011.34
ULR

44th Edition

ULRICH'S™

PERIODICALS
DIRECTORY

2006

International Periodicals Information Since 1932

44th Edition

ULRICH'S™

PERIODICALS
DIRECTORY

2006

International Periodicals Information Since 1932

including
Irregular Serials & Annuals

Volume 1

Classified List of Serials
A-Edu

1-3128

Published by R.R. Bowker LLC
630 Central Avenue, New Providence, NJ 07974

Michael Cairns, President

BowkerLink Publishers' Update System: http://www.bowkerlink.com
Ulrich's Hotline (U.S. only): 1-800-346-6049
Editorial (Canada only, call collect): 1-908-219-0286
Serials Fax (overseas users): (+1) 908-219-0182
Serials E-mail: ulrichs@bowker.com
URL: http://www.ulrichsweb.com
Advertising Sales: 908-219-0072

International Standard Book Number
ISBN10: 0-8352-4768-6 (4-Volume set)
ISBN13: 978-0-8352-4768-9 (4-Volume set)
ISBN 10: 0-8352-4769-4 (Volume 1)
ISBN 13: 978-0-8352-4769-6 (Volume1)
ISBN 10: 0-8352-4770-8 (Volume 2)
ISBN 13: 978-0-8352-4770-2 (Volume 2)
ISBN 10: 0-8352-4771-6 (Volume 3)
ISBN 13: 978-0-8352-4771-9 (Volume 3)
ISBN 10: 0-8352-4772-4 (Volume 4)
ISBN 13: 978-0-8352-4772-6 (Volume 4)

International Standard Serial Number
0000-2100

Library of Congress Control Number
32-16320

Printed and bound in the United States of America

ISBN 0-8352-4768-6

9 780835 247689

Contents

Bowker/Ulrich's Serials Librarianship Award

Presented by the Serials Section
Association for Library Collections and Technical Services (ALCTS)
Division of the American Library Association (ALA)

Sponsored by R.R. Bowker LLC

This annual award is given in recognition of distinguished and ongoing contributions to serials librarianship. Qualified individuals demonstrate leadership in serials-related activities through their participation in professional associations, groups, and/or library education programs; make significant contributions to serials literature; and, in general, strive to enhance our comprehension of the serials world.

AWARD RECIPIENTS

1985 Marcia Tuttle	1996 Jean L. Hirons
1986 Ruth C. Carter	1997 Cindy Hepfer
1987 James P. Danky	1998 Crystal Graham
1988 Marjorie E. Bloss	
1989 John E. Merriman	1999 Regina Romano Reynolds
1990 Jean S. Cook	2000 Trisha L. Davis
1991 Deana L. Astle/Charles A. Hamaker	2001 not awarded
1992 Linda K. Bartley	2002 Eric Lease Morgan
1993 Ann L. Okerson	2003 Frieda Rosenberg
1994 Tina Feick	2004 Pamela Bluh
1995 Peter Gellatly	2005 Dan Tonkery

Preface

In the 74 years since **Ulrich's™ Periodicals Directory** was first published, technology has substantially transformed both the methods and mission of the library and research center. Access, rather than ownership, has become a key consideration. Resource sharing and networking have become common practices in the effort to maintain the flow of quality information. As promising as these changes in collections and services may be, they generate a new set of questions in nearly every sphere of serials management: acquisition; bibliographic control; conservation and preservation; access; standards; and education and training.

At R.R. Bowker, we have set ourselves the task of addressing these transitions by developing and expanding **Ulrich's™ Periodicals Directory** in a variety of ways. Now in its 44th edition, **Ulrich's** has established itself as the premier serials reference source in the world, providing serials users with essential bibliographic and access information that ranges from subscription rates to the latest web sites. For complete details on these changes, please see the User's Guide on pages ix-xv of the prefatory material of Volumes 1-4.

As libraries, institutions, and researchers shift focus from physical ownership of materials to acquiring individual articles on demand, our coverage of document delivery services now includes 17 different services offering the full text of articles from over 42,040 serials listed in **Ulrich's**. For a brief explanation of such services, please refer to the "Document Suppliers" section in the User's Guide, page xiii of the prefatory material. For contact information for these services, please see the company listings section on page xxvi of the prefatory material.

Though the printed serial is by no means on the wane, the use of electronic research tools, whether online or on CD-ROM, continues unabated. There has been a dramatic increase in the use of the Internet as a publishing medium, resulting in new breeds of serials. Electronic publications, such as e-journals and e-zines, emerge every day and are reflected in **Ulrich's**. This edition includes nearly 45,000 serials available exclusively online or in addition to other media. 6,700 serials are indicated as available on CD-ROM. These serials are indicated by a notation in the main entry and a bullet (●) in the TITLE INDEX.

Regardless of the publication medium, serials remain the key tools for scholarship and the primary source of current information and topical news in all fields of endeavor. In toto, the 44th edition of **Ulrich's** contains information on over 188,550 serials published throughout the world, classified and cross-referenced under 900 subject headings. Additionally, each entry is assigned at minimum one Dewey Decimal Classification number from the 22nd edition. Included are serials that are currently available, issued more frequently than once a year and usually published at regular intervals, as well as publications issued annually or less frequently than once a year, or irregularly. While aiming for maximum title coverage, we have established certain criteria for inclusion. We report all publications that meet the definition of a serial except administrative publications of governmental agencies below state level that can be easily found elsewhere. A limited selection of membership directories, comic books, and puzzle and game books is included.

Entries have been updated to reflect the most current information available and nearly 6,000 serials have been added this year, some of which may have since ceased or suspended publication. Included in this edition is cessation or suspension information that has been recorded in our database during the past three years for over 5,880 titles. The ceased or suspended titles are preceded by a dagger (†) in the TITLE INDEX for instant identification.

Users can identify over 3,680 newer serials, which are known to have begun publication since January 1, 2003, by an inverted solid triangle (▼) in both the CLASSIFIED LIST OF SERIALS and the TITLE INDEX. This symbol is

also used to highlight the 219 forthcoming serial launches announced for publication in the years 2005-2006. In addition, over 21,800 refereed serials notations, approximately 84,200 brief descriptions, over 42,600 LC Classification Numbers, and some 18,500 CODEN appear in this edition.

Further facilitating access to serials are indicators found in over 61,300 titles denoting coverage by some 736 abstracting and indexing services, over 16,280 notations of reprint availability, over 84,650 e-mail addresses and over 107,000 URLs (Uniform Resource Locators on the World Wide Web). The number of URLs includes company web sites as well as sites for individual journals. There are many copyright implications associated with the distribution of published material from the Internet and the delivery and sharing of other documents. We therefore provide Copyright Clearance Center notations for over 22,770 registered titles along with over 25,500 Rights & Permissions contact names. When available, we include telephone contact information as well. These data elements make it easy to comply with the law without interrupting the flow of information.

BowkerLink™, a web-based system at http://www.bowkerlink.com, was launched to allow publishers to view, update, and add data to their titles. International data inquiries are mailed to publishers requesting accurate, current information on existing titles, new titles, title changes, and cessations. Updating of the database occurs daily using information received from publishers throughout the year and from serials research conducted in our editorial department. All post office returns are researched, and entries from publishers whose addresses cannot be verified are omitted from the book.

Beginning with the 34th edition, the publication date of **Ulrich's** moved from August to November. Publication in November enables us to provide thousands of updated prices for 2006 since many publishers establish prices for the upcoming year between May and October. Prices set and received by us later than mid-September were not updated for this print edition. However, data are entered as received, so price changes and other information, such as title changes, cessations, and new releases, received after mid-September will appear in issues of the electronic versions of **Ulrich's**. These include **ulrichsweb.com**™, updated weekly on the Internet at http://www.ulrichsweb.com, providing article-level content and linking to journal full-text; Ulrich's Serials Analysis System™, the collection evaluation and reporting tool for library professionals at http://www.ulrichsweb.com/analysis; Ulrich's On Disc, a quarterly CD-ROM from R.R. Bowker; CD-ROM and online versions of Ulrich's from Ovid Technologies; and online from The Dialog Corporation (File No. 480).

Your purchase and use of **Ulrich's** is complemented by access to the **Ulrich's Hotline**, a toll-free number that subscribers may phone for help in solving particular research problems and questions. Canadian users are asked to call a special number collect, and our overseas users are asked to use a designated fax number. (Please refer to page iv for our mailing address, telephone/fax numbers, and e-mail address.) Publishers are encouraged to use **BowkerLink**™ or to e-mail updates as changes to their titles occur, using the e-mail address ulrichs@bowker.com.

As we continue to research, plan, and implement enhancements to the **Ulrich's** database and our database maintenance system, we consider feedback from our users to be essential. Please contact us to let us know your thoughts and suggestions. You may write to us, send us a fax, call us on the telephone, or send us e-mail. Also, be sure to visit the R.R. Bowker home page on the World Wide Web at http://www.bowker.com for the latest news. Please refer to page iv for all contact information.

Gratitude is extended to the entire staff of **Ulrich's** for their unflagging dedication and diligent work in updating and maintaining the serials database in preparation of the 44th edition of **Ulrich's**. Appreciation is also extended to all vendors and service suppliers for working with us to produce this directory. Finally, we thank the various information specialists, serialists, national libraries, and serials publishers throughout the world who have aided us in updating **Ulrich's**. We consider their participation and interest in the dissemination of accurate and comprehensive serials information to be of tremendous value to **Ulrich's** and its users.

This directory offers two primary access methods for locating periodicals: by subject in the CLASSIFIED LIST OF SERIALS (Volumes 1-3), and alphabetically in the TITLE INDEX (Volume 4). Ceased serials are listed in a separate CESSATIONS section (Volume 4) and are also accessible by means of the TITLE INDEX. Other indexes provide listings of selected periodicals in specific categories. These indexes, in Volume 4 are PRODUCER LISTING/SERIALS ON CD-ROM, ONLINE SERVICE LISTING/SERIALS ONLINE, PUBLICATIONS OF INTERNATIONAL ORGANIZATIONS, and ISSN INDEX. See the User's Guide in Volume 4 for a content description and use instructions for the U.S. NEWSPAPERS section.

In addition, separate subheadings for "Abstracting, Bibliographies and Statistics" under major subject headings provide convenient access to these types of publications. Page references for these subheadings are given in the "Subject Guide to Abstracting and Indexing" on page lii. This listing provides an overview of subjects for which abstracting and indexing publications have been identified.

The "User's Guide" is separated into three divisions for ease of use: (I) Section Descriptions, (II) Full Entry Content Description, and (III) Cataloging Rules for Main Entry Title.

Section Descriptions

CLASSIFIED LIST OF SERIALS

This is the main section of the book, containing bibliographic information for currently published serials classified by subject. Entries are arranged alphabetically by title within each subject heading. Subject cross-references in the text direct the user to the location of subheadings.

Volume 1 contains subjects A-Edu, from "Abstracting and Indexing" through "Education." Volume 2 contains subjects Ele-Med, "Electronics" through "Medical Sciences." Volume 3 contains subjects Mee-Z, from "Meetings and Congresses" through "Zoology."

A complete listing of the "Subjects" used in the CLASSIFIED LIST OF SERIALS appears on p. lv. To aid international users, this list is translated into four languages. For additional guidance on the subject classification scheme, the user should also consult the CROSS-INDEX TO SUBJECTS in Volume 4, which contains additional key word references.

Each serial is listed with full bibliographic information only once. If a serial covers several subjects, title cross-references appear under the related headings, directing the user to the heading where the full entry is listed.

New serials beginning publication in the past three years, as well as titles announced for publication in the coming year are highlighted by an inverted triangle symbol (▼) in front of the title.

The "Cataloging Rules for Main Entry Title" section of this "User's Guide" explains the title cataloging rules followed in compiling **Ulrich's**.

CESSATIONS

In this section, entries for serials for which cessation was noted in the past three years are listed alphabetically by title. The cessation entry includes: title, Dewey Decimal Classification number, former frequency of publication, publisher name and address, country-of-publication code, and, if available, other information such as ISSN, subtitle, corporate author, year of first issue, and year ceased. Titles which were originally planned as continuing series but which have closed are included in the CESSATIONS section although back issues may still be available.

If a title has "ceased" because a new title is being used, there will not be an entry in the CESSATIONS section. Instead, the entry is maintained in the CLASSIFIED LIST OF SERIALS under the new title, with a **"Formerly"** or **"Former titles"** indication.

ISSN INDEX

The ISSN INDEX lists serials in order by ISSN number. It includes all serials contained in the **Ulrich's** database, whether current, ceased, or inactive, to which an ISSN has been assigned in our file. A dagger symbol (†) indicates that the title is ceased. If an ISSN appears twice, it usually indicates that the serial has split into two or more parts. Titles that have changed and for which new ISSNs have been assigned will show cross-references from one ISSN to the new ISSN. If no new ISSN has been assigned, the cross-reference is from ISSN to new title. Entries for inactive titles do not appear in the book.

Boldface type indicates the page number where a complete entry can be found for active titles. Titles for which cessation was noted in the last three years have a page reference to the listing in the CESSATIONS INDEX. If no page reference appears for a

ceased title, it means that the cessation was noted more than three years ago and is not listed in this edition. ISSNs of inactive titles likewise do not have page references and are not listed in this book.

A full description of the ISSN and its use is provided on p. xvi.

TITLE INDEX

The TITLE INDEX is the second major access point for serials. To locate a serial by its title, the user should be familiar with title cataloging rules as described in the "Cataloging Rules for Main Entry Titles" paragraphs of this "User's Guide."

The TITLE INDEX lists all current and ceased serials included in this directory. **Boldface** type indicates the page number where the complete entry will be found.

For serials with identical titles published within a country, the city of publication is added in parentheses, and sometimes the year of first publication is given to further distinguish the titles.

If a serial title consists of or contains an acronym, a cross-reference is provided from the full name to the acronym form of the title.

Cross-references are provided from former titles and variant titles, and from the alternate language titles of multi-language publications. Recent title changes are noted, with a reference to the current title. The TITLE INDEX also lists the country code for all serials, along with the ISSN, if known.

The inverted triangle symbol (▼) used in the "Classified List of Serials" to indicate new serials also appears in this index, preceding the title. A dagger (†) appears preceding the title if the publication has ceased. The bullet symbol (●) indicates that the title is available in one or more electronic formats, including online, CD-ROM or e-mail, either exclusively or in addition to printed formats. The arrow symbol (➤) indicates that a title is refereed or peer-reviewed by an editorial board. These symbols appear in a new footer at the bottom of every right-hand page.

CROSS-INDEX TO SUBJECTS

This index lists alphabetically all main subject headings in the **Ulrich's** Subject Authority Database, as well as keyword references that direct users to main or subheadings where publications on those topics are likely to be found. The number following each subject term directs users to the page on which the subject begins within the CLASSIFIED LIST OF SERIALS.

A keyword may refer the user to more than one subject category. In this case, the subject references are listed in alphabetical order and are not necessarily listed in hierarchical order.

Main subject headings appear in uppercase, e.g. AGRICULTURE. Subheadings contain the main subject term in uppercase and the specific subheading term in mixed case, e.g. AGRICULTURE—Agricultural Economics. The keywords, except for acronyms, are displayed entirely in mixed case.

PRODUCER LISTING/SERIALS ON CD-ROM

This section is an alphabetical listing of identified producers of serials on CD-ROM. Entries include the producer address, and contact numbers, and an alphabetical listing of all serial titles known to be available.

ONLINE SERVICE LISTING/SERIALS ONLINE

This section is an alphabetical listing of identified providers of online periodicals. Entries include addresses, contact numbers for the provider, and an alphabetical listing of all titles known to be available, with file names or numbers, if known.

INDEX TO PUBLICATIONS OF INTERNATIONAL ORGANIZATIONS

Complexity of corporate author structure, as well as title page variations in multilingual texts, compound the problems in cataloging publications of international organizations. This special index is provided so that the user may have one reference point for these titles. This index consists of four sections:

European Union
International Congress Proceedings
International Organizations
United Nations

The index contains all current titles listed in the **Ulrich's** database. The user must consult the CLASSIFIED LIST OF SERIALS for the full bibliographic information pertaining to these titles. Page references are provided in bold.

Full Entry Content Description

Basic Information

The following elements are mandatory for listing and appear in all entries: main entry title, frequency of publication, publisher address, country code, and Dewey Decimal Classification number.

Certain electronic journals may not have a physical mailing address; the URL and/or e-mail address provide a means of contacting the publication.

Dewey Decimal Classification Number

The Dewey Decimal number is printed at the top left of each entry. More than one Dewey number may have been assigned if a serial covers several subjects.

LC Classification Number

The Library of Congress classification number, if known, appears directly below the Dewey Decimal number. Shelf numbers are not included.

Country Code

The ISO Country Code is printed at the top center of each entry following the Dewey Decimal number. A complete list of country codes used will be found beginning on page xxii.

ISSN

The ISSN for the main entry title is printed to the right of the country code. Not all publications have been assigned an ISSN, and lack of a number does not render a publication ineligible for listing.

CODEN

The CODEN designation, if known, is printed directly below the country code and ISSN. The CODEN is an alphanumeric code, applied uniquely to a specific publication. Devised by the American Society for Testing and Materials, it is used primarily for scientific and technical titles. New CODEN are assigned by Chemical Abstracts Service.

Title Information

The main title is printed in **boldface** and uppercase as the first item in the entry. Titles are catalogued according to rules described below in the "Cataloging Rules for Main Entry Title" section. For multi-language publications, the parallel language title is also printed in uppercase, immediately following the main entry title, and is separated from it by a slash.

An inverted triangle symbol (▼) printed before the title indicates that the title began publishing within the past three years. This symbol also appears before titles announced for publication in the coming year. An asterisk (*) printed after the title indicates that the address in the entry was not verified by the publisher for this edition.

The subtitle is printed in lowercase after the title. Variant titles are given within the entry and are labeled as such. The Key Title, which is assigned at the time of ISSN assignment by the responsible center of the International Serials Data System, is given only if it is different from the main entry title. Former titles are given at the end of the bibliographic data. See the paragraph below.

Language

The language or languages is given, even if a serial is written in the main language of the country of publication. The order of languages is generally alphabetical and does not represent prominence. If a serial includes abstracts, summaries or sections in additional language(s), that information will be provided as well.

Year First Published

The year first published is given if provided by the publisher. If a title has been suspended and later resumed publication, these dates may be provided as well. If volume numbering was restarted, the notation "N.S." denoting new series precedes the date. If information is lacking, a volume number and specific year may be provided to indicate the approximate age of the publication.

Frequency

The frequency of publication is given in abbreviated form, such as "a." for annual, "irreg." for irregular, "m." for monthly, "3/yr." for three times per year. All abbreviations used are listed in the "General Abbreviations and Special Symbols" on page xix.

Price

Unless otherwise indicated, the price given is the annual price for an individual subscription in the currency of the country of origin. The price in U.S. dollars may also be given if it is provided by the publisher. No attempt is made to convert foreign currency to U.S. dollars. Separate postage information is not given, since postal rates vary widely. A complete list of ISO currency codes used will be found beginning on page xx.

Special Features

A listing of special features may include such items as book or other types of reviews, advertising (usually meaning commercial, not classified advertising), charts, illustrations, bibliography section, article abstracts, and an annual index to the periodical's contents.

Reprint Services

If a serial is known to be available from a reprint service, a code referring to the service appears in the entry. More than one code may be listed. For a list of reprint services and a translation of the codes, please refer to page xxxi.

Pages Per Issue; Columns Per Page

When known, the number of pages per issue (p./no.:) and/or columns per page (cols./p.:) is/are noted.

Refereed Serial

The manuscript peer review and evaluation system is utilized to protect, maintain and raise the quality of scholarly material published in serials. The arrow symbol (➤) appears before the title if a serial is known to be refereed or juried. This information is generally provided by the serial publisher.

Document Type

Notations are included to indicate type of publication, e.g. Academic/Scholarly, Trade, Newsletter, or Abstract/Index. The words "**Document type**" appear in boldface, followed by the document type description, in entries where this information is known. More than one document type may be listed for a single publication, if applicable.

Brief Description

A brief description of the contents and editorial focus of the publication may be provided, preceded by the word "**Description:**" at the end of the bibliographic data. These descriptions were submitted by the publisher or were written by editorial staff after examination of sample copies or publisher catalogs.

Former Titles

Title changes are common phenomena in serials publishing. Many entries contain extensive former title information, providing a history of changes which may be useful for bibliographic record-keeping. Previous titles for the serial are

given, along with their ISSN, if known. ISSN are assigned to specific titles and therefore change with the title. The former titles are preceded by a description of the type of title change. Simple title changes are noted by the words "Formerly" or "Former titles." Other types may include mergers, incorporations or supersessions. Dates provided are generally the date that the change became effective. For mergers and incorporations, date ranges indicate the years of publication for that previous title.

Media

The primary medium is specified for other than the traditional print on paper, with the exception of the notation "Duplicated." Common media listed include Online, CD-ROM, Diskette, Microfilm and Microfiche. Online - full text denotes that the entire text of all the articles of a serial is available online, while Online - full content denotes that the entire content including graphics is available. If a serial is primarily available in Braille or Large Type, that notation will be found here.

Related Titles

This section provides information on all available formats, editions and related publications. Often the title and ISSN are provided. The diamond symbol (♦) indicates that there is a complete listing elsewhere in the CLASSIFIED LIST OF SERIALS. Please refer to the TITLE INDEX for the page number of that listing. When no complete record is available, data such as start year, frequency, or price may be provided.

Information on alternate media editions, such as online, CD-ROM or microform editions, is provided here. Online providers and CD-ROM producer names are given if known to be different from the publisher. Complete address and contact

---

SAMPLE ENTRY

1 641.337   **2** USA   **3** ISSN 1234-5678

4 HD9199.A1   **5** CODEN: COCIEO

6 ► **7** CHINESE JOURNAL OF COFFEE RESEARCH; **8** short articles on coffee research. **9** Key title: Coffee Research **10** (In 3 sections.) **11** Text in Chinese, English. **12** 1987. **13** 24/yr. (in 2 vols.) **14** USD 136 in US and Canada; USD 148 elsewhere (effective 2001) **15** bk.rev. abstr. illus. cum. index: 1987-1997; **16** back issues avail.; reprint service avail. from SWZ,UMI **17** 8 cols./p., 20 p./no. **18** Document type: *Academic/scholarly.*

19 **Description:** Offers articles, coffee news and data analyses to scientists, engineers and research managers.

20 **Supersedes in part** (in 1989): Acta Scientifica Cafe **21** (0000-8888); Which was formerly: Coffee Research Techniques

22 **Media:** Online - full text (from Grinder, Inc.) **23** **Related titles:** CD-ROM ed.: Coffee Research on Disc. 1992. q. USD 32. (from Cafe Institute (File no.42), Platter Corp.); Microfilm ed. (from SMI); Japanese ed.: ISSN 2345-6789. Supplement: Annual Coffee Review. ISSN 6789-1234.

24 **Indexed:** Food Sci.& Tech.Abstr.

25 --- BLDSC (1234.567890), CISTI, GNLM **26** **CCC.**

27 **Published by:** (Coffee Research Institute), **28** Chinese Coffee Inc., **29** 140 US Rte 400, Parsippany, NJ 07974. **30** TEL 908-665-2800, **31** FAX 908-771-7725, **32** Telex 9735 PARV TH, **33** usinfo@coffee.com, **34** http://www. coffeeresearch.com. **35** Eds. Shawn King, Jane Weiner. **36** Pub. Richard Stocker. **37** R&P Ewa Picker TEL 908-665-2875. **38** Adv. contact Sankar Lara **39** adv.: B&W page USD 2,300, color page USD 3,500; trim 7 x 10. **40** circ. 5,000 (paid); 3,200 (controlled) **41** Wire service: SP **42** **Subscr. in the Americas to:** Science Research Centre, Regional Sales Office, PO Box 435, New York, NY 10159-0945. TEL 212-465-7645, FAX 212-576-4785; **43** **Dist. by:** Cafe Distributors, 23 Chen Lu, Beijing 100031, People's Republic of China. TEL 86-10-12345, FAX 86-10-34567. **44** **Co-sponsors:** Chinese Coffee Organization; Chinese Science Society. **Affiliate:** United States Coffee Research Society.

KEY

1 Dewey Decimal Classification
2 ISO Country Code
3 ISSN
4 LC Classification
5 CODEN
6 Refereed Symbol
7 Main Entry Title
8 Subtitle
9 Key Title
10 Bibliographic Note
11 Language
12 First Published
13 Frequency
14 Price
15 Special Features
16 Back Issues & Reprint
17 Page Format
18 Document Type
19 Brief Description
20 Title Changes
21 Former ISSN
22 Media
23 Related Editions
24 Abstracting & Indexing
25 Document Suppliers
26 Copyright Clearance Center
27 Corporate Author
28 Publishing Company
29 Address
30 Telephone
31 Fax
32 Telex
33 E-mail
34 URL
35 Editor
36 Publisher
37 Rights & Permissions Contact
38 Advertising Contact
39 Advertising Rates
40 Circulation
41 Wire Service
42 Subscription
43 Distributor
44 Co-sponsors and other bodies

information for these companies is provided in the ONLINE SERVICE LISTING and CD-ROM PRODUCER LISTING sections, in Volume 4. For publications available in microform, a three-letter code for the vendor or micropublisher is provided. A list of names, addresses, and contact information begins on page xxviii.

Abstracting and Indexing

The notation **"Indexed"** precedes a list of abbreviations for all abstracting and indexing services known to cover the serial on a regular basis. The complete names of the abstracting and indexing services are listed with their abbreviations on page xxxiv. This section also includes status information and related titles. Consult the TITLE INDEX for page references to entries in the CLASSIFIED LIST OF SERIALS for active services.

Document Suppliers

These notations are preceded by an em-dash (—). The presence of a notation indicates the availability of articles from that serial through the specified service, by permission from the copyright holder. Such permissions are subject to change without notice. Articles may be available in paper and/or electronic format, depending on the service. The full names and complete address and contact information for these companies are listed beginning on page xxvi.

The British Library Document Supply Centre shelfmark number, a unique identifier of each serial, appears in parentheses after that organization's code, ex. "BLDSC (0000.000000)." The format of the shelfmark is four digits, a decimal point, then six digits.

The **Ulrich's** database and the individual databases of document suppliers were matched on the presence of ISSNs. When a match was successful, the appropriate document supplier code was noted. Not all serials titles in general or in these individual databses, have ISSNs. Therefore, the absence of one or any document supplier codes in an **Ulrich's** listing does not necessarily mean the title is not available from one or any of these suppliers.

Copyright Clearance Center, Inc.

Copyright Clearance Center, Inc. (CCC), the largest licenser of text reproduction rights in the world, was formed in 1978 to facilitate compliance with U.S. Copyright law. CCC provides licensing systems for reproduction and distribution of copyrighted materials in print and electronic formats. CCC manages rights for over 1.75 million works and represents over 9,600 publishers and hundreds of thousands of authors and other creators, directly or through their representatives. CCC-licensed customers in the U.S. number over 10,000 corporations and subsidiaries, and thousands of government agencies, law firms, document suppliers, libraries, academic institutions, copy shops and bookstores.

The boldfaced **CCC** notation appears in the entries of titles for which the CCC has been authorized by the publisher to grant photocopy permissions on any of their works.

Contact them at 222 Rosewood Dr., Danvers, MA 01923, USA; tel: 978-750-8400; fax: 978-750-4470; URL: http://www.copyright.com.

Publishing Company Information

This section begins with the bold phrase "**Published by**" or "**Address**" if the company name is the same as the title.

Many serials are editorially controlled by a sponsoring organization or corporate author and published by a commercial publisher. In these instances, the commercial publishing company's name and address are given, and the name of the corporate author is given in parentheses immediately preceding. In other instances, either a sponsoring organization or a commercial publishing company has sole responsibility, and only one name is given. We avoid listing printers as publishing companies, preferring the name and address of someone with editorial responsibility. For the same reason, we avoid listing distributors as publishing companies.

Telephone, Fax, Telex Numbers, E-mail, and Web Site Addresses

Telephone, fax, telex numbers and e-mail as well as web site addresses (URLs) are given when provided by the publisher. U.S. and Canadian numbers are given in standard North American format. Toll-free numbers within U.S. and Canada are also included, when available. Numbers in other countries are provided in the same format as supplied by the publisher, resulting in some inconsistencies (e.g. sometimes with a country and/or city code, sometimes without). Users are advised to consult an international operator before placing calls.

Editor

Only one or two names are given when known, preceded by the notation "Ed." or "Eds." Advanced degrees and titles are omitted, except for medical, military and religious titles; absence of a title does not mean that the editor has none.

Publisher

Only one or two names are given when known, preceded by the notation "Pub." or "Pubs." Advanced degrees and titles are omitted, except for medical, military and religious titles; absence of a title does not mean that the publisher has none.

If the publisher is also the editor, and no publishing company name is available, the person's name is given in place of company name with the notation "Ed. & Pub."

Rights and Permissions Contact

A name is given when supplied, preceded by the notation "R&P contact." The telephone number information follows, when known and different from the main number.

Advertising Rates and Contact

When provided by the publisher, the name of the advertising contact, as well as full-page advertising rates and sizes are indicated. Most dimensions are listed in millimeters, except for U.S. publications, the dimensions of which are usually in inches.

Circulation

All circulation figures used are approximate. Circulation is given only if provided by the publisher. The notation "controlled" indicates that the publication is available only to qualified persons, usually members of a particular trade or profession. The notation "paid" indicates that subscribers pay to receive the publication, while the notation "free" indicates that the title is freely distributed.

Wire Services

If a newspaper is known to use one or more news or photo wire services, abbreviations or names of the services used are listed in the entry. Such information is preceded by the words "Wire Service(s)." Abbreviations for wire services used are listed on page xxxii of this volume.

Subscription or Distribution Information

A second address is given only if the address for ordering subscriptions is different from the publishing company's address. Distributors are listed only if we have been informed that a particular organization is the exclusive distributor. Additional subscription and/or distribution offices of international publishers are listed, if known. Telephone and fax numbers and e-mail and URL addresses for subscription and/or distribution offices appear if provided by the publisher.

Other related organizations and companies such as co-sponsors, affiliates, or co-publishers may be noted here.

Newspaper Ownership

The name of the owner(s) of a newspaper is listed, usually accompanied by the owner(s) address, and telephone and fax numbers. The owner address may differ from the newspaper location address. Owner information is preceded by the notation "Owner(s):."

Cataloging Rules for Main Entry Title

The majority of titles in the Ulrich's database were cataloged according to *Anglo-American Cataloging Rules* prior to 1978, the date of the new edition of *Anglo-American Cataloging Rules*. The new *AACR II* reflects a trend toward the Key Title concept of cataloging as used by the International Serials Data System (ISDS) and published in its *International Standard Bibliographic Description for Serials* (1974).

Because recataloging a database the size of Bowker's was not feasible, our cataloging rules were modified but not radically changed. Cross-references are provided in the TITLE INDEX from variant forms of title, such as Key Title, to aid users searching by other methods.

Whenever possible, main entry title cataloging is done from a sample of the title page of the most recent issue, according to the follwoing rules:

Articles at the beginning of titles are omitted, or are bypassed in filing.

Serials with distinctive titles are usually entered under title. For example:

> *Annual Bulletin of Historical Literature*
> *Business Week*
> *Milton Studies*

If a title consists only of a generic term followed by the name of the issuing body, or if the name of the issuing body clarifies the content of the publication, entry is under the name of the issuing body. For example:

> *Newsletter of the American Theological Library Association*

is entered as

> *American Theological Library Association. Newsletter*

> *Economic Performance and Prospects*, issued by the Private Development Corporation of the Philippines

is entered as

> *Private Development Corporation of the Philippines. Economic Performance and Prospects*

A title which consists of a subject modified generic term followed by the name of the issuing body is considered nondistinctive and is entered under the name of the isssuing body. For example:

> *Annual Meeting Scientific Proceedings of the American Animal Hospital Association*

is entered as

> *American Animal Hospital Association. Annual Meeting Scientific Proceedings*

Government publications with nondistinctive titles are entered under the name of the government jurisdiction of the issuing body, although distinctive titles of government organizations may be entered directly under title. For example:

> *Great Britain. Economic and Social Research Council. Annual Report*

but

> *Statistical Abstract of Iceland*

Titles which begin with the initials of the issuing body are entered under the initials. Cross-references from the full name are provided in the TITLE INDEX.

If a geographic name is part of the name of the issuing body, entry will be under the common form of the name of the body.

For example:

University of the West Indies. Vice-Chancellor's Report

not

West Indies. University. Vice-Chancellor's Report

Note, however, that government publications retain similar cataloging as government jurisdiction.

Canada. Statistics Canada. Field Crop Reporting Series

Multilingual titles are entered under the first title given on the title page, or the first title reported by the publisher if the title page is not available. Titles in other languages are entered directly after the main entry title. Cross-references are provided in the TITLE INDEX for each language title.

FILING RULES

Due to the restrictions imposed by computer filing of titles, the following special filing rules should be noted. The majority of punctuation marks are treated as spaces. A combination of punctuation and spaces is treated as one space.

Acronyms and initals are treated as such and are listed at the beginning of each letter of the alphabet.

D H Lawrence Review
D.L.A.N.Y. Newsletter
D N R
Dade County Teacher

Hyphenated words are treated as separate words:

Pre-Text

precedes

Preaching

Initial articles may be provided for a title, but do not affect their alphabetization. Articles and prepositions within titles are alphabetized as words:

Journal of the West

precedes

Journal of Theological Studies

Diacritical marks have been omitted. The German and Scandinavian umlaut has been replaced by the letter "e" following the vowels a, e, o, and u. In Danish, Norwegian, and Swedish, the letter å is sequenced as "aa" and the letter Ø as "oe."

International Standard Serial Number (ISSN)

1. What is the ISSN?

An internationally accepted, concise, unique, and unambiguous code for the identification of serial publications. One ISSN represents one serial title.

The ISSN consists of seven numbers with an eighth check digit calculated according to Modulus 11 and used to verify the number in computer processing. A hyphen is printed after the fourth digit, as a visual aid, and the acronym, ISSN, precedes the number.

2. How did the ISSN evolve as an international system?

The International Organization for Standardization Technical Committee 46 (ISO/TC 46) is the agency responsible for the development of the ISSN as an international standard. The organization responsible for the administration and coordination of ISSN assignments worldwide is the ISSN International Centre in Paris, which is supported by the French government and UNESCO.

ISSNs are assigned by over 50 national centers worldwide. The National Serials Data Program (NSDP) is the U.S. national center. The centers form a network that is coordinated by the ISSN International Centre located in Paris.

The implementation of the ISSN system started with the numbering of 70,000 titles in the serials database of R.R. Bowker (*Ulrich's International Periodicals Directory* and *Irregular Serials and Annuals*). The next serials database numbering was the *New Serials Titles 1950-70* cumulation listing 220,000 titles, cumulated, converted to magnetic tape, and published by R.R. Bowker in collaboration with the Serials Record Division of the Library of Congress. These two databases were used as the starting base for the implementation of the ISSN.

3. What types of publications are assigned ISSNs?

For assignment of an ISSN, a serial is defined as a publication in print or non-print form, issued in successive parts, usually having numerical or chronological designations, and intended to be continued indefinitely.

4. How is the ISSN used?

The ISSN is employed as a component of bar codes and as a tool for the communication of basic information about a serial title and for such processes as ordering, billing, inventory control, abstracting, and indexing. In library processes, the ISSN is used in operations such as acquisitions, claiming, binding, accessioning, shelving, cooperative cataloging, circulation, interlibrary loans, and retrieval of requests.

5. Can a publication have an International Standard Book Number (ISBN) and an ISSN?

Yes! Monographic series (separate works issued indefinitely under a common title, generally in a uniform format with numeric designations) and annuals or titles planned to be issued indefinitely under the same title may be defined as serials. The ISSN is assigned to the serial title, while an ISBN is assigned to each individual title or monograph in the series.

A new ISBN is assigned to each volume or edition by the publisher, while the ISSN, which is assigned by the ISSN International Centre or national ISSN centers, remains the same for each issue. Both numbers should be printed on the copyright page or other appropriate page of each volume, with their acronyms or words preceding each number for immediate identification. With the availability of both an ISSN and ISBN, the problem of defining the overlap of serials and monographs has been resolved.

SAMPLE TITLE

Advances in the Biosciences
ISSN 0065-3446

Vol. 1 Proceedings: Berlin. Schering Symposium of Endocrinology, Berlin. Ed. by Gerhard Raspe. 1969. 40.00 (ISBN 0-08-013395-9). Pergamon.

Vol. 2 Proceedings. Schering Symposium on Biodynamics & Mechanisms of Action of Steroid Hormones, Berlin. Ed. by Gerhard Raspe. 1969. 41.25 (ISBN 0-08-006942-8). Pergamon.

Vol. 3 Proceedings. Schering Workshop on Steroid Metabolism "in Vitro Versus in Vivo," Berlin. Ed. by Gerhard Raspe. 1969. 41.25 (ISBN 0-08-017544-9). Pergamon.

Vol. 4 Proceedings. Schering Symposium on Mechanisms Involved in Conception. Berlin. Ed. by Gerhard Raspe. 1970. text ed. 41.25 (ISBN 0-08-017546-5). Pergamon.

Vol. 25 Development of Responsiveness to Steroid Hormones. Alvin M. Kaye & Myra Kaye et al. LC 79-42938. 1980. 66.00 (ISBN 0-08-024949-X). Pergamon.

ISSN International Centre
20, rue Bachaumont
75002 Paris
France
Tel: +33 (0) 1 44 88 22 20
Fax: +33 (0) 1 40 26 32 43
E-mail: issnic@issn.org
URL: http://www.issn.org

The address for the U.S. national ISSN center is:

National Serials Data Program (NSDP)
Library of Congress
Washington, DC 20540-4160
Tel: 202-707-6452
Fax: 202-707-6333
E-mail: ISSN@loc.gov
URL: http://lcweb.loc.gov/issn

6. Where should the ISSN appear on the serial?

In a prominent position on or in each issue of the serial, such as the front cover, back cover, masthead, title, or copyright pages. The international standard recommendation is that the ISSN of a periodical be printed, whenever possible, in the upper right corner of the front cover.

Promotional and descriptive materials about the serial should include the ISSN.

7. When a title changes, is a new ISSN assigned?

In most instances, a new ISSN is assigned when a title changes. However, the determination is made by the ISSN International Centre or the appropriate national ISSN centers. Publishers should report all the title changes to their respective centers.

8. How does a publisher apply for an ISSN?

The publisher should contact the appropriate national ISSN center or the ISSN International Centre. Centers require bibliographic evidence of a serial, including a copy of the title page and cover. There is no charge to publishers for the assignment of ISSNs.

For full information, publishers should contact the national library or bibliographic center in the country where they are publishing. The address of the ISSN International Centre is:

9. What is SISAC?

SISAC stands for the Serials Industry Systems Advisory Committee. SISAC is an industry group formed to develop voluntary standardized formats for electronically transmitting serials business transaction information. SISAC provides a forum where serial (particularly journal) publishers, library system vendors, and librarians can discuss mutual concerns regarding the electronic transmission of serial information and develop cooperative solutions, in the form of standardized formats, to efficiently address these concerns. *(Reprinted with permission from SISAC.)*

10. What is the SISAC Symbol (SICI) and its relationship to the ISSN?

The Serial Item and Contribution Identifier (SICI) is a serial identification code that follows the ISSN and is a string of letters and/or numbers that uniquely identify a particular issue of a serial. Encoded in the SICI are chronological and enumeration data that identify serials by date and volume/issue numbers. According to SISAC, "the ANSI* standard extends the code down to the article level by adding location number and necessary title information, plus a record validation character. Code 128 is the bar code symbology selected by SISAC for displaying this number string in scannable form. When displayed in the Code 128 symbology, the SICI is called the SISAC symbol." The SICI is the ANSI standard; the SISAC symbol is the bar code. *(Reprinted with permission from SISAC.)*

*ANSI American National Standards Institute. Organization that coordinates the voluntary standards system in the United States. U.S. member of the International Standards Organization (ISO).

Abbreviations
General Abbreviations and Special Symbols

a.	annual	pat.	patents
abstr.	abstracts	play rev.	play reviews (theater reviews)
adv.	advertising	p./no.	pages per issue/number
approx.	approximately	Prof.	Professor
avail.	available	pt.	point type
B&W	Black & White	Pub., Pubs.	Publisher(s)
bi-m.	bimonthly (every two months)	q.	quarterly
bi-w.	biweekly (every two weeks)	R&P	Rights & Permissions
bibl.	bibliographies	rec.rev.	record reviews
bk.rev.	book reviews	rev.	reviews
CCC	Copyright Clearance Center	s-a.	semiannually (twice annually)
c/o	care of	s-m.	semimonthly (twice monthly)
circ.	circulation	s-w.	semiweekly (twice weekly)
cols./p.	columns per page	software rev.	software reviews
cum.index	cumulative index	stat.	statistics
Cy.	County	subscr.	subscription
d.	daily	tel.rev.	television program reviews
dance rev.	dance reviews	3/m.	3 times a month
Dir.	Director	3/w.	3 times a week
dist.	distributed	3/yr.	3 times a year
ed., eds.	edition(s)	tr.lit.	trade literature (manufacturers' catalogs, reader response cards)
Ed., Eds.	Editor(s)		
film rev.	film reviews	tr.mk.	trade marks
fortn.	fortnightly (every two weeks)	video rev.	video reviews
ISSN	International Standard Serial Number	vol., vols.	volume(s)
illus.	illustrations	w.	weekly, week
irreg.	irregular	yr., yrs.	year(s)
m.	monthly, month	✳	not updated / unverified
mkt.	market prices	●	electronic serial
mos.	months	▼	new serial
music rev.	music reviews	†	ceased
N.S.	New Series	◆	complete listing available
no., nos.	number(s)	➤	refereed

Currency Codes

This list of world currencies and their codes is the International Standards Organization (ISO) set of three-letter currency abbreviations. This is the complete list of ISO codes, though not all currencies may be present in **Ulrich's**. The codes are mnemonic in most cases, with the first two letters representing the country name and the third representing the currency name.

CODE	CURRENCY	CODE	CURRENCY
ADP	Andorran Peseta	ERB	Eritrean Birr
AED	United Arab Emirates Dirham	ESP	Spanish Peseta
AFA	Afghanistan Afghani	ETB	Ethiopian Birr
ALL	Albanian Lek	EUR	Euro
AMD	Armenian Dram	FIM	Finnish Markka
ANG	Netherlands Antillian Guilder	FJD	Fiji Dollar
AON	Angolan New Kwanza	FKP	Falkland Islands Pound
ARS	Argentinean Peso	FRF	French Franc
ATS	Austrian Schilling	GBP	British Pound
AUD	Australian Dollars	GEL	Georgian Lari
AWG	Aruban Florin	GHC	Ghanaian Cedi
AZM	Azerbaijan Manat	GIP	Gibraltar Pound
BAD	Bosnian Dinar	GMD	Gambian Dalasi
BBD	Barbados Dollar	GNF	Guinea Franc
BDT	Bangladeshi Taka	GNS	Guinea Syli
BEF	Belgian Franc	GRD	Greek Drachma
BGL	Bulgarian Lev	GTQ	Guatemalan Quetzal
BHD	Bahraini Dinar	GWP	Guinea-Bissau Peso
BIF	Burundi Franc	GYD	Guyanan Dollar
BMD	Bermudan Dollar	HKD	Hong Kong Dollar
BND	Brunei Dollar	HNL	Honduran Lempira
BOB	Bolivian Boliviano	HRK	Croatian Kuna
BPS	British Pounds Sterling	HTG	Haitian Gourde
BRL	Brazilian Real	HUF	Hungarian Forint
BSD	Bahamian Dollar	IDR	Indonesian Rupiah
BTN	Bhutan Ngultrum	IEP	Irish Punt
BWP	Botswanan Pula	ILS	Israeli Shekel
BYB	Belarus Ruble	INR	Indian Rupee
BZD	Belize Dollar	IQD	Iraqi Dinar
CHF	Swiss Franc	IRR	Iranian Rial
CLP	Chilean Peso	ISK	Iceland Krona
CND	Canadian Dollars	ITL	Italian Lira
CNY	Yuan (Chinese) Renminbi	JMD	Jamaican Dollar
COP	Colombian Peso	JOD	Jordanian Dinar
CRC	Costa Rican Colon	JPY	Japanese Yen
CSD	Serbian Dinar	KES	Kenyan Schilling
CUP	Cuban Peso	KGS	Kyrgyzstan Som
CVE	Cape Verde Escudo	KHR	Cambodian New Riel
CYP	Cyprus Pound	KMF	Comoros Franc
CZK	Czech Koruna	KPW	North Korean Won
DEM	Deutsche Mark	KRW	South Korean Won
DJF	Djibouti Franc	KWD	Kuwaiti Dinar
DKK	Danish Krone	KYD	Cayman Islands Dollar
DOP	Dominican Peso	KZT	Kazakhstani Tenge
DZD	Algerian Dinar	LAK	Lao Kip
ECS	Ecuador Sucre	LBP	Lebanese Pound
EEK	Estonian Kroon	LKR	Sri Lanka Rupee
EGP	Egyptian Pound	LRD	Liberian Dollar

LSL	Lesotho Loti		SCR	Seychelles Rupee
LTL	Lithuanian Litas		SDP	Sudanese Pound
LUF	Luxembourg Franc		SEK	Swedish Krona
LVL	Latvian Lat		SGD	Singapore Dollar
LYD	Libyan Dinar		SHP	St. Helena Pound
MAD	Moroccan Dirham		SIT	Slovenian Tolar
MDL	Moldova Leu		SKK	Slovakian Koruna
MGF	Malagasy Franc		SLL	Sierra Leone Leone
MKD	Macedonian Denar		SOS	Somali Schilling
MLF	Mali Franc		SRG	Suriname Guilder
MMK	Myanmar Kyat		STD	Sao Tome and Principe Dobra
MNT	Mongolian Tugrik		SVC	El Salvador Colon
MOP	Macao Pataca		SYP	Syrian Pound
MRK	German Marks		SZL	Swaziland Lilangeni
MRO	Mauritanian Ouguiya		THB	Thai Bhat
MTL	Maltese Lira		TJR	Tajikistan Rubl
MUR	Mauritius Rupee		TMM	Turkemenistan Manat
MVR	Maldive Rufiyaa		TND	Tunisian Dinar
MWK	Malawi Kwacha		TOP	Tongan Pa'anga
MXP	Mexican New Peso		TPE	East Timor Escudo
MYR	Malaysian Ringgit		TRL	Turkish Lira
MZM	Mozambique Metical		TTD	Trinidad and Tobago Dollar
NAD	Namibian Dollar		TWD	Taiwan Dollar
NGN	Nigerian Naira		TZS	Tanzanian Schilling
NIC	Nicaraguan Gold Cordoba		UAK	Ukraine Hryvnia
NLG	Dutch Guilder		UGX	Uganda Shilling
NOK	Norwegian Kroner		USD	US Dollars
NPR	Nepalese Rupee		UYP	Peso Uruguayo
NZD	New Zealand Dollar		UZS	Uzbek Som
OMR	Omani Rial		VEB	Venezuelan Bolivar
PAB	Panamanian Balboa		VND	Vietnamese Dong
PEN	Peruvian New Sol		VUV	Vanuatu Vatu
PGK	Papua New Guinea Kina		WST	Somoan Tala
PHP	Philippine Peso		XAF	CFA Franc BEAC
PKR	Pakistan Rupee		XDR	Special Drawing Rights
PLZ	Polish Zloty		XEC	Eastern Caribbean Dollar
PTE	Portuguese Escudo		XOF	CFA Franc BCEAO
PYG	Paraguay Guarani		XPF	French Polynesian Franc
QAR	Qatari Rial		YER	Yemeni Rial
ROL	Romanian Leu		YUN	Yugoslavian New Dinar
RUR	Russian Ruble		ZAR	South African Rand
RWF	Rwanda Franc		ZMK	Zambian Kwacha
SAR	Saudi Arabian Riyal		ZWD	Zimbabwe Dollar
SBD	Solomon Islands Dollar			

Country of Publication Codes

This list of countries and their codes is the International Standards Organization (ISO) set of three-letter country abbreviations. This is the complete list of ISO codes, though not all countries may be represented in **Ulrich's**. The codes are mnemonic in most cases. The country names listed here may have been shortened to a more common usage form. Country names no longer in use remain on the list to represent any titles that may have ceased while that country name was still in use.

Code Sequence

ABW	Aruba	DEU	Germany	KIR	Kiribati
AFG	Afghanistan	DJI	Djibouti	KNA	Saint Kitts & Nevis
AGO	Angola	DMA	Dominica	KOR	Korea, Republic of
AIA	Anguilla	DNK	Denmark	KWT	Kuwait
ALB	Albania	DOM	Dominican Republic	LAO	Laos
AND	Andorra	DZA	Algeria	LBN	Lebanon
ANT	Netherlands Antilles	ECU	Ecuador	LBR	Liberia
ARE	United Arab Emirates	EGY	Egypt	LBY	Libya
ARG	Argentina	ERI	Eritrea	LCA	St. Lucia
ARM	Armenia	ESH	Western Sahara	LIE	Liechtenstein
ASM	American Samoa	ESP	Spain	LKA	Sri Lanka
ATA	Antarctica	EST	Estonia	LSO	Lesotho
ATF	French Southern Territories	ETH	Ethiopia	LTU	Lithuania
ATG	Antigua & Barbuda	FIN	Finland	LUX	Luxembourg
AUS	Australia	FJI	Fiji	LVA	Latvia
AUT	Austria	FLK	Falkland Islands	MAC	Macau
AZE	Azerbaijan	FRA	France	MAR	Morocco
BDI	Burundi	FRO	Faeroe Islands	MCO	Monaco
BEL	Belgium	FSM	Fed. States of Micronesia	MDA	Moldova
BEN	Benin	GAB	Gabon	MDG	Madagascar
BFA	Burkina Faso	GBR	United Kingdom	MDV	Maldive Islands
BGD	Bangladesh	GEO	Georgia	MEX	Mexico
BGR	Bulgaria	GHA	Ghana	MHL	Marshall Islands
BHR	Bahrain	GIB	Gibraltar	MKD	Macedonia
BHS	Bahamas	GIN	Guinea	MLI	Mali
BIH	Bosnia & Herzegovina	GLP	Guadeloupe	MLT	Malta
BLR	Belarus	GMB	Gambia	MMR	Myanmar
BLZ	Belize	GNB	Guinea-Bissau	MNG	Mongolia
BMU	Bermuda	GNQ	Equatorial Guinea	MNP	Northern Mariana Islands
BOL	Bolivia	GRC	Greece	MOZ	Mozambique
BRA	Brazil	GRD	Grenada	MRT	Mauritania
BRB	Barbados	GRL	Greenland	MSR	Monteserrat
BRD	West Germany	GTM	Guatemala	MTQ	Martinique
BRN	Brunei Darussalam	GUF	French Guiana	MUS	Mauritius
BTN	Bhutan	GUM	Guam	MWI	Malawi
BVT	Bouvet Island	GUY	Guyana	MYS	Malaysia
BWA	Botswana	HKG	Hong Kong	MYT	Mayotte
CAF	Central African Republic	HMD	Heard Island & McDonald Islands	NAM	Namibia
CAN	Canada			NCL	New Caledonia
CCK	Cocos (Keeling) Islands	HND	Honduras	NER	Niger
CHE	Switzerland	HRV	Croatia	NFK	Norfolk Island
CHL	Chile	HTI	Haiti	NGA	Nigeria
CHN	China	HUN	Hungary	NIC	Nicaragua
CIV	Cote D'Ivoire	IDN	Indonesia	NIU	Niue
CMR	Cameroon	IND	India	NLD	Netherlands
COD	Congo, Democratic Republic of	IOT	British Indian Ocean Territory	NOR	Norway
COG	Congo	IRL	Ireland	NPL	Nepal
COK	Cook Islands	IRN	Iran	NRU	Nauru
COL	Colombia	IRQ	Iraq	NZL	New Zealand
COM	Comoros	ISL	Iceland	OMN	Oman
CPV	Cape Verde	ISR	Israel	PAK	Pakistan
CRI	Costa Rica	ITA	Italy	PAN	Panama
CSK	Czechoslovakia	JAM	Jamaica	PCN	Pitcairn
CUB	Cuba	JOR	Jordan	PER	Peru
CXR	Christmas Island	JPN	Japan	PHL	Philippines
CYN	Cayman Islands	KAZ	Kazakstan	PLW	Palau
CYP	Cyprus	KEN	Kenya	PNG	Papua New Guinea
CZE	Czech Republic	KGZ	Kyrgyzstan	POL	Poland
DDR	East Germany	KHM	Cambodia	PRI	Puerto Rico

PRK	Korea, Democratic People's Rep. of	SOM	Somalia	TWN	Taiwan
PRT	Portugal	SPM	Saint Pierre & Miquelon	TZA	Tanzania
PRY	Paraguay	STP	Sao Tome e Principe	UGA	Uganda
PSE	Occupied Palestinian Territory	SUN	U.S.S.R.	UKR	Ukraine
PYF	French Polynesia	SUR	Suriname	UMI	US Minor Islands
QAT	Qatar	SVK	Slovakia	URY	Uruguay
REU	Reunion	SVN	Slovenia	USA	United States
ROM	Romania	SWE	Sweden	UZB	Uzbekistan
RUS	Russia	SWZ	Swaziland	VAT	Vatican City
RWA	Rwanda	SYC	Seychelles	VCT	St. Vincent & Grenadines
SAU	Saudi Arabia	SYR	Syrian Arab Republic	VEN	Venezuela
SCG	Serbia & Montenegro	TCA	Turks & Caicos Islands	VGB	Virgin Islands, British
SDN	Sudan	TCD	Chad	VIR	Virgin Islands, U.S.
SEN	Senegal	TGO	Togo	VNM	Viet Nam
SGP	Singapore	THA	Thailand	VUT	Vanuatu
SGS	South Georgia & Sandwich Islands	TJK	Tajikistan	WLF	Wallis & Futuna
		TKL	Tokelau	WSM	Samoa
SHN	Saint Helena	TKM	Turkmenistan	YEM	Yemen
SJM	Svalbard & Jan Mayen	TNP	East Timor	YUG	Yugoslavia
SLB	Solomon Islands	TON	Tonga	ZAF	South Africa
SLE	Sierra Leone	TTO	Trinidad & Tobago	ZAR	Zaire
SLV	El Salvador	TUN	Tunisia	ZMB	Zambia
SMR	San Marino	TUR	Turkey	ZWE	Zimbabwe
		TUV	Tuvalu		

Country Sequence

AFGHANISTAN	AFG	ECUADOR	ECU	MACAO	MAC
ALBANIA	ALB	EGYPT	EGY	MACEDONIA	MKD
ALGERIA	DZA	EL SALVADOR	SLV	MADAGASCAR	MDG
AMERICAN SAMOA	ASM	EQUATORIAL GUINEA	GNQ	MALAWI	MWI
ANDORRA	AND	ERITREA	ERI	MALAYSIA	MYS
ANGOLA	AGO	ESTONIA	EST	MALDIVE ISLANDS	MDV
ANGUILLA	AIA	ETHIOPIA	ETH	MALI	MLI
ANTARCTICA	ATA	FAEROE ISLANDS	FRO	MALTA	MLT
ANTIGUA & BARBUDA	ATG	FALKLAND ISLANDS	FLK	MARSHALL ISLANDS	MHL
ARGENTINA	ARG	FED. STATES OF MICRONESIA	FSM	MARTINIQUE	MTQ
ARMENIA	ARM	FIJI	FJI	MAURITANIA	MRT
ARUBA	ABW	FINLAND	FIN	MAURITIUS	MUS
AUSTRALIA	AUS	FRANCE	FRA	MAYOTTE	MYT
AUSTRIA	AUT	FRENCH GUIANA	GUF	MEXICO	MEX
AZERBAIJAN	AZE	FRENCH POLYNESIA	PYF	MOLDOVA	MDA
BAHAMAS	BHS	FRENCH SOUTHERN TERRITORIES	ATF	MONACO	MCO
BAHRAIN	BHR	GABON	GAB	MONGOLIA	MNG
BANGLADESH	BGD	GAMBIA	GMB	MONTSERRAT	MSR
BARBADOS	BRB	GEORGIA	GEO	MOROCCO	MAR
BELARUS	BLR	GERMANY	DEU	MOZAMBIQUE	MOZ
BELGIUM	BEL	GHANA	GHA	MYANMAR	MMR
BELIZE	BLZ	GIBRALTAR	GIB	NAMIBIA	NAM
BENIN	BEN	GREECE	GRC	NAURU	NRU
BERMUDA	BMU	GREENLAND	GRL	NEPAL	NPL
BHUTAN	BTN	GRENADA	GRD	NETHERLANDS	NLD
BOLIVIA	BOL	GUADELOUPE	GLP	NETHERLANDS ANTILLES	ANT
BOSNIA & HERZEGOVINA	BIH	GUAM	GUM	NEW CALEDONIA	NCL
BOTSWANA	BWA	GUATEMALA	GTM	NEW ZEALAND	NZL
BOUVET ISLAND	BVT	GUINEA	GIN	NICARAGUA	NIC
BRAZIL	BRA	GUINEA-BISSAU	GNB	NIGER	NER
BRITISH INDIAN OCEAN TERRITORY	IOT	GUYANA	GUY	NIGERIA	NGA
BRUNEI DARUSSALAM	BRN	HAITI	HTI	NIUE	NIU
BULGARIA	BGR	HEARD ISLAND & MCDONALD ISLANDS	HMD	NORFOLK ISLAND	NFK
BURKINA FASO	BFA			NORTHERN MARIANA ISLANDS	MNP
BURUNDI	BDI	HONDURAS	HND	NORWAY	NOR
CAMBODIA	KHM	HONG KONG	HKG	OCCUPIED PALESTINIAN TERRITORY	PSE
CAMEROON	CMR	HUNGARY	HUN		
CANADA	CAN	ICELAND	ISL	OMAN	OMN
CAPE VERDE	CPV	INDIA	IND	PAKISTAN	PAK
CAYMAN ISLANDS	CYM	INDONESIA	IDN	PALAU	PLW
CENTRAL AFRICAN REPUBLIC	CAF	IRAN	IRN	PANAMA	PAN
CHAD	TCD	IRAQ	IRQ	PAPUA NEW GUINEA	PNG
CHILE	CHL	IRELAND	IRL	PARAGUAY	PRY
CHINA	CHN	ISRAEL	ISR	PERU	PER
CHRISTMAS ISLAND	CXR	ITALY	ITA	PHILIPPINES	PHL
COCOS (KEELING) ISLANDS	CCK	JAMAICA	JAM	PITCAIRN	PCN
COLOMBIA	COL	JAPAN	JPN	POLAND	POL
COMOROS	COM	JORDAN	JOR	PORTUGAL	PRT
CONGO	COG	KAZAKHSTAN	KAZ	PUERTO RICO	PRI
CONGO, DEMOCRATIC REPUBLIC OF	COD	KENYA	KEN	QATAR	QAT
		KIRIBATI	KIR	REUNION	REU
COOK ISLANDS	COK	KOREA, DEMOCRATIC PEOPLE'S REP. OF	PRK	ROMANIA	ROM
COSTA RICA	CRI			RUSSIA	RUS
COTE D'IVOIRE	CIV	KOREA, REPUBLIC OF	KOR	RWANDA	RWA
CROATIA	HRV	KUWAIT	KWT	SAINT HELENA	SHN
CUBA	CUB	KYRGYZSTAN	KGZ	SAINT KITTS-NEVIS	KNAI
CYPRUS	CYP	LAOS	LAO	SAINT PIERRE & MIQUELON	SPM
CZECH REPUBLIC	CZE	LATVIA	LVA	SAMOA	WSM
CZECHOSLOVAKIA	CSK	LEBANON	LBN	SAN MARINO	SMR
DENMARK	DNK	LESOTHO	LSO	SAO TOME E PRINCIPE	STP
DJIBOUTI	DJI	LIBERIA	LBR	SAUDI ARABIA	SAU
DOMINICA	DMA	LIBYA	LBY	SENEGAL	SEN
DOMINICAN REPUBLIC	DOM	LIECHTENSTEIN	LIE	SERBIA & MONTENEGRO	SCG
EAST GERMANY	DDR	LITHUANIA	LTU	SEYCHELLES	SYC
EAST TIMOR	TMP	LUXEMBOURG	LUX	SIERRA LEONE	SLE

COUNTRY OF PUBLICATION CODES

SINGAPORE	SGP	TAIWAN	TWN	URUGUAY	URY
SLOVAKIA	SVK	TAJIKISTAN	TJK	US MINOR ISLANDS	UMI
SLOVENIA	SVN	TANZANIA	TZA	UZBEKISTAN	UZB
SOLOMON ISLANDS	SLB	THAILAND	THA	VANUATU	VUT
SOMALIA	SOM	TOGO	TGO	VATICAN CITY	VAT
SOUTH AFRICA	ZAF	TOKELAU	TKL	VENEZUELA	VEN
SOUTH GEORGIA & SANDWICH		TONGA	TON	VIET NAM	VNM
ISLAND	SGS	TRINIDAD & TOBAGO	TTO	VIRGIN ISLANDS, BRITISH	VGB
SPAIN	ESP	TUNISIA	TUN	VIRGIN ISLANDS, U.S.	VIR
SRI LANKA	LKA	TURKEY	TUR	WALLIS & FUTUNA	WLF
ST. LUCIA	LCA	TURKMENISTAN	TKM	WEST GERMANY	BRD
ST. VINCENT & GRENADINES	VCT	TURKS & CAICOS ISLANDS	TCA	WESTERN SAHARA	ESH
SUDAN	SDN	TUVALU	TUV	YEMEN	YEM
SURINAM	SUR	U.S.S.R.	SUN	YUGOSLAVIA	YUG
SVALBARD & JAN MAYEN	SJM	UGANDA	UGA	ZAIRE	ZAR
SWAZILAND	SWZ	UKRAINE	UKR	ZAMBIA	ZMB
SWEDEN	SWE	UNITED ARAB EMIRATES	ARE	ZIMBABWE	ZWE
SWITZERLAND	CHE	UNITED KINGDOM	GBR		
SYRIAN ARAB REPUBLIC	SYR	UNITED STATES	USA		

Document Suppliers

AskIEEE

AskIEEE
10850 Wilshire Blvd, 8th Fl, Los Angeles, CA
90024
TEL 310-445-3891, 800-949-4333
FAX 310-445-3003
E-mail askieee@ieee.org
URL http://ieee.org/services/askieee/

BLDSC

British Library Document Supply Centre
Boston Spa, Wetherby LS23 7BQ, United
Kingdom
TEL 44-1937-546060
FAX 44-1937-546333
TELEX 557381
E-mail dsc-customerservice@bl.uk
URL http://www.bl.uk/services/document/
dsc.html

CASDDS

**Chemical Abstracts Service Document
Detective Service**
2540 Olentangy River Rd, PO Box 3012,
Columbus, OH 43210-0012
TEL 614-447-3670, 800-678-4337
FAX 614-447-3648,
TELEX 684086 via WUI
E-mail dds@cas.org
URL http://www.cas.org/Support/dds.html

CINDOC

**CINDOC Suministro de Documentos
Service**
Joaquin Costa, 22, Madrid 28002, Spain
TEL 34-91-5635482
FAX 34-91-5642644
URL http://www.cindoc.csic.es
E-mail bib-icytfot@cindoc.csic.es

CIS

LexisNexis Academic & Library Solutions
(Subsidiary of: LexisNexis)
4520 East-West Hwy., Ste. 800 Bethesda,
MD 20814
TEL 310-654-1550, 800-638-8380
TELEX 29-2386 CIS UR
E-mail cisinfo@lexis-nexis.com
URL http://www.lexis-nexis.com/academic/
3cis/offprints.asp

CISTI

**CISTI (Canada Institute for Scientific and
Technical Information)**
(Subsidiary of: National Research Council of
Canada)
1200 Montreal Rd., Bldg, M-55, Ottawa, ON
K1A 0S2, Canada
TEL 613-993-9251, 800-668-1222
FAX 613-993-7619
E-mail cisti.producthelp@nrc.ca
URL http://www.nrc.ca/cisti

East View

East View Information Services
3020 Harbor Ln. N., Minneapolis, MN 55447
TEL 763-550-0961, 800-477-1005
FAX 763-559-2931
E-mail eastview@eastview.com
URL http://www.eastview.com/
doc_delivery.asp

Ei

**Elsevier Engineering Information,
Incorporated**
360 Park Ave. S., New York, NY 10010
TEL 800-221-1044
FAX 212-663-3680
E-mail eicustomersupport@elsevier.com
URL http://www.ei.org

GNLM

German National Library of Medicine
Joseph-Stelzman-Str. 9, D-50924, Koeln,
Germany
TEL 49-221-4785600
FAX 49-221-4785697
E-mail zbmed.zbmed@uni-koeln.de
URL http://www.zbmed.de
(Service Suspended for non-German
speaking countries)

Haworth

Haworth Press, Incorporated, The
10 Alice St., Binghamton, NY 13904-1580
TEL 607-722-5857, 800-429-6784
E-mail docdelivery@haworthpress.com
URL http://www.haworthpress.com

IDS

Thomson I S I
(Institute for Scientific Information)
(Subsidiary of: Thomson Corporation)
3501 Market St., Philadelphia, PA 19014
TEL 310-445-3000, 800-603-4367
FAX 856-787-1679
E-mail service@ieonline.com
URL http://www.isidoc.com

IE

Information Express
3221 Porter Dr., Palo Alto, CA 94304
TEL 650-812-3588
FAX 650-812-3573
E-mail service@ieonline.com
URL http://www.ieonline.com

Infotrieve

Infotrieve
10850 Wilshire Blvd 8th Fl, Los Angeles, CA 90024
TEL 310-208-1903, 800-422-4633
FAX 310-208-5971
E-mail info@infotrieve.com,
URL http://www4.infotrieve.com/docdelivery.asp

ingenta

Ingenta.com
(Subsidiary of: Igenta Inc.)
44 Brattle St., 4th Fl., Cambridge, MA 02138
TEL 617-395-4000, 800-296-2221
FAX 617-395-4099
E-mail info@ingenta.com
URL http://www.ingenta.com/

KNAW

NIWI (Netherlands Institute of Scientific Information Services)
Customer Service, 95180, Amsterdam
1090 HD, Netherlands
TEL 31-20-4628628
FAX 31-20-6639257
E-mail info@niwi.knaw.nl
URL http://www.niwi.knaw.nl

Linda Hall

Linda Hall Library of Science, Engineering & Technology, Document Services Department
5109 Cherry St, Kansas City, MO 64110-2498
TEL 816-363-4600, 800-662-1545
FAX 816-926-8785
E-mail requests@lindahall.org
URL http://www.lindahall.org/docserv/

PADDS

Petroleum Abstracts Document Delivery System
Univeristy of Tulsa - McFarlin Library, 2933 E 6th St, Tulsa, OK 74104-3123
TEL 918-631-2231, 800-247-8678
FAX 918-613-3823
URL http://www.pa.utulsa.edu/index.php?textbox=padds.php

Micropublishers and Distributors

AGU   **American Geophysical Union**
No longer a Micropublisher

AIP   **American Institute of Physics**
No longer a Micropublisher

AJP   **American Jewish Periodical Center**
3101 Clifton Ave., Cincinnati, OH 45220
TEL 513-221-1875
FAX 513-221-0519

ALP   **Alpha Com**
Sportallee 6, Hamburg 22335, Germany
TEL 49-40-51302123
FAX 49-40-51302111
URL http://www.alpha-com.de

AMP   **Adam Matthew Publications Ltd.**
Pelham House, London Rd, Marlborough,
Wiltshire SN8 2AA, United Kingdom
TEL 44-1672-511921
FAX 44-1672-511663
E-mail info@ampltd.co.uk
URL http://www.ampltd.co.uk

BHP   **Brookhaven Press**
(Subsidiary of: N M T Corporation)
    PO Box 2287, La Crosse, WI 54602-2287
E-mail brookhaven@nmt.com
URL http://www.brookhavenpress.com

BIO   **Thomson BIOSIS (BioSciences Information
Service of Biological Abstracts)**
No longer a Micropublisher

BNB   **British Library National Bibliographic Service**
Boston Spa, Weyherby, W. Yorkshire LS23 7BQ,
United Kingdom
TEL 44-1937-546585
FAX 44-1937-546586
E-mail nbs-info@bl.uk
URL http://www.bl.uk/

BNQ   **Bibliotheque Nationale du Quebec**
2275 Rue Holt, Montreal, PQ H2G 3H1, Canada
TEL 514-873-1100, 800-363-9028
FAX 514-873-7510
E-mail info@bnquebec.ca
URL http://www.biblinat.gouv.qc.ca/

CDS   **Current Digest of the Soviet Press**
3857 N. High St., Rm. 207, Columbus, OH 43214
TEL 614-292-4234
FAX 614-267-6310
E-mail subscriptions@currentdigest.org
URL http://slavic.osu.edu/

CIS   **LexisNexis Academic & Library Solutions**
(Subsidiary of: LexisNexis)
7500 Old Georgetown Rd., Ste. 1300, Bethesda,
MD 20814-6198
TEL 301-654-1550, 800-638-8380
FAX 301-654-4033
TELEX 29-2386 CIS UR
E-mail academicinfo@lexisnexis.com
URL http://www.lexisnexis.com/academic/
    CISPubs/

CML   **Commonwealth Imaging**
Ste 618, 555 Richmond St, PO Box 215, W
Toronto, ON M5V 3B1, Canada
TEL 416-703-3755 ext 224
FAX 416-703-6426
E-mail nvehrs@westcanadian.com
URL http://www.commonwealthimaging.com/

EVP   **East View Information Services**
3020 Harbor Ln. N., Minneapolis, MN 55447
TEL 763-550-0961, 800-477-1005
FAX 763-559-2931
E-mail microfilm@eastview.com
URL http://www.eastview.com/russian/periodicals/
    microforms/index.asp

FCM   **Fairchild Books**
7 W. 34th St., New York, NY 10001
TEL 212-630-3880, 800-932-4724
FAX 212-630-3868
URL http://www.fairchildbooks.com

GCS   **Preston Microfilming Services**
2215 Queen St. E., Toronto, ON M4E 1E8
TEL 416-699-7154
FAX 416-699-7155
URL http://webhome.idirect.com/~filming

IDC   **I D C Publishers**
Microform production department, PO Box 11205, Leiden 2301 EE, Netherlands
TEL 31-71-5142700
FAX 31-71-5131721
E-mail info@idc.nl
URL http://www.idc.nl

IFA   **International Federation of Film Archives**
1 rue Defacqz, Bruxels 1000, Belgium
TEL 32-2-5343065
FAX 32-2-5344774
E-mail info@fiafnet.org
URL http://www.fiafnet.org/

ILO   **ILO Publications** (International Labour Organizaton)
4, route des Morilons, CH -1211Geneva 22, Switzerland
TEL 301-638-3152
FAX 41-22-7998578
E-mail pubvente@ilo.org
URL http://www.ilo.org/public/english/support/publ/intro/index.htm

IMI   **Irish Microforms, Ltd.**
Unit 7, Southern Cross, Business Park, Bray, Wicklow, Ireland
TEL 353-1-2867055
FAX 353-1-2867095
E-mail griffiths@imagenow.ie

LCP   **The Library of Congress Photoduplication Service**
101 Independence Ave SE, Washington, DC 20540-5230
TEL 202-707-5640
FAX 202-707-1771
E-mail photoduplication@loc.gov
URL http://www.loc.gov/preserve-pds

LIB   **B M I Imaging Systems**
1115 E Arques Ave, Sunnyvale, CA 94805
TEL 408-736-7444, 800-359-3456
FAX 408-736-4397
E-mail info@bmiimaging.com
URL http://www.bmiimaging.com

MIM   **Elsevier**
The Boulevard, Langford Ln., Kidlington, Oxford OX5 1GB, United Kingdom
TEL 44-1865-843000
URL http://www.elsevier.com

MIS   **Moody's Investors Service**
No longer a Micropublisher

MML   **Micromedia, Limited**
(Subsidiary of: ProQuest Information and Learning)
20 Victoria St., Toronto, ON M5C 2N8, Canada
TEL 416-362-5211, 800-387-2689
FAX 416-362-6161
E-mail info@micromedia.on.ca
URL http://www.micromedia.on.ca

MMP   **McLaren Micropublishing Limited**
PO Box 972, Sta. F, Toronto, ON M4Y 2N9, Canada
TEL 416-960-4801
FAX 416-964-3745
E-mail mmicro@interlog.com
URL http://www.mclarenmicropublishing.com

MUE   **University Music Editions**
Box 192, Ft. George Station, New York, NY 10040
TEL 212-569-5340, 800-448-2805
FAX 212-569-1269
E-mail ume@valueweb.net
URL http://www.universitymusicedition.com

NBI   **Newsbank, Incorporated**
4501 Tamiami Trl N., Ste. 316, Naples, FL 34103-3023
TEL 802-875-2910, 800-762-8182
FAX 802-875-2904
E-mail sales@newsbank.com
URL http://www.newsbank.com

NTI   **National Technical Information Service**
(Division of: U. S. Department of Commerce)
5285 Port Royal Rd., Springfield, VA 22161
TEL 703-605-6000
FAX 703-605-6900
TELEX 89-9405
E-mail info@ntis.gov
URL http://www.ntis.gov

NYL   **American Lawyer Media, Incorporated**
No longer a Micropublisher

PMC   **Princeton Microfilm Corp.**
PO Box 2073, Princeton, NJ 08543
TEL 609-452-2066, 800-257-9502
FAX 609-275-6201
E-mail info@princetonmicro.com
URL http://www.princetonmicro.com

PQC   **ProQuest Information & Learning**
300 N Zeeb Rd., PO Box 1346, Ann Arbor, MI 48106-1346
TEL 734-761-4700, 800-521-0600
FAX 734-997-4040, 800-864-0019
E-mail info@il.proquest.com
URL http://www.il.proquest.com/sim/location

PSL   **The Pretoria State Library**
PO Box 397, Pretoria 0001, South Africa
TEL 27-12-3218931
FAX 27-12-3255984
E-mail statelib@statelib.pwv.gov.za

RPI   **Primary Source Microfilm**
(Subsidiary of: Gale Group)
12 Lunar Dr, Woodbridge, CT 06525
TEL 203-397-2600, 800-444-0799
FAX 203-397-3897
E-mail gale.sales@thomson.com
URL http://www.galegroup.com/psm/

MICROPUBLISHERS AND DISTRIBUTORS

SAL   **South African Library**
Queen Victoria St, PO Box 496, Cape Town,
South Africa
TEL 27-21-246320
FAX 27-21-244848

SOC   **Societe Canadienne du Microfilm Inc./
Canadian Microfilming Company Limited**
464, rue Saint-Jean, Ste 110, Montreal, PQ H2Y
2S1, Canada
TEL 514-288-5404
FAX 514-843-4690
E-mail info@socami.qc.ca
URL http://www.socami.qc.ca

SWZ   **Swets Farrington Document Systems**
Postbus 860, Lisse 2160 SZ, Netherlands
TEL 31-252-435111
FAX 31-252-415888
E-mail infolisse@swets-farrington.nl
URL http://www.swets-farrington.nl/

TMI   **Tennessee Microfilms Inc.**
PO Box 23075, Nashville, TN 37202
TEL 615-895-0535

VCI   **VCH Publishers, Incorporated**
No longer a Micropublisher

WMP   **World Microfilm Publications Ltd.**
Microworld House, 4 Foscote Mews, London W9
2HH, United Kingdom
TEL 44-20-75864499
FAX 44-20-77221068
E-mail microworld@ndirect.co.uk
URL http://www.microworld.ndirect.co.uk

WSH   **William S. Hein & Company, Incorporated**
1285 Main St, Buffalo, NY 14209-1987
TEL 716-882-2600, 800-828-7571
FAX 716-883-8100
E-mail mail@wshein.com
URL http://www.wshein.com

WWS   **Lippincott Williams & Wilkins**
No longer a Micropublisher

Reprint Services

CIS   **LexisNexis Academic & Library Solutions**
(Subsidiary of: LexisNexis)
4520 East-West Hwy., Ste. 800, Bethesda, MD 20814
TEL 301-654-1550, 800-638-8380
FAX 301-654-4033
TELEX 29-2386 CIS UR
E-mail cisinfo@lexis-nexis.com
URL http://www.lexisnexis.com/academic/solutions/

HAW   **Haworth Press, Incorporated, The**
10 Alice St., Binghamton, NY 13904-1580
TEL 607-722-5857, 800-429-6784,
FAX 607-722-6362, 607-771-0012, 800-895-0582
TELEX 49 325 99 HAWORTH
E-mail orders@haworthpress.com
URL http://www.haworthpress.com

IRC   **International Reprint Corporation**
287 East H St, Benicia, CA 94510
TEL 707-746-8740
FAX 707-746-1643
E-mail irc@intlreprints.com
URL http://www.intlreprints.com

ISI   **Thomson I S I (Institute for Scientific Information)**
3501 Market St., Philadelphia, PA 19104
TEL 215-386-0100, 800-336-4474
FAX 215-386-2911
E-mail sales@isinet.com
URL http://www.isinet.com

NTI   **National Technical Information Service**
(Division of: U. S. Department of Commerce)
5285 Port Royal Rd., Springfield, VA 22161
TEL 703-605-6000
FAX 703-605-6900
TELEX 89-9405
E-mail info@ntis.gov
URL http://www.ntis.gov

PQC   **ProQuest Information & Learning**
300 N Zeeb Rd., PO Box 1346, Ann Arbor, MI 48106-1346
TEL 734-761-4700, 800-521-0600
FAX 734-997-4040, 800-864-0019
E-mail info@il.proquest.com
URL http://www.umi.com

PSC   **Periodicals Service Company**
11 Main St., Germantown, NY 12526
TEL 518-537-4700
FAX 518-537-5899
E-mail psc@periodicals.com
URL http://www.periodicals.com

SCH   **Schmidt Periodicals GmbH**
Ortsteil Dettendorf, Bad Feilnbach D 83075, Germany
TEL 49-8064221
FAX 49-8064557
E-mail schmidt@periodicals.com
URL http://www.periodicals.com

WSH   **William S. Hein & Company, Incorporated**
1285 Main St, Buffalo, NY 14209-1987
TEL 800-828-7571
FAX 716-883-8100
E-mail mail@wshein.com,
URL http://www.wshein.com

Wire Services

AAP **Australian Associated Press**
9 Lang St, Sydney, NSW 2000, Australia
TEL 61-2-9322-8000
E-mail info@aap.com.au
URL http://aap.com.au

AFP **Agence France-Presse**
Service Communication, 11-15, place de la
Bourse, Paris 75002, France
TEL 33-1-40414646,
FAX 33-1-40414632
E-mail communication@afp.com
URL http://www.afp.com

ANP **Algemeen Nederlands Persbureau
      /Netherlands Press Agency**
Handelskade 49, Rijswijk, 1, Den Haag 2501 AA,
Netherlands
TEL 70-414-1414
E-mail marketing@anp.nl
URL http://www.anp.nl

AP **Associated Press**
450 W. 33rd St., Flr. 7, New York, NY
10001-2606
E-mail info@ap.org
URL http://www.ap.org

APP **Associated Press of Pakistan**
Mashkoor Mahal, I.I. Chundrigar Rd, Karachi,
Pakistan
TEL 92-954-2635695
FAX 92-954-2628118

BNS **Baltic News Service**
Parnu mnt 105, Tallinn 15043, Estonia
TEL 372-6-108-800
FAX 372-610-8811
E-mail bns@bns.ee
URL http://bnsnews.bns.ee

CNS **Copley News Service**
PO Box 120190, San Diego, CA 92112
TEL 619-293-1818
URL http://www.copleynews.com

CaNS **Catholic News Service**
3211 4th St, N E, Washington, DC 20017
TEL 202-541-3250
FAX 202-541-3255
E-mail cns@nccbuscc.org
URL http://www.catholicnews.com

CanP **Canadian Press, The**
36 King St., E., Toronto, ON M5C 2L9, Canada
TEL 416-364-0321, 800-434-7578
FAX 416-364-0207

CiNS **City News Service**
1900 Ave of the Stars Ste 1870, Los Angeles,
CA 90067-4301
TEL 310-201-9120
URL http://www.socalnews.com

DJNS **Dow Jones Newswires**
(Subsidiary of: Dow Jones Company)
1155 Av of the Americas, 3d Fl, New York, NY
10036; 800 Plaza Two, Jersey City, NJ 07311
TEL 201-938-5400, 800-223-2274
FAX 201-938-5600
E-mail newswires@dowjones.com
URL http://www.djnewswires.com

EFE **Agencia EFE**
C/Espronceda, 32, Madrid 28003, Spain
TEL 346-74-00
FAX 346-71-13
E-mail efe@efe.es
URL http://www.efe.es

GNS **Gannett News Service**
7950 Jones Branch Dr, McLean, VA 22107
TEL 703-854-5800
FAX 703-854-2152
URL http://www.gannett.com

JTA **Jewish Telegraphic Agency**
330 Seventh Ave, 11th Fl, New York, NY 10001
TEL 212-643-1890
FAX 212-643-8498
E-mail info@jta.org, Bizmqr@jta.org
URL http://www.jta.org

KR **Knight Ridder Wire Services**
50 W San Fernando St, San Jose, CA 95113
TEL 408-938-7700
URL http://www.kri.com/

LAT-WAT **Los Angeles Times-Washington Post News
      Service**
1150 15th St., N.W., Washington, DC 20071
TEL 202-334-6173
FAX 202-334-5096
E-mail latwp@newsservice.com
URL http://www.newsservice.com

NNS **Newhouse News Service**
1101 Connecticut Ave. NW., Ste. 300,
Washington, DC 20036

NYT **New York Times News Service**
229 W. 43rd St., Rm. 943, New York, NY 10036
TEL 212-556-1927
FAX 212-556-3535

PR **PR Newswire Association LLC**
810 Seventh Ave, 35th Fl, New York, NY 10019
TEL 212-596-1500, 800-832-5522

RN **Reuters Group, PLC**
85 Fleet St., London EC4P 4AJ, United Kingdom
TEL 44-170-250-1122
FAX 44-170-542-8006
TELEX 44-71-250-1122
URL http://www.reuters.com

SAPA **South African Press Association**
Cotswold House, Greenacres Office Park, Cnr.
Victory & Rustenburg Rds, Victory Park, PO Box
7766, Johannesburg 2000, South Africa
TEL 27-11-782-1600
FAX 27-11-782-1587
E-mail comms@sapa.org.za
URL http://www.sapa.org.za/

SHNA **Scripps-Howard Newspaper Alliance -**
Scripps-Howard News Service
1090 Vermont Ave., N.W., Suite 1000,
Washington, DC 20005
TEL 202-408-1484
E-mail copelandp@shns.com
URL http://www.shns.com

SMWS **Scripps-McClatchey Western Service**
1090 Vermont Ave NW Ste 1000, Washington,
DC 20005
TEL 202-408-1484
FAX 202-408-5950

UPI **United Press International**
1510 H St. N.W., Washington, DC 20005
TEL 202-898-8046
FAX 202-898-8138
E-mail jugo@upi.com
URL http://www.upi.com

Abstracting and Indexing Services

This list contains the full names of all abstracting and indexing services whose abbreviations are used in entries in the CLASSIFIED LIST OF SERIALS. For all currently published abstracting and indexing services, please consult the TITLE INDEX for page references to full entries in the CLASSIFIED LIST OF SERIALS. (Bibliographic information on titles for which cessations were noted more than three years ago are not listed in this book. To view information on such titles, one must refer to Ulrich's™ on Disc, Ulrich's Online, or ulrichsweb.com™

A

A&AAb †Astronomy and Astrophysics Abstracts (Supersedes: Astronomischer Jahresbericht)

A&ATA Art and Archaeology Technical Abstracts (Online Edition) (Former titles (until 2002): Art and Archaeology Technical Abstracts (Print Edition); (until 1966): I I C Abstracts)

AAR Accounting Articles (Formerly: C C H Accounting Articles)

ABC †BioCommerce Abstracts (Formerly (until 1997): Abstracts in Biocommerce)

ABCPolSci C S A Political Science & Government (Cambridge Scientific Abstracts) (Formerly (until vol. 32, no. 6, 2000): A B C Pol Sci)

ABCT ARTbibliographies Current Titles (Email Edition) (Formerly (until 2003): ARTbibliographies Current Titles (Print Edition))

ABIPC Abstract Bulletin of Paper Science and Technology (Former titles (until 1998): Institute of Paper Science and Technology. Abstract Bulletin; (until July 1989): Institute of Paper Chemistry. Abstract Bulletin; (until 1958): Institute of Paper Chemistry. Bulletin)

ABIX †A B I X: Australasian Business Intelligence (Former titles: A B I X; (until 1995): Australian Business Index)

ABIn A B I - INFORM (American Business Information)

ABM ARTbibliographies Modern (Supersedes (in 1971): L O M A Literature on Modern Art)

ABRCLP †Abstracts of Book Reviews in Current Legal Periodicals

ABS&EES American Bibliography of Slavic and East European Studies (Formerly (until 1966): American Bibliography of Russian and East European Studies)

ABSML †Abstracts of Bulgarian Scientific Medical Literature (Online Edition) (Former titles (until 1996): Abstracts of Bulgarian Scientific Medical Literature (Print Edition); (until 1968): Abstracts of Bulgarian Scientific Literature. Medicine; (until 1966): Abstracts of Bulgarian Scientific Literature. Medicine and Physical Culture; (until 1963): Abstracts of Bulgarian Scientific Literature. Biology and Medicine)

ABTICS †Abstracts and Book Title Index Card Service (ABTICS)

AC&P †Criminology, Penology & Police Science Abstracts (Formed by the merger of: Police Science Abstracts; Which was formerly: Abstracts on Police Science; Criminology and Penology Abstracts; Abstracts on Criminology and Penology; Excerpta Criminologica)

AD&D †Alcohol, Drugs and Driving (Formerly: Alcohol, Drugs and Driving: Abstracts and Reviews)

ADPA Accounting & Finance Abstracts (Former titles (until 2001): Anbar Accounting & Finance Abstracts; (until 1991): Accounting & Data Processing Abstracts; Which superseded in part: Anbar Management Services Abstracts)

AEA Agricultural Engineering Abstracts

AEBA C S A Agricultural & Environmental Biotechnology Abstracts

AEI Australian Education Index (Online Edition)

AES †Abstracts of English Studies

AESIS †A M F Alert (Australian Mineral Foundation) (Formed by the merger of (1976-1998): A E S I S Quarterly; (1995-1998): A M F Reviews; Which was formerly (1973-1995): Earth Science and Related Information)

AFA American Fisheries Abstracts

AFS †Abstracts of Folklore Studies

AGBP †Guide to Botanical Periodicals (Formerly: Asher's Guide to Botanical Periodicals)

AHCI †Abstracts in Human - Computer Interaction (Formerly: H C I Abstracts)

AHCMS	†Abstracts of Health Care Management Studies (Formerly: Abstracts of Hospital Management Studies)
AIA	†Artificial Intelligence Abstracts (US)
AIAP	Avery Index to Architectural Periodicals
AICP	Anthropological Index Online
AIDS Ab	AIDS Abstracts (Formerly (until 1993): AIDS Information)
AIDS&CR	†AIDS & Cancer Research
AIIM	†Abstracts in Medicine and Key Word Index (Formerly: Abstracts in Internal Medicine)
AIM	†Abridged Index Medicus consists of: †Cumulated Abridged Index Medicus
AIPP	†Roth's American Poetry Annual (Incorporates (1985-1986): Annual Survey of American Poetry; (1983-1986): American Poetry Index; (1984-1986): Annual Index to Poetry in Periodicals)
AIT	†A I T Reports and Publications on Energy. Abstracts (Asian Institute of Technology) (Formerly: A I T Reports and Publications on Renewable Energy Resources. Abstracts)
AJEE	†Abstract Journal in Earthquake Engineering
ALISA	A L I S A (Online) (Australian Library and Information Science Abstracts) (Formerly (until 1996): A L I S A (Print))
ALMD	Australian Legal Monthly Digest
AMB	Abstracts of Military Bibliography (Former titles (until 1976): Resumenes Analiticos sobre Defensa y Seguridad Nacional; (until 1970): Resumenes Analiticos de Bibliografia Militar)
AMED	A M E D (Allied and Complementary Medicine Database)
AMHA	†Adolescent Mental Health Abstracts
AMR	†European Muslims and Christian-Muslim Relations. Abstracts
ANAG	†Abstracts of North American Geology
APC	†Abstracts of Popular Culture
APD	†Acid Precipitation Digest
APEL	Asian - Pacific Economic Literature
API	Architectural Publications Index (Formerly (until 1995): Architectural Periodicals Index; Supersedes: R I B A Library Bulletin)
APIAb	Ei EnCompassLit (Formerly: A P I Lit)
APICat	Technical Literature Abstracts: Catalysts - Zeolites (Online Edition)
APIH&E	Technical Literature Abstracts: Health & Environment (Online Edition)
APIOC	Technical Literature Abstracts: Oilfield Chemicals (Online Edition)
APIPR	Technical Literature Abstracts: Petroleum Refining & Petrochemicals (Online Edition)
APIPS	Technical Literature Abstracts: Petroleum Substitutes (Online Edition)
APITS	Technical Literature Abstracts: Transportation & Storage (Online Edition)
ARDT	†Abstracts on Rural Development in the Tropics
ARG	Abridged Readers' Guide to Periodical Literature
ARI	†Australian Road Index
AS&TI	Applied Science & Technology Index (Supersedes in part: Industrial Arts Index)
ASA	†Australian Speleo Abstracts
ASCA	Personal Alert (Former titles: Research Alert (Philadelphia) (Print Edition); (until 1989): Automatic Subject Citation Alert; A S C A Topics)
ASD	†African Studies Abstracts (Former titles (until 1994): Documentatieblad: The Abstracts Journal of the African Studies Centre Leiden; (until 1980): Afrika Studiecentrum. Documentatieblad)
ASEANManA	A S E A N Management Abstracts (Association of Southeast Asian Nations) (Formerly (until 1982): Management Abstracts of Singapore)
ASFA	Aquatic Sciences & Fisheries Abstracts consists of: A S F A Aquaculture Abstracts (Online Edition) A S F A Marine Biotechnology Abstracts (Online Edition) Aquatic Sciences & Fisheries Abstracts. Part 1: Biological Sciences and Living Resources Aquatic Sciences & Fisheries Abstracts. Part 2: Ocean Technology, Policy and Non-living Resources Aquatic Sciences & Fisheries Abstracts. Part 3: Aquatic Pollution and Environmental Quality
ASG	Abstracts in Social Gerontology (Formerly (until 1990): Current Literature on Aging)
ASI	†Australian Science Index
ASIP	Access: The Supplementary Index to Periodicals (Incorporates (1978-1979): Monthly Periodical Index)
ASLHA	American Speech - Language - Hearing Abstracts
ASSIA	A S S I A (Applied Social Sciences Index & Abstracts) (Supersedes (in 1999): A S S I A: Applied Social Sciences Index & Abstracts (Print))

ASTIS	†A S T I S Bibliography (Arctic Science & Technology Information System) (Supersedes (in 1995): A S T I S Bibliography (Microfiche))
ATA	†Agriculture and Environment for Developing Regions (Former titles (until 1996): Abstracts on Tropical Agriculture; (until 1975): Tropical Abstracts)
ATI	Accounting and Tax Index (Formerly (until 1992): Accountants' Index. Supplement)
AUNI	Air University Library Index to Military Periodicals
AbAn	Abstracts in Anthropology
AbHyg	Abstracts on Hygiene and Communicable Diseases (Former titles: Abstracts on Hygiene; Bulletin of Hygiene)
AcaI	†Academic Index
AcoustA	Acoustics Abstracts (Formerly (until 1967): Acoustics and Ultrasonics Abstracts)
AddicA	Addiction Abstracts
AgBio	AgBiotech News and Information
AgeL	AgeLine
Agr	Agricola C R I S
AgrAg	Agro-Agen
AgrForAb	Agroforestry Abstracts (Online Edition)
AgrLib	Agro-Librex
Agrind	†Agrindex
AltPI	Alternative Press Index
AmH&L	America: History and Life (Formed by the merger of: America: History and Life. Part A: Article Abstracts and Citation; America: History and Life. Part B: Index to Book Reviews; America: History and Life. Part C: American History Bibliography; America: History and Life. Part D: Annual Index) *consists of:* America: History and Life. Annual Index
AmHI	American Humanities Index
AmStI	American Statistics Index
AnBeAb	C S A Animal Behavior Abstracts (Cambridge Scientific Abstracts) (Formerly (until 1974): Behavioural Biology Abstracts, Section A: Animal Behaviour)
AnBrAb	Animal Breeding Abstracts
AnalAb	Analytical Abstracts
AnthLit	Anthropological Literature
ApEcolAb	Ecology Abstracts (Bethesda) (Formerly (until 1980): Applied Ecology Abstracts)
ApMecR	Applied Mechanics Reviews
ApicAb	Apicultural Abstracts
ArcBib	†Arctic Bibliography
ArchI	Architectural Index
ArtHuCI	Arts & Humanities Citation Index

ArtIAb	†Artificial Intelligence Abstracts (UK)
ArtInd	Art Index
Artemisa	Artemisa
AusPAIS	A P A I S: Australian Public Affairs Information Service (Online Edition)

B

B&AI	Biological & Agricultural Index (Formerly (until 1964): Agricultural Index)
B&BAb	Biotechnology & Bioengineering Abstracts *consists of:* †A S F A Marine Biotechnology Abstracts (Print Edition) BioEngineering Abstracts (Online Edition) C S A Agricultural & Environmental Biotechnology Abstracts Genetics Abstracts Medical & Pharmaceutical Biotechnology Abstracts (Online Edition) Microbiology Abstracts: Section A. Industrial & Applied Microbiology
B&I	Business and Industry (Beachwood)
BAS	Bibliography of Asian Studies (Online Edition)
BBCI	Biochemistry and Biophysics Citation Index
BBO	Bibliografia Brasileira de Odontologia (Online Edition)
BCI	Biotechnology Citation Index
BCIRA	†B C I R A Abstracts of International Literature on Metal Castings Production (British Cast Iron Research Association) (Former titles: B C I R A Abstracts of International Foundry Literature; (until 1978): B C I R A Abstracts of Foundry Literature)
BDM&CN	†Bibliography of Developmental Medicine and Child Neurology. Books and Articles Received
BEL&L	Annual Bibliography of English Language and Literature (Formerly (until 1924): Bibliography of English Language and Literature)
BHA	Bibliography of the History of Art (Formed by the merger of (1975-1996): International Repertory of the Literature of Art / Repertoire International de la Litterature de l'Art (RILA); (19??-1996): Repertoire d'Art et d'Archeologie (CD-ROM))
BIM	Bibliography and Index of Micropaleontology (Online Edition)

BIOBASE	BIOBASE *consists of:* Current Advances in Applied Microbiology & Biotechnology Current Advances in Cancer Research Current Advances in Cell & Developmental Biology Current Advances in Clinical Chemistry Current Advances in Ecological & Environmental Sciences Current Advances in Endocrinology & Metabolism Current Advances in Genetics & Molecular Biology Current Advances in Immunology & Infectious Diseases Current Advances in Neuroscience Current Advances in Plant Science Current Advances in Protein Biochemistry Current Advances in Toxicology
BIOSIS Prev	BIOSIS Previews
BLI	Banking Information Index (Formerly (until 1994): Banking Literature Index)
BMAb	Annals of Behavioral Medicine (Incorporates (in 1991): Behavioral Medicine Abstracts; Formerly (until 1985): Behavioral Medicine Update)
BMT	B M T Abstracts (British Maritime Technology Ltd.) (Former titles (until 1986): B S R A. Journal of Abstracts; (until 1970): British Ship Research Association. Journal of Abstracts; (until 1968): British Ship Research Association. Journal; (until 1962): British Shipbuilding Research Association. Journal)
BNI	†B N I (British Newspaper Index)
BPI	Business Periodicals Index (Supersedes in part: Industrial Arts Index)
BPIA	†Business Publications Index and Abstracts
BPRC&P	†Biweekly List of Papers on Radiation Chemistry and Photochemistry (Former titles (until 1978): Biweekly List of Papers on Radiation Chemistry; Weekly List of Papers on Radiation Chemistry; Which incorporated: Index and Cumulative List of Papers on Radiation Chemistry)
BRD	Book Review Digest
BRI	Book Review Index
BRM	†Book Reviews of the Month
BSLBiol	†Abstracts of Bulgarian Scientific Literature. Biology (Formerly: Abstracts of Bulgarian Scientific Literature. Biology and Biochemistry)
BSLEcon	†Abstracts of Bulgarian Scientific Literature. Economics and Law
BSLGeo	†Abstracts of Bulgarian Scientific Literature. Geosciences (Formerly: Abstracts of Bulgarian Scientific Literature. Geology and Geography)
BSLIndus	†Abstracts of Bulgarian Scientific Literature. Industry, Building and Transport
BSLMath	†Abstracts of Bulgarian Scientific Literature. Mathematical and Physical Sciences (Formerly: Abstracts of Bulgarian Scientific Literature. Mathematics, Physics, Astronomy, Geophysics, Geodesy)
BehAb	†Behavioural Abstracts
BibAg	†Bibliography of Agriculture *consists of:* †Bibliography of Agriculture. Annual Cumulative Index
BibCart	Bibliographia Cartographica (Formerly (until 1972): Bibliotheca Cartographica)
BibInd	Bibliographic Index
BibLing	Linguistic Bibliography
BibRep	Human Reproduction Update (Formed by the 1995 merger of: Oxford Review of Reproductive Biology; Bibliography of Reproduction)
BioCN&I	Biocontrol News and Information
BioDAb	†Biodeterioration Abstracts
BioEngAb	BioEngineering Abstracts (Online Edition)
BiolAb	Biological Abstracts (Formed by the 1926 merger of: Abstracts of Bacteriology; Botanical Abstracts)
BiolDig	Biology Digest (Incorporates: Environmental Quality Abstracts)
Biostat	Biostatistica
BldManAb	Chartered Institute of Building. Construction Information Quarterly (Incorporates: Building Management Abstracts; Former titles (until 1999): Construction Information File - C I F; (until 1992): Technical Information Service - T I S; Which was formed by the merger of (1971-1982): Chartered Institute of Building. Estimating Information Service; (1971-1982): Chartered Institute of Building. Site Management Information Service; (1977-1982): Chartered Institute of Building. Maintenance Information Service; (1979-1982): Chartered Institute of Building. Surveying Information Service)
BrArAb	British & Irish Archaeological Bibliography (Online Edition)
BrCerAb	World Ceramics Abstracts (Formerly (until 1989): British Ceramic Abstracts)
BrEdI	British Education Index
BrGeoL	†British Geological Literature
BrHumI	British Humanities Index
BrNI	British Nursing Index (Former titles (until 1997): Nursing and Midwifery Index; (until Dec. 1995): Nursing Bibliography)
BrRB	†British Railways Board. Monthly Review of Technical Literature

BrTechI — Abstracts in New Technologies and Engineering (Former titles (until 1997): Current Technology Index; British Technology Index)

BullT&T — †Bulletin of Chemical Thermodynamics (Former titles (until 1976): Bulletin of Thermodynamics and Thermochemistry; (until 1961): Bulletin of Chemical Thermodynamics; Which superseded: Thermochemical Bulletin and Bulletin of Unpublished Thermal Material)

BusDate — Business Dateline

BusEdI — †Business Education Index

BusI — †Business Index

C

C&CSA — Computer & Communications Security Abstracts (Formerly (until 1999): Computer & Communications Security Reviews)

C&ISA — Computer and Information Systems Abstracts Journal (Former titles (until 1978): Computer and Information Systems; (until 1969): Information Processing Journal)

CA&I — †Children's Authors and Illustrators

CADCAM — †C A D - C A M Abstracts (Computer Aided Design - Computer Aided Manufacturing)

CALL — †C A L L (Current Awareness - Library Literature)

CANZLLI — †Current Australian and New Zealand Legal Literature Index

CBA — Conservation Biology Abstracts

CBCABus — Canadian Business and Current Affairs Business (Supersedes in part (in 1998): C B C A Fulltext; Which was formerly (until 1997): Canadian Business and Current Affairs Fulltext (CD-ROM))

CBCARef — Canadian Business and Current Affairs Reference (Supersedes in part (in 1998): C B C A Fulltext; Which was formerly (until 1997): Canadian Business and Current Affairs - Fulltext (CD-ROM))

CBNB — Chemical Business NewsBase

CBPI — †Canadian Index (Formed by the merger of: Canadian Magazine Index; Canadian News Index; Which was formerly: Canadian Newspaper Index; Canadian Business Index; Which was formerly: Canadian Business Periodicals Index)

CBRC — †Current Book Review Citations

CBRI — Children's Book Review Index

CBTA — Current Biotechnology (Incorporates (1985-2000): Biotechnology: Apparatus, Plant, and Equipment; Which was formerly (until 1991): Biotechnologie; Formerly (until 1990): Current Biotechnology Abstracts)

CCA — †Current Contents Africa (Formerly (until 1978): C C A (Current Contents Africa))

CCI — Chemistry Citation Index

CCIOG — Combined Cumulative Index to Obstetrics and Gynecology

CCIP — Combined Cumulative Index to Pediatrics

CCME — Electronic Current Contents of Periodicals on the Middle East (Formerly: Current Contents of Periodicals on the Middle East)

CCMJ — Current Mathematical Publications (Formed by the merger of (1964-1975): American Mathematical Society. New Publications; (1969-1975): Contents of Contemporary Mathematical Journals)

CCR — †Current Thoughts & Trends (Formerly: Current Christian Abstracts)

CDA — †Child Development Abstracts and Bibliography

CDSP — Current Digest of the Post-Soviet Press (Formerly (until 1992): Current Digest of the Soviet Press; Incorporates: Current Abstracts of the Soviet Press)

CEA — Process and Chemical Engineering (Formerly (until 1991): Chemical Engineering Abstracts)

CEABA — Chemical Engineering and Biotechnology Abstracts (Online Edition)
consists of:
Current Biotechnology
Environmental and Safety Technology
Process and Chemical Engineering
Theoretical Chemical Engineering

CEI — Canadian Business and Current Affairs Education (Formerly (until 1998): Canadian Education Index (CD-ROM Edition))

CERDIC — †Universite de Strasbourg. Centre de Recherche et de Documentation des Institutions Chretiennes. Bulletin du CERDIC

CFA — Canadian Fisheries Abstracts

CHNI — †Consumer Health and Nutrition Index

CIJE — Current Index to Journals in Education

CIN — †Chemical Industry Notes

CINAHL — Cumulative Index to Nursing & Allied Health Literature (Incorporates: Nursing and Allied Health Index; Which was formerly (1956-1976): Nursing Literature Index; (until 1977): Cumulative Index to Nursing Literature)

CIRFAb — †T & D Abstracts (Training & Development) (Supersedes: C I R F Abstracts)

CIS	†Current Index to Statistics
CISA	†Safety and Health at Work (Former titles: C I S Abstracts; Occupational Safety and Health Abstracts)
CISI	C I S Index to Publications of the United States Congress (Congressional Information Service, Inc.)
CJA	Criminal Justice Abstracts (Former titles: Abstracts on Crime and Juvenile Delinquency; Crime and Delinquency Literature; Formed by the merger of: Information Review on Crime and Delinquency; Selected Highlights of Crime and Delinquency)
CJPI	Criminal Justice Periodical Index
CLA	Canon Law Abstracts
CLFP	†Current Literature in Family Planning
CLI	Current Law Index
CLL	Leather Science Abstracts (Formerly (until 1988): Current Leather Literature)
CLOSS	Current Literature on Science of Science (Formerly: Index to Literature on Science of Science)
CLT&T	†Current Literature in Traffic and Transportation
CLitI	†Canadian Literature Index
CMCI	Compumath Citation Index
CMHR	Journal of Prevention and Intervention in the Community (Former titles (until 1996): Prevention in Human Services; (until 1981): Community Mental Health Review)
CMPI	Canadian Music Periodical Index
CPA	Crop Physiology Abstracts
CPE	Contents Pages in Education
CPI	Current Physics Index
CPL	The Catholic Periodical and Literature Index (Former titles: Catholic Periodical Index; Guide to Catholic Literature)
CPLI	†Chicago Psychoanalytic Literature Index
CPM	Contents Pages in Management (Formerly (until 1974): Current Contents in Management)
CPerI	C P I. Q (Formerly (until 1963): Canadian Index to Periodicals and Documentary Films)
CRCL	†Canadian Review of Comparative Literature
CREJ	Contents of Recent Economics Journals
CRFR	†Current References in Fish Research
CRIA	N C B Abstracts (Formerly (until 2000): C R I Abstracts)
CRICC	N C B Current Contents (Formerly (until 2000): C R I Current Contents)
CSI	†Directory of Statistics in Canada (Formerly: Canadian Statistics Index)

CSNB	Chemical Safety NewsBase *consists of:* Chemical Hazards in Industry Hazards in the Office Laboratory Hazards Bulletin
CTA	Calcium and Calcified Tissue Abstracts (Online Edition)
CTD	†Current Titles in Dentistry
CTE	Current Titles in Electrochemistry (Incorporates: Electrochemical News)
CTFA	†Cotton and Tropical Fibres (Formerly (until 1991): Cotton and Tropical Fibres Abstracts)
CTO	†Current Titles in Ocean, Coastal, Lake & Waterway Sciences
CWI	Contemporary Women's Issues
CWPI	†Canadian Women's Periodicals Index (Former titles: Canadian Women's Periodicals: Title Word Index; Canadian Women's Periodicals: K W I C Index)
CZA	Canadian Zoology Abstracts
Cadscan	Cadscan (Formerly (until Oct. 1986): Cadmium Abstracts)
CalPI	California Periodicals Index
CerAb	Ceramic Abstracts (Supersedes in part (in 1922): American Ceramic Society. Journal; Which was formerly (until 1917): American Ceramic Society. Transactions)
ChLitAb	†Children's Literature Abstracts
ChPerI	†Chicano Index (Formerly (until 1989): Chicano Periodical Index)
ChemAb	Chemical Abstracts *consists of:* Chemical Abstracts - Applied Chemistry and Chemical Engineering Sections Chemical Abstracts - Biochemistry Sections Chemical Abstracts - Macromolecular Sections Chemical Abstracts - Organic Chemistry Sections Chemical Abstracts - Physical, Inorganic and Analytical Chemistry Sections Chemical Abstracts - Section Groupings Chemical Abstracts Service Source Index
ChemInfo	ChemInform (Formerly (until 1987): Chemischer Informationsdienst; Which was formed by the merger of (1970-1972): Chemischer Informationsdienst. Organische Chemie; (1970-1972): Chemischer Informationsdienst. Anorganische und Physikalische Chemie)
ChemTitl	†Chemical Titles
ChemoAb	Chemoreception Abstracts (Online Edition)

ABSTRACTING AND INDEXING

Chicano	Chicano Database (Consists of: Chicano Index; Arte Chicano; Chicano Anthology Index; Chicana Studies Index; Hispanic Mental Health Research; Spanish Speaking Mental Health Database)	**CybAb**	†Cybernetics Abstracts (Formerly (until 1965): Theoretical Cybernetics Abstracts)

D

ChrPl	Christian Periodical Index	**DAAI**	Design and Applied Arts Index
ChromAb	Chromatography Abstracts (Former titles (until 1986): Gas and Liquid Chromatography Abstracts; (until 1973): Gas Chromatography Abstracts)	**DBA**	Derwent Biotechnology Abstracts
		DIP	Dietrich's Index Philosophicus
		DM&T	†Aerospace Defense Markets & Technology (Formerly: Defense Markets and Technology)
CivEngAb	C S A Civil Engineering Abstracts (Cambridge Scientific Abstracts)	**DNP**	Digest of Neurology & Psychiatry (Online Edition)
ClinAlert	Clin-Alert	**DPD**	†Data Processing Digest
CommAb	Communication Abstracts	**DSA**	Dairy Science Abstracts
CompAb	Computer Abstracts	**DSHAb**	†D S H Abstracts (Deafness, Speech and Hearing)
CompB	†Computer Business		
CompC	†Computer Contents	**DYW**	†Diversity Your World
CompD	Computer Database	**DentAb**	Dental Abstracts
CompI	†Computer Index	**DentInd**	†Index to Dental Literature
CompIU	†Computer Industry Update	**DiabCont**	†Diabetes Contents
CompLI	Computer Science Index (Former titles (until Dec.2002): Computer Literature Index (Print Edition); (until 1980): Quarterly Bibliography of Computers and Data Processing)	**Djerelo**	Djerelo
		DokArb	†Arbeitsmedizin (Former titles: Beruf und Gesundheit - Occupational Health; (until 1985): Dokumentation Arbeitsmedizin - Documentation Occupational Health)
CompR	Computing Reviews		
ConcrAb	†Concrete Abstracts	**DokStr**	Dokumentation Strasse
Consl	Consumers Index		
Copeia	Copeia Abstracts (Formerly: ABSEARCH Ichthyology and Herpetology)		
			E
CoppAb	†International Copper Information Bulletin (Supersedes: Copper Abstracts; Incorporates: Kupfer - Mitteilungen; Cuivre, Laitons, Alliages - Bibliographie; Rame - Schede Bibliografiche; Cobre - Resumenes Bibliograficos)	**E&CAJ**	Electronics and Communications Abstracts Journal (Former titles (until 1993): Electronics and Communications Abstracts; (until 1992): Electronics and Communications Abstracts Journal; (until 1972): Electronics Abstracts Journal)
CorrAb	Corrosion Abstracts (Incorporates: Corrosion Prevetion Technology; Which was formerly (1978-1995): Corrosion Prevention - Inhibition Digest)	**E&PHSE**	E & P Health, Safety and Environment (Exploration and Production)
		e-psyche	†E-psyche
CurCR	Current Chemical Reactions	**EA**	Ecology Abstracts (Moscow) (Formerly: ABSEARCH Ecology & Plant Science)
CurCont	Current Contents *consists of:* Current Contents: Agriculture, Biology & Environmental Sciences Current Contents: Arts & Humanities Current Contents: Clinical Medicine Current Contents: Engineering, Computing & Technology †Current Contents: Health Services Administration Current Contents: Life Sciences Current Contents: Physical, Chemical & Earth Sciences Current Contents: Social & Behavioral Sciences	**EAA**	Educational Administration Abstracts (Formerly: Educational Abstracts)
		ECER	Exceptional Child Education Resources (Online Edition) (Former titles (until 2004): Exceptional Child Education Resources (Print Edition); (until May 1977): Exceptional Child Education Abstracts)
		ECI	†E C Index (European Communities)
		EEA	Earthquake Engineering Abstracts Database
		EFA	†Essential Fisheries Abstracts
		EI	E I (Online Edition) (Excerpta Indonesica) (Formerly (until 2002): E I (Print Edition))
CurPA	†Current Packaging Abstracts (Formerly (until 1973): Packaging Bulletin)	**EIA**	†Energy Information Abstracts

EIP	Ekistic Index of Periodicals
ELJI	†European Legal Journals Index
ELLIS	†E L L I S (European Legal Literature Information Service)
EMA	C S A Engineered Materials Abstracts *consists of:* C S A Advanced Polymers Abstracts C S A Composites Industry Abstracts C S A World Ceramic Abstracts
EPB	Environmental Issues & Policy Index (Former titles (until Dec. 2002): Environmental Policy Index; (until 2002): Environmental Knowledge Base; Environmental Periodicals Bibliography; (until 1973): Environmental Periodicals)
ERA	Educational Research Abstracts Online
ESPM	Environmental Sciences and Pollution Management
ETA	Educational Technology Abstracts
EZ&PSA	†Essential Ecology, Zoology & Plant Science Abstracts
EduInd	Education Index
EmerIntel	Emerald Fulltext (Former titles: Emerald Intelligence & Fulltext; (until 1999): Emerald)
Emerald	Emerald Management Reviews (Online Edition) (Former titles (until 2002): Emerald Reviews (Online Edition); (until 2001): Anbar International Management Database; (until 1999): Anbar Management Intelligence (CD-ROM Edition)) *consists of:* Accounting & Finance Abstracts Human Resource Management Abstracts Information Management and Technology Abstracts Management Books and Resources †Management Development Abstracts Management of Quality Abstracts Marketing & Logistics Abstracts Operations & Production Management Abstracts Top Management Abstracts
EnerInd	†Energy Information Abstracts Annual (Formed by the 1988 merger of: Energy Index; Energy Information Abstracts Annual)
EnerRA	†Energy Research Abstracts (Formerly (until 1977): E R D A Energy Research Abstracts; (until 1976): E R D A Reports Abstracts)
EnerRev	†Energy Review (Santa Barbara)
EngInd	The Engineering Index Monthly (Former titles (until 1984): Engineering Index Monthly and Author Index; (until 1971): Engineering Index Monthly)
EntAb	Entomology Abstracts

EnvAb	Environment Abstracts (Incorporates (1985-1991): Acid Rain Abstracts; Formerly (until 1974): Environment Information Access)
EnvEAb	Environmental Engineering Abstracts (Online Edition)
EnvInd	Environment Abstracts Annual (Incorporates (in 1990): Acid Rain Abstracts Annual; Which was formerly (until 1988): Acid Rain Annual Index; Incorporates (in 1988): Environment Index)
ErgAb	Ergonomics Abstracts Online
ExcerpMed	Excerpta Medica. Abstract Journals *consists of:* Excerpta Medica. Section 1: Anatomy, Anthropology, Embryology & Histology Excerpta Medica. Section 2: Physiology Excerpta Medica. Section 3: Endocrinology Excerpta Medica. Section 4: Microbiology: Bacteriology, Mycology, Parasitology and Virology Excerpta Medica. Section 5: General Pathology and Pathological Anatomy Excerpta Medica. Section 6: Internal Medicine Excerpta Medica. Section 7: Pediatrics and Pediatric Surgery Excerpta Medica. Section 8: Neurology and Neurosurgery Excerpta Medica. Section 9: Surgery Excerpta Medica. Section 10: Obstetrics and Gynecology Excerpta Medica. Section 11: Otorhinolaryngology Excerpta Medica. Section 12: Ophthalmology Excerpta Medica. Section 13: Dermatology and Venereology Excerpta Medica. Section 14: Radiology Excerpta Medica. Section 15: Chest Diseases, Thoracic Surgery and Tuberculosis Excerpta Medica. Section 16: Cancer Excerpta Medica. Section 17: Public Health, Social Medicine and Epidemiology Excerpta Medica. Section 18: Cardiovascular Diseases and Cardiovascular Surgery Excerpta Medica. Section 19: Rehabilitation and Physical Medicine Excerpta Medica. Section 20: Gerontology and Geriatrics Excerpta Medica. Section 21: Developmental Biology and Teratology Excerpta Medica. Section 22: Human Genetics Excerpta Medica. Section 23: Nuclear Medicine Excerpta Medica. Section 24: Anesthesiology

Excerpta Medica. Section 25: Hematology

Excerpta Medica. Section 26: Immunology, Serology and Transplantation
Excerpta Medica. Section 27: Biophysics, Bio-Engineering and Medical Instrumentation
Excerpta Medica. Section 28: Urology and Nephrology
Excerpta Medica. Section 29: Clinical and Experimental Biochemistry
Excerpta Medica. Section 30: Clinical and Experimental Pharmacology
Excerpta Medica. Section 31: Arthritis and Rheumatism
Excerpta Medica. Section 32: Psychiatry
Excerpta Medica. Section 33: Orthopedic Surgery
†Excerpta Medica. Section 34: Plastic Surgery
Excerpta Medica. Section 35: Occupational Health and Industrial Medicine
Excerpta Medica. Section 36: Health Policy, Economics and Management
†Excerpta Medica. Section 37: Drug Literature Index
Excerpta Medica. Section 38: Adverse Reactions Titles
Excerpta Medica. Section 40: Drug Dependence, Alcohol Abuse and Alcoholism
Excerpta Medica. Section 46: Environmental Health and Pollution Control
Excerpta Medica. Section 48: Gastroenterology
Excerpta Medica. Section 49: Forensic Science Abstracts
Excerpta Medica. Section 50: Epilepsy Abstracts
†Excerpta Medica. Section 51: Mycobacterial Diseases: Leprosy, Tuberculosis and Related Subjects
Excerpta Medica. Section 52: Toxicology
†Excerpta Medica. Section 54: AIDS
†Excerpta Medica. Section 130: Clinical Pharmacology

ExtraMED   ExtraMED

F

F&EA   Fuel and Energy Abstracts (Formerly: Fuel Abstracts and Current Titles)
F&GI   †Farm and Garden Index
F&WA   †Essential Forestry & Wildfire Abstracts
FAMLI   †F A M L I (Family Medicine Literature Index)
FCA   Field Crop Abstracts
FLI   Film Literature Index
FLP   Index to Foreign Legal Periodicals

FLUIDEX   FLUIDEX
consists of:
†Current Fluid Engineering Titles
Fluid Abstracts: Civil Engineering
Fluid Abstracts: Process Engineering
†Industrial Jetting Report
†Pumps and Turbines
†River and Flood Control Abstracts
†Tribology & Corrosion Abstracts
†World Ports and Harbours News
FPA   Forest Products Abstracts
FPRD   †H T F S Digest (Incorporates (1979-1992): Fouling Prevention Research Digest; Former titles (until 1986): Heat Transfer and Fluid Flow Digest; (until 1976): H T F S Digest)
FS&TA   Food Science and Technology Abstracts
FaBeAb   †Faba Bean Abstracts
FamI   Family Index
FemPer   Feminist Periodicals
FiP   Fed in Print (Online Edition) (Formerly: Fed in Print (Print Edition))
FoMM   †Focus On: Molecular Medicine
FoP   Focus On: Psychopharmacology
FoSS&M   Focus On: Sports Science and Medicine
FoVS&M   Focus On: Veterinary Science and Medicine
ForAb   Forestry Abstracts
FutSurv   Future Survey (Formerly: Public Policy Book Forecast)

G

GAA   G A T F World (Graphic Arts Technical Foundation) (Formed by the merger of (1971-1989): E C B Newsletter; (1947-1989): Graphic Arts Abstracts; (1970-1989): G A T F Environmental Control Report; (1970-1989): G A T F (Year))
GALA   †Institute of Paper Science and Technology. Graphic Arts Bulletin (Former titles: Graphic Arts Literature Abstracts; Graphic Arts Progress; Which incorporates (1951-1953): Graphic Arts Index; Which supersedes: P I A Management Reports)
GEOBASE   GEOBASE
consists of:
Ecological Abstracts
Geographical Abstracts: Human Geography
Geographical Abstracts: Physical Geography
Geological Abstracts
Geomechanics Abstracts
International Development Abstracts
Oceanographic Literature Review
GIPL   †Guide to Indian Periodical Literature
GJP   European Psychologist (Formerly (until 1995): German Journal of Psychology)

GLA	†Gay & Lesbian Abstracts
GP&P	†Gas Processing and Pipelining
GPAA	†General Physics Advance Abstracts
GPAI	†Genealogical Periodical Annual Index
GSI	General Science Index
GSS&RPL	Guide to Social Science and Religion (Former titles (until 1988): Guide to Social Science and Religion in Periodical Literature; (until 1970): Guide to Religious and Semi-religious Periodicals)
GSW	GeoScienceWorld
GardL	Garden Literature Index (Formerly (until vol.10, 2001): Garden Literature (Print Edition))
GasAb	†Gas Abstracts
Gdlns	Guidelines
GendWatch	Gender Watch (Formerly: Women 'R')
GenetAb	Genetics Abstracts
GeoRef	Bibliography and Index of Geology (Formed by the merger of (1907-1969): Bibliography of North American Geology; (1933-1969): Bibliography and Index of Geology Exclusive of North America)
GeophysAb	†Geophysical Abstracts
GeosDoc	Geoscience Documentation
GeotechAb	Geotechnical Abstracts

H

H&SSA	Health and Safety Science Abstracts (Online Edition)
H&TI	Hospitality & Tourism Index (Incorporates (1998-Sep.2003): Articles in Hospitality and Tourism; Former titles (until Spring 2003): Lodging, Restaurant and Tourism Index; (until 1995): Lodging and Restaurant Index)
HAPI	Hispanic American Periodicals Index
HBB	†Hungarian Building Bulletin
HDA	Health Devices Alerts
HEA	Higher Education Abstracts (Formerly (until 1984): College Student Personnel Abstracts)
HECAB	†Higher Education Current Awareness Bulletin (Formerly (until 1973): Higher Education)
HGA	†Human Genome Abstracts
HL&ISA	Hungarian Library and Information Science Abstracts
HRA	Human Resources Abstracts (Former titles (until 1975): Poverty and Human Resources Abstracts; (until 1971): Poverty and Human Resources; (until 1970): Poverty and Human Resources Abstracts)

HRIR	†Human Rights Internet Reporter (Formerly: Human Rights Internet Newsletter)
HRIS	T R I S Electronic Bibliographic Data Base (Transportation Research Information Services) (Incorporates (in 1996): Highway Research Abstracts; Which was formerly (1968-1990): H R I S Abstracts)
HelmAb	Helminthological Abstracts (Formerly (until 1989): Helminthological Abstracts. Series A: Animal and Human Helminthology; Which superseded in part (in 1970): Helminthological Abstracts)
HerbAb	Grasslands and Forage Abstracts (Formerly: Herbage Abstracts)
HistAb	Historical Abstracts (Formed by the 2003 merger of: Historical Abstracts: Part A: Modern History Abstracts, 1450-1914; Historical Abstracts: Part B: Twentieth Century Abstracts, 1914 to the Present; Which superseded in part (in 1971): Historical Abstracts)
HlthInd	†Health Index
HongKongiana	†HongKongiana
HortAb	Horticultural Science Abstracts (Formerly (until 2004): Horticultural Abstracts)
HospAb	†Health & Social Care Abstracts (Formerly (until 2003): Health Service Abstracts; Incorporates (1961-1985): Hospital Abstracts; (1974-1985): Current Literature on Health Services; Current Literature on General Medical Practice)
HospI	†International Hospitality and Tourism Database CD-ROM (Formerly (until 1995): Hospitality Index)
HospLI	†Hospital and Health Administration Index (Former titles (until 1995): Hospital Literature Index; Hospital Periodical Literature Index)
HumInd	Humanities Index (Supersedes in part (in 1974): Social Sciences and Humanities Index; Which was formerly (until 1965): International Index)

I

I&DA	Irrigation and Drainage Abstracts
I-WA	Ibis - Wildfowl Abstracts
IAA	International Aerospace Abstracts
IAALC	†Indice Agricola de America Latina y el Caribe (Formerly: Bibliografia Agricola Latinoamericana y del Caribe)
IAB	†Humans & Other Species (Former titles (until 1997): InterActions Bibliography; (until vol.3, 1992): Interactions of Man and Animals)
IABS	Current Awareness in Biological Sciences (Formerly (until 1983): International Abstracts of Biological Sciences)

ABSTRACTING AND INDEXING

IAJS	Index of Articles on Jewish Studies (Online Edition) (Formerly (until 2000): Index of Articles on Jewish Studies (Print Edition))		**IGCS**	†International Guide to Classical Studies
			IHD	Industrial Hygiene Digest
IAOP	International Abstracts in Operations Research		**IHP**	Index to Hebrew Periodicals
			IHTDI	Index to How to Do It Information (Online Edition)
IAPV	Index of American Periodical Verse		**IIBP**	International Index to Black Periodicals Full Text
IBR	I B R. Internationale Bibliographie der Rezensionen Geistes- und Sozialwissenschaftlicher Literatur (Former titles (until 1997): I B R. Internationale Bibliographie der Rezensionen Wissenschaftlicher Literatur; (until 1984): Internationale Bibliographie der Rezensionen Wissenschaftlicher Literatur)		**IIFP**	International Index to Film Periodicals
			IIL	†R S N A Index to Imaging Literature (Radiological Society of North America, Inc.)
			IIMP	International Index to Music Periodicals
			IIPA	International Index to the Performing Arts
			IIPL	†Index to Indian Periodical Literature
IBRH	†Index to Book Reviews in the Humanities		**IIS**	Index to International Statistics
IBSS	International Bibliography of the Social Sciences *consists of:* International Bibliography of the Social Sciences. Anthropology International Bibliography of the Social Sciences. Economics International Bibliography of the Social Sciences. Political Science International Bibliography of the Social Sciences. Sociology		**IITV**	†International Index to Television Periodicals
			IJCS	†Index to Journals in Communication Studies
			IJP	Index to Jewish Periodicals
			ILD	†International Labour Documentation
			ILM	†Index to Little Magazines
IBZ	I B Z - Internationale Bibliographie der Geistes- und Sozialwissenschaftlichen Zeitschriftenliteratur (Former titles (until 2000): I B Z - Internationale Bibliographie der Zeitschriftenliteratur aus Allen Gebieten des Wissens; (until 1984): Internationale Bibliographie der Zeitschriftenliteratur aus Allen Gebieten des Wissens)		**ILP**	Index to Legal Periodicals & Books (Formerly (until 1994): Index to Legal Periodicals)
			ILSA	Indian Library Science Abstracts
			IME	Indice Medico Espanol (Online Edition)
			IMFL	Family & Society Studies Worldwide (Former titles: Family Studies Database; Family Resources; Supersedes: Inventory of Marriage and Family Literature; Which was formerly: International Bibliography of Research in Marriage and the Family)
IBibSS	†International Bibliography of the Social Sciences: Anthropology, Political Science, Economics, Sociology			
IBuildSA	International Building Services Abstracts (E-Mail Edition)			
ICEA	International Civil Engineering Abstracts (Former titles (until 1982): I C E Abstracts; (until 1975): European Civil Engineering Abstracts)		**IMI**	†International Management Information Business Digest
			IMMAb	I M M Abstracts and Index (Institution of Mining and Metallurgy) (Formerly (until 1985): I M M Abstracts)
ICLPL	Index to Canadian Legal Periodical Literature		**INI**	†International Nursing Index
ICM	Children's Magazine Guide (Formerly (until 1981): Subject Index to Children's Magazines)		**INIS AtomInd**	I N I S Atomindex (Online Edition) (International Nuclear Information System) (Formerly (until no.24, vol.28, 1997): I N I S Atomindex (Print); Incorporates (1948-1976): Nuclear Science Abstracts (United States Energy Research and Development Administration); Formerly (until 1968): List of References on Nuclear Energy)
ICUIS	†I C U I S Justice Ministries (Institute on the Church in Urban-Industrial Society) (Supersedes (1970-1978): I C U I S Abstract Service)			
IDIS	I D I S (Iowa Drug Information Service)			
IDP	Index to Dance Periodicals		**INZP**	Te Puna CD-ROM (Former titles: Index New Zealand; (until 1986): Index to New Zealand Periodicals)
IECT	Bibliografia Espanola de Revistas Cientificas de Ciencia y Tecnologia (Formerly (until 1998): Indice Espanol de Ciencia y Tecnologia)		**IPA**	International Pharmaceutical Abstracts
IFP	†Index to Free Periodicals		**IPARL**	Index to Periodical Articles Related to Law

J

JPI	Kokuritsu Kokkai toshokan Zasshi Kiji Sakuin CD-ROM Karento-Ban (National Diet Library) (Formerly (until 2002): N D L CD-ROM - Line Zasshi Kiji Sakuin. Karento-Ban; Which was formed by the merger of (1948-1996): Zasshi Kiji Sakuin. Jinbun Shakai-Hen - Japanese Periodicals Index. Humanities and Social Science; (1950-1996): Zasshi Kiji Sakuin. Gijutsu-Hen - Japanese Periodicals Index. Science and Technology)
JTA	†Japan Technology Series (Formerly (until 1988): Japanese Technical Abstracts)
JW	Journal Watch
JW-C	Journal Watch Cardiology
JW-D	Journal Watch Dermatology
JW-EM	Journal Watch Emergency Medicine
JW-G	Journal Watch Gastroenterology
JW-ID	Journal Watch Infectious Diseases
JW-N	Journal Watch Neurology
JW-P	Journal Watch Psychiatry
JW-WH	Journal Watch Women's Health
JewAb	†Jewish Abstracts

K

KES	†Key to Economic Science (Formerly: Economic Abstracts)
KWIST	Keyword Index to Serial Titles
KWIWR	†Key Word Index of Wildlife Research
Kidney	Kidney (New York, 1992)

L

L&LBA	Linguistics and Language Behavior Abstracts (Incorporates (in 1989, vol.12): Reading Abstracts; Formerly (until 1985): Language and Language Behavior Abstracts)
LAMP	L A M P (Literature Analysis of Microcomputer Publications)
LCR	†Literary Criticism Register
LHB	Laboratory Hazards Bulletin
LHTB	†Library Hi Tech Bibliography
LID&ISL	Lancaster Index to Defence & International Security Literature
LIFT	Literary Journals Index Full Text
LII	†Life Insurance Index
LIMI	Legal Information Management Index
LISA	L I S A: Library & Information Science Abstracts (Supersedes (in 1969): Library Science Abstracts)
LJI	†Legal Journals Index
LOIS	Law Office Information Service
LRI	LegalTrac (Online) (Former titles: LegalTrac (Print); Legal Resource Index)

LT&LA	Language Teaching (Former titles (until 1982): Language Teaching and Linguistics Abstracts; (until 1975): Language-Teaching Abstracts; English Teaching Abstracts)
LeadAb	†Leadscan (Formerly: Lead Abstracts)
LeftInd	Left Index (Online Edition)
LegCont	†Legal Contents (Former titles (until 1980): C C L P: Contents of Current Legal Periodicals; (until 1976: Contents of Current Legal Periodicals; Incorporates: Survey of Law Reviews)
LibLit	Library Literature & Information Science (Formerly (until 1999): Library Literature)
LingAb	Linguistics Abstracts
LogistBibl	Online Logistics Bibliography (Formerly: Bibliography of Logistics Management. Supplement (Print))

M

M&GPA	Meteorological and Geoastrophysical Abstracts
M&MA	Management and Marketing Abstracts (Formerly (until 1976): Marketing Abstracts)
M&PBA	Medical & Pharmaceutical Biotechnology Abstracts (Online Edition)
M&TEA	C S A Mechanical & Transportation Engineering Abstracts (Cambridge Scientific Abstracts)
MA	Mammalogy Abstracts
MAB	†Marine Affairs Bibliography
MAG	†Music Article Guide
MASUSE	M A S Ultra - School Edition
MBA	Microbiology Abstracts *consists of:* Microbiology Abstracts: Section A. Industrial & Applied Microbiology Microbiology Abstracts: Section B. Bacteriology Microbiology Abstracts: Section C. Algology, Mycology and Protozoology
MBF	Materials Business File *consists of:* †Nonferrous Metals Alert †Polymers, Ceramics, Composites Alert †Steels Alert
MCIU	†Microcomputer Industry Update
MCR	Medical Care Research and Review (Former titles (until Mar. 1995): Medical Care Review; Public Health Economics and Medical Care Abstracts)
MEA	Multicultural Education Abstracts
MEA&I	Middle East: Abstracts and Index
MEDLINE	MEDLINE
MEDOC	†Medoc: Index to U S Government Publications in the Medical and Health Sciences

MEDSOC	†Medical Socioeconomic Research Sources (Formerly: Index to the Literature of Medical Socioeconomics)
MELSA	†M E L S A Messenger (Metropolitan Library Service Agency)
METADEX	METADEX *consists of:* Alloys Index Metals Abstracts Metals Abstracts Index
MFA	Surface Finishing Abstracts (Online Edition)
MLA	†M L A Abstracts of Articles in Scholarly Journals
MLA-IB	M L A International Bibliography of Books and Articles on the Modern Languages and Literatures (Modern Language Association of America) (Formerly (until 1956): M L A American Bibliography of Books and Articles on the Modern Languages and Literatures)
MMI	†Michigan Magazine Index
MOS	Methods in Organic Synthesis
MPI	†United Methodist Periodical Index (Formerly: Methodist Periodical Index)
MRD	Media Review Digest (Formerly (until 1974): Multi Media Reviews Index)
MRefA	†Developmental Disabilities Abstracts (Former titles: Mental Retardation and Developmental Disabilities Abstracts; Mental Retardation Abstracts)
MResA	Market Research Abstracts (Online Edition) (Formerly (until 2000): Market Research Abstracts (Print))
MS&D	Medical & Surgical Dermatology
MSB	Mass Spectrometry Bulletin
MSCI	Materials Science Citation Index
MSCT	†Marine Science Contents Tables
MSF	Mystery Short Fiction
MagInd	Magazine Index Plus (Formerly: Magazine Index)
MaizeAb	Maize Abstracts Online
ManagAb	Indian Management Abstracts (Incorporates (1972-1989): Management Abstracts)
ManagCont	†Management Contents
MathR	Mathematical Reviews
MathSciNet	MathSciNet *consists of:* Current Mathematical Publications Mathematical Reviews
MedAb	†Medical Abstract Service
MicrocompInd	Internet & Personal Computing Abstracts (Online Edition)
MinerAb	MinAbs Online (Formerly (until 2004): Mineralogical Abstracts (Print Edition))
MusicInd	Music Index
MycolAb	Abstracts of Mycology

N

NAA	N A A (Nordic Archaeological Abstracts)
NAmW	North American Wildlife & Natural Resources Abstracts
NBA	†Notiziario Bibliografico di Audiologia O R L e Foniatria (Formerly: Notiziario Bibliografico di Audiologia)
NPA	Neuropsychology Abstracts (Formerly (until 1996): PsycSCAN: Neuropsychology)
NPI	†New Periodicals Index
NPPA	†Noise Pollution Publications Abstracts
NPU	Natural Product Updates
NRN	Nutrition Research Newsletter (Incorporates (1981-1998): Food Safety Notebook)
NSA	C S A Neurosciences Abstracts (Online Edition) (Cambridge Scientific Abstracts)
NSCI	Neuroscience Citation Index
NTA	New Testament Abstracts
NemAb	Nematological Abstracts (Supersedes: Helminthological Abstracts. Series B: Plant Nematology; Which was Superseded in part (in 1970): Helminthological Abstracts)
NewsAb	Newspaper Abstracts
NucAcAb	Nucleic Acids Abstracts (Online Edition)
NumL	Numismatic Literature
NurAb	†Nursing Abstracts
NutrAb	Nutrition Abstracts and Reviews *consists of:* Nutrition Abstracts and Reviews. Series A: Human and Experimental Nutrition Abstracts and Reviews. Series B: Livestock Feeds and Feeding

O

OGFA	C S A Oncogenes and Growth Factors Abstracts
ORA	†Oral Research Abstracts
ORMS	Operations Research - Management Science
OTA	Old Testament Abstracts
OceAb	Oceanic Abstracts (Former titles (until 1984): Oceanic Abstracts with Indexes; (until 1972): Oceanic Index; Oceanic Citation Index)
OffTech	†Offshore Technology
OncoAb	†Oncology Abstracts
OphLit	†Ophthalmic Literature
OrnA	Ornithology Abstracts
OrnHort	Ornamental Horticulture
OrnithAb	†Essential Ornithological Abstracts

P

P&BA Paperbase Abstracts (Incorporates (1989-2001): Nonwovens Abstracts; Formerly (until 1995): Paper and Board Abstracts)

PAA&I Documentation in Public Administration (Supersedes: Public Administration Abstracts and Index of Articles)

PABMI †Performing Arts Biography Master Index (Formerly: Theatre, Film, and Television Biographies Master Index)

PAIS P A I S International in Print (Annual) (Public Affairs Information Service) (Former titles (until 1991): P A I S Bulletin; (until 1985): Public Affairs Information Service. Bulletin; (until 1967): Bulletin of the Public Affairs Information Service)

PBA Plant Breeding Abstracts

PC&CA †Abstracts of Research in Pastoral Care and Counseling (Formerly: Pastoral Care and Counseling Abstracts)

PCAb †P C Abstracts

PCI Periodicals Contents Index

PCR2 P C R 2 (Personal Computer Review - Squared)

PE&ON Pharmacoeconomics and Outcomes News (Formerly: PharmacoResources)

PEBNI †Petroleum - Energy Business News Index

PEI Physical Education Index

PGegResA Plant Genetic Resources Abstracts

PGrRegA Plant Growth Regulator Abstracts

PHN&I Postharvest News and Information

PLESA Quarterly Index to Africana Periodical Literature (Formerly: Quarterly Index to Periodical Literature, Eastern and Southern Africa)

PLII †Property & Liability Insurance Index

PMA International Abstracts of Human Resources (Formerly (until 2003): Personnel Management Abstracts)

PMI †Photography Magazine Index

PMPI †Popular Music Periodicals Index

PMR Magazine Article Summaries (Formerly (until 1987): Popular Magazine Review)

PN&I Pig News & Information

PNI Pharmaceutical News Index

PPI †Popular Periodical Index

PRA Peace Research Abstracts Journal

PROMT †Predicasts Overview of Markets and Technology (Formed by the merger of: Chemical Market Abstracts; Equipment Market Abstracts; Which was formerly titled: Electronics Market Abstracts; Electronics and Equipment Market Abstracts)

PSA C S A Worldwide Political Science Abstracts (Cambridge Scientific Abstracts) (Formed by the 2000 merger of: A B C Pol Sci (Online); (1984-2000): Political Science Abstracts (Online); Which superseded: Political Science Abstracts. Annual Supplement (Print); (1967-1980): Political Science, Government, and Public Policy Series. Annual Supplement)

PSI †Philanthropic Studies Index

PST †Packaging Science and Technology Abstracts

PdeR Repere (Online Edition) (Former titles: Repere (Print Edition); (until 1993): Point de Repere; Which was formed by the merger of (1972-1983): Periodex; (1972-1983): Radar (Montreal))

PerIslam †Periodica Islamica

PersLit †Personnel Literature

PetrolAb Petroleum Abstracts

PhilInd Philosopher's Index

PhilipAb Philippine Science and Technology Abstracts (Formerly: Philippine Science and Technology Abstracts Bibliography; Formed by the merger of: Philippine Abstracts; Philippine Science Index)

PhotoAb Imaging Abstracts (Formerly: Photographic Abstracts)

PhotoInd Photography Index

PhysBer †Physics Briefs - Physikalische Berichte (Supersedes: Physikalische Berichte)

Pinpoint †Pinpointer

PlantSci †Plant Science

PollutAb Pollution Abstracts

PopulInd †Population Index (Formerly (until 1937): Population Literature)

PotatoAb Potato Abstracts

PoultAb Poultry Abstracts

Press Press (Formed by the merger of (1946-2001): Printing Abstracts; (1983-2001): World Publishing Monitor; Which was formerly (until 1991): Electronic Publishing Abstracts)

ProtozoAb Protozoological Abstracts

PsyScAP PsycSCAN: Applied Psychology (Online Edition) (Formerly: PsycSCAN: Applied Psychology (Print Edition))

PsyScBA&T PsycSCAN: Behavior Analysis and Therapy

PsyScCP PsycSCAN: Clinical Psychology

PsyScDP PsycSCAN: Developmental Psychology

PsyScLD&MR PsycSCAN: Learning Disorders and Mental Retardation (Former titles: PsycSCAN: Learning and Communication Disorders and Mental Retardation; PsycSCAN: Learning Disabilities - Mental Retardation)

PsycInfo	PsycINFO
PsychoanalAb	Psychoanalytic Abstracts (Formerly (until 1993): PsycSCAN: Psychoanalysis; Psychoanalysis Abstracts)
PsycholAb	Psychological Abstracts
PsycholRG	†Psychological Reader's Guide
PsychopharAb	†Psychopharmacology Abstracts

Q

QAb	†Quality Abstracts
QC&AS	Quality Control and Applied Statistics

R

R&TA	Religious & Theological Abstracts
RA&MP	Review of Aromatic and Medicinal Plants
RAPRA	R A P R A Abstracts (Rubber and Plastics Research Association of Great Britain) consists of: Rapra Abstracts. Additives Rapra Abstracts. Adhesives, Sealants and Coatings Rapra Abstracts. Plastics Materials Rapra Abstracts. Polyurethanes Rapra Abstracts. Rubber Materials
RASB	Russian Academy of Sciences Bibliographies
RCI	Reaction Citation Index
RDA	Rural Development Abstracts
REE&TA	†Rural Extension, Education and Training Abstracts
RGAb	Readers' Guide Abstracts - Full Text (Online Edition)
RGPR	Readers' Guide to Periodical Literature
RGYP	†Reader's Guide for Young People
RHEA	Research into Higher Education Abstracts
RI-1	Religion Index One: Periodicals (Formerly: Index to Religious Periodical Literature)
RI-2	†Religion Index Two: Multi-Author Works
RICS	Isurv Knowledge Alert (Formed by the merger of (1965-2005): R I C S Abstracts and Reviews; (1965-2005): R I C S Weekly Briefing)
RILM	R I L M Abstracts of Music Literature (Repertoire International de Litterature Musicale)
RM&VM	Review of Medical and Veterinary Mycology
RPFIA	Reference Point: Food Industry Abstracts (Former titles: F M I Monthly Index Service; S M I Monthly Index Service (Super Market Institute))
RPP	Review of Plant Pathology (Formerly (until 1970): Review of Applied Mycology)
RRTA	Leisure, Recreation and Tourism Abstracts (Formerly: Rural Recreation and Tourism Abstracts)

Reac	Reactions Weekly (Formerly (until 1990): Reactions)
RefSour	†Reference Sources (Supersedes (1973-1979): Reference Book Review Index)
RefZh	Referativnyi Zhurnal
RefugAb	Refugee Survey Quarterly (Formerly (until 1994): Refugee Abstracts)
RehabLit	†Rehabilitation Literature
Repind	Repindex
ResCtrInd	Resource Center Index (Formerly: Micrographics Index)
RevApplEntom	Review of Agricultural Entomology & Review of Medical and Veterinary Entomology consists of: Review of Agricultural Entomology Review of Medical and Veterinary Entomology
RiceAb	Rice Abstracts
RiskAb	Risk Abstracts (Online Edition)
RoboAb	†Robotics Abstracts (Formerly (until 1989): Robomatix Reporter)

S

S&F	Soils and Fertilizers
S&MA	†Sorghum and Millets (Supersedes (in 1994): Sorghum and Millets Abstracts)
S&VD	The Shock and Vibration Digest
SAA	†Small Animals (Formerly (until 1991): Small Animal Abstracts)
SASA	State Academies of Science Abstracts
SBH	Selected Bibliography of Homosexuality
SBPI	Southern Baptist Periodical Index
SCI	Science Citation Index
SCIMP	†S C I M P (Selective Cooperative Index of Management Periodicals)
SEA	Sociology of Education Abstracts
SEJI	State Education Journal Index and Educators' Guide to Periodicals Research Strategies (Formerly (until 1985): State Education Journal Index)
SENA	Special Educational Needs Abstracts
SFA	†Fisheries Review (Formerly (until 1985): Sport Fishery Abstracts; Incorporates (1972-1985): Fish Health News)
SFSA	Sage Family Studies Abstracts
SIA	Sugar Industry Abstracts (Former titles: Tate and Lyle's Sugar Industry Abstracts; Sugar Industry Abstracts)
SJI	Stamp Journals Index
SJW	†Selected Journals on Water
SLSI	†Sri Lanka Science Index

ABSTRACTING AND INDEXING

SOMA — Educational Management Abstracts (Formerly (2000, until vol.18): School Organisation and Management Abstracts)

SOPODA — †Social Planning - Policy & Development Abstracts (Formerly: Social Welfare, Social Planning, Policy and Social Development)

SPAA — Sage Public Administration Abstracts

SPI — †Sports Periodicals Index

SPPI — South Pacific Periodicals Index (Formerly (until 1978): Bibliography of Periodical Articles Relating to the South Pacific)

SRI — Statistical Reference Index

SRRA — Sage Race Relations Abstracts

SSA — Social Services Abstracts

SSCI — Social Sciences Citation Index

SSI — Social Sciences Index (Supersedes in part (in 1974): Social Sciences and Humanities Index; Which was formerly (until 1965): International Index)

ST&MA — Statistical Theory and Method Abstracts (CD-ROM Edition) (Former titles (until vol.42, 2002): Statistical Theory and Method Abstracts (Print Edition); (until 1964): International Journal of Abstracts)

SUSA — Sage Urban Studies Abstracts

SWA — Studies on Women and Gender Abstracts (Formerly (until 2000): Studies on Women Abstracts)

SWR&A — Social Work Abstracts (Supersedes in part (in 1994): Social Work Research and Abstracts; Which was formerly (until 1977): Abstracts for Social Workers)

SWRA — Water Resources Abstracts (Bethesda, Online Edition) (Formerly (until 1993): Selected Water Resources Abstracts)

Search — †Search (Devon)

SeedAb — Seed Abstracts

SociolAb — Sociological Abstracts

SoftAbEng — †Software Abstracts for Engineers

SoftBase — SoftBase

SolStAb — Solid State and Superconductivity Abstracts (Former titles: Solid State Abstracts Journal; Solid State Abstracts; Incorporates: Science Research Abstracts Journal. Laser and Electro-Optic Reviews, Quantum Electronics, Unconventional Energy Sources; Science Research Abstracts Journal. Superconductivity, Magnetohydrodynamics and Plasma, Theoretical Physics; Which was formerly: Science Research Abstracts, Part A. MHD and Plasma, Superconductivity and Research, and Theoretical Physics; Which incorporated: Theoretical Physics Journal)

SoyAb — Soybean Abstracts (Online Edition)

SpeleolAb — Speleological Abstracts

SportS — SportSearch (Former titles (until 1985): Sport and Fitness Index; (until 1984): Sport and Recreation Index - Index de la Litterature des Sports et des Loisirs; (until 1977): Sport Articles)

T

T&DA — †Training and Development Alert

T&II — †Trade & Industry Index

TCEA — Theoretical Chemical Engineering (Formerly (until 1991): Theoretical Chemical Engineering Abstracts)

TDB — Tropical Diseases Bulletin

TEA — Technical Education & Training Abstracts (Formerly (until 1993): Technical Education Abstracts)

THA — †Tobacco & Health Abstracts (Formerly: Tobacco and Health)

TMA — Top Management Abstracts (Supersedes in part: Anbar Management Services Abstracts)

TOM — T O M (Text on Microfilm)

TOSA — †Tropical Oil Seeds (Formerly (until 1991): Tropical Oil Seeds Abstracts)

TRA — †Transportation Research Abstracts (Formerly: Highway Research Abstracts)

TTI — Textile Technology Index (Formerly: Textile Technology Digest)

TelAb — †Telecommunications Abstracts

Telegen — †Telegen Abstracts (Formerly: Telegen Reporter)

TobAb — Tobacco Abstracts

ToxAb — Toxicology Abstracts

TriticAb — Wheat, Barley and Triticale Abstracts (Formerly: Triticale Abstracts)

U

UAA — †Urban Affairs Abstracts

V

V&AA — Violence & Abuse Abstracts

VITIS — Vitis - Viticulture and Oenology Abstracts (Online Edition) (Formerly (until 2003): Vitis - Viticulture and Oenology Abstracts (Print Edition))

VetBull — Veterinary Bulletin

VirolAbstr — C S A Virology and AIDS Abstracts (Cambridge Scientific Abstracts) (Formerly (until 1988): Virology Abstracts)

W

W&CBA — †Essential Wildlife & Conservation Biology Abstracts

WAA	Aluminum Industry Abstracts (Formerly (until 1991): World Aluminum Abstracts)
WAE&RSA	World Agricultural Economics and Rural Sociology Abstracts (Supersedes: Digest of Agricultural Economics and Marketing)
WBA	World Banking Abstracts
WBSS	†World Bibliography of Social Security
WLA	Wildlife Abstracts
WLR	†Wildlife Review
WMB	World Magazine Bank
WRCInf	Aqualine Abstracts (Formerly (until 1985): W R C Information; Supersedes: Water Pollution Abstracts)
WSA	Women Studies Abstracts
WSCA	World Surface Coating Abstracts (Formerly (until 1969): Review of Current Literature on the Paint and Allied Industries)
WSI	G. K. Hall's Women's Studies Index (Formerly (until 1999): Women's Studies Index (Year))
WTA	World Textile Abstracts (Former titles (until 1969): Textile Abstracts; (until 1967): Journal of the Textile Institute. Abstracts; (until 1956): Journal of the Textile Institute. Proceedings and Abstracts; Which superseded in part (in 1949): Textile Institute. Journal)

WasteInfo	WasteInfo
WatResAb	Hydro-Abstracts (Formerly (until 1980): Water Resources Abstracts)
WeedAb	Weed Abstracts
Weldasearch	Weldasearch Select (Formerly: Weldalert)
WildRev	Wildlife Review Abstracts (Formerly (until 1995): Wildlife Review (Fort Collins))
WorkRelAb	†Work Related Abstracts (Formerly: Employment Relations Abstracts)

Y

YAE&RB	†Association for Education and Rehabilitation of the Blind and Visually Impaired. Yearbook (Incorporates (in 1982): Blindness, Visual Impairment, Deaf-Blindness; Which was formerly: Blindness)

Z

ZentMath	Zentralblatt MATH (Formerly (until 1999): Zentralblatt fuer Mathematik und Ihre Grenzgebiete)
Zincscan	Zincscan (Former titles (until 1986): Zinc Abstracts; (until 1961): Z D A Abstracts)
ZooRec	Zoological Record

Subject Guide to Abstracting and Indexing

The 132 subject headings listed below are major subjects which contain a sub-category headed "Abstracting, Bibliographies, Statistics." This sub-category, which follows the major subject headings in the CLASSIFIED LIST OF SERIALS, identifies publications which abstract and/or index publications in the relevant subject. Bibliographies and statistical publications pertaining to the subject are also included in this sub-category. This guide will enable users to quickly locate subject areas of interest for which abstracting and indexing publications have been identified and to build profiles by combination of relevant subject areas. Page numbers refer to the first page on which the sub-category appears.

Subjects

English	Francais	Deutsch	Español
Abstracting and Indexing Services	Services d'Analyse et d'Indexage	Referate- und Indexdienste	Servicio de Análisis e Indización
Advertising and Public Relations	Publicité et Relations Publiques	Reklamewesen und Public Relations	Relaciones Públicas y Publicidad
Aeronautics and Space Flight	Aéronautique et Astronautique	Luft- und Raumfahrt	Aeronáutica y Vuelo Espacial
Computer Applications	Applications Informatiques	Computer Anwendung	Aplicaciones para Computadoras
Agriculture	Agriculture	Landwirtschaft	Agricultura
Agricultural Economics	Agriculture Économique	Agrarökonomie	Economía Agrícola
Agricultural Equipment	Outillage Agricole	Landwirtschaftsgeräte	Equipo para la Agricultura
Computer Applications	Applications Informatiques	Computer Anwendung	Aplicaciones para Computadoras
Crop Production and Soil	Production Végétale et Terrain	Ernte und Acker	Producción de Cosecha, Tierra
Dairying and Dairy Products	Production Laitière	Milchwirtschaft	Lechería y Productos Lácteos
Feed, Flour and Grain	Pature, Farine et Grain	Futter, Mehl und Getreide	Forraje, Granos y Harina
Poultry and Livestock	Élevage	Geflügel- und Viehwirtschaft	Aves de Corral y Ganadería
Alternative Medicine	Médecine Alternative	Alternative Heilkunde	Medicina Alternativa
Animal Welfare	Protection des Animaux	Tierschutz	Protección a los Animales
Anthropology	Anthropologie	Anthropologie	Antropología
Antiques	Antiquités	Antiquitäten	Antigüedades
Archaeology	Archeologie	Archaeologie	Arqueología
Computer Applications	Applications Informatiques	Computer Anwendung	Aplicaciones para Computadoras
Architecture	Architecture	Architektur	Arquitectura
Computer Applications	Applications Informatiques	Computer Anwendung	Aplicaciones para Computadoras
Art	Art	Kunst	Arte
Computer Applications	Applications Informatiques	Computer Anwendung	Aplicaciones para Computadoras
Arts and Handicrafts	Arts et Métiers	Kunst und Handwerk	Artesanías y Obras Manuales
Astrology	Astrologie	Astrologie	Astrología
Astronomy	Astronomie	Astronomie	Astronomía
Computer Applications	Applications Informatiques	Computer Anwendung	Aplicaciones para Computadoras
Beauty Culture	Soins de Beauté	Schönheitspflege	Belleza Personal
Perfumes and Cosmetics	Parfums et Cosmétiques	Kosmetik und Parfüme	Perfumes y Cosméticos
Beverages	Boissons	Getränke	Bebidas
Bibliographies	Bibliographies	Bibliographien	Bibliografías
Biography	Biographie	Biographie	Biografía
Biology	Biologie	Biologie	Biología
Bioengineering	Biogénie	Bioingenieurwesen	Bio-ingeniería
Biochemistry	Biochimie	Biochemie	Bio-química
Biophysics	Biophysique	Biophysik	Biofísica
Biotechnology	Biotechnologie	Biotechnologie	Biotecnología
Botany	Botanique	Botanik	Botánica
Computer Applications	Applications Informatiques	Computer Anwendung	Aplicaciones para Computadoras
Cytology and Histology	Cytologie et Histologie	Zytologie und Histologie	Citología e Histología
Entomology	Entomologie	Entomologie	Entomología
Genetics	Génétique	Genetik	Genética
Microbiology	Microbiologie	Mikrobiologie	Microbiología
Microscopy	Microscopie	Mikroskopie	Microscopía
Ornithology	Ornithologie	Ornithologie	Ornitología
Physiology	Physiologie	Physiologie	Fisiología
Zoology	Zoologie	Zoologie	Zoología
Birth Control	Limitation des Naissances	Geburtenregelung	Control de Natalidad
Building and Construction	Bâtiment et Construction	Bauwesen	Edificios y Construcción
Carpentry and Woodwork	Charpenterie et Menuiserie	Zimmerhandwerk und Holzbau	Carpintería y Ebanistería
Hardware	Quincaillerie	Metallbaustoffe	Ferretería
Business and Economics	Affaires et Économie	Wirtschaft und Handel	Economía y Negocios
Accounting	Comptabilité	Rechnungswesen	Contabilidad
Banking and Finance	Banque et Finance	Bank- und Finanzwesen	Bancos y Finanzas
Banking and Finance-Computer Applications	Banque et Finance-Applications Informatiques	Bank- und Finanzwesen-Computer Anwendung	Bancos y Finanzas-Aplicaciones para Computadoras
Chamber of Commerce Publications	Publications des Chambres de Commerce	Veröffentlichungen von Handelskammern	Publicaciones de las Cámaras de Comercio
Computer Applications	Applications Informatiques	Computer Anwendung	Aplicaciones para Computadoras
Cooperatives	Coopératives	Genossenschaften	Cooperativas
Domestic Commerce	Commerce Interieur	Binnenhandel	Comercio Interno
Economic Situation and Conditions	Situations et Conditions Économiques	Wirtschaftliche Situation und Verhältnisse	Condiciones y Situaciones Económicas
Economic Systems and Theories, Economic History	Systèmes et Théories Économiques, Histoire Économique	Ökonomische Systeme und Theorien, Wirtschaftsgeschichte	Sistemas y Teorías Economicos, Historia de la Economia
International Commerce	Commerce International	Aussenhandel	Comercio Internacional
International Development and Assistance	Aide et Développement Internationaux	Internationale Entwicklungshilfe	Desarrollo y Asistencia Internacional
Investments	Investissements	Investitionen	Inversiones
Labor and Industrial Relations	Travail et Relations Industrielles	Arbeits und Industrielle Beziehungen	Trabajo y Relaciones Industriales
Macroeconomics	Macroéconomie	Makroökonomie	Macroeconomía
Management	Gestion	Betriebsführung	Gerencia
Marketing and Purchasing	Marketing et Achats	Marketing und Kauf	Ventas y Mercadeo
Office Equipment and Services	Matériel et Entretien de Bureaux	Büroeinrichtung und Service	Equipo y Servicios de Oficinas
Personnel Management	Gestion du Personnel	Personal Führung	Administración de Personal
Production of Goods and Services	Production de Biens et Services	Produktion	Producción de Bienes y Servicios
Public Finance, Taxation	Tresor Publique, Fiscalité	Staatsfinanzen, Steuerwesen	Finanzas Públicas e Impuestos
Small Business	Petites et Moyennes Entreprises	Kleinbetrieb	Pequeños Negocios
Trade and Industrial Directories	Annuaires de Commerce et d'Industrie	Firmenverzeichnisse	Directorios de la Industria y el Comercio

SUBJECTS

Ceramics, Glass and Pottery	Céramique, Verrerie et Poterie	Keramik, Glas und Töpferei	Cerámica, Vidrio y Porcelana
Chemistry	Chimie	Chemie	Química
Analytical Chemistry	Chimie Analytique	Analytische Chemie	Química Analítica
Computer Applications	Applications Informatiques	Computer Anwendung	Aplicaciones para Computadoras
Crystallography	Cristallographie	Kristallographie	Cristalografía
Electrochemistry	Electrochimie	Elektrochemie	Electroquímica
Inorganic Chemistry	Chimie Inorganique	Anorganische Chemie	Química Inorgánica
Organic Chemistry	Chimie Organique	Organische Chemie	Química Orgánica
Physical Chemistry	Physicochimie	Physikalische Chemie	Química Física
Children and Youth	Enfants et Adolescents	Kinder und Jugend	Niños y Jóvenes
About	Au Sujet des	Über	Acerca
For	Pour	Für	Para
Civil Defense	Defense Civile	Ziviler Bevölkerungsschutz	Defensa Civil
Classical Studies	Etudes Classiques	Klassische Studien	Estudios Clásicos
Cleaning and Dyeing	Nettoyage et Teinturerie	Reinigen und Färben	Limpieza y Tintura
Clothing Trade	Vêtement	Bekleidungsgewerbe	Industria del Vestido
Fashions	Mode	Moden	Modas
Clubs	Clubs	Klubs	Clubes
College and Alumni	Université et Diplomés	Universitäten und Hochschul-absolventen	Universidades y Exalumnos
Communications	Communications	Nachrichtentechnik	Comunicaciones
Computer Applications	Applications Informatiques	Computer Anwendung	Aplicaciones para Computadoras
Postal Affairs	Courrier	Postwesen	Correo
Radio	Radio	Rundfunk	Radio
Telephone and Telegraph	Téléphone et Télégraphe	Telephon und Telegraph	Teléfono y Telégrafo
Television and Cable	Télévision	Fernsehen und Bildfrequenzkanal	Cable y Televisión
Video	Vidéo	Video	Video
Computers	Ordinateurs	Computer	Computadoras
Artificial Intelligence	Intelligence Artificielle	Künstliche Intelligenz	Inteligencia Artificial
Automation	Automation	Automatisierung	Automatización
Calculating Machines	Calculateurs	Rechenmaschine	Calculadoras
Circuits	Circuits	Schaltungen	Circuitos
Computer Architecture	Architecture de la Machine	Computer Architektur	Arquitectura de las Computadoras
Computer-Assisted Instruction	Enseignement Assisté par Ordinateur	Computerunterstützter Unterricht	Enseñanza con la Ayuda de las Computadoras
Computer Engineering	Technique Informatique	Computerentwicklung	Ingeniería de las Computadoras
Computer Games	Jeux sur Ordinateurs	Computer Spiele	Juegos para Computadoras
Computer Graphics	Conception Assistée par Ordinateur	Computergraphik	Diseño a través de Computadoras
Computer Industry	Industrie Informatique	Computerbetrieb	Industria de las Computadoras
Computer Industry Directories	Annuaire de l'Industrie Informatique	Computerbetriebverzeichnisse	Directorios de la Industria de las Computadoras
Computer Industry, Vocational Guidance	Industrie Informatique, Orientation Professionnelle	Computerbetrieb Berufsberatung	Guía para la Industria de las Computadoras
Computer Music	Musique sur Ordinateur	Computer Musik	Música a través de Computadoras
Computer Networks	Réseaux d'Ordinateurs	Rechnernetz	Redes de Computadoras
Computer Programming	Programmation Informatique	Computerprogrammierung	Programación de Computadoras
Computer Sales	Ventes d'Ordinateurs	Computervertrieb	Ventas de Computadoras
Computer Security	Sécurité Informatique	Computersicherheit	Seguridad en Computadoras
Computer Simulation	Simulation sur Ordinateurs	Computersimulation	Simulación a través de Computadoras
Computer Systems	Systèmes Informatiques	Computersystemen	Sistemas de Computadoras
Cybernetics	Cybernétique	Kybernetik	Cibernética
Data Base Management	Gestion de Base de Données	Datenbankverwaltung	Bases de Datos
Data Communications, Data Transmission Systems	Communication de données	Datenübertragung, Datenübertragungssystem	Comunicación y Transmisión de Datos
Electronic Data Processing	Traitement de l'Information Electronique	Elektronische Datenverarbeitung	Procesamiento Electrónico de Datos
Hardware	Matériel	Hardware	Equipo Físico
Information Science, Information Theory	Théorie de l'Information	Informationstheorie	Ciencia y Teoría de la Información
Internet	Internet	Internet	Internet
Machine Theory	Théorie de Machine	Maschinetheorie	Teoría de las Máquinas
Microcomputers	Micro-Ordinateurs	Mikrocomputer	Microcomputadoras
Minicomputers	Mini-Ordinateurs	Minicomputer	Minicomputadoras
Personal Computers	Ordinateurs Personnels	Persönlichecomputer	Computadoras Personales
Robotics	Robotique	Robotersysteme	Robótica
Software	Logiciel	Software	Aplicaciones de Computadora
Theory of Computing	Théorie de Traitement	Computertheorie	Teoría de Cálculo
Word Processing	Traitement de Textes	Textverarbeitung	Procesador de Textos
Conservation	Conservation	Landschaftsschutz	Conservación
Consumer Education and Protection	Protection du Consommateur	Verbraucherswirtschaftsschutz	Protección al Consumidor
Criminology and Law Enforcement	Criminologie et Police	Kriminologie und Strafvollzug	Criminología y Acción Policial
Computer Applications	Applications Informatiques	Computer Anwendung	Aplicaciones para Computadoras
Security	Securité	Sicherheit	Seguridad
Dance	Danse	Tanz	Baile
Drug Abuse and Alcoholism	Toxicomanie et Alcoolisme	Rauschgiftsucht und Alkoholismus	Alcoholismo y Drogadicción
Earth Sciences	Sciences Géologiques	Wissenschaften der Erde	Ciencias Geológicas
Computer Applications	Applications Informatiques	Computer Anwendung	Aplicaciones para Computadoras
Geology	Géologie	Geologie	Geología
Geophysics	Géophysique	Geophysik	Geofísica
Hydrology	Hydrologie	Hydrologie	Hidrología
Oceanography	Océanographie	Ozeanographie	Oceanografía
Education	Education	Bildungswesen	Educación
Adult Education	Enseignement des Adultes	Erwachsenenbildung	Educación para Adultos
Computer Applications	Applications Informatiques	Computer Anwendung	Aplicaciones para Computadoras
Guides to Schools and Colleges	Guides des Écoles et Colleges	Führer zur Schulen und Universitäten	Guías de Escuelas y Colegios
Higher Education	Enseignement Supérieur	Hochschulwesen	Educación Superior
International Education Programs	Programmes d'Éducation Internationale	Internazionale Erziehungs-programme	Programas Internacionales de Educación
School Organization and Administration	Organisation et Administration de l'École	Organisation und Verwaltung von dem Schule	Administración y Dirección de Escuelas
Special Education and Rehabilitation	Enseignement Special et Réhabilitation	Fachunterricht und Rehabilitierung	Educación Especial y Rehabilitación
Teaching Methods and Curriculum	Méthodes Pédagogiques et Programmes Scolaires	Lehrmethoden und Lehrplan	Métodos y Planes de Estudio

Electronics	Electronique	Elektronik	Electrónica
Computer Applications	Applications Informatiques	Computer Anwendung	Aplicaciones para Computadoras
Encyclopedias and General Almanacs	Encyclopédies et Almanachs Générales	Enzyklopädien und Allgemeine Nachschlagewerke	Enciclopedias y Almanaques Generales
Energy	Energie	Energie	Energía
Computer Applications	Applications Informatiques	Computer Anwendung	Aplicaciones para Computadoras
Electrical Energy	Energie Électrique	Elektrizitätsenergie	Energía Eléctrica
Geothermal Energy	Energie Géothermique	Thermalenergie	Energía Geotérmica
Hydroelectrical Energy	Energie Hydraulique	Hydroelektroenergie	Energía Hidroeléctrica
Nuclear Energy	Energie Nucléaire	Kernenergie	Energía Nuclear
Solar Energy	Energie Solaire	Sonnenenergie	Energía Solar
Wind Energy	Energie Eolienne	Windenergie	Energía de Viento
Engineering	Ingénierie	Ingenieurwesen	Ingeniería
Chemical Engineering	Génie Chimique	Chemieingenieurwesen	Ingeniería Química
Civil Engineering	Génie Civil	Bauingenieurwesen	Ingeniería Civil
Computer Applications	Applications Informatiques	Computer Anwendung	Aplicaciones para Computadoras
Electrical Engineering	Génie Électrique	Elektrotechnik	Ingeniería Eléctrica
Engineering Mechanics and Materials	Méchanique et Materiels	Ingenieurwesen Mechanik und Materialien	Ingeniería Mecanica y de Materiales
Hydraulic Engineering	Génie Hydraulique	Wasserbau	Ingeniería Hidráulica
Industrial Engineering	Génie Industriel	Industrieingenieurwesen	Ingeniería Industrial
Mechanical Engineering	Génie Mécanique	Maschinenbau	Ingeniería Mecánica
Environmental Studies	Science de l'Environnement	Umweltschutz	Estudios Ambientales
Computer Applications	Applications Informatiques	Computer Anwendung	Aplicaciones para Computadoras
Pollution	Pollution	Umweltverschmutzung	Contaminación
Toxicology and Environmental Safety	Toxicologie et Sécurité de l'Environnement	Toxokologie und Umweltsicherheit	Toxicología y Seguridad Ambiental
Waste Management	Gestion de Déchets	Abfallwirtschaft	Administración de Desperdicios
Ethnic Interests	Ethnologie	Allgemeine Völkerkunde	Publicaciones de Temas Etnicos
Fire Prevention	Prévention d'Incendie	Brandbekämpfung	Prevención del Fuego
Fish and Fisheries	Poisson et Pêche	Fische und Fischerei	Pesca y Pesquerías
Folklore	Folklore	Volkskunde	Folklore
Food and Food Industries	Alimentation et Industries Alimentaires	Nahrungsmittel und Lebensmittel-industrie	Alimentos e Industrias de Alimentos
Bakers and Confectioners	Boulangerie et Confiserie	Bäcker- und Konditorgewerbe	Panaderías y Dulcerías
Grocery Trade	Épicerie	Kolonialwarenhandel	Abacerías
Forest and Forestry	Forêts et Exploitation Forestière	Forstwesen und Waldwirtschaft	Bosques y Selvicultura
Lumber and Wood	Bois	Holz	Maderas
Funerals	Funérailles	Beerdigungen	Funerales
Gardening and Horticulture	Jardinage et Horticulture	Gartenpflege und Gartenbau	Jardinería y Horticultura
Florist Trade	Commerce des Fleurs	Blumenhandel	Comercio de Flores
Genealogy and Heraldry	Généalogie et Science Héraldique	Genealogie und Wappenkunde	Genealogía y Heráldica
Computer Applications	Applications Informatiques	Computer Anwendung	Aplicaciones para Computadoras
General Interest Periodicals (Subdivided by country)	Publications d'Intérêt Général (Selon pays)	Allgemeine Zeitschriften (nach Land)	Periódicos de Interés General (por país)
Geography	Géographie	Geographie	Geografía
Computer Applications	Applications Informatiques	Computer Anwendung	Aplicaciones para Computadoras
Gerontology and Geriatrics	Gérontologie	Gerontologie	Gerontología y Geriátrica
Giftware and Toys	Cadeaux et Jouets	Geschenkartikel und Spielwaren	Juguetes y Regalos
Handicapped	Handicapés	Behinderung	Minusválido
Computer Applications	Applications Informatiques	Computer Anwendung	Aplicaciones para Computadoras
Hearing Impaired	Sourds	Schwerhörigkeit	Discapacitado del Oído
Physically Impaired	Handicapés Physiques	Körperbehinderung	Discapacitado Físicamente
Visually Impaired	Aveugles	Blindheit	Discapacitado Visualmente
Heating, Plumbing, and Refrigeration	Chauffage, Plomberie et Réfrigeration	Heizung, Kühlung und Installation	Calefacción, Plomería y Refrigeración
History	Histoire	Geschichte	Historia
Computer Applications	Applications Informatiques	Computer Anwendung	Aplicaciones para Computadoras
History of Africa	Histoire de l'Afrique	Geschichte-Afrika	Historia de Africa
History of Asia	Histoire de l'Asie	Geschichte-Asien	Historia de Asia
History of Australasia and Other Areas	Histoire de l'Australasie et Autres Pays	Geschichte-Australasien und Andere Gebieten	Historia de Australasia y Otras Areas
History of Europe	Histoire de l'Europe	Geschichte-Europa	Historia de la Europa
History of North and South America	Histoire de l'Amérique du Nord et du Sud	Geschichte-Nord- und Südamerika	Historia de América del Norte y del Sur
History of Near East	Histoire du Proche-Orient	Geschichte-Nahe Osten	Historia del Cercano Oriente
Hobbies	Passe-Temps	Hobbies	Pasatiempos
Home Economics	Gestion Domestique	Hauswirtschaft	Economía Doméstica
Homosexuality	Homosexualité	Homosexualität	Homosexualidad
Hospitals	Hôpitaux	Krankenhäuser	Hospitales
Computer Applications	Applications Informatiques	Computer Anwendung	Aplicaciones para Computadoras
Hotels and Restaurants	Hôtels et Restaurants	Hotels und Restaurants	Restaurantes y Hoteles
Computer Applications	Applications Informatiques	Computer Anwendung	Aplicaciones para Computadoras
Housing and Urban Planning	Logement et Urbanisme	Wohnungswesen und Stadtplanung	Planificación Urbana y Vivienda
Computer Applications	Applications Informatiques	Computer Anwendung	Aplicaciones para Computadoras
How-To and Do-It-Yourself	Bricolage	Selbstanfertigung	Cómo Hacerlo Usted Mismo
Humanities: Comprehensive Works	Humanités: Oeuvres d'Ensemble	Klassische Philologie	Humanidades: Obras Completas
Computer Applications	Applications Informatiques	Computer Anwendung	Aplicaciones para Computadoras
Instruments	Instruments	Instrumente	Instrumentos
Insurance	Assurances	Versicherungswesen	Seguros
Computer Applications	Applications Informatiques	Computer Anwendung	Aplicaciones para Computadoras
Interior Design and Decoration	Agencements Intérieurs et Décoration	Innenarchitektur und Innenausstattung	Diseño Interior y Ornamentación
Furniture and House Furnishings	Meubles et Articles pour la Maison	Möbel und Wohnungseinrichtung	Muebles y Articulos para el Hogar
Jewelry, Clocks and Watches	Bijouterie et Horlogerie	Schmuck und Uhren	Joyería y Relojería
Journalism	Journalisme	Journalismus	Periodismo

SUBJECTS

Labor Unions	Syndicalisme	Gewerkschaften	Sindicatos
Law	Droit	Rechtswissenschaft	Derecho
Civil Law	Droit Civil	Zivilrecht	Derecho Civil
Computer Applications	Applications Informatiques	Computer Anwendung	Aplicaciones para Computadoras
Constitutional Law	Droit Constitutionel	Verfassungsrecht	Derecho Constitucional
Corporate Law	Droit Commercial	Handelsrecht	Derecho Corporativo
Criminal Law	Droit Pénal	Strafrecht	Derecho Criminal
Estate Planning	Succession	Mobiliarvermögensrecht	Planificación de Bienes Raíces
Family and Matrimonial Law	Droit Familial et Matrimonial	Ehegesetz und Familienrecht	Derecho Familial y Matrimonial
International Law	Droit International	Völkerrecht	Derecho Internacional
Judicial Systems	Système Judiciaire	Gerichtswesen	Sistemas Judiciales
Legal Aid	Assistance Judiciaire	Rechtshilfe	Ayuda Legal
Maritime Law	Droit Maritime	Seerecht	Derecho Marítimo
Military Law	Droit Militaire	Kriegsrecht	Derecho Militar
Leather and Fur Industries	Maroquinerie et Fourrure	Leder und Pelz	Pieles y Cuero
Leisure and Recreation	Loisirs et Récréation	Freizeit und Unterhaltung	Tiempo Libre y Recreación
Library and Information Science	Bibliothéconomie et Informatique	Bibliothek- und Informations-wissenschaft	Bibliotecología y Ciencias de la Información
Computer Applications	Applications Informatiques	Computer Anwendung	Aplicaciones para Computadoras
Lifestyle	Divertissement	Lebensstil	Entretenimiento
Linguistics	Linguistique	Sprachwissenschaft	Lingüística
Computer Applications	Applications Informatiques	Computer Anwendung	Aplicaciones para Computadoras
Literary and Political Reviews	Revues Littéraires et Politiques	Literarische und Politische Zeitschriften	Revistas Literarias y Políticas
Literature	Littérature	Literatur	Literatura
Adventure and Romance	Aventure et Romance	Abenteuer und Romantik	Aventura y Romance
Mystery and Detective	Mystère et Policier	Geheimnis und Detektivroman	Misterio y Novela Policiaca
Poetry	Poésie	Poesie	Poesía
Science Fiction, Fantasy, Horror	Science-Fiction, Fantastisque, Horreur	Zukunftsroman, Phantasiegebilde, Grausen	Ciencia Ficción, Fantasía, Horror
Machinery	Machines	Maschinenwesen	Maquinaria
Computer Applications	Applications Informatiques	Computer Anwendung	Aplicaciones para Computadoras
Mathematics	Mathématiques	Mathematik	Matemáticas
Computer Applications	Applications Informatiques	Computer Anwendung	Aplicaciones para Computadoras
Matrimony	Mariage	Ehestand	Matrimonio
Computer Applications	Applications Informatiques	Computer Anwendung	Aplicaciones para Computadoras
Medical Sciences	Médecine	Medizinische Wissenschaften	Ciencias Médicas
Allergology and Immunology	Allergologie et Immunologie	Allergie und Immunologie	Alergología e Imunología
Anaesthesiology	Anesthésiologie	Anaesthesiologie	Anestesiología
Cardiovascular Diseases	Maladies Cardiovasculaires	Kreislauferkrankungen	Enfermedades Cardiovasculares
Chiropractic, Homeopathy, Osteopathy	Chiropraxie, Homéopathie, Ostéopathie	Chiropraktik, Homöopathie, Osteopathie	Quiropráctica, Homeopatía, Osteopatía
Communicable Diseases	Maladies Contagieuses	Infektiöse Krankheiten	Enfermedades Contagiosas
Computer Applications	Applications Informatiques	Computer Anwendung	Aplicaciones para Computadoras
Dentistry	Dentisterie	Zahnmedizin	Odontología
Dermatology and Venereology	Dermatologie et Maladies Vénériennes	Dermatologie und Geschlechtskrankheiten	Dermatología y Venereología
Endocrinology	Endocrinologie	Endokrinologie	Endocrinología
Experimental Medicine, Laboratory Technique	Médecine Expérimentale, Techniques de Laboratoire	Versuchsmedizin, Laboratoriumstechnik	Medicina Experimental, Técnicas del Laboratorio
Forensic Sciences	Médecine Légale	Gerichtliche Medizin	Ciencias Forenses
Gastroenterology	Gastroentérologie	Gastroenterologie	Gastroenterología
Hematology	Hématologie	Hämatologie	Hematología
Hypnosis	Hypnose	Hypnose	Hipnotismo
Internal Medicine	Médecine Interne	Innere Medizin	Medicina Interna
Nurses and Nursing	Personnel et Soins Infirmiers	Krankenpflege	Enfermeros y Enfermería
Obstetrics and Gynecology	Obstétrique et Gynécologie	Gynäkologie und Geburtshilfe	Obstetricia y Ginecología
Oncology	Cancer	Onkologie	Oncología
Ophthalmology and Optometry	Ophtalmologie et Optométrie	Opthalmologie und Optometrie	Oftalmología y Optometría
Orthopedics and Traumatology	Orthopédie et Traumatologie	Orthopädie und Traumatologie	Ortopedia y Traumatología
Otorhinolaryngology	Otorhinolaryngologie	Otorhinolaryngologie	Otorinolaringología
Pediatrics	Pédiatrie	Pädiatrie	Pediatría
Physical Medicine and Rehabilitation	Médecine Physique et Réhabilitation	Physikalische Heilkunde und Rehabilitation	Medicina Física y de Rehabilitación
Psychiatry and Neurology	Psychiatrie et Neurologie	Psychiatrie und Neurologie	Psiquiatría y Neurología
Radiology and Nuclear Medicine	Radiologie et Médecine Nucléaire	Radiologie und Nuklearmedizin	Radiología y Medicina Nuclear
Respiratory Diseases	Maladies Respiratoires	Atmungskrankheiten	Enfermedades Respiratorias
Rheumatology	Rhumatologie	Rheumatologie	Reumatología
Sports Medicine	Médecine du Sport	Sportmedizin	Medicina del Deporte
Surgery	Chirurgie	Chirurgie	Cirugía
Urology and Nephrology	Urologie et Néphrologie	Urologie und Nephrologie	Urología y Nefrología
Meetings and Congresses	Réunions et Congrès	Tagungen und Kongresse	Conferencias y Congresos
Men's Health	Santé de l'Homme	Gesundheit von Männern	Salud de los Hombres
Men's Interests	Publications d'Intérêt Masculin	Männer Interessen	Intereses Masculinos
Men's Studies	Études de l'Homme	Männerstudien	Estudios de los Hombres
Metallurgy	Métallurgie	Metallurgie	Metalurgia
Computer Applications	Applications Informatiques	Computer Anwendung	Aplicaciones para Computadoras
Welding	Soudure	Schweissen	Soldadura
Meteorology	Météorologie	Meteorologie	Meteorología
Computer Applications	Applications Informatiques	Computer Anwendung	Aplicaciones para Computadoras
Metrology and Standardization	Métrologie et Standardisation	Mass- und Gewichtskunde, Normung	Metrología y Normalización
Computer Applications	Applications Informatiques	Computer Anwendung	Aplicaciones para Computadoras
Military	Militaires	Militärwesen	Militares
Mines and Mining Industry	Mines et Resources Minières	Bergwesen und Bergbauindustrie	Minas e Industria Minera
Computer Applications	Applications Informatiques	Computer Anwendung	Aplicaciones para Computadoras
Motion Pictures	Cinéma	Film und Kino	Películas
Museums and Art Galleries	Musées et Galleries	Museen und Kunstgalerien	Museos y Galerías del Arte
Music	Musique	Musik	Música
Computer Applications	Applications Informatiques	Computer Anwendung	Aplicaciones para Computadoras
Native American Studies	Etudes des Amérindiens	Studienfach Eingeborenen Amerikaner	Estudios de los Americanos Nativos
Needlework	Travaux de Couture	Näherei	Bordado
New Age	New Age	New Age	Nueva Epoca
Numismatics	Numismatique	Numismatik	Numismática
Nutrition and Dietetics	Nutrition et Diététique	Ernährung und Diätetik	Dietas y Nutrición
Occupational Health and Safety	Médecine du Travail et Prévention	Berufsgesundheitspflege und Sicherheit	Sanidad y Seguridad en el Trabajo
Occupations and Careers	Emplois et Carrières	Berufe	Empleos y Ocupaciones
Oriental Studies	Études Orientales	Orientalistik	Estudios Orientales

Packaging	Emballage	Verpackung	Empaque
Computer Applications	Applications Informatiques	Computer Anwendung	Aplicaciones para Computadoras
Paints and Protective Coatings	Couleurs et Peintures	Farben und Beläge	Pinturas y Revestimientos Protectores
Paleontology	Paléontologie	Paleontologie	Paleontología
Computer Applications	Applications Informatiques	Computer Anwendung	Aplicaciones para Computadoras
Paper and Pulp	Papier et Pulpe	Papier und Papierstoff	Papel y Pulpa
Parapsychology and Occultism	Parapsychologie et Occultisme	Parapsychologie und Okkultismus	Parapsicología y Ocultismo
Patents, Trademarks and Copyrights	Brevets, Marques Commerciales et Droits d'Auteur	Patente, Schutzmarken und Urheberrechte	Patentes, Marcas Registradas y Derechos de Autor
Petroleum and Gas	Pétrole et Gas Naturel	Petroleum und Gas	Petróleo y Gas Natural
Computer Applications	Applications Informatiques	Computer Anwendung	Aplicaciones para Computadoras
Pets	Animaux Familiers	Haustiere	Mascotas
Pharmacy and Pharmacology	Pharmacie et Pharmacologie	Pharmazie und Pharmakologie	Farmacia y Farmacología
Computer Applications	Applications Informatiques	Computer Anwendung	Aplicaciones para Computadoras
Philately	Philatélie	Briefmarkenkunde	Filatelia
Philosophy	Philosophie	Philosophie	Filosofía
Photography	Photographie	Photographie	Fotografía
Computer Applications	Applications Informatiques	Computer Anwendung	Aplicaciones para Computadoras
Physical Fitness and Hygiene	Santé Physique et Hygiène	Gesundheitszustand und Hygiene	Salud Física e Higiene
Physics	Physique	Physik	Física
Computer Applications	Applications Informatiques	Computer Anwendung	Aplicaciones para Computadoras
Electricity	Electricité	Elektrizität	Electricidad
Heat	Chaleur	Wärme	Calor
Mechanics	Mécanique	Mechanik	Mecánica
Nuclear Physics	Physique Nucléaire	Kernphysik	Física Nuclear
Optics	Optique	Optik	Optica
Sound	Son	Schall	Sonido
Plastics	Plastiques	Kunststoffe	Plásticos
Computer Applications	Applications Informatiques	Computer Anwendung	Aplicaciones para Computadoras
Political Science	Sciences Politiques	Politische Wissenschafte	Ciencias Políticas
Civil Rights	Droits Civiques	Bürgerrechte	Derechos Civiles
International Relations	Relations Internationales	Internationale Beziehungen	Relaciones Internacionales
Population Studies	Démographie	Bevölkerungswissenschaft	Demografía
Printing	Imprimerie	Druck	Imprenta
Computer Applications	Applications Informatiques	Computer Anwendung	Aplicaciones para Computadoras
Psychology	Psychologie	Psychologie	Psicología
Public Administration	Administration Publique	Öffentliche Verwaltung	Administración Pública
Computer Applications	Applications Informatiques	Computer Anwendung	Aplicaciones para Computadoras
Municipal Government	Gouvernement Municipal	Kommunalverwaltung	Gobierno Municipal
Public Health and Safety	Santé Publique et Prévention	Öffentliche Gesundheitspflege	Salud y Seguridad Pública
Publishing and Book Trade	Édition et Commerce du Livre	Verlagswesen und Buchhandel	Editoriales y Ferias de Libros
Computer Applications	Applications Informatiques	Computer Anwendung	Aplicaciones para Computadoras
Real Estate	Immobiliers	Grundbesitz und Immobilien	Bienes Raíces
Computer Applications	Applications Informatiques	Computer Anwendung	Aplicaciones para Computadoras
Religions and Theology	Religions et Théologie	Religion und Theologie	Religión y Teología
Buddhist	Bouddhisme	Buddhist	Budismo
Eastern Orthodox	Églises Orthodoxes	Orthodox	Inglesias Ortodoxas
Hindu	Hindouisme	Hindu	Hinduísmo
Islamic	Islam	Islamische	Islamísmo
Judaic	Judaisme	Jüdäistische	Judaísmo
Protestant	Protestantisme	Evangelische	Iglesia Protestante
Roman Catholic	Catholicisme Romain	Römisch-katholische	Católico Romano
Other Denominations and Sects	Autres	Andere Bekenntnisse und Sekte	Otras Denominaciones y Sectas
Rubber	Caoutchouc	Gummi	Caucho
Computer Applications	Applications Informatiques	Computer Anwendung	Aplicaciones para Computadoras
Sciences: Comprehensive Works	Sciences: Oeuvres d'Ensemble	Wissenschaften: Umfassende Werke	Ciencias: Obras Completas
Computer Applications	Applications Informatiques	Computer Anwendung	Aplicaciones para Computadoras
Shoes and Boots	Chaussures et Bottes	Schuhe und Stiefel	Zapatos y Botas
Singles' Interests and Lifestyles	Intérêts et Style de Vie Célibataire	Ledigenstandinteressen	Intereses y Estilos de Vida de Solteros
Social Sciences: Comprehensive Works	Sciences Sociales: Oeuvres d'Ensemble	Sozialwissenschaften: Umfassende Werke	Ciencias Sociales: Obras Completas
Social Service and Welfare	Service Social et Protection Sociale	Sozialpflege und Fürsorge	Asistencia y Bienestar Social
Sociology	Sociologie	Soziologie	Sociología
Computer Applications	Applications Informatiques	Computer Anwendung	Aplicaciones para Computadoras
Sound Recording and Reproduction	Enregistrement et Reproduction du Son	Tonaufnahme und Tonwiedergabe	Grabaciones y Reproducciones Sonoras
Computer Applications	Applications Informatiques	Computer Anwendung	Aplicaciones para Computadoras
Sports and Games	Sports et Jeux	Sport und Spiele	Deportes y Juegos
Ball Games	Jeux de Balle	Ballspiele	Juegos de Pelota
Bicycles and Motorcycles	Bicyclettes et Motocyclettes	Fahrräder und Motorräder	Bicicletas y Motocicletas
Boats and Boating	Bateaux et Canotage	Boote und Bootfahren	Barcos y Canotaje
Horses and Horsemanship	Equitation	Pferde und Reitsport	Caballos y Equitación
Outdoor Life	Vie en Plein Air	Im Freien	Vida de Campo
Statistics	Statistiques	Statistik	Estadísticas
Technology: Comprehensive Works	Technologie: Oeuvres d'Ensemble	Technologie: Umfassende Werke	Tecnología: Obras Completas
Textile Industries and Fabrics	Textiles	Textil	Telas e Industria Textil
Computer Applications	Applications Informatiques	Computer Anwendung	Aplicaciones para Computadoras
Theater	Théâtre	Theater	Teatro
Tobacco	Tabac	Tabak	Tabaco
Transportation	Transports	Transport	Transporte
Air Transport	Transport Aérien	Luftverkehr	Transporte Aéreo
Automobiles	Automobiles	Kraftfahrzeugen	Automóviles
Computer Applications	Applications Informatiques	Computer Anwendung	Aplicaciones para Computadoras
Railroads	Chemins de Fer	Eisenbahnen	Ferrocarriles
Roads and Traffic	Routes et Circulation	Strassen und Strassenverkehr	Caminos y Tráfico
Ships and Shipping	Navires et Transport Maritimes	Schiffe und Schiffahrt	Barcos y Embarques
Trucks and Trucking	Transports Routiers	Lastkraftwagen	Camiones
Travel and Tourism	Voyages et Tourisme	Reisen und Tourismus	Viaje y Turismo
Airline Inflight and Hotel Inroom	Revues pour Vol de Lignes Aériennes et pour Chambres d'Hôtels	Fluggesellschaft und Hotel Veröffentlichungen	Vuelo en Aerolínea y Cuarto de Hotel
Veterinary Sciences	Science Vétérinaire	Tierheilkunde	Veterinaria
Computer Applications	Applications Informatiques	Computer Anwendung	Aplicaciones para Computadoras
Water Ressources	Ressources en Eau	Wasserwirtschaft	Recursos del Agua
Computer Applications	Applications Informatiques	Computer Anwendung	Aplicaciones de los Computadoras
Women's Health	Santé de la Femme	Gesundheit von Frauen	Salud de las Mujeres
Women's Interests	Publications d'Intérêt Féminin	Fraueninteresse	Intereses Femininos
Women's Studies	Études de la Femme	Frauenstudien	Estudios de las Mujeres

Classified List of Serials
Subjects A-Edu

This section contains bibliographic information for currently published serials, classified by subject. Publisher, address and contact data are provided. See the User's Guide for more information on the many fields included in complete entries.

ABSTRACTING AND INDEXING SERVICES

see also BIBLIOGRAPHIES ; and also Abstracting, Bibliographies, Statistics subheadings under specific subjects

A A A S ANNUAL MEETING PROGRAM - ABSTRACTS OF PAPERS. see *SCIENCES: COMPREHENSIVE WORKS—Abstracting, Bibliographies, Statistics*

A B C NEWS INDEX. see *COMMUNICATIONS—Abstracting, Bibliographies, Statistics*

A B I - INFORM. (American Business Information) see *BUSINESS AND ECONOMICS—Abstracting, Bibliographies, Statistics*

A B S I. (Abstracte in Bibliologie si Stiinta Informarii) see *LIBRARY AND INFORMATION SCIENCES—Abstracting, Bibliographies, Statistics*

A C C CURRENT JOURNAL REVIEW. see *MEDICAL SCIENCES—Abstracting, Bibliographies, Statistics*

A C M ELECTRONIC GUIDE TO COMPUTING LITERATURE; bibliographic listing, author index, keyword index, category index, proper noun subject index, reviewer index, source index. see *COMPUTERS—Abstracting, Bibliographies, Statistics*

A C NIELSEN CHINA MEDIA INDEX. see *COMMUNICATIONS— Abstracting, Bibliographies, Statistics*

A C O G CLINICAL REVIEW. see *MEDICAL SCIENCES— Abstracting, Bibliographies, Statistics*

A E T F A T INDEX; releve des travaux de phanerogamie systematique et des taxons nouveaux concernant l'Afrique au sud du Sahara et Madagascar. see *BIOLOGY—Abstracting, Bibliographies, Statistics*

A L I S A (ONLINE). (Australian Library and Information Science Abstracts) see *LIBRARY AND INFORMATION SCIENCES—Abstracting, Bibliographies, Statistics*

A M E D. (Allied and Complementary Medicine Database) see *ALTERNATIVE MEDICINE—Abstracting, Bibliographies, Statistics*

A P A I S: AUSTRALIAN PUBLIC AFFAIRS INFORMATION SERVICE (ONLINE EDITION). see *PUBLIC ADMINISTRATION—Abstracting, Bibliographies, Statistics*

A R N O V A ABSTRACTS. see *SOCIAL SERVICES AND WELFARE—Abstracting, Bibliographies, Statistics*

A S F A AQUACULTURE ABSTRACTS (ONLINE EDITION). (Aquatic Sciences & Fisheries Abstracts) see *FISH AND FISHERIES—Abstracting, Bibliographies, Statistics*

A S F A MARINE BIOTECHNOLOGY ABSTRACTS (ONLINE EDITION). see *BIOLOGY—Abstracting, Bibliographies, Statistics*

A S S I A. (Applied Social Sciences Index & Abstracts) see *SOCIAL SCIENCES: COMPREHENSIVE WORKS— Abstracting, Bibliographies, Statistics*

A S T I S BIBLIOGRAPHY. see *SCIENCES: COMPREHENSIVE WORKS—Abstracting, Bibliographies, Statistics*

A T PASES. (Adenosine Triphosphatases) see *BIOLOGY—Abstracting, Bibliographies, Statistics*

ABRIDGED BIOGRAPHY AND GENEALOGY MASTER INDEX. see *BIOGRAPHY—Abstracting, Bibliographies, Statistics*

ABRIDGED CATHOLIC PERIODICAL AND LITERATURE INDEX. see *RELIGIONS AND THEOLOGY—Abstracting, Bibliographies, Statistics*

050 011   USA   ISSN 0001-334X
ABRIDGED READERS' GUIDE TO PERIODICAL LITERATURE. Text in English. 1935. 9/yr. (Sep.-May; plus a. & q. cumulation). USD 195 in US & Canada (effective 2006). **Document type:** *Abstract/Index.* **Description:** Indexes selective general interest magazines covered by the unabridged Readers' Guide.
Related titles: ♦ Abridged ed. of: Readers' Guide to Periodical Literature. ISSN 0034-0464.
Published by: H.W. Wilson Co., 950 University Ave, Bronx, NY 10452-4224. TEL 718-588-8400, 800-367-6770, FAX 718-590-1617, 800-590-1617, custserv@hwwilson.com, http://www.hwwilson.com. Ed. Donald Cannon.

ABSTRACT BULLETIN OF PAPER SCIENCE AND TECHNOLOGY. see *PAPER AND PULP—Abstracting, Bibliographies, Statistics*

ABSTRACTA IRANICA. see *HISTORY—Abstracting, Bibliographies, Statistics*

ABSTRACTS IN ANTHROPOLOGY. see *ANTHROPOLOGY— Abstracting, Bibliographies, Statistics*

ABSTRACTS IN MARYLAND ARCHEOLOGY. see *ARCHAEOLOGY—Abstracting, Bibliographies, Statistics*

ABSTRACTS IN NEW TECHNOLOGIES AND ENGINEERING. see *TECHNOLOGY: COMPREHENSIVE WORKS— Abstracting, Bibliographies, Statistics*

ABSTRACTS IN SOCIAL GERONTOLOGY; current literature on aging. see *GERONTOLOGY AND GERIATRICS—Abstracting, Bibliographies, Statistics*

ABSTRACTS OF BULGARIAN SCIENTIFIC LITERATURE. AGRICULTURE AND FORESTRY. VETERINARY MEDICINE. see *VETERINARY SCIENCE—Abstracting, Bibliographies, Statistics*

ABSTRACTS OF BULGARIAN SCIENTIFIC LITERATURE. PHILOSOPHY, SOCIOLOGY, SCIENCE OF SCIENCES, PSYCHOLOGY AND PEDAGOGICS. see *EDUCATION—Abstracting, Bibliographies, Statistics*

ABSTRACTS OF CHINESE GEOLOGICAL LITERATURE. see *EARTH SCIENCES—Abstracting, Bibliographies, Statistics*

ABSTRACTS OF CLINICAL CARE GUIDELINES. see *MEDICAL SCIENCES—Abstracting, Bibliographies, Statistics*

ABSTRACTS OF CURRENT LITERATURE IN TOXICOLOGY. see *ENVIRONMENTAL STUDIES—Abstracting, Bibliographies, Statistics*

ABSTRACTS OF EDUCATIONAL STUDIES AND RESEARCH. see *EDUCATION—Abstracting, Bibliographies, Statistics*

ABSTRACTS OF ENTOMOLOGY. see *BIOLOGY—Abstracting, Bibliographies, Statistics*

ABSTRACTS OF MYCOLOGY. see *BIOLOGY—Abstracting, Bibliographies, Statistics*

ABSTRACTS OF PUBLIC ADMINISTRATION, DEVELOPMENT AND ENVIRONMENT. see *PUBLIC ADMINISTRATION— Abstracting, Bibliographies, Statistics*

ABSTRACTS OF SYMPOSIUM ON PEPTIDE CHEMISTRY/PEPUCHIDO KAGAKU TORONKAI KOEN YOSHISHU. see *FISH AND FISHERIES—Abstracting, Bibliographies, Statistics*

ABSTRACTS OF THE SYMPOSIUM ON ORGANOMETALLIC CHEMISTRY, JAPAN/YUKI KINZOKU KAGAKU TORONKAI KOEN YOSHISHU. see *CHEMISTRY—Abstracting, Bibliographies, Statistics*

ABSTRACTS OF THE TOKYO CONFERENCE ON INSTRUMENTAL ANALYSIS AND ANALYTIC SYSTEMS/BUNSEKI KIKI TO KAISEKI SHISUTEMU NI KANSURU TOKYO TORONKAI KOEN YOSHISHU. see *CHEMISTRY—Abstracting, Bibliographies, Statistics*

ABSTRACTS ON HYGIENE AND COMMUNICABLE DISEASES. see *MEDICAL SCIENCES—Abstracting, Bibliographies, Statistics*

▼ *new title*   ➤ *refereed*   ✳ *unverified*   ♦ *full entry avail.*

A

ABSTRACTS ON THE SYMPOSIUM ON MOLECULAR STRUCTURE/BUNSHI KOZO SOGO TORONKAI KOEN YOSHISHU. see *CHEMISTRY—Abstracting, Bibliographies, Statistics*

016   USA   ISSN 1056-7496
ACADEMIC ABSTRACTS CD-ROM. Text in English. 1991. m. USD 1,799; USD 1,399 for 10 discs. bk.rev. index. **Document type:** *Abstract/Index.* **Description:** Abstracts and indexes over 750 periodicals.
Media: CD-ROM. **Related titles:** Magnetic Tape ed.
Published by: EBSCO Publishing (Subsidiary of: EBSCO Industries, Inc.), 10 Estes St, PO Box 682, Ipswich, MA 01938-0682. TEL 978-356-6500, 800-653-2726, FAX 978-356-6565, ep@epnet.com, http://www.epnet.com. Ed. Melissa Kummerer. **Subscr. to:** Subscription Services, PO Box 1943, Birmingham, AL 35201-1943. TEL 205-991-6600, FAX 205-995-1518.

016   USA
ACADEMIC SEARCH. Text in English. 1993. m. USD 6,000. illus. reprints avail. **Document type:** *Abstract/Index.* **Description:** General index covering over 3000 periodicals.
Media: Online - full content. **Related titles:** CD-ROM ed.
Published by: EBSCO Publishing (Subsidiary of: EBSCO Industries, Inc.), 10 Estes St, PO Box 682, Ipswich, MA 01938-0682. TEL 978-356-6500, 800-653-2726, FAX 978-356-6565, ep@epnet.com, http://www.epnet.com. **Subscr. to:** Subscription Services, PO Box 1943, Birmingham, AL 35201-1943. TEL 205-991-6600, FAX 205-995-1518.

016   USA   ISSN 0095-5698
AI3
ACCESS: THE SUPPLEMENTARY INDEX TO PERIODICALS. Text in English. 1975. s-a. USD 287.50 in North America to institutions; USD 297.50 elsewhere to institutions; USD 895 combined subscription to institutions print & online eds. (effective 2005); includes single user Internet access. illus. Index. reprints avail. **Document type:** *Abstract/Index.* **Description:** Covers regional and city magazines, as well as general interest periodicals not indexed by the H.W. Wilson Company.
Incorporates (1978-1979): Monthly Periodical Index (0197-6567) **Related titles:** Online - full text ed.: USD 495 type 1; USD 795 type 2 (effective 2005); including 15 retrospective years of indexing.
Published by: John Gordon Burke Publisher, Inc., PO Box 1492, Evanston, IL 60204-1492. TEL 847-866-8625, FAX 847-866-6639, info@jgburkepub.com, http://www.jgburkepub.com/access.html; http://jgburkepub.com.

ACCOUNTING & FINANCE ABSTRACTS. see *BUSINESS AND ECONOMICS—Abstracting, Bibliographies, Statistics*

ACCOUNTING AND TAX INDEX. see *BUSINESS AND ECONOMICS—Abstracting, Bibliographies, Statistics*

ACCOUNTING ARTICLES. see *BUSINESS AND ECONOMICS—Abstracting, Bibliographies, Statistics*

ACOUSTICS ABSTRACTS. see *PHYSICS—Abstracting, Bibliographies, Statistics*

ACTA VETERINARIA JAPONICA. see *VETERINARY SCIENCE—Abstracting, Bibliographies, Statistics*

ADHESIVES ABSTRACTS. see *CHEMISTRY—Abstracting, Bibliographies, Statistics*

ADVANCES IN APPLIED CERAMICS; structural, functional and bioceramics. see *CERAMICS, GLASS AND POTTERY—Abstracting, Bibliographies, Statistics*

AERONAUTICAL ENGINEERING: A CONTINUING BIOGRAPHY WITH INDEXES. see *AERONAUTICS AND SPACE FLIGHT—Abstracting, Bibliographies, Statistics*

AEROSPACE AND AVIATION DOCUMENTS CD-ROM. see *AERONAUTICS AND SPACE FLIGHT—Abstracting, Bibliographies, Statistics*

AFRICAN HEALTHLINE. see *MEDICAL SCIENCES—Abstracting, Bibliographies, Statistics*

AFRICAN INDEX MEDICUS. see *MEDICAL SCIENCES—Abstracting, Bibliographies, Statistics*

AFRICAN STUDIES. see *HISTORY—Abstracting, Bibliographies, Statistics*

AGBIOTECH NEWS AND INFORMATION. see *BIOLOGY—Abstracting, Bibliographies, Statistics*

AGE.INFO CD-ROM. see *GERONTOLOGY AND GERIATRICS—Abstracting, Bibliographies, Statistics*

AGELINE. see *GERONTOLOGY AND GERIATRICS—Abstracting, Bibliographies, Statistics*

AGRICULTURAL ABSTRACTS FOR TANZANIA. see *AGRICULTURE—Abstracting, Bibliographies, Statistics*

AGRICULTURAL ENGINEERING ABSTRACTS. see *AGRICULTURE—Abstracting, Bibliographies, Statistics*

AGRICULTURE CHECKLIST. see *AGRICULTURE—Abstracting, Bibliographies, Statistics*

AGRO-AGEN; bibliographic database. see *AGRICULTURE—Abstracting, Bibliographies, Statistics*

AGRO-KONF; bibliographic database. see *AGRICULTURE—Abstracting, Bibliographies, Statistics*

AGRO-LIBREX; bibliographic database. see *AGRICULTURE—Abstracting, Bibliographies, Statistics*

AGROBASE. see *AGRICULTURE—Abstracting, Bibliographies, Statistics*

AGROFORESTRY ABSTRACTS (ONLINE EDITION). see *AGRICULTURE—Abstracting, Bibliographies, Statistics*

AL-AHRAM INDEX/KASHSHAF AL-AHRAM. see *JOURNALISM—Abstracting, Bibliographies, Statistics*

AIDS ABSTRACTS; international literature on acquired immunodeficiency syndrome and related retroviruses. see *MEDICAL SCIENCES—Abstracting, Bibliographies, Statistics*

AIDS & T B WEEKLY ABSTRACTS FROM CONFERENCE PROCEEDINGS. (Tuberculosis) see *MEDICAL SCIENCES—Abstracting, Bibliographies, Statistics*

AIDS & T B WEEKLY ARTICLE SUMMARIES. (Tuberculosis) see *MEDICAL SCIENCES—Abstracting, Bibliographies, Statistics*

AIDSEARCH. see *MEDICAL SCIENCES—Abstracting, Bibliographies, Statistics*

AIR UNIVERSITY LIBRARY INDEX TO MILITARY PERIODICALS. see *MILITARY—Abstracting, Bibliographies, Statistics*

ALLOYS INDEX. see *METALLURGY—Abstracting, Bibliographies, Statistics*

ALT-HEALTH WATCH; alternative health & wellness. see *ALTERNATIVE MEDICINE—Abstracting, Bibliographies, Statistics*

ALUMINUM INDUSTRY ABSTRACTS; a monthly review of the world's technical literature on aluminum. see *METALLURGY—Abstracting, Bibliographies, Statistics*

AMATEUR RADIO SERVICE MASTER FILE UPDATES. see *COMMUNICATIONS—Abstracting, Bibliographies, Statistics*

AMERICA: HISTORY AND LIFE; article abstracts and citations of reviews and dissertations covering the United States and Canada. see *HISTORY—Abstracting, Bibliographies, Statistics*

AMERICA: HISTORY AND LIFE. ANNUAL INDEX. see *HISTORY—Abstracting, Bibliographies, Statistics*

AMERICAN BANKER INDEX. see *BUSINESS AND ECONOMICS—Abstracting, Bibliographies, Statistics*

AMERICAN BOOK PRICES CURRENT. see *PUBLISHING AND BOOK TRADE—Abstracting, Bibliographies, Statistics*

AMERICAN BOOK PRICES CURRENT. FOUR YEAR INDEX. see *PUBLISHING AND BOOK TRADE—Abstracting, Bibliographies, Statistics*

AMERICAN CRYSTALLOGRAPHIC ASSOCIATION. PROGRAM & ABSTRACTS. see *CHEMISTRY—Abstracting, Bibliographies, Statistics*

AMERICAN DRUG INDEX. see *PHARMACY AND PHARMACOLOGY—Abstracting, Bibliographies, Statistics*

AMERICAN FISHERIES ABSTRACTS. see *FISH AND FISHERIES—Abstracting, Bibliographies, Statistics*

AMERICAN HERITAGE CUMULATIVE INDEX. see *HISTORY—Abstracting, Bibliographies, Statistics*

AMERICAN HUMANITIES INDEX. see *HUMANITIES: COMPREHENSIVE WORKS—Abstracting, Bibliographies, Statistics*

011   USA
AMERICAN INFORMATION NEWSLETTER. Text in English. 1991. m. USD 48. back issues avail. **Description:** A newsletter of newsletters; drawn from over 500 other periodicals.

Published by: Paradigm Co., PO Box 45161, Boise, ID 83711. TEL 208-322-7781. Circ: 800.

AMERICAN INSTITUTE FOR CONSERVATION OF HISTORIC AND ARTISTIC WORKS. ABSTRACTS OF PAPERS PRESENTED AT THE ANNUAL MEETING. see *ART—Abstracting, Bibliographies, Statistics*

AMERICAN MATHEMATICAL SOCIETY. ABSTRACTS OF PAPERS PRESENTED. see *MATHEMATICS—Abstracting, Bibliographies, Statistics*

AMERICAN PETROLEUM INSTITUTE. THESAURUS. see *PETROLEUM AND GAS—Abstracting, Bibliographies, Statistics*

AMERICAN SOCIETY FOR MICROBIOLOGY. ABSTRACTS OF THE GENERAL MEETING. see *BIOLOGY—Abstracting, Bibliographies, Statistics*

AMERICAN SPEECH - LANGUAGE - HEARING ABSTRACTS. see *HANDICAPPED—Abstracting, Bibliographies, Statistics*

AMERICAN WELDING SOCIETY ANNUAL MEETING. ABSTRACTS OF PAPERS. see *METALLURGY—Abstracting, Bibliographies, Statistics*

ANALISIS ANUAL DEL MERCADO DEL AZUCAR. see *BUSINESS AND ECONOMICS—Abstracting, Bibliographies, Statistics*

ANALYTICAL ABSTRACTS. see *CHEMISTRY—Abstracting, Bibliographies, Statistics*

ANIMAL BREEDING ABSTRACTS; a monthly abstract of world literature. see *AGRICULTURE—Abstracting, Bibliographies, Statistics*

ANNALES COLLEGII MEDICI UNIVERSITATIS IAGIELLONICAE CRACOVIENSIS. see *MEDICAL SCIENCES—Abstracting, Bibliographies, Statistics*

ANNOTATED INDEX TO INDIAN SOCIAL SCIENCE JOURNALS. see *LIBRARY AND INFORMATION SCIENCES—Abstracting, Bibliographies, Statistics*

ANNUAL INDEX TO MOTION PICTURE CREDITS. see *MOTION PICTURES—Abstracting, Bibliographies, Statistics*

ANTHROPOLOGICAL ABSTRACTS: CULTURAL - SOCIAL ANTHROPOLOGY FROM AUSTRIA, GERMANY, SWITZERLAND. see *ANTHROPOLOGY—Abstracting, Bibliographies, Statistics*

ANTHROPOLOGICAL INDEX ONLINE. see *ANTHROPOLOGY—Abstracting, Bibliographies, Statistics*

ANTHROPOLOGICAL LITERATURE; an index to periodical articles and essays. see *ANTHROPOLOGY—Abstracting, Bibliographies, Statistics*

ANTHROPOLOGISCHER ANZEIGER. see *ANTHROPOLOGY—Abstracting, Bibliographies, Statistics*

ANYAGMOZGATASI ES CSOMAGOLASI SZAKIRODALMI TAJEKOZTATO/ABSTRACT JOURNAL FOR MATERIALS HANDLING AND PACKAGING. see *TRANSPORTATION—Abstracting, Bibliographies, Statistics*

APICULTURAL ABSTRACTS. see *AGRICULTURE—Abstracting, Bibliographies, Statistics*

APPALACHIAN OUTLOOK; new sources of regional information. see *LIBRARY AND INFORMATION SCIENCES—Abstracting, Bibliographies, Statistics*

APPLIED BOTANY ABSTRACTS. see *BIOLOGY—Abstracting, Bibliographies, Statistics*

APPLIED MECHANICS REVIEWS; an assessment of world literature in engineering sciences. see *ENGINEERING—Abstracting, Bibliographies, Statistics*

APPLIED SCIENCE & TECHNOLOGY ABSTRACTS. see *ENGINEERING—Abstracting, Bibliographies, Statistics*

APPLIED SCIENCE & TECHNOLOGY INDEX. see *ENGINEERING—Abstracting, Bibliographies, Statistics*

APPROPRIATE TECHNOLOGY INDEX. see *TECHNOLOGY: COMPREHENSIVE WORKS—Abstracting, Bibliographies, Statistics*

APSTRACTS. see *BIOLOGY—Abstracting, Bibliographies, Statistics*

AQUALINE ABSTRACTS. see *WATER RESOURCES—Abstracting, Bibliographies, Statistics*

AQUATIC BIOLOGY, AQUACULTURE & FISHERIES RESOURCES. see *BIOLOGY—Abstracting, Bibliographies, Statistics*

AQUATIC SCIENCES & FISHERIES ABSTRACTS. PART 1: BIOLOGICAL SCIENCES AND LIVING RESOURCES. see *CONSERVATION—Abstracting, Bibliographies, Statistics*

AQUATIC SCIENCES & FISHERIES ABSTRACTS. PART 2: OCEAN TECHNOLOGY, POLICY AND NON-LIVING RESOURCES. see *WATER RESOURCES—Abstracting, Bibliographies, Statistics*

AQUATIC SCIENCES & FISHERIES ABSTRACTS. PART 3: AQUATIC POLLUTION AND ENVIRONMENTAL QUALITY. see *ENVIRONMENTAL STUDIES—Abstracting, Bibliographies, Statistics*

ARCHITECTURAL INDEX. see *ARCHITECTURE—Abstracting, Bibliographies, Statistics*

ARCTIC & ANTARCTIC REGIONS. see *EARTH SCIENCES—Abstracting, Bibliographies, Statistics*

ART ABSTRACTS. see *ART—Abstracting, Bibliographies, Statistics*

ART AND ARCHAEOLOGY TECHNICAL ABSTRACTS (ONLINE EDITION); abstracts of the technical literature on archaeology, architecture, and the fine and applied arts. see *ART—Abstracting, Bibliographies, Statistics*

ART INDEX. see *ART—Abstracting, Bibliographies, Statistics*

ART PRICE ANNUAL & FALK'S ART PRICE INDEX. see *PRINTING—Abstracting, Bibliographies, Statistics*

ARTBIBLIOGRAPHIES CURRENT TITLES (EMAIL EDITION). see *ART—Abstracting, Bibliographies, Statistics*

ARTBIBLIOGRAPHIES MODERN; abstracts of the current literature of modern art, photography and design. see *ART—Abstracting, Bibliographies, Statistics*

ARTEMISA. see *MEDICAL SCIENCES—Abstracting, Bibliographies, Statistics*

ARTHA SUCHI. see *BUSINESS AND ECONOMICS—Abstracting, Bibliographies, Statistics*

ARTS & HUMANITIES CITATION INDEX. see *ART—Abstracting, Bibliographies, Statistics*

ASIAN ALMANAC; weekly abstracts of Asian affairs. see *POLITICAL SCIENCE—Abstracting, Bibliographies, Statistics*

ASIAN - PACIFIC ECONOMIC LITERATURE. see *BUSINESS AND ECONOMICS—Abstracting, Bibliographies, Statistics*

ASIAN STUDIES W W W MONITOR. (World Wide Web) see *ASIAN STUDIES—Abstracting, Bibliographies, Statistics*

ASSESSMENT REPORT INDEX. see *ENERGY—Abstracting, Bibliographies, Statistics*

ASSOCIATION OF SOUTHERN AFRICAN INDEXERS AND BIBLIOGRAPHERS. NEWSLETTER. see *LIBRARY AND INFORMATION SCIENCES*

ASSOCIATION OF SOUTHERN AFRICAN INDEXERS AND BIBLIOGRAPHERS. PUBLICATIONS. see *LIBRARY AND INFORMATION SCIENCES*

THE ATLANTA CONSTITUTION AND JOURNAL INDEX. see *JOURNALISM—Abstracting, Bibliographies, Statistics*

ATTENDERINGSBULLETIN BIBLIOTHEEK STARING-GEBOUW: LAND, BODEM, WATER. see *ENVIRONMENTAL STUDIES—Abstracting, Bibliographies, Statistics*

AUDIOCASSETTE & C D FINDER. see *EDUCATION—Abstracting, Bibliographies, Statistics*

AUSTRALASIAN RELIGION INDEX. see *RELIGIONS AND THEOLOGY—Abstracting, Bibliographies, Statistics*

AUSTRALIA. BUREAU OF STATISTICS. A GUIDE TO THE CONSUMER INDEX. see *BUSINESS AND ECONOMICS—Abstracting, Bibliographies, Statistics*

AUSTRALIAN AND NEW ZEALAND CITATOR TO UK REPORTS. see *LAW—Abstracting, Bibliographies, Statistics*

AUSTRALIAN AND NEW ZEALAND DIRECTORY OF GENETICS SUPPORT GROUPS, SERVICES AND INFORMATION. see *BIOLOGY—Abstracting, Bibliographies, Statistics*

AUSTRALIAN ARCHITECTURE DATABASE. see *ARCHITECTURE—Abstracting, Bibliographies, Statistics*

AUSTRALIAN CURRENT LAW LEGISLATION. see *LAW—Abstracting, Bibliographies, Statistics*

AUSTRALIAN CURRENT LAW REPORTER. see *LAW—Abstracting, Bibliographies, Statistics*

AUSTRALIAN EDUCATION INDEX (ONLINE EDITION). see *EDUCATION—Abstracting, Bibliographies, Statistics*

AUSTRALIAN FAMILY AND SOCIETY ABSTRACTS. see *SOCIOLOGY—Abstracting, Bibliographies, Statistics*

AUSTRALIAN LEGAL MONTHLY DIGEST. see *LAW—Abstracting, Bibliographies, Statistics*

AUSTRALIAN PATENT ABSTRACTS ON CD-ROM. see *PATENTS, TRADEMARKS AND COPYRIGHTS—Abstracting, Bibliographies, Statistics*

AUSTRALIAN SENTENCING JUDGMENTS BULLETIN. see *LAW—Abstracting, Bibliographies, Statistics*

025.3   AUS   ISSN 0314-3767
AUSTRALIAN SOCIETY OF INDEXERS NEWSLETTER. Text in English. 1977. m. (except Jan.). AUD 22 (effective 2000). adv. bk.rev. back issues avail. **Document type:** *Newsletter, Abstract/Index.* **Description:** Includes information about indexing in all formats, books, databases, periodicales, etc. **Related titles:** Online - full text ed.: Australian Society of Indexers Newsletter Online. ISSN 1326-2718. 1994. **Published by:** Australian Society of Indexers, PO Box R 598, Royal Exchange, NSW 1225, Australia. TEL 61-500-525005, newsletter@aussi.org, http://www.aussi.org/. Ed., R&P, Adv. contact Glenda Browne. Circ: 240 (paid).

AUSTRIAN POLITICIANS, PARTIES AND MAYORS INDEX/OESTERREICHISCHER POLITIKER-, PARTEIEN- UND BUERGERMEISTERINDEX. see *POLITICAL SCIENCE—Abstracting, Bibliographies, Statistics*

AUSZUEGE AUS PRESSEARTIKELN. see *BUSINESS AND ECONOMICS—Abstracting, Bibliographies, Statistics*

AUTOIMMUNE DISEASES. see *MEDICAL SCIENCES—Abstracting, Bibliographies, Statistics*

AUTOMATIZALASI, SZAMITASTECHNIKAI ES MERESTECHNIKAI SZAKIRODALMI TAJEKOZTATO/ AUTOMATION, COMPUTING. COMPUTERS & MEASUREMENT ABSTRACTS. see *PHYSICS—Abstracting, Bibliographies, Statistics*

AVERY INDEX TO ARCHITECTURAL PERIODICALS. see *ARCHITECTURE—Abstracting, Bibliographies, Statistics*

AVIATION MASTER FILE. see *COMMUNICATIONS—Abstracting, Bibliographies, Statistics*

AVIATION TRADESCAN; monthly index and abstracts. see *AERONAUTICS AND SPACE FLIGHT—Abstracting, Bibliographies, Statistics*

B H I NET. see *HUMANITIES: COMPREHENSIVE WORKS*

B H I PLUS. see *HUMANITIES: COMPREHENSIVE WORKS—Abstracting, Bibliographies, Statistics*

B M T ABSTRACTS; international maritime technology. see *TRANSPORTATION—Abstracting, Bibliographies, Statistics*

B S B I ABSTRACTS; abstracts from literature relating to the vascular plants of the British Isles. see *BIOLOGY—Abstracting, Bibliographies, Statistics*

BAHRAIN. EDUCATIONAL DOCUMENTATION LIBRARY. ACQUISITIONS LIST. see *EDUCATION—Abstracting, Bibliographies, Statistics*

BAHRAIN. EDUCATIONAL DOCUMENTATION LIBRARY. BIBLIOGRAPHIC LISTS. see *EDUCATION—Abstracting, Bibliographies, Statistics*

BANYASZATI SZAKIRODALMI TAJEKOZTATO/MINING ABSTRACTS. see *MINES AND MINING INDUSTRY—Abstracting, Bibliographies, Statistics*

BARRON'S INDEX. see *BUSINESS AND ECONOMICS—Abstracting, Bibliographies, Statistics*

BASE DE DONNEES P A S C A L. PLAN DE CLASSEMENT. (Programme Applique a la Selection et la Compilation Automatique de la Literature) see *LIBRARY AND INFORMATION SCIENCES—Computer Applications*

BEILSTEIN ABSTRACTS. see *CHEMISTRY—Abstracting, Bibliographies, Statistics*

BELGIAN PATENTS ABSTRACTS. see *PATENTS, TRADEMARKS AND COPYRIGHTS—Abstracting, Bibliographies, Statistics*

BIBLIOGRAFIE CESKE LINGVISTIKY/BIBLIOGRAPHY OF CZECH LINGUISTICS. see *LINGUISTICS—Abstracting, Bibliographies, Statistics*

BIBLIOGRAFIE CESKE ONOMASTIKY. see *LINGUISTICS—Abstracting, Bibliographies, Statistics*

BIBLIOGRAPHIE DE L'ALGERIE/AL-BIBLIYUGRAFYA AL-DJAZAIRIYAH. see *BIBLIOGRAPHIES*

BIBLIOGRAPHIE ZUR SYMBOLIK, IKONOGRAPHIE UND MYTHOLOGIE. see *ANTHROPOLOGY—Abstracting, Bibliographies, Statistics*

BIBLIOGRAPHIES AND INDEXES IN MEDICAL STUDIES. see *MEDICAL SCIENCES—Abstracting, Bibliographies, Statistics*

BIBLIOGRAPHIES AND INDEXES IN SOCIOLOGY. see *SOCIOLOGY—Abstracting, Bibliographies, Statistics*

BIBLIOGRAPHISCHE INFORMATIONEN ZU MIGRATION UND ETHNIZITAET. see *SOCIOLOGY—Abstracting, Bibliographies, Statistics*

BIBLIOTECA APOSTOLICA VATICANA. CATALOGHI E NORME DI CATALOGAZIONE. see *RELIGIONS AND THEOLOGY—Abstracting, Bibliographies, Statistics*

BIBLIOTECHNOE DELO I BIBLIOGRAFIYA. REFERATIVNO-BIBLIOGRAFICHESKAYA INFORMATSIYA. see *LIBRARY AND INFORMATION SCIENCES—Abstracting, Bibliographies, Statistics*

BIBLIOTHECA IBERO-AMERICANA. see *POLITICAL SCIENCE—Abstracting, Bibliographies, Statistics*

BIOCHEMISTRY AND BIOPHYSICS CITATION INDEX. see *BIOLOGY—Abstracting, Bibliographies, Statistics*

BIOCONTROL NEWS AND INFORMATION. see *AGRICULTURE—Abstracting, Bibliographies, Statistics*

BIOENGINEERING ABSTRACTS (ONLINE EDITION). see *BIOLOGY—Abstracting, Bibliographies, Statistics*

BIOETHICS LITERATURE REVIEW. see *MEDICAL SCIENCES—Abstracting, Bibliographies, Statistics*

BIOFUELS ABSTRACTS. see *ENERGY—Abstracting, Bibliographies, Statistics*

BIOGRAPHY AND GENEALOGY MASTER INDEX. see *BIOGRAPHY—Abstracting, Bibliographies, Statistics*

BIOGRAPHY INDEX; a quarterly index to biographical material in books and magazines. see *BIOGRAPHY—Abstracting, Bibliographies, Statistics*

BIOLOGICAL ABSTRACTS; references, abstracts, and indexes to the world's life sciences research literature. see *BIOLOGY—Abstracting, Bibliographies, Statistics*

BIOLOGICAL ABSTRACTS CUMULATIVE INDEXES. see *BIOLOGY—Abstracting, Bibliographies, Statistics*

BIOLOGICAL ABSTRACTS - R R M (ONLINE EDITION); references and indexes to the world's life science reports, reviews, and meeting literature. (Reports, Reviews, Meetings) see *BIOLOGY—Abstracting, Bibliographies, Statistics*

BIOLOGICAL ABSTRACTS - R R M CUMULATIVE INDEX. (Reports, Reviews, and Meetings) see *BIOLOGY—Abstracting, Bibliographies, Statistics*

BIOLOGICAL & AGRICULTURAL INDEX. see *BIOLOGY—Abstracting, Bibliographies, Statistics*

BIOLOGICAL RHYTHMS. see *BIOLOGY—Abstracting, Bibliographies, Statistics*

BIOLOGY DIGEST. see *BIOLOGY—Abstracting, Bibliographies, Statistics*

BIOPHYSICAL SOCIETY. ANNUAL MEETING. ABSTRACTS. see *BIOLOGY—Abstracting, Bibliographies, Statistics*

BIOSIS EVOLUTIONS. see *BIOLOGY—Abstracting, Bibliographies, Statistics*

BIOSIS PREVIEWS; your complete life sciences database. see *BIOLOGY—Abstracting, Bibliographies, Statistics*

BIOSIS SEARCH GUIDE (YEARS). see *BIOLOGY—Abstracting, Bibliographies, Statistics*

▼ *new title*   ➤ *refereed*   ✱ *unverified*   ◆ *full entry avail.*

A

BIOSIS SERIAL SOURCES. see *BIOLOGY—Abstracting, Bibliographies, Statistics*

BIOTECHNOLOGY & BIOENGINEERING ABSTRACTS. see *CHEMISTRY—Abstracting, Bibliographies, Statistics*

BIOTECHNOLOGY CITATION INDEX. see *BIOLOGY— Abstracting, Bibliographies, Statistics*

BIOTECHNOLOGY INFORMATION. see *BIOLOGY—Abstracting, Bibliographies, Statistics*

BISEIBUTSU KAGAKU BUNRUI KENKYUKAI KOEN YOSHISHU/ABSTRACTS OF ANNUAL MEETING ON MICROBIAL CHEMOTAXONOMY. see *BIOLOGY— Abstracting, Bibliographies, Statistics*

BLACK NEWSPAPER INDEX. see *ETHNIC INTERESTS— Abstracting, Bibliographies, Statistics*

BLATT FUER SORTENWESEN. see *AGRICULTURE— Abstracting, Bibliographies, Statistics*

BLOOD COAGULATION FACTORS; current awareness service for researchers in life sciences. see *MEDICAL SCIENCES—Abstracting, Bibliographies, Statistics*

BOECKH BUILDING COST INDEX. see *BUILDING AND CONSTRUCTION—Abstracting, Bibliographies, Statistics*

BOEI DAIGAKKO KYOKAN KENKYU YOROKU/NATIONAL DEFENSE ACADEMY. DIGEST OF RESEARCHES BY FACULTY MEMBERS. see *MILITARY—Abstracting, Bibliographies, Statistics*

BOLETIN BIBLIOGRAFICO DE LA PREVENCION. see *OCCUPATIONAL HEALTH AND SAFETY—Abstracting, Bibliographies, Statistics*

BOOK REVIEW INDEX; indexes all reviews in over 600 periodicals. see *PUBLISHING AND BOOK TRADE—Abstracting, Bibliographies, Statistics*

BOOK REVIEW INDEX: ANNUAL CUMULATION. see *PUBLISHING AND BOOK TRADE—Abstracting, Bibliographies, Statistics*

BOOKS OF THE SOUTHWEST (ONLINE EDITION); a critical checklist of current Southwestern Americana. see *PUBLISHING AND BOOK TRADE—Abstracting, Bibliographies, Statistics*

THE BOSTON GLOBE INDEX. see *JOURNALISM—Abstracting, Bibliographies, Statistics*

BOTANICAL PESTICIDES ABSTRACTS. see *ENVIRONMENTAL STUDIES—Abstracting, Bibliographies, Statistics*

BOTANISK CENTRALBIBLIOTEK. FORTEGNELSE OVER LOEBENDE PERIODICA VED BOTANISK CENTRALBIBLITEK. see *BIOLOGY—Abstracting, Bibliographies, Statistics*

THE BRAZILIAN BOOK MAGAZINE. see *LITERARY AND POLITICAL REVIEWS—Abstracting, Bibliographies, Statistics*

BREASTFEEDING ABSTRACTS. see *MEDICAL SCIENCES—Abstracting, Bibliographies, Statistics*

BRITISH & IRISH ARCHAEOLOGICAL BIBLIOGRAPHY (ONLINE EDITION). see *ARCHAEOLOGY—Abstracting, Bibliographies, Statistics*

BRITISH EDUCATION INDEX. see *EDUCATION—Abstracting, Bibliographies, Statistics*

BRITISH HUMANITIES INDEX. see *HUMANITIES: COMPREHENSIVE WORKS—Abstracting, Bibliographies, Statistics*

BRITISH LIBRARY. DOCUMENT SUPPLY CENTRE. INDEX OF CONFERENCE PROCEEDINGS. see *MEETINGS AND CONGRESSES—Abstracting, Bibliographies, Statistics*

BRITISH LIBRARY. NAME AUTHORITY LIST. see *LIBRARY AND INFORMATION SCIENCES—Abstracting, Bibliographies, Statistics*

BRITISH NATIONAL BIBLIOGRAPHY FOR REPORT LITERATURE. see *SCIENCES: COMPREHENSIVE WORKS—Abstracting, Bibliographies, Statistics*

BRITISH NURSING INDEX; index of journal articles of interest to nurses, midwives and community staff. see *MEDICAL SCIENCES—Abstracting, Bibliographies, Statistics*

▼ BRITISH POULTRY ABSTRACTS. see *AGRICULTURE— Abstracting, Bibliographies, Statistics*

BULLETIN D'HISTOIRE CISTERCIENNE/CISTERCIAN HISTORY ABSTRACTS. see *RELIGIONS AND THEOLOGY— Abstracting, Bibliographies, Statistics*

BUNSOKU. ENERUGI, GENSHIRYOKU KOGAKU-HEN. see *ENGINEERING—Abstracting, Bibliographies, Statistics*

BUSINESS AND INDUSTRY (BEACHWOOD). see *BUSINESS AND ECONOMICS—Abstracting, Bibliographies, Statistics*

BUSINESS DATELINE. see *BUSINESS AND ECONOMICS— Abstracting, Bibliographies, Statistics*

BUSINESS PERIODICALS INDEX. see *BUSINESS AND ECONOMICS—Abstracting, Bibliographies, Statistics*

BYGGREFERAT; nordiskt litteraturindex. see *BUILDING AND CONSTRUCTION—Abstracting, Bibliographies, Statistics*

BYULLETEN' MEZHDUNARODNYKH NAUCHNYKH S'EZDOV, KONFERENTSII, KONGRESSOV, VYSTAVOK. see *MEETINGS AND CONGRESSES—Abstracting, Bibliographies, Statistics*

C A B ABSTRACTS (ONLINE EDITION). see *AGRICULTURE*

C A SELECTS. see *CHEMISTRY—Abstracting, Bibliographies, Statistics*

C A SELECTS. ACTIVATED CARBON. see *CHEMISTRY— Abstracting, Bibliographies, Statistics*

C A SELECTS. ADSORPTION. see *CHEMISTRY—Abstracting, Bibliographies, Statistics*

C A SELECTS. ALKOXYLATED OLEOCHEMICALS. see *PHARMACY AND PHARMACOLOGY—Abstracting, Bibliographies, Statistics*

C A SELECTS. ALKYLATION & CATALYSTS. see *CHEMISTRY—Abstracting, Bibliographies, Statistics*

C A SELECTS. ALLERGY AND ANTIALLERGIC AGENTS. see *MEDICAL SCIENCES—Abstracting, Bibliographies, Statistics*

C A SELECTS. ANALYTICAL ELECTROCHEMISTRY. see *CHEMISTRY—Abstracting, Bibliographies, Statistics*

C A SELECTS. ANTI-INFLAMMATORY AGENTS AND ARTHRITIS. see *MEDICAL SCIENCES—Abstracting, Bibliographies, Statistics*

C A SELECTS. ANTIBACTERIAL AGENTS. see *CHEMISTRY—Abstracting, Bibliographies, Statistics*

C A SELECTS. ANTIFUNGAL & ANTIMYCOTIC AGENTS. see *BIOLOGY—Abstracting, Bibliographies, Statistics*

C A SELECTS. ANTIOXIDANTS. see *CHEMISTRY—Abstracting, Bibliographies, Statistics*

C A SELECTS. ARTIFICIAL SWEETENERS. see *FOOD AND FOOD INDUSTRIES—Abstracting, Bibliographies, Statistics*

C A SELECTS. ATHEROSCLEROSIS & HEART DISEASE. see *MEDICAL SCIENCES—Abstracting, Bibliographies, Statistics*

C A SELECTS. ATOMIC SPECTROSCOPY. see *PHYSICS—Abstracting, Bibliographies, Statistics*

C A SELECTS. BETA-LACTAM ANTIBIOTICS. see *PHARMACY AND PHARMACOLOGY—Abstracting, Bibliographies, Statistics*

C A SELECTS. BIOGENIC AMINES & THE NERVOUS SYSTEM. see *MEDICAL SCIENCES—Abstracting, Bibliographies, Statistics*

C A SELECTS. BISMUTH CHEMISTRY. see *CHEMISTRY— Abstracting, Bibliographies, Statistics*

C A SELECTS. BLOCK & GRAFT POLYMERS. see *CHEMISTRY—Abstracting, Bibliographies, Statistics*

C A SELECTS. BLOOD COAGULATION. see *MEDICAL SCIENCES—Abstracting, Bibliographies, Statistics*

C A SELECTS. CERAMIC MATERIALS (JOURNALS). see *CERAMICS, GLASS AND POTTERY—Abstracting, Bibliographies, Statistics*

C A SELECTS. CERAMIC MATERIALS (PATENTS). see *CERAMICS, GLASS AND POTTERY—Abstracting, Bibliographies, Statistics*

C A SELECTS. CHELATING AGENTS. see *CHEMISTRY— Abstracting, Bibliographies, Statistics*

C A SELECTS. CHEMICAL ENGINEERING OPERATIONS. see *CHEMISTRY—Abstracting, Bibliographies, Statistics*

C A SELECTS. CHEMICAL INSTRUMENTATION. see *INSTRUMENTS—Abstracting, Bibliographies, Statistics*

C A SELECTS. CHEMICAL VAPOR DEPOSITION. see *CHEMISTRY—Abstracting, Bibliographies, Statistics*

C A SELECTS. COAL SCIENCE AND PROCESS CHEMISTRY. see *CHEMISTRY—Abstracting, Bibliographies, Statistics*

C A SELECTS. COATINGS, INKS, & RELATED PRODUCTS. see *PAINTS AND PROTECTIVE COATINGS—Abstracting, Bibliographies, Statistics*

C A SELECTS. COLLOIDS (APPLIED ASPECTS). see *CHEMISTRY—Abstracting, Bibliographies, Statistics*

C A SELECTS. COLLOIDS (MACROMOLECULAR ASPECTS). see *CHEMISTRY—Abstracting, Bibliographies, Statistics*

C A SELECTS. COLLOIDS (PHYSICOCHEMICAL ASPECTS). see *CHEMISTRY—Abstracting, Bibliographies, Statistics*

C A SELECTS. COLOR SCIENCE. see *CHEMISTRY— Abstracting, Bibliographies, Statistics*

C A SELECTS. COLORANTS AND DYES. see *CLEANING AND DYEING—Abstracting, Bibliographies, Statistics*

C A SELECTS. COMPOSITE MATERIALS (POLYMERIC). see *CHEMISTRY—Abstracting, Bibliographies, Statistics*

C A SELECTS. COMPUTERS IN CHEMISTRY. see *CHEMISTRY—Abstracting, Bibliographies, Statistics*

C A SELECTS. CONDUCTIVE POLYMERS. see *CHEMISTRY—Abstracting, Bibliographies, Statistics*

C A SELECTS. CORROSION. see *CHEMISTRY—Abstracting, Bibliographies, Statistics*

C A SELECTS. CORROSION - INHIBITING COATINGS. see *PAINTS AND PROTECTIVE COATINGS—Abstracting, Bibliographies, Statistics*

C A SELECTS. COSMETIC CHEMICALS. see *BEAUTY CULTURE—Abstracting, Bibliographies, Statistics*

C A SELECTS. CROSSLINKING REACTIONS. see *CHEMISTRY—Abstracting, Bibliographies, Statistics*

C A SELECTS. CRYSTAL GROWTH. see *CHEMISTRY— Abstracting, Bibliographies, Statistics*

C A SELECTS. DETERGENTS, SOAPS, & SURFACTANTS. see *CHEMISTRY—Abstracting, Bibliographies, Statistics*

C A SELECTS. DISTILLATION TECHNOLOGY. see *CHEMISTRY—Abstracting, Bibliographies, Statistics*

C A SELECTS. DRILLING MUDS. see *PETROLEUM AND GAS—Abstracting, Bibliographies, Statistics*

C A SELECTS. DRUG ANALYSIS BIOLOGICAL FLUIDS & TISSUES. see *PHARMACY AND PHARMACOLOGY— Abstracting, Bibliographies, Statistics*

C A SELECTS. DRUG & COSMETIC TOXICITY. see *PHARMACY AND PHARMACOLOGY—Abstracting, Bibliographies, Statistics*

C A SELECTS. ELASTOMERS. see *CHEMISTRY—Abstracting, Bibliographies, Statistics*

C A SELECTS. ELECTRICALLY CONDUCTIVE ORGANICS. see *CHEMISTRY—Abstracting, Bibliographies, Statistics*

C A SELECTS. ELECTROCHEMICAL ORGANIC SYNTHESIS. see *CHEMISTRY—Abstracting, Bibliographies, Statistics*

C A SELECTS. ELECTROCHEMICAL REACTIONS. see *CHEMISTRY—Abstracting, Bibliographies, Statistics*

C A SELECTS. ELECTRODEPOSITION. see *CHEMISTRY— Abstracting, Bibliographies, Statistics*

C A SELECTS. ELECTRON & AUGER SPECTROSCOPY. see *PHYSICS—Abstracting, Bibliographies, Statistics*

C A SELECTS. ELECTRON SPIN RESONANCE (CHEMICAL ASPECTS). see *CHEMISTRY—Abstracting, Bibliographies, Statistics*

C A SELECTS. ELECTRONIC CHEMICALS & MATERIALS. see *CHEMISTRY—Abstracting, Bibliographies, Statistics*

C A SELECTS. EMULSIFIERS AND DEMULSIFIERS. see *CHEMISTRY—Abstracting, Bibliographies, Statistics*

C A SELECTS. EMULSION POLYMERIZATION. see *CHEMISTRY—Abstracting, Bibliographies, Statistics*

C A SELECTS. EPOXY RESINS. see *CHEMISTRY—Abstracting, Bibliographies, Statistics*

C A SELECTS. FATS & OILS. see *CHEMISTRY—Abstracting, Bibliographies, Statistics*

C A SELECTS. FERMENTATION CHEMICALS. see *CHEMISTRY—Abstracting, Bibliographies, Statistics*

C A SELECTS. FIBER - REINFORCED PLASTICS. see *PLASTICS—Abstracting, Bibliographies, Statistics*

C A SELECTS. FLAMMABILITY. see *CHEMISTRY—Abstracting, Bibliographies, Statistics*

C A SELECTS. FLUIDIZED SOLIDS TECHNOLOGY. see *CHEMISTRY—Abstracting, Bibliographies, Statistics*

C A SELECTS. FLUOROPOLYMERS. see *CHEMISTRY— Abstracting, Bibliographies, Statistics*

C A SELECTS. FOOD & FEED ANALYSIS. see *FOOD AND FOOD INDUSTRIES—Abstracting, Bibliographies, Statistics*

C A SELECTS. FOOD, DRUGS, & COSMETICS - LEGISLATIVE & REGULATORY ASPECTS. see *FOOD AND FOOD INDUSTRIES—Abstracting, Bibliographies, Statistics*

C A SELECTS. FOOD TOXICITY. see *CHEMISTRY—Abstracting, Bibliographies, Statistics*

C A SELECTS. FORMULATION CHEMISTRY. see *CHEMISTRY—Abstracting, Bibliographies, Statistics*

C A SELECTS. FREE RADICALS (BIOCHEMICAL ASPECTS). see *BIOLOGY—Abstracting, Bibliographies, Statistics*

C A SELECTS. FREE RADICALS (ORGANIC ASPECTS). see *CHEMISTRY—Abstracting, Bibliographies, Statistics*

C A SELECTS. FUEL & LUBRICANT ADDITIVES. see *CHEMISTRY—Abstracting, Bibliographies, Statistics*

C A SELECTS. FUNGICIDES. see *AGRICULTURE—Abstracting, Bibliographies, Statistics*

C A SELECTS. GASEOUS WASTE TREATMENT. see *CHEMISTRY—Abstracting, Bibliographies, Statistics*

C A SELECTS. HEAT-RESISTANT AND ABLATIVE POLYMERS. see *CHEMISTRY—Abstracting, Bibliographies, Statistics*

C A SELECTS. HERBICIDES. see *AGRICULTURE—Abstracting, Bibliographies, Statistics*

C A SELECTS. HOT-MELT ADHESIVES. see *CHEMISTRY—Abstracting, Bibliographies, Statistics*

C A SELECTS. INFRARED SPECTROSCOPY (ORGANIC ASPECTS). see *CHEMISTRY—Abstracting, Bibliographies, Statistics*

C A SELECTS. INFRARED SPECTROSCOPY (PHYSICOCHEMICAL ASPECTS). see *PHYSICS— Abstracting, Bibliographies, Statistics*

C A SELECTS. INITIATION OF POLYMERIZATION. see *CHEMISTRY—Abstracting, Bibliographies, Statistics*

C A SELECTS. INORGANIC ANALYTICAL CHEMISTRY. see *CHEMISTRY—Abstracting, Bibliographies, Statistics*

C A SELECTS. INORGANIC & ORGANOMETALLIC REACTION SYSTEMS. see *CHEMISTRY—Abstracting, Bibliographies, Statistics*

C A SELECTS. INORGANIC CHEMICALS & REACTIONS. see *CHEMISTRY—Abstracting, Bibliographies, Statistics*

C A SELECTS. INSECTICIDES. see *AGRICULTURE— Abstracting, Bibliographies, Statistics*

C A SELECTS. ION CHROMATOGRAPHY. see *CHEMISTRY—Abstracting, Bibliographies, Statistics*

C A SELECTS. ION-CONTAINING POLYMERS. see *CHEMISTRY—Abstracting, Bibliographies, Statistics*

C A SELECTS. ION EXCHANGE. see *CHEMISTRY—Abstracting, Bibliographies, Statistics*

C A SELECTS. LASER - INDUCED CHEMICAL REACTIONS. see *CHEMISTRY—Abstracting, Bibliographies, Statistics*

C A SELECTS. LIQUID CRYSTALS. see *CHEMISTRY— Abstracting, Bibliographies, Statistics*

C A SELECTS. LUBRICANTS, GREASES, & LUBRICATION. see *CHEMISTRY—Abstracting, Bibliographies, Statistics*

C A SELECTS. MEMBRANE SEPARATION. see *CHEMISTRY—Abstracting, Bibliographies, Statistics*

C A SELECTS. MEMORY & RECORDING DEVICES & MATERIALS. see *CHEMISTRY—Abstracting, Bibliographies, Statistics*

C A SELECTS. METALLO ENZYMES & METALLO COENZYMES. see *CHEMISTRY—Abstracting, Bibliographies, Statistics*

C A SELECTS. MOLECULAR MODELING (BIOCHEMICAL ASPECTS). see *CHEMISTRY—Abstracting, Bibliographies, Statistics*

C A SELECTS. NATURAL PRODUCT SYNTHESIS. see *CHEMISTRY—Abstracting, Bibliographies, Statistics*

C A SELECTS. NEW ANTIBIOTICS. see *PHARMACY AND PHARMACOLOGY—Abstracting, Bibliographies, Statistics*

C A SELECTS. NEW BOOKS IN CHEMISTRY. see *CHEMISTRY—Abstracting, Bibliographies, Statistics*

C A SELECTS. NEW PLASTICS. see *PLASTICS—Abstracting, Bibliographies, Statistics*

C A SELECTS. NONLINEAR OPTICAL MATERIALS. see *PHYSICS—Abstracting, Bibliographies, Statistics*

C A SELECTS. NOVEL NATURAL PRODUCTS. see *CHEMISTRY—Abstracting, Bibliographies, Statistics*

C A SELECTS. NOVEL PESTICIDES & HERBICIDES. see *ENGINEERING—Abstracting, Bibliographies, Statistics*

C A SELECTS. NOVEL POLYMERS FROM PATENTS. see *PATENTS, TRADEMARKS AND COPYRIGHTS—Abstracting, Bibliographies, Statistics*

C A SELECTS. NOVEL SULFUR HETEROCYCLES. see *CHEMISTRY—Abstracting, Bibliographies, Statistics*

C A SELECTS. OCCUPATIONAL EXPOSURE & HAZARDS. see *OCCUPATIONAL HEALTH AND SAFETY—Abstracting, Bibliographies, Statistics*

C A SELECTS. OLEOCHEMICALS CONTAINING NITROGEN. see *CHEMISTRY—Abstracting, Bibliographies, Statistics*

C A SELECTS. OPTICAL AND PHOTOSENSITIVE MATERIALS. see *PHYSICS—Abstracting, Bibliographies, Statistics*

C A SELECTS. OPTIMIZATION OF ORGANIC REACTIONS. see *CHEMISTRY—Abstracting, Bibliographies, Statistics*

C A SELECTS. ORGANIC ANALYTICAL CHEMISTRY. see *CHEMISTRY—Abstracting, Bibliographies, Statistics*

C A SELECTS. ORGANIC OPTICAL MATERIALS. see *CHEMISTRY—Abstracting, Bibliographies, Statistics*

C A SELECTS. ORGANIC REACTION MECHANISMS. see *CHEMISTRY—Abstracting, Bibliographies, Statistics*

C A SELECTS. ORGANIC STEREOCHEMISTRY. see *CHEMISTRY—Abstracting, Bibliographies, Statistics*

C A SELECTS. ORGANO-TRANSITION METAL COMPLEXES. see *CHEMISTRY—Abstracting, Bibliographies, Statistics*

C A SELECTS. ORGANOFLUORINE CHEMISTRY. see *CHEMISTRY—Abstracting, Bibliographies, Statistics*

C A SELECTS. ORGANOMETALLICS IN ORGANIC SYNTHESIS. see *CHEMISTRY—Abstracting, Bibliographies, Statistics*

C A SELECTS. ORGANOPHOSPHORUS CHEMISTRY. see *CHEMISTRY—Abstracting, Bibliographies, Statistics*

C A SELECTS. ORGANOSULFUR CHEMISTRY (JOURNALS). see *CHEMISTRY—Abstracting, Bibliographies, Statistics*

C A SELECTS. ORGANOTIN CHEMISTRY. see *CHEMISTRY—Abstracting, Bibliographies, Statistics*

C A SELECTS. OSTEOPOROSIS & RELATED BONE LOSS. see *MEDICAL SCIENCES—Abstracting, Bibliographies, Statistics*

C A SELECTS. OXIDATION CATALYSTS. see *CHEMISTRY—Abstracting, Bibliographies, Statistics*

C A SELECTS. OXIDE SUPERCONDUCTORS. see *CHEMISTRY—Abstracting, Bibliographies, Statistics*

C A SELECTS. PAINT ADDITIVES. see *PAINTS AND PROTECTIVE COATINGS—Abstracting, Bibliographies, Statistics*

C A SELECTS. PAPER ADDITIVES. see *PAPER AND PULP—Abstracting, Bibliographies, Statistics*

C A SELECTS. PAPER & THIN-LAYER CHROMATOGRAPHY. see *CHEMISTRY—Abstracting, Bibliographies, Statistics*

C A SELECTS. PAPER CHEMISTRY. see *CHEMISTRY— Abstracting, Bibliographies, Statistics*

C A SELECTS. PHARMACEUTICAL CHEMISTRY (JOURNALS). see *PHARMACY AND PHARMACOLOGY—Abstracting, Bibliographies, Statistics*

C A SELECTS. PHARMACEUTICAL CHEMISTRY (PATENTS). see *PHARMACY AND PHARMACOLOGY—Abstracting, Bibliographies, Statistics*

C A SELECTS. PHASE TRANSFER CATALYSIS. see *CHEMISTRY—Abstracting, Bibliographies, Statistics*

C A SELECTS. PHOTOBIOCHEMISTRY. see *CHEMISTRY— Abstracting, Bibliographies, Statistics*

C A SELECTS. PHOTOCATALYSTS. see *CHEMISTRY— Abstracting, Bibliographies, Statistics*

C A SELECTS. PHOTOCHEMICAL ORGANIC SYNTHESIS. see *CHEMISTRY—Abstracting, Bibliographies, Statistics*

C A SELECTS. PHOTORESISTS. see *CHEMISTRY—Abstracting, Bibliographies, Statistics*

C A SELECTS. PHOTOSENSITIVE POLYMERS. see *CHEMISTRY—Abstracting, Bibliographies, Statistics*

C A SELECTS. PLASTIC FILMS. see *PLASTICS—Abstracting, Bibliographies, Statistics*

C A SELECTS. PLASTICS ADDITIVES. see *PLASTICS— Abstracting, Bibliographies, Statistics*

C A SELECTS. PLASTICS FABRICATION & USES. see *PLASTICS—Abstracting, Bibliographies, Statistics*

C A SELECTS. PLASTICS MANUFACTURE & PROCESSING. see *PLASTICS—Abstracting, Bibliographies, Statistics*

C A SELECTS. PLATINUM AND PALLADIUM CHEMISTRY. see *CHEMISTRY—Abstracting, Bibliographies, Statistics*

C A SELECTS PLUS. ADHESIVES. see *CHEMISTRY— Abstracting, Bibliographies, Statistics*

C A SELECTS PLUS. AMINO ACIDS, PEPTIDES AND PROTEINS. see *BIOLOGY—Abstracting, Bibliographies, Statistics*

C A SELECTS PLUS. ANTITUMOR AGENTS. see *MEDICAL SCIENCES—Abstracting, Bibliographies, Statistics*

C A SELECTS PLUS. ASYMMETRIC SYNTHESIS & INDUCTION. see *CHEMISTRY—Abstracting, Bibliographies, Statistics*

C A SELECTS PLUS. BATTERIES & FUEL CELLS. see *CHEMISTRY—Abstracting, Bibliographies, Statistics*

C A SELECTS PLUS. CARBOHYDRATES (CHEMICAL ASPECTS). see *CHEMISTRY—Abstracting, Bibliographies, Statistics*

C A SELECTS PLUS. CARBON & HETEROATOM N M R. see *CHEMISTRY—Abstracting, Bibliographies, Statistics*

C A SELECTS PLUS. CARCINOGENS, MUTAGENS & TERATOGENS. see *MEDICAL SCIENCES—Abstracting, Bibliographies, Statistics*

C A SELECTS PLUS. CATALYSIS (APPLIED & PHYSICAL ASPECTS). see *CHEMISTRY—Abstracting, Bibliographies, Statistics*

C A SELECTS PLUS. CATALYSIS (ORGANIC REACTIONS). see *CHEMISTRY—Abstracting, Bibliographies, Statistics*

C A SELECTS PLUS. CHEMICAL HAZARDS, HEALTH & SAFETY. see *OCCUPATIONAL HEALTH AND SAFETY—Abstracting, Bibliographies, Statistics*

▼ *new title* ➤ *refereed* ✳ *unverified* ◆ *full entry avail.*

C A SELECTS PLUS. CONTROLLED RELEASE TECHNOLOGY. see *CHEMISTRY—Abstracting, Bibliographies, Statistics*

C A SELECTS PLUS. DRUG DELIVERY SYSTEMS & DOSAGE FORMS. see *PHARMACY AND PHARMACOLOGY—Abstracting, Bibliographies, Statistics*

C A SELECTS PLUS. ELECTROPHORESIS. see *CHEMISTRY—Abstracting, Bibliographies, Statistics*

C A SELECTS PLUS. ENVIRONMENTAL POLLUTION. see *ENVIRONMENTAL STUDIES—Abstracting, Bibliographies, Statistics*

C A SELECTS PLUS. ENZYME APPLICATIONS. see *CHEMISTRY—Abstracting, Bibliographies, Statistics*

C A SELECTS PLUS. FLAVORS & FRAGRANCES. see *BEAUTY CULTURE—Abstracting, Bibliographies, Statistics*

C A SELECTS PLUS. FORENSIC CHEMISTRY. see *CHEMISTRY—Abstracting, Bibliographies, Statistics*

C A SELECTS PLUS. GAS CHROMATOGRAPHY. see *CHEMISTRY—Abstracting, Bibliographies, Statistics*

C A SELECTS PLUS. GEL PERMEATION CHROMATOGRAPHY. see *CHEMISTRY—Abstracting, Bibliographies, Statistics*

C A SELECTS PLUS. HIGH PERFORMANCE LIQUID CHROMATOGRAPHY. see *CHEMISTRY—Abstracting, Bibliographies, Statistics*

C A SELECTS PLUS. LIQUID WASTE TREATMENT. see *CHEMISTRY—Abstracting, Bibliographies, Statistics*

C A SELECTS PLUS. MASS SPECTROMETRY. see *CHEMISTRY—Abstracting, Bibliographies, Statistics*

C A SELECTS PLUS. ORGANOSILICON CHEMISTRY. see *CHEMISTRY—Abstracting, Bibliographies, Statistics*

C A SELECTS PLUS. PHARMACEUTICAL ANALYSIS. see *PHARMACY AND PHARMACOLOGY—Abstracting, Bibliographies, Statistics*

C A SELECTS PLUS. PHOTOCHEMISTRY. see *CHEMISTRY—Abstracting, Bibliographies, Statistics*

C A SELECTS PLUS. POLLUTION MONITORING. see *ENVIRONMENTAL STUDIES—Abstracting, Bibliographies, Statistics*

C A SELECTS PLUS. POLYURETHANES. see *CHEMISTRY—Abstracting, Bibliographies, Statistics*

C A SELECTS PLUS. RECOVERY & RECYCLING OF WASTES. see *CHEMISTRY—Abstracting, Bibliographies, Statistics*

C A SELECTS PLUS. SOLID & RADIOACTIVE WASTE TREATMENT. see *CHEMISTRY—Abstracting, Bibliographies, Statistics*

C A SELECTS PLUS. ULTRAFILTRATION. see *CHEMISTRY—Abstracting, Bibliographies, Statistics*

C A SELECTS PLUS. WATER TREATMENT. see *CHEMISTRY—Abstracting, Bibliographies, Statistics*

C A SELECTS PLUS. ZEOLITES. see *CHEMISTRY—Abstracting, Bibliographies, Statistics*

C A SELECTS. POLYACRYLATES (JOURNALS). see *CHEMISTRY—Abstracting, Bibliographies, Statistics*

C A SELECTS. POLYACRYLATES (PATENTS). see *CHEMISTRY—Abstracting, Bibliographies, Statistics*

C A SELECTS. POLYESTERS. see *CHEMISTRY—Abstracting, Bibliographies, Statistics*

C A SELECTS. POLYIMIDES. see *CHEMISTRY—Abstracting, Bibliographies, Statistics*

C A SELECTS. POLYMER BLENDS. see *CHEMISTRY—Abstracting, Bibliographies, Statistics*

C A SELECTS. POLYMER DEGRADATION. see *CHEMISTRY—Abstracting, Bibliographies, Statistics*

C A SELECTS. POLYMER MORPHOLOGY. see *CHEMISTRY—Abstracting, Bibliographies, Statistics*

C A SELECTS. POLYMERIZATION KINETICS & PROCESS CONTROL. see *CHEMISTRY—Abstracting, Bibliographies, Statistics*

C A SELECTS. PORPHYRINS. see *CHEMISTRY—Abstracting, Bibliographies, Statistics*

C A SELECTS. PROSTAGLANDINS. see *CHEMISTRY—Abstracting, Bibliographies, Statistics*

C A SELECTS. PROTON MAGNETIC RESONANCE. see *CHEMISTRY—Abstracting, Bibliographies, Statistics*

C A SELECTS. PSYCHOBIOCHEMISTRY. see *BIOLOGY—Abstracting, Bibliographies, Statistics*

C A SELECTS. QUATERNARY AMMONIUM COMPOUNDS. see *CHEMISTRY—Abstracting, Bibliographies, Statistics*

C A SELECTS. RADIATION CHEMISTRY. see *CHEMISTRY—Abstracting, Bibliographies, Statistics*

C A SELECTS. RADIATION CURING. see *CHEMISTRY—Abstracting, Bibliographies, Statistics*

C A SELECTS. RAMAN SPECTROSCOPY. see *CHEMISTRY—Abstracting, Bibliographies, Statistics*

C A SELECTS. SELENIUM & TELLURIUM CHEMISTRY. see *METALLURGY—Abstracting, Bibliographies, Statistics*

C A SELECTS. SILICAS & SILICATES. see *CHEMISTRY—Abstracting, Bibliographies, Statistics*

C A SELECTS. SILOXANES & SILICONES. see *CHEMISTRY—Abstracting, Bibliographies, Statistics*

C A SELECTS. SILVER CHEMISTRY. see *METALLURGY—Abstracting, Bibliographies, Statistics*

C A SELECTS. SOLAR ENERGY. see *ENERGY—Abstracting, Bibliographies, Statistics*

C A SELECTS. SOLID STATE N M R. (Nuclear Magnetic Resonance) see *CHEMISTRY—Abstracting, Bibliographies, Statistics*

C A SELECTS. SOLVENT EXTRACTION. see *CHEMISTRY—Abstracting, Bibliographies, Statistics*

C A SELECTS. SPECTROCHEMICAL ANALYSIS. see *CHEMISTRY—Abstracting, Bibliographies, Statistics*

C A SELECTS. STEROIDS (BIOCHEMICAL ASPECTS). see *BIOLOGY—Abstracting, Bibliographies, Statistics*

C A SELECTS. STEROIDS (CHEMICAL ASPECTS). see *CHEMISTRY—Abstracting, Bibliographies, Statistics*

C A SELECTS. STRUCTURE - ACTIVITY RELATIONSHIPS. see *CHEMISTRY—Abstracting, Bibliographies, Statistics*

C A SELECTS. SURFACE ANALYSIS. see *CHEMISTRY—Abstracting, Bibliographies, Statistics*

C A SELECTS. SURFACE CHEMISTRY (PHYSICOCHEMICAL ASPECTS). see *CHEMISTRY—Abstracting, Bibliographies, Statistics*

C A SELECTS. SYNFUELS. see *CHEMISTRY—Abstracting, Bibliographies, Statistics*

C A SELECTS. SYNTHETIC HIGH POLYMERS. see *CHEMISTRY—Abstracting, Bibliographies, Statistics*

C A SELECTS. SYNTHETIC MACROCYCLIC COMPOUNDS. see *CHEMISTRY—Abstracting, Bibliographies, Statistics*

C A SELECTS. THERMAL ANALYSIS. see *CHEMISTRY—Abstracting, Bibliographies, Statistics*

C A SELECTS. THERMOCHEMISTRY. see *CHEMISTRY—Abstracting, Bibliographies, Statistics*

C A SELECTS. TRACE ELEMENT ANALYSIS. see *CHEMISTRY—Abstracting, Bibliographies, Statistics*

C A SELECTS. WATER - BASED COATINGS. see *PAINTS AND PROTECTIVE COATINGS—Abstracting, Bibliographies, Statistics*

C A SELECTS. X-RAY ANALYSIS & SPECTROSCOPY. see *PHYSICS—Abstracting, Bibliographies, Statistics*

C I N D A; an index to the literature on microscopic neutron data. see *PHYSICS—Abstracting, Bibliographies, Statistics*

C I S INDEX INDEX. see *PUBLIC ADMINISTRATION—Abstracting, Bibliographies, Statistics*

C I S INDEX TO PUBLICATIONS OF THE UNITED STATES CONGRESS. see *PUBLIC ADMINISTRATION—Abstracting, Bibliographies, Statistics*

C L A S E. (Citas Latinoamericanas en Ciencias Sociales y Humanidades) see *SOCIAL SCIENCES: COMPREHENSIVE WORKS—Abstracting, Bibliographies, Statistics*

C O R E S T A; bulletin d'information. see *TOBACCO—Abstracting, Bibliographies, Statistics*

C P I DIGEST; key to world literature serving the coatings, plastics, fibers, adhesives, and related industries. (Chemical Process Industries) see *PAINTS AND PROTECTIVE COATINGS—Abstracting, Bibliographies, Statistics*

016 USA
C P I. Q. Text in English, French. m. index, cum.index: 1948-1959. **Document type:** *Database, Abstract/Index.* **Description:** Covers more than 400 English- and French-language serials from Canada and the US. **Formerly** (until 1963): Canadian Index to Periodicals and Documentary Films (0527-9259) **Media:** Online - full text. **Related titles:** CD-ROM ed. **Indexed:** RASB. —CISTI. **Published by:** Gale Group (Subsidiary of: Thomson Corporation), 27500 Drake Rd, Farmington Hills, MI 48331-3535. TEL 248-699-4253, 800-347-4253, FAX 248-699-8035, gale.galeord@thomson.com, http://www.galegroup.com.

C R R I ROAD ABSTRACTS. see *ENGINEERING—Abstracting, Bibliographies, Statistics*

C S A ADVANCED POLYMERS ABSTRACTS. see *CHEMISTRY—Abstracting, Bibliographies, Statistics*

C S A AGRICULTURAL & ENVIRONMENTAL BIOTECHNOLOGY ABSTRACTS. see *AGRICULTURE—Abstracting, Bibliographies, Statistics*

C S A ANIMAL BEHAVIOR ABSTRACTS. (Cambridge Scientific Abstracts) see *BIOLOGY—Abstracting, Bibliographies, Statistics*

C S A CIVIL ENGINEERING ABSTRACTS. (Cambridge Scientific Abstracts) see *ENGINEERING—Abstracting, Bibliographies, Statistics*

C S A IMMUNOLOGY ABSTRACTS (ONLINE EDITION). see *MEDICAL SCIENCES—Abstracting, Bibliographies, Statistics*

C S A MECHANICAL & TRANSPORTATION ENGINEERING ABSTRACTS. (Cambridge Scientific Abstracts) see *ENGINEERING—Abstracting, Bibliographies, Statistics*

C S A NEUROSCIENCES ABSTRACTS (ONLINE EDITION). (Cambridge Scientific Abstracts) see *MEDICAL SCIENCES—Abstracting, Bibliographies, Statistics*

C S A ONCOGENES AND GROWTH FACTORS ABSTRACTS. see *MEDICAL SCIENCES—Abstracting, Bibliographies, Statistics*

C S A VIROLOGY AND AIDS ABSTRACTS. (Cambridge Scientific Abstracts) see *BIOLOGY—Abstracting, Bibliographies, Statistics*

C S A WORLD CERAMIC ABSTRACTS. see *CERAMICS, GLASS AND POTTERY—Abstracting, Bibliographies, Statistics*

C S A WORLDWIDE POLITICAL SCIENCE ABSTRACTS. (Cambridge Scientific Abstracts) see *POLITICAL SCIENCE—Abstracting, Bibliographies, Statistics*

C S I R O INSTITUTE OF ENERGY AND EARTH RESOURCES. DIVISION OF GEOMECHANICS. ABSTRACTS OF PUBLISHED PAPERS. (Commonwealth Scientific and Industrial Research Organisation) see *ENGINEERING—Abstracting, Bibliographies, Statistics*

CALCIUM AND CALCIFIED TISSUE ABSTRACTS (ONLINE EDITION). see *BIOLOGY—Abstracting, Bibliographies, Statistics*

CANADA. INLAND WATERS DIRECTORATE. SURFACE WATER DATA. REFERENCE INDEX. CANADA. see *WATER RESOURCES—Abstracting, Bibliographies, Statistics*

CANADA. STATISTICS CANADA. AIR PASSENGER ORIGIN AND DESTINATION. DOMESTIC REPORT. see *TRANSPORTATION—Abstracting, Bibliographies, Statistics*

CANADA. STATISTICS CANADA. SOFTWARE DEVELOPMENT AND COMPUTER SERVICE INDUSTRY/CANADA. STATISTIQUE CANADA. INDUSTRIE DE LA PRODUCTION DE LOGICIELS ET DES SERVICES INFORMATIQUES. see *COMPUTERS—Abstracting, Bibliographies, Statistics*

CANADIAN BUSINESS AND CURRENT AFFAIRS BUSINESS; Canada's premier periodical database. see *BUSINESS AND ECONOMICS—Abstracting, Bibliographies, Statistics*

CANADIAN BUSINESS AND CURRENT AFFAIRS CURRENT EVENTS. see *BUSINESS AND ECONOMICS—Abstracting, Bibliographies, Statistics*

CANADIAN BUSINESS AND CURRENT AFFAIRS EDUCATION. see *EDUCATION—Abstracting, Bibliographies, Statistics*

015   CAN   ISSN 1484-6489
CANADIAN BUSINESS AND CURRENT AFFAIRS REFERENCE; Canada's premier periodical database. Key Title: C B C A Fulltext Reference. Text in English. 1992. m. CND 2,100 to libraries (effective 2005). **Description:** Includes indexing to about 650 active periodicals and a variety of daily news sources. It includes direct access to the full-text content of articles from over 200 active Canadian periodicals. Full-text from another 80 odd publications, those that have ceased between 1993-2002 but which retain historical research value, is also included. With over 4 million records, CBCA Reference is ideal for anyone interested in current events, business, science, the arts, and academic information as produced in Canada.
Supersedes in part (in 1998): C B C A Fulltext (1484-6470); Which was formerly (until 1997): Canadian Business and Current Affairs - Fulltext (CD-ROM) (1206-1816)
Media: Online - full content.
Published by: Micromedia ProQuest (Subsidiary of: ProQuest Information & Learning), 20 Victoria St, Toronto, ON M5C 2N8, Canada. TEL 416-362-5211, FAX 416-362-6161, info@micromedia.ca, http://www.micromedia.ca/ Products_Services/CBCAREF.htm. Ed. Mr. Tom McGreevy.

CANADIAN FISHERIES ABSTRACTS. see *FISH AND FISHERIES—Abstracting, Bibliographies, Statistics*

CANADIAN INCOME TAX RESEARCH INDEX. see *BUSINESS AND ECONOMICS—Abstracting, Bibliographies, Statistics*

CANADIAN INSURANCE. ANNUAL STATISTICAL ISSUE. see *INSURANCE—Abstracting, Bibliographies, Statistics*

CANADIAN MUSIC PERIODICAL INDEX. see *MUSIC—Abstracting, Bibliographies, Statistics*

016   CAN   ISSN 1196-099X
CANADIAN RESEARCH INDEX, MICROLOG/INDEX DE RECHERCHE DU CANADA, MICROLOG; unparalleled access to Canadian government and research publications. Text in English, French. 1979. m. CND 1,000 to libraries (effective 2005). back issues avail. **Document type:** Abstract/Index.
Former titles (until 1992): Microlog: Canadian Research Index (0839-1289); Microlog Index (0707-3135); Publicat Index to Canadian Federal Publications (0384-9813); Urban Canada; Canadian Urban Sources (0917-2775); Profile Index to Canadian and Municipal Government Publications (0316-4068)
Media: Online - full content. **Related titles:** CD-ROM ed.; Microfiche ed.; Online - full text ed.
—BLDSC (5759.176500).
Published by: Micromedia ProQuest (Subsidiary of: ProQuest Information & Learning), 20 Victoria St, Toronto, ON M5C 2N8, Canada. TEL 416-362-5211, 800-387-2689, FAX 416-362-6161, info@micromedia.ca, http://www.micromedia.ca/ Products_Services/CRI.htm. Ed. Brian Terry.

CANADIAN ZOOLOGY ABSTRACTS. see *BIOLOGY—Abstracting, Bibliographies, Statistics*

CANCER EPIDEMIOLOGY. see *MEDICAL SCIENCES—Abstracting, Bibliographies, Statistics*

CANON LAW ABSTRACTS; half-yearly review of periodical literature in canon law. see *RELIGIONS AND THEOLOGY—Abstracting, Bibliographies, Statistics*

CARINDEX: SCIENCE & TECHNOLOGY. see *SCIENCES: COMPREHENSIVE WORKS—Abstracting, Bibliographies, Statistics*

CARINDEX: SOCIAL SCIENCES AND HUMANITIES. see *SOCIAL SCIENCES: COMPREHENSIVE WORKS—Abstracting, Bibliographies, Statistics*

CATALOGO DE LIBROS ANTIGUOS Y MODERNOS. see *PUBLISHING AND BOOK TRADE—Abstracting, Bibliographies, Statistics*

CATALOGUE & INDEX; periodical of C I L I P Cataloguing and Indexing Group. see *LIBRARY AND INFORMATION SCIENCES—Abstracting, Bibliographies, Statistics*

THE CATHOLIC PERIODICAL AND LITERATURE INDEX. see *RELIGIONS AND THEOLOGY—Abstracting, Bibliographies, Statistics*

CELL DIFFERENTIATION. see *BIOLOGY—Abstracting, Bibliographies, Statistics*

CELL MEMBRANES. see *BIOLOGY—Abstracting, Bibliographies, Statistics*

CENTRAL BUILDING RESEARCH INSTITUTE. PUBLICATIONS INDEX. see *BUILDING AND CONSTRUCTION—Abstracting, Bibliographies, Statistics*

CENTRE PROTESTANT D'ETUDES ET DE DOCUMENTATION. LIBRESENS. see *RELIGIONS AND THEOLOGY—Abstracting, Bibliographies, Statistics*

CERAMIC ABSTRACTS. see *CERAMICS, GLASS AND POTTERY—Abstracting, Bibliographies, Statistics*

CHARTERED INSTITUTE OF BUILDING. CONSTRUCTION INFORMATION QUARTERLY. see *BUILDING AND CONSTRUCTION—Abstracting, Bibliographies, Statistics*

CHEMICAL ABSTRACTS. see *CHEMISTRY—Abstracting, Bibliographies, Statistics*

CHEMICAL ABSTRACTS - APPLIED CHEMISTRY AND CHEMICAL ENGINEERING SECTIONS. see *CHEMISTRY—Abstracting, Bibliographies, Statistics*

CHEMICAL ABSTRACTS - BIOCHEMISTRY SECTIONS. see *BIOLOGY—Abstracting, Bibliographies, Statistics*

CHEMICAL ABSTRACTS. COLLECTIVE INDEX. see *CHEMISTRY—Abstracting, Bibliographies, Statistics*

CHEMICAL ABSTRACTS. INDEX GUIDE. see *CHEMISTRY—Abstracting, Bibliographies, Statistics*

CHEMICAL ABSTRACTS - MACROMOLECULAR SECTIONS. see *CHEMISTRY—Abstracting, Bibliographies, Statistics*

CHEMICAL ABSTRACTS - ORGANIC CHEMISTRY SECTIONS. see *CHEMISTRY—Abstracting, Bibliographies, Statistics*

CHEMICAL ABSTRACTS - PHYSICAL, INORGANIC AND ANALYTICAL CHEMISTRY SECTIONS. see *CHEMISTRY—Abstracting, Bibliographies, Statistics*

CHEMICAL ABSTRACTS - SECTION GROUPINGS. see *CHEMISTRY—Abstracting, Bibliographies, Statistics*

CHEMICAL ABSTRACTS SERVICE SOURCE INDEX. see *CHEMISTRY—Abstracting, Bibliographies, Statistics*

CHEMICAL BUSINESS NEWSBASE. see *CHEMISTRY—Abstracting, Bibliographies, Statistics*

CHEMICAL ENGINEERING AND BIOTECHNOLOGY ABSTRACTS (ONLINE EDITION). see *ENGINEERING—Abstracting, Bibliographies, Statistics*

CHEMICAL HAZARDS IN INDUSTRY. see *OCCUPATIONAL HEALTH AND SAFETY—Abstracting, Bibliographies, Statistics*

CHEMICAL SAFETY NEWSBASE. see *OCCUPATIONAL HEALTH AND SAFETY—Abstracting, Bibliographies, Statistics*

CHEMINFORM; selected abstracts in chemistry. see *CHEMISTRY—Abstracting, Bibliographies, Statistics*

CHEMORECEPTION ABSTRACTS (ONLINE EDITION). see *CHEMISTRY—Abstracting, Bibliographies, Statistics*

CHEMTRACTS. see *CHEMISTRY—Abstracting, Bibliographies, Statistics*

CHIKIDAH-I PAYAN'NAMAHHA-YI IRAN/IRANIAN DISSERTATION ABSTRACTS. see *EDUCATION—Abstracting, Bibliographies, Statistics*

CHILD ABUSE, CHILD WELFARE & ADOPTION. see *CHILDREN AND YOUTH—Abstracting, Bibliographies, Statistics*

CHILDREN'S BOOK REVIEW INDEX. see *CHILDREN AND YOUTH—Abstracting, Bibliographies, Statistics*

CHILDREN'S MAGAZINE GUIDE; subject index to children's magazines and web sites. see *CHILDREN AND YOUTH—Abstracting, Bibliographies, Statistics*

CHINA AEROSPACE ABSTRACTS. see *AERONAUTICS AND SPACE FLIGHT—Abstracting, Bibliographies, Statistics*

CHINA MEDICAL ABSTRACTS (INTERNAL MEDICINE). see *MEDICAL SCIENCES—Abstracting, Bibliographies, Statistics*

CHINA MEDICAL ABSTRACTS (SURGERY). see *MEDICAL SCIENCES—Abstracting, Bibliographies, Statistics*

CHINESE FISHERIES ABSTRACTS (CHINESE EDITION). see *FISH AND FISHERIES—Abstracting, Bibliographies, Statistics*

CHINESE FISHERY ABSTRACTS (ENGLISH EDITION). see *FISH AND FISHERIES—Abstracting, Bibliographies, Statistics*

CHINESE SCIENCE ABSTRACTS. PART A; mathematics, mechanics, astronomy and space science, physics, technical sciences. see *SCIENCES: COMPREHENSIVE WORKS—Abstracting, Bibliographies, Statistics*

CHINESE SCIENCE ABSTRACTS. PART B; chemistry, life sciences, earth sciences. see *SCIENCES: COMPREHENSIVE WORKS—Abstracting, Bibliographies, Statistics*

CHLOROPLASTS. see *BIOLOGY—Abstracting, Bibliographies, Statistics*

CHOJU KANKEI TOKEI/ANNUAL STATISTICS OF BIRDS AND ANIMALS. see *BIOLOGY—Abstracting, Bibliographies, Statistics*

CHOLESTEROL & LIPOPROTEINS. see *BIOLOGY—Abstracting, Bibliographies, Statistics*

CHRISTIAN PERIODICAL INDEX; an index to subjects, authors and book reviews. see *RELIGIONS AND THEOLOGY—Abstracting, Bibliographies, Statistics*

CHRISTIAN SCIENCE MONITOR INDEX. see *JOURNALISM—Abstracting, Bibliographies, Statistics*

CHROMATOGRAPHY ABSTRACTS. see *CHEMISTRY—Abstracting, Bibliographies, Statistics*

CITATIONS FOR SERIAL LITERATURE. see *LIBRARY AND INFORMATION SCIENCES—Abstracting, Bibliographies, Statistics*

CLASSIFIED INDEX OF N.L.R.B. AND RELATED COURT DECISIONS. see *BUSINESS AND ECONOMICS—Abstracting, Bibliographies, Statistics*

CLIN-ALERT. see *PHARMACY AND PHARMACOLOGY—Abstracting, Bibliographies, Statistics*

CLINCAL TRIALS INSIGHT CLASSICS. HYPERLIPIDAEMIA. see *MEDICAL SCIENCES—Abstracting, Bibliographies, Statistics*

CLINICAL CYTOGENETICS. see *BIOLOGY—Abstracting, Bibliographies, Statistics*

CLINICAL TRIALS INSIGHT CLASSICS. ANTIBACTERIALS. see *MEDICAL SCIENCES—Abstracting, Bibliographies, Statistics*

CLINICAL TRIALS INSIGHT CLASSICS. ANTITHROMBOTICS. see *MEDICAL SCIENCES—Abstracting, Bibliographies, Statistics*

CLINICAL TRIALS INSIGHT CLASSICS. ANTIVIRALS. see *MEDICAL SCIENCES—Abstracting, Bibliographies, Statistics*

CLINICAL TRIALS INSIGHT CLASSICS. DIABETES. see *MEDICAL SCIENCES—Abstracting, Bibliographies, Statistics*

CLINICAL TRIALS INSIGHT CLASSICS. HEART FAILURE. see *MEDICAL SCIENCES—Abstracting, Bibliographies, Statistics*

CLINICAL TRIALS INSIGHT CLASSICS. HYPERTENSION. see *MEDICAL SCIENCES—Abstracting, Bibliographies, Statistics*

CLINICAL TRIALS INSIGHT CLASSICS. IMMUNOTHERAPEUTICS. VACCINES. see *MEDICAL SCIENCES—Abstracting, Bibliographies, Statistics*

CLINICAL TRIALS INSIGHT CLASSICS. ISCHAEMIC HEART DISEASE. see *MEDICAL SCIENCES—Abstracting, Bibliographies, Statistics*

CLINICAL TRIALS INSIGHT CLASSICS. OBESITY. see *NUTRITION AND DIETETICS—Abstracting, Bibliographies, Statistics*

CLINICAL TRIALS INSIGHT CLASSICS. OBSTRUCTIVE AIRWAYS DISEASE. see *MEDICAL SCIENCES—Abstracting, Bibliographies, Statistics*

CLINICAL TRIALS INSIGHT CLASSICS. PAIN CONTROL. see *MEDICAL SCIENCES—Abstracting, Bibliographies, Statistics*

CLINICAL TRIALS INSIGHT CLASSICS. PEPTIC ULCER DISEASE. see *MEDICAL SCIENCES—Abstracting, Bibliographies, Statistics*

CLINICAL TRIALS INSIGHT CLASSICS. PHARMACOECONOMICS. see *PHARMACY AND PHARMACOLOGY—Abstracting, Bibliographies, Statistics*

CLINICAL TRIALS INSIGHT CLASSICS. RHEUMATIC DISEASE. see *MEDICAL SCIENCES—Abstracting, Bibliographies, Statistics*

A

CLINICAL TRIALS INSIGHT CLASSICS. WOMEN'S HEALTH. see *WOMEN'S HEALTH—Abstracting, Bibliographies, Statistics*

CLINICALS TRIALS INSIGHT CLASSICS. ARRHYTHMIAS. see *MEDICAL SCIENCES—Abstracting, Bibliographies, Statistics*

CLINICALS TRIALS INSIGHT CLASSICS. CANCER CHEMOTHERAPY. see *MEDICAL SCIENCES—Abstracting, Bibliographies, Statistics*

CLOTHING AND TEXTILE ARTS INDEX. see *CLOTHING TRADE—Abstracting, Bibliographies, Statistics*

CLOVER INFORMATION INDEX. see *PUBLISHING AND BOOK TRADE—Abstracting, Bibliographies, Statistics*

COLD SPRING HARBOR LABORATORY. ABSTRACTS OF PAPERS PRESENTED AT MEETINGS. see *BIOLOGY*

COLD SPRING HARBOR LABORATORY. ABSTRACTS OF PAPERS PRESENTED AT THE MEETING ON PROTEOLYSIS & BIOLOGICAL CONTROL. see *BIOLOGY*

COLEGIO OFICIAL DE PSICOLOGOS DE MADRID. SELECCIONES DE PRENSA. see *PSYCHOLOGY— Abstracting, Bibliographies, Statistics*

COLOUR INDEX: ADDITIONS & AMENDMENTS. see *TEXTILE INDUSTRIES AND FABRICS—Abstracting, Bibliographies, Statistics*

COMMODITY YEARBOOK STATISTICAL UPDATE. see *AGRICULTURE—Abstracting, Bibliographies, Statistics*

COMMUNICATION ABSTRACTS; an international information service. see *COMMUNICATIONS—Abstracting, Bibliographies, Statistics*

COMMUNICATION BOOKNOTES QUARTERLY. see *COMMUNICATIONS—Abstracting, Bibliographies, Statistics*

COMMUNICATION SERIALS; an international guide to periodicals in communication, popular culture and the performing arts. see *COMMUNICATIONS—Abstracting, Bibliographies, Statistics*

COMMUNITY CURRENTS; the community development information digest. see *SOCIAL SERVICES AND WELFARE—Abstracting, Bibliographies, Statistics*

COMPACTMATH - COMPACT MATHEMATICS LIBRARY. see *MATHEMATICS—Abstracting, Bibliographies, Statistics*

COMPANIES REGISTERED IN NEW ZEALAND - ADDRESS INDEX. see *BUSINESS AND ECONOMICS—Abstracting, Bibliographies, Statistics*

COMPANIES REGISTERED IN NEW ZEALAND - NOMINAL INDEX. see *BUSINESS AND ECONOMICS—Abstracting, Bibliographies, Statistics*

COMPARATIVE MEDICINE RESEARCH RESOURCES. see *MEDICAL SCIENCES—Abstracting, Bibliographies, Statistics*

COMPENDIUM OF RESEARCH. see *HOUSING AND URBAN PLANNING—Abstracting, Bibliographies, Statistics*

COMPREHENSIVE MEDLINE. see *MEDICAL SCIENCES— Abstracting, Bibliographies, Statistics*

COMPREHENSIVE SUMMARIES OF UPPSALA DISSERTATIONS FROM THE FACULTY OF SCIENCE AND TECHNOLOGY. see *SCIENCES: COMPREHENSIVE WORKS—Abstracting, Bibliographies, Statistics*

COMPUMATH CITATION INDEX. see *COMPUTERS— Abstracting, Bibliographies, Statistics*

COMPUTER ABSTRACTS. see *COMPUTERS—Abstracting, Bibliographies, Statistics*

COMPUTER & CONTROL ABSTRACTS. see *COMPUTERS—Abstracting, Bibliographies, Statistics*

COMPUTER AND INFORMATION SYSTEMS ABSTRACTS JOURNAL. see *COMPUTERS—Abstracting, Bibliographies, Statistics*

COMPUTER SCIENCE INDEX. see *COMPUTERS—Abstracting, Bibliographies, Statistics*

CONFERENCE PAPERS INDEX. see *MEETINGS AND CONGRESSES—Abstracting, Bibliographies, Statistics*

CONGRESS OF HETEROCYCLIC CHEMISTRY. BOOK OF ABSTRACTS/FUKUSOKAN KAGAKU TORONKAI KOEN YOSHISHU. see *CHEMISTRY—Abstracting, Bibliographies, Statistics*

CONGRESSIONAL RECORD SCANNER. see *POLITICAL SCIENCE—Abstracting, Bibliographies, Statistics*

CONSERVATION BIOLOGY ABSTRACTS. see *CONSERVATION—Abstracting, Bibliographies, Statistics*

CONSOLIDATED INDEX TO THE ZIMBABWE LAW REPORTS. see *LAW—Abstracting, Bibliographies, Statistics*

CONSUMERS INDEX; to product evaluations and information sources. see *CONSUMER EDUCATION AND PROTECTION—Abstracting, Bibliographies, Statistics*

CONSUMERS INDEX DATABASE. see *CONSUMER EDUCATION AND PROTECTION—Abstracting, Bibliographies, Statistics*

CONSUMERS REFERENCE DISC. see *CONSUMER EDUCATION AND PROTECTION—Abstracting, Bibliographies, Statistics*

CONTEMPORARY WOMEN'S ISSUES. see *WOMEN'S INTERESTS—Abstracting, Bibliographies, Statistics*

CONTENTS. see *PHARMACY AND PHARMACOLOGY— Abstracting, Bibliographies, Statistics*

CONTENTS PAGES IN EDUCATION. see *EDUCATION— Abstracting, Bibliographies, Statistics*

COPEIA ABSTRACTS. see *BIOLOGY—Abstracting, Bibliographies, Statistics*

CORE JOURNALS IN CARDIOLOGY. see *MEDICAL SCIENCES—Abstracting, Bibliographies, Statistics*

CORE JOURNALS IN CLINICAL NEUROLOGY. see *MEDICAL SCIENCES—Abstracting, Bibliographies, Statistics*

CORE JOURNALS IN DERMATOLOGY. see *MEDICAL SCIENCES—Abstracting, Bibliographies, Statistics*

CORE JOURNALS IN GASTROENTEROLOGY. see *MEDICAL SCIENCES—Abstracting, Bibliographies, Statistics*

CORE JOURNALS IN OBSTETRICS / GYNECOLOGY. see *MEDICAL SCIENCES—Abstracting, Bibliographies, Statistics*

CORE JOURNALS IN OPHTHALMOLOGY. see *MEDICAL SCIENCES—Abstracting, Bibliographies, Statistics*

CORE JOURNALS IN PEDIATRICS. see *MEDICAL SCIENCES—Abstracting, Bibliographies, Statistics*

CORE MEDLINE. see *MEDICAL SCIENCES—Abstracting, Bibliographies, Statistics*

CORROSION ABSTRACTS. see *ENGINEERING—Abstracting, Bibliographies, Statistics*

CREATIVE BOOK SELECTION INDEX. see *PUBLISHING AND BOOK TRADE—Abstracting, Bibliographies, Statistics*

CRIMINAL JUSTICE ABSTRACTS. see *CRIMINOLOGY AND LAW ENFORCEMENT—Abstracting, Bibliographies, Statistics*

CRIMINAL JUSTICE PERIODICAL INDEX. see *CRIMINOLOGY AND LAW ENFORCEMENT—Abstracting, Bibliographies, Statistics*

CROP PHYSIOLOGY ABSTRACTS. see *AGRICULTURE— Abstracting, Bibliographies, Statistics*

CROSSFIRE. see *CHEMISTRY—Abstracting, Bibliographies, Statistics*

CUMULATIVE INDEX OF HOSPITAL LITERATURE. see *HEALTH FACILITIES AND ADMINISTRATION—Abstracting, Bibliographies, Statistics*

CUMULATIVE INDEX TO NURSING & ALLIED HEALTH LITERATURE. see *MEDICAL SCIENCES—Abstracting, Bibliographies, Statistics*

CURRENT ADVANCES IN APPLIED MICROBIOLOGY & BIOTECHNOLOGY. see *BIOLOGY—Abstracting, Bibliographies, Statistics*

CURRENT ADVANCES IN CANCER RESEARCH. see *MEDICAL SCIENCES—Abstracting, Bibliographies, Statistics*

CURRENT ADVANCES IN CELL & DEVELOPMENTAL BIOLOGY. see *BIOLOGY—Abstracting, Bibliographies, Statistics*

CURRENT ADVANCES IN CLINICAL CHEMISTRY. see *CHEMISTRY—Abstracting, Bibliographies, Statistics*

CURRENT ADVANCES IN ECOLOGICAL & ENVIRONMENTAL SCIENCES. see *ENVIRONMENTAL STUDIES—Abstracting, Bibliographies, Statistics*

CURRENT ADVANCES IN GENETICS & MOLECULAR BIOLOGY. see *BIOLOGY—Abstracting, Bibliographies, Statistics*

CURRENT ADVANCES IN IMMUNOLOGY & INFECTIOUS DISEASES. see *MEDICAL SCIENCES—Abstracting, Bibliographies, Statistics*

CURRENT ADVANCES IN NEUROSCIENCE. see *MEDICAL SCIENCES—Abstracting, Bibliographies, Statistics*

CURRENT ADVANCES IN PLANT SCIENCE. see *BIOLOGY—Abstracting, Bibliographies, Statistics*

CURRENT ADVANCES IN PROTEIN BIOCHEMISTRY. see *BIOLOGY—Abstracting, Bibliographies, Statistics*

CURRENT ADVANCES IN TOXICOLOGY. see *ENVIRONMENTAL STUDIES—Abstracting, Bibliographies, Statistics*

CURRENT ANTARCTIC LITERATURE. see *SCIENCES: COMPREHENSIVE WORKS—Abstracting, Bibliographies, Statistics*

CURRENT AWARENESS BULLETIN. see *BUSINESS AND ECONOMICS—Abstracting, Bibliographies, Statistics*

CURRENT AWARENESS IN BIOLOGICAL SCIENCES. see *BIOLOGY—Abstracting, Bibliographies, Statistics*

CURRENT BIBLIOGRAPHIES ON SCIENCE AND TECHNOLOGY: BIOLOGY, PHARMACY AND FOOD SCIENCE. see *BIOLOGY—Abstracting, Bibliographies, Statistics*

CURRENT BIBLIOGRAPHIES ON SCIENCE AND TECHNOLOGY: CHEMISTRY AND CHEMICAL INDUSTRY. see *CHEMISTRY—Abstracting, Bibliographies, Statistics*

CURRENT BIBLIOGRAPHIES ON SCIENCE AND TECHNOLOGY: MECHANICAL ENGINEERING & CONSTRUCTION ENGINEERING. see *METALLURGY— Abstracting, Bibliographies, Statistics*

CURRENT BIBLIOGRAPHY ON SCIENCE AND TECHNOLOGY: CHEMISTRY AND CHEMICAL ENGINEERING (FOREIGN)/KAGAKU GIJUTSU BUNKEN SOKUHO. KAGAKU, KAGAKU KOGYO-HEN (GAIKOKU-HEN). see *CHEMISTRY—Abstracting, Bibliographies, Statistics*

CURRENT BIBLIOGRAPHY ON SCIENCE AND TECHNOLOGY: CHEMISTRY AND CHEMICAL ENGINEERING (JAPANESE)/KAGAKU GIJUTSU BUNKEN SOKUHO KAGAKU. KAGAKU KOGYO-HEN (KOKUNAI-HEN). see *CHEMISTRY—Abstracting, Bibliographies, Statistics*

CURRENT BIBLIOGRAPHY ON SCIENCE AND TECHNOLOGY: CIVIL ENGINEERING AND ARCHITECTURE/KAGAKU GIJUTSU BUNKEN SOKUHO. DOBOKU, KENCHIKU KOGAKU HEN. see *ENGINEERING—Abstracting, Bibliographies, Statistics*

CURRENT BIBLIOGRAPHY ON SCIENCE AND TECHNOLOGY: EARTH SCIENCE, MINING AND METALLURGY/KAGAKU GIJUTSU BUNKEN SOKUHO. KINZOKU KOGAKU, KOZAN KOGAKU, CHIKYU NO KAGAKU-HEN. see *EARTH SCIENCES—Abstracting, Bibliographies, Statistics*

CURRENT BIBLIOGRAPHY ON SCIENCE AND TECHNOLOGY: MECHANICAL ENGINEERING/KAGAKU GIJUTSU BUNKEN SOKUHO. KIKAI KOGAKU-HEN. see *ENGINEERING— Abstracting, Bibliographies, Statistics*

CURRENT BIBLIOGRAPHY ON SCIENCE AND TECHNOLOGY: PURE AND APPLIED PHYSICS/KAGAKU GIJUTSU BUNKEN SOKUHO. BUTSURI, OYOBUTSURI-HEN. see *PHYSICS—Abstracting, Bibliographies, Statistics*

CURRENT BIOLOGY. see *BIOLOGY—Abstracting, Bibliographies, Statistics*

CURRENT BIOTECHNOLOGY. see *BIOLOGY—Abstracting, Bibliographies, Statistics*

CURRENT CHEMICAL REACTIONS. see *CHEMISTRY— Abstracting, Bibliographies, Statistics*

CURRENT CONTENTS: AGRICULTURE, BIOLOGY & ENVIRONMENTAL SCIENCES. see *AGRICULTURE— Abstracting, Bibliographies, Statistics*

CURRENT CONTENTS: CLINICAL MEDICINE. see *MEDICAL SCIENCES—Abstracting, Bibliographies, Statistics*

A

CURRENT CONTENTS: ENGINEERING, COMPUTING & TECHNOLOGY. see ENGINEERING—Abstracting, Bibliographies, Statistics

CURRENT CONTENTS: LIFE SCIENCES. see BIOLOGY—Abstracting, Bibliographies, Statistics

CURRENT CONTENTS OF FOREIGN JOURNALS: MANAGEMENT & ECONOMICS. see BUSINESS AND ECONOMICS—Abstracting, Bibliographies, Statistics

CURRENT CONTENTS ON DISKETTE WITH ABSTRACTS. CLINICAL MEDICINE. see MEDICAL SCIENCES—Abstracting, Bibliographies, Statistics

CURRENT CONTENTS: PHYSICAL, CHEMICAL & EARTH SCIENCES. see CHEMISTRY—Abstracting, Bibliographies, Statistics

CURRENT CONTENTS: SOCIAL & BEHAVIORAL SCIENCES. see PSYCHOLOGY—Abstracting, Bibliographies, Statistics

CURRENT DIGEST OF THE POST-SOVIET PRESS. ANNUAL INDEX. see POLITICAL SCIENCE—Abstracting, Bibliographies, Statistics

CURRENT DIGEST OF THE POST-SOVIET PRESS. QUARTERLY INDEX. see POLITICAL SCIENCE—Abstracting, Bibliographies, Statistics

CURRENT INDEX TO JOURNALS IN EDUCATION. see EDUCATION—Abstracting, Bibliographies, Statistics

CURRENT INDEX TO JOURNALS IN EDUCATION SEMIANNUAL CUMULATION. see EDUCATION—Abstracting, Bibliographies, Statistics

CURRENT INDIAN FORESTRY, ENVIRONMENT & WILDLIFE ABSTRACTS. see FORESTS AND FORESTRY—Abstracting, Bibliographies, Statistics

CURRENT LAW INDEX; multiple access to legal periodicals in print. see LAW—Abstracting, Bibliographies, Statistics

CURRENT LITERATURE ON SCIENCE OF SCIENCE. see SCIENCES: COMPREHENSIVE WORKS—Abstracting, Bibliographies, Statistics

CURRENT MANAGEMENT LITERATURE. see BUSINESS AND ECONOMICS—Abstracting, Bibliographies, Statistics

CURRENT MEDICAL LITERATURE. ALERGOLOGIA. see MEDICAL SCIENCES—Abstracting, Bibliographies, Statistics

CURRENT MEDICAL LITERATURE. ALLERGY. see MEDICAL SCIENCES—Abstracting, Bibliographies, Statistics

CURRENT MEDICAL LITERATURE. ANESTEZJOLOGIA. see MEDICAL SCIENCES—Abstracting, Bibliographies, Statistics

CURRENT MEDICAL LITERATURE. CHIRURGIA. see MEDICAL SCIENCES—Abstracting, Bibliographies, Statistics

CURRENT MEDICAL LITERATURE. CLINICAL NUTRITION. see NUTRITION AND DIETETICS—Abstracting, Bibliographies, Statistics

CURRENT MEDICAL LITERATURE. COLORECTAL CANCER. see MEDICAL SCIENCES—Abstracting, Bibliographies, Statistics

CURRENT MEDICAL LITERATURE. DERMATOLOGIA. see MEDICAL SCIENCES—Abstracting, Bibliographies, Statistics

CURRENT MEDICAL LITERATURE. GASTROENTEROLOGIA. see MEDICAL SCIENCES—Abstracting, Bibliographies, Statistics

CURRENT MEDICAL LITERATURE. GERIATRIA. see GERONTOLOGY AND GERIATRICS—Abstracting, Bibliographies, Statistics

CURRENT MEDICAL LITERATURE. GINEKOLOGIA I POLOZNICTWO. see MEDICAL SCIENCES—Abstracting, Bibliographies, Statistics

CURRENT MEDICAL LITERATURE. HEALTH CARE OF OLDER PEOPLE. see GERONTOLOGY AND GERIATRICS—Abstracting, Bibliographies, Statistics

CURRENT MEDICAL LITERATURE. KARDIOLOGIA. see MEDICAL SCIENCES—Abstracting, Bibliographies, Statistics

CURRENT MEDICAL LITERATURE. LARYNGOLOGIA. see MEDICAL SCIENCES—Abstracting, Bibliographies, Statistics

CURRENT MEDICAL LITERATURE. LECZENIE ZYWIENIOWE. see NUTRITION AND DIETETICS—Abstracting, Bibliographies, Statistics

CURRENT MEDICAL LITERATURE. NEUROLOGIA. see MEDICAL SCIENCES—Abstracting, Bibliographies, Statistics

CURRENT MEDICAL LITERATURE. OKULISTYKA. see MEDICAL SCIENCES—Abstracting, Bibliographies, Statistics

CURRENT MEDICAL LITERATURE. ONKOLOGIA. see MEDICAL SCIENCES—Abstracting, Bibliographies, Statistics

CURRENT MEDICAL LITERATURE. PEDIATRIA. see MEDICAL SCIENCES—Abstracting, Bibliographies, Statistics

CURRENT MEDICAL LITERATURE. PSYCHIATRIA. see MEDICAL SCIENCES—Abstracting, Bibliographies, Statistics

CURRENT MEDICAL LITERATURE. PSYCHIATRY REVIEWS; recent developments in psychiatric care for General Practitioners. see MEDICAL SCIENCES—Abstracting, Bibliographies, Statistics

CURRENT MEDICAL LITERATURE. REUMATOLOGIA. see MEDICAL SCIENCES—Abstracting, Bibliographies, Statistics

CURRENT MEDICAL LITERATURE. UROLOGIA. see MEDICAL SCIENCES—Abstracting, Bibliographies, Statistics

CURRENT OPINION IN IMMUNOLOGY. see MEDICAL SCIENCES—Abstracting, Bibliographies, Statistics

CURRENT PAPERS IN ELECTRICAL & ELECTRONICS ENGINEERING. see ENGINEERING—Abstracting, Bibliographies, Statistics

CURRENT PAPERS IN PHYSICS; containing about 78,000 titles of research articles from the world's physics journals. see PHYSICS—Abstracting, Bibliographies, Statistics

CURRENT PHYSICS INDEX. see PHYSICS—Abstracting, Bibliographies, Statistics

CURRENT PRIMATE REFERENCES. see BIOLOGY— Abstracting, Bibliographies, Statistics

CURRENT RESEARCH IN BRITAIN. BIOLOGICAL SCIENCES. see BIOLOGY—Abstracting, Bibliographies, Statistics

CURRENT RESEARCH IN BRITAIN. HUMANITIES. see HUMANITIES: COMPREHENSIVE WORKS—Abstracting, Bibliographies, Statistics

CURRENT RESEARCH IN BRITAIN. PHYSICAL SCIENCES. see SCIENCES: COMPREHENSIVE WORKS—Abstracting, Bibliographies, Statistics

CURRENT RESEARCH IN BRITAIN. SOCIAL SCIENCES. see SOCIAL SCIENCES: COMPREHENSIVE WORKS— Abstracting, Bibliographies, Statistics

CURRENT TITLES IN ELECTROCHEMISTRY. see CHEMISTRY—Abstracting, Bibliographies, Statistics

CUTTING TECHNOLOGY. see MACHINERY—Abstracting, Bibliographies, Statistics

CYSTIC FIBROSIS. see MEDICAL SCIENCES—Abstracting, Bibliographies, Statistics

CYTOSKELETON. see BIOLOGY—Abstracting, Bibliographies, Statistics

D N A PROBES. (Deoxyribonucleic Acid) see BIOLOGY— Abstracting, Bibliographies, Statistics

D O C P A L RESUMENES SOBRE POBLACION EN AMERICA LATINA/D O C P A L LATIN AMERICAN POPULATION ABSTRACTS. see POPULATION STUDIES—Abstracting, Bibliographies, Statistics

016.05   IDN   ISSN 0854-0306
Z6958.I45
DAFTAR TERBITAN BERKALA INDONESIA YANG TELAH MEMPUNYAI ISSN/LIST OF INDONESIAN SERIALS HAVING ISSN. Text in Indonesian. 1992. biennial. IDR 15,000 domestic; USD 25 foreign (effective 2001). bibl. back issues avail. Document type: Bibliography. Description: Contains listings of publishers in Indonesia with registered ISSN.
Related titles: E-mail ed.; Fax ed.
Published by: Pusat Dokumentasi dan Informasi Ilmiah, Lembaga Ilmu Pengetahuan Indonesia/Center for Scientific Documentation and Information, Indonesian Institute of Science, Jl. Jend. Gatot Subroto 10, Jakarta, 12710, Indonesia. TEL 62-21-5250719, FAX 62-21-5733467, mginting@hotmail.com, info@pdii.lipi.go.id. Ed. Maria Ginting. Circ: 500.

DAIRY SCIENCE ABSTRACTS. see AGRICULTURE— Abstracting, Bibliographies, Statistics

DECLASSIFIED DOCUMENTS ONLINE. see POLITICAL SCIENCE—Abstracting, Bibliographies, Statistics

DEFENCE DOCUMENTS. see MILITARY—Abstracting, Bibliographies, Statistics

DELTA PI EPSILON. INDEX TO DOCTORAL DISSERTATIONS IN BUSINESS EDUCATION. see EDUCATION—Abstracting, Bibliographies, Statistics

DENTAL ABSTRACTS. see MEDICAL SCIENCES—Abstracting, Bibliographies, Statistics

DEPONIROVANNYE NAUCHNYE RABOTY. BIBLIOGRAFICHESKII UKAZATEL'. see SCIENCES: COMPREHENSIVE WORKS—Abstracting, Bibliographies, Statistics

DERWENT BIOTECHNOLOGY ABSTRACTS. see BIOLOGY—Abstracting, Bibliographies, Statistics

DESIGN AND APPLIED ARTS INDEX. see ART—Abstracting, Bibliographies, Statistics

DEUTSCHE NOTAR CD-ROM. see PUBLIC ADMINISTRATION— Abstracting, Bibliographies, Statistics

DIETRICH'S INDEX PHILOSOPHICUS. see RELIGIONS AND THEOLOGY—Abstracting, Bibliographies, Statistics

DIGEST OF NEUROLOGY & PSYCHIATRY (ONLINE EDITION). see MEDICAL SCIENCES—Abstracting, Bibliographies, Statistics

016   JOR
DIRASAT. ANNUAL INDEX. Text in Arabic, English. 1974. a. back issues avail. Document type: Abstract/Index. Description: Indexes all the articles published in all the series of Dirasat journals.
Published by: University of Jordan, Deanship of Academic Research, Dean of Academic Research, Amman, 11942, Jordan. TEL 962-6-5355000 ext 3200, FAX 962-6-5355599, dirasata@ju.edu.jo, http://www.ju.edu.jo/research/dar. Ed. Nabil Shawagfeh.

DIRECTORY OF PUBLISHED PROCEEDINGS. SERIES M L S - MEDICAL, LIFE SCIENCES. see MEDICAL SCIENCES—Abstracting, Bibliographies, Statistics

DIRECTORY OF PUBLISHED PROCEEDINGS. SERIES P C E - POLLUTION CONTROL & ECOLOGY. see ENVIRONMENTAL STUDIES—Abstracting, Bibliographies, Statistics

DIRECTORY OF PUBLISHED PROCEEDINGS. SERIES S E M T - SCIENCE, ENGINEERING, MEDICINE AND TECHNOLOGY. see SCIENCES: COMPREHENSIVE WORKS—Abstracting, Bibliographies, Statistics

DIRECTORY OF PUBLISHED PROCEEDINGS. SERIES S S H - SOCIAL SCIENCES - HUMANITIES. see HUMANITIES: COMPREHENSIVE WORKS—Abstracting, Bibliographies, Statistics

DIRECTORY OF SCIENTIFIC PERIODICALS OF PAKISTAN. see SCIENCES: COMPREHENSIVE WORKS—Abstracting, Bibliographies, Statistics

DISSERTATION ABSTRACTS INTERNATIONAL. SECTION B: PHYSICAL SCIENCES AND ENGINEERING. see SCIENCES: COMPREHENSIVE WORKS—Abstracting, Bibliographies, Statistics

DISSERTATION ABSTRACTS INTERNATIONAL. SECTION C: WORLDWIDE. see HUMANITIES: COMPREHENSIVE WORKS—Abstracting, Bibliographies, Statistics

DISSERTATION ABSTRACTS OF IRANIAN GRADUATES ABROAD/CHIKIDAH-'I PAYAN'NAMAH'HA-YI FARIGH-AL TAHSILAN-I IRANI KHARIJ AZ KISHVAR. see EDUCATION—Abstracting, Bibliographies, Statistics

DISTRICT COURTS JUDGMENTS INDEXES. see LAW—Abstracting, Bibliographies, Statistics

DIZHEN WENZHAI/SEISMOLOGICAL ABSTRACTS. see EARTH SCIENCES—Abstracting, Bibliographies, Statistics

DJERELO. see SCIENCES: COMPREHENSIVE WORKS—Abstracting, Bibliographies, Statistics

DOCUMENTATION IN PUBLIC ADMINISTRATION. see PUBLIC ADMINISTRATION—Abstracting, Bibliographies, Statistics

DOCUMENTATION LIST: AFRICA. see HISTORY—Abstracting, Bibliographies, Statistics

DOCUMENTS; revue des questions allemandes. see HISTORY—Abstracting, Bibliographies, Statistics

▼ new title   ➤ refereed   * unverified   ◆ full entry avail.

A

DOKUMENTATION NATUR UND LANDSCHAFT. see *ENVIRONMENTAL STUDIES—Abstracting, Bibliographies, Statistics*

DOKUMENTATION STRASSE; Kurzauszuege aus dem Schrifttum ueber das Strassenwesen. see *ENGINEERING—Abstracting, Bibliographies, Statistics*

DRUG FILE UPDATE; a current awareness index to publications on drugs and doping in sport. see *SPORTS AND GAMES—Abstracting, Bibliographies, Statistics*

DRUG TARGETING. see *PHARMACY AND PHARMACOLOGY— Abstracting, Bibliographies, Statistics*

E & P HEALTH, SAFETY AND ENVIRONMENT. (Exploration and Production) see *PETROLEUM AND GAS—Abstracting, Bibliographies, Statistics*

E F I - NYTT/E F I - NEWS. see *BUSINESS AND ECONOMICS—Abstracting, Bibliographies, Statistics*

E I (ONLINE EDITION). (Excerpta Indonesica) see *ANTHROPOLOGY—Abstracting, Bibliographies, Statistics*

E I S; digests of environmental impact statements. see *ENVIRONMENTAL STUDIES—Abstracting, Bibliographies, Statistics*

020   USA
E - N F A I S NOTES. Text in English. irreg. (approx. w.). membership only. **Document type:** *Newsletter.* **Description:** Provides news of current developments affecting the information industry, views, comments and opinions.
Supersedes: N F A I S Notes
Media: Online - full text.
Published by: National Federation of Abstracting and Information Services, 1518 Walnut St, Ste 307, Philadelphia, PA 19102. TEL 215-893-1561, FAX 215-893-1564, nfais@nfais.org.

E R I C. (Education Resource Information Center) see *EDUCATION—Abstracting, Bibliographies, Statistics*

E R I C - C U E URBAN DIVERSITY SERIES. see *EDUCATION—Abstracting, Bibliographies, Statistics*

E R I C IDENTIFIER AUTHORITY LIST. see *EDUCATION— Abstracting, Bibliographies, Statistics*

E U D I S E D - EUROPEAN EDUCATIONAL RESEARCH YEARBOOK; project reports - people - contacts. (European Documentation and Information System for Education) see *EDUCATION—Abstracting, Bibliographies, Statistics*

EARTHQUAKE ENGINEERING ABSTRACTS DATABASE. see *ENGINEERING—Abstracting, Bibliographies, Statistics*

EARTHQUAKES AND THE BUILT ENVIRONMENT INDEX. see *ENGINEERING—Abstracting, Bibliographies, Statistics*

ECO-LOG WEEK; a report on waste management and industrial pollution control. see *ENVIRONMENTAL STUDIES— Abstracting, Bibliographies, Statistics*

ECOLOGICAL ABSTRACTS. see *BIOLOGY—Abstracting, Bibliographies, Statistics*

ECOLOGY ABSTRACTS (BETHESDA). see *ENVIRONMENTAL STUDIES—Abstracting, Bibliographies, Statistics*

ECOLOGY ABSTRACTS (MOSCOW). see *BIOLOGY— Abstracting, Bibliographies, Statistics*

ECONOMIC DEVELOPMENT TODAY. see *BUSINESS AND ECONOMICS—Abstracting, Bibliographies, Statistics*

EDITORIALS ON FILE; newspaper editorial reference service with index. see *JOURNALISM—Abstracting, Bibliographies, Statistics*

EDUCATION ABSTRACTS (CD-ROM). see *EDUCATION— Abstracting, Bibliographies, Statistics*

EDUCATION FULL TEXT. see *EDUCATION— Abstracting, Bibliographies, Statistics*

EDUCATION IN KENYA; index of articles on education. see *EDUCATION—Abstracting, Bibliographies, Statistics*

EDUCATION INDEX. see *EDUCATION—Abstracting, Bibliographies, Statistics*

EDUCATION LITERATURE REVIEW. see *EDUCATION— Abstracting, Bibliographies, Statistics*

EDUCATION RESEARCH ABSTRACTS. see *EDUCATION— Abstracting, Bibliographies, Statistics*

EDUCATIONAL ABSTRACTS FOR TANZANIA. see *EDUCATION—Abstracting, Bibliographies, Statistics*

EDUCATIONAL ADMINISTRATION ABSTRACTS. see *EDUCATION—Abstracting, Bibliographies, Statistics*

EDUCATIONAL INDEX OF ARABIC PERIODICALS. see *EDUCATION—Abstracting, Bibliographies, Statistics*

EDUCATIONAL INDEX OF FOREIGN PERIODICALS. see *EDUCATION—Abstracting, Bibliographies, Statistics*

EDUCATIONAL INDICATIVE ABSTRACTS. see *EDUCATION—Abstracting, Bibliographies, Statistics*

EDUCATIONAL INFORMATION ABSTRACTS. see *EDUCATION—Abstracting, Bibliographies, Statistics*

EDUCATIONAL MANAGEMENT ABSTRACTS. see *EDUCATION—Abstracting, Bibliographies, Statistics*

EDUCATIONAL RESEARCH ABSTRACTS ONLINE. see *EDUCATION—Abstracting, Bibliographies, Statistics*

EDUCATIONAL SELECTIVE ABSTRACTS. see *EDUCATION—Abstracting, Bibliographies, Statistics*

EDUCATIONAL TECHNOLOGY ABSTRACTS. see *EDUCATION—Abstracting, Bibliographies, Statistics*

EI ENCOMPASSLIT. see *PETROLEUM AND GAS—Abstracting, Bibliographies, Statistics*

EKISTIC INDEX OF PERIODICALS. see *HOUSING AND URBAN PLANNING—Abstracting, Bibliographies, Statistics*

EKONOMIA ON-LINE. see *BUSINESS AND ECONOMICS— Abstracting, Bibliographies, Statistics*

EKSPRESS-INFORMATSIYA. ASTRONAVTIKA I RAKETODINAMIKA. see *AERONAUTICS AND SPACE FLIGHT—Abstracting, Bibliographies, Statistics*

EKSPRESS-INFORMATSIYA. AVIASTROENIE. see *AERONAUTICS AND SPACE FLIGHT—Abstracting, Bibliographies, Statistics*

EKSPRESS-INFORMATSIYA. DETALI MASHIN. TEKHNOLOGIYA IZGOTOVLENIYA. AVTOMATIZATSIYA PROIZVODSTVA. see *MACHINERY—Abstracting, Bibliographies, Statistics*

EKSPRESS-INFORMATSIYA. GORODSKOI TRANSPORT. see *TRANSPORTATION—Abstracting, Bibliographies, Statistics*

EKSPRESS-INFORMATSIYA. KONTROL'NO-IZMERITEL'NAYA TEKHNIKA. see *INSTRUMENTS—Abstracting, Bibliographies, Statistics*

EKSPRESS INFORMATSIYA. PRAVOVYE VOPROSY OKHRANY OKRUZHAYUSHCHEI SREDY. see *LAW—Abstracting, Bibliographies, Statistics*

EKSPRESS-INFORMATSIYA. RESURSOSBEREGAYUSHCHIE TEKHNOLOGII. see *ENVIRONMENTAL STUDIES— Abstracting, Bibliographies, Statistics*

EKSPRESS-INFORMATSIYA. TARA I UPAKOVKA. KONTEINERY. see *PACKAGING—Abstracting, Bibliographies, Statistics*

EKSPRESS INFORMATSIYA. UPRAVLENIE, LOGISTIKA I INFORMATIKA NA TRANSPORTE. see *TRANSPORTATION—Abstracting, Bibliographies, Statistics*

ELECTRONIC CURRENT CONTENTS OF PERIODICALS ON THE MIDDLE EAST. see *HISTORY—Abstracting, Bibliographies, Statistics*

ELECTRONIC PRODUCT LIBRARY CD-ROM. see *ELECTRONICS*

ELECTRONICS AND COMMUNICATIONS ABSTRACTS JOURNAL. see *COMMUNICATIONS—Abstracting, Bibliographies, Statistics*

ELEKTRONIKAI ES HIRADASTECHNIKAI SZAKIRODALMI/ ELECTRONICS & COMMUNICATIONS ABSTRACTS. see *COMMUNICATIONS—Abstracting, Bibliographies, Statistics*

EMBASE. see *MEDICAL SCIENCES—Abstracting, Bibliographies, Statistics*

EMBASE ALERT. see *MEDICAL SCIENCES—Abstracting, Bibliographies, Statistics*

EMENTARIO DA LEGISLACAO DO PETROLEO. see *LAW—Abstracting, Bibliographies, Statistics*

EMERALD FULLTEXT. see *BUSINESS AND ECONOMICS— Abstracting, Bibliographies, Statistics*

EMERALD MANAGEMENT REVIEWS (ONLINE EDITION). see *BUSINESS AND ECONOMICS—Abstracting, Bibliographies, Statistics*

EMERALD MANAGEMENT REVIEWS (PRINT EDITION). see *BUSINESS AND ECONOMICS—Abstracting, Bibliographies, Statistics*

ENDOCRINE ABSTRACTS. see *MEDICAL SCIENCES— Abstracting, Bibliographies, Statistics*

ENDOTHELIUM. see *BIOLOGY—Abstracting, Bibliographies, Statistics*

ENERGIAIPARI ES ENERGIAGAZDALKODASI TAJEKOZTATO/POWER ENGINEERING ABSTRACTS. see *ENERGY—Abstracting, Bibliographies, Statistics*

ENERGY STORAGE SYSTEMS ABSTRACTS. see *ENERGY—Abstracting, Bibliographies, Statistics*

THE ENGINEERING INDEX ANNUAL. see *ENGINEERING— Abstracting, Bibliographies, Statistics*

ENGINEERING INDEX CUMULATIVE INDEX. see *ENGINEERING—Abstracting, Bibliographies, Statistics*

THE ENGINEERING INDEX MONTHLY. see *ENGINEERING— Abstracting, Bibliographies, Statistics*

ENTOMOLOGY ABSTRACTS. see *BIOLOGY—Abstracting, Bibliographies, Statistics*

ENTREZ DOCUMENT RETRIEVAL SYSTEM. see *BIOLOGY—Abstracting, Bibliographies, Statistics*

ENVIRO - NEWS DIGEST. see *ENVIRONMENTAL STUDIES—Abstracting, Bibliographies, Statistics*

ENVIROFICHE. see *BIOLOGY—Abstracting, Bibliographies, Statistics*

ENVIRONMENT ABSTRACTS. see *CONSERVATION— Abstracting, Bibliographies, Statistics*

ENVIRONMENT ABSTRACTS ANNUAL; a guide to the key environmental literature of the year. see *ENVIRONMENTAL STUDIES—Abstracting, Bibliographies, Statistics*

ENVIRONMENTAL AND SAFETY TECHNOLOGY. see *ENVIRONMENTAL STUDIES—Abstracting, Bibliographies, Statistics*

ENVIRONMENTAL ENGINEERING ABSTRACTS (ONLINE EDITION). see *ENVIRONMENTAL STUDIES—Abstracting, Bibliographies, Statistics*

ENVIRONMENTAL ISSUES & POLICY INDEX. see *ENVIRONMENTAL STUDIES—Abstracting, Bibliographies, Statistics*

ENVIRONMENTAL RESOURCES ABSTRACTS. see *ENVIRONMENTAL STUDIES—Abstracting, Bibliographies, Statistics*

ENVIRONMENTAL SCIENCES AND POLLUTION MANAGEMENT. see *ENVIRONMENTAL STUDIES— Abstracting, Bibliographies, Statistics*

ERGONOMICS ABSTRACTS ONLINE. see *ENGINEERING— Abstracting, Bibliographies, Statistics*

ERHVERVSUDDANNELSERNE. see *EDUCATION—Abstracting, Bibliographies, Statistics*

ERYTHROCYTES. see *MEDICAL SCIENCES—Abstracting, Bibliographies, Statistics*

ESHAMAN.COM. see *COMPUTERS—Abstracting, Bibliographies, Statistics*

ESSAY AND GENERAL LITERATURE INDEX. see *LITERATURE—Abstracting, Bibliographies, Statistics*

ESTETICHESKOE VOSPITANIE; referativno-bibliograficheskaya informatsiya. see *PHILOSOPHY—Abstracting, Bibliographies, Statistics*

ETHNOARTS INDEX. see *ANTHROPOLOGY—Abstracting, Bibliographies, Statistics*

EUROABSTRACTS. see *TECHNOLOGY: COMPREHENSIVE WORKS—Abstracting, Bibliographies, Statistics*

EUROPEAN ASSOCIATION FOR ANIMAL PRODUCTION. ANNUAL MEETING. BOOK OF ABSTRACTS. see AGRICULTURE—Abstracting, Bibliographies, Statistics

EUROPEAN CONGRESS OF CARDIOLOGY. ABSTRACTS OF PAPERS. see MEDICAL SCIENCES—Abstracting, Bibliographies, Statistics

EUROPEAN FOOD RESEARCH AND TECHNOLOGY; international journal of food research and technology. see FOOD AND FOOD INDUSTRIES—Abstracting, Bibliographies, Statistics

EXCEPTIONAL CHILD EDUCATION RESOURCES (ONLINE EDITION). see EDUCATION—Abstracting, Bibliographies, Statistics

EXCEPTIONAL HUMAN EXPERIENCE; studies of the psychic - spontaneous - imaginal. see NEW AGE PUBLICATIONS

EXCERPTA MEDICA. ABSTRACT JOURNALS. see BIOLOGY—Abstracting, Bibliographies, Statistics

EXCERPTA MEDICA. SECTION 1: ANATOMY, ANTHROPOLOGY, EMBRYOLOGY & HISTOLOGY. see BIOLOGY—Abstracting, Bibliographies, Statistics

EXCERPTA MEDICA. SECTION 10: OBSTETRICS AND GYNECOLOGY. see MEDICAL SCIENCES—Abstracting, Bibliographies, Statistics

EXCERPTA MEDICA. SECTION 11: OTORHINOLARYNGOLOGY. see MEDICAL SCIENCES—Abstracting, Bibliographies, Statistics

EXCERPTA MEDICA. SECTION 12: OPHTHALMOLOGY. see MEDICAL SCIENCES—Abstracting, Bibliographies, Statistics

EXCERPTA MEDICA. SECTION 13: DERMATOLOGY AND VENEREOLOGY. see MEDICAL SCIENCES—Abstracting, Bibliographies, Statistics

EXCERPTA MEDICA. SECTION 14: RADIOLOGY. see MEDICAL SCIENCES—Abstracting, Bibliographies, Statistics

EXCERPTA MEDICA. SECTION 15: CHEST DISEASES, THORACIC SURGERY AND TUBERCULOSIS. see MEDICAL SCIENCES—Abstracting, Bibliographies, Statistics

EXCERPTA MEDICA. SECTION 16: CANCER. see MEDICAL SCIENCES—Abstracting, Bibliographies, Statistics

EXCERPTA MEDICA. SECTION 17: PUBLIC HEALTH, SOCIAL MEDICINE AND EPIDEMIOLOGY. see PUBLIC HEALTH AND SAFETY—Abstracting, Bibliographies, Statistics

EXCERPTA MEDICA. SECTION 18: CARDIOVASCULAR DISEASES AND CARDIOVASCULAR SURGERY. see MEDICAL SCIENCES—Abstracting, Bibliographies, Statistics

EXCERPTA MEDICA. SECTION 19: REHABILITATION AND PHYSICAL MEDICINE. see MEDICAL SCIENCES—Abstracting, Bibliographies, Statistics

EXCERPTA MEDICA. SECTION 2: PHYSIOLOGY. see MEDICAL SCIENCES—Abstracting, Bibliographies, Statistics

EXCERPTA MEDICA. SECTION 20: GERONTOLOGY AND GERIATRICS. see GERONTOLOGY AND GERIATRICS—Abstracting, Bibliographies, Statistics

EXCERPTA MEDICA. SECTION 21: DEVELOPMENTAL BIOLOGY AND TERATOLOGY. see BIOLOGY—Abstracting, Bibliographies, Statistics

EXCERPTA MEDICA. SECTION 22: HUMAN GENETICS. see BIOLOGY—Abstracting, Bibliographies, Statistics

EXCERPTA MEDICA. SECTION 23: NUCLEAR MEDICINE. see MEDICAL SCIENCES—Abstracting, Bibliographies, Statistics

EXCERPTA MEDICA. SECTION 24: ANESTHESIOLOGY. see MEDICAL SCIENCES—Abstracting, Bibliographies, Statistics

EXCERPTA MEDICA. SECTION 25: HEMATOLOGY. see MEDICAL SCIENCES—Abstracting, Bibliographies, Statistics

EXCERPTA MEDICA. SECTION 26: IMMUNOLOGY, SEROLOGY AND TRANSPLANTATION. see MEDICAL SCIENCES—Abstracting, Bibliographies, Statistics

EXCERPTA MEDICA. SECTION 27: BIOPHYSICS, BIO-ENGINEERING AND MEDICAL INSTRUMENTATION. see BIOLOGY—Abstracting, Bibliographies, Statistics

EXCERPTA MEDICA. SECTION 28: UROLOGY AND NEPHROLOGY. see MEDICAL SCIENCES—Abstracting, Bibliographies, Statistics

EXCERPTA MEDICA. SECTION 29: CLINICAL AND EXPERIMENTAL BIOCHEMISTRY. see BIOLOGY—Abstracting, Bibliographies, Statistics

EXCERPTA MEDICA. SECTION 3: ENDOCRINOLOGY. see MEDICAL SCIENCES—Abstracting, Bibliographies, Statistics

EXCERPTA MEDICA. SECTION 30: CLINICAL AND EXPERIMENTAL PHARMACOLOGY. see PHARMACY AND PHARMACOLOGY—Abstracting, Bibliographies, Statistics

EXCERPTA MEDICA. SECTION 31: ARTHRITIS AND RHEUMATISM. see MEDICAL SCIENCES—Abstracting, Bibliographies, Statistics

EXCERPTA MEDICA. SECTION 32: PSYCHIATRY. see MEDICAL SCIENCES—Abstracting, Bibliographies, Statistics

EXCERPTA MEDICA. SECTION 33: ORTHOPEDIC SURGERY. see MEDICAL SCIENCES—Abstracting, Bibliographies, Statistics

EXCERPTA MEDICA. SECTION 35: OCCUPATIONAL HEALTH AND INDUSTRIAL MEDICINE. see MEDICAL SCIENCES—Abstracting, Bibliographies, Statistics

EXCERPTA MEDICA. SECTION 36: HEALTH POLICY, ECONOMICS AND MANAGEMENT. see HEALTH FACILITIES AND ADMINISTRATION—Abstracting, Bibliographies, Statistics

EXCERPTA MEDICA. SECTION 38: ADVERSE REACTIONS TITLES. see PHARMACY AND PHARMACOLOGY—Abstracting, Bibliographies, Statistics

EXCERPTA MEDICA. SECTION 4: MICROBIOLOGY: BACTERIOLOGY, MYCOLOGY, PARASITOLOGY AND VIROLOGY. see BIOLOGY—Abstracting, Bibliographies, Statistics

EXCERPTA MEDICA. SECTION 40: DRUG DEPENDENCE, ALCOHOL ABUSE AND ALCOHOLISM. see DRUG ABUSE AND ALCOHOLISM—Abstracting, Bibliographies, Statistics

EXCERPTA MEDICA. SECTION 46: ENVIRONMENTAL HEALTH AND POLLUTION CONTROL. see ENVIRONMENTAL STUDIES—Abstracting, Bibliographies, Statistics

EXCERPTA MEDICA. SECTION 48: GASTROENTEROLOGY. see MEDICAL SCIENCES—Abstracting, Bibliographies, Statistics

EXCERPTA MEDICA. SECTION 49: FORENSIC SCIENCE ABSTRACTS. see MEDICAL SCIENCES—Abstracting, Bibliographies, Statistics

EXCERPTA MEDICA. SECTION 5: GENERAL PATHOLOGY AND PATHOLOGICAL ANATOMY. see BIOLOGY—Abstracting, Bibliographies, Statistics

EXCERPTA MEDICA. SECTION 52: TOXICOLOGY. see ENVIRONMENTAL STUDIES—Abstracting, Bibliographies, Statistics

EXCERPTA MEDICA. SECTION 6: INTERNAL MEDICINE. see MEDICAL SCIENCES—Abstracting, Bibliographies, Statistics

EXCERPTA MEDICA. SECTION 7: PEDIATRICS AND PEDIATRIC SURGERY. see MEDICAL SCIENCES—Abstracting, Bibliographies, Statistics

EXCERPTA MEDICA. SECTION 8: NEUROLOGY AND NEUROSURGERY. see MEDICAL SCIENCES—Abstracting, Bibliographies, Statistics

EXCERPTA MEDICA. SECTION 9: SURGERY. see MEDICAL SCIENCES—Abstracting, Bibliographies, Statistics

EXPRESS BULLETINS; a series of current awareness bulletins for researchers in biology and medicine. see BIOLOGY—Abstracting, Bibliographies, Statistics

F A I ABSTRACT SERVICE. see AGRICULTURE—Abstracting, Bibliographies, Statistics

F I I R O INDUSTRIAL ABSTRACTS. see BUSINESS AND ECONOMICS—Abstracting, Bibliographies, Statistics

F P I: FLOWERING PLANT INDEX. see GARDENING AND HORTICULTURE—Abstracting, Bibliographies, Statistics

F R A N C I S. see SOCIAL SCIENCES: COMPREHENSIVE WORKS—Abstracting, Bibliographies, Statistics

FACHINFORMATION BAHN; Dokumentation der Fachliteratur. see TRANSPORTATION—Abstracting, Bibliographies, Statistics

FAMILY & SOCIETY STUDIES WORLDWIDE. see MATRIMONY—Abstracting, Bibliographies, Statistics

FAMILY INDEX. see SOCIOLOGY—Abstracting, Bibliographies, Statistics

FANATIC READER. see GENERAL INTEREST PERIODICALS—United States

FEDERAL REGISTER SUBJECT INDEX. see LAW—Abstracting, Bibliographies, Statistics

FEDERAL STATUTES ANNOTATIONS. see PUBLIC ADMINISTRATION—Abstracting, Bibliographies, Statistics

FEMINIST PERIODICALS; a current listing of contents. see WOMEN'S STUDIES—Abstracting, Bibliographies, Statistics

FICHIERS-PRESSE. see JOURNALISM—Abstracting, Bibliographies, Statistics

FIELD CROP ABSTRACTS; monthly abstract journal on world annual cereal, legume, root, oilseed and fibre crops. see AGRICULTURE—Abstracting, Bibliographies, Statistics

FIHRIST; index to Arabic periodical literature. see BIBLIOGRAPHIES

FILM INDEX INTERNATIONAL. see MOTION PICTURES—Abstracting, Bibliographies, Statistics

FILM LITERATURE INDEX. see MOTION PICTURES—Abstracting, Bibliographies, Statistics

FILMLOG; index of feature film production and casting in Britain. see MOTION PICTURES—Abstracting, Bibliographies, Statistics

FILMSTRIP AND SLIDE SET FINDER. see EDUCATION—Abstracting, Bibliographies, Statistics

FINANCIAL TIMES INDEX (ANNUAL). see BUSINESS AND ECONOMICS—Abstracting, Bibliographies, Statistics

FINANCIAL TIMES INDEX (MONTHLY). see BUSINESS AND ECONOMICS—Abstracting, Bibliographies, Statistics

FISH & FISHERIES WORLDWIDE. see BIOLOGY—Abstracting, Bibliographies, Statistics

FLUID ABSTRACTS: CIVIL ENGINEERING. see ENGINEERING—Abstracting, Bibliographies, Statistics

FLUID ABSTRACTS: PROCESS ENGINEERING. see ENGINEERING—Abstracting, Bibliographies, Statistics

FOCUS ON CATALYSTS. see CHEMISTRY—Abstracting, Bibliographies, Statistics

FOCUS ON PIGMENTS. see PAINTS AND PROTECTIVE COATINGS—Abstracting, Bibliographies, Statistics

FOCUS ON POWDER COATINGS. see PAINTS AND PROTECTIVE COATINGS—Abstracting, Bibliographies, Statistics

FOCUS ON: SPORTS SCIENCE AND MEDICINE. see MEDICAL SCIENCES—Abstracting, Bibliographies, Statistics

FOCUS ON SURFACTANTS. see CHEMISTRY—Abstracting, Bibliographies, Statistics

FOCUS ON: VETERINARY SCIENCE AND MEDICINE. see VETERINARY SCIENCE—Abstracting, Bibliographies, Statistics

FOOD SCIENCE AND TECHNOLOGY ABSTRACTS. see FOOD AND FOOD INDUSTRIES—Abstracting, Bibliographies, Statistics

FOODINFO. see FOOD AND FOOD INDUSTRIES—Abstracting, Bibliographies, Statistics

FOODS ADLIBRA; key to the world's food literature. see FOOD AND FOOD INDUSTRIES—Abstracting, Bibliographies, Statistics

FOODS ADLIBRA BEVERAGE EDITION. see BEVERAGES—Abstracting, Bibliographies, Statistics

FOODS ADLIBRA FOODSERVICE EDITION. see FOOD AND FOOD INDUSTRIES—Abstracting, Bibliographies, Statistics

FOODS ADLIBRA SEAFOOD EDITION. see FOOD AND FOOD INDUSTRIES—Abstracting, Bibliographies, Statistics

FOOTHILLS INQUIRER. see GENEALOGY AND HERALDRY

▼ *new title* ➤ *refereed* ✱ *unverified* ◆ *full entry avail.*

A

FOREIGN BROADCAST INFORMATION SERVICE DAILY REPORTS. CENTRAL EURASIA. INDEX. see *POLITICAL SCIENCE—Abstracting, Bibliographies, Statistics*

FOREIGN PATENTS INFORMATION BULLETIN. see *PATENTS, TRADEMARKS AND COPYRIGHTS—Abstracting, Bibliographies, Statistics*

FOREST PRODUCTS ABSTRACTS. see *FORESTS AND FORESTRY—Abstracting, Bibliographies, Statistics*

FORESTRY ABSTRACTS; compiled from world literature. see *FORESTS AND FORESTRY—Abstracting, Bibliographies, Statistics*

FRANCE. MINISTERE DE L'AGRICULTURE ET DE LA PECHE. AGRESTE LE BULLETIN. see *AGRICULTURE—Abstracting, Bibliographies, Statistics*

FRENCH PATENTS ABSTRACTS. see *PATENTS, TRADEMARKS AND COPYRIGHTS—Abstracting, Bibliographies, Statistics*

FUEL AND ENERGY ABSTRACTS. see *PETROLEUM AND GAS—Abstracting, Bibliographies, Statistics*

FURO INJEKUSHON BUNSEKI KOENKAI KOEN YOSHISHU/ABSTRACTS OF MEETING ON FLOW INJECTION ANALYSIS. see *CHEMISTRY—Analytical Chemistry*

FUTURE SURVEY; a monthly abstract of books, articles, and reports concerning trends, forecasts, and ideas about the future. see *SCIENCES: COMPREHENSIVE WORKS—Abstracting, Bibliographies, Statistics*

G. K. HALL'S WOMEN'S STUDIES INDEX. see *WOMEN'S STUDIES—Abstracting, Bibliographies, Statistics*

GASTROINTESTINAL HORMONES AND GASTRIC SECRETION. see *MEDICAL SCIENCES—Abstracting, Bibliographies, Statistics*

GAYANA: BOTANICA. see *BIOLOGY—Abstracting, Bibliographies, Statistics*

GENDER WATCH. see *SOCIOLOGY—Abstracting, Bibliographies, Statistics*

GENE THERAPY (SHEFFIELD). see *BIOLOGY—Abstracting, Bibliographies, Statistics*

GENERAL SCIENCE ABSTRACTS. see *SCIENCES: COMPREHENSIVE WORKS—Abstracting, Bibliographies, Statistics*

GENERAL SCIENCE ABSTRACTS - FULL TEXT. see *SCIENCES: COMPREHENSIVE WORKS—Abstracting, Bibliographies, Statistics*

GENERAL SCIENCE INDEX. see *SCIENCES: COMPREHENSIVE WORKS—Abstracting, Bibliographies, Statistics*

GENETICS ABSTRACTS. see *BIOLOGY—Abstracting, Bibliographies, Statistics*

GENETICS SOCIETY OF JAPAN. ABSTRACTS OF THE ANNUAL MEETING/NIHON IDEN GAKKAI TAIKAI PUROGURAMU YOKOSHU. see *BIOLOGY—Abstracting, Bibliographies, Statistics*

GEOGRAPHICAL ABSTRACTS: HUMAN GEOGRAPHY. see *GEOGRAPHY—Abstracting, Bibliographies, Statistics*

GEOGRAPHICAL ABSTRACTS: PHYSICAL GEOGRAPHY. see *GEOGRAPHY—Abstracting, Bibliographies, Statistics*

GEOLOGICAL ABSTRACTS. see *EARTH SCIENCES— Abstracting, Bibliographies, Statistics*

GEOLOGICAL SOCIETY OF AMERICA. ABSTRACTS WITH PROGRAMS. see *EARTH SCIENCES—Abstracting, Bibliographies, Statistics*

GEOLOGICAL SOCIETY OF AUSTRALIA. ABSTRACTS SERIES. see *EARTH SCIENCES—Abstracting, Bibliographies, Statistics*

GEOLOGICAL SOCIETY OF EGYPT. ANNUAL MEETING. ABSTRACTS OF PAPERS. see *EARTH SCIENCES— Abstracting, Bibliographies, Statistics*

GEOMECHANICS ABSTRACTS. see *EARTH SCIENCES—Abstracting, Bibliographies, Statistics*

GEOREF. see *EARTH SCIENCES—Abstracting, Bibliographies, Statistics*

GEOREF SERIALS LIST. see *EARTH SCIENCES—Abstracting, Bibliographies, Statistics*

GEOSCIENCE DOCUMENTATION; a bi-monthly journal for the study of geoscience literature. see *EARTH SCIENCES—Abstracting, Bibliographies, Statistics*

GEOSCIENCEWORLD. see *EARTH SCIENCES—Abstracting, Bibliographies, Statistics*

GEOTECHNICAL ABSTRACTS. see *ENGINEERING— Abstracting, Bibliographies, Statistics*

GEOTECHNICAL SCIENCE LABORATORIES. PUBLICATIONS, REPORTS, AND THESES. see *EARTH SCIENCES— Abstracting, Bibliographies, Statistics*

GEOTHERMAL ENERGY. see *ENERGY—Abstracting, Bibliographies, Statistics*

GEPGYARTASTECHNOLOGIAI ES SZERSZAMGEPIPARI SZAKIRODALMI TAJEKOZTATO/MECHANICAL ENGINEERING & MACHINE TOOL ABSTRACTS. see *ENGINEERING—Abstracting, Bibliographies, Statistics*

GERMAN PATENTS GAZETTE. SECTION 1: CHEMICAL. see *CHEMISTRY—Abstracting, Bibliographies, Statistics*

GERMAN PATENTS GAZETTE. SECTION 3: MECHANICAL AND GENERAL. see *PATENTS, TRADEMARKS AND COPYRIGHTS—Abstracting, Bibliographies, Statistics*

GERMANY. DEUTSCHER BUNDESTAG. WISSENSCHAFTLICHE DIENSTE. NEUE AUFSAETZE IN DER BIBLIOTHEK. see *SCIENCES: COMPREHENSIVE WORKS—Abstracting, Bibliographies, Statistics*

GESELLSCHAFT FUER BIBLIOTHEKSWESEN UND DOKUMENTATION DES LANDBAUES. MITTEILUNGEN. see *AGRICULTURE—Abstracting, Bibliographies, Statistics*

GHANA SCIENCE ABSTRACTS. see *SCIENCES: COMPREHENSIVE WORKS—Abstracting, Bibliographies, Statistics*

GLASS TECHNOLOGY. see *CERAMICS, GLASS AND POTTERY—Abstracting, Bibliographies, Statistics*

GLYCOBIOLOGY RESEARCH. see *BIOLOGY—Abstracting, Bibliographies, Statistics*

GOETEBORG PSYCHOLOGICAL REPORTS. see *PSYCHOLOGY*

GRASSLANDS AND FORAGE ABSTRACTS; monthly abstract journal on grassland husbandry and fodder crop production. see *AGRICULTURE—Abstracting, Bibliographies, Statistics*

GROWTH FACTORS & CYTOKINES - CLINICAL. see *MEDICAL SCIENCES—Abstracting, Bibliographies, Statistics*

GUARDIAN INDEX. see *JOURNALISM—Abstracting, Bibliographies, Statistics*

GUIDE TO SOCIAL SCIENCE AND RELIGION. see *RELIGIONS AND THEOLOGY—Abstracting, Bibliographies, Statistics*

011   USA
GUIDE TO SPECIAL ISSUES AND INDEXES OF PERIODICALS. Text in English. 1962. irreg., latest 1994. **Document type:** Abstract/Index.
Published by: Special Libraries Association, 331 S Patrick St, Alexandria, VA 22314-3501. http://www.sla.org. Ed. Miriam Uhlan.

GUIDE TO U S GOVERNMENT PUBLICATIONS. see *PUBLIC ADMINISTRATION—Abstracting, Bibliographies, Statistics*

GUIDELINES; a subject guide for Australian libraries. see *LIBRARY AND INFORMATION SCIENCES—Abstracting, Bibliographies, Statistics*

HAJOZASI SZAKIRODALMI TAJEKOZTATO/SHIPPING ABSTRACTS. see *TRANSPORTATION—Abstracting, Bibliographies, Statistics*

HANDBOOK OF LATIN AMERICAN STUDIES: A SELECTED AND ANNOTATED GUIDE TO RECENT PUBLICATIONS. see *HISTORY—Abstracting, Bibliographies, Statistics*

HANGKONG WENZHAI/AERONAUTICS ABSTRACTS. see *AERONAUTICS AND SPACE FLIGHT—Abstracting, Bibliographies, Statistics*

HARRIS POLL. see *SOCIOLOGY—Abstracting, Bibliographies, Statistics*

HAZARDS IN THE OFFICE; the newsletter on health and safety in the office. see *OCCUPATIONAL HEALTH AND SAFETY—Abstracting, Bibliographies, Statistics*

HEALTH AND SAFETY SCIENCE ABSTRACTS (ONLINE EDITION). see *PUBLIC HEALTH AND SAFETY—Abstracting, Bibliographies, Statistics*

HEALTH DEVICES ALERTS. see *MEDICAL SCIENCES— Abstracting, Bibliographies, Statistics*

HELICOBACTER. see *BIOLOGY—Abstracting, Bibliographies, Statistics*

HELMINTHOLOGICAL ABSTRACTS. see *BIOLOGY— Abstracting, Bibliographies, Statistics*

HEMOCHROMATOSIS AWARENESS; a quarterly update on hereditary and acquired iron-overload. see *MEDICAL SCIENCES—Abstracting, Bibliographies, Statistics*

HIGH PERFORMANCE LIQUID CHROMATOGRAPHY. see *PHARMACY AND PHARMACOLOGY—Abstracting, Bibliographies, Statistics*

HIGHER EDUCATION ABSTRACTS; abstracts of periodical literature, monographs and conference papers on college students, faculty and administration. see *EDUCATION— Abstracting, Bibliographies, Statistics*

011   IND
THE HINDU INDEX. Text in English. m. (plus a. cumulation). INR 1,500; INR 60 newsstand/cover (effective 2005). **Document type:** Abstract/Index.
Published by: Kasturi & Sons Ltd., Kasturi Bldgs., 859-860 Anna Salai, Chennai, Tamil Nadu 600 002, India. TEL 9144-28589060, FAX 9144-28545703, thehindu@vsnl.com, http://www.thehindu.com.

HISPANIC AMERICAN PERIODICALS INDEX. see *HISTORY—Abstracting, Bibliographies, Statistics*

HISTORICAL ABSTRACTS; bibliography of the world's historical literature. see *HISTORY—Abstracting, Bibliographies, Statistics*

HORTICULTURAL SCIENCE ABSTRACTS. see *GARDENING AND HORTICULTURE—Abstracting, Bibliographies, Statistics*

HOSPITALITY & TOURISM INDEX. see *HOTELS AND RESTAURANTS—Abstracting, Bibliographies, Statistics*

HOUSING ABSTRACTS (H A B S). see *HOUSING AND URBAN PLANNING—Abstracting, Bibliographies, Statistics*

HUMAN REPRODUCTION UPDATE. see *BIOLOGY—Abstracting, Bibliographies, Statistics*

HUMAN RESOURCE MANAGEMENT ABSTRACTS. see *BUSINESS AND ECONOMICS—Abstracting, Bibliographies, Statistics*

HUMAN RESOURCES ABSTRACTS; an international information service. see *BUSINESS AND ECONOMICS—Abstracting, Bibliographies, Statistics*

HUMAN SEXUALITY. see *MEDICAL SCIENCES—Abstracting, Bibliographies, Statistics*

HUMANITIES ABSTRACTS. see *HUMANITIES: COMPREHENSIVE WORKS—Abstracting, Bibliographies, Statistics*

HUMANITIES ABSTRACTS FULL TEXT. see *HUMANITIES: COMPREHENSIVE WORKS—Abstracting, Bibliographies, Statistics*

HUMANITIES INDEX. see *HUMANITIES: COMPREHENSIVE WORKS—Abstracting, Bibliographies, Statistics*

HUNGARIAN LIBRARY AND INFORMATION SCIENCE ABSTRACTS. see *LIBRARY AND INFORMATION SCIENCES—Abstracting, Bibliographies, Statistics*

HUNGARIAN R AND D ABSTRACTS. SCIENCE AND TECHNOLOGY. see *SCIENCES: COMPREHENSIVE WORKS—Abstracting, Bibliographies, Statistics*

I A S C - S C A D BULLETIN. see *LIBRARY AND INFORMATION SCIENCES*

I B R. INTERNATIONALE BIBLIOGRAPHIE DER REZENSIONEN GEISTES- UND SOZIALWISSENSCHAFTLICHER LITERATUR/ INTERNATIONAL BIBLIOGRAPHY OF BOOK REVIEWS OF SCHOLARLY LITERATURE. see *SCIENCES: COMPREHENSIVE WORKS—Abstracting, Bibliographies, Statistics*

I C E L REFERENCES. see *ENVIRONMENTAL STUDIES—Abstracting, Bibliographies, Statistics*

I C H C A NEWS AND CARGO TODAY. see *TRANSPORTATION—Abstracting, Bibliographies, Statistics*

016 USA
I C O N D A: INTERNATIONAL CONSTRUCTION DATABASE. Text in English. 1976. q. (plus a. cumulation).
Media: CD-ROM.
Published by: SilverPlatter Information, Incorporated (Subsidiary of: Ovid Technologies, Incorporated), 100 River Ridge Dr., Norwood, MA 02062. TEL 800-343-0064, sales@ovid.com, http://www.ovid.com.

I C S S R JOURNAL OF ABSTRACTS AND REVIEWS: POLITICAL SCIENCE. see *POLITICAL SCIENCE— Abstracting, Bibliographies, Statistics*

I C S S R JOURNAL OF ABSTRACTS AND REVIEWS: SOCIOLOGY & SOCIAL ANTHROPOLOGY. see *ANTHROPOLOGY—Abstracting, Bibliographies, Statistics*

I D I S. (Iowa Drug Information Service) see *PHARMACY AND PHARMACOLOGY—Abstracting, Bibliographies, Statistics*

I E E E INTERNATIONAL SYMPOSIUM ON INFORMATION THEORY. see *COMPUTERS—Information Science And Information Theory*

I N I S ATOMINDEX (ONLINE EDITION). (International Nuclear Information System) see *PHYSICS—Abstracting, Bibliographies, Statistics*

I T A A PROCEEDINGS (ONLINE). see *CLOTHING TRADE—Abstracting, Bibliographies, Statistics*

I V S ANNUAL. (Index of Veterinary Specialties) see *VETERINARY SCIENCE—Abstracting, Bibliographies, Statistics*

IBIS - WILDFOWL ABSTRACTS. see *BIOLOGY—Abstracting, Bibliographies, Statistics*

ILLINOIS. STATE LIBRARY, SPRINGFIELD. PUBLICATIONS OF THE STATE OF ILLINOIS. see *POLITICAL SCIENCE—Abstracting, Bibliographies, Statistics*

IMAGING ABSTRACTS. see *PHOTOGRAPHY—Abstracting, Bibliographies, Statistics*

THE INDEPENDENT INDEX. see *JOURNALISM—Abstracting, Bibliographies, Statistics*

016 USA ISSN 1041-1321
Z695.93
INDEX AND ABSTRACT DIRECTORY; an international guide to services and serials coverage. Text in English. 1989. biennial. USD 189. **Document type:** *Directory, Abstract/Index.*
Description: Directory of index and abstract services, listing publisher, price and description. Journals included.
Published by: EBSCO Publishing (Subsidiary of: EBSCO Industries, Inc.), 10 Estes St, PO Box 682, Ipswich, MA 01938-0682. TEL 978-356-6500, 800-653-2726, FAX 978-356-6565, ep@epnet.com, http://www.epnet.com. **Subscr. to:** Subscription Services, PO Box 1943, Birmingham, AL 35201-1943. TEL 205-991-6600, FAX 205-995-1518.

INDEX AND ABSTRACTS OF A P I HEALTH-RELATED RESEARCH (YEARS). see *PUBLIC HEALTH AND SAFETY—Abstracting, Bibliographies, Statistics*

INDEX AND DIRECTORY OF INDUSTRY STANDARDS. see *METROLOGY AND STANDARDIZATION—Abstracting, Bibliographies, Statistics*

INDEX ASIA SERIES IN HUMANITIES. see *ASIAN STUDIES—Abstracting, Bibliographies, Statistics*

INDEX CHEMICUS. see *CHEMISTRY—Abstracting, Bibliographies, Statistics*

INDEX DANMARK/GALLUP. see *SOCIOLOGY—Abstracting, Bibliographies, Statistics*

INDEX: FOREIGN BROADCAST INFORMATION SERVICE DAILY REPORTS: EAST ASIA. see *POLITICAL SCIENCE—Abstracting, Bibliographies, Statistics*

INDEX: FOREIGN BROADCAST INFORMATION SERVICE DAILY REPORTS: EASTERN EUROPE. see *POLITICAL SCIENCE—Abstracting, Bibliographies, Statistics*

INDEX: FOREIGN BROADCAST INFORMATION SERVICE DAILY REPORTS: LATIN AMERICA. see *POLITICAL SCIENCE—Abstracting, Bibliographies, Statistics*

INDEX: FOREIGN BROADCAST INFORMATION SERVICE DAILY REPORTS: WESTERN EUROPE. see *POLITICAL SCIENCE—Abstracting, Bibliographies, Statistics*

016 IND ISSN 0250-7595
AI19.I5
INDEX INDIANA. Text in English. 1977. a. INR 105. **Document type:** *Abstract/Index.*
Published by: Central Reference Library, Belvedere, Kolkata, West Bengal 700 027, India. TEL 91-33-479-1721-22. Ed. Y Acharya. Circ: 500.

INDEX INDO-ASIATICUS. see *ASIAN STUDIES—Abstracting, Bibliographies, Statistics*

INDEX INTERNATIONALIS INDICUS. see *ASIAN STUDIES—Abstracting, Bibliographies, Statistics*

INDEX ISLAMICUS; a bibliography of publications on Islam and the Muslim world since 1906. see *ETHNIC INTERESTS—Abstracting, Bibliographies, Statistics*

INDEX MEDICUS INDONESIA. see *MEDICAL SCIENCES—Abstracting, Bibliographies, Statistics*

INDEX OF AFRICAN SOCIAL SCIENCE PERIODICAL ARTICLES. see *POLITICAL SCIENCE—Abstracting, Bibliographies, Statistics*

INDEX OF AMERICAN PERIODICAL VERSE. see *LITERATURE—Abstracting, Bibliographies, Statistics*

INDEX OF ARTICLES ON JEWISH STUDIES (ONLINE EDITION)/RESHIMAT MA'AMARIM BE-MADA'E HA-YAHADUT. see *RELIGIONS AND THEOLOGY— Abstracting, Bibliographies, Statistics*

INDEX OF CONFERENCE PROCEEDINGS (MONTHLY). see *MEETINGS AND CONGRESSES—Abstracting, Bibliographies, Statistics*

INDEX OF CURRENT RESEARCH ON PIGS. see *AGRICULTURE—Abstracting, Bibliographies, Statistics*

INDEX OF ECONOMIC ARTICLES IN JOURNALS AND COLLECTIVE VOLUMES. see *BUSINESS AND ECONOMICS—Abstracting, Bibliographies, Statistics*

INDEX OF FUNGI. see *BIOLOGY—Abstracting, Bibliographies, Statistics*

016.700 ISR
INDEX OF JEWISH ART. Text in English. 1974. irreg. (in 10 vols.), latest vol.24, 1997. Price varies by volume. illus. back issues avail. **Document type:** *Academic/Scholarly.*
Description: Iconographical index of Jewish art.
Published by: Hebrew University of Jerusalem, Center for Jewish Art, Mount Scopus Humanities Bldg., Jerusalem, 91905, Israel. TEL 972-2-5882281, 972-2-5882285, FAX 972-2-5400105, cja@vms.huji.ac.il, http://www.hum.huji.ac.il/cja. Eds. Dr. Bezalel Narkiss, Ruth Jacoby. Circ: 1,000.

INDEX OF MATHEMATICAL PAPERS. see *MATHEMATICS— Abstracting, Bibliographies, Statistics*

INDEX OF MIDDLE ENGLISH PROSE. see *LITERATURE— Abstracting, Bibliographies, Statistics*

INDEX TO BOOK REVIEWS IN RELIGION. see *RELIGIONS AND THEOLOGY—Abstracting, Bibliographies, Statistics*

INDEX TO CHEMICAL REGULATIONS. see *CHEMISTRY— Abstracting, Bibliographies, Statistics*

INDEX TO CHINESE LEGAL PERIODICALS. see *LAW—Abstracting, Bibliographies, Statistics*

016 TWN
▼ **INDEX TO CHINESE PERIODICAL LITERATURE (ONLINE EDITION).** Text in Chinese. 2003. irreg. **Document type:** *Directory, Abstract/Index.*
Media: Online - full content.
Published by: Guoli Zhongyang Tushuguan/National Central Library, 20 Chung Shan S. Rd, Taipei, 100-01, Taiwan. TEL 886-2-2361-9132, FAX 886-2-2311-0155, http://www2.read.com.tw/cgi/ncl3/m_ncl3?e.

INDEX TO CRAFT JOURNALS. see *ARTS AND HANDICRAFTS—Abstracting, Bibliographies, Statistics*

INDEX TO CURRENT URBAN DOCUMENTS. see *PUBLIC ADMINISTRATION—Abstracting, Bibliographies, Statistics*

INDEX TO DANCE PERIODICALS. see *DANCE—Abstracting, Bibliographies, Statistics*

INDEX TO FEDERAL TAX ARTICLES (SUPPLEMENT). see *BUSINESS AND ECONOMICS—Abstracting, Bibliographies, Statistics*

INDEX TO FOREIGN LEGAL PERIODICALS. see *LAW—Abstracting, Bibliographies, Statistics*

016 ISR ISSN 0334-2921
INDEX TO HEBREW PERIODICALS. Text in Hebrew. 1977. a.
Media: Online - full text.
Address: University of Haifa Library, Mt Carmel, Haifa, 31905, Israel. FAX 972-4-8257753, amira@univ.haifa.ac.il, http://libnet.ac.il/~libnet.ihp/. **Affiliate:** University of Haifa Library.

INDEX TO HEBREW PERIODICALS (CD-ROM EDITION). see *BIBLIOGRAPHIES*

INDEX TO HOUSE OF COMMONS PARLIAMENTARY PAPERS. see *POLITICAL SCIENCE—Abstracting, Bibliographies, Statistics*

INDEX TO HOW TO DO IT INFORMATION (ONLINE EDITION); a periodical index. see *HOW-TO AND DO-IT-YOURSELF— Abstracting, Bibliographies, Statistics*

INDEX TO INDIAN ECONOMIC JOURNALS. see *BUSINESS AND ECONOMICS—Abstracting, Bibliographies, Statistics*

INDEX TO INDIAN LEGAL PERIODICALS. see *LAW—Abstracting, Bibliographies, Statistics*

INDEX TO INTERNATIONAL PUBLIC OPINION. see *POLITICAL SCIENCE—Abstracting, Bibliographies, Statistics*

INDEX TO JEWISH PERIODICALS. see *RELIGIONS AND THEOLOGY—Abstracting, Bibliographies, Statistics*

INDEX TO LEGAL CITATIONS AND ABBREVIATIONS. see *LAW—Abstracting, Bibliographies, Statistics*

INDEX TO LEGAL PERIODICALS & BOOKS. see *LAW—Abstracting, Bibliographies, Statistics*

INDEX TO LEGISLATION IN FORCE IN ZIMBABWE. see *LAW—Abstracting, Bibliographies, Statistics*

INDEX TO N A S A NEWS RELEASES AND SPEECHES. see *AERONAUTICS AND SPACE FLIGHT—Abstracting, Bibliographies, Statistics*

051.016 USA ISSN 0163-0466
AI3
INDEX TO NEW ENGLAND PERIODICALS; an index to selected regional publications. Text in English. 1977-1982; resumed 1985. q. (plus a. cumulation). USD 65. back issues avail. **Document type:** *Abstract/Index.*
Published by: Diana Witt Associates, 201 Sheridan Ave, 5, Minneapolis, MN 55405. Ed. Diana Witt. Circ: 185.

INDEX TO NIGERIANA IN SELECTED PERIODICALS. see *HISTORY—Abstracting, Bibliographies, Statistics*

INDEX TO PERIODICAL ARTICLES RELATED TO LAW. see *LAW—Abstracting, Bibliographies, Statistics*

016.059 PHL ISSN 0073-599X
AI3
INDEX TO PHILIPPINE PERIODICALS. Text in English. 1946. q. USD 160 (effective 2006). **Document type:** *Abstract/Index.*
Description: Author subject index to periodicals published in the Philippines.
Formerly (until 1960): Index to Philippine Periodical Literature
Related titles: CD-ROM ed.: USD 40 (effective 2006).
Published by: University of the Philippines, University Library, Gonzalez Hall, cor Apacible St, Quezon City, 1101, Philippines. TEL 632-9818500, FAX 632-9261876, http://www.mainlib.upd.edu.ph/ipp.asp.

INDEX TO PLANT CHROMOSOME NUMBERS. see *BIOLOGY—Abstracting, Bibliographies, Statistics*

INDEX TO REPRODUCTIONS IN ART PERIODICALS. see *ART—Abstracting, Bibliographies, Statistics*

INDEX TO SCIENTIFIC & TECHNICAL PROCEEDINGS. see *SCIENCES: COMPREHENSIVE WORKS—Abstracting, Bibliographies, Statistics*

INDEX TO SCIENTIFIC REVIEWS. see *SCIENCES: COMPREHENSIVE WORKS—Abstracting, Bibliographies, Statistics*

INDEX TO SOCIAL SCIENCES & HUMANITIES PROCEEDINGS. see *SOCIAL SCIENCES: COMPREHENSIVE WORKS—Abstracting, Bibliographies, Statistics*

▼ *new title* ➤ *refereed* * *unverified* ◆ *full entry avail.*

A

016.05 ZAF ISSN 0379-0584
CODEN: ISAPDQ
INDEX TO SOUTH AFRICAN PERIODICALS. Short title: I S A P.
Text in Afrikaans, English. 1945. a. ZAR 200 to individuals;
ZAR 500 private educational institutions; ZAR 1,000 to
institutions (effective 2005). back issues avail. **Document
type:** *Abstract/Index.* **Description:** Provides citations of more
than 260000 articles from more than 600 South African
periodicals from 1940 to the present.
Media: Microfiche. **Related titles:** CD-ROM ed.: (from National
Information Services Corp. (N I S C)); Online - full text ed.:
(from National Information Services Corp. (N I S C)).
—CASDDS.
Published by: National Library of South Africa, PO Box 496,
Cape Town, 8000, South Africa. TEL 27-21-4246320, FAX
27-21-4233359, info@nlsa.ac.za, http://www.nlsa.ac.za. Circ:
350.

▼ **INDEX TO SOUTH ASIAN ECONOMIC JOURNALS.** see
*BUSINESS AND ECONOMICS—Abstracting, Bibliographies,
Statistics*

▼ **INDEX TO SOUTH ASIAN MANAGEMENT JOURNALS.** see
*BUSINESS AND ECONOMICS—Abstracting, Bibliographies,
Statistics*

INDEX TO THE CODE OF FEDERAL REGULATIONS. see
LAW—Abstracting, Bibliographies, Statistics

INDEX TO THE NATIONAL OBSERVER. see
JOURNALISM—Abstracting, Bibliographies, Statistics

016 USA ISSN 0736-6000
Z1314.B4
INDEX TO THE NEWS. Text in English. 19??. a. **Document type:**
Abstract/Index.
Former titles (until 1965): Index, The Record (8756-9450); (until
1959): Index, Bergen Evening Record (8756-9442)
Published by: Johnson Free Public Library, 274 Main St/275
Moore St, Hackensack, NJ 07601. TEL 201-343-4169, FAX
201-343-1395.

INDEX TO THE ST. PAUL PIONEER PRESS. see
JOURNALISM—Abstracting, Bibliographies, Statistics

INDEX TO THE SPORTING NEWS. see *SPORTS AND
GAMES—Abstracting, Bibliographies, Statistics*

INDEX VETERINARIUS; comprehensive monthly subject and
author index to the world's veterinary literature available in
print and on the internet. see *VETERINARY
SCIENCE—Abstracting, Bibliographies, Statistics*

THE INDEXER; the international journal of indexing. see *LIBRARY
AND INFORMATION SCIENCES*

INDEXER LOCATOR. see *LIBRARY AND INFORMATION
SCIENCES*

**INDIA. MINISTRY OF EDUCATION AND SOCIAL WELFARE.
DEPARTMENT OF SOCIAL WELFARE. DOCUMENTATION
SERVICE BULLETIN.** see *SOCIAL SCIENCES:
COMPREHENSIVE WORKS—Abstracting, Bibliographies,
Statistics*

INDIAN ECONOMIC ABSTRACTS. see *BUSINESS AND
ECONOMICS—Abstracting, Bibliographies, Statistics*

INDIAN EDUCATION ABSTRACTS. see *EDUCATION—
Abstracting, Bibliographies, Statistics*

**INDIAN INSTITUTE OF TECHNOLOGY, MADRAS. PH.D.
DISSERTATION ABSTRACTS.** see *TECHNOLOGY:
COMPREHENSIVE WORKS—Abstracting, Bibliographies,
Statistics*

INDIAN LIBRARY SCIENCE ABSTRACTS. see *LIBRARY AND
INFORMATION SCIENCES—Abstracting, Bibliographies,
Statistics*

INDIAN MANAGEMENT ABSTRACTS. see *BUSINESS AND
ECONOMICS—Abstracting, Bibliographies, Statistics*

INDIAN PRESS INDEX. see *JOURNALISM—Abstracting,
Bibliographies, Statistics*

INDIAN PSYCHOLOGICAL ABSTRACTS AND REVIEWS. see
PSYCHOLOGY—Abstracting, Bibliographies, Statistics

INDIAN SCIENCE ABSTRACTS. see *SCIENCES:
COMPREHENSIVE WORKS—Abstracting, Bibliographies,
Statistics*

INDIAN SCIENCE INDEX. SER. B: PRE-MODERN PERIOD. see
*TECHNOLOGY: COMPREHENSIVE WORKS—Abstracting,
Bibliographies, Statistics*

**INDICE DE ARTICULOS SOBRE EDUCACION Y
ADIESTRAMIENTO.** see *EDUCATION—Abstracting,
Bibliographies, Statistics*

016 CUB ISSN 0864-1382
**INDICE GENERAL DE PUBLICACIONES PERIODICAS
CUBANAS.** Text in Spanish. 1970. a. USD 35. index.
Document type: *Abstract/Index.* **Description:** Analytical index
to articles in the social sciences and on general topics
published in Cuban magazines during the preceding year.
Published by: Biblioteca Nacional Jose Marti, Ave. Independencia
y 20 de Mayo, Plaza de la Revolucion, Havana, Cuba. Circ:
500. **Dist. by:** Ediciones Cubanas, Obispo No. 527, Apdo.
605, Havana, Cuba.

INDICE MEDICO ESPANOL (ONLINE EDITION). see *MEDICAL
SCIENCES—Abstracting, Bibliographies, Statistics*

INDIGENOUS KNOWLEDGE INDEX. see *ANTHROPOLOGY—
Abstracting, Bibliographies, Statistics*

**INDONESIAN BIOLOGICAL AND AGRICULTURAL
INDEX/INDEKS BIOLOGI DAN PERTANIAN DE INDONESIA.**
see *AGRICULTURE—Abstracting, Bibliographies, Statistics*

INDUSTRIAL ABSTRACTS FOR TANZANIA. see
*TECHNOLOGY: COMPREHENSIVE WORKS—Abstracting,
Bibliographies, Statistics*

INDUSTRIAL HYGIENE DIGEST. see *OCCUPATIONAL HEALTH
AND SAFETY—Abstracting, Bibliographies, Statistics*

INDUSTRIAL LITERATURE REVIEW; presents catalogs and
brochures to buyers and specifiers in the US industrial
marketplace. see *BUSINESS AND ECONOMICS—Abstracting,
Bibliographies, Statistics*

INFO - A S E A N & PACIFIC RIM. see *BUSINESS AND
ECONOMICS—Abstracting, Bibliographies, Statistics*

INFO - C I S. (Commonwealth of Independent States) see
*BUSINESS AND ECONOMICS—Abstracting, Bibliographies,
Statistics*

INFO - LATINOAMERICA. see *BUSINESS AND
ECONOMICS—Abstracting, Bibliographies, Statistics*

INFO - S A A R C. (South Asian Association of Regional
Cooperation) see *BUSINESS AND ECONOMICS—
Abstracting, Bibliographies, Statistics*

INFOLINGUA. see *LINGUISTICS—Abstracting, Bibliographies,
Statistics*

INFORMATION MANAGEMENT & TECHNOLOGY. see
COMMUNICATIONS

**INFORMATION MANAGEMENT AND TECHNOLOGY
ABSTRACTS.** see *LIBRARY AND INFORMATION
SCIENCES—Abstracting, Bibliographies, Statistics*

**INFORMATION SCIENCE & TECHNOLOGY ABSTRACTS
(ONLINE EDITION).** see *LIBRARY AND INFORMATION
SCIENCES—Abstracting, Bibliographies, Statistics*

INFORMATIONSDIENST F I Z TECHNIK. INSTANDHALTUNG.
see *ENGINEERING—Abstracting, Bibliographies, Statistics*

INFORMATIONSDIENST F I Z TECHNIK. LAERM. see
ENGINEERING—Abstracting, Bibliographies, Statistics

**INFORMATIONSDIENST F I Z TECHNIK.
REGELUNGSTECHNIK.** see *ENGINEERING—Abstracting,
Bibliographies, Statistics*

**INFORMATIONSDIENST PRAXISBEZOGENER LITERATUR IM
WEINBAU.** see *AGRICULTURE—Abstracting, Bibliographies,
Statistics*

**INFORMATSIONNYI BYULLETEN'. BOR'BA S
PRESTUPNOSTYU ZA RUBEZHOM.** see *CRIMINOLOGY
AND LAW ENFORCEMENT—Security*

**INFORMATSIONNYI BYULLETEN'. EKONOMIKA I UPRAVLENIE
V ZARUBEZHNYKH STRANAKH.** see *BUSINESS AND
ECONOMICS—Abstracting, Bibliographies, Statistics*

**INFORMATSIONNYI BYULLETEN'. INOSTRANNAYA PECHAT'
O TEKHNICHESKOM OSNASHCHENII POLITSII
ZARUBEZHNYKH GOSUDARSTV.** see *CRIMINOLOGY AND
LAW ENFORCEMENT—Abstracting, Bibliographies, Statistics*

**INFORMATSIONNYI REFERATIVNYI SBORNIK. EKONOMIYA
ENERGII.** see *ENERGY—Abstracting, Bibliographies,
Statistics*

**INFORMATSIONNYI SBORNIK. EKONOMICHESKAYA NAUKA
SOVREMENNOI ROSSII.** see *BUSINESS AND
ECONOMICS—Abstracting, Bibliographies, Statistics*

**INFORMATSIONNYI SBORNIK. FEDERAL'NYE I
REGIONAL'NYE PROGRAMMY ROSSII.** see *BUSINESS
AND ECONOMICS—Abstracting, Bibliographies, Statistics*

**INFORMATSIONNYI SBORNIK. INTEGRIROVANNAYA
LOGISTIKA.** see *TRANSPORTATION—Abstracting,
Bibliographies, Statistics*

**INFORMATSIONNYI SBORNIK. NOVOSTI ANESTEZIOLOGII I
REANIMATOLOGII.** see *MEDICAL SCIENCES—Abstracting,
Bibliographies, Statistics*

▼ **INFORMATSIONNYI SBORNIK. SERDECHNO-SOSUDISTAYA
KHIRURGIYA. NOVOSTI NAUKI I TEKHNIKI.** see *MEDICAL
SCIENCES—Abstracting, Bibliographies, Statistics*

**INOSTRANNAYA PECHAT' OB EKONOMICHESKOM,
NAUCHNO-TEKHNICHESKOM I VOENNOM POTENTSIALE
GOSUDARSTV-UCHASTNIKOV SNG I TEKHNIKESKIKH
SREDSTVAKH EGO VYIAVLENIYA. SERIYA:
EKONOMICHESKII I NAUCHNO-TEKHNICHESKII
POTENTSIAL.** see *BUSINESS AND ECONOMICS—
Abstracting, Bibliographies, Statistics*

**INOSTRANNAYA PECHAT' OB EKONOMICHESKOM,
NAUCHNO-TEKHNICHESKOM I VOENNOM POTENTSIALE
GOSUDARSTV-UCHASTNIKOV SNG I TEKHNIKESKIKH
SREDSTVAKH EGO VYIAVLENIYA. SERIYA:
TEKHNICHESKIE SREDSTVA RAZVEDYVATELNYKH
SLUZHB ZARUBEZHNYKH GOSUDARSTV.** see *BUSINESS
AND ECONOMICS—Abstracting, Bibliographies, Statistics*

**INOSTRANNAYA PECHAT' OB EKONOMICHESKOM,
NAUCHNO-TEKHNICHESKOM I VOENNOM POTENTSIALE
GOSUDARSTV-UCHASTNIKOV SNG I TEKHNIKESKIKH
SREDSTVAKH EGO VYIAVLENIYA. SERIYA:
VOORUZHENNYE SILY I VOENNO-PROMYSHLENNYI
POTENTSIAL.** see *BUSINESS AND ECONOMICS—
Abstracting, Bibliographies, Statistics*

**INOSTRANNAYA VOENNAYA LITERATURA/FOREIGN MILITARY
LITERATURE INDEX;** annotirovannyi bibliograficheskii
ukazatel'. see *MILITARY—Abstracting, Bibliographies,
Statistics*

INPHARMA WEEKLY; rapid alerts to news on drugs and drug
therapy. see *PHARMACY AND PHARMACOLOGY—
Abstracting, Bibliographies, Statistics*

INSPEC LIST OF JOURNALS AND OTHER SERIAL SOURCES.
see *ENGINEERING—Abstracting, Bibliographies, Statistics*

016 FRA ISSN 1165-4651
INSTITUT APPERT. C T INFOS. (Centre Technique) Text in
French. 1946. m. bk.rev.
Former titles (until 1992): Institut Appert. Bulletin Analytique C T
C P A (1167-9603); Institut Appert. Bulletin Analytique C I E
(0243-5314)
Published by: Institut Appert Cie, 42-44 rue d'Alesia, Paris,
75014, France. Ed. Laurent Weill. Circ: 1,200.

**INSTYTUT HODOWLI I AKLIMATYZACJI ROSLIN.
BIULETYN/INSTITUTE OF PLANT BREEDING AND
ACCLIMATIZATION. BULLETIN.** see *AGRICULTURE—
Abstracting, Bibliographies, Statistics*

**INSTYTUT OBROBKI SKRAWANIEM. PRZEGLAD
DOKUMENTACYJNY.** see *ENGINEERING—Abstracting,
Bibliographies, Statistics*

INSURANCE AND EMPLOYEE BENEFITS LITERATURE. see
INSURANCE—Abstracting, Bibliographies, Statistics

INSURANCE PERIODICALS INDEX. see *INSURANCE—
Abstracting, Bibliographies, Statistics*

INTELLECTUAL PROPERTY REPORTS (NORTH RYDE, 1989);
consolidated index and tables. see *PATENTS, TRADEMARKS
AND COPYRIGHTS—Abstracting, Bibliographies, Statistics*

INTERNATIONAL ABSTRACTS IN OPERATIONS RESEARCH.
see *COMPUTERS—Abstracting, Bibliographies, Statistics*

INTERNATIONAL ABSTRACTS OF HUMAN RESOURCES. see
*BUSINESS AND ECONOMICS—Abstracting, Bibliographies,
Statistics*

INTERNATIONAL AEROSPACE ABSTRACTS. see
*AERONAUTICS AND SPACE FLIGHT—Abstracting,
Bibliographies, Statistics*

**INTERNATIONAL ASSOCIATION FOR DENTAL RESEARCH.
PROGRAM AND ABSTRACTS OF PAPERS.** see *MEDICAL
SCIENCES—Abstracting, Bibliographies, Statistics*

INTERNATIONAL BIOPHYSICS CONGRESS. ABSTRACTS. see
BIOLOGY—Abstracting, Bibliographies, Statistics

▼ **INTERNATIONAL BUILDING SERVICES ABSTRACTS
(E-MAIL EDITION).** see *HEATING, PLUMBING AND
REFRIGERATION—Abstracting, Bibliographies, Statistics*

INTERNATIONAL CIVIL AVIATION ORGANIZATION. INDEX OF I C A O PUBLICATIONS. ANNUAL CUMULATION. see *AERONAUTICS AND SPACE FLIGHT—Abstracting, Bibliographies, Statistics*

INTERNATIONAL CIVIL ENGINEERING ABSTRACTS. see *ENGINEERING—Abstracting, Bibliographies, Statistics*

INTERNATIONAL DEVELOPMENT ABSTRACTS. see *GEOGRAPHY—Abstracting, Bibliographies, Statistics*

INTERNATIONAL FOOD ABSTRACTS. BEVERAGES AND SOFT DRINKS DISK. see *BEVERAGES—Abstracting, Bibliographies, Statistics*

INTERNATIONAL FOOD ABSTRACTS. DAIRY DISK. see *AGRICULTURE—Abstracting, Bibliographies, Statistics*

INTERNATIONAL INDEX TO BLACK PERIODICALS FULL TEXT. see *ETHNIC INTERESTS—Abstracting, Bibliographies, Statistics*

INTERNATIONAL INDEX TO FILM PERIODICALS. see *MOTION PICTURES—Abstracting, Bibliographies, Statistics*

INTERNATIONAL INDEX TO THE PERFORMING ARTS. see *THEATER—Abstracting, Bibliographies, Statistics*

INTERNATIONAL LOGISTICS ABSTRACTS. see *TRANSPORTATION—Abstracting, Bibliographies, Statistics*

INTERNATIONAL MONETARY FUND SURVEY. see *BUSINESS AND ECONOMICS—Abstracting, Bibliographies, Statistics*

INTERNATIONAL PHARMACEUTICAL ABSTRACTS; key to the world's literature of pharmacy. see *PHARMACY AND PHARMACOLOGY—Abstracting, Bibliographies, Statistics*

INTERNATIONAL POLITICAL SCIENCE ABSTRACTS/ DOCUMENTATION POLITIQUE INTERNATIONALE. see *POLITICAL SCIENCE—Abstracting, Bibliographies, Statistics*

INTERNATIONAL REVIEW OF BIBLICAL STUDIES/ INTERNATIONALE ZEITSCHRIFTENSCHAU FUER BIBELWISSENSCHAFT UND GRENZGEBIETE. see *RELIGIONS AND THEOLOGY—Abstracting, Bibliographies, Statistics*

INTERNET & PERSONAL COMPUTING ABSTRACTS (ONLINE EDITION). see *COMPUTERS—Abstracting, Bibliographies, Statistics*

INTESTINAL FUNCTION. see *MEDICAL SCIENCES— Abstracting, Bibliographies, Statistics*

INVERTEBRATE NEUROBIOLOGY. see *BIOLOGY—Abstracting, Bibliographies, Statistics*

IRANIAN GOVERNMENT REPORTS/GUZARISHHA-YI DAWLATI-I IRAN. see *POLITICAL SCIENCE—Abstracting, Bibliographies, Statistics*

IRON METABOLISM. see *BIOLOGY—Abstracting, Bibliographies, Statistics*

IRRIGATION AND DRAINAGE ABSTRACTS. see *AGRICULTURE—Abstracting, Bibliographies, Statistics*

ISRAEL GEOLOGICAL SOCIETY ABSTRACTS. see *EARTH SCIENCES—Abstracting, Bibliographies, Statistics*

▼ **ISURV KNOWLEDGE ALERT.** see *ENGINEERING— Abstracting, Bibliographies, Statistics*

IYAKUHIN FUKUSAYO BUNKEN JOHOSHU. SHOROKUSHU-HEN/ADVERSE REACTION TO DRUGS INFORMATION COMPENDIUM FOR EXPERTS. ABSTRACTS. see *PHARMACY AND PHARMACOLOGY— Abstracting, Bibliographies, Statistics*

IZOBRAZITEL'NOE ISKUSSTVO; referativno-bibliograficheskaya informatsiya. see *ART—Abstracting, Bibliographies, Statistics*

J A E R I REPORTS ABSTRACTS/GENKEN KENKYU SEIKA SHOROKUSYU. (Japan Atomic Energy Research Institute) see *ENERGY—Abstracting, Bibliographies, Statistics*

JAPANESE SYMPOSIUM ON PLASMA CHEMISTRY. ABSTRACT PAPERS/PURAZUMA KAGAKU GODO SHINPOJUMU ABUSUTORAK UTOSHU. see *CHEMISTRY—Abstracting, Bibliographies, Statistics*

JIEFANG RIBAO HEDINGBEN/LIBERATION DAILY BOUND INDEX. see *GENERAL INTEREST PERIODICALS—China*

JINKO KESSHO KOGAKKAI TOKUBETSU KOENKAI KOEN YOSHISHU/ASSOCIATION OF SYNTHETIC CRYSTAL SCIENCE AND TECHNOLOGY. ABSTRACTS OF THE SPECIAL MEETING. see *CHEMISTRY—Abstracting, Bibliographies, Statistics*

JISHIN KOGAKU BUNKEN MOKUROKU/BIBLIOGRAPHY OF EARTHQUAKE ENGINEERING. see *EARTH SCIENCES—Abstracting, Bibliographies, Statistics*

JOURNAL OF ECONOMIC LITERATURE. see *BUSINESS AND ECONOMICS—Abstracting, Bibliographies, Statistics*

JOURNAL OF FERROCEMENT. see *BUILDING AND CONSTRUCTION—Abstracting, Bibliographies, Statistics*

JOURNAL OF HEALTH POPULATION AND NUTRITION. see *MEDICAL SCIENCES—Abstracting, Bibliographies, Statistics*

JOURNAL OF HISTORICAL STUDIES. see *HISTORY— Abstracting, Bibliographies, Statistics*

JOURNAL OF PLANT NUTRITION AND SOIL SCIENCE/ZEITSCHRIFT FUER PFLANZENERNAEHRUNG UND BODENKUNDE. see *BIOLOGY—Abstracting, Bibliographies, Statistics*

JOURNAL OF PREVENTION AND INTERVENTION IN THE COMMUNITY. see *PSYCHOLOGY—Abstracting, Bibliographies, Statistics*

JOURNAL WATCH. see *MEDICAL SCIENCES—Abstracting, Bibliographies, Statistics*

JOURNAL WATCH CARDIOLOGY. see *MEDICAL SCIENCES—Abstracting, Bibliographies, Statistics*

JOURNAL WATCH DERMATOLOGY. see *MEDICAL SCIENCES—Dermatology And Venereology*

JOURNAL WATCH EMERGENCY MEDICINE. see *MEDICAL SCIENCES—Orthopedics And Traumatology*

JOURNAL WATCH GASTROENTEROLOGY. see *MEDICAL SCIENCES—Abstracting, Bibliographies, Statistics*

JOURNAL WATCH INFECTIOUS DISEASES. see *MEDICAL SCIENCES—Abstracting, Bibliographies, Statistics*

JOURNAL WATCH NEUROLOGY. see *MEDICAL SCIENCES—Abstracting, Bibliographies, Statistics*

JOURNAL WATCH PSYCHIATRY. see *MEDICAL SCIENCES—Abstracting, Bibliographies, Statistics*

JOURNAL WATCH WOMEN'S HEALTH. see *WOMEN'S HEALTH—Abstracting, Bibliographies, Statistics*

JOURNALISM AND MASS COMMUNICATION ABSTRACTS; M.A., M.S., and Ph.D. theses in journalism and mass communication. see *JOURNALISM—Abstracting, Bibliographies, Statistics*

JUSTITIELE VERKENNINGEN. see *CRIMINOLOGY AND LAW ENFORCEMENT—Abstracting, Bibliographies, Statistics*

JUTA - STATE LIBRARY INDEX TO THE GOVERNMENT GAZETTE. see *PUBLIC ADMINISTRATION—Abstracting, Bibliographies, Statistics*

K E A RESEARCH PUBLICATIONS. see *EDUCATION— Abstracting, Bibliographies, Statistics*

KAGAKU SHOHO. see *CHEMISTRY—Abstracting, Bibliographies, Statistics*

KARUSHUMU SHINPOJUMU KOEN YOSHI/ABSTRACTS OF CALCIUM SYMPOSIUM. see *BIOLOGY—Abstracting, Bibliographies, Statistics*

KATAB: INDEX ANALYTIQUE BIBLIOGRAPHIQUE. see *BUSINESS AND ECONOMICS—Abstracting, Bibliographies, Statistics*

016.05   IDN   ISSN 0854-6711
KATALOG INDUK MAJALART/UNION CATALOG OF SERIALS. Key Title: Daftar Koleksi Majalah Pusat Dokumentasi dan Informasi Ilmiah Lembaga ilmu Pengetahuan Indonesia. Text in Indonesian. 1971. 3/yr. IDR 30,000 domestic (effective 2001); USD 35 foreign (effective 2000). bibl. back issues avail. **Document type:** *Catalog, Abstract/Index.* **Description:** Includes serials holding of 60 libraries in Indonesia.
Related titles: E-mail ed.; Fax ed.
Published by: Pusat Dokumentasi dan Informasi Ilmiah, Lembaga Ilmu Pengetahuan Indonesia/Center for Scientific Documentation and Information, Indonesian Institute of Science, Jl. Jend. Gatot Subroto 10, Jakarta, 12710, Indonesia. TEL 62-21-5250719, FAX 62-21-5733467, mginting@hotmail.com, info@pdii.lipi.go.id. Ed. Maria Ginting.

KEESING'S RECORD OF WORLD EVENTS. see *POLITICAL SCIENCE—Abstracting, Bibliographies, Statistics*

KENTUCKY PLUMBING-HEATING-COOLING INDEX. see *HEATING, PLUMBING AND REFRIGERATION—Abstracting, Bibliographies, Statistics*

KEW RECORD OF TAXONOMIC LITERATURE RELATING TO VASCULAR PLANTS. see *BIOLOGY—Abstracting, Bibliographies, Statistics*

KEY ABSTRACTS - ANTENNAS & PROPAGATION. see *COMMUNICATIONS—Abstracting, Bibliographies, Statistics*

KEY ABSTRACTS - ARTIFICIAL INTELLIGENCE. see *COMPUTERS—Abstracting, Bibliographies, Statistics*

KEY ABSTRACTS - BUSINESS AUTOMATION. see *COMPUTERS—Abstracting, Bibliographies, Statistics*

KEY ABSTRACTS - COMPUTER COMMUNICATIONS AND STORAGE. see *COMPUTERS—Abstracting, Bibliographies, Statistics*

KEY ABSTRACTS - COMPUTING IN ELECTRONICS & POWER. see *COMPUTERS—Abstracting, Bibliographies, Statistics*

KEY ABSTRACTS - ELECTRONIC CIRCUITS. see *ELECTRONICS*

KEY ABSTRACTS - ELECTRONIC INSTRUMENTATION. see *ELECTRONICS*

KEY ABSTRACTS - FACTORY AUTOMATION. see *COMPUTERS—Abstracting, Bibliographies, Statistics*

KEY ABSTRACTS - HUMAN-COMPUTER INTERACTION. see *COMPUTERS—Abstracting, Bibliographies, Statistics*

KEY ABSTRACTS - MACHINE VISION. see *COMPUTERS— Abstracting, Bibliographies, Statistics*

KEY ABSTRACTS - MEASUREMENTS IN PHYSICS. see *METROLOGY AND STANDARDIZATION—Abstracting, Bibliographies, Statistics*

KEY ABSTRACTS - MICROELECTRONICS & PRINTED CIRCUITS. see *ELECTRONICS*

KEY ABSTRACTS - MICROWAVE TECHNOLOGY. see *ELECTRONICS*

KEY ABSTRACTS - NEURAL NETWORKS. see *COMPUTERS—Abstracting, Bibliographies, Statistics*

KEY ABSTRACTS - ROBOTICS & CONTROL. see *COMPUTERS—Abstracting, Bibliographies, Statistics*

KEY ABSTRACTS - SEMICONDUCTOR DEVICES. see *ELECTRONICS*

KEY ABSTRACTS - SOFTWARE ENGINEERING. see *COMPUTERS—Abstracting, Bibliographies, Statistics*

KEY ABSTRACTS - TELECOMMUNICATIONS. see *COMMUNICATIONS—Abstracting, Bibliographies, Statistics*

KEYWORD INDEX TO SERIAL TITLES. see *LIBRARY AND INFORMATION SCIENCES—Abstracting, Bibliographies, Statistics*

KEYWORD INDEX TO SERIAL TITLES QUARTERLY. see *LIBRARY AND INFORMATION SCIENCES—Abstracting, Bibliographies, Statistics*

KIDNEY (NEW YORK, 1992); a current survey of world literature. see *MEDICAL SCIENCES—Abstracting, Bibliographies, Statistics*

KIKAN KEISEI KENKYUKAI KOEN YOSHISHU/JAPANESE SOCIETY FOR BASIC AND APPLIED ORGAN RESEARCH. ABSTRACTS OF THE MEETING. see *BIOLOGY— Abstracting, Bibliographies, Statistics*

KINDER- UND JUGENDARZT. see *MEDICAL SCIENCES—Abstracting, Bibliographies, Statistics*

KINDEX; an index to legal periodical literature concerning children. see *LAW—Abstracting, Bibliographies, Statistics*

KOHASZATI ES ONTESZETI SZAKIRODALMI TAJEKOZTATO/METALLURGY AND FOUNDRY ABSTRACTS. see *METALLURGY—Abstracting, Bibliographies, Statistics*

KOKAGAKU TORONKAI KOEN YOSHISHU/ABSTRACTS OF SYMPOSIUM ON PHOTOCHEMISTRY. see *CHEMISTRY—Abstracting, Bibliographies, Statistics*

A

▼ *new title*   ➤ *refereed*   ✶ *unverified*   ◆ *full entry avail.*

A

KOKU KISHO NOTO/ABSTRACTS IN AVIATION METEOROLOGY. see *METEOROLOGY—Abstracting, Bibliographies, Statistics*

▼ **KOKURITSU KOKKAI TOSHOKAN ZASSHI KIJI SAKUIN CD-ROM KARENTO-BAN/JAPANESE PERIODICAL INDEX ON CD.** (National Diet Library) see *HUMANITIES: COMPREHENSIVE WORKS—Abstracting, Bibliographies, Statistics*

KOMP'YUTERNYI VESTNIK/COMPUTER BULLETIN. see *COMPUTERS—Abstracting, Bibliographies, Statistics*

KOREA (REPUBLIC). NATIONAL STATISTICAL OFFICE. REPORT ON MINING AND MANUFACTURING SURVEY. see *MINES AND MINING INDUSTRY—Abstracting, Bibliographies, Statistics*

KOREA INSTITUTE FOR NATIONAL UNIFICATION. K I N U RESEARCH ABSTRACTS. see *ASIAN STUDIES— Abstracting, Bibliographies, Statistics*

KOREAN MEDICAL ABSTRACTS. see *MEDICAL SCIENCES—Abstracting, Bibliographies, Statistics*

KOREAN SCIENTIFIC ABSTRACTS. see *SCIENCES: COMPREHENSIVE WORKS—Abstracting, Bibliographies, Statistics*

KORNYEZETVEDELMI SZAKIRODALMI TAJEKOZTATO/ ENVIRONMENTAL CONTROL ABSTRACTS. see *ENVIRONMENTAL STUDIES—Abstracting, Bibliographies, Statistics*

KOTAI NO HANNOSEI TORONKAI KOEN YOKOSHU/ ABSTRACTS OF THE MEETING ON SOLID REACTIVITY. see *CHEMISTRY—Abstracting, Bibliographies, Statistics*

KUL'TURA. KUL'TUROLOGIYA.; referativno-bibliograficheskaya informatsiya. see *HUMANITIES: COMPREHENSIVE WORKS—Abstracting, Bibliographies, Statistics*

KYOKUIKI SEIBUTSU SHINPOJUMU KOEN YOSHISHU/ ABSTRACTS OF THE SYMPOSIUM ON POLAR BIOLOGY. see *BIOLOGY—Abstracting, Bibliographies, Statistics*

KYUSHU UNIVERSITY. RESEARCH INSTITUTE FOR APPLIED MECHANICS. ABSTRACTS OF PAPERS. see *ENGINEERING—Abstracting, Bibliographies, Statistics*

L I S A: LIBRARY & INFORMATION SCIENCE ABSTRACTS. see *LIBRARY AND INFORMATION SCIENCES—Abstracting, Bibliographies, Statistics*

L M S ALERT. IMMUNOTHERAPEUTICS. TRANSPLANT REJECTION. (Literature Monitoring and Evaluation Service) see *MEDICAL SCIENCES—Abstracting, Bibliographies, Statistics*

LABORATORY HAZARDS BULLETIN. see *OCCUPATIONAL HEALTH AND SAFETY—Abstracting, Bibliographies, Statistics*

LANCASTER INDEX TO DEFENCE & INTERNATIONAL SECURITY LITERATURE. see *MILITARY—Abstracting, Bibliographies, Statistics*

LANDOEKONOMISK OVERSIGT. see *AGRICULTURE— Abstracting, Bibliographies, Statistics*

LANGUAGE TEACHING; the international abstracting journal for language teachers and applied linguistics . see *LINGUISTICS—Abstracting, Bibliographies, Statistics*

LATIN AMERICAN INDEX. see *POLITICAL SCIENCE— Abstracting, Bibliographies, Statistics*

LATIN AMERICAN STUDIES. VOLUME 1. see *HISTORY—Abstracting, Bibliographies, Statistics*

LATIN AMERICAN STUDIES. VOLUME 2. see *HISTORY—Abstracting, Bibliographies, Statistics*

LEATHER SCIENCE ABSTRACTS. see *LEATHER AND FUR INDUSTRIES—Abstracting, Bibliographies, Statistics*

LEFT INDEX (ONLINE EDITION); a quarterly index to periodicals of the left. see *POLITICAL SCIENCE—Abstracting, Bibliographies, Statistics*

LEGAL BIBLIOGRAPHY JOURNAL. see *LAW—Abstracting, Bibliographies, Statistics*

LEGAL EDUCATION DIGEST. see *LAW—Abstracting, Bibliographies, Statistics*

LEGAL PERIODICALS IN ENGLISH. see *LAW—Abstracting, Bibliographies, Statistics*

LEGALTRAC (ONLINE). see *LAW—Abstracting, Bibliographies, Statistics*

LEISURE, RECREATION AND TOURISM ABSTRACTS. see *TRAVEL AND TOURISM—Abstracting, Bibliographies, Statistics*

LESBISCH ARCHIVARIA. see *WOMEN'S INTERESTS— Abstracting, Bibliographies, Statistics*

LEUCOCYTES. see *MEDICAL SCIENCES—Abstracting, Bibliographies, Statistics*

LIBRARY LITERATURE & INFORMATION SCIENCE. see *LIBRARY AND INFORMATION SCIENCES—Abstracting, Bibliographies, Statistics*

LICENSEE NAME INDEX TO NON-GOVERNMENT MASTER FREQUENCY DATA BASE. see *COMMUNICATIONS— Abstracting, Bibliographies, Statistics*

LINGUISTICS ABSTRACTS. see *LINGUISTICS—Abstracting, Bibliographies, Statistics*

LINGUISTICS ABSTRACTS ONLINE. see *LINGUISTICS— Abstracting, Bibliographies, Statistics*

LINGUISTICS AND LANGUAGE BEHAVIOR ABSTRACTS. see *LINGUISTICS—Abstracting, Bibliographies, Statistics*

LINX DATABASE. see *LAW—Abstracting, Bibliographies, Statistics*

016 348   GBR   ISSN 1472-1058
KD170
LIST OF STATUTORY PUBLICATIONS. Text in English. 2000. m. **Document type:** *Bibliography.*
Incorporates (1962-2000): List of Instruments Together with the List of Statutory Rules of Northern Ireland (0267-2979); Which was formerly (until 1983): List of Statutory Instruments (0261-829X)
—BLDSC (5270.365000).
Published by: Stationery Office (Norwich), St Crispins House, Duke St, PO Box 29, Norwich, NR3 1PD, United Kingdom. TEL 44-870-600-5522, FAX 44-870-600-5533, customer.services@theso.co.uk, http:// www.thestationeryoffice.com/.

LITERATURSCHAU: SCHWEISSEN UND VERWANDTE VERFAHREN/WELDING AND ALLIED PROCESSES. see *METALLURGY—Abstracting, Bibliographies, Statistics*

LITERATURSCHAU: ZERSTOERUNGSFREIE PRUEFUNG/BULLETIN OF ABSTRACTS: NON-DESTRUCTIVE TESTING. see *ENGINEERING— Abstracting, Bibliographies, Statistics*

LOCAL GOVERNMENT INDEX NEW SOUTH WALES. see *PUBLIC ADMINISTRATION—Abstracting, Bibliographies, Statistics*

LURATHA. see *ANTHROPOLOGY—Abstracting, Bibliographies, Statistics*

LYSOSOMES AND ENDOCYTOSIS. see *BIOLOGY—Abstracting, Bibliographies, Statistics*

M A P S DATA BASE. (Mid-Atlantic Preservation Service) see *COMMUNICATIONS—Abstracting, Bibliographies, Statistics*

016.05   USA
M A S ULTRA - SCHOOL EDITION; Magazine Article Summaries. Text in English. base vol. plus d. updates. **Document type:** *Abstract/Index.*
Media: Online - full content.
Published by: EBSCO Publishing (Subsidiary of: EBSCO Industries, Inc.), 10 Estes St, PO Box 682, Ipswich, MA 01938-0682. TEL 978-356-6500, FAX 978-356-6565, http://www.epnet.com.

M E D I C. (Monthly Ethical Drug Index Complication) see *PHARMACY AND PHARMACOLOGY—Abstracting, Bibliographies, Statistics*

M I M S DISEASE INDEX. see *MEDICAL SCIENCES— Abstracting, Bibliographies, Statistics*

M I M S MEDICAL SPECIALITIES. (Monthly Index of Medical Specialties) see *MEDICAL SCIENCES—Abstracting, Bibliographies, Statistics*

M I R A AUTOMOBILE ABSTRACTS. see *TRANSPORTATION— Abstracting, Bibliographies, Statistics*

M I R A AUTOMOTIVE BUSINESS NEWS. see *BUSINESS AND ECONOMICS—Abstracting, Bibliographies, Statistics*

M I R A VIRTUAL AUTOMOTIVE INFORMATION CENTRE. (Motor Industry Research Association) see *TRANSPORTATION—Abstracting, Bibliographies, Statistics*

M L A INTERNATIONAL BIBLIOGRAPHY OF BOOKS AND ARTICLES ON THE MODERN LANGUAGES AND LITERATURES. see *LITERATURE—Abstracting, Bibliographies, Statistics*

M L B D NEWSLETTER; monthly of indological bibliography. see *RELIGIONS AND THEOLOGY—Abstracting, Bibliographies, Statistics*

M U S E, MUSIC SEARCH; RILM abstracts of music literature. see *MUSIC—Abstracting, Bibliographies, Statistics*

M@BS. see *BUSINESS AND ECONOMICS—Abstracting, Bibliographies, Statistics*

MACROPHAGES. see *MEDICAL SCIENCES—Abstracting, Bibliographies, Statistics*

051 011   USA   ISSN 0895-3376
MAGAZINE ARTICLE SUMMARIES; EBSCO's weekly index to periodical literature. Text in English. 1984. w. USD 1,199. bk.rev. index. **Document type:** *Abstract/Index.*
Formerly (until 1987): Popular Magazine Review (0740-3763)
Related titles: CD-ROM ed.: ISSN 1041-1151. 1989. USD 1,599; Online - full text ed.: ISSN 1058-0255. 1991.
Published by: EBSCO Publishing (Subsidiary of: EBSCO Industries, Inc.), 10 Estes St, PO Box 682, Ipswich, MA 01938-0682. TEL 978-356-6500, 800-653-2726, FAX 978-356-6565, ep@epnet.com, http://www.epnet.com. Ed. Melissa Kummerer. Circ: 3,000. **Subscr. to:** Subscription Services, PO Box 1943, Birmingham, AL 35201-1943. TEL 205-991-6600, FAX 205-995-1518.

MAGAZINE INDEX PLUS. see *PUBLISHING AND BOOK TRADE—Abstracting, Bibliographies, Statistics*

MAIZE ABSTRACTS ONLINE. see *AGRICULTURE—Abstracting, Bibliographies, Statistics*

MALAWI BUREAU OF STANDARDS. LIBRARY. ADDITIONS TO THE LIBRARY. see *METROLOGY AND STANDARDIZATION—Abstracting, Bibliographies, Statistics*

MAMMALOGY ABSTRACTS. see *BIOLOGY—Abstracting, Bibliographies, Statistics*

MAMMARY GLAND. see *BIOLOGY—Abstracting, Bibliographies, Statistics*

MANAGEMENT AND MARKETING ABSTRACTS. see *BUSINESS AND ECONOMICS—Abstracting, Bibliographies, Statistics*

MANAGEMENT BOOKS AND RESOURCES. see *BUSINESS AND ECONOMICS—Abstracting, Bibliographies, Statistics*

MANAGEMENT DATA LIST (ML): ML - MARINE CORPS. see *MILITARY—Abstracting, Bibliographies, Statistics*

MANAGEMENT OF QUALITY ABSTRACTS. see *BUSINESS AND ECONOMICS—Abstracting, Bibliographies, Statistics*

MARINE DATA BASE. see *COMMUNICATIONS—Abstracting, Bibliographies, Statistics*

MARKAZ-I NASHARIYAT-I 'ILMI VA FARHANGI. FIHRIST-I MUNDARIJAT-I MAJALLAH-HA-YI JARI-I/CENTER FOR SCIENTIFIC AND CULTURAL PERIODICALS. TABLE OF CONTENTS OF CURRENT JOURNALS. see *SCIENCES: COMPREHENSIVE WORKS—Abstracting, Bibliographies, Statistics*

MARKET RESEARCH ABSTRACTS (ONLINE EDITION). see *BUSINESS AND ECONOMICS—Abstracting, Bibliographies, Statistics*

MARKETING & LOGISTICS ABSTRACTS. see *BUSINESS AND ECONOMICS—Abstracting, Bibliographies, Statistics*

MARYLAND DOCUMENTS. see *PUBLIC ADMINISTRATION— Abstracting, Bibliographies, Statistics*

MASS COM PERIODICAL LITERATURE INDEX. see *SOCIOLOGY—Abstracting, Bibliographies, Statistics*

MASS SPECTROMETRY BULLETIN. see *CHEMISTRY— Abstracting, Bibliographies, Statistics*

MASTER FREQUENCY DATA BASE (FREQUENCY SEQUENCE). see *COMMUNICATIONS—Abstracting, Bibliographies, Statistics*

MASTER FREQUENCY DATA BASE (SERVICE GROUP CODE SEQUENCE). see *COMMUNICATIONS—Abstracting, Bibliographies, Statistics*

MASTERS ABSTRACTS INTERNATIONAL; catalog of selected masters theses. see EDUCATION—Abstracting, Bibliographies, Statistics

MASTER'S THESES DIRECTORIES. see EDUCATION—Abstracting, Bibliographies, Statistics

MATERIALS BUSINESS FILE. see METALLURGY—Abstracting, Bibliographies, Statistics

MATHEMATICAL REVIEWS; a reviewing journal covering the world literature of mathematical research. see MATHEMATICS—Abstracting, Bibliographies, Statistics

MECHANICAL ENGINEERING ABSTRACTS FROM C S A. see ENGINEERING—Abstracting, Bibliographies, Statistics

MEDIA REVIEW DIGEST; the only complete guide to reviews of non-book media. see MOTION PICTURES—Abstracting, Bibliographies, Statistics

MEDICAL & PHARMACEUTICAL BIOTECHNOLOGY ABSTRACTS (ONLINE EDITION). see MEDICAL SCIENCES—Abstracting, Bibliographies, Statistics

MEDICAL CARE RESEARCH AND REVIEW. see PUBLIC HEALTH AND SAFETY—Abstracting, Bibliographies, Statistics

MEDICAL LITERATURE INDEXING SERVICES IN PAKISTAN. see MEDICAL SCIENCES—Abstracting, Bibliographies, Statistics

MEDICINAL AND AROMATIC PLANTS ABSTRACTS. see MEDICAL SCIENCES—Abstracting, Bibliographies, Statistics

MEDIFAX INDEX. see MEDICAL SCIENCES—Abstracting, Bibliographies, Statistics

MEDITSINSKI PREGLED. see MEDICAL SCIENCES— Abstracting, Bibliographies, Statistics

MEDLINE. see MEDICAL SCIENCES—Abstracting, Bibliographies, Statistics

MELYEPITESI ES VIZEPITESI SZAKIRODALMI TAJEKOZTATO/CIVIL ENGINEERING & HYDRAULIC ENGINEERING ABSTRACTS. see ENGINEERING— Abstracting, Bibliographies, Statistics

MEMBRANY. KRITICHESKIE TEKHNOLOGII. INFORMATSIONNO-ANALITICHESKII ZHURNAL. see ENGINEERING—Abstracting, Bibliographies, Statistics

METAL POWDER REPORT. see METALLURGY—Abstracting, Bibliographies, Statistics

METALS ABSTRACTS. see METALLURGY—Abstracting, Bibliographies, Statistics

METALS ABSTRACTS INDEX. see METALLURGY—Abstracting, Bibliographies, Statistics

METALWORKING ABSTRACTS. see MACHINERY—Abstracting, Bibliographies, Statistics

METEOROLOGICAL AND GEOASTROPHYSICAL ABSTRACTS. see METEOROLOGY—Abstracting, Bibliographies, Statistics

METHODS IN ORGANIC SYNTHESIS. see CHEMISTRY— Abstracting, Bibliographies, Statistics

MEXICO. CENTRO DE INFORMACION TECNICA Y DOCUMENTACION. INDICE DE PELICULAS. see MOTION PICTURES—Abstracting, Bibliographies, Statistics

MEXICO. CENTRO DE INFORMACION TECNICA Y DOCUMENTACION. INDICE DE REVISTAS. SECCION DE EDUCACION Y COMUNICACION. see EDUCATION— Abstracting, Bibliographies, Statistics

MICROBIOLOGY ABSTRACTS: SECTION A. INDUSTRIAL & APPLIED MICROBIOLOGY. see BIOLOGY—Abstracting, Bibliographies, Statistics

MICROBIOLOGY ABSTRACTS: SECTION B. BACTERIOLOGY. see BIOLOGY—Abstracting, Bibliographies, Statistics

MICROBIOLOGY ABSTRACTS: SECTION C. ALGOLOGY, MYCOLOGY AND PROTOZOOLOGY. see BIOLOGY—Abstracting, Bibliographies, Statistics

MILCHWISSENSCHAFT/MILK SCIENCE INTERNATIONAL; journal of nutrition research and food science. see AGRICULTURE—Abstracting, Bibliographies, Statistics

MILITARY SCIENCE INDEX. see MILITARY—Abstracting, Bibliographies, Statistics

MINERALOGICAL SOCIETY OF JAPAN. ANNUAL MEETING ABSTRACTS/NIHON KOBUTSU GAKKAI NENKAI KOEN YOSHISHU. see EARTH SCIENCES—Abstracting, Bibliographies, Statistics

MINSOURCE: MINERALOGICAL ABSTRACTS AND HEY'S MINERAL INDEX ON CD-ROM. see MINES AND MINING INDUSTRY—Abstracting, Bibliographies, Statistics

MIROVOI OKEAN. INFORMATSIONNO-ANALITICHESKII SBORNIK. see EARTH SCIENCES—Abstracting, Bibliographies, Statistics

MITOCHONDRIA. see BIOLOGY—Abstracting, Bibliographies, Statistics

016   USA
MOESSBAUER EFFECT REFERENCE AND DATA JOURNAL. INDEX. Text in English. a. USD 500 domestic; USD 515 foreign (effective 2003). **Document type:** Abstract/Index.
Related titles: Online - full content ed.: USD 300 (effective 2003); ◆ Supplement to: Moessbauer Effect Reference and Data Journal. ISSN 0163-9587.
Published by: University of North Carolina at Asheville, Mossbauer Effect Data Center, One University Heights, CPO #2311, Asheville, NC 28804-8511. TEL 828-251-6617, FAX 828-232-5179, medc@unca.edu, http://www.unca.edu/medc.

MOLECULAR BIOLOGY TECHNIQUES. see BIOLOGY— Abstracting, Bibliographies, Statistics

MONATSSCHRIFT FUER BRAUWISSENSCHAFT (ONLINE EDITION). see BEVERAGES—Abstracting, Bibliographies, Statistics

MULTICULTURAL EDUCATION ABSTRACTS. see EDUCATION—Abstracting, Bibliographies, Statistics

MUNICIPAL ACT AND INDEX TO LOCAL GOVERNMENT LEGISLATION MANUAL. see PUBLIC ADMINISTRATION— Abstracting, Bibliographies, Statistics

MUSIC AND DANCE PERIODICALS; an international directory and guide book. see MUSIC—Abstracting, Bibliographies, Statistics

MUSIC IN PRINT MASTER TITLE INDEX. see MUSIC—Abstracting, Bibliographies, Statistics

MUSIC-IN-PRINT SERIES. see MUSIC—Abstracting, Bibliographies, Statistics

MUSIC INDEX; a subject-author guide to music periodical literature. see MUSIC—Abstracting, Bibliographies, Statistics

MUSIC INDEX ONLINE. see MUSIC—Abstracting, Bibliographies, Statistics

MUSZAKI-GAZDASAGI MAGAZIN/TECHNICAL ECONOMIC DIGEST. see BUSINESS AND ECONOMICS—Abstracting, Bibliographies, Statistics

MUZEINOE DELO I OKHRANA PAMYATNIKOV; referativno-bibliograficheskaya informatsiya. see MUSEUMS AND ART GALLERIES—Abstracting, Bibliographies, Statistics

MUZYKA; referativno-bibliograficheskaya informatsiya. see MUSIC—Abstracting, Bibliographies, Statistics

MYCOBACTERIA. see BIOLOGY—Abstracting, Bibliographies, Statistics

MYSTERY SHORT FICTION. see LITERATURE—Abstracting, Bibliographies, Statistics

N A A. (Nordic Archaeological Abstracts) see ARCHAEOLOGY— Abstracting, Bibliographies, Statistics

N B O ABSTRACTS. see BUILDING AND CONSTRUCTION— Abstracting, Bibliographies, Statistics

N C B ABSTRACTS. see BUILDING AND CONSTRUCTION— Abstracting, Bibliographies, Statistics

N C B CURRENT CONTENTS. see BUILDING AND CONSTRUCTION—Abstracting, Bibliographies, Statistics

N E L M INDEX SERIES. see LITERATURE—Abstracting, Bibliographies, Statistics

THE N E S F A INDEX TO SHORT SCIENCE FICTION. see LITERATURE—Abstracting, Bibliographies, Statistics

N F A I S NEWSLETTER. see LIBRARY AND INFORMATION SCIENCES

025   USA   ISSN 1062-7952
Z695.93
N F A I S YEARBOOK OF THE INFORMATION INDUSTRY (YEAR). Text in English. 1992. a. USD 50 to non-members; USD 40 to members; (effective 1998). **Description:** Discusses the significant events that have influenced the information industry over the past year. Reviews critical issues, national and international policies. Features new technologies, with an emphasis on compact discs.
Published by: (National Federation of Abstracting and Information Services), Information Today, Inc., 143 Old Marlton Pike, Medford, NJ 08055-8750. TEL 609-654-6266; FAX 609-654-4309, custserv@infotoday.com, http://www.infotoday.com. Ed. Arthur W Elias.

N I C E M INDEX TO A V PRODUCERS AND DISTRIBUTORS. see EDUCATION—Abstracting, Bibliographies, Statistics

N T I S ALERTS: AGRICULTURE & FOOD. see AGRICULTURE—Abstracting, Bibliographies, Statistics

N T I S ALERTS: BIOMEDICAL TECHNOLOGY & HUMAN FACTORS ENGINEERING. see MEDICAL SCIENCES—Abstracting, Bibliographies, Statistics

N T I S ALERTS: BUILDING INDUSTRY TECHNOLOGY. see BUILDING AND CONSTRUCTION—Abstracting, Bibliographies, Statistics

N T I S ALERTS: BUSINESS & ECONOMICS. see BUSINESS AND ECONOMICS—Abstracting, Bibliographies, Statistics

N T I S ALERTS: CIVIL ENGINEERING. see ENGINEERING— Abstracting, Bibliographies, Statistics

N T I S ALERTS: COMMUNICATION. see COMMUNICATIONS— Abstracting, Bibliographies, Statistics

N T I S ALERTS: COMPUTERS, CONTROL & INFORMATION THEORY. see COMPUTERS—Abstracting, Bibliographies, Statistics

N T I S ALERTS: ELECTROTECHNOLOGY. see ELECTRONICS

N T I S ALERTS: ENERGY. see ENERGY—Abstracting, Bibliographies, Statistics

N T I S ALERTS: ENVIRONMENTAL POLLUTION & CONTROL. see ENVIRONMENTAL STUDIES—Abstracting, Bibliographies, Statistics

N T I S ALERTS: GOVERNMENT INVENTIONS FOR LICENSING. see TECHNOLOGY: COMPREHENSIVE WORKS—Abstracting, Bibliographies, Statistics

N T I S ALERTS: HEALTH CARE. see PHYSICAL FITNESS AND HYGIENE—Abstracting, Bibliographies, Statistics

N T I S ALERTS: MANUFACTURING TECHNOLOGY. see TECHNOLOGY: COMPREHENSIVE WORKS—Abstracting, Bibliographies, Statistics

N T I S ALERTS: MATERIALS SCIENCES. see ENGINEERING—Abstracting, Bibliographies, Statistics

N T I S ALERTS: OCEAN SCIENCES & ENGINEERING. see EARTH SCIENCES—Abstracting, Bibliographies, Statistics

N T I S ALERTS: TRANSPORTATION. see TRANSPORTATION—Abstracting, Bibliographies, Statistics

N T I S TITLE INDEX. see POLITICAL SCIENCE—Abstracting, Bibliographies, Statistics

NATIONAL ACCOUNTS OF O E C D COUNTRIES. VOLUME 1 MAIN AGGREGATES/COMPTES NATIONAUX DES PAYS DE L'O C D E. VOLUME I. see BUSINESS AND ECONOMICS—Abstracting, Bibliographies, Statistics

NATIONAL ACCOUNTS OF O E C D COUNTRIES. VOLUME 2 DETAILED TABLES. see BUSINESS AND ECONOMICS—Abstracting, Bibliographies, Statistics

NATIONAL CENTER FOR AGRICULTURAL UTILIZATION RESEARCH PUBLICATIONS AND PATENTS. see AGRICULTURE—Abstracting, Bibliographies, Statistics

NATIONAL CHEMICAL INVENTORIES. see CHEMISTRY— Abstracting, Bibliographies, Statistics

NATURAL PRODUCT UPDATES. see CHEMISTRY—Abstracting, Bibliographies, Statistics

NEMATOLOGICAL ABSTRACTS. see BIOLOGY—Abstracting, Bibliographies, Statistics

NEPAL DOCUMENTATION; occasional bibliography. see BUSINESS AND ECONOMICS—Abstracting, Bibliographies, Statistics

▼ new title   ➤ refereed   ＊ unverified   ◆ full entry avail.

A

NERVE CELL BIOLOGY. see *BIOLOGY—Abstracting, Bibliographies, Statistics*

NETHERLANDS PATENTS REPORT. see *PATENTS, TRADEMARKS AND COPYRIGHTS—Abstracting, Bibliographies, Statistics*

NEUROPHYSIOLOGY. see *BIOLOGY—Abstracting, Bibliographies, Statistics*

NEUROPSYCHOLOGY ABSTRACTS. see *MEDICAL SCIENCES—Abstracting, Bibliographies, Statistics*

NEW SOUTH WALES STATUTES ANNOTATIONS. see *LAW—Abstracting, Bibliographies, Statistics*

NEW TESTAMENT ABSTRACTS; a record of current literature. see *RELIGIONS AND THEOLOGY—Abstracting, Bibliographies, Statistics*

THE NEW YORK TIMES INDEX HIGHLIGHTS. see *POLITICAL SCIENCE—Abstracting, Bibliographies, Statistics*

NEW ZEALAND. TABLES OF ACTS AND ORDINANCES AND STATUTORY REGULATIONS IN FORCE. see *PUBLIC ADMINISTRATION—Abstracting, Bibliographies, Statistics*

NEWSLETTER DIGEST. see *BUSINESS AND ECONOMICS—Abstracting, Bibliographies, Statistics*

NEWSPAPER ABSTRACTS. see *JOURNALISM—Abstracting, Bibliographies, Statistics*

THE NEWSPAPER INDEX. see *JOURNALISM—Abstracting, Bibliographies, Statistics*

NIEDEROESTERREICHISCHE LANDES-LANDWIRTSCHAFTSKAMMER. AMTLICHER MARKTBERICHT. see *AGRICULTURE—Abstracting, Bibliographies, Statistics*

NIGERIAN JOURNAL OF SOCIAL SCIENCE RESEARCH ABSTRACTS. see *SOCIAL SCIENCES: COMPREHENSIVE WORKS—Abstracting, Bibliographies, Statistics*

016   NGA   ISSN 0794-6406
AI3
NIGERIAN PERIODICALS INDEX. Text in English. 1986. s-a. NGN 80, USD 50. back issues avail. **Document type:** Abstract/Index. **Description:** Author-subject index with the entries filing in one alphabetical sequence, word-by-word, following ALA filing rules.
Published by: Committee of University Librarians of Nigerian Universities, c/o Dr. H.I. Said, The Library Bayero University, Kano, Nigeria. Ed. B U Nwafor. Circ: 500.

NIHON BAIOREOROJI GAKKAI NENKAI SHOROKUSHU/ JAPANESE SOCIETY OF BIORHEOLOGY. ABSTRACTS OF THE ANNUAL MEETING. see *BIOLOGY—Abstracting, Bibliographies, Statistics*

NIHON BENTOSU GAKKAI TAIKAI/JAPANESE ASSOCIATION OF BENTHOLOGY. ABSTRACTS OF ANNUAL MEETING. see *BIOLOGY—Abstracting, Bibliographies, Statistics*

NIHON BOKIN BOBAI GAKKAI. NENJI TAIKAI YOSHISHU/SOCIETY FOR ANTIBACTERIAL AND ANTIFUNGAL AGENTS, JAPAN. ABSTRACTS OF THE MEETING. see *BIOLOGY—Abstracting, Bibliographies, Statistics*

NIHON CHIKYU KAGAKKAI NENKAI KOEN YOSHISHU/ GEOCHEMICAL SOCIETY OF JAPAN. ABSTRACTS OF REPORTS ON ANNUAL MEETING. see *EARTH SCIENCES—Abstracting, Bibliographies, Statistics*

NIHON CHISHITSU GAKKAI KANTO SHIBU SHINPOJUMU KOEN YOSHISHU/GEOLOGICAL SOCIETY OF JAPAN. ABSTRACTS OF KANTO BRANCH SYMPOSIUM. see *EARTH SCIENCES—Abstracting, Bibliographies, Statistics*

NIHON DOJO BISEIBUTSU GAKKAI KOEN YOSHISHU/SOIL MICROBIOLOGICAL SOCIETY OF JAPAN. ABSTRACTS OF THE ANNUAL MEETING. see *BIOLOGY—Abstracting, Bibliographies, Statistics*

NIHON GYORUI GAKKAI NENKAI KOEN YOSHI/ ICHTHYOLOGY SOCIETY OF JAPAN. ADVANCE ABSTRACTS FOR THE ANNUAL MEETING. see *BIOLOGY—Abstracting, Bibliographies, Statistics*

NIHON IYAKU BUNKEN SHOROKUSHU/JAPAN PHARMACEUTICAL ABSTRACTS. see *PHARMACY AND PHARMACOLOGY—Abstracting, Bibliographies, Statistics*

NIHON JIKKEN DOBUTSU GAKKAI SOKAI KOEN YOSHISHU/JAPANESE ASSOCIATION FOR LABORATORY ANIMAL SCIENCE. ABSTRACTS OF GENERAL MEETING. see *BIOLOGY—Abstracting, Bibliographies, Statistics*

NIHON JINRUI IDEN GAKKAI TAIKAI SHOROKUSHU/JAPAN SOCIETY OF HUMAN GENETICS. ABSTRACTS OF THE ANNUAL MEETING. see *BIOLOGY—Abstracting, Bibliographies, Statistics*

NIHON KAIBOGAKU BUNKENSHU/ABSTRACTS OF JAPANESE ANATOMY. see *MEDICAL SCIENCES—Abstracting, Bibliographies, Statistics*

NIHON KESSHO GAKKAI NENKAI KOEN YOSHISHU/ CRYSTALLOGRAPHIC SOCIETY OF JAPAN. ABSTRACTS OF ANNUAL MEETING. see *CHEMISTRY—Abstracting, Bibliographies, Statistics*

NIHON KONCHU GAKKAI TAIKAI KOEN YOSHI/ ENTOMOLOGICAL SOCIETY OF JAPAN. ABSTRACTS OF ANNUAL MEETING. see *BIOLOGY—Abstracting, Bibliographies, Statistics*

NIHON KOSEIBUTSU GAKKAI NENKAI KOEN YOKOSHU/PALAEONTOLOGICAL SOCIETY OF JAPAN. ABSTRACTS OF THE ANNUAL MEETING. see *PALEONTOLOGY—Abstracting, Bibliographies, Statistics*

NIHON KYUCHAKU GAKKAI KENKYU HAPPYOKAI KOEN YOSHISHU/JAPAN SOCIETY ON ADSORPTION. ABSTRACTS OF THE MEETING. see *CHEMISTRY—Abstracting, Bibliographies, Statistics*

NIHON MAKU GAKKAI NENKAI KOEN YOSHISHU/MEMBRANE SOCIETY OF JAPAN. ABSTRACTS OF ANNUAL MEETING. see *CHEMISTRY—Abstracting, Bibliographies, Statistics*

NIHON MUKIN SEIBUTSU NOTO BAIOROJI GAKKAI SOKAI NITTEI TO SHOROKU/JAPANESE ASSOCIATION OF GERMFREE LIFE AND GNOTOBIOLOGY. ABSTRACTS OF MEETING. see *BIOLOGY—Abstracting, Bibliographies, Statistics*

NIHON RIKUSUI GAKKAI KOEN YOSHISHU/JAPANESE SOCIETY OF LIMNOLOGY. ABSTRACTS OF MEETING. see *EARTH SCIENCES—Abstracting, Bibliographies, Statistics*

NIHON SAIBO SEIBUTSU GAKKAI TAIKAI KOEN YOSHISHU/JAPAN SOCIETY FOR CELL BIOLOGY. ABSTRACTS OF THE MEETING. see *BIOLOGY—Abstracting, Bibliographies, Statistics*

NIHON SEIKAGAKKAI KINKI SHIBU REIKAI YOSHISHU/JAPANESE BIOCHEMICAL SOCIETY, KINKI BRANCH OFFICE. ABSTRACTS OF MEETING. see *FISH AND FISHERIES—Abstracting, Bibliographies, Statistics*

NIHON SEIRI JINRUI GAKKAISHI/JAPANESE JOURNAL OF PHYSIOLOGICAL ANTHROPOLOGY. see *BIOLOGY—Abstracting, Bibliographies, Statistics*

NIHON SENSHOKUTAI KENSA GAKKAI SHOROKUSHU/ JAPANESE ASSOCIATION FOR CHROMOSOME ANALYSIS. ABSTRACT OF ANNUAL MEETING. see *BIOLOGY—Abstracting, Bibliographies, Statistics*

NIHON SHOKUBUTSU BYORI GAKKAI DOJO DENSENBYO DANWAKAI KOEN YOSHISHU/PHYTOPATHOLOGICAL SOCIETY OF JAPAN. ABSTRACTS OF THE MEETING OF SOIL BORNE DISEASE. see *BIOLOGY—Abstracting, Bibliographies, Statistics*

NIHON TANPAKU KOGAKKAI NENKAI PUROGURAMU YOSHISHU/PROTEIN ENGINEERING SOCIETY OF JAPAN. ABSTRACTS OF THE MEETING. see *FISH AND FISHERIES—Abstracting, Bibliographies, Statistics*

NIPPON DOBUTSU KODO GAKKAI TAIKAI HAPPYO YOSHISHU/JAPAN ETHOLOGICAL SOCIETY. ABSTRACTS OF MEETING. see *BIOLOGY—Abstracting, Bibliographies, Statistics*

NITRIC OXIDE. see *BIOLOGY—Abstracting, Bibliographies, Statistics*

NO NO IGAKU SEIBUTSUGAKU KONWAKAI SHOROKU/ABSTRACTS OF CONFERENCE ON MEDICINE AND BIOLOGY OF THE BRAIN. see *BIOLOGY—Abstracting, Bibliographies, Statistics*

016   NOR
NORSKE TIDSSKRIFTARTIKLER (ONLINE EDITION)/ NORWEGIAN INDEX TO PERIODICAL ARTICLES. Text in Norwegian. w. NOK 1,000 (effective 2001). **Document type:** Bibliography.
Formerly: Norske Tidsskriftartikler (Print Edition) (0332-978X)
Media: Online - full content.
Published by: National Library of Norway, Bibliographic Services Department, Solli, PO Box 2674, Oslo, 0203, Norway. TEL 47-23-27-61-19, FAX 47-23-27-60-50, norartikler@nb.no, unni.knutsen@nb.no, http://www.nb.no/baser/norart.

NORTH AMERICAN WILDLIFE & NATURAL RESOURCES ABSTRACTS. see *BIOLOGY—Abstracting, Bibliographies, Statistics*

NORWEGIAN OFFSHORE INDEX. see *PETROLEUM AND GAS—Abstracting, Bibliographies, Statistics*

NOTES AND ABSTRACTS IN AMERICAN AND INTERNATIONAL EDUCATION. see *EDUCATION—Abstracting, Bibliographies, Statistics*

NOTES & COMMENT. see *ENGINEERING—Abstracting, Bibliographies, Statistics*

NOVAYA LITERATURA PO SOTSIAL'NYM I GUMANITARNYM NAUKAM. ISTORIYA. ARKHEOLOGIYA. ETNOLOGIYA; bibliograficheskii ukazatel'. see *ANTHROPOLOGY—Abstracting, Bibliographies, Statistics*

NUCLEIC ACIDS ABSTRACTS (ONLINE EDITION). see *BIOLOGY—Abstracting, Bibliographies, Statistics*

NUTRITION ABSTRACTS AND REVIEWS. SERIES A: HUMAN AND EXPERIMENTAL. see *NUTRITION AND DIETETICS—Abstracting, Bibliographies, Statistics*

NUTRITION ABSTRACTS AND REVIEWS. SERIES B: LIVESTOCK FEEDS AND FEEDING. see *AGRICULTURE—Abstracting, Bibliographies, Statistics*

NYA BYGGREGLER. see *BUILDING AND CONSTRUCTION—Abstracting, Bibliographies, Statistics*

NYUSEN HINYU KENKYUKAI KOEN YOSHISHU/SOCIETY FOR MAMMARY GLANDS AND LACTATION RESEARCH. ABSTRACTS OF THE MEETING. see *MEDICAL SCIENCES—Abstracting, Bibliographies, Statistics*

O E C D HISTORICAL STATISTICS. see *BUSINESS AND ECONOMICS—Abstracting, Bibliographies, Statistics*

O E C S CURRENT AWARENESS BULLETIN. see *BUSINESS AND ECONOMICS—Economic Situation And Conditions*

O J INDEX. (Official Journal of the European Communities) see *POLITICAL SCIENCE—International Relations*

O R REPORTS. (Operating Room) see *HEALTH FACILITIES AND ADMINISTRATION—Abstracting, Bibliographies, Statistics*

OBSTETRIC ANESTHESIA DIGEST. see *MEDICAL SCIENCES—Anaesthesiology*

OBZORNAYA INFORMATSIYA. EKOLOGICHESKAYA EKSPERTIZA. see *ENVIRONMENTAL STUDIES—Abstracting, Bibliographies, Statistics*

OBZORNAYA INFORMATSIYA. EKONOMIKA PRIRODOPOL'ZOVANIYA. see *ENVIRONMENTAL STUDIES—Abstracting, Bibliographies, Statistics*

OBZORNAYA INFORMATSIYA. NAUCHNYE I TEKHNICHESKIE ASPEKTY OKHRANY OKRUZHAYUSHCHEI SREDY. see *ENVIRONMENTAL STUDIES—Abstracting, Bibliographies, Statistics*

OBZORNAYA INFORMATSIYA. PROBLEMY BEZOPASNOSTI POLETOV. see *AERONAUTICS AND SPACE FLIGHT—Abstracting, Bibliographies, Statistics*

OBZORNAYA INFORMATSIYA. PROBLEMY BEZOPASNOSTI PRI CHREZVYCHAINYKH SITUATSIYAKH. see *CIVIL DEFENSE—Abstracting, Bibliographies, Statistics*

OBZORNAYA INFORMATSIYA. PROBLEMY OKRUZHAYUSHCHEI SREDY I PRIRODNYKH RESURSOV. see *ENVIRONMENTAL STUDIES—Abstracting, Bibliographies, Statistics*

OBZORNAYA INFORMATSIYA. TRANSPORT: NAUKA, TEKHNIKA, UPRAVLENIE. see *TRANSPORTATION—Abstracting, Bibliographies, Statistics*

OCCUPATIONAL HEALTH & SAFETY CURRENT CONTENTS. see *OCCUPATIONAL HEALTH AND SAFETY—Abstracting, Bibliographies, Statistics*

OCEANIC ABSTRACTS. see *EARTH SCIENCES—Abstracting, Bibliographies, Statistics*

OCEANOGRAPHIC LITERATURE REVIEW. see *EARTH SCIENCES—Abstracting, Bibliographies, Statistics*

OCEANOGRAPHICAL SOCIETY OF JAPAN. ABSTRACTS ON THE CONFERENCE/NIHON KAIYO GAKKAI TAIKAI KOEN YOSHISHU. see *EARTH SCIENCES—Abstracting, Bibliographies, Statistics*

OLD TESTAMENT ABSTRACTS. see *RELIGIONS AND THEOLOGY—Abstracting, Bibliographies, Statistics*

ONCOGENES. see *MEDICAL SCIENCES—Abstracting, Bibliographies, Statistics*

ONLINE LOGISTICS BIBLIOGRAPHY. see *BUSINESS AND ECONOMICS—Abstracting, Bibliographies, Statistics*

ONOMA. see *LINGUISTICS*

OPERATIONS & PRODUCTION MANAGEMENT ABSTRACTS. see *BUSINESS AND ECONOMICS—Abstracting, Bibliographies, Statistics*

OPERATIONS RESEARCH - MANAGEMENT SCIENCE; international literature digest service. see *BUSINESS AND ECONOMICS—Abstracting, Bibliographies, Statistics*

OPERATIONS RESEARCH - MANAGEMENT SCIENCE YEARBOOK. see *BUSINESS AND ECONOMICS— Abstracting, Bibliographies, Statistics*

ORNAMENTAL HORTICULTURE. see *GARDENING AND HORTICULTURE—Abstracting, Bibliographies, Statistics*

ORNITHOLOGY ABSTRACTS. see *BIOLOGY—Abstracting, Bibliographies, Statistics*

OSTEOPOROSIS. see *MEDICAL SCIENCES—Abstracting, Bibliographies, Statistics*

OXYGEN RADICALS. see *BIOLOGY—Abstracting, Bibliographies, Statistics*

P A I S INTERNATIONAL IN PRINT (ANNUAL). (Public Affairs Information Service) see *POLITICAL SCIENCE—Abstracting, Bibliographies, Statistics*

P A I S INTERNATIONAL IN PRINT (MONTHLY). (Public Affairs Information Service) see *POLITICAL SCIENCE—Abstracting, Bibliographies, Statistics*

P A I S INTERNATIONAL - JOURNALS INDEXED IN (YEAR). (Public Affairs Information Service, Inc.) see *SOCIAL SCIENCES: COMPREHENSIVE WORKS*

PACKAGING MONTH. see *PACKAGING—Abstracting, Bibliographies, Statistics*

PAINT TITLES. see *PAINTS AND PROTECTIVE COATINGS—Abstracting, Bibliographies, Statistics*

PAKISTAN SCIENCE ABSTRACTS. see *SCIENCES: COMPREHENSIVE WORKS—Abstracting, Bibliographies, Statistics*

PAKISTAN VETERINARY INDEX. see *VETERINARY SCIENCE—Abstracting, Bibliographies, Statistics*

PANCREATIC AND SALIVARY SECRETION. see *BIOLOGY—Abstracting, Bibliographies, Statistics*

PAPERBASE ABSTRACTS. see *PAPER AND PULP—Abstracting, Bibliographies, Statistics*

PAPIRIPARI ES NYOMDAIPARI SZAKIRODALMI TAJEKOZTATO/PAPER INDUSTRY & PRINTING ABSTRACTS. see *PAPER AND PULP—Abstracting, Bibliographies, Statistics*

PAPUA NEW GUINEA. NATIONAL STATISTICAL OFFICE. ABSTRACT OF STATISTICS. see *STATISTICS*

PAPUA NEW GUINEA. NATIONAL STATISTICAL OFFICE. CONSUMER PRICE INDEX. see *STATISTICS*

PARASITOLOGY (SHEFFIELD). see *BIOLOGY—Abstracting, Bibliographies, Statistics*

PATENT ABSTRACTS IN ENGLISH. see *PATENTS, TRADEMARKS AND COPYRIGHTS—Abstracting, Bibliographies, Statistics*

PATENTS ABSTRACTS. see *PETROLEUM AND GAS—Abstracting, Bibliographies, Statistics*

PEACE RESEARCH ABSTRACTS JOURNAL. see *POLITICAL SCIENCE—Abstracting, Bibliographies, Statistics*

PEPTIDE INFORMATION. see *BIOLOGY—Abstracting, Bibliographies, Statistics*

PERIODICA. INDICE DE REVISTAS LATINOAMERICANAS EN CIENCIAS. see *SCIENCES: COMPREHENSIVE WORKS—Abstracting, Bibliographies, Statistics*

016.05   USA
PERIODICAL ABSTRACTS. Text in English. 1988. m. price varies. **Document type:** *Abstract/Index.*
Formerly: Periodical Abstracts Ondisc
Media: CD-ROM. **Related titles:** Magnetic Tape ed.; Online - full text ed.: (from The Dialog Corporation).
Published by: ProQuest Information & Learning, 300 N Zeeb Rd., PO Box 1346, Ann Arbor, MI 48106-1346. TEL 734-761-4700, 800-521-0600, info@il.proquest.com, http://www.latimes.com/.

PERIODICAL SOURCE INDEX. see *HISTORY—Abstracting, Bibliographies, Statistics*

PERIODICALS CONTENTS INDEX. see *SOCIAL SCIENCES: COMPREHENSIVE WORKS—Abstracting, Bibliographies, Statistics*

016   USA
PERSONAL ALERT. Text in English. 1965. w. USD 280.
Document type: *Abstract/Index.* **Description:** Reports on all newly published items that match personalized parameters within research specialties in the sciences, social sciences, arts and humanities.
Former titles: Research Alert (Philadelphia) (Print Edition); (until 1989): Automatic Subject Citation Alert; A S C A Topics
Media: Online - full content.
Published by: Thomson I S I (Subsidiary of: Thomson Corporation), 3501 Market St., Philadelphia, PA 19104. TEL 215-386-0100, FAX 215-386-2911.

PESTICIDE INDEX. see *AGRICULTURE—Abstracting, Bibliographies, Statistics*

PESTICIDES ABSTRACTS. see *ENVIRONMENTAL STUDIES—Abstracting, Bibliographies, Statistics*

PETROLEUM ABSTRACTS. see *PETROLEUM AND GAS—Abstracting, Bibliographies, Statistics*

PHARMACEUTICAL NEWS INDEX. see *PHARMACY AND PHARMACOLOGY—Abstracting, Bibliographies, Statistics*

PHARMACOECONOMICS AND OUTCOMES NEWS; rapid alerts to world pharmacoeconomic news, views and practical application. see *PHARMACY AND PHARMACOLOGY— Abstracting, Bibliographies, Statistics*

PHILIPPINE BUSINESS AND INDUSTRY INDEX. see *BUSINESS AND ECONOMICS—Abstracting, Bibliographies, Statistics*

PHILIPPINE INDEX MEDICUS. see *MEDICAL SCIENCES—Abstracting, Bibliographies, Statistics*

PHILIPPINE SCIENCE AND TECHNOLOGY ABSTRACTS. see *SCIENCES: COMPREHENSIVE WORKS—Abstracting, Bibliographies, Statistics*

PHILOSOPHER'S INDEX; an international index to philosophical periodicals and books. see *PHILOSOPHY—Abstracting, Bibliographies, Statistics*

PHYSICAL EDUCATION INDEX. see *EDUCATION—Abstracting, Bibliographies, Statistics*

PHYSICAL REVIEW ABSTRACTS. see *PHYSICS—Abstracting, Bibliographies, Statistics*

PHYSICAL REVIEW - INDEX. see *PHYSICS—Abstracting, Bibliographies, Statistics*

PHYSICS ABSTRACTS. see *PHYSICS—Abstracting, Bibliographies, Statistics*

PHYSICS AND CHEMISTRY OF GLASSES. see *CERAMICS, GLASS AND POTTERY—Abstracting, Bibliographies, Statistics*

PHYSIOTHERAPY IRELAND. see *MEDICAL SCIENCES— Abstracting, Bibliographies, Statistics*

PIG NEWS & INFORMATION. see *AGRICULTURE—Abstracting, Bibliographies, Statistics*

PLANT BIOTECHNOLOGY. see *BIOLOGY—Abstracting, Bibliographies, Statistics*

PLANT BREEDING ABSTRACTS. see *AGRICULTURE— Abstracting, Bibliographies, Statistics*

PLANT GENETIC RESOURCES ABSTRACTS. see *BIOLOGY—Abstracting, Bibliographies, Statistics*

PLANT GROWTH REGULATOR ABSTRACTS. see *AGRICULTURE—Abstracting, Bibliographies, Statistics*

PLAY INDEX. see *LITERATURE—Abstracting, Bibliographies, Statistics*

A

POEMFINDER. see *LITERATURE—Abstracting, Bibliographies, Statistics*

POHYBOVE USTROJI; pokroky ve vyzkumu diagnostice a terapii. see *MEDICAL SCIENCES—Orthopedics And Traumatology*

POLAR AND GLACIOLOGICAL ABSTRACTS. see *EARTH SCIENCES—Abstracting, Bibliographies, Statistics*

POLISH ARCHAEOLOGICAL ABSTRACTS. see *ARCHAEOLOGY—Abstracting, Bibliographies, Statistics*

POLLUTION ABSTRACTS. see *ENVIRONMENTAL STUDIES—Abstracting, Bibliographies, Statistics*

POLSKA BIBLIOGRAFIA ANALITYCZNA MECHANIKI/POLISH SCIENTIFIC ABSTRACTS ON MECHANICS. see *MACHINERY—Abstracting, Bibliographies, Statistics*

POLYMER BLENDS, ALLOYS AND INTERPENETRATING POLYMER NETWORKS ABSTRACTS. see *CHEMISTRY—Abstracting, Bibliographies, Statistics*

POLYMER CONTENTS. see *ENGINEERING—Abstracting, Bibliographies, Statistics*

POPULATION ABSTRACTS. see *POPULATION STUDIES—Abstracting, Bibliographies, Statistics*

POTATO ABSTRACTS. see *AGRICULTURE—Abstracting, Bibliographies, Statistics*

POULTRY ABSTRACTS. see *AGRICULTURE—Abstracting, Bibliographies, Statistics*

PRESS. see *PRINTING—Abstracting, Bibliographies, Statistics*

PROCESS AND CHEMICAL ENGINEERING. see *ENGINEERING—Abstracting, Bibliographies, Statistics*

PRODUKTION VON LEITERPLATTEN UND SYSTEMEN. see *METALLURGY—Abstracting, Bibliographies, Statistics*

PROGRESS IN COAL STEEL AND RELATED SOCIAL RESEARCH; a European journal. see *MINES AND MINING INDUSTRY—Abstracting, Bibliographies, Statistics*

PROLACTIN. see *MEDICAL SCIENCES—Abstracting, Bibliographies, Statistics*

PROSTAGLANDINS - BIOLOGY. see *MEDICAL SCIENCES—Abstracting, Bibliographies, Statistics*

PROTEINS: POST-TRANSLATIONAL PROCESSING. see *BIOLOGY—Abstracting, Bibliographies, Statistics*

PROTOZOOLOGICAL ABSTRACTS. see *BIOLOGY—Abstracting, Bibliographies, Statistics*

PRZEGLAD DOKUMENTACYJNY ELEKTROTECHNIKI. see *ENGINEERING—Abstracting, Bibliographies, Statistics*

PSICODOC; lo mejor de la psicologia al instante. see *PSYCHOLOGY—Abstracting, Bibliographies, Statistics*

PSYCHOANALYTIC ABSTRACTS. see *PSYCHOLOGY— Abstracting, Bibliographies, Statistics*

PSYCHOLOGICAL ABSTRACTS. see *PSYCHOLOGY— Abstracting, Bibliographies, Statistics*

PSYCINFO. see *PSYCHOLOGY—Abstracting, Bibliographies, Statistics*

PSYCSCAN: APPLIED PSYCHOLOGY (ONLINE EDITION). see *PSYCHOLOGY—Abstracting, Bibliographies, Statistics*

PSYCSCAN: CLINICAL PSYCHOLOGY. see *PSYCHOLOGY— Abstracting, Bibliographies, Statistics*

PSYCSCAN: DEVELOPMENTAL PSYCHOLOGY. see *PSYCHOLOGY—Abstracting, Bibliographies, Statistics*

PSYCSCAN: LEARNING DISORDERS AND MENTAL RETARDATION. see *MEDICAL SCIENCES—Abstracting, Bibliographies, Statistics*

PUBLIC TELEVISION TRANSCRIPTS INDEX. see *COMMUNICATIONS—Abstracting, Bibliographies, Statistics*

PURASUMIN BUNKEN MOKUROKU/BIBLIOGRAPHY OF PLASMIN. see *MEDICAL SCIENCES—Abstracting, Bibliographies, Statistics*

A

016.02   KEN   ISSN 1527-5388
Z3503
**QUARTERLY INDEX TO AFRICANA PERIODICAL
LITERATURE.** Text in English. 1991. q. free (effective 2005).
illus. reprints avail. **Document type:** Abstract/Index.
Description: Indexes selected periodicals acquired by the
Nairobi office from 28 African including scholarly journals,
articles on subject areas not found in widely available
literature, and nongovernment publications for scholars of
Africa.
Formerly: Quarterly Index to Periodical Literature, Eastern and
Southern Africa (1018-1555)
Related titles: Online - full content ed.
Published by: U.S. Library of Congress Office, Embassy of the
United States of America, PO Box 30598, Nairobi, Kenya. TEL
254-2-3636300, FAX 254-2-3636321, nairobi@libcon-
kenya.org, http://lcweb2.loc.gov/misc/qsihtml/.

QUEENSLAND COURT OF APPEAL HEADNOTES. see
LAW—Abstracting, Bibliographies, Statistics

QUEENSLAND LEGAL INDEXES. see *LAW—Abstracting,
Bibliographies, Statistics*

R A P R A ABSTRACTS. (Rubber and Plastics Research
Association of Great Britain) see *RUBBER—Abstracting,
Bibliographies, Statistics*

R A P R A REVIEW REPORTS; expert overviews covering the
science and technology of rubbers and plastics. see
PLASTICS—Abstracting, Bibliographies, Statistics

R I L M ABSTRACTS OF MUSIC LITERATURE. (Repertoire
International de Litterature Musicale) see *MUSIC—Abstracting,
Bibliographies, Statistics*

R S A P NEWSLETTER. see *BIBLIOGRAPHIES*

RADIATION RESEARCH SOCIETY. ANNUAL MEETING. see
PHYSICS—Abstracting, Bibliographies, Statistics

RAPRA ABSTRACTS. ADDITIVES. see *PAINTS AND
PROTECTIVE COATINGS—Abstracting, Bibliographies,
Statistics*

**RAPRA ABSTRACTS. ADHESIVES, SEALANTS AND
COATINGS.** see *PAINTS AND PROTECTIVE
COATINGS—Abstracting, Bibliographies, Statistics*

RAPRA ABSTRACTS - CD-ROM. see *RUBBER—Abstracting,
Bibliographies, Statistics*

RAPRA ABSTRACTS. PLASTICS MATERIALS. see
PLASTICS—Abstracting, Bibliographies, Statistics

RAPRA ABSTRACTS. POLYURETHANES. see *PAINTS AND
PROTECTIVE COATINGS—Abstracting, Bibliographies,
Statistics*

RAPRA ABSTRACTS. RUBBER MATERIALS. see
RUBBER—Abstracting, Bibliographies, Statistics

RARE EARTH BULLETIN. see *METALLURGY—Abstracting,
Bibliographies, Statistics*

RASSEGNA MENSILE DI ISRAEL. see *RELIGIONS AND
THEOLOGY—Abstracting, Bibliographies, Statistics*

RAT FUER FORMGEBUNG. LITERATURHINWEISE. see
*TECHNOLOGY: COMPREHENSIVE WORKS—Abstracting,
Bibliographies, Statistics*

REACTION CITATION INDEX. see *CHEMISTRY—Abstracting,
Bibliographies, Statistics*

REACTIONS WEEKLY; rapid alerts to adverse drug experience.
see *PHARMACY AND PHARMACOLOGY—Abstracting,
Bibliographies, Statistics*

016.05   USA
**READERS' GUIDE ABSTRACTS - FULL TEXT (ONLINE
EDITION).** Text in English. 1994. d. USD 3,210 in US &
Canada (effective 2006); price varies. **Document type:**
Abstract/Index. **Description:** Contains full-text articles,
abstracts and indexing for general interest publications.
Media: Online - full text. **Related titles:** CD-ROM ed.: Readers'
Guide Abstracts - Full Text (Mini Edition). CD-ROM DOS
Version). ISSN 1082-3565; Readers' Guide Abstracts - Full
Text (Mega Edition. CD-ROM DOS Version). ISSN 1091-885X;
Readers' Guide Abstracts - Full Text (CD-ROM Windows
Version). ISSN 1093-7811.
Published by: H.W. Wilson Co., 950 University Ave, Bronx, NY
10452-4224. TEL 718-588-8400, 800-367-6770, FAX
718-590-1617, 800-590-1617, custserv@hwwilson.com,
http://www.hwwilson.com/Databases/Readersg.htm.

016.05   USA   ISSN 0034-0464
AI3
READERS' GUIDE TO PERIODICAL LITERATURE. Text in
English. 1900. a. USD 365 in US & Canada (effective 2006).
Document type: Abstract/Index. **Description:** Author and
subject index to selected general interest periodicals of
reference value in libraries.
Related titles: CD-ROM ed.: (from H.W. Wilson, SilverPlatter
Information, Inc.); Magnetic Tape ed.; Online - full text ed.:
USD 1,670 in US & Canada (effective 2006); ♦ Abridged ed.:
Abridged Readers' Guide to Periodical Literature. ISSN
0001-334X.
Indexed: RASB.
—Linda Hall.
Published by: H.W. Wilson Co., 950 University Ave, Bronx, NY
10452-4224. TEL 718-588-8400, 800-367-6770, FAX
718-590-1617, 800-590-1617, custserv@hwwilson.com,
http://www.hwwilson.com/Databases/Readersg.htm. Ed.
Donald Cannon.

REDOC; recreatie en toerisme documentatie. see *LEISURE AND
RECREATION*

REFERATEBLATT ZUR RAUMENTWICKLUNG. see *HOUSING
AND URBAN PLANNING—Abstracting, Bibliographies,
Statistics*

**REFERATIVNYI SBORNIK. FIZIOLOGIYA I PATOLOGIYA
IMMUNNOI SISTEMY. NOVOSTI NAUKI I TEKHNIKI.** see
MEDICAL SCIENCES—Abstracting, Bibliographies, Statistics

**REFERATIVNYI SBORNIK. KLINICHESKAYA
ENDOKRINOLOGIYA. NOVOSTI NAUKI I TEKHNIKI.** see
MEDICAL SCIENCES—Abstracting, Bibliographies, Statistics

▼ **REFERATIVNYI SBORNIK. LUCHEVAYA DIAGNOSTIKA.
NOVOSTI NAUKI I TEKHNIKI.** see *MEDICAL
SCIENCES—Abstracting, Bibliographies, Statistics*

**REFERATIVNYI SBORNIK. MEDITSINA KATASTROF. SLUZHBA
MEDITSINY KATASTROF. NOVOSTI NAUKI I TEKHNIKI.** see
MEDICAL SCIENCES—Abstracting, Bibliographies, Statistics

**REFERATIVNYI SBORNIK. MEDITSINA TRUDA. NOVOSTI
NAUKI I TEKHNIKI.** see *MEDICAL SCIENCES—Abstracting,
Bibliographies, Statistics*

**REFERATIVNYI SBORNIK. PSIKHIATRIYA. NOVOSTI NAUKI I
TEKHNIKI.** see *MEDICAL SCIENCES—Abstracting,
Bibliographies, Statistics*

016   RUS
REFERATIVNYI ZHURNAL. Text in Russian. m. **Document type:**
Abstract/Index.
Media: Online - full text.
Published by: Vserossiiskii Institut Nauchnoi i Tekhnicheskoi
Informatsii (VINITI), Ul Usievicha 20, Moscow, 125190,
Russian Federation. TEL 7-095-1526441, FAX 7-095-9430060,
dir@viniti.ru, http://www.viniti.ru.

REFERATIVNYI ZHURNAL. AKUSTIKA. see *PHYSICS—
Abstracting, Bibliographies, Statistics*

**REFERATIVNYI ZHURNAL. ANALITICHESKAYA KHIMIYA.
OBORUDOVANIE LABORATORII.** see *CHEMISTRY—
Abstracting, Bibliographies, Statistics*

**REFERATIVNYI ZHURNAL. ANTROPOGENOVYI PERIOD.
GEOMORFOLOGIYA SUSHI I MORSKOGO DNA.** see
EARTH SCIENCES—Abstracting, Bibliographies, Statistics

REFERATIVNYI ZHURNAL. ASTRONOMIYA. see
ASTRONOMY—Abstracting, Bibliographies, Statistics

REFERATIVNYI ZHURNAL. ATOMNAYA ENERGETIKA. see
ENERGY—Nuclear Energy

REFERATIVNYI ZHURNAL. AVIASTROENIE. see
TRANSPORTATION—Abstracting, Bibliographies, Statistics

**REFERATIVNYI ZHURNAL. AVIATSIONNYE I RAKETNYE
DVIGATELI.** see *AERONAUTICS AND SPACE
FLIGHT—Abstracting, Bibliographies, Statistics*

REFERATIVNYI ZHURNAL. AVTOMATIKA I TELEMEKHANIKA.
see *COMPUTERS—Abstracting, Bibliographies, Statistics*

**REFERATIVNYI ZHURNAL. AVTOMATIKA I VYCHISLITEL'NAYA
TEKHNIKA.** see *COMPUTERS—Abstracting, Bibliographies,
Statistics*

**REFERATIVNYI ZHURNAL. AVTOMATIKA, TELEMEKHANIKA I
SVIAZ' NA ZHELEZNYKH DOROGAKH.** see
TRANSPORTATION—Abstracting, Bibliographies, Statistics

REFERATIVNYI ZHURNAL. AVTOMOBILESTROENIE. see
TRANSPORTATION—Abstracting, Bibliographies, Statistics

REFERATIVNYI ZHURNAL. AVTOMOBIL'NYE DOROGI. see
TRANSPORTATION—Abstracting, Bibliographies, Statistics

**REFERATIVNYI ZHURNAL. AVTOMOBIL'NYI I GORODSKOI
TRANSPORT.** see *TRANSPORTATION—Abstracting,
Bibliographies, Statistics*

REFERATIVNYI ZHURNAL. AVTOMOBIL'NYI TRANSPORT. see
TRANSPORTATION—Abstracting, Bibliographies, Statistics

REFERATIVNYI ZHURNAL. BIOFIZIKA. see *BIOLOGY—
Abstracting, Bibliographies, Statistics*

**REFERATIVNYI ZHURNAL. BIOGEOGRAFIYA. GEOGRAFIYA
POCHV.** see *BIOLOGY—Abstracting, Bibliographies, Statistics*

▼ **REFERATIVNYI ZHURNAL. BIOKHIMIYA.** see
BIOLOGY—Abstracting, Bibliographies, Statistics

REFERATIVNYI ZHURNAL. BIOLOGIYA. see
BIOLOGY—Abstracting, Bibliographies, Statistics

**REFERATIVNYI ZHURNAL. BIOLOGIYA. FIZIKO-
KHIMICHESKAYA BIOLOGIYA.** see *BIOLOGY—Abstracting,
Bibliographies, Statistics*

**REFERATIVNYI ZHURNAL. BIOLOGIYA. FIZIOLOGIYA I
MORFOLOGIYA CHELOVEKA I ZHIVOTNYKH.** see
BIOLOGY—Abstracting, Bibliographies, Statistics

**REFERATIVNYI ZHURNAL. BIOLOGIYA. GENETIKA:
TSITOLOGIYA.** see *BIOLOGY—Abstracting, Bibliographies,
Statistics*

**REFERATIVNYI ZHURNAL. BIOLOGIYA. OBSHCHIE
PROBLEMY BIOLOGII. RAZDEL -TOM.** see
BIOLOGY—Abstracting, Bibliographies, Statistics

**REFERATIVNYI ZHURNAL. BIOLOGIYA. OBSHCHIE
PROBLEMY BIOLOGII. VYPUSK RAZDELA -TOMA.** see
BIOLOGY—Abstracting, Bibliographies, Statistics

**REFERATIVNYI ZHURNAL. BIOLOGIYA
SEL'SKOKHOZYAISTVENNYKH ZHIVOTNYKH.** see
BIOLOGY—Abstracting, Bibliographies, Statistics

**REFERATIVNYI ZHURNAL. BIONIKA. BIOKIBERNETIKA.
BIOINZHENERIYA.** see *BIOLOGY—Abstracting,
Bibliographies, Statistics*

**REFERATIVNYI ZHURNAL. BIOORGANICHESKAYA KHIMIYA.
MAKROMOLEKULY.** see *CHEMISTRY—Abstracting,
Bibliographies, Statistics*

REFERATIVNYI ZHURNAL. BIOTEKHNOLOGIYA. see
BIOLOGY—Abstracting, Bibliographies, Statistics

REFERATIVNYI ZHURNAL. BOTANIKA. see *BIOLOGY—
Abstracting, Bibliographies, Statistics*

**REFERATIVNYI ZHURNAL. BOTANIKA. VODOROSLI, GRIBY,
LISHAINIKI.** see *BIOLOGY—Abstracting, Bibliographies,
Statistics*

REFERATIVNYI ZHURNAL. BOTANIKA. VYSSHIE RASTENIYA.
see *BIOLOGY—Abstracting, Bibliographies, Statistics*

**REFERATIVNYI ZHURNAL. DVIGATELI VNUTRENNEGO
SGORANIYA.** see *ENGINEERING—Abstracting,
Bibliographies, Statistics*

REFERATIVNYI ZHURNAL. EKOLOGIYA CHELOVEKA. see
*ENVIRONMENTAL STUDIES—Abstracting, Bibliographies,
Statistics*

**REFERATIVNYI ZHURNAL. EKONOMICHESKIE ASPEKTY
ORGANIZATSII I TEKHNIKI SISTEM UPRAVLENIYA.** see
*BUSINESS AND ECONOMICS—Abstracting, Bibliographies,
Statistics*

**REFERATIVNYI ZHURNAL. EKONOMIKA
AGROPROMYSHLENNOGO KOMPLEKSA.** see
AGRICULTURE—Abstracting, Bibliographies, Statistics

**REFERATIVNYI ZHURNAL. EKONOMIKA
NEPROIZVODSTVENNOI SFERY.** see *BUSINESS AND
ECONOMICS—Abstracting, Bibliographies, Statistics*

**REFERATIVNYI ZHURNAL. EKONOMIKA OTRASLEI
KHIMIKO-LESNOGO KOMPLEKSA.** see *BUSINESS AND
ECONOMICS—Abstracting, Bibliographies, Statistics*

**REFERATIVNYI ZHURNAL. EKONOMIKA OTRASLEI LEGKOI
PROMYSHLENNOSTI.** see *BUSINESS AND
ECONOMICS—Abstracting, Bibliographies, Statistics*

**REFERATIVNYI ZHURNAL. EKONOMIKA OTRASLEI
METALLURGICHESKOGO I MASHINOSTROITELNOGO
KOMPLEKSOV.** see *BUSINESS AND ECONOMICS—
Abstracting, Bibliographies, Statistics*

REFERATIVNYI ZHURNAL. EKONOMIKA OTRASLEI PISHCHEVOI PROMYSHLENNOSTI. see *BUSINESS AND ECONOMICS—Abstracting, Bibliographies, Statistics*

REFERATIVNYI ZHURNAL. EKONOMIKA OTRASLEI TOPLIVNO - ENERGETICHESKOGO KOMPLEKSA. see *BUSINESS AND ECONOMICS—Abstracting, Bibliographies, Statistics*

REFERATIVNYI ZHURNAL. EKONOMIKA PROMYSHLENNOSTI. see *BUSINESS AND ECONOMICS—Abstracting, Bibliographies, Statistics*

REFERATIVNYI ZHURNAL. EKONOMIKA STROITEL'STVA. see *BUSINESS AND ECONOMICS—Abstracting, Bibliographies, Statistics*

REFERATIVNYI ZHURNAL. EKONOMIKA TRANSPORTA, SVIAZI I TELEKOMMUNIKATSII. see *BUSINESS AND ECONOMICS—Abstracting, Bibliographies, Statistics*

REFERATIVNYI ZHURNAL. EKSPLUATATSIYA I REMONT SAMOLETOV I DRUGIKH LETATELNYKH APPARATOV. see *TRANSPORTATION—Abstracting, Bibliographies, Statistics*

REFERATIVNYI ZHURNAL. ELEKTRICHESKIE APPARATY. see *ENGINEERING—Abstracting, Bibliographies, Statistics*

REFERATIVNYI ZHURNAL. ELEKTRICHESKIE MASHINY I TRANSFORMATORY. see *ENGINEERING—Abstracting, Bibliographies, Statistics*

REFERATIVNYI ZHURNAL. ELEKTRICHESKIE STANTSII I SETI. see *ENERGY—Abstracting, Bibliographies, Statistics*

REFERATIVNYI ZHURNAL. ELEKTRIFIKATSIYA BYTA. see *ENGINEERING—Abstracting, Bibliographies, Statistics*

REFERATIVNYI ZHURNAL. ELEKTROAKUSTIKA. ZAPIS' I VOSPROIZVEDENIE SIGNALOV. see *ELECTRONICS— Abstracting, Bibliographies, Statistics*

REFERATIVNYI ZHURNAL. ELEKTRONIKA. see *ELECTRONICS—Abstracting, Bibliographies, Statistics*

REFERATIVNYI ZHURNAL. ELEKTROOBORUDOVANIE TRANSPORTA. see *ENGINEERING—Abstracting, Bibliographies, Statistics*

REFERATIVNYI ZHURNAL. ELEKTROPRIVOD I AVTOMATIZATSIYA PROMYSHLENNYKH USTANOVOK. see *ENGINEERING—Abstracting, Bibliographies, Statistics*

REFERATIVNYI ZHURNAL. ELEKTROTEKHNICHESKIE MATERIALY, ELEKTRICHESKIE KONDENSATORY, PROVODA I KABELI. see *ENGINEERING—Abstracting, Bibliographies, Statistics*

REFERATIVNYI ZHURNAL. ELEKTROTEKHNIKA. see *ELECTRONICS*

REFERATIVNYI ZHURNAL. ELEKTROTEKHNOLOGIYA. see *ENGINEERING—Abstracting, Bibliographies, Statistics*

REFERATIVNYI ZHURNAL. ELEKTROVAKUMNYE I GAZORAZRYADNYE PRIBORY I USTROISTVA. see *ELECTRONICS—Abstracting, Bibliographies, Statistics*

REFERATIVNYI ZHURNAL. ENERGETICHESKIE SISTEMY I IKH AVTOMATIZATSIYA. see *ENERGY—Abstracting, Bibliographies, Statistics*

REFERATIVNYI ZHURNAL. ENERGETIKA. see *ENERGY—Abstracting, Bibliographies, Statistics*

REFERATIVNYI ZHURNAL. ENTOMOLOGIYA. see *BIOLOGY—Abstracting, Bibliographies, Statistics*

REFERATIVNYI ZHURNAL. FARMAKOLOGIYA EFFEKTORNYKH SISTEM. KHIMIOTERAPEVTICHESKIE SREDSTVA. see *PHARMACY AND PHARMACOLOGY— Abstracting, Bibliographies, Statistics*

REFERATIVNYI ZHURNAL. FARMAKOLOGIYA OBSHCHAYA. FARMAKOLOGIYA NERVNOI SISTEMY. see *PHARMACY AND PHARMACOLOGY—Abstracting, Bibliographies, Statistics*

REFERATIVNYI ZHURNAL. FARMAKOLOGIYA: TOKSIKOLOGIYA. see *PHARMACY AND PHARMACOLOGY—Abstracting, Bibliographies, Statistics*

REFERATIVNYI ZHURNAL. FITOPATOLOGIYA. see *BIOLOGY—Abstracting, Bibliographies, Statistics*

REFERATIVNYI ZHURNAL. FIZICHESKAYA KHIMIYA: KHIMICHESKAYA TERMODINAMIKA, FIZIKOKHIMICHESKII ANALIZ, RASTVORY, ELEKTROKHIMIYA. see *CHEMISTRY—Abstracting, Bibliographies, Statistics*

REFERATIVNYI ZHURNAL. FIZICHESKAYA KHIMIYA: KINETIKA, KATALIZ, FOTOKHIMIYA, RADYATSIONNAYA KHIMIYA, PLAZMOKHIMIYA. see *CHEMISTRY—Abstracting, Bibliographies, Statistics*

REFERATIVNYI ZHURNAL. FIZICHESKAYA KHIMIYA: KRISTALLOKHIMIYA, KHIMIYA TVERDOGO TELA, GAZY, ZHIDKOSTI, AMORFNYE TELA, POVERKHNOSTNYE YAVLENIYA, KHIMIYA KOLLOIDOV. see *CHEMISTRY— Abstracting, Bibliographies, Statistics*

REFERATIVNYI ZHURNAL. FIZIKA. see *PHYSICS—Abstracting, Bibliographies, Statistics*

REFERATIVNYI ZHURNAL. FIZIKA ATOMA I MOLEKULY. see *PHYSICS—Abstracting, Bibliographies, Statistics*

REFERATIVNYI ZHURNAL. FIZIKA ELEMENTARNYKH CHASTITS I TEORIYA POLEI. see *PHYSICS—Abstracting, Bibliographies, Statistics*

REFERATIVNYI ZHURNAL. FIZIKA GAZOV I ZHIDKOSTEI: TERMODINAMIKA I STATISTICHESKAYA FIZIKA. see *PHYSICS—Abstracting, Bibliographies, Statistics*

REFERATIVNYI ZHURNAL. FIZIKA PLAZMY. see *PHYSICS—Abstracting, Bibliographies, Statistics*

REFERATIVNYI ZHURNAL. FIZIKA TVERDYKH TEL: ELEKTRICHESKIE SVOISTVA. see *PHYSICS—Abstracting, Bibliographies, Statistics*

REFERATIVNYI ZHURNAL. FIZIKA TVERDYKH TEL: MAGNITNYE SVOISTVA. see *PHYSICS—Abstracting, Bibliographies, Statistics*

REFERATIVNYI ZHURNAL. FIZIKA TVERDYKH TEL: STRUKTURA I DINAMIKA RESHETKI. see *PHYSICS—Abstracting, Bibliographies, Statistics*

REFERATIVNYI ZHURNAL. FIZIKA ZEMLI. see *EARTH SCIENCES—Abstracting, Bibliographies, Statistics*

REFERATIVNYI ZHURNAL. FIZIOLOGIYA CHELOVEKA I ZHIVOTNYKH. ENDOKRINNAYA SISTEMA, RAZMNOZHENIE, LAKTATSIYA. see *BIOLOGY—Abstracting, Bibliographies, Statistics*

REFERATIVNYI ZHURNAL. FIZIOLOGIYA CHELOVEKA I ZHIVOTNYKH. KROV', LIMFA, KROVOOBRASHCHENIE, DYKHANIE, POCHKI. see *BIOLOGY—Abstracting, Bibliographies, Statistics*

REFERATIVNYI ZHURNAL. FIZIOLOGIYA CHELOVEKA I ZHIVOTNYKH. NEIROFIZIOLOGIYA, SENSORNYE SISTEMY, V N D, NERVNO-MYSHECHNAYA SISTEMA. see *BIOLOGY—Abstracting, Bibliographies, Statistics*

REFERATIVNYI ZHURNAL. FIZIOLOGIYA CHELOVEKA I ZHIVOTNYKH. OBMEN VESHCHESTV, PITANIE, PISHCHEVARENIE. see *BIOLOGY—Abstracting, Bibliographies, Statistics*

REFERATIVNYI ZHURNAL. FIZIOLOGIYA CHELOVEKA I ZHIVOTNYKH. OBSHCHIE PROBLEMY, VOZRASTNAYA FIZIOLOGIYA. see *BIOLOGY—Abstracting, Bibliographies, Statistics*

REFERATIVNYI ZHURNAL. FIZIOLOGIYA I BIOKHIMIYA RASTENII. see *BIOLOGY—Abstracting, Bibliographies, Statistics*

REFERATIVNYI ZHURNAL. GENERATORY PRYAMOGO PREOBRAZOVANIYA TEPLOVOI I KHIMICHESKOI ENERGII V ELEKTRICHESKUYU. see *ENERGY—Abstracting, Bibliographies, Statistics*

REFERATIVNYI ZHURNAL. GENETIKA CHELOVEKA. see *BIOLOGY—Abstracting, Bibliographies, Statistics*

REFERATIVNYI ZHURNAL. GENETIKA I SELEKTSIYA MIKROORGANIZMOV. see *BIOLOGY—Abstracting, Bibliographies, Statistics*

REFERATIVNYI ZHURNAL. GENETIKA I SELEKTSIYA SEL'SKOKHOZYAISTVENNYKH ZHIVOTNYKH. see *BIOLOGY—Abstracting, Bibliographies, Statistics*

REFERATIVNYI ZHURNAL. GENETIKA I SELEKTSIYA VOZDELYVAEMYKH RASTENII. see *BIOLOGY—Abstracting, Bibliographies, Statistics*

REFERATIVNYI ZHURNAL. GEODEZIYA I AEROS'EMKA. see *EARTH SCIENCES—Abstracting, Bibliographies, Statistics*

REFERATIVNYI ZHURNAL. GEOFIZIKA. see *EARTH SCIENCES—Abstracting, Bibliographies, Statistics*

REFERATIVNYI ZHURNAL. GEOGRAFIYA. see *GEOGRAPHY—Abstracting, Bibliographies, Statistics*

REFERATIVNYI ZHURNAL. GEOGRAFIYA AMERIKI, AVSTRALII, OKEANII I ANTARKTIKI. see *GEOGRAPHY—Abstracting, Bibliographies, Statistics*

REFERATIVNYI ZHURNAL. GEOGRAFIYA STRAN NA TERRITORII BYVSHEGO S S S R. see *GEOGRAPHY— Abstracting, Bibliographies, Statistics*

REFERATIVNYI ZHURNAL. GEOGRAFIYA ZARUBEZHNOI AZII I AFRIKI. see *GEOGRAPHY—Abstracting, Bibliographies, Statistics*

REFERATIVNYI ZHURNAL. GEOGRAFIYA ZARUBEZHNOI EVROPY. see *GEOGRAPHY—Abstracting, Bibliographies, Statistics*

REFERATIVNYI ZHURNAL. GEOKHIMIYA, MINERALOGIYA, PETROGRAFIYA. see *EARTH SCIENCES—Abstracting, Bibliographies, Statistics*

REFERATIVNYI ZHURNAL. GEOLOGICHESKIE I GEOKHIMICHESKIE METODY POISKOV POLEZNYKH ISKOPAEMYKH. see *EARTH SCIENCES—Abstracting, Bibliographies, Statistics*

REFERATIVNYI ZHURNAL. GEOLOGIYA. see *EARTH SCIENCES—Abstracting, Bibliographies, Statistics*

REFERATIVNYI ZHURNAL. GEOMAGNETIZM I VYSOKIE SLOI ATMOSFERY. see *EARTH SCIENCES—Abstracting, Bibliographies, Statistics*

REFERATIVNYI ZHURNAL. GIDROENERGETIKA. see *ENERGY—Abstracting, Bibliographies, Statistics*

REFERATIVNYI ZHURNAL. GIDROGEOLOGIYA, INZHENERNAYA GEOLOGIYA, MERZLOTOVEDENIE. see *EARTH SCIENCES—Abstracting, Bibliographies, Statistics*

REFERATIVNYI ZHURNAL. GORNOE DELO. see *MINES AND MINING INDUSTRY—Abstracting, Bibliographies, Statistics*

REFERATIVNYI ZHURNAL. GORNOE I NEFTEPROMYSLOVOE MASHINOSTROENIE. see *MINES AND MINING INDUSTRY—Abstracting, Bibliographies, Statistics*

REFERATIVNYI ZHURNAL. GORODSKOI TRANSPORT. see *TRANSPORTATION—Abstracting, Bibliographies, Statistics*

REFERATIVNYI ZHURNAL. IKHTIOLOGIYA. see *BIOLOGY—Abstracting, Bibliographies, Statistics*

REFERATIVNYI ZHURNAL. IMMUNOLOGIYA. ALLERGOLOGIYA. see *MEDICAL SCIENCES—Abstracting, Bibliographies, Statistics*

REFERATIVNYI ZHURNAL. INFORMATIKA. see *LIBRARY AND INFORMATION SCIENCES—Abstracting, Bibliographies, Statistics*

REFERATIVNYI ZHURNAL. ISKUSSTVENNYE SOORUZHENIYA NA AVTOMOBIL'NYKH DOROGAKH. see *TRANSPORTATION—Abstracting, Bibliographies, Statistics*

REFERATIVNYI ZHURNAL. ISSLEDOVANIE KOSMICHESKOGO PROSTRANSTVA. see *AERONAUTICS AND SPACE FLIGHT—Abstracting, Bibliographies, Statistics*

REFERATIVNYI ZHURNAL. ISSLEDOVANIE ZEMLI IZ KOSMOSA. see *ASTRONOMY—Abstracting, Bibliographies, Statistics*

REFERATIVNYI ZHURNAL. IZDATEL'SKOE DELO I POLIGRAFIYA. see *PRINTING—Abstracting, Bibliographies, Statistics*

REFERATIVNYI ZHURNAL. KADRY, EKONOMIKA OBRAZOVANIYA. see *BUSINESS AND ECONOMICS— Abstracting, Bibliographies, Statistics*

REFERATIVNYI ZHURNAL. KARTOGRAFIYA. see *GEOGRAPHY—Abstracting, Bibliographies, Statistics*

REFERATIVNYI ZHURNAL. KHIMICHESKOE, NEFTEPERERABATYVAYUSCHCHEE I POLIMERNOE MASHINOSTROENIE. see *ENGINEERING—Abstracting, Bibliographies, Statistics*

REFERATIVNYI ZHURNAL. KHIMIYA. see *CHEMISTRY— Abstracting, Bibliographies, Statistics*

REFERATIVNYI ZHURNAL. KHIMIYA I PERERABOTKA GORYUCHIKH ISKOPAEMYKH I PRIRODNYKH GAZOV. see *CHEMISTRY—Abstracting, Bibliographies, Statistics*

A

REFERATIVNYI ZHURNAL. KHIMIYA I TEKHNOLOGIYA PISHCHEVYKH PRODUKTOV. see *CHEMISTRY— Abstracting, Bibliographies, Statistics*

REFERATIVNYI ZHURNAL. KHIMIYA VYSOKOMOLEKULIARNYKH SOEDINENII. see *CHEMISTRY—Abstracting, Bibliographies, Statistics*

REFERATIVNYI ZHURNAL. KLINICHESKAYA FARMAKOLOGIYA. see *PHARMACY AND PHARMACOLOGY—Abstracting, Bibliographies, Statistics*

REFERATIVNYI ZHURNAL. KLINICHESKAYA IMMUNOLOGIYA I ALLERGOLOGIYA. IMMUNOREABILITATSIYA. IMMUNOFARMAKOLOGIYA. see *MEDICAL SCIENCES—Abstracting, Bibliographies, Statistics*

REFERATIVNYI ZHURNAL. KOMMUNAL'NOE, BYTOVOE I TORGOVOE OBORUDOVANIE. see *MACHINERY— Abstracting, Bibliographies, Statistics*

REFERATIVNYI ZHURNAL. KOMPLEKSNYE I SPETSYALNYE RAZDELY MEKHANIKI. see *PHYSICS—Abstracting, Bibliographies, Statistics*

REFERATIVNYI ZHURNAL. KORROZIYA I ZASHCHITA OT KORROZII. see *METALLURGY—Abstracting, Bibliographies, Statistics*

REFERATIVNYI ZHURNAL. KOTELNYE USTANOVKI I VODOPODGOTOVKA. see *ENERGY—Abstracting, Bibliographies, Statistics*

REFERATIVNYI ZHURNAL. KVANTOVAYA ELEKTRONIKA. KRIOELEKTRONIKA. GOLOGRAFIYA. see *PHYSICS—Abstracting, Bibliographies, Statistics*

REFERATIVNYI ZHURNAL. LEGKAYA PROMYSHLENNOST'. TEKHNOLOGIYA I OBORUDOVANIYE. see *BUSINESS AND ECONOMICS—Abstracting, Bibliographies, Statistics*

REFERATIVNYI ZHURNAL. LEKARTSVENNYE RASTENIYA. see *BIOLOGY—Abstracting, Bibliographies, Statistics*

REFERATIVNYI ZHURNAL. LESOVEDENIE I LESOVODSTVO. see *FORESTS AND FORESTRY—Abstracting, Bibliographies, Statistics*

REFERATIVNYI ZHURNAL. LOKOMOTIVOSTROENIE I VAGONOSTROENIE. see *TRANSPORTATION—Abstracting, Bibliographies, Statistics*

REFERATIVNYI ZHURNAL. MASHINOSTROITEL'NYE MATERIALY, KONSTRUKTSII I RASCHET DETALEI MASHIN. GIDROPRIVOD. see *ENGINEERING—Abstracting, Bibliographies, Statistics*

REFERATIVNYI ZHURNAL. MASHINY I OBORUDOVANIE DLYA TEKSTIL'NOI PROMYSHLENNOSTI. see *TEXTILE INDUSTRIES AND FABRICS—Abstracting, Bibliographies, Statistics*

REFERATIVNYI ZHURNAL. MATEMATICHESKII ANALIZ. see *MATHEMATICS—Abstracting, Bibliographies, Statistics*

REFERATIVNYI ZHURNAL. MATEMATIKA. see *MATHEMATICS—Abstracting, Bibliographies, Statistics*

REFERATIVNYI ZHURNAL. MATERIALY DLYA ELEKTRONIKI. see *ELECTRONICS—Abstracting, Bibliographies, Statistics*

REFERATIVNYI ZHURNAL. MEDITSINA. see *MEDICAL SCIENCES—Abstracting, Bibliographies, Statistics*

REFERATIVNYI ZHURNAL. MEDITSINSKAYA GEOGRAFIYA. see *MEDICAL SCIENCES—Abstracting, Bibliographies, Statistics*

REFERATIVNYI ZHURNAL. MEKHANIKA. see *ENGINEERING—Abstracting, Bibliographies, Statistics*

REFERATIVNYI ZHURNAL. MEKHANIKA DEFORMIRUEMOGO TVERDOGO TELA. see *PHYSICS—Abstracting, Bibliographies, Statistics*

REFERATIVNYI ZHURNAL. MEKHANIKA ZHIDKOSTI I GAZA. see *PHYSICS—Abstracting, Bibliographies, Statistics*

REFERATIVNYI ZHURNAL. MESTOROZHDENIYA GORYUCHIKH POLEZNYKH ISKOPAEMYKH. see *MINES AND MINING INDUSTRY—Abstracting, Bibliographies, Statistics*

REFERATIVNYI ZHURNAL. METALLOVEDENIE I TERMICHESKAYA OBRABOTKA. see *METALLURGY— Abstracting, Bibliographies, Statistics*

REFERATIVNYI ZHURNAL. METALLURGICHESKAYA TEPLOTEKHNIKA. OBORUDOVANIE IZMERENIYA KONTROL I AVTOMATIZATSIYA V METALLURGICHESKOM PROIZVODSTVE. see *METALLURGY—Abstracting, Bibliographies, Statistics*

REFERATIVNYI ZHURNAL. METALLURGIYA. see *METALLURGY—Abstracting, Bibliographies, Statistics*

REFERATIVNYI ZHURNAL. METALLURGIYA TSVETNYKH METALLOV. see *METALLURGY—Abstracting, Bibliographies, Statistics*

REFERATIVNYI ZHURNAL. METEOROLOGIYA I KLIMATOLOGIYA. see *METEOROLOGY—Abstracting, Bibliographies, Statistics*

REFERATIVNYI ZHURNAL. METODY UPRAVLENIYA EKONOMIKOI. see *BUSINESS AND ECONOMICS— Abstracting, Bibliographies, Statistics*

REFERATIVNYI ZHURNAL. METROLOGIYA I IZMERITEL'NAYA TEKHNIKA. see *METROLOGY AND STANDARDIZATION— Abstracting, Bibliographies, Statistics*

REFERATIVNYI ZHURNAL. MIKROBIOLOGIYA OBSHCHAYA. see *BIOLOGY—Abstracting, Bibliographies, Statistics*

REFERATIVNYI ZHURNAL. MIKROBIOLOGIYA PRIKLADNAYA. see *BIOLOGY—Abstracting, Bibliographies, Statistics*

REFERATIVNYI ZHURNAL. MIKROBIOLOGIYA SANITARNAYA I MEDITSINSKAYA. see *BIOLOGY—Abstracting, Bibliographies, Statistics*

REFERATIVNYI ZHURNAL. MIROVAYA EKONOMIKA. SOTSYAL'NO-EKONOMICHESKOE RAZVITIE STRAN MIRA. see *BUSINESS AND ECONOMICS—Abstracting, Bibliographies, Statistics*

REFERATIVNYI ZHURNAL. MOLEKULYARNAYA BIOLOGIYA. see *BIOLOGY—Abstracting, Bibliographies, Statistics*

REFERATIVNYI ZHURNAL. MOLEKULYARNAYA I KLETOCHNAYA IMMUNOLOGIYA. see *MEDICAL SCIENCES—Abstracting, Bibliographies, Statistics*

REFERATIVNYI ZHURNAL. MORFOLOGIYA CHELOVEKA I ZHIVOTNYKH. ANTROPOLOGIYA. see *ANTHROPOLOGY— Abstracting, Bibliographies, Statistics*

REFERATIVNYI ZHURNAL. NARKOLOGICHESKAYA TOKSIKOLOGIYA. see *DRUG ABUSE AND ALCOHOLISM—Abstracting, Bibliographies, Statistics*

REFERATIVNYI ZHURNAL. NASOSOSTROENIE I KOMPRESSOROSTROENIE. KHOLODIL'NOE MASHINOSTROENIE. see *HEATING, PLUMBING AND REFRIGERATION—Abstracting, Bibliographies, Statistics*

REFERATIVNYI ZHURNAL. NAUCHNO-TEKHNICHESKII PROGRESS. INTEGRATSIYA NAUKI S PROIZVODSTVOM. ORGANIZATSIYA I FINANSIROVANIE. see *TECHNOLOGY: COMPREHENSIVE WORKS—Abstracting, Bibliographies, Statistics*

REFERATIVNYI ZHURNAL. NEMETALLICHESKIE POLEZNYE ISKOPAEMYE. see *EARTH SCIENCES—Abstracting, Bibliographies, Statistics*

REFERATIVNYI ZHURNAL. NEORGANICHESKAYA KHIMIYA. KOMPLEKSNYE SOEDINENIYA. RADIOKHIMIYA. see *CHEMISTRY—Abstracting, Bibliographies, Statistics*

REFERATIVNYI ZHURNAL. NETRADITSIONNYE I VOZOBNOVLYAEMYE ISTOCHNIKI ENERGII. see *ENERGY—Abstracting, Bibliographies, Statistics*

REFERATIVNYI ZHURNAL. OBOGASHCHENIE POLEZNYKH ISKOPAEMYKH. see *MINES AND MINING INDUSTRY—Abstracting, Bibliographies, Statistics*

REFERATIVNYI ZHURNAL. OBORUDOVANIE PISHCHEVOI PROMYSHLENNOSTI. see *MACHINERY—Abstracting, Bibliographies, Statistics*

REFERATIVNYI ZHURNAL. OBSHCHAYA EKOLOGIYA. BIOTSENOLOGIYA. GIDROBIOLOGIYA. see *BIOLOGY—Abstracting, Bibliographies, Statistics*

REFERATIVNYI ZHURNAL. OBSHCHAYA GENETIKA. see *BIOLOGY—Abstracting, Bibliographies, Statistics*

REFERATIVNYI ZHURNAL. OBSHCHAYA GEOLOGIYA. see *EARTH SCIENCES—Abstracting, Bibliographies, Statistics*

REFERATIVNYI ZHURNAL. OBSHCHEOTRASLEVYE VOPROSY SOVERSHENSTVOVANIYA KHOZYAISTVENNOGO MEKHANIZMA. see *BUSINESS AND ECONOMICS—Abstracting, Bibliographies, Statistics*

REFERATIVNYI ZHURNAL. OBSHCHIE VOPROSY ENERGETIKI. ENERGETICHESKII BALANS. TOPLIVO. see *ENERGY—Abstracting, Bibliographies, Statistics*

REFERATIVNYI ZHURNAL. OBSHCHIE VOPROSY FIZIKI I FIZICHESKOGO EKSPERIMENTA. see *PHYSICS— Abstracting, Bibliographies, Statistics*

REFERATIVNYI ZHURNAL. OBSHCHIE VOPROSY KHIMICHESKOI TEKHNOLOGII. see *CHEMISTRY— Abstracting, Bibliographies, Statistics*

REFERATIVNYI ZHURNAL. OBSHCHIE VOPROSY KHIMII. FIZICHESKAYA KHIMIYA. STROENIE MOLEKUL. see *CHEMISTRY—Abstracting, Bibliographies, Statistics*

REFERATIVNYI ZHURNAL. OBSHCHIE VOPROSY MATEMATIKI. MATEMATICHESKAYA LOGIKA, TEORIYA CHISEL, ALGEBRA, TOPOLOGIYA, GEOMETRIYA. see *MATHEMATICS—Abstracting, Bibliographies, Statistics*

REFERATIVNYI ZHURNAL. OBSHCHIE VOPROSY MEKHANIKI. OBSHCHAYA MEKHANIKA. see *PHYSICS—Abstracting, Bibliographies, Statistics*

REFERATIVNYI ZHURNAL. OBSHCHIE VOPROSY PATOLOGICHESKOI ANATOMII. see *BIOLOGY—Abstracting, Bibliographies, Statistics*

REFERATIVNYI ZHURNAL. OKEANOLOGIYA. GIDROLOGIYA SUSHI. GLYATSIOLOGIYA. see *EARTH SCIENCES— Abstracting, Bibliographies, Statistics*

REFERATIVNYI ZHURNAL. OKHRANA I ULUCHSHENIE GORODSKOI SREDY. see *ENVIRONMENTAL STUDIES—Abstracting, Bibliographies, Statistics*

REFERATIVNYI ZHURNAL. OKHRANA PRIRODY I VOSPROIZVODSTVO PRIRODNYKH RESURSOV. see *ENVIRONMENTAL STUDIES—Abstracting, Bibliographies, Statistics*

REFERATIVNYI ZHURNAL. ONKOLOGIYA. see *MEDICAL SCIENCES—Abstracting, Bibliographies, Statistics*

REFERATIVNYI ZHURNAL. ONKOLOGIYA EKSPERIMENTAL'NAYA. see *MEDICAL SCIENCES— Abstracting, Bibliographies, Statistics*

REFERATIVNYI ZHURNAL. ONKOLOGIYA KLINICHESKAYA. see *MEDICAL SCIENCES—Abstracting, Bibliographies, Statistics*

REFERATIVNYI ZHURNAL. ONKOLOGIYA: TERAPIYA OPUKHOLEI. see *MEDICAL SCIENCES—Abstracting, Bibliographies, Statistics*

REFERATIVNYI ZHURNAL. OPTIKA I YADERNAYA FIZIKA. see *PHYSICS—Abstracting, Bibliographies, Statistics*

REFERATIVNYI ZHURNAL. ORGANICHESKAYA KHIMIYA. see *CHEMISTRY—Abstracting, Bibliographies, Statistics*

REFERATIVNYI ZHURNAL. ORGANIZATSIYA I BEZOPASNOST' DOROZHNOGO DVIZHENIYA. see *TRANSPORTATION— Abstracting, Bibliographies, Statistics*

REFERATIVNYI ZHURNAL. ORGANIZATSIYA UPRAVLENIYA. see *BUSINESS AND ECONOMICS—Abstracting, Bibliographies, Statistics*

REFERATIVNYI ZHURNAL. POCHVOVEDENIE I AGROKHIMIYA. see *AGRICULTURE—Abstracting, Bibliographies, Statistics*

REFERATIVNYI ZHURNAL. POD'EMNO-TRANSPORTNOE MASHINOSTROENIE. see *ENGINEERING—Abstracting, Bibliographies, Statistics*

REFERATIVNYI ZHURNAL. POLUPROVODNIKOVYE PRIBORY. see *ELECTRONICS—Abstracting, Bibliographies, Statistics*

REFERATIVNYI ZHURNAL. POROSHKOVAYA METALLURGIYA. POKRYTIYA I PLENKI, POLUCHAEMYE FIZIKO-METALLURGICHESKIMI METODAMI. see *METALLURGY—Abstracting, Bibliographies, Statistics*

REFERATIVNYI ZHURNAL. POZHARNAYA BEZOPASNOST'. VYPUSK SVODNOGO TOMA. see *FIRE PREVENTION— Abstracting, Bibliographies, Statistics*

REFERATIVNYI ZHURNAL. POZHARNAYA OKHRANA. SVODNYI TOM. see *FIRE PREVENTION—Abstracting, Bibliographies, Statistics*

016.36337   RUS   ISSN 0202-991X
**REFERATIVNYI ZHURNAL. POZHARNAYA OKHRANA. VYPUSK
SVODNOGO TOMA.** Text in Russian. 1972. m. USD 137
foreign (effective 2006). **Document type:** *Journal,
Abstract/Index.*
Related titles: CD-ROM ed.; Online - full text ed.
Published by: Vserossiiskii Institut Nauchnoi i Tekhnicheskoi
Informatsii (VINITI), Ul Usievicha 20, Moscow, 125190,
Russian Federation. TEL 7-095-1526441, FAX 7-095-9430060,
dir@viniti.ru, http://www.viniti.ru. Dist. by: Informnauka Ltd., Ul
Usievicha 20, Moscow 125190, Russian Federation.
alfimov@viniti.ru.

**REFERATIVNYI ZHURNAL. PRIMENENIE MATEMATICHESKIKH
METODOV V EKONOMICHESKIKH ISSLEDOVANIYAKH I
PLANIROVANII.** see *BUSINESS AND ECONOMICS—
Abstracting, Bibliographies, Statistics*

**REFERATIVNYI ZHURNAL. PRIRODNYE ORGANICHESKIE
SOEDINENIYA I IKH SINTETICHESKIE ANALOGI.** see
CHEMISTRY—Abstracting, Bibliographies, Statistics

**REFERATIVNYI ZHURNAL. PROBLEMY
FUNKTSIONIROVANIYA RYNOCHNOGO KHOZIAISTVA.** see
*BUSINESS AND ECONOMICS—Abstracting, Bibliographies,
Statistics*

**REFERATIVNYI ZHURNAL. PROCHNOST' KONSTRUKTSII I
MATERYALOV.** see *BUILDING AND CONSTRUCTION—
Abstracting, Bibliographies, Statistics*

**REFERATIVNYI ZHURNAL. PROEKTIROVANIE,
KONSTRUIROVANIE, TEKHNOLOGIYA I OBORUDOVANIE
DLYA RADIOTEKHNICHESKOGO PROIZVODSTVA.** see
ELECTRONICS—Abstracting, Bibliographies, Statistics

REFERATIVNYI ZHURNAL. PROGRAMMNOE OBESPECHENIE.
see *COMPUTERS—Abstracting, Bibliographies, Statistics*

**REFERATIVNYI ZHURNAL. PROIZVODSTVO CHUGUNA I
STALI.** see *METALLURGY—Abstracting, Bibliographies,
Statistics*

**REFERATIVNYI ZHURNAL. PROKATNOYE I VOLOCHIL'NOYE
PROIZVODSTVO.** see *METALLURGY—Abstracting,
Bibliographies, Statistics*

REFERATIVNYI ZHURNAL. PROMYSHLENNYI TRANSPORT.
see *TRANSPORTATION—Abstracting, Bibliographies,
Statistics*

REFERATIVNYI ZHURNAL. PSIKHOLOGIYA. see
PSYCHOLOGY—Abstracting, Bibliographies, Statistics

REFERATIVNYI ZHURNAL. RADIATSIONNAYA BIOLOGIYA. see
BIOLOGY—Abstracting, Bibliographies, Statistics

**REFERATIVNYI ZHURNAL. RADIOFIZIKA I FIZICHESKIE
OSNOVY ELEKTRONIKI.** see *PHYSICS—Abstracting,
Bibliographies, Statistics*

**REFERATIVNYI ZHURNAL. RADIOLOKATSIYA,
RADIONAVIGATSIYA, RADIOUPRAVLENIE,
TELEVIZIONNAYA TEKHNIKA.** see *ELECTRONICS—
Abstracting, Bibliographies, Statistics*

**REFERATIVNYI ZHURNAL. RADIOPEREDAYUSHCHIE I
RADIOPRIEMNYE USTROISTVA. RADIOTEKHNICHESKIE
IZMERENIYA.** see *ELECTRONICS—Abstracting,
Bibliographies, Statistics*

**REFERATIVNYI ZHURNAL. RADIOSVYAZ'.
RADIOVESHCHANIE. TELEVIDENIE.** see
COMMUNICATIONS—Abstracting, Bibliographies, Statistics

REFERATIVNYI ZHURNAL. RADIOTEKHNIKA. see
ELECTRONICS—Abstracting, Bibliographies, Statistics

**REFERATIVNYI ZHURNAL. RAKETOSTROENIE I
KOSMICHESKAYA TEKHNIKA.** see *AERONAUTICS AND
SPACE FLIGHT—Abstracting, Bibliographies, Statistics*

**REFERATIVNYI ZHURNAL. RASTENIEVODSTVO
(BIOLOGICHESKIE OSNOVY).** see *BIOLOGY—Abstracting,
Bibliographies, Statistics*

**REFERATIVNYI ZHURNAL. RAZRABOTKA MESTOROZHDENII
TVERDYKH POLEZNYKH ISKOPAEMYKH. OBSHCHIE
PROBLEMY, PROMYSHLENNOST, EKONOMIKA,
STROITELSTVO.** see *MINES AND MINING
INDUSTRY—Abstracting, Bibliographies, Statistics*

**REFERATIVNYI ZHURNAL. RAZRABOTKA MESTOROZHDENII
TVERDYKH POLEZNYKH ISKOPAEMYKH. OSNOVNYE
PROTSESSY.** see *MINES AND MINING INDUSTRY—
Abstracting, Bibliographies, Statistics*

**REFERATIVNYI ZHURNAL. RAZRABOTKA MESTOROZHDENII
TVERDYKH POLEZNYKH ISKOPAEMYKH.
VSPOMOGATELNYE PROTSESSY.** see *MINES AND MINING
INDUSTRY—Abstracting, Bibliographies, Statistics*

**REFERATIVNYI ZHURNAL. RAZRABOTKA NEFTYANYKH I
GAZOVYKH MESTOROZHDENII.** see *PETROLEUM AND
GAS—Abstracting, Bibliographies, Statistics*

**REFERATIVNYI ZHURNAL. REZANIE MATERYALOV. STANKI I
INSTRUMENTY.** see *MACHINERY—Abstracting,
Bibliographies, Statistics*

REFERATIVNYI ZHURNAL. RISK I BEZOPASNOST'. see
*PUBLIC HEALTH AND SAFETY—Abstracting, Bibliographies,
Statistics*

REFERATIVNYI ZHURNAL. ROBOTOTEKHNIKA. see
MACHINERY—Abstracting, Bibliographies, Statistics

REFERATIVNYI ZHURNAL. RUDNYE MESTOROZHDENIYA. see
MINES AND MINING INDUSTRY

REFERATIVNYI ZHURNAL. SETI I SISTEMY SVYAZI. see
COMMUNICATIONS—Abstracting, Bibliographies, Statistics

**REFERATIVNYI ZHURNAL. SILOVAYA
PREOBRAZOVATEL'NAYA TEKHNIKA.** see
ELECTRONICS—Abstracting, Bibliographies, Statistics

**REFERATIVNYI ZHURNAL. SISTEMY, PRIBORY I METODY
KONTROLYA KACHESTVA OKRUZHAYUSHCHEI SREDY.**
see *ENVIRONMENTAL STUDIES—Abstracting,
Bibliographies, Statistics*

**REFERATIVNYI ZHURNAL. STRATIGRAFIYA.
PALEONTOLOGIYA.** see *PALEONTOLOGY—Abstracting,
Bibliographies, Statistics*

**REFERATIVNYI ZHURNAL. STROITEL'NYE I DOROZHNYE
MASHINY.** see *ENGINEERING—Abstracting, Bibliographies,
Statistics*

**REFERATIVNYI ZHURNAL. STROITEL'STVO I
EKSPLUATATSIYA AVTOMOBIL'NYKH DOROG.** see
TRANSPORTATION—Abstracting, Bibliographies, Statistics

**REFERATIVNYI ZHURNAL. STROITELSTVO ZHELEZNYKH
DOROG. PUT' I PUTEVOE KHOZYAISTVO.** see
TRANSPORTATION—Abstracting, Bibliographies, Statistics

REFERATIVNYI ZHURNAL. SUDOSTROENIE. see
TRANSPORTATION—Abstracting, Bibliographies, Statistics

REFERATIVNYI ZHURNAL. SVARKA. see *METALLURGY—
Abstracting, Bibliographies, Statistics*

REFERATIVNYI ZHURNAL. SVERKHPROVODIMOST'. see
PHYSICS—Abstracting, Bibliographies, Statistics

**REFERATIVNYI ZHURNAL. SVETOTEKHNIKA I
INFRAKRASNAYA TEKHNIKA.** see *ENGINEERING—
Abstracting, Bibliographies, Statistics*

REFERATIVNYI ZHURNAL. SVYAZ'. see *COMMUNICATIONS—
Abstracting, Bibliographies, Statistics*

**REFERATIVNYI ZHURNAL. TEKHNICHESKAYA
EKSPLUATATSIYA PODVIZHNOGO SOSTAVA I TYAGA
POEZDOV.** see *TRANSPORTATION—Abstracting,
Bibliographies, Statistics*

REFERATIVNYI ZHURNAL. TEKHNICHESKAYA KIBERNETIKA.
see *COMPUTERS—Abstracting, Bibliographies, Statistics*

**REFERATIVNYI ZHURNAL. TEKHNICHESKII ANALIZ V
METALURGII.** see *METALLURGY—Abstracting,
Bibliographies, Statistics*

**REFERATIVNYI ZHURNAL. TEKHNIKA GEOLOGO-
RAZVEDOCHNYKH RABOT.** see *EARTH
SCIENCES—Abstracting, Bibliographies, Statistics*

**REFERATIVNYI ZHURNAL. TEKHNOLOGICHESKIE ASPEKTY
OKHRANY OKRUZHAYUSHCHEI SREDY.** see
*ENVIRONMENTAL STUDIES—Abstracting, Bibliographies,
Statistics*

**REFERATIVNYI ZHURNAL. TEKHNOLOGIYA I
OBORUDOVANIE KUZNECHNO-SHTAMPOVOCHNOGO
PROIZVODSTVA.** see *METALLURGY—Abstracting,
Bibliographies, Statistics*

**REFERATIVNYI ZHURNAL. TEKHNOLOGIYA I
OBORUDOVANIE LESOZAGOTOVITEL'NOGO,
DEREVOOBRABATYVAYUSHCHEGO I TSELLYULOZNO-
BUMAZHNOGO PROIZVODSTVA.** see *PAPER AND
PULP—Abstracting, Bibliographies, Statistics*

**REFERATIVNYI ZHURNAL. TEKHNOLOGIYA I
OBORUDOVANIE LITEINOGO PROIZVODSTVA.** see
METALLURGY—Abstracting, Bibliographies, Statistics

**REFERATIVNYI ZHURNAL. TEKHNOLOGIYA I
OBORUDOVANIE MEKHANOSBOROCHNOGO
PROIZVODSTVA.** see *MACHINERY—Abstracting,
Bibliographies, Statistics*

**REFERATIVNYI ZHURNAL. TEKHNOLOGIYA I ORGANIZATSIYA
PROIZVODSTVA TEKSTIL'NOI PROMYSHLENNOSTI.** see
*TEXTILE INDUSTRIES AND FABRICS—Abstracting,
Bibliographies, Statistics*

**REFERATIVNYI ZHURNAL. TEKHNOLOGIYA
MASHINOSTROENIYA.** see *ENGINEERING—Abstracting,
Bibliographies, Statistics*

**REFERATIVNYI ZHURNAL. TEKHNOLOGIYA
NEORGANICHESKIKH VESHCHESTV I MATERIALOV.** see
CHEMISTRY—Abstracting, Bibliographies, Statistics

**REFERATIVNYI ZHURNAL. TEKHNOLOGIYA
ORGANICHESKIKH LEKARSTVENNYKH VESHCHESTV,
VETERINARNYKH PREPARATOV I PESTITSIDOV.** see
CHEMISTRY—Abstracting, Bibliographies, Statistics

**REFERATIVNYI ZHURNAL. TEKHNOLOGIYA
ORGANICHESKIKH VESHCHESTV.** see *CHEMISTRY—
Abstracting, Bibliographies, Statistics*

**REFERATIVNYI ZHURNAL. TEKHNOLOGIYA POLIMERNYKH
MATERYALOV: PLASTMASSY, IONOOBMENNYE
MATERYALY.** see *CHEMISTRY—Abstracting, Bibliographies,
Statistics*

**REFERATIVNYI ZHURNAL. TEKHNOLOGIYA POLIMERNYKH
MATERYALOV: PRIRODNYE VYSOKOMOLEKULYARNYE
SOEDINENIYA. KHIMIYA I PERERABOTKA DREVESINY.
KHIMICHESKIE VOLOKNA. TEKSTIL'NYE MATERIALY.
BUMAGA. KOZHA. MEKH.** see *CHEMISTRY—Abstracting,
Bibliographies, Statistics*

**REFERATIVNYI ZHURNAL. TEKHNOLOGIYA POLIMERNYKH
MATERYALOV: REZINA, LAKOKRASOCHNYE MATERIALY
I ORGANICHESKIE POKRYTIYA. VSPOMOGATEL'NYE
MATERIALY DLIA PROIZVODSTVA POLIMEROV I IZDELII
IZ NIKH.** see *CHEMISTRY—Abstracting, Bibliographies,
Statistics*

**REFERATIVNYI ZHURNAL. TEKHNOLOGIYA PROIZVODSTVA
PRODUKTOV BYTOVOI KHIMII. PARFUMERIYA I
KOSMETIKA.** see *CHEMISTRY—Abstracting, Bibliographies,
Statistics*

**REFERATIVNYI ZHURNAL. TEKHNOLOGIYA SILIKATNYKH I
TUGOPLAVKIKH NEMETALLICHESKIKH MATERIALOV.** see
ENGINEERING—Abstracting, Bibliographies, Statistics

**REFERATIVNYI ZHURNAL. TEORETICHESKAYA
RADIOTEKHNIKA. ANTENNY. VOLNOVODY. OB'EMNYE
REZONATORY. RASPROSTRANENIE RADIOVOLN.** see
ELECTRONICS—Abstracting, Bibliographies, Statistics

**REFERATIVNYI ZHURNAL. TEORETICHESKIE I OBSHCHIE
VOPROSY GEOGRAFII.** see *GEOGRAPHY—Abstracting,
Bibliographies, Statistics*

**REFERATIVNYI ZHURNAL. TEORETICHESKIE OSNOVY
TEPLOTEKHNIKI. PROMYSHLENNAYA TEPLOTEKHNIKA.**
see *ENERGY—Abstracting, Bibliographies, Statistics*

**REFERATIVNYI ZHURNAL. TEORIYA METALLURGICHESKIKH
PROTSESSOV.** see *METALLURGY—Abstracting,
Bibliographies, Statistics*

**REFERATIVNYI ZHURNAL. TEORIYA VEROYATNOSTEI I
MATEMATICHESKAYA STATISTIKA.** see *MATHEMATICS—
Abstracting, Bibliographies, Statistics*

REFERATIVNYI ZHURNAL. TEPLOMASSOBMEN. see
ENERGY—Abstracting, Bibliographies, Statistics

**REFERATIVNYI ZHURNAL. TEPLOVYE ELEKTROSTANTSII.
TEPLOSNABZHENIE.** see *ENERGY—Abstracting,
Bibliographies, Statistics*

REFERATIVNYI ZHURNAL. TOKSIKOLOGIYA. see *PHARMACY
AND PHARMACOLOGY—Abstracting, Bibliographies,
Statistics*

**REFERATIVNYI ZHURNAL. TRAKTORY I
SEL'SKOKHOZYAISTVENNYE MASHINY I ORUDIYA.** see
AGRICULTURE—Abstracting, Bibliographies, Statistics

**REFERATIVNYI ZHURNAL. TRANSPORT PROMYSHLENNYKH
PREDPRIYATII. LOGISTIKA. SKLADY. AVTOMATIZATSIYA
POGRUZOCHNO-RAZGRUZOCHNYKH RABOT.** see
TRANSPORTATION—Abstracting, Bibliographies, Statistics

A

REFERATIVNYI ZHURNAL. TRIKOTAZHNAYA, SHVEINAYA I KOZHEVENNO-OBUVNAYA PROMYSHLENNOSTI. see *TEXTILE INDUSTRIES AND FABRICS—Abstracting, Bibliographies, Statistics*

REFERATIVNYI ZHURNAL. TRUBOPROVODNYI TRANSPORT. see *ENGINEERING—Abstracting, Bibliographies, Statistics*

REFERATIVNYI ZHURNAL. TSITOLOGIYA. see *BIOLOGY—Abstracting, Bibliographies, Statistics*

REFERATIVNYI ZHURNAL. TURBOSTROENIE. KOTLOSTROENIE. see *ENGINEERING—Abstracting, Bibliographies, Statistics*

REFERATIVNYI ZHURNAL. UPRAVLENIE PEREVOZOCHNYM PROTSESSOM NA ZHELEZNYKH DOROGAKH. see *TRANSPORTATION—Abstracting, Bibliographies, Statistics*

REFERATIVNYI ZHURNAL. UPRAVLENIE VOZDUSHNYM DVIZHENIEM. ORGANIZATSIYA PEREVOZOK. see *TRANSPORTATION—Abstracting, Bibliographies, Statistics*

REFERATIVNYI ZHURNAL. VIRUSOLOGIYA. see *BIOLOGY—Abstracting, Bibliographies, Statistics*

REFERATIVNYI ZHURNAL. VIRUSOLOGIYA. MIKROBIOLOGIYA. see *BIOLOGY—Abstracting, Bibliographies, Statistics*

REFERATIVNYI ZHURNAL. VODNYE PEREVOZKI. TEKHNICHESKAYA EKSPLUATATSIYA I REMONT FLOTA. see *TRANSPORTATION—Abstracting, Bibliographies, Statistics*

REFERATIVNYI ZHURNAL. VODNYI TRANSPORT. see *TRANSPORTATION—Abstracting, Bibliographies, Statistics*

REFERATIVNYI ZHURNAL. VOLOKONNO-OPTICHESKAYA SVYAZ'. see *PHYSICS—Abstracting, Bibliographies, Statistics*

REFERATIVNYI ZHURNAL. VOPROSY TEKHNICHESKOGO PROGRESSA I ORGANIZATSII PROIZVODSTVA V MASHINOSTROENII. see *ENGINEERING—Abstracting, Bibliographies, Statistics*

REFERATIVNYI ZHURNAL. VOZDUSHNYI TRANSPORT. see *TRANSPORTATION—Abstracting, Bibliographies, Statistics*

REFERATIVNYI ZHURNAL. VYCHISLITEL'NAYA MATEMATIKA. MATEMATICHESKAYA KIBERNETIKA. see *MATHEMATICS—Abstracting, Bibliographies, Statistics*

REFERATIVNYI ZHURNAL. VYCHISLITEL'NYE MASHINY I SISTEMY. see *COMPUTERS—Abstracting, Bibliographies, Statistics*

REFERATIVNYI ZHURNAL. VYCHISLITEL'NYE NAUKI. see *COMPUTERS—Abstracting, Bibliographies, Statistics*

REFERATIVNYI ZHURNAL. VZAIMODEISTVIE RAZNYKH VIDOV TRANSPORTA I KONTEINERNYE PEREVOZKI. see *TRANSPORTATION—Abstracting, Bibliographies, Statistics*

REFERATIVNYI ZHURNAL. YADERNAYA FIZIKA I FIZIKA YADERNYKH REAKTOROV. see *PHYSICS—Abstracting, Bibliographies, Statistics*

REFERATIVNYI ZHURNAL. YADERNYE REAKTORY. see *ENERGY—Abstracting, Bibliographies, Statistics*

REFERATIVNYI ZHURNAL. ZHELEZNODOROZHNYI TRANSPORT. see *TRANSPORTATION—Abstracting, Bibliographies, Statistics*

REFERATIVNYI ZHURNAL. ZOOLOGIYA. see *BIOLOGY—Abstracting, Bibliographies, Statistics*

REFERATIVNYI ZHURNAL. ZOOLOGIYA NAZEMNYKH POZVONOCHNYKH: OBSHCHIE VOPROSY. GERPETOLOGIYA. see *BIOLOGY—Zoology*

REFERATIVNYI ZHURNAL. ZOOLOGIYA NAZEMNYKH POZVONOCHNYKH: ORNITOLOGIYA. see *BIOLOGY—Abstracting, Bibliographies, Statistics*

REFERATIVNYI ZHURNAL. ZOOLOGIYA NAZEMNYKH POZVONOCHNYKH: TERIOLOGIYA, OKHOTOVEDENIE, ZOOPARKI. see *BIOLOGY—Abstracting, Bibliographies, Statistics*

REFERATIVNYI ZHURNAL. ZOOLOGIYA OBSHCHAYA. ZOOLOGIYA BESPOZVONOCHNYKH. see *BIOLOGY—Abstracting, Bibliographies, Statistics*

REFERATIVNYI ZHURNAL. ZOOPARAZITOLOGIYA. see *BIOLOGY—Abstracting, Bibliographies, Statistics*

REFERATOVY VYBER A AKTUALITY Z UROLOGIE/ ABSTRACTS OF UROLOGY. see *MEDICAL SCIENCES—Abstracting, Bibliographies, Statistics*

REFERATOVY VYBER Z ANESTEZIOLOGIE, RESUSCITACE A INTENZIVNI MEDICINY/ABSTRACTS OF ANESTHESIOLOGY AND RESUSCITATION. see *MEDICAL SCIENCES—Abstracting, Bibliographies, Statistics*

REFERATOVY VYBER Z RADIODIAGNOSTIKY (ONLINE EDITION)/ABSTRACTS OF RADIOLOGY. see *MEDICAL SCIENCES—Abstracting, Bibliographies, Statistics*

REFERATOVY VYBER Z REVMATOLOGIE (ONLINE EDITION)/ABSTRACTS OF RHEUMATOLOGY. see *MEDICAL SCIENCES—Abstracting, Bibliographies, Statistics*

REFERENCE POINT: FOOD INDUSTRY ABSTRACTS. see *FOOD AND FOOD INDUSTRIES—Abstracting, Bibliographies, Statistics*

REFUGEE SURVEY QUARTERLY. see *POPULATION STUDIES—Abstracting, Bibliographies, Statistics*

REHABILITATION INDEX. see *MEDICAL SCIENCES— Abstracting, Bibliographies, Statistics*

RELIGION INDEX ONE: PERIODICALS. see *RELIGIONS AND THEOLOGY—Abstracting, Bibliographies, Statistics*

RELIGIOUS & THEOLOGICAL ABSTRACTS. see *RELIGIONS AND THEOLOGY—Abstracting, Bibliographies, Statistics*

RELIGIOUS BOOK REVIEW INDEX. see *RELIGIONS AND THEOLOGY—Abstracting, Bibliographies, Statistics*

RENIN, ANGIOTENSIN & KININS. see *BIOLOGY—Abstracting, Bibliographies, Statistics*

REOROJI TORONKAI KOEN YOSHISHU/ABSTRACTS OF SYMPOSIUM ON RHEOLOGY. see *PHYSICS—Abstracting, Bibliographies, Statistics*

016   CAN   ISSN 1206-1913
REPERE (ONLINE EDITION); index analytique d'articles de periodiques de langue francaise. Text in English. 1983. irreg. CND 375 (effective 2005). index. **Document type:** *Database, Abstract/Index.* **Description:** Online database of articles in French published since 1980 in periodicals in Canada, France, Belgium and Switzerland.
Former titles: Repere (Print Edition) (1198-0281); (until 1993): Point de Repere (0822-8833); Which was formed by the merger of (1972-1983): Periodex (0300-3663); (1972-1983): Radar (Montreal) (0315-2316)
Media: Online - full text. **Related titles:** CD-ROM ed.: ISSN 1196-2143. 1992.
Published by: Services Documentaires Multimedia Inc., 75 Port Royal E, bureau 300, Montreal, PQ H3L 3T1, Canada. TEL 514-382-0895, FAX 514-384-9139, info@sdm.qc.ca, http://www.sdm.qc.ca. Circ: 650.

REPERTOIRE INTERNATIONAL DE LA PRESSE MUSICALE. see *MUSIC—Abstracting, Bibliographies, Statistics*

REPERTORY OF ARTICLES IN THE SOUTH AFRICAN ARCHIVES JOURNAL. see *LIBRARY AND INFORMATION SCIENCES—Abstracting, Bibliographies, Statistics*

REPINDEX. see *ENVIRONMENTAL STUDIES—Abstracting, Bibliographies, Statistics*

REPRODUCTION. ABSTRACT SERIES. see *BIOLOGY— Abstracting, Bibliographies, Statistics*

RESEARCH IN MINISTRY; an index to Doctor of Ministry project reports and theses. see *RELIGIONS AND THEOLOGY—Abstracting, Bibliographies, Statistics*

RESEARCH IN THE HISTORY OF EDUCATION: A LIST OF THESES FOR HIGHER DEGREES IN THE UNIVERSITIES OF ENGLAND AND WALES. see *EDUCATION—Abstracting, Bibliographies, Statistics*

RESEARCH INTO HIGHER EDUCATION ABSTRACTS. see *EDUCATION—Abstracting, Bibliographies, Statistics*

RESOURCES IN EDUCATION. see *EDUCATION—Abstracting, Bibliographies, Statistics*

RESOURCES IN EDUCATION ANNUAL CUMULATION. see *EDUCATION—Abstracting, Bibliographies, Statistics*

RESUMENES ANALITICOS EN EDUCACION. see *EDUCATION—Abstracting, Bibliographies, Statistics*

REVIEW OF AGRICULTURAL ENTOMOLOGY; consisting of abstracts of reviews of current literature on applied entomology throughout the world. see *AGRICULTURE— Abstracting, Bibliographies, Statistics*

REVIEW OF AROMATIC AND MEDICINAL PLANTS. see *BIOLOGY—Abstracting, Bibliographies, Statistics*

REVIEW OF MEDICAL AND VETERINARY ENTOMOLOGY. see *MEDICAL SCIENCES—Abstracting, Bibliographies, Statistics*

REVIEW OF MEDICAL AND VETERINARY MYCOLOGY. see *BIOLOGY—Abstracting, Bibliographies, Statistics*

REVIEW OF PLANT PATHOLOGY; consisting of abstracts and reviews of current literature on plant pathology. see *BIOLOGY—Abstracting, Bibliographies, Statistics*

REVISTA DE COMPENDIOS DE ARTICULOS DE ECONOMIA. see *BUSINESS AND ECONOMICS—Abstracting, Bibliographies, Statistics*

REZA KAGAKU/ABSTRACTS OF RIKEN SYMPOSIUM ON LASER SCIENCE. see *PHYSICS—Abstracting, Bibliographies, Statistics*

RIBOSOMES AND TRANSLATION. see *BIOLOGY—Abstracting, Bibliographies, Statistics*

RICE ABSTRACTS. see *AGRICULTURE—Abstracting, Bibliographies, Statistics*

RINGDOC PROFILE BOOKLETS. see *MEDICAL SCIENCES—Abstracting, Bibliographies, Statistics*

RISK ABSTRACTS (ONLINE EDITION). see *ENVIRONMENTAL STUDIES—Abstracting, Bibliographies, Statistics*

RURAL DEVELOPMENT ABSTRACTS. see *HOUSING AND URBAN PLANNING—Abstracting, Bibliographies, Statistics*

RUSSIAN ACADEMY OF SCIENCES BIBLIOGRAPHIES. see *SOCIAL SCIENCES: COMPREHENSIVE WORKS— Abstracting, Bibliographies, Statistics*

S A E TECHNICAL LITERATURE ABSTRACTS. see *TRANSPORTATION—Abstracting, Bibliographies, Statistics*

S C A D BULLETIN. (Systeme Communautaire d'Acces a la Documentation) see *POLITICAL SCIENCE—Abstracting, Bibliographies, Statistics*

S C E N E S - SCOTTISH ENVIRONMENT NEWS. see *CONSERVATION—Abstracting, Bibliographies, Statistics*

S I D INTERNATIONAL SYMPOSIUM. DIGEST OF TECHNICAL PAPERS. see *COMPUTERS—Abstracting, Bibliographies, Statistics*

S I R S DISCOVERER. (Social Issues Resources Series) see *CHILDREN AND YOUTH—Abstracting, Bibliographies, Statistics*

S I R S DISCOVERER ELEMENTARY EDITION. (Social Issues Resources Series) see *CHILDREN AND YOUTH—Abstracting, Bibliographies, Statistics*

S I R S DISCOVERER MIDDLE EDITION. (Social Issues Resources Series) see *CHILDREN AND YOUTH—Abstracting, Bibliographies, Statistics*

S I R S GOVERNMENT REPORTER. (Social Issues Resources Series) see *SOCIAL SCIENCES: COMPREHENSIVE WORKS—Abstracting, Bibliographies, Statistics*

S I R S INTERACTIVE CITIZENSHIP. see *SOCIAL SCIENCES: COMPREHENSIVE WORKS—Abstracting, Bibliographies, Statistics*

S I R S RENAISSANCE; current perspectives on the arts and humanities. (Social Issues Resources Series) see *HUMANITIES: COMPREHENSIVE WORKS—Abstracting, Bibliographies, Statistics*

S I R S RESEARCHER. (Social Issues Resources Series) see *SOCIAL SCIENCES: COMPREHENSIVE WORKS— Abstracting, Bibliographies, Statistics*

▼ S I R S WEBFIND. see *COMPUTERS—Abstracting, Bibliographies, Statistics*

S K S WEBSELECT. see *COMPUTERS—Abstracting, Bibliographies, Statistics*

S P I N. (Searchable Physics Information Notices) see *PHYSICS—Abstracting, Bibliographies, Statistics*

S S O R YOKOSHU/PROCEEDINGS OF S S O R. see *COMPUTERS—Abstracting, Bibliographies, Statistics*

S T A R (ONLINE). (Scientific and Technical Aerospace Reports) see *AERONAUTICS AND SPACE FLIGHT—Abstracting, Bibliographies, Statistics*

SAGE FAMILY STUDIES ABSTRACTS. see *SOCIOLOGY—Abstracting, Bibliographies, Statistics*

SAGE PUBLIC ADMINISTRATION ABSTRACTS. see *PUBLIC ADMINISTRATION—Abstracting, Bibliographies, Statistics*

SAGE RACE RELATIONS ABSTRACTS. see *SOCIOLOGY—Abstracting, Bibliographies, Statistics*

SAGE URBAN STUDIES ABSTRACTS. see *HOUSING AND URBAN PLANNING—Abstracting, Bibliographies, Statistics*

SAN FRANCISCO CHRONICLE INDEX. see *JOURNALISM—Abstracting, Bibliographies, Statistics*

SAUDI ARABIA. WIZARAT AL-MA'ARIF. AL-ISTIKHLASAT AL-TARBAWIYYAH/SAUDI ARABIA. MINISTRY OF EDUCATION. EDUCATIONAL ABSTRACTS. see *EDUCATION—Abstracting, Bibliographies, Statistics*

SCHOLARS' CHOICE; significant current theological literature from abroad. see *RELIGIONS AND THEOLOGY—Abstracting, Bibliographies, Statistics*

SCHRIFTTUM BAUWESEN: GESAMTAUSGABE. see *BUILDING AND CONSTRUCTION—Abstracting, Bibliographies, Statistics*

SCHWANN C D REVIEW DIGEST - CLASSICAL; the international indexing service - a guide with excerpts to English language reviews of all music recorded on compact and video laser discs. see *MUSIC—Abstracting, Bibliographies, Statistics*

SCHWANN C D REVIEW DIGEST - JAZZ, POPULAR, ETC.; the international indexing service - a guide with excerpts to English language reviews of all music recorded on compact and video laser discs. see *MUSIC—Abstracting, Bibliographies, Statistics*

SCIENCE & TECHNOLOGY ABSTRACTS. see *SCIENCES: COMPREHENSIVE WORKS—Abstracting, Bibliographies, Statistics*

SCIENCE CITATION INDEX. see *SCIENCES: COMPREHENSIVE WORKS—Abstracting, Bibliographies, Statistics*

SCIENCE OF RELIGION; abstracts and index of recent articles. see *RELIGIONS AND THEOLOGY—Abstracting, Bibliographies, Statistics*

SCIENTIFIC AND TECHNICAL PUBLICATIONS IN BULGARIA. see *SCIENCES: COMPREHENSIVE WORKS—Abstracting, Bibliographies, Statistics*

SEA GRANT ABSTRACTS; publications from the nation's Sea Grant programs. see *BIOLOGY—Abstracting, Bibliographies, Statistics*

SECONDARY TEACHERS GUIDE TO FREE CURRICULUM MATERIALS. see *EDUCATION—Abstracting, Bibliographies, Statistics*

SEED ABSTRACTS. see *BIOLOGY—Abstracting, Bibliographies, Statistics*

SEISMOLOGICAL SOCIETY OF JAPAN. PROGRAMME AND ABSTRACTS. see *EARTH SCIENCES—Abstracting, Bibliographies, Statistics*

SELECTED RAND ABSTRACTS; a semiannual guide to publications of the Rand Corporation. see *SCIENCES: COMPREHENSIVE WORKS—Abstracting, Bibliographies, Statistics*

SEL'SKOKHOZYAISTVENNAYA LITERATURA. see *AGRICULTURE—Abstracting, Bibliographies, Statistics*

SERVICIO REFERATIVO DE LA CONSTRUCCION. see *BUILDING AND CONSTRUCTION—Abstracting, Bibliographies, Statistics*

SHANTOU SPECIAL ECONOMIC ZONE YEARBOOK (YEAR). see *BUSINESS AND ECONOMICS—Abstracting, Bibliographies, Statistics*

SHIDA SHOKUBUTSU BUNKEN MOKUROKU/BIBLIOGRAPHY OF PTERIDOPHYTES BY JAPANESE FERNISTS. see *BIOLOGY—Abstracting, Bibliographies, Statistics*

SHOKUBUTSU SOSHIKI SAIBOU BUNSHISEIBUTSU GAKKAI TAIKAI SHINPOJUMU KOEN YOSHISHU/JAPANESE SOCIETY FOR PLANT CELL AND MOLECULAR BIOLOGY. ABSTRACTS OF THE MEETING AND SYMPOSIUM. see *BIOLOGY—Abstracting, Bibliographies, Statistics*

SHORT STORY INDEX; an index to stories in collections and periodicals. see *LITERATURE—Abstracting, Bibliographies, Statistics*

SIGNAL TRANSDUCTION & CYCLIC NUCLEOTIDES. see *BIOLOGY—Abstracting, Bibliographies, Statistics*

SIGNAL'NAYA INFORMATSIYA. KHIMIYA VODY. see *CHEMISTRY—Abstracting, Bibliographies, Statistics*

SIGNAL'NAYA INFORMATSIYA. TOKSIKOLOGIYA LEKARSTVENNAYA. see *PHARMACY AND PHARMACOLOGY—Abstracting, Bibliographies, Statistics*

015.5957　　　　　SGP　　　　　ISSN 0377-7928
AI3
SINGAPORE PERIODICALS INDEX. Text in Chinese, English, Malay. 1969. a. (cumulative vols. issued annually), latest 1981-2000. price varies. **Document type:** *Abstract/Index.*
Related titles: Ed. 1991.
Published by: National Library Board, 91 Stamford Rd, Singapore, 178896, Singapore. TEL 65-546-7225, FAX 65-546-7262. Ed. Hamidale Abdullah. Circ: 250.

SINOPSIS. see *EDUCATION—Abstracting, Bibliographies, Statistics*

SMARTBIX. see *BUSINESS AND ECONOMICS—Abstracting, Bibliographies, Statistics*

SOCIAL SCIENCES CITATION INDEX. see *SOCIAL SCIENCES: COMPREHENSIVE WORKS—Abstracting, Bibliographies, Statistics*

SOCIAL SCIENCES FULL TEXT. see *SOCIAL SCIENCES: COMPREHENSIVE WORKS—Abstracting, Bibliographies, Statistics*

SOCIAL SCIENCES INDEX. see *SOCIAL SCIENCES: COMPREHENSIVE WORKS—Abstracting, Bibliographies, Statistics*

SOCIAL WORK ABSTRACTS. see *SOCIAL SERVICES AND WELFARE—Abstracting, Bibliographies, Statistics*

SOCIETY FOR OLD TESTAMENT STUDY. BOOK LIST. see *RELIGIONS AND THEOLOGY—Abstracting, Bibliographies, Statistics*

SOCIETY FOR RANGE MANAGEMENT. INTERNATIONAL RANGELAND CONGRESS. ABSTRACTS OF PAPERS. see *AGRICULTURE—Abstracting, Bibliographies, Statistics*

SOCIOFILE. see *SOCIOLOGY—Abstracting, Bibliographies, Statistics*

SOCIOKULTURNAYA DEYATELNOST' V SFERE DOSUGA; referativno-bibliograficheskaya informatsiya. see *LEISURE AND RECREATION—Abstracting, Bibliographies, Statistics*

SOCIOLOGICAL ABSTRACTS. see *SOCIOLOGY—Abstracting, Bibliographies, Statistics*

SOCIOLOGY OF EDUCATION ABSTRACTS. see *EDUCATION—Abstracting, Bibliographies, Statistics*

SOFTBASE. see *COMPUTERS—Abstracting, Bibliographies, Statistics*

SOILS AND FERTILIZERS. see *AGRICULTURE—Abstracting, Bibliographies, Statistics*

SOLID STATE AND SUPERCONDUCTIVITY ABSTRACTS. see *PHYSICS—Abstracting, Bibliographies, Statistics*

SOTSIAL'NYE I GUMANITARNYE NAUKI. OTECHESTVENNAYA I ZARUBEZHNAYA LITERATURA. EKONOMIKA; referativnyi zhurnal. see *BUSINESS AND ECONOMICS—Abstracting, Bibliographies, Statistics*

SOTSIAL'NYE I GUMANITARNYE NAUKI. OTECHESTVENNAYA I ZARUBEZHNAYA LITERATURA. FILOSOFIYA; referativnyi zhurnal. see *PHILOSOPHY—Abstracting, Bibliographies, Statistics*

SOTSIAL'NYE I GUMANITARNYE NAUKI. OTECHESTVENNAYA I ZARUBEZHNAYA LITERATURA. GOSUDARSTVO I PRAVO; referativnyi zhurnal. see *LAW—Abstracting, Bibliographies, Statistics*

SOTSIAL'NYE I GUMANITARNYE NAUKI. OTECHESTVENNAYA I ZARUBEZHNAYA LITERATURA. ISTORIYA; referativnyi zhurnal. see *HISTORY—Abstracting, Bibliographies, Statistics*

SOTSIAL'NYE I GUMANITARNYE NAUKI. OTECHESTVENNAYA I ZARUBEZHNAYA LITERATURA. LITERATUROVEDENIE; referativnyi zhurnal. see *LITERATURE—Abstracting, Bibliographies, Statistics*

SOTSIAL'NYE I GUMANITARNYE NAUKI. OTECHESTVENNAYA I ZARUBEZHNAYA LITERATURA. NAUKOVEDENIE; referativnyi zhurnal. see *SCIENCES: COMPREHENSIVE WORKS—Abstracting, Bibliographies, Statistics*

SOTSIAL'NYE I GUMANITARNYE NAUKI. OTECHESTVENNAYA I ZARUBEZHNAYA LITERATURA. SOTSIOLOGIYA; referativnyi zhurnal. see *SOCIOLOGY—Abstracting, Bibliographies, Statistics*

SOTSIAL'NYE I GUMANITARNYE NAUKI. OTECHESTVENNAYA I ZARUBEZHNAYA LITERATURA. YAZYKOZNANIE; referativnyi zhurnal. see *LINGUISTICS—Abstracting, Bibliographies, Statistics*

SOTSIAL'NYE I GUMANITARNYE NAUKI. ZARUBEZHNAYA LITERATURA. VOSTOKOVEDENIE I AFRIKANISTIKA; referativnyi zhurnal. see *ASIAN STUDIES—Abstracting, Bibliographies, Statistics*

SOUTH AFRICAN STUDIES. see *HISTORY—Abstracting, Bibliographies, Statistics*

▼ **SOUTH ASIAN ECONOMIC ABSTRACTS.** see *BUSINESS AND ECONOMICS—Abstracting, Bibliographies, Statistics*

▼ **SOUTH ASIAN MANAGEMENT ABSTRACTS.** see *BUSINESS AND ECONOMICS—Abstracting, Bibliographies, Statistics*

015　　　　　　　FJI　　　　　　ISSN 1011-5110
SOUTH PACIFIC PERIODICALS INDEX. Text in English. 1974. irreg. FJD 15; FJD 7.50 in developing nations (effective 2005). back issues avail. **Document type:** *Abstract/Index.*
Description: Articles concerned with the South Pacific regardless of origin or language.
Formerly (until 1978): Bibliography of Periodical Articles Relating to the South Pacific
Related titles: Microform ed.
Published by: Pacific Information Centre, University of the South Pacific Library, Suva, Fiji. TEL 679-33-13900, FAX 679-33-00830, library@usp.ac.fj.

SOUTHEAST - EAST ASIAN ENGLISH PUBLICATIONS IN PRINT. see *PUBLISHING AND BOOK TRADE—Abstracting, Bibliographies, Statistics*

SOUTHERN BAPTIST PERIODICAL INDEX. see *RELIGIONS AND THEOLOGY—Abstracting, Bibliographies, Statistics*

SOYBEAN ABSTRACTS (ONLINE EDITION). see *BIOLOGY—Abstracting, Bibliographies, Statistics*

SPAIN. MINISTERIO DE AGRICULTURA, PESCA Y ALIMENTACION. BOLETIN MENSUAL DE ESTADISTICA AGRARIA. see *AGRICULTURE—Abstracting, Bibliographies, Statistics*

SPANISH CULTURAL INDEX. see *LITERARY AND POLITICAL REVIEWS—Abstracting, Bibliographies, Statistics*

SPEC-DATA PROGRAM INDEX. see *BUILDING AND CONSTRUCTION—Abstracting, Bibliographies, Statistics*

SPECIAL EDUCATIONAL NEEDS ABSTRACTS. see *EDUCATION—Abstracting, Bibliographies, Statistics*

SPEECH INDEX; an index to 259 collections of orations and speeches for various occasions. see *LINGUISTICS—Abstracting, Bibliographies, Statistics*

SPELEOLOGICAL ABSTRACTS/BULLETIN BIBLIOGRAPHIQUE SPELEOLOGIQUE. see *EARTH SCIENCES—Abstracting, Bibliographies, Statistics*

SPORTS DOCUMENTATION MONTHLY BULLETIN. see *EDUCATION—Abstracting, Bibliographies, Statistics*

015　　　　　　　LKA
SRI LANKA PERIODICALS INDEX. Text in English, Singhalese. 1969. s-a. free on exchange to libraries and research institutes. bibl. **Document type:** *Abstract/Index.*
Formerly (until vol.5): Ceylon Periodical Index
Published by: Department of National Museums, Sir Marcus Fernando Mawatha, P O Box 854, Colombo, 7, Sri Lanka.

STAMPS, COINS, POSTCARDS & RELATED MATERIALS; a directory of periodicals. see *NUMISMATICS—Abstracting, Bibliographies, Statistics*

STATE ACADEMIES OF SCIENCE ABSTRACTS. see *SCIENCES: COMPREHENSIVE WORKS—Abstracting, Bibliographies, Statistics*

STATE BANK OF PAKISTAN. INDEX NUMBERS OF STOCK EXCHANGE SECURITIES. see *BUSINESS AND ECONOMICS—Abstracting, Bibliographies, Statistics*

STATISTICAL REFERENCE INDEX. see *STATISTICS*

STATISTICAL THEORY AND METHOD ABSTRACTS (CD-ROM EDITION). see *MATHEMATICS—Abstracting, Bibliographies, Statistics*

STERN'S SOURCEFINDER; the master directory to human resources and business management information and resources. see *BUSINESS AND ECONOMICS—Abstracting, Bibliographies, Statistics*

STEROID RECEPTORS. see *BIOLOGY—Abstracting, Bibliographies, Statistics*

STEUER UND WIRTSCHAFT INTERNATIONAL. see *BUSINESS AND ECONOMICS—Abstracting, Bibliographies, Statistics*

STEUER- UND WIRTSCHAFTSKARTEI. see *BUSINESS AND ECONOMICS—Abstracting, Bibliographies, Statistics*

STRUCTURAL STATISTICS FOR INDUSTRY AND SERVICES. see *BUSINESS AND ECONOMICS—Abstracting, Bibliographies, Statistics*

STUDIA JEZYKOZNAWCZE. see *LINGUISTICS—Abstracting, Bibliographies, Statistics*

STUDIA POLONO-JUDAICA. SERIES BIBLIOGRAPHICA. see *HISTORY—Abstracting, Bibliographies, Statistics*

STUDIA POLONO-JUDAICA. SERIES LIBRORUM CONGRESSUS. see *HISTORY—Abstracting, Bibliographies, Statistics*

STUDIA ZRODLOZNAWCZE. see *HISTORY—Abstracting, Bibliographies, Statistics*

STUDIES IN BIBLIOGRAPHY AND BOOKLORE; devoted to research in the field of Jewish bibliography. see *RELIGIONS AND THEOLOGY—Abstracting, Bibliographies, Statistics*

STUDIES ON WOMEN AND GENDER ABSTRACTS. see *WOMEN'S STUDIES—Abstracting, Bibliographies, Statistics*

SUBJECT INDEX TO ARTICLES IN NEWSPAPERS IN MAURITIUS. see *JOURNALISM—Abstracting, Bibliographies, Statistics*

SUDAN SCIENCE ABSTRACTS. see *SCIENCES: COMPREHENSIVE WORKS—Abstracting, Bibliographies, Statistics*

SUGAR INDUSTRY ABSTRACTS. see *FOOD AND FOOD INDUSTRIES—Abstracting, Bibliographies, Statistics*

SUOMEN SANOMALEHTIEN MIKROFILMIT/MICROFILMED NEWSPAPERS OF FINLAND. see *JOURNALISM—Abstracting, Bibliographies, Statistics*

SURFACE FINISHING; metal finishing database software. see *METALLURGY—Abstracting, Bibliographies, Statistics*

SURFACE FINISHING ABSTRACTS (ONLINE EDITION). see *METALLURGY—Abstracting, Bibliographies, Statistics*

SURVEY OF ANESTHESIOLOGY. see *MEDICAL SCIENCES—Abstracting, Bibliographies, Statistics*

SURVEY OF OPHTHALMOLOGY. see *MEDICAL SCIENCES—Abstracting, Bibliographies, Statistics*

SYMPOSIUM ON RADIOCHEMISTRY. ABSTRACTS OF PAPERS/HOSHA KAGAKU TORONKAI KOEN YOKOSHU. see *CHEMISTRY—Abstracting, Bibliographies, Statistics*

T O M. (Text on Microfilm) see *EDUCATION—Abstracting, Bibliographies, Statistics*

T R I S ELECTRONIC BIBLIOGRAPHIC DATA BASE. (Transportation Research Information Services) see *TRANSPORTATION—Abstracting, Bibliographies, Statistics*

T V TRANSLATORS ENGINEERING DATA BASE IN ORDER BY STATE, CHANNEL, CALL. see *COMMUNICATIONS—Abstracting, Bibliographies, Statistics*

T V TRANSLATORS ENGINEERING DATA BASE IN ORDER BY STATE, CITY, CHANNEL. see *COMMUNICATIONS—Abstracting, Bibliographies, Statistics*

TAIYOKEI KAGAKU SHINPOJUMU. see *ASTRONOMY—Abstracting, Bibliographies, Statistics*

015.931   NZL   ISSN 1175-1371
TE PUNA CD-ROM. Text in English. 1987. s-a. NZD 992 domestic for 1-8 users license; NZD 1,200 foreign for 1-8 users license; NZD 3,516 domestic for site license; NZD 4,200 foreign for site license; NZD 692 per issue domestic for 1-8 users license; NZD 830 per issue foreign for 1-8 users license; NZD 2,160 per issue domestic for site license; NZD 2,600 per issue foreign for site license (effective 2005). back issues avail.; reprints avail. **Document type:** Abstract/Index. **Description:** Provides access to journal articles, theses, reports, newspapers, books and conference papers about New Zealand or the South Pacific.

Former titles: Index New Zealand (0113-6526); (until 1986): Index to New Zealand Periodicals (0073-5957)
Media: CD-ROM (from R M I T Publishing). **Related titles:** ♦ Online - full content ed.: New Zealand National Bibliography.
Published by: National Library of New Zealand, PO Box 1467, Wellington, 6001, New Zealand. TEL 64-4-4743000, FAX 64-4-4743035, information@natlib.govt.nz, http://www.natlib.govt.nz/. Circ: 400 (controlled).

TECHNICAL EDUCATION & TRAINING ABSTRACTS. see *EDUCATION—Abstracting, Bibliographies, Statistics*

TECHNICAL LITERATURE ABSTRACTS: AUTOMOTIVE. see *PETROLEUM AND GAS—Abstracting, Bibliographies, Statistics*

TECHNICAL LITERATURE ABSTRACTS: CATALYSTS - ZEOLITES (ONLINE EDITION). see *CHEMISTRY—Abstracting, Bibliographies, Statistics*

TECHNICAL LITERATURE ABSTRACTS: FUEL REFORMULATION. see *CHEMISTRY—Abstracting, Bibliographies, Statistics*

TECHNICAL LITERATURE ABSTRACTS: HEALTH & ENVIRONMENT (ONLINE EDITION). see *ENVIRONMENTAL STUDIES—Abstracting, Bibliographies, Statistics*

TECHNICAL LITERATURE ABSTRACTS: NATURAL GAS. see *PETROLEUM AND GAS—Abstracting, Bibliographies, Statistics*

TECHNICAL LITERATURE ABSTRACTS: OILFIELD CHEMICALS (ONLINE EDITION). see *PETROLEUM AND GAS—Abstracting, Bibliographies, Statistics*

TECHNICAL LITERATURE ABSTRACTS: PETROLEUM REFINING & PETROCHEMICALS (ONLINE EDITION). see *PETROLEUM AND GAS—Abstracting, Bibliographies, Statistics*

TECHNICAL LITERATURE ABSTRACTS: PETROLEUM SUBSTITUTES (ONLINE EDITION). see *PETROLEUM AND GAS—Abstracting, Bibliographies, Statistics*

TECHNICAL LITERATURE ABSTRACTS: TRANSPORTATION & STORAGE (ONLINE EDITION). see *TRANSPORTATION—Abstracting, Bibliographies, Statistics*

TECHNICAL LITERATURE ABSTRACTS: TRIBOLOGY. see *CHEMISTRY—Abstracting, Bibliographies, Statistics*

TECHNION - ISRAEL INSTITUTE OF TECHNOLOGY. ABSTRACTS OF RESEARCH THESES. see *EDUCATION—Abstracting, Bibliographies, Statistics*

TEXTILE TECHNOLOGY INDEX. see *TEXTILE INDUSTRIES AND FABRICS—Abstracting, Bibliographies, Statistics*

THAI ABSTRACTS, SERIES A. SCIENCE AND TECHNOLOGY. see *SCIENCES: COMPREHENSIVE WORKS—Abstracting, Bibliographies, Statistics*

THANATOLOGY ABSTRACTS. see *PSYCHOLOGY—Abstracting, Bibliographies, Statistics*

THEORETICAL CHEMICAL ENGINEERING. see *ENGINEERING—Abstracting, Bibliographies, Statistics*

THESIS ABSTRACTS. see *AGRICULTURE—Abstracting, Bibliographies, Statistics*

THYROID HORMONES. see *MEDICAL SCIENCES—Abstracting, Bibliographies, Statistics*

TIMES INDEX. see *JOURNALISM—Abstracting, Bibliographies, Statistics*

THE TIMES LITERARY SUPPLEMENT INDEX. see *LITERATURE—Abstracting, Bibliographies, Statistics*

TISSUE CULTURE. see *BIOLOGY—Abstracting, Bibliographies, Statistics*

TOBACCO ABSTRACTS; world literature on Nicotiana. see *TOBACCO—Abstracting, Bibliographies, Statistics*

TOP MANAGEMENT ABSTRACTS. see *BUSINESS AND ECONOMICS—Abstracting, Bibliographies, Statistics*

TOPICATOR; classified guide to articles in the advertising/communications/marketing periodical press. see *ADVERTISING AND PUBLIC RELATIONS—Abstracting, Bibliographies, Statistics*

TOXICOLOGY ABSTRACTS. see *ENVIRONMENTAL STUDIES—Abstracting, Bibliographies, Statistics*

TRANSIT PLANNING AND RESEARCH REPORTS; an annotated bibliography. see *TRANSPORTATION—Abstracting, Bibliographies, Statistics*

TRANSLATION STUDIES ABSTRACTS. see *LINGUISTICS—Abstracting, Bibliographies, Statistics*

TRANSMITTERS, RECEPTORS & SYNAPSES. see *PHARMACY AND PHARMACOLOGY—Abstracting, Bibliographies, Statistics*

TRAVEL & TOURISM INDEX. see *TRAVEL AND TOURISM—Abstracting, Bibliographies, Statistics*

TROPICAL DISEASES BULLETIN. see *MEDICAL SCIENCES—Abstracting, Bibliographies, Statistics*

TRZISTE STOKE I STOCIH PROIZODA; konjunkturne informacije. see *AGRICULTURE—Abstracting, Bibliographies, Statistics*

TSETSE AND TRYPANOSOMIASIS INFORMATION QUARTERLY. see *MEDICAL SCIENCES—Abstracting, Bibliographies, Statistics*

TUDOMANYOS ES MUSZAKI TAJEKOZTATAS/SCIENTIFIC AND TECHNICAL INFORMATION. see *LIBRARY AND INFORMATION SCIENCES—Abstracting, Bibliographies, Statistics*

TURKISH CHAMBER OF CIVIL ENGINEERS. DIGEST (YEAR); extended summaries from Teknik Dergi/Technical Journal. see *ENGINEERING—Abstracting, Bibliographies, Statistics*

U N B I S PLUS ON CD-ROM. see *POLITICAL SCIENCE—Abstracting, Bibliographies, Statistics*

U S A TODAY INDEX. see *JOURNALISM—Abstracting, Bibliographies, Statistics*

U.S. AGENCY FOR INTERNATIONAL DEVELOPMENT. OFFICE OF HOUSING AND URBAN PROGRAMS. ABSTRACTS. see *HOUSING AND URBAN PLANNING—Abstracting, Bibliographies, Statistics*

U.S. CENTERS FOR DISEASE CONTROL. CONGENITAL MALFORMATIONS SURVEILLANCE. see *BIOLOGY—Abstracting, Bibliographies, Statistics*

U.S. DEPARTMENT OF DEFENSE. INDEX OF SPECIFICATIONS AND STANDARDS. see *METROLOGY AND STANDARDIZATION—Abstracting, Bibliographies, Statistics*

U.S. DEPARTMENT OF DEFENSE. INDEX OF SPECIFICATIONS AND STANDARDS: PART 2, NUMERIC LISTING. see *METROLOGY AND STANDARDIZATION—Abstracting, Bibliographies, Statistics*

U.S. DEPARTMENT OF DEFENSE. INDEX OF SPECIFICATIONS AND STANDARDS: PART 3, FEDERAL SUPPLY CLASS LISTING. see *METROLOGY AND STANDARDIZATION—Abstracting, Bibliographies, Statistics*

U.S. DEPARTMENT OF DEFENSE. INDEX OF SPECIFICATIONS AND STANDARDS: PART 4, NUMERICAL LISTING OF CANCELLED DOCUMENTS. see *METROLOGY AND STANDARDIZATION—Abstracting, Bibliographies, Statistics*

U.S. FOREIGN BROADCAST INFORMATION SERVICE DAILY REPORTS: NEAR EAST AND SOUTH ASIA. INDEX. see *POLITICAL SCIENCE—Abstracting, Bibliographies, Statistics*

U.S. FOREIGN BROADCAST INFORMATION SERVICE DAILY REPORTS: SUB-SAHARAN AFRICA. INDEX. see *POLITICAL SCIENCE—Abstracting, Bibliographies, Statistics*

U.S. GOVERNMENT PERIODICALS INDEX (ONLINE EDITION). see *PUBLIC ADMINISTRATION—Abstracting, Bibliographies, Statistics*

UKAZATEL' BIBLIOGRAFICHESKYKH POSOBII PO SIBIRI I DAL'NEMU VOSTOKU; ezhegodnik. see *SCIENCES: COMPREHENSIVE WORKS—Abstracting, Bibliographies, Statistics*

UKRAINSKYI REFERATYVNYI ZHURNAL. SERIYA 1. PRYRODNYCHI NAUKY, MEDYTSYNA/UKRAINIAN JOURNAL OF ABSTRACTS. SER. 1. PRIRODNICI NAUKI, MEDICINE. see *SCIENCES: COMPREHENSIVE WORKS—Abstracting, Bibliographies, Statistics*

UKRAINSKYI REFERATYVNYI ZHURNAL. SERIYA 2. TEHNIKA, PROMYSLOVIST', SIL'S'KE HOSPODARSTVO/UKRAINIAN JOURNAL OF ABSTRACTS. SER. 2. ENGINEERING, INDUSTRY, AGRICULTURE. see *ENGINEERING—Abstracting, Bibliographies, Statistics*

UKRAINSKYI REFERATYVNYI ZHURNAL. SERIYA 3. SOTSIAL'NI TA HUMANITARNI NAUKY, MYSTETSTVO/ UKRAINIAN JOURNAL OF ABSTRACTS. SER. 3. SOCIAL SCIENCES AND HUMANITIES, ART. see *SOCIAL SCIENCES: COMPREHENSIVE WORKS—Abstracting, Bibliographies, Statistics*

UNIFORM COMMERCIAL CODE LAW JOURNAL. see *LAW—Abstracting, Bibliographies, Statistics*

UNILEX. INTERNATIONAL CASE LAW AND BIBLIOGRAPHY ON THE UN CONVENTION ON CONTRACTS FOR THE INTERNATIONAL SALE OF GOODS. see *LAW—Abstracting, Bibliographies, Statistics*

UNITED METHODIST DIRECTORY & INDEX OF RESOURCES. see *RELIGIONS AND THEOLOGY—Abstracting, Bibliographies, Statistics*

UNITED NATIONS. TRUSTEESHIP COUNCIL. INDEX TO PROCEEDINGS. see *POLITICAL SCIENCE—Abstracting, Bibliographies, Statistics*

UNIVERSAL MILITARY ABSTRACTS. see *MILITARY— Abstracting, Bibliographies, Statistics*

UNIVERSAL SUBJECT LOCATOR. see *LAW—Abstracting, Bibliographies, Statistics*

UNIVERSITY OF DAYTON. SCHOOL OF EDUCATION. ABSTRACTS OF RESEARCH PROJECTS. see *EDUCATION—Abstracting, Bibliographies, Statistics*

UNIVERSITY OF TOKYO. INSTITUTE OF APPLIED MICROBIOLOGY. REPORTS. see *BIOLOGY—Abstracting, Bibliographies, Statistics*

UNIVERZITET U SARAJEVU. DOKTORSKE DISERTACIJE. REZIMEI. see *EDUCATION—Abstracting, Bibliographies, Statistics*

URBADISC CD-ROM. see *HOUSING AND URBAN PLANNING—Abstracting, Bibliographies, Statistics*

URBAN ABSTRACTS. see *HOUSING AND URBAN PLANNING—Abstracting, Bibliographies, Statistics*

VALIDATED ENGINEERING DATA INDEX. see *ENGINEERING—Abstracting, Bibliographies, Statistics*

VALLALATSZERVEZESI ES IPARGAZDASAGI SZAKIRODALMI TAJEKOZTATO/INDUSTRIAL MANAGEMENT ABSTRACTS. see *BUSINESS AND ECONOMICS—Abstracting, Bibliographies, Statistics*

VANYTT; litteratur oever yttre miljoe och arbetsmiljoeteknik. see *ENVIRONMENTAL STUDIES—Abstracting, Bibliographies, Statistics*

VEGYIPARI SZAKIRODALMI TAJEKOZTATO/CHEMICAL ENGINEERING ABSTRACTS. see *CHEMISTRY—Abstracting, Bibliographies, Statistics*

VERENIGING VOOR OPPERVLAKTETECHNIEKEN VAN MATERIALEN. DOCUMENTATIESERVICE. see *METALLURGY—Abstracting, Bibliographies, Statistics*

VERFAHRENSTECHNISCHE BERICHTE/CHEMICAL AND PROCESS ENGINEERING ABSTRACTS. see *ENGINEERING—Abstracting, Bibliographies, Statistics*

050 011   USA   ISSN 0042-4439
Z1231.P2
VERTICAL FILE INDEX; guide to pamphlets and references to current topics. Text in English. 1932. m. (Sep.-July). USD 120 in US & Canada (effective 2006). **Document type:** *Abstract/Index.*
Related titles: Online - full text ed.
—Linda Hall.
Published by: H.W. Wilson Co., 950 University Ave, Bronx, NY 10452-4224. TEL 718-588-8400, 800-367-6770, FAX 718-590-1617, 800-590-1617, custserv@hwwilson.com, http://www.hwwilson.com/print/vfi.html. Ed. Brenda Smith.

VETERINARY BULLETIN; a monthly abstract journal on veterinary science. see *VETERINARY SCIENCE—Abstracting, Bibliographies, Statistics*

VICTORIAN LAW REPORTS CONSOLIDATED INDEX AND TABLES (YEARS). CUMULATIVE SUPPLEMENT. see *LAW—Abstracting, Bibliographies, Statistics*

VICTORIAN STATUTES ANNOTATIONS. see *LAW—Abstracting, Bibliographies, Statistics*

VIKRAM RESEARCH GUIDE. see *SOCIAL SCIENCES: COMPREHENSIVE WORKS—Abstracting, Bibliographies, Statistics*

VIOLENCE & ABUSE ABSTRACTS; current literature in interpersonal violence. see *SOCIOLOGY—Abstracting, Bibliographies, Statistics*

VISION (SHEFFIELD). see *MEDICAL SCIENCES—Abstracting, Bibliographies, Statistics*

VITAL TEXTILE LITERATURE (YEAR). see *TEXTILE INDUSTRIES AND FABRICS—Abstracting, Bibliographies, Statistics*

THE WASHINGTON POST INDEX. see *JOURNALISM— Abstracting, Bibliographies, Statistics*

WASHINGTON SUMMARY. see *POLITICAL SCIENCE— Abstracting, Bibliographies, Statistics*

THE WASHINGTON TIMES INDEX. see *JOURNALISM— Abstracting, Bibliographies, Statistics*

WASTEINFO. see *ENVIRONMENTAL STUDIES—Abstracting, Bibliographies, Statistics*

WATER AND ENERGY ABSTRACTS. see *WATER RESOURCES—Abstracting, Bibliographies, Statistics*

WATER RESOURCES ABSTRACTS (BETHESDA, ONLINE EDITION). see *WATER RESOURCES—Abstracting, Bibliographies, Statistics*

WATER RESOURCES ABSTRACTS. VOLUME 1. see *WATER RESOURCES—Abstracting, Bibliographies, Statistics*

WATER RESOURCES WORLDWIDE. see *WATER RESOURCES—Abstracting, Bibliographies, Statistics*

WEED ABSTRACTS; compiled from world literature. see *AGRICULTURE—Abstracting, Bibliographies, Statistics*

WEED SCIENCE SOCIETY OF AMERICA. ABSTRACTS. see *AGRICULTURE—Abstracting, Bibliographies, Statistics*

WELDASEARCH SELECT; selective dissemination of information. see *METALLURGY—Abstracting, Bibliographies, Statistics*

WESTERN SOCIETY OF PERIODONTOLOGY. JOURNAL. PERIODONTAL ABSTRACTS. see *MEDICAL SCIENCES—Abstracting, Bibliographies, Statistics*

WHAT'S NEW IN W W W SOCIAL SCIENCES NEWSLETTER. (World Wide Web) see *HUMANITIES: COMPREHENSIVE WORKS—Abstracting, Bibliographies, Statistics*

WHEAT, BARLEY AND TRITICALE ABSTRACTS. see *AGRICULTURE—Abstracting, Bibliographies, Statistics*

WHO'S WHO IN THE EGG AND POULTRY INDUSTRIES. see *AGRICULTURE—Abstracting, Bibliographies, Statistics*

WICKS SUBJECT INDEX OF COMMONWEALTH LEGISLATION. see *LAW—Abstracting, Bibliographies, Statistics*

WILDLIFE ABSTRACTS. see *BIOLOGY—Abstracting, Bibliographies, Statistics*

WILDLIFE REVIEW ABSTRACTS; an indexing service for wildlife management. see *CONSERVATION—Abstracting, Bibliographies, Statistics*

WILDLIFE WORLDWIDE. see *BIOLOGY—Abstracting, Bibliographies, Statistics*

WILSON BIOGRAPHIES. see *BIOGRAPHY—Abstracting, Bibliographies, Statistics*

WILSON BUSINESS ABSTRACTS. see *BUSINESS AND ECONOMICS—Abstracting, Bibliographies, Statistics*

WILSON BUSINESS FULL TEXT. see *BUSINESS AND ECONOMICS—Abstracting, Bibliographies, Statistics*

012   USA
WILSON OMNIFILE FULL TEXT MEGA EDITION. Variant title: OmniFile Full Text Mega Edition. Text in English. 1997. base vol. plus d. updates. USD 11,985 in US & Canada (effective 2006). **Document type:** *Abstract/Index.* **Description:** Indexes and abstracts 2,200 journals, of which more than 1,000 are available full text. Includes the most important titles in business, the humanities, and the social sciences, as well as popular magazines.
Media: Online - full text. **Related titles:** CD-ROM ed.: (from H.W. Wilson, SilverPlatter Information, Inc.); Magnetic Tape ed.
Published by: H.W. Wilson Co., 950 University Ave, Bronx, NY 10452-4224. TEL 718-588-8400, 800-367-6770, FAX 718-590-1617, 800-590-1617, custserv@hwwilson.com, http://www.hwwilson.com/Databases/omnifile.htm. Ed. Barbara Bristow.

WIND ENERGY ABSTRACTS; the international wind power abstracts journal. see *ENERGY—Abstracting, Bibliographies, Statistics*

WOMEN STUDIES ABSTRACTS. see *WOMEN'S STUDIES—Abstracting, Bibliographies, Statistics*

WOMEN'S STUDIES INTERNATIONAL (BALTIMORE). see *WOMEN'S STUDIES—Abstracting, Bibliographies, Statistics*

WORLD AGRICULTURAL ECONOMICS AND RURAL SOCIOLOGY ABSTRACTS; abstracts of world literature. see *AGRICULTURE—Abstracting, Bibliographies, Statistics*

WORLD BANKING ABSTRACTS; the international journal of the financial services industry. see *BUSINESS AND ECONOMICS—Banking And Finance*

WORLD CERAMICS ABSTRACTS. see *CERAMICS, GLASS AND POTTERY—Abstracting, Bibliographies, Statistics*

016   USA   ISSN 1080-7950
WORLD MAGAZINE BANK. Text in English. 1995. m.
Media: CD-ROM. **Related titles:** Online - full text ed.
Published by: EBSCO Publishing (Subsidiary of: EBSCO Industries, Inc.), 10 Estes St, PO Box 682, Ipswich, MA 01938-0682. TEL 978-356-6500, 800-653-2726, FAX 978-356-6565, ep@epnet.com, http://www.epnet.com.

WORLD PATENTS INDEX GAZETTE SERVICE. SECTION P: GENERAL. see *PATENTS, TRADEMARKS AND COPYRIGHTS—Abstracting, Bibliographies, Statistics*

WORLD PATENTS INDEX GAZETTE SERVICE. SECTION R: ELECTRICAL. see *PATENTS, TRADEMARKS AND COPYRIGHTS—Abstracting, Bibliographies, Statistics*

WORLD REPORT ON TECHNICAL ADVANCEMENT. see *TECHNOLOGY: COMPREHENSIVE WORKS—Abstracting, Bibliographies, Statistics*

WORLD SURFACE COATING ABSTRACTS. see *PAINTS AND PROTECTIVE COATINGS—Abstracting, Bibliographies, Statistics*

WORLD TEXTILE ABSTRACTS. see *TEXTILE INDUSTRIES AND FABRICS—Abstracting, Bibliographies, Statistics*

X SEN BUNSEKI TORONKAI KOEN YOSHISHU/ABSTRACTS OF ANNUAL CONFERENCE ON X-RAY CHEMICAL ANALYSIS. see *CHEMISTRY—Abstracting, Bibliographies, Statistics*

016   CHN
XINHUA SHUMUBAO. KEJI XINSHU MUBAN/XINHUA CATALOGUE, SCIENCE & TECHNOLOGY. Text in Chinese. 1963. 3/m. CNY 35.04 (effective 2004). **Document type:** *Catalog, Academic/Scholarly.*
Published by: Xinhua Shumubaoshe, 54, Beilishi Lu, Beijing, 100044, China. TEL 86-10-68347639. **Dist. by:** China International Book Trading Corp, 35 Chegongzhuang Xilu, Haidian District, PO Box 399, Beijing 100044, China. TEL 86-10-68412045, FAX 86-10-68412023, cibtc@mail.cibtc.com.cn, http://www.cibtc.com.cn.

016   CHN
XINHUA SHUMUBAO. SHEKE XINSHU MUBAN/XINHUA CATALOGUE, SOCIAL SCIENCE. Text in Chinese. 1963. 3/m. CNY 42 (effective 2004). **Document type:** *Catalog, Academic/Scholarly.*
Published by: Xinhua Shumubaoshe, 54, Beilishi Lu, Beijing, 100044, China. TEL 86-10-68347639. **Dist. by:** China International Book Trading Corp, 35 Chegongzhuang Xilu, Haidian District, PO Box 399, Beijing 100044, China. TEL 86-10-68412045, FAX 86-10-68412023, cibtc@mail.cibtc.com.cn, http://www.cibtc.com.cn.

YEAR BOOK OF DERMATOLOGY AND DERMATOLOGIC SURGERY. see *MEDICAL SCIENCES—Abstracting, Bibliographies, Statistics*

YEAR BOOK OF RHEUMATOLOGY, ARTHRITIS, AND MUSCULOSKELETAL DISEASE. see *MEDICAL SCIENCES—Abstracting, Bibliographies, Statistics*

YIXUE WENZHAI/MEDICAL ABSTRACTS. see *MEDICAL SCIENCES—Abstracting, Bibliographies, Statistics*

YUKI HANNO KAGAKU TORONKAI KOEN YOKOSHU/ ABSTRACTS OF SYMPOSIUM ON ORGANIC REACTIONS. see *CHEMISTRY—Abstracting, Bibliographies, Statistics*

ZAMBIA SCIENCE ABSTRACTS. see *SCIENCES: COMPREHENSIVE WORKS—Abstracting, Bibliographies, Statistics*

▼ *new title*   ➤ *refereed*   ✳ *unverified*   ◆ *full entry avail.*

011.29171 USA ISSN 1066-4858
DK1
ZARUBEZHNAYA PERIODICHESKAYA PECHAT' NA RUSSKOM
YAZYKE. Text in Russian. 1981. q. USD 25 domestic to
individuals; USD 35 foreign to individuals; USD 40 domestic to
institutions; USD 50 foreign to institutions. adv. illus. reprints
avail. Document type: Abstract/Index.
Formerly (until 1992): Abstracts of Soviet and East European
Emigre Periodical Literature (0738-2707)
Indexed: RASB.
Published by: Informatics & Prognostics, 1400 Shattuck Ave, Ste
7 No 10, Berkeley, CA 94709. TEL 510-236-2935, FAX
510-233-0341. Ed. Leonid Khotin. Adv. contact Galina Gezen.
Circ: 150 (paid).

ZEITSCHRIFTENINHALTSDIENST THEOLOGIE; indices
theologici. see RELIGIONS AND THEOLOGY—Abstracting,
Bibliographies, Statistics

ZEITUNGS - DOKUMENTATION BILDUNGSWESEN. see
EDUCATION—Abstracting, Bibliographies, Statistics

ZEITUNGS - INDEX; Verzeichnis wichtiger Aufsaetze aus
deutschsprachigen Zeitungen. see JOURNALISM—
Abstracting, Bibliographies, Statistics

ZENTRALBLATT FUER GEOLOGIE UND PALAEONTOLOGIE.
TEIL I: ALLGEMEINE, ANGEWANDTE, REGIONALE UND
HISTORISCHE GEOLOGIE. see EARTH SCIENCES—
Abstracting, Bibliographies, Statistics

ZENTRALBLATT FUER GEOLOGIE UND PALAEONTOLOGIE.
TEIL II: PALAEONTOLOGIE. see PALEONTOLOGY—
Abstracting, Bibliographies, Statistics

ZENTRALBLATT FUER JUGENDRECHT; Kindheit - Jugend -
Familie. see LAW—Abstracting, Bibliographies, Statistics

ZENTRALBLATT MATH/MATHEMATICS ABSTRACTS. see
MATHEMATICS—Abstracting, Bibliographies, Statistics

ZEOLITY, IKH SVOISTVA I PRIMENENIE; tekushchii ukazatel'
literatury. see EARTH SCIENCES—Geology

ZEORAITO KENKYU HAPPYOKAI KOEN YOKOSHU/JAPAN
ASSOCIATION OF ZEOLITE. ABSTRACTS OF ANNUAL
MEETING. see ENGINEERING—Abstracting, Bibliographies,
Statistics

ZHONGGUO DAODAN YU HANGTIAN WENZHAI/CHINA
ASTRONAUTICS AND MISSILERY ABSTRACTS. see
AERONAUTICS AND SPACE FLIGHT—Abstracting,
Bibliographies, Statistics

ZHONGGUO GUANGXUE YU YINGYONG GUANGXUE
WENZHAI/CHINESE OPTICS AND APPLIED OPTICS
ABSTRACTS. see PHYSICS—Abstracting, Bibliographies,
Statistics

ZHONGGUO NONGYE WENZHAI - NONGYE
GONGCHENG/CHINESE AGRICULTURAL ABSTRACTS -
AGRICULTURAL ENGINEERING. see AGRICULTURE—
Abstracting, Bibliographies, Statistics

ZHONGGUO SHENGWUXUE WENZHAI/CHINESE BIOLOGICAL
ABSTRACTS. see BIOLOGY—Abstracting, Bibliographies,
Statistics

ZHONGGUO SHUXUE WENZHAI/CHINESE MATHEMATICS
ABSTRACTS. see MATHEMATICS—Abstracting,
Bibliographies, Statistics

ZHONGGUO WUJI FENXI HUAXUE WENZHAI/CHINESE
INORGANIC ANALYTICAL CHEMISTRY ABSTRACTS. see
CHEMISTRY—Abstracting, Bibliographies, Statistics

ZHONGGUO WULI WENZHAI/CHINESE PHYSICS ABSTRACTS.
see PHYSICS—Abstracting, Bibliographies, Statistics

016 CHN ISSN 1005-8923
ZHONGGUO XUESHU QIKAN WENZHAI/CHINESE SCIENCE
ABSTRACT. Text in Chinese. 1994. m. CNY 174 domestic;
USD 174 foreign; CNY 14.50 newsstand/cover (effective
2002). 128 p./no.; Document type: Abstract/Index.
Related titles: Online - full content ed. (from WanFang Data
Corp.).
Indexed: RefZh.
—BLDSC (3181.080000).
Address: Hai-dian qu, Xueyuan Nan Lu #86, Beijing, 100081,
China. zlj@public.sti.ac.cn. Ed. Shu Liu. Circ: 1,200 (paid);
300 (controlled).

ZHONGGUO YAOXUE WENZHAI/CHINESE PHARMACEUTICAL
ABSTRACTS. see ALTERNATIVE MEDICINE—Abstracting,
Bibliographies, Statistics

ZHONGGUO YIXUE WENZHAI (ERKEXUE)/CHINA MEDICAL
ABSTRACTS (PEDIATRICS). see MEDICAL
SCIENCES—Abstracting, Bibliographies, Statistics

ZHONGGUO YIXUE WENZHAI (JIHUA SHENGYU, FUCHAN
KEXUE)/CHINA MEDICAL ABSTRACTS (BIRTH CONTROL
AND GYNECOLOGY). see MEDICAL SCIENCES—
Abstracting, Bibliographies, Statistics

ZHONGGUO YIXUE WENZHAI (KOUQIANG YIXUE)/CHINA
MEDICAL ABSTRACTS (STOMATOLOGY). see MEDICAL
SCIENCES—Abstracting, Bibliographies, Statistics

ZHONGGUO YIXUE WENZHAI (NEIKE XUE)/CHINESE
MEDICAL DIGEST (INTERNAL MEDICINE). see MEDICAL
SCIENCES—Abstracting, Bibliographies, Statistics

ZHONGGUO YIXUE WENZHAI (WEISHENGXUE)/CHINESE
MEDICAL DIGEST (HYGIENICS). see PHYSICAL FITNESS
AND HYGIENE—Abstracting, Bibliographies, Statistics

ZIMBABWE RESEARCH INDEX; register of current research in
Zimbabwe. see SCIENCES: COMPREHENSIVE
WORKS—Abstracting, Bibliographies, Statistics

ZOOLOGICAL RECORD. see BIOLOGY—Abstracting,
Bibliographies, Statistics

ZOOLOGICAL RECORD SERIAL SOURCES. see
BIOLOGY—Abstracting, Bibliographies, Statistics

ZUCKERINDUSTRIE; internationales Fachblatt fuer Technik,
Anbau und Wirtschaft. see FOOD AND FOOD
INDUSTRIES—Abstracting, Bibliographies, Statistics

ACCOUNTING

see BUSINESS AND ECONOMICS—Accounting

ADULT EDUCATION

see EDUCATION—Adult Education

ADVENTURE AND ROMANCE

see LITERATURE—Adventure And Romance

ADVERTISING AND PUBLIC RELATIONS

see also BUSINESS AND ECONOMICS—Marketing
And Purchasing

659.1 USA
A B C NEWS BULLETIN. Text in English. 1950. q. free.
Document type: Bulletin. Description: Report on ABC
activities and board actions after each board meeting.
Published by: Audit Bureau of Circulations, 900 N Meacham Rd,
Schaumburg, IL 60173-4968. TEL 847-605-0909, FAX
847-605-0483, http://www.accessabc.com. Ed. Marybeth Meils.
Circ: 12,352.

659.2 296 USA
A J P R S REPORTER. Text in English. s-a. free. Description:
For Jewish public relations professionals.
Published by: (American Jewish Public Relations Society), Neil
Littauer & Associates, Inc., PO Box 560066, Miami, FL
33256-0066. TEL 305-261-0011. Ed. Bettijane Eisenpreis.
Circ: 500.

659 GBR ISSN 1467-2537
A L F. (Account List File) Text in English. 1998. m. Document
type: Journal, Trade.
Formed by the merger of (1988-1998): Account List File
(1465-3834); (1971-1998): B R A D Agencies and Advertisers
(1356-496X); Which was formerly (until 1994): B R A D
Advertiser & Agency List (0144-6126)
Published by: B R A D Group (Subsidiary of: Emap Media Ltd.),
33-39 Bowling Green Ln, London, EC1R ODA, United
Kingdom. TEL 44-20-7505-8000, FAX 44-20-7833-8201,
http://www.brad.co.uk.

659.1 DEU
A U M A INFOBLAETTER; Daten und Fakten ueber Messen und
Ausstellungen im In- und Ausland. Text in German. m. free.
Document type: Newsletter. Description: Preliminary figures
and information on trade shows and exhibitions in Germany
and worldwide.
Formerly: A U M A Informationsblaetter
Published by: Ausstellungs- und Messe-Ausschuss der
Deutschen Wirtschaft e.V./Association of the German Trade
Fair Industry, Lindenstr 8, Cologne, 50674, Germany. TEL
49-221-20907-0, FAX 49-221-2090712, info@auma.de,
http://auma.de.

659.1 DEU
A U M A - MITTEILUNGEN. Text in German. m. free. Document
type: Newsletter. Description: Information for AUMA
members and the press regarding the work of AUMA.

Published by: Ausstellungs- und Messe-Ausschuss der
Deutschen Wirtschaft e.V./Association of the German Trade
Fair Industry, Lindenstr 8, Cologne, 50674, Germany. TEL
49-221-20907-0, FAX 49-221-2090712, info@auma.de,
http://www.auma.de. Circ: 1,700.

659.1 DNK ISSN 0903-3459
A V HAANDBOGEN MED PRODUCENTERNES KATALOG. Text
in Danish. 1987. a.
Published by: Grafiske Haandboeger, Finsensvej 80,
Frederiksberg, 2000, Denmark. TEL 45-38-88-32-22, FAX
45-38-88-30-38. Ed. Svend Erik Pedersen. adv.: B&W page
DKK 9,950, color page DKK 11,900. Circ: 7,000.

659.1 USA
A W N Y MATTERS. Text in English. 1988. m. membership. adv.
Document type: Newsletter. Description: Informs members
of relevant news and developments on and in the industry.
Published by: Advertising Women of New York, 153 E 57th St,
New York, NY 10022. TEL 212-593-1950, FAX 212-759-2865.
Ed. Phylis Goldberg. Circ: 800.

659 USA
THE AD AGE DAILY WORLD WIRE. Text in English. ceased
2003 (Jan. 17); resumed 199?. d. (Tue.-Fri.). USD 1,195 to
individuals Site license (effective 2002). Description:
Highlights news about product launches, accounts won and
lost, key personnel changes, innovative marketing initiatives,
regulatory changes and trends within broadcast, print and
interactive media.
Media: Online - full text. Related titles: E-mail ed.
Published by: Crain Communications, Inc., 711 Third Ave, New
York, NY 10017-4036. TEL 212-210-0280, info@crain.com,
http://adage.com/about_us/subscriptions/aadww_sub.html,
http://www.crain.com. Ed. Scott Donaton.

659 USA
AD AGE GLOBAL. Variant title: Adageglobal. Text in English.
1997. N.S. 2000 (June). m. USD 49 domestic; USD 79 in
Canada; USD 99 foreign (effective 2001). Document type:
Magazine, Trade. Description: Provides an international
perspective on the advertising industry for global
decision-makers, presents the shifts in continental marketing
and advertising alliances, and the drivers of the worldwide
trends.
Formerly (until Sep. 2000): Advertising Age International
(1524-8984); Incorporates: Euromarketing (0952-3820)
Related titles: Online - full text ed. (from EBSCO Publishing,
Gale Group, H.W. Wilson, O C L C Online Computer Library
Center, Inc.).
Indexed: BPI.
—BLDSC (0678.253220). CCC.
Published by: Crain Communications, Inc., 711 Third Ave, New
York, NY 10017-4036. TEL 212-210-0280, info@crain.com,
http://www.crain.com. Ed. Stefano Hatfield. Circ: 25,230.

659.2 USA
AD AGENCY INSIDER; what's new and what's working for
growing agencies. Text in English. m. USD 349 (effective
2001). Document type: Newsletter, Trade. Description:
Provides practical agency management tips and techniques to
improve billings and profits.
Published by: InfoCom Group, 5900 Hollis St, Ste L, Emeryville,
CA 94608-2008. TEL 510-596-9300, 800-959-1059, FAX
510-596-9331, webmgr@infocomgroup.com,
http://www.infocomgroup.com/aai.html.

659 USA ISSN 0190-7166
AD $ SUMMARY. Text in English. q.
Published by: Competitive Media Reporting, 11 W 42nd St, 11th
Fl, New York, NY 10036. TEL 212-789-1400.

659.1 332.1 USA
AD IDEAS. (Avail. in 6 industry categories.) Text in English. m.
USD 395. Document type: Trade. Description: Provides an
ongoing review of trends in newspaper advertising, reprinting
and commenting on current ads in specific industries.
Examines design, effectiveness and other criteria, and
presents advice on ad strategies and the latest advertising
updates.
Formerly: Ad Trends
Published by: National System, Inc., 56 Worthington Access Dr,
Maryland Heights, MO 63043-3806. TEL 800-231-8179, FAX
314-205-1996. Ed., R&P Jeff Wingbermuehle. Pub. Chase
McKeague.

380.1 IRL ISSN 1649-1432
AD MAG. Text in English. 2000. w. adv. Document type:
Magazine, Trade.
Former titles (until 2001): Ireland Ads (1649-0940); (until 2001):
Dublin Ads (1393-9998)
Published by: Hoson Company, 3-7 Camden Pl., Dublin, 2,
Ireland. TEL 353-1-4784322, FAX 353-1-4781055,
editor@hoson.com, http://www.hoson.com.

659.1 USA
AD - MAG✶. Text in English. 11/yr.
Published by: Advertising Club of Greater St. Louis, P O Box
25880, St. Louis, MO 63136-0880. TEL 314-231-4185, FAX
314-231-4188. Circ: 1,200.

659.1 AUS ISSN 0814-6942
AD NEWS. Text in English. 1928. 25/yr. AUD 90 domestic; AUD 120 in New Zealand; AUD 135 in Asia; AUD 180 elsewhere (effective 2005). adv. illus.; stat. **Document type:** *Magazine, Trade.* **Description:** Serves the advertising, marketing and media industries nationally.
Former titles (until 1984): Advertising News (0814-6934); (until 1971): Advertising and Newspaper News (0001-8929)
Related titles: Online - full text ed.
Indexed: ABIX, BusI.
Published by: Yaffa Publishing Group Pty Ltd., 17-21 Bellevue St, Surry Hills, NSW 2010, Australia. TEL 61-2-92812333, FAX 61-2-92812750, yaffa@yaffa.com.au, http://www.adnews.com.au, http://www.yaffa.com.au. Ed. Edward Charles. Pub. Jeremy Light. Adv. contact James Yaffa. B&W page AUD 3,850, color page AUD 5,340; trim 258 x 358. Circ: 7,550.

659.1 AUS ISSN 0816-3650
AD NEWS HANDBOOK. Text in English. a. AUD 50 domestic; AUD 75 foreign (effective 2005). adv. **Document type:** *Directory, Trade.*
Published by: Yaffa Publishing Group Pty Ltd., 17-21 Bellevue St, Surry Hills, NSW 2010, Australia. TEL 61-2-92812333, FAX 61-2-92812750, yaffa@yaffa.com.au, http://www.yaffa.com.au. Pub. Jeremy Light. Adv. contact Michelle Beckley.

AD NEWS PROMOTIONAL PRODUCTS DIRECTORY. see *BUSINESS AND ECONOMICS—Trade And Industrial Directories*

659.143 USA
AD - TIER NEWSLETTER. Text in English. 1981. m. membership. adv. **Document type:** *Newsletter.* **Description:** Information on cable advertising.
Published by: Cabletelevision Advertising Bureau (CAB), 830 Third Ave, Frnt 2, New York, NY 10022-7522. TEL 212-508-1200. Ed. Steve Raddoclk. Pub., Adv. contact Steve Raddock. Circ: 2,100.

659 USA
AD TRENDS: HOME CENTER✶. Text in English. 1940. m. looseleaf. USD 64.55 (effective 2001). **Description:** Covers all phases of newspaper advertising and merchandising from leading home centers throughout the U.S. and Canada as gleaned from over 100 daily newspapers.
Published by: National Research Bureau, 320 Valley St, Burlington, IA 52601-5513. TEL 319-752-5415, FAX 319-752-3421. Ed. Teresa Levinson.

659 USA
AD TRENDS: SHOPPING CENTER✶. Text in English. 1940. m. looseleaf. USD 42.25 (effective 2001). **Description:** Covers all phases of newspaper advertising and merchandising from leading shopping centers throughout the U.S. and Canada as gleaned from over 100 daily newspapers.
Published by: National Research Bureau, 320 Valley St, Burlington, IA 52601-5513. TEL 319-752-5415, FAX 319-752-3421. Ed. Teresa Levinson.

ADAD; working the media substance since 1917. see *COMMUNICATIONS*

659.1 AUS ISSN 0311-2225
ADBRIEF. Text in English. 1972. w. AUD 440 (effective 1999). bk.rev. **Document type:** *Newsletter.* **Description:** Covers advertising, media news and developments.
Incorporates: Inside Advertising and Media
Related titles: Online - full text ed.
—CCC.
Published by: Newsletter Information Services, PO Box 2095, Manly, NSW 2095, Australia. TEL 61-2-9977-7500, FAX 61-2-9977-3310, customer.support@newsinfo.com.au, http://www.newsinfo.com.au. Ed. Simon Canning. Circ: 550.

380.1029 AUS ISSN 0819-6648
ADBRIEF REGISTER: AGENCIES & MARKETERS. Text in English. 1986. 3/yr. AUD 395, USD 237 per issue (effective 1999). **Document type:** *Directory.* **Description:** Lists advertising agencies, advertising consultancies, media-buying and sales promotion companies, and national and regional advertisers.
Related titles: Diskette ed.
Published by: Newsletter Information Services, PO Box 2095, Manly, NSW 2095, Australia. TEL 61-2-9977-7500, FAX 61-2-9977-3310, customer.support@newsinfo.com.au, http://www.newsinfo.com.au. Ed. Anna Lockwood.

ADBUSTERS; journal of the mental environment. see *ENVIRONMENTAL STUDIES*

659.1 USA
ADCLUBBER. Text in English. 1918. 6/yr. membership. adv. **Document type:** *Newsletter.*
Published by: Advertising Club of Metropolitan Washington, 717 Princess St, Alexandria, VA 22314. TEL 703-683-5954, FAX 703-683-5480, info@dcadclub.com, http://www.dcadclub.com. Ed., R&P Carol Deck. Adv. contact Pat Wilson. Circ: 800 (controlled).

659.1 USA
ADCOM NET. Text in English. 1991. d. free. adv. **Document type:** *Trade.*
Supersedes (in 1996): Ad - Com Magazine (1061-3242)
Media: Online - full text.
Published by: Publitech, Inc., PO Box 840, Sherborn, MA 01770. TEL 508-651-3932, publisher@adcom.net, http://www.adcom.net. Ed. Carl B E Shedd. Pub., R&P Carl B.E. Shedd.

659.1 USA ISSN 0001-8066
ADCRAFTER; the voice of advertising in Detroit. Text in English. 1907. bi-w. USD 30; USD 60 combined subscription Adcrafter & Roster (effective 2005). adv. bk.rev. **Document type:** *Magazine, Trade.*
Published by: Adcraft Club of Detroit, 3011 W Grand Blvd, Ste 1715, Detroit, MI 48202-3000. TEL 313-872-7850, FAX 313-872-7858, adcraft@adcraft.org, http://www.adcraft.org. Ed., R&P Robert Guerrini. Pub. Steve Brown. Adv. contact William Jentzen. color page USD 1,630, B&W page USD 730; trim 8.5 x 11. Circ: 3,200 (paid).

659.1 NLD ISSN 0165-0726
ADFORMATIE. Text in Dutch. 1973. w. (Thu.). EUR 160; EUR 49 to students (effective 2005). adv. **Document type:** *Trade.*
Indexed: ChLitAb.
—IE, Infotrieve.
Published by: Adformatie Groep (Subsidiary of: Wolters Kluwer N.V.), Postbus 75462, Amsterdam, 1070 AL, Netherlands. TEL 31-20-5733644, FAX 31-20-6793581, http://www.adformatie.nl. Ed. Michael van Os. Pub. Berend Jan Veldkamp.

659.1 NLD ISSN 1389-1294
ADFORMATIE BUREAUBIJLAGE. Text in Dutch. 1984. a. EUR 99 (effective 2005); includes supplement. **Description:** Offers a comprehensive overview of the 600 largest advertising agencies involved with the Dutch marketplace.
Former titles (until 1997): Jaarboek Reclamebranche (1383-5599); (until 1996): Adformatie Bureau Bijlage (1387-8859)
Related titles: Supplement(s): Adfo Bureaubijlage Update.
Published by: Adformatie Groep (Subsidiary of: Wolters Kluwer N.V.), Postbus 75462, Amsterdam, 1070 AL, Netherlands. TEL 31-20-5733636, FAX 31-20-6711894, http://www.adformatie.nl/bureaubijlage/. Ed. Sacha Naaraat. Pub. Berend Jan Veldkamp.

659.1 658 GBR ISSN 1353-7318
ADLINE; the marketing magazine for the regions. Text in English. 1980. m. GBP 20. **Document type:** *Trade.*
Published by: Adline Publishing Ltd., 361 Moseley Rd, Birmingham, Worcs B12 9DE, United Kingdom. TEL 0121-446-4466, FAX 0121-446-4462. Ed. Tony Murrey. Circ: 11,225 (controlled).

659.1 658.8 GBR ISSN 0001-8295
HF5801
ADMAP. Text in English. 1964. m. (11/yr.). USD 430 (effective 2004). adv. bk.rev. charts; illus.; stat. back issues avail. **Document type:** *Magazine, Trade.* **Description:** Coverage includes advertising, marketing, research and media planning. Aimed at senior practitioners in these industries.
Related titles: Online - full text ed.
Indexed: ADPA, Emerald, IndBusRep, M&MA, MResA.
—BLDSC (0681.910000), IE, Infotrieve, ingenta. **CCC.**
Published by: N T C Publications Ltd. (Subsidiary of: World Advertising Research Center Ltd.), PO Box 69, Henley-on-Thames, Oxon RG9 1GB, United Kingdom. orders@warc.com, http://store.warc.com/productinfo/3.asp, http://www.warc.com. adv.: B&W page GBP 1,210, color page GBP 1,940; trim 21 x 29.7. Circ: 2,500 (paid).

659.1 NZL ISSN 0112-6997
ADMEDIA. Text in English. 1985. 11/yr. NZD 185 domestic; NZD 310 foreign (effective 2000). adv. bk.rev. back issues avail. **Document type:** *Trade.* **Description:** Covers advertising and media industry news and features for senior executives.
Related titles: Online - full text ed.: (from EBSCO Publishing, Gale Group, ProQuest Information & Learning); ♦ Includes: Agencies & Clients. ISSN 0112-8876; Supplement(s): Fastline.
Indexed: ABIn, INZP, WBA, WMB.
—BLDSC (0678.180000).
Published by: Profile Publishing Ltd., Wellesley St, PO Box 5544, Auckland, New Zealand. TEL 64-9-630-8940, FAX 64-9-630-1046, info@profile.co.nz, http://www.profile.co.nz/. Ed. Paul Panckhurst. Pub. Reg Birchfield. Circ: 1,174.

ADMISSIONS MARKETING REPORT. see *EDUCATION—School Organization And Administration*

659.1 CAN
ADNEWS INSIGHT✶. Text in English. 1981. m. (d. fax subscriptions). CND 195; CND 260 foreign. adv. **Document type:** *Trade.* **Description:** Offers marketing news and information of interest to national advertisers, agencies and media.
Former titles: Adnews (0712-9041); (until 1981): Stimulus Adnews (0711-2297)
Published by: Bale Communications, 80 Park Lawn Rd, Ste 212, Toronto, ON M8Y 3H8, Canada. TEL 416-498-5164, FAX 416-498-6845. Ed. Mike Deibert. Circ: 6,700 (paid).

659.1 GBR ISSN 1350-1402
ADS INTERNATIONAL✶; the magazine for advertising creativity. Text in English. 1988. q. GBP 15. adv. bk.rev. illus. **Document type:** *Trade.*
Formerly (until 1993): HotAds International (0962-7316)
Indexed: DAAI.
—CCC.
Published by: Datateam Publishing Ltd, 15a London Rd, Maidstone, Kent ME16 8LY, United Kingdom. TEL 44-1622-687031, FAX 44-1622-757646, info@datateam.co.uk, http://www.datateam.co.uk/home/home.htm. Ed. Dan Foulkes. Pub. Robert T Prior. R&P Penelope Foulkes. Adv. contact Lawrence McAlister. color page GBP 990. Circ: 7,000.

659.1 ZAF ISSN 1022-6982
ADVANTAGE. Text in English. 1994. m. ZAR 441 domestic; ZAR 528 foreign (effective 2003). adv. illus. **Document type:** *Trade.* **Description:** Overview of advertising, marketing, publishing, and the Internet.
Published by: Primedia Publishing, 366 Pretoria Ave, Ferndale, Randburg, Transvaal 2194, South Africa. TEL 27-11-787-5725, FAX 27-11-787-5776, http://www.primemags.co.za. Ed. John Farquhari. Pub. S Sordon. Adv. contact S Weir. Circ: 3,000.

659.1 NLD ISSN 0001-8856
ADVERTENTIEBLAD. Text in Dutch. 1952. w. USD 20. adv.
Published by: B. V. Rotadruk, Postbus 16, Axel, Netherlands. Ed. Chr van Breemen. Circ: (controlled).

659.1 USA ISSN 1078-6678
HF5805
ADVERTISER & AGENCY RED BOOKS PLUS. Text in English. q. USD 1,295 (effective 1999). **Document type:** *Directory.* **Description:** Features the complete databases of all three Red Books: Standard Directory of Advertisers; Standard Directory of Advertising Agencies; and Standard Directory of International Advertisers and Agencies. Provides insight into the world's top agencies, advertisers, their products, and what media they use.
Media: CD-ROM.
Published by: LexisNexis (Subsidiary of: LexisNexis North America), PO Box 7587, Charlottesville, VA 22906-7587. TEL 434-972-7600, 800-446-3410, llp.customer.support@lexis-nexis.com, http://www.lexislawpublishing.com.

659.1 GBR ISSN 0065-3578
HF5802
ADVERTISER'S ANNUAL. Text in English. 1925. a., latest vol.77, 2002-2003. GBP 260 (effective 2002). adv. **Document type:** *Directory.* **Description:** Lists 4,000 major UK advertisers and 12,000 brands. Includes advertising agencies and their clients; sponsorship consultants; recruitment agencies. ABC/VFD audited newspapers and periodicals; TV and radio advertising listings.
—BLDSC (0712.238000).
Published by: Hollis Publishing Ltd., Harlequin House, 7 High St, Teddington, Middx TW11 8EL, United Kingdom. TEL 44-20-8977-7711, FAX 44-20-8977-1133, orders@hollis-pr.co.uk., http://www.hollis-pr.com/publications/advertisers.htm, http://www.hollis-pr.co.uk/. Ed. Nesta Hollis. Adv. contact Jane Ireland. B&W page GBP 800, color page GBP 1,200; 125 x 245. Circ: 1,100.

659.1 USA ISSN 0001-8899
HF5801 CODEN: ADVAAQ
ADVERTISING AGE; the international newspaper of marketing. Text in English. 1930. w. USD 178.50 domestic; USD 198 in Canada; USD 349 in Europe & Mexico; USD 419 elsewhere (effective 2005). adv. bk.rev. charts; illus.; tr.lit. Index. back issues avail.; reprints avail. **Document type:** *Newspaper, Trade.* **Description:** Reports on all aspects of advertising, including interactive media, marketing research, sales promotion, and brand management.
Incorporates: Advertising Age's Focus (0264-1755)
Related titles: Microfiche ed.: (from CIS); Microform ed.: (from PQC); Online - full text ed.: ISSN 1557-7414 (from EBSCO Publishing, Factiva, Florida Center for Library Automation, Gale Group, H.W. Wilson, LexisNexis, Northern Light Technology, Inc., O C L C Online Computer Library Center, Inc., ProQuest Information & Learning); Supplement(s): Forbes Critical Mass.
Indexed: ABIn, Acal, B&I, BLI, BPI, BPIA, BusI, CADCAM, ChPerI, CurPA, LRI, M&MA, MASUSE, MEDLINE, MagInd, PMR, PROMT, PSI, RASB, ResCtrInd, SRI, T&II, TelAb.
—BLDSC (0712.250000), CASDDS. **CCC.**
Published by: Crain Communications, Inc., 1155 Gratiot Ave, Detroit, MI 48207-2997. TEL 313-446-6000, http://www.adage.com/, http://www.crain.com. Eds. Scott Donaton, Rance Crain, David Klein. Pub. Jill Manee. Adv. contact Paul Audino. B&W page USD 20,090, color page USD 26,205. Circ: 79,500 (paid).

659.1 USA
ADVERTISING AGE CHINA. Text in English. m. **Document type:** *Newsletter, Trade.*
Media: Online - full text.
Published by: Crain Communications, Inc., 360 N Michigan Ave, Chicago, IL 60601-3806. TEL 312-649-5200, FAX 312-280-3183, info@crain.com, http://www.crain.com.

A

659.1 USA ISSN 0747-3168
ADVERTISING & GRAPHIC ARTS TECHNIQUES* . Text in English. 1966. m. USD 10. adv. bk.rev. bibl.; charts; illus.; tr.lit. back issues avail. **Document type:** *Trade.*
Former titles: Advertising Techniques (0001-0235); A A T: Ad Art Techniques
Published by: Advertising Trade Publications, Inc., c/o Dan Barron, Ed, 456 Glenbrook Rd, Stamford, CT 06906-1800. TEL 212-889-6500, FAX 212-889-6504. Circ: 3,766.

659.111 USA ISSN 1528-6428
ADVERTISING & MARKETING REVIEW. Text in English. 1975. m. USD 18. adv. back issues avail. **Document type:** *Magazine, Trade.* **Description:** Serves the advertising and marketing community in Colorado and the organizations that participate in the industry.
Formerly: Colorado M A C News
Related titles: Online - full text ed.
Address: 622 Gardenia Ct, Golden, CO 80401. TEL 303-277-9840, FAX 303-278-9909, kencuster@aol.com, http://www.ad-mkt-review.com. Ed., Pub., R&P, Adv. contact Ken Custer. B&W page USD 1,000, color page USD 1,100; trim 10.88 x 8.38. Circ: 4,000 (controlled).

657 USA ISSN 1534-7311
HF5821
➤ **ADVERTISING & SOCIETY REVIEW.** Text in English. 2000. irreg. **Document type:** *Journal, Academic/Scholarly.* **Description:** Publishes diverse points of view about advertising, both pro and con, with the goal of fostering a better understanding about the role of advertising.
Media: Online - full content (from EBSCO Publishing, Project MUSE). **Related titles:** Online - full text ed.: (from O C L C Online Computer Library Center, Inc.).
Published by: Advertising Educational Foundation, 220 E. 42nd St., Ste. 3300, New York, NY 10017-5806. TEL 212-986-8060, FAX 212-986-8061, sk@aef.com, http://muse.jhu.edu/journals/advertising_and_society_review/toc/asr4.1.html, http://www.aef.com. Ed. William M. O'Barr.

659.13 IND
ADVERTISING BRIEF. Text in English. 1997. bi-m. INR 390, USD 55 (effective 1999). bk.rev.; music rev.; play rev.; tel.rev. charts; illus.; mkt.; maps. 40 p./no. 5 cols./p.; back issues avail. **Document type:** *Proceedings, Trade.* **Description:** Provides information to the advertising and media industry in India.
Published by: Mid-Day Publications Ltd., Unit No.4, Steelmade Industrial Estate, Marol Maroshi Rd., Mumbai, Maharashtra 400 059, India. TEL 91-22-850-4895, FAX 91-22-850-3164, dotcom@mid-day.mailserve.net, upclose@vsnl.com, http://www.mid-day.com/brief/index.asp. Ed. Anil Thakraney. Pub. Hoshie Ghaswalla. adv.: B&W page INR 76,000, color page INR 95,000. Circ: 9,000 (paid); 1,000 (controlled). **Dist. by:** Dangat Newspaper Agency, Bazargate, Fort, Mumbai, Maharashtra 400 001, India. TEL 91-22-262-1235, FAX 91-22-2691236.

659.1 USA
ADVERTISING CLUB OF NEW YORK. NEWSLETTER. Text in English. q. membership only. adv. **Document type:** *Newsletter.*
Published by: Advertising Club of New York, 235 Park Ave S, New York, NY 10003-1405. TEL 212-533-8080. Adv. contact Madhn Malhan.

659.1 USA ISSN 0193-4457
ADVERTISING - COMMUNICATIONS TIMES; business newspaper for the advertising general industry, corporations in Philadelphia, Eastern PA., N.J., and Del. Text in English. 1977. m. USD 39 (effective 2005). adv. tr.lit. back issues avail. **Document type:** *Newspaper, Trade.*
Related titles: Online - full text ed.: (from ProQuest Information & Learning).
Indexed: ABIn.
Published by: Advertising - Communications Times Inc., 121 Chestnut St, Philadelphia, PA 19106. TEL 215-629-1666, FAX 215-923-8358, adcommtimes@aol.com. Pub., R&P Joseph H Ball. adv.: page USD 4,480. Circ: 42,000.

659.1 340 USA ISSN 0277-9943
ADVERTISING COMPLIANCE SERVICE NEWSLETTER. Text in English. 1981. bi-m. USD 545 (effective 2005). adv. **Document type:** *Newsletter, Trade.* **Description:** Aimed at attorneys representing advertisers, advertising agencies, marketers, publishers or broadcasters. Covers the latest developments in the broad advertising law area.
Published by: JLCom Publishing Co., LLC, 26 Hawthorn Dr, Succasunna, NJ 07876-2112. TEL 888-235-2997, FAX 973-252-7552, lawpublish@aol.com, http://www.lawpublish.com. Ed., Pub., R&P, Adv. contact John Lichtenberger.

659.1 USA
ADVERTISING COUNCIL. ANNUAL REPORT. Text in English. 1986. a. **Document type:** *Corporate.*
Former titles: Report to the American People (1061-2912); (until 1987): Advertising Council. Annual Report (0898-3739)
Published by: Advertising Council, 261 Madison Ave, New York, NY 10016-2303. TEL 212-992-1500.

659.1 USA
ADVERTISING CREATIVITY NEWSLETTER. Text in English. 1990. a. looseleaf. USD 19.95 (effective 2000). **Document type:** *Newsletter.* **Description:** Covers various aspects of advertising and public relations.
Published by: Prosperity & Profits Unlimited Distribution Services, PO Box 416, Denver, CO 80201-0416. TEL 303-575-5676. Ed. A. Doyle. R&P A Doyle. Circ: 4,000 (paid).

659.14 330.9 GBR ISSN 0968-2163
ADVERTISING EXPENDITURE FORECASTS. Text in English. 1987. 2/yr. GBP 325 (effective 2000). **Document type:** *Trade.* **Description:** Expenditure by medium in 48 countries to 2002, with backdata to 1988. Includes commentary and advertising forecasts.
Published by: Zenith Media, Bridge House, 63-65 N. Wharf Rd, London, W2 1LA, United Kingdom. TEL 44-20-7224-8500, FAX 44-20-7298-6902, publications@zenithmedia.co.uk, http://www.zenithmedia.com. Ed., Pub. Adam Smith.

659.1 GBR ISSN 1369-3530
THE ADVERTISING FORECAST. Text in English. 1978. q. GBP 825 (effective 2000). **Document type:** *Trade.* **Description:** Provides a guide to budgeting, forecasting and risk analysis in the advertising business.
Formerly: Forecast of Advertising Expenditure (0263-8118)
Related titles: Online - full text ed.: (from EBSCO Publishing).
—CCC.
Published by: (Advertising Association), N T C Publications Ltd. (Subsidiary of: World Advertising Research Center Ltd.), PO Box 69, Henley-on-Thames, Oxon RG9 1GB, United Kingdom. TEL 44-1491-411000, FAX 44-1491-571188, ntc@ntc.co.uk.

ADVERTISING, MARKETING, AND PUBLIC RELATIONS RESOURCES; an internet miniguide. see *BUSINESS AND ECONOMICS—Abstracting, Bibliographies, Statistics*

659.1 USA
ADVERTISING RESEARCH FOUNDATION. TRANSCRIPT PROCEEDINGS. Text in English. irreg. USD 75 to non-members; USD 50 to members. adv. **Document type:** *Proceedings.*
Published by: Advertising Research Foundation, 641 Lexington Ave, 11th Fl, New York, NY 10022. TEL 212-751-5656, FAX 212-319-5265.

659.1 USA
ADVERTISING VIA TELEMARKETING SCRIPT - PRESENTATIONS NEWSLETTER. Text in English. 1990. biennial. looseleaf. USD 39.95 (effective 2000). **Document type:** *Newsletter, Trade.* **Description:** Covers script presentations for telemarketing to various types of businesses.
Published by: Alfreda Doyal, PO Box 416, Denver, CO 80201. TEL 303-575-5676, FAX 970-292-2136, mail@curriculumresourceonline.com, http://www.telemarketingscripts.20m.com. Ed. A Doyle. R&P A. Doyle. Circ: 5,000.

659.1 GBR ISSN 0955-0704
ADVERTISING WORKS. Text in English. 1981. biennial. GBP 48 (effective 2000). **Document type:** *Trade.* **Description:** Twenty case histories from the IPA's most recent advertising effectiveness awards.
—BLDSC (0712.287150), IE, ingenta.
Published by: (Institute of Practitioners in Advertising), N T C Publications Ltd. (Subsidiary of: World Advertising Research Center Ltd.), Farm Rd, Henley-on-Thames, Oxon RG9 1EJ, United Kingdom. TEL 44-1491-411000, FAX 44-1491-571188, ntc_publications@compuserve.com.

659.1 IND ISSN 0001-8988
ADVERTLINK* ; a newspaper on advertising and marketing. Text in English. 1957. fortn. INR 15. adv. bk.rev. bibl.; charts; illus.; mkt.; pat.; tr.lit.; tr.mk.; stat. **Document type:** *Newspaper.*
Published by: Dhiren Mitra Ed. & Pub., 45, Raja Rammohan Sarani, Kolkata, West Bengal 700 009, India. Circ: 1,653.

659 USA ISSN 1549-9553
▼ **ADWEEK.** Text in English. 2003. w. USD 149 domestic; USD 199 in Canada; USD 319 elsewhere; USD 3.95 newsstand/cover (effective 2005). **Document type:** *Magazine, Trade.*
Formed by the merger of (1960-2003): Adweek: Eastern Edition (0199-2864); Which was formerly (until 1979): A N N Y (Advertising news of New York) (0001-2041); (197?-2003): Adweek: Midwest Edition (0276-6612); Which was formerly (until 1981): Adweek. Midwest Advertising News (0199-8188); (19??-2003): Adweek: New England Edition (0888-0840); Which was formerly (until 1986): New England Advertising Week (0028-4653); Which incorporated (1972-1987): Ad East (0192-7922); (1980-2003): Adweek: Southeast Edition (8756-6389); Which was formerly (until 198?): Adweek. Southeast Advertising News (0270-8302); (until 19??): Southern Advertising/Markets (0192-6438); (1979-2003): Adweek: Southwest Edition (0746-892X); Which was formerly (until 198?): Adweek. Southwest Advertising News (0194-3553); (1970-2003): Adweek: Western Edition; Which was formerly (until 19??): Adweek. Western Advertising News (0199-4743); (until 1980): M A C (0194-4789)
Related titles: ♦ Online - full text ed.: Adweek (Online Edition).
Indexed: BPI.
—CCC.
Published by: V N U Business Publications (Subsidiary of: V N U Business Media), 770 Broadway, New York, NY 10003-9595. TEL 646-654-5420, FAX 646-654-5365, info@adweek.com, bmcomm@vnuinc.com, http://www.adweek.com, http://www.vnubusinessmedia.com/. Ed. Sidney Holt. Pub. Ami Brophy. Circ: 26,591 (paid). **Subscr. to:** PO Box 16719, North Hollywood, CA 91615-6719. TEL 800-562-2706, FAX 818-487-4501.

659 USA
ADWEEK (ONLINE EDITION). Text in English. w. USD 149 combined subscription domestic print & online eds. (effective 2003). adv. back issues avail. **Document type:** *Magazine, Trade.*
Media: Online - full text (from EBSCO Publishing, Gale Group, H.W. Wilson, O C L C Online Computer Library Center, Inc., ProQuest Information & Learning). **Related titles:** ♦ Print ed.: Adweek. ISSN 1549-9553; Regional ed(s).: Adweek: Eastern Edition; Adweek: Midwest Edition; Adweek: New England Edition; Adweek: Southeast Edition; Adweek: Western Edition; Adweek: Southwest Edition.
Published by: V N U eMedia (Subsidiary of: V N U Business Media), 770 Broadway, New York, NY 10003 . TEL 646-654-4500, FAX 646-654-7212, info@adweek.com, http://www.adweek.com, http://www.vnuemedia.com/.

ADWEEK DIRECTORY. see *BUSINESS AND ECONOMICS—Trade And Industrial Directories*

AFRICA & MIDDLE EAST MARKET & MEDIAFACT. see *STATISTICS*

659 NZL ISSN 0112-8876
AGENCIES & CLIENTS; the credentials book. Text in English. a., latest 1999, 14th ed. NZD 104.95 domestic; NZD 119.95 foreign (effective 2000). **Document type:** *Trade.* **Description:** Provides details on agency executives, billings, media mix, clients, and brands in 3 categories: Agencies, Direct Agencies & Media Independents. Also includes listings of the creative portfolio services to agencies, animation, audio, production and pos-production companies, and a display showcase for Photographers & Illustrators.
Related titles: ♦ Issued with: AdMedia. ISSN 0112-6997.
Published by: Profile Publishing Ltd., Wellesley St, PO Box 5544, Auckland, New Zealand. TEL 64-9-6301040, FAX 64-9-630-1046, info@profile.co.nz, http://www.profile.co.nz/. Adv. contact Niki O'Brien.

659.1 DEU ISSN 0178-658X
AGENTUREN UND MARKEN ADRESS. Text in German. 1967. 4/yr. EUR 270; EUR 160 newsstand/cover (effective 2004). adv. **Document type:** *Directory, Trade.*
Formerly (until 1985): Media-Adress (0170-4281)
Published by: Media-Daten Verlag GmbH (Subsidiary of: Springer Science+Business Media), Postfach 1546, Wiesbaden, 65173, Germany. TEL 49-611-78780, FAX 49-611-7878465, info@media-daten.de, http://www.media-daten.de. Ed. Sabine Ratzler. Pub. Jan Peter Kruse. Adv. contact Sabine Schueler. B&W page EUR 2,905, color page EUR 4,135. Circ: 1,649 (paid).

659.1 ITA
AGENZIE E CLIENTI. Text in Italian. 1983. 2/yr. EUR 165 per vol.. adv. **Document type:** *Directory.*
Published by: Strategia Editoriale, Piazza della Repubblica 32, Milan, MI 20124, Italy. TEL 39-02-67151202, FAX 39-02-66980255, info@strategia.it, http;//www.strategia.it. Ed. Adolfo Galleazzi.

▼ **AIRCRAFT OWNER;** the monthly buyers guide for aviation products and services. see *TRANSPORTATION—Air Transport*

659.1 SVK
ALMANACH REKLAMY. Text in Slovak. a. **Document type:** *Directory, Trade.*
Published by: Sanoma Magazines Slovakia s.r.o., Kopcianska 6, Bratislava 5, 85101, Slovakia. sanomaslovakia@sanomaslovakia.sk, http://www.sanoma.sk.

659.1 ITA
AMERICA. Text in Italian. 4/yr.
Indexed: BRD, RGAb.
Address: Corso Vercelli, 2, Milan, MI 20145, Italy. TEL 2-49-82-890, FAX 2-469-65-37. Ed. Paolo Galli. Circ: 3,000.

659 USA ISSN 0883-2404
AMERICAN ACADEMY OF ADVERTISING. PROCEEDINGS OF THE CONFERENCE. Text in English. 1977. a. free membership (effective 2005).
Former titles (until 1985): American Academy of Advertising. Proceedings of the Convention (0883-8666); (until 1983): American Academy of Advertising. Proceedings of the Conference (0738-1638); (until 1982): American Academy of Advertising. Proceedings of the Annual Conference (0148-4044)
—BLDSC (6842.935500), IE.
Published by: American Academy of Advertising, c/o Dr Dennis G Martin, Brigham Young University, Department of Communications, E-509 HFAC, Provo, UT 84602-6403. http://advertising.utexas.edu/AAA/proceedings.html.

741.67 USA ISSN 1052-0236
T223.V1
AMERICAN CORPORATE IDENTITY. Text in English. 1986. a. USD 59.95 (effective 2000). **Document type:** *Trade.* **Description:** Reports corporations' visual identities, such as signage, stationery, trademarks, and packaging.
Published by: Art Direction Book Co., Inc., 456 Glenbrook Rd., Glenbrook, CT 06906. TEL 203-353-1441, FAX 203-353-1371. Ed. David E Carter. Pub. Don Barron. Circ: 6,000 (paid).

659 USA
AMERICAN COUNCIL OF HIGHWAY ADVERTISERS. NEWSLETTER* . Text in English. m. **Document type:** *Newsletter.*
Formerly: Roadside Business Association. Newsletter
Published by: American Council of Highway Advertisers, 1421 Prince St, 330, Alexandria, VA 22314. TEL 703-548-9256, FAX 410-867-1764, rico45acp@aol.com. Ed. Richard Roberts. R&P R R Roberts.

AMERICAN NEWS - SAN BERNARDINO. see *ETHNIC INTERESTS*

AMERICAS MARKET & MEDIAFACT. see *STATISTICS*

741.67 USA
NC1001.5
ANDY AWARDS CREATIVE BOOK. Text in English. a. USD 25. adv. **Description:** Showcases winners of the International Andy Award.
Formerly: Andy Awards Souvenir Journal (0270-2525)
Published by: Advertising Club of New York, 235 Park Ave S, New York, NY 10003-1405. TEL 212-533-1570. Adv. contact Madhn Malhan. Circ: 2,000.

659.13 CZE
ANNONCE; noviny po bezplatnou soukromu inzerci. Text in Czech. 1990. 3/w. USD 743. adv. back issues avail. **Document type:** *Newspaper.* **Description:** Publishes personal, real estate, cars, business cooperation ads, as well as commercial and display ads.
Published by: Annonce Prague, Na Porici 30, Prague, 11406, Czech Republic. TEL 42-24-812459, FAX 42-24-811264. Ed. Josef Kudlacek. Adv. contact Hanka Nekvapilova. Circ: 60,000.

659.132 DEU
ANNONCE. Text in German. 2/w. adv. **Document type:** *Bulletin, Consumer.* **Description:** Filled with announcements and advertisements.
Published by: Annonce D. Cohnen Verlags GmbH, Juelicher Str 40-42, Aachen, 52070, Germany. TEL 49-241-508892, FAX 49-241-902400, service@annonce.de, http://www.annonce.de.

659 FRA ISSN 0982-9822
ANNONCES. Text in French. 1945. w. adv. **Document type:** *Newspaper.*
Published by: Editions G. N. Carre, 36 rue de Malte, Paris, 75011, France. TEL 48-05-30-30, FAX 48-05-29-75. Circ: 8,000.

659 SWE ISSN 1653-1973
ANNONSOEREN. Text in Swedish. 1991. bi-m.
Supersedes (in 2004): Saelj- och Marknadsfoering (1650-4658); Which was formerly (until 2002): Saelj- och Markenadsstrategi (1104-9537); (until 1994): Saelj (1102-2728); and incorporated (in 2002): Info (0019-9656); Which was formerly (1926-1955): Annosoeren (1103-0704)
Related titles: Online - full text ed.
Published by: Sveriges Annonsoerer, Drottninggatan 71 C, PO Box 1327, Stockholm, 11183, Sweden. TEL 46-8-54525230, FAX 46-8-235510, info@annons.se, http://www.annons.se. Ed. Bugge Woldner.

659.1 658.8 ESP ISSN 0214-4905
ANUNCIOS; semanario de la publicidad. Text in Spanish. 1980. 45/yr. adv. **Document type:** *Trade.* **Description:** Covers marketing and advertising.
—CCC.
Published by: Publicaciones Profesionales S.A., Principe de Vergara, 15, 3o izda., Madrid, 28001, Spain. TEL 34-1-4357847, FAX 34-1-5753284. Ed. Javier Castro. Pub. Luis Muniz. Adv. contact Esther Valdivia. Circ: 5,000.

659.1 ROM ISSN 1221-5805
ANUNT DE LA A LA Z. Text in Romanian. 1990. w. **Document type:** *Magazine, Consumer.*
Address: Aleea Dealul Mitropoliei nr. 5, sector 4, Bucharest, Romania. TEL 40-21-3366545, FAX 40-21-3363866.

659.1314 DEU ISSN 0173-1882
APOTHEKE HEUTE; Schaufenster - Werbung - Einrichtung - Marketing. Text in German. 1950. q. EUR 6; EUR 3.50 newsstand/cover (effective 2006). **Document type:** *Journal, Trade.* **Description:** Explores store window-dressing and advertising in pharmacies.
Former titles: Schaufenster (Stuttgart) (0173-2110); Aktuelle Schaufenster (0568-7632)
Related titles: ♦ Supplement to: Deutsche Apotheker Zeitung. ISSN 0011-9857.
—BLDSC (1568.907000), GNLM.
Published by: Deutscher Apotheker Verlag, Postfach 101061, Stuttgart, 70009, Germany. TEL 49-711-25820, FAX 49-711-2582290, daz@deutscher-apotheker-verlag.de, http://www.deutscher-apotheker-verlag.de. Ed. Peter Ditzel.

DER APOTHEKEN-FAX-BRIEF. see *PHARMACY AND PHARMACOLOGY*

APPAREL PRODUCTION NEWS. see *CLOTHING TRADE*

ARKANSAS PRESS ASSOCIATION DIRECTORY. see *JOURNALISM*

ARKANSAS PUBLISHER. see *JOURNALISM*

ARKANSAS PUBLISHER WEEKLY. see *JOURNALISM*

659.1 DEU
ART DIRECTORS CLUB JAHRBUCH. Text in German. 1965. a. EUR 108 (effective 2004). adv. back issues avail. **Document type:** *Yearbook, Trade.*
Published by: (Art Directors Club Deutschland), Verlag Hermann Schmidt Mainz, Robert-Koch-Str 8, Mainz, 55129, Germany. TEL 49-6131-506030, FAX 49-6131-506080, info@typografie.de, http://www.typografie.de/verlagsverzeichnis/werbung/656-8.html. Circ: 5,000.

THE ART OF SELF PROMOTION; nuts and bolts for manageable marketing. see *BUSINESS AND ECONOMICS—Small Business*

ASIA PACIFIC MARKET & MEDIAFACT. see *STATISTICS*

ASIA PACIFIC PUBLIC RELATIONS JOURNAL. see *POLITICAL SCIENCE*

ASIAN BRAND NEWS; the essential read for marketing professionals. see *BUSINESS AND ECONOMICS—Marketing And Purchasing*

070 JPN
ASIAN MEDIA DIRECTORY* . Text in English. 1974. a. USD 90. adv. **Document type:** *Directory.*
Formerly: Asian Press and Media Directory
Published by: Syme Media Enterprises Ltd., c/o Intercontinental Marketing Corp, I.P.O. Box 5056, Tokyo, 100-30, Japan.

659.1 HKG ISSN 1561-7351
ASIAN P R NEWS; the essential read for business communications. Text in English. bi-w. HKD 2,250 domestic; USD 288 foreign (effective 2000). adv. **Document type:** *Magazine, Trade.* **Description:** Delivers hard news on the major players of the day and addresses the issues that challenge the public relations industry.
Published by: Media & Marketing Ltd., 28/F, Dorset House, 979 Kings Rd, Quarry Bay, Hong Kong. TEL 852-2577-2628, FAX 852-2576-9171, askme@media.com.hk, http://www.media.com.hk. Ed. Sharon Desker Shaw. Pub. Ken McKenzie. Adv. contact Steve Bruce. B&W page HKD 5,608, color page HKD 8,018; trim 181 x 260. Circ: 300 (paid and controlled).

659.14 DNK ISSN 0108-3120
AUDIO VISUELLE MEDIA. Variant title: A V M Scandinavia (Dansk Udg.). Text in Danish. 11/yr. DKK 300 (effective 2000). adv. **Document type:** *Newspaper.*
Related titles: Norwegian ed.: Audiovisuelle Medier. ISSN 0804-0281.
Published by: Specialbladsforlaget, Finsensvej 80, Frederiksberg, 2000, Denmark. TEL 45-38-88-32-22, FAX 45-38-88-30-38. Ed. Per Rahauge Rasmussen. adv.: B&W page DKK 21,900, color page DKK 25,950; trim 360 x 265. Circ: 11,164.

659.1 USA
AUDIT BUREAU OF CIRCULATIONS. ANNUAL CONFERENCE RECAP. Text in English. a. **Document type:** *Newsletter.*
Formerly: Audit Bureau of Circulations. Annual Meeting. Proceedings
Published by: Audit Bureau of Circulations, 900 N Meacham Rd, Schaumburg, IL 60173-4968. TEL 847-605-0909, FAX 847-605-0483, http://www.accessabc.com.

AUSTRALIA. BUREAU OF STATISTICS. SELECTED BUSINESS SERVICES, AUSTRALIA. see *BUSINESS AND ECONOMICS—Abstracting, Bibliographies, Statistics*

659 AUS ISSN 0067-1606
AUSTRALIAN ADVERTISING RATE AND DATA SERVICE. Abbreviated title: A.A.R.D.S. Text in English. 1935. m. (11/yr.). AUD 4,117.58 for Print & Online Eds. (effective 2001). adv. **Document type:** *Trade.* **Description:** Contains comprehensive listings, including contact details and advertising rates, of all known Australian newspapers and magazines, radio and television stations, and outdoor media.
Related titles: Online - full content ed.
Published by: Reed Business Information Pty Ltd (Subsidiary of: Reed Business Information International), Locked Bag 2999, Chatswood, NSW 2067, Australia. customerservice@reedbusiness.com.au, http://www.reedbusiness.com.au. Ed. Michael Rafferty. Pub. Barrie Parsons. Adv. contact Dennis Russell.

659 760 AUS ISSN 1324-1613
AUSTRALIAN CREATIVE. Text in English. 1995. s-a. AUD 32 domestic; AUD 42 in New Zealand; AUD 48 in Asia; AUD 64 elsewhere (effective 2005). adv. **Document type:** *Trade.* **Description:** For creative executives and production managers in advertising agencies, design studios, production houses and marketing companies.
Published by: Yaffa Publishing Group Pty Ltd., 17-21 Bellevue St, Surry Hills, NSW 2010, Australia. TEL 61-2-92812333, FAX 61-2-92812750, yaffa@yaffa.com.au, http://www.yaffa.com.au. Ed. Robyn Gower. Pub. Jeremy Light. Adv. contact James Yaffa. B&W page AUD 2,000, color page AUD 2,690; trim 210 x 297. Circ: 8,043.

AUSTRALIAN JOURNAL OF COMMUNICATION. see *COMMUNICATIONS*

AUTO - CENTRUM. see *TRANSPORTATION—Automobiles*

AUTO FOTO. see *TRANSPORTATION—Automobiles*

658.8 AUS ISSN 1325-9210
B & T WEEKLY. (Broadcasting and Television) Text in English. 1950. w. AUD 161.70 (effective 2001). adv. bk.rev. charts; illus. back issues avail. **Document type:** *Trade.* **Description:** Covers advertising, public relations, journalism and marketing.
Former titles: Broadcasting (0005-268X); Television
Related titles: Online - full text ed.: (from EBSCO Publishing, Gale Group, LexisNexis).
Indexed: ABIX.
Published by: Reed Business Information Pty Ltd (Subsidiary of: Reed Business Information International), Locked Bag 2999, Chatswood, NSW 2067, Australia. customerservice@reedbusiness.com.au, http://www.reedbusiness.com.au. Ed. Lara Sinclair. Pub., R&P Barrie Parsons. Adv. contact Dennis Russell. B&W page AUD 3,090, color page AUD 4,345; 220 x 305. Circ: 6,906.

659.1 AUS ISSN 0810-669X
B & T YEAR BOOK. Text in English. 1958. a. AUD 198.66 (effective 2001). adv. back issues avail. **Document type:** *Trade.* **Description:** Comprehensive contact information for all major media, advertising and marketing services, and related industries.
Formerly: Broadcasting and Television Year Book (0084-8093)
Published by: Reed Business Information Pty Ltd (Subsidiary of: Reed Business Information International), Locked Bag 2999, Chatswood, NSW 2067, Australia. customerservice@reedbusiness.com.au, http://www.reedbusiness.com.au. Ed. Michael Rafferty. Pub. Barrie Parsons. Adv. contact Dennis Russell. Circ: 3,500 (paid).

659.1029 USA
B M A MEMBERSHIP DIRECTORY AND RESOURCE GUIDE. Text in English. 1986. a. USD 75 membership academic; USD 150 membership business (effective 2000). 200 p./no.; **Document type:** *Directory, Trade.* **Description:** Includes company addresses, phone numbers, titles, and a yellow pages section of services for business communications professionals.
Former titles: B M A Membership Directory and Yellow Pages; B - P A A Membership Directory and Yellow Pages
Related titles: Online - full content ed.
Published by: Business Marketing Association, 400 N Michigan Ave, 15th Fl, Chicago, IL 60611-4104. TEL 312-409-4262, 800-664-4262, FAX 312-409-4266, bma@marketing.org, http://www.marketing.org/resourcedirectorycategories.html. Ed. Barbara Waldorf. Circ: 5,000.

659.1 USA
B P A INTERNATIONAL. ANNUAL REPORT. Text in English. a. **Document type:** *Corporate.*
Formerly: Business Publications Audit of Circulations. Annual Report
Published by: B P A International, 2 Corporate Dr., Ste 900, Shelton, CT 06484-6259. TEL 212-779-3200, FAX 212-725-1721.

B2B E-NEWSLETTER. see *BUSINESS AND ECONOMICS*

BACON'S NEWSPAPER - MAGAZINE DIRECTORY. see *BUSINESS AND ECONOMICS—Trade And Industrial Directories*

BANK ADVERTISING NEWS; the independent national newspaper of financial marketing. see *BUSINESS AND ECONOMICS—Banking And Finance*

BEGA DISTRICT NEWS. see *GENERAL INTEREST PERIODICALS—Australia*

659.1 DEU
BERLINER TYPE. Text in German. a. **Document type:** *Directory, Trade.* **Description:** Contains documentation and articles on actual trends in corporate photography, catalogues, sales folders, image brochures, presentations and annual reports.
Published by: Varus Verlag, Konrad-Zuse-Platz 1-3, Bonn, 53227, Germany. TEL 49-228-944660, FAX 49-228-9446666, info@varus.com, http://www.varus.com.

A

▼ new title ➤ refereed * unverified ♦ full entry avail.

659.1 658 AUT
BESTSELLER. Text in German. m. EUR 56 domestic; EUR 97 foreign (effective 2005). adv. **Document type:** *Magazine, Trade.*
Indexed: RASB.
Published by: Manstein Zeitschriften Verlagsgesellschaft mbH, Brunner Feldstr 45, Perchtoldsdorf, N 2380, Austria. TEL 43-1-866480, FAX http://www.manstein.at, 43-1-86648100, office@manstein.at, http://www.manstein.at/Magazine/Bestseller/. Ed. Maximilian Mondel. Adv. contact Martina Hofmann. B&W page EUR 2,690, color page EUR 4,250; trim 210 x 280. Circ: 12,800 (paid and controlled).

659.3 USA ISSN 1082-9660
BIG PICTURE. Text in English. 1996. bi-m. USD 42 domestic; USD 97 in Canada; USD 145 elsewhere (effective 2005). adv. **Document type:** *Magazine, Trade.* **Description:** Covers digitally printed visual communications for fine art, retail advertising, trade shows, and photographic applications. Explains the digital processes from image capture and retouching to color management, image processing, output and display.
Related titles: Online - full content ed.; Special ed(s).: Big Picture. Buyer's Guide.
—CCC.
Published by: S T Media Group International, Inc., 407 Gilbert Ave, Cincinnati, OH 45202. TEL 513-421-2050, FAX 513-421-5144, http://www.bigpicture.net. Ed. Greg Sharpless. Pub. Steve Duccilli. adv.: B&W page USD 6,176, color page USD 7,476. Circ: 32,000 (paid and controlled).

BILBOERSEN. see *TRANSPORTATION—Automobiles*

659.1 USA
BODY COPY∗. Text in English. 1989. bi-m. USD 20. **Description:** Provides highlights on the people working in advertising. Articles are written by industry professionals.
Published by: Breznan Publishing Company, Inc., 11190 Carpenter Rd, Flushing, MI 48433-9746. TEL 213-470-9809. Ed. David Breznau.

BOOT FOTO. see *SPORTS AND GAMES—Boats And Boating*

659.1 BWA
BOTSWANA ADVERTISER. Text in English. w.
Address: Broadhurst, Nakedi Rd 5647, PO Box 130, Gaborone, Botswana.

659.1 658 JPN
BRAIN∗ /BUREIN. Text in Japanese. 1961. m. JPY 17,820. back issues avail.
Indexed: e-psyche.
Published by: Seibundo Shinkosha Inc., 3-3-11 Hongo, Bunkyoku, Tokyo, 164-0013, Japan. Ed. H Hayakawa. Circ: 40,000.

659 GBR ISSN 0965-9390
BRAND STRATEGY. Text in English. 1991. m. GBP 345 in Europe; GBP 365 elsewhere (effective 2000). stat. back issues avail. **Document type:** *Newsletter.* **Description:** Provides news and information especially relevant to individuals involved in brand management and new product development.
Related titles: Online - full text ed.: (from EBSCO Publishing, Gale Group, Northern Light Technology, Inc., O C L C Online Computer Library Center, Inc., ProQuest Information & Learning).
Indexed: ABIn.
—IE.
Published by: Centaur Publishing, St Giles House, 50 Poland St, London, W1V 4AX, United Kingdom. TEL 44-20-79704000, FAX 44-20-7970-4009, joannap@centaur.co.uk. Ed. Joanna Perkin. Circ: 563 (paid).

659.1 USA ISSN 1064-4318
HF5801 CODEN: BANDEN
BRANDWEEK; the newsweekly of marketing communications . Text in English. 1980. w. (46/yr.). USD 149 domestic; USD 342 in Canada; USD 319 foreign; USD 3.95 per issue (effective 2005). adv. bk.rev. charts; illus.; stat. back issues avail.; reprints avail. **Document type:** *Magazine, Trade.* **Description:** Contains news briefs, trends, new campaigns and promotions, and new product news on marketer/retailer relationships, successful media strategies, agency/client relationships, and global marketing.
Incorporates (in 2003): Adweek Magazines' Technology Marketing (1536-2272); Which had former titles (until 1997): Marketing Computers (0895-5697); (until 1987): Adweek's Computer and Electronics Marketing (0884-5549); (until 1985): Computer and Electronics Marketing (8750-1848); Which incorporated (1983-1985): Computer Advertising News (8750-9288); Former titles (until 1992): Adweek's Marketing Week (0892-8274); (until 1986): Adweek (National Marketing Edition) (0888-3718); Which superseded (in 1985): Ad Forum (0274-6328)
Related titles: Microform ed.: (from PQC); Online - full text ed.: (from bigchalk, EBSCO Publishing, Factiva, Florida Center for Library Automation, Gale Group, H.W. Wilson, Northern Light Technology, Inc., O C L C Online Computer Library Center, Inc., ProQuest Information & Learning).
Indexed: ABIn, B&I, BPI, BPIA, LRI, T&II.
—BLDSC (2269.980000), IE, ingenta. **CCC.**
Published by: V N U Business Publications (Subsidiary of: V N U Business Media), 770 Broadway, New York, NY 10003-9595. TEL 646-654-7604, 800-722-6658, info@brandweek.com, bmcomm@vnuinc.com, http://www.brandweek.com, http://www.vnubusinessmedia.com/. Ed. Karen Benezra. Pub., Adv. contact Charlotte Erwin TEL 323-525-2276. B&W page USD 9,450, color page USD 14,540. Circ: 24,103 (paid). **Subscr. to:** PO Box 16749, North Hollywood, CA 91615-9465.

THE BRANDWEEK DIRECTORY. see *BUSINESS AND ECONOMICS—Trade And Industrial Directories*

BRIEFING; publicidade - media - marketing. see *BUSINESS AND ECONOMICS—Marketing And Purchasing*

BRITAIN'S ADVERTISING INDUSTRY (YEAR). see *BUSINESS AND ECONOMICS—Trade And Industrial Directories*

BRITISH RATE AND DATA. see *BIBLIOGRAPHIES*

659.1 004.6 USA ISSN 1539-3690
HF6146.I58
BROADBAND ADVERTISING. Text in English. 2001. m. USD 1,095; USD 1,490 combined subscription print & e-mail eds. (effective 2005). adv. **Document type:** *Newsletter, Trade.*
Formed by the merger of (1980-2001): Cable T V Advertising (0270-885X); (1998-2001): Internet Advertising (1523-584X)
Related titles: E-mail ed.: USD 995 (effective 2005).
Published by: Kagan Research, LLC, One Lower Ragsdale Dr, Bldg One, Ste 130, Monterey, CA 93940. TEL 831-624-1536, FAX 831-625-3225, info@kagan.com, http://www.kagan.com. Pub. Paul Kagan. adv.: page USD 3,670.

659.1 USA
BULLDOG REPORTER; an insider's report on agency and corporate media relations. Text in English. 1979. bi-w. USD 549 (effective 2003). adv. cum.index. back issues avail. **Document type:** *Newsletter, Trade.* **Description:** Provides up to date information on the movements and placement of the most influential media professionals in the business.
Related titles: Regional ed(s).: Bulldog Reporter (East Coast Edition); Bulldog Reporter (West Coast Edition).
Published by: InfoCom Group, 5900 Hollis St, Ste L, Emeryville, CA 94608-2008. TEL 510-596-9300, 800-959-1059, FAX 510-596-9331, webmgr@infocomgroup.com, http://www.infocomgroup.com. Ed. Clare Curley. Pub. Margaret Beck.

659.1 USA ISSN 1529-5133
Z284
BULLDOG REPORTER'S BOOK MARKETING AND PUBLICITY; what's new and what's working to increase book sales. Text in English. 1998. fortn. USD 299 domestic; USD 319 in Canada & Mexico; USD 339 elsewhere (effective 2000). back issues avail. **Document type:** *Newsletter, Trade.*
Published by: InfoCom Group, 5900 Hollis St, Ste L, Emeryville, CA 94608-2008. TEL 510-596-9300, 800-959-1059, FAX 510-596-9331, bmp@infocomgroup.com, http://www.infocomgroup.com/, http://infocomgroup.com. Ed. Kristin Benden. Pub. James Sinkinson.

BURRELLE'S CHESAPEAKE BAY MEDIA DIRECTORY (YEAR); DE, MD, VA, DC. see *BUSINESS AND ECONOMICS—Trade And Industrial Directories*

BURRELLE'S MEDIA DIRECTORY (CD-ROM EDITION). see *COMMUNICATIONS*

BURRELLE'S MEDIA DIRECTORY. VOL 1, NEWSPAPERS & RELATED MEDIA. see *COMMUNICATIONS*

BURRELLE'S MEDIA DIRECTORY. VOL 2, MAGAZINES & NEWSLETTERS. see *COMMUNICATIONS*

BURRELLE'S MEDIA DIRECTORY. VOL 3, BROADCAST & RELATED MEDIA. see *COMMUNICATIONS*

BURRELLE'S MIDWEST MEDIA DIRECTORY (YEAR); IL, WI, IN, MI, OH. see *BUSINESS AND ECONOMICS—Trade And Industrial Directories*

BURRELLE'S MINNESOTA MEDIA DIRECTORY (YEAR). see *BUSINESS AND ECONOMICS—Trade And Industrial Directories*

BURRELLE'S NEW ENGLAND MEDIA DIRECTORY (YEAR). see *BUSINESS AND ECONOMICS—Trade And Industrial Directories*

BURRELLE'S SOUTHEAST MEDIA DIRECTORY (YEAR); FL, GA, NC, SC, TN. see *BUSINESS AND ECONOMICS—Trade And Industrial Directories*

BURRELLE'S TEXAS MEDIA DIRECTORY (YEAR). see *BUSINESS AND ECONOMICS—Trade And Industrial Directories*

BURRELLE'S WEST MEDIA DIRECTORY (YEAR); CA, OR, WA, AZ. see *BUSINESS AND ECONOMICS—Trade And Industrial Directories*

659.1 USA ISSN 1070-0250
BUSINESS LIFE MAGAZINE - GREENSBORO; the business magazine of the Piedmont Triad. Text in English. 1989. m. USD 24 (effective 2005). adv. bk.rev.; software rev.; video rev. illus. back issues avail. **Document type:** *Magazine, Trade.* **Description:** Contains people-oriented business information.
Related titles: Online - full text ed.
Published by: Business Life Magazine (Greensboro), 4101 A Piedmont Pkwy, Greensboro, NC 27410. TEL 336-812-8801, FAX 336-812-8832, info@bizlife.com, http://www.bizlife.com. Ed. Lynne Brandon. Pub. Robert Kober. R&P Kay M Meekins. Adv. contact Robert Gainey. B&W page USD 2,750; trim 10.88 x 8.38. Circ: 13,000.

659.1 658.8 GBR ISSN 1470-708X
BUSINESS RATIO. ADVERTISING AGENCIES. Text in English. 1984. a. GBP 275 (effective 2001). charts; stat. **Document type:** *Trade.* **Description:** Examines the industry structure of advertising agencies, market size and trends, recent developments and prospects, and major company profiles.
Former titles (until 2000): Business Ratio Plus: Advertising Agencies (1357-1648); (until 1993): Business Ratio Report: Advertising Agencies (0267-0402)
Published by: The Prospect Shop Ltd., Field House, 72 Oldfield Rd, Hampton, Middx TW12 2HQ, United Kingdom. TEL 44-20-8461-8730, 44-20-8481-8720, FAX 44-20-8783-1940, info@theprospectshop.co.uk.

659.1 GBR ISSN 1470-7098
BUSINESS RATIO. PUBLIC RELATIONS CONSULTANCIES. Text in English. 1987. a. GBP 275 (effective 2001). **Document type:** *Trade.*
Former titles (until 2000): Business Ratio Plus: Public Relations Consultancies (1356-0158); (until 1994): Key Note Report: Public Relations Consultancies (0963-441X); (until 1989): Business Ratio Report: Public Relations Consultants (0952-4371)
Published by: The Prospect Shop Ltd., Field House, 72 Oldfield Rd, Hampton, Middx TW12 2HQ, United Kingdom. TEL 44-20-8461-8730, 44-20-8481-8720, FAX 44-20-8783-1940, info@theprospectshop.co.uk.

659.1 GBR
BUSINESS RATIO REPORT: SIGN AND STREET FURNITURE MANUFACTURERS; an industry sector analysis. Text in English. 1987. a. **Document type:** *Trade.*
Formerly (until 1992): Business Ratio Report: Signs and Street Furniture (0952-0775)
Published by: The Prospect Shop Ltd., Field House, 72 Oldfield Rd, Hampton, Middx TW12 2HQ, United Kingdom. TEL 44-20-8461-8730, 44-20-8481-8720, FAX 44-20-8783-1940, info@theprospectshop.co.uk.

659.111 USA
THE BUSINESS - TO - BUSINESS MARKETER. Text in English. 1977. m. USD 75 membership academic; USD 150 membership corporate (effective 2000). adv. bk.rev. charts; illus.; tr.lit. **Document type:** *Newsletter, Trade.* **Description:** Contains business-to-business marketing, advertising and public relations news.
Former titles: Business - to - Business Marketing Communications; Communicator (Alexandria, 1977); B - P A A Communicator (0896-7849)
Related titles: Online - full content ed.: B 2 B Marketer.
Published by: Business Marketing Association, 400 N Michigan Ave, 15th Fl, Chicago, IL 60611-4104. TEL 312-409-4262, 800-664-4262, FAX 312-409-4266, bma@marketing.org, http://205.158.47.30/frames/learninglibrary.html, http://www.marketing.org. Ed. Rick Kean. Circ: 4,500.

659.1 USA ISSN 0095-5531
HF5843
BUYERS' GUIDE TO OUTDOOR ADVERTISING. Text in English. s-a. USD 425 (effective 1998). **Document type:** *Directory.*
Published by: Competitive Media Reporting, 11 W 42nd St, 11th Fl, New York, NY 10036. TEL 212-789-1400.

BUZZ (ROCHESTER); perspectives on marketing technology. see *BUSINESS AND ECONOMICS—Marketing And Purchasing*

659 SWE ISSN 1650-7924
BYRAABOKEN. Text in Swedish. 1987. a. SEK 695 (effective 2004).
Formerly (until 2001): Reklambyraaer i Sverige (0284-0413)
Related titles: Online - full text ed.
Published by: Sveriges Reklamfoerbund/Association of Advertising Companies, Sveavaegen 34, Stockholm, 11134, Sweden. TEL 46-8-6790800, FAX 46-8-6790801, http://www.reklam.se.

659.1 CAN
C C A B CIRCULATE. Text in English. 1973 (vol.4). q. **Document type:** *Newsletter.*
Published by: Canadian Circulations Audit Board, Inc., 90 Eglinton Ave E, Ste 980, Toronto, ON M4P 2Y3, Canada. TEL 416-487-2418, FAX 416-487-6405, info@bpai.com, http://www.bpai.com. Ed. Patrick Sweeney. Circ: 4,000.

659.1 CAN ISSN 1704-3816
C C N MATTHEWS C C E DIRECTORY. Key Title: CCNMatthews CCE Directory. Text in English. 1993. s-a. **Document type:** *Directory, Trade.*

Formerly (until 2002): Matthews C C E Directory (1192-6325)
Published by: C C N Matthews, 8th Fl 48 Yonge St, Toronto, ON M5E 1G6, Canada. TEL 416-362-0885, FAX 416-362-6669, info@ccnmatthews.com, http://www.cdn-news.com/.

C M A COMMUNICATOR. see *BUSINESS AND ECONOMICS—Marketing And Purchasing*

659.2 BEL ISSN 0778-1032
C V NEWS. (Curriculum Vitae) Variant title: Curriculum Vitae News. Text in Dutch. 1990. w. (50/yr). bk.rev. back issues avail. **Document type:** *Newsletter, Trade.* **Description:** News of the advertising, marketing and media professions.
Related titles: Supplement(s): BEF 300 per vol. (effective 2000).
Published by: C V News, Rijkendalstraat 12, Strombeek, 1853, Belgium. TEL 32-2-267-5653, FAX 32-2-267-1813. Ed. Josephine Overeem. Circ: 500 (paid).

384.555 USA
CABLE T V FACTS. Text in English. 1983. a. USD 10 to non-members (effective 1998). adv. **Document type:** *Directory.*
Published by: Cabletelevision Advertising Bureau (CAB), 830 Third Ave, Frnt 2, New York, NY 10022-7522. TEL 212-508-1200, FAX 212-832-3268. Ed., Pub., Adv. contact Steve Raddock.

659 070 GBR ISSN 0008-2309
PN4701 CODEN: CMPGBW
CAMPAIGN (LONDON, 1968); the national weekly of the communications business, embracing advertising, marketing, newspapers and magazines, television, radios and posters. Text in English. 1968. w. GBP 129 domestic; GBP 164 in Europe & Ireland; GBP 237 elsewhere (effective 2004). adv. bk.rev. illus. reprints avail. **Document type:** *Magazine, Trade.*
Related titles: Online - full text ed.: (from EBSCO Publishing, Florida Center for Library Automation, Gale Group, LexisNexis, Northern Light Technology, Inc., O C L C Online Computer Library Center, Inc., ProQuest Information & Learning).
Indexed: ABIn, ADPA, B&I, DAAI, Emerald, IndBusRep, M&MA, PhotoAb.
—BLDSC (3016.300000). **CCC.**
Published by: Haymarket Business Publications Ltd., 174 Hammersmith Rd, London, W6 7JP, United Kingdom. TEL 44-20-82675000, FAX 44-20-82674268, campaign@haynet.com, hpg@haymarketgroup.com, http://www.haymarketgroup.com. Ed. Claire Beale TEL 44-20-82674893. Pub. Petra Green TEL 44-20-82674867. Adv. contact Gena Merson TEL 44-20-82674923. Circ: 16,452 (paid). **Dist. by:** Frontline, Park House, 117 Park Rd, Peterborough, Cambs PE1 2TS, United Kingdom. TEL 44-1733-555161, FAX 44-1733-562788.

659 AUS ISSN 1030-004X
CAMPAIGN BRIEF (SYDNEY). Text in English. 1986. a. AUD 35 per issue (effective 2000); free with magazine subscription. adv. **Document type:** *Directory, Trade.* **Description:** Contains directory of advertising, media PR industry and associated industries—From advertising agencies to voice overs—For the West Australian industry only.
Published by: Campaign Brief Pty. Ltd., Campaign Brief House, 29-31 Myrtle St, North Sydney, NSW 2060, Australia. TEL 61-2-9954-0042, FAX 61-2-9954-0263, cbperth@ozemail.com.au. Ed. Kim Shaw. Circ: 2,000. **Subscr. to:** PO Box 699, West Perth, W.A. 6872, Australia.

659 AUS ISSN 1444-5743
CAMPAIGN BRIEF (WEST PERTH). Text in English. 1984. 6/yr. AUD 42 domestic includes Local Trade Directory (effective 2000).. adv. back issues avail. **Document type:** *Trade.* **Description:** Focuses on creative issues in production of TV, print and cinema advertising, for everyone involved in the creative processes.
Former titles (until 1998): Campaign Brief W A (1444-5751); (until 1996): Campaign Brief (0816-4789)
Published by: Campaign Brief Pty. Ltd., Level 1, Forest Centre, 14-16 Rowland St., Subiaco, W.A. 6005, Australia. TEL 61-8-93809044, FAX 61-8-93809069, cbperth@ozemail.com.au. Ed. Kim Shaw. Pubs. Kim Shaw, Michael Lynch. Adv. contact Michael Lynch. B&W page AUD 1,400, color page AUD 2,000; trim 240 x 330. Circ: 2,000 (paid). **Subscr. to:** PO Box 699, West Perth, W.A. 6872, Australia.

659 AUS
CAMPAIGN BRIEF ASIA. Text in English. 1996 (Oct.). q. AUD 28 domestic (effective 2000). adv. **Document type:** *Trade.*
Published by: Campaign Brief Pty. Ltd., Level 1, Forest Centre, 14-16 Rowland St., Subiaco, W.A. 6005, Australia. TEL 61-8-93809044, FAX 61-8-93809069, http://www.campaignbrief.com/html/home.asp. Eds., Pubs. Kim Shaw, Michael Lynch. adv.: color page USD 2,000. Circ: 3,000 (paid).

659 AUS
CAMPAIGN BRIEF - AUSTRALIA. Text in English. 1987. 10/yr. AUD 55 domestic (effective 2000). adv. **Document type:** *Trade.*
Published by: Campaign Brief Pty. Ltd., Level 1, Forest Centre, 14-16 Rowland St., Subiaco, W.A. 6005, Australia. TEL 61-8-93809044, FAX 61-8-93809069, cbperth@ozemail.com.au. Ed. Michael Lynch. Pubs. Kim Shaw, Michael Lynch. adv.: color page AUD 2,100. Circ: 5,000 (paid).

658 MEX ISSN 1563-7026
CAMPECHE COLONIAL; revista mensual de publicidad. Text in Spanish. irreg. free (effective 2001). adv.
Media: Online - full text.
Published by: Alpha One Publicidad, Calle 10 No. 471 Altos, Col. San Roman, Campeche, Campeche, Mexico. TEL 52-9-8163603, alphaone64@yahoo.com, http://www.geocities.com/MadisonAvenue/Boardroom/4238/index.html.

CAMPGROUND & COTTAGE RESORT MANAGEMENT. see *TRAVEL AND TOURISM*

CAPELL'S CIRCULATION REPORT, INC.; the newsletter of magazine circulation. see *PUBLISHING AND BOOK TRADE*

659.1 658 USA ISSN 1076-6081
CARD TALK. Text in English. 1980. q. USD 15; USD 18 foreign (effective 1997). adv. bk.rev. back issues avail. **Document type:** *Newsletter.* **Description:** Covers facests of business cards including their use as effective tools for advertising, marketing, promotion, sales, public relations and networking.
Published by: American Business Card Club, PO Box 460297, Aurora, CO 80046-0297. TEL 303-690-6496. Ed., Pub., R&P, Adv. contact Avery N Pitzak. Circ: 500 (paid).

CERCA E TROVA; settimanale di inserzioni gratuite. see *GENERAL INTEREST PERIODICALS—Italy*

659.1 USA
CHICAGO ADVERTISING & MEDIA. Text in English. s-m. USD 25. adv. tr.lit.
Published by: K B Communications, PO Box 5353, Chicago, IL 60680-5353. TEL 630-271-1133, FAX 630-271-1144. Ed. Joe Brar. Circ: 10,000.

659.1 GBR ISSN 0953-7457
CHINA MEDIA BOOK ✱ ; China's advertising rates & media. Text in English. 1988. biennial. GBP 75. **Document type:** *Trade.*
Published by: Anglo-Chinese Publications Ltd., 17 Belmont, Lansdown Rd, Bath, Avon BA1 5DZ, United Kingdom. TEL 44-1225-339516. Ed. Marcus H Langston. Circ: 1,500.

659.1 200 USA ISSN 0744-4370
CHRISTIAN ADVERTISING FORUM ✱ . Text in English. 1981. bi-m. USD 18. adv.
Address: PO Box 21433, Roanoke, VA 24018-0145. Ed. Stephen M Wike. Circ: 2,460.

659.1 USA ISSN 1081-1346
CLASSIFIED COMMUNICATION ✱ ; the newsletter for small budget advertising. Text in English. 1990. m. USD 33; USD 45 in Canada; USD 55 elsewhere. bk.rev. **Document type:** *Newsletter.*
Published by: Classified Communication Inc., PO Box 4177, Prescott, AZ 86302-4177. TEL 520-778-6788, FAX 520-445-0517, classcomm@aol.com. Ed., Pub. Agnes Franz. R&P Magda Gregory.

CLUB MODELE. see *CLOTHING TRADE—Fashions*

659.1029 USA
HF5827.4
CO-OP ADVERTISING PROGRAM SOURCEBOOK (YEAR). Text in English. 1981. s-a. USD 637 (effective 2005). adv. 960 p./no.; **Document type:** *Directory.* **Description:** Used to find manufacturers' co-op programs that retailers and wholesalers use to fund advertising and promotional campaigns. Details over 5,000 programs, including the way the programs work, rules for eligibility, creative materials available, timing, and reimbursement.
Formerly (until 1997): Co-op Source Directory (0736-0878)
Related titles: Magnetic Tape ed.
Published by: National Register Publishing (Subsidiary of: Marquis Who's Who), 562 Central Ave, New Providence, NJ 07974. TEL 800-473-7020, FAX 908-673-1189, NRPsales@marquiswhoswho.com, http://www.co-opsourcebook.com, http://www.nationalregisterpub.com. Circ: 2,872. **Subscr. to:** Reed Reference Publishing, Order Dept, Box 31, New Providence, NJ 07974-9903. TEL 800-521-8110.

741.67 746.92 700 FRA ISSN 1152-8885
COLLECTOR. Text in French. 1990. q. adv. **Description:** Devoted to mass-media images (advertising, graphic arts, fashion, contemporary art).
Published by: Editions du Triangle Rose, 45 rue Sedaine, Paris, Cedex 11 75557, France. TEL 43-57-52-05, FAX 43-57-80-40. Ed. Pascal Le Coq. Circ: 10,000.

COLOR NEWS. see *BEAUTY CULTURE*

COMMUNICARE; Journal of Communication Sciences. see *COMMUNICATIONS*

659.1 NLD ISSN 1381-4974
COMMUNICATIE; vakblad voor communicatie professionals. Text in Dutch. 1963. m. (11/yr). EUR 135 to individuals; EUR 49 to students; EUR 15 per issue (effective 2005). adv. illus. **Document type:** *Journal, Trade.* **Description:** Offers communications professionals information on interesting cases, interviews with industry leaders, and news of developments and innovations in the field.
Formed by the 1995 merger of: Communicatief (0922-2944); P R en V (0927-619X); Which was formerly (until 1991): P R en Voorlichting (0165-7232); (until 1979): Provisorium (0928-5342)
Related titles: ♦ Online - full content ed.: Communicatie Online.
—IE, Infotrieve.
Published by: Kluwer B.V. (Subsidiary of: Wolters Kluwer N.V.), Postbus 23, Deventer, 7400 GA, Netherlands. TEL 31-570-673449, FAX 31-570-691555, http://www.communicatieonline.nl/, http://www.kluwer.nl. Ed. Rocco Mooij. Pub. Rogier Mulder. Adv. contact Ilja van Zijl. Circ: 3,600 (paid and controlled).

COMMUNICATIO SOCIALIS; internationale Zeitschrift fuer Kommunikation in Religion, Kirche und Gesellschaft. see *RELIGIONS AND THEOLOGY—Roman Catholic*

659.1 760 USA ISSN 0010-3519
NC997.A1
COMMUNICATION ARTS. Text in English. 1959. 8/yr. USD 53 domestic; USD 70 in Canada; USD 110 elsewhere (effective 2004). adv. bk.rev.; software rev. illus. back issues avail.; reprints avail. **Document type:** *Magazine, Trade.* **Description:** Publishers articles on graphic design firms, advertising agencies and illustrated studies of outstanding people in the field. For designers, art directors, design firms, corporate design departments, agencies, and everyone involved in visual communications.
Formerly (until 1969): C A Magazine (0884-0008)
Related titles: CD-ROM ed.; Online - full text ed.
Indexed: ABIPC, ABM, ArtInd, DAAI, GALA, RASB.
—BLDSC (3359.339000), IE, Infotrieve, ingenta.
Address: 110 Constitution Dr, Menlo Park, CA 94025. TEL 650-326-6040, 800-258-9111, FAX 650-326-1648, ca@commarts.com, http://www.commarts.com/CA. adv.: B&W page USD 8,550, color page USD 11,330. Circ: 90,000 (paid).

659.1 333.7 USA
COMMUNICATOR (SCOTTSDALE). Text in English. a. membership. **Description:** Presents membership activities and news.
Formerly: Communicators Showcase
Published by: Utility Communicators International, c/o Robert Janke, 5525 E Grandview Rd, Scottsdale, AZ 85254. TEL 602-971-1989.

COMMUNICATOR'S NOTEBOOK. see *JOURNALISM*

659.1 USA
COMMUNIQUE. Text in English. 3/yr. free to members. **Description:** For advertising and public relations employees in the insurance industry.
Formerly: Life Communications
Published by: Insurance and Financial Communicators Association, PO Box 387, East Rutherford, NJ 07073. TEL 201-939-4739, FAX 201-584-0254, http://www.ifcaonline.org. Ed. Carol Morgan.

659.1 360 USA
COMMUNITY FOCUS. Text in English. q. free. **Document type:** *Newsletter.* **Description:** Informs First Nationwide employees and the public about the community-service events the bank sponsors throughout the nation.
Published by: California Federal Bank, Corporate Communications, 135 Main St, San Francisco, CA 94105-1817. TEL 415-904-1203. Ed. Mary Rische.

COMPENDIUM OF GOVERNMENT ISSUES AFFECTING DIRECT MARKETING. see *BUSINESS AND ECONOMICS—Marketing And Purchasing*

COMPUTER FEATURES DIRECTORY. see *COMPUTERS—Computer Industry Directories*

659 ARG ISSN 0326-3185
COMUNICACION; del area latinoamericana. Text in Spanish. 1980. m.
Published by: Editorial Profesionales Publicitarios, P B, Viamonte, 1653, Capital Federal, Buenos Aires 1055, Argentina. Ed. Juan Carlos Escalera Moya.

659.1 COL ISSN 0120-1638
COMUNICACION INTEGRAL. Text in Spanish. 1974. q. COP 400, USD 12. adv. bk.rev.
Published by: Entropia Grupo de Comunicacion Empresarial Integral, Apartado Aereo 3139, Medellin, ANT, Colombia. Ed. Humberto Lopez. Circ: 2,500.

COMUNICACION Y SOCIEDAD. see *COMMUNICATIONS*

COMUNICARTE. see *COMMUNICATIONS*

A

658.0071 USA
CONSULTING SUCCESS ONLINE. Text in English. 1983. q. USD 50 membership (effective 2005). back issues avail. **Document type:** *Newsletter.* **Description:** Includes tips on managing small businesses, pricing services, marketing, what's new in the field of writing and communications consulting and networking for new members.
Former titles: Consulting Success; Professional Writing Consultant
Media: Online - full text.
Published by: Association of Professional Communication Consultants, 211 E 28 St, Tulsa, OK 74114. TEL 918-743-4793, http://www.consultingsuccess.org/publications/consultingsuccess/index.htm. Ed. Betsy Frick. Circ: 200.

659.143 USA ISSN 0738-291X
CONTACTS; the media pipeline for public relations people. Text in English. 1970. w. USD 443 (effective 2005). cum.index. back issues avail. **Document type:** *Newsletter, Trade.* **Description:** Outlines the information needs of editors, writers and producers of magazines (consumer & trade), newspapers, TV & radio, providing contact information.
Published by: MerComm, Inc., 500 Executive Blvd, Ste 200, Ossining, NY 10562. TEL 914-923-9400, FAX 914-923-9484, rwitt@mercommawards.com. Ed. Nora Madonik. Pub. Reni L Witt. Circ: 5,000 (paid).

659 ESP
CONTROL. Text in Spanish. 1962. m. adv.
Formerly: Control de Publicidad y Ventas (0573-8636)
—CCC.
Published by: P C Disc S.A., Ferraz, 11 Piso 1, Madrid, 28008, Spain. TEL 1-247-30-00, FAX 1-248-11-23. Ed. Francisco Javier San Roman y Perez. Circ: 5,000.

659.1314 USA
THE CORPORATE LOGO; the monthly sales magazine for promotional product distributors. Text in English. 13/yr. USD 85 domestic; USD 100 in Canada; USD 150 elsewhere (effective 2005). adv. **Document type:** *Magazine, Trade.* **Description:** Covers news and trends affecting the promotional products marketplace, selling strategies, ideas and techniques to help every distributor increase his or her bottom line.
Published by: Virgo Publishing, Inc., 3300 N. Central Ave., Ste 300, Phoenix, AZ 85012. TEL 480-990-1101, FAX 480-990-0819, tcl@vpico.com, cs@vpico.com, http://www.corporatelogo.com, http://www.vpico.com. adv.: B&W page USD 3,760, color page USD 4,950; bleed 8.375 x 11.125. Circ: 20,000.

659.1 FRA ISSN 1268-6905
CORRESPONDANCE DE LA PUBLICITE; quotidien d'information et de documentation professionnelles. Text in French. d. adv. **Description:** Provides professional news and data on the advertising industry.
Published by: Societe Generale de Presse et d'Editions, 13 av. de l'Opera, Paris, 75001, France. TEL 33-1-40151715, FAX 33-1-40151789. Ed. Etienne Lacour. Pub. Marianne Berard Quelin. Circ: 3,000.

659.1 658.8 USA
COUNSEL✶. Text in English. 1974. q. membership. **Description:** For marketing and public relations officials.
Published by: National Council for Marketing and Public Relations, 4602 W 21st St, CIR, Greeley, CO 80634-3277. Ed. Geraldine Gallagher. Circ: 2,000.

659.1 USA ISSN 0011-0027
COUNSELOR (LANGHORNE). Text in English. 1954. m. USD 75 (effective 2005). adv. bk.rev. **Document type:** *Magazine, Trade.* **Description:** Publishes news for professionals in promotional marketing and specialty advertising management who are listed with the Advertising Specialty Institute.
Published by: Advertising Specialty Institute, 4800 Street Rd, Trevose, PA 19053. TEL 215-953-4000, FAX 215-953-3034, info@asicentral.com, http://www.promomart.com, http://www.asicentral.com. Ed. Richard Kern. Pub. Rick Fairfield. Circ: 9,000 (controlled).

CRAP HOUND. see *ART*

659.1 USA ISSN 0737-5883
CREATIVE; the magazine of promotion and marketing. Text in English. 1966. bi-m. USD 30 domestic; USD 50 foreign; USD 4 newsstand/cover (effective 2004). adv. bk.rev. **Document type:** *Magazine, Trade.* **Description:** Published in the interest of sales promotion and marketing executives who manage point-of-purchase displays, trade show exhibits and sales promotion programs.
Formerly: Creative Signs and Displays
Related titles: Microfiche ed.: (from PQC); Online - full text ed.
Published by: Magazines Creative, Inc., 42 W 38th St, New York, NY 10018. TEL 212-840-0160, FAX 212-819-0945, creativemag@comvision.com, http://www.creativemag.com. Ed. David H Flaserstein. adv.: B&W page USD 1,910; trim 8.25 x 10.875. Circ: 15,000.

659.1 IRL
CREATIVE. Text in English. fortn.
Published by: Concept & Realisation Ltd., 23 The Mews, Upper Mount St., Dublin, 2, Ireland. TEL 762212, FAX 761204. Ed. Garrett Stokes.

CREATIVE MARKETING; incentives in retail promotion. see *BUSINESS AND ECONOMICS—Marketing And Purchasing*

659.1 USA ISSN 1064-3915
CREATIVE NEW JERSEY. Text in English. 1987. bi-m. USD 14.95. **Document type:** *Trade.* **Description:** Reports on the State's advertising industry and related businesses.
Published by: Carlsun Publications, 4 New St, Ramsey, NJ 07446. TEL 201-670-8688, FAX 201-670-4484. Ed. Sally Jane Gellert. adv.: B&W page USD 1,746; trim 16 x 9.75. Circ: 17,882.

CREATIVE REVIEW. see *BUSINESS AND ECONOMICS—Marketing And Purchasing*

659.1 USA ISSN 1541-3403
HF5801
CREATIVITY. Text in English. 1993. 10/yr. USD 99 combined subscription domestic print & online eds.; USD 109.95 combined subscription in Canada print & online eds.; USD 139.95 combined subscription elsewhere print & online eds. (effective 2005). adv. **Document type:** *Magazine, Trade.* **Description:** Covers technological developments affecting the advertising design field.
Formerly (until 2001): Advertising Age's Creativity (1072-9119)
Related titles: Online - full text ed.: (from EBSCO Publishing, Factiva).
—CCC.
Published by: Crain Communications, Inc., 1155 Gratiot Ave, Detroit, MI 48207-2997. TEL 313-446-6000, info@crain.com, http://www.getcreativity.com, http://www.crain.com. Ed. Ann Diez. adv.: color page USD 8,300, B&W page USD 6,500; trim 11 x 14.5. Circ: 25,582 (controlled).

740 USA ISSN 0097-6075
NC997
CREATIVITY (GLENBROOK). Text in English. 1971. a. USD 62.95 (effective 2000). **Document type:** *Trade.* **Description:** Examines advertising art.
Supersedes (1960-1965): Advertising Directions
Related titles: Online - full text ed.
Published by: (Art Direction Magazine), Art Direction Book Co., Inc., 456 Glenbrook Rd., Glenbrook, CT 06906. TEL 203-353-1441, FAX 203-353-1371. Circ: 6,700.

659.2 USA
CRISIS MANAGEMENT REPORTER; damage control when you need it. Text in English. m. USD 190; USD 210 foreign (effective 1999). index. **Document type:** *Newsletter.* **Description:** For the investor relations or public relations professional who may have to face answering to stockholders, government regulators, the public, and the press regarding such issues as minority group relations, labor unrest, product tampering, community protests, and financial malfeasance.
Published by: Kennedy Information Inc., One Kennedy Place, Rte 12 S, Fitzwilliam, NH 03447. TEL 603-585-3101, 800-531-0007, FAX 603-585-9555, http://www.kennedyinfo.com. Ed. Gerald Murray.

659.2 USA ISSN 1528-3836
CRISIS MANAGER. Text in English. 2000. m. free. bk.rev. **Document type:** *Newsletter, Trade.* **Description:** Covers everything from crisis case histories, book reviews, analyses of current breaking crises, and editorials on the state of crisis management today.
Media: Online - full content. **Related titles:** E-mail ed.
Published by: Bernstein Crisis Management LLC, 1013 Orange Ave, Monrovia, CA 91016-3724. TEL 626-305-9277, FAX 877-471-1573, jonathan@bernsteincrisismanagement.com, http://www.bernsteincom.com/newsletter.html.

CROSS AND TALK; for communications between you and the world. see *COMMUNICATIONS*

D M A STATISTICAL FACT BOOK. see *BUSINESS AND ECONOMICS—Marketing And Purchasing*

DAGENS MEDIA; affaerstidningen om marknadsfoering och medieval. see *BUSINESS AND ECONOMICS—Marketing And Purchasing*

DALTONS WEEKLY; your perfect partner for buying and selling. see *REAL ESTATE*

659.1 DNK ISSN 1602-9992
DANSK ANNONCOERFORENING. ANNONCOERGUIDE. Text in Danish. 1979. a. DKK 395 per issue (effective 2004). **Document type:** *Directory, Trade.*
Former titles (until 2001): Annoncoerforenings Bureaufortegnelse (0108-2191); (until 1980): Fortegnelse over Reklamebureauer - Konsulenter og Specialvirksomhede i Danmark (0108-2183); Which was formed by the merger of (196?-1979): Oversigt over Autoriserede Reklamebureauer i Danmark (0902-4670); Which was formerly (until 1976): Oversigt over Reklamebureauer i Danmark (0902-3984); (19??-1979): Fortegnelse over Konsulenter og Specialvirksomheder i Markedsfoering og Reklame
Published by: Dansk Annoncoerforening/Association of Danish Advertisers, Soeborg Hovedgade 65B, Soeborg, 2860, Denmark. TEL 45-39-274346, FAX 45-39-274946, daf@annoncoer.dk, http://www.annoncoer.dk.

659.1 658.8 DNK ISSN 0109-0968
DANSK FAGPRESSEKATALOG. Text in Danish. 1984. a. DKK 295 (effective 2004). adv. **Document type:** *Catalog.* **Description:** Provides price and media information on Danish business and trade papers.
Related titles: Online - full text ed.: 1984.
Published by: Dansk Fagpresse Service, Pressens Hus, Skindergade 7, Copenhagen K, 1159, Denmark. TEL 45-33-974000, FAX 45-33-912670, df@danskfagpresse.dk, http://www.danskfagpresse.dk. adv.: B&W page DKK 12,500, color page DKK 14,900; trim 210 x 297. Circ: 950 (paid); 3,050 (controlled).

DANSK PRESSE. see *JOURNALISM*

659.1 ITA ISSN 0038-9501
DATI E TARIFFE PUBBLICITARIE; prontuario dei mezzi pubblicitari italiani. Text in Italian. 1963. 4/yr. EUR 620 (effective 2005). adv. **Document type:** *Directory, Trade.*
Related titles: Online - full text ed.: EUR 1,100 (effective 2005).
Published by: Strategia Editoriale, Piazza della Repubblica 32, Milan, MI 20124, Italy. TEL 39-02-67151202, FAX 39-02-66980255, info@strategia.it, http://www.strategia.it.

659.1 USA ISSN 1070-7409
DELANEY REPORT. Text in English. 1990. w. USD 265; USD 348 by fax. **Document type:** *Newsletter.* **Description:** Covers news, trends in marketing, advertising, and media.
Related titles: Fax ed.
Address: 149 Fifth Ave, New York, NY 10010. TEL 212-979-7881, FAX 212-979-0691. Ed., Pub., R&P Thomas F Delaney.

DEMEURES ET CHATEAUX. see *REAL ESTATE*

741.6029 USA ISSN 1092-1389
TS23
THE DESIGN FIRM DIRECTORY - GRAPHIC DESIGN EDITION; a listing of firms and consultants in graphic design in the U.S. Text in English. 1979. a. USD 59 (effective 1998). **Document type:** *Directory.*
Supersedes in part (in 1997): Design Firm Directory - Graphic and Industrial Design Edition (0889-7611); Which superseded in part (in 1986): Design Directory (0195-4326)
Published by: Wefler & Associates, Inc., 6 Milburn Park., Evanston, IL 60201-1744. TEL 847-475-1866. Ed., Pub. W Daniel Wefler. Circ: 1,000.

659.1 DEU
DEUTSCHER KOMMUNIKATIONSVERBAND B D W. JAHRBUCH. Text in German. a. **Document type:** *Yearbook, Trade.* **Description:** Covers trends and developments in one-to-one and business-to-business and business-to-consumer communications.
Published by: (Deutscher Kommunikationsverband B D W e.V.), Varus Verlag, Konrad-Zuse-Platz 1-3, Bonn, 53227, Germany. TEL 49-228-944660, FAX 49-228-9446666, info@varus.com, http://www.varus.com.

659 DEU ISSN 0934-9057
DEUTSCHER VERTRIEBS- UND VERKAUFS-ANZEIGER; Zeitschrift fuer Handel, Dienstleistung und Industrie. Text in German. 1988. m. adv. **Document type:** *Magazine, Trade.*
Related titles: Online - full text ed.
Published by: Gesellschaft fuer Unternehmensberatung im Telefonverkauf und Aussendienst GmbH, Hunaeusstr 10, Celle, 29227, Germany. TEL 49-5141-85011, FAX 49-5141-85933, info@guta.de, http://www.guta.de. Adv. contact Gabriele Lechner. B&W page EUR 13,910.40, color page EUR 17,388; trim 280 x 420. Circ: 135,050 (controlled).

659.1 DEU ISSN 0082-1802
DEUTSCHER WERBEKALENDER; Taschenbuch fuer Marketing und Werbung. Text in German. 1964. a. EUR 36 (effective 2004). adv. **Document type:** *Directory, Trade.*
Published by: Verlagsgruppe Handelsblatt GmbH, Kasernenstr 67, Duesseldorf, 40213, Germany. TEL 49-211-8870, FAX 49-211-371792, leser-service@vhb.de, http://www.absatzwirtschaft.de/dwk, http://www.vhb.de. adv.: B&W page EUR 1,600, color page EUR 2,890. Circ: 4,780 (paid and controlled).

659.1 USA
DIAMOND TRAIL NEWS. Text in English. 1975. w. USD 22 in state; USD 28 out of state; USD 50 foreign (effective 2000). bk.rev. back issues avail. **Document type:** *Newspaper.*
Address: P O Box 267, Sully, IA 50251-0267. TEL 641-594-4488, FAX 641-594-4498, DTNews@aol.com. Ed., Pub., R&P Mark Davitt. Circ: 1,800 (paid).

DIRECT LINE. see *BUSINESS AND ECONOMICS—Marketing And Purchasing*

DIRECT MARKETING (ONLINE EDITION); using direct response advertising to enhance marketing database. see *BUSINESS AND ECONOMICS—Marketing And Purchasing*

DIRECT MARKETING ASSOCIATION. ANNUAL REPORT. see *BUSINESS AND ECONOMICS—Marketing And Purchasing*

DIRECT MARKETING MARKET PLACE; the networking source of the direct marketing industry. see *BUSINESS AND ECONOMICS—Marketing And Purchasing*

659.1 658 USA
DIRECT RESPONSE SPECIALIST✶ . Text in English. 1982. m. USD 77 (effective 1997). adv. bk.rev. back issues avail. **Document type:** *Newsletter.* **Description:** Discusses effective response and profit techniques.
Formerly (until 1987): Mail Order Connection
Published by: Galen Stilson Ed. & Pub., 4036 Mermoor Ct, Palm Harbor, FL 34685-1105. TEL 813-786-1411, FAX 813-785-7049, gstilson@mindspring.com.

659.1 658 USA ISSN 1087-2183
DIRECTION (ALLENDALE). Text in English. 1979. bi-m. USD 40; USD 50 foreign (effective 1999). adv. bk.rev. back issues avail. **Document type:** *Newsletter.* **Description:** Provides tips on how to better influence buying decisions, with emphasis on more productive and profitable use of direct mail, sales promotion, publicity and other marketing tools.
Published by: Direct Marketing Consultants, Inc., 705 Franklin Tpke, Allendale, NJ 07401-1637. TEL 201-327-9213, FAX 201-327-9213. Ed., R&P Hugh P Curley. Circ: 4,927.

DIRECTIONS (NEW YORK). see *BUSINESS AND ECONOMICS—Marketing And Purchasing*

659.2 MEX
DIRECTORIO M P M - AGENCIAS Y ANUNCIANTES/M P M - MEXICAN ADVERTISING AGENCIES DIRECTORY; personal y cuentas. (Medios Publicitarios Mexicanos) Text in Spanish. 1964. s-a. USD 80; USD 60 newsstand/cover (effective 2001). adv. **Document type:** *Directory, Trade.*
Published by: Medios Publicitarios Mexicanos S.A., Av Eugenia 811, Col. Del Valle, Mexico City, DF 03100, Mexico. TEL 52-5-5523-3342, FAX 52-5-5523-3379, http://www.mpm.com.mx. Ed. Fernando A Villamil. Circ: 1,500.

DIRECTORIO M P M - MEDIOS IMPRESOS/M P M - MEXICAN PRINT MEDIA RATES & DATA; tarifas y datos-anuncio exterior, periodicos y revistas. (Medios Publicitarios Mexicanos) see *ADVERTISING AND PUBLIC RELATIONS—Abstracting, Bibliographies, Statistics*

DIRECTORY OF ADVERTISING AGENCIES. see *BUSINESS AND ECONOMICS—Trade And Industrial Directories*

659.1029 USA
DIRECTORY OF MAILING LIST COMPANIES. Text in English. 1955. irreg., latest vol.13, 1999. USD 50 (effective 2000). adv. **Document type:** *Directory.* **Description:** Provides the names and addresses of more than 1,000 mailing list specialists. Includes list brokers, compilers and owners as well as list management companies, co-operative mailers, package insert programs and card deck mailers, with name of contacts, phone numbers and types of lists carried.
Formerly (until 1991): Directory of Mailing List Houses (0419-2923)
Published by: Todd Publications, 500, Millwood, NY 10546-0500. TEL 914-358-6213, FAX 914-358-1059, toddpub@aol.com, http://www.toddpublications.com. Ed., Pub., R&P, Adv. contact Barry Klein.

DIRECTORY OF MAJOR MAILERS & WHAT THEY MAIL (YEAR). see *BUSINESS AND ECONOMICS—Trade And Industrial Directories*

DIRECTORY WORLD'S YELLOW PAGES INDUSTRY SOURCE BOOK. see *BUSINESS AND ECONOMICS—Trade And Industrial Directories*

659.1 GBR
THE DOOR-TO-DOOR MARKETING HANDBOOK. Text in English. 1989. a. free. adv. back issues avail. **Document type:** *Directory, Trade.* **Description:** Contains a list of companies able to deliver advertising and promotional materials to households throughout the UK, along with background information.
Formerly: Letterbox Marketing Handbook
Published by: Association of Household Distributors Ltd., 7 Parsonage Pl, Tring, Herts HP23 5AT, United Kingdom. TEL 44-1442-890991, FAX 44-1442-890992, ahd@epinet.co.uk, http://www.ahd.org.uk. Ed., Adv. contact Shelley Radice. Circ: 3,000 (controlled).

659.1 DEU
DOPPELPUNKT. Text in German. 1984. m. adv. **Document type:** *Magazine, Trade.*
Published by: Neue Toene Werner Mende Verlag oHG, Am Haag 10, Reichenberg, 97234, Germany. TEL 49-931-69469, FAX 49-931-69470, http://www.doppelpunkt.de. adv.: B&W page EUR 1,340, color page EUR 2,365. Circ: 44,817 (controlled).

659.1 340 USA
DO'S AND DON'TS IN ADVERTISING. Text in English. 1949. base vol. plus m. updates. looseleaf. USD 500; USD 350 renewals (effective 2000); CBBB members get reduced rate or free subscription dependent on dues schedule. **Document type:** *Corporate.* **Description:** Contains numerous Federal Trade Commission, Food and Drug Administration, Federal Communications Commission, and other agency regulations and guides. Summarizes key legal decisions, and state and federal laws affecting advertising. Over 4,000 pages updated monthly.
Published by: Council of Better Business Bureaus, Publications Department, 4200 Wilson Blvd, Arlington, VA 22203-1804. TEL 703-276-0100. Ed. Wendi Dee. R&P Steven B Davis.

354.35 USA ISSN 0363-2830
DOWNTOWN PROMOTION REPORTER. Text in English. 1976. m. USD 189 (effective 2005). illus. 12 p./no.; back issues avail.; reprints avail. **Document type:** *Newsletter, Trade.* **Description:** Focuses on bringing more people downtown for shopping, sales and special events. Covers tested promotional ideas, public relations, increasing participation, image building, seasonal promotions.
Published by: (Downtown Research & Development Center), Alexander Communications Group, Inc., 28 W 25th St, 8th Fl, New York, NY 10010. TEL 212-228-0246, 212-232-4317, FAX 212-228-0376, info@downtowndevelpment.com, info@alexcommgrp.com, http://www.downtowndevelopment.com/, http://www.alexcommgrp.com. Ed. Mary Klein. Pub. Margaret Dewitt.

E & W P.O.S.; das Insider-Magazin fuer Verkaufsprofis. (Elektro und Wirtschaft) see *BUSINESS AND ECONOMICS—Marketing And Purchasing*

659.132 USA
THE E-ZINE ADSOURCE DIRECTORY WEEKLY. Text in English. 1998. w. free. **Description:** Covers all aspects of advertising via e-zines.
Media: Online - full text.
Published by: Upstat, Inc., 7654 W. Moorefield Dr., Frankfort, IL 60423-7500. TEL 770-682-3016, FAX 770-682-5860, editor@ezineadsource.com, http://www.ezineadsource.com. Ed. John Nesbit.

EDITOR & PUBLISHER; the newsmagazine of the fourth estate since 1894. see *JOURNALISM*

EDITOR & PUBLISHER - FREE PAPER PUBLISHER COMMUNITY PUBLICATIONS YEAR BOOK; a media buyers guide. see *JOURNALISM*

659.1 GBR ISSN 0268-7542
EDITORS MEDIA DIRECTORIES. VOL. 1: NATIONAL MEDIA. Text in English. m. (in 6 vols.). GBP 575 for all 6 vols. (effective 2002); price varies each vol. adv. **Document type:** *Directory.* **Description:** Access to the entire UK media, with detailed editorial listings of more than 42,000 contacts and freelancers at over 14,000 publications, stations and programs.
Published by: Media Information Ltd., Chess House, 34 Germain St, Chesham, Bucks HP5 1SJ, United Kingdom. TEL 44-1494-797230, FAX 44-870-736-0011, editors@waymaker.co.uk, editors@mediainfo.co.uk, http://www.editorsmediadirectories.com/. Ed. Helen Buckhurst.

659.1 GBR ISSN 0268-7550
EDITORS MEDIA DIRECTORIES. VOL. 2: BUSINESS AND PROFESSIONAL. Text in English. q. GBP 175; GBP 475 for all 6 vols.. adv. **Document type:** *Directory.*
Published by: Media Information Ltd., Chess House, 34 Germain St, Chesham, Bucks HP5 1SJ, United Kingdom. TEL 44-1494-797230, FAX 44-1494-797-224, editors@mediainfo.co.uk. Ed. Helen Buckhurst.

659.1 GBR ISSN 0268-7569
EDITORS MEDIA DIRECTORIES. VOL. 3: PROVINCIAL NEWSPAPERS & TOWN GUIDE. Text in English. 3/yr. GBP 170; GBP 475 for all 6 vols. adv. **Document type:** *Directory.*
Published by: Media Information Ltd., Chess House, 34 Germain St, Chesham, Bucks HP5 1SJ, United Kingdom. TEL 44-1494-797230, FAX 44-1494-797-224, editors@mediainfo.co.uk. Ed. Helen Buckhurst.

659.1 GBR ISSN 0268-7577
EDITORS MEDIA DIRECTORIES. VOL. 4: CONSUMER & LEISURE MAGAZINES. Text in English. q. GBP 150; GBP 475 for all 6 vols. adv. **Document type:** *Directory.*
Published by: Media Information Ltd., Chess House, 34 Germain St, Chesham, Bucks HP5 1SJ, United Kingdom. TEL 44-1494-797230, FAX 44-1494-797-224, editors@mediainfo.co.uk. Ed. Helen Buckhurst.

659.1 GBR
EDITORS MEDIA DIRECTORIES. VOL.5: RADIO AND T V PROGRAMMES. Text in English. s-a. GBP 130; GBP 475 for all 6 vols. adv. **Document type:** *Directory.*
Formerly: Editors Media Directories. Vol. 5: Broadcast Media (0268-7585)
Published by: Media Information Ltd., Chess House, 34 Germain St, Chesham, Bucks HP5 1SJ, United Kingdom. TEL 44-1494-797230, FAX 44-1494-797-224, editors@mediainfo.co.uk. Ed. Helen Buckhurst.

659.1 GBR
EDITORS MEDIA DIRECTORIES. VOL. 6: FREELANCERS, WRITERS' GUILDS & LONDON CORRESPONDENTS OF FOREIGN PRESS. Text in English. a. GBP 110; GBP 475 for all 6 vols. adv. **Document type:** *Directory.*
Formerly: Editors Media Directories. Vol. 6: Writers' Guilds and London Correspondents of Foreign Press (0268-7631)
Published by: Media Information Ltd., Chess House, 34 Germain St, Chesham, Bucks HP5 1SJ, United Kingdom. TEL 44-1494-797230, FAX 44-1494-797-224, editors@mediainfo.co.uk. Ed. Helen Buckhurst.

659.1 ITA ISSN 0393-9170
ELECTRONIC MASS MEDIA AGE. Text in Italian. 1985. m. USD 50. adv. back issues avail. **Document type:** *Magazine, Consumer.*
Published by: Systems Comunicazioni, Via Olanda 6, Vigano di Gaggiano, MI 20083, Italy. TEL 39-02-92270757, FAX 39-02-90841682, info@systems.it, http://www.systems.it. Ed. M Dipisa. Circ: 4,800.

659.1 658.8 AUS
EQUINE OZ✶ . Text in English. m. **Description:** Provides news, fulltext articles about equestrian events worldwide.
Media: Online - full text.
Published by: Laurel Enterprises, PO Box 234, Dee Why, NSW 2099, Australia. TEL 61-2-9369-2433, FAX 61-2-9389-5450, Mark.Williams@equineoz.com.au, laurel@equinesoz.com.au, http://www.equineoz.com.au/. Ed. Mark Williams.

659.1 796.72 USA
ERNIE SAXTON'S MOTORSPORTS SPONSORSHIP - MARKETING NEWS; the latest marketing promotion & sponsorship news in all forms of motorsports. Text in English. 1985. m. USD 89.95 domestic; USD 99.95 foreign (effective 2000). adv. bk.rev. **Document type:** *Newsletter, Trade.* **Description:** Lists motorsports marketing news and sponsorship opportunities and offers advice.
Published by: Ernie Saxton Communications, 1448 Hollywood Ave, Langhorne, PA 19047-7417. TEL 215-752-7797, FAX 215-752-1518. Ed. Marilyn Saxton. Adv. contact Ernie Saxton.

659.1 658 DEU
ETAT-KALKULATOR. Text in German. 1980. 2/yr. EUR 78; EUR 57 newsstand/cover (effective 2005). adv. **Document type:** *Journal, Trade.*
Published by: Creativ Collection Verlag GmbH, Basler Landstr 61, Freiburg Im Breisgau, 79111, Germany. TEL 49-761-479240, FAX 49-761-4792411, info@creativcollection.com, http://www.creativcollection.com. Ed. Matthias Prosch. Adv. contact Matthias A Prosch. B&W page EUR 1,100, color page EUR 2,000. Circ: 4,000 (controlled).

659.132 CAN ISSN 1205-7142
ETHNIC MEDIA & MARKETS. Text in English. 1995. s-a. CND 109.50 domestic (effective 2000); included with subscr to Canadian Advertising Rates & Data. **Document type:** *Directory, Trade.* **Description:** Lists advertising contacts and rates of noteworthy Canadian periodicals that cater to ethnic minorities.
Related titles: ♦ Supplement to: Canadian Advertising Rates and Data. ISSN 0038-9498.
—CISTI.
Published by: C A R D, the Media Information Network (Subsidiary of: Rogers Media Publishing Ltd), Subscriber Services, Maclean Hunter Bldg, 777 Bay St, 8th Fl, Toronto, ON M5W 1A7, Canada. TEL 416-596-2790, FAX 416-596-5158, http://www.cardmedia.com/products/products.htm. Adv. contact Lucia De Stefano.

659.1 GBR
EUROMARKETING VIA EMAIL. Text in English. 1987. w. GBP 195, USD 295 (effective 1999). software rev. back issues avail. **Document type:** *Newsletter, Trade.* **Description:** Covers the most significant news and developments in marketing, advertising and media across Europe.
Formerly: Euromarketing (0952-3820)
Media: Online - full text (from Factiva, Gale Group, O C L C Online Computer Library Center, Inc.). **Related titles:** E-mail ed.
Indexed: B&I.
Published by: Crain Communications, Inc. (London), New Garden House, 78 Hatton Garden, London, EC1N 8JD, United Kingdom. TEL 44-20-7457-1400, FAX 44-20-7457-1440, 76544.1460@compuserve.com, http://www.crain.co.uk. Ed., Pub. Bill Britt.

659.1 GBR ISSN 0951-7758
EUROPEAN ADVERTISING & MEDIA FORECAST. Text in English. 1986. bi-m. GBP 1,190 (effective 2000). **Document type:** *Trade.* **Description:** Presents data, forecasts and expert analyses covering advertising expenditures and media developments in 22 countries.
Related titles: Online - full text ed.: (from EBSCO Publishing).
—CCC.

▼ new title ➤ refereed ✶ unverified ♦ full entry avail.

A

Published by: (Advertising Association), N T C Publications Ltd. (Subsidiary of: World Advertising Research Center Ltd.), PO Box 69, Henley-on-Thames, Oxon RG9 1GB, United Kingdom. TEL 44-1491-411000, FAX 44-1491-571188, ntc@ntc.co.uk. **Co-sponsor:** Advertising Informaion Group.

EUROPEAN MEDIA DIRECTORY. see *BUSINESS AND ECONOMICS—Trade And Industrial Directories*

659.1 DEU ISSN 1435-5264
EUROPEAN PROMOTIONAL PRODUCTS INDUSTRY. Abbreviated title: E P P I. Text in English. 1998. bi-m. EUR 26 (effective 2000). adv. **Document type:** *Magazine, Trade.*
Published by: W A Verlag GmbH, Waltherstr 80, Cologne, 51069, Germany. TEL 49-221-689110, FAX 49-221-6891110, info@wa-verlag-koeln.de, http://www.werbeartikel-verlag.de. Ed. Michael Scherer. Pub. Klaus Stallbaum. Adv. contact Serkan Karabulut. Circ: 6,700 (paid and controlled).

659 338 GBR ISSN 0924-5855
EUROPEAN SIGN MAGAZINE. Text in English; Summaries in French, German. 1987. bi-m. GBP 45 in the European Union; GBP 55 in Europe; USD 120 elsewhere. adv. **Document type:** *Magazine, Trade.* **Description:** Covers all aspects of signmaking and the sign business.
Published by: C M P Information Ltd. (Subsidiary of: United Business Media), Sovereign House, Sovereign Way, Tonbridge, Kent TN9 1RW, United Kingdom. TEL 44-1732-377391, FAX 44-1732-377552, enquiries@cmpinformation.com, http://www.cmpinformation.com. Ed. Karen Charlesworth. Adv. contact Richard Langrish. page GBP 5,250; trim 297 x 210. Circ: 7,000.

659.1 FRA ISSN 1145-6167
EVENEMENTIEL✶. Text in French. 11/yr. **Description:** Dedicated to publicity through sponsorship, conventions and product launches.
Address: 86 rue du President Wilson, Levallois Perret, 92300, France. TEL 45-45-67-66, FAX 45-45-07-37. Ed. Yves Barraud. Circ: 13,000.

659.2 USA ISSN 0271-3659
EXECUTIVE SPEAKER. Text in English. 1980. m. USD 216 domestic; USD 251 foreign (effective 2000). bk.rev.; software rev.; Website rev. index. 12 p./no.; **Document type:** *Newsletter, Trade.* **Description:** Serves as a clearinghouse and digest for recent speeches by executives. Features examples of the best openings, closings and quotations from speeches along with a line or two of analysis that points out what made the quotation effective.
Related titles: Online - full text ed.: (from LexisNexis).
Published by: Executive Speaker Co., PO Box 292437, Dayton, OH 45429. TEL 937-294-8493, FAX 937-294-6044, mail@executive-speaker.com, http://www.executive-speaker.com. Ed., Pub. Robert O Skovgard.

EXHIBIT CITY NEWS. see *MEETINGS AND CONGRESSES*

EXHIBITOR MAGAZINE; the magazine for trade show and event marketing management. see *BUSINESS AND ECONOMICS—Marketing And Purchasing*

659.2 USA
EXPERT P R; tips, notes and news firm industry insiders. (Public Relations) Variant title: ExpertPR. Text in English. 2001 (Apr.). w. free. **Document type:** *Newsletter, Trade.* **Description:** Provides updates on the latest news and events in the public relations industry.
Media: Online - full content.
Published by: MediaMap, Inc., 311 Arsenal St, Watertown, MA 02472. TEL 617-393-3200, FAX 617-393-3250, editor@mediamap.com, http://www.mediamap.com/expertpr/.

659.1 BEL
F E D M A - MEMBERSHIP NEWS. Abstracts and contents page in English. 1976. m. membership. bk.rev. **Document type:** *Newsletter.*
Formerly (until 1997): F E D M A - Gram
Related titles: E-mail ed.; Online - full text ed.
Published by: Federation of European Direct Marketing, Av de Tervuren 439, Brussels, 1150, Belgium. TEL 32-2-7794268, FAX 32-2-7794269, info@fedma.org, http://www.fedma.org. Ed., Adv. contact Margrethe Saxegaard. Circ: 1,000.

FACILITIES AND DESTINATIONS; the bible for convention, exposition and event management. see *BUSINESS AND ECONOMICS—Management*

FACILITIES AND EVENT MANAGEMENT. see *BUSINESS AND ECONOMICS—Management*

FASHION WATCH. see *CLOTHING TRADE—Fashions*

FASTLINE: DIXIE EDITION. see *TRANSPORTATION—Trucks And Trucking*

FASTLINE: TENNESSEE (TRUCK EDITION). see *TRANSPORTATION—Trucks And Trucking*

FEATURE NEWS PUBLICITY OUTLETS. see *JOURNALISM*

659.1 332 USA ISSN 0748-1845
HF6161. B2
FINANCIAL ADVERTISING REVIEW; the monthly report on advertising by banks, savings & loans, and credit unions. Text in English. 1986. m. USD 294; USD 30 per issue (effective 2004). back issues avail.; reprints avail. **Document type:** *Newsletter, Trade.* **Description:** Covers advertising and marketing programs successfully implemented in the financial industry, with emphasis on print advertising, featuring more than 100 examples of the nation's best print, radio, outdoor and direct-mail financial advertising campaigns.
Related titles: Microform ed.: (from PQC); Online - full text ed.
Indexed: BLI.
—CCC.
Published by: The Business Word, Inc., 11211 E Arapahoe Rd, Ste 101, Centennial, CO 80112-3851. TEL 303-290-8500, 800-328-3211, FAX 303-290-9025, far/businessword@businessword.com, customer.service@businessword.com, http://www.businessword.com/pubs/far.html. Ed. Pamela Moore. Pub. Donald E L Johnson. Circ: 1,100 (paid and controlled).

FINANCIAL SURVEY. SIGN & STREET FURNITURE MANUFACTURERS & DISTRIBUTORS; company data for success. see *BUSINESS AND ECONOMICS—Trade And Industrial Directories*

659.1 DEU
FINDLING; Marktplatz fuer kostenlose private Kleinanzeigen. Text in German. 1985. 2/w. looseleaf. adv. **Document type:** *Consumer.*
Published by: Dolmen Verlag GmbH, Untertuerkheimer Str 39-41, Saarbruecken, 66117, Germany. TEL 49-681-9535300, FAX 49-681-9535305. Ed. Martin Welker. Adv. contact Hans Martin Knerr. Circ: 37,976.

741.67 760 SWE ISSN 0345-7850
FOERBUNDET FOER ART, BILD, COPY OCH DESIGN. MEDDELANDET. Text in Swedish. 1958-1987; resumed 1988. m. adv. bk.rev.
Published by: Sveriges Reklamfoerbund/Association of Advertising Companies, Sveavaegen 34, Stockholm, 11134, Sweden. TEL 46-8-6790800, FAX 46-8-6790801, http://www.reklam.se. Circ: 2,000.

FORMER SOVIET UNION MARKETING, MEDIA & ADVERTISING DIRECTORY. see *BUSINESS AND ECONOMICS—Marketing And Purchasing*

FREELANCE WRITER'S REPORT. see *JOURNALISM*

FRIDAY REPORT. see *BUSINESS AND ECONOMICS—Marketing And Purchasing*

659 658 USA ISSN 1549-344X
HC79.H53
FUTURE OF TECHNOLOGY ADVERTISING & MARKETING REPORT (YEAR). Text in English. a. USD 2,295 (effective 2003 & 2004).
Published by: SIMBA Information (Subsidiary of: R.R. Bowker LLC), 60 Long Ridge Rd., Ste 300, Stamford, CT 06902. TEL 203-325-8193, 800-307-2529, FAX 203-325-8915, info@simbanet.com, http://www.simbanet.com.

659.1 DEU ISSN 0936-8159
G W A. Text in German. a. EUR 75.50 to non-members; EUR 50 to members (effective 2005). **Document type:** *Journal, Trade.*
Former titles (until 198?): Werbeagenturen der G W A (0720-7220); (until 1980): G W A mit Sicherheit Werben (0171-8215)
Published by: Gesamtverband Werbeagenturen e.V., Friedensstr 11, Frankfurt am Main, 60311, Germany. TEL 49-69-2560080, FAX 49-69-236883, info@gwa.de, http://www.gwa.de.

659.1 USA
GEIGER REPORT. Text in English. fortn. USD 75 (effective 2001).
Address: 4924 Emerson Ave S, Minneapolis, MN 55409. TEL 612-825-3217. Ed., Pub. Bob Geiger. Circ: 350.

DIE GESCHAEFTSIDEE; Fachmagazin fuer Unternehmensgruendung und neue Maerkte. see *BUSINESS AND ECONOMICS—Small Business*

659.1 658.8 ITA
GLOBAL. Text in Italian. 1988. 4/yr. USD 175; includes Media Key and TV Key. adv.
Related titles: ♦ Supplement to: Media Key.
Published by: Media Key s.r.l., Via Lippi Filippino, 33 C, Milan, MI 20131, Italy. TEL 39-2-70638348, FAX 39-2-2363662. Ed. Roberto Albano. Adv. contact Silvana Catazzina. Circ: 9,500.

659.111 USA
THE GLOBE (ROLLINSVILLE); I C O M's monthly electronic newsletter. Text in English. 1950. a., latest 2001. free. adv. 16 p./no. 3 cols./p.; back issues avail. **Document type:** *Newsletter.*
Formerly: Agency Expertise
Media: Online - full text.
Published by: ICOM - International Communications Agency Network, Inc., Box 490, 1649 County Rd 12, Rollinsville, CO 80474-0490. TEL 303-258-9511, FAX 303-258-3090, info@icomagencies.com, gburandt@eagle-access.net, http://www.icomagencies.com. Eds. Gary Burandt TEL 303-258-9511, Leslee Rockwell. Pub. Jennifer Turco. R&P Gary Burandt TEL 303-258-9511.

659.2 CHN ISSN 1005-3239
GONGGUAN SHIJIE/PUBLIC RELATIONS WORLD. Text in Chinese. 1993. m. CNY 69.60, USD 33.60 domestic (effective 2005). **Document type:** *Journal, Academic/Scholarly.*
Address: 30, Taihua Jie, 3F, Bangonglou, Shijiazhuang, 050051, China. TEL 86-311-7872870, FAX 86-311-7019380, prmaginhebei@sina.com, http://ggsj.periodicals.net.cn/. **Dist. by:** China International Book Trading Corp, 35 Chegongzhuang Xilu, Haidian District, PO Box 399, Beijing 100044, China. TEL 86-10-68412045, FAX 86-10-68412023, cibtc@mail.cibtc.com.cn, http://www.cibtc.com.cn.

659.1 340 USA
GOVERNMENT REPORT. Text in English. 1960. 9/yr. free membership (effective 2005). back issues avail. **Document type:** *Newsletter.* **Description:** Monitors state and federal legislation and regulatory activity affecting the advertising industry.
Formerly: Washington Report (Washington, 1960)
Published by: American Advertising Federation, 1101 Vermont Ave, N W, Ste 500, Washington, DC 20005. TEL 202-898-0089, FAX 202-898-0159, aaf@aaf.org, http://www.aaf.org/. Ed. Andrea Croot. Circ: 3,000.

▼ **GRAPHIC & DESIGN BUSINESS.** see *ART*

GRAPHIC DESIGN: U S A. see *PRINTING*

GRAPHIS; international journal of visual communication. see *ART*

GRAPHIS DESIGN; international annual of design and illustration. see *ART*

659.1 VEN
GUIA VENEZOLANA DE PUBLICIDAD Y MERCADEO. Text in Spanish. 1967. a. VEB 400, USD 60. adv.
Published by: M.G. Ediciones Especializadas, S.A., Av. Maturin, No. 15, Urb. Los Cedros, El Bosque, Caracas, 1050, Venezuela. Ed. Montserrat Giol. Circ: 2,000.

LA GUIDA AGENZIE. see *BUSINESS AND ECONOMICS—Trade And Industrial Directories*

659.1 FRA ISSN 1295-8239
GUIDE STRATEGIES MULTIMEDIA. Text in French. 1999. a. **Document type:** *Directory.* **Description:** Lists agencies, design firms, and marketing communication companies using all media.
Published by: Groupe Strategies SA (Subsidiary of: Reed Business Information France), 2 rue Maurice Hartmann, BP62, Issy-les-Moulinaux, Cedex 92133, France. TEL 33-1-46294629, FAX 33-1-40930314, ogm@groupe-strategies.fr, infos@groupe-strategies.fr, http://www.groupe-strategies.fr. Circ: 12,000 (paid). **Subscr. to:** 99 rue d'Amsterdam, Paris 75008 , France.

659.1 CHN ISSN 1002-5685
GUOJI XINWENJIE/INTERNATIONAL COMMUNICATION JOURNAL. Text in Chinese. 1961. q.
Related titles: Online - full text ed.: (from East View Information Services).
Published by: Zhongguo Renmin Daxue/Renmin University of China, Keyan Bangonglou, Donglou, Beijing, 100872, China. TEL 86-10-62511076, http://www.ruc.edu.cn/.

H M C NEWS. see *PHARMACY AND PHARMACOLOGY*

HAUSTIER ANZEIGER. see *PETS*

741.67 360 USA ISSN 8756-4513
HEALTHCARE ADVERTISING REVIEW; creative forum for the people who plan and create healthcare advertising programs. Text in English. 1985. bi-m. USD 294 domestic; USD 304 in Canada; USD 309 elsewhere (effective 2005). back issues avail. **Document type:** *Magazine, Trade.* **Description:** Covers advertising and marketing programs successfully implemented in the health care industry, with emphasis on print advertising.
Related titles: Online - full text ed.: USD 294 (effective 2004).
—CCC.
Published by: The Business Word, Inc., 11211 E Arapahoe Rd, Ste 101, Centennial, CO 80112-3851. TEL 303-290-8500, 800-328-3211, FAX 303-290-9025, customer.service@businessword.com, http://businessword.com/index.php/weblog/publications/content/8/, http://www.businessword.com. Pub. Donald E L Johnson. Circ: 1,200 (paid).

HISPANIC MARKET WEEKLY. see *BUSINESS AND ECONOMICS—Marketing And Purchasing*

659 USA
HISPANICAD.COM. Text in English. 1999. d. free.
Media: Online - full text.

Published by: Hispanic Media Sales Inc., 1 Chardonnay Rd, Cortland Manor, NY 10567. TEL 914-734-8264, FAX 914-737-3234, http://www.hispanicad.com.

659.2029 GBR ISSN 0962-3590
HD59.6.E85
HOLLIS EUROPE; the directory of European public relations & PR networks. Text in English. 1990. a., latest vol.13, 2002-2003. GBP 185 per vol. (effective 2002). adv. **Document type:** *Directory.* **Description:** Provides a reference to public-relations consultancies across 30 countries of Western, Central, and Eastern Europe, public affairs and sponsorship contacts, public-relations contacts in Europe's leading companies, research and information soures, and services to the public-relations industry in Europe.
Published by: Hollis Publishing Ltd., Harlequin House, 7 High St, Teddington, Middx TW11 8EL, United Kingdom. TEL 44-20-8977-7711, FAX 44-20-8977-1133, orders@hollis-pr.co.uk, http://www.hollis-pr.com/publications/europe.html, http://www.hollis-pr.co.uk/. Ed. Helen Evans. Pub. Rosemary Sarginson. adv.: B&W page GBP 1,300, color page GBP 2,250; 179 x 265. Circ: 1,500.

659.1029 GBR ISSN 1351-5691
HOLLIS SPONSORSHIP & DONATIONS YEARBOOK. Text in English. 1993. a., latest 2002, 10th Ed. GBP 115 per vol.; GBP 80 per vol. to non-profit organizations (effective 2002). adv. **Document type:** *Directory.* **Description:** Lists companies that sponsor events and make corporate donations; also gives sponsorship opportunities in the arts, sports, charities, education and media sector.
—BLDSC (4322.403100).
Published by: Hollis Publishing Ltd., Harlequin House, 7 High St, Teddington, Middx TW11 8EL, United Kingdom. TEL 44-20-8977-7711, FAX 44-20-8977-1133, orders@hollis-pr.co.uk, http://www.hollis-pr.com/publications/spons.htm, http://www.hollis-pr.co.uk/. adv.: B&W page GBP 1,200, color page GBP 1,750; 179 x 265. Circ: 3,000.

338.0029 GBR ISSN 1354-2397
HOLLIS SPONSORSHIP NEWSLETTER. Text in English. 1994. m. (10/yr.). GBP 250; GBP 175 to non-profit organizations (effective 2000). **Document type:** *Newsletter.* **Description:** Provides the latest news, developments, and trends, along with expert analysis, commentary, and information on the sponsorship industry.
Published by: Hollis Publishing Ltd., Harlequin House, 7 High St, Teddington, Middx TW11 8EL, United Kingdom. TEL 44-20-8977-7711, FAX 44-20-8977-1133, orders@hollis-pr.co.uk, http://www.hollis-pr.co.uk/. Pub. Rosemary Sarginson.

658.0029 GBR ISSN 1364-9000
HM263
HOLLIS UK PRESS & PUBLIC RELATIONS ANNUAL. Text in English. 1967. a. (plus q. updates), latest vol.34. GBP 137.50 includes website access and updates (effective 2002). adv. bk.rev. bibl. index. back issues avail. **Document type:** *Directory.* **Description:** Provides a guide to press contacts, public relations departments, news and information sourcces, public relations consultancies, and other services to communications and the media.
Formerly (until 1994): Hollis Press & Public Relations Annual (0073-3059); Incorporates: Contact: The U K News Contact Directory
Related titles: Online - full text ed.
—BLDSC (4322.403600).
Published by: Hollis Publishing Ltd., Harlequin House, 7 High St, Teddington, Middx TW11 8EL, United Kingdom. TEL 44-20-8977-7711, FAX 44-20-8977-1133, orders@hollis-pr.co.uk, http://www.hollis-pr.com/publications/presspublic.htm, http://www.hollis-pr.co.uk/. Ed. Sarah Hughes. Pub. Gary Zabel. adv.: B&W page GBP 1,130; 115 x 174. Circ: 4,500.

HONEY KONTAKT. see *MEN'S INTERESTS*

659.1 AUT
HORIZONT. Text in German. 1991. w. EUR 75 domestic; EUR 123 foreign (effective 2005). adv. **Document type:** *Magazine, Trade.*
Related titles: Online - full text ed.
Published by: Manstein Zeitschriften Verlagsgesellschaft mbH, Brunner Feldstr 45, Perchtoldsdorf, N 2380, Austria. TEL 43-1-866480, FAX http://www.manstein.at, 43-1-86648100, office@manstein.at, http://www.horizont.at. Ed. Maximilian Mondel. Adv. contact Martina Hofmann. B&W page EUR 3,250, color page EUR 5,105; trim 271 x 396. Circ: 14,400 (paid and controlled).

659.1 DEU ISSN 0175-7989
HORIZONT (FRANKFURT). Text in German. 1954. w. EUR 149 domestic; EUR 216.40 foreign; EUR 3.50 newsstand/cover (effective 2003). adv. bk.rev. **Document type:** *Magazine, Trade.* **Description:** Provides information on all important processes in marketing communications.
Incorporates (1954-1991): Neue Werbung (0028-3452)
Related titles: Online - full text ed.: (from LexisNexis).
—CCC.
Published by: Deutscher Fachverlag GmbH, Mainzer Landstr 251, Frankfurt Am Main, 60326, Germany. TEL 49-69-759501, FAX 49-69-75952999, info@horizont.net, info@dfv.de, http://www.dfv.de, http://www.horizont.net. Ed. Chr Ickstadt. Adv. contact Manfred Winter. B&W page EUR 5,635, color page EUR 7,180; trim 286 x 330. Circ: 17,601.

▼ **HOUSTON HOUSINGUIDE.** see *BUILDING AND CONSTRUCTION*

659.1 USA ISSN 1084-2241
I A A WORLD NEWS. Text in English. 1960; N.S. 1988. q. USD 80 (effective 2000). bk.rev. charts; illus.; mkt.; tr.lit. reprint service avail. from PQC. **Document type:** *Newsletter.* **Description:** For IAA members in international marketing and communications.
Formerly (until vol.7, no.1, 1994): International Advertiser (0885-3363); Incorporates: United Nations Report; Advertising World (0163-9412); International Marketing Report (0198-6228)
Indexed: ATI, BPI, ManagCont, PAIS, PROMT, RASB, T&II.
Published by: International Advertising Association, 521 Fifth Ave, Rm 1807, New York, NY 10175-0003. TEL 212-557-1133, FAX 212-983-0455, TELEX 237969, webmaster@iaaglobal.org. Ed., R&P Pamela Yaeger. Circ: 5,000.

659.1 IRL
I A P I BUSINESS READERSHIP SURVEY. (Institute of Advertising Practitioners in Ireland) Text in English. 1987. biennial. **Document type:** *Bulletin.*
Published by: I A P I, 8 Upper Fitzwilliam St., Dublin, 2, Ireland. TEL 353-1-6765991, FAX 353-1-6614589, info@iapi.com, http://www.iapi.ie. Ed., R&P Ian Fox. Circ: 200 (controlled).

659.111 USA
I C O M NEWSLETTER. Text in English. 1950. m. adv. **Document type:** *Newsletter.*
Formerly: International Federation of Advertising Agencies. Newsletter
Published by: International Communications Agency Network, Inc., 1649 County Rd 12, PO Box 490, Rollinsville, CO 80474-0490. TEL 303-258-9511, FAX 303-258-3090, globe@icomagencies.com, http://www.icomagencies.com. Ed., R&P Leslee T Alexander.

659.1 070 IND ISSN 0073-4284
I N F A PRESS AND ADVERTISERS YEAR BOOK. Text in English. 1962. a. USD 100 (effective 2000). adv. **Document type:** *Yearbook, Trade.* **Description:** Year book on advertising, media planning, sales promotion and publicity in India.
Published by: (India News and Feature Alliance), I N F A Publications, Jeevan Deep Bldg. Parliament St., New Delhi, 110 001, India. TEL 91-11-3733330, FAX 91-11-3746788. Ed. Mr. Inderjit. Pub. Poonam I Kaushisk. Adv. contact Anand Kumar. Circ: 5,000.

I.P. MARK. (Informacion de Publicidad y Marketing) see *BUSINESS AND ECONOMICS—Marketing And Purchasing*

ICOGRADA MESSAGE BOARD. see *ART*

659.1 740 JPN ISSN 0019-1299
NC997.A1
IDEA✶ ; international advertising art. Text in English, Japanese. 1953. bi-m. JPY 23,640. adv. index. back issues avail. **Description:** International graphic design magazine.
Indexed: ABM, BiolAb, DAAI, RASB.
—BLDSC (4362.362000).
Published by: Seibundo Shinkosha Inc., 3-3-11 Hongo, Bunkyoku, Tokyo, 164-0013, Japan. Ed. Minoru Takita. Circ: 32,000.

659.1 USA ISSN 0896-1441
IDEAS. Text in English. 1950. m. membership. stat. back issues avail. **Document type:** *Trade.*
Former titles: Ideas Newsletter; I N P A Advertising Newsletter (0019-0152)
Related titles: Online - full text ed.
Published by: International Newspaper Marketing Association, 10300 North Central Expressway, Ste 467, Dallas, TX 75231. TEL 214-373-9111, FAX 214-373-9112, inma@inma.org, http://www.inma.org. Ed. Dawn McMullan. Pub., R&P Earl Wilkinson. Circ: 1,300.

659.1 DEU ISSN 0176-859X
IDEEN ARCHIV. Text in German. 1979. m. looseleaf. back issues avail. **Document type:** *Journal, Academic/Scholarly.*
Published by: Bergmoser und Hoeller Verlag GmbH, Karl-Friedrich-Str 76, Aachen, 52072, Germany. TEL 49-241-93888123, FAX 49-241-93888134, kontakt@buhv.de, http://www.buhv.de. Circ: 1,400.

IKONOMICHESKI ZHIVOT. see *BUSINESS AND ECONOMICS*

THE IMAGE MAKERS SOURCE; the Madison Avenue handbook. see *PHOTOGRAPHY*

INDUSTRIAL EXCHANGE & MART. see *MACHINERY*

659.1 CAN
INFO PRESSE COMMUNICATIONS; le seul magazine d'affaires francophones des communications au Canada. Text in French. 1985. m. CND 59; CND 125 foreign (effective 1999). adv. back issues avail. **Description:** Trade magazine on advertising, marketing and the media in Quebec and Canada.
Formerly: Info Presse Canada (0827-4711)
Indexed: PdeR.
Published by: Editions Info Presse, 4316 rue St Laurent, Montreal, PQ H2W 1Z3, Canada. TEL 514-842-5873, FAX 514-842-2422. Ed. Bruno Gautier. Circ: 8,000.

659 ITA
INFORMAZIONI E ORIENTAMENTI. Text in Italian. bi-m.
Address: Via Guglielmo Marconi, 67-2, Bologna, BO 40122, Italy. Ed. Giuliano Cazzola.

INSIDE. see *INTERIOR DESIGN AND DECORATION*

659.1 USA
INSIDE IMPACT. Text in English. 1987. q. USD 25. adv.
Published by: Impact Advertising Inc., 1546 Main St, Dunedin, FL 34698. TEL 813-736-6228, FAX 813-734-9368. Ed. Bruce Cohen. Circ: 4,498.

659.1 AUT
INSIDER. Text in German. 25/yr.
Published by: Insider Verlag, Cobenzlgasse 66, Vienna, W 1190, Austria. TEL 01-326054, FAX 01-327338. Ed. Inge Weinlich. Circ: 3,000.

659.1 GBR ISSN 1351-4598
INSTITUTE OF PUBLIC RELATIONS. HANDBOOK (YEAR). Text in English. a. GBP 30. **Document type:** *Directory.*
Published by: (Institute of Public Relations), Kogan Page Ltd., 120 Pentonville Rd, London, N1 9JN, United Kingdom. FAX 44-20-7837-6348. R&P Linda Batman.

659.1 FRA ISSN 0154-1617
INTER FORAIN. Text in French. 24/yr. **Description:** Commercial and artistic magazine relating to exhibitions, fairs and foreign festivals.
Address: B.P. 52, Avignon, Cedex 84005, France. TEL 90-82-54-03, TELEX 432 770. Ed. Michel Pierre. Circ: 27,420.

659.111 USA
INTERACTIVE ADVERTISING & BRANDING NEWS. Text in English. 1986. bi-w. USD 499 (effective 2004). **Document type:** *Newsletter, Trade.* **Description:** Provides news, analysis, and opinion for the exploding business of electronic advertising, shopping and commerce.
Former titles: Electronic Advertising & Marketplace Report (1092-0188); Electronic Marketplace Report (1071-247X); (until 1993): Electronic Directory and Classified Report
Related titles: Online - full text ed.: (from EBSCO Publishing, Gale Group).
Indexed: CompD.
—CCC.
Published by: SIMBA Information (Subsidiary of: R.R. Bowker LLC), 60 Long Ridge Rd., Ste 300, Stamford, CT 06902. TEL 203-325-8193, 800-307-2529, 888-269-5372, FAX 203-325-8915, info@simbanet.com, http://www.simbanet.com. Ed. Linda Kopp.

INTERACTIVE GLOBAL NEWS. see *BUSINESS AND ECONOMICS—International Commerce*

659.2 USA ISSN 1099-6893
INTERACTIVE PUBLIC RELATIONS NEWSLETTER. Abbreviated title: i-PR. Text in English. 1995. m. back issues avail. **Document type:** *Newsletter.*
Media: E-mail.
Published by: Xpress Press Service, 4741 Sarazen Dr, Hollywood, FL 33021. TEL 654-989-3338, FAX 954-989-3331, 800-713-7701, news@xpresspress.com, http://www.xpresspress.com/ipr.html. Ed. Tina Koening.

659.1 CAN ISSN 1197-7825
INTERCESSOR. Text in English. 1930. bi-m. back issues avail. **Document type:** *Newsletter.*
Published by: Inter-Varsity Christian Fellowship of Canada, 64 Prince Andrew Pl, Toronto, ON M3C 2H4, Canada. TEL 905-884-6880, FAX 905-884-6550, ivcfnat@hookup.net, http://www.ivcf.ca. Ed., R&P Rob Regier. Pub. Jim Berney. Circ: 3,000.

659.1 AUT
INTERN. Text in German. w. EUR 285 domestic; EUR 350 foreign (effective 2005). adv. **Document type:** *Newsletter, Trade.*
Published by: Manstein Zeitschriften Verlagsgesellschaft mbH, Brunner Feldstr 45, Perchtoldsdorf, N 2380, Austria. TEL 43-1-866480, FAX http://www.manstein.at, 43-1-86648100, office@manstein.at, http://www.manstein.at/Magazine/intern/. Ed. Rainer Seebacher. Adv. contact Martina Hofmann. B&W page EUR 1,660, color page EUR 2,390; trim 210 x 297. Circ: 1,650 (paid and controlled).

A

▼ new title ➤ refereed ✶ unverified ♦ full entry avail.

659.1 GBR ISSN 0265-0487
HF5801
➤ **INTERNATIONAL JOURNAL OF ADVERTISING**; the quarterly review of marketing communications. Text in English. 1982. q. USD 160 to individuals; USD 304 to institutions (effective 2004). adv. bk.rev. charts; illus.; stat. index, cum.index. reprints avail. **Document type:** *Academic/Scholarly.* **Description:** Aimed at both academics and practitioners. It is international in scope and covers a wide range of advertising and marketing issues, including: advertising technologies, role of the media, market sectors, advertising effectiveness, agency relationships and marketing.
Formerly: Journal of Advertising (0261-9903); Which superseded (1978-1980): Advertising Magazine; Which was formerly: Advertising; (1964-1978): Advertising Quarterly (0001-8961)
Related titles: Online - full text ed.: 1982 (from EBSCO Publishing).
Indexed: ABIn, ADPA, AcaI, BAS, BPI, BPIA, BusI, CPM, ESPM, Emerald, LRI, M&MA, MResA, ManagCont, PAIS, RiskAb, SSCI, T&II.
—BLDSC (4541.575000), IE, Infotrieve, ingenta. **CCC.**
Published by: (Advertising Association), N T C Publications Ltd. (Subsidiary of: World Advertising Research Center Ltd.), Farm Rd, Henley-on-Thames, Oxon RG9 1EJ, United Kingdom. TEL 44-1491-411000, FAX 44-1491-571188, orders@warc.com, http://store.warc.com/ProductInfo/30.asp, http://www.warc.com. Ed. Douglas West. R&P Katherine Goldsmith. Adv. contact Tim Clifton. Circ: 800.

➤ **INTERNATIONAL JOURNAL OF MARKET RESEARCH.** see *BUSINESS AND ECONOMICS—Marketing And Purchasing*

659.1 USA ISSN 1069-4277
HF5826.5
INTERNATIONAL MEDIA GUIDE. BUSINESS - PROFESSIONAL. THE AMERICAS. Variant title: I M G Business Publications. The Americas(International Media Guide). Text in English. 1971. a. USD 300 domestic; USD 311 in Canada & Mexico; USD 329 elsewhere (effective 2001). adv. **Document type:** *Directory, Trade.* **Description:** Lists more than 3,000 business and professional trade publications from North and South America and the Caribbean.
Former titles (until 1989): Media Guide International. Business - Professional Publications. Latin America (1069-4269); International Media Guide. Business - Professional Publications. Latin America (1069-4250); (1979-1984): Media Guide International. Business - Professional Publications. Latin America (0730-5257); Supersedes in part: Media Guide International. Business - Professional Publications Edition (0164-1743); Media Guide International. Business Publications Edition (0098-9398); Newsmedia Guide International
Published by: S R D S, 1700 Higgins Rd, Des Plaines, IL 60018-5605. TEL 847-357-5000, 800-851-7737, FAX 847-375-5001, http://www.srds.com. Ed. Debbie Dunkleberger. R&P, Adv. contact Carolyn Adams. B&W page USD 2,950, color page USD 4,450; trim 8.5 x 11. Circ: 1,500 (paid).

▼ **INTERNET MEDIA REVIEW.** see *COMPUTERS—Internet*

INTERNET YELLOW PAGES (YEAR): BUSINESS MODELS AND MARKET OPPORTUNITIES. see *BUSINESS AND ECONOMICS—Computer Applications*

INTRODUCTION TO MAIL ORDER. see *BUSINESS AND ECONOMICS—Small Business*

INVESTOR RELATIONS MAGAZINE. see *BUSINESS AND ECONOMICS—Investments*

INVESTOR RELATIONS NEWSLETTER. see *BUSINESS AND ECONOMICS—Investments*

IOWA HOME-BASED BUSINESS DIRECTORY. see *BUSINESS AND ECONOMICS—Trade And Industrial Directories*

659.1 ISR ISSN 0792-7185
ISRAEL ADVERTISING. Text in English. q. free. adv. **Document type:** *Directory.*
Published by: Jerusalem Marketing Group, P O Box 23859, Jerusalem, 91237, Israel. TEL 972-50-266598, FAX 972-2-6250946. Ed. S I Gottlieb.

JAARBOEK DIRECT MARKETING. see *BUSINESS AND ECONOMICS—Marketing And Purchasing*

659.1 700 DEU ISSN 1616-2528
HF5802
JAHRBUCH DER WERBUNG/ADVERTISER'S ANNUAL. Text in German. 1964. a. EUR 89 (effective 2005). adv. bk.rev. **Document type:** *Directory, Trade.* **Description:** Provides overview of advertising developments in the German speaking world.
Former titles (until 1999): Jahrbuch der Werbung in Deutschland, Oesterreich und der Schweiz (0932-6251); (until 1975): Werbung in Deutschland (0083-8012)
Related titles: CD-ROM ed.: ISSN 1616-251X.
Published by: Econ Verlag, Friedrichstr 126, Berlin, 10117, Germany. TEL 49-30-23456300, FAX 49-30-23456303, isabel.hagemann@econ-verlag.de, http://www.jdw.de, http://www.econ-verlag.de. adv.: color page EUR 3,470; trim 161 x 248. Circ: 4,000.

659 JPN ISSN 0918-4406
HF5415.12.J3
JAPAN (YEAR) MARKETING AND ADVERTISING YEARBOOK. Text in English. 1972. a. JPY 8,400 domestic; JPY 8,000 foreign (effective 2000). adv. bk.rev. charts; illus.; stat. back issues avail. **Document type:** *Directory, Trade.* **Description:** Explains marketing and advertising trends in Japan on the basis of statistical data.
Former titles (until 1991): Dentsu Japan Marketing - Advertising (0386-6076); (until 1972): Industrial Japan (0019-8439)
Indexed: BAS, KES, PAIS.
Published by: Dentsu Inc., 11-10 Tsuki-Ji 1-chome, Chuo-ku, Tokyo, 104-0045, Japan. TEL 81-3-5551-5585, FAX 81-3-5551-2014, http://www.dentsu.co.jp. Ed. Yasumichi Yamaguchi TEL 81-3-5551-5925. R&P, Adv. contact Honda Akiko. B&W page JPY 200,000, color page JPY 30,000; trim 205 x 155. Circ: 10,000.

659.1 JPN
JAPAN ADVERTISING FEDERATION. AIMS AND ORGANIZATION. Text in Japanese. irreg.
Published by: Japan Advertising Federation/Zennihon Kokoku Renmei, Kochiwa Bldg, 4-8-12 Ginza, Chuo-ku, Tokyo, 104-0061, Japan. TEL 03-562-2966.

JIM ROMENESKO'S MEDIA NEWS. see *JOURNALISM*

JONESREPORT PLUS FOR SHOPPING CENTER MARKETING & MANAGEMENT. see *BUSINESS AND ECONOMICS—Marketing And Purchasing*

659.1 USA ISSN 0091-3367
HF5801
➤ **JOURNAL OF ADVERTISING.** Text in English. 1972. q. USD 76 domestic to individuals; USD 96 foreign to individuals; USD 149 domestic to institutions; USD 184 foreign to institutions (effective 2006). adv. bk.rev. charts; illus. Index. reprint service avail. from PQC,PSC. **Document type:** *Journal, Academic/Scholarly.* **Description:** Contributes to the development of advertising theory and its relationship to advertising practices and processes.
Related titles: CD-ROM ed.; Microform ed.: (from PQC); Online - full text ed.: ISSN 1557-7805. 2003 (Mar.) (from EBSCO Publishing, Gale Group, H.W. Wilson, Northern Light Technology, Inc., O C L C Online Computer Library Center, Inc., ProQuest Information & Learning, Swets Information Services).
Indexed: ABIn, ADPA, ASCA, AcaI, AgeL, ArtHuCI, BPIA, BusI, CommAb, CurCont, Emerald, HistAb, L&LBA, ManagAb, ManagCont, PAIS, PsycInfo, PsycholAb, SFSA, SOPODA, SSCI, V&AA, e-psyche.
—BLDSC (4918.949000), IDS, IE, Infotrieve, ingenta. **CCC.**
Published by: M.E. Sharpe, Inc., 80 Business Park Dr, Armonk, NY 10504. TEL 914-273-1800, 800-541-6563, FAX 914-273-2106, journalofadvertising@bus.iastate.edu, custserv@mesharpe.com, http://www.mesharpe.com/mall/results1.asp?acr=joa. Ed. Russell N Laczniak. R&P Elizabeth Granda TEL 914-273-1800 ext 118. Adv. contact Barbara Ladd TEL 914-273-1800 ext 121. page USD 300. Circ: 1,850 (paid).

659.1 GBR ISSN 0021-8499
HF5801 CODEN: JADRAV
JOURNAL OF ADVERTISING RESEARCH. Text in English. 1960. q. USD 265 in North America to institutions; GBP 175 elsewhere to institutions; USD 285 combined subscription in North America to institutions print & online eds.; GBP 180 combined subscription elsewhere to institutions print & online eds. (effective 2005). charts; illus. index, cum.index. reprint service avail. from PQC,ISI. **Document type:** *Journal, Trade.*
Related titles: Microform ed.: (from PQC); Online - full text ed.: ISSN 1740-1909. USD 240 in North America to institutions; GBP 155 elsewhere to institutions (effective 2005) (from bigchalk, EBSCO Publishing, Florida Center for Library Automation, Gale Group, Northern Light Technology, Inc., O C L C Online Computer Library Center, Inc., Swets Information Services).
Indexed: ABIn, ASCA, ASEANManA, AcaI, AgeL, BPI, BPIA, BusI, CIS, CPM, CommAb, CurCont, ESPM, Emerald, JCQM, KES, M&MA, MResA, ManagCont, ORMS, PsySCAP, PsycInfo, PsycholAb, RiskAb, SCIMP, SSCI, SUSA, T&II, e-psyche.
—BLDSC (4918.950000), IDS, IE, Infotrieve, ingenta. **CCC.**
Published by: (Advertising Research Foundation USA), Cambridge University Press, The Edinburgh Bldg, Shaftesbury Rd, Cambridge, CB2 2RU, United Kingdom. TEL 44-1223-312393, FAX 44-1223-315052, journal@thearf.org, journals@cambridge.org, http://titles.cambridge.org/journals/journal_catalogue.asp?historylinks=ALPHA&mnemonic=JAR, http://www.cup.cam.ac.uk/. Ed. Arthur J Kover. Circ: 3,000 (paid). **Subscr. to:** Cambridge University Press, 100 Brook Hill Dr, West Nyack, NY 10994. TEL 845-353-7500, FAX 845-353-4141, journals_subscriptions@cup.org

741.67 150.19 USA ISSN 1057-7408
HF5415.32
➤ **JOURNAL OF CONSUMER PSYCHOLOGY.** Text in English. 1992. q. USD 500 in US & Canada to institutions; USD 530 elsewhere to institutions; USD 525 combined subscription in US & Canada to institutions print & online eds.; USD 555 combined subscription elsewhere to institutions print & online eds. (effective 2006). adv. back issues avail.; reprint service avail. from PSC. **Document type:** *Journal, Academic/Scholarly.* **Description:** Publishes original data and theoretical, methodological and review papers on the role of advertising in consumer psychology, the development and change of consumer attitudes, choice and decision processes.
Related titles: Online - full text ed.: ISSN 1532-7663. USD 475 worldwide to institutions (effective 2006) (from EBSCO Publishing, Gale Group, O C L C Online Computer Library Center, Inc., Swets Information Services).
Indexed: ABIn, BibInd, CurCont, FamI, H&TI, PsycInfo, PsycholAb, RILM, SSCI, e-psyche.
—BLDSC (4965.214000), IE, Infotrieve, ingenta. **CCC.**
Published by: (Society for Consumer Psychology), Lawrence Erlbaum Associates, Inc., 10 Industrial Ave, Mahwah, NJ 07430-2262. TEL 201-258-2200, 800-926-6579, FAX 201-236-0072, journals@erlbaum.com, http://www.leaonline.com/loi/jcp. Ed. Robert Wyer. adv.: page USD 450; trim 7 x 10.

659.1 USA ISSN 1064-1734
HF5801
JOURNAL OF CURRENT ISSUES & RESEARCH IN ADVERTISING. Text in English. 1978. s-a. USD 28 domestic; USD 35 foreign (effective 2005). back issues avail.; reprint service avail. from PSC. **Document type:** *Magazine, Trade.*
Formerly (until 1992): Current Issues and Research in Advertising (0163-3392)
Related titles: Online - full text ed.: (from EBSCO Publishing).
Indexed: ABIn, BPI, CommAb, PRA, SPAA, V&AA.
—BLDSC (4965.880000), IE, Infotrieve, ingenta.
Published by: C T C Press, PO Box 200159, Columbia, SC 29229-0159. TEL 803-754-3112, FAX 803-754-3013, cbarnett@ctcpress.com, http://www.ctcpress.com. Eds. Claude R Martin, James Leigh. Circ: 347 (paid); 352 (paid and free); 5 (free).

659.1 USA ISSN 1525-2019
HF5801
➤ **JOURNAL OF INTERACTIVE ADVERTISING.** Text in English. 2000. s-a. free (effective 2005). **Document type:** *Journal, Academic/Scholarly.*
Media: Online - full content.
Published by: (Michigan State University, Department of Advertising), University of Texas at Austin, Department of Advertising, 1 University Station A1200, Austin, TX 78712. TEL 512-471-1101, FAX 512-471-7018, advertising@mail.utexas.edu, http://www.jiad.org, http://uts.cc.utexas.edu/~tecas/leckopen.html. Eds. Hairong Li, John D. Leckenby.

➤ **JOURNAL OF INTERNATIONAL SELLING & SALES MANAGEMENT.** see *BUSINESS AND ECONOMICS—Marketing And Purchasing*

659.1 658 USA ISSN 1049-6491
HF5415.34 CODEN: JPRMEP
➤ **JOURNAL OF PROMOTION MANAGEMENT**; innovations in planning & applied research. Abbreviated title: J P M. Text in English. 1991. q. USD 265 combined subscription domestic to institutions print & online eds.; USD 357.75 combined subscription in Canada to institutions print & online eds.; USD 384.25 combined subscription elsewhere to institutions print & online eds. (effective academic year 2005 - 2006). adv. 120 p./no. 1 cols./p.; back issues avail.; reprint service avail. from HAW. **Document type:** *Journal, Academic/Scholarly.* **Description:** Directed to professionals in advertising, public relations, and personal sales as well as academicians, teachers, and researchers.
Related titles: Microfiche ed.: (from PQC); Microform ed.; Online - full text ed.: ISSN 1540-7594. free to institutions (effective 2003); free with print subs. (from EBSCO Publishing, O C L C Online Computer Library Center, Inc., Swets Information Services).
Indexed: BLI, CommAb, DIP, IBR, IBZ, M&MA.
—BLDSC (5042.768000), Haworth, IE, ingenta. **CCC.**
Published by: Best Business Books (Subsidiary of: Haworth Press, Inc.), 10 Alice St, Binghamton, NY 13904. TEL 607-722-5857, 800-429-6784, FAX 607-771-0012, 800-896-0582, getinfo@haworthpress.com, http://www.haworthpress.com/web/JPM. Ed. Richard Alan Nelson. Pub. William Cohen. R&P Ruth Ann Heath TEL 607-722-5857 ext 316. Adv. contact Rebecca Miller-Baum TEL 607-722-5857 ext 337. B&W page USD 315, color page USD 550; trim 4.375 x 7.125. Circ: 101 (paid).

659.2 USA ISSN 1062-726X
HM263
➤ **JOURNAL OF PUBLIC RELATIONS RESEARCH.** Text in English. 1989. q. USD 525 in US & Canada to institutions; USD 555 elsewhere to institutions; USD 550 combined subscription in US & Canada to institutions print & online eds.; USD 580 combined subscription elsewhere to institutions print & online eds. (effective 2006). adv. back issues avail.; reprint service avail. from PSC. **Document type:** *Journal, Academic/Scholarly.* **Description:** Research in public relations theory, examinations of methodology and motivations, improvements in public relations strategies, as well as critical articles on the history, ethics and philosophy of public relations.
Formerly (until 1992): Public Relations Research Annual (1042-1408)
Related titles: Online - full text ed.: ISSN 1532-754X. USD 495 worldwide to institutions (effective 2006) (from EBSCO Publishing, Gale Group, O C L C Online Computer Library Center, Inc., Swets Information Services).
Indexed: ABIn, CommAb, PsycInfo, PsycholAb, V&AA.
—BLDSC (5043.646000), IE, Infotrieve, ingenta. **CCC.**
Published by: (Association for Education in Journalism and Mass Communication), Lawrence Erlbaum Associates, Inc., 10 Industrial Ave, Mahwah, NJ 07430-2262. TEL 201-258-2200, 800-926-6579, FAX 201-236-0072, journals@erlbaum.com, http://www.leaonline.com/loi/jprr. Ed. Linda Aldoory. adv.: page USD 350; trim 5 x 8.

➤ **K F Z BOERSE.** (Kraftfahrzeug) see *TRANSPORTATION—Automobiles*

659 USA ISSN 1522-3000
KAGAN'S ADVERTISING FORECASTS. Variant title: Advertising Forecasts. Text in English. 19??. a. USD 1,395 (effective 2005). **Document type:** *Directory, Trade.* **Description:** Provides historical data and trend analysis focused on where the advertising money is going.
Published by: Kagan Research, LLC, One Lower Ragsdale Dr, Bldg One, Ste 130, Monterey, CA 93940. TEL 831-624-1536, FAX 831-625-3225, info@kagan.com, http://www.kagan.com.

KAGAN'S MEDIA MERGERS & ACQUISITIONS. see *COMMUNICATIONS*

659.1 658.8 USA ISSN 0160-8932
KEY (BATTLEGROUND). Text in English. 1960-1990; resumed 1993. m. free (effective 2000). adv. bk.rev. stat.; tr.lit. index. **Document type:** *Newsletter.* **Description:** Includes marketing and advertising tips and techniques for mail order firms, Internet companies, self-publishers and small businesses.
Incorporates: Mail Order Product (0162-8496)
Indexed: SPAA.
Published by: Owen Communications Corporation, Battle Ground, WA 98604-0010. TEL 360-887-8646, http://www.mailmaxx.com. Ed., Pub., R&P, Adv. contact Brooks Owen. Circ: 10,000.

659.1 GBR
KEY NOTE MARKET ASSESSMENT. ADVERTISING AGENCIES. Text in English. irreg., latest 2000, Mar. GBP 730 per issue (effective 2002). **Document type:** *Trade.* **Description:** Provides an overview of a specific UK market segment and includes executive summary, market definition, market size, industry background, competitor analysis, current issues, forecasts, company profiles, and more.
Former titles (until 2000): Key Note Market Report: Advertising Agencies (1464-1178); Key Note Report: Advertising Agencies (0266-1985)
Related titles: CD-ROM ed.; Online - full text ed.
Published by: Key Note Ltd., Field House, 72 Oldfield Rd, Hampton, Mddx TW12 2HQ, United Kingdom. TEL 44-20-8481-8750, FAX 44-20-8783-0049, info@keynote.co.uk, http://www.keynote.co.uk.

659.1 658 GBR
KEY NOTE MARKET ASSESSMENT. INTERNET ADVERTISING. Text in English. 2001. irreg., latest 2001, Dec. GBP 730 per issue (effective 2002). **Description:** Provides an in-depth strategic analysis across a broad range of industries and contains an examination on the scope, dynamics and shape of key UK markets in the consumer, financial, lifestyle and business to business sectors.
Published by: Key Note Ltd., Field House, 72 Oldfield Rd, Hampton, Mddx TW12 2HQ, United Kingdom. TEL 44-20-8481-8750, FAX 44-20-8783-0049, info@keynote.co.uk, http://www.keynote.co.uk. Ed. Simon Taylor.

659.1 GBR
KEY NOTE MARKET REPORT: P R CONSULTANCIES. Variant title: P R Consultancies. Text in English. irreg., latest vol.2, 1990. GBP 265 (effective 1999). **Document type:** *Trade.*
Published by: Key Note Ltd., Field House, 72 Oldfield Rd, Hampton, Mddx TW12 2HQ, United Kingdom. TEL 44-20-8481-8750, FAX 44-20-8783-0049, info@keynote.co.uk, http://www.keynote.co.uk.

659.1 808.8 USA
KINGSWOOD KRANIUM. Text in English. 1995. m. **Description:** A lighthearted humor magazine.
Media: Online - full text.
Published by: Kingswood Advertising, Inc., Cricket Terrace Center, Ardmore, PA 19003. webczar@kingswood.com, http://www.kingswood.com. Ed. Adam Bailine.

KOEHLER RUNDSCHAU. see *PAPER AND PULP*

659.1 DEU
KOMMUNIKATIONSVERBAND.DE JAHRBUCH. Text in German. a. **Document type:** *Journal, Trade.*
Published by: (kommunikationsverband.de), Varus Verlag, Konrad-Zuse-Platz 1-3, Bonn, 53227, Germany. TEL 49-228-94466-0, FAX 49-228-9446666, info@varus.com, http://www.kommunikationsverband.de, http://www.varus.com.

659.132 DEU ISSN 0721-975X
DER KONTAKTER; der Nachrichten-Dienst fuer die Werbebranche. Text in German. 1961. w. adv. **Document type:** *Journal, Trade.* **Description:** Provides insider news and information for the advertising industry.
Published by: Maerkte und Medien Verlagsgesellschaft mbH (Subsidiary of: Sueddeutscher Verlag GmbH), Karlstr 41, Munich, 80333, Germany. TEL 49-89-5485205, FAX 49-89-54852520, kontakt@kontakter.de, http://www.kontakter.de. Ed. Andreas Knaut. Adv. contact Karl-Heinz Panse.

KRESS REPORT. see *COMMUNICATIONS*

659.1 JPN
KYOWA HAKKO KOGYO. ANNUAL REPORT. Text in Japanese. a. **Document type:** *Corporate.* **Description:** Features advertising art from Japan.
Published by: Kyowa Hakko Kogyo Co. Ltd., 1-6-1 Ote-Machi, Chiyoda-ku, Tokyo, 100-8185, Japan. TEL 81-3-3282-1903, FAX 81-3-3282-0990, http://www.kyowa.co.jp. Circ: 10,000 (controlled).

659 305.868 USA
LATINO BUYER MAGAZINE. Text in English. 2000. bi-m. adv.
Related titles: Online - full text ed.
Published by: LatinoBuyer Magazine, Inc., P O Box 56538, Miami, FL 33256-5358. TEL 305-665-6438, 800-853-0997, FAX 305-665-7409, info@latinobuyer.com, ads@latinobuyer.com, http://www.latinobuyer.com. adv.: page USD 2,800; 7.5 x 10.111.

070.5 USA
LAUNCH PAD. Text in English. 1996. 3/yr. free. **Document type:** *Newsletter.* **Description:** Report on activities of ABC subsidiary, the Audit Bureau of Verification Services.
Published by: Audit Bureau of Circulations, 900 N Meacham Rd, Schaumburg, IL 60173-4968. TEL 847-605-0909, FAX 847-605-0483, http://www.accessabc.com. Ed. Mary E Metzger.

THE LAW OF ADVERTISING. see *LAW*

659.1 DEU
LEIPZIGER MESSEJOURNAL. Text in English. a.
Indexed: KES.
Published by: Leipziger Messeamt, Markt 11-15, Leipzig, 04109, Germany. Ed. Ines Schymura.

LESSONS OF YELLOW PAGES COMPETITION. see *BUSINESS AND ECONOMICS—Trade And Industrial Directories*

LIBRARY P R NEWS. see *LIBRARY AND INFORMATION SCIENCES*

659.1 DEU
LICENSING & MERCHANDISING. Text in German. m. adv. **Document type:** *Magazine, Trade.*
Published by: W A Verlag GmbH, Waltherstr 80, Cologne, 51069, Germany. TEL 49-221-689110, FAX 49-221-6891110, info@wa-verlag-koeln.de, http://www.werbeartikel-verlag.de. Ed. Michael Scherer. Pub. Klaus Stallbaum. Adv. contact Serkan Karabulut.

659.1 USA
LIFESTYLE MEDIA RELATIONS REPORTER. Variant title: Bulldog Reporter's Lifestyle Media Relations Reporter. Text in English. fortn. USD 549 (effective 2003). back issues avail. **Document type:** *Newsletter, Trade.* **Description:** Contains updates and pitching intelligence on the most influential consumer media and journalists in the United States.
Published by: InfoCom Group, 5900 Hollis St, Ste L, Emeryville, CA 94608-2008. TEL 510-596-9300, 800-959-1059, FAX 510-596-9331, webmgr@infocomgroup.com, http://www.infocomgroup.com/lifestyle.html. Ed. Meghan Collins. Pub. James Sinkinson.

659.1 GBR ISSN 0967-0041
LIFESTYLE POCKET BOOK. Text in English. a. GBP 24 (effective 2000). **Document type:** *Trade.* **Description:** Provides a detailed statistical profile of the British at work and play.
—**CCC.**
Published by: (Advertising Association), N T C Publications Ltd. (Subsidiary of: World Advertising Research Center Ltd.), Farm Rd, Henley-on-Thames, Oxon RG9 1EJ, United Kingdom. TEL 44-1491-411000, FAX 44-1491-571188, info@ntc.co.uk.

659.1 USA ISSN 1045-9723
LINK (TROY); news, views, and trends of the Yellow Pages industry. Text in English. 1989. 10/yr. USD 90 domestic; USD 120 in Canada & Mexico; USD 150 elsewhere. adv. back issues avail. **Document type:** *Trade.* **Description:** Addresses news and issues related to the Yellow Pages advertising medium.
Published by: Yellow Pages Publishers Association, 820 Kirts Blvd, Ste 100, Troy, MI 48084-4836. TEL 248-244-6200, FAX 248-244-6226, barbier@yppa.geis.com, http://www.yppa.org. Ed. Charles Laughlin. Pub. James C Logan. R&P, Adv. contact Christine Barbier TEL 248-244-6211. Circ: 3,000.

LOBBYING IN THE EUROPEAN UNION. see *BUSINESS AND ECONOMICS—Marketing And Purchasing*

659.1 DEU
LOGO TOTAL. Text in German. q. EUR 0.50 newsstand/cover (effective 2003). adv. **Document type:** *Magazine, Consumer.*
Published by: Der Heisse Draht Verlag GmbH und Co., Drostestr 14-16, Hannover, 30161, Germany. TEL 49-511-390910, FAX 49-511-39091252, zentrale@dhd.de, http://www.dhd.de. Adv. contact Kai Burkhardt. B&W page EUR 2,857, color page EUR 3,215. Circ: 80,000 (paid and controlled).

LOGO4HANDY. see *COMMUNICATIONS—Telephone And Telegraph*

659.1 DEU
LOGODAY. Text in German. m. EUR 2 newsstand/cover (effective 2003). adv. **Document type:** *Magazine, Consumer.*
Published by: Der Heisse Draht Verlag GmbH und Co., Drostestr 14-16, Hannover, 30161, Germany. TEL 49-511-390910, FAX 49-511-39091252, zentrale@dhd.de, http://www.dhd.de. Adv. contact Kai Burkhardt. B&W page EUR 3,438, color page EUR 3,796. Circ: 95,000 (paid and controlled).

659.1 GBR ISSN 0305-1765
LOUGHTON REVIEW. Text in English. 1968. m. free. back issues avail.
Published by: Monkswood Press, Caxton House, Old Station Rd, Loughton, Essex IG10 4PE, United Kingdom. TEL 0181-502-0236, FAX 0181-508-2834. Ed. A T Harvey. Circ: 17,700 (controlled).

659 USA
THE LOWBROW LOWDOWN. Text in English. 2000. w. back issues avail. **Document type:** *Newsletter, Trade.* **Description:** Comments on recent news stories about advertising and marketing.
Media: Online - full content. **Related titles:** E-mail ed.
Published by: The Lowbrow Lowdown TEL 201-536-8718, kate@lowbrowlowdown.com, http://www.lowbrowlowdown.com. Ed., Pub. Kate Kaye.

659.143 USA ISSN 0893-0260
LURZER'S INTERNATIONAL ARCHIVE; ads, TV and posters world-wide. Variant title: Archive Magazine. Text in English. 1984. bi-m. USD 48 (effective 2000). adv. illus.; tr.lit. back issues avail. **Document type:** *Trade.* **Description:** Presents international TV commercials and print ad campaigns. Covers 24 categories of ads.
Related titles: Video ed.
Published by: American Showcase Inc., 915 Broadway, 14th Fl, New York, NY 10010-7108. TEL 212-673-6600, 800-989-9494, FAX 212-673-9795, TELEX 880356. Ed. Walter Lurzer. Pub. Ira Shapiro. R&P Ann Middlebrook. Adv. contact Karen Hadam. Circ: 9,500. **Subscr. to:** P O Box 450, Congers, NY 10920-9970.

659.1 IRL ISSN 0790-2751
M A P S. (Media, Advertising, Promotions & Sponsorship) Text in English. 1984. a. **Document type:** *Directory, Trade.*
Published by: (Association of Advertisers in Ireland), Mac Communications, Taney Hall, Eglinton Terrace, Dundrum, Dublin, Dublin 14, Ireland. TEL 353-1-2960000, FAX 353-1-2960383, info@maccommunications.ie. Ed. Sarah McQuaid. Circ: 2,000 (controlled).

659.1 DEU ISSN 0723-3361
M + A REPORT; das Magazin fuer Messen, Events und Marketing. Text in German. 1919. 8/yr. EUR 68.48; EUR 78 in Europe; EUR 83 elsewhere; EUR 10.60 newsstand/cover (effective 2000). adv. bk.rev. back issues avail. **Document type:** *Trade.* **Description:** Trade magazine for fairs, exhibitions, events, and marketing professionals.
Incorporates (1919-1990): M und A Infos
Indexed: RASB.
—**CCC.**
Published by: M + A Verlag fuer Messen, Ausstellungen und Kongresse GmbH (Subsidiary of: Deutscher Fachverlag GmbH), Postfach 200128, Frankfurt Am Main, 60605, Germany. TEL 49-69-759502, FAX 49-69-75951280, muareport-redaktion@dfv.de, http://www.mua.expobase.com, http://www.m-a.com. Ed. Freya Goettlich. Adv. contact Jutta Fautz. B&W page EUR 2,520.67, color page EUR 3,180.24; trim 297 x 210. Circ: 12,298 (controlled).

M D - MARKETING DIGEST; Fachbereichszeitschrift der Fachhochschule fuer Wirtschaft, Pforzheim. see *BUSINESS AND ECONOMICS—Marketing And Purchasing*

A

070.5 USA
M P A: SALES EDGE. Text in English. 1973. irreg. free to members. index. back issues avail. **Document type:** *Newsletter.*
Former titles: M P A Newsletter of Research (0895-1861); (until 1985): Magazine Newsletter of Research
Published by: Magazine Publishers of America, 919 Third Ave, New York, NY 10022. TEL 212-872-3700, FAX 212-888-4217. Circ: 18,000.

M P R EXCHANGE. see *HEALTH FACILITIES AND ADMINISTRATION*

MACCLESFIELD EXPRESS ADVERTISER. see *JOURNALISM*

659.111 GBR
THE MAGAZINE HANDBOOK (YEAR). Text in English. 1991. a. GBP 25. index. **Document type:** *Bulletin.*
Published by: Periodical Publishers Association, Queens House, 28 Kingsway, London, WC2B 6JR, United Kingdom. TEL 44-20-7404-4166, FAX 44-20-7404-4167, info1@ppa.co.uk, http://www.ppa.co.uk. Ed. Phil Cutts. Pub. Peter Dear. Circ: 6,000 (controlled).

659.111 GBR ISSN 0956-9855
MAGAZINE NEWS. Text in English. 1989. 5/yr. adv. **Document type:** *Trade.*
—CCC.
Published by: Periodical Publishers Association, Queens House, 28 Kingsway, London, WC2B 6JR, United Kingdom. TEL 44-20-7404-4166, FAX 44-20-7404-4167, info1@ppa.co.uk, http://www.ppa.co.uk. Ed. Daska Davis. Pub. Nicholas Mazur. Adv. contact Antony Hill. color page GBP 1,260; trim 210 x 296. Circ: 10,194 (controlled).

MAGNET MARKETING & SALES. see *BUSINESS AND ECONOMICS—Marketing And Purchasing*

659.1 USA
MAIL ADVERTISING SERVICE ASSOCIATION INTERNATIONAL. PERFORMANCE PROFILES. Text in English. a. USD 500 to non-members; USD 300 to members. **Description:** Annual report on operating and financial ratios for mailing service industry.
Formerly: Mail Advertising Service Association International. Sales Personnel Compensation Survey
Published by: Mailing & Fulfillment Service Association, 1421 Prince St, Ste 410, Alexandria, VA 22314. http://www.mfsanet.org/.

659.1 USA
MAIL ADVERTISING SERVICE ASSOCIATION INTERNATIONAL. POSTSCRIPTS. Text in English. s-w. membership. **Description:** Presents association and industry news. Includes member news, equipment exchange listings, meetings, postal information and industrial information.
Published by: Mailing & Fulfillment Service Association, 1421 Prince St, Ste 410, Alexandria, VA 22314. http://www.mfsanet.org/.

659.1 USA
MAIL ADVERTISING SERVICE ASSOCIATION INTERNATIONAL. QUARTERLY BUSINESS OUTLOOK. Text in English. q. membership.
Published by: Mailing & Fulfillment Service Association, 1421 Prince St, Ste 410, Alexandria, VA 22314. http://www.mfsanet.org/.

659.133 ESP ISSN 1135-7029
MAIL MARKETING. Text in Spanish. 1996. m. USD 240 foreign. adv. bk.rev. back issues avail. **Document type:** *Newsletter.*
Related titles: Online - full text ed.
Published by: Ediciones Comunicacion y Negocios, Pablo Vidal, 8-2o, Madrid, 28043, Spain. TEL 34-41-413-4034, FAX 34-91-519-5440, mail.marketing@mad.servicom.es, http://www.marketingdirecto.com. Ed., Pub., R&P Javier Piedrahita. Circ: 1,000.

659.1029 USA ISSN 1040-1296
MAIL ORDER PRODUCT GUIDE. Text in English. 1989. irreg. USD 75 (effective 2000). adv. **Document type:** *Directory.*
Published by: Todd Publications, 500, Millwood, NY 10546-0500. TEL 914-358-6213, FAX 914-358-1059, toddpub@aol.com, http://www.toddpublications.com. Ed., Pub., R&P, Adv. contact Barry Klein. Circ: 4,000.

659 USA ISSN 1521-6683
MAJOR MARKETING CAMPAIGNS ANNUAL. Text in English. 1998. a. USD 170 (effective 2005). **Description:** Provides an in-depth analysis of recent marketing campaigns.
Published by: Gale Research Co. (Subsidiary of: Gale Group), 27500 Drake Rd, Farmington Hills, MI 48331-3535. TEL 248-699-4253, http://www.gale.com.

MANAGEMENT IN NIGERIA. see *BUSINESS AND ECONOMICS—Management*

659.1 USA ISSN 0193-3116
MANHATTAN CATALOGUE. Text in English. 1979. 5/yr. USD 5.
Published by: Manhattan Catalogue, Inc., 141 Eighth Ave, New York, NY 10011. Ed. Gene Chase. Circ: 20,000.

659.1 DNK ISSN 0105-9424
MARKEDSFOERING. Text in Danish. 1927. 30/yr. DKK 900, USD 70 (effective 2000). adv. bk.rev. charts; illus.; mkt.; tr.lit. index.
Formerly: Dansk Reklame (0011-6459)
—CCC.
Published by: (Dansk Markedsfoerings Forbund), Specialbladsforlaget, Finsensvej 80, Frederiksberg, 2000, Denmark. Ed. Svend Erik Pedersen. Circ: 8,507.

659 DEU ISSN 0172-2441
MARKEN HANDBUCH FIRMEN, MARKEN, WERBEAGENTUREN. Text in German. 1962. 2/yr. adv. **Document type:** *Trade.*
Incorporates (1962-1988): Europa Handbuch (0723-7758); Which was formerly (until 1981): Europa Handbuch der Werbegesellschaften (0085-0349); Formerly (until 1979): Marken-Handbuch der Werbung und Etatbetreuung (0085-3119)
Published by: Team Verlag GmbH und Fachzeitschriften KG, Auwanne 19, Karlstein, 63791, Germany. Ed. Horst P Czerner. Circ: 2,500.

MARKENARTIKEL. see *BUSINESS AND ECONOMICS—Marketing And Purchasing*

659.1 USA ISSN 1061-7159
HF5826.5
MARKETER'S GUIDE TO MEDIA. Text in English. 1978. a. (Feb.). USD 129 (effective 2005). adv. charts. back issues avail.; reprints avail. **Description:** Guide to media rates, advertising opportunities, and audience demographics.
Former titles (until 1992): Mediaweek's Guide to Media (1057-1280); (until 1991): Adweek's Marketer's Guide to Media (0888-5494); (until 1986): Adweek's Media Cost Guide (0886-2788); Media Cost Guide
—CCC.
Published by: V N U Business Publications (Subsidiary of: V N U Business Media), 770 Broadway, New York, NY 10003-9595. TEL 646-654-5870, FAX 646-654-5518, http://www.vnubusinessmedia.com/. Ed. Katherine Moore. **Subscr. to:** PO Box 2006, Lakewood, NJ 08701.

MARKETING; Zeitschrift fuer Forschung und Praxis. see *BUSINESS AND ECONOMICS—Marketing And Purchasing*

MARKETING & CREATIVE HANDBOOK. see *BUSINESS AND ECONOMICS—Marketing And Purchasing*

659.1 BEL ISSN 0779-0619
MARKETING BOOK. Text in Dutch, French. 1992. a. EUR 425 domestic; EUR 550 foreign (effective 2005); incl. Media Marketing, MM News, Marketing Book, & Media Plan. **Document type:** *Directory.* **Description:** Covers all Belgian marketing, advertising and public relations agencies.
Related titles: ♦ Supplement to: Media & Marketing. ISSN 0777-0812.
Published by: Editions Dupuis S.A., Rue Jules Destree 52, Marcinelle, 6001, Belgium. TEL 32-71-600500, FAX 32-71-600599, dupuis@dupuis.be, http://www.dupuis.com/servlet/jpecat?pgm=ENH_SENG&lang=UK. Adv. contact Marie Laurence Decoster. Circ: 2,000 (paid).

MARKETING CONSENSUS GUIDE. see *BUSINESS AND ECONOMICS—Marketing And Purchasing*

659.1 658.8 PRT ISSN 0871-4932
MARKETING E PUBLICIDADE. Text in Portuguese. 1985. m. EUR 2.44 newsstand/cover (effective 2004). **Document type:** *Magazine, Trade.*
Published by: Edicoes Expansao Economica Lda., Rue Mario Castelhano, 40-1, Queluz de Baixo, Barcarena, 2749-502, Portugal. TEL 351-21-496-95-40, FAX 351-21-436-95-39, webmaster@expansao.iol.pt, http://www.marketingepublicidade.iol.pt, http://www.expansao.iol.pt. Ed. Rosa Goncalves. Adv. contact Hugo Santinho. Circ: 2,500.

MARKETING MAGAZINE; Canada's weekly newspaper for marketing, advertising and sales executives. see *BUSINESS AND ECONOMICS—Marketing And Purchasing*

659.1 IRL ISSN 0332-267X
MARKETING OPINION. Text in English. 1980. 12/yr.
Address: 12 Magennis Pl., Dublin, Ireland. TEL 1-719-896, FAX 1-719-562. Ed. Derek Garvey.

658 USA ISSN 1065-9994
HE8700.8
THE MARKETING PULSE; the exclusive insight provider to the entertainment, marketing, advertising and media industries. Text in English. 1979. bi-m. USD 300; USD 330 foreign. bk.rev. charts; stat. back issues avail. **Document type:** *Newsletter.* **Description:** Provides analysis of and recommendations for the marketing media, advertising, and entertainment industries. Includes news, research, and forecasting for key decision makers.
Former titles (until 1989): Media Report; Media Science Reports; Media Science Newsletter (0194-1607)
Published by: Unlimited Positive Communications, Inc., 7 Innis Ave, New Paltz, NY 12561. TEL 914-255-2222, FAX 914-255-2231, gdnem1@ix.netcom.com. Ed. Bill Harvey. R&P Russ Norman. Circ: 475.

MARKETING WITH HONORS; directory of awards competitions. see *BUSINESS AND ECONOMICS—Marketing And Purchasing*

659.1 USA
▼ **MARKETING Y MEDIOS.** Text in English. 2004. m. USD 49; free to qualified personnel (effective 2005). adv. **Document type:** *Magazine, Trade.* **Description:** Covers marketing, advertising and media that target the U.S. Hispanic population.
Published by: V N U Business Publications (Subsidiary of: V N U Business Media), 770 Broadway, New York, NY 10003-9595. TEL 646-654-5780, FAX 646-654-5813, editorial@marketingymedios.com, http://www.marketingymedios.com. Pub., Adv. contact Michael Hatherill. B&W page USD 8,100, color page USD 11,500; trim 8.375 x 10.875. Circ: 18,000 (paid and controlled).

659.1 FIN ISSN 1237-6655
MARKKINOINTI & MAINONTA. Text in Finnish. 1952. 43/yr. EUR 132 (effective 2005). adv. bk.rev.; film rev. charts; illus.; stat.; tr.lit. **Document type:** *Magazine, Trade.* **Description:** A weekly news and trade magazine specializing in advertising, marketing and related media.
Formerly: Mainosuutiset (0025-0864)
Related titles: Online - full text ed.
Published by: Talentum Oyj, Malminkatu 30, PO Box 920, Helsinki, 00101, Finland. TEL 358-240-4240, FAX 358-240-424130, seppo.maattanen@marmai.fi, info@talentum.fi, http://www.marmai.fi, http://www.talentum.fi. Ed. Seppo Maattanen. adv.: color page EUR 6,690; 252 x 368. Circ: 11,631 (paid).

659.1 HKG ISSN 1562-1138
MEDIA; Asia's media & marketing newspaper. Text in English. 1974. bi-w. HKD 638 domestic; USD 100 in Asia; USD 120 elsewhere. adv. charts; mkt.; stat.; tr.lit. back issues avail. **Document type:** *Newspaper, Trade.* **Description:** Covers the advertising, media, and marketing industries in China, Hong Kong, Indonesia, Japan, Korea, Malaysia, the Philippines, Singapore, Taiwan, Thailand and Vietnam. Includes the latest news, current trends, analysis of advertising campaigns and case studies.
Formerly: Media and Marketing
Related titles: E-mail ed.; Online - full text ed.: (from EBSCO Publishing, Factiva, O C L C Online Computer Library Center, Inc., ProQuest Information & Learning); Ed.: Zhongguohua. ISSN 1561-9990. 1995.
Indexed: ABIn, HongKongiana.
Published by: Media & Marketing Ltd., 28/F, Dorset House, 979 Kings Rd, Quarry Bay, Hong Kong. TEL 852-2565 2780, FAX 852-2968 0755, askme@media.com.hk, http://www.media.com.hk. Ed. Suzanne Miao. Pub. Ken McKenzie. Adv. contact Steve Bruce. B&W page HKD 47,578, color page HKD 67,048; trim 38 x 28.5. Circ: 11,000.

659.111 BEL ISSN 0777-0812
MEDIA & MARKETING. Text in Dutch, French. 1984. m. illus. **Document type:** *Trade.* **Description:** Covers the Belgian and international media and marketing scene.
Former titles (until 1989): Media Magazine (0774-8175); (until 1986): Media Marketing (0773-6630)
Related titles: ♦ Supplement(s): Marketing Book. ISSN 0779-0619; ♦ Media Plan. ISSN 0776-5738.
Indexed: B&I, CPerI.
Published by: Editions Dupuis S.A., Rue Jules Destree 52, Marcinelle, 6001, Belgium. TEL 32-71-600500, FAX 32-71-600599, dupuis@dupuis.be, http://www.dupuis.com/servlet/jpecat?pgm=ENH_SENG&lang=UK. Ed. Xavier Dupuis. Adv. contact Marie Laurence Decoster. Circ: 7,500 (paid).

659.1 658.8 GBR
MEDIA & MARKETING EUROPE. Text in English. 1989. m. GBP 95 in United Kingdom; GBP 137.50 elsewhere; GBP 5 newsstand/cover in United Kingdom (effective 1999). **Document type:** *Magazine, Trade.* **Description:** Offers news and features for European advertisers and agencies.
Indexed: B&I.
Published by: Emap Media Ltd. (Subsidiary of: Emap Business Communications Ltd.), 33-39 Bowling Green Ln, London, EC1R 0DA, United Kingdom. TEL 44-20-7505-8000, FAX 44-20-7505-8504, traceyt@media.emap.co.uk, http://www.emap.com. Ed. Tracey Taylor. Circ: 10,600. **Subscr. to:** Readerlink Ltd., Audit House, 260 Field End Rd, Ruislip, Mddx HA4 9LT, United Kingdom. TEL 44-20-8956-3000.

659.1 HKG
MEDIA CHINA. Text in Chinese. bi-m. adv. **Document type:** *Magazine, Trade.* **Description:** Focuses on analysis and trends in the advertising and marketing industries in the Greater China market.
Published by: Media & Marketing Ltd., 28/F, Dorset House, 979 Kings Rd, Quarry Bay, Hong Kong. TEL 852-2577-2628, FAX 852-2576-9171, askme@media.com.hk, http://www.media.com.hk. Ed. Iris Lai. Pub. Ken McKenzie. Adv. contact Steve Bruce. B&W page HKD 18,778, color page HKD 22,782; trim 180 x 287. Circ: 1,308 (paid and controlled).

MEDIA-DATEN: DEUTSCHLAND OST. see *BUSINESS AND ECONOMICS—Trade And Industrial Directories*

659.1 380 DEU ISSN 0946-7637
MEDIA DATEN: REGIONALE MAERKTE UND MEDIEN✶. Text in German. 1987. 2/yr. **Document type:** *Directory, Trade.*
Formerly (until 1994): Media Daten: Regionale Medien und Maerkte (0934-4861)
Published by: Media-Daten Verlag GmbH (Subsidiary of: Springer Science+Business Media), Abraham-Lincoln-Str 46, Wiesbaden, 65189, Germany. TEL 49-611-78780, FAX 49-611-7878465, info@media-daten.de, http://www.media-daten.de. Circ: 1,200 (paid).

659.1 DEU ISSN 0934-3822
MEDIA DATEN: VERBREITUNGSATLAS - ANZEIGENBLAETTER✶. Text in German. 1978. a. **Document type:** *Directory, Trade.*
Formerly (until 1988): Media Daten: Anzeigenblaetter (0170-4036)
Published by: Media-Daten Verlag GmbH (Subsidiary of: Springer Science+Business Media), Postfach 1546, Wiesbaden, 65173, Germany. TEL 49-611-78780, FAX 49-611-7878465, info@media-daten.de, http://www.media-daten.de. Circ: 1,500 (paid).

659.1 658 NZL ISSN 0113-2202
MEDIA DIRECTORY. Text in English. 1973. s-a. NZD 260. adv. **Document type:** *Directory.* **Description:** Directory listing all magazines, newspapers, radio stations and TV channels.
Published by: A G B McNair Ltd., c/o Ed. Scanlan, Ed., 129-157 Hurstmere Rd, Takapuna, Auckland, New Zealand. TEL 64-9-4862144, FAX 64-9-4863836, scanlane@acnielsen.co.nz. R&P, Adv. contact Ed Scanlan. Circ: 2,000 (paid).

659.111 DEU ISSN 1430-1474
MEDIA FACTS. Text in German. 1995. m. **Document type:** *Journal, Trade.*
Published by: Deutscher Fachverlag GmbH, Mainzer Landstr 251, Frankfurt Am Main, 60326, Germany. TEL 49-69-759501, FAX 49-69-75952050, 49-69-75952999, info@dfv.de, http://www.dfv.de.

659.1 ITA ISSN 0394-9575
MEDIAFORUM. Text in Italian. 1970. w. adv. bk.rev.
Related titles: Supplement(s): Quaderni Media.
Published by: Ediforum srl, Via Pietrasanta 14, Edificio 7, Milan, MI 20141, Italy. TEL 39-02-535981, FAX 39-02-53598247, redazione@ediforum.it, http://www.dailymedia.it. Ed. Enrico Robbiati. Circ: 9,000.

659.111 USA ISSN 0024-9793
MEDIA INDUSTRY NEWSLETTER. Abbreviated title: M I N. Text in English. 1948. w. looseleaf. USD 895 (effective 2005). bk.rev. charts; stat.; illus. index. back issues avail.; reprints avail. **Document type:** *Newsletter, Trade.* **Description:** Provides current news and information about the marketing and advertising trends in the media industry, especially magazine and newspaper publications.
Incorporates in part (in 2002): m i n's New Media Report; Which incorporated (1994-1997): Interactive Video News (1076-4526); Which was formed by the merger of (1993-1994): Video Services News (1067-3849); (1990-1994): Video Marketing Newsletter (0196-4429); Formerly: Magazine Industry Newsletter
Related titles: Online - full text ed.: (from Gale Group, O C L C Online Computer Library Center, Inc., ProQuest Information & Learning).
Indexed: ABIn.
—CCC.
Published by: Access Intelligence, LLC (Subsidiary of: Veronis, Suhler & Associates Inc.), 1201 Seven Locks Rd, Ste 300, Potomac, MD 20854. TEL 301-354-2000, 800-777-5006, FAX 301-340-1451, aduff@phillips.com, clientservices@accessintel.com, http://www.minonline.com/, http://www.pbimedia.com. Eds. Steve Cohn, Steven Cohn. Pub. Diane Schwartz. Circ: 2,143.

659.1 GBR ISSN 0266-8688
MEDIA INTERNATIONAL. Text in English. 1973. m. GBP 42; GBP 76 foreign (effective 1999). adv. bk.rev. **Document type:** *Trade.* **Description:** Written for personnel in companies that advertise internationally and agencies who are involved in media decisions for international advertising campaigns.
Related titles: Online - full text ed.
Indexed: RASB.
Published by: Reed Business Information Ltd. (Subsidiary of: Reed Business), Quadrant House, The Quadrant, Brighton Rd, Sutton, Surrey SM2 5AS, United Kingdom. TEL 44-208-652-3500, FAX 44-208-652-8977, rbp.subscriptions@rbi.co.uk, rbi.subscriptions@qss-uk.com, http://www.reedbusiness.com, http://www.reedinfo.co.uk/. Ed., R&P Penny Wilson. Pub. Leon Clifford. Adv. contact Charlotte Davies. Circ: 12,502. **Subscr. to:** Quadrant Subscription Services, PO Box 302, Haywards Heath, W Sussex RH16 3YY, United Kingdom. TEL 44-1444-445566, FAX 44-1444-445447.

659.1 USA
MEDIA MARKET GUIDE✶. Text in English. 1969. q. USD 675. adv. **Document type:** *Directory.*
Published by: Media Market Resources, Inc., 365 Union, Littleton, NH 03561. TEL 603-444-5720, 800-242-9618, FAX 603-444-2872, info@mediamarket.com. Ed. Robert Herbst. Pub. Martin Herbst. R&P, Adv. contact Amy Konikowsky. Circ: 1,200.

659.143 USA
MEDIA MATTERS. Text in English. 1986. bi-m. USD 175; USD 88 to students. adv. back issues avail. **Document type:** *Newsletter, Trade.* **Description:** Provides original commentary, analyses, and forecasts on all aspects of media and advertising.
Published by: Media Dynamics, Inc., 570 7th Ave Rm 1906, New York, NY 10018-1619. TEL 212-704-0024, FAX 212-704-0023, info@mediadynamicsinc.com, http://www.mediadynamicsinc.com. Ed. Carol Williams. Pub. Ed Papazian. R&P Mary Ellen Pastor. Adv. contact Barbara Llull.

659.1 DEU ISSN 0720-3519
HF5843
MEDIA PLAKAT. Text in German. 1961. a. EUR 169 (effective 2003). adv. **Document type:** *Directory, Trade.* **Description:** Advertising rates and prices for billboarding and outdoor advertising.
Supersedes in part (in 1979): Media-Fakten (0543-2413)
Published by: Media-Daten Verlag GmbH (Subsidiary of: Springer Science+Business Media), Postfach 1546, Wiesbaden, 65173, Germany. TEL 49-611-78780, FAX 49-611-7878465, info@media-daten.de, http://www.media-daten.de. adv.: B&W page EUR 1,930, color page EUR 3,160. Circ: 1,500 (paid).

659.111 BEL ISSN 0776-5738
MEDIA PLAN. Text in Dutch, French. 1989. a. (Jan.), latest 2005. EUR 425 domestic; EUR 550 foreign (effective 2005); incl. Media Marketing, MM News, Marketing Book, & Media Plan. **Document type:** *Directory.* **Description:** Provides data on all Belgian print and broadcast media.
Related titles: ♦ Supplement to: Media & Marketing. ISSN 0777-0812.
Published by: Editions Dupuis S.A., Rue Jules Destree 52, Marcinelle, 6001, Belgium. TEL 32-71-600500, FAX 32-71-600599, dupuis@dupuis.be, http://www.dupuis.com/servlet/jpecat?pgm=ENH_SENG&lang=UK. Adv. contact Marie Laurence Decoster. Circ: 3,000 (paid).

MEDIA PROFESSIONAL. see *JOURNALISM*

659.2 USA
MEDIA RELATIONS INSIDER. Text in English. 2000. m. USD 399 (effective 2003). **Document type:** *Newsletter, Trade.*
Published by: InfoCom Group, 5900 Hollis St, Ste L, Emeryville, CA 94608-2008. TEL 510-596-9300, 800-959-1059, FAX 510-596-9331, webmgr@infocomgroup.com, http://www.infocomgroup.com.

659.2 USA
MEDIA RELATIONS REPORT. Text in English. s-m. USD 347. **Document type:** *Newsletter, Trade.* **Description:** Provides news on media contact changes, placement opportunities, and insights from journalists that will help you target your releases.
Published by: Lawrence Ragan Communications, Inc., 316 N Michigan Ave, Ste 300, Chicago, IL 60601. TEL 312-960-4106, 800-878-5331, FAX 312-960-4106, http://www.ragan.com.

659.1320948 DNK ISSN 0076-5821
Z6941
MEDIA SCANDINAVIA; a Scandinavian advertising media directory. Text in Danish, English. 1948. a. DKK 650 (effective 2000). adv. **Document type:** *Directory.*
Former titles (until 1967): Media (0903-5001); (until 1962): Bladlisten (0903-4986); (until 1960): Eberlins Bladliste (0903-4951)
Related titles: CD-ROM ed.
Published by: Danske Reklame- og Relationsbureauers Brancheforening/Danish Association of Advertising and Relationship Agencies, Badstuestraede 20, Copenhagen K, 1209, Denmark. TEL 45-33-13-44-44, FAX 45-33-11-63-03, drrb@drrb.dk, www.drrb.dk. Eds. Finn Kern, Lone Ellebo. Adv. contact K Persson. page DKK 1,750. Circ: 2,500.

659.1 DEU ISSN 0173-5993
HN460.M3
MEDIA SPECTRUM; Kommentare, Meinungen, Analysen. Text in German. 1963. m. **Document type:** *Trade.* **Description:** For media planners and other media people.
—IE, Infotrieve.
Published by: Media-Daten Verlag GmbH (Subsidiary of: Springer Science+Business Media), Postfach 1546, Wiesbaden, 65173, Germany. TEL 49-611-78780, FAX 49-611-7878465, info@media-daten.de, http://www.media-daten.de. Circ: 2,050.

659.1 CZE ISSN 1210-8294
MEDIA TARIF. Text in Czech. 1993. 2/yr. CZK 3,190 (effective 2001). adv. **Document type:** *Magazine, Trade.*
Published by: Strategie Praha s.r.o., Drtinova 8, Prague 5, 150 00, Czech Republic. TEL 420-2-57323578, FAX 420-2-57018362, mediatarif@istrategie.cz, strategie.praha@istrategie.cz, http://www.istrategie.cz. adv.: page CZK 67,250.

659.1 GBR ISSN 0963-0023
MEDIA WEEK. Text in English. 1985. w. GBP 99 (effective 2005). adv. charts; stat. back issues avail. **Document type:** *Magazine, Trade.* **Description:** Provides weekly news and analysis of all the important media issues facing advertisers, agencies and media owners.
Related titles: Online - full text ed.
Indexed: B&I, M&MA.
—BLDSC (5525.263000).
Published by: Quantum Business Media Ltd., Quantum House, 19 Scarbrook Rd, Croydon, Surrey CR9 1LX, United Kingdom. TEL 44-20-85654200, FAX 44-20-85654444, enquiries@quantumbusinessmedia.com, http://www.mediaweek.co.uk, http://www.quantumbusinessmedia.com. Ed. Susannah Richmond. Pub. Karen Needham. Adv. contact Elizabeth Houghton. Circ: 16,754.

MEDIAFIGYELO. see *BUSINESS AND ECONOMICS—Marketing And Purchasing*

659.1 FIN
MEDIAHELMI. Text in Finnish. 3/yr. **Document type:** *Trade.*
Published by: Helsinki Media Company Oy, PL 2, Helsinki, 00040, Finland. TEL 358-9-1201, FAX 358-9-120-5988. Ed. Eija Soratie.

659.1 NLD ISSN 0168-8235
MEDIAMARKT. Text in Dutch. 1975. m. adv. charts; illus. **Document type:** *Trade.*
Former titles (until 1984): Ariadne (0922-3800); (until 1982): Ariadne - Revue der Reclame (0165-4152); Formed by the merger of (1973-1975): M M D Ariadne (0922-3797); Kontekst (0922-3916); Which was formerly (1938-1972): Revue der Reclame (0035-1881)
Published by: Samsom Uitgeverij B.V. (Subsidiary of: Wolters Kluwer N.V.), Postbus 4, Alphen aan den Rijn, 2400 MA, Netherlands. TEL 31-172-466321, FAX 31-172-435527. Circ: 3,500.

070.5 CHE
MEDIAPERFORMANCE. Text in French, German. 1968. a. CHF 220 (effective 2001). **Document type:** *Directory, Trade.* **Description:** Detailed coverage of Swiss newspapers' circulation sorted according to geographic area.
Former titles: Verbreitungsdaten der Schweizer Presse; Streudaten der Schweizer Presse
Related titles: Online - full text ed.
Published by: Verband Schweizerischer Werbegesellschaften/Association des Societes Suisses de Publicite, Av des Mousquines 4, Case Postale 339, Lausanne, 1001, Switzerland. TEL 41-21-2136141, FAX 41-21-3126709, dcl@vsw-assp.ch, http://www.vsw-assp.ch. Circ: 500.

659.1 USA ISSN 1055-176X
HF6146.T42
MEDIAWEEK; the news magazine of the media . Text in English. 1966. w. (Mon.). USD 149 domestic; USD 319 elsewhere; USD 3.95 newsstand/cover (effective 2005). adv. illus. index. back issues avail.; reprints avail. **Document type:** *Magazine, Trade.*
Former titles (until 1990): Marketing and Media Decisions (0195-4296); (until 1979): Media Decisions (0025-6900)
Related titles: Microfiche ed.: (from CIS); Microform ed.: (from PQC); Online - full text ed.: (from EBSCO Publishing, Florida Center for Library Automation, Gale Group, H.W. Wilson, Northern Light Technology, Inc., O C L C Online Computer Library Center, Inc., ProQuest Information & Learning, The Dialog Corporation).
Indexed: ABIn, AcaI, BPI, BPIA, BusI, LRI, ManagCont, PROMT, SRI, T&II.
—BLDSC (5525.385900). **CCC.**
Published by: V N U Business Publications (Subsidiary of: V N U Business Media), 770 Broadway, New York, NY 10003-9595. TEL 646-654-7601, FAX 646-654-5351, mburgi@mediaweek.com, bmcomm@vnuinc.com, http://www.mediaweek.com, http://www.vnubusinessmedia.com. Ed. Michael Burgi. Pub. Linda D'Adamo. adv.: B&W page USD 7,980, color page USD 12,140; trim 10.88 x 8.38. Circ: 21,978 (paid).

MEDICAL NEWS REPORT. see *BUSINESS AND ECONOMICS—Marketing And Purchasing*

MEDIEN DIALOG; Gespraech - Diskussion - Meinung - Information. see *COMMUNICATIONS—Television And Cable*

659.143 DEU
MEDIENREPORT. Text in German. 1974. m. tr.lit. back issues avail. **Document type:** *Newsletter, Trade.*
Published by: Medienreport Verlags GmbH, Hegnacher Str 30, Waiblingen, 71336, Germany. TEL 49-7151-23331, FAX 49-7151-23338, http://www.medienreport.de. Ed. Rolf G Lehmann. Circ: 1,500.

659.132 PRT
MEIOS. Text in Portuguese. 1992. m. EUR 15 (effective 2005). **Document type:** *Bulletin, Trade.* **Description:** Publishes information on advertising and advertising agencies.
Related titles: Online - full text ed.
Published by: Associacao da Imprensa nao Diaria, Rua Gomez Freire No. 183, 4 Esquerdo, Lisbon, 1169-041, Portugal. TEL 351-21-3555092, FAX 351-21-3142199, revistameios@aind.pt, http://www.aind.pt/revmeios.html. Ed. Ana Cristina Cruz. Adv. contact Joana Ramada Curto. Circ: 1,200.

▼ new title ➤ refereed ✶ unverified ♦ full entry avail.

659.1 USA ISSN 0889-2776
HM263
METRO CALIFORNIA MEDIA. Text in English. 1979. a. USD 345 (effective 2005). **Document type:** *Directory, Trade.* **Description:** Covers key personnel in media located in California.
Formerly: California Publicity Outlets
Published by: Bacon's Information, Inc., 332 S Michigan Ave, Ste 900, Chicago, IL 60604. TEL 312-922-2400, 800-621-0561, FAX 312-987-9773, directories@bacons.com, http://www.bacons.com. Pub. Ruth McFarland. R&P Ruth Cox McFarland TEL 312-986-2728. Circ: 3,000.

659 700 USA
METRO'S PLUS BUSINESS. Text in English. 1934. m. USD 60 (effective 1999). adv. bk.rev.; software rev. charts; illus.; mkt.; stat. back issues avail. **Document type:** *Trade.* **Description:** Spotlights the newspaper industry, special sections, advertising, marketing and designs.
Related titles: Online - full text ed.
Published by: Metro Creative Graphics, Inc., 519, 8th Ave., 18th Fl, New York, NY 1000110018-4577. TEL 800-223-1600, FAX 212-967-4602, TELEX 421947, alexachang@metrocreativegraphics.com, http://www.metrocreativegraphics.com. Ed., Adv. contact Alexandra Chang. Circ: 7,000.

MIDI MEDIA. see *BUSINESS AND ECONOMICS—Marketing And Purchasing*

659.1 BRA
MIDIA. Text in Portuguese. 1977. a. free.
Published by: Editora Rural, Rua Gabriela 333, Porto Alegre, RGS, Brazil.

659.1 ITA ISSN 0392-5498
MILLIMETRO; periodico di informazioni aziendali di marketing e di pubblicita. Text in Italian. 1964. q. adv. bk.rev. **Document type:** *Corporate.*
Published by: St. Paul's International, Via Giotto, 36, Milan, MI 20145, Italy. TEL 39-2-48071, FAX 39-2-48008247, TELEX 332232 EPI I. Ed. Giuseppe Altamore. Circ: 5,000.

MISSOURI PRESS NEWS. see *JOURNALISM*

MONDAY REPORT ON RETAILERS. see *BUSINESS AND ECONOMICS—Marketing And Purchasing*

659 USA ISSN 1557-5152
MOTIVATION STRATEGIES. Text in English. 1998. q. adv. **Document type:** *Magazine, Trade.* **Description:** Covers incentives, including merchandise, travel, recognition, debit cards, and online award systems. Return-on-investment and research. Motivational meetings. Performance improvement strategies encompassing tracking systems, marketing communications, online applications, etc., designed to achieve critical business objectives.
Published by: Selling Communications, Inc., One Bridge St, Ste 77, Irvington, NY 10533. TEL 914-591-7600, FAX 914-591-7699, selling@sellingcommunications.com, http://www.sellingcommunications.com/Motivation_Strategies.440.0.html. Adv. contact Jim Kilmetis TEL 914-591-7600 ext 229. B&W page USD 6,000; 7 x 10. Circ: 25,000.

MOTORRAD BOERSE. see *SPORTS AND GAMES—Bicycles And Motorcycles*

MOTORRAD FOTO. see *SPORTS AND GAMES—Bicycles And Motorcycles*

659.1 DEU
MUENCHNER SCHAUKASTERL. Text in German. 1975. w.
Published by: Muenchner Schaukasterl Verlag GmbH, Simplonstr 2, Munich, 81825, Germany. TEL 089-429129. Ed. Harald Richter. Circ: 50,000.

070.5 USA ISSN 1554-8961
HF5861
▼ **MULTICHANNEL MERCHANT.** Text in English. 2005. m. USD 85 domestic; USD 96 foreign; free to qualified personnel (effective 2005). adv. bk.rev. reprint service avail. from PQC. **Document type:** *Magazine, Trade.* **Description:** Catalog executives publication that covers news, trends, technologies and strategies for improving market share and profitability.
Formed by the merger of (1983-2005): Catalog Age (0740-3119); (1993-2005): Operatons & Fulfillment (1069-6083)
Related titles: Online - full text ed.: (from EBSCO Publishing, Gale Group, H.W. Wilson, O C L C Online Computer Library Center, Inc., ProQuest Information & Learning).
Indexed: ABIn, B&I, BPI, PSI, SoftBase.
—BLDSC (3074.082000), IE, ingenta. **CCC.**
Published by: Primedia Business Magazines & Media, Inc. (Subsidiary of: Primedia, Inc.), 11 River Bend Dr S, Stamford, CT 06907. TEL 203-358-9900, FAX 203-358-5811, inquiries@primediabusiness.com, http://multichannelmerchant.com, http://www.primediabusiness.com. Ed. Sherry Chiger TEL 203-358-4386. adv.: B&W page USD 2,965, color page USD 3,830; 14.25 x 10.88. Circ: 14,193 (controlled). **Subscr. to:** PO Box 12993, Overland Park, KS 66282-2993. TEL 800-441-0294, FAX 913-967-1331.

659.1 USA ISSN 0743-0795
MULTINATIONAL P R REPORT. Text in English. 1984. m. USD 105 (effective 2004). bk.rev. **Document type:** *Newsletter, Trade.* **Description:** News for professionals in public relations.
Published by: Pigafetta Press, PO Box 39244, Washington, DC 20016. TEL 202-244-2580, FAX 202-244-2581, http://www.prplace.com. Ed. John M Reed.

MURRAY REGION TOURIST NEWS. see *TRAVEL AND TOURISM*

MYHANDY. see *COMMUNICATIONS—Telephone And Telegraph*

659.1 USA
N A D CASE REPORTS. (Council of Better Business Bureaus, Inc.) Text in English. 1973. 10/yr. USD 1,000 (effective 1998). Jan issue includes year case summary. 90 p./no.; **Document type:** *Corporate.* **Description:** Promotes truth and accuracy in advertising. Each issue discusses specifically which national ads have been challenged, by whom, and gives the outcome of the challenge.
Related titles: CD-ROM ed.
Published by: Council of Better Business Bureaus, Inc., National Advertising Division, 845 Third Ave, New York, NY 10022. TEL 212-705-0100, FAX 212-832-1296, http://www.bbb.org. Ed. Wendi Dee. R&P Bruce Hopewell. Circ: 5,700.

070.5 USA
N A P R BULLETIN. Text in English. 1950. m. looseleaf. USD 135 membership (effective 2001). back issues avail. **Document type:** *Newsletter, Trade.*
Published by: National Association of Publishers' Representatives, PO Box 3139, New York, NY 10163. TEL 212-685-3254, FAX 212-685-2963, info@naprassoc.org, http://www.naprassoc.org. Ed. Thomas F Kenny. Circ: 300.

N Y AUCTION ADVERTISER. see *BUSINESS AND ECONOMICS—Marketing And Purchasing*

659.1 RUS
NARUZHNAYA REKLAMA ROSSII. Text in Russian. m.
Published by: Naruzhnaya Rekama Rossii, Tverskoi bul 6, Moscow, 103009, Russian Federation. TEL 7-095-2028595, 7-095-2918023, mediarama@ftcenter.ru, http://www.signs.ru. Ed. Eduard Chumakov.

659.1 340 USA
NATIONAL ADVERTISING DIVISION CASE REPORT. Text in English. 10/yr. USD 2,500 (effective 2001). **Description:** A summary of cases where national advertising claims have been challenged and the issues resolved by the industry's self-regulatory body.
Published by: Council of Better Business Bureaus, Publications Department, 4200 Wilson Blvd, Arlington, VA 22203-1804. TEL 703-276-0100. Ed. Wendi Dee. R&P Steven B Davis. Circ: 1,000.

659.1029 CAN ISSN 0077-5177
HF5808.C2
NATIONAL LIST OF ADVERTISERS. Text in English. 1936. a. CND 230 (effective 2003). adv. **Document type:** *Directory, Trade.* **Description:** Lists names, addresses, brand names, personnel, etc. of over 3,000 national advertisers.
Published by: C A R D, the Media Information Network (Subsidiary of: Rogers Media Publishing Ltd), Subscriber Services, Maclean Hunter Bldg, 777 Bay St, 8th Fl, Toronto, ON M5W 1A7, Canada. TEL 416-596-2790, FAX 416-596-5158, http://www.cardmedia.com/products/products.htm. Ed. Nancy Remnant. Adv. contact Lucia De Stefano. B&W page CND 1,856, color page CND 3,644; trim 200 x 273.

NATIONAL NEWS. see *COMMUNICATIONS—Television And Cable*

THE NATIONAL P R PITCH BOOK. BUSINESS & CONSUMER EDITION. see *BUSINESS AND ECONOMICS—Trade And Industrial Directories*

THE NATIONAL P R PITCH BOOK. COMPUTERS & TECHNOLOGY EDITION. see *BUSINESS AND ECONOMICS—Trade And Industrial Directories*

THE NATIONAL P R PITCH BOOK. HEALTH, FITNESS & MEDICINE EDITION. see *BUSINESS AND ECONOMICS—Trade And Industrial Directories*

THE NATIONAL P R PITCH BOOK. INVESTMENT, BANKING & FINANCIAL SERVICES EDITION. see *BUSINESS AND ECONOMICS—Trade And Industrial Directories*

THE NATIONAL P R PITCH BOOK. ISSUES, POLICY & POLITICS EDITION. see *BUSINESS AND ECONOMICS—Trade And Industrial Directories*

THE NATIONAL P R PITCH BOOK. TRAVEL, HOSPITALITY & DESTINATIONS EDITION. see *BUSINESS AND ECONOMICS—Trade And Industrial Directories*

NATIONAL RADIO PUBLICITY OUTLETS. see *COMMUNICATIONS—Radio*

659.1 GRC
NEA DIMOSSIOTIS. Text in Greek. 1958. m. USD 50. adv. bk.rev. stat. back issues avail.
Former titles: Dimossiotis (0012-2920); Dimossiotis-Provoli
Published by: Imera Publishing Co., 61 Mihalakopoulou St, Patras, 262 21, Greece. Ed. Andrew C Rizopoulos. Circ: 2,500. **Subscr. to:** 5 Miltiadou St, Holargos, Athens 155 62, Greece.

659.2 370.1 USA ISSN 1076-254X
NETWORK (ROCKVILLE). Text in English. 1959. 11/yr. free to members. **Document type:** *Newsletter, Trade.*
Formerly: Paragraphs (0031-1669)
Published by: National School Public Relations Association, 15948 Derwood Rd, Rockville, MD 20855-2123. TEL 301-519-0496, FAX 301-519-0494, nspra@nspra.org, http://www.nspra.org. Circ: 1,800 (paid and controlled).

659.2 USA ISSN 0077-9024
Z6953.N6
NEW YORK PUBLICITY OUTLETS. Text in English. 1954. a. USD 345 (effective 2005). **Document type:** *Directory, Trade.* **Description:** Covers key personnel in media located within the state of New York.
Published by: Bacon's Information, Inc., 332 S Michigan Ave, Ste 900, Chicago, IL 60604. TEL 312-922-2400, 800-621-0561, FAX 312-987-9773, directories@bacons.com, http://www.bacons.com. Pub. Ruth McFarland. R&P Ruth Cox McFarland TEL 312-986-2728. Circ: 4,000.

659.1 070.172 USA
NEWSPAPER ASSOCIATION OF AMERICA. NEWSPAPER ADVERTISING PLANBOOK. Text in English. a.
Supersedes (in 1992): Newspaper Advertising Bureau. Newspaper Advertising Planbook
Published by: Newspaper Association of America, 1921 Gallows Rd, Ste 600, Vienna, VA 22182-3900. TEL 703-902-1600, FAX 703-917-0636, http://www.naa.org.

659.1 JPN
NIKKEI IMAGE CLIMATE FORECAST. Text in Japanese. m.?. **Document type:** *Newsletter.* **Description:** Analysis of trends and consumer behavior as they affect corporate image strategies.
Published by: Nihon Keizai Shimbun Inc., 1-9-5 Ote-Machi, Chiyoda-ku, Tokyo, 100-0004, Japan. TEL 81-3-32700251, FAX 81-3-52552661.

659.1 JPN
NIKKEI RYUTSU SHIMBUN/NIKKEI MARKETING JOURNAL. Text in Japanese. 1971. 3/w. adv. **Document type:** *Newspaper.* **Description:** Japan's leading source of information on distribution market.
Published by: Nihon Keizai Shimbun Inc., 1-9-5 Ote-Machi, Chiyoda-ku, Tokyo, 100-0004, Japan. TEL 81-3-32700251, FAX 81-3-52552661. Ed. Shunsaku Ikeda. Adv. contact Hiroshi Sekino. B&W page JPY 3,270,000; trim 533 x 385. Circ: 318,677.

659.1 RUS
NOVAYA POLIGRAFIYA. Text in Russian. m.
Address: Ul Petrovka 26, k 302, 304, Moscow, 101429, Russian Federation. TEL 7-095-9236974. Ed. V V Kazartseva. Circ: 3,000.

659.1 740 DEU ISSN 1438-1753
NC997.A1
NOVUM; Forum fuer Kommunikations-Design. Text in English, German. 1924. m. EUR 101.40; EUR 144 elsewhere; EUR 82.80 to students (effective 2002). adv. bk.rev. abstr.; illus. **Document type:** *Magazine, Trade.*
Former titles (until 1996): Novum Gebrauchsgraphik (0302-9794); (until 1974): Novum (0340-1987); Gebrauchsgraphik (0016-5743)
Indexed: ABM, ArtInd, DAAI, IBR, RASB.
—BLDSC (6180.443000), IE, Infotrieve. **CCC.**
Published by: (New Media Magazine Verlag GmbH), S M G - Stiebner Medien GmbH, Nymphenburger Str 86, Munich, 80636, Germany. TEL 49-89-1257378, FAX 49-89-12162282, ulrich@novumnet.de, verlag@stiebner.com, http://www.novumnet.de, http://www.stiebner.com. Eds. Erhardt D Stiebner, Stefan Benaburger, Bettina Ulrich. Adv. contact Christine Moosman. Circ: 8,000.

659.2 ESP ISSN 0211-2000
NUEVA PUBLICIDAD. Text in Spanish. 1970. q. **Document type:** *Trade.* **Description:** Covers all communications areas, including photography and graphic arts.
Published by: Asociacion Espanola de Profesionales de Publicidad, Jardin de San Federico, 5 6o, Madrid, 28009, Spain. TEL 401-15-13. Circ: 2,000.

O C S NOUVELLES. see *COMMUNICATIONS*

O P M A OVERSEAS MEDIA GUIDE. see *BUSINESS AND ECONOMICS—Trade And Industrial Directories*

O'DWYER'S DIRECTORY OF PUBLIC RELATIONS EXECUTIVES. see *BUSINESS AND ECONOMICS—Trade And Industrial Directories*

O'DWYER'S DIRECTORY OF PUBLIC RELATIONS FIRMS. see *BUSINESS AND ECONOMICS—Trade And Industrial Directories*

O'DWYER'S NEW YORK PUBLIC RELATIONS DIRECTORY. see *BUSINESS AND ECONOMICS—Trade And Industrial Directories*

659.1 USA
O'DWYER'S P R MARKETPLACE. Text in English. 1987. bi-w. USD 24 (effective 2001). adv. **Document type:** *Newsletter, Trade.* **Description:** Lists public relations jobs and people available.
Published by: J.R. O'Dwyer Co., Inc., 271 Madison Ave, Ste 600, New York, NY 10016. TEL 212-679-2471, john@odwyerpr.com, http://www.odwyerpr.com. Ed. Jack O'Dwyer.

659 USA
O'DWYER'S P R NEWSLETTER. Text in English. 1968. w. looseleaf. USD 295 (effective 2005). bk.rev. **Document type:** *Newsletter, Trade.* **Description:** Provides the latest news and information on public relations firms and professionals.
Former titles: Jack O'Dwyer's Newsletter (0047-1690); Jack O'Dwyer's P R Newsletter
Related titles: E-mail ed.; Online - full text ed.: (from LexisNexis).
Published by: J.R. O'Dwyer Co., Inc., 271 Madison Ave, Ste 600, New York, NY 10016. TEL 212-679-2471, FAX 212-683-2750, jack@odwyerpr.com, john@odwyerpr.com, http://www.odwyerpr.com. Ed., Pub. Jack O'Dwyer. Circ: 20,000 (paid).

659.2 USA ISSN 1043-2957
O'DWYER'S P R SERVICES REPORT. (Public Relations) Text in English. 1987. m. USD 60 (effective 2005). adv. **Document type:** *Magazine, Trade.* **Description:** Publishes articles on current topics and trends of interest to PR professionals, including profiles of firms, discussions of legal and financial issues.
Related titles: Online - full text ed.: (from LexisNexis).
Published by: J.R. O'Dwyer Co., Inc., 271 Madison Ave, Ste 600, New York, NY 10016. TEL 212-679-2471, FAX 212-683-2750, kevin@odwyerpr.com, john@odwyerpr.com, htpp://www.odwyerpr.com, http://www.odwyerpr.com. Pub. Jack O'Dwyer. Circ: 4,000.

659 HRV ISSN 1331-0097
OGLASNIK. Text in Croatian. 1991. 3/w. adv. **Document type:** *Newspaper, Consumer.*
Address: Savska 41/IV, Zagreb, 10000, Croatia. TEL 385-1-6102800, FAX 385-1-6102850, mkopriv@oglasnik.hr, http://mir.oglasnik.hr. adv.: page HRK 8,300.

OKLAHOMA PUBLISHER. see *PUBLISHING AND BOOK TRADE*

OMNIBUS. see *TRANSPORTATION*

659.1 USA
ONE. A MAGAZINE. Text in English. 4/yr. USD 40 domestic; USD 50 foreign (effective 2005). adv. **Document type:** *Magazine, Trade.* **Description:** Contains articles written exclusively for and by people who produce creative advertising work.
Published by: The One Club for Art & Copy, 32 E 21st St, New York, NY 10010. TEL 212-979-1900, FAX 212-979-5006, one.amagazine@oneclub.com, http://www.oneclub.com/onemag.htm. Ed. Warren Berger. Adv. contact Kevin Swanepoel.

659.1 USA
OUTDOOR ADVERTISING EXPENDITURE REPORT. Text in English. q. stat. **Document type:** *Newsletter.*
Published by: Outdoor Advertising Association of America, 1850 M St, N W, Ste 1040, Washington, DC 20036. TEL 202-833-5566, FAX 202-833-1522.

659.1 GBR ISSN 0048-251X
OVERSEAS ADVERTISING. Text in English. 1971 (vol.8). m. GBP 17, USD 50. adv. illus.
Incorporates: Far East (0014-7532)
Related titles: Microfilm ed.: (from PQC).
Indexed: Englnd.
Published by: New Product Newsletter Co. Ltd., 1a Chesterfield St, London, W1X 7HF, United Kingdom. Ed. H R Vaughan. Circ: 7,000.

659.1 GBR
P E D INDUSTRIAL SELECTOR. Text in English. 1976. 9/yr. **Document type:** *Trade.*
Published by: Wilmington Publishing, Wilmington House, Church Rd, Dartford, Kent UA2 7EF, United Kingdom. TEL 44-1322-277788, FAX 44-1322-276476. Circ: 56,323.

P M C OF N Y NEWSLETTER. see *BUSINESS AND ECONOMICS—Marketing And Purchasing*

659.1 USA
P-O-P DESIGN; products and news for high-volume producers of displays, signs and fixtures. (Point-of-Purchase) Text in English. 1994. 9/yr. USD 59 (effective 2000). adv. back issues avail. **Document type:** *Journal, Trade.* **Description:** Publishes developments and advancements in materials, processes, systems, equipment and services.
Formerly: P-O-P & Sign Design (1081-2660)
Published by: Hoyt Publishing Co., 7400 Skokie Blvd, Skokie, IL 60077-3339. TEL 847-675-7400, FAX 847-675-7494, getinfo@hoytpub.com. Ed. William Schober. Pub., R&P, Adv. contact Dan Ashenden. Circ: 20,006.

659.2 USA
P R AGENCY INSIDER; what's new and what's working for growing pr agencies. (Public Relations) Text in English. m. USD 349 (effective 2001). **Document type:** *Newsletter, Trade.* **Description:** Provides practical public relations agency management tips and techniques.
Published by: InfoCom Group, 5900 Hollis St, Ste L, Emeryville, CA 94608-2008. TEL 510-596-9300, 800-959-1059, FAX 510-596-9331, webmgr@infocomgroup.com, http://www.infocomgroup.com/prai.html.

659.2 AUT
P R ALMANACH. (Public Relations) Text in German. 1997. a. EUR 36 (effective 2005). adv. **Document type:** *Directory, Trade.*
Published by: Manstein Zeitschriften Verlagsgesellschaft mbH, Brunner Feldstr 45, Perchtoldsdorf, N 2380, Austria. TEL 43-1-866480, FAX http://www.manstein.at, 43-1-86648100, office@manstein.at. Ed. Gertrude Mayer. Adv. contact Martina Hofmann.

659.2 USA
P R - CHICAGO. Text in English. m.
Address: 30 N Michigan Ave, 508, Chicago, IL 60602-3404. TEL 312-372-7744. Ed. Carla Brock.

659.2 USA
P R INTELLIGENCE REPORT. Text in English. s-m. USD 279. **Document type:** *Newsletter.* **Description:** Provides the details, insights and information you need to improve your career.
Published by: Lawrence Ragan Communications, Inc., 316 N Michigan Ave, Ste 300, Chicago, IL 60601. TEL 312-960-4106, 800-878-5331, FAX 312-960-4106, http://www.ragan.com.

659.1 CHE
P R MAGAZIN. Text in German. m.
Published by: Zollinger & Partner AG, Steinacherstr. 105, Zurich, 8804, Switzerland. TEL 01-7812563, FAX 01-7812570. Ed. Hans Zollinger. Circ: 3,000.

659.1 DEU ISSN 0342-8702
P R - MAGAZIN; das Magazin der Kommunikationsbranche. Text in German. 1969. m. EUR 162; EUR 48 to students (effective 2002). adv. bk.rev. **Document type:** *Magazine, Trade.*
Incorporates (1964-1981): Format (0015-7759)
Indexed: KES.
—IE, Infotrieve. **CCC.**
Published by: Verlag Rommerskirchen und Co. KG, Mainzer Str 16-18, Remagen, 53424, Germany. TEL 49-2228-931-0, FAX 49-2228-931149, prmagazin@rommerskirchen.com, info@rommerskirchen.com, http://www.rommerskirchen.com. Ed. Thomas Rommerskirchen. Circ: 8,000.

659.2 USA ISSN 1546-0193
HM263.A1
P R NEWS. (Public Relations) Variant title: Phillips P R News. Text in English. 1944. w. looseleaf. USD 697 domestic (effective 2005). **Document type:** *Newsletter, Trade.* **Description:** Publishes for public relations, public affairs and communications executives. Reports public relations techniques and trends, case studies of programs and news of the industry.
Formerly (until 1992): Public Relations News (0033-3697); Incorporates (1993-2001): Healthcare P R & Marketing News (1072-3684); Which was formerly (until 1993): Healthcare P R News (1068-0403); Incorporates (until 199?): P R News Media Hot Sheet (1520-8419)
Related titles: Online - full text ed.: (from bigchalk, Gale Group, LexisNexis, ProQuest Information & Learning).
Indexed: ABIn.
—**CCC.**
Published by: Access Intelligence, LLC (Subsidiary of: Veronis, Suhler & Associates Inc.), 1201 Seven Locks Rd, Ste 300, Potomac, MD 20854. TEL 301-354-2000, 800-777-5006, FAX 301-340-1451, smclaughlin@phillips.com, clientservices@accessintel.com, http://www.prandmarketing.com/cgi/catalog/info?PRN, http://www.pbimedia.com. Ed. Peggy Stuntz. Pub. Diane Schwartz.

659 GBR
P R PLANNER - EUROPE. Text in English. 1974. a. looseleaf. GBP 545. **Document type:** *Directory.* **Description:** Complete list of European trade and consumer publications. Four key markets are classified for 14 European countries.
Related titles: CD-ROM ed.
Published by: Media Information Ltd., Chess House, 34 Germain St, Chesham, Bucks HP5 1SJ, United Kingdom. FAX 44-1494-797-224, prplanner@mediainfo.co.uk. Ed. Helen Buckhurst.

659 GBR
P R PLANNER - U.K. Text in English. 1966. a. looseleaf. GBP 355. **Document type:** *Directory.* **Description:** Contains over 300 classified lists of magazines and more than 12,000 editors and specialist writers on newspapers, magazines, radio and TV.
Related titles: CD-ROM ed.
Published by: Media Information Ltd., Chess House, 34 Germain St, Chesham, Bucks HP5 1SJ, United Kingdom. TEL 44-1494-797260, FAX 44-1494-7972243, prplanner@mediainfo.co.uk. Ed. Helen Buckhurst.

659.1 DEU
P R REPORT. Text in German. 1965. w. EUR 187.50 domestic; EUR 216.50 foreign (effective 2005). adv. **Document type:** *Magazine, Trade.* **Description:** Contains the latest news, in-depth analysis, top columnists, and reviews of public relations campaigns and job opportunities.
Published by: Haymarket Media GmbH, Mexikoring 33, Hamburg, 22297, Germany. TEL 49-40-69206200, FAX 49-40-69206333, redaktion.prreport@haymarket.de, info@haymarket.de, http://www.prreport.de. Ed. Sebastian Vesper. Adv. contact Enno Arp. color page EUR 4,300; trim 210 x 280. Circ: 7,266 (paid and controlled).

659.2 USA ISSN 0048-2609
P R REPORTER; weekly newsletter of public relations, public affairs & communication. Text in English. 1958. w. USD 225 (effective 2005). **Document type:** *Newsletter, Trade.*
Published by: Lawrence Ragan Communications, Inc., 316 N Michigan Ave, Ste 300, Chicago, IL 60601. TEL 312-960-4140, FAX 312-960-4106, http://www.ragan.com.

659.2 CHE ISSN 0033-3727
P R REVUE; Schweizerisches Magazin fuer Public Relations/periodique suisse de relations publiques. Text in French, German, Italian. 1954. m. CHF 185. adv. bk.rev. **Document type:** *Trade.*
Indexed: KES.
Published by: (Schweizerische Public Relations Gesellschaft/Swiss Public Relations Society), Rheintaler Druckerei und Verlags AG, c/o Perex Communications, Helvetiastr 45, Bern, 3005, Switzerland. TEL 031-3528818. Ed. Angela Kreis Muzzulini.

659.1 USA ISSN 1091-5583
HD59.6.U6
P R WATCH; public interest reporting on the public relations industry. Text in English. 1993. q. USD 35 to individuals; USD 60 to non-profit organizations; USD 200 to corporations. bk.rev. **Document type:** *Newsletter.* **Description:** Discusses developments and trends in the public relations industry from a populist and public-interest perspective.
Published by: Center for Media & Democracy, Inc., 520 University Ave., Ste. 227, Madison, WI 53703-4929. TEL 608-260-9713, FAX 608-260-9714, http://www.prwatch.org. Ed. John C Stauber. Circ: 4,000.

659.2 GBR ISSN 0267-6087
P R WEEK (UK EDITION). (Public Relations) Text in English. 1984. w. (47/yr.). GBP 111 domestic; GBP 154 in Europe; GBP 206 elsewhere (effective 2004). adv. bk.rev. stat. back issues avail. **Document type:** *Magazine, Trade.* **Description:** Provides the latest news and information on all aspects of the public relations business.
Related titles: Online - full content ed.; Online - full text ed.: (from Gale Group, LexisNexis).
Indexed: M&MA.
—BLDSC (6579.243000). **CCC.**
Published by: Haymarket Business Publications Ltd., 174 Hammersmith Rd, London, W6 7JP, United Kingdom. TEL 44-20-8943-5000, 44-20-82675000, FAX 44-20-82674268, prweek@haynet.com, admin.prweek@haynet.com, http://www.prweek.com, http://www.haymarketgroup.com, http://www.factiva.com. Ed. Gidon Freeman TEL 44-20-82674370. Pub. Peter Goldstein TEL 44-20-82674682. Adv. contact Ben Smith TEL 44-20-82674372. Circ: 17,000 weekly (paid).

659.2 USA ISSN 1524-1696
HD59
P R WEEK (US EDITION). (Public Relations) Text in English. 1998. w. (49/yr.). USD 128 domestic; USD 233 in Canada; USD 357 elsewhere; USD 4 newsstand/cover (effective 2003). adv. back issues avail. **Document type:** *Magazine, Trade.* **Description:** Provides the latest news, in-depth analysis, top columnists, and reviews of campaigns and job opportunities for public relations professionals throughout the United States.
Related titles: Online - full text ed.: (from EBSCO Publishing, Florida Center for Library Automation, Gale Group, ProQuest Information & Learning).
Indexed: ABIn.
Published by: PR Publications Ltd., 220 Fifth Ave, New York, NY 10001. TEL 212-532-9200, FAX 212-532-6765, http://www.prweekus.com. Ed. Julia Hood. Pub. Julie Moore. Adv. contact Kevin Redmile. B&W page USD 4,845, color page USD 5,485; trim 10.875 x 15.

▼ new title ➤ refereed ∗ unverified ♦ full entry avail.

A

659.1 USA
P S A. (Public Service Advertising) Text in English. 1982. q. USD 20. adv. tr.lit.
Published by: Doug Wyles Publication, Inc., 49 W 76th St, New York, NY 10023. TEL 212-877-4800. Ed. Cyndy Floor. Circ: 14,600.

659.1 DEU ISSN 1436-6193
P S I JOURNAL; internationales Magazin fuer Werbeartikel. Text in English, French, German. 1960. m. adv. bk.rev. back issues avail. **Document type:** *Magazine, Trade.*
Formerly (until 1998): P S I Nachrichten (0179-4388)
Published by: Praesent Service Institut (Subsidiary of: Reed Business Information GmbH), Voelkingerstr 4, Duesseldorf, 40219, Germany. TEL 49-211-901910, FAX 49-211-90191180, http://www.psi-messe.com. Ed. Manfred Schloesser. Pub. Reiner Klein. R&P Monika Mueller. Adv. contact Tanja Damrath. B&W page EUR 1,099, color page EUR 1,941; trim 185 x 260. Circ: 6,500 (controlled).

659.1 RUS
PABLISITI. Text in Russian. m.
Address: Pr-t Lenina 69, korp 2, Ekaterinburg, 620075, Russian Federation. termekt@rosincom.ru. Ed. Nikolai Kozariichuk.

070 659.2 USA
PARTYLINE; the weekly roundup of media placement opportunities. Text in English. 1960. w. looseleaf. USD 200 (effective 2005). back issues avail. **Document type:** *Newsletter, Trade.* **Description:** For public relations professionals.
Formerly (until 1990): P R A's Party Line (Public Relations Aids) (0030-8226)
Published by: PartyLine Publishing, 35 Sutton Pl, New York, NY 10022-2464. byarmon@1x.netcom.com, http://www.partylinepublishing.com. Ed., Pub., R&P Morton Yarmon. Circ: 1,500 (paid).

PFERDE-ANZEIGER. see *SPORTS AND GAMES—Horses And Horsemanship*

PHARMA-MARKETING JOURNAL. see *BUSINESS AND ECONOMICS—Marketing And Purchasing*

659 658 GBR ISSN 1744-0696
▼ ➤ **PLACE BRANDING.** Text in English. 2004 (Nov.). q. USD 170 in North America to individuals based at universities or other educational establishment; GBP 95 in Europe to individuals based at universities or other educational establishment; GBP 110 elsewhere to individuals based at universities or other educational establishment; USD 340 in North America to institutions; GBP 190 in Europe to institutions; GBP 205 elsewhere to institutions (effective 2005). **Document type:** *Journal, Academic/Scholarly.* **Description:** Provides ministries, governments, civil servants, agencies and consultants with the latest thinking and most valuable lessons on how places can better manage their images for economic, social and cultural development.
Related titles: Online - full text ed.
—BLDSC (6506.730000).
Published by: Palgrave Macmillan Ltd. (Subsidiary of: Macmillan Publishers Ltd.), Houndmills, Basingstoke, Hants RG21 6XS, United Kingdom. TEL 44-1256-329242, FAX 44-1256-810526, journal-info@palgrave.com, http://www.palgrave-journals.com/.

➤ **PLAYBACK**; Canada's broadcast and production journal. see *COMMUNICATIONS—Television And Cable*

➤ **POPKULTUR.** see *MUSIC*

659.1 USA
POPULAR LIFE∗. Text in English. 1990. q. USD 8; USD 2 newsstand/cover. **Description:** Publishes collections of advertisements from the past to criticize the social evils of consumer society today.
Address: 96 Hillside Ave, Rochester, NY 14610-2411. Ed. Mary Arp. Circ: 88.

659.2 HRV ISSN 1331-6834
POSLOVNI SAVJETNIK. Text in Croatian. 1951. m. **Document type:** *Magazine, Trade.*
Former titles (until 1998): Progresov Poslovni Savjetnik (1331-4122); (until 1997): Progresov Porezni Savjetnik (1331-2219); (until 1996): Progres Informacije (1330-738X)
Published by: Progres d.o.o., Varsavska 2, Zagreb, 10000, Croatia. TEL 385-1-4432301, FAX 385-1-4432889. Ed. Ljubo Jurcic.

741.67 658 USA ISSN 1097-3389
PRACTICE BUILDERS. Key Title: Practice Builder Association's What's Working. Variant title: What's Working. Text in English. 1983. m. (except Nov.-Dec. combined). USD 194 (effective 2000). adv. back issues avail. **Document type:** *Newsletter.* **Description:** Covers innovative marketing and promotional strategies for healthcare professionals to help build their practices in an effective yet ethical way.
Formerly (until 199?): Practice Builder (0883-3036)
Address: 1 Macarthur Pl., Ste. 200, Santa Ana, CA 92707-5941. TEL 949-253-7900, FAX 949-252-1002, sam_jones@practicebuilders.com, http://www.practicebuilders.com. Ed. Michael Riley. Pub. S.L. Jones. R&P, Adv. contact S L Jones.

659.1 RUS
PRAKTIKA REKLAMY. Text in Russian. m. USD 275 in United States.
Address: Kashirskoe shosse 12, kom 10, Moscow, 115230, Russian Federation. TEL 7-095-1116260. Ed. Yu A Grishin. **US dist. addr.:** East View Information Services, 3020 Harbor Ln. N., Minneapolis, MN 55447. TEL 612-550-0961.

659.1 DEU ISSN 0723-9408
PRAXIS DER WERBUNG. Short title: P W. Text in German. 1980. m. **Document type:** *Trade.*
Published by: Suedwestdeutsche Akademie fuer Marketing und Kommunikation e.V., Koenigstr 1B, Stuttgart, 70173, Germany. TEL 49-711-291714. Ed. Oliver Apfel.

659.1 USA ISSN 1072-7531
HF5718.22
PRESENTATIONS; technology and techniques for effective communication. Text in English. 1988. m. USD 69 domestic; USD 95 in Canada; USD 120 elsewhere; free to qualified personnel (effective 2005). adv. bk.rev. illus. reprints avail. **Document type:** *Magazine, Trade.* **Description:** Provides expert intelligence necessary to make better presentations and more cost-effective decisions about product selection.
Former titles (until 1993): Presentation Products (1070-6089); (until 1992): Presentation Products Magazine (1041-9780)
Related titles: Microform ed.: (from PQC); Online - full text ed.: (from EBSCO Publishing, Gale Group, Northern Light Technology, Inc., O C L C Online Computer Library Center, Inc., ProQuest Information & Learning).
Indexed: ABIn, C&ISA, CCR, E&CAJ, IAA, InfoSAb, Microcompind, SoftBase.
—BLDSC (6609.746000), IE. **CCC.**
Published by: V N U Business Publications (Subsidiary of: V N U Business Media), 50 S Ninth St, Minneapolis, MN 55402. FAX 612-333-6526, tsimons@presentations.com, bmcomm@vnuinc.com, http://www.presentations.com/, http://www.vnubusinessmedia.com/. Ed. Tad Simons. Pub., Adv. contact Richard Ausman TEL 612-340-4901. page USD 12,190; trim 8 x 10.75. Circ: 75,000 (controlled). **Subscr. to:** PO Box 2086, Skokie, IL 60076-7986.

PRIMA COMUNICAZIONE. see *COMMUNICATIONS*

PRINCIPAL COMMUNICATOR. see *EDUCATION*

659 AUS ISSN 1448-4404
▼ **PRISM.** Text in English. 2003. a. free (effective 2005). **Document type:** *Journal, Trade.*
Media: Online - full text.
Published by: Bond University, School of Humanities and Social Sciences, Gold Coast, QLD 4229, Australia. TEL 61-7-5595250320, FAX 61-7-55952545, http://www.bond.edu.au. Ed. Elspeth Tilley.

PRIVAT. see *MEN'S INTERESTS*

LE PRODUCTION MAKERS SOURCE. see *COMMUNICATIONS—Video*

659.1 658 USA
PROFESSIONAL ADVISOR. Text in English. 1977. m. USD 120 (effective 1997). adv. bk.rev. back issues avail. **Document type:** *Newsletter.* **Description:** Covers the marketing of consulting, seminars, information products, and services.
Former titles: Professional Consultant (0272-8559); Professional Consultant and Information Marketing Report; Professional Consultant and Seminar Business Report
Published by: Bernard Hale Zick, Ed. & Pub., PO Box 6339, Kingwood, TX 77325-6399. TEL 281-358-0409, 800-677-3253, bernard@zick.com, http://www.zick.com.

659.1 GBR
PROFILE. Text in English. 1982. q. GBP 55 to non-members; free to members (effective 2005). adv. bk.rev. back issues avail. **Document type:** *Magazine, Trade.* **Description:** Features interviews, case-studies, profiles, style guides and comment.
Former titles (until 1999): The Institute of Public Relations. Journal; (until 1993): Public Relations (0263-6166)
—IE, Infotrieve. **CCC.**
Published by: Institute of Public Relations, The Old Trading House, 15 Northburgh St, London, EC1V 0PR, United Kingdom. TEL 44-20-72535151, FAX 44-20-74900588, RichardG@cipr.co.uk, info@ipr.org.uk, http://www.cipr.co.uk/direct/publications.asp?v1=profile, http://www.ipr.org.uk/. Ed. Gro Elin Hansen.

659.1 USA ISSN 1040-7480
PROFILES IN HEALTHCARE MARKETING; the latest trends in healthcare marketing, promotion & public relations. Text in English. 1984. bi-m. USD 294 (effective 2005). back issues avail.; reprints avail. **Document type:** *Newsletter, Trade.* **Description:** Provides up-close case studies of successful and not-so-successful hospital marketing and public relations campaigns. Includes reprints of actual ads, press releases, brochures, and story boards.
Formerly (until 1981): Profiles in Hospital Marketing (0275-9632)
Related titles: Online - full text ed.
Indexed: MEDLINE.
—**CCC.**
Published by: The Business Word, Inc., 11211 E Arapahoe Rd, Ste 101, Centennial, CO 80112-3851. TEL 303-290-8500, 800-328-3211, FAX 303-290-9025, plmoore@businessword.com, customer.service@businessword.com, http://www.businessword.com. Pub. Donald E L Johnson. Circ: 700 (paid).

PROMAX INTERNATIONAL. see *COMMUNICATIONS—Television And Cable*

659.1 USA ISSN 1047-1707
HF5837 CODEN: PROMFN
PROMO; promotion marketing worldwide. Text in English. 1987. m. USD 72 domestic; USD 111 in Canada; USD 182 foreign; free domestic to qualified personnel (effective 2004). adv. bk.rev. charts; tr.lit. back issues avail. **Document type:** *Magazine, Trade.* **Description:** Serving marketing execs at Fortune 1000 companies with news and how-to articles pertaining to creating and implementing successful brand marketing strategies.
Related titles: Online - full text ed.: (from EBSCO Publishing, Florida Center for Library Automation, Gale Group, H.W. Wilson, O C L C Online Computer Library Center, Inc.).
Indexed: B&I, BPI.
—**CCC.**
Published by: Primedia Business Magazines & Media, Inc. (Subsidiary of: Primedia, Inc.), 9800 Metcalf Ave, Overland Park, KS 66212-2216. TEL 913-341-1300, FAX 913-967-1898, kerryj_smith@intertec.com, inquiries@primediabusiness.com, http://www.promomagazine.com/, http://www.primediabusiness.com. Ed. Kathleen Joyce. Pub. Lisa Perrin. adv.: B&W page USD 4,353, color page USD 6,075; trim 10.88 x 8.5. Circ: 25,300 (paid and controlled). **Subscr. to:** PO Box 12993, Overland Park, KS 66282-2993. TEL 800-441-0294, FAX 913-967-1331.

659.1 USA ISSN 1072-3293
PROMOTIONAL PRODUCTS BUSINESS. Text in English. 1976. m. USD 48 domestic to members; USD 60 in Canada & Mexico to members; USD 65 elsewhere to members; USD 62 domestic to non-members; USD 74 in Canada & Mexico to non-members; USD 79 elsewhere to non-members (effective 2005). adv. bk.rev. **Document type:** *Magazine, Trade.* **Description:** Provides in-depth communication with association members and others in the specialty advertising and promotional product industry.
Former titles: National Products Business; Specialty Advertising Business (0195-0495)
Published by: Promotional Products Association International, 3125 Skyway Circle N, Irving, TX 75038-3526. TEL 972-258-3046, FAX 972-258-3012, http://www.ppa.org/Publications/PPB/. Ed. Lisa Horn. Pub., R&P Tina Filepski. Adv. contact Melissa McGrath Klusmeyer. Circ: 13,000 (paid and controlled).

PROTECTING THE ENVIRONMENT (YEAR). see *ENVIRONMENTAL STUDIES*

659.1 BEL ISSN 0771-3819
PUB. Text in Flemish, French. 1976. 19/yr. EUR 132.78; EUR 219.07 combined subscription incl. Agency Book (effective 2005). **Document type:** *Trade.* **Description:** News on advertising, marketing, and other aspects of communications and media.
Related titles: Supplement(s): Agency Book.
Published by: Editions Kluwer (Subsidiary of: Wolters Kluwer Belgique), Avenue Louise 326, Brussels, 1050, Belgium. TEL 32-800-16868, FAX 32-2-3003003, customer@editionskluwer.be, http://www.editionskluwer.be/ek/home.asp. Eds. Jean-Michel Stichelbaut, Mark Anthierens. Adv. contact Gerda Bourdeaud'hui. Circ: 5,000.

659.1 BEL
PUB CREATIVE BOOK. Text in Dutch, French. 1978. a. EUR 118.42 (effective 2003). adv. **Document type:** *Directory.*
Former titles: Pub Creative and Print Production Book (0778-2101); (until 1989): Pub Annuaire Creatif - Kreatief Jaarboek Pub (0778-2098)
Published by: Editions Kluwer (Subsidiary of: Wolters Kluwer Belgique), Avenue Louise 326, Brussels, 1050, Belgium. TEL 32-800-16868, FAX 32-2-3003003, packnews@wkb.be, http://www.editionskluwer.be/ek/home.asp. Ed. Bernard Lefevre. Adv. contact Gerda Bourdeaud'hui.

659.1 BEL ISSN 0778-1946
PUB MEDIABOOK. Text in Dutch, French. 1984. a. EUR 130.56 (effective 2003). adv. **Description:** Covers advertising and the media in Belgium and Luxembourg.

Published by: Editions Kluwer (Subsidiary of: Wolters Kluwer Belgique), Avenue Louise 326, Brussels, 1050, Belgium. TEL 32-800-16868, FAX 32-2-3003003, customer@editionskluwer.be, http://www.editionskluwer.be/ek/home.asp. Ed. Bernard Lefevre. Adv. contact Gerda Bourdeaud'hui.

659.1 658.8   ITA
PUBBLICITA ITALIA. Text in Italian. 1989. 45/yr. adv. **Document type:** *Trade.*
Published by: Marketing Finanza Italia s.r.l., Via Alessandro Stradella, 3, Milan, MI 20129, Italy. TEL 39-02-9400554, FAX 39-02-29401816, redapi@tin.it, http://www.pubblicitaitalia.it. Ed. Lillo Perri. Adv. contact Daniele Monai. Circ: 7,678.

PUBLIC EYE. see *LIBRARY AND INFORMATION SCIENCES*

659.1   DEU   ISSN 1430-5828
PUBLIC RELATIONS∗ . Text in German. 1994. a. **Document type:** *Directory, Trade.* **Description:** Deals with the topic of quality in public relations, including the relationship between agencies and customers.
Published by: E C O N Verlag GmbH, Friedrichstr 126, Berlin, 10117, Germany. TEL 49-30-23456300, FAX 49-30-23456303, sabine.kahl@ullstein-buchverlage.de, http://www.econ-verlag.de. Adv. contact Barbara Lampe. Circ: 2,500 (paid).

659.2   DEU   ISSN 0949-8052
PUBLIC RELATIONS FORUM; fuer Wissenschaft und Praxis. Text in German. 1995. q. adv. **Document type:** *Magazine, Trade.*
Related titles: Online - full text ed.
Published by: (Deutsche Public Relations Gesellschaft), Antim Verlag GmbH, Breite Gasse 38, Nuernberg, 90402, Germany. TEL 49-911-22814, FAX 49-911-22815. Adv. contact Lydia Kastenhuber. B&W page EUR 1,800, color page EUR 2,700; trim 176 x 260. Circ: 8,500 (controlled).

659.2   IND   ISSN 0033-3689
HD59
PUBLIC RELATIONS JOURNAL OF INDIA. Text in English. 1970. 5/yr. INR 18, USD 12. adv. bk.rev. illus. index.
Published by: P. R. Publications, 16-199 Lane No 7 Joshi Rd., Karol Bagh, New Delhi, 110 005, India. Ed. Roshan Lan.

659.2   USA   ISSN 0033-3700
HM263   CODEN: PREUEU
PUBLIC RELATIONS QUARTERLY. Text in English. 1955. q. USD 65 domestic; USD 70 in Canada & Mexico; USD 77 elsewhere (effective 2005). bk.rev. charts; illus.; stat. index. 48 p./no. 2 cols./p.; back issues avail.; reprint service avail. from PQC. **Document type:** *Magazine, Trade.* **Description:** Contains articles on the theory and practice of public relations, marketing public affairs, education and organizational communication.
Incorporates: International Public Relations Review (0020-8434)
Related titles: Microform ed.: (from PQC); Online - full text ed.: (from bigchalk, EBSCO Publishing, Florida Center for Library Automation, Gale Group, H.W. Wilson, Northern Light Technology, Inc., O C L C Online Computer Library Center, Inc., ProQuest Information & Learning).
Indexed: ABIn, ADPA, ASEANManA, ATI, BPI, BPIA, BusI, CommAb, ManagCont, T&II.
—BLDSC (6968.600000), IE, Infotrieve, ingenta. **CCC.**
Published by: Hudson Associates, 44 W Market St, Box 311, Rhinebeck, NY 12572-0311. TEL 845-876-2081, FAX 845-876-2561, prquarterly@aol.com, hphudson@aol.com, http://www.newsletter-clearinghse.com. Ed. Elaine Newman. Pub. Howard Penn Hudson. Adv. contact Nicole Lapierre. Circ: 5,000 (paid).

659.2   GBR   ISSN 0363-8111
HM263   CODEN: PREREL
PUBLIC RELATIONS REVIEW. Text in English. 1975. 5/yr. EUR 133 in Europe to individuals; JPY 17,700 in Japan to individuals; USD 148 to individuals except Europe and Japan; EUR 381 in Europe to institutions; JPY 50,600 in Japan to institutions; USD 427 to institutions except Europe and Japan (effective 2006). adv. bk.rev. bibl.; illus. back issues avail.; reprint service avail. from PQC,ISI. **Document type:** *Trade.* **Description:** Features in-depth analyses of measurements and evaluations, public relations education, public policy, history and bibliographies.
Related titles: Microform ed.: (from PQC); Online - full text ed.: (from EBSCO Publishing, Florida Center for Library Automation, Gale Group, H.W. Wilson, IngentaConnect, Northern Light Technology, Inc., O C L C Online Computer Library Center, Inc., ScienceDirect, Swets Information Services).
Indexed: ABIn, ASCA, AgeL, ArtHuCI, BPI, BPIA, BusI, CIJE, CommAb, CurCont, HRA, ManagCont, PAIS, PRA, PSA, SOPODA, SSCI, T&II, e-psyche.
—BLDSC (6968.680000), IE, Infotrieve, ingenta. **CCC.**
Published by: Elsevier Ltd. (Subsidiary of: Elsevier Science & Technology), The Boulevard, Langford Ln, Kidlington, Oxford, OX5 1GB, United Kingdom. TEL 44-1865-843000, FAX 44-1865-843010, http://www.elsevier.com/locate/pubrev. Ed. Ray E Hiebert. Circ: 2,500. **Subscr. to:** Elsevier BV, PO Box 211, Amsterdam 1000 AE, Netherlands. TEL 31-20-485-3757, FAX 31-20-485-3432, nlinfo-f@elsevier.nl, http://www.elsevier.nl.

PUBLIC RELATIONS SOCIETY OF AMERICA DIRECTORY. see *BUSINESS AND ECONOMICS—Trade And Industrial Directories*

659.2   USA   ISSN 1082-9113
HD59
PUBLIC RELATIONS STRATEGIST. Text in English. 1995. q. USD 100 domestic; USD 110 in Canada; USD 120 elsewhere (effective 2005). adv. **Document type:** *Magazine, Trade.*
Related titles: Online - full text ed.: (from EBSCO Publishing, Factiva, ProQuest Information & Learning).
—Infotrieve.
Published by: The Public Relations Society of America, Inc., 33 Maiden Ln, 11th Fl, New York, NY 10038-5150. TEL 212-460-1400, FAX 212-995-0757, john.elsasser@prsa.org, http://www.prsa.org/_Publications/magazines/strategist.asp?ident=m2. Ed. John Elsasser TEL 212-460-1419. Pub. Fraser P Seitel. Adv. contact Anne Fetsch. page USD 5,500.

659.2   USA   ISSN 1080-6792
HD59
PUBLIC RELATIONS TACTICS. Text in English. 1994. m. USD 75 domestic to non-members; USD 85 in Canada to non-members; USD 95 elsewhere to non-members; USD 24 to students (effective 2005). adv. bk.rev. back issues avail. **Document type:** *Newspaper, Trade.* **Description:** Includes news, trends, and how-to information for public relations practitioners.
Related titles: Online - full text ed.: (from EBSCO Publishing, Northern Light Technology, Inc., ProQuest Information & Learning).
Published by: The Public Relations Society of America, Inc., 33 Maiden Ln, 11th Fl, New York, NY 10038-5150. TEL 212-460-1400, FAX 212-995-0757, john.elsasser@prsa.org, http://www.prsa.org. Ed. John Elsasser TEL 212-460-1419. adv.: B&W page USD 3,000. Circ: 25,000.

659.1   USA
PUBLIC SERVICE ADVERTISING BULLETIN. Text in English. bi-m. free (effective 2005). **Document type:** *Bulletin.*
Published by: Advertising Council, 261 Madison Ave, New York, NY 10016-2303. TEL 212-922-1500. Ed. Joan McLaughlin.

070.5   CAN   ISSN 0836-5024
HF3221
PUBLICATION PROFILES. Text in English. 1980. a. CND 107.50 domestic (effective 2001); included with subscr to Canadian Advertising Rates & Data. adv. **Document type:** *Directory, Trade.* **Description:** Examines consumer, agriculture and business magazines in Canada.
Formerly: Media Editorial Profile Edition (0228-5215)
Related titles: ♦ Supplement to: Canadian Advertising Rates and Data. ISSN 0038-9498.
—CISTI.
Published by: C A R D, the Media Information Network (Subsidiary of: Rogers Media Publishing Ltd), Subscriber Services, Maclean Hunter Bldg, 777 Bay St, 8th Fl, Toronto, ON M5W 1A7, Canada. TEL 416-596-2790, FAX 416-596-5158, http://www.cardmedia.com/products/products.htm. Ed. Nancy Remnant. Adv. contact Lucia De Stefano. B&W page CND 4,338, color page CND 5,996; trim 204 x 274. Circ: 5,215.

659.1   VEN
PUBLICIDAD Y MERCADEO. Text in Spanish. 1961. m. USD 40. adv.
Published by: M.G. Ediciones Especializadas, S.A., Av. Maturin, No. 15, Urb. Los Cedros, El Bosque, Caracas, 1050, Venezuela. Ed. Montserrat Giol. Circ: 3,250.

659.1   USA
PUBLICITY AND MEDIA RESOURCES FOR PUBLISHERS∗ . Text in English. 1958-1979; resumed 1988. biennial. USD 200. adv. bk.rev. index.
Former titles (until 1992): Advertising and Publicity Resources for Scholarly Books; Ad Guide: An Advertiser's Guide to Scholarly Periodicals (0065-3586)
Published by: Association of American University Presses, 71 W 23rd St., New York, NY 10010. TEL 212-941-6610. Ed. Chris Terry. Circ: (controlled).

381.45002   USA
PUBLISHERS INFORMATION BUREAU REPORT; magazine advertising expenditures. (In seven industry sections: Apparel, Business-Financial, Drugs-Toiletries, Food-Beverages, General, Home-Building, Transportation-Agriculture) Text in English. 1948. m. looseleaf. adv. charts; stat. back issues avail. **Document type:** *Trade.* **Description:** Contains advertising expenditures and trade publication provided on a monthly basis to members.
Former titles: P I B Monthly; P I B Monthly Service - Leading National Advertisers Monthly Service; P I B Monthly (0030-7998)
Related titles: Fax ed.; Microfilm ed.
Published by: Publishers' Information Bureau Inc., 919 Third Ave, 22nd Fl, New York, NY 10022. TEL 212-872-3700, FAX 212-888-4217, http://www.magazine.org.

659.1   ITA   ISSN 0033-3999
PUBLITRANSPORT. Text in Italian. 1961. q. free. adv.
Description: Features articles on advertising displayed on public transportation.

Published by: Impresa Generale Pubblicita, Piazza Cavour, 1, Milan, MI 20121, Italy. TEL 654651. Ed. Fabrizio du Chene de Vere. Circ: 4,600.

LA PULCE; il settimanale di annunci gratuiti. see *GENERAL INTEREST PERIODICALS—Italy*

659.1   GBR
QUARTERLY SUMMARY OF BRANDS AND ADVERTISERS. Text in English. 1992. q. GBP 1,065 (effective 1999). back issues avail. **Document type:** *Trade.*
Related titles: CD-ROM ed.
Published by: A.C. Nielson - Meal Ltd., Kings Court, 185 Kings Rd, 2nd Fl, Reading, Berks RG1 4EX, United Kingdom. TEL 44-800-328-4477, FAX 44-1189-596579, geoff.nightingale@acnielsen.co.uk. R&P Geoff Nightingale. Circ: 200 (paid).

659.1   GBR   ISSN 0951-7766
QUARTERLY SURVEY OF ADVERTISING EXPENDITURE. Text in English. 1984. q. GBP 595 (effective 2000). stat. **Document type:** *Trade.* **Description:** Provides accurate, up-to-date and detailed analysis of advertising expenditure trends in the UK.
Formerly (until 1987): Quarterly Review of Advertising Statistics (0266-5646)
Related titles: Online - full text ed.: (from EBSCO Publishing).
—CCC.
Published by: (Advertising Association), N T C Publications Ltd. (Subsidiary of: World Advertising Research Center Ltd.), PO Box 89, Henley-on-Thames, Oxon RG9 1GB, United Kingdom. TEL 44-1491-411000, FAX 44-1491-571188, ntc@ntc.co.uk.

659.1   USA
R A B INSTANT BACKGROUND; profiles of 50 businesses. Text in English. 1970. s-a. USD 50 per vol.. **Description:** Describes businesses in summary format.
Published by: Radio Advertising Bureau, 261 Madison Ave, 23rd Fl, New York, NY 10016-2303. TEL 212-681-7200, FAX 212-681-7223.

659.1 200   USA
R C C COUNSELOR. Text in English. 4/yr. membership. **Document type:** *Newsletter.* **Description:** Covers events within the Council and its chapters, with special emphasis on religious public relations.
Published by: Religion Communicators Council, 475 Riverside Dr., Ste. 1305, New York, NY 10115-0075. Circ: 800.

R F D NEWS. see *AGRICULTURE*

RADIO AD BIZ. see *COMMUNICATIONS—Radio*

659.142   USA
RADIO ADVERTISING BUREAU. RETAIL MARKETING KIT. Text in English. m.
Published by: Radio Advertising Bureau, 261 Madison Ave, 23rd Fl, New York, NY 10016-2303. TEL 212-681-7200, FAX 212-681-7223.

RADIO CO-OP SOURCES. see *COMMUNICATIONS—Radio*

659.2   USA
RADIO - T V INTERVIEW REPORT; the magazine talk show producers read to find guests. Text in English. 1986. s-m. adv. bk.rev. **Document type:** *Trade.* **Description:** Lists authors, experts, entrepreneurs and others available for radio and TV appearances.
Published by: Bradley Communications Corp., PO Box 1206, Lansdowne, PA 19050. TEL 610-259-1070, FAX 610-284-3704, http://www.rtir.com. Ed., Pub. Stephen Hall Harrison. adv.: page USD 549. Circ: 5,000 (controlled).

RAGAN'S ANNUAL REPORT REVIEW. see *JOURNALISM*

659.2   USA
RAGAN'S PUBLIC RELATIONS REVIEW. Text in English. bi-m. USD 249 (effective 1999). **Document type:** *Newsletter.* **Description:** Focuses on issues facing public relations practitioners.
Published by: Lawrence Ragan Communications, Inc., 316 N Michigan Ave, Ste 300, Chicago, IL 60601. TEL 312-960-4106, 800-878-5331, FAX 312-960-4106, http://www.ragan.com.

659.132   CAN   ISSN 0706-8085
REACHING THE MANITOBA MARKET. Text in English. 1977. a. free. adv. **Document type:** *Directory.*
Published by: Manitoba Community Newspapers Association, 310 275 Portage Ave, Winnipeg, MB R3B 2B3, Canada. TEL 204-947-1691, FAX 204-947-1919, http://www.mana.com. Ed. Clint Szakacs. Circ: 1,500.

REDAKTIONS ADRESS. see *BUSINESS AND ECONOMICS—Trade And Industrial Directories*

659.1   DEU   ISSN 0932-1543
REDEN-BERATER; Handbuch fuer erfolgreiche Reden im Betrieb, in der Oeffentlichkeit und im Privatleben. Text in German. 1987. 7/yr. looseleaf. **Document type:** *Bulletin.* **Description:** How-to publication on public speaking and speechwriting.

▼ *new title*   ➤ *refereed*   ∗ *unverified*   ◆ *full entry avail.*

A

Published by: V N R Verlag fuer die Deutsche Wirtschaft AG, Theodor-Heuss-Str 2-4, Bonn, 53095, Germany. TEL 49-228-8205-0, FAX 49-228-364411. Ed. F Franken.

659.2 NLD ISSN 0034-3218
REGELRECHT. Text in Dutch. 1955. 11/yr. free.
Published by: Honeywell B.V., Marketing Division, Postbus 12683, Amsterdam (ZO), 1100 AR, Netherlands. Ed. G J V D Kempen. Circ: 1,500.

659.1 BEL
REKLAAM IS SUCCES. Text in French. 1934. w. adv. **Document type:** *Newspaper, Trade.*
Related titles: Diskette ed.
Address: Otterstraat 167, Turnhout, 2300, Belgium. TEL 32-14-411411, FAX 32-14-422932, info@reklaamissucces.be, http://www.reklaamissucces.be. Adv. contact Buntinx Willy.

REKLAMA NEDELI. see *BUSINESS AND ECONOMICS*

REKLAMODATEL'. see *BUSINESS AND ECONOMICS—Marketing And Purchasing*

659.1 FRA ISSN 0246-7143
RELATIONS PRESSE. Text in French. 1965. 4/yr. adv. **Document type:** *Newspaper.*
Published by: Information Presse et Communication, 9 rue de Duras, Paris, 75008, France. TEL 33-1-42650803, FAX 33-1-42660767, relationspresse.ipc@wanadou.fr. Ed. Jerome Saczewski. Adv. contact Charles Juster. Circ: 600.

659.2 FRA ISSN 0034-3811
RELATIONS PUBLIQUES INFORMATIONS. Text in French. 1956. w. adv. bk.rev.
—CCC.
Published by: (E P C I), I S E R P, 87 bis rue Carnot, Levallois Perret, 92300, France. Ed. Philippe A Boiry. Circ: 1,800.

659.1 USA
REMINDER PLUS. Text in English. w. USD 22; free to qualified personnel. adv.
Published by: Hipple Printing Co., Inc., 333 W Dakota, Pierre, SD 57501. TEL 605-224-7301. Ed. Terry Hipple. Circ: 18,800.

659.2 381.1 BEL ISSN 1372-3294
RENDEVENEMENT (FRENCH EDITION). Text in French. 1995. 9/yr. (plus 20 e-mails). EUR 56 (effective 2005). adv. illus.; tr.lit. **Document type:** *Trade.* **Description:** Covers all aspects of arranging and marketings conventions, meetings, trade shows, and marketing presentations.
Related titles: Dutch ed.: Rendevenement (Dutch Edition). ISSN 1372-3286.
Published by: Professional Media Group, Torhoutsesteenweg 226 bus 2/6, Zedelgem, B-8210, Belgium. TEL 32-50-240404, FAX 32-50-240445, info@pmgroup.be, http://www.rendevenement.be/?lang=f, http://www.pmgroup.be. Ed. Inez Costenoble. adv.: color page EUR 2,575; trim 297 x 210.

RENTAL MANAGEMENT. see *BUSINESS AND ECONOMICS—Marketing And Purchasing*

RESEARCH. see *BUSINESS AND ECONOMICS—Marketing And Purchasing*

659.1 658.8 USA ISSN 1523-7656
HF6146.B74
RESPONSE MAGAZINE; multi-channel direct advertising. Text in English. 1992. m. USD 45 domestic; USD 60 in Canada & Mexico; USD 115 elsewhere (effective 2005). adv. charts. back issues avail. **Document type:** *Magazine, Trade.* **Description:** Delivers timely news, trends, and analysis of the direct response television industry. Covers home shopping, infomercials, DRTV, and online merchandising.
Formerly: Response T V (1077-5439)
Related titles: Online - full text ed.: (from EBSCO Publishing, Florida Center for Library Automation, Gale Group, O C L C Online Computer Library Center, Inc.).
Indexed: B&I.
—CCC.
Published by: Advanstar Communications, Inc., 201 Sandpointe Ave, Ste 600, Santa Ana, CA 92707-8700. TEL 714-513-8400, FAX 714-513-8454, jyarrington@advanstar.com, info@advanstar.com, http://www.responsemagazine.com, http://www.advanstar.com. Ed. Thomas Haire TEL 714-513-8850. Pub. John Yarrington TEL 714-513-8624. adv.: B&W page USD 4,840, color page USD 6,095; trim 8.25 x 11. Circ: 24,000 (controlled).

659.1 SWE ISSN 0036-1887
RESUME; nyhetstidningen om medier och marknadskommunikation. Text in Swedish. 1950. 40/yr. SEK 1,990 domestic; SEK 2,272 elsewhere (effective 2004). adv. illus. **Document type:** *Newsletter, Trade.*
Related titles: Online - full text ed.: ISSN 1402-4950.
Published by: Resume Foerlag AB, Gamla Brogatan 26, Stockholm, 11390, Sweden. TEL 46-8-7363000, FAX 46-8-7365004, red@resume.se, http://www.resume.se. Ed., Pub. Viggo Cavling. Adv. contact Jesper Gravestam TEL 46-8-6623192. B&W page SEK 34,500, color page SEK 42,500; trim 258 x 364. Circ: 9,900 (paid).

659.1 USA ISSN 1099-4408
RETAIL AD WORLD. Text in English. 1941. m. USD 299 in US & Canada; USD 349 elsewhere (effective 2000). illus. reprint service avail. from PQC. **Document type:** *Journal, Trade.* **Description:** Presents information and advice on how to create successful ads, campaigns, special events, and direct mail promotions.
Former titles (until 1998): Retail Ad Week (0735-7087); (until 1971): Retail Advertising Week (0034-5997)
Related titles: Microform ed.: (from PQC).
Published by: Visual Reference Publications, Inc., 302 Fifth Ave, New York, NY 10001. TEL 212-279-7000, 800-251-4545, FAX 212-279-7014, retailreporting@retailreporting.com, http://www.retailreporting.com.

659.1 ESP ISSN 0211-3333
REVISTA INTERNACIONAL DE COMUNICACION Y RELACIONES PUBLICAS/INTERNATIONAL MAGAZINE OF COMMUNICATIONS AND PUBLIC RELATIONS. Key Title: R P Internacional de Relaciones Publicas. Short title: Relaciones Publicas. Text in English, Spanish. 1962. q. bk.rev. bibl.; charts; illus.; stat.; tr.lit. index. **Description:** Presents research and disseminates knowledge in the areas of communication and public relations.
Formerly (until 1979): R P. Tecnicas de Relaciones Publicas (1137-2664)
—CCC.
Address: Jose Ortega y Gasset, 50, Madrid, 28006, Spain. TEL 34-1-4022609, FAX 34-1-4022614. Ed. Fernando Lozano Dominguez. Adv. contact Paloma Almagro. Circ: 30,000 (paid).

659 658 COL ISSN 0120-5293
REVISTA PUBLICIDAD Y MERCADEO. Text in Spanish. 1979. m. USD 270; USD 8 newsstand/cover; COP 125,000 per issue (effective 1998). adv. bk.rev.; software rev. bibl.; stat. back issues avail. **Document type:** *Trade.* **Description:** Specializes in national and international information about advertising, marketing, mass media and other related areas.
Published by: Ediciones y Eventos Ltda., Calle 39 No. 14-80, Barrio Teusaquillo, Bogota, CUND, Colombia. TEL 57-1-2885723, FAX 57-1-2885723, edyev@sol1.telecom.com.co. Ed. Leonor Puentes Anaya. Pub. Nohra Canete. Adv. contact Maria Cristina Decala. page USD 14,000; trim 275 x 205. Circ: 2,500.

S A M MAGAZINE. (Sales Advertising Marketing) see *BUSINESS AND ECONOMICS—Marketing And Purchasing*

659.1 ZAF
S A R A D. (South African Rates and Data) Text in English. 1972. bi-m. ZAR 950 (effective 2000). adv. **Document type:** *Trade.*
Related titles: Online - full content ed.
Published by: S A R A D Publishing Co (Pty) Ltd, PO Box 2647, Randburg, Gauteng 2125, South Africa. TEL 27-11-787-2070, FAX 27-11-787-2070, sarad@sarad.co.za, saradnet@icon.co.za, http://www.sarad.co.za. Ed. Kirsten Calitz. Circ: 750.

659.15 GBR
S D E A DIRECTORY OF SHOPFITTINGS AND DISPLAY EQUIPMENT. Text in English. 1980. a. GBP 15 (effective 2000). adv. **Document type:** *Directory.*
Former titles: S D E A Catalogue of Shopfittings and Display; S D E A Members Catalogue of Shopfittings and Display
Published by: Shop and Display Equipment Association, 24 Croydon Rd, Caterham, Surrey CR3 6YR, United Kingdom. TEL 44-1883-348911, FAX 44-1883-343435. Ed. Lawrence Cutler. Circ: 11,000.

S P A N CONNECTION. see *PUBLISHING AND BOOK TRADE*

S P WEEKLY; voice of the industry. (Service Provider Weekly) see *BUSINESS AND ECONOMICS—Marketing And Purchasing*

015 USA ISSN 1539-3011
HF5905
S R D S CIRCULATION (YEAR). Text in English. 1962. a. USD 312 (effective 2005). adv. stat. **Document type:** *Directory, Trade.* **Description:** Contains listings of more than 1,600 daily newspapers and newspaper groups. Provides county-by-county analyses of daily newspaper circulation figures for each state.
Formerly (until 1996): Circulation (Year) (0569-6704); Incorporates (1959-1990): Newspaper Circulation Analysis (0585-0428)
Published by: S R D S, 1700 Higgins Rd, Des Plaines, IL 60018-5605. TEL 847-375-5000, FAX 847-375-5001, jlevy@srds.com, http://www.srds.com. adv.: B&W page USD 5,955, color page USD 9,535; trim 11 x 8.5. Circ: 2,038 (controlled and free).

659.132 USA
S R D S INTERACTIVE ADVERTISING SOURCE. Text in English. 1996. q. USD 561 domestic; USD 571 in Canada & Mexico; USD 654 elsewhere (effective 2001). adv. **Document type:** *Directory, Trade.* **Description:** Compiles over 4000 online and other interactive advertising opportunities. Includes advertising rates, traffic information, key contacts and audience profiles.
Formerly: Interactive Advertising Source
Related titles: Supplement(s): S R D S' URLink.

Published by: S R D S, 1700 Higgins Rd, Des Plaines, IL 60018-5605. TEL 847-375-5060, 800-851-7737, FAX 847-375-5004, prome@srds.com, http://www.srds.com. Adv. contact Valerie Rome. B&W page USD 1,206, color page USD 2,730.

659.1 658.8 USA
SALES AND IDEA BOOK. Text in English. s-a.
Published by: Newspaper Association of America, 1921 Gallows Rd, Ste 600, Vienna, VA 22182-3900. TEL 703-902-1600, FAX 703-917-0636, http://www.naa.org.

SALES AND SERVICE FOR AN UNFAIR ADVANTAGE. see *BUSINESS AND ECONOMICS—Marketing And Purchasing*

SAM; what matters most in sales, advertising & marketing today. (Sales, Advertising and Marketing) see *BUSINESS AND ECONOMICS—Marketing And Purchasing*

SAMMLER MARKT. see *ANTIQUES*

SAN DIEGO CREATIVE DIRECTORY. see *BUSINESS AND ECONOMICS—Trade And Industrial Directories*

659.1 DEU ISSN 0933-016X
SCHAUFENSTER & SHOP DESIGN; die internationale Fachzeitschrift des Visual Merchandising. Text in Dutch, English, French, German, Italian, Spanish. 1950. m. USD 100 (effective 2000). adv. bk.rev. bibl.; illus. **Document type:** *Trade.* **Description:** Reports on trends, innovations and new products.
Formerly (until 1988): Schaufenster (0036-5939)
—CCC.
Published by: L I S Verlag GmbH, Theresienstr 9, Passau, 94032, Germany. TEL 49-851-93200-0, FAX 49-851-9320049, info@s-sd.com, http://www.s-sd.com. Ed. Peter Schwibach. Circ: 11,000.

SECONDAMANO; il giornale di piccoli annunci. see *GENERAL INTEREST PERIODICALS—Italy*

SECONDAMANO (BOLOGNA - MODENA - REGGIO); il giornale di piccoli annunci. see *GENERAL INTEREST PERIODICALS—Italy*

SECONDAMANO (GENOVA); il giornale di piccoli annunci. see *GENERAL INTEREST PERIODICALS—Italy*

SECONDAMANO (MONZA - BRIANZA); il giornale di inserzioni gratuite. see *GENERAL INTEREST PERIODICALS—Italy*

SECONDAMANO (PARMA); il giornale di piccoli annunci. see *GENERAL INTEREST PERIODICALS—Italy*

SECONDAMANO (PIACENZA); il giornale di piccoli annunci. see *GENERAL INTEREST PERIODICALS—Italy*

SECONDAMANO (TURIN); il giornale di piccoli annunci. see *GENERAL INTEREST PERIODICALS—Italy*

659.2 USA ISSN 1092-6267
SELLING TO KIDS. Text in English. 1996. bi-w. USD 495 domestic; USD 530 foreign (effective 1999). **Document type:** *Newsletter, Trade.* **Description:** Contains practical advice on how to prosper in the constantly changing kids' marketplace.
Incorporates (1998-2001): Kids T V (1461-6009)
Published by: E P M Communications, 160 Mercer St, 3rd Fl, New York, NY 10012-3212. TEL 212-941-0099, FAX 212-941-1622, pstuntz@phillips.com, info@epmcom.com, http://www.prandmarketing.com, http://www.epmcom.com.

659.143 USA ISSN 1074-5297
PN1993
SHOOT. Text in English. 1960. w. USD 125 domestic; USD 218 in Canada; USD 330 to Mexico, Central America, Caribbean, Colombia, Venezuela; USD 418 to Europe, South America, United Kingdom, Mediterranean; USD 516 elsewhere (effective 2005). adv. back issues avail.; reprints avail. **Document type:** *Magazine, Trade.* **Description:** For the commercial production and advertising industries. Special feature issues cover industry events such as the Clio Awards, NAB Convention, ITS Convention, and SMPTE.
Formerly (until 1994): Back Stage Shoot (1055-9825)
Related titles: Online - full text ed.: (from EBSCO Publishing, Florida Center for Library Automation, Gale Group, O C L C Online Computer Library Center, Inc.).
Indexed: IIPA.
—CCC.
Published by: V N U Business Publications (Subsidiary of: V N U Business Media), 770 Broadway, New York, NY 10003-9595. TEL 646-654-5780, shoot@shootonline.com, bmcomm@vnuinc.com, http://www.shootonline.com/, http://www.vnubusinessmedia.com/. Ed. Robert Goldrich. Pub. Roberta Griefer. Adv. contact Patti Fahn. color page USD 5,455. Circ: 13,971 (paid and controlled). **Subscr. to:** PO Box 2069, Marion, OH 43306-4169. TEL 800-745-8922.

SHOW BIZ NEWS AND MODEL NEWS. see *THEATER*

SHOWFAX. see *MEETINGS AND CONGRESSES*

SHOWS & EXHIBITIONS. see *MEETINGS AND CONGRESSES*

659.132 ZAF
SIGN & GRAPHICS. Text in English. 1995. bi-m. ZAR 108.32; ZAR 350 foreign (effective 1997). adv. back issues avail. **Description:** Includes information pertaining to the signage industry and buyers of signage.
Published by: Graphix Publications (Pty) Ltd., PO Box 751119, Garden View, 2047, South Africa. TEL 27-11-622-4800, FAX 27-11-622-2480, sticklan@aztec.co.za. Ed. Lucia Kaszinska. Pub. Brian Stickland. Adv. contact Dyecan Copeland. page ZAR 5,007. Circ: 3,500.

659 USA ISSN 0895-0555
SIGN BUILDER ILLUSTRATED; the how-to magazine. Text in English. 1987. m. USD 3.75 newsstand/cover. adv. charts; illus.; stat.; tr.lit. back issues avail. **Document type:** *Magazine, Trade.* **Description:** Acts as a "how-to" publication for the sign industry.
Related titles: Online - full text ed.: (from ProQuest Information & Learning).
Indexed: ABIn.
Published by: Simmons-Boardman Publishing Corp., 345 Hudson St, 12th Fl, New York, NY 10014-4502. TEL 212-620-7200, FAX 212-633-1863, http://www.signshop.com. Adv. contact Mel Katz TEL 212-620-7247. B&W page USD 2,110, color page USD 3,025; trim 8.125 x 10.875. Circ: 19,000.

659.15 686.2 USA ISSN 0893-9888
HF5841
SIGN BUSINESS. Text in English. 1986. m. USD 38 in US & Canada; USD 85 elsewhere (effective 2005). adv. illus. back issues avail.; reprints avail. **Document type:** *Magazine, Trade.* **Description:** For businesses engaged in the design, production, sales and maintenance of all types of interior and exterior signs.
Published by: National Business Media, Inc., PO Box 1416, Broomfield, CO 80038. TEL 303-469-0424, FAX 303-469-5730, sbeditor@nbm.com, http://www.nbm.com/signbusiness. Ed. Eddie Wieber. adv.: B&W page USD 4,275, color page USD 5,265; trim 10.88 x 8.13. Circ: 20,000 (controlled).

659.1 GBR
SIGN UPDATE. Text in English. 1990. bi-m. GBP 16.50, USD 20.50 (effective 2001). adv. bk.rev.; software rev.; Website rev. tr.lit.; mkt. 100 p./no. 3 cols./p.; back issues avail. **Document type:** *Magazine, Trade.*
Related titles: CD-ROM ed.; Diskette ed.; E-mail ed.
Address: Allens Orchard, Chipping Warden, Banbury, OX17 1LX, United Kingdom. TEL 44-1295-660666, FAX 44-1295-660866, magazine@sign-update.co.uk, http://www.sign-update.co.uk. Ed., Pub. Roger Hinchliffe. R&P Ron Hills. Adv. contact Tracey Ward. B&W page GBP 495, color page GBP 880; trim 210 x 297. Circ: 7,188.

659.132 GBR ISSN 0049-0466
SIGN WORLD. Text in English. 1964. 10/yr. GBP 17.75 domestic; GBP 21.75 foreign (effective 2005). adv. bk.rev. illus. **Document type:** *Magazine, Trade.* **Description:** Publishes articles and news of developments and products in the sign field.
—CCC.
Published by: A.E. Morgan Publications Ltd., Stanley House, 9 West St, Epsom, Surrey KT18 7RL, United Kingdom. TEL 44-1372-741411, FAX 44-1372-744493, valerie@aemorgan.co.uk. Ed. Michael Connolly. Pub. Terence Morgan. Adv. contact Derek Pearson. color page GBP 1,165; 180 x 260. Circ: 5,000.

659.1 658 USA ISSN 0270-4757
HF5841
SIGNCRAFT; the guide to profitable and creative sign production. Text in English. 1980. 7/yr. USD 35 domestic; USD 44 foreign; USD 5.95 newsstand/cover (effective 2005). adv. **Document type:** *Magazine, Trade.* **Description:** Focuses on design, technique and business management in the commercial sign shop industry.
—CCC.
Published by: Signcraft Publishing Co., Inc., 10271 Deer Run Farms Rd, Fort Myers, FL 33912. TEL 941-939-4644, 800-204-0204, FAX 941-939-0607, signcraft@signcraft.com, http://www.signcraft.com. Ed., R&P Tom McIltrot. Adv. contact Michelle DiGiacomo. Circ: 13,500 (paid).

659.1029 GBR ISSN 0261-8974
SIGNMAKERS AND SUPPLIERS DIRECTORY. Text in English. 1971. a. GBP 6.50 (effective 1999). adv. illus. index. **Document type:** *Directory.* **Description:** Lists suppliers of goods and services for the sign industry.
Formerly (until 1978): Sign Makers and Suppliers Year Book and Directory
Published by: A.E. Morgan Publications Ltd., Stanley House, 9 West St, Epsom, Surrey KT18 7RL, United Kingdom. TEL 44-1372-741411, FAX 44-1372-744493. Ed. Michael Connolly. Pub. Terence Morgan. Adv. contact Julia Dempster. B&W page GBP 490, color page GBP 770; trim 130 x 190.

659 CZE ISSN 1212-0588
SIGNMAKING. Text in Czech. 1997. q. CZK 200; CZK 50 newsstand/cover (effective 2001). adv. **Document type:** *Magazine, Trade.*
Published by: Strategie Praha s.r.o., Drtinova 8, Prague 5, 150 00, Czech Republic. TEL 420-2-57323578, FAX 420-2-57018362, strategie.praha@istrategie.cz, http://www.istrategie.cz. Ed. Marek Stonis. adv.: page CZK 35,000.

659.15 USA ISSN 0037-5063
SIGNS OF THE TIMES; the industry journal since 1906. Text in English. 1906. 13/yr. USD 39 domestic; USD 59 in Canada; USD 62 elsewhere (effective 2005). adv. bk.rev. stat.; tr.lit. index. back issues avail. **Document type:** *Magazine, Trade.* **Description:** Contains articles on the design and manufacture of all types of signs.
Related titles: Microform ed.: (from PQC); ♦ Spanish ed.: Signs of the Times & Screen Printing en Espanol. ISSN 1091-0832.
Indexed: CERDIC, DAAI.
—CCC.
Published by: S T Publications Inc. (Subsidiary of: S T Media Group International, Inc.), 407 Gilbert Ave, Cincinnati, OH 45202. TEL 513-421-2050, FAX 513-421-5144, wade.swormstedt@stmediagroup.com, http://www.signweb.com. Ed. Darek Johnson. Pub. Wade Swormstedt. adv.: B&W page USD 3,902, color page USD 4,902. Circ: 18,100.

SIGNS OF THE TIMES & SCREEN PRINTING EN ESPANOL. see *PRINTING*

SMART; occasioni tutte da vedere. see *GENERAL INTEREST PERIODICALS—Italy*

659 CAN ISSN 1480-2821
THE SOURCES HOTLINK. Text in English. 1996. q. CND 20 (effective 2004). adv. bk.rev. **Document type:** *Newsletter.* **Description:** Offers hints and tips on gaining positive news coverage.
Published by: Sources Publishing, 489 College St, Ste 305, Toronto M6G 1A5, ON M6G 1A5, Canada. TEL 416-964-7799, FAX 416-964-8763, sources@sources.com, http://www.sources.com. Ed. Kirsten Cowan. Pub. Barrie Zwicker. R&P Ulli Deimer. Adv. contact Michelle Hernandez. Circ: 1,200 (paid).

SOUTH EAST MAGAZINE. see *LITERARY AND POLITICAL REVIEWS*

657.1 ZAF
SOUTHERN AFRICAN PUBLIC RELATIONS JOURNAL. Cover title: Southern African P R J. Text in English. 1995. m. (11/yr.). ZAR 131.10; ZAR 160 foreign. bk.rev. **Description:** Covers issues relating to public relations in southern Africa including case studies, workshops, reports, conference and seminar information, professional profiles, and features on various industry sectors.
Published by: Journal Workshop, Cramerview, PO Box 387, Bryanston, Johannesburg 2060, South Africa. TEL 27-11-706-4978, FAX 27-11-706-22310, saprj@icon.co.za. Ed., Pub., R&P Karen de Wet. Adv. contact Lyn Aitken. B&W page ZAR 3,795, color page ZAR 4,740; trim 250 x 190. Circ: 4,509.

659.1 USA
SOUTHERN CALIFORNIA MEDIA DIRECTORY. Text in English. 1967. a. looseleaf. adv. **Document type:** *Directory.* **Description:** Lists media outlets: newspapers, radio and television stations, bureaus and wire services.
Published by: Public Communications of Los Angeles, 1910 W Sunset Blvd, Ste 460, Los Angeles, CA 90026-3247. TEL 213-387-7252, FAX 213-413-4026, webmaster@pcla.org, http://www.pcla.org. Ed. Diana Gentry. R&P Mike Ferguson. Adv. contact Lisa Guilford.

659.1 371.42 GBR
SPONSORSHIP AND FUNDING GUIDE. Text in English. a. GBP 8.99 per issue (effective 2004). adv. **Document type:** *Directory.*
Former titles (until 2002): Sponsorship and Funding Directory; Sponsorship for Students (Year)
—BLDSC (8419.217000).
Published by: (Careers and Occupational Information Centre), Hobsons PLC, Bateman St, Cambridge, Cambs CB2 1LZ, United Kingdom. TEL 44-1223-460366, FAX 44-1223-301506. Ed. Wendy Frankiss. Pub. David Harrington. Adv. contact Adrian Kimpton. **Dist. by:** Biblios Publishers' Distribution Services Ltd., Star Rd, Partridge Green, W Sussex RH13 8LD, United Kingdom. TEL 44-1403-710851, FAX 44-1403-711143. **Co-sponsor:** Careers Research and Advisory Centre, Employment Department Group.

SPONSORSHIP NEWS; the first magazine devoted to sponsorship. see *SPORTS AND GAMES*

THE SPONSORSHIP REPORT. see *SOCIAL SERVICES AND WELFARE*

STANDARD DIRECTORY OF ADVERTISERS (ADVERTISING AGENCIES). see *BUSINESS AND ECONOMICS—Trade And Industrial Directories*

STANDARD DIRECTORY OF ADVERTISERS (BUSINESS CLASSIFICATIONS EDITION). see *BUSINESS AND ECONOMICS—Trade And Industrial Directories*

STANDARD DIRECTORY OF ADVERTISING AGENCIES; the agency red book. see *BUSINESS AND ECONOMICS—Trade And Industrial Directories*

STANDARD DIRECTORY OF INTERNATIONAL ADVERTISERS AND AGENCIES; the international red book. see *BUSINESS AND ECONOMICS—Trade And Industrial Directories*

657 658 USA ISSN 1086-704X
HF5845
STORE WINDOWS. Text in English. 1995 (no.8). irreg.
Formerly (until no.8, 1995): Store Windows That Sell (1086-7023)
Published by: Visual Reference Publications, Inc., 302 Fifth Ave, New York, NY 10001. TEL 212-279-7000, 800-251-4545, FAX 212-279-7014.

659.1 ITA
STRATEGIA. Text in Italian. 1973. m. (11/yr.). EUR 100 (effective 2005). adv. bk.rev. charts; illus.; stat. back issues avail. **Document type:** *Trade.* **Description:** Covers Italian and international current events.
Indexed: DM&T.
Published by: Strategia Editoriale, Piazza della Repubblica 32, Milan, MI 20124, Italy. TEL 39-02-67151202, FAX 39-02-66980255, info@strategia.it, http://www.strategia.it. Ed. Ivana Pasian. Circ: 8,623.

659.1 FRA ISSN 0180-6424
STRATEGIES; le premier journal professionnel de la communication. Text in French. 1971. w. charts; illus. **Document type:** *Trade.* **Description:** Reports on issues and trends in communication, the media, and marketing.
Published by: Groupe Strategies SA (Subsidiary of: Reed Business Information France), 2 rue Maurice Hartmann, BP62, Issy-les-Moulinaux, Cedex 92133, France. TEL 33-1-46294629, FAX 33-1-40930314, infos@groupe-strategies.fr, http://www.groupe-strategies.fr. Circ: 14,405. **Subscr. to:** 99 rue d'Amsterdam, Paris 75008 , France.

659 330.9 USA
STREAMING MEDIA ADVERTISING FORECAST (YEAR). Text in English. a. USD 1,195 (effective 2004 & 2005).
Published by: SIMBA Information (Subsidiary of: R.R. Bowker LLC), 60 Long Ridge Rd., Ste 300, Stamford, CT 06902. TEL 203-325-8193, 800-307-2529, FAX 203-325-8915, info@simbanet.com, http://www.simbanet.com.

659.111 USA
THE SUMMIT COLLECTION; a collection of fine stores and services. Text in English.
Published by: Summit Downtown, Inc, 71 Summit Ave, Summit, NJ 07901.

659.1 SUR
SURINAME. ADVERTENTIEBLAD; national gazette. Text in Dutch. s-w. USD 400 (effective 2000). adv. **Document type:** *Government.* **Description:** Publishes official notices of the Republic, including laws, licensing requirements, court decisions, balances of the Central Bank, company statutes and other official announcements.
Published by: N.V. Drukkerij & Uitgeverij D A G, Gravenstraat 120, PO Box 56, Paramaribo, Suriname. TEL 597-473501, 597-471223, FAX 597-454782, 597-454782. Ed., Adv. contact Edward D Findlay. Circ: 1,000.

T V & CABLE PUBLICITY OUTLETS - NATIONWIDE. see *COMMUNICATIONS—Television And Cable*

TAEGLICH KRESS. see *COMMUNICATIONS*

TAIPEI HUA K'AN/TAIPEI PICTORIAL. see *GENERAL INTEREST PERIODICALS—Taiwan*

659.1 KWT
TARGET ADVERTISING NEWS. Text in English. fortn. **Document type:** *Newspaper.*
Published by: Basel Al Abduljalil, P O Box 27927, Safat, 13001, Kuwait. TEL 965-2408105, FAX 965-2408108. adv.: color page KWD 4,750. Circ: 50,000.

TARGET MARKETING; the leading magazine for integrated database marketing. see *BUSINESS AND ECONOMICS—Marketing And Purchasing*

659.2 070.5 FRA ISSN 0038-9579
TARIF MEDIA. Text in French. 1961. 6/yr. EUR 836 (effective 2005). Supplement avail. **Document type:** *Consumer.* **Description:** Supplies the advertising industry with facts on French national and local press, trade, technical and professional publications, television listings. Includes advertising rates, formats, circulation, geographical and social breakdown on French media.
—CCC.

▼ new title ➤ refereed ✶ unverified ♦ full entry avail.

Published by: Societe Tarif Media S.A., 43 rue du Colonel Pierre Avia, Paris, 75015, France. TEL 33-1-41335419, FAX 33-1-41861869, betsabe.desantigny@tarifmedia.com, http://www.tarifmedia.com. Eds. Betsabe Desantigny, Corinne Mulot. Adv. contact Eric Lahurte. Circ: 1,750.

658   USA
TECHNOLOGY ADVERTISING & BRANDING REPORT. Text in English. 24/yr. USD 549 (effective 2004). **Document type:** *Newsletter.*
Published by: SIMBA Information (Subsidiary of: R.R. Bowker LLC), 60 Long Ridge Rd., Ste 300, Stamford, CT 06902. TEL 203-325-8193, 800-307-2529, FAX 203-325-8915, info@simbanet.com, http://www.simbanet.com. Ed. Linda Kopp.

TELEPHONE ORGANIZATION OF THAILAND. ANNUAL REPORT. see *COMMUNICATIONS—Telephone And Telegraph*

TELEVISION IN ASIA PACIFIC TO THE YEAR... see *COMMUNICATIONS—Television And Cable*

TELEVISION IN EUROPE TO THE YEAR... see *COMMUNICATIONS—Television And Cable*

659.1 658.8   ITA
TODAY FAX. Text in Italian. 1989. d. **Document type:** *Newsletter.*
Related titles: Fax ed.
Published by: Marketing Finanza Italia s.r.l., Via Alessandro Stradella, 3, Milan, MI 20129, Italy. TEL 39-02-9400554, FAX 39-02-29401816, http://www.pubblicitaitalia.it. Ed. Lillo Perri. Circ: 4,500.

659.1 760   JPN
TOKYO ART DIRECTORS ANNUAL/A D C NENKAN. Text in English, Japanese. 1957. a. USD 257. adv. back issues avail.
Formerly: Annual of Advertising Art in Japan (0548-1643)
Published by: (Art Directors Club of Tokyo), Bijutsu Shuppan-sha, Inaoka Bldg, 2-36 Kanda-Jinbo-cho, Chiyoda-ku, Tokyo, 1010051, Japan. TEL 03-3234-2151, FAX 03-3234-9451. Circ: 4,000. **Dist. by:** International Marketing Corp., I.P.O. Box 5056, Tokyo 100-30, Japan. TEL 81-3-3661-7458, FAX 81-3-3667-9646.

TOP 50 EUROPEAN MEDIA OWNERS. see *COMMUNICATIONS*

659.1   USA   ISSN 0145-5559
T391
TRADESHOW. Text in English. a. adv. **Document type:** *Trade.*
Published by: Reed Business Information (Subsidiary of: Reed Business), 5700 Wilshire Blvd, Ste 120, Los Angeles, CA 90036. TEL 323-965-2093, FAX 323-965-5334, http://www.tradeshowweek.com, http://www.reedbusiness.com. Ed. Carol Andrews. Pub. Irene Sperling.

TRADESHOW DIRECTORY. see *BUSINESS AND ECONOMICS—Trade And Industrial Directories*

658.8   USA   ISSN 0733-0170
TRADESHOW WEEK; since 1971, the only weekly source of news & statistics on the tradeshow industry. Text in English. 1971. 51/yr. USD 439 domestic; USD 459 foreign; USD 15 newsstand/cover domestic (effective 2005). Incl. TSW's Services Directory, TSW's Major Exhibit Hall Directory, Tradeshow Week 200.. adv. abstr. s-a. index. 25 p./no. 3 cols./p.; back issues avail.; reprints avail. **Document type:** *Magazine, Trade.* **Description:** Informs and inspires corporate exhibitors, show organizers and suppliers about the trends, news, ideas, and issues shaping the exposition industry in the US and abroad.
Related titles: Online - full text ed.: (from Florida Center for Library Automation, Gale Group, O C L C Online Computer Library Center, Inc., ProQuest Information & Learning); ♦ Supplement(s): Tradeshow Week's Buyer's Guide. ISSN 1099-3061; ♦ Tradeshow Week's Major Exhibit Hall Directory.
Indexed: ABIn.
—CCC.
Published by: Reed Business Information (Subsidiary of: Reed Business), 5700 Wilshire Blvd, Ste 120, Los Angeles, CA 90036. TEL 323-965-2093, FAX 323-965-5334, aschaffer@reedbusiness.com, http://www.tradeshowweek.com, http://www.reedbusiness.com. Ed. Michael Hart TEL 323-965-5305. Pub. Adam Schaffer TEL 323-965-2093. Circ: 2,100 (paid). Subscr. to: Reed Business Information, PO Box 16447, North Hollywood, CA 91615-6447. TEL 800-375-4212, FAX 818-487-4550, http://www.pubservice.com/CH.htm.

658.8   USA   ISSN 1099-3061
AS6
TRADESHOW WEEK'S BUYER'S GUIDE. Text in English. a. USD 150 (effective 2004); free with subscr. to Tradeshow Week.
Related titles: ♦ Supplement to: Tradeshow Week. ISSN 0733-0170.
Published by: Reed Business Information (Subsidiary of: Reed Business), 5700 Wilshire Blvd, Ste 120, Los Angeles, CA 90036. TEL 323-965-2093, FAX 323-965-5334, http://www.reedbusiness.com.

658.8   USA
TRADESHOW WEEK'S MAJOR EXHIBIT HALL DIRECTORY. Text in English. a. USD 175 per vol. (effective 2004). **Document type:** *Directory.*
Related titles: ♦ Supplement to: Tradeshow Week. ISSN 0733-0170.
Published by: Reed Business Information (Subsidiary of: Reed Business), 5700 Wilshire Blvd, Ste 120, Los Angeles, CA 90036. TEL 323-965-2093, FAX 323-965-5334, http://www.reedbusiness.com. Ed. Michael Hart TEL 323-965-5305.

TRAFFIC AUDIT BUREAU. ANNUAL REPORT. see *TRANSPORTATION—Roads And Traffic*

TRAFFIC AUDIT BUREAU. NEWSLETTER. see *TRANSPORTATION—Roads And Traffic*

659.1   DEU   ISSN 1436-798X
TRANSFER - WERBEFORSCHUNG UND PRAXIS. Text in English, German. 1956. q. EUR 65; EUR 50 to students; EUR 17.50 newsstand/cover (effective 2005). adv. **Document type:** *Magazine, Trade.* **Description:** Covers new developments, strategies, and research in the advertising and marketing fields.
Former titles (until 1999): Werbeforschung und Praxis (0256-4033); (until 1985): W W G Information (0252-8045)
Related titles: Online - full text ed.
Published by: (Deutsche Werbewissenschaftliche Gesellschaft e.V.), Varus Verlag, Konrad-Zuse-Platz 1-3, Bonn, 53227, Germany. TEL 49-228-944660, FAX 49-228-9446666, info@varus.com, http://www.varus.com/seiten/transfer.html. adv.: color page EUR 2,500; B&W page EUR 1,500; 175 x 248. Circ: 7,120 (paid and controlled). **Co-sponsor:** Oesterreichische Werbewissenschaftliche Gesellschaft.

U K MEDIA DIRECTORY. see *BUSINESS AND ECONOMICS—Trade And Industrial Directories*

U K MEDIA YEARBOOK. see *COMMUNICATIONS*

U K TELEVISION FORECASTS. see *COMMUNICATIONS— Television And Cable*

659   USA   ISSN 1070-9096
HF5801
U S AD REVIEW. Variant title: USadreview. Text in English. q. USD 199 in US & Canada; USD 299 elsewhere (effective 2000). **Document type:** *Journal, Trade.* **Description:** Provides a comprehensive collection of the most interesting and dynamic print advertising in America.
Published by: Visual Reference Publications, Inc., 302 Fifth Ave, New York, NY 10001. TEL 212-279-7000, 800-251-4545, FAX 212-279-7014, retailreporting@retailreporting.com, http://www.retailreporting.com.

U S REAL ESTATE REGISTER. see *REAL ESTATE*

UNIWERSYTET JAGIELLONSKI. OSRODEK BADAN PRASOZNAWCZYCH. ZESZYTY PRASOZNAWCZE. see *JOURNALISM*

659.1 363.6   USA
UTILITY COMMUNICATORS INTERNATIONAL. NEWSLETTER. Text in English. 6/yr. membership. **Document type:** *Newsletter.* **Description:** Includes information on advertising and public relations as well as association news and developments.
Formerly: Public Utilities Communicators Association. Newsletter
Published by: Utility Communicators International, c/o Robert Janke, 5525 E Grandview Rd, Scottsdale, AZ 85254. TEL 602-971-1989, robertjanke@compuserve.com. Ed. Robert Janke. Circ: 400.

659.1   USA
V I P ADDRESS BOOK UPDATE. Text in English. 1988. a. USD 24.95 per issue (effective 2003). adv. **Document type:** *Directory.*
Related titles: ♦ Supplement to: (Year) V I P Address Book. ISSN 1043-0261.
Published by: Associated Media Companies, Ltd., PO Box 489, Gleneden Beach, OR 97388-0489. TEL 541-764-4233, 800-258-0615, vipaddress@isp.com, http:// www.vipaddress.com. Ed. James M Wiggins. Adv. contact Adele M Cooke.

V M & S D. (Visual Merchandising & Store Design) see *INTERIOR DESIGN AND DECORATION*

659.1   DEU
VIERTELJAHRESHEFTE FUER MEDIA- UND WERBEWIRKUNG. Text in German. 1969. q. **Document type:** *Trade.*
Formerly: Vierteljahreshefte fuer Mediaplanung
Published by: Heinrich Bauer Verlag, Burchardstr 11, Hamburg, 20077, Germany. TEL 49-40-30190, FAX 49-40-326589. Ed. Gabriele Kaplitza. Circ: 3,000.

659.1   USA   ISSN 0042-5915
VIEWS & REVIEWS (NEW YORK, 1937). Text in English. 1937. 6/yr. USD 249 in US & Canada; USD 299 elsewhere (effective 2000). illus. **Document type:** *Journal, Trade.* **Description:** Provides information on and examples of top-notch window and in-store display ideas.
Published by: Visual Reference Publications, Inc., 302 Fifth Ave, New York, NY 10001. TEL 212-279-7000, 800-251-4545, FAX 212-279-7014, retailreporting@retailreporting.com, http://www.retailreporting.com.

659.2   ZAF
VOX COM. Text in English. 1991. irreg. (approx a.). **Document type:** *Newsletter.*
Supersedes (in 1993): Songusa Newsletter
Published by: National Public Relations Association of South Africa, c/o SA Communication Service, Private Bag X745, Pretoria, 0001, South Africa.

659.1   DEU   ISSN 0042-9538
HF5415.12.G4
W & V. (Werben und Verkaufen) Text in German. 1963. w. EUR 165 domestic; EUR 200 foreign (effective 2005). adv. bk.rev. charts; illus.; mkt.; pat.; tr.lit.; tr.mk. **Document type:** *Magazine, Trade.* **Description:** Provides information on all aspects of sales and marketing.
Related titles: Online - full text ed.: (from LexisNexis, O C L C Online Computer Library Center, Inc.). —IE, Infotrieve. **CCC.**
Published by: Europa Fachpresse Verlag GmbH (Subsidiary of: Sueddeutsche Verlag), Emily-Noether-Str 2-E, Munich, 80992, Germany. TEL 49-89-5485200, FAX 49-89-54852108, webmaster@efv.de, http://www.wuv.de. Ed. Andreas Werb. Adv. contact Ulrich Weise. B&W page EUR 4,370; trim 202 x 262. Circ: 22,261.

659   USA
THE WAHLSTROM REPORT. Text in English. **Description:** Covers news and trends about advertising in print or electronic telephone directories.
Media: Online - full content. **Related titles:** E-mail ed.
Published by: Wahlstrom & Company, 1290 E Main St, Stamford, CT 06902. TEL 203-348-7347, 800-348-7347, webmaster@wahlstrom.com, http://www.wahlstrom.com/.

659.1   USA
WASHINGTON MORNING LINE✶ . Text in English. m. membership. **Description:** Provides news and information of relevance and interest to members.
Published by: American Council of Highway Advertisers, 1421 Prince St, 330, Alexandria, VA 22314. TEL 301-261-9197, FAX 410-867-1764, rico45acp@aol.com.

WEB ADVERTISING (YEAR); market analysis & forecast. see *COMPUTERS—Internet*

659.2   AUS   ISSN 1441-7472
THE WELL; the newsletter of Jackson Wells Morris. Text in English. 1992. q. **Document type:** *Newsletter.* **Description:** Discusses news in the public relations industry with relevance to the company.
Media: Online - full text.
Published by: Jackson Wells Communications, Gateway Court, 81-91 Military Rd, Neutral Bay, NSW 2089, Australia. TEL 61-2-990-44333, FAX 61-2-990-44555, jwc@jackwell.com.au, http://www.jackwell.com.au/news.htm.

659.1   CHE
WERBE WOCHE. Text in German. 46/yr. **Document type:** *Trade.*
Published by: Verlag Media-Daten AG, Kanzleistr 80, Zuerich, 8026, Switzerland. TEL 41-1-2417776, FAX 41-1-2417884. Ed. Ursula Klein. Circ: 4,100.

659.1   AUT
WERBEALMANACH. Text in German. 1978. a. adv. **Document type:** *Directory, Trade.*
Published by: Manstein Zeitschriften Verlagsgesellschaft mbH, Brunner Feldstr 45, Perchtoldsdorf, N 2380, Austria. TEL 43-1-866480, FAX http://www.manstein.at, 43-1-86648100, office@manstein.at, http://www.manstein.at/Magazine/ WerbeAlmanach/. Eds. Brigitte Rohrer, Gertrude Mayer. Circ: 2,800.

659.1   DEU   ISSN 1435-9715
DAS WERBEARTIKEL MAGAZIN. Text in German. 1989. 4/yr. adv. **Document type:** *Magazine, Trade.*
Formerly (until 1998): Werbeartikel Wirtschaft (0945-7976)
Published by: W A Verlag GmbH, Waltherstr 80, Cologne, 51069, Germany. TEL 49-221-689110, FAX 49-221-6891110, info@wa-verlag-koeln.de, http://www.werbeartikel-verlag.de. Ed. Michael Scherer. Pub. Klaus Stallbaum. Adv. contact Serkan Karabulut. Circ: 29,920 (paid).

659.1   DEU   ISSN 1439-3026
WERBEARTIKEL NACHRICHTEN. Text in English, French, German. 1983. 10/yr. back issues avail. **Document type:** *Journal, Trade.*
Formerly (until 1998): Werbeartikel Nachrichten fuer Insider (0945-7984)

Published by: W A Verlag GmbH, Waltherstr 80, Cologne, 51069, Germany. TEL 49-221-689110, FAX 49-221-6891110, info@wa-verlag-koeln.de, http://www.werbeartikel-nachrichten.de, http://www.werbeartikel-verlag.de. Ed. Michael Scherer. Pub. Klaus Stallbaum. Adv. contact Serkan Karabulut. Circ: 97,000 (paid).

659.1 DEU ISSN 0930-4487
WERBEBERATER - IDEENSERVICE FUER ERFOLGREICHE WERBUNG UND OEFFENTLICHKEITSARBEIT. Text in German. 1984. m. looseleaf. back issues avail. **Document type:** *Bulletin.*
Published by: V N R Verlag fuer die Deutsche Wirtschaft AG, Theodor-Heuss-Str 2-4, Bonn, 53095, Germany. TEL 49-228-8205-0, FAX 49-228-364411. Ed. Norman Rentrop.

659.1 DEU
WERBUNG IN DEUTSCHLAND (YEAR). Text in German. a. **Document type:** *Corporate.*
Published by: Zentralverband der Deutschen Werbewirtschaft, Villichgasse 17, Bonn, 53177, Germany. TEL 49-228-82092-0, FAX 49-228-357583. Ed. Volker Nickel.

363.7282 USA
WESTERN SLOPE BARGAIN HUNTER ✶ . Text in English. 1970. w. USD 20. adv. bk.rev. back issues avail. **Document type:** *Newspaper.* **Description:** Contains classified advertisements, with an emphasis on recycling, collections, local services and opportunities.
Published by: Bargain Hunter, PO Box 2110, Glenwood Springs, CO 81602-2110. TEL 970-945-6235, FAX 970-945-5140, dpuddu@cjnetworks.com, http://searchcolorado.com. Ed. Dave Pudda. Adv. contact H Cochran. Circ: 10,000.

659.1071 USA ISSN 1083-9119
HF5815.U5
WHERE SHALL I GO TO STUDY ADVERTISING & PUBLIC RELATIONS?. Text in English. 1965. a. USD 5 domestic; USD 7.50 foreign (effective 2000 - 2001). adv. **Document type:** *Directory.* **Description:** Aimed at students and counselors seeking information on U.S. universities that have advertising and public relations education programs.
Former titles: Where Shall I Go to College to Study Advertising and Public Relations?; (until 1992): Where Shall I Go to College to Study Advertising?
Published by: Advertising Education Publications, PO Box 68232, Lubbock, TX 79414. TEL 806-798-0616, FAX 806-798-0616, bilross@lsu.edu, http://www.mcom.ttu.edu/wsig/, http://www.mcom.ttu.edu/wsiq?/. Ed. Billy I Ross. Adv. contact Keith F Johnson. Circ: 3,000 (paid).

WHITE PAGES & DIRECTORY LISTINGS (YEAR). see *BUSINESS AND ECONOMICS—Trade And Industrial Directories*

659.1029 USA ISSN 1058-9201
HF5863
WHO'S WHO; The M F S A blue ribbon buyers' guide to mailing and fulfillment companies. Text in English. 1990. a. free to members (effective 2005); USD 65. adv. **Document type:** *Directory.*
Published by: M F S A - Mailing & Fulfillment Service Association, 1421 Prince St, Ste 410, Alexandria, VA 22314-2806. TEL 703-836-9200, 800-333-6272, FAX 703-548-8204, mfsa-mail@mfsanet.org, http://www.mfsanet.org/pages/index.cfm?pageid=1. Pub. Anita Shelton.

659.025 HUN
WHO'S WHO IN ADVERTISING AND MEDIA/KI KICSODA A REKLAM ES MEDIA VILAGABAN. Text in Hungarian. 1999. a. **Document type:** *Directory.*
Related titles: ♦ Supplement to: Budapest Business Journal. ISSN 1216-7304.
Published by: New World Publishing Inc., Szent Istvan Korut 11, III emelet, Budapest, 1055, Hungary. TEL 36-1-374-3344, FAX 361-374-3345, editor@bbj.hu, http://www.ceebiz.com.

WHO'S WHO IN PUBLIC RELATIONS (INTERNATIONAL). see *BIOGRAPHY*

659.1 NLD ISSN 0927-1392
WIE WERKT WAAR IN DE RECLAME. Text in Dutch. 1986. s-a. EUR 130 (effective 2005). **Document type:** *Directory, Trade.* **Description:** Lists important persons at the 600 largest advertising agencies in the Netherlands.
Related titles: Supplement(s): Wie Werkt Waar in de Reclame (Diskette). ISSN 1566-9351. 1995.
Published by: Adformatie Groep (Subsidiary of: Wolters Kluwer N.V.), Postbus 75462, Amsterdam, 1070 AL, Netherlands. TEL 31-20-5733644, FAX 31-20-6793581, http://www.adformatie.nl.

659.1 GBR ISSN 0000-0213
Z6956.E5
WILLINGS PRESS GUIDE; a guide to the press of the United Kingdom and to the principal publications of Europe, the Americas, Australasia, Asia, Africa and the Middle East. Text in English. 1874. a. (in 2 vols.). GBP 225, USD 380; GBP 170 for individual vols. (effective 2000). adv. subject index. **Document type:** *Directory.* **Description:** Information on publications in the UK and overseas. Includes information on publishers and services to the publishing industry.
—BLDSC (9319.000000), Linda Hall.
Published by: Hollis Publishing Ltd., Harlequin House, 7 High St, Teddington, Middx TW11 8EL, United Kingdom. TEL 44-20-8977-7711, FAX 44-20-8977-1133, orders@hollis-pr.co.uk, http://www.hollis-pr.co.uk/. Ed. Nesta Hollis. Pub. Gary Zabel. adv.: B&W page GBP 800, color page GBP 1,750; 185 x 275. Circ: 4,500 (paid).

659.1 DEU ISSN 0934-585X
WOERKSHOP/WORKSHOP; alles, was Werbern Erfolg bringt. Text in German. 1988. 4/yr. EUR 30 in Europe to institutions; USD 38 elsewhere to institutions; EUR 12 newsstand/cover (effective 2006). adv. illus. **Document type:** *Journal, Trade.*
Published by: G I T Verlag GmbH (Subsidiary of: Wiley - V C H Verlag GmbH & Co. KGaA), Roesslerstr 90, Darmstadt, 64293, Germany. TEL 49-6151-80900, FAX 49-6151-8090146, info@gitverlag.com, http://www.gitverlag.com. Ed. Dr. Sonja Andres. Adv. contact Helga Kritzler. color page EUR 3,150; trim 215 x 295. Circ: 9,500.

WOHNMOBIL MARKT. see *SPORTS AND GAMES—Outdoor Life*

(YEAR) WOMEN'S VOLLEYBALL MEDIA GUIDE. see *SPORTS AND GAMES—Ball Games*

WORLDWIDE YELLOW PAGES MARKETS (YEAR). see *BUSINESS AND ECONOMICS—Trade And Industrial Directories*

659.1 USA ISSN 1043-0261
CT120
(YEAR) V I P ADDRESS BOOK. Text in English. 1988. a. USD 94.95 per issue (effective 2003). adv. index. **Document type:** *Directory.* **Description:** Contains more than 28,000 names of people who make a difference.
Related titles: ♦ Supplement(s): V I P Address Book Update.
Published by: Associated Media Companies, Ltd., PO Box 489, Gleneden Beach, OR 97388-0489. TEL 541-764-4233, 800-258-0615, vipaddress@isp.com, http://www.vipaddress.com. Ed., Pub. James M Wiggins. R&P, Adv. contact Adele M Cooke.

YELLOW PAGES & DIRECTORY REPORT; the newsletter for the yellow page & directory publishing industry. see *BUSINESS AND ECONOMICS—Trade And Industrial Directories*

YELLOW PAGES MARKET FORECAST (YEAR). see *BUSINESS AND ECONOMICS—Trade And Industrial Directories*

YELLOW PAGES SALES & MARKETING. see *BUSINESS AND ECONOMICS—Trade And Industrial Directories*

659.1 USA ISSN 1043-4933
YELLOW SHEET (BALLWIN) ✶ ; the practical newsletter on agency management. Text in English. 1984. m. USD 119. adv. index. back issues avail. **Document type:** *Newsletter.* **Description:** For owners and managers of small advertising agencies.
Published by: Communications Management Inc., 14208 Willow Bend Park, Apt 5, Chesterfield, MO 63017-8258. Ed., R&P, Adv. contact George Johnson.

659.1042083 GBR
YOUNG CONSUMERS. Text in English. 1999. q. USD 345 (effective 2005). adv. **Document type:** *Journal, Trade.* **Description:** Draws on the experience and knowledge of kids and youth marketers, advertising agencies, market researchers and the very best academic research. It provides practical guidance on the latest ideas alongside articles that represent fundamental new thinking.
Formerly (until 2004): International Journal of Advertising & Marketing to Children (1464-6676)
Related titles: Online - full text ed.: (from EBSCO Publishing).
—BLDSC (4541.576000). **CCC.**
Published by: World Advertising Research Center Ltd., Farm Road, Henley on Thames, Oxon RG9 1GB, United Kingdom. TEL 44-1491411000, FAX 44-1491418600, enquiries@warc.com, http://www.warc.com/, http://store.warc.com/productinfo/35.asp. Eds. Barbie Clarke, Dr. Brian Young. adv.: page GBP 250.

659.1 DEU
ZENTRALVERBAND DER DEUTSCHEN WERBEWIRTSCHAFT. SERVICE. Text in German. 6/yr. **Document type:** *Bulletin.*
Formerly: Zentralausschuss der Werbewirtschaft Service
Published by: Zentralverband der Deutschen Werbewirtschaft, Villichgasse 17, Bonn, 53177, Germany. TEL 49-228-82092-0, FAX 49-228-357583.

659.1 CHN ISSN 1005-9156
ZHONGGUO GUANGGAO/CHINA ADVERTISING. Text in Chinese. 1981. m. (bi-m. until 2001). CNY 144 (effective 2004). illus. 128 p./no.; **Document type:** *Journal, Academic/Scholarly.*
Address: 200, Ninghai Dong Lu, Shexin Dasha 1805-Shi, Shanghai, 200021, China. TEL 86-21-63552298, FAX 86-21-63551811, china-ad@online.sh.cn; china-ad@ad-cn.net, http://www.ad-cn.net/. **Dist. in China by:** China Books & Periodicals Inc, 360 Swift Ave., Ste. 48, S San Fran, CA 94080-6220. TEL 415-282-2994; **Dist. overseas by:** China International Book Trading Corp, 35 Chegongzhuang Xilu, Haidian District, PO Box 399, Beijing 100044, China. TEL 86-10-68412045, FAX 86-10-68412023, cibtc@mail.cibtc.com.cn, http://www.cibtc.com.cn.

659.1 DEU
ZIELGRUPPEN HANDBUCH. Text in German. 1967. 2/yr. free. **Document type:** *Catalog.* **Description:** Includes information about direct marketing and AZ products and services.
Published by: A Z Bertelsmann Direct GmbH, Carl Bertelsmann Str 161 s, Guetersloh, 33311, Germany. TEL 49-5241-805438, FAX 49-5241-809336, http://www.az.bertelsmann.de. Circ: 25,000.

659.1 DEU
ZIMPEL. TEIL 6: ANZEIGENBLAETTER. Text in German. base vol. plus s-a. updates. **Document type:** *Directory.*
Published by: Verlag Dieter Zimpel (Subsidiary of: Springer Science+Business Media), Angererstr 36, Munich, 80796, Germany. TEL 49-89-3073445, FAX 49-89-302409. **Subscr. to:** Gabler Verlag, Abraham-Lincoln-Str 46, Wiesbaden 65189, Germany. TEL 49-611-7878297, FAX 49-611-7878466.

ZOO (LONDON,1999). see *ART*

659.132 DEU
ZWEITE HAND. Text in German. 1983. 3/w. adv. **Document type:** *Trade.*
Related titles: Online - full text ed.
Published by: Zweite Hand Verlag, Am Treptower Park 75, Berlin, 12435, Germany. TEL 49-30-534310, FAX 49-3053431112, zweitehand@zweitehand.de, http://www.zweitehand.de. Ed. Mathias Pilarski. Pubs. Herbert Borrmann, Konrad Boerries. Adv. contact Susanne Allgaier Parda.

ADVERTISING AND PUBLIC RELATIONS—Abstracting, Bibliographies, Statistics

659.1021 USA
A B C BLUE BOOK: CANADIAN DAILY NEWSPAPERS. Text in English. 1970. s-a. looseleaf. USD 55 to members (effective 1999). stat. **Document type:** *Abstract/Index.* **Description:** Publishes six-month circulation for Canadian daily newspapers.
Published by: Audit Bureau of Circulations, 900 N Meacham Rd, Schaumburg, IL 60173-4968. TEL 847-605-0909, FAX 847-605-0483, http://www.accessabc.com.

016.6591 USA
A B C BLUE BOOK: CANADIAN WEEKLY NEWSPAPERS. Text in English. 1969. s-a. looseleaf. USD 55 to members (effective 1999). stat. **Document type:** *Abstract/Index.* **Description:** Publishes six-month circulation averages for Canadian weekly newspapers.
Published by: Audit Bureau of Circulations, 900 N Meacham Rd, Schaumburg, IL 60173-4968. TEL 847-605-0909, FAX 847-605-0483, http://www.accessabc.com.

016.6591 USA
A B C BLUE BOOK: U S DAILY NEWSPAPERS. Text in English. 1969. s-a. looseleaf. USD 415 to members (effective 1999). stat. **Description:** Publishers' statements of circulation data.
Published by: Audit Bureau of Circulations, 900 N Meacham Rd, Schaumburg, IL 60173-4968. TEL 847-605-0909, FAX 847-605-0483, http://www.accessabc.com.

016.6591 USA
A B C BLUE BOOK: U S WEEKLY NEWSPAPERS. Text in English. 1969. s-a. looseleaf. USD 100 to members (effective 1999). stat. **Description:** Publishers' statements of circulation data.
Published by: Audit Bureau of Circulations, 900 N Meacham Rd, Schaumburg, IL 60173-4968. TEL 847-605-0909, FAX 847-605-0483, http://www.accessabc.com.

ADVERTISING, MARKETING, AND PUBLIC RELATIONS RESOURCES; an internet miniguide. see *BUSINESS AND ECONOMICS—Abstracting, Bibliographies, Statistics*

659.1021 GBR ISSN 0951-774X
ADVERTISING STATISTICS YEARBOOK (YEAR). Text in English. 1986. a. GBP 125 per issue (effective 2000). **Document type:** *Trade.* **Description:** Describes advertising and media trends and analyzes ad statistics.
—BLDSC (0712.285400). **CCC.**
Published by: (Advertising Association), N T C Publications Ltd. (Subsidiary of: World Advertising Research Center Ltd.), Farm Rd, Henley-on-Thames, Oxon RG9 1EJ, United Kingdom. TEL 44-1491-411000, FAX 44-1491-571188, ntc@ntc.co.uk.

AFRICA & MIDDLE EAST MARKET & MEDIAFACT. see *STATISTICS*

A

A

AMERICAS MARKET & MEDIAFACT. see *STATISTICS*

ASIA PACIFIC MARKET & MEDIAFACT. see *STATISTICS*

659.1021 USA
AUDIT BUREAU OF CIRCULATIONS. ANNUAL REPORT. Text in English. a. free. back issues avail. **Document type:** *Corporate.*
Published by: Audit Bureau of Circulations, 900 N Meacham Rd, Schaumburg, IL 60173-4968. TEL 847-605-0909, FAX 847-605-0483, http://www.accessabc.com. Circ: 15,000.

659.1021 USA
AUDIT BUREAU OF CIRCULATIONS. PUBLISHER'S STATEMENTS. Text in English. 1983. s-a. looseleaf. USD 2 (effective 1999). stat. **Document type:** *Abstract/Index.* **Description:** Publishers' statements of newspaper and magazine circulation data.
Published by: Audit Bureau of Circulations, 900 N Meacham Rd, Schaumburg, IL 60173-4968. TEL 847-605-0909, FAX 847-605-0483, http://www.accessabc.com.

659.1021 USA
AUDIT BUREAU OF CIRCULATIONS. SUPPLEMENTAL DATA REPORTS. Text in English. 1968. a. looseleaf. USD 2.75 (effective 1999); per periodical title. back issues avail. **Document type:** *Abstract/Index.* **Description:** Audited circulation information in addition to the contents of audit reports for selected publications.
Published by: Audit Bureau of Circulations, 900 N Meacham Rd, Schaumburg, IL 60173-4968. TEL 847-605-0909, FAX 847-605-0483, http://www.accessabc.com.

016.6591 CAN ISSN 0038-9498
HF5801
CANADIAN ADVERTISING RATES AND DATA. Text in English. 1928. m. CND 525; CND 225 newsstand/cover (effective 2001). adv. **Description:** Aimed at media planning and buying executives, contains rates, circulation, and closing dates.
Formed by the merger of: Standard Rate and Data Service. Canadian Advertising; Standard Rate and Data Service. Canadian Media Rates and Data
Related titles: ♦ Supplement(s): Publication Profiles. ISSN 0836-5024; ♦ Ethnic Media & Markets. ISSN 1205-7142.
Indexed: KES.
—CISTI. **CCC.**
Published by: C A R D, the Media Information Network (Subsidiary of: Rogers Media Publishing Ltd), Subscriber Services, Maclean Hunter Bldg, 777 Bay St, 8th Fl, Toronto, ON M5W 1A7, Canada. TEL 416-596-2790, FAX 416-596-5158, http://www.cardmedia.com. Adv. contact Lucia De Stefano. B&W page CND 4,463, color page CND 5,069; trim 210 x 297. Circ: 4,544.

659.1021 USA ISSN 1186-2955
CANADIAN CIRCULATION OF U S MAGAZINES. Text in English. 1983. a. USD 30 to members (effective 1999). stat. **Description:** Provides comparative figures and circulation trends in Canadian markets.
Published by: Audit Bureau of Circulations, 900 N Meacham Rd, Schaumburg, IL 60173-4968. TEL 847-605-0909, FAX 847-605-0483, http://www.accessabc.com. Ed. Chris Hodges.

659.1021 USA ISSN 1043-7495
CANADIAN NEWSPAPER CIRCULATION FACT BOOK. Text in English. 1971. a. USD 52 (effective 1999). stat. **Document type:** *Abstract/Index.* **Description:** Circulation data for all ABC-member Canadian newspapers by market, county and province.
Former titles (until 1988): Canadian Daily - Weekly Newspaper Circulation Factbook (0278-162X); (until 1980): A B C Factbook (0098-2520)
Indexed: SRI.
Published by: Audit Bureau of Circulations, 900 N Meacham Rd, Schaumburg, IL 60173-4968. TEL 847-605-0909, FAX 847-605-0483, http://www.accessabc.com.

659.1021 USA
COUNTY PENETRATION REPORTS; a tabulation of county circulation data for daily and weekly newspapers. Text in English. 1981. a. looseleaf. membership only. **Document type:** *Abstract/Index.* **Description:** Shows county penetration of ABC-member newspapers.
Related titles: Diskette ed.
Published by: Audit Bureau of Circulations, 900 N Meacham Rd, Schaumburg, IL 60173-4968. TEL 847-605-0909, FAX 847-605-0483, http://www.accessabc.com.

016.6591 MEX ISSN 0185-9099
DIRECTORIO M P M - MEDIOS AUDIO-VISUALES/M P M - MEXICAN AUDIOVISUAL MEDIA RATES & DATA; tarifas y datos-cine, radio y television. (Medios Publicitarios Mexicanos) Text in Spanish. 1958. q. USD 120; USD 60 newsstand/cover (effective 2001). adv. **Document type:** *Directory, Trade.*
Supersedes in part (in 1974): Directorio de Medios Publicitarios Mexicanos (0038-9528)
Published by: Medios Publicitarios Mexicanos S.A., Av Eugenia 811, Col. Del Valle, Mexico City, DF 03100, Mexico. TEL 52-5-5523-3342, FAX 52-5-5523-3379, http://www.mpm.com.mx. Ed. Fernando A Villamil. Circ: 1,200.

016.6591 MEX ISSN 0186-7792
DIRECTORIO M P M - MEDIOS IMPRESOS/M P M - MEXICAN PRINT MEDIA RATES & DATA; tarifas y datos-anuncio exterior, periodicos y revistas. (Medios Publicitarios Mexicanos) Text in Spanish. 1958. q. USD 120; USD 60 newsstand/cover (effective 2001). adv. illus. **Document type:** *Directory, Trade.*
Supersedes in part (in 1974): Directorio de Medios Publicitarios Mexicanos (0038-9528)
Published by: Medios Publicitarios Mexicanos S.A., Av Eugenia 811, Col. Del Valle, Mexico City, DF 03100, Mexico. TEL 52-5-5523-3342, FAX 52-5-5523-3379, http://www.mpm.com.mx. Ed. Fernando A Villamil. Circ: 1,200.

659.1021 USA ISSN 1082-4634
F A S - F A X: CANADIAN DAILY NEWSPAPERS. Text in English. 1970. s-a. looseleaf. USD 36 to non-members; USD 12 to members (effective 1999). stat. **Document type:** *Abstract/Index.* **Description:** Six-month circulation figures for Canadian ABC-member newspapers.
Related titles: Diskette ed.
Indexed: SRI.
Published by: Audit Bureau of Circulations, 900 N Meacham Rd, Schaumburg, IL 60173-4968. TEL 708-605-0909, FAX 708-605-0483. Circ: 1,298.

016.6591 USA
F A S - F A X REPORTS: BUSINESS PUBLICATIONS. Text in English. 1969. s-a. looseleaf. USD 75 to non-members; USD 25 to members (effective 1999). back issues avail. **Document type:** *Abstract/Index.* **Description:** Six-month circulation figures for ABC-member business periodicals.
Related titles: Diskette ed.
Published by: Audit Bureau of Circulations, 900 N Meacham Rd, Schaumburg, IL 60173-4968. TEL 847-605-0909, FAX 847-605-0483, http://www.accessabc.com.

659.1021 USA
F A S - F A X REPORTS: MAGAZINE, FARM AND RELIGIOUS PUBLICATIONS. Text in English. 1969. s-a. looseleaf. USD 120 to non-members; USD 37 to members (effective 1999). back issues avail. **Document type:** *Abstract/Index.* **Description:** Six-month circulation information on ABC-member periodicals.
Former titles: F A S - F A X Reports: Magazine - Farm; Key Note Report: Periodicals
Indexed: SRI.
Published by: Audit Bureau of Circulations, 900 N Meacham Rd, Schaumburg, IL 60173-4968. TEL 847-605-0909, FAX 847-605-0483, http://www.accessabc.com.

659.1021 USA
F A S - F A X: UNITED STATES AND CANADIAN WEEKLY NEWPAPERS. Text in English. 1969. s-a. looseleaf. USD 36 to non-members; USD 12 to members (effective 1999). **Document type:** *Abstract/Index.* **Description:** Six-month circulation figures for ABC-member newspapers.
Related titles: Diskette ed.
Indexed: SRI.
Published by: Audit Bureau of Circulations, 900 N Meacham Rd, Schaumburg, IL 60173-4968. TEL 847-605-0909, FAX 847-605-0483, http://www.accessabc.com.

659.1021 USA
F A S - F A X: UNITED STATES DAILY NEWSPAPERS. Text in English. 1969. s-a. looseleaf. USD 120 to non-members; USD 40 to members (effective 1999). stat. **Document type:** *Abstract/Index.* **Description:** Six-month circulation figures for ABC-member newspapers.
Related titles: Diskette ed.
Indexed: SRI.
Published by: Audit Bureau of Circulations, 900 N Meacham Rd, Schaumburg, IL 60173-4968. TEL 847-605-0909, FAX 847-605-0483, http://www.accessabc.com.

016.6591 USA ISSN 1071-4553
P94.5.H58
HISPANIC MEDIA & MARKET SOURCE. Text in English. q. USD 271 domestic; USD 274 in Canada & Mexico; USD 306 elsewhere (effective 2001). adv. **Document type:** *Directory, Trade.* **Description:** Provides media planners and buyers with more than 2300 listings that contain rates and information on Hispanic media, including radio, T.V., newspapers, business and consumer publications, and direct mail lists.
Formerly (until vol.6, no.4, 1993): Hispanic Media and Markets (1044-0933)
Published by: S R D S, 1700 Higgins Rd, Des Plaines, IL 60018-5605. TEL 847-357-5000, 800-851-7737, FAX 847-357-5009, ebeer@srds.com, http://www.srds.com. Pub., R&P Elisa N Beerbohm. adv.: B&W page USD 2,280, color page USD 4,285; trim 11 x 10.31.

659.1021 USA ISSN 1073-8002
HF5826.5
INTERNATIONAL MEDIA GUIDE. BUSINESS/PROFESSIONAL, ASIA/PACIFIC, MIDDLE EAST/AFICA. Cover title: Business Professional Publications. Asia-Pacific/Middle East-Africa. Variant title: I M G Business Publications. Asia Pacific/Middle East/Africa(International Media Guide). Text in English. 1971. a. USD 300 domestic; USD 311 in Canada & Mexico; USD 329 elsewhere (effective 2001). adv. **Document type:** *Directory, Trade.* **Description:** Provides comprehensive bibliographic and advertising information for 4,000 trade publications in 57 categories.
Formed by the 1991 merger of: International Media Guide. Business - Professional. Asia - Pacific (1073-8010); Which was formerly: International Media Guide. Business - Professional Publications. Asia, Australasia and U S S R (1073-8029); (1983-1979): Media Guide International Edition: Business - Professional Publications. Asia, Australasia and USSR (0730-5249); International Media Guide. Business - Professional. Middle East - Africa (1073-7995); Which was formerly: International Media Guide. Business - Professional Publications. Middle East - Africa (1073-824X); (until 1984): Media Guide International Edition: Business - Professional Publications. Middle East - Africa (0730-5265); Both of which superseded in part: Media Guide International. Business - Professional Publications Edition (0164-1743); Which was formerly: Media Guide International. Business Publications Edition (0098-9398); Newsmedia Guide International
Published by: S R D S, 1700 Higgins Rd, Des Plaines, IL 60018-5605. TEL 847-357-5000, 800-851-7737, FAX 847-375-5001, http://www.srds.com. Ed. Debbie Dunkleberger. R&P, Adv. contact Carolyn Adams. B&W page USD 2,950, color page USD 4,450; trim 8.5 x 11. Circ: 1,500 (paid).

016.6591 USA
INTERNATIONAL MEDIA GUIDE. BUSINESS - PROFESSIONAL. EUROPE. Variant title: I M G Business Publications. Professional. Europe(International Media Guide). Text in English. 1971. a. USD 300 domestic; USD 311 in Canada & Mexico; USD 329 elsewhere (effective 2001). adv. **Document type:** *Directory, Trade.* **Description:** Lists more than 6,000 European business and professional trade publications, with bibliographic and advertising information.
Formerly: Media Guide International. Business - Professional Publications. Europe (0730-5273); Supersedes in part: Media Guide International. Business - Professional Publications Edition (0164-1743); Which was formerly: Media Guide International. Business Publications Edition (0098-9398); Newsmedia Guide International
Published by: S R D S, 1700 Higgins Rd, Des Plaines, IL 60018-5605. TEL 847-357-5000, 800-851-7737, FAX 847-375-5001, http://www.srds.com. Ed. Debbie Dunkleberger. R&P, Adv. contact Carolyn Adams. B&W page USD 2,950, color page USD 4,450; trim 8.5 x 11. Circ: 1,500 (paid).

016.6591 USA
Z6953.8
INTERNATIONAL MEDIA GUIDE. CONSUMER MAGAZINES WORLDWIDE. Variant title: I M G Consumer Magazines Worldwide(International Media Guide). Text in English. 1976. a. USD 300 domestic; USD 311 in Canada & Mexico; USD 329 elsewhere (effective 2001). adv. **Document type:** *Directory, Trade.* **Description:** Lists some 4,500 top consumer magazines published worldwide, giving bibliographic and advertising information.
Former titles: International Media Guide. Consumer Magazines Edition; (until 1982): Media Guide International. Consumer Magazines Edition (0730-238X); Media Guide International. Airline Inflight - Travel Magazines Edition; Media Guide International. Airline Inflight Magazines Edition (0145-9864)
Published by: S R D S, 1700 Higgins Rd, Des Plaines, IL 60018-5605. TEL 847-357-5000, 800-851-7737, FAX 847-375-5001, http://www.srds.com. Ed. Debbie Dunkleberger. R&P, Adv. contact Carolyn Adams. B&W page USD 2,950, color page USD 4,450; trim 8.5 x 11. Circ: 1,500 (paid).

016.6591 USA ISSN 1070-3195
Z6941
INTERNATIONAL MEDIA GUIDE. NEWSPAPERS WORLDWIDE. Variant title: I M G Newspapers Worldwide(International Media Guide). Text in English. 1972. a. USD 300 domestic; USD 311 in Canada & Mexico; USD 329 elsewhere (effective 2001). adv. **Document type:** *Directory, Trade.* **Description:** Lists ad rates and technical information on newspapers throughout the world, complete addresses with contacts.
Former titles (until 1983): Media Guide International. Newspapers - Newsmagazines Edition (0093-9447); Newsmedia Guide International; Newspapers and Newsmagazines Worldwide
Published by: S R D S, 1700 Higgins Rd, Des Plaines, IL 60018-5605. TEL 847-357-5000, 800-851-7737, FAX 847-375-5001, http://www.srds.com. Ed. Debbie Dunkleberger. R&P, Adv. contact Carolyn Adams. B&W page USD 2,950. Circ: 2,000 (paid).

659.1021 IRL
IRELAND. CENTRAL STATISTICS OFFICE. ADVERTISING AGENCIES INQUIRY. Text in English. a. charts; stat. **Document type:** *Government.* **Description:** Presents details of the gross amount charged by advertising agencies.

Former titles: Ireland. Central Statistics Office. Business of Advertising Agencies - Results for Respondents to Inquiry (0791-3516); (until 1984): Ireland. Central Statistics. Business of Advertising Agencies - Results of Inquiry (0791-3508); (until 1974): Ireland. Central Statistics Office. Return for Advertising Agencies for Year (0791-3494); (until 1959): Ireland. Central Statistics Office. Inquiry into Advertising Agencies Activities (0075-0581)
Published by: Central Statistics Office/Eire, An Phriomh-Oifig Staidrimh, Skehard Rd., Cork, Ireland. TEL 353-21-4535000, FAX 353-21-4535555, information@cso.ie, http://www.cso.ie.

659.1021 USA
MAGAZINE MARKET COVERAGE REPORT. Text in English. 1983. a. (in 2 vols.). looseleaf. USD 80 to individuals (effective 1999). stat. **Description:** Matches magazine circulation to DMA or MSA markets. Includes market data.
Related titles: Diskette ed.
Published by: Audit Bureau of Circulations, 900 N Meacham Rd, Schaumburg, IL 60173-4968. TEL 847-605-0909, FAX 847-605-0483, http://www.accessabc.com.

659.1021 USA ISSN 1044-6079
PN4888.C59
MAGAZINE TREND REPORT. Text in English. 1980. a. USD 75 (effective 1999). **Document type:** *Trade.* **Description:** Provides five years of circulation and ad rate figures for all ABC-audited US and Canadian consumer magazines with ad revenue.
Related titles: Diskette ed.
Indexed: SRI.
Published by: Audit Bureau of Circulations, 900 N Meacham Rd, Schaumburg, IL 60173-4968. TEL 847-605-0909, FAX 847-605-0483, http://www.accessabc.com.

659.1021 USA
MAIL ADVERTISING SERVICE ASSOCIATION INTERNATIONAL. WAGE AND SALARY, AND FRINGE BENEFITS SURVEY. Text in English. a. USD 375 to non-members; USD 200 to members. **Description:** Report of wages and salaries in the mailing services industry.
Formerly: Mail Advertising Service Association International. Wage and Salary Survey
Published by: Mailing & Fulfillment Service Association, 1421 Prince St, Ste 410, Alexandria, VA 22314. http://www.mfsanet.org/.

016.6591 CHE
MEDIA-DATEN (ZURICH); directory of Swiss media. Text in German. 1976. s-a. USD 250 (effective 1999). adv. **Document type:** *Trade.*
Published by: Verlag Media-Daten AG, Kanzleistr 80, Zuerich, 8026, Switzerland. TEL 41-1-2417776, FAX 41-1-2417884. Ed. Otto Eisenegger. Circ: 1,200.

016.6591 DEU ISSN 0931-3265
MEDIA-DATEN: ZEITUNGEN - ANZEIGENBLAETTER. Text in German. 1961. 7/yr. EUR 525; EUR 209 newsstand/cover (effective 2003). adv. **Document type:** *Directory, Trade.*
Supersedes in part (in 1986): Media-Daten: Zeitungen - Radio - T V - Anzeigenblaetter (0931-3184); Which was formerly (until 1980): Media-Daten: Zeitungen, Radio und T V (0170-4184); Which superseded in part (in 1976): Media-Daten (0543-2405)
Published by: Media-Daten Verlag GmbH (Subsidiary of: Springer Science+Business Media), Postfach 1546, Wiesbaden, 65173, Germany. TEL 49-611-78780, FAX 49-611-7878465, info@media-daten.de, http://www.media-daten.de. adv.: B&W page EUR 2,905, color page EUR 4,135. Circ: 1,293 (paid).

659.1021 USA
NEWSPAPER CIRCULATION RATE BOOK. Text in English. 1972. a. USD 11 to members (effective 1999). stat. **Document type:** *Abstract/Index.* **Description:** Provides single-copy and home-delivery rate data for all ABC-audited daily newspapers.
Formerly: Daily Newspaper Circulation Rate Book
Related titles: Diskette ed.
Published by: Audit Bureau of Circulations, 900 N Meacham Rd, Schaumburg, IL 60173-4968. TEL 847-605-0909, FAX 847-605-0483, http://www.accessabc.com.

016.6591 USA ISSN 1080-1936
HF5905
PRODUCTION PLANNING SYSTEM. Variant title: MediaScope Production Planning System. Text in English. 4/yr. USD 882 (effective 2001). **Document type:** *Trade.* **Description:** Assembles lists with detailed print production information and calculates common advertising sizes for multiple publications.
Media: Diskette. **Related titles:** Diskette ed.: ISSN 1080-2401.
Published by: S R D S, 1700 Higgins Rd, Des Plaines, IL 60018-5605. TEL 847-357-5000, 800-851-7737, FAX 847-375-5001, http://www.srds.com.

659.142021 USA
RADIO ADVERTISING BUREAU. RADIO FACTS. Text in English. a. **Description:** Provides a statistical overview of the U.S. commercial radio industry with comparison of radio advertising to advertising in other media.
Published by: Radio Advertising Bureau, 261 Madison Ave, 23rd Fl, New York, NY 10016-2303. TEL 212-681-7200, FAX 212-681-7223. Circ: 40,000.

659.1021 ZAF
S A A R F ALL MEDIA & PRODUCT SURVEY. Short title: S A A R F A M P S. Text in English. 1975. s-a. ZAR 2,275 (effective 2001). charts; stat. **Description:** Survey of consumables, usage of media products and services.
Formerly: All Media and Product Survey (0379-637X)
Related titles: Online - full text ed.
Published by: S A Advertising Research Foundation, PO Box 98874, Sloane Park, Johannesburg 2152, South Africa. TEL 27-11-463-5340, FAX 27-11-463-5010, saarf@saarf.co.za, http://www.saarf.co.za. Ed. Piet Smit.

659.1021 ZAF
S A A R F TELEVISION AUDIENCE MEASUREMENT SURVEY. Text in English. 1989. w. ZAR 8,630 (effective 1999). charts.
Formerly: A M P S Meter Weekly Reports
Related titles: Diskette ed.; Online - full text ed.
Published by: S A Advertising Research Foundation, PO Box 98874, Sloane Park, Johannesburg 2152, South Africa. TEL 27-11-463-5340, FAX 27-11-463-5010. Ed. Piet Smit. Circ: 80.

016.6591 USA ISSN 1529-6490
HF5905 CODEN: BPUSE4
S R D S BUSINESS PUBLICATION ADVERTISING SOURCE. Text in English. 1919. m. USD 682 domestic; USD 762 in Canada & Mexico; USD 1,386 elsewhere (effective 2001). adv. **Document type:** *Directory, Bibliography.* **Description:** For planners and buyers of business and classified advertising. Provides rates and data on more than 9700 listings, along with other needed information (e.g., circulation, advertising page dimensions) in standardized segments.
Former titles (until 1995): Business Publication Advertising Source (1071-4642); (until Oct.1993): Business Publication Rates and Data (0038-948X); Incorporates: Business Classified Rates and Data
Related titles: CD-ROM ed.
Published by: S R D S, 1700 Higgins Rd, Des Plaines, IL 60018-5605. TEL 847-375-5060, 800-851-7737, FAX 847-375-5001, lalbr@srds.com, http://www.srds.com. Pub., R&P Stephen Davis. adv.: B&W page USD 5,595, color page USD 9,350; trim 11 x 10.31.

016.6591 USA ISSN 1533-8029
HF5905
S R D S COMMUNITY PUBLICATION ADVERTISING SOURCE. Text in English. 1945. s-a. USD 194 (effective 2005). adv. stat. **Document type:** *Directory, Trade.* **Description:** Compiles information on more than 3000 metropolitan and nonmetropolitan newspapers, including advertising rates, page sizes and formats, and circulation.
Former titles: Community Publication Advertising Source (1079-9745); (until 1994): Community Publication Source (1071-4650); (until 1993): Community Publication Rates and Data (0162-8887); Weekly Newspaper and Shopping Guide Rates and Data (0162-8895); Weekly Newspaper Rates and Data (0038-9587)
Published by: S R D S, 1700 Higgins Rd, Des Plaines, IL 60018-5605. TEL 847-375-5000, 800-232-0772, ext 8020, FAX 847-375-5001, http://www.srds.com. Pub. Elisa N Beerbohm. adv.: B&W page USD 1,580, color page USD 3,415; trim 11 x 10.31.

016.6591 USA ISSN 1086-8208
HF5905
S R D S CONSUMER MAGAZINE ADVERTISING SOURCE. Text in English. 1919. q. USD 748 (effective 2005). adv. stat. **Document type:** *Directory, Trade.* **Description:** Provides rates and data on more than 3,200 consumer magazines, both US and international. Includes information on circulation, page dimensions, and personnel.
Former titles (until 1995): Consumer Magazine and Agri-Media Source (1071-4537); (until Oct. 1993): Consumer Magazine and Agri-Media Rates and Data (0746-2522); (until 1983): Consumer Magazine and Farm Publication Rates and Data (0038-9595)
Related titles: CD-ROM ed.
Published by: S R D S, 1700 Higgins Rd, Des Plaines, IL 60018-5605. TEL 847-375-5000, 800-232-0772, ext 8020, FAX 847-375-5001, srobe@srds.com, http://www.srds.com. Pub., R&P Sarah Roberson. adv.: B&W page USD 6,550, color page USD 11,010; trim 11 x 10.31.

016.6591 USA ISSN 1071-4561
HF5861 CODEN: DMLSES
S R D S DIRECT MARKETING LIST SOURCE. Text in English. 1967. bi-m. USD 586 (effective 2004). adv. stat. Supplement avail. **Document type:** *Directory, Trade.* **Description:** Lists more than 27,000 mailing lists available, divided into three sections: business, consumer, and farm, as well as Canadian and international lists. Includes relevant rates and data.
Formerly (until 1993): Direct Mail List Rates and Data (0419-182X)
Related titles: ♦ Supplement(s): S R D S The Bullet. ISSN 1067-1641.
Published by: S R D S, 1700 Higgins Rd, Des Plaines, IL 60018-5605. TEL 847-375-5060, 800-851-7737, FAX 847-375-5001, rroth@srds.com, http://www.srds.com. Pub. Ruth Rothseid. adv.: B&W page USD 2,495, color page USD 4,905; trim 11 x 10.31.

016.6591 USA
S R D S MEXICAN AUDIOVISUAL MEDIA RATES & DATA. Text in Spanish. 4/yr. USD 126 (effective 2001). adv. **Document type:** *Directory, Trade.* **Description:** Provides advertising and media information on over 900 radio and television stations throughout Mexico.
Published by: S R D S, 1700 Higgins Rd, Des Plaines, IL 60018-5605. TEL 847-357-5000, 800-851-7737, FAX 847-375-5001, http://www.srds.com/product_info/mexican/index.html.

016.6591 USA
S R D S MEXICAN PRINT MEDIA RATES & DATA. Text in Spanish. 4/yr. USD 126 (effective 2001). adv. **Document type:** *Directory, Trade.* **Description:** Contains information on over 400 Mexican newspapers, consumer magazines, business publications, outdoor and transit advertising alternatives.
Published by: S R D S, 1700 Higgins Rd, Des Plaines, IL 60018-5605. TEL 847-357-5000, 800-851-7737, FAX 847-375-5001, http://www.srds.com.

016.6591 USA ISSN 1529-6482
HF5905
S R D S NEWSPAPER ADVERTISING SOURCE. Text in English. 1919. m. USD 772 (effective 2005). adv. stat. **Document type:** *Directory, Trade.* **Description:** Lists rates and data for more than 1,800 newspapers in the US, listed by state and city.
Former titles (until 1995): Newspaper Advertising Source (1071-4529); (until 1993): Newspaper Rates and Data (0038-9544)
Related titles: Online - full text ed.
Published by: S R D S, 1700 Higgins Rd, Des Plaines, IL 60018-5605. TEL 847-375-5000, 800-232-0772, ext 8020, FAX 847-375-5001, http://www.srds.com. Pub. Elisa N Beerbohm. R&Ps Elisa N Beerbohm, Sarah Roberson. adv.: B&W page USD 5,780, color page USD 7,640; trim 11 x 10.31.

659.1021 USA ISSN 1078-7887
HF5813.U6
S R D S OUT-OF-HOME ADVERTISING SOURCE. Text in English. 1990. a. USD 299 domestic; USD 301 in Canada & Mexico; USD 307 elsewhere (effective 2001). adv. **Document type:** *Directory, Trade.* **Description:** Provides more than 2,500 listings that contain advertising rates and data for "out-of-home media" in the nontraditional media marketplace.
Formerly (until 1995): Advertising Options Plus (1058-2592)
Published by: S R D S, 1700 Higgins Rd, Des Plaines, IL 60018-5605. TEL 847-375-5060, 800-851-7737, FAX 847-375-5001, srobe@srds.com, ebeer@srds.com, http://www.srds.com. Pub. Elisa N Beerbohm. Adv. contact Maria Kilinski. B&W page USD 2,315, color page USD 4,110; trim 11 x 10.31. Circ: 2,000.

016.6591 USA
HF5905
S R D S PRINT MEDIA PRODUCTION SOURCE. Text in English. 1967. q. USD 401 domestic; USD 415 in Canada & Mexico; USD 563 elsewhere (effective 2001). adv. bibl. **Document type:** *Directory, Trade.* **Description:** Lists more than 8,700 business, consumer, and newspaper advertising opportunities, giving production information on each. Includes trim sizes, R.O.P. guidelines, insert specs, material specifications (including film and proofing requirements), personnel to contact, and issue and closing dates.
Former titles: Print Media Production Source (1071-4545); (until 1993): Print Media Production Data (0555-1633)
Related titles: CD-ROM ed.
Published by: S R D S, 1700 Higgins Rd, Des Plaines, IL 60018-5605. TEL 847-375-5060, 800-851-7737, FAX 847-375-5001, lalbr@srds.com, http://www.srds.com. Pub. Stephen Davis. adv.: B&W page USD 1,230, color page USD 4,230.

016.659142 USA ISSN 1529-6512
HF5905
S R D S RADIO ADVERTISING SOURCE. Text in English. 1929. m. USD 490 domestic; USD 497 in Canada & Mexico; USD 601 elsewhere (effective 2001). adv. **Document type:** *Directory, Trade.* **Description:** Lists and provides important information on more than 10,000 radio stations, networks, syndiators, rep firms and group owners, arranged geographically by state and city. Includes demographic and socioeconomic data.
Former titles: Radio Advertising Source (1071-4707); Spot Radio Rates and Data (0038-9560)
Published by: S R D S, 1700 Higgins Rd, Des Plaines, IL 60018-5605. TEL 847-375-5060, 800-851-7737, FAX 847-375-5001, srobe@srds.com, http://www.srds.com. Pub. Sarah Roberson. adv.: B&W page USD 3,060, color page USD 6,195; trim 11 x 10.31.

016.6591 USA
HF5905
S R D S TECHNOLOGY MEDIA SOURCE. Text in English. 1990. a. USD 291 in North America; USD 302 elsewhere (effective 2001). adv. **Document type:** *Directory, Trade.* **Description:** Contains rates and data for for more than 3,300 business and consumer publications and direct-mail lists.

▼ new title ➤ refereed ✶ unverified ♦ full entry avail.

Former titles: Technology Media Source (1071-4588); (until 1993): S R D S Media and Market Planner. Technology Market (1064-5721)
Published by: S R D S, 1700 Higgins Rd, Des Plaines, IL 60018-5605. TEL 847-375-5060, 800-851-7737, FAX 847-375-5001, lalbr@srds.com, http://www.srds.com. Pub. Stephen Davis. adv.: B&W page USD 5,595, color page USD 9,350; trim 11 x 10.31.

659.1021 USA ISSN 1067-1641
HF5863 CODEN: BULLE7
S R D S THE BULLET; the latest in list activity. (Standard Rate and Data Service) Key Title: The Bullet. Text in English. 1991. bi-m. free with subscr. to Direct Marketing List Source. adv. stat. **Document type:** *Trade.*
Related titles: ♦ Supplement to: S R D S Direct Marketing List Source. ISSN 1071-4561.
—CASDDS.
Published by: S R D S, 1700 Higgins Rd, Des Plaines, IL 60018-5605. TEL 847-375-5060, 800-851-7737, FAX 847-375-5001, rroth@srds.com, http://www.srds.com. Pub. Ruth Rothseid.

659.1021 ZAF
SOUTH AFRICA. STATISTICS SOUTH AFRICA. CENSUS OF PROFESSIONAL AND BUSINESS SERVICES - ADVERTISING PRACTITIONERS AND ALLIED SERVICES AND MARKETING RESEARCH SERVICES. Text in English. irreg., latest 1987. ZAR 10 (effective 2000). **Document type:** *Government.*
Former titles: South Africa. Statistics South Africa. Census of Business Services - Advertising Practitioners and Allied Services and Marketing Research Services; (until Aug. 1998): South Africa. Central Statistical Service. Census of Business Services - Advertising Practitioners and Allied Services and Marketing Research Services
Published by: Statistics South Africa/Statistieke Suid-Afrika, Private Bag X44, Pretoria, 0001, South Africa. TEL 27-12-310-8911, FAX 27-12-310-8500, info@statssa.pwv.gov.za, http://www.statssa.gov.za.

016.659142 USA ISSN 1076-3988
HF5905
T V & CABLE SOURCE. Text in English. 1947. q. USD 464 domestic; USD 473 in Canada & Mexico; USD 573 elsewhere (effective 2001). adv. **Document type:** *Directory, Trade.* **Description:** Aimed at planners and buyers of television advertising. Lists more than 4,000 TV stations, networks, and cable systems geographically by DMAs.
Former titles: Spot T V & Cable Source (1071-4596); (until 1993): Spot Television Rates and Data (0038-9552)
Published by: S R D S, 1700 Higgins Rd, Des Plaines, IL 60018-5605. TEL 847-375-5060, 800-851-7737, FAX 847-375-5001, srobe@srds.com, ebeer@srds.com, http://www.srds.com. Pub. Elisa N Beerbohm. R&P Sarah Roberson. adv.: B&W page USD 4,800, color page USD 7,925; trim 11 x 10.31.

016.659 USA ISSN 0040-9340
TOPICATOR; classified guide to articles in the advertising/communications/marketing periodical press. Text in English. 1965. bi-m. USD 110 (effective 2001). 30 p./no.; back issues avail. **Document type:** *Abstract/Index.* **Description:** Indexes articles from periodicals in the fields of advertising, public relations, marketing, journalism, broadcasting, electronic media, and general communications.
Address: PO Box 757, Terrebonne, OR 97760-0757. TEL 541-923-7334, topicator@yahoo.com. Ed., Pub., R&P Wendell E Wolles. Circ: 150 (paid).

WEB AD MONTHLY; the technology and business of web advertising. see *COMPUTERS—Internet*

016.659 USA ISSN 0043-4558
WHAT'S NEW IN ADVERTISING AND MARKETING. Text in English. 1945. q. USD 20 to non-profit organizations; USD 30 to corporations; USD 40 foreign to corporations. adv. bk.rev. abstr. **Document type:** *Bibliography.* **Description:** Lists current materials in advertising, marketing and communication.
Media: Duplicated (not offset).
Indexed: PAIS.
—CCC.
Published by: Special Libraries Association, Advertising and Marketing Division, c/o Johnn Patton, Suffolk Cooperative Library System, 627 N Sunrise Service Rd, Bellport, NY 11713. TEL 516-286-1600, FAX 516-286-1647. Ed. Brady Leyser. Circ: 400 (paid).

AERONAUTICS AND SPACE FLIGHT

see also ENGINEERING—Mechanical Engineering ; TRANSPORTATION—Air Transport

629.13 USA ISSN 0882-9365
A A H S JOURNAL. Text in English. 1956. q. USD 49; USD 64 foreign (effective 1998). adv. bk.rev. illus. reprints avail. **Document type:** *Newsletter, Academic/Scholarly.*
Formerly (until 1980): American Aviation Historical Society Journal (0002-7553)
Indexed: AUNI, AmH&L, HistAb, RASB.
—CISTI, Linda Hall.
Published by: American Aviation Historical Society, 2333 Otis St, Santa Ana, CA 92704. TEL 714-549-4818, http://cwalton.jovanet.com/aahs/. Ed., R&P Albert Hansen. Adv. contact John Dzurica.

629.1 USA
A A S ASTRODYNAMICS CONFERENCE. PROCEEDINGS. (American Astronautical Society) Text in English. 1975. biennial. price varies. cum.index. back issues avail. **Document type:** *Proceedings.*
Related titles: ♦ Series of: Advances in the Astronautical Sciences. ISSN 0065-3438.
Indexed: Englnd, IAA.
Published by: (American Astronautical Society, Inc.), Univelt, Inc., PO Box 28130, San Diego, CA 92198-0130. TEL 760-746-4005, FAX 760-746-3139, 76121.1532@compuserve.com, http://www.univelt.com. Ed., Pub., R&P Robert H Jacobs.

624.9 USA
A A S / G S F C INTERNATIONAL SYMPOSIUM ON SPACEFLIGHT DYNAMICS. Text in English. 1993. irreg., latest vol.100, 1998, parts 1 and 2. price varies. illus. back issues avail. **Document type:** *Proceedings.*
Related titles: Microfiche ed.; ♦ Series of: Advances in the Astronautical Sciences. ISSN 0065-3438.
Published by: (American Astronautical Society, Inc.), Univelt, Inc., PO Box 28130, San Diego, CA 92198-0130. TEL 760-746-4005, FAX 760-746-3139, 76121.1532@compuserve.com, http://www.univelt.com. Ed., Pub., R&P Robert H Jacobs.

629.1 USA ISSN 0730-3564
➤ **A A S HISTORY SERIES.** (American Astronautical Society) Text in English. 1977. irreg. (approx. 1-2/yr.), latest vol.24, 2001. price varies. bibl.; charts; illus. cum.index. back issues avail. **Document type:** *Monographic series, Academic/Scholarly.* **Description:** Comprises historical volumes on space flight and related fields. Compiles monographs of proceedings, including, as a subseries, historical symposia of the International Academy of Astronautics.
Related titles: ♦ Supplement to: Advances in the Astronautical Sciences. ISSN 0065-3438.
Indexed: BiolAb, BrCerAb, C&ISA, CerAb, CorrAb, CurCont, E&CAJ, EMA, Englnd, IAA, Inspec, M&TEA, MBF, METADEX, WAA.
—BLDSC (0537.620000), CISTI, Ei.
Published by: (American Astronautical Society, Inc.), Univelt, Inc., PO Box 28130, San Diego, CA 92198-0130. TEL 760-746-4005, FAX 760-746-3139, http://www.univelt.com. Ed. Donald C Elsder. Circ: 400.

629.45 USA
A A S I ONLINE NEWS. (Artemis Society International) Text in English. 1997. irreg. back issues avail. **Document type:** *Newsletter, Internal.* **Description:** Covers news and information for members of Artemis Society International which promotes space travel and permanent, self-supporting lunar settlements.
Media: Online - full text.
Published by: Artemis Society International, P O Box 940825, Plano, TX 75094-0825. newsmonger@asi.org, pr-asi@tlrc.com, http://www.asi.org/adb/06/09/04/.

629.4 USA ISSN 0065-7417
TL787
A A S MICROFICHE SERIES. (American Astronautical Society) Text in English. 1968. irreg., latest vol.80, 1999. price varies. bibl.; charts; illus. cum.index: 1954-1978; 1979-1985; 1986-1992. **Document type:** *Proceedings.* **Description:** Comprises proceedings volumes on microfiche, as well as supplements to hard-copy proceedings volumes.
Media: Microfiche. **Related titles:** ♦ Supplement to: Advances in the Astronautical Sciences. ISSN 0065-3438; ♦ Supplement(s): Spaceflight Mechanics. ISSN 1081-6003.
Indexed: ChemAb, Englnd, IAA, Inspec.
—BLDSC (0537.663000).
Published by: (American Astronautical Society, Inc.), Univelt, Inc., PO Box 28130, San Diego, CA 92198-0130. TEL 760-746-4005, FAX 760-746-3139, 76121.1532@compuserve.com, http://www.univelt.com. Ed., Pub., R&P Robert H Jacobs. Circ: 400.

629.13 GBR ISSN 0967-246X
A A S U MEMO. Text in English. irreg.
—BLDSC (0537.691500).
Published by: University of Southampton, Department of Aeronautics and Astronautics, Highfield, Southhampton, SO17 1BJ, United Kingdom. TEL 44-1703-595000, FAX 44-1703-593058, http://www.soton.ac.uk/genesis/index.htm.

629.13 GBR ISSN 0404-4967
A A S U REPORT. Text in English. irreg. **Document type:** *Monographic series.*
—BLDSC (0537.692000).
Published by: University of Southampton, Department of Aeronautics and Astronautics, Highfield, Southhampton, SO17 1BJ, United Kingdom. TEL 44-1703-595000, FAX 44-1703-593058, http://www.soton.ac.uk/genesis/index.htm.

358.4 USA
A G A R D BULLETIN✶. (Advisory Group for Aerospace Research and Development) Text in English. q. **Document type:** *Bulletin, Government.* **Description:** Describes AGARD programs and lists meetings and publications.
Published by: U.S. National Aeronautics and Space Administration, Scientific and Technical Information Office, 7121 Standard Dr, Hanover, MD 21076-1320. help@sti.nasa.gov, http://www.sti.nasa.gov. **Co-sponsor:** NATO Advisory Group for Research and Development.

358.4 USA
A G A R D HIGHLIGHTS✶. (Advisory Group for Aerospace Research and Development) Text in English. s-a. **Document type:** *Bulletin, Government.* **Description:** Presents highlights of AGARD activities.
Published by: U.S. National Aeronautics and Space Administration, Scientific and Technical Information Office, 7121 Standard Dr, Hanover, MD 21076-1320. help@sti.nasa.gov, http://www.sti.nasa.gov. **Co-sponsor:** NATO Advisory Group for Aerospace Research and Development.

629 FRA ISSN 0376-4435
CODEN: AGAMDF
A G A R D MANUAL. (Advisory Group for Aerospace Research and Development) Text in English. irreg. **Document type:** *Monographic series.*
—BLDSC (0735.925000), CISTI.
Published by: North Atlantic Treaty Organization, Research and Technology Organization, 7, rue Ancelle, Neuilly-sur-Seine, 92200, France.

358.4 FRA
➤ **A G A R D REPORTS.** (Advisory Group for Aerospace Research and Development) Text in English. q. back issues avail. **Document type:** *Academic/Scholarly.* **Description:** Lists classified AGARD publications announced in Scientific and Technical Aerospace Reports (STAR) during the preceding quarter.
Media: Online - full text.
—BLDSC (7368.510000).
Published by: North Atlantic Treaty Organization, Research and Technology Organization, 7, rue Ancelle, Neuilly-sur-Seine, 92200, France. TEL 33-1-55612295, 33-1-55612297, FAX 33-1-55612299, 33-1-55612298, help@sti.nasa.gov, http://www.sti.nasa.gov, http://www.rta.nato.int.

629.1 USA ISSN 0273-4508
TL875 CODEN: CPSCDO
A I A A - A S M E - A S C E - A H S STRUCTURES, STRUCTURAL DYNAMICS, AND MATERIALS CONFERENCE. COLLECTION OF TECHNICAL PAPERS. Text in English. 1976. a. USD 7,500; USD 8,500 combined subscription print & online eds. (effective 2005). reprint service avail. from PQC. **Document type:** *Proceedings.*
Former titles: A I A A - A S M E Structures, Structural Dynamics, and Materials Conference. Collection of Technical Papers (0161-5750); A I A A - A S M E - S A E Structures, Structural Dynamics, and Materials Conference. Proceedings (0160-855X)
Indexed: CivEngAb, Englnd, IAA.
—CASDDS, Ei. **CCC.**
Published by: American Institute of Aeronautics and Astronautics, Inc., 1801 Alexander Bell Dr, Ste 500, Reston, VA 20191. TEL 703-264-7500, FAX 703-264-7551, custserv@aiaa.org, http://www.aiaa.org.

629.1325 USA ISSN 0001-1444
A I A A BULLETIN. (American Institute of Aeronautics and Astronautics) Text in English. 1996. m. USD 163 in North America to institutions; USD 200 elsewhere to institutions (effective 2005). **Document type:** *Trade.*
Media: Online - full content.
—CCC.
Published by: American Institute of Aeronautics and Astronautics, Inc., 1801 Alexander Bell Dr, Ste 500, Reston, VA 20191. TEL 703-264-7500, FAX 703-264-7551, custserv@aiaa.org, http://www.aiaa.org. Ed. Christine Williams. Pub. Robert Dickman.

629.1 USA ISSN 0001-1452
TL501.A688 CODEN: AIAJAH
➤ **A I A A JOURNAL**; devoted to aerospace research and development. Text in English. 1963. m. USD 1,305 in North America to non-members; USD 1,425 elsewhere to non-members; USD 75 in North America to members; USD 135 elsewhere to members; USD 1,500 combined subscription in North America to non-members print & online eds.; USD 1,640 combined subscription elsewhere to non-members print & online eds.; USD 70 combined subscription in North America to members print & online eds.; USD 135 combined subscription elsewhere to members print & online eds. (effective 2006). bk.rev. charts; illus. index. reprint service avail. from PQC. **Document type:** *Journal, Academic/Scholarly.* **Description:** Covers new theoretical developments and experimental results on aeroacoustics, aerodynamics, combustion, fundamentals of propulsion, fluid mechanics, aerospace environment, marine technology, lasers, plasmas, and magnetohydrodynamics, research instrumentation, structural mechanics and thermophysics.

Formed by the merger of (1934-1963): Journal of the Aerospace Sciences (0095-9820); Which was formerly (until 1958): Journal of the Aeronautical Sciences (0095-9812); (1945-1963): A R S Journal (0097-4056); Which was formerly (until 1959): Jet Propulsion (0095-8751); (until 1954): American Rocket Society. Journal (0095-9073)
Related titles: Microform ed.: (from PMC, PQC); Online - full text ed.: ISSN 1533-385X. USD 1,305 to non-members; USD 75 to members (effective 2006) (from EBSCO Publishing, Gale Group, IngentaConnect).
Indexed: AS&TI, ASCA, AcoustA, ApMecR, BMT, BrCerAb, C&ISA, CCI, CMCI, CerAb, ChemAb, CivEngAb, CorrAb, CurCont, E&CAJ, EMA, ESPM, Englnd, ExcerpMed, FLUIDEX, H&SSA, IAA, ISMEC, ISR, Inspec, M&TEA, MBF, METADEX, MSCI, MathR, RefZh, S&VD, SCI, SolStAb, WAA, ZentMath.
—BLDSC (0772.610000), AskIEEE, CASDDS, CISTI, Ei, IDS, IE, Infotrieve, ingenta, Linda Hall. **CCC.**
Published by: American Institute of Aeronautics and Astronautics, Inc., 1801 Alexander Bell Dr, Ste 500, Reston, VA 20191. TEL 703-264-7500, FAX 703-264-7551, custserv@aiaa.org, http://www.aiaa.org. Eds. Christine Williams, Gerard M Faeth. Pub. Robert Dickman. Circ: 3,400 (paid).

629.1 USA ISSN 0001-1460
TL501.A688
➤ **A I A A STUDENT JOURNAL.** Text in English. 1963. q. USD 25 to non-members; free to members (effective 2006). adv. bk.rev. charts; illus. reprint service avail. from PQC. **Document type:** *Academic/Scholarly.* **Description:** Features articles pertinent to the aerospace student's professional development.
Related titles: Microform ed.: (from PQC).
Indexed: CivEngAb, IAA, M&TEA, RefZh.
—BLDSC (0772.810000), CISTI, IE, Infotrieve, Linda Hall. **CCC.**
Published by: American Institute of Aeronautics and Astronautics, Inc., 1801 Alexander Bell Dr, Ste 500, Reston, VA 20191. TEL 703-264-7500, FAX 703-264-7551, custserv@aiaa.org, http://www.aiaa.org/content.cfm?pageid=322&lupubid=2. Ed. Patrick Gouhin. Circ: 9,000.

629.13 USA
CODEN: AAPRAQ
A I A A TECHNICAL MEETING PAPERS. Text in English. 1963. irreg. USD 7,500; USD 8,500 combined subscription print & online eds. (effective 2006). **Document type:** *Proceedings, Trade.*
Formerly: A I A A Paper (0146-3705); Which incorporated: Guidance Control and Flight Mechanics Conference. Proceedings (0072-7946); Aerodynamics Deceleration Systems Conference. Papers Presented (0065-3675)
Related titles: ♦ CD-ROM ed.: American Institute of Aeronautics and Astronautics. Meeting Papers on Disc. ISSN 1087-7215; Microfiche ed.; Online - full text ed.
Indexed: Englnd, IAA.
—CASDDS, CISTI. **CCC.**
Published by: American Institute of Aeronautics and Astronautics, Inc., 1801 Alexander Bell Dr, Ste 500, Reston, VA 20191. TEL 703-264-7500, FAX 703-264-7551, custserv@aiaa.org, http://www.aiaa.org. Circ: 100.

629.1 USA ISSN 0898-509X
A I A UPDATE. Text in English. 10/yr. free. **Document type:** *Newsletter.*
Published by: Aerospace Industries Association of America, 1000 Wilson Blvd., Ste. 1700, Arlington, VA 22209-3928. TEL 202-371-8400, FAX 202-371-8470, http://www.aia-aerospace.org. Ed. Janet Neale. Circ: 6,000.

629 USA
A L A MAGAZINE. Text in Spanish. 1993. m. USD 25 (effective 2002). **Description:** Educational publication focused on primary aviation activities and areas of aviation responsibility, including new products and services, technological advances and current events affecting aviation. Reaches the professional aviation environment in Latin America and Spain.
Published by: Asociacion Latinoamericana de Aeronautica/Latin American Aeronautical Association, 2514 Gravel Rd, Fort Worth, TX 76118. TEL 817-284-0431, FAX 817-284-0433, http://www.ala-internet.com/alanew.

629.1 USA
A M F I INDUSTRY NEWS. Text in English. 1972. bi-m. looseleaf. membership. adv. bk.rev. **Document type:** *Newsletter.* **Description:** Information and news pertaining to aviation maintenance industry.
Formerly: Aviation Maintenance Foundation. Industry News
Published by: Aviation Maintenance Foundation International, PO Box 2826, Redmond, WA 98073. TEL 360-658-8980, FAX 360-658-7274. Ed. R Kost. Circ: 6,000.

387.7 AUS ISSN 1442-6056
A O P A; the aviation magazine in Australia. Text in English. 1950. m. AUD 71.40 (effective 1999). adv. back issues avail. **Document type:** *Consumer.*
Related titles: Online - full text ed.
Published by: Aircraft Owners and Pilots Associations, Hangar 600, Prentice St., Bankstown Airport, NSW 2200, Australia. TEL 61-2-9791-9099, FAX 61-3-9791-9355, mail@aopa.com.au, http://www.aopa.com.au. Ed., R&P David Palmer. Adv. contact Sharon Molgate. B&W page AUD 750, color page AUD 1,350; trim 210 x 297. Circ: 7,500.

629.132 USA
A O P A FLIGHT TRAINING. Text in English. 1989. m. USD 21.95 (effective 2005). adv. bk.rev. charts; illus.; mkt.; stat. back issues avail. **Document type:** *Magazine, Consumer.* **Description:** Provides how-to and operational information for pilots in various stages of receiving, renewing or upgrading their certification. Covers careers, safety, techniques, regulations, and aircraft.
Formerly: Flight Training (1047-6415); Incorporates (1968-1989): N A F I Newsletter
Published by: Aircraft Owners and Pilots Association, 421 Aviation Way, Frederick, MD 21701. TEL 301-695-2350, FAX 301-695-2180, flighttraining@aopa.org, inforequest@aopa.org, http://www.ftmag.com/, http://www.aopa.org. Eds. Mike Collins, Thomas B Haines. Pub. Phil Boyer. Adv. contact Dave Speer. B&W page USD 5,210, color page USD 7,285; trim 7.88 x 10.5. Circ: 82,000 (paid and controlled).

629.132 DEU
A O P A LETTER. (Aircraft Owners and Pilots Association) Text in German. 1989. bi-m. EUR 2.80 newsstand/cover (effective 2004). adv. **Document type:** *Magazine, Trade.*
Published by: A O P A Germany - Verband der Allgemeinen Luftfahrt e.V., Ausserhalb 27, Egelsbach-Flugplatz, 63329, Germany. TEL 49-6103-42081, FAX 49-6103-42083, info@aopa.de, http://www.aopa.de. adv.: B&W page EUR 1,314, color page EUR 2,183. Circ: 9,897 (controlled).

629.13 AUS ISSN 0002-2691
A O P A MAGAZINE. Text in English. 1948. m. AUD 96. adv. bk.rev. illus.; pat. **Document type:** *Trade.* **Description:** Covers all aspects of interest for general aviators.
Published by: Aircraft Owners and Pilots Association of Australia, PO Box 26, Georges Hall, NSW 2198, Australia. TEL 61-2-97919099, FAX 61-2-97919355, editor@aopa.com.au, http://www.aopa.com.au/. Ed., R&P Mark Barnett. Adv. contact Jeff Self. B&W page AUD 750, color page AUD 1,350. Circ: 11,000.

629.132 USA ISSN 0001-2084
HD8039.A4
A O P A PILOT. Text in English. 1958. m. USD 39 to members; USD 21 to qualified organizations (effective 2005). adv. bk.rev. charts; illus.; stat.; tr.lit. Index. reprints avail. **Document type:** *Magazine, Consumer.*
Indexed: CLT&T, HRIS.
—Linda Hall.
Published by: Aircraft Owners and Pilots Association, 421 Aviation Way, Frederick, MD 21701. TEL 301-695-2350, FAX 301-695-2180, pilot@aopa.org, http://www.aopa.org/pilot. Ed. Thomas B Haines. Pub. Phil Boyer. Circ: 340,000 (paid and controlled).

629.132 USA
TL726.2
A O P A'S AIRPORT DIRECTORY. Text in English. 1989. a. USD 39 (effective 2000). adv. **Document type:** *Directory.*
Formerly: A O P A's Aviation U S A (1056-7704); Which was formed by the 1989 merger of: A O P A Handbook for Pilots (0568-3785); A O P A's Airport U S A (0271-065X); Which was formerly: A O P A Airport Directory (0065-4906)
Published by: Aircraft Owners and Pilots Association, 421 Aviation Way, Frederick, MD 21701. TEL 301-695-2000. Pub. Phil Boyer. R&P Tom Haines. Adv. contact Dave Speer. Circ: 300,000.

A P M BULLETIN. see *ANTIQUES*

629.13 CZE
A R T I REPORTS. (Aeronautical Research and Test Institute) Text in English; Summaries in Czech, French, German. 1960. irreg. (2-3/yr.). USD 12 (effective 2002). back issues avail. **Document type:** *Academic/Scholarly.*
Related titles: Microfilm ed.
Published by: Vyzkumny a Zkusebni Letecky Ustav, Beranovych 130, Letnany, Prague 9, 199 05, Czech Republic. TEL 42-2-72115111, FAX 42-2-86920518. Ed., R&P Ladislav Vymetal TEL 42-2-72115223.

797.5 629.13 ITA ISSN 1121-8703
A S AVIAZIONE SPORTIVA. Text in Italian. 1991. m. (10/yr.). EUR 40 domestic (effective 2004). adv. 96 p./no.; back issues avail. **Document type:** *Magazine, Consumer.* **Description:** Includes articles on aviation, old and new planes, flight simulation, engines, accessories, and techniques.
Published by: (Inveric Aviazione S.r.l.), Gruppo Editoriale Olimpia SpA, Via E Fermi 24, Loc Osmannoro, Sesto Fiorentino, FI 50129, Italy. TEL 39-055-30321, FAX 39-055-3032280, http://www.edolimpia.it. Adv. contact Gianna Vannucci. color page EUR 650; 210 x 275. Circ: 30,000. **Dist. by:** Parrini & C, Piazza Colonna 361, Rome, RM 00187, Italy. TEL 39-06-695141.

629 USA
A T M GLOBAL. Text in English. 1992. w. USD 699 in North America; USD 799 elsewhere (effective 2004). **Document type:** *Newsletter.* **Description:** For air traffic managers, airport and airline executives, equipment and systems suppliers, builders, safety consultants and engineers.
Formerly: A T C Market Report (1070-5740)
Related titles: Online - full text ed.: (from LexisNexis, ProQuest Information & Learning).
Indexed: ABIn.
—**CCC.**
Published by: McGraw-Hill Companies, Aviation Week, 1200 G St, N W, Ste 200, Washington, DC 20005. TEL 202-383-2374, 202-383-2350, FAX 202-383-2438, http://www.aviationnow.com/avnow.

629.1 USA ISSN 1041-6706
A W A NEWS✶. Text in English. 1938. 6/yr. membership. adv. bk.rev.
Former titles: Aviation - Space Writers Association Newsletter; Aviation - Space Writers Association News
Published by: Aviation - Space Writers Association, 6540 50th St., N., Oakdale, MN 55128-1708. TEL 614-221-1900, FAX 614-221-1989. Circ: 1,500.

613.69 USA ISSN 1057-5561
ACCIDENT PREVENTION. Text in English. 1948. m. USD 240 to non-members; free to members (effective 2004). bk.rev. reprint service avail. from PQC. **Document type:** *Newsletter.* **Description:** Focuses on the flight deck.
Formerly (until vol.44, no.11, 1987): Accident Prevention Bulletin (0898-5774)
Indexed: RefZh.
Published by: Flight Safety Foundation, Inc., 601 Madison St, Ste 300, Alexandria, VA 22314-1756. TEL 703-739-6700, FAX 703-739-6708, setze@flightsafety.org, http://www.flightsafety.org/ap_home.html. Ed. Roger Rozelle. Circ: 2,400 (paid).

629.4 GBR ISSN 0094-5765
TL787 CODEN: AASTCF
➤ **ACTA ASTRONAUTICA.** Summaries in English, French, German, Russian. 1955. 24/yr. EUR 3,520 in Europe to institutions; JPY 467,500 in Japan to institutions; USD 3,938 to institutions except Europe and Japan (effective 2006). adv. illus. Index. back issues avail.; reprints avail. **Document type:** *Proceedings, Academic/Scholarly.* **Description:** Publishes contributions in all fields of basic engineering, life and social sciences and space technology pertaining to the peaceful scientific exploration of space, its exploitation for human welfare and progress, and the conception, design, development and operation of earth-based or spaceborne systems.
Supersedes (in 1974): Astronautica Acta (0004-6205)
Related titles: Microform ed.: (from PQC); Online - full text ed.: (from EBSCO Publishing, Gale Group, IngentaConnect, ScienceDirect, Swets Information Services).
Indexed: ASCA, ApMecR, BiolAb, BrCerAb, C&ISA, CerAb, ChemAb, CivEngAb, CorrAb, CurCont, E&CAJ, EMA, ESPM, Englnd, H&SSA, IAA, IAOP, ISR, Inspec, M&GPA, M&TEA, MBF, METADEX, RiskAb, SCI, SSCI, SolStAb, WAA.
—BLDSC (0596.750000), AskIEEE, CASDDS, CISTI, Ei, IDS, IE, Infotrieve, ingenta, Linda Hall. **CCC.**
Published by: (International Academy of Astronautics FRA), Pergamon (Subsidiary of: Elsevier Science & Technology), The Boulevard, Langford Ln, East Park, Kidlington, Oxford OX5 1GB, United Kingdom. TEL 44-1865-843000, FAX 44-1865-843010, http://www.elsevier.com/locate/actaastro. Ed. Jean-Pierre Marec. **Subscr. to:** Elsevier BV, PO Box 211, Amsterdam 1000 AE, Netherlands. TEL 31-20-485-3757, FAX 31-20-485-3432, nlinfo-f@elsevier.nl, http://www.elsevier.nl.

629.4 USA ISSN 1041-102X
CODEN: ADASED
AD ASTRA; to the stars: the magazine of the National Space Society . Text in English. 1989. 6/yr. USD 45 to individuals; USD 60 to institutions; USD 20 to students (effective 2005). adv. bk.rev. illus. reprints avail. **Document type:** *Magazine.* **Description:** Features articles on space and exploration, astronomy, satellites and technology, commercial space, and educational activities.
Related titles: Online - full text ed.: (from H.W. Wilson, O C L C Online Computer Library Center, Inc.).
Indexed: ABS&EES, Acal, CivEngAb, GSI, IAA, Maglnd, RGAb, RGPR.
—BLDSC (0678.160000), IE, Infotrieve, ingenta, Linda Hall.
Published by: National Space Society, 1620 I St., N.W., Ste 615, Washington, DC 20003-4316. TEL 202-429-1600, FAX 202-463-8497, nsshq@nss.org, http://www.nss.org/adastra/aaindex.html. Ed. Anthony Duignan-Cabrera. Adv. contact Truby Chiaviello. Circ: 26,800 (paid and free).

629.13 DEU ISSN 0001-8279
DER ADLER; Monatszeitschrift fuer Luftsport und Luftfahrt. Text in German. 1926. m. adv. bk.rev. charts; illus. index. **Document type:** *Magazine, Consumer.*
—**CCC.**
Published by: Baden-Wuerttembergischer Luftfahrtverband e.V., Herdweg 77, Stuttgart, 70193, Germany. TEL 49-711-227620, FAX 49-711-2276244, info@bwlv.de, http://www.bwlv.cc/verband_adler.php, http://www.bwlv.de. Ed. Klaus Michael Hallmayer. Circ: 12,000.

ADVANCED COMPOSITES MONTHLY. see *ENGINEERING—Engineering Mechanics And Materials*

629.4 GBR ISSN 0273-1177
QB495 CODEN: ASRSDW
➤ **ADVANCES IN SPACE RESEARCH.** Text in English. 1981. 27/yr. EUR 3,640 in Europe to institutions; JPY 483,400 in Japan to institutions; USD 4,072 elsewhere to institutions (effective 2006); Subscr. incls.: C O S P A R Information Bulletin. illus. Index. back issues avail.; reprints avail. **Document type:** *Proceedings, Academic/Scholarly.* **Description:** Covers the progress on an international scale of all kinds of fundamental research carried out with the use of balloons, rockets, or rocket propelled vehicles.
Formed by the merger of (1978-1980): Advances in Space Exploration (0164-0046); (1963-1980): Life Sciences and Space Research (0075-9422); (1960-1980): Space Research (0371-232X)
Related titles: Microform ed.: (from PQC); Online - full text ed.: (from EBSCO Publishing, Gale Group, IngentaConnect, ScienceDirect, Swets Information Services).
Indexed: AESIS, ASCA, BiolAb, BrCerAb, C&ISA, CIN, CerAb, ChemAb, ChemTitl, CivEngAb, CorrAb, E&CAJ, EMA, ESPM, EngInd, EnvEAb, GEOBASE, IAA, ISR, Inspec, M&GPA, M&TEA, MBF, METADEX, MSB, PhysBer, PollutAb, RefZh, SCI, WAA.
—BLDSC (0711.490000), AskIEEE, CASDDS, CISTI, Ei, IDS, IE, Infotrieve, ingenta, Linda Hall. **CCC.**
Published by: (International Council of Scientific Unions FRA), Pergamon (Subsidiary of: Elsevier Science & Technology), The Boulevard, Langford Ln, East Park, Kidlington, Oxford OX5 1GB, United Kingdom. TEL 44-1865-843000, FAX 44-1865-843010, http://www.elsevier.com/locate/asr, http://www.elsevier.nl. Ed. M A Shea. **Subscr. to:** Elsevier BV, PO Box 211, Amsterdam 1000 AE, Netherlands. nlinfo-f@elsevier.nl.

629.4 USA ISSN 0065-3438
TL787.A6 CODEN: ADASA9
ADVANCES IN THE ASTRONAUTICAL SCIENCES. Text in English. 1957. q., latest vol.107, 2001, pts.1-2. USD 155 domestic; USD 170 elsewhere (effective 2004); price varies. adv. bk.rev. bibl.; charts; illus. cum.index: 1954-1978; 1979-1985; 1986-1992. back issues avail. **Document type:** *Proceedings, Academic/Scholarly.* **Description:** Publishes the proceedings of major technical conferences in the field of space. For universities, research establishments, libraries, and the aerospace industry.
Related titles: Microfiche ed.; ♦ Series: American Astronautical Society. Proceedings of the Annual Meeting. ISSN 0516-9593; ♦ A A S Astrodynamics Conference. Proceedings; ♦ Guidance and Control. ISSN 1057-493X; ♦ Spaceflight Mechanics. ISSN 1081-6003; ♦ A A S / G S F C International Symposium on Spaceflight Dynamics; ♦ Supplement(s): A A S Microfiche Series. ISSN 0065-7417; ♦ Science and Technology Series. ISSN 0278-4017; ♦ A A S History Series. ISSN 0730-3564; ♦ Space Safety and Rescue (Year).
Indexed: BiolAb, BrCerAb, C&ISA, CerAb, ChemAb, CorrAb, E&CAJ, EMA, EngInd, IAA, ISMEC, Inspec, M&TEA, MBF, METADEX, SolStAb, WAA.
—BLDSC (0699.300000), CASDDS, CISTI, Ei, IE, ingenta, Linda Hall. **CCC.**
Published by: (American Astronautical Society, Inc.), Univelt, Inc., PO Box 28130, San Diego, CA 92198-0130. TEL 760-746-4005, FAX 760-746-3139, 76121.1532@compuserve.com, http://www.univelt.com. Ed. Kathleen C Howell. Pub., R&P Robert H Jacobs. Circ: 400.

629.133 USA
AERO. Text in English. 1992. q. free to qualified personnel. illus. **Document type:** *Trade.* **Description:** Provides operators of Boeing- and McDonnell Douglas-designed aircraft with supplemental technical information to promote the continuous safety and efficiency of their daily fleet operations.
Formerly (until 1998): Airliner (1065-9757)
Related titles: Online - full text ed.
—BLDSC (0719.902000).
Published by: (Customer Services Division), Boeing Commercial Airplanes Group, MC 2M 89, PO Box 3707, Seattle, WA 98124-2207. TEL 206-544-8237, FAX 206-544-9178, aeromagazine@boeing.com, http://www.boeing.com/commercial/aeromagazine. Ed. Leslie Nichols. Pub. Steve Smith.

629.13 USA ISSN 1547-4542
TL501.A2354
▼ **AERO-ASTRO.** Text in English. 2003 (Nov.). a. free (effective 2003).
Published by: Massachusetts Institute of Technology, Department of Aeronautics and Astronautics, Rm 33 412, Cambridge, MA 02139. TEL 617-253-2424, http://web.mit.edu/aeroastro/www. Ed. Ian Waitz.

629.132 387.71 USA
AERO INFORMATION MAGAZINE. Text in English. 1998. q. free. bk.rev. charts; illus. back issues avail. **Document type:** *Academic/Scholarly.* **Description:** Discusses all aspects of aviation safety for commercial airline pilots.
Media: Online - full text.
Published by: Proactive Information Corporation safepic@safepic.com, http://www.safeaim.com. Ed. E R Hanson.

629.13 NLD ISSN 1381-8600
AERO-JOURNAAL✶. Text in Dutch. 1987. m. USD 37. adv. back issues avail. **Description:** Contains news, information, interviews, association policy statements, and other items relating to flying, including gliding and ballooning.
Related titles: Diskette ed.: 1987.
Published by: (Koninklijke Nederlandse Vereniging voor Luchtvaart), Printing & Projects, Josef Israelplein 8, The Hague, 2596 AS, Netherlands. TEL 31-5700-11341, FAX 31-5700-14741. **Subscr. to:** KNVvL, Jozef Israelsplein 8, The Hague 2596 AS, Netherlands. TEL 31-70-3245457, FAX 31-70-3240230.

AERO MECHANIC. see *LABOR UNIONS*

629.13 USA ISSN 1530-9339
AERO - NEWS NETWORK. Variant title: Aero - News Network Daily News Brief. A N N. Text in English. 1999. d. free. **Document type:** *Trade.*
Media: Online - full content.
Address: PO Box 9132, Winter Haven, FL 33883-9132. TEL 863-299-8680, FAX 863-294-3678, editor@aero-news.net, http://www.aero-news.net/. Ed. Jim Campbell.

629.13 POL ISSN 0867-6720
TL500 CODEN: TLASB3
AERO-TECHNIKA LOTNICZA. Text in Polish. 1936. m. USD 42. adv. bk.rev. **Description:** Covers air technics and history of airplane.
Former titles (until 1990): Technika Lotnicza i Astronautyczna (0040-1145); (until 1966): Technika Lotnicza (0371-6368)
Indexed: ChemAb, IAA.
—CASDDS, CISTI, Linda Hall.
Published by: Oficyna Wydawnicza SIMP Press Ltd., ul Swietokrzyska 14a, Warsaw, 00050, Poland. Ed. W J Gawrych. Circ: 3,500. **Dist. by:** Ars Polona, Krakowskie Przedmiescie 7, Warsaw, Poland.

629.1 ARG ISSN 0001-9127
TL504
AEROESPACIO/AEROSPACE; revista nacional aeronautica y espacial - national aeronautic and space review. Text in English, Spanish. 1931. bi-m. USD 48. adv. bk.rev. charts; illus. index. back issues avail. **Description:** Articles on aerospace news, civil, military, entrepreneurial, sports and airborne and ground equipment, air and anti-air weapons. Includes defense matters and aerospace systems.
Former titles (until 1967): Revista Nacional de Aeronautica y Espacial (0325-3082); (until 1962): Revista Nacional de Aeronautica
Indexed: IAA.
Published by: Fuerza Aerea Argentina, Paraguay, 748 Piso 3, Capital Federal, Buenos Aires 1057, Argentina. TEL 54-114-3222753, FAX 54-114-181256, TELEX 39-21763 AEROESPACIO. Ed. Jorge Di Paolo. Circ: 24,000. **Subscr. to:** Casilla de Correo 37, Suc. 12B, Buenos Aires 1412, Argentina.

629.1 GBR ISSN 0265-8569
AEROGRAM. Text in English. 1977. s-a. free. adv. bk.rev. **Document type:** *Academic/Scholarly.*
Indexed: RefZh.
Published by: Cranfield University, College of Aeronautics, Cranfield, Bedford, MK43 0AL, United Kingdom. TEL 44-1234-750111, FAX 44-1234-751640, TELEX 825172 CITECH G, aerogram@cranfield.ac.uk, http://www.cranfield.ac.uk/coa/aerogram/aerog-l.htm. Ed., R&P Ron G Wingrove. Circ: 5,000 (controlled).

613 BGR ISSN 0861-1432
QB1
AEROKOSMICHESKI IZSLEDVANIYA V BULGARIYA/AEROSPACE RESEARCH IN BULGARIA. Text in Bulgarian. 1970. a.
Formerly (until 1990): Space Research of Bulgaria (0204-9104)
Indexed: RefZh.
—Linda Hall.
Published by: Bulgarska Akademiya na Naukite/Bulgarian Academy of Sciences, 6 Moskovska St, Sofia, 1000, Bulgaria. TEL 359-2-981-33-47, FAX 359-2-979-34-67, http://www.space.bas.bg.

629.13 RUS ISSN 1680-5291
AEROKOSMICHESKII KUR'ER/AEROSPACE COURIER. Text in Russian. 1998. bi-m. **Document type:** *Journal.*
Published by: Izdatel'skii Dom Sozvezdie 4, ul M Gruzinskaya, d 52, Moscow, 123557, Russian Federation. http://www.aerosc.net/html/english/index.html.

629.1 RUS
AEROKOSMOS. Text in Russian. w. USD 525 in United States.
Published by: I T A R - T A S S, Tverskoi bulvar 10-12, Moscow, 125993, Russian Federation. TEL 7-095-2025474, FAX 7-095-2024937. **US dist. addr.:** East View Information Services, 3020 Harbor Ln. N., Minneapolis, MN 55447. TEL 612-550-0961.

629.13 DEU ISSN 0341-1281
TL503
AEROKURIER. Text in German. 1957. m. EUR 49.90; EUR 4.50 newsstand/cover (effective 2004). adv. bk.rev. bibl.; charts; illus.; stat.; tr.mk. index. **Document type:** *Magazine, Trade.* **Description:** Civil aviation news, events and products for all size planes.
Formerly: Deutscher Aerokurier (0012-107X)
Indexed: ExcerpMed.
—IE, Infotrieve, Linda Hall. **CCC.**
Published by: (Deutscher Aero Club e.V.), Vereinigte Motor-Verlage GmbH & Co. KG, Leuschnerstr 1, Stuttgart, 70174, Germany. TEL 49-711-18201, FAX 49-228-9565245, aerokurier@compuserve.com, internet-redaktion@motor-presse-stuttgart.de, http://www.aerokurier.rotor.com, http://www.motorpresse.de. Ed. Volker K Thomalla. Pub. Peter Paul Pietsch. Adv. contact Reinhard Wittstamm. B&W page EUR 3,456, color page EUR 6,400; trim 185 x 248. Circ: 28,742 (paid and controlled).

629.13 GBR
AEROMART. Text in English. m. GBP 17; GBP 27 in Europe; USD 70 in US & Canada; GBP 29 elsewhere. **Document type:** *Trade.*
Published by: Wilmington Publishing Ltd. (Subsidiary of: Wilmington Group Plc), Maidstone Rd, Footscray, Sidcup, Kent DA14 5HZ, United Kingdom. TEL 44-20-82697720, FAX 44-20-82697730, aeromart@wilmington.co.uk.

629.47 RUS ISSN 1681-5173
AEROMEKHANIKA I GAZOVAYA DINAMIKA. Text in Russian. 2001. q. **Document type:** *Journal, Academic/Scholarly.*
Indexed: RefZh.
Published by: Redaktsiya Zhurnala Aeromekhanika i Gazovaya Dinamika, Michurinskii pr-t, dom 1, komn 3, Moscow, 119899, Russian Federation. TEL 7-095-9390265.

AEROMILITARIA; Air-Britain military aviation historical journal. see *MILITARY*

629.1 ITA ISSN 0394-820X
AERONAUTICA E DIFESA. Text in Italian. 1986. m. EUR 33.75 domestic; EUR 48.50 foreign (effective 2004). adv. bk.rev.
Published by: Edizioni Monografie s.r.l., P.O. Box 2446, Rome, RM 00100, Italy. TEL 39-06-5180534, FAX 39-06-51600013, aerodife@tin.it. Ed. Claudio Tatangelo. Circ: 60,000 (paid).

629.1 ZAF ISSN 0257-8573
AERONAUTICA MERIDIANA. Text in English; Summaries in Afrikaans, English. 1980. a. ZAR 20, USD 10. back issues avail. **Document type:** *Academic/Scholarly.*
Formerly: Aeronautical Society of South Africa. Journal (0250-3786)
Indexed: ISAP, Inspec.
—AskIEEE, Linda Hall.
Published by: Aeronautical Society of South Africa, c/o School of Mechanical Engineering, University of Pretoria, Pretoria, 0002, South Africa. TEL 27-12-420-2014, FAX 27-12-342-1379. Ed. E H Mathews. Circ: 1,000.

629.13 629.47 JPN
AERONAUTICAL AND SPACE SCIENCES JAPAN. Text in Japanese. m. **Document type:** *Journal, Academic/Scholarly.*
—BLDSC (0724.590000).
Published by: Nihon Koku Uchu Gakkai/Japan Society for Aeronautical and Space Sciences, Ohkami Meiwa Bldg. 3F, 1-18-2 Shimbashi, Minato-ku, Tokyo, 105-0004, Japan. http://www.jsass.or.jp/web/.

AERONAUTICAL ENGINEERING: A CONTINUING BIOGRAPHY WITH INDEXES. see *AERONAUTICS AND SPACE FLIGHT—Abstracting, Bibliographies, Statistics*

629.13254 USA
AERONAUTICAL INFORMATION MANUAL; official guide to basic flight information and A T C procedures. Text in English. base vol. plus irreg. updates. looseleaf. USD 88 (effective 2001). **Document type:** *Government.* **Description:** Provides the aviation community with basic flight information and ATC procedures for use in the National Airspace System (NAS) of the United States.
Published by: U.S. Government Printing Office, 732 N Capitol St NW, Washington, DC 20401. TEL 202-512-1800, FAX 202-512-2250, http://www.gpo.gov.

629.1 USA
AERONAUTICAL INFORMATION PUBLICATION. Short title: U.S. A I P. Text in English. base vol. plus q. updates. looseleaf. USD 105 (effective 2001). **Document type:** *Government.* **Description:** Lists F.A.A. regulations and data required for safe aircraft operations in the U.S. National Airspace System.
Formerly: U.S. Aeronautical Information Publication
Published by: U.S. Federal Aviation Administration, 800 Independence Ave S W, Washington, DC 20591. TEL 202-267-3484. **Subscr. to:** U.S. Government Printing Office, Superintendent of Documents, PO Box 371954, Pittsburgh, PA 15250-7954. TEL 202-512-1800, FAX 202-512-2250.

629.13   GBR   ISSN 0001-9240
TL501   CODEN: AENJAK
➤ **THE AERONAUTICAL JOURNAL.** Text in English. 1897.
12/yr. GBP 299 (effective 2004). bk.rev. charts; illus. Index.
reprints avail. **Document type:** *Journal, Academic/Scholarly.*
Description: Covers all aspects of aerospace technology and
engineering.
Incorporates: Aeronautical Quarterly (0001-9259)
Related titles: Microform ed.: (from PMC, PQC).
Indexed: AS&TI, ASCA, ApMecR, BMT, CISA, ChemAb,
CivEngAb, CurCont, ESPM, EngInd, ExcerpMed, FLUIDEX,
H&SSA, IAA, ISR, Inspec, M&TEA, MathR, RefZh, S&VD,
SCI.
—BLDSC (0725.400000), CISTI, Ei, IDS, IE, Infotrieve, ingenta,
Linda Hall. **CCC.**
Published by: Royal Aeronautical Society, 4 Hamilton Pl, London,
W1J 7BQ, United Kingdom. TEL 44-20-7670-4300, FAX
44-20-7670-4309, publications@raes.org.uk,
raes@raes.org.uk, http://www.raes.org.uk/First/publications/
aerospace_journal.htm, http://www.aerosociety.com. Ed. J L
Stollery. Pub. Keith Mans. R&P Mr. C S Male TEL
44-20-7670-4352. Adv. contact David Holmes TEL
44-1485-528020. Circ: 1,500. **Subscr. addr.:** RAES
Subscriptions Dept, Customer Interface, Bradley Pavillions,
Bradley Stoke North, Bristol BS32 0PP, United Kingdom. TEL
44-1454-642485, FAX 44-1454-620080, cihotline@aol.com.

➤ **AERONAUTICAL NEWSLETTER;** New Jersey Aviation News.
see *TRANSPORTATION—Air Transport*

629.1   GBR   ISSN 0269-8900
AERONAUTICAL SATELLITE NEWS. Text in English. 1986. bi-m.
free. adv. charts; illus.; stat. back issues avail. **Document
type:** *Trade.* **Description:** Promotes the development of
aeronautical satellite communications.
Related titles: Supplement(s): Aero Industry.
Published by: (International Maritime Satellite Organization),
Inmarsat, 99 City Rd, London, EC1Y 1AX, United Kingdom.
TEL 44-20-8728-1449, FAX 44-20-7728-1344, TELEX 297201
INMSAT G, emma_kelly@inmarsat.org. Ed. Emma Kelly. Adv.
contact Peter Honeywell. Circ: 13,000 (controlled).

629.13   BEL   ISSN 0065-3713
AERONOMICA ACTA. Text in Dutch, English, French; Prefatory
materials in Multiple languages. 1959. irreg., latest 1985. price
varies.
—Linda Hall.
Published by: Institut d'Aeronomie Spatiale de Belgique, Av
Circulaire 3, Brussels, 1180, Belgium.

AEROPHILE. see *HOBBIES*

629.1   GBR   ISSN 1741-4016
TL501
AEROPLANE. Text in English. 1973. m. GBP 36.72 domestic;
USD 70.83 in United States (effective 2004). adv. reprint
service avail. from PQC. **Document type:** *Magazine,
Consumer.* **Description:** Authoritative magazine for
enthusiasts of vintage aircraft featuring aeronautical nostalgia,
preservation and recollections.
Formerly (until 1998): Aeroplane Monthly (0143-7240)
Related titles: Microform ed.: (from PQC).
Indexed: RefZh.
—BLDSC (0727.987000), CISTI, IE. **CCC.**
Published by: I P C Country & Leisure Media Ltd. (Subsidiary of:
I P C Media Ltd.), King's Reach Tower, Stamford St, London,
SE1 9LS, United Kingdom. TEL 44-870-4445000, FAX
44-20-72617900, aeroplane_monthly@ipcmedia.com,
http://www.aeroplanemonthly.com, http://www.ipcmedia.com.
Ed. Mike Oakey TEL 44-20-72615849. Pub. Fiona Mercer TEL
44-20-79077261. Adv. contact Lee Morris TEL
44-20-72616459. color page GBP 1,029. Circ: 37,694. **Dist.
by:** I P C Media Ltd., Perrymount Rd, Haywards Heath RH16
3DA, United Kingdom. TEL 44-1444-475675, FAX
44-1444-445599, ipcsubs@qss-uk.com.

629.13   USA   ISSN 0740-722X
TL501.A688   CODEN: ASAEA4
➤ **AEROSPACE AMERICA.** Text in English. 1932. m. USD 163
in North America to non-members; USD 200 elsewhere to
non-members; free to members (effective 2006). adv. bk.rev.
bibl.; charts; illus.; stat.; tr.lit. index. reprint service avail. from
PQC. **Document type:** *Journal, Academic/Scholarly.*
Description: Provides coverage of key issues affecting the
aerospace field. Includes analytical coverage of aeronautics,
space, defense, design, electronics, computer applications,
and science, highlighting the principal technologies involved
and their implications for both industry and the individual
aerospace professional.
Former titles (until 1983): Astronautics and Aeronautics
(0004-6213); (until 1963): Astronautics and Aerospace
Engineering (0278-856X); Which was formed by the 1963
merger of (1957-1963): Astronautics (0097-7152);
(1958-1963): Aesrospace Engineering (0096-669X); Which
was formerly (until 1958): Aeronautical Engineering Review
(0096-4352)
Related titles: Microform ed.: (from PQC); Online - full text ed.:
(from LexisNexis).

Indexed: ABS&EES, AMB, AS&TI, ASCA, ApMecR, BrCerAb,
C&ISA, CerAb, ChemAb, CivEngAb, CorrAb, CurCont,
E&CAJ, EMA, EngInd, ExcerpMed, IAA, ISMEC, ISR, M&TEA,
MBF, METADEX, NPPA, RefZh, RoboAb, S&VD, SCI, SSCI,
SolStAb, WAA.
—BLDSC (0729.852000), CASDDS, CISTI, Ei, IDS, IE,
Infotrieve, ingenta, Linda Hall. **CCC.**
Published by: American Institute of Aeronautics and Astronautics,
Inc., 1801 Alexander Bell Dr, Ste 500, Reston, VA 20191. TEL
703-264-7500, FAX 703-264-7551, custserv@aiaa.org,
http://www.aiaa.org. Ed. Elaine J Camhi. Pub. Robert
Dickman. Adv. contacts Howard O'Brien, Terry Stoneberg.
B&W page USD 3,200, color page USD 4,100. Circ: 41,000
(controlled).

➤ **AEROSPACE AND ELECTRONICS COST INDICES.** see
BUSINESS AND ECONOMICS—Domestic Commerce

629.132   JPN
AEROSPACE ANNUAL JAPAN. Text in Japanese. 1954. a. JPY
10,000. adv. **Document type:** *Directory.* **Description:** Covers
Japanese aviation policy and administration, airline business,
aircraft manufacturing, air sports and self-defence air force.
Former titles: Koku nenkan/Aviation Annual of Japan
(0389-4185); (until 1975): Koku uchu nenkan/Aerospace
Annual Japan (0389-4177); (until 1963): Koku Nenkan/Air
Annual Japan (0389-4169)
Published by: Nihon Koku Kyokai/Japan Aeronautic Association,
18-2, Shimbashi 1-Chome, Minato-ku, Tokyo, 105-0004 ,
Japan. TEL 81-3-3502-1201, FAX 81-3-3503-1375,
http://www.aero.or.jp/.

629.1   CHN   ISSN 1004-9711
TL789.8.C55   CODEN: ACEECG
AEROSPACE CHINA. Text in English. 1992. s-a. USD 50
(effective 1999). **Description:** Covers China's space activities,
achievements, science and technology, experiments, satellites
and missiles.
Related titles: Online - full text ed.: (from East View Information
Services); ◆ Chinese ed.: Zhongguo Hangtian. ISSN
1002-7742.
Published by: Hangtian Gongye Zong Gongsi, Xinxi
Yanjiu-suo/China Aerospace Corporation, Institute for
Astronautics Information, 1 Binhe Lu, Hepingli, PO Box 1408,
Beijing, 100013, China. TEL 86-10-6837-2847, FAX
86-10-8422-1606, TELEX 210471 IAI CN,
duyq@mimi.cnc.ac.cn., http://www.space.cetin.net.cn. Ed. Xue
Fuxing.

629.1   USA   ISSN 1553-8591
HD9711.5.U58
AEROSPACE DAILY & DEFENSE REPORT. Text in English.
1973 (vol.61). d. (Mon-Fri). USD 1,785 domestic email or print
ed.; USD 2,185 foreign email or print ed. (effective 2005).
Website rev. charts; tr.lit. **Document type:** *Newsletter, Trade.*
Former titles (until 2004): Aerospace Daily (0193-4546); Missile -
Space Daily
Related titles: Online - full text ed.: (from EBSCO Publishing,
Northern Light Technology, Inc.).
—BLDSC (1838.703000), IE, Linda Hall. **CCC.**
Published by: McGraw-Hill Companies, Inc., 1200 G St NW Ste
200, Washington, DC 20005. TEL 609-426-7070, FAX
609-426-7087, aerospacedaily@AviationNow.com,
http://www.aviationnow.com/aviationnow/
aerospacedaily_marketing_page.jsp, http://www.mcgraw-
hill.com. Ed. Lee Ewing TEL 202-383-2363.

629.1   USA   ISSN 0736-2536
TL671.2
AEROSPACE ENGINEERING MAGAZINE. Text in English. 1981.
9/yr. USD 75 in North America to non-members; USD 135
elsewhere to non-members; free to members (effective 2005).
adv. bk.rev. illus. Index. back issues avail.; reprints avail.
Document type: *Magazine, Trade.* **Description:** Covers
advances in aerospace technology that can be applied to the
design of new or improved vehicles or systems. Bibliographic
article abstracts are online.
Formerly: S A E in Aerospace Engineering.
Related titles: Microfiche ed.; Microfilm ed.; Online - full text ed.:
(from Questel Orbit Inc.).
Indexed: ASCA, BrCerAb, C&ISA, CerAb, CivEngAb, CorrAb,
E&CAJ, EMA, EngInd, IAA, M&TEA, MBF, METADEX, RefZh,
SolStAb, WAA.
—BLDSC (0729.861000), CISTI, Ei, IDS, IE, Infotrieve, ingenta,
Linda Hall. **CCC.**
Published by: Society of Automotive Engineers, 400
Commonwealth Dr, Warrendale, PA 15096-0001. TEL
724-776-4841, FAX 724-776-9765, aero@sae.org,
advertising@sae.org, http://www.sae.org/aeromag. Eds. Jean
Broge, Kevin Jost. Pub. Tom Drozda. Adv. contact Marcie
Hineman. Circ: 24,177.

629.13   GBR   ISSN 1369-3522
AEROSPACE EUROPE. Text in English. 1947. a., latest vol.55,
2002/2003. GBP 104 per vol. (effective 2002). adv. bk.rev.
Document type: *Directory, Trade.* **Description:** Gives
comprehensive coverage to the European aerospace and
airport services markets.
Formerly: Aviation Europe (0143-1145); Incorporates: Sell's
British Aviation (0080-8695)

Published by: C M P Information Ltd. (Subsidiary of: United
Business Media), Sovereign House, Sovereign Way,
Tonbridge, Kent TN9 1RW, United Kingdom. TEL
44-1732-377391, FAX 44-1732-377552,
indistry@ubminternational.com, http://www.ubminfo.com/
productview.asp?id=1, http://www.cmpinformation.com,
http://www.look4industry.co.uk. Ed. Philip Dury TEL
44-1732-377542. Pub. Elaine Soni TEL 44-1732-377423. R&P
Rachel Wichall TEL 44-1732-377627. Adv. contact Sarah
Thompson TEL 44-1732-377576. page GBP 1,155. Circ:
1,500.

AEROSPACE FACTS AND FIGURES. see *AERONAUTICS AND
SPACE FLIGHT—Abstracting, Bibliographies, Statistics*

629.1   GBR   ISSN 1467-5072
AEROSPACE INTERNATIONAL. Text in English. 1945. m. GBP
95 (effective 1999); free to members. adv. bk.rev. illus.
Document type: *Trade.* **Description:** Contains a roundup of
the previous months news, including industry, air transport,
defence, spaceflight, general aviation, who's news, milestones,
safety and e-business. Plus in-depth features, letters and
aerospace calendar.
Formerly (until 1997): Aerospace (0305-0831); Which
incorporated (in 1987): Tech Air (0040-0831); Which was
formerly: Society of Licensed Aircraft Engineers and
Technologists. Journal
Indexed: BrTechI, CoppAb, IAA, M&TEA, METADEX, RefZh.
—BLDSC (0729.873100), CISTI, Ei, IDS, IE, Linda Hall. **CCC.**
Published by: Royal Aeronautical Society, 4 Hamilton Pl, London,
W1J 7BQ, United Kingdom. TEL 44-20-7670-4300, FAX
44-20-7670-4309, publications@raes.org.uk,
raes@raes.org.uk, http://www.raes.org.uk/First/publications/
aerospace_journal.htm, http://www.aerosociety.com. Ed. I
Sheppard. Pub. Keith Mans. Adv. contact David Holmes TEL
44-1485-528020. Circ: 19,000. **Subscr. addr.:** RAES
Subscriptions Dept, Customer Interface, Bradley Pavillions,
Bradley Stoke North, Bristol BS32 0PP, United Kingdom. TEL
44-1454-642485, FAX 44-1454-620080, cihotline@aol.com.

629.1   JPN
AEROSPACE JAPAN WEEKLY. Text in English. 1988. w. JPY
185,000. adv. **Document type:** *Newsletter.*
Published by: Ikaros Publications Ltd., 3-2 Kagura-Zaka,
Shinjuku-ku, Tokyo, 162-0825, Japan. TEL 81-3-3267-2832,
FAX 81-3-3267-2787. Ed., R&P Koji Hoashi. Adv. contact
Kinsaku Endo. Circ: 500.

629.1   RUS
AEROSPACE JOURNAL. Text in English, Russian. bi-m. USD
145 in United States. **Document type:** *Academic/Scholarly.*
Indexed: IAA.
Published by: Military Parade Ltd., Ul Mosfil'movskaya 35, str 1,
Moscow, 117330, Russian Federation. TEL 7-095-1439652,
FAX 7-095-1439660, http://www.milparade.ru/aerospace. Ed. G
Lyssenko. **US dist. addr.:** East View Information Services,
3020 Harbor Ln. N., Minneapolis, MN 55447. TEL
612-550-0961.

629.1   USA
AEROSPACE MANAGEMENT AND LAW. Text in English. 1991.
irreg. price varies. **Document type:** *Monographic series.*
Published by: Praeger Publishers (Subsidiary of: Greenwood
Publishing Group Inc.), 88 Post Rd W, Box 5007, Westport,
CT 06881-5007. TEL 203-226-3571, FAX 203-222-1502.

629.47   USA   ISSN 0741-8779
AEROSPACE MATERIAL SPECIFICATIONS. Variant title: A M S
Index of Aerospace Material Specifications. Text in English.
s-a.
—BLDSC (0729.884000). **CCC.**
Published by: Society of Automotive Engineers, 400
Commonwealth Dr, Warrendale, PA 15096-0001. TEL
724-776-4841, FAX 724-776-0790, magazines@sae.org,
http://www.sae.org.

629.1   CAN
AEROSPACE NEWS AND COMMENT. Text in English. 4/yr. CND
35 to non-members (effective 1999). adv. **Document type:**
Newsletter. **Description:** Provides an overview of issues and
events currently affecting the Canadian aerospace industry.
Formerly: Aerospace News
Published by: Aerospace Industries Association of
Canada/Association des Industries Aerospatiales du Canada,
60 Queen St, Ste 1200, Ottawa, ON K1P 5Y7, Canada. FAX
613-232-1142, info@aiac.ca. Ed. Doug Caie. R&P Peter Boag
TEL 613-232-4297. Adv. contact Sandra Sutcliffe. B&W 1/2
page CND 550. Circ: 2,400 (controlled).

629   USA   ISSN 1054-7045
AEROSPACE PRODUCTS; components and systems technology.
Text in English. 1986. q. adv.
—CCC.
Published by: Phillips International Inc., 1201 Seven Locks Rd,
Ste 300, Potomac, MD 20854. TEL 301-340-2100. Ed. Dave
Jensen. Circ: (controlled).

629.1   GBR
AEROSPACE REVIEW. Text in English. 1950. s-a. free. illus. back
issues avail. **Document type:** *Trade.* **Description:** News and
technical reviews of avionics systems and equipment
manufactured by Smiths Industries.

▼ *new title*   ➤ *refereed*   ✶ *unverified*   ◆ *full entry avail.*

A

Former titles: Aerospace and Defence Review; Aviation Review (0374-2490)
Indexed: Inspec.
—BLDSC (0729.912800).
Published by: Smiths Industries Aerospace, 765 Finchley Rd, London, NW11 8DS, United Kingdom. TEL 44-20-8458-3232, FAX 44-20-8209-0526, plc@smithsind.co.uk, http://www.smithsind-aerospace.co.uk. Ed. S Broadbent. R&P R Plumley. Circ: 6,500 (controlled). **Dist. addr. in US:** Publicity Dept., Smith Industries Aerospace, 4141 Eastern Ave S E, Grand Rapids, MI 49518-8727.

629.13 GBR ISSN 1465-5497
AEROSPACE RISK. Text in English. 1999. m.
—BLDSC (0729.914000). **CCC.**
Published by: L L P - Informa Business Publishing Plc., 69-77 Paul St, London, EC2A 4LQ, United Kingdom. TEL 44-20-7553-1751, FAX 44-20-7553-1974. Adv. contact Stuart Burchell TEL 44-20-7553-1684.

629.13 FRA ISSN 1270-9638
TL501 CODEN: ARSTFZ
➤ **AEROSPACE SCIENCE AND TECHNOLOGY.** Text in English. 1997. 8/yr. EUR 307 in Europe to institutions; JPY 40,600 in Japan to institutions; USD 343 elsewhere to institutions (effective 2006). charts; illus. index. reprints avail. **Document type:** *Journal, Academic/Scholarly.* **Description:** Covers all fields of aerospace research from fundamental research to industrial applications.
Formed by the merger of (1977-1997): Recherche Aerospaciale (0034-1223); (1977-1997): Zeitschrift fuer Flugwissenschaften und Weltraumforschung (0342-068X); Which was formed by the merger of (1953-1977): Zeitschrift fuer Flugwissenschaften (0044-2739); (1957-1977): Raumfahrtforschung (0034-0103); Which was formerly (until 1964): Raketentechnik und Raumfahrtforschung (0370-3525)
Related titles: Online - full text ed.: (from EBSCO Publishing, Gale Group, IngentaConnect, ScienceDirect, Swets Information Services).
Indexed: ASCA, ApMecR, BrCerAb, C&ISA, CMCI, Cadscan, CerAb, ChemAb, CivEngAb, CorrAb, CurCont, E&CAJ, EMA, EngInd, ExcerpMed, FLUIDEX, IAA, INIS AtomInd, ISMEC, ISR, Inspec, LeadAb, M&TEA, MBF, METADEX, MSCI, MathR, RefZh, SCI, SolStAb, WAA, Zincscan.
—BLDSC (0729.917000), AskIEEE, CASDDS, CISTI, Ei, IDS, IE, Infotrieve, ingenta, Linda Hall. **CCC.**
Published by: (France. Office National d'Etudes et de Recherches Aerospatiales), Elsevier France, Editions Scientifiques et Medicales (Subsidiary of: Elsevier Science & Technology), 23 Rue Linois, Paris, 75724, France. TEL 33-1-71724600, FAX 33-1-71724650, academic@elsevier-fr.com, http://www.elsevier.com/locate/aescte. Eds. Fred Thomas, M. de Gliniasty. **Subscr. to:** Elsevier BV, PO Box 211, Amsterdam 1000 AE, Netherlands. TEL 31-20-485-3757, FAX 31-20-485-3432, nlinfo-f@elsevier.nl, http://www.elsevier.nl. **Co-sponsor:** Forschungsanstalt fur Luft -und Raumfahrt - Deutsche Gesellschaft fur Luft- und Raumfahrt, GW.

629.1 TWN
AEROSPACE TECHNOLOGY. Text in Chinese. 1985. bi-m. adv. **Description:** Covers technical developments and engineering issues in Asia-Pacific aerospace industry.
Published by: Tzeng Brothers Information Group, P.O. Box 43-345, 7G-09 World Trade Ctr., Taipei, 105, Taiwan. TEL 2-999-2969, FAX 2-999-2989. Ed. G L Wang. Pub. James Y.C. Tzeng. Adv. contact James Y C Tzeng. B&W page USD 2,000, color page USD 3,000; trim 287 x 215. Circ: 9,100.

629.1 GBR ISSN 1478-2774
AEROSPACE TESTING INTERNATIONAL. Text in English. 2002 (July). q. GBP 35, USD 55 (effective 2004). **Document type:** *Magazine, Trade.* **Description:** Covers the very latest news plus in-depth features and industry interviews on the latest echnology and solutions for the aerospace testing community.
Published by: AutoIntermediates Ltd. (Subsidiary of: U K & International Press), Abinger House, Church St, 120 South St, Dorking, Surrey RH4 1DF, United Kingdom. TEL 44-1306-743744, FAX 44-1306-742525, info@ukintpress.com, http://www.ukintpress.com/.

629.1 USA
AEROSPACE TESTING SEMINAR. PROCEEDINGS. Text in English. 1975. a. USD 115 to non-members; USD 85 to members (effective 2003). **Document type:** *Proceedings, Trade.*
Media: CD-ROM.
—BLDSC (6836.170000).
Published by: Institute of Environmental Sciences and Technology, 5005 Newport Dr, Ste 506, Rolling Meadows, IL 60008-3841. TEL 847-255-1561, FAX 847-255-1699, iest@iest.org, http://www.iest.org. R&P Julie Kendrick. **Co-sponsor:** Aerospace Corporation.

001.942 JPN
AEROSPACE U F O NEWS. Text in Japanese; Summaries in English. 1974 (vol.6). q. membership. bk.rev. illus.
Formerly (until 1982): U F O News
Published by: (International U F O Observer Corps.), C B A International, Naka, P.O. Box 12, Yokohama, 231, Japan. Ed. Yusuke J Matsumura. Circ: 35,000.

629.13 USA
AEROTECH NEWS AND REVIEW. Text in English. 1997. w. adv.
Related titles: Online - full content ed.: Aerotech News Online.
Address: 456 East Ave, K-4, Ste 8, Lancaster, CA 93535. TEL 661-945-5634, http://www.aerotechnews.com/index.html. Ed. Stuart Ibberson.

629.13 ITA ISSN 0365-7442
TL504 CODEN: ATMSCD
AEROTECNICA, MISSILI E SPAZIO. Text in English, Italian; Summaries in English. 1920. q. free to members. adv. bk.rev. abstr.; bibl.; charts; illus. index.
Formed by the merger of: Aerotecnica (0001-9453); Missili e Spazio (0026-6019); Which was formerly: Missili (0369-2175)
Related titles: Microform ed.: 1920 (from PQC).
Indexed: ChemAb, CurCont, IAA, Inspec, ZentMath.
—CASDDS, CISTI, Linda Hall.
Published by: Associazione Italiana di Aeronautica e Astronautica, Via Nazionale 200, Rome, 00184, Italy. TEL 39-06-4825050, FAX 39-06-4825012, http://www.aidaa.it/. Ed. Vittorio Giavotto. Circ: 1,000.

387.7 CUB ISSN 0001-9461
AEROVOZ✶. Text in Spanish. 1945. m. USD 1. adv. charts; illus.
Published by: Sindicato Nacional de Trabajadores de la Aviacion, Palacio de los Trabajadores, San Carlos y Penalver, Ciudad de La Habana, Cuba. Ed. Gustavo Mas Aguilar. Circ: 3,000.

387.7 IRL ISSN 0001-9550
AERSCEALA; staff journal of Aer Lingus. Text in English, Irish. 1948. bi-m. free. adv. **Document type:** *Newsletter.* **Description:** Covers news and areas of interest to serving and retired airline staff.
Published by: Aer Lingus, Communications Department, Dublin Airport PA6-07, Dublin, Ireland. TEL 353-1-8862326, FAX 353-1-8863160. Ed. Collette Kearney. Circ: 9,000 (controlled).

629.132 USA ISSN 0740-1434
AG-PILOT INTERNATIONAL; aviation in agriculture worldwide. Text in English. 1978. 12/yr. USD 34.95 in North America; USD 49.95 elsewhere (effective 2000). adv. bk.rev. bibl.; charts; illus.; stat.; tr.lit. **Document type:** *Trade.* **Description:** Information on agri-aviation for ag pilots, chemical dealers and consultants.
Published by: Graphics Plus, PO Box 1607, Mt. Vernon, WA 98273-1607. TEL 206-336-3336, FAX 206-336-2506, agpilot@cnw.com. Ed. Tom J Wood. R&P Thomas J Wood. Adv. contacts Corrie Warren, Tom J Wood. B&W page USD 2,670, color page USD 3,730; trim 10.88 x 8.5. Circ: 4,494 (paid).

AGARDOGRAPH. see *MILITARY*

629.1 USA ISSN 0745-4864
AGRICULTURAL AVIATION. Text in English. 1974. bi-m. USD 30 domestic; USD 45 foreign (effective 2005). **Document type:** *Magazine, Trade.*
Formerly: W A A (0192-6845)
Indexed: Agr.
—CISTI.
Published by: (National Agricultural Aviation Association), Naylor Publications, Inc., 5950 NW 1st Pl, Gainesville, FL 32607-6018. TEL 800-369-6220, information@agaviation.org, http://www.agaviation.org, http://www.naylor.com. Ed. Natalie Lutz. Pub. Chris Hodges TEL 800-369-6220 ext 3368. Circ: 6,500 (controlled).

629.13 FRA ISSN 1166-0422
AILES MAGAZINE. Text in French. 1984. m. EUR 60 domestic; EUR 82 foreign. back issues avail. **Description:** Covers light and microlight aircraft.
Former titles (until 1991): U L M Ailes Magazine (0764-3977); (until 1986): U L M Mag (0756-9785)
Published by: ConceptAir, 44 rue de Groussay, Rambouillet, 78120, France. ailesmag@alfa-zulu.com. Ed. Alain Yves Berger. Circ: 25,000.

613.69 USA
AIR ACCIDENTS & THE NEWS MEDIA✶. Text in English. 1965. irreg. USD 5. bk.rev.
Formerly: Air Accidents and the Newswriter
Published by: Aviation - Space Writers Association, 6540 50th St., N., Oakdale, MN 55128-1708. TEL 614-221-1900, FAX 614-221-1989. Circ: 1,500.

629.13 USA ISSN 0400-8456
THE AIR ALMANAC. Text in English. 1937. a. USD 53 (effective 2002). back issues avail. **Document type:** *Government.* **Description:** Contains the astronomical data required for air navigation.
—Linda Hall.
Published by: U.S. Naval Observatory, c/o Dr D D McCarthy, Department of the Navy, Washington, DC 20392-5100. http://itsofficial.net. **Subscr. also to:** U.S. Government Printing Office, Superintendent of Documents. **Co-sponsor:** H.M. Nautical Almanac Office (UK).

AIR & SPACE LAW. see *TRANSPORTATION—Air Transport*

AIR AND SPACE LAWYER. see *LAW*

THE AIR & SPACE POWER JOURNAL. see *MILITARY*

AIR & SPACE POWER JOURNAL ESPANOL. see *MILITARY*

AIR & SPACE POWER JOURNAL IN PORTUGUESE. see *MILITARY*

629.13 USA
TL501
AIR & SPACE - SMITHSONIAN. Text in English. 1986. bi-m. USD 24 domestic; USD 30 foreign; USD 3.99 newsstand/cover (effective 2005). adv. bk.rev.; software rev.; video rev.; film rev. bibl.; illus. back issues avail.; reprints avail. **Document type:** *Magazine, Consumer.* **Description:** Discusses the design and history of all types of aircraft and space vehicles.
Formerly: Air & Space (0193-8304)
Related titles: Online - full text ed.
Indexed: ASIP, AmH&L, BRI, CBRI, CLT&T, CivEngAb, HRIS, HistAb, IAA, M&TEA, MASUSE.
—BLDSC (0774.132000), Infotrieve, ingenta, Linda Hall. **CCC.**
Published by: Smithsonian Institution, Air & Space Magazine, Victor Bldg., 7100 MRC 951, P O Box 37012, Washington, DC 20013-7012. TEL 800-766-2149, FAX 202-275-1886, airspacedt@aol.com, http://www.airspacemag.com. Ed. George C Larson. Pub. Amy Wilkins. R&P Sheila Brannum. Adv. contact Thomas Madden. B&W page USD 10,920, color page USD 16,305; trim 8.38 x 10.88. Circ: 222,305 (paid). **Subscr. to:** PO Box 420113, Palm Coast, FL 32142-0013. **Dist. in UK by:** Seymour Distribution Ltd, 86 Newman St, London W1T 3EX, United Kingdom. TEL 44-20-73968000, FAX 44-20-73968002.

629.1 GBR ISSN 0950-7434
AIR-BRITAIN DIGEST. Text in English. 1948. q. GBP 15; includes Air-Britain News. **Description:** Publishes articles on historical and contemporary aviation worldwide.
Published by: Air-Britain (Historians) Ltd., 1 East St, Tonbridge, Kent TN9 1AR, United Kingdom. Circ: 4,000.

629.1 GBR ISSN 0950-7442
AIR-BRITAIN NEWS. Text in English. 1964. m. GBP 15; includes Air-Britain Digest. **Description:** News on civil registers worldwide.
Published by: Air-Britain (Historians) Ltd., 1 East St, Tonbridge, Kent TN9 1AR, United Kingdom.

629.1325 USA
AIR BULLETIN. Text in English. 1997. w. free. illus. back issues avail. **Document type:** *Bulletin.* **Description:** Features international airline industry news, daily headlines, aircraft and airline safety.
Media: Online - full text.
Published by: ConnexWorks Inc. bulletin@airconnex.com, http://www.airconnex.com.

AIR CADET; the journal for air minded youth. see *CHILDREN AND YOUTH—For*

387.7 CAN ISSN 0568-3424
AIR CANADA. ANNUAL REPORT✶. Text in English, French. a.
Published by: Air Canada, Air Canada Centre, Stn St. Laurent, P O Box 14000, Montreal, PQ H4Y 1H4, Canada. TEL 514-879-7766.

387.744 USA ISSN 0002-2241
AIR CLASSICS. Text in English. 1963. m. USD 36.95 (effective 2005). adv. bk.rev.; film rev. charts; illus. **Document type:** *Magazine, Consumer.*
Related titles: Online - full text ed.: (from bigchalk, Northern Light Technology, Inc., ProQuest Information & Learning).
Indexed: HistAb.
Published by: Challenge Publications, Inc., 9509 Vassar Ave, Ste A, Chatsworth, CA 91311-0883. moleary@challengeweb.com, http://www.challengeweb.com. Ed. Michael O'Leary. Pub. Edwin Schnepf. Adv. contact George Hulett. Circ: 120,000 (paid).

629.13 GBR ISSN 0143-5450
AIR ENTHUSIAST; the historic aviation journal. Text in English. 1977. bi-m. GBP 29.70 domestic; GBP 36.70 in United States; GBP 4.95 newsstand/cover (effective 2003). adv. charts; illus. 84 p./no.; back issues avail. **Document type:** *Consumer.*
—CISTI.
Published by: Key Publishing Ltd., PO Box 100, Stamford, Lincs PE9 1XQ, United Kingdom. TEL 44-1780-755131, FAX 44-1780-757261, ann.saundry@keypublishing.com, http://www.keypublishing.com. Ed. Ken Ellis. Pub. Ann Saundry. Adv. contact Emma White. Circ: 10,000. **Subscr. in N. America to:** Air Enthusiast, Key Publishing Ltd, PO Box 100, Avenel, NJ 07001. **Dist. by:** Seymour Distribution Ltd, 86 Newman St, London W1T 3EX, United Kingdom. TEL 44-20-73968000, FAX 44-20-73968002.

629.13 FRA ISSN 1240-3113
TL502
AIR & COSMOS - AVIATION MAGAZINE INTERNATIONAL. Text in French. 1963. w. adv. bk.rev. bibl.; charts; illus.
Formed by the merger of (1963-1992): Air et Cosmos (0044-6971); (1964-1992): Aviation Magazine International (0005-2132); Which incorporated (1953-1967): Air Transport Magazine (0002-256X)

Indexed: BrCerAb, C&ISA, CerAb, CivEngAb, CorrAb, DM&T, E&CAJ, EMA, IAA, KES, M&TEA, MBF, METADEX, PROMT, RefZh, SolStAb, WAA.
—CISTI, IE, Infotrieve, Linda Hall. **CCC.**
Published by: Groupe Revenu Francais, 1 bis av. de la Republique, Paris, 75011, France. TEL 33-1-49293200, FAX 33-1-49293201. Ed. Pierre Langereux. Adv. contact Robert Monteux. Circ: 40,034. **Subscr. to:** B. P. 540, Sainte Genevieve Cedex 60732, France.

AIR FAN; mensuel de l'aeronautique militaire internationale. see *MILITARY*

AIR FORCE COMPTROLLER. see *MILITARY*

AIR FORCE MAGAZINE; the force behind the force. see *MILITARY*

AIR FORCE TIMES (U.S. EDITION). see *MILITARY*

387.7 GBR ISSN 0306-5634
UG630.A1
AIR INTERNATIONAL. Text in English. 1971. m. GBP 36 domestic in the UK, US & Canada; GBP 42 in Europe; GBP 42.80 elsewhere (effective 2005). adv. bk.rev. bibl.; charts; illus. s-a. index. back issues avail.; reprints avail. **Document type:** *Magazine, Trade.* **Description:** International military and civil aerospace news and analysis of current and historical events.
Formerly: Air Enthusiast (0044-6963)
Related titles: Online - full text ed.
Indexed: BrCerAb, C&ISA, CerAb, CivEngAb, CorrAb, DM&T, E&CAJ, EMA, IAA, M&TEA, MBF, METADEX, PROMT, SolStAb, WAA.
—BLDSC (0776.340000), CISTI, IE, Infotrieve, ingenta, Linda Hall.
Published by: Key Publishing Ltd., PO Box 100, Stamford, Lincs PE9 1XQ, United Kingdom. TEL 44-1780-755131, FAX 44-1780-757261, malcolm.english@keypublishing.com, http://www.airinternational.com/, http://www.keypublishing.com. Ed. Malcolm English. Pub. Richard Cox. Adv. contact Al Evans. Circ: 16,014. **Subscr. in US to:** Key Publishing Ltd., PO Box 100, Avenel, NJ 07001. TEL 800-688-6247. **Dist. by:** Seymour Distribution Ltd, 86 Newman St, London W1T 3EX, United Kingdom. FAX 44-207-396-8002, enquiries@seymour.co.uk.

331.1 629.1 USA ISSN 1056-5051
CODEN: BABUFF
AIR JOBS DIGEST. Text in English. 1986. m. USD 96 in North America; USD 154.20 elsewhere (effective 2000). adv. **Document type:** *Newspaper.* **Description:** Lists current open positions in the entire aviation and aerospace industry, including corporate, commercial and government aviation.
Published by: World Air Data, PO Box 42724, Washington, DC 20015. TEL 301-990-6800, FAX 301-990-8484. Ed. Ellis H Hammond.

629.13 GBR
THE AIR LETTER; world aviation, space and electronics day by day. Text in English. 1932. d. GBP 785 domestic; GBP 785 in Europe; USD 1,655 in United States; GBP 930 elsewhere (effective 2001). charts; illus.; stat. 8 p./no.; back issues avail.; reprints avail. **Document type:** *Newsletter, Trade.* **Description:** Information guide to the international aerospace, air transport and defense industries.
Formerly (until Sep. 1993): Interavia Air Letter (0020-5176)
Related titles: E-mail ed.: GBP 935 domestic; GBP 935 in Europe; USD 1,980 in United States; GBP 1,100 rest of world (effective 2001); Fax ed.: GBP 785 domestic; GBP 785 in Europe; USD 1,655 in United States; GBP 930 rest of world (effective 2001); ♦ Online - full content ed.: Air Letter On-Line.
Published by: The Air Letter, 50-52 Upper Village Rd, Sunninghill, Berks SL5 7AQ, United Kingdom. TEL 44-1344-874866, FAX 44-1344-874543, info@airletter.com, http://www.airletter.com. Ed. Andrew Campbell. Pub., Adv. contact Tim O'Shea. Circ: (controlled).

629.1325 GBR
AIR LETTER ON-LINE. Text in English. d. GBP 935 domestic; GBP 935 in Europe; USD 1,980 in United States; GBP 1,100 rest of world (effective 2001).
Media: Online - full content. **Related titles:** E-mail ed.: GBP 935 domestic; GBP 935 in Europe; USD 1,980 in United States; GBP 1,100 rest of world (effective 2001); Fax ed.: GBP 785 domestic; GBP 785 in Europe; USD 1,655 in United States; GBP 930 rest of world (effective 2001); ♦ Print ed.: The Air Letter.
Published by: The Air Letter, 50-52 Upper Village Rd, Sunninghill, Berks SL5 7AQ, United Kingdom. TEL 44-1344-874866, FAX 44-1344-874543, info@airletter.com, http://www.airletter.com.

387.72 USA ISSN 0002-242X
TL501
AIR LINE PILOT; the magazine of professional flight deck crews. Text in English. 1932. 10/yr. USD 32 domestic; USD 45 foreign; USD 22 to students (effective 2005). bk.rev. charts; illus.; stat. Index. 40 p./no. 3 cols./p.; reprint service avail. from PQC. **Document type:** *Magazine, Trade.* **Description:** Covers air safety and technology, industry developments, labor union issues, airline industry regulations and economics, airline pilot profession.
Incorporates: Tech Talk (Herndon) (0040-0858)
Related titles: Microfilm ed.: (from PQC).
Indexed: AUNI, CLT&T, HRIS.
—BLDSC (0776.349600), IE, Infotrieve, ingenta, Linda Hall.
Published by: Air Line Pilots Association, A F L - C I O, 535 Herndon Pkwy, PO Box 1169, Herndon, VA 20172. TEL 703-481-4460, FAX 703-464-2114, magazine@alpa.org, http://www.alpa.org. Ed. J Gary DiNunno. Adv. contact Lara Engebretson. Circ: 85,000 (paid and free).

629.1 USA
AIR MARKET NEWS. Text in English. 1982. bi-m. free to qualified personnel. adv. tr.lit. **Document type:** *Magazine, Trade.*
Published by: General Publications, Inc., PO Box 480, Hatch, NM 87937-0480. TEL 505-267-1030, FAX 505-267-1920. Ed. Dixie Binning. Pub. Jennifer Prill. Circ: 18,500 (controlled).

AIR MEDICAL JOURNAL. see *MEDICAL SCIENCES*

629.13 GBR ISSN 1360-4635
AIR NAVIGATION INTERNATIONAL. Text in English. 1995. fortn. GBP 445, USD 668 (effective 2000). **Document type:** *Newsletter, Trade.* **Description:** Reports on the latest technical news regarding the key FANS elements - communications, navigation and surveillance, as well as related systems.
Related titles: E-mail ed.; Fax ed.
Published by: Reed Business Information Ltd. (Subsidiary of: Reed Business), Quadrant House, The Quadrant, Brighton Rd, Sutton, Surrey SM2 5AS, United Kingdom. TEL 44-208-652-3500, FAX 44-208-652-8977, rbi.subscriptions@qss-uk.com, http://www.reedbusiness.co.uk/. Ed. Emma Kelly. **Subscr. to:** Quadrant Subscription Services, PO Box 302, Haywards Heath, W Sussex RH16 3YY, United Kingdom. TEL 44-1444-445566, FAX 44-1444-445447.

629.13 GBR ISSN 0965-1896
AIR PICTORIAL INTERNATIONAL. Text in English. 1939. m. GBP 31.80; GBP 39 per issue foreign; GBP 2.65 newsstand/cover (effective 1999). adv. bk.rev. illus.; stat. index. **Document type:** *Consumer.* **Description:** Directed to the air enthusiast to inform about all aspects of aviation.
Formerly (until 1992): Air Pictorial (0002-2462)
—CISTI, IE, Infotrieve. **CCC.**
Published by: H P C Publishing, Drury Ln, St Leonards-on-Sea, E Sussex TN38 9BJ, United Kingdom. TEL 44-1424-720477, FAX 44-1424-443693. Ed. Barry Wheeler. Pub. Derek Knoll. Adv. contact Rosemary Beckwith. Circ: 19,000. **Dist. by:** Seymour Distribution Ltd, 86 Newman St, London W1T 3EX, United Kingdom. FAX 44-207-396-8002, enquiries@seymour.co.uk.

387.7 USA ISSN 1044-016X
UG633.A1
➤ **AIR POWER HISTORY**; the journal of air and space history. Text in English. 1954. q. USD 35 to individuals; USD 45 to institutions; USD 25 to students (effective 2005). adv. bk.rev. charts; illus.; maps. cum.index: 1954-1972, 1973-1983. 72 p./no.; back issues avail.; reprint service avail. from PQC,ISI. **Document type:** *Journal, Academic/Scholarly.* **Description:** Focuses on military history of aeronautics of space flight. Audience is both military and academics.
Former titles (until 1989): Aerospace Historian (0001-9364); Airpower History (0277-9048)
Related titles: Microform ed.: (from PQC); Online - full text ed.: (from bigchalk, EBSCO Publishing, Florida Center for Library Automation, Gale Group, Northern Light Technology, Inc., O C L C Online Computer Library Center, Inc., ProQuest Information & Learning).
Indexed: ABM, AMB, AUNI, AmH&L, BAS, BRI, CBRI, HistAb, LID&ISL, RASB, SPPI.
Published by: Air Force Historical Foundation, 1535 Command Drive, Ste A122, Andrews AFB, MD 20762-7002. TEL 301-981-2139, 301-736-1959, FAX 301-981-3574, airpowerhistory@yahoo.com, bingem@andrews.af.mil, bausumh@vmi.edu, http://www.afhistoricalfoundation.com. Ed. Jacob Neufeld. Pub. Brian S Gunderson. R&P Col. Joseph A Marston. Adv. contact Mark D Mandeles. page USD 1,400. Circ: 7,000 (paid). **Subscr. to:** Air Power History, VMI Parade Ground, Lexington, VA 24450. TEL 540-464-7468, FAX 540-464-7330.

629.13 ITA
AIR PRESS. Text in Italian. 1959. w. EUR 690 (effective 2005). adv. **Document type:** *Magazine, Consumer.*
Published by: Editoriale Aeronautica s.r.l., Via Appia Nuova, 96, Rome, RM 00183, Italy. TEL 39-06-7000894, FAX 39-06-70490271, air_press@virgilio.it, http://www.airpress.it/airpress/PUB/airpress.asp?doc=1. Ed. Oscar Dariz. Adv. contact Roberta Digregorio. Circ: 2,000.

629.1 USA ISSN 1044-727X
KF2406.A15
AIR SAFETY WEEK; the newsletter of air safety regulation. Text in English. 1987. w. USD 997 (effective 2005). index. back issues avail. **Document type:** *Newsletter, Trade.* **Description:** Reports on developments in air safety regulation, focusing on regulatory authorities in the US.
Incorporates (1993-1997): C N S Outlook (1072-5393); Formerly (until 1989): Air Safety Law and Technology (0893-1003)
Related titles: Online - full text ed.: (from Data-Star, Gale Group, LexisNexis, Northern Light Technology, Inc., ProQuest Information & Learning, The Dialog Corporation).
Indexed: ABIn.
—**CCC.**
Published by: Access Intelligence, LLC (Subsidiary of: Veronis, Suhler & Associates Inc.), 1201 Seven Locks Rd, Ste 300, Potomac, MD 20854. TEL 301-354-2000, 800-777-5006, FAX 301-424-2058, jbrain@pbimedia.com, clientservices@accessintel.com, http://www.pbimedia.com/cgi/catalog/info?ASW. Ed. David Evans.

629.13 USA ISSN 1097-3133
AIR SHOWS. Text in English. 1984. q. USD 35 to members (effective 2000). adv. **Document type:** *Trade.* **Description:** Contains industry news, views, trends and education.
Formerly: I C A S News (0746-2743)
Published by: International Council of Air Shows, 751 Miller Dr, S E, No F4, Leesburg, VA 20175-8993. TEL 703-779-8510, icas@airshows.org, http://www.airshows.org. Ed., R&P, Adv. contact Mary Jackson. Circ: 1,200.

797.5 CHE
AIR SPORTS INTERNATIONAL. Text in English. m. charts; illus. back issues avail. **Document type:** *Magazine, Consumer.* **Description:** Presents all FAI-recognized air sports, including ballooning, aerobatics, and skydiving.
Related titles: Online - full text ed.
Published by: Federation Aeronautique International, Av Mon Repos 24, Lausanne, 1005, Switzerland. TEL 41-21-345-1070, FAX 41-21-345-1077, editor.airsports@fai.org, http://airsports.fai.org/home.html, http://www.fai.org. Ed., Pub. Dev Atul.

629.1 USA ISSN 0192-8740
TL725.3.T7
AIR TRAFFIC CONTROL ASSOCIATION. FALL CONFERENCE PROCEEDINGS. Text in English. 1977. a. USD 30 (effective 2000). back issues avail. **Document type:** *Proceedings.*
—BLDSC (1075.097500).
Published by: Air Traffic Control Association, Inc., 1101 King St, Ste 300, Arlington, VA 22314-2944. TEL 703-299-2430, FAX 703-299-2437, atca@worldnet.att.net, info@atca.org, http://www.atca.org. Ed. G A Hartl. Circ: 1,200.

AIR TRAFFIC MANAGEMENT. see *TRANSPORTATION—Air Transport*

AIR TRAFFIC MANAGEMENT YEARBOOK. see *TRANSPORTATION—Air Transport*

387.7 USA ISSN 0002-2543
HE9761.1
AIR TRANSPORT WORLD. Text in English. 1964. m. USD 60 domestic; USD 85 in Canada; USD 100 elsewhere; free to qualified personnel (effective 2005). adv. charts; illus.; tr.lit. Index. back issues avail.; reprint service avail. from PQC. **Document type:** *Magazine, Trade.* **Description:** Reports on managerial, technical and operational advances, and developments and trends in the airline industries that supply the airlines with equipment and services.
Related titles: Microform ed.: (from PQC); Online - full text ed.: (from bigchalk, EBSCO Publishing, Factiva, Florida Center for Library Automation, Gale Group, H.W. Wilson, Northern Light Technology, Inc., O C L C Online Computer Library Center, Inc., ProQuest Information & Learning, The Dialog Corporation); ♦ Supplement(s): World Airline Report.
Indexed: ABIn, ABS&EES, B&I, BPI, BrCerAb, BusI, C&ISA, CLT&T, CerAb, CorrAb, E&CAJ, EIA, EMA, EnerInd, EnvAb, HRIS, IAA, M&TEA, MBF, METADEX, PAIS, PROMT, RASB, RefZh, SRI, SolStAb, T&II, TelAb, WAA.
—BLDSC (0776.800000), IE, Infotrieve, ingenta, Linda Hall. **CCC.**
Published by: A T W Media Group (Subsidiary of: Penton Media, Inc.), 1350 Connecticut Ave, NW, Ste 902, Washington, DC 20036. TEL 202-659-8500, FAX 202-659-1554, http://www.atwonline.com/. Eds. Perry Flint, J A Donoghue. Pub. William A Freeman III. adv.: B&W page USD 7,995, color page USD 9,945. Circ: 3,742 (paid); 40,700 (controlled).

629.44 GBR
AIRCLAIMS SPACE INTELLIGENCER NEWSLETTER. Text in English. m. GBP 100 (effective 2003). **Document type:** *Newsletter, Trade.* **Description:** Provides a current digest of major space news.
Media: E-mail.
Published by: Airclaims Limited, Cardinal Point, Newall Rd, Heathrow Airport, London, TW6 2AS, United Kingdom. TEL 44-20-8897-1066, FAX 44-20-8897-0300, ian.sheppard@airclaims.co.uk, http://www.airclaims.co.uk.

A

▼ new title ➤ refereed ✶ unverified ♦ full entry avail.

A

629.1 CAN ISSN 0443-7926
AIRCRAFT ACCIDENT DIGEST. Text in English. 1951. irreg., latest 1996. USD 49. reprints avail.
Related titles: French ed.: Recueil d'Accidents d'Aviation. ISSN 1014-4536; Spanish ed.: Recompilacion de Accidentes de Aviacion. ISSN 1014-4544; ♦ Series of: I C A O Circulars. ISSN 1014-4412.
Published by: International Civil Aviation Organization, External Relations and Public Information Office, 999 University St, Montreal, PQ H3C 5H7, Canada. TEL 514-954-8022, FAX 514-954-6769, sales_unit@icao.org, icaohq@icao.int.

629.13 AUS ISSN 1327-5437
AIRCRAFT & AEROSPACE ASIA PACIFIC. Text in English. 1918. 10/yr. USD 63 domestic; USD 80 in New Zealand; USD 95 in Asia; USD 125 elsewhere (effective 2005). adv. bk.rev. abstr.; bibl.; charts; illus.; stat. **Document type:** *Journal, Trade.* **Description:** Covers the Asia Pacific aviation industry with reports and analysis.
Former titles (until 1995): Aircraft & Aerospace (1032-9366); Which incorporated: Aviation News; (until 1988): Aircraft (1032-9358)
Related titles: Online - full text ed.
Indexed: ABIX, AMB.
—IE, Infotrieve.
Published by: Yaffa Publishing Group Pty Ltd., 17-21 Bellevue St, Surry Hills, NSW 2010, Australia. TEL 61-2-92812333, FAX 61-2-92812750, yaffa@yaffa.com.au, http://www.yaffa.com.au/mags/airmag.htm. Circ: 12,453.

AIRCRAFT ECONOMICS. see *TRANSPORTATION—Air Transport*

629.1 GBR
➤ **AIRCRAFT ENGINEERING AND AEROSPACE TECHNOLOGY**; an international journal. Text in English. 1929. 6/yr. EUR 3,098.29 in Europe; USD 3,159 in North America; AUD 3,579 in Australasia; GBP 2,173.91 in UK & elsewhere (effective 2006). bk.rev. charts; illus.; pat.; tr.lit. index. reprint service avail. from PSC. **Document type:** *Journal, Academic/Scholarly.* **Description:** Covers the materials and technologies employed in the aircraft and aerospace industry.
Formerly: Aircraft Engineering (0002-2667)
Related titles: Online - full text ed.: (from bigchalk, EBSCO Publishing, Emerald Group Publishing Limited, Gale Group, IngentaConnect, O C L C Online Computer Library Center, Inc., ProQuest Information & Learning, Swets Information Services).
Indexed: ABIn, ASCA, BrCerAb, BrTechI, C&ISA, CerAb, ChemAb, CivEngAb, CorrAb, E&CAJ, EMA, ESPM, EmerIntel, EngInd, ExcerpMed, H&SSA, IAA, Inspec, M&TEA, MBF, METADEX, PROMT, RefZh, SolStAb, WAA.
—BLDSC (0780.070000), AskIEEE, CISTI, Ei, IDS, IE, ingenta, Linda Hall. **CCC.**
Published by: Emerald Group Publishing Limited, 60-62 Toller Ln, Bradford, W Yorks BD8 9BY, United Kingdom. TEL 44-1274-777700, FAX 44-1274-785200, infomation@emeraldinsight.com, http://www.emeraldinsight.com/aeat.htm. Ed. Terry Savage. Pub. Vicky Williams. R&P Mr. James Bender. **Subscr. addr. in Australia:** Emerald Group Publishing Ltd., PO Box 1567, Toowong, QLD 4066, Australia. TEL 61-3870-7144, FAX 61-3870-4013; **Subscr. addr. in N America:** Emerald Group Publishing Ltd., 44 Brattle St, 4th Fl, Cambridge, MA 02138. TEL 617-497-2175, 888-622-0075, FAX 617-354-6875.

629.13 GBR ISSN 0002-2675
AIRCRAFT ILLUSTRATED. Text in English. 1968. m. GBP 43.20 domestic; GBP 55.50 in Europe; GBP 61.50 elsewhere; GBP 3.35 per issue (effective 2005). bk.rev.; film rev. charts; illus. index. 100 p./no.; reprint service avail. from PQC. **Document type:** *Magazine, Consumer.* **Description:** Contains news and features on military and civil aviation subjects, and superb aerial phoyography.
—CCC.
Published by: Ian Allan Publishing Ltd., Riverdene Business Park, Riverdene Industrial Estate, Molesey Rd, Walton-on-Thames, Surrey KT12 4RG, United Kingdom. TEL 44-1932-266600, FAX 44-1932-266601, info@ianallanpub.co.uk, http://www.ianallan.com/publishing/airillus/index.htm. Ed. Allan Burney. R&P David Allan. Adv. contact Richard Cochrane. Circ: 40,000 (paid). **Dist. by:** MarketForce UK Ltd, 247 Tottenham Court Rd, London, Middx W1T 7AU, United Kingdom. TEL 44-207-2615199, FAX 44-207-2617341.

629.1 GBR ISSN 1463-8932
AIRCRAFT INTERIORS INTERNATIONAL. Text in English. 1998. q. GBP 65, USD 100 (effective 2004). **Document type:** *Magazine, Trade.* **Description:** Covers the latest trends and developments in aircraft interior design, cabin brand development and completion.
Indexed: RefZh.
Published by: AutoIntermediates Ltd. (Subsidiary of: U K & International Press), Abinger House, Church St, 120 South St, Dorking, Surrey RH4 1DF, United Kingdom. TEL 44-1306-743744, FAX 44-1306-742525, info@ukintpress.com, http://www.ukintpress.com/.

629.13 387.7 GBR ISSN 0967-439X
AIRCRAFT TECHNOLOGY ENGINEERING & MAINTENANCE. Text in English. 1992. bi-m. GBP 100 domestic; GBP 115, USD 185 foreign (effective 2001). adv. software rev. charts; illus.; mkt.; stat.; tr.lit. back issues avail. **Document type:** *Trade.* **Description:** International air transport magazine covering aircraft manufacturing and the maintenance. Aimed at airline senior executives, OEM management and aftermarket service companies.
Related titles: Online - full text ed.; Supplement(s): Quality and Training; Commuter and Regional Aircraft.
Indexed: BrCerAb, C&ISA, CerAb, CivEngAb, CorrAb, E&CAJ, EMA, IAA, M&TEA, MBF, METADEX, SolStAb, WAA.
—Linda Hall.
Published by: Aviation Industry Press, 31 Palace St, London, SW1E 5HW, United Kingdom. TEL 44-20-7828-3805, 44-20-7828-4370, FAX 44-20-7828-9154, 44-20-7828-9154, atem@aviation-industry.com, http://www.aviation-industry.com. Ed. Paul Copping. Pub. Simon Barker. R&P Martin Fendt. Adv. contact Simon N Barker. B&W page GBP 3,988, color page GBP 6,138; trim 8.27 x 10.95. Circ: 13,000.

629.1 387.7 CAN ISSN 1014-0107
AIRCRAFT TYPE DESIGNATORS/DESIGNADORES DE TIPOS DE AERONAVE/INDICATIFS DE TYPE D'AERONEF. Text in English, French, Russian, Spanish. 1967. irreg., latest vol.25, 1997. USD 27.
Related titles: Diskette ed.: USD 200.
Published by: International Civil Aviation Organization, External Relations and Public Information Office, 999 University St, Montreal, PQ H3C 5H7, Canada. TEL 514-954-8022, FAX 514-954-6769, sales_unit@icao.org, icaohq@icao.int.

387.7 GBR ISSN 0966-0348
AIRCRAFT VALUE JOURNAL✶. Text in English. 1992. m. GBP 200, USD 320. charts; stat. back issues avail. **Document type:** *Trade.* **Description:** Reviews aircraft value by type for the aviation financing community.
Indexed: RefZh.
Published by: Aircraft Value Analysis Co., 23 Cherry Lane, Bearley, Startford-upon-Avon CV37 OSX, United Kingdom. TEL 44-1789-730283, FAX 44-1773-828603. Ed. Paul Leighton.

AIRFLOW. see *SPORTS AND GAMES—Outdoor Life*

AIRFORCE; the magazine of Canada's air force heritage. see *MILITARY*

AIRFORCES MONTHLY; the world's leading military aviation magazine. see *MILITARY*

629.132 USA
AIRLINE FLEET & SEM DIRECTORY. Text in English. a. USD 24.95 to members; USD 29.95 to non-members (effective 2001). **Document type:** *Directory.*
Published by: Aviation Information Resources, Inc. (AIR, Inc.), Ailine Pilots Careers, 3800 Camp Creek Pkwy S W Ste 18-100, Atlanta, GA 30331-6228. TEL 404-592-6500, FAX 404-592-6515. Circ: 10,000 (paid).

629.132 USA
AIRLINE INFORMATION & ADDRESS DIRECTORY. Text in English. 1993. a. USD 28.95, USD 33.95 (effective 2001).
Media: Online - full content.
Published by: Aviation Information Resources, Inc. (AIR, Inc.), Ailine Pilots Careers, 3800 Camp Creek Pkwy S W Ste 18-100, Atlanta, GA 30331-6228. TEL 404-592-6500, FAX 404-592-6515. Circ: 10,000 (paid).

AIRLINE MODELER. see *HOBBIES*

AIRLINE NINETY TWO; revista de aviacion comercial y aeropuertos. see *TRANSPORTATION—Air Transport*

629.132 USA
AIRLINE PILOT APPLICATION HANDBOOK. Text in English. 1991. a. USD 29.95 to members; USD 34.95 to non-members (effective 2001).
Media: Online - full content.
Published by: Aviation Information Resources, Inc. (AIR, Inc.), Ailine Pilots Careers, 3800 Camp Creek Pkwy S W Ste 18-100, Atlanta, GA 30331-6228. TEL 404-592-6500, FAX 404-592-6515. Circ: 10,000 (paid).

629.132 USA ISSN 1095-4317
AIRLINE PILOT CAREERS; a magazine for the current and future airline pilot. Text in English. 1983. m. USD 39.95 domestic; USD 49.95 in Canada; USD 59.95 elsewhere (effective 2000). adv. bk.rev. index. 40 p./no.; back issues avail. **Document type:** *Magazine, Trade.* **Description:** Each issue offers in-depth information on a major airline and one of its regional partners. Features include airline history and projections, pilot interviews and a Q&A from a major recruiter.
Former titles (until 1996): Career Pilot (1048-8898); (until 1989): Piloting Careers (0745-4996)
Related titles: Online - full text ed.
Indexed: CLT&T, HRIS.
Published by: Aviation Information Resources, Inc. (AIR, Inc.), Ailine Pilots Careers, 3800 Camp Creek Pkwy S W Ste 18-100, Atlanta, GA 30331-6228. TEL 404-592-6500, 800-538-5627, FAX 404-592-6515, jetjobs@airapps.com, http://www.jet-jobs.com. Ed. Jane Dacher. Pub. Kit Darby. R&P Montina L Waymire TEL 404-592-6500 ext 159. Adv. contact Debbie Kellie TEL 800-538-5627 ext 121. Circ: 11,000 (paid).

629.132 USA ISSN 1098-0490
AIRLINE PILOT JOB MONTHLY. Text in English. 1992. m. USD 99 (effective 2000). adv. **Document type:** *Newsletter, Trade.* **Description:** Covers pilot hiring, industry news, statistics and trends that affect pilot hiring at over 200 airlines.
Related titles: Online - full text ed.
Published by: Aviation Information Resources, Inc. (AIR, Inc.), Ailine Pilots Careers, 3800 Camp Creek Pkwy S W Ste 18-100, Atlanta, GA 30331-6228. TEL 404-592-6500, 800-538-5627, FAX 404-592-6515, jetjobs@airapps.com, http://www.jet-jobs.com. Ed., R&P Montina L Waymire TEL 404-592-6500 ext 159. Pub. Kit Darby. Adv. contact Debbie Kellie TEL 800-538-5627 ext 121. Circ: 10,000 (paid).

AIRLINER WORLD; the global airline scene. see *TRANSPORTATION—Air Transport*

AIRLINERS; the world's airline magazine. see *TRANSPORTATION—Air Transport*

621.133 387.74 DEU
AIRLINERS IN SERVICE AROUND THE WORLD SERIES. Text in English, German. 1999. irreg., latest vol.2. USD 23.95, EUR 21. charts; illus.; stat. **Document type:** *Monographic series, Trade.* **Description:** Each volume traces the development and history of a particular airliner.
Published by: NARA-Verlag, Postfach 1241, Allershausen, 85388, Germany. TEL 49-8166-68530, FAX 49-8166-68530, NARA-international@t-online.de, http://www.NARA-international.de. Pub. J Krauthauser.

629.133 USA
AIRLINERTECH SERIES. Text in English. irreg. USD 16.95 per vol. domestic; GBP 9.95 per vol. in Europe. charts; illus. back issues avail. **Document type:** *Monographic series, Consumer.* **Description:** Discusses and describes in considerable detail the history and technical specifications of a noteworthy commercial airliner. Includes development history and later modifications.
Published by: Specialty Press, 11605 Kost Dam Rd, North Branch, MN 55056. TEL 651-583-3239. **in UK & rest of Europe:** Airlife Publishing Ltd, 101 Longden Rd, Shrewsbury SY3 9EB, United Kingdom.

AIRMAN; official magazine of the U.S. Air Force. see *MILITARY*

629.13 USA ISSN 1057-963X
TL710
AIRMAN'S INFORMATION MANUAL; official guide to basic flight information and A T C procedures. Text in English. s-a. (plus updates 4/yr.). USD 58; USD 72.50 foreign. **Document type:** *Government.* **Description:** Contains the fundamentals required in order to fly in the U.S. National Airspace System; also contains items of interest to pilots concerning health and flight safety.
Former titles: Airman's Information Manual. Basic Flight Information and A T C Procedures; Airman's Information Manual. Part 1: Basic Flight Information and ATC Procedures; Airman's Information Manual. Part 1:Basic Flight Manual and ATC Procedures (0002-2764)
Published by: U.S. Federal Aviation Administration, 800 Independence Ave S W, Washington, DC 20591. TEL 202-655-4000. **Subscr. to:** U.S. Government Printing Office, Superintendent of Documents.

629.132 AUS ISSN 1321-0564
AIRNEWS. Text in English. 1950. q. AUD 30; AUD 65 membership; AUD 5 newsstand/cover (effective 2001). adv. 28 p./no.; **Document type:** *Newsletter.* **Description:** Reports on members activities & topics relevant to Australian pilots.
Published by: Australian Women Pilots' Association, c/o Sue Alexander, Ed., 1-39 Narong Road, Caulfield North, VIC 3161, Australia. airnewseditor@optusnet.com.au, http://www.awpa.org.au. Ed., R&P, Adv. contact Sue Alexander. B&W page AUD 300, color page AUD 360; 19 x 27. Circ: 700 (controlled).

387.74 USA ISSN 1072-1797
TI 725.3.M2A65
AIRPORT BUSINESS. Text in English. 1993. 10/yr. USD 55 domestic; USD 68 in US & Canada; USD 99 elsewhere (effective 2005). adv. charts; illus.; stat. back issues avail.; reprints avail. **Document type:** *Magazine, Trade.* **Description:** An on-going source of how-to information for managers of airports and airport-based businesses. Covers management, finance and funding, regulations, community relations, sales and marketing, operations, maintenance, security, fuel, and ground service.
Formed by the 1993 merger of: F B O - Fixed Base Operator (0893-3081); Airport Services (1041-4231); Which was formerly (until 1988): Airport Services Management (0002-2829)

Related titles: Online - full text ed.: (from EBSCO Publishing, Gale Group, ProQuest Information & Learning).
Indexed: RASB.
—CCC.
Published by: Cygnus Business Media, Inc., 1233 Janesville Ave, Fort Atkinson, WI 53538-0803. TEL 800-547-7377, FAX 920-568-2244, paul.bowers@cygnuspub.com, http://www.airportbusiness.com. Ed. John Infanger. Circ: 17,510 (controlled); 78 (paid).

387.736 GBR
TL725.A1
AIRPORTS INTERNATIONAL MAGAZINE. Text in English. 1968. 9/yr. USD 175; USD 19 newsstand/cover (effective 2003). adv. bk.rev. stat. back issues avail.; reprints avail. **Document type:** *Magazine, Trade.* **Description:** Focuses on airport construction and development throughout the world.
Former titles (until 1971): Airports International Directory (0261-6513); Airports International (0002-2853)
Related titles: Online - full text ed.: (from Factiva, Gale Group, O C L C Online Computer Library Center, Inc.).
Indexed: B&I, HRIS.
—BLDSC (0785.070000), IE, ingenta. **CCC.**
Published by: Key Publishing Ltd., PO Box 100, Stamford, Lincs PE9 1XQ, United Kingdom. TEL 44-1780-755131, FAX 44-1780-757261, ann.saundry@keypublishing.com, http://www.airportsinternational.co.uk, http://www.keypublishing.com. Ed. Tom Allett. Adv. contact David Plant. Circ: 13,962.

358.4 USA ISSN 1067-1048
TL685.3
AIRPOWER; the story of combat aviation. Text in English. 1971. bi-m. USD 25; USD 31 foreign (effective 1998). adv. bk.rev. charts; illus. **Document type:** *Consumer.*
Related titles: Online - full text ed.: (from bigchalk, Florida Center for Library Automation, Gale Group).
Published by: Sentry Books, Inc., 10718 White Oak Ave, Box 3324, Granada Hills, CA 91344. TEL 818-368-2012. Ed. Joseph V Mizrahi. Adv. contact Ed Jacobs. page USD 500. Circ: 80,000.

629.13 USA
AIRSHIP. Text in English. bi-m. USD 15 domestic membership; USD 25 foreign membership (effective 2000). illus. **Document type:** *Newsletter.* **Description:** Discusses the history of Naval Air Station Lakehurst, a mooring site for airships in Lakehurst, NJ.
Published by: Navy Lakehurst Historical Society, PO Box 328, Lakehurst, NJ 08733. TEL 732-244-8861, 609-567-4082, FAX 732-244-8897, info@nlhs.com, http://www.nlhs.com/nlhsmemb.htm.

358.4 GBR
AIRSHOW AND DEFENSE EXPO INTERNATIONAL. Text in English. 1996. 9/yr. GBP 100, USD 190, EUR 160 (effective 2002). adv. illus.; tr.lit. back issues avail. **Document type:** *Magazine, Trade.* **Description:** Contains news regarding the business of professional/trade/aerospace/defense exhibitions, shows and conferences.
Formerly: Airshow International (1465-3109)
Published by: Harper Broadbent, 35 Bromley Road, Bingley, West Yorkshire, BD16 4DA, United Kingdom. svb@globalnet.co.uk, http://www.harperbroadbent.com. Ed. Brian Walters. Pub., R&P Steve Broadbent. Adv. contact Viv Harper. Circ: 2,500 (paid and controlled).

797.5 USA
AIRSHOW PROFESSIONAL; the catalog of professional airshow performers & support services. Text in English. USD 12 (effective 2001). adv. **Document type:** *Catalog, Trade.* **Description:** Provides information on airshow performers and services.
Published by: Flyer Publications, Inc., PO Box 199, Oregon, WI 53575-0199. TEL 608-835-7063, FAX 608-835-3323, weiman@mailbag.com, http://www.wanews.com/airpro.

629.132 797 AUS ISSN 0156-6016
AIRSPORT. Text in English. 1968. m. AUD 95 (effective 1999). adv. back issues avail. **Document type:** *Newsletter.* **Description:** Covers amateur aircraft construction and operation.
Published by: Sport Aircraft Association of Australia, PO Box 169, Clifton Hill, VIC 3068, Australia. TEL 61-3-9482-4716, FAX 61-3-9482-3936. Ed. Graeme Goates. Adv. contact Martin Hone. Circ: 2,000.

AIRWAYS; a global review of commercial flight. see *TRANSPORTATION—Air Transport*

629.47 RUS ISSN 1727-6853
➤ **AKTUAL'NYE PROBLEMY AVIATSIONNYKH I AEROKOSMICHESKIKH SISTEM: PROTSESSY, MODELI, EKSPERIMENT/ACTUAL PROBLEMS OF AVIATION AND AEROSPACE SYSTEMS: PROCESSES, MODELS, EXPERIMENT.** Text in Russian, English. 1995. s-a. USD 80 foreign (effective 2005). **Document type:** *Journal, Academic/Scholarly.* **Description:** Presents papers in areas of theory, design and technology of aircraft engines; materials, information and computing systems, experimental investigations.
Published by: (Embry-Riddle Aeronautical University USA, International Federation of Nonlinear Analysts DEU, Academy of Non-Linear Sciences), Kazanskii Gosudarstvennyi Tekhnicheskii Universitet im. A.N. Tupoleva/Kazan Aviation Institute, Adamuck, 4-6, Kazan-15, 420015, Russian Federation. TEL 7-8432-361648, FAX 7-8432-367621, lyudmila.kuzmina@ksu.ru, http://www.kcn.ru/tat_en/science/ans/journals/rasj.html. Ed. G L Degtyarev. **Co-publisher:** Academy of Non-Linear Sciences.

001.942 USA
ALIEN HIDEOUT WEEKLY EZINE. Text in English. w. **Document type:** *Newsletter.* **Description:** Aimed at all levels of interest in UFOs and aliens.
Media: Online - full text.
Address: http://www.geocities.com/area51/lair/7676. Ed. Karl Jones.

ALIENS (AUCKLAND). see *ASTRONOMY*

629.133 USA ISSN 1541-0455
TL721.5
AMERICAN AIRCRAFT & AIRSHOW MAGAZINE. Text in English. 2002 (July). q. USD 20 domestic; USD 30 foreign (effective 2002).
Published by: Air Data Publishing, P.O. Box 1330, Powderly, TX 75473. TEL 903-732-3509. Ed. Roger E. Stewart.

629.4 USA ISSN 0516-9593
AMERICAN ASTRONAUTICAL SOCIETY. PROCEEDINGS OF THE ANNUAL MEETING. Text in English. 1957. irreg. price varies. cum.index. back issues avail. **Document type:** *Proceedings.*
Related titles: ♦ Series of: Advances in the Astronautical Sciences. ISSN 0065-3438.
Published by: (American Astronautical Society, Inc.), Univelt, Inc., PO Box 28130, San Diego, CA 92198-0130. TEL 760-746-4005, FAX 760-746-3139, 76121.1532@compuserve.com, http://www.univelt.com. Ed., Pub., R&P Robert H Jacobs.

629.133 USA ISSN 0733-4249
TL716.A1 CODEN: PFASDL
AMERICAN HELICOPTER SOCIETY. ANNUAL FORUM. PROCEEDINGS. Text in English, 1943. a. USD 180 to non-members; USD 135 to members. back issues avail. **Document type:** *Proceedings.*
Formerly: American Helicopter Society. National Forum. Proceedings (0065-8510)
Indexed: AcoustA, CivEngAb, EngInd.
—BLDSC (1085.665000), IE, ingenta, Linda Hall.
Published by: American Helicopter Society, Inc., 217 N Washington St, Alexandria, VA 22314. TEL 703-684-6777, FAX 703-739-9279. Circ: 650.

629.133 USA ISSN 0002-8711
TL716.A1 CODEN: JHESAK
AMERICAN HELICOPTER SOCIETY. JOURNAL. Text in English. 1956. q. USD 95 domestic; USD 115 foreign; USD 20 per issue domestic; USD 25 per issue foreign (effective 2005). illus. reprints avail. **Document type:** *Journal.*
Indexed: ASCA, AcoustA, ApMecR, BrCerAb, C&ISA, CerAb, CorrAb, CurCont, E&CAJ, EMA, EngInd, IAA, ISMEC, ISR, Inspec, M&TEA, MBF, METADEX, RefZh, SCI, SolStAb, WAA.
—BLDSC (4686.350000), AskIEEE, CISTI, IDS, IE, Infotrieve, ingenta, Linda Hall.
Published by: American Helicopter Society, Inc., 217 N Washington St, Alexandria, VA 22314. TEL 703-684-6777, FAX 703-739-9279, staff@vtol.org, http://www.vtol.org/journal/. Ed. Gopal Gaonkar. Circ: 3,000 (paid).

629.13 629.4 USA ISSN 1087-7215
TL505
AMERICAN INSTITUTE OF AERONAUTICS AND ASTRONAUTICS. MEETING PAPERS ON DISC. Text in English. 1996. irreg. USD 7,500 (effective 2005). **Document type:** *Academic/Scholarly.*
Media: CD-ROM. **Related titles:** ♦ Print ed.: A I A A Technical Meeting Papers.
—Linda Hall.
Published by: American Institute of Aeronautics and Astronautics, Inc., 1801 Alexander Bell Dr, Ste 500, Reston, VA 20191. TEL 703-264-7500, FAX 703-264-7551, custserv@aiaa.org, http://www.aiaa.org.

629.1 USA
AMERICAN SOCIETY OF MECHANICAL ENGINEERS. AEROSPACE DIVISION. NEWSLETTER. Text in English. a. free membership (effective 2003).
Related titles: Online - full text ed.
Published by: A S M E International, Three Park Ave, New York, NY 10016-5990. TEL 212-591-7722, FAX 212-591-7674, infocentral@asme.org, http://www.asme.org/divisions/aerospace/newsletter/index.html. **Subscr. to:** 22 Law Dr, PO Box 2900, Fairfield, NJ 07007-2900. TEL 973-882-1170, 973-882-1167, 800-843-2763, 95-800-843-2763, FAX 973-882-1717.

620.11 USA ISSN 0733-4230
CODEN: ASADD4
AMERICAN SOCIETY OF MECHANICAL ENGINEERS. AEROSPACE DIVISION. PUBLICATION AD. Text in English. irreg., latest vol.67, 2003. USD 140 to non-members; USD 70 to members (effective 2003). **Document type:** *Monographic series.*
Indexed: BrCerAb, C&ISA, CerAb, CorrAb, E&CAJ, EMA, IAA, ISMEC, M&TEA, MBF, METADEX, SolStAb, WAA.
—BLDSC (1745.202000), CISTI, IE, ingenta. **CCC.**
Published by: A S M E International, Three Park Ave, New York, NY 10016-5990. infocentral@asme.org, http://www.asme.org. **Subscr. to:** 22 Law Dr, PO Box 2900, Fairfield, NJ 07007-2900. TEL 973-882-1170, 973-882-1167, 800-843-2763, 95-800-843-2763, FAX 973-882-1717.

341.47 CAN ISSN 0701-158X
K1
➤ **ANNALS OF AIR AND SPACE LAW/ANNALES DE DROIT AERIEN ET SPATIAL.** Text in English, French. 1976. a., latest vol.26, 2002. CND 100 (effective 2002). adv. bk.rev. cum.index: 1976-1987. back issues avail.; reprint service avail. from WSH. **Document type:** *Monographic series, Academic/Scholarly.*
Related titles: Online - full text ed.
Indexed: CLI, FLP, ICLPL, ILP, LRI, PCI.
—BLDSC (1035.800000). **CCC.**
Published by: McGill University, Institute of Air and Space Law, 3661 Peel St, Montreal, PQ H3A 1X1, Canada. TEL 514-398 5095, FAX 514-398 8197, maria.damico@mcgill.ca, http://www.iasl.mcgill.ca/publications/annals/index.htm. Eds. Dimitri Maniatis, Michael Milde TEL 514-398-5093. R&P Michael Milde TEL 514-398-5093. Adv. contact Maria D'Amico. Circ: 1,200.

629.13 USA ISSN 1062-6174
ANNALS OF BALLOON HISTORY AND MUSEOLOGY. Text in English. 1991. irreg. USD 30; USD 35 foreign (effective 1998). bk.rev. **Document type:** *Academic/Scholarly.* **Description:** Scholarly essays on history of the free balloon and the collecting of related material.
Address: 15155 County Rd 32, Mayer, MN 55360. TEL 612-657-2237. Ed. Paul Maravelas.

629.1 USA ISSN 1093-9288
TK2901 CODEN: PBAAE8
ANNUAL BATTERY CONFERENCE ON APPLICATIONS AND ADVANCES. Text in English. 1986. a. USD 182 per vol. to institutions (effective 2004). **Document type:** *Proceedings, Trade.*
Formerly (until 1995): Battery Conference on Applications and Advances. Proceedings (1089-8182)
Related titles: Online - full text ed.: (from I E E E).
—BLDSC (1075.714000). **CCC.**
Published by: Institute of Electrical and Electronics Engineers, Inc., 3 Park Ave, 17th Fl, New York, NY 10016-5997. TEL 212-419-7900, 800-678-4333, FAX 212-752-4929, customer.service@ieee.org, http://www.ieee.org.

629.1325 USA
ANNUAL F A A COMMERCIAL AVIATION FORECAST CONFERENCE PROCEEDINGS. Text in English. 197?. a.
Formerly: Annual F A A Aviation Forecast Conference Proceedings
Published by: U.S. Federal Aviation Administration, 800 Independence Ave S W, Washington, DC 20591. TEL 202-267-8017, FAX 202-366-7060, http://www.faa.gov. **Dist. by:** U.S. Government Printing Office, Superintendent of Documents, PO Box 371954, Pittsburgh, PA 15250-7954. TEL 202-512-1800, FAX 202-512-2250, orders@gpo.gov, http://www.access.gpo.gov.

387.7 USA ISSN 0003-5823
ANTIQUE AIRPLANE ASSOCIATION NEWS. Text in English. 1953. q. USD 36 membership (effective 1999); includes APM Bulletin and International Antique Airplane Digest. adv. bk.rev. charts; illus.; tr.lit. **Description:** Presents articles, photos and drawings of antique and classical airplanes of past and present.
Published by: Antique Airplane Association, Inc., 22001 Bluegrass Rd, Ottumwa, IA 52501-8569. TEL 515-938-2773. Ed., Pub., R&P Robert L Taylor. Adv. contact L Reis. Circ: 5,000.

629.1 BRA ISSN 0103-5002
TL525.B8
ANUARIO AEROSPACIAL BRASILEIRO/BRAZILIAN AEROSPACE YEARBOOK; diretorio aerospacial brasileiro. Text in Portuguese; Summaries in English. 1983. a. per issue exchange basis. adv. charts; illus.; stat. **Document type:** *Directory.* **Description:** Contains sector analysis, performance statistics, trend indicators, data on aircraft fleets, and supply and service company listings.
Published by: Aviacao em Revista Editora Ltda., Rua da Consolacao, 1992 Andar 10, Consolacao, Sao Paulo, SP 01302-001, Brazil. aviacaoemrevista@uol.com.br. Ed., Pub., R&P Helcio Estrella. Adv. contact Francisco Carlos Alves. B&W page USD 6,300, color page USD 7,400; trim 280 x 210. Circ: 24,000.

▼ *new title* ➤ *refereed* ✱ *unverified* ♦ *full entry avail.*

A

359 USA ISSN 1094-0405
VG93
APPROACH; the naval aviation safety review. Text in English. 1995. bi-m. USD 50 (effective 2001). charts; illus. back issues avail. **Document type:** *Government.*
Supersedes in part (in 1997): Approach Mech (1086-928X); Which was formed by the merger of (1955-1995): Approach (0570-4979); (1968-1995): Mech (0025-6471)
Related titles: Online - full content ed.; Online - full text ed.: (from EBSCO Publishing, Florida Center for Library Automation, Gale Group, ProQuest Information & Learning).
Indexed: AIAP, IUSGP, RefZh.
—Linda Hall.
Published by: Naval Safety Center (Subsidiary of: U.S. Department of the Navy), 375 A St, Norfolk, VA 23511. TEL 757-444-3520, http://safetycenter.navy.mil/publications/approach/ApproachDefault.htm, http://www.safetycenter.navy.mil/. Circ: 13,000. **Subscr. to:** U.S. Government Printing Office, Superintendent of Documents, PO Box 371954, Pittsburgh, PA 15250-7954. TEL 202-512-1800, FAX 202-512-2250, orders@gpo.gov, http://www.access.gpo.gov.

629.13 387.71 GBR
ARAB AVIATION REVIEW; an air transport and aerospace quarterly magazine. Text in Arabic; Summaries in Arabic, English. 1990. q. USD 30. adv. charts; illus.; stat. back issues avail. **Document type:** *Trade.* **Description:** Covers all aspects of the aerospace industry and includes important issues concerning economic, commercial, legal, managerial and operational aspects of air transport operations, aerospace and military aviation. Aims to promote and enhance business links between international and Arab aviation companies.
Published by: Communications Enterprises, Crown House, Crown Ln, Farnham Royal, Slough, East Burnham, Bucks SL2 3SQ, United Kingdom. TEL 44-1753-648-701, FAX 44-1753-648-707, info@makkahadv.com. Ed., Pub. Mohammed Salahuddin. adv.: B&W page USD 2,200, color page USD 3,000; trim 210 x 290. Circ: 9,300.

629.1 GBR ISSN 0262-4923
ARCHIVE (AIR-BRITAIN); civil aviation historical quarterly. Text in English. 1980. q. GBP 14. illus.
Published by: Air-Britain (Historians) Ltd., 1 East St, Tonbridge, Kent TN9 1AR, United Kingdom. Circ: 1,500. **Subscr. to:** 15 Mallory Close, St Athan, Barry, S Glam CF6 9JJ, United Kingdom.

355.31 CHE ISSN 0252-9793
HD9743.A1
ARMADA INTERNATIONAL. Text in English. 1977. 6/yr. CHF 156 in Europe; USD 156 elsewhere (effective 2001). adv. charts; illus. back issues avail.; reprints avail. **Document type:** *Magazine, Trade.* **Description:** International news of weapon systems and armed forces.
Related titles: Online - full text ed.: (from EBSCO Publishing, Gale Group, Northern Light Technology, Inc., O C L C Online Computer Library Center, Inc., ProQuest Information & Learning); French ed.; German ed.
Indexed: ABIn, AMB, AUNI, BAS, BrCerAb, C&ISA, CerAb, CivEngAb, CorrAb, DM&T, E&CAJ, EMA, IAA, LID&ISL, M&TEA, MBF, METADEX, PROMT, SolStAb, WAA.
—BLDSC (1682.400000), IE, Infotrieve, ingenta, Linda Hall.
Address: Thurgauerstr 39, Zurich, 8050, Switzerland. TEL 41-1-3085050, FAX 41-1-3085055, mail@armada.ch, http://www.armada.ch. Ed. Eric Biass. Pub. Caroline Schwegler. R&P, Adv. contact Peter Stierlin. color page USD 8,130; 210 x 297. Circ: 21,382 (controlled).

ARMY AVIATION. see *MILITARY*

ARMY FLIER. see *MILITARY*

387.7 USA ISSN 0004-2617
ARNOLD AIR LETTER. Text in English. 1950. q. USD 5 to non-members. adv. charts; illus.
Published by: Arnold Air Society, National Publications Headquarters, AFROTC Det 045, San Jose State University, One Washington Sq, San Jose, CA 95192-0051. TEL 214-886-5200. Ed. Col Randal G Kelly. Circ: 7,500.

629.13 SGP ISSN 0129-1289
ASIA - PACIFIC AVIATION AND ENGINEERING JOURNAL. Text in English. 1976. 4/yr. USD 90. adv. **Document type:** *Academic/Scholarly.*
Formerly (until Dec. 1987): Aircraft Engineer (0129-9913)
Published by: Singapore Institute of Aerospace Engineers, Airline House A 5F, 25 Airline Rd, Singapore, 819829, Singapore. TEL 542-0688, FAX 542-9034. Ed. Poon Chia Wee. Circ: 10,000.

ASIAN AIRLINES & AEROSPACE. see *TRANSPORTATION—Air Transport*

629.1 SGP ISSN 0129-9972
ASIAN AVIATION. Text in English. 1981. m. SGD 70 in Asia & the Pacific; SGD 75 elsewhere; free elsewhere to qualified personnel. adv. bk.rev. back issues avail. **Document type:** *Trade.* **Description:** Activities of the aerospace industry of the Asia-Pacific region: airlines, air forces, airports and space communications.
Related titles: Online - full text ed.: (from LexisNexis).
Indexed: BAS.
Published by: Asian Aviation Publications Pte. Ltd., Thye Hong Centre, 2 Leng Kee Rd 04-01, Singapore, 159086, Singapore. TEL 65-474-7088, FAX 65-479-6668. Ed. Colin Gibson. Circ: 10,951 (controlled).

ASIAN DEFENCE AND DIPLOMACY. see *MILITARY*

ASSOCIATION TECHNIQUE MARITIME ET AERONAUTIQUE, PARIS. BULLETIN. see *TRANSPORTATION—Ships And Shipping*

629.4 028.5 USA
ASTRO-NEWS. Text in English. 1985. q. free to members. back issues avail. **Document type:** *Newsletter.* **Description:** Organizational newsletter giving updates on space-related news, program and membership activities.
Published by: Young Astronaut Council, 5200 27th St NW, Washington, DC 20015-1326. TEL 202-682-1984, FAX 202-775-1773. Ed., R&P Cecelia Blalock.

629.4 AUS ISSN 0312-8121
ASTRONAUTICAL SOCIETY OF WESTERN AUSTRALIA. NEWS BULLETIN. Text in English. 1976. m. AUD 25 domestic; AUD 35 foreign (effective 2000). bk.rev. back issues avail. **Document type:** *Bulletin.* **Description:** Discusses space exploration.
Indexed: RefZh.
Published by: Astronautical Society of Western Australia, PO Box 278, South Perth, W.A. 6151, Australia. Ed., Pub. Jos Heyman. Circ: 50 (paid); 30 (controlled).

629.4 POL ISSN 0004-623X
ASTRONAUTYKA. Text in Polish. 1958. bi-m. USD 16.20. bk.rev. charts; illus. **Description:** Popular-scientific magazine devoted to astronautics and space research.
Indexed: IBR.
Published by: Polskie Towarzystwo Astronautyczne/Polish Astronautical Society, Ul Z. Krasinskiego 54, Warsaw, 01755, Poland. TEL 48-22-3082703. Ed. Pawel Elsztein. Circ: 3,000. **Dist. by:** Ars Polona, Krakowskie Przedmiescie 7, Warsaw, Poland.

629.1 797.5 CAN
ATLANTIC INFLIGHT✶. Text in English. 1978. q. looseleaf. CND 15 (effective 1999). adv. bk.rev. stat.; tr.lit. **Document type:** *Newsletter.* **Description:** Provides coverage of hang gliding and paragliding events in Atlantic Canada.
Published by: Hang Gliding and Paragliding Association of Atlantic Canada, Diligent River, NS BOM-1HO, Canada. TEL 902-254-2972. Ed. Michael Fuller. R&P Chris Walters. Circ: 25 (controlled).

AUDITS OF AIRLINES, WITH CONFORMING CHANGES. see *INSURANCE*

629.13 AUS
AUSTRALIA. AERONAUTICAL RESEARCH LABORATORIES. AERODYNAMICS NOTE. Text in English. irreg.
—BLDSC (0726.105000).
Published by: Aeronautical and Maritime Research Laboratories, 506 Lorimer St, Fishermans Bend, VIC 3207, Australia. http://www.dsto.defence.gov.au/amrl/index.html.

629.13 AUS ISSN 0365-0049
AUSTRALIA. AERONAUTICAL RESEARCH LABORATORIES. AERODYNAMICS REPORT. Text in English. 1949. irreg.
—BLDSC (0726.110000).
Published by: Aeronautical and Maritime Research Laboratories, 506 Lorimer St, Fishermans Bend, VIC 3207, Australia. http://www.dsto.defence.gov.au/amrl/index.html.

629.13 AUS ISSN 0430-6082
AUSTRALIA. AERONAUTICAL RESEARCH LABORATORIES. STRUCTURES AND MATERIALS REPORT. Text in English. 1940. irreg.
—BLDSC (0726.190000), CISTI.
Published by: Aeronautical and Maritime Research Laboratories, 506 Lorimer St, Fishermans Bend, VIC 3207, Australia. http://www.dsto.defence.gov.au/amrl/index.html.

629.13 AUS ISSN 0313-7554
AUSTRALIA. AERONAUTICAL RESEARCH LABORATORIES. STRUCTURES NOTE. Text in English. 1975. irreg.
—BLDSC (0726.195300).
Published by: Aeronautical and Maritime Research Laboratories, 506 Lorimer St, Fishermans Bend, VIC 3207, Australia. http://www.dsto.defence.gov.au/amrl/index.html.

629.13 AUS ISSN 0365-1592
AUSTRALIA. AERONAUTICAL RESEARCH LABORATORIES. STRUCTURES TECHNICAL MEMORANDUM. Text in English. irreg.
—BLDSC (0726.195700).
Published by: Aeronautical and Maritime Research Laboratories, 506 Lorimer St, Fishermans Bend, VIC 3207, Australia. http://www.dsto.defence.gov.au/amrl/index.html.

629.13 AUS
AUSTRALIA. AERONAUTICAL RESEARCH LABORATORIES. SYSTEMS NOTE. Text in English. 1955. irreg.
—BLDSC (0726.196000).
Published by: Aeronautical and Maritime Research Laboratories, 506 Lorimer St, Fishermans Bend, VIC 3207, Australia. http://www.dsto.defence.gov.au/amrl/index.html.

629.13 AUS
AUSTRALIA. AERONAUTICAL RESEARCH LABORATORIES. SYSTEMS REPORT. Text in English. 1954. irreg.
—BLDSC (0726.197000).
Published by: Aeronautical and Maritime Research Laboratories, 506 Lorimer St, Fishermans Bend, VIC 3207, Australia. http://www.dsto.defence.gov.au/amrl/index.html.

AUSTRALIAN AEROSPACE INDUSTRY CAPABILITY DIRECTORY. see *BUSINESS AND ECONOMICS—Trade And Industrial Directories*

629.1325 AUS ISSN 0813-0876
AUSTRALIAN AVIATION. Text in English. 1977. m. (11/yr.). AUD 72.60 domestic; AUD 88 in Asia & the Pacific; AUD 110 elsewhere (effective 2004). adv. **Document type:** *Magazine, Trade.* **Description:** Reports on all facets of the aviation and aerospace environment here in Australia and as well as events overseas. Contains dedicated news and regular feature sections each issue on the airlines, airliner development, military aviation, defence policy, aerospace industry, general aviation and helicopters.
Formerly (until 1981): Australian Aviation & Defence (0159-611X)
Published by: Aerospace Publications Pty. Ltd., PO Box 1777, Fyshwick, ACT 2609, Australia. TEL 61-2-62800111, FAX 61-2-62800007, mail@ausaviation.com.au, http://www.ausaviation.com.au/index.html. adv.: B&W page AUD 2,300, color page AUD 3,200; trim 20.6 x 27.6. Circ: 15,756.

629.13 AUS
AUSTRALIAN AVIATION ANNUAL. Text in English. 1960. a. **Document type:** *Trade.* **Description:** Lists the names and addresses of every flying training school and every helicopter operator, plus detailing the personnel, fleet and major achievements of every airline in Australasia, the ADF Order of Battle, statistics and a complete list of the region's military aircraft.
Formerly: Australian Aviation Yearbook (0084-7232)
Published by: Aerospace Publications Pty. Ltd., PO Box 1777, Fyshwick, ACT 2609, Australia. TEL 61-2-62800111, FAX 61-2-62800007, http://www.ausaviation.com.au/annual/annualindex.

629.13 AUS ISSN 0004-9123
AUSTRALIAN FLYING. Text in English. 1961. bi-m. AUD 35 domestic; AUD 45 in New Zealand; AUD 52 in Asia; AUD 70 elsewhere (effective 2005). adv. bk.rev. illus. **Document type:** *Magazine, Consumer.* **Description:** Industry magazine devoted to the needs of today's aviation professional. Covers both civil and military flying disciplines, from fixed-wing to helicopter operations.
Published by: Yaffa Publishing Group Pty Ltd., 17-21 Bellevue St, Surry Hills, NSW 2010, Australia. TEL 61-2-92812333, FAX 61-2-92812750, yaffa@yaffa.com.au, http://www.yaffa.com.au/mags/flymag.htm. Ed. Doug Nancarrow. Pub. Tracy Yaffa. Adv. contact Tiffany Palmer. B&W page AUD 1,765, color page AUD 2,475; trim 210 x 273. Circ: 11,335.

629.13 AUS ISSN 0004-9204
AUSTRALIAN GLIDING. Text in English. 1950. m. AUD 28.80 domestic; AUD 40.50 foreign; Includes Yearbook. adv. bk.rev. charts; illus.; stat. **Document type:** *Newsletter.* **Description:** Carries world wide news, technical and semi-technical features.
Indexed: SportS.
Published by: Gliding Federation of Australia, 130 Wirraway Rd, Essendon Airport, VIC 3041, Australia. TEL 61-3-9379-7411, FAX 61-3-9379-5519, AGeditor@gfa.on.net, http://www.gfa.org.au. Ed. Noel Matthews. R&P D E Thomas. Adv. contact Ray Munn. page AUD 240; trim 185 x 255. Circ: 3,500 (paid).

629.13 AUS ISSN 0084-7364
AUSTRALIAN GLIDING YEARBOOK. Text in English. 1969. a. AUD 5. adv. bk.rev. **Description:** Contains detailed information on all gliding clubs in Australia, complete gliding statistics, lists of national and international records, competition numbers, etc.
Published by: Gliding Federation of Australia, 130 Wirraway Rd, Essendon Airport, VIC 3041, Australia. TEL 61-3-9379-7411, FAX 61-3-9379-5519, AGeditor@gfa.on.net, http://www.gfa.org.au. Ed. Noel Matthews. R&P E R N Thomas. Adv. contact Ray Munn. page AUD 120; trim 185 x 255. Circ: 3,500 (paid).

001.94 AUS ISSN 0156-742X
TL789.6.A8
AUSTRALIAN INTERNATIONAL U F O FLYING SAUCER RESEARCH. Text in English. 1978. q. AUD 15 to members (effective 2000). **Document type:** *Newsletter.*
Published by: Australian Flying Saucer Society, GPO Box 2004, Adelaide, SA 5001, Australia. Ed., Pub. Colin Norris.

001.942 AUS
AUSTRALIAN U F O BULLETIN. Text in English. 1972. q. AUD 15, USD 20 (effective 1999). adv. bk.rev. charts. **Document type:** *Bulletin.*
Published by: Victorian U.F.O. Research Society, PO Box 1043, Moorabbin, VIC 3189, Australia. TEL 61-3-95922502, FAX 61-3-95922502, vufors@ozemail.com.au, http://www.ozemail.com.au/~vufors. Ed., R&P Judith M Magee. Circ: 500.

629.4 FIN ISSN 0356-021X
AVARUUSLUOTAIN/RYMDSONDEN. Text in Finnish; Summaries in English. 1971. q. EUR 22. adv. bk.rev. **Document type:** *Magazine, Academic/Scholarly.*
Formerly (until 1972): A T S Luotain
Published by: Suomen Avaruustutkimusseura ry/Saellskapet foer Astronautisk Forskning i Finland, PO Box 503, Helsinki, 00101, Finland. TEL 358-9-19294660, FAX 358-9-19294603. Ed. Tero Siili. Circ: 200 (controlled).

629.78 FIN ISSN 1236-9403
AVARUUSUUTISET. Text in Finnish. 1993. bi-m. **Document type:** *Journal, Trade.*
Published by: Tekes, PO Box 69, Helsinki, 001011, Finland. TEL 358-10-5215856, FAX 358-10-5215901, tekes@tekes.fi, http://www.tekes.fi. Ed. Pauli Stigell.

629.13 ITA
AVIA✶ . Text in Italian. 1960. m. adv. bk.rev. illus.
Published by: Aeronews, Aeroporto Fiumicino, Rome, RM, Italy. Ed. Romano Nodari.

629.1 BRA ISSN 0102-4876
TL525.B8
AVIACAO EM REVISTA/AVIATION MAGAZINE. Text in Portuguese; Summaries in English. 1938. m. (except Nov.-Dec. combined). USD 100. adv. bk.rev. illus. **Document type:** *Trade.* **Description:** Covers the aviation industry, airlines, airports, air cargo, training, market, technology and sport flying.
Formerly: Aviacao e Astronautica (0005-206X)
Published by: Aviacao em Revista Editora Ltda., Rua da Consolacao, 1992 Andar 10, Consolacao, Sao Paulo, SP 01302-001, Brazil. aviacaoemrevista@uol.com.br. Ed., Pub., R&P Helcio Estrella. Adv. contact Francisco Carlos Alves. B&W page USD 5,700, color page USD 6,750; trim 280 x 210. Circ: 24,000.

AVIACION. see *MILITARY*

629.13 ARG ISSN 0045-1177
AVIACION Y ASTRONAUTICA✶ . Text in Spanish. 1971 (vol.11). bi-m. ARS 25, USD 8. adv. bibl.; charts; illus.; tr.lit.
Address: Avda. Belgrano, 1735, Capital Federal, Buenos Aires 1093, Argentina. Ed. Gilberto Julian Riega.

629.13 FRA
AVIAGUIDE; ou voler en Ile-de-France?. Text in French. 1980. s-a. adv. back issues avail. **Document type:** *Directory.* **Description:** Provides information on where to rent a light aircraft (or helicopter) and where to learn to pilot an aircraft as well as corresponding prices.
Published by: 1013 Editions, 7 rue de Blaru, Jeufosse, 78270, France. TEL 30-98-92-92, FAX 30-98-93-13. Ed. Christian Sainderichin. Circ: 2,500 (paid).

629.1 RUS
AVIAKOSMICHESKAYA TEKHNIKA I TEKHNOLOGIYA. Text in Russian. q. USD 299.95 in United States. **Document type:** *Academic/Scholarly.*
Published by: Rossiiskaya Inzhenernaya Akademiya, Sektsiya Aviakosmicheskaya, Sokol'nicheskii val 37-10, Moscow, 107313, Russian Federation. TEL 7-095-4974961, FAX 7-095-4934388. **US dist. addr.:** East View Information Services, 3020 Harbor Ln. N., Minneapolis, MN 55447. TEL 612-550-0961.

629.1 RUS
AVIAKOSMICHESKOE PRIBOROSTROENIE. Text in Russian. 2002. m. USD 375 in United States (effective 2004).
Published by: NauchTekhLitIzdat, Alymov per, dom 17, str 2, Moscow, 107258, Russian Federation. TEL 7-095-2690004, FAX 7-095-3239010, pribor@tgizdat.ru, http://www.tgizdat.ru. **Dist. by:** East View Information Services, 3020 Harbor Ln. N., Minneapolis, MN 55447. TEL 800-477-1005, FAX 800-800-3839, eastview@eastview.com, http://www.eastview.com.

629.132 RUS
AVIAMASTER. Text in Russian. bi-m. USD 95 in United States.
Published by: Vostochnyi Gorizont, Novodmitrovskaya ul 5-a, Moscow, 125015, Russian Federation. TEL 7-095-2341678, FAX 7-095-2851687, tmaver@dol.ru. Ed. A N Perevozchikov. **US dist. addr.:** East View Information Services, 3020 Harbor Ln. N., Minneapolis, MN 55447. TEL 612-550-0961, FAX 612-559-2931.

629 RUS ISSN 1726-6173
AVIAPANORAMA. Text in Russian. 1996. bi-m. USD 53 foreign (effective 2004). **Document type:** *Academic/Scholarly.*
Indexed: RefZh.
Published by: Aviapanorama Media Ltd, ul L Chaikinoi, dom 6, Moscow, 125315, Russian Federation. aviapanorama@mail.ru, http://www.aviapanorama.ru. Ed. Timofei Zabaluev. **Dist. by:** Informnauka Ltd., Ul Usievicha 20, Moscow 125190, Russian Federation. alfimov@viniti.ru.

343.097 USA
AVIATION ACCIDENT LAW & PRACTICE. Text in English. 1963. 2 base vols. plus updates 2/yr. looseleaf. USD 731 base vol(s). (effective 2003).
Published by: Matthew Bender & Co., Inc. (Subsidiary of: LexisNexis North America), 1275 Broadway, Albany, NY 12204. international@bender.com, http://bender.lexisnexis.com. Ed. Lee Kreindler.

AVIATION AND ENVIRONMENT NEWS. see *ENVIRONMENTAL STUDIES*

343.097 GBR ISSN 1352-4003
AVIATION & SPACE LAW REPORTS. Text in English. 1994. m. (plus a. cumulation). GBP 295, USD 445; includes cumulation. **Document type:** *Academic/Scholarly.*
Published by: Lloyds of London Press Ltd., Sheepen Pl, Cochester, Essex C03 3LP, United Kingdom.

629.1029 USA ISSN 0001-0502
TL512
AVIATION BUYERS DIRECTORY. Key Title: A B D. Text in English. 1949. q. USD 45 (effective 1999). adv. **Document type:** *Directory.*
Formerly: Aviation Business Directory
Media: Duplicated (not offset).
Published by: Air Service Directory, Inc., 280 N. Bedford Rd., Ste. 301, Mount Kisco, NY 10549-1148. TEL 914-835-7200, abd50@aol.com, aviation@buyers.com, http://www.aviationbuyers.com. Ed. Robert Annis. Pub. Jerry Greenwald. R&P Rick Greenwald. Circ: 20,500 (controlled).

629.1325 CAN ISSN 1496-7863
AVIATION CANADA (OTTAWA). Text in English. 1994. q. CND 16.90 domestic; USD 21 in United States; CND 34 overseas; CND 4.50 newsstand/cover (effective 2000). **Description:** Covers general, commercial and recreational aviation in Canada.
Formerly (until 2001): Aviation Quarterly (1198-676X)
Indexed: CPerl.
—BLDSC.
Published by: Aviation Canada Media Inc., 72 Sunnyside Ave, Ottawa, ON K1S 0R1, Canada. TEL 613-730-9439, FAX 613-730-1321, info@aviationcanada.ca, http://www.aviationcanada.ca. Ed., R&P, Adv. contact Bob Baglow.

629.132 USA ISSN 0147-9911
TL721.4
THE AVIATION CONSUMER. Text in English. 1971. m. USD 84 in US & Canada; USD 102 elsewhere (effective 2006). back issues avail.; reprints avail. **Document type:** *Magazine, Consumer.*
Published by: Belvoir Media Group, LLC, 800 Connecticut Ave, Norwalk, CT 06854-1631. TEL 203-857-3100, 800-424-7887, FAX 203-857-3103, customer_service@belvoir.com, http://www.aviationconsumer.com, http://www.belvoir.com. Circ: 12,000 (paid).

AVIATION EDUCATION NEWS. see *TRANSPORTATION—Air Transport*

629.13 333.79 USA
AVIATION FACILITIES ENERGY ASSOCIATION. ANNUAL REPORT. Text in English. a.
Published by: Aviation Facilities Energy Association, Atlanta Airlines Terminal Corp, Box 415171, Atlanta, GA 30320. TEL 404-530-2105.

629.13 333.79 USA
AVIATION FACILITIES ENERGY ASSOCIATION. ENERGY CONSUMPTION ANALYSIS REPORT. Text in English. a.
Published by: Aviation Facilities Energy Association, Atlanta Airlines Terminal Corp, Box 415171, Atlanta, GA 30320. TEL 404-530-2105.

629.13 AUS ISSN 0815-4392
TL529
AVIATION HERITAGE. Text in English. 1960. q. AUD 45 domestic; AUD 55 in the Pacific Rim; AUD 68 elsewhere in the Pacific Rim (effective 2000). bk.rev. 44 p./no.; back issues avail. **Document type:** *Journal, Academic/Scholarly.* **Description:** Covers Australian and Pacific Islands historical events and personalities.
Formerly: Aviation Historical Society of Australia. Journal (0045-1185)
Published by: Aviation Historical Society of Australia, PO Box 2007, South Melbourne, VIC 3205, Australia. TEL 61-39-5834072, FAX 61-39-5834072, auster@primus.com.au. Ed. William Barker.

387.7 NZL ISSN 0110-5493
AVIATION HISTORICAL SOCIETY OF NEW ZEALAND. JOURNAL. Text in English. 1958. a. NZD 40. adv. bk.rev. bibl.; charts; illus. index. **Document type:** *Academic/Scholarly.*
Indexed: INZP.
—CCC.
Published by: Aviation Historical Society of New Zealand, Private Box 12-009, Wellington, 6038, New Zealand. TEL 64-4-471-4070, FAX 64-4-471-0395. Ed. C F L Jenks. Circ: 400.

629.13 USA ISSN 1076-8858
TL515
AVIATION HISTORY. Text in English. 1990. bi-m. USD 29.95; USD 4.99 newsstand/cover (effective 2005). adv. bk.rev.; software rev. illus.; maps. back issues avail. **Document type:** *Magazine, Consumer.* **Description:** Feature articles and departments cover the development of commercial, military, high performance and experimental aviation, profiles of planes and personalities, aerial oddities, heritage, events and aviation artwork.
Former titles: Aviation (1067-4799); Aviation Heritage (1054-335X)
Related titles: Online - full text ed.: (from bigchalk, EBSCO Publishing, ProQuest Information & Learning).
Indexed: MASUSE.
—CCC.
Published by: Primedia History Group (Subsidiary of: Primedia Enthusiast Media), 741 Miller Dr, S E, Ste D-2, Leesburg, VA 20175. TEL 703-771-9400, 800-358-6327, FAX 703-779-8310, http://www.historynet.com. Eds. Arthur H Sanfelici, Roger Vance. Pub. Joe Peckle. Adv. contact Tamra Varda. B&W page USD 1,927, color page USD 2,884. Circ: 90,000 (paid).

629.1 USA
AVIATION ILLUSTRATED MAGAZINE✶ . Text in English. 1995. bi-m. USD 19.95 domestic; USD 31.95 foreign; USD 4.95 newsstand/cover. adv. bk.rev.; video rev. back issues avail.
Formerly: Aviation Art Show Case
Media: Online - full text.
Published by: Vector Publishing Group, 221 Town Ctr W 233, Santa Maria, CA 93458-5083. TEL 805-928-7115, FAX 805-928-7685, http://www.avationillustrated.com. Adv. contact Maria Binde.

629.13 CAN
AVIATION IN CANADA. Text in English. 1993. irreg. CND 48, USD 58; USD 67 foreign. **Description:** Describes the Canadian aviation industry from its earliest years to present with up to 75 years of operating and financial data and information on key markets, airports, air regulation and Canada's safety record.
Related titles: French ed.
Published by: Statistics Canada, Operations and Integration Division, Circulation Management, Jean Talon Bldg, 2 C12, Tunney's Pasture, Ottawa, ON K1A 0T6, Canada. TEL 613-951-7277, 800-267-6677, FAX 613-951-1584, http://www.statcan.ca.

AVIATION INTERNATIONAL NEWS; the newsmagazine of corporate, business and regional aviation. see *TRANSPORTATION—Air Transport*

629.1 USA ISSN 1090-221X
TL671.9
AVIATION MAINTENANCE. Text in English. 1982. m. USD 109; free to qualified personnel (effective 2005). **Document type:** *Magazine, Trade.* **Description:** Publishes for aviation service professionals in commercial, corporate and military aviation maintenance.
Formerly (until 1996): Aviation Equipment Maintenance (0745-0214)
—CCC.
Published by: Access Intelligence, LLC (Subsidiary of: Veronis, Suhler & Associates Inc.), 1201 Seven Locks Rd, Ste 300, Potomac, MD 20854. TEL 301-354-2000, 800-777-5006, FAX 301-762-3068, am@pbimedia.com, clientservices@accessintel.com, http://www.aviationmx.com, http://www.pbimedia.com. Ed. Matt Turber TEL 301-354-2000. Pub. Nancy O'Brien. Circ: 25,000 (controlled).

629.134 USA
AVIATION MAINTENANCE ALERTS. Text in English. m. USD 41 (effective 2001). **Document type:** *Government.*
Published by: Federal Aviation Administration, Aviation Data Systems Branch, AFS-620, P O Box 25082, Oklahoma City, OK 73125-5029. **Subscr. to:** U.S. Government Printing Office, Superintendent of Documents, PO Box 371954, Pittsburgh, PA 15250-7954. TEL 202-512-1800, FAX 202-512-2250, orders@gpo.gov, http://www.access.gpo.gov.

629.1 USA
AVIATION MAINTENANCE FOUNDATION INTERNATIONAL. INDUSTRY REPORT. Text in English. a. **Document type:** *Trade.*
Published by: Aviation Maintenance Foundation International, PO Box 2826, Redmond, WA 98073. TEL 360-658-8980, FAX 360-658-7274.

AVIATION MASTER FILE. see *COMMUNICATIONS—Abstracting, Bibliographies, Statistics*

▼ new title ➤ refereed ✶ unverified ♦ full entry avail.

A

629.132 USA ISSN 0005-2140
AVIATION MECHANICS BULLETIN. Text in English. 1953. bi-m. USD 280 worldwide to non-members; free to members (effective 2005). reprint service avail. from PQC. **Document type:** *Magazine, Trade.* **Description:** For aviation maintenance technicians, with an emphasis on airline and corporate operations.
Former titles (until 1960): Aviation; Mechanic's Bulletin
Indexed: RefZh.
—Linda Hall.
Published by: Flight Safety Foundation, Inc., 601 Madison St, Ste 300, Alexandria, VA 22314-1756. TEL 703-739-6700, FAX 703-739-6708, http://flightsafety.org/aviation_mech.html. Circ: 2,500 (paid).

616.980711 USA ISSN 0067-2661
AVIATION MEDICAL EDUCATION SERIES. Text in English. 1965. irreg. **Document type:** *Monographic series, Government.*
Published by: (Aviation Medicine Office), U.S. Federal Aviation Administration, 800 Independence Ave S W, Washington, DC 20591. TEL 202-655-4000.

387.7 USA ISSN 0145-1014
AVIATION MONTHLY; monthly aviation safety summary and consumer report. Text in English. 1973. m. USD 39 domestic; USD 49 in Canada; USD 59 elsewhere (effective 2000). stat. back issues avail. **Description:** Publishes aviation accident report briefs.
Formerly (until 1976): M A S S Report
Indexed: Englnd.
Published by: Peter Katz Productions, Inc., PO Box 831, White Plains, NY 10602-0831. TEL 914-949-7443. Ed. Peter J Katz. Circ: 18,000.

629.1325 CAN ISSN 1184-0366
AVIATION REVIEW. Text in English. 1980. q. free to members. **Document type:** *Journal, Academic/Scholarly.*
Published by: Western Canada Aviation Museum, 958 Ferry Rd., Winnipeg, MB, Canada. TEL 204-786-5503, FAX 204-775-4761, info@wcam.mb.ca, http://www.wcam.mb.ca/.

629.132 USA ISSN 0277-1764
AVIATION SAFETY; the twice-monthly journal of accident prevention. Text in English. 1981. m. USD 84 in US & Canada; USD 102 elsewhere (effective 2006). **Document type:** *Magazine, Trade.* **Description:** Offers professional and recreational pilots important safety information, tips, and related news.
—BLDSC (1838.578000), IE, ingenta.
Published by: Belvoir Media Group, LLC, 800 Connecticut Ave, Norwalk, CT 06854-1631. TEL 203-857-3100, 800-424-7887, FAX 203-857-3103, customer_service@belvoir.com, http://www.aviationsafetymagazine.com, http://www.belvoir.com. Ed. Mark M Lacagnina.

629.1 USA
AVIATION SPACE WRITERS ASSOCIATION. YEARBOOK AND DIRECTORY✱; including roster of membership. Text in English. 1938. a. USD 95. adv. **Document type:** *Directory.*
Formerly: Aviation Space Writers Association Manual
Published by: Aviation - Space Writers Association, 6540 50th St., N., Oakdale, MN 55128-1708. TEL 614-221-1900, FAX 614-221-1989. Ed. Madeline Field. Circ: 1,200.

AVIATION STRATEGY. see *TRANSPORTATION—Air Transport*

629.1 AUS ISSN 1322-8242
AVIATION TRADER. Text in English. 1988. m. AUD 24 domestic; AUD 57 foreign; AUD 2.50 newsstand/cover; NZD 3.95 newsstand/cover in New Zealand (effective 1999). adv. 32 p./no. 7 cols./p.; back issues avail. **Document type:** *Magazine, Trade.*
Related titles: Online - full text ed.
Published by: Helix Aviation Pty. Ltd., PO Box 266, Lismore, 2480, Australia. TEL 61-2-66-222133, FAX 61-2-66-222123, aviation@nor.com.au, http://www.aviationtrader.com.au. Ed. Pat Gosling. Pub. Kevin Gosling. Adv. contact Sharon Fletcher. B&W page AUD 131,850, color page AUD 1,570; trim 263 x 380. Circ: 10,419.

629.13 USA ISSN 0005-2175
TL501
AVIATION WEEK & SPACE TECHNOLOGY. Text in English. 1916. w. USD 98 domestic; USD 109 in Canada & Mexico; USD 160 in Europe; USD 175 elsewhere (effective 2004). adv. charts; illus. back issues avail.; reprints avail. **Document type:** *Magazine, Trade.* **Description:** Provides current news and information related to the aviation and aerospace industry.
Former titles (until 1960): Aviation Week, Including Space Technology (1042-1688); (until 1958): Aviation Week (0097-7128); Which was formed by the merger of (1943-1947): Aviation News (0190-3624); (1922-1947): Aviation (0097-7098)
Related titles: CD-ROM ed.; Microfilm ed.: (from PQC); Online - full text ed.: (from bigchalk, EBSCO Publishing, LexisNexis, O C L C Online Computer Library Center, Inc., ProQuest Information & Learning).
Indexed: ABIn, ABS&EES, AIA, AMB, AS&TI, ASCA, AcaI, ApMecR, B&I, BMT, BPI, BiolDig, BrCerAb, BrTechI, BusI, C&CSA, C&ISA, CADCAM, CLT&T, CerAb, ChemAb, CivEngAb, CorrAb, DM&T, E&CAJ, EEA, EMA, Englnd, EnvAb, ExcerpMed, FLUIDEX, HRIS, HlthInd, IAA, ISR, LID&ISL, LRI, M&TEA, MASUSE, MBF, MEA&I, METADEX, MagInd, PMR, PRA, PROMT, RASB, RGAb, RGPR, RefZh, SRI, SolStAb, T&II, TelAb, WAA.
—BLDSC (1838.695000), CISTI, Ei, IDS, IE, Infotrieve, ingenta, Linda Hall. **CCC.**
Published by: McGraw-Hill Companies, Inc., 1221 Ave of the Americas, New York, NY 10020. TEL 800-525-5003, feedback@aviationnow.com, http://www.aviationnow.com/avnow, http://www.mcgraw-hill.com. Ed. David North. Pub. Kenneth Gazzola. adv.: B&W page USD 13,155, color page USD 15,335. Circ: 107,000 (paid).

387.7 USA ISSN 1538-7267
AVIATION WEEK'S BUSINESS AND COMMERCIAL AVIATION. Text in English. 1958. m. USD 54 domestic; USD 58 in Canada & Mexico; USD 79 elsewhere (effective 2005). adv. bk.rev. illus. back issues avail. **Document type:** *Magazine, Trade.* **Description:** Covers current industry news. Provides readers with vital information to help them operate aircraft with greater safety and efficiency. Has a strong editorial focus on how-to operations.
Formerly (until 1966): Business and Commercial Aviation (0191-4642)
Related titles: Microform ed.: (from PQC); Online - full text ed.: (from EBSCO Publishing, LexisNexis, ProQuest Information & Learning, The Dialog Corporation); Supplement(s): Annual Purchase Planning Handbook.
Indexed: ABIn, AS&TI, BusI, CLT&T, Englnd, HRIS, ISR, LRI, RefZh, SRI, T&II.
—BLDSC (2933.180000), CISTI, IE, Infotrieve, ingenta. **CCC.**
Published by: McGraw-Hill Companies, Inc., 1221 Ave of the Americas, New York, NY 10020. TEL 212-512-2000, FAX 212-426-7087, customer.service@mcgraw-hill.com, http://www.aviationnow.com/content/publication/b_ca/bca.htm, http://www.mcgraw-hill.com. Ed. Jim Mathews TEL 202-383-2374. Circ: 50,000 (controlled).

387.7 623 USA ISSN 1545-486X
AVIATION WEEK'S HOMELAND SECURITY & DEFENSE. Text in English. 2002. w. USD 595 domestic; USD 675 overseas (effective 2002).
Related titles: E-mail ed.: USD 595 (effective 2002).
Published by: McGraw-Hill Companies, Inc., 1221 Ave of the Americas, New York, NY 10020. http://www.aviationnow.com/avnow/spSec/hs.jsp.

629.1325 331.1 USA
AVIATIONCAREER.NET. Text in English. m. USD 29; USD 15 to students (effective 2001). **Document type:** *Consumer.*
Published by: World Employment Database, Inc., Box 550010, Fort Lauderdale, FL 33355. TEL 954-472-6684, FAX 954-472-8524, editor@aviationcareer.net, http://www.aviationcareer.net. Ed. Janice C Wood.

629.13 ZAF
THE AVIATOR. Text in English. bi-m. ZAR 80 domestic membership; ZAR 200 foreign membership (effective 2000). illus. back issues avail. **Document type:** *Journal.* **Description:** Discusses news, events, and activities at the SOuth African Airways Museum Society, an organization dedicated to preserving South Africa's civil aviation heritage by restoring classic passenger airliners.
Related titles: Online - full content ed.
Published by: South African Airways Museum Society, PO Box 10411, Aston Manor, 1630, South Africa. FAX 27-11-972-8589, barryn@tnet.co.za, http://www.tnet.co.za/SAAM/Aviator/Current/body.htm, http://www.saamuseum.co.za.

658 USA ISSN 0195-0347
AVIATORS HOT LINE. Text in English. 1978. m. USD 21.95 (effective 2002). adv. back issues avail.; reprints avail. **Document type:** *Magazine, Trade.* **Description:** National and international marketplace for active buyers and sellers of corporate and general aircraft, parts and services.
Published by: Heartland Aviation Group (Subsidiary of: Heartland Communications Group, Inc.), 1003 Central Ave, Fort Dodge, IA 50501. TEL 515-955-1600, 800-247-2000, FAX 800-247-2000, ahlsales@aviatorshotline.com, http://www.aviatorshotline.com. adv.: color page USD 1,150, B&W page USD 660. Circ: 30,000.

629.1 RUS ISSN 0202-2745
AVIATSIONNAYA I RAKETNAYA TEKHNIKA; ekspress-informatsiya po materialam inostrannoi pechati. Text in Russian. s-m. USD 155 in United States. **Document type:** *Academic/Scholarly.*
—East View.
Published by: T.S.A.G.I., Ul Radio 17, Moscow, 107005, Russian Federation. TEL 7-095-2634039. **US dist. addr.:** East View Information Services, 3020 Harbor Ln. N., Minneapolis, MN 55447. TEL 612-550-0961.

629.1 RUS ISSN 0869-530X
AVIATSIONNAYA PROMYSHLENNOST'. Text in Russian. m. USD 169.95 in United States. **Document type:** *Academic/Scholarly.*
—East View.
Published by: Assotsiatsiya Aviatekhinform, Gzhel'skii per 13-a, Moscow, 107120, Russian Federation. TEL 7-095-2789128, FAX 7-095-2332323. **US dist. addr.:** East View Information Services, 3020 Harbor Ln. N., Minneapolis, MN 55447. TEL 612-550-0961.

629.132 UKR
AVIATSIYA I VREMYA. Text in Ukrainian. bi-m. USD 130 in United States.
Published by: Tsentr AeroHobbi, A-ya 166, Kiev, 252062, Ukraine. TEL 380-441-3047. **US dist. addr.:** East View Information Services, 3020 Harbor Ln. N., Minneapolis, MN 55447. TEL 612-550-0961.

629.73 ITA ISSN 1124-5433
AVIOFLAP. Text in Italian. 1993. m. EUR 41.32 domestic; EUR 56.41 foreign (effective 2000). **Document type:** *Magazine.* **Description:** Contains articles on commercial, civil and military aircraft, aviation, and air shows.
Published by: Coop CELI, Via Salaria 825, Rome, 00138, Italy. flap@eureka.it, http://www.flap.it.

629.1325 USA
AVION ONLINE NEWSPAPER. Text in English. w.
Media: Online - full content.
Published by: Embry-Riddle Aeronautical University, 600 S. Clyde Morris Blvd., Daytona Beach, FL 32114-3900. http://www.db.erau.edu/campus/student/sga/avion.html.

629.13 USA ISSN 1085-9284
AVIONICS MAGAZINE. Text in English. 1977. m. USD 80 (effective 2005); free to qualified personnel. adv. bk.rev. charts; illus.; pat.; stat. Index. back issues avail. **Document type:** *Magazine, Trade.* **Description:** Reports on technical, business and regulatory developments in all areas of avionics, including free flight, satellite navigation and positioning, airborne systems, ground navigation aids, air traffic control and management, and test and maintenance.
Former titles (until 1991): Avionics (0273-7639); (until 1980): Avionics Report (0191-2143)
Indexed: BrCerAb, C&ISA, CerAb, CivEngAb, CorrAb, E&CAJ, EMA, IAA, M&TEA, MBF, METADEX, WAA.
—BLDSC (1839.162000), CISTI, IE, Infotrieve, ingenta, Linda Hall. **CCC.**
Published by: Access Intelligence, LLC (Subsidiary of: Veronis, Suhler & Associates Inc.), 1201 Seven Locks Rd, Ste 300, Potomac, MD 20854. TEL 301-354-2000, 800-777-5006, FAX 301-762-3068, clientservices@accessintel.com, http://www.avionicsmagazine.com/, http://www.pbimedia.com. Ed. David Jensen TEL 301-354-1820. Pub. Daniel E Comiskey TEL 301-354-1812. Circ: (controlled).

629.132 USA
AVIONICS MAINTENANCE CONFERENCE. BOOKLET. Text in English. irreg.
Published by: Avionics Maintenance Conference, c/o Aeronautical Radio, Inc, 2551 Riva Rd, Annapolis, MD 21401. TEL 301-266-4116.

629.1 USA
AVIONICS MAINTENANCE CONFERENCE. CONFERENCE PROGRAM. Text in English. a.
Published by: Avionics Maintenance Conference, c/o Aeronautical Radio, Inc, 2551 Riva Rd, Annapolis, MD 21401. TEL 301-266-4116.

629.1 USA
AVIONICS MAINTENANCE CONFERENCE. CONFERENCE REPORT. Text in English. a.
Published by: Avionics Maintenance Conference, c/o Aeronautical Radio, Inc, 2551 Riva Rd, Annapolis, MD 21401. TEL 301-266-4116.

629.13 USA ISSN 0567-2899
AVIONICS NEWS MAGAZINE✱. Text in English. 1959. m. free. adv.
Published by: Aircraft Electronics Association, 4217 S Hocker Dr, Independence, MO 64055-4723. TEL 816-373-6565, FAX 816-478-3100. Ed. Monte R Mitchell. Circ: 4,500.

629.13 USA
AVSTOP MAGAZINE ONLINE. Text in English. d. adv. **Document type:** *Journal.*
Media: Online - full content.
Address: avstop@avstop.com, http://avstop.com/.

629.1325 USA
AVWEB. Text in English. 1995. w. **Document type:** *Consumer.*
Address: 800 Connecticut Ave, Norwalk, CT 06854. http://www.avweb.com, http://www.avweb.com/. Ed. Glenn Pew.

629 UKR
AVYABIZNES. Text in Ukrainian. q. USD 95 in United States. **Document type:** *Trade.*
Published by: Assotsiatsiya Transportnoyi Aviatsii Ukrainy, Basseinaya ul 9, Kiev, Ukraine. TEL 380-244-9191. **US dist. addr.:** East View Information Services, 3020 Harbor Ln. N., Minneapolis, MN 55447. TEL 612-550-0961.

B A R T INTERNATIONAL. (Business Aviation & Regional Transport) see *TRANSPORTATION—Air Transport*

629.1029 GBR
B H A B INFORMATION HANDBOOK. Text in English. 1972. a. GBP 7.50 per issue domestic; GBP 9 per issue in United States (effective 2000). stat.; tr.lit. **Document type:** *Trade.*
Description: Reference guide for civil helicopter users.
Published by: British Helicopter Advisory Board, Graham Ste., W. Entrance, Fairoaks Airport, Chobham, Woking, Surrey GU24 8HX, United Kingdom. TEL 44-1276-856100, FAX 44-1276-856126. Ed. J P W Friedberger. Adv. contact J Walsh. Circ: 2,000.

629.132 DEU
B L N - BAYERISCHE LUFTSPORT-NACHRICHTEN. Text in German. 1962. bi-m. **Document type:** *Newsletter.*
Published by: (Deutscher Aero Club e.V.), Luftsport-Verband Bayern e.V., Prinzregentenstr 120, Munich, 81677, Germany. TEL 089-45503216, FAX 089-45503211. Ed. Juergen Woerdehoff.

001.942 GBR ISSN 1466-8017
B U F O R A BULLETIN. Text in English. 1989. 8/yr. GBP 20 (effective 2001). adv. bk.rev. back issues avail.
Supersedes: U F O Times (0958-4846); Which was formed by the 1989 merger of: Journal of Transient Aerial Phenomena (0143-8840); And B U F O R A Bulletin (0265-1947); Which was formerly (until 1981): B U F O R A Journal (0306-798X)
Published by: British Unidentified Flying Object Research Association, BM BUFORA, London, WC1N 3XX, United Kingdom. enquiries@bufora.org.uk, http://www.bufora.org.uk. Ed. Mr. M Hudson. Circ: 400 (paid).

629.13 GBR
B W P A GAZETTE. Text in English. a. free. adv. **Document type:** *Trade.*
Published by: British Women Pilots Association, Brooklands Museum, Brooklands Rd, Weybridge, Surrey KT13 0QN, United Kingdom. enquiries@bwpa.demon.co.uk, http://www.bwpa.com. Ed., Adv. contact Clare Walker. Circ: 2,000.

629.132 GBR
B W P A NEWSLETTER. Text in English. 1955. q. membership. adv. bk.rev. **Document type:** *Newsletter.*
Former titles: B W P A Magazine
Media: Duplicated (not offset).
Published by: British Women Pilots Association, Brooklands Museum, Brooklands Rd, Weybridge, Surrey KT13 0QN, United Kingdom. enquiries@bwpa.demon.co.uk, http://www.bwpa.com. Ed., Adv. contact Sue Chase. Circ: 500.

629.1 ISR
BA'AVIR. Text in Hebrew. 1987. bi-m.
Published by: Baavir Publications, P O Box 1173, Rehovot, 76111, Israel. TEL 03-959976.

BACKYARD FLYER. see *HOBBIES*

BALLOON LIFE; the magazine for hot air ballooning. see *SPORTS AND GAMES*

797.5 USA ISSN 0194-6854
BALLOONING. Text in English. 1977 (vol.10). bi-m. USD 45; USD 50 in Canada & Mexico; USD 85 elsewhere (effective 1999). adv. bk.rev. charts; illus.; tr.lit. reprints avail. **Document type:** *Newsletter.*
Published by: (Balloon Federation of America), Ballooning Magazine, PO Box 400, Indianola, IA 50125. FAX 515-961-3537, ballon-fed@bfa.ycg.org, http://www.bfa.net/publications.htm. Circ: 5,100.

629.1 FRA ISSN 1024-5464
BAROMETRE DU TRANSPORT AERIEN/AVIATION INDUSTRY BAROMETER. Text in English, French. 1994. q. 40 p./no.; **Description:** Analysis of current trends in the aviation industry.
Published by: Institut du Transport Aerien, 103 rue la Boetie, Paris, 75008, France. TEL 33-1-43593868, FAX 33-1-43594737, TELEX 642 584F.

629.1 CHN ISSN 1001-5965
CODEN: BHHDE8
➤ **BEIJING HANGKONG HANGTIAN DAXUE XUEBAO/BEIJING UNIVERSITY OF AERONAUTICS AND ASTRONAUTICS. JOURNAL.** Text in Chinese; Abstracts in English. 1956-1960; resumed 1980. q. CNY 96; CNY 8 newsstand/cover (effective 2005). charts; illus. **Document type:** *Journal, Academic/Scholarly.* **Description:** Contains original papers on aeronautics and astronautics.
Related titles: Online - full content ed.: (from WanFang Data Corp.); Online - full text ed.: (from East View Information Services).
Indexed: BrCerAb, C&ISA, CIN, CerAb, ChemAb, ChemTitl, CivEngAb, CorrAb, E&CAJ, EMA, EngInd, IAA, Inspec, M&TEA, MBF, METADEX, RefZh, SolStAb, WAA.
—BLDSC (4707.892700), AskIEEE, CASDDS, IE, ingenta, Linda Hall.
Published by: Beijing Hangkongtian Daxue/Beijing University of Aeronautics and Astronautics, 37 Xueyuan Rd, Haidian District, Beijing, 100083, China. TEL 86-10-82317826, FAX 86-10-82317850, jbuaa@buaa.edu.cn, http://bhxb.buaa.edu.cn, http://www.buaa.edu.cn/. Ed. Gao Zhentong.

629.1 ISR ISSN 0302-8194
TL527.I75
BIAF/ISRAEL AVIATION AND SPACE MAGAZINE. Text in Hebrew. 1972. q. USD 35 (effective 2001). adv. bk.rev. bibl.; charts; illus. back issues avail. **Document type:** *Trade.*
Description: Covers current developments in military and civil aviation and aerospace in Israel and the world, as well as historical topics.
Published by: (Israel Society of Aeronautics and Astronautics), Yehuda Borovik Ed. & Pub., P O Box 3144, Rishon Le Zion, 75131, Israel. TEL 972-3-9664030, FAX 972-3-9649599, biaf@befeqint.net. Circ: 2,000.

358.4 ISR ISSN 0006-3878
BIT'ON HEL HA-AVIR/ISRAEL AIR FORCE MAGAZINE. Text in Hebrew. 1948. bi-m. USD 50. adv. bk.rev.; film rev. charts; illus.; stat. **Description:** New products and technical reports for the ministry and airforce members.
Indexed: PROMT.
Published by: (Israel. Air Force of Israel), Ministry of Defense Publishing House, P O Box 01560, Zahal - Idf, Israel. TEL 972-3-5694153. Ed. Marav Halperin. Circ: 30,000.

629.13 GBR ISSN 1366-6665
BLUE PRINT. (Monthly and Quarterly supplements avail.) Text in English. 1987. 50/yr. GBP 310 domestic; USD 496 foreign; GBP 10, USD 14 newsstand/cover (effective 2001 - 2002). charts; mkt.; stat. back issues avail. **Document type:** *Newsletter, Trade.* **Description:** Contains articles on aircraft fleet acquisitions, general airline news, and airline industry news. Aimed at owners and operators, including leasing companies, financiers and insurers.
Related titles: Online - full text ed.
Published by: Airclaims Limited, Cardinal Point, Newall Rd, Heathrow Airport, London, TW6 2AS, United Kingdom. TEL 44-20-8897-1066, FAX 44-20-8897-0300, ian.sheppard@airclaims.co.uk, http://www.airclaims.co.uk. Eds. Julius Themistocleous, Richard Maslen. Pub. Ian Sheppard. Circ: 400 (paid).

629.4 GBR ISSN 0007-084X
CODEN: JBISAW
➤ **BRITISH INTERPLANETARY SOCIETY JOURNAL.** Abbreviated title: J B I S. Text in English. 1934. bi-m. GBP 290, USD 536 (effective 2005). bk.rev. illus.; abstr. Index. 72 p./no. 2 cols./p.; back issues avail.; reprint service avail. from PQC. **Document type:** *Journal, Academic/Scholarly.*
Related titles: Microform ed.: (from PQC).
Indexed: CurCont, EngInd, ExcerpMed, IAA, Inspec, RASB.
—BLDSC (4718.000000), AskIEEE, Ei, IE, Infotrieve, ingenta, Linda Hall. **CCC.**
Published by: British Interplanetary Society, 27-29 S Lambeth Rd, London, SW8 1SZ, United Kingdom. TEL 44-20-77353160, FAX 44-20-78201504, jbis@bis-spaceflight.com, mail@bis-spaceflight.com, http://bis-spaceflight.com/publicB.htm. Ed. A R Martin. Circ: 1,500.

629.1 USA ISSN 1059-3977
BUCKEYE PIETENPOL ASSOCIATION NEWSLETTER. Text in English. 1983. q. USD 10 domestic; USD 12 in Canada & Mexico; USD 14 elsewhere (effective 2000). adv. bk.rev. back issues avail. **Document type:** *Newsletter.* **Description:** Covers Pietenpol airplanes and their designer, Bernard H. Pietenpol.
Published by: Buckeye Pietenpol Association, 7 Crosswinds Dr., St. Louis, MO 63132-4303. TEL 314-677-1669, gmaclaren@aol.com, http://users.aol.com/bpanews. Ed., R&P Grant E MacLaren. Circ: 1,000 (paid).

629.1 USA ISSN 0361-5065
TL609
BUOYANT FLIGHT. Text in English. 1952. bi-m. looseleaf. USD 15. bk.rev. bibl.; illus. back issues avail.
Indexed: SportS.
Published by: Lighter Than Air Society, 526 S. Main St., Ste. 232, Akron, OH 44311-4403. Ed. Eric Brothers. Circ: 900.

629.133 USA
BUSINESS AIR. Text in English. 1991. m. USD 39.95 domestic; USD 113 foreign (effective 2002). adv. back issues avail.; reprints avail. **Document type:** *Magazine, Trade.*
Published by: Heartland Aviation Group (Subsidiary of: Heartland Communications Group, Inc.), 1003 Central Ave, Fort Dodge, IA 50501. TEL 515-955-1600, 800-247-2000, FAX 515-574-2199, flying@businessair.com, http://www.businessair.com. adv.: page USD 2,150; trim 8 x 10.75. Circ: 27,700.

387.7 CAN ISSN 1207-1978
TL501
➤ **C A H S JOURNAL.** Text in English. 1963. q., latest vol.39, no.4. CND 35 domestic; USD 35 foreign (effective 1999 - 2000). bk.rev. illus. index, cum.index. back issues avail. **Document type:** *Journal, Academic/Scholarly.* **Description:** Aims to record Canada's aviation history.
Related titles: Microform ed.: (from MML).
Indexed: AmH&L, HistAb.
—CISTI.
Published by: Canadian Aviation Historical Society, Sta A, P O Box 224, Willowdale, ON M2N 5S8, Canada. TEL 416-410-9774, 905-294-4438, FAX 905-294-5845, cahsnatsec@mail.cahs.com, http://www.cahs.com/journal00.html. Ed. W J Wheeler. R&P G E Rice. Circ: 1,300.

629.1 USA
C.A.L. - N-X-211 COLLECTORS SOCIETY. NEWSLETTER. Text in English. 1989. m. looseleaf. USD 25 (effective 2000). adv. bk.rev. back issues avail. **Document type:** *Newsletter.*
Description: Directed to educate readers about the life and times of Charles A. Lindbergh.
Published by: C.A.L. - N-X-211 Collectors Society, 727 Younkin Pkwy S, Columbus, OH 43207-4788. TEL 614-497-9517. Ed. Mort Kuff. Pub. Dick Hoerle. Adv. contact Dan Clemons. Circ: 250 (paid).

796.154 FRA
C I A M FLYER. Text in English. 1990. a. free. illus. back issues avail. **Document type:** *Magazine, Consumer.* **Description:** Discusses news and topics of interest to the FAI Aeromodelling Commission, whose members build and fly model aircraft that are designed in accordance with aeronautical principles.
Media: Online - full content.
Published by: F A I Aeromodelling Commission, 93 bd du Montparnasse, Paris, 75006, France. JackSile@aol.com, http://www.fai.org/aeromodelling/about. Ed. Jack Sile TEL 44-1449-675190. **Co-sponsor:** Federation Aeronautique International.

629.13 URY ISSN 0797-0072
CODEN: CCIAEE
C I D A E. Text in Spanish, English, French, Portuguese. 1976. a. free. bk.rev. **Document type:** *Government.* **Description:** Covers doctrine, legislation and jurisprudence on aerospace issues.
Published by: Direccion General de Aviacion Civil, Centro de Investigacion y Difusion Aeronautico Espacial, Carlos Ouijano 1182, Colonia, 959, Montevideo, 11103, Uruguay. TEL 598-2-900-0904, FAX 598-2-908-2446, TELEX 22631 DIRACIV UY, cidae@adinet.com.uy. Circ: 600.

629.4 FRA ISSN 1283-9817
C N E S MAGAZINE. Text in French, English. 1997. q.
Indexed: RefZh.
Published by: Centre National d'Etudes Spatiales, 18 ave Edouard Belin, Toulouse, Cedex 31401, France. TEL 33-05-61273131, FAX 33-05-61273179, http://www.cnes.fr.

629.4 FRA ISSN 0964-2749
C O S P A R COLLOQUIA SERIES. Text in English. 1990. irreg. price varies. **Document type:** *Monographic series, Academic/Scholarly.*
—BLDSC (3477.218000), IE, ingenta.
Published by: (Committee on Space Research), Elsevier France, Editions Scientifiques et Medicales (Subsidiary of: Elsevier Science & Technology), 23 Rue Linois, Paris, 75724, France. TEL 33-1-71724600, FAX 33-1-71724650, http://www.elsevier.fr.

629.13 GBR ISSN 0045-8732
TL787
➤ **C O S P A R INFORMATION BULLETIN.** (COmmittee on SPAce Research) Text in English, French. 1960. 3/yr. only avail. with subscr. to Advances in Space Research. adv. reprint service avail. from PQC. **Document type:** *Bulletin, Academic/Scholarly.* **Description:** Covers the latest developments in scientific space activities.
Related titles: Microfilm ed.: (from PQC); Online - full text ed.: (from EBSCO Publishing, Gale Group, IngentaConnect, ScienceDirect, Swets Information Services).
—BLDSC (3477.220000), IE, Linda Hall. **CCC.**
Published by: (International Council of Scientific Unions FRA), Pergamon (Subsidiary of: Elsevier Science & Technology), The Boulevard, Langford Ln, East Park, Kidlington, Oxford OX5 1GB, United Kingdom. TEL 44-1865-843000, FAX 44-1865-843010, http://www.elsevier.com/locate/cospar. Ed. R A Harrison. Circ: 2,300. **Subscr. to:** Elsevier BV, PO Box 211, Amsterdam 1000 AE, Netherlands. TEL 31-20-485-3757, FAX 31-20-485-3432, nlinfo-f@elsevier.nl, http://www.elsevier.nl.

614.85 387.7 629.1 USA ISSN 1057-5553
CABIN CREW SAFETY. Text in English. 1956. bi-m. USD 280 to non-members (effective 2005). reprint service avail. from PQC. **Document type:** *Newsletter.* **Description:** Focuses attention on the cabin crew, especially in airline operations, but the special requirements of corporate operations are also presented.
Former titles (until vol.22, no.6, 1987): Cabin Crew Safety Bulletin (0898-5758); (until 1975): Cabin Crew Safety Exchange
Indexed: RefZh.
Published by: Flight Safety Foundation, Inc., 601 Madison St, Ste 300, Alexandria, VA 22314-1756. TEL 703-739-6700, FAX 703-739-6708, http://www.flightsafety.org/ccs_home.html. Ed. Roger Rozelle. Circ: 2,250.

▼ new title ➤ refereed ✶ unverified ♦ full entry avail.

A

629.1 CHN ISSN 1001-4381
CAILIAO GONGCHENG/JOURNAL OF MATERIAL ENGINEERING. Text in Chinese. 1956. m. CNY 60 domestic; USD 4 per issue foreign; USD 5 per issue domestic (effective 2000).
Related titles: Online - full content ed.: (from WanFang Data Corp.); Online - full text ed.: (from East View Information Services).
Indexed: BrCerAb, C&ISA, CerAb, CivEngAb, CorrAb, E&CAJ, EMA, Englnd, IAA, M&TEA, MBF, METADEX, SolStAb, WAA.
—BLDSC (5012.229000).
Published by: Beijing Hangkong Cailian Yanjiuyuan/Beijing Institute of Aeronautical Materials, Beijing, 100095, China. TEL 86-1-62456622.

629.1 GBR
CAMBRIDGE AEROSPACE SERIES. Text in English. irreg., latest vol.7, 1997. **Document type:** *Monographic series.*
Indexed: CCMJ.
—BLDSC (3015.939050).
Published by: University of Cambridge, Press Syndicate, The Pitt Bldg, Trumpington St, Cambridge, Cambs CB2 1RP, United Kingdom. TEL 44-1223-315052, http://publishing.cambridge.org/series/caes. **Dist. addr. in N America:** Cambridge University Press Distribution Center, 110 Brookhill Dr., West Nyack, NY 10994-2140. TEL 800-872-7423, subscriptions_newyork@cambridge.org.

629.13 CAN ISSN 0008-2821
CODEN: CSPJAE
CANADIAN AERONAUTICS AND SPACE JOURNAL. Text in English, French. 1955. q. CND 90 domestic; USD 80 foreign (effective 2001). bk.rev. bibl.; charts; illus. index. back issues avail.; reprint service avail. from PQC. **Description:** Devoted to timely reporting on a variety of topics of interest to the international aerospace community.
Related titles: Microfiche ed.: (from MML); Microfilm ed.: (from MML); Microform ed.: (from MML, PQC).
Indexed: AMB, ApMecR, BrCerAb, C&ISA, CBCARef, CBPI, CerAb, CivEngAb, CorrAb, CurCont, E&CAJ, EMA, ESPM, Englnd, ForAb, H&SSA, IAA, IBR, Inspec, M&TEA, MBF, METADEX, SolStAb, WAA.
—BLDSC (3016.600000), CISTI, Ei, IE, Infotrieve, ingenta, Linda Hall. **CCC.**
Published by: Canadian Aeronautics and Space Institute, 1750 Courtwood Crescent, Suite 105, Ottawa, ON K2C 2B5, Canada. TEL 613-234-0191, FAX 613-234-9039, casi@casi.ca, http://www.casi.ca/index.php?pg=casj. Ed. Stewart W Baillie. R&P Ian Ross. Circ: 2,000.

629.13 CAN ISSN 1487-5381
HE9769.C2
CANADIAN CIVIL AIRCRAFT REGISTER (CD-ROM EDITION). Text in English. 1929. m. price varies. reprints avail.
Formerly (until 1998): Canadian Civil Aircraft Register (Print Edition) (0527-6497)
Related titles: Diskette ed.; Magnetic Tape ed.; Microfiche ed.
—**CCC.**
Published by: Transport Canada, Aircraft Registration, A A R R C, 200 Kent St, Ottawa, ON K1A 0N8, Canada. TEL 613-990-1118, FAX 613-990-6215. Circ: 900.

629.132 CAN
CANADIAN FLIGHT*. Text in English. 1964. m. CND 45, USD 45. adv. illus. back issues avail. **Document type:** *Trade.*
Formerly: Canadian General Aviation News (0226-5648)
Related titles: ♦ Includes: Canadian Homebuilt Aircraft News. ISSN 0820-5639; ♦ Canadian Ultralight News. ISSN 0821-6673.
Published by: (Canadian Owners & Pilots Association), Canadian Flight Publishing Co., 75 Albert St, Ste 1001, Ottawa, ON K1P 5E7, Canada. TEL 613-234-4901, FAX 613-236-8646, editorial@copanational.org, advertising@copanational.org. Ed., R&P Doris Ohlmann. Pub. Garth Wallace. Adv. contact Cathy Kennedy. Circ: 18,000; 17,000 (paid).

629.13 CAN
CANADIAN FLIGHT ANNUAL*. Text in English. 1955. a. CND 5. adv. bk.rev.; film rev. illus. **Document type:** *Directory.*
Supersedes (in 1995): Canadian Flight (0008-3577)
—CISTI. **CCC.**
Published by: (Canadian Owners and Pilots Association), Canadian Flight Publishing Co., 75 Albert St, Ste 1001, Ottawa, ON K1P 5E7, Canada. TEL 613-236-4901, FAX 613-236-8646, editorial@copanational.org, advertising@copanational.org. Ed., R&P Doris Ohlman. Pub. Garth Wallace. Adv. contact Cathy Stanfield. Circ: 25,000.

629.132 CAN ISSN 0820-5639
CANADIAN HOMEBUILT AIRCRAFT NEWS*. Text in English. m. illus. **Description:** Contains information of interest to pilots of homebuilt aircraft.
Related titles: ♦ Issued with: Canadian Flight.
Published by: Canadian Flight Publishing Co., 75 Albert St, Ste 1001, Ottawa, ON K1P 5E7, Canada. TEL 613-565-0881, FAX 613-236-8846. Ed. Doris Ohlman.

629.13 CAN ISSN 0703-8992
CODEN: CJRSDP
CANADIAN JOURNAL OF REMOTE SENSING. Text in English. 1975. bi-m. CND 155 domestic to individuals; USD 100 foreign to individuals (effective 2001). adv. charts; illus.; stat. back issues avail. **Description:** Devoted to timely reporting on topics of interests to the international remote sensing community.
Related titles: Online - full text ed.: (from EBSCO Publishing).
Indexed: ASFA, Agr, CBCARef, CivEngAb, CurCont, ESPM, Englnd, ExcerpMed, ISMEC, Inspec, M&GPA, M&TEA, OceAb, PollutAb, SWRA.
—BLDSC (3035.450000), AskIEEE, CISTI, Ei, IE, Infotrieve, ingenta, Linda Hall. **CCC.**
Published by: (Canadian Remote Sensing Society), Canadian Aeronautics and Space Institute, 1750 Courtwood Crescent, Suite 105, Ottawa, ON K2C 2B5, Canada. TEL 613-234-0191, FAX 613-234-9039, publications@casi.ca, casi@casi.ca, http://www.casi.ca/index.php?pg=cjrs. Ed. Joseph Buckley. R&P Ian Ross.

CANADIAN MUSEUM OF FLIGHT & TRANSPORTATION. MUSEUM NEWSLETTER. see *MUSEUMS AND ART GALLERIES*

629.132 CAN ISSN 0821-6673
CANADIAN ULTRALIGHT NEWS*. Text in English. 1982. m.
Related titles: ♦ Issued with: Canadian Flight.
Published by: Canadian Flight Publishing Co., 75 Albert St, Ste 1001, Ottawa, ON K1P 5E7, Canada. TEL 613-565-0881, FAX 613-236-8646. Ed. Doris Ohlmann.

629.13 GBR
A CAREER IN AVIATION. Text in English. a. 50 p./no. 2 cols./p.; **Document type:** *Academic/Scholarly.*
Published by: British Women Pilots Association, Brooklands Museum, Brooklands Rd, Weybridge, Surrey KT13 0QN, United Kingdom. enquiries@bwpa.demon.co.uk, http://www.bwpa.com. Ed., Adv. contact Clare Walker. Circ: 1,000.

CAREER PILOT JOB REPORT (ONLINE). see *OCCUPATIONS AND CAREERS*

629.132 919.704 ANT
CARIBBEAN AVIATION AND TOURISM NEWS/NOTICIERO AERONAUTICO Y TURISMO CARIBENSE. Text in English, Spanish. 1981. m. free. adv.
Formerly: Caribbean Aviation News
Published by: International Caribbean Federation of AeroClubs, Fosfaatweg 27, Willemstad, Curacao, Netherlands Antilles. TEL 599-9-681910, FAX 599-9625962, TELEX 390-1080 AFRO NA. Eds. Elba Serrano, Henry Veeris. Circ: 15,000.

358.4 AUS
CARRIER AVIATION NEWS. Text in English. 1996. bi-m. (plus d. updates). free. adv. **Document type:** *Newsletter.* **Description:** Contains current locations of aircraft carriers, news, features, photos, statistics, and links to all carrier sites.
Media: Online - full text.
Address: GPO Box 2204, Adelaide, SA 5001, Australia. TEL 61-8-8276-8661, davemc@geocities.com, http://www.carries-aviation-news.com/. Ed., Pub., Adv. contact David McCandless.

629.1 CHN ISSN 1000-8829
TJ212
CEKONG JISHU/MEASUREMENT & CONTROL TECHNOLOGY. Text in Chinese. 1982. m. USD 34.80; USD 2.90 newsstand/cover (effective 2001). adv. back issues avail. **Document type:** *Academic/Scholarly.*
Related titles: Online - full content ed.: (from WanFang Data Corp.); Online - full text ed.: (from East View Information Services).
Published by: (Zhongguo Hangkong Gongye Zonggongsi), Beijing Changcheng Hangkong Cekong Jishu Yanjiusuo/Beijing Measurement and Control Technology Research Institute, PO Box 2351, Beijing, 100022, China. TEL 86-1-65686291, FAX 86-1-65670337, TELEX 210411 CIFAI CN, cmct@public.fhnet.cn.net, http://www.mct.com.cn. Ed. Ning Zhou. Circ: 10,000; 6,000 (paid). **Dist. by:** China International Book Trading Corp, 35 Chegongzhuang Xilu, Haidian District, PO Box 399, Beijing 100044, China. TEL 86-10-68412045, FAX 86-10-68412023, cibtc@mail.cibtc.com.cn, http://www.cibtc.com.cn.

629.4 FRA ISSN 1269-6161
CENTRE NATIONAL D'ETUDES SPATIALES. RAPPORT D'ACTIVITE. Text in English, French. 1962. a. free. **Document type:** *Corporate.*
Published by: Centre National d'Etudes Spatiales, 18 ave Edouard Belin, Toulouse, Cedex 31401, France. TEL 33-05-61273131. Ed. Alain Benssoussan. R&P J L Astor. Circ: 3,500.

697 USA ISSN 0745-3523
CESSNA OWNER MAGAZINE. Text in English. 1974. m. USD 44 domestic membership; USD 59 foreign membership (effective 2003). adv. **Document type:** *Consumer.* **Description:** Provides information to Cessna owners and other enthusiasts about the joys and rewards of flying Cessna airplanes. Provides information on flight safety, places to fly, tips on maintenance and repairs, FAA airworthiness alerts, and service difficulty reports.
Published by: Cessna Owner Organization, N 7450 Aanstad Rd, PO Box 5000, Iola, WI 54945-5000. TEL 888-692-3776, jenniferj@cessnaowner.org, http://www.cessnaowner.org/. Ed. Thomas Block. Pub. Jennifer Julin. Adv. contact Trevor Janz. B&W page USD 949, color page USD 1,085; trim 10.88 x 8.13. Circ: 5,975.

629.13 ITA
CHI E CHI DELL'AERONAUTICA E DELLO SPAZIO. Text in English, Italian. 1992. a. **Document type:** *Directory, Consumer.*
Published by: Crisalide Press, Via Brusuglio 66, Milan, MI 20161, Italy. TEL 39-02-6464663, FAX 39-02-6461622, http://www.crisalidepress.it. Ed. Alberto Schieppati. Circ: 50,000.

CHIKYU DENJIKI CHIKYU WAKUSEIKEN GAKKAI KAIHO/SOCIETY OF GEOMAGNETISM AND EARTH, PLANETARY AND SPACE SCIENCES. NEWS. see *EARTH SCIENCES—Geophysics*

CHIKYU DENJIKI CHIKYU WAKUSEIKEN GAKKAI KOENKAI KOEN YOKOSHU/SOCIETY OF GEOMAGNETISM AND EARTH, PLANETARY AND SPACE SCIENCES. PREPRINTS OF THE MEETING. see *EARTH SCIENCES—Geophysics*

629.1 CHN ISSN 1003-6008
CHINA AERO INFORMATION/ZHONGGUO HANGKONG XINXI. Text in English. m. USD 482.40; USD 40.20 newsstand/cover (effective 2001). adv. **Document type:** *Academic/Scholarly.*
Related titles: Online - full text ed.
Published by: (Hangkong Hangtian Gongye-bu/Aviation Industries of China, Keji Qingbao Yanjiusuo/China Aero-Information Center), Aviation Industry Press, 14 Xiaoguan Dongli, Anwai, Beijing, 100029, China. TEL 86-1-6491-8417, FAX 86-1-6491-8417, cai@iag.com.cn, http://www.iag.com. Ed. Zhang Yong. Adv. contact Zhiyuan Xiao. **Dist. by:** China International Book Trading Corp, 35 Chegongzhuang Xilu, Haidian District, PO Box 399, Beijing 100044, China. TEL 86-10-68412045, FAX 86-10-68412023, cibtc@mail.cibtc.com.cn, http://www.cibtc.com.cn.

CHINA AEROSPACE ABSTRACTS. see *AERONAUTICS AND SPACE FLIGHT—Abstracting, Bibliographies, Statistics*

629.1 CHN
CHINA AEROSPACE DATABASE. Text in Chinese. a. USD 1,000. **Description:** Covers aerospace and rocketry in China.
Related titles: CD-ROM ed.; English ed.: USD 500.
Published by: Hangtian Gongye Zong Gongsi, Xinxi Yanjiu-suo/China Aerospace Corporation, Institute for Astronautics Information, 1 Binhe Lu, Hepingli, PO Box 1408, Beijing, 100013, China. TEL 86-10-6837-2847, FAX 86-10-8422-1606, duyq@mimi.cnc.ac.cn, http://www.space.cetin.net.cn.

387.7 CHN
CHINAERO. Text in Chinese, English. 2000 (Apr.). m. CNY 880 domestic; USD 100 foreign (effective 2000). adv. back issues avail. **Document type:** *Academic/Scholarly.* **Description:** Provides foreign firms and Chinese users and manufacturers with information of the latest development of the Chinese aviation market, including scientific data.
Published by: Beijing Wide-Chance Technical Center, Rm A415 Jucai Office Building, No.76 Caoyuan Hutong, Dongcheng District, Beijing, 100007, China. TEL 86-10-6407-3318, FAX 86-10-840-18095, chinaero@public2.east.cn.net, http://www.chinaero.com. Ed. Mr. Zhang Wong. Pub. Liyuan Wang. adv.: B&W page USD 500, color page USD 800. Circ: 1,000.

629.13 CHN ISSN 1000-9361
TL501 CODEN: CJAEEZ
CHINESE JOURNAL OF AERONAUTICS. Text and summaries in English. 1988. q. CNY 120; USD 30 newsstand/cover (effective 2005). adv. back issues avail. **Document type:** *Academic/Scholarly.* **Description:** Covers aeronautical research in China, including fluid mechanics and aerodynamics, flight dynamics and testing, aircraft propulsion systems, auto control and avionics, aerospace manufacturing and materials. Compared with Acta Aeronautica et Astronautica Sinica, Chinese Journal of Aeronautics lays more emphasis on international exchange, while the publication of any paper not be repeated in the two journals.
Related titles: Online - full content ed.: (from WanFang Data Corp.); Online - full text ed.: (from East View Information Services); ♦ Chinese ed.: Hangkong Xuebao. ISSN 1000-6893.
Indexed: ApMecR, BrCerAb, C&ISA, CerAb, CivEngAb, CorrAb, E&CAJ, EMA, Englnd, IAA, M&TEA, MBF, METADEX, RefZh, WAA.
—BLDSC (3180.290500), CISTI, IE, ingenta, Linda Hall. **CCC.**

Published by: Press of Acta Aeronautica et Astronautica Sinica, 37 Xueyuan Rd, Beijing, 100083, China. TEL 86-10-82317058, FAX 86-10-82318016, wxy@hkxb.net.cn, aaas@buaa.edu.cn, http://hkxb-e.periodicals.net.cn/, http://www.hkxb.net.cn/hkxb. Circ: 300. **Co-sponsor:** Chinese Society of Aeronautics and Astronautics/Zhongguo Hangkong Xuehui.

629.1 USA ISSN 0887-9680
UG633
CITIZEN AIRMAN. Text in English. 1949. bi-m. USD 18 (effective 2001). back issues avail. **Document type:** *Government.* **Description:** Contains complete and up-to-date information of interest to the Air Reserve Forces.
Related titles: Online - full text ed.: (from EBSCO Publishing, Gale Group, ProQuest Information & Learning).
Indexed: AUNI.
Published by: U.S. Air Force - Reserves, HQ AFRES - PAR, 155 Second St., Robins Afb, GA 31098-1635. TEL 912-327-1773, FAX 913-327-1772. Ed. Cliff Tyler. Circ: 80,000. **Subscr. to:** U.S. Government Printing Office, Superintendent of Documents.

CIVIL AIRCRAFT AIRWORTHINESS INFORMATION AND PROCEDURES. see *TRANSPORTATION—Air Transport*

629.1 PAK
CIVIL AVIATION IN PAKISTAN: HALF-YEARLY NEWSLETTER. Text in English. 1971. s-a. charts; stat. **Document type:** *Newsletter.*
Incorporates: Forward (0015-8615); Forward: P I D C Journal (0429-2405)
Published by: Department of Civil Aviation, Karachi 4, Pakistan.

629.13 NZL ISSN 1172-9643
CLASSIC WINGS DOWNUNDER. Text in English. 1994. q. NZD 42 domestic; AUD 36 in Australia; NZD 54 elsewhere; NZD 7.95, AUD 6.90, USD 5.95, CND 7.95 newsstand/cover (effective 2002). adv. illus. back issues avail. **Document type:** *Magazine, Consumer.* **Description:** Provides information for pilots, restorers and lovers of old aircraft world-wide; contains in-depth articles on war-bird and vintage aircraft featuring stunning air-to-air photography and comprehensive news coverage from around the world, with a unique focus on what's happening "Down-under." Official magazine of the Australian and New Zealand Warbird Associations.
Published by: New Zealand Warbirds Association, P.O. Box 534, Blenheim, New Zealand. TEL 64-3-578-9609, FAX 64-3-577-6451, 877-577-8560, admin@classicwings.com, http://www.classicwings.com. Ed. Graham Orphan. Circ: 24,000. **Subscr. to:** PO Box 1356, Moonpark, CA 93020-1356. **Dist. in N. America by:** Ingram Distributors, PO Box 7000, La Vergne, TN 37086-7000.; **Dist. in the UK by:** Comag, Tavistock Works, Tavistock Rd, W Drayton, Middx UB7 7QX, United Kingdom.

629.13 USA ISSN 0742-1508
COCKPIT. Text in English. q.
Indexed: BrCerAb, C&ISA, CerAb, CivEngAb, CorrAb, E&CAJ, EMA, IAA, M&TEA, MBF, METADEX, SolStAb, WAA.
—CISTI, Linda Hall.
Published by: Society of Experimental Test Pilots, Box 986, Lancaster, CA 93584-0986. TEL 661-942-9574, FAX 661-940-0398, setp@setp.org, http://www.setp.org.

629.132 NOR ISSN 0332-9798
COCKPIT FORUM. Text in Norwegian. 1973. bi-m. membership. adv. bk.rev. **Document type:** *Trade.*
—CCC.
Published by: Norsk Flygerforbund, Elgveien 9, Stokke, 3160, Norway. TEL 47-67-58-11-85, FAX 47-67-58-11-82. Ed., Adv. contact Erlend Larsen. Circ: 2,400.

629.1 USA ISSN 1071-3816
CODE ONE. Text in English. 1985. q. USD 20 domestic; USD 30 foreign (effective 2004). illus. back issues avail. **Document type:** *Magazine, Trade.* **Description:** Covers military aviation, with particular emphasis on the F-16 family of planes.
Related titles: Online - full text ed.
—Linda Hall.
Published by: Lockheed Martin TAS (Subsidiary of: Lockheed Martin), Mail Zone 1503, Box 748, Ft. Worth, TX 76101-0748. TEL 817-777-5542, FAX 817-763-4797, erichehs@lmtas.com, eric.hehs@lmco.com, http://www.codeonemagazine.com. Ed. Eric Hehs. Circ: 40,000.

341.47 USA ISSN 0069-5831
COLLOQUIUM ON THE LAW OF OUTER SPACE. PROCEEDINGS. Text in English. 1958. a. USD 84.95 to non-members; USD 64.95 to members. back issues avail.; reprint service avail. from PQC. **Document type:** *Proceedings, Academic/Scholarly.* **Description:** Covers the latest developments in the legal aspects of astronautics, space travel and exploration.
Indexed: IAA.
—BLDSC (6842.900000).
Published by: (International Aeronautical Federation), American Institute of Aeronautics and Astronautics, Inc., 1801 Alexander Bell Dr, Ste 500, Reston, VA 20191. TEL 703-264-7500, FAX 703-264-7551, custserv@aiaa.org, http://www.aiaa.org. **Co-sponsor:** International Institute of Space Law.

358.4 629.133 USA ISSN 1367-8418
UG1240
COMBAT AIRCRAFT. Text in English. 1997. bi-m. USD 29.95 domestic; GBP 19.95 in United Kingdom; USD 39 in Europe; GBP 2.70 newsstand/cover. **Document type:** *Consumer.*
Published by: Airtime Publishing Inc., 120 East Ave, Norwalk, CT 06851. **Subscr. to:** 10 Bay St, Westport, CT 06880. **Dist. in UK by:** M M C Ltd., Octagon House, White Hart Meadows, Ripley, Woking, Surrey GU23 6HR, United Kingdom. TEL 44-1483-211222, FAX 44-1483-224541.

358.4 USA ISSN 1063-8970
THE COMBAT EDGE. Text in English. 1961. m. USD 47 (effective 2001). **Document type:** *Government.* **Description:** Focuses on leadership and flight safety; includes weapons, ground, maintenance and general safety.
Formerly (until 1992): T A C Attack (Tactical Air Command) (0494-3880)
Related titles: Online - full text ed.: (from bigchalk, EBSCO Publishing, Factiva, Gale Group, Northern Light Technology, Inc., ProQuest Information & Learning).
Indexed: AUNI.
Published by: U.S. Department of the Air Force, HQ ACC PAVM, Attn: Barbara Taylor, HQ ACC/SEP, 175 Sweeney Blvd, Langley Afb, VA 23665-2700. TEL 804-764-3658, FAX 804-764-3102, http://www.acc.af.mil/public/combat-edge. Ed. Lt Col Adrian Robbe. R&P Lt.Col. Nelson L Beard. Circ: 13,000. **Non-military persons & institutions subscr. to:** U.S. Government Printing Office, Superintendent of Documents, PO Box 371954, Pittsburgh, PA 15250-7954. TEL 202-512-1800, FAX 202-512-2250, orders@gpo.gov, http://www.access.gpo.gov.

629.133 USA
COMMERCIAL AIRCRAFT. Text in English. a. USD 29.95; USD 59.95 combined subscription print, CD-ROM & online eds. (effective 2002). adv. **Document type:** *Magazine, Trade.* **Description:** Provides detailed information on all the major passenger and cargo aircraft flown throughout the world.
Related titles: CD-ROM ed.; Online - full text ed.
Published by: Pyramid Media Group, 666 Fifth Ave, Ste 230, New York, NY 10103. TEL 212-332-0909, FAX 212-315-1534, info@pyramid.ch, http://www.pyramid.ch. Ed., Pub. Aram Gesar. Adv. contact Martin Brennan.

629.13 USA
COMMONWEALTH OF PENNSYLVANIA AERONAUTICAL CHART✶. Text in English. a. free.
Published by: Department of Transportation, Bureau of Aviation, 555 Walnut St, Harrisburg, PA 17101-1907.

629.1 USA
COMMONWEALTH OF PENNSYLVANIA. AIRPORT DIRECTORY✶. Text in English. a. free. **Document type:** *Directory.*
Published by: Department of Transportation, Bureau of Aviation, 555 Walnut St, Harrisburg, PA 17101-1907.

358.4 GBR
CONCISE AEROSPACE; aerospace news from the commonwealth of independent states. Text in English. 1993. m. USD 1,000 domestic; GBP 625 elsewhere (effective 2005). adv. back issues avail. **Document type:** *Newsletter, Trade.* **Description:** Contains news, features and editorials about the aerospace and aviation industries in the Russian Federation, the former CIS and Eastern Europe. Also covers civil and military aviation, space and the political context of business operating in this region.
Formerly (until 1997): Concise (1350-2859)
Related titles: Fax ed.; Online - full text ed.
Published by: Bracora Ltd., Lower Court, Staverton, Glos GL51 0TW, United Kingdom. TEL 44-1242-680519, FAX 44-1242-680793, info@conciseb2b.com, http://www.conciseb2b.com/oaerospace.html. Ed., R&P Steve Thomson. Pub. Robert Hadfield. Adv. contact Vicky Darwin. Circ: 150 (paid).

629.1 USA
CONFERENCE ON SPACE SIMULATION. PROCEEDINGS. Text in English. biennial, latest vol.21, 2000. USD 100 per vol. to non-members; USD 75 per vol. to members (effective 2003). **Document type:** *Proceedings, Academic/Scholarly.*
Media: CD-ROM.
Published by: Institute of Environmental Sciences and Technology, 5005 Newport Dr, Ste 506, Rolling Meadows, IL 60008-3841. TEL 847-255-1561, FAX 847-255-1699, iest@iest.org, http://www.iest.org. R&P Julie Kendrick. **Co-sponsors:** U.S. National Aeronautics and Space Administration, Public Affairs Office; American Society for Testing and Materials; American Institute of Aeronautics and Astronautics, Inc.

629.1 BEL ISSN 0772-6880
CONTACT. Text in Dutch, French. q. EUR 20 domestic membership; EUR 30 in Europe membership; EUR 40 foreign membership (effective 2005). bk.rev. illus. back issues avail. **Document type:** *Magazine.* **Description:** Keeps members informed of association activities, and discusses the history of civil and military aviation in Belgium.
Published by: Belgian Aviation History Association, Rue Montoyer 1/32, Boite 10, Bruxelles, 1000, Belgium. e-baha@yahoogroups.com, http://www.baha.be.

629.13 USA
CONTACT! (TUCSON); experimental aircraft and powerplant newsforum for designers and builders. Text in English. 1990. bi-m. USD 20 domestic; CND 28 in Canada; USD 41 elsewhere (effective 2001). 20 p./no.; back issues avail.; reprints avail. **Document type:** *Journal, Consumer.* **Description:** Promotes the experimental development, expansion and exchange of aeronautical concepts, information, and experience.
Published by: (Aeronautics Education Enterprises), Michael C. Myal, Ed. & Pub., 2900 E Weymouth, Tucson, AZ 85716. TEL 520-881-2232, FAX 520-795-6776, contact1@dcnet2000.com, contact1@Flash.net, http://www.nonprofitnet.com/contact/. Circ: 1,200.

629.13 GBR
CONTROL COLUMN. Text in English. 1967. 8/yr. GBP 3.60, USD 8. adv. bk.rev. back issues avail.
Published by: Control Column Publications, 127 Hawton Rd, Newark, Notts NG24 4QG, United Kingdom. Ed. Neville Franklin. Circ: 1,200.

387.7 CAN ISSN 0010-8073
THE CONTROLLER; journal of air traffic control. (Includes Annual Conference Proceedings) Text in English. 1961. q. USD 40 to non-members; USD 30 to members (effective 2005). adv. bk.rev.; film rev. charts; illus. **Document type:** *Journal, Trade.*
Indexed: HRIS, IAA, Inspec.
—CISTI, IE, Infotrieve.
Published by: International Federation of Air Traffic Controllers' Associations, 1255 University St, Ste 408, Montreal, PQ H3B 3B6, Canada. TEL 514-866-7040, FAX 514-866-7612, office@ifatca.org, subscribe@ifatca.org, http://www.the-controller.net, http://www.ifatca.org/. adv.: B&W page CHF 2,900; trim 185 x 265. Circ: 5,000.

629.1 USA ISSN 0736-4709
TL722
CORPORATE AVIATION SAFETY SEMINAR. PROCEEDINGS. Text in English. 1955. a., latest 1992, 37th, Baltimore, MD. reprint service avail. from PQC. **Document type:** *Proceedings.*
Former titles (until 23rd, 1978): Corporate Aircraft Safety Seminar; (until 14th, 1969): Business Aircraft Safety Seminar
—Ei.
Published by: Flight Safety Foundation, Inc., 601 Madison St, Ste 300, Alexandria, VA 22314-1756. TEL 703-739-6700, FAX 703-739-6708. Ed. Roger Rozelle.

629.4 RUS ISSN 0010-9525
QC801 CODEN: CSCRA7
➤ **COSMIC RESEARCH.** Text in English. 1963. bi-m. EUR 3,125, USD 2,818, GBP 1,958 to institutions (effective 2005). back issues avail. **Document type:** *Journal, Academic/Scholarly.* **Description:** Covers physical phenomena in outer space.
Related titles: Online - full text ed.: ISSN 1608-3075. EUR 3,125, USD 2,818, GBP 1,958 to institutions (effective 2005) (from EBSCO Publishing, Gale Group, IngentaConnect, Kluwer Online, O C L C Online Computer Library Center, Inc., Springer LINK, Swets Information Services); ♦ Translation of: Kosmicheskie Issledovaniya. ISSN 0023-4206.
Indexed: ApMecR, BibLing, CivEngAb, CurCont, EnerRA, EngInd, Inspec.
—BLDSC (0411.075000), AskIEEE, CISTI, IE, Infotrieve, ingenta, Linda Hall. **CCC.**
Published by: (Rossiiskaya Akademiya Nauk/Russian Academy of Sciences), M A I K Nauka - Interperiodica, Profsoyuznaya ul 90, Moscow, 117997, Russian Federation. TEL 7-095-3347420, FAX 7-095-3360666, compmg@maik.ru, http://www.maik.ru/journals/cosres.htm. Ed. Timur M Eneev. R&P Vladimir I Vasil'ev. **Subscr. to:** Interperiodica, PO Box 1831, Birmingham, AL 35201-1831. TEL 205-995-1567, 800-633-4931, FAX 205-995-1588; Springer-Verlag Dordrecht, Journals Department, PO Box 322, Dordrecht, Netherlands. TEL 31-78-6576392, FAX 31-78-6576474.

➤ **CROSS & COCKADE INTERNATIONAL.** see *MILITARY*

629.1 USA ISSN 1527-5264
CROSSLINK. Text in English. 2000 (Winter). s-a. **Document type:** *Magazine, Trade.* **Description:** Provides detailed updates on the corporation's evolving capabilities and ongoing achievements in aerospace technology.
Related titles: Online - full content ed.: ISSN 1527-5272.
Indexed: BrCerAb, C&ISA, CerAb, CorrAb, E&CAJ, EMA, IAA, M&TEA, MBF, METADEX, WAA.
—Linda Hall.
Published by: Aerospace Press, Box 92957, Los Angeles, CA 90009-2957. crosslink@aero.org, http://www.aero.org/publications/crosslink/index.html. Eds. Gabriel Spera, Donna J Born.

629.1 GBR ISSN 0263-3043
CROYDON AIRPORT SOCIETY JOURNAL. Text in English. 1981. s-a. GBP 12.50, USD 30 to members (effective 1992). adv. bk.rev. index. back issues avail. **Document type:** *Academic/Scholarly.* **Description:** Contains historical information about Croydon Airport.
Published by: Croydon Airport Society, 193 Commonside E, Mitcham, Surrey CR4 1HB, United Kingdom. TEL 44-20-8648-3906, FAX 44-20-8770-4750. Ed., R&P Peter G Cooksley. Adv. contact Tom Samson. Circ: 800 (controlled).

A

629.13   NLD   ISSN 0926-2571
D D A MAGAZINE. Text in Dutch. bi-m. illus. back issues avail.
Document type: *Magazine.* **Description:** Carries news of the
Dutch Dakota Association, an organization dedicated to
preserving, flying, and exhibiting classic DC-3 and C-47
airplanes. Includes related articles on historical aviation and
present-day flights with historic aircraft.
Formerly (until 1989): Dakota Magazine (0926-2563)
Published by: Dutch Dakota Association, PO Box 75090,
Schiphol, 1117 ZP, Netherlands. TEL 31-20-374-7700, FAX
31-20-405-0221, dda@xs4all.nl, http://www.xs4all.nl/~dda/UK/
orge/member.htm, http://www.xs4all.nl/~dda/index.htm.

629.1   DEU   ISSN 0178-6326
D G L R BERICHT. Text in German. irreg. **Document type:**
Monographic series, Trade.
—BLDSC (3579.420000), IE, ingenta.
Published by: Deutsche Gesellschaft fuer Luft- und Raumfahrt
Lilienthal-Oberth e.V., Godesberger Allee 70, Bonn, 53175,
Germany. TEL 49-228-308050, FAX 49-228-3080524,
geschaeftsstelle@dglr.de, http://www.dglr.de. R&P Marlis
Mess.

629.13   DEU   ISSN 0070-4083
D G L R JAHRBUECHER. Text in German. 1952. a. price varies.
index. **Document type:** *Proceedings, Trade.*
Formerly: Wissenschaftliche Gesellschaft fuer Luft- und
Raumfahrt. Jahrbuecher
—Linda Hall.
Published by: Deutsche Gesellschaft fuer Luft- und Raumfahrt
Lilienthal-Oberth e.V., Godesberger Allee 70, Bonn, 53175,
Germany. TEL 49-228-308050, FAX 49-228-3080524,
geschaeftsstelle@dglr.de, http://www.dglr.de. R&P Marlis
Mess.

D H S; Die Flugzeuge der Nationalen Volksarmee.
(Diensthabendes System) see *MILITARY*

629.13   DEU   ISSN 0938-2194
D L R - JAHRESBERICHT. Text in German. 1969. a. free.
Document type: *Corporate.*
Formerly: D F V L R Jahresbericht (0070-3966)
—CISTI, Linda Hall.
Published by: Deutsches Zentrum fuer Luft- und Raumfahrt e.V.,
Linder Hoehe, Cologne, 51147, Germany. TEL 49-2203-6010,
FAX 49-2203-6013249, pressestelle@dlr.de, http://www.dlr.de.
Circ: 5,000.

629.13   DEU   ISSN 0939-298X
CODEN: MDFREV
D L R - MITTEILUNGEN. Text in German. 1964. irreg. price
varies. **Document type:** *Monographic series,*
Academic/Scholarly. **Description:** Presents new findings in
the DLR research fields of aerospace, energetics and traffic.
Former titles (until 1990): D F V L R - Mitteilungen (0176-7739);
(until 1978): Deutsche Luft- und Raumfahrt. Mitteilung
(0070-4253); Which superseded in part: D F L Bericht
(0366-9017)
Indexed: ZentMath.
—CASDDS, CISTI, Ei. **CCC.**
Published by: Deutsches Zentrum fuer Luft- und Raumfahrt e.V.,
Linder Hoehe, Cologne, 51147, Germany. TEL 49-2203-6010,
FAX 49-2203-67310, pressestelle@dlr.de, http://www.dlr.de.

629.13   DEU   ISSN 0937-0420
TL526.G3   CODEN: DLRNE2
D L R - NACHRICHTEN. Text in German. 1969. q. free. bibl.;
charts; illus. **Document type:** *Bulletin, Academic/Scholarly.*
Description: Covers all aspects of aerospace research and
technology, energetics and traffic research. Includes European
space projects and reports of events.
Formerly (until 1989): D F V L R - Nachrichten (0011-4901);
Which was formed by the merger of (1956-1969): D V L -
Nachrichten (0414-9122); (1964-1969): Deutsche
Forschungsanstalt fuer Luft- und Raumfahrt. Mitteilungen
(0178-6814)
Indexed: ApMecR, CivEngAb, EngInd, FLUIDEX, IAA, M&TEA,
RefZh.
—BLDSC (3605.683000), CINDOC, CISTI, Ei, Linda Hall. **CCC.**
Published by: Deutsches Zentrum fuer Luft- und Raumfahrt e.V.,
Linder Hoehe, Cologne, 51147, Germany. TEL 49-2203-6010,
FAX 49-2203-67310, pressestelle@dlr.de, http://www.dlr.de/dlr-
nachrichten. Ed. Sabine Hoffmann. Circ: 10,000.

629.1   DNK   ISSN 0109-6605
DANSK RUMFORSKNINGINSTITUT. PUBLIKATIONER. Text in
Danish. irreg. **Document type:** *Government.*
Published by: Dansk Rumforskninginstitut/Danish Space
Research Institute, Juliane Maries Vej 30, Copenhagen Oe,
2100, Denmark. TEL 45-35-32-58-30, FAX 45-35-36-24-75,
username@dsri.dk, http://www.dsri.dk.

623.451   CHN   ISSN 1004-7182
DAODAN YU HANGTIAN YUNZAI JISHU/MISSILES AND
SPACE VEHICLES. Text in Chinese. 1972. bi-m. USD 25.20;
CNY 8, USD 4.20 newsstand/cover (effective 2001). back
issues avail. **Document type:** *Academic/Scholarly.*
Related titles: Online - full content ed.: (from WanFang Data
Corp.); Online - full text ed.: (from East View Information
Services).

Published by: Zhongguo Yunzai Huojian Jishu Yanjiuyuan, 9200
Xinxiang 21 Fenxiang, Beijing, 100076, China. TEL
86-1-68383377. Ed. Lunxian Tan. **Dist. by:** China International
Book Trading Corp, 35 Chegongzhuang Xilu, Haidian District,
PO Box 399, Beijing 100044, China. TEL 86-10-68412045,
FAX 86-10-68412023, cibtc@mail.cibtc.com.cn,
http://www.cibtc.com.cn.

DE L'AUTOMOBILE ET DE L'AERONAUTIQUE. see
TRANSPORTATION—Automobiles

355.27   GBR
DEFENCE HELICOPTER; serving the military and parapublic
communities. Text in English. 1982. bi-m. GBP 80 in United
Kingdom; USD 130 foreign (effective 2003). adv. back issues
avail.; reprints avail. **Document type:** *Magazine, Trade.*
Description: Provides unclassified sources of information on
military helicopters.
Former titles (until 2003, vol.22, no.3): Defence & Public Service
Helicopter (1478-758X); (until 2002, vol.21, no.5): Defence
Helicopter (0963-116X); (until 1990): Defence Helicopter World
(0263-5062); Air Ambulance Special Report
Related titles: Online - full text ed.; ◆ Supplement(s): Shephard's
Civil Helicopter Handbook. ISSN 1365-649X; ◆ Shephard's
Military Helicopter Handbook. ISSN 1365-6600.
Indexed: BrCerAb, C&ISA, CerAb, CivEngAb, CorrAb, E&CAJ,
EMA, IAA, LID&ISL, M&TEA, MBF, METADEX, RefZh,
SolStAb, WAA.
—BLDSC (3541.615600), IE, ingenta, Linda Hall. **CCC.**
Published by: Shephard Press Ltd., 111 High St, Burnham,
Bucks SL1 7JZ, United Kingdom. TEL 44-1628-604311,
800-873-2147, FAX 44-1628-664334, 44-1628-664075,
heli-uv@shepard.co.uk, publishing@shephard.co.uk,
http://www.shephard.co.uk/pubs/dpsh/. Ed. Andy Healey. Pub.
John Woolley. Adv. contact Sandy Doyle. B&W page GBP
5,040, color page GBP 6,720; trim 205 x 273. Circ: 10,200.

355   USA
DEFENSE AND AEROSPACE AGENCIES BRIEFING. Text in
English. m. looseleaf. **Document type:** *Newsletter.*
Description: Traces and analyzes the activities of nearly 100
U.S. government agencies, facilities, and other contracting
offices.
Published by: Teal Group Corp., 3900 University Dr, Ste 220,
Fairfax, VA 22030. TEL 703-385-1992, FAX 703-691-9591.

355   USA
DEFENSE AND AEROSPACE COMPANIES BRIEFING. Text in
English. m. looseleaf. **Document type:** *Newsletter.*
Description: Reports on US and international companies,
organizations, and universities that do a major portion of their
business in the defense and aerospace sector.
Published by: Teal Group Corp., 3900 University Dr, Ste 220,
Fairfax, VA 22030. TEL 703-385-1992, FAX 703-691-9591.

355   USA   ISSN 0889-0404
UA23
DEFENSE DAILY. Text in English. 1959. d. (245 iss./yr.). USD
1,997 (effective 2005). charts; illus. **Document type:**
Newsletter, Trade.
Incorporates (1993-1998): C 4 I News (1071-1317); (1991-1998):
Tactical Technology (1059-0552); Former titles (until 1981):
Defense - Space Business Daily; Space Business Daily News
Service (0038-6243)
Related titles: Online - full text ed.: (from bigchalk, Florida Center
for Library Automation, Gale Group, LexisNexis, O C L C
Online Computer Library Center, Inc., ProQuest Information &
Learning, The Dialog Corporation).
Indexed: DM&T.
—CCC.
Published by: Access Intelligence, LLC (Subsidiary of: Veronis,
Suhler & Associates Inc.), 1201 Seven Locks Rd, Ste 300,
Potomac, MD 20854. TEL 301-354-2000, 800-777-5006, FAX
301-762-3068, clientservices@accessintel.com,
http://www.pbimedia.com/cgi/catalog/info?DD.

629.1   NLD
DELFT UNIVERSITY. SERIES 1: AERODYNAMICS. Text in
Dutch. 1997. irreg., latest vol.16, 1998. price varies.
Document type: *Monographic series.* **Description:** Examines
issues in aeronautical engineering in theory and practice with
regard to principles of aerodynamics.
Published by: Delft University Press (Subsidiary of: Technische
Universiteit Delft/Delft University of Technology), PO Box 98,
Delft, 2600 MG, Netherlands. TEL 31-15-278-3254, FAX
31-15-2781661, dup@dup.tudelft.nl.

629.1   NLD
DELFT UNIVERSITY. SERIES 2: FLIGHT MECHANICS. Text in
Dutch. 1997. irreg., latest vol.3, 1998. price varies. **Document**
type: *Monographic series.* **Description:** Examines issues in
aeronautical engineering with regard to flight mechanics.
Published by: Delft University Press (Subsidiary of: Technische
Universiteit Delft/Delft University of Technology), PO Box 98,
Delft, 2600 MG, Netherlands. TEL 31-15-278-3254, FAX
31-15-2781661, dup@dup.tudelft.nl.

629.1   NLD
DELFT UNIVERSITY. SERIES 3: CONTROL AND SIMULATION.
Text in Dutch. 1997. irreg., latest vol.5, 1998. price varies.
Document type: *Monographic series.* **Description:** Examines
issues in aeronautical engineering with regard to control and
simulation.
Published by: Delft University Press (Subsidiary of: Technische
Universiteit Delft/Delft University of Technology), PO Box 98,
Delft, 2600 MG, Netherlands. TEL 31-15-278-3254, FAX
31-15-2781661, dup@dup.tudelft.nl.

629.1   NLD
DELFT UNIVERSITY. SERIES 5: AEROSPACE STRUCTURES
AND COMPUTATIONAL MECHANICS. Text in Dutch. 1997.
irreg., latest vol.4, 1998. price varies. **Document type:**
Monographic series. **Description:** Examines issues in
aerospace engineering, both theoretical and in practice, with
regard to the design of aeronautical structures and
computational mechanics.
Published by: Delft University Press (Subsidiary of: Technische
Universiteit Delft/Delft University of Technology), PO Box 98,
Delft, 2600 MG, Netherlands. TEL 31-15-278-3254, FAX
31-15-2781661, dup@dup.tudelft.nl.

629.1   NLD
DELFT UNIVERSITY. SERIES 7: AEROSPACE MATERIALS.
Text in Dutch. 1997. irreg., latest vol.11, 1998. price varies.
Document type: *Monographic series.* **Description:** Discusses
and explores issues in aeronautical engineering with regard to
new materials used in the construction of aircraft.
Published by: Delft University Press (Subsidiary of: Technische
Universiteit Delft/Delft University of Technology), PO Box 98,
Delft, 2600 MG, Netherlands. TEL 31-15-278-3254, FAX
31-15-2781661, dup@dup.tudelft.nl.

629.1   NLD
DELFT UNIVERSITY. SERIES 8: AERODYNAMICS AND
SATELLITE SYSTEMS. Text in Dutch. 1997. irreg., latest
vol.3, 1998. price varies. **Document type:** *Monographic*
series. **Description:** Explores practical and theorectical issues
in aerospace and aeronautical engineering with regard to
satellite systems and aerodynamics.
Published by: Delft University Press (Subsidiary of: Technische
Universiteit Delft/Delft University of Technology), PO Box 98,
Delft, 2600 MG, Netherlands. TEL 31-15-278-3254, FAX
31-15-2781661, dup@dup.tudelft.nl.

629.1 387.7   CAN   ISSN 1014-0123
DESIGNATORS FOR AIRCRAFT OPERATING AGENCIES,
AERONAUTICAL AUTHORITIES AND SERVICES. Text in
English, French, Russian, Spanish. 1959. irreg., latest vol.118,
2001. USD 67 (effective 2002).
Related titles: Diskette ed.: USD 200.
Published by: International Civil Aviation Organization, External
Relations and Public Information Office, 999 University St,
Montreal, PQ H3C 5H7, Canada. TEL 514-954-8022, FAX
514-954-6769, sales_unit@icao.org, icaohq@icao.int.

629.13   DEU   ISSN 1434-8454
TL507   CODEN: FDFREM
DEUTSCHES ZENTRUM FUER LUFT- UND RAUMFAHRT.
FORSCHUNGSBERICHTE. Text in English, German. 1964.
irreg. price varies. index. **Document type:** *Monographic*
series, Academic/Scholarly. **Description:** Presents new
findings in the research fields of aerospace, energetics and
traffic.
Former titles (until 1997): D L R - Forschungsberichte
(0939-2963); (until 1989): D F V L R - Forschungsberichte
und D F V L R - Mitteilungen (0171-1342); (until 1978):
Deutsche Luft- und Raumfahrt Forschungsberichte
(0070-4245); Which superseded in part (1954-1964): D F L
Bericht (0366-9017)
Indexed: ApMecR, BrCerAb, C&ISA, CCMJ, CerAb, ChemAb,
CivEngAb, CorrAb, E&CAJ, EMA, IAA, ISMEC, M&GPA,
M&TEA, MBF, METADEX, MathR, SolStAb, WAA, ZentMath.
—BLDSC (4011.171250), CISTI, Ei, IE, Linda Hall. **CCC.**
Published by: Deutsches Zentrum fuer Luft- und Raumfahrt e.V.,
Linder Hoehe, Cologne, 51147, Germany. TEL 49-2203-6010,
FAX 49-2203-6014745, werner.wilke@dlr.de, http://www.dlr.de.

629.1   USA
DIGITAL AVIONICS SYSTEMS CONFERENCE. PROCEEDINGS.
Text in English. a. USD 434 per vol.; USD 217 per vol. to
members (effective 2004). **Document type:** *Proceedings,*
Trade. **Description:** Covers the impact of open systems
architectures on the avionics industry, the impact of avionic on
profitability and performance, and the impact of new
technologies on the marketplace are highlighted.
Related titles: CD-ROM ed.
Published by: Institute of Electrical and Electronics Engineers,
Inc., 3 Park Ave, 17th Fl, New York, NY 10016-5997. TEL
212-419-7900, 800-678-4333, FAX 212-752-4929,
customer.service@ieee.org, http://www.ieee.org. **Co-sponsor:**
I E E E Aerospace and Electronic Systems Society.

DIRECTORY OF BRITISH AVIATION (YEARS). see
TRANSPORTATION—Air Transport

629.1 FRA
DIRECTORY OF RUSSIAN SPACE INDUSTRY. Text in French. 1993. biennial. illus. **Document type:** *Directory.* **Description:** Lists 100 Russian space organizations and firms. Includes a short space glossary and acronym list.
Published by: (European Space Agency, Publications Division/Agence Spatiale Europeenne NLD), Sevig Press Publishing, 6 rue Bellart, Paris, 75015, France. TEL 33-1-42732837, FAX 33-1-42732095. Ed., R&P Dick Shirvanian. Adv. contact Anayis Khedjian.

629.13 USA
THE DIRIGO FLYER. Text in English. m. USD 25 domestic membership (effective 2000). illus. back issues avail. **Document type:** *Journal.* **Description:** Documents the history of aviation in Maine, along with historic buildings, photographs, and other memorabilia.
Published by: Maine Aviation Historical Society, Maine Air Museum, PO Box 2641, Bangor, ME 04402. TEL 207-854-9972, pshaw@maine.rr.com, townsend@acadia.net, http://www.acadia.net/mahs. Ed. Leo Boyle TEL 207-854-9972.

358.4 USA ISSN 1061-1231
THE DISPATCH (MIDLAND); American airpower a proud heritage. Text in English. 1976. q. USD 38 (effective 1999). adv. bk.rev. charts; illus.; stat. **Description:** Covers WWII aviation history (1939-1945).
Formerly: C A F Dispatch
Published by: Confederate Air Force, PO Box 62000, Midland, TX 79711-2000. TEL 432-563-1000, FAX 432-563-8046. Ed. Kay Crites. Circ: 7,000.

629.132 FRA ISSN 0764-9185
DOCAVIA. Text in French. 198?. irreg. adv. **Document type:** *Monographic series, Trade.* **Description:** Covers aviation topics.
Published by: Editions Lariviere, Espace Clichy, 12 rue Mozart, Clichy, Cedex 92587, France. TEL 33-1-41403360, FAX 33-1-47376498, abo@editions-lariviere.fr, http://www.editions-lariviere.fr. Ed. Michel Benichou. R&P Isabelle Leguillon TEL 33-1-41403388. Adv. contact Ollivier Adda.

629.1 DEU ISSN 0948-7050
DOKUMENTE DER LUFT- UND RAUMFAHRTINDUSTRIE. Text in Multiple languages. 1994. irreg. **Document type:** *Monographic series.*
—BLDSC (3616.370000).
Published by: Daimler-Benz Aerospace AG, Postfach 801109, Munich, 81663, Germany. TEL 49-89-60734651, FAX 49-89-60734655, beate.strauss@hg.dasa.de, http//www.dasa.com.

629.44 AUS
DRAGONDAILY. Text in English. d. **Document type:** *Academic/Scholarly.* **Description:** Provides information on the latest developments in the People's Republic of China's space technologies and research.
Media: Online - full content.
Published by: Space Daily, PO Box A447, Sydney South, NSW 2000, Australia. TEL 61-2-9360-2257, simon@spacer.com, http://www.spacedaily.com/china.html.

629.1 USA ISSN 1548-7547
TL685.15
E A A SPORT PILOT & LIGHT SPORT AIRCRAFT. Text in English. 1981 (Jan.). m. USD 40 (effective 2004). adv. bk.rev. index. back issues avail. **Document type:** *Magazine, Trade.* **Description:** Technical magazine covering home-building aircraft. Includes plans and design information, and news on ultralights and kit planes.
Former titles (until 2004): Experimenter (1084-6441); (until 1995): E A A Experimenter (0894-1289); (until 1987): E A A Light Plane World (8750-7579); (until 1985): Ultralight and the Light Plane; (until 1984): Ultralight (0279-3792)
Indexed: IHTDI.
Published by: Experimental Aircraft Association, Inc., PO Box 3086, Oshkosh, WI 54903-3086. TEL 414-426-4800, FAX 414-426-4828, http://www.eaa.org/. Ed. Mary Jones. Circ: 18,000.

629.13 NLD ISSN 1013-9036
E C S L NEWS. (European Centre for Space) Text in English, French. 1989. q. free. illus. **Document type:** *Newsletter.*
—Linda Hall.
Published by: European Space Agency, Publications Division/Agence Spatiale Europeenne, Keplerlaan 1, Noordwijk, 2200 AG, Netherlands. TEL 31-1719-86555, FAX 31-1719-58433. Ed. D Guyenne. Circ: 3,300.

E E E LINKS; electronic packaging and space parts. see *ELECTRONICS*

629.13 NLD ISSN 0258-025X
TL858
E S A ANNUAL REPORT. (European Space Agency) Text in English. 1975. a.
Related titles: Online - full text ed.: ISSN 1608-4748. 199?; French ed.: E S A Rapport Annuel. ISSN 0252-936X. 1974.
—BLDSC (3810.923200), CISTI.
Published by: European Space Agency, Publications Division/Agence Spatiale Europeenne, Keplerlaan 1, Noordwijk, 2200 AG, Netherlands. TEL 31-71-5653400, FAX 31-71-5655433, http://esapub.esrin.esa.it/publicat/epdgi.html.

629 NLD ISSN 0250-1589
TL789.8.E9
E S A - B R. (European Space Agency) Variant title: European Space Agency. Brochure. Text in English. 1979. irreg.
—BLDSC (3830.130000).
Published by: European Space Agency, Publications Division/Agence Spatiale Europeenne, Keplerlaan 1, Noordwijk, 2200 AG, Netherlands. TEL 31-71-5653400, FAX 31-71-5655433, http://esapub.esrin.esa.it/publicat/epdgi.html.

629.1 NLD ISSN 0376-4265
TL787 CODEN: ESABD8
E S A BULLETIN. (European Space Agency) Text in English, French. 1966. q. free. bibl.; illus. **Document type:** *Bulletin.*
Formerly (1968-1975): E S R O - E L D O Bulletin (0012-799X)
Related titles: Online - full text ed.: ISSN 1608-4713.
Indexed: ASCA, BrCerAb, C&ISA, CerAb, CivEngAb, CorrAb, CurCont, E&CAJ, EMA, EnvAb, ErgAb, IAA, Inspec, M&TEA, MBF, METADEX, RefZh, SolStAb, TelAb, WAA.
—BLDSC (3810.923300), AskIEEE, CISTI, Ei, IDS, IE, Infotrieve, ingenta, Linda Hall. **CCC.**
Published by: European Space Agency, Publications Division/Agence Spatiale Europeenne, Keplerlaan 1, Noordwijk, 2200 AG, Netherlands. TEL 31-071-5153400, FAX 31-071-5655433. Eds. B Battrick, T D Guyenne. Circ: 25,000.

629 NLD ISSN 1010-5301
E S A - F (ENGLISH EDITION). (European Space Agency) Variant title: European Space Agency. Folder. Text in English. 1986. irreg.
Related titles: French ed.: E S A - F (French Edition). ISSN 1010-5298.
—BLDSC (3830.140000).
Published by: European Space Agency, Publications Division/Agence Spatiale Europeenne, Keplerlaan 1, Noordwijk, 2200 AG, Netherlands. TEL 31-71-5653400, FAX 31-71-5655433, http://esapub.esrin.esa.it/publicat/epdgi.html.

629.13 NLD ISSN 0256-596X
EARTH OBSERVATION QUARTERLY. Text in English. 1983. q. free. illus. **Document type:** *Magazine, Trade.*
Related titles: Online - full text ed.: ISSN 1608-4780.
Indexed: EnvAb, FCA, FLUIDEX, ForAb, GEOBASE, I&DA, IAA, M&GPA, S&F, TriticAb.
—BLDSC (3643.200000), CIS, Linda Hall.
Published by: European Space Agency, Publications Division/Agence Spatiale Europeenne, Keplerlaan 1, Noordwijk, 2200 AG, Netherlands. TEL 31-1719-86555, FAX 31-1719-85433. Ed. T D Guyenne. Circ: 12,000.

629.13 USA
EARTH OBSERVER. Text in English. 1989. bi-m. free. **Document type:** *Government.*
Related titles: Online - full text ed.
Indexed: RefZh.
Published by: U.S. National Aeronautics and Space Administration, Earth Observing System Project, Goddard Space Flight Center, Greenbelt, MD 20771. TEL 301-614-5559, FAX 301-614-5620, cgriner@pop900.gsfc.nasa.gov, http://eospso.gsfc.nasa.gov/earth_observ.html. Ed. Charlotte Griner. Circ: 7,000.

590 USA ISSN 0424-9399
EMPORIA STATE RESEARCH STUDIES. Text in English. irreg., latest 1996. USD 3 per issue. index. back issues avail. **Document type:** *Academic/Scholarly.*
Indexed: MLA, MLA-IB.
—Linda Hall.
Published by: (Emporia State University), Emporia State University Press, 1200 Commercial, Emporia, KS 66801-5087. TEL 316-341-5208, FAX 316-341-5997. Ed., R&P John O Schwenn. Circ: 2,000.

629.13 GBR
ENGINE YEARBOOK (YEAR). Text in English. a. **Document type:** *Trade.* **Description:** Examines many aspects of the aircraft engine business, from manufacturing through maintenance. Also covers the specialist component and service sectors.
Published by: Aviation Industry Press, 31 Palace St, London, SW1E 5HW, United Kingdom. TEL 44-20-7828-4376, FAX 44-20-7828-9154, atem@aviation-industry.com, http://www.aviation-industry.com. Ed. Paul Copping. Pub. Simon Barker. R&P Martin Fendt. Adv. contact Simon N Barker.

629.1 USA ISSN 1093-4804
ENGINEERING, CONSTRUCTION, AND OPERATIONS IN SPACE. Text in English. 1988. biennial, latest 1994. USD 161 domestic; USD 193.20 foreign (effective 2003). **Document type:** *Proceedings, Trade.*
Related titles: Online - full text ed.
—BLDSC (3758.610000). **CCC.**
Published by: American Society of Civil Engineers, 1801 Alexander Bell Dr, Reston, VA 20191-4400. TEL 703-295-6300, 800-548-2723, FAX 703-295-6222, http://www.pubs.asce.org, http://www.asce.org.

629.1 DEU
EUROCOPTER INTERN. Text in German. 1992. m. **Document type:** *Corporate.*
Published by: Eurocopter Deutschland GmbH, Postfach 801140, Munich, 81611, Germany. Ed. Alfred Beck. Circ: 4,500.

629.1 FRA ISSN 0531-7444
EUROPEAN ORGANISATION FOR CIVIL AVIATION EQUIPMENT. GENERAL ASSEMBLY. ANNUAL REPORT. Text in English, French. 1964. a. price varies.
Published by: European Organization for Civil Aviation Equipment/Organisation Europeenne pour l'Equipement de l'Aviation Civile, 17 rue Hamelin, Paris, Cedex 16 75783, France. TEL 33-1-45057188, FAX 33-1-45057230, eurocae@compuserve.com, http://www.eurocae.org. Circ: 200.

629.13 NLD ISSN 0379-4059
EUROPEAN SPACE AGENCY. PROCEDURES, STANDARDS AND SPECIFICATIONS SERIES. Key Title: E S A - P S S. Text in Dutch. 1978. irreg. price varies.
—BLDSC (3830.148000), CISTI.
Published by: European Space Agency, Publications Division/Agence Spatiale Europeenne, Keplerlaan 1, Noordwijk, 2200 AG, Netherlands. TEL 31-071-5653400, FAX 31-071-5655433.

629.13 NLD ISSN 0379-4075
EUROPEAN SPACE AGENCY. SCIENTIFIC AND TECHNICAL MEMORANDA. Key Title: E S A - S T M. Text in Dutch. 1964. irreg.
Supersedes in part: E S A Scientific - Technical Reports, Notes and Memoranda; Formerly (until 1975): E S R O Scientific - Technical Reports, Notes and Memoranda
Indexed: Englnd.
—BLDSC (3830.151000).
Published by: European Space Agency, Publications Division/Agence Spatiale Europeenne, Keplerlaan 1, Noordwijk, 2200 AG, Netherlands. TEL 31-071-5653400, FAX 31-071-5655433.

629.13 NLD ISSN 0379-4067
CODEN: ESSTFI
EUROPEAN SPACE AGENCY. SCIENTIFIC AND TECHNICAL REPORTS. Key Title: E S A - S T R. Text in Dutch. 1964. irreg.
Supersedes in part: E S A Scientific - Technical Reports, Notes and Memoranda; Formerly (until 1975): E S R O Scientific - Technical Reports, Notes and Memoranda
Indexed: CIN, ChemAb, ChemTitl, Englnd.
—BLDSC (3830.152000), CASDDS.
Published by: European Space Agency, Publications Division/Agence Spatiale Europeenne, Keplerlaan 1, Noordwijk, 2200 AG, Netherlands. TEL 31-071-5653400, FAX 31-071-5655433.

629.1 FRA ISSN 0765-0574
TL788.3
EUROPEAN SPACE DIRECTORY. Text in French. 1986. a. adv. **Document type:** *Directory.* **Description:** Lists 300 company profiles of European space firms and agencies.
—BLDSC (3830.180000), IE, ingenta.
Published by: Sevig Press Publishing, 6 rue Bellart, Paris, 75015, France. TEL 33-1-42732837, FAX 33-1-42732095. Ed., R&P Dick Shirvanian. Adv. contact Anayis Khedjian. Circ: 4,000.

629 POL ISSN 1231-1952
HT395.E8
EUROPEAN SPATIAL RESEARCH AND POLICY. Text in English. 1994. s-a. EUR 25 foreign (effective 2005). bk.rev.
Description: Covers the theoretical and empirical aspects of spatial analyses by defining the concepts of space, environment, society, and economy at the local, regional, and supranational level.
Indexed: SUSA.
—BLDSC (3830.232060), IE, ingenta.
Published by: Wydawnictwo Uniwersytetu Lodzkiego/Lodz University Press, ul Jaracza 34, Lodz, 90262, Poland. TEL 48-42-6332279, FAX 48-42-6331671, esrap@krysia.uni.lodz.pl, wdwul@krysia.uni.lodz.pl, http://www.geo.uni.lodz.pl/esrp/, http://www.uni.lodz.pl/ulinfo/wyd-ul.htm. Ed. Tadeusz Marszal.
Dist. by: Ars Polona, Krakowskie Przedmiescie 7, Warsaw, Poland. TEL 48-22-9263914, FAX 48-22-9265334, arspolona@arspolona.com.pl, http://www.arspolona.com.pl.

629.13 USA ISSN 1062-8576
EXPERIMENTAL ROCKET FLYER. Text in English. 1992. q. USD 45 (effective 1998). adv. bk.rev.; software rev. charts; illus. back issues avail. **Description:** Covers experimental rocket construction, suppliers, launchings and results. Specializing in rockets traveling 20,000 to 2,000,000 feet altitude sub-orbital.
Related titles: Online - full text ed.
Published by: California Rocketry, PO Box 1242, Claremont, CA 91711. FAX 877-441-1776, 1rocket@gte.net, http://www.usrockets.com. Ed. Jerry Irvine. adv.: page USD 600; trim 11 x 8.5. Circ: 4,000 (paid).

629.13 USA ISSN 1544-6921
EXPORT AEROSPACE NEWS. Text in English. q.
Related titles: Online - full text ed.: ISSN 1544-693X.

▼ new title ➤ refereed ✶ unverified ♦ full entry avail.

A

Published by: U. S. Department of Commerce, International Trade Administration, Office of Aerospace, 1401 Constitution Ave. NW Rm. 2128, Washington, DC 20230. TEL 202-482-1228, FAX 202-482-3113, http://www.ita.doc.gov/aerospace.

796.154 USA
EXTREME ROCKETRY. Text in English. 2000. 9/yr. USD 39.95 domestic; USD 59.95 in Canada (effective 2003). adv. **Document type:** *Magazine, Consumer.* **Description:** Provides information and content on building and launching model rockets.
Related titles: Online - full text ed.
Published by: RocketeerMedia, 3020 Bryant Ave, Las Vegas, NV 89102. TEL 702-233-8222, FAX 702-877-1211, info@extremerocketry.com, http://www.extremerocketry.com. Ed., Pub. Brent McNeely.

387.7 USA
EXXON AVIATION NEWS DIGEST. Text in English. 1947. w. stat.
Formerly: Esso Aviation News Digest (0014-0996)
Published by: (Exxon Aviation Marketing Affiliates), Exxon Company USA, 800 Bell St, Box 2180, Houston, TX 77252-2180. TEL 713-656-3636. Circ: 10,000.

F-40; Die Flugzeuge der Bundeswehr. see *MILITARY*

629.1325 387.7 USA ISSN 0276-9212
F A A AVIATION FORECASTS. (Federal Aviation Administration) Text in English. 1989. a.
Published by: Federal Aviation Administration, Office of Aviation Policy and Plans, 800 Independence Ave SW, Washington, DC 20591. TEL 202-267-3355, http://apo.faa.gov/pubs.asp, http://apo.faa.gov/pubs.asp?Lev2=1.

629.1 CAN
F A N S FACTS SHEET. (Future Air Navigation Systems) Text in English. bi-m. USD 50 (effective 2000). **Document type:** *Trade.* **Description:** Intended to increase the awareness and understanding of the ICAO Future Air Navigation Systems concept and its impact on airline operations.
Published by: International Air Transport Association, 800 Place Victoria, P O Box 113, Montreal, PQ H4Z 1M1, Canada. TEL 514-874-0202, FAX 514-874-9633.

629.13 FRA ISSN 1293-5476
F A S T AIRBUS TECHNICAL DIGEST. (Flight, Airworthiness, Support and Techology) Text in French. 1983. 2/yr. free. illus. back issues avail. **Document type:** *Bulletin, Trade.* **Description:** Provides articles on the subjects of flight, airworthiness, support and technology, to inform and assist operators of mainly (but not only) Airbus aircraft.
Formerly: F A S T Technical Magazine
Related titles: Online - full text ed.
Published by: Airbus Industrie, Customer Services, 1 rond-point Maurice Bellonte, Blagnac, Cedex 31707, France. TEL 33-5-61933929, FAX 33-5-61932767, TELEX AIRBU 530526F, fast.digest@airbus.fr, http://www.airbus.com. Ed. Denis Dempster. Circ: 30,000.

F M T. see *HOBBIES*

629.13 FRA ISSN 0757-4169
FANA DE L'AVIATION. Text in French. 1969. m. EUR 67.99 (effective 2002). adv. bk.rev. **Document type:** *Magazine, Trade.*
Former titles (until 1983): Fanatique de l'Aviation (0337-8861); (until 1975): Album du Fanatique de l'Aviation (0337-8853)
Published by: Editions Lariviere, Espace Clichy, 12 rue Mozart, Clichy, Cedex 92587, France. TEL 33-1-41403366, FAX 33-1-47376498, abo@editions-lariviere.fr, http://www.editions-lariviere.fr. Ed. Bertrand de Cerval. Adv. contact Ollivier Adda. Circ: 43,000.

629.13 GBR ISSN 0071-402X
FARNBOROUGH AIR SHOW (PUBLIC PROGRAMME). Text in English. biennial. **Document type:** *Catalog.*
Published by: Society of British Aerospace Companies Ltd., Duxbury House, 60 Petty France, London, SW1H 9EU, United Kingdom. TEL 44-171-227-1000. Ed. Susan Godfrey.

797.5 USA ISSN 1549-4756
FAST FACTS. Variant title: I C A S Fact Facts(International Council of Air Shows). Text in English. 1998. bi-w. free to members (effective 2004). **Document type:** *Newsletter.*
Media: Online - full content.
Published by: International Council of Air Shows, 751 Miller Dr, S E, No F4, Leesburg, VA 20175-8993. TEL 703-779-8510, FAX 703-779-8511, icas@airshows.org, http://www.airshows.org/FastFacts/Defaulttff.htm.

629.1325 USA
FEDERAL AVIATION ADMINISTRATION AIRWORTHINESS DIRECTIVES. BOOK 2, LARGE AIRCRAFT. Text in English. base vol. plus irreg. updates. looseleaf. USD 299 (effective 2001). **Document type:** *Government.*
Published by: U.S. Federal Aviation Administration, 800 Independence Ave S W, Washington, DC 20591. http://www.faa.gov. **Subscr. to:** U.S. Government Printing Office, Superintendent of Documents, PO Box 371954, Pittsburgh, PA 15250-7954. TEL 202-512-1800, FAX 202-512-2250, orders@gpo.gov, http://www.access.gpo.gov.

629.1325 USA
FEDERAL AVIATION ADMINISTRATION AIRWORTHINESS DIRECTIVES. BOOK 2, SMALL AIRCRAFT, ROTORCRAFT, GLIDERS, AND BALLOONS. Text in English. base vol. plus irreg. updates. looseleaf. USD 276 (effective 2001). s.a. indexes. **Document type:** *Government.*
Published by: U.S. Federal Aviation Administration, 800 Independence Ave S W, Washington, DC 20591. **Subscr. to:** U.S. Government Printing Office, Superintendent of Documents, PO Box 371954, Pittsburgh, PA 15250-7954. TEL 202-512-1800, FAX 202-512-2250, orders@gpo.gov, http://www.access.gpo.gov.

629.1325 USA
FEDERAL AVIATION REGULATIONS. PART 1, DEFINITIONS AND ABBREVIATIONS. Text in English. base vol. plus irreg. updates. looseleaf. USD 36 (effective 2001). **Document type:** *Government.*
Related titles: Online - full content ed.
Published by: U.S. Federal Aviation Administration, Aircraft Certification Service, 800 Independence Ave, SW, Ste 819, Washington, DC 20591. http://www.airweb.faa.gov/Regulatory_and_Guidance_Library/rgFAR.nsf/MainFrame?OpenFrameSet, http://www.faa.gov/avr/air/airhome.htm. **Subscr. to:** U.S. Government Printing Office, Superintendent of Documents, PO Box 371954, Pittsburgh, PA 15250-7954. TEL 202-512-1800, FAX 202-512-2250, orders@gpo.gov, http://www.access.gpo.gov.

629.1325 USA
FEDERAL AVIATION REGULATIONS. PART 11, GENERAL RULE-MAKING PROCEDURES. Text in English. base vol. plus irreg. updates. looseleaf. USD 30 (effective 2001). **Document type:** *Government.*
Related titles: Online - full content ed.
Published by: U.S. Federal Aviation Administration, Aircraft Certification Service, 800 Independence Ave, SW, Ste 819, Washington, DC 20591. http://www.airweb.faa.gov/Regulatory_and_Guidance_Library/rgFAR.nsf/MainFrame?OpenFrameSet, http://www.faa.gov/avr/air/airhome.htm. **Subscr. to:** U.S. Government Printing Office, Superintendent of Documents, PO Box 371954, Pittsburgh, PA 15250-7954. TEL 202-512-1800, FAX 202-512-2250, orders@gpo.gov, http://www.access.gpo.gov.

629.1325 USA
FEDERAL AVIATION REGULATIONS. PART 119, CERTIFICATION: AIR CARRIERS AND COMMERCIAL OPERATORS. Text in English. base vol. plus irreg. updates. looseleaf. USD 35 (effective 2001). **Document type:** *Government.*
Published by: U.S. Federal Aviation Administration, Aircraft Certification Service, 800 Independence Ave, SW, Ste 819, Washington, DC 20591. http://www.faa.gov/avr/air/airhome.htm. **Subscr. to:** U.S. Government Printing Office, Superintendent of Documents, PO Box 371954, Pittsburgh, PA 15250-7954. TEL 202-512-1800, FAX 202-512-2250, orders@gpo.gov, http://www.access.gpo.gov.

629.1325 USA
FEDERAL AVIATION REGULATIONS. PART 121, CERTIFICATION AND OPERATIONS: DOMESTIC, FLAG, AND SUPPLEMENTAL AIR CARRIERS AND COMMERCIAL OPERATORS OF LARGE AIRCRAFT. Text in English. base vol. plus irreg. updates. looseleaf. USD 92 (effective 2001). **Document type:** *Government.*
Published by: U.S. Federal Aviation Administration, Aircraft Certification Service, 800 Independence Ave, SW, Ste 819, Washington, DC 20591. http://www.faa.gov/avr/air/airhome.htm. **Subscr. to:** U.S. Government Printing Office, Superintendent of Documents, PO Box 371954, Pittsburgh, PA 15250-7954. TEL 202-512-1800, FAX 202-512-2250, orders@gpo.gov, http://www.access.gpo.gov.

629.1325 USA
FEDERAL AVIATION REGULATIONS. PART 125, CERTIFICATION AND OPERATIONS: AIRPLANES HAVING A SEATING CAPACITY OF 20 OR MORE PASSENGERS OR A MAXIMUM PAYLOAD CAPACITY OF 6,000 POUNDS OR MORE. Text in English. base vol. plus irreg. updates. looseleaf. USD 64 (effective 2001). **Document type:** *Government.*
Published by: U.S. Federal Aviation Administration, Aircraft Certification Service, 800 Independence Ave, SW, Ste 819, Washington, DC 20591. http://www.faa.gov/avr/air/airhome.htm. **Subscr. to:** U.S. Government Printing Office, Superintendent of Documents, PO Box 371954, Pittsburgh, PA 15250-7954. TEL 202-512-1800, FAX 202-512-2223, orders@gpo.gov, http://www.access.gpo.gov.

629.1325 USA
FEDERAL AVIATION REGULATIONS. PART 129, OPERATIONS: FOREIGN AIR CARRIERS AND FOREIGN OPERATORS OF UNITED STATES-REGISTERED AIRCRAFT ENGAGED IN COMMON CARRIAGE. Text in English. base vol. plus irreg. updates. looseleaf. USD 26 (effective 2001). **Document type:** *Government.*
Published by: U.S. Federal Aviation Administration, Aircraft Certification Service, 800 Independence Ave, SW, Ste 819, Washington, DC 20591. http://www.faa.gov/avr/air/airhome.htm. **Subscr. to:** U.S. Government Printing Office, Superintendent of Documents, PO Box 371954, Pittsburgh, PA 15250-7954. TEL 202-512-1800, FAX 202-512-2250, orders@gpo.gov, http://www.access.gpo.gov.

629.1325 USA
FEDERAL AVIATION REGULATIONS. PART 13, INVESTIGATIVE AND ENFORCEMENT PROCEDURES. Text in English. base vol. plus irreg. updates. looseleaf. USD 22 (effective 2001). **Document type:** *Government.*
Published by: U.S. Federal Aviation Administration, Aircraft Certification Service, 800 Independence Ave, SW, Ste 819, Washington, DC 20591. http://www.faa.gov/avr/air/airhome.htm. **Subscr. to:** U.S. Government Printing Office, Superintendent of Documents, PO Box 371954, Pittsburgh, PA 15250-7954. TEL 202-512-1800, FAX 202-512-2250, orders@gpo.gov, http://www.access.gpo.gov.

629.1325 USA
FEDERAL AVIATION REGULATIONS. PART 135, AIR TAXI OPERATORS AND COMMERCIAL OPERATORS. Text in English. base vol. plus irreg. updates. looseleaf. USD 80 (effective 2001). **Document type:** *Government.*
Published by: U.S. Federal Aviation Administration, Aircraft Certification Service, 800 Independence Ave, SW, Ste 819, Washington, DC 20591. http://www.faa.gov/avr/air/airhome.htm. **Subscr. to:** U.S. Government Printing Office, Superintendent of Documents, PO Box 371954, Pittsburgh, PA 15250-7954. TEL 202-512-1800, FAX 202-512-2250, orders@gpo.gov, http://www.access.gpo.gov.

629.1325 USA
FEDERAL AVIATION REGULATIONS. PART 145, REPAIR STATIONS. Text in English. base vol. plus irreg. updates. USD 34 (effective 2001). **Document type:** *Government.*
Published by: U.S. Federal Aviation Administration, Aircraft Certification Service, 800 Independence Ave, SW, Ste 819, Washington, DC 20591. http://www.faa.gov/avr/air/airhome.htm. **Subscr. to:** U.S. Government Printing Office, Superintendent of Documents, PO Box 371954, Pittsburgh, PA 15250-7954. TEL 202-512-1800, FAX 202-512-2250, orders@gpo.gov, http://www.access.gpo.gov.

629.1325 USA
FEDERAL AVIATION REGULATIONS. PART 21, CERTIFICATION PROCEDURES FOR PRODUCTS AND PARTS. Text in English. base vol. plus irreg. updates. looseleaf. USD 38 (effective 2001). **Document type:** *Government.*
Published by: U.S. Federal Aviation Administration, Aircraft Certification Service, 800 Independence Ave, SW, Ste 819, Washington, DC 20591. http://www.faa.gov/avr/air/airhome.htm. **Subscr. to:** U.S. Government Printing Office, Superintendent of Documents, PO Box 371954, Pittsburgh, PA 15250-7954. TEL 202-512-1800, FAX 202-512-2250, orders@gpo.gov, http://www.access.gpo.gov.

629.1325 USA
FEDERAL AVIATION REGULATIONS. PART 23, AIRWORTHINESS STANDARDS: NORMAL, UTILITY, ACROBATICS, AND COMMUTER CATEGORY AIRPLANES. Text in English. base vol. plus irreg. updates. looseleaf. USD 36 (effective 2001). **Document type:** *Government.*
Published by: U.S. Federal Aviation Administration, Aircraft Certification Service, 800 Independence Ave, SW, Ste 819, Washington, DC 20591. http://www.faa.gov/avr/air/airhome.htm. **Subscr. to:** U.S. Government Printing Office, Superintendent of Documents, PO Box 371954, Pittsburgh, PA 15250-7954. TEL 202-512-1800, FAX 202-512-2250, orders@gpo.gov, http://www.access.gpo.gov.

629.1325 USA
FEDERAL AVIATION REGULATIONS. PART 25, AIRWORTHINESS STANDARDS: TRANSPORT CATEGORY AIRPLANES. Text in English. base vol. plus irreg. updates. looseleaf. USD 47 (effective 2001). **Document type:** *Government.*
Published by: U.S. Federal Aviation Administration, Aircraft Certification Service, 800 Independence Ave, SW, Ste 819, Washington, DC 20591. http://www.faa.gov/avr/air/airhome.htm. **Subscr. to:** U.S. Government Printing Office, Superintendent of Documents, PO Box 371954, Pittsburgh, PA 15250-7954. TEL 202-512-1800, FAX 202-512-2250, orders@gpo.gov, http://www.access.gpo.gov.

629.1325 USA
FEDERAL AVIATION REGULATIONS. PART 27, AIRWORTHINESS STANDARDS: NORMAL CATEGORY ROTORCRAFT. Text in English. base vol. plus irreg. updates. looseleaf. USD 39 (effective 2001). **Document type:** *Government.*
Published by: U.S. Federal Aviation Administration, Aircraft Certification Service, 800 Independence Ave, SW, Ste 819, Washington, DC 20591. http://www.faa.gov/avr/air/airhome.htm. **Subscr. to:** U.S. Government Printing Office, Superintendent of Documents, PO Box 371954, Pittsburgh, PA 15250-7954. TEL 202-512-1800, FAX 202-512-2250, orders@gpo.gov, http://www.access.gpo.gov.

629.1325 USA
FEDERAL AVIATION REGULATIONS. PART 29, AIRWORTHINESS STANDARDS: TRANSPORT CATEGORY ROTORCRAFT. Text in English. base vol. plus irreg. updates. looseleaf. USD 28 (effective 2001). **Document type:** *Government.*
Published by: U.S. Federal Aviation Administration, Aircraft Certification Service, 800 Independence Ave, SW, Ste 819, Washington, DC 20591. http://www.faa.gov/avr/air/airhome.htm. **Subscr. to:** U.S. Government Printing Office, Superintendent of Documents, PO Box 371954, Pittsburgh, PA 15250-7954. TEL 202-512-1800, FAX 202-512-2250, orders@gpo.gov, http://www.access.gpo.gov.

629.134 USA
FEDERAL AVIATION REGULATIONS. PART 33, AIRWORTHINESS STANDARDS: AIRCRAFT ENGINES. Text in English. base vol. plus irreg. updates. looseleaf. USD 28 (effective 2001). **Document type:** *Government.*
Published by: U.S. Federal Aviation Administration, Aircraft Certification Service, 800 Independence Ave, SW, Ste 819, Washington, DC 20591. http://www.faa.gov/avr/air/airhome.htm. **Subscr. to:** U.S. Government Printing Office, Superintendent of Documents, PO Box 371954, Pittsburgh, PA 15250-7954. TEL 202-512-1800, FAX 202-512-2250, orders@gpo.gov, http://www.access.gpo.gov.

629.13254 USA
FEDERAL AVIATION REGULATIONS. PART 61, CERTIFICATION: PILOTS, FLIGHT INSTRUCTORS, AND GROUND INSTRUCTORS. Text in English. base vol. plus irreg. updates. looseleaf. USD 59 (effective 2001). **Document type:** *Government.*
Published by: U.S. Federal Aviation Administration, Aircraft Certification Service, 800 Independence Ave, SW, Ste 819, Washington, DC 20591. http://www.faa.gov/avr/air/airhome.htm. **Subscr. to:** U.S. Government Printing Office, Superintendent of Documents, PO Box 371954, Pittsburgh, PA 15250-7954. TEL 202-512-1800, FAX 202-512-2250, orders@gpo.gov, http://www.access.gpo.gov.

629.13254 USA
FEDERAL AVIATION REGULATIONS. PART 65, CERTIFICATION: AIRMEN OTHER THAN FLIGHT CREWMEMBERS. Text in English. base vol. plus irreg. updates. looseleaf. USD 36 (effective 2001). **Document type:** *Government.*
Published by: U.S. Federal Aviation Administration, Aircraft Certification Service, 800 Independence Ave, SW, Ste 819, Washington, DC 20591. http://www.faa.gov/avr/air/airhome.htm. **Subscr. to:** U.S. Government Printing Office, Superintendent of Documents, PO Box 371954, Pittsburgh, PA 15250-7954. TEL 202-512-1800, FAX 202-512-2250, orders@gpo.gov, http://www.access.gpo.gov.

629.1325 USA
FEDERAL AVIATION REGULATIONS. PART 71, DESIGNATION OF FEDERAL AIRWAYS, AREA LOW ROUTES, CONTROLLED AIRSPACE, REPORTING POINTS, JET ROUTES, AND AREA HIGH ROUTES. Text in English. base vol. plus irreg. updates. USD 29 (effective 2001).
Published by: U.S. Federal Aviation Administration, Aircraft Certification Service, 800 Independence Ave, SW, Ste 819, Washington, DC 20591. http://www.faa.gov/avr/air/airhome.htm. **Subscr. to:** U.S. Government Printing Office, Superintendent of Documents, PO Box 371954, Pittsburgh, PA 15250-7954. TEL 202-512-1800, FAX 202-512-2250, orders@gpo.gov, http://www.access.gpo.gov.

629.1325 USA
FEDERAL AVIATION REGULATIONS. PART 91, GENERAL OPERATING AND FLIGHT RULES. Text in English. base vol. plus irreg. updates. looseleaf. USD 157 (effective 2001). **Document type:** *Government.*
Published by: U.S. Federal Aviation Administration, Aircraft Certification Service, 800 Independence Ave, SW, Ste 819, Washington, DC 20591. http://www.faa.gov/avr/air/airhome.htm. **Subscr. to:** U.S. Government Printing Office, Superintendent of Documents, PO Box 371954, Pittsburgh, PA 15250-7954. TEL 202-512-1800, FAX 202-512-2250, orders@gpo.gov, http://www.access.gpo.gov.

629.1325 USA
FEDERAL AVIATION REGULATIONS. PART 93, SPECIAL AIR TRAFFIC RULES AND AIRPORT TRAFFIC PATTERNS. Text in English. base vol. plus irreg. updates. looseleaf. USD 68 (effective 2001). **Document type:** *Government.*
Published by: U.S. Federal Aviation Administration, Aircraft Certification Service, 800 Independence Ave, SW, Ste 819, Washington, DC 20591. http://www.faa.gov/avr/air/airhome.htm. **Subscr. to:** U.S. Government Printing Office, Superintendent of Documents, PO Box 371954, Pittsburgh, PA 15250-7954. TEL 202-512-1800, FAX 202-512-2250, orders@gpo.gov, http://www.access.gpo.gov.

001.942 CHN ISSN 1001-7674
FEIDIE TANSUO/JOURNAL OF U F O RESEARCH. Text in Chinese. bi-m. USD 11.40; USD 1.90 newsstand/cover (effective 2001). **Document type:** *Academic/Scholarly.*
Related titles: Online - full text ed.: (from East View Information Services).
Published by: Gansu Kexue Jishu Chubanshe, Lanzhou, Gansu 730000, China. gstp@public.lz.gs.cn. **Dist. by:** China International Book Trading Corp, 35 Chegongzhuang Xilu, Haidian District, PO Box 399, Beijing 100044, China. TEL 86-10-68412045, FAX 86-10-68412023, cibtc@mail.cibtc.com.cn, http://www.cibtc.com.cn.

623.451 CHN ISSN 1009-1319
FEIHANG DAODAN/WINGED MISSILES JOURNAL. Text in Chinese. m. CNY 80 (effective 2004). back issues avail. **Document type:** *Journal, Academic/Scholarly.*
Related titles: Online - full text ed.: (from East View Information Services, WanFang Data Corp.).
Published by: Zhongguo Hangtianke Gongjituan, Di-3 Yanjiuyuan Di-31-Suo, 7254 Xinxiang 4-Fenxiang, Beijing, 100074, China. TEL 81-10-68376009, 310feihang@sina.com, http://fhdd.periodicals.net.cn/default.html. **Dist. by:** China International Book Trading Corp, 35 Chegongzhuang Xilu, Haidian District, PO Box 399, Beijing 100044, China. TEL 86-10-68412045, FAX 86-10-68412023, cibtc@mail.cibtc.com.cn, http://www.cibtc.com.cn.

629.132 CHN ISSN 1002-0853
FEIXING LIXUE/FLIGHT DYNAMICS. Text in Chinese. 1983. q. **Document type:** *Journal, Academic/Scholarly.*
Related titles: Online - full text ed.: (from East View Information Services, WanFang Data Corp.).
Indexed: BrCerAb, C&ISA, CerAb, CorrAb, E&CAJ, EMA, IAA, M&TEA, MBF, METADEX, RefZh, WAA.
—BLDSC (3951.004500), IE, Linda Hall.
Published by: (Hangkong Hangtianbu Feixing Shiyan Yanjiuyuan), Feixing Lixue Zazhishe, Liangyan-qu, PO Box 73, Xi'an, 710089, China. TEL 86-29-86838449, FAX 86-29-86838915, fhlx@chinajournal.net.cn, http://fxlx.periodicals.net.cn/default.html. **Dist. by:** China International Book Trading Corp, 35 Chegongzhuang Xilu, Haidian District, PO Box 399, Beijing 100044, China. TEL 86-10-68412045, FAX 86-10-68412023, cibtc@mail.cibtc.com.cn, http://www.cibtc.com.cn.

FIJI. BUREAU OF STATISTICS. AIRCRAFT STATISTICS. see *AERONAUTICS AND SPACE FLIGHT—Abstracting, Bibliographies, Statistics*

629.4 USA ISSN 0899-4161
TL787
FINAL FRONTIER✶; the magazine of space exploration. Text in English. 1988. bi-m. USD 14.95. adv. bk.rev. **Document type:** *Consumer.* **Description:** Seeks to broaden the base of space enthusiasts among the general public, as well as to provide information to aerospace professionals.
—Linda Hall.
Published by: Final Frontier Publishing, Inc., The Brooklyn College Science Fiction Society, Central Depository, Boylan Hall, Bedford Ave and Ave H, Brooklyn, NY 11210. TEL 612-822-9600, FAX 612-822-9640. Ed. Leonard David. Circ: 90,000.

387.7 BRA ISSN 0046-404X
FLAP INTERNACIONAL; revista latinoamericana de aviacao. Text in Portuguese. 1962. m. adv. charts; illus.; stat. **Description:** Provides current trade information, news and articles to airline pilots and professionals related to the aeronautics field.
Published by: Grupo Editorial Spagat Ltda., Rua Professor Artur Ramos, 183 Andar 10, Jd Paulistano, Sao Paulo, SP 01454-011, Brazil. TEL 55-11-8164455, FAX 55-11-2104186. Ed. Carlos Andre Spagat. Circ: 42,000.

629.13 DEU ISSN 0001-9445
FLIEGER-REVUE; Magazin fuer Luft- und Raumfahrt. Text in German. 1952. m. EUR 42 domestic; EUR 58.80 foreign; EUR 4 newsstand/cover (effective 2005). adv. bk.rev. charts; illus. index. **Document type:** *Magazine, Consumer.* **Description:** Covers civilian and military aviation, general aviation, and developments in the aviation and space industries.
Former titles (until 1970): Aerosport (0323-7931); (until 1960): Fluegel der Heimat (0426-6218)
—CCC.
Published by: Moeller Druck und Verlag GmbH, Oraniendamm 48, Berlin, 13469, Germany. TEL 49-30-419090, FAX 49-30-41909299, redaktion@fliegerrevue.de, info@moellerdruck.de, http://www.fliegerrevue.de, http://www.moellerdruck.de. adv.: B&W page EUR 3,010, color page EUR 4,360; trim 179 x 259. Circ: 21,048 (paid and controlled).

629.1 DEU ISSN 1438-0978
FLIEGERKALENDER. Text in German. 1979. a. EUR 13.90 (effective 2006). abstr.; charts; illus.; stat. **Document type:** *Magazine, Trade.*
Published by: Verlag E.S. Mittler und Sohn GmbH, Striepenweg 31, Hamburg, 21147, Germany. TEL 49-40-7971303, FAX 49-40-79713324, Vertrieb@koehler-mittler.de, http://www.koehler-mittler.de. Ed. Hans M Namislo. Adv. contact Rainer Metzner. Circ: 5,500.

629.132 DEU ISSN 0170-5504
FLIEGERMAGAZIN. Text in German. m. EUR 48.60 domestic; EUR 67.44 foreign; EUR 4.35 newsstand/cover (effective 2003). adv. **Document type:** *Magazine, Consumer.*
Incorporates (1921-1980): Der Flieger (0015-3680)
—CCC.
Published by: Jahr Top Special Verlag, Jessenstr 1, Hamburg, 22767, Germany. TEL 49-40-38906271, FAX 49-40-38906301, http://www.flieger-m.de/, http://www.jahr-tsv.de. Ed. Juergen Schelling. Adv. contact Klaus Macholz. B&W page EUR 3,540, color page EUR 6,192; trim 196 x 260. Circ: 28,150 (paid).

629.13 GBR ISSN 0015-3710
TL501
FLIGHT INTERNATIONAL. Text in English. 1909. w. EUR 140 in Europe eurozone; USD 149 in United States; GBP 92 in the UK & elsewhere (effective 2004). adv. bk.rev. charts; illus. index. reprint service avail. from PQC. **Document type:** *Magazine, Trade.* **Description:** Provides in-depth technical reporting on world aerospace news geared toward the professional.
Related titles: Microform ed.: (from PQC); Online - full text ed.: (from Data-Star, EBSCO Publishing, Florida Center for Library Automation, Gale Group, H.W. Wilson, LexisNexis, O C L C Online Computer Library Center, Inc., ProQuest Information & Learning).
Indexed: AS&TI, AUNI, B&I, BrCerAb, BrTechI, C&ISA, CLT&T, CerAb, ChemAb, CivEngAb, CorrAb, DM&T, E&CAJ, EMA, EngInd, HRIS, IAA, M&TEA, MBF, METADEX, PROMT, RASB, RefZh, SolStAb, WAA, WTA.
—BLDSC (3951.010000), CISTI, IE, Infotrieve, ingenta, Linda Hall. **CCC.**
Published by: Reed Business Information Ltd. (Subsidiary of: Reed Business), Quadrant House, The Quadrant, Brighton Rd, Sutton, Surrey SM2 5AS, United Kingdom. TEL 44-20-86523500, FAX 44-20-86528932, http://www.flightinternational.com, http://www.reedbusiness.co.uk/. Ed. Murdo Morrison TEL 44-20-8652-3882. Adv. contact Richard Thiele TEL 44-20-8652-3315. Circ: 50,500. **Subscr. to:** Quadrant Subscription Services, Rockwood House, 9-17 Perrymount Rd, Haywards Heath, W. Sussex RH16 3DH, United Kingdom. TEL 44-20-8652-3500, FAX 44-20-8652-8932, rbi.subscriptions@qss-uk.com.

629.13 USA ISSN 1095-1075
FLIGHT JOURNAL; exploring the aviation adventure. Text in English. 1996. bi-m. USD 19.95 domestic; USD 23.95 in Canada; USD 29.95 elsewhere; USD 4.95 newsstand/cover (effective 2005). adv. bk.rev. illus. **Document type:** *Magazine, Consumer.* **Description:** Covers current and historic aviation and personalities.
Formerly: Flight (1087-0822)
Related titles: Online - full text ed.: (from bigchalk, Northern Light Technology, Inc., ProQuest Information & Learning).
Published by: Air Age Media, 100 E Ridge, Ridgefield, CT 06877-4606. TEL 203-431-9000, FAX 203-431-3000, flightjournal@airage.com, http://www.flightjournal.com, http://www.airage.com. Ed. Budd Davisson. adv.: B&W page USD 1,785, color page USD 2,680. Circ: 40,000 (paid).

FLIGHT PARAMEDIC NEWS. see *MEDICAL SCIENCES*

FLIGHT PHYSICIAN. see *MEDICAL SCIENCES*

629.132 GBR ISSN 0015-3737
FLIGHT SAFETY BULLETIN. Text in English. 1965. q. GBP 12; GBP 18 foreign (effective 2001). adv. bk.rev. illus.; stat. back issues avail. **Document type:** *Bulletin.* **Description:** Contains articles, statistics, and accident details of UK general aviation accidents and incidents. Aims to foster the development of general aviation and its safety by encouraging competence among pilots and operators.
Indexed: ESPM, H&SSA.
Published by: General Aviation Safety Council, Rochester Airport, Chatham, Kent ME5 9SD, United Kingdom. TEL 44-1634-200203, FAX 44-1634-200203, editor@gen-av-safety.demon.co.uk, johncampbell@gen-av-safety.demon.co.uk. Ed. Nigel Everett. Adv. contact Andrew Dent TEL 44-1993-891000. Circ: 14,500.

629.13 USA ISSN 1057-5588
TL553.5
FLIGHT SAFETY DIGEST. Text in English. 1970. m. USD 520 to non-members (effective 2005); free to members. illus. reprint service avail. from PQC. **Document type:** *Magazine, Trade.* **Description:** Analyzes controversial industry issues, shares observations of important influences, describes the latest innovations in training, technology or management.
Former titles (until 1988): F S F Flight Safety Digest (0898-5715); Flight Safety Digest (0736-7554); (until 1982): Flight Safety Facts and Reports (0098-7182); (until 1974): Flight Safety Facts and Analysis (0894-4571)
Indexed: CLT&T, HRIS, RefZh.
—BLDSC (3952.120000).
Published by: Flight Safety Foundation, Inc., 601 Madison St, Ste 300, Alexandria, VA 22314-1756. TEL 703-739-6700, FAX 703-739-6708, http://www.flightsafety.org. Ed. Roger Rozelle. Circ: 2,700.

FLIGHT SIMULATOR WORLD. see *COMPUTERS—Computer Games*

629.1 USA
FLIGHT TEST NEWS. Text in English. 1981. m. looseleaf. free to members (effective 2005). back issues avail. **Document type:** *Newsletter.*
Formerly: Society of Flight Test Engineers Newsletter
Related titles: CD-ROM ed.

Published by: Society of Flight Test Engineers, 44814 N Elm Ave, Lancaster, CA 93534. TEL 661-949-2095, FAX 661-949-2096, sfte@sfte.org, http://www.sfte.org/. Ed. John Minor. Circ: 1,200.

629.13   USA
FLIGHTLINES. Text in English. 10/yr. adv. **Document type:** *Newsletter.*
Published by: Kent Publications, Inc. (Woodmere), PO Box 364, Woodmere, NY 11598-0364. Pub. Bernard Kovit.

629.132   AUS   ISSN 1320-5870
FLIGHTPATH. Text in English. q. AUD 30 domestic; AUD 40 in New Zealand; AUD 50 in Asia; AUD 60 elsewhere (effective 2005). adv. **Document type:** *Magazine, Consumer.* **Description:** For pilots and aircraft owners, civil and military air crews, as well as enthusiasts who have a fascination with flight.
Incorporates: AirPower
Published by: Yaffa Publishing Group Pty Ltd., 17-21 Bellevue St, Surry Hills, NSW 2010, Australia. TEL 61-2-92812333, FAX 61-2-92812750, yaffa@yaffa.com.au, http://www.yaffa.com.au. Ed. Rob Fox. Pub. Tracy Yaffa. Adv. contact Tiffany Palmer. B&W page AUD 1,330, color page AUD 1,795; trim 210 x 297.

629.13   AUT
FLUG-INFORMATIONEN. Text in German. 1950. q. membership. bk.rev. **Document type:** *Bulletin.* **Description:** Contains information on Austrian aviation history.
Formerly: Flugsport-Informationen (0015-4598)
Published by: Oesterreichisches Luftfahrt Archiv, Kreuzgasse 63, Vienna, W 1100, Austria. Ed. Reinhard Keimel. Circ: 300.

629.13   DEU   ISSN 0015-4547
TL503
FLUG REVUE. Text in German. 1968. m. EUR 49.90; EUR 4.50 newsstand/cover (effective 2005). adv. bk.rev. illus. index. back issues avail. **Document type:** *Magazine, Consumer.* **Description:** Contains research information on all aspects of air and space travel.
Formed by the 1968 merger of: Flugwelt International (0935-0640); Which superseded (1949-1962): Flugwelt (0935-0632); And: Flugrevue International (0935-0667); Which was formerly (until 1963): Flug - Revue (0935-3860); (1949-1956): Weltluftfahrt (0935-3496); (1908-1944): Flugsport (0935-3488)
Indexed: BrCerAb, C&ISA, CLT&T, CerAb, CivEngAb, CorrAb, E&CAJ, EMA, IAA, M&TEA, MBF, METADEX, RefZh, SolStAb, WAA.
—CISTI, IE, Infotrieve, Linda Hall. **CCC.**
Published by: Vereinigte Motor-Verlage GmbH & Co. KG, Leuschnerstr 1, Stuttgart, 70174, Germany. TEL 49-711-18201, FAX 49-711-1821779, http://www.flug-revue.rotor.com/FRheft/frnewhe.htm, http://www.motorpresse.de. Ed. Norbert Burgner. Pub. Peter Paul Pietsch. Adv. contact Reinhard Wittstamm. B&W page EUR 5,030, color page EUR 9,400; trim 185 x 248. Circ: 39,730 (paid and controlled).

629.1   DEU   ISSN 0938-3883
FLUGPOST; Informationsdienst Luftfahrt. Text in German. 1989. w. EUR 350 (effective 2005). **Document type:** *Newsletter, Consumer.*
Published by: Aviatic Verlag GmbH, Kolpingring 16, Oberhaching, 82041, Germany. TEL 49-89-6138900, FAX 49-89-61389010, aviatic@aviatic.de, http://www.aviatic.de/flugpost/. Ed., Pub. Peter Pletschacher.

629.1   DEU
FLUGSICHERHEITSMITTEILUNGEN (FSM). Text in German. 1972. irreg. free. back issues avail. **Document type:** *Government.* **Description:** Covers basic theoretical information for training of pilot students and flight safety.
Published by: Luftfahrt-Bundesamt, Postfach 3054, Braunschweig, 38020, Germany. TEL 49-531-2355-0, FAX 49-531-2355751, info@lba.de, http://www.lba.de. Ed., R&P Ernst Boller TEL 49-531-2355549. Circ: 27,000.

629.1   AUT
FLUGSPORTZEITUNG. Text in German. 1972. m. adv. bk.rev. **Document type:** *Journal, Consumer.*
Published by: Verlag Karl Berger, Spratzerner Kirchenweg 51, Postfach 398, St. Poelten, N 3101, Austria. TEL 43-2742-353422, FAX 43-2742-353422, flugsportzeitung@aon.at, http://members.aon.at/flugsportzeitung/index.htm. Ed., Adv. contact Karl Berger. Circ: 2,400.

629.133   DEU   ISSN 1617-0725
FLUGZEUG CLASSIC. Text in German. 2000. 10/yr. EUR 44.10; EUR 4.90 newsstand/cover (effective 2003). adv. **Document type:** *Magazine, Consumer.*
Incorporates (1985-2001): Flugzeug (0933-8454)
Published by: GeraNova Zeitschriftenverlag GmbH, Innsbrucker Ring 15, Munich, 81673, Germany. TEL 49-89-13069911, FAX 49-89-13069910, info@geranova.de, http://www.geranova-verlag.de/magazine/flugzeugclassic.asp. Ed. Peter Pletschacher. adv.: B&W page EUR 1,372, color page EUR 1,784. Circ: 27,410 (paid and controlled).

629.1   DEU   ISSN 0947-627X
FLY AND GLIDE. Text in German. 1975. m. EUR 48.60 domestic; EUR 67.44 foreign; EUR 4.05 newsstand/cover (effective 2003). adv. **Document type:** *Magazine, Consumer.*
Former titles (until 1994): Drachenflieger Magazin (0175-1492); (until 1983): Drachenflieger (0722-8589); (until 1980): Drachenflieger-Magazin (0343-3447)
Published by: Jahr Top Special Verlag, Jessenstr 1, Hamburg, 22767, Germany. TEL 49-40-38906271, FAX 49-40-38906301, redaktion@fly-and-glide.de, erichsen@jahr-tsv.de, http://www.jahr-tsv.de. Ed. Carolin Rochelt. Adv. contact Heiko Rottmann TEL 49-40-38906283. B&W page EUR 1,700, color page EUR 2,880; trim 185 x 248. Circ: 22,783 (paid).

FLYER; the magazine for pilots. see *TRANSPORTATION—Air Transport*

629.13   SWE   ISSN 0281-8760
FLYG; flygets aarsbok. Text in Swedish. 1948-1971; resumed 1979. a. SEK 335 (effective 2000). bk.rev. **Document type:** *Monographic series, Academic/Scholarly.* **Description:** Features articles on all aspects of aviation with emphasis on recent events.
Formerly (until 1982): I Luften
Published by: Bevingade Ord, Martinvaegen 36, Bromma, 16155, Sweden. TEL 46-8-37-70-50, FAX 46-8-37-17-70, bevingat@telia.com. Ed. P Kristoffersson. Circ: 5,000. **Dist. by:** Soerlins Foerlag, Fack 434, Noerrkoeping 60105, Sweden.

629.132   SWE   ISSN 0284-1215
FLYGBRANSCHEN. Text in Swedish. 1987. m. SEK 295 (effective 1991).
Address: Bollgrand 18, Ekeroe, 17836, Sweden.

629.1309   SWE   ISSN 0345-3413
FLYGHISTORISK REVY. Text in Swedish. 1962. irreg.
Formerly (until vol.13, 1966): Meddelande fraan Svensk Flyghistorisk Foerening
Published by: Svensk Flyghistorisk Foerening/Swedish Aviation Historical Society, PO Box 10267, Stockholm, 10055, Sweden. sffkansli@telia.com, http://www.sff.n.se.

629.132   SWE   ISSN 1101-3915
FLYGLEDAREN; tidning foer Svensk Flygledarfoerening. Text in Swedish. 1977. q. SEK 360 to members (effective 1990).
Address: A T S, Fack 54, Malmo-sturup, 23032, Sweden.

629.13   SWE   ISSN 0015-4784
FLYGREVYN. Text in Swedish. 1951. 8/yr. SEK 345 domestic; SEK 410 in Scandinavia; SEK 520 in Europe; SEK 620 elsewhere (effective 2002). adv. bk.rev. illus. **Document type:** *Consumer.*
(until 1967): K S A K - Nytt; (until 1957): Flygrevyn; Former titles (until 1955): Looping
Published by: Flygrevyn Forlag AB, Oevre Vaelsta Gaard, Tungelsta, 13792, Sweden. TEL 46-8-500-379-00, FAX 46-8-500-379-01, http://www.flygtorget.se/hangaren/flygrevyn.flygrevyn.index.html.

629.1   SWE   ISSN 0284-8821
FLYGTEKNIKERNS VAERLD. Text in Swedish. 1974. q.
Formerly (until 1985): Teknikerns Vaerld
Published by: Svensk Flygteknikerfoerening (SFF), c/o SRAT, Magnus Ladulaasgatan 8, PO Box 38401, Stockholm, 10064, Sweden. TEL 46-8-4424460, FAX 46-8-4424480, http://www.sff.cc/Service/FTV/ftv.html. Eds. Tobias Albrecht TEL 46-411-44989, Leif Samuelsson.

629.13   USA   ISSN 0015-4806
TL501
FLYING. Text in English. 1927. m. USD 14.97 domestic; USD 22.97 foreign; USD 4.50 newsstand/cover (effective 2005). adv. bk.rev. charts; illus.; stat.; tr.lit. index. reprint service avail. from PQC. **Document type:** *Magazine, Consumer.* **Description:** Discusses topics in general (private and corporate) aviation and reviews new aircraft and equipment. Covers safety and flying techniques.
Related titles: Microform ed.: (from MIM, PQC); Online - full text ed.: (from America Online, Inc., O C L C Online Computer Library Center, Inc., The Dialog Corporation).
Indexed: ARG, BRI, CBRI, CLT&T, CivEngAb, ConsI, IAA, MagInd, PMR, RGAb, RGPR, SPI, SportS.
—CISTI, IE, Infotrieve, Linda Hall.
Published by: Hachette Filipacchi Media U.S., Inc. (Subsidiary of: Hachette Filipacchi Medias S.A.), 1633 Broadway, New York, NY 10019. TEL 212-767-6000, FAX 212-767-4932, flyedit@hfmus.com, http://www.flyingmag.com, http://www.hfmus.com. Ed. J Mac McClellan. Pub. Dick Koenig. adv.: B&W page USD 15,670, color page USD 23,520; trim 7.88 x 10.5. Circ: 305,763 (paid).

629.13   GBR   ISSN 0262-8201
FLYING M. Text in English. 1980 (vol.5). 3/yr. membership. adv. bk.rev. illus.
Published by: Society of Friends of the Royal Air Force Museum, Royal Air Force Museum, Grahame Park Way, London, NW9 5LL, United Kingdom. Ed. Peter Silver. Circ: 2,300.

358.4   USA   ISSN 0279-9308
UG633
FLYING SAFETY. Text in English. 1944. m. USD 32 domestic; USD 40 foreign (effective 2005). bk.rev. illus.; charts. back issues avail.; reprint service avail. from PQC. **Document type:** *Government.* **Description:** Covers the many fields of flight, aircraft engineering, flight training, and safety both in the air and on the ground.
Formerly (until vol.37, 1981): Aerospace Safety (0001-9429)
Related titles: Microform ed.: (from MIM, PQC); Online - full text ed.: (from EBSCO Publishing, Northern Light Technology, Inc., O C L C Online Computer Library Center, Inc., ProQuest Information & Learning).
Indexed: AUNI, ESPM, H&SSA, IUSGP, RefZh.
—BLDSC (3964.128000), IE, Infotrieve, Linda Hall.
Published by: U.S. Air Force Safety Agency, 9700 G Ave, S E, Ste 282, Kirtland AFB, NM 87117-5670. TEL 505-846-0931, http://afsafety.af.mil/magazine/htdocs/fsmfirst.htm. Circ: 18,350.
Subscr. to: U.S. Government Printing Office, Superintendent of Documents, PO Box 371954, Pittsburgh, PA 15250-7954. TEL 202-512-1800, FAX 202-512-2250, orders@gpo.gov, http://www.access.gpo.gov.

001.94   USA   ISSN 0898-3798
FLYING SAUCER DIGEST. Text in English. 1967. q. USD 12. adv. bk.rev. back issues avail. **Document type:** *Newsletter.*
Formerly: U F O Journal (Cleveland)
Published by: United Aerial Phenomena Agency, PO Box 347032, Cleveland, OH 44134-7032. Ed., Adv. contact Allan J Manak.

001.942   GBR   ISSN 0015-4881
TL789
FLYING SAUCER REVIEW. Abbreviated title: F S R. Text in English. 1955. q. GBP 15 domestic; GBP 18, USD 35 foreign (effective 2001). adv. back issues avail. **Document type:** *Consumer.* **Description:** Serves as an international journal of cosmology and eschatology, and for the discussion of reports of unidentified flying objects and their alien occupants. Carries the latest U.F.O. reports from all parts of the English-speaking world and includes information directly translated from numerous languages worldwide.
—BLDSC (3964.145000).
Published by: F S R Publications Ltd., PO Box 162, High Wycombe, Bucks HP13 5DZ, United Kingdom. TEL 44-1923-779018, fsr_fsr@hotmail.com, http://www.corpex.com/users/archmage/fsr/fsrhome.htm. Ed., R&P, Adv. contact Gordon W Creighton. Circ: 3,500.

387.706594   AUS
FLYING START. Text in English. a. AUD 5.90 newsstand/cover (effective 2002). adv. **Document type:** *Magazine, Consumer.*
Published by: Khandu Publishing, PO Box 731, Mt. Eliza, VIC 3930, Australia. TEL 61-3-9775-2466, FAX 61-3-9775-2488.

629.13   NOR   ISSN 0332-6934
FLYNYTT. Text in Norwegian. 1929. 6/yr. NOK 200 domestic; NOK 265 in Europe; NOK 275 elsewhere (effective 2001). adv. bk.rev.; video rev.; software rev. bibl.; charts; illus.; maps; pat.; stat.; tr.lit.; mkt. 72 p./no. 3 cols./p.; back issues avail. **Document type:** *Magazine, Trade.*
—CCC.
Published by: Norsk Aero Klubb, Tollbugata 3, Oslo, 0152, Norway. TEL 47-23-10-29-00, FAX 47-23-10-29-01, flynytt@nak.no, http://www.flynytt.no. Ed., R&P Rolf Liland TEL 47-91-31-87-37. Pub., Adv. contact Arne Mathisen TEL 47-23-10-29-50. color page NOK 14,500, color page USD 1,543; trim 210 x 297. Circ: 6,200 (controlled). **Co-sponsor:** Norges Luftsportsforbund/Norwegian Air Sports Association.

629.1 790.13   GBR   ISSN 0262-6950
TL501
FLYPAST; the UK's top selling aviation monthly. Text in English. 1980. m. GBP 35 domestic; EUR 63.98 in Europe; USD 68.97 in United States; GBP 43 in Canada (effective 2003). adv. bk.rev. bibl.; illus. Index. back issues avail.; reprints avail. **Document type:** *Magazine.*
Published by: Key Publishing Ltd., PO Box 100, Stamford, Lincs PE9 1XQ, United Kingdom. TEL 44-1780-755131, FAX 44-1780-757261, flypast@keypublishing.com, ann.saundry@keypublishing.com, http://www.flypast.com, http://www.keypublishing.com. Ed. Ken Ellis. Pub. Richard Cox. Adv. contact Emma White. Circ: 44,081. **Dist. by:** Seymour Distribution Ltd, 86 Newman St, London W1T 3EX, United Kingdom. FAX 44-207-396-8002, enquiries@seymour.co.uk.

629.1325   DNK   ISSN 0015-492X
FLYV. Text in Danish. 1928. m. DKK 450 (effective 2004). adv. bk.rev.; film rev. charts; illus.; stat.; tr.lit. index. **Document type:** *Trade.* **Description:** Provides information about general aviation, military aviation, commercial aviation, air traffic, gliding, sport flying, home-building of aircraft and ballooning in Denmark and abroad.
—CCC.
Published by: Kongelig Dansk Aeroklub, Lufthavnsvej 28, Roskilde, 4000, Denmark. TEL 45-46-141500, FAX 45-46-191316, flyv@kda.dk, kda@kda.dk, http://www.kda.dk. Ed. Knud Larsen TEL 45-46-141502. Adv. contact Jacob Tornvig. Circ: 8,500 (controlled).

FOREIGN AIRWORTHINESS DIRECTIVES. C A A ADDITIONAL AIRWORTHINESS DIRECTIVES. see *TRANSPORTATION—Air Transport*

FORST, HOLZ UND JAGD TASCHENBUCH. see *FORESTS AND FORESTRY*

FRANCE. DIRECTION GENERALE DE L'AVIATION CIVILE. BULLETIN STATISTIQUE. see *AERONAUTICS AND SPACE FLIGHT—Abstracting, Bibliographies, Statistics*

629.13   FRA   ISSN 0078-3781
TL502   CODEN: ORATAQ
FRANCE. OFFICE NATIONAL D'ETUDES ET DE RECHERCHES AEROSPATIALES. NOTES TECHNIQUES. Text in French; Summaries in English. 1946. irreg. (approx. 15/yr.). index, cum.index: 1950-1987. **Document type:** *Academic/Scholarly.* **Description:** Presents works of a high technical level with documents concerning aerodynamics, energetics, materials, structures, physics, computer sciences, automatic systems and test instrumentation.
Formerly (until 1963): France. Office National d'Etudes et de Recherches Aeronautiques. Note Technique (0369-7614)
Indexed: ApMecR, CivEngAb, RefZh.
—CASDDS, CISTI, Linda Hall.
Published by: Office National d'Etudes et de Recherches Aerospatiales, 29 av. de la Division Leclerc, Chatillon, Cedex 92322, France. TEL 33-1-46733780, http://www.onera.fr. R&P Khoa Dang Tran. Circ: 230.

629.13   FRA   ISSN 0078-379X
TL507
FRANCE. OFFICE NATIONAL D'ETUDES ET DE RECHERCHES AEROSPATIALES. PUBLICATIONS. Text in French; Summaries in English. 1946. irreg. (approx. 5/yr.). index, cum.index: 1947-1987. **Document type:** *Academic/Scholarly.* **Description:** Results of studies and work of primary importance concerning aerodynamics, energetics, materials, structures, physics, computer sciences, automatic systems and test instrumentation.
Formerly (until 1963): France, Office National d'Etudes et de Recherches Aeronautiques. Publications (0369-7622)
Indexed: ApMecR, RefZh.
—CISTI, Linda Hall.
Published by: Office National d'Etudes et de Recherches Aerospatiales, 29 av. de la Division Leclerc, Chatillon, Cedex 92322, France. TEL 33-1-46733780, http://www.onera.fr. R&P Khoa Dang Tran. Circ: 230.

629.1   CAN   ISSN 0317-056X
TL545
FROM THE GROUND UP. Text in English. 1947. irreg., latest vol.28. CND 39.95 (effective 2000). **Document type:** *Academic/Scholarly.* **Description:** Discusses in-depth all subjects related to aircraft operation: theory of flight, aero engines, meteorology, navigation, radio and radio navigation, air safety and aeronautical facilities.
Published by: Aviation Publishers Co. Ltd., P O Box 1361, Sta B, Ottawa, ON K1P 5R4, Canada. TEL 613-244-8280, FAX 613-244-8281, aviationpub@igs.net, http://www.aviationpublishers.com. Ed. I L Peppler. Pub., R&P Graeme H Peppler. Circ: 12,000 (paid).

FUERZA AEREA. see *MILITARY*

001.94   USA
FUND FOR U F O RESEARCH QUARTERLY REPORT. Text in English. 1980. q. USD 15 contribution (effective 2000). **Document type:** *Newsletter.* **Description:** Publishes current scientific research into unidentified flying objects, as well as periodic special reports and monographs.
Published by: Fund for U F O Research, PO Box 277, Mt. Rainier, MD 20712. TEL 703-684-6032, FAX 703-684-6082, http://www.fufo.com. Ed. Rob Swiatek. Circ: 1,200.

629.1   USA
G A C I A C BULLETIN. Text in English. q. **Document type:** *Government.*
Media: Online - full text.
Published by: U.S. Department of Defense, Guidance and Control Information Analysis Center, c/o Chalmer George, AMC Smart Weapons Management Office, Attn.: AMSMI-SW, Redstone Arsenal, AL 35898-5222. TEL 205-876-3788, 4860287510, http://gaciac.iitri.com/bulletins.html.

629.13   VEN
GACETA AEREA/AIR GAZETTE. Text in Spanish. 1971. m. USD 90. adv.
Address: Edif. La Carlota Ofc. 8-D Piso 8, Ave. Libertador cruce con Acacias, Apdo 68075, Caracas, DF 1062-A, Venezuela. Ed. Miguel Antoni. Circ: 4,500.

629.1   USA
GASBAG. Text in English. q. USD 28 to members (effective 2000). adv. bk.rev. bibl.; illus. **Description:** Covers technology of lighter-than-air flight.
Incorporates (1974-1996): Aerostation (0741-5974)
Published by: Association of Balloon and Airship Constructors, PO Box 3841, City Of Industry, CA 91744-0841. TEL 619-581-1721, FAX 619-581-1721, http://www.sdic.net/piolenc/abac.htm. Eds. F Marc de Piolenc, Laurie Soffe. Pub., R&P, Adv. contact F Marc de Piolenc. Circ: 100 (paid).

629.13   GBR
GATWICK NEWS. Text in English. 1982. w. GBP 25. adv. bk.rev.; film rev.; play rev. stat.; tr.lit. back issues avail. **Document type:** *Newspaper.*
Published by: Malmoss Ltd., 31-33 Station Rd, Horley, Surrey RH6 9HW, United Kingdom. TEL 44-1293-775000, FAX 44-1293-775444. Ed. Jackie Pond. Circ: 23,000.

629.13   USA   ISSN 1536-8513
GENERAL AVIATION NEWS. Text in English. 1949. bi-m. USD 35 domestic; USD 45 in Canada (effective 2005). adv. bk.rev.; software rev.; video rev.; Website rev. charts; illus.; stat.; tr.lit.; mkt. 72 p./no. 4 cols./p.; back issues avail.; reprints avail. **Document type:** *Magazine, Trade.* **Description:** Covers the general aviation scene, from business flying to recreational activities, with technical and personality features, product reviews, air show news, and other topics of interest to plane owners, airport operators, pilots.
Former titles (until 2001): The Flyer (1531-2364); (until 1997): General Aviation News and Flyer (1052-9136); (until 1990): Western Flyer (0274-9645); Incorporates: General Aviation News (0191-927X)
Published by: Flyer Media, Inc., PO Box 39099, Lakewood, WA 98439-0099. TEL 253-471-9888, 800-426-8538, FAX 253-471-9911, comments@generalaviationnews.com, http://www.generalaviationnews.com. Pubs. Ben Sclair, Robyn Sclair. R&P Ben Sclair. Adv. contacts Dave Mathews, Larry Price, Tom Brun. color page USD 3,150, B&W page USD 2,250; 10 x 13. Circ: 50,000 (paid and controlled).

GLOBAL JOURNAL ON AIR & SPACE LAW. see *TRANSPORTATION—Air Transport*

629.1325   USA   ISSN 1089-988X
QH657
➤ **GRAVITATIONAL AND SPACE BIOLOGY BULLETIN.** Text in English. 1988. s-a. back issues avail. **Document type:** *Academic/Scholarly.* **Description:** Reports research in space and gravitational biology to further understanding of the biological effects of gravity and space flight on plants and animals. For individuals interested in basic and applied fields of space and gravitational and related environmental life sciences.
Formerly (until 1996): A S G S B Bulletin (0898-4697)
Related titles: Online - full content ed.
Published by: American Society of Gravitational and Space Biology, PO Box 12247, Rosslyn, VA 22219. TEL 202-628-1500, FAX 202-628-1509, dbeem@aibs.org. Ed. Thora W Halstead. Circ: 500.

629.1325   USA
GREAT AIRLINERS SERIES. Text in English. 1996. irreg., latest vol.7, 2000. USD 27.95 per vol. (effective 2000). bibl.; charts; illus.; stat. back issues avail. **Document type:** *Monographic series, Consumer.* **Description:** Each volume describes in detail the design, construction, commercial profitability, and history of a particular airliner type. Information on each aircraft built, including operational history, manufacturer's serial number, and ultimate fate is given. Individual airplanes include: Vol. 1: Convair 880 & 990; Vol. 2: Douglas DC-8; Vol. 3: Boeing 747 SP; Vol. 4: McDonnell Douglas DC-9; Vol. 5: Lockheed L-188 Electra. Forthcoming are: Vol. 6: McDonnell Douglas DC-10; Vol. 7: Boeing 720; vol.8: Lockheed L-1011.
Published by: World Transport Press, PO Box 821208, Pembroke Pines, FL 33082-1208. airliner@bellsouth.net, http://www.airlinersonline.com. Subscr. to: PO Box 52-1238, Miami, FL 33152-1238. TEL 305-477-7163, 800-845-6711, FAX 305-599-1995.

GREAT BRITAIN. CIVIL AVIATION AUTHORITY. AIRWORTHINESS NOTICES. see *TRANSPORTATION—Air Transport*

GREAT BRITAIN. CIVIL AVIATION AUTHORITY. APPROVED AERIAL POSITIONS. see *TRANSPORTATION—Air Transport*

GREAT BRITAIN. CIVIL AVIATION AUTHORITY. CIVIL AVIATION PUBLICATIONS. see *TRANSPORTATION—Air Transport*

GREAT BRITAIN. CIVIL AVIATION AUTHORITY. TYPE CERTIFICATE DATA SHEETS. see *TRANSPORTATION—Air Transport*

GREAT BRITAIN. DEPARTMENT OF THE ENVIRONMENT, TRANSPORT AND THE REGIONS. AVIATION CONSULTATION PAPERS. see *TRANSPORTATION—Air Transport*

001.94   USA
GROUND SAUCER WATCH NEWSLETTER✶. Text in English. 1973. 3/yr. USD 4.50. bk.rev. illus. **Document type:** *Newsletter.*
Published by: Civilian Aerial Phenomena Research Organization, 1634 E Monte Cristo Ave, Phoenix, AZ 85022-3300. Ed. William Spaulding. Circ: 1,500.

629.1   USA   ISSN 1544-1067
GROUND SUPPORT MAGAZINE. Short title: G S E Today. Text in English. 1993. m. USD 55 (effective 2005); free to qualified personnel. adv. **Document type:** *Magazine, Trade.* **Description:** Connects airlines, manufacturers, suppliers, airports and regulatory bodies in the ground support industry.

Formerly (until 2003): Ground Support Equipment Today (1093-9482)
Related titles: Online - full text ed.: (from Gale Group, ProQuest Information & Learning).
Indexed: BrCerAb, C&ISA, CerAb, CorrAb, E&CAJ, EMA, IAA, M&TEA, MBF, METADEX, WAA.
—Linda Hall.
Published by: Cygnus Business Media, Inc., 1233 Janesville Ave, Fort Atkinson, WI 53538-0803. TEL 920-563-1698, 800-547-7377, FAX 920-568-2244, http://www.groundsupportmagazine.com, http://www.cygnusb2b.com/index.cfm. Ed. Karen Reinhardt. Pub. Holly Hoffer. Circ: 15,000 (controlled).

629.13   FRA
GROUPEMENT DES INDUSTRIES FRANCAISES AERONAUTIQUES ET SPATIALES. INFO. Key Title: G I F A S Info. Text in French. 1946. m. charts; illus.; stat. **Document type:** *Newsletter.*
Former titles (until 2000): Groupement des Industries Francaises Aeronautiques et Spatiales. Lettre (1266-4812); (until 1993): Lettre Hebdomadaire - G I F A S (1247-9802); (until 1989): Informations Aeronautiques et Spatiales. Lettre Hebdomadaire (0399-4864); Which supersedes in part (in 1976): Informations Aeronautiques (0399-4856); Which was formerly (until 1976): Informations Aeronautiques Francaises (0399-4848); (until 1956): Informations Aeronautiques (0399-483X)
Related titles: English ed.: G I F A S Newsletter. ISSN 1266-4820.
Published by: Groupement des Industries Francaises Aeronautiques et Spatiales, 4 rue Galilee, Paris, Cedex 16 75782, France. TEL 33-1-44431752, FAX 33-1-44431756, com@gifas.asso.fr, http://www.gifas.asso.fr. Ed. Patrick Guerin. Circ: 3,500.

GUANGZHOU MINHANG/GUANGZHOU CIVIL AVIATION. see *TRANSPORTATION—Air Transport*

629.13   BRA   ISSN 0104-4958
GUIA DE AVIACAO AGRICOLA/AGRICULTURAL AVIATION GUIDE. Text in Portuguese; Summaries in English. 1992. a. adv. **Document type:** *Directory.* **Description:** Provides information on sales, services available, fleets, companies and personnel in the industry.
Published by: Aviacao em Revista Editora Ltda., Rua da Consolacao, 1992 Andar 10, Consolacao, Sao Paulo, SP 01302-001, Brazil. aviacaoemrevista@uol.com.br. Ed., Pub., R&P Helcio Estrella. Adv. contact Francisco Carlos Alves. B&W page USD 4,500, color page USD 4,950; trim 280 x 210. Circ: 10,000.

629.13   BRA   ISSN 0104-4974
GUIA DE OFICINAS E MANUTENCAO/WORKSHOP AND MAINTENANCE GUIDE. Text in Portuguese; Summaries in English. 1991. a. adv. **Document type:** *Directory.* **Description:** Contains analysis, performance statistics, trend indicators, company data, services and supply listings.
Published by: Aviacao em Revista Editora Ltda., Rua da Consolacao, 1992 Andar 10, Consolacao, Sao Paulo, SP 01302-001, Brazil. aviacaoemrevista@uol.com.br. Ed., Pub., R&P Helcio Estrella. Adv. contact Francisco Carlos Alves. B&W page USD 4,500, color page USD 4,950; trim 280 x 210. Circ: 10,000.

629.132   BRA   ISSN 0104-7957
GUIA DO AEROCLUBES E AERODESPORTOS/AEROCLUBS AND AIR SPORTS GUIDE. Text in Portuguese; Summaries in English. 1990. a. adv. **Document type:** *Directory.* **Description:** Provides analyses, fleet data, company, club, manufacturer listings, air sport associations, parachuting clubs and ballon activities.
Published by: Aviacao em Revista Editora Ltda., Rua da Consolacao, 1992 Andar 10, Consolacao, Sao Paulo, SP 01302-001, Brazil. aviacaoemrevista@uol.com.br. Ed., Pub., R&P Helcio Estrella. Adv. contact Francisco Carlos Alves. B&W page USD 4,500, color page USD 4,950; trim 280 x 210. Circ: 10,000.

629.1   USA   ISSN 1057-493X
TL787.A6
GUIDANCE AND CONTROL. Text in English. 1979. a., latest vol.121, 2005. price varies. back issues avail. **Document type:** *Proceedings.*
Related titles: ◆ Series of: Advances in the Astronautical Sciences. ISSN 0065-3438.
Indexed: EngInd, IAA.
—CCC.
Published by: (American Astronautical Society, Inc.), Univelt, Inc., PO Box 28130, San Diego, CA 92198-0130. TEL 760-746-4005, FAX 760-746-3139, 76121.1532@compuserve.com, http://www.univelt.com. Eds. Robert D Culp, William Frazier. Pub. Robert H Jacobs.

629.132   GBR
GUILD NEWS. Text in English. 1956. bi-m. membership. bk.rev. back issues avail. **Document type:** *Academic/Scholarly.* **Description:** Includes records of the guild's technical and social activities.
Incorporates: Guild of Air Pilots and Air Navigators. Journal

▼ *new title*   ➤ *refereed*   ✶ *unverified*   ◆ *full entry avail.*

A

Published by: Guild of Air Pilots and Air Navigators, Cobham House, 291 Grays Inn Rd, London, Mddx WC1X 8QF, United Kingdom. TEL 44-171-837-3323, FAX 44-171-833-3190. Ed. H O Field. Circ: 2,000.

629.1 CHN ISSN 1000-4009
GUOJI HANGKONG/INTERNATIONAL AVIATION. Text in Chinese. 1956. m. CNY 108 (effective 2004). 68 p./no.; **Document type:** *Journal, Academic/Scholarly.* **Description:** Covers the aviation, aerospace, air transportation, military and defense industries, including topics such as new products, financial and trade information, coming events, and general industry news.
Related titles: Online - full text ed.: (from East View Information Services).
—CCC.
Published by: Zhongguo Hangkong Gongye Fazhan Yanjiu Zhongxin, 14, Anwai Xiaoguan Dongli, Beijing, 100029, China. TEL 86-10-64916901, FAX 86-10-64918417, http://www.aeroinfo.com.cn/magazine/inter_aviation/inter_aviation.asp. Circ: 57,379. **Dist. by:** China International Book Trading Corp, 35 Chegongzhuang Xilu, Haidian District, PO Box 399, Beijing 100044, China. TEL 86-10-68412045, FAX 86-10-68412023, cibtc@mail.cibtc.com.cn, http://www.cibtc.com.cn.

662.666 CHN ISSN 1006-2793
GUTI HUOJIAN JISHU/JOURNAL OF SOLID ROCKET TECHNOLOGY. Text in Chinese. 1978. q. CNY 5 per issue (effective 2000). back issues avail. **Document type:** *Academic/Scholarly.*
Related titles: Online - full content ed.: (from WanFang Data Corp.); Online - full text ed.: (from East View Information Services).
Indexed: BrCerAb, C&ISA, CerAb, CivEngAb, CorrAb, E&CAJ, EMA, Englnd, IAA, M&TEA, MBF, METADEX, SolStAb, WAA.
—BLDSC (5065.370000), IE, ingenta, Linda Hall.
Published by: Zhongguo Hangtian Gongye Zonggongsi, Di 4 Yanjiuyuan/China Aerospace Corporation, No.4 Research Academy, PO Box 120, Xian, 710025, China. TEL 86-29-3603254. Ed. Kexi Zhao.

629.133 USA
H A C TECHLINE✶. Text in English. 1977. q. looseleaf. USD 10; USD 15 foreign. adv. bk.rev. back issues avail. **Document type:** *Newsletter.* **Description:** Covers amateur-built sport aircraft in the form of authentically scaled replicas of old civil and military aircraft.
Published by: Historical Aircraft Corporation, 2636 N Rd, Hotchkiss, CO 81419-9758. Ed., R&P, Adv. contact Warren Eberspacher. Circ: 100 (paid).

HANDBOOK ON RADIO FREQUENCY SPECTRUM REQUIREMENTS FOR CIVIL AVIATION. see *COMMUNICATIONS—Radio*

HANG GLIDING. see *SPORTS AND GAMES—Outdoor Life*

629.13 USA
HANGAR HAPPENIN'S; what's happening in and about the Yankee Air Museum. Text in English. m. membership. illus. 12 p./no.; back issues avail. **Document type:** *Newsletter, Consumer.* **Description:** Discusses activities and events at the Yankee Air Force, an organization dedicated to the restoration, preservation, and exhibition of classic military airplanes.
Related titles: Online - full content ed.: free.
Published by: Yankee Air Force, 2041 A St - East Access, Willow Run Airport, Belleville, MI 48111. TEL 734-483-4030, FAX 734-483-5076, seaton@provide.net, yankeeairmuseum@provide.net, http://www.yankeeairmuseum.org.

629.13 CHN ISSN 1003-6660
HANGKONG BIAOZHUNHUA YU ZHILIANG/AERONAUTIC STANDARDIZATION AND QUALITY. Text in Chinese. 1972. bi-m. CNY 4 per issue (effective 2000). back issues avail. **Document type:** *Academic/Scholarly.*
Related titles: Online - full content ed.: (from WanFang Data Corp.); Online - full text ed.: (from East View Information Services).
Published by: Zhongguo Hangtian Gongye Zonggongsi, Di 301 Yanjiusuo, PO Box 1665, Beijing, 100028, China. TEL 86-1-64663322 ext 3307. Ed. Guoying Chen.

629.13 CHN ISSN 1005-5053
➤ **HANGKONG CAILIAO XUEBAO/JOURNAL OF AERONAUTICAL MATERIALS.** Text in Chinese. 1981. q. CNY 5 (effective 2003). 62 p./no.; back issues avail. **Document type:** *Journal, Academic/Scholarly.*
Related titles: Online - full content ed.: (from WanFang Data Corp.); Online - full text ed.: (from East View Information Services).
Indexed: BrCerAb, C&ISA, CerAb, CivEngAb, CorrAb, E&CAJ, EMA, Englnd, IAA, Inspec, M&TEA, MBF, METADEX, RefZh, SolStAb, WAA.
—BLDSC (4918.979000), IE, ingenta.
Published by: Zhongguo Hangkong Xuehui/Chinese Society of Aeronautics and Astronautics, PO Box 81-62, Beijing, 100095, China. TEL 86-10-62456622 ext 5228, FAX 86-10-62456212, hkclxb@biam.ac.cn.

629.1 CHN
HANGKONG DANG'AN/AERONAUTICS ARCHIVES. Text in Chinese. bi-m.
Published by: Hangkong Hangtian-bu, Dang'an-guan/Ministry of Aero-Space Industry, Archives, PO Box 33, no.11, Beijing, 100712, China. TEL 4013322. Ed. Ju Hongfu.

629.13 CHN ISSN 1000-8055
HANGKONG DONGLI XUEBAO/JOURNAL OF AEROSPACE POWER. Text in Chinese. 1986. q. back issues avail. **Document type:** *Academic/Scholarly.*
Related titles: Online - full content ed.: (from WanFang Data Corp.); Online - full text ed.: (from East View Information Services).
Indexed: BrCerAb, C&ISA, CerAb, CivEngAb, CorrAb, E&CAJ, EMA, Englnd, IAA, M&TEA, MBF, METADEX, SolStAb, WAA.
—BLDSC (4919.300000), Linda Hall.
Published by: Zhongguo Hangkong Xuehui/Chinese Society of Aeronautics and Astronautics, 37 Xueyuan Lu, Beijing, 100083, China. Ed. Chuan Jun Cao.

HANGKONG HANGTIAN YIYAO/AEROSPACE MEDICINE. see *MEDICAL SCIENCES*

629.13 CHN ISSN 1002-6061
HANGKONG JICE JISHU/AERONAUTICAL METROLOGY AND MEASUREMENT TECHNIQUE. Text in Chinese. 1962. bi-m. CNY 3.50 per vol. domestic; USD 4 per vol. foreign (effective 2000). back issues avail. **Document type:** *Academic/Scholarly.*
Related titles: Online - full text ed.: (from East View Information Services).
Published by: Changcheng Jiliang Ceshi Jishu Yanjiusuo, Beijing, 100095, China. TEL 86-1-62456633 ext 366, FAX 86-1-62452909.

629.13 CHN ISSN 1003-5451
HANGKONG JINGMI ZHIZAO JISHU/AVIATION PRECISION MANUFACTURING TECHNOLOGY. Text in Chinese. bi-m. CNY 4 per issue domestic (effective 2000). back issues avail. **Document type:** *Academic/Scholarly.*
Related titles: Online - full content ed.: (from WanFang Data Corp.); Online - full text ed.: (from East View Information Services).
Published by: (Zhongguo Hangkong Gongye Zonggongsi), Hangkong Jizai Shebei Zhizao Jishu Zhongxin (Subsidiary of: Zhongguo Hangkong Gongye Zonggongsi), PO Box 2559-9, Beijing, 100076, China. TEL 86-1-6838040. Ed. Daohong Wang.

HANGKONG JUNYI/FLIGHT SURGEON. see *MEDICAL SCIENCES—Surgery*

629.1325 CHN ISSN 1007-5453
HANGKONG KEXUE JISHU/AERONAUTICAL SCIENCE AND TECHNOLOGY. Text in Chinese. 1989. bi-m. CNY 48 (effective 2004). **Document type:** *Academic/Scholarly.*
Related titles: Online - full content ed.; Online - full text ed.: (from East View Information Services).
Published by: Zhongguo Hangkong Gongye Fazhan Yanjiu Zhongxin, 14, Anwai Xiaoguan Dongli, Beijing, 100029, China. TEL 86-10-64910703, FAX 86-10-64918417, http://www.aeroinfo.com.cn/magazine/aero_science/aero_science.asp. **Dist. by:** China International Book Trading Corp, 35 Chegongzhuang Xilu, Haidian District, PO Box 399, Beijing 100044, China. TEL 86-10-68412045, FAX 86-10-68412023, cibtc@mail.cibtc.com.cn, http://www.cibtc.com.cn.

629.1 CHN ISSN 1000-6885
HANGKONG MOXING/MODEL AIRPLANE. Text in Chinese. q. **Document type:** *Academic/Scholarly.*
Published by: Zhongguo Hangkong Xuehui/Chinese Society of Aeronautics and Astronautics, 37 Xueyuan Lu, Beijing, 100083, China. TEL 86-10-62017322.

629.1 CHN
TL671.28 CODEN: HZGOEO
HANGKONG WEIZIU YU GONGCHENG/AVIATION ENGINEERING AND MAINTENANCE. Text in Chinese. 1956. bi-m. CNY 60 (effective 2004). adv. 56 p./no.; back issues avail. **Document type:** *Journal, Academic/Scholarly.* **Description:** Reports on aviation and aerospace production and marketing activities, including advanced manufacturing technology, material engineering and management.
Formerly: Hangkong Zhizao Gongcheng/Aviation Production Engineering (1001-1765)
Related titles: Online - full content ed.: (from WanFang Data Corp.); Online - full text ed.: (from East View Information Services).
Indexed: Englnd.
Published by: (Zhongguo Hangkong Gongye Zonggongsi, Zhongguo Hangkong Xinxi Zhongxin/China Aero-Information Center), Zhongguo Hangkong Gongye Fazhan Yanjiu Zhongxin, 14, Anwai Xiaoguan Dongli, Beijing, 100029, China. TEL 86-10-64910703, FAX 86-10-64918417, http://www.aeroinfo.com.cn/magazine/aviation_engineer/aviation_engineer.asp. adv.: B&W page USD 2,200, color page USD 3,500; trim 10.75 x 8. Circ: 10,000. **Dist. by:** China International Book Trading Corp, 35 Chegongzhuang Xilu, Haidian District, PO Box 399, Beijing 100044, China. TEL 86-10-68412045, FAX 86-10-68412023, cibtc@mail.cibtc.com.cn, http://www.cibtc.com.cn.

HANGKONG WENZHAI/AERONAUTICS ABSTRACTS. see *AERONAUTICS AND SPACE FLIGHT—Abstracting, Bibliographies, Statistics*

629.1 CHN ISSN 1000-6893
HANGKONG XUEBAO/ACTA AERONAUTICA ET ASTRONAUTICA SINICA. Text in Chinese; Summaries in Chinese, English. 1965. bi-m. USD 31.20; USD 5.20 newsstand/cover (effective 2001). **Document type:** *Academic/Scholarly.* **Description:** Covers aeronautical research in China, including fluid mechanics and aerodynamics, flight dynamics and testing, aircraft propulsion systems, autocontrol and avionics, aerospace manufacturing and materials.
Related titles: CD-ROM ed.; Online - full content ed.: (from WanFang Data Corp.); Online - full text ed.: (from East View Information Services); ♦ English ed.: Chinese Journal of Aeronautics. ISSN 1000-9361.
Indexed: ApMecR, BrCerAb, C&ISA, CerAb, CivEngAb, CorrAb, E&CAJ, EMA, Englnd, IAA, M&TEA, MBF, METADEX, RefZh, SolStAb, WAA.
—BLDSC (0588.200000), CISTI, IE, ingenta, Linda Hall.
Published by: Press of Acta Aeronautica et Astronautica Sinica, 37 Xueyuan Rd, Beijing, 100083, China. TEL 86-10-82317058, FAX 86-10-82318016, aaas@buaa.edu.cn, http://www.chinainfo.gov.cn/periodical/hkxb, http://www.hkxb.net.cn/hkxb. Ed. De Chao Zhu. Pub. Xiao Yong Wu. R&P Xiao-Yong Wu TEL 86-10-82317058. Circ: 2,000 (paid); 1,000 (controlled). **Dist. overseas by:** China International Book Trading Corp, 35 Chegongzhuang Xilu, Haidian District, PO Box 399, Beijing 100044, China. TEL 86-10-68412045, FAX 86-10-68412023, cibtc@mail.cibtc.com.cn, http://www.cibtc.com.cn.
Co-sponsor: Zhongguo Hangkong Xuehui/Chinese Society of Aeronautics and Astronautics.

629.1 CHN ISSN 1000-0119
TL504
HANGKONG ZHISHI/AEROSPACE KNOWLEDGE. Text in Chinese. 1958. m. USD 28.80; USD 2.40 newsstand/cover (effective 2001). adv. bk.rev. back issues avail. **Document type:** *Consumer.* **Description:** Covers the aerospace field in China and abroad, providing scientific, technical, and management information. Reports on China's air force, civil aviation, and aerospace industry, and introduces aerial sports, including ultralight aircraft, airships, balloons, gliding, and parachuting.
Related titles: Online - full text ed.
—Linda Hall.
Published by: (Zhongguo Hangkong Xuehui/Chinese Society of Aeronautics and Astronautics), Hangkong Zhishi Zazhishe/Aerospace Knowledge Press, 37 Xueyuan Lu, Beijing, 100083, China. FAX 86-1-8232-8259, http://www.aerospace.jsinfo.net. Ed., Pub., R&P, Adv. contact Xie Chu TEL 86-10-8231-7055. B&W page USD 500, color page USD 2,000; trim 279 x 208. Circ: 320,000. **Dist. overseas by:** China International Book Trading Corp, 35 Chegongzhuang Xilu, Haidian District, PO Box 399, Beijing 100044, China. TEL 86-10-68412045, FAX 86-10-68412023, cibtc@mail.cibtc.com.cn, http://www.cibtc.com.cn.

629.1 CHN
CODEN: HGJIEO
➤ **HANGKONG ZHIZAO JISHU/AERONAUTICAL MANUFACTURING TECHNOLOGY.** Text in Chinese. 1958. bi-m. USD 12; USD 2 newsstand/cover (effective 2001). adv. back issues avail. **Document type:** *Academic/Scholarly.* **Description:** Caters to the top management of the Ministry of Aero-space Industry, the Air Force and other national defense administrations, scientific researchers, and engineers and technical personnel in China.
Formerly: Hangkong Gongyi Jishu/Aeronautical Manufacturing Technology (1000-8756)
Related titles: Online - full content ed.: (from WanFang Data Corp.); Online - full text ed.: (from East View Information Services).
—BLDSC (0725.450000), IE, ingenta.
Published by: (Zhongguo Hangkong Gongye Zhizao Gongcheng Yanjiusuo), Zhongguo Hangkong Gongye Di-1-Ji Tuangongsi, PO Box 340, Beijing, 100024, China. TEL 86-1-65761731-2332 ext 2358, FAX 86-1-65762306, amt@public.sti.ac.cn. adv.: B&W page USD 1,500, color page USD 2,500. Circ: 80,000. **Overseas subscr. to:** China National Publishing Industry Trading Corporation. **Dist. by:** China International Book Trading Corp, 35 Chegongzhuang Xilu, Haidian District, PO Box 399, Beijing 100044, China. TEL 86-10-68412045, FAX 86-10-68412023, cibtc@mail.cibtc.com.cn, http://www.cibtc.com.cn.

629.1325 CHN ISSN 1004-6518
HANGKONG ZHOUKAN/AVIATION NEWS WEEKLY. Text in Chinese. 1963. w. CNY 208 (effective 2004). **Document type:** *Journal, Academic/Scholarly.*

Published by: Zhongguo Hangkong Gongye Fazhan Yanjiu Zhongxin, 14, Anwai Xiaoguan Dongli, Beijing, 100029, China. TEL 86-10-64916904, FAX 86-10-64918417, http://www.aeroinfo.com.cn/magazine/aviation_weekly/aviation_weekly.asp. **Dist. by:** China International Book Trading Corp, 35 Chegongzhuang Xilu, Haidian District, PO Box 399, Beijing 100044, China. TEL 86-10-68412045, FAX 86-10-68412023, cibtc@mail.cibtc.com.cn, http://www.cibtc.com.cn.

629.1   CHN   ISSN 1000-7474
TL789.8.C55
HANGTIAN/ASTRONAUTICS. Text in Chinese. bi-m. CNY 1.60 per issue.
Published by: Zhongguo Yuhang Xuehui/Chinese Astronautic Society, 2 Yuetan Beixiaojie, Beijing, 100830, China. TEL 894602. Ed. Li Longyuan.

616.98021   CHN   ISSN 1002-0837
HANGTIAN YIXUE YU YIXUE GONGCHENG/SPACE MEDICINE & MEDICAL ENGINEERING. Text in Chinese. 1988. bi-m. CNY 72 domestic; USD 30.60 foreign (effective 2005).
Document type: *Academic/Scholarly.*
Related titles: Online - full text ed.: (from East View Information Services, WanFang Data Corp.).
Indexed: BrCerAb, C&ISA, CerAb, CivEngAb, CorrAb, E&CAJ, EMA, EngInd, IAA, M&TEA, MBF, METADEX, SolStAb, WAA.
—BLDSC (8361.603300), IE, ingenta, Linda Hall.
Published by: Hangtian Yixue Gongcheng Yanjiusuo, PO Box 5104-25, Beijing, 100094, China. TEL 86-10-66365788, FAX 86-10-62585031, su_hongyu@126.com, http://htyxyyxgc.periodicals.net.cn/. Ed. Jinhe Wei. **Dist. by:** China International Book Trading Corp, 35 Chegongzhuang Xilu, Haidian District, PO Box 399, Beijing 100044, China. TEL 86-10-68412045, FAX 86-10-68412023, cibtc@mail.cibtc.com.cn, http://www.cibtc.com.cn.

629.132   MEX
HELICE. Text in Spanish. 1959. bi-m. MXP 27. adv. bk.rev. charts; illus.; stat.
Published by: Mexican Air Line Pilots Association, c/o Capt. J.J. Castillo A., Ave. PALOMAS 110, Lomas de Sotelo, Mexico City, DF 11200, Mexico. FAX 52-5-202-25-73, TELEX 17-63-468 ASPAME. Ed. Capt R Rebollo. Circ: 2,000 (controlled).

629.133   CHE   ISSN 1019-1178
HELICO REVUE. Text in French. q. CHF 46 (effective 1998).
Related titles: German ed.: ISSN 1019-1186.
Published by: Editions Jean Ducret, Case Postale 121, Lausanne, 1010, Switzerland. Eds. Irene Ducret, Jean Ducret. Pub. Irene Ducret.

HELICOPTER ASSOCIATION INTERNATIONAL. MAINTENANCE UPDATE. see *TRANSPORTATION—Air Transport*

629.133   USA
HELICOPTER ASSOCIATION INTERNATIONAL. PRELIMINARY ACCIDENT REPORTS. Text in English. q. USD 50 to non-members; USD 25 to members (effective 2000).
Document type: *Newsletter, Trade.* **Description:** Includes National Transportation Safety Board preliminary accident reports as well as quarterly accident summary statistics.
Published by: Helicopter Association International, 1635 Prince St, Alexandria, VA 22314-2818. TEL 703-683-4646, 800-435-4976, FAX 703-683-4745, marilyn.mckinnis@rotor.com, http://www.rotor.com. Ed., R&P Richard Wright. Pub. Roy D Resavage. Circ: 2,400.

355.27   GBR
HELICOPTER INTERNATIONAL MAGAZINE. Text in English. 1977. bi-m. GBP 23 in Europe; GBP 33, USD 55 elsewhere (effective 2000 - 2001). adv. bk.rev. back issues avail.
Document type: *Trade.* **Description:** International news coverage of the military and commercial helicopter industry and operators worldwide.
Formerly: Helicopter Magazine (0143-1005)
Related titles: Online - full text ed.
Indexed: PROMT, RefZh.
—CISTI, IE.
Published by: Avia Press Associates, 75 Elm Tree Rd, Locking, Weston-super-Mare, Somers BS24 8EL, United Kingdom. TEL 44-1934-822524, FAX 44-1934-822400, sales@aviapress.fsnet.co.uk, http://www.aviapress.freeserve.co.uk/. Ed., Pub., R&P Elfan ap Rees. Adv. contact Julie Appleford. B&W page GBP 3,060, B&W page USD 5,050, color page GBP 4,228, color page USD 6,975. Circ: 25,000 (paid).

629.133   USA   ISSN 0363-8227
HELICOPTER NEWS. Text in English. 1975. bi-w. USD 797 (effective 2005). bk.rev. **Document type:** *Newsletter, Trade.*
Media: E-mail.
Indexed: ABIn.
—CCC.
Published by: Access Intelligence, LLC (Subsidiary of: Veronis, Suhler & Associates Inc.), 1201 Seven Locks Rd, Ste 300, Potomac, MD 20854. TEL 301-354-2000, 800-777-5006, FAX 301-762-3068, clientservices@accessintel.com, http://www.pbimedia.com/cgi/catalog/info?HN. Ed. Chuck Steele. Circ: 700.

629.133   USA   ISSN 1042-2048
TL716.5
HELICOPTER SAFETY. Text in English. 1967. bi-m. USD 280 worldwide to non-members; USD 120 worldwide to members (effective 2005). bk.rev. illus. reprint service avail. from PQC.
Document type: *Newsletter, Trade.* **Description:** Highlights the broad spectrum of real-world helicopter operations.
Formerly (until vol.13, no.5, 1987): Helicopter Safety Bulletin (0898-8145)
Indexed: RefZh.
Published by: Flight Safety Foundation, Inc., 601 Madison St, Ste 300, Alexandria, VA 22314-1756. TEL 703-739-6700, FAX 703-739-6708, setze@flightsafety.org, http://www.flightsafety.org. Ed. Roger Rozelle. Circ: 2,750.

629.133   GBR
HELIDATA NEWS & CLASSIFIED. Text in English. 1980. bi-w. looseleaf. GBP 200 in Europe; GBP 250, USD 450 elsewhere (effective 2000 - 2001). adv. bk.rev. back issues avail.
Document type: *Newsletter, Trade.* **Description:** Contains helicopter news and marketing support classified covering the international military and commercial helicopter industry.
Formerly: HeliData (0951-9904)
Published by: Avia Press Associates, 75 Elm Tree Rd, Locking, Weston-super-Mare, Somers BS24 8EL, United Kingdom. TEL 44-1934-822524, FAX 44-1934-822400, helidata@aviapress.fsnet.co.uk, http://www.helidata.rotor.com. Ed., Pub., R&P Elfan ap Rees. Adv. contact Wendy Reed. B&W page GBP 3,060, B&W page USD 5,050, color page GBP 4,228, color page USD 6,975. Circ: 11,500.

HELIPORT DEVELOPMENT GUIDE. see *TRANSPORTATION—Air Transport*

HIGH TECHNOLOGY CAREERS. see *OCCUPATIONS AND CAREERS*

387.7   USA   ISSN 0018-2443
HISTORICAL AVIATION ALBUM∗ **.** Text in English. 1965. a. price varies. charts; illus.; stat.; tr.mk. **Document type:** *Consumer.* **Description:** Short stories on airplanes and aviation history. Includes production statistics.
Related titles: Microform ed.: 1965 (from PQC).
Published by: Sunshine House, PO Box 665, Destin, FL 32540-0665. TEL 812-232-3076. Ed. Alan Abel. Circ: 3,500.

HONG KONG OBSERVATORY. NEWSLETTER FOR THE AVIATION COMMUNITY; weather on wings. see *METEOROLOGY*

629.1 621.3   CHN   ISSN 1007-2276
➤ **HONGWAI YU JIGUANG GONGCHENG/INFRARED AND LASER ENGINEERING.** Text in Chinese; Abstracts in English. 1972. bi-m. USD 120 (effective 2000 - 2001). adv. 96 p./no.; back issues avail. **Document type:** *Journal, Academic/Scholarly.* **Description:** Focuses on the applications of infrared, laser and optoelectronic technology to space, satellites, tactical missiles and other weapons systems, as well as several advance experiment methods and new materials of this field.
Related titles: CD-ROM ed.; Online - full content ed.; Online - full text ed.: (from East View Information Services).
Indexed: BrCerAb, C&ISA, CerAb, CorrAb, E&CAJ, EMA, IAA, Inspec, M&TEA, MBF, METADEX, RefZh, WAA.
—BLDSC (4499.370000), IE, ingenta, Linda Hall.
Published by: Zhongguo Hangtianke Gongjituan, Tianjin Jinhang Jishu Wuli Yanjiusuo/China Aerospace Science and Industry Corporation, Tianjin Jinhang Institute of Technical Physics, PO Box 225 32, Tianjin, 300192, China. TEL 86-22-23666400, FAX 86-22-23363423, duyq@mimi.cnc.ac.cn, irla@vip.sina.com. Eds. Jin Li, Jinfeng Feng, Shuzhen He, Xueyan Zhao, Zheng Zhai Yuan. Pub. Zailong Sun. Adv. contacts An Bo, Xueyan Zhao. page CNY 8,000. Circ: 2,000. **Subscr. to:** An Bo, Dept. of Documentation, PO Box 1408, Beijing 100013, China. TEL 86-1-68372847, FAX 86-1-64227606. **Co-sponsors:** Chinese Society of Astronautics; Speciality Society of Opto-Electronic Technology.

629.1   USA
HORIZONS (TORRANCE). Text in English. 1988. m. free. back issues avail. **Description:** Covers contracts and product news, aerospace industry trends, and human interest articles for employees.
Published by: Allied-Signal Aerospace Company, 2525 W 190th St, Torrance, CA 90504. TEL 213-512-1928, FAX 213-512-2490. Ed. Gary Lutz. Circ: 56,000.

629.133   GBR   ISSN 0144-3755
HOVERCRAFT BULLETIN; a bi-monthly summary of world hovercraft news and events. Text in English. 1971. bi-m. looseleaf. GBP 25; GBP 30 foreign (effective 2000). adv. bk.rev. illus.; pat.; tr.lit. back issues avail. **Document type:** *Bulletin.* **Description:** Covers the latest developments in hovercraft technology.
Formerly: U K H S Bulletin
Published by: Hovercraft Society, Argus Gate, Chark Ln, Lee-on-the-Solent, Hamps PO13 9NY, United Kingdom. TEL 44-705-601310, warwick@hovercraft-museum.org, http://www.hovercraft-museum.org. Ed. Chris Potter. Adv. contact Warwick Jacobs. B&W page GBP 100, color page GBP 300. Circ: 300.

629.3   GBR   ISSN 0957-4263
THE HOVERCRAFT MUSEUM NEWSLETTER. Text in English. 1987. q. GBP 10 (effective 2000). adv. **Document type:** *Newsletter.*
Published by: Hovercraft Society, Argus Gate, Chark Ln, Lee-on-the-Solent, Hamps PO13 9NY, United Kingdom. TEL 44-705-601310, http://www.hovercraft-museum.org. Ed. Chris Potter. Adv. contact Warwick Jacobs. B&W page GBP 150, color page GBP 300. Circ: 300.

629.45   GBR   ISSN 1468-9456
➤ **HUMAN FACTORS AND AEROSPACE SAFETY;** an international journal. Text in English. 2000. q. GBP 75 to individuals; GBP 120 to institutions (effective 2006). bk.rev. 90 p./no.; back issues avail. **Document type:** *Journal, Academic/Scholarly.* **Description:** Contains both formal research and practitioner papers, describing new research in the area of human factors and aerospace safety, and activities such as successful safety and regulatory initiatives or accident case studies.
Indexed: ErgAb, HRIS, IAA, PsycInfo, PsycholAb.
—BLDSC (4336.076000), IE, Linda Hall. **CCC.**
Published by: Ashgate Publishing Ltd (Subsidiary of: Gower Publishing Co. Ltd.), Gower House, Croft Rd, Aldershot, Hants GU11 3HR, United Kingdom. TEL 44-1252-331551, FAX 44-1252-317446, info@ashgate.com, http://www.ashgate.com/subject_area/aviation/aviation_journals.htm. Eds. Don Harris, Helen C Muir. R&P Jacquie Cox TEL 44-1252-331551.

614.85 629.1   USA   ISSN 1057-5545
HUMAN FACTORS & AVIATION MEDICINE. Text in English. 1957. bi-m. USD 280 worldwide to non-members; USD 120 worldwide to members (effective 2005). bk.rev. reprint service avail. from PQC. **Document type:** *Newsletter, Trade.* **Description:** Allows specialists, researchers, and physicians to present information critical to the training, performance and health of aviation professionals.
Former titles (until vol.34, no.6, 1987): Human Factors and Aviation Medicine Bulletin (0898-5723); (until vol.34, no.4, 1987): Human Factors Bulletin
Indexed: RefZh.
Published by: Flight Safety Foundation, Inc., 601 Madison St, Ste 300, Alexandria, VA 22314-1756. TEL 703-739-6700, FAX 703-739-6708, setze@flightsafety.org, http://www.flightsafety.org. Ed. Roger Rozelle. Circ: 2,400 (controlled).

HUNTING REVIEW. see *PETROLEUM AND GAS*

001.942   FRA   ISSN 0246-6287
HYPOTHESES EXTRATERRESTRES; revue de l'Univers O.V.N.I. Text in French. 1971. q. FRF 50. bk.rev.
Formerly (until 1980): Extraterrestres (0399-5216)
Published by: G.E.O.S.-France, 39 Rue de Fretay, Villejust, 91140, France. Ed. L Gerard. Circ: 5,000.

I A T A - I A L AIR DISTANCES. see *TRANSPORTATION—Air Transport*

387.7   CAN   ISSN 1014-8876
                                         CODEN: ICJOEP
I C A O JOURNAL. Text in English. 1946. m. (10/yr.). USD 25 domestic; GBP 25 foreign; USD 3 newsstand/cover (effective 2005). adv. charts; illus. reprints avail. **Document type:** *Magazine, Trade.*
Former titles (until 1990): I C A O Bulletin (0018-8778); (until 1952): I C A O Monthly Bulletin (0256-8128); (until 1948): P I C A O Monthly Bulletin (0256-8136)
Related titles: Microfiche ed.: (from CIS); Online - full text ed.: ISSN 1564-4510; French ed.; Spanish ed.
Indexed: BrCerAb, C&ISA, CLT&T, CerAb, CorrAb, E&CAJ, EMA, ESPM, EnvAb, H&SSA, HRIS, IAA, IIS, M&GPA, M&TEA, MBF, METADEX, RefZh, RiskAb, TelAb, WAA.
—BLDSC (4360.220750), CISTI, IE, ingenta, Linda Hall. **CCC.**
Published by: International Civil Aviation Organization, External Relations and Public Information Office, 999 University St, Montreal, PQ H3C 5H7, Canada. TEL 514-954-8219, FAX 514-954-6077, icaohq@icao.int, http://www.icao.int/cgi/goto.pl?icao/en/jr/jr.cfm. Ed. Eric MacBurnie.

336.2   CAN
I C A O'S POLICIES ON TAXATION IN THE FIELD OF INTERNATIONAL AIR TRANSPORT. Text in English, Arabic, French, Russian, Spanish. irreg., latest 2000, 3rd ed. free on request (effective 2001).
Published by: International Civil Aviation Organization, c/o Document Sales Unit, 999 University St, Montreal, PQ H3C 5H7, Canada. TEL 514-954-8022, FAX 514-954-6769, TELEX 05-24513, icaohq@icao.int.

629.1   GBR   ISSN 0308-7247
I C AERO REPORT. Text in English. irreg. **Document type:** *Monographic series.*
—CISTI.
Published by: Imperial College of Science, Technology and Medicine, Department of Aeronautics (Subsidiary of: University of London), University of London, Prince Consort Rd, London, SW7 2BY, United Kingdom. R&P Sue Clarke.

I E E E - A E S C O N AEROSPACE AND ELECTRONICS CONFERENCE. RECORD. see *ENGINEERING—Electrical Engineering*

▼ *new title*   ➤ *refereed*   ∗ *unverified*   ♦ *full entry avail.*

A

629.1 USA
I E E E - A E S S DAYTON CHAPTER SYMPOSIUM. Text in English. 1979. a. **Document type:** *Monographic series, Trade.*
Former titles (until 1984): I E E E - A E S S Symposium (Proceedings); (until 1980): I E E E - A E S S Seminar
Related titles: CD-ROM ed.; Microfiche ed.
Published by: Institute of Electrical and Electronics Engineers, Inc., 3 Park Ave, 17th Fl, New York, NY 10016-5997. TEL 800-678-4333, customer.service@ieee.org, http://www.ieee.org. **Co-sponsor:** Aerospace and Electronic Systems Society, Dayton Section.

629.1 USA
I E E E - A I A A DIGITAL AVIONICS SYSTEMS CONFERENCE. PROCEEDINGS. Variant title: A I A A - I E E E Digital Avionics Systems Conference. Proceedings. (Publication alternates between IEEE and AIAA) Text in English. 1975. a. USD 434 per vol. to institutions; USD 217 per vol. to members (effective 2004). **Document type:** *Proceedings, Trade.*
Former titles (until 1981): A I A A - I E E E Digital Avionics Systems Conference. Technical Papers; (until 1979): Digital Avionics Systems Conference (Publication); (until 1977): A I A A Digital Avionics Systems Conference (Preprints)
Related titles: CD-ROM ed.; Microfiche ed.
Indexed: Englnd.
—BLDSC (4362.787700).
Published by: Institute of Electrical and Electronics Engineers, Inc., 3 Park Ave, 17th Fl, New York, NY 10016-5997. TEL 212-419-7900, 800-678-4333, FAX 212-752-4929, customer.service@ieee.org, http://www.ieee.org. **Co-sponsors:** Aerospace and Electronic Systems Society; American Institute of Aeronautics and Astronautics, Inc.

I E E E AEROSPACE AND ELECTRONIC SYSTEMS MAGAZINE. see *ELECTRONICS*

629.4 USA ISSN 1095-323X
TL693 CODEN: NASEA9
I E E E AEROSPACE CONFERENCE. PROCEEDINGS. Text in English. a. USD 672 per vol. to non-members; USD 336 per vol. to members (effective 2004). **Document type:** *Proceedings, Trade.*
Former titles (until 1997): I E E E National Aerospace and Electronics Conference. Proceedings (0547-3578); National Aerospace Electronics Conference. Proceedings; National Aerospace and Electronics Conference. Record (0065-373X)
Related titles: CD-ROM ed.; Microfiche ed.; Online - full text ed.: (from I E E E).
Indexed: Englnd, IAA, Inspec.
—BLDSC (4362.787692), IE, ingenta, Linda Hall. **CCC.**
Published by: Institute of Electrical and Electronics Engineers, Inc., 3 Park Ave, 17th Fl, New York, NY 10016-5997. TEL 212-419-7900, 800-678-4333, FAX 212-752-4929, customer.service@ieee.org, http://www.ieee.org. **Co-sponsor:** Aerospace and Electronic Systems Society.

629.47 USA ISSN 0275-9306
TL1100 CODEN: PRICDT
I E E E POWER ELECTRONICS SPECIALISTS CONFERENCE. RECORD. Short title: P E S C Record. Text in English. 1970. a. USD 418; USD 209 to members (effective 2004). illus. **Document type:** *Proceedings, Trade.*
Former titles: I E E E Power Processing and Electronics Specialists Conference. Record (0090-2381); (until 1971): Power Conditioning Specialists Conference. Record (0079-4414)
Related titles: CD-ROM ed.; Microfiche ed.; Online - full text ed.: (from I E E E).
Indexed: C&ISA, E&CAJ, Englnd, Inspec, SolStAb.
—BLDSC (4363.015000), Ei, IE, ingenta. **CCC.**
Published by: Institute of Electrical and Electronics Engineers, Inc., 3 Park Ave, 17th Fl, New York, NY 10016-5997. TEL 212-419-7900, 800-678-4333, FAX 212-752-4929, customer.service@ieee.org, http://www.ieee.org. **Co-sponsor:** Aerospace and Electronic Systems Society.

629.1 621.381 USA ISSN 1097-5764
I E E E RADAR CONFERENCE. PROCEEDINGS. Text in English. 1991. a. USD 196 to institutions (effective 2001). **Description:** Provides a global perspective of affordable radar systems for the new millennium, emphasizing both leading-edge technology and new applications.
Former titles (until 1995): I E E E National Radar Conference. Record (1083-2033); (until 1991): I E E E National Radar Conference. Proceedings (0896-9817)
Related titles: CD-ROM ed.
Published by: Institute of Electrical and Electronics Engineers, Inc., 3 Park Ave, 17th Fl, New York, NY 10016-5997. TEL 800-678-4333, customer.service@ieee.org, http://www.ieee.org. **Co-sponsor:** I E E E Aerospace and Electronic Systems Society.

I E E E TRANSACTIONS ON AEROSPACE AND ELECTRONIC SYSTEMS. see *ENGINEERING—Electrical Engineering*

629.132 USA ISSN 0894-6620
I F R; the magazine for the accomplished pilot. (Instrument Flight Rule) Text in English. 1985. m. USD 59 in US & Canada; USD 77 elsewhere (effective 2006). adv. **Document type:** *Magazine, Trade.*
Published by: Belvoir Media Group, LLC, 800 Connecticut Ave, Norwalk, CT 06854-1631. TEL 203-857-3100, 800-424-7887, FAX 203-857-3103, customer_service@belvoir.com, http://www.ifr-magazine.com/, http://www.belvoir.com. Ed. Paul Berge. Pub. Robert Englander. Circ: 25,000. **Subscr. to:** 8586 Potter Park Rd, Ste 119, Sarasota, FL 34238. TEL 941-552-5700.

629.132 USA ISSN 0896-9868
I F R REFRESHER. Text in English. 1987. m. USD 59 in US & Canada; USD 77 elsewhere (effective 2006). **Document type:** *Magazine, Consumer.* **Description:** Written for instrument pilots who care passionately about staying proficient and who are willing to put their brains and their egos on the line once a month to prove it.
Published by: Belvoir Media Group, LLC, 800 Connecticut Ave, Norwalk, CT 06854-1631. TEL 203-857-3100, 800-424-7887, FAX 203-857-3103, customer_service@belvoir.com, http://www.ifr-refresher.com/, http://www.belvoir.com. Ed. Russell Lawton. Circ: 15,000.

629.132 USA ISSN 1536-3066
I S A NEWS. (International Society of Women Airline Pilots) Text in English. 1979. 3/yr. free to individual members (effective 2005). Website rev. 24 p./no. 3 cols./p.; back issues avail.; reprints avail. **Document type:** *Newsletter, Trade.*
Related titles: Video ed.
Published by: International Society of Women Airline Pilots, 2250 E Tropicana Ave, Ste 19-395, Las Vegas, NV 89119. nonrev4funn@aol.com, http://www.iswap.org/html/newsletter.html. Ed., Pub., R&P Jennifer Neal. Circ: 560.

387.7 FRA ISSN 1011-615X
I.T.A. ETUDES ET DOCUMENTS/I.T.A. STUDIES AND REPORTS. Text in English, French. 1986. bi-m. membership. charts; illus.; stat. index, cum.index: 1961-1971. **Document type:** *Monographic series.*
Formed by the 1986 merger of: I.T.A. Documents (0248-577X); I.T.A. Etudes
Published by: Institut du Transport Aerien, 103 rue la Boetie, Paris, 75008, France. TEL 33-1-43593868, FAX 33-1-43594737.

629.1 FRA ISSN 0766-2750
I.T.A. PRESS (EDITION FRANCAISE). Text in French. 1986. s-m. looseleaf. **Document type:** *Newsletter.*
Formerly (until 1983): Institut du Transport Aerien. Communication (0755-5148)
Published by: Institut du Transport Aerien, 103 rue la Boetie, Paris, 75008, France. TEL 33-1-43593868, FAX 33-1-43594737.

629.1 FRA ISSN 0766-3366
I.T.A. PRESS (ENGLISH EDITION). Text in French. 1983. bi-m. **Document type:** *Newsletter.*
Formerly (until 1984): Institut du Transport Aerien. Newsletter (0755-513X)
Published by: Institut du Transport Aerien, 103 rue la Boetie, Paris, 75008, France. TEL 33-1-43593868, FAX 33-1-43594737.

629.13 FRA ISSN 0018-8786
ICARE; revue de l'aviation francaise. Text in French. 1957. q. adv. bk.rev. bibl.; illus. back issues avail. **Document type:** *Trade.*
—CISTI. **CCC.**
Published by: Syndicat National des Pilotes de Ligne Francais, Tour Essor 93 - Espace Jean Mermoz, 14-16 rue de Scandicci, Pantin, Cedex 93508, France. TEL 33-1-49422089, FAX 33-1-48917289, http://www.revue-icare.com/. Ed., R&P Francois Rude. Pub. Hughes Gendre. Adv. contact Jean Delattre. Circ: 9,000.

IKOMAYAMA UCHU KAGAKUKAN NYUSU. see *MUSEUMS AND ART GALLERIES*

629.13 FIN ISSN 0019-252X
ILMAILU. Text in Finnish. 1938. 11/yr. EUR 68 (effective 2005). adv. bk.rev. charts; illus. **Document type:** *Magazine, Consumer.*
—**CCC.**
Published by: Suomen Ilmailuliitto/Finnish Aeronautical Association, Malmi Airport, Helsinki, 00830, Finland. TEL 358-9-35093444, FAX 358-9-35093440, ilmailu@ilmailuliitto.fi, http://www.ilmailuliitto.fi/. Ed. Tero Tuominen. Circ: 10,600 (controlled).

IN FLIGHT U S A. see *TRANSPORTATION—Air Transport*

629.133 387.7 GBR
INCAMERA. Text in English. 1998. irreg., latest vol.3. GBP 16.99, USD 24.95 (effective 2001). illus. **Document type:** *Consumer.* **Description:** Illustrates the color schemes of classic airliners that are no longer in production.
Published by: Scoval Publishing Ltd., Scoval Publishing Ltd, Ponteland, PO Box 36, Newcastle upon Tyne, Tyne and Wear NE20 9WE, United Kingdom. TEL 44-1661-820838, FAX 44-1661-822911. Eds. John Wess, Scott Henderson. **Dist. in the US by:** Airways International, Inc.. TEL 208-263-5906, 208-263-2098.

INDEX TO N A S A NEWS RELEASES AND SPEECHES. see *AERONAUTICS AND SPACE FLIGHT—Abstracting, Bibliographies, Statistics*

629.1 IND ISSN 0376-5466
TL789.8.I5
INDIA. DEPARTMENT OF SPACE. ANNUAL REPORT. Text in English. 1973. a. free. **Document type:** *Government.*
Related titles: Hindi ed.
Published by: Department of Space, Antariksh Bhavan, New Bel Rd., Bangalore, Karnataka 560 094, India. TEL 080-3334474, FAX 080-3332253. Ed. S Krish Namurthy. Circ: 5,000 (controlled).

629.1 IND ISSN 0970-6674
INDIAN AIRMAN AND SPACEMAN. Text in English. 1947. m. USD 60. adv.
Published by: A. Devi Biren Roy Trust, Roy Mansions, Behala, Kolkata, West Bengal 700 034, India. Ed. Biren Roy. Adv. contact T K Ghosh. Circ: 2,000.

629.13 FRA ISSN 0761-0718
INFO-PILOTE. Text in French. 1985. m. adv. **Description:** Focuses on French aeronautics for managers, employees, and students working in the field.
Published by: Air Press, 67 av. de la Republique, Paris, 75011, France. TEL 33-1-43-56-00-04, FAX 33-1-43-56-68-00. Circ: 38,876.

001.942 BEL
INFORESPACE. Text in French. 1972. bi-m. USD 30. adv. **Document type:** *Bulletin.* **Description:** Features research on various extra-terrestrial phenomena.
Published by: Societe Belge d'Etude des Phenomenes Spatiaux, Av Paul Janson 74, Brussels, 1070, Belgium. FAX 25-20-73-93. Adv. contact Michel Bougard. Circ: 2,000.

629.44 USA
INFORMATION PLUS REFERENCE SERIES. SPACE EXPLORATION; are the gains worth the cost?. Text in English. biennial. USD 40 per vol. (effective 2004). **Document type:** *Monographic series, Academic/Scholarly.*
Related titles: Online - full content ed.; ♦ Series of: Information Plus Reference Series.
Published by: Gale Group (Subsidiary of: Thomson Corporation), 27500 Drake Rd, Farmington Hills, MI 48331-3535. TEL 248-699-4253, 800-877-4253, FAX 248-699-8035, 800-414-5043, galeord@gale.com, http://www.galegroup.com.

629.13 ESP ISSN 0020-1006
INGENIERIA AERONAUTICA Y ASTRONAUTICA. Text in Spanish. 1949. q. adv. bk.rev. charts; illus. index. **Document type:** *Academic/Scholarly.*
Indexed: IAA, IECT.
—BLDSC (4501.810000), CINDOC, IE, ingenta.
Published by: Asociacion de Ingenieros Aeronauticos, Hermosilla, 30 1o, Madrid, 28001, Spain. TEL 34-1-4353021, FAX 34-1-4358283. Ed., R&P Anibal Isidoro Carmona. Circ: 2,000.

629.1 USA ISSN 1092-9185
INSIDE AVIATION/AEROSPACE I T. (Information Technology) Text in English. 1997. bi-w.
Related titles: Online - full text ed.
Published by: McGraw-Hill Companies, Aviation Week, 1200 G St, N W, Ste 200, Washington, DC 20005. TEL 202-383-2374, FAX 202-383-2438, http://www.aviationnow.com/avnow.

INSIDE F A A. (Federal Aviation Administration) see *TRANSPORTATION—Air Transport*

629.4 CAN ISSN 0823-048X
INSTITUTE FOR AEROSPACE RESEARCH. AERONAUTICAL NOTES✶. Key Title: Aeronautical Note. Text in English. irreg. free. adv. **Document type:** *Government.*
Formerly (until June 1990): National Aeronautical Establishment. Aeronautical Notes
—**CCC.**
Published by: National Research Council of Canada, Institute for Aerospace Research, Montreal Rd, Ottawa, ON K1A 0R6, Canada. TEL 613-993-9101. Pub. Jonathan Rath. Adv. contact Jeff Mackwood.

629.13 USA
INSTITUTE OF NAVIGATION. NATIONAL TECHNICAL MEETING PROCEEDINGS. Text in English. a. price varies. adv. **Document type:** *Proceedings.*
Supersedes (in 1984): National Aerospace Meeting. Proceedings
Indexed: Englnd.
—BLDSC (6848.168500).
Published by: Institute of Navigation, 3975 University Dr, Ste 390, Fairfax, VA 22030-2520. TEL 703-383-9688, FAX 703-383-9689, meetings@ion.org, http://www.ion.org. Ed. Lisa Beaty. Pub. Wendy Hickman. Adv. contact Jennifer Murphy Smith.

629.1 IND ISSN 0257-3423
TL501
➤ **INSTITUTION OF ENGINEERS (INDIA). AEROSPACE ENGINEERING DIVISION. JOURNAL.** Text in English. 1978. s-a. INR 80, USD 25 (effective 2000). adv. charts; illus. index. **Document type:** *Academic/Scholarly.*

Indexed: BrCerAb, C&ISA, CerAb, CorrAb, E&CAJ, EEA, EMA, EngInd, IAA, M&TEA, MBF, METADEX, RefZh, WAA.
—CISTI, Ei, Linda Hall.
Published by: (Aerospace Engineering Division), Institution of Engineers (India), 8 Gokhale Rd., Kolkata, West Bengal 700 020, India. TEL 91-33-2235068, 91-33-2238314, FAX 91-33-2238345, technical@ieindia.org, http://www.ieindia.org. Ed., Pub. B C Thakurta. Adv. contact S S Basu. Circ: 2,000.

629.1   GBR   ISSN 0954-4100
TJ1   CODEN: PMGEEP
➤ **INSTITUTION OF MECHANICAL ENGINEERS. PROCEEDINGS. PART G: JOURNAL OF AEROSPACE ENGINEERING.** Text in English. 1989. bi-m. GBP 669 (effective 2005). bk.rev. illus. back issues avail.; reprints avail.
Document type: *Journal, Academic/Scholarly.* **Description:** Communicates ideas on both theoretical and practical aspects of all types of civil and military air- and spacecraft and their support systems.
Supersedes in part (in 1989): Institution of Mechanical Engineers. Proceedings. Part D: Transport Engineering (0265-1904); Which superseded in part (1847-1982): Institution of Mechanical Engineers. Proceedings (0020-3483)
Related titles: Online - full text ed.: (from EBSCO Publishing, Gale Group, IngentaConnect, O C L C Online Computer Library Center, Inc., ProQuest Information & Learning, Swets Information Services); ◆ Series: Institution of Mechanical Engineers. Proceedings.
Indexed: AS&TI, ASCA, ApMecR, BrCerAb, BrTechI, C&ISA, CMCI, CerAb, CivEngAb, CorrAb, CurCont, E&CAJ, EMA, ESPM, H&SSA, IAA, ISMEC, Inspec, M&TEA, MBF, METADEX, SolStAb, WAA.
—BLDSC (6724.900870), AskIEEE, CISTI, Ei, IDS, IE, Infotrieve, ingenta, Linda Hall. **CCC.**
Published by: (Institution of Mechanical Engineers), Professional Engineering Publishing Ltd., Northgate Ave, Bury St Edmunds, Suffolk IP32 6BW, United Kingdom. TEL 44-1284-705271, FAX 44-1284-768219, journals@pepublishing.com, http://www.pepublishing.com/journal2.asp?id=23, http://www.imeche.org.uk. Ed. J Hodgkinson. Pub. Rosie Grimes. Circ: 800. **Subscr. in the Americas:** PO Box 361, Birmingham, AL 35201-0361. TEL 800-633-4931, FAX 205-995-1588.

629.13   CHE   ISSN 1423-3215
TL500
INTERAVIA; business & technology . Text in English. 1992. m. USD 150 in Europe; USD 175 rest of world (effective 2002). adv. Website rev. abstr.; charts; illus. index. 50 p./no. 2 cols./p.; reprints avail. **Document type:** *Magazine, Trade.* **Description:** Covers all aspects of aerospace technology, avionics and commercial aviation.
Formerly (until 1994): Interavia, Aerospace World (1023-5043); Which was formed by the merger of (1946-1992): Interavia (0020-5168); (1987-1992): Aerospace World (1423-3223)
Related titles: Microform ed.: 1946 (from PQC); Online - full text ed.: 1946 (from EBSCO Publishing, Florida Center for Library Automation, Gale Group, H.W. Wilson, O C L C Online Computer Library Center, Inc., ProQuest Information & Learning, The Dialog Corporation).
Indexed: ABIn, AMB, AUNI, BPI, BrCerAb, C&ISA, CLT&T, CerAb, CivEngAb, CompD, CorrAb, E&CAJ, EMA, HRIS, IAA, Inspec, LID&ISL, M&TEA, MBF, METADEX, PROMT, SolStAb, WAA.
—AskIEEE, CISTI, Infotrieve, Linda Hall.
Published by: Aerospace Media Publishing SA, 33 Route de l'Aeroport, PO Box 56, Geneva 15, 1215, Switzerland. TEL 41-22-7882788, FAX 41-22-7882726, interavia@swissonline.ch, http://www.aerospacemedia.com. Ed. Oliver Sutton. Pub. Robert Monteux. R&P Pierre Condom. Adv. contact Cyril Mikailoff. Circ: 21,000 (paid).

INTERNATIONAL AEROSPACE ABSTRACTS. see *AERONAUTICS AND SPACE FLIGHT—Abstracting, Bibliographies, Statistics*

387.7   USA   ISSN 0270-5176
TL553.5
INTERNATIONAL AIR SAFETY SEMINAR PROCEEDINGS. Text in English. 1949. a. price varies. reprint service avail. from PQC. **Document type:** *Proceedings, Trade.*
Former titles (until 9th, 1957): Annual International Air Safety Seminar; (until 6th, 1955): Annual Air Safety Seminar
Related titles: Microform ed.: (from PQC).
Indexed: CLT&T, EngInd.
—BLDSC (1086.500000), Ei, IE, ingenta.
Published by: Flight Safety Foundation, Inc., 601 Madison St, Ste 300, Alexandria, VA 22314-1756. TEL 703-739-6700, FAX 703-739-6708. Ed. Roger Rozelle.

387.7   USA
INTERNATIONAL ANTIQUE AIRPLANE DIGEST. Text in English. q. USD 36 membership (effective 1999); includes APM Bulletin and Antique Airplane Association News. adv. **Document type:** *Newsletter.* **Description:** Historical aviation articles, photos, aircraft company histories and biographical stories on pioneer aviators.
Published by: Antique Airplane Association, Inc., 22001 Bluegrass Rd, Ottumwa, IA 52501-8569. TEL 515-938-2773. Pub. Robert L Taylor. Adv. contact L Reis.

INTERNATIONAL AVIATION NEWS. see *TRANSPORTATION—Air Transport*

629.132   CAN   ISSN 0074-2287
INTERNATIONAL CIVIL AVIATION ORGANIZATION. AIR NAVIGATION PLAN. AFRICA - INDIAN OCEAN REGION. Text in English, French, Spanish. 1954. irreg., latest vol.26, 1989. USD 75.
Published by: International Civil Aviation Organization, External Relations and Public Information Office, 999 University St, Montreal, PQ H3C 5H7, Canada. TEL 514-954-8022, FAX 514-954-6769, sales_unit@icao.org, icaohq@icao.int.

629.132   CAN   ISSN 0074-2295
INTERNATIONAL CIVIL AVIATION ORGANIZATION. AIR NAVIGATION PLAN. CARIBBEAN AND SOUTH AMERICAN REGIONS. Text in English. 1956. irreg., latest vol.14, 1991. USD 58.
Formed by the 1968 merger of: International Civil Aviation Organization. Air Navigation Plan. Caribbean Region (0534-8056); International Civil Aviation Organization. Air Navigation Plan. South American - South Atlantic Region (0534-8080)
Related titles: French ed.; Spanish ed.
Published by: International Civil Aviation Organization, External Relations and Public Information Office, 999 University St, Montreal, PQ H3C 5H7, Canada. TEL 514-954-8022, FAX 514-954-6769, sales_unit@icao.org, icaohq@icao.int.

629.132   CAN   ISSN 0304-7652
TL500.5
INTERNATIONAL CIVIL AVIATION ORGANIZATION. AIR NAVIGATION PLAN. EUROPEAN REGION. Text in English. irreg. (in 2 vols.), latest 1985, 23rd ed. looseleaf. USD 146; includes binders.
Related titles: French ed.; Russian ed.; Spanish ed.
Published by: International Civil Aviation Organization, External Relations and Public Information Office, 999 University St, Montreal, PQ H3C 5H7, Canada. TEL 514-954-8022, FAX 514-954-6769, sales_unit@icao.org, icaohq@icao.int.

629.132   CAN   ISSN 1014-0034
INTERNATIONAL CIVIL AVIATION ORGANIZATION. AIR NAVIGATION PLAN. MIDDLE EAST AND ASIA REGIONS. Text in English. 1967. irreg., latest vol.15, 1989. USD 58.
Formerly: International Civil Aviation Organization. Air Navigation Plan. Middle East and South East Asia Regions (0074-2317)
Related titles: Arabic ed.; French ed.; Spanish ed.
Published by: International Civil Aviation Organization, External Relations and Public Information Office, 999 University St, Montreal, PQ H3C 5H7, Canada. TEL 514-954-8022, FAX 514-954-6769, sales_unit@icao.org, icaohq@icao.int.

629.132   CAN   ISSN 0074-2325
INTERNATIONAL CIVIL AVIATION ORGANIZATION. AIR NAVIGATION PLAN. NORTH ATLANTIC, NORTH AMERICAN AND PACIFIC REGIONS. Text in English. 1956. irreg., latest vol.13, 1990. USD 49.
Formed by the 1967 merger of: I C A O. Air Navigation Plan. North Atlantic Region (0534-8064); I C A O. Air Navigation Plan. Pacific Region (0534-8072)
Related titles: French ed.; Spanish ed.
Published by: International Civil Aviation Organization, External Relations and Public Information Office, 999 University St, Montreal, PQ H3C 5H7, Canada. TEL 514-954-8022, FAX 514-954-6769, sales_unit@icao.org, icaohq@icao.int.

INTERNATIONAL CIVIL AVIATION ORGANIZATION. ASSEMBLY. MINUTES OF THE PLENARY MEETINGS. see *TRANSPORTATION—Air Transport*

629.1   CAN   ISSN 0074-2384
INTERNATIONAL CIVIL AVIATION ORGANIZATION. ASSEMBLY. REPORT OF THE TECHNICAL COMMISSION. Text in English. 1947. irreg., latest vol.31, 1995. USD 11. **Document type:** *Proceedings.*
Related titles: Arabic ed.: At-Taqrir - Al-Gamiyyat al-Umumiyyat ad-Dawarat. Al-Lagnat al-Fanmiyyat. ISSN 1014-4927; French ed.: Organisation de l'Aviation Civile Internationale. Assemble. Rapport et Procedes Verbaux de la Commission Technique. ISSN 1014-0387; Russian ed.: Mezhdunarodnaya Organizatsiya Grazhdanskoi Aviatsii. Assambleya. Doklady i Protokoly Tekhnicheskoi Komissii. ISSN 1014-0395; Spanish ed.: Organizacion de Aviacion Civil Internacional. Asamblea. Informe y Actas de la Comision Tecnica. ISSN 1014-0379.
Published by: International Civil Aviation Organization, External Relations and Public Information Office, 999 University St, Montreal, PQ H3C 5H7, Canada. TEL 514-954-8022, FAX 514-954-6769, sales_unit@icao.org, icaohq@icao.int.

629.1   CAN
INTERNATIONAL CIVIL AVIATION ORGANIZATION. COMMITTEE ON AVIATION ENVIRONMENTAL PROTECTION. REPORT OF THE MEETING. Text in English. 1986. irreg., latest vol.3, 1995. USD 29. back issues avail.
Related titles: French ed.; Russian ed.; Spanish ed.
Published by: International Civil Aviation Organization, External Relations and Public Information Office, 999 University St, Montreal, PQ H3C 5H7, Canada. TEL 514-954-8022, FAX 514-954-6769, sales_unit@icao.org, icaohq@icao.int.

INTERNATIONAL CIVIL AVIATION ORGANIZATION. COUNCIL. ANNUAL REPORT. see *TRANSPORTATION—Air Transport*

629.13   CAN
INTERNATIONAL CIVIL AVIATION ORGANIZATION. COUNCIL TO CONTRACTING STATES ON CHARGES FOR AIRPORTS AND AIR NAVIGATION SYSTEMS. STATEMENTS. Text in English. irreg., latest vol.5, 1997. USD 5.
Related titles: Arabic ed.; French ed.; Russian ed.; Spanish ed.
Published by: International Civil Aviation Organization, External Relations and Public Information Office, 999 University St, Montreal, PQ H3C 5H7, Canada. TEL 514-954-8022, FAX 514-954-6769, sales_unit@icao.org, icaohq@icao.int.

INTERNATIONAL CIVIL AVIATION ORGANIZATION. DIGESTS OF STATISTICS. SERIES R. CIVIL AIRCRAFT ON REGISTER. see *TRANSPORTATION—Abstracting, Bibliographies, Statistics*

INTERNATIONAL CIVIL AVIATION ORGANIZATION. GENERAL CONCEPT OF SEPARATION PANEL. REPORT OF THE MEETING. see *TRANSPORTATION—Air Transport*

INTERNATIONAL CIVIL AVIATION ORGANIZATION. INDEX OF I C A O PUBLICATIONS. ANNUAL CUMULATION. see *AERONAUTICS AND SPACE FLIGHT—Abstracting, Bibliographies, Statistics*

387.7   CAN
INTERNATIONAL CIVIL AVIATION ORGANIZATION. LOCATION INDICATORS. Text in English, French, Russian, Spanish. irreg., latest vol.92, 1999. USD 49 (effective Nov. 2000).
Related titles: Diskette ed.
Published by: International Civil Aviation Organization, External Relations and Public Information Office, 999 University St, Montreal, PQ H3C 5H7, Canada. TEL 514-954-8022, FAX 514-954-6769, sales_unit@icao.org, icaohq@icao.int, http://www.icao.org/.

INTERNATIONAL CIVIL AVIATION ORGANIZATION. REPORT OF THE AIR NAVIGATION CONFERENCE. see *TRANSPORTATION—Air Transport*

621.1 387.7   CAN
INTERNATIONAL CIVIL AVIATION ORGANIZATION. SPECIAL COMMITTEE FOR THE MONITORING AND CO-ORDINATION OF DEVELOPMENT AND TRANSITION PLANNING FOR THE FUTURE AIR NAVIGATION SYSTEM (FANS - PHASE II). REPORT OF THE MEETING. Text in English. irreg., latest 1993. USD 54. **Document type:** *Proceedings.*
Formerly: International Civil Aviation Organization, Special Committee on Future Air Navigation Systems (FANS). Report of the Meeting
Related titles: French ed.; Russian ed.; Spanish ed.
Published by: International Civil Aviation Organization, External Relations and Public Information Office, 999 University St, Montreal, PQ H3C 5H7, Canada. TEL 514-954-8022, FAX 514-954-6769, sales_unit@icao.org, icaohq@icao.int.

629.1   CAN   ISSN 0074-2570
INTERNATIONAL CIVIL AVIATION ORGANIZATION. TECHNICAL PANEL ON SUPERSONIC TRANSPORT. REPORT OF MEETING. Text in English. irreg., latest 1973, 4th, Montreal. price varies.
Related titles: French ed.; Spanish ed.; Russian ed.
Published by: International Civil Aviation Organization, External Relations and Public Information Office, 999 University St, Montreal, PQ H3C 5H7, Canada. TEL 514-954-8022, FAX 514-954-6769, sales_unit@icao.org, icaohq@icao.int.

INTERNATIONAL CIVIL AVIATION ORGANIZATION. VISUAL AIDS PANEL. REPORT OF THE MEETING. see *TRANSPORTATION—Air Transport*

629.1   USA   ISSN 0730-2010
TL566
INTERNATIONAL CONGRESS ON INSTRUMENTATION IN AEROSPACE SIMULATION FACILITIES. RECORD. Key Title: I C I A S F Record. Text in English. 1964. biennial. price varies.
Formerly (until 1966): International Congress on Instrumentation in Aerospace Simulation Facilities. Proceedings (0730-1790)
Indexed: CivEngAb, EngInd.
—BLDSC (4362.045300), Ei, IE, ingenta. **CCC.**
Published by: Institute of Electrical and Electronics Engineers, Inc., 345 E 47th St, New York, NY 10017-2394. TEL 800-678-4333, customer.service@ieee.org, http://www.ieee.org. **Co-sponsor:** Aerospace and Electronic Systems Society.

629.132   USA
INTERNATIONAL COUNCIL OF AIRCRAFT OWNER AND PILOT ASSOCIATIONS BULLETIN. Text in English. m. free. **Document type:** *Bulletin.* **Description:** Details membership activities.
Published by: International Council of Aircraft Owner and Pilot Associations, 421 Aviation Way, Fredrick, MD 21701. TEL 301-695-2221, FAX 301-695-2375. Ed. Steven J Brown.

▼ *new title*   ➤ *refereed*   ✱ *unverified*   ◆ *full entry avail.*

A

629.4 USA
INTERNATIONAL DEVELOPMENT IN SPACE STATION AND SPACE TECHNOLOGIES. Text in English. irreg., latest 1984, 35th, Lausanne. USD 94.50 to non-members; USD 64.50 to members. reprint service avail. from PQC. **Document type:** *Academic/Scholarly.* **Description:** Selected papers from IAF meetings.
Formerly: International Astronautical Federation (I A F). International Congress. Invited Papers
Published by: (International Astronautical Federation), American Institute of Aeronautics and Astronautics, Inc., 1801 Alexander Bell Dr, Ste 500, Reston, VA 20191. TEL 703-264-7500, FAX 703-264-7551, custserv@aiaa.org, http://www.aiaa.org. Ed. Luigi G Napolitano.

INTERNATIONAL DIRECTORY OF AIRCRAFT AND AVIATION EQUIPMENT & ACCESSORIES IMPORTERS. see *BUSINESS AND ECONOMICS—Trade And Industrial Directories*

INTERNATIONAL DIRECTORY OF CIVIL AIRCRAFT (YEAR). see *TRANSPORTATION—Air Transport*

INTERNATIONAL DIRECTORY OF MILITARY AIRCRAFT (YEAR). see *MILITARY*

629.1 USA ISSN 0364-0418
INTERNATIONAL FLIGHT INFORMATION MANUAL. Text in English. a. looseleaf. USD 59; USD 73.75 foreign. Supplement avail. **Document type:** *Government.* **Description:** Used as a preflight and training guide by U.S. nonscheduled commercial carriers, business operations, and private aviators for flights beyond U.S. airspace.
—Linda Hall.
Published by: U.S. Federal Aviation Administration, 800 Independence Ave S W, Washington, DC 20591. TEL 202-655-4000. **Subscr. to:** U.S. Government Printing Office, Superintendent of Documents. TEL 202-512-3238.

629.13 USA ISSN 0020-675X
TL501
INTERNATIONAL FLYING FARMER. Text in English. 1947. 6/yr. USD 25 domestic; USD 30 in Canada; USD 35 elsewhere (effective 2005). adv. bk.rev. illus.; mkt.; pat. **Document type:** *Newsletter, Trade.* **Description:** Focuses on aviation and agriculture and on how they are intertwined. Includes profiles of members.
—CISTI.
Published by: International Flying Farmers, Inc., PO Box 9124, Wichita, KS 67277-0124. TEL 316-943-4234, FAX 316-943-4235, support@flyingfarmers.org, http://www.flyingfarmers.org. Ed. Deanne Earwood. Pub., R&P Kathy Marsh. Circ: 2,000.

358.4 USA
INTERNATIONAL GUIDE TO UNMANNED VEHICLES. Text in English. 1997. a. charts; illus. **Document type:** *Trade.* **Description:** Describes remote control and other pilotless military aircrafts.
Published by: McGraw-Hill Companies, Inc., 1200 G St NW Ste 200, Washington, DC 20005. http://www.aviationnow.com/, http://www.mcgraw-hill.com.

620.1 USA
TL589 CODEN: PIISEF
INTERNATIONAL INSTRUMENTATION SYMPOSIUM (CD-ROM). Text in English. 1987. a. USD 80 to non-members; USD 70 to members (effective 2004). back issues avail.; reprint service avail. from PQC,ISI. **Document type:** *Proceedings, Trade.*
Formerly (until 2002): International Instrumentation Symposium (Print) (0277-7576); Which superseded in part: Instrumentation in the Aerospace Industry (0096-7238); Fundamentals of Test Measurement (0891-4052); Fundamentals of Aerospace Instrumentation (0094-3975); Former titles: Advances in Test Measurement. Proceedings (0568-0204); I S A Aerospace Instrumentation Symposium. Proceedings (0536-2008)
Media: CD-ROM. **Related titles:** Microform ed.: (from PQC).
Indexed: CIN, ChemAb, ChemTitl, Engind, Inspec.
—BLDSC (6846.335000), CASDDS, Ei. **CCC.**
Published by: The Instrumentation, Systems and Automation Society, 67 Alexander Dr, Research Triangle Park, NC 27709. TEL 919-549-8411, FAX 919-549-8288, info@isa.org, http://www.isa.org.

INTERNATIONAL JOURNAL OF AEROACOUSTICS. see *PHYSICS—Sound*

629.13 GBR ISSN 1743-5447
▼ ➤ **INTERNATIONAL JOURNAL OF AERODYNAMICS.** Text in English. 2005. q. USD 450 to institutions; USD 545 to institutions print & online eds. (effective 2005). **Document type:** *Journal, Academic/Scholarly.*
Related titles: Online - full text ed.: ISSN 1743-5455. USD 450 to institutions (effective 2005).
Published by: Inderscience Publishers, IEL Editorial Office, PO Box 735, Olney, Bucks MK46 5WB, United Kingdom. TEL 44-1234-240519, FAX 44-1234-240515, info@inderscience.com, https://www.inderscience.com/browse/index.php?journalID=140, http://www.inderscience.com. Ed. Dr. Mohammed A Dorgham. **Subscr. to:** World Trade Centre Bldg, 29 route de Pre-Bois, Case Postale 896, Geneva 15 1215, Switzerland. FAX 41-22-7910885, subs@inderscience.com.

➤ **THE INTERNATIONAL JOURNAL OF AVIATION PSYCHOLOGY.** see *TRANSPORTATION—Air Transport*

629.13 ISR ISSN 0334-0082
➤ **INTERNATIONAL JOURNAL OF TURBO AND JET ENGINES.** Text in English. 1983. q. USD 370 (effective 2005). adv. bk.rev. back issues avail. **Document type:** *Academic/Scholarly.*
Indexed: ASCA, ApMecR, BrCerAb, C&ISA, CerAb, CivEngAb, CorrAb, E&CAJ, EMA, IAA, M&TEA, MBF, METADEX, SolStAb, WAA.
—BLDSC (4542.696200), CISTI, IE, Infotrieve, ingenta, Linda Hall.
Published by: Freund Publishing House, Ltd., P O Box 35010, Tel Aviv, 61350, Israel. TEL 972-3-5628540, FAX 972-3-5628538, h_freund@netvision.net.il, http://www.freundpublishing.com. Ed. B Gal-Or.

629.134 USA
➤ **INTERNATIONAL JOURNAL OF WEIGHT ENGINEERING.** Text in English. 1943. 3/yr. USD 30 (effective 2000). adv. illus. **Document type:** *Academic/Scholarly.*
Former titles: Journal of Weight Engineering; (until 1981): S.A.W.E. Journal (0583-9270)
Indexed: BMT, CivEngAb, IAA.
—CISTI.
Published by: Society of Allied Weight Engineers, Inc., 204 Hubbard St, Glastonbury, CT 06033-3063. TEL 860-633-0850, FAX 860-633-8971, saweed@aol.com. Ed., Adv. contact Robert W Ridenour. Circ: 1,000 (controlled).

629.1 USA ISSN 0364-6742
TL725.A1
INTERNATIONAL NOTICES TO AIRMEN. Text in English. 1973. fortn. USD 55; USD 68.75 foreign. back issues avail. **Document type:** *Government.* **Description:** Alerts pilots traveling in U.S. airspace to temporary hazardous conditions, changes in facility operational data, and foreign entry procedures and regulations.
Formerly (until 1975): International Notams
—Linda Hall.
Published by: U.S. Federal Aviation Administration, 800 Independence Ave S W, Washington, DC 20591. TEL 202-655-4000. **Subscr. to:** U.S. Government Printing Office, Superintendent of Documents.

629.132 387.7 USA
INTERNATIONAL OPERATIONS BULLETIN. Text in English. 1982. q. membership only. bk.rev. **Document type:** *Bulletin.* **Description:** Timely operational information for professional aircrews of business aircraft that fly internationally.
Formerly: I B A C International Update
Published by: (International Business Aviation Council), National Business Aviation Association, 1200 18th St, N W, Ste 400, Washington, DC 20036-2506. TEL 202-783-9000, FAX 202-331-8364, http://www.nbaa.org. Ed. William H Stine II. Circ: 4,000.

INTERNATIONAL RADAR CONFERENCE. RECORD. see *COMMUNICATIONS*

629.132 USA ISSN 1088-8128
INTERNATIONAL SOCIETY OF AIR SAFETY INVESTIGATORS. FORUM. Text in English. 1977. q.
—CISTI.
Published by: International Society of Air Safety Investigators, Pakr Center, 107 E Holly Ave Ste 11, Sterling, VA 20164. TEL 703-430-9668, FAX 703-430-4970, isasihq@isasi.org, http://www.isasi.org/.

629.1 GBR ISSN 0958-9058
INTERNATIONAL SPACE DIRECTORY. Text in English. 1988. a. adv. **Document type:** *Directory, Trade.*
Published by: Parker Publications Ltd., 42 Keephatch Rd, Wokingham, Berks RG40 1QD, United Kingdom. TEL 44-118-9774000, FAX 44-118-9774001, editorial@spaceandcommunications.com, jalexan808@aol.com, http://www.spaceandcommunications.com. Ed. Mark Williamson. Pub., Adv. contact Julie Alexander. R&P Ian Parker.

629.13 USA
INTERNATIONAL SPACE INDUSTRY REPORT✶. Text in English. 1998. bi-w. USD 99; USD 7.50 newsstand/cover; USD 139 foreign (effective 1998). software rev. charts; stat. back issues avail.
Related titles: Online - full text ed.
Published by: Launchspace Publications, PO Box 3411, Northbrook, IL 60065-3411. TEL 703-749-2324, FAX 703-749-3177, info@launchspace.com, http://www.launchspace.com. R&P Milan Rudzika. adv.: color page USD 6,950; trim 14.38 x 10.75.

001.942 USA ISSN 0730-174X
TL789.A1
INTERNATIONAL U F O REPORTER. Text in English. 1976. 4/yr. USD 25. adv. bk.rev.
Formerly (until 1982): Second Look; Which incorporates: Frontiers of Science; Probe
Indexed: CCMJ, RefZh.
Published by: Center for U F O Studies, 2457 W Peterson Ave, Ste 6, Chicago, IL 60659-4118. TEL 312-271-3611. Ed. Jerome Clark. Circ: 2,000.

629.13 DEU ISSN 0579-6938
INTERNATIONALER WELTKONGRESS DER U F O-FORSCHER. DOKUMENTARBERICHT. Text in German. a. **Document type:** *Proceedings.*
Published by: Ventla-Verlag, Hohenzollernstr 9, Guetersloh, 33330, Germany. TEL 49-5241-24750, FAX 49-5241-28520.

629.13 GBR ISSN 0020-9597
INTERPLANETARY NEWS; Britain's space monthly. Text in English. 1957. m. GBP 6. adv. bk.rev.
Related titles: Microfiche ed.
Published by: Interplanetary Space Travel Research Association (United Kingdom), 21 Hargwyne St, London, SW9 9RQ, United Kingdom. Ed. Mike Parry. Circ: (controlled).

001.94 USA
INTERSPACE - LINK CONFIDENTIAL NEWSLETTER; the link. Text in English. 1983. m. USD 100 domestic; USD 125 foreign (effective 2001). adv. back issues avail. **Document type:** *Newsletter.* **Description:** Keeps readers current on UFOs, space, science, and spiritual teachings.
Indexed: RefZh.
Published by: (National Investigation Committee on Unidentified Flying Objects), N I C U F O Publishing, 9101 Topanga Canyon Blvd., Apt. 209, Chatsworth, CA 91311-5763. TEL 818-989-5942, FAX 818-981-2165, http://www.nicufo.org. Ed., Pub., Adv. contact Frank Stranges. Circ: 300 (paid).

629.13 ISR
➤ **ISRAEL ANNUAL CONFERENCE ON AEROSPACE SCIENCES. PROCEEDINGS.** Text in English. 1958. a., latest 40th proceedings. USD 155 (effective 2000). adv. **Document type:** *Proceedings, Academic/Scholarly.*
Formerly (until 1994): Israel Annual Conference on Aviation and Astronautics. Collection of Papers (0075-0972)
Indexed: ApMecR, IAA.
—BLDSC (4583.602000).
Published by: Technion - Israel Institute of Technology, Faculty of Aerospace Engineering, Technion City, Haifa, 32000, Israel. TEL 972-4-8292260, FAX 972-4-8231848, alice@aerodyne.technion.ac.il, http://ae-www.technion.ac.il. Circ: 1,000 (paid).

629.13 ITA ISSN 1120-6977
VK4
➤ **ISTITUTO ITALIANO DI NAVIGAZIONE. ATTI.** Text in Italian. 1959. q. EUR 21 (effective 2004). adv. bk.rev. illus. **Document type:** *Proceedings, Academic/Scholarly.* **Description:** Includes texts of conferences, articles about navigation, problems and proposals, as well as pertinent news articles.
Formerly (until 1967): Istituto Italiano di Navigazione. Notiziario (1120-6985)
Published by: Istituto Italiano di Navigazione, Via Cremona 15B, Rome, 00161, Italy. http://www.iin.it. Ed. Adolfo Gambardella. Adv. contact Antonino Biccairri. Circ: 750.

629.1 ESP ISSN 0213-1250
ITAVIA. Text in Spanish. 1973. 3/yr. free.
Indexed: IECT, RefZh.
—CINDOC.
Published by: Asociacion y Colegio de Ingenieros Tecnicos Aeronauticos, Hortaleza, 61, Madrid, 2804, Spain. TEL 34-1-91-522-0604, 34-1-91-522-0918, FAX 34-1-91-522-5357.

629.1 RUS ISSN 0579-2975
CODEN: IVUAAV
➤ **IZVESTIYA VYSSHIKH UCHEBNYKH ZAVEDENII. AVIATSIONNAYA TEKHNIKA.** Text in Russian. 1958. q. USD 221 foreign (effective 2005). **Document type:** *Journal, Academic/Scholarly.*
Indexed: BrCerAb, C&ISA, CerAb, CivEngAb, CorrAb, CurCont, E&CAJ, EMA, IAA, Inspec, M&TEA, MBF, METADEX, RefZh, SolStAb, WAA.
—BLDSC (0077.360000), CASDDS, CISTI, East View, IDS, Linda Hall. **CCC.**
Published by: Kazanskii Gosudarstvennyi Tekhnicheskii Universitet im. A.N. Tupoleva/Kazan Aviation Institute, Adamuck, 4-6, Kazan-15, 420015, Russian Federation. TEL 7-8432-361648, FAX 7-8432-367621, lyudmila.kuzmina@ksu.ru, http://www.kai.ru/kai/main.en.html. Ed. N. Vakhitov. **US dist. addr.:** East View Information Services, 3020 Harbor Ln. N., Minneapolis, MN 55447. TEL 800-477-1005, FAX 800-800-3839, eastview@eastview.com, http://www.eastview.com.

➤ **J A R AMENDMENT SERVICE TO REGULATORY DOCUMENTS.** see *TRANSPORTATION—Air Transport*

➤ **J A S M A: JOURNAL OF THE JAPAN SOCIETY OF MICROGRAVITY APPLICATION.** see *PHYSICS*

629.13 IRN ISSN 1735-2134
➤ **J A S T.** Text in English. q. **Document type:** *Journal, Academic/Scholarly.* **Description:** Covers aerodynamics, propulsion, guidance and control, structures, design and industrial studies. Established to distribute information of significant researches, theoretical works, technical and methodological applications, case studies, short communications and surveys and reviews concerned with the traditional or modern Aerospace Engineering.
—BLDSC (4663.149550).
Published by: Journal of Aerospace Science and Technology, Azadi Ave, P O Box 11365-8639, Tehran, Iran. TEL 98-21-6164936, FAX 98-21-6022731, jast@sharif.edu, intjast@yahoo.com, http://ae.sharif.edu. Ed. Karim Mazaheri.

629.13 ITA ISSN 0394-3437
J P 4 MENSILE DI AERONAUTICA. (Jet Petrol Quattro) Text in Italian; Summaries in English. 1972. m. bk.rev. index. **Document type:** *Consumer.* **Description:** Deals with every aspect of civilian and military aviation. Covers commercial aviation, technology and space.
Published by: Edizioni Aeronautiche Italiane Srl, Casella Postale 1550, Florence, 50133, Italy. TEL 39-055-574774, FAX 39-055570103, edai@edai.it, http://www.edai.it/. Ed. Paolo Gianvanni. R&P Randa Eid. Adv. contact Daniela Mingaia TEL 39-055-2094724. Circ: 27,250.

629.13 DEU ISSN 0021-3896
JAEGERBLATT; offizielles Organ der Gemeinschaft der Jagdflieger - Vereinigung der Flieger Deutscher Streitkraefte. Text in German. 1952. bi-m. adv. bk.rev. illus. **Document type:** *Magazine, Consumer.*
—CCC.
Published by: Gemeinschaft der Jagdflieger - Vereinigung der Flieger Deutscher Streitkraefte e.V., Dahlienweg 1, Sankt Augustin, 53757, Germany. TEL 49-2241-203629, FAX 49-2241-922609, GOverhoff@t-online.de, http://www.fliegergemeinschaft.de. Ed., R&P, Adv. contact Gert Overhoff.

629.1 GBR
JANE'S AERO-ENGINES. Text in English. s-a. GBP 795, USD 1,265, AUD 2,070 (effective 2004). **Document type:** *Trade.* **Description:** Provides a source for information on civil and military engines throughout the world that are in production or still in service.
Related titles: CD-ROM ed.: GBP 1,165, USD 1,865, AUD 3,030 (effective 2004); Online - full text ed.: GBP 1,250, USD 1,999, AUD 3,250 (effective 2004).
Published by: Jane's Information Group, Sentinel House, 163 Brighton Rd, Coulsdon, Surrey CR5 2YH, United Kingdom. TEL 44-20-87003700, FAX 44-20-87631006, info@janes.co.uk, http://jae.janes.com/, http://www.janes.com. **Dist. in Asia by:** Jane's Information Group Asia, 60 Albert St, #15-01 Albert Complex, Singapore 189969, Singapore. TEL 65-331-6280, FAX 65-336-9921, info@janes.com.sg; **Dist. in Australia by:** Jane's Information Group Australia, PO Box 3502, Rozelle, NSW 2039, Australia. TEL 61-2-8587-7900, FAX 61-2-8587-7901, info@janes.thomson.com.au; **Dist. in the Americas by:** 1340 Braddock Pl, Ste 300, Alexandria, VA 22314-1651. TEL 703-683-3700, 800-824-0768, FAX 703-836-0297, 800-836-0297, info@janes.com.

JANE'S AIR AND SYSTEMS LIBRARY. see *MILITARY*

JANE'S AIR-LAUNCHED WEAPONS. see *MILITARY*

JANE'S AIR TRAFFIC CONTROL. see *TRANSPORTATION—Air Transport*

629.134 GBR
JANE'S AIRCRAFT COMPONENT MANUFACTURERS. Text in English. m. GBP 1,175, USD 1,875, AUD 3,055 (effective 2004). **Document type:** *Trade.* **Description:** Provides details of all the major companies involved in the manufacturing and distribution of aircraft parts from airframes, power units and engines to hydraulics and cabin equipment.
Media: Online - full content. **Related titles:** CD-ROM ed.: GBP 1,175, USD 1,875, AUD 3,055 (effective 2004).
Published by: Jane's Information Group, Sentinel House, 163 Brighton Rd, Coulsdon, Surrey CR5 2YH, United Kingdom. TEL 44-20-87003700, FAX 44-20-87631006, info@janes.co.uk, http://jacm.janes.com/, http://www.janes.com. **Dist. in Asia by:** Jane's Information Group Asia, 60 Albert St, #15-01 Albert Complex, Singapore 189969, Singapore. TEL 65-331-6280, FAX 65-336-9921, info@janes.com.sg; **Dist. in Australia by:** Jane's Information Group Australia, PO Box 3502, Rozelle, NSW 2039, Australia. TEL 61-2-8587-7900, FAX 61-2-8587-7901, info@janes.thomson.com.au; **Dist. in the Americas by:** 1340 Braddock Pl, Ste 300, Alexandria, VA 22314-1651. TEL 703-683-3700, 800-824-0768, FAX 703-836-0297, 800-836-0297, info@janes.com.

629.133 GBR ISSN 1361-6684
JANE'S AIRCRAFT UPGRADES. Text in English. 1992. a. GBP 385, USD 590, AUD 1,000 per issue (effective 2004); price varies per vol.. adv. back issues avail. **Document type:** *Yearbook, Trade.* **Description:** Covers air upgrade programs for aircraft no longer in production.
Formerly (until 1995): Jane's Civil and Military Aircraft Upgrades (0969-0417)
Related titles: CD-ROM ed.: USD 1,340 in the Americas; GBP 835 elsewhere (effective 2002); Online - full text ed.: USD 1,465 in the Americas; GBP 915 elsewhere (effective 2002).
—BLDSC (4645.946000).
Published by: Jane's Information Group, Sentinel House, 163 Brighton Rd, Coulsdon, Surrey CR5 2YH, United Kingdom. TEL 44-20-87003700, FAX 44-20-87631006, info@janes.co.uk, http://catalog.janes.com/catalog/public/index.cfm?fuseaction=home.ProductInfoBrief&product_id=80, http://www.janes.com. Ed. Simon Michell. Pub. Karen Heffer. Adv. contact Richard West. page GBP 4,000; trim 12 x 8. **Dist. in Asia by:** Jane's Information Group Asia, 60 Albert St, #15-01 Albert Complex, Singapore 189969, Singapore. TEL 65-331-6280, FAX 65-336-9921, info@janes.com.sg; **Dist. in Australia by:** Jane's Information Group Australia, PO Box 3502, Rozelle, NSW 2039, Australia. TEL 61-2-8587-7900, FAX 61-2-8587-7901, info@janes.thomson.com.au; **Dist. in the Americas by:** 1340 Braddock Pl, Ste 300, Alexandria, VA 22314-1651. TEL 703-683-3700, 800-824-0768, FAX 703-836-0297, 800-836-0297, info@janes.com.

629.133 GBR ISSN 0075-3017
TL501
JANE'S ALL THE WORLD'S AIRCRAFT. Text in English. 1909. a. USD 725 per issue in the Americas; BHD 1,210 per issue in Australia & New Zealand; GBP 465 per issue elsewhere (effective 2005). adv. index. **Document type:** *Trade.* **Description:** Publishes technical details of all piloted aircraft, powered and unpowered, currently under development, in production or available in assembly kit production in 172 countries worldwide.
Related titles: CD-ROM ed.: USD 1,385 in the Americas; GBP 865 elsewhere (effective 2002); Microfiche ed.: USD 3,075 in the Americas for complete set 1909-1993; GBP 1,975 elsewhere for complete set 1909-1993; USD 525 in the Americas per set; GBP 345 elsewhere per set (effective 2002); Microfiche sets are cumulative and available for each of the following years 1909-1919, 1920-1929, 1930-1939, 1940-1949, 1950-1959, 1960-1969, 1970-1979, and 1980-1993; Online - full text ed.: GBP 950 elsewhere; USD 1,520 in the Americas (effective 2002).
—BLDSC (4646.000000), IE, Infotrieve, Linda Hall. **CCC.**
Published by: Jane's Information Group, Sentinel House, 163 Brighton Rd, Coulsdon, Surrey CR5 2YH, United Kingdom. TEL 44-20-87003700, FAX 44-20-87631006, customerservices.uk@janes.com, info@janes.co.uk, http://catalogue.janes.com/jawa_trans.shtml, http://www.janes.com. Ed. Paul Jackson. Adv. contact Janine Boxall TEL 44-20-87003852. **Dist. in Asia by:** Jane's Information Group Asia, 60 Albert St, #15-01 Albert Complex, Singapore 189969, Singapore. TEL 65-331-6280, FAX 65-336-9921, info@janes.com.sg; **Dist. in Australia by:** Jane's Information Group Australia, PO Box 3502, Rozelle, NSW 2039, Australia. TEL 61-2-8587-7900, FAX 61-2-8587-7901, info@janes.thomson.com.au; **Dist. in the Americas by:** 1340 Braddock Pl, Ste 300, Alexandria, VA 22314-1651. TEL 703-683-3700, 800-824-0768, FAX 703-836-0297, 800-836-0297, info@janes.com.

629.1 GBR ISSN 0264-794X
JANE'S AVIONICS. Text in English. 1982. a. USD 610 per issue in the Americas; AUD 1,035 per issue in Australia & New Zealand; GBP 395 per issue elsewhere (effective 2005 - 2006). adv. index. **Document type:** *Yearbook, Trade.* **Description:** Covers civil and military airborne electronic equipment; provides technical details and manufacturer contact information.
Related titles: CD-ROM ed.: USD 1,340 in the Americas; GBP 835 elsewhere (effective 2002); Online - full text ed.: USD 1,465 in the Americas; GBP 915 elsewhere (effective 2002).
—BLDSC (4646.620000).
Published by: Jane's Information Group, Sentinel House, 163 Brighton Rd, Coulsdon, Surrey CR5 2YH, United Kingdom. TEL 44-20-87003700, FAX 44-20-87631006, customerservices.uk@janes.com, info@janes.co.uk, http://catalogue.janes.com/avionics_trans.shtml, http://www.janes.com. Ed. Edward Downs. Adv. contact Janine Boxall TEL 44-20-87003852. **Dist. in Asia by:** Jane's Information Group Asia, 60 Albert St, #15-01 Albert Complex, Singapore 189969, Singapore. TEL 65-331-6280, FAX 65-336-9921, info@janes.com.sg; **Dist. in Australia by:** Jane's Information Group Australia, PO Box 3502, Rozelle, NSW 2039, Australia. TEL 61-2-8587-7900, FAX 61-2-8587-7901, info@janes.thomson.com.au; **Dist. in the Americas by:** 1340 Braddock Pl, Ste 300, Alexandria, VA 22314-1651. TEL 703-683-3700, 800-824-0768, FAX 703-836-0297, 800-836-0297, info@janes.com.

JANE'S C 4 I SYSTEMS. see *MILITARY*

JANE'S ELECTRO-OPTIC SYSTEMS. see *MILITARY*

629.133 327.12 GBR
JANE'S ELECTRONIC MISSION AIRCRAFT. Text in English. s-a. GBP 792, USD 1,265, AUD 2,070 (effective 2004). **Document type:** *Magazine, Trade.* **Description:** Covers the electronic mission systems installed in military, paramilitary and civilian fixed-wing aircraft, helicopters and unmanned aerial vehicles and aerostats that have a primary electronic mission. Contents includes: Airborne early warning; psychological warfare; radar surveillance/multisensor systems; command and control; electronic warfare; signals intelligence; radar and electronic warfare training; research and development.
Related titles: CD-ROM ed.: GBP 1,165, USD 1,865, USD 3,030 (effective 2004); Online - full content ed.: GBP 1,250, USD 1,999, AUD 3,250 (effective 2004).
Published by: Jane's Information Group, Sentinel House, 163 Brighton Rd, Coulsdon, Surrey CR5 2YH, United Kingdom. TEL 44-20-87003700, FAX 44-20-87631006, info@janes.co.uk, http://jema.janes.com/, http://www.janes.com.

629.133 GBR
JANE'S HELICOPTER MARKETS AND SYSTEMS. Text in English. s-a. GBP 815, USD 1,305, AUD 2,120 (effective 2004). **Document type:** *Trade.* **Description:** Provides a comprehensive resource on the world's manned and unmanned helicopters and engines in use, in production, under development or being upgraded.
Related titles: CD-ROM ed.: GBP 1,175, USD 1,875, USD 3,055 (effective 2004); Online - full text ed.: GBP 1,270, USD 2,030, AUD 3,300 (effective 2004).
Published by: Jane's Information Group, Sentinel House, 163 Brighton Rd, Coulsdon, Surrey CR5 2YH, United Kingdom. TEL 44-20-87003700, FAX 44-20-87631006, info@janes.co.uk, http://jhms.janes.com/, http://www.janes.com. **Dist. in Asia by:** Jane's Information Group Asia, 60 Albert St, #15-01 Albert Complex, Singapore 189969, Singapore. TEL 65-331-6280, FAX 65-336-9921, info@janes.com.sg; **Dist. in Australia by:** Jane's Information Group Australia, PO Box 3502, Rozelle, NSW 2039, Australia. TEL 61-2-8587-7900, FAX 61-2-8587-7901, info@janes.thomson.com.au; **Dist. in the Americas by:** 1340 Braddock Pl, Ste 300, Alexandria, VA 22314-1651. TEL 703-683-3700, 800-824-0768, FAX 703-836-0297, 800-836-0297, info@janes.com.

629.1 GBR ISSN 1467-1662
TL512
JANE'S INTERNATIONAL A B C AEROSPACE DIRECTORY. Text in English. 1936. a. GBP 515, USD 810, AUD 1,340 per issue for 2005-2006 Edition (effective 2005). adv. index. **Document type:** *Directory, Trade.* **Description:** Lists companies, manufacturers, governmental and official organizations in all areas of aerospace-related activities. Includes company name, senior personnel, and product, service description.
Former titles (until 1994): International A B C Aerospace Directory (0967-6481); Interavia A B C Aerospace Directory; Interavia A B C (0074-1116)
Related titles: CD-ROM ed.: GBP 940, USD 1,510, AUD 2,445 (effective 2005); Online - full text ed.: GBP 1,015, USD 1,625, AUD 2,640 (effective 2005).
Indexed: BusI, T&II.
Published by: Jane's Information Group, Sentinel House, 163 Brighton Rd, Coulsdon, Surrey CR5 2YH, United Kingdom. TEL 44-20-87003700, FAX 44-20-87631006, info@janes.co.uk, http://abc.janes.com/, http://www.janes.com. Ed. Peter Partridge. Pub. Karen Heffer. **Dist. in Asia by:** Jane's Information Group Asia, 60 Albert St, #15-01 Albert Complex, Singapore 189969, Singapore. TEL 65-331-6280, FAX 65-336-9921, info@janes.com.sg; **Dist. in Australia by:** Jane's Information Group Australia, PO Box 3502, Rozelle, NSW 2039, Australia. TEL 61-2-8587-7900, FAX 61-2-8587-7901, info@janes.thomson.com.au; **Dist. in the Americas by:** 1340 Braddock Pl, Ste 300, Alexandria, VA 22314-1651. TEL 703-683-3700, 800-824-0768, FAX 703-836-0297, 800-836-0297, info@janes.com.

629.1 GBR ISSN 1352-0660
JANE'S SPACE DIRECTORY. Text in English. a. GBP 375, USD 590, AUD 980 per issue for 2005-2006 Edition (effective 2005). **Document type:** *Directory, Trade.* **Description:** Includes extensive detail on civil and military satellites, orbital and sub-orbital launch vehicles.
Former titles: Interavia Space Directory; (until 1988): Jane's Spaceflight Directory
Related titles: CD-ROM ed.: GBP 910, USD 1,450, AUD 2,370 (effective 2005); Online - full text ed.: GBP 980, USD 1,570, AUD 2,545 (effective 2005).
—BLDSC (4647.097300).
Published by: Jane's Information Group, Sentinel House, 163 Brighton Rd, Coulsdon, Surrey CR5 2YH, United Kingdom. TEL 44-20-87003700, FAX 44-20-87631006, info@janes.co.uk, http://jsd.janes.com/, http://www.janes.com. Ed. David Baker. **Dist. in Asia by:** Jane's Information Group Asia, 60 Albert St, #15-01 Albert Complex, Singapore 189969, Singapore. TEL 65-331-6280, FAX 65-336-9921, info@janes.com.sg; **Dist. in Australia by:** Jane's Information Group Australia, PO Box 3502, Rozelle, NSW 2039, Australia. TEL 61-2-8587-7900, FAX 61-2-8587-7901, info@janes.thomson.com.au; **Dist. in the Americas by:** 1340 Braddock Pl, Ste 300, Alexandria, VA 22314-1651. TEL 703-683-3700, 800-824-0768, FAX 703-836-0297, 800-836-0297, info@janes.com.

359.94834 GBR
JANE'S UNMANNED AERIAL VEHICLES AND TARGETS. Text in English. s-a. GBP 8,350, USD 1,335, AUD 2,170 (effective 2004). **Document type:** *Trade.* **Description:** Covers over 180 UAVs, 120 aerial targets and 240 subsystems, including full vehicle and target listing includes information on development, mission payloads, guidance and control, operational status, specifications, customers, and contractors together with photographs for impartial assessment and comparison. Each entry details the manufacturer, complete with contact information and the civil and military organizations using the aircraft.

▼ *new title* ➤ *refereed* ✶ *unverified* ♦ *full entry avail.*

A

Related titles: CD-ROM ed.: GBP 1,205, USD 1,930, AUD 3,135 (effective 2004); Online - full content ed.: GBP 1,305, USD 2,090, AUD 3,395 (effective 2004).
Published by: Jane's Information Group, Sentinel House, 163 Brighton Rd, Coulsdon, Surrey CR5 2YH, United Kingdom. TEL 44-20-87003700, FAX 44-20-87631006, info@janes.co.uk, http://juav.janes.com/, http://www.janes.com.

JAPAN AVIATION NEWS. see *TRANSPORTATION—Air Transport*

629.13   JPN   ISSN 0549-3811
TL501   CODEN: TJASAM
➤ **JAPAN SOCIETY FOR AERONAUTICAL AND SPACE SCIENCES. TRANSACTIONS.** Text in English. 1958. q. abstr.; charts; illus. **Document type:** *Journal, Academic/Scholarly.*
Related titles: Online - full text ed.: (from J-Stage).
Indexed: ASCA, ApMecR, BrCerAb, C&ISA, CerAb, ChemAb, CivEngAb, CorrAb, CurCont, E&CAJ, EMA, EngInd, IAA, ISMEC, ISR, Inspec, JCT, JTA, M&TEA, MBF, METADEX, RefZh, SCI, SolStAb, WAA.
—BLDSC (8973.950000), AskIEEE, CASDDS, CISTI, Ei, IDS, IE, Infotrieve, ingenta, Linda Hall. **CCC.**
Published by: Nihon Koku Uchu Gakkai/Japan Society for Aeronautical and Space Sciences, Ohkami Meiwa Bldg. 3F, 1-18-2 Shimbashi, Minato-ku, Tokyo, 105-0004, Japan. TEL 81-3-35010463, JSASS@capj.or.jp, http://tjsass.jstage.jst.go.jp, http://www.jsass.or.jp/web/.

➤ **JOINT AVIATION AUTHORITIES. CERTIFICATION INFORMATION - PROCEDURES.** see *TRANSPORTATION—Air Transport*

➤ **JOINT AVIATION AUTHORITIES. GENERAL INFORMATION - PROCEDURES. INFORMATION LEAFLETS.** see *TRANSPORTATION—Air Transport*

➤ **JOINT AVIATION AUTHORITIES. MAINTENANCE INFORMATION - PROCEDURES.** see *TRANSPORTATION—Air Transport*

➤ **JOINT AVIATION AUTHORITIES. NOTICE OF PROPOSED AMENDMENT SCHEME.** see *TRANSPORTATION—Air Transport*

➤ **JOINT AVIATION AUTHORITIES. REGULATORY DOCUMENTS.** see *TRANSPORTATION—Air Transport*

629.1325   USA
JONATHAN'S SPACE REPORT. Text in English. 1989. w. free. back issues avail.
Media: Online - full content.
Published by: Harvard-Smithsonian Center for Astrophysics, 60 Garden St, MS 6, Cambridge, MA 02138. jmcdowell@cfa.harvard.edu, http://hea-www.harvard.edu/QEDT/jcm/space/jsr/jsr.html. Ed. Jonathan McDowell.

001.942   DEU   ISSN 0723-7766
JOURNAL FUER U F O - FORSCHUNG. Text in German; Summaries in English. 1980. bi-m. EUR 21; EUR 3.50 newsstand/cover (effective 2005). adv. bk.rev. **Document type:** *Magazine, Consumer.*
Published by: Gesellschaft zur Erforschung des U F O - Phaenomens - G E P e.V., Luisenstr 4, Luedenscheid, 58511, Germany. TEL 49-2351-23377, FAX 49-2351-23335, jufof@ufo-forschung.de, info@ufo-forschung.de, http://www.jufof.de, http://gep.alien.de. Ed. Hans-Werner Peiniger. Circ: 400.

629.1   USA   ISSN 1542-9423
▼ **JOURNAL OF AEROSPACE COMPUTING, INFORMATION, AND COMMUNICATION.** Text in English. 2004 (Jan.). irreg. USD 380 to non-members; USD 40 to members (effective 2006).
Media: Online - full content.
Indexed: C&ISA, E&CAJ, IAA.
Published by: American Institute of Aeronautics and Astronautics, Inc., 1801 Alexander Bell Dr, Ste 500, Reston, VA 20191. TEL 703-264-7500, FAX 703-264-7551, custserv@aiaa.org, http://www.aiaa.org/jacic/index.cfm. Ed. Lyle N. Long.

JOURNAL OF AEROSPACE ENGINEERING. see *ENGINEERING—Civil Engineering*

629.13   IND
TL504   CODEN: JANIAK
JOURNAL OF AEROSPACE SCIENCES AND TECHNOLOGIES. Text in English. 1949. q. INR 400 domestic; USD 105 foreign (effective 2005). adv. bk.rev. index. **Document type:** *Academic/Scholarly.*
Formerly (until 2004): Aeronautical Society of India. Journal (0001-9267)
Indexed: ApMecR, C&ISA, CivEngAb, CorrAb, E&CAJ, EMA, EngInd, IAA, Inspec, M&TEA, METADEX, SolStAb, WAA.
—BLDSC (4919.700000), CISTI, Ei, IE, Infotrieve, ingenta, Linda Hall.
Published by: (Aeronautical Society of India), H P C Publishers Distributors Pvt. Ltd., 4805 Bharat Ram Rd, 24 Darya Ganj, New Delhi, 110 002, India. TEL 91-11-23254401, FAX 91-11-23274405, hpc@vsnl.com, hpcpd@hpc.cc. Ed. P J Lalvani. Circ: 1,800.

387.7   USA   ISSN 0021-8650
TL725.3.T7
JOURNAL OF AIR TRAFFIC CONTROL. Text in English. 1958. q. USD 35 domestic to non-members; USD 45 foreign to non-members (effective 2005). adv. bk.rev.; film rev. charts; illus. index. back issues avail. **Document type:** *Magazine, Trade.* **Description:** Dedicated to the progress in the art and science of air traffic control.
Indexed: BrCerAb, C&ISA, CLT&T, CerAb, CivEngAb, CorrAb, E&CAJ, EMA, ESPM, H&SSA, HRIS, IAA, M&TEA, MBF, METADEX, SolStAb, WAA.
—IE, Infotrieve, Linda Hall.
Published by: Air Traffic Control Association, Inc., 1101 King St, Ste 300, Arlington, VA 22314-2944. TEL 703-299-2430, FAX 703-299-2437, info@atca.org, http://www.atca.org/static2_item.asp?item_ID=24,17. Ed. Suzette Matthews. Adv. contact Judy Gibbons. color page USD 3,000, B&W page USD 1,800. Circ: 4,000 (paid).

JOURNAL OF AIR TRANSPORTATION. see *TRANSPORTATION*

629.13   USA   ISSN 0021-8669
TL501   CODEN: JAIRAM
➤ **JOURNAL OF AIRCRAFT**; devoted to aeronautical science and technology. Text in English. 1963. bi-m. USD 715 in North America to non-members; USD 775 elsewhere to non-members; USD 825 combined subscription in North America to non-members print & online eds.; USD 890 combined subscription elsewhere to non-members print & online eds.; USD 60 combined subscription in North America to members print & online eds.; USD 90 combined subscription elsewhere to members print & online eds. (effective 2006). charts; illus. index. reprint service avail. from PQC. **Document type:** *Journal, Academic/Scholarly.*
Description: Covers advanced design concepts and operating advances in aircraft. Papers on military and civilian aircraft, ground effect machines, V/STOL and supersonic and hypersonic aircraft, with emphasis on practical engineering.
Related titles: Microform ed.: (from PQC); Online - full content ed.: ISSN 1533-3868. USD 730 to non-members; USD 65 to members (effective 2006); Online - full text ed.: (from EBSCO Publishing, Gale Group).
Indexed: AS&TI, ASCA, ApMecR, BrCerAb, C&ISA, CerAb, CivEngAb, CorrAb, CurCont, E&CAJ, EMA, EngInd, H&SSA, IAA, ISMEC, ISR, Inspec, M&GPA, M&TEA, MBF, METADEX, RefZh, S&VD, SCI, SolStAb, WAA.
—BLDSC (4926.700000), CISTI, Ei, IDS, IE, Infotrieve, ingenta, Linda Hall. **CCC.**
Published by: American Institute of Aeronautics and Astronautics, Inc., 1801 Alexander Bell Dr, Ste 500, Reston, VA 20191. TEL 703-264-7500, FAX 703-264-7551, custserv@aiaa.org, http://www.aiaa.org/publications/index.hfm?pub=5&lupublicationid=22. Ed. Thomas M Weeks. Adv. contacts Howard O'Brien, Terry Stoneberg. Circ: 30,000 (paid).

629.4   USA   ISSN 0021-9142
                                        CODEN: JALSA6
➤ **JOURNAL OF ASTRONAUTICAL SCIENCES.** Text in English. 1954. q. USD 160 domestic; USD 180 foreign (effective 2005). illus.; charts; stat. cum.index: 1954-1979. 200 p./no. 1 cols./p.; back issues avail.; reprints avail. **Document type:** *Journal, Academic/Scholarly.*
Related titles: Microfilm ed.
Indexed: AS&TI, ASCA, BrCerAb, C&ISA, CCMJ, CerAb, CivEngAb, CorrAb, CurCont, E&CAJ, EMA, ESPM, EngInd, H&SSA, IAA, ISR, Inspec, M&GPA, M&TEA, MBF, METADEX, MathR, MathSciNet, RefZh, SCI, SolStAb, WAA.
—BLDSC (4947.450000), AskIEEE, CISTI, Ei, IDS, IE, Infotrieve, ingenta, Linda Hall. **CCC.**
Published by: American Astronautical Society (Springfield), 6352 Rolling Mill Place, Ste 102, Springfield, VA 22152-2354. TEL 703-866-0020, FAX 703-866-3526, aas@astronautical.org, http://www.astronautical.org. Ed. Kathleen Howell. Circ: 1,800.

387.7   USA   ISSN 1065-1136
➤ **JOURNAL OF AVIATION-AEROSPACE EDUCATION & RESEARCH.** Text in English. 3/yr. **Document type:** *Journal, Academic/Scholarly.*
Indexed: BrCerAb, C&ISA, CerAb, CorrAb, E&CAJ, EMA, IAA, M&TEA, MBF, METADEX, SolStAb, WAA.
—BLDSC (4949.980000), IE, ingenta, Linda Hall.
Published by: Embry-Riddle Aeronautical University, 600 S Clyde Morris Blvd, Daytona Beach, FL 32114. TEL 386-226-6986, FAX 386-226-6299, http://www.erau.edu/er/faculty/jaaer/. Ed. William Kohlruss.

➤ **JOURNAL OF FLOW VISUALIZATION AND IMAGE PROCESSING.** see *ENGINEERING—Mechanical Engineering*

629.1   USA   ISSN 0731-5090
TL676   CODEN: JGCODS
➤ **JOURNAL OF GUIDANCE, CONTROL, AND DYNAMICS**; devoted to the technology of dynamics and control. Text in English. 1978. bi-m. USD 730 in North America to institutions; USD 790 elsewhere to institutions; USD 840 combined subscription in North America to institutions print & online eds.; USD 910 combined subscription elsewhere to institutions print & online eds.; USD 65 combined subscription in North America to members print & online eds.; USD 95 combined subscription elsewhere to members print & online eds. (effective 2006). bk.rev. charts; illus. index. back issues avail. **Document type:** *Journal, Academic/Scholarly.* **Description:** Covers dynamics, guidance, control, navigation, optimization, electronics, and information processing related to aeronautical and astronautical systems. Focuses on technical knowledge, exploratory developments, design criteria, and applications.
Formerly: Journal of Guidance and Control (0162-3192)
Related titles: Microform ed.; Online - full text ed.: ISSN 1533-3884. USD 730 to non-members; USD 65 to members (effective 2006) (from EBSCO Publishing, Gale Group).
Indexed: AS&TI, ASCA, ApMecR, BrCerAb, C&ISA, CMCI, CerAb, CivEngAb, CorrAb, CurCont, E&CAJ, EMA, ESPM, EngInd, H&SSA, IAA, ISMEC, ISR, Inspec, M&TEA, MBF, METADEX, RefZh, SCI, SolStAb, WAA, ZentMath.
—BLDSC (4996.561000), AskIEEE, CISTI, Ei, IDS, IE, Infotrieve, ingenta, Linda Hall. **CCC.**
Published by: American Institute of Aeronautics and Astronautics, Inc., 1801 Alexander Bell Dr, Ste 500, Reston, VA 20191. TEL 703-264-7500, FAX 703-264-7551, custserv@aiaa.org, http://www.aiaa.org/publications/index.hfm?pub=5&lupublicationid=23. Ed. George T Schmidt. Pub. Cort Durocher. Adv. contact Howard O'Brien. Circ: 2,200 (paid).

➤ **JOURNAL OF NAVIGATION.** see *TRANSPORTATION—Ships And Shipping*

629.1   USA   ISSN 0748-4658
TL780   CODEN: JPPOEL
➤ **JOURNAL OF PROPULSION AND POWER**; devoted to aerospace propulsion and power. Text in English. 1985. bi-m. USD 790 domestic to non-members; USD 850 foreign to non-members; USD 910 combined subscription domestic to non-members print & online eds.; USD 980 combined subscription foreign to non-members print & online eds.; USD 55 combined subscription domestic to members print & online eds.; USD 85 combined subscription foreign to members print & online eds. (effective 2006). charts; illus. index. back issues avail. **Document type:** *Journal, Academic/Scholarly.* **Description:** Covers advances in airbreathing electric and exotic propulsion, solid and liquid rockets, fuels and propellants, power generation, and the application of aerospace technology to terrestrial energy systems.
Related titles: Microform ed.; Online - full text ed.: ISSN 1533-3876. USD 790 to non-members; USD 55 to members (effective 2006) (from EBSCO Publishing, Gale Group).
Indexed: ASCA, ASFA, ApMecR, BrCerAb, C&ISA, CIN, CMCI, CerAb, ChemAb, ChemTitl, CivEngAb, CorrAb, CurCont, E&CAJ, EMA, ESPM, EngInd, H&SSA, IAA, ISMEC, ISR, M&TEA, MBF, METADEX, MSB, SCI, SolStAb, WAA.
—BLDSC (5042.795000), CASDDS, CISTI, Ei, IDS, IE, Infotrieve, ingenta, Linda Hall. **CCC.**
Published by: American Institute of Aeronautics and Astronautics, Inc., 1801 Alexander Bell Dr, Ste 500, Reston, VA 20191. TEL 703-264-7500, FAX 703-264-7551, custserv@aiaa.org, http://www.aiaa.org. Ed. Vigor Yang. Circ: 1,600 (paid).

629.1 330   USA   ISSN 1529-353X
➤ **JOURNAL OF SPACE COMMERCE.** Text in English. 2000. a. **Document type:** *Academic/Scholarly.*
Media: Online - full content.
Published by: Institute for Advanced Interdisciplinary Research, Box 591351, Houston, TX 77259-1351. http://www.systems.org/HTML/scommerce/default.htm.

➤ **JOURNAL OF SPACE LAW.** see *LAW—International Law*

629.1   JPN   ISSN 0911-551X
                                        CODEN: JSTSF7
JOURNAL OF SPACE TECHNOLOGY AND SCIENCE. Text in English. 2/yr. USD 50. **Document type:** *Academic/Scholarly.*
Indexed: C&ISA, CivEngAb, E&CAJ, IAA.
—CISTI, Linda Hall.
Published by: Japanese Rocket Society/Nihon Roketto Kyokai, c/o Business Center for Academic Societies Japan, 5-16-9 Honkomagome, Bunkyo-ku, Tokyo, 113-0021, Japan. TEL 81-3-5814-5811, FAX 81-3-5814-5822, TELEX 2722268 BCJSP. Ed. Yoshiaki Ohkami.

629.13 USA ISSN 0022-4650
TL787.A62 CODEN: JSCRAG
➤ **JOURNAL OF SPACECRAFT AND ROCKETS**; devoted to astronautical science and technology. Text in English. 1964. bi-m. USD 680 domestic to institutions; USD 740 foreign to institutions; USD 780 combined subscription domestic to institutions print & online eds.; USD 850 combined subscription foreign to institutions print & online eds.; USD 55 combined subscription domestic to members print & online eds.; USD 85 combined subscription foreign to members print & online eds. (effective 2006). charts; illus. index. reprint service avail. from PQC. **Document type:** *Journal, Academic/Scholarly.* **Description:** Advancement of the science and technology related to spacecraft and missile systems and their associated missions and performance through the dissemination of original archival papers describing significant advances in space sciences, and the application of space technology to other fields.
Related titles: Microform ed.: (from PQC); Online - full text ed.: ISSN 1533-6794. USD 680 to institutions; USD 55 to members (effective 2006) (from EBSCO Publishing, Gale Group, IngentaConnect).
Indexed: AS&TI, ASCA, ApMecR, BrCerAb, C&ISA, CIN, Cadscan, CerAb, ChemAb, ChemTitl, CivEngAb, CorrAb, CurCont, E&CAJ, EMA, ESPM, Englnd, H&SSA, IAA, ISMEC, ISR, Inspec, LeadAb, M&TEA, MBF, METADEX, MSB, RefZh, S&VD, SCI, SolStAb, WAA, Zincscan.
—BLDSC (5066.100000), CASDDS, CISTI, Ei, IDS, IE, Infotrieve, ingenta, Linda Hall. **CCC.**
Published by: American Institute of Aeronautics and Astronautics, Inc., 1801 Alexander Bell Dr, Ste 500, Reston, VA 20191. TEL 703-264-7500, FAX 703-264-7551, custserv@aiaa.org, http://www.aiaa.org/publications/jornals/spacecraft-scope.html. Ed. E Vincent Zoby. Circ: 2,200 (paid).

629.13 IND ISSN 0971-1600
TL795
JOURNAL OF SPACECRAFT TECHNOLOGY. Text in English. 1991. s-a. **Description:** Devoted exclusively to research and development in the field of spacecraft technology and is meant for circulation amongst the professionals in the field.
Indexed: BrCerAb, C&ISA, CerAb, CivEngAb, CorrAb, E&CAJ, EMA, IAA, Inspec, M&GPA, M&TEA, MBF, METADEX, SolStAb, WAA.
—BLDSC (5066.103000), CISTI, IE, Infotrieve, ingenta, Linda Hall.
Published by: Indian Space Research Organisation Satellite Centre, Library & Documentation, Airport Rd, Vimanapura Post, Bangalore, 560 017, India. TEL 91-80-5083413, FAX 91-80-5083403, info@isro.org, jst@isac.ernet.in, http://www.isro.org.

629.1 CHN ISSN 1671-1793
➤ **JOURNAL OF SYSTEMS ENGINEERING AND ELECTRONICS.** Text in English. 1979. q. CNY 160 (effective 2004). **Document type:** *Journal, Academic/Scholarly.* **Description:** Covers academic exchanges in the field of high technology, and technological developments relevant to China's space undertaking.
Former titles: Chinese Journal of Systems Engineering and Electronics (1004-4132)
Related titles: Online - full content ed.: (from WanFang Data Corp.); Online - full text ed.: (from East View Information Services); ♦ Chinese ed.: Xitong Gongcheng yu Dianzi Jishu. ISSN 1001-506X.
Indexed: BrCerAb, C&ISA, CerAb, CorrAb, E&CAJ, EMA, Englnd, IAA, Inspec, M&TEA, MBF, METADEX, WAA.
—BLDSC (5068.073510), AskIEEE, CISTI, Ei.
Published by: (Ministry of Aero-Space Industry), Kexue Chubanshe/Science Press, 16 Donghuang Cheng Genbei Jie, Beijing, 100717, China. TEL 86-10-64000246, FAX 86-10-64030255, http://www.sciencep.com/. Ed. Dingchang Chen. **Dist. by:** China International Book Trading Corp, 35 Chegongzhuang Xilu, Haidian District, PO Box 399, Beijing 100044, China. TEL 86-10-68412045, FAX 86-10-68412023, cibtc@mail.cibtc.com.cn, http://www.cibtc.com.cn.

001.94 USA ISSN 0730-5478
TL789.A1
JOURNAL OF U F O STUDIES. Text in English. 1979-1983; N.S. 1989. a. USD 21. bk.rev. bibl.; illus.
Published by: Center for U F O Studies, 2457 W Peterson Ave, Ste 6, Chicago, IL 60659-4118. TEL 312-271-3611. Ed. Stuart Appelle. Circ: 500.

KEPLERIAN ELEMENTS. see *COMMUNICATIONS—Radio*

629.1 GBR ISSN 1366-042X
KEY NOTE MARKET REPORT: AEROSPACE. Variant title: Aerospace. Text in English. irreg., latest 1988, Dec. GBP 340 per issue (effective 2002). **Document type:** *Trade.* **Description:** Provides an overview of a specific UK market segment and includes executive summary, market definition, market size, industry background, competitor analysis, current issues, forecasts, company profiles, and more.
Formerly (until 1996): Key Note Report: Aerospace (0954-8262)
Related titles: CD-ROM ed.; Online - full text ed.
Published by: Key Note Ltd., Field House, 72 Oldfield Rd, Hampton, Mddx TW12 2HQ, United Kingdom. TEL 44-20-8481-8750, FAX 44-20-8783-0049, info@keynote.co.uk, http://www.keynote.co.uk. Ed. Phillippa Smith.

KISHO EISEI SENTA GIJUTSU HOKOKU/METEOROLOGICAL SATELLITE CENTER TECHNICAL NOTE. see *METEOROLOGY*

KISHO EISEI SENTA NYUSU/METEOROLOGICAL SATELLITE CENTER NEWS. see *METEOROLOGY*

629.132 745.5 USA ISSN 0891-1851
KITPLANES; the independent voice for homebuilt aviation. Text in English. 1984. m. USD 29.95 domestic; USD 41.95 foreign (effective 2006). adv. illus. 100 p./no.; reprints avail. **Document type:** *Magazine, Consumer.* **Description:** Provides tips and other information to persons interested in designing, building and flying their own aircraft. Covers theory, practical application, how-to, and in-flight reports.
Related titles: Online - full text ed.: (from Gale Group).
Indexed: IHTDI.
—CCC.
Published by: (Kitplanes Acquisitions Co.), Aviation Publishing Group, PO Box 65656, Greenwich, CT 06856. TEL 203-661-6111, editorial@kitplanes.com, http://www.kitplanes.com. Eds. Brian Clark, Marc Cook. Pub. Cindy Pedersen. adv.: B&W page USD 4,170, color page USD 6,290. Circ: 70,000 (paid).

629.132 ISR ISSN 0792-4836
K'NAFAYIM. Text in Hebrew. 1988. q. membership. adv. bk.rev.
Formerly: Termica
Published by: Aero Club of Israel, P O Box 26261, Tel Aviv, 63432, Israel. TEL 972-3-5175038, FAX 972-3-5177280. Ed. Arik Sinai. Circ: 6,000.

629.1 JPN ISSN 0023-284X
KOKU GIJUTSU/AIRCRAFT ENGINEERING. Text in Japanese. 1955. m. JPY 9,960. adv. bk.rev. cum.index. **Document type:** *Academic/Scholarly.*
—BLDSC (1838.220000), CISTI, Linda Hall. **CCC.**
Published by: Nihon Koku Gijutsu Kyokai/Japan Aeronautical Engineers' Association, 1-6-6 Haneda Airport, Ota-ku, Tokyo, 144-0041, Japan. TEL 81-3-3747-7600, FAX 81-3-3747-7570, jaeam@mx2.alpha-web.ne.jp, http://www.jaea.or.jp/. Ed. T Yamaguchi. Circ: 20,000.

KOKU KISHO NOTO/ABSTRACTS IN AVIATION METEOROLOGY. see *METEOROLOGY—Abstracting, Bibliographies, Statistics*

629.13 JPN ISSN 0389-4010
KOKU UCHU GIJUTSU KENKYUJO HOKOKU/NATIONAL AEROSPACE LABORATORY. TECHNICAL REPORT. Text in English, Japanese. 1963. irreg.
Formerly: Koku Gijutsu Kenkyujo Hokoku (0452-294X)
Indexed: RefZh.
—BLDSC (8717.410000), CISTI.
Published by: Kagaku Gijutsucho Koku Uchu Gijutsu Kenkyujo/National Aerospace Laboratory, 7-44-1 Jindaiji-Higashi-Machi, Chofu-shi, Tokyo-to 182-0012, Japan. TEL 81-422-40-3081, FAX 81-422-40-3008.

629.13 JPN ISSN 0289-260X
KOKU UCHU GIJUTSU KENKYUJO TOKUBETSU SHIRYO/NATIONAL AEROSPACE LABORATORY. SPECIAL PUBLICATION. Text in English, Japanese. 1983. irreg.
—BLDSC (8379.490000), CISTI.
Published by: Kagaku Gijutsucho Koku Uchu Gijutsu Kenkyujo/National Aerospace Laboratory, 7-44-1 Jindaiji-Higashi-Machi, Chofu-shi, Tokyo-to 182-0012, Japan. TEL 81-422-40-3081, FAX 81-422-40-3008.

629.1 CHN ISSN 0254-6124
QB495 CODEN: KKXUDK
➤ **KONGJIAN KEXUE XUEBAO/CHINESE JOURNAL OF SPACE SCIENCE.** Text in Chinese; Summaries in English. 1981. bi-m. CNY 60 (effective 2004). adv. **Document type:** *Journal, Academic/Scholarly.* **Description:** Deals with various aspects of space sciences, including physics, chemistry, astrophysics, geology, medicine, and biology in space, space material science, space sensing, space probing technology, and analysis of space observations.
Related titles: Online - full text ed.: (from East View Information Services); ♦ Partial translation of: Chinese Astronomy and Astrophysics. ISSN 0275-1062.
Indexed: Inspec, RefZh.
—AskIEEE, CASDDS, Linda Hall.
Published by: Kexue Chubanshe/Science Press, 16 Donghuang Cheng Genbei Jie, Beijing, 100717, China. TEL 86-10-64000246, FAX 86-10-64030255, http://www.sciencep.com/. Circ: 6,000. **Dist. by:** China International Book Trading Corp, 35 Chegongzhuang Xilu, Haidian District, PO Box 399, Beijing 100044, China. TEL 86-10-68412045, FAX 86-10-68412023, cibtc@mail.cibtc.com.cn, http://www.cibtc.com.cn.

629.4 RUS ISSN 0023-4206
QB500 CODEN: KOISAW
KOSMICHESKIE ISSLEDOVANIYA. Text in Russian. 1963. bi-m. USD 228 foreign (effective 2005). bk.rev. index. **Document type:** *Journal, Academic/Scholarly.* **Description:** Covers physical phenomena in outer space.
Related titles: Online - full text ed.; ♦ English Translation: Cosmic Research. ISSN 0010-9525.
Indexed: BiolAb, CIN, ChemAb, ChemTitl, CivEngAb, IAA, Inspec, M&TEA, MSB, RefZh.
—BLDSC (0092.540000), AskIEEE, CASDDS, CISTI, East View, Linda Hall. **CCC.**
Published by: (Rossiiskaya Akademiya Nauk/Russian Academy of Sciences), Izdatel'stvo Nauka, Profsoyuznaya ul 90, Moscow, 117864, Russian Federation. TEL 7-095-3347151, FAX 7-095-4202220, secret@naukaran.ru, http://www.maik.ru/cgi-bin/list.pl?page=kosiss, http://www.naukaran.ru. **Dist. by:** M K - Periodica, ul Gilyarovskogo 39, Moscow 129110, Russian Federation. TEL 7-095-2845008, FAX 7-095-2813798, info@periodicals.ru, http://www.mkniga.ru.

629.13 RUS ISSN 0130-2701
TL504
KRYL'YA RODINY/WINGS OF THE MOTHERLAND. Text in Russian. 1950. m. USD 99.95. bk.rev. bibl.; illus.
Related titles: Microfiche ed.: (from EVP); Online - full text ed.: (from East View Information Services).
Indexed: BrCerAb, CerAb, CivEngAb, CorrAb, EMA, IAA, M&TEA, MBF, METADEX, RefZh, WAA.
—East View, Linda Hall.
Published by: Rossiiskaya Oboronnaya Sportivno-Tekhnicheskaya Organizatsiya, Novoryazanskaya ul 26, Moscow, 107066, Russian Federation. TEL 7-095-2616890, FAX 7-095-2676545. Ed. A I Krikunenko. Circ: 80,000. **US dist. addr.:** East View Information Services, 3020 Harbor Ln. N., Minneapolis, MN 55447. TEL 612-550-0961.

629.13 SWE ISSN 0280-1078
KUNGLIGA TEKNISKA HOEGSKOLAN. FLYGTEKNISK INSTITUTIONEN. K T H AERO MEMO F I. Text in English, Swedish. 1948. irreg. **Document type:** *Monographic series.*
—CISTI.
Published by: Kungliga Tekniska Hoegskolan, Institutionen foer Flygteknik/Royal Institute of Technology, Division of Aeronautics, Stockholm, 10784, Sweden. Circ: 35.

629.13 USA
LANDINGS.COM. Text in English. 1994. d. adv.
Media: Online - full content.
Address: 6280 S. Valley View Blvd., Ste. 314, Las Vegas, NV 89118 . landings@landings.com, landings-ops@landings.com, http://www.landings.com/.

629.4 USA
LAUNCHSPACE. Text in English. 1997. bi-m. adv. **Document type:** *Bulletin, Trade.* **Description:** Trade publication that reaches the entire group of engineers, scientists and other technical professionals that make up the space industry.
Related titles: Online - full text ed.
Indexed: IAA.
Published by: Launchspace Publications, 2206 Bryant St, San Francisco, CA 94110. TEL 703-749-2324, josh@newspace.com, http://www.launchspace.com. Ed. Joshua Cohen. Adv. contact Ryan Kraven. Circ: 80,000 (controlled).

629.13092 USA ISSN 0274-9319
KF2400.A15
LAWYER - PILOTS BAR ASSOCIATION JOURNAL. Key Title: L P B A Journal. Text in English. 1959. q. USD 55. bk.rev. illus. index. **Description:** Covers legal aspects of aeronautics, aviation law and regulations, product liability and aviation safety.
Formerly (until 1980): Legal Eagles News (0024-0354)
Published by: Lawyer - Pilots Bar Association, c/o Yodice Associates, 500 E St SW Ste 930, Washington, DC 20024. TEL 202-863-1000, FAX 202-484-1312. Ed. Jacob I Rosenbaum. Circ: 1,600.

629.13 USA
LEADING EDGE (OJAI). Text in English. d. adv. **Description:** Covers the leading edge of aviation, space and defense technology news.
Media: Online - full text.
Address: P O Box 1748, Ojai, CA 93024-1748. TEL 805-639-7901, FAX 805-646-0315, editor@AeroSpaceNews.com, http://www.AeroSpaceNews.com/. Ed., Pub. Craig Schmitman.

LEADING EDGE (WRIGHT-PATTERSON AIR FORCE BASE). see *MILITARY*

629.13 CZE ISSN 1211-877X
➤ **LETECKY ZPRAVODAJ.** Text in Czech; Summaries in English. 1957. q. USD 12 (effective 2001); or exchange basis (effective 2001). charts; illus. back issues avail. **Document type:** *Journal, Academic/Scholarly.* **Description:** Publishes articles about building and testing of aircraft and their parts and research on aviation.
Formerly (until 1997): V Z L U Zpravodaj (0044-5355)
Related titles: Microform ed.
Indexed: CivEngAb, IAA.
—CISTI, Linda Hall.
Published by: Vyzkumny a Zkusebni Letecky Ustav, Beranovych 130, Letnany, Prague 9, 199 05, Czech Republic. TEL 42-2-72115223, FAX 42-2-86920518, TELEX 121893. Ed. Ladislav Vymetal TEL 42-2-72115223. Circ: 200.

▼ new title ➤ refereed ✶ unverified ♦ full entry avail.

A

629.13 CZE ISSN 0024-1156
TL504
LETECTVI A KOSMONAUTIKA; polularne odborny ctrnactidenik. Text in Czech. 1921. fortn. CZK 109, USD 50.60 (effective 1996). adv. bk.rev.
Formerly: Kridla Vlasti
—IE, Infotrieve.
Published by: (Aeroklub), Vydavatelstvi Magnet Press, Vladislavova 26, Prague, 11366, Czech Republic. TEL 42-2-24239435, FAX 42-2-261226. Ed. Josef Fryha. Circ: 58,000.

629.132 USA ISSN 0278-8950
TL671.9
LIGHT PLANE MAINTENANCE; the monthly maintenance report to pilots and aircraft owners. Text in English. 1987. m. USD 74 in US & Canada; USD 91 elsewhere (effective 2006). **Document type:** *Magazine, Consumer.* **Description:** Devoted to showing plane owners how to save money on maintenance, legally, by doing it themselves.
Indexed: IHTDI.
Published by: Belvoir Media Group, LLC, 800 Connecticut Ave, Norwalk, CT 06854-1631. TEL 203-857-3100, 800-424-7887, FAX 203-857-3103, customer_service@belvoir.com, https://secure.palmcoastd.com/pcd/document?iMag_id=01057, http://www.belvoir.com. Ed. John Likokis.

629.1325 USA ISSN 0364-5282
LOCATION IDENTIFIERS. Text in English. triennial. USD 34 (effective 2001). **Document type:** *Government.* **Description:** Lists identifiers authorized by the Federal Aviation Administration, Department of the Navy, and Transport Canada. Also lists U.S. airspace fixes and procedure codes and includes guidelines for requesting identifiers and procedures for making assignments.
Related titles: Online - full text ed.: ISSN 1555-0540.
Published by: U.S. Federal Aviation Administration, 800 Independence Ave S W, Washington, DC 20591. http://www.faa.gov/ATpubs/LID/LIDHME.htm. **Subscr. to:** U.S. Government Printing Office, Superintendent of Documents, PO Box 371954, Pittsburgh, PA 15250-7954. TEL 202-512-1800, FAX 202-512-2250, orders@gpo.gov, http://www.access.gpo.gov.

387.72 GBR ISSN 0024-5798
TL501
LOG. Text in English. 1937. bi-m. GBP 14; GBP 22 foreign. adv. bk.rev. charts; illus. **Document type:** *Trade.*
Indexed: CLT&T, HRIS.
—Linda Hall.
Published by: British Air Line Pilots Association (B.A.L.P.A.), 81 New Rd, Harlington, Hayes, Mddx UB3 9BG, United Kingdom. TEL 44-181-476-4000, FAX 44-181-476-4077, TELEX 265871 MONREF G, ginaalexander@balpa.org.uk. Ed. I G Frow. Circ: 9,000.

629.13 USA
LOST BIRDS; discover aviation archaeology. Text in English. 1998. q. USD 19.95; USD 23.45 foreign (effective 2000). illus.; stat. back issues avail. **Document type:** *Consumer.* **Description:** Chronicles military and civilian aircraft lost to accidents or training.
Published by: Vision Entertainment, Inc., 3172 N Rainbow Blvd, 266, Las Vegas, NV 89108. TEL 888-502-4757, visionentr@aol.com, http://www.lostbirds.com.

629.1325 POL ISSN 1732-5323
LOTNICTWO. Text in Polish. 1998. m. EUR 56 foreign (effective 2005). **Document type:** *Journal.*
Formerly (until 2003): Lotnictwo Wojskowe (1505-1196)
Published by: Wydawnictwo Magnum-X, ul Skrajna 1/25, Warsaw, 03209, Poland. TEL 48-22-8103330. **Dist. by:** Ars Polona, Krakowskie Przedmiescie 7, Warsaw, Poland. TEL 48-22-9263914, FAX 48-22-9265334, arspolona@arspolona.com.pl, http://www.arspolona.com.pl.

629.13 NLD ISSN 1381-9100
LUCHTVAARTKENNIS; luchtvaarthistorisch tijdschrift. Text in Dutch. 1951. bi-m. looseleaf. bk.rev. bibl.; charts; illus. index. back issues avail. **Description:** Deals with Dutch aviation history, society and the Dutch branch of Air Britain.
Formerly (until 1987): Maandelijkse Mededelingen (1381-9119)
Published by: Kononklijke Nederlandse Vereniging voor Luchtvaart, Afdeling Luchtvaartkennis, Jozef Israelsplein 8, The Hague, 2596 AS, Netherlands. TEL 31-70-3245457, FAX 31-70-3240230. Ed. H J Hazewinkel. Circ: 300.

629.13 DEU ISSN 0173-6264
TL503
LUFT- UND RAUMFAHRT. Text in German. 1968. bi-m. EUR 27.60 domestic; EUR 32.40 foreign; EUR 4.60 newsstand/cover (effective 2005). adv. bk.rev. **Document type:** *Magazine, Trade.*
Formerly (until 1980): D G L R Mitteilungen (0418-8640)
Indexed: BrCerAb, C&ISA, CerAb, CivEngAb, CorrAb, E&CAJ, EMA, IAA, M&TEA, MBF, METADEX, RefZh, SolStAb, WAA. —CISTI, Linda Hall. **CCC.**
Published by: (Deutsche Gesellschaft fuer Luft- und Raumfahrt Lilienthal-Oberth e.V.), Aviatic Verlag GmbH, Kolpingring 16, Oberhaching, 82041, Germany. TEL 49-89-6138900, FAX 49-89-61389010, aviatic@aviatic.de, http://www.aviatic.de/luft/index.html. Ed. Peter Pletschacher. Circ: 4,000.

LUFTFAHRT JOURNAL. see *TRANSPORTATION—Air Transport*

797.5 DEU
LUFTSPORT; das Magazin fuer den Luftsport. Text in German. 1987. 9/yr. adv. **Document type:** *Magazine, Consumer.*
Published by: V L S - Verlag Luftsport GmbH, Postfach 100764, Duisburg, 47007, Germany. TEL 49-203-3639980, FAX 49-203-3639988, Verlag-Luftsport@t-online.de, http://www.magazin-luftsport.de. Adv. contact Heike Moeller TEL 49-203-36399820. B&W page EUR 2,480, color page EUR 3,902. Circ: 49,400 (controlled).

629.13 DEU ISSN 0015-3699
LUFTWAFFE*. Text in German. 1965. m. adv. bk.rev. illus. **Document type:** *Magazine, Government.*
Formerly: Fliegerkurier
Published by: A. Bernecker Verlag, Unter dem Schoeneberg 1, Melsungen, 34212, Germany. TEL 49-5661-7310, FAX 49-5661-731111, http://www.bernecke.de. Circ: 36,000.

629.132 USA ISSN 0199-5243
M A P A LOG MAGAZINE. Text in English. 1981 (vol.4). m. (except Oct.). free to members (effective 2003). adv. bk.rev. 64 p./no.
Published by: Mooney Aircraft Pilots Association, 149 Heimer Rd, Ste 560, San Antonio, TX 78232. TEL 210-525-8008, FAX 210-525-8085, http://www.mooneypilots.com.

001.942 USA
M U F O N - INTERNATIONAL U F O SYMPOSIUM PROCEEDINGS. Text in English. 1971. a. USD 25 (effective 2001). back issues avail. **Document type:** *Proceedings.*
—BLDSC (5981.940000).
Published by: Mutual U F O Network, Inc., c/o John Schnessler, PO Box 369, Morrison, CO 80465-0369. TEL 303-932-7709, FAX 303-932-9279, mufonhq@aol.com, http://www.mufon.com. Eds. Barbra H Maher Jr., Irena Scott. Adv. contact John Schnessler. Circ: 1,000.

001.94 USA ISSN 0270-6822
TL789.A1
M U F O N U F O JOURNAL. Text in English. 1967. m. USD 30 domestic; USD 35 foreign (effective 2001). adv. bk.rev. back issues avail.; reprints avail. **Document type:** *Bulletin.* **Description:** News and investigations of sightings of UFO phenomena.
Formerly: Skylook (0049-0687)
Indexed: MagInd.
Published by: Mutual U F O Network, Inc., c/o John Schnessler, PO Box 369, Morrison, CO 80465-0369. TEL 303-932-7709, FAX 303-932-9279, mufonhq@aol.com, http://www.mufon.com. Ed. Dwight Connelly. Circ: 4,000.

629.31 SWE ISSN 0280-8498
MACH. Text in Swedish. 1980. q. free (effective 2005). adv. bk.rev. back issues avail. **Document type:** *Trade.*
Media: Online - full text.
Address: PO Box 5002, Bromma, 16105, Sweden. FAX 46-8-178855, hakan.ahlstrom@mach-flyg.com, http://www.mach-flyg.com. Eds. Krister B Lundberg, Haakan Ahlstroem TEL 46-8-178855. R&P Haakan Ahlstroem TEL 46-8-178855.

629.1 ESP
MACH 82. Text in Spanish. 6/yr.
Published by: Spanish Union of Airline Pilots, Grl. Diaz Porlier 49, int. 4o, Madrid, 28001, Spain. TEL 1-402-28-35. Ed. J A Silva. Circ: 30,000.

629.133 USA ISSN 1543-8805
MALIBU MIRAGE. Running title: MMOPA(Malibu Mirage Owners and Pilots Association). Text in English. q. free to members (effective 2003).
Formerly: Malibu Mirage Owners and Pilots Association Newsletter
Published by: Malibu Mirage Owners and Pilots Association, P. O. Box 1288, Green Valley, AZ 85622. TEL 520-399-1121, FAX 520-648-3823, http://www.mmopa.com. Ed. Jeff Schweitzer.

MANDATORY AIRCRAFT MODIFICATIONS AND INSPECTIONS SUMMARY. see *TRANSPORTATION—Air Transport*

629.44 520 AUS
MARDAILY. Text in English. d. **Document type:** *Academic/Scholarly.* **Description:** Covers the latest news and developments in man's exploration of Mars, the technologies involved, and the latest scientific advancements and research.
Media: Online - full content.
Published by: Space Daily, PO Box A447, Sydney South, NSW 2000, Australia. TEL 61-2-9360-2257, simon@spacer.com, http://www.spacedaily.com/.

MARITIME COMMAND TRIDENT. see *MILITARY*

MARKET INTELLIGENCE REPORTS: AIRBORNE ELECTRONICS FORECAST. see *ELECTRONICS*

629.1 USA
MARKET INTELLIGENCE REPORTS: AIRBORNE RETROFIT AND MODERNIZATION FORECAST. Text in English. base vol. plus m. updates. looseleaf. USD 1,585 (effective 2003). abstr.; charts; illus.; mkt.; stat. back issues avail. **Document type:** *Trade.* **Description:** Highlights military and commercial aircraft business opportunities; analyzes airframes, propulsion, electronics, avionics and armaments as funded or speculative R&M projects.
Formerly: D M S Market Intelligence Reports: Airborne Retrofit and Modernization Forecast
Related titles: CD-ROM ed.: USD 1,525 (effective 2001); Online - full content ed.: USD 1,695 (effective 2001).
Published by: Forecast International/D M S, 22 Commerce Rd, Newtown, CT 06470. TEL 203-426-0800, FAX 203-426-0223, info@forecast1.com, sales@forecast1.com, http://www.forecast1.com. Eds. Bill Dane, Ray Jaworowski. R&P Ray Peterson.

355 USA ISSN 0194-469X
MARKET INTELLIGENCE REPORTS: AIRCRAFT FORECAST, CIVIL AND MILITARY. Text in English. base vol. plus m. updates. looseleaf. USD 1,785 (effective 2005). back issues avail. **Description:** Provides analysis of military, commercial, business and general aviation aircraft programs (including many in Russia, Eastern Europe and China). Includes a 10-year forecast.
Formerly: D M S Market Intelligence Reports: Aircraft Forecast, Civil and Military
Related titles: CD-ROM ed.: USD 1,625 (effective 2001); Online - full content ed.: USD 1,795 (effective 2001).
—**CCC.**
Published by: Forecast International/D M S, 22 Commerce Rd, Newtown, CT 06470. TEL 203-426-0800, FAX 203-426-0223, info@forecast1.com, sales@forecast1.com, https://www.forecast1.com/fistore/prod.cfm?ProductID=1, http://www.forecast1.com. Eds. Bill Dane, Ray Jaworowski. R&P Ray Peterson.

MARKET INTELLIGENCE REPORTS: ANTI-SUBMARINE WARFARE FORECAST. see *MILITARY*

355 USA
MARKET INTELLIGENCE REPORTS: CIVIL AIRCRAFT FORECAST. Text in English. base vol. plus m. updates. looseleaf. USD 1,585 (effective 2003). abstr.; charts; illus.; mkt.; stat. back issues avail. **Document type:** *Trade.* **Description:** Reports on the worldwide commercial aircraft market, such as large and regional transports, bizjets, rotorcraft and general aviation aircraft, with 10-year forecasts.
Formerly: D M S Market Intelligence Reports: Civil Aircraft Forecast
Related titles: CD-ROM ed.: USD 1,525 (effective 2001); Online - full content ed.: USD 1,695 (effective 2001).
Published by: Forecast International/D M S, 22 Commerce Rd, Newtown, CT 06470. TEL 203-426-0800, FAX 203-426-0223, info@forecast1.com, sales@forecast1.com, http://www.forecast1.com. Eds. Bill Dane, Ray Jaworowski. R&P Ray Peterson.

MARKET INTELLIGENCE REPORTS: DEFENSE & AEROSPACE COMPANIES. see *MILITARY*

MARKET INTELLIGENCE REPORTS: FOREIGN MILITARY MARKETS: N A T O & EUROPE. see *MILITARY*

MARKET INTELLIGENCE REPORTS: MILITARY AIRCRAFT FORECAST. see *MILITARY*

MARKET INTELLIGENCE REPORTS: MISSILE FORECAST. see *MILITARY*

MARKET INTELLIGENCE REPORTS: SPACE SYSTEMS FORECAST. see *MILITARY*

629.1 USA
MARKET INTELLIGENCE REPORTS: WORLD AIRLINE MAINTENANCE FORECAST. Text in English. base vol. plus q. updates. looseleaf. USD 1,685 (effective 2003). abstr.; charts; illus.; mkt.; stat. **Document type:** *Trade.* **Description:** Provides a 10-year forecast of the demand for transport aircraft maintenance by region, worldwide.
Formerly: D M S Market Intelligence Reports: World Airline Maintenance Forecast
Published by: Forecast International/D M S, 22 Commerce Rd, Newtown, CT 06470. TEL 203-426-0800, FAX 203-426-0223, info@forecast1.com, sales@forecast1.com, http://www.forecast1.com. Ed., R&P Ray Peterson.

629.1 USA
MARKET INTELLIGENCE REPORTS: WORLD COMMERCIAL AIRCRAFT - ENGINE ORDERS & OPTIONS. Text in English. base vol. plus q. updates. looseleaf. USD 1,235 (effective 2003). abstr.; charts; illus.; mkt.; stat. **Document type:** *Trade.* **Description:** Lists all available orders and options for commercial transport aircraft worldwide.
Formerly: D M S Market Intelligence Reports: World Commercial Aircraft - Engine Orders & Options

Published by: Forecast International/D M S, 22 Commerce Rd, Newtown, CT 06470. TEL 203-426-0800, FAX 203-426-0223, info@forecast1.com, sales@forecast1.com, http://www.forecast1.com. Eds. Bill Dane, Ray Jaworowski. R&P Ray Peterson.

629.1325   USA
MARTIAN CHRONICLE. Text in English. 1995. s-a.
Media: Online - full content.
Published by: Jet Propulsion Laboratory, California Institute of Technology, National Aeronautics and Space Administration, 4800 Oak Grove Rd, Pasadena, CA 91109. TEL 818-354-4321, http://www.jpl.nasa.gov/marshron. Ed. Stephen J Edberg.

629.1   USA
MASSACHUSETTS INSTITUTE OF TECHNOLOGY. FLIGHT TRANSPORTATION LABORATORY. F T L REPORTS AND MEMORANDA. Text in English. 1966. irreg. price varies. charts; illus.
Formerly: Massachusetts Institute of Technology. Flight Transportation Laboratory. F T L Reports
Published by: (Flight Transportation Laboratory), Massachusetts Institute of Technology, Department of Aeronautics and Astronautics, Rm 33 412, Cambridge, MA 02139. TEL 617-253-2424. Ed. Robert W Simpson.

629.1   USA
MECHANIST∗. Text in English. m.
Published by: International Association of Machinists and Aerospace Workers, 900 Machinists Pl., Upper Marboro, MD 20772. TEL 301-967-4500.

METEOROLOGICAL SATELLITE CENTER. MONTHLY REPORT. see *METEOROLOGY*

629.1   USA   ISSN 0539-8703
MICHIGAN AVIATION. Text in English. 1961. bi-m. free. bk.rev. illus.
Published by: Aeronautics Commission, 2700 E Airport Service Dr, Capital City Airport, Lansing, MI 48906. TEL 517-335-9283, FAX 517-321-6422. Ed. Kenneth Schaschl. Circ: 17,000 (controlled).

MICRO. see *ELECTRONICS*

629.1   GBR   ISSN 0968-3100
MICROLIGHT FLYING. Text in English. 1980. bi-m. GBP 43 to non-members (effective 2001). adv. bk.rev. 60 p./no. 3 cols./p.; back issues avail. Document type: *Consumer.*
Formerly: Flightline (0266-0504)
Published by: (British Microlight Aircraft Association), Pagefast Ltd., 4-6 Lansil Way, Lansil Industrial Estate, Lancaster, LA1 3QY, United Kingdom. TEL 44-1524-841010, FAX 44-1524-841578, microlight@pagefast.co.uk, office@pagefast.co.uk, http://www.pagefast.co.uk. Ed. David Bremner. Pub., R&P Norman Burr. Adv. contact Wendy Burr. B&W page GBP 215; trim 210 x 297. Circ: 4,100 (paid).

355   USA   ISSN 1046-9079
UG485
MILITARY & AEROSPACE ELECTRONICS. Text in English. 1990. m. USD 140 domestic; USD 210 in Canada; USD 280 elsewhere; USD 15 per issue domestic; free to qualified personnel (effective 2005). adv. Document type: *Newspaper, Trade.* Description: For designers, buyers and specifiers of electronic components and subsystems. Includes product and technology applications, military and defense industry news, design development briefs and new product updates.
Related titles: Online - full text ed.: (from EBSCO Publishing, Factiva, Florida Center for Library Automation, Gale Group, O C L C Online Computer Library Center, Inc.).
Indexed: BrCerAb, C&ISA, CerAb, CorrAb, E&CAJ, EMA, IAA, M&TEA, MBF, METADEX, SolStAb, WAA.
—BLDSC (5767.974500), IE, Linda Hall. **CCC.**
Published by: PennWell Corp., 1421 S Sheridan Rd, Tulsa, OK 74112. TEL 918-835-3161, FAX 918-831-9804, Headquarters@PennWell.com, http://www.milaero.com, http://www.pennwell.com. Ed. John Keller. adv.: B&W page USD 11,610, color page USD 13,630. Circ: 38,000 (controlled).

MILITARY & COMMERCIAL FIBER BUSINESS. see *MILITARY*

MILITARY PARADE. see *MILITARY*

MILITARY SPACE. see *MILITARY*

MODEL AIRPLANE NEWS. see *HOBBIES*

MODELE MAGAZINE; revue des modeles d'avions. see *HOBBIES*

LE MODELE REDUIT D'AVION. see *HOBBIES*

MOUNTAIN PILOT; the mountains aviation magazine. see *TRANSPORTATION—Air Transport*

629   USA   ISSN 1077-9647
MUSEUM OF FLIGHT NEWS. Text in English. 1979. bi-m. USD 40 (effective 1999). adv. bk.rev. illus. Document type: *Newsletter.*
Formerly: Air Museum News
Published by: Museum of Flight Foundation, 9404 E Marginal Way, So, Seattle, WA 98108. TEL 206-764-5700, FAX 206-764-5707. Ed. Hollis M Palmer. R&P Hollis Palmer TEL 206-764-5703. Circ: 23,000.

629.1   USA
MX MAGAZINE. Text in English. q. adv. Document type: *Magazine, Trade.* Description: Provides a source of aviation maintenance information for management and technicians.
Published by: Professional Aviation Maintenance Association, 717 Princess St., Alexandria, VA 22314-2221. TEL 202-730-0260, FAX 202-730-0259, hq@pama.org, http://www.pama.org. Adv. contact Christina Vloet TEL 202-730-0262. B&W page USD 2,260, color page USD 3,000.

387.7   USA
N A A A NEWSLETTER. Text in English. w. Document type: *Newsletter.*
Published by: National Agricultural Aviation Association, 1005 E St S E, Washington, DC 20003. TEL 202-546-5722, FAX 202-546-5726. Ed. Jim Boillot.

629.13   JPN   ISSN 0023-2726
N A L NEWS/KOGIKEN NYUSU. Text in Japanese. 1958. m. abstr. Document type: *Newsletter.*
Indexed: RefZh.
Published by: National Aerospace Laboratory/Kagaku Gijutsucho Koku Uchu Gijutsu Kenkyujo, 7-44-1 Jindaiji-Higashi-Machi, Chofu-shi, Tokyo-to 182-0012, Japan. TEL 0422-47-5911. Ed. Kingo Takasawa.

629.13   USA   ISSN 0191-7811
N A S A. CONFERENCE PUBLICATION. (National Aeronautics and Space Administration) Text in English. 1977. irreg. Document type: *Proceedings, Academic/Scholarly.*
Related titles: Series: N A S A. Joint University Program for Air Transportation Research. ISSN 1043-0954. 1980.
—BLDSC (6015.366000), CISTI, IE, ingenta.
Published by: U.S. National Aeronautics and Space Administration, Scientific and Technical Information Office, 7121 Standard Dr, Hanover, MD 21076-1320. TEL 301-621-0390, FAX 301-621-0134, help@sti.nasa.gov, http://www.sti.nasa.gov.

629.13   USA   ISSN 0077-3093
N A S A FACTS. Text in English. irreg.
Published by: U.S. National Aeronautics and Space Administration, Code FEO-2, Washington, DC 20546. TEL 202-755-2320. Dist. by: U.S. Government Printing Office, Superintendent of Documents, PO Box 371954, Pittsburgh, PA 15250-7954. TEL 202-512-1800, FAX 202-512-2250, orders@gpo.gov, http://www.access.gpo.gov.

629.1   USA
N A S A O NEWSLETTER. Text in English. m. USD 70. Document type: *Newsletter.* Description: Reports on current aviation issues and developments, state agency activities, pertinent congressional news and general items of interest.
Published by: National Association of State Aviation Officials, 8401 Colesville Rd, Ste 505, Silver Spring, MD 20910. TEL 301-588-0587, FAX 301-585-1803. Ed., R&P Stacey Moye.

629.13   USA   ISSN 0148-8589
N A S A REFERENCE PUBLICATION. (National Aeronautics and Space Administration) Text in English. 1977. irreg. Document type: *Monographic series.*
—BLDSC (6015.428000), CISTI.
Published by: N A S A Headquarters, Code FEO-2, 300 E. St. SW., Washington, DC 20546. http://science.nasa.gov.

629.1   USA
N A S A SCIENTIFIC AND TECHNICAL PUBLICATIONS CATALOG∗. Text in English. a. Document type: *Catalog, Government.* Description: Lists N.A.S.A. publications from four report series entered into the S.T.I. Database during the previous year.
Published by: U.S. National Aeronautics and Space Administration, Scientific and Technical Information Office, 7121 Standard Dr, Hanover, MD 21076-1320. help@sti.nasa.gov, http://www.sti.nasa.gov.

629.13   USA   ISSN 0145-319X
TL521.3.T4
N A S A TECH BRIEFS. Text in English. 1963. m. USD 75 domestic; USD 195 foreign; free to qualified personnel (effective 2005). adv. back issues avail. Document type: *Magazine, Trade.* Description: Includes technical information for engineering solutions, design and manufacturing.
Formerly (until 1976): N A S A Tech Brief (0096-7491)
Related titles: Online - full text ed.: (from bigchalk, ProQuest Information & Learning).
Indexed: BrCerAb, C&ISA, CerAb, CivEngAb, CorrAb, E&CAJ, EMA, IAA, Inspec, M&TEA, MBF, METADEX, SoftBase, SolStAb, WAA.
—IE, Infotrieve, Linda Hall. **CCC.**

Published by: (U.S. National Aeronautical and Space Administration), Associated Business Publications, 317 Madison Ave, Ste 1900, New York, NY 10017-5391. TEL 212-490-3999, 800-944-6272, FAX 212-986-7864, help@sti.nasa.gov, http://www.nasatech.com. Ed. Linda L. Bell. Pub. Joseph T Pramberger. adv.: B&W page USD 10,395, color page USD 12,475. Circ: 205,000.

629.13   USA   ISSN 0148-8341
TL521.3   CODEN: NTPADG
N A S A. TECHNICAL PAPER. (National Aeronautics and Space Administration) Text in English. 1977. irreg.
Indexed: ESPM.
—BLDSC (6015.474000), CISTI.
Published by: U.S. National Aeronautics and Space Administration, Scientific and Technical Information Office, 7121 Standard Dr, Hanover, MD 21076-1320. help@sti.nasa.gov, http://www.sti.nasa.gov.

629.1   USA
N A S A TECHNICAL REPORTS SERVER. Abbreviated title: N T R S. Text in English. irreg. Document type: *Academic/Scholarly.*
Media: Online - full content.
Published by: NASA Center for AeroSpace Information, 7121 Standard Dr, Hanover, MD 21076-1320. TEL 301-621-0390, help@sti.nasa.gov, http://ntrs.nasa.gov/, http://www.sti.nasa.gov/.

629   USA   ISSN 0899-5257
N A S A THESAURUS. (National Aeronautics and Space Administration Thesaurus) Text in English. triennial. USD 209 per issue (effective 2004).
Published by: N A S A Scientific and Technical Information, 7121 Standard Dr, Hanover, MD 21076-1320. FAX 301-621-0134.

629.1   USA
N A S A THESAURUS SUPPLEMENT. PART 1. HIERARCHICAL LISTING∗. Text in English. irreg., latest no.4, Jul. 1996. back issues avail. Document type: *Abstract/Index.* Description: Compiles aerospace engineering terms and lists any changes in their definitions. Used both when entering documents into and retrieving documents from the NASA STI database.
Related titles: Online - full text ed.
Published by: U.S. National Aeronautics and Space Administration, Scientific and Technical Information Office, 7121 Standard Dr, Hanover, MD 21076-1320. help@sti.nasa.gov, http://www.sti.nasa.gov.

629.1   USA
N A S A THESAURUS SUPPLEMENT. PART 2. ACCESS VOCABULARY∗. Text in English. irreg., latest no.4, Jul. 1996. back issues avail. Document type: *Abstract/Index.* Description: Compiles aerospace engineering terms and lists any changes in their definitions. Used both to enter and retrieve documents from the N.A.S.A. S.T.I. database.
Related titles: Online - full text ed.
Published by: U.S. National Aeronautics and Space Administration, Scientific and Technical Information Office, 7121 Standard Dr, Hanover, MD 21076-1320. help@sti.nasa.gov, http://www.sti.nasa.gov.

629.1   USA
N A S A THESAURUS SUPPLEMENT. PART 3. DEFINITIONS. Text in English. irreg., latest 1994. Document type: *Abstract/Index.* Description: Compiles aerospace engineering terms and lists any changes in their definitions. Used both to enter and retrieve documents from the N.A.S.A. S.T.I. database.
Related titles: Online - full text ed.
Published by: U.S. National Aeronautics and Space Administration, Scientific and Technical Information Office, 7121 Standard Dr, Hanover, MD 21076-1320. help@sti.nasa.gov, http://www.sti.nasa.gov.

629.13071   USA
N A S A UNIVERSITY PROGRAMS REPORT∗. Variant title: Greenbook. Text in English. a. charts; stat. Document type: *Directory, Government.* Description: Compiles active projects and related statistics of the NASA University Program for the previous fiscal year.
Published by: U.S. National Aeronautics and Space Administration, Scientific and Technical Information Office, 7121 Standard Dr, Hanover, MD 21076-1320. help@sti.nasa.gov, http://www.sti.nasa.gov.

387.7   USA   ISSN 1091-1553
N B A A DIGEST. Text in English. m. membership.
Formerly: Business Aviation Digest
Published by: National Business Aviation Association, 1200 18th St, N W, Ste 400, Washington, DC 20036-2506. TEL 202-783-9000, FAX 202-331-8364, http://www.nbaa.org.

629   NLD   ISSN 0369-478X
CODEN: NCRAAT
N L R REPORT. Text in English. irreg.
Indexed: BrCerAb, C&ISA, CerAb, CorrAb, E&CAJ, EMA, IAA, M&TEA, MBF, METADEX, SolStAb, WAA.
Published by: Nationaal Lucht -en Ruimtevaartlaboratorium/ National Aerospace Laboratory, Postbus 90502, Amsterdam, 1006, Netherlands. TEL 31-20-5113113, FAX 31-20-5113210.

▼ *new title*   ➤ *refereed*   ∗ *unverified*   ◆ *full entry avail.*

A

629.13 USA
N S S D C NEWS. (National Space Science Data Center) Text in English. q. back issues avail. **Document type:** *Newsletter, Government.*
Media: Online - full text.
Published by: N A S A Goddard Space Flight Center, National Space Science Data Center, Code 633, Greenbelt Rd, Greenbelt, MD 20771. TEL 301-286-7355, FAX 301-286-1771, beall@ndadsb.gsfc.nasa.gov, joseph.h.king@gsfc.nasa.gov, http://nssdc.gsfc.nasa.gov/nssdc_news/.

NAGOYA KOKU KISHOHYO/NAGOYA DATA OF AERONAUTICAL METEOROLOGY. see *METEOROLOGY*

629.13 CHN ISSN 1001-4926
NANCHANG HANGKONG GONGYE XUEYUAN XUEBAO/NANCHANG INSTITUTE OF AERONAUTICAL TECHNOLOGY. JOURNAL. Text in Chinese. 1987. q. back issues avail. **Document type:** *Academic/Scholarly.*
Related titles: Online - full content ed.: (from WanFang Data Corp.); Online - full text ed.: (from East View Information Services).
Published by: Nanchang Hangkong Gongye Xueyuan, Shanghai lu, Nanchang, Zhejiang 330034, China. TEL 86-791-8223348.

629.1 CHN ISSN 1005-2615
TL504 CODEN: NHHXEU
NANJING HANGKONG HANGTIAN DAXUE XUEBAO/NANJING UNIVERSITY OF AERONAUTICS AND ASTRONAUTICS. JOURNAL. Text in Chinese. 1956. bi-m. USD 31.20; USD 5.20 newsstand/cover (effective 2001). adv. bk.rev. **Document type:** *Journal, Academic/Scholarly.* **Description:** Comprehensive academic publication which deals mainly with research achievements in aeronautics, civil aviation, astronautics, and their theoretical basis.
Formerly (until vol.25, no.2, 1993): Nanjing Hangkong Xueyuan Xuebao (1000-1956)
Related titles: Online - full content ed.: (from WanFang Data Corp.); Online - full text ed.: (from East View Information Services).
Indexed: BrCerAb, C&ISA, CIN, CerAb, ChemAb, ChemTitl, CivEngAb, CorrAb, E&CAJ, EMA, ESPM, EngInd, H&SSA, IAA, Inspec, M&GPA, M&TEA, MBF, METADEX, RefZh, SolStAb, WAA, ZentMath.
—BLDSC (4828.679300), AskIEEE, CASDDS, Linda Hall.
Published by: Nanjing Hangkong Daxue/Nanjing University of Aeronautics and Astronautics, 29 Yudao St, Nanjing, 210016, China. TEL 86-25-4892726, FAX 86-25-4494880, TELEX 34155 NAINJ CN, tnc01@nuaa.edu.cn, http://njhkht.periodicals.com.cn/default.html. Ed. Xiong Chunru. Circ: 1,200. **Dist. by:** China International Book Trading Corp, 35 Chegongzhuang Xilu, Haidian District, PO Box 399, Beijing 100044, China. TEL 86-10-68412045, FAX 86-10-68412023, cibtc@mail.cibtc.com.cn, http://www.cibtc.com.cn.

629.1 CHN ISSN 1005-1120
NANJING UNIVERSITY OF AERONAUTICS AND ASTRONAUTICS. TRANSACTIONS. Text in English. 1982. s-a. USD 80. adv. bk.rev. **Document type:** *Academic/Scholarly.* **Description:** Publishes papers on special subject research and reviews in the science and technology of aeronautics, civil aviation, and astronautics.
Formerly (until 1993): Nanjing Aeronautical Institute. Journal (English Edition)
Indexed: BrCerAb, C&ISA, CerAb, CivEngAb, CorrAb, E&CAJ, EMA, ESPM, EngInd, H&SSA, IAA, Inspec, M&TEA, MBF, METADEX, MathR, MathSciNet, RefZh, SolStAb, WAA, ZentMath.
—BLDSC (8983.730000), AskIEEE, CISTI, Linda Hall.
Published by: Nanjing Hangkong Hangtian Daxue, 29 Yudao St, Nanjing, Jiangsu 210016, China. TEL 025-4892726, FAX 025-4494880, TELEX 34155 NAINJ CN, tnc01@nuaa.edu.cn. Ed. Xiong Chunru. Circ: 900.

629.4 USA
NATIONAL AERONAUTICS. Text in English. 1922. 6/yr. USD 34 membership (effective 2000). adv. stat. 8 p./no.; **Document type:** *Newsletter, Trade.* **Description:** Includes industry news, membership benefits, awards coverage, records and competition.
Former titles: For the Record (Arlington); (until 1974): National Aeronautics (0005-2116)
—CISTI.
Published by: National Aeronautic Association, 1737 King St., Ste. 220, Alexandria, VA 22314-2760. TEL 703-527-0226, FAX 703-527-0229, naa@naa-usa.org, http://www.naa-usa.org. Ed. Jim Way. adv.: page USD 1,800; bleed 8.5 x 11. Circ: 3,500.

629.13 IND ISSN 0077-2976
NATIONAL AEROSPACE LABORATORIES. ANNUAL REPORT. Text in English. 1961. a. per issue exchange basis. **Document type:** *Corporate, Government.*
Formerly: National Aeronautical Laboratory. Annual Report
Published by: National Aeronautical Laboratory, Kodihalli, P O Box 1779, Bangalore, Karnataka 560 017, India. TEL 91-80-508-6080, FAX 91-80-527-0670, goudar@css.cmmmacs.ernet.in. Circ: 500. **Affiliate:** Council of Scientific and Industrial Research.

629.13 IND
NATIONAL AEROSPACE LABORATORIES. COMBINED AEROSPACE REPORTS ADDITIONS. Text in English. m. per issue exchange basis. **Document type:** *Monographic series, Government.*
Formerly: National Aeronautical Laboratory. Current Scientific and Technical Reports
Published by: National Aeronautical Laboratory, Kodihalli, P O Box 1779, Bangalore, Karnataka 560 017, India. TEL 91-80-508-6080, FAX 91-80-527-0670, goudar@css.cmmmacs.ernet.in, http://www.cmmacs.ernet.in/nal/publn.html.

NATIONAL BUSINESS AIRCRAFT ASSOCIATION. MAINTENANCE AND OPERATIONS BULLETIN. see *TRANSPORTATION—Air Transport*

NATIONAL DEFENSE; NDIA's business and technology journal . see *MILITARY*

629.13 POL
NATIONAL REPORT OF SPACE RESEARCH IN POLAND. Text in Polish, English. biennial. **Document type:** *Monographic series, Academic/Scholarly.*
Published by: Polska Akademia Nauk, Komitet Badan Kosmicznych i Satelitarnych, Palac Kultury i Nauki, pok 2507, Warsaw, Poland. TEL 48-22-6208021, jblecki@cbk.waw.pl. Ed. Jan Blecki.

359 USA ISSN 0028-1417
VG93
NAVAL AVIATION NEWS. Text in English. 1917. bi-m. USD 16 domestic; USD 20 foreign (effective 2005). bk.rev. illus. index. back issues avail. **Document type:** *Magazine, Government.* **Description:** Presents articles of interest on all phases of Navy and Marine air activity.
Related titles: Online - full text ed.: (from bigchalk, EBSCO Publishing, Florida Center for Library Automation, Gale Group, Northern Light Technology, Inc., ProQuest Information & Learning).
Indexed: DM&T, IUSGP, PROMT, RefZh.
—IE, Linda Hall.
Published by: U.S. Department of the Navy, Naval Historical Center, 805 Kidder Breese Street SE, Washington Navy Yard, DC 20374-5060. TEL 202-433-4407, FAX 202-433-2343, nannews@navy.mil, http://www.history.navy.mil/branches/nhcorg5.htm, http://www.history.navy.mil/index.html. Ed. Sandy Russell. Circ: 30,000 (controlled). **Subscr. to:** U.S. Government Printing Office, Superintendent of Documents, PO Box 371954, Pittsburgh, PA 15250-7954. TEL 202-512-1800, FAX 202-512-2250, orders@gpo.gov, http://www.access.gpo.gov.

NAVIGATION; revue technique de navigation aerienne, maritime, spatiale et terrestre. see *TRANSPORTATION—Ships And Shipping*

629.13 USA ISSN 0028-1522
VK1 CODEN: NAVIB3
NAVIGATION (WASHINGTON). Text in English. 1946. q. subscr. incld. with membership. adv. bk.rev. bibl.; illus. Index. back issues avail. **Document type:** *Journal, Academic/Scholarly.*
Indexed: ASFA, AUNI, BibCart, BrCerAb, C&ISA, CerAb, CivEngAb, CorrAb, E&CAJ, EMA, ESPM, HRIS, IAA, ISMEC, Inspec, M&TEA, MBF, METADEX, MathR, OceAb, SolStAb, WAA.
—BLDSC (6066.000000), AskIEEE, CISTI, Ei, IE, Infotrieve, ingenta, Linda Hall. **CCC.**
Published by: Institute of Navigation, 3975 University Dr, Ste 390, Fairfax, VA 22030-2520. TEL 703-383-9688, FAX 703-383-9689, membership@ion.org, http://www.ion.org. Circ: 3,000.

629.132 USA ISSN 0028-1581
➤ **NAVIONEERS.** Text in English. 1960. bi-m. USD 15 to non-members. adv. illus. cum.index: 1961-1996. back issues avail. **Document type:** *Newsletter, Academic/Scholarly.*
Published by: American Navion Society, 2706 Skyline Dr, Grand Junction, CO 81506. TEL 970-243-8513, fls@gjct.net. Ed. Hugh Smith. R&P, Adv. contact Jerry Feather. Circ: 1,200. **Subscr. to:** PO Box 148, Grand Jct, CO 81502-0148.

629.1 AUT
NEUE FLIEGER REVUE✶. Text in German. 8/yr. **Document type:** *Magazine, Consumer.*
Published by: Oesterreichischer Aero-Club, Herbeckstr 27, Vienna, 1180, Austria. TEL 43-1-47846820, FAX 43-1-478468283. Circ: 31,500 (paid).

NEUES VON ROHDE UND SCHWARZ. see *COMMUNICATIONS*

NEW BOOKS RECEIVED BY THE FACULTY LIBRARY. see *AERONAUTICS AND SPACE FLIGHT—Abstracting, Bibliographies, Statistics*

629.13 USA
NEW JERSEY AVIATION NEWS. Text in English. 1962. q. free (effective 2005). bk.rev. 4 p./no. 3 cols./p.; **Document type:** *Newsletter, Government.* **Description:** News of general aviation activities in New Jersey.
Former titles: New Jersey Aviation; New Jersey Aviation News and Views; Flight Log
Related titles: Supplement(s): New Jersey Aviation Bulletin.
Published by: (Division of Aeronautics), Department of Transportation, 1035 Parkway Ave, PO Box 610, Trenton, NJ 08625-0610. TEL 609-530-2900, FAX 609-530-4549, mjstoddard@juno.com, http://www.njaviation.com. Ed., R&P Mike Stoddard TEL 973-377-8955. Circ: 13,000 (controlled and free).

614.8 NZL ISSN 0112-8949
TL553.5
NEW ZEALAND FLIGHT SAFETY. Text in English. 1972. 2/yr. NZD 20; NZD 23 foreign. illus. **Document type:** *Government.* **Description:** To promote safety in the New Zealand civil aviation system by providing safety information.
Formerly: Flight Safety
Published by: Civil Aviation Authority of New Zealand, PO Box 31-441, Lower Hutt, New Zealand. FAX 64-4-5692-024. Ed. C F L Jenks. Circ: 9,500.

614.8 NZL ISSN 1171-1558
NEW ZEALAND FLIGHT SAFETY SUPPLEMENT. Text in English. 1992. every 6 wks. NZD 20; NZD 23 foreign; with parent title. **Document type:** *Government.* **Description:** Provides safety information for the New Zealand civil aviation system.
Published by: Civil Aviation Authority of New Zealand, PO Box 31-441, Lower Hutt, New Zealand. FAX 64-4-5692-024. Ed. C F L Jenks.

629.1325 NZL
NEW ZEALAND SPORT FLYING. Text in English. q. NZD 6.95 newsstand/cover. **Document type:** *Magazine, Consumer.*
Published by: New Zealand Aviation News Ltd., PO Box 209, Morrinsville, 2251, New Zealand. TEL 64-7-889-7949, FAX 64-7-889-7949.

629.13 JPN ISSN 1344-6460
TL504 CODEN: NKGAB8
NIHON KOKU UCHU GAKKAI ROMBUNSHU/JAPAN SOCIETY FOR AERONAUTICAL AND SPACE SCIENCES. Text in Japanese; Summaries in English. 1934. m. JPY 10,000 membership (effective 2005). adv. abstr.; bibl.; charts; illus. **Document type:** *Journal, Academic/Scholarly.*
Supersedes in part (in 1999): Nihon Koku Uchu Gakkaishi (0021-4663)
Related titles: Online - full content ed.; Online - full text ed.: (from J-Stage).
Indexed: BrCerAb, C&ISA, CerAb, CivEngAb, CorrAb, E&CAJ, EMA, IAA, INIS AtomInd, Inspec, JPI, JTA, M&TEA, MBF, METADEX, WAA.
—BLDSC (4805.980000), AskIEEE, CISTI, Linda Hall. **CCC.**
Published by: Nihon Koku Uchu Gakkai/Japan Society for Aeronautical and Space Sciences, Ohkami Meiwa Bldg. 3F, 1-18-2 Shimbashi, Minato-ku, Tokyo, 105-0004, Japan. TEL 81-3-35010463, JSASS@capj.or.jp, http://jjsass.jstage.jst.go.jp, http://www.jsass.or.jp/web/. Ed. Toshio Nagashima. Pub. Takenory Nishi.

629.132 USA ISSN 0273-608X
NINETY-NINE NEWS. Text in English. 1929. 6/yr. USD 20 domestic to non-members; USD 30 foreign to non-members (effective 2000). adv. bk.rev. illus. cum.index: 1929-1984. back issues avail. **Document type:** *Newsletter, Consumer.* **Description:** Includes news and articles of interest to women pilots.
Published by: (International Women Pilots), The Ninety-Nines, Inc., 7100 Terminal Dr., Will Rogers Airport, PO Box 965, Oklahoma City, OK 73159. TEL 405-685-7969, FAX 405-685-7985, editor99news@aol.com, http://www.ninety-nines.org/99news.html. Ed. Betty Rowley. R&P Lu Hollander. Adv. contact John Shoemaker. Circ: 7,000.

629.13092 USA ISSN 1523-6412
NORTHERN PILOT; the magazine for backcountry aviation enthusiasts. Text in English. 1999. bi-m. USD 19 domestic; USD 28 in Canada; USD 35 elsewhere (effective 2000). adv. **Document type:** *Magazine, Consumer.* **Description:** Contains information to increase public awareness of general and commercial aviation by promoting safe and neighbor-friendly flying practices and addressing public concerns or questions on local aviation-related issues.
Published by: Frostbite Publications, LLC, PO Box 220168, Anchorage, AK 99522-0168 . TEL 907-258-6898, FAX 907-258-4354, info@northernpilot.com, http://www.northernpilot.com. Adv. contact Peter M Diemer.

629.1 USA
NORTHROP GRUMMAN REVIEW MAGAZINE. Text in English. q. free domestic to members. **Document type:** *Magazine, Trade.*
Published by: Northrop Grumman Corp., 1840 Century Park, E, Los Angeles, CA 90067-2199. TEL 310-553-6262, FAX 310-201-3023, http://www.northropgrumman.com. Ed. Gina Ceron. Circ: 40,000 (free).

629.13 USA ISSN 1057-9621
TL710
NOTICES TO AIRMEN. Text in English. fortn. USD 208; USD 260 foreign. back issues avail. **Document type:** *Government.* **Description:** Contains all NOTAMs.

Former titles: Airman's Information Manual. Notices to Airmen; (until May 1978): Airman's Information Manual. Part 3A: Notices to Airmen
Related titles: Online - full text ed.: ISSN 1555-0311. —Linda Hall.
Published by: U.S. Federal Aviation Administration, Planning, Publications & Analysis Division, Publication Branch, ATX 420, 800 Independence Avenue SW, Washington, DC 20591. TEL 202-655-4000. **Subscr. to:** U.S. Government Printing Office, Superintendent of Documents.

001.942 ITA
NOTIZIARIO U F O. (Unidentified Flying Objects) Text in Italian; Summaries in English. 1966. bi-m. EUR 22 (effective 2004). adv. bk.rev.; film rev. bibl.; illus. back issues avail. **Document type:** Bulletin, Consumer.
Published by: Centro Ufologico Nazionale/National Ufological Center, Casella Postale 823, Bologna, 40100, Italy. TEL 39-051-6235536, http://www.cun-italia.net/centrou.htm. Ed. Roberto Pinotti. Circ: 50,000.

629.1 ITA ISSN 0393-1005
NOVA ASTRONAUTICA. Text in English, Italian. 1981. q. EUR 65 (effective 2005). adv. bk.rev. back issues avail. **Document type:** Newsletter, Consumer. **Description:** Covers studies and experiments on Non Newtonian Propulsion of the new ASPS prototype SC23.
Related titles: Online - full text ed.
Published by: Associazione Sviluppo Propulsione Spaziale/Association for the Development of Space Propulsion, Via Nino Martoglio 22, Rome, 00137, Italy. TEL 39-06-87131068, http://www.asps.it. Circ: 900.

629.4 RUS ISSN 1561-1078
NOVOSTI KOSMONAVTIKI. Text in Russian; Contents page in English. 1991. m. USD 222 foreign (effective 2005). adv. charts; illus.; stat. back issues avail. **Document type:** Journal. **Description:** Provides news on Russian and international astronautics: manned missions, spacecrafts and satellites, probes, and launch vehicles.
Related titles: Partial English translation(s):.
Indexed: RefZh.
Address: ul Vorontsovo pole, dom 3, Moscow, 109028, Russian Federation. TEL 7-095-2306350, FAX 7-095-9178681, nk@novosti-kosmonavtiki.ru, http://www.novosti-kosmonavtiki.ru. Ed., Adv. contact Igor Marinin. page USD 4,500. Circ: 5,000 (paid). **US dist. addr.:** East View Information Services, 3020 Harbor Ln. N., Minneapolis, MN 55447. TEL 800-477-1005, FAX 800-800-3839, eastview@eastview.com, http://www.eastview.com.

629.13 FRA
O N E R A SCIENTIFIC AND TECHNICAL ACTIVITIES. Text in French. 1969. a. free. **Document type:** Corporate.
Formerly: Office National d'Etudes et de Recherches Aerospatiales. Activites (1169-7830)
Related titles: English ed.: France. Nation Office of Aerospace Studies and Research. Activities. ISSN 1169-7857. —BLDSC.
Published by: Office National d'Etudes et de Recherches Aerospatiales, 29 av. de la Division Leclerc, Chatillon, Cedex 92322, France. TEL 33-1-46733780, FAX 33-1-46734141, http://www.onera.fr. Ed. Khoa Dang-Tran. R&P Khoa Dang Tran. Circ: 2,400.

001.94 GBR ISSN 0262-7795
O S E A P CENTRE UPDATE. Text in English. 1982. irreg. GBP 5. bk.rev.
Published by: Organisation for Scientific Evaluation of Aerial Phenomena, 2 Acer Ave, Crewe, Ches, United Kingdom. Ed. David L Rees. Circ: 135.

001.94 GBR ISSN 0262-5954
O S E A P JOURNAL. Text in English. 1982. irreg. GBP 5.
Published by: Organisation for Scientific Evaluation of Aerial Phenomena, 2 Acer Ave, Crewe, Ches, United Kingdom. Ed. Mark A Tyrrell. Circ: 135.

OLTRE; la conoscenza. see PARAPSYCHOLOGY AND OCCULTISM

629.13 NLD ISSN 1562-8019
TL787
ON STATION. Text in English. 1999. q. back issues avail. **Document type:** Newsletter.
Related titles: Online - full text ed.: ISSN 1608-4764. —BLDSC (6256.750500), Linda Hall.
Published by: European Space Agency, Publications Division/Agence Spatiale Europeenne, Keplerlaan 1, Noordwijk, 2200 AG, Netherlands. TEL 31-71-5653400, FAX 31-71-5655433, http://esapub.esrin.esa.it/onstation/onstation.htm. Eds. Andrew Wilson, Brigitte Kaldeich.

ONZE LUCHTMACHT. see MILITARY

629.132 USA
ORGANIZATION OF BLACK AIRLINE PILOTS. CONVENTION JOURNAL. Text in English. a. **Document type:** Newsletter.
Published by: Organization of Black Airline Pilots, PO Box 5793, Englewood, NJ 07631. TEL 201-568-8145. Ed. Raymond Washington.

629.132 USA
ORGANIZATION OF BLACK AIRLINE PILOTS. NEWSLETTER. Text in English. 1981. q. free to members. bk.rev. **Document type:** Newsletter, Trade.
Published by: Organization of Black Airline Pilots, PO Box 5793, Englewood, NJ 07631. TEL 201-568-8145. Ed. Eddie Raynord Hadden.

629.13 CAN ISSN 0843-1566
OUTBOUND. Text in English. 1969. q. free to members. bk.rev. bibl. back issues avail. **Document type:** Academic/Scholarly. **Description:** Covers the society's affairs and general items of aviation interest.
Published by: Canadian Aviation Historical Society, Sta A, P O Box 224, Willowdale, ON M2N 5S8, Canada. TEL 905-683-9069. Ed. W J Wheeler. R&P G E Rice. Circ: 1,350.

629.13 387.7 USA ISSN 1086-0983
TL671.9
OVERHAUL & MAINTENANCE; the magazine for m & o management. Text in English. bi-m. USD 54 domestic; USD 59 in Canada & Mexico; USD 79 elsewhere (effective 2005). illus. **Document type:** Trade. **Description:** Covers all aspects of aircraft maintenance.
Related titles: Online - full text ed.: (from EBSCO Publishing, ProQuest Information & Learning). —CCC.
Published by: McGraw-Hill Companies, Inc., 1221 Ave of the Americas, New York, NY 10020. TEL 212-512-2000, 800-525-5003, http://www.aviationnow.com/content/publication/om/om.htm, http://www.mcgraw-hill.com. Pub. Mark Lipowicz TEL 212-904-6425.

629.13 USA ISSN 0092-3591
TL521
OVERVIEW OF THE F A A ENGINEERING & DEVELOPMENT PROGRAMS. Text in English. 1974. irreg. free to qualified personnel. illus. Supplement avail. **Document type:** Monographic series, Government.
Published by: U.S. Federal Aviation Administration, 800 Independence Ave S W, Washington, DC 20591. TEL 202-655-4000.

629.1 USA ISSN 0896-8926
CODEN: ISWRE7
P A M A NEWS. Text in English. 1978. 10/yr. USD 35. adv. back issues avail. **Document type:** Newsletter, Trade. **Description:** Industry journal for aviation maintenance personnel.
Published by: Professional Aviation Maintenance Association, 717 Princess St., Alexandria, VA 22314-2221. TEL 202-730-0260, FAX 202-730-0259, hq@pama.org, http://www.pama.org. Ed. Peter Rohrbach. Circ: 4,000 (paid).

629.133343 AUS ISSN 1441-1121
PACIFIC FLYER. Text in English. m. AUD 66 domestic; AUD 78 in Asia & the Pacific; AUD 99.50 elsewhere (effective 2004). adv. **Document type:** Magazine, Consumer. **Description:** Contains articles and features for recreational pilots.
Formerly (until 1998): Pacific Ultralights Monthly (1321-781X)
Published by: Khandu Publishing, PO Box 731, Mt. Eliza, VIC 3930, Australia. TEL 61-3-9775-2466, FAX 61-3-9775-2488, info@pacificflyer.com.au, http://www.pacificflyer.com.au. Ed. Angela Smith. adv.: B&W page AUD 396, color page AUD 744; bleed 216 x 291.

629.13 NZL ISSN 1174-8052
PACIFIC WINGS. Text in English. 1932. m. NZD 66 domestic; AUD 66 in Australia; NZD 99 elsewhere; NZD 7.95 newsstand/cover (effective 2001). adv. bk.rev. charts; illus.; stat. back issues avail. **Document type:** Magazine, Consumer. **Description:** Covers both civil and military aviation within New Zealand.
Former titles (until 1998): New Zealand Wings (0110-1471); (until 1973): Wings (0043-5899) —CCC.
Published by: N.Z. Wings Ltd., Harewood, PO Box 39099, Christchurch, New Zealand. TEL 64-3-3590250, FAX 64-3-3590471, info@nzwing.co.nz, http://www.nzwings.co.nz. Ed., Pub., R&P Callum Macpherson TEL 64-6-3646283. Adv. contact Kevin Walsh. B&W page NZD 1,000, color page NZD 1,750; trim 210 x 297. Circ: 20,000.

629.1 JPN ISSN 0912-490X
PAIROTTO. Text in Japanese. 1965. 3/yr.
Indexed: RefZh.
Published by: Nihon Pairotto Kyokai/Japanese Pilots Association, 4-5 Koji-Machi, Chiyoda-ku, Tokyo, 102-0083, Japan.

PARACHUTIST. see SPORTS AND GAMES

PEGASUS JOURNAL. see MILITARY

629.13 USA ISSN 0888-3467
PERFORMANCE MATERIALS. Text in English. 1986. bi-w. looseleaf. USD 577 in North America to institutions; USD 657 elsewhere to institutions (effective 2001). back issues avail.
Formerly: Report on Performance Materials
Related titles: E-mail ed.: USD 840 (effective 2000); Online - full text ed.: (from Florida Center for Library Automation, Gale Group).

Published by: Technical Insights (Subsidiary of: Frost & Sullivan), 7550 IH 10 West, Ste 400, San Antonio, TX 78229. TEL 212-850-8600, FAX 212-850-8800, insights@wiley.com, http://www.wiley.com/technical_insights. Ed. Harry Goldstein. Pub. Paul Majchrzyk. Circ: 6,000.

629.13 NLD ISSN 1381-1827
TL504
PILOOT EN VLIEGTUIG; het complete luchtvaart magazine. Text in Dutch. 1994. m. EUR 64.50; EUR 6.45 newsstand/cover (effective 2005). adv. bk.rev. illus. **Document type:** Consumer. **Description:** Provides useful information for pilots and student pilots.
Incorporates (1999-2000): Luchtvaartwereld (Maarssen) (1566-0257); (1987-2000): Luchtvaart (0921-7258); Which was formed by the 1986 merger of: Luchtvaartwereld (0921-724X); Vliegtuigparade (0165-3040)
Published by: Reed Business Information bv (Subsidiary of: Reed Business), Postbus 4, Doetinchem, 7000 BA, Netherlands. TEL 31-314-349911, FAX 31-314-343991, karel.campers@reedbusiness.nl, info@reedbusiness.nl, http://www.pilootenvliegtuig.nl/, http://www.reedbusiness.nl. Ed. Ruud Vos. Circ: 10,100.

629.132 GBR ISSN 0300-1695
TL721.4
PILOT (CLAPHAM). Text in English. 1967. m. GBP 39 domestic; GBP 55 foreign; GBP 3.40 newsstand/cover (effective 2005). adv. bk.rev.; software rev.; video rev.; Website rev. illus. index. back issues avail. **Document type:** Magazine, Consumer.
Indexed: RefZh.
—IE, Infotrieve.
Published by: Archant Specialist Ltd. (Subsidiary of: Archant), The Mill, Bearwalden Business Park, Royston Rd, Wendens Ambo, Essex CB11 4GB, United Kingdom. TEL 44-1799-544200, farine.clarke@archant.co.uk, http://www.pilotweb.co.uk, http://www.archant.co.uk/. Ed. Dave Calderwood. Adv. contact Dave Foster. B&W page GBP 1,300, color page GBP 1,900; trim 216 x 279. Circ: 22,332 (paid). **Dist. by:** Comag, Tavistock Works, Tavistock Rd, W Drayton, Middx UB7 7QX, United Kingdom. TEL 44-1895-444055, FAX 44-1895-433605.

PILOT GETAWAYS. see TRAVEL AND TOURISM

629.13092 USA
PILOT JOURNAL. Text in English. 2000. q. USD 25; USD 5.99 newsstand/cover (effective 2001). adv. **Document type:** Magazine, Consumer.
Address: 12121 Wilshire Blvd, Ste 1200, Los Angeles, CA 90025. TEL 310-826-5008, editors@pilotjournals.com, http://www.pilotjournals.com. Ed., Pub. Steve Werner.

629 USA ISSN 0897-7666
PILOT'S AUDIO UPDATE. Text in English. 1979. m. USD 96 (effective 2006). **Document type:** Magazine, Consumer. **Description:** Reviews old procedures and new regulations related to general aviation.
Media: Audio CD.
Published by: Belvoir Media Group, LLC, 800 Connecticut Ave, Norwalk, CT 06854-1631. TEL 203-857-3100, 800-424-7887, FAX 203-857-3103, customer_service@belvoir.com, https://www.ezsubscription.com/cgi-bin/formgen.exe/add?db=PILOT&key=7WWW05, http://www.belvoir.com.

629.132 GBR ISSN 1470-2673
PILOT'S LEARN TO FLY GUIDE. Text in English. 1999. a. GBP 4.95 newsstand/cover (effective 2001). adv. **Document type:** Magazine, Consumer. **Description:** Provides articles and information for people learning to fly and those wishing to brush up on their skills.
Published by: Pilot Publishing Company Ltd. (Subsidiary of: Archant Specialist Ltd.), Clockhouse, 28 Old Town, London, SW4 0LB, United Kingdom. TEL 44-171-498-2506, FAX 44-20-7498-6920. Adv. contact Brian Harriss TEL 44-20-7613-0717.

629.132 USA ISSN 1052-5580
PIPERS MAGAZINE. Text in English. m. USD 42 domestic; USD 57 foreign (effective 2000). adv.
Published by: (Pipers Owner Society), Jones Publishing, Inc., N 7450 Aanstad Rd, PO Box 5000, Iola, WI 54945. TEL 715-445-5000, 800-331-0038, FAX 715-445-4053, jonespub@jonespublishing.com, http://www.jonespublishing.com. Ed. John Kronschnabl. Pub. Joe Jones. Adv. contact Trevor Janz.

629.13 USA ISSN 0032-0617
TL721.4
PLANE AND PILOT. Text in English. 1965. m. USD 11.97 domestic; USD 21.97 foreign; USD 4.99 newsstand/cover (effective 2005). adv. bk.rev. illus. reprint service avail. from PQC. **Document type:** Magazine, Consumer.
Incorporates (in 1987): Homebuilt Aircraft; Airways (0002-287X)
Related titles: Microform ed.: (from PQC); Online - full text ed.: (from ProQuest Information & Learning).
Indexed: IHTDI, SportS.

Published by: Werner Publishing Corporation, 12121 Wilshire Blvd., Ste 1220, Los Angeles, CA 90025. TEL 310-820-1500, 800-283-4330, FAX 303-604-7644, 310-826-5008, editors@planeandpilotmag.com, http://www.planeandpilotmag.com. Eds. Lyn Freeman, Steve Werner. Pub. Steve Werner. Circ: 134,000.

629.132 USA
PLANE TALK. Text in English. m.
Published by: Avionics Maintenance Conference, c/o Aeronautical Radio, Inc, 2551 Riva Rd, Annapolis, MD 21401. TEL 301-266-4116.

629.13 DEU ISSN 1632-2266
PLANET AEROSPACE (FRENCH EDITION); mensuel d'information aeronautique et spatiale. Text in French. 1970. q. EUR 17.64 in Europe; EUR 19.60 elsewhere; EUR 4.90 newsstand/cover (effective 2005). adv. bk.rev. **Document type:** *Magazine, Trade.*
Former titles (until 1999): Revue Aerospatiale (0994-9003); (until 1983): Aerospatiale (0065-3780)
Indexed: RefZh.
—IE, Infotrieve. **CCC.**
Published by: GeraNova Zeitschriftenverlag GmbH, Innsbrucker Ring 15, Munich, 81673, Germany. TEL 49-89-13069911, FAX 49-89-13069910, info@geranova.de, http://www.planet-aerospace.com, http://www.geranova-verlag.de. Ed. Alexis von Croy. Adv. contact Norbert Stahl. color page EUR 15,820; bleed 210 x 280. Circ: 58,000 (paid).

387.7 DEU ISSN 1616-7880
PLANET AEROSPACE (GERMAN EDITION); aeronautics - space defence. Text in German. 1935. 4/yr. EUR 21 in Europe; EUR 23 elsewhere; EUR 5.80 newsstand/cover (effective 2003). adv. back issues avail. **Document type:** *Magazine, Trade.*
Description: Portrays the benefits of aviation, spaceflight and defense technologies and clarifies these with actual examples.
Former titles: Aerospace (0949-7064); (until 1994): Dornier Post (0012-5563)
Indexed: AMB, BrCerAb, C&ISA, CerAb, CivEngAb, CorrAb, E&CAJ, EMA, EngInd, IAA, M&TEA, MBF, METADEX, MedAb, WAA.
—BLDSC (6508.242500), Linda Hall. **CCC.**
Published by: (Daimler-Benz Aerospace AG), Residence Verlag GmbH, Gruener Weg 12, Moehnesee, 59519, Germany. Ed. Gilles Patri TEL 33-1-42242121. Circ: 140,500.

PLANETARY REPORT. see *ASTRONOMY*

629.1 RUS ISSN 1684-1301
POLET; obshcherossiiskii nauchno-tekhnicheskii zhurnal. Text in Russian. 1998. m. USD 542 foreign (effective 2004). **Document type:** *Journal.*
Indexed: RefZh.
Published by: Izdatel'stvo Mashinostroenie, Stromynskii per 4, Moscow, 107076, Russian Federation. TEL 7-095-2683858, mashpubl@mashin.ru, http://www.mashin.ru. **Dist. by:** M K - Periodica, ul Gilyarovskogo 39, Moscow 129110, Russian Federation. TEL 7-095-2845008, FAX 7-095-2813798, info@periodicals.ru, http://www.mkniga.ru.

629.13 GBR ISSN 0032-4493
POPULAR FLYING. Text in English. 1957. bi-m. membership. adv. bk.rev. charts; illus. **Document type:** *Trade.*
Published by: Popular Flying Association, Terminal Bldg, Shoreham Airport, Shoreham-by-Sea, W Sussex BN43 5FF, United Kingdom. TEL 44-1273-461616, FAX 44-1273-463390. Ed. John Catchpole. R&P A Preston. Adv. contact Yvette Savile Barton. B&W page GBP 535, color page GBP 700; trim 210 x 297. Circ: 8,000.

629.13 POL ISSN 0373-5982
TL787.P67 CODEN: POASBE
➤ **POSTEPY ASTRONAUTYKI/PROGRESS IN ASTRONAUTICS.** Text in English, Polish. 1967. a., latest vol.26, 1999. PLZ 2.50, USD 4. adv. bk.rev. abstr.; bibl.; charts; illus. back issues avail. **Document type:** *Journal, Academic/Scholarly.* **Description:** Publishes original scientific papers devoted to a broad range of astonautics research.
Indexed: IAA.
—CASDDS, CISTI, Linda Hall.
Published by: Polska Akademia Nauk, Centrum Badan Kosmicznych/Polish Academy of Sciences, Space Research Center, Ul Bartycka 18 a, Warsaw, 00716, Poland. TEL 48-22-8403766, FAX 48-22-8403131, wp@cbk.waw.pl. Ed. Marek Banaszkiewicz. Circ: 200. **Subscr. to:** Polskie Towarzystwo Astronautyczne, Ul Z. Krasinskiego 54, Warsaw 01755, Poland. TEL 48-22-6852703.

629.13 NLD ISSN 1018-8657
TL790 CODEN: PRFUEZ
PREPARING FOR THE FUTURE: E S A TECHNOLOGY QUARTERLY. Text in English. 1991. q. free.
Indexed: BrCerAb, C&ISA, CerAb, CivEngAb, CorrAb, E&CAJ, EMA, IAA, M&TEA, MBF, METADEX, SolStAb, WAA.
—BLDSC (6607.876580), CISTI, Linda Hall.
Published by: European Space Agency, Publications Division/Agence Spatiale Europeenne, Keplerlaan 1, Noordwijk, 2200 AG, Netherlands. TEL 31-071-5653677, FAX 31-071-5655433. Ed. M Perry. Circ: 25,000.

PREVISIONS GLISSANTES DETAILLEES EN PERSPECTIVES SECTORIELLES (VOL.16): CONSTRUCTION AEROSPATIALE. see *BUSINESS AND ECONOMICS—Economic Situation And Conditions*

PROBE REPORT. see *PARAPSYCHOLOGY AND OCCULTISM*

629.1 RUS
PROBLEMY AVYATSIONNOI I KOSMICHESKOI TEKHNIKI. Text in Russian. irreg.
Published by: Izdatel'stvo Zarubezhnaya Radioelektronika, Ul Annenskaya 21, Moscow, 127521, Russian Federation. TEL 7-095-2198244. **US dist. addr.:** East View Information Services, 3020 Harbor Ln. N., Minneapolis, MN 55447. TEL 612-550-0961.

PROBLEMY KOSMICHESKOI BIOLOGII. see *BIOLOGY*

629.1 GBR ISSN 0376-0421
CODEN: PAESD6
➤ **PROGRESS IN AEROSPACE SCIENCES.** Text in English, French, German. 1961. 8/yr. EUR 1,519 in Europe to institutions; JPY 201,700 in Japan to institutions; USD 1,698 to institutions except Europe and Japan (effective 2006). illus. Index. reprints avail. **Document type:** *Academic/Scholarly.* **Description:** Focuses on the application of recent developments and research in the aerospace sciences to problems encountered in industry, research establishments and universities.
Formerly: Progress in Aeronautical Sciences (0079-6026)
Related titles: Microfilm ed.: (from PQC); Online - full text ed.: (from EBSCO Publishing, Gale Group, IngentaConnect, ScienceDirect, Swets Information Services).
Indexed: ASCA, ApMecR, BrCerAb, C&ISA, CerAb, CivEngAb, CorrAb, CurCont, E&CAJ, EMA, EngInd, IAA, ISR, Inspec, M&TEA, MBF, METADEX, RefZh, SCI, SolStAb, WAA.
—BLDSC (6865.902000), CISTI, Ei, IDS, IE, Infotrieve, ingenta, Linda Hall. **CCC.**
Published by: Pergamon (Subsidiary of: Elsevier Science & Technology), The Boulevard, Langford Ln, East Park, Kidlington, Oxford OX5 1GB, United Kingdom. TEL 44-1865-843000, FAX 44-1865-843010, http://www.elsevier.com/locate/paerosci. Ed. A B Haines. **Subscr. to:** Elsevier BV, PO Box 211, Amsterdam 1000 AE, Netherlands. TEL 31-20-485-3757, FAX 31-20-485-3432, nlinfo-f@elsevier.nl, http://www.elsevier.nl.

629.133 USA
PROP-LINERS OF AMERICA. NEWSLETTER. Text in English. 1999. quadrennial. free. **Document type:** *Newsletter, Consumer.* **Description:** Discusses the group's efforts to acquire and restore a rare Convair 240, a twin piston-engined airliner that once flew with American Airlines, along with related topics and issues of interest.
Media: Online - full content.
Published by: Prop-Liners of America, 21 Clearview Dr, Stafford Springs, CT 06076. TEL 860-684-4988, wbradshaw@prop-liners.com, http://www.prop-liners.com/newsletter.htm, http://www.propliners.com. Ed. Bill Bradshaw.

PROPEL; tidsskrift for civil og militaer flyvning. see *MILITARY*

629.133 GBR ISSN 0269-4018
PROPLINER; the international review of piston-engined and turboprop transport aircraft. Text in English. 1979. q. GBP 16 domestic; GBP 19 foreign (effective 2002). adv. charts; illus. back issues avail. **Document type:** *Consumer.*
Published by: Propliner Magazine Ltd., Vale Rd, 3 Castle Woods, Redlynch, Salisbury, Wilts SP5 2PY, United Kingdom. TEL 44-1725-513856, FAX 44-1725-513857. Ed., R&P, Adv. contact Tony Merton Jones. Circ: 4,000. **Subscr. to:** New Roots, Sutton Green, New Roots, Sutton Green Rd, Guildford, Surrey GU4 7QD, United Kingdom.

PTISI KAI DIASTIMA/FLIGHT AND SPACE. see *MILITARY*

629.1 USA ISSN 1065-7738
TL787
➤ **QUEST (GRAND FORKS)**; the history of spaceflight quarterly. Text in English. 1992. q. USD 30 domestic; USD 35 in Canada & Mexico; USD 45 elsewhere (effective 2004). adv. illus. back issues avail. **Document type:** *Journal, Academic/Scholarly.* **Description:** Chronicles the past international achievements in the fields of both manned and unmanned spaceflight. Preserves these histories and provides a network for correspondence with others who share a similar interest.
Formerly (1992): Lift Off (1060-7692)
Indexed: AmH&L, CivEngAb, HistAb, IndIslam.
—Linda Hall.
Published by: University of North Dakota, Space Studies Department, Stephen Johnson, University of N. Dakota, Grand Forks, ND 58202. TEL 719-487-9833, FAX 701-777-3711, quest@spacebusiness.com, http://www.spacebusiness.com/quest/. Ed. Stephen Johnson. R&P, Adv. contact Suezette Bieri. Circ: 1,500 (paid).

➤ **R & D CONTRACTS MONTHLY**; a continuously up-dated sales and R & D tool for all research organizations and manufacturers. (Research & Development) see *SCIENCES: COMPREHENSIVE WORKS*

➤ **R E M E JOURNAL.** see *ENGINEERING—Mechanical Engineering*

629.44 AUS
R L V ALERT. (Rocket Launched Vehicles) Text in English. d. **Document type:** *Academic/Scholarly.* **Description:** Covers the latest rocket launches and payloads, including research vehicles, data and other related fields.
Media: Online - full content.
Published by: Space Daily, PO Box A447, Sydney South, NSW 2000, Australia. TEL 61-2-9360-2257, simon@spacer.com, http://www.spacedaily.com/.

629.135 USA ISSN 0193-4422
R T C A DIGEST. Text in English. 1965. bi-m. free to members (effective 2005). adv. **Document type:** *Newsletter, Consumer.*
Published by: (Radio Technical Commission for Aeronautics), R T C A, Inc., 1828 L St NW, Ste. 805, Washington, DC 20036-5133. TEL 202-833-9339, FAX 202-833-9434, info@rtca.org, http://www.rtca.org. Ed. Jerry Bryant. adv.: page USD 750. Circ: 1,000 (paid and controlled).

629.13 358.4 FRA ISSN 1562-2312
R T O EDUCATIONAL NOTES. (Research and Technology Organization) Text in English. 1965. irreg. **Document type:** *Monographic series.*
Formerly (until 1998): A G A R D Advisory Report (0549-7221)
Indexed: Inspec.
—CISTI, ingenta.
Published by: North Atlantic Treaty Organization, Research and Technology Organization, 7, rue Ancelle, Neuilly-sur-Seine, 92200, France. TEL 33-1-55612295, 33-1-55612297, FAX 33-1-55612299, 33-1-55612298, http://www.rta.nato.int.

R T O LECTURE SERIES. (Research and Technology Organization) see *MILITARY*

629.135 USA
RADIO TECHNICAL COMMISSION FOR AERONAUTICS. PROCEEDINGS OF THE ANNUAL TECHNICAL SYMPOSIUM. Short title: R T C A Proceedings. Text in English. 1955. a. USD 40 (effective 1999). **Document type:** *Proceedings.*
Formerly: Radio Technical Commission for Aeronautics. Proceedings of the Annual Assembly Meeting (0145-9589)
—BLDSC (6809.630000), Linda Hall.
Published by: (Radio Technical Commission for Aeronautics), R T C A, Inc., 1828 L St NW, Ste. 805, Washington, DC 20036-5133. TEL 202-833-9339, FAX 202-833-9434, TELEX 2407254, http://www.rtca.org. Ed. Malia Richmond-Crum. R&P Malia Richmond Crum. Circ: 500.

RAPID NOTICE NEWS SERVICE. see *PHILATELY*

629.13 NLD ISSN 1013-9044
CODEN: RESKEZ
REACHING FOR THE SKIES; E S A space transportation systems. Text in English, French. 1989. q. free. illus.
Related titles: Online - full content ed.: ISSN 1608-4756.
Indexed: BrCerAb, C&ISA, CerAb, CivEngAb, CorrAb, E&CAJ, EMA, IAA, M&TEA, MBF, METADEX, SolStAb, WAA.
Published by: European Space Agency, Publications Division/Agence Spatiale Europeenne, Keplerlaan 1, Noordwijk, 2200 AG, Netherlands. TEL 31-071-5653403, FAX 31-071-5655433. Eds. D Guyenne, N Longdon. Circ: 20,000.

629.1 CHE
REGA. Text in French, German, Italian. 1972. s-a. **Document type:** *Magazine, Corporate.*
Address: Postfach 1414, Zuerich, 8058, Switzerland. TEL 41-1-6543311, FAX 41-1-6543788, http://www.rega.com. Ed. Norbert Hobmeier. Adv. contact Walter Stuenzi. Circ: 1,194,000.

629.136 FRA ISSN 0034-320X
REGARDS SUR LE COMITE D'ETABLISSEMENT D'ORLY SUD. Text in French. 1966. q. free. adv.
—**CCC.**
Published by: Comite d'Etablissement Air France-Orly Sud, Extension Est, Batiment CRP, Aerogare d'Orly Sud, France. Ed. M Alain Lemaitre. Circ: 8,000 (controlled).

629 DEU
REUSS JAHRBUCH DER LUFT- UND RAUMFAHRT; German Aerospace Annual. Text in German. 1951. a. adv. bk.rev. index. **Document type:** *Directory.*
Formerly: Jahrbuch der Luftfahrt und Raumfahrt (0075-269X)
—CISTI.
Published by: Suedwestdeutsche Verlagsanstalt GmbH, R1, 4-6, Mannheim, 68161, Germany. TEL 0621-3922882, FAX 0621-3922800. Ed. Tilman Reuss.

629.13 USA ISSN 0279-4519
REVISTA AEREA; voz aeronautica de America Latina, Espana y las Filipinas. Text in Spanish, English. 1937. 4/yr. USD 50 (effective 2005). adv. bk.rev. illus. back issues avail. **Document type:** *Magazine, Trade.* **Description:** Covers aviation and aerospace developments (military, commercial, and business) worldwide for senior Latin American business executives, government officials, and other ranking aerospace decision makers.

Formerly: Aero Digest
Published by: Strato Publishing Co., Inc., 405 East 56th St., Ste 4E, New York, NY 10022-2430. TEL 212-371-7392, FAX 212-371-1224, strato310@aol.com, http://www.revistaaerea.com. Ed., Pub., R&P Elaine Asch-Root. Adv. contact Ines Trevino. B&W page USD 6,300, color page USD 9,865; trim 8.13 x 10.88. Circ: 11,200 (paid and free).

629.13 COL ISSN 0034-6942
REVISTA AERONAUTICA; al servicio de la aviacion colombiana. Text in Spanish. 1947. q. USD 28. adv. bk.rev. charts; illus. index. **Document type:** *Government.*
Published by: Fuerza Aerea Colombiana, Apartado Aereo 51097, Bogota, DE, Colombia. Ed. Alvaro Baquero. Circ: 20,000.

629.13 ESP ISSN 0034-7647
TL504
REVISTA DE AERONAUTICA Y ASTRONAUTICA. Text in Spanish. 1932. m. EUR 18.12 domestic; EUR 38.50 in Europe; EUR 42.10 elsewhere (effective 2001). adv. bk.rev. back issues avail. **Document type:** *Government.*
Formerly: Revista de Aeronautica
Indexed: AMB, BrCerAb, C&ISA, CerAb, CivEngAb, CorrAb, DIP, E&CAJ, EMA, IAA, IECT, M&TEA, MBF, METADEX, SolStAb, WAA.
—CINDOC, CISTI, Linda Hall. **CCC.**
Published by: Ministerio del Aire/Spanish Airforce, Princesa, 88, Madrid, 28008, Spain. TEL 34-91-5442819, FAX 34-91-5442819. Ed. Col Francisco Eytor Coira. R&P Antonio Alonso Ibanez. Adv. contact Juan Pedro Aguilar Moreno. page ESP 90,000. Circ: 10,000 (paid).

629.13 PRT ISSN 0034-9208
REVISTA DO AR. Text in Portuguese. 1937. q. adv. bk.rev. charts; illus.
Published by: Aero Club de Portugal, Rua General Pimenta de Castro, 4-C, Lisbon, 1700, Portugal. TEL 351-21-840-5317, FAX 351-21-840-5572, aecp@aecp.pt, http://www.aecp.pt/. Ed. Jose Augusto Rosa. Circ: 5,000.

629.13 FRA ISSN 1144-2158
REVUE FRANCAISE DE DROIT AERIEN ET SPATIAL. Text in French. 1946. q. adv. bk.rev. index. reprint service avail. from SCH. **Document type:** *Journal.*
Formerly (until 1989): Revue Francaise de Droit Aerien (0035-287X)
Indexed: FLP, IBR, RASB.
—IE, Infotrieve. **CCC.**
Published by: (Association d'Etudes et de Documentation de Droit Aerien), Editions A. Pedone, 13 rue Soufflot, Paris, 75005, France. TEL 33-1-43540597, FAX 33-1-46340760, editions-pedone@wanadoo.fr, http://bief.org/pedone/index.cfm. Ed. A Garnault. Circ: 1,000.

REVUE GENERALE DES ROUTES. see *TRANSPORTATION—Roads And Traffic*

REVUE ROUMAINE DES SCIENCES TECHNIQUES. SERIE DE MECANIQUE APPLIQUEE. see *ENGINEERING—Mechanical Engineering*

533.6 DEU ISSN 0172-3898
RHEINISCH-WESTFAELISCHEN TECHNISCHEN HOCHSCHULE AACHEN. AERODYNAMISCHES INSTITUT. ABHANDLUNGEN. Text in German. 1921. irreg. **Document type:** *Monographic series, Academic/Scholarly.*
—BLDSC (0539.460000), CISTI.
Published by: Rheinisch-Westfaelischen Technischen Hochschule Aachen, Aerodynamisches Institut, Wuellnerstr 5-7, Aachen, 52062, Germany. http://www.aia.rwth-aachen.de.

629.13 ITA ISSN 0391-6162
RIVISTA AERONAUTICA. Text in Italian; Summaries in English, French, German, Spanish. 1977. bi-m. EUR 18.07 domestic; EUR 43.89 foreign (effective 2004). adv. bk.rev. bibl.; charts; illus. index. **Document type:** *Magazine, Consumer.*
Description: Covers modern aviation, space technology, history of aviation and world-wide air forces.
Formerly (until 1976): Rivista Aeronautica - Missilistica (0035-5747)
Indexed: AMB, ASCA, ApMecR, ChemAb, DIP, IBR, RefZh.
—CISTI, IDS, Linda Hall.
Published by: Ministero della Difesa, Aeronautica, Viale dell' Universita 4, Rome, 00185, Italy. TEL 39-06-49865495, FAX 39-06-4456302, http://www.rivista.aeronautica.difesa.it. Ed. Leonardo Tricarico. Pub. Adelchi Pillinini. Circ: 21,000.

629 JPN ISSN 0485-2877
ROCKET NEWS. Text in Japanese. 1957. m. JPY 300 per issue to non-members. abstr. **Document type:** *Newsletter.*
Indexed: BrCerAb, C&ISA, CerAb, CorrAb, E&CAJ, EMA, IAA, M&TEA, MBF, METADEX, WAA.
Published by: Japanese Rocket Society/Nihon Roketto Kyokai, c/o Business Center for Academic Societies Japan, 5-16-9 Honkomagome, Bunkyo-ku, Tokyo, 113-0021, Japan. TEL 81-3-5814-5811, FAX 81-3-5814-5822. Ed. Y Morita. Circ: 600.

629.133 USA ISSN 1066-8098
TL716.A1 CODEN: RWINEI
ROTOR & WING; serving the worldwide helicopter industry. Text in English. 1967. m. free to qualified personnel. adv. illus. back issues avail.; reprints avail. **Document type:** *Magazine, Trade.* **Description:** Covers technical and business developments in helicopter manufacturing and operations.
Former titles (until 1992): Rotor and Wing International (0191-6408); Rotor and Wing (0035-8452)
Related titles: Online - full text ed.; Supplement(s): World Helicopter Resource; Rotor & Wing Annual Buyer's Guide.
Indexed: HRIS.
—BLDSC (8025.720000), CISTI, IE, ingenta. **CCC.**
Published by: Access Intelligence, LLC (Subsidiary of: Veronis, Suhler & Associates Inc.), 1201 Seven Locks Rd, Ste 300, Potomac, MD 20854. TEL 301-354-2000, 800-777-5006, FAX 301-762-3068, rjones@pbimedia.com, clientservices@accessintel.com, http://www.rotorandwing.com, http://www.pbimedia.com. Ed. Douglas Nelms. Adv. contact Wiley Loughran. B&W page USD 8,190, color page USD 10,275; bleed 8.5 x 11. Circ: 33,000 (controlled).

629.13 USA
ROTOR BREEZE. Text in English. 1951. bi-m. free. **Document type:** *Newsletter.*
Published by: Bell Helicopter Textron, Inc., Dept. H3, Box 482, Ft. Worth, TX 76101. Ed. Susan Green.

ROTOR ROSTER. see *TRANSPORTATION—Air Transport*

629.133 USA ISSN 1041-2735
ROTORCRAFT. Text in English. 1963. 9/yr. USD 35 membership; USD 39 in Mexico membership; USD 41 in Canada membership; USD 49 elsewhere membership (effective 2000). adv. bk.rev. illus. back issues avail. **Document type:** *Academic/Scholarly.* **Description:** Features gyroplanes and helicopters built by amateur enthusiasts.
Formerly (until 1988): Popular Rotorcraft Flying (0032-4620)
Published by: Popular Rotorcraft Association, PO Box 68, Mentone, IN 46539-0068. TEL 219-353-7227, FAX 219-353-7227, prahq@aol.com, http://www.pra.org. Ed., R&P, Adv. contact Stephanie Gremminger. Pub. Paul Abbott. B&W page USD 960. Circ: 5,000.

ROYAL AERONAUTICAL DIRECTORY OF EUROPEAN AVIATION. see *TRANSPORTATION—Air Transport*

629.4 NLD ISSN 1382-2446
RUIMTEVAART. Text in Dutch. 1952. bi-m.
Indexed: BrCerAb, C&ISA, CerAb, CorrAb, E&CAJ, EMA, IAA, M&TEA, MBF, METADEX, WAA.
—BLDSC (8048.805000), IE, Infotrieve.
Published by: Nederlandse Vereniging voor Ruimtevaart, Zonnenburg 2, Utrecht, 3512 NL, Netherlands. TEL 31-30-2311360, info@ruimtevaart-nvr.nl.

629.13 USA ISSN 1068-7998
TL504
➤ **RUSSIAN AERONAUTICS - IZ. V U Z.** Text in English. 1966. q. USD 2,065 per vol. in US & Canada; USD 2,345 per vol. elsewhere (effective 2006). bk.rev. abstr.; charts; illus. index. back issues avail. **Document type:** *Journal, Academic/Scholarly.* **Description:** Presents reports on the research being conducted at Tupolev Kazan Aviation Institute. Articles may cover aerodynamics, structural mechanics, instrumentation, automation and aeronautics, and communications systems.
Formerly (until 1992): Soviet Aeronautics - Iz. V U Z (0364-8117)
Indexed: ApMecR, EngInd, IAA, Inspec, MathR.
—BLDSC (0420.752000), AskIEEE, CISTI, IE, ingenta, Linda Hall. **CCC.**
Published by: (Ministerstvo Vysshego i Srednego Spetsial'nogo Obrazovaniya RUS), Allerton Press, Inc., 18 W 27th St, New York, NY 10001. TEL 646-424-9686, FAX 646-424-9695, journals@allertonpress.com, http://allertonpress.com/journals/aer.htm, http://www.allertonpress.com. Ed. Dr. Vyacheslav A Firsov.

629.13 USA ISSN 0191-6319
TL553.5 CODEN: SAFJDH
S A F E JOURNAL. Text in English. 1967. 2/yr. USD 25 domestic; USD 30 foreign (effective 2005). adv. bk.rev. **Document type:** *Journal, Trade.* **Description:** Provides a multidisciplinary forum for sharing ideas and information on human safety.
Indexed: ESPM, ErgAb, ExcerpMed, H&SSA, HRIS, IAA.
—BLDSC (8065.300000), CISTI, IE, Infotrieve, ingenta, Linda Hall.
Published by: S A F E Association, PO Box 130, Creswell, OR 97426-0130. TEL 541-895-3012, FAX 541-895-3014, safe@usit.net, safe@peak.org, http://www.safeassociation.com. Ed., Adv. contact Jeani Benton. Circ: 1,000 (paid and controlled).

629.13 USA ISSN 0743-846X
TL697.S3
➤ **S A F E SYMPOSIUM PROCEEDINGS.** Text in English. a. USD 27.50 domestic; USD 30 foreign (effective 2005). **Document type:** *Proceedings, Academic/Scholarly.*
—Linda Hall.
Published by: S A F E Association, PO Box 130, Creswell, OR 97426-0130. TEL 541-895-3012, FAX 541-895-3014, safe@peak.org, http://www.safeassociation.com. Ed. Jeani Benton. Circ: 1,000.

629.1 USA
S A W E NEWSLETTER. Text in English. 1966. q. USD 30 (effective 2001); includes International Journal of Weight Engineering. bk.rev. **Document type:** *Newsletter.*
Published by: Society of Allied Weight Engineers, Inc., 204 Hubbard St, Glastonbury, CT 06033-3063. TEL 860-633-0850, FAX 860-633-8971, saweed@aol.com. Ed. Robert W Ridenour. Circ: 1,000 (controlled).

629.13 USA
S C A N. (Selected Current Aerospace Notices) Text in English. s-m. back issues avail. **Document type:** *Abstract/Index.* **Description:** Keeps readers aware of the latest additions to the NASA STI Database, arranged in 191 aerospace-related categories.
Related titles: Online - full text ed.
Published by: U.S. National Aeronautics and Space Administration, Scientific and Technical Information Office, 7121 Standard Dr, Hanover, MD 21076-1320. TEL 301-621-0390, FAX 301-621-0134, help@sti.nasa.gov, http://www.sti.nasa.gov/scan/scan.html. Circ: (controlled).

S C S I SAFETY MONITOR. (Southern California Safety Institute) see *OCCUPATIONAL HEALTH AND SAFETY*

629.13 FRA ISSN 0750-7569
S N E C M A INFORMATIONS; journal d'information du personnel. Text in French. 1953. q. free. bk.rev. charts; illus.; stat. index.
Formerly: S N E C M A (0036-1720)
—**CCC.**
Published by: Societe Nationale d'Etude et de Construction de Moteurs d'Aviation, 2 bd. General Martial Valin, Paris, Cedex 15 75724, France. FAX 40-60-81-02. Ed. Nicole Spodek. Circ: 22,000.

S P A R C JIMUKYOKUHO/S P A R C NEWS. see *ASTRONOMY*

629.1 387.7 USA ISSN 0894-5667
TL726.2
S P A WATER LANDING DIRECTORY. Text in English. biennial. USD 38 to non-members; USD 19 to members (effective 2000). adv. **Document type:** *Directory.* **Description:** Lists landing areas and regulations by state, with descriptions of facilities and services available. Also lists bodies of water that are open or off limits.
Formerly: Seaplane Landing Directory
Related titles: Special ed(s).: Seaplane Base Directory.
Published by: Seaplane Pilots Association, 4315 Highland Park Blvd, C, Lakeland, FL 33813-7588. TEL 301-695-2083, FAX 301-695-2375, spa@aopa.org. Ed. Michael Volk. Pub. Roger Myers. Circ: 3,000.

S T A R (ONLINE). (Scientific and Technical Aerospace Reports) see *AERONAUTICS AND SPACE FLIGHT—Abstracting, Bibliographies, Statistics*

001.942 DNK ISSN 0904-2598
S U F O I NEWS. Text in English. 1974-1982; resumed 1987. irreg. bk.rev.; software rev.; video rev. **Document type:** *Newsletter, Consumer.* **Description:** Excerpts from the Danish magazine U F O Nyt.
Formerly (until 1979): Skandinavisk U F O Information. Newsletter (0904-258X)
Published by: Skandinavisk U F O Information, PO Box 6, Gentofte, 2820, Denmark. info@sufoi.dk, http://www.sufoi.dk.

001.94 DNK ISSN 1396-545X
S U F O I NYHEDSBREV. (Skandinavisk U F O Information) Text in Danish. 1996. 6/m. **Document type:** *Newsletter, Consumer.*
Published by: Skandinavisk U F O Information, PO Box 6, Gentofte, 2820, Denmark. info@sufoi.dk, http://www.sufoi.dk.

629.1 USA
S U R V I A C BULLETIN. Text in English. bi-m. **Document type:** *Government.*
Media: Online - full text.
Published by: U.S. Department of Defense, Survivability - Vulnerability Information Analysis Center ryan_linda@bah.com, http://surviac.flight.wpafb.af.mil/curr_awar/surviac_bulletin/bulletins.html.

629.133 GBR ISSN 0036-2735
TL760.A1
SAILPLANE AND GLIDING. Text in English. 1950. bi-m. GBP 18.50; GBP 2.75 newsstand/cover (effective 1999). adv. bk.rev. charts; illus.; stat. index. reprint service avail. from PQC. **Document type:** *Consumer.*
Related titles: Microfilm ed.: (from PQC).
Indexed: RASB, SportS.
Published by: British Gliding Association, British Gliding Association, Kimberley House, 47 Vaughan Way, Leicester, LE1 4SE, United Kingdom. TEL 44-116-2531051, FAX 44-116-2515939, bgahq@aol.co.uk, http://www.gliding.co.uk. Ed. Gillian Bryce Smith. Adv. contact Debbie Carr. Circ: 8,500.

▼ new title ➤ refereed ✶ unverified ♦ full entry avail.

A

629.1325 RUS ISSN 0869-5946
SAMOLET. Text in Russian. bi-m. USD 75 in United States.
—East View.
Published by: Komissiya Sodeistviya Konversii, Obshchestvo Avyastroitelei, Leningradskii pr-t 24-a, Moscow, 125040, Russian Federation. TEL 7-095-2149919, FAX 7-095-2142288. **US dist. addr.:** East View Information Services, 3020 Harbor Ln. N., Minneapolis, MN 55447. TEL 612-550-0961.

629.1 RUS
SAMOLETY MIRA. Text in Russian. m. USD 159.95 in United States.
Published by: Firma Universal'nyi Servis, A-ya 36, Moscow, 107392, Russian Federation. TEL 7-095-1680776. Ed. E T Astakhova. **US dist. addr.:** East View Information Services, 3020 Harbor Ln. N., Minneapolis, MN 55447. TEL 612-550-0961.

629.19 USA
SAMOLYOT/AIRCRAFT. Text in English. m. adv. **Document type:** *Trade.* **Description:** Covers the past, present and future of the aviation and aerospace industries in Russia; includes interviews.
Published by: Aviation Maintenance Foundation International, PO Box 2826, Redmond, WA 98073. TEL 360-658-8980, FAX 360-658-7274. **Co-sponsor:** Russian Aeronautical Society.

SATNEWS ONLINE MAGAZINE. see *COMMUNICATIONS—Television And Cable*

SAVUNMA VE HAVACILIK; defence and aerospace. see *MILITARY*

SCALE AIRCRAFT MODELLING. see *HOBBIES*

629.13 USA ISSN 0278-4017
CODEN: AASTBE
SCIENCE AND TECHNOLOGY SERIES. Text in English. 1964. irreg. (approx. 4-5/yr.), latest vol.103, 2001. price varies. bibl.; charts; illus. cum.index 1954-1978; 1979-1985; 1986-1992. back issues avail. **Document type:** *Proceedings, Academic/Scholarly.*
Former titles (until 1976): Science and Technology (San Diego) (0080-7451); (until 1972): A A S Science and Technology Series (0065-7425)
Related titles: Microfiche ed.; ♦ Series: Space Safety and Rescue (Year); ♦ Supplement to: Advances in the Astronautical Sciences. ISSN 0065-3438.
Indexed: BiolAb, BrCerAb, C&ISA, CerAb, ChemAb, CivEngAb, CorrAb, CurCont, E&CAJ, EMA, EngInd, IAA, Inspec, M&TEA, MBF, METADEX, SolStAb, WAA.
—BLDSC (8134.283000), CISTI, Ei, Linda Hall. **CCC.**
Published by: (American Astronautical Society, Inc.), Univelt, Inc., PO Box 28130, San Diego, CA 92198-0130. TEL 760-746-4005, FAX 760-746-3139, 76121.1532@compuserve.com, http://www.univelt.com. Ed., Pub. Robert H Jacobs. Circ: 400.

629.13 629.14 USA
SCIENCE@NASA. (National Aeronautic and Space Administration) Text in English. d. free (effective 2003).
Description: Provides informative scientific and research-level articles based on the activities of the National Aeronautics and Space Administration.
Media: Online - full content.
Published by: N A S A Headquarters, Code FEO-2, 300 E. St. SW., Washington, DC 20546. phillips@spacesciences.com, http://science.nasa.gov.

629.13 NLD ISSN 0927-3417
SCRAMBLE. Text in Dutch. 1979. m. EUR 43.20 domestic; EUR 48.50 in Belgium; GBP 40.50 in United Kingdom; EUR 61.50 in Europe; EUR 95 elsewhere (effective 2005). adv. illus. back issues avail. **Document type:** *Consumer.* **Description:** Reports on developments in civil and military aviation and includes high-quality illustrations for the aviation enthusiast.
Published by: Dutch Aviation Society, PO Box 75545, Schiphol, 1118 ZN, Netherlands. FAX 31-84-7383905, info@scramble.nl, http://www.scamble.nl/. Circ: 3,000 (paid).

SCREAMING EAGLE. see *MILITARY*

629.1 CHN ISSN 1006-1630
SHANGHAI HANGTIAN/AEROSPACE SHANGHAI. Text in Chinese. 1984. bi-m. CNY 7 newsstand/cover (effective 2002). **Document type:** *Journal, Academic/Scholarly.*
Related titles: Online - full content ed.: (from WanFang Data Corp.); Online - full text ed.: (from East View Information Services).
—BLDSC (0729.918000).
Published by: Shanghai Hangtianju Di-807 Yanjiusuo, 408 Guilin Lu, Zhonghelou, Shanghai, 200233, China. TEL 86-21-64832184, FAX 86-21-64362404, shz@sh.cetin.net.cn, http://shht.periodicals.com.cn/default.html, http://www.sh.cetin.net.cn/dzqk/. **Dist. by:** China International Book Trading Corp, 35 Chegongzhuang Xilu, Haidian District, PO Box 399, Beijing 100044, China. TEL 86-10-68412045, FAX 86-10-68412023, cibtc@mail.cibtc.com.cn, http://www.cibtc.com.cn.

SHAWCROSS & BEAUMONT AIR LAW. see *TRANSPORTATION—Air Transport*

629.1 GBR ISSN 1351-3478
SHEPHARD'S UNMANNED VEHICLES HANDBOOK. Text in English. 1994. q. GBP 60 domestic; USD 90 foreign (effective 2003). **Document type:** *Directory.* **Description:** Contains comprehensive directory of unmanned aerial vehicles, along with their payloads and groundstations.
—Infotrieve, Linda Hall.
Published by: Shephard Press Ltd., 111 High St, Burnham, Bucks SL1 7JZ, United Kingdom. TEL 44-1628-604311, FAX 44-1628-664334, publishing@shephard.co.uk, http://www.shephard.co.uk. Ed. James Masey. Pub. Sandy Doyle. Adv. contact Mike Wild.

629.1325 CHN
SHIJIE HANGKONG HANGTIAN BOLAN/AEROSPACE WORLD. Text in Chinese. m. CNY 153.60 (effective 2004). **Document type:** *Academic/Scholarly.*
Related titles: Online - full content ed.
Address: PO Box 1408, Beijing, 100013, China. http://www.space.cetin.net.cn/docs/bolan/bl99.htm. **Dist. by:** China International Book Trading Corp, 35 Chegongzhuang Xilu, Haidian District, PO Box 399, Beijing 100044, China. TEL 86-10-68412045, FAX 86-10-68412023, cibtc@mail.cibtc.com.cn, http://www.cibtc.com.cn.

629.134 JPN
SHOGEKI KOGAKU SHINPOJUMU. Text in English, Japanese. 1974. a. **Document type:** *Proceedings.* **Description:** Covers shock engineering.
Published by: Institute of Space and Aeronautical Science/Uchu Kagaku Kenkyujo, 1-1 Yoshinodai 3-chome, Sagamihara-shi, Kanagawa-ken 229-0022, Japan. FAX 0427-57-4779. Ed. Takashi Abe.

SILVER WINGS. see *MILITARY*

629.13 GBR
SKYPORT. Text in English. 1976. w. GBP 40. adv. bk.rev. **Document type:** *Newspaper.*
Published by: Skyport Ltd., Red House, 360 Cranford Ln, Hayes, Mddx UB3 5HD, United Kingdom. TEL 44-181-759-1235, FAX 44-181-759-7739. Ed., Pub. Nigel Botherway. Adv. contact Sunita Parekh. Circ: 36,000.

387.7 IND ISSN 0970-8502
SKYWAYS; aviation magazine of Asia. Text in English. 1947. m. USD 50. adv. bk.rev. illus.
Formerly (until Jan. 1976): Asian and Indian Skyways (0004-4539)
—CISTI.
Published by: Aeronautical Publications of India Pvt. Ltd., Old Santacruz Airport, Mumbai, Maharashtra 400 029, India. TEL 11-6124448, FAX 22-942222, TELEX 011-71086-AWIB-IN. Ed. D M Heble. Adv. contact D De St. Rotta. Circ: 9,980.

387.7 USA ISSN 1051-6956
SKYWAYS; journal of the airplane 1920-1940. Text in English. 1987. q. USD 35 domestic; USD 40 foreign (effective 2003). adv. bk.rev.; software rev.; video rev.; film rev. bibl.; charts; illus.; tr.lit. 80 p./no. 2 cols./p.; back issues avail. **Document type:** *Journal, Consumer.* **Description:** Contains information on the restoration, reproduction and modelling of airplanes, 1920-1940.
—CISTI.
Published by: World War I Aeroplanes, Inc., 15 Crescent Rd, Poughkeepsie, NY 12601-4490. TEL 914-473-3679. Ed. David W Ostrowski. R&P Leonard E Opdycke TEL 845-473-3679. Adv. contact Beverly Williams TEL 845-473-3679. B&W 1/4 page USD 55. Circ: 1,200.

629.13 USA ISSN 0197-7245
SMITHSONIAN STUDIES IN AIR AND SPACE. Text in English. 1977. irreg., latest vol.7, 1990. free. reprint service avail. from PQC. **Document type:** *Monographic series.*
—Linda Hall.
Published by: Smithsonian Institution Press, 750 Ninth St., N. W., Suite 4300, Washington, DC 20560-0950. TEL 202-275-2233, FAX 202-275-2274. Ed. Diane Tyler. Circ: 1,600.

629.133 USA ISSN 0037-7503
TL760.A1
SOARING. Text in English. 1937. m. free membership (effective 2005). adv. bk.rev. charts; illus.; stat. reprints avail. **Document type:** *Magazine, Trade.* **Description:** Describes the thrill of all types of gliding and soaring, along with special events catering to this avocation. Covers flying techniques and safety.
Indexed: BAS, MagInd, SPI, SportS.
—Linda Hall.
Published by: Soaring Society of America, Inc, PO Box 2100, Hobbs, NM 88241-2100. TEL 505-392-1177, FAX 505-392-8154, info@ssa.org, http://www.ssa.org/magazine/. Circ: 14,881.

629.13 BRA ISSN 0037-8666
SOCIEDADE BRASILEIRA DE ESTUDOS SOBRE DISCOS VOADORES. BOLETIM. Text in Portuguese; Summaries in English. 1957. irreg. per issue exchange basis. bk.rev. illus.; stat. cum.index: 1957-1987. **Document type:** *Bulletin.*
Description: Explores the phenomenon of extraterrestrial crafts landing on Earth.
Media: Duplicated (not offset). **Related titles:** Microfilm ed.
Published by: Sociedade Brasileira de Estudos Sobre Discos Voadores, Correio Largo do Machado, Centro, Caixa Postal 16 017, Rio De Janeiro, RJ 20001-970, Brazil. Ed. W Buhler. Circ: 400.

629.13 USA ISSN 0742-3705
SOCIETY OF EXPERIMENTAL TEST PILOTS. SYMPOSIUM PROCEEDINGS. Variant title: Report to the Aerospace Profession. S E T P Technical Review. Text in English. 1964. a.
Supersedes in part (in 1967): Society of Experimental Test Pilots. Technical Review (0096-8781)
Indexed: BrCerAb, C&ISA, CerAb, CorrAb, E&CAJ, EMA, IAA, M&TEA, MBF, METADEX, WAA.
—BLDSC (8585.676700), CISTI, IE, Linda Hall.
Published by: Society of Experimental Test Pilots, Box 986, Lancaster, CA 93584-0986. TEL 661-942-9574, FAX 661-940-0398, setp@setp.org, http://www.setp.org.

629.1 USA ISSN 1050-9690
SOCIETY OF FLIGHT TEST ENGINEERS. ANNUAL SYMPOSIUM PROCEEDINGS. Text in English. 1970. a. USD 60 (effective 2005). illus. **Document type:** *Proceedings.*
—BLDSC (1534.963000), IE, ingenta.
Published by: Society of Flight Test Engineers, 44814 N Elm Ave, Lancaster, CA 93534. TEL 661-949-2095, FAX 661-949-2096, sfte@sfte.org, http://www.sfte.org/papers/index.html.

629.1 USA
SOCIETY OF FLIGHT TEST ENGINEERS. NEWSLETTER. Text in English. 1970. m. USD 25. **Document type:** *Newsletter.*
Published by: Society of Flight Test Engineers, 44814 N Elm Ave, Lancaster, CA 93534. TEL 661-949-2095, FAX 661-949-2096, sfte@sfte.org, http://www.sfte.org/.

001.942 USA
SOLAR SPACE LETTER. Text in English. 1960. 6/yr. USD 12; USD 15 foreign. adv. bk.rev. **Document type:** *Newsletter.*
Address: PO Box 332, Cornville, AZ 86325-0332. Ed., R&P Robert Short. Circ: 2,000.

629.13 551.6 JPN ISSN 0289-3347
SORA TO UMI/SKY AND MARINE. Text in Japanese; Summaries in English. 1980. a. JPY 2,000.
Indexed: ASFA, ESPM.
Published by: Koku Uchu Riyo Suisan Kaiyo Kenkyukai/Society of Airborne, Satellite Physical and Fishery Oceanography, Tokai Daigaku Kaiyogakubu Kaiyo Kagakuka, 20-1 Ori-Do 3-chome, shimizu-shi, Shizuoka-ken 424-0902, Japan.

629.132 790.1 ZAF ISSN 0256-0593
SOUTH AFRICAN AERONEWS. Text in English. 1983. 11/yr. ZAR 30, USD 13. adv. bk.rev. back issues avail. **Document type:** *Newsletter.*
Published by: Aero Club of South Africa, PO Box 1993, Halfway House, 1685, South Africa. FAX 27-11-8052765. Ed. M A van Ginkel. Circ: 5,000.

SOUTHERN AVIATOR; smart birds fly south. see *TRANSPORTATION*

629.1 USA ISSN 0738-0968
TL787
SPACE AGE TIMES; the international publication of space news, benefits and education. Text in English. 1974. bi-m. USD 26; USD 32 foreign. adv. bk.rev.; film rev. charts; illus.; stat.; tr.lit. back issues avail. **Description:** Worldwide coverage of space news exploration for both the professional and the layman.
Related titles: ♦ Cumulative ed(s).: U S S E A Update. ISSN 0741-4587.
Published by: U S Space Education Association, News Operations Division, PO Box 249, Rheems, PA 17570-0249. TEL 717-367-5196. Ed. Stephen M Cobaugh. R&P Debra Palmisano. Adv. contact Ronald Palmisano. Circ: 1,500.

629.1 GBR ISSN 1462-8112
SPACE BUSINESS INTERNATIONAL. Text in English. 1998. q. USD 95 (effective 2000). adv. **Document type:** *Magazine, Trade.* **Description:** Offers comprehensive and insightful coverage of the space industry, with an in-depth focus on the satellite communications and aerospace businesses.
Published by: SPACE.com, Space House, 27 Boltro Rd, Haywards Heath, W Sussex RH16 1BP, United Kingdom. TEL 44-1444-454590, FAX 44-1444-454561, spacebusint@btinternet.com, http://www.spacebusint.com. Ed. Mike Blackwell. Adv. contact Andrew Gotla. page USD 7,500. Circ: 15,000 (paid and controlled).

629.13 USA ISSN 0741-1731
SPACE CALENDAR. Text in English. 1982. w. USD 79 domestic to individuals; USD 139 foreign to individuals; USD 139 domestic to institutions; USD 199 foreign to institutions. back issues avail. **Document type:** *Newsletter.* **Description:** Covers space-related events and news worldwide.
Related titles: Fax ed.; Online - full text ed.
Published by: Space Age Publishing Company, 75-5751 Kuakini Hwy., Ste. 201, Kaulua-kona, HI 96740. TEL 808-326-2014, FAX 808-326-1825, spaceage@ilhawaii.net. Ed., Pub. Steve Durst. Circ: 625.

SPACE CAREERS. see *OCCUPATIONS AND CAREERS*

629.1 USA
SPACE.COM. Text in English. 1999. d. adv. **Document type:** *Consumer.* **Description:** Focuses on news, entertainment, information and education concerning space and space-related subjects.
Incorporates (1989-200?): SpaceViews (1086-654X)
Media: Online - full content.
Address: 120 W 45th St, New York, NY 10036. TEL 212-703-5800, FAX 212-703-5900, info@space.com, http://www.space.com.

384.51 NLD ISSN 0924-8625
TK5104 CODEN: SPCCEJ
➤ **SPACE COMMUNICATIONS**; an international journal. Text in English. 1983. q. EUR 412, USD 493 combined subscription print & online eds. (effective 2006). adv. illus. index. back issues avail.; reprints avail. **Document type:** *Journal, Academic/Scholarly.* **Description:** Covers all aspects of the satellite communications: technical, financial and legal.
Formerly (until 1990): Space Communication and Broadcasting (0167-9368)
Related titles: Online - full text ed.: (from EBSCO Publishing, Gale Group, IngentaConnect, O C L C Online Computer Library Center, Inc., Swets Information Services).
Indexed: ABIn, ASCA, B&BAb, BrCerAb, C&ISA, CerAb, CivEngAb, CommAb, CorrAb, CurCont, E&CAJ, EMA, EngInd, IAA, Inspec, M&TEA, MBF, METADEX, MSCI, SolStAb, WAA.
—BLDSC (8361.592000), AskIEEE, CISTI, Ei, IDS, IE, Infotrieve, ingenta, Linda Hall. **CCC.**
Published by: I O S Press, Nieuwe Hemweg 6B, Amsterdam, 1013 BG, Netherlands. TEL 31-20-6883355, FAX 31-20-6203419, info@iospress.nl, order@iospress.nl, http://www.iospress.nl/html/09248625.php. Eds. M Bousquet, W T Brandon. R&P Ms. Carry Koolbergen TEL 31-20-6382189. Adv. contact Ms. Jolijn van Eunen. Circ: 300. **Subscr. to:** I O S Press, Inc, 4502 Rachael Manor Dr., Fairfax, VA 22032-3631. iosbooks@iospress.com; Kinokuniya Co. Ltd., Shinjuku 3-chome, Shinjuku-ku, Tokyo 160-0022, Japan. FAX 81-3-3439-1094, journal@kinokuniya.co.jp, http://www.kinokuniya.co.jp; Globe Publication Pvt. Ltd., C-62 Inderpuri, New Delhi 100 012, India. TEL 91-11-579-3211, 91-11-579-3212, FAX 91-11-579-8876, custserve@globepub.com, http://www.globepub.com.

629.13 USA ISSN 0584-6099
SPACE CONGRESS. PROCEEDINGS. Text in English. 1964. a. USD 80 (effective 2004).
Related titles: CD-ROM ed.: USD 50 (effective 2004).
—BLDSC (6849.277000).
Published by: Canaveral Council of Technical Societies, PO Box 245, Cape Canaveral, FL 32920-0245. http://www.canaveralcts.org.

629.13 USA ISSN 1048-2652
SPACE FAX DAILY. Text in English. 1984. d. USD 195 to individuals; USD 570 foreign to individuals; USD 295 to institutions; USD 670 foreign to institutions. **Document type:** *Newsletter.* **Description:** Provides information on the developments and technology of the space industry.
Formerly: Space Daily (0749-6575)
Related titles: Fax ed.; Online - full text ed.
Published by: Space Age Publishing Company, 75-5751 Kuakini Hwy., Ste. 201, Kaulua-kona, HI 96740. TEL 808-326-2014, FAX 808-326-1825, spaceage@ilhawaii.net. Ed., Pub. Steve Durst.

629.4 JPN
SPACE IN JAPAN. Text in English. biennial. JPY 1,500. illus. **Description:** Covers Japan's space development policies, national organizations for space activities, international cooperation projects; profiles of members; addresses of related organizations; information on and brief histories of space development.
Published by: Kagaku Gijutsu-cho/Science and Technology Agency, 2-1 Kasumigaseki 2-chome, Chiyoda-ku, Tokyo, 100-0013, Japan. TEL 03-3581-5271. **Subscr. to:** Keidanren (Federation of Economic Organizations), 1-9-4 Ote-Machi, Chiyoda-ku, Tokyo 100-0004, Japan.

629.1 AUS ISSN 1329-4857
SPACE INDUSTRY NEWS. Abbreviated title: SpIN. Text in English. 1985. q. 12 p./no.; back issues avail. **Document type:** *Newsletter.*
Former titles (until Dec. 1997): C S I R O Space Industry News (1037-5759); (until 1990): C O S S A Space Industry News (0816-7044)
Related titles: Online - full text ed.
Indexed: AESIS.
Published by: Cooperative Research Centre for Satellite Systems, GPO Box 1483, Canberra, ACT 2601, Australia. TEL 61-2-62818520, FAX 61-2-62818521, satsys@crcss.csiro.au, http://www.crcss.csiro.au/about/spin/spin.htm, http://www.crcss.csiro.au/default.htm. Eds. Jeff Kingwell, Wayne Deeker. Circ: 2,500.

629.41 330 USA
SPACE NEWS (NEW YORK). Text in English. w. adv. **Description:** Covers the business aspect of the international space industry.
Published by: SPACE.com, 120 W 45th St, New York, NY 10036. TEL 212-703-5800, FAX 212-703-5900, info@space.com, advertising@hq.space.com, http://www.space.com.

629.1 USA ISSN 1046-6940
TL787
SPACE NEWS (SPRINGFIELD). Text in English. 1989. 48/yr. (Mon.). USD 139 domestic; USD 159 in Canada; USD 199 elsewhere (effective 2005). adv. charts. reprint service avail. from PQC. **Document type:** *Newspaper.* **Description:** Covers the international politics and business of the space industry.
Related titles: Microform ed.; Online - full text ed.
Indexed: B&I, BiolDig, BrCerAb, C&ISA, CerAb, CivEngAb, CorrAb, E&CAJ, EMA, IAA, M&TEA, MBF, METADEX, SolStAb, WAA.
—IE, Linda Hall. **CCC.**
Published by: Imaginova Corp., 470 Park Ave. S., New York, NY 10016. TEL 212-703-5800, FAX 212-703-5802, spacenewshelp@imaginova.com, info@hq.space.com, http://www.spacenews.com, http://www.imaginova.com/. Circ: 13,417.

629.1 GBR ISSN 0265-9646
TL787 CODEN: SPCPEO
➤ **SPACE POLICY.** Text in English. 1985. 4/yr. EUR 213 in Europe to individuals; JPY 28,100 in Japan to individuals; USD 237 to individuals except Europe and Japan; EUR 1,255 in Europe to institutions; JPY 166,700 in Japan to institutions; USD 1,405 to institutions except Europe and Japan (effective 2006). adv. bk.rev. illus. Index. reprints avail. **Document type:** *Academic/Scholarly.* **Description:** Takes an interdisciplinary approach to space activities and developments in their industrial, economic, political, legal and social contexts.
Related titles: Microform ed.: (from PQC); Online - full text ed.: (from EBSCO Publishing, Gale Group, IngentaConnect, ScienceDirect, Swets Information Services).
Indexed: ASCA, BrCerAb, C&ISA, CerAb, CivEngAb, CommAb, CorrAb, CurCont, E&CAJ, EAA, EMA, IAA, LID&ISL, M&TEA, MBF, METADEX, PAIS, PSA, RASB, SSCI, TelAb, WAA.
—BLDSC (8361.604500), CISTI, IDS, IE, Infotrieve, ingenta, Linda Hall. **CCC.**
Published by: Pergamon (Subsidiary of: Elsevier Science & Technology), The Boulevard, Langford Ln, East Park, Kidlington, Oxford OX5 1GB, United Kingdom. TEL 44-1865-843000, FAX 44-1865-843010, http://www.elsevier.com/locate/spacepol. Ed. Frances Brown. **Subscr. to:** Elsevier BV, PO Box 211, Amsterdam 1000 AE, Netherlands. TEL 31-20-485-3757, FAX 31-20-485-3432, nlinfo-f@elsevier.nl, http://www.elsevier.nl.

629.13 USA ISSN 0733-8678
SPACE PRESS* . Text in English. 1981. m. USD 50. adv. bk.rev. charts; illus.; pat.; stat. **Document type:** *Newsletter.* **Description:** Complete coverage of all US and international space news.
Published by: Vernuccio Publications, 3148 Fairmount Ave, Bronx, NY 10465-1415. TEL 212-724-5919. Ed. Frank V Vernuccio Jr. Circ: 1,000.

629.1 USA ISSN 0743-8982
SPACE R & D ALERT* . Text in English. 1982. bi-m. USD 195. adv. bk.rev. back issues avail.
Formerly: Space Journal (0736-0789)
Related titles: Online - full text ed.: 1982.
Published by: Aerospace Communications, c/o Jeffrey K Manber, Ed, 519 N Alfred St, Alexandria, VA 22314-2226. Ed. Jeffrey K Manber. Circ: 3,500.

SPACE RESEARCH IN JAPAN. see *ASTRONOMY*

629.44 GBR ISSN 1366-6827
SPACE REVIEW. Text in English. 1988. m. GBP 600 (effective 2003). **Document type:** *Journal, Trade.* **Description:** Provides data and statistics on the launching and operating of satellites, with particular emphasis on communication satellites.
Published by: Airclaims Limited, Cardinal Point, Newall Rd, Heathrow Airport, London, TW6 2AS, United Kingdom. TEL 44-20-8897-1066, FAX 44-20-8897-0300, ian.sheppard@airclaims.co.uk, http://www.airclaims.co.uk.

624.9 USA
SPACE SAFETY AND RESCUE (YEAR). Text in English. 1974. a. illus. back issues avail. **Document type:** *Proceedings.*
Formerly (until 1976): Space Rescue and Safety
Related titles: Microfiche ed.; ♦ Series of: Science and Technology Series. ISSN 0278-4017; ♦ Supplement to: Advances in the Astronautical Sciences. ISSN 0065-3438.
Published by: (American Astronautical Society, Inc.), Univelt, Inc., PO Box 28130, San Diego, CA 92198-0130. TEL 760-746-4005, FAX 760-746-3139, 76121.1532@compuserve.com, http://www.univelt.com. Ed., Pub., R&P Robert H Jacobs.

629.1325 USA
SPACE SCIENCE NEWS. Text in English. 1996. irreg.
Media: Online - full content.
Published by: N A S A Marshall Space Flight Center, Space Sciences Laboratory, Huntsville, AL 12345. gregory.wilson@msfc.nasa.gov, http://science.nasa.gov. Ed. Gregory Wilson.

SPACE SCIENCE REVIEWS. see *ASTRONOMY*

629.13 GBR
SPACE TECHNOLOGY (LONDON). Text in English. 2000. irreg., latest vol.1. price varies. **Document type:** *Monographic series, Academic/Scholarly.*
Published by: Imperial College Press (Subsidiary of: World Scientific Publishing Co. Pte. Ltd.), 57 Shelton St, London, WC2H 9HE, United Kingdom. TEL 44-20-7836-3954, FAX 44-20-7836-2002, edit@icpress.co.uk, geetha@icpress.co.uk, http://www.wspc.com.sg/books/series/st_series.shtml, http://www.icpress.co.uk/. Ed. Anthony K Hyder.

621.48 USA
CODEN: SNPSEG
SPACE TECHNOLOGY AND APPLICATIONS INTERNATIONAL FORUM (YEAR). Text in English. 1984. a. (in 2 vols.). price varies. **Document type:** *Proceedings.*
Former titles: Symposium on Space Nuclear Systems. Proceedings; Space Nuclear Power Systems (1041-2824)
Indexed: IAA.
—CASDDS, CISTI.
Published by: Institute for Space Nuclear Power Studies, University of New Mexico, Albuquerque, NM 87131. TEL 505-277-2813. Ed. Mohamed S El Genk.

629.1 JPN ISSN 1347-3832
SPACE TECHNOLOGY JAPAN. Text in English. irreg. **Document type:** *Journal, Academic/Scholarly.*
Media: Online - full content.
Published by: Nihon Koku Uchu Gakkai/Japan Society for Aeronautical and Space Sciences, Ohkami Meiwa Bldg. 3F, 1-18-2 Shimbashi, Minato-ku, Tokyo, 105-0004, Japan. TEL 81-3-35010463, JSASS@capj.or.jp, http://stj.jstage.jst.go.jp/, http://www.jsass.or.jp/web/.

629.1 NLD ISSN 0924-4263
➤ **SPACE TECHNOLOGY LIBRARY.** Text in English. 1987. irreg., latest vol.17, 2004. price varies. **Document type:** *Monographic series, Academic/Scholarly.*
—BLDSC (8361.660200), CISTI.
Published by: Springer-Verlag Dordrecht (Subsidiary of: Springer Science+Business Media), Van Godewijckstraat 30, Dordrecht, 3311 GX, Netherlands. TEL 31-78-6576050, FAX 31-78-6576474, http://www.springeronline.com. Ed. J R Wertz.

629.4 USA
SPACE TIMES (SPRINGFIELD). Text in English. 1962. bi-m. USD 80 domestic to institutions; USD 95 foreign to institutions (effective 2005). bk.rev. charts; illus. 24 p./no. 3 cols./p.; back issues avail.; reprints avail. **Document type:** *Magazine, Academic/Scholarly.* **Description:** Dedicated to advancing all space activities. Readers include space professionals, space enthusiasts, educators, students and anyone interested in the space program and space exploration.
Formerly (until 1986): A A S Newsletter (0001-0227)
—**CCC.**
Published by: American Astronautical Society (Springfield), 6352 Rolling Mill Place, Ste 102, Springfield, VA 22152-2354. TEL 703-866-0020, FAX 703-866-3526, aas@astronautical.org, http://www.astronautical.org. Ed. Roger Launius. Circ: 1,600.

629.1 USA ISSN 0889-6054
SPACE TODAY; covering space from earth to the edge of the universe. Text in English. 1986. m. USD 34.95. adv. bk.rev. index. back issues avail. **Document type:** *Bulletin.* **Description:** Space news, astronomy, sciences and flights.
Published by: Arcsoft Publishers, 8000 Carnostie Dr., Laurinburg, NC 28352-7805. TEL 410-742-9009. Ed. Anthony R Curtis. Circ: 5,000.

629.1 GBR
SPACE: UK. Text in English. 1999. 3/yr. free. bk.rev.; software rev. back issues avail. **Document type:** *Government.*
Related titles: Online - full text ed.
Published by: British National Space Centre, 151 Buckingham Palace Rd, London, SW1W 9SS, United Kingdom. TEL 44-171-215-0807, FAX 44-171-215-0938, information@bnsc-hg.ccmail.compuserve.com, http://www.bnsc.gov.uk. Ed. Brian Mairs. Circ: 10,000.

629.44 USA
SPACEANTHOLOGY.COM. Text in English. 2000. **Document type:** *Magazine, Consumer.* **Description:** Informs the general public about the science behind aerospace issues, space exploration and space development.
Media: Online - full content.

▼ new title ➤ refereed ✶ unverified ♦ full entry avail.

Address: P O Box 22703, Newport News, VA 23609. editor@spaceanthology.com, http://www.spaceanthology.com. Ed. E. Ward.

629.44 520 AUS
SPACEDAILY. Text in English. d. **Document type:** *Academic/Scholarly.* **Description:** Covers news, events, and editorial articles on the issues of space, engineering, design, science and other technical details.
Media: Online - full content.
Published by: Space Daily, PO Box A447, Sydney South, NSW 2000, Australia. TEL 61-2-9360-2257, simon@spacer.com, http://www.spacedaily.com/.

629.4 GBR ISSN 0038-6340
TL787 CODEN: SPFLAN
SPACEFLIGHT; the magazine of astronautics and outer space. Text in English. 1956. m. GBP 43, USD 80 membership; GBP 15, USD 54 to students (under 22 years); GBP 29, USD 54 to senior citizens (over 65 years) (effective 2004). adv. bk.rev.; software rev. charts; illus. index. 48 p./no.; back issues avail.; reprint service avail. from PQC. **Document type:** *Magazine, Consumer.* **Description:** Explores all aspects of space flight and space exploration.
Incorporates: Space Education (0261-1813)
Related titles: Microform ed.: (from PQC); Online - full text ed.: (from H.W. Wilson, O C L C Online Computer Library Center, Inc.).
Indexed: AS&TI, ApMecR, BrArAb, BrCerAb, BrTechI, C&ISA, CerAb, ChemAb, CivEngAb, CorrAb, E&CAJ, EMA, EngInd, IAA, IBR, Inspec, M&TEA, MBF, METADEX, SolStAb, WAA.
—BLDSC (8361.700000), CISTI, IE, Infotrieve, ingenta. **CCC.**
Published by: British Interplanetary Society, 27-29 S Lambeth Rd, London, SW8 1SZ, United Kingdom. TEL 44-20-77353160, FAX 44-20-78201504, sf@bis-spaceflight.com, mail@bis-spaceflight.com, http://www.bis-spaceflight.com/publicA.htm, http://bis-spaceflight.com. Ed., Adv. contact Clive Simpson. Circ: 8,000. **Dist. by:** Lakeside Publishing Services, Unit 1D. Tideway Industrial Estate, 87 Kirtling St, London SW8 5BP, United Kingdom. TEL 44-20-77206680, FAX 44-20-74989616.

629.4 USA ISSN 1081-6003
SPACEFLIGHT MECHANICS. Text in English. 1991. a. price varies. charts; illus. back issues avail. **Document type:** *Proceedings, Academic/Scholarly.*
Related titles: ♦ Series of: Advances in the Astronautical Sciences. ISSN 0065-3438; ♦ Supplement to: A A S Microfiche Series. ISSN 0065-7417.
Indexed: IAA.
—CCC.
Published by: (American Astronautical Society, Inc.), Univelt, Inc., PO Box 28130, San Diego, CA 92198-0130. TEL 760-746-4005, FAX 760-746-3139, 76121.1532@compuserve.com, http://www.univelt.com. Ed., Pub., R&P Robert H Jacobs.

629.44 330 AUS
SPACEMART. Text in English. d. adv. **Document type:** *Academic/Scholarly.* **Description:** Details the business-end of space travel and space science.
Media: Online - full content.
Published by: Space Daily, PO Box A447, Sydney South, NSW 2000, Australia. TEL 61-2-9360-2257, simon@spacer.com, http://www.spacemart.com/, http://www.spacedaily.com/.

629.44 USA
SPACEWARN BULLETIN. Text in English. m. back issues avail. **Document type:** *Bulletin, Government.* **Description:** Provides brief description of satellites and space probes launched during the preceding month.
Media: Online - full text.
Published by: N A S A Goddard Space Flight Center, National Space Science Data Center, Code 633, Greenbelt Rd, Greenbelt, MD 20771. TEL 301-286-7355, FAX 301-286-1771, wwas@nssdca.gsfc.nasa.gov, joseph.h.king@gsfc.nasa.gov, http://nssdc.gsfc.nasa.gov/spacewarn/.

629.1 USA ISSN 1076-609X
SPACEWATCH. Text in English. 1984. m. membership. adv. **Document type:** *Newsletter.*
Published by: United States Space Foundation, 310 S 14th St, Colorado Springs, CO 80904-4009. TEL 719-576-8000, FAX 719-576-8801. Pub. Richard P MacLeod. R&P Steve Eisenhart. Adv. contact Beth-Ann Lipskin.

SPINOFF. see *TECHNOLOGY: COMPREHENSIVE WORKS*

629.13 USA ISSN 0038-7835
GV758 CODEN: SCOPER
SPORT AVIATION. Variant title: E A A Sport Aviation. Text in English. 1953. m. USD 40 membership (effective 2005). adv. bk.rev. charts; illus. 136 p./no. 3 cols./p.; reprints avail. **Document type:** *Magazine, Consumer.* **Description:** Covers a wide variety of recreational aviation topics ranging from building and restoring to flying adventures and education.
Related titles: CD-ROM ed.
Indexed: IHTDI, PMR, SportS.
Published by: Experimental Aircraft Association, Inc., 3000 Poberezny Rd, Oshgosh, WI 54901. TEL 920-426-4800, FAX 920-426-4873, editorial@eaa.org, editorial@eaa.org, http://www.eaa.org/benefits/sportaviation/index.html. Ed. Scott M Spangler. Pub. Tom Poberezny. Adv. contact Julie Russo. B&W page USD 3,555, color page USD 52,000. Circ: 170,000 (paid).

SPORT ROCKETRY. see *HOBBIES*

SPORTPARACHUTIST. see *SPORTS AND GAMES—Outdoor Life*

629.132 USA ISSN 0279-1749
TL721.4
SPORTSMAN PILOT✶. Text in English. 1981. q. USD 8 domestic; USD 9 foreign (effective 2000). adv. bk.rev. **Document type:** *Consumer.*
Published by: Jack B. Cox, Ed. & Pub., PO Box 400, Asheboro, NC 27204-0400. TEL 920-231-6657. Circ: 3,000.

629.45 FRA ISSN 1273-8476
SPOUTNIK MAGAZINE; histoires de la conquete spatiale. Text in French. 1997. q.
Published by: Editions Explorer France, Le Prologue 1 voie no. 1, Labege, Cedex 31312, France. TEL 33-5-61004848, FAX 33-5-61004738. Ed. Catherine Dorr. Pub. Laurent Husson.

629.44 AUS
STATIONDAILY. Text in English. d. **Document type:** *Academic/Scholarly.* **Description:** Covers news and events on orbital crafts, including the International Space Station, space tourism, and the latest science.
Media: Online - full content.
Published by: Space Daily, PO Box A447, Sydney South, NSW 2000, Australia. TEL 61-2-9360-2257, simon@spacer.com, http://www.space-travhttp://www.space-travel.com/el.com/, http://www.spacedaily.com/.

001.942 ESP
STENDEK. Text in Spanish. 1970. 4/yr. USD 12. bk.rev. **Description:** Covers unidentified flying objects.
Published by: Centro de Estudios Interplanetarios de Barcelona, Apto. 282, Barcelona, Spain. Ed. Pedro Redon. Circ: 1,400.

629.4 NLD ISSN 0926-7093
➤ **STUDIES IN ASTRONAUTICS.** Text in English. 1979. irreg., latest vol.4, 1990. price varies. **Document type:** *Monographic series, Academic/Scholarly.* **Description:** Reviews topics in astronautics.
—CISTI.
Published by: Elsevier BV (Subsidiary of: Elsevier Science & Technology), Radarweg 29, Amsterdam, 1043 NX, Netherlands. TEL 31-20-4853911, FAX 31-20-4852457, nlinfo-f@elsevier.nl, http://www.elsevier.nl.

➤ **SURINAM. CENTRAAL BUREAU LUCHTKARTERING. JAARVERSLAG.** see *GEOGRAPHY*

629.1309 SWE ISSN 1100-9837
➤ **SVENSK FLYGHISTORISK TIDSKRIFT.** Text in Swedish. 1970. 6/yr. SEK 300 domestic; SEK 370 in Scandinavia; SEK 410 elsewhere (effective 2004). adv. bk.rev. **Document type:** *Academic/Scholarly.*
Former titles (until 1990): Flyghistorisk Maanadsblad (0345-3421); (until 1971): Flyghistorisk Tidskrift
Published by: Svensk Flyghistorisk Foerening/Swedish Aviation Historical Society, PO Box 10267, Stockholm, 10055, Sweden. sven.stridsberg@geol.lu.se, sffkansli@telia.com, http://www.sff.n.se. Ed., R&P Sven Stridsberg. Circ: 5,400.

629.13 ISR ISSN 0072-9302
CODEN: TIDRAR
T.A.E. REPORT. Text in English. 1959. irreg. USD 20.
Indexed: ApMecR.
—Linda Hall.
Published by: Technion - Israel Institute of Technology, Department of Aeronautical Engineering, Haifa, Israel. TEL 04-292260, FAX 04-231848, TELEX 46406-TECON-IL. Circ: 100.

629.4 CHN
TAIKONG TANSUO/EXPLORATION OF OUTER SPACE. Text in Chinese. m. USD 28.80; USD 2.40 newsstand/cover (effective 2001). **Document type:** *Academic/Scholarly.*
Published by: Zhongguo Yuhang Xuehui/Chinese Astronautic Society, 2 Yuetan Beixiaojie, Beijing, 100830, China. **Dist. by:** China International Book Trading Corp, 35 Chegongzhuang Xilu, Haidian District, PO Box 399, Beijing 100044, China. TEL 86-10-68412045, FAX 86-10-68412023, cibtc@mail.cibtc.com.cn, http://www.cibtc.com.cn.

629.13 UAE
AL-TAIRAN AL-MADANI/CIVIL AVIATION. Text in Arabic. 1980. m. free. **Description:** Covers civil aviation matters in the U.A.E., including safety awareness.
Published by: Civil Aviation Administration, PO Box 20, Abu Dhabi, United Arab Emirates. TEL 757500. Ed. Ali Bin Khalfan Al Dahiri. Circ: 1,000.

629.13 GBR
TECH LOG. Text in English. 1970. m. membership. adv. **Document type:** *Newsletter, Trade.* **Description:** Deals with technical and legal matters facing membership. Also covers aircraft maintenance techniques.
Published by: Association of Licensed Aircraft Engineers (1981), Bourn House, 8 Park St, Bagshot, Surrey GU19 5AQ, United Kingdom. TEL 44-1276-474888, FAX 44-1276-452767. Ed. Gerry Evans. R&P, Adv. contact Wendy Evans. page GBP 100. Circ: 1,800.

629.132 USA ISSN 0744-8996
TL760.A1
➤ **TECHNICAL SOARING.** Text in English. 1976. q. free membership (effective 2005). illus. back issues avail.; reprints avail. **Document type:** *Magazine, Consumer.*
Indexed: SportS.
—BLDSC (8726.780000), CISTI, IE, ingenta.
Published by: Technical Soaring Society of America, Inc., PO Box 2100, Hobbs, NM 88241-2100. TEL 505-392-1177, FAX 503-392-8154, magazine@ssa.org, http://www.ssa.org. Ed. Mark Kennedy. Circ: 750.

629.45 RUS ISSN 0868-8060
TEKHNIKA VOZDUSHNOGO FLOTA. Text in Russian. bi-m. USD 229.95 in United States.
Indexed: RefZh.
—East View.
Published by: Tsentral'nyi Aerogidrodinamicheskii Institut im. N.E. Zhukovskogo, Ul Radio 17, Moscow, 107005, Russian Federation. TEL 7-095-2634039. **US dist. addr.:** East View Information Services, 3020 Harbor Ln. N., Minneapolis, MN 55447. TEL 612-550-0961.

629.78 FIN ISSN 1235-9572
TEKNO NYT. Text in Finnish. 1992. irreg. **Document type:** *Monographic series, Trade.*
Published by: Tekes, PO Box 69, Helsinki, 001011, Finland. TEL 358-10-5215856, FAX 358-10-5215901, tekes@tekes.fi, http://www.tekes.fi.

629.78 FIN ISSN 1239-758X
TEKNOLOGIAKATSAUS. Text in Finnish. 1985. irreg. **Document type:** *Monographic series, Trade.*
Formerly (until 1996): Julkaisu - Tekes (0782-5420)
Published by: Tekes, PO Box 69, Helsinki, 001011, Finland. TEL 358-10-5215856, FAX 358-10-5215901, tekes@tekes.fi, http://www.tekes.fi.

TELESCOPIUM. see *ASTRONOMY*

629.1 USA ISSN 0193-4120
TA171
TEST ENGINEERING & MANAGEMENT. Text in English. 1959. bi-m. USD 50 domestic; USD 60 foreign; free to qualified personnel (effective 2005). adv. bk.rev. charts; illus.; tr.lit. index. 24 p./no. 3 cols./p.; back issues avail. **Document type:** *Magazine, Trade.* **Description:** Exchange of ideas and information among reliability, qualification testing professionals. Covers shock and vibration testing; model analysis, materials testing, climatics testing, product and package testing, automotive testing, biomedical testing, and stress screening.
Formerly (until 1963): Test Engineering (0097-3882)
Indexed: BrCerAb, C&ISA, CerAb, CivEngAb, CorrAb, CurPA, E&CAJ, EMA, EngInd, IAA, M&TEA, MBF, METADEX, SolStAb, WAA.
—BLDSC (8796.361000), CISTI, Ei (8796.361000), IE, Infotrieve, ingenta, Linda Hall.
Published by: Mattingley Publishing Co., Inc., 3756 Grand Ave, Ste 205, Oakland, CA 94610. TEL 510-839-0909, FAX 510-839-2950, testmag@testmagazine.biz, testmag@mattingley-publ.com, http://twstmagazine.biz, http://www.mattingley-publ.com. adv.: B&W page USD 3,250; trim 8 x 10.88. Circ: 9,000 (controlled).

629.13 NLD ISSN 0040-6023
THERMIEK. Text in Dutch. 1964. 5/yr. EUR 20 domestic; EUR 30 in Europe; EUR 35 elsewhere. adv. bk.rev. **Description:** Includes gliding news and activities, reports of events, championships, technical information, new designs, safety information, and list of events.
—IE.
Published by: Koninklijke Nederlandse Vereniging voor Luchtvaart, Afdeling Zweefvliegen/Royal Netherlands Aeronautical Association, Postbus 484, Arnhem, 6800 AL, Netherlands. TEL 31-26-3514515, FAX 31-26-3510446, info@thermiekfotowedstrijd.nl, knvvlsz@xs4all.nl, http://www.thermiekfotowedstrijd.nl.

629.44 522 USA
TODAY AT N A S A. Text in English. d. free. illus. back issues avail. **Document type:** *Newsletter, Government.* **Description:** Informs the public of NASA's activities, plans, and accomplishments. Discusses matters of manned and unmanned space exploration.
Media: Online - full content.
Published by: U.S. National Aeronautics and Space Administration, Public Affairs Office, Headquarters Bldg, Code P, 300 E St, SW, Washington, DC 20546. comments@hq.nasa.gov, http://www.nasa.gov. Eds. Brian Dunbar, Sudha V Chudamani.

629.1325 USA
TODAY@NASA.GOV. Text in English. 1996. d.
Media: Online - full content.
Published by: U.S. National Aeronautics and Space Administration, Code FEO-2, Washington, DC 20546. TEL 202-453-1533, http://www.nasa.gov/today/index.html.

629.1325 GBR
TODAY'S PILOT; Europe's best G A magazine. Text in English. 2000 (Nov.). m. GBP 33.60 domestic; GBP 39.60 in Europe; GBP 38.40 in US & Canada; GBP 48 elsewhere (effective 2003). back issues avail.; reprints avail. **Document type:** *Magazine, Consumer.* **Description:** Covers topics of interest to the recreational aviator.
Published by: Key Publishing Ltd., PO Box 100, Stamford, Lincs PE9 1XQ, United Kingdom. TEL 44-1780-755131, FAX 44-1780-757261, todayspilot@keypublishing.com, ann.saundry@keypublishing.com, http://www.todayspilot.co.uk/, http://www.keypublishing.com. Ed. Dave Unwin. Pub. Ann Saundry. Adv. contact Ian Swain. Circ: 15,000.

629.132 CAN
TOWLINE. Text in English. irreg. (approx. 6/yr.). membership.
Published by: Edmonton Soaring Club, P O Box 472, Edmonton, AB T5J 2K1, Canada. Ed. Marty Slater. Circ: 100.

629.1 USA ISSN 0041-0365
TRADE-A-PLANE. Text in English. 1937. 36/yr. USD 42 in United States; USD 168 in Canada & Mexico; USD 210 elsewhere; USD 53 in United States for 12 issues; USD 53 in Canada & Mexico for 12 issues; USD 70 elsewhere for 12 issues (effective 2001); Print subscr. includes free online access. adv. **Document type:** *Newspaper.* **Description:** Provides buying and selling information for general aviation.
Related titles: Online - full text ed.: USD 29; USD 2.95 per month (effective 2001).
Address: 174 Fourth St, Crossville, TN 38555. TEL 931-484-5137, 800-337-5263, FAX 931-484-2532, 800-423-9030, subs@trade-a-plane.com, http://www.trade-a-plane.com. Circ: 211,080.

629.1325 355 387.7 GBR
TRANSMIT; the journal of the Guild of Air Traffic Control Officers. Text in English. 1961. q. GBP 20; GBP 5 newsstand/cover (effective 2000). adv. video rev. charts; illus.; stat.; tr.lit. back issues avail. **Document type:** *Magazine, Trade.* **Description:** Air traffic management technical and professional issues targeted at air traffic control officers.
Related titles: Online - full text ed.
Published by: (The/U K Guild of Air Traffic Control Officers), G A T C O, 47 Heathfield Green, Midhurst, Sussex GU29 9QA, United Kingdom. TEL 44-1730-814364, FAX 44-1730-814364, transmit@gatco.org, http://www.gatco.org. Ed. Michael L Burlyn. adv.: color page GBP 400. Circ: 400 (paid); 2,600 (controlled).

629.1 CHN ISSN 1001-4055 CODEN: TUJIEG
➤ **TUIJIN JISHU/JOURNAL OF PROPULSION TECHNOLOGY.** Text in Chinese. 1980. bi-m. USD 120 (effective 1998 & 1999). adv. **Document type:** *Academic/Scholarly.* **Description:** Carries theses, research papers, reports in theoretical studies, design, experiment, manufacture and application of propulsion technology in the field of propulsion systems for missiles, launch vehicles and spacecrafts.
Related titles: Online - full text ed.: (from East View Information Services).
Indexed: BrCerAb, C&ISA, CerAb, ChemAb, CivEngAb, CorrAb, E&CAJ, EMA, EngInd, IAA, M&TEA, MBF, METADEX, SolStAb, WAA.
—BLDSC (5042.800000), CASDDS, IE, ingenta, Linda Hall.
Published by: Zhongguo Hangtian Gongye Zonggongsi, Di 3 Yanjiuyuan 31 Yanjiushuo/China Aerospace Corporation, No.3 Third Research Academy, No.31 Institute, PO Box 7208 26, Beijing, 100074, China. TEL 86-10-6837-6141, FAX 86-10-6837-4052, TELEX 222832 AHY CN. Ed., R&P Yaosong Dai TEL 86-10-6837-7584. Adv. contact Shi Yahong. Circ: 2,000.

➤ **TURBULENCE.** see *METROLOGY AND STANDARDIZATION*

➤ **TURKISH DEFENCE & AEROSPACE UPDATE.** see *MILITARY*

629.1325 USA
TYPE CERTIFICATION DATA SHEET AND SPECIFICATIONS. VOLUME 1, SINGLE-ENGINE AIRPLANES. Text in English. base vol. plus m. updates. looseleaf. USD 465 (effective 2001). **Document type:** *Government.*
Related titles: ◆ Microfiche ed.: Type Certification Data Sheet and Specifications, Volumes 1 - 6.
Published by: U.S. Federal Aviation Administration, 800 Independence Ave S W, Washington, DC 20591. http://www.faa.gov. **Subscr. to:** U.S. Government Printing Office, Superintendent of Documents, PO Box 371954, Pittsburgh, PA 15250-7954. TEL 202-512-1800, FAX 202-512-2250, orders@gpo.gov, http://www.access.gpo.gov.

629.1325 USA
TYPE CERTIFICATION DATA SHEET AND SPECIFICATIONS. VOLUME 2, SMALL MULTIENGINE AIRPLANES. Text in English. base vol. plus m. updates. looseleaf. USD 435 (effective 2001). **Document type:** *Government.*
Related titles: ◆ Microfiche ed.: Type Certification Data Sheet and Specifications, Volumes 1 - 6.
Published by: U.S. Federal Aviation Administration, 800 Independence Ave S W, Washington, DC 20591. http://www.faa.gov. **Subscr. to:** U.S. Government Printing Office, Superintendent of Documents, PO Box 371954, Pittsburgh, PA 15250-7954. TEL 202-512-1800, FAX 202-512-2250, orders@gpo.gov, http://www.access.gpo.gov.

629.1325 USA
TYPE CERTIFICATION DATA SHEET AND SPECIFICATIONS. VOLUME 3, LARGE MULTIENGINE AIRPLANES. Text in English. base vol. plus m. updates. looseleaf. USD 470 (effective 2001). **Document type:** *Government.*
Related titles: ◆ Microfiche ed.: Type Certification Data Sheet and Specifications, Volumes 1 - 6.
Published by: U.S. Federal Aviation Administration, 800 Independence Ave S W, Washington, DC 20591. http://www.faa.gov. **Subscr. to:** U.S. Government Printing Office, Superintendent of Documents, PO Box 371954, Pittsburgh, PA 15250-7954. TEL 202-512-1800, FAX 202-512-2250, orders@gpo.gov, http://www.access.gpo.gov.

629.1325 USA
TYPE CERTIFICATION DATA SHEET AND SPECIFICATIONS. VOLUME 4, ROTORCRAFT, GLIDERS, BALLOONS, AND AIRSHIPS. Text in English. base vol. plus m. updates. looseleaf. USD 445 (effective 2001). **Document type:** *Government.*
Related titles: ◆ Microfiche ed.: Type Certification Data Sheet and Specifications, Volumes 1 - 6.
Published by: U.S. Federal Aviation Administration, 800 Independence Ave S W, Washington, DC 20591. http://www.faa.gov. **Subscr. to:** U.S. Government Printing Office, Superintendent of Documents, PO Box 371954, Pittsburgh, PA 15250-7954. TEL 202-512-1800, FAX 202-512-2250, orders@gpo.gov, http://www.access.gpo.gov.

629.1325 USA
TYPE CERTIFICATION DATA SHEET AND SPECIFICATIONS. VOLUME 5, AIRCRAFT ENGINES AND PROPELLERS. Text in English. base vol. plus m. updates. looseleaf. USD 460 (effective 2001). **Document type:** *Government.*
Related titles: ◆ Microfiche ed.: Type Certification Data Sheet and Specifications, Volumes 1 - 6.
Published by: U.S. Federal Aviation Administration, 800 Independence Ave S W, Washington, DC 20591. http://www.faa.gov. **Subscr. to:** U.S. Government Printing Office, Superintendent of Documents, PO Box 371954, Pittsburgh, PA 15250-7954. TEL 202-512-1800, FAX 202-512-2250, orders@gpo.gov, http://www.access.gpo.gov.

629.1325 USA
TYPE CERTIFICATION DATA SHEET AND SPECIFICATIONS, VOLUMES 1 - 6. Text in English. base vol. plus m. updates. USD 260 (effective 2001). **Document type:** *Government.*
Media: Microfiche. **Related titles:** ◆ Print ed.: Type Certification Data Sheet and Specifications. Volume 1, Single-Engine Airplanes; ◆ Type Certification Data Sheet and Specifications. Volume 2, Small Multiengine Airplanes; ◆ Type Certification Data Sheet and Specifications. Volume 3, Large Multiengine Airplanes; ◆ Type Certification Data Sheet and Specifications. Volume 4, Rotorcraft, Gliders, Balloons, and Airships; ◆ Type Certification Data Sheet and Specifications. Volume 5, Aircraft Engines and Propellers.
Published by: U.S. Federal Aviation Administration, 800 Independence Ave S W, Washington, DC 20591. http://www.faa.gov. **Subscr. to:** U.S. Government Printing Office, Superintendent of Documents, PO Box 371954, Pittsburgh, PA 15250-7954. TEL 202-512-1800, FAX 202-512-2250, orders@gpo.gov, http://www.access.gpo.gov.

001.94 USA
TL789.A1
U F O; a forum for extraordinary theories and phenomena The Science and Phenomena Magazine. Text in English. 1986. bi-m. USD 19.99 domestic; USD 35 foreign (effective 2001). adv. bk.rev.; film rev. bibl.; charts; illus.; pat.; stat. 80 p./no.; back issues avail. **Document type:** *Magazine.* **Description:** Affords a journalistic and cultural view of UFO reports, theories and ideas. Covers broad range of approaches.
Published by: U F O Media Group, PO Box 66970, Los Angeles, CA 90066-0970. TEL 310-827-0505. Ed. Vicki Cooper Ecker. Pub. William Birnes. Circ: 24,000.

001.942 SWE ISSN 0284-9291
U F O - AKTUELLT. (Unidentified Flying Object) Text in Swedish. 1980. q. SEK 190 domestic; SEK 250 foreign; SEK 47.50 newsstand/cover (effective 2001). adv. bk.rev.; video rev. charts; illus. 32 p./no. 3 cols./p.; back issues avail. **Document type:** *Newspaper.* **Description:** Covers investigations of alleged sightings of UFOs, interviews and articles for the general public.
Formerly (until 1984): U F O - Sverige - Aktuellt (0280-0136)
Related titles: Online - full text ed.

Published by: U F O - Sweden, PO Box 175, Sala, 73323, Sweden. TEL 46-08-892053, FAX 46-021-124111, clas.svahn@dn.se, http://www.ufo.se. Ed., Pub., R&P, Adv. contact Hakan Ekstrand TEL 46-021-137003. B&W page SEK 3,500, color page SEK 4,500. Circ: 1,700 (paid); 1,300 (controlled). **Dist. by:** Interpress AB, Fack 901760, Stockholm 12032, Sweden. TEL 46-8-6025560, FAX 46-8-7220028.

001.942 USA
U F O DIGEST; online webzine. (Unidentified Flying Object) Text in English. 1999. m. USD 4.99 (effective 1999). **Document type:** *Newsletter.* **Description:** Deals exclusively with UFO sightings and encounters.
Media: Online - full text.
Address: PO Box 146, Minot, ND 58702. TEL 701-420-1069, 877-536-3806, greyfox@netinc.ca, http://www.ufodigest.com/. Ed. Dirk Vander Ploeg.

U F O ENCOUNTER; journal of U F O research Queensland. (Unidentified Flying Object) see *NEW AGE PUBLICATIONS*

001.942 USA
U F O JOURNAL OF FACTS. Text in English. q. USD 19.95 (effective 2001). **Document type:** *Consumer.* **Description:** Contains color pictures and UFO reports.
Published by: UFO Photo Archives, PO Box 17206, Tucson, AZ 85710 . Ed. Wendelle C Stevens.

001.942 USA
U F O MAGAZINE; the science & phenomena magazine. Text in English. 1986. bi-m. USD 24.99; USD 19.99 for 5 issues (effective 2003). bk.rev.; film rev.; Website rev. 80 p./no.; back issues avail. **Document type:** *Magazine, Consumer.*
Address: PO Box 66970, Los Angeles, CA 90066. TEL 310-827-0505, FAX 310-827-6865, vecker@attbi.com, http://www.ufomag.com. Ed. Vicki Ecker. Pub. Bill Birnes. Adv. contact Tom Chambers. Circ: 50,000.

001.942 ITA ISSN 1128-6709
U F O NETWORK. Text in Italian. 1999. m.
Published by: Futuro, Via Appia Nuova 59, Roma, 00183, Italy. mbalien@tin.it.

001.94 USA
U F O NEWSCLIPPING SERVICE. (Unidentified Flying Object) Text in English. 1969. m. USD 55 domestic; USD 80 foreign (effective 2000). bk.rev. back issues avail. **Document type:** *Newsletter.* **Description:** Reports on current worldwide UFO sightings.
Address: 2 Caney Valley Dr, Plumerville, AR 72127. TEL 501-354-2558, ufons@webtv.net. Ed., Pub. Lucius Farish. Circ: 550 (paid).

001.94 DNK ISSN 0049-4976
U F O - NYT. Text in Danish. 1958. q. DKK 267 (effective 2004). adv. bk.rev. illus. back issues avail. **Document type:** *Consumer.* **Description:** Covers unidentified flying objects.
Published by: Skandinavisk U F O Information, PO Box 6, Gentofte, 2820, Denmark. info@sufoi.dk, http://www.ufo.dk/ magasin/unyt-dk.htm, http://www.sufoi.dk. Ed. Kim Moeller Hansen. Circ: 1,500.

001.94 DNK ISSN 0902-2341
U F O VISION. Text in Danish. 1987-1992; resumed 1997. a. price varies. adv. bk.rev. back issues avail. **Document type:** *Consumer.*
Published by: Skandinavisk U F O Information, PO Box 6, Gentofte, 2820, Denmark. info@sufoi.dk, http://www.sufoi.dk/ salg/uvis-an1.htm.

U K ADDITIONAL REQUIREMENTS AND SPECIAL CONDITIONS. see *TRANSPORTATION—Air Transport*

620.419 GBR ISSN 1462-8600
U K SPACE INDEX. Text in English. a. **Document type:** *Directory.*
Formerly: Space and Education; Supersedes in part (in 1992): Directory of U K Space Capabilities
—BLDSC (8361.577250).
Published by: British National Space Centre, 151 Buckingham Palace Rd, London, SW1W 9SS, United Kingdom. TEL 44-171-215-0807, FAX 44-171-215-0936, http:// www.bnsc.gov.uk/.

629.132 USA
U S AIRLINE SALARY SURVEY. Text in English. a. USD 35 to members; USD 40 to non-members (effective 2001).
Media: Online - full content.
Published by: Aviation Information Resources, Inc. (AIR, Inc.), Ailine Pilots Careers, 3800 Camp Creek Pkwy S W Ste 18-100, Atlanta, GA 30331-6228. TEL 404-592-6500, FAX 404-592-6515.

629.13 USA ISSN 0091-0805
TL521
U.S. NATIONAL AERONAUTICS AND SPACE ADMINISTRATION. SCIENTIFIC AND TECHNICAL INFORMATION OFFICE. N A S A S P. (National Aeronautics and Space Administration Special Publication) Text in English. 1962. irreg. price varies. back issues avail. **Document type:** *Monographic series.*

A

—BLDSC (6015.470000), CISTI.
Published by: U.S. National Aeronautics and Space Administration, Scientific and Technical Information Office, 7121 Standard Dr, Hanover, MD 21076-1320. TEL 301-621-0390, FAX 301-621-0134, help@sti.nasa.gov, http://www.hq.nasa.gov/office/hqlibrary/ic/ic2.htm#pubs, http://www.sti.nasa.gov.

629.13 USA ISSN 0499-9320
TL521.3.T4 CODEN: NATMA4
U.S. NATIONAL AERONAUTICS AND SPACE ADMINISTRATION. TECHNICAL MEMORANDUM*. Key Title: N A S A Technical Memorandum. Text in English. irreg. **Document type:** *Monographic series, Government.*
Related titles: Microfiche ed.
Indexed: ASFA, BiolAb, BrCerAb, C&ISA, CIN, CerAb, ChemAb, ChemTitl, CivEngAb, CorrAb, E&CAJ, EMA, ESPM, GEOBASE, IAA, M&TEA, MBF, METADEX, SolStAb, WAA.
—BLDSC (6015.473500), CASDDS, CISTI, Ei.
Published by: U.S. National Aeronautics and Space Administration, Scientific and Technical Information Office, 7121 Standard Dr, Hanover, MD 21076-1320. help@sti.nasa.gov, http://www.sti.nasa.gov.

629.13 USA ISSN 0077-3131
U.S. NATIONAL AERONAUTICS AND SPACE ADMINISTRATION. TECHNICAL NOTES*. Text in English. irreg. **Document type:** *Government.*
Indexed: ApMecR, BiolAb, BrCerAb, C&ISA, CerAb, CivEngAb, CorrAb, E&CAJ, EMA, IAA, M&TEA, MBF, METADEX, SolStAb, WAA.
—CISTI.
Published by: U.S. National Aeronautics and Space Administration, Scientific and Technical Information Office, 7121 Standard Dr, Hanover, MD 21076-1320. help@sti.nasa.gov, http://www.sti.nasa.gov.

U.S. NATIONAL AERONAUTICS AND SPACE ADMINISTRATION. VIDEO CATALOG. see *AERONAUTICS AND SPACE FLIGHT—Abstracting, Bibliographies, Statistics*

629.1 USA ISSN 0741-4587
U S S E A UPDATE; the bulletin of important space news, politics, and information. Text in English. 1980. m. USD 26; USD 32 foreign. back issues avail. **Document type:** *Newsletter.* **Description:** Provides information on space legislation, workshops and conferences.
Related titles: ♦ Cumulative ed. of: Space Age Times. ISSN 0738-0968.
Published by: U S Space Education Association, News Operations Division, PO Box 249, Rheems, PA 17570-0249. TEL 717-367-5196. Ed. Stephen M Cobaugh. R&P Debra Palmisano. Circ: 1,500.

UCHU KOKU KANKYO IGAKU. see *MEDICAL SCIENCES*

001.94 DNK ISSN 1396-5697
UFOLOGISK TIDSSKRIFT; fagtidsskrift for dansk og udenlandsk ufoforskning. Text in Danish. 1996. irreg., latest vol.2.
Published by: Skandinavisk U F O Information, PO Box 6, Gentofte, 2820, Denmark. info@sufoi.dk, http://www.sufoi.dk.

629.1325 USA
ULTRAFLIGHT MAGAZINE. Text in English. m. USD 34.95 domestic; USD 45 in Canada; USD 85 elsewhere; USD 3.50, CND 5.95 newsstand/cover (effective 2001). **Document type:** *Consumer.* **Description:** Contains informative articles and aviation tips, covering wide range of powered flight vehicles.
Published by: Magazine & Design, Inc., PO Box 7008, St Petersburg, FL 33734. ultraflight@ultraflight.com, http://www.ultraflight.com. Adv. contact AnnaMarie Switz TEL 252-353-7065.

797.55 USA ISSN 0883-7937
ULTRALIGHT FLYING!; international magazine of ultralight aviation. Text in English. 1976. m. USD 36.95 domestic; USD 41.95 in Canada & Mexico; USD 44.95 elsewhere; USD 5 per issue (effective 2005). adv. bk.rev. illus. reprints avail. **Document type:** *Magazine, Consumer.* **Description:** For enthusiasts of ultralight and microlight aviation.
Formerly: Glider Rider
Published by: Glider Rider, Inc., Dept N, PO Box 6009, Chattanooga, TN 37401. TEL 423-629-5375, FAX 423-629-5379, contact@ulflyingmag.com, http://www.ultralightflying.com. Eds. Sharon Wilcox, Scott Wilcox. Pub. Tracy Knauss. R&P Scott Wilcox. Adv. contact David Prestridge. Circ: 15,500 (paid).

629.132 USA
UNITED STATES PILOTS ASSOCIATION NEWS. Text in English. bi-m. USD 35. adv. **Document type:** *Newsletter.* **Description:** Covers activities, operations, and meetings of the association, a non-profit group of state pilot organizations and their members united for mutual support, aviation safety and education. Contains news, aviation events, and relevant legislation.
Published by: United States Pilots Association, 483 S. Kirkwood Rd., Ste. 10, St. Louis, MO 63122. TEL 314-849-8772. Ed. Steve Uslan. Pub. Pam Uslan. R&P Jan Hoynacki TEL 417-338-2225. Adv. contact Jeff Griffiths. Circ: 20,000 (controlled).

629.1 USA
UNITED STATES SPACE FOUNDATION. NATIONAL SPACE SYMPOSIUM PROCEEDINGS REPORTS. Text in English. 1984. a. USD 50. adv. **Document type:** *Proceedings.*
Formerly: United States Space Foundation. National Space Symposium Reports
Published by: United States Space Foundation, 310 S 14th St, Colorado Springs, CO 80904-4009. TEL 719-576-8000, FAX 719-576-8801, http://www.inovatec.com/ussf.org, http://www.ussf.org/. Ed., R&P Steve Eisenhart. Pub. Richard P MacLeod. Adv. contact Beth-Ann Lipskin. Circ: 1,400.

629.1 GBR
UNIVERSITY OF SOUTHAMPTON. DEPARTMENT OF AERONAUTICS AND ASTRONAUTICS. TECHNICAL REPORT. Text in English. irreg. **Document type:** *Monographic series.*
—BLDSC (8723.401500).
Published by: University of Southampton, Department of Aeronautics and Astronautics, Highfield, Southhampton, SO17 1BJ, United Kingdom. TEL 44-1703-595000, FAX 44-1703-593058, dm@aero.soton.ac.uk, http://www.soton.ac.uk/genesis/index.htm.

629.13 CAN ISSN 1483-457X
UNIVERSITY OF TORONTO. INSTITUTE FOR AEROSPACE STUDIES. GRADUATE STUDIES AND RESEARCH PROGRESS REPORT. Text in English. 1952-199?; resumed 1992. a. free. **Document type:** *Academic/Scholarly.*
Formerly (until 1994): University of Toronto. Institute for Aerospace Studies. Annual Progress Report (0082-5239)
—BLDSC (4207.423500), CISTI, Linda Hall.
Published by: University of Toronto, Institute for Aerospace Studies, 4925 Dufferin St, Downsview, ON M3H 5T6, Canada. TEL 416-667-7700, FAX 416-667-7799, http://www.utias.utoronto.ca. Circ: 1,000.

629.1 629.13 USA ISSN 0896-8454
CODEN: VGRMEQ
V-GRAM. Text in English. 1980. q.
Indexed: Inspec.
—Linda Hall.
Published by: Jet Propulsion Laboratory, California Institute of Technology, National Aeronautics and Space Administration, 4800 Oak Grove Rd, Pasadena, CA 91109. TEL 818-354-4321.

629.1 IND
➤ **VAYU AEROSPACE REVIEW.** Text in English. 1974. bi-m. INR 250 domestic; USD 40 foreign (effective 2000). adv. bk.rev. **Document type:** *Academic/Scholarly.*
Published by: Society For Aerospace Studies, D-43, Sujan Singh Park, New Delhi, 110 003, India. TEL 91-11-4626183, FAX 91-11-4628615, TELEX 031-63358-LTAIN, vschopra@mailcity.com. Ed. Vikramjit S Chopra. adv.: B&W page USD 1,950, color page USD 3,300. Circ: 20,000 (paid and controlled).

358.4 NLD ISSN 0042-3122
VEILIG VLIEGEN; flight, ground and maintenance safety journal. Text in Dutch. 1953. m. bk.rev. illus. index.
—IE, Infotrieve.
Published by: Koninklijke Luchtmacht, Afdeling Bedrijfsveiligheid Koninklijke Luchtmachtstaf/Royal Netherlands Air Force, Binckhorstlaan 135, Postbus 20703, The Hague, 2500 ES, Netherlands. TEL 70-3492358, FAX 70-3492500, TELEX 43393. Ed. R A Gebhardt. Circ: 5,000 (controlled).

629.133 USA ISSN 0042-4455
TL716.A1 CODEN: VEFLAD
VERTIFLITE. Text in English. 1955. q. USD 90 domestic to members; USD 110 foreign to members (effective 2005). adv. bk.rev. illus. Index. reprints avail. **Document type:** *Magazine, Trade.*
Related titles: Online - full text ed.
Indexed: BrCerAb, C&ISA, CerAb, CivEngAb, CorrAb, E&CAJ, EMA, Englnd, HRIS, IAA, M&TEA, MBF, METADEX, RefZh, WAA.
—BLDSC (9216.900000), CISTI, IE, Infotrieve, ingenta, Linda Hall.
Published by: American Helicopter Society, Inc., 217 N Washington St, Alexandria, VA 22314. TEL 703-684-6777, FAX 703-739-9279, staff@vtol.org, http://www.vtol.org/vertiflite/. Ed. L. Kim Smith. Pub. Rhett Flater. Circ: 6,000 (paid and controlled).

629.1 RUS
VESTNIK AVIATSII I KOSMONAVTIKI; vserossiiskii aerokosmicheskii zhurnal. Text in Russian. 1997. 6/yr. USD 172 foreign (effective 2005). **Document type:** *Journal.* **Description:** Designed for fans of aircraft and professionals. Analytical, information clauses, historical materials.
Address: Ul Viktorenko 7, Moscow, 125319, Russian Federation. TEL 7-095-1577546, FAX 7-095-5039168. Ed. Sergei Skrynnikov TEL 7-095-9740111. Circ: 14,500. **Dist. by:** East View Information Services, 3020 Harbor Ln. N., Minneapolis, MN 55447. TEL 763-550-0961, FAX 763-559-2931, eastview@eastview.com, http://www.eastview.com.

629.45 RUS
VESTNIK AVYATSII I KOSMONAVTIKI. Text in English, Russian. bi-m. USD 115 in United States.
Indexed: RefZh.
Address: Volokolamskoe shosse 4, Moscow, 125871, Russian Federation. TEL 7-095-1959470, FAX 7-095-1959471. Ed. S Skrynnikov. **US dist. addr.:** East View Information Services, 3020 Harbor Ln. N., Minneapolis, MN 55447. TEL 612-550-0961.

629.13 RUS ISSN 1025-6768
TL504
VESTNIK VOZDUSHNOGO FLOTA. Text in Russian. 1918. m. USD 133. **Document type:** *Trade.* **Description:** Covers Russian military and commercial aviation.
Formerly (until 1995): Aviatsiya i Kosmonavtika (0373-9821)
Related titles: Microfiche ed.: (from EVP).
Indexed: LID&ISL, RASB, RefZh.
—CISTI.
Address: Krasnoarmeiskaya ul 4, Moscow, 125167, Russian Federation. TEL 7-095-2121550, FAX 7-095-2125680. **US dist. addr.:** East View Information Services, 3020 Harbor Ln. N., Minneapolis, MN 55447. TEL 612-550-0961.

629.133 DNK ISSN 0109-8330
VETERANFLY KLUBBEN. Text in Danish. 1969. q. DKK 300 to members (effective 1997). adv. bk.rev. illus. **Document type:** *Newsletter.*
Formerly: K Z and Veteranfly Klubben
Published by: K Z & Veteranfly Klubben, Nygade 12 A, PO Box 104, Aabenraa, 6200, Denmark. TEL 45-74-22-22-66, FAX 45-74-62-80-69. Ed. Tine Atterman. Adv. contact Lisbeth Seemann. Circ: 1,000.

629.1 745.1 USA ISSN 0091-6943
TL506.A1
VINTAGE AIRPLANE. Text in English. 1972. m. USD 27 (effective 2000). adv.
Indexed: IHTDI.
—CISTI.
Published by: (Antique Classic Division), Experimental Aircraft Association, Inc., PO Box 3086, Oshkosh, WI 54903-3086. TEL 414-426-4800, http://www.eaa.org, http://www.eaa.org/. Ed. H G Frautshy. Circ: 10,000.

629.13 USA
VOLANDO. Text in Spanish. 1989. q. adv. **Description:** For professional agricultural and air tanker pilots of all Spanish and Portuguese speaking countries.
Published by: Tomelupa, PO Box 71, Sedro Woolley, WA 98284. TEL 877-778-0044, FAX 877-778-0035, agpilot78@aol.com. Ed., Pub. Tom J Wood. adv.: B&W page USD 2,970, color page USD 4,310; trim 8.5 x 10.875.

629.1 ESP
VOLAR. Text in Spanish. 1988. 12/yr. adv. **Document type:** *Consumer.* **Description:** Covers sport flying and parachuting.
Published by: Trade Zap, S.L., C. las Llamas, 5, S. Sebastian De Los Reyes, (Madrid) 28707, Spain. TEL 34-1-6570116, FAX 34-1-6570202. Ed. Enrique Jimenez. Adv. contact Chony Zapico. Circ: 10,600.

797.5 BOL ISSN 1609-6487
VOLAR; la revista de aeronautica de Bolivia. Text in Spanish. 1997. bi-m. USD 20 (effective 2003). adv.
Media: Online - full text.
Published by: Zeta & P Editores, Calle Velasco 580, 1er. Piso, Of 2, Santa Cruz de la Sierra, Bolivia. TEL 591-3-539900, FAX 591-3-539990, http://www.bolivianet.com/volar/cont.htm. Ed. Miguel Zabala Bishop.

629.133 ITA ISSN 1121-5607
VOLARE. Text in Italian. 1983. m. EUR 60 domestic; EUR 89 foreign (effective 2005). adv. **Document type:** *Magazine, Consumer.*
Published by: Editoriale Domus, Via Gianni Mazzocchi 1/3, Rozzano, MI 20089, Italy. TEL 39-02-824721, editorialedomus@edidomus.it, http://www.edidomus.it. Ed. Francesco Giaculli. Circ: 26,024.

629.1 BEL ISSN 0377-8312
CODEN: LSVDDQ
VON KARMAN INSTITUTE FOR FLUID DYNAMICS. LECTURE SERIES. Text in English. 1965. irreg. (approx 10/yr.). EUR 1,169 (effective 2003). back issues avail. **Document type:** *Monographic series, Academic/Scholarly.*
Related titles: Microfiche ed.: (from NTI).
—BLDSC (5180.590000), CISTI, IE, ingenta, Linda Hall.
Published by: Von Karman Institute for Fluid Dynamics/Institut von Karman de Dynamique des Fluides, Ch de Waterloo 72, Rhode-Saint-Genese, 1640, Belgium. TEL 32-2-3599611, FAX 32-2-3599600, biblio@vki.ac.be, http://www.vki.ac.be. Adv. contact Christelle Debeer.

387.7 USA ISSN 0736-198X
TL506.A1
W W I AERO; the journal of the early aeroplane (1900-1918). Text in English. 1961. q. USD 35 domestic; USD 40 foreign (effective 2003). adv. bk.rev.; software rev.; video rev.; film rev. bibl.; charts; illus.; tr.lit. 144 p./no. 2 cols./p.; back issues avail. **Document type:** *Journal, Consumer.* **Description:** Covers restoration, reproduction and modelling of early airplanes, 1900-1918.
Formerly: World War I Aeroplanes

Published by: World War I Aeroplanes, Inc., 15 Crescent Rd, Poughkeepsie, NY 12601-4490. TEL 914-473-3679. Ed., Pub., R&P Leonard E Opdycke TEL 845-473-3679. Adv. contact Beverly Williams TEL 845-473-3679. B&W 1/4 page USD 55. Circ: 1,500.

629.1 USA
UG1240
WARBIRDS INTERNATIONAL. Text in English. 9/yr. USD 21.95; USD 39.95 foreign (effective 1999). adv. **Document type:** *Consumer.*
Formerly: Air Progress Warbirds International (0885-2502)
Published by: Challenge Publications, Inc., 9509 Vassar Ave., Ste. A, Chatsworth, CA 91311-0883. TEL 818-887-0550, FAX 818-884-1343, mail@challengeweb.com, moleary@challengeweb.com, http://www.challengeweb.com. Ed. Michael O'Leary. Pub. Edwin Schnepf. R&P Susan Duprey. Adv. contact Michael Astamendi. Circ: 47,736.

629.133 USA
WARBIRDTECH SERIES. Text in English. irreg. USD 16.95, GBP 9.95 per vol.. charts; illus. back issues avail. **Document type:** *Monographic series, Consumer.* **Description:** Presents in considerable detail the history and technical specifications of a noteworthy military aircraft. Includes regular missions and special variants.
Published by: Specialty Press, 11605 Kost Dam Rd, North Branch, MN 55056. TEL 651-583-3239. **in UK & rest of Europe:** Airlife Publishing Ltd, 101 Longden Rd, Shrewsbury SY3 9EB, United Kingdom.

629.13 POL ISSN 1425-2104
➤ **WARSAW UNIVERSITY OF TECHNOLOGY. INSTITUTE OF AERONAUTICS AND APPLIED MECHANICS. RESEARCH BULLETIN.** Text in English. 1992. irreg., latest vol.12, 2001. bk.rev. illus. 220 p./no. 2 cols./p.; back issues avail. **Document type:** *Bulletin, Academic/Scholarly.*
Published by: (Politechnika Warszawska, Instytut Aeronautyki i Mechaniki Stosowanej/Warsaw University of Technology, Institute of Aeronautics and Applied Mechanics), Oficyna Wydawnicza Politechniki Warszawskiej/Publishing House of the Warsaw University of Technology, ul Polna 50, Warsaw, 00644, Poland. oficyna@wpw.pw.edu.pl. Ed. Zdobyslaw Goraj.

629.1 USA ISSN 0739-6538
WASHINGTON REMOTE SENSING LETTER. Text in English. 1981. 4/m. USD 1,010 in North America; USD 1,100 elsewhere (effective 2004). bk.rev.; software rev.; Website rev. bibl.; stat.; tr.lit. 4 p./no.; back issues avail.; reprints avail. **Document type:** *Newsletter.* **Description:** Includes applications of satellite photography of the earth; also covers related programs of world governments and the private sector.
Related titles: E-mail ed.: USD 3,500 site only email delivery; USD 15,000 global email delivery (effective 2004).
Published by: Felsher Publishing Co., P O Box 20, Germantown, DC 20875-0020. TEL 202-393-3640, FAX 301-428-0557. Ed., Pub. Murray Felsher.

629.1 387.7 USA ISSN 0733-1754
TL684
WATER FLYING. Text in English. bi-m. USD 17.50; USD 3.95 newsstand/cover (effective 2001). adv. **Document type:** *Trade.* **Description:** Covers regulatory, operational, safety, and industry developments. Includes regional reports.
Published by: Seaplane Pilots Association, 4315 Highland Park Blvd, C, Lakeland, FL 33813-7588. TEL 301-695-2083, FAX 301-695-2375, waterflying@seaplanes.org, http://www.seaplanes.org. Circ: 7,500 (controlled).

629.1 387.7 USA ISSN 0193-4198
TL684
WATER FLYING ANNUAL. Text in English. a. USD 10 to non-members (effective 2000). bk.rev. **Document type:** *Trade.* **Description:** Features reports, tips, and techniques to improve seaplane flying. Includes listings of training facilities.
Published by: Seaplane Pilots Association, 4315 Highland Park Blvd, C, Lakeland, FL 33813-7588. TEL 301-695-2083, FAX 301-695-2375. Circ: 8,000.

629.13 DEU ISSN 0043-2172
U3 CODEN: WHTCAK
WEHRTECHNIK; Quartalsschrift fuer wirtschaftliche Fragen der Verteidigung, Luftfahrt und Industrie. Text in German. 1956. q. EUR 40 domestic; EUR 45 foreign (effective 2003). adv. bk.rev. charts; illus. back issues avail. **Document type:** *Magazine, Trade.* **Description:** Covers defense and economics, aerospace technology and electronics.
Formerly (until 1969): Wehrtechnische Monatshefte (0341-9991); Incorporates (1957-1975): Wehr und Wirtschaft (0043-2113)
Indexed: ExcerpMed, IBR, Inspec, LID&ISL, PAIS, RASB, RefZh. —IE, Infotrieve, Linda Hall. **CCC.**
Published by: (Deutsche Gesellschaft fuer Wehrtechnik e.V.), Wehr und Wissen Verlagsgesellschaft mbH, Heilsbachstr 26, Bonn, 53123, Germany. TEL 49-228-6483-0, FAX 49-228-6483-109, marketing@moench-group.com, http://www.monch.com. Ed. Hans Joachim Wagner. Adv. contact Christa Andre TEL 49-228-6483137. B&W page USD 5,550, color page USD 9,000; trim 7.3125 x 10.1666. Circ: 14,821.

629.1 DEU
DIE WELT DER LUFTSCHIFFE. Text in German. 1963. 3/yr. **Document type:** *Bulletin.*
Published by: Verein der Luftschiffahrt e.V., Falkentaler Steig 108, Berlin, 13465, Germany.

629.13 330 CAN ISSN 1499-2396
WESTERN CANADIAN AEROSPACE INDUSTRY CAPABILITIES GUIDE. Text in English. 1999. biennial.
Published by: Western Economic Diversification Canada, 700-601 West Hastings St, Price Waterhouse Building, Vancouver, BC V6B 5G9, Canada. TEL 604-666-6256, FAX 604-666-2353.

629.1 GBR
WHAT'S NEW IN U K AEROSPACE. Text in English. bi-m. **Document type:** *Newsletter.*
Former titles: Society of British Aerospace Companies. Agenda; (until 1993): S B A C News
Published by: Society of British Aerospace Companies Ltd., Duxbury House, 60 Petty France, London, SW1H 9EU, United Kingdom. TEL 44-171-227-1000. Ed. Susan Godfrey. Circ: 1,500.

358.4 PAK
WINGS; world review of aviation & defence. Cover title: Monthly Wings. Text in English. 1979. m. PKR 400 domestic; USD 100 foreign (effective 2000). adv. bk.rev. illus. **Document type:** *Trade.* **Description:** Covers news of the aviation, air transport and defense and aerospace sectors in Pakistan and throughout the world.
Published by: Phoenix Publications Co., Chundrigar Rd., Muhammadi House 101, Karachi, 74000, Pakistan. TEL 92-21-2412591, FAX 92-21-2420797. Ed., Pub. Javed Mushtaq. Adv. contact Haseeb Ahmed. Circ: 5,000.

629.13 AUS ISSN 0043-5880
WINGS. Text in English. 1940. q. AUD 10 domestic; AUD 15 foreign (effective 2001). adv. bk.rev. illus. **Description:** Keeps readers up-to-date on current aviation both military and civil.
Related titles: Online - full text ed.: (from Northern Light Technology, Inc.).
Published by: Royal Australian Air Force Association (New South Wales Division) Inc., PO Box A 2147, Sydney South, NSW 1235, Australia. TEL 61-2-92999290, FAX 61-2-92996560. Ed. D Hornsey. Circ: 10,000. **Co-sponsor:** Australian Flying Corps.

358.4 USA ISSN 1067-0637
TL501
WINGS (GRANADA HILLS). Text in English. 1971. bi-m. USD 25; USD 31 foreign (effective 1998). adv. bk.rev. charts; illus.; stat. back issues avail. **Document type:** *Consumer.*
Related titles: Online - full text ed.
Indexed: BiolDig.
Published by: Sentry Books, Inc., 10718 White Oak Ave, Box 3324, Granada Hills, CA 91344. TEL 818-368-2012. Ed. Joseph V Mizrahi. Adv. contact Ed Jacobs. page USD 500. Circ: 60,000.

629.13 USA
WINGS CLUB. BULLETIN. Text in English. m. **Document type:** *Bulletin.*
Published by: Wings Club, 52 Vanderbilt Ave, 18th Fl, New York, NY 10017. TEL 212-867-1770.

359 USA ISSN 0274-7405
VG93
➤ **WINGS OF GOLD.** Text in English. 1975. q. USD 35 (effective 2003). bk.rev. charts; illus. 80 p./no. 2 cols./p.; back issues avail. **Document type:** *Magazine, Academic/Scholarly.*
Related titles: Online - full text ed.: (from bigchalk, Northern Light Technology, Inc., ProQuest Information & Learning).
Published by: (Association of Naval Aviation, Inc.), Wings of Gold, Inc. (Subsidiary of: Association of Naval Aviation, Inc.), 2550 Huntington Ave, 201, Alexandria, VA 22303-1400. TEL 703-960-2490, FAX 703-960-4490, zip@anahq.org, http://www.anahq.org. Ed., R&P Zip Rausa TEL 703-960-2490. Adv. contact Linda Bubien TEL 858-793-0770. Circ: 9,200 (paid).

629.1325 USA ISSN 1069-8736
TL553
WOMAN PILOT. Text in English. 1993. bi-m.
Published by: Aviatrix Publishing, Incorporated, PO Box 485, Arlington Heights, IL 60006-0485. publisher@womanpilot.com, http://www.womanpilot.com. Circ: 6,000.

629.1325 USA ISSN 1064-4997
WONDERFUL WORLD OF FLYING. Text in English. 1987. q. USD 29.95 per vol. (effective 2000). adv. back issues avail. **Description:** Illustrates ways in which pilots can improve their flying skills, becoming safer and more proficient. Aircraft of all types, modern and antique, large and small, are featured.
Former titles: Wide World of Flying; A B C Wide World of Flying
Media: Video.
Published by: Aviation Media Inc, 610 Minuet Ln., Ste. A, Charlotte, NC 28217-2713. TEL 800-772-WWOF, steve.kahn@wwof.com, http://www.wwof.com. Ed., Pub. Stephen Kahn TEL 914-524-0344.

387.7 355 USA
WORLD AEROSPACE & DEFENSE INTELLIGENCE (ONLINE EDITION). Text in English. w. USD 495 (effective 2003). **Description:** Covers the major developments and budgets of the civil and military industries.
Formerly (until 199?): World Aerospace & Defense Intelligence (Print)
Media: Online - full content.
Published by: Forecast International/D M S, 22 Commerce Rd, Newtown, CT 06470. TEL 203-426-0800, FAX 203-426-0223, info@forecast1.com, sales@forecast1.com, http://www.forecast1.com. Ed. Stuart Slade. R&P Ray Peterson.

629.133 GBR ISSN 1369-6483
WORLD AIRCRAFT INFORMATION FILES. Text in English. 1997. w. GBP 1.70 newsstand/cover (effective 2000). **Document type:** *Consumer.* **Description:** Contains detailed reference information on key aspects of aviation - past and present - from fighters, air forces and aces, to airlines, accidents and technology.
Published by: Bright Star Publishing plc, 179 Dalling Rd, London, W6 0ES, United Kingdom. aviation@midsubs.com, http://www.brightstar.co.uk. **Dist. by:** Comag, Tavistock Works, Tavistock Rd, W Drayton, Middx UB7 7QX, United Kingdom. TEL 44-1895-444055, FAX 44-1895-433602.

WORLD AIRLINE FLEETS NEWS. see *TRANSPORTATION—Air Transport*

WORLD AIRLINE REPORT. see *TRANSPORTATION*

629.13 ZAF ISSN 0261-2399
WORLD AIRNEWS. Text in English. 1972. m. ZAR 110 in South Africa & Namibia (effective 2000); ZAR 175, USD 2.50 elsewhere. adv. bk.rev. illus. back issues avail. **Document type:** *Trade.* **Description:** Contains articles, news items, photography, pertaining to commercial and avocational aviation technology and activities in Africa.
Incorporates: African Air Transport (0261-2313); Wings Over Africa (0043-5910)
Indexed: CLT&T, ISAP.
Published by: T C E Publications Ltd, PO Box 35082, Northway, 4065, South Africa. TEL 27-31-564-1319, FAX 27-31-563-7115, tom@airnews.co.za. Ed., Pub., R&P, Adv. contact Tom Chalmers. B&W page USD 2,100, color page USD 3,480; trim 185 x 255. Circ: 13,367 (paid and controlled).

629.132 USA ISSN 0888-5265
WORLD AIRSHOW NEWS; the trade magazine for the airshow entertainment industry. Text in English. 1986. bi-m. USD 20 (effective 2001). adv. bk.rev. **Document type:** *Trade.* **Description:** All known airshow producers in North Americans. Also reaching performers, support services professionals and corporate sponsors.
Published by: Flyer Publications, Inc., PO Box 199, Oregon, WI 53575-0199. TEL 608-835-7063, FAX 608-835-3323, weiman@mailbag.com, http://www.wanews.com. Ed., Pub. Dave Weiman. adv.: color page USD 1,016; trim 10 x 7.5. Circ: 3,000.

387.7 629.13 USA ISSN 0890-510X
TL537
WORLD AND UNITED STATES AVIATION AND SPACE RECORDS. Text in English. a. (plus q. updates). USD 24.95 domestic to non-members; USD 30.95 foreign to non-members; USD 21.95 newsstand/cover (effective 2001). adv. illus.; stat. 448 p./no. 2 cols./p.; **Description:** Showcases records for every flying machine, from model aircraft to the space shuttle, piston-engined craft to jetliners.
Published by: National Aeronautic Association, 1737 King St., Ste. 220, Alexandria, VA 22314-2760. TEL 703-527-0226, FAX 703-527-0229, http://www.naa-usa.org/website/html/records/recordsbook.htm. Ed. Art Greenfield. adv.: page USD 5,500; 5.5 x 8.5.

629.13 USA ISSN 1549-8727
TL512
WORLD AVIATION DIRECTORY & AEROSPACE DATABASE. Text in English. 1940. s-a. USD 259 (effective 2005). adv. pat. index. **Document type:** *Directory, Trade.* **Description:** Lists the people, companies, products and services in aviation, defense and aerospace.
Former titles (until Win. 2003): Aviation Week's World Aviation Directory (1541-146X); (until 2001): World Aviation Directory (0043-826X); Incorporates (1955-1987): Aviation Week and Space Technology Marketing Directory; Which was formerly: Aviation Week and Space Technology. Buyers Guide
Related titles: CD-ROM ed.: USD 795 (effective 2004); Online - full text ed.: USD 995 (effective 2004).
—CCC.
Published by: McGraw-Hill Companies, Aviation Week, 1200 G St, N W, Ste 200, Washington, DC 20005. TEL 202-383-2374, FAX 202-383-2438, http://www.aviationnow.com/aviationnow/wad_marketing_page.jsp, http://www.aviationnow.com/avnow. Ed. Bert J Shayte. Pub. Charles Hull. Circ: 15,000.

A

629.1 GBR ISSN 1368-485X
WORLD DIRECTORY OF LEISURE AVIATION. Text in English. 1992. a. GBP 5.95 domestic; USD 14 foreign (effective 2001). adv. 1 cols./p.; **Document type:** *Magazine, Consumer.* **Description:** Directory of all kinds of leisure aircraft and associated equipment.
Related titles: Online - full content ed.: Widola.com; French ed.; German ed.
Published by: Pagefast Ltd., 4-6 Lansil Way, Lansil Industrial Estate, Lancaster, LA1 3QY, United Kingdom. TEL 44-1524-841010, FAX 44-1524-841578, wdla@pagefast.co.uk, office@pagefast.co.uk, http://www.widola.com/, http://www.pagefast.co.uk. Eds. Martine Coulon, Willi Tacke. Pub., R&P Norman Burr. Adv. contact Wendy Burr. B&W page USD 1,915, color page USD 3,825; trim 297 x 210. Circ: 40,000 (paid).

358.4 USA
WORLD MILITARY AVIATION (YEAR). Cover title: Naval Institute Guide to World Military Aviation. Text in English. biennial. USD 159.95 (effective 1999). illus. **Description:** Covers military combat, transport, and rescue aircraft worldwide.
Published by: (Naval Institute), Naval Institute Press, 291 Maryland Ave, Annapolis, MD 21402. TEL 410-268-6110, FAX 410-269-7940, webmaster@usni.org, http://www.nip.org. Ed. Rene J Francillon. R&P Susan Todd Brook. **Orders to:** 2062 Generals Hwy, Annapolis, MD 21401. TEL 800-233-8764.

629.4 USA
WORLD SPACE SYSTEMS BRIEFING. Text in English. m. looseleaf. **Document type:** *Newsletter.* **Description:** Identifies and analyzes emerging programs and services, with an eye toward helping contractors get in on the bottom floor.
Published by: Teal Group Corp., 3900 University Dr, Ste 220, Fairfax, VA 22030. TEL 703-385-1992, FAX 703-691-9591.

629.1 USA ISSN 0737-8548
WORLD SPACEFLIGHT NEWS. Text in English. m. USD 30.
Published by: Randall M. Schuler, Ed. & Pub., PO Box 98, Sewell, NJ 08080. TEL 609-478-6396.

629.13 CHN ISSN 1004-731X
T57.62
➤ **XITONG FANGZHEN XUEBAO/JOURNAL OF SYSTEM SIMULATION.** Text in Chinese; Abstracts in English. 1989. m. CNY 12, USD 12 newsstand/cover (effective 2002). back issues avail. **Document type:** *Academic/Scholarly.* **Description:** Covers all important subjects related to system simulation, such as theory and methodology of modeling and simulation, credibility evaluation of simulation, V&A, simulation computer and software, artificial intelligence, simulator for training and system research and operation, DIS, simulation-based design, virtual prototype, virtual reality and visualization, and applications of simulation technology to industry, communication, aero-space, military, and national economics.
Related titles: Online - full content ed.: (from WanFang Data Corp.); Online - full text ed.: (from East View Information Services).
Indexed: Englnd, Inspec.
—BLDSC (5068.060500).
Published by: Zhongguo Xitong Fangzhen Xuehui/Chineae Association for System Simulation, PO Box 3929, Beijing, 100854, China. xtfzxb@public3.bta.net.cn, simulate@163.net. Eds. Jing-lian Ma, Jin Wan. Adv. contact Jing-lian Ma. Circ: 2,000 (paid); 150 (controlled).

629.1 CHN ISSN 1007-2330
TL698 CODEN: YCGOFH
➤ **YUHANG CAILIAO GONGYI/AEROSPACE MATERIALS & TECHNOLOGY.** Text in Chinese; Summaries in English. 1971. bi-m. USD 17.40; USD 2.90 newsstand/cover (effective 2001). **Document type:** *Academic/Scholarly.* **Description:** A scientific journal focusing on aerospace materials and technology.
Related titles: Online - full content ed.: (from WanFang Data Corp.); Online - full text ed.: (from East View Information Services).
Indexed: BrCerAb, C&ISA, CerAb, CivEngAb, CorrAb, E&CAJ, EMA, IAA, M&TEA, MBF, METADEX, SolStAb, WAA.
—BLDSC (0729.883100), CASDDS, IE, Linda Hall.
Published by: Hangtian Gongye Zong Gongsi, Hangtian Cailiao ji Gongyi Yanjiu-suo/China Aerospace Corporation, Aerospace Research Institute of Materials and Processing Technology, PO Box 9200-73, Beijing, 100076, China. TEL 86-1-68383269, 86-1-68383269, FAX 86-1-64227606, duyq@mimi.cnc.ac.cn, anb@ns.iai.canet.cn. Ed. Li Hong. **Subscr. to:** An Bo, Dept. of Documentation, PO Box 1408, Beijing 100013, China. TEL 86-1-68372847, FAX 86-1-64227606. **Dist. by:** China International Book Trading Corp, 35 Chegongzhuang Xilu, Haidian District, PO Box 399, Beijing 100044, China. TEL 86-10-68412045, FAX 86-10-68412023, cibtc@mail.cibtc.com.cn, http://www.cibtc.com.cn.

629.13 CHN ISSN 1000-7202
YUHANG JICE JISHU/JOURNAL OF ASTRONAUTIC METROLOGY AND MEASUREMENT. Text in Chinese. 3/yr. USD 12; USD 2 newsstand/cover (effective 2001). back issues avail. **Document type:** *Academic/Scholarly.*
Related titles: Online - full content ed.: (from WanFang Data Corp.); Online - full text ed.: (from East View Information Services).
Published by: Zhongguo Hangtian Keji Jituan Gongsi, PO Box 9200-24, Beijing, 100076, China. TEL 86-1-68383695, FAX 86-1-68383627. Ed. Wenlong Shao. **Dist. by:** China International Book Trading Corp, 35 Chegongzhuang Xilu, Haidian District, PO Box 399, Beijing 100044, China. TEL 86-10-68412045, FAX 86-10-68412023, cibtc@mail.cibtc.com.cn, http://www.cibtc.com.cn.

629.1 CHN ISSN 1000-1328
TL787
YUHANG XUEBAO/JOURNAL OF ASTRONAUTICS. Text in Chinese. 1980. q. USD 37.80; USD 6.30 newsstand/cover (effective 2001). adv.
Related titles: Online - full content ed.: (from WanFang Data Corp.); Online - full text ed.: (from East View Information Services).
Indexed: BrCerAb, C&ISA, CerAb, CorrAb, E&CAJ, EMA, Englnd, IAA, M&TEA, MBF, METADEX, RefZh, WAA.
—BLDSC (4947.498000), Linda Hall.
Published by: (Zhongguo Yuhang Xuehui/Chinese Astronautic Society), Yuhang Xuebao Bianjibu, PO Box 838, Beijing, 100830, China. TEL 86-1-68768107, FAX 86-1-68768107, sh708@263.net. Ed. Zhuang Fenggan. Circ: 1,200. **Dist. outside China by:** China International Book Trading Corp, 35 Chegongzhuang Xilu, Haidian District, PO Box 399, Beijing 100044, China. TEL 86-10-68412045, FAX 86-10-68412023, cibtc@mail.cibtc.com.cn, http://www.cibtc.com.cn.

ZHENDONG CESHI YU ZHENDUAN/ VIBRATION,MEASUREMENT AND DIAGNOSIS. see *ENGINEERING—Mechanical Engineering*

621.811 CHN ISSN 1004-4523
CODEN: ZXUEEA
ZHENDONG GONGCHENG XUEBAO/JOURNAL OF VIBRATION ENGINEERING. Text in Chinese. 1987. q. USD 120 (effective 2000). adv. **Document type:** *Academic/Scholarly.* **Description:** Covers vibration theory and applications for researchers, managers, faculty members and students in the field of aeronautics and astronautics, mechanical engineering, civil engineering, electronic engineering, machinery, and more.
Related titles: Diskette ed.; E-mail ed.; Fax ed.; Online - full text ed.: (from East View Information Services).
Indexed: ApMecR, BrCerAb, C&ISA, CerAb, CivEngAb, CorrAb, E&CAJ, EMA, Englnd, IAA, M&TEA, MBF, METADEX, RefZh, WAA.
—BLDSC (5072.475000), Linda Hall.
Published by: (Zhongguo Zhendong Gongcheng Xuehui/Chinese Vibration Engineering Society), Nanjing Hangkong Daxue/Nanjing University of Aeronautics and Astronautics, 29 Yudao St, Nanjing, 210016, China. TEL 86-25-4892135, FAX 86-25-4599621, csve@dns.nuaa.edu.cn. Ed. Zhu Jincai. Circ: 3,000.

ZHONGGUO DAODAN YU HANGTIAN WENZHAI/CHINA ASTRONAUTICS AND MISSILERY ABSTRACTS. see *AERONAUTICS AND SPACE FLIGHT—Abstracting, Bibliographies, Statistics*

629.13 TWN ISSN 1022-0666
ZHONGGUO HANGKONG TAIKONG XUEHUI XUEKAN/AERONAUTICAL AND ASTRONAUTICAL SOCIETY OF THE REPUBLIC OF CHINA. TRANSACTIONS. Text in Chinese. 1970. s-a.
Formerly (until 1993): Zhongguo Hangkong-Taikongxue Hui Huikan (0379-7252)
Indexed: BrCerAb, C&ISA, CerAb, CorrAb, E&CAJ, EMA, IAA, M&TEA, MBF, METADEX, WAA.
—BLDSC (8885.160000), Linda Hall.
Published by: Zhongguo Hangkong Taikong Xuehui/Aeronautical and Astronautical Society of the Republic of China, Chu Hsing Rd, Room 229, Bldg. 52, 195 Sec. 4, Chutung, Hsinchu, 310, Taiwan. TEL 886-3-5918710, FAX 886-3-5827714, aasrc@itri.org.tw, http://www.cast.itri.org.tw/aasrc/.

629.1 CHN ISSN 1002-7742
ZHONGGUO HANGTIAN. Text in Chinese; Summaries in English. 1977. m. USD 240 (effective 1999). adv. **Description:** Introduces both civil and military applications of space science and technology; provides the latest information on Chinese launch vehicles, satellites and rockets.
Formerly (until Jul. 1991): Shijie Daodan yu Hangtian (1001-4144)
Related titles: Online - full text ed.: (from East View Information Services); ♦ English ed.: Aerospace China. ISSN 1004-9711.
—BLDSC (0729.855500), IE, ingenta.
Published by: Hangtian Gongye Zong Gongsi, Xinxi Yanjiu-suo/China Aerospace Corporation, Institute for Astronautics Information, 1 Binhe Lu, Hepingli, PO Box 1408, Beijing, 100013, China. TEL 86-10-6837-3440, FAX 81-10-8422-1606, duyq@mimi.cnc.ac.cn, http://www.space.cetin.net.cn. Ed. Li Enzhong. R&P, Adv. contact An Bo. color page USD 4,500.

629.1 CHN ISSN 1000-758X
QB495 CODEN: JKKJEK
➤ **ZHONGGUO KONGJIAN KEXUE JISHU/CHINESE SPACE SCIENCE AND TECHNOLOGY.** Text in Chinese. 1981. bi-m. USD 17.40; USD 2.90 newsstand/cover (effective 2004). bk.rev. abstr. 72 p./no.; **Document type:** *Journal, Academic/Scholarly.* **Description:** Covers system integration and subsystem design of spacecraft, sounding rockets; astrodynamics; reentry and recovery techniques; space electronics; remote sensing from space power supply; materials used and processed in space; space medicine and biology; space environment simulation and more.
Related titles: Online - full text ed.: (from East View Information Services, WanFang Data Corp.).
Indexed: BrCerAb, C&ISA, CerAb, CivEngAb, CorrAb, E&CAJ, EMA, IAA, M&TEA, MBF, METADEX, WAA.
—Linda Hall.
Published by: Zhongguo Kongjian Jishu Yanjiuyuan/Chinese Academy of Space Technology, PO Box 9622, Beijing, 100086, China. TEL 86-1-6837-8141, FAX 86-1-6837-8745, zgkj@chinajournal.net.cn, http://zgkjkxjs.periodicals.net.cn/default.html. Ed. Shenyuan Hou. Circ: 1,500. **Dist. by:** China International Book Trading Corp, 35 Chegongzhuang Xilu, Haidian District, PO Box 399, Beijing 100044, China. TEL 86-10-68412045, FAX 86-10-68412023, cibtc@mail.cibtc.com.cn, http://www.cibtc.com.cn.

629.1 CHN ISSN 1001-5000
TL504
ZHONGGUO MINHANG XUEYUAN XUEBAO/CIVIL AVIATION INSTITUTE OF CHINA. JOURNAL. Text in Chinese; Abstracts in English. 1984. q. USD 10. adv. **Document type:** *Academic/Scholarly.* **Description:** Covers aeronautical power and mechanical devices, aircraft maintenance, automatic control, electrical engineering, communication, air transportation, and other related disciplines.
Related titles: Online - full text ed.: (from East View Information Services).
Published by: Zhongguo Minhang Xueyuan/Civil Aviation Institute of China, Zhangguizhuang Jichang (Airport), Tianjin 300300, China. TEL 491750, FAX 022-493347. Ed. Zai Jian Ping. Adv. contact Yatian Li. page USD 500. Circ: 1,000.

ZHONGHUA HANGKONG HANGTIAN YIXUE ZAZHI/CHINESE JOURNAL OF AEROSPACE MEDICINE. see *MEDICAL SCIENCES*

AERONAUTICS AND SPACE FLIGHT—Abstracting, Bibliographies, Statistics

016.6291 USA ISSN 0163-4941
Z5063.A2
AERONAUTICAL ENGINEERING: A CONTINUING BIOGRAPHY WITH INDEXES✶. Text in English. 1970. m. index. back issues avail. **Document type:** *Catalog, Abstract/Index.*
Formerly: Aeronautical Engineering: A Special Biography with Indexes
Media: Online - full text.
—Linda Hall.
Published by: U.S. National Aeronautics and Space Administration, Scientific and Technical Information Office, 7121 Standard Dr, Hanover, MD 21076-1320. help@sti.nasa.gov, http://www.sti.nasa.gov. **Co-sponsor:** U.S. Federal Aviation Administration.

016.6291 GBR
AEROSPACE AND AVIATION DOCUMENTS CD-ROM. Short title: A & A. Text in English. 1982. m. adv. **Document type:** *Abstract/Index.*
Formerly (until 199?): Aerospace and Aviation Documents Microfile
Media: CD-ROM.
Published by: Technical Indexes Ltd., c/o Sopie Johnson, Willoughby Rd, Bracknell, Berks RG12 8DW, United Kingdom. TEL 44-1344-426311, FAX 44-1344-424971, http://www.tionestop.com. Adv. contact Mark Winslett.

629.13021 USA ISSN 0898-4425
TL501
AEROSPACE FACTS AND FIGURES. Text in English. 1945. a. USD 35 (effective 2000). charts. **Document type:** *Trade.*
Indexed: SRI.
—Linda Hall.
Published by: Aerospace Industries Association of America, 1000 Wilson Blvd., Ste. 1700, Arlington, VA 22209-3928. TEL 202-371-8561, FAX 202-371-8470, http://www.aia-aerospace.org. Ed. David Napier.

AEROSPACE MEDICINE AND BIOLOGY; a continuing bibliography. see *MEDICAL SCIENCES—Abstracting, Bibliographies, Statistics*

016.6291 USA ISSN 0899-1928
AVIATION TRADESCAN; monthly index and abstracts. Text in English. 1984. m. USD 175 (effective 2003). abstr. 25 p./no.; back issues avail.; reprints avail. **Document type:** *Directory, Abstract/Index.* **Description:** Provides monthly indexing and brief abstracts for over 70 aviation-aerospace publications.
Related titles: Diskette ed.

Published by: Aerospace Research Group, Inc., 11 Atlantic Ave, Nanuet, NY 10954-3302. tradescan@aol.com. Ed., Pub., R&P Catherine Heinzer. Circ: 500 (paid).

016.62913 CHN ISSN 1002-6592
TL501
CHINA AEROSPACE ABSTRACTS. Text in English. 1988. q. USD 140. index. **Document type:** *Abstract/Index.*
Related titles: Online - full text ed.; Chinese ed.: Zhongguo Hangkong Wenzhai. ISSN 1002-6606.
Published by: (Aviation Industries of China, China Aero-Information Center), Hangkong Gongye Chubanshe/Aviation Industry Press, 14 Xiaoguan Dongli, Andingmenwai, Beijing, 100029, China. TEL 86-1-64918404, FAX 86-1-64918420. Ed. Wang Mei.

016.6294 RUS ISSN 0132-1668
TL787.7
EKSPRESS-INFORMATSIYA. ASTRONAVTIKA I RAKETODINAMIKA. Text in Russian. 1960. 24/yr. USD 156 foreign (effective 2006). **Document type:** *Journal, Abstract/Index.*
—East View.
Published by: Vserossiiskii Institut Nauchnoi i Tekhnicheskoi Informatsii (VINITI), Ul Usievicha 20, Moscow, 125190, Russian Federation. TEL 7-095-1526441, FAX 7-095-9430060, dir@viniti.ru, http://www.viniti.ru. **Dist. by:** Informnauka Ltd., Ul Usievicha 20, Moscow 125190, Russian Federation. alfimov@viniti.ru.

016.62913 RUS ISSN 0207-5008
TL504
EKSPRESS-INFORMATSIYA. AVIASTROENIE. Text in Russian. 1964. 48/yr. USD 90 foreign (effective 2006). **Document type:** *Journal, Abstract/Index.*
—East View. **CCC.**
Published by: Vserossiiskii Institut Nauchnoi i Tekhnicheskoi Informatsii (VINITI), Ul Usievicha 20, Moscow, 125190, Russian Federation. TEL 7-095-1526441, FAX 7-095-9430060, dir@viniti.ru, http://www.viniti.ru. **Dist. by:** Informnauka Ltd., Ul Usievicha 20, Moscow 125190, Russian Federation. alfimov@viniti.ru.

629.13021 FJI ISSN 0256-8071
FIJI. BUREAU OF STATISTICS. AIRCRAFT STATISTICS. Text in English. a., latest 1994. USD 5 (effective 2000). **Document type:** *Government.* **Description:** Contains information on the operations of both domestic and international airlines.
Published by: Bureau of Statistics, c/o Librarian, Govt. Bldg. 5, PO Box 2221, Suva, Fiji. TEL 679-315-822, FAX 679-303-656.

387.7021 FRA ISSN 0181-1517
TL502
FRANCE. DIRECTION GENERALE DE L'AVIATION CIVILE. BULLETIN STATISTIQUE. Text in French. 1960. a. free.
Published by: Direction Generale de l'Aviation Civile, Service de Coordination Economique, Europeenne et Internationale, Bureau Statistiques, 48 rue Camille Desmoulins, Issy-les-Moulineaux, Cedex 92452, France. TEL 41-09-49-80, FAX 41-09-48-83. Circ: 600.

016.6291 CHN ISSN 1006-2130
HANGKONG WENZHAI/AERONAUTICS ABSTRACTS. Text in Chinese. m. USD 190. **Document type:** *Abstract/Index.*
Formerly: Guowai Hangkong Wenxhai - Foreign Aeronautics Abstracts (1002-6614)
Published by: (Aviation Industries of China, China Aero-Information Center), Hangkong Gongye Chubanshe/Aviation Industry Press, 14 Xiaoguan Dongli, Andingmenwai, Beijing, 100029, China. TEL 86-1-64918404, FAX 86-1-64918417. Ed. Gao Yingjun.

016.62913 CAN ISSN 1200-5800
INDEX OF AIRWORTHINESS DIRECTIVES APPLICABLE IN CANADA/INDEX DES CONSIGNES DE NAVIGABILITE EN VIGUEUR AU CANADA. Text in English, French. 1994. q. CND 210 (effective 2004).
Published by: Transport Canada, Aviation Regulation, Tower C, Place de Ville, 330 Sparks St, Ottawa, ON K1A 0N5, Canada. TEL 613-990-2309, http://www.tc.gc.ca. **Subscr. to:** Canadian Government Publishing Centre, Publishing and Depository Services, Public Works and Government Services Canada, Ottawa, ON K1A 0S5, Canada. TEL 613-941-5995, 800-635-7943, FAX 613-954-5779, 800-565-7757, publications@pwgsc.gc.ca, http://publications.gc.ca.

016.6291 USA
INDEX TO N A S A NEWS RELEASES AND SPEECHES✶. Text in English. a. free. **Document type:** *Catalog, Abstract/Index.* **Description:** Lists news releases from selected NASA agencies.
Published by: U.S. National Aeronautics and Space Administration, Scientific and Technical Information Office, 7121 Standard Dr, Hanover, MD 21076-1320. help@sti.nasa.gov, http://www.sti.nasa.gov.

016.62913 USA ISSN 0020-5842
TL500 CODEN: IAEAA8
➤ **INTERNATIONAL AEROSPACE ABSTRACTS.** Text in English. 1961. m. (13 issues). USD 2,550 combined subscription print & online eds. (effective 2006). illus. a. index in Print & on CD-ROM. back issues avail.; reprints avail. **Document type:** *Abstract/Index.* **Description:** For professionals in aerospace or other high-tech fields. Provides abstracts of papers and articles, including bibliographic information listed under 75 subject headings.
Related titles: CD-ROM ed.: (from The Dialog Corporation); Magnetic Tape ed.; Microform ed.: (from PMC); Online - full content ed.: ISSN 1555-6670. USD 1,905 (effective 2006).
Indexed: PhotoAb, RASB.
—BLDSC (4535.620000), Linda Hall. **CCC.**
Published by: (American Institute of Aeronautics and Astronautics, Inc.), C S A Journal Division (Subsidiary of: Cambridge Information Group), 7200 Wisconsin Ave, Ste 715, Bethesda, MD 20814. TEL 301-961-6798, 800-843-7751, FAX 301-961-6799, journals@csa.com, http://www.csa.com.

016.3877 CAN ISSN 0074-249X
Z5063.A1
INTERNATIONAL CIVIL AVIATION ORGANIZATION. INDEX OF I C A O PUBLICATIONS. ANNUAL CUMULATION. Text in English. irreg., latest 1986. USD 9. back issues avail. **Document type:** *Abstract/Index.*
Published by: International Civil Aviation Organization, External Relations and Public Information Office, 999 University St, Montreal, PQ H3C 5H7, Canada. TEL 514-954-8022, FAX 514-954-6769, sales_unit@icao.org, icaohq@icao.int.

016.6291 IND
NATIONAL AEROSPACE LABORATORIES. COMBINED AEROSPACE BOOK ADDITIONS. Text in English. s-m. per issue exchange basis. **Document type:** *Government.*
Formerly: National Aeronautical Laboratory. Recent Book Additions
Published by: National Aeronautical Laboratory, Kodihalli, P O Box 1779, Bangalore, Karnataka 560 017, India. TEL 91-80-508-6080, FAX 91-80-527-0670, goudar@css.cmmmacs.ernet.in, http://www.cmmacs.ernet.in/nal/publn.html.

016.62913 ISR
NEW BOOKS RECEIVED BY THE FACULTY LIBRARY. Text in English. 1956. q. free.
Published by: Technion - Israel Institute of Technology, Faculty of Aeronautical Engineering, Kiryat Hatechnion, Haifa, 32000, Israel. Ed. Mariuca Stanciu. Circ: 300.

016.6291 RUS ISSN 0235-5000
OBZORNAYA INFORMATSIYA. PROBLEMY BEZOPASNOSTI POLETOV. Text in Russian. 1971. m. USD 129 foreign (effective 2006). **Document type:** *Journal, Academic/Scholarly.*
—East View.
Published by: Vserossiiskii Institut Nauchnoi i Tekhnicheskoi Informatsii (VINITI), Ul Usievicha 20, Moscow, 125190, Russian Federation. TEL 7-095-1526441, FAX 7-095-9430060, dir@viniti.ru, http://www.viniti.ru. **Dist. by:** Informnauka Ltd., Ul Usievicha 20, Moscow 125190, Russian Federation. alfimov@viniti.ru.

REFERATIVNYI ZHURNAL. AVIASTROENIE. see *TRANSPORTATION—Abstracting, Bibliographies, Statistics*

016.6291 RUS ISSN 0373-6407
REFERATIVNYI ZHURNAL. AVIATSIONNYE I RAKETNYE DVIGATELI. Text in Russian. 1961. m. USD 151 foreign (effective 2006). **Document type:** *Journal, Abstract/Index.*
Related titles: CD-ROM ed.; Online - full text ed.
—East View.
Published by: Vserossiiskii Institut Nauchnoi i Tekhnicheskoi Informatsii (VINITI), Ul Usievicha 20, Moscow, 125190, Russian Federation. TEL 7-095-1526441, FAX 7-095-9430060, dir@viniti.ru, http://www.viniti.ru. **Dist. by:** Informnauka Ltd., Ul Usievicha 20, Moscow 125190, Russian Federation. alfimov@viniti.ru.

016.62913 RUS ISSN 0034-2408
REFERATIVNYI ZHURNAL. ISSLEDOVANIE KOSMICHESKOGO PROSTRANSTVA. Text in Russian. 1964. m. USD 469 foreign (effective 2006). **Document type:** *Abstract/Index.*
Related titles: CD-ROM ed.; Online - full text ed.
—East View.
Published by: Vserossiiskii Institut Nauchnoi i Tekhnicheskoi Informatsii (VINITI), Ul Usievicha 20, Moscow, 125190, Russian Federation. TEL 7-095-1526441, FAX 7-095-9430060, dir@viniti.ru, http://www.viniti.ru. Ed. Yurii Arskii. **Dist. by:** Informnauka Ltd., Ul Usievicha 20, Moscow 125190, Russian Federation. alfimov@viniti.ru.

016.6291 RUS ISSN 0207-1371
TL787.7
REFERATIVNYI ZHURNAL. RAKETOSTROENIE I KOSMICHESKAYA TEKHNIKA. Text in Russian. 1961. m. USD 212 foreign (effective 2006). **Document type:** *Journal, Abstract/Index.*
Formerly: Referativnyi Zhurnal. Raketostroenie
Related titles: CD-ROM ed.; Online - full text ed.
Indexed: ChemAb.
—East View, Linda Hall.
Published by: Vserossiiskii Institut Nauchnoi i Tekhnicheskoi Informatsii (VINITI), Ul Usievicha 20, Moscow, 125190, Russian Federation. TEL 7-095-1526441, FAX 7-095-9430060, dir@viniti.ru, http://www.viniti.ru. **Dist. by:** Informnauka Ltd., Ul Usievicha 20, Moscow 125190, Russian Federation. alfimov@viniti.ru.

016.62913 USA ISSN 1548-8837
TL500 CODEN: STAEA5
➤ **S T A R (ONLINE).** (Scientific and Technical Aerospace Reports) Text in English. 1963. m. illus. index. back issues avail.; reprint service avail. from PQC. **Document type:** *Academic/Scholarly.* **Description:** Announces abstracts and indexes reports issued by NASA and similar government agencies, as well as from universities, independent research organizations, and industry.
Formerly (until 1996): S T A R (Print) (0036-8741)
Media: Online - full content. **Related titles:** Microform ed.: (from NTI, PMC, PQC).
Indexed: ChemAb, ErgAb, FLUIDEX, MSB, PhotoAb.
—CASDDS, Linda Hall.
Published by: U.S. National Aeronautics and Space Administration, Scientific and Technical Information Office, 7121 Standard Dr, Hanover, MD 21076-1320. help@sti.nasa.gov, http://www.sti.nasa.gov.

016.6291 USA
U.S. NATIONAL AERONAUTICS AND SPACE ADMINISTRATION. VIDEO CATALOG✶. Text in English. irreg. free. **Document type:** *Catalog, Government.* **Description:** Lists all N.A.S.A.-produced videotapes.
Related titles: Online - full text ed.
Published by: U.S. National Aeronautics and Space Administration, Scientific and Technical Information Office, 7121 Standard Dr, Hanover, MD 21076-1320. help@sti.nasa.gov, http:/www.sti.nasa.gov, http://www.sti.nasa.gov.

016.6291 CHN ISSN 1005-7870
ZHONGGUO DAODAN YU HANGTIAN WENZHAI/CHINA ASTRONAUTICS AND MISSILERY ABSTRACTS. Text in Chinese, English. 1994. bi-m. USD 250 (effective 1999). index. **Document type:** *Abstract/Index.* **Description:** Cites the aerospace-related books, technical papers, standards, conference papers, and journals recently produced in China.
Related titles: CD-ROM ed.
Published by: Hangtian Gongye Zong Gongsi, Xinxi Yanjiu-suo/China Aerospace Corporation, Institute for Astronautics Information, 1 Binhe Lu, Hepingli, PO Box 1408, Beijing, 100013, China. TEL 86-10-6837-2847, FAX 86-10-8422-1606, duyq@mimi.cnc.ac.cn, http://www.space.cetin.net.cn. Ed. An Bo. adv.: color page USD 1,000.

AERONAUTICS AND SPACE FLIGHT—Computer Applications

629.130285 USA
COMPUTER SECURITY APPLICATIONS CONFERENCE. Text in English. 1985. a. price varies. adv. **Document type:** *Proceedings.* **Description:** Contains technical papers and tutorials that address the application of computer security technologies in the aerospace and other environments.
Former titles (until 1988): Aerospace Computer Security Applications Conference; (until 1987): Aerospace Computer Security Conference
Indexed: Englnd, Inspec.
Published by: (Institute of Electrical and Electronics Engineers, Inc.), I E E E Computer Society, 10662 Los Vaqueros Circle, PO Box 3014, Los Alamitos, CA 90720-1314. TEL 714-821-8380, FAX 714-821-4010. Ed. Cat Harris. Pub. Matt Loeb. Adv. contact Frieda Koester.

E S A - I R S NEWS & VIEWS. (European Space Agency - Information Retrieval Service) see *LIBRARY AND INFORMATION SCIENCES—Computer Applications*

629.130285 USA
LOCKHEED M S C STAR. (Missiles and Space Company) Text in English. 1955. fortn. free. adv. illus. back issues avail.
Published by: Lockheed Missiles and Space Co., Inc., Department of Public Relations, PO Box 3504 1111 Lockheed Way, Sunnyvale, CA 94088-3504. TEL 408-742-7441, FAX 408-743-2239. Ed. Mark van Wyk. Circ: 31,000.

629.1300285 621.39 USA
POSITION, LOCATION, AND NAVIGATION SYMPOSIUM. Text in English. a. USD 212; USD 106 to members (effective 2004). **Document type:** *Proceedings, Trade.*
Indexed: IAA.
Published by: Institute of Electrical and Electronics Engineers, Inc., 3 Park Ave, 17th Fl, New York, NY 10016-5997. TEL 212-419-7900, 800-678-4333, FAX 212-752-4929, customer.service@ieee.org, http://www.ieee.org.

629.130285 USA
U.S. FEDERAL AVIATION ADMINISTRATION. SYSTEMS RESEARCH AND DEVELOPMENT. REPORT F A A - R D. Text in English. 1958. irreg. price varies. **Document type:** *Monographic series, Government.*

▼ new title ➤ refereed ✶ unverified ♦ full entry avail.

A

Published by: (Systems Research and Development Service), U.S. Federal Aviation Administration, 800 Independence Ave S W, Washington, DC 20591. TEL 202-655-4000. **Subscr. to:** National Technical Information Service, Government Research Center, 5285 Port Royal Rd, Springfield, VA 22161. TEL 703-605-6060, 800-363-2068, http://www.ntis.gov.

AGRICULTURAL ECONOMICS

see AGRICULTURE—Agricultural Economics

AGRICULTURAL EQUIPMENT

see AGRICULTURE—Agricultural Equipment

AGRICULTURE

see also AGRICULTURE—Agricultural Economics ; AGRICULTURE—Agricultural Equipment ; AGRICULTURE—Computer Applications ; AGRICULTURE—Crop Production And Soil ; AGRICULTURE—Dairying And Dairy Products ; AGRICULTURE—Feed, Flour And Grain ; AGRICULTURE—Poultry And Livestock ; FOOD AND FOOD INDUSTRIES ; FORESTS AND FORESTRY ; GARDENING AND HORTICULTURE

630   USA   ISSN 0001-0073
A A E A BYLINE∗ . Text in English. 1924. 10/yr. membership. bk.rev. **Document type:** Newsletter, Trade.
Media: Duplicated (not offset).
Published by: American Agricultural Editors Association, PO Box 162585, Austin, TX 78716-2585. TEL 512-474-2041, FAX 512-474-77787. Ed. Denise C Terrell. Circ: 600.

A A G BIJDRAGEN. see HISTORY—History Of Europe

630 338.1   USA
A A N TODAY. Text in English. bi-m. **Document type:** Bulletin.
Published by: American Association of Nurserymen, 1250 I St, N W, Ste 500, Washington, DC 20005. TEL 202-789-2900. Ed. Angela Hutcherson.

A B C BLUE BOOK: U S AND CANADIAN FARM PUBLICATIONS. see AGRICULTURE—Abstracting, Bibliographies, Statistics

A C D I - V O C A WORLD REPORT. see BUSINESS AND ECONOMICS—International Development And Assistance

630   AUS   ISSN 1031-8194
A C I A R MONOGRAPH SERIES. Text in English. 1986. irreg.
Indexed: BIOSIS Prev, ZooRec.
—BLDSC (0576.823000), IE, ingenta.
Published by: Australian Centre for International Agricultural Research, PO Box 1571, Canberra, ACT 2601, Australia. TEL 61-2-62170500, FAX 61-2-62170501, http://www.aciar.gov.au/publications/db/types.asp?typeID=2.

630   AUS   ISSN 0813-7234
S540.8.A8
A C I A R NEWSLETTER. Text in English. 1980. s-a.
Related titles: Online - full content ed.
—CISTI.
Published by: Australian Centre for International Agricultural Research, PO Box 1571, Canberra, ACT 2601, Australia. TEL 61-2-62170500, FAX 61-2-62170501, http://www.aciar.gov.au/publications/aciar/index.htm.

630   AUS
A C I A R PARTNERS MAGAZINE. Text in English. a.
Related titles: Online - full text ed.
Published by: Australian Centre for International Agricultural Research, PO Box 1571, Canberra, ACT 2601, Australia. TEL 61-2-62170500, FAX 61-2-62170501, http://www.aciar.gov.au/publications/partners/index.htm.

630   AUS   ISSN 1038-6920
                                           CODEN: AIAPE5
A C I A R PROCEEDINGS. Text in English. 1985. irreg.
Indexed: BIOSIS Prev.
—BLDSC (0576.825900), IE, ingenta.
Published by: Australian Centre for International Agricultural Research, PO Box 1571, Canberra, ACT 2601, Australia. TEL 61-2-62170500, FAX 61-2-62170501, http://www.aciar.gov.au/publications/db/types.asp?typeID=1.

630   AUS   ISSN 0816-7923
A C I A R TECHNICAL REPORTS SERIES. Text in English. 1985. irreg. **Document type:** Monographic series.
Indexed: BIOSIS Prev.
—CISTI.
Published by: Australian Centre for International Agricultural Research, PO Box 1571, Canberra, ACT 2601, Australia. TEL 61-2-62170500, FAX 61-2-62170501, http://www.aciar.gov.au/publications/db/types.asp?typeID=3.

630   AUS   ISSN 0819-7857
A C I A R WORKING PAPERS. Text in English. 1987. irreg.
Published by: Australian Centre for International Agricultural Research, PO Box 1571, Canberra, ACT 2601, Australia. TEL 61-2-62170500, FAX 61-2-62170501, http://www.aciar.gov.au/publications/db/types.asp?typeID=9.

333.79   USA   ISSN 1046-0993
A E R O SUN TIMES∗ . Text in English. 1973. q. USD 15; USD 20 in Canada; USD 25 foreign. adv. bk.rev. bibl.; charts; illus. 15 p./no.; back issues avail. **Document type:** Newsletter.
Description: Information on sustainable agriculture, renewable energy and conservation, multi-modal transportation, and community self-reliance.
Indexed: EIA, EnvAb, NPI.
Published by: Alternative Energy Resources Organization, 432 N Last Chance Gulch St, Helena, MT 59601-5014. TEL 406-443-7272, FAX 406-442-9120, aero@desktop.org. Ed., R&P, Adv. contact Melinda Artz. Circ: 800.

630   MAR
A F A A NEWSLETTER/A F A A BULLETIN D'INFORMATION. Text in Arabic, English, French. 1978. s-a. MAD 80, USD 10. adv. bk.rev. back issues avail. **Document type:** Newsletter.
Published by: Association of Faculties of Agriculture in Africa, Instituts, B P 8642, Rabat, Morocco. TEL 774702. Ed. A O Tantawy. Circ: 1,000. **Affiliate:** Institut Agronomique et Veterinaire Hassan II.

630   CAN
A F H R C FACTSHEETS. (Atlantic Food and Horticulture Research Centre) Text in English. 3/yr. free. **Document type:** Government.
Supersedes in part (in 1994): Agriscope (1181-814X)
Media: Online - full text.
—CISTI.
Published by: Agriculture Canada, Kentville Research Station, Kentville, NS B4N 1J5, Canada. TEL 902-679-5333, FAX 902-679-2311, http://res.agr.ca/kentville/pubs/agindex.htm. Ed. Charlie Embree.

630   GTM   ISSN 0001-1274
A G A. Text in Spanish. 1970 (vol.18). m.
Published by: Asociacion General de Agricultores, 9A. Calle 3-43, Guatemala City 1, Guatemala. Ed. Mario Alvarado Rubio. Circ: 1,000.

630   AUS   ISSN 0728-859X
A I A S OCCASIONAL PUBLICATION. (Australian Institute of Agricultural Science) Text in English. 1982. irreg. **Document type:** Monographic series.
Indexed: NutrAb, PN&I.
—BLDSC (0772.934000).
Published by: Australian Institute of Agricultural Science and Technology, Level 1, Rear 671 Glenferrie Rd, Hawthorn, VIC 3122, Australia. TEL 61-3-98153600, FAX 61-3-98153633, members@aiast.com.au, http://www.aiast.com.au/.

630 658   CUB   ISSN 0514-9797
A N A P. Text in Spanish. 1961. m. USD 20 in North America; USD 26 in South America; USD 29 in Europe; USD 41 elsewhere. illus. **Description:** Official organ of the Cuban farmers. Contains information, interviews and features about national events.
Published by: (Asociacion Nacional de Agricultores Pequenos, Departamento de Exportacion), Ediciones Cubanas, Obispo No. 527, Apdo. 605, Havana, Cuba. Ed. Ricardo Machado. Circ: 90,000.

A O S A - S C S T SEED TECHNOLOGIST NEWS. see BIOLOGY—Botany

630   ZAF   ISSN 1021-2752
A R D R I NEWS. (Agricultural and Rural Development Research Institute) Text in English. 1980. s-a. free. bk.rev. **Document type:** Newsletter. **Description:** Provides information to practitioners and decision-makers in the area of agriculture and rural and community development, and fosters awareness of the institute's activities and resources.
Published by: University of Fort Hare, Agricultural and Rural Development Research Institute, Private Bag X1314, Alice, Ciskei 5700, South Africa. TEL 0404-31154, FAX 0404-31730. Ed. Barbara Morrow. Circ: 1,000 (controlled).

630   ETH
A R D U PUBLICATION. Text in English. 1966. irreg. price varies. charts. cum.index.
Supersedes: C A D U Publications (0069-3405)
Published by: Arussi Rural Development Unit, PO Box 3376, Addis Ababa, Ethiopia.

338.1   USA
A R S QUARTERLY REPORT. (Agriculture Research Service) Text in English. a. **Document type:** Government.
Description: Provides up-to-date information on current projects in the chief scientific research agency of the U.S.D.A.
Related titles: Online - full text ed.
Published by: U.S. Department of Agriculture, Agricultural Research Service, 5601 Sunnyside Ave, Beltsville, MD 20705-5130. TEL 301-344-2769, hbecker@asrr.arsusda.gov, http://www.ars.usda.gov, http://www.ars.usda.gov/main/main.htm. Ed. Hank Becker.

630.715   LKA
A R T I NEWS LETTER. Text in English, Singhalese. 1973. q. free. adv. abstr.; stat. **Document type:** Newsletter.
Published by: Agrarian Research and Training Institute, 114 Wijerama Mawatha, Colombo, 7, Sri Lanka. Ed. S B K Bandara. Circ: 1,200.

630   USA   ISSN 0743-5673
A S A E MEMBER ROSTER. Text in English. 1984. a. USD 16.50 to members (effective 2004).
—CCC.
Published by: American Society of Agricultural Engineers, 2950 Niles Rd, St. Joseph, MI 49085-9659. TEL 269-429-0300, FAX 269-429-3852, hq@asae.org, http://www.asae.org.

A S A E MONOGRAPH SERIES. see ENGINEERING

630   USA   ISSN 0066-0566
S1   CODEN: AASPC3
A S A SPECIAL PUBLICATION. (American Society of Agronomy) Text in English. 1963. irreg., latest vol.57, 1994. adv. **Document type:** Monographic series, Trade.
Indexed: Agr, BIOSIS Prev, BiolAb, S&F, SoyAb.
—BLDSC (1738.600000), CASDDS, CISTI, Ei, IE, ingenta.
CCC.
Published by: American Society of Agronomy, Inc., 677 S Segoe Rd, Madison, WI 53711. TEL 608-273-8080, FAX 608-273-2021, http://www.agronomy.org. Adv. contact Keith R Schlesinger.

A S E A N FOOD JOURNAL. see NUTRITION AND DIETETICS

630   JPN   ISSN 0917-1150
A T I C INFORMATION/A T I C JOHO. Text in Japanese. 1987. 5/yr. stat.
Published by: Agricultural Development Technical Information Center/Tochi Kairyo Gijutsu Joho Senta, 34-4 Shinbashi 5-chome, Minato-ku, Tokyo, 105-0004, Japan.

630 634.9 636   SWE   ISSN 0284-6160
A T L; lantbrukets affaerstidning. (Annonsblad till Tidskrift foer Landtmaen) Variant title: Annonsblad till Tidskrift foer Landtmaen. Text in Swedish. 1884. 2/w. SEK 488 (effective 2005). adv. **Document type:** Magazine, Trade. **Description:** Concerned with agriculture, forestry and animal husbandry in Sweden and elsewhere.
Formerly (until 1988): Annonsblad till Tidskrift foer Landtmaen (0282-1451)
Related titles: Online - full content ed.
Published by: (Lantbrukarnas Riksfoerbund/Federation of Swedish Farmers), L R F Media AB, Murmansgatan 119, PO Box 6044, Malmo, 20011, Sweden. TEL 46-40-6016400, FAX 46-50-6016499, alt@lrfmedia.lrf.se, lrfmedia@lrfmedia.lrf.se, http://www.atl.nu, http://www.media.lrf.se. Ed. Olle Sjoekvist TEL 46-40-6016461. Adv. contacts Christer Karlsson TEL 46-8-58836801, Nils Adlercreutz. B&W page SEK 19,400, color page SEK 26,200; trim 243 x 360. Circ: 61,100.

630   TWN   ISSN 0258-3089
A V R D C REPORT. Key Title: Progress Report - Asian Vegetable Research and Development Center. Text in English. 1986. a. USD 10 domestic; USD 12 foreign (effective 2000). **Document type:** Academic/Scholarly. **Description:** Covers the research and development on improving vegetable crops in the tropics and subtropics, including collection and enhancement of germplasm, varietal improvement, pest and disease management, production technology improvement, agricultural biotechnology, environment and nutrition, and technology transfer.
Indexed: IIS, PGegResA, RPP.
—CISTI.
Published by: Asian Vegetable Research and Development Center, Shanhua, PO Box 42, Tainan, 741, Taiwan. TEL 886-6-5837801, FAX 886-6-5830009, avrdcbox@betra.avrdc.org.tw, http://www.avrdc.org.tw. Ed., R&P, Adv. contact David Abbass TEL 886-65837801 ext 550.

630   DNK   ISSN 0107-0304
AARSSKRIFT FOR TOENDER LANDBRUGSSKOLE. Text in Danish. 1979. a. DKK 50. illus.
Published by: Toender Landbrugsskole, Vestre Omfartsvej, Tonder, 6270, Denmark.

638.1   FRA   ISSN 0373-4625
ABEILLE DE FRANCE ET L'APICULTEUR. Text in French. 1922. m. EUR 28 domestic; EUR 37 foreign (effective 2005). adv. bk.rev. charts; illus. **Description:** Information of interest to apiculturists, agriculturalists, nature lovers and botanists.
Formerly: Abeille de France (0001-3137)
Indexed: ApicAb, SIA.
Published by: Union Nationale de l'Apiculture Francaise, 26 rue des Tournelles, Paris, 75004, France. TEL 33-1-48874715. Circ: 38,000.

638.1   FRA   ISSN 1293-8874
ABEILLES & FLEURS, REVUE FRANCAISE D'APICULTURE; mensuel d'information apicole. Text in French. 1998. m. EUR 25.92 domestic; EUR 36.59 foreign (effective 2005). adv. illus. **Document type:** Magazine, Trade. **Description:** Information of interest to the apiculturist.

Formed by the merger of (1953-1998): Abeilles et Fleurs (0765-8702); (1946-1998): La Revue Francaise d'Apiculture (0035-2853)
Indexed: ApicAb, SIA.
—CISTI.
Published by: Union Nationale de l'Apiculture Francaise, 26 rue des Tournelles, Paris, 75004, France. TEL 33-1-48874715. Circ: 10,000.

630 634 ROM ISSN 1010-3589
CODEN: BASSDO
ACADEMIA DE STIINTE AGRICOLE SI SILVICE. BULETIN INFORMATIV. Text in French. 1970. a. per issue exchange basis. **Document type:** *Bulletin.*
Indexed: FCA, HerbAb, PotatoAb.
—CASDDS.
Published by: Academia de Stiinte Agricole si Silvice, Bd. Marasti 61, Bucharest, 71331, Romania. Ed. Ileana Muresan.

630 363.7 FRA ISSN 0989-6988
S5 CODEN: CRAFEQ
ACADEMIE D'AGRICULTURE DE FRANCE. COMPTES RENDUS. Text in French. 1761. bi-m. bk.rev. bibl.; charts; stat. **Document type:** *Proceedings.* **Description:** website includes French and English summaries of papers.
Former titles (until 1986): Academie d'Agriculture de France. Comptes Rendus des Seances (0001-3986); (until 1915): Societe Royale et Centrale d'Agriculture. Bulletin des Seances (0151-1335)
Indexed: AEA, ASFA, AbHyg, AgBio, AgrForAb, AnBrAb, BIOSIS Prev, BioCN&I, BiolAb, CIN, CPA, ChemAb, ChemTitl, DBA, DSA, ESPM, ExcerpMed, FCA, FPA, FS&TA, ForAb, HerbAb, HortAb, I&DA, IndVet, MaizeAb, NemAb, NutrAb, OrnHort, PBA, PGegResA, PGrRegA, PHN&I, PN&I, PotatoAb, PoultAb, RA&MP, RDA, RPP, RRTA, RefZh, RevApplEntom, RiceAb, S&F, SIA, SeedAb, SoyAb, TDB, TriticAb, VITIS, VetBull, WAE&RSA, WeedAb.
—BLDSC (3369.043000), CASDDS, CISTI, IE, ingenta, Linda Hall. **CCC.**
Published by: Academie d'Agriculture de France, 18 rue de Bellechasse, Paris, 75007, France. TEL 33-1-47051037, FAX 33-1-45550978, murielle.macherat@paris.inra.fr, http://www.academie-agrculture.fr. Ed. Georges Pedro. Circ: 1,000.

ACCADEMIA DELLE SCIENZE DI SIENA DETTA DE FISIOCRITICI. ATTI. see *MEDICAL SCIENCES*

630 ESP
ACCION COOPERATIVA. Text in Spanish. 12/yr.
Address: Campo de Tajonar, Valle De Aranguren, Navarra 31192, Spain. TEL 948-299400, FAX 948-299420. Ed. J Sarasa Murugarren. Circ: 140,000.

630 BRA ISSN 0100-560X
HD1875.P35
ACOMPANHAMENTO DA SITUACAO AGROPECUARIA DO PARANA. Text in Portuguese. 1974. m. free or exchange basis. charts; stat. **Description:** Provides an economical outlook of yielded crops and market prices, in addition to other date statistics, regarding the state of Parana.
Former titles (until 1976, vol.2, no.4): Acompanhamento da Situacao das Culturas; (until 1976, vol.2, no.3): Situacao das Culturas; (until 1975): Relatorio da Situacao das Culturas
Published by: Secretaria de Estado da Agricultura, Rua dos Funcionarios, 1559, Cabral, Caixa Postal 464, Curitiba, PR 80035-050, Brazil. http://www.pr.gov.br/sima. Circ: 3,500.

630 USA
ACREAGE. Text in English. m. USD 14.95 domestic; USD 22.95 per academic year in Canada & Mexico; USD 39.95 per academic year elsewhere (effective 2004). adv. **Document type:** *Trade.*
Published by: Heartland Ag-Business Group, Inc., 1003 Central Ave, Fort Dodge, IA 50501. TEL 515-955-1600, 800-673-4763, aginfo@agdeal.com, http://www.agdeal.com. adv.: B&W page USD 1,000, color page USD 1,665; trim 7.75 x 10.75.

630 USA
ACREAGE MAGAZINE. Text in English. 1978. m. USD 5. adv. back issues avail.
Published by: Argus Observer, 1160 S W 4th St, Box 130, Ontario, OR 97914-0130. TEL 503-889-5387, FAX 503-889-3347. Ed. Eric Ellis. Adv. contact Linda Warren. Circ: 56,292.

ACTA AGROBOTANICA. see *BIOLOGY—Botany*

630 HUN ISSN 0238-0161
S16.H8 CODEN: AAHUEX
ACTA AGRONOMICA HUNGARICA; an international multidisciplinary journal in agricultural science. Text in English. 1950. q. USD 320 (effective 2006). adv. bk.rev. bibl.; charts; illus.; maps. index. 120 p./no.; **Document type:** *Journal, Academic/Scholarly.* **Description:** Publishes papers on applied and basic research in plant genetics, breeding, cultivation, taxonomy, physiology, biochemistry, ecology, and cenology. Covers phytotomy, phytogeography, and phytopathology. Includes zootomy, geography, pathology, biology, genetics, and breeding, soil science and virology.
Formerly (until 1985): Academiae Scientiarum Hungaricae. Acta Agronomica (0001-513X)
Related titles: Online - full text ed.: ISSN 1588-2527 (from EBSCO Publishing, Swets Information Services).
Indexed: AEA, AgBio, AgrForAb, AnBrAb, BIOSIS Prev, BioCN&I, BiolAb, CIN, CPA, CTFA, ChemAb, ChemTitl, CurCont, DSA, FCA, FS&TA, ForAb, HerbAb, HortAb, I&DA, IBR, IBZ, IndVet, MaizeAb, NutrAb, OrnHort, PBA, PGegResA, PGrRegA, PHN&I, PotatoAb, PoultAb, RA&MP, RDA, RPP, RevApplEntom, RiceAb, S&F, S&MA, SIA, SeedAb, SoyAb, TOSA, TriticAb, VITIS, VetBull, WAE&RSA, WeedAb.
—BLDSC (0590.200000), CASDDS, CISTI, IE, ingenta, KNAW, Linda Hall. **CCC.**
Published by: (Agricultural Research Institute, Magyar Tudomanyos Akademia/Hungarian Academy of Sciences), Akademiai Kiado Rt. (Subsidiary of: Wolters Kluwer N.V.), Prielle Kornelia U. 19, Budapest, 1117, Hungary. TEL 36-1-4648282, FAX 36-1-4648221, journals@akkrt.hu, http://www.akkrt.hu. Ed. Zoltan Bedo.

630 571.4 POL ISSN 1234-4125
ACTA AGROPHYSICA. Text in Polish. 1994. irreg., latest vol.82, 2003. price varies. **Document type:** *Monographic series, Academic/Scholarly.*
Indexed: AgrAg, AgrLib.
Published by: Polska Akademia Nauk, Instytut Agrofizyki/Polish Academy of Sciences, Institute of Agrophysics, ul Doswiadczalna 4, PO Box 201, Lublin, 20290, Poland. TEL 48-81-7445061, FAX 48-81-7445067, editor@demeter.ipan.lublin.pl, http://www.ipan.lublin.pl.

ACTA SCIENTIARUM. see *BIOLOGY*

630 SVK ISSN 1335-2555
➤ **ACTA TECHNOLOGICA AGRICULTURAE**; vedecky casopis pre machanizaciu pol'nohospodarstva/the scientific journal for agricultural engineering. Text in Slovak, English. 1998. s-a. SKK 60 (effective 2001 - 2002). back issues avail. **Document type:** *Journal, Academic/Scholarly.*
Indexed: AEA, AnBrAb, DSA, FCA, FPA, HerbAb, HortAb, I&DA, MaizeAb, NutrAb, PHN&I, PotatoAb, RefZh, S&F, SIA, SeedAb, TriticAb, WAE&RSA, WeedAb.
—BLDSC (0664.500000), CISTI, IE, ingenta.
Published by: Slovenska Pol'nohospodarska Univerzita v Nitre/Slovak University of Agriculture in Nitra, Tr. A. Hlinku 2, Nitra, 949 76, Slovakia. TEL 42-37-65117514, FAX 421-37-6511560. Ed. Jozef Lobotka.

630 CZE ISSN 1211-8516
CODEN: AUASFV
ACTA UNIVERSITATIS AGRICULTURAE ET SILVICULTURAE MENDELIANAE BRUNENSIS. Text and summaries in Czech, English. 1994. q. USD 20 (effective 2005). adv. charts; stat. index. **Document type:** *Academic/Scholarly.*
Formed by the merger of (1919-1994): Acta Universitatis Agriculturae. Series A. Facultas Agronomica (0524-7403); (1987-1994): Acta Universitatis Agriculturae. Series B. Facultas Horticulturae (0862-2558); (1965-1994): Acta Universitatis Agriculturae. Series D. Facultas Agroeconomica (0524-7446); (1992-1994): Acta Universitatis Agriculturae. Facultas Silviculturae et Technologiae Ligni (1211-2984); Which was formerly (1919-1992): Acta Universitatis Agriculturae. Series C. Facultas Silviculturae (0524-7438)
Indexed: AEA, AgBio, AgrForAb, AnBrAb, BioCN&I, BiolAb, CIN, CPA, ChemAb, ChemTitl, CurCont, DSA, ExcerpMed, FCA, FPA, FS&TA, FaBeAb, ForAb, HelmAb, HerbAb, HortAb, I&DA, IndVet, MaizeAb, NutrAb, OrnHort, PBA, PGegResA, PGrRegA, PHN&I, PN&I, PotatoAb, PoultAb, ProtozoAb, RM&VM, RPP, RRTA, RevApplEntom, RiceAb, S&F, SIA, SeedAb, SoyAb, TriticAb, VITIS, VetBull, WAE&RSA, WeedAb, ZooRec.
—BLDSC (0584.352000), CASDDS, CISTI.
Published by: Mendelova Zemedelska a Lesnicka Univerzita v Brne, Zemedelska 1, Brno, 61300, Czech Republic. FAX 420-5-45211128, http://www.mendelu.cz/veda/acta. Ed. Ladislav Zeman. Circ: 400.

631 SWE ISSN 1401-6249
ACTA UNIVERSITATIS AGRICULTURAE SUECIAE. AGRARIA. Variant title: Agraria. Text in English. 1996. irreg. **Document type:** *Academic/Scholarly.*
Indexed: AEA, AgBio, AgrForAb, AnBrAb, BioCN&I, CPA, DSA, FCA, FPA, ForAb, HelmAb, HerbAb, HortAb, I&DA, IndVet, MaizeAb, NutrAb, OrnHort, PBA, PGegResA, PGrRegA, PHN&I, PN&I, PotatoAb, PoultAb, ProtozoAb, RA&MP, RDA, RM&VM, RPP, RRTA, RiceAb, S&F, SIA, SeedAb, SoyAb, TriticAb, VetBull, WAE&RSA, WeedAb, ZooRec.
—CINDOC, CISTI.
Published by: Sveriges Lantbruksuniversitet, SLU/Swedish University of Agricultural Sciences, PO Box 7070, Uppsala, 75007, Sweden. TEL 46-18-671010, FAX 46-18-672000, publikationstjanst@slu.se, http://www.slu.se.

630 FRA ISSN 0338-182X
ACTION AGRICOLE DE TARN ET GARONNE. Text in French. 1972. 23/yr.
Related titles: ♦ Supplement(s): Tempe Informations. ISSN 0338-1811.
Published by: Action Agricole de, 420 av. de Monclar, Montauban, Cedex 82017, France. TEL 63-63-11-15, FAX 63-20-15-65. Ed. Paul Couronne. Circ: 10,186.

630 FRA ISSN 0767-8711
ACTION AGRICOLE DE TOURAINE. Text in French. 1944. w.
Address: 30 rue de la Prefecture, Tours, 37000, France. TEL 47-05-54-72, FAX 47-05-58-17. Ed. Michel Gerbault. Circ: 7,000.

630 FRA ISSN 0750-862X
ACTION AGRICOLE PICARDE. Text in French. 1945. w. **Document type:** *Magazine, Consumer.*
Address: 19 bis Rue Alexandre Dumas, Amiens, 80096 Cedex 3, France. TEL 33-3-22533050, FAX 33-3-22533051, daniel.rigaux@aapicarde.fr, http://www.aapicarde.fr. Circ: 5,500.

630 FRA
ACTION PAYSANNE. Text in French. 47/yr.
Address: 5 rue A Deforges, Manosque, 04100, France. TEL 92-72-00-44, FAX 92-72-58-73. Ed. T Trellu. Circ: 2,100.

630 CAN
AD-VISER. Text in English. 1965. s-m. CND 33. adv. **Document type:** *Consumer.*
Address: 1320 36 St N, Lethbridge, AB T1H 5H8, Canada. TEL 403-328-5114, FAX 403-328-5443. Ed., Pub., R&P Rick Gillis. Adv. contact Al Such. Circ: 19,200.

ADVANCES IN AGRICULTURAL BIOTECHNOLOGY. see *BIOLOGY—Biotechnology*

630 EGY ISSN 1110-5585
ADVANCES IN AGRICULTURAL RESEARCH/GADID FI AL-BUHUTH AL-ZIRA'IYYAT. Text in English. 1996. 3/yr. EGP 20 (effective 2004). **Document type:** *Journal, Academic/Scholarly.*
Published by: Alexandria University, Faculty of Agriculture, Saba Basha, Plant Protection Department, Alexandria, Egypt. TEL 20-3-5870605, 20-3-5871646, http://derp.sti.sci.eg/data/0240.htm. Ed. Dr. Hasan Aly Abdel-Hamid Mussbah.

630 EGY ISSN 1110-6425
ADVANCES IN AGRICULTURAL RESEARCH IN EGYPT. Text in English. 1998. s-a. **Document type:** *Journal, Academic/Scholarly.*
—CISTI.
Published by: The Agricultural Research Center, Central Agricultural Pesticides Laboratory, Giza, Egypt. TEL 20-2-5732231, http://derp.sti.sci.eg/data/0211.htm.

630 IND ISSN 0971-6394
ADVANCES IN AGRICULTURAL RESEARCH IN INDIA. Text in English. 1994. s-a. USD 240 (effective 2004). **Document type:** *Academic/Scholarly.*
Indexed: AEA, AgBio, AgrForAb, AnBrAb, BioCN&I, CPA, DSA, FCA, FPA, FS&TA, ForAb, HerbAb, HortAb, I&DA, MaizeAb, NemAb, NutrAb, OrnHort, PBA, PGegResA, PGrRegA, PHN&I, PotatoAb, PoultAb, RA&MP, RDA, RPP, RevApplEntom, RiceAb, S&F, SIA, SeedAb, SoyAb, TriticAb, WAE&RSA, WeedAb.
—BLDSC (0697.812000).
Published by: Pragati Prakashan, c/o K.K. Mittal, Business Manager, P O Box 62, Meerut, Uttar Pradesh 250 001, India. TEL 91-121-640642, FAX 91-121-663838. **Subscr. to:** Scientific Publishers, 5-A New Pali Rd., Near Hotel Taj Hari Mahal, PO Box 91, Jodhpur, Rajasthan 342 003, India. TEL 91-291-2433323, FAX 91-291-2512580, info@scientificpub.com, http://www.scientificpub.com.

630 664 SGP ISSN 1793-0855
ADVANCES IN AGRICULTURAL SCIENCE & TECHNOLOGY. Text in English. 2002. irreg., latest vol.1, 2002. price varies. **Document type:** *Monographic series, Academic/Scholarly.* **Description:** Covers wide aspects of agricultural science and technology, including proteomics, synthetic biology, nanotechnology and related fields.
Published by: World Scientific Publishing Co. Pte. Ltd., 5 Toh Tuck Link, Singapore, 596224, Singapore. TEL 65-466-5775, FAX 65-467-7667, wspc@wspc.com.sg, series@wspc.com.sg, http://www.worldscibooks.com/series/aast_series.shtml, http://www.worldscientific.com. Eds. Xiangzhong Jerry Yang, Xiusheng Harrison Yang. **Dist. by:** World Scientific Publishing Co., Inc., 1060 Main St, River Edge, NJ 07661. TEL 201-487-9655, 800-227-7562, FAX 201-487-9656, 888-977-2665; World Scientific Publishing Ltd., 57 Shelton St, London WC2H 9HE, United Kingdom. TEL 44-20-78360888, FAX 44-20-78362020, sales@wspc.co.uk.

630 POL ISSN 1230-1353
➤ **ADVANCES IN AGRICULTURAL SCIENCES.** Text in Polish; Summaries in English. 1993. a. price varies. **Document type:** *Academic/Scholarly.*
Indexed: AbHyg, AgrAg, AgrForAb, AgrLib, AnBrAb, BioCN&I, DSA, FCA, IndVet, NutrAb, PN&I, PoultAb, RefZh, S&F, SIA, SoyAb, VetBull.
—BLDSC (0697.815000).
Published by: Akademia Rolnicza w Szczecinie/Agricultural University of Szczecin, Dzial Wydawnictw, Ul Doktora Judyma 22, Szczecin, 71466, Poland. TEL 48-91-4541639, FAX 48-91-4541642, TELEX 0425494 AR, fizj@demeter.zoo.ar.szczecin.pl. Ed. Wieslaw F Skrzypczak.

A

338.1 IND
ADVANCES IN AGRICULTURE RESEARCH IN INDIA. Text in English. s-a. USD 120 (effective 2005). **Description:** Reports useful experiments and field trials in agronomy, agricultural economics, agricultural engineering, Indian agricultural development, news agricultural production strategy, irrigation, hortifulture, landscape & gardening, soil & water conservation, fisheries, dairy science, vetenary science etc.
Published by: International Book Distributors, 9/3, Rajpur Rd., First Fl, Dehra Dun, Uttar Pradesh 248 001, India. ibdbooks@sancharnet.in. Ed. Y P S Pundir.

630 USA ISSN 0065-2113
S405 CODEN: ADAGA7
➤ **ADVANCES IN AGRONOMY.** Text in English. 1949. irreg., latest vol.79, 2003. USD 134.95 per vol. vol.81 (effective 2004). reprint service avail. from ISI. **Document type:** *Academic/Scholarly.* **Description:** Major reviews deal with the current topics of interest to agronomists, as well as crop and soil scientists. The subjects covered are varied and exemplary of the myriad subject matter dealt with by this long-running serial.
Related titles: Online - full text ed.: (from ScienceDirect).
Indexed: AEA, ASCA, AgBio, Agr, B&AI, BIOSIS Prev, BioCN&I, BiolAb, CIN, CPA, ChemAb, ChemTitl, FCA, ForAb, HerbAb, HortAb, I&DA, ISR, MSB, MaizeAb, NutrAb, PBA, PCI, PGegResA, PGrRegA, PotatoAb, RA&MP, RPP, RevApplEntom, RiceAb, S&F, SCI, SIA, SeedAb, SoyAb, TriticAb, WAE&RSA, WeedAb.
—BLDSC (0698.000000), CASDDS, CISTI, IE, ingenta, Linda Hall. **CCC.**
Published by: (American Society for Agronomy, Inc.), Academic Press (Subsidiary of: Elsevier Science & Technology), 525 B St, Ste 1900, San Diego, CA 92101-4495. apsubs@acad.com, http://www.academicpress.com. Ed. Donald Sparks.

338.17 USA ISSN 1068-4883
ADVANCES IN STRAWBERRY RESEARCH. Text in English. 1982. a. USD 100 (effective 2004). back issues avail. **Document type:** *Journal.* **Description:** Publishes articles and reports related to a variety of aspects of strawberry research to promote and improve the industry and industry practices.
Formerly (until 1992): Advances in Strawberry Production (0732-3506)
Indexed: Agr.
—CISTI.
Published by: North American Strawberry Growers Association, 526 Brittany Dr, State College, PA 16803-1420. TEL 814-238-3364, FAX 814-238-7051, info@nasga.org, http://www.nasga.org/journals/main.htm. Ed. Dr. Gail R. Nonnecke.

630 664 GBR ISSN 0266-8017
AFRICAN FARMING AND FOOD PROCESSING. Text in English. 1978. bi-m. adv. back issues avail. **Document type:** *Magazine, Trade.* **Description:** Covers the agricultural and primary food-processing industries in English-speaking nations in Africa.
Formerly (until 1984): West African Farming and Food Processing (0143-1307)
Indexed: AEA, AbHyg, AnBrAb, BioCN&I, CPA, DSA, FCA, FS&TA, HelmAb, HerbAb, HortAb, I&DA, IndVet, MaizeAb, NemAb, NutrAb, OrnHort, PHN&I, PN&I, PoultAb, ProtozoAb, RDA, RPP, RRTA, RevApplEntom, RiceAb, S&F, TOSA, VetBull, WAE&RSA, WeedAb.
—BLDSC (0732.443000), IE, ingenta.
Published by: Alain Charles Publishing Ltd., Alain Charles House, 27 Wilfred St, London, SW1E 6PR, United Kingdom. TEL 44-20-78347676, FAX 44-20-79730076, post@alaincharles.com, http://www.alaincharles.com/africa/af.htm. Ed. Jonquil L Phelan. Adv. contact Claire Laudrum. Circ: 10,516.

AFRICAN STUDY MONOGRAPHS. see *ANTHROPOLOGY*

AFRICAN STUDY MONOGRAPHS. SUPPLEMENTARY ISSUE. see *ANTHROPOLOGY*

630 USA ISSN 0161-5408
AG ALERT. Text in English. 1974. w. free membership (effective 2005). adv. **Document type:** *Newspaper, Trade.* **Description:** Provides news and information on California agriculture.
Indexed: RevApplEntom.
Published by: California Farm Bureau Federation, 2300 River Plaza Dr, Sacramento, CA 95833-3293. TEL 916-561-5550, FAX 916-561-5695, agalert@cfbf.com, http://www.cfbf.com/agalert. Ed. Steve Adler. Pub. Ann Smith. Adv. contact Dennis Duncan. Circ: 45,000 (controlled).

630 570 USA
THE AG BIOETHICS FORUM. Text in English. 1988. s-a. free. **Description:** Covers bioethical issues pertaining to agriculture, food, animals and the environment.
Related titles: Online - full text ed.
Published by: Iowa State University, Bioethics Program, 402 Catt Hall, I S U, Ames, IA 50011. TEL 515-294-5400, FAX 515-294-0780, bioethics@iastate.edu, http://www.bioethics.iastate.edu. Ed. Gary Comstock.

630.24 668.6 JPN ISSN 0029-5426
CODEN: NOJID9
AG-CHEM AGE/NOYAKU JIDAI. Text in Japanese. 1954. s-a. free. adv. **Document type:** *Newsletter.* **Description:** Examines research in agricultural chemicals.
Indexed: RefZh.
—CASDDS.
Published by: Nippon Soda Co. Ltd., New Otemachi Bldg, 2-2-1 Ote-Machi, Chiyoda-ku, Tokyo, 100-0004, Japan. TEL 03-3245-6178, FAX 03-3245-6289. Ed. Koji Kikkawa. Circ: 10,000.

630 USA ISSN 0899-7535
AG FOCUS. Text in English. 1924. m. USD 50 (effective 2005). adv. charts; illus.; tr.lit. 2 p./no.; **Document type:** *Newsletter.* **Description:** Educational information for agricultural producers.
Formerly: Orange County Farm News (0030-4271)
Indexed: Agr.
Published by: Cornell Cooperative Extension, 420 E Main St, Batavia, NY 14020. TEL 716-433-8839, FAX 716-438-0275, wjg1@cornell.edu, http://www.cce.cornell.edu/programs/nw-ny-dairy-fieldcrops/agfocus.htm. adv.: page USD 200. Circ: 1,000 (paid and free).

338.1 USA
AG INDUSTRIAL MATERIALS & PRODUCTS. Text in English. q. USD 25; USD 40 foreign. **Document type:** *Newspaper, Trade.* **Description:** Covers the latest developments in the rapidly growing field of new non-food industrial and consumer products made from renewable agricultural materials.
Published by: New Uses Council, PO Box 8340, St. Louis, MO 63132-0340. TEL 314-434-5556. **Subscr. to:** C A for the Self-Employed, 2626 E 82nd St, Ste 325, Minneapolis, MN 55425. TEL 800-445-1525, FAX 612-854-8458.

630 USA
AG JOURNAL (HARLINGTON). Text in English. 1989. m. USD 1 per issue. adv. **Document type:** *Newspaper.*
Published by: Freedom Newspapers, Inc., 1310 S Commerce, Harlingen, TX 78550. TEL 210-430-6211, FAX 210-430-6213. Ed. Gary Long. Adv. contact Marcia Bleier. B&W page USD 99,450; trim 13 x 10. Circ: 33,132.

630 USA
AG JOURNAL (LA JUNTA). Text in English. 1949. w. (Fri.). USD 35 (effective 2005). adv. illus.; mkt. back issues avail. **Document type:** *Newspaper, Trade.* **Description:** Covers agriculture related issues and people. Focus is on ranching, farming, legislation, and the environment.
Formerly (until Sep. 1997): Arkansas Valley Journal (0004-1890)
Related titles: Microform ed.; Online - full text ed.
Address: 617 Raton Ave, Ste 4, PO Box 500, La Junta, CO 81050-0500. TEL 719-384-8121, FAX 719-384-2867, journal@ria.net, http://www.agjournalonline.com. Pub., R&P Pat R Ptolemy. Circ: 10,000 (paid). Wire service: AP.

AG-PILOT INTERNATIONAL; aviation in agriculture worldwide. see *AERONAUTICS AND SPACE FLIGHT*

630 NZL
AG TRADER. Text in English. m. NZD 25 (effective 2005); distr. free with Straight Furrow. **Document type:** *Newspaper, Trade.*
Published by: New Zealand Rural Press Ltd., PO Box 971, Hamilton, New Zealand. agtrader@ruralpress.com, http://www.ruralpress.com/. Adv. contact Rebecca Stuart TEL 64-7-8386206. Circ: 82,000 (free).

630 USA
AG WEEKLY; plus Farm Times. Text in English. w. USD 35 (effective 2005). **Document type:** *Newspaper, Trade.*
Incorporates: Farm Times, Incorporated; (until 1994): Farm Times
Related titles: Online - full content ed.
Published by: Lee Publications, Inc (Subsidiary of: Lee Enterprises, Inc.), 311 Main Ave., W, Twin Falls, ID 83301. TEL 208-735-3256, FAX 208-734-9667, agweekly@magicvalley.com, http://www.agweekly.com/. Ed. Carol Ryan Dumas. Pub. Brian Kroshus TEL 208-735-3254. Circ: 32,000.

636 USA
AG YOUTH MAGAZINE. Text in English. 1988. 7/yr. USD 20 domestic (effective 2001). adv. **Document type:** *Magazine, Consumer.* **Description:** Covers agricultural events and activities, and success stories about young people in agriculture.
Published by: Ag Youth, P O Box 339, Sentinel, OK 73664. TEL 800-599-6884, FAX 580-393-4471, agyouth@pldi.net, http://www.agyouth.com/contents.html. adv.: B&W page USD 485.

630 660.6 CAN
AGBIOTECH BULLETIN (ONLINE). Text in English. 1993. 10/yr. 12 p./no.; **Description:** Offers the latest news on agricultural biotechnology, with special reference to the Saskatchewan and Canadian scene. Key topic areas include regulations, upcoming events, trends, financial news, issues, opportunities, resources and people.
Formerly (until 1999): AgBiotech Bulletin (Print) (1206-4106)
Media: Online - full text.
Published by: Ag-West Biotech Inc., 101-111 Research Dr, Saskatoon, SK S7N 3R2, Canada. TEL 306-975-1939, FAX 306-975-1966, agwest@agwest.sk.ca, http://www.agwest.sk.ca.

AGBIOTECH NEWS AND INFORMATION. see *BIOLOGY—Abstracting, Bibliographies, Statistics*

630 USA
CODEN: BRPOEF
AGBIOTECH REPORTER; agricultural research - business. Text in English. 1984. m. USD 297 in North America to institutions & government; USD 524 in North America to libraries; USD 589 elsewhere (effective 2005). adv. tr.lit. back issues avail.; reprints avail. **Document type:** *Newsletter, Trade.* **Description:** Current scientific and business news in the specific field of agricultural biotechnology.
Former titles (until 199?): Biotech Reporter (1069-4773); (until 1993): AgBiotechnology News (0899-3998); (until 1987): Agricultural Biotechnology News (0748-822X); Agricultural Biotechnology
Related titles: Online - full text ed.: (from EBSCO Publishing).
Indexed: ASCA, Agr, BCI, CBTA, Telegen.
—BLDSC (6001.753900), CISTI, IE.
Published by: Scissortail Productions, Llc. (Subsidiary of: T & F Informa plc), 2302 W 1st St, Cedar Falls, IA 50613-2282. TEL 319-277-3599, FAX 319-277-3783, agrausa@cfu.net, http://www.bioreporter.com, http://www.agra-usa.com/. Eds. Andy Apel, Mary Shepherd. Adv. contact Steve Karr. Circ: 1,500.

630 USA
AGFOCUS. Text in English. 1974. m. USD 59 (effective 1998). adv. back issues avail. **Document type:** *Newsletter.* **Description:** Covers commercial agriculture and rural land use issues.
Former titles: AgImpact; Genesee County Trends
Published by: Cornell Cooperative Extension, 420 E Main St, Batavia, NY 14020. TEL 716-343-3040, FAX 716-439-8455. Ed., R&P Nathan Herendeen TEL 716-433-2651. Adv. contact Wendy Garrett. Circ: 1,000 (controlled). **Co-sponsor:** Cooperative Extension Associations.

630 338.1 USA ISSN 1080-8639
AGLETTER. Text in English. 1949. q. looseleaf. free (effective 2005). charts; stat.; mkt. 4 p./no.; reprint service avail. from CIS. **Document type:** *Newsletter, Trade.*
Formerly (until 1995): Agricultural Letter (0002-1512)
Related titles: Microfiche ed.: (from CIS).
Indexed: AmStI.
—CISTI.
Published by: Federal Reserve Bank of Chicago, Public Information Center, PO Box 834, Chicago, IL 60690. TEL 312-322-5111, FAX 312-322-5515, http://www.chicagofed.org/economic_research_and_data/ag_letter.cfm. R&P Marlene Murray TEL 312-322-2384. Circ: 12,100.

630 FRA ISSN 0339-4409
AGRA ALIMENTATION✶. Text in French. 1964. 45/yr.
Address: 82 rue de Monceau, Paris, 75008, France. TEL 43-87-39-59, FAX 43-87-79-11, TELEX 650 452 AGRAPRS. Ed. G Chalencon. Circ: 1,500.

AGRAFOOD EAST EUROPE. see *BUSINESS AND ECONOMICS—Trade And Industrial Directories*

630 GBR ISSN 1361-9810
AGRAFOOD EUROPE. Text in English. m. GBP 434 domestic; GBP 512 in Europe; GBP 558 elsewhere (effective 2005). **Document type:** *Trade.* **Description:** Comprehensive monthly report on agricultural markets, policy and trade in the European Union.
Formerly: European Agribusiness (1350-4460); Supersedes (in 1992): Green Europe (0141-2213)
—CISTI.
Published by: Agra Europe (London) Ltd. (Subsidiary of: T & F Informa plc), 80 Calverley Rd, Tunbridge Wells, Kent TN1 2UN, United Kingdom. TEL 44-1892-533813, FAX 44-1892-544895, marketing@agra-net.com, http://www.agra-net.com.

AGRAFOOD LATIN AMERICA. see *FOOD AND FOOD INDUSTRIES*

630 RUS
AGRANYI ZHURNAL. Text in Russian. m. **Document type:** *Journal.*
Published by: Press - VideoTsentr Ministerstva Sel'skogo Khozyaistvo Rossiskoi Federatsii, Orlikov per 1/11, Moscow, 107139, Russian Federation. TEL 7-095-2074979, moafvc@dol.ru.

630 AUT
AGRAR POST; unabhaengige oesterreichische Zeitschrift. Text in German. m. **Document type:** *Journal, Trade.*
Published by: Agrar Post Verlag Dr. Bruno Mueller GmbH, Schulstr 64, Langenzersdorf, N 2103, Austria. TEL 43-2244-4647, FAX 43-2244-464723. Circ: 65,000.

630   CHE   ISSN 1022-663X
TX657.O64   CODEN: MFTNF2
AGRARFORSCHUNG. Text in German. 1994. 11/yr. CHF 59 domestic; CHF 65 foreign (effective 2003). adv. bk.rev. index. **Document type:** *Journal, Academic/Scholarly.* **Description:** Swiss agricultural research journal covering animal and plant production, environment, agricultural economics and engineering, and food.
Formed by the merger of (1887-1994): Landwirtschaftliches Jahrbuch der Schweiz (0023-8171); (1962-1994): Schweizerische Landwirtschaftliche Forschung (0036-763X); Landwirtschaft Schweiz (1013-3054); Which was formed by the merger of: Schweizerische Landwirtschaftliche Monatshefte (0036-7648); Mitteilungen fuer die Schweizerische Landwirtschaft (0540-4789)
Indexed: AEA, AbHyg, AgBio, AgrForAb, AnBrAb, BioCN&I, BiolAb, CPA, ChemAb, DSA, FCA, FS&TA, ForAb, HelmAb, HerbAb, HortAb, I&DA, IndVet, MaizeAb, NemAb, NutrAb, OrnHort, PBA, PGegResA, PHN&I, PN&I, PotatoAb, PoultAb, ProtozoAb, RA&MP, RM&VM, RPP, RRTA, RevApplEntom, S&F, SIA, SeedAb, SoyAb, TriticAb, VetBull, WAE&RSA, WeedAb.
—CASDDS, CISTI, IE, Infotrieve, Linda Hall.
Published by: Eidgenoessische Forschungsanstalt fuer Nutztiere, Posieux, 1725, Switzerland. TEL 41-26-4077221, FAX 41-26-4077300, agrarforschung@rap.admin.ch, http://www.agrarforschung.ch. Ed. Andrea Leuenberger.
Co-sponsor: Bundesamt fuer Landwirtschaft.

630   DEU   ISSN 0945-4888
AGRARIA; Studien zur Agraroekologie. Text in German. 1991. irreg., latest vol.30, 2002. price varies. **Document type:** *Monographic series, Academic/Scholarly.*
Published by: Verlag Dr. Kovac, Arnoldstr 49, Hamburg, 22763, Germany. TEL 49-40-3988800, FAX 49-40-39888055, info@verlagdrkovac.de, http://www.verlagdrkovac.de/2-1.htm.

630   USA
AGRARIAN ADVOCATE. Text in English. 1979. q. free membership (effective 2005). adv. bk.rev. tr.lit. back issues avail. **Document type:** *Newsletter, Trade.*
Formerly: California Agrarian Action Project. Newsletter
Published by: Community Alliance with Family Farmers, PO Box 363, Davis, CA 95617. TEL 530-756-8518, FAX 530-756-7857, caff@caff.org, http://www.caff.org. Ed. Will Stockwin. R&P Thomas Nelson. Adv. contact Aileen Vance. Circ: 5,000 (paid and controlled).

630   NLD   ISSN 1380-6335
AGRARISCH DAGBLAD. Text in Dutch. 1987. 5/w. EUR 325.95 (effective 2003). adv. illus. **Document type:** *Newspaper, Trade.* **Description:** For farmers, managers and investors in the agricultural sector.
Published by: Reed Business Information bv (Subsidiary of: Reed Business), Hanzestraat 1, Doetinchem, 7006 RH, Netherlands. TEL 31-314-349911, FAX 31-314-343839, info@reedbusiness.nl, http://product.reedbusiness.nl/nstd/Agrarisch%20dagblad.pdf, http://www.reedbusiness.nl. Ed. B. Westenbrink. Circ: 25,000.

630   NLD   ISSN 0925-837X
AGRARISCH ONDERWIJS. Text in Dutch. 1958. 20/yr. adv. bk.rev.
Former titles (until 1990): Land- en Tuinbouwonderwijs (0169-0973); (until 1984): Maandblad voor het Land- en Tuinbouwonderwijs (0024-8657)
Published by: Educatieve Partners Nederland, Postbus 666, Houten, 3990 DR, Netherlands. TEL 31-3403-59777, FAX 31-3403-59700. Ed. P J Boetzkes. Circ: 1,451.

630 340   NLD   ISSN 0167-4242
K16
AGRARISCH RECHT. Text in Dutch. 1940. m. adv. index.
Formerly (until 1982): Pacht (0165-7186)
Indexed: ELLIS.
—IE, Infotrieve.
Published by: (Instituut voor Agrarisch Recht), Kluwer B.V. (Subsidiary of: Wolters Kluwer N.V.), Postbus 23, Deventer, 7400 GA, Netherlands. TEL 31-570-673449, FAX 31-570-691555, juridisch@kluwer.nl, http://www.kluwer.nl. Circ: 1,400.

630   AUT   ISSN 0002-0710
AGRARISCHE RUNDSCHAU. Text in German. 1947. 6/yr. EUR 43.50 domestic; EUR 53 foreign (effective 2004). adv. bk.rev. index. **Document type:** *Magazine, Trade.*
Indexed: RRTA, WAE&RSA.
Published by: (Oesterreichische Gesellschaft fuer Land- und Forstwirtschaftspolitik), Oesterreichischer Agrarverlag GmbH, Achauer Str 49a, Leopoldsdorf, N 2333, Austria. TEL 43-2235-4040, FAX 43-2235-404929, office@agrarverlag.at, http://www.agrarverlag.at. Ed. Ernst Scheiber. Adv. contact Romana Hummer. B&W page EUR 2,157; trim 180 x 266. Circ: 4,000 (paid and controlled).

630   AUT
AGRARISCHES INFORMATIONSZENTRUM. Text in German. d. **Document type:** *Journal, Trade.*
Published by: Verein Agrarisches Informationszentrum, Schauflergasse 6, Vienna, 1014, Austria. TEL 43-1-5331843, FAX 43-1-5350438, pressedienst@aiz.info, http://www.aiz.info. Ed. Christian Posekany.

AGRARMAERKTE IN ZAHLEN. DEUTSCHLAND. see *AGRICULTURE—Abstracting, Bibliographies, Statistics*

630   DEU
AGRARMEGA ZINE. Text in English, German. w. **Description:** Dedicated to the German farming population.
Media: Online - full text.
Address: Germany. master@la-net.de, http://www.agrar-net.com/mega. Ed. Hans Peter Langwieser.

630   RUS   ISSN 1023-1668
S13   CODEN: VSNLAF
AGRARNAYA NAUKA/AGRARIAN SCIENCE. Text in Russian. 1956. bi-m. USD 105 foreign (effective 2004). **Document type:** *Academic/Scholarly.* **Description:** Covers aspects of agrarian scientist cooperation, agrarian science, information in agroindustrial system, market, agrarian reform, epidemiology and virus control, plant growing by ecologically safe technology.
Formerly (until 1992): Vestnik Sel'skokhozyaistvennoi Nauki (0206-6335)
Indexed: AEA, AgrForAb, AnBrAb, BioCN&I, BiolAb, CPA, ChemAb, DSA, FCA, FS&TA, ForAb, HerbAb, HortAb, I&DA, IndVet, MaizeAb, PGrRegA, PHN&I, PN&I, PotatoAb, PoultAb, RASB, RefZh, SIA, SeedAb, SoyAb, TriticAb, VetBull, WAE&RSA, WeedAb.
—CASDDS, CISTI, Linda Hall. **CCC.**
Published by: (Akademiya Sel'skokhozyaistvennykh Nauk), Izdatel'stvo Kolos, Sadovaya-Spasskaya 18, Moscow, 107807, Russian Federation. TEL 7-095-2072057, FAX 7-095-9753731. Ed. V B Zil'berkvit. Circ: 2,000. **Dist. by:** Informnauka Ltd., Ul Usievicha 20, Moscow 125190, Russian Federation. alfimov@viniti.ru.

630 340   DEU   ISSN 0340-840X
K1
AGRARRECHT. Text in German. m. EUR 166.80 domestic; EUR 178.20 foreign; EUR 15 newsstand/cover (effective 2004). adv. back issues avail. **Document type:** *Journal, Trade.*
Indexed: AEA, AbHyg, AgBio, DSA, ELLIS, ExcerpMed, ForAb, HortAb, I&DA, IBR, IBZ, IndVet, NutrAb, RDA, RRTA, S&F, SIA, VetBull, WAE&RSA.
—CCC.
Published by: (Deutsche Gesellschaft fuer Agrarrecht), Landwirtschaftsverlag GmbH, Huelsebrockstr 2, Muenster, 48165, Germany. TEL 49-2501-801-0, FAX 49-2501-801204, zentrale@lv-h.de, http://www.lv-h.de. Ed. Bernold Bendel. Adv. contact Reinhard Geissel. B&W page EUR 960, color page EUR 1,584. Circ: 1,633.

AGRARSOZIALE GESELLSCHAFT. ARBEITSBERICHT. see *SOCIOLOGY*

AGRARSOZIALE GESELLSCHAFT. KLEINE REIHE. see *SOCIOLOGY*

AGRARSOZIALE GESELLSCHAFT. LAENDLICHER RAUM. RUNDBRIEF. see *SOCIOLOGY*

AGRARSOZIALE GESELLSCHAFT. MATERIALSAMMLUNG. see *SOCIOLOGY*

630   DEU   ISSN 0931-1378
AGRARSPECTRUM. Text in German. 1981. irreg., latest vol.37, 2004. price varies. **Document type:** *Monographic series, Academic/Scholarly.*
Published by: D L G Verlags GmbH, Eschborner Landstr 122, Frankfurt Am Main, 60489, Germany. TEL 49-69-247880, FAX 49-69-24788480, dlg-verlag@dlg-frankfurt.de, http://www.dlg-verlag.de.

630 314   LUX   ISSN 1607-2308
AGRARSTATISTIK. VIERTELJAHRESBULLETIN/ AGRICULTURAL STATISTICS. QUARTERLY BULLETIN/STATISTIQUES AGRICOLES. BULLETIN TRIMESTRIEL. Text in German. 2000. q.
Published by: European Commission, Office for Official Publications of the European Union, 2 Rue Mercier, Luxembourg, L-2985, Luxembourg. TEL 352-29291, FAX 352-2929-1, http://publications.eu.int.

630   DEU   ISSN 0179-2903
AGRARTECHNIK. Text in German. 1922. 11/yr. EUR 79.80 domestic; EUR 89.60 foreign; EUR 7.45 newsstand/cover (effective 2004). adv. mkt.; stat. **Document type:** *Magazine, Trade.*
Former titles (until 1985): Agrartechnik International (0179-289X); (until 1984): Agrartechnik International. Ausgabe A (0341-695X); Landmaschinen Markt (0023-7981)
Indexed: AEA, RRTA, VetBull, WAE&RSA.
—CCC.
Published by: Deutscher Landwirtschaftsverlag GmbH, Kabelkamp 6, Hannover, 30179, Germany. TEL 49-511-678060, FAX 49-511-67806200, agrartechnik@mail.ct-net.de, dlv.hannover@dlv.de, http://www.agrartechnikonline.de, http://www.dlv.de. Ed. Dieter Daenzer. Adv. contact Tobias Voelk. B&W page EUR 3,078, color page EUR 4,514; trim 188 x 270. Circ: 10,443 (controlled).

631.1   DEU
AGRARTECHNIK AKTUELL. Text in German. fortn. adv. **Document type:** *Newsletter, Trade.*
Published by: Deutscher Landwirtschaftsverlag GmbH, Kabelkamp 6, Hannover, 30179, Germany. TEL 49-511-678060, FAX 49-511-67806200, dlv.hannover@dlv.de, http://www.dlv.de. adv.: B&W page EUR 1,960, color page EUR 2,940. Circ: 7,492 (controlled).

630   HUN   ISSN 0002-1105
S16.H8
AGRARTORTENETI SZEMLE/AGRICULTURAL HISTORY REVIEW; historia rerum rusticarum. Text in Hungarian; Summaries in English. 1957. q. USD 30. adv. bk.rev. illus. index. **Document type:** *Academic/Scholarly.*
Indexed: AmH&L, CurCont, HistAb, RASB, WAE&RSA.
—CISTI. **CCC.**
Published by: (Magyar Tudomanyos Akademia/Hungarian Academy of Sciences), Magyar Mezogazdasagi Muzeum/Hungarian Agricultural Museum, PO Box 129, Budapest, 1367, Hungary. TEL 36-1-3430573, FAX 36-1-3439120. Eds. Gyorgy Feher TEL 36-1-3438485, Sandor Zsarnoczai. R&P, Adv. contact Gyorgy Feher TEL 36-1-3438485. Circ: 500 (paid).

630   DEU   ISSN 0002-1121
HD101
AGRARWIRTSCHAFT; Zeitschrift fuer Betriebswirtschaft, Marktforschung und Agrarpolitik. Text in German; Summaries in English. 1952. 8/yr. EUR 112; EUR 12 newsstand/cover (effective 2004). adv. bk.rev. bibl.; charts; mkt.; stat. index. reprints avail. **Document type:** *Journal, Trade.*
Related titles: Supplement(s): Agrarwirtschaft. Sonderheft. ISSN 0515-6866. 1954.
Indexed: AEA, AbHyg, AgBio, AnBrAb, BiolAb, DSA, ELLIS, FCA, FPA, FS&TA, ForAb, HerbAb, HortAb, I&DA, IBR, KES, MaizeAb, NemAb, NutrAb, PBA, PGegResA, PHN&I, PN&I, PROMT, PotatoAb, PoultAb, RASB, RDA, RRTA, RevApplEntom, S&F, SIA, SeedAb, SoyAb, TDB, TOSA, TriticAb, WAE&RSA, WeedAb.
—BLDSC (0738.600000), CISTI, IE, Infotrieve, ingenta. **CCC.**
Published by: (Institut fuer Landwirtschaftliche Marktforschung Braunschweig), Deutscher Fachverlag GmbH, Mainzer Landstr 251, Frankfurt Am Main, 60326, Germany. TEL 49-69-759501, FAX 49-69-75952999, agrar@dfv.de, info@dfv.de, http://www.agroonline.de/agrarwirtschaft, http://www.dfv.de. Ed. Dirk Manegold. adv.: B&W page EUR 921, color page EUR 1,803. Circ: 992 (paid and controlled).

630   DEU   ISSN 1435-6201
AGRARWISSENSCHAFTLICHE FORSCHUNGSERGEBNISSE. Variant title: Schriftenreihe Agrarwissenschaftliche Forschungsergebnisse. Text in German. 1992. irreg., latest vol.26, 2004. price varies. **Document type:** *Monographic series, Academic/Scholarly.*
Published by: Verlag Dr. Kovac, Arnoldstr 49, Hamburg, 22763, Germany. TEL 49-40-3988800, FAX 49-40-39888055, info@verlagdrkovac.de, http://www.verlagdrkovac.de/2-2.htm.

630   CAN   ISSN 0833-8353
AGRI-COM. Text in French. 1983. s-m. CND 15 (effective 1998). adv. **Document type:** *Newspaper.*
Published by: Union des Cultivateurs Franco-Ontariens, 2474 rue Champlain, Clarence Creek, ON K0A 1N0, Canada. TEL 613-488-2929, FAX 613-488-2541, http://www.info.agricom@atreide.net. Ed., R&P Pierre Glaude. Adv. contact Jean Claude Clark. Circ: 5,300.

630 658   USA
AGRI-CULTURE. Text in English. 1950. m. USD 24 (effective 2000). adv. **Document type:** *Newspaper.*
Formerly: Iowa County Farmer
Address: PO Box 208, Marengo, IA 52301. TEL 319-642-5506, FAX 319-642-5509. Ed., R&P Dan Adix. Pub. Michael Simmons. Adv. contact Paul Thompson. Circ: 10,000 (paid).

630   CAN   ISSN 1489-923X
AGRI DIGEST. Text in English. 1990. 6/yr. CND 10, USD 15; (effective Jan. 1997). adv. bk.rev. mkt.; tr.lit. 24 p./no. 6 cols./p.; **Description:** Focus on production and marketing technology relating to agriculture, particularly in British Columbia.
Formerly (until 1998): British Columbia Agri Digest (1184-2164); Which was formed by the 1990 merger of: B.C. Farm Business Digest (1184-2180); British Columbia Dairy Digest (1182-011X); British Columbia Growers Digest (1184-2172)
—CISTI.
Published by: BC Interior Agri Publications, RR#2, S-26, C-32, Chase, BC V0E 1M0, Canada. TEL 250-679-5362, FAX 250-679-5362, frankay@mail.ocis.net. Ed., Pub. Fran Kay. Adv. contact Ralph Terpstra. page CND 1,275; trim 11.5 x 17. Circ: 7,500 (controlled).

630   CAN   ISSN 1193-8277
HD9014.C2
AGRI-FOOD PERSPECTIVES. Text in English. q. charts; illus.; stat. **Document type:** *Government.* **Description:** Outlook for major Canadian food commodities.

▼ *new title*   ➤ *refereed*   ✳ *unverified*   ◆ *full entry avail.*

A

Former titles: Canada. Agriculture Canada. Market Outlook and Analysis Division. Policy Branch. Market Commentary (0823-4760); Canada. Agriculture Canada. Market Commentary; (until 1982): Canada. Agriculture Canada. Marketing and Trade Division. Animal and Animal Products: Outlook
Related titles: French ed.: Perspectives Agro-Alimentaire. ISSN 1193-8285; Supplement(s): Animal and Animal Products Outlook.
Indexed: CBPI, CSI, FS&TA, PoultAb, WAE&RSA.
Published by: Agriculture Canada, Policy Branch, 930 Carling Ave, Ottawa, ON K1A 0C7, Canada. TEL 613-995-5880, FAX 613-996-9564, TELEX 053-3283. Circ: 4,000.

630 FIN ISSN 1459-2029
▼ **AGRI-FOOD RESEARCH & NEWS.** Text in English. 2003. 10/yr. EUR 60 to individuals; EUR 120 to institutions; EUR 30 to students (effective 2004). **Document type:** *Journal, Academic/Scholarly.* **Description:** Contains summaries of ongoing research and development.
Media: Online - full content.
Published by: International Society Of Food, Agriculture and Environment, Meri-Rastilantie 3 C, Helsinki, 00980, Finland. TEL 358-9-3231768, isfae@isfae.org, http://www.isfae.org/isfae/2004/issue3/index.php.

630 CAN ISSN 1192-7704
AGRI-FOOD RESEARCH IN ONTARIO/RECHERCHE AGRO-ALIMENTAIRE EN ONTARIO. Text in English. 1978. q. free. illus. index, cum.index. **Document type:** *Government.* **Description:** Semi-technical reviews of research projects in agriculture funded by the Ministry.
Former titles (until 1993): Highlights of Agricultural and Food Research in Ontario; Highlights of Agricultural Research in Ontario (0706-5213)
Indexed: AEA, AgBio, BioCN&I, DSA, FCA, HerbAb, HortAb, IndVet, MaizeAb, PBA, PN&I, ProtozoAb, RPP, RefZh, RevApplEntom, S&F, TriticAb, WAE&RSA, WeedAb.
—BLDSC (0738.874500), CISTI. **CCC.**
Published by: Ministry of Agriculture, Food & Rural Affairs, Research and Corporate Services Division, Research Branch, 1 Stone Rd W 4th Fl NW, Guelph, ON N1G 4Y2, Canada. TEL 519-826-4191, FAX 519-826-4211, research@omafra.gov.on.ca. Ed. Robyn Meerveld. Circ: 8,300.

630 CAN
AGRI-FOOD TRADE UPDATE. Text in English. q. **Document type:** *Newsletter.*
Formerly: Ontario Ministry of Agriculture, Food and Rural Affairs. Agricultural Trade Update.; Ontario. Ministry of Agriculture and Food. Agricultural Trade Update
Published by: Ministry of Agriculture, Food and Rural Affairs (Toronto), Policy Analysis Branch, Legislative Bldg, Queen s Park, Toronto, ON M7A 2B2, Canada. TEL 416-326-3229, FAX 416-326-9892. Ed. Laurinda Lang.

630 CHE
AGRI-HEBDO. Text in German. w.
Address: Case Postale 247, Lausanne 6, 1000, Switzerland. TEL 021-6177457, FAX 021-262292. Ed. Janine Rouiler. Circ: 20,200.

630 660.6 BEL ISSN 1370-8821
AGRI-INDUSTRY EUROPE✱. Text in Dutch. m. (11/yr.). **Document type:** *Bulletin.* **Description:** Provides a comprehensive update on the European Union initiatives in agricultural research, development and legislation, with emphasis on biotechnology.
Related titles: CD-ROM ed.; Online - full text ed.; French ed.: Europe Agro-Industry. ISSN 1371-290X.
Published by: Europe Information Service SA, Av Adolphe Lacomble 66-68, Brussels, 1030, Belgium. TEL 32-2-7377709, FAX 32-2-7326757, eis@eis.be, http://www.eis.be.

630 378 USA ISSN 0882-9292
AGRI-NATURALIST. Text in English. 1893. 3/yr. USD 10. **Document type:** *Government.* **Description:** Provides students, faculty, and staff with a source of information about the College's activities.
Former titles (until 1984): Buckeye Triune (0274-9785); (until 1975): Ag Student (0090-3388)
Published by: Ohio State University, College of Agriculture, 204 Agriculture Administration Bldg, 2120 Fyffe Rd, Columbus, OH 43210. TEL 614-292-0202. Ed. Robert Agunga. Circ: 2,000.

630 USA
AGRI-NEWS (BILLINGS). Text in English. 1967. w. USD 26 (effective 2000). adv. bk.rev. **Document type:** *Newspaper.* **Description:** Reports general agriculture news in Montana, Wyoming, and the western Dakotas, and Nebraska.
Published by: Western Livestock Reporter, Inc., PO Box 30755, Billings, MT 59107-0759. TEL 406-259-5406, FAX 406-259-6888, bestnwet@imt.net, http://www.cattleplus.com. Ed. Linda Grosskopf. Pub. Pat Goggins. Adv. contacts Jan Sattler, Marsha Christenson. page USD 1,142; 16 x 11. Circ: 26,000.

630 658 USA ISSN 0744-5598
AGRI-NEWS (DES MOINES). Text in English. 1983. w. USD 26 subscr - mailed; USD 36 subscr - mailed for 2 yrs. (effective 2005). **Document type:** *Newsletter, Trade.* **Description:** Provides economic information on agriculture in Iowa and nationwide, crop and livestock information for Iowa and the US.
Published by: Iowa Agricultural Statistics, 210 Walnut St, Rm 833, Des Moines, IA 50309. TEL 515-284-4340, FAX 515-284-4342, http://www.cattleplus.com. Circ: 1,000. Wire service: AP.

630 USA ISSN 0745-3450
AGRI NEWS (ROCHESTER). Text in English. 1976. w. (Thu.). USD 31.95 (effective 2005). adv. **Document type:** *Newspaper, Trade.* **Description:** Features news and information of importance to farm households and agribusiness in southern and central Minnesota and northern Iowa.
Published by: Post - Bulletin Company, PO Box 6118, Rochester, MN 55903-6118. TEL 507-285-7707, news@agrinews.com, http://www.agrinews.com. Ed. Kelly J Boldan. R&P Kelly Boldan. Circ: 17,698.

630 FRA ISSN 0002-1199
AGRI-PICK-UP; hebdomadaire d'information agricole. Text in French. 1963. w.
—CCC.
Address: 6 rue Henri Barbusse, Draveil, 91210, France. Ed. Jean P Jamet.

AGRI-PLASTICS REPORT. see *PLASTICS*

630 BEL ISSN 1021-4240
AGRI-SERVICE INTERNATIONAL✱. Text in English. 1979. fortn. **Document type:** *Trade.* **Description:** Covers the European Union agricultural policies and related issues.
Related titles: French ed.: Agromonde Services. ISSN 0259-756X.
Published by: Europe Information Service SA, Rue de la Loi 200, Brussels, 1049, Belgium. TEL 32-2-242-6020, FAX 32-2-242-9410.

630 USA ISSN 0887-2910
AGRI-TIMES NORTHWEST. Text in English. 1984. s-m. USD 20 (effective 1997). adv. bk.rev. **Document type:** *Newspaper.* **Description:** Contains news of interest to farmers in eastern Washington, eastern Oregon and northern Idaho.
Published by: J - A Publishing Corp., 211 S E Court, Box 189, Pendleton, OR 97801-0189. TEL 503-276-7845, FAX 503-276-7964. Ed. Virgil Rupp. Adv. contact Bill Johnson. Circ: 3,000.

630 USA
AGRI-VIEW. Text in English. 1952. w. (Thu.). USD 24 farmers in WI, MI, MN, IA & IL; USD 30 non-farmers in WI; USD 54 elsewhere (effective 2005). **Document type:** *Newspaper, Trade.*
Contact Owner: Capital Newspapers, Inc., 2001 Fish Hatchery Rd, Madison, WI 53713. TEL 608-250-4162, FAX 608-250-4155, http://www.agriview.com. Circ: 46,500 (paid).

630 CHE
AGRI-WOCHE. Text in German. w.
Address: Rte de Chantemerle 41, Postfach 918, Fribourg 1, 1700, Switzerland. TEL 037-267313, FAX 037-267574. Ed. Beat Andrey.

630 DEU ISSN 0938-0337
S7 CODEN: AGRREE
➤ **AGRIBIOLOGICAL RESEARCH**; Zeitschrift fuer Agrarbiologie - Agrikulturchemie - Oekologie. Text in German; Summaries in English, French. 1953. q. adv. bk.rev. charts; illus. index. **Document type:** *Journal, Academic/Scholarly.* **Description:** Contains original articles by experts in agricultural research in the fields of cattle, feed, and soil.
Formerly (until 1990): Landwirtschaftliche Forschung (0023-8147)
Indexed: AEA, ASCA, ASFA, BiolAb, CIN, CPA, ChemAb, ChemTitl, CurCont, DSA, ESPM, ExcerpMed, FCA, FS&TA, HGA, HerbAb, HortAb, IBR, ISR, IndVet, MSB, MaizeAb, NutrAb, OrnHort, PBA, PGegResA, PN&I, PotatoAb, PoultAb, RM&VM, RPP, RiceAb, S&F, SCI, SWRA, SeedAb, TriticAb, VetBull, WeedAb.
—CASDDS, CISTI, IDS, Linda Hall. **CCC.**
Published by: V D L U F A Verlag, Siebengebirgsstr 200, Bonn, 53229, Germany. TEL 49-228-4342511, FAX 49-228-4342474, info@vdlufa.de, http://www.vdlufa.de. Ed. M Kirchgessner.

630 POL ISSN 1640-4734
AGRICOLA. Text in Polish. 1988. q. **Document type:** *Journal, Academic/Scholarly.*
Published by: Szkola Glowna Gospodarstwa Wiejskiego (SGGW)/Warsaw Agricultural University, Ul Nowoursynowska 166, Warsaw, 02787, Poland. TEL 48-22-8439041, FAX 48-22-8471562, jmw_wyd@alpha.sggw.waw.pl, http://www.sggw.waw.pl.

630 ITA
AGRICOLTORE (MILAN). Text in Italian. 1919. s-m. adv.
Published by: Unione Provinciale Agricoltori di Milano, Via Giuseppe Ripamonti, 35, Milan, MI 20136, Italy. TEL 39-02-5830-2096. Ed. Marcello Bosio. Circ: 4,500.

630 ITA ISSN 0002-1202
AGRICOLTORE (PERUGIA); periodico degli agricoltori umbri. Text in Italian. 1944. m. membership. adv. bk.rev. charts; illus.; stat. **Description:** Provides information for agriculturalists and farmers.
Related titles: Microform ed.
Published by: Unione Provinciale degli Agricoltori di Perugia, Via Manzoni, 223, Ponte S. Giovanni, PG 06087, Italy. TEL 39-075-5990584, FAX 39-075-5990485. Ed. Antonio Margiotta. Circ: 2,000.

630 ITA ISSN 0515-6912
AGRICOLTORE BRESCIANO. Text in Italian. 1953. w. (50/yr.). adv.
Published by: Unione Provinciale Agricoltori di Brescia, Via Creta, 50, Brescia, BS 25124, Italy. TEL 39-030-222861. Ed. Lucio Binacchi. Circ: 9,000.

630 ITA
AGRICOLTORE CUNEENSE✱. Text in Italian. m.
Published by: Unione Provinciale Agricoltori di Cuneo, Cuneo, CN 12100, Italy. Ed. Ettore Bandiera.

630 ITA ISSN 0400-7719
AGRICOLTORE DI TERRA DI LAVORO. Text in Italian. 1955. m.
Published by: Unione Provinciale Agricoltori di Caserta, Via Nazario Sauro 22, Caserta, CE 81100, Italy. TEL 39-0823-327181, FAX 39-0823-326411, caserta@confagricoltura.it, http://www.confagricoltura.it. Ed. Cesare A Martucci.

630 ITA
AGRICOLTORE MONREGALESE✱. Text in Italian. m.
Address: Corso Statuto 38, Mondovi, CN 12048, Italy. Ed. Carlo Nan.

631 CHE
AGRICOLTORE TICINESE. Text in Italian. w. adv. **Document type:** *Newspaper, Trade.*
Address: Via Gorelle, Casa postale 447, S. Antonino, 6592, Switzerland. TEL 41-91-8519092, FAX 41-91-8519098, agri@ticino.com. Adv. contact Roger Hauser. Circ: 6,156 (paid and controlled).

630 ITA
AGRICOLTORE VERONESE✱. Text in Italian. a.
Published by: Unione Provinciale Agricoltori di Verona, Via Antonio Locatelli, 3, Verona, VR 37122, Italy.

338.1 631.1 630 ITA
AGRICOLTURA (BOLOGNA). Text in Italian. 1953. m. EUR 21 domestic; EUR 42 foreign (effective 2005). adv. bk.rev. charts; illus.; maps; stat.; tr.lit. **Document type:** *Magazine, Trade.* **Description:** Provides information on economics, technical aspects and experimentation for the community of farmers.
Related titles: Fax ed.
Indexed: ForAb, OrnHort, RPP, RevApplEntom, WeedAb.
Published by: Assessorato Agricoltura Regione Emilia-Romagna, Via Silvani 6, Bologna, BO 40122, Italy. TEL 39-051-284017, FAX 39-051-284666, agriweb@ermesagricoltura.it, http://www.ermesagricoltura.it/wcm/ermesagricoltura/rivista.

630 ITA ISSN 1593-0017
AGRICOLTURA (MILAN). Text in Italian. 2001. bi-m. EUR 80 (effective 2005). **Document type:** *Magazine, Consumer.*
Published by: IPSOA Editore (Subsidiary of: Wolters Kluwer Italia Srl), Strada 1, Palazzo F6, Milanofiori, Assago, MI 20090, Italy. TEL 39-02-82476888, FAX 39-02-82476436, http://www.ipsoa.it.

630 ITA ISSN 0002-1237
AGRICOLTURA (ROME)✱; attualita italiane e straniere. Text in English, French, Italian. 1952. m. free. adv. bk.rev. charts; illus. index.
Formerly: Agricoltura Italiana (0515-6920)
Indexed: ApicAb, ChemAb, I&DA, WAE&RSA.
Published by: (Istituto di Tecnica e Propaganda Agraria), I S M E A, Via Cornelio Celso, 6, Rome, RM 00161, Italy. Ed. Giuseppe Calabrese. Circ: 10,000.

630 ITA ISSN 0002-1245
AGRICOLTURA ARETINA. Text in Italian. 1945. m. adv.
Published by: Unione Provinciale Agricoltori di Arezzo, Corso Italia, 205, Arezzo, AR 52100, Italy. TEL 39-0575-22280. Ed. Umberto Moretti. Circ: 22,280.

630 ITA
AGRICOLTURA DEL FRIULI-VENEZIA GIULIA✱. Text in Italian. 1979 (vol.11). q. membership.
Published by: Federazione Regionale delle Unioni Agricoltori del Friuli-Venezia Giulia, Via D Moro, 18, Udine, UD 33100, Italy. Ed. G Scorzon.

630 ITA ISSN 0400-776X
AGRICOLTURA DELLE VENEZIE. Text in Italian. 1947. m. bk.rev. reprint service avail. from ISI.
Indexed: ChemAb, PBA, SFA, WildRev.
Published by: Consulta per l'Agricoltura e le Foreste delle Venezie, Corso del Popolo 85-e, Mestre, VE 30173, Italy. Circ: 1,500.

630 ITA ISSN 0002-127X
CODEN: AGITD8
AGRICOLTURA D'ITALIA. Text in Italian. 1954. m. (11/yr.). adv. charts; illus. **Document type:** *Trade.* **Description:** For farmers, breeders, and agricultural technicians. Contains news about atomic energy applied to agriculture and about all agricultural problems.
Indexed: ForAb.
—CASDDS.
Published by: (Istituto di Studi Nucleari per l'Agricoltura), Gruppo Editoriale Gesualdi, Via Quattro Novembre, 152, Rome, RM 00187, Italy. TEL 39-06-6784964, FAX 39-06-6782994. Ed. Gemma Gesualdi. Circ: 25,000.

630 590 ITA ISSN 1592-8764
AGRICOLTURA E ZOOTECNICA BIOLOGICA. Key Title: A.Z.Bio. Text in Italian. 2001. m. (11/yr.). EUR 62 domestic; EUR 110 foreign (effective 2005). 72 p./no.; **Document type:** *Magazine, Trade.*
Published by: Il Sole 24 Ore Edagricole, Via Goito 13, Bologna, BO 40126, Italy. TEL 39-051-62267, FAX 39-051-490200, http://www.edagricole.it. Ed. Giorgio Setti. Circ: 7,000.

630 ITA
AGRICOLTURA MANTOVANA. Text in Italian. 1946. 48/yr. adv.
Published by: Unione Provinciale degli Agricoltori di Mantova, Via Luca Fancelli 4, Mantova, MN 46100, Italy. TEL 39-0376-330711, FAX 39-0376-330754. Ed. Pietro Guandalini. Circ: 4,500.

630 ITA ISSN 0394-0438
CODEN: AGIPAR
AGRICOLTURA MEDITERRANEA; international journal of agricultural science. Text in Italian. 1871. q. **Document type:** *Academic/Scholarly.*
Formerly (until 1986): Agricoltura Italiana (0375-8389)
Indexed: AEA, AgBio, AgrForAb, AnBrAb, BiolAb, CPA, ChemAb, DSA, ExcerpMed, FCA, HelmAb, HerbAb, HortAb, I&DA, IndVet, MaizeAb, NutrAb, OrnHort, PBA, PGegResA, PGrRegA, PHN&I, PN&I, PotatoAb, PoultAb, ProtozoAb, RA&MP, RPP, RRTA, RevApplEntom, RiceAb, S&F, SIA, SeedAb, SoyAb, TriticAb, VITIS, VetBull, WAE&RSA, WeedAb.
—BLDSC (0739.811000), CASDDS, IE, ingenta.
Published by: (Universita degli Studi di Pisa), Pacini Editore SpA, Via A. Gherardesca 1, Ospedaletto, PI 56121, Italy. TEL 39-050-313011, FAX 39-050-3130300, pacini.editore@pacinieditore.it, http://www.pacinionline.it. Ed. Ranieri Favilli.

630 ITA ISSN 0365-2653
AGRICOLTURA NUOVA. Text in Italian. 1949. m. (11/yr.). free to members. adv. bk.rev. **Document type:** *Magazine, Trade.*
Published by: Associazione Nazionale Giovani Agricoltori/National Association of Young Farmers, Corso Vittorio Emanuele 101, Rome, 00186, Italy. http://www.agricolturanuova.crol.it. Ed. Elisabetta Tufarelli. adv.: page EUR 1,300. Circ: 50,000.

631 BEL
L'AGRICULTEUR✶. Text in French. 1892. w. includes Alliance Agricole. adv. bk.rev.
Published by: Belgische Boerenbond, Minderbroedersstraat 8, Leuven, 3000, Belgium. TEL 32-16-242200, FAX 32-16-242266. Ed. S Minten. Circ: 2,700.

630 FRA ISSN 0293-9428
AGRICULTEUR CHARENTAIS. Text in French. w.
Address: 2 av. de Fetilly, La Rochelle, Cedex 9 17074, France. TEL 46-67-25-22, TELEX AGRICHA 790 750 F. Ed. Claude Belliard. Circ: 9,800.

630 FRA
AGRICULTEUR D'ANJOU. Text in French. m.
Address: 7 av. Jean Joxe, BP 248, Angers, Cedex 1 49002, France. TEL 41-32-43-43, FAX 41-32-43-70, TELEX 720 823. Ed. Francois Merle. Circ: 13,329.

630 FRA ISSN 1148-8247
AGRICULTEUR DE L'AISNE. Text in French. 1951. w. adv. **Document type:** *Newspaper.*
Address: 38 place E. Herriot, Laon, Cedex 02007, France. TEL 33-3-23225050, FAX 33-3-23237541. Ed. J L Martin. Adv. contact P Perbereau. Circ: 6,600.

630 FRA ISSN 0751-6231
AGRICULTEUR NORMAND. CALVADOS. Text in French. 1969. w.
Published by: Agriculteur Normand, 19 quai de Juillet, Caen, 14000, France. TEL 31-70-88-00, FAX 31-82-29-63. Ed. Francois Durand. Circ: 28,507.

630 FRA ISSN 0751-6266
AGRICULTEUR NORMAND. MANCHE. Text in French. 1969. w.
Published by: Agriculteur Normand, 19 quai de Juillet, Caen, 14000, France. TEL 31-70-88-00, FAX 31-82-29-63.

630 FRA ISSN 0751-624X
AGRICULTEUR NORMAND. ORNE. Text in French. 1969. w.
Published by: Agriculteur Normand, 19 quai de Juillet, Caen, 14000, France. TEL 31-70-88-00, FAX 31-82-29-63.

630 FRA ISSN 0758-380X
AGRICULTEUR PROVENCAL. Text in French. w.
Published by: Maison des Agriculteurs, 22 av. Pontier, Aix-en-Provence, 13626, France. TEL 42-21-23-18, FAX 42-23-14-18. Ed. Alain Poisson. Circ: 12,000.

630 FRA ISSN 0339-4433
AGRICULTEURS DE FRANCE. Text in French. 1867. 6/yr. adv. **Document type:** *Newspaper.*
Former titles (until 1965): Revue des Agriculteurs de France (1155-0937); (until 1962): Agriculture Pratique (0365-2688)
—CISTI.
Published by: Societe des Agriculteurs de France, 8 rue d'Athenes, Paris, 75009, France. TEL 33-1-44531515, FAX 33-1-44531525. Pub. Jean-Francois Colomer. Circ: 5,000.

630 VEN ISSN 0002-1326
AGRICULTOR VENEZOLANO✶. Text in Spanish. 1970 (vol.34). bi-m. free. charts; illus.
Published by: Ministerio de Agricultura y Cria, Centro Simon Bolivar Torre Norte 16o, Caracas, DF 1010, Venezuela. Circ: 15,000.

630 636 ESP ISSN 0002-1334
AGRICULTURA; revista agropecuaria. Text in Spanish. 1929. m. EUR 40 domestic; EUR 48 in Portugal; EUR 60.10 elsewhere (effective 2005). adv. bk.rev. illus.; stat. index. back issues avail.
Indexed: AEA, AgBio, AgrForAb, AnBrAb, BioCN&I, BioDAb, BiolAb, CPA, ChemAb, DSA, FCA, FPA, ForAb, HerbAb, HortAb, I&DA, IECT, IndVet, MaizeAb, NemAb, NutrAb, OrnHort, PBA, PGegResA, PGrRegA, PHN&I, PN&I, PotatoAb, PoultAb, RDA, RPP, RRTA, RefZh, RevApplEntom, RiceAb, S&F, SIA, SeedAb, SoyAb, TDB, TriticAb, WAE&RSA, WeedAb.
—CINDOC, CISTI. **CCC.**
Published by: Editorial Agricola Espanola S.A., Caballero de Gracia, 24-3, Madrid, 28013, Spain. TEL 34-91-5211633, FAX 34-91-5224872, redaccion@editoria.agricola.com, http://www.editorialagricola.com/agricultura.htm. Ed. Cristobal de la Puerta Castello. Circ: 6,300.

630 MOZ
AGRICULTURA. Text in Portuguese. 1982. q.
Published by: Instituto Nacional de Investigacao Agronomica, Centro de Documentacao e Informacao, C.P. 3658, Maputo 11, Mozambique. TEL 1-460100.

630 DOM ISSN 0365-2750
AGRICULTURA. Text in Spanish. 1905. m.
Formerly: Revista de Agricultura (0370-3312)
—CISTI, Linda Hall.
Published by: Secretaria de Estado de Agricultura y Colonizacion, Santo Domingo, Dominican Republic. Ed. Miguel Rodriguez Jr.

630 USA ISSN 0002-1350
AGRICULTURA DE LAS AMERICAS. Text in Spanish. 1952. bi-m. free to qualified personnel. adv. bk.rev. charts; illus. reprint service avail. from PQC. **Document type:** *Trade.*
Related titles: Microfilm ed.: (from PQC).
Indexed: DSA, FCA, HerbAb.
—Linda Hall. **CCC.**
Published by: Keller International Publishing Corp., 150 Great Neck Rd, Great Neck, NY 11021. TEL 516-829-9210, FAX 516-824-5414, http://www.kellerpubs.com. Ed. Victor Prieto. Adv. contact Orlando Llerandi. Circ: 38,144.

630 ESP ISSN 0213-3385
S253
AGRICULTURA, LA PESCA Y LA ALIMENTACION ESPANOLAS. Text in Spanish. 1963. a. price varies. illus.; charts; stat. **Document type:** *Monographic series, Government.*
Former titles (until 1982): Agricultura y la Pesca Espanolas en (Year) (0212-1182); (until 1980): Agricultura Espanola (0065-440X)
Indexed: ASFA, ESPM, WAE&RSA.
Published by: (Spain. Secretaria General Tecnica), Ministerio de Agricultura Pesca y Alimentacion, Centro de Publicaciones, Paseo Infanta Isabel 1, Madrid, 28014, Spain. TEL 34-91-3475550, FAX 34-91-3475722, mllopisj@mapya.es, http://www.mapya.es. Ed. Porfirio Sanchez Rodriguez. R&P Juan Carlos Palacios Lopez.

630 MDA
AGRICULTURA MOLDOVEI/AGRIKULTURA MOLDOVEI: ZHURNAL DLYA FERMEROV; revista pentru fermieri. Text in Moldavian, Russian. 1956. bi-m. USD 220 foreign (effective 2005). illus. 28 p./no.; back issues avail. **Document type:** *Magazine, Trade.*
Formerly (until 1990): Sel'skoe Hozyaistvo Moldavii
Address: ul Pushkin 22, Chisinau, Moldova. TEL 373-2-234524. Ed. E Dimitrenco. **US dist. addr.:** East View Information Services, 3020 Harbor Ln. N., Minneapolis, MN 55447. TEL 800-477-1005, FAX 800-800-3839, eastview@eastview.com, http://www.eastview.com.

630 PRT
AGRICULTURA NOVA. Text in Portuguese. 12/yr.
Address: Rua 9 de Abril 132 r-c 1-2o, Porto, 4200, Portugal. TEL 2-814944, FAX 2-817813, TELEX 28388. Ed. Adelaide Maria.

630 ROM ISSN 1220-7578
AGRICULTURA ROMANIEI. Text in Romanian. 1974. w.
Published by: Ministerul Agriculturii si Alimentatiei, Calea Serban Voda 30-32, Sector 4, Bucharest, Romania. TEL 176020. Ed. Lucian Rosca. Circ: 70,000.

630 CHL ISSN 0365-2807
S15 CODEN: AGTCA9
AGRICULTURA TECNICA. Text in Spanish; Summaries in English, Spanish. 1941. q. USD 11 domestic; USD 55 foreign (effective 2004). bk.rev. bibl.; illus. index, cum.index: 1965-1980. back issues avail. **Description:** Presents the results of land and cattle studies from the institute and Chilean universities.
Formerly (until 1942): Boletin de Sanidad Vegetal (0716-3827)
Related titles: Online - full text ed.: ISSN 0717-6333. 2000. free (effective 2005) (from SciELO).
Indexed: AEA, AgBio, AgrForAb, Agrind, AnBrAb, BibAg, BioCN&I, BiolAb, CPA, ChemAb, DSA, FCA, FPA, FS&TA, ForAb, HerbAb, HortAb, I&DA, IAALC, INIS AtomInd, IndVet, MaizeAb, NemAb, NutrAb, OrnHort, PBA, PGegResA, PGrRegA, PHN&I, PotatoAb, RA&MP, RDA, RPP, RevApplEntom, RiceAb, S&F, SIA, SeedAb, SoyAb, TriticAb, VITIS, VetBull, WAE&RSA, WeedAb.
—BLDSC (0742.000000), CASDDS, CISTI, IE, ingenta, Linda Hall.
Published by: Instituto de Investigaciones Agropecuarias, Casilla 439, Correo, 3, Santiago, Chile. TEL 56-2-5417223, FAX 56-2-5417667, http://www.scielo.cl/. Ed. Nora Aedo. Circ: 1,500.

630 MEX ISSN 0568-2517
CODEN: ATMXAQ
AGRICULTURA TECNICA EN MEXICO. Text in Spanish; Summaries in English, Spanish. 1955. s-a. USD 12. index. back issues avail. **Document type:** *Academic/Scholarly.*
Indexed: AEA, AgBio, AnBrAb, BibAg, BioCN&I, BiolAb, CPA, ChemAb, DSA, FCA, ForAb, HerbAb, HortAb, I&DA, MaizeAb, OrnHort, PBA, PGegResA, PGrRegA, PotatoAb, RA&MP, RDA, RPP, RefZh, RevApplEntom, RiceAb, S&F, S&MA, SIA, SeedAb, SoyAb, TDB, TOSA, TriticAb, VITIS, VetBull, WAE&RSA, WeedAb.
—CASDDS.
Published by: Instituto Nacional de Investigaciones Forestales, Agricolas y Pecuarias, Vocalia Division Agricola, Apdo. Postal 6-882, Mexico City, DF 06600, Mexico. Ed. Marino Gonzalez Camarillo. Pub. Matilde Marquez Sanchez. Circ: 1,000 (controlled).

630 CZE ISSN 0231-5742
AGRICULTURA TROPICA ET SUBTROPICA. Text in Multiple languages. 1967. a.
Indexed: AEA, AgrForAb, AnBrAb, CPA, DSA, FCA, ForAb, HerbAb, HortAb, I&DA, IndVet, MaizeAb, NutrAb, OrnHort, PBA, PGrRegA, PHN&I, PN&I, PotatoAb, PoultAb, RA&MP, RDA, RPP, RiceAb, S&F, SIA, SeedAb, TDB, TriticAb, VetBull, WAE&RSA, WeedAb, ZooRec.
—BLDSC (0742.070000).
Published by: Ceska Zemedelska Univerzita v Praze, Kamycka 129, Prague 6, 16521, Czech Republic. TEL 420-2-24381111, http://www.czu.cz.

630 HRV ISSN 1331-7768
S13 CODEN: PJZSAZ
AGRICULTURAE CONSPECTUS SCIENTIFICUS. Text in Serbo-Croatian; Summaries in English. 1939. q. USD 50. bk.rev. back issues avail.
Formerly (until 1996): Poljoprivredna Znanstvena Smotra (0370-0291)
Related titles: Online - full text ed.: ISSN 1331-7776.
Indexed: AEA, AgBio, AgrForAb, AnBrAb, BIOSIS Prev, BioCN&I, BiolAb, CPA, DSA, FCA, FS&TA, ForAb, HerbAb, HortAb, I&DA, IndVet, MaizeAb, NemAb, NutrAb, OrnHort, PBA, PGegResA, PGrRegA, PHN&I, PN&I, PoultAb, RPP, RRTA, RevApplEntom, S&F, SIA, SeedAb, SoyAb, TriticAb, VITIS, VetBull, WAE&RSA, WeedAb.
—CASDDS, CISTI.
Published by: Fakultet Poljoprivrednih Znanosti, Simunska 25, Zagreb, 41000, Croatia. http://www.agr.hr/smotra/index.htm. Ed. Franjo Satovic. Circ: 1,000.

AGRICULTURAL ABSTRACTS FOR TANZANIA. see *AGRICULTURE—Abstracting, Bibliographies, Statistics*

630 570 IND ISSN 0970-1907
CODEN: ABRSEG
➤ **AGRICULTURAL AND BIOLOGICAL RESEARCH.** Text in English. 1985. s-a. INR 750, USD 100 to individuals; INR 350, USD 50 to institutions (effective 2003). adv. bk.rev. abstr. **Document type:** *Journal, Academic/Scholarly.* **Description:** An international journal on agricultural and biological research including environmental and toxicological studies.
Indexed: BIOSIS Prev, BiolAb, FS&TA, ZooRec.
—BLDSC (0742.710000).
Published by: Young Environmentalist Association, 64 Khurshed Bagh, Lucknow, Uttar Pradesh 226 004, India. TEL 91-522-2682610, amishrao@chmcc.org. Ed., R&P, Adv. contact Anil Mishra. page INR 2,000. Circ: 1,000.

▼ new title ➤ refereed ✶ unverified ♦ full entry avail.

A

630 FIN ISSN 1459-6067
S269.F5 CODEN: AFSFFB
➤ **AGRICULTURAL AND FOOD SCIENCE (PRINT).** Text in English; Summaries in Finnish. 1992. q., latest vol.11, 2002. EUR 50 combined subscription domestic to individuals print & online; EUR 84 combined subscription foreign to individuals print & online; EUR 50 domestic to institutions print only; EUR 84 foreign to institutions print only; EUR 270 combined subscription to institutions print & online; EUR 25 combined subscription to members (effective 2005). charts; illus. index. back issues avail. **Document type:** *Journal, Academic/Scholarly.*
Former titles (until 2004): Agricultural and Food Science in Finland (1239-0992); (until vol.5, 1996): Agricultural Science in Finland (0789-600X); Which was formed by the merger of (1962-1992): Annales Agriculturae Fenniae (0570-1538); (1929-1992): Journal of Agricultural Science in Finland (0782-4386)
Related titles: Online - full text ed.: Agricultural and Food Science (Online). ISSN 1795-1895. 1998 (from Gale Group, IngentaConnect).
Indexed: AEA, ASCA, ASFA, AbHyg, AgBio, AnBrAb, BIOSIS Prev, BioCN&I, BiolAb, CIN, CPA, ChemAb, ChemTitl, CurCont, DBA, DSA, ESPM, EnvEAb, FCA, FPA, FS&TA, ForAb, H&SSA, HerbAb, HortAb, I&DA, IABS, IndVet, MaizeAb, NemAb, NutrAb, OrnHort, PBA, PGegResA, PGrRegA, PHN&I, PN&I, PollutAb, PotatoAb, PoultAb, RA&MP, RDA, RM&VM, RPP, RefZh, RevApplEntom, RiceAb, S&F, SIA, SWRA, SeedAb, SoyAb, TriticAb, VetBull, WAE&RSA, WeedAb, ZooRec.
—BLDSC (0742.864000), CASDDS, CISTI, IDS, IE, ingenta, Linda Hall. **CCC.**
Published by: M T T Agrifood Research Finland/Maa- ja Elintarviketalouden Tutkimuskeskus, Editorial Office, Jokioinen, 31600, Finland. TEL 358-3-41882347, FAX 358-3-41882339, sari.torkko@mtt.fi, http://www.mtt.fi/afs/. Eds. Ilkka P Laurila, Sari Torkko. R&P Sari Torkko. Circ: 600. **Co-sponsor:** Scientific Agricultural Society of Finland.

➤ **AGRICULTURAL AND FOREST METEOROLOGY.** see *METEOROLOGY*

➤ **AGRICULTURAL & VETERINARY CHEMICALS.** see *AGRICULTURE—Crop Production And Soil*

630 TWN ISSN 0300-550X
S19 CODEN: CHNHAN
➤ **AGRICULTURAL ASSOCIATION OF CHINA. JOURNAL/CHUNG HUA NUNG HSUEH HUI PAO.** Text in Chinese; Summaries in English. 1918; N.S. 1953. bi-m. TWD 200, USD 7 per issue (effective 2000). adv. abstr. cum.index. **Document type:** *Academic/Scholarly.*
Indexed: AIAP, ASCA, BAS, BIOSIS Prev, BiolAb, CPA, CurCont, ExcerpMed, FCA, HerbAb, HortAb, LeadAb, MaizeAb, PBA, PGrRegA, PN&I, RPP, RevApplEntom, S&F, S&MA, SeedAb, TOSA, TriticAb, WeedAb, Zincscan.
—CISTI, Linda Hall.
Published by: Agricultural Association of China/Chung Hua Nung Hsueh Yeh, 14 Wenchow St, Taipei, 106, Taiwan. TEL 886-2-2363-6681, FAX 886-2-2367-7128, agrchina@ms22.hinet.net. Ed. Chung-Kee Yeh. Pub. Pso-kwei Peng. R&P, Adv. contact Huei-Mei Hung TEL 886-2-2363-6681. Circ: 3,000.

➤ **AGRICULTURAL AVIATION.** see *AERONAUTICS AND SPACE FLIGHT*

➤ **AGRICULTURAL CHEMICAL NEWS.** see *CHEMISTRY—Organic Chemistry*

630 KEN
AGRICULTURAL DEVELOPMENT CORPORATION. ANNUAL REPORT. Text in English. 1966. a. free.
Published by: Agricultural Development Corporation, Development House, PO Box 47101, Nairobi, Kenya. Circ: 500.

630 PAK
AGRICULTURAL DEVELOPMENT IN PAKISTAN. Text in English. 1967. a. USD 15.
Published by: Press Corporation of Pakistan, P O Box 3138, Karachi, 75400, Pakistan. TEL 21-455-3703, FAX 21-7736198. Ed. Saeed Hafeez. Circ: 10,000.

630.7 USA ISSN 0732-4677
S530
THE AGRICULTURAL EDUCATION MAGAZINE. Text in English. 1929. bi-m. USD 10 domestic; USD 20 foreign (effective 2005). adv. bk.rev. illus. index. reprint service avail. from PQC. **Document type:** *Magazine, Trade.*
Formerly (until 1980): Agricultural Education (0002-144X)
Related titles: Microform ed.: (from PQC); Online - full text ed.: (from H.W. Wilson, O C L C Online Computer Library Center, Inc., ProQuest Information & Learning).
Indexed: ABIn, Agr, BibAg, CIJE, CurCont, EduInd, F&GI, RASB.
—BLDSC (0745.880000), CISTI, IE, ingenta, Linda Hall.
Published by: Agricultural Education Magazine, Inc., Department of Agricultural Education and Studies, Iowa State University, 201 Curtiss Hall, Ames, IA 50011. TEL 515-294-5904, FAX 515-294-0530, http://www.ageds.iastate.edu. Ed. Jamie Cano. R&P Louis Riesenberg. adv.: B&W page USD 1,000. Circ: 4,500 (paid).

630 LKA ISSN 1391-0671
➤ **AGRICULTURAL ENGINEERING.** Text in English. 1977. a. LKR 100; USD 18 foreign (effective 1999). adv. bk.rev. abstr.; charts; illus.; mkt.; tr.lit. **Document type:** *Monographic series, Academic/Scholarly.* **Description:** Covers research articles related to agricultural engineering, technical notes, news, students information etc. Audience: researchers, professional and business personnel in agriculture.
Related titles: CD-ROM ed.; Online - full text ed.
Indexed: FCA, SLSI.
Published by: Agricultural Engineering Society of Sri Lanka, Department of Agricultural Engineering, Faculty of Agriculture, University of Peradeniya, Peradeniya, 20400, Sri Lanka. TEL 94-8-388923, FAX 94-8-388041, aessl@ageng.pdn.ac.lk. Ed. P M K Alahakoon.

630 620 USA ISSN 0733-1770
AGRICULTURAL ENGINEERING INDEX (YEARS). Text in English. irreg., latest vol.5. USD 41.25 to non-members (effective 2001). **Document type:** *Abstract/Index.* **Description:** Lists over 10,000 books, articles, and technical papers published by selected U.S. and foreign agricultural engineering technical societies during a five-year period.
—CISTI. **CCC.**
Published by: American Society of Agricultural Engineers, 2950 Niles Rd, St. Joseph, MI 49085-9659. TEL 269-429-0300, FAX 269-429-3852, hq@asae.org, http://asae.org/, http://www.asae.org. R&P Sandy Rutter.

630 620 THA ISSN 0858-2114
CODEN: IAEJE5
➤ **AGRICULTURAL ENGINEERING JOURNAL.** Text in English. 1992. 4/yr. USD 135 in Asia to institutions; USD 150 elsewhere to institutions (effective 2004). **Document type:** *Academic/Scholarly.* **Description:** Covers soil and water engineering, farm machinery, farm structures, post-harvest technology, and food processing and emerging technologies.
Indexed: AEA, ASFA, B&BAb, BioEngAb, BrCerAb, C&ISA, CPA, CerAb, CorrAb, E&CAJ, EMA, ESPM, EnvEAb, FCA, H&SSA, HerbAb, HortAb, I&DA, IAA, M&TEA, MBF, METADEX, MaizeAb, NutrAb, OrnHort, PBA, PGegResA, PHN&I, PN&I, PollutAb, RRTA, RiceAb, S&F, SWRA, SeedAb, TriticAb, WAA, WAE&RSA, WeedAb.
—BLDSC (4535.648600), CISTI, Ei.
Published by: Asian Association for Agricultural Engineering, c/o Agricultural Systems & Engineering, Asian Institute of Technology, Klong Luang, PO Box 4, Pathumthani, 12120, Thailand. TEL 66-2-524-5479, FAX 66-2-524-6200, TELEX 84276 TH, salokhe@ait.ac.th, aaae@ait.ac.th, http://www.ait.ac.th. Ed. V M Salokhe. Circ: 300 (paid).

630 IND ISSN 0970-2962
AGRICULTURAL ENGINEERING TODAY. Text in English. 1976. bi-m. USD 70 (effective 2000). back issues avail. **Document type:** *Academic/Scholarly.*
Indexed: AEA, CTFA, ISA, S&F, SeedAb, SoyAb, TOSA.
Published by: (Indian Society of Agricultural Engineers), Scientific Publishers, 5-A New Pali Rd., Near Hotel Taj Hari Mahal, PO Box 91, Jodhpur, Rajasthan 342 003, India. TEL 91-291-2433323, FAX 91-291-2512580, info@scientificpub.com, http://www.scientificpub.com. Circ: 3,000.

630 IND
AGRICULTURAL EXTENSION REVIEW. Text in English. bi-m. INR 12. adv. **Document type:** *Government.*
Published by: Ministry of Agriculture and Rural Development, Directorate of Extension, Krishi Vistar Bhawan, Dr. K.S. Krishnan Marg, Pusa, New Delhi, 110 012, India. TEL 91-11-603568. Circ: 4,000.

630 USA ISSN 0002-1482
S1
➤ **AGRICULTURAL HISTORY.** Text in English. 1927. q. USD 49 to indviduals for membership; USD 172 to institutions for membership (effective 2005 & 2006). adv. bk.rev. bibl.; illus. Index. 136 p./no.; back issues avail.; reprints avail. **Document type:** *Journal, Academic/Scholarly.* **Description:** Covers economic, social, historical, political, technological and scientific developments throughout the world and throughout history as they relate to agriculture.
Related titles: Microform ed.: (from PQC); Online - full text ed.: USD 150 to institutions (effective 2005 & 2006) (from Chadwyck-Healey Inc., EBSCO Publishing, Florida Center for Library Automation, Northern Light Technology, Inc., O C L C Online Computer Library Center, Inc., ProQuest Information & Learning, Swets Information Services).
Indexed: ABS&EES, AEA, ASCA, Agr, AmH&L, AmHI, ArtHuCI, B&AI, BAS, BibAg, BiolAb, BrArAb, CJA, ChPerI, CurCont, DIP, DSA, EnvAb, FCA, ForAb, GEOBASE, GardL, HistAb, HortAb, HumInd, I&DA, IBR, IBSS, IBZ, NumL, OrnHort, PBA, PCI, RASB, RDA, RILM, RPP, RRTA, RefSour, S&F, SIA, SRRA, SSCI, SeedAb, TriticAb, VetBull, WAE&RSA.
—BLDSC (0747.400000), CISTI, IDS, IE, Infotrieve, ingenta, Linda Hall. **CCC.**
Published by: (Agricultural History Society), University of California Press, Journals Division, 2000 Center St, Ste 303, Berkeley, CA 94704-1223. TEL 510-643-7154, FAX 510-642-9917, journals@ucpress.edu, http://ucpress.edu/journals/ah/, http://www.ucpress.edu/journals. Ed. Claire Strom. adv.: page USD 325; 4.5 x 7.5. Circ: 1,200 (paid).

630 GBR ISSN 0002-1490
S419
AGRICULTURAL HISTORY REVIEW. Text in English. 1953. s-a. GBP 15 membership (effective 2005). adv. bk.rev. bibl.; charts. cum.index vols. 1-35. back issues avail.; reprint service avail. from PQC. **Document type:** *Journal, Academic/Scholarly.* **Description:** Publishes articles, reviews, bibliographies, and conference reports.
Related titles: Microform ed.: (from PQC).
Indexed: ASCA, AmH&L, ArtHuCI, BibInd, BrArAb, BrHumI, CJA, CurCont, DSA, ESPM, HistAb, MEA&I, NumL, PCI, RASB, RiskAb, S&F, SSCI.
—BLDSC (0747.500000), CISTI, IDS, IE, Infotrieve, ingenta. **CCC.**
Published by: British Agricultural History Society, c/o University of Exeter, Department of History, Amory Building, Rennes Dr, Exeter, EX4 4RJ, United Kingdom. TEL 44-1392-263284, FAX 44-1392-263305, BAHS@exeter.ac.uk, http://www.bahs.org.uk/agrev.htm. Ed. R W Hoyle. R&P M Overton. Circ: 850.

AGRICULTURAL INFORMATION RESOURCE CENTERS (YEAR); a world directory. see *LIBRARY AND INFORMATION SCIENCES*

630 AUS ISSN 0814-8066
AGRICULTURAL LAND BULLETIN. Text in English. 1983. irreg. price varies. **Document type:** *Bulletin, Government.* **Description:** Description and methodology of the Department of Agriculture's land classification mapping program.
Published by: Department of Agriculture, Locked Bag 21, Orange, NSW 2800, Australia. TEL 61-63-913433. Ed. Ling Sim. Circ: 500.

AGRICULTURAL LAW. see *LAW*

AGRICULTURAL LAW (NEW YORK). see *LAW*

630 340 USA
AGRICULTURAL LAW (SPRINGFIELD). Text in English. 1992. q. looseleaf. USD 68; USD 38 to non-profit organizations (effective 2006). back issues avail. **Document type:** *Newsletter, Trade.*
Published by: Illinois State Bar Association, Illinois Bar Center, 424 S Second St, Springfield, IL 62701. TEL 217-525-1760, 800-252-8908, sanderson@isba.org, http://www.isba.org. Ed. Paul Meints.

630 340 USA ISSN 1051-2780
KF1681.A15
AGRICULTURAL LAW DIGEST. Text in English. 1989. 24/yr. looseleaf. USD 110 (effective 2005). adv. s-a. index. back issues avail. **Document type:** *Newsletter, Trade.* **Description:** Publishes articles on current developments in agricultural law.
Related titles: CD-ROM ed.; Online - full content ed.
Published by: Agricultural Law Press, 2585 Bowmont Dr, Eugene, OR 97405-1407. TEL 541-302-1667, FAX 541-302-1958, aglaw@aol.com, http://www.agrilawpress.com. Ed., R&P Robert P Achenbach Jr. Circ: 263 (paid).

630 340 USA
AGRICULTURAL LAW NEWSLETTER. Text in English. q. membership. **Document type:** *Newsletter.*
Published by: (AgLaw Committee), Missouri Bar, PO Box 119, Jefferson City, MO 65102. TEL 314-635-4128, FAX 314-635-2811. Ed. Ernest H Van Hooser.

630 658.8 IND ISSN 0002-1555
AGRICULTURAL MARKETING; devoted to the problems of agricultural marketing in India. Text in English, Hindi. 1958. q. USD 36 (effective 2006). adv. charts; illus.; mkt. **Document type:** *Government.*
Indexed: AgrForAb, DSA, HortAb, I&DA, NutrAb, OrnHort, PHN&I, PN&I, PotatoAb, PoultAb, RA&MP, RDA, RiceAb, S&F, SIA, SeedAb, SoyAb, TriticAb, WAE&RSA.
—BLDSC (0750.390000), IE, ingenta.
Published by: (India. Directorate of Marketing & Inspection), Ministry of Agriculture, Dept. of Agriculture and Cooperation, Directorate of Marketing and Inspection, Head Office NH IV, Faridabad, New Delhi, 121 001, India. TEL 91-5412392, FAX 91-412394. Eds. Dr. Nafees Ahmad, Shri Lallan Rai. Circ: 500. **Subscr. to:** I N S I O Scientific Books & Periodicals, P O Box 7234, Indraprastha HPO, New Delhi 110 002, India. info@insio.com, http://www.insio.com.

630 USA ISSN 0002-158X
AGRICULTURAL NEWS (LAFAYETTE). Short title: Ag News. Text in English. 1917. m. USD 5 to members (effective 1999). adv. charts; illus.; stat. back issues avail. **Document type:** *Consumer.* **Description:** Covers farm management, dairy, field crops, fruits and vegetables, and woodlot, nursery and greenhouse management.
Incorporates (1915-1970): Cayuga County Farm and Home News (0008-865X)
Indexed: SoyAb, WeedAb.
Published by: (Cooperative Extension Association of Cayuga, Onondaga, Oswego Counties, Agricultural Division), A G Service Publications, Sentinel Heights Rd., Lafayette, NY 13084. TEL 315-677-7818, FAX 315-677-3852. Ed., R&P Keith Severson TEL 315-963-7286. Adv. contact Robert C Watson. Circ: 3,000 (paid). **Subscr. to:** 1050 W Genesee St, Syracuse, NY 13204.

AGRICULTURAL REGIONS OF CYPRUS. see *AGRICULTURE—Abstracting, Bibliographies, Statistics*

AGRICULTURAL RESEARCH AND EXTENSION NETWORK. PAPERS. see *BUSINESS AND ECONOMICS—International Development And Assistance*

630 GUY ISSN 0065-4523
AGRICULTURAL RESEARCH GUYANA. Text in English. 1967. a. free. bk.rev.
Indexed: Agrind.
Published by: National Agricultural Research Institute, Mon Repos, East Coast Demerara, Guyana. TEL 592-20-2249, FAX 592-20-4481. Circ: 150.

630 CYP ISSN 1018-9475
S322.C8
AGRICULTURAL RESEARCH INSTITUTE. ANNUAL REVIEW. Text in English. 1962. a. free. bk.rev. back issues avail.; reprints avail. **Document type:** *Monographic series, Government.* **Description:** Outlines the year's research activities.
Formerly (until 1991): Cyprus. Agricultural Research Institute. Annual Report (0070-2307)
Indexed: AnBrAb, BiolAb, FCA, FS&TA, HortAb, RPP, RevApplEntom, WeedAb.
—BLDSC (7785.939200), CISTI.
Published by: Ministry of Agriculture Natural Resources and the Environment, Agricultural Research Institute, PO Box 22016, Nicosia, 1516, Cyprus. TEL 357-22-403107, FAX 357-22-316770, library@arinet.ari.gov.cy, http://www.ari.gov.cy. Ed. A P Mavrogenis. Circ: 1,200.

630 CYP ISSN 0253-6749
CODEN: MRCIEJ
➤ **AGRICULTURAL RESEARCH INSTITUTE. MISCELLANEOUS REPORTS.** Text in English, Greek. 1980. irreg., latest vol.86, 2002. free. bibl.; charts; illus.; stat. back issues avail.; reprints avail. **Document type:** *Monographic series, Academic/Scholarly.*
Indexed: AgBio, CPA, DSA, FCA, FS&TA, HerbAb, HortAb, NemAb, NutrAb, OrnHort, PBA, PGrRegA, PotatoAb, RA&MP, RPP, S&F, SoyAb, TriticAb, WeedAb.
—CISTI.
Published by: Ministry of Agriculture Natural Resources and the Environment, Agricultural Research Institute, PO Box 22016, Nicosia, 1516, Cyprus. TEL 357-22-403107, FAX 357-22-316770, library@arinet.ari.gov.cy, http://www.ari.gov.cy. Ed. A P Mavrogenis. Circ: 400.

630 IRL ISSN 0269-4433
AGRICULTURAL RESEARCH INSTITUTE OF NORTHERN IRELAND. ANNUAL REPORT. Text in English. 1928. a.
Related titles: Online - full text ed.
—BLDSC (1100.000000).
Published by: Agricultural Research Institute of Northern Ireland, Hillsborough, BT26 6DR, Ireland. TEL 353-2892-682484, FAX 353-2892-689594, http://www.arini.ac.uk/annrep.htm, http://www.arini.ac.uk/index.htm.

630 CAN ISSN 0706-425X
AGRICULTURAL RESEARCH INSTITUTE OF ONTARIO. ANNUAL REPORT. Text in English, French. 1962. a. free. **Document type:** *Government.* **Description:** Includes summaries of selected research programs in all areas of agriculture research, listings of projects funded by the Ministry, publications resulting from research completed during the period and reports on research programs and projects approved by the ARIO and funded by the Ministry.
Formerly: Ontario. Agricultural Research Institute. Report (0078-4664)
Media: Online - full text.
Indexed: HortAb.
—CISTI.
Published by: Ministry of Agriculture, Food & Rural Affairs, Education, Research and Laboratories Division, 1 Stone Rd W, 4th Fl N W, Guelph, ON N1G 4Y2, Canada. TEL 519-826-4191, FAX 519-826-4211, meervel@omafra.gov.on.ca, http://www.gov.on.ca/omafra/english/research/index.html. Ed. Robyn Meerwald. Circ: 900.

630 CYP ISSN 0070-2315
CODEN: CYABAP
➤ **AGRICULTURAL RESEARCH INSTITUTE. TECHNICAL BULLETIN.** Text in English. 1966. irreg., latest vol.211, 2001. free. bibl.; charts; illus.; stat. back issues avail.; reprints avail. **Document type:** *Monographic series, Academic/Scholarly.*
Indexed: AnBrAb, BiolAb, CPA, DSA, FCA, FS&TA, FaBeAb, HerbAb, HortAb, I&DA, IndVet, NutrAb, OrnHort, PBA, PGrRegA, PHN&I, PotatoAb, PoultAb, RPP, S&F, SeedAb, SoyAb, TriticAb, WeedAb.
—BLDSC (8618.200000), CISTI, IE, ingenta.
Published by: Ministry of Agriculture Natural Resources and the Environment, Agricultural Research Institute, PO Box 22016, Nicosia, 1516, Cyprus. TEL 357-22-403107, FAX 357-22-316770, library@arinet.ari.gov.cy, http://www.ari.gov.cy. Ed. A P Mavrogenis. Circ: 400.

630 600 ISR ISSN 0333-578X
AGRICULTURAL RESEARCH ORGANIZATION. SCIENTIFIC ACTIVITIES. Text in English. 1971. triennial. USD 25 (effective 1996). **Document type:** *Academic/Scholarly.*
Published by: (Institute for Technology and Storage of Agricultural Products), Agricultural Research Organization, Volcani Center, P O Box 6, Bet Dagan, 50250, Israel. TEL 972-3-9683111, FAX 972-3-993998, TELEX 381746. Ed. Y Russo Aro. Circ: 2,500.

630 ISR ISSN 0334-2484
AGRICULTURAL RESEARCH ORGANIZATION. SPECIAL PUBLICATIONS. Text in English, Hebrew. 1971. every 3 yrs. USD 25 per issue. **Document type:** *Academic/Scholarly.*
Indexed: BiolAb.
—CISTI.
Published by: (Publications Department), Agricultural Research Organization, Volcani Center, P O Box 6, Bet Dagan, 50250, Israel. TEL 972-3-9683216, FAX 972-3-993998.

630 ZWE
AGRICULTURAL RESEARCH TRUST (ZIMBABWE). SUMMER REPORT. Variant title: A R T Summer Report. Text in English. 1981. a. adv. illus. **Document type:** *Trade.*
Related titles: ♦ Supplement to: The Farmer. ISSN 1011-0488.
Published by: (Agricultural Research Trust (Zimbabwe)), Modern Farming Publications, Agriculture House, Moffat St., PO Box 1622, Harare, Zimbabwe. TEL 263-4-753278, FAX 263-4-750754. Adv. contact Michael Rook. B&W page ZWD 9,911, color page ZWD 11,946; trim 216 x 280.

630 ZWE
AGRICULTURAL RESEARCH TRUST (ZIMBABWE). WINTER REPORT. Variant title: A R T Winter Report. Text in English. 1981. a. adv. illus. **Document type:** *Trade.*
Related titles: ♦ Supplement to: The Farmer. ISSN 1011-0488.
Published by: (Agricultural Research Trust (Zimbabwe)), Modern Farming Publications, Agriculture House, Moffat St., PO Box 1622, Harare, Zimbabwe. TEL 263-4-753278, FAX 263-4-750754. Adv. contact Michael Rook. B&W page ZWD 9,911, color page ZWD 11,946; trim 216 x 280.

630 IND ISSN 0253-1496
AGRICULTURAL REVIEWS. Text in English. 1980. q. USD 75 foreign (effective 2006). **Document type:** *Academic/Scholarly.* **Description:** Publishes review articles reporting original research with a new theory on all aspects of plant and soil sciences, animal husbandry, and veterinary and dairy sciences.
Indexed: AEA, AgBio, AgrForAb, AnBrAb, BioCN&I, BiolAb, CPA, CTFA, ChemAb, DSA, FCA, FPA, FS&TA, ForAb, HerbAb, HortAb, I&DA, IndVet, MaizeAb, NemAb, NutrAb, OrnHort, PBA, PGegResA, PGrRegA, PHN&I, PN&I, PotatoAb, PoultAb, ProtozoAb, RA&MP, RDA, RPP, RevApplEntom, RiceAb, S&F, S&MA, SIA, SeedAb, SoyAb, TriticAb, VetBull, WAE&RSA, WeedAb.
—BLDSC (0754.120000), CISTI, IE, ingenta, Linda Hall.
Published by: Agricultural Research Communication Centre, 1130 Sadar Bazar, Post Office Marg, Karnal, Haryana 132 001, India. TEL 91-184-255080. Ed. R Sahay. **Subscr. to:** I N S I O Scientific Books & Periodicals, P O Box 7234, Indraprastha HPO, New Delhi 110 002, India. info@insio.com, http://www.insio.com.

630 AUS ISSN 1030-4614
CODEN: SDPGFD
AGRICULTURAL SCIENCE. Text in English. 1935. q. adv. bk.rev. index. back issues avail. **Document type:** *Journal, Trade.* **Description:** Aims to promote the advancement of agricultural science in Australia and New Zealand, to further the interests of both institutes, and provide a medium for communication among members and all those interested in agriculture.
Formerly (until 1987): Australian Institute of Agricultural Science. Journal (0045-0545)
Indexed: AEA, AgBio, Agr, AgrForAb, AnBrAb, BAS, BioCN&I, BiolAb, CPA, ChemAb, CurCont, DSA, FCA, FPA, FS&TA, ForAb, HerbAb, HortAb, I&DA, IndVet, NutrAb, PBA, PHN&I, PN&I, RA&MP, RDA, RPP, RRTA, RevApplEntom, S&F, S&MA, SeedAb, SoyAb, TOSA, TriticAb, VetBull, WAE&RSA, WeedAb.
—BLDSC (0754.180000), CASDDS, CISTI, IE, ingenta, Linda Hall. **CCC.**
Published by: Australian Institute of Agricultural Science and Technology, Level 1, Rear 671 Glenferrie Rd, Hawthorn, VIC 3122, Australia. TEL 61-3-98153600, FAX 61-3-98153633, members@aiast.com.au, http://www.aiast.com.au/journal.html. Ed. Ted Hayes. Circ: 4,500.

630 636 IND ISSN 0253-150X
CODEN: ASDIDY
AGRICULTURAL SCIENCE DIGEST. Text in English. 1981. q. USD 75 foreign (effective 2006). **Document type:** *Academic/Scholarly.* **Description:** Features original research notes and short communications on plant and soil sciences.
Indexed: AEA, AgrForAb, BIOSIS Prev, BioCN&I, BiolAb, CIN, CPA, CTFA, ChemAb, ChemTitl, FCA, FPA, FS&TA, ForAb, HerbAb, HortAb, I&DA, IndVet, MaizeAb, NutrAb, OrnHort, PBA, PGegResA, PGrRegA, PHN&I, PotatoAb, PoultAb, RA&MP, RDA, RPP, RevApplEntom, RiceAb, S&F, S&MA, SIA, SeedAb, SoyAb, TDB, TOSA, TriticAb, VITIS, VetBull, WAE&RSA, WeedAb.
—CASDDS, Linda Hall.
Published by: Agricultural Research Communication Centre, 1130 Sadar Bazar, Post Office Marg, Karnal, Haryana 132 001, India. TEL 91-184-255080. Ed. B S Dahiya. **Subscr. to:** I N S I O Scientific Books & Periodicals, P O Box 7234, Indraprastha HPO, New Delhi 110 002, India. info@insio.com, http://www.insio.com.

630 IND ISSN 0971-6289
➤ **AGRICULTURAL SCIENCE SOCIETY OF NORTHEAST INDIA. JOURNAL.** Variant title: Journal of the Agricultural Science Society of Northeast India. Text in English. 1979. s-a. INR 400 domestic; USD 50 foreign (effective 2000). adv. bk.rev. Index. **Document type:** *Journal, Academic/Scholarly.* **Description:** Promotes research articles and scientific culture involving all disciplines of agriculture and allied sciences.
Indexed: AEA, AgBio, BioCN&I, CPA, DSA, FCA, FPA, ForAb, HortAb, I&DA, MaizeAb, NutrAb, PBA, PGrRegA, PHN&I, PotatoAb, RA&MP, RDA, RPP, RiceAb, S&F, SIA, SeedAb, SoyAb, TDB, TriticAb, WAE&RSA, WeedAb, ZooRec.
—BLDSC (4679.820000).
Published by: Agricultural Science Society of Northeast India, Assam Agricultural University, Jorhat, 785 013, India. TEL 91-376-320947, FAX 91-376-320965, pkb@aau.ren.nie.in. Ed. S K Dutta. Pub., R&P, Adv. contact P K Barua. B&W page INR 5,000. Circ: 50 (paid); 450 (controlled).

630 IND ISSN 0002-1679
AGRICULTURAL SITUATION IN INDIA. Text in English. 1948. m. USD 36 (effective 2006). bk.rev. abstr.; charts; stat. index. **Document type:** *Government.*
Indexed: AEA, ARDT, ATA, AgrForAb, BAS, BioDAb, CTFA, DSA, FPA, ForAb, HortAb, I&DA, ILD, MaizeAb, PAA&I, RASB, RDA, REE&TA, RRTA, RiceAb, S&F, S&MA, TOSA, TriticAb, WAE&RSA.
—BLDSC (0755.400000), IE, ingenta.
Published by: (India. Ministry of Agriculture, India. Directorate of Economics and Statistics), Scientific Publishers, 5-A New Pali Rd., Near Hotel Taj Hari Mahal, PO Box 91, Jodhpur, Rajasthan 342 003, India. TEL 91-291-2433323, FAX 91-291-2512580, info@scientificpub.com, http://www.scientificpub.com. Ed. Brajesh Kumar Gautam. Circ: 975. **Subscr. to:** I N S I O Scientific Books & Periodicals, P O Box 7234, Indraprastha HPO, New Delhi 110 002, India. info@insio.com, http://www.insio.com.

630 LUX ISSN 1025-6660
HD1920.5
AGRICULTURAL SITUATION IN THE EUROPEAN UNION/LAGER DER LANDWIRTSCHAFT IN DER EUROPEISCHEN UNION/SITUATION DE L'AGRICULTURE DANS L'UNION EUROPEENNE/SITUAZIONE DELL'AGRICOLTURA NELL'UNIONE EUROPEA. Text in English. 1975. a.
Formerly (until 1994): Agricultural Situation in the Community (1010-0806)
—BLDSC (0755.390000).
Published by: European Commission, Office for Official Publications of the European Union, 2 Rue Mercier, Luxembourg, L-2985, Luxembourg. FAX 352-43032500, idea@opoce.cec.eu.int, http://europa.eu.int.

630 NGA ISSN 0065-454X
AGRICULTURAL SOCIETY OF NIGERIA. PROCEEDINGS. Text in English. 1962. a. free. adv. bk.rev. **Document type:** *Proceedings.*
Published by: Agricultural Society of Nigeria, c/o Dr. T.I. Ashaye, PMB 5029, Ibadan, Oyo, Nigeria. Ed. Q B Anthonio. Circ: 1,000.

630 TTO ISSN 0368-1327
AGRICULTURAL SOCIETY OF TRINIDAD & TOBAGO. JOURNAL✶. Text in English. 1894. q. TTD 14, USD 7. adv. index.
Formerly: Agricultural Society of Trinidad & Tobago. Proceedings (0370-2030)
Indexed: AnBrAb, BiolAb, CurCont, DSA, FCA, HerbAb, HortAb, PBA, RPP, RRTA, S&F, WAE&RSA.
—CISTI.
Published by: Agricultural Society of Trinidad & Tobago, 112 St Vincent St, St Clair, Port-of-Spain, Trinidad, Trinidad & Tobago. TEL 868-627-3087, agrisoc@tstt.net.tt. Ed. Leo C Nanton. Circ: 2,680.

AGRICULTURAL SPRAY ADJUVANTS. see *CHEMISTRY—Organic Chemistry*

AGRICULTURAL STATISTICS OF GREECE. see *AGRICULTURE—Abstracting, Bibliographies, Statistics*

AGRICULTURAL STATISTICS OF SARAWAK. see *AGRICULTURE—Abstracting, Bibliographies, Statistics*

631 GBR ISSN 0140-4822
AGRICULTURAL SUPPLY INDUSTRY. Abbreviated title: A S I. Text in English. 1971. w. GBP 180 in Europe; GBP 215 in the Middle East; USD 410 in US & Canada; JPY 45,600 in Japan; GBP 231 rest of world (effective 2001). adv. bk.rev. 8 p./no. 3 cols./p.; back issues avail.; reprints avail. **Document type:** *Newsletter.* **Description:** Aimed at manufacturers and distributors of agrochemicals, fertilizers, animal feeds, animal health products, seeds and grain.
Related titles: Online - full text ed.: (from Data-Star, Gale Group).

Indexed: PROMT.
Published by: P J B Publications Ltd. (Subsidiary of: T & F Informa plc), 5th Fl, Telephone House, 69-77 Paul Street, London, EC2A 4LQ, United Kingdom. TEL 44-20-70176979, FAX 44-20-70176969, info@pjbpubs.com, http://www.pjbpubs.com. Ed. Jamie Day. Pub. Dr. Philip Brown. R&P Annette Watts TEL 44-20-83328961. Adv. contact Gail de Souza TEL 44-20-83328967. Circ: 1,419 (paid). **Subscr. addr. in N America:** Pharmabooks Ltd., 270 Madison Ave., # 4, New York, NY 10016-0601.

630 NLD ISSN 0308-521X
S3 CODEN: AGSYD5
➤ **AGRICULTURAL SYSTEMS.** Text in English. 1976. 12/yr. EUR 2,609 in Europe to institutions; JPY 346,500 in Japan to institutions; USD 2,918 elsewhere to institutions; EUR 357 in Europe to qualified personnel; JPY 47,200 in Japan to qualified personnel; USD 399 elsewhere to qualified personnel (effective 2006). adv. bk.rev. charts; illus. index. back issues avail. **Document type:** *Journal, Academic/Scholarly.* **Description:** Presents the results of studies concerning the whole or parts of the food chain from production to consumption.
Incorporates (in 1988): Agricultural Administration and Extension (0269-7475); Which was formerly (until 1986): Agricultural Administration (0309-586X)
Related titles: Microform ed.: (from PQC); Online - full text ed.: (from EBSCO Publishing, Gale Group, IngentaConnect, ScienceDirect, Swets Information Services).
Indexed: AEA, ASCA, AbHyg, AgBio, Agr, AgrForAb, AnBrAb, ApicAb, BIOBASE, BibAg, BioCN&I, BiolAb, CPA, CTFA, CurCont, DSA, EPB, EnvAb, FCA, FPA, ForAb, GEOBASE, HerbAb, HortAb, I&DA, IABS, IAOP, ISR, IndVet, MaizeAb, NemAb, NutrAb, OrnHort, PBA, PGegResA, PHN&I, PN&I, PlantSci, PotatoAb, PoultAb, ProtozoAb, RDA, REE&TA, RPP, RevApplEntom, RiceAb, S&F, SCI, SFA, SIA, SSCI, SeedAb, SoyAb, TDB, TriticAb, VetBull, WAE&RSA, WeedAb, WildRev.
—BLDSC (0757.410000), CISTI, IDS, IE, Infotrieve, ingenta. **CCC.**
Published by: Elsevier BV (Subsidiary of: Elsevier Science & Technology), Radarweg 29, Amsterdam, 1043 NX, Netherlands. TEL 31-20-4853911, FAX 31-20-4852457, nlinfo-f@elsevier.nl, http://www.elsevier.com/locate/agsy, http://www.elsevier.nl. Eds. J. Hansen, M. K. Van Ittersum, P. K. Thornton.

630 PRK
AGRICULTURAL WORKING PEOPLE OF KOREA✶. Text in Korean. 1973 (no.30). m. charts; illus.
Published by: Central Committee of the Union of Agricultural Working People of Korea, Pyongyang, Korea, N.

630 NGA ISSN 0331-0965
AGRICULTURE. Text in English. 1969. bi-m. KES 6, USD 24. adv. bk.rev.
Published by: Joe Obateru & Co., PO Box 472, Okitipupa, Ondo State, Nigeria. Ed. Tayo Obateru. Circ: 20,000.

630 ITA ISSN 1564-3123
AGRICULTURE 21. Text in Italian. 1998. m. back issues avail.
Media: Online - full text. **Related titles:** Italian ed.: ISSN 1564-3131; Spanish ed.: Agricultura 21. ISSN 1564-314X.
Published by: Food and Agriculture Organization of the United Nations, Sales and Marketing Group, Viale delle Terme di Caracalla, Rome, 00100, Italy. FAX 39-06-57053360, ag21@fao.org, http://www.fao.org/ag/magazine/default.htm/.

630 IND ISSN 0002-1725
AGRICULTURE AND AGRO-INDUSTRIES JOURNAL. Text in English. 1968. m. adv. charts; mkt.; stat. **Document type:** *Academic/Scholarly.*
Indexed: ExcerpMed, FS&TA.
—CISTI.
Published by: Chary Publications Pvt Ltd, 311 Raikar Chambers, Govandi East, Mumbai, Maharashtra 400088, India. Ed. S T Chary. Circ: 4,000.

630 GBR
SB4 CODEN: AGINEP
AGRICULTURE & EQUIPMENT INTERNATIONAL; the journal of international crop and animal husbandry. Text in English. 1949. bi-m. GBP 92, USD 161 (effective 2002). adv. bk.rev. charts; illus.; stat. **Document type:** *Academic/Scholarly.* **Description:** Publishes technical articles on agriculture and related disciplines for persons working in countries other than their own.
Formed by the 1992 merger of: Farm Equipment International; Agriculture International (0269-2457); Which was formed by the merger of: Livestock International (0306-8560); World Crops (0043-8391)
Related titles: Microfiche ed.: (from PQC); Microfilm ed.: (from PQC).
Indexed: AEA, ARDT, AnBrAb, B&AI, BAS, BioCN&I, DBA, EPB, EngInd, FCA, FS&TA, HerbAb, MaizeAb, PotatoAb, RASB, SFA, SeedAb, WAE&RSA, WeedAb, WildRev.
—CISTI, IE, Linda Hall. **CCC.**

Published by: Research Information Ltd., Grenville Court, Britwell Rd, Burnham, Bucks SL1 8DF, United Kingdom. TEL 44-1628-600499, FAX 44-1628-600488, info@researchinformation.co.uk, http://www.researchinformation.co.uk/. Ed. George Macpherson. Pub. Kumar Patel TEL 44-20-8328-2470. Adv. contact Ras Patel. B&W page GBP 576. Circ: 4,800.

630 CAN ISSN 1496-9920
AGRICULTURE AND FOOD (YEAR) ANNUAL PERFORMANCE REPORT. Text in English. 1915. a.
Former titles (until 2000): Agriculture and Food (Year) Annual Report (1492-6571); (until 1999): British Columbia. Ministry of Agriculture and Food. Annual Report (1492-0964); (until 1998): British Columbia. Ministry of Agriculture, Fisheries and Food. Annual Report (1197-0650); (until 1991): Ministry of Agriculture and Fisheries. Annual Report (0835-4871); (until 1984): Ministry of Agriculture and Food. Annual Report (0710-8664); (until 1979): British Columbia Ministry of Agriculture. Annual Report (0702-9993); (until 1979): British Columbia Ministry of Agriculture. Report (0701-788X); British Columbia Department of Agriculture. Report (0383-3143); Department of Agriculture. Annual Report (0383-3151); Report of the Department of Agriculture
—CISTI.
Published by: British Columbia, Ministry of Agriculture, Food and Fisheries, 808 Douglas St, Victoria, BC V8W 2Z7, Canada. TEL 250-387-1023, FAX 250-387-1522, http://www.gov.bc.ca/bvprd/bc/channel.do?action=ministry&channelID=-8377&navId=NAV_ID_province.

630 635 JPN ISSN 0369-5247
CODEN: NOOEAJ
AGRICULTURE AND HORTICULTURE✶ /NOKO TO ENGEI. Text in Japanese. 1926. m. JPY 17,700.
Indexed: FCA, HerbAb, HortAb, OrnHort, PBA, RiceAb, S&F.
—CASDDS, CISTI.
Published by: Seibundo Shinkosha Inc., 3-3-11 Hongo, Bunkyoku, Tokyo, 164-0013, Japan. Ed. Toshikuni Numaho. Circ: 100,000.

630 NLD ISSN 0889-048X
HD1401 CODEN: AHVAEO
➤ **AGRICULTURE AND HUMAN VALUES.** Text in English. 1984. q. EUR 325, USD 328, GBP 200 combined subscription to institutions print & online eds. (effective 2005). adv. reprint service avail. from PSC. **Document type:** *Journal, Academic/Scholarly.* **Description:** Seeks to create educational and scholarly junctures among the humanities, the social sciences, food and nutrition studies, and the agricultural disciplines, and to promote and ethical, social, and biological understanding of agriculture.
Related titles: Online - full text ed.: ISSN 1572-8366 (from EBSCO Publishing, Gale Group, IngentaConnect, Kluwer Online, O C L C Online Computer Library Center, Inc., ProQuest Information & Learning, Springer LINK, Swets Information Services).
Indexed: ABIn, AgBio, Agr, AgrForAb, AnBrAb, BibLing, BioCN&I, CurCont, DSA, EPB, FCA, FPA, FS&TA, ForAb, HerbAb, HortAb, I&DA, IndVet, JEL, MaizeAb, NutrAb, PBA, PGegResA, PHN&I, PN&I, PhilInd, PotatoAb, PoultAb, ProtozoAb, RA&MP, RDA, RI-1, RI-2, RPP, RRTA, RefZh, RevApplEntom, RiceAb, S&F, SFA, SSCI, SeedAb, SoyAb, TDB, VetBull, WAE&RSA, WeedAb.
—BLDSC (0759.530000), CISTI, IE, Infotrieve, ingenta. **CCC.**
Published by: (Agriculture, Food, and Human Value Society), Springer-Verlag Dordrecht (Subsidiary of: Springer Science+Business Media), Van Godewijckstraat 30, Dordrecht, 3311 GX, Netherlands. TEL 31-78-6576050, FAX 31-78-6576474, http://springerlink.metapress.com/openurl.asp?genre=journal&issn=0889-048X, http://www.springeronline.com. Ed. Laura B DeLind.

➤ **AGRICULTURE CHECKLIST.** see *AGRICULTURE—Abstracting, Bibliographies, Statistics*

630 FRA ISSN 0395-7152
AGRICULTURE DE GROUPE. Text in French. 1953. bi-m. adv. **Description:** Explores the world of agriculture; its economy, production costs, laws and regulations, choices.
Formerly (until 1962): Union des Ententes et Communautes Rurales. Bulletin de Liaison (0997-4164)
Indexed: SoyAb.
Published by: Groupements Agricoles pour l'Exploitation en Commun, Service de Publications, 11 rue de la Baume, Paris, 75008, France. TEL 33-1-53891228, FAX 33-1-45630932. Ed. Bernadette Weber. Pub. Pierre Lenoir.

630 FRA ISSN 0821-2732
AGRICULTURE DE LA NIEVRE. Text in French. 1981. w.
Published by: Maison de l'Agriculture, Place de Chantefois, Nevers, 58000, France. TEL 86-60-30-30. Ed. Philippe Richard. Circ: 7,600.

AGRICULTURE DECISIONS. see *LAW*

630 FRA
AGRICULTURE DROMOISE. Text in French. 1952. w.
Address: 2 bd. Vauban, BP 121, Valence, Cedex 26001, France. TEL 75-42-04-00, FAX 75-42-07-88. Ed. Freddy Martin Rosset. Circ: 8,088.

630 NLD ISSN 0167-8809
S601 CODEN: AEENDO
➤ **AGRICULTURE, ECOSYSTEMS & ENVIRONMENT.** Text in English. 1982. 24/yr. EUR 2,138 in Europe to institutions; JPY 283,400 in Japan to institutions; USD 2,395 to institutions except Europe and Japan (effective 2006). adv. bk.rev. bibl.; illus. index. back issues avail.; reprints avail. **Document type:** *Journal, Academic/Scholarly.* **Description:** Concerned with the interaction of methods of agricultural production, agroecosystems and the environment.
Incorporates (1979-1985): Protection Ecology (0378-4339); Formed by the merger of (1974-1982): Agriculture and Environment (0304-1131); (1974-1982): Agro-Ecosystems (0304-3746)
Related titles: Microform ed.: (from PQC); Online - full text ed.: (from EBSCO Publishing, Gale Group, IngentaConnect, ScienceDirect, Swets Information Services); ♦ Series: Applied Soil Ecology. ISSN 0929-1393.
Indexed: AEA, APD, ASCA, ASFA, AbHyg, AgBio, Agr, AgrForAb, AnBrAb, ApEcolAb, B&AI, BIOBASE, BIOSIS Prev, BioCN&I, BiolAb, CIN, CPA, CTFA, ChemAb, ChemTitl, CivEngAb, CurCont, DBA, DSA, EIA, EPB, ESPM, EnerInd, EngInd, EntAb, EnvAb, EnvEAb, EnvInd, ExcerpMed, FCA, FLUIDEX, FPA, FS&TA, FaBeAb, ForAb, GEOBASE, HelmAb, HerbAb, HortAb, I&DA, IABS, ISR, IndVet, Inspec, M&GPA, MaizeAb, NemAb, NutrAb, OrnHort, PBA, PGegResA, PGrRegA, PHN&I, PN&I, PlantSci, PollutAb, PotatoAb, PoultAb, RA&MP, RDA, RM&VM, RPP, RRTA, RevApplEntom, RiceAb, S&F, S&MA, SCI, SFA, SIA, SSCI, SWRA, SeedAb, SoyAb, TDB, TriticAb, VITIS, VetBull, WAE&RSA, WeedAb, WildRev, ZooRec.
—BLDSC (0760.380000), CASDDS, CISTI, Ei, IDS, IE, Infotrieve, ingenta, Linda Hall. **CCC.**
Published by: Elsevier BV (Subsidiary of: Elsevier Science & Technology), Radarweg 29, Amsterdam, 1043 NX, Netherlands. TEL 31-20-4853911, FAX 31-20-4852457, nlinfo-f@elsevier.nl, http://www.elsevier.com/locate/agee, http://www.elsevier.nl. Ed. M R Carter.

630 CAN ISSN 1491-6819
AGRICULTURE, FOOD AND BEVERAGES. Text in English. 1997. irreg. **Document type:** *Government.*
Published by: Agriculture and Agri-Food Canada, Southern Crop Protection and Food Research Centre, 1391 Sandford St, London, ON N5V 4T3, Canada. TEL 519-457-1470, FAX 519-457-3997, http://www.agr.gc.ca/.

630 FRA
AGRICULTURE - HORIZON. Text in French. 1893. w.
Address: B.P. 757, Arras, Cedex 62031, France. TEL 33-1-21502474, FAX 33-1-21240393. Ed. Roland Beugin. Circ: 44,477.

AGRICULTURE IN DENMARK. see *AGRICULTURE—Abstracting, Bibliographies, Statistics*

630 JPN ISSN 0018-3490
AGRICULTURE IN HOKKAIDO/HOKUNO. Text in Japanese. 1934. m. JPY 800 newsstand/cover. index.
Published by: Hokunokai, 1-1, Nishi 7-chome, Kita 1-jo, Chuo-ku, Sapporo-shi, Hokkaido 060, Japan. Circ: 1,600.

630 JOR
AGRICULTURE IN JORDAN/ZIRA'AT FI EL-URDON. Text in Arabic. 1965. q.
Published by: Ministry of Agriculture, P O Box 2099, Amman, Jordan.

630 GBR ISSN 0268-876X
AGRICULTURE IN SCOTLAND. Text in English. 1949. a. price varies. **Document type:** *Government.*
Indexed: RASB.
Published by: Scottish Office, Agriculture and Fisheries Department, Pentland House, 47 Robb's Loan, Edinburgh, EH14 1TY, United Kingdom. **Subscr. to:** H.M.S.O., 71 Lothian Rd, Edinburgh, Midlothian EH3 9AZ, United Kingdom.

630 GBR ISSN 0956-2567
HD1930.I6
AGRICULTURE IN THE UNITED KINGDOM. Text in English. a.
—BLDSC (0764.018500).
Published by: The Stationery Office, St. Clements House, 2-16 Colegate, Norwich, NR3 1BQ, United Kingdom. TEL 44-01603-723017, http://www.hmso.gov.uk.

630 AUS
CODEN: RBPVEW
AGRICULTURE TODAY. Text in English. 1992. m. adv. **Document type:** *Newspaper, Trade.* **Description:** Advisory, management and research newspaper for primary agricultural producers.
Formerly (until 2002): N S W Agriculture Today (1038-8613)
—CISTI.
Published by: Rural Press Ltd. (Subsidiary of: Agricultural Publishers Pty. Ltd.), 159 Bells Line of Rd., PO Box 999, North Richmond, NSW 2754, Australia. TEL 61-2-45704444, FAX 61-2-45704630, http://www.ruralpress.com/publications/detail.asp?publication_id=73. Ed. Guy Rowlinson. Adv. contact Rhonda Johnston TEL 61-2-67667488. B&W page AUD 1,365, color page AUD 2,015; trim 232 x 380. Circ: 38,376 (paid).

630 AUS ISSN 1440-4125
AGRICULTURE VICTORIA RUTHERGLEN RESEARCH REPORT. Text in English. 1982. biennial. free. back issues avail. **Document type:** *Government.* **Description:** Discusses research on various aspects of grain, sheep, and cattle.
Former titles (until 1998): Institute for Integrated Agricultural Development. Research Report; Rutherglen Research Institute. Research Report (0814-4990); Rutherglen, Australia. Research Station. Digest of Recent Research (0080-5009)
Published by: Australia Department of Natural Resources and Environment Victoria, Chiltern Valley Rd, RMB 1145, Rutherglen, VIC 3685, Australia. TEL 61-2-6030-4500, FAX 61-2-6030-4600, http://www.nre.vic.gov.au/profiles/avruther.htm. Ed. Garry McDonald. Circ: 1,000.

630 AUS ISSN 0726-934X
AGRICULTURE WESTERN AUSTRALIA. FARMNOTE. Text in English. irreg. AUD 56 domestic for Farmnotes, Primary Focus and Journal of Agriculture; AUD 66 foreign for Farmnotes, Primary Focus and Journal of Agriculture (effective 2001). 4 p./no.; **Document type:** *Monographic series, Government.*
Related titles: Online - full content ed.: 1989.
—BLDSC (3896.230000).
Published by: Department of Agriculture (Western Australia), 3 Baron-Hay Court, South Perth, W.A. 6151, Australia. TEL 61-8-93683333, FAX 61-8-9474-2018, enquiries@agric.wa.gov.au, http://www.agric.wa.gov.au/agency/pubns/farmnote/. R&P C Harris TEL 61-8-9368-3944.

AGRIDEV WEEKLY BULLETIN. see *AGRICULTURE—Abstracting, Bibliographies, Statistics*

630 SWE ISSN 0044-6831
AGRIFACK. Text in Swedish. 1942. 11/yr. SEK 300 (effective 2001). adv. bk.rev. **Document type:** *Newspaper, Trade.* **Description:** Covers agriculture, forestry, food & nutrition, economics and labor conditions.
Address: Lilla Nygatan 14, Fack 2062, Stockholm, 10312, Sweden. TEL 46-8-613-49-00, FAX 46-8-20-20-81, agrifack@saco.se, http://www.agrifack.com. Ed., Adv. contact Lars-Erik Liljebaeck. Pub. Helmer Svensson. B&W page SEK 10,000, color page SEK 13,600; trim 185 x 255. Circ: 5,900.

630 ZAF ISSN 1021-4895
AGRIFOKUS/AGRIFOCUS. Text in Afrikaans, English. 1992. q.
Indexed: ISAP.
Published by: Transvaalse Landbou-ontwikkelingsinstituut/ Transvaal Agricultural Development Institute, Privaatsak X180, Pretoria, 0001, South Africa.

630 NAM
AGRIFORUM. Text mainly in Afrikaans; Text occasionally in English. 1990. m. NAD 4.80 newsstand/cover. adv. illus.
Published by: Namibia Agricultural Union, Private Bag 13255, Windhoek, 9000, Namibia. Ed. R Erasmus.

630.658 CAN
AGRILINE; daily commodity news. Text in English. 5/w. CND 399 domestic; USD 399 foreign (effective 2001). **Document type:** *Newsletter.* **Description:** Contains information on Canadian commodity trade, agriculture, prices, crop conditions and agribusiness.
Published by: Century Publishing Co., PO Box 444, Winnipeg, MB R3C 2H6, Canada. TEL 204-943-8861, FAX 204-944-8033. Pub. Morris Dorosh. R&P Shelley Penner.

659.1 BWA
AGRINEWS. Text in English. 1971. m. **Description:** Contains technical information about agriculture and rural development.
Address: Private Bag 003, Gaborone, Botswana. Circ: 6,000.

630 664 639.2 634.9 ITA ISSN 1020-0320
AGRIS. Text in English. a. USD 825 (effective 2005).
Media: CD-ROM (from SilverPlatter Information, Inc.).
Published by: Food and Agriculture Organization of the United Nations, Sales and Marketing Group, Viale delle Terme di Caracalla, Rome, 00100, Italy. http://www.fao.org.

630 ESP ISSN 0211-030X
AGRISHELL; revista de fitopatologia y agricultura. Text in Spanish. 1973. 3/yr. free. bk.rev. illus.
Indexed: IECT.
—CCC.
Published by: Shell Espana S.A., Barquillo, 17, Madrid, 28004, Spain. TEL 34-91-521-4741, TELEX 27734 SHELL E. Ed. Alfonso Alvarez Valdes. Circ: 10,000.

631 CUB ISSN 1025-0247
AGRISOST. Text in Spanish. 1997. s-a.
Media: Online - full text.
Published by: Instituto Superior Pedagogico "Jose Marti", Departamento de Agronomia, Carr. Circunvalacion Norte km.5, Camaguey, 74670, Cuba. http://www.ceniai.inf.cu/dpub/agrisost/. Ed. Oscar L Parrado Alvarez.

630 USA
AGRISURFER; more grain, less chaff. Text in English. w. **Description:** A guide to all that's new and interesting in the online world of agriculture.
Media: Online - full text.
Address: 605 N Park Ave, Tifton, GA 31794. TEL 917-388-9399, agrisurfer@agrisurfer.com, http://agrisurfer.com/subscribe_agrisurfer.html.

630 CAN ISSN 1200-8001
AGRIVIEW. Text in English. m. free. **Document type:** *Government.* **Description:** Serves as the official department newspaper. Covers programs and services for Saskatchewan farmers and food organizations.
—CISTI.
Published by: Agriculture and Food, Communications Branch, B5 Walter Scott Bldg, 3085 Albert St, Regina, SK S4S 0B1, Canada. TEL 306-787-5140, FAX 306-787-0216, lstinson@agr.gov.sk.ca, http://www.agr.gov.sk.ca.

630 USA ISSN 1053-9603
AGRIVIEW. Text in English. 1942. s-m. USD 10 (effective 2005). adv. mkt.; stat. 12 p./no. 5 cols./p.; back issues avail. **Document type:** *Newsletter, Trade.* **Description:** Focuses on Vermont agriculture.
Related titles: Online - full text ed.
Published by: Vermont Agency of Agriculture, Food and Markets, 116 State St, Drawer 20, Montpelier, VT 05620-2901. TEL 802-828-2500, FAX 802-828-3831, Bosma@agr.state.vt.us, http://www.state.vt.us/agric/agriview.htm. Ed. Mark Bosma. Circ: 4,000 (paid).

630 CAN ISSN 1480-0268
AGRIVISION. Text in English. 1995. a.
—CISTI.
Published by: Agriculture and Agri-Food Canada, Southern Crop Protection and Food Research Centre, 1391 Sandford St, London, ON N5V 4T3, Canada. TEL 519-457-1470, FAX 519-457-3997.

630 CAN ISSN 0228-5584
AGRIWEEK; Canada's agribusiness authority since 1967. Text in English. 1967. w. CND 135 domestic; USD 135 foreign (effective 2001). **Document type:** *Newsletter.* **Description:** Contains information on Canadian agriculture and agribusiness, commodity trade, prices, crop conditions, and government policy.
Related titles: E-mail ed.
—CISTI. **CCC.**
Published by: Century Publishing Co., PO Box 444, Winnipeg, MB R3C 2H6, Canada. TEL 204-943-8861, FAX 204-944-8033, http://www.agriweek.com. Pub. Morris Dorosh. R&P Shelley Penner.

630 634.9 CHL ISSN 0716-1689
AGRO-CIENCIA. Text in English, Spanish. 1985. s-a.
Indexed: ASFA, ESPM, FCA, FPA, FS&TA, I&DA, IndVet, OrnHort, PN&I.
Published by: Universidad de Concepcion, Facultad de Ciencias Agropecuarias y Forestales, Avenida Vicente Mendez 595, Casilla 537, Chillan, Chile. TEL 56-42-208743, FAX 56-42-275305, aciencia@chillan.udec.cl, http://www.chillan.udec.cl/agrociencia/. Ed. Sergio Recabarren.

AGRO-ECOLOGY NEWS AND PERSPECTIVES; science and education for a sustanaible agriculture. see *ENVIRONMENTAL STUDIES*

664 ITA ISSN 1722-6996
CODEN: AIHTEI
AGRO FOOD INDUSTRY HI-TECH. Text in English. 1990. bi-m. EUR 42 domestic; EUR 75 foreign (effective 2005). adv. bk.rev. Index. back issues avail. **Document type:** *Journal, Trade.* **Description:** Presents technical developments in the food industry, cosmetic, chemical, pharmaceutical, agrochemicals and nutritional fields.
Formerly (until 1991): Agro-Industry Hi-Tech (1120-6012)
Related titles: Online - full text ed.: (from EBSCO Publishing).
Indexed: AEA, ASCA, AbHyg, AgBio, Agr, BCI, BioCN&I, CEABA, CIN, CPA, ChemAb, ChemTitl, DSA, FCA, FPA, FS&TA, ForAb, HerbAb, HortAb, I&DA, IndVet, MaizeAb, NutrAb, PBA, PGegResA, PGrRegA, PHN&I, PotatoAb, PoultAb, RA&MP, RDA, RM&VM, RPP, RevApplEntom, RiceAb, S&F, SIA, SeedAb, SoyAb, TDB, TriticAb, WAE&RSA, WeedAb.
—BLDSC (0764..552000), CASDDS, IDS, IE, ingenta.
Published by: Tekno Scienze s.r.l., Via Aurelio Saffi 23, Milan, MI 20123, Italy. TEL 39-02-4818011, FAX 39-02-4818070, http://www.teknoscienze.com. Ed. Carla Scesa. R&P, Adv. contact Michaela Carmagnola. B&W page USD 1,680; trim 210 x 297. Circ: 7,000.

630 338.1 FRA ISSN 1166-7729
AGRO MAGAZINE; revue mensuelle technique and economique en agro-industrie et agro-alimentaire. Text in French. 1937. 11/yr. adv. bk.rev. charts; illus.; tr.lit.
Formerly (until 1992): Agriculture (0002-1709)
Indexed: BiolAb, RASB.
—CCC.
Published by: Editagro, 64 rue la Boetie, Paris, 75008, France. TEL 33-1-45610406, FAX 33-1-42251770. Ed. J Billiemaz. Circ: 7,500.

630 CAN ISSN 0065-4655
AGRO-NOUVELLES. Text in French. 1965. 11/yr. adv. bk.rev. **Document type:** *Bulletin.*
Published by: Ordre des Agronomes du Quebec, 1001 rue Sherbrooke E, Bur 810, Montreal, PQ H2L 1L3, Canada. TEL 800-361-3833, agronome@oaq.qc.ca, http://www.oaq.qc.ca/, http://www.oag.gc.ca/. Ed., Adv. contact Claudine Lussier. Circ: (controlled).

631 NGA
AGRO-SCIENCE: JOURNAL OF TROPICAL AGRICULTURE, FOOD, ENVIRONMENTAL AND EXTENSION. Text in English. 2000. s-a. NGN 750 in Africa; USD 90 elsewhere (effective 2004). back issues avail. **Document type:** *Journal, Academic/Scholarly.*
Related titles: Online - full text ed.
Published by: University of Nigeria, Department of Animal Science, Nsukka, Nigeria. misunn@aol.com, http://www.inasp.info/ajol/journals.html. Ed. G. Igboeli.

630 BEL ISSN 0002-1814
AGRO-SERVICE/LANDBOUW SERVICE. Text in French. 1954. bi-m. adv. bk.rev. charts; illus.; stat. **Document type:** *Government.*
Related titles: Dutch ed.
Published by: Nationale Centrale Landbouw-Service, Spastraat 8, Brussels, 1040, Belgium. Ed. M Speeckaert. Circ: 2,000.

630 POL ISSN 1230-1825
AGRO SERWIS. Text in Polish. 1992. bi-m. PLZ 24; USD 10 in United States. adv. bk.rev. index. back issues avail. **Description:** Provides information, summaries, reports, forecast for farmers, agricultural firms, students.
Published by: Biznes - Press Ltd., pok. 302, Ul Swietokrzyska 20, Warsaw, 00002, Poland. TEL 48-22-272401, FAX 48-22-272401. Adv. contact Teresa Gosiorowska. B&W page PLZ 1,500. Circ: 25,000.

630 MEX
AGRO-SINTESIS; agricultura-ganaderia-avicultura. Text in Spanish. 1969. m. USD 20. adv. bk.rev. abstr.; illus.; stat.; tr.lit. index. back issues avail.
Published by: Editorial Ano Dos Mil, S.A., Indianapolis 70, Mexico City, DF 03810, Mexico. Ed. Juan Francisco Gonzalez Inigo. Circ: 13,000.

630 CHL ISSN 0304-8802
CODEN: AGSUDR
➤ **AGRO SUR.** Text and summaries in English, Spanish. 1973. 2/yr. CLP 6,000 domestic to individuals; USD 40 foreign to individuals; CLP 10,000 domestic to institutions; USD 50 foreign to institutions (effective 2005); or exchange basis. bk.rev. abstr.; charts; illus. index, cum.index: 1974-1980, 1989-1998. **Document type:** *Journal, Academic/Scholarly.* **Description:** Includes research papers in agriculture produced by the faculty and external researchers, both from Chile and other countries.
Indexed: AEA, ASFA, AgBio, AgrForAb, Agrind, AnBrAb, B&AI, BibAg, BioCN&I, BiolAb, CPA, ChemAb, DSA, ESPM, FCA, FPA, FS&TA, ForAb, HerbAb, HortAb, I&DA, IAALC, IBR, IndVet, MBA, MaizeAb, NemAb, NutrAb, OrnHort, PBA, PGegResA, PGrRegA, PHN&I, PN&I, PotatoAb, PoultAb, RDA, RPP, RevApplEntom, S&F, SIA, SWRA, SeedAb, TDB, TriticAb, VITIS, VetBull, WAE&RSA, WeedAb.
—BLDSC (0764.552500), CASDDS, CINDOC, CISTI, IE, ingenta.
Published by: Universidad Austral de Chile, Facultad de Ciencias Agrarias, Casilla 567, Valdivia, Chile. TEL 56-63-221239, FAX 56-63-221068, aellies@uach.cl. Ed. Dr. Luis L Latrille. R&P Achim Ellies TEL 56-63-221054. Circ: 300 (paid); 200 (controlled).

338.1 RUS
AGRO XXI; nauchno-prakticheskii zhurnal. Text in Russian. 1999. s-a. USD 148 in United States (effective 2004). 144 p./no.; **Document type:** *Journal, Trade.* **Description:** Topical news from Russia and abroad on plant protection and quarantine, general problems of plant growing and genetic engineering.
Published by: Agrorus', Mosfil'movskaya ul, 52, Moscow, 119590, Russian Federation. TEL 7-095-9379812, FAX 7-095-2326825, agrorus@agrorus.com, http://www.agrorus.com. Circ: 1,000.
Dist. by: East View Information Services, 3020 Harbor Ln. N., Minneapolis, MN 55447. TEL 800-477-1005, FAX 800-800-3839, eastview@eastview.com, http://www.eastview.com.

▼ **AGROALIMENTACION & DESARROLLO SUSTENTABLE**; revista de educacion agroalimentare. see *NUTRITION AND DIETETICS*

630 USA ISSN 0002-1822
S33 CODEN: AGBOBO
➤ **AGROBOREALIS.** Text in English. 1969. s-a. free. charts; illus.; stat. back issues avail. **Document type:** *Journal, Academic/Scholarly.*
Indexed: Agr, BIOSIS Prev, BiolAb, CurCont, EnvAb, ExcerpMed, FCA, FPA, FS&TA, ForAb, HerbAb, HortAb, I&DA, IndVet, MaizeAb, NutrAb, OrnHort, RefZh, S&F, SFA, TriticAb, VetBull, WildRev.
—BLDSC (0764.555000), CISTI, Linda Hall.

Published by: University of Alaska at Fairbanks, Agricultural and Forestry Experiment Station, 305 O'Neill Building, P O Box 757140, Fairbanks, AK 99775-7140. TEL 907-474-7083, FAX 907-474-6567, fynrpub@aurora.alaska.edu, http://www.uaf.edu/salrm/afes/pubs/agro/index.html. Ed. Deirdre Helfferich. Circ: 4,000 (controlled).

630 668.6 SVK ISSN 0002-1830
CODEN: AGROB2

AGROCHEMIA/AGRICULTURAL CHEMICALS. Text in Czech, Slovak; Summaries in English. 1961. m. SKK 96; USD 27 foreign (effective 2000). adv. bk.rev. charts; illus.; pat. **Document type:** *Trade.*
Related titles: Microfilm ed.: (from PMC).
Indexed: AEA, BiolAb, CIN, ChemAb, ChemTitl, ExcerpMed, FCA, HerbAb, HortAb, IndVet, MaizeAb, PGrRegA, RM&VM, RPP, RevApplEntom, S&F, TriticAb, WAE&RSA, WeedAb.
—CASDDS, CISTI, Linda Hall.
Published by: (Vyzkumny Ustav Agrochemicke Technologie), V U C H T a.s., Novelova 34, Bratislava, 83603, Slovakia. TEL 33-14-41, FAX 42-7-594-43. Circ: 5,000. **Dist. by:** Slovart G.T.G. s.r.o., Krupinska 4, PO Box 152, Bratislava 85299, Slovakia. TEL 421-2-63839472, FAX 421-2-63839485, http://www.slovart-gtg.sk. **Co-sponsor:** Slovchemia.

630 668.6 ITA ISSN 0002-1857
S583 CODEN: AGRCAX

➤ **AGROCHIMICA**; rivista internazionale di chimica vegetale, pedologia e fertilizzazione del suolo. Text in English, French, German, Italian, Spanish. 1956. bi-m. EUR 129 domestic; EUR 155 foreign (effective 2003). adv. bk.rev. abstr.; bibl.; illus. index. back issues avail.; reprint service avail. from ISI. **Document type:** *Academic/Scholarly.* **Description:** Devoted to original research in the field of plant chemistry, soil science and fertilization.
Indexed: ASCA, ASFA, AgBio, AgrForAb, BBCI, BIOBASE, BioDAb, BiolAb, CCI, CIN, CPA, Cadscan, ChemAb, ChemTitl, CurCont, DSA, ESPM, ExcerpMed, FCA, FPA, FaBeAb, ForAb, HerbAb, HortAb, I&DA, IABS, LeadAb, MBA, MaizeAb, NemAb, NutrAb, OrnHort, PBA, PGegResA, PGrRegA, PHN&I, PlantSci, PoultAb, RA&MP, RPP, RefZh, RevApplEntom, RiceAb, S&F, S&MA, SIA, SWRA, SeedAb, SoyAb, TriticAb, VITIS, WeedAb, Zincscan.
—BLDSC (0764.600000), CASDDS, CISTI, IDS, IE, Infotrieve, ingenta, Linda Hall.
Published by: (Universita degli Studi di Pisa), Gruppo Agrochimica, Via del Borghetto, 80, Pisa, PI 56124, Italy. TEL 39-050-971921, FAX 39-050-598614. Ed. R Riffaldi. Circ: 500. **Subscr. to:** Pacini Editore SpA.

630 MEX ISSN 1405-3195
S539.M6

➤ **AGROCIENCIA.** Text in English, Spanish; Summaries in Spanish, English. 1966. bi-m. MXP 350 domestic to individuals; USD 80 foreign to individuals; MXP 700 domestic to institutions; USD 100 foreign to institutions (effective 2000). adv. bk.rev. abstr.; charts; illus. Index. back issues avail. **Document type:** *Journal, Academic/Scholarly.* **Description:** Presents original papers in plant protection, animal science, crop science, animal and plant breeding, crop physiology, water resources, meteorology and microclimate, crop production, soil science, agricultural development and economics, genetic and natural resources, and forestry.
Formed by the 1996 merger of (1990-1994): Agrociencia. Fitociencia (0188-302X); (1990-1993): Agrociencia. Agua, Suelo, Clima (0188-3089); (1991-1992): Agrociencia. Ciencia Animal (0188-3038); (1991-1993): Agrociencia. Recursos Naturales Renovables (0188-3062); (1990-1993): Agrociencia. Socioeconomica (0188-3070); (1990-1993): Agrociencia. Matematicas Aplicada, Estadisticas y Computacion (0188-3054); (1990-1993): Agrociencia. Proteccion Vegetal (0188-3046); Which superseded in part (in 1990): Agrociencia (0185-0288)
Related titles: E-mail ed.; Online - full text ed.: free (effective 2005).
Indexed: AEA, AgBio, Agr, AgrForAb, AnBrAb, BioCN&I, BiolAb, CIS, CPA, CurCont, DSA, FCA, FPA, FS&TA, ForAb, HelmAb, HerbAb, HortAb, I&DA, IndVet, MaizeAb, NutrAb, OrnHort, PBA, PGegResA, PGrRegA, PHN&I, PN&I, PotatoAb, PoultAb, RA&MP, RDA, RPP, RRTA, RevApplEntom, RiceAb, S&F, SIA, SeedAb, SoyAb, TDB, TriticAb, VetBull, WAE&RSA, WeedAb, ZooRec.
—BLDSC (0764.621500), CISTI.
Published by: Colegio de Postgraduados, Programa de Genetica I R E G E P, Chapingo, MEX 56230, Mexico. TEL 52-595-48944, FAX 52-595-48944, leopoldo@colpos.colpos.mx, http://www.colpos.mx/agrocien/agrociencia.htm. Ed. Dr. Leopoldo E Mendoza-Onofre. Circ: 700 (paid); 800 (controlled).

630 URY ISSN 1510-0839

➤ **AGROCIENCIA.** Text in Spanish; Summaries in English. 1997. bi-m. back issues avail. **Document type:** *Journal, Academic/Scholarly.*
Indexed: AEA, AgBio, AgrForAb, AnBrAb, BioCN&I, CPA, DSA, FCA, FPA, ForAb, HerbAb, HortAb, I&DA, INIS AtomInd, IndVet, MaizeAb, NutrAb, OrnHort, PBA, PGegResA, PGrRegA, PHN&I, PN&I, PoultAb, RDA, RPP, RiceAb, S&F, SeedAb, SoyAb, TriticAb, WAE&RSA, WeedAb.
—CISTI.
Published by: Universidad de la Republica, Facultad de Agronomia, Av. G Garzon, 780, Montevideo, 12908, Uruguay. TEL 598-2-3078868, FAX 598-2-3078868, biblio@fagro.edu.uy.

630 DOM ISSN 0376-4974

AGROCONOCIMIENTO. Text in Spanish. 1976. m. USD 12. adv. bk.rev. **Description:** Contains agricultural news and technical information.
Address: Apdo 345 2, Santo Domingo, Dominican Republic. Ed. Domingo Marte. Circ: 10,000.

630 MEX ISSN 1605-4881

AGROCULTURA. Text in English. 1999. bi-m. MXP 120 (effective 2001). adv.
Media: Online - full text. **Related titles:** Print ed.
Published by: Grupo Editorial Eikon, SA de CV, Privada Paris 2472, Col. Los Arcos, Guadalajara, Jalisco, 44520, Mexico. TEL 52-3-6159307, FAX 52-3-6153299, http://www.agrored.com.mx/Agrocultura/. adv.: B&W page MXP 8,740, color page MXP 11,650; 20.6 x 27.5.

630 COL

AGRODIARIO. Text in Spanish. 1980. m.
Address: Calle 15 No. 8-94 Of. 506, Apartado Aereo 24215, Bogota, CUND, Colombia. TEL 57-1-281-5528. Circ: 10,000.

AGROFORESTERIA EN LAS AMERICAS. see *FORESTS AND FORESTRY*

631 GBR ISSN 0967-649X

AGROFORESTRY NEWS. Text in English. 1992. quadrennial. GBP 20 domestic; GBP 24 foreign to individuals; GBP 34 foreign to institutions (effective 2004).
Published by: Agroforestry Research Trust, 46 Hunters Moon Dartington, Totnes, Devon, TQ9 6JT, United Kingdom. TEL 44-14-1803-8476, FAX 44-14-1803-8407, mail@agroforestry.co.uk, http://www.agroforestry.co.uk.

630 634.9 NLD ISSN 0167-4366
CODEN: AGSYE6

➤ **AGROFORESTRY SYSTEMS.** Text in English. 1982. 9/yr. EUR 968, USD 988, GBP 638 combined subscription to institutions print & online eds. (effective 2005). adv. back issues avail.; reprint service avail. from PSC. **Document type:** *Journal, Academic/Scholarly.* **Description:** Publishes research concerning agroforestry and other sustainable land management systems which combine agriculture, animal husbandry and trees on the same unit of land.
Incorporates (1972-1999): Agroforestry Forum (0966-8616); Which was formerly (until 1992): Agroforestry in the U K
Related titles: Microform ed.: (from PQC); Online - full text ed.: ISSN 1572-9680 (from EBSCO Publishing, Gale Group, IngentaConnect, Kluwer Online, O C L C Online Computer Library Center, Inc., Springer LINK, Swets Information Services).
Indexed: AEA, ARDT, ASCA, ASFA, AgBio, Agr, AgrForAb, AnBrAb, B&AI, BIOBASE, BIOSIS Prev, BibLing, BioCN&I, BiolAb, CPA, CurCont, DSA, EPB, EngInd, EnvAb, FCA, FPA, ForAb, GEOBASE, GardL, HerbAb, HortAb, I&DA, IABS, ILD, MaizeAb, NemAb, NutrAb, OrnHort, PBA, PGegResA, PGrRegA, PN&I, PlantSci, PoultAb, RA&MP, RDA, RPP, RefZh, RevApplEntom, RiceAb, S&F, SFA, SIA, SSCI, SWA, SeedAb, SoyAb, TDB, TriticAb, VITIS, WAE&RSA, WeedAb, WildRev.
—BLDSC (0764.730000), CISTI, Ei, IDS, IE, Infotrieve, ingenta. **CCC.**
Published by: (International Council for Research in Agroforestry), Springer-Verlag Dordrecht (Subsidiary of: Springer Science+Business Media), Van Godewijckstraat 30, Dordrecht, 3311 GX, Netherlands. TEL 31-78-6576050, FAX 31-78-6576474, http://springerlink.metapress.com/openurl.asp?genre=journal&issn=0167-4366, http://www.springeronline.com. Ed. P K Ramachandran Nair.

630 KEN ISSN 1013-9591

AGROFORESTRY TODAY. Text in English. 1979. q. USD 40 to individuals; USD 60 to institutions (effective 1999). adv. **Document type:** *Newsletter.* **Description:** Initiates, stimulates and supports research leading to more sustainable and productive land use in developing countries through integration of trees in land use systems.
Former titles (until 1989): I C R A F Newsletter and Agroforestry Review; Agroforestry Review; I C R A F Newsletter (0255-8173)
Related titles: ♦ Spanish ed.: Bean Program Annual Report. ISSN 0120-2243; Spanish ed.: Informe Anual del Programa de Frijol. ISSN 0120-2235; Ed.: Agroforesterie Aujourd'hui. ISSN 1015-3225.
Indexed: AEA, ARDT, AgrForAb, FPA, ForAb, HerbAb, HortAb, OrnHort, PBA, PHN&I, RA&MP, RDA, SeedAb, TDB, TriticAb, WAE&RSA, WeedAb.
—CISTI, IE.
Published by: International Centre for Research in Agroforestry, PO Box 30677, Nairobi, Kenya. TEL 254-2-521450, FAX 254-2-521001, TELEX 22048, icraf@cgiar.org, http://www.chiar.org/icraf. Ed., R&P, Adv. contact Debra Lodoen. Circ: 6,000 (controlled).

630 668.6 HUN ISSN 0002-1873
CODEN: AKTLAU

AGROKEMIA ES TALAJTAN/AGROCHEMISTRY AND SOIL SCIENCE. Text in Hungarian; Summaries in English. 1951. q. USD 100 (effective 2006). bk.rev. bibl.; charts; illus.; maps. index, cum.index. back issues avail. **Document type:** *Journal, Academic/Scholarly.* **Description:** Publishes original papers in the fields of soil science, agricultural chemistry, soil microbiology and soil biochemistry.
Related titles: Online - full text ed.: ISSN 1588-2713.
Indexed: AEA, BioCN&I, BiolAb, CIN, CPA, ChemAb, ChemTitl, CurCont, FCA, FPA, ForAb, HerbAb, HortAb, I&DA, MaizeAb, NemAb, OrnHort, PBA, PGegResA, PotatoAb, RPP, RRTA, RevApplEntom, S&F, SIA, SeedAb, SoyAb, TriticAb, WAE&RSA, WeedAb.
—CASDDS, CISTI, Linda Hall. **CCC.**
Published by: (Magyar Tudomanyos Akademia/Hungarian Academy of Sciences, Agrokemiai Kutato Intezet), Akademiai Kiado Rt. (Subsidiary of: Wolters Kluwer N.V.), Prielle Kornelia U. 19, Budapest, 1117, Hungary. TEL 36-1-4648282, FAX 36-1-4648221, journals@akkrt.hu, http://www.akkrt.hu. Ed. Gyorgy Varallyay. Circ: 1,500.

630 668.6 RUS ISSN 0002-1881
S583 CODEN: AGKYAU

AGROKHIMIYA. Text in Russian. 1964. m. USD 397 foreign (effective 2005). bk.rev. index. **Document type:** *Journal, Academic/Scholarly.* **Description:** Publishes the results of theoretical and experimental studies and reviews on the current problems of soil chemistry and fertility, plant nutrition, plant protection and plant growth regulators, application of fertilizers, ecology, and ecotoxicology.
Related titles: Online - full text ed.; ♦ English Translation: Eurasian Soil Science. ISSN 1064-2293.
Indexed: AbHyg, AgBio, ApicAb, BIOSIS Prev, BioCN&I, BiolAb, CPA, CTFA, ChemAb, DBA, FCA, FPA, FS&TA, FaBeAb, ForAb, HerbAb, HortAb, I&DA, MaizeAb, NemAb, NutrAb, OrnHort, PBA, PGegResA, PGrRegA, PHN&I, PN&I, PotatoAb, PoultAb, RA&MP, RM&VM, RPP, RefZh, RevApplEntom, RiceAb, S&F, S&MA, SIA, SeedAb, SoyAb, TriticAb, VITIS, WAE&RSA, WeedAb.
—BLDSC (0005.250000), CASDDS, CISTI, East View, IE, ingenta, KNAW, Linda Hall. **CCC.**
Published by: (Rossiiskaya Akademiya Nauk/Russian Academy of Sciences), Izdatel'stvo Nauka, Profsoyuznaya ul 90, Moscow, 117864, Russian Federation. TEL 7-095-3347151, FAX 7-095-4202220, secret@naukaran.ru, http://www.maik.ru/cgi-bin/list.pl?page=agro, http://www.naukaran.ru. **Dist. by:** M K - Periodica, ul Gilyarovskogo 39, Moscow 129110, Russian Federation. TEL 7-095-2845008, FAX 7-095-2813798, info@periodicals.ru, http://www.mkniga.ru. **Co-sponsor:** Ministerstvo Sel'skogo Khozyaistva Rossiiskoi Federatsii.

630 DNK ISSN 0906-0081

AGROLOGISK (ODENSE); tidsskrift om markbrug. Text in Danish. 1983. m. DKK 595 domestic; DKK 775 in Europe; DKK 979 elsewhere (effective 2005). adv. illus. **Document type:** *Magazine, Trade.*
Formerly (until 1990): Agrologisk Tidsskrift Marken (0108-8459)
Related titles: Online - full text ed.
Published by: Dansk Agrar Forlag A-S (Subsidiary of: FagbladsGruppen A/S), Birk Centerpark 36, Herning, 7400, Denmark. TEL 45-76-207970, FAX 45-96-265296, agrologisk@agrar.dk, post@agrar.dk, http://www.agrar.dk/agrologisk.asp. Eds. Knud E Madsen, Niels Damgaard Hansen. adv.: page DKK 8,900; 270 x 184. Circ: 3,300.

630 COL ISSN 0120-9965
CODEN: ETSEED

AGRONOMIA COLOMBIANA. Text in English. 1983. s-a.
Indexed: ASFA, BioCN&I, CPA, ESPM, FCA, HerbAb, HortAb, MaizeAb, NemAb, OrnHort, PBA, PGegResA, PGrRegA, PHN&I, PotatoAb, RDA, RPP, RiceAb, S&F, SIA, SeedAb, WAE&RSA, WeedAb.
—CISTI, Linda Hall.
Published by: Universidad Nacional de Colombia, Facultad de Agronomia, Ciudad Universitaria, Apartado Aereo 14490, Santafe de Bogota, Colombia. TEL 0571-3165100, FAX 0571-3165176.

630 CRI ISSN 0377-9424
CODEN: AGCODV

AGRONOMIA COSTARRICENSE. Variant title: Revista de Ciencias Agricolas. Text in Spanish. 1977. s-a. CRC 1,000 domestic; USD 30 foreign (effective 2000). adv. charts; illus. index. **Document type:** *Academic/Scholarly.*
Related titles: Online - full text ed.: (from Gale Group).
Indexed: AgBio, AgrForAb, AnBrAb, BioCN&I, BioDAb, BiolAb, CPA, ChemAb, CurCont, DSA, FCA, FPA, ForAb, HerbAb, HortAb, I&DA, INIS AtomInd, IndVet, MaizeAb, NemAb, NutrAb, OrnHort, PBA, PGegResA, PGrRegA, PHN&I, PotatoAb, PoultAb, RDA, RM&VM, RPP, RRTA, RevApplEntom, RiceAb, S&F, SIA, SeedAb, SoyAb, VetBull, WAE&RSA, WeedAb.
—CASDDS, CISTI, Linda Hall.
Published by: Editorial de la Universidad de Costa Rica, Apdo. 75-2060, Ciudad Universitaria Rodrigo Facio Brenes, San Pedro de Montes de Oca, San Jose, 2050, Costa Rica. TEL 506-207-4000, FAX 506-207-5535, cmmoreno@cariari.ucr.ac.cr, http://www.ucr.ac.cr/. R&P Mario Murillo TEL 506-2075003. Adv. contact Cristina Moreno Murillo.

630 MOZ ISSN 0044-6858
CODEN: AMOCBR
AGRONOMIA MOCAMBICANA. Variant title: Instituto de Investigacao Agronomica de Mocambique. Comunicacoes. Text in Portuguese; Summaries in English, Portuguese. 1967. irreg., latest vol.2, 1974. price varies. charts; illus.; stat. index.
Indexed: BiolAb, ChemAb.
—CISTI.
Published by: Instituto Nacional de Investigacao Agronomica, Centro de Documentacao e Informacao, C.P. 3658, Maputo 11, Mozambique. Circ: 400.

630 BRA ISSN 0365-2726
O AGRONOMICO; boletim tecnico informativo do Instituto Agronomico. Key Title: Agronomico. Text in Portuguese. 1949. m. bk.rev. abstr. **Document type:** *Bulletin, Trade.*
Indexed: ATA, BibAg, BiolAb, ChemAb, FCA, HortAb, MaizeAb, OrnHort, PBA, RPP, RefZh, SeedAb, SoyAb, TriticAb.
—CISTI.
Published by: Instituto Agronomico, Servico de Divulgacao Tecnico-Cientifica, Caixa Postal 28, Campinas, SP 13020-902, Brazil. TEL 55-19-32315422, FAX 55-19-32314943, public@iac.sp.gov.br, http://www.iac.sp.gov.br. Ed. Angela M C Furlani. Circ: 2,000.

631 CIV ISSN 1015-2288
AGRONOMIE AFRICAINE. Text in French. 1989. 3/yr.
Related titles: Online - full text ed.: (from International Network for the Availability of Scientific Publications, African Journals Online).
Published by: Association Ivoirienne des Sciences Agronomiques, 20 BP 703, Abidjan, 20, Ivory Coast. http://www.inasp.info/ajol/journals.html. Ed. Ake Severin.

630 FIN ISSN 0781-8718
AGRONOMILIITTO. YEARBOOK. Text in Finnish. a. **Document type:** *Catalog, Academic/Scholarly.*
Published by: Agronomiliitto/Finnish Association of Academic Agronomists, P Makasiinkatu 6 A 8, Helsinki, 00130, Finland. TEL 358-9-2511160, FAX 358-9-25111610. Ed. Markku Pulkkinen.

630 HRV ISSN 0002-1954
AGRONOMSKI GLASNIK. Text in Serbo-Croatian; Summaries in English, French, German. 1938. bi-m. USD 26.70. adv. bk.rev. abstr.; bibl.; charts; illus.
Indexed: AEA, AgBio, AnBrAb, BioCN&I, BiolAb, CPA, ChemAb, DSA, FCA, FPA, FS&TA, ForAb, HerbAb, HortAb, I&DA, MaizeAb, NutrAb, OrnHort, PBA, PGegResA, PGrRegA, PHN&I, PN&I, PotatoAb, RA&MP, RPP, RRTA, RevApplEntom, S&F, SIA, SeedAb, SoyAb, TriticAb, VITIS, WAE&RSA, WeedAb.
—CISTI.
Published by: Savez Poljoprivrednih Inzenjera i Tehnicara Hrvatske, Berislaviceva 6, Zagreb, Croatia. Ed. Ivan Novak.

630 USA ISSN 0065-4663
CODEN: AGRYAV
AGRONOMY: A SERIES OF MONOGRAPHS. Text in English. 1949. irreg., latest vol.33, 1992. USD 600 (effective 2005). adv. **Document type:** *Monographic series.*
Indexed: Agr, BIOSIS Prev, BiolAb, ChemAb.
—BLDSC (0770.900000), CASDDS, CISTI, IE, ingenta. **CCC.**
Published by: American Society of Agronomy, Inc., 677 S Segoe Rd, Madison, WI 53711. TEL 608-273-8080, FAX 608-273-2021. Adv. contact Keith R Schlesinger.

630 ZWE
AGRONOMY INSTITUTE. ANNUAL REPORT. Text in English. a. free. back issues avail.
Published by: (Zimbabwe. Information Services), Ministry of Lands Agriculture and Rural Resettlement, Research and Specialist Services, Causeway, PO Box 8108, Harare, Zimbabwe. Circ: 250.

630 USA ISSN 0002-1962
S22 CODEN: AGJOAT
➤ **AGRONOMY JOURNAL**; an international journal of agriculture and natural resource sciences. Text in English. 1907. bi-m. USD 50 to members; USD 600 to non-members (effective 2005). adv. charts; illus. index. 2 cols./p.; back issues avail.; reprints avail. **Document type:** *Journal, Academic/Scholarly.*
Description: Contains papers on all aspects of crop and soil sciences including crop physiology, production, and management along with their relationship to soil fertility and climatic conditions.
Incorporates (1988-1999): Journal of Production Agriculture (0890-8524); Formerly: American Society of Agronomy. Journal (0095-9650)
Related titles: CD-ROM ed.; Microfilm ed.: (from PMC); Online - full content ed.: ISSN 1435-0645 (from HighWire Press); Online - full text ed.: (from bigchalk, EBSCO Publishing, H.W. Wilson, O C L C Online Computer Library Center, Inc., ProQuest Information & Learning).
Indexed: AEA, ASCA, ASFA, AgBio, Agr, AgrForAb, AnBrAb, B&AI, BIOBASE, BIOSIS Prev, BibAg, BioCN&I, BiolAb, CIN, CIS, CPA, CTFA, Cadscan, ChemAb, ChemTitl, CurCont, DBA, DSA, EPB, ESPM, Englnd, EnvAb, EnvInd, ExcerpMed, F&GI, FCA, FS&TA, FaBeAb, ForAb, HerbAb, HortAb, I&DA, IABS, INIS AtomInd, ISR, IndVet, LeadAb, M&GPA, MaizeAb, NemAb, NutrAb, OrnHort, PBA, PCI, PGegResA, PGrRegA, PHN&I, PN&I, PlantSci, PotatoAb, PoultAb, RA&MP, RDA, RM&VM, RPP, RRTA, RefZh, RevApplEntom, RiceAb, S&F, S&MA, SCI, SIA, SWRA, SeedAb, SoyAb, TOSA, TriticAb, VetBull, WAE&RSA, WeedAb, Zincscan.
—BLDSC (0771.200000), CASDDS, CISTI, Ei, IDS, IE, Infotrieve, ingenta, Linda Hall. **CCC.**
Published by: American Society of Agronomy, Inc., 677 S Segoe Rd, Madison, WI 53711. TEL 608-273-8080, FAX 608-273-2021, journals@agronomy.org, http://agron.scijournals.org/, http://www.agronomy.org. Eds. Calvin H Pearson, K A Barbarick. adv.: color page USD 3,215, B&W page USD 1,190. Circ: 7,650 (paid).

630.658 EST ISSN 1406-894X
▼ ➤ **AGRONOMY RESEARCH.** Text in English. 2003. s-a. **Document type:** *Monographic series, Academic/Scholarly.*
Description: Intended for publication broad-spectrum original articles in actual problems of modern agriculture incl. crop and animal science, genetics, economics, technical aspects, agriculture and environmental relations, etc.
Related titles: Online - full text ed.: free (effective 2005).
Indexed: B&BAb, BioEngAb, EntAb, FCA, RefZh.
Published by: Eesti Pollumajandusulikool/Estonian Agricultural University, Kreutzwaldi 64, Tartu, 51014, Estonia. TEL 372-7-313001, FAX 372-7-313069, agronomy@eau.ee, info@eau.ee, http://www.eau.ee/~agronomy.

631 PER ISSN 1609-9680
AGRONOTICIAS. Text in Spanish. 2000. m. PEN 150 domestic; USD 120 in South America; USD 150 in North America; USD 180 in Europe; USD 220 in Asia (effective 2003).
Media: Online - full text.
Address: Jr. Pablo Bermudez No. 285, Ofic. 202 Jesus Maria, Lima, 11, Peru. TEL 51-1-4338632, FAX 51-1-4339574, agronoticias@terra.com.pe, http://barrioperu.terra.com.pe/agronoticias/.

630 VEN
AGROPECUARIO (VENEZUELA). Text in Spanish. 24/yr.
Published by: Venozolana de Prensa, Calle 5 no. 9-27, Calabozo, Gurico 2312, Venezuela. Ed. Gontran Carcia.

630 POL ISSN 1230-7866
AGROPROLOG. Text in Polish. 1990. m.
Published by: Zwiazek Przedsiebiorstw Rolnych, Ul Wspolna 30, Warsaw, 00930, Poland. TEL 48-22-628-7889, TELEX 812400. Ed. Bozena Kopka. Circ: 40,000.

630 PRT ISSN 0002-1970
CODEN: AGLSAH
AGROS; revista tecnico-cientifica. Text in Portuguese; Summaries in English. 1917. a. adv. bibl.; charts; illus.; mkt. back issues avail. **Document type:** *Academic/Scholarly.*
Related titles: Fax ed.; Online - full text ed.
Indexed: BiolAb, ChemAb.
—CASDDS, CISTI.
Published by: Instituto Superior de Agronomia, Associacao dos Estudantes, Tapada da Ajuda, Lisbon, 1300, Portugal. TEL 351-21-3625986, FAX 351-21-3625986, aeisa@isa.utl.pt, http://www.aewww.isu.utl.pt. Ed., Pub. Hugo Eichmann. Circ: 1,000.

630 COL ISSN 0044-6882
AGROSINTESIS. Text in Spanish. 1968. m. adv.
Related titles: Microform ed.: (from PQC).
Address: Apartado Aereo 24 215, Bogota, CUND, Colombia. Ed. Carlos Giraldo. Circ: 5,000.

630 668.6 POL ISSN 1732-2634
CODEN: AGROD4
AGROTECHNIKA; poradnik nawozenia i ochrony roslin. Text in Polish. 1961. m. EUR 32 foreign (effective 2005). adv. bk.rev. charts; illus. index, cum.index. **Document type:** *Magazine, Trade.* **Description:** Covers tillage, fertilization and protection of plants in the field.
Former titles (until 2004): Agro Chemia Technika (1731-1136); (until 2003): Agrochemia (0002-1849)
Indexed: AgrLib, BiolAb, CPA, ExcerpMed, FCA, FaBeAb, HerbAb, PN&I, PotatoAb, SIA, SeedAb.
—CASDDS, CISTI.
Published by: Hortpress Sp. z o.o., ul Kopernika 34, Warsaw, 00336, Poland. TEL 48-22-8261626, FAX 48-22-8264362, agro@hortpress.com, info@hortpress.com, http://www.hortpress.com. Ed. Janusz Nuckowski. Circ: 30,000. **Dist. by:** Ars Polona, Krakowskie Przedmiescie 7, Warsaw, Poland. TEL 48-22-9263914, FAX 48-22-9265334, arspolona@arspolona.com.pl, http://www.arspolona.com.pl.

630 CUB ISSN 0568-3114
CODEN: AGCUDF
AGROTECNIA DE CUBA. Abstracts and contents page in English. 1963. q. USD 32 in South America; USD 34 in North America; USD 36 elsewhere. **Description:** Offers initiatives to the science of agronomy.
Indexed: Agrind, BioCN&I, ChemAb, FCA, HerbAb, HortAb, MaizeAb, PGrRegA, PotatoAb, RPP, RevApplEntom, RiceAb, SeedAb, WeedAb.
—CASDDS.
Published by: Centro de Informacion y Documentacion Agropecuario, Gaveta Postal 4149, Havana, 4, Cuba. **Dist. by:** Ediciones Cubanas, Obispo No. 527, Apdo. 605, Havana, Cuba.

630 HRV ISSN 0002-1989
AGROTEHNICAR; Jugoslavenski list za mehanizaciju u poljoprivredi. Text in Serbo-Croatian. 1965. m. USD 23.70. adv. bk.rev.
Published by: Novinski Izdavacki Zavod za Poljoprivredu, Trg Republike 3-I, Zagreb, 41000, Croatia. Ed. Mile Culjat. Circ: 20,000.

630 CYP ISSN 0002-1997
AGROTIS/COUNTRYMAN. Text in Greek. 1943. q. free. **Document type:** *Government.*
Published by: Press and Information Office, Editorial Office, Nicosia, Cyprus. TEL 357-2-446981, FAX 357-2-453730, TELEX 2526 PIONIC. Ed. Tasos Koualis. Circ: 6,500.

631.091 BRA ISSN 0103-3816
CODEN: AGROE5
AGROTROPICA. Text in English, French, Portuguese, Spanish; Summaries in English. 1971. 3/yr. BRL 40, USD 60 (effective 2001). index, cum.index: 1971-1975. back issues avail.
Formerly (until 1989): Revista Theobroma (0370-7962)
Indexed: AEA, ATA, AgBio, AgrForAb, Agrind, BibAg, BioCN&I, BiolAb, CPA, ChemAb, DSA, ExcerpMed, FCA, FS&TA, ForAb, HerbAb, HortAb, I&DA, IAALC, MaizeAb, NutrAb, PBA, PGegResA, PGrRegA, PHN&I, PotatoAb, ProtozoAb, RDA, RM&VM, RPP, RevApplEntom, S&F, SIA, SeedAb, TOSA, WAE&RSA, WeedAb.
—BLDSC (0771.856000), CASDDS, CISTI, IE, ingenta, Linda Hall.
Published by: Centro de Pesquisas do Cacau/Cacao Research Center, Caixa Postal 7, Itabuna, BA 45600-970, Brazil. TEL 55-73-214-3217, 55-73-2143220, FAX 55-73-2143218, TELEX 0732157 CLRC BR, agrotrop@cepec.gov.br, http://www.cepec.gov.br/agrotrop. Eds. Miguel Moreno Ruiz, Paulo Dos Santos Terra. Circ: 650. **Co-sponsor:** Comissao Executiva do Plano da Lavoura Cacaueira.

630 660 GBR ISSN 0268-313X
AGROW; world crop protection news. Text in English. 1985. bi-w. GBP 525, EUR 890, USD 1,050, JPY 167,000 (effective 2005). adv. bk.rev. 24 p./no. 2 cols./p.; back issues avail.; reprints avail. **Document type:** *Newsletter.* **Description:** Covers the agrochemical market, including company news, legislation and product development. Targets industry executives.
Related titles: Online - full text ed.: (from Data-Star).
—BLDSC (0771.865000), CISTI, IE, Infotrieve. **CCC.**
Published by: P J B Publications Ltd. (Subsidiary of: T & F Informa plc), 5th Fl, Telephone House, 69-77 Paul Street, London, EC2A 4LQ, United Kingdom. TEL 44-20-70176979, FAX 44-20-70176969, info@pjbpubs.com, http://www.pjbpubs.com/agrow/index.htm. Ed. Jackie Bird. Pub. Dr. Philip Brown. R&P Annette Watts TEL 44-20-83328961. Adv. contact Tom Jamison TEL 44-20-83328871. Circ: 1,723 (paid). **Subscr. addr. in N America:** Pharmabooks Ltd., 270 Madison Ave., # 4, New York, NY 10016-0601.

630 CAN ISSN 1188-8822
AGVANCE. Text in English, French. 1991. irreg. **Document type:** *Newsletter.*
Related titles: Online - full text ed.: ISSN 1495-0111.
Published by: Agriculture and Agri-Food Canada, Research Branch, Sir John Carling Bldg, 930 Carling Ave, Ottawa, ON K1A 0C5, Canada. TEL 613-759-6610, FAX 613-759-6726, publications@agr.gc.ca, http://res2.agr.gc.ca/ns/index_e.htm, http://www.agr.gc.ca.

338.17 USA
AGVENTURES. Text in English. bi-m. USD 21 domestic; USD 30 foreign (effective 2004). adv. back issues avail. **Document type:** *Magazine, Consumer.* **Description:** Explores the profitability of various agricultural ventures.
Indexed: Agr.
Published by: Schatz Publishing Group, 11950 W. Highland Ave., Blackwell, OK 74631-6511. TEL 580-628-4551, 888-474-6397, FAX 580-628-2011, AgVentures@aol.com, http://www.agventures.com/. adv.: B&W page USD 495; 7 x 9.75.

630 USA ISSN 0884-6162
AGWEEK. Text in English. 1984. w. adv. bk.rev. **Document type:** *Newspaper, Trade.* **Description:** Cointain agriculture news, markets, commentary and common sense.
Formerly (until 1985): Farm and Home (8750-1783)
Related titles: Online - full text ed.: (from The Dialog Corporation).
Indexed: B&I.
—CISTI.
Published by: Knight-Ridder Inc., PO Box 6008, Grand Forks, ND 58201-6008. TEL 701-780-1242, FAX 701-780-1123, http://www.agweek.com. Ed. Kim K Deats. Pub. Michael Maidenberg. R&P, Adv. contact Mark Steinke TEL 701-780-1179. Circ: 30,000.

▼ new title ➤ refereed ✶ unverified ♦ full entry avail.

A

630 NGA ISSN 0065-471X
AHMADU BELLO UNIVERSITY. INSTITUTE FOR AGRICULTURAL RESEARCH. ANNUAL REPORT. Text in English. 1962-1968; N.S. 1980. a. USD 20. **Document type:** *Corporate.* **Description:** Overview and research highlights of eight research programs of the Institute for Agricultural Research in Nigeria.
Indexed: FCA, HerbAb, RPP.
Published by: Ahmadu Bello University, Institute for Agricultural Research, PMB 1044, Samaru-Zaria, Kaduna, Nigeria. FAX 234-69-50563. Ed. Bolaji Adeniji.

630 UKR
AHROTEKHSERVIS. Text in Ukrainian. 3/m.
Published by: Derzhavnyi Kontsern Ukrahrotekhservis, Ul Suvorova 9, Kiev, Ukraine. TEL 380-44-293-3896. **US dist. addr.:** East View Information Services, 3020 Harbor Ln. N., Minneapolis, MN 55447. TEL 612-550-0961.

630 FRA ISSN 0002-2136
AIN AGRICOLE. Text in French. 1944. w. adv. bk.rev.
—CCC.
Published by: Societe d Editions et de Publicite Agricole du Department de l (Subsidiary of: Agri-Media), 4 av. du Champ de Foire, Bourg En Bresse, Cedex 01003, France. FAX 74-22-47-20. Ed. Alain Silvestre. Circ: 10,000.

AJIKEN WORLD TRENDS. see *BUSINESS AND ECONOMICS*

630 POL ISSN 0137-1754
S13
AKADEMIA ROLNICZA, POZNAN. ROCZNIKI. ROLNICTWO. Text in Polish; Summaries in English. 1966. irreg. price varies. **Document type:** *Academic/Scholarly.* **Description:** Works on field and plants cultivation, genetics and breeding of plants, pedology, agro-chemistry, agro-microbiology and mechanization farming.
Indexed: AgrAg, AgrLib, BibAg.
Published by: (Akademia Rolnicza im. Augusta Cieszkowskiego w Poznaniu), Wydawnictwo Akademii Rolniczej w Poznaniu, ul Witosa 45, Poznan, 61693, Poland. TEL 48-61-487809, FAX 48-61-487802, wgolab@owl.au.poznan.pl, wydar@au.poznan.pl, http://swan.au.poznan.pl/bib/bghome.html. R&P Elzbieta Zagorska TEL 48-61-487806.

630 POL ISSN 0208-8436
CODEN: RRPNDH
AKADEMIA ROLNICZA, POZNAN. ROCZNIKI. ROZPRAWY NAUKOWE. Text in Polish; Summaries in English. 1959. irreg. price varies. **Document type:** *Monographic series, Academic/Scholarly.* **Description:** Covers biology, zoology, agriculture, food technology, wood technology, animal husbandry, animal breeding, horticulture, forestry, soil science, and agricultural technics.
Indexed: AgrAg, AgrLib, BibAg, WeedAb.
—CASDDS.
Published by: (Akademia Rolnicza im. Augusta Cieszkowskiego w Poznaniu), Wydawnictwo Akademii Rolniczej w Poznaniu, ul Witosa 45, Poznan, 61693, Poland. TEL 48-61-487809, FAX 48-61-487802, wgolab@owl.au.poznan.pl, wydar@au.poznan.pl, http://swan.au.poznan.pl/bib/bghome.html. R&P Elzbieta Zagorska TEL 48-61-487806.

630 POL ISSN 0137-2149
Z5055.P6
➤ **AKADEMIA ROLNICZA W SZCZECINIE. INFORMATORY.** Text in Polish. 1968. irreg. price varies. bk.rev. **Document type:** *Academic/Scholarly.*
Indexed: ChemAb, FCA, NutrAb, PotatoAb.
Published by: Akademia Rolnicza w Szczecinie/Agricultural University of Szczecin, Dzial Wydawnictw, Ul Doktora Judyma 22, Szczecin, 71466, Poland. TEL 48-91-4541639, FAX 48-91-4541642, TELEX 0425494 AR, fizj@demeter.zoo.ar.szczecin.pl. Ed. Wieslaw F Skrzypczak.

630 POL ISSN 0239-6467
CODEN: RZARB8
➤ **AKADEMIA ROLNICZA W SZCZECINIE. ROZPRAWY.** Text in Polish; Abstracts in English. 1966. irreg. price varies. bk.rev. **Document type:** *Academic/Scholarly.*
Indexed: AgBio, AgrLib, AnBrAb, BioCN&I, CPA, ChemAb, DSA, FCA, ForAb, HerbAb, HortAb, I&DA, IndVet, NemAb, NutrAb, OrnHort, PBA, PGegResA, PGrRegA, PN&I, PotatoAb, PoultAb, ProtozoAb, RPP, RefZh, RevApplEntom, S&F, SIA, SeedAb, TriticAb, VetBull, WAE&RSA, WeedAb.
—CASDDS, CISTI.
Published by: Akademia Rolnicza w Szczecinie/Agricultural University of Szczecin, Dzial Wydawnictw, Ul Doktora Judyma 22, Szczecin, 71466, Poland. TEL 48-91-4541639, FAX 48-91-4541642, TELEX 0425494 AR, fizj@demeter.zoo.ar.szczecin.pl. Ed. Wieslaw F Skrzypczak.

630 POL ISSN 0867-7964
AKADEMIA ROLNICZA WE WROCLAWIU. ZESZYTY NAUKOWE. Text in Polish. irreg. **Document type:** *Academic/Scholarly.*
Formerly (until 1972): Wyzsza Szkola Rolnicza. Zeszyty Naukowe (0867-065X)
Related titles: ♦ Series: Akademia Rolnicza we Wroclawiu. Zeszyty Naukowe. Rolnictwo. ISSN 0137-1959; ♦ Akademia Rolnicza we Wroclawiu. Zeszyty Naukowe. Mechanizacja Rolnictwa. ISSN 0867-3756; ♦ Akademia Rolnicza we Wroclawiu. Zeszyty Naukowe. Melioracja. ISSN 0137-1967; ♦ Akademia Rolnicza we Wroclawiu. Zeszyty Naukowe. Monografie. ISSN 0867-2393; ♦ Akademia Rolnicza we Wroclawiu. Zeszyty Naukowe. Nauki Humanistyczne. ISSN 1234-8333; ♦ Akademia Rolnicza we Wroclawiu. Zeszyty Naukowe. Weterynaria. ISSN 0137-1975; ♦ Akademia Rolnicza we Wroclawiu. Zeszyty Naukowe. Technologia Zywnosci. ISSN 0209-0503; ♦ Akademia Rolnicza we Wroclawiu. Zeszyty Naukowe. Inzynieria Srodowiska. ISSN 1230-4484; ♦ Akademia Rolnicza we Wroclawiu. Zeszyty Naukowe. Zootechnika; ♦ Akademia Rolnicza we Wroclawiu. Zeszyty Naukowe. Geodezja i Urzadzenia Rolne. ISSN 0209-0511; ♦ Akademia Rolnicza we Wroclawiu. Zeszyty Naukowe. Rozprawy; ♦ Akademia Rolnicza we Wroclawiu. Zeszyty Naukowe. Konferencje. ISSN 1232-3071; ♦ Akademia Rolnicza we Wroclawiu. Zeszyty Naukowe. Bibliografie. ISSN 1427-5805.
Indexed: NutrAb, ZooRec.
—BLDSC (9512.152000), CISTI.
Published by: Akademia Rolnicza we Wroclawiu/Agricultural University of Wroclaw, Ul Norwida 25, Wroclaw, 50375, Poland. TEL 48-71-3205101, wyd@ozi.ar.wroc.pl. **Subscr. to:** Wydawnictwo Akademii Rolniczej we Wroclawiu, ul Sopocka 23, Wroclaw 50344, Poland.

AKADEMIA ROLNICZA WE WROCLAWIU. ZESZYTY NAUKOWE. BIBLIOGRAFIE. see *AGRICULTURE—Abstracting, Bibliographies, Statistics*

630 POL ISSN 1232-3071
AKADEMIA ROLNICZA WE WROCLAWIU. ZESZYTY NAUKOWE. KONFERENCJE. Text in Polish. 1994. irreg. price varies. **Document type:** *Academic/Scholarly.*
Related titles: ♦ Series of: Akademia Rolnicza we Wroclawiu. Zeszyty Naukowe. ISSN 0867-7964.
Indexed: AgrLib.
Published by: Akademia Rolnicza we Wroclawiu/Agricultural University of Wroclaw, Ul Norwida 25, Wroclaw, 50375, Poland. TEL 48-71-3205101, wyd@ozi.ar.wroc.pl. **Subscr. to:** Wydawnictwo Akademii Rolniczej we Wroclawiu, ul Sopocka 23, Wroclaw 50344, Poland.

630 POL ISSN 0867-2393
AKADEMIA ROLNICZA WE WROCLAWIU. ZESZYTY NAUKOWE. MONOGRAFIE. Text in Polish; Summaries in English. 1990. irreg. price varies. **Document type:** *Monographic series.*
Related titles: ♦ Series of: Akademia Rolnicza we Wroclawiu. Zeszyty Naukowe. ISSN 0867-7964.
Indexed: AgrLib.
Published by: Akademia Rolnicza we Wroclawiu/Agricultural University of Wroclaw, Ul Norwida 25, Wroclaw, 50375, Poland. TEL 48-71-3205101, wyd@ozi.ar.wroc.pl. Circ: 300. **Subscr. to:** Wydawnictwo Akademii Rolniczej we Wroclawiu, ul Sopocka 23, Wroclaw 50344, Poland.

630 POL ISSN 0137-1959
CODEN: ZNARBC
AKADEMIA ROLNICZA WE WROCLAWIU. ZESZYTY NAUKOWE. ROLNICTWO. Text in Polish; Summaries in English. 1955. irreg. price varies. **Document type:** *Academic/Scholarly.*
Formerly (until 1973): Wyzsza Szkola Rolnicza we Wroclawiu. Zeszyty Naukowe. Rolnictwo (0520-9307)
Related titles: ♦ Series of: Akademia Rolnicza we Wroclawiu. Zeszyty Naukowe. ISSN 0867-7964.
Indexed: AEA, AgrAg, AgrLib, DSA, FCA, REE&TA, TriticAb.
—CASDDS, CISTI.
Published by: Akademia Rolnicza we Wroclawiu/Agricultural University of Wroclaw, Ul Norwida 25, Wroclaw, 50375, Poland. TEL 48-71-3205101, wyd@ozi.ar.wroc.pl. Circ: 350. **Subscr. to:** Wydawnictwo Akademii Rolniczej we Wroclawiu, ul Sopocka 23, Wroclaw 50344, Poland.

630 POL
AKADEMIA ROLNICZA WE WROCLAWIU. ZESZYTY NAUKOWE. ROZPRAWY. Text in Polish. 1977. irreg. price varies. **Document type:** *Academic/Scholarly.*
Former titles (until 1994): Akademia Rolnicza we Wroclawiu. Zeszyty Naukowe. Rozprawa Habilitacyjna (0867-1427); (until 1990): Akademia Rolnicza we Wroclawiu. Zeszyty Naukowe. Rozprawy (0209-1321)
Related titles: ♦ Series of: Akademia Rolnicza we Wroclawiu. Zeszyty Naukowe. ISSN 0867-7964.
Indexed: AgrAg, AgrLib.
—CISTI.
Published by: Akademia Rolnicza we Wroclawiu/Agricultural University of Wroclaw, Ul Norwida 25, Wroclaw, 50375, Poland. TEL 48-71-3205101, wyd@ozi.ar.wroc.pl. Circ: 300. **Subscr. to:** Wydawnictwo Akademii Rolniczej we Wroclawiu, ul Sopocka 23, Wroclaw 50344, Poland.

630 BLR ISSN 1029-6891
CODEN: VBYSA6
➤ **AKADEMIYA AGRARNYKH NAVUK RESPUBLIKI BELARUSI. VESTSI.** Text in Belorussian, Russian; Summaries in English. 1963. q. USD 20 (effective 1999). bibl.; charts; illus. index. **Document type:** *Academic/Scholarly.* **Description:** Covers economics and information technologies; arable farming and plant growth; animal breeding and veterinary medicine; poultry farming; processing of agricultural produces; mechanization; engineering and automation.
Former titles (until 1996): Akademiya Agrarnykh Navuk Belarusi. Vestsi (1024-5898); (until 1992): Akademiya Navuk Belarusskai S.S.R. Seriya Sel'skogaspadarchykh Navuk. Vestsi (0321-1657)
Related titles: Diskette ed.
Indexed: AEA, AgBio, AnBrAb, BioCN&I, BiolAb, CIN, CPA, ChemAb, ChemTitl, DSA, FCA, FS&TA, HelmAb, HerbAb, HortAb, I&DA, IndVet, MaizeAb, NemAb, NutrAb, OrnHort, PBA, PGrRegA, PHN&I, PN&I, PotatoAb, PoultAb, ProtozoAb, RA&MP, RDA, RM&VM, RPP, RefZh, S&F, SIA, SeedAb, SoyAb, TriticAb, VetBull, WAE&RSA, WeedAb.
—BLDSC (0037.097000), CASDDS, CISTI. **CCC.**
Published by: Akademiya Agrarnykh Navuk Respubliki Belarusi, Kasintsa 103, Minsk, 220108, Belarus. TEL 375-172-773790, FAX 375-172-786921, agrec@belpak.minsk.by. Ed. V S Antonuk. Pub. V Sidorovich. R&P V Bulanchikov. Circ: 350. **Dist. by:** Belsausdruk, Pr F Skaryny 79, Minsk 220041, Belarus.

630 580 JPN ISSN 0385-3152
AKITA-KEN KAJU SHIKENJUO KENKYUU HUOKOKU/AKITA FRUIT-TREE EXPERIMENT STATION. BULLETIN. Text in Japanese. 1969. a.
Indexed: AEA, BioCN&I, CPA, HortAb, PBA, PGegResA, PHN&I, RPP, S&F, SeedAb, WAE&RSA.
—Linda Hall.
Published by: Akita Prefectural College of Agriculture, 2-2 Ohgata-mura, Akita 010-04, Japan.

630 580 JPN ISSN 1346-1443
AKITA KENRITSU DAIGAKU TANKI DARGAKUBU KIYO/AKITA PREFECTURAL COLLEGE OF AGRICULTURE. BULLETIN. Text and summaries in Japanese. 1975. a. back issues avail.
Formerly (until 2000): Akita Kenritsu Nogyo Tanki Daigaku Kenkyu Hokoku (0389-8423)
Indexed: AEA, AnBrAb, BiolAb, CPA, ExcerpMed, FCA, HerbAb, HortAb, I&DA, IBSS, IndVet, NutrAb, PBA, PN&I, PoultAb, RefZh, S&F, TriticAb, VetBull, WAE&RSA, WeedAb.
—Linda Hall.
Published by: Akita Prefectural College of Agriculture, 2-2 Ohgata-mura, Akita 010-04, Japan. Circ: 550.

630 NLD ISSN 0169-0116
AKKERBOUW (DOETINCHEM). Text in Dutch. 1971. bi-w. EUR 167.63 (effective 2005). adv. bk.rev. charts; illus.; tr.lit. index. **Document type:** *Trade.* **Description:** For the large arable farming specialist; information about cultural, technical, financial and mechanization aspects.
Related titles: ♦ Supplement to: Boerderij. ISSN 0006-5617.
Published by: Reed Business Information bv (Subsidiary of: Reed Business), Hanzestraat 1, Doetinchem, 7006 RH, Netherlands. info@reedbusiness.nl, http://www.reedbusiness.nl. Adv. contact Cor van Nek. B&W page EUR 2,074, color page EUR 3,199; trim 290 x 225. Circ: 15,570.

630 BEL ISSN 1373-2722
AKKERBOUW & VEETEELT. Text in Dutch. 1998. m. (except Jan. & Aug.). bk.rev. back issues avail. **Document type:** *Consumer.*
Published by: Rekad N.V., Geelsweg 47A, Herentals, 2200, Belgium. TEL 32-14-286070, FAX 32-14-214774, info@rekad.be, http://rekad.be. Adv. contact Hilde Provoost. Circ: 7,500.

630 634.9 635 USA ISSN 1072-074X
ALABAMA AGRICULTURAL EXPERIMENT STATION. RESEARCH REPORT SERIES. Text in English. 1983. irreg., latest vol.7, 1991.
Media: Online - full content.
Indexed: BioCN&I, ForAb, HortAb, OrnHort, PotatoAb, WAE&RSA, WeedAb.
—Linda Hall.
Published by: Alabama Agricultural Experiment Station, 107 Comer Hall, Auburn, AL 36849. TEL 334-844-2345, FAX 334-844-5892, http://www.ag.auburn.ed/resinfo/publications. Ed. J R Roberson. Circ: 4,000.

630 USA
ALABAMA FARMER. Text in English. 1985. m. USD 21.95 in state; USD 30 out of state; USD 75 foreign (effective 2001). **Document type:** *Newspaper.* **Description:** Contains national and local news about dairy products, cattle, cotton, row crops, poultry, and swine.
Published by: Farm Progress Companies, 191 S Gary Ave, Carol Stream, IL 60188. TEL 630-690-5600, FAX 630-462-2869. Ed. Donna Sandusky. adv.: B&W page USD 1,218. Circ: 37,057.

ALASKA AGRICULTURAL STATISTICS. see *AGRICULTURE—Abstracting, Bibliographies, Statistics*

ALASKA FARM REPORTER. see *AGRICULTURE—Abstracting, Bibliographies, Statistics*

630 CAN ISSN 0702-3030
ALBERTA AGRICULTURE. ANNUAL REPORT. Text in English. 1905. a. free.
Former titles (until 1972): Alberta. Department of Agriculture. Annual Report (0702-3022); (until 1969): Alberta. Water Resources Division. Annual Report (0065-597X)
Published by: Department of Agriculture, Publishing Branch, 7000 113th St, Edmonton, AB T6H 5T6, Canada. TEL 403-427-2121, FAX 403-427-2861. Circ: (controlled).

630 CAN
ALBERTA AGROLOGIST. Text in English. 1947. 5/yr. free to members (effective 2004). adv. bk.rev. **Document type:** *Newsletter.* **Description:** For professionals in the agriculture and food industry in Alberta.
Formerly: A I A Newsletter
Published by: Alberta Institute of Agrologists, #375, 13220 St Albert Trail, Edmonton, AB T5L 4W1, Canada. TEL 780-432-0663, FAX 780-439-8414, PAg@aia.ab.ca, http://www.aia.ab.ca. Ed. Ken Davies. Circ: 1,300 (controlled).

630 658 LUX
ALCOVIT. Text in German. 1959. 10/yr. adv. **Description:** Covers farm management, including breeding, animal nutrition, plant and grain production, and algritultural news reports.
Formerly: Conseiller Alcovit Protector
Published by: Moulins de Kleinbettingen, 7 rue Laduno, Erpeldange-ettelbruck, L-9147, Luxembourg. TEL 352-810344, FAX 352-817863. Ed. Rudy Peters. adv.: B&W page EUR 984, color page EUR 1,484; 315 x 440. Circ: 10,500.

630 ISR
ALEI ESEV. Text in Hebrew. 1979. q. membership only. bk.rev. **Document type:** *Newsletter.*
Published by: Weed Science Society of Israel, Department of Ornamental Horticulture, Volcani Centre, P O Box 6, Bet Dagan, 50250, Israel. TEL 972-3-9683500, FAX 972-3-9660589. Ed. Menashe Horowitz.

630 PER ISSN 1021-1810
ALERTA AGRARIO. Text in Spanish. 1987. m. **Document type:** *Bulletin.* **Description:** Reviews rural problems.
Published by: Centro Peruano de Estudios Sociales, Ave. Salaverry, 818, Jesus Maria, Lima, 11, Peru. TEL 51-14-336610, FAX 51-14-331744, alerta@cepes.org.pe. Ed. Bertha Consiglieri. Circ: 100,000.

630 EGY ISSN 0044-7250
S19 CODEN: AAGRAF
➤ **ALEXANDRIA JOURNAL OF AGRICULTURAL RESEARCH.** Text in English; Summaries in Arabic, English. 1953. 3/yr. EGP 20 domestic; USD 60 foreign (effective 2004). adv. abstr.; bibl.; charts; illus.; stat. back issues avail. **Document type:** *Journal, Academic/Scholarly.* **Description:** Publishes papers in agricultural science and related subjects, including agricultural engineering, food science, floriculture and horticulture, plant pathology, forestry and wood technology, soil and water science.
Indexed: AEA, AbHyg, AgBio, AgrForAb, AnBrAb, BioCN&I, BioDAb, BiolAb, CPA, CTFA, ChemAb, DSA, FCA, FPA, FS&TA, FaBeAb, ForAb, HerbAb, HortAb, I&DA, IndVet, MaizeAb, NemAb, NutrAb, OrnHort, PBA, PGegResA, PGrRegA, PHN&I, PotatoAb, PoultAb, RA&MP, RDA, REE&TA, RM&VM, RPP, RevApplEntom, RiceAb, S&F, SIA, SeedAb, SoyAb, TDB, TriticAb, VetBull, WAE&RSA, WeedAb, ZooRec.
—BLDSC (0786.940000), CASDDS, CISTI, Ei, IE, ingenta.
Published by: University of Alexandria, Faculty of Agriculture, c/o Dr. Abdel-Mugid, Alexandria, Egypt. TEL 20-3-5971960, sfawzy@alexnet.com.eg, http://derp.sti.sci.eg/data/0056.htm. Ed. Dr. Abdel-Mugid Muhammad Qamara. Circ: 1,000.

630 USA ISSN 1522-0648
ALFA FRIENDS AND FAMILY. Text in English. 1946. q. USD 2 newsstand/cover; free to members (effective 2005). adv. tr.lit. back issues avail. **Document type:** *Magazine, Trade.*
Former titles: Alfa News (1065-7673); Alabama Farm Bureau News
Published by: Alabama Farmers Federation, 2108 E South Blvd, Montgomery, AL 36191-0001. TEL 334-288-3900, FAX 334-284-3957, jhelms@alfafarmers.org/, http://www.alfafarmers.org. Ed. Jeff Helms. Adv. contact Ken Workman. B&W page USD 3,235, color page USD 3,985. Circ: 150,000 (controlled).

ALIMARKET. see *FOOD AND FOOD INDUSTRIES*

ALIMARKET REVISTA. see *FOOD AND FOOD INDUSTRIES*

630 FIN ISSN 1239-4602
ALIMENTA. Text in Finnish. 1907. 6/yr. adv. bk.rev. illus.; stat. **Document type:** *Magazine, Academic/Scholarly.*
Formerly (until 1996): Maatalous (0024-8827)
Indexed: BiolAb.
—CISTI.
Published by: Agronomiliitto/Finnish Association of Academic Agronomists, P Makasiinikatu 6 A 8, Helsinki, 00130, Finland. TEL 358-9-2511160, FAX 358-9-25111610. Ed. Pekka Rinne. Adv. contact Juha Halminen. Circ: 5,400.

630 976 USA ISSN 1082-1570
ALL AROUND KENTUCKY. Text in English. 1937. bi-m. USD 0.50 (effective 2005). adv. illus. **Document type:** *Newsletter, Trade.* **Description:** Newsletter on issues affecting the farming and agricultural population of the state, with editorial column on commodities and market analysis. Also articles on travel, outdoor activities and sports in Kentucky.
Formerly (until 1995): Kentucky Farm Bureau News (0023-0200)
Published by: Kentucky Farm Bureau Federation, PO Box 20700, Louisville, KY 40220. TEL 502-495-5000, FAX 502-495-5114, ghuddleston@kyfb.com, http://www.kyfb.com. Ed. Rachel Kamuf. Adv. contact Scott Weining. B&W page USD 2,890, color page USD 3,490; trim 10 x 14. Circ: 376,000 (paid).

630 HUN
ALLAMI GAZDASAG/STATE FARMING. Text in Hungarian. 1946. m. USD 26.
Indexed: RASB.
Published by: General Direction of State Farming, Akademia utca 1-3, Budapest, 1054, Hungary. TEL 112-4617, FAX 111-4877. Ed. Mrs. P Gorgenyi.

630 DEU
ALLGAEUER BAUERNBLATT. Text in German. 1923. w. EUR 98 (effective 2004). adv. **Document type:** *Newspaper, Trade.*
Published by: A V A - Agrar Verlag Allgaeu GmbH, Porschestr 2, Kempten, 87437, Germany. TEL 49-831-571420, FAX 49-831-79008, bauernblatt@ava-verlag.de, info@ava-verlag.de, http://www.allgaeuer-bauernblatt.de, http://www.ava-verlag.de. Ed. Hannes Stich. Pub. Wolfgang Kuehnle. adv.: B&W page EUR 3,342, color page EUR 4,673. Circ: 11,040 (paid and controlled).

630 AUT
ALLGEMEINE BAUERN ZEITUNG✶ **.** Text in German. q.
Published by: Kaertner Bauerbund, c/o Kartner Landes-Ausstellung, Spitalgasse 14, Klagenfurt, K 9020, Austria. TEL 0463-511710, FAX 0463-502018. Ed. Horst Reichmann. Circ: 32,000.

638.1 DEU ISSN 0002-5828
CODEN: ADIMBW
ALLGEMEINE DEUTSCHE IMKERZEITUNG; ueberregionale Imkerfachzeitschrift. Text in German. 1967. m. EUR 31.20; EUR 2.95 newsstand/cover (effective 2004). adv. charts; illus. **Document type:** *Newspaper, Trade.* **Description:** Discusses bee culture.
Indexed: ApicAb, ChemAb, ExcerpMed.
—CASDDS, CISTI. **CCC.**
Published by: Deutscher Landwirtschaftsverlag GmbH, Berliner Str 112A, Berlin, 13189, Germany. TEL 49-30-29397450, FAX 49-30-29397459, bienenredaktion@dlv.de, dlv.berlin@dlv.de, http://www.adiz-online.de, http://www.dlv.de. Ed. Juergen Schwenkel. adv.: B&W page EUR 1,352, color page EUR 2,267. Circ: 8,815 (paid and controlled).

631 BEL
L'ALLIANCE AGRICOLE. Text in French. 1929. w. includes Agriculteur. adv. mkt. back issues avail. **Document type:** *Newspaper.* **Description:** Includes technical, economic, and political information about agriculture.
Published by: Alliance Agricole Belge, Rue de la Science 25, Brussels, 1040, Belgium. TEL 32-2-2307495, FAX 32-2-2304251. Ed., Pub. Etienne de Paul. Adv. contact Luc Raulier. B&W page BEF 41,040, color page BEF 65,000; trim 380 x 255. Circ: 12,000.

630 AUT
ALM UND BERGBAUER. Text in German. 1948. m. bk.rev. **Document type:** *Journal, Trade.*
Formerly: Alm und Weide (0044-7374)
Indexed: RRTA, WAE&RSA.
Published by: Oesterreichische Arbeitsgemeinschaft fuer Alm und Weide, Gilmstrasse 2 - Stoecklgebaeude, Innsbruck, T 6020, Austria. TEL 43-1-512-5083908, FAX 43-1-512-5083905. Ed. Dieter Putz. Circ: 5,000.

ALMANAC FOR FARMERS AND CITY FOLK. see *ENCYCLOPEDIAS AND GENERAL ALMANACS*

630 DEU ISSN 0002-6298
DER ALMBAUER; Mitteilungen fuer Alm-, Berg- und Gruenlandbauern und ueber Forstrechte. Text in German. 1948. m. EUR 24; EUR 2.25 newsstand/cover (effective 2004). adv. bk.rev. illus. **Document type:** *Magazine, Trade.*
—CCC.
Published by: (Almwirtschaftlicher Verein Oberbayern), Deutscher Landwirtschaftsverlag GmbH, Lothstr 29, Munich, 80797, Germany. TEL 49-89-127051, FAX 49-89-12705335, dlv.muenchen@dlv.de, http://www.dlv.de. adv.: B&W page EUR 1,004, color page EUR 1,706. Circ: 2,398 (paid).

638.1 AUT ISSN 0002-6352
ALPENLAENDISCHE BIENENZEITUNG. Text in German. 1912. 11/yr. EUR 17.50 domestic; EUR 21.40 foreign (effective 2005). adv. bk.rev. index. **Document type:** *Magazine, Trade.*
Indexed: ApicAb.
Published by: Leopold Stocker Verlag, Hofgasse 5, Graz, St 8011, Austria. TEL 43-316-821636, FAX 43-316-835612, stocker-verlag@stocker-verlag.com, http://www.landwirt.com/ez/index.php/article/articleview/140/1/63/?name=zeitschriften, http://www.stocker-verlag.com. Ed. Josef Gstrein. Adv. contact Manuela Jantscher. B&W page EUR 340, color page EUR 750; trim 137 x 205. Circ: 6,000 (paid and controlled).

630 IND ISSN 0970-4671
ALTERNATIVE - APPROPRIATE TECHNOLOGIES IN AGRICULTURE. Text in English. 1980. 4/yr. INR 570, USD 95 (effective 2000). adv. abstr.; bibl. index.
Published by: K.K. Roy (Private) Ltd., 55 Gariahat Rd., P O Box 10210, Kolkata, West Bengal 700 019, India. R&P M Misra TEL 91-33-475-4872. Circ: 1,690.

630 USA ISSN 1545-8741
HD1751
▼ **AMBER WAVES**; the economics of food, farming, natural resources and rural America. Text in English. 2003 (Feb.). 5/yr. USD 49.95 domestic; USD 99.90 foreign (effective 2004). illus. **Description:** Offers a window into the broad range of ERS research and analysis. Food, farming, natural resources, and rural America are covered.
Formed by the 2003 merger of: Agricultural Outlook; Food Review; Rural America
Related titles: Online - full text ed.: (from H.W. Wilson).
Indexed: Agr, PAIS.
—CISTI.
Published by: U.S. Department of Agriculture, Economic Research Service, 1800 M St, N W, Ste 3, Washington, DC 20036-5828. TEL 703-605-6060, 800-999-6779, FAX 703-605-6880, ersinfo@ers.usda.gov, http://www.ers.usda.gov/publications/Magazines.htm. Ed. Sheila Sankaran.

630 USA
▼ **AMERICAN ACREAGE.** Text in English. 2003. m. **Document type:** *Magazine, Trade.*
Media: Online - full content.
Published by: Gazette Communications, PO Box 5279, Des Moines, IA 52406-5279. TEL 800-475-6655, http://www.iowafarmer.com/.

630 USA ISSN 0161-8237
AMERICAN AGRICULTURIST. Text in English. 1842. m. USD 23 in state; USD 30 out of state (effective 2005). adv. bk.rev. illus.; mkt.; stat. 60 p./no.; reprints avail. **Document type:** *Magazine, Trade.* **Description:** Supplies the information needs of farm operators in New York.
Formerly: American Agriculturist and Rural New Yorker (0002-7219); Incorporates (in 1964): Rural New Yorker
Related titles: Microform ed.: (from PQC).
—Linda Hall.
Published by: Farm Progress Companies, 191 S Gary Ave, Carol Stream, IL 60188. TEL 630-462-2892, FAX 630-462-2867, info@farmprogress.com, http://www.americanagriculturist.com, http://www.farmprogress.com/. Ed. John Vogel. Pub. Jeff M Lapin. Adv. contact Tom Shearing. B&W page USD 3,470, color page USD 4,860. Circ: 32,000 (paid and controlled).

630 338.1 USA
AMERICAN ASSOCIATION OF NURSERYMEN UPDATE. Text in English. every 3 wks. **Document type:** *Bulletin.*
Published by: American Association of Nurserymen, 1250 I St, N W, Ste 500, Washington, DC 20005. TEL 202-789-2900. Ed. Angela Hutcherson.

630 338.1 USA
AMERICAN ASSOCIATION OF NURSERYMEN WHO'S WHO IN THE NURSERY INDUSTRY MEMBER DIRECTORY. Text in English. a. USD 150 to non-members. adv. **Document type:** *Directory.*
Former titles: American Association of Nurserymen Directory for the Nursery Industry and Related Associations; American Association of Nurserymen Membership Directory; Allied Landscape Industry Member Directory (0098-793X)
Published by: American Association of Nurserymen, 1250 I St, N W, Ste 500, Washington, DC 20005. TEL 202-789-2900. Circ: 3,500.

638.1 USA ISSN 0002-7626
SF521 CODEN: ABJOAS
AMERICAN BEE JOURNAL. Text in English. 1861. m. USD 22.95 domestic; USD 39.65 foreign (effective 2005). adv. bk.rev. abstr.; charts; illus.; stat. index. 80 p./no. 3 cols./p.; reprint service avail. from PQC. **Document type:** *Magazine, Trade.* **Description:** Magazine for hobby and professional beekeepers. Topics include management, honey processing, marketing, disease control.
Related titles: Microfilm ed.: (from PMC, PQC).
Indexed: AEA, ASCA, AbHyg, AgBio, Agr, AgrForAb, AnBrAb, ApicAb, B&BAb, BibAg, BioCN&I, BiolAb, CPA, ChemAb, ChemoAb, CurCont, EntAb, F&GI, FCA, FPA, ForAb, HortAb, IndVet, MaizeAb, NutrAb, OrnHort, PBA, PGegResA, PHN&I, PoultAb, ProtozoAb, RA&MP, RDA, RM&VM, RRTA, RevApplEntom, S&F, SIA, SSCI, SeedAb, TDB, VetBull, WAE&RSA, WeedAb.
—BLDSC (0810.750000), CASDDS, CISTI, IDS, IE, Infotrieve, ingenta, Linda Hall. **CCC.**

A

A

Published by: Dadant & Sons, Inc., 51 South Second St., Hamilton, IL 62341. TEL 217-847-3324, FAX 217-847-3660, ABJ@dadant.com, abj@dadant.com, http://www.dadant.com. Ed., R&P Joe M Graham TEL 217-847-3324. Adv. contact Marta Menn. page USD 876.15. Circ: 11,000 (paid).

638.1 USA ISSN 0014-9438
AMERICAN BEEKEEPING FEDERATION. NEWSLETTER. Text in English. 1943. bi-m. USD 35 membership (effective 2005). adv. bk.rev. **Document type:** *Newsletter, Trade.* **Description:** Keeps members current on activities of the organization and of happenings in the honey and beekeeping industry in the USA.
Indexed: ApicAb.
—CISTI.
Published by: American Beekeeping Federation, Inc., P.O. Box 1337, Jesup, GA 31598-1337. TEL 912-427-4233, FAX 912-427-8447, info@abfnet.org, http://www.abfnet.org. Ed. Troy H Fore Jr. Adv. contact Christina Wright. Circ: 2,000 (paid and controlled).

630 USA ISSN 0198-8816
AMERICAN CHIANINA JOURNAL. Text in English. 1973. 8/yr. USD 25 (effective 1998). adv. back issues avail. **Document type:** *Trade.*
Published by: American Chianina Association, PO Box 890, Platte City, MO 64079. TEL 816-431-2808, FAX 816-431-5381. Ed. Tammy Scott. Pub., R&P, Adv. contact Terry Atchison. Circ: 2,500.

AMERICAN FARMER SERIES. see *LITERATURE*

334.683 338.1 USA
AMERICAN FARMLAND TRUST. Text in English. 1981. q. (Jan., Apr., July, Oct.). USD 20 to members (effective 2005). **Document type:** *Magazine, Trade.*
Address: 1200 18th St, N W, Ste. 800, Washington, DC 20036. TEL 202-331-7300, FAX 202-659-8339, info@farmland.org, http://www.farmland.org. Ed. Chris Soto. Circ: 50,000 (paid and controlled).

630 338.642 USA ISSN 1089-8492
AMERICAN OSTRICH★ . Text in English. 1987. m. USD 80; USD 120 foreign (effective 1998). adv. bk.rev. back issues avail. **Document type:** *Trade.* **Description:** Covers alternative agriculture.
Formerly: Ostrich Report
Published by: American Ostrich Association, PO Box 162627, Fort Worth, TX 76161-2627. TEL 817-232-1200, FAX 817-232-1390, aoa@flash.net, http://www.ostriches.org. Ed., R&P, Adv. contact Janis L Gary. Circ: 4,500.

630 USA ISSN 1064-7473
HD1476.U5
AMERICAN SMALL FARM. Text in English. 1992. m. USD 18 (effective 2005). adv. bk.rev. **Document type:** *Magazine, Consumer.* **Description:** Focuses on production agriculture by the small-acreage farmer and rancher.
Address: 267 Broad St, Westerville, OH 43081. TEL 614-895-3755, FAX 614-895-3757, http://www.smallfarm.com. Ed. Andy Stevens. Adv. contact Marti Smith. B&W page USD 4,545, color page USD 5,885; trim 10.5 x 7.88. Circ: 67,000 (paid and controlled).

630 USA ISSN 0149-9890
CODEN: AAEPCZ
AMERICAN SOCIETY OF AGRICULTURAL ENGINEERS. ANNUAL MEETING PAPERS. Text in English. 1957. a., latest 2002. USD 1,600 (effective 2004). **Document type:** *Trade.* **Description:** Publishes full-text papers presented at its meetings and specialty conferences.
Related titles: Microfiche ed.: USD 14,000 (effective 2004).
Indexed: AEA, Agr, AgrForAb, BioCN&I, CPA, DSA, EngInd, FCA, FPA, ForAb, HortAb, I&DA, IndVet, MaizeAb, NutrAb, OrnHort, PBA, PHN&I, PN&I, PotatoAb, PoultAb, RA&MP, RDA, RPP, RevApplEntom, RiceAb, S&F, S&MA, SIA, SeedAb, SoyAb, TriticAb, VetBull, WAE&RSA, WeedAb.
—BLDSC (6369.640000), CISTI. **CCC.**
Published by: American Society of Agricultural Engineers, 2950 Niles Rd, St. Joseph, MI 49085-9659. TEL 269-429-0300, FAX 269-429-3852, hq@asae.org, http://www.asae.org/pubs/meeting.html. R&P Sandy Rutter.

630 USA ISSN 1061-1827
Z5074.E6
AMERICAN SOCIETY OF AGRICULTURAL ENGINEERS. COMPREHENSIVE INDEX OF PUBLICATIONS. Text in English. 1979. a. USD 6 to non-members; USD 2 to members (effective 2001). **Description:** Provides a keyword listing of all publications available from the Society.
Formerly (until 1984): Comprehensive Index of A S A E Publications (0889-6798)
Related titles: Online - full text ed.: USD 135 to non-members; USD 30 to members (effective 2000).
—Linda Hall.
Published by: American Society of Agricultural Engineers, 2950 Niles Rd, St. Joseph, MI 49085-9659. TEL 269-429-0300, FAX 269-429-3852, hq@asae.org, http://asae.org/, http://www.asae.org. R&P Sandy Nalepa.

630 USA ISSN 0001-2351
S671 CODEN: TAAEAJ
➤ **AMERICAN SOCIETY OF AGRICULTURAL ENGINEERS. TRANSACTIONS.** Key Title: Transactions of the A S A E. (Consists of Divisional Transactions: Power & Machinery; Soil & Water; Structure & Environment; Electrical & Electronic Systems - Emerging Technologies; Food and Process Engineering) Text in English. 1958. bi-m. USD 337 domestic to non-members; USD 385 foreign to non-members; USD 111 to members (effective 2005). illus. cum.index: 1907-1960, 1961-1970, 1971-1980, 1981-1985. back issues avail.; reprints avail. **Document type:** *Journal, Academic/Scholarly.* **Description:** Addresses irrigation, drainage, farm buildings and equipment, agricultural machinery, biological engineering, food engineering, aquaculture, electronics, forestry and knowledge systems.
Related titles: Microfiche ed.
Indexed: AEA, AIA, ASCA, ASFA, AbHyg, AgBio, Agr, AgrForAb, AnBrAb, B&AI, BIOBASE, BiolAb, BrCerAb, C&ISA, CEABA, CMCI, CPA, CTFA, CerAb, ChemAb, CivEngAb, CorrAb, CurCont, DSA, E&CAJ, EIA, EMA, ESPM, EngInd, EnvAb, EnvEAb, ExcerpMed, FCA, FLUIDEX, FPA, FS&TA, ForAb, GEOBASE, HelmAb, HerbAb, HortAb, I&DA, IAA, IABS, IAOP, ISMEC, ISR, IndVet, M&GPA, M&TEA, MBF, METADEX, MaizeAb, NemAb, NutrAb, OrnHort, PBA, PGegResA, PGrRegA, PHN&I, PN&I, PlantSci, PollutAb, PotatoAb, PoultAb, ProtozoAb, RA&MP, RM&VM, RPP, RevApplEntom, RiceAb, S&F, S&MA, SCI, SIA, SWRA, SeedAb, SolStAb, SoyAb, TOSA, TriticAb, VetBull, WAA, WAE&RSA, WTA, WeedAb.
—BLDSC (8894.650000), CASDDS, CINDOC, CIS, CISTI, Ei, IDS, IE, ingenta, Linda Hall. **CCC.**
Published by: American Society of Agricultural Engineers, 2950 Niles Rd, St. Joseph, MI 49085-9659. TEL 269-429-0300, FAX 269-429-3852, hq@asae.org, http://www.asae.org. Ed. Glenn Laing. Pub. Donna M. Hull. R&P Sandy Rutter. Circ: 1,200 (paid and controlled).

630 USA ISSN 0003-116X
➤ **AMERICAN SOCIETY OF FARM MANAGERS AND RURAL APPRAISERS. JOURNAL.** Key Title: A S F M R A Journal. Text in English. 1937. a. USD 28 (effective 2005). stat.; tr.lit. cum.index: nos.1-41 (1937-1977), nos.42-57 (1978-1987). 2 cols./p.; back issues avail. **Document type:** *Journal, Academic/Scholarly.* **Description:** Contains articles of interest to farm managers, rural appraisers, agricultural consultants, and other agricultural professionals.
Related titles: CD-ROM ed.; Online - full content ed.; Online - full text ed.
Indexed: Agr.
Published by: American Society of Farm Managers and Rural Appraisers, 950 S Cherry St, Ste 508, Denver, CO 80246-2664. TEL 303-758-3513, FAX 303-758-0190, asfmra@agri-associations.org, http://www.asfmara.org. Ed. Cheryl Cooley. Circ: 3,000.

➤ **ANALES CIENTIFICOS.** see *SCIENCES: COMPREHENSIVE WORKS*

➤ **ANDELSBLADET.** see *BUSINESS AND ECONOMICS—Cooperatives*

630 IND ISSN 0003-2956
CODEN: AAGJAP
ANDHRA AGRICULTURAL JOURNAL. Text in English. 1954. q. USD 40 (effective 2006). adv. charts; illus.
Indexed: AnalAb, BiolAb, ChemAb, FCA, FS&TA, PBA, RPP, S&F, WeedAb.
—CASDDS, CISTI.
Published by: Andhra Agricultural Union, Agricultural College Campus Bapatla, Guntur, Andhra Pradesh 522 101, India. Ed. I V Subba Rao. Circ: 2,000. **Subscr. to:** I N S I O Scientific Books & Periodicals, P O Box 7234, Indraprastha HPO, New Delhi 110 002, India. info@insio.com, http://www.insio.com.

630 IND ISSN 0003-2964
ANDHRA PRADESH PRODUCTIVITY COUNCIL. TARGET. Text in English. 1961. s-a. INR 6. adv. bk.rev.
Formerly: Andhra Pradesh Productivity Council. Journal
Published by: Andhra Pradesh Productivity Council, 10-1-200, A.C. Guards, P O Box 21, Hyderabad, Andhra Pradesh 500 004, India. Ed. S Rajagopala Reddi. Circ: 1,000.

630 GBR
ANGLIA FARMER AND CONTRACTOR. Text in English. m. GBP 18 (effective 1998). adv. **Document type:** *Bulletin.* **Description:** Covers all aspects of agriculture.
Published by: B C Publications, 16C Market Pl, Diss, Norfolk IP22 3AB, United Kingdom. FAX 44-1379-650480. Ed. Roger Turff. Adv. contact Jenny Holkham. Circ: 7,600 (controlled).

630 CHN ISSN 1000-2197
ANHUI NONGXUEYUAN XUEBAO/ANHUI AGRICULTURAL COLLEGE. JOURNAL. Text in Chinese. 1957. q. CNY 5 newsstand/cover (effective 2004). **Document type:** *Journal, Academic/Scholarly.*
Related titles: Online - full content ed.: (from WanFang Data Corp.); Online - full text ed.: (from East View Information Services).
Indexed: RefZh.
—BLDSC (0902.916850), IE.
Published by: Anhui Nongxueyuan/Anhui Agricultural College, 130, Changjiang Xilu, Hefei, Anhui 230036, China. TEL 86-551-2810205, ahnydxxb@mail.hf.ah.cn, http://ahnydxxb.periodicals.net.cn/default.html, http://www.ahau.edu.cn/.

630 CHN ISSN 0517-6611
ANHUI NONGYE KEXUE/ANHUI AGRICULTURAL SCIENCE. Text in Chinese. q.
Related titles: Online - full text ed.: (from East View Information Services).
—BLDSC (4935.373000), IE, ingenta.
Published by: Anhui Sheng Nongye Kexueyuan/Anhui Provincial Academy of Agricultural Science, Silihe, Hefei Xijiao (west Suburb), Anhui 230031, China. TEL 257273. Ed. Zhang Zhengzhong.

ANIMAL BREEDING ABSTRACTS; a monthly abstract of world literature. see *AGRICULTURE—Abstracting, Bibliographies, Statistics*

630 FRA
ANJOU AGRICOLE. Text in French. w.
Address: 14 av. Joxe, Angers, Cedex 49006, France. TEL 41-88-98-53. Circ: 11,293.

630 POL ISSN 0365-1118
S13 CODEN: ACEAA2
ANNALES UNIVERSITATIS MARIAE CURIE-SKLODOWSKA. SECTIO E. AGRICULTURA. Text in English, Polish; Summaries in English, French, German. 1946. a. price varies. **Document type:** *Academic/Scholarly.*
Indexed: AEA, AnBrAb, BiolAb, CPA, ChemAb, DSA, ExcerpMed, FCA, ForAb, HerbAb, HortAb, I&DA, MaizeAb, NutrAb, OrnHort, PBA, PGrRegA, PHN&I, PotatoAb, PoultAb, RM&VM, RPP, RefZh, RevApplEntom, S&F, SIA, SeedAb, SoyAb, TriticAb, WAE&RSA, WeedAb.
—CASDDS, CISTI, Linda Hall.
Published by: Uniwersytet Marii Curie-Sklodowskiej w Lublinie, Wydawnictwo, pl M Curie Sklodowskiej 5, Lublin, 20031, Poland. TEL 48-81-375304, FAX 48-81-336699. Ed. Adam Szember. Circ: 650.

630 570 IND ISSN 0971-9660
ANNALS OF AGRI BIO RESEARCH; an international journal of basic and applied agriculture and biology. Text in English. 1996. a. INR 600, USD 60 (effective 2003). adv. bk.rev. **Document type:** *Academic/Scholarly.*
Indexed: AEA, ASFA, AgBio, AgrForAb, AnBrAb, B&BAb, BioCN&I, CPA, DSA, ESPM, EntAb, FCA, FPA, FS&TA, ForAb, HGA, HerbAb, HortAb, I&DA, IndVet, MBA, MaizeAb, NemAb, NutrAb, OrnHort, PBA, PGegResA, PGrRegA, PHN&I, PotatoAb, PoultAb, ProtozoAb, RA&MP, RDA, RPP, RevApplEntom, RiceAb, S&F, SIA, SeedAb, SoyAb, TriticAb, VetBull, WAE&RSA, WeedAb.
—BLDSC (1035.275000), IE, ingenta.
Published by: Agri Bio Research Publishers, 121 Mohalla Chaudharian, Hisar, 125 001, India. TEL 91-1662-37530, bajdasch@nde.vsnl.com. Ed. B D Chaudhary. Circ: 500.

630 IND ISSN 0970-3179
CODEN: AAGREJ
ANNALS OF AGRICULTURAL RESEARCH. Text in English. 1980. q. USD 150 (effective 2006). **Document type:** *Journal, Academic/Scholarly.*
Indexed: AEA, AgBio, AgrForAb, BioCN&I, CPA, DSA, FCA, FPA, ForAb, HerbAb, HortAb, I&DA, MaizeAb, NemAb, NutrAb, OrnHort, PBA, PGegResA, PGrRegA, PHN&I, PotatoAb, PoultAb, RA&MP, RDA, RM&VM, RPP, RevApplEntom, RiceAb, S&F, SIA, SeedAb, SoyAb, TriticAb, WAE&RSA, WeedAb.
Published by: (Indian Society of Agricultural Science), H P C Publishers Distributors Pvt. Ltd., 4805 Bharat Ram Rd, 24 Darya Ganj, New Delhi, 110 002, India. TEL 91-11-3254401, FAX 91-11-619-3511, hpcpd@giasdl01.vsnl.net.in, hpcpd@hpc.cc, http://www.hpc.cc, http://www.bizdelhi.com/publisher/hpc, http://www.indianindustry.com. **Subscr. to:** I N S I O Scientific Books & Periodicals, P O Box 7234, Indraprastha HPO, New Delhi 110 002, India. info@insio.com, http://www.insio.com.

630 EGY ISSN 0570-1783
ANNALS OF AGRICULTURAL SCIENCE/HAWLIYAT AL-'LUM AL-ZIRA'IYYAT. Text in English. 1956. s-a. EGP 20 (effective 2004). **Document type:** *Academic/Scholarly.*
Indexed: AEA, AgBio, AgrForAb, BioCN&I, CPA, DSA, FCA, FPA, FS&TA, ForAb, HelmAb, HerbAb, HortAb, I&DA, IndVet, MaizeAb, NemAb, NutrAb, OrnHort, PBA, PGegResA, PGrRegA, PHN&I, PotatoAb, PoultAb, RA&MP, RDA, RM&VM, RPP, RiceAb, S&F, SIA, SeedAb, SoyAb, TriticAb, VetBull, WAE&RSA, WeedAb, ZooRec.
—BLDSC (1035.500000), CISTI, IE, ingenta.
Published by: Ain Shams University, Faculty of Agriculture, Shoubra El-Kheima, Hadayek Shoubra, P O Box 68, Cairo, 11241, Egypt. TEL 20-2-4820230, FAX 20-2-4444460, info@asunet.shams.edu.eg, http://derp.sti.sci.eg/data/0059.htm, http://asunet.shams.eun.eg. Ed. Dr. Muhammad El-Sawi.

630 EGY ISSN 1110-0419
ANNALS OF AGRICULTURAL SCIENCE, MOSHTOHOR/ HAWLIYYAAT AL-'ULUM AL-ZIRA'IYYAT BI-MUSTUHUR. Text in English. 1973. q. EGP 5 newsstand/cover (effective 2004). **Document type:** *Academic/Scholarly.*
Indexed: ASFA, ESPM, SWRA.
Published by: Zagazig University, Faculty of Agriculture, Banha Branch, Mushtuhur, Tukh, Kalubia, Egypt. TEL 20-13-460306, FAX 20-13-467786, http://derp.sti.sci.eg/data/0060.htm. Ed. Dr. Muhammad El-Saeid Ahmad Zaki.

660 BGD ISSN 1025-482X
ANNALS OF BANGLADESH AGRICULTURE. Text and summaries in English. 1991. s-a. BDT 200 domestic; USD 80 foreign (effective 2000). abstr.; charts; stat. back issues avail. **Document type:** *Academic/Scholarly.* **Description:** Covers all aspects of agriculture with research articles production, crop and pest control, to social issues confronting agricultural area.
Indexed: AgBio, AgrForAb, CPA, FCA, ForAb, HerbAb, HortAb, I&DA, MaizeAb, NemAb, OrnHort, PBA, PGegResA, PGrRegA, PHN&I, PotatoAb, PoultAb, RA&MP, RDA, RPP, RevApplEntom, RiceAb, S&F, SIA, SeedAb, SoyAb, TriticAb, WAE&RSA, WeedAb.
—BLDSC (1038.650000).
Published by: Bangabandhu Sheikh Mujibur Rahman Agricultural University, Salna, Gazipur, 1703, Bangladesh. TEL 880-2-9332127, ipsa@dhaka.agni.com. Ed. A M Ashraful Kamal. Circ: 300.

631.091 PHL ISSN 0116-0710
CODEN: ATREDV
➤ **ANNALS OF TROPICAL RESEARCH.** Text in English. 1979. s-a. USD 30; USD 25 to libraries; USD 20 to students. abstr. index. back issues avail. **Document type:** *Academic/Scholarly.*
Indexed: AnBrAb, FCA, FPA, FS&TA, IPP, PBA, PHN&I, RDA, RPP, RevApplEntom, RiceAb, WAE&RSA, WeedAb, ZooRec.
—BLDSC (1045.200000).
Published by: Visayas State College of Agriculture, Baybay, Leyte Province 6521, Philippines. TEL 63-53-335-2617, visca@sat.vitanet.org. Ed., R&P Jose R Pardales Jr. Circ: 500.

630 639.2 333.72 HKG ISSN 0441-1641
S322.H6
ANNUAL DEPARTMENTAL REPORT BY THE DIRECTOR OF AGRICULTURE AND FISHERIES. Text in English. 1965. a. **Document type:** *Government.*
Indexed: ESPM.
—BLDSC (1083.970000), CISTI.
Published by: Agriculture, Fisheries and Conservation Department, 5/F, Cheung Sha Wan Government Offices, 303 Cheung Sha Wan Rd, Kowloon, Hong Kong. http://www.afcd.gov.hk/web/index_c.htm.

630 915.2 JPN
ANNUAL REVIEW OF AGRICULTURE IN KINKI DISTRICT/KINKI NOGYO JOSEI HOKOKU. Text in Japanese. 1964. a.
Published by: Kinki Agricultural Administration Bureau/Kinki Nosei-kyoku, Shimochoja-machi Sagaru, Nishinotoin-dori, Kamigyo-ku, Kyoto-shi, 602, Japan.

ANVIL MAGAZINE. see *METALLURGY*

630 JPN ISSN 0003-6331
AOMORI NOGYO. Text in Japanese. 1950. m. JPY 350 newsstand/cover.
Published by: Aomoriken Nogyo Kairyo Fukyukai/Aomori Prefecture Agricultural Improvement and Propagation Association, Aomoriken Norinbu, 1-1 Nagashima 1-chome, Aomori-shi, Aomori-ken 030-0861, Japan. Ed. Yotsuo Katsurahara. Circ: 96,000.

638.1 ITA ISSN 0003-6455
APIACTA; an international technical magazine of apicultural and economic information. Text in English, French, Spanish. 1966. q. USD 28 (effective 1999). adv. bk.rev. back issues avail. **Document type:** *Bulletin.* **Description:** Discusses bee culture.
Related titles: Microform ed.: (from PQC).
Indexed: ApicAb, BiolAb, ExcerpMed, RevApplEntom, SIA, ZooRec.
—BLDSC (1567.975000), CISTI, Linda Hall.
Published by: "Apimondia" International Federation of Beekeepers' Associations/Federation Internationale des Associations d'Apiculture, Corso Vittorio Emanuele II, 101, Rome, RM 00186, Italy. TEL 39-06-6852286, FAX 39-06-6852868, apimondia@mclink.it. Ed. Ms. E Dumitrascu. Adv. contact Cristian Constantinescu. Circ: 1,000.

APICULTURAL ABSTRACTS. see *AGRICULTURE—Abstracting, Bibliographies, Statistics*

638.1 ITA
APIMONDIA INTERNATIONAL BEEKEEPING CONGRESS. PROCEEDINGS. Text in Multiple languages. 1958 (17th). biennial. price varies. **Document type:** *Proceedings.*
Published by: "Apimondia" International Federation of Beekeepers' Associations/Federation Internationale des Associations d'Apiculture, Corso Vittorio Emanuele II, 101, Rome, RM 00186, Italy. TEL 39-06-6852286, FAX 39-06-6852286, apimondia@mclink.it.

630 CHE
APPENZOELLER BUUR. Text in German. w.
Address: Engelgasse 3, Appenzell, 9050, Switzerland. TEL 071-871922, FAX 071-873753. Ed. Walter Koller. Circ: 5,200.

630 USA ISSN 0883-8542
➤ **APPLIED ENGINEERING IN AGRICULTURE.** Text in English. 1985. 6/yr. USD 111 domestic to non-members; USD 132 foreign to non-members; USD 58 to members (effective 2004). **Document type:** *Journal, Academic/Scholarly.* **Description:** Presents the latest technical developments in every area of engineering for agriculture.
Indexed: AEA, ASFA, AbHyg, AgBio, Agr, AgrForAb, AnBrAb, B&BAb, BibAg, BioEngAb, BrCerAb, C&ISA, CPA, CTFA, CerAb, CivEngAb, CorrAb, CurCont, DSA, E&CAJ, EMA, ESPM, Englnd, FCA, FPA, FS&TA, ForAb, HerbAb, HortAb, I&DA, IAA, ISMEC, IndVet, Inspec, M&TEA, MBF, METADEX, MaizeAb, NemAb, NutrAb, OrnHort, PGrRegA, PHN&I, PN&I, PotatoAb, PoultAb, RA&MP, RDA, RM&VM, RPP, RRTA, RevApplEntom, RiceAb, S&F, S&MA, SIA, SWRA, SeedAb, SolStAb, SoyAb, TDB, TriticAb, VITIS, VetBull, WAA, WAE&RSA, WeedAb.
—BLDSC (1572.350000), CISTI, Ei, IE, Infotrieve, ingenta, Linda Hall. **CCC.**
Published by: American Society of Agricultural Engineers, 2950 Niles Rd, St. Joseph, MI 49085-9659. TEL 269-429-0300, FAX 269-429-3852, hq@asae.org, http://www.asae.org/pubs/style/appl.html. Ed. Melissa Miller. R&P Sandy Nalepa. Circ: 700.

630 USA
APPLY. Text in English. 2001. 9/yr. free to qualified personnel (effective 2005). adv. **Document type:** *Magazine, Trade.*
Related titles: ♦ Supplement to: Farm Industry News. ISSN 0892-8312.
Published by: Primedia Business Magazines & Media, Inc. (Subsidiary of: Primedia, Inc.), 7900 International Dr, Ste 300, Minneapolis, MN 55425. TEL 952-851-9329, FAX 952-851-4601, app2mag@aol.com, inquiries@primediabusiness.com, http://www.apply-mag.com, http://www.primediabusiness.com. Ed. Den Gardner. Pub. Greg Frey TEL 952-851-4613. Adv. contact Cindy Kramer. B&W page USD 3,050, color page USD 4,050; 7 x 10. Circ: 20,000. **Subscr. to:** 2104 Harvell Circle, Bellevue, NE 68005. TEL 402-505-7173, 866-505-7173, FAX 402-293-0741.

639.3 FRA ISSN 0295-0448
AQUA REVUE. Text in French. 1985. 8/yr. bk.rev. **Document type:** *Newspaper.* **Description:** Explores marine and continental aquaculture.
Indexed: ASFA, ESPM, RefZh.
—BLDSC (1581.864250).
Published by: Societe SEA - R, 37 avenue de la Tranchee, Tours, 37100, France. TEL 33-2-47054060, FAX 33-2-47054077. Ed. Bernard Marie Thomas. R&P Marianne Kany. Adv. contact Nathalie Bleau. Circ: 2,300.

630.658 590 THA ISSN 0859-600X
AQUACULTURE ASIA. Text in English; Section in Chinese, Thai. q. USD 30 in Asia & the Pacific; USD 50 elsewhere (effective 2002). adv. bk.rev. **Description:** Provides information to farmers to improve their production and farm management practices.
Indexed: ESPM.
—BLDSC (1581.866032), IE, ingenta.
Published by: Network of Aquaculture Centres in Asia-Pacific, PO Box 1040, Bangkok, 10903, Thailand. TEL 66-2-5611728, FAX 66-2-5611727, naca@enaca.org, publications@enaca.org, http://www.enaca.org/AquacultureAsia/. adv.: B&W page USD 350.

AQUACULTURE OUTLOOK. see *FISH AND FISHERIES*

630 BHR
ARAB AGRICULTURE YEARBOOK/AL-ZIRA'AH AL-ARABIYYAH. Text in Arabic, English. 1985. a. BHD 17, USD 45 (effective 2000). adv. illus.; stat. **Document type:** *Directory.* **Description:** Comprehensive guide to all sectors of agriculture in the Arab world, including North Africa and Somalia, covering government ministries, farm consultancy services, international suppliers of machinery, food processing and storage equipment, investment opportunities and agricultural scientists.
Related titles: ♦ Supplement to: Arab World Agribusiness.
Published by: Fanar Publishing W L L, Bahrain Tower 8th Fl., PO Box 10131, Manama, Bahrain. TEL 973-213900, FAX 973-211765. Ed. Abdul Wahed Alwani. adv.: B&W page USD 1,925, color page USD 2,530; trim 210 x 270. Circ: 12,000.

630 EGY ISSN 1110-2675
ARAB UNIVERSITIES JOURNAL OF AGRICULTURAL SCIENCES/MAGALLAT ITIHAD AL-GAMI'AT AL-'ARABIYYAT LIL-DIRASAT WA-AL-BUHUT AL-ZIRA'IYYAT. Text in English. 1993. s-a. **Document type:** *Journal, Academic/Scholarly.*
Indexed: AgBio, AgrForAb, AnBrAb, BioCN&I, CPA, DSA, FCA, FPA, ForAb, HelmAb, HerbAb, HortAb, I&DA, IndVet, MaizeAb, NemAb, OrnHort, PBA, PGegResA, PGrRegA, PHN&I, PotatoAb, PoultAb, RA&MP, RM&VM, RPP, S&F, SIA, SeedAb, SoyAb, TDB, TriticAb, WAE&RSA, WeedAb.
Published by: Arab Universities Union of Agricultural Sciences, Hadayek Shobra, 11241 Faculty of Agriculture, Ain Shams University, P O Box 68, Cairo, Egypt. TEL 20-2-4441554, FAX 20-2-4444460, http://derp.sti.sci.eg/data/0238.htm. Ed. Dr. Hasan Ahmad Ghallab.

630 BHR
ARAB WORLD AGRIBUSINESS/AL-ZIRA'AH FI-L-ALAM AL-ARABI. Text in Arabic, English. 1984. 9/yr. USD 65 (effective 2000). back issues avail. **Document type:** *Trade.*
Related titles: ♦ Supplement(s): Arab Agriculture Yearbook.
Indexed: FS&TA, IndVet.
Published by: Fanar Publishing W L L, Bahrain Tower 8th Fl., PO Box 10131, Manama, Bahrain. TEL 973-213900, FAX 973-211765. Ed. Abdul Wahed Alwani. Circ: 16,000.

631 DEU ISSN 0365-1665
ARBEITEN DER D L G. Text in German. 1894. irreg., latest vol.197, 2004. price varies. **Document type:** *Monographic series, Academic/Scholarly.*
Published by: D L G Verlags GmbH, Eschborner Landstr 122, Frankfurt Am Main, 60489, Germany. TEL 49-69-247880, FAX 49-69-24788480, dlg-verlag@dlg-frankfurt.de, http://www.dlg-verlag.de.

ARBEITSKREISE ZUR LANDENTWICKLUNG IN HESSEN. DORFENTWICKLUNG. see *SOCIOLOGY*

ARBEITSKREISE ZUR LANDENTWICKLUNG IN HESSEN. LANDNUTZUNG. see *SOCIOLOGY*

ARBEITSKREISE ZUR LANDENTWICKLUNG IN HESSEN. STALLBAU UND TECHNIK. see *SOCIOLOGY*

ARBEITSKREISE ZUR LANDENTWICKLUNG IN HESSEN. WOHNEN UND WOHNUMWELT. see *SOCIOLOGY*

631 DEU ISSN 0178-0867
ARCHIV DER D L G. Variant title: Deutsche Landwirtschafts Gesellschaft. Archiv. Text in German. 19??. irreg., latest vol.98, 2004. price varies. **Document type:** *Monographic series, Academic/Scholarly.*
Published by: D L G Verlags GmbH, Eschborner Landstr 122, Frankfurt Am Main, 60489, Germany. TEL 49-69-247880, FAX 49-69-24788480, dlg-verlag@dlg-frankfurt.de, http://www.dlg-verlag.de.

630 GBR ISSN 0323-5408
CODEN: APPZAJ
ARCHIV FUER PHYTOPATHOLOGIE UND PFLANZENSCHUTZ/ ARCHIVES OF PHYTOPATHOLOGY AND PLANT PROTECTION. Text in German; Summaries in English, German, Russian. 1965. bi-m. GBP 993, USD 1,486 combined subscription to institutions print & online eds. (effective 2006). bk.rev. charts; illus.; stat. index. reprint service avail. from PSC. **Document type:** *Journal, Academic/Scholarly.* **Description:** Publishes original papers and reviews covering all scientific aspects of modern plant protection.
Formerly (until 1972): Archiv fuer Pflanzenschutz (0003-9349)
Related titles: Online - full text ed.: ISSN 1477-2906. GBP 943, USD 1,412 to institutions (effective 2006) (from EBSCO Publishing, Gale Group, IngentaConnect, O C L C Online Computer Library Center, Inc., Swets Information Services).
Indexed: AEA, ASCA, AgBio, AgrForAb, BioCN&I, BioDAb, CPA, ChemAb, CurCont, DBA, ExcerpMed, FCA, FPA, FS&TA, FaBeAb, ForAb, HerbAb, HortAb, I&DA, MaizeAb, NemAb, OrnHort, PBA, PGegResA, PGrRegA, PHN&I, PotatoAb, RA&MP, RM&VM, RPP, RevApplEntom, RiceAb, S&F, SIA, SeedAb, TriticAb, WeedAb, ZooRec.
—BLDSC (1639.700000), CASDDS, CISTI, IE, Infotrieve, ingenta, Linda Hall. **CCC.**
Published by: (Akademie der Landwirtschaftswissenschaften CHE), Taylor & Francis Ltd (Subsidiary of: Taylor & Francis Group), 4 Park Sq, Milton Park, Abingdon, OX14 4RN, United Kingdom. TEL 44-1235-828600, FAX 44-1235-829000, info@tandf.co.uk, http://www.tandf.co.uk/journals/titles/03235408.html. Eds. Dieter Spaar, Theo Wetzel. **Subscr. in N America to:** Taylor & Francis Inc., Customer Services Dept, 325 Chestnut St, 8th Fl, Philadelphia, PA 19106. TEL 215-625-8900, 800-354-1420, FAX 215-625-8914, customerservice@taylorandfrancis.com; **Subscr. to:** Journals Customer Service, Rankine Rd, Basingstoke, Hants RG24 8PR, United Kingdom. TEL 44-1256-813000, FAX 44-1256-330245, enquiry@tandf.co.uk.

630 MDG
ARCHIVES DU FO FI FA. Text in French. a.
Published by: Centre d'Information et de Documentation Scientifique et Technique, BP 6224, Antananarivo, 101, Madagascar. TEL 33288.

630 FRA ISSN 0750-1536
ARDENNE AGRICOLE. Text in French. 1944. w.
Address: 1 av. du Petit Bois, BP 416, Charleville-Mezieres, Cedex 08105, France. TEL 24-33-53-00. Ed. Albert Molie. Circ: 6,000.

AL-ARDH. see *LABOR UNIONS*

▼ *new title* ➤ *refereed* ✶ *unverified* ♦ *full entry avail.*

630 ARG
ARGENTINA. SECRETARIA DE ESTADO DE AGRICULTURA Y GANADERIA. COMUNICADO DE PRENSA. Text in Spanish. 1979 (no.107). irreg. stat.
Media: Duplicated (not offset).
Published by: Secretaria de Estado de Agricultura y Ganaderia, Avda. Paseo Colon, 922, Capital Federal, Buenos Aires 1063, Argentina.

630 ARG
ARGENTINA. SERVICIO NACIONAL DE ECONOMIA Y SOCIOLOGIA RURAL. PUBLICACION E S R. Text in Spanish. irreg.
Published by: Servicio Nacional de Economia y Sociologia Rural, Avda. Paseo Colon, 974, Capital Federal, Buenos Aires 1063, Argentina.

630 USA ISSN 1557-1831
ARIZONA AGRICULTURE. Text in English. 1948. m. USD 150 to non-members; USD 112 to members (effective 2005). adv. bk.rev. charts; illus.; pat.; stat.; tr.lit. back issues avail. **Document type:** *Newspaper.* **Description:** Covers legislative, regulatory and economic issues impacting Arizona agriculturalists.
Formerly (until 2005): Arizona Farm Bureau News (0274-7014)
Published by: Arizona Farm Bureau Federation, 325 S Higley Rd, Higley, AZ 85236. TEL 480-635-3604, FAX 480-635-3781, http://www.azib.org. Ed. Neil Schneider. Pub. Jim Klinker. Circ: 3,000 (paid and controlled).

630 USA ISSN 0744-5474
ARIZONA LAND AND PEOPLE. Text in English. 1949. a. free. bk.rev. **Document type:** *Consumer.* **Description:** Highlights and describes for a key audience the programs and activities of the college.
Formerly: Progressive Agriculture in Arizona (0033-0744)
Indexed: B&AI, BiolAb, CurCont, EIA, EnerInd, FCA, HerbAb, OrnHort.
—CISTI.
Published by: University of Arizona, College of Agriculture, Tucson, AZ 85721. TEL 602-621-7176. Ed. S McGinley. Circ: 5,500.

630 USA
ARKANSAS FARMER. Text in English. 1985. m. USD 21.95 in state; USD 30 out of state (effective 2001). adv. illus.; mkt. reprints avail. **Document type:** *Newspaper.* **Description:** Contains agricultural news and features for Arkansas's commercial farm and ranch operators.
Formerly (until 1992): Arkansas Farm and Country
Published by: Farm Progress Companies, 191 S Gary Ave, Carol Stream, IL 60188. TEL 630-462-2892, 800-477-1737, FAX 630-462-2885, http://www.farmprogress.com/. Ed. Ken Bretches. Pub. Allan Johnson. Adv. contact Don Tourte. B&W page USD 2,100, color page USD 2,900; trim 10.75 x 8. Circ: 67,514.

AROMATIC NEWS; news from the Aromatic News Project. see *BIOLOGY—Botany*

630 IND ISSN 0971-7730
ASIAN AGRI-HISTORY. Text in English. 1997. q. INR 270 domestic to individuals; USD 15 to individuals in South Asia; USD 25 elsewhere to individuals; INR 1,250 domestic to institutions; USD 60 to institutions in South Asia; USD 90 elsewhere to institutions (effective 2004). adv. back issues avail. **Document type:** *Journal.* **Description:** Publishes articles on the agricultural heritage of South and Southeast Asia.
Indexed: AmH&L, GEOBASE.
Published by: Asian Agri-History Foundation, 47 ICRISAT Colony-I, Brig. Sayeed Rd., Secunderabad, Andhra Pradesh 500 009, India. TEL 91-40-27755774, FAX 91-40-27750630, info@agri-history.org, http://www.agri-history.org/publications.htm. adv.: B&W page USD 100; 14 x 19.8.

631.8 TWN
ASIAN AND PACIFIC COUNCIL. FOOD AND FERTILIZER TECHNOLOGY CENTER. EXTENSION - TECHNICAL BULLETIN. Text in Chinese. 1970. s-m. free. bibl.; charts; illus.; stat.
Indexed: AEA, AgrForAb, AnBrAb, BioCN&I, DSA, FCA, ForAb, HerbAb, HortAb, I&DA, IndVet, NutrAb, OrnHort, PHN&I, RDA, RPP, RRTA, RevApplEntom, RiceAb, S&F, SoyAb, TriticAb, WAE&RSA, WeedAb.
Published by: Asian and Pacific Council, Food and Fertilizer Technology Center, 14 Wenchow St, 5th Fl, Taipei, Taiwan. FAX 02-362-0478. Circ: 4,300 (controlled).

630 TWN ISSN 1010-142X
ASIAN VEGETABLE RESEARCH AND DEVELOPMENT CENTER. TECHNICAL BULLETIN. Text in English. 1975. irreg. price varies. **Document type:** *Bulletin, Academic/Scholarly.*
Published by: Asian Vegetable Research and Development Center, Shanhua, PO Box 42, Tainan, 741, Taiwan. TEL 886-6-5837801, FAX 886-6-5830009, avrdcbox@betra.avrdc.org.tw, http://www.avrdc.org.tw. Ed., R&P, Adv. contact David Abbass TEL 886-65837801 ext 550.

ASOCIACION INTERAMERICANA DE BIBLIOTECARIOS, DOCUMENTALISTAS Y ESPECIALISTAS EN INFORMACION AGRICOLA. BOLETIN INFORMATIVO. see *LIBRARY AND INFORMATION SCIENCES*

630 020 CRI
ASOCIACION INTERAMERICANA DE BIBLIOTECARIOS, DOCUMENTALISTAS Y ESPECIALISTAS EN INFORMACION AGRICOLA. BOLETIN TECNICO. Text in Spanish. 1966. irreg. membership. **Description:** Directory of AIBDEIA corporation and individual members.
Former titles: Asociacion Interamericana de Bibliotecarios, Documentalistas y Especialistas en Informacion Agricola. Boletin Especial; Asociacion Interamericana de Bibliotecarios y Documentalistas Agricolas. Boletin Especial (0074-0748) —Linda Hall.
Published by: Asociacion Interamericana de Bibliotecarios Documentalistas y Especialistas en Informacion Agricola, Apartado Postal 55, Coronado, San Jose 2200, Costa Rica. TEL 506-2160290, FAX 506-2160291, aibda@iica.a.cr. Ed. Carlos F Molestina. Circ: 250.

ASOCIACION INTERAMERICANA DE BIBLIOTECARIOS Y DOCUMENTALISTAS AGRICOLAS. REVISTA. see *LIBRARY AND INFORMATION SCIENCES*

630 URY ISSN 0044-9326
ASOCIACION RURAL DEL URUGUAY. REVISTA. Text in Spanish. 1872. s-m. abstr.; bibl.; illus.; stat.; tr.lit.
Published by: Asociacion Rural del Uruguay, Av. Uruguay, 864, Montevideo, 11102, Uruguay. TEL 598-2-9020484, FAX 598-2-9020489, http://www.aru.com.uy. Circ: 5,000.

630 EGY ISSN 1110-0486
ASSIUT JOURNAL OF AGRICULTURAL SCIENCES. Text in English. 1970. q. **Document type:** *Journal, Academic/Scholarly.*
Related titles: ♦ Arabic ed.: Magallat Asyut al-'ulum al-zira'iyyat. ISSN 0258-3275.
Indexed: AEA, AgBio, AgrForAb, AnBrAb, BioCN&I, CPA, DSA, FCA, FPA, ForAb, HerbAb, HortAb, I&DA, IndVet, MaizeAb, NemAb, NutrAb, OrnHort, PBA, PGegResA, PGrRegA, PHN&I, PotatoAb, PoultAb, RA&MP, RDA, RM&VM, RPP, RiceAb, S&F, SIA, SeedAb, SoyAb, TriticAb, VetBull, WAE&RSA, WeedAb.
—BLDSC (1746.672070), IE, ingenta.
Published by: Assiut University, Faculty of Agriculture, c/o Dr. A.A. Eisaa, Editor, Assiut, 71515, Egypt. TEL 20-88-332631, FAX 20-88-331384, sup@aun.eun.eg, http://derp.sti.sci.eg/data/0068.htm, http://www.aun.eun.eg.

630 070.48 FRA
ASSOCIATION DES JOURNALISTES AGRICOLES. ANNUAIRE. Text in French. a.
Published by: Association des Journalistes Agricoles, 9 rue Papillon, Paris, 75009, France. Circ: 2,000.

630 FRA ISSN 0221-508X
AURORE PAYSANNE. Text in French. 24/yr.
Address: 24 rue des Ingrains, BP 213, Chateauroux, Cedex 36028, France. TEL 54-22-20-07. Circ: 7,900.

630 DEU ISSN 0045-0049
AUSBILDUNG UND BERATUNG IN LAND- UND HAUSWIRTSCHAFT; Monatsschrift fuer Lehr- und Beratungskraefte. Text in German. 1948. 11/yr. **Document type:** *Trade.*
Indexed: IBR, IBZ, RRTA, VITIS, WAE&RSA.
—CCC.
Published by: (Land- und Hauswirtschaftlicher Auswertungs- und Informationsdienst), Landwirtschaftsverlag GmbH, Huelsebrockstr 2, Muenster, 48165, Germany. TEL 49-2501-801-0, FAX 49-2501-801204, TELEX 892665-LANDV-D, zentrale@landwirtschaftsverlag.com, zentrale@lv-h.de, http://www.landwirtschaftsverlag.com. **Subscr. to:** Postfach 480249, Muenster 48079, Germany.

638.1 AUS ISSN 1329-0231
AUSSIE BEE. Text in English. 1997. q. AUD 30, USD 26.50 (effective 1999). adv. charts; illus.; maps; stat. index. back issues avail. **Document type:** *Bulletin.* **Description:** Presents articles on biology, species, history and commercial uses of Australian native bees.
Published by: Australian Native Bee Research Centre, PO Box 74, North Richmond, NSW 2754, Australia. TEL 61-2-45761495, FAX 61-2-45761196, anbrc@zeta.org.au, http://www.zeta.org.au/~anbrc/. Ed., R&P Anne Dollin. Adv. contact Paul Wagner. Circ: 500 (paid).

638.1 AUS ISSN 0004-8313
AUSTRALASIAN BEEKEEPER. Text in English. 1899. m. AUD 35, USD 38 domestic; USD 36 foreign (effective 2000). adv. bk.rev. charts; illus.; mkt.; stat. index. **Document type:** *Trade.*
Indexed: ApicAb, ForAb, HortAb.
Published by: Pender Beekeeping Supplies Pty. Ltd., Private Mail Bag 19, Maitland, NSW 2320, Australia. TEL 61-49-327244, FAX 61-49-327621. Ed. R Gulliford. R&P Allen Clarke. Adv. contact Joyce Gardner. Circ: 2,000 (paid).

600 AUS ISSN 1032-2469
AUSTRALIA. BUREAU OF RURAL RESOURCES. PROCEEDINGS. Text in English. 1988. q. **Document type:** *Monographic series, Academic/Scholarly.*
Indexed: ASFA.
Published by: Department of Agriculture, Fisheries, and Forestry, Bureau of Rural Sciences, Edmund Barton Building, Broughton Street, Barton, GPO Box 858, Canberra, ACT 2601, Australia. TEL 61-2-6272-4282, FAX 61-2-6272-4747, http://www.affa.gov.au.

630 639.2 AUS
AUSTRALIA. BUREAU OF RURAL SCIENCES. REPORT. Text in English. irreg.
Formerly: Australia. Bureau of Resource Sciences. Report
Published by: Department of Agriculture, Fisheries, and Forestry, Bureau of Rural Sciences, Edmund Barton Building, Broughton Street, Barton, GPO Box 858, Canberra, ACT 2601, Australia. http://www.affa.gov.au. **Subscr. to:** Publications Sales, PO Box 6103, West Footscray, VIC 3012, Australia. TEL 1-800-020157, FAX 61-3-83798201, sales@brs.gov.au, http://www.affashop.gov.au.

AUSTRALIA. BUREAU OF STATISTICS. AGRICULTURAL INDUSTRIES, FINANCIAL STATISTICS, AUSTRALIA, PRELIMINARY. see *AGRICULTURE—Abstracting, Bibliographies, Statistics*

AUSTRALIA. BUREAU OF STATISTICS. AGRICULTURE, AUSTRALIA. see *AGRICULTURE—Abstracting, Bibliographies, Statistics*

AUSTRALIA. BUREAU OF STATISTICS. AUSTRALIAN FARMING IN BRIEF. see *AGRICULTURE—Abstracting, Bibliographies, Statistics*

AUSTRALIA. BUREAU OF STATISTICS. DIRECTORY OF AGRICULTURAL AND RURAL STATISTICS. see *AGRICULTURE—Abstracting, Bibliographies, Statistics*

AUSTRALIA. BUREAU OF STATISTICS. PRINCIPAL AGRICULTURAL COMMODITIES, AUSTRALIA, PRELIMINARY. see *AGRICULTURE—Abstracting, Bibliographies, Statistics*

630 AUS
AUSTRALIAN & NEW ZEALAND OLIVEGROWER & PROCESSOR/AUSTRALIAN AND NEW ZEALAND OLIVEGROWER AND PROCESSOR. Text in English. 1994. bi-m. AUD 35 domestic; AUD 53.50 in New Zealand; AUD 59.50 elsewhere (effective 2004). **Document type:** *Magazine, Trade.*
Former titles: Australian Olivegrower & Processor (1448-5486); Which incorporated: Australian Olive Industry Journal; (until 2003): Australian Olive Grower (1448-5478); Which incorporated (2002-200?): Australian Smallfarmer (1447-591X); (until 1997): Olives Australia (1448-546X)
Published by: Ryan Publications Pty. Ltd., PO Box 3013, Norwood, SA 5067, Australia. admin@olivegrower.com.au, http://www.olivegrower.com.au/.

AUSTRALIAN AND NEW ZEALAND WINE INDUSTRY JOURNAL. see *BEVERAGES*

638.1 AUS ISSN 0045-0294
AUSTRALIAN BEE JOURNAL. Text in English. 1918. m. AUD 30. **Document type:** *Trade.*
Indexed: ApicAb, FPA, ForAb.
Published by: Victorian Apiarist's Association, c/o Mrs. Judy Graves, 23 McBride Rd, Upper Beaconsfield, VIC 3808, Australia.

630 AUS ISSN 0810-8315
AUSTRALIAN CENTRE FOR INTERNATIONAL AGRICULTURAL RESEARCH. ANNUAL REPORT. Text in English. 1982. a.
—BLDSC (1112.302700), CISTI.
Published by: Australian Centre for International Agricultural Research, PO Box 1571, Canberra, ACT 2601, Australia. TEL 61-2-62170500, FAX 61-2-62170501, http://www.aciar.gov.au.

630 AUS ISSN 1036-6474
CODEN: PCNSEW
AUSTRALIAN FARM JOURNAL. Text in English. 1991. m. AUD 83.40; AUD 6.95 newsstand/cover (effective 2005). adv. bk.rev. illus. Index. back issues avail. **Document type:** *Magazine, Trade.* **Description:** Covers the marketing and sustainability issues associated with broad acre primary production including grains, wool, sheep meat, beef cattle, and plantation timber, as well as reviewing emerging alternative industries.
Formed by the merger of (1980-1991): Farm (0725-3338); (1977-1991): Australian Rural Times (1034-5809); Which was formerly (until 1989): National Farmer (0155-2201)
—CISTI.
Published by: Rural Press Ltd. (Subsidiary of: Agricultural Publishers Pty. Ltd.), 10 Sydenham St., PO Box 254, Moonee Ponds, VIC 3039, Australia. TEL 61-3-92870900, FAX 61-3-93705622, http://afj.farmonline.com.au/home.asp, http://www.ruralpress.com/. Ed. Patrick Francis. Adv. contact Donna Clarke. page USD 2,843.10. Circ: 6,495.

630 AUS ISSN 0004-9409
S17 CODEN: AJAEA9
➤ **AUSTRALIAN JOURNAL OF AGRICULTURAL RESEARCH.** Text in English. 1950. m. AUD 200 combined subscription in Australia & New Zealand to individuals for print & online eds.; USD 200 combined subscription elsewhere to individuals for print & online eds.; AUD 1,190 combined subscription in Australia & New Zealand to institutions for print & online eds.; USD 1,115 combined subscription elsewhere to institutions for print & online eds. (effective 2004). adv. bibl.; charts; illus. Index. back issues avail. **Document type:** *Journal, Academic/Scholarly.* **Description:** Covers the physical, chemical, or biological aspects of an agricultural system.
Related titles: Microform ed.: (from PQC); Online - full text ed.: AUD 180 in Australia & New Zealand to individuals; USD 160 elsewhere to individuals; AUD 1,070 in Australia & New Zealand to institutions; USD 990 elsewhere to institutions (effective 2004) (from EBSCO Publishing, O C L C Online Computer Library Center, Inc., Swets Information Services).
Indexed: AEA, ASCA, ASFA, AgBio, Agr, AgrForAb, AnBrAb, AnalAb, ApicAb, B&AI, BIOBASE, BIOSIS Prev, BibAg, BioCN&I, BioDAb, BiolAb, CBTA, CIN, CPA, CTFA, Cadscan, ChemAb, ChemTitl, CurCont, DBA, DSA, EIA, EPB, ESPM, EnerInd, EngInd, EnvAb, EnvEAb, EnvInd, ExcerpMed, FCA, FS&TA, ForAb, GEOBASE, HelmAb, HerbAb, HortAb, I&DA, IABS, INIS AtomInd, ISR, IndVet, LeadAb, M&GPA, M&TEA, MaizeAb, NemAb, NutrAb, OrnHort, PBA, PGegResA, PGrRegA, PHN&I, PN&I, PlantSci, PollutAb, PotatoAb, PoultAb, ProtozoAb, RA&MP, RDA, RM&VM, RPP, RefZh, RevApplEntom, RiceAb, S&F, S&MA, SCI, SIA, SWRA, SeedAb, SoyAb, TTI, TriticAb, VITIS, VetBull, WAE&RSA, WTA, WeedAb, Zincscan.
—BLDSC (1802.000000), CASDDS, CIS, CISTI, Ei, IDS, IE, Infotrieve, ingenta, Linda Hall. **CCC.**
Published by: (C S I R O Australia), C S I R O Publishing, 150 Oxford St, PO Box 1139, Collingwood, VIC 3066, Australia. TEL 61-3-96627628, FAX 61-3-96627611, publishing@csiro.au, http://www.publish.csiro.au/journals/ajar/. Circ: 850.

344.94043 AUS
AUSTRALIAN QUARANTINE AND INSPECTION SERVICE. BULLETIN. Text in English. 1989. m. **Document type:** *Bulletin, Government.* **Description:** Summarizes information and news from AQIS for individuals and organizations involved in quarantine and inspection matters.
Formerly (until 2002): A Q I S Bulletin (1033-9280)
Indexed: IndVet, RPP, RevApplEntom.
—CISTI.
Published by: Australian Quarantine and Inspection Service, Edmund Barton Bldg, Broughton St, Barton, GPO Box 858, Canberra, ACT 2601, Australia. TEL 61-2-6272-5156, FAX 61-2-6272-4494, carson.creagh@agis.gov.au, http://www.affa.gov.au/content/output.cfm?ObjectID=D2C48F86-BA1A-11A1-A2200060A1B00050. Ed., R&P Carson Creagh. Circ: 3,000.

630 AUS ISSN 0819-2995
AUSTRALIAN RURAL SCIENCE ANNUAL; a forum for rural thought. Text in English. 1963. a. AUD 2.50. adv. bk.rev. **Description:** Informs the public and primary producers of scientific research and development in the rural sector of Australia.
Formerly (until 1987): Chiasma (0084-8735)
Published by: (University of New England, Rural Science Undergraduates' Society), Percival Publishing Co. Pty. Ltd., 862-870 Elizabeth St, Waterloo Dc, NSW 2017, Australia. Ed. Deborah Streeter. Circ: 1,500.

630 AUT
AUSTRIA. BUNDESMINISTERIUM FUER LAND- UND FORSTWIRTSCHAFT. JAHRESBERICHT. Text in German. a. free. **Document type:** *Government.*
Media: Online - full content.
Published by: Bundesministerium fuer Land- und Forstwirtschaft, Umwelt und Wasserwirtschaft, Stubenring 1, Vienna, 1012, Austria. TEL 43-1-711006762, FAX 43-1-711005198, manfred.dietrich@bmlf.gv.at, http://www.bmlf.gv.at. Ed. Manfred Dietrich. Circ: 1,600.

630 FRA ISSN 0988-9256
AUVERGNE AGRICOLE. Text in French. w.
Address: 10-12 Au Marx Dormof, B.P. 479, Clermont-Ferrand, 63013, France. TEL 73-43-44-30, FAX 73-34-02-40. Ed. M Francois Charles. Circ: 10,500.

630 MEX ISSN 0188-7890
AVANCES EN INVESTIGACION AGROPECUARIA. Text in English, French, Spanish; Summaries in English. 1992. 3/yr. (Spanish 2/yr.; English 1/yr.). MXP 30, USD 40 (effective 1994). charts; stat. index. back issues avail. **Document type:** *Academic/Scholarly.* **Description:** Includes a wide spectrum of topics related to agriculture in the tropics. Considers economics, technology, computer technology, or anything which affects agriculture or animal production in the tropics.
Indexed: AgBio, AnBrAb, HelmAb, IndVet, NutrAb, PN&I, PoultAb, ProtozoAb.
Published by: University of Colima, Coordinacion General de Investigacion Cientifica, Justo Sierra 592, Colima, 28010, Mexico. TEL 331-4-11-33, FAX 331-2-75-81, hummel@volcan.ucol.mx. Ed. Janet Hummel. Circ: 250.
Subscr. to: Apdo. Postal 22, Colima 28045, Mexico.

630 FRA
AVENIR AGRICOLE DE LA MAYENNE✶. Text in French. w.
Published by: Avenir Agricole de la, 3 rue Saint-Andre, BP 0325, Laval, Cedex 53003, France. TEL 43-49-56-00, FAX 43-49-56-19. Ed. D Legoy. Circ: 13,000.

630 FRA ISSN 0998-0210
AVENIR AGRICOLE DE L'ARDECHE. Text in French. 1885. w.
Address: 4 av. de l'Europe Unie, B.P. 139, Privas, Cedex 07000, France. TEL 75-64-60-62. Circ: 6,018.

630 FRA ISSN 1148-3121
AVENIR AGRICOLE ET RURAL DE LA HAUTE MARNE. Text in French. w. **Document type:** *Newspaper.*
Former titles (until 1990): Avenir Paysan et Rural de la Haute Marne (0154-7461); (until 1977): Avenir Paysan de la Haute Marne (0154-7453)
Published by: Maison de l'Agriculture (Chaumont), 26 av. du 109 E Ri, Chaumont, 52000, France. TEL 25-32-19-91, FAX 25-31-40-54. Ed. Patrice Zehr. Circ: 2,600.

630 ITA ISSN 0005-2361
AVVENIRE AGRICOLO (PARMA). Text in Italian. 1892. m. free. adv. bk.rev. illus.
Indexed: ChemAb.
—BLDSC (1840.250000).
Published by: Consorzio Agrario Provinciale, Viale Gramsci, 26-C, Parma, PR 43100, Italy. TEL 0521-4981, TELEX 0521-550097. Ed. Domenico Fini. Circ: 1,300.

630 EGY ISSN 1110-1563
AL AZHAR JOURNAL OF AGRICULTURAL RESEARCH/ MAGALLAR AL-AZHAR LIL-BEHUTH AL-ZIRA'IYYAT. Text in English. 1984. s-a. **Document type:** *Journal, Academic/Scholarly.*
Published by: Al-Azhar University, Faculty of Agriculture, Al-Nasr Rd, Nasr City, Cairo, Egypt. TEL 20-2-4024132, FAX 20-2-4024190, http://derp.sti.sci.eg/data/0252.htm. Ed. Dr. Maher Amin Wali.

630 AUT ISSN 1026-6275
B A L VEROEFFENTLICHUNGEN. Text in German. 1949. irreg., latest vol.36, 2002. price varies. adv. **Document type:** *Monographic series, Government.*
Formerly (until 1989): Bundesanstalt fuer Alpenlaendische Landwirtschaft. Veroeffentlichungen (1010-6146)
Indexed: AnBrAb, FCA, HerbAb, HortAb, IndVet, MaizeAb, NutrAb, PN&I, PotatoAb, S&F, VetBull, WAE&RSA.
—CISTI.
Published by: Bundesanstalt fuer Alpenlaendische Landwirtschaft Gumpenstein, Irdning, St 8952, Austria. TEL 43-3682-22451, FAX 43-3682-2461488, office@bal.bmlf.gv.at, http://www.bal.bmlf.gv.at. Ed., R&P Kurt Chytil TEL 43-3682-22451. Adv. contact Eva Rainer. Circ: 500.

B & B AGRAR; die Zeitschrift fuer Bildung und Beratung. (Bildung und Beratung) see *NUTRITION AND DIETETICS*

630 AUS
BACK PADDOCK. Text in English. 1995. q. AUD 230. **Document type:** *Newsletter.* **Description:** Presents agri-political information regarding Australian agriculture and horticulture.
Published by: South Australian Farmers' Federation, Halifax St, PO Box 6014, Adelaide, SA 5000, Australia. TEL 8-82325555, FAX 8-82321331, adeegan@saff.com.au. Ed. Alexia Deegan. Circ: 6,000.

630 DEU ISSN 0936-4838
BADISCHE BAUERN ZEITUNG. Text in German. 1948. w. EUR 79.80 domestic; EUR 113.40 foreign; EUR 1.55 newsstand/cover (effective 2004). adv. **Document type:** *Newspaper, Trade.*
Related titles: Online - full text ed.
Published by: Badischer Landwirtschafts Verlag GmbH, Friedrichstr 43, Freiburg Im Breisgau, 79098, Germany. TEL 49-761-271330, FAX 49-761-2021887, vertrieb@blv-freiburg.de, http://www.badische-bauern-zeitung.de. Ed. Richard Bruskowski. Adv. contact Karin Wirbals-Langner. B&W page EUR 2,684, color page EUR 4,034. Circ: 16,906 (paid).

630 IND
BALIRAJA; magazine devoted to modern commercial agriculture. Text in Marathi. 1970. m. INR 250 (effective 2001). adv. bk.rev. abstr.; illus.; maps. 108 p./no. 2 cols./p.; back issues avail. **Document type:** *Magazine, Consumer.* **Description:** Devoted to the progress of modern agriculture and rural marketing in Maharashtra.
Published by: P.B. Bhosale Ed. & Pub., 1384 Shukrawar Peth, Nawa Vishnu Chowk, Pune, Maharashtra 411 002, India. TEL 91-20-4485803, FAX 91-020-4485803, balirajamag@usa.net, agrindia@pn2.vsnl.net, http://www.baliraja.com. Ed., Pub. P B Bhosale. R&P, Adv. contact N P Bhosale. B&W page INR 8,000, color page INR 16,000; trim 170 x 230.

BANGLADESH AGRICULTURAL SCIENCES ABSTRACTS. see *AGRICULTURE—Abstracting, Bibliographies, Statistics*

630 BGD
➤ **BANGLADESH INSTITUTE OF NUCLEAR AGRICULTURE. ANNUAL REPORT.** Text in English. 1982. a. BDT 100 per issue domestic; USD 15 per issue foreign (effective 2001). **Document type:** *Academic/Scholarly.* **Description:** Covers research work on nuclear applications in agriculture.
Published by: Bangladesh Institute of Nuclear Agriculture, PO Box 4, Mymensingh, 2200, Bangladesh. TEL 880-91-54401, FAX 880-91-54091, bina@bdmail.net. Ed. M A Hamid. Circ: 100.

630 BGD ISSN 0379-4296
S322.B26 CODEN: BJAGAQ
BANGLADESH JOURNAL OF AGRICULTURAL SCIENCES. Text in English. 1974. s-a. BDT 60 to individuals; BDT 200 to institutions.
Indexed: BiolAb, ChemAb, FCA, FS&TA, INIS AtomInd, ZooRec.
—CASDDS, Linda Hall.
Published by: Bangladesh Agricultural University Old Boys' Association, c/o Dept. of Soil Science, Agricultural University, Mymensingh, Bangladesh. Ed. M Eaqub. Circ: 300.
Co-sponsor: Bangladesh Agricultural University.

BANGLADESH JOURNAL OF BIOLOGICAL SCIENCES. see *BIOLOGY*

630.715 BGD ISSN 1011-3916
S544.5.B3
BANGLADESH JOURNAL OF EXTENSION EDUCATION. Text in English. 1986. s-a.
Published by: Bangladesh Agricultural University, Department of Agricultural Extension and Teachers' Training, Mymesingh, 2202, Bangladesh.

630 BGD ISSN 0258-7130
➤ **BANGLADESH JOURNAL OF NUCLEAR AGRICULTURE.** Text in English. 1985. a. BDT 100 domestic; USD 15 foreign (effective 2003). **Document type:** *Academic/Scholarly.* **Description:** Covers research papers on nuclear applications in agriculture.
Published by: Bangladesh Institute of Nuclear Agriculture, PO Box 4, Mymensingh, 2200, Bangladesh. TEL 880-91-54401, 880-91-54402, 880-91-55032, 880-91-55059, 880-91-54047, FAX 880-91-54091, bina@bdmail.net. Ed. M A Hamid. Circ: 400.

633.72 BGD
BANGLADESH TEA RESEARCH INSTITUTE. ANNUAL REPORT✶. Text in English. 1973. irreg. BDT 20.
Published by: Bangladesh Tea Research Institute (Subsidiary of: Interface Technologies Corporation), Srimangal, Sylhet, Bangladesh.

BANKRUPTCY PRACTICE SERIES. CHAPTER 12: FARM REORGANIZATIONS. see *LAW*

BAUEN FUER DIE LANDWIRTSCHAFT. see *BUILDING AND CONSTRUCTION*

630 AUT ISSN 0005-6561
DER BAUER; Mitteilungsblatt der Oberoesterreichischen Landwirtschaftskammer. Text in German. 1948. w. EUR 25 (effective 2005). adv. bk.rev. **Document type:** *Newspaper, Trade.*
Published by: Landwirtschaftskammer fuer Oberoesterreich, Auf der Gugl 3, Linz, O 4021, Austria. TEL 43-732-69021363, FAX 43-732-69021707, ref-presse@lk-ooe.at, http://www.lk-ooe.at. Ed. Heinz Krichbaumer. Adv. contact Michael Schwabegger. page EUR 3,350; trim 196 x 260. Circ: 42,000 (paid and controlled).

630 BEL
DER BAUER; Wochenschrift fuer den praktischen Landwirt und die Familie auf dem Land. Text in German. 1923. w. adv. bk.rev.
Published by: Belgische Boerenbond, Minderbroedersstraat 8, Leuven, 3000, Belgium. TEL 32-87-552446, FAX 32-87-742311. Ed. Frans Sterckx. Circ: 2,300.

630 DEU ISSN 0947-9767
BAUERNBLATT. Text in German. 1850. w. EUR 71 domestic; EUR 115 foreign; EUR 1.30 newsstand/cover (effective 2004). adv. **Document type:** *Newspaper, Trade.*
Former titles (until 1993): Bauernblatt fuer Schleswig-Holstein und Mecklenburg-Vorpommern (0947-9759); (until 1992): Bauernblatt fuer Schleswig-Holstein (0936-4668)
Published by: Bauernband Schleswig-Holstein, Jungfernsteig 25, Rendsburg, 24768, Germany. TEL 49-4331-12770, redaktion@bauernblattsh.de, bvsh@bauernverbandsh.de, http://www.bauernblattsh.de. Ed. Rainer Mohrmann. Adv. contact Ute Moellhof. B&W page EUR 2,851.56, color page EUR 4,155.56; trim 198 x 276. Circ: 26,593 (paid and controlled).

630 CHE
BAUERNBLATT DER NORDWESTSCHWEIZ. Text in German. w.
Address: Obere Steingrubenstr 55, Postfach 63, Solothurn, 4504, Switzerland. TEL 065-233657, FAX 065-235893. Ed. Urs Nussbaumer. Circ: 4,007.

A

059 DEU ISSN 0945-3822
BAUERNKALENDER. Text in German. 1992. a. adv. **Document type:** *Journal, Trade.*
Formed by the merger of (1951-1992): Der Landwirt. Ausgabe Nordbaden (0341-8170); (1951-1992): Der Landwirt. Ausgabe Wuerttemberg-Hohenzollern (0945-3814); (1951-1992): Der Landwirt. Ausgabe Suedbaden (0945-3806); (1944-1992): Schwaebischer Bauernkalender (0945-3792)
Published by: Verlag Eugen Ulmer GmbH, Wollgrasweg 41, Stuttgart, 70599, Germany. TEL 49-711-4507-0, FAX 49-711-4507-120, info@ulmer.de, http://www.ulmer.de. adv.: B&W page EUR 2,952, color page EUR 4,077. Circ: 76,000 (controlled).

630 CHE
BAUERNSPIEGEL. Text in German. m.
Address: Postfach, Muenchenbuchsee, 3053, Switzerland. TEL 031-8693504. Ed. H P Rueb. Circ: 5,000.

630 DEU ISSN 0941-2239
BAUERNZEITUNG. Text in German. 1960. w. EUR 74 (effective 2004). adv. **Document type:** *Newspaper, Trade.*
Formerly: Neue Deutsche Bauernzeitung
Related titles: Online - full text ed.
Indexed: RASB.
Published by: Deutscher Bauernverlag GmbH, Wilhelmsaue 37, Berlin, 10713, Germany. TEL 49-30-464060, FAX 49-30-46406205, info@bauernverlag.de, http://www.bauernzeitung.de, http://www.bauernverlag.de. adv.: B&W page EUR 4,950, color page EUR 7,864.80; trim 202 x 310. Circ: 31,377 (paid and controlled).

631 CHE ISSN 1420-1410
BAUERNZEITUNG. Text in German. 1994. w. CHF 72 (effective 2002). adv. **Document type:** *Newspaper, Trade.*
Formed by the merger of (1912-1994): Zentralblatt Land- und Milchwirtschaft (1420-231X); Which was formerly (until 1968): Schweizerisches Zentralblatt der Milchproduzenten (1420-2336); (until 1959): Schweizerisches Zentralblatt fuer Milchwirtschaft (1420-2328); (1975-1994): Brugg-Informationen (1420-1399); Which was formed by the merger of (1901-1975): Schweizerische Bauernzeitung (1420-1313); (1911-1975): Schweizerische Landwirtschaftliche Marktzeitung (1420-1453)
Related titles: Online - full text ed.
Published by: Schweizer Agrarmedien GmbH, Thunstr. 78, Bern 16, 3000, Switzerland. TEL 41-31-9583333, FAX 41-31-9583334, verlag@bauernzeitung.ch, verlag@diegruene.ch, http://www.bauernzeitung.ch, http://www.diegruene.ch. adv.: page CHF 7,095; 290 x 430.

631 CHE ISSN 1420-7990
BAUERNZEITUNG NORDWESTSCHWEIZ, BERN UND FREIBURG. Text in German. 1996. w. CHF 87 (effective 2002). adv. **Document type:** *Newspaper, Trade.*
Formed by the merger of (1995-1996): BauernZeitung Bern und Freiburg (1420-794X); (1910-1996): Bauernblatt der Nordwestschweiz (1420-7982)
Published by: Schweizer Agrarmedien GmbH, Thunstr. 78, Bern 16, 3000, Switzerland. TEL 41-31-9583333, FAX 41-31-9583334, redaktion.be@bauernzeitung.ch, verlag@diegruene.ch, http://www.bauernzeitung.ch/nw/default.htm, http://www.diegruene.ch. Ed. Alois Heinzer.

630 CHE ISSN 1422-5271
BAUERNZEITUNG ZENTRALSCHWEIZ AARGAU. Text in German. 1994. w. CHF 87 (effective 2002). **Document type:** *Newspaper, Trade.*
Formerly (until 1996): Bauernzeitung Zentralschweiz (1420-2190); Which was formed by the merger of (186?-1994): Landwirt (1420-1615); (1867-1994): Innerschweizer Bauernzeitung (1420-1623); Which was formerly (until 1935): Urschweizer Bauernzeitung (1420-245X)
Published by: Luzerner Bauernverband, Schellenrain 5, Postfach, Sursee, 6210, Switzerland. TEL 41-41-9258040, FAX 41-41-9217337, bauernzeitung.sursee@luzernerbauern.ch, http://www.bauernzeitung.ch/za/default.htm. Ed. Josef Scherer-Sigrist TEL 41-41-9258029. Circ: 12,000.

630 NZL
BAY OF PLENTY FARMER. Text in English. 1982. m. adv. back issues avail. **Description:** Covers national and regional issues and events in agriculture and horticulture.
Published by: Hauraki Publishers Ltd., P.O. Box 363, Thames, New Zealand. Ed. Stephen D Hill. Circ: 16,000.

638.1 DEU ISSN 0724-8857
BAYERISCHES BIENEN-BLATT; Fachblatt fuer Bienenzucht. Text in German. 1973. q. membership. adv. bk.rev. **Document type:** *Corporate.*
Published by: Verband Bayerischer Bienenzuechter e.V., Spitzwegstr 6, Muehldorf, 84453, Germany. TEL 08631-5363, FAX 08631-5392. Ed. Eduard Wimmer. Circ: 5,700.

053.1 DEU ISSN 0005-7169
BAYERISCHES LANDWIRTSCHAFTLICHES WOCHENBLATT. Text in German. 1810. w. looseleaf. EUR 99.80 domestic; EUR 122 foreign; EUR 2.40 newsstand/cover (effective 2004). adv. bk.rev. illus.; mkt. **Document type:** *Newspaper, Trade.*
Related titles: Online - full text ed.
—CCC.
Published by: (Bayerischer Bauernverband), Deutscher Landwirtschaftsverlag GmbH, Lothstr 29, Munich, 80797, Germany. TEL 49-89-127051, FAX 49-89-12705335, blw@dlv.de, dlv.muenchen@dlv.de, http://www.wochenblatt-dlv.de, http://www.dlv.de. Ed. Johannes Urban. Adv. contact Henning Stemmler. B&W page EUR 9,424, color page EUR 15,475; trim 212 x 310. Circ: 106,698 (paid).

630 DEU ISSN 0341-2776
BAYRISCHER BAUERNKALENDER. Text in German. 1946. a. EUR 8.61 per issue (effective 2004). adv. **Document type:** *Journal, Trade.*
Published by: Deutscher Landwirtschaftsverlag GmbH, Lothstr 29, Munich, 80797, Germany. TEL 49-89-127051, FAX 49-89-12705335, dlv.muenchen@dlv.de, http://www.dlv.de. adv.: B&W page EUR 3,643, color page EUR 5,566. Circ: 68,000 (controlled).

630 COL ISSN 0120-2243
SB327
BEAN PROGRAM ANNUAL REPORT. Cover title: Beans. Text in Spanish. 1969. a. bk.rev. **Document type:** *Yearbook, Corporate.* **Description:** Detailed progress report primarily for the information of research collaborators in the bean network.
Related titles: ◆ English ed.: Agroforestry Today. ISSN 1013-9591; Spanish ed.: Informe Anual del Programa de Frijol. ISSN 0120-2235; Ed.: Agroforesterie Aujourd'hui. ISSN 1015-3225.
Published by: (Bean Program), Centro Internacional de Agricultura Tropical/International Center for Tropical Agriculture, Publications Unit, Apartado Aereo 6713, Cali, VALLE, Colombia. TEL 57-2-4450000, FAX 57-2-4450073, TELEX 05769 CIAT CO, ciat-comunicaciones@cgiar.org, http://www.ciat.cgiar.org/. Ed. Cesar Cardona.

630 GBR
BEDFORDSHIRE AND HUNTINGDONSHIRE FARMER. Text in English. m. membership. adv. back issues avail.
Contact: National Farmers Union, Agriculture House, 164 Shaftesbury Ave, London, WC2H 8HL, United Kingdom. TEL 44-20-73317200, FAX 44-20-73317401, NFU@nfuonline.com, http://www.nfu.org.uk/. Ed. R Payne. Circ: 2,200.

630 NOR ISSN 0806-1866
BEDRE GARDSDRIFT. Text in Norwegian. 1981. 10/yr. NOK 399 domestic; NOK 449 elsewhere (effective 2005). adv. **Document type:** *Magazine, Trade.*
Former titles (until 1991): K. K. Heje (0801-8766); (until 1990): K. K. Heje Driftsteknikk (0333-4821)
Related titles: Online - full text ed.
Published by: Vanebo Fagpresse AS, PO Box 130, Kirkenaer, 2260, Norway. TEL 47-62-941000, FAX 47-62-941010, hans@vanebo.no, firmapost@vanebo.no, http://www.gardsdrift.no, http://www.vanebo.no. Ed. Hans Degerdal TEL 47-62-941013. Adv. contact Roy Utgaard TEL 47-62-946995. B&W page NOK 8,900, color page NOK 13,400; 190 x 265.

638.1 GBR ISSN 0005-7703
BEE CRAFT. Text in English. 1919. m. GBP 18 in British Isles; GBP 24 in Europe; USD 51 in United States; AUD 90 in Australia; GBP 36 rest of world (effective 2004). adv. bk.rev. illus. index. 36 p./no. 2 cols./p.; back issues avail. **Document type:** *Magazine, Consumer.* **Description:** Contains beginners' notes, practical suggestions, scientific works, seasonal checks, accounts of honey collection in different areas, a calendar of events, and readers' letters.
Indexed: ApicAb, RevApplEntom.
Published by: (British Bee-Keepers Association), Bee Craft Ltd., The Company Secretary Alison Mouser, 79 Strathcona Ave, Bookham, Leatherhead, Surrey, KT23 4HR, United Kingdom. TEL 44-1372-451891, secretary@hotmail.com, secretary@hotlmail.com, http://www.bee-craft.com. Ed. Mrs. Claire Waring. Pub., R&P Miss Alison Mouser. Adv. contact Mrs. Pam Todd TEL 44-1904-707408. Circ: 4,500 (paid).

638.1 USA ISSN 1071-3190
SF521
BEE CULTURE; the magazine of American beekeeping. Text in English. 1872. m. USD 21.50 domestic; USD 36.50 foreign (effective 2005). adv. bk.rev. charts; illus.; stat. index. back issues avail.; reprint service avail. from PQC. **Document type:** *Magazine, Trade.* **Description:** Provides beekeeping information for the beginner, sideliner and commercial beekeeper.
Formerly (until 1992): Gleanings in Bee Culture (0017-114X)
Related titles: Microform ed.: (from PQC); Online - full text ed.: (from Northern Light Technology, Inc., ProQuest Information & Learning).
Indexed: ABIn, ApicAb, B&AI, BiolAb, ChemAb, F&GI, RevApplEntom.
—CISTI, Linda Hall.
Published by: A.I. Root Co., PO Box 706, Medina, OH 44258-0706. TEL 330-725-6677, 800-289-7668, FAX 330-725-5624, beeculture@airoot.com, http://www.beeculture.com, http://www.airoot.com. Ed., R&P Kim Flottum TEL 330-725-6677. Pub. John Root. adv.: page USD 812. Circ: 12,500 (paid).

638.1 GBR ISSN 0005-772X
CODEN: BEWOAN
➤ **BEE WORLD**; the international link between beekeeping science and practice. Text in English. 1919. q. GBP 50 (effective 2004). adv. bk.rev. bibl.; charts; illus.; mkt. index., cum.index: 1919-1949. 2 cols./p.; back issues avail. **Document type:** *Journal, Academic/Scholarly.* **Description:** Contains topical articles and reviews for beekeepers and scientists-truly international scope.
Related titles: Online - full text ed.: (from Gale Group).
Indexed: ASCA, AgBio, Agr, AgrForAb, ApicAb, B&AI, BibAg, BioCN&I, BiolAb, CPA, ChemAb, CurCont, EntAb, F&GI, FCA, FPA, ForAb, HelmAb, HerbAb, HortAb, ISR, IndVet, MaizeAb, NutrAb, OrnHort, PBA, PGegResA, PHN&I, PoultAb, ProtozoAb, RA&MP, RDA, RRTA, RefZh, RevApplEntom, S&F, SCI, SIA, SoyAb, VetBull, WAE&RSA, WeedAb, ZooRec.
—BLDSC (1876.000000), CISTI, IDS, IE, Infotrieve, ingenta, Linda Hall. **CCC.**
Published by: International Bee Research Association, 18 North Rd, Cardiff, Wales CF10 3DT, United Kingdom. TEL 44-2920-372409, FAX 44-2920-665522, mail@ibra.org.uk, http://www.ibra.org.uk. Ed. Dr. Pamela A Munn. adv.: page GBP 145; trim 120 x 175. Circ: 1,200.

638.1 GBR ISSN 0005-7754
BEEKEEPING. Text in English. 1934. 10/yr. GBP 8.50 to non-members; GBP 11.50 foreign to non-members. adv. bk.rev. index. **Document type:** *Bulletin.* **Description:** Discusses bee culture.
Indexed: ApicAb.
Published by: Devon Beekeepers Association, c/o Brian Gant, Ed, Leat Orchard, Grange Rd, Buckfast, Devon TQ11 0EH, United Kingdom. TEL 44-1364-642233, FAX 44-1364-342233, 106213.3313@compuserve.com. R&P, Adv. contact Brian Gant. Circ: 1,000 (paid).

638.1 CAN ISSN 0838-0937
BEEKEEPING NOTES. Text in English. 3/yr. (plus irreg. updates). free. **Document type:** *Newsletter.*
Published by: Department of Agriculture and Marketing, Kentville Agricultural Centre, Kentville, NS B4N 1J5, Canada. TEL 902-679-6029, FAX 902-679-6062, drogers@gov.ns.ca. Ed. R E L Dick Rogers. Circ: 650.

638.1 ZWE
BEELINE. Text in English. 1963. q. ZWD 100 (effective 1993). bk.rev. **Document type:** *Newsletter, Academic/Scholarly.*
Indexed: SIA.
Published by: Zimbabwe Beekeepers Council, Highlands, PO Box HG 255, Harare, Zimbabwe. TEL 263-4-490625, FAX 263-4-490625, athol@msasa.samara.co.zw. Ed. Athol Desmond. adv.: B&W page ZWD 136. Circ: 400.

638.1 GBR ISSN 1477-6588
BEES FOR DEVELOPMENT JOURNAL; the journal for sustainable beekeeping. Text in English. 1983. q. GBP 20 in United Kingdom; USD 38 elsewhere (effective 2004 & 2005). adv. bk.rev.; video rev.; software rev. index. 16 p./no. 3 cols./p.; back issues avail. **Document type:** *Journal, Trade.* **Description:** Provides information on sustainable, low-technology beekeeping.
Former titles (until March 2002): Beekeeping & Development (1369-9555); (until 1990): Newsletter for Beekeepers in Tropical and Subtropical Countries (0256-4424)
Related titles: Online - full content ed.; French ed.: ISSN 1369-9415.
Indexed: RefZh.
Published by: Bees for Development, Troy, Monmouth, NP25 4AB, United Kingdom. TEL 44-1600-713648, FAX 44-1600-716167, info@beesfordevelopment.org, http://www.beesfordevelopment.org. Ed., R&P Nicola Bradbear. Adv. contact Helen Jackson. B&W page GBP 200, color page GBP 300. Circ: 5,000 (paid).

630 CAN
BEESCENE. Text in English. q. CND 20, USD 30 (effective 1997). adv. illus.; mkt.; stat.; tr.lit. back issues avail. **Document type:** *Trade.*
Published by: (British Columbia Honey Producers Association), BC Interior Agri Publications, RR#2, S-26, C-32, Chase, BC V0E 1M0, Canada. TEL 250-679-5362, FAX 250-679-5362, frankay@mail.ocis.net. Ed., Pub., Adv. contact Fran Kay. page CND 500; trim 10.75 x 8.25. Circ: 850 (paid).

638.1 USA ISSN 1063-939X
BEESCIENCE. Text in English. 1990. 4/yr. USD 30. **Document type:** *Academic/Scholarly.*
—BLDSC (1875.650000).
Published by: Wicwas Press. L.L.C., 175 Alden Ave., New Haven, CT 06515-2109. TEL 203-250-7575, FAX 203-250-7575. Ed. Lawrence J Connor.

630 DEU ISSN 0522-604X
BEHOERDEN UND ORGANISATIONEN DER LAND- FORST- UND ERNAEHRUNGSWIRTSCHAFT. Text in German. 195?. a. EUR 132.50 (effective 2003). adv. **Document type:** *Directory, Trade.*
Published by: B. Behr's Verlag GmbH & Co. KG, Averhoffstr. 10, Hamburg, 22085, Germany. TEL 49-40-2270080, FAX 49-40-2201091, info@behrs.de, http://www.behrs.de. Adv. contact Frau Haertel.

630 CHN ISSN 1000-6966
BEIJING NONGYE/BEIJING AGRICULTURE. Text in Chinese. m.
Related titles: Online - full text ed.: (from East View Information Services).
Published by: Beijing Shi Nongye Ju, 19 Beisanhuan Donglu, Dewai, Beijing, 100029, China. TEL 2012244. Ed. Li Hushan.

630 CHN ISSN 1001-8344
BEIJING NONGYE KEXUE/BEIJING AGRICULTURAL SCIENCE. Text in Chinese. 1983. bi-m. CNY 3.50 per issue (effective 2003).
Related titles: Online - full text ed.: (from East View Information Services).
Indexed: AgBio, BioCN&I, CPA, FCA, ForAb, HortAb, I&DA, MaizeAb, NutrAb, OrnHort, PBA, PGegResA, PGrRegA, PHN&I, RPP, RevApplEntom, RiceAb, S&F, SIA, SeedAb, SoyAb, TriticAb, WAE&RSA.
—BLDSC (1878.325400).
Published by: Beijing Shi Nonglin Kexueyuan, Nongye Keji Qingbaosuo/Beijing Academy of Agriculture and Forestry Sciences, Institute of Agricultural Science and Technology Information, Haidian-qu Banjing, Beijing, 100089, China. TEL 86-10-88444803, FAX 86-10-88444805, nkybjs@sina.com.

630 BLZ
BELIZE. DEPARTMENT OF AGRICULTURE. ANNUAL REPORT AND SUMMARY OF STATISTICS. Text in English. 1937. a. USD 2. stat.
Indexed: FCA, HerbAb, RPP.
Published by: Ministry of Natural Resources, Department of Agriculture, Belmopan, Belize. Circ: 350.

630 NLD ISSN 0160-3612
CODEN: BSARDN
➤ **BELTSVILLE SYMPOSIA IN AGRICULTURAL RESEARCH.** Text in Dutch. 1977. irreg., latest vol.14, 1991. price varies. back issues avail. **Document type:** *Proceedings, Academic/Scholarly.*
Indexed: BIOSIS Prev, BiolAb, CIN, ChemAb, ChemTitl.
—CASDDS, CISTI. **CCC.**
Published by: (U.S. Department of Agriculture USA, Beltsville Agricultural Research Center), Springer-Verlag Dordrecht (Subsidiary of: Springer Science+Business Media), Van Godewijckstraat 30, Dordrecht, 3311 GX, Netherlands. TEL 31-78-6576050, FAX 31-78-6576474, http://www.springeronline.com.

630.285 ISR
BEN-GURION UNIVERSITY OF THE NEGEV. INSTITUTES FOR APPLIED RESEARCH. SCIENTIFIC ACTIVITIES. Text in English. 1973. irreg., latest 1999. free. **Document type:** *Academic/Scholarly.* **Description:** Publishes short summaries of research projects conducted at the institutes, covering findings in chemistry and applications of chemical technology, and agriculture, applied biology and biotechnology.
Formerly: Ben-Gurion University of the Negev. Research and Development Authority. Applied Research Institute. Scientific Activities; Which superseded: Negev Institute for Arid Zone Research, Beer-Sheva, Israel. Report for Year (0077-6467)
Indexed: FCA, HerbAb, HortAb.
Published by: Ben Gurion University of the Negev, Institutes for Applied Research, P O Box 653, Beersheba, 84105, Israel. TEL 972-7-6461931, FAX 972-7-6472969, iar@bgumail.bgu.ac.il. Ed. Dorot Imber. Circ: 1,000.

630 USA
BENEFITS ADVISOR. Variant title: Michigan Farm News Rural Living. Text in English. 1923. q. membership (effective 2005). adv. **Document type:** *Magazine, Consumer.* **Description:** Covers the benefits of Michigan Farm Bureau membership.
Former titles (until 2001): Rural Living (Lansing) (0743-9962); (until 1981): Michigan Farm News (0026-2161)
Published by: Michigan Farm Bureau, PO Box 30960, Lansing, MI 48909. mifarmnews@aol.com, http://www.michiganfarmbureau.com. Ed. Paul Jackson. Pub. Dennis Rudat. Adv. contact Tim Rogers. B&W page USD 2,075, color page USD 2,675. Circ: 46,762.

630 DEU ISSN 0005-9080
HD1951 CODEN: BERLAN
➤ **BERICHTE UEBER LANDWIRTSCHAFT.** Summaries in English, French, German. 1907. 3/yr. EUR 277.20 domestic; EUR 283.20 foreign (effective 2005). bk.rev. charts; illus. index. back issues avail.; reprint service avail. from ISI. **Document type:** *Journal, Academic/Scholarly.*
Indexed: AEA, ASCA, ASFA, AbHyg, AgBio, AnBrAb, BIOSIS Prev, BiolAb, CPA, ChemAb, CurCont, DIP, DSA, ESPM, ExcerpMed, FCA, FS&TA, ForAb, HerbAb, HortAb, I&DA, IBR, IBZ, IndVet, KES, MaizeAb, NutrAb, OrnHort, PAIS, PBA, PGegResA, PHN&I, PN&I, PotatoAb, PoultAb, RA&MP, RDA, RPP, RRTA, RevApplEntom, RiceAb, S&F, SSCI, SoyAb, TriticAb, VITIS, VetBull, WAE&RSA, WeedAb.
—BLDSC (1936.500000), CASDDS, CISTI, IDS, IE, Infotrieve, ingenta. **CCC.**
Published by: (Germany. Bundesministerium fuer Ernaehrung, Landwirtschaft und Forsten), Landwirtschaftsverlag GmbH, Huelsebrockstr 2, Muenster, 48165, Germany. TEL 49-2501-27500, FAX 49-2501-27551, 511@bmvel.bund.de, zentrale@lv-h.de, http://www.verbraucherministerium.de/index-000B9B8146A2119391806521C0A8D816.html, http://www.lv-h.de. Eds. F Quadflieg, J Blasum. Circ: 1,620.

630 DEU ISSN 0301-2689
CODEN: BELWAQ
BERICHTE UEBER LANDWIRTSCHAFT. SONDERHEFTE. Text in German. irreg., latest vol.205, 1991. price varies. reprint service avail. from ISI. **Document type:** *Monographic series.*
Indexed: BIOSIS Prev, BiolAb, CurCont, ForAb, IBR, IBZ, ILD, RASB, S&F, WAE&RSA.
Published by: Landwirtschaftsverlag GmbH, Huelsebrockstr 2, Muenster, 48165, Germany. TEL 49-2501-801-0, FAX 49-2501-801204, zentrale@landwirtschaftsverlag.com, zentrale@lv-h.de, http://www.landwirtschaftsverlag.com. Circ: 1,600.

630 GBR ISSN 0954-9609
BERKS, BUCKS AND OXON FARMER. Text in English. 1962. m. adv.
Formerly (until 1988): Oxford and Berkshire Farmer; Incorporates: Oxford Farmer; Berkshire Farmer; Oxfordshire Farmer (0030-7688)
Published by: County Farmers Publications Ltd., 55 Goldington Rd, Bedford, Beds MK40 3LU, United Kingdom. TEL 44-1234-351401, FAX 44-1234-328615. Ed. T Bewley. Circ: 4,100.

630 639.2 BMU
BERMUDA. DEPARTMENT OF AGRICULTURE AND FISHERIES. MONTHLY BULLETIN. Text in English. 1914. m. free. back issues avail. **Document type:** *Bulletin, Trade.*
Former titles: Bermuda. Department of Agriculture, Fisheries and Parks. Monthly Bulletin; Farmers' Bulletin; Bermuda. Department of Agriculture. Agricultural Bulletin
Indexed: AgrForAb, ForAb, RPP, RevApplEntom, WildRev.
Published by: Department of Agriculture and Fisheries, PO Box HM 834, Hamilton, HMCX, Bermuda. TEL 441-236-4201, FAX 441-236-7582. Ed. Peggy Daniels. Circ: 1,274.

630 639.2 BMU
BERMUDA. DEPARTMENT OF AGRICULTURE AND FISHERIES. REPORT FOR THE YEAR. Text in English. 1905. a. back issues avail. **Document type:** *Government.*
Former titles: Bermuda. Department of Agriculture, Fisheries and Parks. Report for the Year; Bermuda. Department of Agriculture and Fisheries. Report for the Year
Indexed: BiolAb, FCA, HerbAb, HortAb, MaizeAb, RPP.
—BLDSC (7674.425000).
Published by: Department of Agriculture and Fisheries, PO Box HM 834, Hamilton, HMCX, Bermuda. TEL 441-236-4201, FAX 441-236-7582. Ed., R&P Peggy Daniels. Circ: 250.

630 CAN
BETTER FARMING; the new business magazine for Ontario agriculture. Text in English. 1999. 10/yr. CND 26 domestic; CND 58 in United States; CND 99 foreign (effective 2001). **Document type:** *Magazine, Trade.* **Description:** Covers news and issues of interest to the farmers of Ontario, Canada.
Published by: AgMedia Co-operative Inc., 21400 Service Rd, RR 2, Vankleek Hill, ON K0B 1R0, Canada. TEL 613-678-2232, FAX 613-678-5993, editor@betterfarming.com, admin@betterfarming.com, http://www.betterfarming.com/index.htm, http://www.betterfarming.com/contact.htm. Pub., Adv. contact Paul Nolan TEL 519-763-0444.

BHARTIYA KRISHI ANUSANDHAN PATRIKA; quarterly research journal of plant and animal sciences. see *BIOLOGY—Zoology*

638.1 DEU ISSN 0006-212X
DIE BIENE; ueberregionale Fachzeitschrift fuer Imker. Text in German. 1864. m. EUR 31.70 domestic; EUR 35.40 foreign; EUR 2.90 newsstand/cover (effective 2004). adv. bk.rev. charts; illus.; stat. **Document type:** *Magazine, Trade.*
Indexed: ApicAb, RevApplEntom.
—CCC.
Published by: (Deutscher Imkerbund e.V.), Deutscher Landwirtschaftsverlag GmbH, Kabelkamp 6, Hannover, 30179, Germany. TEL 49-511-678060, FAX 49-511-67806200, js-bienenredaktion@t-online.de, dlv.hannover@dlv.de, http://www.diebiene.de, http://www.dlv.de. Ed. Juergen Schwenkel. adv.: B&W page EUR 1,352, color page EUR 2,267; trim 185 x 260. Circ: 11,200 (paid and controlled).

638.1 DEU
DAS BIENENMUETTERCHEN. Text in German. 1955. 10/yr. adv. back issues avail. **Document type:** *Newspaper.* **Description:** News for beekeepers worldwide.
Published by: Internationaler Bund der Sklaenarbienenzuechter e.V., Pommernstr 3, Waldshut-Tiengen, 79761, Germany. TEL 41-41-628913641, FAX 41-41-628913641. Ed. Gerhard Fasolin. Circ: 2,000.

638.1 DEU
BIENENPFLEGE; die Zeitschrift fuer den Imker. Text in German. m. **Document type:** *Magazine, Trade.*
Indexed: RefZh.
Published by: Landesverband Wuerttembergischer Imker e.V., Olgastr. 23, Reichenbach, 73262, Germany. guidoeich@t-online.de, http://www.imker-landesverband-wuerttemberg.de/pflege/pflege.html. Ed. Guido Eich.

638.1 AUT ISSN 0006-2146
BIENENVATER. Text in German. 1869. m. adv. bk.rev. illus. index. **Document type:** *Magazine, Trade.* **Description:** Covers bee keeping.
Indexed: ApicAb, RefZh.
Published by: Oesterreichischer Imkerbund, Georg-Coch-Platz 3-11 A, Vienna, W 1010, Austria. TEL 43-1-5125429, FAX 43-1-51254294, oesterr.imkerbund@aon.at, http://www.imkerbund.at. Ed. Hans Hutsteiner. Circ: 27,000.

638.1 AUT ISSN 0006-2154
BIENENWELT; Fachzeitschrift fuer den Imker. Text in German. 1959. 11/yr. EUR 17.50 domestic; EUR 21.40 foreign (effective 2005). adv. bk.rev. illus. index. **Document type:** *Magazine, Trade.*
Indexed: ApicAb, ChemAb.
—CISTI.
Published by: Leopold Stocker Verlag, Hofgasse 5, Graz, St 8011, Austria. TEL 43-316-821636, FAX 43-316-835612, stocker-verlag@stocker-verlag.com, http://www.stocker-verlag.com/landwirtschaftliche-Zeitschriften-47-10/Bienenwelt.html. Ed. Simon Stolz. Adv. contact Thomas Muehlbacher. Circ: 4,000.

638.1 NLD ISSN 0926-3357
BIJEN; maandblad voor imkers. Text in Dutch. 1898; N.S. 1992. 11/yr. adv. bk.rev. illus. **Description:** Magazine about beekeeping, includes announcements of activities and lectures.
Formed by the 1992 merger of: Bijenteelt (0166-5820); Which was formerly (1922-1964): St. Ambrosius (0927-6661); Bijenteelt - Maandschrift voor Bijenteelt (0166-6444); Which was formerly: Maandschrift voor Bijenteelt (0024-8681)
Indexed: ApicAb.
Published by: (Vereniging tot Bevordering der Bijenteelt in Nederland), Bijen, Postbus 90, Bennekom, 6720 AB, Netherlands. TEL 31-317-422422, FAX 31-317-424180, bijenhuis@tip.nl. Ed. M L Boerjan. R&P M.L. Boerjan. Circ: 8,000. **Co-sponsors:** Imkersbonden ABTB Limburgse Land- en Tuinbouwbond; Bond van Bijenhouders van de ZLTO.

630 CHE
BIO AKTUELL/BIO ACTUALITES; Informationsbulletin fuer Biobaeurinnen und Biobauern. Text in French, German. 10/yr. CHF 39; CHF 46 foreign (effective 1999). **Document type:** *Bulletin.* **Description:** Information bulletin for organic agriculture producers.
Published by: Forschungsinstitut fuer Biologischen Landbau, Ackerstr., Frick, 5262, Switzerland. TEL 41-62-8657272, FAX 41-62-8657273, admin@fibl.ch. Ed. Marcus Baer. adv.: B&W page CHF 1,294; trim 268 x 186. Circ: 7,100. **Co-sponsor:** Vereinigung Schweizer Biolandbau-Organisationen.

BIOCONTROL NEWS AND INFORMATION. see *AGRICULTURE—Abstracting, Bibliographies, Statistics*

630 635 GBR ISSN 0144-8765
CODEN: BIAHDP
➤ **BIOLOGICAL AGRICULTURE AND HORTICULTURE;** an international journal of sustainable production systems. Text in English. 1982. 4/yr. USD 219 to institutions (effective 2005). adv. bk.rev. abstr.; bibl.; charts; illus.; maps. index. back issues avail. **Document type:** *Journal, Academic/Scholarly.* **Description:** Covers the field of sustainable agriculture.
Related titles: Microform ed.
Indexed: AEA, ASCA, ASFA, AgBio, Agr, AgrForAb, AnBrAb, BIOSIS Prev, BibAg, BioCN&I, BiolAb, CPA, ChemAb, CurCont, DIP, DSA, EPB, EntAb, ExcerpMed, FCA, FPA, ForAb, GEOBASE, GardL, HelmAb, HerbAb, HortAb, I&DA, IBR, IBZ, IndVet, MaizeAb, NemAb, NutrAb, OrnHort, PBA, PGegResA, PGrRegA, PHN&I, PN&I, PotatoAb, PoultAb, RA&MP, RDA, RM&VM, RPP, RefZh, RevApplEntom, RiceAb, S&F, SIA, SeedAb, SoyAb, TriticAb, VITIS, WAE&RSA, WeedAb.
—BLDSC (2074.200000), CASDDS, CISTI, IDS, IE, Infotrieve, ingenta, Linda Hall. **CCC.**
Published by: A B Academic Publishers, PO Box 42, Bicester, Oxon OX26 6NW, United Kingdom. bahjournal@btopenworld.com, http://www.bahjournal.btinternet.co.uk/. Ed. P J C Harris.

630 USA
BIOLOGICAL FARMING NEWS. Text in English. 1970. 5/yr. USD 10 (effective 1998). bk.rev. **Document type:** *Newspaper.* **Description:** Offers resources and services advocating a biological approach to agriculture as an alternative to organic or chemical farming.
Address: 7100C 2nd St, N W, Albuquerque, NM 87107. TEL 505-761-1454, FAX 505-761-1458. Ed., Pub., R&P Leland B Taylor. Circ: 25,000.

630 BRA ISSN 0366-0567
QH1 CODEN: BIOGAL
BIOLOGICO. Text in Portuguese; Summaries in English. 1935. s-a. BRL 10, USD 7 (effective 1999). bibl.; illus. index. cum.index. **Document type:** *Academic/Scholarly.*
Indexed: AbHyg, AgBio, AgrForAb, BioCN&I, BiolAb, ChemAb, DSA, FCA, ForAb, HelmAb, HerbAb, HortAb, I&DA, IndVet, NutrAb, OrnHort, PBA, PGegResA, PN&I, PotatoAb, PoultAb, ProtozoAb, RA&MP, RDA, RM&VM, RPP, RevApplEntom, S&F, SIA, SeedAb, SoyAb, TDB, TOSA, TriticAb, VetBull, WAE&RSA, WeedAb, ZooRec.
—CASDDS, CISTI, Linda Hall.

A

▼ new title ➤ refereed ✶ unverified ♦ full entry avail.

A

Published by: Instituto Biologico, Av Rodrigues Alves 1252 04014-002, Centro, Caixa Postal 12 898, Sao Paulo, SP 01059-970, Brazil. TEL 55-11-5729822, FAX 55-11-5709704. Ed. Marcia Maria Reboucas. Circ: 1,200.

630 634.9 DEU ISSN 0067-5849
S231 CODEN: MBBLA9
BIOLOGISCHE BUNDESANSTALT FUER LAND- UND FORSTWIRTSCHAFT, BERLIN-DAHLEM. MITTEILUNGEN. Text and summaries in English, German. 1906. irreg. price varies. illus. **Document type:** *Monographic series, Academic/Scholarly.* **Description:** Publication devoted to biological research in agriculture and forestry.
Indexed: BIOSIS Prev, BioCN&I, BiolAb, DBA, FCA, FPA, FS&TA, ForAb, HerbAb, HortAb, PBA, RPP, RefZh, RevApplEntom, S&F, VITIS, WeedAb, ZooRec.
—BLDSC (5833.900000), CISTI, IE, ingenta, Linda Hall. **CCC.**
Published by: Biologische Bundesanstalt fuer Land- und Forstwirtschaft, Messeweg 11-12, Braunschweig, 38104, Germany. TEL 49-531-2995, FAX 49-531-2993000, pressestelle@bba.de, http://www.bba.de/mitteil/mitteil.htm.

632 DEU ISSN 0521-2804
BIOLOGISCHE BUNDESANSTALT FUER LAND- UND FORSTWIRTSCHAFT. JAHRESBERICHT. Text in German. 19??. a. **Document type:** *Monographic series, Academic/Scholarly.*
—BLDSC (4633.000000).
Published by: Biologische Bundesanstalt fuer Land- und Forstwirtschaft, Messeweg 11-12, Braunschweig, 38104, Germany. TEL 49-531-2995, FAX 49-531-2993000, pressestelle@bba.de, http://www.bba.de.

BIOMETEOROLOGY BULLETIN. see *METEOROLOGY*

BIORESOURCE TECHNOLOGY. see *BIOLOGY—Biotechnology*

BIOTECHNOLOGY AND GENETIC ENGINEERING REVIEWS. see *BIOLOGY—Biotechnology*

BIOTECHNOLOGY IN AGRICULTURE AND FORESTRY. see *BIOLOGY—Biotechnology*

BIOTECHNOLOGY IN AGRICULTURE SERIES. see *BIOLOGY—Biotechnology*

BIOTECHNOLOGY INDUSTRY GUIDE. see *BIOLOGY*

630 IND ISSN 0971-1724
BIRSA AGRICULTURAL UNIVERSITY. JOURNAL OF RESEARCH. Text in English. 1989. s-a. INR 25.
Formerly (until 1991): B A U Journal of Research (0971-1201)
Indexed: AEA, AgBio, AgrForAb, AnBrAb, BioCN&I, CPA, DSA, FCA, FPA, ForAb, HelmAb, HerbAb, HortAb, I&DA, IndVet, MaizeAb, NemAb, NutrAb, OrnHort, PBA, PGegResA, PGrRegA, PHN&I, PN&I, PotatoAb, PoultAb, ProtozoAb, RA&MP, RDA, RM&VM, RPP, RevApplEntom, RiceAb, S&F, SIA, SeedAb, SoyAb, TDB, TriticAb, VetBull, WAE&RSA, WeedAb.
—BLDSC (5049.840000), IE, ingenta.
Published by: Birsa Agricultural University, Ranchi, Bihar 834 006, India. Ed. A A Khan.

638.1 SWE ISSN 0006-3886
BITIDNINGEN. Text in Swedish. 1902. m. SEK 300 (effective 2000). adv. bk.rev. abstr.; charts; illus.; mkt. index. **Document type:** *Trade.*
Indexed: RevApplEntom.
Published by: Sveriges Biodlares Riksfoerbund (SBR), Trumpetarevaegen 5, Mantorp, 59020, Sweden. FAX 46-582-61-16-82, osterlund@bt.biodlarna.se. Ed., Adv. contact Erik Oesterlund. Circ: 13,000.

BLATT FUER SORTENWESEN. see *AGRICULTURE—Abstracting, Bibliographies, Statistics*

630 AUT ISSN 0006-4742
BLICK INS LAND; das Magazin fuer den laendlichen Raum. Text in German. 1966. m. adv. illus. **Document type:** *Consumer.*
Published by: (Universitaet fuer Bodenkultur Wien), S P V Printmedien GmbH, Margaretenstr 22, 2nd Fl, Vienna, N 1040, Austria. TEL 43-1-5812890, FAX 43-1-581289023, http://www.blickinsland.at. Ed. Klaus Orthaber. Adv. contact Doris Daettel. B&W page EUR 8,590, color page EUR 9,400; trim 200 x 264. Circ: 212,000 (paid and controlled).

631 ZAF
BLOEMFONTEIN AGRICULTURAL SHOW CATALOGUE. Text in Afrikaans, English. a. adv.
Published by: Dryer Advertising, 21-25 Kruase St, PO Box 286, Bloemfontein, South Africa. Ed. F de Jaeger.

631 AUT ISSN 0006-5471
CODEN: BODEA2
➤ **DIE BODENKULTUR**; Austrian journal of agricultural research. Text in English, German. 1949. 4/yr. EUR 171; EUR 47 newsstand/cover (effective 2005). bk.rev. charts; illus.; abstr. back issues avail. **Document type:** *Journal, Academic/Scholarly.* **Description:** Provides an international outlet for new research in all areas of agronomy, ecology and related sciences.
Indexed: AEA, ASCA, ASFA, AgBio, AgrForAb, AnBrAb, BIOBASE, BIODAb, BiolAb, CIN, CPA, ChemAb, ChemTitl, CurCont, DBA, DSA, ESPM, ExcerpMed, FCA, FS&TA, ForAb, HerbAb, HortAb, I&DA, IABS, IBR, ISR, IndVet, MaizeAb, NutrAb, OrnHort, PBA, PGegResA, PGrRegA, PHN&I, PN&I, PlantSci, PotatoAb, PoultAb, RA&MP, RASB, RDA, RM&VM, RPP, RRTA, RefZh, RevApplEntom, RiceAb, S&F, SCI, SIA, SWRA, SeedAb, SoyAb, TriticAb, VITIS, VetBull, WAE&RSA, WeedAb.
—BLDSC (2116.790000), CASDDS, CISTI, IE, ingenta, Linda Hall.
Published by: (Institut fuer Agraroekonomik), Facultas Verlags- und Buchhandels AG, Berggasse 5, Vienna, W 1090, Austria. TEL 43-1-3105356-0, FAX 43-1-3197050, verlag@facultas.at, http://www.boku.ac.at/bokujournal/, http://www.wuv.at. Ed. Hans Karl Wytrzens. Pub. Sigrid Neulinger. Circ: 2,122.

630 BEL ISSN 0772-7054
DE BOER EN DE TUINDER. Text in Dutch. 1891. w. adv. bk.rev.
Formerly: Boer (0006-5595); Incorporating (since Jan. 1, 1976): Ons Fruitteeltblad (0030-266X); Tuinbouwberichten (0041-3976)
Indexed: AEA, HortAb, PGrRegA, S&F, WeedAb.
Published by: Belgische Boerenbond, Minderbroedersstraat 8, Leuven, 3000, Belgium. TEL 32-87-552446, FAX 32-87-742311. Ed. F Hofkens. Circ: 50,000.

630 ZAF ISSN 0259-0204
DIE BOER - THE FARMER. Text in Afrikaans, English. 1974. m. ZAR 22 domestic; ZAR 57 in Africa; ZAR 60 elsewhere. adv. bk.rev. **Document type:** *Newspaper.* **Description:** Reports topical news of current events, background information, and advice to farmer readers from the council chambers of organized agriculture at the national level.
Published by: South African Agricultural Union/Suid-Afrikaanse Landbou Unie, PO Box 1508, Pretoria, 0001, South Africa. TEL 27-12-3226980, FAX 27-12-3200557, lynette.salu@agriinfo.co.za. Ed., Adv. contact Lynette van Hoven. R&P Lynnette van Hoven. B&W page ZAR 6,480, color page ZAR 8,640; trim 210 x 298. Circ: 42,000 (paid).

630 NLD ISSN 0006-5617
BOERDERIJ; onafhankelijk weekblad voor de landbouw. Text in Dutch. 1915. w. EUR 142.50 (effective 2005). adv. bk.rev. charts; illus.; mkt. **Document type:** *Trade.* **Description:** General agricultural trade news plus politics, technical, financial and family information.
Incorporates (1992-1996): Vleesvee (1383-7206)
Related titles: Online - full content ed.; ♦ Supplement(s): Akkerbouw (Doetinchem). ISSN 0169-0116; ♦ Varkenshouderij. ISSN 0169-0167; ♦ Veehouderij. ISSN 0169-0213.
Indexed: ExcerpMed.
—CISTI, IE, Infotrieve.
Published by: Reed Business Information bv (Subsidiary of: Reed Business), Hanzestraat 1, Doetinchem, 7006 RH, Netherlands. boerderij@reedbusiness.nl, www.zibb.nl/landbouw. Ed. Henk E P Dokter. adv.: B&W page EUR 4,720, color page EUR 5,950; 194 x 260. Circ: 58,426.

630 ZAF
BOERE WEEKBLAD. Text in Afrikaans. 1994. w. ZAR 270.32; ZAR 556.40 foreign (effective 1998). illus.
Incorporates: Farmers Weekly (Afrikaans Edition)
Published by: Republican Press (Pty) Ltd., PO Box 32083, Mobeni, 4060, South Africa. TEL 27-31-4503100, FAX 27-31-4508200. Ed. Corrie Venter. R&P Roy Minnaar TEL 27-11-7287245. Adv. contact T Anderson.

BOLETIM METEOROLOGICO PARA A AGRICULTURA. see *METEOROLOGY*

630 570 ESP
BOLETIN DE AGRICULTURA BIOLOGICO-DINAMICA. Text in Spanish. 1986. q. **Document type:** *Bulletin.*
Published by: Editorial Rudolf Steiner, Guipuzcoa, 11-1 izda, Madrid, 28020, Spain. TEL 34-1-2531481. Ed. Antonio Malagon Golderos.

630 ESP
BOLETIN DE AVISOS. Text in Spanish. m. free (effective 2002).
Published by: Generalitat Valenciana, Conselleria de Agricultura, Pesa y Alimentacion. Secretaria General, C. Amadeo de Saboya, 2, Valencia, 46010, Spain. TEL 34-963-866912, FAX 34-963-866907, http://www.gva.es/agricultura/publica.htm.

630 CHL ISSN 0716-5579
BOLETIN DE COMERCIO EXTERIOR DEL SECTOR PESQUERO. Text in Spanish. 1985. m.
Indexed: ESPM.
Published by: Ministerio de Agricultura, Oficina de Estudios y Politicas Agrarias, Teatinos 40, Piso 8, Santiago, Chile. TEL 56-2-397-3000, FAX 56-2-397-3044, http://www.odepa.gob.cl/.

630 COL
BOLETIN DE PRENSA. Text in Spanish. irreg.
Published by: Comite Nacional por la Salvacion Agropecuaria, Carrera 4C No. 33-48, Ibague, TOL, Colombia. TEL 57-982-658058. Ed. Angel Maria Caballero.

630 ARG ISSN 0084-7968
HD9044.A78
BOLSA DE CEREALES. NUMERO ESTADISTICO. Text in Spanish. 1937. a.
Published by: Bolsa de Cereales, Avda. Corrientes, 119, 1o Piso, Capital Federal, Buenos Aires 1043-AAB, Argentina. TEL 54-11-4312-6516, FAX 54-11-4312-3611, mrava@bc.org.ar, http://www.bolcereales.com.

630 FRA
BON CULTIVATEUR DE L'EST. Text in French. 1820. m.
Published by: H. Burcier Ed. & Pub., 6 rue des Michottes, Nancy, 54000, France. Circ: 5,200.

630 NOR ISSN 0332-8414
BONDEBLADET. Text in Norwegian. 1974. w. NOK 580 (effective 2001). adv. charts; illus. back issues avail.
Formed by the 1974 merger of: Norges Bondeblad (0029-1684); Produsenten
—**CCC.**
Published by: Norwegian Farmers Union, Schweigaardsgt 34 C, Postboks 9367, Groenland, Oslo, 0135, Norway. TEL 47-22-05-47-67, FAX 47-22-17-25-05, post@bondebladet.no, http://www.bondebladet.no. Eds. Jon Lauritzen, Bendik Bendiksen. Adv. contact Truls J Aasterud. color page NOK 38,000, B&W page NOK 30,650;. Circ: 87,063.

630 NOR ISSN 0800-2126
BONDEVENNEN. Text in Norwegian. 1898. w. (fortn. in summer months). NOK 400 (effective 2000). adv. **Document type:** *Journal, Trade.*
Published by: Bondevennen B.A., Postboks 208, Stavanger, 4001, Norway. FAX 47-51-88-74-53. Ed. Oeyvind Bergoey. Circ: 8,000.

DE BOOMKWEKERIJ (DOETINCHEM). see *GARDENING AND HORTICULTURE*

BOTSWANA. MINISTRY OF AGRICULTURE. AGRICULTURAL STATISTICS. see *AGRICULTURE—Abstracting, Bibliographies, Statistics*

630.21 BWA ISSN 0068-0478
BOTSWANA. MINISTRY OF AGRICULTURE. ANNUAL REPORT. Text in English. 1947. a. free. charts. **Document type:** *Government.*
Indexed: FCA, HerbAb.
Published by: Ministry of Agriculture, Division of Planning and Statistics, Private Bag 0033, Gaborone, Botswana. TEL 267-328780, FAX 267-328847, TELEX 2752 SACCAR BD. Ed. Henry G Jobeta. R&P Dan B Gombalume. **Subscr. to:** Government Printer, Private Bag 0081, Gaborone, Botswana. TEL 267-353202, FAX 267-312001, http://www.gov.bw.

630 FRA ISSN 1257-144X
BOURBONNAIS RURAL. Text in French. 1972. w. adv. **Document type:** *Newspaper.*
Address: BP 12, Desertines, 03630, France. TEL 33-4-70051046, FAX 33-4-70053598. Ed. Jean Paul Bourdier. Adv. contact M Chambenoit. Circ: 9,640 (controlled).

630 570 BRA ISSN 0006-8705
SB13 CODEN: BRGTAF
BRAGANTIA. Text in English, Portuguese; Abstracts in English. 1941. 3/yr. BRL 70 domestic; USD 80 foreign (effective 2004). bibl.; charts; illus. index. back issues avail. **Document type:** *Government.*
Related titles: Online - full text ed.: free (effective 2005) (from SciELO).
Indexed: AEA, ATA, AgBio, AgrForAb, BIOSIS Prev, BibAg, BiolAb, CIN, CPA, CTFA, ChemAb, ChemTitl, FCA, FPA, ForAb, GEOBASE, HerbAb, HortAb, I&DA, MaizeAb, NemAb, NutrAb, OrnHort, PBA, PGegResA, PGrRegA, PHN&I, PotatoAb, RPP, RevApplEntom, RiceAb, S&F, SIA, SeedAb, SoyAb, TOSA, TriticAb, VITIS, WTA, WeedAb.
—CASDDS, CISTI, Linda Hall.
Published by: Instituto Agronomico, Servico de Divulgacao Tecnico-Cientifica, Caixa Postal 28, Campinas, SP 13020-902, Brazil. TEL 55-19-32315422, FAX 55-19-32314943, public@iac.sp.gov.br, http://www.scielo.br/scielo.php?script=sci_serial&pid=0006-8705&lng=en&nrm=iso, http://www.iac.sp.gov.br. Ed. Angela M C Furlani. Circ: 1,000.

636.082 JPN ISSN 1344-7610
CODEN: BRSCES
➤ **BREEDING SCIENCE.** Text and summaries in English. 1951. q. JPY 8,000 membership (effective 2004). adv. back issues avail. **Document type:** *Journal, Academic/Scholarly.* **Description:** Publishes original contributions related to breeding.
Supersedes in part (in 1998): Ikushugaku Zasshi/Japanese Journal of Breeding (0536-3683)
Related titles: Online - full text ed.: ISSN 1347-3735. free (effective 2005) (from J-Stage).
Indexed: AEA, ASCA, AgBio, AgrForAb, BIOBASE, BIOSIS Prev, BiolAb, CIN, CPA, ChemAb, ChemTitl, CurCont, DSA, FCA, FS&TA, ForAb, HerbAb, HortAb, IABS, MaizeAb, NemAb, OrnHort, PBA, PGegResA, PGrRegA, PHN&I, PlantSci, PotatoAb, RA&MP, RPP, RRTA, RevApplEntom, RiceAb, S&F, S&MA, SIA, SSCI, SeedAb, SoyAb, TOSA, TriticAb, VITIS, WeedAb.

—BLDSC (2277.716000), CASDDS, CISTI, IDS, IE, ingenta. **CCC.**
Published by: Nihon Ikushu Gakkai/Japanese Society of Breeding, c/o Nakanishi Printing Co., Ltd., Shimotachiuri Ogawa-Higashi, Kamikyo-ku, Kyoto, 602-8048, Japan. TEL 81-75-4153661, FAX 81-75-4153662, jsb@nacos.com, http://jsbbs.jstage.jst.go.jp/, http://www.nacos.com/jsb/. Ed. Kazutoshi Okuno. Circ: 2,000.

630 DEU
BREMER LANDWIRTSCHAFTLICHE RUNDSCHAU. Text in German. 1960. bi-m. adv. **Document type:** *Journal, Trade.*
Published by: Landwirtschaftskammer Bremen, Ellhornstr 30, Bremen, 28195, Germany. TEL 49-421-1675750, FAX 49-421-1675759, lwk-bremen@t-online.de, http://www.lwk-bremen.de/rundschau.htm. adv.: B&W page EUR 380, color page EUR 650. Circ: 1,340 (controlled).

630 340 DEU ISSN 0947-4358
BRIEFE ZUM AGRARRECHT. Text in German. 1993. m. EUR 44.50; EUR 4.10 newsstand/cover (effective 2004). adv. 48 p./no.; **Document type:** *Journal, Trade.*
Published by: Deutscher Landwirtschaftsverlag GmbH, Berliner Str 112A, Berlin, 13189, Germany. TEL 49-30-29397450, FAX 49-30-29397459, dlv.berlin@dlv.de, http://www.agrarrecht.de, http://www.dlv.de. Ed. Klaus Boehme. adv.: page EUR 332; trim 122 x 178. Circ: 2,500 (paid).

638.1 GBR ISSN 0007-0327
BRITISH BEE JOURNAL. Text in English. 1873. m. GBP 8.40; GBP 12, GBP 22.50 foreign; GBP 0.50 newsstand/cover. adv. bk.rev. charts; illus. **Document type:** *Trade.*
Indexed: ApicAb.
Published by: British Bee Publications Ltd., 46 Queen St, Geddington, Nr. Kettering, Northants NN14 1AZ, United Kingdom. TEL 44-1536-742250. Ed. Cecil C Tonsley. Circ: 3,500.

BRITISH COLUMBIA. MINISTRY OF AGRICULTURE AND FOOD. ANNUAL STATISTICS (YEAR). see *AGRICULTURE—Abstracting, Bibliographies, Statistics*

630 CAN ISSN 0706-9308
BRITISH COLUMBIA. MINISTRY OF AGRICULTURE FISHERIES AND FOOD D.A.T.E. PROGRAM REPORT. Text in English. 1974. a. CND 5. **Document type:** *Government.*
Former titles: British Columbia. Ministry of Agriculture and Food D.A.T.E. Program Report; British Columbia. Ministry of Agriculture D.A.T.E. Program Report
—CISTI.
Published by: Ministry of Agriculture, Food and Fisheries, Stn Prov Govt, PO Box 9058, Victoria, BC V8W 9E2, Canada. Ed. Reg Miller. Circ: 1,300. **Orders to:** W A I R, 742 Vanalman Ave, Victoria, BC V8V 1X4, Canada.

632.9 CAN ISSN 0228-8117
BRITISH COLUMBIA. MINISTRY OF AGRICULTURE FISHERIES AND FOOD. FIELD CROP PRODUCTION GUIDE TO WEED, DISEASE, INSECT, BIRD AND RODENT CONTROL. Text in English. a. CND 10. **Document type:** *Government.*
Former titles (until 1980): British Columbia. Department of Agriculture. Guide to Field Crop Weed, Disease, Insect, Rodent Control Recommendations (0706-4322); (until 1978): British Columbia. Department of Agriculture. Field Crop Control Recommendations (0706-4330); (until 1973): British Columbia. Department of Agriculture. Recommendations for Field Crops (0706-4349); (until 1971): British Columbia. Department of Agriculture. Field Crop Recommendations (0713-0090)
Published by: Ministry of Agriculture, Food and Fisheries, Stn Prov Govt, PO Box 9058, Victoria, BC V8W 9E2, Canada.

BRITISH COLUMBIA. MINISTRY OF AGRICULTURE FISHERIES AND FOOD. MUSHROOM PRODUCTION GUIDE. see *GARDENING AND HORTICULTURE*

BRITISH COLUMBIA. MINISTRY OF AGRICULTURE FISHERIES AND FOOD. NURSERY CROP PRODUCTION GUIDE FOR COMMERCIAL GROWERS. see *GARDENING AND HORTICULTURE*

630 CAN ISSN 0711-7590
BROADWATER MARKET LETTER✶; a weekly summary of farm commodity prices, management suggestions, market trends and policies. Text in English. 1974. w. CND 149, USD 159. **Document type:** *Newsletter.* **Description:** Informs farmers, ranchers, and agri-business subscribers about the week's activities in local and world commodity markets.
Related titles: Fax ed.: 1974.
Published by: DePutter Publishing Ltd., 190 Wortley Rd, London, ON N6C 6A2, Canada. TEL 519-663-2224, FAX 519-663-9124. Ed. John Deputter. Pub. Jon Deputter.

661.073 630.24 ISR ISSN 0007-2192
BROMIDES IN AGRICULTURE. Text in English. 1960. 2/yr. free. bk.rev. abstr.; charts; illus.
Published by: Dead Sea Bromine Company Ltd., P O Box 180, Beersheba, 84101, Israel. TEL 972-7-797630, FAX 972-7-297846. Ed. Yuval Cohen. Circ: 1,500.

630 USA ISSN 0007-2834
BUCKEYE FARM NEWS. Text in English. 1919. 18/yr. USD 5 to non-members; free to members (effective 2005). adv. bk.rev. illus. index. **Document type:** *Magazine, Trade.*
Formerly: Ohio Farm Bureau News
Related titles: Online - full text ed.
Published by: Ohio Farm Bureau Federation, Inc., 2 Nationwide Plz, PO Box 182383, Columbus, OH 43218-2383. TEL 614-249-2400, FAX 614-249-2200, lsnyder@ofbf.org, http://www.ofbf.org. Ed. Joe Cornely. adv.: B&W page USD 1,785. Circ: 58,115 (controlled).

630 ALB
BUJQESIA SOCIALISTE✶. Text in Albanian. m. USD 3.08.
Indexed: RASB.
Published by: Ministria e Bujqesise/Ministry of Agriculture, c/o Publishing and Information Center for Agriculture, Tirana, Albania. TELEX 4209. Ed. Faik Labinoti.

630 ALB
BUJQESTA SHQIPTARE/ALBANIAN AGRICULTURE. Text in Albanian. m. USD 3.08.
Published by: Center of Information and Agrifood Formation, c/o Kastriot Ahmati, Ed, Rr Skender Kosturi, Tirana, Albania. TEL 355-42-28422, FAX 355-42-28422.

630 334.683 ALB ISSN 0563-573X
CODEN: BSBUAY
BULETINI I SHKENCAVE BUJQESORE/BULLETIN DES SCIENCES AGRICOLES. Text in Albanian; Summaries in French. 1962. q. USD 8.
Indexed: ChemAb, FCA, HortAb, S&F, SeedAb, TriticAb.
—BLDSC (2366.249500), CASDDS, Linda Hall.
Published by: Center of Information and Agrifood Formation, c/o Kastriot Ahmati, Ed, Rr Skender Kosturi, Tirana, Albania. TEL 355-42-28422, FAX 355-42-28422.

630 636.089 BGR ISSN 1310-0351
➤ **BULGARIAN JOURNAL OF AGRICULTURAL SCIENCE.** Text in English. 1995. 6/yr. EUR 200 foreign (effective 2005). abstr.; bibl.; illus. 118 p./no. 2 cols./p.; reprints avail. **Document type:** *Journal, Academic/Scholarly.* **Description:** Includes papers covering all areas of agriculture and veterinary science. Aimed at scientific researchers in Bulgaria and abroad.
Indexed: AEA, AbHyg, AgBio, AgrForAb, AnBrAb, BioCN&I, CPA, DSA, FCA, FPA, FS&TA, ForAb, HelmAb, HerbAb, HortAb, I&DA, INIS AtomInd, IndVet, MaizeAb, NemAb, NutrAb, OrnHort, PBA, PGegResA, PGrRegA, PHN&I, PN&I, PotatoAb, PoultAb, ProtozoAb, RA&MP, RDA, RM&VM, RPP, RevApplEntom, RiceAb, S&F, SIA, SeedAb, SoyAb, TriticAb, VITIS, VetBull, WAE&RSA, WeedAb.
—BLDSC (2366.686500), CISTI, IE, ingenta.
Published by: Natzionalen Tzentar za Agrarni Nauki/National Center for Agrarian Sciences of Bulgaria, Souhodolska St 30, Sofia, 1373, Bulgaria. TEL 359-2-2929481, FAX 359-2-211905, aa@bgcict.acad.bg, http://bjas.hit.bg. Eds. Iliana Nikolova, Dr. Tsvetan Tsvetkov.

630 FRA ISSN 0007-4055
BULLETIN AGRICOLE DES HAUTES PYRENEES. Text in French. 1941. 10/yr.
Address: 34 Place du Foirail, Tarbes, 65000, France. TEL 33-62-935552. Ed. Alain Fontaine. Circ: 9,500.

631 RWA ISSN 0557-8213
BULLETIN AGRICOLE DU RWANDA/RWANDA AGRICULTURAL BULLETIN. Text in French. 1968. 4/yr. adv.
Published by: (Rwanda. Ministere de l'Agriculture, de l'Elevage et des Forets), O C I R, BP 104, Kigali - Gikondo, Rwanda. Ed. Augustin Nzindukiyimana. Circ: 800.

630 CAN ISSN 0007-4446
LE BULLETIN DES AGRICULTEURS. Text in English. 1917. m. CND 34.95 domestic; CND 64 foreign (effective 2003). adv. bk.rev. **Document type:** *Magazine, Trade.*
Related titles: Microfiche ed.; Online - full text ed.: (from Micromedia ProQuest, ProQuest Information & Learning).
Indexed: PdeR.
—CISTI.
Published by: Rogers Media Publishing Ltd, 1001 boul de Maisonneuve Ouest, Rm 1100, Montreal, PQ H3A 3E1, Canada. TEL 514-845-5141, FAX 514-845-6261, info@lebulletin.com, http://www.lebulletin.com, http://www.rogers.com. Ed. Sylvie Bouchard. Pub. Simon Guertin. adv.: B&W page CND 3,450, color page CND 4,395; trim 10.75 x 8. Circ: 35,067 (paid).

630 BWA ISSN 0256-7512
S542.B55
BULLETIN OF AGRICULTURAL RESEARCH IN BOTSWANA. Text in English. 1983. q. free. charts; bibl.; illus.; stat. back issues avail. **Document type:** *Bulletin, Government.*
Indexed: ISAP.
Published by: Ministry of Agriculture, Division of Planning and Statistics, Private Bag 0033, Gaborone, Botswana. TEL 267-328780, FAX 267-328847, TELEX 2752 SACCAR BD. Ed. Lobisa L Setshwaelo. R&P Dan B Gombalume. Circ: 250. **Subscr. to:** Government Printer, Private Bag 0081, Gaborone, Botswana. TEL 267-353202, FAX 267-312001, http://www.gov.bw.

630 IND
BULLETIN OF AGRICULTURE PRICES. Text in English. w. INR 150, USD 54 (effective 1993).
Published by: Ministry of Agriculture, Department of Agriculture and Cooperation, Directorate of Economics and Statistics, A-2E-3 Kasturba Gandhi Marg Barracks, New Delhi, 110 001, India. TEL 11-381523. Ed. Brajesh Kumar Gautam. Circ: 370. **Dist. by:** Controller of Publications, Civil Lines, New Delhi 110 006, India.

633.1 IND ISSN 0007-4896
SB183 CODEN: BUGTA2
BULLETIN OF GRAIN TECHNOLOGY. Text in English. 1963. 3/yr. USD 15 to non-members. adv. bk.rev. abstr.; bibl.; charts; illus.; stat. cum.index. back issues avail.
Indexed: BiolAb, ChemAb, ExcerpMed, FCA, FS&TA, HerbAb, NutrAb, RevApplEntom, RiceAb, S&F, ZooRec.
—CASDDS, CISTI.
Published by: Foodgrain Technologists' Research Association of India, Hapur, Uttar Pradesh, India. Ed. Dr. N S Agarwal. Circ: 750.

638.1 FRA ISSN 0335-3710
CODEN: BTAPDO
BULLETIN TECHNIQUE APICOLE. Text in French. 1973. q. adv. bk.rev. cum.index: 1973-1995. back issues avail. **Document type:** *Bulletin.* **Description:** Publishes information on the science of beekeeping.
Related titles: Fax ed.; Online - full text ed.
Indexed: ApicAb, BiolAb, RefZh, SIA.
—CASDDS, CISTI. **CCC.**
Published by: Centre Apicole, Office pour l'Information et la Documentation en Apiculture, Echauffour, Ste Gauburge, 61370, France. TEL 33-2-33340580, FAX 33-2-33344634, opida@apiservices.com, http://www.beeculture.com/opida, http://www.apiculture.com/opida. Ed. Francoise Jeanne. Pub. Michel Bocquet. R&P, Adv. contact Raymond Bartlet. Circ: 3,000. **Dist. by:** O.P.I.D.A., Centre Agricole, Echauffour 61370, France.

630 AUT ISSN 1026-6267
BUNDESANSTALT FUER ALPENLAENDISCHE LANDWIRTSCHAFT. BERICHT. Text in German. 1989. irreg. price varies. adv. back issues avail. **Document type:** *Monographic series, Government.*
Published by: Bundesanstalt fuer Alpenlaendische Landwirtschaft Gumpenstein, Irdning, St 8952, Austria. TEL 43-3682-22451, FAX 43-3682-2461488, office@bal.bmlf.gv.at, http://www.bal.bmlf.gv.at. Ed., R&P Kurt Chytil TEL 43-3682-22451. Adv. contact Eva Rainer. Circ: 500.

630 AUT ISSN 0007-6244
BURGENLAENDISCHE LANDWIRTSCHAFTSKAMMER. MITTEILUNGSBLATT. Text in German. 1957. fortn. free to qualified personnel. adv. bk.rev. illus.; mkt.; pat. **Document type:** *Bulletin, Trade.*
Published by: Burgenlaendische Landwirtschaftskammer, Esterhazystr 15, Eisenstadt, B 7001, Austria. TEL 43-2682-702, FAX 43-2682-702190, hans.weiss@lk-bgld.at, http://www.lk-bgld.at. Ed. Hans Weiss. Circ: 39,000.

630 AUT
BURGENLAENDISCHER AGRARKURIER. Text in German. m. **Document type:** *Journal, Trade.*
Published by: Bauernbund Burgenland, Esterhazystr 15, Eisenstadt, 7000, Austria. http://www.oevp-burgenland.at/bauernbund/.

338.1 BFA
BURKINA FASO. SERVICE DES STATISTIQUES AGRICOLES. ANNUAIRE. Text in French. 1970. a.
Formerly: Upper Volta. Service des Statistiques Agricoles. Annuaire
Published by: Service des Statistiques Agricoles, Ministere de l'Agriculture et de l'Elevage, BP 7010, Ouagadougou, Burkina Faso. Circ: 500.

630 USA ISSN 0195-1246
BUSINESS FARMER. Text in English. 1925. w. (Fri.). USD 26.95 subscr - mailed (effective 2005). adv. bk.rev. **Document type:** *Newspaper.*
Published by: Business Farmer, Inc., PO Box 770, Scottsbluff, NE 69361. TEL 307-532-2184, FAX 308-635-2348, craig@businessfarmer.com, http://www.businessfarmer.com. Circ: 3,300.

BUSINESS RATIO. THE AGRICULTURAL EQUIPMENT INDUSTRY. see *MACHINERY*

630 ISL ISSN 1012-6910
CODEN: BUVIEE
BUVISINDI/ICELANDIC AGRICULTURAL SCIENCES. Text in English, Multiple languages; Summaries in English. 1969-1986; resumed 1988. irreg. (1-2/yr.). free. **Document type:** *Academic/Scholarly.* **Description:** Publishes original research concerning Icelandic agriculture.
Formerly (until 1986): Islenzkar Landbunadarrannsoknir (0368-0142)

▼ new title ➤ refereed ✶ unverified ♦ full entry avail.

Indexed: AgBio, AnBrAb, BIOSIS Prev, BiolAb, CPA, FCA, FPA, ForAb, HelmAb, HerbAb, HortAb, IndVet, NemAb, NutrAb, PBA, PGegResA, PGrRegA, PN&I, PoultAb, ProtozoAb, RPP, RefZh, RevApplEntom, S&F, SeedAb, SoyAb, TriticAb, VetBull, ZooRec.
—BLDSC (4361.454000), CISTI.
Published by: Rannsoknastofnun Landbunadarins/Agricultural Research Institute, Keldnaholti, Reykjavik, 112, Iceland. TEL 354-577-1010, FAX 354-577-1020, rsj@rala.is, gudrun@rala.is, http://www.rala.is. Eds. Fridrik Palmason, Tryggvi Gunnarsson. Circ: 600 (controlled).

630 CAN
C A A R COMMUNICATOR. Text in English. 1980. 5/yr. CND 22.50 (effective 2004). adv. back issues avail. **Document type:** *Magazine, Trade.* **Description:** For retailers of fertilizers and chemicals in Canada, their suppliers, and manufacturers.
Formerly: W F C D Communicator (0822-8183)
—CISTI.
Published by: (Canadian Association of Agri-Retailers), Issues Ink, 203-897 Corydon Ave, Winnipeg, MB R3M 0W7, Canada. TEL 204-453-1965, FAX 204-475-5247, issues@issuesink.com, http://www.issuesink.com. Ed., Adv. contact Robynne Anderson. R&P Erin Brand TEL 204-453-1965. Circ: 3,800.

016.63 USA
C A B ABSTRACTS (ONLINE EDITION). Text in English. 1973.
Formerly: C A B Abstracts (Print Edition)
Media: Online - full content.
Published by: CABI Publishing North America (Subsidiary of: CAB International), 875 Massachusetts Ave, 7th Fl, Cambridge, MA 02139. publishing@cabi.org, cabi-nao@cabi.org, http://www.cabi-publishing.org/.

630 GBR ISSN 0953-5586
C A P LEGISLATION QUARTERLY. (Common Agricultural Policy) Text in English. q. looseleaf. GBP 374; GBP 392 in Europe; GBP 437 elsewhere (effective 2000). **Document type:** *Trade.*
Published by: Agra Europe (London) Ltd. (Subsidiary of: T & F Informa plc), 80 Calverley Rd, Tunbridge Wells, Kent TN1 2UN, United Kingdom. TEL 44-1892-533813, FAX 44-1892-544895, 100637.3460@compuserve.com, marketing@agra-net.com.

630 341 GBR ISSN 0142-5633
C A P MONITOR; a continuously up-dated information service on the Common Agricultural Policy of the European Union. (Common Agricultural Policy) Text in English. 1978. base vol. plus irreg. updates. looseleaf. GBP 890 base vol(s). domestic basic vol. & first year updates; GBP 990 base vol(s). in Europe basic vol. & first year updates; GBP 1,088 base vol(s). elsewhere basic vol. & first year updates; GBP 1,012 updates domestic for 2005 updates (renewals only); GBP 1,100 updates in Europe for 2005 updates (renewals only); GBP 1,203 updates elsewhere for 2005 updates (renewals only) (effective 2005). **Document type:** *Trade.* **Description:** Continuously updated reference and guide to the Common Agricultural Policy of the European Union.
—BLDSC (3050.622300).
Published by: Agra Europe (London) Ltd. (Subsidiary of: T & F Informa plc), 80 Calverley Rd, Tunbridge Wells, Kent TN1 2UN, United Kingdom. TEL 44-1892-533813, FAX 44-1892-544895, marketing@agra-net.com, http://www.agra-net.com.

630 TTO ISSN 1018-1210
C A R A P H I N NEWS. Text in English. 1989. 3/yr. free in the Caribbean; USD 10 outside the Caribbean (effective 2001). adv. bk.rev. back issues avail. **Document type:** *Newsletter, Trade.*
Formerly: I I C A Miscellaneous Publication (0534-5391)
Indexed: AgBio, AgrForAb, BioCN&I, CPA, FPA, ForAb, HortAb, IndVet, OrnHort, PBA, PGegResA, PGrRegA, PHN&I, RPP, RRTA, RevApplEntom, RiceAb, S&F, SIA, WAE&RSA, WeedAb.
—BLDSC (3050.952500), CISTI.
Published by: Inter-American Institute for Cooperation on Agriculture, Caribbean Animal and Plant Health Information Network, PO Box 1318, Port of Spain, WI, Trinidad & Tobago. TEL 868-628-4403, FAX 868-628-7086, iicabar@caribsurf.com, http://www.iicasaninet.net. Ed., R&P Sandra Vokaty. Circ: 1,200; 1,200 (controlled).

630 FRA ISSN 1167-3702
C F C A ACTUALITES. Text in French. bi-m.
—CISTI.
Published by: (Confederation Francaise de la Cooperation Agricole), Societe de Diffusion d'Informations Agricoles et de Presse (SODIAP), 49 avenue de la Grande Armee, Paris, 75116, France. TEL 33-1-44175700, FAX 33-1-44175701. Ed. Irene de Bretteville. Adv. contact Brigitte Verron.

630 COL
C I A T EN PERSPECTIVA; informe anual. Text in Spanish. 1980. a.
Related titles: ♦ English ed.: C I A T in Perspective.
Published by: Centro Internacional de Agricultura Tropical/International Center for Tropical Agriculture, Publications Unit, Apartado Aereo 6713, Cali, VALLE, Colombia. TEL 57-2-4450000, FAX 57-2-4450073, ciat-comunicaciones@cgiar.org, http://www.ciat.cgiar.org. Circ: 3,000 (controlled).

630 COL
S540.8.C45
C I A T IN PERSPECTIVE; annual report. Text in English. 1980. a. free. **Document type:** *Corporate.* **Description:** Presents highlights of CIAT activities.
Formerly: C I A T Report (0120-3169); Supersedes: Centro Internacional de Agricultura Tropical. Annual Report; C I A T Highlights
Related titles: ♦ Spanish ed.: C I A T en Perspectiva.
Indexed: AnBrAb, BiolAb, HerbAb, PBA.
—CISTI.
Published by: (Distribucion de Publicaciones), Centro Internacional de Agricultura Tropical/International Center for Tropical Agriculture, Publications Unit, Apartado Aereo 6713, Cali, VALLE, Colombia. TEL 57-2-4450000, FAX 57-2-4450073, ciat@cgiar.org, ciat-comunicaciones@cgiar.org, http://www.ciat.cgiar.org/. Ed. Nathan C Russell. Circ: 2,000 (controlled).

630 600 PHL ISSN 0115-0405
CODEN: CSCJDK
C L S U SCIENTIFIC JOURNAL. Text in English. 1966. 2/yr. PHP 30, USD 10. back issues avail. **Document type:** *Academic/Scholarly.*
Indexed: IPP.
—CASDDS.
Published by: Central Luzon State University, c/o Estefania W. Kollin, Publications House, Munoz, Nueva Ecija, Philippines. Ed. Carminia Leabres Ramos. Circ: 4,000.

630 PHL ISSN 0116-7847
CODEN: CJANES
C M U JOURNAL OF SCIENCE. Text in English. 1979. q. PHP 60, USD 4. back issues avail.
Formerly (until vol.9, 1987): C M U Journal of Agriculture, Food and Nutrition (0115-4931)
Indexed: AgBio, AgrForAb, BioCN&I, CPA, DSA, FCA, ForAb, HerbAb, HortAb, I&DA, IPP, IndVet, MaizeAb, NutrAb, PN&I, PotatoAb, RDA, RRTA, S&F, SIA, SeedAb, SoyAb, WAE&RSA.
—CCC.
Published by: Central Mindanao University, University Town, Musuan, Bukidnon 8710, Philippines. Ed. Herminio M Pava. Circ: 350.

630 AUS ISSN 1329-6671
SB111.A2
C S I R O TROPICAL AGRICULTURE. TROPICAL AGRICULTURE TECHNICAL MEMORANDUM. Text in English. 1976. irreg. price varies. **Document type:** *Monographic series.*
Formerly (until 1997): Commonwealth Scientific and Industrial Research Organization. Division of Tropical Crops and Pastures. Tropical Agronomy Technical Memorandum (0157-9711)
Indexed: AEA, AgrForAb, BIOSIS Prev, BiolAb, CPA, FCA, ForAb, HerbAb, I&DA, IndVet, MaizeAb, PBA, PGegResA, RPP, S&F, SAA, SeedAb, SoyAb, TriticAb, VetBull, WeedAb.
—BLDSC (9053.700000), CASDDS, CISTI.
Published by: C S I R O Tropical Agriculture, 306 Carmody Rd, Brisbane, St Lucia, QLD 4067, Australia. TEL 61-7-32142200, FAX 61-7-32142288, library@tag.csiro.au, http://www.tag.csiro.au. R&P Marshall Mackay.

630 636.089 613.2 GBR
▼ **CAB REVIEWS: PERSPECTIVES IN AGRICULTURE, VETERINARY SCIENCE, NUTRITION AND NATURAL RESOURCES.** Text in English. forthcoming 2006. base vol. plus irreg. updates. GBP 600, USD 1,050 to institutions (effective 2005). **Document type:** *Database, Academic/Scholarly.* **Description:** Focuses on animal science and veterinary medicine; applied plant sciences; agriculture; nutrition and food science; natural resources and environmental sciences.
Media: Online - full text.
Published by: CABI Publishing (Subsidiary of: CAB International), CAB International, Wallingford, Oxfordshire OX10 8DE, United Kingdom. TEL 44-1491-832111, FAX 44-1491-833508, publishing@cabi.org, http://www.cabi-publishing.org/. Ed. David Hemming. Pub. David Smith TEL 44-1491-829325.

630 ESP ISSN 0214-8161
CADERNOS DO AREA DE CIENCIAS AGRARIAS. Text in Spanish. 1981. a.
—CINDOC.
Published by: (Instituto Gallego de Informacion), Seminario de Estudos Galegos, Monte do Gozo San Marcos s-n, Santiago De Compostela, (La Coruna) 15771, Spain.

630 FRA ISSN 1166-7699
S5
CAHIERS D'ETUDES ET DE RECHERCHES FRANCOPHONES. AGRICULTURES. Key Title: Agricultures (Montrouge). Variant title: Cahiers Agricultures. Text in French. 1992. 6/yr. EUR 70 combined subscription in the European Union to individuals print & online eds.; EUR 80 combined subscription elsewhere to individuals print & online eds.; EUR 115 combined subscription in the European Union to institutions print & online eds.; EUR 125 combined subscription elsewhere to institutions print & online eds.; EUR 50 combined subscription in the European Union to students print & online eds.; EUR 55 combined subscription elsewhere to students print & online eds. (effective 2005). **Document type:** *Journal, Academic/Scholarly.* **Description:** Takes a multidisciplinary approach to agronomic research and rural development.
Related titles: Online - full text ed.
Indexed: AEA, AgBio, AgrForAb, AnBrAb, BIOSIS Prev, BioCN&I, BiolAb, CPA, DSA, FCA, FPA, FS&TA, ForAb, HelmAb, HerbAb, HortAb, I&DA, IndVet, MaizeAb, NemAb, NutrAb, OrnHort, PBA, PGegResA, PGrRegA, PHN&I, PN&I, PotatoAb, PoultAb, ProtozoAb, RA&MP, RDA, RPP, RRTA, RevApplEntom, RiceAb, S&F, SIA, SeedAb, SoyAb, TDB, TriticAb, VetBull, WAE&RSA, WeedAb.
—BLDSC (2948.610500), CISTI, IE, ingenta.
Published by: John Libbey Eurotext, 127 Avenue de la Republique, Montrouge, 92120, France. TEL 33-1-46730660, FAX 33-1-40840999, contact@jle.com, http://www.john-libbey-eurotext.fr. Ed. Rene Lesel. **Subscr. to:** A T E I, 3 av. Pierre Kerautret, Romainville 92230, France. TEL 33-1-48408686, FAX 33-1-48400731, atei@club-internet.fr.

630 FRA ISSN 1022-1379
CAHIERS OPTIONS MEDITERRANEENNES. Text in French, English. 1993. irreg., latest vol.54, 2001. **Document type:** *Monographic series.*
Indexed: AEA, ASFA, AgBio, AgrForAb, AnBrAb, CPA, DSA, ESPM, FCA, FPA, ForAb, HerbAb, HortAb, I&DA, IndVet, MaizeAb, NemAb, NutrAb, OrnHort, PBA, PGegResA, PGrRegA, PHN&I, PN&I, PoultAb, ProtozoAb, RA&MP, RDA, RPP, RRTA, RevApplEntom, S&F, SIA, SeedAb, SoyAb, TriticAb, VetBull, WAE&RSA, WeedAb, ZooRec.
Published by: Centre International de Hautes Etudes Agronomiques Mediterraneennes, Institut Agronomique Mediterraneen de Montpellier/International Centre for Advanced Mediterranean Agronomic Studies, 3191 route de Mende, Montpellier Cedex 5, 34093, France. TEL 33-4-67046000, FAX 33-4-67542527. Ed. Mr. Chioccioli. Pub. Mr. Lerin.

630 EGY ISSN 0526-8613
CODEN: CAABAR
CAIRO UNIVERSITY. FACULTY OF AGRICULTURE. BULLETIN. Text in English; Summaries in Arabic, English. 1950. irreg. USD 120 (effective 2001). bk.rev. back issues avail. **Document type:** *Bulletin, Academic/Scholarly.*
Related titles: Diskette ed.; E-mail ed.
Indexed: AEA, AgBio, AgrForAb, AnBrAb, BioCN&I, CPA, DSA, FCA, FPA, FS&TA, ForAb, HerbAb, HortAb, I&DA, IndVet, MaizeAb, NutrAb, OrnHort, PBA, PGegResA, PGrRegA, PHN&I, PotatoAb, PoultAb, RA&MP, RDA, RM&VM, RPP, RevApplEntom, RiceAb, S&F, SIA, SeedAb, SoyAb, TDB, TriticAb, VetBull, WAE&RSA, WeedAb, ZooRec.
—BLDSC (2507.380000), IE, ingenta.
Published by: Cairo University, Faculty of Agriculture, Gameaat El-Qahera Str, Giza, Egypt. TEL 20-2-5701235, 20-2-5724107, http://derp.sti.sci.eg/data/0077.htm. Ed. Dr. Samir Abdel-Wahhab Abou-El-Rous. Circ: 300 (paid).

630 NCL ISSN 1292-9239
CALEDONIE AGRICOLE. Text in French. 1983. bi-m. XPF 3,000 (effective 2000); EUR 25.14. adv. **Document type:** *Bulletin.*
Former titles (until 1998): Agri Infos (1257-0397); Chambre d'Agriculture New Caledonia. Bulletin
Published by: Chambre d'Agriculture New Caledonia, PO Box 111, Noumea, 98845, New Caledonia. TEL 687-272056, FAX 687-284587. Ed. G Roucou. Pub. A Mazurier. Adv. contact Ann Marie Brot. Circ: 3,500.

630 USA ISSN 0575-5298
CALIFORNIA AGRICULTURAL DIRECTORY (YEAR); including Oregon & Washington. Text in English. 1963. a. USD 30. **Document type:** *Directory.*
Published by: California Farm Bureau Federation, 2300 River Plaza Dr, Sacramento, CA 95833-3293. FAX 916-561-5695, http://www.cfbf.com. Ed. Clark Biggs. Circ: 1,000.

630 USA ISSN 0008-0845
S1 CODEN: CAGRA3
➤ **CALIFORNIA AGRICULTURE**; reports of progress in research. Text in English. 1946. bi-m. USD 24 foreign (effective 2004); Free upon request in the U.S.. charts; illus.; stat. index. back issues avail.; reprints avail. **Document type:** *Journal, Academic/Scholarly.* **Description:** Reports of progress in research and reviews from Division of Agriculture and Natural Resources, University of California.
Related titles: Online - full text ed.

Indexed: AEA, ASFA, AbHyg, AgBio, Agr, AgrForAb, AnBrAb, BioCN&I, BiolAb, CPA, CTFA, CalPI, ChemAb, CurPA, DBA, DSA, EIA, ESPM, EntAb, EnvAb, EnvEAb, ExcerpMed, FCA, FPA, FS&TA, ForAb, HelmAb, HerbAb, HortAb, I&DA, IndVet, MBA, MaizeAb, NemAb, NutrAb, OrnHort, PBA, PGegResA, PGrRegA, PHN&I, PN&I, PollutAb, PotatoAb, PoultAb, ProtozoAb, RASB, RPP, RRTA, RevApplEntom, RiceAb, S&F, SFA, SIA, SWRA, SeedAb, SoyAb, TriticAb, VITIS, VetBull, WAE&RSA, WeedAb, WildRev, ZooRec.
—BLDSC (3011.000000), CASDDS, CIS, CISTI, IE, ingenta, Linda Hall.
Published by: University of California at Oakland, Division of Agriculture and Natural Resources, 1111 Franklin St, 6th Fl, Oakland, CA 94607-5200. TEL 510-987-0044, FAX 510-465-2659, calag@ucop.edu, http://californiaagriculture.ucop.edu/, http://www.ucanr.org. Circ: 18,484.

630 USA ISSN 0008-1051
CALIFORNIA FARMER; the business magazine for commercial agriculture. Text in English. 1854. 15/yr. USD 23.95 in state (effective 2005). adv. illus.; mkt. reprints avail. **Document type:** *Magazine, Trade.* **Description:** Covers farming and ranching, marketing, and legislation for farmers and ranchers in California.
Related titles: Microfilm ed.: (from LIB).
Indexed: CalPI, EnvAb, EnvInd, F&GI.
Published by: Farm Progress Companies, 191 S Gary Ave, Carol Stream, IL 60188-2095. TEL 630-462-2229, FAX 630-462-2202, swyant@farmprogress.com, info@farmprogress.com, http://www.farmprogress.com, http://www.farmprogress.com/. Ed. Len Richardson TEL 925-687-1662. Adv. contact Don Tourte. B&W page USD 2,150, color page USD 2,650; trim 10.5 x 14.5. Circ: 40,000 (paid).

630 USA ISSN 0008-1124
CALIFORNIA GRANGE NEWS. Text in English. 1932. bi-m. USD 7 (effective 2005). adv. bk.rev. illus. **Document type:** *Magazine, Trade.*
Published by: California State Grange, 2101 Stockton Blvd, Sacramento, CA 95817. TEL 916-454-5805, FAX 916-739-8189, jdhartz@grangeonline.com, http://www.grange.org. Ed., Adv. contact J D Hartz. Pub. Thomas Stefenoni. col. inch USD 15. Circ: 21,210 (paid and controlled).

631 USA ISSN 0744-2653
CALIFORNIA ORNAMENTAL CROPS REPORT. Text in English. s-w. looseleaf. USD 132. back issues avail. **Document type:** *Newspaper, Government.* **Description:** Presents lists of shipping points, market conditions, price ranges, product quality, and wholesale markets pertaining to cut flowers in- and out-of-state.
Published by: (U.S. Department of Agriculture), Federal-State Market News Service (Sacramento), 630 Sansome St, Rm 727, San Francisco, CA 94111. TEL 415-705-1300, FAX 415-705-1301. Circ: 150.

631 USA ISSN 0194-8504
CALIFORNIA STRAWBERRY REPORT. Text in English. s-w. looseleaf. USD 99; USD 198 foreign. back issues avail. **Document type:** *Government.* **Description:** Presents lists of shipments, market conditions, wholesale prices, product quality, and produce distribution of this fruit from and throughout the state.
Published by: (U.S. Department of Agriculture), Federal-State Market News Service (Sacramento), 630 Sansome St, Rm 727, San Francisco, CA 94111. TEL 415-705-1300, FAX 415-705-1301. Circ: 100.

630 USA
CALIFORNIA VEGETABLE JOURNAL. Text in English. **Document type:** *Magazine, Trade.* **Description:** Covers news and issues of interest to vegetable farmers and crop growers in California.
Published by: Rincon Publishing, 1419 E. Valley Rd., Santa Barbara, CA 93108-1204. TEL 805-684-6581, FAX 805-684-1535, rincon@rinconpublishing.com, http://www.rinconpublishing.com/cvj/vegetable_journal.html.

630 635 GBR ISSN 0954-9617
CAMBRIDGESHIRE FARMERS. Text in English. 1947. m. adv. bk.rev.
Formerly: Cambridgeshire Farmers' Journal
Published by: County Farmers Publications Ltd., 55 Goldington Rd, Bedford, Beds MK40 3LU, United Kingdom. TEL 44-1234-351401, FAX 44-1234-328614. Ed. D Brown. Circ: 3,450.

630 CMR ISSN 0527-4257
S19
CAMEROUN AGRICOLE, PASTORALE ET FORESTIER ✶. Text in French. 1957. 6/yr. adv.
Published by: Chambre d'Agriculture et des Forets du Cameroun, Parc Repiquet, BP L89, Yaounde, Cameroon.

630 ESP
CAMP VALENCIA. Text in Spanish. 1977. m.
Published by: Unio de Llavrador i Ramaders del Pais Valencia, Avellanas, 17 3o, Valencia, 46003, Spain. TEL 6-931-31-93, FAX 6-391-59-47. Ed. Eloi Casanovas. Circ: 10,000.

983 CHL ISSN 0008-2341
CAMPESINO. Text in Spanish. 1838. m. CLP 10,000 (effective 2002). adv. abstr.; illus.; stat. index.
Published by: Sociedad Nacional de Agricultura, Casilla 40-D, Tenderini, 187, Santiago, Chile. TEL 56-2-6396710, info@sna.cl, http://www.sna.cl. Ed. Patricio Montt. Circ: 5,000.

630 332 ESP ISSN 0212-2146
CAMPO; boletin de informacion agraria. Text in Spanish. 1967. q. free. charts; illus.; stat. cum.index.
Indexed: IECT.
—CINDOC.
Published by: Banco de Bilbao - Vizcaya, Servicio de Estudios, Gran Via 1, Bilbao, 48001, Spain. TEL 94-447 71 00, TELEX 32055 BB AC. Ed. Sabino Larrea Ereno.

630 MEX ISSN 0008-2473
EL CAMPO; revista mensual agricola y ganadera. Text in Spanish. 1924. m. MXP 750. adv. bk.rev.
Published by: Publicaciones Armol, S.A., Mar Negro No. 147, Apdo. Postal 17-506, Mexico City, DF 11410, Mexico. Ed. Armando Palafox Flores. Circ: 35,000.

630 USA ISSN 0211-4704
CAMPO Y MECANICA; journal of popular farm science and rural life. Text in Spanish. 1960. 4/yr. free to qualified personnel.
Related titles: ♦ German ed.: Flur und Furche. ISSN 0015-4733; ♦ English ed.: Furrow. ISSN 0016-3112; ♦ Swedish ed.: Faran; ♦ Spanish ed.: Surco Argentina; ♦ Norwegian ed.: Fara; ♦ Spanish ed.: Surco Mexicana; Afrikaans ed.: 1895; Danish ed.: 1895; Dutch ed.: 1895; French ed.: 1895; Italian ed.: 1895; Portuguese ed.: 1895.
Published by: John Deere Publishing, One John Deere Place, Moline, IL 61265. TEL 309-765-8000. Ed. Jean Claude Hiron. Circ: 203,000.

338.1 CAN ISSN 1207-621X
CANADA. AGRICULTURE & AGRI-FOOD CANADA. POLICY BRANCH. BI-WEEKLY BULLETIN. Text in English. 1988. bi-w. free (effective 2004). **Description:** Provides market information and analysis on specific issues covering domestic and international grains, oilseeds, and pulse and special crop markets.
Related titles: Online - full text ed.: ISSN 1494-1805.
—CISTI.
Published by: Agriculture & Agri-Food Canada, Market Analysis Division, 500-303 Main St, Winnipeg, MB R3C 3G7, Canada. bulletin@agr.gc.ca.

638.1 CAN ISSN 0576-4688
CANADIAN BEEKEEPING. Text in English. 1968. 6/yr. CND 21.40 domestic; USD 20 in United States; CND 60 foreign (effective 2005). adv. **Document type:** *Trade.*
Indexed: ApicAb, SIA.
—CISTI.
Published by: Beekeeping Industry in Canada, P O Box 678, Tottenham, ON L0G 1W0, Canada. TEL 905-936-4975. Ed. W J R Arnott. adv.: B&W page CND 420.

571.2 578 CAN
CODEN: CPDSAS
CANADIAN PLANT DISEASE SURVEY. Text in English. 1921. q. free. charts; illus. index, cum.index: 1954-1994. **Document type:** *Government.* **Description:** Reports the occurrence and severity of plant diseases in each province of Canada.
Media: Diskette. **Related titles:** E-mail ed.
Indexed: ASCA, ASFA, Agr, BiolAb, CurCont, FCA, ForAb, HerbAb, HortAb, ISR, MBA, MaizeAb, PBA, PlantSci, RPP, S&F, SeedAb, SoyAb, TriticAb.
Published by: Agriculture and Agri-Food Canada, Southern Crop Protection and Food Research Centre, 1391 Sandford St, London, ON N5V 4T3, Canada. TEL 519-457-1470, FAX 519-457-3997, hiltons@em.agr.ca, http://res.agr.ca/lond/pmrc/pmrchome.html, http://www.agr.gc.ca/. Ed., Pub. Stephanie Hilton. Circ: 800.

630 CAN ISSN 0841-209X
CANOLA GUIDE. Text in English. 1987. 7/yr. adv. **Document type:** *Trade.* **Description:** Published for canola growers in western Canada interested in increasing the efficiency and profitability of their operations.
Related titles: ♦ Supplement to: Country Guide. ISSN 0383-7114.
—CISTI.
Published by: Farm Business Communications, P O Box 6600, Winnipeg, MB R3C 3A7, Canada. TEL 204-944-5761, FAX 204-942-8463. Ed. Bill Strautman. Adv. contact Tom Mumby. Circ: 25,641.

630 CHN ISSN 0258-4069
CANSANG TONGBAO/SERICULTURE BULLETIN. Text in Chinese; Summaries in Chinese, English. 1954. q. CNY 20 (effective 2001). adv. 64 p./no.; **Document type:** *Bulletin.*
Related titles: Online - full text ed.: (from East View Information Services).
Published by: Zhejiang Cansang Xuehui/Zhejiang Sericulture Society, Huajiachi Campus, Zhejiang University, 268 Kaixuan Rd, Hangzhou, Zhejiang 310029, China. TEL 86-571-86433341, FAX 86-571-86433341. Ed. Xu Junliang. Adv. contact Jinhua Hu. Circ: 4,000.

630 634.9 USA ISSN 0740-3704
CAPITAL PRESS; regional Oregon, Idaho, Washington, N. California agricultural-forest weekly. Text in English. 1928. w. (Fri.). USD 44 (effective 2005). adv. 56 p./no.; back issues avail. **Document type:** *Newspaper.*
Published by: Press Publishing Co., 1400 Broadway, N.E., Salem, OR 97303. TEL 503-364-4431, FAX 503-370-4383, newsroom@capitalpress.com, http://www.capitalpress.com. Ed., Pub. Elaine Shein. Adv. contact Greg Hains. Circ: 36,328. Wire service: AP.

THE CARETAKER GAZETTE; number 1 source for caretaker jobs!. see *OCCUPATIONS AND CAREERS*

630 570 HND ISSN 0008-8692
CODEN: CEIBAR
➤ **CEIBA.** Text in English, Spanish. 1950. s-a. USD 20 (effective 2000). adv. bk.rev. charts; illus. cum.index. reprint service avail. from PQC. **Document type:** *Academic/Scholarly.*
Related titles: Microform ed.: (from PQC).
Indexed: AgrForAb, AnBrAb, BioCN&I, BiolAb, CPA, ChemAb, DSA, FCA, ForAb, HerbAb, HortAb, I&DA, MaizeAb, NutrAb, OrnHort, PBA, PGegResA, PN&I, PotatoAb, PoultAb, RA&MP, RDA, RPP, RefZh, RevApplEntom, RiceAb, S&F, SFA, SeedAb, TriticAb, WAE&RSA, WeedAb, WildRev, ZooRec.
—CINDOC, CISTI, Linda Hall.
Published by: (Escuela Agricola Panamericana), Zamorano Academic Press, Apdo. 93, Tegucigalpa D C, Honduras. TEL 504-7766140, FAX 504-7766240, apitty@zamorano.edu.hn. Ed., R&P, Adv. contact Abelino Pitty. Circ: 1,000.

➤ **CENICAFE.** see *FOOD AND FOOD INDUSTRIES*

➤ **CENSO AGROPECUARIO.** see *AGRICULTURE—Abstracting, Bibliographies, Statistics*

➤ **CENSUS OF AGRICULTURE. VOLUME 3: SPECIAL STUDIES. FARM AND RANCH IRRIGATION SURVEY.** see *AGRICULTURE—Abstracting, Bibliographies, Statistics*

630 USA ISSN 1085-4975
CENTER FOR RURAL AFFAIRS NEWSLETTER; a newsletter surveying events affecting rural America. Text in English. 1974. m. free. **Document type:** *Newsletter.* **Description:** Covers agricultural and policy issues of interest to family farmers and ranchers, small businesses, and rural communities.
Published by: Center for Rural Affairs, PO Box 405, Walthill, NE 68067. TEL 402-846-5428, FAX 402-846-5420, info@cfra.org, http://www.cfra.org. Ed., Pub., R&P Marie Powell. Circ: 7,000.

630 TWN ISSN 0258-3070
CODEN: RBMBDO
CENTERPOINT. Text in English. 1981. 3/yr. **Document type:** *Newsletter, Academic/Scholarly.* **Description:** Contains the latest news about the association and the vegetable research field.
Published by: Asian Vegetable Research and Development Center, Shanhua, PO Box 42, Tainan, 741, Taiwan. TEL 886-6-5837801, FAX 886-6-5830009, avrdcbox@netra.avrdc.org.tw, http://www.avrdc.org.tw. Ed. Ming-Tong Kow. Pub., R&P Yu-Shing Kow TEL 886-2-2362-8148 ext 11. Adv. contact Fu-Jung Chien.

630 NZL
CENTRAL DISTRICTS FARMER. Text in English. w. **Document type:** *Newspaper, Trade.*
Published by: Manawatu Standard Ltd (Subsidiary of: Independent Newspapers Ltd.), 57-64 The Sq, PO Box 3, Palmerston North, New Zealand. TEL 64-6-3235839, FAX 64-6-3509541, cdfarmer@inspire.net.nz. Ed. Peter Keane. Circ: 13,344.

630 IND ISSN 0374-7115
CENTRAL PLANTATION CROPS RESEARCH INSTITUTE. ANNUAL REPORT. Text in English. 1970. a. free. **Document type:** *Corporate.*
Indexed: BiolAb.
Published by: Central Plantation Crops Research Institute, KSD District, Kasaragod, Kerala 671 124, India. TEL 91-499-430893, FAX 91-499-430322, TELEX 08001202 PALM IN, cpcri@x400.nicgw.nic.in. Circ: 450.

338.1 IND
CENTRAL PLANTATION CROPS RESEARCH INSTITUTE. NEWSLETTER. Text in English, Hindi. 1975. q. free. **Document type:** *Newsletter.*
Published by: Central Plantation Crops Research Institute, KSD District, Kasaragod, Kerala 671 124, India. TEL 91-499-430893, FAX 91-499-430322, cpcri@x400.nicgw.nic.in. Ed. A R S Menon.

630 580 IND
CENTRAL PLANTATION CROPS RESEARCH INSTITUTE. RESEARCH HIGHLIGHTS. Text in English. 1980. a. free. **Document type:** *Corporate.*
Published by: Central Plantation Crops Research Institute, KSD District, Kasaragod, Kerala 671 124, India. TEL 91-499-430893, FAX 91-499-430322, cpcri@400.nicgw.nic.in. Circ: 400.

A

630 622 636 381   AUS
CENTRAL QUEENSLAND NEWS. Text in English. 1937. s-w. AUD 29.50.
Published by: Central Queensland News Publishing Co., PO Box 259, Emerald, QLD 4720, Australia. Ed. Peter Cliff. Circ: 4,717.

638.2   IND   ISSN 0304-6818
SF542.75.I52
CENTRAL SERICULTURAL RESEARCH AND TRAINING INSTITUTE. ANNUAL REPORT. Key Title: Annual Report - Central Sericultural Research and Training Institute. Text in English. 1964. a. INR 100, USD 20 (effective 1999). **Document type:** *Government.*
Published by: Central Sericultural Research & Training Institute, Srirampuram, Manandavadi Rd., Mysore, Karnataka 570 008, India. FAX 91-821-480845, TELEX 0846 203 CSRI IN, csrti@nicfos.ernet.in. Circ: 300 (controlled).

630   GBR
CENTRAL SOUTHERN FARMER. Text in English. 1964. m. adv.
Formerly: Surrey N.F.U. Journal (0039-6176)
Published by: County Farmers Publications Ltd., 55 Goldington Rd, Bedford, Beds MK40 3LU, United Kingdom. TEL 44-1234-351401, FAX 44-1234-328614. Ed. N Errington. Circ: 2,500.

630   GBR
CENTRE FOR AGRICULTURAL STRATEGY SERIES. Text in English. irreg., latest no.38, 1999, June. price varies. back issues avail. **Document type:** *Monographic series.*
Description: Profiles the state of agriculture in individual countries, with particular emphasis on the developing nations.
Published by: Centre for Agricultural Strategy, 1 Earley Gate, The University, Whiteknights Rd, PO Box 237, Reading, RG6 6AR, United Kingdom. TEL 44-118-9318150, FAX 44-118-9353423, casagri@reading.ac.uk, http://www.rdg.ac.uk/AgriStrat/.

354.69   MDG
CENTRE NATIONAL DE RECHERCHES APPLIQUES AU DEVELOPPEMENT RURAL. DEPARTEMENT DE RECHERCHES AGRONOMIQUES. RAPPORT ANNUEL. Text in French. a.
Published by: Centre National de la Recherche Appliquee au Developpement Rural, Departement de Recherches Agronomiques, BP 1690, Antananarivo, Madagascar.

630   MDG
CENTRE NATIONAL DE RECHERCHES APPLIQUES AU DEVELOPPEMENT RURAL. DEPARTEMENT DE RECHERCHES AGRONOMIQUES. RAPPORT D'ACTIVITE. Text in French. irreg.
Published by: Centre National de la Recherche Appliquee au Developpement Rural, Departement de Recherches Agronomiques, BP 1690, Antananarivo, Madagascar.

630   ESP
CENTRO DE EDAFOLOGIA Y BIOLOGIA APLICADA DEL SEGURA. MONOGRAFIAS. Text in Spanish. 1950. irreg. price varies. **Document type:** *Monographic series, Academic/Scholarly.*
Published by: Centro de Edafologia y Biologia Aplicada del Segura, Avda. de la Fama, 1, Murcia, 30080, Spain.

630   MEX   ISSN 0084-8697
CENTRO DE INVESTIGACIONES AGRICOLAS DE TAMAULIPAS. INFORME ANUAL DE LABORES. Text in Spanish. 1968. a. free.
Published by: Centro de Investigaciones Agricolas de Tamaulipas, Apdo. Postal 172, Rio Bravo, TAMAULIPAS, Mexico.

631.091   BRA
CENTRO DE PESQUISA AGROFLORESTAL DA AMAZONIA ORIENTAL. BOLETIM DE PESQUISA. Text in Portuguese; Summaries in English, Portuguese. 1976. irreg. price varies. bibl.; charts; stat. **Document type:** *Bulletin.*
Former titles (until 1992): Centro de Pesquisa Agropecuaria do Tropico Umido. Boletim de Pesquisa (0100-8102); (until 1980): Instituto de Pesquisa Agropecuaria do Norte. Boletim Tecnico
Indexed: AEA, ATA, Agrind, BibAg, HerbAb, IndVet, NutrAb, ProtozoAb, S&F, SIA, VetBull.
Published by: Empresa Brasileira de Pesquisa Agropecuaria, Centro de Pesquisa Agroflorestal da Amazonia Oriental (Subsidiary of: Empresa Brasileira de Pesquisa Agropecuaria), Trav,Dr.Eneas Pinheiro s/n - Marco, Belem, PA 66095-100, Brazil. TEL 55-91-2766333, FAX 55-91-2760323, sac@cpatu.embrapa.br, http://www.embrapa.br. Circ: 1,000.

630   BRA   ISSN 0100-0845
CODEN: BTCPBW
CENTRO DE PESQUISAS DO CACAU. BOLETIM TECNICO. Text in Portuguese. 1970. irreg. BRL 5, USD 10 per issue (effective 2001). **Document type:** *Bulletin.*
Indexed: BiolAb, S&F, WeedAb.
—CISTI, Linda Hall.

Published by: (Brazil. Comissao Executiva do Plano da Lavoura Cacaueira), Centro de Pesquisas do Cacau/Cacao Research Center, Caixa Postal 7, Itabuna, BA 45600-970, Brazil. TEL 55-73-214-3217, FAX 55-73-2143218, agrotrop@cepec.gov.br, http://www.cepec.gov.br/agrotrop. Eds. Miguel Moreno Ruiz, Paulo Dos Santos Terra. Circ: 400.

630   BRA   ISSN 0102-4256
SB268.B6
CENTRO DE PESQUISAS DO CACAU. INFORME DE PESQUISAS. Text in Portuguese. 1963. a.
Formerly: Centro de Pesquisas do Cacau. Informe Tecnico (0100-5065)
Indexed: AEA, BiolAb.
—CISTI, Linda Hall.
Published by: (Brazil. Comissao Executiva do Plano da Lavoura Cacaueira), Centro de Pesquisas do Cacau/Cacao Research Center, Caixa Postal 7, Itabuna, BA 45600-970, Brazil. TEL 55-73-214-3217, FAX 55-73-2143218, http://www.cepec.gov.br/agrotrop. Eds. Miguel Moreno Ruiz, Paulo Dos Santos Terra.

631   DOM   ISSN 1560-5744
CENTRO PARA EL DESARROLLO AGROPECUARIO Y FORESTAL. BOLETIN. Key Title: Boletin CEDAF. Text in Spanish. 1988. m. back issues avail.
Formerly (until 1998): Fundacion de Desarrollo Agropecuario. Boletin (1018-4546)
Related titles: Online - full text ed.: ISSN 1684-0038. 2001.
Published by: Centro para el Desarrollo Agropecuario y Forestal, C. Jose Amado Soler, 50, Ensanche Paraiso, Santo Domingo, Dominican Republic. TEL 809-5440616, FAX 809-5444727, cedaf@cedaf.org.do, http://www.cedaf.org.do/publica/boletines.htm.

CESKA ZEMEDELSKA A POTRAVINARSKA BIBLIOGRAFIE. see *AGRICULTURE—Abstracting, Bibliographies, Statistics*

630   ARG   ISSN 0325-7932
CHACRA Y CAMPO MODERNO. Text in Spanish. 1930. m. adv. illus. **Document type:** *Magazine, Consumer.* **Description:** Covers farming and the countryside.
Former titles (until 199?): Campo Moderno y Chacra (0325-7940); (until 1975): Chacra y Campo Moderno (1514-2442); (until 1974): Chacra (0009-0913)
Published by: Editorial Atlantida S.A., Azopardo 579, 3 piso, Capital Federal, Buenos Aires 1307, Argentina. TEL 54-11-4331-3865, FAX 54-11-4343-1362, info@atlantidadigital.com.ar, http://www.atlantida.com.ar. Ed. Constancio C Vigil. Circ: 35,000.

630   FRA   ISSN 0396-7883
CHAMBRES D'AGRICULTURE. Text in French. 1929. m. (11/yr.).
Former titles: Chambres d'Agriculture. Circulaire (1155-6986); (until 1941): Agriculture en Temps de Guerre (1155-6994); Which was formed by the merger of: Chambres d'Agriculture. Serie E, Faits et Documents (1155-7044); Chambres d'Agriculture. Serie C, les Pouvoirs Publics (1155-7028); Chambres d'Agriculture. Serie A, les Travaux des Chambres d'Agriculture (1155-7001)
Indexed: AEA, AbHyg, AgBio, DSA, FPA, FS&TA, ForAb, HortAb, IndVet, MaizeAb, NutrAb, PBA, PGegResA, PHN&I, PN&I, PoultAb, RDA, RPP, RRTA, S&F, SIA, SoyAb, TriticAb, VetBull, WAE&RSA.
—BLDSC (3129.550000).
Published by: Assemblee Permanente des Chambres d'Agriculture, Maison des Chambres d'Agriculture, 9 av. George V, Paris, 75008, France. TEL 33-1-47235540, FAX 33-1-47238497. Ed. Lucien Bourgeois. Pub. L Goupilleau.

CHARTERED INSTITUTE OF PUBLIC FINANCE AND ACCOUNTANCY. COUNTY FARMS STATISTICS. ACTUALS. see *AGRICULTURE—Abstracting, Bibliographies, Statistics*

630   USA
CHAUTAUQUA COUNTY AGRICULTURAL NEWS. Text in English. 1918. m. USD 10 (effective 2005). adv. **Document type:** *Newsletter, Trade.* **Description:** Contains information on dairy, livestock, farm business, free fruits and business management.
Published by: Cornell Cooperative Extension Association of Chautauqua County, 3542 Turner Rd, Ste 1, Jamestown, NY 14701-9608. TEL 716-664-9502, FAX 716-664-6327. Ed. Andrew Dufresne. Adv. contact Emily Runge. Circ: 700 (paid).

630   GBR   ISSN 0954-9641
CHESHIRE FARMER. Text in English. 1963. m. adv.
Published by: County Farmers Publications Ltd., 55 Goldington Rd, Bedford, Beds MK40 3LU, United Kingdom. TEL 44-1234-351401, FAX 44-1234-328614. Ed. R Bacon. Circ: 3,000.

630   CHL   ISSN 0379-5845
S193
CHILE AGRICOLA; la revista agreocologica. Text in Spanish. 1975. 8/yr., latest vol.16, no.249, 2001. USD 37 domestic; USD 75 in the Americas; USD 85 in Europe (effective 2001). adv. bk.rev. index. 48 p./no.; back issues avail. **Document type:** *Magazine, Trade.* **Description:** Covers agricultural economics, equipment, crop production and soil, dairying and dairy products, feed, flour, and animals.

Address: Casilla 2, Correo, 13, Teresa Vial 1172, Santiago, Chile. TEL 56-2-5222627, chilagric@chile.com. Ed., Adv. contact Raul Gonzalez Valenzuela. Pub. Ricardo Gonzalez Hidalgo. B&W page USD 870, color page USD 1,440; 27.5 x 21.5. Circ: 7,000 (paid).

630   CHL
CHILE. INSTITUTO DE INVESTIGACIONES AGROPECUARIAS. MEMORIA ANUAL. Text in Spanish. 1965. a. per issue exchange basis.
Indexed: AnBrAb, VITIS.
Published by: Instituto de Investigaciones Agropecuarias, Casilla 439, Correo, 3, Santiago, Chile. TEL 5417223, FAX 56-2-5417667.

CHILE. INSTITUTO NACIONAL DE ESTADISTICAS. ESTADISTICAS AGROPECUARIAS. see *AGRICULTURE— Abstracting, Bibliographies, Statistics*

CHINA FOOD & AGRICULTURE. see *FOOD AND FOOD INDUSTRIES*

630   CHN
CHINESE ACADEMIC JOURNALS FULL-TEXT DATABASE. AGRICULTURE. Text in Chinese, English. m. USD 120 for the 1st series; USD 6 for each additonal series (effective 2003). **Document type:** *Academic/Scholarly.* **Description:** Covers agriculture, forestry, livestock, fishing, aquatic product, plant protection, horticulture, irrigation works, ecology, agricultural Machine, biology.
Media: CD-ROM (from Tsinghua Tongfang Optical Disc Co., Ltd.).
Related titles: ♦ Online - full content ed.: C N K I Web; Online - full text ed.: (from East View Information Services); (from East View Information Services); ♦ Print ed.: Dalian Shuichan Xueyuan Xuebao. ISSN 1000-9957; ♦ Jiangsu Linye Keji. ISSN 1001-7380; ♦ Zhejiang Nongye Xuebao. ISSN 1004-1524; ♦ Beifang Yuanyi. ISSN 1001-0009.
Published by: Tsinghua Tongfang Optical Disc Co., Ltd., Room 1300, Huaye Building, Tsing Hua University, PO BOX 84-48, Beijing, 100084, China. TEL 86-1-62791819, FAX 86-1-62791944, Beijing@cnki.net, http://www.cnki.net.
Co-sponsor: Tsinghua University.

630 660.6   GBR   ISSN 1479-2362
▼ **CHINESE JOURNAL OF AGRICULTURAL BIOTECHNOLOGY.** Text in English. 2004 (Apr.). 3/yr. USD 710 in the Americas to institutions except Canada; GBP 405 elsewhere to institutions; USD 760 combined subscription in the Americas to institutions except Canada; print & online eds.; GBP 435 combined subscription elsewhere to institutions print & online eds. (effective 2006). **Document type:** *Journal, Academic/Scholarly.* **Description:** Features high quality Chinese research translated into English and presented alongside specially commissioned material to provide a wider context.
Related titles: Online - full text ed.: USD 605 in the Americas to institutions except Canada; GBP 345 elsewhere to institutions (effective 2006) (from EBSCO Publishing, Gale Group, IngentaConnect, Swets Information Services).
—BLDSC (3180.290570), IE. **CCC.**
Published by: CABI Publishing (Subsidiary of: CAB International), CAB International, Wallingford, Oxfordshire OX10 8DE, United Kingdom. TEL 44-1491-832111, FAX 44-1491-833508, cabi@cabi.org, http://www.cabi-publishing.org/. Ed. R Hull. Pub. Sarah Peck TEL 44-1491-829304.

630 643.9   USA   ISSN 0199-0217
CHRISTMAS TREES MAGAZINE; a magazine of plantation management for Christmas tree growers. Text in English. 1973. q. USD 16 domestic; USD 17 in Canada & Mexico; USD 35 elsewhere; USD 4 per issue domestic (effective 2004). adv. back issues avail. **Document type:** *Magazine, Trade.* **Description:** Covers various aspects of the grower's operations from planting, insect and weed control, to shearing, shaping and marketing. For Christmas tree growers, wholesale and retail.
Published by: Tree Publishers, Inc., PO Box 107, Lecompton, KS 66050-0107. ctreesmag@aol.com, http://www.christmastreesmagazine.com/. Ed., Adv. contact Catherine Wright Howard. Pub. Chuck Wright. Circ: 4,748 (paid).

630   BRA   ISSN 0045-6888
CODEN: CIAGDX
➤ **CIENCIA AGRONOMICA.** Text in Portuguese; Summaries in English. 1971. s-a. USD 10 (effective 2002). bibl.; charts; illus. **Document type:** *Journal, Academic/Scholarly.*
Indexed: AnBrAb, BiolAb, CPA, ChemAb, FCA, ForAb, HortAb, I&DA, IndVet, OrnHort, PBA, PGegResA, PHN&I, RefZh, S&F, SeedAb, WAE&RSA.
—CASDDS, CISTI.
Published by: Universidade Federal do Ceara, Centro de Ciencias Agrarias, Ave. Mister Hull, Benfica, Caixa Postal 12168, Fortaleza, CE 60021-970, Brazil. TEL 55-88-2889732, FAX 55-88-2889419, ccapesq@ufc.br, http://sw.npd.ufc.br/ccapesquisa. Ed., R&P Sebastiao Medeiro Filho. Circ: 700.

630   PAN   ISSN 0258-6452
CIENCIA AGROPECUARIA. Text in Spanish; Summaries in English. 1978. a. USD 3.50. abstr.; bibl.; charts.
Indexed: AnBrAb, DSA, FCA, HerbAb, MaizeAb, PBA, PotatoAb, RPP, RefZh, RevApplEntom, RiceAb, WeedAb.

Published by: Instituto de Investigacion Agropecuaria de Panama, Centro de Informacion Documental Agropecuaria, Apdo. 6-4391, El Dorado, Panama City, 6a, Panama. TELEX 3677 PG. Ed. Elizabeth de Ruiloba. Circ: 1,000.

630 BRA ISSN 1413-7054
S15 CODEN: CIAGFZ
CIENCIA E AGROTECNOLOGIA. Text in Portuguese. 1977. q.
Formerly (until 1995): Ciencia e Pratica (0100-3267)
Indexed: AEA, AgBio, AgrForAb, AnBrAb, BIOSIS Prev, BioCN&I, BiolAb, CPA, DSA, FCA, FPA, ForAb, HerbAb, HortAb, I&DA, IndVet, MaizeAb, NemAb, NutrAb, OrnHort, PBA, PGegResA, PGrRegA, PHN&I, PN&I, PotatoAb, PoultAb, RA&MP, RDA, RM&VM, RPP, RiceAb, S&F, SIA, SeedAb, SoyAb, TDB, TriticAb, VITIS, VetBull, WAE&RSA, WeedAb.
Published by: Universidade Federal de Lavras, Campus Universitario, CP 37, Lavras, MG 37200-000, Brazil. TEL 55-35-38291122, FAX 55-35-38291100, http://www.ufla.br.

630 CHL ISSN 0304-5609
CODEN: CINADC
➤ **CIENCIA E INVESTIGACION AGRARIA.** Text in Spanish; Summaries in English. 1974. 3/yr. CLP 12,000; USD 50 foreign. adv. bk.rev. stat. **Document type:** *Academic/Scholarly.* **Description:** Original papers on agricultural research including soil sciences, crop sciences, animal sciences, fruit culture and technology, and agricultural economics.
Indexed: AgBio, AgrForAb, AnBrAb, B&AI, BioCN&I, CPA, ChemAb, DSA, FCA, FPA, FS&TA, ForAb, HerbAb, HortAb, I&DA, IndVet, MaizeAb, NutrAb, OrnHort, PBA, PGegResA, PGrRegA, PHN&I, PotatoAb, PoultAb, RA&MP, RDA, RM&VM, RPP, RevApplEntom, S&F, SIA, SeedAb, SoyAb, TriticAb, VetBull, WAE&RSA, WeedAb.
—CASDDS, CINDOC.
Published by: Pontificia Universidad Catolica de Chile, Facultad de Agronomia, Casilla 114-D, Santiago, Chile. TEL 56-2-6865704, FAX 56-2-5526005, rcia@puc.cl. Ed. Gaston Pichard. R&P Catalina Bay Schmith. Adv. contact Catalina Bay-Schmith. Circ: 300.

630 636.08 BRA ISSN 0103-8478
CODEN: CIRUEP
➤ **CIENCIA RURAL.** Text and summaries in English, Portuguese. 1971. bi-m. USD 30 domestic; USD 45 foreign (effective 2003). adv. bk.rev. bibl.; charts; illus. 200 p./no.; back issues avail. **Document type:** *Journal, Academic/Scholarly.*
Formerly (until 1990, vol.20): Centro de Ciencias Rurais. Revista (0085-5901)
Related titles: Online - full text ed.: free (effective 2005) (from H.W. Wilson).
Indexed: AEA, AbHyg, AgBio, AgrForAb, AnBrAb, BioCN&I, CPA, ChemAb, DSA, FCA, FPA, ForAb, HelmAb, HerbAb, HortAb, I&DA, IndVet, M&GPA, MaizeAb, NemAb, NutrAb, OrnHort, PBA, PGegResA, PGrRegA, PHN&I, PN&I, PotatoAb, PoultAb, ProtozoAb, RA&MP, RDA, RM&VM, RPP, RevApplEntom, RiceAb, S&F, SIA, SeedAb, SoyAb, TDB, TriticAb, VetBull, WAE&RSA, WeedAb, WildRev, ZooRec.
—CASDDS, CISTI.
Published by: Universidade Federal de Santa Maria, Centro de Ciencias Rurais, Campus Universitario, Santa Maria, RGS 97105-900, Brazil. TEL 55-55-220-8698, FAX 55-55-220-8695, TELEX 552230 UFSM BR, rudi@ccr.ufsm.br, http://www.ufsm.br/ccr/revista/. Ed., Adv. contact Rudi Weiblen TEL 55-55-2208034. Circ: 1,200 (controlled).

630 CUB
CIENCIA Y TECNICA EN LA AGRICULTURA. SERIE: APICULTURA. Abstracts and contents page in English. 1985. a. USD 6 in the Americas; USD 7 in Europe.
Indexed: Agrind, SIA.
Published by: Centro de Informacion y Documentacion Agropecuario, Gaveta Postal 4149, Havana, 4, Cuba. **Dist. by:** Ediciones Cubanas, Obispo No. 527, Apdo. 605, Havana, Cuba.

630 CUB ISSN 0255-8602
S15 CODEN: CAGRD6
CIENCIAS DE LA AGRICULTURA. Text in Spanish; Summaries in English. 1966. irreg. USD 16 in North America; USD 18 in South America; USD 19 in Europe; USD 21 elsewhere. bibl.; charts; illus.
Formerly (until 1977): Revista de Agricultura (0034-7671)
Indexed: AnBrAb, BioDAb, ChemAb, EIP, ExcerpMed, FCA, HerbAb, HortAb, I&DA, INIS AtomInd, IndVet, MaizeAb, PBA, PGrRegA, RPP, RevApplEntom, S&F, SIA, SeedAb, SoyAb, TriticAb, VetBull, WeedAb.
—CISTI.
Published by: Academia de Ciencias de Cuba, Capitolio, Havana, 12400, Cuba. acc@ceniai.cu, http://www.cuba.cu/ciencia/acc/.

630 MEX ISSN 0084-8689
CIRCULAR C I A T. Text in Spanish. 1968. a. free.
Published by: Centro de Investigaciones Agricolas de Tamaulipas, Apdo. Postal 172, Rio Bravo, TAMAULIPAS, Mexico.

634.6 IDN ISSN 0854-5006
COCOINFO INTERNATIONAL. Text in English. 1993. s-a. USD 25 in Asia & the Pacific; USD 30 elsewhere (effective 2001). **Description:** Promotes processing and marketing of coconut products, featuring technology corner, face to face interview with prominent figure in coconut industry, market outlook, coco events, and statistics.
Published by: Asian and Pacific Coconut Community, 3rd Fl., Lina Bldg., Jl H R Rasuna Said Kav B 7, Kuningan, Jakarta, 12920, Indonesia. TEL 62-21-5221712, FAX 62-21-5221714, apcc@indo.net.id, http://www.apcc.org.sg/.

634 LKA ISSN 0255-4119
COCONUT BULLETIN. Text in English. 1960. s-a. LKR 10, USD 2.50 (effective 2000). adv. abstr.; charts; illus.; stat. cum.index. **Document type:** *Bulletin.* **Description:** Source of information for coconut growers.
Formerly (until 1983): Ceylon Coconut Planters' Review (0009-0816)
Indexed: ATA, AgrForAb, BiolAb, ChemAb, FCA, HortAb, ISA, SLSI, TOSA.
—CISTI.
Published by: Coconut Research Institute, Bandirippuwa Estate, Lunuwila, Sri Lanka. TEL 94-31-253795, FAX 94-31-57391. Circ: 1,500.

634 LKA
COCONUT RESEARCH INSTITUTE. ANNUAL REPORT. Text in English. a. USD 10 (effective 2000). **Document type:** *Corporate.* **Description:** Contains details of experiments, research findings and different activities and programs.
Published by: Coconut Research Institute, Bandirippuwa Estate, Lunuwila, Sri Lanka. TEL 94-31-253795, FAX 94-31-57391.

630 FJI
COCONUT TELEGRAPH. Text in English. 1975. m. **Description:** Serves widely-scattered rural communities.
Address: Vanua Levu, PO Box 249, Savusavu, Fiji. Ed. Mrs. Lema Low.

634 LKA ISSN 0255-4100
CODEN: COCSEK
COCOS. Text in English. 1950. a. LKR 20, USD 5 (effective 2000). adv. bibl.; charts; illus. cum.index every 10 yrs. back issues avail.; reprints avail. **Description:** Technical articles and research notes on coconuts.
Formerly (until 1983): Ceylon Coconut Quarterly (0009-0824)
Indexed: AEA, ATA, AgBio, AgrForAb, BioCN&I, BiolAb, CPA, ChemAb, FCA, HortAb, I&DA, ISA, PBA, PHN&I, RDA, RPP, RevApplEntom, S&F, SIA, SLSI, SeedAb, TDB, TOSA, WAE&RSA.
—CISTI. **CCC.**
Published by: Coconut Research Institute, Bandirippuwa Estate, Lunuwila, Sri Lanka. TEL 94-31-55300, FAX 94-31-57391, dircri@sri.lanka.net. Ed. C Jayasehera. Circ: 500.

630 BRA
COLECCAO C E D E S. GRANDES TEMAS✶. Text in Portuguese. 1982. irreg.
Published by: Camara de Estudos e Debates Economicos e Sociais, c/o Paulo Robello de Castro, Rua da Quitanda, 68 Andar 4, Centro, Rio De Janeiro, RJ 20011-030, Brazil.

630 COL
COLEGA AGROPECUARIO. Text in Spanish. 1976. irreg.
Published by: Sociedad de Ingenieros Agronomos de Antioquia, Apdo. Aereos 51185, Calle 54, 45-36, Medellin, ANT, Colombia. **Co-sponsors:** Colegio de Medicos Veterinarios y Zootecnistas de Antioqua; Asociacion Nacional de Tecnologos Agropecuarios.

630 ZAF
COLIMPEX AGRICULTURAL EXECUPAD. Text in Afrikaans, English. a. adv.
Published by: Colimpex Africa (Pty) Ltd., PO Box 5838, Johannesburg, 2000, South Africa.

630 GBR
COLLEGE FARM GUIDE (YEAR). Text in English. a.
Formerly (until 1998): College Farm (Year)
—BLDSC (3311.068000).
Published by: Harper Adams University College, Edgmond, Newport, Shropshire, TF10 8NB, United Kingdom. TEL 44-1952-820280, FAX 44-1952-814783, hrlrobinson@harper-adams.ac.uk, http://www.harper-adams.ac.ul/.

630 USA
COLLEGE OF AGRICULTURAL, CONSUMER AND ENVIRONMENTAL SCIENCES. RESEARCH PROGRESS. Text in English. 1888. biennial. free. **Document type:** *Academic/Scholarly.*
Formerly: Illinois Agricultural Experiment Station. Research Progress (0887-7300)
Related titles: CD-ROM ed.
—Linda Hall.
Published by: (Office of Research and Information Services), University of Illinois at Urbana-Champaign, College of Agricultural, Consumer and Environmental Sciences, 211 Mumford Hall, 1301 W Gregory Dr, Urbana, IL 61801. TEL 217-244-2830, c-frank@uiuc.edu. Ed. Tina Prow. Circ: 1,700.

630 FRA ISSN 0293-1915
CODEN: COLIEZ
LES COLLOQUES DE L'INRA. Text in French. 1981. irreg. price varies. **Document type:** *Monographic series.*
Indexed: BIOSIS Prev, ESPM, VITIS, ZooRec.
—BLDSC (3313.554000), CISTI, IE, ingenta. **CCC.**
Published by: Institut National de la Recherche Agronomique (INRA), Service des Publications, Route de Saint Cyr, Versailles, Cedex 78026, France. TEL 33-1-30833406, FAX 33-1-30833449, inra-editions@versailles.inra.fr, http://www.inra.fr/index.html.

630 USA
COLORADO FARMER - STOCKMAN. Text in English. 1947. 14/yr. USD 21.95 in state; USD 30 out of state (effective 2001). charts; illus.; mkt.; stat. reprints avail. **Document type:** *Trade.* **Description:** Covers ranching and farming practices, marketing, and legislation for ranchers and farmers in Colorado.
Formerly: Colorado Rancher and Farmer (0010-1729)
Published by: Farm Progress Companies, 191 S Gary Ave, Carol Stream, IL 60188. TEL 630-462-2892, FAX 630-462-2885, info@farmprogress.com, http://www.farmprogress.com/. Ed. Joan Waldoch. Pub. Allan Johnson. Adv. contact Jess Lapin. Circ: 3,421 (paid).

630 ITA
COLTIVATORE ENNESE. Text in Italian. 1951. bi-m. membership.
Published by: Federazione Provinciale Coltivatori Diritti di Enna, Via Roma, 429, Enna, EN 94100, Italy. Ed. Giuseppe Pergola.

630 ITA
COLTIVATORE MARCHIGIANO. Text in Italian. m.
Address: Via Dell' Industria, 18, Ancona, AN 60127, Italy. Ed. Alberto Castellucci.

630 ITA
COLTIVATORE REGGIANO. Text in Italian. 1953. s-m. adv.
Published by: Federazione Provinciale Coltivatori Diretti di Reggio Emilia, Via B Ricasoli, 4, Reggio Emilia, RE 42100, Italy. Ed. Ugo Saoncella. Circ: 8,300.

630 ITA
COLTIVATORI CUNEESI. Text in Italian. 1946. 26/yr. adv.
Published by: Federazione Provinciale Coltivatori Diretti di Cuneo, Corso Giolitti, 21, Cuneo, CN 12100, Italy. TEL 39-171-64591, FAX 39-171-697134. Ed. A Cantamessa. Circ: 59,000.

630 USA ISSN 0010-1877
THE COLUMBIA BASIN FARMER. Text in English. 1957. m. USD 12 (effective 2005). adv. illus.; mkt. back issues avail. **Document type:** *Magazine, Trade.* **Description:** Offers features on local growers, agricultural technology, new farming methods, crops, prices, and legislative news.
Published by: Basin Publishing Co., P.O. Box O, Othello, WA 99344. farmer@othellooutlook.com, outlook@cbnn.net, http://www.othellooutlook.com. Ed. Louann Morgan. Pub. Bill Edlin. Circ: 10,000.

COMMODITY FUTURES FORECAST SERVICE. see *BUSINESS AND ECONOMICS—Investments*

COMMUNITY TRANSPORTATION REPORTER; the magazine of community transit industry. see *TRANSPORTATION*

COMPENDIUM OF IRISH ECONOMIC AND AGRICULTURE STATISTICS (YEAR). see *AGRICULTURE—Abstracting, Bibliographies, Statistics*

630 ESP ISSN 1138-2775
COMUNITAT VALENCIANA AGRARIA. Text in Spanish, Catalan. 1994. q.
Indexed: IECT.
—CINDOC.
Published by: Generalitat Valenciana, Conselleria de Agricultura, Pesa y Alimentacion. Secretaria General, C. Amadeo de Saboya, 2, Valencia, 46010, Spain. TEL 34-963-866912, FAX 34-963-866907, patri.mujeriego@agricultura.m400.gva.es, http://www.gva.es/agricultura/publica.htm.

630 USA ISSN 1014-1588
CONFERENCE REGIONALE DE LA F A O POUR L'AFRIQUE. RAPPORT. Text in French. 1960. biennial.
Related titles: ♦ English ed.: F A O Regional Conference for Africa. Report. ISSN 0429-9353.
Published by: Food and Agriculture Organization of the United Nations, c/o Bernan Associates, 4611 F Assembly Dr, Lanham, MD 20706-4391.

630 USA ISSN 1014-4080
CONFERENCE REGIONALE DE LA F A O POUR L'ASIE ET LE PACIFIQUE. RAPPORT. Text in French. biennial.
Related titles: ♦ English ed.: F A O Regional Conference for Asia and the Pacific. Report. ISSN 1010-0997; Chinese ed.: Lianheguo Liangshi ji Nongye Zuzhi. Dayanghou Quyu Huiyi Baogao. Liangnong Zuzhi. ISSN 1014-6628. 1980.
Published by: Food and Agriculture Organization of the United Nations, c/o Bernan Associates, 4611 F Assembly Dr, Lanham, MD 20706-4391.

A

630 USA ISSN 1014-2398
CONFERENCE REGIONALE DE LA F A O POUR LE PROCHE-ORIENT. RAPPORT. Text in French. 1949. biennial.
Related titles: ♦ English ed.: F A O Regional Conference for the Near East. Report. ISSN 0427-8089.
Published by: Food and Agriculture Organization of the United Nations, c/o Bernan Associates, 4611 F Assembly Dr, Lanham, MD 20706-4391.

630 BRA
CONFLITOS NO CAMPO - BRASIL. Text in Portuguese. irreg.
Published by: Comissao Pastoral da Terra, Rua 19 No. 35 Centro, St Central, Caixa Postal 749, Goiania, GO 74001-970, Brazil. TEL 062-224-4436, FAX 062-225-4967.

630 USA ISSN 1059-8723
CONNECTICUT WEEKLY AGRICULTURAL REPORT. Text in English. 1920. w. USD 10 (effective 1999). adv. **Document type:** *Bulletin.*
Formerly: Connecticut Market Bulletin (0161-5858)
Published by: Department of Agriculture, 165 Capitol Ave., Rm. 401, Hartford, CT 06106-1630. TEL 860-713-2503, FAX 860-713-2516. Ed. Robert Pellegrino. Adv. contact Patricia Bussa. Circ: 2,200.

630 BFA
CONSTRUIRE ENSEMBLE. Text in French. bi-m. XOF 2,500.
Published by: Centre d'Etudes Economiques et Sociales d'Afrique, BP 305, Bobo Dioulasso, Burkina Faso.

CONSUMPTIE VAN VOEDINGSMIDDELEN IN NEDERLAND. see *AGRICULTURE—Abstracting, Bibliographies, Statistics*

630 ITA ISSN 1121-8592
IL CONTOTERZISTA; rivista per l'impresa agromeccanica. Text in Italian. 1992. m. (11/yr.). EUR 62 domestic; EUR 110 foreign (effective 2005). adv. **Document type:** *Magazine, Trade.* **Description:** For and about farm-contractors.
Published by: Il Sole 24 Ore Edagricole, Via Goito 13, Bologna, BO 40126, Italy. TEL 39-051-62267, FAX 39-051-490200, http://www.edagricole.it. Ed. Giorgio Setti. Circ: 13,500.

630 334.683 CAN ISSN 0315-1204
COOPERATEUR AGRICOLE. Text in French. 1972. 9/yr. CND 10. adv. **Document type:** *Trade.*
Published by: Cooperative Federee de Quebec, P O Box 500, Youville Sta, Montreal, PQ H2P 2W2, Canada. TEL 514-384-6450, coopagri@coopfed.qc.ca, http://www.coopfed.qc.ca. Ed. Patrick Dupuis. Pub. Mario Dumais. Adv. contact Andre Leger. Circ: 23,293.

630 334.683 ITA
COOPERATIVA (MACERATA). Text in Italian. q.
Address: Via Carducci, 20, Macerata, MC 62100, Italy. Ed. Franco Ortenzi.

630 IND ISSN 0302-7767
HD2951
COOPERATIVE PERSPECTIVE. Text in English. 1966. q. INR 60 to students; INR 120 to institutions. adv. bk.rev. charts; stat. cum.index vols. 1-13. back issues avail. **Document type:** *Academic/Scholarly.*
Formerly (Feb.-Apr. 1973): Cooperative Information Bulletin (0009-9805)
Published by: Vaikunth Mehta National Institute of Cooperative Management, University Rd., Pune, Maharashtra 411 007, India. TEL 327974, FAX 327726, vmnicom@mah.n.c.in. adv.: page INR 1,500. Circ: 225.

630 334.683 ITA
COOPERATORE AGRICOLO. Text in Italian. 3/yr.
Published by: Consorzio Agricolo Provinciale, Ancona, AN 60100, Italy. Ed. Antonio Liguori.

570 630 USA ISSN 1067-585X
CODEN: CORFFN
CORNELL FOCUS. Text in English. 1934. 3/yr. free. charts; illus. index. **Document type:** *Academic/Scholarly.*
Former titles (until vol.20, no.4, 1991): New York's Food and Life Sciences Quarterly (0361-5367); (until 1970): New York's Food and Life Sciences (0028-7938); (until 1968): Farm Research (0096-1124)
Indexed: ASFA, AgBio, Agr, AgrForAb, BiolAb, BiolDig, DSA, ESPM, EnvAb, EnvInd, FCA, FPA, FS&TA, ForAb, HerbAb, HortAb, I&DA, IndVet, NutrAb, OrnHort, PBA, PGrRegA, PN&I, PotatoAb, RA&MP, RPP, RRTA, S&F, SFA, SIA, SWRA, WAE&RSA, WRCInf, WeedAb, WildRev.
—BLDSC (3470.942400), CISTI, IE, ingenta, Linda Hall.
Published by: Cornell University, Agricultural Experiment Station, 1150 Comstock Hall, College of Agriculture & Life Sciences, Ithaca, NY 14853. TEL 607-255-1876, FAX 607-255-9873. Ed. Elizabeth Bauman. Circ: 5,000 (controlled).

630 GBR ISSN 0954-9668
CORNISH FARMER AND GROWER. Text in English. 1964. m. adv.
Published by: County Farmers Publications Ltd., 55 Goldington Rd, Bedford, Beds MK40 3LU, United Kingdom. TEL 44-1234-351401, FAX 44-1234-328614. Ed. Alison Best. Circ: 2,700.

COTTON DIGEST INTERNATIONAL. see *TEXTILE INDUSTRIES AND FABRICS*

COTTON: REVIEW OF THE WORLD SITUATION. see *TEXTILE INDUSTRIES AND FABRICS*

630 664 USA ISSN 1070-0021
COUNCIL FOR AGRICULTURAL SCIENCE AND TECHNOLOGY. ISSUE PAPERS. Text in English. 1993. irreg. USD 100 includes Task Force Reports, Issue Papers, and Special Publications (effective 2005). **Document type:** *Monographic series.*
—CISTI.
Published by: Council for Agricultural Science and Technology, 4420 W Lincoln Way, Ames, IA 50014-2447. TEL 515-292-2125, FAX 515-292-4512, cast@cast-science.org, http://www.cast-science.org. R&P Linda M Chimenti.

630 664 USA ISSN 0194-407X
S1
COUNCIL FOR AGRICULTURAL SCIENCE AND TECHNOLOGY. SPECIAL PUBLICATIONS. Text in English. irreg. USD 100 includes Task Force Reports, Issue Paper and Special Publications (effective 2000). **Description:** Series of occasional reports on issues in food and agricultural science.
Indexed: Agr.
—CISTI.
Published by: Council for Agricultural Science and Technology, 4420 W Lincoln Way, Ames, IA 50014-2447. TEL 515-292-2125, FAX 515-292-4512, cast@cast-science.org, http://www.cast-science.org. R&P Linda M Chimenti.

630 664 USA ISSN 0194-4088
CODEN: RCATEQ
COUNCIL FOR AGRICULTURAL SCIENCE AND TECHNOLOGY. TASK FORCE REPORTS. Text in English. irreg. USD 100 includes Task Force Reports, Issue Papers, and and Special Publications (effective 2005). **Description:** Broad scientific documents written by groups of scientists.
Incorporates (1976-1994): Comments From C A S T (0194-4096)
Indexed: AbHyg, Agr, BIOSIS Prev, BiolAb, FS&TA, I&DA, IndVet, RM&VM, RRTA, VetBull, WAE&RSA.
—CISTI, ingenta.
Published by: Council for Agricultural Science and Technology, 4420 W Lincoln Way, Ames, IA 50014-2447. TEL 515-292-2125, FAX 515-292-4512, cast@cast-science.org, http://www.cast-science.org. R&P Linda M Chimenti.

COUNTRY FOLK. see *LIFESTYLE*

630 USA ISSN 0191-8907
COUNTRY FOLKS. (Avail. in 4 editions: East, West, Pennsylvania, New England) Text in English. 1974. w. USD 25 (effective 1997). **Description:** Covers all aspects of agriculture.
Published by: Lee Publications, Inc., 6113 State Hwy 5, Palatine Bridge, NY 13428. TEL 515-673-3237, 800-836-2888, FAX 518-673-2381, ctryfks@telenet.net, subscriptions@leepub.com. Ed. Janice Handy.

COUNTRY FOLKS GROWER. see *GARDENING AND HORTICULTURE*

630 USA ISSN 1054-9064
COUNTRY FOLKS OF PENNSYLVANIA. Text in English. 1945. w. USD 25; USD 1 newsstand/cover (effective 1997). bk.rev. back issues avail. **Document type:** *Newspaper.*
Formerly (until 1990): Farm and Home News (1040-8525)
Published by: Lee Publications, Inc., 6113 State Hwy 5, Palatine Bridge, NY 13428. TEL 515-673-3237, 800-836-2888, FAX 518-673-2381. Ed. Janice Handy. adv.: B&W page USD 665; trim 14 x 10.25. Circ: 10,465.

630 CAN ISSN 0383-7114
COUNTRY GUIDE; the farm magazine. Text in English. 1882. m. (11/yr.). CND 19.50, USD 50. adv. bk.rev. charts; illus.; mkt.; pat.; stat. **Document type:** *Trade.*
Related titles: Microfilm ed.: (from CML, SOC); Microform ed.: (from PQC); ♦ Supplement(s): Canola Guide. ISSN 0841-209X.
Indexed: CBCARef, CBPI.
—CISTI, Linda Hall. **CCC.**
Published by: Farm Business Communications, P O Box 6600, Winnipeg, MB R3C 3A7, Canada. TEL 204-944-5761, FAX 204-942-8463. Ed. Dave Wreford. Adv. contact Tom Mumby. Circ: 73,994.

630 CAN ISSN 0011-0183
COUNTRY LIFE IN BRITISH COLUMBIA. Text in English. 1915. m. CND 10, USD 20. adv. bk.rev. illus. **Description:** News and features concerning farming in B.C. covering a wide spectrum of commodities such as beef, tree fruits, and dairy.
—CISTI.
Published by: Country Life Ltd., 10317 158A Street, Surrey, BC V4N 2M5, Canada. TEL 604 951-4444, FAX 604 951-4445, countrylife@telus.net. Ed., Pub. Peter Wilding. Circ: 9,060.

630 USA ISSN 0011-0205
COUNTRY LIVING (COVINGTON). Text in English. 1945. m. USD 10.95 (effective 2001). adv. bk.rev.
Published by: Arens Corp., 395 S High St, Covington, OH 45318. TEL 937-473-2020. Ed. Gary Godfrey. Circ: 17,448.

630 USA
THE COUNTRY TODAY. Text in English. 1977. w. USD 23 domestic; USD 155 foreign (effective 2000). adv. illus. **Document type:** *Newspaper, Trade.* **Description:** Contains agricultural news, features, market information for farmers and rural residents.
Related titles: Microfilm ed.
Published by: Eau Claire Press Company, 701 S Farwell, Eau Claire, WI 54702. TEL 715-833-9270, FAX 715-833-9273, countrytoday@ecol.net, http://www.ecol.net. Ed. Jim Massey. Pub. Pieter Graaskamp TEL 715-833-9275. Adv. contact Marion Loew. Circ: 27,483 (paid).

COUNTRY WOMAN. see *WOMEN'S INTERESTS*

630 AUS ISSN 0011-0264
COUNTRYMAN. Text in English. 1885. w. AUD 65. adv. bk.rev. charts; illus.; stat. **Document type:** *Newspaper.*
Published by: West Australian Newspapers, 219 St Georges Terrace, Perth, W.A. 6000, Australia. FAX 09-482-3324. Ed. John Dare. Circ: 15,000.

630 USA ISSN 0739-4330
COUNTY AGENTS DIRECTORY; the reference book for agricultural extension workers. Text in English. 1915. biennial. USD 23.95. **Document type:** *Directory.*
Published by: Doane Agricultural Service Co., 11701 Borman Dr, Ste 300, St. Louis, MO 63146-4199. TEL 314-569-2700, FAX 314-569-1083. Ed. Kristine Myszka. Circ: 3,000.

630 FRA ISSN 1241-3992
COURRIER DE L'ENVIRONNEMENT DE L'I N R A. (Institut National de la Recherche Agronomique) Text in French. 1987. 3/yr. free (effective 2004).
Formerly (until 1993): Courrier de la Cellule Environnement (0995-1083)
Indexed: AbHyg, AgBio, AgrForAb, AnBrAb, BioCN&I, DSA, FPA, ForAb, HerbAb, HortAb, I&DA, MaizeAb, PBA, PGegResA, PN&I, S&F, TriticAb, WAE&RSA, WeedAb.
—CISTI.
Published by: Institut National de la Recherche Agronomique, Mission Environnement-Societe, 147, rue de l'Universite, Paris, 75338 Cedex 07, France. TEL 33-1-42759249, FAX 33-1-42759508, lecourrier@paris.inra.fr, http://www.infra.fr/dpenv/. Circ: 11,500.

630 ITA
CRONACHE DELL'AGRICOLTURA. Text in Italian. 1949. m. adv.
Published by: Unione Provinciale Agricoltori di Torino, Corso V. Emanuele 58, Turin, TO 10121, Italy. TEL 39-11-530616. Ed. M G Calzoni. Circ: 16,500.

631 IND ISSN 0011-1872
CROPS IN INDIA. Text in English. 1968. q. INR 8. charts; stat.
Published by: Agro-Service, 3491 Gali Bajrangbali, Chawri Bazar, New Delhi, 110 006, India. Ed. H K Tiwari.

630 635 FRA ISSN 0263-9459
CODEN: CRUNDD
➤ **CRUCIFERAE NEWSLETTER.** Text in English. 1976-1991; resumed 1993. a. EUR 150 (effective 2002). bk.rev. **Document type:** *Newsletter, Academic/Scholarly.* **Description:** Contains research notes, news items, and information on cruciferous crops and related species.
Indexed: AEA, AgBio, AgrForAb, BioCN&I, CPA, ChemAb, FCA, FPA, FS&TA, ForAb, HortAb, I&DA, NutrAb, OrnHort, PBA, PGegResA, PGrRegA, PHN&I, RA&MP, RPP, RevApplEntom, RiceAb, S&F, SIA, SeedAb, SoyAb, TriticAb, WAE&RSA, WeedAb.
—BLDSC (3489.871500), CASDDS, IE, ingenta.
Published by: European Association for Research on Plant Breeding, INRA - Station d'Amelioration des Plantes, Domaine de la Motte, BP 29, Le Rheu, 35653, France. TEL 33-2-99285100, FAX 33-2-99285120, TELEX 740 060 F. Circ: 500.

630 ESP ISSN 1139-1456
CUADERNOS DE AGRICULTURA, PESCA Y ALIMENTACION. Text in Spanish. 1998. m. price varies. **Document type:** *Monographic series, Government.*
—CINDOC.
Published by: Ministerio de Agricultura Pesca y Alimentacion, Centro de Publicaciones, Paseo Infanta Isabel 1, Madrid, 28014, Spain. TEL 34-91-3475550, FAX 34-91-3475722, mllopisj@mapya.es, http://www.mapya.es.

CUBA. CENTRO DE INFORMACION Y DOCUMENTACION AGROPECUARIO. BOLETIN DE RESENAS. SERIE: MEJORAMIENTO ANIMAL. see *BIOLOGY—Zoology*

630 CUB ISSN 0253-5785
CODEN: CEAGD5
CUBA. MINISTERIO DE EDUCACION SUPERIOR. CENTRO AGRICOLA. Text in Spanish. 3/yr. USD 20 in the Americas; USD 24 in Europe; in N. and S. America; Europe $24.

Indexed: AEA, AgBio, AgrForAb, BioCN&I, CPA, FCA, ForAb, HerbAb, HortAb, I&DA, INIS AtomInd, MaizeAb, NemAb, OrnHort, PBA, PGegResA, PGrRegA, PHN&I, PN&I, PotatoAb, PoultAb, RA&MP, RPP, RRTA, RiceAb, S&F, SIA, SeedAb, TriticAb, WAE&RSA, WeedAb.
—CASDDS, CISTI.
Published by: (Cuba. Ministerio de Educacion Superior), Ediciones Cubanas, Obispo No. 527, Apdo. 605, Havana, Cuba.

630 CUB
CUBA. MINISTERIO DE LA AGRICULTURA. CENTRO DE INFORMACION Y DIVULGACION AGROPECUARIO. NOTICIERO AGROPECUARIO. SUPLEMENTO. Text in Spanish. m.
Published by: Centro de Informacion y Documentacion Agropecuario, Gaveta Postal 4149, Havana, 4, Cuba.

630 CUB
CUBA. MINISTERIO DE LA AGRICULTURA. CENTRO DE INFORMACION Y DOCUMENTACION AGROPECUARIO. EXTRANJERAS. Text in Spanish. w.
Published by: Centro de Informacion y Documentacion Agropecuario, Gaveta Postal 4149, Havana, 4, Cuba.

630 CUB
CUBA. MINISTERIO DE LA AGRICULTURA. CENTRO DE INFORMACION Y DOCUMENTACION AGROPECUARIO. NOTICIERO AGROPECUARIO. Text in Spanish. irreg.
Published by: Centro de Informacion y Documentacion Agropecuario, Gaveta Postal 4149, Havana, 4, Cuba.

CUBA. MINISTERIO DE LA AGRICULTURA. CENTRO DE INFORMACION Y DOCUMENTACION AGROPECUARIO. NOTICIERO AGROPECUARIO. SUPLEMENTO AGROMETEOROLOGICO. see *METEOROLOGY*

630 CUB ISSN 0864-0408
➤ **CUBAN JOURNAL OF AGRICULTURAL SCIENCE.** Text in English. 1967. 4/yr. USD 80 (effective 2004). adv. bk.rev. abstr. 120 p./no. 2 cols./p.; reprints avail. **Document type:** *Journal, Academic/Scholarly.*
Formerly (until 1972): Revista Cubana de Ciencia Agricola (English Edition) (0253-5815)
Related titles: ♦ Spanish ed.: Revista Cubana de Ciencia Agricola. ISSN 0034-7485.
Indexed: AEA, AbHyg, AgBio, AgrForAb, AnBrAb, BIOSIS Prev, BioCN&I, BiolAb, CPA, CurCont, DSA, FCA, FPA, FS&TA, ForAb, HelmAb, HerbAb, HortAb, I&DA, IndVet, MaizeAb, NutrAb, OrnHort, PBA, PGegResA, PGrRegA, PN&I, PoultAb, RDA, RPP, RevApplEntom, RiceAb, S&F, SIA, SeedAb, SoyAb, TriticAb, VetBull, WAE&RSA, WeedAb.
—BLDSC (3490.855000), IE, ingenta.
Published by: Instituto de Ciencia Animal, Tulipan No. 1011 e-47 y Loma, Nuevo Vedado, Havana, Cuba. TEL 53-62-99180, FAX 53-73-35382, ica@ceniai.inf.cu. Ed. Rafael Herrera.

630 ESP
CUENCA AGRARIA. Text in Spanish. 12/yr.
Address: Teruel, 1 1o, Cuenca, 16004, Spain. TEL 66-27-77-77, FAX 66-21-13-60. Circ: 6,000.

630 ESP ISSN 0011-2747
CULTIVADOR MODERNO; revista de agricultura ganaderia y mechanizacion. Text in Spanish. 1911. m. (11/yr.). adv. bk.rev. bibl. **Description:** Covers agriculture with emphasis on livestock, machinery and equipment.
Indexed: IECT.
Published by: Raul Maria Mir Rague Ed. & Pub., Escoles Pies, 45, Barcelona, 08017, Spain. TEL 93-212-43-67, FAX 93-418-92-79. Circ: 11,000.

630 COL ISSN 0122-8056
CULTIVANDO AFINIDADES; boletin sobre cooperacion en investigacion agricola. Text in Spanish. 1982. 2/yr. free. 16 p./no.; **Document type:** *Bulletin.* **Description:** Highlights CIAT's current research activities and results and their impact on agricultural development.
Formerly (until 1996): C I A T International (Spanish Edition) (0120-4084)
Indexed: HerbAb.
—CISTI.
Published by: (Unidad de Comunicaciones), Centro Internacional de Agricultura Tropical/International Center for Tropical Agriculture, Publications Unit, Apartado Aereo 6713, Cali, VALLE, Colombia. TEL 57-2-4450000, FAX 57-2-4450073, ciat-comunicaciones@cgiar.org, http://www.ciat.cgiat.org/. Ed. Nathan Russell. Circ: 4,000.

630 USA ISSN 1065-1691
CULTIVAR. Text in English. 1981. s-a. free. bk.rev. back issues avail. **Document type:** *Newsletter.* **Description:** For researchers, farmers and gardeners interested in agro-ecological approaches to farming and gardening. Addresses issues related to sustainable agriculture. Reports on research and activities of the Center for Agroecology & Sustainable Food Systems.
Indexed: PHN&I, RPP, RevApplEntom, TriticAb.
—BLDSC (3491.617200).
Published by: University of California at Santa Cruz, Center for Agroecology & Sustainable Food Systems, 1156 High St, Santa Cruz, CA 95064. TEL 831-459-3240, FAX 831-459-2799, http://www.ucsc.edu/casfs. Ed., R&P Martha Brown TEL 831-459-3376. Circ: 5,000.

631.5 FRA ISSN 1143-7405
CULTIVAR; cultiver, gerer, entreprendre. Text in French. 1968. bi-m. bk.rev. **Description:** Information on agronomy and agricultural production.
Former titles (until 1989): Cultivar 2000 (1143-7391); (1988-1989): Cultivar 2000, Grandes Cultures, Elevages (0983-0979); Which was formed by the merger of: Elevage 2000 (0298-4326); Agromais (0290-1846); Cultivar (0045-9216)
Indexed: AEA, AnBrAb, BioCN&I, DSA, FCA, HerbAb, HortAb, I&DA, IndVet, MaizeAb, NemAb, NutrAb, OrnHort, PBA, PN&I, PotatoAb, ProtozoAb, RPP, S&F, SoyAb, TriticAb, WAE&RSA, WeedAb.
—CISTI.
Published by: Agri Terroir Communication, 61, Rue du XXe-Corps-Americain, Metz, 57000, France. TEL 33-03-87691818, FAX 33-03-87691814, infocentre@editions-mirabelle.com, http://www.editions-mirabelle.com. Ed. Antoine Herve. Circ: 50,000.

630 BRA ISSN 0104-1010
CULTURA AGRONOMICA. Text in Portuguese. 1992. a.
Indexed: AEA, AgrForAb, AnBrAb, BioCN&I, CPA, ESPM, FCA, ForAb, HerbAb, HortAb, I&DA, MaizeAb, NutrAb, OrnHort, PBA, PGegResA, PGrRegA, PHN&I, PN&I, PotatoAb, RA&MP, RDA, RM&VM, RPP, RiceAb, S&F, SIA, SWRA, SeedAb, SoyAb, TriticAb, WAE&RSA, WeedAb.
—CISTI.
Published by: Universidade Estadual Paulista "Julio de Mesquita Filho" , Faculdade de Engenharia, Avenida Brasil Centro 56, Caixa Postal 31, Ilha Solteira, SP 15385-000, Brazil. TEL 55-18-3743-1000, FAX 55-18-3742-2735, enes@agr.feis.unesp.br, http://www.feis.unesp.br/. Ed. Enes Furlani Jr.

630 USA ISSN 1048-4876
HT401
CULTURE AND AGRICULTURE. Text in English. 1977. s-a. USD 60 to institutions (effective 2006). **Document type:** *Journal, Academic/Scholarly.*
Related titles: Online - full text ed.: ISSN 1556-486X.
Indexed: AnthLit, WAE&RSA.
—BLDSC (3491.668560), IE, ingenta. **CCC.**
Published by: (American Anthropological Association), University of California Press, Journals Division, 2000 Center St, Ste 303, Berkeley, CA 94704-1223. TEL 510-643-7154, FAX 510-642-9917, journals@ucpress.edu, http://www.anthrosource.net/loi/cag, http://www.ucpress.edu/journals. Eds. James H McDonald, Laura J Levi.

630 GBR
CUMBRIA FARMER. Text in English. 1972. m. adv.
Published by: County Farmers Publications Ltd., 55 Goldington Rd, Bedford, Beds MK40 3LU, United Kingdom. TEL 44-1234-351401, FAX 44-1234-328614. Ed. R Bacon. Circ: 4,050.

630 GBR
CUMBRIAN FARMING* . Text in English. q. adv. **Document type:** *Magazine.*
Published by: Cambrian Press, 3 Chatsworth Sq, Carlisle, Cumbria CA1 1HB, United Kingdom. TEL 44-1228-47144, FAX 44-1228-514747. Ed. Tony Thornton. Adv. contact A Taylor. Circ: 8,560.

630 IND ISSN 0971-6947
CODEN: OAREEJ
➤ **CURRENT AGRICULTURAL RESEARCH.** Text in English. 1988. q. USD 100 (effective 1996). bk.rev. **Document type:** *Academic/Scholarly.*
Formerly (until 1995): Orissa Journal of Agricultural Research (0970-728X)
Indexed: AEA, Agrind, CIN, ChemAb, ChemTitl, FCA, HortAb, MaizeAb, PBA, PHN&I, RDA, RPP, RevApplEntom, RiceAb, SeedAb, TriticAb, WAE&RSA, WeedAb.
—BLDSC (3494.110000), CASDDS.
Published by: Association of Agricultural Scientists, College of Agriculture Bldg., Orissa University of Agriculture & Technology, Bhubaneswar, Orissa 751 003, India. Ed. D Mishra. Circ: 300.

630 IND ISSN 0254-1092
CODEN: CUAGEG
CURRENT AGRICULTURE. Text in English. 1977. s-a. USD 50 (effective 2000). **Document type:** *Academic/Scholarly.*
Indexed: AEA, AbHyg, AgBio, AgrForAb, BioCN&I, CPA, FCA, FPA, FS&TA, ForAb, HelmAb, HerbAb, HortAb, I&DA, IndVet, MaizeAb, OrnHort, PBA, PGegResA, PGrRegA, PHN&I, PN&I, PotatoAb, RA&MP, RDA, RPP, RiceAb, S&F, SIA, SeedAb, TDB, TriticAb, WAE&RSA, WeedAb.
—BLDSC (3494.120000), CASDDS, Linda Hall.
Published by: H P C Publishers Distributors Pvt. Ltd., 4805 Bharat Ram Rd, 24 Darya Ganj, New Delhi, 110 002, India. TEL 91-11-3254401, FAX 91-11-619-3511, hpcpd@nda.vsnl.net.in, hpcpd@hpc.cc, http://www.hpc.cc, http://www.bizdelhi.com/publisher/hpc, http://www.indianindustry.com. **Co-publisher:** Indian Society of Salinity Research Scientists.

630 631 PAK
CURRENT AGRO-TECHNOLOGY FOR POTATO PRODUCTION. Text in English. 1981. irreg.
Published by: Pakistan Agricultural Research Council, Plot 20, G-5-1, P O Box 1031, Islamabad, Pakistan. Ed. Mahfooz Ali Shah. Circ: 1,000.

CURRENT CONTENTS: AGRICULTURE, BIOLOGY & ENVIRONMENTAL SCIENCES. see *AGRICULTURE—Abstracting, Bibliographies, Statistics*

630 IND ISSN 0256-6885
CODEN: CREREE
CURRENT RESEARCH REPORTER. Text in English. 1985. s-a. INR 30 domestic to individuals; USD 20 foreign to individuals; INR 50 domestic to institutions; USD 50 foreign to institutions. **Description:** Publishes papers on original research in the field of agricultural science and technology.
Indexed: SIA.
—CASDDS.
Published by: Mahatma Phule Agricultural University, Rahuri, Dist-Ahmednagar, Maharashtra 413 722, India.

CYPRUS. DEPARTMENT OF STATISTICS AND RESEARCH. AGRICULTURAL STATISTICS. see *AGRICULTURE—Abstracting, Bibliographies, Statistics*

CYPRUS. DEPARTMENT OF STATISTICS AND RESEARCH. CENSUS OF AGRICULTURE. see *AGRICULTURE—Abstracting, Bibliographies, Statistics*

630 DEU ISSN 0173-654X
D B V INFORMATIONEN. Text in German. w. looseleaf. **Document type:** *Bulletin.*
Published by: Deutscher Bauernverband e.V., Godesberger Allee 142-148, Bonn, 53175, Germany. TEL 0228-8198240, FAX 0228-8198231.

630 DEU ISSN 0341-0412
S7
D L G - MITTEILUNGEN. Text in German. 1885. m. EUR 74.40 domestic (effective 2005). adv. bk.rev. abstr.; illus.; stat. index. **Document type:** *Magazine, Trade.*
Incorporates (1981-1997): P S P Pflanzenschutz-Praxis (0723-0311); Formerly: Deutsche Landwirtschafts-Gesellschaft. Mitteilungen der D L G (0341-0404); Which incorporated (in 1990): Agrar-Inform (0863-4491); Which was formerly: Kooperation (0023-3811)
Indexed: AEA, DSA, ExcerpMed, FCA, FaBeAb, HerbAb, IndVet, MaizeAb, PBA, PGrRegA, RASB, RRTA, TriticAb, WAE&RSA, WeedAb.
—BLDSC (3605.640000), IE, Infotrieve, ingenta. **CCC.**
Published by: (Deutsche Landwirtschafts-Gesellschaft e.V.), Landwirtschaftsverlag GmbH, Huelsebrockstr 2, Muenster, 48165, Germany. TEL 49-2501-27500, FAX 49-2501-27551, zentrale@lv-h.de, http://www.dlg-mitteilungen.de, http://www.lv-h.de. Ed. Thomas Preusse. Adv. contact Reinhard Geissel. color page EUR 5,491.50, B&W page EUR 3,328.50. Circ: 17,605 (paid). **Subscr. to:** Postfach 480249, Muenster 48079, Germany.

631 DEU ISSN 0340-787X
D L Z AGRARMAGAZIN; die landwirtschaftliche Zeitschrift fuer Management, Produktion und Technik. Text in German. 1949. m. EUR 60; EUR 5.80 newsstand/cover (effective 2005). adv. bk.rev. **Document type:** *Magazine, Trade.*
Formerly (until 1994): D L Z (0011-5010)
Related titles: Online - full text ed.
Indexed: AEA, ChemAb, DSA, RRTA, RefZh, WAE&RSA.
—CISTI, IE. **CCC.**
Published by: Deutscher Landwirtschaftsverlag GmbH, Lothstr 29, Munich, 80797, Germany. TEL 49-89-127051, FAX 49-89-12705335, reddlz@dlv.de, dlv.muenchen@dlv.de, http://www.dlz-agrarmagazin.de, http://www.dlv.de. Ed. Willi Weber. Adv. contact Henning Stemmler. B&W page EUR 5,778, color page EUR 9,418; trim 188 x 270. Circ: 71,080 (paid and controlled).

DAKOTA COUNSEL. see *ENERGY*

630 USA ISSN 1069-5397
DAKOTA FARMER. Text in English. 1927. 15/yr. USD 23.95 domestic; USD 45 elsewhere (effective 2005). adv. illus.; mkt. **Document type:** *Magazine, Trade.* **Description:** Provides local and timely crop and livestock production practices for farm operators in the Dakotas.
Former titles (until 1993): Dakota Grower and Rancher (1064-6760); (until 1992): Dakota Wallace Farmer (1048-5775)
Related titles: ♦ Supplement(s): Dairy Producer.

▼ new title ➤ refereed * unverified ♦ full entry avail.

A

Published by: Farm Progress Companies, 191 S Gary Ave, Carol Stream, IL 60188-2095. TEL 630-462-2229, FAX 630-462-2202, info@farmprogress.com, http:// www.dakotafarmer.com, http://www.farmprogress.com/. Ed. Lon Tonneson TEL 218-236-8420. Adv. contact Don Tourte. B&W page USD 1,850, color page USD 2,350; trim 10.5 x 14.5. Circ: 23,000 (paid and controlled).

638.1   DNK   ISSN 0900-5749
DANSK BIAVL. Text in Danish. 1977. m. DKK 60. illus.
Former titles (until 1984): Dansk-Biavl og Miljoe (0108-3139); (until 1981): Danske Biavl (0106-9128)
Indexed: ApicAb.
Published by: Danske Biavleres Landsforening D.B.L., Sjaellandsgade 4, Avlum, 7490, Denmark.

630   DNK   ISSN 0904-9363
DANSK LANDBRUG. Text in Danish. 1979. 25/yr. DKK 375 (effective 2001). adv. **Document type:** Newspaper.
Description: latest agricultural news.
Formerly: Jysk Landbrug
Published by: Vest Media A-S, Storegade 28, Skansen, Varde, 6800, Denmark. TEL 45-75-22-44-33, 45-75-22-44-00, FAX 45-75-21-00-50, 45-75-22-44-77, dansk-landbrug@vestmedia.dk, dansk-landbrug.dk. Ed. Erik Halden. Circ: 115,712 (controlled).

630   PER   ISSN 1017-9011
HD1901
DEBATE AGRARIO. Text in Spanish. 1987. q. USD 40.
Description: Deals with rural issues.
Indexed: AEA, AgrForAb, DSA, FPA, ForAb, HAPI, HortAb, I&DA, NutrAb, PBA, PGegResA, PHN&I, RDA, RRTA, RiceAb, S&F, SIA, SoyAb, TDB, WAE&RSA.
Published by: Centro Peruano de Estudios Sociales, Ave. Salaverry, 818, Jesus Maria, Lima, 11, Peru. TEL 51-14-336610, FAX 51-14-331744, feguren@cepes.org.pe. Ed. Fernando Eguren L.

636.294   CAN
DEERFARMERS' DIGEST. Text in English. m. free (effective 2000). **Description:** Provides news, information and how-to articles about raising deer on farms and ranches.
Media: Online - full text. **Related titles:** Print ed.
Published by: Deer Farmers' Information Network, Box 8220, Edmonton, AB T6H 4P1, Canada. TEL 780-430-8245, FAX 780-434-0412, 800-267-9997, info@deerfarmer.com, http://www.deerfarmer.com/library/digest/. Ed., Pub. Russell Sawchuk.

630   FRA   ISSN 0249-7336
DEFENSE AGRICOLE DE LA BEAUCE ET DU PERCHE. Text in French. 1904. m.
Address: 15 Place des Halles, Chartres, Cedex 28004, France. TEL 37-20-30-40. Ed. Jean Claude Moriceau. Circ: 3,373.

630   FRA   ISSN 1162-9908
DEFENSE PAYSANNE DU LOT. Text in French. 24/yr.
Published by: Defense Paysanne du, 430 av. Jean Jaures, Cahors, Cedex 46004, France. TEL 65-22-55-30, TELEX 533 725 AGRI LOT. Ed. M Marchais. Circ: 15,974.

630   PAK
DEHI RAZAKAR. Text in Urdu. 1969. fortn. PKR 100; PKR 200 foreign (effective 1998). **Document type:** Newspaper.
Description: Discusses various aspects of agriculture, economic planning, social welfare and farm management, as well as issues such as literacy, youth development, civil defence, farm forestry and environmental safety.
Published by: National Farm Guide Council of Pakistan, c/o Mohammad Anwer Chaudhry, Ed., 405, Ferozepur Rd., Lahore, 54600, Pakistan. TEL 92-42-5864155, FAX 92-42-5864155. Ed. Anwar Chaudhry. Pub. Mohammad Anwer Chaudhry. Circ: (controlled).

630   USA
DEL-MAR-VA HEARTLAND✶. Text in English. 1983 (vol.9). 3/yr. USD 2 per issue. adv. bk.rev. illus.
Published by: Heartland Publications, Ltd., PO Box 249, Denton, MD 21629. TEL 301-479-2061. Ed. Kristen Dukes. Circ: 105,000.

630   USA
DELAWARE AG NEWS. Text in English. 1984. m. free.
Document type: Government. **Description:** Provides news about Delaware Department of Agriculture services and activities. Includes calendar of events, legislative updates, and features on local topics.
Formerly (until 1994): Delaware Agenda
Published by: Department of Agriculture, 2320 S DuPont Hwy, Dover, DE 19901. TEL 302-739-4811, FAX 302-697-6287. Ed. Vicki Davis.

630   USA   ISSN 0194-2964
DELMARVA FARMER. Text in English. 1978. w. USD 24 domestic; USD 50 in Canada; USD 60 elsewhere (effective 2003). **Document type:** Newspaper, Consumer.
Related titles: Supplement(s): Mid-Atlantic Poultry Farmer; Mid-Atlantic Beef & Dairy; Next Generation; Horsin' Around.

Published by: American Farm Publications, Inc., 505 Brookletts Ave, PO Box 2026, Easton, MD 21601. TEL 800-634-5021, FAX 410-822-5068, http://www.americanfarm.com. Ed. Mark Powell. Pub. E. Ralph Hostetter. Circ: 10,000.

630   CAN
DELORAINE TIMES & STAR. Text in English. w. CND 25 in city; CND 30 elsewhere (effective 2000). adv. **Document type:** Newspaper. **Description:** Local news and photos, editorial comment, agriculture-related articles.
Related titles: Microfilm ed.
Published by: D T S Publishing, Ltd., 122 Broadway St N, P O Box 407, Deloraine, MB R0M 0M0, Canada. TEL 204-747-2249, FAX 204-747-3999. Ed., Pub., R&P, Adv. contact Bev Lischka. Circ: 1,350.

630   ARG   ISSN 0011-7978
DELTA. Text in Spanish. 1933. fortn. adv. mkt.
Published by: Periodico Delta S.C.A., General Mitre 320, Tigre, Argentina. Eds. Julio Cesar Comte, Rosalia K De Mikler. Circ: 5,000.

630   USA
DELTA AGRICULTURAL DIGEST. Text in English. a. USD 14.95. adv. **Document type:** Trade.
Formerly: Delta Digest
Published by: Farm Press (Subsidiary of: Primedia Business Magazines & Media, Inc.), PO Box 1420, Clarksdale, MS 38614. TEL 601-624-8503, FAX 601-627-1977. Ed. Forrest Laws. Pub. Mike Gonitzke. R&P, Adv. contact Darrah Parker. Circ: 20,000. **Subscr. to:** Primedia Business Magazines & Media, Inc., PO Box 12993, Overland Park, KS 66282-2993. TEL 800-441-0294, FAX 913-967-1331, inquiries@primediabusiness.com, http:// www.primediabusiness.com.

630   USA   ISSN 0011-8036
DELTA FARM PRESS. Text in English. 1944. w. USD 38 domestic; USD 189 foreign; free to qualified personnel in MO, MS, LA, AR, or TN (effective 2005). adv. charts; stat.
Document type: Magazine, Trade. **Description:** Covers theregion's major crops, plus the legislative, environmental and regulatory issues that affect their businesses; includes marketing, research and technology updates, along with features on area farmers and agribusiness news.
Related titles: Online - full text ed.: (from bigchalk, Factiva, H.W. Wilson, O C L C Online Computer Library Center, Inc.).
Indexed: B&AI.
—CCC.
Published by: Primedia Business Magazines & Media, Inc. (Subsidiary of: Primedia, Inc.), 9800 Metcalf Ave, Overland Park, KS 66212-2216. TEL 913-341-1300, FAX 913-967-1898, gfrey@primedia.com, inquiries@primediabusiness.com, http://www.deltafarmpress.com/, http:// www.primediabusiness.com. Eds. Elton Robinson, Hembree Brandon. Pub. Greg Frey TEL 952-851-4613. Adv. contact Glenn Luedke. Circ: 27,010 (controlled).

DEMOCRACIA NA TERRA. see POLITICAL SCIENCE

DENMARK. DANMARKS STATISTIK. LANDBRUGSSTATISTIK. see AGRICULTURE—Abstracting, Bibliographies, Statistics

630 639.2   DNK   ISSN 1398-3172
DENMARK. MINISTERIET FOR FOEDEVARER, LANDBRUG OG FISKERI. STRUKTURDIREKTORATET. KORTLAEGNING.
Text in Danish. 1976. a. free. **Document type:** Government.
Description: Contains inventory of current food, agricultural and fisheries research projects financed by the ministry.
Former titles (until 1997): Denmark. Ministeriet for Foedevarer, Landbrug og Fiskeri. Forskningssekretariatet. Kortlaegning (1397-3797); Landbrugs- og Fiskeriministeriet, Forskningssekretariatet. Kortlaegning (0906-1770); Landbrugets Samraad for Forskning og Forsoeg. Kortlaegning (0105-4244)
Published by: Ministeriet for Foedevarer, Landbrug og Fiskeri, Direktoratet for FoedevareErhverv/Ministry of Food, Agriculture and Fisheries, Directorate for Food, Fisheries and Agri Business, Kampmannsgade 3, Copenhagen V, 1780, Denmark. dffe@dffe.dk, http://www.dffe.dk. Ed. Poul Hoffmann. Circ: 400.

630   GBR   ISSN 0954-9684
DERBYSHIRE FARMER. Text in English. 1973 (vol.27). m. adv.
Published by: County Farmers Publications Ltd., 55 Goldington Rd, Bedford, Beds MK40 3LU, United Kingdom. TEL 44-1234-351401, FAX 44-1234-328614. Ed. P Hudson. Circ: 2,900.

630   DEU   ISSN 0343-3846
DEUTSCHE BAUERN-KORRESPONDENZ. Text in German. 1948. m. adv. bk.rev. stat. index. **Document type:** Journal, Trade.
Indexed: ExcerpMed, RRTA, WAE&RSA.
Published by: Deutscher Bauernverband e V., Godesberger Allee 142-148, Bonn, 53175, Germany. TEL 49-30-31904407, FAX 49-30-31904431, presse@bauernverband.de, http://www.bauernverband.de. Circ: (controlled).

630   DEU   ISSN 0938-8818
DEUTSCHE LANDWIRT✶; Monatszeitung des Verbandes Deutscher Landwirte. Text in German. 1990. m. adv. bk.rev. back issues avail. **Document type:** Newspaper, Trade.
Published by: Verband Deutscher Landwirte, Dresdner Str 46, Dittmansdorf, 09526, Germany. TEL 49-37360-6344, FAX 49-37360-6366, info@deutsche-landwirte.de, http://www.deutsche-landwirte.de. Circ: 50,000.

630   DEU   ISSN 1610-8930
DEUTSCHER LANDWIRTSCHAFTS GESELLSCHAFT. JAHRESBERICHT. Text in German. 197?. a. **Document type:** Yearbook, Trade.
Former titles (until 2002): D L G Jahresbericht (1616-2447); (until 1998): Deutscher Landwirtschafts Gesellschaft. Jahresbericht (0724-0651)
Published by: D L G Verlags GmbH, Eschborner Landstr 122, Frankfurt Am Main, 60489, Germany. TEL 49-69-247880, FAX 49-69-24788480, dlg-verlag@dlg-frankfurt.de, http://www.dlg-verlag.de.

638.1   DEU   ISSN 0943-2914
DEUTSCHES BIENEN JOURNAL. Text in German. 1993. m. EUR 33.50 (effective 2005). adv. **Document type:** Magazine, Trade.
Formed by the merger of (1886-1993): Neue Bienen Zeitung (0863-3584); Which was formerly (until 1990): Garten und Kleintierzucht. Ausgabe C: Imker (0433-1826); (until 1962): Leipziger Bienenzeitung (0323-6684); (1990-1993): Deutsches Imker Journal (0938-197X); Which was formed by the merger of (1949-1990): Nordwestdeutsche Imkerzeitung (0938-1988); (1967-1990): Allgemeine Deutsche Imkerzeitung; Which was formed by the merger of (1950-1967): Deutsche Bienenwirtschaft (0418-8241); (1949-1967): Westfaelische Bienenzeitung (0372-7254); (1949-1967): Suedwestdeutscher Imker (0371-4683)
—CISTI. **CCC.**
Published by: Deutscher Bauernverlag GmbH, Wilhelmsaue 37, Berlin, 10713, Germany. TEL 49-30-464060, FAX 49-30-46406205, bienenjournal@bauernverlag.de, info@bauernverlag.de, http://www.bienenjournal.de, http://www.bauernverlag.de. adv. B&W page EUR 1,700, color page EUR 2,737.50. Circ: 18,488 (paid and controlled).

DEVELOPING ECONOMIES. see BUSINESS AND ECONOMICS—International Development And Assistance

630 338.91   NLD
DEVELOPMENT ORIENTED RESEARCH IN AGRICULTURE. Text in English. 1988. irreg., latest vol.5, 1994. price varies. back issues avail. **Document type:** Monographic series.
Description: Publishes monographic studies on topics in agricultural development.
Published by: (Koninklijk Instituut voor de Tropen/Royal Tropical Institute), K I T Publishers, Mauritskade 63, PO Box 95001, Amsterdam, 1090 HA, Netherlands. TEL 31-20-568-8272, FAX 31-20-568-8286, TELEX 15080 KIT NL, kitpress@kit.nl, publishers@kit.nl, http://www.kit.nl. Pub. Ron Smit. **Dist. in US & Canada by:** Eiron Inc., PO Box 40072, Washington, DC 20016. TEL 202-966-3240.

DEVELOPMENTS IN AGRICULTURAL AND MANAGED FOREST ECOLOGY. see FORESTS AND FORESTRY

630   GBR   ISSN 0012-169X
DEVON FARMER. Text in English. m. adv.
Published by: County Farmers Publications Ltd., 55 Goldington Rd, Bedford, Beds MK40 3LU, United Kingdom. TEL 44-1234-351401, FAX 44-1234-328614. Ed. A Gibson. Circ: 7,100.

630.24 668.6   MEX
DICCIONARIO DE ESPECIALIDADES AGROQUIMICAS. Text in Spanish. 1984. a. USD 37. adv.
Formerly: Diccionario Agroquimico
Published by: Ediciones P L M S.A. de C.V., San Bernardino 17, Col del Valle, Mexico City, DF 03100, Mexico. TEL 687-1766, FAX 536-5027. Ed. Luis Hochstein. Circ: 5,000.

630   FRA
DICTIONNAIRE - ANNUAIRE DE L'AGRICULTURE ET DE L'AGRO-ALIMENTAIRE; organismes - dirigeants - fournisseurs. Short title: Dic-Agri. Text in French. 1966. a. index. **Document type:** Directory. **Description:** Catalogs agricultural unions, professional associations, specialized schools on the national, regional and departmental levels, as well as 3000 French and European food companies.
Formerly: Dictionnaire - Annuaire de l'Agriculture
Published by: Editions et Publications Specialisees, 25 rue de Madrid, Paris, 75008, France. TEL 33-1-44707494, FAX 33-1-44707499. Pub. Jacques Baret.

630   FRA   ISSN 0012-2483
DICTIONNAIRE PERMANENT: ENTREPRISE AGRICOLE. Text in French. 1969. 2 base vols. plus m. updates. looseleaf. EUR 271 base vol(s). (effective 2004). bibl. index, cum.index.
Description: Discusses legal and fiscal problems linked with agricultural activities.
Related titles: CD-ROM ed.; Online - full text ed.
Indexed: RRTA, WAE&RSA.

Published by: Editions Legislatives, 80 Avenue de la Marne, Montrouge, Cedex 92546, France. TEL 33-1-40923636, FAX 33-1-40923663, infocom@editions-legislatives.fr, http://www.editions-legislatives.fr. Ed. Guy Chesne. Pub. Michel Vaillant. Circ: 4,000.

349 FRA ISSN 1290-6115
DICTIONNAIRE PERMANENT: SOCIAL AGRICOLE. Text in French. 1956. base vol. plus m. updates. looseleaf. EUR 305 base vol(s). (effective 2004). bibl. index, cum.index.
Description: Presents social legislation pertaining to agriculture.
Formerly: Dictionnaire Permanent: Rural (0012-2505)
Published by: Editions Legislatives, 80 Avenue de la Marne, Montrouge, Cedex 92546, France. TEL 33-1-40923636, FAX 33-1-40923663, infocom@editions-legislatives.fr, http://www.editions-legislatives.fr. Pub. Michel Vaillant. Circ: 2,800.

630 JOR ISSN 1026-3764
CODEN: DSNJDI
➤ **DIRASAT. AGRICULTURAL SCIENCES.** Text in Arabic, English. 1974. 3/yr. JOD 13.50 domestic to individuals; JOD 16.50 domestic to institutions; USD 45 foreign (effective 2002). illus. index, cum.index. back issues avail. **Document type:** *Journal, Academic/Scholarly.* **Description:** Presents research papers and articles in agricultural and animal sciences.
Supersedes in part (in 1996): Dirasat. Series B: Pure and Applied Sciences (0253-424X)
Indexed: AEA, AgBio, AgrForAb, AnBrAb, BIOSIS Prev, BioCN&I, BiolAb, CPA, DSA, FCA, ForAb, HelmAb, HerbAb, HortAb, I&DA, IBSS, IndVet, MaizeAb, NemAb, NutrAb, OrnHort, PBA, PGegResA, PGrRegA, PHN&I, PotatoAb, PoultAb, RA&MP, RDA, RM&VM, RPP, RevApplEntom, RiceAb, S&F, SIA, SeedAb, SoyAb, TDB, TriticAb, VITIS, VetBull, WAE&RSA, WeedAb.
—CASDDS, CISTI.
Published by: University of Jordan, Deanship of Academic Research, Dean of Academic Research, Amman, 11942, Jordan. TEL 962-6-5355000 ext 3200, FAX 962-6-5355599, dirasatab@ju.edu.jo, http://www.ju.edu.jo/research/dar. Ed. Nabil Shawagfeh. Circ: 1,000 (controlled).

630 COL
DIRECTORIO AGROPECUARIO DE COLOMBIA. Text in Spanish. biennial. COP 3,000, USD 10.
Published by: (Sociedad de Agricultores de Colombia), Corporacion Editorial Interamericana, Ave. Jimenez, 403, Of 907, PO Box 14965, Bogota, CUND 1, Colombia.

DIRECTORY OF COCONUT TRADERS AND EQUIPMENT MANUFACTURERS. see *BUSINESS AND ECONOMICS—Trade And Industrial Directories*

DIRECTORY OF INTERNATIONAL COCONUT RESEARCH WORKERS. see *BUSINESS AND ECONOMICS—Trade And Industrial Directories*

630 340 ITA ISSN 1720-4445
DIRITTO DELL'AGRICOLTURA. Text in Italian. 1992. 3/yr. EUR 62 domestic to individuals; EUR 73 domestic to institutions; EUR 82 foreign (effective 2004). **Document type:** *Journal, Trade.*
Published by: Edizioni Scientifiche Italiane SpA, Via Chiatamone 7, Naples, NA 80121, Italy. TEL 39-081-7645443, FAX 39-081-7646477, info@esispa.com, http://www.esispa.com.

630 ESP ISSN 1132-0176
DISTRIBUCION Y CONSUMO. Text in Spanish. 1984. m. (11/yr.). free. **Document type:** *Trade.*
Formerly (until 1991): Mercaconsumo (1130-8273)
Related titles: CD-ROM ed.: 1997.
—CINDOC.
Published by: Empresa Nacional Mercasa, Paseo Habana, 180, Madrid, 28036, Spain. TEL 34-91-3500609, http://www.mercasa.es/es/publicaciones/htm/index2.html. Ed. I Olivares. Circ: 10,034.

632.7 GBR ISSN 1369-104X
DISTRIBUTION MAPS OF PLANT PESTS. Text in English. 1951. s-a. looseleaf. USD 830 combined subscription in the Americas to institutions except Canada; print & online eds.; GBP 475 combined subscription elsewhere to institutions print & online eds. (effective 2006). back issues avail. **Document type:** *Academic/Scholarly.* **Description:** Comprises maps giving the world distribution, together with supporting references, of a particular arthropod pest.
Formerly until (1996): Distribution Maps of Pests (0952-634X)
Related titles: Online - full text ed.: 2006.
Indexed: ForAb, PHN&I, RPP, RefZh, RevApplEntom, RiceAb, SoyAb, TriticAb, ZooRec.
—CISTI. **CCC.**
Published by: CABI Publishing (Subsidiary of: CAB International), CAB International, Wallingford, Oxfordshire OX10 8DE, United Kingdom. TEL 44-1491-832111, FAX 44-1491-833508, cabi@cabi.org, http://www.cabi-publishing.org/. **Subscr. addr. in N America:** CABI Publishing North America, 875 Massachusetts Ave, 7th Fl, Cambridge, MA 02139. TEL 617-395-4056, 800-528-4841, FAX 617-354-6875, cabi-nao@cabi.org.

334 DMA
DOMINICA CO-OPERATIVE NEWSLETTER. Text in English. 1980. q. free. charts. **Document type:** *Newsletter.*
Supersedes: Dominica. Registrar of Co-Operative Societies. Report
Published by: Ministry of Community Development and Women's Affairs, Co-operative Division, Government Headquarters, Kennedy Ave., Roseau, Dominica. TEL 809-448-2401, FAX 809-448-7397, cuffyw@cwdom.dm. Ed. Washbourne N Cuffy.

630 CHN ISSN 1005-9369
CODEN: DNDXEA
➤ **DONGBEI NONGYE DAXUE XUEBAO/NORTHEAST AGRICULTURAL UNIVERSITY. JOURNAL.** Text in Chinese; Abstracts in English. 1957. q. CNY 26 domestic; USD 60 foreign (effective 2003). **Document type:** *Academic/Scholarly.* **Description:** Covers scientific experiment results in the fields of agronomy, animal science, veterinary science, farm machinery, biotechnology, horticulture, and agricultural economics.
Formerly (until Mar. 1994): Dongbei Nongxueyuan Xuebao - Northeast Agricultural College. Journal (0253-228X)
Related titles: Online - full text ed.: (from East View Information Services); ♦ English ed.: Northeast Agricultural University. Journal. ISSN 1006-8104.
Indexed: AnBrAb, BioCN&I, CPA, DSA, HortAb, MaizeAb, PN&I, PoultAb, RPP, RevApplEntom, S&F, SeedAb, SoyAb, VetBull, WeedAb.
—CASDDS.
Published by: Dongbei Nongye Daxue, Editorial Dept. of Journal of Northeast Agricultural University, Xiangfang-qu, Harbin, Heilongjiang 150030, China. TEL 86-451-5390553, FAX 86-451-5390553, xuebao@neau.edu.cn. Ed. Li Wenxiong. Circ: 6,000.

630 GBR ISSN 0012-5598
DORSET FARMER. Text in English. 1962. m. adv.
Published by: County Farmers Publications Ltd., 55 Goldington Rd, Bedford, Beds MK40 3LU, United Kingdom. TEL 44-1234-351401, FAX 44-1234-328614. Ed. R A MacDonald. Circ: 2,250.

630 FRA ISSN 1257-4627
LES DOSSIERS DE L'ENVIRONNEMENT DE L'I N R A. (Institut National de la Recherche Agronomique) Text in French. 1992. irreg., latest vol.26, 2004. price varies. **Document type:** *Monographic series.*
Formerly (until 1993): Les Dossiers de la Cellule Environnement (1244-7986)
Indexed: DSA, ForAb, HerbAb, HortAb, S&F, WAE&RSA, WeedAb.
Published by: Institut National de la Recherche Agronomique, Mission Environnement-Societe, 147, rue de l'Universite, Paris, 75338 Cedex 07, France. TEL 33-1-42759249, FAX 33-1-42759508, http://www.infra.fr/dpenv/. **Subscr. to:** I N R A Editions, Route de Saint-Cyr, Versailles 78026 Cedex, France. TEL 33-1-30833406, FAX 33-1-30833449, INRA-Editions@versailles.inra.fr.

630 RUS ISSN 0235-2451
DOSTIZHENIYA NAUKI I TEKHNIKI A P K. (Agro-Promyshlennyi Kompleks) Text in Russian. 1987. bi-m. USD 143 foreign (effective 2003).
Indexed: RefZh.
—East View.
Address: Sadovaya-Spasskaya 18, Moscow, 107807, Russian Federation. TEL 7-095-2072291, FAX 7-095-2072870. Ed. Vladimir I Nikiforov. Circ: 1,600. **Dist. by:** M K - Periodica, ul Gilyarovskogo 39, Moscow 129110, Russian Federation. TEL 7-095-2845008, FAX 7-095-2813798, info@periodicals.ru, http://www.mkniga.ru; **US dist. addr.:** East View Information Services, 3020 Harbor Ln. N., Minneapolis, MN 55447. TEL 612-550-0961.

DOWN TO EARTH. see *CHEMISTRY*

THE DRAKE JOURNAL OF AGRICULTURAL LAW. see *LAW*

630 ESP
DRECERA. Text in Spanish. m.
Formerly (until 1993): Forum Agrari
Published by: Confederation and Professional Agricultural Organizations of Catalunya, Pza. Sant Josep Oriol 4, Barcelona, 08002, Spain. TEL 3-301-17-40, FAX 3-317-30-05. Ed. Ferran de Muller. Circ: 60,000.

DU SOL A LA TABLE. see *ENVIRONMENTAL STUDIES*

630 ARG
E A G PUBLICACIONES. Text in Spanish. charts; stat.
Formed by the merger of: S E A G Boletin del Maiz (0036-1232); S E A G Boletin del Trigo (0036-1240); S E A G Boletin del Algodon (0036-1224)
Media: Duplicated (not offset).
Published by: (Argentina. Servicio Nacional de Economia y Sociologia Rural), Secretaria de Estado de Agricultura y Ganaderia, Avda. Paseo Colon, 922, Capital Federal, Buenos Aires 1063, Argentina.

630 DEU ISSN 1682-1130
➤ **E-JOURNAL - C I G R.** (Commission Internationale du Genie Rural) Variant title: Agricultural Engineering International. Text in English. 1999. irreg. free (effective 2004). **Document type:** *Journal.* **Description:** Provides a forum for the exchange of research results and other general information among agricultural engineers and others interested in agricultural engineering subjects around the world.
Media: Online - full content.
Indexed: Agr, FCA.
Published by: Internationale Kommission fuer Agrartechnik/International Commission of Agricultural Engineering, c/o Peter Schulze Lammers, Institut fuer Landtechnik, Universitaet Bonn, Nussallee 5, Bonn, 53115, Germany. TEL 49-228-732389, FAX 49-228-739644, ejournal@cigr.agen.tamu.edu, cigr@uni-bonn.de, http://cigr-ejournal.tamu.edu/. Ed. Rosana Moreira.

028.1 USA ISSN 1098-4399
Z5852
E-STREAMS (CONTOOCOOK); electronic reviews of science and technology references covering engineering, agriculture, medicine and science. Text in English. 1998. m. free. bk.rev. back issues avail. **Document type:** *Academic/Scholarly.*
Media: Online - full text. **Related titles:** Online - full text ed.
Indexed: BRI, CBRI.
Published by: Yankee Book Peddler, Inc., 999 Maple St, Contoocook, NH 03229. TEL 603-746-3102, FAX 603-746-5628, estreams@ybp.com, http://www.e-streams.com. Ed. H Robert Malinowsky. Pub. Glen Secor. R&P Jennifer Goodrich.

THE EARLY BIRD. see *HISTORY—History Of North And South America*

630 JPN ISSN 0913-7815
EARTH/CHIJO. Text in Japanese. 1947. m.
Related titles: Online - full text ed.: (from Northern Light Technology, Inc.).
Indexed: BiolDig.
Published by: Ie-No-Hikari Coop-Publishing Association, 11 Ichigaya-Funagawara-Machi, Shinjuku-ku, Tokyo, 162-0826, Japan. TEL 03-3266-9000, FAX 03-3266-9048, TELEX 22367. Ed. Takeshi Nogami.

630 KEN ISSN 0012-8325
S17 CODEN: EAFJAU
➤ **EAST AFRICAN AGRICULTURAL AND FORESTRY JOURNAL.** Text in English. 1935. q. KES 4,000, GBP 40, USD 62 (effective 2004). adv. bk.rev. index, cum.index. back issues avail.; reprints avail. **Document type:** *Journal, Academic/Scholarly.* **Description:** Publishes original research in agriculture, veterinary science, forestry and, allied subjects.
Formerly (until 1960): East African Agricultural Journal of Kenya, Tanganyika, Uganda and Zanzibar (0367-0074)
Related titles: Microfilm ed.; Online - full text ed.: (from International Network for the Availability of Scientific Publications, African Journals Online).
Indexed: ASFA, AnBrAb, B&AI, BiolAb, CTFA, ChemAb, DSA, ESPM, FCA, FPA, FS&TA, ForAb, HerbAb, HortAb, IBR, IndVet, NutrAb, PBA, PLESA, PoultAb, RPP, RevApplEntom, S&F, S&MA, SFA, VetBull, WeedAb.
—CASDDS, CISTI, Linda Hall.
Published by: (Veterubart Research Department), Kenya Agricultural Research Institute, PO Box 30148, Nairobi, Kenya. TEL 0154-328801, FAX 254-0154-32090, TELEX 25287 KARI HQ KE, odalis@arcc.or.ke, http://www.inasp.info/ajol/journals.html. Ed. J O Mugah. Circ: 1,000.

630 GBR
EAST ANGLIAN FARMER & GROWER. Text in English. m. adv. **Document type:** *Trade.*
Formed by the Dec. 1992 merger of: Bedfordshire and Huntingdonshire Farmer and Grower; Cambridgeshire Farmer and Grower
Published by: West Country Magazines, N R U, Agriculture House, Willie Snaith Rd, Newmarket, Cambs CB8 7SN, United Kingdom. TEL 44-1638-667662, FAX 44-1638-666442. Ed. R Tuner. Adv. contact C Newman. Circ: 46,437.

630 GBR
EAST OF ENGLAND SHOW CATALOGUE. Text in English. 1968. a. GBP 3. adv.
Published by: East of England Agricultural Society, East Of England Agricultural Society, East Of England Showground, Oundle Rd, Alwalton, Peterborough, PE2 6XE, United Kingdom. FAX 0733-370038. Ed. Tonie Gibson. Circ: 6,000.

630 GBR ISSN 0954-9692
EAST RIDING FARMER. Text in English. 1949. m. adv.
Published by: County Farmers Publications Ltd., 55 Goldington Rd, Bedford, Beds MK40 3LU, United Kingdom. TEL 44-1234-351401, FAX 44-1234-328614. Ed. A Hepworth. Circ: 2,000.

630 GBR ISSN 0012-8546
EAST SUSSEX FARMER. Text in English. 1964. m. adv.
Published by: County Farmers Publications Ltd., 55 Goldington Rd, Bedford, Beds MK40 3LU, United Kingdom. TEL 44-1234-351401, FAX 44-1234-328614. Ed. N Errington. Circ: 1,550.

A

A

630 338.1 FRA ISSN 1273-7011
ECHO DES M.I.N.; mensuel de la filiere fruits et legumes. Text in French. 1985. m. EUR 50.31 domestic; EUR 76.99 in the European Union and Switzerland; EUR 85.37 elsewhere (effective 2000). index. **Document type:** *Trade.* **Description:** Offers news on the culture and consumption of fruits and vegetables and economic analysis in the French and international market.
Published by: Echo Edition, 1405 rte de Noves, BP 12, Morieres-les-Avignon, 84310, France. TEL 33-4-90335656, FAX 33-4-90335151, echo@wanadoo.fr. Ed. Jean Harzig. Pub. Jean-Luc Gregorini. R&P Jean Luc Gregorini. Adv. contact Laurence Marneys.

630 SWE ISSN 1404-2347
CODEN: CRSCE5
ECOLOGY AND CROP PRODUCTION SCIENCE. Text in English. 1988. irreg. price varies. **Document type:** *Monographic series, Academic/Scholarly.*
Formerly (until 1999): Crop Production Science (1100-1186)
—CISTI.
Published by: Sveriges Lantbruksuniversitet, Institutionen foer Ekologi och Vaextproduktionslaera/Swedish University of Agricultural Sciences, Department of Ecology and Crop Production Science, PO Box 7043, Uppsala, 75007, Sweden. TEL 46-18-671000, FAX 46-18-672890, http://www.evp.slu.se. Circ: 500.

630 DEU ISSN 1016-5061
ECOLOGY AND FARMING. Text in English. 1982. 3/yr. adv. bk.rev. back issues avail. **Document type:** *Bulletin, Trade.* **Description:** Charts the progress of organic agriculture on an international basis.
Supersedes: International Federation of Organic Agricultural Movements. Bulletin (0195-0304)
Related titles: ♦ German ed.: Oekologie und Landbau. ISSN 1015-2423.
—CISTI.
Published by: International Federation of Organic Agriculture Movements, c/o Oekozentrum Imsbach, Theley, Tholey, 66636, Germany. TEL 49-6853-919890, FAX 49-6853-919899, headoffice@ifoam.org. Ed. Joy Marchand. R&P B. Geier. Adv. contact B Geier.

631 ESP ISSN 1135-6863
EDAFOLOGIA. Text in Spanish. 1995. q.
Related titles: Online - full text ed.
Indexed: IECT.
—CINDOC.
Published by: Universidad de Granada, Facultad de Ciencias, Depto de Edafologia y Quimica Agricola, Granda, Andalucia 18071, Spain. TEL 34-958-248537, FAX 34-958-244160, decacien@goliat.ugr.es, http://www.ugr.es/. Ed. Juan Antonio Fernandez Garcia.

630 EST ISSN 1406-4049
EESTI POLLUMAJANDUSULIKOOLI. TEADUSTOODE KOGUMIK/ESTONIAN AGRICULTURAL UNIVERSITY. TRANSACTIONS. Text in Estonian. 1992. irreg. **Document type:** *Monographic series, Academic/Scholarly.*
Indexed: AEA, AbHyg, AgBio, AgrForAb, BioCN&I, CPA, DSA, ESPM, FCA, FPA, ForAb, HerbAb, HortAb, I&DA, MaizeAb, NemAb, NutrAb, OrnHort, PBA, PGegResA, PGrRegA, PHN&I, PollutAb, PotatoAb, ProtozoAb, RA&MP, RM&VM, RPP, RRTA, S&F, SIA, SeedAb, SoyAb, TriticAb, WAE&RSA, WeedAb, ZooRec.
Published by: Eesti Pollumajandusulikool/Estonian Agricultural University, Kreutzwaldi 64, Tartu, 51014, Estonia. http://www.eau.ee.

630 DNK ISSN 0013-2187
EFFEKTIVT LANDBRUG/PRODUCTIVE FARMING. Text in Danish. 1949-1956; resumed 1964. w. DKK 485 (effective 2004). adv. charts; illus. **Document type:** *Trade.* **Description:** Focus on the supply, processing and marketing sectors of Danish agriculture, including information about products and methods of significance to farmers in Denmark.
Former titles (until 1970): Traktor- og Landbrugsbladet (0041-0977); (until 1951): Traktorbladet
Published by: Landbrugnet Fyn A/S, Odensevej 29, Langeskov, 5550, Denmark. TEL 45-70-151237, FAX 45-70-151247, effektivt@landbrugnet.dk, http://www.landbrugnet.dk. Ed. Jacob Lund-Larsen TEL 45-63-382534. Adv. contact Kjeld Birk TEL 45-75-411045. Circ: 22,000 (controlled).

630 TUR ISSN 1018-8851
EGE UNIVERSITESI. ZIRAAT FAKULTESI. DERGISI. Text in Turkish. 3/yr.
Indexed: AgBio, AgrForAb, AnBrAb, BioCN&I, CPA, DSA, FCA, FPA, FS&TA, ForAb, HerbAb, HortAb, I&DA, IndVet, MaizeAb, NemAb, OrnHort, PBA, PGegResA, PGrRegA, PHN&I, PotatoAb, PoultAb, RA&MP, RPP, RRTA, RefZh, S&F, SIA, SeedAb, SoyAb, TriticAb, VITIS, WAE&RSA, ZooRec.
—BLDSC (9514.610000), IE.
Published by: Ege Universitesi, Ziraat Fakultesi, Izmir, Bornova, 35100, Turkey.

630 TUR ISSN 0367-1577
EGE UNIVERSITESI. ZIRAAT FAKULTESI. YAYINLARI. Text in Turkish. irreg.
Indexed: ZooRec.
Published by: Ege Universitesi, Ziraat Fakultesi, Izmir, Bornova, 35100, Turkey.

630 EGY ISSN 1110-6336
EGYPTIAN JOURNAL OF AGRICULTURAL RESEARCH. Text in English. 195?. q. **Document type:** *Journal, Academic/Scholarly.*
Supersedes in part (in 1990): Agricultural Research Review (1110-0389)
Indexed: AgBio, AgrForAb, AnBrAb, BioCN&I, CPA, DSA, FCA, FPA, ForAb, HelmAb, HerbAb, HortAb, I&DA, IndVet, MaizeAb, NemAb, OrnHort, PBA, PGegResA, PGrRegA, PHN&I, PotatoAb, PoultAb, ProtozoAb, RA&MP, RM&VM, RPP, S&F, SIA, SeedAb, SoyAb, TDB, TriticAb, WAE&RSA, WeedAb.
—BLDSC (3664.259500), CISTI, IE.
Published by: The Agricultural Research Center, Central Agricultural Pesticides Laboratory, Giza, Egypt. TEL 20-2-5732231, http://derp.sti.sci.eg/data/0212.htm. Ed. Dr. Muhsen A El-Gendi.

630 EGY ISSN 1110-6158
EGYPTIAN JOURNAL OF AGRONEMATOLOGY/AL-MAGALLAT AL-MISRIYYAT LIL-NIMATULUGIYA AL-ZIRA'IYYAT. Text in English. 1997. s-a. **Document type:** *Journal, Academic/Scholarly.*
Published by: Egyptian Society for Nematology, Plant Protection Dept, Faculty of Agriculture, Cairo University, Giza, Egypt. sanaaharoon@hotmail.com, http://derp.sti.sci.eg/data/0322.htm.

630 EGY ISSN 0379-3575
CODEN: EJAGDS
➤ **EGYPTIAN JOURNAL OF AGRONOMY/AL-MAGALLAT AL-MISRIYYAT LI-L-MAHASIL.** Text in English; Summaries in Arabic, English. 1976. a. USD 57 (effective 2003). charts; illus. reprint service avail. from IRC. **Document type:** *Journal, Academic/Scholarly.*
Indexed: AgBio, CIN, CPA, ChemAb, ChemTitl, FCA, HerbAb, HortAb, I&DA, MaizeAb, PBA, PGegResA, PGrRegA, PHN&I, RPP, S&F, SIA, SeedAb, SoyAb, TriticAb.
—BLDSC (3664.260000), CASDDS, CISTI, IE, Linda Hall.
Published by: (Egyptian Society of Crop Science, Research Department), National Information and Documentation Centre (NIDOC), Tahrir St., Dokki, Awqaf P.O., Giza, Egypt. TEL 20-2-3371696, FAX 20-2-3371746, http://derp.sti.sci.eg/data/0106.htm. Ed. Dr. Helal El-Sayed El-Hattab. Circ: 1,000.

630 EGY ISSN 1110-1571
EGYPTIAN JOURNAL OF APPLIED SCIENCE/AL-MAGALLAT AL-MISRIYYAT LIL-'LUM AL-TATBIIQIYYAT. Text in English. 1986. m. **Document type:** *Journal, Academic/Scholarly.*
Published by: Zagazig University, Faculty of Agriculture, Banha Branch, Mushtuhur, Zagazig, Egypt. TEL 20-55-323490, 20-55-345452, http://derp.sti.sci.eg/data/0218.htm. Ed. Dr. Abdel-Hamid Hasan Salem.

630 JPN ISSN 0424-6829
S405 CODEN: ECPMAZ
EHIME DAIGAKU NOGAKUBU KIYO/EHIME UNIVERSITY. MEMOIRS. SECTION 6. Text in Japanese. 1948. irreg. **Document type:** *Academic/Scholarly.*
Former titles (until 1954): Matsuyama Agricultural College. Scientific Reports (0371-098X); (until 1948): Ehime Agricultural College. Scientific Reports (0371-2532)
Indexed: AgBio, CPA, HortAb, PGrRegA, PHN&I, S&F, VITIS, WAE&RSA.
—BLDSC (5580.900000), CISTI.
Published by: Ehime Daigaku, Nogakubu/Ehime University, College of Agriculture, 3-5-7 tarumi, Matsuyama-shi, Ehime, 790-8566, Japan. TEL 81-89-9469806, FAX 81-89-9414175, http://web.agr.ehime-u.ac.jp/memoirs/memoirs/memoirs.htm, http://web.agr.ehime-u.ac.jp/index.html.

630 ESP ISSN 0211-0946
EINA; unio de pagesos-baix llobregat. Text in Catalan. 1983. bi-m. adv. **Document type:** *Trade.*
Published by: Edicions la Terra S.L., Avinguda Francesc Cambo, 14 3-B, Barcelona, 08003, Spain. TEL 34-93-2680900, FAX 34-93-2684893, http://www.uniopagesos.es/unio. Ed. Montserrat Lligades. Adv. contact Josep M Escola. Circ: 600.

630 NLD ISSN 0926-9142
EKOLAND; vakblad voor de biologische landbouw. Text in Dutch. 1980. 11/yr. EUR 57.50 (effective 2005). adv. bk.rev. **Document type:** *Trade.*
Formerly (until 1981): Boerenbrief (0926-9150)
Published by: (Stichting Ekoland), Uitgeverij van Westering bv, Postbus 16, Baarn, 3740 AA, Netherlands. TEL 31-35-5423281, FAX 31-35-5424119, redactie@ekoland.nl, administratie@ekoland.nl, http://www.ekoland.nl/. Ed. Peter Brul. Pub., R&P, Adv. contact Jaap van Westering. Circ: 4,150.

631.584 POL ISSN 1426-2940
EKOLAND; kwartalnik rolnictwa ekologicznego. Text in Polish. 1990. q. PLZ 20; PLZ 5 newsstand/cover (effective 2002). adv. bk.rev. abstr.; charts; illus. back issues avail. **Document type:** *Bulletin.* **Description:** Covers organic agriculture and horticulture. For scientists, research workers, students, farmers, gardeners, food producers.
Indexed: AgrLib.
Published by: Ekoland Stowarzyszenie Producentow Zywnosci Metodami Ekologicznymi/Ekoland, Association of Organic Producers, ul. Waszyngtona 42/13, Warszawa, 03910, Poland. ekoland@ekoland.org.pl, http://www.ekoland.org.pl. Ed., R&P, Adv. contact Waldemar Fortuna. page PLZ 50; 400 x 600. Circ: 2,000.

630 BRA ISSN 1516-5604
EMBRAPA MANDIOCA E FRUTICULTURA. BOLETIM DE PESQUISA. Text in Portuguese. 1981. irreg. price varies. **Document type:** *Bulletin, Government.*
Formerly: Brazil. Centro Nacional de Pesquisa de Mandioca e Fruticultura Tropical. Boletim de Pesquisa (0101-5117)
Indexed: ChemAb, FCA, HortAb, PBA, PGrRegA, S&F.
—CISTI.
Published by: Empresa Brasileira de Pesquisa Agropecuaria, Centro Nacional de Pesquisa de Mandioca e Fruticultura Tropical (Subsidiary of: Empresa Brasileira de Pesquisa Agropecuaria), Rua Embrapa s/n, Cruz das Almas, BA 44380-000, Brazil. TEL 55-75-621-8000, FAX 55-75-621-1118, sac@cnpmf.embrapa.br, http://www.cnpmf.embrapa.br. Circ: 500.

639.2 630 BRA ISSN 1516-5612
EMBRAPA MANDIOCA E FRUTICULTURA. CIRCULAR TECNICA. Text in Portuguese. 1980. irreg. price varies. **Document type:** *Government.*
Formerly (until 1999): Brazil. Centro Nacional de Pesquisa de Mandioca e Fruticultura Tropical. Circular Tecnica (0100-8064)
Indexed: AgrForAb, CPA, FCA, HortAb, I&DA, PGrRegA, PHN&I, S&F, WAE&RSA.
—BLDSC (3265.124770), CISTI.
Published by: Empresa Brasileira de Pesquisa Agropecuaria, Centro Nacional de Pesquisa de Mandioca e Fruticultura Tropical (Subsidiary of: Empresa Brasileira de Pesquisa Agropecuaria), Rua Embrapa s/n, Cruz das Almas, BA 44380-000, Brazil. TEL 55-75-621-8000, FAX 55-75-621-1118, sac@cnpmf.embrapa.br, http://www.cnpmf.embrapa.br.

630 BRA ISSN 1516-5744
EMBRAPA MANDIOCA E FRUTICULTURA. COMUNICADO TECNICO. Text in Portuguese. 1975. irreg. price varies. **Document type:** *Monographic series, Government.*
Formerly (until 1999): Brazil. Centro Nacional de Pesquisa de Mandioca e Fruticultura Tropical. Comunicado Tecnico (0100-8854)
Indexed: ChemAb, FCA, HortAb, S&F, SoyAb.
—CISTI.
Published by: Empresa Brasileira de Pesquisa Agropecuaria, Centro Nacional de Pesquisa de Mandioca e Fruticultura Tropical (Subsidiary of: Empresa Brasileira de Pesquisa Agropecuaria), Rua Embrapa s/n, Cruz das Almas, BA 44380-000, Brazil. TEL 55-75-621-8000, FAX 55-75-621-1118, sac@cnpmf.embrapa.br, http://www.cnpmf.embrapa.br.

630 BRA ISSN 1516-5728
EMBRAPA MANDIOCA E FRUTICULTURA. DOCUMENTOS. Abbreviated title: C N P M F Documentos. Text in Portuguese. 1981. irreg., latest vol.92, 2000, June.
Formerly (until 1999): Centro Nacional de Pesquisa de Mandioca e Fruticultura Tropical. Documento (0101-7411)
Indexed: FCA, HortAb, PBA, PGegResA.
—BLDSC (3612.103130).
Published by: Empresa Brasileira de Pesquisa Agropecuaria, Centro Nacional de Pesquisa de Mandioca e Fruticultura Tropical (Subsidiary of: Empresa Brasileira de Pesquisa Agropecuaria), Rua Embrapa s/n, Cruz das Almas, BA 44380-000, Brazil. TEL 55-75-621-8000, FAX 55-75-621-1118, sac@cnpmf.embrapa.br, http://www.cnpmf.embrapa.br. Circ: 500.

630 BRA ISSN 1516-5752
EMBRAPA MANDIOCA E FRUTICULTURA. PESQUISA EM ANDAMENTO. Text in Portuguese. 1980. irreg. price varies. **Document type:** *Monographic series.*
Formerly (until 1999): Pesquisa em Andamento - Mandioca e Fruticultura (0100-8161)
Indexed: AEA, AnBrAb, ProtozoAb.
—CISTI.
Published by: Empresa Brasileira de Pesquisa Agropecuaria, Centro Nacional de Pesquisa de Mandioca e Fruticultura Tropical (Subsidiary of: Empresa Brasileira de Pesquisa Agropecuaria), Rua Embrapa s/n, Cruz das Almas, BA 44380-000, Brazil. TEL 55-75-621-8000, FAX 55-75-621-1118, sac@cnpmf.embrapa.br, http://www.cnpmf.embrapa.br.

630 BRA ISSN 1516-5736
EMBRAPA MANDIOCA E FRUTICULTURA. RELATORIO TECNICO ANUAL. Text in Portuguese. 1977. a., latest 1994. abstr.; bibl.; charts. **Document type:** *Government.*
Formerly (until 1994): Central Nacional de Pesquisa de Mandioca e Fruticultura Tropical. Relatorio Tecnico Anual (0101-2711)
Indexed: ChemAb.
Published by: Empresa Brasileira de Pesquisa Agropecuaria, Centro Nacional de Pesquisa de Mandioca e Fruticultura Tropical (Subsidiary of: Empresa Brasileira de Pesquisa Agropecuaria), Rua Embrapa s/n, Cruz das Almas, BA 44380-000, Brazil. TEL 55-75-621-8000, FAX 55-75-621-1118, sac@cnpmf.embrapa.br, http://www.cnpmf.embrapa.br. Circ: 1,000.

630 637 USA ISSN 0886-9693
EMPIRE STATE FARMER. Text in English. 1978. s-m. (1st & 3rd Wed.). free. adv. back issues avail. **Document type:** *Newspaper, Trade.*
Formerly: North Country Farmer (Adams)
Published by: Journal Publishing Co., Inc., 7 Main St., Adams, NY 13605. TEL 315-232-2141, FAX 315-232-4586. Ed., Pub. Karl A Fowler. adv.: B&W page USD 480, color page USD 630. Circ: 10,000 (free).

630 BRA ISSN 0101-7683
EMPRESA CAPIXABA DE PESQUISA AGROPECUARIA. COMUNICADO TECNICO. Text in Portuguese. 1979. irreg. **Document type:** *Monographic series.*
Formerly (until 1981): Empresa Capixaba de Pesquisa Agropecuaria. Comunicado E M C A P A (0100-8609)
Indexed: HortAb.
—BLDSC (3397.482000), CISTI.
Published by: Empresa Capixaba de Pesquisa Agropecuaria, Caixa Postal 391, Vitoria, ES 29 001-97, Brazil. FAX 55-27-2223848, emcapa02@npd.ufes.br.

630 BRA ISSN 0100-896X
EMPRESA DE PESQUISA AGROPECUARIA DO ESTADO DO RIO DE JANEIRO. COMUNICADO TECNICO. Text in Portuguese. 1978. 3/w. **Document type:** *Monographic series.*
Indexed: CPA, FCA, HerbAb, HortAb, I&DA, MaizeAb, NutrAb, PBA, PGegResA, RDA, RPP, RiceAb, S&F, SIA, SeedAb, SoyAb, WAE&RSA.
—BLDSC (3397.650000).
Published by: Empresa de Pesquisa Agropecuaria do Rio de Janeiro, Alameda Sao Boaventura 770, Fonseca - Niteroi, RJ 24 120-191, Brazil. TEL 55-21-26271588, webmaster@pesagro.rj.gov.br, http://www.pesagro.com.

630 BRA ISSN 0101-3769
EMPRESA DE PESQUISA AGROPECUARIA DO RIO DE JANEIRO. INFORME TECNICO. Text in Portuguese. 1980. 3/w.
Indexed: DSA, IndVet, NutrAb, WAE&RSA.
—BLDSC (4498.889300).
Published by: Empresa de Pesquisa Agropecuaria do Rio de Janeiro, Alameda Sao Boaventura 770, Fonseca - Niteroi, RJ 24 120-191, Brazil. TEL 55-21-26271588, webmaster@pesagro.rj.gov.br, http://www.pesagro.com.

539.7 630 BRA ISSN 0100-3593
CODEN: ENAGDM
ENERGIA NUCLEAR E AGRICULTURA. Text and summaries in English, Portuguese. 1979. s-a. USD 30. bk.rev. bibl.; charts; illus.; stat. back issues avail.
Indexed: Agrind, BiolAb, ChemAb, ExcerpMed.
—CASDDS, CISTI.
Published by: Universidade de Sao Paulo, Centro de Energia Nuclear na Agricultura, Av Centenario, 303, S Dimas, Caixa Postal 96, Piracicaba, SP 13416-000, Brazil. Ed. Frederico Maximiliano Wiendl. Circ: 400.

ENERGY IN WORLD AGRICULTURE. see *ENERGY*

630 BRA ISSN 0100-6916
CODEN: EARIDM
➤ **ENGENHARIA AGRICOLA.** Text in Portuguese, English. 1971. 3/yr. BRL 15, USD 8.06 (effective 2001). adv. Website rev. 150 p./no.; back issues avail. **Document type:** *Journal, Academic/Scholarly.* **Description:** Presents original papers in agricultural engineering.
Related titles: Online - full text ed.: free (effective 2005).
Indexed: AEA, AgrForAb, AnBrAb, CPA, DSA, FCA, FPA, FS&TA, ForAb, HerbAb, HortAb, I&DA, MaizeAb, NutrAb, PBA, PHN&I, PN&I, PotatoAb, PoultAb, RA&MP, RDA, RPP, RevApplEntom, RiceAb, S&F, SIA, SeedAb, SoyAb, TOSA, TriticAb, WAE&RSA, WeedAb.
—CASDDS.
Published by: Associacao Brasileira de Engenharia Agricola/Brazilian Agricultural Engineering Society, Departamento de Engenharia Rural - UNESP, Faculdade de Ciencias Agrarias e Veterinarias, Via de Acesso Prof. Paulo D. Castellane, km 5, Jaboticabal, SP 14884-900, Brazil. TEL 55-16-32033341, sbea.jab@netsite.com.br, http://www.scielo.br/scielo.php/script_sci_serial/pid_0100-6916/lng_en/nrm_iso, http://www.sbea.org.br. Ed. Jose Renato Zanini. R&P Irenilza Dealencar Naas TEL 55-19-37881039. Adv. contact Carlos Eduardo A Furlani.

630 FRA
ENSEMBLE. Text in French. 11/yr.
Address: La Noelle, Ancenis, 44150, France. TEL 40-98-91-60, FAX 40-98-91-64, TELEX 710 645. Ed. Robert Rene. Circ: 15,000.

630 334.683 FRA ISSN 1143-7588
ENTRAID' CENTRE-OUEST. Text in French. 1984. 11/yr. FRF 275 (effective 1999). adv. **Document type:** *Newspaper.* **Description:** For cooperatives and development groups of farmers.
Address: Agropole, B.P. 129, Poitiers, 86004, France. TEL 33-5-49447448, FAX 33-5-49447446. Ed. Pascal Bordeau. Circ: 5,000.

630 FRA ISSN 0242-9063
ENTRAID'OC. Text in French. 11/yr.
Address: 26 place Marnac, BP 5, Ramonville-St Agne, 31520, France. TEL 61-75-86-30, FAX 61-75-64-28. Ed. Jean Gaffet. Circ: 13,000.

630 FRA ISSN 0397-197X
ENTRAID'OUEST. Text in French. 1973. 11/yr. FRF 250 (effective 1997). adv. bk.rev. **Document type:** *Newspaper.*
Formerly (until 1974): Federation Departementale des C.U.M.A. d'Ille et Vilaine. Bulletin de Liaison (0397-1988)
Address: 65 rue de Saint Brieuc, Rennes, Cedex 35042, France. TEL 33-2-99546312, FAX 33-2-99546309. Ed. J F Bourblanc. Pub. Alain Hindre. Adv. contact Laurence Guilmois. Circ: 18,000.

▼ **ENTREPRENEURS DES TERRITOIRES.** see *LABOR UNIONS*

630 BEL ISSN 1371-144X
ENTREPRISE AGRICOLE. Text in French. 1993. m. (11/yr.). EUR 42.50 (effective 2004). back issues avail. **Document type:** *Consumer.* **Description:** Covers agriculture in general.
Published by: Rekad N.V., Geelsweg 47A, Herentals, 2200, Belgium. TEL 32-14-286070, FAX 32-14-214774, info@rekad.be, http://rekad.be. Ed. Jomi Memschoote. Circ: 10,500.

630 DEU ISSN 0343-6462
ENTWICKLUNG UND LAENDLICHER RAUM. Text in English, German; Summaries in English, French. 1967. bi-m. EUR 34; EUR 5.50 newsstand/cover (effective 2004). adv. bk.rev. abstr.; illus.; stat. index. 36 p./no.; back issues avail. **Document type:** *Magazine, Trade.*
Formerly: Landwirt im Ausland (0047-4002)
Related titles: English ed.: Agriculture and Rural Development. ISSN 1619-8891. EUR 22; EUR 11.50 newsstand/cover (effective 2004); French ed.: Agriculture et Developpement Rural. ISSN 1619-8905. EUR 22; EUR 11.50 newsstand/cover (effective 2004).
Indexed: AEA, ARDT, AgBio, AgrForAb, AnBrAb, DSA, ExcerpMed, FCA, FPA, ForAb, HerbAb, HortAb, I&DA, IBR, IBZ, IndVet, MaizeAb, NutrAb, PBA, PGegResA, PHN&I, PotatoAb, PoultAb, RA&MP, RDA, REE&TA, RM&VM, RRTA, RiceAb, S&F, SIA, SeedAb, SoyAb, TDB, TriticAb, VetBull, WAE&RSA.
—BLDSC (3790.935000), IE, ingenta. **CCC.**
Published by: D L G Verlags GmbH, Eschborner Landstr 122, Frankfurt Am Main, 60489, Germany. TEL 49-69-247880, FAX 49-69-24788480, a.wilcke@dlg-frankfurt.de, dlg-verlag@dlg-frankfurt.de, http://www.rural-development.de, http://www.dlg-verlag.de. Ed. A Wilcke. Adv. contact S Pierre-Louis TEL 49-69-24788466. color page EUR 1,199; trim 190 x 262. Circ: 6,000. **Co-sponsor:** Deutsche Landwirtschafts-Gesellschaft e.V.

631.3 USA
EQUIPMENT CATALOG. Text in English. a. adv. **Document type:** *Catalog, Trade.* **Description:** Provides information about equipment and services for the grain, feed, milling and seed industries.
Published by: Country Journal Publishing Company, 3065 Pershing Ct, Decatur, IL 62526-1564. TEL 217-877-9660, FAX 217-877-6647. Pub. Mark Avery. Adv. contact Deb Coontz. B&W page USD 450, color page USD 600.

630 VEN
ERA AGRICOLA; una vision alternativa del campo venezolano. Text in Spanish. q. VEB 395; USD 15 in Latin America; USD 20 elsewhere. adv. bk.rev. illus.
Published by: Fundacion la Era Agricola, Apdo. Postal 456, Merida, 5101-A, Venezuela. TEL 074-527401, FAX 074-527402. Ed. Alfredo Lascoutx. Circ: 5,300.

630 DEU ISSN 0014-0309
ERWERBS - OBSTBAU; Berichte aus Wissenschaft und Praxis. Text in German. 1959. bi-m. EUR 353.27 combined subscription to institutions print & online eds. (effective 2005). adv. bk.rev. charts; illus. index. back issues avail. **Document type:** *Journal, Academic/Scholarly.*
Related titles: Online - full text ed.: ISSN 1439-0302 (from EBSCO Publishing, Springer LINK, Swets Information Services).
Indexed: AEA, AgBio, AgrForAb, BIOBASE, BioCN&I, CPA, DBA, FS&TA, HortAb, I&DA, NutrAb, OrnHort, PBA, PGegResA, PGrRegA, PHN&I, RA&MP, RDA, RPP, RRTA, RefZh, RevApplEntom, S&F, SIA, SeedAb, TriticAb, VITIS, WAE&RSA, WeedAb.
—CISTI, IE, Infotrieve. **CCC.**
Published by: Springer-Verlag (Subsidiary of: Springer Science+Business Media), Tiergartenstr 17, Heidelberg, 69121, Germany. TEL 49-6221-3450, FAX 49-6221-345229, http://www.springer.de. Ed. Werner Dierend. Adv. contact Stephan Kroeck TEL 49-30-827875739. **Subscr. to:** Springer GmbH Auslieferungsgesellschaft, Haberstr 7, Heidelberg 69126, Germany. TEL 49-6221-345-0, FAX 49-6221-345-4229, subscriptions@springer.de.

631.5 DEU
ERZEUGERPREISE FUER PRODUKTE AUS OEKOLOGISCHEM ANBAU. Text in German. w. **Document type:** *Bulletin, Trade.*
Published by: Zentrale Markt und Preisberichtstelle GmbH, Rochusstr 2, Bonn, 53123, Germany. TEL 49-228-9777173, FAX 49-228-9777179, info@zmp.de, http://www.zmp.de.

630 FRA ISSN 1763-5179
L'ESPACE ALPIN. Text in French. 1938. bi-m. adv. **Document type:** *Corporate.*
Formerly (until 2003): Le Sillon Alpin (0765-166X)
Published by: Sillon Alpin, 8 ter rue Capitaine de Brisson, Gap, Cedex 05010, France. TEL 33-4-92525300, FAX 33-4-92525309. Ed., R&P, Adv. contact Michel Orciere. Circ: 2,000.

630 FRA
ESPACE OUEST - ILLE ET VILAINE - COTES D'ARMOR - FINISTERE. Text in French. 50/yr.
Published by: Espace Ouvert, 22 av. Janvier, Rennes, Cedex 35007, France. TEL 99-29-58-88, FAX 99-31-18-19. Ed. Yves Dibout. Circ: 29,000.

630 GBR
ESSEX YOUNG FARMER. Text in English. 10/yr. **Document type:** *Newsletter.*
Address: 2 East Hill, Colchester, Essex CO1 2QL, United Kingdom. TEL 01206-861574, FAX 01206-862537. Ed. Tony Phelps. Circ: 2,500.

630 ARG ISSN 0325-1799
ESTACION EXPERIMENTAL REGION AGROPECUARIA PERGAMINO. INFORME TECNICO. Summaries in English. 1960. irreg. per issue exchange basis.
Formerly: Estacion Experimental Agropecuaria Pergamino. Informe Tecnico (0020-0832)
Related titles: Microfilm ed.
Indexed: AnBrAb, BibAg, DSA, FCA, HerbAb, I&DA, MaizeAb, NutrAb, PBA, PN&I, PoultAb, RPP, S&MA, WeedAb.
—BLDSC (4498.890000).
Published by: Instituto Nacional de Tecnologia Agropecuaria, Estacion Experimental Regional Agropecuaria, C.C.31, Pergamino, 2700, Argentina. Circ: 2,000 (controlled).

ESTADISTICA PANAMENA. SITUACION ECONOMICA. SECCION 352. HOJA DE BALANCE DE ALIMENTOS. see *AGRICULTURE—Abstracting, Bibliographies, Statistics*

630 338.1 PRT ISSN 0870-2594
ESTADO DAS CULTURAS E PREVISAO DE COLHEITAS. Text in Portuguese. 1945. m. bk.rev. charts; stat. **Document type:** *Government.* **Description:** Describes the development of the major agricultural crops.
Formerly: Folha Mensal do Estado das Culturas e Previsao de Colheitas (0014-1178)
Published by: Instituto Nacional de Estatistica, Ave. Antonio Jose de Almeida 2, Lisbon, 1000-043, Portugal. TEL 351-21-8426100, FAX 351-21-8426380, ine@ine.pt, http://www.ine.pt/. Circ: 1,200.

ESTATE PLANNING FOR FARMERS AND RANCHERS. see *LAW—Estate Planning*

630 MEX ISSN 1405-2466
S451.7
ESTUDIOS AGRARIOS (MEXICO, D.F.). Text in Spanish. 1995. q. back issues avail.
Related titles: Online - full text ed.
Published by: Procuraduria Agraria, Motolinia No. 11, 6o. Piso, Col. Centro, Mexico, D.F., 06000, Mexico. TEL 56-5-2379033, FAX 56-5-5211140, dgea@ri.redint.com, http://www.pa.gob.mx/publica/paota.htm. Ed. Froylan Hernandez Lara.

630 ESP ISSN 0210-4830
S469.S7
➤ **ESTUDIS D'HISTORIA AGRARIA.** Text in Catalan; Summaries in English. 1978. a. back issues avail. **Document type:** *Monographic series, Academic/Scholarly.* **Description:** Covers agricultural history and economics.
—CINDOC.
Published by: (Centre d'Estudis Historics Internacionals), Universitat de Barcelona, Servei de Publicacions, Gran Via Corts Catalanes 585, Barcelona, 08007, Spain. TEL 34-93-4021100, http://www.publicacions.ub.es.

630 BRA
ESTUDOS SOCIEDADE E AGRICULTURA. Text in Portuguese. 1993. irreg.
Published by: (Curso de Pos-graduacao em Desenvolvimento Agricola), Universidade Federal Rural do Rio de Janeiro, Departamento de Letras e Ciencias Sociais, Av Presidente Vargas, 417, 6-9 Andares, Centro, Rio De Janeiro, RJ 20071-003, Brazil. TEL 55-21-2248477.

630 ETH ISSN 0257-2605
ETHIOPIAN JOURNAL OF AGRICULTURAL SCIENCES. Text in English. 1979. s-a. USD 20. **Document type:** *Academic/Scholarly.* **Description:** Fosters scientific communication and promotes the dissemination and application of research findings through research and review articles, and short communications on agricultural development-technology; animal and crop improvement, nutrition, protection and management.
Address: PO Box 5509, Addis Ababa, Ethiopia. Ed. Dr. Hailu Gebre Mariam. Circ: 500. **Co-sponsors:** Alemaya University of Agriculture; Addis Ababa University; Ethiopian Science and Technology Commission; Institute of Agricultural Research.

▼ new title ➤ refereed ✶ unverified ♦ full entry avail.

630 FRA ISSN 0983-3846
EURE AGRICOLE. Text in French. 1945. w.
Published by: Agricole, 1 bis rue de la Justice, BP 185, Evreux, Cedex 27001, France. TEL 32-39-36-72. Ed. Pierre Roussel. Circ: 5,003.

630 GBR ISSN 1478-0917
➤ **EUROCHOICES**; the European agri-food & rural resources issues periodical. Text in English. 2001. 3/yr. EUR 30 in Europe to individuals eurozone; USD 30 in United States to individuals; GBP 20 elsewhere to individuals; EUR 120 in Europe to institutions eurozone; USD 120 in United States to institutions; GBP 80 elsewhere to institutions (effective 2005). back issues avail. **Document type:** *Journal, Academic/Scholarly.* **Description:** Aims to bring current research and policy deliberations on agri-business and rural resource issues to a wide readership, both technical & non-technical.
Published by: (European Association of Agricultural Economists), Queen's University Belfast, Department of Agricultural and Food Economics, Newforge Ln, Belfast, BT9 5PX, United Kingdom. TEL 44-28-90255204, http://eurochoices.org/.

630 HUN ISSN 1416-6194
AZ EUROPAI UNIO AGRARGAZDASAGA. Text in Hungarian. 1993. m. free. abstr. **Document type:** *Journal, Government.*
Former titles (until 1996): Europai Unio Mezogazdasaga (1218-7941); (until 1995): Ek-Agrarszemle (1217-6230)
Published by: Orszagos Mezogazdasagi Konyvtar es Dokumentacios Kozpont, Attila ut 93, Budapest, 1253, Hungary. TEL 36-1-4894900, FAX 36-1-3569928, http://www.omgk.hu. Ed. Erika Gulacsi Papay.

630 639.2 BEL ISSN 1372-5327
EUROPE AGRI. Text in English. fortn. (22/yr.). EUR 670 (effective 2000). **Document type:** *Bulletin, Trade.* **Description:** Presents European policy and regulations in the agri-foods, non-food processing and biotechnology sectors; research and developmental programs; and business news.
Related titles: CD-ROM ed.; Online - full text ed.: (from Gale Group, O C L C Online Computer Library Center, Inc.); French ed.: Europe Agro. ISSN 1372-5319.
Indexed: B&I.
Published by: Europe Information Service SA, Av Adolphe Lacomble 66-68, Brussels, 1030, Belgium. TEL 32-3-737-7709, FAX 32-3-732-6757, eis@eis.be, http://www.eis.be. Pub. Eric Damiens.

630 BEL ISSN 1560-1862
EUROPEAN COMMISSION. DIRECTORATE-GENERAL OF AGRICULTURE. NEWSLETTER. Text in English. 1998. m. **Document type:** *Newsletter.*
—BLDSC (6107.256600), CISTI.
Published by: European Commission, Directorate-General of Agriculture, Rue de la Loi 130, 2nd Flr, Brussels, 1049, Belgium. TEL 32-2-2953240, FAX 32-2-2957540, agri-library@cec.eu.int, http://europa.eu.int/comm/agriculture/publi/newsletter/index_en.htm, http://europa.eu.int/comm/dgs/agriculture/index_en.htm.

630 338.91 NLD
EUROPEAN PERSPECTIVES ON RURAL DEVELOPMENT. Text in English. 1994. irreg., latest 2003. **Document type:** *Monographic series, Academic/Scholarly.* **Description:** Discusses issues relating to different aspects of European rural development.
Published by: (Circle for Rural European Studies), Koninklijke Van Gorcum BV/Royal Van Gorcum BV, PO Box 43, Assen, 9400 AA, Netherlands. TEL 31-592-379555, FAX 31-592-372064, info@vangorcum.nl, http://www.vangorcum.nl.

630 310 LUX ISSN 1015-9924
EUROSTAT AGRICULTURAL PRICES. PRICE INDICES AND ABSOLUTE PRICES./EUROSTAT. AGRARPREISE. PREISINDIZES UND ABSOLUTE PREISE/EUROSTAT. PRIX AGRICOLES. INDICES DE PRIX ET PRIX ABSOLUS; quarterly statistics. Text in English, French. 1990. q.
—CISTI.
Published by: European Commission, Statistical Office of the European Communities, Rue Alcide de Gasperi, Luxembourg, 2920, Luxembourg. TEL 352-4301-34526, FAX 352-4301-32600, eurostat-infodesk@cec.eu.int, http://www.europa.eu.int/comm/eurostat.

EUROSTAT STATISTICS IN FOCUS. AGRICULTURE AND FISHERIES. see *AGRICULTURE—Abstracting, Bibliographies, Statistics*

EUROSTAT STATISTIK KURZ GEFASST. LANDWIRTSCHAFT UND FISCHEREI. see *AGRICULTURE—Abstracting, Bibliographies, Statistics*

630 FRA ISSN 1626-6838
EUROVIN - NEWS. Text in French; Summaries in English, German, Italian, Spanish. 1968. 6/yr. EUR 110 (effective 2001). adv. **Document type:** *Bulletin.*
Former titles (until 1999): Cahier de Conjoncture des Regions Viticoles Europeennes (1249-2353); (until 1992): Situation du Marche Vinicole (0223-4580)
Published by: Institut Europeen de Conjoncture Viti-Vinicole, Ecole Nationale de Formation Agronomique, BP 87, Castanet Tolosan, Cedex 31326, France. TEL 33-5-61753280, FAX 33-5-61753274, iecv@sicoval.fr. Ed., R&P, Adv. contact Jean Dubos. Circ: 5,000.

630.0742 GBR ISSN 0014-4797
S3 CODEN: EXAGAL
➤ **EXPERIMENTAL AGRICULTURE.** Text in English. 1965. q. GBP 240 to institutions; USD 388 in North America to institutions; GBP 254 combined subscription to institutions print & online eds.; USD 420 combined subscription in North America to institutions print & online eds. (effective 2006). adv. bk.rev. bibl.; charts; illus. back issues avail.; reprint service avail. from PSC. **Document type:** *Journal, Academic/Scholarly.* **Description:** Discusses the agronomy of crops. Includes information on the food, forage, and industrial crops of the warmer regions of the Earth.
Related titles: Microform ed.: (from PQC); Online - full text ed.: ISSN 1469-4441. GBP 214 to institutions; USD 358 in North America to institutions (effective 2006) (from EBSCO Publishing, O C L C Online Computer Library Center, Inc., Swets Information Services).
Indexed: AEA, ASCA, ASFA, Agr, AgrForAb, AnBrAb, B&AI, BIOBASE, BIOSIS Prev, BibAg, BioCN&I, BiolAb, CIN, CIS, CPA, CTFA, Cadscan, ChemAb, ChemTitl, CurCont, DSA, ESPM, EngInd, FCA, FS&TA, ForAb, HerbAb, HortAb, I&DA, IABS, ISR, IndVet, LeadAb, MaizeAb, NemAb, NutrAb, OrnHort, PBA, PCI, PGegResA, PGrRegA, PlantSci, PollutAb, PotatoAb, RA&MP, RDA, RPP, RRTA, RefZh, RevApplEntom, RiceAb, S&F, S&MA, SCI, SWRA, SeedAb, SoyAb, TOSA, TriticAb, VITIS, VetBull, WAE&RSA, WeedAb, Zincscan.
—BLDSC (3838.600000), CASDDS, CISTI, Ei, IDS, IE, Infotrieve, ingenta, Linda Hall. **CCC.**
Published by: Cambridge University Press, The Edinburgh Bldg, Shaftesbury Rd, Cambridge, CB2 2RU, United Kingdom. TEL 44-1223-312393, FAX 44-1223-315052, journals@cambridge.org, http://uk.cambridge.org/journals/eag. Ed. M K Carr. R&P Linda Nicol TEL 44-1223-325757. Adv. contact Rebecca Curtis TEL 44-1223-325757. **Subscr. to:** Cambridge University Press, 100 Brook Hill Dr, West Nyack, NY 10994. TEL 845-353-7500, FAX 845-353-4141, journals_subscriptions@cup.org

630 FRA ISSN 0983-6233
EXPLOITANT AGRICOLE DE SAONE ET LOIRE. Text in French. w.
Formerly (until 1947): Saone et Loire Agricole et Viticole (0983-6225)
Published by: Maison de l'Agriculture (Macon), 59 rue du 19 Mars 1962, BP 522, Macon, Cedex 71010, France. TEL 85-38-50-66, FAX 85-39-46-77, TELEX 351 928. Ed. Lucette Pagnier. Circ: 14,548.

630 FRA ISSN 1266-1791
EXPLOITANT AGRICOLE DU GARD. Text in French. 1959. w. adv. bk.rev. **Document type:** *Newspaper.*
Published by: L'Exploitant Agricole, MAS de l'agriculture, 1120 route de Saint-Gilles, Nimes, Cedex 9 30932, France. TEL 33-4-66045040, FAX 33-4-66045031, lexploit@club-internet.fr. Ed. Pierre Lalanne. Circ: 2,200 (controlled).

630 FRA ISSN 0755-284X
EXPLOITANT FAMILIAL. Text in French. 1960. m. adv.
Published by: (Federation des Syndicats Agricoles), Agence Centrale de Publicite, 100 rue de Bordeaux, Angouleme, 16000, France. TEL 45-95-01-88, FAX 45-38-37-74. Ed. Alain Giagnerot. Circ: 66,000.

630 BRA ISSN 0014-5394
EXTENSAO EM MINAS GERAIS. Text in Portuguese. fortn. free. adv.
Published by: Empresa de Assistencia Tecnica e Extensao Rural do Estado de Minas Gerais, Assessoria de Relacoes Publicas & Imprensa, Av Raja Gabaglia, 1626 Andar 1, S Lucia, Belo Horizonte, MG 30350-540, Brazil. TEL 55-31-349-8000, FAX 55-31-349-8250. Ed. Harildo Norberto Ferreira. Circ: 4,500 (controlled).

630 USA
EXTENSION NEWS - ALBANY - RENSSELAER - SARATOGA - WASHINGTON COUNTIES. Text in English. 1918. m. membership. adv. charts; illus.
Formerly: Albany County Agriculture News (0002-466X)
Media: Duplicated (not offset).
Published by: Cooperative Extension Association of Albany County, Agricultural Division, Martin Rd, Voorheesville, Albany, NY 12186. TEL 518-765-3635. Ed. John E Gergen. Circ: 5,000.

630 307.141 MOZ ISSN 1027-5797
EXTRA; revista para o desenvolvimento rural integrado e a extensas rural em mozambique. Text in Portuguese. 1989. q. MZM 480,000 domestic; USD 40 foreign. **Document type:** *Bulletin.*
Published by: Centro de Formacao Agraria, Av. das FPLM, 3658, Maputo, Mozambique. TEL 258-1-460219, 258-1-460137, FAX 258-1-460220, 258-1-460187. Pub. Diogo Milagre.

630 USA ISSN 1020-8712
F A O AGRICULTURAL INFORMATION MANAGEMENT SERIES. Text in English. a. USD 14 (effective 2002). **Description:** It describes an approach to assess locations and areal expanses that have potential for the production of bambara groundnut across the world.
Published by: Food and Agriculture Organization of the United Nations, c/o Bernan Associates, 4611 F Assembly Dr, Lanham, MD 20706-4391. TEL 301-459-7666, FAX 301-459-0056, publications-sales@fao.org, http://www.fao.org.

630 ITA ISSN 0259-2770
F A O BETTER FARMING SERIES. Text in English. 1976. irreg. **Document type:** *Monographic series, Academic/Scholarly.*
Related titles: French ed.: Serie F A O, Apprentissage Agricole. ISSN 1014-4129; Spanish ed.: Serie Mejores Cultivos. ISSN 1014-4137.
Indexed: ESPM.
Published by: Food and Agriculture Organization of the United Nations, Via delle Terme di Caracalla, Rome, RM 00100, Italy. TEL 39-06-5705-1, FAX 39-06-5705-3152, FAO-HQ@fao.org, http://www.fao.org.

630 ITA ISSN 0259-2568
F A O LAND AND DEVELOPMENT SERIES. (Food and Agriculture Organization) Text in Italian. 1977. irreg., latest vol.9, 1993.
Related titles: Spanish ed.: Coleccion F A O, Fomento de Tierras Aguas. ISSN 1014-319X; French ed.: Collection F A O, Mise en Valeur des Terres et des Eaux. ISSN 1014-3203.
Published by: Food and Agriculture Organization of the United Nations, Sales and Marketing Group, Viale delle Terme di Caracalla, Rome, 00100, Italy. TEL 39-06-57054350, FAX 39-06-57053360.

350 630 USA ISSN 1014-6679
F A O LEGISLATIVE STUDY. Text in English, French. 1957. irreg., latest vol.68, 1999. price varies. **Document type:** *Monographic series.*
Former titles (until 1986): Food and Agriculture Organization of the United Nations. Legislative Study (0253-021X); (until 1971): F A O Legislative Series (0071-7045)
Indexed: ASFA, ESPM, FPA, ForAb, I&DA, IndVet, NutrAb, PBA, PGegResA, PHN&I, RDA, S&F, SFA, SeedAb, VetBull, WAE&RSA, WeedAb, WildRev.
—CISTI, Linda Hall.
Published by: Food and Agriculture Organization of the United Nations, c/o Bernan Associates, 4611 F Assembly Dr, Lanham, MD 20706-4391. TEL 301-459-7666, FAX 301-459-0056.

630 USA ISSN 0429-9353
F A O REGIONAL CONFERENCE FOR AFRICA. REPORT. Text in English. 1960. biennial. USD 12 (effective 2000).
Related titles: ♦ French ed.: Conference Regionale de la F A O pour l'Afrique. Rapport. ISSN 1014-1588.
Published by: Food and Agriculture Organization of the United Nations, c/o Bernan Associates, 4611 F Assembly Dr, Lanham, MD 20706-4391. TEL 301-459-7666, FAX 301-459-0056.

630 USA ISSN 1010-0997
F A O REGIONAL CONFERENCE FOR ASIA AND THE PACIFIC. REPORT. Text in English. 1949. biennial. USD 12 (effective 2000).
Formerly (until 1979): F A O Regional Conference for Asia and the Far East. Report (0427-8070)
Related titles: ♦ French ed.: Conference Regionale de la F A O pour l'Asie et le Pacifique. Rapport. ISSN 1014-4080; Chinese ed.: Lianheguo Liangshi ji Nongye Zuzhi. Dayanghou Quyu Huiyi Baogao. Liangnong Zuzhi. ISSN 1014-6628. 1980.
—CISTI.
Published by: Food and Agriculture Organization of the United Nations, c/o Bernan Associates, 4611 F Assembly Dr, Lanham, MD 20706-4391. TEL 301-459-7666, FAX 301-459-0056.

630 USA ISSN 1010-1403
F A O REGIONAL CONFERENCE FOR EUROPE. REPORT. Text in English. biennial. USD 11 (effective 2000).
Related titles: French ed.: Conference Regionale de la F A O pour l'Europe. Rapport. ISSN 1014-4056; Spanish ed.: Conferencia Regional de la F A O para Europa. Informe. ISSN 1014-4064.
Published by: Food and Agriculture Organization of the United Nations, c/o Bernan Associates, 4611 F Assembly Dr, Lanham, MD 20706-4391. TEL 301-459-7666, FAX 301-459-0056. **Co-sponsor:** UN Economic Commission for Europe.

630 USA ISSN 1020-2889
F A O REGIONAL CONFERENCE FOR LATIN AMERICA AND THE CARIBBEAN. REPORT. Text in English. 1962. biennial. price varies.
Formerly (until 1984): F A O Regional Conference for Latin America. Report (1010-1381)
Indexed: WAE&RSA.
Published by: Food and Agriculture Organization of the United Nations, c/o Bernan Associates, 4611 F Assembly Dr, Lanham, MD 20706-4391. TEL 301-459-7666, FAX 301-459-0056.

630   USA   ISSN 0427-8089
HD2056.5
F A O REGIONAL CONFERENCE FOR THE NEAR EAST.
REPORT. Text in English. 1962. biennial. USD 12 (effective 2000).
Related titles: ♦ French ed.: Conference Regionale de la F A O pour le Proche-Orient. Rapport. ISSN 1014-2398.
Published by: Food and Agriculture Organization of the United Nations, c/o Bernan Associates, 4611 F Assembly Dr, Lanham, MD 20706-4391. TEL 301-459-7666, FAX 301-459-0056.

630   USA   ISSN 0532-0313
F A O TERMINOLOGY BULLETIN. (Food and Agriculture Organization) Text in English. irreg., latest vol.32, 1995. price varies. Document type: Monographic series.
Indexed: FS&TA.
Published by: Food and Agriculture Organization of the United Nations, c/o Bernan Associates, 4611 F Assembly Dr, Lanham, MD 20706-4391. FAX 301-459-0056, http://www.fao.org.

630   ITA   ISSN 0259-2533
F A O TRAINING SERIES. Text in English. 19??. irreg. price varies. Document type: Monographic series, Academic/Scholarly.
Indexed: ESPM.
Published by: Food and Agriculture Organization of the United Nations, Via delle Terme di Caracalla, Rome, RM 00100, Italy. TEL 39-06-5705-1, FAX 39-06-5705-3152, FAO-HQ@fao.org, http://www.fao.org.

630   BRA   ISSN 0104-9089
F E P A G R O BOLETIM. Text in Portuguese. 1977-1983; N.S. 1995. irreg. Document type: Monographic series, Academic/Scholarly.
Formerly (until 1995): Instituto de Pesquisas Agronomicas. Boletim Tecnico (0100-3062)
Indexed: ESPM, FCA, HortAb, I&DA, MaizeAb, NutrAb, PBA, RiceAb, S&F, SoyAb.
—CISTI.
Published by: Fundacao Estadual de Pesquisa Agropecuaria, Secretaria da Ciencia e Tecnologia, Rua Goncalves Dias, 570, Bairro Menino Deus, Porto Alegre, RS 90130-060, Brazil. TEL 55-512-33-5411, FAX 55-512-337607, fepagro@fepagro.rs.gov.br, http://www.fepagro.rs.gov.br.

630.7   USA
F F A ADVISORS MAKING A DIFFERENCE. Text in English. bi-m. membership only. Document type: Newsletter.
Formerly: Future Farmers of America. Between Issues
Published by: National F F A Organization, 6060 FFA Dr, PO Box 68960, Indianapolis, IN 46268. TEL 317-802-4266, FAX 317-802-5266, http://www.ffa.org. Ed. Randy Bernhardt. Circ: (controlled).

630.71   USA   ISSN 1069-806X
F F A NEW HORIZONS. (Future Farmers of America) Text in English. 1952. bi-m. USD 2 to non-members; USD 6 to members (effective 2005). adv. bk.rev. illus. Document type: Magazine, Consumer. Description: Covers activities of the FFA, new and improved methods in agriculture and managing a business, hobbies, and sports stories for youth 14-21 years of age.
Formerly (until 1990): National Future Farmer (0027-9315)
Published by: National F F A Organization, 6060 FFA Dr, PO Box 68960, Indianapolis, IN 46268. TEL 317-802-4266, FAX 317-802-6052, ndunckel@ffa.org, http://www.ffa.org. Ed. Erich Gaukel. Pub. Julie Adams. Circ: 462,000 (paid).

633.6 664.1   GBR   ISSN 0014-6048
F.O. LICHT'S EUROPAEISCHES ZUCKERJOURNAL. Variant title: Europaisches Zuckerjournal. Text in German. 1963. 36/yr. GBP 1,397 in Europe; GBP 1,456 elsewhere (effective 2005). Document type: Journal.
Related titles: ♦ English ed.: F.O. Licht's International Sugar and Sweetener Report. ISSN 0940-8541.
Indexed: CPA, DBA, SeedAb.
Published by: Agra Europe (London) Ltd. (Subsidiary of: T & F Informa plc), 80 Calverley Rd, Tunbridge Wells, Kent TN1 2UN, United Kingdom. TEL 44-1892-533813, FAX 44-1892-544895, marketing@agra-net.com, http://www.agra-net.com.

633.6 664.1   GBR   ISSN 0940-8541
F.O. LICHT'S INTERNATIONAL SUGAR AND SWEETENER REPORT. Variant title: International Sugar and Sweetener Report. Text in English. 1961. 36/m. GBP 1,397 in Europe; GBP 1,456 elsewhere (effective 2005). charts; stat. back issues avail. Document type: Newsletter, Trade. Description: Contains analysis and reporting on the world sugar and sweetener markets, with production, consumption and trade statistics.
Formerly: F.O. Licht's International Sugar Report
Related titles: Online - full text ed.; ♦ German ed.: F.O. Licht's Europaeisches Zuckerjournal. ISSN 0014-6048.
Indexed: RRTA, SIA, WAE&RSA.
—CISTI.

Published by: Agra Europe (London) Ltd. (Subsidiary of: T & F Informa plc), 80 Calverley Rd, Tunbridge Wells, Kent TN1 2UN, United Kingdom. TEL 44-1892-533813, FAX 44-1892-544895, marketing@agra-net.com, http://www.agra-net.com. Ed. Helmut Ahfield.

630   BRA   ISSN 0100-2694
FACULDADE DE CIENCIAS AGRARIAS DO PARA. BOLETIM. Text in Portuguese; Abstracts in English. 1972. irreg., latest vol.28, 1998. USD 3 (effective 1999). bibl.; charts; stat. Document type: Bulletin. Description: Covers agriculture, forestry and veterinary science.
Formerly: Escola de Agronomia da Amazonia. Boletim
Indexed: FCA, FPA, ForAb, HortAb, IndVet, MaizeAb, RPP, S&F, SeedAb, WAE&RSA, WeedAb.
Published by: (Brazil. Servicio de Documentacao e Informacao), Ministerio de Educacao, Faculdade de Ciencias Agrarias do Para, Comercio, Caixa Postal 917, Belem, PA 66017-970, Brazil. TEL 55-91-2744518, fcap@supridad.com.br. Ed. Marly Sampaio.

630 570   COL   ISSN 0304-2847
S15
FACULTAD NACIONAL DE AGRONOMIA MEDELLIN. REVISTA. Key Title: Revista Facultad Nacional de Agronomia. Text in English; Summaries in English, Spanish. 1939. s-a. COP 15,000 domestic; USD 20 foreign (effective 2000). cum.index: 1939-1981. back issues avail. Document type: Academic/Scholarly.
Indexed: AEA, AgBio, AnBrAb, BioCN&I, BiolAb, CPA, DSA, FCA, FPA, ForAb, HerbAb, HortAb, I&DA, IndVet, MaizeAb, NemAb, NutrAb, PBA, PGegResA, PGrRegA, PHN&I, PN&I, PotatoAb, PoultAb, RDA, RPP, RevApplEntom, S&F, SIA, SeedAb, VetBull, WAE&RSA.
—Linda Hall.
Published by: Universidad Nacional de Colombia, Facultad de Ciencias Agropecuarias, Apartado 568, Medellin, Colombia. TEL 57-4-2607333 ext 106, FAX 57-4-2300420, rvergara@perseus.unalmed.edu.co. Ed. Miryam Ospina. Circ: 700 (controlled).

630   SWE   ISSN 1403-1744
FAKTA. JORDBRUK. Text in Swedish. 1998. 20/yr. SEK 372 (effective 2003). back issues avail. Document type: Monographic series, Academic/Scholarly.
Formed by the merger of (1983-1998): Fakta. Ekonomi (0280-7122); (1982-1998): Fakta. Husdjur (0280-7130); (1982-1998): Fakta. Mark - Vaexter (0280-7106); (1983-1998): Fakta. Teknik (0280-7149)
Published by: Sveriges Lantbruksuniversitet, SLU/Swedish University of Agricultural Sciences, PO Box 7070, Uppsala, 75007, Sweden. TEL 46-18-671010, FAX 46-18-672000, publikationstjanst@slu.se, http://www.slu.se/forskning/fakta/faktajordbruk/index.html. Ed. Eva Ronquist.

630   GBR   ISSN 0266-8025
FAR EASTERN AGRICULTURE. Text in English. 1983. bi-m. GBP 48, USD 78, EUR 80 (effective Oct. 2002). adv. back issues avail. Document type: Magazine, Trade. Description: Covers all sectors of agriculture in Southeast Asia from machinery and equipment, grain and crops, irrigation, agri-chemicals, livestock breeding and processing with regular coverage of news and events in each product area.
Related titles: Chinese ed.: Dong Nong Ye. ISSN 0950-527X.
Indexed: AEA, DSA, FCA, HortAb, IndVet, PN&I, PoultAb, RDA, RM&VM, RPP, RevApplEntom, S&F, WAE&RSA, WeedAb.
—CISTI.
Published by: Alain Charles Publishing Ltd., Alain Charles House, 27 Wilfred St, London, SW1E 6PR, United Kingdom. TEL 44-20-78347676, FAX 44-20-79730076, post@alaincharles.com, http://www.alaincharles.com/asia/fea.htm. Ed. Louise Brownlee. Adv. contact Loic Barroche. Circ: 9,146.

630   USA
FARA; journal of popular farm science and rural life. Text in Norwegian. 1978. 4/yr. free to qualified personnel.
Related titles: ♦ German ed.: Flur und Furche. ISSN 0015-4733; ♦ English ed.: Furrow. ISSN 0016-3112; ♦ Swedish ed.: Faran; ♦ Spanish ed.: Surco Argentina; ♦ Spanish ed.: Campo y Mecanica. ISSN 0211-4704; ♦ Spanish ed.: Surco Mexicana; Afrikaans ed.: 1895; Danish ed.: 1895; Dutch ed.: 1895; French ed.: 1895; Italian ed.: 1895; Portuguese ed.: 1895.
Published by: John Deere Publishing, One John Deere Place, Moline, IL 61265. TEL 309-765-8000. Ed. Jean Claude Hiron. Circ: 34,500.

630   USA
FARAN; a journal of popular farm science and rural life. Text in Swedish. 1975. 4/yr. free to qualified personnel.
Related titles: ♦ German ed.: Flur und Furche. ISSN 0015-4733; ♦ English ed.: Furrow. ISSN 0016-3112; ♦ Spanish ed.: Surco Mexicana; ♦ Spanish ed.: Surco Argentina; ♦ Norwegian ed.: Fara; ♦ Spanish ed.: Campo y Mecanica. ISSN 0211-4704; Afrikaans ed.: 1895; Danish ed.: 1895; Dutch ed.: 1895; French ed.: 1895; Italian ed.: 1895; Portuguese ed.: 1895.
Published by: John Deere Publishing, One John Deere Place, Moline, IL 61265. TEL 309-765-8000. Ed. Jean Claude Hiron. Circ: 26,500.

630   GBR
FARM ADVERTISER. Text in English. m. adv.
Published by: C M P Information Ltd. (Subsidiary of: United Business Media), Oliver's Pl, Eastway, Fulwood, P O Box 18, Preston, Lancs PR2 9GU, United Kingdom. enquiries@cmpinformation.com, http://www.cmpinformation.com. Pub. Peter Walker. Adv. contact Julie Kightly.

630   GBR   ISSN 1368-3160
FARM AND COUNTRY RETAILER. Text in English. 1997. bi-m. GBP 30 domestic; GBP 40 foreign (effective 2000). adv. mkt.; stat.; tr.lit. back issues avail. Document type: Trade. Description: Contains new product information, industry and legislative news, company profiles, and special features.
Formed by the merger of (1995-1997): Country and Equestrian Retailer (1358-8885); (1995-1997): Animal Health News and Agritrade Review (1360-0346)
—CCC.
Published by: John C. Alborough Ltd., John C Alborough Ltd, Lion House, Needham Market, Suffolk IP6 8NT, United Kingdom. TEL 44-1449-723800, FAX 44-1449-723801. Ed. Anna Barsby. Pub. John C Alborough. Adv. contact Ces Kerridge. B&W page GBP 520, color page GBP 840; trim 210 x 297. Circ: 4,000 (controlled).

630 664   IRL   ISSN 0791-6477
CODEN: FFOOE4
FARM & FOOD. Text in English. 1960. 3/yr. EUR 15.50 (effective 2005). reprint service avail. from PQC. Document type: Academic/Scholarly.
Former titles (until 1991): Farm and Food Research (0046-3302); (until 1970): Farm Research News (0430-0866)
Indexed: AEA, AbHyg, AgBio, AgrForAb, AnBrAb, BioCN&I, CPA, DSA, FCA, FS&TA, ForAb, HelmAb, HerbAb, HortAb, I&DA, INIS AtomInd, IndVet, MaizeAb, NutrAb, OrnHort, PBA, PHN&I, PN&I, PST, PotatoAb, PoultAb, RM&VM, RPP, RRTA, RevApplEntom, RiceAb, S&F, SFA, SIA, SoyAb, TriticAb, VetBull, WAE&RSA, WeedAb, WildRev.
—BLDSC (3870.870000), CISTI, IE, ingenta. CCC.
Published by: Teagasc, Oak Park, Carlow, Ireland. TEL 353-59-9170200, FAX 353-59-9182097, publications@hq.teagasc.ie, http://www.teagasc.ie. Circ: 4,500.

630   GBR
FARM AND FOOD NEWS. Abbreviated title: F A F S. Text in English. 1966. 3/yr. (plus annual report). EUR 10; EUR 20 foreign (effective 2001). bk.rev.; Website rev. back issues avail. Document type: Journal.
Formerly: Farm and Food Society Newsletter
Published by: Farm and Food Society, 4 Willifield Way, London, NW11 7XT, United Kingdom. http://www.fafs.org. Ed. J Bower.

630   CAN
FARM AND FOOD REPORT. Text in English. 1978. w. free. back issues avail. Document type: Government. Description: Presents general agriculture topics for farmers, such as the effect of diet on young horses, vegetable oil based fuels, and short articles on various related topics.
Published by: Agriculture and Food, B5 Walter Scott Bldg, 3085 Albert St, Regina, SK S4S 0B1, Canada. FAX 306-787-0216, lstinson@agr.gov.sk.ca, http://www.agr.gov.sk.ca/saf.

630   USA   ISSN 1541-2768
S113   CODEN: SDFHAT
FARM AND HOME RESEARCH; agricultural experiment station quarterly. Text in English. 1949. q. free. Document type: Journal, Trade. Description: Reports research done in the experiment station to assist farmers, ranchers and consumers in developing economic, human, and natural resources.
Formerly (until 1998): South Dakota Farm & Home Research (0038-3295)
Indexed: ASCA, AgeL, Agr, BiolAb, CurCont, DSA, ExcerpMed, FCA, HerbAb, NutrAb, PBA.
—CISTI, Linda Hall.
Published by: South Dakota Agricultural Experiment Station, South Dakota State University, Box 2207, Brookings, SD 57007. TEL 605-688-4149, FAX 605-688-4018, http://www.abs.sdstate.edu/abs/farm&home. Ed. Barbara Hartinger. Circ: 6,600. Subscr. to: South Dakota State University Farm and Home Research, ACC, Box 2231, Brookings, SD 57007.

630   USA   ISSN 0192-5237
FARM AND RANCH∗. Text in English. 1970. s-m. USD 10. adv.
Related titles: Microfilm ed.: 1970 (from PQC).
Published by: Farm & Ranch Weekly, Inc., PO Box 2368, Dallas, TX 75221. TEL 817-562-2814. Ed. Bill Dutton. Circ: 8,200.

630   USA   ISSN 0744-9852
FARM AND RANCH GUIDE. Text in English. 1980. bi-w. (Fri.). USD 32.95 (effective 2005). adv. Document type: Newspaper, Trade.
Address: 4023 State St, Bismarck, ND 58501. TEL 701-255-4905, FAX 701-255-2312, http://www.farmandranchguide.com. Ed. Mark Conlon. Pub. David Borlaug. Adv. contact Cliff Meyer. Circ: 46,000.

▼ *new title*   ➤ *refereed*   ∗ *unverified*   ♦ *full entry avail.*

A

630 USA ISSN 0276-170X
S521.5.A2
FARM & RANCH LIVING. Text in English. 1978. bi-m. USD 14.98 domestic; CND 19.98 in Canada; USD 25.98 newsstand/cover elsewhere (effective 2005). illus. back issues avail. **Document type:** *Magazine, Consumer.* **Description:** Offers photo-tours of farms and ranches, including visits with the owners.
Published by: Reiman Publications, LLC (Subsidiary of: Reader's Digest Association), 5400 S 60th St, Greendale, WI 53129. TEL 414-423-0100, 800-344-6913, FAX 414-423-8463, editors@farmandranchliving.com, subscriberservices@reimanpub.com, http://www.farmandranchliving.com, http://www.reimanpub.com. Ed. Nick Pabst. Circ: 400,000 (paid). **Subscr. to:** PO Box 997, Greendale, WI 53129.

630 USA
FARM & RANCH NEWS. Text in English. 1974. m. (1st. of mo.). USD 12.50 (effective 2005). adv. **Document type:** *Newspaper.*
Address: PO Box 160, Lithia, FL 33547-0160. TEL 813-737-6397, flabest@aol.com. Ed., Pub., Adv. contact George Parker Jr. col. inch USD 7.50. Circ: 5,500 (paid).

FARM ANTIQUES NEWS. see *ANTIQUES*

430 USA
FARM BROADCASTERS LETTER. Text in English. 1953. w. **Document type:** *Government.* **Description:** Includes information for and about farm broadcasters. Highlights developments at U.S.D.A. and in agriculture.
Published by: U.S. Department of Agriculture, Office of Public Affairs, 14th St & Independence Ave, S W, Washington, DC 20250-1300. TEL 202-720-7762, FAX 202-690-1131. Ed. Vic Powell. Circ: 1,200.

630 USA ISSN 0197-5617
FARM BUREAU NEWS. Text in English. 1921. 23/yr. USD 30 domestic; USD 63 foreign (effective 2005). illus. **Document type:** *Newsletter, Trade.* **Description:** Reports legislative and regulatory developments affecting farmers and ranchers.
Formerly: American Farm Bureau Federations Official News Letter (0002-8398)
Related titles: Online - full text ed.
—CISTI.
Published by: American Farm Bureau Federation, 600 Maryland Ave, S W, Ste 800, Washington, DC 20024. TEL 202-484-3600, FAX 202-406-3604, fbnews@fb.com, http://www.fb.com/. Ed. Lynne Finnerty. Circ: 50,000 (paid).

630 USA
FARM BUREAU'S RURAL ROUTE. Text in English. 1930. q. membership. adv. **Description:** Contains articles about the organization's programs, activities, and views concerning public policy issues.
Former titles: Agventure (0887-9133); (until 1986): Badger Farm Bureau News (0005-3740)
Published by: Wisconsin Farm Bureau Federation, PO Box 5550, Madison, WI 53705. TEL 608-833-8070, FAX 608-829-4256. Ed. Tom Thieding. Circ: 54,000.

630 USA ISSN 0896-1883
FARM CHRONICLE. Text in English. 1981. w. USD 10.50 (effective 2000). adv. **Document type:** *Trade.* **Description:** Contains national and local news of interest to people in Virginia, Maryland and North Carolina.
Formerly: Farm and Country
Published by: Lee Newspapers, Ltd., PO Box 460, Culpeper, VA 22701. TEL 540-829-1010, FAX 540-829-1013. Ed. Tom Green. Pub. Fred Lee. Adv. contact Tom Mahoney. Circ: 14,500.

630 GBR ISSN 0144-0675
FARM CONTRACTOR AND LARGE-SCALE FARMER. Text in English. 1971. m. USD 55. adv. bk.rev. charts; illus.; stat.; tr.lit. **Document type:** *Trade.* **Description:** Supplies coverage of new machines, new techniques and business management for agricultural contractors and large-scale farmers.
Indexed: AEA.
Published by: A C P Publishers Ltd., Iron Down House, Deddington, Banbury, Oxon OX15 0PJ, United Kingdom. TEL 44-1869-338936, FAX 44-1869-338578. Ed. A Collier. Adv. contact M Benjamin. Circ: 10,167.

630 CAN
FARM FOCUS. Text in English. 1975 (vol.3). s-m. CND 20. adv. illus. **Document type:** *Trade.* **Description:** Trade journal serving the maritime province's agricultural industry.
Published by: Fundy Group Publications, 2 Second St, P O Box 128, Yarmouth, NS B5A 4B1, Canada. TEL 902-742-7111. Ed. Heather Jones. Circ: 8,500.

630 USA
FARM FORUM. Text in English. w. (Fri.). USD 167.44 (effective 2005). **Document type:** *Newspaper, Trade.*
Published by: Knight Ridder, Inc., 124 S. Second St., Aberdeen, Brown, SD 57401-6010. TEL 605-225-4100, FAX 605-225-0421, circulation@aberdeennews.com, http://www.aberdeennews.com. Ed. Cindi Eikamp. Pub. Adrian Pratt. Adv. contact Christy Orwig. Circ: 40,000 (paid).

630.658 USA
▼ **FARM FUTURES DAILY.** Text in English. 2004. d. USD 65 (effective 2005). **Document type:** *Newsletter, Trade.* **Description:** Provides information on corn, soybean and wheat, as well as information on a wide range of other topics.
Published by: Farm Progress Companies, 191 S Gary Ave, Carol Stream, IL 60188. TEL 630-462-2892, FAX 630-462-2867, info@farmprogress.com, http://www.farmprogress.com/.

630 CAN ISSN 0705-8748
FARM GATE; regional country news. Text in English. 1977. m. CND 12. adv. **Document type:** *Newspaper.* **Description:** Information for farmers about innovations, equipment and sustainable agricultural methods.
—CISTI.
Published by: Metroland Printing, Publishing and Distributing Ltd., 15 King St, Elmira, ON N3B 2R1, Canada. TEL 519-669-5155, 800-645-7355, FAX 519-669-5928, country@eedy.com, enews@bond.net. Ed. Kate Monk. Adv. contact Jim Beckett. Circ: 25,000.

630 PAK
FARM GUIDE. Variant title: Quarterly Farm Guide. Text in English. 1970. q. PKR 100; PKR 200 foreign (effective 1999). **Document type:** *Newspaper.* **Description:** Discusses various aspects of agriculture, farm forestry and farm management from an international perspective, as well as relevant issues such as literacy, youth development, civil defence, and environmental safety.
Published by: National Farm Guide Council of Pakistan, c/o Mohammad Anwer Chaudhry, Ed., 405, Ferozepur Rd., Lahore, 54600, Pakistan. TEL 92-42-5864155, FAX 92-42-5864155. Ed. Mohammad Anwer Chaudhry.

631 USA ISSN 0892-8312
S671.F37
FARM INDUSTRY NEWS. Text in English. 1967. 11/yr. free domestic to qualified personnel in the Midwest (CO, IA, IL, IN, KS, MI, MN, MO, MT, ND, NE, OH, OK, SD, TX, WI and WY; USD 25 domestic elsewhere in the US; USD 35 foreign (effective 2005). adv. bk.rev. illus.; tr.lit. back issues avail. **Document type:** *Magazine, Trade.* **Description:** Deals with product news and technology for high income midwestern farmer.
Incorporates: Farm Industry News - West (0161-4339); Former titles: Farm Industry News - Sunbelt; Farm Industry News - South (0161-4347); Farm Industry News - Midwest (0199-6924); Which superseded (in 1979): Farm Industry News (0014-7990)
Related titles: Online - full text ed.: (from bigchalk, EBSCO Publishing, Florida Center for Library Automation, Gale Group, H.W. Wilson, O C L C Online Computer Library Center, Inc., ProQuest Information & Learning); ♦ Supplement(s): Apply.
Indexed: ABIn, B&AI, F&GI, RASB.
—**CCC.**
Published by: Primedia Business Magazines & Media, Inc. (Subsidiary of: Primedia, Inc.), 9800 Metcalf Ave, Overland Park, KS 66212-2216. TEL 913-341-1300, FAX 913-967-1898, kmcmahon@primediabusiness.com, inquiries@primediabusiness.com, http://farmindustrynews.com/, http://www.primediabusiness.com. Ed. Karen McMahon. Pub. Greg Frey TEL 952-851-4613. adv.: B&W page USD 19,800, color page USD 23,400. Circ: 245,010 (controlled). **Subscr. to:** PO Box 12993, Overland Park, KS 66282-2993. TEL 800-441-0294, FAX 913-967-1331.

630 USA ISSN 0014-8008
CODEN: AJCHEW
FARM JOURNAL; the magazine of American agriculture. Text in English. 1877. 12/yr. USD 24.75 domestic; USD 55 foreign (effective 2005). adv. bk.rev. illus. Supplement avail.; reprint service avail. from PQC. **Document type:** *Magazine, Trade.* **Description:** Contains news and feature material dealing with agricultural production, technology and policy as well as general information of interest to farm families.
Related titles: Microform ed.: (from PQC); Online - full text ed.: (from Factiva, Gale Group, LexisNexis, O C L C Online Computer Library Center, Inc., ProQuest Information & Learning); Supplement(s): In the Country.
Indexed: BusI, MagInd, PMR, T&II.
—CISTI, Linda Hall. **CCC.**
Published by: Farm Journal Media, 1818 Market St., 31st Fl, Philadelphia, PA 19103-3654. TEL 215-557-8900, 800-523-1538, FAX 215-568-5012, kfreiberg@farmjournal.com, http://www.farmjournal.com, http://www.agweb.com. Ed. Karen Freiberg. Pub. Steve Custer. adv.: B&W page USD 35,935, color page USD 47,000; trim 10.5 x 7.88. Circ: 443,000 (paid and controlled).

FARM LAW. see *LAW*

630 658 GBR ISSN 0014-8059
➤ **FARM MANAGEMENT.** Text in English. 1967. q. GBP 35 domestic to non-members; GBP 38 in Europe to non-members; GBP 40 elsewhere to non-members; free to members (effective 2005). adv. bk.rev. charts; illus.; stat. index. **Document type:** *Magazine, Academic/Scholarly.* **Description:** Reports on agriculture business management in its widest sense, including production, marketing and agricultural merchandising. It brings both new developments and succcessful achievements in agricultiral business management before readers.
Indexed: AEA, AgBio, AgrForAb, AnBrAb, DSA, ForAb, HortAb, I&DA, IAOP, IndVet, MaizeAb, NutrAb, PBA, PGegResA, PHN&I, PN&I, PotatoAb, PoultAb, RDA, REE&TA, RICS, RRTA, RevApplEntom, S&F, SIA, SoyAb, TriticAb, VetBull, WAE&RSA, WeedAb.
—BLDSC (3880.300000), CISTI, IE, ingenta.
Published by: Institute of Agricultural Management, Farm Management Unit, The University of Reading, Reading, Berks RG6 6AT, United Kingdom. TEL 44-1189-316578, FAX 44-1189-756467, iagrm@rdg.ac.uk, http://www.rdg.ac.uk/iagrm. Ed. Martyn Warren. R&P, Adv. contact David Ansell. Circ: 2,000.

630 USA
FARM TALK. Text in English. 1974. w. USD 30 KS, AR & MO states; USD 38 elsewhere (effective 2005). **Document type:** *Magazine, Trade.*
Published by: Farm Talk Publishing (Subsidiary of: H D S Corp.), 1801 S 59 Hwy, Box 601, Parsons, KS 67357. TEL 316-421-9450, FAX 316-421-9473, farmtalk@terraworld.com. Ed. Mark Parker. Circ: 10,000 (paid).

630 AUS
FARM WEEKLY. Text in English. 1921. w. AUD 146.80; AUD 2.95 newsstand/cover (effective 2005). adv. bk.rev. charts; illus.; mkt. **Document type:** *Newspaper, Trade.* **Description:** Information for the farming community including market news, livestock and crop information, new machinery, agripolitical commentary, and in-depth local and national news analysis.
Former titles (until 1994): Elders Weekly; Western Farmer and Grazier (0311-7804); (until 1974): Wesfarmers News (0043-2865)
Published by: Rural Press Ltd. (Subsidiary of: Agricultural Publishers Pty. Ltd.), GPO Box 1268, Victoria Park East, W.A. 6981, Australia. TEL 61-8-94733100, 800-804-538, FAX 800-242-348, 61-8-93615055, http://fw.farmonline.com.au/home.asp, http://www.ruralpress.com/. Ed. Rick Lee TEL 61-8-94724238. Adv. contact Wendy Gould TEL 61-8-94724237. Circ: 13,667.

630 USA ISSN 1535-010X
FARM WORLD. Text in English. 1955. w. (except for Christmas week). USD 28.50 IN, OH, KY, MI, TN, IL, WV; USD 38 elsewhere (effective 2005). adv. bk.rev. **Document type:** *Newspaper, Consumer.*
Formerly (until 2001): FarmWeek (0164-8640); Which superseded in part (in Sep. 1978): Eastern Indiana Farmer (0420-3690)
Related titles: Online - full content ed.: Farm World Online.
Published by: D M G World Media, Inc., 27 N Jefferson St, PO Box 90, Knightstown, IN 46148-0120. TEL 765-345-5133, 800-876-5133, FAX 765-345-3398, davidb@farmworldonline.com, http://www.farmworldonline.com. Ed. David Blower Jr. Pub. Richard Lewis. Adv. contact Toni Hodson. Circ: 33,000 (paid). Wire service: AP.

630 658 CAN
FARMER. Text in English. m. adv.
Published by: Gordon Publishing and Printing, 228 Main St., Bible Hill, NS B2N 4H2, Canada. TEL 902-895-7946, FAX 902-893-1427. Ed. Peter Heckhert. Circ: 2,550.

630 GBR
THE FARMER. Text in English. 22/yr. adv.
Published by: Farmer, Chronicle House, Castle Foregate, Shrewsbury, Shrops SY1 2DN, United Kingdom. TEL 44-1743-363222, FAX 44-1743-232305. Ed. Chris Brandon. Adv. contact Angela Rogers. Circ: 18,291.

631 JAM ISSN 0014-8350
FARMER. Text in English. bi-m. JMD 2. adv. illus. index.
Indexed: ChemAb, HortAb, PBA.
—CISTI.
Published by: Jamaica Agricultural Society, N. Parade, Kingston, Jamaica.

631 ZWE ISSN 1011-0488
THE FARMER; Zimbabwe farming news magazine. Text in English. 1928. w. (Thu.). ZWD 157; ZWD 218 elsewhere (effective 1999). adv. bk.rev. charts; illus.; mkt. Supplement avail. **Document type:** *Trade.* **Description:** Disseminates information of interest to farmers in Zimbabwe, promoting the adoption, implementation and application of improved farming practices.
Formerly: Rhodesian Farmer (0035-4775); Incorporates: Tobacco News
Related titles: ♦ Supplement(s): Cattleman of the Year; ♦ Agricultural Research Trust (Zimbabwe). Summer Report; ♦ Agricultural Research Trust (Zimbabwe). Winter Report.
Published by: (Commercial Farmers' Union), Modern Farming Publications, Agriculture House, Moffat St., PO Box 1622, Harare, Zimbabwe. TEL 263-4-753278, FAX 263-4-750754, TELEX 22084 CFU ZW. Ed. Felicity Wood. Adv. contact Michael Rook. B&W page ZWD 9,911, color page ZWD 11,946; trim 216 x 280. Circ: 6,000 (paid).

633.18 GUY
FARMER. Text in English. 1959 (vol.8). q. USD 1. adv. stat.
Formerly (until 1975): Rice Review (0035-497X)
Published by: (Guyana Rice Producers Association), New Guyana Co. Ltd., Government Industrial Estate, Lot 8, East Bank Demerara, Guyana. TEL 592-2-62471. Circ: 4,000.

630 USA ISSN 1069-5400
THE FARMER (MINNESOTA). Text in English. 15/yr. USD 23.95 (effective 2005). adv. illus. **Document type:** *Magazine, Trade.* **Description:** Provides timely and local crop and livestock production practices to farm operators in Minnesota.
Formed by the merger of (1992-1993): Minnesota Farmer (1064-6752); Which was formerly (until 1992): Minnesota Wallaces Farmer (1049-8214); (1992-1993): U S Agriculture (1066-1301); Which was formed by the merger of (1935-1992): Farmer (0896-5579); (1980-1992): Dakota Farmer (0198-6171)
Related titles: Supplement(s): Daily Producer.
Published by: Farm Progress Companies, 191 S Gary Ave, Carol Stream, IL 60188-2095. TEL 630-462-2229, FAX 630-462-2202, info@farmprogress.com, http://www.the-farmer.com, http://www.farmprogress.com/. Ed. Paula Mohr. Adv. contact Don Tourte. B&W page USD 2,350, color page USD 2,850; trim 10.5 x 14.5. Circ: 30,000.

631 IND ISSN 0014-8369
FARMER AND PARLIAMENT. Text in English, Hindi. 1966. m. USD 10 (effective 2000). adv.
Published by: Farmers' Parliamentary Forum, Deen Dayal Upadhay Marg, 215 Rouse Ave., New Delhi, 110 002, India. Ed. S.N. Bhalla. Pub. S N Bhalla. Circ: 2,000. **Dist. by:** H P C Publishers Distributors Pvt. Ltd., 4805 Bharat Ram Rd, 24 Darya Ganj, New Delhi 110 002, India. TEL 91-11-325-4401, FAX 91-11-619-3511.

630 GBR
FARMER BUSINESS IN WALES. Text in English. 1967. 4/yr. membership. adv. bk.rev.
Published by: Welsh Agricultural Organisation Society Ltd., Brynawel, Box 8, Aberystwyth, United Kingdom. Ed. J Kendall. Circ: 9,000.

630 658 CAN ISSN 1185-2178
FARMER - RANCHER. Text in English. q. adv. **Document type:** *Trade.*
Formerly (until 1990): Northwest Farmer - Rancher (0822-5737)
Related titles: Microfilm ed.: (from CML).
Published by: Battlefords Publishing Ltd., P O Box 1029, Battleford, SK S9A 3E6, Canada. TEL 306-445-7261, FAX 306-445-3223. Ed. Lorne Cooper. Pub., R&P Steven Dills. Adv. contact Alana Schweitzer. Circ: 15,602.

630 USA ISSN 0739-9235
FARMER-STOCKMAN OF THE MIDWEST. Text in English. 1927. w. (Mon.). USD 18 in KS & NE; USD 22 in other states; USD 28 in Canada (effective 2004); USD 0.50 newsstand/cover. **Document type:** *Newspaper, Trade.*
Published by: Nebraska Farmer Stockman Inc., PO Box 349, Belleville, KS 66935. TEL 785-527-2244. Ed., Pub. Mark Miller. Adv. contact Paul Haase. Circ: 5,000 (paid).

630 GBR ISSN 1074-0163
FARMER TO FARMER. Text in English. 8/yr. **Document type:** *Newsletter.*
Published by: B H R Communications, County Mills, Worcester, WR1 3NU, United Kingdom. TEL 01905-25541, FAX 01905-723412, TELEX 338266. Ed. Sylvia Powell.

630 USA ISSN 0745-211X
FARMERS' ADVANCE. Text in English. 1898. w. USD 24.95. adv. **Document type:** *Newsletter.* **Description:** Farm and auction guide for Michigan, Indiana and Ohio.
Formerly: Farmers' Advance News (0273-7949)
Published by: Camden Publications, P O Box 130, Camden, MI 49232-0008. TEL 517-368-0365, FAX 517-368-5131. Ed. John Snyder. Pub. Kurt Greenhoe. Adv. contact Debbie Peiffer. Circ: 20,000 (paid).

630 640 USA ISSN 0889-5619
FARMERS AND CONSUMERS MARKET BULLETIN. Text in English. 1917. bi-w. USD 20 out of state; free in state (effective 2005). adv. illus. **Document type:** *Bulletin, Trade.* **Description:** Provides agriculture features and stories for Georgia residents.
Published by: Georgia Department of Agriculture, 19 Martin Luther King Jr Dr, S N, Atlanta, GA 30334-4250. TEL 404-656-3685, FAX 404-651-7957, cmoore@agr.state.ga.us, http://www.agr.state.ga.us/mbindex.html. Ed., R&P Carlton B Moore. Circ: 156,000 (paid and free).

630 GBR ISSN 0014-8393
FARMERS CLUB. JOURNAL. Text in English. 1842. bi-m. GBP 15 (effective 2002). adv. bk.rev. 24 p./no. 8 cols./p.; **Document type:** *Journal.*
Indexed: FCA, HerbAb, PBA, RRTA, WAE&RSA.
Published by: Farmers Club, 3 Whitehall Court, London, SW1A 2EL, United Kingdom. TEL 44-20-7930-3751, FAX 44-20-7839-7864. Ed., Adv. contact D A Gomery TEL 44-1892-853187. Circ: 5,800.

630 USA ISSN 1088-7733
FARMER'S EXCHANGE. Text in English. 1926. w. USD 25 (effective 2005). adv. 48 p./no. 6 cols./p.; **Document type:** *Newspaper, Trade.* **Description:** Covers general agricultural news for northern Indiana and southern Michigan counties.
Published by: Exchange Publishing Corp., 19401 Industrial Dr, New Paris, IN 46553. TEL 574-831-2138, FAX 574-831-2131, http://www.farmers-exchange.net. Ed. Jerry Goshert. Pub. Steve E. Yeater. Circ: 14,500 (paid and free).

630 USA
FARMERS' EXCHANGE (FAYETTEVILLE). Text in English. 1987. m. free to qualified personnel. adv. 64 p./no.; **Document type:** *Magazine, Consumer.*
Formerly: Tennessee Farmer's Exchange
Published by: Exchange, Inc., 404 S Main St, PO Box 490, Fayetteville, TN 37334. TEL 931-433-9737, FAX 931-433-0053. Pub. Bill Thomas. Adv. contact Jim Bowers. Circ: 30,000.

630 TWN ISSN 0014-8415
CODEN: FIVEEU
FARMERS' FRIEND✶. Key Title: Nong You. Text in Chinese. 1940. m. TWD 72, USD 1.80. adv. bk.rev. abstr.; charts; illus.; stat. index; cum.index.
Address: Box 16, Nei-Hsin, Taichung, Taiwan. Ed. Yen Chun Hsiung. Circ: 18,000.

630 GBR ISSN 0014-8423
FARMERS GUARDIAN. Text in English. 1958. w. GBP 70 domestic; USD 148 foreign; GBP 0.65 newsstand/cover (effective 2000). adv. bk.rev. illus. **Document type:** *Newspaper, Trade.* **Description:** News briefs, articles, editorial, and opinions on the legislative, regulatory, health, and market forecasting issues that affect the financial and operational aspects of agricultural businesses.
Related titles: Microform ed.; Online - full text ed.: (from Gale Group, Northern Light Technology, Inc., ProQuest Information & Learning).
Indexed: ABIn.
—BLDSC (3894.500000).
Published by: C M P Information Ltd. (Subsidiary of: United Business Media), Oliver's Pl, Eastway, Fulwood, P O Box 18, Preston, Lancs PR2 9GU, United Kingdom. http://www.cmpinformation.com. Ed., R&P Michael Finch. Pub. Peter Walker. Adv. contact Julie Kightly. Circ: 54,799.

630 GBR
FARMERS GUIDE. Text in English. 1979. m. adv. **Document type:** *Trade.* **Description:** Regional farming publication for agriculture in the eastern counties.
Formerly (until 1992): East Anglian Farmers Guide
Published by: Early Bird Farming Publications Ltd., Parkside, London Rd, Ipswich, Suffolk IP2 0SS, United Kingdom. TEL 44-1473-691888, FAX 44-1473-691886. Ed. Jane Potts. adv.: B&W page GBP 724, color page GBP 850. Circ: 22,000.

630 USA ISSN 0192-6322
FARMERS HOT LINE. Text in English. 63/yr. USD 39.95 (effective 2000). adv. **Document type:** *Journal, Trade.* **Description:** For dealers, manufacturers, and other machinery purchasing decision makers. Designed to bring together buyers and sellers of farm machinery and related services.
Published by: Heartland Ag-Business Group, Inc., 1003 Central Ave, Fort Dodge, IA 50501. TEL 515-574-2161, 800-673-4763, FAX 515-574-2181. Ed., Pub., R&P, Adv. contact Sandra J Simonson. Circ: 40,000.

630 USA ISSN 1521-6802
FARMER'S MARKET ONLINE. Text in English. 1994. w.
Media: Online - full content.
Published by: Hofferber, P.O. Box 441, Baker City, OR 97814-0441. http://www.FarmersMarketOnline.com, http://www.farmersmarketonline.com/. Ed. Michael Hofferber.

630 USA
THE FARMER'S PRIDE. Text in English. s-m. USD 19.50. **Document type:** *Newspaper.*
Published by: Farmland Publications, 316 Public Sq., Columbia, KY 42728. TEL 270-384-9454, 800-489-9454, FAX 270-384-9343. Ed. Diane Neat. Pub. Sharon Burton. Adv. contact Jada Coomer. Circ: 15,000 (paid).

336.225 USA ISSN 0499-647X
KF6369.8.F3
FARMERS' TAX GUIDE. Text in English. 1955. a.
Published by: U.S. Internal Revenue Service, 1111 Constitution Ave, N W, Washington, DC 20224. TEL 800-829-1040, http://www.irs.gov.

630 GBR ISSN 0014-8474
FARMERS WEEKLY. Text in English. 1934. w. GBP 96.20 domestic; EUR 243 in Europe euro zone; USD 243 in United States; GBP 162 elsewhere (effective 2005). adv. **Document type:** *Trade.* **Description:** Provides news and business, technical livestock, arable and machinery information to farmers and supply and advisory people.
Related titles: Online - full text ed.: (from EBSCO Publishing, Gale Group, H.W. Wilson, LexisNexis, O C L C Online Computer Library Center, Inc.).
Indexed: AgrForAb, AnBrAb, B&AI, BrTechI, CBNB, DSA, FCA, FS&TA, HerbAb, HortAb, M&TEA, MASUSE, RICS, RRTA, RefZh, RevApplEntom, SIA, WAE&RSA.
—BLDSC (3895.500000), CISTI, IE. **CCC.**
Published by: Reed Business Information Ltd. (Subsidiary of: Reed Business), Quadrant House, The Quadrant, Brighton Rd, Sutton, Surrey SM2 5AS, United Kingdom. TEL 44-20-86523500, FAX 44-20-86528932, farmers.weekly@rbi.co.uk, http://www.fwi.co.uk/, http://www.reedbusiness.co.uk/. Ed., R&P Stephen Howe TEL 44-20-8652-4912. Pub. Roger Williams. Adv. contact Vic Bunby TEL 44-20-8652-4030. Circ: 99,000. **Subscr. to:** Quadrant Subscription Services, PO Box 302, Haywards Heath, W Sussex RH16 3YY, United Kingdom. TEL 44-1444-475603, FAX 44-1444-445447, rbi.subscriptions@qss-uk.com.

630 ZAF ISSN 0014-8482
FARMER'S WEEKLY (ENGLISH EDITION). Text in English. 1911. w. ZAR 270.32; ZAR 556.40 overseas. adv. bk.rev. illus.; mkt. index. **Document type:** *Trade.* **Description:** Covers all aspects of farming in South Africa.
Related titles: Afrikaans ed.: Farmer's Weekly (Afrikaans edition). ISSN 1023-7879.
Indexed: AnBrAb, FS&TA, ISAP, SIA.
Published by: Republican Press (Pty) Ltd., PO Box 32083, Mobeni, 4060, South Africa. TEL 27-31-4508100, FAX 27-31-4508200. Ed. Corrie Venter. R&P Roy Minnaar TEL 27-11-7287245. Adv. contact T Anderson. Circ: 24,000.

630 GBR
FARMERS WEEKLY INTERACTIVE. Text in English. d. GBP 125 per service; GBP 300 full service. **Description:** Provides independent, topical information for the agricultural industry. Inludes a news service, a weather service providing a full national and regional four day weather forecast, a daily markets service providing guide to prices and trends, with commentaries on key markets in the UK and worldwide.
Media: Online - full text.
Published by: Reed Business Information Ltd. (Subsidiary of: Reed Business), Quadrant House, The Quadrant, Brighton Rd, Sutton, Surrey SM2 5AS, United Kingdom. TEL 44-20-86523500, FAX 44-20-86528932, http://www.fwi.co.uk, http://www.reedbusiness.co.uk/. Pub. Julian Westaway.

630 USA
FARMERS WEEKLY REVIEW. Text in English. 1921. w. USD 13.50 (effective 2001). adv. bk.rev. 16 p./no. 5 cols./p.; **Document type:** *Newspaper, Trade.* **Description:** Includes items of regional interest, including local government and business.
Related titles: Microform ed.
Published by: Farmers Weekly Review, Inc., 100 Manhattan Rd, Joliet, IL 60433. TEL 815-727-4811, FAX 815-727-5570. Ed., Pub. Patrick J Cleary. Adv. contact Debbie Werner. page USD 640; 10 x 16. Circ: 12,200 (paid and controlled).

630 KEN
FARMER'S WORLD; Kenya's farm magazine. Text in English, Swahili. 1977. m. adv. charts; illus.; stat.
Formerly: Farmer's Voice
Published by: (Kenya Grain Growers Co-operative Union), Oryx Publications Ltd., PO Box 40106, Nairobi, Kenya. Circ: 7,500.

630 USA ISSN 0091-1305
FARMFUTURES; the farm business magazine. Text in English. 1972-1999; resumed 2004. 9/yr. adv. bk.rev. charts. back issues avail. **Document type:** *Magazine, Trade.* **Description:** The business magazine of American agriculture, edited expressly for the operators of large, fulltime farming businesses.
—CISTI.
Published by: Farm Progress Companies, 191 S Gary Ave, Carol Stream, IL 60188. TEL 630-462-2230, FAX 630-462-2869, http://www.farmfutures.com/ME2/default.asp. Ed. Mike Wilson. Adv. contact Rhoda Ludwig. color page USD 1,850; trim 8.25 x 10.5. Circ: 212,000.

630 AUS ISSN 1038-1678
FARMING AHEAD. Text in English. 1983. m. AUD 163.90 membership (effective 2000); includes Kondinin Group Update. adv. software rev. mkt.; stat.; illus. **Document type:** *Magazine, Consumer.* **Description:** Covers cropping, cattle, and sheep management, pasture management, machinery, with equipment evaluations, research reports, farm computing and technology articles, marketing and finance tips, and rural research reports.
Former titles (until 1992): Kondinin Group Talk (1033-9078); (until 1988): Group Talk (0814-4613)
Indexed: AgrForAb, ForAb, HortAb, OrnHort, RPP, S&F.
—CISTI.
Published by: Kondinin Group, 4/398 Great Eastern Hwy, RedCliffe, W.A. 6104, Australia. TEL 61-8-9478-3343, FAX 61-8-9748-3353, Nicole@condinin.au, joanne@kondinin.com.au, http://www.kondinin.com.au/farmingahead. Ed., R&P Nicole Baxter. Adv. contact Carole King. page USD 3,200. Circ: 29,000 (controlled).

630 GBR
FARMING ECHO. Text in English. m. **Document type:** *Bulletin.*
Published by: Lincolnshire Publishing Ltd., Brayford Wharf East, Lincoln, LN5 7AT, United Kingdom. TEL 44-1522-525252, FAX 44-1522-545759. Ed. Cliff Smith. Circ: 65,000.

630 GBR
FARMING LIFE. Text in English. 104/yr.

Address: 51-67 Donegall St, Belfast, Co Antrim BT1 2GB, United Kingdom. TEL 0232-244441, FAX 0232-230715. Ed. David McCoy. Circ: 62,000.

630 USA ISSN 1539-7432
FARMING MAGAZINE; people, land, and community. Text in English. 2001 (Summer). q. USD 18 (effective 2001). adv.
Published by: Friends of the Agarians, P. O. Box 85, Mt. Hope, OH 44660.

630 GBR ISSN 0265-1645
FARMING NEWS. Text in English. 1983. w. GBP 70 domestic; USD 101 foreign; GBP 1.40 newsstand/cover (effective 2000). adv. **Document type:** *Newspaper, Trade.*
Related titles: Online - full text ed.: (from LexisNexis, Northern Light Technology, Inc.).
Published by: C M P Information Ltd. (Subsidiary of: United Business Media), Riverbank House, Angel Ln, Tonbridge, Kent TN9 1SE, United Kingdom. TEL 44-1732-364422, FAX 44-1732-377675, enquiries@cmpinformation.com, http://www.farmgate.co.uk, http://www.cmpinformation.com. Ed. James Van der Bos. Adv. contact David Bentley. Circ: 71,000. **Subscr. to:** Marlowe House, 109 Station Rd, Sidcup, Kent DA15 7ET, United Kingdom. TEL 44-20-8309-7000. **Dist. by:** Seymour Distribution Ltd, 86 Newman St, London W1T 3EX, United Kingdom. FAX 44-207-396-8002, enquiries@seymour.co.uk.

630 AUS
FARMING ONLINE. Text in English. d. free. **Document type:** *Trade.* **Description:** Serves Australian farmers and agriculture.
Media: Online - full text.
Published by: Rural Press Ltd. (Subsidiary of: Agricultural Publishers Pty. Ltd.), 10 Sydenham St., PO Box 254, Moonee Ponds, VIC 3039, Australia. TEL 61-3-92870900, FAX 61-3-93705622, http://www.farmonline.com.au/, http://www.ruralpress.com/.

630 GBR
FARMING REVIEW. (Covers 5 counties) Text in English. 1982. m.
Published by: Community Media Ltd., 32 Waterloo St, Weston-Super-Mar, BS2 31LW, United Kingdom. Ed. David Parker. Circ: 12,500.

630 AUS
FARMING SMALL AREAS. Text in English. q. free. **Document type:** *Magazine, Trade.*
Published by: Rural Press Ltd. (Subsidiary of: Agricultural Publishers Pty. Ltd.), 159 Bells Line of Rd., PO Box 999, North Richmond, NSW 2754, Australia. TEL 61-2-45704444, FAX 61-2-45704630, http://www.ruralpress.com/. Ed. Kim-Cherie Davidson. Adv. contact Roland Cowley. Circ: 53,918.

630 CAN ISSN 0838-8512
FARMING TODAY (WELLINGTON-WATERLOO-PERTH EDITION). Text in English. 1978. s-m. USD 10.
Published by: Wenger Publications, P O Box 130, Mount Forest, ON N0G 2L0, Canada. TEL 519-291-1660. Ed. Vaugham Douglas. Circ: 15,999.

630 USA ISSN 0272-3417
FARMING UNCLE; periodical for natural people and mother nature lovers. Text in English. 1977. q. USD 8 domestic; USD 13 foreign (effective 2004). adv. bk.rev. illus.; stat. back issues avail. **Description:** Features articles on the appreciation of nature and wildlife and its relationship to operating a self-sufficient agricultural enterprise.
Indexed: AltPI.
Address: P O Box 427, New York, NY 10458. Ed., Pub. Louis Toro. adv.: B&W page USD 4,750; trim 8 x 5. Circ: 1,000.

630 GBR
FARMING WALES/YR AMAETHWR. Text in English. 1992. m. membership. adv. bk.rev. **Document type:** *Trade.*
Published by: National Farmer's Union, Village, Swansea, 24 Tawe Business Park, Phoenix Way, Enterprise Park, Llansam, Swansea, SA7 9LB, United Kingdom. TEL 44-1792-774848, FAX 44-1792-774758. Ed. Keith Jones. Adv. contact Caroline Herbert. Circ: 14,000.

630 GBR ISSN 1364-9515
FARMLAND MARKET. Text in English. 1974. s-a. GBP 90 domestic; EUR 158 in Europe; USD 156.75 in United States; GBP 95 elsewhere (effective 2003). **Document type:** *Trade.* **Description:** Source of reference on prices and trends in the U.K. for those involved in agricultural land and property sales.
Indexed: RICS.
Published by: (Royal Institute of Chartered Surveyors), Reed Business Information Ltd. (Subsidiary of: Reed Business), Quadrant House, The Quadrant, Brighton Rd, Sutton, Surrey SM2 5AS, United Kingdom. TEL 44-20-86523500, FAX 44-20-86528932, rbi.subscriptions@qss-uk.com, http://www.reedbusiness.co.uk/. Ed. Andrew Shirley TEL 44-20-8652-4920. Pub. Roger Williams. **Subscr. to:** Quadrant Subscription Services, Rockwood House, 9-17 Perrymount Rd, Haywards Heath, W. Sussex RH16 3DH, United Kingdom. TEL 44-20-8652-3500, FAX 44-20-8652-8932.

338 630 USA ISSN 0093-5832
FARMLAND NEWS. Text in English. 1959. w. USD 29 (effective 2005). adv. illus. 40 p./no.; back issues avail. **Document type:** *Newspaper.* **Description:** Covers rural human interest.
Formerly (until 1971): Farmland (0014-8539)
—CISTI, Linda Hall.
Address: PO Box 240, Archbold, OH 43502-0240. TEL 419-445-9456, FAX 419-445-4444, ads@farmlandnews.com, http://www.farmlandnews.com. Ed. Jed W Grisez. Pub. O Roger Taylor. R&P Jed. W Grisez. Adv. contact Doug Nutter. col. inch USD 8.75. Circ: 5,011 (paid); 158 (free).

630 AUS
FARMS & FARM MACHINERY. Text in English. 1988. m. AUD 65; AUD 6 newsstand/cover (effective 2003). adv. **Document type:** *Trade.* **Description:** Designed for the rural market, covering farming equipment and properties for sale across Australia.
Published by: A C P Trader International Group (Subsidiary of: A C P Publishing Pty. Ltd.), 54-58 Park St, Sydney, NSW 1028, Australia. TEL 61-2-92828000, FAX 61-2-92674361, http://www.farmhub.com.au/mag-ffmaus.asp, http://www.tradergroup.com.au/. Ed. Peter Lawson-Hanscombe. Adv. contact Rick Smith. B&W page AUD 1,340, color page AUD 1,970; trim 262 x 362. Circ: 15,534. **Subscr. to:** Magshop, Reply Paid 4967, Sydney, NSW 2001, Australia. TEL 61-2-9282800, magshop@acp.com.au, http://magshop.com.au.

630 USA
FARMS AND LAND IN FARMS, FINAL ESTIMATES. Text in English. every 5 yrs. **Document type:** *Government.*
Published by: U.S. Department of Agriculture, National Agricultural Statistics Service, 1400 Independence Ave, S W, Washington, DC 20250-2000. nass@nass.usda.gov, http://www.usda.gov/nass.

630 GBR ISSN 0014-8547
FARMWEEK. Text in English. 1961. w. GBP 0.60 newsstand/cover. adv. bk.rev. abstr.; charts; mkt.; stat. **Document type:** *Newspaper, Trade.*
Incorporating: Farmer's Journal
Indexed: HortAb, SeedAb, WeedAb.
Published by: (Ulster Farmers Union), Morton Newspapers Ltd., 14 Church St, Portadown, Craigavon, Co Armagh, N Ireland BT62 3HY, United Kingdom. TEL 44-1762-339421, FAX 44-1762-350203, ed@farmweek.com, http://www.farmweek.com. Ed. Hal Crowe. Adv. contact Diane McCartney. Circ: 13,800.

630 ESP
FASAGA - ANDALUCIA. Text in Spanish. 12/yr.
Address: Edif. Jerez 74 planta 2a, Jerez De La Frontera, Cadiz 11407, Spain. TEL 56-30-79-00.

630 BGD
FASHAL. Text in Bengali. 1965. w.
Address: Motijheel C-A, 28 J Toyenbee Circular Rd, Dhaka, 1000, Bangladesh. TEL 2-233099. Ed. Ershad Mazumdar. Circ: 8,000.

630 USA
FASTLINE: WISCONSIN EDITION. Text in English. 1988-198?; resumed 1994. m. USD 10 (effective 2000). **Description:** Designed to the farming industry.
Former titles: Farmers Fastline: Wisconsin Edition; (until 1989): Wisconsin Farmers Fastline
Published by: Fastline Publications, Inc., 4900 Fox Run Rd, Buckner, KY 40010. TEL 800-626-6409, FAX 502-222-0615, info@fastlinepub.com, http://www.fastlinepublications.com. Ed., Pub., R&P William G Howard. Circ: 22,000.

630 EGY ISSN 1110-7790
FAYOUM JOURNAL OF AGRICULTURAL RESEARCH AND DEVELOPMENT/MAGALLAT AL-FAYYOUM AL-BIHUTH WA AL-TANMIYYAT AL-ZIRAA'IYYAT. Text in English. 1985. s-a. **Document type:** *Journal, Academic/Scholarly.*
Published by: Cairo University, Faculty of Agriculture, Fayyoum Branch, Fayyoum, Egypt. TEL 20-84-343721, FAX 20-84-334964, http://derp.sti.sci.eg/data/0368.htm. Ed. Dr. Farghal Abdel-Hafizh Zaid.

630 FRA ISSN 0396-8936
FEDERATION NATIONALE DES AGRICULTEURS MULTIPLICATEURS DE SEMENCES. BULLETIN. Text in French. 1962. 6/yr. adv. bibl.; stat. **Document type:** *Bulletin.* **Description:** Technical information on seed producing, means to guarantee yield and quality in producing fields, economic information on market situation, and general information on regulation and findings that may influence seed growing.
—BLDSC (2512.140000).
Published by: Federation Nationale des Agriculteurs Multiplicateurs de SEMENCES, 74 rue Jean-Jacques Rousseau, Paris, 75001, France. TEL 33-1-44827333, FAX 33-1-44827340, fnams-paris@wanadoo.fr. Ed. Georges Sicard, R&P Daniel Dattee. Adv. contact Catherine Guy. Circ: 30,000.

630 USA ISSN 0274-7308
FENCE POST ∗. Text in English. 1980. w. USD 14. adv. **Document type:** *Newspaper.*
Indexed: WildRev.
Published by: John Walker, PO Box 488, Windsor, CO 80550-0488. TEL 303-686-5694, FAX 303-686-5694. Ed. Duane McCormick. Circ: 10,000.

630 658 TWN ISSN 0017-8195
S471.T28
FENGNIAN/HARVEST; friend to the farmers. Text in Chinese. 1951. s-m. TWD 650 domestic (effective 1999); TWD 30 newsstand/cover; USD 67 foreign (effective 1999). adv. charts; illus.; stat. cum.index. **Document type:** *Government.* **Description:** Provides information for families involved in agriculture. Suggests agricultural techniques, examines production and marketing of specific crops. Coverage includes livestock, irrigation, automation, and news of the industry.
Related titles: Fax ed.
Indexed: BioCN&I.
Published by: (Council of Agriculture), Harvest Farm Magazine, 14 Wenchow St, Taipei, Taiwan. TEL 886-2-2362-8148, FAX 886-2-2363-6724, h3628148@ms15.hinet.net, http://www.coa.gov.tw/ch/fst/index.htm. Ed. Ming Tang Kao. Pub. Pi Phong Hong. adv.: B&W page USD 640, color page USD 1,454.50; trim 190 x 260. Circ: 15,000.

630 ESP
FERIAS, MERCADOS Y MATADEROS. Text in Spanish. 52/yr.
Published by: Ferias Mercados y Mataderos, Gran Via, 49, Apartado 125, Salamanca, 37001, Spain. TEL 23-27-05-87, FAX 23-21-00-99. Ed. E Ferreira Carretero.

630 USA ISSN 0071-4607
TP963.A1 CODEN: PFRWAD
FERTILIZER INDUSTRY ROUND TABLE. PROCEEDINGS. Text in English. 1955. a. USD 35 (effective 2000). **Document type:** *Proceedings.*
Indexed: Agr.
—BLDSC (6841.440000), CASDDS, CISTI, Linda Hall.
Published by: Fertilizer Industry Round Table, 1914 Baldwin Mill Rd, Forest Hill, MD 21050. silbersack@clearviewcatv.net silbersack@clearviewcatv.net, http://www.firt.org. Ed. Terri Silbersack. Circ: 300.

▼ **FIELD & FEAST.** see *FOOD AND FOOD INDUSTRIES*

630 GBR
FIFE FARMER. Text in English. m. adv. **Document type:** *Trade.*
Published by: Angus County Press Ltd., Forfar, Angus DD8 1BU, United Kingdom. TEL 01307-464899, FAX 01307-466923. Ed. Ian Wallace. Adv. contact Linda Ruston. Circ: 7,000.

630 FJI ISSN 0015-0886
S400.F5 CODEN: FJAJAB
FIJI AGRICULTURAL JOURNAL. Text in English. N.S. 1970. s-a. FJD 2. back issues avail.
Indexed: AgrForAb, AnBrAb, BiolAb, ChemAb, DSA, FCA, FS&TA, HerbAb, HortAb, IndVet, PBA, PN&I, RPP, RRTA, RevApplEntom, S&F, SPPI, SoyAb, VetBull, WAE&RSA, WeedAb.
—CASDDS, CISTI, Linda Hall.
Published by: Ministry of Agriculture & Fisheries, PO Box 358, Suva, Fiji. Ed. Param Sivan. Circ: 600.

630 FJI ISSN 0071-4844
FIJI. MINISTRY OF AGRICULTURE & FISHERIES. ANNUAL REPORT. Text in English. 1906. a. FJD 1.
Formerly: Fiji. Department of Agriculture. Annual Report
Indexed: FCA, HerbAb, NutrAb, RPP, RevApplEntom.
Published by: Ministry of Agriculture & Fisheries, PO Box 358, Suva, Fiji.

630 FJI
FIJI. MINISTRY OF AGRICULTURE & FISHERIES. ANNUAL RESEARCH REPORT. Text in English. N.S. 1969. a. FJD 2, USD 3.75 per issue.
Formerly: Fiji. Department of Agriculture. Annual Research Report.
Published by: Ministry of Agriculture & Fisheries, PO Box 358, Suva, Fiji.

FINANCIAL SURVEY. AGRICULTURAL GROWERS & MERCHANTS; company data for success. see *BUSINESS AND ECONOMICS—Trade And Industrial Directories*

630 338 332.7 IND ISSN 0015-2110
HG2051.I4
FINANCING AGRICULTURE. Text in English. 1969. q. INR 75, USD 35 (effective 1999). bk.rev. **Document type:** *Newspaper, Consumer.* **Description:** Comments on the agricultural economic situation and related topics.
Indexed: BAS, HortAb, PHN&I, RDA, RRTA, WAE&RSA.
Published by: Agricultural Finance Corporation Ltd., Dhanraj Mahal 1st Fl., Chatrapati Shivaji Maharaj Marg, Mumbai, Maharashtra 400 001, India. TEL 91-22-202-8924, FAX 91-22-202-8966, TELEX 11 85849 AFCO IN, afcl@bom2.vsnl.net-in. Ed. Subash Chandra Wadhwa. Circ: 5,000.

FINLAND. MINISTRY OF AGRICULTURE AND FORESTRY. INFORMATION CENTRE. STATISTICS. MAATILATILASTOLLINEN VUOSIKIRJA/YEARBOOK OF FARM STATISTICS. see *AGRICULTURE—Abstracting, Bibliographies, Statistics*

FINLAND. MINISTRY OF AGRICULTURE AND FORESTRY. INFORMATION CENTRE. STATISTICS. TIETOKAPPA. see *AGRICULTURE—Abstracting, Bibliographies, Statistics*

630 USA ISSN 0747-1114
FIRELANDS FARMER✶. Text in English. 1971. w. USD 20. adv. bk.rev. **Document type:** *Newspaper.*
Published by: Thomas Mezick, PO Box 146, New London, OH 44851-0146. TEL 419-929-8043, FAX 419-929-3800. Ed. Cleve Canham. Adv. contact Amy Cawrse. Circ: 4,150.

630 USA
FLORIDA AGRICULTURAL RESEARCH. Text in English. 1956. q. free. charts; illus.; stat.
Former titles (until 1987): University of Florida. Institute of Food and Agricultural Sciences. Research (0894-0673); (until 1986): Florida Agricultural Research (0734-8444); Supersedes (in 1982): Sunshine State Agricultural Research Report (0039-5447)
Indexed: BiolAb, ChemAb, FCA, HerbAb, PBA.
—CISTI, Linda Hall.
Published by: (Agricultural Experiment Station), University of Florida, Institute of Food and Agricultural Sciences, Press Room, McCarty Hall, Gainesville, FL 32611. TEL 904-392-1733. Ed. Chuck Woods. Circ: 8,000.

580 630 USA ISSN 0071-5948
CODEN: FPBRAE
FLORIDA. DIVISION OF PLANT INDUSTRY. BIENNIAL REPORT. Text in English. 1916. biennial. **Document type:** *Government.*
Indexed: BiolAb, RPP.
—CISTI, Linda Hall.
Published by: Department of Agriculture and Consumer Services, Division of Plant Industry, 1911 S W 34th St, Box 147100, Gainesville, FL 32614-7100. TEL 904-372-3505, FAX 904-955-2301. Ed. Maeve McConnell.

630 USA
FLORIDA FARMER. Text in English. m. USD 21.95 in state; USD 30 out of state (effective 2001). adv. **Document type:** *Trade.*
Published by: Farm Progress Companies, 191 S Gary Ave, Carol Stream, IL 60188. TEL 630-462-2892, FAX 630-462-2885, swyant@farmprogress.com, http://www.farmprogress.com/. Ed. Pam Golden TEL 850-682-0608. Pub. Allan Johnson. Adv. contact Don Tourte. B&W page USD 2,100, color page USD 5,000.

630 USA ISSN 1531-2356
CODEN: FGRAAE
FLORIDA GROWER. Text in English. 1907. m. USD 19.95 domestic; USD 28 in Canada; USD 39 foreign; free to qualified personnel (effective 2005). adv. bk.rev. illus. reprint service avail. from PQC. **Document type:** *Magazine, Trade.* **Description:** Covers growing, harvesting, processing, packing, shipping and marketing of Florida citrus and vegetables.
Formerly: Florida Grower and Rancher (0015-4091); Incorporates (in 1979): Florida Field Report (0015-4075)
Related titles: Microform ed.: (from PQC); Online - full text ed.
Indexed: ChemAb.
Published by: Meister Media Worldwide, 37733 Euclid Ave, Willoughby, OH 44094-5992. TEL 440-942-2000, FAX 440-942-0662, flg_circ@floridagrower.net, info@meistermedia.com, http://www.meistermedia.com. Ed. Charlotte Sine. Pub. Gerry Bagdon. Circ: 14,000 (paid and controlled).

338.1 USA ISSN 0046-4120
FLORIDA MARKET BULLETIN. Text in English. 1978 (vol.20). m. free. adv. illus.; tr.lit. **Document type:** *Government.* **Description:** Contains news and classified ads relating to Florida agriculture.
Formerly: Florida. Department of Agriculture and Consumer Services. Market Bulletin
Published by: Department of Agriculture and Consumer Services, 407 S. Calhoun St., # 234, Tallahassee, FL 32399-6555. http://www.fl-ag.com. Ed. Galen Moses. Circ: 20,000 (controlled).

630 USA ISSN 0015-3869
FLORIDAGRICULTURE. Text in English. 1943. m. free to members (effective 2004). adv. illus. back issues avail. **Document type:** *Magazine, Trade.* **Description:** Covers FFB activities, agriculture in Florida, and environmental issues.
Published by: Florida Farm Bureau Federation, PO Box 147030, Gainesville, FL 32614-7030. TEL 352-374-1521, FAX 352-374-1530, ealbanesi@sfbcic.com, http://floridafarmbureau.org, http://www.fb.com/flfb. Ed. Ed Albanesi. Adv. contact De Ann Holton. page USD 2,320, color page USD 2,709. Circ: 143,000 (controlled).

630 USA ISSN 0745-8355
FOCUS ON FARMING. Text in English. 1979. bi-w. (Mon.). USD 17.50 (effective 2005). adv. 24 p./no. 5 cols./p.; **Document type:** *Newspaper.*
Published by: Community Newspapers, 6 Central St, Moravia, NY 13118. TEL 315-497-1551, comnews@sccinternet.com. Ed. Bernard F McGuerty III TEL 315-497-1551. Pub., R&P, Adv. contact Butch McGuerty. B&W page USD 45,224. Circ: 15,000 (paid).

630 MOZ
FOLHAS VERDES. Text in Portuguese. 1993. m. free. **Document type:** *Newsletter, Consumer.* **Description:** Summerizes the activities and events of the Ministry of Agriculture and Fisheries.
Published by: Centro de Documentacao e Informacao do Sector Agrario, PO Box 1406, Maputo, Mozambique. TEL 258-1-460187, FAX 258-1-460137. Ed. Felix Alexandre Senete. Circ: 175.

630 VEN
FOMENTO AGROPECUARIO. Text in Spanish. 1976. m. free. charts; illus.; stat.
Published by: Banco Central de Venezuela, Av Urdaneta Esq Las Carmelitas, Caracas, 1010, Venezuela. TEL 58-212-8015111, FAX 58-212-8611649, info@bcv.org.ve, http://www.bcv.org.ve.

630 VEN
FONAIAP DIVULGA. Text in Spanish. 1981. 4/yr. VEB 1,200, USD 25. adv. bk.rev. illus.
Indexed: BioCN&I, BioDAb, DSA, FCA, HortAb, IndVet, RPP, RevApplEntom, RiceAb, WeedAb.
Published by: Fondo Nacional de Investigaciones Agropecuarias, Apdo. 2103, Maracay, 2105, Venezuela. FAX 58-43-836312. Ed. Josefa Saavedra. Circ: 5,000.

630 664 USA ISSN 1029-8622
FOOD, AGRICULTURE AND THE ENVIRONMENT. Text in English. irreg. **Document type:** *Monographic series, Academic/Scholarly.*
Indexed: GEOBASE.
—BLDSC (3977.003910).
Published by: International Food Policy Research Institute, 2033 K St, N W, Ste 400, Washington, DC 20006-1002. TEL 202-862-5600, FAX 202-467-4439, ispri-info@cgiar.org, http://www.cgiar.org/ifpri.

630 JPN ISSN 0915-5457
FOOD AND AGRICULTURAL POLICY RESEARCH CENTER. STUDY GROUP ON INTERNATIONAL ISSUES. REPORT. Key Title: Report of Study Group on International Issues, FAPRC. Text in English. 1989. irreg.
Published by: Food and Agriculture Policy Research Center, Japan/Shokuryo, Nogyo Seisaku Kenkyu Senta. Kokusai Bukai, 8th Fl Yushima Tokyo Bldg, 37-4 Yushima 4-chome, Tokyo, Bunkyo-ku 113-0034, Japan. TEL 81-3-3839-6802.

FOOD AND AGRICULTURE ORGANIZATION OF THE UNITED NATIONS. ASIA AND THE PACIFIC COMMISSION ON AGRICULTURAL STATISTICS. PERIODIC REPORT. see *AGRICULTURE—Abstracting, Bibliographies, Statistics*

630 USA ISSN 0532-0208
FOOD AND AGRICULTURE ORGANIZATION OF THE UNITED NATIONS. BASIC TEXTS. Text in English, French, Spanish. 1960. irreg. **Document type:** *Monographic series.*
Published by: Food and Agriculture Organization of the United Nations, c/o Bernan Associates, 4611 F Assembly Dr, Lanham, MD 20706-4391. TEL 301-459-7666, FAX 301-459-0056.

630 USA ISSN 0071-6944
FOOD AND AGRICULTURE ORGANIZATION OF THE UNITED NATIONS CONFERENCE. REPORT. Text in English. biennial (29th session). price varies.
Related titles: Microfiche ed.: (from CIS).
Indexed: ChemAb, IIS, NutrAb.
Published by: Food and Agriculture Organization of the United Nations, c/o Bernan Associates, 4611 F Assembly Dr, Lanham, MD 20706-4391. TEL 301-459-7666, FAX 301-459-0056.

630 THA ISSN 1014-191X
FOOD AND AGRICULTURE ORGANIZATION OF THE UNITED NATIONS. REGIONAL OFFICE FOR ASIA AND THE PACIFIC. PUBLICATION. Abbreviated title: R A P A Publication. Text in English. 1983. irreg.
Formerly (until 1986): Food and Agriculture Organization of the United Nations. Regional Office for Asia and the Pacific. Monograph (1014-1928)
Indexed: AEA, AbHyg, AgrForAb, AnBrAb, FCA, FPA, ForAb, HerbAb, HortAb, I&DA, IndVet, PGegResA, RDA, RRTA, RiceAb, S&F, WAE&RSA.
Published by: Food and Agriculture Organization of the United Nations, Regional Office for Asia and the Pacific, Maliwan Mansion, 39 Phra Atit Rd, Bangkok, 10200, Thailand. TEL 66-2-6974000, FAX 66-2-6974445, fao-rap@fao.org, http://www.fao.or.th/Publications/publications.htm.

630 THA ISSN 1020-1009
FOOD AND AGRICULTURE ORGANIZATION OF THE UNITED NATIONS. REGIONAL OFFICE FOR ASIA AND THE PACIFIC. REPORT. Abbreviated title: R A P A Report. Text in English. 1987. irreg.
Indexed: ESPM.
Published by: Food and Agriculture Organization of the United Nations, Regional Office for Asia and the Pacific, Maliwan Mansion, 39 Phra Atit Rd, Bangkok, 10200, Thailand. TEL 66-2-6974000, FAX 66-2-6974445.

630 IND ISSN 0015-6396
CODEN: FFAGDB
FOOD FARMING AND AGRICULTURE. Text in English. 1968. m. abstr.; bibl.; charts; illus.; stat. cum.index.
Indexed: ChemAb, FCA, HerbAb, NutrAb.
—CASDDS.
Address: c/o L.K. Pandeya, Ed., Block F, 105-C New Alipore Rd., Kolkata, West Bengal 700 053, India.

FOOD SCIENCE AND AGRICULTURAL CHEMISTRY. see *FOOD AND FOOD INDUSTRIES*

FOODWATCH UPDATE. see *CONSUMER EDUCATION AND PROTECTION*

630 AUS
FORAGE. Text in English. 1958. a. free. adv.
Published by: University of Melbourne, School of Agriculture, Parkville, VIC 3052, Australia. Circ: 1,500. **Co-sponsor:** La Trobe University, School of Forestry.

630 USA
FORAGE FARMER✶. Text in English. q. **Document type:** *Newsletter, Trade.*
Published by: International Silo Association, 332 Brookview Dr., Luxemburg, WI 54217-1079. cropstorage@cs.com, http://www.silo.org.

FORD ALMANAC; for farm and home. see *ENCYCLOPEDIAS AND GENERAL ALMANACS*

FOREIGN AGRICULTURAL TRADE OF THE UNITED STATES/U.S. AGRICULTURAL TRADE UPDATE. see *BUSINESS AND ECONOMICS—International Commerce*

FOREST, TREES AND LIVELIHOODS. see *FORESTS AND FORESTRY*

630 SWE ISSN 1400-8688
FORSKNINGSNYTT OM OEKOLOGISK LANDBRUK I NORDEN. Text in Multiple languages. 1987. q. SEK 390 (effective 2003). **Description:** Research news about ecological farming in the Nordic countries.
Formerly (until 1995): Alternativodlingsbrevet (1100-7133)
Indexed: HortAb, RA&MP, RPP, S&F, WeedAb.
Published by: Sveriges Lantbruksuniversitet, Centrum foer Uthaalligt Lantbruk/Swedish University of Agricultural Sciences. Centre for Sustainable Agriculture, PO Box 7047, Uppsala, 75047, Sweden. FAX 46-18-673571, http://www.cul.slu.se. Ed. Karin Ullven TEL 46-18-671696.

630 AUT ISSN 0015-8224
DER FORTSCHRITTLICHE LANDWIRT. Text in German. 1917. 24/yr. EUR 63.40 domestic; EUR 77.90 foreign (effective 2005). adv. bk.rev. index. **Document type:** *Magazine, Trade.*
Indexed: RefZh.
Published by: Leopold Stocker Verlag, Hofgasse 5, Graz, St 8011, Austria. TEL 43-316-821636, FAX 43-316-835612, stocker-verlag@stocker-verlag.com, http://www.stocker-verlag.com/landwirtschaftliche-Zeitschriften-36-10/Der-fortschrittliche-Landwirt.html. Ed. Anton Stock. Adv. contact Thomas Muehlbacher. B&W page EUR 2,390, color page EUR 3,700; trim 190 x 260. Circ: 37,000 (paid and controlled).

631.3 FRA ISSN 0429-2766
FOURRAGES. Text in English. 1960. quadrennial.
Indexed: AgBio, AgrForAb, AnBrAb, CPA, DSA, FCA, ForAb, HerbAb, HortAb, I&DA, MaizeAb, PBA, PGegResA, RM&VM, RRTA, S&F, SIA, SeedAb, SoyAb, TriticAb, WAE&RSA, WeedAb.
—CISTI.
Published by: Institut National de la Recherche Agronomique (INRA), Service des Publications, Route de Saint Cyr, Versailles, Cedex 78026, France. TEL 33-1-30833406, FAX 33-1-30833449, inra-editions@versailles.inra.fr, http://www.inra.fr/index.html.

630 580 HRV ISSN 1330-2884
CODEN: FHJUDA
FRAGMENTA PHYTOMEDICA ET HERBOLOGICA. Text in Croatian. 1971. s-a. USD 10. abstr.; illus. back issues avail. **Document type:** *Journal, Academic/Scholarly.*
Former titles (until 1993): Fragmenta Herbologica (1330-2906); (until 1991): Fragmenta Herbologica Iugoslavica (0350-3615)
Indexed: BiolAb, CPA, ChemAb, FCA, ForAb, HortAb, MaizeAb, PBA, RPP, RevApplEntom, SoyAb, TriticAb, WeedAb.
—CASDDS, CISTI.
Published by: Institute for Plant Protection, Faculty of Agricultural Sciences, Simunska c 25-V, Zagreb, 41000, Croatia. Circ: 500.

630 FRA ISSN 0152-3295
FRANCE. MINISTERE DE L'AGRICULTURE ET DE LA FORET. BULLETIN D'INFORMATION. Cover title: B I M A. Text in French. 1944. w. (40/yr.). EUR 36 in the European Union; EUR 56 elsewhere (effective 2003). charts; illus.; stat. **Document type:** *Bulletin.* **Description:** Covers the principal measures taken and decisions made by the Ministry in agricultural and social matters.

A

Former titles (until 1975): France. Ministere de l'Agriculture et du Developpement Rural. Bulletin d'Information (0395-8256); (until 1944): France. Ministere de l'Agriculture. Bulletin d'Information. Bulletin (0373-4994)
Published by: Ministere de l'Agriculture et de la Foret, 78 rue de Varenne, Paris, 75007, France. **Subscr. to:** Lavoisier, Lavoisier - Dept Abonnements, 14 rue de Provigny, Cachan 94236, France. TEL 33-1-47406700, FAX 33-1-47406702, abo@lavoisier.fr.

FRANCE. MINISTERE DE L'AGRICULTURE ET DE LA PECHE. AGRESTE INFO; la statistique agricole. see *AGRICULTURE—Abstracting, Bibliographies, Statistics*

630 ISL ISSN 0016-1209
S11
FREYR. Text in Icelandic. 1904. m. USD 45 (effective 1998). adv. bk.rev. illus.; mkt.; stat.
Indexed: RASB.
Published by: Baendasamtoek Islands/Farmers Association of Icelandd, PO Box 7080, Reykjavik, Iceland. TEL 354-551-9200, FAX 354-562-3058. Eds. Askell Thorisson, Matthias Eggertsson. Circ: 2,500.

630 USA
FRONT PORCH. Text in English. 1935. 6/yr. USD 12 to members (effective 2005). adv. **Document type:** *Newspaper.* **Description:** Features Farm Bureau activities; also farming, farming business, and culturally related stories,.
Formerly: Farm Bureau Press
Published by: Arkansas Farm Bureau Federation, 10720 Kanis Road, Little Rock, AR 72211. TEL 501-224-4400, FAX 501-228-1557, audie.ayer@arfb.com, http://www.arfb.com/publications/front_porch/default.asp. Ed., Pub. A Audie Ayer. adv.: B&W page USD 3,010, color page USD 3,635; 12.5 x 9.38. Circ: 235,500 (controlled).

638.1 FRA ISSN 0429-7857
FRUITS ET ABEILLES. Text in French. m.
Indexed: ApicAb.
Published by: Union des Federations Arboricoles et Apicoles, 24 rue St-Wolfgang, Weyersheim, 67720, France. Ed. Gerard Weibel.

630 DEU ISSN 1615-9373
FUEHRUNGSKRAEFTE UND MANAGEMENT. Text in German. 2000. q. EUR 22.50 domestic; EUR 24.50 foreign (effective 2003). adv. **Document type:** *Magazine, Trade.*
Formed by the merger of (1955-2000): Der Gartenbauingenieur (0016-4763); (1965-2000): Agraringenieur, Agrarmanager (0341-2520); Which was formerly (until 1972): Der Agraringenieur (0002-1059)
Published by: B A I Verlag GmbH, Konrad Adenauer Str 18, Habichtswald, 34317, Germany. TEL 49-5606-56675, FAX 49-5606-56674, info@agraring.de, http://www.agraring.de. adv.: page EUR 818.07. Circ: 1,750 (paid and controlled).

630 CHN ISSN 0429-8047
FUJIAN NONGYE/FUJIAN AGRICULTURE. Text in Chinese. m. CNY 12.
Related titles: Online - full text ed.: (from East View Information Services).
Published by: (Fujian Sheng Nongye Ting/Fujian Provincial Bureau of Agriculture), Fujian Nongye Bianjibu, 153 Guping Lu, Fuzhou, Fujian 350003, China. TEL 556106. Ed. Chen Qingshou. Circ: 78,000.

630 631 CHN ISSN 1006-7817
CODEN: FCNHAL
FUJIAN NONGYE DAXUE XUEBAO/FUJIAN AGRICULTURAL UNIVERSITY. JOURNAL. Text in Chinese; Abstracts in English. q. USD 24. adv. **Document type:** *Academic/Scholarly.* **Description:** Covers crop production, fruit trees, tea, vegetables, flowers, bees, animal husbandry and veterinary science, food engineering, plant protection, soil and plant nutrient, as well as agricultural economics.
Formerly (until 1994): Fujian Nongxueyuan Xuebao - Fujian Agricultural College. Journal (0427-7082)
Indexed: AEA, AgBio, AgrForAb, AnBrAb, B&BAb, BioCN&I, CPA, DSA, ESPM, FCA, FPA, FS&TA, ForAb, HerbAb, HortAb, I&DA, IndVet, MBA, MaizeAb, NemAb, NutrAb, OrnHort, PBA, PGegResA, PGrRegA, PHN&I, PN&I, PollutAb, PoultAb, RA&MP, RDA, RPP, RefZh, RevApplEntom, RiceAb, S&F, SIA, SeedAb, SoyAb, TriticAb, VetBull, WAE&RSA, WeedAb. —CASDDS.
Published by: Fujian Nongye Daxue, Jinshan, Fuzhou, Fujian 350002, China. TEL 86-591-3741213, FAX 86-591-3710251. Ed. Li Wenshan. Circ: 2,000. **Dist. overseas by:** China International Book Trading Corp, 35 Chegongzhuang Xilu, Haidian District, PO Box 399, Beijing 100044, China. TEL 86-10-68412045, FAX 86-10-68412023, cibtc@mail.cibtc.com.cn, http://www.cibtc.com.cn.

630 CHN ISSN 0253-2301
CODEN: FNKED9
FUJIAN NONGYE KEJI/FUJIAN AGRICULTURAL SCIENCE AND TECHNOLOGY. Text in Chinese. 1973. bi-m. CNY 30, USD 14.40 (effective 2004). adv. **Document type:** *Journal, Academic/Scholarly.*
Related titles: Online - full content ed.: (from WanFang Data Corp.); Online - full text ed.: (from East View Information Services).
Indexed: AgBio, AgrForAb, AnBrAb, BioCN&I, CPA, FCA, HortAb, MaizeAb, NemAb, OrnHort, PBA, PGrRegA, PN&I, PoultAb, RA&MP, RiceAb, S&F, SIA, SeedAb, TriticAb, WAE&RSA. —CASDDS.
Published by: Fujian Nongye Kexueyuan/Fujian Academy of Agricultural Science, 247 Wusi Rd, Fuzhou, Fujian 350003, China. TEL 86-591-841771, fjnykj@163.net, faas@pub1.fz.fj.cn, http://fjnykj.periodicals.net.cn/default.html. Ed. Wang Jinghui. **Dist. outside of China by:** China International Book Trading Corp, 35 Chegongzhuang Xilu, Haidian District, PO Box 399, Beijing 100044, China. TEL 86-10-68412045, FAX 86-10-68412023, cibtc@mail.cibtc.com.cn, http://www.cibtc.com.cn/.

630 CHN ISSN 1000-7121
FUJIAN SHENG NONGKEYUAN XUEBAO/FUJIAN ACADEMY OF AGRICULTURAL SCIENCE. JOURNAL. Text in Chinese. 1986. q. CNY 1.20 newsstand/cover. **Document type:** *Academic/Scholarly.*
Indexed: AEA, AgBio, AgrForAb, AnBrAb, BioCN&I, CPA, FCA, FPA, FS&TA, ForAb, HortAb, I&DA, IndVet, MaizeAb, NemAb, NutrAb, OrnHort, PBA, PGegResA, PGrRegA, PHN&I, PN&I, PotatoAb, PoultAb, RA&MP, RPP, RevApplEntom, RiceAb, S&F, SIA, SeedAb, SoyAb, TDB, TriticAb, VetBull, WeedAb.
Published by: Fujian Sheng Nongkeyuan, Qingbao Suo/Fujian Academy of Agricultural Science, Information Institute, 247 Wusi Rd, Fuzhou, Fujian 350003, China. TEL 86-591-784-1771. Ed. Wang Jinghui.

630 JPN
FUKUI UNIVERSITY. FACULTY OF EDUCATION. MEMOIRS. SERIES 3: APPLIED SCIENCE AND AGRICULTURAL SCIENCE. Text in Japanese; Summaries in English, Japanese. a. free. **Document type:** *Academic/Scholarly.*
Published by: Fukui University, Faculty of Education/Fukui Daigaku Kyoikugakubu, 9-1 Bunkyo 3-chome, Fukui-shi, 910-0017, Japan. Ed. Terutsugu Ando.

630 VEN ISSN 0029-4160
FUNDACION SERVICIO PARA EL AGRICULTOR. NOTICIAS AGRICOLAS. Text in Spanish. 1955. bi-m. USD 15. adv. charts; illus. index. cum.index every 3 yrs.
Published by: Fundacion Servicio para el Agricultor, Estacion Experimental de Cagua, Carretera via La Sengundera Km. 3, Cagua, (Estado Aragua), Venezuela. TEL 58-44-79184, FAX 58-44-75607. Ed. Hector Ayala. Circ: 10,000.

630 USA ISSN 0016-3112
FURROW; a journal of popular farm science and rural life. Text in English. 1895. 8/yr. free to qualified personnel (effective 2005). illus. reprint service avail. from PQC. **Document type:** *Magazine, Trade.*
Related titles: Microform ed.: (from PQC); ♦ German ed.: Flur und Furche. ISSN 0015-4733; ♦ Swedish ed.: Faran; ♦ Norwegian ed.: Fara; ♦ Spanish ed.: Surco Argentina; ♦ Spanish ed.: Campo y Mecanica. ISSN 0211-4704; ♦ Spanish ed.: Surco Mexicana; Afrikaans ed.: 1895; Danish ed.: 1895; Dutch ed.: 1895; French ed.: 1895; Italian ed.: 1895; Portuguese ed.: 1895; ♦ Regional ed(s).: Surco Latinoamericana; ♦ Sulco; ♦ Voor; ♦ Sillon.
Indexed: AEA, CPL, F&GI, IFP, OTA. —CISTI, Linda Hall.
Published by: John Deere Publishing, 11145 Thompson Ave, Lenexa, KS 66219. TEL 800-387-7691, FAX 651-644-3416, http://www.deere.com. Ed. Andy Markwart. Circ: 1,500,000 (free).

630 USA
FURROW (AUSTRALIAN - NEW ZEALAND EDITION). Text in English. 1978. 3/yr. free.
Published by: John Deere Publishing, One John Deere Place, Moline, IL 61265. TEL 309-765-8000. Ed. G R Sollenberger. Circ: 40,000.

630 USA
FURROW (UNITED KINGDOM EDITION); journal of popular farm science and rural life. Text in English. 1973. 4/yr. free to qualified personnel.
Indexed: ISAP.
Published by: John Deere Publishing, One John Deere Place, Moline, IL 61265. TEL 309-765-8000. Ed. Jean Claude Hiron. Circ: 52,000.

630 USA ISSN 0748-1578
CODEN: FTRSER
FUTURES (EAST LANSING). Text in English. 1967. q. Single copy free. reprint service avail. from PQC,ISI.
Formerly: Michigan Science in Action (0076-809X)
Indexed: ABCPolSci, ABIn, AEA, AbHyg, AgBio, Agr, AnBrAb, BrRB, CLOSS, CPM, CREJ, DSA, EAA, F&GI, FCA, ForAb, HerbAb, HortAb, IndVet, MMI, ManagCont, NemAb, NutrAb, OrnHort, PBA, PN&I, PoultAb, RPP, RRTA, S&F, SCIMP, SeedAb, T&II, VITIS, WAE&RSA, WeedAb. —BLDSC (4060.645000), CISTI, Linda Hall.
Published by: Michigan State University, Agricultural Experiment Station, 310 Agriculture Hall, East Lansing, MI 48824-1039. TEL 517-432-1555, FAX 517-355-1804. Ed. Jamie Depolo. Circ: 5,000 (controlled).

630 MEX ISSN 0187-4381
GACETA AGRICOLA. Text in Spanish. 1956. every 10 days. MXP 2,000, USD 30. adv. bk.rev.
Address: Av. La Paz 1522, Apdo. Postal 5-225, Guadalajara, JALISCO 45000, Mexico. Ed. Francisco Sainz Ibarra. Circ: 30,000.

630 ESP ISSN 0016-3864
GACETA RURAL; semanario de informacion agropecuaria. Text in Spanish. 1945. w. adv. bk.rev. bibl.; stat. **Document type:** *Newspaper, Trade.* **Description:** Presents general information on agriculture in Spain.
Published by: Gestora Editorial Rural S.L., Avda Ramon y Cajal, 5, Madrid, 28016, Spain. TEL 34-1-3440462, FAX 34-1-3440463. Ed. Ana de Rojas. Circ: 2,500.

GAMMA FIELD SYMPOSIA. see *BIOLOGY—Biophysics*

630 636 VEN ISSN 0046-5399
GANAGRINCO; ganaderia - agricultura - industria - comercio. Text in Spanish; Summaries in English, Spanish. q. USD 6. adv. illus.; charts.
Address: Ed. Rafael Salom, Apdo. de Correos 3318, Caracas, 101, Venezuela. Circ: 2,000.

630 PRT ISSN 0378-8032
S18 CODEN: GOSADL
GARCIA DE ORTA: SERIE DE ESTUDOS AGRONOMICOS. Text in Portuguese. 1953. irreg., latest vol.20, 1998. price varies. back issues avail. **Document type:** *Academic/Scholarly.*
Supersedes in part (in 1973): Garcia de Orta (0016-4569)
Indexed: AEA, FCA, FPA, FS&TA, HortAb, MaizeAb, PHN&I, S&F, SeedAb, TriticAb. —BLDSC (4069.982000), CASDDS, CISTI.
Published by: Instituto de Investigacao Cientifica Tropical, Rua da Junqueira, 30, Lisbon, 1349-007, Portugal. TEL 351-21-3622621, FAX 351-21-3631460, iict@iict.pt. Circ: 1,000. **Subscr. to:** Centro de Documentacao e Informacao, Rua de Jau, 47, Lisbon 1300, Portugal. TEL 351-21-3644846, FAX 351-21-3628218.

GARDEN TO KITCHEN NEWSLETTER. see *NUTRITION AND DIETETICS*

630 FRA ISSN 1245-1606
GASCON MAGAZINE. Text in French. 1991. bi-m.
Related titles: ♦ Supplement to: Terres d'Ariege. ISSN 0750-8093.
Published by: Terres d, 32 av. du General de Gaulle, BP 7, Foix, Cedex 09001, France. TEL 61-65-20-00, FAX 61-02-89-60.

630 ITA
GAZZETTA AGRICOLA. Text in Italian. 1945. 28/yr.
Address: Via Guidelli, 10, Reggio Emilia, RE 42100, Italy. TEL 39-241, FAX 53-105. Ed. Marco Benati. Circ: 8,000.

630 ITA
GAZZETTINO AGRICOLO DI PARMA. Text in Italian. 1947. w. adv.
Published by: Unione Provinciale Agricoltori di Parma, Viale Gramsci 26b, Parma, PR 43100, Italy. TEL 39-0521-290516, FAX 39-0521-291153, parma@confagricoltura.it, http://www.confagricoltura.org. Ed. Massimo Dall'Olio. Circ: 6,500 (controlled).

638.1 USA
GEORGIA BEEKEEPERS ASSOCIATION. NEWSLETTER. Text in English. 1997. m. free to members. **Document type:** *Newsletter.* **Description:** Provides information about bees and news for the members of the association.
Media: Online - full text.
Published by: Georgia Beekeepers Association, Inc., 528 Bridge Ave, Forest Park, GA 30050. TEL 409-366-6405, beewares@aol.com, http://www.georgiahoney.com/gbanews.htm.

630 USA ISSN 0735-696X
S451.G4
GEORGIA FARM BUREAU NEWS; the voice of Georgia farmers. Text in English. 1938. 6/yr. USD 15 (effective 2005). adv. **Document type:** *Magazine, Trade.* **Description:** Information on the financial, legislative, and policy issues affecting Georgia agriculture.
Published by: Georgia Farm Bureau Federation, PO Box 7068, Macon, GA 31209. paul@gfb.org, http://www.gfb.org/gfbnews.html. Ed., R&P Jennifer Whittaker. Pub. Paul Beliveau. Adv. contact Lili Davis. Circ: 60,000 (paid).

630 USA ISSN 0016-8254
GEORGIA FARMER. Text in English. 1956. m. USD 12; USD 25 foreign. adv. **Document type:** *Newspaper.*
Published by: Farm Progress Companies, 191 S Gary Ave, Carol Stream, IL 60188. TEL 630-462-2892, FAX 630-462-2885, http://www.farmprogress.com/. Ed. Donna Sandusky. adv.: B&W page USD 3,000, color page USD 8,400. Circ: 18,000.

630 USA ISSN 0016-8262
GEORGIA FUTURE FARMER. Text in English. 1942. 2/yr.
Published by: Future Farmers of America, Georgia Association, 1766 Twin Towers East, Atlanta, GA 30334. Ed. Curtis Corbin. Circ: 18,000.

630 USA
GEORGIA NEIGHBORS. Text in English. 3/yr. USD 15 to non-members; free to members (effective 2005). **Description:** Features on rural life and places of interest around Georgia.
Published by: Georgia Farm Bureau Federation, PO Box 7068, Macon, GA 31209. Ed. Jennifer Whittaker. Circ: 412,600.

630 ESP ISSN 1132-810X
GEORGICA. Text in Spanish. 1992. a. back issues avail.
Indexed: AgBio, AnBrAb, CPA, ForAb, HerbAb, HortAb, I&DA, IECT, PBA, PGegResA, PHN&I, S&F, SIA, SeedAb, WAE&RSA.
—CINDOC, CISTI.
Published by: Universidad de Zaragoza, Escuela Universitaria de Estudios Sociales, Violante de Hundria, 23, Zaragoza, 50009, Spain. TEL 34-976-761028, FAX 34-976-761029, websociales@posta.unizar.es, http://www.unizar.es/.

338 630 DEU ISSN 0722-8333
Q180.G4
GERMANY. BUNDESMINISTERIUM FUER ERNAEHRUNG, LANDWIRTSCHAFT UND FORSTEN. AGRARBERICHT DER BUNDESREGIERUNG. Text in German. 1956. a. **Document type:** *Government.*
Related titles: Online - full text ed.
Indexed: WAE&RSA.
Published by: Bundesministerium fuer Verbraucherschutz, Ernaehrung und Landwirtschaft, Rochusstr 1, Bonn, 53123, Germany. http://www.verbraucherministerium.de.

GESELLSCHAFT FUER BIBLIOTHEKSWESEN UND DOKUMENTATION DES LANDBAUES. MITTEILUNGEN. see *AGRICULTURE—Abstracting, Bibliographies, Statistics*

630 CAN
GESTION ET TECHNOLOGIE AGRICOLES. Text in English. 1975. 10/yr. CND 18.70 (effective 2000). adv. **Document type:** *Newspaper.*
Published by: Courrier de Saint-Hyacinthe, 655 Sainte Anne, St Hyacinthe, PQ J2S 5G4, Canada. TEL 514-773-6028. Ed. Benoit Chartier. R&P Guy Roy. Adv. contact Paul Paradis. Circ: 20,000 (paid).

638.1 GHA
GHANA BEE NEWS. Text in English. 1981. q. USD 9. adv. bk.rev. illus. back issues avail.
Published by: Technology Consultancy Centre, University of Science and Technology, Kumasi, Ghana. Ed. Celia Till. Circ: 1,200.

630 GHA ISSN 0046-5917
GHANA FARMER; Ministry of Agriculture review on agricultural development. Text in English. 1932-1974; resumed 1978. 3/yr. adv. bk.rev. **Document type:** *Bulletin, Government.*
Indexed: FCA, HerbAb, HortAb, PBA.
Published by: Ministry of Agriculture, Information Support Unit, PO Box 299, Accra, Ghana. Ed. J Agbebkewu. Circ: 3,000.

630 GHA ISSN 0855-0042
S379.G4 CODEN: GJASAF
➤ **GHANA JOURNAL OF AGRICULTURAL SCIENCE.** Text in English; Summaries in English, French. 1968. 3/yr. USD 35 (effective 2003). bk.rev. index. **Document type:** *Trade.* **Description:** Publishes papers on agricultural science and related disciplines. Focuses on original research and new investigations into changes in subsistence agriculture.
Related titles: Online - full text ed.: (from International Network for the Availability of Scientific Publications, African Journals Online).
Indexed: AnBrAb, BiolAb, ChemAb, DSA, FCA, HerbAb, HortAb, IndVet, NutrAb, PBA, RPP, RRTA, RevApplEntom, S&F, VetBull, WAE&RSA, WeedAb.
Published by: (South Africa. Council for Scientific and Industrial Research ZAF), National Science and Technology Press, PO Box M 32, Accra, Ghana. TEL 233-21-778808, FAX 223-21-777655, http://www.csir.org.gh. Ed. D K Acquaye. R&P F J K Adotevi. Circ: 500.

➤ **GHANA. METEOROLOGICAL DEPARTMENT. AGROMETEOROLOGICAL BULLETIN.** see *METEOROLOGY*

631 DEU ISSN 0179-0145
GIESSENER SCHRIFTEN ZUR AGRAR- UND ERNAEHRUNGSWIRTSCHAFT. Text in German. 1971. irreg., latest vol.32, 2002. **Document type:** *Monographic series, Academic/Scholarly.*
Published by: D L G Verlags GmbH, Eschborner Landstr 122, Frankfurt Am Main, 60489, Germany. TEL 49-69-247880, FAX 49-69-24788480, dlg-verlag@dlg-frankfurt.de, http://www.dlg-verlag.de.

630 JPN ISSN 0072-4513
CODEN: GNKEAH
GIFU DAIGAKU NOGAKUBU KENKYU HOKOKU/GIFU UNIVERSITY. FACULTY OF AGRICULTURE. RESEARCH BULLETIN. Text and summaries in English, Japanese. 1951. irreg., latest vol.28, 1969. free. **Document type:** *Bulletin.*
Indexed: AEA, AgBio, AnBrAb, BioCN&I, BiolAb, CIN, CPA, ChemAb, ChemTitl, DSA, FCA, FPA, FS&TA, ForAb, HerbAb, HortAb, I&DA, IndVet, NutrAb, OrnHort, PBA, PGrRegA, PHN&I, PoultAb, RDA, RPP, RRTA, RevApplEntom, RiceAb, S&F, S&MA, VetBull, WAE&RSA, ZooRec.
—BLDSC (7722.000000), CASDDS, IE, ingenta.
Published by: Gifu Daigaku, Nogakubu/Gifu University, Faculty of Agriculture, 1-1 Yanagi-To, Gifu-shi, 501-1112, Japan. Ed. Hironori Sakurai. Circ: 750.

GINSENG REVIEW. see *PHARMACY AND PHARMACOLOGY*

630 AUS ISSN 0158-3840
GIPPSLAND FARMER. Text in English. 1981. m. adv. back issues avail. **Document type:** *Newspaper.* **Description:** Concentrates on issues affecting the Gippsland farmer.
Published by: Rural Press Ltd. (Subsidiary of: Agricultural Publishers Pty. Ltd.), 159 Bells Line of Rd., PO Box 999, North Richmond, NSW 2754, Australia. TEL 61-2-45704444, FAX 61-2-45704630, http://www.ruralpress.com/. Circ: 12,000.

630 SCG ISSN 0017-0976
GLASNIK POLJOPRIVREDNE PROIZVODNJE, PRERADE I PLASMANA. Text in Serbo-Croatian. 1952. m. YUN 550.
Indexed: RASB.
Published by: Privredni Pregled, Marsala Birjuzova 3-5, Belgrade, 11000. Ed. Slobodan Sindovic.

630 NGA ISSN 1596-2903
➤ **GLOBAL JOURNAL OF AGRICULTURAL SCIENCES.** Text in English. 2002. s-a. NGN 750 per issue domestic; USD 25 per issue foreign (effective 2003). bk.rev. back issues avail.; reprints avail. **Document type:** *Journal, Academic/Scholarly.*
Related titles: Online - full text ed.: (from International Network for the Availability of Scientific Publications, African Journals Online).
Published by: Global Journal of Pure and Applied Sciences, c/o Prof. Barth N. Ekwueme,, University of Calabar, Department of Geology, PO Box 3651, Calabar, Nigeria. ekwueme@unical.anpa.net.ng, http://www.inasp.info/ajol/. Eds. Leonard N Agwunobi, Barth N Ekwueme.

630 USA
GLOBE ADVERTISER. Text in English. 1977. w. free. adv. **Document type:** *Newspaper.*
Former titles (until 1994): Heartland Journal (Mason City); Rural Life
Published by: Globe Gazette, 300 N Washington Ave, Mason City, IA 50401. TEL 515-421-0546, FAX 515-421-0516. Ed. Kevin Baskins. Pub. Howard Query. Adv. contact Byron Wooten. Circ: 16,303.

630 BRA ISSN 0102-6178
GLOBO RURAL. Text in Portuguese. 1985. m. BRL 87 (effective 2005). adv. illus. back issues avail. **Document type:** *Magazine, Consumer.* **Description:** For a professional rural audience and others interested in this lifestyle. Covers cattle, breeding, fruticulture, horticulture, ecology and soil management.
Related titles: Online - full text ed.; ♦ Supplement(s): Globo Rural Cozinha da Fazenda. ISSN 0104-4044; ♦ Globo Rural Especial Como Criar. ISSN 0104-5288; ♦ Globo Rural Responde. ISSN 0104-3544.
Published by: Editora Globo S.A., Av. Jaguare, 1487, Sao Paulo, SP 05346 902, Brazil. TEL 55-11-37677852, FAX 55-11-37677771, atendimento@edglobo.com.br, http://revistagloborural.globo.com/, http://editoraglobo.globo.com/. Ed. Paulo de Oliveira Soares. adv.: page USD 42,700; trim 274 x 208. Circ: 164,000 (paid).

GLOBO RURAL COZINHA DA FAZENDA. see *HOME ECONOMICS*

630 BRA ISSN 0104-5288
GLOBO RURAL ESPECIAL COMO CRIAR. Variant title: Como Criar. Text in Portuguese. 199?. a. adv. illus. **Document type:** *Consumer.*
Related titles: ♦ Supplement to: Globo Rural. ISSN 0102-6178.
Published by: Editora Globo S.A., Rua Domingos Sergio dos Anjos, 277, Pirituba, Jd S Elias, Sao Paulo, SP 05136-170, Brazil. TEL 55-11-3766-3000, atendimento@edglobo.com.br, http://www.editoraglobo.com.br, http://editoraglobo.globo.com/. Pub. Jose Francisco Queiroz.

630 BRA ISSN 0104-3544
GLOBO RURAL RESPONDE. Text in Portuguese. 199?. a. adv. illus. **Document type:** *Consumer.*
Related titles: ♦ Supplement to: Globo Rural. ISSN 0102-6178.
Published by: Editora Globo S.A., Rua Domingos Sergio dos Anjos, 277, Pirituba, Jd S Elias, Sao Paulo, SP 05136-170, Brazil. TEL 55-11-836-5000, atendimento@edglobo.com.br, http://www.editoraglobo.com.br, http://editoraglobo.globo.com/. Pub. Jose Francisco Queiroz.

630 GBR ISSN 0954-9714
GLOUCESTERSHIRE AND NORTH AVON FARMER. Text in English. 1962. m. adv.
Formerly: Gloucestershire Farmer (0017-131X)
Published by: County Farmers Publications Ltd., 55 Goldington Rd, Bedford, Beds MK40 3LU, United Kingdom. TEL 44-1234-351401, FAX 44-1234-328614. Ed. T Bawley. Circ: 2,600.

630.075 USA
GOOD EARTH ASSOCIATION. NEWSLETTER. Text in English. 1984. biennial. USD 10 to members (effective 1999). adv. bk.rev. **Document type:** *Newsletter.* **Description:** News of the organization, which operates a living farm museum displaying historical farm equipment, farming data, recipes, ecology information, etc.
Published by: Good Earth Association, 202 E. Church St., Pocohontas, AR 72455-2899. TEL 870-892-8329, FAX 870-892-8681, dwater@tcac.net. Ed. D L Waterworttisr. R&P Gladys Nelson TEL 870-647-2009. Adv. contact Donald Waterworth. Circ: 500.

630 IND
GRAMEEN DUNIYA. Text in Hindi. 1973. w. INR 200; INR 3 newsstand/cover. adv. **Document type:** *Newspaper.*
Published by: M.M.G. Publications, 199 C.M.-I., Jhandewalan Extn., New Delhi, 110 055, India. TEL 7779843. Ed. Sanjay Gupta. Pub. M M Gupta. Adv. contact Ajay Gupta.

630 IND
GRAMLOK. Text in Hindi. 1975. fortn. INR 100; INR 5 newsstand/cover. adv. 4 cols./p.
Published by: Gramlok Prakashan, Vishwasnagar Shahdara, 5-32 Patel Gali, New Delhi, 110 032, India. TEL 2208405. Ed. Krishan Kumar. Pub. Raghunath Basak. Adv. contact K R Nair. B&W page INR 13,000, color page INR 26,000; 200 x 325. Circ: 49,415.

630 USA ISSN 0279-9391
GRANGE ADVOCATE. Key Title: Grange Advocate Aggressive for Rural Pennsylvania. Text in English. 1904. m. membership. adv. back issues avail. **Document type:** *Newsletter, Trade.* **Description:** Deals with general news and personnel of farming industry with an emphasis on rural issues.
Former titles: Grange Advocate for Rural Pennsylvania (0164-4955); Pennsylvania Grange News
Related titles: Online - full text ed.
Published by: Pennsylvania State Grange, 1604 N Second St, Harrisburg, PA 17102. TEL 717-234-5001, FAX 717-234-7654, Advocate@pagrange.org. adv.: page USD 500; 10 x 10.5. Circ: 20,000 (controlled).

630 GBR ISSN 0142-5242
CODEN: GFSCDW
➤ **GRASS AND FORAGE SCIENCE.** Text in English. 1946. q. GBP 490 combined subscription in Europe to institutions print & online eds.; USD 904 combined subscription in the Americas to institutions & Caribbean (print & online eds.); GBP 538 combined subscription elsewhere to institutions print & online eds. (effective 2006). adv. bk.rev. bibl.; charts; illus. index. **Document type:** *Journal, Academic/Scholarly.* **Description:** Disseminates the results of research and development in all aspects of grass and forage utilization and reviews the state of knowledge on relevant topics.
Formerly (until vol.34, 1979): British Grassland Society. Journal (0007-0750)
Related titles: Microform ed.: (from PQC); Online - full text ed.: ISSN 1365-2494. 1998. GBP 465 in Europe to institutions; USD 858 in the Americas to institutions & Caribbean; GBP 511 elsewhere to institutions (effective 2006) (from Blackwell Synergy, EBSCO Publishing, Gale Group, IngentaConnect, O C L C Online Computer Library Center, Inc., Swets Information Services).
Indexed: AEA, AEBA, ASCA, AgBio, Agr, AgrForAb, B&AI, BIOBASE, BIOSIS Prev, BibAg, BiolAb, CIN, CPA, ChemAb, ChemTitl, CurCont, DSA, ESPM, FCA, FPA, ForAb, GEOBASE, GenetAb, HerbAb, HortAb, I&DA, IABS, IAOP, ISR, IndVet, M&PBA, MaizeAb, NemAb, NutrAb, OrnHort, PBA, PCI, PGegResA, PGrRegA, PHN&I, PN&I, PlantSci, PoultAb, RPP, RevApplEntom, S&F, SCI, SIA, SeedAb, SoyAb, TriticAb, VetBull, WAE&RSA, WeedAb.
—BLDSC (4213.320000), CASDDS, CISTI, IDS, IE, Infotrieve, ingenta, Linda Hall. **CCC.**
Published by: (European Grassland Federation, British Grassland Society), Blackwell Publishing Ltd., 9600 Garsington Rd, Oxford, OX4 2ZG, United Kingdom. TEL 44-1865-776868, FAX 44-1865-714591, customerservices@oxon.blackwellpublishing.com, http://www.blackwellpublishing.com/journals/GFS. Ed. John A Milne TEL 44-118-9318189. Pub. Elaine Stott. R&P Sophie Savage. Adv. contact Jenny Applin. Circ: 1,530.

630 GBR ISSN 1744-6961
GRASSLAND SCIENCE. Text in English. q. USD 282 combined subscription in the Americas to institutions & Caribbean; GBP 146 combined subscription elsewhere to institutions (effective 2006). **Description:** Presents knowledge, ideas, and philosophies on better management and use of grasslands, forage crops and turf plants for both agricultural and non-agricultural purposes across the world.
Related titles: Online - full text ed.: ISSN 1744-697X. USD 268 in the Americas to institutions; GBP 139 elsewhere to institutions (effective 2006) (from Blackwell Synergy, EBSCO Publishing, O C L C Online Computer Library Center, Inc.).
—**CCC.**
Published by: (Japanese Society of Grassland Science JPN), Blackwell Publishing Ltd., 9600 Garsington Rd, Oxford, OX4 2ZG, United Kingdom. TEL 44-1865-776868, FAX 44-1865-714591, customerservices@oxon.blackwellpublishing.com, http://www.blackwellpublishing.com/journals/GRS.

▼ new title ➤ refereed ✶ unverified ♦ full entry avail.

630 GBR ISSN 1359-3919
HD1921
GREAT BRITAIN. MINISTRY OF AGRICULTURE, FISHERIES AND FOOD. DIGEST OF AGRICULTURAL CENSUS STATISTICS. Text in English. 1972. a. GBP 22 (effective 1998). reprint service avail. from PQC.
Formerly (until 1992): Great Britain. Ministry of Agriculture, Fisheries and Food. Agricultural Statistics. United Kingdom (0065-4590)
—CISTI, Linda Hall. **CCC.**
Published by: Stationery Office, 51 Nine Elms Ln, London, SW8 5DA, United Kingdom. book.orders@theso.co.uk, http://www.national-publishing.co.uk.

630 333.1 GBR
GREAT BRITAIN. NATURAL RESOURCES INSTITUTE. BULLETIN. Text in English. 1987. irreg. **Document type:** *Monographic series.* **Description:** Presents the results of research covering topics relevant to development issues in agriculture, especially sustainable resource management.
Formerly: Great Britain. Overseas Development Natural Resources Institute. Bulletin (0952-8245)
Related titles: CD-ROM ed.; Online - full text ed.
Indexed: FCA, FS&TA, IndVet, MaizeAb, NutrAb, PGegResA, PHN&I, ProtozoAb, RDA, RM&VM, RevApplEntom, SeedAb, ZooRec.
Published by: Natural Resources Institute, Central Ave, Chatham Maritime, Kent, ME4 4TB, United Kingdom. TEL 44-1634-880088, FAX 44-1634-880066, publications@nri.org, http://www.nri.org.

GREECE. NATIONAL STATISTICAL SERVICE. REVISED AGRICULTURAL PRICE INDICES. see *AGRICULTURE—Abstracting, Bibliographies, Statistics*

630 BEL ISSN 0250-5886
HD1920.5.Z8
GREEN EUROPE; newsletter on the common agricultural policy. Text in English. 1979. m. free. **Document type:** *Newsletter.*
Formerly: Newsletter on the Common Agricultural Policy
Related titles: Microfiche ed.: (from CIS); Danish ed.: Gronne Europa. ISSN 1012-2087; French ed.: Europe Verte. ISSN 1012-2125; German ed.: Grunes Europa. ISSN 1012-2095; Greek ed.: Prasine Europe. ISSN 1012-2109; Italian ed.: ISSN 1012-2133; Portuguese ed.: ISSN 1012-215X; Spanish ed.: Europa Verde. ISSN 1012-2079; Dutch ed.: Groen Europa. ISSN 1012-2141.
Indexed: DSA, IIS, PotatoAb, RRTA, WAE&RSA.
—CISTI.
Published by: European Commission, Rue de la Loi - Wetstraat 200, Brussels, 1049, Belgium. **Dist. by:** European Commission, Office for Official Publications of the European Union, 2 Rue Mercier, Luxembourg L-2985, Luxembourg.

630 USA ISSN 0149-5569
GREEN MARKETS. Text in English. 1977. w. USD 915 domestic; USD 940 in Canada; USD 1,220 elsewhere (effective 2005). **Document type:** *Newsletter, Trade.* **Description:** Presents news and insight on fertilizer prices, company plans, plant start-ups and closings, international tenders, joint ventures, mergers and acquisitions, litigation, key personnel changes etc.
Related titles: CD-ROM ed.; Online - full content ed.: USD 957 (effective 2003).
—CISTI. **CCC.**
Published by: Pike & Fischer, Inc. (Subsidiary of: The Bureau of National Affairs, Inc.), 1010 Wayne Ave, Ste 1400, Silver Spring, MD 20910. TEL 301-562-1530, FAX 301-562-1521, http://greenmarkets.pf.com. Ed. Steve Seay.

630 USA ISSN 0895-772X
GREEN MARKETS DEALER REPORT. Text in English. 1987. w. USD 299 (effective 2005). **Document type:** *Newsletter, Trade.* **Description:** Contains industry news, market intelligence and in-depth analysis on the ag-chem and fertilizer industry.
Related titles: Online - full content ed.: USD 345 (effective 2003).
—CCC.
Published by: Pike & Fischer, Inc. (Subsidiary of: The Bureau of National Affairs, Inc.), 1010 Wayne Ave, Ste 1400, Silver Spring, MD 20910. TEL 301-562-1530, 800-255-8131, FAX 301-562-1521, pike@pf.com, http://www.pf.com. Ed. Steve Seay.

630 GBR ISSN 0017-4092
GREENSWARD. Text in English. 1962. a., latest vol.43, 2000. GBP 2, USD 6 to non-members (effective 2001). adv. bk.rev. abstr.; charts. back issues avail. **Document type:** *Proceedings.*
Indexed: DSA, FCA, HerbAb.
Published by: South West Scotland Grassland Society, Auchincruive, Ayr, Scotland KA6 5HW, United Kingdom. TEL 44-1292-525325, FAX 44-1292-525333, L.Reid@ed.sac.ac.uk. Ed., Adv. contact Gordon Tiley. Circ: 800.

638.1 DNK ISSN 1397-9868
GROEN VIDEN, HUSDYRBRUG. Text in Danish. 1976. irreg. (approx.10/yr.). DKK 125; DKK 20 per issue (effective 2002).
Supersedes in part (in 1998): Groen Viden, Landbrug (0903-0727); Which was formerly (until 1987): Statens Planteavlsforsoeg. Meddelelse (0105-6514)
Indexed: AEA, AgBio, AnBrAb, CPA, DSA, FCA, HerbAb, I&DA, IndVet, NutrAb, PN&I, PoultAb, S&F, SIA, SoyAb, TriticAb, VetBull, WAE&RSA.
—CISTI.
Published by: Ministeriet for Foedevarer, Landbrug og Fiskeri, Danmarks Jordbrugsforskning/Ministry of Food, Agriculture and Fisheries. Danish Institute of Agricultural Sciences, PO Box 50, Tjele, 8830, Denmark. TEL 45-8999-1900, FAX 45-8999-1919, http://www.agrsci.dk/djfpublikation/default.htm.

630 DNK ISSN 1397-985X
GROEN VIDEN, MARKBRUG. Text in Danish. 1976. irreg. (approx.15-20/yr). DKK 225; DKK 10 per issue (effective 2002).
Supersedes in part (in 1997): Groen Viden, Landbrug (0903-0727); Which was formerly (until 1987): Statens Planteavlsforsoeg. Meddelelse (0105-6514)
Indexed: AEA, CPA, DSA, FCA, HerbAb, HortAb, I&DA, MaizeAb, NemAb, NutrAb, OrnHort, PBA, PHN&I, PN&I, PotatoAb, RA&MP, RPP, S&F, SIA, SeedAb, TriticAb, WAE&RSA, WeedAb.
—CISTI.
Published by: Ministeriet for Foedevarer, Landbrug og Fiskeri, Danmarks Jordbrugsforskning/Ministry of Food, Agriculture and Fisheries. Danish Institute of Agricultural Sciences, PO Box 50, Tjele, 8830, Denmark. TEL 45-8999-1900, FAX 45-8999-1919, http://www.agrsci.dk/djfpublikation/default.htm.

630 BEL
GROENE KRANT. Text in Dutch. 1973. m. adv. bk.rev. **Document type:** *Newspaper.*
Published by: K.L.J. Kring - Groene (B.J.B.), Waversebaan 99, Postbus 107, Oud-Heverlee, 3050, Belgium. TEL 32-16-479999. Ed. Wim Veulemans. Circ: 3,500.

GROENTEN & FRUIT. ALGEMEEN. see *GARDENING AND HORTICULTURE*

630 DEU ISSN 0946-6592
GROSSVERBRAUCHER INTERN. Text in German. w. **Document type:** *Bulletin, Trade.*
Published by: Zentrale Markt und Preisberichtstelle GmbH, Rochusstr 2, Bonn, 53123, Germany. TEL 49-228-9777173, FAX 49-228-9777179, info@zmp.de, http://www.zmp.de.

338 NZL
GROWER (WELLINGTON). Text in English. 11/yr.
Published by: (New Zealand Vegetable and Potato Growers Federation), Vegetable Producers Publishing Co, P.O. Box 10232, Huddert Parker Bldg, Post Office Sq, Wellington, New Zealand. comgrow@xtra.co.nz, http://www.thegrower.co.nz. Circ: 4,500.

631.091 COL ISSN 0122-8048
SB111.A2
GROWING AFFINITIES; a bulletin about cooperation in agricultural research. Text in English. 1982. 2/yr. free. **Document type:** *Bulletin.* **Description:** Highlights CIAT's current research activities and CIAT's relationship with other related organizations.
Formerly (until 1996): C I A T International (English Edition) (0120-4092)
Indexed: NutrAb, RDA, SeedAb, WAE&RSA.
—CISTI.
Published by: (Unidad de Comunicaciones), Centro Internacional de Agricultura Tropical/International Center for Tropical Agriculture, Publications Unit, Apartado Aereo 6713, Cali, VALLE, Colombia. TEL 415-833-6626, FAX 57-2-4450073, TELEX 05769 CIAT, ciat-comunicaciones@cgiar.org, n.russel@cgnet.com, http://www.ciat.cgiar.org. Ed. Nathan Russell. Circ: 3,000.

GROWING EDGE MAGAZINE; indoor & outdoor gardening for today's grower. see *GARDENING AND HORTICULTURE*

630 664 GTM
GUATEMALA. MINISTERIO DE AGRICULTURA, GANADERIA Y ALIMENTACION. DIRECCION GENERAL DE SERVICIOS AGRICOLAS. MEMORIA DE LABORES. Text in Spanish. a. **Description:** Provides information on projects of the ministry.
Published by: Ministerio de Agricultura, Ganaderia y Alimentacion, Direccion General de Servicios Agricolas, Palacio Nacional, Guatemala City, Guatemala.

GUIA DE AVIACAO AGRICOLA/AGRICULTURAL AVIATION GUIDE. see *AERONAUTICS AND SPACE FLIGHT*

630 CAN
GUIDE DE L'AGRICULTURE DU QUEBEC. Text in English. 1992. a. CND 25.
Published by: Les Productions CT Enr., 1048 rue d' Avaugour, Chicoutimi, PQ G7H 2T1, Canada. TEL 514-856-7821, FAX 514-359-0836. Ed. Martine Breton. adv.: B&W page CND 1,030, color page CND 1,330; trim 10.88 x 8.25. Circ: 5,000.

630 MWI ISSN 0542-3007
S338.M28
GUIDE TO AGRICULTURAL PRODUCTION IN MALAWI. Text in English. 1968. a. **Document type:** *Government.*
Published by: Ministry of Agriculture, Extension Aids Branch, PO Box 594, Lilongwe, Malawi. TEL 265-720933. Circ: 5,000. **Orders to:** Government Printer, PO Box 37, Zomba, Malawi. TEL 265-50-523155.

630 070 GBR ISSN 0072-8969
GUILD OF AGRICULTURAL JOURNALISTS YEAR BOOK✶ . Text in English. 1958. a. GBP 5.
Published by: Lancer Public Relations, 26 Kingsfield Ave, Ipswich, Suffolk IP1 3TA, United Kingdom.

GUNMAKEN NOGYO KISHO SAIGAI SOKUHO/GUNMA PREFECTURE. NEWS OF AGRICULTURAL METEOROLOGY DISASTER. see *METEOROLOGY*

630 551.5 CHN ISSN 1000-6427
GUOWAI NONGXUE - NONGYE QIXIANG/FOREIGN AGRICULTURE - AGRICULTURAL METEOROLOGY. Text in Chinese. q.
Published by: Zhongguo Nongye Kexueyuan/Chinese Academy of Agricultural Sciences, Chinese Society for Horticultural Science, 30 Baishiqiao Lu, Beijing, 100081, China. TEL 8314433. Ed. Zhu Lukuan.

630 JPN ISSN 0570-4561
CODEN: NENGEM
GYOMU NENPO - AOMORI-KEN RINGO SHIKENJO/AOMORI APPLE EXPERIMENT STATION. ANNUAL REPORT. Text in Japanese. 1931. a.
—BLDSC (1107.430000), CISTI.
Published by: Aomori-ken Ringo Shikenjo/Aomori Apple Experiment Station, Kuroishi, Japan. http://hello.net.pref.aomori.jp/ken/ringo-siken/.

630 GBR
H S E AGRICULTURE INFORMATION SHEET. Text in English. N.S. 1996. irreg., latest vol.1, 1996. **Description:** Contains notes on good practices which are not compulsory but which may be helpful.
Formerly (until 1995): H S E Agriculture Sheet
—BLDSC (4335.321530).
Published by: Health and Safety Executive, Rose Ct, 2 Southwark Bridge, London, SE1 9HS, United Kingdom. TEL 44-1541-545500, FAX 44-114-2892333.

HABITATION. see *FOOD AND FOOD INDUSTRIES*

630 GBR ISSN 0017-7121
HAMPSHIRE FARMER. Text in English. m. adv.
Published by: County Farmers Publications Ltd., 55 Goldington Rd, Bedford, Beds MK40 3LU, United Kingdom. TEL 44-1234-351401, FAX 44-1234-328614. Ed. N Errington. Circ: 2,300.

630.658 351 NLD
HANDBOEK AGRARISCH ONDERNEMEN. Text in Dutch. 1994. s-a. looseleaf. adv. illus.; stat. index. back issues avail. **Document type:** *Journal, Trade.* **Description:** Provides a reference guide on agricultural topics and informs Dutch farmers of regulations.
Published by: Reed Business Information bv (Subsidiary of: Reed Business), Hanzestraat 1, Doetinchem, 7006 RH, Netherlands. TEL 31-314-349911, FAX 31-314-343839, info@reedbusiness.nl, http://www.reedbusiness.nl. Ed. R Smeele. Pub. J Bobbink. Circ: 1,000 (paid).

630 NLD
HANDBOEK VAN ZIEKTEN, PLAGEN EN ONKRUIDEN. Text in Dutch. 1980. m. looseleaf. illus. **Document type:** *Trade.* **Description:** Covers all aspects of crop protection, control of diseases, pests and weeds (excluding cultivation under glass), as well as approved materials, legislation and safety matters.
Former titles: Beheersen van Ziekten, Plagen en Onkruiden; Akkerbouwpraktijk
Published by: Reed Business Information bv (Subsidiary of: Reed Business), Hanzestraat 1, Doetinchem, 7006 RH, Netherlands. TEL 31-314-349911, FAX 31-314-343839, info@reedbusiness.nl, http://www.reedbusiness.nl. Ed. S Wit.

630 ISL ISSN 0251-1940
HANDBOK BAENDA. Text in Icelandic. 1951. a. ISK 2,250, USD 30 (effective 2000). back issues avail.; reprints avail. **Document type:** *Trade.* **Description:** Contains advice and other material of interest to the farming industry in Iceland.
Published by: Farmers Union of Iceland, PO Box 7080, Reykjavik, 127, Iceland. TEL 354-563-0300, FAX 354-562-3058, bbl@bondi.is, http://www.bondi.is. Ed. Matthias Eggertsson. Circ: 2,200.

HARD- EN ZACHTFRUIT. see *GARDENING AND HORTICULTURE*

630 CAN ISSN 1190-8416
S522.C2 CODEN: HARSEI
HARROWSMITH COUNTRY LIFE. Text in English. 1976. 6/yr. CND 21.38 domestic; CND 25 foreign; CND 3.75 newsstand/cover (effective 1999). adv. bk.rev. bibl.; charts; illus.; stat.; tr.lit. index. back issues avail.; reprint service avail. from PQC.
Formerly (until 1994): Harrowsmith (0381-6885)

Related titles: Microfiche ed.: (from MML, PQC); Microform ed.: (from MML); Online - full text ed.: (from EBSCO Publishing).
Indexed: ASIP, CBCARef, CBPI, CPerl, IHTDI.
—CISTI. **CCC.**
Published by: Malcolm Publishing Inc., 11 450 Albert Hudon Blvd, Montreal, PQ H1G 3J9, Canada. TEL 514-327-4464, FAX 514-327-7592, hclmag@globetrotter.net. Ed. Tom Cruickshank. Pub., R&P Michael Paradis. Adv. contact Yolanda Thornton. B&W page CND 6,300, color page CND 7,900; trim 10.75 x 7.88. Circ: 180,000 (paid).

630 663 USA
HARVEST (LAKEVILLE-MIDDLEBORO). Text in English. 1980. bi-m. **Document type:** *Newsletter.* **Description:** For growers in the Ocean Spray cooperative. Provides information on business, entomology, horticulture, environment and equipment.
Published by: Ocean Spray, One Ocean Spray Dr, Lakeville, MA 02349. TEL 508-946-7246, FAX 508-947-9791. Ed., R&P Judith Duffy. Circ: 2,000.

630 USA ISSN 1089-4640
HARVEST STATES AGRIVISIONS✶. Text in English. 1927. bi-m. USD 4 to members (effective 1998). adv. bk.rev. charts; illus.; stat. **Document type:** *Journal, Trade.*
Former titles (until Nov. 1992): Harvest States Journal; Co-Op Country News; Farmers Union Herald (0014-8458)
Published by: Harvest States Cooperatives, 5500 Cenex Dr, Inver Grove Heights, MN 55077-1733. FAX 612-641-3731, http://www.harveststates.com. Ed., R&P Alison Cummings. Circ: 15,000.

630 IND ISSN 0017-8225
HARVESTER; agricultural engineering journal. Text in English. 1968. q. INR 40. adv. bk.rev. bibl.; charts; stat. **Description:** Published with the interest of informing and edifying the prairie family.
Published by: (Agricultural Engineering Society), Indian Society of Engineers, 5 Lindsay St., Kolkata, West Bengal 700 016, India. Ed. M K Diwan. Circ: 3,100.

630 300 636.089 IND ISSN 0379-4008
HARYANA AGRICULTURAL UNIVERSITY. JOURNAL OF RESEARCH. Text in English. 1971. q. INR 200, USD 60. adv. abstr.; bibl.; charts. **Document type:** *Academic/Scholarly.* **Description:** Contains original research articles and notes on agriculture, animal and veterinary sciences, basic sciences, social sciences and home science.
Indexed: AEA, AgrForAb, AnBrAb, BioCN&I, BiolAb, CIN, CPA, CTFA, ChemAb, ChemTitl, DSA, FCA, FPA, FS&TA, ForAb, HerbAb, HortAb, I&DA, IndVet, MaizeAb, NemAb, NutrAb, OrnHort, PBA, PGegResA, PGrRegA, PHN&I, PN&I, PotatoAb, PoultAb, RA&MP, RDA, RPP, RevApplEntom, RiceAb, S&F, S&MA, SIA, SeedAb, SoyAb, TDB, TriticAb, VetBull, WAE&RSA, WeedAb, ZooRec.
Published by: Haryana Agricultural University, Hisar, Haryana 125 004, India. Circ: 500.

630 ISR ISSN 0017-8314
S19
HASSADEH✶ /FIELD; a monthly review of settlement and agriculture. Text in English, Hebrew. 1920. m. USD 150. adv. bk.rev. abstr.; bibl.; charts; illus.; stat. index. **Document type:** *Academic/Scholarly.*
Indexed: AEA, AnBrAb, BioCN&I, BiolAb, CPA, CTFA, ChemAb, DSA, FCA, HerbAb, HortAb, IHP, IndVet, MaizeAb, NutrAb, OrnHort, PGrRegA, PHN&I, PoultAb, RPP, RevApplEntom, SoyAb, WeedAb.
—CISTI.
Published by: G.K. Hassadeh Monthly Review Ltd., c/o Israel Association of Periodical Press (IAAP), 93 Arlozarez St, Tel Aviv, 62098, Israel. TEL 972-3-6929978, FAX 972-3-6929979. Ed. J M Margalit. Adv. contact Guy Klug. Circ: 8,000 (controlled).

630 FRA
HAUTE LOIRE PAYSANNE. Text in French. w.
Address: Hotel Interconsulaire, Bd. Bertrand, B.P. 63, Le Puy, Cedex 43002, France. TEL 71-02-60-44. Ed. G Assezat. Circ: 5,000.

630 FRA
HAUTE SAONE AGRICOLE BELFORT AGRICULTURE. Text in French. w.
Published by: Agricole Belfort Agriculture, 22 place du Champ de Foire, BP 251, Vesoul, Cedex 70005, France. TEL 84-76-07-36, FAX 84-76-76-36. Ed. Laurent Le Gall. Circ: 6,600.

HEALTHY HARVEST. see *PUBLIC HEALTH AND SAFETY*

630 CHN ISSN 1000-1573
QE1 CODEN: JCUGEX
HEBEI NONGYE DAXUE XUEBAO/HEBEI UNIVERSITY OF AGRICULTURE. JOURNAL. Text in Chinese; Abstracts in English. 1959. q. CNY 16, USD 40 (effective 1997 & 1998). **Document type:** *Academic/Scholarly.* **Description:** Covers crop cultivation, fruit, vegetables, and plant protection, pesticide, husbandry and veterinary, food processing and sanitation.
Related titles: Online - full text ed.: (from East View Information Services).
Indexed: AgBio, AgrForAb, AnBrAb, BioCN&I, CPA, FCA, ForAb, HortAb, IndVet, MaizeAb, NemAb, NutrAb, OrnHort, PBA, PGegResA, PGrRegA, PHN&I, PN&I, PotatoAb, PoultAb, RA&MP, RPP, RefZh, RevApplEntom, RiceAb, S&F, SIA, SeedAb, TriticAb, VetBull, WeedAb, ZooRec.
—BLDSC (4682.050000), CASDDS.
Published by: Hebei Nongye Daxue/Hebei University of Agriculture, Nanguan, Baoding, Hebei 071001, China. TEL 86-312-2091322, FAX 86-312-2025635. Ed. Yiyuan He. Circ: 2,500. **Dist. overseas by:** China International Book Trading Corp, 35 Chegongzhuang Xilu, Haidian District, PO Box 399, Beijing 100044, China.

HEBREW UNIVERSITY OF JERUSALEM. AUTHORITY FOR RESEARCH AND DEVELOPMENT. CURRENT RESEARCH. see *MEDICAL SCIENCES*

630 CHN ISSN 1000-2340
HENAN NONGYE DAXUE XUEBAO/HENAN AGRICULTURAL UNIVERSITY. JOURNAL. Text in Chinese. 1960. q. CNY 20 (effective 2003). 100 p./no.; **Document type:** *Journal, Academic/Scholarly.*
Formerly (until Dec.1984): Henan Nongxueyuan Xuebao
Related titles: Online - full text ed.: (from East View Information Services).
Indexed: AEA, AgBio, AgrForAb, AnBrAb, BioCN&I, CPA, FCA, ForAb, HortAb, I&DA, IndVet, MaizeAb, NutrAb, OrnHort, PBA, PGegResA, PGrRegA, PHN&I, PN&I, PoultAb, ProtozoAb, RA&MP, RDA, RPP, RefZh, RiceAb, S&F, SeedAb, TriticAb, VetBull, WAE&RSA, WeedAb.
Published by: Henan Nongye Daxue/Henan Agricultural University, Wehua Lu, Zhengzhou, 450002, China. hnauxb@henau.edu.cn, http://nnxb.chinajournal.net.cn. Ed. Bailiang Zhang. **Dist. by:** China Publication Foreign Trade Company, PO Box 782, Beijing 100011, China. TEL 86-10-3832058.

630 531.64 CHN ISSN 1000-8551
S589.5 CODEN: HEXUEE
HENONG XUEBAO/ACTA AGRICULTURAE NUCLEATAE SINICA. Text in Chinese, English; Abstracts in English. 1987. q. CNY 10. **Document type:** *Academic/Scholarly.* **Description:** Publishes researches on the use of nuclear technology in various branches of agriculture, biology and animal sciences.
Related titles: Online - full text ed.: (from East View Information Services).
Indexed: CIN, ChemAb, ChemTitl, FCA, HortAb, INIS AtomInd, IndVet, MaizeAb, NutrAb, PGrRegA, RiceAb, S&F, SIA, SeedAb, TriticAb.
—BLDSC (0588.940000), CASDDS, Linda Hall.
Published by: Zhongguo Nongye Kexueyuan, Yuanzineng Liyong Yanjiusuo/Chinese Academy of Agricultural Sciences, Institute of Nuclear Energy Utilization, PO Box 5109, Beijing, 100094, China. TEL 2581177. Ed. Xu Guanren.

630 GBR ISSN 0018-0688
HEREFORDSHIRE FARMER. Text in English. 1948. m. adv.
Published by: County Farmers Publications Ltd., 55 Goldington Rd, Bedford, Beds MK40 3LU, United Kingdom. TEL 44-1234-351401, FAX 44-1234-328614. Ed. P Hudson. Circ: 1,900.

630 GBR
HERTFORDSHIRE FARMER. Text in English. 1948. m. adv. back issues avail.
Published by: Eastern Counties N.F.U. Journals Ltd., 55 Goldington Rd, Bedford, MK40 3LU, United Kingdom. Ed. D Green. Circ: 2,100.

630 USA ISSN 0018-1471
HIGH PLAINS JOURNAL. (In 5 regional eds.: Western Kansas; Eastern Kansas & Missouri; Nebraska, Iowa & South Dakota; Colorado & Wyoming; Oklahoma, Texas, New Mexico) Text in English. 1883. w. USD 59; USD 2 newsstand/cover (effective 2005). adv. bk.rev. illus.; mkt. 120 p./no. 5 cols./p.; back issues avail.; reprints avail. **Document type:** *Magazine, Consumer.* **Description:** Covers agricultural matters throughout the entire Plains region.
Related titles: Online - full text ed.
Published by: High Plains Publishers, Inc., 1500 E Wyatt Earp Blvd, Box 760, Dodge City, KS 67801-0760. TEL 620-227-7171, 800-452-7171, FAX 620-227-7173, journal@hpj.com, http://www.hpj.com. Ed. Holly Martin. Pub. Duane Ross. Adv. contact Tom Taylor. B&W page USD 10,474.80, color page USD 12,124.40; trim 10 x 14. Circ: 53,300 (paid).

630 634.9 PHL
HIGHLIGHTS. Text in English. 1982. a. free. **Description:** Summary of the proceedings of the annual regional R&D symposium.
Formerly (until 1989): Highlights from the Philippine Agriculture, Environment, and Natural Resources Research and Development Network (0116-9440)
—BLDSC (4307.499200).
Published by: Philippine Council for Agriculture Forestry & Natural Resources Research & Development, Department of Science & Technology, Los Banos, Laguna 4030, Philippines. TEL 63-49-536-0014, FAX 63-49-536-0016, pcarrd@pcarrd.dost.gov.ph, http://www.pcarrd.dost.gov.ph. Ed. Erlinda Belen.

630 USA ISSN 0018-1668
CODEN: HARAAS
➤ **HIGHLIGHTS OF AGRICULTURAL RESEARCH.** Text in English. 1954. q. free (effective 2004). charts; illus.; stat. **Document type:** *Journal, Academic/Scholarly.*
Indexed: AEA, AgBio, Agr, BioCN&I, ChemAb, DSA, EnvAb, FCA, FS&TA, HortAb, IndVet, MaizeAb, NutrAb, OrnHort, PBA, PHN&I, PoultAb, RM&VM, RPP, RevApplEntom, S&F, WAE&RSA, WeedAb.
—BLDSC (4307.530000), CASDDS, CIS, CISTI, IE.
Published by: Alabama Agricultural Experiment Station, 107 Comer Hall, Auburn, AL 36849. TEL 334-844-2345, FAX 334-844-5892. Circ: 10,500.

630 AUS
HILLS FARMER. Text in English. m. adv. **Document type:** *Newspaper, Trade.* **Description:** Specialist publication for the small farmers in the Adelaide region who produce a hugely diverse range of high value commodities.
Published by: Rural Press Ltd. (Subsidiary of: Agricultural Publishers Pty. Ltd.), 159 Bells Line of Rd., PO Box 999, North Richmond, NSW 2754, Australia. TEL 61-2-45704444, FAX 61-2-45704630, http://www.ruralpress.com/. Circ: 7,000 (controlled).

630 IND ISSN 0018-1889
HIMACHAL AGRICULTURAL NEWSLETTER. Text in English. 1969. q. charts; illus. **Document type:** *Newsletter.*
Published by: Department of Agriculture, c/o G.S. Agarval, Agricultural Information Officer, Simla, Himachal Pradesh, India. Ed. Rattan S Himesh.

630 IND ISSN 0970-0595
CODEN: HJARAN
➤ **HIMACHAL JOURNAL OF AGRICULTURAL RESEARCH.** Text and summaries in English. 1971. s-a. INR 200, INR 400 to institutional members (effective 2003). adv. bk.rev. **Document type:** *Journal, Academic/Scholarly.* **Description:** Publishes research on agricultural, veterinary, animal and home sciences.
Indexed: AEA, AgrForAb, AnBrAb, BioCN&I, BiolAb, CPA, DSA, FCA, FPA, ForAb, HerbAb, HortAb, I&DA, ISA, IndVet, MaizeAb, NutrAb, OrnHort, PBA, PGegResA, PGrRegA, PHN&I, PotatoAb, PoultAb, RA&MP, RDA, RPP, RRTA, RevApplEntom, RiceAb, S&F, SIA, SeedAb, SoyAb, TDB, TriticAb, VetBull, WAE&RSA, WeedAb.
Published by: H.P. Agriculture University, Himachal Pradesh Krishi Vishvavidyalaya, c/o Hirday Paul Singh, Directorate of Research, Palanpur, Himachal Pradesh 176 062, India. TEL 91-189-30406, FAX 91-1894-30511, dr@hpkv.hp.nic.in. Ed. Hirday Paul Singh. Circ: 300 (paid).

630 JPN ISSN 0073-229X
CODEN: HIROAO
HIROSAKI UNIVERSITY. FACULTY OF AGRICULTURE. BULLETIN/HIROSAKI DAIGAKU NOGAKUBU GAKUJUTSU HOKOKU. Text in English, Japanese; Summaries in English. 1955. s-a. **Document type:** *Bulletin, Academic/Scholarly.*
Indexed: AnBrAb, BioDAb, BiolAb, CIN, ChemAb, ChemTitl, DSA, ExcerpMed, FCA, FS&TA, HerbAb, HortAb, I&DA, MaizeAb, NutrAb, PBA, PGrRegA, RPP, RiceAb, S&F, TriticAb, WAE&RSA.
—CASDDS, CISTI.
Published by: Hirosaki Daigaku, Nogakubu/Hirosaki University, Faculty of Agriculture, 3 Bunkyo-cho, Hirosaki, Aomori-ken, 036, Japan. Ed. Eiji Bekki. Circ: 470.

630 900 ESP ISSN 1139-1472
HD2021 CODEN: NHAGEC
➤ **HISTORIA AGRARIA**; revista cuatrimestral del seminario de historia agraria. Text in Spanish; Abstracts in English, Spanish. 1991. s-a. USD 45 foreign to individuals; USD 70 foreign to institutions; USD 25 newsstand/cover foreign (effective 2001). adv. bk.rev. bibl. index, cum.index: 1991-1992. **Document type:** *Academic/Scholarly.* **Description:** Specializes in the history of agriculture, economy and rural society of Spain and Latin America.
Formerly (until 1998): Noticiario de Historia Agraria (1132-1261)
Indexed: AbHyg, AmH&L, AnBrAb, DIP, FCA, ForAb, GEOBASE, HistAb, I&DA, IBR, IBSS, IBZ, PHN&I, S&F, SOPODA, SSA, TriticAb, WAE&RSA.
—CINDOC.
Published by: (Universidad de Murcia, Facultad de Economia y Empresa), Universidad de Murcia, Servicio de Publicaciones, Edificio Saavedra Fajardo, C/ Actor Isidoro Maiquez 9, Murcia, 30007, Spain. TEL 34-968-363887, FAX 34-968-363414, jcarrion@fcu.um.es, servpubl@um.es, http://www.um.es/spumweb. Ed. Jose Miguel Martinez Carrion. Adv. contact Maria Paz Chivite Jimenez. Circ: 800.

630.09 IND ISSN 0378-7524
HISTORY OF AGRICULTURE. Text in English. 1973. q. USD 67 (effective 2000). adv. bk.rev. index.
Indexed: AmH&L, HistAb.
—BLDSC (4317.770000).
Published by: (International Association for the History of Agriculture), K.K. Roy (Private) Ltd., 55 Gariahat Rd., P O Box 10210, Kolkata, West Bengal 700 019, India. R&P M Misra TEL 91-33-475-4872. Circ: 1,980.

638.1 CAN
HIVE LIGHTS. Text in English. 1986. q. CND 20; USD 20 foreign. adv. bk.rev. back issues avail. **Document type:** *Trade.*
Published by: Canadian Honey Council, R R 2 S 26 C 32, Chase, BC V0E 1M0, Canada. TEL 250-679-5362, FAX 250-679-5394. Ed., Pub., Adv. contact Fran Kay. Circ: 750.

HOBBY FARMS. see *BUSINESS AND ECONOMICS*

630 DEU ISSN 1434-7717
HOF DIREKT. Text in German. 1997. bi-m. EUR 45.60 domestic; EUR 47.40 foreign; EUR 7 newsstand/cover (effective 2005). adv. **Document type:** *Magazine, Trade.*
Published by: Landwirtschaftsverlag GmbH, Huelsebrockstr 2, Muenster, 48165, Germany. TEL 49-2501-801-0, FAX 49-2501-801204, hofdirektredaktion@wochenblatt.com, zentrale@lv-h.de, http://www.hofdirekt.com, http://www.lv-h.de.

630 DEU ISSN 0340-9783
CODEN: HOARDR
HOHENHEIMER ARBEITEN. Text in German. 1961. irreg. (not numbered after vol.132), latest 1996. bk.rev. **Document type:** *Monographic series, Academic/Scholarly.*
Indexed: AnBrAb, ChemAb, S&F.
—CASDDS.
Published by: (Universitaet Hohenheim), Verlag Eugen Ulmer GmbH, Wollgrasweg 41, Stuttgart, 70599, Germany. TEL 49-711-4507-0, FAX 49-711-4507-120, info@ulmer.de.

630 JPN ISSN 1345-661X
HOKKAIDO DAIGAKU DAIGAKUIN NOGAKU KENKYUKA HOBUN KIYO/HOKKAIDO UNIVERSITY. GRADUATE SCHOOL OF AGRICULTURE. MEMOIRS. Text in Japanese. 1951. s-a. **Document type:** *Journal, Academic/Scholarly.*
Formerly (until 2000): Hokkaido Daigaku Nogakubu Hobun Kiyo/Hokkaido University. Faculty of Agriculture. Memoirs (0367-5726)
Indexed: RefZh.
—BLDSC (5616.905500), CISTI, Linda Hall.
Published by: Hokkaido Daigaku, Nogakubu/Hokkaido University, Faculty of Agriculture, Kita 9, Nishi 9, Kita-ku, Sapporo, 060-8589, Japan. TEL 81-11-7062417, FAX 81-11-7160879, kouryu@general.hokudai.ac.jp, http://www.hokudai.ac.jp/agricu..

HOKKAIDO KYOIKU DAIGAKU KIYO. DAI-2-BU, B. SEIBUTSUGAKU, CHIGAKU, NOGAKU-HEN/HOKKAIDO UNIVERSITY OF EDUCATION. JOURNAL. SECTION 2 B. BIOLOGY, GEOLOGY, AND AGRICULTURE. see *BIOLOGY*

HOKKAIDO NO NOGYO KISHO/HOKKAIDO JOURNAL OF AGRICULTURAL METEOROLOGY. see *METEOROLOGY*

630 JPN ISSN 0367-5955
CODEN: HKNSBV
HOKKAIDO NOGYO SHIKENJO KENKYU HOKOKU/NATIONAL AGRICULTURAL RESEARCH CENTER FOR HOKKAIDO REGION. RESEARCH BULLETIN. Text in Japanese; Summaries in English. 1905. irreg. exchange basis. **Document type:** *Bulletin, Government.*
Formerly (until 1972): Hokkaido Nogyo Shikenjo Iho (0018-3415)
Related titles: Microform ed.; Online - full content ed.
Indexed: AEA, AgBio, AnBrAb, BioCN&I, BiolAb, CPA, ChemAb, DSA, FCA, FS&TA, HerbAb, HortAb, I&DA, MaizeAb, NemAb, NutrAb, PBA, PGegResA, PGrRegA, PHN&I, PotatoAb, RPP, RefZh, RevApplEntom, RiceAb, S&F, SIA, SeedAb, SoyAb, TriticAb, WAE&RSA, WeedAb.
—BLDSC (7724.000000), CISTI, IE.
Published by: National Agricultural Research Center for Hokkaido Region, 1, Hitsujigaoka, Toyohira-ku, Sapporo-shi, Hokkaido 062-8555, Japan. TEL 81-11-851-9141, FAX 81-11-859-2178, http://ss.cryo.affrc.go.jp/kikaku/info/houkoku.htm. Ed. Shigeo Komuro. Circ: 1,000. **Dist. in US by:** New York Agricultural Experiment Station, 630 W North St, Geneva, NY 14456.

630 JPN ISSN 0386-2224
HOKKAIDO NOGYO SHIKENJO KENKYU SHIRYO/NATIONAL AGRICULTURAL RESEARCH CENTER FOR HOKKAIDO REGION. MISCELLANEOUS PUBLICATION. Text in Japanese. 1973. irreg. **Document type:** *Academic/Scholarly.*
Published by: National Agricultural Research Center for Hokkaido Region, 1, Hitsujigaoka, Toyohira-ku, Sapporo-shi, Hokkaido 062-8555, Japan. TEL 81-11-851-9141, FAX 81-11-859-2178, http://ss.cryo.affrc.go.jp/kikaku/info/shiryo.htm.

630 JPN ISSN 0441-0750
HOKKAIDO NOGYO SHIKENJO NENPO/NATIONAL AGRICULTURAL RESEARCH CENTER FOR HOKKAIDO REGION. ANNUAL REPORTS. Text in Japanese. 1973. a. **Document type:** *Academic/Scholarly.*
Published by: National Agricultural Research Center for Hokkaido Region, 1, Hitsujigaoka, Toyohira-ku, Sapporo-shi, Hokkaido 062-8555, Japan. TEL 81-11-851-9141, FAX 81-11-859-2178, http://ss.cryo.affrc.go.jp/.

630 JPN ISSN 1345-6601
CODEN: JFAGAI
HOKKAIDO UNIVERSITY. GRADUATE SCHOOL OF AGRICULTURE. JOURNAL/HOKKAIDO DAIGAKU DAIGAKUIN NOGAKU KENKYUKA KIYO. Text in English. 1902. irreg. per issue exchange basis. charts; illus. **Document type:** *Academic/Scholarly.*
Former titles (until 1999): Hokkaido University. Faculty of Agriculture. Journal (0018-344X); (until 1945): Hokkaido Imperial University. Faculty of Agriculture. Journal (0368-2072); (until 1928): Hokkaido Imperial University. College of Agriculture. Journal (0368-1718); (until 1917): Tohoku Imperial University. College of Agriculture. Journal (0368-1726)
Indexed: ABIPC, AEA, AgrForAb, AnBrAb, BIOSIS Prev, BiolAb, CPA, ChemAb, FCA, ForAb, HerbAb, HortAb, I&DA, IndVet, MaizeAb, OrnHort, PBA, PGegResA, PGrRegA, PHN&I, PotatoAb, RDA, RPP, RefZh, RevApplEntom, RiceAb, S&F, SFA, SeedAb, WAE&RSA, WildRev, ZooRec.
—BLDSC (4757.603000), CASDDS, CISTI, IE, Linda Hall.
Published by: (Hokkaido Daigaku, Daigakuin, Nogaku Kenkyuka/Hokkaido University, Graduate School of Agriculture), Hokkaido University, Faculty of Agriculture/Hokkaido Dagaiku Nogakubu, Nishi-9-chome, Kita 9-jo, Kita-ku, Sapporo, 060-8589, Japan.

630 USA ISSN 0018-4748
HOOSIER FARMER. Text in English. 1919. q. USD 2 to members (effective 2005). adv. **Document type:** *Magazine, Trade.*
Description: Covers general Indiana farm news as well as news about organized farm activities. Stories focus on Farm Bureau members, informing them of policies and programs adopted to improve the economic and social welfare of member families.
Published by: Indiana Farm Bureau, Inc., PO Box 1290, Indianapolis, IN 46206-1290. TEL 317-692-7824, FAX 317-692-7854, askus@infarmbureau.org, infinfo@farmbureau.com, http://www.infarmbureau.org, http://www.farmbureau.com. Ed. Lew Middleton. adv.: B&W page USD 3,371. Circ: 280,000 (paid and controlled).

630 FRA ISSN 1147-7598
HORIZONS CENTRE ILE-DE-FRANCE (EDITION EURE ET LOIR). Text in French. 1946. w. adv. bk.rev. **Document type:** *Newspaper.*
Formerly: Agriculture d'Eure et Loir
Published by: Horizons Centre Ile-de-France (Edition), 6 rue Francis Vovelle, BP 195, Chartres, Cedex 28004, France. TEL 37-28-40-93, FAX 37-34-58-39. Ed. Joannes Cote. Circ: 16,000.

630 FRA ISSN 1147-758X
HORIZONS CENTRE ILE-DE-FRANCE (EDITION LOIR-ET-CHER). Text in French. 1968. w.
Formerly (until 1990): Information Agricole de Loir et Cher (0337-1719)
Address: 15 av. de Vendome, Blois, Cedex 41000, France. TEL 54-78-51-20, FAX 54-78-31-03. Ed. Marie Odile Beaudoux. Circ: 5,000.

630 FRA ISSN 1147-7563
HORIZONS CENTRE ILE-DE-FRANCE (EDITION SEINE-ET-MARNE). Text in French. w.
Formerly (until 1990): Sillon de Seine et Marne (0751-6355)
Published by: Horizons Centre Ile-de-France (Edition), 418 av. Aristide Briand, Le Mee-sur-Seine, 77350, France. TEL 64-39-95-94, FAX 64-39-62-52. Circ: 5,100.

630 635 JPN ISSN 0911-6494
HOUJYOU. Text in Japanese. 1963. a. donation. **Document type:** *Bulletin.*
Published by: Kagawa Prefecture Agricultural Experiment Station/Kagawa-ken Nogyo Shikenjo, Busshozan-cho, Takamatsu-shi, Kagawa-ken, Japan. TEL 81-878-89-1121, FAX 81-878-89-1125. Ed. Kazunori Obika. Circ: 200.

630 CHN ISSN 1000-7091
S19
HUABEI NONGXUE BAO/NORTH CHINA AGRICULTURE JOURNAL. Text in Chinese. 1986. q. USD 30. adv. **Document type:** *Academic/Scholarly.*
Related titles: Online - full text ed.: (from East View Information Services).
Indexed: AEA, AgBio, AgrForAb, AnBrAb, BioCN&I, CPA, FCA, FPA, ForAb, HelmAb, HerbAb, HortAb, I&DA, IndVet, MaizeAb, NemAb, NutrAb, OrnHort, PBA, PGegResA, PGrRegA, PHN&I, PN&I, PotatoAb, PoultAb, RA&MP, RPP, RiceAb, S&F, SIA, SeedAb, SoyAb, TriticAb, VetBull, WeedAb.
Published by: Hebei Academy of Agricultural and Forestry Sciences, 24 Jichang Lu, Shijiazhuang, Hebei 050051, China. TEL 86-316-7042853. Ed. Li Guangmin. Pub. Sun Limin. R&P, Adv. contact Limin Sun. Circ: 5,000.

HUAFEI DAOBAO. see *ENGINEERING—Chemical Engineering*

HUAFEI SHICHANG ZHOUBAO. see *ENGINEERING—Chemical Engineering*

630 CHN ISSN 1001-411X
HUANAN NONGYE DAXUE XUEBAO/SOUTH CHINA AGRICULTURAL UNIVERSITY. JOURNAL. Text in Chinese. 1984. q. CNY 5 newsstand/cover (effective 2004). **Document type:** *Journal, Academic/Scholarly.*
Related titles: Online - full content ed.: (from WanFang Data Corp.); Online - full text ed.: (from East View Information Services).
Indexed: AgBio, AgrForAb, AnBrAb, B&BAb, BioCN&I, CPA, DSA, ESPM, EntAb, FCA, FPA, ForAb, HelmAb, HerbAb, HortAb, I&DA, IndVet, MaizeAb, NemAb, OrnHort, PBA, PGegResA, PGrRegA, PHN&I, PN&I, PotatoAb, PoultAb, ProtozoAb, RA&MP, RRTA, RefZh, S&F, SIA, SeedAb, SoyAb, TDB, TriticAb, WAE&RSA, WeedAb.
Published by: Huanan Nongye Daxue/South China Agricultural University, Wushan Road, Tianhe District, Guangzhou, 510642, China. TEL 86-20-85280069, FAX 86-20-85281885, journal@scau.edu.cn, zyx@scau.edu.cn, http://hnnydxxb.periodicals.net.cn/default.html, http://www.scau.edu.cn/.

630 CHN ISSN 1000-2421
HUAZHONG NONGYE DAXUE XUEBAO/HUAZHONG AGRICULTURAL UNIVERSITY. JOURNAL. Text in Chinese. 1956. bi-m. **Document type:** *Journal, Academic/Scholarly.*
Related titles: Online - full text ed.: (from East View Information Services, WanFang Data Corp.).
Indexed: AgBio, AgrForAb, AnBrAb, BioCN&I, CPA, DSA, FCA, FPA, ForAb, HelmAb, HerbAb, HortAb, I&DA, IndVet, MaizeAb, NemAb, OrnHort, PBA, PGegResA, PGrRegA, PHN&I, PN&I, PotatoAb, PoultAb, ProtozoAb, RA&MP, RPP, S&F, SIA, SeedAb, SoyAb, TriticAb, WAE&RSA, WeedAb.
—BLDSC (4758.966600), IE.
Published by: Huazhong Nongye Daxue, Editorial Department of Journal of Huazhong Agricultural University, Wuhan, Hubei 430070, China. hnlkxb@mail.hzau.de, http://hznydx.wanfangdata.com.cn/default.html. **Dist. by:** China International Book Trading Corp, 35 Chegongzhuang Xilu, Haidian District, PO Box 399, Beijing 100044, China. TEL 86-10-68412045, FAX 86-10-68412023, cibtc@mail.cibtc.com.cn, http://www.cibtc.com.cn.

630 CHN ISSN 1007-1032
HUNAN NONGYE DAXUE XUEBAO/HUNAN AGRICULTURAL UNIVERSITY. JOURNAL (NATURAL SCIENCES). Text in Chinese. 1956. bi-m.
Formerly (until 1994): Hunan Nongxueyuan Xuebao/Hunan Agricutural College. Journal (1000-5021)
Related titles: Online - full content ed.: (from WanFang Data Corp.); Online - full text ed.: (from East View Information Services).
Indexed: AgBio, AgrForAb, AnBrAb, BioCN&I, CPA, DSA, FCA, ForAb, HelmAb, HerbAb, HortAb, I&DA, IndVet, MaizeAb, OrnHort, PBA, PGegResA, PGrRegA, PHN&I, PN&I, PotatoAb, PoultAb, RA&MP, RM&VM, RPP, RefZh, S&F, SIA, SeedAb, SoyAb, TDB, TriticAb, WAE&RSA, WeedAb.
—BLDSC (4759.156150), IE.
Published by: Hunan Nongye Daxue/Hunan Agricultural University, Furong-qu, Changsha, 410128, China. TEL 86-731-4618035, FAX 86-731-4618098, hnauxb@public.cs.hn.cn, http://hunannydx.wanfangdata.com.cn/default.html.

630 HUN ISSN 0864-7410
HUNGARIAN AGRICULTURAL ENGINEERING. Text in English. 1988. a. free. charts; stat. **Document type:** *Proceedings.*
Indexed: FS&TA.
—CISTI.
Published by: (Magyar Tudomanyos Akademia/Hungarian Academy of Sciences), Hungarian Institute of Agricultural Engineering, Tessedik S utca 4, Godollo, 2101, Hungary. fmmi@elender.hu. Ed. Laszlo Toth. Pub. Dr. L Fenyvesi.

HUNGARY. KOZPONTI STATISZTIKAI HIVATAL. MEZOGAZDASAGI ELELMISZERIPARI STATISZTIKAI EVKONYV/HUNGARY. CENTRAL STATISTICAL OFFICE. YEARBOOK OF AGRICULTURAL STATISTICS. see *AGRICULTURE—Abstracting, Bibliographies, Statistics*

HUNGARY. KOZPONTI STATISZTIKAI HIVATAL. MEZOGAZDASAGI ELELMISZERIPARI STATISZTIKAI ZSEBKONYV. see *AGRICULTURE—Abstracting, Bibliographies, Statistics*

HUNGER NEWS & HOPE. see *SOCIAL SERVICES AND WELFARE*

632.7 GBR
I B R A CONFERENCE ON TROPICAL BEES. Text in English. irreg., latest 2000. price varies. back issues avail. **Document type:** *Proceedings, Academic/Scholarly.*
Formerly: International Conference on Apiculture in Tropical Climates. Proceedings
Published by: International Bee Research Association, 18 North Rd, Cardiff, Wales CF10 3DT, United Kingdom. TEL 44-2920-372409, FAX 44-2920-665522, mail@ibra.org.uk, http://www.ibra.org.uk. Ed. Dr. Pamela A Munn.

I C A C RECORDER. see *TEXTILE INDUSTRIES AND FABRICS*

630 IND
I C A R NEWS. Text in English, Hindi. irreg.
Published by: Indian Council of Agricultural Research, Krishi Anusandhan Bhavan, Pusa, New Delhi, 110 012, India. TEL 91-11-5731350, FAX 91-11-5731282, http://icar.org.in/.

I C R A - AGRIMISSIO INFORMATION. see *RELIGIONS AND THEOLOGY—Roman Catholic*

I D E OCCASIONAL PAPERS SERIES. see *BUSINESS AND ECONOMICS*

I D E RESEARCH SERIES/KENKYU-SOSHO. see *BUSINESS AND ECONOMICS*

I D E SYMPOSIUM PROCEEDINGS. see *BUSINESS AND ECONOMICS*

630 USA
I F A COOPERATOR. Text in English. 1935. 4/yr. USD 1. adv. illus. **Document type:** *Newsletter, Trade.*
Formerly: Intermountain Farmer (0020-5672)
Published by: Intermountain Farmers Association, 1147 West 2100 South, Salt Lake City, UT 84119. TEL 801-972-2122, FAX 801-972-2186. Ed., R&P, Adv. contact Bonnie Humphrey. Circ: 7,250.

I F A D UPDATE. see *BUSINESS AND ECONOMICS—International Development And Assistance*

630 FRA
I F A P NEWSLETTER: WORLD FARMER. Text in French. 198?. bi-m. **Document type:** *Newsletter.* **Description:** News on the activities of IFAP and its member organizations throughout the world.
Formerly: I F A P Newsletter (Print Edition) (0984-9963)
Media: Online - full text.
Published by: International Federation of Agricultural Producers/Federation Internationale des Producteurs Agricoles, 60 Rue Saint-Lazare, Paris, 75009, France. TEL 33-1-45260553, FAX 33-1-48747212, ifap@ifap.org, http://www.ifap.org. Circ: 1,500.

630 USA
IDAHO FARMER - STOCKMAN. Text in English. 1895. m. USD 21.95 in state; USD 30 out of state; USD 75 foreign (effective 2001). adv. **Document type:** *Trade.*
Former titles: Idaho Farmer (1073-189X); (until 1993): Idaho Farmer - Stockman (1041-1682); (until 1977): Gem State Rural; Western Farmer and Agricultural Age
Published by: Farm Progress Companies, 191 S Gary Ave, Carol Stream, IL 60188. FAX 435-753-1388. Ed. Ron Daines. Circ: 8,568 (paid).

630 CHL ISSN 0073-4675
S15 CODEN: IDESBG
➤ **IDESIA.** Text in Spanish; Summaries in English. 1970. a. USD 6 per vol. (effective 2001). bk.rev. charts; bibl.; illus.; stat. **Document type:** *Academic/Scholarly.* **Description:** Covers agronomic research and scientific papers and reports.
Indexed: AEA, AgBio, AgrForAb, BIOSIS Prev, BioCN&I, BiolAb, CPA, ChemAb, FCA, FPA, FS&TA, ForAb, HerbAb, HortAb, I&DA, NemAb, OrnHort, PBA, PGegResA, PHN&I, PotatoAb, RA&MP, RDA, RPP, RevApplEntom, S&F, SIA, SeedAb, TDB, TriticAb, WAE&RSA, WeedAb.
—CASDDS, CISTI.
Published by: Universidad de Tarapaca, Facultad de Agronomia, Casilla 6-D, Arica, Chile. TEL 56-58-205502, FAX 56-58-220035, fagron@alpaca.quipu.uta.cl. Ed. Mauricio Jimenez. Circ: 1,000.

630 JPN ISSN 0913-7823
IE-NO-HIKARI/LIGHT OF HOME. Text in Japanese. 1925. m.
Published by: Ie-No-Hikari Coop-Publishing Association, 11 Ichigaya-Funagawara-Machi, Shinjuku-ku, Tokyo, 162-0826, Japan. TEL 03-3266-9000, FAX 03-3266-9048. Ed. Toshio Horie.

630 NGA ISSN 0331-6351
IFE JOURNAL OF AGRICULTURE. Text in English. 1967. a. NGN 1.50. bk.rev. **Document type:** *Academic/Scholarly.*
Formerly (until 1979): University of Ife. Faculty of Agriculture. Annual Research Report (0579-7195)
Indexed: RDA, WAE&RSA.
—CISTI.
Published by: Obafemi Awolowo University, Ile Ife, Osun State, Nigeria. Ed. A E Akingbohungbe. Circ: 500.

630 ISR
IKKARE YISRA'EL. Text in Hebrew. irreg. free.
Published by: Farmers in Israel Association, P O Box 209, Tel Aviv, 61001, Israel. TEL 03-252227.

IKUSHUGAKU KENKYU/BREEDING RESEARCH. see *BIOLOGY*

630 USA ISSN 0194-7443
ILLINOIS AGRI NEWS. Text in English. 1977. w. USD 23 (effective 2005). adv. back issues avail. **Document type:** *Newspaper, Trade.* **Description:** Serves farm families in the state of Illinois.
Related titles: Microfilm ed.
Published by: Agri-News Publications, 420 Second St., Lasalle, IL 61301-2334. TEL 815-223-2558, FAX 815-223-5997, editorial@agrinews-pub.com, agrinews@theramp.net, http://www.agrinews-pubs.com. Ed. Jim Henry. Pub., R&P Lynn Barker. Adv. contact Marguerite Allen. B&W page USD 5,430.90, color page USD 6,030.90. Circ: 35,000 (paid).

630 USA
ILLINOIS FARMWEEK. Text in English. 1974. w. USD 75 (effective 1998). adv. **Document type:** *Newspaper.* **Description:** Covers the latest news on farm production and marketing, economics, research and legislation.
Published by: Illinois Farm Bureau, 1701 Towanda Ave, Bloomington, IL 61701. TEL 309-557-2238, FAX 309-557-2559. Ed. David McClelland. Adv. contact Bob Standard. Circ: 87,650.

630 USA ISSN 0032-6615
ILLINOIS PRAIRIE FARMER. Text in English. 1841. 14/yr. USD 23.95 in state; USD 32 out of state (effective 2005). adv. bk.rev. charts; illus.; stat.; tr.lit. index. reprint service avail. from PQC. **Document type:** *Magazine, Trade.* **Description:** Serves commercial farmers and ranchers in Illinois, emphasizes coverage of production, management, marketing, public policy and rural lifestyle.
Related titles: Microform ed.: (from PQC); (from PQC).
Indexed: F&GI.
—CISTI.
Published by: Farm Progress Companies, 191 S Gary Ave, Carol Stream, IL 60188. TEL 630-690-5600, FAX 630-462-2869, info@farmprogress.com, http://www.prairiefarmer.com. Ed. Cherry Brieser Stout. adv.: B&W page USD 6,240, color page USD 8,735; trim 8 x 10.75. Circ: 40,000.

638.1 DEU ISSN 0019-2732
CODEN: IMKRA3
IMKERFREUND; Bienenzeitung zur Wahrung und Foerderung der Interessen der Bienenzuechter. Text in German. 1945. m. EUR 32.20; EUR 3.10 newsstand/cover (effective 2004). adv. bk.rev. charts; illus.; mkt.; tr.lit. **Document type:** *Newspaper, Consumer.*
Indexed: ApicAb, BiolAb.
—CCC.
Published by: (Landesverband Bayerischer Imker e.V.), Deutscher Landwirtschaftsverlag GmbH, Lothstr 29, Munich, 80797, Germany. TEL 49-89-127051, FAX 49-89-12705335, dlv.muenchen@dlv.de, http://www.imkerfreund.de, http://www.dlv.de. adv.: B&W page EUR 842, color page EUR 1,487. Circ: 15,078 (paid and controlled).

630 USA ISSN 0749-1573
IMPACT (ATHENS). Text in English. 1890. a. free. illus. back issues avail.
Formerly: University of Georgia. Agricultural Experiment Stations. Annual Report
Media: Online - full text.
Indexed: MaizeAb.
—CISTI, Linda Hall.
Published by: (Georgia Agricultural Experiment Stations), University of Georgia, College of Agriculture, Division of Agricultural Communications, Athens, GA 30602. TEL 404-542-3621, http://www.ces.uga.edu/ces/pubs.html. Ed. Kathleen Sheridan. Circ: 10,000.

630 CAN ISSN 1709-8785
▼ **IMPLEMENT SUCCESS.** Text in English. 2003. bi-m. CND 250 membership (effective 2005). **Document type:** *Magazine, Trade.*
Published by: Agricultural Manufacturers of Canada, Stockman's Arena, Regina Exhibition Park, PO Box 636, Station Main, Regina, SK S4P 3A3, Canada. TEL 306-522-2710, FAX 306-781-7293, pima@pima.ca, http://www.pima.ca. Circ: 2,000 (controlled).

630 IND ISSN 0084-781X
INDIAN AGRICULTURE IN BRIEF. Text in English. 1958. a. INR 200, USD 72. **Document type:** *Government.*
Published by: Ministry of Agriculture, Department of Agriculture and Cooperation, Directorate of Economics and Statistics, A-2E-3 Kasturba Gandhi Marg Barracks, New Delhi, 110 001, India. TEL 11-381523. Ed. Brajesh Kumar Gautam. Circ: 900.

630 IND
INDIAN AGRICULTURE REVIEW. Text in English. 1993. a. INR 250, USD 55 (effective 2000). adv. abstr.; charts; illus. reprint service avail. from PQC. **Document type:** *Trade.*
Related titles: Microfilm ed.: (from PQC).
Published by: Technical Press Publications, Eucharistic Congress Bldg. No.1, 5/1 Convent St, Colaba, Mumbai, Maharashtra 400 039, India. TEL 91-22-2021446, FAX 91-22-2871499. Ed., Pub. J P de Sousa. adv.: B&W page INR 1,750, color page INR 2,250; trim 18 x 23. Circ: 12,000.

630 IND ISSN 0019-4336
CODEN: INAGAT
INDIAN AGRICULTURIST. Text in English. 1957. q. INR 160, USD 50. adv. bk.rev. abstr.; charts; illus. index. **Description:** Provides forum for association and gives conference information as well as research data in the agricultural field.
Indexed: AEA, ASFA, AgBio, AgrForAb, BAS, BioCN&I, BiolAb, CPA, CTFA, ChemAb, ESPM, FCA, FPA, FS&TA, ForAb, HerbAb, HortAb, I&DA, MaizeAb, NemAb, NutrAb, OrnHort, PBA, PGegResA, PGrRegA, PHN&I, PotatoAb, PoultAb, RA&MP, RDA, RM&VM, RPP, RevApplEntom, RiceAb, S&F, SIA, SWRA, SeedAb, SoyAb, TOSA, TriticAb, WAE&RSA, WeedAb.
—CASDDS, CISTI, Linda Hall.
Published by: (Agricultural Society of India), Calcutta University Press, Sri Sibendra Nath Kanjilal, 48 Hazra Rd., Kolkata, West Bengal 700 019, India. Ed. Dr. A K Sarkar. Circ: 600.

638.1 IND ISSN 0019-4425
INDIAN BEE JOURNAL. Text in English. 1938. q. USD 40 to individuals (effective 2003). adv. bk.rev. abstr.; charts; illus.; stat. index.
Indexed: ApicAb, BiolAb, ChemAb, HortAb, RevApplEntom, SIA, ZooRec.
Published by: All-India Bee Keepers Association, c/o Dept. of Zoology, Agricultural University, Hisar, Haryana 125 004, India. Ed. R C Sihagr. Circ: 700.

634 IND ISSN 0367-7281
INDIAN COCONUT JOURNAL. Text in English. N.S. 1947. m. INR 75, USD 100 (effective 2001). adv. bk.rev. mkt.; stat. 24 p./no. 3 cols./p.; **Document type:** *Journal, Government.*
Formerly: Coconut Bulletin (0010-0145)
Indexed: AEA, AgrForAb, BioCN&I, BiolAb, CPA, FS&TA, HortAb, NutrAb, OrnHort, PBA, PHN&I, RA&MP, RDA, RPP, RevApplEntom, S&F, SeedAb, WAE&RSA, WeedAb.
—BLDSC (4394.000000), IE, ingenta.
Published by: Department of Agriculture, Coconut Development Board, Ernakulam, Cochin, Kerala 11, India. TEL 91-484-371265, FAX 91-484-371902, cdbkochi@vsnl.com, http://www.coconutboard.nic.in. Ed. T B NandaKumar. Pub. Dr. R K Singh. Circ: 3,000.

630 IND
INDIAN FARMER TIMES. Text in English. 1983. m. INR 55. adv. bk.rev. illus.
Published by: Farmers Welfare Trust Society (WAFM), 6-B Regal Bldg., New Delhi, 110 001, India. Ed. Jagdeesh Kodesia. Circ: 3,500.

630 IND
INDIAN FARMERS' DIGEST. Text in English. m. INR 100; INR 10 newsstand/cover (effective 2003). **Document type:** *Journal.*
Published by: G. B. Pant University of Agriculture and Technology, C/o Dr. K.K. Singh, O.I.C Telecom Unit, Pantnagar, Udhamsingh Nagar, Uttaranchal 263 145, India. TEL 91-5944-33671, FAX 91-5944-33473, kks@gbpuat.ernet.in, http://www.gbpuat.ac.in.

631 IND ISSN 0019-4786
S17
INDIAN FARMING. Text in English. 1940. m. USD 45 to institutions (effective 2006). adv. bk.rev. charts; illus. index. reprint service avail. from PQC. **Document type:** *Academic/Scholarly.* **Description:** Covers agriculture, animal husbandry and allied subjects.
Related titles: Microform ed.: (from PQC).
Indexed: AEA, ASFA, AgrForAb, AnBrAb, BioCN&I, BiolAb, CTFA, ChemAb, DSA, ESPM, ExcerpMed, FCA, FPA, FS&TA, ForAb, HerbAb, HortAb, IndVet, MaizeAb, NutrAb, PN&I, PotatoAb, PoultAb, ProtozoAb, RASB, RDA, RiceAb, S&F, S&MA, SFA, SeedAb, SoyAb, TOSA, TriticAb, VetBull, WAE&RSA, WeedAb.
—Linda Hall.
Published by: Indian Council of Agricultural Research, Krishi Anusandhan Bhavan, Pusa, New Delhi, 110 012, India. http://www.scientificpub.com/bookdetails.php?booktransid=442&bookid=438. Ed. Ashok Singh. Adv. contact S K Joshi. Circ: 51,200. **Subscr. to:** Scientific Publishers, 5-A New Pali Rd., Near Hotel Taj Hari Mahal, PO Box 91, Jodhpur, Rajasthan 342 003, India. TEL 91-291-2433323, FAX 91-291-2512580, info@scientificpub.com, http://www.scientificpub.com.

INDIAN FORESTER. see *FORESTS AND FORESTRY*

INDIAN JOURNAL OF AGRICULTURAL BIOCHEMISTRY. see *BIOLOGY—Biochemistry*

630 IND ISSN 0971-8664
➤ **INDIAN JOURNAL OF AGRICULTURAL MARKETING.** Text in English. 1986. 3/yr. INR 300 to individuals; GBP 35 foreign to individuals (effective 2003). adv. bk.rev. mkt.; stat.; tr.lit. **Document type:** *Academic/Scholarly.* **Description:** Covers all aspects of agricultural marketing useful for academics administrators, researchers, traders, etc.
Indexed: AEA, DSA, PHN&I, RDA, TriticAb, WAE&RSA.
—BLDSC (4409.970000), IE, ingenta.
Published by: Indian Society of Agricultural Marketing, 57, IV Seminary Hills, Nagpur, Maharashtra 440 006, India. TEL 91-712-558-767, FAX 91-712-549-236. Ed. S S Acharya. Pub. T Satyanarayana. adv.: B&W page USD 100. Circ: 1,000 (paid).

630 IND ISSN 0367-8245
S19 CODEN: IJARC2
INDIAN JOURNAL OF AGRICULTURAL RESEARCH; journal of plant and soil science. Text in English. 1967. q. INR 600 domestic; USD 70 foreign (effective 2004). bk.rev. abstr. **Document type:** *Academic/Scholarly.* **Description:** Publishes original research articles by eminent scientists and book reviews on all aspects of Plant and Soil sciences.
Formerly (until 1971): Indian Journal of Science and Industry. Section A. Agricultural Sciences (0367-8296); Which superseded in part (in 1970): Indian Journal of Science and Industry (0019-5618)

A

Indexed: AEA, ASFA, AgBio, AgrForAb, BIOSIS Prev, BioCN&I, BiolAb, CPA, CTFA, ChemAb, CurCont, DSA, ESPM, FCA, FPA, FS&TA, ForAb, HerbAb, HortAb, I&DA, ISR, MBA, MaizeAb, NutrAb, OrnHort, PBA, PGegResA, PGrRegA, PHN&I, PollutAb, PotatoAb, RA&MP, RDA, RPP, RRTA, RevApplEntom, RiceAb, S&F, S&MA, SIA, SWRA, SeedAb, SoyAb, TOSA, TriticAb, VITIS, WAE&RSA, WeedAb.
—BLDSC (4409.980000), CASDDS, CISTI, IE, Infotrieve, ingenta, Linda Hall.
Published by: Agricultural Research Communication Centre, 1130 Sadar Bazar, Post Office Marg, Karnal, Haryana 132 001, India. TEL 91-184-255080. Ed. Dr. Kirti Singh. Circ: 1,500.

630.2 IND ISSN 0019-5022
S19 CODEN: IJASA3
➤ **INDIAN JOURNAL OF AGRICULTURAL SCIENCES.** Text in English. 1931. m. USD 100 to institutions (effective 2006). adv. bk.rev. bibl.; charts; illus.; stat. index. reprint service avail. from PQC. **Document type:** *Journal, Academic/Scholarly.*
Description: Devoted to experimental agriculture. Publishes original articles in all branches of agriculture, including cytology, genetics, breeding, agronomy, soil science, water use, microbiology, plant diseases and pests, agricultural engineering, education, and economics.
Related titles: Microform ed.: (from PQC).
Indexed: AEA, ASCA, ASFA, AgBio, AgrForAb, Agrind, B&BAb, BIOBASE, BIOSIS Prev, BioCN&I, BiolAb, CIN, CPA, CTFA, ChemAb, ChemTitl, CurCont, ESPM, EngInd, ExcerpMed, FCA, FPA, FS&TA, ForAb, HerbAb, HortAb, I&DA, IABS, IndVet, LeadAb, MBA, MaizeAb, NemAb, NutrAb, OrnHort, PBA, PGegResA, PGrRegA, PHN&I, PlantSci, PollutAb, PotatoAb, PoultAb, RA&MP, RDA, RM&VM, RPP, RevApplEntom, RiceAb, S&F, S&MA, SFA, SIA, SPPI, SWRA, SeedAb, SoyAb, TDB, TOSA, TriticAb, VITIS, WAE&RSA, WeedAb, WildRev, Zincscan, ZooRec.
—BLDSC (4410.000000), CASDDS, CISTI, Ei, IDS, IE, Infotrieve, ingenta, Linda Hall.
Published by: (Indian Council of Agricultural Research), Scientific Publishers, 5-A New Pali Rd., Near Hotel Taj Hari Mahal, PO Box 91, Jodhpur, Rajasthan 342 003, India. TEL 91-291-2433323, FAX 91-291-2512580, info@scientificpub.com, http://www.scientificpub.com/bookdetails.php?booktransid=309&bookid=305. Ed. Ashok Singh. Adv. contact S K Joshi. Circ: 2,000.

630 IND ISSN 0537-197X
SB4 CODEN: IJAGAZ
➤ **INDIAN JOURNAL OF AGRONOMY.** Text in English. 1956. q. USD 250 to institutions (effective 2006). adv. bk.rev. back issues avail. **Document type:** *Journal, Academic/Scholarly.*
Description: Features research papers in the areas of crop production and soil for use of scientists in the field of agronomy, plant physiology and soil science.
Indexed: AEA, ASCA, AgBio, AgrForAb, BIOSIS Prev, BiolAb, CIN, CPA, CTFA, ChemAb, ChemTitl, CurCont, DSA, FCA, FPA, ForAb, HerbAb, HortAb, I&DA, MaizeAb, NutrAb, OrnHort, PBA, PGegResA, PGrRegA, PHN&I, PN&I, PotatoAb, PoultAb, RA&MP, RDA, RPP, RevApplEntom, RiceAb, S&F, S&MA, SIA, SeedAb, SoyAb, TOSA, TriticAb, WAE&RSA, WeedAb.
—BLDSC (4410.100000), CASDDS, CISTI, IDS, IE, Infotrieve, ingenta, Linda Hall. **CCC.**
Published by: Indian Society of Agronomy, Division of Agronomy, Indian Agricultural Research Institute, New Delhi, 110 012, India. TEL 91-11-25842283, ipsahlaw@nda.vsnl.net.in, http://www.scientificpub.com/bookdetails.php?booktransid=310&bookid=306, http://www.socagron.com. Ed. R C Gautam. Pub. I P S Ahlawat. Circ: 2,200 (paid); 50 (controlled).

630 IND ISSN 0971-2062
INDIAN JOURNAL OF DRYLAND AGRICULTURAL RESEARCH AND DEVELOPMENT. Text in English. 1986. s-a. USD 50 (effective 2003). **Document type:** *Academic/Scholarly.*
Indexed: AbHyg, AgrForAb, AnBrAb, BioCN&I, CPA, FCA, FPA, ForAb, HerbAb, HortAb, I&DA, MaizeAb, OrnHort, PBA, PGegResA, PHN&I, RA&MP, RM&VM, S&F, SeedAb, SoyAb, TDB, TriticAb, WAE&RSA, WeedAb.
Published by: (Indian Society of Dryland Agriculture), H P C Publishers Distributors Pvt. Ltd., 4805 Bharat Ram Rd, 24 Darya Ganj, New Delhi, 110 002, India. TEL 91-11-3254401, FAX 91-11-619-3511, hpcpd@hpc.cc, http://www.bizdelhi.com/publisher/hpc, http://www.indianindustry.com. **Subscr. to:** Scientific Publishers, 5-A New Pali Rd., Near Hotel Taj Hari Mahal, PO Box 91, Jodhpur, Rajasthan 342 003, India. info@scientificpub.com, http://www.scientificpub.com.

632.6257 IND ISSN 0303-6960
QL391.N4 CODEN: IJNEDT
➤ **INDIAN JOURNAL OF NEMATOLOGY.** Text in English. 1971. s-a. INR 500, USD 100 (effective 2001). adv. bk.rev. bibl.; charts; illus. back issues avail. **Document type:** *Journal, Academic/Scholarly.*
Indexed: AgBio, AgrForAb, BioCN&I, BiolAb, CPA, FCA, FPA, ForAb, HerbAb, HortAb, I&DA, MaizeAb, NemAb, OrnHort, PBA, PGegResA, PHN&I, PN&I, PotatoAb, PoultAb, RA&MP, RPP, RevApplEntom, RiceAb, S&F, SIA, SeedAb, SoyAb, TriticAb, WeedAb, ZooRec.
—CISTI.
Published by: (Division of Nematology), Indian Agricultural Research Institute, Nematological Society of India, c/o General Secretary, I.A.R.I., New Delhi, 110 012, India. Ed. Dr. Gopal Swarup. Pub. Dr. R V Singh. Circ: 500.

630 IND ISSN 0970-308X
➤ **INDIAN SOCIETY FOR COTTON IMPROVEMENT. JOURNAL.** Text in English. 1976. 3/yr. (in 26 vols.). INR 300, USD 35 (effective 2001). bk.rev. 2 cols./p.; back issues avail. **Document type:** *Journal, Academic/Scholarly.*
Indexed: ISA, TTI.
Published by: Indian Society for Cotton Improvement, c/o Central Institute for Research on Cotton Technology, Adenwala Rd., Matunga, Mumbai, Maharashtra 400 019, India. TEL 91-22-4127273, FAX 91-22-4130835, circot@vsnl.com. Ed. V Sundaram. Pub. S N Nagwekar. R&P A J Shaikh.

631 IND ISSN 0019-638X
S590 CODEN: JINSA4
➤ **INDIAN SOCIETY OF SOIL SCIENCE. JOURNAL.** Text in English. 1953. q. USD 160 to institutions (effective 2005). adv. bk.rev. illus. index. **Document type:** *Academic/Scholarly.*
Indexed: AEA, ATA, AgBio, AgrForAb, BiolAb, CIN, CPA, ChemAb, ChemTitl, EngInd, ExcerpMed, FCA, FPA, ForAb, HerbAb, HortAb, I&DA, INIS AtomInd, ISA, MaizeAb, NemAb, OrnHort, PBA, PGegResA, PGrRegA, PotatoAb, PoultAb, RA&MP, RDA, RPP, RevApplEntom, RiceAb, S&F, S&MA, SIA, SeedAb, SoyAb, TOSA, TriticAb, VITIS, WAE&RSA, WeedAb.
—BLDSC (4769.000000), CASDDS, CISTI, IE, ingenta, Linda Hall.
Published by: (Indian Society of Soil Science), Scientific Publishers, 5-A New Pali Rd., Near Hotel Taj Hari Mahal, PO Box 91, Jodhpur, Rajasthan 342 003, India. TEL 91-291-2433323, FAX 91-291-2512580, info@scientificpub.com, http://www.scientificpub.com/bookdetails.php?booktransid=341&bookid=337. Ed. T D Biswas. R&P G Narayanasamy. Adv. contact G. Narayanasamy. Circ: 2,500 (paid).

630 USA ISSN 0745-7103
CODEN: PHESDL
INDIANA AGRI-NEWS. Text in English. 1982. w. USD 15 (effective 2000). adv. **Document type:** *Newspaper.*
Description: Farm and rural community magazine.
Published by: Agri-News Publications, 420 Second St., Lasalle, IL 61301-2334. TEL 815-223-2558, FAX 815-223-5997, agrinews@theramp.net, http://www.agrinews-pubs.com. Ed. Jim Henry. Pub., R&P Lynn Barker. Adv. contact Sue Cheslic. Circ: 22,000.

630 USA ISSN 0073-6783
INDIANA. AGRICULTURAL EXPERIMENT STATION. INSPECTION REPORT. Text in English. 1956. irreg. price varies.
Indexed: Agr.
—Linda Hall.
Published by: Purdue University, Agricultural Experiment Station, c/o Donna Southard, W, Lafayette, IN 47907. TEL 317-494-5962, FAX 317-496-1117.

630 USA ISSN 0073-6791
INDIANA. AGRICULTURAL EXPERIMENT STATION. RESEARCH BULLETIN. Text in English. 1957. irreg. (12-15/yr.). **Document type:** *Academic/Scholarly.*
Published by: Purdue University, Agricultural Experiment Station, c/o Donna Southard, W, Lafayette, IN 47907. TEL 317-494-5962, FAX 317-496-1117. R&P Eldon Ortman. Circ: 2,500.

630 USA
INDIANA AGRINEWS. Text in English. 1982. w. (Fri.). USD 15 domestic; USD 100 foreign (effective 2005). adv. **Document type:** *Newspaper.*
Published by: AgriNews Publications, 420 Second St, La Salle, IL 61301. TEL 815-223-2558, 800-772-9354, FAX 815-223-5997, indianaagrinews@mw.net, http://www.agrinews-pubs.com. Pub. Lynn Barker. adv.: B&W page USD 1,965, color page USD 2,755. Circ: 23,000 (controlled and free). Wire service: AP.

630 USA ISSN 0162-7104
INDIANA PRAIRIE FARMER. Text in English. 1841. m. (except Jan.-Mar., s-m.). USD 23.95 (effective 2005). adv. **Document type:** *Magazine, Trade.* **Description:** Local and timely crop and livestock production practices are emphasized by staff editors who live and work in the area. Management, government, rural lifestyle, and economic issues are also regularly featured.
Published by: Farm Progress Companies, 191 S Gary Ave, Carol Stream, IL 60188-2095. TEL 630-462-2229, FAX 630-462-2202, tbeckman@farmprogress.com, info@farmprogress.com, http://www.indianaprairiefarmer.com. Eds. Paul Queck, Thomas Bechman. Pub. Allan Johnson. adv.: B&W page USD 2,150, color page USD 2,650; trim 10.5 x 14.5. Circ: 23,000 (paid).

INDONESIAN BIOLOGICAL AND AGRICULTURAL INDEX/INDEKS BIOLOGI DAN PERTANIAN DE INDONESIA. see *AGRICULTURE—Abstracting, Bibliographies, Statistics*

INDUSTRIES ALIMENTAIRES ET AGRICOLES. see *FOOD AND FOOD INDUSTRIES*

338.1 URY
INFOPESCA. NOTICIAS COMERCIALES. Text in English, Spanish. bi-w. **Description:** Covers the prices of products and by-products of the world-wide markets.
Published by: Infopesca, Julio Herrera y Obes 1296, Casilla de Correo 7086, Montevideo, 11200, Uruguay. TEL 598-2-902-8701, FAX 598-2-903-0501, infopesca@infopesca.org, http://www.infopesca.org/not-com.htm.

630 PAN
INFORMACION AGRICOLA PANAMENA. Text in Spanish. 1981. bi-m.
Published by: Instituto de Investigacion Agropecuaria de Panama, Centro de Informacion Documental Agropecuaria, Apdo. 6-4391, El Dorado, Panama City, 6a, Panama. Ed. Vielka Chang Yau. Circ: 250.

630 FRA ISSN 0019-994X
INFORMATION AGRICOLE. Text in French. m. adv. charts; illus.; stat.; tr.lit.
Indexed: DSA, NutrAb, RRTA, WAE&RSA.
—CISTI. **CCC.**
Published by: Federation Nationale des Syndicats d'Exploitants Agricoles, 11 rue de la Baume, Paris, 75008, France. TEL 33-1-53834747. Ed. Yves Salmon.

630 FRA
INFORMATION AGRICOLE DU CHER. Text in French. w. **Document type:** *Newspaper.*
Published by: Information Agricole du, 3 rue Volta, Bourges, Cedex 18002, France. TEL 48-70-14-54, FAX 48-65-01-29. Ed. Maryvonne Langlois. Pub. Berry Republichin. Circ: 7,100.

630 FRA ISSN 1157-2507
INFORMATION AGRICOLE DU RHONE. Text in French. w.
Published by: Information Agricole du, 4 Place Gensoul, Lyon, 69002, France. TEL 78-42-65-92, FAX 78-42-61-63. Ed. Paul Lormage. Circ: 9,087.

630 635 DEU
INFORMATION SOURCES IN AGRICULTURE AND HORTICULTURE✶. Text in English. 1984. irreg., latest vol.2, 1994. GBP 55, USD 110. **Document type:** *Directory.*
Description: Emphasizes practical techniques and research, as well as the economic and environmental impacts of agriculture. Topics surveyed include organic farming, biotechnology, management practice.
Published by: K.G. Saur Verlag GmbH (Subsidiary of: Gale Group), Ortlerstr 8, Munchen, 81373, Germany. TEL 49-89-769020, FAX 49-89-76902150, info@saur.de, http://www.saur.de.

INFORMATIONSDIENST PRAXISBEZOGENER LITERATUR IM WEINBAU. see *AGRICULTURE—Abstracting, Bibliographies, Statistics*

630 ITA ISSN 0020-0689
L'INFORMATORE AGRARIO. Text in Italian. 1945. w. (51/yr.). EUR 79 domestic (effective 2005). adv. bk.rev. charts; illus.; mkt.; stat. index. **Document type:** *Newspaper, Consumer.*
Description: Covers the technical, economic and political aspects of all the branches of agriculture and breeding.
Related titles: CD-ROM ed.
Indexed: AEA, AbHyg, AgBio, AgrForAb, AnBrAb, ApicAb, BioCN&I, CPA, DSA, FCA, FPA, FaBeAb, ForAb, HelmAb, HerbAb, HortAb, I&DA, IndVet, MaizeAb, NemAb, NutrAb, OrnHort, PBA, PGegResA, PGrRegA, PHN&I, PN&I, PotatoAb, PoultAb, RA&MP, RASB, RDA, RM&VM, RPP, RRTA, RevApplEntom, RiceAb, S&F, S&MA, SIA, SeedAb, SoyAb, TriticAb, VITIS, VetBull, WAE&RSA, WeedAb.
—BLDSC (4496.750000), IE, ingenta.
Published by: Edizioni L' Informatore Agrario S.p.A., Via Bencivegna Giordani 16, Verona, 37133, Italy. TEL 39-045-8057511, FAX 39-045-597510, informatoreagrario@informatoreagrario.it, http://www.informatoreagrario.it. Ed., R&P Giovanni Rizzotti. Pub. Elena Rizzotti. Adv. contact Giuseppe Colombo Manfroni. Circ: 39,634 (controlled).

INFORMATORE FITOPATOLOGICO. see *BIOLOGY—Botany*

630.5 BRA ISSN 0100-3364
HD1875.M5
INFORME AGROPECUARIO. Text in Portuguese. 1975. irreg. BRL 12 per issue (effective 2004). adv. **Document type:** *Journal, Academic/Scholarly.*
Formerly (until no.2, 1976): Informe Agropecuario: Conjuntura e Estatistica
Indexed: AEA, AgBio, AgrForAb, Agrind, AnBrAb, BioCN&I, CPA, DSA, FCA, FPA, ForAb, HerbAb, HortAb, I&DA, IBR, IndVet, MaizeAb, NemAb, NutrAb, OrnHort, PBA, PGegResA, PGrRegA, PHN&I, PN&I, PotatoAb, PoultAb, ProtozoAb, RA&MP, RDA, RPP, RevApplEntom, RiceAb, S&F, S&MA, SIA, SeedAb, SoyAb, TDB, TriticAb, VetBull, WAE&RSA, WeedAb.
—BLDSC (4498.311000).
Published by: Empresa de Pesquisa Agropecuaria de Minas Gerais, Av Jose Candido da Silveira 1647, Cidade Nova, Belo Horizonte, MG 31170-000, Brazil. sac@epamig.br. Ed. Gustavo de Jesus Werneck. Circ: 3,000.

630 MEX
INGENIERIA AGRONOMICA. Text in Spanish. 1975. q. MXP 150, USD 14. charts; illus.
Published by: Colegio de Ingenieros Agronomos de Mexico, A.C., Sindicalismo 92, Mexico City 18, DF, Mexico.

630 FRA ISSN 1264-9147
CODEN: INGEFO
INGENIERIES. Text in French. 6/yr. EUR 62.50 in the European Union; EUR 74.70 elsewhere (effective 2003).
Indexed: ASFA, ESPM.
—CASDDS.
Published by: Lavoisier, 11 rue Lavoisier, Paris, 75008, France. TEL 33-1-42653995, FAX 33-1-42650246, info@lavoisier.fr, http://www.lavoisier.fr. **Subscr. to:** Lavoisier - Dept Abonnements, 14 rue de Provigny, Cachan 94236, France. TEL 33-1-47406700, FAX 33-1-47406702, abo@lavoisier.fr.

630 ESP
INSTITUT AGRICOLA CATALA DE SANT ISIDRE. CALENDARI DEL PAGES. Text in Spanish. 1856. a.
Published by: Institut Agricola Catala de Sant Isidre, Placa Sant Josep Oriol, 4, Barcelona, 08002, Spain. TEL 93-301-16-36, FAX 93-317-30-05, http://www.institutagricola.org. Ed. Ferran de Muller.

630 RWA
INSTITUT DES SCIENCES AGRONOMIQUES DU RWANDA. DEPARTEMENT DES PRODUCTIONS VEGETALES. COMPTE RENDU DES TRAVAUX. Text in French. a.
Published by: Institut des Sciences Agronomiques, Departement des Productions Vegetales, BP 138, Butare, Rwanda.

630 TUN ISSN 0365-4761
SB29.T8
INSTITUT NATIONAL DE LA RECHERCHE AGRONOMIQUE DE TUNISIE. ANNALES. Text in French; Summaries in English. 1920. a. price varies. **Document type:** *Government.*
Description: Scientific journal publishing the results of Tunisian agricultural research and focusing on the improvement of animal and plant production in Tunisia.
Indexed: AgBio, AnBrAb, BioCN&I, CPA, DSA, FCA, FPA, HerbAb, HortAb, NutrAb, OrnHort, PBA, PGegResA, RPP, RevApplEntom, S&F, SeedAb, TriticAb.
—BLDSC (0925.100000).
Published by: (Service de Documentation), Institut National de la Recherche Agronomique de Tunisie, Rue Hedi Karray, 2080 Ariana, Tunis, Tunisia. TEL 230024, FAX 231693. Circ: 800.

630 TUN ISSN 0020-238X
INSTITUT NATIONAL DE LA RECHERCHE AGRONOMIQUE DE TUNISIE. DOCUMENTS TECHNIQUES. Text in French; Summaries in English. 1963. irreg., latest vol.107, 1991. price varies. **Document type:** *Government.* **Description:** Technical journal intended to help Tunisian farmers improve crop and livestock productivity through improved management.
Indexed: BiolAb.
Published by: (Service de Documentation), Institut National de la Recherche Agronomique de Tunisie, Rue Hedi Karray, 2080 Ariana, Tunis, Tunisia. TEL 230024, FAX 231693. Circ: 500.

630 COD
INSTITUT NATIONAL POUR L'ETUDE ET LA RECHERCHE AGRONOMIQUE. RAPPORT ANNUEL. Cover title: Rapport pour l'Exercice. Text in French. a. illus.
Published by: Institut National pour l'Etude et la Recherche Agronomique, BP 1513, Kisangani, Congo, Dem. Republic.

631 GRC ISSN 0365-5814
SB599 CODEN: APYBAQ
INSTITUT PHYTOPATHOLOGIQUE BENAKI. ANNALES. NOUVELLE SERIE. Text in English. N.S. 1935. irreg., latest vol.18, no.1, 1997. EUR 23 (effective 2002). charts; illus. index. back issues avail. **Document type:** *Journal, Academic/Scholarly.*
Related titles: Greek ed.: Benakeio Futopathologico Institouto. chorika. ISSN 1107-3721; English ed.
Indexed: ASFA, BIOSIS Prev, BioCN&I, BioDAb, BiolAb, ChemAb, DBA, ESPM, ForAb, HortAb, MaizeAb, OrnHort, PBA, PGrRegA, PHN&I, PotatoAb, RPP, RevApplEntom, S&F, TriticAb, VITIS, WeedAb, ZooRec.
—BLDSC (0933.000000), CASDDS, CISTI.
Published by: Institut Phytopathologique Benaki/Benaki Phytopathological Institute, 8 Delta St, Kifissia, Athens 145 61, Greece. FAX 30-1-807-7506, bpilibr@otenet.gr. R&P A S Alivizatos TEL 30-1-807-9603. Circ: 700.

630 296 ISR ISSN 0334-9942
INSTITUTE FOR AGRICULTURAL RESEARCH ACCORDING TO THE TORAH. BULLETIN. Text in Hebrew. 1980. bi-m. ILS 50. adv. bk.rev. **Document type:** *Bulletin.* **Description:** Examines religious issues affecting farmers and consumers, to foster observance of Jewish law in matters pertaining to agriculture, food production and consumerism.
Indexed: IHP, S&F.
Published by: Institute for Agricultural Research According to the Torah, Nahal Soreq Municipal Bldg., Yad Benjamin, 76812, Israel. TEL 972-8-591167, FAX 972-8-594172. Ed. Elyakim Shlanger. adv.: B&W page ILS 2,000. Circ: 3,000 (paid).

INSTITUTE OF AGRICULTURE AND ANIMAL SCIENCE. JOURNAL. see *VETERINARY SCIENCE*

INSTITUTE OF BREWING. JOURNAL. see *BEVERAGES*

630 IND ISSN 0257-3431
S671
➤ **INSTITUTION OF ENGINEERS (INDIA). AGRICULTURAL ENGINEERING DIVISION. JOURNAL.** Text in English. 1983. s-a. INR 80, USD 25 (effective 2000). adv. **Document type:** *Academic/Scholarly.*
Indexed: Englnd, RefZh.
—CISTI, Ei, Linda Hall.
Published by: (Agricultural Engineering Division), Institution of Engineers (India), 8 Gokhale Rd., Kolkata, West Bengal 700 020, India. TEL 91-33-2235068, 91-33-2238314, FAX 91-33-2238345, technical@ieindia.org, http://www.ieindia.org. Ed., Pub. B C Thakurta. Adv. contact S S Basu. Circ: 2,000.

630 BRA ISSN 0020-3653
SB599 CODEN: AIBOA3
INSTITUTO BIOLOGICO. ARQUIVOS. Text in Portuguese; Summaries in English. 1928. s-a. BRL 20 (effective 1999). illus. index. **Document type:** *Academic/Scholarly.*
Indexed: AgBio, AgrForAb, AnBrAb, BioCN&I, BiolAb, ChemAb, DSA, ExcerpMed, FCA, FPA, ForAb, HelmAb, HerbAb, HortAb, IndMed, IndVet, MEDLINE, MaizeAb, NemAb, NutrAb, OrnHort, PBA, PHN&I, PN&I, PoultAb, ProtozoAb, RA&MP, RM&VM, RPP, RevApplEntom, RiceAb, S&F, S&MA, SIA, SeedAb, SoyAb, TDB, TOSA, TriticAb, VetBull, WeedAb, ZooRec.
—BLDSC (1687.000000), CASDDS, CISTI.
Published by: Instituto Biologico, Av Rodrigues Alves 1252 04014-002, Centro, Caixa Postal 12 898, Sao Paulo, SP 01059-970, Brazil. TEL 55-11-5729822, FAX 55-11-5709704. Ed. Marcia Maria Reboucas.

630 COL ISSN 0538-0391
INSTITUTO COLOMBIANO AGROPECUARIO. BOLETIN TECNICO. Text in Spanish. 1977 (no.45). irreg. illus.
Indexed: BiolAb.
Published by: Instituto Colombiano Agropecuario, Apdo. Aereo 151123, El Dorado, Bogota, Colombia. FAX 57-1-2673013. Circ: 2,500.

630 ESP ISSN 0374-8189
INSTITUTO DE ECONOMIA Y PRODUCCIONES GANADERAS DEL EBRO. COMUNICACIONES. Text in Spanish. 1970. irreg., latest vol.11, 1980. free.
Indexed: AnBrAb, BiolAb, WAE&RSA.
Published by: Instituto de Economia y Producciones Ganaderas del Ebro, Miguel Servet, 177, Zaragoza, 50013, Spain. Circ: 500.

630 ESP ISSN 0375-3417
INSTITUTO DE ECONOMIA Y PRODUCCIONES GANADERAS DEL EBRO. TRABAJOS. Text in Spanish. 1970. irreg., latest vol.63, 1988. free.
Indexed: AnBrAb, BiolAb, IECT, WAE&RSA.
Published by: Instituto de Economia y Producciones Ganaderas del Ebro, Miguel Servet, 177, Zaragoza, 50013, Spain. Ed. M Ocana. Circ: 500.

630 MOZ ISSN 0077-1791
INSTITUTO DE INVESTIGACAO AGRONOMICA DE MOCAMBIQUE. CENTRO DE DOCUMENTACAO AGRARIA. MEMORIAS. Text in Portuguese; Summaries in English, French, Portuguese. 1966. irreg., latest vol.5, 1974. price varies. illus. index.
Indexed: BiolAb.
Published by: Instituto Nacional de Investigacao Agronomica, Centro de Documentacao e Informacao, C.P. 3658, Maputo 11, Mozambique. Circ: 500.

631.091 PRT ISSN 0871-1763
INSTITUTO DE INVESTIGACAO CIENTIFICA TROPICAL. COMUNICACOES. SERIE DE CIENCIAS AGRARIAS. Text in Portuguese. 1989. irreg., latest vol.20. price varies. back issues avail. **Document type:** *Monographic series.*
Published by: Instituto de Investigacao Cientifica Tropical, Rua da Junqueira, 30, Lisbon, 1349-007, Portugal. TEL 351-21-3622621, FAX 351-21-3631460, iict@iict.pt. Circ: 1,000. **Subscr to:** Centro de Documentacao e Informacao, Rua de Jau, 47, Lisbon 1300, Portugal. TEL 351-21-3644846, FAX 351-21-3628218.

630 ESP ISSN 1134-4903
INSTITUTO DE RECURSOS NATURALES Y AGROBIOLOGIA DE SEVILLA. MEMORIA. Text in Spanish. 1967. a.
Formerly (until 1989): Centro de Edafologia y Biologia Aplicada del Cuarto. Memoria (1134-489X)
—CINDOC.
Published by: Consejo Superior de Investigaciones Cientificas, Instituto de Recursos Naturales y Agrobiologia de Sevilla, Avenida de Reina Mercedes, 10, Sevilla, 41012, Spain. TEL 95-4624711, FAX 95-4624002, http://www.irnase.csic.es.

630 BRA ISSN 0103-5215
INSTITUTO DO DESENVOLVIMENTO ECONOMICO-SOCIAL DO PARA. PARA AGRARIO. Text in Portuguese. 1986. s-a. bibl.; charts; stat. **Document type:** *Government.*
Published by: Instituto do Desenvolvimento Economico Social do Para, Av Nazare, 871, Nazare, Belem, Para 66035170, Brazil. TEL 55-91-2244411, FAX 55-91-2253414.

630 330.9 MEX
INSTITUTO NACIONAL DE INVESTIGACIONES FORESTALES, AGRICOLAS Y PECUARIAS. FOLLETOS DE INVESTIGACION. Text in Spanish; Summaries in English, Spanish. 1979. irreg. free. charts. **Document type:** *Academic/Scholarly.*
Formerly (until 1985): Instituto Nacional de Investigaciones Agricolas. Folletos de Investigacion
Indexed: BiolAb.
Published by: Instituto Nacional de Investigaciones Forestales, Agricolas y Pecuarias, Vocalia Division Agricola, Apdo. Postal 6-882, Mexico City, DF 06600, Mexico. Circ: 3,000.

630 MEX
INSTITUTO NACIONAL DE INVESTIGACIONES FORESTALES, AGRICOLAS Y PECUARIAS. TEMAS DIDACTICOS. Text in Spanish. 1976. irreg. free. charts. **Document type:** *Academic/Scholarly.*
Formerly (until 1985): Instituto Nacional de Investigaciones Agricolas. Temas Didacticos
Published by: Instituto Nacional de Investigaciones Forestales, Agricolas y Pecuarias, Vocalia Division Agricola, Apdo. Postal 6-882, Mexico City, DF 06600, Mexico. Circ: 3,000.

630 ARG ISSN 0325-1772
INSTITUTO NACIONAL DE TECNOLOGIA AGROPECUARIA. ESTACION EXPERIMENTAL REGIONAL AGROPECUARIA. BOLETIN DE DIVULGACION TECNICA. Text in Spanish. 1970. irreg.
Formerly: Instituto Nacional de Tecnologia Agropecuaria. Estacion Experimental Regional Agropecuaria. Publicacion Tecnica
Indexed: BiolAb, DSA, FCA, HerbAb, RevApplEntom, S&F, WAE&RSA.
Published by: Instituto Nacional de Tecnologia Agropecuaria, Estacion Experimental Regional Agropecuaria, Casilla de Correos 31, Pergamino, Buenos Aires 2700, Argentina. Circ: 1,500.

630 664 PRT ISSN 0365-2971
INSTITUTO SUPERIOR DE AGRONOMIA. ANAIS. Text in English, French, Portuguese; Summaries in English, French. 1920. a. price varies. back issues avail. **Document type:** *Academic/Scholarly.*
Published by: Instituto Superior de Agronomia, Tapada da Ajuda, Lisbon Codex, 1399, Portugal. FAX 351-1-3635031, TELEX 44700 ISATEL. Ed. R P Ricardo. Circ: 900.

630 IND ISSN 0020-4919
INTENSIVE AGRICULTURE. Text in English. 1963. bi-m. INR 12. bk.rev. charts; illus. **Description:** Contains information on practical aspects of farming told in a very simple language and supported by helpful pictures.
Formerly: Extension (0421-9724)
—CISTI.
Published by: Ministry of Agriculture and Rural Development, Directorate of Extension, Krishi Vistar Bhawan, Dr. K.S. Krishnan Marg, Pusa, New Delhi, 110 012, India. TEL 603568. Ed. Shukla Hazra. adv.: page INR 2,000; 210 x 270. Circ: 12,000.

630.71 NER ISSN 0534-4727
INTER-AFRICAN CONFERENCE ON INDUSTRIAL COMMERCIAL AND AGRICULTURAL EDUCATION MEETING✶. Text in English, French. 1954. irreg. **Document type:** *Proceedings.*
Published by: (Commission for Technical Co-Operation in Africa South of the Sahara), Maison de l'Afrique, BP 878, Niamey, Niger.

630 USA ISSN 1072-2610
INTERFAX. FOOD & AGRICULTURE REPORT. Text in English. w. stat. **Document type:** *Trade.* **Description:** Offers a comprehensive review of the food and agriculture industry in Russia and the CIS. Covers all aspects of the industry including the import and export of raw materials and processed goods, sowing and production forecasts, and harvest and consumption statistics.
Related titles: E-mail ed.; Fax ed.; Online - full content ed.
Contact: Interfax America, Inc. (Subsidiary of: Interfax Ltd.), 3025 S Parker Rd, Ste 737, Aurora, CO 80014-2925. TEL 303-825-1510, FAX 303-825-1513, america@interfax.com, http://www.interfax.com. **Dist. in Germany Austria and Switzerland by:** Interfax Deutschland GmbH, IndustriestraBe 6, Kronberg/Tx 61476 , Germany. TEL 49-61-7361369, FAX 49-61-7361206; **Dist. in Western Europe by:** Interfax Europe Ltd., 1st Fl, 50 Hans Crescent, Knightsbridge, London SW1X 0N, United Kingdom. TEL 44-20-7581-5550, FAX 44-20-7581-4490.

INTERNATIONAL ASSOCIATION OF AGRICULTURAL INFORMATION SPECIALISTS. QUARTERLY BULLETIN. see *LIBRARY AND INFORMATION SCIENCES*

638.1 ROM ISSN 0074-2007
INTERNATIONAL BEEKEEPING CONGRESS. REPORTS. Text in Romanian. biennial. price varies. adv. **Document type:** *Proceedings.*
Published by: International Federation of Beekeepers' Associations "Apimondia", Bd. Ficusului 42, Bucharest, 71544, Romania. TEL 40-1-6330918, FAX 40-1-63129492, TELEX 10998 IITEA R. Ed. Erika Dumitrascu. Adv. contact Paltin Nottara.

▼ new title ➤ refereed ✶ unverified ♦ full entry avail.

A

630 SYR ISSN 0254-8313
INTERNATIONAL CENTER FOR AGRICULTURAL RESEARCH IN THE DRY AREAS. ANNUAL REPORT. Text in English. 1978. a.
—BLDSC (4538.416800), CISTI.
Published by: International Center for Agricultural Research in the Dry Areas, PO Box 5466, Aleppo, Syria. TEL 963-21-2213433, FAX 963-21-2213490, icarda@cgiar.org, http://www.icarda.cgiar.org.

630 KEN
INTERNATIONAL CENTRE FOR RESEARCH IN AGROFORESTRY. ANNUAL REPORT. Text in English. 1979. a. free. **Document type:** *Corporate.*
Published by: International Centre for Research in Agroforestry, PO Box 30677, Nairobi, Kenya. TEL 254-2-521450, FAX 254-2-521001, icraf@cgiar.org. Ed. Bernardette Hince. R&P Bernadette Hince. Circ: 3,000.

INTERNATIONAL COTTON ADVISORY COMMITTEE. PROCEEDINGS. see *TEXTILE INDUSTRIES AND FABRICS*

INTERNATIONAL FLYING FARMER. see *AERONAUTICS AND SPACE FLIGHT*

630 GBR ISSN 1560-2192
➤ **INTERNATIONAL INSTITUTE FOR ENVIRONMENT AND DEVELOPMENT. DISCUSSION PAPER.** Text in English. 1998. 2/yr. GBP 8 (effective 1999). **Document type:** *Monographic series, Academic/Scholarly.* **Description:** The series aims to analyze the effectiveness of international initiatives in sustainable development and natural resource management in the context of rural livelihood.
Indexed: FPA, RDA, WAE&RSA.
Published by: International Institute for Environment and Development, 3 Endsleigh St, London, WC1H ODD, United Kingdom. TEL 44-171-388-2117, FAX 44-171-388-2826, sustag@iiee.org, http://www.iied.org.

354.3 GBR ISSN 1357-9258
INTERNATIONAL INSTITUTE FOR ENVIRONMENT AND DEVELOPMENT. SUSTAINABLE AGRICULTURE PROGRAMME. GATEKEEPER SERIES. Text in English. 1987. 3/yr. price varies. **Document type:** *Monographic series, Academic/Scholarly.* **Description:** Publishes research aimed at policy makers on promoting the development of socially and environmentally aware agriculture.
Related titles: Online - full content ed.
Indexed: AgrForAb, ForAb, HortAb, I&DA, IndVet, ProtozoAb, RDA, RevApplEntom, RiceAb, S&F, WAE&RSA, WeedAb.
—BLDSC (4089.225100), ingenta.
Published by: (Sustainable Agriculture Programme), International Institute for Environment and Development, 3 Endsleigh St, London, WC1H ODD, United Kingdom. TEL 44-20-73882117, FAX 44-20-73882826, sustag@iied.org, mailbox@iied.org, info@iied.org, http://www.iied.org/agri/gatekeepers/gatekeep.html. Ed. Fiona Hall. R&P Simon Ferrigno TEL 44-7872-7214. Circ: 250 (paid); 1,500 (controlled).

630 NGA ISSN 1013-0322
S540.8.I57
INTERNATIONAL INSTITUTE OF TROPICAL AGRICULTURE. ANNUAL REPORT AND RESEARCH HIGHLIGHTS. Text in English. 1984. a. USD 10. **Document type:** *Corporate.*
Formed by the merger of (1976-1984): International Institute of Tropical Agriculture. Annual Report (0257-8387); (1968-1984): International Institute of Tropical Agriculture. Research Highlights (0331-4340)
Related titles: French ed.: ISSN 1115-8891.
Indexed: I&DA, MaizeAb.
—BLDSC (1311.505000), CISTI.
Published by: International Institute of Tropical Agriculture, PMB 5320, Ibadan, Oyo, Nigeria. TEL 234-2-241-2626, TELEX 31417 TROPIB NG, iita@cgnet.com, iita@cgiar.org. Ed. Jack Reeves.

338.1 GBR ISSN 1462-4605
S493 CODEN: IJARD3
➤ **INTERNATIONAL JOURNAL OF AGRICULTURAL RESOURCES, GOVERNANCE AND ECOLOGY.** Abbreviated title: I J A R G E. Text in English. q. USD 450 to institutions; USD 545 combined subscription to institutions print & online eds. (effective 2005). **Document type:** *Journal, Academic/Scholarly.* **Description:** Proposes and fosters discussion on the evolution and governance of agricultural resources, with emphasis on the implications that policy choices have on both the welfare of humans and the ecology of the planet.
Related titles: Online - full text ed.: ISSN 1741-5004. USD 450 to institutions (effective 2005) (from EBSCO Publishing).
Indexed: Agr, AgrForAb, BrCerAb, C&ISA, CerAb, CorrAb, E&CAJ, EMA, EPB, ESPM, EnvEAb, ForAb, GEOBASE, I&DA, IAA, M&TEA, MBF, METADEX, NutrAb, PGegResA, PN&I, PollutAb, RDA, RRTA, S&F, SWRA, SolStAb, SoyAb, WAA, WAE&RSA, WRCInf.
—BLDSC (4541.610000), Linda Hall.
Published by: Inderscience Publishers, IEL Editorial Office, PO Box 735, Olney, Bucks MK46 5WB, United Kingdom. TEL 44-1234-240519, FAX 44-1234-240515, ijarge@inderscience.com, editor@inderscience.com, http://www.inderscience.com/ijarge. Ed. Dr. Mohammed A Dorgham. **Subscr. to:** World Trade Centre Bldg, 29 route de Pre-Bois, Case Postale 896, Geneva 15 1215, Switzerland. FAX 41-22-7910885, subs@inderscience.com.

630 570 PAK ISSN 1560-8530
➤ **INTERNATIONAL JOURNAL OF AGRICULTURE AND BIOLOGY.** Text in English. 1999. q. INR 600 domestic to individuals; USD 125 foreign to individuals; INR 1,000 domestic to institutions; USD 150 foreign to institutions (effective 2003). **Document type:** *Journal, Academic/Scholarly.* **Description:** Publishes original research papers, review articles, short communications, status papers and continuing education articles on all aspects of agriculture, biology and other life sciences.
Indexed: AgBio, AgrForAb, AnBrAb, BioCN&I, CPA, DSA, FCA, FPA, ForAb, HelmAb, HerbAb, HortAb, I&DA, IndVet, MaizeAb, NutrAb, OrnHort, PBA, PGegResA, PGrRegA, PHN&I, PotatoAb, PoultAb, ProtozoAb, RA&MP, RDA, RPP, RiceAb, S&F, SIA, SeedAb, SoyAb, TDB, TriticAb, VetBull, WAE&RSA, WeedAb.
—BLDSC (4541.607000).
Published by: Friends Science Publishers, 399 #B, Peoples Colony No.1, Faisalabad, 38090, Pakistan. TEL 92-41-546079, fspublishers@ijab.org, http://www.ijab.org. Ed. Dr. Zafar I Randhawa. **Subscr. to:** C/o Dr. Zafar I. Randhawa, EIC, Department of Vet. Parasitology, University of Agriculture, Faisalabad 380 040, Pakistan.

631 NGA ISSN 1595-9716
➤ **INTERNATIONAL JOURNAL OF AGRICULTURE AND RURAL DEVELOPMENT.** Text in English. 2000. a. NGN 600 domestic to individuals; USD 50 in Africa to individuals; USD 100 elsewhere to individuals; NGN 1,000 domestic to institutions; USD 60 in Africa to institutions; USD 120 elsewhere to institutions (effective 2004). back issues avail. **Document type:** *Academic/Scholarly.* **Description:** Designed to provide information in the areas of agriculture and rural development in the tropics.
Related titles: Online - full text ed.: (from International Network for the Availability of Scientific Publications, African Journals Online).
Indexed: FCA.
Published by: Federal University of Technology, School of Agriculture and Agricultural Technology, PMB 1526, Owerri, Nigeria. TEL 236-83-230974, http://www.inasp.info/ajol/journals/ijard/about.html. Ed. U. Herbert.

631 FIN ISSN 1459-0255
➤ **INTERNATIONAL JOURNAL OF FOOD, AGRICULTURE AND ENVIRONMENT.** Text in English. 2002. q. EUR 60 to individuals; EUR 120 to institutions; EUR 30 to students (effective 2004). adv. **Document type:** *Journal, Academic/Scholarly.* **Description:** Contains research, critical reviews and short communications on food science and technology, agriculture, animal science, human nutrition and environmental disciplines.
Related titles: Online - full text ed.: ISSN 1459-0263.
Indexed: AEBA, ASFA, B&BAb, ESPM, EntAb, EnvEAb, FCA, FS&TA, GenetAb, H&SSA, M&GPA, PollutAb, SWRA.
—BLDSC (4984.536750), CISTI, IE.
Published by: (International Society Of Food, Agriculture and Environment), World Food RD Ltd., Meri-Rastilantie 3C, Helsinki, 00980, Finland. editorial@world-food.net, info@world-food.net, http://world-food.net. Eds. Dr. Ramdane Dris, Dr. Shri Mohan Jain.

➤ **INTERNATIONAL JOURNAL OF SOCIOLOGY OF AGRICULTURE AND FOOD/REVISTA INTERNACIONAL DE SOCIOLOGIA SOBRE AGRICULTURA Y ALIMENTOS.** see *SOCIOLOGY*

630 IND ISSN 0254-8755
CODEN: IJTADD
INTERNATIONAL JOURNAL OF TROPICAL AGRICULTURE. Text in English. 1983. q. USD 220 to institutions (effective 2003). adv. bk.rev. back issues avail. **Document type:** *Academic/Scholarly.* **Description:** Original research papers, critical reviews and short communications dealing with all aspects of fundamental and applied tropical agriculture.
Indexed: AEA, AgBio, AgrForAb, AnBrAb, BIOSIS Prev, BioCN&I, BiolAb, CIN, CPA, CTFA, ChemAb, ChemTitl, CurCont, DSA, EngInd, FCA, FPA, FS&TA, ForAb, HerbAb, HortAb, I&DA, IndVet, MaizeAb, NemAb, NutrAb, OrnHort, PBA, PGegResA, PGrRegA, PHN&I, PotatoAb, PoultAb, RA&MP, RDA, RPP, RevApplEntom, RiceAb, S&F, S&MA, SIA, SeedAb, SoyAb, TDB, TriticAb, VITIS, VetBull, WAE&RSA, WeedAb.
—BLDSC (4542.696100), CASDDS, CISTI, Ei.
Published by: Scientific Publishers, 5-A New Pali Rd., Near Hotel Taj Hari Mahal, PO Box 91, Jodhpur, Rajasthan 342 003, India. TEL 91-291-2433323, FAX 91-291-2512580, info@scientificpub.com, http://www.scientificpub.com. Circ: 1,000.

630 011 USA
INTERNATIONAL SOCIETY OF CITRICULTURE. PROCEEDINGS. Text in English. 1973. irreg. price varies. back issues avail. **Document type:** *Proceedings.* **Description:** Publishes papers presented at International Society of Citriculture congresses.
Indexed: BiolAb, HortAb.
Published by: International Society of Citriculture, c/o Charlie Coggins, Department of Botany and Plant Sciences, University of California, Riverside, CA 92521-0124. TEL 909-787-4412, FAX 909-787-4437, charles.coggins@ucr.edu, http://www.lal.ufl.edu/isc_citrus_homepage.htm. Circ: 1,000.

630 CHL
INVESTIGACION Y PROGRESO AGROPECUARIO KAMPENAIKE. Text in Spanish. 1988. irreg. USD 4.50; USD 6 foreign.
Published by: (Chile. Estacion Experimental Kampenaike), Instituto de Investigaciones Agropecuarias, Casilla 439, Correo, 3, Santiago, Chile. Circ: 1,000.

630 USA ISSN 0097-3416
CODEN: IWRBBR
IOWA AGRICULTURE AND HOME ECONOMICS EXPERIMENT STATION. RESEARCH BULLETIN. Text in English. 1911. irreg. per issue exchange basis. charts; illus.; stat. cum.index. back issues avail. **Document type:** *Bulletin.* **Description:** Includes reports of research in the agricultural and biological sciences of interest primarily to scientific and professional workers.
Indexed: BibAg, BiolAb, ChemAb, CurCont.
—CISTI, Linda Hall.
Published by: (Iowa Agriculture and Home Economics Experiment Station), Iowa State University of Science and Technology, 304 Curtiss Hall, Ames, IA 50011. TEL 515-294-5616, FAX 515-294-8662. Ed. Carol A Greiner. Circ: (controlled).

630 USA ISSN 0361-199X
CODEN: IWSRBC
IOWA AGRICULTURE AND HOME ECONOMICS EXPERIMENT STATION. SPECIAL REPORT. Text in English. 1936. irreg. per issue exchange basis. charts; illus.; stat. cum.index. back issues avail. **Document type:** *Monographic series.* **Description:** Includes papers, technical and semitechnical reports in the agricultural and biological sciences of interest primarily to specialized audiences.
Formerly: Agricultural and Home Economics Experiment Station. Special Report (0097-5125)
Indexed: BibAg, BiolAb, CurCont, NutrAb, SCI.
—CISTI, Linda Hall.
Published by: (Iowa Agriculture and Home Economics Experiment Station), Iowa State University of Science and Technology, 304 Curtiss Hall, Ames, IA 50011. TEL 515-294-5616, FAX 515-294-8662. Ed. Carol A Greiner.
Co-sponsor: Iowa Cooperative Extension Service in Agriculture and Home Economics.

630 USA
IOWA AGRICULTURIST✶. Text in English. 1901. s-a. USD 10. adv. illus. back issues avail. **Description:** Designed for students and faculty in Iowa State University's College of Agriculture. Covers the innovations, achievements, history and concerns within agriculture and focuses on how these issues relate to ISU.
Published by: Iowa Agriculturist, Inc., Student Publications, Ames, IA 50011. TEL 515-294-9381. Adv. contact Danielle McGuire. Circ: 2,500 (controlled).

630 USA ISSN 0021-051X
IOWA FARM BUREAU SPOKESMAN. Text in English. 1934. w. free membership only (effective 2005). adv. charts; illus. **Document type:** *Newspaper.*
Published by: (Iowa Farm Bureau Federation), Spokesman Press, Inc., 606 Eighth St, Grundy Center, IA 50638. TEL 515-225-5532, FAX 515-225-5419, http://www.iowafarmbureau.com. Ed. Dale Johnson. Pub. Charles M Allen. Adv. contact John Doak. Circ: 98,000 (paid).

630 USA
IOWA FARMER TODAY. Text in English. 1984. w. USD 35 domestic; USD 70 foreign; free to qualified personnel (effective 2005). adv. **Document type:** *Magazine, Trade.* **Description:** Covers Iowa's farmers and agribusiness. Contains production, policy, equipment, marketing and rural living information.
Published by: Lee Agri-Media, Inc., PO Box 5279, Cedar Rapids, IA 52406-5279. TEL 800-475-6655, FAX 319-398-8482, news@iowafarmer.com, http://www.iowafarmer.com. Circ: 70,000 (controlled).

IOWA R E C NEWS. (Rural Electric Cooperative) see *ENERGY—Electrical Energy*

630 IRN ISSN 1013-9885
CODEN: IAGRE5
➤ **IRAN AGRICULTURAL RESEARCH/TAHQIQAT KISHAVARZAI-I IRAN.** Text in English; Summaries in English, Persian, Modern. 1981. s-a. USD 50 to individuals; USD 100 to institutions. **Document type:** *Academic/Scholarly.* **Description:** Publishes original research articles and notes pertaining to agricultural science.

Supersedes: Iranian Journal of Agricultural Research (0376-4524)
Related titles: Microform ed.
Indexed: AEA, AgBio, AnBrAb, BioCN&I, BiolAb, CIN, CPA, ChemAb, ChemTitl, DSA, FCA, FS&TA, HerbAb, HortAb, I&DA, IndVet, MaizeAb, NutrAb, OrnHort, PBA, PGegResA, PGrRegA, PHN&I, PotatoAb, PoultAb, RA&MP, RDA, RPP, RevApplEntom, RiceAb, S&F, SeedAb, TriticAb, VetBull, WAE&RSA, WeedAb.
—BLDSC (4567.522550), CASDDS, Linda Hall.
Published by: Shiraz University, College of Agriculture, Shiraz, Iran. TEL 98-71-28193, FAX 98-71-28193. Ed. M Khosh Khui. R&P J Jamalian.

630 IRN ISSN 1017-5652
CODEN: IRJADJ
IRANIAN JOURNAL OF AGRICULTURAL SCIENCES. Text in Persian, Modern; Abstracts in English. 1969. q. IRR 1,000 to individuals; IRR 800 to students. **Description:** Presents technical research studies in the agricultural sciences. Discusses ways of improving productivity in terms of crop yield and livestock.
Formerly: University of Teheran. Agricultural College Publication
Indexed: AEA, AgBio, AgrForAb, AnBrAb, BioCN&I, BiolAb, CPA, DSA, FCA, FS&TA, ForAb, HerbAb, HortAb, I&DA, IndVet, M&GPA, MaizeAb, NemAb, NutrAb, OrnHort, PBA, PGegResA, PGrRegA, PHN&I, PotatoAb, PoultAb, RA&MP, RDA, RPP, RRTA, RevApplEntom, RiceAb, S&F, SIA, SeedAb, SoyAb, TriticAb, VetBull, WAE&RSA, WRCInf, WeedAb.
Published by: University of Teheran, College of Agriculture, Centre for Scientific and Technical Publications, Karaj, Iran. Ed. H Oloumi Sadeghi. Circ: 1,000.

338.1 IRL
IRELAND. DEPARTMENT OF AGRICULTURE, FOOD AND RURAL DEVELOPMENT. STATEMENT OF STRATEGY. Text in English. irreg.
—BLDSC (8438.394060).
Published by: Department of Agriculture, Food & Rural Development/An Roinn Talmhaiochta Bia Agus Forbartha Tuaithe, Agriculture House, Kildare St, Dublin, Dublin 2, Ireland. TEL 353-1-607-2000, information@daff.irlgov.ie, http://www.irlgov.ie/daff/.

638.1 IRL ISSN 0021-1079
THE IRISH BEEKEEPER. Text in English. 1947. m.
Indexed: ApicAb.
Published by: Federation of Irish Beekeeping Associations, St Elmo, Marlborough Rd., Glenageary, Co. Dublin, Ireland. TEL 353-1-2809520. Ed. Graham Hall. Circ: 1,200. **Subscr. to:** S. Reddy, 8 Tower View Park, Kildare, Ireland.

630 IRL ISSN 0790-679X
IRISH CO-OPERATIVE ORGANISATION SOCIETY. ANNUAL REPORT. Text in English. 1895. a. **Document type:** *Corporate.*
Former titles (until 1986): Irish Co-operative Organisation Society. Annual Report and Accounts (0790-6781); (until 1985): Irish Co-operative Organisation Society. Annual Report (0790-6773); (until 1980): Irish Agricultural Organisation Society. Annual Report (0790-455X); (until 1965): Irish Agricultural Organisation Society. Report (0790-4541); (until 1901): Irish Agricultural Organisation Society. Annual Report (0075-0719)
Published by: Irish Co-operative Organisation Society Ltd., Plunkett House, 84 Merrion Sq., Dublin, 2, Ireland. TEL 353-1-6764783, FAX 353-1-6624502, info@icos.ie, http://www.icos.ie.

630 IRL ISSN 0021-1168
IRISH FARMERS' JOURNAL. Text in English. 1948. w. EUR 135 in Ireland; EUR 130 Northern Ireland; EUR 210 in United Kingdom; IEP 324 in the European Union; IEP 352 rest of world (effective 2005); for 52 weeks. adv. bk.rev. reprint service avail. from PQC. **Document type:** *Newspaper, Trade.* **Description:** Provides a focus for open debate on agricultural development in Ireland.
Related titles: Online - full content ed.
Published by: Agricultural Trust, Irish Farm Centre, Bluebell, Dublin, Dublin 12, Ireland. TEL 353-1-4199599, FAX 353-1-4520876, http://www.farmersjournal.ie. Ed. Matthew Dempsey TEL 353-1-4199500. Adv. contact John Gill. B&W page EUR 7,800; trim 290 x 360. Circ: 69,867.

630 IRL ISSN 0332-2408
IRISH FARMERS MONTHLY. Text in English. 1977. m. adv. bk.rev.
Published by: I F P Media, 31 Deansgrange Rd., Blackrock, Co. Dublin, Ireland. TEL 353-1-2893305, FAX 353-1-2896406, http://www.ifpmedia.com. Ed. Margaret Donnelly. Adv. contacts David Markey, John Sheehan. B&W page EUR 1,990, color page EUR 2,625; trim 210 x 297. Circ: 24,000.

630 IRL ISSN 0791-6833
CODEN: IAFREY
➤ **IRISH JOURNAL OF AGRICULTURAL AND FOOD RESEARCH.** Text in English. 1992. 2/yr. EUR 70 (effective 2005). illus.; stat. index. **Document type:** *Academic/Scholarly.* **Description:** Covers agricultural research, including plant and animal sciences, food science, soils, engineering, buildings, economics, and sociology.
Formed by the merger of (1977-1992): Irish Journal of Food Science and Technology (0332-0375); (1967-1992): Irish Journal of Agricultural Economics and Rural Sociology (0021-1249); (1962-1992): Irish Journal of Agricultural Research (0578-7483)
Indexed: AEA, ASCA, AbHyg, AgBio, Agr, AgrForAb, AnBrAb, BIOSIS Prev, BioCN&I, BiolAb, CIN, CPA, ChemAb, ChemTitl, CurCont, DSA, ExcerpMed, FCA, FPA, FS&TA, ForAb, HerbAb, HortAb, I&DA, ISR, IndVet, MaizeAb, NemAb, NutrAb, OrnHort, PBA, PHN&I, PN&I, PotatoAb, PoultAb, RM&VM, RPP, RevApplEntom, S&F, SCI, SIA, SeedAb, SoyAb, TriticAb, VetBull, WAE&RSA, WeedAb.
—BLDSC (4571.850000), CASDDS, CISTI, IDS, IE, ingenta. **CCC.**
Published by: Teagasc, Oak Park, Carlow, Ireland. TEL 353-59-9170200, FAX 353-59-9182097, publications@hq.teagasc.ie, http://www.teagasc.ie/research/journal.htm. Ed. J P Hanrahan. Circ: 1,300.

631.6 627 GBR ISSN 1531-0353
TC801
➤ **IRRIGATION AND DRAINAGE.** Text in English, French. 1952. 5/yr. USD 425 to institutions; USD 468 combined subscription to institutions print & online eds. (effective 2006). adv. bk.rev. **Document type:** *Journal, Academic/Scholarly.* **Description:** Contains articles on irrigation, drainage, river training and flood control.
Former titles (until 2000): I C I D Journal (0971-7412); (until 1995): I C I D Bulletin (0300-2810); (until 1969): I C I D Annual Bulletin
Related titles: Online - full content ed.: ISSN 1531-0361. USD 425 to institutions (effective 2006); Online - full text ed.: (from EBSCO Publishing, Swets Information Services, Wiley InterScience).
Indexed: AEA, Agr, CPA, CurCont, ESPM, FCA, HortAb, I&DA, MaizeAb, S&F, SWRA, WAE&RSA.
—BLDSC (4580.946000), CISTI, IE, Linda Hall. **CCC.**
Published by: (International Commission on Irrigation and Drainage/Commission Internationale des Irrigations et du Drainage IND), John Wiley & Sons Ltd. (Subsidiary of: John Wiley & Sons, Inc.), The Atrium, Southern Gate, Chichester, West Sussex PO19 8SQ, United Kingdom. TEL 44-1243-779777, FAX 44-1243-775878, customer@wiley.co.uk, http://www.wileyeurope.com/WileyCDA/WileyTitle/productCd-IRD.html, http://www.wiley.co.uk. Circ: 2,900. **Subscr. addr. in the Americas:** John Wiley & Sons, Inc., 111 River St, Hoboken, NJ 07030-5774. TEL 201-748-6645, FAX 201-748-6088, subinfo@wiley.com.

▼ ➤ **IRRIGATION & WATER RESOURCES.** see *WATER RESOURCES*

631.7 DEU ISSN 0342-7188
S612 CODEN: IRSCD2
➤ **IRRIGATION SCIENCE.** Text in English. 1978. q. EUR 628 combined subscription to institutions print & online eds. (effective 2005). adv. reprint service avail. from ISI. **Document type:** *Journal, Academic/Scholarly.* **Description:** Publishes original contributions and short communications with an emphasis placed on physical and chemical aspects of water status and movement in the plant-soil-atmosphere system.
Related titles: Microform ed.: (from PQC); Online - full text ed.: ISSN 1432-1319 (from EBSCO Publishing, Springer LINK, Swets Information Services).
Indexed: AEA, AESIS, ASCA, ASFA, Agr, AgrForAb, BIOSIS Prev, BiolAb, CPA, CTFA, ChemAb, CivEngAb, CurCont, ESPM, EngInd, EnvAb, FCA, FLUIDEX, ForAb, GEOBASE, HerbAb, HortAb, I&DA, IAOP, ISR, M&TEA, MaizeAb, OrnHort, PBA, PGegResA, PGrRegA, PotatoAb, RA&MP, RiceAb, S&F, S&MA, SCI, SWRA, SoyAb, TriticAb, VITIS, WAE&RSA.
—BLDSC (4581.580000), CASDDS, CISTI, Ei, IDS, IE, Infotrieve, ingenta, Linda Hall. **CCC.**
Published by: Springer-Verlag (Subsidiary of: Springer Science+Business Media), Tiergartenstr 17, Heidelberg, 69121, Germany. TEL 49-6221-3450, FAX 49-6221-345229, http://link.springer.de/link/service/journals/00271/index.htm. Ed. Robert G Evans. Adv. contact Stephan Kroeck TEL 49-30-827875739. **Subscr. in the Americas to:** Springer-Verlag New York, Inc., Journal Fulfillment, PO Box 2485, Secaucus, NJ 07096-2485. TEL 800-777-4643, 201-348-4033, FAX 201-348-4505, journals@springer-ny.com, http://www.springer-ny.com; **Subscr. to:** Springer GmbH Auslieferungsgesellschaft, Haberstr 7, Heidelberg 69126, Germany. TEL 49-6221-345-0, FAX 49-6221-345-4229, subscriptions@springer.de.

630 SYR
IRSHAD AL-ZIRAI. Text in Arabic. 6/yr. adv.
Published by: Ministry of Agriculture, Damascus, Syria.

630 CAN ISSN 0823-7735
ISLAND FARMER. Text in English. 1974. w. adv.
—CISTI.
Published by: Island Press Ltd., P O Box 790, Montague, PE C0A 1R0, Canada. TEL 902-838-2515, FAX 902-838-4392. Adv. contact Barb Donnelly. Circ: 2,261.

630 338.95694 ISR ISSN 0793-4971
ISRAEL AGRITECHNOLOGY FOCUS. Text in English. 1993. q. ILS 79, USD 28.90. adv. charts; illus.; stat.; tr.lit. index. back issues avail. **Document type:** *Trade.* **Description:** Covers farming technology and agriculture and agricultural R&D in Israel, business ventures and investments in agriculture.
Formerly: Focus on Israel Agritechnology
Indexed: FCA, RDA, S&F, WAE&RSA.
Published by: Global Link Ltd., P O Box 57179, Tel Aviv, 61571, Israel. TEL 972-3-5628511, FAX 972-3-5628512. Ed. Nicky Blackburn. Pub. Tamara Genosar. R&P Michael Eilan. Adv. contact Haim Heller.

ISRAEL. CENTRAL BUREAU OF STATISTICS. AGRICULTURAL STATISTICS QUARTERLY. see *AGRICULTURE—Abstracting, Bibliographies, Statistics*

630 ISR
ISRAEL. RURAL PLANNING AND DEVELOPMENT AUTHORITY. AGRICULTURAL AND RURAL ECONOMIC REPORT. Text in Hebrew. a. free.
Former titles: Israel. Rural Planning and Development Authority. Agricultural and Rural Development Report; Israel. Agriculture and Settlement Planning and Development Center. Agricultural and Rural Development Report; Israel. Agricultural and Settlement Planning and Development Center. Statistical Series for the Agricultural Year (0075-0964); Israel. Agricultural and Settlement Planning and Development Center. Statistical Series of the Budgetary Year (0075-1294)
Published by: Ministry of Agriculture, Rural Planning and Economic Development, Hakirya, P O Box 7011, Tel Aviv, Israel. Circ: 500.

630 ITA ISSN 1125-4718
➤ **ITALIAN JOURNAL OF AGRONOMY**; an official journal of the Italian Society of Agronomy. Text in English. 1997. s-a. EUR 36 in the European Union to individuals; EUR 42 elsewhere to individuals; EUR 60 in the European Union to institutions; EUR 70 elsewhere to institutions (effective 2003). Website rev. **Document type:** *Academic/Scholarly.* **Description:** Publishes papers in the fields of agronomy and crop science.
Indexed: AgBio, CPA, FCA, HerbAb, HortAb, I&DA, MaizeAb, NutrAb, OrnHort, PBA, PGegResA, PGrRegA, PHN&I, PotatoAb, RA&MP, S&F, SIA, SeedAb, SoyAb, TriticAb, WeedAb.
—BLDSC (4588.339450), IE, ingenta.
Published by: (Societa Italiana di Agronomia), Forum Societa Editrice Universitaria Udinese, Via Larga 38, Udine, UD 33100, Italy. TEL 39-0432-2600, FAX 39-0432-296756, forum@forumeditrice.it, t, http://www.forumeditrice.it. Ed. Giuseppe Zerbi. Adv. contact Paolo Ceccon TEL 39-432-558613.

630 ITA ISSN 1120-8945
S235
ITALY. ISTITUTO NAZIONALE DI STATISTICA. STATISTICHE DELL'AGRICOLTURA, ZOOTECNIA E MEZZI DI PRODUZIONE. Text in Italian. 1940. a. **Document type:** *Government.*
Former titles (until 1985): Italy. Istituto Centrale di Statistica. Statistiche Agrarie (1120-8937); (until 1983): Italy. Istituto Centrale di Statistica. Annuario di Statistica Agraria (0075-1669); (until 1950): Annuario Statistico dell'Agricoltura Italiana (1120-8929)
Indexed: RASB.
—CISTI.
Published by: Istituto Nazionale di Statistica, Via Cesare Balbo 16, Rome, 00184, Italy. FAX 39-06-46735198. Circ: 1,500.

IVORY COAST. MINISTERE DE L'AGRICULTURE. ANNUAIRE DES STATISTIQUES AGRICOLES. see *AGRICULTURE—Abstracting, Bibliographies, Statistics*

IWATE HORTICULTURE EXPERIMENT STATION. BULLETIN. see *AGRICULTURE—Crop Production And Soil*

630 JPN ISSN 1340-6108
J I R C A S INTERNATIONAL SYMPOSIUM SERIES. Text in English. 1967. a. reprint service avail. from ISI. **Document type:** *Proceedings, Government.*
Formerly (until no.26, 1993): Tropical Agriculture Research Series (0388-9386)
Indexed: AEA, AbHyg, AgBio, Agr, AgrForAb, BioCN&I, CPA, FCA, FPA, FS&TA, ForAb, HerbAb, HortAb, I&DA, IndVet, MaizeAb, NutrAb, PBA, PGegResA, PGrRegA, PHN&I, PotatoAb, RA&MP, RDA, RM&VM, RPP, RefZh, RevApplEntom, RiceAb, S&F, SIA, SeedAb, SoyAb, TDB, TriticAb, WAE&RSA, WeedAb.
—BLDSC (4669.175000), CASDDS, CISTI.
Published by: Ministry of Agriculture, Forestry and Fisheries, Japan International Research Center for Agricultural Sciences/Norinsuisan-sho Kokusai Norinsuisangyo Kenkyu Center, Tsukuba, Ibaraki 305, Japan. TEL 81-298-38-6304, FAX 81-298-38-6316, head@ss.jircas.affrc.go.jp, http://ss.jircas.affrc.go.jp/index.sjis.html. Ed. Nobuyoshi Maeno.

630 JPN ISSN 1340-7686
J I R C A S JOURNAL; for scientific papers. Text in English. 1971. s-a.
Formerly (until 1994): Tropical Agriculture Research Center. Technical Bulletin (0388-9394)

A

Indexed: AEA, AgBio, AgrForAb, AnBrAb, BioCN&I, CPA, FCA, ForAb, HelmAb, HerbAb, HortAb, I&DA, MaizeAb, NutrAb, OrnHort, PBA, PGegResA, PHN&I, RA&MP, RDA, RPP, RefZh, RevApplEntom, RiceAb, S&F, SIA, SeedAb, SoyAb, TriticAb, WAE&RSA, WeedAb.
—CISTI, IE, ingenta.
Published by: Ministry of Agriculture, Forestry and Fisheries, Japan International Research Center for Agricultural Sciences/Norinsuisan-sho Kokusai Norinsuisangyo Kenkyu Center, Tsukuba, Ibaraki 305, Japan. TEL 81-298-38-6304, FAX 81-298-38-6316, head@ss.jircas.affrc.go.jp, http://ss.jircas.affrc.go.jp/index.sjis.html. R&P Nobuyoshi Maeno.

630 IND ISSN 0021-3713
J N K V V NEWS. Text in English. 1967. q. free.
Published by: Jawaharlal Nehru Krishi Vishwa Vidyalaya, c/o Information and Public Relations Office, Jabalpur, Madhya Pradesh 482 004, India. Ed. S D N Tiwari. Circ: 1,100.

630 IND ISSN 0021-3721
S17 CODEN: JNRJAW
J N K V V RESEARCH JOURNAL. Text in English. 1967. q. USD 6. adv. bk.rev.
Indexed: AEA, AgBio, AgrForAb, AnBrAb, BioCN&I, BiolAb, CPA, ChemAb, DSA, FCA, ForAb, HelmAb, HerbAb, HortAb, I&DA, IndVet, MaizeAb, NemAb, NutrAb, OrnHort, PBA, PGegResA, PGrRegA, PHN&I, PN&I, PotatoAb, PoultAb, RA&MP, RDA, RM&VM, RPP, RevApplEntom, RiceAb, S&F, SIA, SeedAb, SoyAb, TDB, TriticAb, VetBull, WAE&RSA, WeedAb.
—CASDDS, CISTI.
Published by: Jawaharlal Nehru Krishi Vishwa Vidyalaya, c/o Information and Public Relations Office, Jabalpur, Madhya Pradesh 482 004, India. Ed. Dr. K G Nema. Circ: 500.

631 SWE ISSN 1401-4955
J T I - RAPPORT. KRETSLOPP & AVFALL. Text in Swedish. 1972. irreg. SEK 125 domestic; SEK 155 foreign (effective 2002). **Document type:** *Monographic series, Trade.*
Supersedes in part (in 1996): J T I - Rapport (0346-7597)
Related titles: Online - full content ed.
Published by: Institutet foer Jordbruks- och Miljoeteknik/Swedish Institute of Agricultural and Environmental Engineering, PO Box 7033, Uppsala, 75007, Sweden. TEL 46-18-30-33-00, FAX 46-18-30-09-56, http://www.jti.slu.se/publikat/rapporter/rapporter.htm.

631 SWE ISSN 1401-4963
J T I - RAPPORT. LANTBRUK & INDUSTRI. Text in Swedish. 1972. irreg. SEK 125 domestic; SEK 155 foreign (effective 2002). **Document type:** *Monographic series, Trade.*
Supersedes in part (in 1996): J T I - Rapport (0346-7597)
Related titles: Online - full content ed.
Published by: Institutet foer Jordbruks- och Miljoeteknik/Swedish Institute of Agricultural and Environmental Engineering, PO Box 7033, Uppsala, 75007, Sweden. TEL 46-18-30-33-00, FAX 46-18-30-09-56, http://www.jti.slu.se/publikat/rapporter/rapporter.htm.

JAARSTATISTIEK VAN DE VEEVOEDERS. see *AGRICULTURE—Abstracting, Bibliographies, Statistics*

630 JAM
JAMAICA AGRICULTURAL SOCIETY. MINUTES OF THE HALF-YEARLY MEETING. Text in English. s-a.
Published by: Jamaica Agricultural Society, N. Parade, Kingston, Jamaica.

630 JPN ISSN 0021-3551
CODEN: JARJA9
JAPAN AGRICULTURAL RESEARCH QUARTERLY. Abbreviated title: J A R Q. Text in English. 1966. q. free (effective 2004). charts; illus.; stat. index. back issues avail.; reprint service avail. from ISI. **Document type:** *Government.* **Description:** Disseminates information on the achievements and trends of agricultural research in Japan and overseas countries.
Related titles: Online - full text ed.: free (effective 2005).
Indexed: AEA, ASCA, AbHyg, AgBio, AgrForAb, AnBrAb, BIOSIS Prev, BioCN&I, BiolAb, CIN, CPA, ChemAb, ChemTitl, CurCont, DSA, ExcerpMed, FCA, FPA, FS&TA, ForAb, HelmAb, HerbAb, HortAb, I&DA, IndVet, MaizeAb, NemAb, NutrAb, OrnHort, PBA, PGegResA, PGrRegA, PHN&I, PN&I, PotatoAb, PoultAb, ProtozoAb, RA&MP, RDA, RM&VM, RPP, RefZh, RevApplEntom, RiceAb, S&F, S&MA, SIA, SeedAb, SoyAb, TriticAb, VetBull, WAE&RSA, WeedAb.
—BLDSC (4647.780000), CASDDS, CISTI, IDS, IE, ingenta, Linda Hall.
Published by: Ministry of Agriculture, Forestry and Fisheries, Japan International Research Center for Agricultural Sciences/Norinsuisan-sho Kokusai Norinsuisangyo Kenkyu Center, Tsukuba, Ibaraki 305, Japan. TEL 81-298-38-6304, FAX 81-298-38-6316, TELEX 3652456-TARCJP-J, head@ss.jircas.affrc.go.jp, http://ss.jircas.affrc.go.jp/index.sjis.html. Ed., Pub., R&P Kunio Tsubota. Circ: 2,100.

630 634.9 JPN ISSN 0446-5458
JAPAN. NORIN-SHO NENPO/JAPAN. MINISTRY OF AGRICULTURE AND FORESTRY. ANNUAL REPORT. Text in Japanese. 1953. irreg., latest 1997. JPY 6,000. bk.rev. illus.; stat. **Document type:** *Government.*
Supersedes: Norin Suisan Nenkan
Published by: (Association of Agriculture & Forestry Statistics, Japan. Ministry of Agriculture and Forestry), Government Publications Service Center

630 JPN
JAPANESE JOURNAL OF RURAL ECONOMICS. Text in English. 1999. a. **Document type:** *Journal, Academic/Scholarly.*
Published by: Nihon Nogyo Keizai Gakkai/Agricultural Economic Society of Japan, c/o Center for Academic Publications Japan, 2-4-16 Yayoi, Bunkyo-ku, Tokyo, 113-0032, Japan. http://edpex104.bcasj.or.jp/aesj/index.htm.

630 FRA ISSN 0396-7425
JEUNES AGRICULTEURS. Text in French. 1947. m. adv. **Document type:** *Newspaper, Trade.* **Description:** Discusses such themes as agricultural enterprise, the setting up of young farmers and CNJA's vision of agricultural development.
Published by: Centre National des Jeunes Agriculteurs, 14 rue la Boetie, Paris, 75008, France. TEL 33-1-42651751, FAX 33-1-40170866, philippe.kros@wanadoo.fr. Ed., R&P Philippe Kroslakova. Adv. contact Christophe Joret. Circ: 30,000.

630 CHN ISSN 1002-1302
S542.C4
JIANGSU NONGYE KEXUE/JIANGSU AGRICULTURAL SCIENCES. Text in Chinese; Summaries in English. 1979. bi-m. adv. **Document type:** *Academic/Scholarly.*
Related titles: Online - full text ed.: (from East View Information Services).
Indexed: AEA, AgBio, AgrForAb, AnBrAb, BioCN&I, CPA, FCA, FS&TA, HerbAb, HortAb, I&DA, IndVet, MaizeAb, NutrAb, OrnHort, PBA, PGegResA, PGrRegA, PHN&I, PN&I, PoultAb, RA&MP, RDA, RPP, RevApplEntom, RiceAb, S&F, SeedAb, SoyAb, TriticAb, WAE&RSA, WeedAb.
—BLDSC (4668.456000).
Published by: (Jiangsusheng Nongye Kexueyuan/Jiangsu Academy of Agricultural Sciences), Jiangsu Nongye Kexue Bianjibu, Xiaolingwei, Nanjing, Jiangsu, 210014, China. Ed. Ma Yikang.

630 CHN ISSN 1000-4440
➤ **JIANGSU NONGYE XUEBAO/JIANGSU JOURNAL OF AGRICULTURAL SCIENCES.** Text in Chinese; Abstracts in English. 1985. q. CNY 4 per issue. **Document type:** *Academic/Scholarly.* **Description:** Contains research papers on various aspects of agricultural sciences.
Related titles: CD-ROM ed.; Online - full text ed.: (from East View Information Services).
Indexed: AEA, AgBio, AgrForAb, AnBrAb, BioCN&I, CPA, DSA, FCA, FPA, ForAb, HerbAb, HortAb, I&DA, IndVet, MaizeAb, NemAb, NutrAb, OrnHort, PBA, PGegResA, PGrRegA, PHN&I, PN&I, PotatoAb, PoultAb, RA&MP, RDA, RM&VM, RPP, RevApplEntom, RiceAb, S&F, SIA, SeedAb, SoyAb, TriticAb, VetBull, WAE&RSA, WeedAb.
—BLDSC (4668.459000), CISTI.
Published by: Jiangsu Sheng Nongye Kexueyuan/Jiangsu Academy of Agricultural Sciences, Xiaolingwei, Nanjing, Jiangsu 210014, China. TEL 86-25-4390285. Ed. Gao Liangzhi.

630 CHN ISSN 1000-2286
JIANGXI NONGYE DAXUE XUEBAO/ACTA AGRICULTURAE UNIVERSITATIS JIANGXIENSIS. Text in Chinese. 1979. bi-m. **Document type:** *Journal, Academic/Scholarly.*
Related titles: Online - full content ed.: (from WanFang Data Corp.); Online - full text ed.: (from East View Information Services).
Indexed: AEA, ASFA, AgBio, AgrForAb, AnBrAb, BioCN&I, CPA, DSA, ESPM, EnvEAb, FCA, FPA, ForAb, HelmAb, HerbAb, HortAb, I&DA, IndVet, M&GPA, MaizeAb, NemAb, NutrAb, OrnHort, PBA, PGegResA, PGrRegA, PHN&I, PN&I, PollutAb, PotatoAb, PoultAb, ProtozoAb, RA&MP, RDA, RM&VM, RPP, RRTA, RefZh, RiceAb, S&F, SIA, SWRA, SeedAb, SoyAb, TriticAb, VetBull, WAE&RSA, WeedAb, ZooRec.
—BLDSC (0588.690000).
Published by: Jiangxi Nongye Daxue, Nanchang, Jiangxi 330045, China. TEL 86-791-3813246, FAX 86-791-3813740, http://jxnydxxb.periodicals.com.cn/default.html. **Dist. by:** China International Book Trading Corp, 35 Chegongzhuang Xilu, Haidian District, PO Box 399, Beijing 100044, China. TEL 86-10-68412045, FAX 86-10-68412023, cibtc@mail.cibtc.com.cn, http://www.cibtc.com.cn.

630 CHN ISSN 1000-5684
S19 CODEN: JNDXUEB
➤ **JILIN NONGYE DAXUE XUEBAO/JILIN UNIVERSITY OF AGRICULTURE. JOURNAL.** Text in Chinese. bi-m. CNY 60 (effective 2003). **Document type:** *Journal, Academic/Scholarly.*
Related titles: CD-ROM ed.; Microfilm ed.; Online - full content ed.: (from WanFang Data Corp.); Online - full text ed.: (from East View Information Services).
Indexed: AEA, AgBio, AgrForAb, AnBrAb, BioCN&I, CPA, DSA, FCA, ForAb, HelmAb, HerbAb, HortAb, I&DA, IndVet, MaizeAb, NemAb, NutrAb, OrnHort, PBA, PGegResA, PGrRegA, PHN&I, PN&I, PotatoAb, PoultAb, ProtozoAb, RA&MP, RDA, RM&VM, RPP, RefZh, RevApplEntom, RiceAb, S&F, SIA, SeedAb, SoyAb, TDB, TriticAb, VetBull, WAE&RSA, WeedAb, ZooRec.
—BLDSC (4809.594000).
Published by: Jilin Nongye Daxue/Jilin University of Agriculture, Donghuan Lunan, Changchun, Jilin 130118, China. TEL 86-431-4531241, jlndxb@vip.sina.com, http://jlnydxxb.periodicals.net.cn. Ed. Aiqun Zhao.

630 635 634.9 712 DNK ISSN 0906-7043
JORD OG VIDEN; information, politik og debat for jordbrugsakademikere. Text in Danish. 1855. 17/yr. DKK 770 domestic; DKK 920 foreign; DKK 390 in Europe to students; DKK 640 elsewhere to students (effective 2004). adv. bk.rev. bibl.; charts; illus. index. 32 p./no. 4 cols./p.; **Document type:** *Bulletin, Trade.*
Former titles (until 1992): Ugeskrift for Jordbrug (0106-0546); (until Jan. 1979): Ugeskrift for Agronomer, Hortonomer, Forstkandidater og Licentiater (0106-0538); (until 1976): Ugeskrift for Agronomer og Hortonomer (0106-0074); Which was formed by the merger of (1947-1971): Horticultura (0018-5272); (1967-1971): Ugeskrift for Agronomer (0041-5774); Which was formerly (until 1967): Ugeskrift for Landmaend (0909-8046)
Indexed: FCA, HerbAb, HortAb, S&F, WeedAb.
—CISTI.
Published by: Jordbrugsakademikernes Forbund, Frederiksberg Alle 3, Copenhagen V, 1621, Denmark. TEL 45-20-212800, FAX 45-20-212810, jogv@jordbrugsakademikerne.dk, post@jordbrugsakademikerne.dk, http://www.jordbrugsakademikerne.dk. Ed. Marianne Tinggaard. adv.: B&W page DKK 14,500, color page DKK 19,900; trim 264 x 187. Circ: 6,055.

630 JOR
JORDAN. DEPARTMENT OF STATISTICS. AGRICULTURAL STATISTICAL YEARBOOK AND AGRICULTURAL SAMPLE SURVEY. Text in Arabic, English. 1966. a. USD 15 (effective 2000). **Document type:** *Government.*
Published by: Department of Statistics, P O Box 2015, Amman, Jordan. TEL 962-6-842171, FAX 962-6-833518.

630 634.9 DNK ISSN 0107-6108
JORDBRUG OESTJYLLAND (MIDT): SAMTLIGE LANDBRUG, SKOVBRUG OG GARTNERIER. Text in Danish. 1980. fortn. adv. illus.
Published by: Jordbrug Oestjylland (Midt), c/o Bo Eriksson, Fussingsvej 21, Horsens, 8700, Denmark.

630 363.7 DNK ISSN 1399-8323
JORDBRUG OG MILJOE. Text in Danish. 1999. irreg. back issues avail. **Document type:** *Monographic series, Government.*
Related titles: Online - full text ed.: ISSN 1399-9443.
Published by: Miljoeministeriet, Danmarks Miljoeundersoegelser/Ministry of the Environment, National Environmental Research Institute, Denmark, Frederiksborgvej 399, PO Box 358, Roskilde, 4000, Denmark. TEL 45-46-301200, FAX 45-46-301114, dmu@dmu.dk, http://www.dmu.dk.

630 SWE ISSN 0345-5718
JORDBRUKSAKTUELLT. Text in Swedish. 1962. 18/yr. SEK 250 in Scandinavia; SEK 300 in Europe. adv.
Address: Naebbtrogsgatan 2, Fack 8120, Orebro, 70008, Sweden. TEL 46-19-13-07-80, FAX 46-19-10-17-75, jordbruks@ja.se, http://www.ja.se. Ed. Peter Lsjoesten. Adv. contact Peter Sjoesten. B&W page SEK 25,250, color page SEK 32,560; trim 370 x 250. Circ: 100,800.

630 FRA ISSN 0021-7778
JOURNAL DE LA CORSE AGRICOLE. Text in French. 1965. m.
Published by: (Mutualite Sociale Agricole de la Corse), Imprimerie Siciliano, B.P. 255, Ajaccio, Corsica 20179, France. TEL 95-21-01-84, FAX 95-21-37-49. Circ: 3,800.

641.22 FRA ISSN 1274-2244
CODEN: JSTTFA
➤ **JOURNAL DES SCIENCES ET TECHNIQUES DE LA TONNELLERIE/JOURNAL OF COOPERAGE SCIENCES AND TECHNIQUES.** Text in French, English. 1995. a. EUR 20 domestic; EUR 24 foreign (effective 2003). **Document type:** *Journal, Academic/Scholarly.*
Related titles: Online - full text ed.
Indexed: FPA, ForAb, HortAb, NutrAb, VITIS.
—BLDSC (5056.689700), CASDDS.
Published by: Vigne et Vin Publications Internationales, 42 rue Marsan, Bordeaux, 33300, France. TEL 33-5-57876869, FAX 33-5-57876848, vvpi@wanadoo.fr, http://www.vigne-vin.com.

630 658 FRA ISSN 0446-9739
JOURNAL DU FERMIER ET DU METAYER. Text in French. 1948. m. adv.
Published by: F.N.S.E.A., Section Nationale des Fermiers et Metayers, 11 rue de la Baume, Paris, 75008, France. Ed. Aline Guyvarc'h.

641.22 FRA ISSN 1151-0285
CODEN: JISVE8
JOURNAL INTERNATIONAL DES SCIENCES DE LA VIGNE ET DU VIN. Text in French, English. 1967. q. EUR 80 domestic; EUR 95 foreign (effective 2005). adv. bk.rev. Supplement avail. **Document type:** *Academic/Scholarly.* **Description:** Discusses viticulture and enology.
Formerly: Connaissance de la Vigne et du Vin (0010-597X)

Indexed: AEA, AgBio, AnalAb, BIOSIS Prev, BiolAb, CIN, CPA, ChemAb, ChemTitl, CurCont, FPA, FS&TA, ForAb, HortAb, I&DA, MSB, NutrAb, PBA, PGegResA, PGrRegA, PHN&I, RPP, RevApplEntom, S&F, SIA, SeedAb, VITIS, WeedAb.
—BLDSC (5007.686250), CASDDS, IE, ingenta. **CCC.**
Published by: (Association des Anciens Eleves de l'Institut d'Oenologie de Bordeaux), Vigne et Vin Publications Internationales, 42 rue Marsan, Bordeaux, 33300, France. TEL 33-5-57876869, FAX 33-5-57876848, vvpi@wanadoo.fr, http://www.vigne-vin.com/. Ed. Aline Lonvaud-Funel. Circ: 1,500.

JOURNAL OF AGRICULTURAL AND ENVIRONMENTAL ETHICS. see *PHILOSOPHY*

630 641.3 USA ISSN 1049-6505
S494.5.I47 CODEN: JFOIEU
➤ **JOURNAL OF AGRICULTURAL & FOOD INFORMATION.** Abbreviated title: J A F I. Text in English. q. USD 95 combined subscription domestic to institutions print & online eds.; USD 128.25 combined subscription in Canada to institutions print & online eds.; USD 137.75 combined subscription elsewhere to institutions print & online eds. (effective 2006). adv. 120 p./no. 1 cols./p.; back issues avail.; reprint service avail. from HAW. **Document type:** *Journal, Academic/Scholarly.* **Description:** Provides a forum for the communication of research, innovative practice, and informed opinion on all aspects of agricultural and food information.
Formerly (until 1991): Journal of Food and Agricultural Info
Related titles: Microform ed.: (from PQC); Online - full text ed.: ISSN 1540-4722. 2002. free to institutions (effective 2003); free with print subs. (from EBSCO Publishing, O C L C Online Computer Library Center, Inc., Swets Information Services).
Indexed: ASFA, Agr, BibAg, BioCN&I, BrCerAb, C&ISA, CerAb, CorrAb, E&CAJ, EMA, ESPM, EnvAb, FCA, FS&TA, ForAb, H&SSA, H&TI, HRA, HerbAb, HortAb, IAA, IBR, IBZ, InfoSAb, Inspec, LISA, M&TEA, MBF, METADEX, OrnHort, RefZh, S&F, WAA, WAE&RSA.
—BLDSC (4920.050000), AskIEEE, Haworth, IE, Infotrieve, Linda Hall. **CCC.**
Published by: Haworth Information Press (Subsidiary of: Haworth Press, Inc.), 10 Alice St, Binghamton, NY 13904. TEL 607-722-5857, 800-429-6784, FAX 607-771-0012, 800-895-0582, getinfo@haworthpress.com, http://www.haworthpress.com/web/JAFI. Eds. Amy Blair, Anita M Ezzo. Pub. William Cohen. R&P Ruth Ann Heath TEL 607-722-5857 ext 316. Adv. contact Rebecca Miller-Baum TEL 607-722-5857 ext 337. B&W page USD 315, color page USD 550; trim 4.375 x 7.125. Circ: 150 (paid).

➤ **JOURNAL OF AGRICULTURAL AND URBAN ENTOMOLOGY.** see *BIOLOGY—Entomology*

➤ **JOURNAL OF AGRICULTURAL EDUCATION.** see *EDUCATION*

630.711 NLD
➤ **JOURNAL OF AGRICULTURAL EDUCATION AND EXTENSION**; international journal on changes in agricultural knowledge and action systems. Text in English. 1994. q. bk.rev. **Document type:** *Academic/Scholarly.* **Description:** Publishes articles on topical issues in agricultural higher and secondary education and extension.
Formerly (until vol. 4, no. 4, 1998): European Journal of Agricultural Education and Extension (1381-2335)
Related titles: Diskette ed.
Indexed: Agr, CIJE, DSA, PGegResA, RDA, RevApplEntom, SeedAb, WAE&RSA, WeedAb.
—BLDSC (4920.880000), IE, ingenta, KNAW.
Address: Group Communication and Innovation Studies, Hollandseweg 1, Wageningen, 6706 KN, Netherlands. TEL 31-317-482599, FAX 31-317-484791, Annemarie.Wagemakers@Alg.VLK.WAU.NL, http://www.bib.wau.nl/ejae/. Ed. Jet Proose. Circ: 250 (paid).

630 IND ISSN 0256-6524
JOURNAL OF AGRICULTURAL ENGINEERING. Text in English. 1964. q. USD 100 (effective 2003). adv. bk.rev. bibl.; charts; illus.
Indexed: IAOP, S&F.
Published by: Indian Society of Agricultural Engineers, Satya Mansion, Flat nos. 305-306 Community Centre, Ranjit Nagar, New Delhi, 100 008, India. TEL 11-5709003. Ed. A P Bhatnagar. Circ: 1,000. **Subscr. to:** Scientific Publishers, 5-A New Pali Rd., Near Hotel Taj Hari Mahal, PO Box 91, Jodhpur, Rajasthan 342 003, India. TEL 91-291-2433323, FAX 91-291-2512580, info@scientificpub.com, http:// www.scientificpub.com.

JOURNAL OF AGRICULTURAL LENDING. see *BUSINESS AND ECONOMICS—Banking And Finance*

630 EGY ISSN 1110-032X
JOURNAL OF AGRICULTURAL RESEARCH/MAGALLAT AL-BIHUD AL-ZIRAA'IYYAT GAAMI'AT TANTAA. Text in English. 1975. q. **Document type:** *Journal, Academic/Scholarly.*
Published by: Tanta University, Faculty of Agriculture, Kafr El-Shaikh, Tanta, Egypt. TEL 20-40-322762, http://derp.sti.sci.eg/data/0154.htm. Ed. Dr. Muhammad Aly El-Ashri.

630 TWN ISSN 0376-477X
S278.F6 CODEN: CHNCDB
JOURNAL OF AGRICULTURAL RESEARCH OF CHINA. Key Title: Zhonghua Nongye Yanjiu. Text in Chinese, English. 1950. q. free. **Document type:** *Academic/Scholarly.*
Formerly (until vol.23, 1974): Journal of Taiwan Agricultural Research (0022-4847)
Indexed: AEA, AgBio, AgrForAb, BAS, BioCN&I, BiolAb, CPA, FCA, FPA, ForAb, HerbAb, HortAb, I&DA, MaizeAb, NemAb, OrnHort, PBA, PGegResA, PGrRegA, PHN&I, PN&I, PotatoAb, PoultAb, RA&MP, RM&VM, RPP, RRTA, RevApplEntom, RiceAb, S&F, S&MA, SIA, SeedAb, SoyAb, TOSA, TriticAb, WAE&RSA, WeedAb, ZooRec.
—BLDSC (4922.870000), CASDDS, CISTI, IE, ingenta.
Published by: Taiwan Agricultural Research Institute, 189 Chung-cheng Rd, Wufeng, Taipei, Taiwan. FAX 866-4-333-8162. Pub. Chien Yih Lin.

363.11963 USA ISSN 1074-7583
S565 CODEN: JASHFD
➤ **JOURNAL OF AGRICULTURAL SAFETY AND HEALTH.** Text in English. 1995. q. USD 109 domestic to non-members; USD 119 foreign to non-members; USD 56 to members (effective 2004). bk.rev.; video rev. abstr.; illus. index. reprints avail. **Document type:** *Journal, Academic/Scholarly.* **Description:** Focuses on the unique needs and concerns of safety and health as they relate to agriculture.
Related titles: Online - full content ed.
Indexed: AEA, ASFA, AbHyg, AgBio, Agr, AnBrAb, DSA, EPB, ESPM, EngInd, ErgAb, FPA, ForAb, H&SSA, HerbAb, HortAb, IndMed, IndVet, MEDLINE, MaizeAb, PBA, PHN&I, PN&I, PotatoAb, PoultAb, RDA, RM&VM, RPP, RRTA, RevApplEntom, RiskAb, SoyAb, TDB, ToxAb, WAE&RSA, WeedAb.
—BLDSC (4922.980000), CISTI, IE, Infotrieve, ingenta. **CCC.**
Published by: American Society of Agricultural Engineers, 2950 Niles Rd, St. Joseph, MI 49085-9659. TEL 269-429-0300, FAX 269-429-3852, hq@asae.org, http://www.asae.org. Ed. Dennis Murphy. R&P Sandy Rutter. Circ: 400.

630 GBR ISSN 0021-8596
S3 CODEN: JASIAB
➤ **JOURNAL OF AGRICULTURAL SCIENCE.** Text in English. 1905. bi-m. GBP 448 to institutions; USD 722 in North America to institutions; GBP 494 combined subscription to institutions print & online eds.; USD 795 combined subscription in North America to institutions print & online eds. (effective 2006). adv. bk.rev. bibl.; charts; illus. index. back issues avail.; reprint service avail. from PSC. **Document type:** *Journal, Academic/Scholarly.* **Description:** Covers research in pure and applied sciences relating to agricultural problems.
Formerly (until 1999): Review of Reserch Work at the Faculty of Agriculture (0354-3498)
Related titles: Microform ed.: (from PMC, PQC); Online - full text ed.: ISSN 1469-5146. GBP 432 to institutions; USD 694 in North America to institutions (effective 2006) (from EBSCO Publishing, O C L C Online Computer Library Center, Inc., Swets Information Services).
Indexed: AEA, ASCA, ASFA, AgBio, Agr, AgrForAb, AnBrAb, ApicAb, B&AI, BIOBASE, BIOSIS Prev, BibAg, BioCN&I, BiolAb, CADCAM, CBTA, CIN, CIS, CPA, CTFA, ChemAb, ChemTitl, CurCont, DBA, DSA, EPB, ESPM, EngInd, EnvAb, EnvEAb, ExcerpMed, FCA, FPA, FS&TA, FaBeAb, ForAb, GEOBASE, HelmAb, HerbAb, HortAb, I&DA, IABS, ISR, IndVet, MaizeAb, NAA, NemAb, NutrAb, OrnHort, PBA, PGegResA, PGrRegA, PHN&I, PN&I, PlantSci, PollutAb, PotatoAb, PoultAb, ProtozoAb, RA&MP, RPP, RefZh, RevApplEntom, RiceAb, S&F, S&MA, SCI, SFA, SIA, SPPI, SWRA, SeedAb, SoyAb, TOSA, TriticAb, VITIS, VetBull, WAE&RSA, WeedAb, WildRev, ZooRec.
—BLDSC (4923.000000), CASDDS, CISTI, Ei, IDS, IE, Infotrieve, ingenta, Linda Hall. **CCC.**
Published by: Cambridge University Press, The Edinburgh Bldg, Shaftesbury Rd, Cambridge, CB2 2RU, United Kingdom. TEL 44-1223-312393, FAX 44-1223-315052, journals@cambridge.org, http://uk.cambridge.org/journals/ags. Eds. Julian Wiseman, Robert Naylor. R&P Linda Nicol TEL 44-1223-325757. Adv. contact Rebecca Curtis TEL 44-1223-325757. **Subscr. to:** Cambridge University Press, 100 Brook Hill Dr, West Nyack, NY 10994. TEL 845-353-7500, FAX 845-353-4141, journals_subscriptions@cup.org

638.1 POL ISSN 1643-4439
➤ **JOURNAL OF AGRICULTURAL SCIENCE.** Text and summaries in English, Polish. 1957. s-a. PLZ 15, EUR 15 per issue (effective 2003). back issues avail. **Document type:** *Journal, Academic/Scholarly.*
Formerly: Pszczelnicze Zeszyty Naukowe (0552-4563)
Indexed: AgrAg, AgrLib, FS&TA, ZooRec.
Published by: (Pszczelnicze Towarzystwo Naukowe), Instytut Sadownictwa i Kwiaciarstwa, Oddzial Pszczelnictwa w Pulawach/Institute of Pomology and Floriculture, Division of Apiculture, ul. Kazimierska 2, Pulawy, 24-100, Poland. TEL 48-81-8864208, FAX 48-81-8864209, opisk@man.pulawy.pl, opisk@man.pulawy.pl. Eds. Teresa Szczesna, Wojciech Skowronek.

630 IRN ISSN 1680-7073
JOURNAL OF AGRICULTURAL SCIENCE AND TECHNOLOGY. Text in English. 2000. q. **Document type:** *Journal, Academic/Scholarly.*
—BLDSC (4923.025100).
Published by: University of Tarbiat Modarres, Faculty of Agriculture, PO Box 14115-336, Tehran, Iran. TEL 98-21-4196408, FAX 98-21-4196524, jastiran@modares.ac.ir, http://www.modares.ac.ir. Ed. K Poustini.

630 EGY ISSN 1110-0346
JOURNAL OF AGRICULTURAL SCIENCES. Text in English. 1976. q. **Document type:** *Journal, Academic/Scholarly.*
Published by: Mansoura University, Faculty of Agriculture, University Campus, Mansoura, Egypt. TEL 20-50-345274, FAX 20-50-345268, http://derp.sti.sci.eg/data/0155.htm. Ed. Dr. M S El-Gendi.

631.091 363.7 ITA ISSN 1590-7198
CODEN: RSTTAP
JOURNAL OF AGRICULTURE AND ENVIRONMENT FOR INTERNATIONAL DEVELOPMENT. Text in English, French, Spanish; Summaries in English. 1907. q. EUR 41.30 per issue domestic; EUR 46.50 per issue foreign (effective 2003). bk.rev. abstr.; bibl.; charts; illus.; stat. index. back issues avail. **Document type:** *Journal, Academic/Scholarly.*
Former titles: Rivista di Agricoltura Subtropicale e Tropicale (0035-6026); (until 1944): Agricoltura Coloniale (0394-2945)
Indexed: AEA, ATA, AbHyg, AgrForAb, AnBrAb, B&AI, BioCN&I, BiolAb, CPA, ChemAb, CurCont, DSA, ExcerpMed, FCA, FPA, FS&TA, ForAb, HelmAb, HerbAb, HortAb, I&DA, IndVet, MaizeAb, NutrAb, OrnHort, PBA, PGegResA, PHN&I, PotatoAb, ProtozoAb, RDA, RPP, RRTA, RefZh, RevApplEntom, S&F, S&MA, SeedAb, TDB, TriticAb, VetBull, WAE&RSA, WeedAb.
—CASDDS, CISTI.
Published by: Istituto Agronomico per l'Oltremare di Firenze, Via Antonio Cocchi 4, Florence, 50131, Italy. TEL 39-055-50611, FAX 39-055-5061333, rivtrop@iao.florence.it, http://www.iao.florence.it. Ed., R&P Alice Perlini. Circ: 800.

631.091 DEU
➤ **JOURNAL OF AGRICULTURE AND RURAL DEVELOPMENT IN THE TROPICS AND SUBTROPICS.** Text in English. 2002. 2/yr. EUR 30; EUR 20 newsstand/cover (effective 2004). **Document type:** *Journal, Academic/Scholarly.*
Formed by the merger of (1966-2002): Der Tropenlandwirt (0041-3186); (1963-2002): Beitraege zur Tropischen Landwirtschaft und Veterinaermedizin (0301-567X); Which was formerly (until 1973): Beitraege zur Tropischen und Subtropischen Landwirtschaft und Tropenveterinaermedizin (0005-8203)
—BLDSC (4925.785000).
Published by: Kassel University Press GmbH, Diagonale 10, Kassel, 34127, Germany. TEL 49-561-8042159, FAX 49-561-8043429, geschaeftsfuehrung@upress.uni-kassel.de, http://web1.150025.vserver.de/trop/default.php?language= de&cPath=9, http://www.upress.uni-kassel.de. **Co-sponsor:** Deutsches Institut fuer Tropische und Subtropische Landwirtschaft.

631 NGA ISSN 1595-7470
JOURNAL OF AGRICULTURE AND SOCIAL RESEARCH. Text in English. 2001. s-a. NGN 400 to individuals; NGN 800 to institutions (effective 2004). **Description:** Publishes articles on agriculture, home economics/food science, forestry, wildlife and fisheries, environment and waste management, economics, urban and Regional planning, sociology and other relevant social and applied sciences.
Related titles: Online - full text ed.: (from International Network for the Availability of Scientific Publications, African Journals Online).
Published by: University of Ibadan, Faculty of Agriculture and Forestry, Ibadan, Nigeria. http://www.inasp.info/ajol/journals/ jasr/about.html, http://www.ui.edu.ng/. Ed. O. Oladele.
Co-publisher: Federal University of Technology, School of Agriculture and Agricultural Technology.

630 IRQ ISSN 1012-3474
CODEN: JAWPEM
JOURNAL OF AGRICULTURE AND WATER RESEARCH. PLANT PRODUCTION✶. Text in Arabic, English. 1986. s-a. IQD 5, USD 15 to individuals; to individuals; institutions $50.
Indexed: Agrind, BiolAb, ChemAb, HerbAb.
—CASDDS.
Published by: Scientific Research Council, Agricultural and Water Resources Research Center, Jadiriyah, P O Box 2441, Baghdad, Iraq. TELEX 213976 SR IK. Ed. Semir A Al-Shaker. Circ: 500.

630 IRQ ISSN 1012-3482
CODEN: JWSREQ
JOURNAL OF AGRICULTURE AND WATER RESOURCES RESEARCH. SOIL AND WATER RESOURCES✶. Text in Arabic, English. 1986. s-a. IQD 5, USD 15 to individuals; to individuals; institutions $50.
Indexed: AEA, Agrind, BiolAb, ChemAb, HerbAb, I&DA.
—CASDDS.
Published by: Scientific Research Council, Agricultural and Water Resources Research Center, Jadiriyah, P O Box 2441, Baghdad, Iraq. TELEX 213976 SR IK. Ed. Semir A Al-Shaker. Circ: 500.

JOURNAL OF AGROMEDICINE; interface of human health & agriculture. see *OCCUPATIONAL HEALTH AND SAFETY*

A

630 PAK ISSN 1812-5379
➤ **JOURNAL OF AGRONOMY.** Text in English. 2002. q. USD 350 (effective 2005). **Document type:** *Journal, Academic/Scholarly.* **Description:** Publishes articles, reviews and short communications of a high scientific and ethical standard in the field of crop sciences.
Formerly (until 2004): Pakistan Journal of Agronomy (1680-8207)
Related titles: Online - full text ed.: ISSN 1812-5417. free (effective 2005).
Indexed: FCA.
Published by: Asian Network for Scientific Information, 308-Lasani Town, Sargodha Rd, Faislabad, 38090, Pakistan. TEL 92-41-2001145, FAX 92-41-731433, http://www.ansinet.org/c4p.php?j_id=ja, http://www.ansinet.net.

638.1 GBR ISSN 0021-8839
QL563 CODEN: JACRAQ
➤ **JOURNAL OF APICULTURAL RESEARCH.** Text in English. 1962. q. GBP 125 (effective 2004). adv. bibl.; charts; illus. index. 2 cols./p.; back issues avail. **Document type:** *Journal, Academic/Scholarly.* **Description:** Contains original scientific research on bees and beekeeping.
Related titles: Online - full text ed.: (from Gale Group).
Indexed: ASCA, ASFA, AgBio, Agr, AgrForAb, ApicAb, BIOSIS Prev, BioCN&I, BiolAb, CIN, CPA, ChemAb, ChemTitl, CurCont, EntAb, FCA, FPA, FS&TA, ForAb, HerbAb, HortAb, ISR, IndVet, MaizeAb, NutrAb, OrnHort, PGegResA, ProtozoAb, RM&VM, RefZh, RevApplEntom, SCI, SIA, SeedAb, TDB, TriticAb, VetBull, WeedAb.
—BLDSC (4939.600000), CASDDS, CISTI, IDS, IE, Infotrieve, ingenta, Linda Hall. **CCC.**
Published by: International Bee Research Association, 18 North Rd, Cardiff, Wales CF10 3DT, United Kingdom. TEL 44-2920-372409, FAX 44-2920-665522, mail@ibra.org.uk, http://www.ibra.org.uk. Eds. Dr. Keith S Delaplane, Dr. Pamela A Munn. Adv. contact Dr. Pamela A Munn. page GBP 145; trim 130 x 200. Circ: 500.

630 USA ISSN 1051-0834
S494.5.C6A27
➤ **JOURNAL OF APPLIED COMMUNICATIONS.** Text in English. 1990. q. USD 75 (effective 2005). bk.rev.; Website rev.; software rev.; video rev. index. back issues avail. **Document type:** *Journal, Academic/Scholarly.* **Description:** Covers a variety of applied communications research conducted at land-grant and public agencies internationally that deal with public comminication issues in agriculture and natural resourses.
Indexed: Agr, CIJE.
Published by: Agricultural Communicators in Education, PO Box 110811, Gainesville, FL 32611. TEL 352-392-9588, FAX 352-392-7902, ace@mail.ifas.ufl.edu, http://www.aceweb.org/JAC/jac.html. Ed. Linda Foster Benedict. Circ: 740 (paid).

631 HRV ISSN 1332-9049
JOURNAL OF CENTRAL EUROPEAN AGRICULTURE. Text in Multiple languages. 2000. quadrennial. free (effective 2005). back issues avail.
Media: Online - full text.
Indexed: AgBio, AnBrAb, BioCN&I, CPA, DSA, FCA, HerbAb, HortAb, IndVet, MaizeAb, OrnHort, PBA, PGrRegA, PHN&I, PotatoAb, RM&VM, RRTA, S&F, SIA, SeedAb, SoyAb, TriticAb, WAE&RSA, WeedAb.
Published by: Sveuciliste U Zagrebu, Agronomski Fakultet/University of Zagreb, Faculty of Agriculture, Svetosimunska 25, Zagreb, 100000, Croatia. TEL 385-1-2393777, FAX 385-1-2315300, http://www.agr.hr/jcea/.

JOURNAL OF ENVIRONMENTAL EXTENSION. see *ENVIRONMENTAL STUDIES*

JOURNAL OF ENVIRONMENTAL SCIENCE AND HEALTH. PART B: PESTICIDES, FOOD CONTAMINANTS, AND AGRICULTURAL WASTES. see *ENVIRONMENTAL STUDIES*

JOURNAL OF GINSENG RESEARCH. see *PHARMACY AND PHARMACOLOGY*

638.2 JPN ISSN 1346-8073
SF541 CODEN: NISZAQ
➤ **JOURNAL OF INSECT BIOTECHNOLOGY AND SERICOLOGY.** Text in English, Japanese. 1930. bi-m. JPY 7,500 (effective 1999). adv. bk.rev. index. **Document type:** *Academic/Scholarly.* **Description:** Contains research articles on sericultural science and insect utilization.
Supersedes in part (in 2000): Nippon Sanshigaku Zasshi/Journal of Sericultural Science of Japan (0037-2455)
Related titles: Online - full text ed.: (from J-Stage).
Indexed: A&ATA, Agr, BIOSIS Prev, BiolAb, CIN, ChemAb, ChemTitl, FCA, INIS AtomInd, TTI, WTA, ZooRec.
—BLDSC (5064.010000), CASDDS, CISTI, IE, ingenta, Linda Hall. **CCC.**
Published by: Nihon Sanshi Gakkai/Japanese Society of Sericultural Science, National Institute of Sericultural & Entomological Science, 1-2 Owashi, Tsukuba-shi, Ibaraki-ken 305-0851, Japan. TEL 81-29-8386158, FAX 81-29-8386159, stakeda@affrc.go.jp, http://www.affrc.go.jp:8001/jsss/. Ed. Toshihiko Iizuka. Adv. contact Atsunobu Haga. Circ: 1,300.

630.071 USA ISSN 1077-0755
S544
➤ **JOURNAL OF INTERNATIONAL AGRICULTURAL AND EXTENSION EDUCATION.** Text in English. 1994. 3/yr. USD 45 to individuals; USD 75 to libraries; USD 20 per issue (effective 2005). **Document type:** *Journal, Academic/Scholarly.* **Description:** Articles intended for publication should focus on international agricultural education and/or international extension education with implications for developed and developing countries.
Related titles: Diskette ed.: USD 15 (effective 2002); E-mail ed.: USD 10 (effective 2002); Online - full content ed.
Indexed: IBSS.
Published by: Association of International Agricultural and Extension Education, 2116 TAMU, College Station, TX 77843-2116. TEL 979-862-1507, FAX 979-845-6296, nplace@mail.ifas.ufl.edu, http://www.aiaee.org/journal.html, http://ag.arizona.edu/aiaee/index.htm. Ed. Gary J Wingenbach. Circ: 175 (paid).

➤ **JOURNAL OF IRRIGATION AND DRAINAGE ENGINEERING.** see *ENGINEERING—Civil Engineering*

630 IND ISSN 0378-2395
CODEN: JMAUDA
➤ **JOURNAL OF MAHARASHTRA AGRICULTURAL UNIVERSITIES.** Text in English. 1976. 3/yr. INR 800, USD 120. bk.rev. charts; illus.; stat. back issues avail. **Document type:** *Academic/Scholarly.*
Formerly (until 1976): Research Journal of Mahatma Phule Agricultural University (0378-6404)
Indexed: AEA, AgBio, AgrForAb, AnBrAb, BIOSIS Prev, BioCN&I, BiolAb, CIN, CPA, CTFA, ChemAb, ChemTitl, DSA, FCA, FPA, ForAb, HelmAb, HerbAb, HortAb, I&DA, IndVet, MaizeAb, NemAb, NutrAb, OrnHort, PBA, PGegResA, PGrRegA, PHN&I, PotatoAb, PoultAb, RA&MP, RDA, REE&TA, RM&VM, RPP, RefZh, RevApplEntom, RiceAb, S&F, S&MA, SIA, SeedAb, SoyAb, TDB, TOSA, TriticAb, VITIS, VetBull, WAE&RSA, WeedAb, ZooRec.
—BLDSC (4819.230000), CASDDS, CISTI, IE, ingenta, Linda Hall.
Published by: Poona Agricultural College, Pune, Maharashtra 411 005, India. TEL 5537033. Ed. N B Pawar. Circ: 1,200.
Co-sponsors: Mahatma Phule Agricultural University Rahuri; Marathwada Krishi Vidyapeeth Parbhani; Konkan Krishi Vidyapeeth, Dapoli; Punjabrao Krishi Vidyapeeth, Akola.

630 BGR ISSN 1311-0489
JOURNAL OF MOUNTAIN AGRICULTURE IN THE BALKANS. Text in Bulgarian, English. bi-m. USD 96 foreign (effective 2002). **Document type:** *Journal, Academic/Scholarly.* **Description:** Covers basic and applied research relevant to agriculture in the mountain areas; publishes papers and short communications on stockbreeding, forage production, and ecological issues.
Indexed: RefZh, VITIS.
Published by: Research Institute of Mountain Stockbreeding and Agriculture, 281 Vasil Levski St., Troyan, 5600, Bulgaria. TEL 359-670-22802, FAX 359-670-23032, iusba@iusba.bia-bg.com, rimsa@rimsa.org, http://www.rimsa.org/en/. **Dist. by:** Sofia Books, ul Silivria 16, Sofia 1404, Bulgaria. TEL 359-2-9586257, info@sofiabooks-bg.com, http://www.sofiabooks-bg.com.

630 MYS ISSN 1511-2780
CODEN: JOPRFO
JOURNAL OF OIL PALM RESEARCH. Text in English. 1989. s-a. MYR 20, USD 15 (effective 2000). bk.rev. back issues avail. **Document type:** *Academic/Scholarly.*
Formerly: Eleais (0128-1828)
Indexed: AEA, AgBio, Agr, BioCN&I, CIN, CPA, ChemAb, ChemTitl, DSA, FPA, FS&TA, ForAb, HortAb, I&DA, MaizeAb, PBA, PGegResA, PGrRegA, PHN&I, RA&MP, RM&VM, RPP, S&F, SIA, SeedAb, SoyAb, WAE&RSA, WeedAb.
—BLDSC (5026.303500), CASDDS, IE, ingenta.
Published by: Lembaga Minyak Sawit Malaysia/Malaysian Palm Oil Board (Subsidiary of: Kementerian Perusahaan Utama, Malaysia/Ministry of Primary Industries, Malaysia), PO Box 10620, Kuala Lumpur, 50720, Malaysia. TEL 60-3-89259155, 60-3-89259775, FAX 60-3-89259446, http://mpob.gov.my. Circ: 800.

JOURNAL OF PALYNOLOGY. see *BIOLOGY—Botany*

JOURNAL OF PEST SCIENCE. see *BIOLOGY—Entomology*

630 IND
JOURNAL OF RESEARCH A N G R A U. Text in English. q. INR 60 to individuals; INR 150 to institutions. **Document type:** *Academic/Scholarly.*
Formerly: Journal of Research A P A U (0970-0226)
Indexed: AEA, AgBio, AgrForAb, AnBrAb, BioCN&I, CPA, DSA, FCA, FPA, FS&TA, ForAb, HerbAb, HortAb, I&DA, IndVet, MaizeAb, NemAb, NutrAb, OrnHort, PBA, PGegResA, PGrRegA, PHN&I, PotatoAb, PoultAb, RA&MP, RDA, RM&VM, RPP, RevApplEntom, RiceAb, S&F, SIA, SeedAb, SoyAb, TDB, TriticAb, VetBull, WAE&RSA, WeedAb.
—BLDSC (5049.817000).
Published by: Acharya N G Ranga Agricultural University, Rajendrangar, Hyderabad, Andhra Pradesh 500 030, India.

630 IND ISSN 0258-1728
CODEN: JRAUDB
JOURNAL OF RESEARCH - ASSAM AGRICULTURAL UNIVERSITY. Text in English. 1980. s-a. **Document type:** *Journal, Academic/Scholarly.*
—BLDSC (5049.830000).
Published by: Assam Agricultural University, Directorate of Research, Jorhat, Assam, India. http://www.aau.ac.in/research.

630 GBR ISSN 1366-9338
➤ **JOURNAL OF RURAL MANAGEMENT AND HUMAN RESOURCES.** Text in English. 1975 (vol.4). a. GBP 10 to individuals; GBP 35 to institutions (effective 2003). adv. bk.rev. **Document type:** *Academic/Scholarly.* **Description:** Seeks to provide an outlet to put forward the results of new research, review papers, information, and commentary relevant to agricultural staffing and agricultural business management.
Former titles (until 1996): Agricultural Manpower (0260-2040); Journal of Agricultural Labour Science
Indexed: AEA, DSA, REE&TA, WAE&RSA.
—BLDSC (8052.491500), CISTI, IE, ingenta.
Published by: Agricultural Manpower Society, University of Reading, Earley Gate, PO Box 236, Reading, Berks RG6 6AT, United Kingdom. TEL 44-118-9318492. Ed., R&P, Adv. contact Mike Robinson. Circ: 200. **Subscr. to:** c/o AW Hales, Secy, Secretary Reading Agricultural Consultants, Races Farm, Aston St, Aston Tirroid, Didcot, Oxon OX11, United Kingdom.

630 SCG ISSN 0354-5695
CODEN: APNAA2
JOURNAL OF SCIENTIFIC AGRICULTURAL RESEARCH. Text in Serbian; Summaries in English. 1934. q. YUN 870; USD 150 foreign (effective 1999). bk.rev.
Former titles (until 1993): Arhiv za Poljoprivredne Nauke (0004-1262); (until 1948): Archiv za Poljoprivredne Nauke i Techniku (0365-5601)
Indexed: AnBrAb, BiolAb, CPA, ChemAb, CurCont, DSA, FCA, FS&TA, HerbAb, HortAb, MaizeAb, NutrAb, PGrRegA, PN&I, RPP, SeedAb, SoyAb, TriticAb, WeedAb.
—CASDDS, CISTI, Linda Hall.
Published by: Savez Poljoprivrednih Inzenjera i Tehnicara Jugoslavije/Association of Agricultural Engineers and Technicians of Yugoslavia, Kneza Milosa 9-1, Belgrade, 11000. TEL 381-3244317, FAX 381-3244317. Ed. Zivorad Videnovic. R&P Dragustin Nedeljkovic. Circ: 1,100.

630 CHN ISSN 1002-2481
JOURNAL OF SHANXI AGRICULTURAL SCIENCE. Text in Chinese. 1961. q. CNY 16 (effective 2000 - 2001). **Document type:** *Academic/Scholarly.*
Related titles: Online - full text ed.: (from East View Information Services).
Published by: Shanxi Nongye Kexueyuan/Shanxi Academy of Agricultural Sciences, 4 Wucheng Lu, Taiyuan, Shanxi 030006, China. TEL 86-351-7075565, 86-351-7089783, FAX 86-351-17089781, sxnyzzs@public.ty.sx.cn, http://www.chinainfo.gov.cn. Ed. Wenze Yan.

JOURNAL OF SOIL AND WATER CONSERVATION IN INDIA. see *CONSERVATION*

638 363.7 333.77 USA ISSN 1044-0046
S494.5.S86 CODEN: JSAGEB
➤ **JOURNAL OF SUSTAINABLE AGRICULTURE;** innovations for the long-term and lasting maintenance and enhancement of agricultural resources, production and environmental quality. Abbreviated title: J S A. Text in English. 1990. q. (in 2 vols.). USD 320 combined subscription domestic to institutions print & online eds.; USD 432 combined subscription in Canada to institutions print & online eds.; USD 464 combined subscription elsewhere to institutions print & online eds. (effective academic year 2005 - 2006). adv. bk.rev. 120 p./no. 1 cols./p.; back issues avail.; reprint service avail. from HAW. **Document type:** *Journal, Academic/Scholarly.* **Description:** Deals with the study and application of sustainable agriculture for solutions to the problems of resource depletion and environmental misuse.
Related titles: Microfiche ed.: (from PQC); Microform ed.; Online - full text ed.: ISSN 1540-7578. free to institutions (effective 2003); free with print subs. (from EBSCO Publishing, O C L C Online Computer Library Center, Inc., Swets Information Services).
Indexed: AEA, ASCA, ASFA, AgBio, Agr, AgrForAb, AnBrAb, BioCN&I, BiolDig, CPA, CurCont, DSA, EIA, EPB, ESPM, EnvAb, EnvEAb, FCA, FPA, FS&TA, ForAb, GEOBASE, GardL, HerbAb, HortAb, I&DA, IBR, IBZ, IndVet, M&TEA, MaizeAb, NemAb, NutrAb, OrnHort, PAIS, PBA, PGegResA, PGrRegA, PHN&I, PN&I, PollutAb, PotatoAb, PoultAb, RA&MP, RDA, RPP, RefZh, RevApplEntom, RiceAb, S&F, SIA, SOPODA, SSCI, SWRA, SeedAb, SoyAb, TDB, TriticAb, VetBull, WAE&RSA, WeedAb.
—BLDSC (5067.730000), Haworth, IDS, IE, Infotrieve, ingenta. **CCC.**

Published by: Food Products Press (Subsidiary of: Haworth Press, Inc.), 10 Alice St, Binghamton, NY 13904-1580. TEL 607-722-5857, 800-429-6784, FAX 607-771-0012, 800-895-0582, getinfo@haworthpress.com, http://www.haworthpressinc.com/store/product.asp?sku=J064, http://www.haworthpress.com/. Ed. Raymond P Poincelot. Pub. William Cohen. R&P Ruth Ann Heath TEL 607-722-5857 ext 316. Adv. contact Rebecca Miller-Baum TEL 607-722-5857 ext 337. B&W page USD 315, color page USD 550; trim 4.375 x 7.125. Circ: 285 (paid).

➤ **JOURNAL OF TEA SCIENCE/CHAYE KEXUE.** see *FOOD AND FOOD INDUSTRIES*

630 664 GBR ISSN 0022-5142
TX341 CODEN: JSFAAE
➤ **JOURNAL OF THE SCIENCE OF FOOD AND AGRICULTURE.** Text in English. 1950. 15/yr. USD 2,795 to institutions; USD 3,075 combined subscription to institutions print & online eds. (effective 2006). adv. abstr.; bibl.; charts; illus. index. back issues avail.; reprint service avail. from ISI. **Document type:** *Journal, Academic/Scholarly.* **Description:** Publishes original research and critical reviews in agriculture and food science, with particular emphasis on interdisciplinary studies at the agriculture-food interface.
Related titles: Microform ed.: (from PQC); Online - full text ed.: ISSN 1097-0010. 1996. USD 2,795 to institutions (effective 2006) (from EBSCO Publishing, Gale Group, IngentaConnect, Swets Information Services, Wiley InterScience).
Indexed: AEA, ASCA, ASFA, AbHyg, AgBio, Agr, AgrForAb, AnBrAb, AnalAb, B&AI, BIOBASE, BIOSIS Prev, BioCN&I, BiolAb, BrTechI, CBTA, CCI, CEA, CEABA, CIN, CPA, CTFA, Cadscan, ChemAb, ChemTitl, CurCont, DBA, DSA, ESPM, EngInd, ExcerpMed, FCA, FPA, FS&TA, FaBeAb, ForAb, GEOBASE, HerbAb, HortAb, I&DA, IABS, ISR, IndMed, IndVet, LeadAb, MEDLINE, MSB, MaizeAb, NutrAb, OrnHort, PBA, PCI, PGegResA, PGrRegA, PHN&I, PN&I, PlantSci, PollutAb, PotatoAb, PoultAb, RA&MP, RASB, RDA, RM&VM, RPP, RRTA, RefZh, RevApplEntom, RiceAb, S&F, S&MA, SCI, SFA, SIA, SPPI, SWRA, SeedAb, SoyAb, TCEA, TDB, TOSA, TriticAb, VITIS, VetBull, WAE&RSA, WTA, WeedAb, WildRev, Zincscan, ZooRec.
—BLDSC (5055.000000), CASDDS, CINDOC, CISTI, Ei, GNLM, IDS, IE, Infotrieve, ingenta, Linda Hall. **CCC.**
Published by: (Society of Chemical Industry), John Wiley & Sons Ltd. (Subsidiary of: John Wiley & Sons, Inc.), The Atrium, Southern Gate, Chichester, West Sussex PO19 8SQ, United Kingdom. TEL 44-1243-779777, FAX 44-1243-775878, customer@wiley.co.uk, http://www3.interscience.wiley.com/cgi-bin/jhome/1294, http://www.wiley.co.uk. Ed. D S Reid. adv.: B&W page GBP 650, color page GBP 1,550; trim 210 x 297. Circ: 1,250. **Subscr in the Americas to:** John Wiley & Sons, Inc., 111 River St, Hoboken, NJ 07030-5774. TEL 800-225-5945, subinfo@wiley.com.

630 IND ISSN 0971-636X
CODEN: ARJKAQ
➤ **JOURNAL OF TROPICAL AGRICULTURE.** Text in English. 1962. s-a. INR 300 domestic; USD 75 foreign (effective 2001). bk.rev. charts; illus.; abstr. 100 p./no. 2 cols./p.; back issues avail. **Document type:** *Journal, Academic/Scholarly.*
Formerly (until vol.30, 1993): Agricultural Research Journal of Kerala (0002-1628)
Indexed: AgBio, AgrForAb, AnBrAb, BioCN&I, BiolAb, CPA, ChemAb, ChemTitl, DSA, FCA, FPA, ForAb, HerbAb, HortAb, I&DA, MaizeAb, NemAb, NutrAb, OrnHort, PBA, PGegResA, PGrRegA, PHN&I, PoultAb, RA&MP, RDA, RPP, RRTA, RefZh, RevApplEntom, RiceAb, S&F, SIA, SeedAb, SoyAb, TOSA, WAE&RSA, WeedAb, ZooRec.
—BLDSC (5070.660000), CASDDS.
Published by: Kerala Agricultural University, College of Horticulture, Mannuthy, Trichur, Kerala 680651, India. TEL 91-487-370086, FAX 91-487-370150, TELEX 887-268 KAU IN, kaujta@123india.com. Ed. A I Jose. Circ: 500 (paid and controlled). **Dist. by:** H P C Publishers Distributors Pvt. Ltd., 4805 Bharat Ram Rd, 24 Darya Ganj, New Delhi 110 002, India. TEL 91-11-325-4402, FAX 91-11-686-3511.

630 MYS ISSN 1394-9829
S3
➤ **JOURNAL OF TROPICAL AGRICULTURE AND FOOD SCIENCE.** Text in English, Malay. 1973. s-a., latest vol.30, no.2, 2002. MYR 40 domestic; USD 40 foreign (effective 2004). charts; illus.; abstr. 250 p./no. 2 cols./p.; back issues avail. **Document type:** *Journal, Academic/Scholarly.* **Description:** Publishes results of scientific studies in the fields of tropical agriculture and food science.
Former titles (until vol.24, no.2, 1996): M A R D I Research Journal - Jurnal Penyelidikan M A R D I (0128-0686); (until vol.15, no.2, 1987): M A R D I Research Bulletin (0126-5709)
Indexed: AgrForAb, BIOSIS Prev, BiolAb, FS&TA, HerbAb, HortAb, PN&I, PoultAb, RiceAb, S&F, ZooRec.
—BLDSC (5070.662000), CASDDS, CISTI, IE, ingenta.
Published by: Malaysian Agricultural Research & Development Institute/Institut Penyelidikan dan Kemajuan Pertanian Malaysia, PO Box 12301, General Post Office, Kuala Lumpur, 50774, Malaysia. TEL 60-3-89437226, FAX 60-3-89487630, TELEX MARDI-MA-37115, publicat@mardi.my, http://www.mardi.my. Ed. Embi Yusoff. R&P Rohani Mahmood. Circ: 500.

638.1 CHE ISSN 0368-4040
JOURNAL SUISSE D'APICULTURE. Text in French. 1879. 10/yr. CHF 48 (effective 2001). adv. **Document type:** *Journal, Trade.* **Description:** Focuses on bee culture.
Indexed: ApicAb, ChemAb.
Published by: Societe Romande d'Apiculture, c/o Andre Perrin, Biorda 19, Riaz, 1632, Switzerland. TEL 41-26-9120336, FAX 41-26-9120671. Ed. Michel Breganti. Circ: 4,500.

630 ESP
JOVENES AGRICULTORES. Text in Spanish. 1978. m. (11/yr.). free (effective 2005). adv. illus. **Document type:** *Trade.*
Published by: Asociacion Agraria Jovenes Agricultores (ASAJA), Agustin de Bethencourt, 17-2o, Madrid, 28003, Spain. TEL 34-91-5336764, FAX 34-91-5349286, asajanet@asaja.com, http://www.asajanet.com/listado/Listado.html?sec=6001. Ed. Pilar Sanchez Munoz. Adv. contact Fernanda Pastor. Circ: 22,000.

630 FRA ISSN 0222-979X
JURA AGRICOLE ET RURAL. Text in French. w.
Published by: Agricole et Rural, 455 rue du Colonel de Casteinau, BP 420, Lons-le-Saunier, Cedex 39006, France. TEL 84-24-44-70. Ed. Marc Derudet. Circ: 4,665.

660.6 IDN ISSN 0853-8360
➤ **JURNAL BIOTEKNOLOGI PERTANIAN**; Indonesian Agricultural Biotechnology. Text in English, Indonesian; Abstracts in English, Indonesian. 1996. s-a. IDR 12,000 domestic; USD 12 foreign (effective 2002). abstr.; charts; illus. **Document type:** *Journal, Academic/Scholarly.* **Description:** Publishes primary research articles of agricultural biotechnology. Aims to disseminate agricultural research results to the users, including researchers, research managers, and educators at home as well as abroad.
Related titles: Online - full text ed.
Published by: Agency for Agricultural Research & Development, Jl Ir H Juanda 20, Bogor, 16122, Indonesia. TEL 62-251-321746, FAX 62-251-326561, pustaka@bogor.net, http://pustaka.bogor.net. Ed. Sugiono Morljopawiro.

630 IDN ISSN 0216-4418
HF5616.I6
➤ **JURNAL PENELITIAN DAN PENGEMBANGAN PERTANIAN.** Text in Indonesian, English. 1982. q. IDR 12,000 domestic; USD 12 foreign (effective 2002). abstr.; charts; illus. **Document type:** *Journal, Academic/Scholarly.* **Description:** Publishes review articles on agricultural research and development. The purpose of the journal is to disseminate agricultural research and developments to users, namely decision makers, research managers, and extentionists in Indonesia as well as abroad.
Indexed: AEA, AgBio, AgrForAb, AnBrAb, BioCN&I, CPA, DSA, FCA, ForAb, HerbAb, HortAb, I&DA, IndVet, MaizeAb, NemAb, NutrAb, OrnHort, PBA, PGegResA, PHN&I, PN&I, RA&MP, RDA, RM&VM, RPP, RRTA, RevApplEntom, RiceAb, S&F, SeedAb, SoyAb, TDB, WAE&RSA, WeedAb.
Published by: Agency for Agricultural Research & Development, Jl Ir H Juanda 20, Bogor, 16122, Indonesia. TEL 62-251-321746, FAX 62-251-326561, pustaka@bogor.net, http://pustaka.bogor.net. Ed. Surachmat Kusumo.

633.63 FIN ISSN 0789-2667
JUURIKASSARKA. Text in Finnish. 1981. q. adv. **Document type:** *Journal, Trade.* **Description:** Concerned with sugar beet growing from seed to harvest, economy and sugar processing.
Formerly (until 1988): Juurikas (0358-545X)
Related titles: Swedish ed.: Betfaeltet. ISSN 0789-2616. 1981.
Published by: Sokerijuurikkaan Tutkimuskeskus, Korvenkylaentie 201, Kotalato, 25170, Finland. TEL 358-2-7708200, FAX 358-2-7708282, http://www.sjt.fi. Ed., R&P Kyosti Raininko TEL 358-2-770-8200. Adv. contact Sirkua Raininko.

630 NLD
K L V UPDATE. Text in Dutch. 1887. 4/yr. EUR 61 (effective 2003). adv. bk.rev. abstr.; bibl.; charts. index.
Former titles (until 2002): L T Journaal (0927-6203); (until 1992): Landbouwkundig Tijdschrift (0927-6955); (until 1983): Landbouwkundig Tijdschrift. P T (0165-5221); Landbouwkundig Tijdschrift (0023-7787); (until 1924): Cultura
Indexed: BiolAb, ChemAb, DSA, ELLIS, ExcerpMed, FCA, FS&TA, HerbAb, KES, NutrAb, RRTA, S&F, WAE&RSA.
—CISTI.
Published by: Koninklijk Landbouwkundige Vereniging/Royal Netherlands Society of Agricultural Sciences, Postbus 79, Wageningen, 6700 AB, Netherlands. TEL 31-317-483487, FAX 31-317-483976. Ed. A Boon. Circ: 7,000 (paid).

630 FIN ISSN 1239-0429
K M VET. (Kaytannon Maamies) Text in Finnish. 1995. 7/yr. EUR 53 (effective 2001). adv. **Document type:** *Magazine, Consumer.*
Related titles: ♦ Supplement to: Kaytannon Maamies. ISSN 0022-9571.
Published by: Yhtyneet Kuvalehdet Oy/United Magazines Ltd., Maistraatinportti 1, Helsinki, 00015, Finland. TEL 358-9-15661, FAX 358-9-145650, http://www.kaytannonmaamies.fi/kmvet/index.html, http://www.kuvalehdet.fi/. Ed. Pentti Torma. adv.: color page EUR 1,310; 280 x 217. Circ: 6,780 (paid).

630 SWE ISSN 1102-9056
K S L A NYTT. Text in Swedish. 1992. q. free (effective 2004). **Document type:** *Newsletter.*
Related titles: Online - full text ed.; English ed.
Published by: Kungliga Skogs- och Lantbruksakademien/Royal Swedish Academy of Agriculture and Forestry, Drottninggatan 95 B, PO Box 6806, Stockholm, 11386, Sweden. TEL 46-8-54547700, FAX 46-8-54547710, akademien@ksla.se, http://www.ksla.se.

A

630 DEU ISSN 0945-2370
S674.43.G3
K T B L ARBEITSPAPIERE. Text in German. 1972. irreg. price varies. **Document type:** *Monographic series, Trade.*
Formerly (until 1992): Kuratorium fuer Technik und Bauwesen in der Landwirtschaft. Arbeitspapier (0930-0295)
Indexed: AEA, DSA, HortAb, IndVet, NutrAb, OrnHort, PHN&I, RPP, WAE&RSA, WeedAb.
—BLDSC (5118.756000).
Published by: Kuratorium fuer Technik und Bauwesen in der Landwirtschaft e.V., Bartningstr 49, Darmstadt, 64289, Germany. TEL 49-6151-70010, FAX 49-6151-7001123, ktbl@ktbl.de, http://www.ktbl.de. R&P Harald Kuehner.

630 DEU ISSN 0173-2811
K T B L - SCHRIFTEN. Text in German. 1972. irreg. price varies. charts; illus. **Document type:** *Monographic series, Academic/Scholarly.*
Formed by the merger of (1969-1972): K T B L Bauschriften (0173-2854); (1970-1972): K T B L Flugschrift (0173-2846); Which was formerly (1968-1970): K T L Flugschrift (0173-2838); (1954-1968): Kuratoriums fuer Technik in der Landwirtschaft. Flugschrift (0452-8948); (1969-1972): K T B L Berichte ueber Landtechnik (0173-2889); Which was formerly (1967-1969): K T L Berichte ueber Landtechnik (0173-2870); (1948-1967): Berichte ueber Landtechnik (0173-2862); (1969-1972): K T B L Manuskriptdruck (0173-2919); Which was formerly (1966-1969): K T L Manuskriptdruck (0173-2900); (1960-1966): Kuratorium fuer Technik in der Landwirtschaft. Manuskriptdruck (0173-2897)
Indexed: AEA, DSA, ExcerpMed, FCA, HerbAb, IndVet, MaizeAb, NutrAb, PHN&I, PN&I, PoultAb, RRTA, RevApplEntom, S&F, SeedAb, TriticAb, VetBull, WAE&RSA.
—BLDSC (5118.768000), IE, ingenta.
Published by: Kuratorium fuer Technik und Bauwesen in der Landwirtschaft e.V., Bartningstr 49, Darmstadt, 64289, Germany. TEL 49-6151-70010, FAX 49-6151-7001123, ktbl@ktbl.de, http://www.ktbl.de. R&P Harald Kuehne. Circ: 800. **Co-sponsor:** Bundesministerium fuer Ernaehrung, Landwirtschaft und Forsten.

630 DEU
K T B L SONDERVEROEFFENTLICHUNGEN. Text in German. irreg. price varies. **Document type:** *Monographic series, Trade.*
Published by: Kuratorium fuer Technik und Bauwesen in der Landwirtschaft e.V., Bartningstr 49, Darmstadt, 64289, Germany. TEL 49-6151-70010, FAX 49-6151-7001123, ktbl@ktbl.de, http://www.ktbl.de. R&P Harald Kuehner.

630 AUT
KAERNTER BAUER. Text in German. 1844. w. EUR 40 (effective 2005). adv. bk.rev. **Document type:** *Newspaper, Trade.*
Published by: Kammer fuer Land- und Forstwirtschaft Kaernten, Museumgasse 5, Klagenfurt, K 9010, Austria. TEL 43-463-5850, FAX 43-463-5851219, presse@lk-kaernten.at, http://www.lk-kaernten.at. Ed. Rudolf Fritzer. adv.: B&W page EUR 2,240, color page EUR 3,136; trim 200 x 263. Circ: 28,000 (controlled).

630 JPN ISSN 0368-5128
KAGAWA DAIGAKU NOGAKUBU GAKUJUTSU HOKOKU/KAGAWA UNIVERSITY. FACULTY OF AGRICULTURE. TECHNICAL BULLETIN. Text in Japanese. 1950. irreg. **Document type:** *Bulletin, Academic/Scholarly.*
Formerly (until 1955): Kagawa Kenritsu Noka Daigaku Gakujutsu Hokoku/Kagawa Agricultural College. Technical Bulletin (0368-5993)
Indexed: AgBio, AgrForAb, CPA, FCA, FPA, ForAb, HortAb, I&DA, INIS AtomInd, IndVet, MaizeAb, OrnHort, PBA, PGegResA, PGrRegA, PHN&I, PoultAb, RA&MP, RM&VM, RPP, RRTA, RefZh, S&F, SIA, SeedAb, SoyAb, TriticAb, VITIS, WAE&RSA, WeedAb.
—BLDSC (8625.910000), CISTI. **CCC.**
Published by: Kagawa Daigaku, Nogakubu/Kagawa University, Faculty of Agriculture, 2393, Ikenobe, Miki-cho, Kita-gun, Kagawa, 761-0795, Japan. TEL 81-87-8913008, FAX 81-87-8913021, http://ci.nii.ac.jp/vol_issue/nels/AN00038339_jp.html, http://www.ag.kagawa-u.ac.jp/index2.html.

630 JPN ISSN 0453-0764
CODEN: KDNKAO
KAGAWA DAIGAKU NOGAKUBU KIYO/KAGAWA UNIVERSITY. FACULTY OF AGRICULTURE. MEMOIRS. Text in Japanese. 1955. irreg. **Document type:** *Academic/Scholarly.*
Formerly (until 1955): Kagawa Kenritsu Noka Daigaku Kiyo/Kagawa Agricultural College. Memoirs (0368-6000)
Indexed: BioCN&I, CPA, HortAb, PGrRegA, SeedAb.
—**CCC.**

▼ new title ➤ refereed ✶ unverified ♦ full entry avail.

Published by: Kagawa Daigaku, Nogakubu/Kagawa University, Faculty of Agriculture, 2393, Ikenobe, Miki-cho, Kita-gun, Kagawa, 761-0795, Japan. TEL 81-87-8913008, FAX 81-87-8913021, http://www.ag.kagawa-u.ac.jp/index2.html.

630.2 JPN ISSN 0374-8804
CODEN: KNKHA2
KAGAWA PREFECTURE AGRICULTURAL EXPERIMENT STATION. BULLETIN. Text in Japanese; Summaries in English, Japanese. 1949. a. donation. **Document type:** *Bulletin.*
Indexed: BiolAb.
—BLDSC (2597.852000), CASDDS.
Published by: Kagawa Prefecture Agricultural Experiment Station/Kagawa-ken Nogyo Shikenjo, Busshozan-cho, Takamatsu-shi, Kagawa-ken, Japan. TEL 81-878-89-1121, FAX 81-878-89-1125. Ed. Kazunori Obika. Circ: 600.

630 JPN ISSN 0453-0845
KAGOSHIMA DAIGAKU NOGAKUBU GAKUJUTSU HOKOKU/KAGOSHIMA UNIVERSITY. FACULTY OF AGRICULTURE. BULLETIN. Text in Japanese. 1952. irreg. **Document type:** *Bulletin, Academic/Scholarly.*
Indexed: AgBio, AnBrAb, CPA, FCA, FPA, ForAb, HortAb, I&DA, IndVet, NemAb, PBA, PGrRegA, PHN&I, PN&I, RRTA, RefZh, S&F, SIA, SoyAb, WAE&RSA, WeedAb, ZooRec.
—BLDSC (2507.000000), CISTI.
Published by: Kagoshima Daigaku, Nogakubu/Kagoshima University, Faculty of Agriculture, 21-24 Korimo-To 1-chome, Kagoshima, 890-0065, Japan. TEL 81-99-2858515, FAX 81-99-2858525.

630 JPN ISSN 0453-0853
S19 CODEN: MAKUA6
KAGOSHIMA UNIVERSITY. FACULTY OF AGRICULTURE. MEMOIRS/KAGOSHIMA DAIGAKU NOGAKUBU KIYO. Text in Japanese. 1952. a. exchange basis. bibl.; charts; illus. **Document type:** *Journal, Academic/Scholarly.*
Indexed: AbHyg, AgBio, AnBrAb, BAS, BIOSIS Prev, BiolAb, CIN, CPA, ChemAb, ChemTitl, DSA, ExcerpMed, FCA, FPA, ForAb, HortAb, IndVet, NutrAb, OrnHort, PBA, PGegResA, PGrRegA, RM&VM, RefZh, RevApplEntom, RiceAb, S&F, SIA, SeedAb, SoyAb, VetBull, WAE&RSA, ZooRec.
—BLDSC (5592.000000), CASDDS, CISTI.
Published by: Kagoshima Daigaku, Nogakubu/Kagoshima University, Faculty of Agriculture, 21-24 Korimo-To 1-chome, Kagoshima, 890-0065, Japan. TEL 81-99-2858515, FAX 81-99-2858525, agrsyomu@kuas.kagoshima-u.ac.jp, http://www.agri.kagoshima-u.ac.jp/. Ed. Masao Akuzawa. Circ: 1,000.

630 JPN ISSN 1347-3549
KAJU KENKYUSHO KENKYU HOKOKU/NATIONAL INSTITUTE OF FRUIT TREE SERVICE. BULLETIN. Text in Japanese. 2002. irreg. free (effective 2004).
Indexed: AgBio, BioCN&I, CPA, HortAb, OrnHort, PBA, PGegResA, PGrRegA, PHN&I, S&F, SIA, SeedAb, WAE&RSA, ZooRec.
—CISTI.
Published by: Nougyo Seibutsukei Tokutei Sangyo Gijutsu Kenkyu Kiko Kaju Kenkyusho/National Agricultural Research Organization. National Institute of Fruit Tree Science, 2-1 Fujimoto, Tsukuba, Ibaraki, 305-8605, Japan. http://www.fruit.affrc.go.jp/index-e.html.

630 JPN ISSN 0388-8231
KANAGAWA-KEN NOGYO SOGO KENKYUJO KENKYU HOKOKU/KANAGAWA-KEN AGRICULTURAL RESEARCH INSTITUTE OF KANAGAWA PREFECTURE. BULLETIN. Text in Japanese. a. **Document type:** *Academic/Scholarly.*
Incorporates (1973-1995): Kanagawa-ken Sangyo Senta Shiken Kenkyu Hokoku (0388-824X); (in 1994): Kanagawa-ken Engei Shikenjo Kenkyu Hokoku (0374-8731); Which was formerly (1953-1961): Kanagawa-ken Nogyo Shikenjo Engei Bunjo Kenkyu hokoku (0451-3193); Former titles (until 1970): Kanagawa-ken Nogyo Shikenjo Kenkyu Hokoku (0388-8223); (until 1961): Kanagawa-ken Nogyo Shikenjo nogyo Shiken Seiseki
Indexed: SoyAb.
—CISTI.
Published by: Kanagawa-Ken Nogyo Sogo Kenkyujo/Kanagawa Prefecture Agricultural Research Institute, 1617 Kamikisawa, Hiratsuka-si, Kanagawa-Ken, Japan. TEL 81-463-58-0333, FAX 81-463-58-4254.

630.7 367 USA
KANSAS 4-H JOURNAL. Text in English. 1950. 10/yr. USD 6. adv. bk.rev. **Document type:** *Newsletter.* **Description:** Serves as a communication link for Kansas 4-H'ers.
Published by: Kansas 4-H Foundation Inc., Umberger Hall, Rm 116, Kansas State University, Manhattan, KS 66506-3417. TEL 913-532-5881, FAX 913-532-6963. Ed., R&P Rhonda Atkinson. Circ: 13,200.

338.1 USA
KANSAS AGRICULTURE ANNUAL REPORT AND FARM FACTS. Text in English. 1872. a. free. illus.; stat. **Document type:** *Government.*
Former titles (until 1981): Kansas. State Board of Agriculture. Annual Report and Farm Facts (0196-0954); Formed by the merger of: Kansas. State Board of Agriculture. Annual Report; Farm Facts; Formerly (until 1976): Kansas Agriculture Report (0091-6900); Supersedes: Kansas. State Board of Agriculture. Biennial Report to the Governor
—CISTI, Linda Hall.
Published by: State Board of Agriculture, 901 S Kansas Ave, Topeka, KS 66612-1280. TEL 913-296-3556, FAX 913-296-2247. Ed. Carole A Jordan. Circ: 8,000.

630 USA ISSN 0091-9586
KANSAS COUNTRY LIVING. Text in English. 1951. m. USD 10 (effective 2005). adv. tr.lit. **Document type:** *Magazine, Consumer.*
Formerly: Kansas Electric Farmer (0022-8540)
Media: Duplicated (not offset).
Published by: Kansas Electric Cooperatives, Inc., 7332 S.W. 21st St., Topeka, KS 66615. TEL 785-478-4554, FAX 785-478-4852, kec@kec.org, http://www.kec.org. Circ: 80,000 (paid).

630 USA
KANSAS FARMER. Text in English. 1864. m. USD 23.95 in state (effective 2005). adv. bk.rev. charts; illus.; stat.; tr.lit. **Document type:** *Magazine, Trade.* **Description:** Covers all phases of farming. Special assignments go to agricultural college scientists and other specialists.
Former titles: Kansas Farmer-Stockman (0451-4041); Kansas Farmer (0022-8583)
Related titles: ♦ Supplement(s): Dairy Producer; ♦ Hog Producer; ♦ Beef Producer; Irrigation Extra.
—Linda Hall.
Published by: Farm Progress Companies, 191 S Gary Ave, Carol Stream, IL 60188-2095. TEL 515-278-7786, 630-462-2229, FAX 630-462-2202, info@farmprogress.com, http://www.kansasfarmer.com, http://www.farmprogress.com/. Ed. Bill Spiegel. Adv. contact Terry Butzirus. B&W page USD 1,950, color page USD 2,450; trim 10.5 x 14.5. Circ: 19,000 (paid).

630 USA ISSN 1077-0453
KANSAS LIVING*. Text in English. q.
Published by: Kansas Farm Bureau, 2627 KFB Plaza, Manhattan, KS 66502-8155. Ed. John Schlageck. Circ: 130,000.

630 IND
KARSHAKAN. Text in Malayalam. m. INR 150 for 2 yrs.; INR 8 newsstand/cover. adv. **Description:** Agricultural magazine.
Published by: Rashtra Deepika Ltd., Deepika Bldg., C.M.S. College Rd., P O Box 7, Kottayam, Kerala 686 001, India. TEL 91-481-566706, FAX 91-481-567947. adv.: page INR 18,000; 170 x 230. Circ: 40,000.

630 IND
KARSHAKASREE; farmers' monthly. Text in Malayalam. 1995. m.
Published by: Malayala Monorama Co. Ltd., P O Box 26, Kottayam, Kerala 686 001, India. TEL 91-481-563646, FAX 91-481-562479, TELEX 0888-201-MNR-IN. Ed. K M Mathew. Pub. Jacob Mathew. adv.: B&W page INR 10,000, color page INR 20,000. Circ: 45,000.

630 THA ISSN 0075-5192
CODEN: KASJAP
KASETSART JOURNAL. Text in English, Thai. 1961. s-a. **Document type:** *Academic/Scholarly.*
Indexed: AEA, APEL, AgBio, AgrForAb, AnBrAb, BioCN&I, CIN, CPA, ChemAb, ChemTitl, DSA, FCA, FPA, ForAb, HelmAb, HerbAb, HortAb, I&DA, INIS AtomInd, IndVet, MaizeAb, NemAb, NutrAb, OrnHort, PBA, PGegResA, PGrRegA, PHN&I, PN&I, PotatoAb, PoultAb, ProtozoAb, RA&MP, RDA, RM&VM, RPP, RevApplEntom, RiceAb, S&F, SIA, SeedAb, SoyAb, TDB, TriticAb, VetBull, WAE&RSA, WeedAb, ZooRec.
—CASDDS, CISTI.
Published by: Kasetsart University, 50 Phahonyothin Rd, Chatuchak, Bangkok, 10900, Thailand. TEL 66-2-5790113, FAX 66-2-5798781, http://www.ku.ac.th.

630 THA ISSN 0125-3697
➤ **KASIKORN.** Text in Thai. 1928. bi-m. THB 35 (effective 2001). adv. bk.rev. bibl.; charts; illus.; stat.; tr.lit. 112 p./no.; back issues avail. **Document type:** *Magazine, Government.* **Description:** Agriculture, fish, livestock.
Published by: Department of Agriculture, Bangkhen, Bangkok, 10900, Thailand. TEL 02-579-5369, pannew@doa.go.th. Ed., Adv. contact Pannee Wichachoo TEL 662-561-2825. Circ: 8,000 (paid).

630 CHE
KATHOLISCHER SCHWEIZERBAUER. Text in German. 14/yr.
Address: St Galler Str 35, Tuebach, 9327, Switzerland. TEL 071-411795. Ed. Notker Angehr Zahner. Circ: 198,000.

630 FIN ISSN 0022-9571
KAYTANNON MAAMIES. Variant title: K M. Text in Finnish. 1952. 15/yr. EUR 109 (effective 2005). adv. charts; illus. index. **Document type:** *Magazine, Trade.* **Description:** For the professional farmer.
Related titles: ♦ Supplement(s): K M Vet. ISSN 1239-0429.
—CISTI.
Published by: Yhtyneet Kuvalehdet Oy/United Magazines Ltd., Maistraatinportti 1, Helsinki, 00015, Finland. TEL 358-9-15661, FAX 358-9-145650, http://www.kuvalehdet.fi/. Ed. Pentti Torma. adv.: color page EUR 3,380, B&W page EUR 2,500; trim 280 x 217. Circ: 24,481.

630 GBR ISSN 0023-0022
KENT FARMER. Text in English. 1952. m. adv.
Published by: County Farmers Publications Ltd., 55 Goldington Rd, Bedford, Beds MK40 3LU, United Kingdom. TEL 44-1234-351401, FAX 44-1234-328614. Ed. N Errington. Circ: 3,300.

KENTUCKY AGRICULTURAL STATISTICS. see *AGRICULTURE—Abstracting, Bibliographies, Statistics*

630 USA ISSN 1098-0350
KENTUCKY FARMER. Text in English. 1841. m. USD 21.95 in state; USD 30 out of state; USD 2 newsstand/cover (effective 2001); free to qualified personnel. adv. charts; illus.; mkt.; pat. **Document type:** *Trade.*
Incorporates (1989-1997): Kentucky Prairie Farmer
Published by: Farm Progress Companies, 191 S Gary Ave, Carol Stream, IL 60188. TEL 630-462-2892, info@farmprogress.com, http://www.farmprogress.com/. Ed. Tim Sickman TEL 502-266-9556. adv.: B&W page USD 1,515. Circ: 12,000.

KENYA. CENTRAL BUREAU OF STATISTICS. AGRICULTURAL CENSUS (LARGE FARM AREAS). see *AGRICULTURE—Abstracting, Bibliographies, Statistics*

630 KEN ISSN 0023-0421
KENYA FARMER. Text in English; Text occasionally in Swahili. 1954. m. KES 120. adv.
Incorporates: Mkulima wa Kenya
Published by: Agricultural Society of Kenya, PO Box 30176, Nairobi, Kenya. Ed. Fred Nyanga Origa. Circ: 20,000.

630 KEN
KENYA. MINISTRY OF AGRICULTURE. SCIENTIFIC RESEARCH DIVISION. ANNUAL REPORT*. Text in English. 196?. a.
Formerly: Kenya. Ministry of Agriculture. Research Division. Annual Report
Indexed: FCA, HerbAb, RPP.
Published by: Ministry of Agriculture, Scientific Research Division, Nairobi, Kenya. **Subscr. to:** Government Printing and Stationery Dept., Government Printing and Stationery Dept., Box 30128, Nairobi, Kenya.

KEXUE ZHIFU YU SHENGHUO/SCIENCE PROSPERITY AND LIFE. see *SCIENCES: COMPREHENSIVE WORKS*

630 AZE
KHEIAT. Text in Azerbaijani. w. USD 299 in United States.
Published by: Ministry of Agriculture, Metbuat pr 529, Baku, 370146, Azerbaijan. TEL 994-12-382545. **US dist. addr.:** East View Information Services, 3020 Harbor Ln. N., Minneapolis, MN 55447. TEL 612-550-0961.

630 IND ISSN 0023-1088
KHETI. Text in Hindi. 1948. m. INR 180, USD 45 (effective 2000). adv. bk.rev. charts; illus. index. **Document type:** *Government.* **Description:** Caters to the needs of progressive farmers, research workers and students.
Incorporates: Pashupalan (0031-2606)
Indexed: AEA.
Published by: Indian Council of Agricultural Research, Krishi Anusandhan Bhavan, Pusa, New Delhi, 110 012, India. Ed. Jagdeep Saxena. Adv. contact S K Joshi. Circ: 45,100.

630 BLR
S13
KHOZYAIN (MINSK). Text in Russian. 1925. m.
Formerly (until 1991): Sel'skoe Khozyaistvo v Belorussii (0131-6311)
Indexed: RASB.
Published by: Ministry of Agriculture and Food, Vul Bogdanovicha 15, Minsk, 220040, Belarus. TEL 0172-2318692. Ed. I F Kravtsov. Circ: 25,500. **US dist. addr.:** East View Information Services, 3020 Harbor Ln. N., Minneapolis, MN 55447. TEL 612-550-0961.

630 RUS ISSN 0868-7188
S13
KHOZYAIN (MOSCOW). Text in Russian. 1963. bi-m. USD 95 in North America.
Formerly (until no.11, 1990): Agropromyshlennyi Kompleks Rossii (0235-2613)
Indexed: RASB.
—CISTI.
Published by: Ministerstvo Sel'skogo Khozyaistva i Prodovol'stviya Rossii, Sadovaya-Spasskaya 18, Moscow, 107807, Russian Federation. TEL 7-095-2075493. Ed. A S Ryabokon'. Circ: 7,760. **US dist. addr.:** East View Information Services, 3020 Harbor Ln. N., Minneapolis, MN 55447. TEL 612-550-0961.

630 RUS
KHRANENIE I PERERABOTKA SEL'KHOZSYR'YA. Text in Russian. 1993. bi-m. USD 105 in North America (effective 2000).
Indexed: FS&TA, RefZh.
—BLDSC (0396.250000).
Published by: Izdatel'stvo Pishchevaya Promyshlennost', Sadovaya-Spasskaya 18, kom 601-606, Moscow, 107807, Russian Federation. TEL 7-095-2071770, FAX 7-095-2077958. **Dist. by:** East View Information Services, 3020 Harbor Ln. N., Minneapolis, MN 55447. TEL 763-550-0961, FAX 763-559-2931.

630 KEN
KILIMO NEWS. Text in English. 1979. q. KES 200 (effective 2001). adv. **Document type:** *Newsletter, Government.* **Description:** Gathers and disseminates information on recent technologies farmers in Kenya can use to boost their crop production.
Related titles: Diskette ed.
Published by: Ministry of Agriculture, Agricultural Information Center, PO Box 66730, Nairobi, Kenya. TEL 446464, FAX 446465. Circ: 2,000.

630 SAU ISSN 1018-3590
CODEN: JKSAFS
➤ **KING SAUD UNIVERSITY JOURNAL. AGRICULTURAL SCIENCES.** Key Title: Majallat Jami'at al-Malik Sa'ud, al-'Ulum al-Zira'iyyah. (Other sections avail.: Administrative Sciences, Architecture and Planning, Arts, Computer and Information Sciences, Educational Sciences and Islamic Studies, Engineering Sciences, Science) Text in Arabic, English. 1989. s-a. USD 5 (effective 2001). charts; illus. back issues avail. **Document type:** *Journal, Academic/Scholarly.*
Indexed: AEA, AnBrAb, BioCN&I, DSA, FCA, FS&TA, ForAb, HerbAb, HortAb, I&DA, IndVet, NutrAb, OrnHort, PBA, PHN&I, PotatoAb, PoultAb, RDA, RPP, RevApplEntom, S&F, SeedAb, SoyAb, TriticAb, WAE&RSA, WeedAb.
—CASDDS, Linda Hall.
Published by: King Saud University, University Libraries, P O Box 22480, Riyadh, 11495, Saudi Arabia. TEL 966-1-4676148, FAX 966-1-4676162. Ed. Khalid A. Al-Hamoudi. R&P Dr. Sulaiman Saleh Al-Ogle. Circ: 2,000.

630 JPN ISSN 0385-311X
CODEN: KCNKDK
KINKI CHUGOKU AGRICULTURAL RESEARCH/KINKI CHUGOKU NOGYO KENKYU. Text in Japanese; Contents page in English, Japanese. 1962. s-a. JPY 2,000 (effective 1999). **Document type:** *Academic/Scholarly.*
Formerly (until 1973): Chugoku Agricultural Research (0009-6229)
Indexed: PoultAb, SoyAb, TriticAb.
—CISTI.
Published by: Kinki Chugoku Agricultural Research Association, c/o Chugoku National Agricultural Experiment Station, Nishi-Fukatsu-cho, Fukuyama-shi, Hiroshima-ken 721-8514, Japan. FAX 81-849-24-7893. Ed. Masaki Yoshimura. Circ: 1,150.

630 JPN ISSN 1347-1244
KINKI CHUUGOKU SHIKOKU NOUGYOU KENKYUU SENTA KENKYUU HOUKOKU/NATIONAL AGRICULTURAL RESEARCH CENTER FOR WESTERN REGION. BULLETIN. Text in Japanese. 2002 (Mar.). a.
Formed by the merger of (1953-2001): Shikoku Nogyo Shikenjo Hokoku/Shikoku National Agricultural Experiment Station. Bulletin (0037-3702); (1987-2001): Chugoku Nogyo Shikenjo Kenkyu Hokoku/Chugoku National Agricultural Experiment Station. Bulletin (0913-4239); Which was formed by the merger of (1967-1987): Chugoku Nogyo Shikenjo Hokoku. D, Kikaku Renrakushitsu, Kaku-bu/Chugoku National Agricultural Experiment Station. Bulletin. Series D, Department of Research Planning and Coordination (0385-6569); (1967-1987): Chugoku Nogyo Shikenjo Hokoku. A, Sakumo/Chugoku National Agricultural Experiment Station. Bulletin. Series A, Department of Agronomy (0366-7227); (1952-1987): Chugoku Nogyo Shikenjo Hokoku. E, Kankyobu/Chugoku National Agricultural Experiment Station. Bulletin. Series E, Department of Plant Protection and Soil Management (0366-726X); Both of which superseded in part (in 1966): Chugoku Nogyo Shikenjo Hokoku. A Sakumotsubu, Kankyobu/Chugoku Agricultural Experiment Station. Bulletin. Series A Crop Division and Environment Division (0385-6577); (1952-1987): Chugoku Nogyo Shikenjo Hokoku. B, Chikusanbu/Chugoku National Agricultural Experiment Station. Bulletin. Series B, Department of Animal Industry (0366-7464); (1952-1987): Chugoku Nogyo Shikenjo Hokoku. C, Nogyo Keieibu/Chugoku National Agricultural Experiment Station. Bulletin. Series C, Department of Rural Economy (0385-6550); Both of which superseded in part (in 1960): Chugoku Nogyo Shikenjo Hokoku/Chugoku Agricultural Experiment Station. Bulletin (0366-6247); Which was formerly (until 1953): Chugoku Shikoku Nogyo Shikenjo Hokoku/Chugoku Agricultural Experiment Station. Bulletin (0385-6607)
Related titles: Online - full content ed.
Indexed: AgBio, AnBrAb, BioCN&I, CPA, DSA, FCA, HerbAb, HortAb, I&DA, IndVet, MaizeAb, OrnHort, PBA, PGrRegA, PHN&I, PN&I, PoultAb, RA&MP, RPP, RRTA, S&F, SIA, SeedAb, TriticAb, WAE&RSA.
—BLDSC (2629.470000), CISTI.
Published by: Nougyou Gijutsu Kenkyuu Kikou, Kinki Chuugoku Shikoku Nougyou Kenkyuu Senta/National Agricultural Research Organization, National Agricultural Research Center for Western Region, 6-12-1 Nishi-fukatsucho, Fukuyama, Hiroshima 721-8514, Japan. TEL 81-84-9234100, www@cgk.affrc.go.jp, http://wenarc.naro.affrc.go.jp/labo/2/1.html, http://wenarc.naro.affrc.go.jp/top.html.

630 JPN ISSN 0453-8889
CODEN: KDNOA2
KINKI DAIGAKU. NOGAKUBU KIYO/KINKI UNIVERSITY. FACULTY OF AGRICULTURE. MEMOIRS. Text in Multiple languages. 1960. a.
Indexed: AgBio, AnBrAb, BioCN&I, CPA, ESPM, FCA, FPA, ForAb, HerbAb, HortAb, I&DA, MaizeAb, NutrAb, PBA, PGegResA, PGrRegA, PHN&I, PotatoAb, PoultAb, RA&MP, RDA, RPP, RRTA, RiceAb, S&F, SoyAb, TriticAb, WAE&RSA, WeedAb, ZooRec.
—BLDSC (5592.500000), CISTI, IE, ingenta.
Published by: Kinki Daigaku, Nogakubu/Kinki University, Faculty of Agriculture, Department of Agronomy, Nara, 631-8505, Japan.

630 USA ISSN 0023-1746
HD1751
KIPLINGER AGRICULTURE LETTER. Text in English. 1929. fortn. USD 56 (effective 2005). **Document type:** *Newsletter, Trade.* **Description:** News and summary forecasts for agriculturists and businesspersons who deal with agriculture.
Related titles: Online - full text ed.: (from Florida Center for Library Automation, Gale Group, H.W. Wilson, LexisNexis, ProQuest Information & Learning).
Indexed: B&AI.
—**CCC.**
Published by: Kiplinger Washington Editors, Inc., 1729 H St, N W, Washington, DC 20006. FAX 202-331-1206, http://www.kiplinger.com/. Eds. Priscilla Biandin, Knight A Kiplinger. Pub. Knight A Kiplinger.

630 IND
KISAN WORLD. Text in English. 1974. m. INR 20, USD 16. adv. bk.rev. illus. **Document type:** *Newspaper.*
Indexed: FCA, HerbAb.
Published by: Sakthi Sugars Ltd., 101 Mount Rd., Guindy, Chennai, Tamil Nadu 600 032, India. TEL 91-422-2350212. Ed. N Mahalingam. Pub. K P Ganesan. Circ: 30,000.

630 IRN
KISHAVARAZ. Text in Persian, Modern. 1989 (vol.10). m. IRR 350 per issue.
Published by: F. Gulafra, Vali Asar Rd., Opp Fatimi Rd., Blk.4, Teheran, Iran.

KISHO TO NOSAGYO/METEOROLOGY AND AGRICULTURE. see *METEOROLOGY*

630 IND
KISSAN BHAARTI. Text in Hindi. m. INR 100 domestic; INR 10 newsstand/cover domestic (effective 2003).
Published by: G. B. Pant University of Agriculture and Technology, C/o Dr. K.K. Singh, O.I.C Telecom Unit, Pantnagar, Udhamsingh Nagar, Uttaranchal 263 145, India. TEL 91-5944-33671, FAX 91-5944-33473, kks@gbpuat.ernet.in, http://www.gbpuat.ac.in.

630 SVN ISSN 0023-2238
KMECKI GLAS. Text in Slovenian. 1943. w. SIT 987, USD 77. adv.
Published by: C Z P Kmecki Glas, Celovska 43, Box 47, Ljubljana, 61001, Slovenia. TEL 061-328670, FAX 061-321-651. Ed. Rajko Ocepek. Circ: 35,000.

630 570 JPN ISSN 0452-2370
CODEN: KNGKAP
KOBE UNIVERSITY. FACULTY OF AGRICULTURE. SCIENCE REPORTS. Text in English, Japanese; Summaries in English. 1953. a. per issue exchange basis.
Indexed: AEA, AnBrAb, BioCN&I, BiolAb, DSA, FCA, FPA, FS&TA, ForAb, HortAb, NutrAb, PBA, PGrRegA, RefZh, RiceAb, WildRev, ZooRec.
—BLDSC (8152.377000), CASDDS, CISTI, ingenta.
Published by: Kobe Daigaku, Nogakubu/Kobe University, Faculty of Agriculture, 1 Rokko-Dai-cho, Nada-ku, Kobe-shi, Hyogo-ken 657-0013, Japan. FAX 078-871-8450. Circ: 800.

630 570 JPN ISSN 0389-0473
CODEN: KDGHBF
KOCHI DAIGAKU GAKUJUTSU KENKYU HOKOKU. NOGAKU/KOCHI UNIVERSITY. AGRICULTURAL SCIENCE. RESEARCH REPORTS. Text in English, Japanese; Summaries in English. 1952. a. free. **Document type:** *Bulletin.*
Supersedes in part (in 1969): Kochi Daigaku Gakujutsu Kenkyu Hokoku. Shizen Kagaku 2 (0389-0236); Which superseded in part (in 1961): Kochi Daigaku Gakujutsu Kenkyu Hokoku (0452-246X)
Indexed: BiolAb, HortAb, OrnHort, RPP.
—BLDSC (7762.399500), CASDDS.
Published by: Kochi Daigaku/Kochi University, 5-1 Akebono-cho 2-chome, Kochi-shi, Kochi-ken 780-8520, Japan. TEL 0888-44-0111, FAX 0888-64-5200.

630 620 JPN ISSN 0450-6219
KOCHI UNIVERSITY. FACULTY OF AGRICULTURE. MEMOIRS. Text in English, Japanese; Summaries in English. 1956. a. free.
Indexed: BiolAb, RefZh.
Published by: Kochi Daigaku, Nogakubu/Kochi University, Faculty of Agriculture, 5-1 Akebono-cho 2-chome, Kochi-shi, Kochi-ken 780-8520, Japan. FAX 0888-64-5200.

630 334 FIN ISSN 1456-7210
S16.F5
KODIN PELLERVO. Text in Finnish. 1899. m. EUR 73 (effective 2005). adv. **Document type:** *Magazine, Consumer.*
Formerly (until 1999): Pellervo (0031-4188)
Published by: Pellervo-Seura ry/Confederation of Finnish Cooperatives, Simonkatu 6, PO Box 77, Helsinki, 00101, Finland. TEL 358-9-4767501, FAX 358-9-6948845, finnvoop@pellervo.fi, http://www.pellervo.fi/pellervo/pellervo.htm. Ed. Kaisu Rasanen. Adv. contact Merja Sainio. B&W page EUR 1,631, color page EUR 2,556; 185 x 270. Circ: 40,000.

630 JPN ISSN 0387-3773
KOKUSAI NORINGYO KYORYOKU. Text in Japanese. 1989. q. **Document type:** *Magazine, Trade.*
Incorporates (1978-1997): Kokusai noringyo Kyoryoku Joho/Association for International Cooperation of Agriculture & Forestry. Newsletter (0286-0058); (1992-1997): Roshia, Too no Nogyo/Agriculture in the Former USSR and East Europe (0918-2047); Which was formerly (1989-1992): Soren, To-O no Nogyo/Agriculture in USSR and East Europe (0915-5740)
—BLDSC (4539.465400).
Published by: Kokusai Noringyo Kyoryoku Kyokai/Association for International Cooperation of Agriculture & Forestry, Ichibancho 19, Chiyoda-ku, Tokyo, 102-0082, Japan. TEL 81-3-32637377, FAX 81-3-32345137, http://www.aicaf.or.jp/.

630 AUS
KONDININ GROUP UPDATE. Text in English. q. AUD 163.90 membership (effective 2000); includes Farming Ahead (ISSN 1038-1678). **Document type:** *Newsletter, Trade.* **Description:** Discusses news and issues of the Kondinin Group, an independent organization providing financial and research information to agricultural businesses.
Published by: Kondinin Group, 4/398 Great Eastern Hwy, RedCliffe, W.A. 6104, Australia. TEL 61-8-9478-3343, FAX 61-8-9748-3353, joanne@kondinin.com.au, http://www.kondinin.com.au/membership.

630.711 636.07 DNK ISSN 1600-2490
KONGELIGE VETERINAER- OG LANDBOHOEJSKOLE. DE STUDERENDES RAAD. TVAERFAGLIGT RUSUDVALG. BRUGSANVISNING I KVL. Text in Danish. 1981. a. DKK 30.
Former titles (until 1998): Kongelige Veterinaer- og Landbohoejskole. De Studerendes Raad. Tvaerfagligt Rusudvalg. Haandbog (1395-654X); (until 1994): Kongelige Veterinaer- og Landbohoejskole. Haandbog (0109-4998); (until 1982): Haandbog for Studerende ved Landbohoejskolen (0902-2716)
Published by: Kongelige Veterinaer- og Landbohoejskole, Studerendes Raad, Dyrlaegevej 9, Frederiksberg, 1870, Denmark. TEL 45-35-28-21-54, FAX 45-35-28-21-52, http://www.dsr.kvl.dk. Circ: 1,500.

630 DNK ISSN 0906-9550
KONGELIGE VETERINAER- OG LANDBOHOEJSKOLE. JORDBRUGSTEKNISK INSTITUT. RAPPORT. Text in Multiple languages. 1959. irreg. price varies. **Document type:** *Monographic series.*
Former titles (until 1991): Kongelige Veterinaer- og Landbohoejskole. Jordbrugsteknisk Institut. Meddelelse (0106-8237); (until 1966): Kongelige Veterinaer- og Landbohoejskole. Afdelingen for Landbrugsmaskiner. Meddelelse (0589-6770)
Indexed: AEA.
Published by: Kongelige Veterinaer- og Landbohoejskole, Institut for Jordbrugsvidenskab/Royal Veterinary and Agricultural University. Department of Agricultural Sciences, Thorvaldsensvej 40, Frederiksberg C, 1871, Denmark. TEL 45-35-28-34-96, FAX 45-35-28-34-60.

KONGETSU NO TENKO TO NORIN SAGYO/MONTHLY NEWS OF WEATHER, AGRICULTURE AND FORESTRY. see *METEOROLOGY*

KONINKLIJK INSTITUUT VOOR DE TROPEN. CRITICAL REVIEWS AND ANNOTATED BIBLIOGRAPHIES. see *AGRICULTURE—Abstracting, Bibliographies, Statistics*

630 KOR ISSN 0259-6148
S471.K8 CODEN: LECOE3
KOREA (REPUBLIC). MINISTRY OF AGRICULTURE AND FORESTY, RURAL DEVELOPMENT ADMINISTRATION. ANNUAL REPORT. Text in English. 1958. a. free. **Document type:** *Government.*
Former titles (until 1984): Korea (Republic). Office of Rural Development. Research Report (0259-6571); Korea (Republic). Office of Rural Development. Agricultural Research Report (0075-6865)
Related titles: Microfiche ed.
Indexed: AnBrAb, ExcerpMed, HortAb, NutrAb, PotatoAb, PoultAb, VetBull.

—CASDDS, CISTI.
Published by: Ministry of Agriculture & Forestry, Office of Rural Development, 250 Seodungdong Auweon, Kyeonggido, 441 707, Korea, S. FAX 82-331-293-9359, itcc@chollian.net, http://www.rda.go.kr. Ed. Kun Hwan Yun. Circ: 1,230.

KOTI. see *HOME ECONOMICS*

630 RUS
KREST'YANSKAYA GAZETA. Text in Russian. 1906. w. USD 150 in North America.
Related titles: Microfilm ed.: (from PQC).
Indexed: RASB.
Published by: Izdatel'stvo Podmoskov'e, Ul 1905 Goda 7, Moscow, 123022, Russian Federation. TEL 7-095-2569100. Ed. Konstantin Lysenko. Circ: 91,340. **Dist. by:** East View Information Services, 3020 Harbor Ln. N., Minneapolis, MN 55447. TEL 763-550-0961, FAX 763-559-2931.

630 IND ISSN 0970-8650
KRISHAK JAGAT. Text in Hindi. 1946. w. INR 250. adv. bk.rev. **Document type:** *Newspaper.* **Description:** Coverage of agriculture, animal husbandry, dairy, poultry and other agro-industries.
Address: 14 Indira Press Complex, M.P. Nagar, P O Box 37, Bhopal, Madhya Pradesh 462 011, India. TEL 91-755-768452, FAX 91-755-5553913. Ed., Pub. Vijay Kumar Bondriya. Adv. contact Sunil Gangrade. B&W page INR 22,800, color page INR 40,000; 280 x 420. Circ: 51,436.

630 IND ISSN 0023-4710
KRISHAK SAMACHAR. Text in Hindi. 1956. m. INR 10, USD 2. adv. bk.rev. abstr.; bibl.; charts; illus.; stat.
Related titles: English ed.
Published by: Bharat Krishak Samaj/Farmer's Forum, India, A-1 Nizamuddin West, New Delhi, 110 013, India. TEL 11-619508. Ed. K Prabhakar Reddy. Circ: 30,000.

630 IND
KRISHAK SANDESH. Text in Hindi. 1987. fortn. INR 2 newsstand/cover. adv. 12 p./no.
Address: 81-L Block, Sri Ganganagar, 335 001, India. TEL 24569. Ed. Santosh Sharma. Pub. Brij Bhushan Sharma.

630 SWE ISSN 1402-0386
KUNGLIGA SKOG- OCH LANTBRUKSAKADEMIEN. SKOGS- OCH LANTBRUKSHISTORISKA MEDDELANDEN. Text in Swedish. 1992. irreg., latest vol.27, 2003. price varies. **Document type:** *Monographic series, Academic/Scholarly.*
Formerly (until 1997): Skogs-och Lantbrukshistoriska Meddelanden: utgivna av Kungliga Skogs- och Lantbruksakademiens Bibliotek (1102-9048)
Related titles: ♦ Supplement to: Kungliga Skogs- och Lantbruksakademiens Tidskrift. ISSN 0023-5350.
Published by: Kungliga Skogs- och Lantbruksakademien/Royal Swedish Academy of Agriculture and Forestry, Drottninggatan 95 B, PO Box 6806, Stockholm, 11386, Sweden. TEL 46-8-54547700, FAX 46-8-54547710, akademien@ksla.se, http://www.ksla.se.

630 634.9 SWE ISSN 0023-5350
S11
KUNGLIGA SKOGS- OCH LANTBRUKSAKADEMIENS TIDSKRIFT/ACADEMIE ROYALE D'AGRICULTURE ET DE SYLVICULTURE DE SUEDE. ANNALES/KOENIGLICHE SCHWEDISCHE AKADEMIE DER LAND- UND FORSTWIRTSCHAFT. ZEITSCHRIFT/ROYAL SWEDISH ACADEMY OF AGRICULTURE AND FORESTRY. JOURNAL. Text in Swedish; Summaries in English, German. 1877. irreg. (15-20 times a year). SEK 350 (effective 2004); includes irreg. supplements. bibl.; charts; illus. index. back issues avail. **Document type:** *Academic/Scholarly.*
Former titles (until 1956): Kungl. Landtbruksakademiens Tidskrift (0368-6086); (until 1938): Kungl. Landtbruks-akademiens Handlingar och Tidskrift
Related titles: ♦ Supplement(s): Kungliga Skog- och Lantbruksakademien. Skogs- och Lantbrukshistoriska Meddelanden. ISSN 1402-0386; Kungliga Skogs- och Lantbruksakademiens Tidskrift, Supplement. ISSN 0075-7233.
Indexed: AbHyg, AgBio, AgrForAb, AnBrAb, BioCN&I, BiolAb, CPA, ChemAb, DSA, FCA, FPA, FS&TA, ForAb, HerbAb, HortAb, I&DA, IndVet, NemAb, NutrAb, OrnHort, PBA, PGegResA, PHN&I, PN&I, PotatoAb, PoultAb, RDA, RPP, RRTA, RefZh, RevApplEntom, S&F, SFA, TriticAb, VetBull, WAE&RSA, WeedAb, WildRev.
—CISTI, Linda Hall.
Published by: Kungliga Skogs- och Lantbruksakademien/Royal Swedish Academy of Agriculture and Forestry, Drottninggatan 95 B, PO Box 6806, Stockholm, 11386, Sweden. TEL 46-8-54547700, FAX 46-8-54547710, akademien@ksla.se, http://www.ksla.se.

630 JPN ISSN 0023-5725
KUSUNOKI NOHO✶. Text in Japanese. 1947. m. JPY 800, USD 2.30. adv. bk.rev. abstr.; charts; illus. index.
Published by: Nishimura Shoten, 1-10 Kanda-Nishiki-cho, Chiyoda-ku, Tokyo, 101-0054, Japan. Ed. Ikuo Uesugi. Circ: 800.

KUWAIT. CENTRAL STATISTICAL OFFICE. AGRICULTURAL STATISTICS BULLETIN/KUWAIT. AL-IDARAH AL-MARKAZIYYAH LIL-IHSA'. NASHRAH AL-IHSA'AT AL-ZIRA'IYYAH. see *AGRICULTURE—Abstracting, Bibliographies, Statistics*

630 JPN ISSN 0451-1476
QP141.A1 CODEN: KDSKAF
KYOTO DAIGAKU SHOKURYO KAGAKU KENKYUSHO HOKOKU/KYOTO UNIVERSITY. RESEARCH INSTITUTE FOR FOOD SCIENCE. BULLETIN. Text in English, Japanese; Summaries in English. 1949. a. free. bk.rev. back issues avail. **Document type:** *Academic/Scholarly.*
Indexed: ASFA, B&BAb, ChemAb, ChemoAb, ESPM, FS&TA, MBA, NutrAb, RefZh, VITIS.
—BLDSC (2695.000000), CASDDS, CISTI.
Published by: Kyoto University, Research Institute for Food Science/Kyoto Daigaku Shokuryo Kagaku Kenkyusho, Gokasho, Uji, 6110011, Japan. TEL 81-774-38-3702, FAX 81-774-38-3702. Ed. Tomohiko Mori. Circ: 800.

KYOTO FURITSU DAIGAKU GAKUJUTSU HOKOKU. NINGEN KANKYOGAKU, NOGAKU/KYOTO PREFECTURAL UNIVERSITY. SCIENTIFIC REPORTS: AGRICULTURE. see *ENVIRONMENTAL STUDIES*

630 JPN ISSN 0388-2330
S405 CODEN: MAGKAO
KYOTO UNIVERSITY. COLLEGE OF AGRICULTURE. MEMOIRS/KYOTO DAIGAKU NOGAKUBU KIYO. Text in English. 1926. s-a. per issue exchange basis.
Indexed: ABIPC, BiolAb, DSA, EnvAb, FPA, FS&TA, ForAb, HerbAb, HortAb, I&DA, PBA, RevApplEntom, S&F, VITIS.
—CASDDS.
Published by: Kyoto University, College of Agriculture/Kyoto Daigaku Nogakubu, Kita-Shirakawaoiwake-cho, Sakyo-ku, Kyoto-shi, 606-8224, Japan. FAX 075-753-6025. Ed. Kanji Nakato. Circ: 700.

630 JPN ISSN 0286-8180
KYUSHU TOKAI DAIGAKU NOGAKUBU KIYO/KYUSHU TOKAI UNIVERSITY. FACULTY OF AGRICULTURE. PROCEEDINGS. Text in Japanese. 1982. a. **Document type:** *Proceedings, Academic/Scholarly.*
Indexed: AgBio, AnBrAb, CPA, DSA, FCA, ForAb, HerbAb, HortAb, OrnHort, PBA, PGegResA, PotatoAb, PoultAb, RefZh, S&F, SeedAb, SoyAb, WAE&RSA, WeedAb.
—CISTI.
Published by: Kyushu Tokai Daigaku, Nogakubu/Kyushu Tokai University, School of Agriculture, Choyo-mura Aso-gun, Kumamoto, 869-1404, Japan. http://www.ktokai-u.ac.jp/~nougaku/nougaku.htm.

630 JPN ISSN 0023-6152
S3 CODEN: JFAKAU
➤ **KYUSHU UNIVERSITY. FACULTY OF AGRICULTURE. JOURNAL/KYUSHU DAIGAKU NOGAKUBU KIYO.** Text in English, French, German. 1923. q. per issue exchange basis. bibl.; illus. index. **Document type:** *Academic/Scholarly.*
Indexed: AEA, ASCA, ASFA, AgBio, AgrForAb, AnBrAb, BIOSIS Prev, BioCN&I, BiolAb, CIN, CPA, ChemAb, ChemTitl, CurCont, DBA, DSA, ESPM, EntAb, EnvEAb, FCA, FPA, FS&TA, ForAb, HerbAb, HortAb, I&DA, ISR, IndVet, M&GPA, MaizeAb, NemAb, NutrAb, OrnHort, PBA, PGegResA, PGrRegA, PHN&I, PN&I, PollutAb, PotatoAb, PoultAb, RA&MP, RDA, RPP, RRTA, RefZh, RevApplEntom, RiceAb, S&F, SCI, SFA, SIA, SWRA, SeedAb, SoyAb, TriticAb, VITIS, VetBull, WAE&RSA, WeedAb, WildRev, ZooRec.
—BLDSC (4743.000000), CASDDS, IDS, IE, ingenta, Linda Hall.
Published by: Kyushu University, Faculty of Agriculture/Kyushu Daigaku Nogakubu, 6-10-1 Hakozaki, Higashi-ku, Fukuoka-shi, 812-0053, Japan.

630 JPN ISSN 1347-0159
KYUSHU UNIVERSITY. FACULTY OF AGRICULTURE. SCIENCE BULLETIN/KYUUSHUU DAIGAKU DAIGAKUIN NOUGAKU KENKYUUIN KANZEI ZASSHI. Text in Japanese. 1924. s-a.
Formerly (until 2000): Kyushu Daigaku Nogakubu Gakugei Zasshi (0368-6264)
Indexed: AEA, ASFA, AgBio, AgrForAb, AnBrAb, BIOSIS Prev, BioCN&I, BiolAb, CPA, DSA, ESPM, FCA, FPA, FS&TA, ForAb, HerbAb, HortAb, I&DA, MaizeAb, NutrAb, OrnHort, PBA, PGegResA, PHN&I, PollutAb, PotatoAb, RA&MP, RDA, RefZh, RiceAb, S&F, SIA, SeedAb, SoyAb, TriticAb, VITIS, WAE&RSA, WeedAb, ZooRec.
—BLDSC (8137.000000), CISTI, IE, ingenta, Linda Hall.
Published by: Kyushu University, Faculty of Agriculture/Kyushu Daigaku Nogakubu, 6-10-1 Hakozaki, Higashi-ku, Fukuoka-shi, 812-0053, Japan.

630 JPN ISSN 0915-499X
SB111.A2
➤ **KYUSHU UNIVERSITY. INSTITUTE OF TROPICAL AGRICULTURE. BULLETIN/NETTAI NOGAKU KENKYU.** Text in English. 1975. a. exchange basis. back issues avail. **Document type:** *Bulletin, Academic/Scholarly.* **Description:** Covers tropical crop production, soil, and water conservation.
Indexed: AgBio, AgrForAb, BIOSIS Prev, BioCN&I, BiolAb, CPA, FCA, ForAb, HerbAb, HortAb, I&DA, MaizeAb, OrnHort, PBA, PGegResA, PGrRegA, PotatoAb, RA&MP, RPP, RevApplEntom, RiceAb, S&F, SIA, SeedAb, SoyAb, WeedAb, ZooRec.
—BLDSC (2585.195000).
Published by: Kyushu University, Institute of Tropical Agriculture/Kyushu Daigaku Nettai Nogaku Kenkyu Senta, Hakozaki, Higashi-ku, Fukuoka-shi, 812-8581, Japan. TEL 81-92-642-3076, FAX 81-92-642-3077, mmatsu@agr.kyushu-u.ac.jp, http://www.ita.agr.kyushu-u.ac.jp. Ed., Pub. Hisashi Yahata. R&P Masaru Matsumoto. Circ: 400.

639 JPN ISSN 1346-9177
KYUUSHUU OKINAWA NOUGYOU KENKYUU SENTA HOUKOKU/NATIONAL AGRICULTURAL RESEARCH CENTER FOR KYUSHU OKINAWA REGION. BULLETIN. Text in Japanese. 1951. irreg. **Document type:** *Bulletin, Academic/Scholarly.*
Former titles (until 2001): Kyushu Nogyo Shikenjo Hokoku (0376-0685); (until 1969): Kyushu Nogyo Shikenjo (0451-162X)
Indexed: AEA, AgBio, BioCN&I, CPA, DSA, FCA, HerbAb, HortAb, I&DA, MaizeAb, NemAb, NutrAb, PBA, PGegResA, PGrRegA, PHN&I, PN&I, RPP, RiceAb, S&F, SIA, SeedAb, SoyAb, TriticAb, WAE&RSA, WeedAb, ZooRec.
—BLDSC (2629.460000), CISTI.
Published by: National Agricultural Research Center for Kyushu Okinawa Region, Nishigoshi, Kikuchi, Kumamoto Prefecture 861-1192, Japan.

L E I - DRAAD. see *AGRICULTURE—Abstracting, Bibliographies, Statistics*

631 334.683 FIN ISSN 0355-0680
L O A. Key Title: L o A. Lantmaen och Andelsfolk. Variant title: Nya LoA. Text in Swedish. 1919. 11/yr. EUR 52.50 (effective 2005). adv. index. **Document type:** *Magazine, Trade.*
Former titles (until 1969): Lantmaen och Andelsfolk; (until 1965): Tidskrift foer Lantmaen och Andelsfolk; (until 1960): Lantmaen och Andelsfolk
Related titles: Online - full text ed.; ♦ Includes: M T. Mejeritidskrift foer Finlands Svenskbygd. ISSN 0782-2383.
Indexed: RefZh.
Published by: Svenska Lantbruksproducenternas Centralfoerbund/Central Union of Swedish-Speaking Agricultural Producers in Finland, Fredriksgatan 61 A 34, Helsinki, 00100, Finland. TEL 358-9-5860460, FAX 358-9-6941358, http://www.slc.fi/loa/. Ed. Ingvar Andersson. Adv. contact Lisbeth Loennqvist TEL 358-9-8039553. color page EUR 1,690, B&W page EUR 830; 185 x 258.

630 DEU ISSN 1439-6424
L W - LANDWIRTSCHAFTLICHES WOCHENBLATT HESSEN, RHEILAND-PFALZ. HESSENBAUER (AUSGABE SUED). Text in German. 1792. w. adv. **Document type:** *Newspaper, Trade.*
Former titles (until 2000): Hessenbauer - Ausgabe Sued (0723-3647); (until 1981): Der Hessenbauer. Ausgabe Regierung-Bezirk Darmstadt (0171-1652); Which superseded in part (in 1978): Der Hessenbauer (0170-561X)
Published by: Landwirtschaftsverlag Hessen GmbH, Taunusstr 151, Friedrichsdorf, 61381, Germany. TEL 49-6172-7106193, FAX 49-6172-7106199, lw-redaktion@lv-hessen.de, harald.niese@lv-hessen.de, http://www.lw-wochenblatt.de. Ed. Cornelius Mohr. Adv. contact Christa Schweitzer. B&W page EUR 2,530, color page EUR 4,224; trim 192 x 275. Circ: 15,384 (paid).

630 DEU ISSN 1439-6416
L W - LANDWIRTSCHAFTLICHES WOCHENBLATT HESSEN, RHEINLAND-PFALZ. HESSENBAUER (AUSGABE NORD). Text in German. 1792. w. adv. **Document type:** *Newspaper, Trade.*
Formerly (until 2000): Hessenbauer - Ausgabe Nord (0723-3639)
Published by: Landwirtschaftsverlag Hessen GmbH, Taunusstr 151, Friedrichsdorf, 61381, Germany. TEL 49-6172-7106193, FAX 49-6172-7106199, lw-redaktion@lv-hessen.de, harald.niese@lv-hessen.de, http://www.lw-wochenblatt.de. Ed. Cornelius Mohr. Adv. contact Christa Schweitzer. B&W page EUR 2,530, color page EUR 4,224; trim 192 x 275. Circ: 13,720 (paid and controlled).

630 USA ISSN 0093-4909
LACKAWANNA - WAYNE - PIKE - SUSQUEHANNA FARM & HOME NEWS✶. Text in English. 1947. m. USD 5. adv. illus.; stat.
Published by: Farm & Home Publications, 10 Lourdes Rd, Binghamton, NY 13905-4293. Ed. Bernard M Swartz. Circ: 2,100.

630 AUT
HD1931
LAENDLICHER RAUM. Text in German. 1953. m. free. bk.rev. charts; illus.; stat. index. **Document type:** *Government.*
Formerly (until 2000): Der Foerderungsdienst (0015-525X)
Media: Online - full text.
Indexed: AEA, AgBio, AnBrAb, BioCN&I, CPA, DSA, FCA, ForAb, HerbAb, HortAb, I&DA, IndVet, MaizeAb, NutrAb, OrnHort, PBA, PGrRegA, PHN&I, PN&I, PotatoAb, PoultAb, REE&TA, RM&VM, RPP, RRTA, RefZh, RevApplEntom, S&F, SIA, SeedAb, SoyAb, TriticAb, VetBull, WAE&RSA, WeedAb.

—BLDSC (3985.800000), CISTI, IE.
Published by: Bundesministerium fuer Land- und Forstwirtschaft, Umwelt und Wasserwirtschaft, Stubenring 1, Vienna, 1012, Austria. TEL 43-1-711006762, FAX 43-1-711005198, http://www.laendlicher-raum.at, http://www.bmlf.gv.at. Ed. Manfred Dietrich.

630 FRA
L'AGRI... Text in French. 1947. w. **Document type:** *Newspaper.*
Address: 77 av. Victor Dalbiez, Perpignan, Cedex 66027, France. TEL 33-4-68850202, FAX 33-4-68852425. Ed. Jean Pierre Cot. Circ: 9,000 (paid).

630 CHN ISSN 1007-7561
LAINGYOU SHIPIN KEJI/SCIENCE AND TECHNOLOGY OF CEREALS, OILS AND FOODS. Text in Chinese. bi-m. CNY 6 per issue domestic (effective 2000). back issues avail. **Document type:** *Academic/Scholarly.*
Related titles: Online - full content ed.: (from WanFang Data Corp.); Online - full text ed.: (from East View Information Services).
Published by: Guojia Liangshi Shubei Ju, Baiwon Zhuang Dajie 11, Beijing, 100037, China. TEL 86-1-68324027. Ed. Chang Rui Lin.

338.17 FRA ISSN 1625-9548
LAMY PRODUITS ET BIENS DE GRANDE CONSOMMATION. Text in French. 2000. q. EUR 495.85 (effective 2004).
Media: CD-ROM. **Related titles:** Online - full text ed.; Print ed.
Published by: Lamy S.A. (Subsidiary of: Wolters Kluwer France), 21/23 rue des Ardennes, Paris, 75935 Cedex 19, France. TEL 33-1-825080800, FAX 33-1-44721388, lamy@lamy.fr, http://www.lamy.fr.

630 GBR ISSN 0955-0011
LANCASHIRE FARMER. Text in English. 1962. m. adv.
Published by: County Farmers Publications Ltd., 55 Goldington Rd, Bedford, Beds MK40 3LU, United Kingdom. TEL 44-1234-351401, FAX 44-1234-328614. Ed. R Bacon. Circ: 4,150.

630 USA ISSN 0023-7485
LANCASTER FARMING. Text in English. 1955. w. (Sat.). USD 40 domestic in MD, DE, NJ, NY, OH, PA, VA, WV; USD 50 elsewhere (effective 2005). adv. bk.rev. illus.; mkt. reprint service avail. from PQC. **Document type:** *Newspaper, Trade.*
Description: Covers high-production agriculture for the northeast and mid-Atlantic states.
Related titles: Microform ed.: (from PQC).
Address: 1 E Main St, Box 609, Ephrata, PA 17522. TEL 717-626-1164, FAX 717-733-6058, farming@lancasterfarming.com, http://www.lancasterfarming.com. Ed. Andy Andrews. Pub. William Burgess. Adv. contact Gary Myer TEL 717-721-4414. Circ: 50,000 (paid).

630 AUS ISSN 0023-7523
THE LAND. Text in English. 1911. w. (Thu.). AUD 170.40; AUD 3 newsstand/cover (effective 2005). adv. bk.rev. illus. **Document type:** *Newspaper, Consumer.* **Description:** Provides a forum for debate on a host of rural and agricultural issues as well as information for people whose life and work revolve around the land.
Published by: Rural Press Ltd. (Subsidiary of: Agricultural Publishers Pty. Ltd.), 159 Bells Line of Rd., PO Box 999, North Richmond, NSW 2754, Australia. TEL 61-2-45704444, FAX 61-2-45704630, editorial.theland@ruralpress.com, http://www.theland.com.au, http://www.ruralpress.com/. Ed. Andrew Marshall. Adv. contact Roland Cowley. Circ: 55,586 (paid).

630 USA ISSN 0279-1633
THE LAND. Text in English. 1976. w. USD 20 (effective 2005); free to qualified personnel. adv. bk.rev. **Document type:** *Magazine, Trade.* **Description:** Local and regional agricultural news and features: rural people and their activities and involvements, including profiles. Also carries columns by area people, market projections, and a Washington report via correspondent.
Related titles: Online - full text ed.
Published by: Mankato Free Press Co., PO Box 3169, Mankato, MN 56002-3169. TEL 507-345-4523, FAX 507-345-1027, kschulz@the-land.com. Ed. Kevin Schulz. Adv. contact Kim Henrickson. B&W page USD 2,950, color page USD 3,740. Circ: 33,000 (paid and free).

630 634.9 DEU ISSN 1439-3239
LAND & FORST. Text in German. 1847. w. EUR 74; EUR 1.55 newsstand/cover (effective 2004). adv. bk.rev. illus.; mkt. **Document type:** *Magazine, Trade.* **Description:** Covers all aspects of agriculture and farming. Includes list of prices, reports of events, questions and answers and weather forecasts.
Formerly (until 1997): Hannoversche Land- und Forstwirtschaftliche Zeitung (0017-7466)
Related titles: Online - full text ed.
—CCC.
Published by: (Landwirtschaftskammer Hannover), Deutscher Landwirtschaftsverlag GmbH, Kabelkamp 6, Hannover, 30179, Germany. TEL 49-511-678060, FAX 49-511-67806200, dlv.hannover@dlv.de, http://www.landundforst.de, http://www.dlv.de. Ed. Wulf Obermeier. Adv. contact Werner Reinfelder. B&W page EUR 4,590, color page EUR 6,372; trim 190 x 270. Circ: 49,773 (paid and controlled).

630 GBR
LAND CONTRACTOR. Text in English. 4/yr.
Address: Huts Corner, Tilford Rd, Hindhead, Surrey GU26 6SF, United Kingdom. TEL 0428-605360, FAX 0428-606351. Ed. Don Gomery. Circ: 3,500.

630 SWE
LAND LANTBRUK. Text in Swedish. 1994. 48/yr. SEK 1,248 (effective 2005). adv. **Document type:** *Magazine, Trade.*
Supersedes in part: Land (0023-7531)
Related titles: Online - full content ed.
Published by: L R F Media AB, Gaevlegatan 22, Stockholm, 11392, Sweden. TEL 46-8-58836600, FAX 46-8-58836989, landlantbruk@lrfmedia.lrf.se, lrfmedia@lrfmedia.lrf.se, http://www.lantbruk.com, http://www.media.lrf.se. Eds. Anders Ahlberg TEL 46-8-58836757, Sven Olov Loeoev TEL 46-8-58836726. Pub. Anders Ahlberg TEL 46-8-58836757. Adv. contact Christer Karlsson TEL 46-8-58836801. B&W page SEK 29,800, color page SEK 36,000; trim 237 x 320. Circ: 123,200.

630 AUT
LAND UND RAUM. Text in German. 4/yr. EUR 12.35 domestic; EUR 13.80 foreign; EUR 3.63 newsstand/cover (effective 2005). **Document type:** *Journal, Trade.*
Formerly: Laendlicher Raum
Published by: Oesterreichisches Kuratorium fuer Landtechnik und Landentwicklung, Gusshausstr 5, Vienna, W 1040, Austria. TEL 43-1-5051891, FAX 43-1-5053175, office@oekl.at, http://www.oekl.at/publikationen/landraum/. Ed. Eva-Maria Munduch-Bader. Circ: 1,300 (paid and controlled).

630 BEL
LANDBODE✶. Text in Flemish. 24/yr. adv.
Address: Kapellelei 14, Mortsel, 2640, Belgium. Circ: 5,500.

LANDBOHISTORISK TIDSSKRIFT. see *HISTORY—History Of Europe*

LANDBOUW-ECONOMISCH INSTITUUT. MEDEDELINGEN. see *AGRICULTURE—Abstracting, Bibliographies, Statistics*

630 NLD
LANDBOUW-ECONOMISCH INSTITUUT. ONDERZOEKVERSLAG. Text in Dutch; Text occasionally in English. 1992 (no.92). irreg., latest vol.153, 1996. price varies. back issues avail. **Document type:** *Government.* **Description:** Publishes the results of statistical, econometric and environmental research on topics and issues pertaining to agriculture in the Netherlands and Europe.
Indexed: DSA, WAE&RSA.
Published by: Landbouw-Economisch Instituut, Burgemeester Patijnlaan 19, The Hague, 2585 BE, Netherlands. TEL 31-70-330-8330, FAX 31-70-361-5624, postmaster@lei.dlo.nl, http://www.lei.dlo.nl/lei.

630 NLD ISSN 0927-7838
HET LANDBOUWBLAD; agrarisch vakblad voor Noord-Nederland. Text in Dutch. 1903. w. (Sat.). EUR 79.50 (effective 2005). adv. bk.rev. illus.; stat. 7 cols./p.; **Document type:** *Newspaper, Trade.* **Description:** Covers agricultural, economic and social news and issues for farmers in the northern portion of the Netherlands.
Formerly (until 1993): Fries Landbouwblad (0016-1373); Incorporates (1988-1999): Noordoogst (1380-4278); Which was formerly (until 1994): Landbode (Editie Drenthe - Groningen) (0923-3229); Which was formed by the merger of (1970-1988): Landbode - Drents Landbouwblad (0165-6635); (1970-1988): Landbode - Groninger Landbouwblad (0165-6732); Incorporates (1919-1969): Groninger Landbouwblad (0017-4521); (1985-2000): Boer en Bedrijf (1568-0789); (1947-1994): Ons Platteland (0927-782X); Which was formerly (until 1992): Ons Friese Platteland (0166-3046)
Published by: Noordelijke Land- en Tuinbouw Organisatie, Postbus 186, Drachten, 9200 AD, Netherlands. TEL 31-512-305250, FAX 31-512-305251, hlb@nlto.nl, info@nlto.nl, http://www.nlto.nl/hetlandbouwblad/. adv.: B&W page EUR 1,671.60. Circ: 20,219.

630 ZAF ISSN 0023-7779
LANDBOUWEEKBLAD. Text in Afrikaans. 1919. w. ZAR 361.41 domestic; ZAR 1,263.69 foreign (effective 2000). adv. bk.rev. charts; illus. **Document type:** *Trade.*
Indexed: ISAP, SFA.
Published by: National Magazines (Subsidiary of: National Media Ltd.), PO Box 1802, Cape Town, 8000, South Africa. TEL 27-21-406-2202, FAX 27-21-406-2924, lbw@landbou.com, http://www.landbou.com. Ed. Tean du Preez. Circ: 43,400.

630 BEL ISSN 0772-7240
LANDBOUWLEVEN. Text in Dutch. 1951. w. EUR 43 (effective 2005). adv. charts; illus.; mkt.; maps; stat. **Document type:** *Newspaper.*
Related titles: ♦ French ed.: Sillon Belge.
Published by: Landelijke Uitgeverijen, Leon Grosjeanlaan 92, Brussels, 1140, Belgium. TEL 32-2-730-3301, FAX 32-2-726-9134 02/726.91.34, http://www.landbouwleven.be/landbouw/index.htm. Pub., R&P Andre de Mol TEL 32-2-7303301. Adv. contact Sylvie Eyben TEL 32-2-7303316. B&W page EUR 1,600, color page EUR 2,462; trim 260 x 380. Circ: 44,395.

630 SUR
LANDBOUWPROEFSTATION SURINAME. JAARVERSLAG/ AGRICULTURAL EXPERIMENT STATION SURINAME. ANNUAL REPORT. Text in Dutch; Summaries in English. 1903. a. SRG 15. charts; illus.; stat. **Document type:** *Government.*
Indexed: FCA, HerbAb, HortAb.
Published by: (Surinam. Landbouwproefstation), Department of Agriculture and Fisheries, Agricultural Experiment Station, PO Box 160, Paramaribo, Suriname. Circ: 500.

630 DNK ISSN 0108-2744
LANDBRUG FYN; fynsk landbrugs eget blad. Text in Danish. 1981. w. DKK 250 (effective 2004). adv. illus. **Document type:** *Bulletin, Trade.*
Published by: Landbrug Fyn A/S, Odensevej 29, Langeskov, 5550, Denmark. TEL 45-70-151237, FAX 45-70-151247, fyn@landbrugnet.dk, http://www.landbrugnet.dk. Ed. Erik Hansen TEL 45-63-382535. Adv. contact Bettina Ravn TEL 45-63-382520. Circ: 16,107.

630 DNK ISSN 1395-377X
LANDBRUG SYD; landbrugets eget blad i Syd- og Soenderjylland. Text in Danish. 1994. w. DKK 250 (effective 2004). adv. **Document type:** *Trade.*
Published by: Landbrug Syd ApS (Subsidiary of: Landbrug Fyn A/S), Skolegade 1A, Broerup, 6650, Denmark. TEL 45-75-381500, FAX 45-75-381516, syd@landbrugnet.dk, http://www.landbrugnet.dk. Ed. John Ankersen. Adv. contact Betina D Joergensen TEL 45-76-603042. Circ: 25,249.

630.60489 DNK ISSN 0302-4946
S245
LANDBRUGSAARBOG; noeglen til dansk landbrug. Text in Danish. 1899. a., latest vol.103, 2002. DKK 299 (effective 2005).
Formerly (until 1966): Landoekonomisk Aarbog (0105-0036)
Related titles: Online - full content ed.: ISSN 1602-1118.
—CISTI.
Published by: Det Kongelige Danske Landhusholdningsselskab/ Royal Danish Agricultural Society, Jacob Gades Alle 12, Vejen, 6600, Denmark. TEL 45-43-411769, FAX 45-43-410210, lhs@1769.dk, http://www.landbrugsaarbogen.dk, http://www.1769.dk.

630 DNK ISSN 1603-4236
▼ **LANDBRUGSAVISEN.** Text in Danish. 2003. w. **Document type:** *Trade.*
Formed by the merger of (1956-2003): Landsbladet (0455-2741); (1971-2003): Landbrugsmagasinet (0109-0240)
Related titles: Online - full content ed.
Published by: (Dansk Landbrug/Danish Agriculture), Dansk Landbrugs Medier, Vester Farimagsgade 6, Copenhagen V, 1606, Denmark. TEL 46-33-394700, post@landbrugsavisen.dk, http://www.landbrugsavisen.dk. Ed. Henning Lisberg TEL 46-33-394749. Adv. contact Jesper Jessig TEL 46-33-394719. Circ: 66,000.

382.4109489 DNK ISSN 0106-3812
HD9015.D4
LANDBRUGSEKSPORTEN. Text in Danish. 1960. a. free.
Description: Gives statistics on the Danish annual agricultural commodity trade.
—CISTI.
Published by: Landbrugets Afsaetningsudvalg, Afdeling for Markedsanalyse, Axelborg, Axeltorv 3, Copenhagen V, 1609, Denmark. TEL 45-3314-5672, FAX 45-3313-3650, kcm@landbrug.dk, http://www.landbrug.dk. Circ: 1,400.

630 NOR ISSN 0023-7833
LANDBRUKSTIDENDE. Text in Norwegian. 1899. w. adv. illus.; stat.
Incorporates (1895-1904): Landmanden (0809-2435); Formerly (until 1901): Jordbrugerens Blad (0809-2427)
—CCC.
Published by: Landbrukssamvirkets Informasjonskontor Midt-Norge AS, Bromstadveien 37, Trondheim, 7005, Norway. http://www.gaardsplassen.no. Ed. Ole T Hofstad. Adv. contact Borgny Losen TEL 47-73-90-31-57. color page NOK 13,200; 246 x 370.

LANDESFORSCHUNGSANSTALT FUER LANDWIRTSCHAFT UND FISHEREI MECKLENBURG-VORPOMMERN. MITTEILUNGEN. see *FISH AND FISHERIES*

630 CHE
LANDFREUND PLUS; das schweizer Agrarmagazin. Text in German. 1923. m. CHF 98 with Top Agrar; CHF 149 with Profil (effective 2001). **Document type:** *Magazine, Trade.*
Former titles (until 2001): Landfreund (1420-5351); (until 1981): Praktische Landwirtschaft, Landfreund (1420-584X); (until 1978): Neue Landfreund (1420-5858); (until 1970): Landfreund (1420-5866)

Published by: Schweizer Bauer, Dammweg 9, Bern, 3001, Switzerland. TEL 41-31-3303444, FAX 41-31-3303648, office@landfreund.ch, lf.leserservice@btm.ch. Ed. Max Welter. R&P Ulrich Utiger. Circ: 18,000 (paid and controlled).

LANDOEKONOMISK OVERSIGT. see *AGRICULTURE—Abstracting, Bibliographies, Statistics*

630 FIN ISSN 0023-8015
LANDSBYGDENS FOLK. Text in Swedish. 1947. w. EUR 45 (effective 2004). adv. **Document type:** *Newspaper, Trade.*
Formerly: Svenska Lantbruksproducenternas Centralfoerbund. Publication (0355-0788)
Published by: Svenska Lantbruksproducenternas Centralfoerbund/Central Union of Swedish-Speaking Agricultural Producers in Finland, Fredriksgatan 61 A 34, Helsinki, 00100, Finland. TEL 358-9-5860460, FAX 358-9-6941358, http://www.slc.fi/lf/lf.asp. Ed. Mikael Jern TEL 358-9-58604608. Adv. contact Bjarne Jansson TEL 358-9-58604630. Circ: 10,500.

LANDSCAPE HISTORY. see *HISTORY*

630 AUT
LANDTECHNISCHE SCHRIFTENREIHE. Text in German. irreg., latest vol.222, 2004. price varies. adv. **Document type:** *Monographic series, Trade.*
Published by: Oesterreichisches Kuratorium fuer Landtechnik und Landentwicklung, Gusshausstr 5, Vienna, W 1040, Austria. TEL 43-1-5051891, FAX 43-1-5053175, office@oekl.at, http://www.oekl.at/publikationen/lts/.

630 DEU ISSN 0023-8104
DAS LANDVOLK; Agrar- und wirtschaftspolitisches Medium. Text in German. 1952. every 3 wks. EUR 11.50 (effective 2004). adv. bk.rev. **Document type:** *Newspaper, Trade.* **Description:** Contains articles and items for farmers featuring news on agricultural economy, prices, market, production.
—CCC.
Published by: (Verband der Niedersaechsischen Landvolkes e.V.), Deutscher Landwirtschaftsverlag GmbH, Kabelkamp 6, Hannover, 30179, Germany. TEL 49-511-678060, FAX 49-511-67806200, dlv.hannover@dlv.de, http://www.dlv.de. adv.: B&W page EUR 4,374, color page EUR 6,048; 315 x 470. Circ: 80,245 (paid and controlled).

630 GBR ISSN 1363-8300
➤ **LANDWARDS**; the journal for professional scientists, engineers and technologists in agriculture, forestry, environment and amenity. Text in English. 1944. bi-m. GBP 52; GBP 12 newsstand/cover (effective 2003). adv. bk.rev. charts; illus.; stat. index. **Document type:** *Journal, Academic/Scholarly.* **Description:** Contains conference papers, refereed scientific papers and technical and news articles.
Formerly (until 1996): Agricultural Engineer (0308-5732); Which incorporated (1938-1988): Soil and Water (0309-023X); Which was formerly: Institution of Agricultural Engineers. Journal and Proceedings (0020-3238)
Related titles: Microfilm ed.: (from PQC).
Indexed: AEA, Agr, AgrForAb, AnBrAb, CPA, DSA, FCA, FPA, ForAb, HerbAb, HortAb, I&DA, IAOP, IndVet, OrnHort, PHN&I, PN&I, PotatoAb, RDA, RevApplEntom, S&F, SIA, TriticAb, WAE&RSA, WeedAb.
—CISTI, IE, Infotrieve, Linda Hall. **CCC.**
Published by: Institution of Agricultural Engineers, West End Rd, Silsoe, Bedford, Beds MK45 4DU, United Kingdom. TEL 44-1525-861096, FAX 44-1525-861660, secretary@iagre.org, http://www.iagre.org. Ed. Brian D Whitney. R&P, Adv. contact Brian Whitney. Circ: 2,000 (paid).

630 634.9 AUT ISSN 0047-4010
DIE LANDWIRTSCHAFT; Fachzeitschrift fuer die Gesamtinteressen der Land- und Forstwirtschaft. Text in German. 1971. m. adv. charts; illus. **Document type:** *Magazine, Trade.*
Indexed: PBA.
Published by: Niederoesterreichische Landes-Landwirtschaftskammer, Wiener Str 64, St. Poelten, 3100, Austria. TEL 43-2742-2599300, FAX 43-2742-2591009, office@lk-noe.at, http://www.lk-noe.at. Ed. Gerd Rittenauer. Adv. contact Lieselotte Domanski. Circ: 65,000 (controlled).

630 LUX
LANDWIRTSCHAFT AKTUELL. Text in German. m.
Address: 10 rue Principale, Stolzembourg, 9463, Luxembourg. TEL 84-67-7.

630 AUT
LANDWIRTSCHAFTLICHE BLAETTER. Text in German. 1864. w. free. **Document type:** *Trade.*
Published by: Landeslandwirtschaftskammer fuer Tirol, Brixnerstr 1, Innsbruck, T 6020, Austria. TEL 43-512-5929-216, FAX 43-512-5929-208, presse@lk-tirol.at.

630 AUT ISSN 1010-1330
LANDWIRTSCHAFTLICHE MITTEILUNGEN. Text in German. 1884. fortn. adv. bk.rev. **Document type:** *Newspaper, Trade.* **Description:** Covers news and information of interest to farmers. Features crop production, livestock, market news, agricultural economics and politics. Includes calendar of events.
Published by: Landeskammer fuer Land- und Forstwirtschaft in Steiermark, Hamerlinggasse 3, Graz, St 8010, Austria. TEL 43-316-80500, FAX 43-316-80501512, office@lk-stmk.at, http://www.lk-stmk.at. Ed. Rosemarie Wilhelm. Adv. contact Andrea Kratzer. color page EUR 6,434; trim 275 x 394. Circ: 60,000 (controlled).

630 DEU ISSN 0023-8163
LANDWIRTSCHAFTLICHE ZEITSCHRIFT RHEINLAND. Text in German. 1833. w. **Document type:** *Newsletter, Trade.* **Description:** Provides various agricultural information about the region: on farming, marketing, government policies, and industry. Includes association news, events, questions and answers.
Published by: Rheinischer Landwirtschaftsverlag GmbH, Rochusstr 18, Bonn, 53123, Germany. TEL 49-228-5200635, FAX 49-228-5200660. Ed. Stefan Sallen. Circ: 22,000.

630 DEU
LANDWIRTSCHAFTLICHER TASCHENKALENDER FUER WESER - EMS. Text in German. 1948. a. **Document type:** *Trade.*
Published by: Landwirtschaftsverlag Weser-Ems GmbH, Mars-la-Tour-Str 4, Oldenburg, 26121, Germany. TEL 49-441-801231, FAX 49-441-801239. Ed. H H Kowalewsky. Circ: 9,000.

630 DEU ISSN 0940-967X
LANDWIRTSCHAFTLICHES WOCHENBLATT. Text in German. 1885. w. EUR 79.80 domestic; EUR 128.40 foreign; EUR 1.65 newsstand/cover (effective 2004). adv. bk.rev. illus.; mkt.; tr.lit. **Document type:** *Magazine, Trade.*
Formerly (until 1991): Wuerttembergisches Wochenblatt fuer Landwirtschaft (0043-9606)
—CCC.
Published by: Verlag Eugen Ulmer GmbH, Wollgrasweg 41, Stuttgart, 70599, Germany. TEL 49-711-45070, FAX 49-711-4507120, redaktion-lw@bwagrar.de, info@ulmer.de, http://www.bwagrar.de, http://www.ulmer.de. adv.: B&W page EUR 6,732, color page EUR 10,332. Circ: 54,512 (paid and controlled).

630 DEU ISSN 0342-765X
LANDWIRTSCHAFTLICHES WOCHENBLATT WESTFALEN-LIPPE: AUSGABE A. Text in German. 1844. w. EUR 80.40 domestic; EUR 144.60 foreign; EUR 1.70 newsstand/cover (effective 2003). adv. bk.rev. **Document type:** *Newspaper, Trade.*
—CCC.
Published by: Landwirtschaftsverlag GmbH, Huelsebrockstr 2, Muenster, 48165, Germany. TEL 49-2501-801-0, FAX 49-2501-801351, zentrale@lv-h.de, http://www.lv-h.de. Ed. Franz Josef Budde. Adv. contact Klaus Kauther. B&W page EUR 5,858, color page EUR 9,668. Circ: 63,366 (paid and controlled).

630 AUT
LANDWIRTSCHAFTS ZEITUNG. Text in German. 1929. w. (Fri.). **Document type:** *Newspaper, Trade.*
Formerly (until 1996): Oberoesterreichische Landwirtschafts Zeitung
Published by: Oberoesterreichischer Bauern- und Nebenerwerbsbauernbund, Harrachstr 12, Linz, O 4010, Austria. TEL 43-732-7738660, office@ooe.bauernbund.at, http://www.ooe.bauernbund.at. Ed. Franz Hofer. Pub. Markus Rosinger. Adv. contact Josef Meisinger. Circ: 38,600.

630 DEU ISSN 0047-4029
S7
LANDWIRTSCHAFTSBLATT WESER-EMS. Text in German. 1853. w. adv. **Document type:** *Newspaper.*
Published by: (Landwirtschaftskammer Weser-Ems GmbH), Landwirtschaftsverlag Weser-Ems GmbH, Mars-la-Tour-Str 4, Oldenburg, 26121, Germany. TEL 49-441-801231, FAX 49-441-801239. Ed. Walter Hollweg. Adv. contact Ute Pluemer. Circ: 23,800.

LANDWORKER. see *LABOR UNIONS*

360 364.9 SWE ISSN 1402-0645
LANTBRUKSMAGASINET. Text in Swedish. 1995. 8/yr. SEK 260 (effective 2001). adv. **Document type:** *Magazine, Trade.* **Description:** Covers agriculture and forestry in Sweden and other countries.
Published by: Svenska Media Resia AB, PO Box 63, Ljusdal, 82722, Sweden. TEL 46-651-150-50, FAX 46-651-133-33, post@svenskamediaresia.se, http://www.svenskamediaresia.se. Ed., Pub. Mikael Sagstroem. Adv. contact Tommy Flodberg. B&W page SEK 18,900, color page SEK 22,900; trim 185 x 270. Circ: 26,500.

630 SWE ISSN 0282-4132
LANTBRUKSPRAKTIKA; med Lantbrukstekniska Kalendern. Text in Swedish. 1942. a. SEK 119 (effective 1998). adv.
Published by: Lantbrukstekniska Foerlaget, Fack 150, Lindesberg, 71123, Sweden. TEL 46-58-11-55-50, FAX 46-58-11-44-00, http://www.lantbruksnet.se. Ed. Hans Falck. Adv. contact Brita Falck. B&W page SEK 3,900.

630 SWE ISSN 0023-8430
LANTMAESTAREN. Text in Swedish. 1938. q. SEK 100; SEK 25 newsstand/cover (effective 2001). adv. charts; illus. **Document type:** *Magazine, Trade.*
Published by: Sveriges Lantmaestarfoerbund, c/o LIME AB, Tejarps Gaard, Klaagerup, 23041, Sweden. TEL 46-40-40-86-80, FAX 46-40-40-86-86. Ed. Agneta Lillehoeoek. Adv. contact Goeran Maansson. B&W page SEK 7,400, color page SEK 10,000; trim 184 x 270. Circ: 4,500 (paid and controlled).

630 SWE ISSN 0023-8449
LANTMANNEN; sveriges ledande lantbruksmagasin. Text in Swedish. 1879. m. SEK 749 (effective 2005). adv. bk.rev. charts; illus.; tr.lit. index. **Document type:** *Magazine, Trade.*
Formed by the merger of: Svenskt Land; Which was formerly (until 1935): Landtmannen - Tidskrift foer Landtmaen; Landtmannen; Which was formerly (until 1917): Tidskrift foer Landtmaen; Incorporates (in 1990): Teknik i Jord och Skog (0282-8618); Which was formerly (until 1985): Traktor Journalen (0021-7433)
Indexed: ChemAb, FCA, HerbAb, NAA, PBA.
—CISTI.
Published by: (Lantbrukarnas Riksfoerbund/Federation of Swedish Farmers), L R F Media AB, Gaevlegatan 22, Stockholm, 11392, Sweden. TEL 46-8-58836600, FAX 46-8-58836989, lantmannen@lrfmedia.lrf.se, lrfmedia@lrfmedia.lrf.se, http://www.lantmannen.com, http://www.media.lrf.se. Ed. Anders Ahlberg TEL 46-8-58836757. Adv. contact Birgit Emilsson TEL 46-40-6016455. B&W page SEK 10,200, color page SEK 13,700; trim 185 x 270. Circ: 10,400.

LATHYRUS LATHYRISM NEWSLETTERS. see *BIOLOGY—Botany*

630 BRA ISSN 0023-9135
S15
LAVOURA. Text in Portuguese. 1897. bi-m. BRL 20 (effective 2001). adv. bk.rev. bibl.; charts; illus.; stat. back issues avail. **Document type:** *Magazine, Consumer.*
Indexed: IBR.
—CISTI, Linda Hall.
Published by: Sociedade Nacional de Agricultura, Av General Justo, 171, Centro, Rio De Janeiro, RJ 20021-130, Brazil. TEL 55-21-25330088, FAX 55-21-22404189, snafagram@snagricultura.org.br, http://www.snagricultura.org.br/lavoura. Ed. Antonio Mello Alvarenga Neto. R&P Cristina Lucia Baran. Adv. contact Silvia Mara.

630 PRT
LAVRADOR. Text in Portuguese. 6/yr.
Address: Avda. Aliados 107-9, Lisbon, Portugal. TEL 21021, TELEX 25108.

630 AUS
LEADING EDGE. Text in English. 1970. s-a. AUD 40; AUD 60 foreign (effective 1998). adv. bk.rev. **Document type:** *Newsletter, Consumer.* **Description:** Includes agricultural engineering news, research, and stories.
Formerly (until 1998): Agricultural Engineering Australia (0044-6807)
Indexed: AEA, Agr, DSA, EPB, FCA, FPA, ForAb, HortAb, IAOP, MaizeAb, OrnHort, PHN&I, RPP, RevApplEntom, RiceAb, S&F, SIA, SeedAb, TriticAb, WeedAb.
—CISTI.
Published by: Society for Engineering in Agriculture, Institution of Engineers, 11 National Circuit, Barton, ACT 2600, Australia. TEL 61-6-2706555, FAX 61-6-2731488, TELEX AA62758. Ed. Geoffrey Hamilton. R&P, Adv. contact F Williams. Circ: 600.

630 DEU ISSN 0023-9917
LEBENDIGE ERDE; Biologisch-Dynamische Landwirtschaft, Ernaehrung, Kultur. Text in German. 1950. bi-m. EUR 36 domestic; EUR 41 foreign; EUR 6 newsstand/cover (effective 2005). adv. bk.rev. **Document type:** *Journal, Academic/Scholarly.*
Indexed: RefZh.
Published by: Forschungsring fuer Biologisch-Dynamische Wirtschaftsweise e.V., Brandschneise 2, Darmstadt, 64295, Germany. TEL 49-6155-84120, FAX 49-6155-846911, Redaktion@LebendigeErde.de, Info@Forschungsring.de, http://www.lebendigeerde.de, http://www.forschungsring.de. Adv. contact Michael Weiler. page EUR 580; trim 180 x 232. Circ: 8,500.

630 ITA
LEGA CONTADINA. Text in Italian. bi-m.
Published by: Rura Grafica s.r.l., c/o Rag. Tenneriello, Via Di Sant Angela Merici, 96, Rome, RM 00162, Italy. Ed. Ricci Sante. Circ: 12,500.

630 GBR ISSN 0306-0160
LEICESTERSHIRE, NORTHAMPTONSHIRE & RUTLAND FARMER. Text in English. 1954. m. adv.
Formerly: Leicestershire Farmer (0024-0656)
Published by: County Farmers Publications Ltd., 55 Goldington Rd, Bedford, Beds MK40 3LU, United Kingdom. TEL 44-1234-351401, FAX 44-1234-328614. Ed. S Fisher. Circ: 4,100.

630   RUS
LESNAYA GAZETA. Text in Russian. 1926. 104/yr. USD 220 in North America.
Related titles: Microfilm ed.: (from EVP).
Address: Novocheremushkinskaya ul 69 korp a, Moscow, 117418, Russian Federation. TEL 7-095-3325295. Ed. G M Nadareishvili. Dist. by: East View Information Services, 3020 Harbor Ln. N., Minneapolis, MN 55447. TEL 763-550-0961, FAX 763-559-2931.

630   RUS   ISSN 0132-828X
LESNAYA NOV'. Text in Russian. 1918. m. USD 147 in North America.
Indexed: RASB.
Published by: Profizdat, Myasnitskaya ul 13, Moscow, 101000, Russian Federation. TEL 7-095-1289485. Dist. by: East View Information Services, 3020 Harbor Ln. N., Minneapolis, MN 55447. TEL 763-550-0961, FAX 763-559-2931.

631   FRA   ISSN 1157-0059
LA LETTRE DE CIRCUITS CULTURE. Text in French. 1991. w. EUR 342 domestic; EUR 410 foreign (effective 2002).
Published by: Agri Terroir Communication, 61, Rue du XXe-Corps-Americain, Metz, 57000, France. TEL 33-03-87691818, FAX 33-03-87691814, infocentre@editions-mirabelle.com, http://www.editions-mirabelle.com.

630   FRA
LETTRE DES I T P A; hommes et agriculture. (Ingenieurs et Techniciens pour l'Agriculture) Text in French. 1949. q. adv. bk.rev. bibl.; charts; illus.; stat.
Former titles: I T P A Letters; Hommes et Agriculture; Technique et Pratique Agricoles (0040-1226)
Indexed: IBZ.
Published by: Ecole Superieure d'Agriculture, BP 201, Val de Reuil, 27100, France. Ed. M Havard. Circ: 2,000.

630   LUX   ISSN 0455-8154
DE LETZEBURGER BAUER. Text in German. 1944. w. adv. bk.rev. Description: Covers national and international agricultural problems.
Published by: Centrale Paysanne, 12 bd. d'Avranches, Luxembourg, L-2980, Luxembourg. TEL 352-4181-61262, FAX 400375, letzeburger.bauer@netline.lu. Ed. Guy Tabourin. Circ: 8,500.

630   BEL
LEVEND LAND. Text in Dutch. 1971. m. adv. bk.rev.
Published by: Belgische Boerenbond, Minderbroedersstraat 8, Leuven, 3000, Belgium. TEL 32-16-242165, FAX 32-16-242168, TELEX 23119 AVV B.

LIBERIA. MINISTRY OF AGRICULTURE. STATISTICAL HANDBOOK. see AGRICULTURE—Abstracting, Bibliographies, Statistics

LIBYA. CENSUS AND STATISTICS DEPARTMENT. AGRICULTURAL CENSUS. see AGRICULTURE—Abstracting, Bibliographies, Statistics

630   LBY   ISSN 1010-3740
                                        CODEN: LJAGD3
LIBYAN JOURNAL OF AGRICULTURE. Text in English. 1971. a.
—CASDDS.
Published by: Al-Fateh University, Faculty of Agriculture, P O Box 13040, Tripoli, Libya. TEL 36010, TELEX 20629.

630 570 333.72   NOR   ISSN 0801-1524
LIDIA (AS). Text in English. 1986. irreg. Document type: Academic/Scholarly.
—BLDSC (5208.501000).
Published by: Agricultural University of Norway, Department of Biology and Nature Conservation, PO Box 5003, As, 1432, Norway. TEL 47-64-948900, FAX 47-64-947505, ina@nlh.no, http://www.nlh.no/.

630 051   NZL
LIFESTYLE FARMER. Text in English. bi-m. NZD 25; NZD 5.50 newsstand/cover (effective 2005). Document type: Newspaper, Trade. Description: Contains practical farming information and advice articles specifically for the small block holders.
Related titles: Online - full content ed.
Published by: New Zealand Rural Press Ltd., PO Box 4233, Auckland, 1001, New Zealand. lifestylefarmer.nz@ruralpress.com, http://www.lifestyle-farmer.co.nz, http://www.ruralpress.com/. Ed. Rachel Wike. Adv. contact Patricia Mawhinney TEL 64-9-3769792. Circ: 10,000.

630   GBR   ISSN 0955-6893
LINCOLNSHIRE FARMER. Text in English. 1925. m. adv.
Former titles (until 1989): Lincolnshire Farmer and Record (0955-002X); Lincolnshire Record
Published by: County Farmers Publications Ltd., 55 Goldington Rd, Bedford, Beds MK40 3LU, United Kingdom. TEL 44-1234-351401, FAX 44-1234-328614. Ed. S Fisher. Circ: 4,550.

LIVING HISTORICAL FARMS BULLETIN. see MUSEUMS AND ART GALLERIES

630   USA   ISSN 0024-5313
LIVINGSTON COUNTY AGRICULTURAL NEWS. Text in English. 1918. m. USD 10 (effective 1999). adv. illus. Document type: Newsletter.
Media: Duplicated (not offset).
Published by: Cooperative Extension Association of Livingston County, Agricultural Division, 158 S Main St, Mount Morris, NY 14510. TEL 716-658-4110, FAX 716-658-4707. Ed., Pub., R&P, Adv. contact David L Thorp TEL 716-658-3250. Circ: 225 (controlled).

630   NLD   ISSN 1380-426X
LOONBEDRIJF; periodiek gewijd aan de belangen van het loonbedrijf in agrarisch- en grondverzetwerk. Text in Dutch. 1948. m. EUR 65 (effective 2005). adv. Document type: Bulletin, Trade. Description: Covers the integrated management of enterprise, business, and employment aimed at farm contractors as well as professional inforemation about agriculture.
Formerly (until 1981): Loonbedrijf in Land- en Tuinbouw (0024-6468)
Published by: (Vereniging voor Cultuurtechnische Werken en Grondverzet, Meststoffendistributie en Loonwerken in de Agrarische Sector in Nederland), Stichting Cumela Pers, Postbus 1156, Nijkerk, 3860 BD, Netherlands. TEL 31-33-2474950, FAX 31-33-2474951, loonbedrijf@cumela.nl, info@cumela.nl, http://www.cumela.nl. Ed. Toon van der Stok. adv.: B&W page EUR 968, color page EUR 1,268; trim 200 x 270. Circ: 3,400.

630   USA   ISSN 0024-6735
S67   CODEN: LOAGAZ
➤ **LOUISIANA AGRICULTURE.** Text in English. 1957. q. free in state. charts; illus. Document type: Journal, Academic/Scholarly. Description: Publishes results of research in agricultural sciences.
Indexed: AEA, ASFA, AgBio, Agr, AgrForAb, AnBrAb, BioCN&I, BiolAb, CPA, CTFA, CurCont, DSA, ESPM, EnvAb, EnvInd, ExcerpMed, FCA, FPA, FS&TA, ForAb, HelmAb, HerbAb, HortAb, I&DA, IndVet, MaizeAb, NemAb, NutrAb, OrnHort, PBA, PGegResA, PGrRegA, PHN&I, PollutAb, PoultAb, RA&MP, RDA, RPP, RevApplEntom, RiceAb, S&F, SIA, SWRA, SeedAb, SoyAb, TriticAb, VetBull, WAE&RSA, WeedAb, ZooRec.
—BLDSC (5294.950000), CASDDS, CIS, IE, ingenta.
Published by: (Louisiana Agricultural Experiment Station), Louisiana State University, Agricultural Center, PO Box 25203, Baton Rouge, LA 70894-5203. TEL 225-578-4161, FAX 225-578-4143, http://www.lsuagcenter.com/Communications/LouisianaAgriculture/agmag/index.asp, http://www.agctr.lsu.edu/. Ed. Linda Foster Beredict. Circ: 5,000 (controlled).

630   USA   ISSN 0024-6808
LOUISIANA FARMER. Text in English. m. USD 21.95 in state; USD 30 out of state; USD 75 foreign (effective 2001). Document type: Newspaper.
Formerly (until 1965): Louisiana Farm and Ranch (0092-7538)
Published by: Farm Progress Companies, 191 S Gary Ave, Carol Stream, IL 60188. TEL 504-488-4718, FAX 504-482-8950, info@farmprogress.com, http://www.farmprogress.com/. Ed. Carroll Smith. adv.: B&W page USD 1,009. Circ: 12,500.

630   USA   ISSN 0279-8824
LOUISIANA MARKET BULLETIN. Text in English. 1916. fortn. USD 10. adv. Description: News of the Louisiana agriculture industry.
Published by: Department of Agriculture and Forestry, PO Box 3534, Baton Rouge, LA 70821-3534. TEL 504-922-1284. Ed. Renee M Tull. Circ: 25,000.

630   ZWE
LOWVELD RESEARCH STATIONS. ANNUAL REPORT. Text in English. a. free. back issues avail.
Indexed: BiolAb.
Published by: (Zimbabwe. Information Services), Ministry of Lands Agriculture and Rural Resettlement, Research and Specialist Services, Causeway, PO Box 8108, Harare, Zimbabwe. Circ: 250.

630   USA   ISSN 0091-4460
M A F E S RESEARCH HIGHLIGHTS. Text in English. 1939. q. free. charts; illus. index. back issues avail. Document type: Government. Description: Deals with agricultural research.
Formerly: Mississippi Farm. Research (0026-6221)
Related titles: Online - full text ed.
Indexed: Agr, BibAg, CTFA, HortAb, OrnHort, WAE&RSA.
—CISTI, Linda Hall.
Published by: Mississippi Agricultural and Forestry Experiment Station, Box 9625, 210 Bost Bldg, Extension Dr, Mississippi State, MS 39762-9740. TEL 601-325-1714, FAX 601-325-1710, rebekahr@ext.msstate.edu, anne@mafes.msstate.edu, http://www.aac.msstate.edu/majes/highlights, http://mafes.msstate.edu. Ed. Rebekah Ray. R&P Bob Ratliff. Circ: 10,500.

630   MYS   ISSN 0127-4007
➤ **M A R D I REPORT/LAPORAN M A R D I.** Text in English, Malay. 1975. irreg. (7-8/yr.), latest vol.197, 2002. price varies. abstr.; illus.; charts. back issues avail. Document type: Bulletin, Academic/Scholarly.

Published by: Malaysian Agricultural Research & Development Institute/Institut Penyelidikan dan Kemajuan Pertanian Malaysia, PO Box 12301, General Post Office, Kuala Lumpur, 50774, Malaysia. TEL 60-3-89437226, FAX 60-3-89487630, TELEX MARDI-MA-37115, publicat@mardi.my, http://www.mardi.my. R&P Rohani Mahmood. Circ: 500.

630   MYS
M P O B TECHNOLOGY. (Malaysian Palm Oil Board) Text in English. 1981. irreg., latest vol.21, 1998. MYR 10 per issue (effective 2000). Document type: Monographic series, Academic/Scholarly.
Formerly: P O R I M Technology (0127-0257)
—BLDSC (6554.518000).
Published by: Lembaga Minyak Sawit Malaysia/Malaysian Palm Oil Board (Subsidiary of: Kementerian Perusahaan Utama, Malaysia/Ministry of Primary Industries, Malaysia), PO Box 10620, Kuala Lumpur, 50720, Malaysia. TEL 60-3-89259155, 60-3-89259775, FAX 60-3-89259446, http://mpob.gov.my/mpobtech.htm.

630   EST   ISSN 0235-6899
MAAKODU. Text in Estonian. m. USD 149 in North America.
—CISTI.
Published by: Redaktsiya Maakodu, Lai 39, Tallin, Estonia. TEL 370-6411161. Ed. Arvo Sirindi. Dist. by: East View Information Services, 3020 Harbor Ln. N., Minneapolis, MN 55447. TEL 763-550-0961, FAX 763-559-2931.

630   FIN   ISSN 0355-3787
MAASEUDUN TULEVAISUUS. Text in Finnish. 1916. 3/w. EUR 121 domestic; EUR 150 in Europe; EUR 220 elsewhere (effective 2005). adv. Document type: Newspaper, Consumer.
Related titles: Online - full content ed.: ISSN 1458-8021.
Published by: Maataloustuottajain Keskusliitto/Central Union of Agricultural Producers and Forest Owners, Simonkatu 6, Helsinki, 00100, Finland. TEL 358-20-4131, FAX 358-20-4132409, http://www.maaseuduntulevaisuus.fi/, http://www.mtk.fi. Ed. Lauri Kontro. R&P Kimmo Varjovaara. Adv. contact Hannu Toivonen TEL 358-9-1311-5237. Circ: 82,080.

MADAGASCAR. MINISTERE DE LA PRODUCTION AGRICOLE ET DU PATRIMOINE FONCIER. STATISTIQUES AGRICOLES. ANNUAIRE. see AGRICULTURE—Abstracting, Bibliographies, Statistics

638.1   IND   ISSN 0970-0919
MADHUPRAPANCHA. Text in English. 1981. q. INR 10. illus. back issues avail.
Published by: South Kanara Bee-Keepers' Co-operative Society Ltd., No. L 386, Puttur, D.K., Karnataka 574 201, India. Ed. Srimivasa Rae. Circ: 1,000.

MADHYA PRADESH. DIRECTORATE OF AGRICULTURE. AGRICULTURAL STATISTICS. see AGRICULTURE—Abstracting, Bibliographies, Statistics

630   IDN   ISSN 0024-9556
MADJALAH PERTANIAN✶ . Text in Indonesian. 1949. irreg. (4-12/yr.). free. charts; stat.
Published by: Directorate of Agriculture Extension/Direktorat Penyaluhan Pertanian, Jalan Ragunan, Pasarminggu, Jakarta, Indonesia. Ed. Soekandar Wiriaatmadja. Circ: 6,000.

630   IND   ISSN 0024-9602
S17   CODEN: MAAJAP
➤ **MADRAS AGRICULTURAL JOURNAL.** Text in English. 1973 (vol.60). m. INR 60 to individuals; INR 150 to institutions. adv. charts; stat. Document type: Academic/Scholarly.
Indexed: AEA, AgBio, AgrForAb, AnBrAb, BioCN&I, BiolAb, CPA, CTFA, ChemAb, DBA, DSA, ExcerpMed, FCA, FPA, FS&TA, ForAb, HerbAb, HortAb, I&DA, MaizeAb, NemAb, NutrAb, OrnHort, PBA, PGegResA, PGrRegA, PHN&I, PN&I, PotatoAb, PoultAb, RA&MP, RDA, RPP, RRTA, RevApplEntom, RiceAb, S&F, S&MA, SIA, SeedAb, SoyAb, TDB, TOSA, TriticAb, WAE&RSA, WeedAb, ZooRec.
—BLDSC (5331.000000), CASDDS, CISTI, IE, ingenta.
Published by: Madras Agricultural Students' Union, Agricultural University Campus, Coimbatore, Tamil Nadu 641 003, India. Ed. M Stephen Dorairaj.

630   EGY   ISSN 0258-3275
                                        CODEN: AJASDK
MAGALLAT ASYUT AL-'ULUM AL-ZIRA'IYYAT. Text in Arabic. 1970. irreg. Document type: Journal, Academic/Scholarly.
Related titles: ◆ English ed.: Assiut Journal of Agricultural Sciences. ISSN 1110-0486.
—Linda Hall.
Published by: Assiut University, Faculty of Agriculture, c/o Dr. A.A. Eisaa, Editor, Assiut, 71515, Egypt. TEL 20-88-332631, FAX 20-88-331384, sup@aun.eun.eg, http://www.aun.eun.eg.

630   LBN   ISSN 0076-2369
MAGON. SERIE SCIENTIFIQUE✶ . Text and summaries in English, French. 1965. irreg., latest vol.33, 1970. free.
—CISTI.
Published by: Institut de Recherches Agronomiques, Laboratoire Regional Veterinaire, Fanar, Lebanon.

▼ *new title*   ➤ *refereed*   ✶ *unverified*   ◆ *full entry avail.*

A

630 LBN ISSN 0076-2377
MAGON. SERIE TECHNIQUE✱. Text in Arabic, English, French; Summaries in English, French. 1965. irreg., latest vol.11, 1970. free.
Indexed: BiolAb.
—CISTI.
Published by: Institut de Recherches Agronomiques, Laboratoire Regional Veterinaire, Fanar, Lebanon.

MAGYAR MEZOGAZDASAGI BIBLIOGRAFIA. see *AGRICULTURE—Abstracting, Bibliographies, Statistics*

630 HUN ISSN 0521-4238
S227
MAGYAR MEZOGAZDASAGI MUZEUM KOZLEMENYEI/ HUNGARIAN AGRICULTURAL MUSEUM. PROCEEDINGS. Text mainly in Hungarian; Summaries in English, German. 1966. biennial. USD 35 (effective 2001). illus. **Document type:** *Proceedings.* **Description:** Essays in agricultural history.
Indexed: AmH&L, HistAb.
—CISTI.
Published by: Magyar Mezogazdasagi Muzeum/Hungarian Agricultural Museum, PO Box 129, Budapest, 1367, Hungary. TEL 36-1-3430573, FAX 36-1-3439120. Ed. Sandor Oroszi. R&P Gyorgy Feher TEL 36-1-3438485. Circ: 700.

630.724 USA
MAINE AGRICULTURAL AND FOREST EXPERIMENT STATION. ANNUAL REPORT. Text in English. 1886. a. free. illus. back issues avail.
Formerly: Maine Agricultural Experiment Station. Annual Report
Related titles: Microfilm ed.; Online - full text ed.
Published by: Maine Agricultural and Forest Experiment Station, University of Maine, 5782 Winslow Hall, Rm 1, Orono, ME 04469-5782. TEL 207-581-3227, maes2@maine.edu, http://www.umaine.edu/mafes/electron.htm. Ed. J R Round. Circ: 1,500.

630 USA ISSN 1070-1516
MAINE AGRICULTURAL AND FOREST EXPERIMENT STATION. MISCELLANEOUS REPORT. Text in English. 1948. irreg., latest vol.426, 2001. free.
Former titles (until 1993): Maine Agricultural Experiment Station. Miscellaneous Report (0734-9564); (until 1982): Life Sciences and Agriculture Experiment Station. Miscellaneous Report (0094-436X); (until 1971): Maine Agricultural Experiment Station. Miscellaneous Report (0094-4378)
Related titles: Microfilm ed.
Indexed: ASFA, SFA, WildRev.
—CISTI.
Published by: Maine Agricultural and Forest Experiment Station, University of Maine, 5782 Winslow Hall, Rm 1, Orono, ME 04469-5782. TEL 207-581-3211, maes2@maine.edu, http://www.umaine.edu/mafes/publicat.htm. Ed. Barbara Harrity.

630 USA ISSN 1070-1524
S69.E1 CODEN: TBMSEU
MAINE AGRICULTURAL AND FOREST EXPERIMENT STATION. TECHNICAL BULLETIN. Text in English. 1962. irreg., latest vol.179, 2001. free. **Document type:** *Bulletin.*
Formerly (until 1994): Maine Agricultural Experiment Station. Technical Bulletin (0734-9556)
Related titles: Microfilm ed.
Indexed: AEA, AgBio, BioCN&I, BiolAb, DSA, FCA, FS&TA, ForAb, HerbAb, HortAb, I&DA, PHN&I, PotatoAb, RevApplEntom, S&F, SFA, SeedAb, WAE&RSA, WeedAb, WildRev, ZooRec.
—BLDSC (8630.019000), CISTI.
Published by: Maine Agricultural and Forest Experiment Station, University of Maine, 5782 Winslow Hall, Rm 1, Orono, ME 04469-5782. TEL 207-581-3227, maes2@maine.edu, http://www.umaine.edu/mafes/publicat.htm. Ed. Barbara Harrity.

630 635 USA ISSN 0891-9194
MAINE ORGANIC FARMER AND GARDENER. Text in English. 1974. q. USD 12 domestic; USD 18 foreign (effective 2001). adv. bk.rev. illus. index. cum.index. back issues avail. **Document type:** *Newspaper, Consumer.* **Description:** News, articles, announcements, and instruction on environmental, agricultural issues, farming and gardening.
Published by: Maine Organic Farmers and Gardeners Association, PO Box 170, Unity, ME 04988. TEL 207-568-4142, MOFGA@mofga.org, mofga@mofga.org, http://www.mofga.org. Ed., R&P Jean English. Adv. contact Janice Clark. Circ: 5,000 (paid and controlled).

630 UAE ISSN 1021-1357
S471.U65
➤ **MAJALLAT AL-IMARAT LIL-'ULUM AL-ZIRA'IYYAH/ EMIRATES JOURNAL OF AGRICULTURAL SCIENCES.** Text in Arabic, English. 1988. s-a. per issue exchange basis. **Document type:** *Journal, Academic/Scholarly.*
Indexed: AEA, AgBio, AgrForAb, AnBrAb, CPA, DSA, FCA, FS&TA, ForAb, HortAb, I&DA, IndVet, NutrAb, OrnHort, PBA, PGegResA, PGrRegA, PoultAb, S&F, SeedAb, TDB, TriticAb, WAE&RSA.
Published by: United Arab Emirates University, College of Food Systems, PO Box 17555, Al-ain, United Arab Emirates. TEL 971-3-7051442, FAX 971-3-7632384, ejas@uaeu.ac.ae, http://www.agri.uaeu.ac.ae/research/ejas.html, http://www.cfs.uaeu.ac.ae. Ed. Ahmed S. Hussein. Circ: 2,000.

630 UGA ISSN 0075-4730
MAKERERE UNIVERSITY. FACULTY OF AGRICULTURE. HANDBOOK✱. Text in English. 1963. irreg.
Published by: Makerere University, Faculty of Agriculture, PO Box 7062, Kampala, Uganda.

630 UGA ISSN 0075-4773
MAKERERE UNIVERSITY. FACULTY OF AGRICULTURE. TECHNICAL BULLETIN. Text in English. 1962. irreg.
Published by: Makerere University, Faculty of Agriculture, PO Box 7062, Kampala, Uganda.

630 MWI
MALAWI. DEPARTMENT OF AGRICULTURAL RESEARCH. ANNUAL REPORT. Text in English. a. MWK 10; price varies.
Incorporates (in 1975): Agricultural Research Council of Malawi. Annual Report (0065-4515); Formerly (1963-1969): Malawi. Department of Agriculture. Annual Report (0076-3047)
Indexed: AnBrAb, BiolAb, DSA, FCA, HerbAb, RPP, RevApplEntom, SFA.
Published by: (Malawi. Library System), Ministry of Agriculture, Department of Agricultural Research, PO Box 158, Lilongwe, Malawi. TEL 265-767222. **Orders to:** Government Printer, PO Box 37, Zomba, Malawi. TEL 265-50-523155.

MALAWI. NATIONAL STATISTICAL OFFICE. NATIONAL SAMPLE SURVEY OF AGRICULTURE. see *AGRICULTURE—Abstracting, Bibliographies, Statistics*

630 639.2 MYS
MALAYSIA. MINISTRY OF AGRICULTURE. TECHNICAL AND GENERAL BULLETINS. Text in English. 1957; N.S. 1973. irreg.
Former titles: Malaysia. Ministry of Agriculture. Technical Bulletins; Malaysia. Ministry of Agriculture and Rural Development. Technical Bulletins
Indexed: AnBrAb, RevApplEntom, S&F.
Published by: Ministry of Agriculture, Publications Unit, Wisma Tani, Jalan Sultan Salahuddin, Kuala Lumpur, 50624, Malaysia.

630 MYS ISSN 0025-1321
S17 CODEN: MAGJAL
MALAYSIAN AGRICULTURAL JOURNAL. Text in English. 1912. s-a. USD 26. adv. bk.rev. charts; illus.; stat. index.
Related titles: Microfiche ed.: (from BHP).
Indexed: AnBrAb, BIOSIS Prev, BioCN&I, BiolAb, ChemAb, DSA, FCA, FS&TA, HerbAb, HortAb, IndVet, NutrAb, PBA, RPP, RRTA, RevApplEntom, S&F, TOSA, VetBull, WAE&RSA, WeedAb.
—CASDDS, CISTI.
Published by: Ministry of Agriculture, Publications Unit, Wisma Tani, Jalan Sultan Salahuddin, Kuala Lumpur, 50624, Malaysia. Ed. S Thamutaram. Circ: 1,500 (controlled).

570 MYS ISSN 0126-8643
CODEN: MABIDU
➤ **MALAYSIAN APPLIED BIOLOGY JOURNAL✱.** Text in English. 1972. s-a. USD 50. adv. bk.rev. **Document type:** *Academic/Scholarly.*
Formerly (until 1977): Malaysian Agricultural Research Journal (0126-5458)
Indexed: Agr, AnBrAb, BAS, BIOSIS Prev, BiolAb, DSA, ExcerpMed, FCA, FS&TA, HerbAb, IndVet, NutrAb, SFA, TriticAb, VetBull, WildRev, ZooRec.
—BLDSC (5356.064000), IE, ingenta, Linda Hall.
Published by: Malaysian Society of Applied Biology, c/o Pusat Pengajian BioSains dan Bioteknologi, Fakulti Sains dan Teknologi, Universiti Kebangsaan Malaysia, 43600 UKM Bangi, Selangor, Malaysia. TEL 60-3-89293815, FAX 60-3-89252698, nazlina@ukm.my. Ed., R&P Syed Jalaludin. Circ: 500.

634 MYS ISSN 0126-5601
MALAYSIAN PINEAPPLE. Text and summaries in English. 1971. irreg., latest vol.2, 1972. illus.
Published by: Malayan Pineapple Industry Board, Pineapple Research Station, P.O. Box 101, Pekan Nenas, Johor, Malaysia. Circ: 1,500.

MALAYSIAN RUBBER BOARD. PLANTERS BULLETIN. see *RUBBER*

630 BRA ISSN 0102-8901
MANCHETE RURAL. Text in Portuguese. 1975. m. USD 42. **Document type:** *Trade.* **Description:** For people who deal with agriculture, cattle raising and related industries.
Formerly (until 1987): Agricultura de Hoje (0100-5707)
Published by: Bloch Editores S.A., Edificio Manchete, Rua do Russel, 766-804, Gloria, Rio De Janeiro, RJ 22210010, Brazil. TEL 021-5554000, FAX 021-2059998, Ed. Paulo Roque. Circ: 70,000.

MANEJO INTEGRADO DE PLAGAS. see *BIOLOGY—Biotechnology*

630 CAN ISSN 0084-3865
S147
MANITOBA AGRICULTURE YEARBOOK. Text in English. 1907. a. CND 10 domestic; CND 9.35 foreign (effective 2000). **Document type:** *Government.* **Description:** Major responsibility is to acquire and provide selected data on Manitoba agriculture for use by government, farm organizations and farmers, researchers and the general public.
—CISTI.
Published by: Manitoba Agriculture and Food, Program & Policy Analysis Branch, 810 401 York Ave, Winnipeg, MB R3C 0P8, Canada. TEL 204-945-3503, FAX 204-948-2844, jhoney@agr.gov.mb.ca. Ed. Janet Honey. Circ: 2,000 (paid and controlled).

638.1 CAN ISSN 0708-3483
MANITOBA BEEKEEPER. Text in English. 1979. q. looseleaf. CND 20; USD 30 foreign (effective 2001). bk.rev. **Document type:** *Newsletter.* **Description:** Provides technical information related to honey production and beekeeping.
—CISTI.
Published by: Manitoba Beekeepers' Association, P O Box 1448, Steinback, MB R0A 2A0, Canada. TEL 204-326-3763, hlaird@mb.sympatico.ca, manbeekr@mb.sympatico.ca. Ed. Ron Rudiak. R&P Don Dixon. Adv. contact Lois Simpson. Circ: 300.

630 CAN ISSN 0025-2239
MANITOBA CO-OPERATOR. Text in English. 1925. w. (Thurs.). CND 39.90 domestic; USD 80 in United States; USD 150 elsewhere; CND 1.50 newsstand/cover domestic (effective 2001). adv. bk.rev. **Document type:** *Newspaper.* **Description:** Published in the interests of agriculture in the province of Manitoba featuring comment of local, national, and international events relevant to farming. Also featured are news and articles of interest to farm families 4-H reports and commodity market commentary. Annual magazine supplements provide farmers with complete telephone listings of services available to them and an annual crop planning supplement.
Related titles: CD-ROM ed.
—CISTI.
Published by: (Manitoba Pool Elevators), Agricore Co-operative Ltd., 220 Portage Ave, P O Box 9800, Sta Main, Winnipeg, MB R3C 3K7, Canada. TEL 204-954-1400, FAX 204-954-1422, news@co-operator.mb.ca. Ed., Pub. John Morriss. adv.: B&W page USD 2,997, color page USD 3,847; 11 x 8.5. Circ: 14,199.

630 FRA ISSN 0295-7841
MARAICHER NANTAIS. Text in French. 1962. 11/yr.
Address: 22 bd. Benoni Goulin, Nantes, Cedex 2 44062, France. Ed. L Bureau. Circ: 3,000.

630 FRA
MARCHES. Text in French. 1872. 5/w. adv. **Document type:** *Trade.*
Formerly: Marches Agricoles-l'Echo des Halles (0397-5754); Formed by the merger of: Marches Agricoles: Alimentaires et Fonciers; Echo des Halles
Related titles: Microfiche ed.
—CCC.
Published by: Agro-Business Communication, 84 bd. de Sebastopol, Paris, 75003, France. TEL 33-1-42742800, FAX 33-1-42742895, TELEX 240 660. Ed. Rene Charles Millet. Circ: 18,196.

MARKET TRENDS. see *AGRICULTURE—Abstracting, Bibliographies, Statistics*

630 FRA ISSN 0758-5691
MARNE AGRICOLE. Text in French. w.
Published by: Maison des Agriculteurs (Reims), Rue Leon Patoux, BP 326, Reims, Cedex 51061, France. TEL 26-04-74-51, TELEX MARAGRI 830 487. Ed. Pierre Flandre. Circ: 8,775.

631.584 USA
MARY JANE'S FARM. Text in English. q. USD 5.75 newsstand/cover domestic; USD 7.75 newsstand/cover in Canada (effective 2004); free with their product purchase of $50.
Address: 1000 Wild Iris Ln, Moscow, ID 83843. TEL 888-750-6004, maryjane@maryjanesfarm.org, http://www.maryjanesfarm.org. Ed. Jane Mary Butters.

630 USA ISSN 0279-7895
MARYLAND FARMER. Text in English. 1978. m. USD 21.95 in state; USD 30 out of state (effective 2001). adv. **Document type:** *Newspaper.*
Published by: Farm Progress Companies, 191 S Gary Ave, Carol Stream, IL 60188. TEL 630-462-2892, FAX 630-462-2885, info@farmprogress.com, http://www.farmprogress.com/. Ed. John Vogel. adv.: B&W page USD 3,300, color page USD 7,920. Circ: 18,000.

630 DNK ISSN 1395-8526
MASKINBLADET; landbrugets nyhedsmagasin. Text in Danish. 17/yr. DKK 365 domestic; DKK 839 in Europe; DKK 1,077 elsewhere (effective 2005). adv. **Document type:** *Newsletter, Trade.*

Related titles: Online - full text ed.
Published by: FagbladsGruppen A/S, Birk Centerpark 36, Herning, 7400, Denmark. TEL 45-96-265299, FAX 45-96-265296, mail@maskinbladet.dk, http://www.maskinbladet.dk, http://www.fbg.dk. Ed. Niels Damgaard Hansen. Adv. contact Brian V Oerskov. page DKK 31,320. Circ: 52,716.

MASSACHUSETTS AGRICULTURE (YEAR) ANNUAL REPORT. see *AGRICULTURE—Abstracting, Bibliographies, Statistics*

630 DEU
MATERIALEN ZUR MARKTBERICHTERSTATTUNG. Text in German. irreg., latest vol.32, 2000. **Document type:** *Bulletin, Trade.*
Indexed: DSA, PotatoAb, PoultAb, RA&MP, WAE&RSA.
Published by: Zentrale Markt und Preisberichtstelle GmbH, Rochusstr 2, Bonn, 53123, Germany. TEL 49-228-9777173, FAX 49-228-9777179, info@zmp.de, http://www.zmp.de.

630 MUS ISSN 0368-9042
CODEN: MDARA2
MAURITIUS CHAMBER OF AGRICULTURE. ANNUAL REPORT. Text in English. 1853. a. USD 3 (effective 2000). **Document type:** *Corporate.* **Description:** Annual review of Mauritian sugar industry and agricultural diversification, including tea, tobacco and other crops, with a comprehensive statistical bulletin.
Formerly: Mauritius Chamber of Agriculture. President's Report
Published by: Mauritius Chamber of Agriculture, PO Box 312, Port Louis, Mauritius. TEL 230-208-0747, FAX 230-208-1269, mca312@bow.intnet.mu, http://www.prosi.intnet.mu. Ed. Axel Pellegrin. Circ: 1,000.

630 MUS
S338.M3
MAURITIUS. MINISTRY OF AGRICULTURE, FOOD TECHNOLOGY AND NATURAL RESOURCES. ANNUAL REPORT. Text in English. 1913. a. MUR 50 (effective 2000). **Document type:** *Bulletin, Corporate.*
Former titles: Mauritius. Ministry of Agriculture, Fisheries and Cooperatives. Annual Report; Mauritius. Ministry of Agriculture and Natural Resources. Annual Report (0304-775X); Mauritius. Ministry of Agriculture, Fisheries and Natural Resources. Annual Report; Mauritius. Ministry of Agriculture and Natural Resources and the Environment. Annual Report
Indexed: BiolAb.
—CISTI.
Published by: Ministry of Agriculture, Food Technology and Natural Resources, Agricultural Services, Reduit, Mauritius. TEL 454-1091, FAX 464-4898. Ed. Lam Thuon Nine. R&P J C Appapoulay.

630 MUS
MAURITIUS. MINISTRY OF AGRICULTURE, FOOD TECHNOLOGY AND NATURAL RESOURCES. TECHNICAL BULLETIN. Text in English. 1979. a. free. **Document type:** *Bulletin, Corporate.*
Former titles: Mauritius. Ministry of Agriculture, Fisheries and Cooperatives. Technical Bulletin; Mauritius. Ministry of Agriculture and Natural Resources. Technical Bulletin; Mauritius. Ministry of Agriculture, Fisheries and Natural Resources. Technical Bulletin; Mauritius. Ministry of Agriculture and Natural Resources and the Environment. Technical Bulletin
Published by: Ministry of Agriculture, Food Technology and Natural Resources, Agricultural Services, Reduit, Mauritius. TEL 454-1091, FAX 464-4898, TELEX 2124427. Ed. Lam Thuon Nine. R&P J C Appapoulay.

630 658 MEX
MAYO AGRICOLA. Text in Spanish. 1962. q. bk.rev. index.
Published by: Distrito de Riego No. 38, Rio Mayo, Pesquera y Jimenez, Navojoa, SONORA, Mexico. Circ: (controlled).

630 OMN
AL-MAZARI'. Text in Arabic. w.
Published by: Ministry of Agriculture and Fisheries, Ruwi, P O Box 467, Muscat, Oman. TEL 696300, TELEX 3503. Ed. Khalid Az Zubaidi.

638.1 FIN ISSN 0783-3377
MEHILAINEN. Text in Finnish; Abstracts occasionally in English, Swedish. 1984. bi-m. EUR 38 (effective 2005). adv. bk.rev. index. back issues avail. **Document type:** *Newsletter.* **Description:** Focuses on beekeeping both as profession and hobby.
Formed by the merger of (1946-1984): Mehilaistalous (0355-0516); (1966-1984): Mehilaishotaja (0543-3843)
Published by: Suomen Mehilaishoitajain Liitto SML r.y./Finnish Beekeepers' Association, Kasarmikatu 26 C 34, Helsinki, 00130, Finland. TEL 358-9-661281, FAX 358-9-661283, http://www.hunaja.net/smlkoti/lehti/lehti.htm. Ed. Lauri Ruottinen. adv.: B&W page EUR 740. Circ: 4,000.

630 ISR ISSN 0334-7532
S542.I75
MEHKAR HAKLA'I BE-YISRAEL/ISRAEL AGRESEARCH. Text in Hebrew. 1986. s-a. USD 20 (effective 1997). **Document type:** *Government.*
Indexed: IHP.
Published by: Agricultural Research Organization, Volcani Center, P O Box 6, Bet Dagan, 50250, Israel. TEL 972-3-9683216, FAX 972-3-9693998. Ed. Yona Rousso.

638.1 TUR ISSN 1302-5821
MELLIFERA/JOURNAL OF BEEKEEPING IN TURKEY; Turkiye agrcilik dergisi. Text in Turkish. s-a. USD 20 (effective 2004).
Related titles: Online - full text ed.: (from EBSCO Publishing).
Indexed: FCA, ZooRec.
Published by: Turkiye Kalkinma Vakfi Yadinidir, Kirkpinar Sokak No. 20/6, Cankaya, Ankara, 06540, Turkey. TEL 90-312-4404500, FAX 90-312-4404232, mellifera@ktg.com.tr, http://www.tkv-dft.org/publications/index.htm.

630 IDN ISSN 0125-9318
MENARA PERKEBUNAN. Text in English. 1958. s-a. USD 25. charts; stat. **Document type:** *Academic/Scholarly.*
Supersedes (1926-1957): Bergcultures
Related titles: Microfiche ed.: (from IDC).
Indexed: ATA, BioCN&I, CPA, FCA, FPA, HerbAb, HortAb, RAPRA, RPP, RRTA, RevApplEntom, S&F, WAE&RSA, WeedAb.
Published by: Indonesian Biotechnology Research Institute for Estate Crops/Unit Penelitian Bioteknologi Perkebunan, Jl. Taman Kencana 1, Bogor, 1651, Indonesia. TEL 62-251-324048, FAX 62-251-328516, TELEX 48369-AARD-IA, briec@indo.net.id. Circ: 500.

338.1 630 LUX ISSN 1014-8159
MERCADOS AGRARIOS. PRECIOS/AGRARMARKTE. PREISE/AGRICULTURAL MARKETS. PRICES/ LANDBRUGSMARKEDER. PRISER/MARCHES AGRICOLES. PRIX/MERCADOS AGRICOLAS. PRECOS/MERCATI AGRICOLI. PREZZI. Text in Multiple languages. 1990. 5/yr. **Description:** Contains data on the recorded prices of the various markets of the European Union.
—CISTI.
Published by: European Commission, Office for Official Publications of the European Union, 2 Rue Mercier, Luxembourg, L-2985, Luxembourg. FAX 352-2929-1, opoce-info-info@cec.eu.int, http://publications.eu.int.

630 ARG ISSN 0328-2708
HD1856
MERCOSUR AGROPECUARIO; actualidad y perspectivas. Text in Spanish. 1995. irreg.
Published by: Secretaria de Agricultura Ganaderia y Pesca, Of. 162, Avda. Paseo Colon, 982 Piso 3, Capital Federal, Buenos Aires 1063, Argentina. TEL 54-114-3492753, FAX 54-114-3492742.

METSATILASTOLLINEN VUOSIKIRJA/FINNISH STATISTICAL YEARBOOK OF FORESTRY. see *FORESTS AND FORESTRY*

630 RUS ISSN 0235-7801
S13 CODEN: MAZHEC
MEZHDUNARODNYI AGROPROMYSHLENNYI ZHURNAL; nauchno-proizvodstvennyi zhurnal po obmenu dostizheniyami nauki i peredovogo opyta v agrompromyshlennom komplekse stran. Text in Russian. 1957. bi-m. bk.rev. charts. index.
Formerly (until 1989): Mezhdunarodnyi Sel'skokhozyaistvennyi Zhurnal (0026-1882)
Indexed: AEA, AgBio, AgrForAb, AnBrAb, BioCN&I, BiolAb, CPA, ChemAb, DSA, FCA, FS&TA, ForAb, HerbAb, HortAb, I&DA, IndVet, MaizeAb, NutrAb, OrnHort, PBA, PGegResA, PGrRegA, PHN&I, PN&I, PotatoAb, PoultAb, RA&MP, RASB, RDA, RPP, RRTA, RefZh, RevApplEntom, S&F, SIA, SeedAb, SoyAb, TriticAb, VetBull, WAE&RSA, WeedAb.
—BLDSC (0107.860000), CISTI, East View.
Published by: (Sovet Ekonomicheskoi Vzaimopomoshchi, Komitet po Sotrudnichestvu v Oblasti Agropromyshlennogo Kompleksa), Mezhdunarodnyi Agropromyshlennyi Zhurnal, Sadovaya-Spasskaya 18, Moscow, 107807, Russian Federation. TEL 7-095-2073211, FAX 7-095-2072870. Ed. Georgii P Rudenko. Circ: 3,500. **Dist. in U.S. by:** Victor Kamkin Inc., 220 Girard St, Ste 1, Gaithersburg, MD 20877.

630 USA ISSN 1063-598X
S451.M5
MICHIGAN FARM NEWS. Text in English. 1923. 20/yr. free to members. adv. **Document type:** *Newspaper, Trade.*
Supersedes in part (in 1990): Rural Living (Lansing) (0743-9962); Which was formerly (until 1981): Michigan Farm News (0026-2161)
Published by: Michigan Farm Bureau, PO Box 30960, Lansing, MI 48909. mfbinfo@aol.com, http://www.michiganfarmbureau.com. Ed. Paul Jackson. Pub. Dennis Rudat. Adv. contact Tim Rogers. B&W page USD 2,180, color page USD 2,830. Circ: 48,000 (controlled).

630 USA ISSN 0026-2153
MICHIGAN FARMER. Text in English. 1841. m. USD 23.95 (effective 2005). adv. bk.rev. charts; illus.; stat. **Document type:** *Magazine, Trade.*
Related titles: Microfilm ed.; Microform ed.: (from PQC).
Published by: Farm Progress Companies, 191 S Gary Ave, Carol Stream, IL 60188-2095. TEL 630-462-2229, FAX 630-462-2202, info@farmprogress.com, http://www.michiganfarmer.com/ME2/Audiences/Default.asp, http://www.farmprogress.com/. Eds. Dean Peterson, Jennifer Vincent. Adv. contact Don Tourte. B&W page USD 1,350, color page USD 1,850; trim 10.5 x 14.5. Circ: 12,000 (paid).

630 GBR
MID-WEST FARMER. Text in English. 8/yr.
Address: Holmer Rd, Hereford, HR4 9UJ, United Kingdom. TEL 432-274413, FAX 432-50514. Ed. Richard Winterbourn.

630 USA
MIDAMERICA FARMER GROWER. Text in English. 1983. w. USD 21 (effective 2005). adv. **Document type:** *Magazine, Trade.* **Description:** For farmers in Illinois, Southwest Indiana, Missouri, Kentucky, Arkansas and Tennessee who farm 220 or more acres. Covers news, events, shows, workshops and insect and weed control.
Published by: S J S Publishing Co., Inc., 19 N Main, Perryville, MO 63775. TEL 314-547-2244, FAX 314-547-5663. Ed., Pub. John LaRose. Adv. contact Lisa LaRose. B&W page USD 1,998, color page USD 2,448. Circ: 24,000.

630 USA
MIDWEST BULLSEYE. Text in English. m. USD 24 for 2 yrs. domestic; USD 70 for 2 yrs. foreign; free to qualified personnel (effective 2004). adv. **Document type:** *Magazine, Trade.*
Published by: Lee Agri-Media, Inc., PO Box 239, Tekamah, Burt, NE 68061. TEL 402-374-2226, FAX 402-374-2739, http://www.midwestbullseye.com. Ed. Mark Jackson. Circ: 30,000 (paid and controlled).

630 USA
MIDWEST MESSENGER (NORTH EDITION). Text in English. bi-w. USD 38.60 in state; USD 36.08 out of state; free domestic to qualified personnel (effective 2005). **Document type:** *Newspaper, Trade.* **Description:** Covers North East Nebraska and parts of Iowa; and contains photos, event calendar, farm and local news, auctions, and much more.
Related titles: Regional ed(s).: Midwest Messenger (South Edition); Midwest Messenger (West Edition); Midwest Messenger (Iowa Edition).
Published by: Lee Agri-Media, Inc., 4023 State St, Bismark, ND 58503. TEL 701-255-4905, support@midwestmessenger.com, http://www.midwestmessenger.com. Ed. Mark Jackson. Pub. Bret McCormick. Circ: 188,263 (paid and free).

630 635.67 ZAF ISSN 1012-6775
MIELIES - MAIZE; lyfblad van die nasionale Mielieprodusente-organisasie. Key Title: Mielies (Pretoria). Text in Afrikaans, English. 1963. m. ZAR 75 domestic; ZAR 160 foreign; ZAR 1.14 newsstand/cover. adv. bk.rev. illus.; mkt.; stat. **Document type:** *Trade.* **Description:** Covers commercial, agricultural, and technical news relating to commercial grain crops and their production in the summer grain areas of South Africa.
Incorporates: Maize News - Mielienuus (0026-3559); Former titles (1969-1980): Landman (0023-7965); Sampi-News - Sampi-Nuus
Published by: Grain S A/Graan S A, PO Box 88, Bothaville, South Africa. TEL 27-56-514-2145, FAX 27-56-515-3613, nampo@mielies.co.za. Ed. Peter Maartens. Adv. contact Johan Vanonselen. B&W page ZAR 4,145, color page ZAR 5,740; trim 210 x 298. Circ: 22,000.

MILCHWISSENSCHAFT/MILK SCIENCE INTERNATIONAL; journal of nutrition research and food science. see *AGRICULTURE—Abstracting, Bibliographies, Statistics*

334.683 EGY ISSN 1110-0257
MINIA JOURNAL OF AGRICULTURAL RESEARCH AND DEVELOPMENT/MAGALLAT AL-BUHUTH WA AL-TANMIYYAT AL-ZIRAA'IYYAT BIL-MINIYAA. Text in English. 1974. s-a. free. **Document type:** *Journal, Academic/Scholarly.*
Published by: Minia University, Faculty of Agriculture, Minia University Campus, Minia, Egypt. http://derp.sti.sci.eg/data/0178.htm. Ed. Dr. El-Saeid Abdel-Al Muftah.

630 BRA ISSN 0100-9974
MINISTERIO DE EDUCACAO. FACULDADE DE CIENCIAS AGRARIAS DO PARA. INFORME TECNICO. Text in Portuguese. 1979. irreg., latest vol.24, 1998. USD 2. abstr.; charts; stat. **Document type:** *Monographic series.* **Description:** Covers agriculture, forestry and veterinary science.
Published by: (Brazil. Servicio de Documentacao e Informacao), Ministerio de Educacao, Faculdade de Ciencias Agrarias do Para, Comercio, Caixa Postal 917, Belem, PA 66017-970, Brazil. TEL 55-91-2744518, FAX 55-91-2743814, TELEX 091-1892 FAGP, fcap@supridad.com.br. Ed. Marly Sampaio.

630 USA ISSN 0362-8167
CODEN: MXSBAE
MINNESOTA AGRICULTURAL EXPERIMENT STATION. STATION BULLETIN. Text in English. 1888. irreg. (approx. 3/yr.). price varies. **Document type:** *Monographic series, Academic/Scholarly.*
Related titles: Microfilm ed.
Indexed: BiolAb.

A

—CISTI.
Published by: (Minnesota Agricultural Experiment Station), University of Minnesota, Coffey Hall, 1420 Eckles Ave, Ste 240, St. Paul, MN 55108-6070. TEL 612-625-4272, FAX 612-625-2207, lae@umn.edu, http://www.maes.umn.edu. Ed., R&P Larry A Etkin TEL 612-625-4272.

630 USA
MINNESOTA FARM GUIDE. Text in English. bi-w. (Fri.). free qualified MN farmers or ranchers; USD 32.95 (effective 2005). **Document type:** *Newspaper, Trade.*
Related titles: Online - full content ed.
Published by: Lee Agri-Media, Inc., 4023 State St, Bismark, ND 58503. TEL 701-255-4905, FAX 701-255-2312, office@farmandranchguide.com, http://www.minnesotafarmguide.com, http://www.agads.com. Ed. Mark Conlon. Circ: 245,000 (controlled and free).

630 EGY ISSN 1110-0265
MINUFIYA JOURNAL OF AGRICULTURAL RESEARCH/ MAGALLAT AL-MINUFIYYAT LIL-BIHUO AL-ZIRAA'IYYAT. Text in English. 1978. s-a. **Document type:** *Journal, Academic/Scholarly.*
Published by: Munoufiya University, Faculty of Agriculture, Munoufiya University Shebin El-Kom, Munoufiya, Egypt. http://derp.sti.sci.eg/data/0176.htm. Ed. Dr. Maher M El-Shennawi.

630 FRA ISSN 0026-5810
MIROIR DU CENTRE; agricole, artistique, economique, universitaire. Text in French. 1963. m. adv. bk.rev.; film rev. illus.; tr.lit.
Published by: Office Publicitaire du Centre, 14 place Jourdan, Limoges, Cedex 87003, France. Ed. Camille Rivet. Circ: 80,000.

634 USA ISSN 0898-0497
MISSISSIPPI AGRICULTURAL AND FORESTRY EXPERIMENT STATION. BULLETIN. Text in English. 1888. irreg. **Document type:** *Bulletin, Trade.*
Formerly (until 1970): Mississippi Agricultural Experiment Station. Bulletin (0096-7696)
—BLDSC (2617.880000), CISTI, Linda Hall.
Published by: Mississippi Agricultural and Forestry Experiment Station, Box 9625, 210 Bost Bldg, Extension Dr, Mississippi State, MS 39762-9740. TEL 662-325-3005, FAX 662-325-3001, anne@mafes.msstate.edu, http://mafes.msstate.edu.

630 USA
MISSISSIPPI FARM COUNTRY. Text in English. 1922. bi-m. USD 2 (effective 2004). adv. bk.rev. illus. **Document type:** *Newspaper, Trade.*
Former titles: Mississippi Farm Bureau Country (1079-963X); (until 1995): Mississippi Farm Bureau News (0026-6205)
Related titles: Microfilm ed.
Published by: Mississippi Farm Bureau Federation, PO Box 1972, Jackson, MS 39215-1972. TEL 601-977-4153. Ed. Glynda Phillips. Adv. contact Paul Hurst. Circ: 230,464.

630 USA
MISSISSIPPI FARMER. Text in English. m. USD 21.95 in state; USD 30 out of state (effective 2001). adv. **Document type:** *Newspaper.*
Published by: Farm Progress Companies, 191 S Gary Ave, Carol Stream, IL 60188. TEL 630-462-2892, FAX 630-462-2885, http://www.farmprogress.com/. Ed. Eva Ann Dorris TEL 662-489-1777. Adv. contact Don Tourte. B&W page USD 2,100, color page USD 5,000. Circ: 12,500.

630 636 USA ISSN 0279-2346
MISSOURI. DEPARTMENT OF AGRICULTURE. WEEKLY MARKET SUMMARY. Text in English. 1981. w. USD 18 (effective 2000). **Document type:** *Government.*
Published by: Department of Agriculture, 1616 Missouri Blvd, Box 630, Jefferson City, MO 65102. TEL 573-751-4211, FAX 573-751-2868. Ed. Sam Shelton. Circ: 1,750.

630 USA ISSN 0026-668X
MISSOURI RURALIST. Text in English. 1859. 15/yr. USD 23.95 in state (effective 2005). adv. bk.rev. charts; illus.; stat. **Document type:** *Magazine, Trade.*
Related titles: Microfilm ed.
Published by: Farm Progress Companies, 191 S Gary Ave, Carol Stream, IL 60188-2095. TEL 630-462-2229, FAX 630-462-2202, info@farmprogress.com, http://www.rpl.com/au, http://www.farmprogress.com/. Ed. Jerilyn Johnson. adv.: B&W page USD 2,050, color page USD 2,550; trim 10.5 x 14.5. Circ: 20,000 (paid).

630 JPN ISSN 0544-6066
MIYAZAKI DAIGAKU NOGAKUBU. KENKYU HOKOKU/MIYAZAKI UNIVERSITY. FACULTY OF AGRICULTURE. BULLETIN. Text in Japanese. 1955. irreg.
Indexed: AgBio, AgrForAb, AnBrAb, BioCN&I, CPA, DSA, FCA, FS&TA, ForAb, HerbAb, HortAb, I&DA, INIS AtomInd, IndVet, MaizeAb, NemAb, OrnHort, PBA, PGrRegA, PHN&I, PN&I, RPP, RRTA, RefZh, S&F, SeedAb, SoyAb, TriticAb, WAE&RSA, WeedAb, ZooRec.
—BLDSC (2507.235000), CISTI, IE.
Published by: Miyazaki Daigaku Nogakubu, Gakuen-kibanadai, Miyazaki, 889-2192, Japan. TEL 81-985582811, FAX 81-985582884.

630 IND
THE MODERN KHETI. Text in Panjabi. 1987. m. INR 35; USD 20 foreign. adv. back issues avail. **Document type:** *Trade.* **Description:** Deals with agriculture and farms such as crops, dairy, fishery, floriculture and hotriculture.
Related titles: Fax ed.
Published by: Mehram Group of Publications, Panduser, Nabha, Patiala, Punjab 147 201, India. TEL 01765-20595, FAX 91-01765-20678. Ed. Karamjit Singh TEL 91-01765-20595. R&P G S Bir. Adv. contact G.S. Bir. B&W page INR 14,000, color page INR 28,000; trim 240 x 180. Circ: 74,500.

MOGJAE GONGHAG/JOURNAL OF THE KOREAN WOOD SCIENCE AND TECHNOLOGY. see *FORESTS AND FORESTRY—Lumber And Wood*

630 ITA ISSN 0026-9484
MONDO AGRICOLO; settimanale di tecnica, economia e politica agraria. Text in Italian. 1950. fortn. EUR 31 domestic; EUR 62 foreign; EUR 1.54 per issue (effective 2005). adv. bk.rev. illus.
Related titles: Online - full text ed.
Indexed: RefZh.
Published by: (Confederazione Generale Agricoltura Italiana), Societa Editrice Periodici Enotria, Corso Vittorio Emanuele II, 101, Rome, RM 00186, Italy. TEL 39-6-6852374, FAX 39-6-68308578, immco@mbox.vol.it, http://www.mondoagricolo.crol.it., http://www.confagricoltura.it/. Ed. Augusto Bocchini. adv.: color page EUR 4,300; bleed 200 x 267. Circ: 45,000.

630 ESP ISSN 1575-6106
CODEN: MINIB8
MONOGRAFIAS I N I A. FORESTAL. Text in Spanish. 1973. irreg. price varies. **Document type:** *Monographic series, Government.*
Supersedes in part (in 1998): Instituto Nacional de Investigaciones Agrarias. Coleccion Monografias (0210-3354)
Indexed: ForAb, IECT, PBA, RefZh, S&F, SeedAb.
—CASDDS, CINDOC, CISTI.
Published by: (Spain. Instituto Nacional de Investigaciones Agrarias), Ministerio de Agricultura Pesca y Alimentacion, Centro de Publicaciones, Paseo Infanta Isabel 1, Madrid, 28014, Spain. TEL 34-91-3475550, FAX 34-91-3475722, mllopisj@mapya.es, http://www.mapya.es. R&P Carmen Montejo.

630 USA ISSN 0886-3075
MONTANA FARM BUREAU SPOKESMAN. Text in English. 1919. q. USD 25 to non-members; USD 4 to members (effective 2005). adv. back issues avail. **Document type:** *Magazine, Trade.* **Description:** Features the various meetings of the Montana Farm Bureau and the policies adopted. Discusses social and economic farm problems.
Supersedes (in 1985): Montana Agriculture (0026-9905)
Published by: Montana Farm Bureau Federation, 502 S 19th., Ste 104, Bozeman, MT 59718. TEL 406-587-3153, FAX 406-587-0319, info@mfbf.org, MFFarmB@AOL.com, http://www.mfbf.org. Ed. Rebecca Colnar. Pub. J T Cummins Jr. adv.: B&W page USD 525; trim 11 x 8.5. Circ: 12,000 (controlled).

MONTHLY SUMMARY OF EXPORT CREDIT GUARANTEE PROGRAM ACTIVITY. see *BUSINESS AND ECONOMICS—International Commerce*

630 FRA ISSN 0750-2389
MOSELLE AGRICOLE. Text in French. w.
Published by: Agricole, 64 av. Andre Malraux, Metz, Cedex 1 57045, France. TEL 87-63-31-33. Ed. M Forte. Circ: 14,586.

630 IND ISSN 0047-8539
CODEN: MJASAD
MYSORE JOURNAL OF AGRICULTURAL SCIENCES. Text in English. 1967. q. USD 60 (effective 2000). bk.rev. index. reprint service avail. from PQC,ISI. **Document type:** *Academic/Scholarly.*
Related titles: Microfilm ed.: (from PQC).
Indexed: AEA, AgrForAb, BioCN&I, BiolAb, CPA, CTFA, ChemAb, ChemTitl, CurCont, DSA, ExcerpMed, FCA, FPA, FS&TA, FaBeAb, ForAb, HelmAb, HerbAb, HortAb, I&DA, INIS AtomInd, IndVet, MaizeAb, NemAb, NutrAb, OrnHort, PBA, PGegResA, PGrRegA, PHN&I, PN&I, PotatoAb, PoultAb, RA&MP, RDA, RM&VM, RPP, RRTA, RevApplEntom, RiceAb, S&F, S&MA, SFA, SIA, SeedAb, SoyAb, TOSA, TriticAb, VetBull, WAE&RSA, WeedAb, WildRev, ZooRec.
—BLDSC (5997.500000), CASDDS, CISTI, Linda Hall.
Published by: University of Agricultural Sciences Bangalore, Communication Centre, Hebbal, Bangalore, Karnataka 560 024, India. Ed. B S Siddaramiah. Circ: 600. **Dist. overseas by:** H P C Publishers Distributors Pvt. Ltd., 4805 Bharat Ram Rd, 24 Darya Ganj, New Delhi 110 002, India. TEL 91-11-325-4401, 91-11-686-4511.

N A A A NEWSLETTER. see *AERONAUTICS AND SPACE FLIGHT*

630 GBR
N A A C NEWSLETTER; contracting bulletin. Text in English. 12/yr. membership. **Document type:** *Newsletter, Trade.* **Description:** Contains information about all aspects of contracting operations.
Published by: National Association of Agricultural Contractors, Samuelson House, Orton Centre, Peterborough, PE2 5LT, United Kingdom. TEL 44-1733-362920, FAX 44-1733-362021, jill.hewitt@naac.co.uk, http://www.naac.co.uk. Ed., Adv. contact Jill Hewitt. Circ: 600 (controlled).

630.7 USA ISSN 0149-4910
➤ **N A C T A JOURNAL.** Text in English. 1957. q. USD 35 to libraries (effective 2005). adv. bk.rev. cum.index: 1957-1965. reprint service avail. from PQC,ISI. **Document type:** *Journal, Academic/Scholarly.* **Description:** Presents articles and research on agricultural instruction at the college level.
Formerly: National Association of Colleges and Teachers of Agriculture. Journal (0027-8602)
Related titles: Microfilm ed.: 1957 (from PQC); Online - full text ed.: (from ProQuest Information & Learning).
Indexed: Agr, CurCont, ISR.
—BLDSC (6011.330000), IE, ingenta.
Published by: National Association of Colleges and Teachers of Agriculture, c/o Dr Rick Parker, Editor, 151 West 100 South, Rupert, ID 83350. TEL 208-436-0692, FAX 208-436-1384, nactaeditor@pmt.org, nactasec@pmt.org, http://www.nactateachers.org/nacjournal.htm. Ed. Rick Parker. Circ: 1,500 (paid).

630 ZAF ISSN 0028-128X
N A U N L U. Text in Afrikaans, English. 1951. m. free. adv. illus. **Document type:** *Newsletter.* **Description:** News and information journal for farmers in Natal, covering activities of Natal Agriculture Union and affiliations such as farmers' association, cooperatives, producer organizations.
Published by: Natal Agricultural Union, PO Box 186, Pietermaritzburg, KwaZulu-Natal 3200, South Africa. Ed. S Shone. Circ: 9,200.

630 CAN ISSN 0848-8851
N B I A NEWSLETTER. Text in English, French. 1989. q. looseleaf. free. bk.rev. back issues avail. **Document type:** *Newsletter.* **Description:** For professional agrologists in Atlantic Canada.
Published by: New Brunswick Institute of Agrologists, P O Box 20280, Fredericton, NB E3B 4Z7, Canada. TEL 506-452-3260, FAX 506-452-3316. Ed. Dr. Warren K Coleman. Circ: 200 (controlled).

630 USA ISSN 1055-2634
N F O REPORTER. Text in English. 1956. 10/yr. USD 1 to members; USD 5 to non-members. **Document type:** *Trade.* **Description:** Covers group marketing and price negotiation and other topics of interest to family farmers.
Published by: National Farmers Organization, 528 Billy Sunday Rd., Ste. 100, Ames, IA 50010-8087. TEL 515-292-2000, 800-247-2110, FAX 515-292-7106, nfo@netins.net, http://nfo.org. Ed., R&P Perry Garner TEL 515-292-2000 ext.271. Circ: 20,000.

630 GBR ISSN 1460-3845
N F U BUSINESS. Text in English. s-m. adv. **Document type:** *Trade.*
Published by: National Farmers Union, Agriculture House, 164 Shaftesbury Ave, London, WC2H 8HL, United Kingdom. TEL 44-20-73317200, FAX 44-20-73317401, NFU@nfuonline.com, http://www.nfu.org.uk/. Ed. John Ford. Adv. contact John Smith. Circ: 83,151.

630 GBR
N F U COUNTRYSIDE. Text in English. m. **Document type:** *Consumer.*
Published by: National Farmers Union, Agriculture House, 164 Shaftesbury Ave, London, WC2H 8HL, United Kingdom. TEL 44-20-73317200, FAX 44-20-73317401, NFU@nfuonline.com, http://www.nfu.org.uk/. Circ: 60,000 (controlled).

630 GBR
N F U MAGAZINE. Text in English. q. GBP 9.20; GBP 12 in Europe; GBP 18 elsewhere. **Document type:** *Trade.*
Former titles: British Farmer and Grower Magazine (1364-7849); (until 1996): British Farmer (0267-6338); (until 1985): British Farmer and Stockbreeder (0007-0688); (until 1971): Farmer and Stock Breeder (0425-760X)
Indexed: DSA, FCA, FS&TA, HerbAb, RRTA, WAE&RSA.
—CISTI.
Published by: National Farmers Union, Agriculture House, 164 Shaftesbury Ave, London, WC2H 8HL, United Kingdom. TEL 44-20-73317200, FAX 44-20-73317401, NFU@nfuonline.com, http://www.nfu.org.uk/. Ed. Sara Cushing. Circ: 83,550.

630 GBR
N F U REGIONAL JOURNAL - CENTRAL. Text in English. 1992. m. membership. adv. **Document type:** *Trade.* **Description:** Local information for members of the National Farmers' Union.
Formerly: Central Region Farmer

Contact Corp. Auth.: National Farmers Union, Agriculture House, 164 Shaftesbury Ave, London, WC2H 8HL, United Kingdom. TEL 44-20-73317200, FAX 44-20-73317401, NFU@nfuonline.com, http://www.nfu.org.uk/. Ed. Tom Bewley. Adv. contact Jan Milner. page GBP 340; trim 176 x 240. Circ: 6,500 (paid).

N G F A DIRECTORY - YEARBOOK (YEAR). see *BUSINESS AND ECONOMICS—Trade And Industrial Directories*

630 USA
N G F A GRAIN BOOK (YEAR). Text in English. 1993. irreg. (2-3/yr.). USD 450 (effective 1999). charts; stat.; tr.lit. **Document type:** *Trade.* **Description:** Contains general grain business text and aims at grain elevator operators, managers and traders.
Related titles: Online - full text ed.
Published by: National Grain and Feed Association, 1250 Eye St N W, Ste 1003, Washington, DC 20005. TEL 202-289-0873, FAX 202-289-5388, ngfa@ngfa.org, http://www.ngfa.org. Ed. Randall C Gordon. Circ: 2,750.

N G F A NEWSLETTER. see *BUSINESS AND ECONOMICS—Trade And Industrial Directories*

630 NOR ISSN 0805-7028
N I L F - RAPPORT. (Norsk Institutt for Landbruksoekonomisk Forskning) Text in Multiple languages. 1987. irreg. price varies. back issues avail. **Document type:** *Monographic series, Academic/Scholarly.*
Supersedes in part (in 1995): Norsk Institutt for Landbruksoekonomisk Forskning. Forskningsmelding A (0802-0337); Which was formed by the merger of (1952-1987): Norsk Institutt for Landbruksoekonomisk Forskning. F 2 (0801-8626); (1970-1987): Norsk Institutt for Landbruksoekonomisk Forskning. I 7 (0801-8596); Which incorporated (1981-1985): Budsjettnemmda for Jordbruket. Utredninger (0800-7675); Supersedes in part (in 1995): Norsk Institutt for Landbruksoekonomisk Forskning. Forskningsmelding B (0801-8553); Which was formerly (until 1987): Norsk Institutt for Landbruksoekonomisk Forskning. F-3 (0801-8561); (until 1985): Norges Landbruksoekonomiske Institutt. F-3 (0801-860X); (1958-1965): Norges Landbruksoekonomiske Institutt. Stensilert Saermelding (0801-8618); Superseded in part (1988-1995): Norsk Institutt for Landbruksoekonomisk Forskning. C (0802-2577)
Related titles: Online - full text ed.
Indexed: DSA, HortAb, RA&MP, WAE&RSA.
Published by: Norsk Institutt for Landbruksoekonomisk Forskning (NILF)/Norwegian Agricultural Economics Research Institute (NILF), Schweigaards Gate 33B, Postboks 8024, Dep, Oslo, 0030, Norway. TEL 47-22-367200, FAX 47-22-367299, postmottak@nilf.no, http://www.nilf.no, http://www.nilf.no/.

630 NLD ISSN 1573-5214
S11 CODEN: NETMAW
➤ **N J A S WAGENINGEN JOURNAL OF LIFE SCIENCES.** Cover title: N J A S. Text in English. 1953. q. EUR 140 domestic; EUR 180 foreign (effective 2003). adv. bk.rev. abstr.; bibl.; charts; illus. Index. back issues avail.; reprint service avail. from PQC. **Document type:** *Journal, Academic/Scholarly.*
Formerly (until 2003): Netherlands Journal of Agricultural Science (0028-2928)
Related titles: Microform ed.: (from PQC).
Indexed: AEA, ASCA, ASFA, AgBio, AgrForAb, AnBrAb, BIOSIS Prev, BioCN&I, BiolAb, CIN, CPA, CTFA, Cadscan, ChemAb, ChemTitl, CurCont, DSA, EIA, ESPM, EnerInd, EngInd, EntAb, ExcerpMed, FCA, FPA, FS&TA, FaBeAb, ForAb, GEOBASE, HerbAb, HortAb, I&DA, IBR, IBZ, ISR, IndVet, LeadAb, MaizeAb, NutrAb, OrnHort, PBA, PGegResA, PHN&I, PN&I, PollutAb, PotatoAb, PoultAb, RA&MP, RDA, RPP, RRTA, RevApplEntom, RiceAb, S&F, S&MA, SCI, SFA, SIA, SWRA, SeedAb, SoyAb, TriticAb, VetBull, WAE&RSA, WeedAb, WildRev, Zincscan, ZooRec.
—BLDSC (6077.000000), CASDDS, CISTI, Ei, IDS, IE, ingenta, Linda Hall.
Published by: Koninklijk Landbouwkundige Vereniging/Royal Netherlands Society of Agricultural Sciences, Postbus 79, Wageningen, 6700 AB, Netherlands. TEL 31-317-485191, FAX 31-317-483976, office@klv.nl, http://www.klv.nl. Eds. JF Wienk, PC Struik. Pub., Adv. contact Marian Bos-Boers. B&W page EUR 400; 13 x 19.

➤ **N T I S ALERTS: AGRICULTURE & FOOD.** see *AGRICULTURE—Abstracting, Bibliographies, Statistics*

630 COD
N U K T A. Text in French. w.
Address: 14 Chaussee de Kasenga, BP 3805, Lubumbashi, Congo, Dem. Republic. Ed. Ngoy Bunduki.

NAFO - NYTT. see *LABOR UNIONS*

630 CHN ISSN 1000-2030
S19 CODEN: NNDXEI
➤ **NANJING NONGYE DAXUE XUEBAO/NANJING AGRICULTURAL UNIVERSITY. JOURNAL.** Text in Chinese. 1956-1957; resumed 1980. q. CNY 32 (effective 2003). **Document type:** *Academic/Scholarly.* **Description:** Covers original research papers, literature reviews and brief information on different fields of agriculture science.
Formerly (until 1985): Nanjing Agricultural College. Journal (0465-7918)
Related titles: CD-ROM ed.; Online - full content ed.; Online - full text ed.: (from East View Information Services).
Indexed: AEA, AgBio, AnBrAb, B&BAb, BioCN&I, CIN, CPA, ChemAb, ChemTitl, DSA, ESPM, EntAb, FCA, FPA, FS&TA, ForAb, HelmAb, HortAb, I&DA, IndVet, MaizeAb, NemAb, NutrAb, OrnHort, PBA, PGegResA, PGrRegA, PHN&I, PN&I, PoultAb, ProtozoAb, RA&MP, RDA, RM&VM, RPP, RRTA, RefZh, RevApplEntom, RiceAb, S&F, SIA, SeedAb, SoyAb, TDB, TriticAb, VetBull, WAE&RSA, WeedAb, ZooRec.
—BLDSC (4828.675700), CASDDS, IE, ingenta.
Published by: Nanjing Nongye Daxue/Nanjing Agricultural University, Weigang, Nanjing, Jiangsu 210095, China. TEL 86-25-4395214, FAX 86-25-4396734, nauxb@mail.njau.edu.cn, http://www.njau.edu.cn. Ed. Xiaobo Zheng. Circ: 1,500.

659.1 USA
NATIONAL AGRI-MARKETING ASSOCIATION NEWS* **.** Text in English. fortn. membership. bk.rev. **Description:** Includes association and industry developments, as well as employment opportunities and calendar of events.
Published by: National Agri-Marketing Association, 11020 King St, Ste 205, Shawnee Mission, KS 66210-1201. TEL 913-492-0220, FAX 913-492-5147.

NATIONAL AGRICULTURAL PLASTICS CONGRESS. PROCEEDINGS. see *PLASTICS*

630 USA ISSN 1045-1579
S541
NATIONAL AGRICULTURAL RESEARCH AND EXTENSION USERS ADVISORY BOARD. REPORT TO THE PRESIDENT AND CONGRESS - UNITED STATES. Text in English. a.
Published by: National Agricultural Research and Extension Users Advisory Board, Rm 432 A, Admin Bldg, USDA, 14th St & Independence Ave, S W, Washington, DC 20250.

630 LKA
CODEN: NASJAO
NATIONAL AGRICULTURAL SOCIETY OF SRI LANKA. JOURNAL. Text in English. 1964. a. USD 18 (effective 2004). adv. illus. **Document type:** *Academic/Scholarly.*
Formerly: National Agricultural Society of Ceylon. Journal (0547-3616)
Indexed: ATA, BiolAb, ChemAb, DSA, FCA, FS&TA, HerbAb, HortAb, PBA, RPP, RRTA, SLSI, WAE&RSA.
—CASDDS.
Published by: National Agricultural Society of Sri Lanka, Faculty of Agriculture, University of Sri Lanka, Peradeniya, Sri Lanka. gunasenah@yahoo.com. Ed. H P M Gunasena. R&P, Adv. contact H.P.M. Gunasena. Circ: 400.

NATIONAL CENTER FOR AGRICULTURAL UTILIZATION RESEARCH PUBLICATIONS AND PATENTS. see *AGRICULTURE—Abstracting, Bibliographies, Statistics*

630 USA ISSN 1092-8545
HD1485.F34
NATIONAL FARMERS UNION NEWS; for family farmers and rural Americans. Text in English. 1948. m. USD 10 (effective 1999 & 2000). bk.rev. charts; stat. back issues avail. **Document type:** *Newsletter.* **Description:** Provides public-policy issues affecting family farmers.
Formerly (until 1996): National Farmers Union Washington Newsletter (0027-9226)
Related titles: Online - full text ed.
Published by: National Farmers Union, 11900 E Cornell Ave, Aurora, CO 80014-3194. TEL 303-337-5500, FAX 303-368-1390, nfu@nfu.org, http://www.nfu.org. Ed., R&P Marilyn Wentz. Circ: 30,000 (paid).

NATIONAL HONEY REPORT. see *AGRICULTURE—Agricultural Economics*

630 570 JPN
S494.5.I5
NATIONAL INSTITUTE FOR AGRO-ENVIRONMENTAL SCIENCES. ANNUAL REPORT. Text in English. 1995. a.
Formerly: National Institute of Agro-Environmental Sciences. Annual Report (1342-6648)
—CISTI, Linda Hall.
Published by: National Institute for Agro-Environmental Sciences/Nogyo Kankyo Gijutsu Kenkyusho, 3-1-3 Kannondai, Tsukuba, 305-8604, Japan. TEL 81-29-8388148, FAX 81-29-8388199.

NATIONAL INSTITUTE OF AGROBIOLOGICAL RESOURCES. ANNUAL REPORT. see *BIOLOGY*

631.86029 USA ISSN 1073-0540
HD9003
NATIONAL ORGANIC DIRECTORY. Text in English. 1983. a. USD 49.95 in US & Canada (effective 2000). adv. **Document type:** *Directory.*
Former titles (until 1995): National Directory of Organic Wholesalers (1066-2162); Organic Wholesalers Directory and Yearbook - Organic Food and Farm Supplies; C A N Directory - Wholesalers of Organic Produce and Products; C A A P Directory - Wholesalers of Organic Produce and Products
Published by: Community Alliance with Family Farmers, PO Box 363, Davis, CA 95617. TEL 530-756-8518, 800-852-3832, FAX 530-756-7857. Ed. Judy Sams. Adv. contact Aileen Vance. Circ: 2,000.

630 TWN
SB13 CODEN: KTNYA8
NATIONAL TAIWAN UNIVERSITY. COLLEGE OF AGRICULTURE. ANNUAL REPORT. Text in Chinese. 1946. a. free. **Document type:** *Bulletin.*
Formerly (until 1997): National Taiwan University. College of Agriculture. Memoirs (0077-5819)
Indexed: AEA, AgBio, AnBrAb, BiolAb, CIN, CPA, ChemAb, ChemTitl, ESPM, ExcerpMed, FCA, FPA, ForAb, HelmAb, HerbAb, HortAb, IndVet, OrnHort, PHN&I, PN&I, PollutAb, RPP, RevApplEntom, RiceAb, S&F, SFA, SWRA, SeedAb, TOSA, VITIS, VetBull, WeedAb, WildRev, ZooRec.
—CASDDS, CISTI.
Published by: National Taiwan University, College of Agriculture, 1, Sec 4, Roosevelt Rd, Taipei, Taiwan. Ed. Wu Cho Chen. Circ: 500.

630 NLD ISSN 0169-1449
NATIONALE RAAD VOOR LANDBOUWKUNDIG ONDERZOEK. JAARVERSLAG/NATIONAL COUNCIL FOR AGRICULTURAL RESEARCH. ANNUAL REPORT. Text in Dutch. 1957. a.
—BLDSC (4610.972000).
Published by: Nationale Raad voor Landbouwkundig Onderzoek/National Council for Agricultural Research, PO Box 20401, The Hague, 2500 EK, Netherlands. TEL 31-70-3785653, FAX 31-70-3786149, http://www.agro.nl.

NATUR UND RECHT; Zeitschrift fuer das gesamte Recht zum Schutze der natuerlichen Lebensgrundlagen und der Umwelt. see *LAW*

630 FRA
NATURE ET PROGRES; la revue de la bio. Text in French. 1964. bi-m. EUR 5 newsstand/cover (effective 2002). adv. **Document type:** *Journal, Academic/Scholarly.* **Description:** Provides a forum to discuss the environment, agriculture and health issues.
Former titles (until 2002): La Revue de Nature & Progres (1627-2889); (until 2001): Nature et Progres (0182-7146)
—BLDSC (6046.510000), IE, ingenta.
Published by: Nature & Progres, 68 Bd Gambetta, Uzes, 30700, France. TEL 33-4-66032340, FAX 33-4-66032341, nature.et.progres@wanadoo.fr. Ed. Didier Dillen. Pub., Adv. contact Marc Durand.

630 BIH ISSN 0351-4471
NAUCNA SVESKA. Text in Serbo-Croatian; Summaries in English. 1979. a. BAD 12,000, USD 40. back issues avail.
Published by: A I P K Istrazivacko Razvojni Institut, 4 Jula 19, Banja Luka, 78000, Bosnia Herzegovina. TEL 078 42-792. Ed. Jovan Kondic. Circ: 400.

630 IND
NAVEENA VELAANMAI. Text in Tamil. 1994 (Apr.). m. INR 110 (effective 2000).
Address: 17 Aziz Mulk First St, Thousand Lights, Chennai, Tamil Nadu 600 006, India. TEL 91-44-8220979, FAX 91-44-8254745, meenaari@hotmail.com, http://www.intamn.com/velanmy/. Ed. Haridasan V.

630 GRC ISSN 0028-1727
CODEN: NAEPO9
NEA AGROTIKI EPITHEORESIS; agricultural and farming review. Text in Greek; Summaries in English, French. 1947. bi-m. USD 31 foreign. adv. bk.rev. abstr.; bibl.; illus.; stat. index. **Document type:** *Newspaper.*
Published by: (Committee of Greek Agronomists), Spiros Spirou Ltd., 5 Markoni St, Athens, 122 42, Greece. TEL 30-1-3472-821, FAX 30-1-3471-890, TELEX 219133 SPIR GR. Ed., Adv. contact George Spirou. Circ: 7,300.

630 USA ISSN 0745-6522
NEBRASKA FARM BUREAU NEWS. Text in English. 1960. m. free to members (effective 2005). adv. **Document type:** *Magazine, Trade.* **Description:** News of state and national events and legislation affecting farmers and ranchers.
Formerly (until 1983): Nebraska Agriculture (0279-1080)
Published by: Nebraska Farm Bureau Federation, PO Box 80299, Lincoln, NE 68501. TEL 402-421-4405, tinah@nefb.org, http://www.nefb.org. Ed., Adv. contact Tina Henderson. Circ: 58,000 (paid and controlled).

631 USA ISSN 1049-1880
S1
NEBRASKA FARMER. Text in English. 1859. 15/yr. USD 23.95 in state (effective 2005). adv. **Document type:** *Magazine, Trade.* **Description:** Covers ranching and farming practices, marketing, legislation, and technology updates for farmers and ranchers in Nebraska.
—Linda Hall.
Published by: (Nebraska Farmer Co.), Farm Progress Companies, 191 S Gary Ave, Carol Stream, IL 60188-2095. TEL 630-462-2229, FAX 630-462-2202, info@farmprogress.com, http://www.nebraskafarmer.com, http://www.farmprogress.com/. adv.: B&W page USD 2,950, color page USD 3,450; trim 10.5 x 14.5. Circ: 30,000 (paid).

630 051 USA
NEBRASKA FENCE POST; celebrating our rural lifestyle. Text in English. w. (Sat.). USD 34; USD 0.50 newsstand/cover (effective 2005). **Document type:** *Newspaper, Consumer.*
Published by: Swift Newspapers, Inc., 500 Double Eagle Ct., Reno, NV 89511. TEL 702-850-7676, FAX 702-850-7677, nfp@thefencepost.com, http://www.thefencepost.com. Ed. Julie Hothan. Pub. Gary Sweeney. Circ: 15,000 (paid).

338.1 334.683 USA
NEBRASKA UNION FARMER. Text in English. 1914. q. free to members. **Document type:** *Magazine, Trade.*
Published by: Nebraska Farmers' Union, 1305 Plum St., Lincoln, NE 68502. TEL 402-476-8815, FAX 402-476-8859, nefu@aol.com. Ed. Pat Craycraft. Circ: 3,000 (free).

630 USA ISSN 0162-3974
NEIGHBORS. Text in English. 1975. m. USD 2 (effective 2005). adv. **Document type:** *Magazine, Trade.*
Published by: Alabama Farmers Federation, 2108 E South Blvd, Montgomery, AL 36191-0001. jhelms@alfafarmers.org, http://www.alfafarmers.org. Ed. Jeff Helms. Circ: 150,000 (paid and controlled).

NEKAZAL ELIKAGAI SEKTOREAREN ESTATISTIKA URTEKARIA E.A.E./ANUARIO ESTADISTICO DEL SECTOR AGROALIMENTARIO C.A.P.V. see *AGRICULTURE—Abstracting, Bibliographies, Statistics*

NEMATOLOGY; international journal of fundamental and applied nematological research. see *BIOLOGY—Zoology*

631.091 JPN ISSN 0021-5260
CODEN: NENOA8
NETTAI NOGYO/JAPANESE JOURNAL OF TROPICAL AGRICULTURE. Text in English, Japanese; Summaries in English. 1957. q. subscr. incld. with membership. adv. charts; illus. **Document type:** *Journal, Academic/Scholarly.*
Indexed: AEA, AgBio, AgrForAb, BioCN&I, BiolAb, CIN, CPA, ChemAb, ChemTitl, CurCont, DSA, FCA, FPA, FS&TA, ForAb, HerbAb, HortAb, I&DA, MaizeAb, NutrAb, OrnHort, PBA, PGegResA, PGrRegA, PHN&I, PN&I, PotatoAb, RA&MP, RDA, RPP, RevApplEntom, RiceAb, S&F, SIA, SeedAb, SoyAb, TDB, TriticAb, WAE&RSA, WeedAb.
—BLDSC (4658.950000), CASDDS, IE, ingenta. **CCC.**
Published by: Nippon Nettai Nogyo Gakkai/Tropical Agriculture Research Association of Japan, Tokyo University of Agriculture, Faculty of International Agriculture & Food Studies, 1-1-1 Setagaya-ku, Tokyo, 156-8502, Japan. TEL 81-3-54772404, FAX 81-3-54774032, jsta@midori.h.chiba-u.ac.jp, koshio@nodai.ac.jp, http://wwwsoc.nii.ac.jp/jsta/content/netunou.html, http://wwwsoc.nii.ac.jp/jsta/index.html. Circ: 800.

638.1 DEU
NEUE BIENENZUCHT. Text in German. 1974. m. bk.rev.
Formerly: Bienenzucht
Indexed: ApicAb, RefZh.
Published by: Landesverband Schleswig-Holsteinischer Imker, Theodor Heuss Ring 55, Bad Segeberg, 23795, Germany. Ed. Horst Sigfert. Circ: 4,000.

630 DEU ISSN 0937-9851
DIE NEUE D L. Text in German. 1955. bi-m. bk.rev. **Document type:** *Newsletter, Trade.*
Former titles (until 1989): D L Quer (0935-5529); (until 1988): D L. Deutsche Landjugend (Ausgabe Bayern) (0935-5510); (until 1980): Deutsche Landjugend (0170-0642)
Published by: Bund der Deutschen Landjugend im Deutschen Bauernverband e.V., Reinhardtstr 18, Berlin, 10117, Germany. TEL 49-30-31904253, FAX 49-30-31904206, info@landjugend.de, http://www.landjugend.de. Ed. Jochen Heimberg. Adv. contact Monika Baaken. Circ: 11,000.

630 DEU ISSN 0863-2847
NEUE LANDWIRTSCHAFT; das Fachmagazin fuer den Agrarmanager. Text in German. 1990. m. EUR 67.30 domestic (effective 2004). adv. 104 p./no.; **Document type:** *Journal, Trade.*
Incorporates: Feldwirtschaft (0014-9799); Tierzucht (0373-1677)
Indexed: AEA, AnBrAb, DSA, FCA, HerbAb, HortAb, I&DA, IndVet, MaizeAb, NutrAb, PN&I, PotatoAb, PoultAb, RPP, RRTA, RevApplEntom, S&F, SIA, TriticAb, VetBull, WAE&RSA, WeedAb.
—BLDSC (6077.626100), CISTI, IE, ingenta.
Published by: Deutscher Landwirtschaftsverlag GmbH, Berliner Str 112A, Berlin, 13189, Germany. TEL 49-30-293974-50, FAX 49-30-29397459, dlv.berlin@dlv.de, http://www.neuelandwirtschaft.de, http://www.dlv.de. Eds. Klaus Boehme, Manfred Grund. adv.: B&W page EUR 2,829, color page EUR 4,555. Circ: 13,691 (paid and controlled).

630 AUT
NEUES LAND. Text in German. 1934. w. adv. bk.rev. **Document type:** *Newsletter.*
Formerly: Steirisches Bauernbuendler
Published by: Steirischer Bauernbund, Reitschulgasse 3, Graz, St 8010, Austria. TEL 43-316-826361, FAX 43-316-826361-16. Ed. Fred Strohmeier. Pub. Alois Puntigam. R&P Raimund Samel. Adv. contact Josef Trattner.

630 USA ISSN 0899-8434
NEVADA FARM BUREAU'S AGRICULTURE & LIVESTOCK JOURNAL. Text in English. 1932. m. free to members. adv. bk.rev. illus. **Document type:** *Newspaper.* **Description:** Provides news, features and information of interest to Nevada farmers and ranchers and other members.
Published by: Nevada Farm Bureau Federation, 2165 Green Vista Dr, Sparks, NV 89431. TEL 775-674-4000, http://www.fb.com/nvfb. Ed., Pub. Doug Bussleman. R&P, Adv. contact Edward K Foster TEL 800-992-1106. Circ: 8,739 (paid).

630 IND ISSN 0971-0647
CODEN: NEAGEP
NEW AGRICULTURIST. Text in English. 1990. s-a. INR 200 domestic to individuals; USD 100 foreign to individuals; INR 1,000 domestic to institutions; USD 200 foreign to institutions (effective 2003). adv. back issues avail. **Document type:** *Academic/Scholarly.*
Indexed: AEA, AgBio, AgrForAb, BioCN&I, CIN, CPA, ChemAb, ChemTitl, FCA, FS&TA, ForAb, HerbAb, HortAb, I&DA, MaizeAb, NutrAb, PBA, PGegResA, PGrRegA, PHN&I, PotatoAb, RA&MP, RDA, RPP, S&F, SIA, SeedAb, SoyAb, TriticAb, WAE&RSA, WeedAb, ZooRec.
—BLDSC (6081.775000), CASDDS. **CCC.**
Published by: Bioved Research Society, c/o Brijesh K. Dwivedi General Secretary, Teliarganj, U.P., 133/42, MLN Rd, Allahabad, Uttar Pradesh 211 002, India. bioved2003@yahoo.com. Ed. B K Dwivedi. adv.: page INR 3,000.

630 GBR
NEW AGRICULTURIST. Text in English. 1998. 6/yr. bk.rev. back issues avail. **Description:** Features news, focus articles, debate and other perspectives on all aspects of agriculture.
Media: Online - full text.
Published by: Wren Media, Fressinglfield Eye, Suffolk IP21 5SA, United Kingdom. TEL 44-1379-586787, FAX 44-1379-586755, M.Pickstock@wrenmedia.co.uk, http://www.new-agri.co.uk/. Ed. Michael Pickstock.

630 USA
NEW ENGLAND FARM BULLETIN AND GARDEN GAZETTE. Text in English. 1976. m. USD 17 (effective 2000). adv. bk.rev. index. **Document type:** *Newsletter.*
Formerly: New England Farm Bulletin (0279-9162)
Published by: Jacob's Meadow, Inc., PO Box 67, Taunton, MA 02780-0067. TEL 508-878-7075. Ed. Pam Comstock. Circ: 17,000.

630 USA ISSN 0193-0923
NEW ENGLAND FARMER. Text in English. 1822. m. USD 21.95 in state; USD 30 out of state (effective 2001). adv. bk.rev. charts. reprint service avail. from PQC. **Document type:** *Newspaper, Trade.*
Related titles: Microform ed.: 1822 (from PQC); (from PQC); Supplement(s): Grow; Farm Show Program; The Sugarmaker; Empire Farm Days.
Published by: Farm Progress Companies, P.O. Box 38, Huntington, VT 05462. Eds. John Vogel, Kelly Fuerstenberg TEL 203-440-0368. adv.: B&W page USD 1,346. Circ: 17,000 (paid and controlled).

630 USA ISSN 0077-832X
S89
➤ **NEW HAMPSHIRE. AGRICULTURAL EXPERIMENT STATION, DURHAM. RESEARCH REPORTS.** Text in English. 1961. irreg., latest 1996. free. **Document type:** *Academic/Scholarly.*
Indexed: Agr, CurCont.
—CISTI.
Published by: University of New Hampshire, Agricultural Experiment Station, Durham, NH 03824. TEL 603-862-1452.

630 USA ISSN 0077-8338
NEW HAMPSHIRE. AGRICULTURAL EXPERIMENT STATION, DURHAM. STATION BULLETINS. Text in English. 1888. irreg. free. **Document type:** *Bulletin.*
Indexed: CurCont.
—CISTI, Linda Hall.
Published by: University of New Hampshire, Agricultural Experiment Station, Durham, NH 03824. TEL 603-862-1452. Circ: 100.

630 USA
NEW HOLLAND NEWS. Text in English. 1960. 8/yr. adv. **Document type:** *Trade.* **Description:** Presents articles on crops, animals, farm people and rural life.
Former titles: Ford New Holland News; Sperry New Holland News
Indexed: F&GI.
Published by: New Holland, Inc., PO Box 1895, New Holland, PA 17557. TEL 717-354-1121, http://www.newholland.com/na. Ed. Gary Martin. Circ: 400,000 (controlled).

NEW JERSEY ADMINISTRATIVE CODE. AGRICULTURE. see *LAW*

630 USA ISSN 0898-8765
NEW JERSEY FARMER. Text in English. 1988. m. USD 20 domestic; USD 30 in Canada; USD 40 foreign (effective 2003). adv. **Document type:** *Newspaper, Consumer.* **Description:** Focuses on New Jersey's principal agricultural interests and on agri-political issues.
Published by: American Farm Publications, Inc., 505 Brookletts Ave, PO Box 2026, Easton, MD 21601. TEL 800-634-5021, FAX 410-822-5068, http://www.americanfarm.com. Ed. Mark Powell. Pub. E. Ralph Hostetter. Circ: 5,000.

630 ITA ISSN 1594-5685
NEW MEDIT. Text in Multiple languages. 1990. 4/yr. EUR 45 domestic; EUR 55 foreign (effective 2005). **Document type:** *Magazine, Consumer.*
Formerly (until 2001): Medit (1120-6403)
Indexed: AEA, AgBio, AnBrAb, CPA, DSA, FCA, FPA, ForAb, HerbAb, HortAb, I&DA, JEL, MaizeAb, NutrAb, OrnHort, PBA, PGegResA, PHN&I, PN&I, PoultAb, RDA, RRTA, RevApplEntom, S&F, SIA, SeedAb, TDB, TriticAb, WAE&RSA.
—BLDSC (6084.485900), IE.
Published by: (International Centre of Further Study of Mediterranean Agriculture), Edizioni Dedalo, Casella Postale BA-19, Bari, BA 70123, Italy. TEL 39-080-5311413, FAX 39-080-5311414, info@edizionidedalo.it, http://www.edizionidedalo.it. Circ: 3,000.

NEW MEXICO AGRICULTURAL STATISTICS. see *AGRICULTURE—Abstracting, Bibliographies, Statistics*

630 USA ISSN 0028-6192
NEW MEXICO FARM & RANCH. Text in English. 1944. m. USD 24 (effective 2004). adv. bk.rev. illus. **Document type:** *Magazine, Trade.* **Description:** News and information on agriculture in New Mexico including legislation and farm bureau actions.
Published by: (New Mexico Farm & Livestock Bureau), New Mexico Farm & Ranch, Inc., 421 N Water St, Las Cruces, NM 88001. TEL 505-526-5521, FAX 505-525-0858. R&P, Adv. contact Erik Ness. B&W page USD 600, color page USD 800. Circ: 15,000 (paid).

630 USA ISSN 0548-5967
S93 CODEN: NEXRAX
NEW MEXICO STATE UNIVERSITY. AGRICULTURAL EXPERIMENT STATION. RESEARCH REPORT. Text in English. 1955. irreg. (10-20/yr.), latest vol.678, 1993. **Document type:** *Academic/Scholarly.*
Indexed: ASCA, BiolAb, CurCont, NutrAb.
—CISTI, Linda Hall.
Published by: New Mexico State University, Agricultural Experiment Station, Drawer 3AI, Las Cruces, NM 88003-0003. TEL 505-646-2701. Ed. Terry Canup.

630 AUS ISSN 0156-255X
HD2155.N47
NEW SOUTH WALES. DEPARTMENT OF AGRICULTURE. ANNUAL REPORT. Text in English. 1890. a. AUD 16. back issues avail.
Indexed: BiolAb.
—CISTI.
Published by: Department of Agriculture, Locked Bag 21, Orange, NSW 2800, Australia. TEL 61-63-913433. Ed. D Harris. Circ: 1,500.

630 AUS ISSN 0369-5867
NEW SOUTH WALES. DEPARTMENT OF AGRICULTURE. SCIENCE BULLETIN. Text in English. 1912. irreg. price varies. **Description:** Contains major research reports, reviews and monographs.
Published by: Department of Agriculture, Locked Bag 21, Orange, NSW 2800, Australia. TEL 61-63-913433. Ed. E Roberts. Circ: 750.

630 AUS ISSN 0311-8576
CODEN: TBAWDF
NEW SOUTH WALES. DEPARTMENT OF AGRICULTURE. TECHNICAL BULLETIN. Text in English. 1974. irreg. price varies. **Description:** Discusses soundly designed and executed agricultural programs or reviews.
—CASDDS, CISTI.
Published by: Department of Agriculture, Locked Bag 21, Orange, NSW 2800, Australia. TEL 61-63-913433. Ed. E Roberts. Circ: 750.

NEW YORK AGRICULTURAL STATISTICS. see *AGRICULTURE—Abstracting, Bibliographies, Statistics*

630 USA
NEW YORK FARMER✱. Text in English. m. USD 12; USD 25 foreign. **Document type:** *Newspaper.*
Related titles: Microform ed.: (from PQC).
Published by: Rural Press U S A, 1101 Spring Forest Rd, Ste 101, Raleigh, NC 27615. TEL 919-676-3276, 800-477-1737, FAX 919-676-9803. Ed. Linda Goodwin. Pub. Jeff Tennant. adv.: B&W page USD 1,218. Circ: 17,000.

630 NZL ISSN 0028-8233
CODEN: NEZFA7

➤ **NEW ZEALAND JOURNAL OF AGRICULTURAL RESEARCH.** Text in English. 1958. q. NZD 200, USD 135 combined subscription to individuals print & online eds.; NZD 425, USD 305 combined subscription to institutions print & online eds. (effective 2006). adv. bibl.; charts; illus. Index. back issues avail. **Document type:** *Journal, Academic/Scholarly.* **Description:** Publishes papers on all aspects of animal and pastoral science relevant to temperate and sub-tropical regions.
Related titles: Online - full text ed.: NZD 170, USD 115 to individuals; NZD 360, USD 260 to institutions (effective 2006) (from EBSCO Publishing).
Indexed: AEA, ASCA, ASFA, AgBio, AgrForAb, AnBrAb, B&AI, BIOBASE, BIOSIS Prev, BioCN&I, BiolAb, CIN, CPA, ChemAb, ChemTitl, CurCont, DBA, DSA, EIA, ESPM, EnerInd, EngInd, EntAb, EnvAb, EnvEAb, ExcerpMed, FCA, FPA, FS&TA, ForAb, GEOBASE, HelmAb, HerbAb, HortAb, I&DA, IABS, ISR, IndVet, MaizeAb, NemAb, NutrAb, PBA, PGegResA, PN&I, PlantSci, PollutAb, PotatoAb, PoultAb, RA&MP, RM&VM, RPP, RevApplEntom, S&F, SCI, SIA, SWRA, SeedAb, SoyAb, TOSA, Telegen, TriticAb, VITIS, VetBull, WAE&RSA, WTA, WeedAb.
—BLDSC (6092.500000), CASDDS, CISTI, Ei, IDS, IE, Infotrieve, ingenta, Linda Hall. **CCC.**
Published by: R S N Z Publishing, PO Box 598, Wellington, New Zealand. TEL 64-4-4727421, FAX 64-4-4731841, sales@rsnz.org, http://www.rsnz.govt.nz/publish/nzjar/. Ed. David Swain. Circ: 600. **Subscr. in the Americas to:** R S N Z Publishing, PO Box 7075, Lawrence, KS 66044-7075. TEL 785-843-1235, FAX 785-843-1274, sir@allenpress.com.

630 NZL ISSN 0114-0671
CODEN: NZJSEF

➤ **NEW ZEALAND JOURNAL OF CROP AND HORTICULTURAL SCIENCE.** Text in English. 1973. q. NZD 200, USD 135 combined subscription to individuals print & online eds.; NZD 425, USD 305 combined subscription to institutions print & online eds. (effective 2006). adv. back issues avail. **Document type:** *Journal, Academic/Scholarly.* **Description:** Publishes research papers concerned with all aspects of horticulture and crops, with a special focus on kiwifruit and apples.
Formerly (until 1990): New Zealand Journal of Experimental Agriculture (0301-5521)
Related titles: Online - full text ed.: NZD 170, USD 115 to individuals; NZD 360, USD 260 to institutions (effective 2004) (from EBSCO Publishing).
Indexed: AEA, ASCA, ASFA, AgBio, AnBrAb, ApicAb, BIOBASE, BIOSIS Prev, BioCN&I, BiolAb, CIN, CPA, ChemAb, ChemTitl, CurCont, DSA, ESPM, EntAb, ExcerpMed, FCA, FPA, FS&TA, ForAb, GEOBASE, GenetAb, HGA, HerbAb, HortAb, I&DA, ISR, IndVet, MBA, MaizeAb, NemAb, NutrAb, OrnHort, PBA, PGegResA, PGrRegA, PHN&I, PN&I, PlantSci, PotatoAb, RA&MP, RM&VM, RPP, RefZh, RevApplEntom, RiceAb, S&F, SCI, SIA, SPPI, SWRA, SeedAb, SoyAb, TriticAb, VITIS, VetBull, WAE&RSA, WeedAb.
—BLDSC (6093.300000), CASDDS, CISTI, IDS, IE, Infotrieve, ingenta, Linda Hall. **CCC.**
Published by: R S N Z Publishing, PO Box 598, Wellington, New Zealand. TEL 64-4-4727421, FAX 64-4-4731841, sales@rsnz.org, http://www.rsnz.govt.nz/publish/nzjchs/. Ed. S Stanislawek. Circ: 400. **Subscr. in the Americas to:** R S N Z Publishing, PO Box 7075, Lawrence, KS 66044-7075. TEL 785-843-1235, FAX 785-843-1274, sir@allenpress.com.

630 310 NZL
NEW ZEALAND. STATISTICS NEW ZEALAND. AGRICULTURAL PRODUCTION STATISTICS. Text in English. **Document type:** *Government.* **Description:** Provides aggregate totals for fundamental agricultural data to be used as benchmarks for inter-censal estimates.
Published by: Statistics New Zealand/Te Tari Tatau, PO Box 2922, Wellington, New Zealand. TEL 64-4-495-4600, FAX 64-4-473-2626, info@stats.govt.nz, http://www.stats.govt.nz.

630 640 USA ISSN 1061-7760
NEWS & VIEWS (BELMONT). Text in English. 1917. 10/yr. USD 6 (effective 1998). adv. charts; stat. back issues avail. **Document type:** *Newsletter.*
Former titles: Allegany County Cooperative Extension News; Allegany County Farm and Home News
Related titles: Online - full text ed.
Indexed: BibAg.
Published by: Cornell Cooperative Extension of Allegany County, 5435A County Rd 48, Belmont, NY 14813. TEL 716-268-7644. Ed. Paul Westfall. Circ: 500.

630 USA ISSN 0886-814X
S494.5.I5
NEWS C A S T. Text in English. 1974. q. USD 100 includes Task Force Reports, Issue Papers, and Special Publications (effective 2000). **Description:** News of interest to CAST members, and summaries of CAST publications.
Published by: Council for Agricultural Science and Technology, 4420 W Lincoln Way, Ames, IA 50014-2447. TEL 515-292-2125, FAX 515-292-4512, cast@cast-science.org, http://www.cast-science.org. Ed. Robert J Ver Straeten. R&P Linda M Chimenti. Circ: 4,000.

NIEDEROESTERREICHISCHE LANDES-LANDWIRTSCHAFTSKAMMER. AMTLICHER MARKTBERICHT. see *AGRICULTURE—Abstracting, Bibliographies, Statistics*

NIGERIA. METEOROLOGICAL SERVICE. AGROMETEOROLOGICAL BULLETIN. see *METEOROLOGY*

630 NGA ISSN 0300-368X
NIGERIAN AGRICULTURAL JOURNAL. Text in English. 1964. s-a. USD 8. adv. bk.rev. illus. **Document type:** *Academic/Scholarly.*
Related titles: Online - full text ed.: (from International Network for the Availability of Scientific Publications, African Journals Online).
Indexed: BiolAb, FCA, HerbAb, PBA, RPP, WeedAb.
Published by: Agricultural Society of Nigeria, c/o Dr. T.I. Ashaye, PMB 5029, Ibadan, Oyo, Nigeria. Ed. Q B O Anthonio. Circ: 1,000.

NIHON DANI GAKKAISHI/ACAROLOGICAL SOCIETY OF JAPAN. JOURNAL. see *BIOLOGY—Entomology*

630 JPN ISSN 0385-8634
CODEN: NDNHDH
NIIGATA DAIGAKU NOGAKUBU KENKYU HOKOKU/NIIGATA UNIVERSITY. FACULTY OF AGRICULTURE. BULLETIN. Text in English, Japanese. 1951. s-a. per issue exchange basis. **Document type:** *Academic/Scholarly.*
Formerly (until 1977): Niigata Agricultural Science
Indexed: AEA, AgBio, AgrForAb, AnBrAb, BioCN&I, CIN, CPA, ChemAb, ChemTitl, DSA, ExcerpMed, FCA, FPA, ForAb, HerbAb, HortAb, I&DA, IndVet, NutrAb, OrnHort, PBA, PGrRegA, PHN&I, PN&I, PotatoAb, PoultAb, RPP, RefZh, RevApplEntom, RiceAb, S&F, SIA, SeedAb, SoyAb, TriticAb, VetBull, WAE&RSA, WeedAb.
—BLDSC (2507.237000), CASDDS, CISTI.
Published by: Niigata Daigaku, Nogakubu/Niigata University, Faculty of Agriculture, 8050 Igarashi 2, Niigata-shi, 950-22181, Japan. Ed. Atsushi Suzuki. Circ: 500.

631.5814 USA ISSN 0091-9993
NO-TILL FARMER. Text in English. 1972. 12/yr. USD 37.95; USD 4 newsstand/cover (effective 2005). adv. bk.rev. 16 p./no.; **Document type:** *Magazine, Consumer.* **Description:** For farmers who are interested in all aspects of no-till farming, regardless of their level of expertise.
Indexed: F&GI.
—**CCC.**
Published by: Lessiter Publications, 225 Regency Court, Ste 200, Brookfield, WI 53045. TEL 262-782-4480, 800-645-8455, FAX 262-782-1252, info@lesspub.com, http://www.no-tillfarmer.com, http://www.lesspub.com/afj. Ed., Pub. Frank Lessiter. Circ: 5,500 (paid).

630 664.9 SWE ISSN 0281-8205
NOETKOETT; aktuellt om svensk noetkoettsproduktion. Text in Swedish. 1982. bi-m. adv. back issues avail. **Document type:** *Magazine, Trade.* **Description:** Focuses on agriculture, agricultural equipment and economics, animal feed and welfare, food and food industries.
Published by: (Nordiska Avelsfoereningen foer Biffraser), Svensk Mjoelk AB/Swedish Dairy Association, Torsgatan 14, Stockholm, 10546, Sweden. notkott@svenskmjolk.se, info@svenskmjolk.se, http://www.svenskmjolk.se. Ed. Lena Widebaeck TEL 46-16-163442. Adv. contact Marie Louise Ankersten TEL 46-16-163516. B&W page SEK 4,830, color page SEK 8,000; trim 185 x 270. Circ: 6,300. **Co-sponsor:** Sveriges Koettproducenters Intressefoerening.

630 JPN ISSN 0387-2335
CODEN: NDGKAM
NOGYO DOBOKU GAKKAI ROMBUNSHU/JAPANESE SOCIETY OF IRRIGATION, DRAINAGE AND RECLAMATION ENGINEERING. TRANSACTIONS. Text in Japanese. 1960. bi-m. JPY 15,900 to non-members; JPY 7,950 to members (effective 2005).
Formerly (until 1965): Nogyo Doboku Kenkyu. Bessatsu (0549-5652)
Indexed: INIS AtomInd, RefZh.
—BLDSC (8975.120000), CISTI, IE, Linda Hall. **CCC.**
Published by: Japanese Society of Irrigation Drainage and Reclamation Engineering/Nogyo Doboku Gakkai, Nogyo Doboku Kaikan, 34-4 Shinbashi 5-chome, Minato-ku, Tokyo, 105-0004, Japan. TEL 81-3-34363418, FAX 81-3-34358494, suido@jsidre.or.jp, http://www.jsidre.or.jp/.

630 JPN ISSN 0369-5123
CODEN: NOGDAA
NOGYO DOBOKU GAKKAI-SHI/JAPANESE SOCIETY OF IRRIGATION, DRAINAGE AND RECLAMATION ENGINEERING. JOURNAL. Text in Japanese. 1929. m. **Document type:** *Journal, Academic/Scholarly.*
—BLDSC (4809.463000), CISTI, Linda Hall. **CCC.**
Published by: Nogyo-Doboku Gakkai/Japanese Society of Irrigation, Drainage and Reclamation Engineering, c/o Nogyo-doboku Kaikan, 34-4 Shinbashi 5-Chome, Minato-ku, Tokyo, 105-0004, Japan. TEL 81-3-34363418, FAX 81-3-34358494, suido@jsidre.or.jp, http://www.jsidre.or.jp/publ/jrnal.htm.

630 570 JPN ISSN 0911-9450
S589.7 CODEN: NKGHEW
NOGYO KANKYO GIJUTSU KENKYUSHO HOKOKU/NATIONAL INSTITUTE FOR AGRO-ENVIRONMENTAL SCIENCES. BULLETIN. Text in English, Japanese; Summaries in English. 1986. irreg. free. back issues avail. **Document type:** *Bulletin, Academic/Scholarly.*
Indexed: BIOSIS Prev, BiolAb, CIN, ChemAb, ChemTitl, RefZh, S&F, VITIS, ZooRec.
—BLDSC (2640.020000), CASDDS, CISTI, Linda Hall.
Published by: National Institute for Agro-Environmental Sciences/Nogyo Kankyo Gijutsu Kenkyusho, 3-1-3 Kannondai, Tsukuba, 305-8604, Japan. TEL 81-29-8388148, FAX 81-29-8388199. Circ: 1,000.

NOGYO KISHO KENKYU SHUROKU/COLLECTED PAPERS OF AGRICULTURAL METEOROLOGY. see *METEOROLOGY*

NOGYO KISHO NENPO/ANNUAL REPORT OF AGRICULTURAL METEOROLOGY. see *METEOROLOGY*

NOGYO SEIBUTSU SHIGEN KENKYUJO KENKYU SHIRYO/NATIONAL INSTITUTE OF AGROBIOLOGICAL RESOURCES. MISCELLANEOUS PUBLICATION. see *BIOLOGY*

NOGYO SEIBUTSU SHIGEN KENKYUJO NENPO/NATIONAL INSTITUTE OF AGROBIOLOGICAL RESOURCES. ANNUAL REPORT. see *BIOLOGY*

NOGYO SEIBUTSU SHIGEN KENKYUJO NYUSU/NATIONAL INSTITUTE OF AGROBIOLOGICAL RESOURCES. NEWS. see *BIOLOGY*

630 JPN
NOGYO SOGO KENKYUJO NENPO/NATIONAL RESEARCH INSTITUTE OF AGRICULTURAL ECONOMICS. ANNUAL REPORT. Text in Japanese. 1949. a. **Document type:** *Government.*
Formerly: National Research Institute of Agriculture. Annual Report
Indexed: RASB.
Published by: Norinsuisan-sho, Norim Suisam Seisaku Kemkyujo/Ministry of Agriculture, Forestry and Fisheries - Policy Reserach Institute, 2-1 Nishigahara 2-chome, Kita-ku, Tokyo, 114-0024, Japan. TEL 81-3-3910-3946. Ed. Kazuo Nonaka.

630 NGA ISSN 0331-6742
NOMA. Text in English. 1978. a. USD 25. bk.rev. charts. **Document type:** *Academic/Scholarly.* **Description:** Contains general-interest articles on agriculture.
Formerly (until 1978): Samaru Agricultural Newsletter (0036-3731)
Media: Duplicated (not offset).
Indexed: AnBrAb, BiolAb, DSA, HortAb, RRTA, RevApplEntom, S&F, WAE&RSA.
—CISTI.
Published by: Ahmadu Bello University, Institute for Agricultural Research, PMB 1044, Samaru-Zaria, Kaduna, Nigeria. FAX 234-69-50563. Ed. T O Fadiji.

630 CHN ISSN 1002-7785
NONGCUN DASHIJIE. Text in Chinese. bi-m.
Published by: (Nongcun Dashijie Bianjibu), Xinhua News Agency, 57 Xuanwumen Xidajie, Beijing, 100803, China. Ed. Zhao Huaiqing.

630 333.7932 CHN ISSN 1006-8910
NONGCUN DIANGONG. Text in Chinese. m. CNY 3 per issue domestic (effective 2000). back issues avail. **Document type:** *Academic/Scholarly.*
Related titles: Online - full content ed.: (from WanFang Data Corp.); Online - full text ed.: (from East View Information Services).
Published by: Guojia Dianli Gongsi, Nongdian Gongzuobu, Xu Dong Lu, Wuyi, 430077, China. TEL 86-27-86772556. Eds. Meng Xiang Zhao, Zhong Fu Li.

630 CHN ISSN 0577-5825
NONGCUN KEXUE SHIYAN/AGRICULTURAL EXPERIMENT. Text in Chinese. m.
Published by: Jilin Keji Baokan She, 8 Minkang Lu, Changchun, Jilin 130041, China. TEL 853243. Ed. Zhang Jiugui.

630 CHN ISSN 1002-6827
NONGCUN SHIYONG GONGCHENG JISHU/PRACTICAL RURAL ENGINEERING TECHNOLOGY. Text in Chinese. 1986. bi-m. **Document type:** *Academic/Scholarly.*
Related titles: Online - full text ed.: (from East View Information Services).
Published by: Zhongguo Nongye Gongcheng Yanjiu Shejiyuan/Chinese Research and Design Institute of Agricultural Engineering, Nongzhanguan Nanlu, Beijing, 100026, China. TEL 5003366. Ed. Wang Songtao.

630 CHN
NONGMIN RIBAO/FARMER'S DAILY. Text in Chinese. 1980. 6/w. CNY 198 (effective 2004). adv. **Document type:** *Newspaper, Consumer.* **Description:** Provides national coverage of agricultural issues, technologies and other related issues.
Related titles: Online - full content ed.

Published by: Nongmin Ribaoshe, 1, Zhaowai Balizhuang Beili, Beijing, 100025, China. TEL 86-10-85834401, FAX 86-10-85815102, http://www.farmers.net.cn/. **Dist. by:** China International Book Trading Corp, 35 Chegongzhuang Xilu, Haidian District, PO Box 399, Beijing 100044, China. TEL 86-10-68412045, FAX 86-10-68412023, cibtc@mail.cibtc.com.cn, http://www.cibtc.com.cn.

630 CHN ISSN 1000-7741
NONGMIN WENZHAI/FARMER'S DIGEST. Text in Chinese. 1984. m. CNY 1.80 newsstand/cover. adv. **Document type:** *Journal, Academic/Scholarly.* **Description:** Presents a broad selection of information and new technologies published in China's newspapers and magazines.
Published by: Zhongguo Nongcun Zazhishe, 61 Fuxing Lu, Beijing, 100036, China. TEL 86-10-68271458, prcd@sohu.com, http://nmwz.periodicals.net.cn/. Ed. Zhonghua Sun. Circ: 1,800,000.

632.95 668.65 CHN ISSN 1008-7303
NONGYAOXUE XUEBAO/CHINESE JOURNAL OF PESTICIDE SCIENCE. Text in Chinese. 1999 (Jun.). q. CNY 15 newsstand/cover (effective 2002). **Document type:** *Journal, Academic/Scholarly.*
Related titles: Online - full content ed.: (from WanFang Data Corp.); Online - full text ed.: (from East View Information Services).
Indexed: ASFA, B&BAb, ESPM, EntAb, PollutAb, RefZh, SWRA, ZooRec.
—BLDSC (3180.471000).
Published by: Zhongguo Nongye Daxue, 2, Yuanmingyuanxi Road, Haidian District, Beijing, 100094, China. TEL 86-2-62632619, FAX 86-2-62893003, nyxuebao@263.net, http://periodicals.wanfangdata.com.cn/gyjs.asp?ID=80352. Ed. Wanyi Chen. **Dist. by:** China International Book Trading Corp, 35 Chegongzhuang Xilu, Haidian District, PO Box 399, Beijing 100044, China. TEL 86-10-68412045, FAX 86-10-68412023, cibtc@mail.cibtc.com.cn, http://www.cibtc.com.cn.

630 CHN ISSN 1002-6819
NONGYE GONGCHENG XUEBAO/CHINESE SOCIETY OF AGRICULTURAL ENGINEERING. TRANSACTIONS. Text mainly in Chinese; Text occasionally in English. bi-m. **Document type:** *Journal, Academic/Scholarly.*
Related titles: Online - full content ed.: (from WanFang Data Corp.); Online - full text ed.: (from East View Information Services).
Indexed: AEA, ASFA, AgBio, AgrForAb, AnBrAb, BioCN&I, BrCerAb, C&ISA, CPA, CerAb, CorrAb, DSA, E&CAJ, EMA, ESPM, EnvEAb, FCA, FPA, ForAb, HerbAb, HortAb, I&DA, IAA, IndVet, M&TEA, MBF, METADEX, MaizeAb, NutrAb, OrnHort, PBA, PGegResA, PGrRegA, PHN&I, PN&I, PotatoAb, PoultAb, RA&MP, RDA, RPP, RRTA, RefZh, RiceAb, S&F, SIA, SWRA, SeedAb, SolStAb, SoyAb, TDB, TriticAb, VetBull, WAA, WAE&RSA, WeedAb.
—BLDSC (8912.478000), Linda Hall.
Published by: Zhongguo Nongye Gongcheng Xuehui/Chinese Society of Agricultural Engineering, Zhaoyang District, Nongzhanguan Nan Road, Beijing, 100026, China. http://www.chinainfo.gov.cn/periodical/nygcxb/index.htm.

NONGYE HUANJING KEXUE XUEBAO/JOURNAL OF AGRO-ENVIRONMENT SCIENCE. see *ENVIRONMENTAL STUDIES*

NONGYE KAOGU/AGRICULTURAL ARCHAEOLOGY. see *ARCHAEOLOGY*

630 CHN ISSN 1000-6400
S471.C6
NONGYE KEJI TONGXUN/AGRICULTURAL SCIENCE AND TECHNOLOGY BULLETIN. Text in Chinese. m.
Related titles: Online - full text ed.: (from East View Information Services).
Indexed: HortAb, MaizeAb, RevApplEntom, TriticAb, WeedAb.
Published by: Zhongguo Nongye Kexueyuan/Chinese Academy of Agricultural Sciences, Chinese Society for Horticultural Science, 30 Baishiqiao Lu, Beijing, 100081, China. TEL 8314433. Ed. Hou Liande.

630 CHN ISSN 1002-4840
NONGYE QUHUA/AGRICULTURAL REGIONAL PLANNING. Text in Chinese. 1987. bi-m. CNY 2 per issue. bk.rev. **Document type:** *Academic/Scholarly.*
Published by: (Quhua Suo), Zhongguo Nongye Kexueyuan/Chinese Academy of Agricultural Sciences, Chinese Society for Horticultural Science, 30 Baishiqiao Lu, Beijing, 100081, China. TEL 01-8316540, FAX 01-831654. Ed. Li Yingzhong.

630 660.6 CHN ISSN 1006-1304
NONGYE SHENGWU JISHU XUEBAO/JOURNAL OF AGRICULTURAL BIOTECHNOLOGY. Text in Chinese. 1993. bi-m. CNY 72 (effective 2005). **Document type:** *Journal, Academic/Scholarly.*
Related titles: Online - full text ed.: (from East View Information Services, WanFang Data Corp.).
Indexed: AgBio, BioCN&I, CPA, FCA, HortAb, MaizeAb, PBA, PGegResA, PGrRegA, PoultAb, S&F, SIA, SeedAb, SoyAb, TriticAb, WeedAb.
—BLDSC (6117.305000).

Published by: Zhongguo Nongye Daxue, 2, Yuanmingyuanxi Road, Haidian District, Beijing, 100094, China. nsjxb@mail.cau.edu.cn, http://nyswjsxb.periodicals.net.cn/. Ed. Jilun Li. **Dist. by:** China International Book Trading Corp, 35 Chegongzhuang Xilu, Haidian District, PO Box 399, Beijing 100044, China. TEL 86-10-68412045, FAX 86-10-68412023, cibtc@mail.cibtc.com.cn, http://www.cibtc.com.cn.

630 TWN
NONGYE SHIJIE/AGRICULTURE WORLD. Text in Chinese. m. TWD 1,000; TWD 100 newsstand/cover (effective 2002). **Document type:** *Journal, Academic/Scholarly.*
Related titles: Online - full content ed.
Address: Hankou Road, Section 3, 55 Lane, no.21, Taizhong, Taiwan. TEL 886-4-22932036, FAX 886-4-22931449, agric729@ms11.hinet.net, http://www.agriworld.com.tw/.

630 CHN
NONGYE ZHISHI/AGRICULTURAL KNOWLEDGE. Text in Chinese. 1950. m. USD 18. **Document type:** *Academic/Scholarly.* **Description:** Introduces popular agricultural science knowledge.
Published by: Shandong Nongye Zhishi Zazhishe, 21 Minziqian Rd, Jinan, Shandong 250100, China. TEL 86-531-8930447. Ed. Yang Lijian. Pub. Liu Zongquan. Circ: 650,000.

630 DNK
NORD- MIDT- OG VESTSJAELLANDS LANDBRUGS-NYT. Text in Danish. w. adv.
Published by: Lolland-Falsters Erververvsforlag ApS, Marrebaeck, Vaeggerlose, 4873, Denmark. Circ: 16,933.

630 NOR ISSN 0029-1226
NORDEN; nord-Norges landbrukstidsskrift. Text in Norwegian. 1896. 16/yr. NOK 390; NOK 450 foreign (effective 1999). adv. bk.rev. illus.; stat. index. **Document type:** *Newsletter, Trade.*
Published by: A-L Landbrukstidsskriftet Norden, Vaagenes Forskningsstasjon, Bodoe, N-8010, Norway. TEL 47-75-58-80-90, FAX 47-75-58-80-99, post@norden-bodo.no. Ed. Haakon Renolen. Circ: 3,500.

630 DNK ISSN 0048-0495
S11 CODEN: NOJOAO
NORDISK JORDBRUKSFORSKNING. Text in Danish, English, Norwegian, Swedish. 1918. q. DKK 240 (effective 1998). bk.rev. **Document type:** *Abstract/Index.*
Indexed: AEA, AgBio, AnBrAb, BioCN&I, BiolAb, CPA, ChemAb, DSA, FCA, ForAb, HerbAb, HortAb, I&DA, IndVet, MaizeAb, NemAb, NutrAb, PBA, PGrRegA, PHN&I, PN&I, PotatoAb, PoultAb, RASB, RPP, RRTA, RevApplEntom, S&F, SeedAb, SoyAb, TriticAb, WAE&RSA, WeedAb.
—CASDDS.
Published by: Nordiske Jordbrugeres Forening, Mariendalsvej 27 2, Frederiksberg, 2000, Denmark. TEL 45-3888-6688, FAX 45-3888-6611, NJF-GS@inet.uni2.dk, http://www.njf.dk. Ed. Jens Wulff. Circ: 2,800.

630 GBR ISSN 0955-0208
NORFOLK FARMER. Text in English. m. adv.
Formerly: Norfolk Farmers' Union Gazette
Published by: County Farmers Publications Ltd., 55 Goldington Rd, Bedford, Beds MK40 3LU, United Kingdom. TEL 44-1234-351401, FAX 44-1234-328614. Ed. D Brown. Circ: 2,400.

630 690 NOR ISSN 0802-8532
NORGES LANDBRUKSHOEGSKOLE. INSTITUTT FOR TEKNISKE FAG. RAPPORTER/AGRICULTURAL UNIVERSITY OF NORWAY. DEPARTMENT OF AGRICULTURAL ENGINEERING. RESEARCH REPORTS. Text in Norwegian; Summaries in English. 1990. irreg. **Document type:** *Monographic series, Academic/Scholarly.* **Description:** Contains reports from research projects.
—CISTI.
Published by: Norges Landbrukshoegskole, Institutt for Tekniske Fag, Postboks 5065, Aas, 1432, Norway. TEL 47-64-94-87-94, FAX 47-64-94-88-10. Ed. Oluf Berentsen.

NORIN SUISAN TOKEI GEPPO/MONTHLY STATISTICS ON AGRICULTURE, FORESTRY AND FISHERIES. see *AGRICULTURE—Abstracting, Bibliographies, Statistics*

NORIN SUISAN TOSHO SHIRYO GEPPO. see *AGRICULTURE—Abstracting, Bibliographies, Statistics*

630 639.2 634.9 JPN ISSN 0387-1452
NORINSHO KOHO/AGRICULTURE, FORESTRY, FISHERY. Variant title: A F F. Text in Japanese. 1970. m. JPY 8,424; JPY 610 newsstand/cover (effective 2002). **Document type:** *Journal, Government.*
Published by: Association of Agriculture & Forestry Statistics, 3-9-13, Shimo-Meguro, Meguro-ku, Tokyo, 153-0064, Japan. TEL 81-3-3492-2990, FAX 81-3-3492-2971, henshu@aafs.or.jp, http://www.aafs.or.jp/.

630 NOR ISSN 0805-9691
NORSK INSTITUTT FOR LANDBRUKSOEKONOMISK FORSKNING. NOTAT. Text in Norwegian. 1995. irreg. price varies. back issues avail. **Document type:** *Monographic series, Academic/Scholarly.*

Supersedes in part (in 1995): Norsk Institutt for Landbruksoekonomisk Forskning. A (0802-0337); Which was formed by the merger of (1952-1987): Norsk Institutt for Landbruksoekonomisk Forskning. F 2 (0801-8626); (1970-1987): Norsk Institutt for Landbruksoekonomisk Forskning. I 7 (0801-8596); Which incorporated (1981-1985): Budsjettnemnda for Jordbruket. Utredninger (0800-7675); Supersedes in part (in 1995): Norsk Institutt for Landbruksoekonomisk Forskning. B (0801-8553); Which was formerly (until 1987): Norsk Institutt for Landbruksoekonomisk Forskning. F-3 (0801-8561); (until 1985): Norsk Institutt for Landbruksoekonomiske Institutt. F-3 (0801-860X); (1968-1965): Norsk Institutt for Landbruksoekonomiske Institutt. Stensilert Saermelding (0801-8618); Supersedes in part (in 1995): Norsk Institutt for Landbruksoekonomisk Forskning. C (0802-2577)
Related titles: Online - full text ed.
Indexed: WAE&RSA.
Published by: Norsk Institutt for Landbruksoekonomisk Forskning (NILF)/Norwegian Agricultural Economics Research Institute (NILF), Schweigaards Gate 33B, Postboks 8024, Dep, Oslo, 0030, Norway. TEL 47-22-367200, FAX 47-22-367299, postmottak@nilf.no, http://www.nilf.no, http://www.nilf.no/.

630 NOR ISSN 0332-5474
NORSK LANDBRUK. Text in Norwegian. 1882. fortn. NOK 682 (effective 2001). adv. charts; illus.; mkt. 64 p./no.; back issues avail. **Document type:** *Trade.*
Indexed: FCA, HerbAb, HortAb, PBA, SeedAb, TriticAb.
—CISTI. **CCC.**
Published by: A-S Landbruksforlaget, Schweigaard gt. 34A, Postboks 9303, Groenland, Oslo, 0135, Norway. TEL 47-23-15-89-21, FAX 47-23-15-89-20, norsk.landbruk@landbruksforlaget.no, http://www.landbruksforlaget.no. Ed. Marianne Roehme TEL 47-23-15-89-82. Adv. contact Torstein Forseth TEL 47-23-15-89-90. B&W page NOK 7,800, color page NOK 12,000; 185 x 260. Circ: 16,863.

630 USA ISSN 0744-5466
NORTH CAROLINA. DEPARTMENT OF AGRICULTURE. AGRICULTURAL REVIEW. Key Title: Agricultural Review (Raleigh). Text in English. 1925. m. free. adv. **Document type:** *Newspaper, Government.* **Description:** Editorial and classified advertising for farmers.
—Linda Hall.
Published by: Department of Agriculture, 2 W Edenton St, Raleigh, NC 27601. TEL 919-733-4216, jim_knight@ncdamail.agr.state.nc.us, http://www.agr.state.nc.us. Ed., R&P James S Knight TEL 919-733-4216. Circ: 70,700. **Subscr. to:** PO Box 27647, Raleigh, NC 27611.

630 USA ISSN 0744-9593
NORTH CAROLINA FARM BUREAU NEWS. Text in English. 1936. m. (11/yr.). free membership (effective 2005). adv. back issues avail. **Document type:** *Magazine, Consumer.*
Published by: North Carolina Farm Bureau Federation, Box 27766, Raleigh, NC 27611. TEL 919-782-1705, FAX 919-783-3593, ncfbfed@ncfb.com, http://www.ncfb.com/. Ed., R&P Chris Street. adv.: B&W page USD 4,009, color page USD 4,956; trim 10.75 x 8. Circ: 410,000 (paid).

630 USA
NORTH CAROLINA FARMER★. Text in English. 1980. m. USD 12. adv. **Document type:** *Newspaper.* **Description:** Covers people and progress in agriculture, innovative farm operations, crop and livestock improvements and management, farm business, and marketing.
Supersedes: Carolina Farmer (North Carolina Edition) (0744-2033)
Published by: Rural Press U S A, 1101 Spring Forest Rd, Ste 101, Raleigh, NC 27615. TEL 919-621-0991, 800-477-1737, FAX 919-676-9803. Ed. Richard Davis. Pub. Jeff Tennant. Adv. contact Blake Lewis. B&W page USD 1,515. Circ: 30,000.

630 USA
NORTH CAROLINA SEED LAW. Text in English. 1953. irreg. free. **Document type:** *Government.* **Description:** Provides seed law information to the North Carolina seed industry.
Published by: Department of Agriculture, PO Box 27647, Raleigh, NC 27611. TEL 919-733-7125, http://www.agr.state.nc.us. R&P James S Knight TEL 919-733-4216. Circ: (controlled).

630 640 USA
NORTH COUNTRY FARM NEWS★. Text in English. 1956. m. adv. bk.rev. **Description:** Informs agricultural producers on how to improve agricultural productivity and improve environmental quality.
Former titles (until Jan. 1979): Extension; (until Jan. 1975): Clinton County Cooperative Extension News; Clinton County Agricultural News
Published by: Clinton County Cooperative Extension, 6064 State Rte 22, Ste 5, Plattsburgh, NY 12901-6222. Ed. Beth Spaugh. Circ: 900 (controlled).

338.17 USA
NORTH DAKOTA AGRICULTURAL RESEARCH. Text in English. 1997. irreg. bk.rev. **Document type:** *Journal.* **Description:** Focuses on research related to the production and processing of agricultural products and societal issues important to the community.

Media: Online - full content.
Indexed: Agr.
Published by: North Dakota State University, Agriculture Communications Office, Fargo, ND 58105-5655. ndarjour@ndsuext.nodak.edu, http://www.ag.ndsu.nodak.edu/ndagres/ndagres.htm. Ed. Dr. Albert Schneider.

NORTH DAKOTA AGRICULTURAL STATISTICS. see *AGRICULTURE—Abstracting, Bibliographies, Statistics*

603 353.9 USA ISSN 1550-5618
S99
NORTH DAKOTA. DEPARTMENT OF AGRICULTURE. BIENNIAL REPORT OF THE COMMISSIONER OF AGRICULTURE. Text in English. 1890. biennial. free. illus.; stat. **Document type:** *Government.*
Former titles (until 1999): North Dakota. Department of Agriculture. Biennial Report (0362-9643); North Dakota. Department of Agriculture. Annual Report (0093-8203)
—CISTI.
Published by: Department of Agriculture, 600 E Blvd, 6th Fl, Bismarck, ND 58505-0020. TEL 701-224-2231, FAX 701-224-4567. Ed. Ellen Delp. Circ: 600.

630 GBR
NORTH EAST FARMER. Text in English. m. adv. **Document type:** *Newsletter.*
Formerly: East Riding Farmers Journal
Address: 207 Tadcaster Rd, York, 402 1UB, United Kingdom. TEL 44-1904-451550, FAX 44-1904-451560. Ed. Kevin Pearce. Adv. contact Carol Makepeace. Circ: 2,500.

630 USA
NORTH IOWA FARMER. Text in English. m. free. adv. **Document type:** *Newspaper.*
Published by: Globe Gazette, 300 N Washington Ave, Mason City, IA 50401. TEL 515-421-0546, FAX 515-421-0516. Ed. Kevin Baskins. Pub. Howard Query. Adv. contact Byron Wooten. Circ: 10,777.

630 GBR ISSN 0306-0675
NORTH RIDING AND DURHAM FARMER. WHOLE EDITION. Text in English. 1962. m. adv.
Incorporates: North Riding and Durham Farmer. North Riding Edition; Formerly: North Riding and Durham Farmer. Durham Edition
Published by: County Farmers Publications Ltd., 55 Goldington Rd, Bedford, Beds MK40 3LU, United Kingdom. TEL 44-1234-351401, FAX 44-1234-328614. Ed. A Hepworth. Circ: 4,250.

630 GBR
NORTH WALES FARMING NEWS✶. Text in English. 1973. m. GBP 1.24.
Published by: Mellison Ltd., 63 Cambrian Dr, Rhos On Sea, Colwyn Bay, Clwyd LL28 4TA, United Kingdom. Ed. G E Walters.

630 USA
NORTH WEST COMMODITY CORNER. Text in English. 1992. w. USD 85 domestic; USD 90 in Canada & Mexico; USD 115 elsewhere (effective 2001). charts; illus.; mkt.; maps; stat. back issues avail. **Document type:** *Newsletter, Government.*
Media: Fax. **Related titles:** Fax ed.; Online - full text ed.
Published by: U.S. Department Of Agriculture, Livestock & Grain Market News Branch, 1428 S. Pioneer Way, Moses Lake, WA 98837. http://www.ams.usda.gov/lsg/mncs/pdf%5Fweekly/compweekly.htm, http://www.ams.usda.gov/lsg/mncs/pdf%5Fweekly/compweekly.htm. Circ: 300.

630 CHN ISSN 1006-8104
NORTHEAST AGRICULTURAL UNIVERSITY. JOURNAL. Text in English. 1994. s-a. USD 40 (effective 2003). back issues avail. **Document type:** *Academic/Scholarly.*
Related titles: Online - full content ed.: (from WanFang Data Corp.); Online - full text ed.: (from East View Information Services); ♦ Chinese ed.: Dongbei Nongye Daxue Xuebao. ISSN 1005-9369.
Indexed: AEA, AgBio, AnBrAb, BioCN&I, CPA, DSA, FCA, ForAb, HerbAb, HortAb, I&DA, IndVet, MaizeAb, NutrAb, OrnHort, PBA, PGegResA, PGrRegA, PHN&I, PN&I, PotatoAb, PoultAb, RA&MP, RPP, RefZh, RevApplEntom, RiceAb, S&F, SIA, SeedAb, SoyAb, TDB, TriticAb, VetBull, WAE&RSA, WeedAb.
—BLDSC (4834.146000).
Published by: Northeast Agricultural University, Xiangfang-qu, Harbin, 150030, China. TEL 86-451-5390553, FAX 86-451-5390639, slbl@public.hr.hl.cn, http://www.neau.edu.cn. Ed. Li Jun Xing.

338.1 639.2 AUS
NORTHERN TERRITORY. DEPARTMENT OF PRIMARY INDUSTRY AND FISHERIES. TECHNICAL ANNUAL REPORT. Text in English. 1989. a. AUD 8 (effective 2001). **Document type:** *Government.*
Published by: Australia. Department of Primary Industry and Fisheries, PO Box 990, Darwin, N.T. 0801, Australia. TEL 61-889-992202, FAX 61-889-992307, hassan.bajhau@nt.gov.au, http://www.dpif.nt.gov.au/dpif/pubcat. Ed. H Bajhau. R&P Hassan Bajhau.

338.1 639.2 AUS ISSN 1032-0393
NORTHERN TERRITORY. DEPARTMENT OF PRIMARY INDUSTRY AND FISHERIES. TECHNICAL BULLETIN. Text in English. 1979. irreg. AUD 6 per issue (effective 2001). **Document type:** *Monographic series, Government.*
Former titles (until 1988): Northern Territory. Division of Primary Production. Technical Bulletin (1031-9581); (until 1987): Northern Territory. Department of Primary Production. Technical Bulletin (0158-2763)
Indexed: AgBio, AgrForAb, CPA, ForAb, HerbAb, HortAb, IndVet, OrnHort, PBA, RevApplEntom, S&F, SeedAb, WAE&RSA, WeedAb.
—CISTI.
Published by: Australia. Department of Primary Industry and Fisheries, PO Box 990, Darwin, N.T. 0801, Australia. TEL 61-889-992202, FAX 61-889-992307, hassan.bajhau@nt.gov.au, http://www.dpif.nt.gov.au/dpif/pubcat. Ed. H Bajhau. R&P Hassan Bajhau.

630 GBR ISSN 0955-0216
NORTHUMBERLAND FARMER. Text in English. 1958. m. adv.
Published by: County Farmers Publications Ltd., 55 Goldington Rd, Bedford, Beds MK40 3LU, United Kingdom. TEL 44-1234-351401, FAX 44-1234-328614. Ed. A Hepworth. Circ: 1,750.

630 USA
NORTHWESTERN ILLINOIS FARMER; the original farm family newspaper. Text in English. 1867. w. (Wed.). USD 20 (effective 2005). adv. **Document type:** *Newspaper, Consumer.*
Address: PO Box 536, Lena, IL 61048-0536. TEL 815-369-2811, FAX 815-369-2816. Ed., Pub. Norman C. Templin. adv.: col. inch USD 8. Circ: 11,000 (paid).

NORWAY. STATISTISK SENTRALBYRAA. JORDBRUKSSTATISTIKK/STATISTICS NORWAY. AGRICULTURAL STATISTICS. see *AGRICULTURE—Abstracting, Bibliographies, Statistics*

630 FRA ISSN 0299-3635
NOTRE TERROIR. Text in French. 1987. 24/yr.
Address: 1 rue du Chateau, Chambery, 73000, France. TEL 33-17-36. Ed. M Donzel. Circ: 5,000.

630 GBR ISSN 0955-0224
NOTTINGHAMSHIRE FARMER. Text in English. 1949. m. adv. index. **Document type:** *Trade.*
Formerly: Nottinghamshire Farmers' Journal
Published by: County Farmers Publications Ltd., 55 Goldington Rd, Bedford, Beds MK40 3LU, United Kingdom. TEL 44-1234-351401, FAX 44-1234-328614. Ed. S Fisher. Circ: 1,600.

630 CAN ISSN 0833-8485
NOVA SCOTIA INSTITUTE OF AGROLOGISTS NEWSLETTER. Text in English. q. looseleaf. free. back issues avail. **Document type:** *Newsletter.*
Published by: Nova Scotia Institute of Agrologists, P O Box 550, Truro, NS B2N 5E3, Canada. TEL 902-893-6520. Eds. Campbell Gunn, Laurie Eagles. Circ: 350.

630 338.642 HRV ISSN 0353-7838
NOVOGRADISKI GLASNIK. Text in Croatian. 1974. s-m.
Formerly (until 1990): N G Novine (0351-6857)
Published by: Narodno Sveuciliste "Matija Antun Reljkovic", Reljkoviceva 4, Nova Gradiska, 55400, Croatia. TEL 055 63-762.

630 RUS
NOVYI SEMLEVLADELETS. Text in Russian. m. USD 125 in United States.
Published by: Agrofirma Semko, Pr-t Mira, Moscow, 129223, Russian Federation. TEL 7-095-9394806, FAX 7-095-2166355. Ed. V I Stepanenko. **US dist. addr.:** East View Information Services, 3020 Harbor Ln. N., Minneapolis, MN 55447. TEL 612-550-0961.

630 POL ISSN 0029-5396
S13
NOWE ROLNICTWO✶. Text in Polish. 1951. s-m. PLZ 600. adv. bk.rev. bibl.; charts; illus.; stat. index.
Indexed: RASB.
Published by: Polskie Towarzystwo Nauk Agrotechnicznych, ul Akademicka 13, Lublin, 20934, Poland. Ed. Rudolf Kowalski. Circ: 19,000. **Dist. by:** Ars Polona, Krakowskie Przedmiescie 7, Warsaw, Poland.

NUCLEUS. see *ENERGY—Nuclear Energy*

NUTRITION SOCIETY OF INDIA. PROCEEDINGS. see *NUTRITION AND DIETETICS*

630 ZAF ISSN 0029-7321
O T KANER. (Oostelike Transvaalse) Text in Afrikaans. 1956. bi-m. membership. adv. bk.rev. illus.; stat. back issues avail.
Published by: O T K (Koop) Bpk, PO Box 100, Bethal, Mpumalanga 2310, South Africa. TEL 01361-71000, FAX 01361-5776. Ed. Werner A Ras. Circ: 11,000.

630 ZAF
O V K NUUS/O V K NEWS. Text in English. 1993. irreg. free. adv. illus. **Document type:** *Newsletter, Consumer.*
Former titles (until Dec. 1998): O V K Boerenuus; Oos-Vrystaat Boerenuus
Published by: O V K Bedryf bpk/O V K Operations Ltd, Posbus 96, Ladybrand, 9745, South Africa. TEL 27-51-924-0630, FAX 27-51-924-0338, mcf@ovk.co.za. Ed., R&P, Adv. contact M C C Fourie. Circ: 2,500.

OBST- UND WEINBAU. see *BEVERAGES*

630 DEU ISSN 0179-7077
OBSTBAU. Text in German. 1976. m.
Indexed: AEA, FS&TA, I&DA.
Published by: Fachgruppe Obstbau im Bundesausschuss fuer Obst und Gemuese, Godesberger Allee 142-148, Bonn, 53175, Germany.

630 CHE
OBWALDNER BAUERNBLATT. Text in German. m. **Document type:** *Newspaper, Trade.*
Address: Tellenstr 39, Kaegiswil, 6056, Switzerland. TEL 41-41-6601651. Ed. Peter Krummenacher. Circ: 1,050.

630 POL ISSN 0029-8239
OCHRONA ROSLIN. Text in Polish. 1956. m. PLZ 72 domestic; EUR 18 foreign (effective 2005). adv. **Document type:** *Journal, Academic/Scholarly.*
Indexed: AEA, AbHyg, AgBio, AgrForAb, AgrLib, BioCN&I, CPA, FCA, FPA, FaBeAb, ForAb, HelmAb, HerbAb, HortAb, MaizeAb, NemAb, NutrAb, OrnHort, PBA, PGegResA, PGrRegA, PHN&I, PN&I, PotatoAb, RA&MP, RM&VM, RPP, RevApplEntom, RiceAb, S&F, SIA, SeedAb, TriticAb, WAE&RSA, WeedAb.
—BLDSC (6235.120000).
Published by: Wydawnictwo Plantpress sp. z o.o., ul J Lea 116, Krakow, 30133, Poland. wydawnictwo@haslo.pl, ogloszenia@haslo.pl. adv.: B&W page USD 1,400. Circ: 1,200.

630 DEU ISSN 1015-2423
OEKOLOGIE UND LANDBAU. Text in German. 1977. q. adv. bk.rev. abstr.; bibl.; stat. back issues avail. **Document type:** *Bulletin, Trade.*
Formerly (until 1988): I F O A M (0171-7456)
Related titles: ♦ English ed.: Ecology and Farming. ISSN 1016-5061.
Indexed: DSA, ExcerpMed, FCA, PoultAb, RefZh, VITIS.
—CISTI.
Published by: (International Federation of Organic Agriculture Movements), Stiftung Oekologie und Landbau, Postfach 1516, Bad Duerkheim, 67089, Germany. TEL 49-6322-98970224, FAX 49-6322-989701, info@soel.de, http://www.soel.de. Ed. Immo Luenzer. R&P, Adv. contact Minou Yussefi. Circ: 5,000.
Co-sponsor: Research Institute of Organic Agriculture.

630 AUT
OESTERREICHISCHE BAUERNZEITUNG. Text in German. w. EUR 60 (effective 2004). adv. **Document type:** *Newspaper, Trade.*
Formerly: Oesterreichische Bauerbuendler
Published by: (Niederoesterreichischer Bauernbund), Oesterreichischer Agrarverlag GmbH, Achauer Str 49a, Leopoldsdorf, N 2333, Austria. TEL 43-2235-4040, FAX 43-2235-404929, office@agrarverlag.at, http://www.agrarverlag.at. adv.: B&W page EUR 13,746, color page EUR 16,353. Circ: 147,317 (paid and controlled).

630 AUT
OESTERREICHISCHES RAIFFEISENBLATT. Text in German. m. EUR 60 domestic; EUR 67 foreign (effective 2004). adv. **Document type:** *Magazine, Trade.*
Published by: Oesterreichischer Agrarverlag GmbH, Achauer Str 49a, Leopoldsdorf, N 2333, Austria. TEL 43-2235-4040, FAX 43-2235-404929, office@agrarverlag.at, http://www.agrarverlag.at/raiffeisenblatt/index.html. Ed. Robert Bzoch.

630 USA ISSN 0078-3951
CODEN: OARBB7
➤ **OHIO AGRICULTURAL RESEARCH AND DEVELOPMENT CENTER, WOOSTER. RESEARCH BULLETIN.** Text in English. 1888. irreg., latest 2001. free (effective 2005). bibl.; charts; illus. **Document type:** *Bulletin, Academic/Scholarly.*
Indexed: Agr, BiolAb, CurCont, ExcerpMed, FCA, ForAb, HerbAb, MaizeAb, NutrAb, PBA, RRTA, RefZh, RevApplEntom, S&F, SeedAb, WAE&RSA.
—BLDSC (7730.720000), CISTI, Linda Hall.
Published by: Ohio State University, Ohio Agricultural Research and Development Center, Wooster, 1680 Madison Ave, Wooster, OH 44691-4096. TEL 330-263-3701, FAX 330-263-3688, oardc@osu.edu. Ed. Joy Ann Fischer. Circ: 1,100.

630 USA ISSN 0078-396X
CODEN: OARCBA
➤ **OHIO AGRICULTURAL RESEARCH AND DEVELOPMENT CENTER, WOOSTER. RESEARCH CIRCULAR.** Text in English. 1888. irreg., latest vol.299, 1999. free. bibl.; charts; illus. back issues avail. **Document type:** *Bulletin, Academic/Scholarly.*

A

Indexed: AEA, Agr, BiolAb, CPA, CurCont, FCA, FPA, ForAb, HerbAb, HortAb, IndVet, NutrAb, PBA, PGrRegA, PHN&I, RPP, RRTA, RefZh, RevApplEntom, S&F, VetBull, WAE&RSA, WeedAb.
—CISTI, Linda Hall.
Published by: Ohio State University, Ohio Agricultural Research and Development Center, Wooster, 1680 Madison Ave, Wooster, OH 44691-4096. TEL 330-263-3777. Ed. Joy Ann Fischer. Circ: 1,100.

630 USA ISSN 0030-0896
OHIO FARMER. Text in English. 1848. 12/yr. USD 23.95 (effective 2005). adv. bk.rev. charts; illus.; stat. **Document type:** *Magazine, Trade.* **Description:** Family farm journal covering all aspects of farming. Deals with technical farm problems, labor, equipment, techniques, and marketing.
Related titles: Microfilm ed.; Microform ed.: (from PQC).
—CISTI. **CCC.**
Published by: Farm Progress Companies, 191 S Gary Ave, Carol Stream, IL 60188-2095. TEL 630-462-2229, FAX 630-462-2202, http://www.ohiofarmer.com, http://www.farmprogress.com/. Ed. Tim White. adv.: B&W page USD 1,950, color page USD 2,450; trim 10.5 x 14.5. Circ: 20,000 (paid).

630 USA ISSN 0749-4009
OHIO GRANGER. Text in English. 1898. bi-m. free to members (effective 2005). adv. **Document type:** *Magazine, Trade.*
Former titles (until 1984): Ohio Grange (0030-0926); (until 1969): Ohio State Grange Monthly
Indexed: CLT&T.
Published by: Ohio State Grange, 121, Fredericktown, OH 43019-0121. Ed. Jim Grafton. Circ: 10,000 (controlled).

630 634.9 USA ISSN 0736-8003
OHIO STATE UNIVERSITY. AGRICULTURAL RESEARCH AND DEVELOPMENT CENTER, WOOSTER. SPECIAL CIRCULAR. Text in English. 1925. irreg., latest vol.156, 1996. free. bibl.; charts; illus. back issues avail. **Document type:** *Bulletin, Trade.* **Description:** In-depth, specialized examinations of individual topics in various disciplines of the agricultural sciences.
Indexed: AEA, AbHyg, AgBio, Agr, AgrForAb, AnBrAb, BioCN&I, CPA, CTFA, DSA, FCA, FPA, ForAb, HerbAb, HortAb, I&DA, IndVet, MaizeAb, NemAb, NutrAb, OrnHort, PBA, PGegResA, PGrRegA, PHN&I, PN&I, PoultAb, RA&MP, RPP, RiceAb, S&F, SIA, SeedAb, SoyAb, TriticAb, VetBull, WAE&RSA, WeedAb.
—BLDSC (8366.120000), CISTI, IE, ingenta, Linda Hall.
Published by: Ohio State University, Ohio Agricultural Research and Development Center, Wooster, 1680 Madison Ave, Wooster, OH 44691-4096. TEL 330-263-3775. Ed. Joy Ann Fischer. Circ: 2,500.

630 USA ISSN 1082-7854
OHIO'S COUNTRY JOURNAL. Text in English. 1992. m. USD 12 (effective 1999). adv.
Published by: Agri Communicators, Inc., 1625 Bethel Rd., Columbus, OH 43220-2071. TEL 614-481-6000, FAX 614-487-8205. Ed. Tim Reeves. Pub. Ed Johnson. Adv. contact Jill Davis. Circ: 16,100 (paid).

630 MYS ISSN 1511-7634
OIL PALM BULLETIN. Text in English. 1980. s-a. MYR 10 newsstand/cover (effective 2002). **Document type:** *Bulletin.*
Formerly: P O R I M Bulletin (0127-0249)
Indexed: AEA, AgBio, BioCN&I, CPA, DSA, FCA, FPA, HortAb, I&DA, NutrAb, PBA, PGrRegA, PHN&I, RDA, S&F, SIA, WAE&RSA.
—BLDSC (6252.207000), IE, ingenta.
Published by: Lembaga Minyak Sawit Malaysia/Malaysian Palm Oil Board (Subsidiary of: Kementerian Perusahaan Utama, Malaysia/Ministry of Primary Industries, Malaysia), PO Box 10620, Kuala Lumpur, 50720, Malaysia. TEL 60-3-89259155, 60-3-89259775, FAX 60-3-89259446, http://mpob.gov.my.

630 GBR
OILSEEDS AND INDUSTRIAL CROPS. Text in English. 1983. q. GBP 19. adv. **Document type:** *Trade.*
Formerly: Oilseeds (0265-0002)
Indexed: WAE&RSA.
Published by: Processors & Growers Research Organisation, 34 Cavendish Rd, London, NW6 7XP, United Kingdom. TEL 0181-459-5330. Ed. Herbert Daybell. Adv. contact Tony Smith. Circ: 12,000 (controlled).

630 FRA ISSN 0030-1523
OISE AGRICOLE. Text in French. 1915. w. adv. bk.rev.
Published by: Peasants Organizations, Rue Frere-Gagne, BP 463, Beauvais, Cedex 60021, France. FAX 44-89-45-50. Ed. A Devooght. Circ: 6,378.

630 JPN ISSN 0474-0254
CODEN: ODNGAM
OKAYAMA DAIGAKU NOGAKUBU GAKUJUTSU HOKOKU/OKAYAMA UNIVERSITY. FACULTY OF AGRICULTURE. SCIENTIFIC REPORTS. Text in Japanese. 1952. s-a.
Indexed: AgBio, AgrForAb, AnBrAb, CPA, DSA, FCA, FPA, ForAb, HerbAb, HortAb, I&DA, INIS AtomInd, MaizeAb, NemAb, OrnHort, PBA, PGegResA, PGrRegA, PHN&I, PN&I, RA&MP, RM&VM, S&F, SIA, SeedAb, SoyAb, TriticAb, WAE&RSA.
—BLDSC (8196.550000), IE.
Published by: Okayama Daigaku, Nogakubu/Okayama University, Faculty of Agriculture, 1-1-1 Tsushima-naka, Okayama, Japan. TEL 81-86-2521111, FAX 81-86-2528388, http://www.okayama-u.ac.jp/user/agr/.

630 USA ISSN 1544-6476
OKLAHOMA COUNTRY. Text in English. 1947. q. USD 15 to non-members; free to members (effective 2005). adv. 36 p./no. 3 cols./p.; back issues avail. **Document type:** *Magazine, Trade.* **Description:** Documents the impact of federal and state legislation on agricultural and rural areas.
Former titles (until 2003): Oklahoma Farm Bureau Journal (1091-921X); (until 1996): Farm Bureau Journal (1077-1859); (until 1989): Oklahoma Farm Bureau Farmer (0048-1599)
Related titles: Microfiche ed.
Published by: Oklahoma Farm Bureau, 2501 N Stiles, Oklahoma City, OK 73105. TEL 405-523-2300, FAX 405-523-2362, mikenichols@okfb.org, nicola_freeman@okfb.org, http://www.okfarmbureau.org. R&P, Adv. contact Mike Nichols TEL 405-523-2345. page USD 1,500; 9.375 x 9.75. Circ: 158,000 (paid and controlled).

OLEO REVISTA. see *FOOD AND FOOD INDUSTRIES*

630 ZAF ISSN 0259-9341
ONS EIE. Text in Afrikaans, English. 1965. bi-m. membership. adv. charts; illus.; mkt.; tr.lit. back issues avail. **Document type:** *Newsletter, Trade.* **Description:** Covers agricultural and related topics, as well as news of the company.
Published by: Suidwes Investments Ltd./Suitwes Beleggings Beperk, PO Box 5, Leeudoringstad, 2660, South Africa. TEL 27-53-115-78, FAX 27-53-831-2370, adrit@admin.Suidwes.co.za. Ed., R&P, Adv. contact Adri Theron. B&W page ZAR 2,750, color page ZAR 3,850; trim 210 x 297. Circ: 8,000 (controlled). **Subscr. to:** PO Box 150, Kimberley 8300, South Africa.

631 CAN
ONTARIO FARMER. Text in English. 1968. w. CND 35. **Document type:** *Trade.*
Formed by the merger of: Ontario Farmer (Eastern Edition) (0831-3873); Which was formerly: Eastern Ontario Farmer (0380-0067); Ontario Farmer (Western Edition) (0831-3865); Which was formerly: Western Ontario Farmer (0049-7460)
Indexed: SSA.
—CISTI.
Published by: Bowes Publishers Ltd., PO Box 7400, London, ON N5Y 4X3, Canada. TEL 519-473-0010, FAX 519-473-2256. Ed. Paul Mahon. Pub. Mervyn J Hawkins. Circ: 35,398.

630 CAN
ONTARIO. MINISTRY OF AGRICULTURE, FOOD AND RURAL AFFAIRS. AGRI-FOOD TRADE UPDATE. Text in English. q. free. **Document type:** *Government.*
Formerly: Ontario. Ministry of Agriculture and Food. Agri-Food Trade Update (1183-1588)
—CISTI.
Published by: Ministry of Agriculture, Food and Rural Affairs (Toronto), Policy Analysis Branch, Legislative Bldg, Queen s Park, Toronto, ON M7A 2B2, Canada. TEL 416-326-3210, FAX 416-326-9892.

630 CAN
ONTARIO. MINISTRY OF AGRICULTURE, FOOD AND RURAL ANALYSIS. AGRI-FOOD OUTLOOK AND POLICY REVIEW. Text in English. bi-m. charts; stat. **Document type:** *Newsletter.*
Formerly: Ontario. Ministry of Agriculture and Food. Agri-Food Outlook and Policy Review (1180-2936)
—CISTI.
Published by: Ministry of Agriculture, Food and Rural Analysis (Toronto), Policy Analysis Branch, Legislative Bldg, Queen s Park, Toronto, ON M7A 2B2, Canada. TEL 416-326-3210, FAX 416-326-9892. Ed. Martin Jaeger.

635 NLD ISSN 1566-2616
OOGST LANDBOUW; landbouw weekblad. Text in Dutch. 1988. w. (49/yr.). EUR 105.40 (effective 2005). adv. bk.rev. illus. Supplement avail. **Document type:** *Magazine, Trade.*
Supersedes in part (in 1998): Oogst (0923-0769); Which incorporated (1946-1987): Boer en Tuinder (0006-5609)
Related titles: Regional ed(s).: Westweek. ISSN 0929-8290; G L T O Nieuws. ISSN 1389-8140; Zuidland; Land & Vee.
Indexed: ELLIS.
—IE.
Published by: (Land- en Tuinbouw Organisatie Nederland), Stichting AgriPers, Postbus 29745, The Hague, 2502 LS, Netherlands. TEL 31-70-3382888, FAX 31-70-3382844, info@agripers.nl, http://www.agripers.nl. Circ: 59,536.

635 NLD ISSN 1566-2624
OOGST TUINBOUW; tuinbouw weekblad. Text in Dutch. 1988. w. (49/yr.). EUR 105.40 (effective 2005). adv. bk.rev. illus. **Document type:** *Magazine, Consumer.*
Supersedes in part (in 1998): Oogst (0923-0769); Which incorporated (1946-1987): Boer en Tuinder (0006-5609)
Related titles: Supplement(s): Oogst Plus voor de Sierteelt.
—IE.
Published by: (Land- en Tuinbouw Organisatie Nederland), Stichting AgriPers, Postbus 29745, The Hague, 2502 LS, Netherlands. TEL 31-70-3382888, FAX 31-70-3382844, info@agripers.nl, http://www.agripers.nl. Circ: 12,341.

630 IND
OOSAMALA. Text in Marathi. m.
Published by: V.S. Kane Ed. & Pub., White House Tilak Rd., Pune, Maharashtra 411 030, India. Circ: 2,000.

630 FRA ISSN 1016-121X
S5
OPTIONS MEDITERRANEENNES. SERIE A: SEMINAIRES MEDITERRANEENS. Text in French, English. 1963. irreg., latest vol.44, 2001. adv. bk.rev. abstr.; bibl.; charts; illus. **Document type:** *Monographic series, Academic/Scholarly.*
Supersedes in part (in 1989): Options Mediterraneennes. Serie Etudes (0253-1542); Which was formerly (until 1981): Options Mediterraneennes (0025-8261); Mediterranea
Indexed: AbHyg, AgBio, AgrForAb, AnBrAb, CPA, DSA, FCA, ForAb, HelmAb, HerbAb, HortAb, I&DA, IndVet, MaizeAb, NemAb, NutrAb, OrnHort, PBA, PGegResA, PGrRegA, PHN&I, PN&I, RA&MP, RM&VM, RPP, RRTA, RevApplEntom, S&F, S&MA, SIA, SeedAb, SoyAb, TDB, TriticAb, VetBull, WAE&RSA, WeedAb.
—CISTI.
Published by: Centre International de Hautes Etudes Agronomiques Mediterraneennes, Institut Agronomique Mediterraneen de Montpellier/International Centre for Advanced Mediterranean Agronomic Studies, 3191 route de Mende, Montpellier Cedex 5, 34093, France. TEL 33-4-67046000, FAX 33-4-67542527, TELEX 58672 IAMZ E, http://www.iamm.fr. Ed. Mr. Chioccioli. Pub. Mr. Lerin. Circ: 500.

630 FRA ISSN 1016-1228
OPTIONS MEDITERRANEENNES. SERIE B: ETUDES ET RECHERCHES. Text in French, English. 1963. irreg., latest vol.34, 2001. **Document type:** *Monographic series, Academic/Scholarly.*
Supersedes in part (in 1989): Options Mediterraneennes. Serie Etudes (0253-1542); Which was formerly (until 1981): Options Mediterraneennes (0025-8261); Mediterranea
Indexed: AEA, AgrForAb, AnBrAb, DSA, ForAb, HerbAb, HortAb, IndVet, MaizeAb, NutrAb, PBA, PGegResA, PotatoAb, RPP, RRTA, RevApplEntom, RiceAb, SeedAb, SoyAb, TriticAb, VetBull, WAE&RSA.
—CISTI.
Published by: Centre International de Hautes Etudes Agronomiques Mediterraneennes, Institut Agronomique Mediterraneen de Montpellier/International Centre for Advanced Mediterranean Agronomic Studies, 3191 route de Mende, Montpellier Cedex 5, 34093, France. TEL 33-4-67046000, FAX 33-4-67542527. Ed. Mr. Chioccioli. Pub. Mr. Lerin. Circ: 500.

630 NLD ISSN 0030-4239
ORANG PELADANG. Text in Dutch. 1912. bi-m. adv. **Document type:** *Academic/Scholarly.*
Published by: Deventer Landbouwers Vereniging Nji Sri, Postbus 27, Deventer, Netherlands. Ed. Robert van Donk. Circ: 750.

630 USA ISSN 0162-5179
OREGON FARM BUREAU NEWS. Text in English. 1948. s-m. free to members (effective 2005). adv. **Document type:** *Newsletter, Trade.*
Published by: Oregon Farm Bureau Federation, 3415 Commercial St, S E, Ste G, Salem, OR 97302-4668. TEL 503-399-1701, FAX 503-399-8082, http://www.oregonfb.org. Eds. Anne Marie Moss, Dave Dillon. R&P Dave Dillon. Circ: 11,000 (controlled).

630 USA ISSN 0030-4697
OREGON GRANGE BULLETIN. Text in English. 1900. m. USD 15 to non-members; free to members (effective 2005). adv. bk.rev. illus. **Document type:** *Bulletin, Consumer.*
Related titles: Online - full content ed.
Published by: Oregon State Grange, 643 Union St, NE, Salem, OR 97301-2462. TEL 503-316-0106, FAX 503-316-0109, gbulletin@grange.com, osgrange@grange.org, http://www.grange.org/Oregon/bulletin/, http://www.grange.org/Oregon/index.php. Eds. Chris Rea, John Fine. adv.: page USD 770. Circ: 16,000 (paid and free).

630 635 333.72 GBR ISSN 1464-1224
ORGANIC FARMING; Soil Association's journal for organic horticulture & agriculture. Text in English. 1983. q. GBP 15 domestic to individuals; GBP 17 foreign to individuals; GBP 18 domestic to institutions; USD 20 foreign to institutions; GBP 3.95 newsstand/cover (effective 2002). adv. bk.rev. illus.; mkt.; stat.; tr.lit. cum.index. back issues avail. **Document type:** *Newsletter, Trade.* **Description:** Provides technical information, news, and commentary on the principles, practice, and politics of organic farming and growing.
Formerly (until 1998): New Farmer and Grower (0952-1402)
Indexed: AEA, DSA, EPB, FCA, GardL, IndVet, PHN&I, RPP, S&F, WAE&RSA.
—BLDSC (6287.585000), IE, ingenta.
Published by: Soil Association, 40-56 Victoria St, Bristol, BS1 6BY, United Kingdom. TEL 44-117-929-0661, FAX 44-117-925-2504, soilassoc@gn.apc.org, http://www.soilassociation.org. Ed. Peter Mundy TEL 44-117-914-2416. Adv. contact Martin Trowell TEL 44-117-914-2446. B&W page GBP 260, color page GBP 500; trim 270 x 180. Circ: 5,500 (paid).

ORGANIC GROWING (ULVERSTONE). see *GARDENING AND HORTICULTURE*

630 GBR ISSN 1473-8392
ORGANIC LIFE. Text in English. 2001. bi-m. GBP 14.99 (effective 2004).
Address: Aldbury House, Dower Mews, Berkhamsted, Herts, HP4 2BL, United Kingdom.

630 USA
ORGANIC NEWS; working to promote organic farming and gardening in New Jersey. Variant title: N O F A - N J's Organic News. Text in English. q. free membership (effective 2004). adv. 12 p./no.; **Document type:** *Newsletter.*
Description: Discusses the association's activities and profiles members.
Published by: Northeast Organic Farming Association of New Jersey, 60 S. Main St., Pennington, NJ 08334. TEL 609-737-6848, FAX 609-737-2366, nofainfo@nofanj.org, http://www.nofanj.org, http://www.nofanj.org/. Ed., Adv. contact Mike Zazzara. page USD 85. Circ: 500 (paid).

630 USA
ORGANIC PERSPECTIVES. Text in English. bi-m. **Document type:** *Newsletter, Government.* **Description:** Contains reports on organics from around the world and covers items of interest about the U.S. national organic program and the domestic organic industry, including a list of upcoming conferences, trade shows and other events.
Related titles: Online - full content ed.
Published by: U.S. Department of Agriculture, Foreign Agricultural Service, AgExport Services, 1400 Independence Ave SW, Washington, DC 20250-1051. info@fas.usda.gov, http://www.fas.usda.gov/agx/organics/newsletter.htm. Ed. Angela Thomas TEL 202-720-1533.

ORGANIC PRODUCTS RETAILER. see *FOOD AND FOOD INDUSTRIES*

631 USA
ORNAMENTAL CROPS NATIONAL MARKET TRENDS. Text in English. 1968. w. looseleaf. USD 96; USD 192 foreign. back issues avail. **Document type:** *Newsletter, Government.*
Description: Offers news briefs on production projections, price ranges, available supplies, and trading activity for decorative greens and cut flowers throughout the United States with lists of imports from abroad.
Published by: (U.S. Department of Agriculture), Federal-State Market News Service (Sacramento), 630 Sansome St, Rm 727, San Francisco, CA 94111. TEL 415-705-1300, FAX 415-705-1301. Circ: 175.

630 NZL
OTAGO SOUTHLAND FARMER. Text in English. fortn.
Document type: *Newspaper, Consumer.*
Published by: Southland Times Co Ltd, 67 Esk St, P.O. Box 805, Invercargill, New Zealand. TEL 64-3-418-1115, FAX 64-3-418-1173, newspapersales@stl.co.nz. Ed., R&P Charmaine Dillon TEL 64-3-2181909. Adv. contact Ragwyn Williamson. Circ: 19,132.

630 GBR ISSN 0030-7270
CODEN: OUAGA8
➤ **OUTLOOK ON AGRICULTURE**; an international review of agricultural science, economics and policy. Text in English. 1956. q. USD 342 combined subscription in United States to institutions print & online eds.; EUR 346 combined subscription to institutions in the Eurozone; print & online eds.; GBP 225 combined subscription elsewhere to institutions print & online eds. (effective 2005). bibl.; charts; illus.; abstr. index. back issues avail. **Document type:** *Journal, Academic/Scholarly.* **Description:** Contains scientific and economic analysis of current developments in agricultural science.
Related titles: Online - full text ed.: 2000 (from EBSCO Publishing, Gale Group, IngentaConnect, Swets Information Services).
Indexed: AEA, ASCA, AgBio, Agr, AgrForAb, AnBrAb, BIOSIS Prev, BibAg, BioCN&I, BiolAb, CPA, ChemAb, CurCont, DBA, DSA, EIA, EnerInd, FCA, FS&TA, ForAb, HerbAb, HortAb, I&DA, IBSS, ISR, IndVet, MaizeAb, NemAb, NutrAb, OrnHort, PBA, PGegResA, PHN&I, PN&I, PotatoAb, PoultAb, RA&MP, RDA, RM&VM, RPP, RRTA, RevApplEntom, RiceAb, S&F, SCI, SIA, SSCI, SeedAb, SoyAb, TDB, TriticAb, VetBull, WAE&RSA, WeedAb.
—BLDSC (6314.500000), CASDDS, CISTI, IE, Infotrieve, ingenta, Linda Hall. **CCC.**
Published by: I P Publishing Ltd., Coleridge House, 4-5 Coleridge Gardens, London, NW6 3HQ, United Kingdom. TEL 44-20-7372-2600, FAX 44-20-7372-2253, JEdmondIP@aol.com, http://www.ippublishing.com/general_agriculture.htm. Ed. David Lister. R&P John Edmondson. **Subscr. to:** Extenza - Turpin, Pegasus Dr, Stratton Business Park, Biggleswade, Beds SG18 8TQ, United Kingdom.

630 ITA ISSN 1593-8697
P A. PREVIDENZA AGRICOLA; mensile ENPAIA. Text in Italian. 1951. m. free to members. bk.rev. charts; illus.; stat.
Document type: *Magazine, Government.*
Formerly (until 1987): Previdenza Agricola (0032-8057)
Published by: Ente Nazionale di Previdenza e di Assistenza per gli Impiegati dell'Agricoltura, Viale Beethoven 48, Rome, 00144, Italy. TEL 39-06-54581, FAX 39-06-5926295, http://www.enpaia.it. Ed. Donato De Leonardis. Circ: 25,000.

630 PHL ISSN 0116-3140
THE P C A R R D MONITOR. Text in English. 1973. q. free. bk.rev. **Document type:** *Newsletter, Government.*
Formerly (until 1982): Philippine Council for Agriculture, Forestry, and National Resources Research and Development. Monitor (0115-0529)
Indexed: FCA, HerbAb, HortAb, IPP, NutrAb, PBA, RDA, RRTA, RevApplEntom, RiceAb, WAE&RSA.
—CISTI.
Published by: Philippine Council for Agriculture Forestry and Natural Resources Research and Development, Los Banos, Laguna 4030, Philippines. FAX 63-49-536-0016, TELEX 40860 PARRS PM, pcarrd@pcarrd.dost.gov.ph, http://www.pcarrd.dost.gov.ph. Ed. Erinda H Belen. Circ: 4,000.

338.1 USA
P D A TODAY. (Pennsylvania Department of Agriculture) Text in English. 1915. q. free. **Document type:** *Newsletter, Government.*
Former titles (until Dec. 1998): Pennsylvania Agriculture News (1043-6235); (until Dec. 1989): Agriculture News Bulletin
Published by: Department of Agriculture, 2301 N Cameron St, Harrisburg, PA 17110-9408. TEL 717-787-5085, FAX 717-787-1039, jbucher@state.pa.us, http://www.pda.state.pa.us. Ed. Jasmine Bucher. Circ: 7,000.

630 IND ISSN 0378-813X
P K V RESEARCH JOURNAL. (Punjabrao Krishi Vidyapeeth) Text in English. 1972. s-a. INR 75 to non-members; INR 50 to members. **Document type:** *Academic/Scholarly.* **Description:** Devoted to research in the field of agricultural sciences. Contains original research, research notes and review papers.
Indexed: AEA, ASFA, AgrForAb, AnBrAb, BIOSIS Prev, BioCN&I, CPA, DSA, ESPM, EntAb, FCA, FPA, ForAb, HelmAb, HerbAb, HortAb, I&DA, IndVet, MaizeAb, NutrAb, OrnHort, PBA, PGegResA, PGrRegA, PHN&I, PollutAb, PotatoAb, PoultAb, RA&MP, RDA, RM&VM, RPP, RevApplEntom, RiceAb, S&F, SIA, SeedAb, SoyAb, TriticAb, VetBull, WAE&RSA, WeedAb, ZooRec.
Published by: Agricultural University, Akola, Maharashtra 444 104, India. TEL 58419, TELEX 0725-215 PKV IN. Ed. R S Bonde.

630 338.91 GBR ISSN 1357-938X
P L A NOTES. (Participatory Learning and Action) Text in English. 1988. 3/yr. GBP 20, USD 30 (effective 2001). bk.rev.; Website rev. back issues avail. **Document type:** *Academic/Scholarly.*
Description: Enables practitioners of participatory methodologies throughout the world to share their field experiences, conceptual reflections and methodological innovations.
Formerly: R R A Notes
Indexed: AgrForAb, RDA, RevApplEntom, RiceAb, TDB, WAE&RSA, WeedAb.
—BLDSC (6506.505000).
Published by: (Sustainable Agriculture Programme), International Institute for Environment and Development, 3 Endsleigh St, London, WC1H ODD, United Kingdom. TEL 44-20-73882117, FAX 44-20-73882826, sustag@iied.org, info@iied.org, http://www.iied.org/resource/. Circ: 600 (paid); 1,700 (controlled).

630 MYS ISSN 0127-2209
TP684.P3
P O R I M OCCASIONAL PAPER. Text in English. 1982. irreg., latest vol.39, 1998. MYR 10 per issue (effective 2000).
Document type: *Monographic series, Academic/Scholarly.*
Indexed: RDA, S&F.
—BLDSC (6554.515000).
Published by: Lembaga Minyak Sawit Malaysia/Malaysian Palm Oil Board (Subsidiary of: Kementerian Perusahaan Utama, Malaysia/Ministry of Primary Industries, Malaysia), PO Box 10620, Kuala Lumpur, 50720, Malaysia. TEL 60-3-89259155, 60-3-89259775, FAX 60-3-89259446, http://mpob.gov.my/summary_paper.htm.

630 PHL ISSN 0117-522X
PACIFIC JOURNAL OF SCIENCE AND TECHNOLOGY. Text in English. 1965. s-a. PHP 100, USD 25 (effective 2000). bk.rev. back issues avail. **Description:** Publishes original scientific reports of experiments on any field of study geared toward rural development in the tropical setting, particularly the Pacific Basin.
Formerly (until 1992): Researcher (0048-7341)
Media: Duplicated (not offset).
Published by: University of Eastern Philippines, Research Center, University Town, Northern Samar, 6400, Philippines. Ed. Julita R Calonge. Circ: 3,000.

PADDESTOELEN; onafhankelijke vakkrant voor Nederland en België. see *GARDENING AND HORTICULTURE*

633.51 PAK ISSN 0030-9699
PAKISTAN COTTONS. Text in English. 1958. q. PKR 26. adv. charts; illus.; stat. index.
Supersedes: Pakistan Cotton Bulletin (0479-2327)
Indexed: CTFA, ChemAb, FCA, HerbAb, I&DA, PBA, S&F, SeedAb, TTI.
Published by: Pakistan Central Cotton Committee, c/o Secretary, Moulvi Tamizuddin Khan Rd., Karachi 1, Pakistan. TEL 524104-6. Ed. S Zain Idris Mirza.

PAKISTAN. FOOD AND AGRICULTURE DIVISION. AGRICULTURAL STATISTICS OF PAKISTAN. see *AGRICULTURE—Abstracting, Bibliographies, Statistics*

630 PAK ISSN 0251-0480
CODEN: PJARDC
PAKISTAN JOURNAL OF AGRICULTURAL RESEARCH. Text in English. 1949. q. PKR 60. adv. abstr.; charts; illus. reprint service avail. from PQC. **Document type:** *Academic/Scholarly.*
Former titles: Journal of Agricultural Research (0368-1157); West Pakistan Journal of Agricultural Research (0043-3179); Agriculture Pakistan (0002-1776)
Related titles: Microform ed.: (from PQC).
Indexed: AEA, AgBio, AnBrAb, B&AI, BibAg, BioCN&I, BiolAb, CIN, CPA, CTFA, ChemAb, ChemTitl, DSA, FCA, FS&TA, HerbAb, HortAb, I&DA, INIS AtomInd, IndVet, MaizeAb, NutrAb, PBA, PGegResA, PGrRegA, PHN&I, PotatoAb, PoultAb, RA&MP, RDA, RM&VM, RPP, RRTA, RevApplEntom, RiceAb, S&F, S&MA, SIA, SeedAb, SoyAb, TOSA, TriticAb, VetBull, WAE&RSA, WeedAb, ZooRec.
—CASDDS, CISTI, Linda Hall.
Published by: Pakistan Agricultural Research Council, Plot 20, G-5-1, P O Box 1031, Islamabad, Pakistan. Ed. Sabiha Amin. Circ: 1,000.

630 PAK ISSN 0552-9034
S471.P16
PAKISTAN JOURNAL OF AGRICULTURAL SCIENCES. Text in English. 1965. q. USD 50 (effective 1999 & 2000). adv. bk.rev.
Document type: *Academic/Scholarly.*
Indexed: AEA, AgBio, AgrForAb, AnBrAb, ApicAb, BioCN&I, BiolAb, CPA, ChemAb, DSA, FCA, FPA, ForAb, HerbAb, HortAb, I&DA, IndVet, MaizeAb, NutrAb, OrnHort, PBA, PGegResA, PGrRegA, PHN&I, PotatoAb, PoultAb, RDA, RPP, RRTA, RevApplEntom, RiceAb, S&F, SIA, SeedAb, SoyAb, TDB, TriticAb, VetBull, WAE&RSA, WeedAb, ZooRec.
—BLDSC (6340.894600), IE, ingenta.
Published by: University of Agriculture, Dept. of Livestock Management, Faisalabad, Pakistan. Ed. Bakht Baidar Khan.
Co-sponsor: Capricorn Computers.

630 PAK ISSN 1023-1072
SB610
PAKISTAN JOURNAL OF AGRICULTURE, AGRICULTURAL ENGINEERING AND VETERINARY SCIENCES. Text in English. 1985. s-a. adv. back issues avail. **Document type:** *Journal, Academic/Scholarly.* **Description:** Original research papers in agricultural and veterinary sciences, including agricultural engineering.
Published by: Sindh Agriculture University, Tandojam, 70050, Pakistan. TEL 92-2233-5869, FAX 92-2233-5300. Ed., R&P Dr. Bherulal Devrajani TEL 92-2233-5460. Circ: 1,000.

630 AUT
DIE PALETTE; Monatsmagazin fuer Geld & Leben. Text in German. m. EUR 30 (effective 2004). adv. **Document type:** *Magazine, Consumer.*
Published by: Oesterreichischer Agrarverlag GmbH, Achauer Str 49a, Leopoldsdorf, N 2333, Austria. TEL 43-2235-4040, FAX 43-2235-404929, office@agrarverlag.at, http://www.agrarverlag.at. Eds. Kurt Quendler, Margret Oberhofer. adv.: B&W page EUR 2,270, color page EUR 4,020; trim 175 x 260. Circ: 30,000 (paid and controlled).

630 MYS ISSN 0127-3329
HD9490.5.P34
PALM OIL DEVELOPMENTS. Text in English. 1984. s-a. MYR 10 per issue (effective 2000). **Document type:** *Academic/Scholarly.*
Indexed: AbHyg, DSA, HortAb, NutrAb, SoyAb, WAE&RSA.
—BLDSC (6345.562095).
Published by: Lembaga Minyak Sawit Malaysia/Malaysian Palm Oil Board (Subsidiary of: Kementerian Perusahaan Utama, Malaysia/Ministry of Primary Industries, Malaysia), PO Box 10620, Kuala Lumpur, 50720, Malaysia. TEL 60-3-89259775, FAX 60-3-89259446, http://mpob.gov.my/homepage96/podev.html.

630 PAN
PANAMA. INSTITUTO DE INVESTIGACION AGROPECUARIA. INFORME ANUAL. Text in Spanish. 1976. a.
Published by: Instituto de Investigacion Agropecuaria de Panama, Centro de Informacion Documental Agropecuaria, Apdo. 6-4391, El Dorado, Panama City, 6a, Panama. Ed. Tomas Noriega.

630 PAN
PANAMA. INSTITUTO DE INVESTIGACION AGROPECUARIA. MEMORIA. FORO NACIONAL DE INFORMACION DOCUMENTAL. Text in Spanish. 1980. a.
Formerly: Panama. Instituto de Investigacion Agropecuaria. Memoria. Reunion Panamena de Informacion Agricola

Published by: Instituto de Investigacion Agropecuaria de Panama, Centro de Informacion Documental Agropecuaria, Apdo. 6-4391, El Dorado, Panama City, 6a, Panama. Ed. Vielka Chang Yau. Circ: 300. **Co-sponsor:** Grupo Panameno de Informacion Agricola.

630 IND
PANTNAGAR NEWS. Text in English. q. (a. also avail.).
Published by: G. B. Pant University of Agriculture and Technology, C/o Dr. K.K. Singh, O.I.C Telecom Unit, Pantnagar, Udhamsingh Nagar, Uttaranchal 263 145, India. TEL 91-5944-33671, FAX 91-5944-33473, kks@gbpuat.ernet.in, http://www.gbpuat.ac.in.

630 PNG ISSN 0256-954X
CODEN: PNGFEZ
➤ **PAPUA NEW GUINEA JOURNAL OF AGRICULTURE, FORESTRY AND FISHERIES.** Text in English. 1935. a. PGK 37 domestic; PGK 40 foreign (effective 2002). bk.rev. abstr.; charts; illus. cum.index. back issues avail. **Document type:** *Academic/Scholarly.* **Description:** Publishes research papers on primary industry subjects.
Former titles (until 1984): Papua New Guinea Agricultural Journal (0031-1464); (until 1954): Papua and New Guinea Agriculture Gazette (0370-078X); (until 1941): New Guinea Agricultural Gazette (0369-3716)
Indexed: ASFA, BiolAb, ChemAb, CurCont, DSA, FCA, FPA, ForAb, HerbAb, HortAb, IndVet, NutrAb, PoultAb, RPP, RRTA, RevApplEntom, RiceAb, S&F, SFA, WAE&RSA, ZooRec.
—BLDSC (6404.513450), CASDDS.
Published by: Department of Agriculture and Livestock, Publication Section, PO Box 417, Konedobu NCD, Papua New Guinea. TEL 675-320-2886, FAX 675-320-2883, dalit@daltron.com.pg. Ed. Chris Dekuku. Circ: 300 (paid).

638.1 RUS
PASEKA. Text in Russian. m. USD 99.95 in United States.
Published by: Rospchelovodsoyuz, Leninskii Prospekt 20, Moscow, 117071, Russian Federation. TEL 7-095-2509443, FAX 7-095-9542266. Ed. I I Khutornyi. **US dist. addr.:** East View Information Services, 3020 Harbor Ln. N., Minneapolis, MN 55447. TEL 612-550-0961.

630 COL ISSN 1012-7410
PASTURAS TROPICALES. Text in English, French, Portuguese, Spanish; Summaries in English, Spanish. 1979. 3/yr. COP 18,000 domestic; USD 50 in developing nations (effective 2001). **Description:** Accumulates scientific articles, research notes and comments about pasture research in the tropics.
Former titles: Pasturas Tropicales. Boletin; Pastos Tropicales. Boletin Informativo (0120-1484)
Indexed: AgrForAb, BioCN&I, CPA, DSA, FCA, ForAb, HerbAb, HortAb, MaizeAb, NemAb, NutrAb, PBA, PGegResA, PHN&I, RDA, RPP, RevApplEntom, RiceAb, S&F, SIA, SeedAb, SoyAb, WAE&RSA, WeedAb.
Published by: (Unidad de Comunicaciones), Centro Internacional de Agricultura Tropical/International Center for Tropical Agriculture, Publications Unit, Apartado Aereo 6713, Cali, VALLE, Colombia. TEL 57-2-4450000, FAX 57-2-4450073, ciat-comunicaciones@cgiar.org, http://www.ciat.cgiar.org/. Ed. Alberto Ramirez. Circ: 700.

630 FRA ISSN 1145-6639
PAYSAN BRETON (EDITION COTES-DU-NORD). Text in French. 1945. w.
Supersedes in part (in 1961): Paysan Breton (0996-1615)
Published by: Paysan Breton, BP 224, Plerin, 22192, France.

630 FRA ISSN 1145-6620
PAYSAN BRETON (EDITION FINISTERE). Text in French. 1945. w. **Document type:** *Magazine, Trade.*
Supersedes in part (in 1961): Paysan Breton (0996-1615)
Published by: Paysan Breton, BP 224, Plerin, 22192, France.

630 FRA ISSN 1156-8461
PAYSAN BRETON (EDITION MORBIHAN). Text in French. w.
Published by: Paysan Breton, BP 224, Plerin, 22192, France. Ed. M Gouerou. Circ: 80,910.

630 FRA
PAYSAN D'AUVERGNE. Text in French. w.
Published by: Maison des Paysans, R.N. 89, Marmilhat, 63370, France. TEL 73-91-23-33. Ed. Herve de Puytorac. Circ: 10,166.

630 FRA ISSN 1148-7488
PAYSAN DU MIDI. Text in French. 1946. w. **Document type:** *Newspaper.*
Address: Parc Marcel Dessault, 4 rue Jacqueline Auriol, St Jean de Vedas, 34430, France. TEL 33-04-67070366, FAX 33-04-67070371. Ed. M Ponce. Circ: 12,000.

630 FRA ISSN 0755-7027
PAYSAN LORRAIN. Text in French. 1946. 50/yr.
Address: 5 rue de la Vologne, Laxou, Cedex 54524, France. TEL 83-96-51-16, FAX 83-96-31-50. Ed. Jean Luc Masson. Circ: 4,000.

630 FRA ISSN 0221-0037
PAYSAN MORBIHANNAIS. Text in French. 1946. 24/yr.
Address: B.P. 183, Vannes, 56000, France. Circ: 14,714.

630 FRA ISSN 0181-8880
PAYSAN SAVOYARD. Text in French. 1945. 22/yr.
Address: 52 av. des Iles, BP 327, Annecy, Cedex 74037, France. TEL 50-52-82-40. Circ: 6,000.

630 FRA
PAYSAN TARNAIS LA MILLIASOLLE. Text in French. w.
Address: BP 42, Albi, Cedex 81002, France. TEL 63-54-39-81, FAX 63-47-09-87. Ed. Pierre Chavanon. Circ: 7,850.

630 FRA ISSN 0241-9092
PAYSAN VOSGIEN. Text in French. 1946. w.
Address: La Colombiere, Rue Andre Vith, Epinal, Cedex 88025, France. TEL 29-33-01-23. Circ: 3,630.

630 FRA ISSN 1245-0855
PAYSANS DE LA LOIRE. Text in French. 1945. w.
Published by: Paysans de la, 43 av. Albert Raimond, BP 50, Saint-Priest-en-Jarez, Cedex 42272, France. TEL 77-79-15-22, FAX 77-79-17-82. Ed. Erick Roizard. Circ: 11,286.

638.1 HRV ISSN 0031-3416
PCELA. Text in Croatian. 1881. m. index.
Indexed: ApicAb.
Published by: Pcelarski Savez Hrvatske, 8 Maja 1945, 26, Zagreb, 41000, Croatia. TEL (041) 272-383. Ed. Koviljka Majnaric. **Co-sponsor:** Savez Pcelara Bosne i Hercegovine.

638.1 RUS ISSN 0369-8629
PCHELOVODSTVO. Text in Russian. 1921. bi-m. USD 82 (effective 1998).
Indexed: ApicAb, BiolAb, ForAb, RASB, RefZh, SIA.
—CISTI, East View.
Published by: Izdatel'stvo Kolos, Sadovaya-Spasskaya 18, Moscow, 107807, Russian Federation. TEL 7-095-2072125, FAX 7-095-2072870. Ed. Irina Yu Vereshchaka. Circ: 88,000. **Dist. by:** M K - Periodica, ul Gilyarovskogo 39, Moscow 129110, Russian Federation. TEL 7-095-2845008, FAX 7-095-2813798, info@periodicals.ru, http://www.mkniga.ru; **Dist. in U.S. by:** Victor Kamkin Inc., 220 Girard St, Ste 1, Gaithersburg, MD 20877.

630 GBR
PEA & BEAN PROGRESS. Text in English. 1982. 3/yr. adv. **Document type:** *Trade.*
Former titles: Vegetable Grower (0264-8857); (until 1982): Processors and Growers Research Organisation. News Letter (0308-2504); (until 1973): Pea Growers Research Organisation. News Letter
Indexed: FCA, HortAb, PBA, RPP.
Published by: Processors & Growers Research Organisation, 34 Cavendish Rd, London, NW6 7XP, United Kingdom. TEL 0181-459-5330. Ed. Herbert Daybell. Adv. contact Tony Smith. Circ: 5,500.

630 USA ISSN 0889-5929
PENN STATE AGRICULTURE. Text in English. 1953. s-a. free (effective 2002). illus. 36 p./no. 3 cols./p.; back issues avail. **Document type:** *Magazine, Consumer.*
Supersedes (1968-1984): Science in Agriculture (0048-9670)
Related titles: Online - full content ed.
Indexed: Agr, BiolAb, BiolDig, ExcerpMed, FCA, HerbAb, HortAb, IndVet, NutrAb, RPP, RRTA, S&F, VetBull, WAE&RSA.
—Linda Hall.
Published by: Pennsylvania State University, Agricultural Experiment Station, Agricultural Administration Bldg, University Park, PA 16802. TEL 814-865-4700, ecm3@psu.edu, http://aginfo.psu.edu/psa, http://www.cas.psu.edu. Ed., R&P Eston Martz TEL 814-863-3587. Circ: 24,000.

630 USA ISSN 0031-4471
S1
PENNSYLVANIA FARMER. Text in English. 1877. 12/yr. USD 19.95. adv. bk.rev. charts; illus.; stat.; tr.lit.
Published by: Farm Progress Companies, 191 S Gary Ave, Carol Stream, IL 60188. TEL 630-690-5600, FAX 630-462-2869. Ed. John Vogel. adv.: B&W page USD 3,300, color page USD 4,620; trim 10 x 7. Circ: 40,738; 38,699 (paid).

630 USA ISSN 0891-6705
PENNSYLVANIA STATE UNIVERSITY. AGRICULTURAL EXTENSION SERVICE. CIRCULAR. Text in English. 1953. irreg. **Document type:** *Monographic series.*
Indexed: Agr.
Published by: Pennsylvania State University, Agricultural Extension Service, 112 Agricultural Administration Bldg, University Park, PA 16802-2602. TEL 814-865-6713, 877-345-0691, FAX 814-863-5560, agpubsdist@psu.edu, http://pubs.cas.psu.edu/catalog.html.

630 ITA ISSN 1120-2955
PERITO AGRARIO. Text in Italian. 1953. 6/yr. EUR 5 (effective 2005). adv. **Document type:** *Magazine, Trade.*
Published by: (Collegio Nazionale dei Periti Agrari), Iacico Srl, Via Angelo Poliziano 80, Rome, 00184, Italy. TEL 39-06-4873183, FAX 39-06-4873144, www.iacico@networld.it. Ed. Piero Pecciarini. Circ: 12,000 (paid).

630 712 USA ISSN 0897-7348
THE PERMACULTURE ACTIVIST. Text in English. 1985. 4/yr., latest vol.46, 2001. USD 23 in North America; USD 36 elsewhere (effective 2004). adv. bk.rev. Alternative Press Index. 68 p./no.; back issues avail. **Document type:** *Magazine, Trade.* **Description:** Propounds the four-point ethic of permaculture: care of the earth, care of people, distribution of surplus to assist others, and limiting of consumption and describes a design system for landscape and human settlements.
Indexed: AltPI, EPB, GardL.
Published by: The Permaculture Activist, PO Box 1209, Black Mountain, NC 28711-1209. TEL 828-669-6336, FAX 828-669-5068, pcactivist@mindspring.com, pcactiv@metalab.unc.edu, Http://www.permacultureactivist.net, http://metalab.unc.edu/pc-activist. Ed., Pub. Peter Bane. Adv. contact Keith Johnson. Circ: 5,000 (paid).

630 NLD ISSN 0031-5869
PERSOVERZICHT. Text in Dutch. 1955. fortn. index. 20 p./no.; **Document type:** *Newsletter.*
Published by: Hoofdproductschap voor Akkerbouw, Stadhoudersplantsoen 12, The Hague, Netherlands. TEL 31-70-3708319, 31-70-3708708, FAX 31-70-3708444, voorlichting@hpa.agro.nl, http://www.hpa.ul. Ed. H R Mulder. Circ: 260.

630 FRA ISSN 0399-8533
CODEN: CBLKAE
PERSPECTIVES AGRICOLES. Text in French. 11/yr. adv.
—BLDSC (6428.137400), CISTI, IE, ingenta.
Published by: Societe les Editions et Publications Agricoles Francaises, 3 rue des Freres Perier, Paris, 75116, France. TEL 33-1-64992224, FAX 33-1-64993330. Ed. Elisabeth Fabre. Adv. contact M Seroux. Circ: 21,000. **Subscr. to:** Boigneville 91720, France.

630 IDN
PERTANI P T. Text in Indonesian. 1974. m.
Address: Jalan Pasar Minggu, Kalibata, P.O. Box 247 KBY, Jakarta Belatan, Indonesia. TEL 021-793108, TELEX 47249. Ed. Ir Rusli Yahya.

630 MYS
S3 CODEN: PERTDY
➤ **PERTANIKA JOURNAL OF TROPICAL AGRICULTURAL SCIENCE.** Text and summaries in English, Malay. 1978. irreg. (1-2/yr.), latest vol.25, 2002. USD 60 (effective 2002). adv. bk.rev. **Document type:** *Academic/Scholarly.*
Supersedes in part (in 1993): Pertanika (0126-6128)
Related titles: Microfilm ed.
Indexed: ASFA, Agrind, AnBrAb, ApicAb, BiolAb, CIN, CPA, ChemAb, ChemTitl, FCA, FPA, FS&TA, ForAb, HerbAb, HortAb, I&DA, IndVet, NutrAb, PBA, PGegResA, PST, PoultAb, REE&TA, RPP, RevApplEntom, RiceAb, S&F, SeedAb, TOSA, TriticAb, VetBull, WAE&RSA, WeedAb.
—BLDSC (6428.183070), CASDDS.
Published by: (Agricultural University of Malaysia/Universiti Pertanian Malaysia), Universiti Pertanian Malaysia Press, 43400 UPM, Serdang, Selangor, Malaysia. TEL 603-8946-8855, FAX 603-8941-6172. Ed. Ruth Kiew. Circ: 400.

630 BRA ISSN 0100-204X
S475.B7 CODEN: PEABBT
➤ **PESQUISA AGROPECUARIA BRASILEIRA/BRAZILIAN JOURNAL OF AGRICULTURAL RESEARCH.** Text in Portuguese; Abstracts in English. 1966. m. BRL 48 domestic; USD 180 foreign (effective 2003). adv. bk.rev. abstr.; charts; illus. back issues avail. **Document type:** *Academic/Scholarly.*
Formerly (until 1978): Pesquisa Agropecuaria. Serie Agronomia; Incorporates (in 1978): Pesquisa Agropecuaria Brasileira. Serie Veterinaria-Zootecnia; Which was formed by the 1977 merger of: Pesquisa Agropecuaria Brasileira. Serie Veterinaria; Pesquisa Agropecuaria Brasileira. Serie Zootenia
Related titles: Online - full text ed.: ISSN 1678-3921. free (effective 2005) (from SciELO).
Indexed: AEA, ASCA, AgBio, AgrForAb, AnBrAb, BioCN&I, BiolAb, CPA, CTFA, Cadscan, ChemAb, CurCont, DSA, FCA, FPA, FS&TA, ForAb, HelmAb, HerbAb, HortAb, I&DA, IndVet, LeadAb, MaizeAb, NemAb, NutrAb, OrnHort, PBA, PGegResA, PGrRegA, PHN&I, PN&I, PotatoAb, PoultAb, ProtozoAb, RA&MP, RDA, RM&VM, RPP, RevApplEntom, RiceAb, S&F, S&MA, SIA, SeedAb, SoyAb, TOSA, TriticAb, VetBull, WAE&RSA, WeedAb, Zincscan, ZooRec.
—BLDSC (6428.230000), CASDDS, CINDOC, CISTI, IDS, IE, ingenta.
Published by: Empresa Brasileira de Pesquisa Agropecuaria, Parque Estacao Biologica - PqEB s-n, Brasilia, 70770-901, Brazil. TEL 55-61-4484433, FAX 55-61-3471041, pab@spi.imbrapa.br, http://www.scielo.br/pab, http://www.embrapa.br. Circ: 1,600 (controlled).

630 BRA ISSN 0104-9070
PESQUISA AGROPECUARIA GAUCHA. Text in Portuguese. 1995. s-a. USD 35. **Description:** Publishes original articles and reviews in the fields of agronomy, renewable natural resources, veterinary and animal science and related subjects.

Indexed: AEA, AgBio, AgrForAb, AnBrAb, BioCN&I, CPA, DBA, DSA, FCA, FS&TA, ForAb, HelmAb, HerbAb, HortAb, I&DA, IndVet, MaizeAb, NemAb, NutrAb, OrnHort, PBA, PGegResA, PGrRegA, PHN&I, PN&I, PoultAb, ProtozoAb, RA&MP, RDA, RM&VM, RPP, RevApplEntom, RiceAb, S&F, SeedAb, SoyAb, TriticAb, VetBull, WAE&RSA, WeedAb.
Published by: Fundacao Estadual de Pesquisa Agropecuaria, Secretaria da Ciencia e Tecnologia, Rua Goncalves Dias, 570, Bairro Menino Deus, Porto Alegre, RS 90130-060, Brazil. TEL 55-512-33-5411, FAX 55-512-337607.

630 BRA ISSN 0100-8501
CODEN: PAPEDJ
PESQUISA AGROPECUARIA PERNAMBUCANA. Text in Portuguese; Summaries in English. 1977. s-a. free. bk.rev. back issues avail.
Indexed: BiolAb, CPA, ChemAb, FCA, ForAb, HerbAb, HortAb, I&DA, MaizeAb, PBA, PGegResA, PotatoAb, S&F, SIA, SeedAb.
—CASDDS.
Published by: Empresa Pernambucana de Pesquisa Agropecuaria, Divisao de Informacao e Documentacao, Av General San Martin, 1371, Bonji, S Martin, Recife, PE 50761-000, Brazil. TEL 081-445-2200, FAX 081-227-4017. Ed. Jose Bahia de Oliveira. Circ: 1,000.

630 540 GBR
THE PESTICIDE MANUAL. Text in English. 1983. irreg., latest vol.12, 2000, Nov. GBP 165 per issue (effective 2003). 1250 p./no.; **Document type:** *Trade.* **Description:** Contains comprehensive data on active ingredients used in crop protection and pest control.
Formerly (until 1994): Agrochemicals Handbook
Related titles: CD-ROM ed.; Online - full text ed.: Pesticide Fact File.
Published by: British Crop Protection Council, Bear Farm, Binfield, Bracknell, Berks RG42 5QE, United Kingdom. TEL 44-118-934-2727, FAX 44-118-934-1998, publications@BCPC.org, http://www.bcpc.org. Ed. Clive Tomlin.

630 PHL
S17 CODEN: PHAGAU
➤ **THE PHILIPPINE AGRICULTURAL SCIENTIST**; an international journal of tropical agriculture and related sciences. Text in English. 1911. q. PHP 600 domestic; USD 200 foreign (effective 2002). bk.rev. charts; illus. Index. 120 p./no.; **Document type:** *Academic/Scholarly.* **Description:** Original research papers and notes on original fundamental or applied research and, to a limited extent, critical research reviews, professorial chair lectures or book reviews on tropical agricultural science and related areas, including agroecosystems, food science, engineering, biotechnology, economics, extension, rural sociology, development communication, and agroforestry.
Formerly (until 1999): Philippine Agriculturist (0031-7454)
Indexed: AEA, AbHyg, AgBio, AgrForAb, AnBrAb, BAS, BioCN&I, BiolAb, CPA, CTFA, ChemAb, CurCont, DSA, ExcerpMed, FCA, FS&TA, ForAb, HelmAb, HerbAb, HortAb, I&DA, IPP, IndVet, MaizeAb, NemAb, NutrAb, OrnHort, PBA, PGegResA, PGrRegA, PHN&I, PN&I, PotatoAb, PoultAb, RA&MP, RDA, RPP, RevApplEntom, RiceAb, S&F, SIA, SeedAb, TriticAb, VITIS, VetBull, WAE&RSA, WeedAb, ZooRec.
—BLDSC (6453.000000), CASDDS, CISTI, IE, ingenta, Linda Hall.
Published by: University of the Philippines at Los Banos, College of Agriculture, College, Laguna, 4031, Philippines. capao@mudspring.uplb.edu.ph, http://www.uplb.edu.ph/journal/philagri/. Ed., R&P, Adv. contact Ofelia K Bautista. Circ: 20,000 (paid). **Co-sponsor:** Central Experiment Station.

➤ **PHILIPPINE JOURNAL OF VETERINARY AND ANIMAL SCIENCES.** see *VETERINARY SCIENCE*

➤ **PHILIPPINES. DEPARTMENT OF AGRICULTURE. BUREAU OF AGRICULTURAL STATISTICS. DEVELOPMENT INDICATORS IN PHILIPPINE AGRICULTURE.** see *AGRICULTURE—Abstracting, Bibliographies, Statistics*

➤ **PHILIPPINES. DEPARTMENT OF AGRICULTURE. BUREAU OF AGRICULTURAL STATISTICS. SELECTED STATISTICS IN AGRICULTURE.** see *AGRICULTURE—Abstracting, Bibliographies, Statistics*

630 USA ISSN 0191-7935
PHOTO STAR. Text in English. 1895. w. USD 25. adv. **Document type:** *Newspaper.*
Address: 307 State St, Box B, Willshire, OH 45898. TEL 419-495-2696, FAX 419-495-2143. Ed. Judith E Bunner. Adv. contact John Bunner. Circ: 11,000.

630 330.9 ITA ISSN 0392-5056
IL PICENTINO. Text in Italian. 1845. q. adv. bk.rev. bibl.; charts. **Document type:** *Academic/Scholarly.* **Description:** Features financial, agricultural and historical news in the province of Salerno and surrounding areas.
Published by: Societa Economica della Provincia di Salerno, Biblioteca Provinciale di Salerno, Via Valerio Laspro, Salerno, SA 84100, Italy. Ed. Luigi Postiglione. Circ: 500.

636.2 GBR
PIG INDUSTRY. Text in English. 1985. m. GBP 20 domestic; GBP 30 in Europe. adv. **Document type:** *Bulletin.* **Description:** Contains news about the pig industry.
Formerly: National Pig News
Published by: (British Pig Association), B C Publications, 16C Market Pl, Diss, Norfolk IP22 3AB, United Kingdom. FAX 44-1379-650480. Ed., Pub., R&P Brian Chester. Adv. contact Nigel Filby. Circ: 7,800 (controlled).

PLANT BREEDING ABSTRACTS. see *AGRICULTURE—Abstracting, Bibliographies, Statistics*

570 POL ISSN 1429-3862
SB123 CODEN: HRANAX
PLANT BREEDING AND SEED SCIENCE/HODOWLA ROSLIN I NASIENNICTWO. Text and summaries in English. 1957. s-a. EUR 44 foreign (effective 2005). adv. bk.rev. reprints avail. **Document type:** *Journal, Academic/Scholarly.* **Description:** Contains basic publications on plant breeding, seed production and such related areas as genetics, botany, physiology, biochemistry, phytopathology.
Formerly (until 1995): Hodowla Roslin, Aklimatyzacja i Nasiennictwo (0018-3040)
Indexed: AgBio, AgrAg, AgrLib, BiolAb, CPA, ChemAb, ExcerpMed, FCA, FS&TA, ForAb, HerbAb, HortAb, MaizeAb, NutrAb, OrnHort, PBA, PGegResA, PHN&I, PotatoAb, RA&MP, RPP, RefZh, RevApplEntom, S&F, SIA, SeedAb, SoyAb, TriticAb, WeedAb.
—CASDDS, CISTI.
Published by: Instytut Hodowli i Aklimatyzacji Roslin/Plant Breeding and Acclimatization Institute, Radzikow, Blonie, 05870, Poland. TEL 48-22-7253611, FAX 48-22-7254714, postbox@ihar.edu.pl, http://www.ihar.edu.pl. Ed. Henryk J Czembor. R&P, Adv. contact Roman Osinski. Circ: 1,300. **Dist. by:** Ars Polona, Krakowskie Przedmiescie 7, Warsaw, Poland. TEL 48-22-9263914, FAX 48-22-9265334, arspolona@arspolona.com.pl, http://www.arspolona.com.pl.

PLANT CELL, TISSUE AND ORGAN CULTURE; an international journal on in vitro culture of higher plants. see *BIOLOGY—Cytology And Histology*

PLANT GROWTH REGULATOR ABSTRACTS. see *AGRICULTURE—Abstracting, Bibliographies, Statistics*

630 CZE ISSN 1214-1178
S13 CODEN: ROVYAM
➤ **PLANT, SOIL AND ENVIRONMENT.** Variant title: Plant Production. Text and summaries in Czech, English. 1954. m. USD 195 in Europe; USD 214 elsewhere (effective 2004). adv. charts; illus. **Document type:** *Journal, Academic/Scholarly.* **Description:** Publishes original scientific papers, results of research, review of articles and analyses from experimental biology, agronomy, natural resources and the environment.
Formerly (until 2003): Rostlinna Vyroba (0370-663X)
Indexed: AEA, ASCA, AgBio, AgrForAb, BioCN&I, BiolAb, CIN, CPA, ChemAb, ChemTitl, CurCont, DSA, ExcerpMed, FCA, FPA, FS&TA, FaBeAb, ForAb, HerbAb, HortAb, I&DA, MaizeAb, NemAb, NutrAb, OrnHort, PBA, PGegResA, PGrRegA, PHN&I, PotatoAb, RA&MP, RASB, RM&VM, RPP, RRTA, RefZh, RevApplEntom, RiceAb, S&F, SIA, SeedAb, SoyAb, TriticAb, WAE&RSA, WeedAb.
—BLDSC (6523.614000), CASDDS, CISTI, IDS, IE, ingenta.
Published by: Ceska Akademie Zemedelskych Ved, Ustav Zemedelskych a Potravinarskych Informaci/Czech Academy of Agricultural Sciences, Institute of Agricultural and Food Information, Slezska 7, Prague 2, 120 56, Czech Republic. TEL 420-2-227010352, FAX 420-2-227010116, editor@uzpi.cz, http://www.cazv.cz, http://www.uzpi.cz. Ed. Eva Stribrna. Circ: 350.

630 MYS ISSN 0126-575X
S295 CODEN: PLTRBH
➤ **PLANTER.** Text in English. 1920. a. MYR 150; MYR 170 foreign (effective 1999). bk.rev. reprints avail. **Document type:** *Monographic series, Academic/Scholarly.*
Related titles: Microfilm ed.
Indexed: AEA, ATA, AgBio, AgrForAb, AnBrAb, BioCN&I, CPA, ExcerpMed, FCA, FPA, FS&TA, ForAb, HerbAb, HortAb, I&DA, NemAb, NutrAb, OrnHort, PBA, PGegResA, PGrRegA, PHN&I, RA&MP, RDA, RPP, RRTA, RevApplEntom, S&F, SIA, SeedAb, TDB, TOSA, WAE&RSA, WeedAb.
—BLDSC (6524.800000), CASDDS, IE, ingenta.
Published by: Incorporated Society of Planters, PO Box 10262, Kuala Lumpur, 50708, Malaysia. TEL 60-3-242-5561, FAX 60-3-242-6898, isphq@tm.net.my, http://www.isphq.com. Ed. W T Perera. R&P W.T. Perera TEL 60-3-242-5668. Circ: 3,900.

➤ **PLASTICULTURE**; les plastiques dans l'agriculture - plastics in agriculture and horticulture - los plasticos en la agricultura - Kunststoffe im Landbau. see *PLASTICS*

630 NLD
PLATTELANDS POST MAGAZINE; agrarisch vakblad. Text in Dutch. 1948. m. (10/yr.). EUR 36.50 (effective 2005). adv. mkt. 64 p./no. 4 cols./p.; back issues avail. **Document type:** *Newspaper.* **Description:** Covers agricultural topics in the Dutch flat lands.
Published by: Eisma B.V. Publishers, Archimedesweg 20, Postbus 340, Leeuwarden, 8901 BC, Netherlands. TEL 31-58-2954854, FAX 31-58-2954875, businessmedia@eisma.nl, http://www.eisma.nl/businessmedia/index.asp. Ed., Adv. contact Rinus van Wezel. Pub. Minne Hovenga. Circ: 8,000.

630 663 664 HRV ISSN 0352-1753
PODRAVKA; znanstveno-strucni casopis. Text in Croatian; Summaries in English. 1983. s-a. USD 10. back issues avail.
Indexed: NutrAb.
Published by: R.O. Istrazivanja i Razvoj, Marinkoivca 32, Koprivnica, 43300, Croatia. TEL 043-827-144, FAX 043-827-169, TELEX 23348 YU POD KC. Ed. Ante Babic. Circ: 1,000.

634 LKA
POL PAWATH. Text in Singhalese. irreg. (1-2/yr.). LKR 10 (effective 2000). back issues avail. **Description:** Contains valuable information and advice for coconut growers.
Published by: Coconut Research Institute, Bandirippuwa Estate, Lunuwila, Sri Lanka. TEL 94-31-253795, FAX 94-31-57391.

630 ITA ISSN 1722-4365
POLITICA AGRICOLA INTERNAZIONALE/INTERNATIONAL AGRICULTURAL POLICY. Text in Multiple languages. 2002. q. EUR 60 domestic (effective 2004). **Document type:** *Magazine, Consumer.*
Published by: Edizioni L' Informatore Agrario S.p.A., Via Bencivegna Giordani 16, Verona, 37133, Italy. TEL 39-045-8057511, FAX 39-045-597510, informatoreagrario@informatoreagrario.it, http://www.informatoreagrario.it.

630 HRV ISSN 1330-7142
POLJOPRIVREDA (OSIJEK). Text in Croatian, English. 1982. s-a. 50 p./no. 2 cols./p.; **Document type:** *Journal, Academic/Scholarly.* **Description:** Presents scientific professional papers in the field of agriculture.
Formerly (until 1995): Znanost i Praksa u Poljoprivredi i Prehrambenoj Tehnologiji (0352-1346); Which was formed by the merger of (1976-1982): Poljoprivredni Fakulteta u Osijeku. Zbornik Radova (0350-8595); (1971-1982): Poljoprivredni Institut Osijek. Zbornik Radova (0350-7211)
Indexed: AEA, ASFA, AgBio, AgrForAb, AnBrAb, BioCN&I, CPA, DSA, ESPM, FCA, FS&TA, ForAb, HerbAb, HortAb, I&DA, IndVet, MaizeAb, NutrAb, OrnHort, PBA, PGegResA, PHN&I, PN&I, PotatoAb, PoultAb, RA&MP, RPP, RefZh, S&F, SIA, SeedAb, SoyAb, TriticAb, VetBull, WAE&RSA, WeedAb.
—CISTI.
Published by: Poljoprivredni Fakultet u Osijeku/Faculty of Agriculture in Osijek, Trg. sv. Trojstva 3, Osijek, 31000, Croatia. TEL 385-31-224210, FAX 385-31-207017, studentska@pfos.hr, http://suncokret.pfos.hr.

630 SVK ISSN 0551-3677
POLNOHOSPODARSTVO/AGRICULTURE. Text in Slovak; Abstracts and contents page in English. 1954. m. USD 95 (effective 2001). bk.rev. bibl.; charts. **Document type:** *Journal.* **Description:** Presents research on plant and animal production, mechanization of agriculture, primarily focusing on Slovakia. Also examines the development of agricultural science, both in the region and abroad.
Indexed: AnBrAb, BiolAb, CPA, ChemAb, ChemTitl, DSA, ExcerpMed, FCA, FS&TA, FaBeAb, ForAb, HerbAb, HortAb, INIS AtomInd, IndVet, MaizeAb, NutrAb, OrnHort, PBA, PGrRegA, PN&I, PotatoAb, PoultAb, RASB, RPP, SFA, SeedAb, SoyAb, TriticAb, VITIS, VetBull, WeedAb, ZooRec.
—BLDSC (6544.500000), CISTI, IE, ingenta.
Published by: Ministerstvo Polnohospodarstva Slovenskej Respubliki, Vyskumny Ustav Zivocisnej Vyroby, Hlohovska 2, Nitra, 94992, Slovakia. FAX 421-37-6546361. Ed. Jan Plesnik. **Dist. by:** Fortis-CS, Stavitelska 1, Bratislava 83104, Slovakia.

630.7 IND ISSN 0032-4299
POONA AGRICULTURAL COLLEGE MAGAZINE. Text in English, Hindi, Marathi. 1970 (vol.60). irreg. INR 12, USD 5. bibl.; charts; illus.
Indexed: BiolAb, ChemAb.
—CISTI.
Published by: Mahatma Phule Krishi Vidyapeeth, Ahmednagar Dist., Rahuri, Maharashtra 413 722, India.

630 POL ISSN 0137-6780
PORADNIK GOSPODARSKI; czasopismo rolnikow i organizacji rolniczych. Text in Polish. 1889. m. USD 87 foreign (effective 2000). adv. bk.rev. illus. back issues avail. **Description:** Guide for farmers and their families.
Indexed: AgrLib.
Address: Ul Mickiewicza 33, Poznan, 60837, Poland. TEL 48-61-8476001. Ed. Wawrzyniec Trawinski. Adv. contact Aleksandra Szymanowska. Circ: 10,000.

PORTUGAL. INSTITUTO NACIONAL DE ESTATISTICA. ESTATISTICAS AGRICOLAS. see *AGRICULTURE—Abstracting, Bibliographies, Statistics*

PORTUGAL. INSTITUTO NACIONAL DE ESTATISTICA. INQUERITO AO GANHO DOS TRABALHADORES AGRICOLAS. see *AGRICULTURE—Abstracting, Bibliographies, Statistics*

▼ new title ➤ refereed ✶ unverified ♦ full entry avail.

A

630   POL   ISSN 0032-5457
                                      CODEN: PNROAB
➤ **POSTEPY NAUK ROLNICZYCH.** Text in Polish; Summaries in English. 1949. bi-m. PLZ 60, USD 20 (effective 2000). adv. bk.rev. charts; illus. index. **Document type:** *Monographic series, Academic/Scholarly.* **Description:** Provides articles reviewing the most recent achievements in agricultural sciences with special emphasis on the important scientific problems for Polish agriculture.
Formerly (until 1954): Postepy Wiedzy Rolniczej (0370-2650)
Indexed: AgrLib, AnBrAb, BiolAb, ChemAb, FCA, HerbAb, RASB, RPP, RRTA, WAE&RSA.
—CASDDS, CISTI.
Published by: Polska Akademia Nauk, Wydzial Nauk Rolniczych Lesnych i Weterynaryjnych, Palac Kultury i Nauki, Warsaw, 00901, Poland. TEL 48-22-6204292, FAX 48-22-6204292, http://www.warman.net.pl/alf/psjc, http://www.warman.net.pl/atf/psjc. Ed., R&P Henryk Okruszko. Circ: 250. **Dist. by:** DABOR - Oficyna Wydawniczo-Poligraficzna, ul Kazury 22-27, Warsaw 02795, Poland. TEL 48-22-6491899.

632   POL   ISSN 1427-4337
SB950.A2   CODEN: PPLPF3
POSTEPY W OCHRONIE ROSLIN/PROGRESS IN PLANT PROTECTION. Text in Polish; Summaries in English. 1957. a. USD 50 per vol. (effective 2005). illus. index. **Document type:** *Journal, Academic/Scholarly.*
Formerly (until vol.36, 1996): Instytut Ochrony Roslin. Biuletyn (0020-448X)
Indexed: AEA, AgBio, AgrForAb, AgrLib, BioCN&I, BiolAb, CPA, DSA, FCA, FS&TA, ForAb, HelmAb, HerbAb, HortAb, MaizeAb, NemAb, NutrAb, OrnHort, PBA, PGegResA, PGrRegA, PHN&I, PN&I, PotatoAb, ProtozoAb, RA&MP, RM&VM, RPP, RefZh, RevApplEntom, S&F, SIA, SeedAb, SoyAb, TriticAb, WAE&RSA, WeedAb, ZooRec.
—CASDDS, CISTI.
Published by: Instytut Ochrony Roslin/Institute of Plant Protection, ul Miczurina 20, Poznan, 60318, Poland. TEL 48-61-8649173, FAX 48-61-8676301, D.Wolna@ior.poznan.pl, http://www.ior.poznan.pl/wydaw/Wyd-PO.htm. Ed. Stefan Pruszynski. Circ: 1,000.

POSTHARVEST BIOLOGY AND TECHNOLOGY. see *BIOLOGY—Biotechnology*

635.21   GBR
POTATO MAGAZINE. Text in English. 6/yr. **Description:** Serves the potato industry, including growers and traders.
Address: 78a Ashby Rd, Spilsby, Lincs PE23 5DW, United Kingdom. TEL 0359-41663, FAX 0790-53556. Ed. Fid Backhouse. Circ: 20,000.

635.21 380.141   GBR   ISSN 1365-571X
POTATO MARKETS WEEKLY. Text in English. 1975. w. GBP 1,595 domestic; GBP 1,842 in Europe; GBP 1,927 elsewhere; GBP 1,755 combined subscription domestic print & online eds.; GBP 2,002 combined subscription in Europe print & online eds.; GBP 2,087 combined subscription elsewhere print & online eds. (effective 2005). back issues avail. **Document type:** *Newsletter, Trade.* **Description:** Extensive overview of production, price and market information from European, North America and the major producing countries. Includes futures prices from London, Hanover and Amsterdam.
Formerly: Potato Markets (0141-2221)
Related titles: Fax ed.; Online - full content ed.
—CISTI.
Published by: Agra Europe (London) Ltd. (Subsidiary of: T & F Informa plc), 80 Calverley Rd, Tunbridge Wells, Kent TN1 2UN, United Kingdom. TEL 44-1892-533813, FAX 44-1892-544895, marketing@agra-net.com, http://www.agra-net.com. Ed. Guy Faulkner.

630   GBR   ISSN 0961-7655
POTATO REVIEW. Text in English. 1990. 6/yr. GBP 31 domestic; EUR 61.13 in Europe; USD 67.04 elsewhere (effective 2003). bk.rev. **Document type:** *Magazine, Trade.* **Description:** Serves the potato industry with information about market trends, and technical and scientific developments in the potato crop.
Address: Docwra's, Guestwick, Dereham, Norfolk NR20 5AL, United Kingdom. TEL 44-1362-683363, FAX 44-1362-680078, edit@potatoreview.com, http://www.potatoreview.com/. Ed. David Mossman. Adv. contact Hazel Hescott TEL 44-1454-615118. Circ: 12,000. **Subscr. to:** c/o Gillian Davison, Barnside, Nairdwood Way, Great Missenden, Bucs HP16 0QW, United Kingdom. TEL 44-1494-864121, FAX 44-1494-868731, subs@potatoreview.com.

630   CAN
POTATOES IN CANADA. Text in English. 1981. a. free with subscr. to Top Crop Manager. adv. illus. back issues avail. **Document type:** *Trade.*
Related titles: ◆ Supplement to: Top Crop Manager. ISSN 1488-4313.
Published by: Annex Publishing & Printing, Inc., 222 Argyle Ave, Delhi, ON N4B 2Y2, ON N4B 2Y2, Canada. TEL 519-582-2513, 800-265-2827, FAX 519-582-4040, sfredericks@annexweb.com, http://www.annexweb.com. Circ: 3,014.

630   POL   ISSN 0079-4708
S13   CODEN: PTPWAX
➤ **POZNANSKIE TOWARZYSTWO PRZYJACIOL NAUK. KOMISJA NAUK ROLNICZYCH I LESNYCH. PRACE.** Text in Polish; Summaries in English, German. 1950. s-a., latest vol.93, 2002. price varies. bibl.; charts; illus. **Document type:** *Monographic series, Academic/Scholarly.*
Indexed: AEA, AgrAg, AgrLib, AnBrAb, CIN, CPA, ChemAb, ChemTitl, DSA, FCA, FPA, ForAb, HerbAb, HortAb, I&DA, IndVet, MaizeAb, NutrAb, OrnHort, PBA, PGegResA, PGrRegA, PHN&I, PN&I, PotatoAb, PoultAb, RPP, RRTA, S&F, SIA, SeedAb, SoyAb, TriticAb, VetBull, WAE&RSA, WeedAb.
—CASDDS.
Published by: (Poznanskie Towarzystwo Przyjaciol Nauk, Komisja Nauk Rolniczych i Lesnych), Poznanskie Towarzystwo Przyjaciol Nauk/Poznan Society for the Advancement of the Arts and Sciences, ul Sew Mielzynskiego 27-29, Poznan, 61725, Poland. TEL 48-61-8527441, FAX 48-61-8522205, sekretariat@ptpn.poznan.pl, wydawnictwo@ptpn.poznan.pl, http://www.ptpn.poznan.pl. Ed. Andrzej Wojciechowski. Circ: 200. **Dist. by:** Ars Polona, Krakowskie Przedmiescie 7, Warsaw, Poland. TEL 48-22-9263914, FAX 48-22-9265334, arspolona@arspolona.com.pl, http://www.arspolona.com.pl.

630   USA
THE PRAIRIE STAR. Text in English. bi-w. (Fri.). free qualified farmers or ranchers; USD 29.50 subscr - mailed others; USD 75 subscr - mailed in Canada (effective 2005). **Document type:** *Newspaper, Trade.*
Published by: Lee Agri-Media, Inc., 4023 State St, Bismark, ND 58503. TEL 701-255-4905, editor@theprairiestar.com, http://www.theprairiestar.com. Ed. Shannon Burkdoll. Adv. contact Maureen Iregoin. Circ: 18,000 (controlled and free).

630   USA   ISSN 1385-2256
S494.5.P73   CODEN: PRAGF3
PRECISION AGRICULTURE. Text in English. 1998. 6/yr. EUR 445, USD 466, GBP 293 combined subscription to institutions print & online eds. (effective 2005). adv. back issues avail.; reprint service avail. from PSC. **Description:** Provides an effective forum for disseminating original and fundamental research and experience in the rapidly advancing area of precision farming.
Related titles: Online - full text ed.: ISSN 1573-1618 (from EBSCO Publishing, Gale Group, IngentaConnect, Kluwer Online, O C L C Online Computer Library Center, Inc., Ovid Technologies, Inc., Springer LINK, Swets Information Services).
Indexed: AEA, Agr, BIOBASE, BibLing, CPA, ESPM, FCA, GEOBASE, HerbAb, HortAb, I&DA, M&GPA, MaizeAb, NemAb, PBA, PHN&I, PotatoAb, RA&MP, RPP, RefZh, S&F, SIA, SWRA, SoyAb, TriticAb, WAE&RSA, WTA, WeedAb.
—BLDSC (6603.995020), IE, Infotrieve, ingenta. **CCC.**
Published by: Springer-Verlag New York, Inc. (Subsidiary of: Springer Science+Business Media), 233 Spring St, New York, NY 10013. TEL 212-460-1500, FAX 212-460-1575, service@springer-ny.com, http://springerlink.metapress.com/openurl.asp?genre=journal&issn=1385-2256, http://www.springer-ny.com. Ed. John Stafford. **Subscr. to:** Journal Fulfillment, PO Box 2485, Secaucus, NJ 07096-2485. TEL 201-348-4033, FAX 201-348-4505, journals@springer-ny.com.

PRECOS E RENDIMENTOS NA AGRICULTURA. see *AGRICULTURE—Abstracting, Bibliographies, Statistics*

630.7   FRA   ISSN 0339-0055
PRESENCE DE L'ENSEIGNEMENT AGRICOLE PRIVE. Text in French. 1975. bi-m. adv.
Published by: Conseil National de l'Enseignement Agricole Prive, 277 rue Saint-Jacques, Paris, 75005, France. TEL 33-1-53737420, FAX 33-1-53737430, cneap@cneap-scolanet.org, http://cneap.scolanet.org. Ed. Sophie de Ravinel. Pub. Yvon LeNoncy. Adv. contact Danielle Champagnat.

PRINCE EDWARD ISLAND. DEPARTMENT OF AGRICULTURE. AGRICULTURAL STATISTICS. see *AGRICULTURE—Abstracting, Bibliographies, Statistics*

630   ZAF   ISSN 1024-1558
PROAGRI; agricultural technology for the farmer. Text in Afrikaans, English. 1994. 9/yr. USD 25 foreign. adv. cum.index (1994-1998). back issues avail. **Document type:** *Trade.* **Description:** Informs farmers on technological developments, products, and services of importance to agriculture.
Related titles: Online - full text ed.
Indexed: ISAP.
Published by: Prima Business Consultants (Pty.) Ltd., PO Box 72691, Lynnwood Ridge, Pretoria 0040, South Africa. TEL 27-12-809-0150, FAX 27-12-809-0149, info@proagri.co.za, http://www.proagri.co.za. Ed. A.F. Rall. R&P A F Rall. Adv. contact Pieter Rall. page USD 1,000; trim 210 x 297. Circ: 44,000.

631   TKM   ISSN 0032-9428
S612   CODEN: POSPBR
PROBLEMY OSVOENIYA PUSTYN'. Text in Russian; Abstracts and contents page in English. 1967. bi-m. USD 149. bk.rev. abstr.; charts; illus. index. **Document type:** *Academic/Scholarly.* **Description:** Focuses on results of scientific research of desert territories in the former Soviet Union and abroad.
Indexed: BIOSIS Prev, BiolAb, HortAb, ZooRec.
—CCC.
Published by: (Institut Pustny'), Akademiya Nauk Turkmenistana, Bitarapt Tyrkmenistan 15, Ashgabat, 744000, Turkmenistan. TEL 3632-357256. Ed A Babaev. Circ: 800. **US dist. addr.:** East View Information Services, 3020 Harbor Ln. N., Minneapolis, MN 55447. TEL 612-550-0961.

PRODUCAO AGRICOLA MUNICIPAL; culturas temporarias e permanentes. see *AGRICULTURE—Abstracting, Bibliographies, Statistics*

630   CAN   ISSN 1183-9929
PRODUCTEUR PLUS. Text in French. 1991. 8/yr. CND 34.95 (effective 1999). adv. **Document type:** *Trade.*
—CISTI.
Published by: Editions Imago Inc., P O Box 147, Farnham, PQ J2N 2R4, Canada. TEL 514-293-8282, FAX 514-293-8554. Ed., Pub., R&P Leonard Pigeon. Adv. contact Bertrand Beaumont. Circ: 22,290.

630   DEU   ISSN 0937-1583
PROFI; magazin fuer agrartechnik. Text in German. m. EUR 79.20 domestic; EUR 95.40 foreign; EUR 7.20 newsstand/cover (effective 2003). adv. **Document type:** *Magazine, Trade.*
—CCC.
Published by: Landwirtschaftsverlag GmbH, Huelsebrockstr 2, Muenster, 48165, Germany. TEL 49-2501-801-0, FAX 49-2501-801204, service@profi.com, zentrale@lv-h.de, http://www.profi.com, http://www.lv-h.de. adv.: B&W page EUR 4,940, color page EUR 7,904. Circ: 53,394.

631.091   COL
PROGRAMA DE FORRAJES TROPICALES. INFORME BIANUAL. Text in Spanish. 1975. a. **Document type:** *Corporate.* **Description:** Detailed progress report primarily for information for research collaborators in the tropical pastures network.
Formerly: Programa de Pastos Tropicales. Informe Anual (0120-2391)
Related titles: English ed.: Tropical Forages Program Annual Report.
Published by: (Unidad de Comunicaciones), Centro Internacional de Agricultura Tropical/International Center for Tropical Agriculture, Publications Unit, Apartado Aereo 6713, Cali, VALLE, Colombia. TEL 57-2-4450000, FAX 57-2-4450073, http://www.ciat.cgiar.org/. Ed. Carlos E Lascano. Circ: 250.

630   USA
PROGRESSIVE FARMER (MIDSOUTH). Text in English. 1886. m. USD 18 domestic; USD 26 foreign (effective 2005). **Document type:** *Magazine, Trade.*
Published by: Progressive Farmer, Inc., 2100 Lakeshore Drive, Birmingham, AL 35209. TEL 205-445-6416, 800-357-4466, progressivefarmer@timeinc.com, http://www.progressivefarmer.com. Eds. Jack Odle, Victoria G Myers. Pub. Bruce Thomas. Circ: 450,000 (paid).

630   USA   ISSN 1073-0656
PROGRESSIVE FARMER (MIDWEST). Text in English. m. USD 18 domestic; USD 26 foreign (effective 2005). **Document type:** *Magazine, Trade.*
Formerly (until 199?): Progressive Farmer. Corn Soybeans Midwest (1056-2249)
Published by: Progressive Farmer, Inc., 2100 Lakeshore Drive, Birmingham, AL 35209. TEL 205-445-6416, 800-357-4466, progressivefarmer@timeinc.com, http://www.progressivefarmer.com. Ed. Dan Miller. Pub. Bruce Thomas. Circ: 600,000 (paid).

630   USA
PROGRESSIVE FARMER (SOUTHEAST). Text in English. m. USD 18 domestic; USD 26 foreign (effective 2005). **Document type:** *Magazine, Trade.*
Published by: Progressive Farmer, Inc., 2100 Lakeshore Drive, Birmingham, AL 35209. TEL 205-445-6416, 800-357-4466, progressivefarmer@timeinc.com, http://www.progressivefarmer.com.

630   USA   ISSN 0033-0760
PROGRESSIVE FARMER (SOUTHWEST). Text in English. 1886. 10/yr. USD 18 domestic; USD 26 foreign (effective 2005). adv. bk.rev. charts; illus.; stat.; tr.lit. index. back issues avail.; reprints avail. **Document type:** *Magazine, Trade.* **Description:** Covers all issues affecting farmers.
Related titles: Microform ed.: (from PQC); Online - full text ed.: (from ProQuest Information & Learning); Supplement(s): Rural Sportsman.
Indexed: ABIn.
—Linda Hall. **CCC.**

A

Published by: Progressive Farmer, Inc., 2100 Lakeshore Drive, Birmingham, AL 35209. TEL 205-445-6416, 800-357-4466, progressivefarmer@timeinc.com, http://www.progressivefarmer.com. Eds. Jack Odle, Victoria G Myers. Pub. Bruce Thomas. adv.: B&W page USD 36,890, color page USD 51,960; trim 8 x 10.5. Circ: 630,000.

630   PAK
PROGRESSIVE FARMING. Text in English. 1981. bi-m. PKR 15. adv. bk.rev.
Indexed: BiolAb, ChemAb, ForAb, HortAb, NutrAb, RiceAb.
Published by: Pakistan Agricultural Research Council, Plot 20, G-5-1, P O Box 1031, Islamabad, Pakistan. Ed. Syed Athar Hosain. Circ: 1,000.

630 658   UKR
PROPOZYTSIYA. Text in Ukrainian. 1994. m. UAK 56 domestic; USD 60 foreign (effective 2003). adv. illus.; mkt. 118 p./no. 3 cols./p.; Document type: Magazine. Description: Focuses on agricultural business.
Related titles: Online - full content ed.
Published by: Kompaniya Univest Marketing, Dmytrivska vul 44 b, Kiev, 01054, Ukraine. TEL 380-44-2358118, FAX 380-44-2358162, propozitsiya@univest-group.com, univest@carrier.kiev.ua, http://www.propozitsiya.com, http://www.univest-group.com. Eds. Oleg Ermolenko, Olga Sidorenko. Adv. contact Igor Skazatniy TEL 380-44-235-8161. Circ: 22,000.

630   IRL
PROVINCIAL FARMER. Text in English. 1983. m. adv. back issues avail. Document type: Magazine, Trade.
Published by: Meath Chronicle Ltd., Market Sq., Navan, Co Meath, Ireland. TEL 353-46-9079699, FAX 353-46-9023565, info@meath-chronicle.ie, http://www.meath_chronicle.ie. Adv. contact Paul Luddy. B&W page EUR 2,025, color page EUR 2,158; 260 x 346. Circ: 50,000.

PUERTO RICO. OFICINA DE ESTADISTICAS AGRICOLAS. BOLETIN SEMESTRAL DE ESTADISTICAS AGRICOLAS. see AGRICULTURE—Abstracting, Bibliographies, Statistics

630   IND   ISSN 0048-6019
S17   CODEN: JRPUAF
PUNJAB AGRICULTURAL UNIVERSITY. JOURNAL OF RESEARCH. Text and summaries in English. 1964. q. INR 45. bk.rev. Document type: Academic/Scholarly.
Indexed: AEA, AgBio, AgrForAb, AnBrAb, ApicAb, BioCN&I, BiolAb, CIN, CIS, CPA, CTFA, ChemAb, ChemTitl, DSA, FCA, FPA, FS&TA, ForAb, HerbAb, HortAb, I&DA, IndVet, MaizeAb, NemAb, NutrAb, OrnHort, PBA, PGegResA, PGrRegA, PHN&I, PotatoAb, PoultAb, ProtozoAb, RA&MP, RDA, RM&VM, RPP, RRTA, RefZn, RevApplEntom, RiceAb, S&F, S&MA, SIA, SeedAb, SoyAb, TDB, TOSA, TriticAb, VetBull, WAE&RSA, WeedAb.
—CASDDS, Linda Hall.
Published by: Punjab Agricultural University, Department of Entomology, Ludhiana, Punjab 141 004, India. Ed. K L Dua. Circ: 500.

PUNJAB FRUIT JOURNAL. see GARDENING AND HORTICULTURE

PUNJAB HORTICULTURAL JOURNAL. see GARDENING AND HORTICULTURE

630   CAN   ISSN 1480-0764
QUARTERLY AGRI-FOOD TRADE HIGHLIGHTS. Text in English. 1997. quadrennial.
—CISTI.
Published by: Agriculture and Agri-Food Canada, Economic and Policy Analysis Directorate, 960 Carling Ave, Bldg 74, Ottawa, PQ K1A OC6, Canada. TEL 613-759-1746, FAX 613-759-7090.

630   DEU
➤ QUARTERLY JOURNAL OF INTERNATIONAL AGRICULTURE/JOURNAL TRIMESTRIEL D'AGRICULTURE INTERNATIONALE. Text in English; Summaries in English, French, German. 1962. q. EUR 98 to non-members; EUR 78 to members; EUR 29 newsstand/cover (effective 2004). bk.rev. abstr.; bibl.; stat. index. back issues avail. Document type: Journal, Academic/Scholarly.
Formerly: Zeitschrift fuer Auslaendische Landwirtschaft (0049-8599)
Indexed: AEA, ARDT, ASFA, AgrForAb, AnBrAb, BAS, DIP, DSA, ESPM, EngInd, FCA, ForAb, GEOBASE, HerbAb, HortAb, I&DA, IBR, IBZ, ILD, JEL, MaizeAb, NutrAb, PAIS, PBA, PHN&I, PollutAb, PotatoAb, PoultAb, RASB, RDA, REE&TA, RRTA, RiceAb, S&F, SWRA, SoyAb, TDB, TriticAb, WAE&RSA.
—BLDSC (7191.600000), CISTI, Ei, IE, ingenta. CCC.
Published by: D L G Verlags GmbH, Eschborner Landstr 122, Frankfurt Am Main, 60489, Germany. TEL 49-69-247880, FAX 49-69-24788480, dlg-verlag@dlg-frankfurt.de, http://www.agrar.hu-berlin.de/qjia, http://www.dlg-verlag.de. Ed. Dieter Elz. Circ: 500.

630   CAN   ISSN 0701-6557
S159
QUEBEC (PROVINCE). MINISTERE DE L'AGRICULTURE. RAPPORT ANNUEL: MERITE AGRICOLE. Text in English. 1972. a. CND 5. illus.
Formerly: Quebec (Province). Ministere de l'Agriculture. Rapport du Merite Agricole
—CISTI.
Published by: Ministere de l'Agriculture, des Pecheries et de l'Alimentation Quebec, 200 Chemin Ste Foy, 1er etage, Quebec, PQ G1R 4X6, Canada. TEL 418-380-2110, FAX 418-380-2176, info@agr.gouv.qc.ca, http://www.agr.gouv.qc.ca.

630   CAN   ISSN 0714-9158
QUEBEC FARMERS' ADVOCATE. Text in English. 1980. m. (11/yr.) CND 22 (effective 2001). adv. bk.rev. illus.; stat.; tr.lit. Document type: Newspaper. Description: Provides information, news and current events for the English-speaking farmers of Quebec.
Formerly: Quebec Farmers Association. Newsletter (0226-7705)
—CISTI.
Published by: Le Defenseur des Agriculteurs du Quebec Inc., P O Box 80, Ste Anne De Bellevue, PQ H9X 3L4, Canada. TEL 514-457-2010, FAX 514-398-7972. Ed. Susanne Brown. Pub. Hugh Maynard. adv.: B&W page CND 650, color page CND 1,550; 13.5 x 10.25. Circ: 4,000.

630   AUS   ISSN 0727-6273
QUEENSLAND. DEPARTMENT OF PRIMARY INDUSTRIES. INFORMATION SERIES. Text in English. 1982. irreg.
Document type: Monographic series, Government.
Indexed: ESPM.
Published by: Queensland, Department of Primary Industries, 80 Ann St., GPO Box 46, Brisbane, QLD 4001, Australia. TEL 61-7-34046999, FAX 61-7-34046900, callweb@dpi.qld.gov.au, http://www.dpi.qld.gov.au.

630   AUS   ISSN 0727-6281
QUEENSLAND. DEPARTMENT OF PRIMARY INDUSTRIES. PROJECT REPORT. Text in English. 1977. irreg.
Formerly (until 1982): Queensland. Department of Primary Industries. Agriculture Branch. Project Report (0155-3712)
Published by: Queensland, Department of Primary Industries, 80 Ann St., GPO Box 46, Brisbane, QLD 4001, Australia. TEL 61-7-34046999, FAX 61-7-34046900, callweb@dpi.qld.gov.au, http://www.dpi.qld.gov.au.

338.1   AUS   ISSN 0728-0696
QUEENSLAND DEPARTMENT OF PRIMARY INDUSTRIES. STUDY TOUR REPORT. Text in English. 1981. 3/w.
Indexed: ESPM.
Published by: Queensland, Department of Primary Industries, 80 Ann St., GPO Box 46, Brisbane, QLD 4001, Australia. TEL 61-7-34046999, FAX 61-7-34046900, callweb@dpi.qld.gov.au, http://www.dpi.qld.gov.au.

630   AUS
QUEENSLAND FARMER. Text in English. m. adv. Document type: Newspaper, Consumer. Description: Focuses on research, extension and management within the agricultural industries of Queensland.
Published by: Rural Press Ltd. (Subsidiary of: Agricultural Publishers Pty. Ltd.), 10 Sydenham St., PO Box 254, Moonee Ponds, VIC 3039, Australia. farmer.qcl@ruralpress.com, http://www.ruralpress.com/. Eds. Ian Morgan TEL 81-7-49543534, Jason Rickett TEL 61-7-47213344. Circ: 10,000.

630   AUS
▼ QUEENSLAND SMART FARMER. Text in English. 2005. bi-m. adv. Document type: Magazine, Trade.
Published by: Rural Press Ltd. (Subsidiary of: Agricultural Publishers Pty. Ltd.), Cnr Finucane Rd. and Delaney St., PO Box 586, Orminston, QLD 4160, Australia. TEL 61-7-38268200, http://www.qldsmartfarmer.com.au/, http://www.ruralpress.com/. Adv. contact Rod Hibberd. page AUD 1,400; bleed 280 x 345.

QUICK FROZEN FOODS INTERNATIONAL. see FOOD AND FOOD INDUSTRIES

630   KOR
R D A JOURNAL OF AGRICULTURAL SCIENCE. (Rural Development Administration) Text in Korean. 1958. s-a. free. adv. Document type: Academic/Scholarly.
Formerly (until 1993): R D A Research Reports
Indexed: AgBio, DSA, I&DA, PGrRegA, RA&MP, RPP, RevApplEntom, RiceAb, VetBull.
Published by: Rural Development Administration, Research Support Division, Suwon, 441707, Korea, S. TEL 82-331-292-4251, FAX 82-331-291-6067. Ed. Yu Ki Hong. Pub. Young Sun Park.

630 664   ITA   ISSN 1020-3737
R E U TECHNICAL SERIES. Text in Italian. 1995. irreg.
Formerly: R E U R Technical Series (1024-2368)
Indexed: AEA, AnBrAb, DSA, HerbAb, HortAb, NutrAb, RRTA, S&F, WAE&RSA.
—BLDSC (7785.537500).

Published by: Food and Agriculture Organization of the United Nations, Regional Office for Europe, Publications Division, Viale delle Terme di Caracalla, Rome, 00100 , Italy. TEL 39-57974350, FAX 39-57975155, publications-sales@fao.org, http://www.fao.org.

630 659   USA   ISSN 0481-5084
R F D NEWS. Text in English. 1958. s-m. USD 12 (effective 2000). adv. bk.rev. tr.lit. Document type: Newspaper.
Published by: Gazette Publishing Co., Inc., 131 E Main St, Box 367, Bellevue, OH 44811. TEL 419-483-7410, FAX 419-483-3617. Ed., R&P, Adv. contact Tom Ackerman. Pub. Tom Smith. Circ: 71,920.

630   IND
RAJASTHAN JOURNAL OF AGRICULTURAL SCIENCES. Text in English. 1970. s-a. INR 15. bibl.; charts.
Indexed: BiolAb.
Published by: Rajasthan Agricultural Research Workers Association, Government Agricultural Research Station, Durgapur, Jaipur, Rajasthan, India. Ed. R L Mathur.

630   JPN   ISSN 0388-0028
AS541
RAKUNO GAKUEN DAIGAKU KIYO. JINBUN SHAKAI KAGAKU HEN/RAKUNO GAKUEN UNIVERSITY. CULTURAL AND SOCIAL SCIENCES. Text mainly in Japanese; Text occasionally in English, German; Summaries in English. 1961. a. per issue exchange basis (effective 2003). Document type: Academic/Scholarly.
Supersedes in part: College of Dairy Agriculture, Hokkaido. Journal (0069-570X)
—BLDSC (4845.550000), CISTI.
Published by: Rakuno Gakuen Daigaku/Rakuno Gakuen University, 582-1 Bunkyodai Midori-cho, Ebetsu-shi, Hokkaido 069, Japan. Ed. Kazuo Horiuchi. Circ: 1,000.

RAMING VAN DE BEDRIJFSUITKOMSTEN VAN DE BEDRIJVEN MET GROENTEELT IN DE OPEN GROND, FRUIT- EN BLOEMBOLLENT. see AGRICULTURE—Abstracting, Bibliographies, Statistics

338.1 630   CAN   ISSN 0827-4053
THE RAM'S HORN; a monthly newsletter of food system analysis. Text in English. 1980. m. CND 24 domestic; USD 25 in United States; USD 30 elsewhere (effective 2005). bk.rev. illus. reprints avail. Document type: Magazine, Trade.
Description: Presents a critique of the agribusiness status quo, and acts as a watchdog on such topics as food labeling, irradiation, additives, and genetic engineering. Also features pieces about economic alternatives like farmer's markets and urban gardening.
Published by: Ram's Horn, S-6, C-27, RR#1, Sorrento, BC V0E 2W0, Canada. TEL 250-675-4866, FAX 250-675-4866, ramshorn@ramshorn.ca, ramshorn@ramshorn.bc.ca, http://www.ramshorn.ca. Ed. Cathleen Kneen.

600 658   AUS   ISSN 0812-4930
RANGE MANAGEMENT NEWSLETTER. Text in English. 1975. 3/yr. AUD 30; AUD 35 foreign (effective 1999). adv.
Document type: Newsletter. Description: For scientific and management groups in the pastoral industries of Australia.
Indexed: AgrForAb, ForAb, HerbAb, NutrAb, PGegResA, RRTA, S&F, WeedAb.
Published by: Australian Rangeland Society, c/o CSIRO, PO Box 2111, Alice Springs, N.T. 0871, Australia. TEL 61-8-89500137, FAX 61-8-89529587. Ed. Gary Bastin. R&P Gary Bastim. Circ: 550.

RANGELAND ECOLOGY & MANAGEMENT. see BIOLOGY

RANGELAND JOURNAL. see CONSERVATION

RASSEGNA TECNICA DEL FRIULI VENEZIA GIULIA. see ENGINEERING—Civil Engineering

630 340   DEU   ISSN 0486-1469
K18
RECHT DER LANDWIRTSCHAFT; Zeitschrift fuer Landwirtschafts- und Agrarumweltrecht. Text in German. 1949. m. EUR 171 (effective 2005). Document type: Newsletter, Trade.
Indexed: IBR, IBZ.
—CCC.
Published by: Agricola-Verlag GmbH, Postfach 2133, Butjadingen-Stollhamm, 26964, Germany. info@agricola-verlag.de, http://www.agricola-verlag.de.

630   USA
THE RECORD (GAINSVILLE). Text in English. 1965. w. (Thu.) USD 0.50 newsstand/cover; USD 20 in state; USD 25 subscr - mailed elsewhere (effective 2005). adv. bk.rev. Document type: Newspaper. Description: General news and some agricultural news.
Former titles: Record - Farm and Ranch; Independent Farmer and Rancher
Published by: Santa Fe Publishing Co., Inc., 620 N. Main St., Gainsville, FL 32602. TEL 352-377-2444, FAX 352-338-1986, record620@aol.com. Ed. Marcy Yozgat. Pub. Constance D Rowe. Circ: 6,800 (paid).

▼ new title   ➤ refereed   * unverified   ◆ full entry avail.

A

631 DOM ISSN 1684-0046
RED DE DESARROLLO TECNOLOGICO DE FRUTALES. HOJA DIVULGATIVA. Key Title: Hoja Divulgativa - REDFRUIT. Text in Spanish. 2000. irreg. back issues avail.
Published by: Centro para el Desarrollo Agropecuario y Forestal, C. Jose Amado Soler, 50, Ensanche Paraiso, Santo Domingo, Dominican Republic. TEL 809-5440616, FAX 809-5444727, cedaf@cedaf.org.do, http://www.cedaf.org.do/publica/boletines.htm.

630 658 CAN
RED DEER ADVOCATE PLUS. Text in English. 1967. w. CND 83.46. adv.
Related titles: Microfilm ed.: (from CML, SOC).
Published by: Canwest Publishers Ltd., 2950 Bremner Ave, Bag 5200, Red Deer, AB T4N 5G3, Canada. TEL 403-343-2400, FAX 403-342-4051. Circ: 40,457.

630 AUS ISSN 1329-184X
REFORM (KINGSTON). Text in English. 1997. q. **Description:** Covers issues related to the rural and agricultural areas of Australia, including rural life, healthcare, finances, laws and regulations.
Related titles: Online - full text ed.
Published by: National Farmers Federation, PO Box E10, Kingston, ACT 2604, Australia. TEL 61-2-6273-3855, FAX 61-2-6273-2331, nff@nff.org.au, http://www.nff.org.au/reform/.

630 AUS ISSN 1440-396X
REGIONAL REVIEW. Text in English. 1998. m. **Description:** Provides update information of seasonal conditions across New South Wales focusing on agriculture and livestock.
Media: Online - full text.
Published by: NSW Agriculture, PO Box 413, Darlinghurst, NSW 2010, Australia. TEL 61-2-9296-1555, http://www.agric.nsw.gov.au/climate/rr/.

636 FRA ISSN 1279-6530
RENCONTRES AUTOUR DES RECHERCHES SUR LES RUMINANTS. Variant title: Rencontres Recherche Ruminants. Text in French. 1994. irreg.
Indexed: AgBio, AnBrAb, DSA, HerbAb, IndVet, MaizeAb, S&F, WAE&RSA.
—BLDSC (7356.906700).
Published by: (France. Institut National de la Recherche Agronomique (INRA)), Institut de l'Elevage, 149 Rue de Bercy, Paris, 75595 Cedex 12, France. TEL 33-1-40045150, FAX 33-1-40045275, http://www.inst-elevage.asso.fr.

630 USA ISSN 0090-8932
TS1980
RENDER; the national magazine of rendering. Text in English. 1959. bi-m. free to qualified personnel. adv. illus.; stat.; tr.lit. **Document type:** *Magazine, Trade.* **Description:** Promotes the exchange of ideas on management, operations, research and development, environmental controls, quality assurance, and marketing among all facets of the rendering industry in North America.
Supersedes (in 1972): Renderer (0034-4362)
—CISTI.
Published by: (National Renderers Association), Sierra Publishing, 2820 Birch Ave, Camino, CA 95709. TEL 530-644-8428, FAX 530-644-8429, editors@rendermagazine.com, http://www.rendermagazine.com. Ed., Pub. Tina Caparella. adv.: B&W page USD 1,494; trim 11 x 8.5. Circ: 6,500 (controlled).

630 363.7 GBR ISSN 1742-1705
S605.5 CODEN: AJAAEZ
➤ **RENEWABLE AGRICULTURE AND FOOD SYSTEMS.** Text in English. 1986. q. USD 210 in the Americas to institutions except Canada; GBP 120 elsewhere to institutions; USD 230 combined subscription in the Americas to institutions except Canada; print & online eds.; GBP 130 combined subscription elsewhere to institutions print & online eds. (effective 2006). adv. bk.rev. illus. back issues avail.; reprints avail. **Document type:** *Journal, Academic/Scholarly.* **Description:** Publishes original research and review articles on the economic, ecological, and environmental impacts of agriculture; the effective use of renewable resources and biodiversity in agro-ecosystems; and the technological and sociological implications of sustainable food systems.
Formerly (until 2004): American Journal of Alternative Agriculture (0889-1893)
Related titles: Online - full text ed.: ISSN 1742-1713. USD 175 in the Americas to institutions except Canada; GBP 100 elsewhere to institutions (effective 2006) (from EBSCO Publishing, Gale Group, IngentaConnect, Ovid Technologies, Inc., Swets Information Services).
Indexed: AEA, ASCA, ASFA, AgBio, Agr, AgrForAb, AnBrAb, B&AI, BibAg, BioCN&I, CPA, DSA, EPB, ESPM, EngInd, EnvAb, EnvEAb, FCA, FPA, FS&TA, ForAb, GEOBASE, GardL, HerbAb, HortAb, I&DA, M&GPA, MaizeAb, NemAb, NutrAb, OrnHort, PBA, PHN&I, PN&I, PollutAb, PotatoAb, PoultAb, RA&MP, RDA, REE&TA, RPP, RRTA, RefZh, RevApplEntom, RiceAb, S&F, SSCI, SeedAb, SoyAb, TDB, TriticAb, VetBull, WAE&RSA, WeedAb.
—BLDSC (7364.184500), CISTI, Ei, IE, Infotrieve, ingenta. CCC.

Published by: CABI Publishing (Subsidiary of: CAB International), CAB International, Wallingford, Oxfordshire OX10 8DE, United Kingdom. TEL 44-1491-832111, FAX 44-1491-833508, cabi@cabi.org, http://www.cabi-publishing.org/. Ed. J W Doran. adv.: B&W page GBP 225, B&W page USD 360; 170 x 225. Circ: 1,000. **Subscr. addr. in N. America:** CABI Publishing North America, 875 Massachusetts Ave, 7th Fl, Cambridge, MA 02139. TEL 617-395-4056, 800-528-4841, FAX 617-354-6875, cabi-nao@cabi.org.

630 CHN
RENSHEN YANJIU/GINSENG STUDIES. Text in Chinese. q.
Published by: Jilin Renshen Yanjiusuo/Jilin Ginseng Research Institute, 37-12 Longquan Lu, Tonghua, Jilin 134001, China. TEL 4835. Ed. Zhou Wenhao.

RESALE WEEKLY. see *BUILDING AND CONSTRUCTION*

630 658 USA ISSN 1061-7795
RESISTANT PEST MANAGEMENT. Text in English. 1989. s-a. free. adv. bk.rev. **Document type:** *Newsletter.*
Former titles: Pest Resistance Management; Pesticide Resistance Management
Indexed: AgBio, BioCN&I, FCA, MaizeAb, PBA, PHN&I, RPP, RevApplEntom, WeedAb.
Published by: Michigan State University, B-11 Pesticide Research Center, East Lansing, MI 48824-1311. TEL 517-355-1768, FAX 517-353-5598, 22513mew@msu.edu, http://www.msstate.edu/entomology/ENTPLP.html. Ed. Mark E Whalon. Adv. contact Andrea Coombs. Circ: 1,600.

630 FRA ISSN 0995-6069
REVEIL LOZERE. Text in French. 1969. 48/yr.
Formerly (until 1989): Reveil Agricole (0995-6077)
Published by: Societe d Edition et de Publication Agricole de, 9 place au Ble, Mende, 48000, France. TEL 66-49-18-92, FAX 66-49-00-52. Ed. Anselme Rousset. Circ: 5,000.

630 SCG ISSN 0354-5865
REVIJA AGRONOMSKA SAZNANJA✶. Text in Serbian; Summaries in English. 1994. q. YUN 200; USD 40 foreign.
Published by: Vojvodjansko Drustvo za Poljoprivrednu Tehniku/Voivodina's Society of Agricultural Engineers, c/o Institute for Agricultural Mechanisation, P.O. Box 41, Belgrade-Zemun. FAX 381-21-59989, vlazic@polj.ns.ac.yu, mmartog@uns.ns.ac.yu. Ed. Milan Martinov. R&P Veselin Lazic. Circ: 500. **Co-sponsor:** Yugoslav Scientific Society of Agricultural Engineers.

630 ARG ISSN 0080-2069
CODEN: RAARA2
REVISTA AGRONOMICA DEL NOROESTE ARGENTINO. Text in Spanish. 1953. irreg. ARS 1,000. bk.rev.
Indexed: ATA, BIOSIS Prev, BiolAb, DSA, FCA, HerbAb, HortAb, RPP, RRTA, VITIS, WAE&RSA.
—CASDDS, CINDOC.
Published by: Universidad Nacional de Tucuman, Facultad de Agronomia y Zootecnia, Casilla de Correos 125, San Miguel De Tucuman, Tucuman 4000, Argentina. Circ: 350.

630 CRI ISSN 0048-7597
REVISTA AGROPECUARIA; al servicio de la agricultura y la ganaderia centroamericana. Text in Spanish. 1969. q. USD 6. adv. bk.rev. illus.
Indexed: FCA.
Published by: Editora Latina Ltda., San Rafael Abajo de Desamparados, San Jose, Costa Rica. Ed. J Luis Burgos Murillo. Circ: 5,000.

REVISTA BRASILEIRA DE AGROMETEOROLOGIA. see *METEOROLOGY*

630 BRA ISSN 0100-3518
SB195 CODEN: RBARDC
REVISTA BRASILEIRA DE ARMAZENAMENTO. Text in English. 1976. s-a.
Indexed: AEA, AgrForAb, BioCN&I, CPA, FCA, FPA, FS&TA, HerbAb, HortAb, MaizeAb, NutrAb, OrnHort, PBA, PGegResA, PGrRegA, PHN&I, RA&MP, RDA, RM&VM, RPP, RefZh, RevApplEntom, RiceAb, S&F, SIA, SeedAb, SoyAb, TriticAb, WAE&RSA, ZooRec.
—BLDSC (7843.600000), CINDOC, CISTI.
Published by: Centro Nacional de Trein Armazenagem-Centreinar, Campus da Univ. Fed. Vicosa, Vicosa, MG, 36571-000, Brazil. TEL 55-31-891-2270, FAX 55-31-891-1943, centrein@mail.ufv.br. Ed. Paulo Cesar Correa. Circ: 3,000.

630 628 BRA ISSN 1415-4366
➤ **REVISTA BRASILEIRA DE ENGENHARIA AGRICOLA E AMBIENTAL.** Abbreviated title: Agriambi. Text in Portuguese. 1997. q. **Document type:** *Journal, Academic/Scholarly.* **Description:** Publishes original scientific and technical articles in the areas of irrigation and drainage engineering, agricultural meteorology and climatology, soil and water management, rural constructions and ambient, storage and processing of agricultural products, environmental control and management, automation and instrumentation, energy in agriculture and agricultural machines.
Related titles: Online - full text ed.: free (effective 2005).
Indexed: AbHyg, AgBio, AgrForAb, AnBrAb, CPA, DSA, ESPM, EnvEAb, FCA, FPA, ForAb, HerbAb, HortAb, I&DA, MaizeAb, OrnHort, PBA, PGegResA, PHN&I, PN&I, PotatoAb, PoultAb, RRTA, S&F, SIA, SeedAb, SoyAb, TDB, TriticAb, WAE&RSA, WeedAb.
Published by: Universidade Federal de Campina Grande, Centro de Ciencias e Tecnologia, Departamento de Engenharia Agricola, Caixa Postal 10078, Campina Grande, PB 58109-970, Brazil. TEL 55-83-3101056, FAX 55-83-3101185, agriambi@agriambi.com.br, http://www.scielo.br/scielo.php/script_sci_serial/pid_1415-4366/lng_en/nrm_iso/lng_en.

630 BRA ISSN 0034-737X
S15 CODEN: RCERA2
➤ **REVISTA CERES;** orgao de divulgacao tecnico-cientifica em ciencias agrarias. Text in English, Portuguese, Spanish; Summaries in English. 1939. bi-m. USD 40 (effective 2002). abstr.; bibl.; charts; illus. index. back issues avail. **Document type:** *Journal, Academic/Scholarly.* **Description:** Publishes research papers on agriculture and related fields.
Formerly (until 1944): Ceres (0366-5798)
Indexed: AEA, AgBio, AgrForAb, AnBrAb, BioCN&I, BiolAb, CIN, CPA, ChemAb, ChemTitl, DSA, FCA, FPA, FS&TA, ForAb, HelmAb, HerbAb, HortAb, I&DA, IndVet, MaizeAb, NemAb, NutrAb, OrnHort, PBA, PGegResA, PGrRegA, PHN&I, PN&I, PotatoAb, PoultAb, RA&MP, RDA, RPP, RefZh, RevApplEntom, RiceAb, S&F, SFA, SIA, SeedAb, SoyAb, TriticAb, VetBull, WAE&RSA, WeedAb, WildRev, ZooRec.
—BLDSC (7848.000000), CASDDS, CINDOC, CISTI, IE, ingenta, Linda Hall.
Published by: Universidade Federal de Vicosa, Vicosa, MG 36570-000, Brazil. TEL 55-31-8992136, FAX 55-31-8992205, ceres@mail.ufv.br. Ed. Clibas Vieira. Circ: 1,100 (controlled).

630 CUB ISSN 1010-2760
REVISTA CIENCIAS TECNICAS AGROPECUARIAS. Text in Spanish. 4/yr. USD 42 in the Americas; USD 48 in Europe; USD 28 elsewhere (effective 2000). adv. back issues avail. **Document type:** *Academic/Scholarly.*
—CISTI.
Published by: Universidad Agraria de la Habana, Direccion de Informacion Cientifico-Tecnica, Apdo. Postal 18-19, San Jose de las Lajas, La Habana, Cuba. TEL 53-64-63013 ext 291, FAX 53-7-240942, TELEX 056-113, jargen@main.isch.edu.cu. Ed. Pedro Paneque Rondon. Pub. Arturo R. Martinez. Adv. contact Nelson Napoles Hernandez. B&W page USD 96; trim 21 x 29.7. **Dist. by:** Ediciones Cubanas, Obispo No. 527, Apdo. 605, Havana, Cuba.

630 CUB ISSN 0034-7485
➤ **REVISTA CUBANA DE CIENCIA AGRICOLA.** Text in Spanish. 1967. 4/yr. USD 80 (effective 2003). adv. bk.rev. charts; illus.; stat. index. **Document type:** *Academic/Scholarly.* **Description:** Covers animal nutrition, genetics, pasture and forage production. Includes information about milk, beef, poultry and swine production; biochemistry, conservation, weeds and pests, soils, fertilizers and mechanization.
Related titles: ♦ English ed.: Cuban Journal of Agricultural Science. ISSN 0864-0408.
Indexed: ASCA, AgrForAb, AnBrAb, BiolAb, CIN, ChemAb, ChemTitl, CurCont, DSA, ExcerpMed, FCA, FS&TA, ForAb, HerbAb, IAALC, IndVet, MaizeAb, NutrAb, PBA, PoultAb, RRTA, RiceAb, S&F, SIA, SeedAb, SoyAb, VetBull, WAE&RSA, WeedAb.
—CINDOC, CISTI.
Published by: Instituto de Ciencia Animal, Tulipan No. 1011 e-47 y Loma, Nuevo Vedado, Havana, Cuba. TEL 53-62-99180, FAX 53-73-35382, ica@ceniai.inf.cu. Ed. Rafael Herrera. R&P Dulce Maria Vento. Adv. contact Maria Teresa Perez. B&W page USD 20, color page USD 100. Circ: 250 (paid).

630 BRA ISSN 0034-7655
CODEN: RAPCAW
➤ **REVISTA DE AGRICULTURA.** Text in English, Portuguese, Spanish; Summaries in English, Portuguese, Spanish. 1926. 3/yr. BRL 30 in Mercosul; USD 60 elsewhere (effective 2003). adv. bk.rev. bibl.; charts; illus. index. back issues avail. **Document type:** *Journal, Academic/Scholarly.*
Related titles: E-mail ed.; Microfilm ed.
Indexed: AEA, AgBio, AgrForAb, AnBrAb, BioCN&I, BiolAb, CIN, CPA, ChemAb, ChemTitl, CurCont, DSA, FCA, FPA, ForAb, HerbAb, HortAb, I&DA, IndVet, MaizeAb, NemAb, NutrAb, OrnHort, PBA, PGegResA, PGrRegA, PHN&I, PotatoAb, PoultAb, RA&MP, RDA, RM&VM, RPP, RevApplEntom, RiceAb, S&F, SIA, SeedAb, SoyAb, TobAb, TriticAb, VetBull, WAE&RSA, WeedAb, ZooRec.
—CASDDS, Linda Hall.
Published by: Associacao de Estudos de Agricultura, Centro, Caixa Postal 60, Piracicaba, SP 13400-970, Brazil. TEL 55-19-34223604, FAX 55-19-34267136, mabgomes@carpa.ciagri.usp.br. Ed., R&P Frederico Pimentel Gomes. Adv. contact Mrs. Marli Debem Gomes TEL 55-19-34340535. B&W page USD 400; trim 190 x 130. Circ: 600.

630 PRT ISSN 0871-018X
➤ **REVISTA DE CIENCIAS AGRARIAS.** Text in English, French, Portuguese. 1903. 4/yr. GBP 20 domestic; USD 60 foreign (effective 2000). adv. **Document type:** *Academic/Scholarly.*
Related titles: Online - full text ed.

Indexed: BIOSIS Prev, BiolAb, FPA, ForAb, HortAb, IndVet, PBA, PGegResA, ProtozoAb, S&F, SeedAb, VITIS, VetBull, WeedAb, WildRev.
Published by: Sociedade de Ciencias Agarias, Rua Junqueira, 299, Lisbon, 1300, Portugal. TEL 351-21-3633719, FAX 351-21-3622518, http://agricultura.isa.utl.pt/scap. Ed. Mendes Ferrao. Pub. A. Pimenta Castro. Adv. contact A Pimenta Castro.

343.076 URY ISSN 0797-292X
REVISTA DE DERECHO AGRARIO - URUGUAY. Text in Spanish. 1985. irreg., latest vol.8. price varies. **Document type:** *Trade.* **Description:** Discusses agricultural law.
Published by: Fundacion de Cultura Universitaria, Casilla de Correo Central, Veinticinco De Mayo, 568, Montevideo, 11003, Uruguay. TEL 598-2-9161152, FAX 598-2-9152549, fcuventa@multi.com.uy, http://www.fcu.com.uy.

REVISTA DE DERECHO Y REFORMA AGRARIA. see *LAW*

630 ESP ISSN 1139-7748
REVISTA DE DESARROLLO RURAL Y COOPERATIVISMO AGRARIO. Text in Spanish. 1998. a.
Related titles: Online - full text ed.: ISSN 1139-8507. 1998.
—CINDOC.
Published by: Universidad de Zaragoza, Departamento de Produccion Animal y Ciencia de los Alimentos, Miguel Servet, 177, Zaragoza, 55013, Spain. saezen@posta.unizar.es, http://cederul.unizar.es/revista/. Ed. Enrique Saez Olivito.

REVISTA DE DIREITO AGRARIO. see *LAW*

630 ESP
REVISTA DE L'INSTITUT. Text in Spanish. 4/yr.
Published by: Association of Agricultural Traders in Catalunya, Placa Sant Josep Oriol, 4, Barcelona, 08002, Spain. TEL 3-30-11-740, FAX 3-317-30-05. Circ: 3,000.

630 MEX ISSN 0034-9097
HD1792
REVISTA DEL MEXICO AGRARIO✶. Text in Spanish. 1967. 6/yr. USD 12.
Indexed: PAIS.
Published by: Confederacion Nacional Campesina, Apdo. Postal 59-007, Mexico, D.F., 10200, Mexico. Ed. Hugo Tulio Melendez. **Subscr. to:** Libreria Mexico Agraria, Apdo. Postal 59-007, Mexico City 1, DF, Mexico.

630 BRA ISSN 0100-607X
REVISTA DO SETOR DE CIENCIAS AGRARIAS. Text in Portuguese; Summaries in English, Portuguese. 1979. biennial. adv. bibl.; charts; illus. **Document type:** *Academic/Scholarly.* **Description:** Articles and scientific notes in the area of agronomy, forestry, and veterinarian sciences.
Related titles: CD-ROM ed.
Indexed: AEA, AgBio, AgrForAb, AnBrAb, BioCN&I, CPA, DSA, FCA, FPA, ForAb, HerbAb, HortAb, I&DA, IndVet, MaizeAb, NemAb, NutrAb, OrnHort, PBA, PGegResA, PGrRegA, PHN&I, PN&I, PotatoAb, PoultAb, RA&MP, RPP, RRTA, S&F, SeedAb, SoyAb, TDB, VetBull, WAE&RSA.
Published by: Universidade Federal do Parana, Sector de Ciencias Agrarias, Centro, Caixa Postal 672, Curitiba, PR 81531-990, Brazil. TEL 55-41-2535552, FAX 55-41-2535552. Ed. Vismar da Costa Lima Neto. Circ: 800.

630 330.1 ARG
REVISTA INTERDISCIPLINARIA DE ESTUDIOS AGRARIOS. Variant title: Cuadernos del P I E A. Programa Interdisciplinario de Estudios Agrarios. Cuadernos. Text in Spanish. 1996. 3/yr. USD 26 (effective 2003). bk.rev. **Document type:** *Academic/Scholarly.*
Published by: Instituto de Investigaciones de Historia Economica y Social, Fac. de Ciencias Economicas UBA, Avda. Cordoba, 2122 Piso 2, Buenos Aires, 1120, Argentina. piea@interlink.com.ar.

630 COL ISSN 0035-0222
REVISTA NACIONAL DE AGRICULTURA. Text in Spanish. 1906. q. COP 36,000, USD 160; or exchange basis. adv. bk.rev. charts; illus. **Document type:** *Trade.* **Description:** Publishes articles on all aspects of price policy, credit, land tenure reform, research extension, natural resources management, marketing, foreign trade, and public investment. Analyzes the effects of these factors on agricultural production.
Indexed: AgBio, BiolAb, ChemAb, DSA, ForAb, HortAb, NutrAb, RDA, RiceAb, TriticAb, WAE&RSA.
—BLDSC (7868.300000), CISTI, IE, ingenta.
Published by: Sociedad de Agricultores de Colombia, Carrera 7a, 24-89 Piso 44, Bogota, DE, Colombia. TEL 57-1-2813313, FAX 57-1-2844572, socdeagr@impsat.net.co, http://www.sociedadagricultores.org.co. Ed. Gabriel Martinez Pelaez. Adv. contact Ruth Ortega. Circ: 2,000.

581 630 CUB ISSN 0138-6492
REVISTA PLANTAS MEDICINALES. Abstracts and contents page in English. 1981. a. USD 6 in the Americas; USD 9 in Europe. abstr.
Indexed: Agrind.
—CISTI.

Published by: Centro de Informacion y Documentacion Agropecuario, Gaveta Postal 4149, Havana, 4, Cuba. **Dist. by:** Ediciones Cubanas, Obispo No. 527, Apdo. 605, Havana, Cuba.

630 BRA
REVISTA REALIDADE RURAL/RURAL REALTY. Text in Portuguese. 1963. m.
Published by: Cooperativa Central dos Produtores Rurais de Minas Gerais, Rua Itambe, 40, Floresta, Belo Horizonte, MG 30150-150, Brazil. Ed. Jose P Campos. Circ: 30,000.

630 FRA ISSN 0999-212X
REVUE AGRICOLE DE L'AUBE. Text in French. 1862. w.
Formerly (until 1928): Revue Agricole du Comice Departmental de l'Aube (0999-2111); (until 1902): Bulletin Agricole (0999-2103); (until 1875): Revue Agricole du Department de l'Aube (0999-209X)
Published by: Revue Agricole de l, 2 bis rue Jeanne d'Arc, BP 4017, Troyes, Cedex 10013, France. TEL 25-73-30-55, FAX 25-73-12-63. Ed. G Menuel. Circ: 5,000.

630 CHE ISSN 0375-1325
CODEN: RSAGB
REVUE SUISSE D'AGRICULTURE. Text in French; Summaries in English, German, Italian. 1969. bi-m. CHF 46 (effective 2001). adv. bk.rev. illus. **Document type:** *Journal, Academic/Scholarly.*
Supersedes in part (in 1969): Agriculture Romande (0515-7412)
Indexed: AEA, AgBio, AnBrAb, BioCN&I, BiolAb, CPA, DBA, DSA, FCA, FS&TA, ForAb, HelmAb, HerbAb, HortAb, I&DA, IndVet, MaizeAb, NutrAb, PBA, PGegResA, PGrRegA, PHN&I, PN&I, PotatoAb, RA&MP, RASB, RDA, RM&VM, RPP, RRTA, RefZh, RevApplEntom, S&F, SIA, SeedAb, SoyAb, TriticAb, VITIS, VetBull, WAE&RSA, WeedAb.
—BLDSC (7953.345000), CISTI, IE, Infotrieve, ingenta, Linda Hall.
Published by: A M T R A - Association pour la Mise en Valeur des Travaux de la Recherche Agronomique, Case Postale 516, Nyon 1, 1260, Switzerland. TEL 44-22-3634151, FAX 41-22-3634155. Ed. Andre Maillard. Adv. contact Eliane Rohrer. B&W page CHF 1,503; trim 250 x 180. Circ: 5,000.

630 DEU
RHEINISCHES GENOSSENSCHAFTSBLATT. Text in German. m. adv. bk.rev.
Published by: Genossenschaftsverband Rheinland e.V., Postfach 101562, Cologne, 50455, Germany. TEL 49-221-20140, FAX 49-221-236581.

630 CAN ISSN 0844-3823
LE RICHELIEU DIMANCHE. Text in French. 1936. w. CND 48, USD 270 (effective 2000). adv. 8 cols./p.; **Document type:** *Newspaper.*
Formerly: Richelieu Agricole
Related titles: Microfilm ed.
Published by: Promotion G.& P. Inc., 84 Richelieu St, Saint Jean Sur Richelieu, PQ J3B 6X3, Canada. TEL 514-347-5371, FAX 514-347-4539. Ed. Robert Paradis. Adv. contact Bernard Paradis. Circ: 35,795.

630 ITA ISSN 0391-8688
RISICOLTORE; mensile d'informazioni agricole, industriali, e commerciali. Text in Italian. 1956. m. free. adv. bk.rev. **Document type:** *Newspaper.* **Description:** Deals with rice and grain growing; includes political, technical and economic factors pertaining to agriculture.
Published by: Ente Nazionale Risi, Piazza Pio XI, 1, Milan, MI 20123, Italy. TEL 39-02-8855111, FAX 39-02-865503, info@enterisi.it, http://www.enterisi.it. Ed., R&P Paolo Viana. Adv. contact Donata Zanardo. Circ: 30,000.

630 USA
RIVERSIDE COUNTY AGRICULTURE✶. Text in English. 1946. m. USD 5 to non-members. adv. bk.rev. illus.
Former titles: Riverside County Farm and Agricultural Business News (0035-5690); Riverside County Farm Bureau News
Published by: (Riverside County Farm Bureau, Inc.), Riverside County Publishing Co., 7190 Jurupa Ave, Riverside, CA 92504-1016. Ed. Robert Eli Perkins. Circ: 3,277.

630 340 ITA ISSN 0391-8696
K22
RIVISTA DI DIRITTO AGRARIO. Text in Italian. 1922. q. EUR 72.30 in the European Union; EUR 108.46 elsewhere (effective 2002). adv. **Description:** Presents research, legislation, and judicial decisions regarding agrarian law.
Indexed: DIP, ELLIS, IBR, IBZ, RASB.
—IE, Infotrieve.
Published by: (Istituto di Diritto Agrario Internazionale e Comparato), Casa Editrice Dott. A. Giuffre (Subsidiary of: LexisNexis Europe and Africa), Via Busto Arsizio, 40, Milan, MI 20151, Italy. TEL 39-02-28089200, FAX 39-02-38009582, giuffre@giuffre.it, http://www.giuffre.it. Ed. Marco Goldoni. Circ: 1,800.

630 900 ITA ISSN 0557-1359
S419
➤ **RIVISTA DI STORIA DELL'AGRICOLTURA.** Text in Italian; Summaries in English. 1961. s-a. bibl.; illus.; maps. cum.index: 1961-1995. back issues avail. **Document type:** *Journal, Academic/Scholarly.* **Description:** Covers history of agriculture, agricultural technologies, the rural world, and agricultural literature.
Indexed: RASB.
Published by: Accademia dei Georgofili, Logge Uffizi Corti, Florence, FI 50122, Italy. TEL 39-055-212114, FAX 39-055-2302754, accademia@georgofili.it, http://www.georgofili.it. Ed. Giovanni Cherubini. Circ: 300. **Dist. by:** Studio Editoriale Fiorentino, Italy. TEL 39-55-481460, FAX 39-55481460.

630 USA
ROCKY MOUNTAIN FARMERS UNION. Text in English. 1912. bi-m. USD 7 (effective 2005). charts; illus. **Document type:** *Magazine, Trade.*
Formerly: Rocky Mountain Union Farmer (0035-7650)
Address: 5655 S Yosemite St, Ste 400, Greenwood Village, CO 80111. TEL 303-752-5800, FAX 303-752-5810, rmfu@aol.com, rmfu@rmfu.org, http://www.rmfu.org. Eds. Ann Lynn Eschbach, Marilyn Wentz. Pub. John Stencel. R&P Marilyn Wentz. Circ: 8,000 (paid).

630 ITA
LA ROMAGNA AGRICOLA E ZOOTECNICA. Text in Italian. 1915. a. free.
Published by: Azienda Agraria Sperimentale Marani, Via Romea Nord, 248, Ravenna, RA 48100, Italy. TEL 0544 451041, FAX 0544-451448. Circ: 1,000.

638.1 ROM ISSN 1220-2525
ROMANIA APICOLA. Text in Romanian. 1926. m. **Description:** Review of apiculture.
Former titles (until 1989): Apicultura in Romania (0378-2425); (until 1975): Apicultura (0518-1305); (until 1948): Romania Apicola (1220-2517)
Indexed: RefZh.
Published by: Asociatia Crescatorilor de Albine din Romania/Beekeeping Association of Romania, Masaryk Thomas 17, Bucharest, 70231, Romania. TEL 40-21-2114750. Circ: 25,000.

630 RUS ISSN 0869-6128
CODEN: DRASE8
ROSSIISKAYA AKADEMIYA SEL'SKOKHOZYAISTVENNYKH NAUK. DOKLADY. Text in Russian. 1936. bi-m. USD 173 foreign (effective 2005). bk.rev. charts. index. **Document type:** *Journal, Academic/Scholarly.*
Formerly: Vsezoyuznaya Akademiya Sel'skokhozyaistvennykh Nauk im. V.I. Lenina. Doklady (0042-9244)
Related titles: ♦ English Translation: Russian Agricultural Sciences. ISSN 1068-3674.
Indexed: AgBio, CIN, CPA, CTFA, ChemAb, ChemTitl, HortAb, I&DA, NutrAb, PGrRegA, PotatoAb, RefZh, SoyAb, TriticAb, VetBull, WeedAb.
—BLDSC (0055.460000), CASDDS, CISTI, East View, Linda Hall. **CCC.**
Published by: Rossiiskaya Akademiya Sel'skokhozyaistvennykh Nauk/Russian Academy of Agricultural Sciences, Ul Krzhizhanovskogo 15, k 2, Moscow, 117218, Russian Federation. TEL 7-095-2077660. Ed. Nadezhda S Markova. Circ: 1,300. **US dist. addr.:** East View Information Services, 3020 Harbor Ln. N., Minneapolis, MN 55447. TEL 800-477-1005, FAX 800-800-3839, eastview@eastview.com, http://www.eastview.com.

338.1 RUS ISSN 0869-3730
ROSSIISKAYA AKADEMIYA SEL'SKOKHOZYAISTVENNYKH NAUK. VESTNIK. Text in Russian. m. USD 149 in United States.
Indexed: RefZh.
—East View.
Published by: Rossiiskii Akademii Sel'skokhozyaistvennykh Nauk, Ul Krzhizhanovskogo 15, Moscow, 117218, Russian Federation. TEL 7-095-2086014. **US dist. addr.:** East View Information Services, 3020 Harbor Ln. N., Minneapolis, MN 55447. TEL 612-550-0961.

630 GBR ISSN 0080-4134
S3 CODEN: JRAGAY
ROYAL AGRICULTURAL SOCIETY OF ENGLAND. JOURNAL. Text in English. 1839. a. GBP 55 to individual members (effective 2005). adv. index. reprint service avail. from ISI. **Document type:** *Journal, Academic/Scholarly.* **Description:** Contains practical self-help articles that can be swiftly implemented on the farm. It also includes comment pieces on the industry as well as case studies on science and technology at work in agriculture.
Media: Online - full content. **Related titles:** Microform ed.: (from PMC).
Indexed: AEA, AbHyg, AgBio, AnBrAb, BiolAb, CPA, DSA, Englnd, FCA, FS&TA, ForAb, GEOBASE, HerbAb, HortAb, I&DA, IndVet, MaizeAb, NemAb, NutrAb, PAIS, PBA, PCI, PGegResA, PHN&I, PN&I, PoultAb, RDA, RICS, RPP, RRTA, RevApplEntom, S&F, SIA, SeedAb, TriticAb, VetBull, WAE&RSA, WeedAb.
—BLDSC (4851.000000), CISTI, Ei, IE, Infotrieve, ingenta, Linda Hall.

A

Published by: Royal Agricultural Society of England, National Agricultural Centre, Stoneleigh Park, Warks CV8 2LZ, United Kingdom. TEL 44-24-76696969, info@rase.org.uk, http://www.rase.org.uk/activities/publications/RASE_journal/index.asp. R&P Alan Spedding. Circ: 16,000.

630   ZAF
ROYAL AGRICULTURAL SOCIETY OF NATAL. ROYAL SHOW PROGRAMME. Text in English. a. ZAR 4. adv.
Formerly: Royal Agricultural Society of Natal. Royal Show Catalogue
Published by: Royal Agricultural Society of Natal, PO Box 524, Pietermaritzburg, KwaZulu-Natal 3200, South Africa. TEL 27-331-56274, FAX 27-331-943540. Circ: 500.

630   GBR
ROYAL BATH & WEST SHOW CATALOGUE. Text in English. 1852. a. GBP 2 (effective 2000). adv. **Document type:** Catalog.
Formerly: Bath and West Show Catalogue
Published by: Royal Bath and West of England Society, The Showground, Shepton Mallet, Somers BA4 6QN, United Kingdom. TEL 44-1749-822200, FAX 44-1749-823169, general.office@bathandwest.co.uk, http://www.bathandwest.co.uk. Ed. Louise Boyce. R&P Martyn Rayner. Circ: 3,000.

630   GBR
ROYAL HIGHLAND NEWS. Text in English. 1969. 3/yr. free to members. adv. **Document type:** Newsletter. **Description:** Review of the society's activities.
Former titles (until 1992): Royal Highland and Agricultural Society of Scotland. Review; Royal Highland and Agricultural Society of Scotland. Show Guide and Review
Published by: Royal Highland and Agricultural Society of Scotland, Royal Highland Centre, Ingliston, Edinburgh EH28 8NF, United Kingdom. TEL 44-131-335-6200, FAX 44-131-333-5236. Ed., R&P, Adv. contact Ross Muir. Circ: 16,000.

ROYAL TROPICAL INSTITUTE. BULLETIN. see ANTHROPOLOGY

630 624   JPN
RURAL AND ENVIRONMENTAL ENGINEERING. Abbreviated title: R E E. Text in English. 1982. s-a. JPY 4,000 foreign to individuals; JPY 6,000 foreign to institutions. **Description:** Covers land consolidation, rural planning, environmental sciences, irrigation and water management.
Formerly (until 1996): Journal of Irrigation Engineering and Rural Planning (0287-8607)
Indexed: Agr, EngInd.
—BLDSC (8052.419500), IE, ingenta, Linda Hall. **CCC.**
Published by: Japanese Society of Irrigation Drainage and Reclamation Engineering/Nogyo Doboku Gakkai, Nogyo Doboku Kaikan, 34-4 Shinbashi 5-chome, Minato-ku, Tokyo, 105-0004, Japan. TEL 81-3-34363418, FAX 81-3-34358494, yositake@jsidre.or.jp, suido@jsidre.or.jp, http://www.jsidre.or.jp Ed., R&P Sschiko Yoshitake. **Subscr. to:** Maruzen Co., Ltd., 3-10 Nihonbashi, 2-Chome, Chuo-ku, Tokyo 103, Japan.

RURAL AREAS NEWSLINK. see ENVIRONMENTAL STUDIES

RURAL AREAS NEWSLINK (GERMAN EDITION). see ENVIRONMENTAL STUDIES

RURAL BUILDER. see BUILDING AND CONSTRUCTION

630   USA   ISSN 1063-5866
HN90.C6
RURAL CONDITIONS AND TRENDS. Text in English. 1990. q. USD 26; USD 52 foreign (effective 1999). illus. reprints avail. **Description:** Analyzes statistical data obtained from a number of federal sources. Describes conditions and trends of rural America in terms of employment and unemployment, industry, earnings, income poetry, and population.
Indexed: AmStl, CIJE, PAIS.
Published by: U.S. Department of Agriculture, Economic Research Service, 1800 M St, N W, Rm 3100, Washington, DC 20036. TEL 202-694-5050, ersinfo@ers.usda.gov, http://www.ers.usda.gov/. Ed. Doug Bowers. **Dist. by:** U.S. Department of Agriculture, National Agricultural Statistics Service, 5285 Port Royal Rd, Springfield, VA 22161. TEL 703-605-6220, 800-999-6779, FAX 603-605-6900, nass@nass.usda.gov, http://www.usda.gov/nass.

630 334   USA   ISSN 1088-8845
HD1491.U5
RURAL COOPERATIVES. Text in English. 1934. bi-m. USD 23 (effective 2005). charts; illus. reprint service avail. from CIS. **Document type:** Magazine, Trade. **Description:** Directed to cooperatives' hired professional management and its elected leadership. Reports actions by cooperatives, USDA's Rural Developments, RBS and Cooperative Services activities, and perspectives of leaders on problems, issues, and challenges facing cooperatives' member-owners.
Former titles (until 1996): Farmer Cooperatives (0364-0736); (until 1976): News for Farmer Cooperatives (0028-9035)
Related titles: Microform ed.: (from CIS); Online - full content ed.; Online - full text ed.: (from EBSCO Publishing, Florida Center for Library Automation, Gale Group, ProQuest Information & Learning).

Indexed: AgBio, Agr, AgrForAb, AmStl, BibAg, DSA, F&GI, HortAb, IUSGP, NutrAb, PAIS, PHN&I, RDA, TriticAb, WAE&RSA.
—Linda Hall.
Published by: U.S. Department of Agriculture, Rural Business - Cooperative Service, Stop 3250, Washington, DC 20250-3250. TEL 202-720-7558, FAX 202-720-4641, http://www.rurdev.usda.gov/rbs/pub/openmag.htm. Ed. Daniel Campbell. Circ: 7,000. **Subscr. to:** U.S. Government Printing Office, Superintendent of Documents, PO Box 371954, Pittsburgh, PA 15250-7954. TEL 202-512-1800, FAX 202-512-2250, orders@gpo.gov, http://www.access.gpo.gov.

630   USA
RURAL DEVELOPMENT PERSPECTIVES. Text in English. 1997. 3/yr.
Indexed: Agr, CIJE, PAIS.
Published by: U.S. Department of Agriculture, Economic Research Service, 1800 M St, N W, Rm 3100, Washington, DC 20036. TEL 202-694-5050, ersinfo@ers.usda.gov, http://www.ers.usda.gov/.

630   UGA   ISSN 0080-4851
RURAL DEVELOPMENT RESEARCH PAPER. Text in English. 1965. irreg. price varies.
Published by: Department of Rural Economy, PO Box 7062, Kampala, Uganda.

▼ **RURAL EUROPE**; agri-environment and rural development policy. see ENVIRONMENTAL STUDIES

338.01   AUS   ISSN 0812-1729
RURAL INDUSTRY DIRECTORY. Text in English. 1958. a. AUD 24.95. **Document type:** Directory.
Former titles: Australian Agriculture, Fisheries and Forestry Directory (0067-2106); Australian Primary Industry Organizations
—CCC.
Published by: Department of Primary Industries and Energy, GPO Box 858, Canberra, ACT 2600, Australia.

630   NZL   ISSN 0113-7646
RURAL NEWS; the business of farming. Text in English. 1989. s-m. (except Dec. & Jan.). NZD 80; NZD 3.95 newsstand/cover (effective 2002). adv. illus. 32 p./no. 7 cols./p.; **Document type:** Newspaper. **Description:** Provides news of farming and agricultural issues. Informs the agricultural industry of all matters of significant news affecting the industry.
Published by: Rural News Ltd., 11th Fl, Patent House, 57 Fort St, PO Box 3855, Auckland 1, New Zealand. TEL 64-9-3070399, FAX 64-9-3070122, rural_news@clear.net.nz. Ed. David Anderson. Pub., Adv. contact Brian Hight. page NZD 4,286; trim 290 x 420. Circ: 93,883 (controlled).

RURAL POLICY MATTERS. see EDUCATION

▼ **RURAL REALITIES.** see SOCIOLOGY

630   AUS   ISSN 1034-6074
S381   CODEN: RUREEM
RURAL RESEARCH∗ . Text in English. 1952. q. AUD 25 (effective 1996). charts; illus. cum.index every 10 yrs. **Document type:** Academic/Scholarly.
Formerly (until 1972): Rural Research in C.S.I.R.O. (0036-0090)
Indexed: AEA, AESIS, Agr, AgrForAb, BioCN&I, DSA, FCA, FS&TA, ForAb, Gdlns, IndVet, NutrAb, OrnHort, PBA, RM&VM, RPP, RevApplEntom, S&F, VetBull, WAE&RSA, WBA, WMB.
Published by: Kondinin Group, 4/398 Great Eastern Hwy, RedCliffe, W.A. 6104, Australia. TEL 61-9-4783343, FAX 61-9-4783353, kgperth@ozemail.com.au. Ed. R Taylor. Circ: 20,000.

630   CAN   ISSN 1197-124X
RURAL ROOTS. Text in English. 1991. w. CND 32 (effective 1999). adv. bk.rev. **Document type:** Newspaper.
Related titles: Microform ed.
Published by: Prince Albert Daily Herald, 30 10th St E, P O Box 550, Prince Albert, SK S6V 5R9, Canada. TEL 306-764-4276, 800-667-8245, FAX 306-763-3331, pa.dailyherald@sksympatico.ca. Ed. Ruth Griffiths. Pub. Bob Gibb. Adv. contact Len Haubrich. Circ: 6,600 (paid); 24,107 (controlled).

THE RURAL SOCIOLOGIST. see SOCIOLOGY

RURAL SOCIOLOGY; devoted to scientific study of rural and community life. see SOCIOLOGY

630   GBR   ISSN 0141-898X
RURAL TECHNOLOGY GUIDE. Text in English. 1977. irreg. price varies. **Document type:** Monographic series. **Description:** Describes how to make devices or utilize appropriate technologies designed to assist rural industries and communities in developing countries.
Related titles: CD-ROM ed.; Online - full text ed.
Indexed: FCA, ForAb, HerbAb, RRTA, WAE&RSA.
—CISTI.

Published by: Natural Resources Institute, Central Ave, Chatham Maritime, Kent, ME4 4TB, United Kingdom. TEL 44-1634-880088, FAX 44-1634-880066, publications@nri.org, http://www.nri.org.

630   CAN   ISSN 1493-7883
RURAL TIMES. Text in English. 1999. q.
Published by: Agriculture and Agri-Food Canada, Rural Secretariat, 1525 Carling Ave, 3rd Flr, Ottawa, ON K1A 0C5, Canada. TEL 888-781-2222, FAX 800-884-9899, rs@agr.gc.ca, http://www.rural.gc.ca.

630.97132   CAN   ISSN 0700-5385
RURAL VOICE. Text in English. 1975. m. USD 16.05; CND 20 foreign. adv. bk.rev. back issues avail. **Document type:** Trade. **Description:** Addresses the people and issues central to agriculture and the family farm.
—CISTI.
Published by: North Huron Publishing Company Inc., 136 Queen St, P O Box 429, Blyth, ON N0M 1H0, Canada. TEL 519-523-4311, FAX 519-523-9140. Ed., Pub. Keith Roulston. Adv. contact Gerry Fortune. Circ: 15,000.

630   NZL   ISSN 1171-4425
RURAL WOMAN; official journal of Rural Women New Zealand. Text in English. 1933. bi-m. NZD 15 domestic; NZD 22.50 foreign (effective 2000). adv. back issues avail. **Document type:** Newsletter.
Formerly (until 1991): New Zealand Countrywoman (0028-8039)
—CCC.
Published by: Rural Woman New Zealand, Thorndon, PO Box 12021, Wellington, New Zealand. TEL 64-4-473-5524, FAX 64-4-472-8946, ruralwomen@clear.net.nz, http://www.ruralwomen.org. Ed., R&P, Adv. contact Tess Casey. Circ: 6,000 (controlled).

630   ARG
HD1861
RURALIA; revista argentina de estudios agrarios. Text in Spanish. 1990. a.
Related titles: Online - full text ed.: ISSN 0327-9596.
Published by: Ediciones Imago Mundi, Sanchez De Loria, 1821, Capital Federal, Buenos Aires 1241, Argentina. FAX 54-114-7756937, TELEX 18937 FLACS AR. Ed. Osvaldo Barsky.

630   USA   ISSN 1068-3674
S3
➤ **RUSSIAN AGRICULTURAL SCIENCES.** Text in English. 1976. m. USD 2,225 per vol. in US & Canada; USD 2,580 per vol. elsewhere (effective 2006). charts; illus.; stat.; abstr.; maps. index. back issues avail. **Document type:** Journal, Academic/Scholarly. **Description:** Covers agronomy, soil science, irrigation and erosion, plant diseases, animal breeding, and fertilizers.
Formerly (until 1993): Soviet Agricultural Sciences (0735-2700)
Related titles: ♦ Translation of: Rossiiskaya Akademiya Sel'skokhozyaistvennykh Nauk. Doklady. ISSN 0869-6128.
Indexed: AEA, AgBio, AgrForAb, AnBrAb, BIOSIS Prev, BioCN&I, BiolAb, CPA, DSA, ExcerpMed, FCA, FPA, FS&TA, ForAb, HelmAb, HerbAb, HortAb, I&DA, IndVet, MaizeAb, NutrAb, OrnHort, PBA, PGegResA, PGrRegA, PHN&I, PN&I, PotatoAb, PoultAb, ProtozoAb, RA&MP, RM&VM, RPP, RRTA, RevApplEntom, RiceAb, S&F, SIA, SeedAb, SoyAb, TriticAb, VetBull, WAE&RSA, WeedAb.
—BLDSC (0420.752100), CISTI, IE, ingenta. **CCC.**
Published by: (Rossiiskaya Akademiya Sel'skokhozyaistvennykh Nauk/Russian Academy of Agricultural Sciences RUS), Allerton Press, Inc., 18 W 27th St, New York, NY 10001. TEL 646-424-9686, FAX 646-424-9695, journals@allertonpress.com, http://www.allertonpress.com/journals/agr.htm. Ed. Natalya S Markova.

630   FRA   ISSN 0338-5353
RUSTICA; l'hebdo jardin. Text in French. 1928. w. EUR 72 domestic; EUR 102 newsstand/cover foreign (effective 2005). **Document type:** Magazine, Consumer.
Former titles: Rustica Hebdo (0338-5353); (until 1973): Rustica (0338-5345)
Published by: Rustica S.A., 15-27 rue Moussorgski, Paris, 75895 Cedex 18, France. TEL 33-1-53263300, FAX 33-1-53263301, http://www.rustica.fr/. Ed. Janine Dorbeaux. Adv. contact Luc Debasquiat. Circ: 350,000. **Subscr. to:** Service Abonnements, BP 200, Sainte Genevieve Cedex 60732, France.

630 636   RWA
RWANDA. MINISTERE DE L'AGRICULTURE ET DE L'ELEVAGE. RAPPORT ANNUEL. Text in French. a.
Published by: Ministere de l'Agriculture et de l'Elevage, BP 621, Kigali, Rwanda.

630   RUS   ISSN 0233-7754
RYBOLOV. Text in Russian. 1985. bi-m. USD 95 in United States (effective 2000).
Indexed: ASFA, ESPM.
Published by: Redaktsiya Rybolov, Sadovaya-Spasskaya 18, Moscow, 107807, Russian Federation. TEL 7-095-2072110. Ed. A V Golovanov. **Dist. by:** East View Information Services, 3020 Harbor Ln. N., Minneapolis, MN 55447. TEL 763-550-0961, FAX 763-559-2931.

636.08 THA ISSN 1029-7073
S A B R A O JOURNAL OF BREEDING AND GENETICS. Text in English. 1969. s-a. USD 30. **Document type:** *Academic/Scholarly.* **Description:** Devoted to the basic and practical aspects of breeding research in economic organisms.
Former titles (until 1998): S A B R A O Journal (1010-3902); (until 1974): S A B R A O Newsletter (1010-4674)
Indexed: ASFA, AgBio, Agr, AnBrAb, B&BAb, CPA, FCA, GenetAb, HGA, HerbAb, HortAb, MaizeAb, OrnHort, PBA, PGegResA, PGrRegA, PotatoAb, PoultAb, RA&MP, RPP, RiceAb, S&F, SeedAb, SoyAb, TriticAb, WAE&RSA, WeedAb.
—BLDSC (8062.390300), CISTI, IE, ingenta.
Published by: Society for the Advancement of Breeding Researches in Asia and Oceania, c/o Prof. Sumin Smutkupt Secretary-General, Dept. of Applied Radiation & Isotopes, Faculty of Science, Kasetsart University, Bangkok, 10900, Thailand. TEL 66-2-5795530, FAX 66-2-5795530, fscisil@nontri.ku.ac.th. Ed., R&P R.N. Oram TEL 66-2-62465255. Adv. contact R N Oram.

338.1 GBR
S A C REVIEW. Text in English. 1988. a. **Document type:** *Academic/Scholarly.*
Formerly: Edinburgh School of Agriculture. Annual Review (0953-6884)
—BLDSC (7786.666000).
Published by: S A C, King's Buildings, West Mains Rd, Edinburgh, EH9 3JG, United Kingdom. TEL 44-131-535-4000, FAX 44-131-535-4246.

630 ZAF
S A CO-OP. (South Africa - Suid Afrika) Text in English. 1977. m. free to members. adv. bk.rev. illus. 32 p./no.; back issues avail. **Document type:** *Magazine, Trade.* **Description:** Promotes agricultural companies and cooperatives.
Formerly: N T K - Nuus (0250-1236)
Related titles: Afrikaans ed.: S A Koops.
Published by: (Northern Transvaal Co-Op Ltd.), Mediacom C C, PO Box 1432, Northcliff, Johannesburg 2115, South Africa. mediacom@intekom.co.za. Ed. Willie Louw. R&P Peter Smith TEL 27-18-293-0622. Adv. contact Jana Greenall. B&W page ZAR 4,550, color page ZAR 6,600; trim 185 x 265. Circ: 19,550. **Co-sponsor:** Free State Co-op.

630.9 AUS ISSN 1324-2083
SH318.S68
S A R D I RESEARCH REPORT SERIES. (South Australian Research and Development Institute) Text in English. 1995. irreg.
Indexed: ESPM, ZooRec.
Published by: South Australian Research and Development Institute, GPO Box 397, Adelaide, SA 5001, Australia. TEL 61-8-8303-9400, FAX 61-8-8303-9309, pirsa.sardi@saugov.sa.gov.au, http://www.sardi.sa.gov.au.

630 USA
S L O COUNTY FARMER & RANCHER MAGAZINE. (San Luis Obispo) Text in English. 2002. m. free to members; USD 1 newsstand/cover (effective 2005). adv. 16 p./no.; **Document type:** *Magazine, Trade.*
Related titles: Online - full content ed.
Published by: San Luis Obispo County Farm Bureau, 651 Tank Farm Rd, San Luis Obispo, CA 93401. TEL 805-543-3654, FAX 805-543-3697, info@slofarmbureau.org, http://www.slofarmbureau.org. Ed. Mark Souder. adv.: page USD 500. Circ: 3,000 (paid).

630 CHL
S N A BOLETIN DE MERCADO. Text in Spanish. m.
Published by: Sociedad Nacional de Agricultura, Casilla 40-D, Tenderini, 187, Santiago, Chile. TEL 56-2-6396710, info@sna.cl, http://www.sna.cl.

630 CHL
S N A BOLETIN ECONOMICO. Text in Spanish. m.
Published by: Sociedad Nacional de Agricultura, Casilla 40-D, Tenderini, 187, Santiago, Chile. TEL 56-2-6396710, info@sna.cl, http://www.sna.cl.

630 CHL
S N A VOCERO AGRICOLA. Text in Spanish. m.
Published by: Sociedad Nacional de Agricultura, Casilla 40-D, Tenderini, 187, Santiago, Chile. TEL 56-2-6396710, info@sna.cl, http://www.sna.cl.

630 NCL ISSN 1019-6234
S P C AGRICULTURAL NEWS. Text in English. 1992. s-a. **Document type:** *Newsletter.*
Related titles: French ed.: Bulletin de l'Agriculture. ISSN 1025-4935.
Published by: Secretariat of the Pacific Community, PO Box D5, Noumea, Cedex 98848, New Caledonia. TEL 687-262000, FAX 687-263818, spc@spc.int, http://www.spc.int.

630 DEU
SAARLAENDISCHES BAUERNBLATT. Text in German. fortn.
Published by: Bauernbund Saar e.V., Heinestr 2-4, Saarbruecken, 66121, Germany. TEL 62964.

630 RUS
SAD I OGOROD. Text in Russian. bi-m. USD 95 in United States (effective 2000).

Published by: Izdatel'stvo Kolos, Sadovaya-Spasskaya 18, Moscow, 107807, Russian Federation. TEL 7-095-2071740, FAX 7-095-2072870. Ed. S I Yakovleva. **Dist. by:** East View Information Services, 3020 Harbor Ln. N., Minneapolis, MN 55447. TEL 763-550-0961, FAX 763-559-2931.

630 RUS
SADOVOD K.M.K. Text in Russian. 1990. m.
Published by: Zavodoupravlenie K.M.K., Pl Pobedy, Novokuznetsk, Kemerovskaya Oblast' 654000, Russian Federation. Ed. M P Merenkov.

630 JPN ISSN 0581-2801
CODEN: SDNID7
SAGA DAIGAKU NOGAKUBU IHO/SAGA UNIVERSITY. FACULTY OF AGRICULTURE. BULLETIN. Text in English, Japanese; Summaries in English. s-a. per issue exchange basis. back issues avail. **Document type:** *Bulletin, Academic/Scholarly.*
Indexed: AEA, AgBio, AnBrAb, BiolAb, CPA, FCA, FS&TA, ForAb, HortAb, I&DA, MaizeAb, NutrAb, OrnHort, PBA, PGegResA, PGrRegA, PHN&I, PoultAb, RDA, RPP, RiceAb, S&F, SIA, SeedAb, SoyAb, TriticAb, WAE&RSA, WeedAb.
—BLDSC (2507.239000), CISTI.
Published by: Saga Daigaku, Nogakubu/Saga University, Faculty of Agriculture, 1 Honjo-machi, Saga-shi, Saga-ken 840, Japan. Ed. Teru Yanagita. Circ: 500.

630 IND
SAKSHI FARM WEEKLY. Text in Hindi. 1964. w. INR 65; INR 1.50 newsstand/cover. 12 p./no. 5 cols./p.
Published by: Vijay Kumar Bhatia Ed. & Pub., 38-18 East Patel Nagar, New Delhi, 110 008, India. TEL 5711319. adv.: page INR 12,000. Circ: 47,207.

630 NGA ISSN 0331-7285
SAMARU JOURNAL OF AGRICULTURAL RESEARCH. Text in English. 1981. a. USD 30 per issue. **Document type:** *Academic/Scholarly.* **Description:** Publishes the results of agricultural research concerning arable savannah land.
Indexed: FS&TA, I&DA, MaizeAb, RiceAb, S&F, S&MA, SeedAb, TOSA, TriticAb.
—CISTI.
Published by: Ahmadu Bello University, Institute for Agricultural Research, PMB 1044, Samaru-Zaria, Kaduna, Nigeria. FAX 234-69-50563. Ed. A M Emechebe.

630 NGA ISSN 0080-5769
SAMARU MISCELLANEOUS PAPERS. Text in English. 1963. irreg. USD 20. **Document type:** *Monographic series, Academic/Scholarly.* **Description:** Publishes research papers on agricultural topics of local interest.
Indexed: BiolAb, RDA, RRTA, WAE&RSA.
Published by: Ahmadu Bello University, Institute for Agricultural Research, PMB 1044, Samaru-Zaria, Kaduna, Nigeria. FAX 234-69-50563.

630 SWE ISSN 1651-6745
SAMSPEL; om levande naturresurser. Text in Swedish; Summaries in English. 2001. q. free (effective 2003). adv. **Description:** Overview of ongoing research.
Formerly (until 2003): Forskning Paagaar (1650-6359)
Related titles: Online - full content ed.
Published by: Sveriges Lantbruksuniversitet, Informationsavdelingen/Swedish University of Agricultural Sciences, Sveriges Lantbruksuniversitet, Informationsavdelingen, PO Box 7077, Stockholm, 75007, Sweden. samspel@slu.se, http://www.slu.se/samspel. Ed. Mikael Propst TEL 46-18-671413. Pub. Mikael Jansson. Adv. contact Marie Oestlund TEL 46-18-671727. page SEK 17,000; 187 x 257. Circ: 12,500.

631 USA ISSN 0273-6004
SAN FRANCISCO WHOLESALE ORNAMENTAL CROPS REPORT. Text in English. 1968. w. looseleaf. USD 96. back issues avail. **Document type:** *Government.* **Description:** Presents lists of price ranges and offerings of cut flowers, potted plants and greens on the flower market.
Published by: (U.S. Department of Agriculture), Federal-State Market News Service (Sacramento), 630 Sansome St, Rm 727, San Francisco, CA 94111. TEL 415-705-1300, FAX 415-705-1301. Circ: 135.

SAN JOAQUIN AGRICULTURAL LAW REVIEW. see *LAW.*

630 CHE ISSN 1424-6341
ST. GALLER BAUER. Text in German. 1913. w. **Document type:** *Newspaper, Trade.*
Address: Magdenauerstr. 2, Flawil, 9230, Switzerland. TEL 41-71-3946015, FAX 41-71-835210, sgbauer@bauern-sg.ch. Ed. H Peter. Circ: 11,861.

638.1 FRA ISSN 0036-4568
LA SANTE DE L'ABEILLE. Text in French. 1967. bi-m. adv. bibl.; charts; illus. index. **Document type:** *Newspaper.* **Description:** News of interest to the apiculturist.
Indexed: ApicAb, BiolAb, RefZh, RevApplEntom.
—CCC.

Published by: Federation Nationale des Organisations Sanitaires Apicoles Departementales (F.N.O.S.A.D.), Quartier Chapitre, Riez, 04500, France. TEL 33-4-92777572, FAX 33-4-92778100, sante-de-labeille@wanadoo.fr, http://www.agriculture.com/sante-de-labeille. Ed. Jean Paul Faucon. Circ: 10,000.

630 MYS ISSN 0080-6420
S322.S3
SARAWAK. DEPARTMENT OF AGRICULTURE. RESEARCH BRANCH. ANNUAL REPORT. Text in English. 1962. a., latest 1996. MYR 25 newsstand/cover (effective 2001). back issues avail. **Document type:** *Government.*
Indexed: FCA, HerbAb, HortAb, RPP, RevApplEntom.
Published by: Department of Agriculture, Agricultural Research Centre, Peti Sura 977, Kuching, Sazawak 93720, Malaysia. TEL 60-82-611171, FAX 60-82-611178, kgiparc@sarawaknet.gov.my. Circ: 350.

630 ITA ISSN 0391-8726
SARDEGNA AGRICOLTURA. Text in Italian. 1970. bi-m. adv.
Address: Piazza Annunziata, 4, Cagliari, CA 09123, Italy. TEL 39-70-274096. Ed. Flavio Siddi. Circ: 3,000.

630 PAK ISSN 1016-4383
➤ **SARHAD JOURNAL OF AGRICULTURE.** Text in English. 1985. bi-m. PKR 1,600; USD 150 foreign; PKR 400 newsstand/cover (effective 2003). adv. abstr.; bibl.; charts; illus.; stat. back issues avail. **Document type:** *Magazine, Academic/Scholarly.* **Description:** Publishes research articles in the field of agricultural sciences.
Indexed: AEA, AbHyg, AgBio, AgrForAb, AnBrAb, BioCN&I, CPA, DSA, FCA, FPA, FS&TA, ForAb, HerbAb, HortAb, I&DA, IndVet, MaizeAb, NemAb, NutrAb, OrnHort, PBA, PGegResA, PGrRegA, PHN&I, PotatoAb, PoultAb, ProtozoAb, RA&MP, RDA, RM&VM, RPP, RRTA, RevApplEntom, RiceAb, S&F, SIA, SeedAb, SoyAb, TDB, TriticAb, VetBull, WAE&RSA, WeedAb, ZooRec.
—BLDSC (8076.048000), IE, ingenta.
Published by: N.W.F.P. Agricultural University, Peshawar, Pakistan. TEL 91-9216572 ext 275, FAX 91-9216520, vc@vcnwfp.psw.erum.com.pk. Ed., R&P Dr. Sher Hassan. adv.: B&W page PKR 12,000. Circ: 150 (controlled).

➤ **SARMA.** see *LABOR UNIONS*

630 ESP
SARRO. Text in Catalan. 1997. s-a. adv. **Document type:** *Trade.*
Published by: (Federacio Catalana de Caca, Territorial de Girona), Edicions la Terra S.L., Avinguda Francesc Cambo, 14 3-B, Barcelona, 08003, Spain. TEL 34-93-2680900, FAX 34-93-2684893, http://www.uniopagesos.es/unio. Adv. contact Josep M Escola. Circ: 15,000.

SASKATCHEWAN AGRICULTURE AND FOOD. AGRICULTURAL STATISTICS. see *AGRICULTURE— Abstracting, Bibliographies, Statistics*

630 CAN ISSN 0713-1844
SASKATCHEWAN AGRICULTURE AND FOOD. ANNUAL REPORT. Text in English. 1905. a. free. adv. charts; illus. back issues avail. **Document type:** *Government.*
Formerly: Saskatchewan. Department of Agriculture. Annual Report (0319-3578)
Related titles: Microfiche ed.
—CISTI.
Published by: Agriculture and Food, Communications Branch, B5 Walter Scott Bldg, 3085 Albert St, Regina, SK S4S 0B1, Canada. TEL 306-787-5150, FAX 306-787-0216, library@agr.gov.sk.ca, http://www.agr.gov.sk.ca/saf. Adv. contact Harvey Johnson. Circ: 500.

SASKATCHEWAN CROP INSURANCE CORPORATION. ANNUAL REPORT. see *INSURANCE*

630 658 CAN
SASKATCHEWAN FARM LIFE. Text in English. 1982. fortn. CND 33.68. adv. back issues avail.
Published by: Farm Life Publications, 75 Lenore Dr, 4, Saskatoon, SK S7K 7Y1, Canada. TEL 306-242-5723, FAX 306-668-6164. Ed. Larry Hiatt. Circ: 160,000 (controlled).

SASKATCHEWAN GRAIN CAR CORPORATION. ANNUAL REPORT. see *TRANSPORTATION*

630 ROM ISSN 1220-8140
SATUL ROMANESC. Text in Romanian. w.
Published by: Federation of Agricultural Companies of Rumania, Piata Presei Libere 1, Bucharest, 71341, Romania. Ed. Titu Constantin. Circ: 80,000.

630 SCG ISSN 0350-1205
CODEN: SAPOAB
SAVREMENA POLJOPRIVREDA/CONTEMPORARY AGRICULTURE; Jugoslovenski casopis za poljoprivredu. Text in Serbo-Croatian; Summaries in English. 1953. m. YUN 120, USD 22.75. bibl.; charts; illus.; pat.; stat.
Formerly (until 1959): Poljoprivreda Vojvodine
Indexed: AnBrAb, FCA, HerbAb, HortAb, INIS AtomInd, PBA, RASB, S&F, WeedAb.
—CISTI.

A

Published by: Dnevnik, Bulevar 23 Oktobra 31, Novi Sad. Ed. Miloje Saric.

338.432 DEU ISSN 0303-2612
SCHWAEBISCHER BAUER. Text in German. 1949. w. EUR 79.80 domestic; EUR 128.40 foreign (effective 2004). adv. **Document type:** *Magazine, Trade.*
Published by: Verlag Eugen Ulmer GmbH, Wollgrasweg 41, Stuttgart, 70599, Germany. TEL 49-711-45070, FAX 49-711-4507120, info@ulmer.de, http://www.bwagrar.de, http://www.ulmer.de. adv.: B&W page EUR 2,728, color page EUR 4,448. Circ: 18,138 (paid and controlled).

630 CHE ISSN 1420-0546
SCHWEIZER BAUER; die unabhaengige Zeitung fuer die Landwirtschaft. Text in German. 1846. 2/w. CHF 144 (effective 2002). adv. bk.rev. **Document type:** *Newspaper, Trade.*
Former titles (until 1901): Schweizer Bauer und Bernische Blaetter fuer Landwirthschaft (1421-167X); (until 1897): Bernische Blaetter fuer Landwirthschaft (1421-1548); (until 1857): Bernische Blaetter fuer Landwirthschaft, Wald- und Gartenbau (1421-153X); (until 1849): Wochenblatt fuer Landwirthschaft und Gartenbau (1421-1521)
Related titles: Online - full text ed.
Address: Dammweg 9, Bern, 3001, Switzerland. TEL 41-31-3303444, FAX 41-31-3303395, sb@btm.ch, http://www.schweizerbauer.ch. Ed. Rudolf Haudenschild. R&P Ulrich Utiger. Circ: 28,500.

630 CHE ISSN 0377-5070
SCHWEIZER LANDTECHNIK. Text in German. 1939. 11/yr. CHF 60 domestic; CHF 80 foreign (effective 2001). **Document type:** *Magazine, Trade.*
Former titles (until 1971): Der Traktor und die Landmaschine (1423-0925); (until 1955): Der Traktor (1423-0933)
Related titles: French ed.: Technique Agricole; Supplement(s): F A T - Berichte. ISSN 1018-502X. 1970.
Indexed: AEA, DSA, FCA, NutrAb, PHN&I, RefZh, RevApplEntom, SoyAb, TriticAb, WAE&RSA, WeedAb.
Published by: Schweizerischer Verband fuer Landtechnik, Ausserdorfstr 31, Postfach 55, Riniken, 5223, Switzerland. TEL 41-56-4412022, FAX 41-56-4416731, zs@agrartechnik.ch, http://www.agrartechnik.ch. Ed. J Fischer.

638.1 CHE ISSN 0036-7540
SCHWEIZERISCHE BIENEN-ZEITUNG; monats zeitschrift des vereins deutschschweizerischer bienenfreunde. Text in German. 1863. m. CHF 40 (effective 2001). adv. bk.rev. charts; illus. index. 64 p./no. 3 cols./p.; **Document type:** *Magazine, Trade.* **Description:** Features news and information on breeding, behavior, honey and pollen production of bees; includes reports and a calendar of events.
Indexed: ApicAb, BiolAb, ChemAb.
—BLDSC (8114.700000), IE, ingenta. **CCC.**
Published by: Verein Deutschschweizerischer und Raetoromanischer Bienenfreunde, Krattigstr 55, Spiez, 3700, Switzerland. TEL 41-33-6549330, FAX 41-33-6549331, info@swissbee.ch, http://www.swissbee.ch. Ed. Berchtold Lehnherr. adv.: B&W page CHF 1,050; trim 135 x 193. Circ: 16,000. **Subscr. to:** I P O Service, Industriestr 5, Boesingen 3178, Switzerland. TEL 41-31-7409760, FAX 41-31-7409776.

630 CHE
SCHWEIZERISCHER VERBAND INGENIEUR-AGRONOMEN UND LEBENSMITTEL-INGENIEURE. JOURNAL. Text in French, German. q. CHF 107.50 to members (effective 2000). adv. **Document type:** *Journal, Trade.*
Formerly: Schweizerischer Verband Ingenieur-Agronomen und Lebensmittel-Ingenieure. Bulletin
Published by: Schweizerischer Verband Ingenieur-Agronomen und Lebensmittel-Ingenieure, Laenggasse 79, Zollikofen, 3052, Switzerland. TEL 41-31-9110668, FAX 41-31-9114925, svial@pop.agri.ch, http://combi.agri.ch/svial. Ed., R&P Oskar Meyer. Adv. contact Marianne Moser. Circ: 2,500.

630 BRA ISSN 0103-9016
CODEN: SGRIEF
➤ **SCIENTIA AGRICOLA.** Text in English, Portuguese; Summaries in English, Portuguese. 1944. 4/yr. BRL 65 domestic; BRL 80 foreign (effective 2000). bibl.; illus.; stat. back issues avail. **Document type:** *Academic/Scholarly.* **Description:** Publishes articles that contribute to the to the scientific development of agricultural sciences.
Formerly (until 1992): Escola Superior de Agricultura "Luiz de Queiroz". Anais (0071-1276)
Related titles: Online - full text ed.: free (effective 2005) (from SciELO).
Indexed: AEA, AgBio, AgrForAb, Agrind, AnBrAb, BibAg, BioCN&I, BiolAb, CPA, CTFA, ChemAb, ChemTitl, CurCont, DSA, FCA, FPA, ForAb, HerbAb, HortAb, I&DA, INIS AtomInd, IndVet, MaizeAb, NemAb, NutrAb, OrnHort, PBA, PGegResA, PGrRegA, PHN&I, PN&I, PotatoAb, PoultAb, ProtozoAb, RA&MP, RDA, RM&VM, RPP, RevApplEntom, RiceAb, S&F, S&MA, SIA, SeedAb, SoyAb, TDB, TriticAb, VetBull, WAE&RSA, WeedAb.
—BLDSC (8169.270000), CASDDS, IE, ingenta.
Published by: Universidade de Sao Paulo, Escola Superior de Agricultura "Luiz de Queiroz", Centro, Caixa Postal 9, Piracicaba, Sao Paulo 13400970, Brazil. TEL 55-19-4294373, FAX 55-19-4220711, TELEX 19-1141 EALQ, scientia@carpa.ciagri.usp.br, http://www.scielo.br/, http://www.esalq.usp.br/scientia. Ed. Klaus Reichardt. Circ: 500.

630 IND
SCIENTIFIC HORTICULTURE. Text and summaries in English. a. USD 35 (effective 2001).
Formerly (until 1992): Scientific Publishers
Indexed: CPA, FCA, NutrAb, OrnHort, PBA, PGegResA, PGrRegA, PHN&I, RPP, RevApplEntom, SeedAb, SoyAb.
Published by: Scientific Publishers, 5-A New Pali Rd., Near Hotel Taj Hari Mahal, PO Box 91, Jodhpur, Rajasthan 342 003, India. TEL 91-291-2433323, FAX 91-291-2512580, info@scientificpub.com, http://www.scientificpub.com. Ed. S P Singh.

630 ITA ISSN 0036-8881
SCIENZA E TECNICA AGRARIA; rivista mensile di agricoltura meridionale. Text in Italian. 1961. m. adv. charts; illus.; stat. index.
Published by: Associazioni Provinciale Dottori in Scienze Agrarie e Scienze Forestali, Viale JFKennedy 86, Bari, BA 70124, Italy. info@adafba.it, http://www.adafba.it. Ed. Nicola Matarrese.

638.1 GBR ISSN 0370-8918
CODEN: SCBKAB
SCOTTISH BEEKEEPER. Text in English. 1924. m. GBP 15 to members (effective 2001). adv. **Document type:** *Newsletter.*
—CISTI.
Published by: Scottish Beekeepers' Association, c/o Enio Brown, Milton House, Main St, Scotlandwell, Kinross-Shire KY13 9JA, United Kingdom. TEL 44-1505-702680, apissgot@aol.com. Ed. A.E. McArthur. R&P A E McArthur. Adv. contact Enio Brown.

630 GBR
SCOTTISH COUNTRY BUSINESS REFERENCE BOOK. Text in English. 1990. a. GBP 10.50 per issue in United Kingdom; USD 20 per issue rest of world (effective 2000). adv. charts; illus.; stat. back issues avail. **Document type:** *Trade.* **Description:** Contains reference and articles predominately for farmers and also contains a diary section.
Published by: G B Ford Associates, 8 Osborne Terr, Edinburgh, EH12 5HG, United Kingdom. TEL 44-131-346-0549, FAX 44-131-346-0549. Ed., Pub., Adv. contact G B Ford. B&W page GBP 900, color page GBP 1,875; trim 148 x 210. Circ: 6,500 (controlled); 500 (paid).

630 GBR ISSN 0036-9195
THE SCOTTISH FARMER. Text in English. 1893. w. GBP 55; GBP 1.40 newsstand/cover; GBP 75 foreign (effective 1999). adv. bk.rev. charts; illus.; mkt.; pat.; stat.; tr.mk. **Document type:** *Newspaper.*
Indexed: IndVet, RICS, VetBull.
—CCC.
Published by: Caledonian Magazines Ltd., 6th Fl, 195 Albion St, Glasgow, G1 1QQ, United Kingdom. TEL 44-141-302-7700, FAX 44-141-302-7799, info@calmags.co.uk. Ed. A Fletcher. R&P Mike Ure. Adv. contact Karen Coyle. Circ: 24,881.

SEED SCIENCE AND TECHNOLOGY. see *BIOLOGY—Botany*

630 USA ISSN 1096-0724
SB114.A1 CODEN: JSTEDV
➤ **SEED TECHNOLOGY.** Text in English. 1908. a., latest vol.23, no.2. USD 50 domestic; USD 60 foreign (effective 2005). cum.index: 1908-1937, 1938-1959. **Document type:** *Journal, Academic/Scholarly.*
Formerly: Journal of Seed Technology (0146-3071); Which superseded (in 1976): Association of Official Seed Analysts. Proceedings (0097-1324)
Indexed: AEA, AgBio, Agr, AgrForAb, BioCN&I, BiolAb, CPA, ChemAb, FCA, ForAb, HerbAb, HortAb, MaizeAb, NemAb, OrnHort, PBA, PGegResA, PGrRegA, PHN&I, PotatoAb, RA&MP, RPP, RevApplEntom, RiceAb, S&F, SIA, SeedAb, SoyAb, TriticAb, WAE&RSA, WeedAb.
—BLDSC (8218.173000), CASDDS, CISTI, IE, Infotrieve, ingenta, Linda Hall.
Published by: Association of Official Seed Analysts / Society of Commercial Seed Technologists, PMB #411, 1763 E University Blvd, Ste A, Las Cruces, NM 88001. TEL 505-522-1437, aosaoffice@earthlink.net, http:// www.aosaseed.com/journal.html. Ed. Dennis Tekrony. Circ: 400.

338.1 USA
SEED TODAY. Text in English. q. adv. **Document type:** *Magazine, Trade.* **Description:** Provides news, profiles, equipment and plant information for plant operations management in the seed processing industry.
Published by: Country Journal Publishing Company, 3065 Pershing Ct, Decatur, IL 62526-1564. TEL 217-877-9660, FAX 217-877-6647. Pub. Mark Avery. Adv. contact Deb Coontz. B&W page USD 500, color page USD 1,000.

635 970.1 USA ISSN 1083-8074
SEEDHEAD NEWS. Text in English. 1983 (January). q. USD 25 (effective 2004). adv. bk.rev. back issues avail. **Document type:** *Newsletter.* **Description:** Discusses efforts to conserve seeds of crops grown by Native Americans in the Southwest U.S.
Published by: Native Seeds - Search, 526 N Fourth Ave, Tucson, AZ 85705. TEL 520-622-5561, FAX 520-522-5591, info@nativeseeds.org, http://www.nativeseeds.org. Eds. Evelyn Rens, Shannon Scott, Suzanne Nelson. Pubs., R&Ps Shannon Scott, Suzanne Nelson. Adv. contact Suzanne Nelson. Circ: 4,600 (paid).

SEIBUTSU TO KISHO. see *METEOROLOGY*

630 BRA ISSN 0037-1122
CODEN: SEVAAR
SEIVA. Text in Portuguese; Summaries in English. 1940. q. BRL 15, USD 3. charts; illus. index.
Media: Duplicated (not offset).
Indexed: BiolAb, ChemAb, FCA, HerbAb, HortAb, PBA, RiceAb, S&F.
—CISTI.
Published by: Universidade Federal de Vicosa, Diretorio Central dos Estudiantes, Vicosa, MG 36570-000, Brazil. Circ: 4,000.

630 JPN ISSN 0387-4338
SEKAI NO NORINSUISAN/WORLD AGRICULTURE, FORESTRY AND FISHERIES. Text in Japanese. 1952. m. JPY 6,000 domestic; JPY 9,000 foreign (effective 2001). adv. bk.rev. 48 p./no.; **Document type:** *Bulletin.*
Formerly: F A O Information (0014-5629)
Published by: Japan F A O Association/Kokusai Shokuryo Nogyo Kyokai, Bajichikusan-Kaikan, 1-2 Kanda-Surugadai, Chiyoda-ku, Tokyo, 101-0062, Japan. TEL 81-3-3294-2425, FAX 81-3-3294-2427, jpnfao@mb.infoweb.ne.jp, http://www.fao-kyokai.or.jp. Ed. Keisuke Yoshimura. Adv. contact Maiko Mori. Circ: 1,400.

SELF-EMPLOYED COUNTRY; communicating for agriculture and the self-employed. see *BUSINESS AND ECONOMICS—Small Business*

SEL'SKOKHOZYAISTVENNAYA LITERATURA. see *AGRICULTURE—Abstracting, Bibliographies, Statistics*

630 RUS
SEM'YA. ZEMLYA. UROZHAI. Text in Russian. m. USD 99 in United States.
Address: Ul Pashpilevskaya 106, Krasnodar, 350000, Russian Federation. TEL 7-8612-553556, FAX 7-8612-553085. Ed. F Bezruk. **US dist. addr.:** East View Information Services, 3020 Harbor Ln. N., Minneapolis, MN 55447. TEL 612-550-0961.

630 ITA ISSN 0037-234X
SENTINELLA AGRICOLA; periodico cremonese di tecnica e divulgazione agraria fondato nel 1896. Text in Italian. 1896. m. free. adv. bk.rev. illus.; stat. index. **Document type:** *Bulletin.*
Published by: Servizio Provinciale Agricoltura Foresta Alimentazione, Via Monteverdi, 17, Cremona, CR 26100, Italy. FAX 39-372-457167. Ed. Paolo Baccolo. Circ: 1,033.

SEOUL NATIONAL UNIVERSITY. FACULTY PAPERS. BIOLOGY AND AGRICULTURE SERIES. see *BIOLOGY*

630 KOR ISSN 1013-4077
S19 CODEN: SNYOEF
SEOUL NATIONAL UNIVERSITY JOURNAL OF AGRICULTURAL SCIENCES/SOUL TAE-NONGHAK YON'GU CHI. Text in English, Korean. 1976. s-a. per issue exchange basis. **Document type:** *Academic/Scholarly.*
Former titles (until 1988): Seoul National University. Agricultural Research (0255-7010); Seoul National University. College of Agriculture. Bulletin
Indexed: ApicAb, FCA, PGrRegA.
—CISTI.
Published by: Seoul National University, College of Agriculture, 103 Seodoon-dong, Suwon, 170, Korea, S. FAX 0331-293-5928. Circ: 800.

630 USA
SERIE DE INVESTIGACIONES Y DESARROLLO. Short title: S I D. Text in Spanish. 1984. irreg. price varies.
Published by: (Instituto Interamericano de Cooperacion Agricola), Organization of American States/Organizacion de los Estados Americanos, General Secretariat, Department of Publications, 1889 F St, N W, Washington, DC 20006-4499. TEL 202-458-3527, FAX 202-458-3534. **Dist. by:** Center for Promotion and Distribution of Publications, PO Box 66398, Washington, DC 20035.

630 USA ISSN 0192-4184
SEVEN COUNTY FARM AND HOME NEWS. Text in English. 1947. m. adv.
Formerly: Columbia - Luzerne - Wyoming - Lycoming Farm and Home News
Published by: Farm & Home Publications, 10 Lourdes Rd, Binghamton, NY 13905-4293. Ed. Bernard M Swartz. Circ: 3,100.

SEYCHELLES. PRESIDENT'S OFFICE. STATISTICS DIVISION. AGRICULTURE SURVEY. see *AGRICULTURE—Abstracting, Bibliographies, Statistics*

052 054.1 SYC
SEYCHELLOIS. Text in English, French. 1928. d. SCR 48. adv.
Indexed: RASB.
Published by: (Seychelles Farmers Association), Seychellois Press Ltd., PO Box 32, Victoria, Mahe, Seychelles. Ed. G de Comarmond. Circ: 1,800. **Co-sponsor:** Seychelles Copra Association.

630 CHN ISSN 1000-193X
SHANGHAI NONGXUEYUAN XUEBAO/SHANGHAI AGRICULTURAL INSTITUTE. JOURNAL. Text in Chinese. 1983. q. CNY 2.50. adv.
Related titles: Online - full text ed.: (from East View Information Services).
Indexed: AEA, AgBio, AgrForAb, AnBrAb, BioCN&I, CPA, DSA, FCA, FS&TA, ForAb, HelmAb, HerbAb, HortAb, I&DA, IndVet, MaizeAb, NutrAb, OrnHort, PBA, PGegResA, PGrRegA, PHN&I, PN&I, PotatoAb, PoultAb, ProtozoAb, RA&MP, RDA, RM&VM, RPP, RRTA, RiceAb, S&F, SIA, SeedAb, SoyAb, TriticAb, VetBull, WAE&RSA, WeedAb, ZooRec.
—BLDSC (4874.740000).
Published by: Shanghai Nongxueyuan/Shanghai Agricultural College, No 31 Qishen Lu, Shanghai, 201101, China. TEL 923010. Ed. Wu Jinkang. Circ: 1,000.

630 CHN ISSN 1000-3924
CODEN: SHNXED
SHANGHAI NONGYE XUEBAO/ACTA AGRICULTURAE SHANGHAI. Text in Chinese. 1985. q. CNY 10, USD 4.23 newsstand/cover (effective 2002). **Document type:** *Academic/Scholarly.*
Related titles: Online - full content ed.: (from WanFang Data Corp.); Online - full text ed.: (from East View Information Services).
Indexed: AEA, AbHyg, AgBio, AgrForAb, AnBrAb, BioCN&I, CPA, DSA, FCA, ForAb, HelmAb, HerbAb, HortAb, I&DA, IndVet, MaizeAb, NemAb, NutrAb, OrnHort, PBA, PGegResA, PGrRegA, PHN&I, PN&I, PotatoAb, PoultAb, ProtozoAb, RA&MP, RDA, RM&VM, RPP, RRTA, RiceAb, S&F, SIA, SeedAb, SoyAb, TDB, TriticAb, VetBull, WAE&RSA, WeedAb, ZooRec.
—BLDSC (0589.070000), CISTI, IE, ingenta.
Published by: Shanghai-shi Nongkexue Xinxisuo, 2901 Bei Zhai Lu, Shanghai, 201106, China. TEL 86-21-62208660 ext 3175, FAX 86-21-62206698, http://shnyxb.periodicals.com.cn/default.html. **Dist. by:** China International Book Trading Corp, 35 Chegongzhuang Xilu, Haidian District, PO Box 399, Beijing 100044, China. TEL 86-10-68412045, FAX 86-10-68412023, cibtc@mail.cibtc.com.cn, http://www.cibtc.com.cn.

630 CHN ISSN 1006-9739
SHANXI AGRICULTURE/SHANXI NONGYE. Text in Chinese. 1993. bi-m. CNY 18 (effective 2000 - 2001). **Document type:** *Bulletin, Academic/Scholarly.*
Formerly: Shanxi Nongye - Shanxi Agriculture (0488-5368)
Related titles: Online - full text ed.: (from East View Information Services).
Published by: Shanxi Nongye Kexueyuan/Shanxi Academy of Agricultural Sciences, 4 Wucheng Lu, Taiyuan, Shanxi 030006, China. TEL 86-351-7075565, 86-351-7089783, FAX 86-351-17089781, sxnyzzs@public.ty.sx.cn, http://www.chinainfo.gov.cn. Ed. Wenze Yan. Adv. contact Dehui Chai.

630 CHN ISSN 1000-162X
SHANXI NONGYE DAXUE XUEBAO/SHANXI UNIVERSITY OF AGRICULTURE. JOURNAL. Text in Chinese. s-a.
Related titles: Online - full text ed.: (from East View Information Services).
Published by: Shanxi Nongye Daxue/Shanxi University of Agriculture, Taigu Xian (county), Shanxi 030801, China. TEL 22902. Ed. Chen Zhen.

630 CHN ISSN 1000-1700
SHENYANG NONGYE DAXUE XUEBAO/SHENYANG AGRICULTURAL UNIVERSITY. JOURNAL. Text in Chinese. 1986. q. **Document type:** *Journal, Academic/Scholarly.*
Related titles: Online - full text ed.: (from East View Information Services, WanFang Data Corp.).
Indexed: ZooRec.
—BLDSC (4874.935100), IE.
Published by: Shenyang Nongye Daxue/Shenyang Agricultural University, 120, Dongling Road, Shenyang, 110161, China. TEL 86-24-88421508, http://synydxxb.wanfangdata.com.cn/default.html, http://www.syau.edu.cn/. **Dist. by:** China International Book Trading Corp, 35 Chegongzhuang Xilu, Haidian District, PO Box 399, Beijing 100044, China. TEL 86-10-68412045, FAX 86-10-68412023, cibtc@mail.cibtc.com.cn, http://www.cibtc.com.cn.

630 CHN ISSN 1002-4433
SHIJIE NONGYE/WORLD AGRICULTURE. Text in Chinese. 1979. m. CNY 5, USD 2.40 per issue (effective 2003). adv. **Document type:** *Academic/Scholarly.* **Description:** Introduces the current advances in agriculture, animal husbandry and fishery.
Related titles: Online - full text ed.: (from East View Information Services).
Published by: Zhongguo Nongye Chubanshe/China Agricultural Press, Zhaoyang-qu, 18, Maizidian Jie, Beijing, 100026, China. TEL 86-10-65064142, FAX 86-10-65005665, sj-ny@sohu.com, http://shijny.periodicals.net.cn/default.html. Eds. Cai Shenglin, Wang Qiang. adv.: page USD 5,000. Circ: 10,000. **Dist. by:** China International Book Trading Corp, 35 Chegongzhuang Xilu, Haidian District, PO Box 399, Beijing 100044, China. TEL 86-10-68412045, FAX 86-10-68412023, cibtc@mail.cibtc.com.cn, http://www.cibtc.com.cn.

630 JPN ISSN 0583-0621
S19 CODEN: SDNOAM
SHINSHU DAIGAKU NOGAKUBU KIYO/SHINSHU UNIVERSITY. FACULTY OF AGRICULTURE. JOURNAL. Text in Japanese. 1951. a. **Document type:** *Journal, Academic/Scholarly.*
Supersedes in part (in 1958): Shinshu Daigaku Kiyo/Shinshu University. Journal (0559-8575)
Indexed: AgBio, AnBrAb, CPA, DSA, FCA, FPA, ForAb, HerbAb, HortAb, IndVet, MaizeAb, NutrAb, PBA, PGegResA, PGrRegA, PHN&I, PotatoAb, PoultAb, RA&MP, RDA, RPP, RRTA, RiceAb, S&F, SIA, SeedAb, VetBull, WAE&RSA, WeedAb.
—BLDSC (4743.300000).
Published by: Shinshu Daigaku, Nogakubu/Shinshu University, Faculty of Agriculture, 8304 Minami-minaowa, Kami-ina, Nagano, 399-4598, Japan. TEL 81-265-771300, http://karamatsu.shinshu-u.ac.jp/.

SHIYONGJUN XUEBAO/ACTA EDULIS FUNGI. see *BIOLOGY—Botany*

630 JPN ISSN 0918-6638
SHOKUBUTSU KOJO GAKKAISHI/JAPANESE SOCIETY OF HIGH TECHNOLOGY IN AGRICULTURE. JOURNAL. Text in Japanese. 1991. s-a. **Document type:** *Journal, Academic/Scholarly.*
Indexed: AgBio, BioCN&I, CPA, FCA, ForAb, HerbAb, HortAb, I&DA, NutrAb, OrnHort, PBA, PGegResA, PGrRegA, PHN&I, PotatoAb, RA&MP, RPP, S&F, SeedAb, TriticAb, WAE&RSA, WeedAb.
—BLDSC (4888.600000). **CCC.**
Published by: Nihon Shokubutsu Kojo Gakkai/Japanese Society of High Technology in Agriculture, 317, Nishino, Numazu-city, Shizuoka 410-0395, Japan. FAX 81-55-9681156, shita@fb.u-tokai.ac.jp, http://shita.jp/journal/index-j.htm.

SHOKUHIN SOGO KENKYUJO KENKYU HOKOKU/NATIONAL FOOD RESEARCH INSTITUTE. REPORT. see *FOOD AND FOOD INDUSTRIES*

SHOKURYO, SONO KAGAKU TO GIJUTSU/FOOD, IT'S SCIENCE AND TECHNOLOGY. see *FOOD AND FOOD INDUSTRIES*

630 USA ISSN 1093-9520
SHOW ME MISSOURI FARM BUREAU. Text in English. 1921. 6/yr. USD 30 membership (effective 2005). adv. **Document type:** *Magazine, Trade.*
Formerly (until 1997): Missouri F B News (0026-6574)
Related titles: Microfiche ed.
Published by: Missouri Farm Bureau Federation, PO Box 658, Jefferson City, MO 65102. TEL 573-893-1400, FAX 573-893-1470, mo@momail.com, http://www.mofb.com. Circ: 105,000.

630 RUS ISSN 0370-8799
CODEN: SBVSAQ
SIBIRSKII VESTNIK SEL'SKOKHOZYAISTVENNOI NAUKI/SIBERIAN BULLETIN OF AGRICULTURAL SCIENCE. Text in Russian. 1971. s-a.
Indexed: RefZh, ZooRec.
—BLDSC (0164.099000), CISTI.
Published by: Izdatel'stvo Nauka, Sibirskoye Otdeleniye, Novosibirskaya oblast', P.O. Box 45, Krasnoobsk, 633128, Russian Federation. TEL 7-3832-483762. Ed. P. Goncharov.

630 DEU
SICHER LEBEN (HANNOVER). Text in German. 1965. bi-m.
Published by: Hannoversche Landwirtschaftliche Berufsgenossenschaft, Im Haspelfelde 24, Hannover, 30173, Germany. TEL 0511-8073-0, FAX 0511-8073-498.

630 DEU
SICHER LEBEN (SPEYER). Text in German. 1965. 6/yr. **Document type:** *Bulletin.*
Published by: Landwirtschaftliche Berufsgenossenschaft Rheinhessen-Pfalz, Speyer, 67343, Germany. TEL 06232-911205, FAX 06232-911187. Ed. Richard Binz. Circ: 18,000.

630 CHN ISSN 1000-2650
SICHUAN NONGYE DAXUE XUEBAO/SICHUAN AGRICULTURAL UNIVERSITY. JOURNAL. Text in Chinese. 1983. q. CNY 5 newsstand/cover (effective 2005). **Document type:** *Journal, Academic/Scholarly.*
Related titles: Online - full text ed.: (from East View Information Services, WanFang Data Corp.).
Indexed: AgBio, AgrForAb, AnBrAb, BioCN&I, CPA, FCA, ForAb, HerbAb, HortAb, IndVet, MaizeAb, OrnHort, PBA, PGegResA, PGrRegA, PN&I, PoultAb, RA&MP, S&F, SIA, SeedAb, TriticAb, WeedAb.
—BLDSC (8271.622800), IE.
Published by: Sichuan Nongye Daxue/Sichuan Agricultural University, Yucheng-qu, Ya'an, 625014, China. TEL 86-835-2242295, FAX 86-835-2242742, jsau@sicau.edu.cn, http://scnydxxb.periodicals.net.cn/.

SICKLE & SHEAF. see *CLUBS*

630 SLE
SIERRA LEONE AGRICULTURAL JOURNAL✶. Text in English. 1972. s-a. SLL 2, USD 6. adv. bk.rev. charts; illus. **Document type:** *Journal, Academic/Scholarly.*
Indexed: FCA, HerbAb, RRTA, WAE&RSA.
Published by: Sierra Leone Agricultural Society, University of Sierra Leone, Njala University College, Private Mail Bag, Freetown, Sierra Leone.

SIGMUL BYEONG GWA NONG-EOB/RESEARCH IN PLANT DISEASE. see *BIOLOGY—Botany*

630 USA
SILLON; a journal of popular farm science and rural life. Text in French. 1970. 4/yr. free to qualified personnel.
Related titles: ♦ Regional ed(s).: Furrow. ISSN 0016-3112; ♦ Surco Latinoamericana; ♦ Sulco; ♦ Voor.
Indexed: RILM.
Published by: John Deere Publishing, One John Deere Place, Moline, IL 61265. TEL 309-765-8000. Ed. Jean Claude Hiron. Circ: 140,000.

630 BEL
SILLON BELGE. Text in French. 1932. 49/yr. EUR 40 (effective 2002). adv. **Document type:** *Newspaper.*
Related titles: ♦ Dutch ed.: Landbouwleven. ISSN 0772-7240.
Published by: Editions Rurales, Leon Grosjeanlaan 92, Brussels, 1140, Belgium. TEL 02-730-3300, FAX 02-726-9134, TELEX 25882, erulu@euronet.be. Ed. A Demol. Adv. contact Sylvie Eyben. Circ: 43,346.

630 FRA ISSN 0152-6456
SILLON DES LANDES ET DES PYRENEES. EDITION 64. Text in French. 1968. w.
Formerly (until 1978): Sillion des Landes et des Pyrenees (0152-6421)
Published by: Societe d'Editions Agricoles du Basin de l'Adour, 124 bd. Tourasse, Pau, 64000, France. TEL 59-02-35-55. Ed. J L Dumontier Beroulet. Circ: 20,000.

630 RUS ISSN 0037-5322
SIL'S'KE BUDIVNYTSTVO. Text in Ukrainian. 1951. m. illus.
Indexed: RASB.
Published by: Izdatel'stvo Kniga, Moscow, 125047, Russian Federation.

630 UKR ISSN 0235-635X
SIL'S'KI OBRII. Text in Ukrainian. m. USD 150 in United States (effective 2000).
Address: Ul Pavlovskaya 11g, Kiev, Ukraine. TEL 293-53-80.
Dist. by: East View Information Services, 3020 Harbor Ln. N., Minneapolis, MN 55447. TEL 763-550-0961, FAX 763-559-2931.

630 CHL ISSN 0037-5403
CODEN: SMNTAW
SIMIENTE. Text in Spanish. 1930. q. CLP 9,000 domestic; USD 40 foreign; CLP 7.50 to students (effective 2005). adv. bk.rev. bibl.; charts; illus.; stat. **Description:** Technical articles on agricultural science and engineering. Includes news of and for members.
Related titles: Online - full text ed.
Indexed: BiolAb, ChemAb, FCA, HerbAb, HortAb, MaizeAb, PGrRegA, PotatoAb, S&F, SeedAb, TriticAb, WeedAb.
—CASDDS.
Published by: Sociedad Agronomica de Chile, Calle Mac Iver 120, Of.36, Santiago, Chile. http://www.sach.cl/simiente.htm. Ed. Elena Dagnino. Circ: 2,000.

630 CAN ISSN 0225-7211
SIMMENTAL COUNTRY. Text in English. 1973. m. (11/yr). CND 38; USD 55 in United States; CND 80 elsewhere (effective 1999). adv. **Document type:** *Newspaper.*
Formerly (until 1979): Simmental Scene (0318-0913)
—CISTI.
Published by: (Canadian Simmental Association), Simmental Country Ltd., 13 4101 19th St N E, Calgary, AB T2E 7C4, Canada. TEL 403-250-5255, FAX 403-250-5121, country@simmental.com. Ed., Pub. Gaylene Groeneveld. adv.: B&W page CND 675; trim 10.75 x 8.38. Circ: 4,355.

630 IDN
SINAR JAYA. Text in Indonesian. fortn. adv.
Address: Jalan Sultan Aqung 67 A, Jakarta Selatan, Indonesia. Ed. Suryono Projopranoto.

630 639.2 636.089 SGP ISSN 0129-6485
S322.S55 CODEN: SJPIDP
SINGAPORE JOURNAL OF PRIMARY INDUSTRIES. Text in English. 1973. a. SGD 15 (effective 1999). adv. back issues avail.

Indexed: AgBio, AgrForAb, AnBrAb, BioCN&I, BiolAb, ChemAb, DSA, ForAb, HelmAb, HortAb, I&DA, IndVet, NutrAb, OrnHort, PBA, PGrRegA, PHN&I, PN&I, PoultAb, ProtozoAb, RPP, RevApplEntom, S&F, SFA, TDB, VITIS, VetBull, WAE&RSA. —BLDSC (8285.464000), CASDDS, CISTI.
Published by: Ministry of National Development, Primary Production Department, National Development Bldg, 5 Maxwell Rd 03-00, Singapore, 069110, Singapore. FAX 65-2206068, TELEX RS-28851-PPD. Ed. Tan Hock Seng. Circ: 500.

SITUATION ET STATISTIQUES MONDIALES DU SECTEUR VITICOLE. see *AGRICULTURE—Abstracting, Bibliographies, Statistics*

630.9489 DNK ISSN 0900-3460
SKALMEJEN. Text in Danish. 1984. q. DKK 25 (effective 1998). illus. **Document type:** *Newsletter, Consumer.*
Published by: Ringsted Museum og Forening, c/o Kirsten Henriksen, Koegevej 41, Ringsted, 4100, Denmark.

630 USA
SMALL FARM DIGEST. Text in English. q. **Document type:** *Newsletter, Government.*
Formed by the merger of: Small-Scale Agriculture Today; Small and Part Time Farms
Related titles: Online - full text ed.
Published by: U.S. Department of Agriculture, Cooperative State Research, Education and Extension Service, Stop 3250, Washington, DC 20250-3250. solson@reeusda.gov, http://www.reeusda.gov/agsys/sfd/. Ed. Stephanie K Olson.

630 USA
SMALL FARM NEWS. Text in English. 1981. q. free. bk.rev. 12 p./no.; **Document type:** *Newsletter, Trade.* **Description:** Provides information to extension workers, researchers, and operators of small farms and related businesses.
Published by: Small Farm Center, University of California at Davis, One Shields Ave, Davis, CA 95616-8699. TEL 530-752-8136, FAX 530-752-7716, sfcenter@ucdavis.edu, http://www.sfc.ucdavis.edu/pubs/SFNews/news.htm. Circ: 5,000 (controlled).

630 USA ISSN 1079-9729
SMALL FARM TODAY; the how-to magazine of alternative and traditional crops, livestock and direct marketing. Text in English. 1984. bi-m. USD 23.95 domestic; USD 33.95 foreign; USD 4.95 newsstand/cover (effective 2005). adv. bk.rev.; video rev. illus. 80 p./no.; back issues avail. **Document type:** *Magazine, Trade.* **Description:** To promote and preserve small farming and rural living by providing both traditional and non-traditional farming alternatives adaptable to small acreages.
Formerly (until 1992): Missouri Farm (0892-6301)
Indexed: Agr.
Published by: Missouri Farm Publishing, Inc., 3903 W Ridge Trail Rd, Clark, MO 65243-9525. TEL 573-687-3525, FAX 573-687-3148, smallfarm@socket.net, http://www.smallfarmtoday.com. Ed., Pub. Ron Macher. R&P Paul Berg. Adv. contact Jeff Macher. B&W page USD 915, color page USD 1,270; trim 8.5 x 11. Circ: 12,500 (paid and controlled).

630 USA ISSN 0743-9989
SMALL FARMER'S JOURNAL; featuring practical horse-farming. Text in English. 1976. q. USD 30 domestic; USD 40 in Canada & Mexico; USD 45 elsewhere (effective 2005). adv. bk.rev. illus. 132 p./no.; back issues avail. **Document type:** *Trade.*
—CISTI.
Published by: Small Farmers Journal, Inc., PO Box 1627, Sisters, OR 97759-1627. TEL 541-549-2064, 800-876-2893, FAX 541-549-4403, agrarian@smallfarmersjournal.com, http://www.smallfarmersjournal.com. Ed., Pub. Lynn R Miller. Adv. contact Amy Ferris. Circ: 40,000.

630 AUS ISSN 1441-3701
SMALL FARMS. Text in English. m. free domestic; AUD 3 per issue in Asia & the Pacific; AUD 4.50 per issue elsewhere (effective 2004). adv. **Document type:** *Magazine, Trade.*
Address: PO Box 225, Bowral, NSW 2576, Australia. TEL 61-2-48617778, FAX 61-2-48617779, smallfarms@bigpond.com, http://www.smallfarms.net/.

363.7 CAN ISSN 0383-6312
SMALLHOLDER. Text in English. 1973. 3/yr. CND 16; CND 2.75 per issue (effective 2004). adv. bk.rev. bibl.; illus. **Document type:** *Newsletter.* **Description:** Reader's exchange on topics of interest to people living rural lifestyles; covers gardening, homestead skills, environment and more.
Published by: Smallholder Publishing Collective, Argenta, BC V0G 1B0, Canada. Circ: 700.

630 GBR ISSN 0265-7473
SMALLHOLDER; for practical smallfarming today. Text in English. 1981. m. GBP 26.10 domestic; GBP 38.16 in Europe; GBP 49.15 elsewhere (effective 2003). adv. bk.rev. illus. cum.index. back issues avail. **Document type:** *Newspaper, Consumer.* **Description:** Presents news and views for farmers of small holdings, with articles on poultry, sheep, pigs, dairy, and produce.
Related titles: Online - full content ed.
Published by: Newsquest Media Group (Subsidiary of: Gannett Newspapers), Falmouth Business Park, Bickland Water Rd, Falmouth, Cornwall, TR11 4SZ, United Kingdom. TEL 44-1326-213333, FAX 44-1326-212108, edit@smallholder.co.uk, packet@packetseries.co.uk, http://www.smallholder.co.uk, http://www.newsquest.co.uk/. Ed. Liz Wright. adv.: B&W page GBP 350, color page GBP 575; trim 210 x 297. Circ: 12,000 (paid).

630 ARG ISSN 0037-864X
SOCIEDAD RURAL ARGENTINA. BOLETIN. Text in Spanish. 1958. 9/yr. ARS 20,000. adv. **Document type:** *Bulletin.*
Indexed: ZooRec.
Published by: Sociedad Rural Argentina, Florida, 460, Capital Federal, Buenos Aires 1005, Argentina. Circ: 15,000.

SOCIETE D'HORTICULTURE ET D'HISTOIRE NATURELLE DE L'HERAULT. ANNALES. see *SCIENCES: COMPREHENSIVE WORKS*

630 GBR ISSN 0967-0548
HD1401
SOCIO-ECONOMIC SERIES. Text in English. 1993. irreg. price varies. **Document type:** *Monographic series.* **Description:** Covers a wide range of development issues in agriculture from reviews to practical field projects.
Related titles: CD-ROM ed.; Online - full text ed.
Indexed: FPA, RDA.
—BLDSC (6180.547900).
Published by: Natural Resources Institute, Central Ave, Chatham Maritime, Kent, ME4 4TB, United Kingdom. TEL 44-1634-880088, FAX 44-1634-880066, publications@nri.org, http://www.nri.org.

SOCIOLOGIJA SELA; casopis za istrazivanje prostornoga i sociokulturnog razvoja/quaterly for spatial and sociocultural development studies. see *SOCIOLOGY*

630 SVN ISSN 0350-1655
SODOBNO KMETIJSTVO. Text in Slovenian. 1950. m. SIT 1,584, USD 107. adv.
Formerly: Socialisticno Kmetijstvo
Indexed: AEA, AgBio, AnBrAb, BioCN&I, CPA, DSA, FCA, ForAb, HelmAb, HerbAb, HortAb, I&DA, IndVet, MaizeAb, NemAb, NutrAb, OrnHort, PBA, PGegResA, PGrRegA, PHN&I, PN&I, PotatoAb, PoultAb, RA&MP, RASB, RDA, RPP, RRTA, RevApplEntom, S&F, SIA, SeedAb, SoyAb, TriticAb, VetBull, WAE&RSA, WeedAb.
Published by: C Z P Kmecki Glas, Celovska 43, Box 47, Ljubljana, 61001, Slovenia. TEL 061-328670, FAX 061-321-651. Ed. Rajko Ocepek. Circ: 1,000.

630 NLD ISSN 0167-1987
CODEN: SOTRD5
➤ **SOIL & TILLAGE RESEARCH.** Text in Dutch. 1981. 10/yr. EUR 1,856 in Europe to institutions; JPY 246,700 in Japan to institutions; USD 2,076 to institutions except Europe and Japan (effective 2006). adv. bk.rev. bibl.; abstr. index. reprints avail. **Document type:** *Academic/Scholarly.* **Description:** Covers changes in the physical, chemical and biological parameters of soil environment caused by soil tillage and field traffic. Examines the effects and interactions on crop establishment, root development and plant growth.
Incorporates (1988-1997): Soil Technology (0933-3630)
Related titles: Microform ed.: (from PQC); Online - full text ed.: (from EBSCO Publishing, Gale Group, IngentaConnect, ScienceDirect, Swets Information Services).
Indexed: AEA, AESIS, ASCA, Agr, AgrForAb, BIOBASE, BIOSIS Prev, BioCN&I, BiolAb, CPA, CTFA, ChemAb, CurCont, EPB, ESPM, Englnd, EnvAb, ExcerpMed, FCA, FLUIDEX, FPA, ForAb, GEOBASE, HerbAb, HortAb, I&DA, IABS, ISR, MaizeAb, NemAb, OrnHort, PBA, PGegResA, PN&I, PlantSci, PotatoAb, PoultAb, RDA, RPP, RRTA, RiceAb, S&F, S&MA, SCI, SIA, SSCI, SWRA, SeedAb, SoyAb, TTI, TriticAb, VITIS, WAE&RSA, WeedAb.
—BLDSC (8321.760000), CASDDS, CISTI, Ei, IDS, IE, Infotrieve, ingenta, Linda Hall. **CCC.**
Published by: (International Soil Tillage Research Organisation), Elsevier BV (Subsidiary of: Elsevier Science & Technology), Radarweg 29, Amsterdam, 1043 NX, Netherlands. TEL 31-20-4853911, FAX 31-20-4852457, nlinfo-f@elsevier.nl, http://www.elsevier.com/locate/still, http://www.elsevier.nl. Eds. A. J. Franzluebbers, M R Carter, M Kutilek.

630 GBR ISSN 0038-1314
SOMERSET FARMER. Text in English. 1962. m. adv.
Published by: County Farmers Publications Ltd., 55 Goldington Rd, Bedford, Beds MK40 3LU, United Kingdom. TEL 44-1234-351401, FAX 44-1234-328614. Ed. A A Gibson. Circ: 4,600.

630 AUT ISSN 1018-1954
SORTENVERSUCHSERGEBNISSE. Text in German. 1950. a. price varies. adv. 50 p./no. 3 cols./p.; back issues avail. **Document type:** *Academic/Scholarly.*
Former titles (until 1989): Bundesanstalt fuer Alpenlaendische Landwirtschaft Gumpenstein. Versuchsergebnisse; Bundesanstalt fuer Alpine Landwirtschaft. Versuchsergebnisse
Indexed: FCA, PBA, PGrRegA, PotatoAb.
—BLDSC (8328.673150).
Published by: Bundesanstalt fuer Alpenlaendische Landwirtschaft Gumpenstein, Irdning, St 8952, Austria. TEL 43-3682-22451, FAX 43-3682-2461488, office@bal.bmlf.gv.at, http://www.bal.bmlf.gv.at. Ed., R&P Kurt Chytil TEL 43-3682-22451. Adv. contact Eva Rainer. Circ: 250.

630 ZAF
SOUTH AFRICA. DEPARTMENT OF AGRICULTURE. AGRICULTURAL BULLETINS. Text in English. 1925. irreg. (10-12/yr.). price varies. charts; illus.; stat. **Document type:** *Bulletin, Government.*
Former titles: South Africa. Department of Agriculture and Fisheries. Agricultural Bulletins; South Africa. Department of Agricultural Technical Services. Agricultural Bulletins (0002-1393)
Related titles: Afrikaans ed.
Indexed: BiolAb, PBA.
Published by: Department of Agriculture, Private Bag X144, Pretoria, 0001, South Africa. TEL 27-12-3197141, FAX 27-12-3232516. Circ: 1,100.

630 ZAF
SOUTH AFRICA. DEPARTMENT OF AGRICULTURE. ANNUAL REPORT OF THE DIRECTOR-GENERAL. Text in English. 1960. a. price varies. **Document type:** *Government.*
Former titles: South Africa. Department of Agriculture. Annual Report of the Chief; South Africa. Department of Agricultural Development. Annual Report of the Chief for Agricultural Development; South Africa. Department of Agriculture and Water Supply. Annual Report of the Superintendent-General (1017-4575); (until 1985): South Africa. Department of Agriculture and Water Supply. Annual Report of the Head of the Department (1010-1942); (until 1984): South Africa. Department of Agriculture. Report of the Secretary for Agricultural Technical Services; (until 1981): South Africa. Department of Agriculture and Fisheries. Report of the Secretary for Agricultural Technical Services; South Africa. Department of Agricultural Technical Services. Report of the Secretary for Agricultural Technical Services (0081-2153)
Indexed: AnBrAb, IndVet, RPP, WeedAb.
Published by: Department of Agriculture, Private Bag X144, Pretoria, 0001, South Africa. TEL 27-12-3197141, FAX 27-12-3232516. R&P M A Fourie. Circ: 1,000.

630 ZAF
SOUTH AFRICA. DEPARTMENT OF AGRICULTURE. OFFICIAL LIST OF PROFESSIONAL RESEARCH WORKERS, LECTURING STAFF AND EXTENSION WORKERS IN THE AGRICULTURAL FIELD. Text in English. 1965. a. free. **Document type:** *Government.*
Former titles: South Africa. Department of Agriculture and Fisheries. Official List of Professional Research Workers, Lecturing Staff and Extension Workers in the Agricultural Field; South Africa. Department of Agricultural Technical Services. Official List of Professional Research Workers, Lecturing Staff and Extension Workers in the Agricultural Field
Published by: Department of Agriculture, Private Bag X144, Pretoria, 0001, South Africa. TEL 27-12-3197141, FAX 27-12-3232516. R&P Ronelle Hechter. Circ: (controlled).

630 ZAF
CODEN: TCSFDR
SOUTH AFRICA. DEPARTMENT OF AGRICULTURE. TECHNICAL COMMUNICATION. Text in English. 1960. irreg. price varies. **Document type:** *Government.*
Former titles (until no.238, 1994): South Africa. Department of Agricultural Development. Technical Communication (1019-3111); (until no.220, 1990): South Africa. Department of Agriculture and Water Supply. Technical Communication (1012-7100); (until 1984): South Africa. Department of Agriculture. Technical Communication (0255-0164); (until 1981): South Africa. Department of Agriculture and Fisheries. Technical Communication (0253-2840); South Africa. Department of Agricultural Technical Services. Technical Communication (0081-217X)
Indexed: BiolAb, FS&TA, RPP.
—CASDDS.
Published by: Department of Agriculture, Private Bag X144, Pretoria, 0001, South Africa. TEL 27-12-3197141, FAX 27-12-3232516. R&P Ronelle Hechter. Circ: 1,100.

SOUTH AFRICA. STATISTICS SOUTH AFRICA. STATISTICAL RELEASE. AGRICULTURAL SURVEY. see *AGRICULTURE—Abstracting, Bibliographies, Statistics*

638.1 ZAF ISSN 0038-2019
SOUTH AFRICAN BEE JOURNAL. Text in Afrikaans, English. 1911. bi-m. ZAR 110 (effective 1997). adv. bk.rev. stat. **Document type:** *Trade.*
Indexed: ApicAb, BioCN&I, ISAP.
Published by: South African Federation of Beefarmers' Associations, PO Box 41, Modderfontein, 1645, South Africa. TEL 27-11-8822646, lear@ae.aeci.co.za. Circ: 500.

630.715 ZAF ISSN 0301-603X
SOUTH AFRICAN JOURNAL OF AGRICULTURAL EXTENSION/SUID-AFRIKAANSE TIJDSKRIF VIR LANDBOUVOORLIGTING. Text and summaries in Afrikaans, English. 1972. a. ZAR 50. adv. bk.rev. bibl. author index: vols.1-22. back issues avail. **Document type:** *Academic/Scholarly.* **Description:** Promotes the adoption of sound farming practices by the creation of scientific guidelines for agricultural development.
Formerly: South African Society for Agricultural Extension. Journal
Related titles: Online - full text ed.: (from International Network for the Availability of Scientific Publications, African Journals Online).
Indexed: ISAP, RDA, WAE&RSA.
Published by: South African Society for Agricultural Extension/Suid-Afrikaanse Vereniging vir Landbouvoorligting, University of Pretoria, Pretoria, 0002, South Africa. TEL 27-12-420-3246, FAX 27-12-420-3247. Ed. C A J Botha. Circ: (controlled).

630.715 ZAF
SOUTH AFRICAN SOCIETY FOR AGRICULTURAL EXTENSION. CONFERENCE PROCEEDINGS/SUID-AFRIKAANSE VERENIGING VIR LANDBOUVOORLIGTING. KONFERENSIEHANDELINGE. Text in Afrikaans, English. a. ZAR 50. **Document type:** *Proceedings.*
Published by: South African Society for Agricultural Extension/Suid-Afrikaanse Vereniging vir Landbouvoorligting, University of Pretoria, Pretoria, 0002, South Africa. TEL 27-12-420-3246, FAX 27-12-420-3247. Ed. C A J Botha.

630 USA ISSN 0889-1834
SOUTH CAROLINA FARMER✶. Text in English. m. USD 12; USD 25 foreign. **Document type:** *Newspaper.*
Supersedes: Carolina Farmer (South Carolina Edition) (0893-7508)
Published by: Rural Press U S A, 1101 Spring Forest Rd, Ste 101, Raleigh, NC 27615. TEL 919-676-3276, 800-477-1737, FAX 919-676-9803. Ed. R Davis. Pub. Jeff Tennant. adv.: B&W page USD 1,218. Circ: 11,000.

630 USA ISSN 1079-8889
SOUTH CAROLINA Y F AND F F A. Text in English. 1950. q. USD 0.50. adv. tr.lit. **Document type:** *Trade.*
Formerly: South Carolina Young Farmer and Future Farmer (0038-3201)
Published by: South Carolina Young Farmers and Future Farmers, 109 Barre Hall, Clemson, SC 29634. TEL 803-734-8426, FAX 803-734-3525, TGLDDN@clemson.edu. Ed. Tommy Gladden. Circ: 8,000 (controlled).

630 USA ISSN 0745-8797
SOUTH DAKOTA UNION FARMER. Text in English. 1918. m. USD 1. adv.
Published by: Farmers Educational & Cooperative Union of America, South Dakota Division, PO Box 1388, Huron, SD 57350. Ed. Charles W Groth. Circ: 16,007.

630 GBR ISSN 0953-7546
SOUTH EAST FARMER. Text in English. 1979. m. GBP 50 domestic; GBP 70 foreign (effective 2003). adv. **Document type:** *Trade.* **Description:** Contains news, intelligence and features for farmers and growers in S E England.
Published by: Evegate Publishing Ltd., PO Box 53, Ashford, Kent TN23 1WE, United Kingdom. TEL 44-1233-656644, cliver@southeastbusiness.net, http://www.southeastfamer.net. Ed. John Harvey. Adv. contact Jamie McGrorty. Circ: 13,000.

630 GBR
SOUTH EAST REGION N F U JOURNAL. Text in English. 12/yr. adv. **Document type:** *Trade.*
Published by: Bailey Newspaper Group, Agriculture House, Station Rd, Liss, Hants GU33 7AR, United Kingdom. TEL 44-1730-893723, FAX 44-1730-892622. Ed. Sue Acworth. Adv. contact Jan Milner.

630 GBR
SOUTH WEST FARMER. Text in English. 1981. m. adv. bk.rev.
Published by: West of England Newspapers Ltd., Burrington Way, Plymouth, PL5 3LN, United Kingdom. TEL 44-1752-777151, FAX 44-1752-780680. Ed. David Husband. Circ: 30,000.

630 USA ISSN 0194-0937
SOUTHEAST FARM PRESS. Text in English. 1974. s-m. USD 34; free to qualified personnel (effective 2005). adv. stat. **Document type:** *Magazine, Trade.*
Related titles: Online - full text ed.: (from bigchalk, EBSCO Publishing, Factiva, H.W. Wilson, O C L C Online Computer Library Center, Inc., ProQuest Information & Learning).
Indexed: ABIn, B&AI.
—CCC.
Published by: Primedia Business Magazines & Media, Inc. (Subsidiary of: Primedia, Inc.), 14920 US Highway 61, PO Box 1420, Clarksdale, MS 38614. TEL 662-624-8503, FAX 662-627-1977, inquiries@primediabusiness.com, http://www.southeastfarmpress.com, http://www.primediabusiness.com. Eds. Paul Hollis, Hembree Brandon. Pub. Greg Frey. adv.: color page USD 5,554, B&W page USD 4,764. Circ: 53,000 (paid).

630 AUS
SOUTHERN COUNTRY. Text in English. m. adv. **Document type:** *Newspaper, Trade.* **Description:** Caters to the needs and specialities of farmers in the south east region of South Australia and Western Victoria.
Published by: Rural Press Ltd. (Subsidiary of: Agricultural Publishers Pty. Ltd.), 159 Bells Line of Rd., PO Box 999, North Richmond, NSW 2754, Australia. TEL 61-2-45704444, FAX 61-2-45704630, http://www.ruralpress.com/. Circ: 4,000 (controlled).

630 USA ISSN 0038-4100
SOUTHERN FARMER. Text in English. m. USD 23.95 (effective 2005). adv. **Document type:** *Magazine, Trade.*
Contact Owner: Farm Progress Companies, 191 S Gary Ave, Carol Stream, IL 60188-2095. TEL 630-462-2229, FAX 630-462-2202, swyant@farmprogress.com, info@farmprogress.com, http://www.southern-farmer.com, http://www.farmprogress.com/. adv.: col. inch USD 2,650, B&W page USD 2,150; trim 10.5 x 14.5. Circ: 25,000 (paid and controlled).

630 USA ISSN 0192-4168
SOUTHERN TIER TOWN AND COUNTRY LIVING✶. Text in English. 1947. m. USD 5. adv. stat.; illus.
Published by: Farm & Home Publications, 10 Lourdes Rd, Binghamton, NY 13905-4293. Ed. Bernard M Swartz. Circ: 2,600.

630 USA ISSN 0194-0945
SOUTHWEST FARM PRESS. Text in English. 1974. s-m. USD 36 domestic; USD 179 foreign; free to qualified personnel in TX, OK, NM, or KS (effective 2005). adv. charts; illus.; tr.lit. **Document type:** *Magazine, Trade.* **Description:** Covers the varied, highly productive agriculture of the soutwestern states, including production, management, research and legislative/regulatory issues affecting growers of key cotton, wheat, grain sorghum, rice, peanuts, pecans, soybeans, corn and vegetable/citrus crops.
Related titles: Online - full text ed.: (from bigchalk, EBSCO Publishing, Factiva, Gale Group, H.W. Wilson, O C L C Online Computer Library Center, Inc., ProQuest Information & Learning).
Indexed: ABIn, B&AI.
—CCC.
Published by: Primedia Business Magazines & Media, Inc. (Subsidiary of: Primedia, Inc.), 14920 US Highway 61, PO Box 1420, Clarksdale, MS 38614. TEL 662-624-8503, FAX 662-627-1977, gfrey@primedia.com, inquiries@primediabusiness.com, http://southwestfarmpress.com/, http://www.primediabusiness.com. Eds. Ron Smith, Hembree Brandon. Pub. Greg Frey. Adv. contact Kevin Hudson. color page USD 8,631. Circ: 47,100 (paid).

630 ESP
SPAIN. MINISTERIO DE AGRICULTURA, PESCA Y ALIMENTACION. BOLETIN. Text in Spanish. 1993. m. price varies. illus.; charts; stat. **Document type:** *Bulletin, Government.*
Published by: (Spain. Secretaria General Tecnica), Ministerio de Agricultura Pesca y Alimentacion, Centro de Publicaciones, Paseo Infanta Isabel 1, Madrid, 28014, Spain. TEL 34-91-3475550, FAX 34-91-3475722, mllopisj@mapya.es, http://www.mapya.es. R&P Miguel Llopis.

SPAIN. MINISTERIO DE AGRICULTURA, PESCA Y ALIMENTACION. BOLETIN MENSUAL DE ESTADISTICA AGRARIA. see *AGRICULTURE—Abstracting, Bibliographies, Statistics*

630 ESP
SPAIN. MINISTERIO DE AGRICULTURA, PESCA Y ALIMENTACION. INSTITUTO DE REFORMA Y DESARROLLO AGRARIO. HOJAS DIVULGADORAS. Text in Spanish. 1918. 20/yr. price varies. **Document type:** *Bulletin, Academic/Scholarly.* **Description:** Technical bulletin for farmers.
Formerly: Spain. Ministerio de Agricultura, Pesca y Alimentacion. Servicio de Extension Agraria. Hojas Divulgadoras
Indexed: AnBrAb, DSA, FCA, HerbAb, IndVet, PotatoAb, RM&VM.
Published by: (Spain. Instituto de Reforma y Desarrollo Agrario), Ministerio de Agricultura Pesca y Alimentacion, Centro de Publicaciones, Paseo Infanta Isabel 1, Madrid, 28014, Spain. TEL 34-91-3475550, FAX 34-91-3475722, mllopisj@mapya.es, http://www.mapya.es. Ed. Felicisimo Gonzalez Rodriquez. R&P Juan Carlos Palacios Lopez. Circ: 40,000.

SPAIN. MINISTERIO DE AGRICULTURA PESCA Y ALIMENTACION. SECRETARIA GENERAL TECNICA. ANUARIO DE ESTADISTICA AGROALIMENTARIA. see *AGRICULTURE—Abstracting, Bibliographies, Statistics*

630.658 CAN
SPECIALTY FARMS. Text in English. 7/yr. CND 17.50 domestic; USD 45 foreign (effective 2005). **Document type:** *Magazine, Trade.*
Published by: Annex Publishing & Printing, Inc., 222 Argyle Ave, Delhi, ON N4B 2Y2, ON N4B 2Y2, Canada. TEL 519-582-2513, 800-265-2827, FAX 519-582-4040, sfredericks@annexweb.com, http://www.annexweb.com. Ed. Margaret Land. Circ: 3,500.

638.1 USA ISSN 0190-6798
THE SPEEDY BEE; the beekeepers' newspaper. Text in English. 1972. m. USD 17.25; USD 1.75 newsstand/cover (effective 2005). adv. bk.rev. **Document type:** *Magazine, Trade.* **Description:** Covers the beekeeping and honey industry.
Indexed: ApicAb.
Published by: Fore's Honey Farms, Inc., PO Box 1317, Jesup, GA 31598. TEL 912-427-4018, FAX 912-427-8447, troyfore@bellsouth.net, troyfore@jesup.net, http://www.speedybee.net. Ed., Pub., R&P Troy H Fore Jr. Adv. contact Donna Brooks. Circ: 1,500.

633.83 IND ISSN 0970-5805
HD9210.I5
SPICE INDIA. Text in English. m. INR 50 (effective 2000). adv. bk.rev. **Document type:** *Government.*
Former titles: Cardamom (0970-5449); (until Nov. 1976): Cardamom News (0008-6274)
Related titles: Hindi ed.; Kannada ed.; Malayalam ed.; Nepali ed.; Tamil ed.; Telugu ed.
Indexed: CWI.
Published by: Ministry of Commerce, Spices Board, N.H. Bypass, Palarivattom P.O., P O Box 2277, Cochin, Kerala 682 025, India. TEL 91-484-33610, FAX 91-484-331429, sbhochn@giasmd01.vsnl.net.in, http://www.indianspices.com. Ed. P S Sreekantan Thampi. Circ: 12,000.

633.83 IND
SPICES MARKET. Text in English. w. INR 200 (effective 2000). **Document type:** *Government.*
Published by: Ministry of Commerce, Spices Board, N.H. Bypass, Palarivattom P.O., P O Box 2277, Cochin, Kerala 682 025, India. TEL 91-484-333610, FAX 91-484-331429, sbhochn@giasmd01.vsnl.net.in, spicesboard@vsnl.com, mail@indianspices.com, http://www.indianspices.com. Ed. P S Sreekantan Thampi. Circ: 1,500.

630 CAN ISSN 1498-2579
SPOTLIGHT ON RESEARCH. Text in English. 2001. a.
Published by: Agriculture and Agri-Food Canada, Research Branch, Sir John Carling Bldg, 930 Carling Ave, Ottawa, ON K1A 0C5, Canada. TEL 613-759-6610, FAX 613-759-6726, publications@agr.gc.ca, http://www.agr.gc.ca.

630 LKA ISSN 1391-6947
➤ **SRI LANKA DEPARTMENT OF AGRICULTURE. ANNALS.** Text and summaries in English. 1999. a., latest vol.5, 2003. LKR 500 domestic; USD 10 foreign (effective 2004 - 2005). back issues avail. **Document type:** *Proceedings, Academic/Scholarly.* **Description:** Publishes research articles relevant to agriculture development in Sri Lanka including crop production, pest management, harvest and food processing, etc. Intended for agriculture research, professionals, academics and university students.
Formerly (until vol.3, 2001): Department of Agriculture. Proceedings of the Annual Symposium
Indexed: AgBio, AgrForAb, BioCN&I, CPA, FCA, HelmAb, HerbAb, HortAb, I&DA, MaizeAb, NemAb, OrnHort, PBA, PGegResA, PGrRegA, PHN&I, PN&I, PotatoAb, PoultAb, S&F, SIA, SeedAb, WAE&RSA, WeedAb.
Published by: Sri Lanka Department of Agriculture, ASDA Secretariat, P O Box 21, Peradeniya, 20400, Sri Lanka. asda1@slnet.lk, dgagri@srilanka.net, http://www.agridept.gov.lk. Circ: 500 (free).

630 GBR ISSN 0955-0267
STAFFORDSHIRE FARMER. Text in English. m. adv.
Published by: County Farmers Publications Ltd., 55 Goldington Rd, Bedford, Beds MK40 3LU, United Kingdom. TEL 44-1234-351401, FAX 44-1234-328614. Ed. P Hudson. Circ: 3,650.

630 382 USA ISSN 0844-3955
STAT (BLAINE)✶. Text in English. 1988. w. USD 260 domestic; USD 340 foreign (effective 2000). adv. **Description:** Specializes in peas, beans, lentils, canaryseed, millet, and sunflower market analysis.
Published by: Stat Publishing, 250 H St, Blaine, WA 98230-4033. TEL 604-535-8505, FAX 604-531-8818, publisher@statpub.com, http://statpub.com/stat. Ed. Brian Clancey. Pub. P B Clancey. Circ: 1,000.

630 USA ISSN 0081-4539
S401.U6 CODEN: FAONEY
STATE OF FOOD AND AGRICULTURE. Text in English. 1947. a. USD 55 (effective 2000). **Document type:** *Monographic series.*
Related titles: Microfiche ed.: (from CIS); Spanish ed.: Estado Mundial de la Agricultura y la Alimentacion. ISSN 0251-1371; French ed.: Situation Mondiale de l'Alimentation et de l'Agriculture. ISSN 0251-1460.
Indexed: BIOSIS Prev, FS&TA, IIS, IndVet, NutrAb, RDA, TDB, VetBull, WAE&RSA.
—Linda Hall.
Published by: Food and Agriculture Organization of the United Nations, c/o Bernan Associates, 4611 F Assembly Dr, Lanham, MD 20706-4391. TEL 301-459-7666, FAX 301-459-0056.

STATISTICAL OFFICE OF THE EUROPEAN COMMUNITIES. STATISTICAL YEARBOOK. AGRICULTURE. see *AGRICULTURE—Abstracting, Bibliographies, Statistics*

▼ new title ➤ refereed ✶ unverified ♦ full entry avail.

A

STATISTICAL YEAR BOOK OF INDONESIA. see *POPULATION STUDIES—Abstracting, Bibliographies, Statistics*

STATISTIK AUSTRIA. LANDWIRTSCHAFTLICHE MASCHINENZAEHLUNG. see *AGRICULTURE—Abstracting, Bibliographies, Statistics*

STATISTISCHES JAHRBUCH UEBER ERNAEHRUNG, LANDWIRTSCHAFT UND FORSTEN DER BUNDESREPUBLIK DEUTSCHLAND. see *AGRICULTURE—Abstracting, Bibliographies, Statistics*

638.1 CAN
STING. Text in English. 1983. bi-m. membership. adv. bk.rev. back issues avail. **Document type:** *Newspaper.* **Description:** Provides updates, management techniques, meeting dates, programs, reports to advance and promote apiculture in Ontario for both hobbyists and commercial producers.
Published by: Ontario Beekeepers Association, Bayfield, ON N0M 1G0, Canada. TEL 519-565-2622, FAX 519-565-5452, ontbee@tcc.on.ca, http://www.tcc.on.ca/~ontbee. Ed., Adv. contact Pat Westlake. Circ: 460.

630 AUS ISSN 1321-0157
STOCK AND LAND. Text in English. 1914. w. AUD 92.82; AUD 2.10 newsstand/cover (effective 2005). adv. bk.rev. mkt. **Document type:** *Newspaper, Trade.* **Description:** Business and livestock information for farmers and graziers.
Formerly: Angus News
Published by: Rural Press Ltd. (Subsidiary of: Agricultural Publishers Pty. Ltd.), 10 Sydenham St., PO Box 254, Moonee Ponds, VIC 3039, Australia. TEL 61-3-92870900, FAX 61-3-93705622, http://www.stockandland.com, http://www.ruralpress.com/. Ed. John Carson. Adv. contact Craig Davidson. Circ: 12,304.

STOCKMAN - GRASS FARMER. see *AGRICULTURE—Poultry And Livestock*

630 USA ISSN 0097-1251
S43
STORRS AGRICULTURAL EXPERIMENT STATION. BULLETIN. Text in English. 1888. irreg., latest vol.476, 1988. **Document type:** *Bulletin.*
Indexed: Agr, BiolAb.
—BLDSC (2770.500000), CISTI, Linda Hall.
Published by: Storrs Agricultural Experiment Station, Agricultural Publications, U-35, 1376 Storrs Rd., University of Connecticut, Storrs, CT 06269-4035. TEL 203-486-3336. Circ: 300.

630 USA ISSN 0069-8997
CODEN: CASRBU
STORRS AGRICULTURAL EXPERIMENT STATION. RESEARCH REPORT. Text in English. 1964. irreg., latest vol.85, 1992. **Document type:** *Academic/Scholarly.*
Indexed: Agr, BiolAb, ExcerpMed, SFA, WildRev, ZooRec.
—BLDSC (7766.270000), Linda Hall.
Published by: Storrs Agricultural Experiment Station, Agricultural Publications, U-35, 1376 Storrs Rd., University of Connecticut, Storrs, CT 06269-4035. TEL 203-486-3336. Circ: 300.

630 DNK ISSN 0908-0058
STORSTROEMS AMTS LANDBRUGS-NYT. Text in Danish. w. adv.
Published by: Lolland-Falsters Erververvsforlag ApS, Marrebaeck, Vaeggerlose, 4873, Denmark. Circ: 10,323.

630 658 USA ISSN 0039-4432
S1
SUCCESSFUL FARMING; for families that make farming their business . Text in English. 1902. m. USD 15.95 domestic; USD 27.95 foreign (effective 2005). adv. illus. reprints avail. **Document type:** *Magazine, Trade.* **Description:** Offers practical help for business farmers with decisions that affect both their business's profitability and their families.
Related titles: Microfiche ed.: (from NBI); Online - full text ed.: Agriculture Online (from Florida Center for Library Automation, Gale Group, Northern Light Technology, Inc., O C L C Online Computer Library Center, Inc., ProQuest Information & Learning).
Indexed: ABIn, ARG, MagInd, RGAb, RGPR.
—CISTI, Linda Hall.
Published by: Meredith Corp., 1716 Locust St, Des Moines, IA 50309-3023. TEL 515-284-3000, 800-556-9184, FAX 515-284-3563, gene.johnston@meredith.com, http://www.agriculture.com, http://www.meredith.com. Ed. Loren Kruse. Pub. Tom Davis. Adv. contact Scott Mortimer. B&W page USD 39,910, color page USD 57,090; trim 8 x 10.5. Circ: 485,000 (paid).

630 ITA ISSN 1120-5857
SUEDTIROLER LANDWIRT; Fachblatt der Suedtiroler Bauern und Genossenschaften. Text in German. 1947. s-m. adv. bk.rev. abstr.; charts; illus.; mkt.; stat. cum.index.
Formerly: Landwirt (0023-8112)
Related titles: Microform ed.
Published by: Suedtiroler Bauernbundgenossenschaft, Bolzano, BZ 39100, Italy. TELEX 981171. Ed. L Michael Pohl. Circ: 19,000.

630 USA ISSN 0039-467X
SUFFOLK COUNTY AGRICULTURAL NEWS. Text in English. 1917. m. USD 25 in state; USD 30 out of state. adv. bk.rev. charts; illus.; tr.lit.
Formerly: Suffolk County Farm News
Published by: Cooperative Extension Association of Suffolk County, 246 Griffing Ave, Riverhead, NY 11901. TEL 516-727-7850, FAX 516-727-7130. Ed. William J Sanok. Circ: 1,300.

630 GBR ISSN 0955-0275
SUFFOLK FARMER. Text in English. m. adv.
Published by: County Farmers Publications Ltd., 55 Goldington Rd, Bedford, Beds MK40 3LU, United Kingdom. TEL 44-1234-351401, FAX 44-1234-328614. Ed. D Brown. Circ: 2,300.

630 GBR
SUFFOLK SCENE. Text in English. 4/yr. bk.rev.
Address: Suffolk, 30 Lower Brook St, Ipswich, Suffolk IP4 1AN, United Kingdom. TEL 473-230023, FAX 473-225296, TELEX 98172. Ed. Peter Hopper. Circ: 57,000.

630 664.1 GBR ISSN 1468-6031
SB226 CODEN: SUCAEE
SUGAR CANE INTERNATIONAL; the journal of cane agriculture. Text in English. 1983. bi-m. GBP 300 worldwide (effective 2005). adv. bk.rev. abstr.; charts; illus.; pat.; stat. **Document type:** *Journal, Academic/Scholarly.* **Description:** Contains current information for all involved in growing or studying sugar cane.
Formerly (until 1999): Sugar Cane (0265-7406)
Indexed: AEA, AgBio, AgrForAb, BioCN&I, CPA, FCA, FPA, ForAb, HortAb, I&DA, MaizeAb, NemAb, NutrAb, PBA, PGegResA, PGrRegA, PHN&I, RA&MP, RDA, RPP, RefZh, RevApplEntom, S&F, SIA, SeedAb, WAE&RSA, WeedAb.
—BLDSC (8511.650000), CASDDS, IE, ingenta, Linda Hall.
Published by: International Media Ltd. (Subsidiary of: Agra Europe (London) Ltd.), 80 Calverley Rd, Tunbridge Well, Kent TN1 2UN, United Kingdom. TEL 44-1892-533813, FAX 44-1892-544895, marketing@agra-europe.com, http://www.agra-net.com. Ed. John Blackwell. Adv. contact Mark Jones. Circ: 300.

630 USA ISSN 0730-6490
TP375 CODEN: PSPCE4
SUGAR PROCESSING RESEARCH CONFERENCE. PROCEEDINGS. Text in English. 1982. biennial. price varies. back issues avail. **Document type:** *Proceedings, Academic/Scholarly.*
Formerly: Technical Session on Cane Sugar Refining Research. Proceedings
Indexed: Agr, CIN, ChemAb, ChemTitl.
—CASDDS, CISTI.
Published by: U.S. Department of Agriculture, Agricultural Research Service (New Orleans), Robert E. Lee Boulevard, New Orleans, LA 70124. TEL 504-286-4329, FAX 504-282-5387, spri@srrc.ars.usda.gov, http://www.spriinc.org/.

631.091 USA ISSN 0199-8498
SUGAR PRODUCER; representing the sugar beet industry in the United States. Text in English. 1976. 8/yr. USD 15.95 (effective 2005). adv. **Document type:** *Magazine, Trade.*
Published by: Harris Publishing, Inc. (Idaho Falls), 360 B St, Idaho Falls, ID 83402-3547. TEL 208-524-7000, FAX 208-522-5241. Ed. Gary Fairbourn. Pub. Jason Harris. Adv. contact Richard Holley. B&W page USD 3,087, color page USD 4,723. Circ: 15,500 (paid and controlled).

633.61 PHL ISSN 0039-4769
SUGARCANE FARMERS' BULLETIN. Text in English. 1964-1977; resumed. bi-m. PHP 12. bk.rev. charts; illus. index. **Document type:** *Bulletin.*
Published by: Philippine Sugar Regulatory Administration, North Ave, Diliman, Quezon City Mm, 1128, Philippines. Ed. Antonina P Pamaran. Circ: 7,000.

624 JPN ISSN 0914-4218
SUIRIHO. Text in Japanese. 1982. a. JPY 1,500.
Published by: Nogyo Doboku Gakkai, Nogyo Suiri Kenkyu Bukai/Japanese Society of Irrigation, Drainage and Reclamation Engineering, Society for the Study of Agricultural Water Use, Nogyo Daigaku Nogyo Kogakka, Tochi Kairyogaku Kenkyushitsu, 1-1 Sakuragaoka 1-chome, Setagaya-ku, Tokyo, 156-0054, Japan.

630 USA
SULCO; journal of popular farm science and rural life. Text in Portuguese. 1973. 4/yr. free to qualified personnel.
Related titles: ♦ Regional ed(s).: Furrow. ISSN 0016-3112; ♦ Surco Latinoamericana; ♦ Voor; ♦ Sillon.
Published by: John Deere Publishing, One John Deere Place, Moline, IL 61265. TEL 309-765-8000. Ed. Jean Claude Hiron. Circ: 11,000.

630 USA ISSN 0160-0680
CODEN: SUAGDL
➤ **SULPHUR IN AGRICULTURE.** Text in English. 1977. biennial. free to qualified personnel. bk.rev. back issues avail. **Document type:** *Academic/Scholarly.* **Description:** Provides information about sulphur in plant and animal nutrition; the use of sulphur and sulphur compounds as soil amendments; the technology, use and marketing of sulphur-containing fertilizers; and other aspects of sulphur in agriculture.
Supersedes: Sulphur Institute Journal (0039-4904)
Indexed: BiolAb, ChemAb, FCA, HerbAb, HortAb, S&F, TriticAb, WAE&RSA.
—CASDDS, CISTI, Linda Hall.
Published by: Sulphur Institute, 1140 Connecticut Ave, N W, Ste 612, Washington, DC 20036-4012. TEL 202-331-9660, FAX 202-293-2940, TELEX 440472, sulphur@sulphurinstitute.org. Ed., R&P Donald L Messick. Circ: 3,000 (controlled).

➤ **SUNNSEIT'N;** Die Fachzeitschrift fuer baeuerliche Vermieter. see *TRAVEL AND TOURISM*

➤ **SUO;** mires and peat. see *FORESTS AND FORESTRY*

631 ARG ISSN 0328-4247
SUPER CAMPO. Text in Spanish. 1994. m. adv. **Document type:** *Magazine, Trade.* **Description:** Specializes in agricultural and farming topics.
Related titles: Online - full text ed.
Published by: Editorial Perfil S.A., Chacabuco 271, Buenos Aires, Buenos Aires 1069, Argentina. TEL 54-11-4341-9000, FAX 54-11-4341-9090, supercampo@perfil.com.ar, correo@perfil.com.ar, http://www.supercampo.uol.com.ar, http://www.perfil.com.ar. Ed. Daniel Valerio. Circ: 29,000 (paid).

630 USA
SUPIMA ASSOCIATION OF AMERICA NEWSLETTER. Text in English. 1954. m. looseleaf. free. charts; stat. back issues avail. **Document type:** *Newsletter.*
Published by: Supima Association of America, 4141 E Broadway Rd, Phoenix, AZ 85040. TEL 602-437-1364, FAX 602-437-0143, TELEX 5106005606 (SUPIMA PHX), mlsupima@amug.org, http://www.supimacotton.org. Ed. Matt Laughlin. Circ: 2,600.

630 USA
SURCO ARGENTINA; journal of popular farm science and rural life. Text in Spanish. 1959. 2/yr. free to qualified personnel.
Related titles: ♦ German ed.: Flur und Furche. ISSN 0015-4733; ♦ English ed.: Furrow. ISSN 0016-3112; ♦ Swedish ed.: Faran; ♦ Norwegian ed.: Fara; ♦ Spanish ed.: Campo y Mecanica. ISSN 0211-4704; ♦ Spanish ed.: Surco Mexicana; Afrikaans ed.: 1895; Danish ed.: 1895; Dutch ed.: 1895; French ed.: 1895; Italian ed.: 1895; Portuguese ed.: 1895.
Published by: John Deere Publishing, One John Deere Place, Moline, IL 61265. TEL 309-752-8000. Ed. G R Souenberger. Circ: 19,100.

630 USA
SURCO LATINOAMERICANA; journal of popular farm science and rural life. Text in Spanish. 1965. 4/yr. free to qualified personnel.
Related titles: ♦ Regional ed(s).: Furrow. ISSN 0016-3112; ♦ Sulco; ♦ Voor; ♦ Sillon.
Published by: John Deere Publishing, One John Deere Place, Moline, IL 61265. TEL 309-765-8000. Ed. G R Souenberger. Circ: 24,800.

630 USA
SURCO MEXICANA; journal of popular farm science and rural life. Text in Spanish. 1952. 4/yr. free to qualified personnel.
Formerly: Surco John Deere
Related titles: ♦ German ed.: Flur und Furche. ISSN 0015-4733; ♦ English ed.: Furrow. ISSN 0016-3112; ♦ Swedish ed.: Faran; ♦ Spanish ed.: Surco Argentina; ♦ Norwegian ed.: Fara; ♦ Spanish ed.: Campo y Mecanica. ISSN 0211-4704; Afrikaans ed.: 1895; Danish ed.: 1895; Dutch ed.: 1895; French ed.: 1895; Italian ed.: 1895; Portuguese ed.: 1895.
Published by: John Deere Publishing, One John Deere Place, Moline, IL 61265. TEL 309-765-8000. Ed. Carolos MacDonado. Circ: 55,000.

630 ESP
SURCOS DE ARAGON. Text in Spanish. 12/yr.
Published by: Departamento de Agricultura Ganaderia y Montes, Edif. Pignatelli, Paseo Maria Agustin, Zaragoza, 50004, Spain. TEL 76-22-43-00, FAX 76-47-07-48. Ed. I Palacio Espanol.

630 SUR ISSN 0039-6133
S201
SURINAAMSE LANDBOUW/SURINAM AGRICULTURE. Text in English. 1953. irreg. (2-3/yr.). SRG 15. bk.rev. abstr.; bibl.; charts; illus.; stat. index. cum.index. **Document type:** *Academic/Scholarly.*
Indexed: BibAg, BiolAb, ChemAb, FCA, HerbAb, HortAb, NutrAb, PGrRegA, ProtozoAb, WeedAb.
—CISTI.
Published by: Department of Agriculture and Fisheries, Agricultural Experiment Station, PO Box 160, Paramaribo, Suriname. Circ: 600.

630　　　　　　GBR
SUSTAINABLE RURAL DEVELOPMENT SERIES. Text in English. irreg., latest vol.2, 1995. price varies. **Document type:** *Monographic series, Academic/Scholarly.*
Published by: CABI Publishing (Subsidiary of: CAB International), CAB International, Wallingford, Oxfordshire OX10 8DE, United Kingdom. TEL 44-1491-832111, FAX 44-1491-833508, cabi@cabi.org, http://www.cabi-publishing.org/. **Dist. in N America:** Oxford University Press, 2001 Evans Rd, Cary, NC 27513. TEL 919-677-0977, 800-852-7323, FAX 919-677-1714.

630　　　　　　SWE　　　　　　ISSN 1404-5974
SVERIGES LANTBRUKSUNIVERSITET. FAELTFORSKNINGSENHETEN. RAPPORT. Text in Swedish. 2000. a. prce varies.
Supersedes in part (1973-1998): Vaextodling (1100-1151)
—CISTI.
Published by: Sveriges Lantbruksuniversitet, Faeltforskningsenheten, PO Box 7043, Uppsala, 75007, Sweden. TEL 46-18-671427, http://www.ffe.slu.se.

630　　　　　　SWE　　　　　　ISSN 1404-2339
SVERIGES LANTBRUKSUNIVERSITET. INSTITUTIONEN FOER EKOLOGI OCH VAEXTPRODUKTIONSLAERA. RAPPORT. Text in Swedish; Summaries in English. 1973. irreg.
Supersedes in part (in 1999): Vaextodling (1100-1151); Former titles (until 1988): Sveriges Lantbruksuniversitet. Institutionen foer Vaextodling. Rapport (0348-1034); (until 1988): Lantbrukshoegskolan. Institutionen foer Vaextodling. Rapporter och Avhandlingar (0346-7236)
Indexed: BiolAb, FCA, HortAb, PBA, PotatoAb, TriticAb, WeedAb.
—CISTI.
Published by: Sveriges Lantbruksuniversitet, Institutionen foer Ekologi och Vaextproduktionslaera/Swedish University of Agricultural Sciences, Department of Ecology and Crop Production Science, PO Box 7043, Uppsala, 75007, Sweden. TEL 46-18-671000, FAX 46-18-672890, http://www.evp.slu.se.

630 690　　　　SWE　　　　　　ISSN 1104-7321
SVERIGES LANTBRUKSUNIVERSITET. INSTITUTIONEN FOER JORDBRUKETS BIOSYSTEM OCH TEKNOLOGI. SPECIALMEDDELANDE/SWEDISH UNIVERSITY OF AGRICULTURAL SCIENCES. DEPARTMENT OF AGRICULTURAL BIOSYSTEMS AND TECHNOLOGY. SPECIAL REPORT. Cover title: Specialmeddelande - J B T. Text in Swedish; Summaries in English. 1971. irreg. (5-6/yr.), latest vol.241, 2002. price varies. back issues avail. **Document type:** *Monographic series, Academic/Scholarly.* **Description:** For scientists, consultants and teachers on research results in farm-building technology and environment.
Former titles (until 1994): Sveriges Lantbruksuniversitet. Insittutionen foer Lantbrukets Byggnadsteknik (LBT). Specialmeddelande (0348-0593); (until 1977): Lantbrukshoegskolan. Institutionen foer Lantbrukets Byggnadsteknik (LBT). Specialmeddelande (0346-7686)
Indexed: AEA, AbHyg, AnBrAb, BrCerAb, C&ISA, CerAb, CorrAb, DSA, E&CAJ, EMA, FPA, HerbAb, HortAb, I&DA, IAA, IndVet, M&TEA, MBF, METADEX, NutrAb, PN&I, PoultAb, RA&MP, RRTA, SolStAb, VetBull, WAA, WAE&RSA.
—BLDSC (8404.955000), CISTI, Linda Hall.
Published by: Sveriges Lantbruksuniversitet, Institutionen foer Jordbrukets Biosystem och Teknologi/Swedish University of Agricultural Sciences. Department of Agricultural Biosystems and Technology, Slottsvaegen 1, PO Box 43, Alnarp, 23053, Sweden. TEL 46-40-415000, FAX 46-40-460421, info@jbt.slu.se, http://www.jbt.slu.se/publicering/index.htm. Circ: 300.

630　　　　　　SWZ
SWAZILAND. MINISTRY OF AGRICULTURE. AGRICULTURAL RESEARCH DIVISION. ANNUAL REPORT. Text in English. 1960. a., latest 1988. back issues avail. **Document type:** *Government.*
Former titles (until 1977): University of Botswana, Lesotho and Swaziland. Agricultural Research Division. Annual Report; (until 1971): Swaziland. Ministry of Agriculture. Agricultural Research Division. Annual Report; Swaziland. Department of Agriculture. Research Division. Annual Report (0586-125X)
Indexed: BiolAb, FCA, HerbAb, HortAb.
Published by: Ministry of Agriculture, Agricultural Research Division, c/o Chief Research Officer, PO Box 4, Malkerns, Swaziland. TEL 268-83017, TELEX 22589 WD.

354.68　　　　SWZ
SWAZILAND. MINISTRY OF AGRICULTURE. ANNUAL REPORT. Text in English. 1967. a. stat. **Document type:** *Government.*
Indexed: AnBrAb, FCA, HerbAb, HortAb, RevApplEntom.
Published by: Ministry of Agriculture, Mbabane, Swaziland.

SWEDEN. STATISTISKA CENTRALBYRAAN. JORDBRUKSSTATISTISK AARSBOK. see *AGRICULTURE—Abstracting, Bibliographies, Statistics*

SWEDEN. STATISTISKA CENTRALBYRAAN. STATISTISKA MEDDELANDEN. SERIE J, JORDBRUK, SKOGSBRUK OCH FISKE. see *AGRICULTURE—Abstracting, Bibliographies, Statistics*

630　　　　　　FRA　　　　　　ISSN 0766-7302
LE SYNDICAT AGRICOLE (EDITION PAS-DE-CALAIS). Text in French. 1944. w.

Incorporates in part: Le Syndicat Agricole (Edition Lille) (0991-7144)
Published by: Syndicat Agricole, 44 rue Jean-sans-Peur, Lille, Cedex 59024, France. TEL 20-54-85-97, FAX 20-54-55-72. Ed. C Durlin. Circ: 14,000.

631　　　　　　NLD　　　　　　ISSN 0928-9526
SYSTEMS APPROACHES FOR SUSTAINABLE AGRICULTURAL DEVELOPMENT. Text in English. 1992. irreg., latest vol.8, 2000. price varies. **Document type:** *Monographic series.* **Description:** Integrates disciplines related to systems approaches for sustainable agricultural development, in particular from the technical and socio-economic sciences.
Indexed: BIOSIS Prev.
—BLDSC (8589.323500), ingenta. **CCC.**
Published by: Springer-Verlag Dordrecht (Subsidiary of: Springer Science+Business Media), Van Godewijckstraat 30, Dordrecht, 3311 GX, Netherlands. TEL 31-78-6576050, FAX 31-78-6576474, http://www.springeronline.com. Ed. Frits W T Penning de Vries.

630　　　　　　SVK　　　　　　ISSN 0491-9424
SZABAD FOLDMUVES✳ . Text in Slovak. 1950. w.
Published by: Ministerstvo Podmospodarstva a Vyzivy, Dobrovicova 12, Bratislava, 80000, Slovakia.

SZCZECINSKIE ROCZNIKI NAUKOWE, NAUKI PRZYRODNICZE I ROLNICZE. see *BIOLOGY—Botany*

630　　　　　　POL　　　　　　ISSN 0239-8613
　　　　　　　　　　　　　　　　　　CODEN: ZNWNDA
SZKOLA GLOWNA GOSPODARSTWA WIEJSKIEGO. ROZPRAWY NAUKOWE I MONOGRAFIE/WARSAW AGRICULTURAL UNIVERSITY. TREATISES AND MONOGRAPHS. Text in English, Polish. 1957. irreg., latest vol.262, 2003. USD 10 per issue (effective 2003). **Document type:** *Monographic series, Academic/Scholarly.*
Formerly (until 1980): Akademia Rolnicza, Warsaw. Zeszyty Naukowe. Rozprawy Naukowe (0512-4646)
Indexed: AgrLib.
—CASDDS, CISTI, Linda Hall.
Published by: Szkola Glowna Gospodarstwa Wiejskiego (SGGW)/Warsaw Agricultural University, Ul Nowoursynowska 166, Warsaw, 02787, Poland.

T U I A F P W INFORMATION. see *LABOR UNIONS*

630　　　　　　TWN　　　　　　ISSN 0494-5263
TAIWAN AGRICULTURAL RESEARCH INSTITUTE. ANNUAL REPORT. Key Title: Nianbao - Taiwan Sheng Nongye Shiyansuo. Text in Chinese. 1946. a. charts; illus.; stat.
—BLDSC (1464.490000), CISTI.
Published by: Taiwan Agricultural Research Institute, 189 Chung-cheng Rd, Wufeng, Taipei, Taiwan. FAX 04-3338162. Ed. Ching Liang Liaw. Pub. Chien Yih Lin.

630 580　　　　TWN
TAIWAN AGRICULTURAL RESEARCH INSTITUTE. RESEARCH SUMMARY. Text in Chinese. irreg., latest 1975, June.
Published by: Taiwan Agricultural Research Institute, 189 Chung-cheng Rd, Wufeng, Taipei, Taiwan. FAX 04-3338162. Pub. Chien Yih Lin.

TAIWAN NONGYE HUAXUE YU SHIPIN KEXUE/TAIWANESE JOURNAL OF AGRICULTURAL CHEMISTRY AND FOOD SCIENCE. see *FOOD AND FOOD INDUSTRIES*

630　　　　　　CHN
TAIWAN NONGYE QINGKUANG/TAIWAN AGRICULTURAL INFORMATION. Text in Chinese. q. CNY 3.20.
Published by: Fujian Sheng Nongye Kexueyuan, Keji Qingbao Suo/Fujian Academy of Agricultural Science, Science and Technology Information Institute, 41 Hualin Lu, Fuzhou, Fujian 350003, China. TEL 571771. Ed. He Shukai. **Dist. overseas by:** Jiangsu Publications Import & Export Corp., 56 Gao Yun Ling, Nanjing, Jiangsu, China.

630　　　　　　TWN
TAIZHONG-QU NONGQING YUEKAN. Text in Chinese. 1999 (Oct.). m. **Document type:** *Journal, Academic/Scholarly.*
Media: Online - full content.
Published by: Taizhong-qu Nongye Gailiangchang/Taichung District Agricultural Improvement Station, Lane 361, 200, Chia-Tung Road Sec 1, Ta-Tsun, 515, Taiwan. TEL 886-4-8523101, FAX 886-4-8525841, tdais110@ms6.hinet.net, http://www.tdais.gov.tw/search/book4/book4.htm.

630　　　　　　TWN　　　　　　ISSN 0255-5905
S19　　　　　　　　　　　　　　　CODEN: TCNPEX
TAIZHONG-QU NONGYE GAILIANG CHANG YANJIU HUIBAO/TAICHUNG DISTRICT AGRICULTURAL IMPROVEMENT STATION. BULLETIN. Text in Chinese; Abstracts in English. 1976. irreg. **Document type:** *Bulletin, Academic/Scholarly.*
Indexed: AEA, BIOSIS Prev, BiolAb, CPA, FCA, HortAb, OrnHort, PBA, PHN&I, RPP, RiceAb, S&F, SeedAb, WAE&RSA, ZooRec.
—CISTI.

Published by: Taizhong-qu Nongye Gailiangchang/Taichung District Agricultural Improvement Station, Lane 361, 200, Chia-Tung Road Sec 1, Ta-Tsun, 515, Taiwan. TEL 886-4-8523101, FAX 886-4-8525841, tdais110@ms6.hinet.net, http://www.tdais.gov.tw/search/issn/search-i2.html.

630　　　　　　TWN
TAIZHONG-QU NONGYE ZHUANXUN. Text in Chinese. 1992. q. **Document type:** *Journal, Academic/Scholarly.*
Published by: Taizhong-qu Nongye Gailiangchang/Taichung District Agricultural Improvement Station, Lane 361, 200, Chia-Tung Road Sec 1, Ta-Tsun, 515, Taiwan. TEL 886-4-8523101, FAX 886-4-8525841, tdais110@ms6.hinet.net, http://www.tdais.gov.tw/search/book1/book1.htm.

630　　　　　　JPN　　　　　　ISSN 0082-156X
　　　　　　　　　　　　　　　　　　CODEN: TDNHAC
TAMAGAWA UNIVERSITY. FACULTY OF AGRICULTURE. BULLETIN. Text in English, German, Japanese; Summaries in English, German. 1960. a. avail. on exchange.
Indexed: BIOSIS Prev, BiolAb, ExcerpMed, FCA, HerbAb, HortAb, PBA, RPP, VITIS, WeedAb, ZooRec.
—BLDSC (2507.350000), CASDDS, CISTI, Linda Hall.
Published by: Tamagawa University, Faculty of Agriculture/Tamagawa Daigaku Nogakubu, 6-1-1 Tamagawagakuen, Machida-shi, Tokyo-to 194-0041, Japan.

630 070　　　　DEU　　　　　　ISSN 0082-1845
TASCHENBUCH FUER AGRARJOURNALISTEN. Text in German. 1957. a. EUR 52 (effective 2003). **Document type:** *Bulletin, Trade.*
Published by: (Verband der Agrarjournalisten), B. Behr's Verlag GmbH & Co. KG, Averhoffstr. 10, Hamburg, 22085, Germany. TEL 49-40-2270080, FAX 49-40-2201091, info@behrs.de, http://www.behrs.de.

630　　　　　　GBR
TAYSIDE FARMER. Text in English. q. adv. **Document type:** *Trade.*
Published by: Angus County Press Ltd., Forfar, Angus DD8 1BU, United Kingdom. TEL 01307-464899, FAX 01307-466923. Ed. Ian Wallace. Adv. contact Linda Ruxton. Circ: 7,000.

633.72　　　　BGD
TEA JOURNAL OF BANGLADESH✳ . Text in English. 1963. s-a. BDT 7 per issue. adv. bk.rev. abstr.; bibl.; charts; illus. index; cum.index.
Formerly: Tea Journal of Pakistan (0040-0351)
Indexed: ChemAb, HortAb, S&F.
Published by: Bangladesh Tea Research Institute (Subsidiary of: Interface Technologies Corporation), Srimangal, Sylhet, Bangladesh. Ed. S H Chaudhury. Circ: 500.

633.72　　　　MWI
TEA RESEARCH FOUNDATION. QUARTERLY NEWSLETTER. Text in English. 1952. q. USD 72; USD 80 in Africa; USD 81.50 in Europe; USD 81.50 in the Middle East; USD 81.50 in India; USD 83 elsewhere. back issues avail. **Document type:** *Newsletter, Trade.* **Description:** Covers tea growing and manufacturing in regions with a single rainy season.
Formerly: Tea Research Station. Quarterly Newsletter (0040-0378)
Indexed: AEA, ATA, CPA, FCA, ForAb, HortAb, I&DA, MaizeAb, OrnHort, PBA, PGegResA, PHN&I, RDA, RPP, RevApplEntom, S&F, WAE&RSA, WeedAb.
—BLDSC (7196.690000).
Published by: Tea Research Foundation of Central Africa, PO Box 51, Mulanje, Malawi. TEL 265-462277. Ed. A M Whittle. Circ: 450.

630 664　　　　IRL　　　　　　ISSN 0791-4695
TEAGASC ANNUAL REPORT. Text in English. 1990. a. **Document type:** *Government.*
Formed by the 1990 merger of: Foras Taluntais. Annual Report (0790-7400); A C O T Annual Report (0332-379X)
Indexed: AnBrAb, DSA, NutrAb.
—CISTI.
Published by: Teagasc, Oak Park, Carlow, Ireland. TEL 353-1-6376000, FAX 353-1-6688023.

630 664　　　　IRL　　　　　　ISSN 0791-7376
TEAGASC RESEARCH REPORT. Text in English. a. EUR 6.50 (effective 2005). **Document type:** *Academic/Scholarly.* **Description:** Annual research report covering approximately 400 research projects in agriculture and food.
Formed by the merger of (197?-1992): Food Science and Technology Research Report (0790-2999); (1971-1992): Economics and Rural Welfare Research Report (0332-0251); Which was formerly: Foras Taluntais. Rural Economics Division. Research Report (0332-0200); (1961-1962): Foras Taluntais. Rural Economics Division. Technical Progress Report (0429-0313); (1971-1992): Animal Production Research Report (0332-1207); Which was formerly (1960-1970): Foras Taluntais. Animal Husbandry and Dairying Division and Animal Sciences Division. Research Report (0429-0283); (1971-1992): Horticulture Research Report (0790-2964); Which was formerly: Foras Taluntais. Horticulture and Forestry Division. Research Report (0332-1258); (1960-1961): Foras Taluntais. Horticulture and Forestry Division. Technical Progress Report (0532-1093); (1971-1992): Plant Sciences and Crop Husbandry Research Report (0790-2956); Which was formerly: Foras Taluntais. Plant Sciences and Crop

Husbandry Division. Research Report (0332-1053); (1960-1971): Foras Taluntais. Plant Sciences and Crop Husbandry Division. Technical Progress Report (0429-0291); (1981-1992): Soils and Grassland Production Research Report (0790-2980); Which was (until 1981): Soils Research Report (0790-2972); (until 1971): Foras Taluntais. Soils Division. Research Report (0332-1002); (1960-1961): Foras Taluntais. Soils Division. Technical Progress Report (0429-0321) —CISTI.
Published by: Teagasc, Oak Park, Carlow, Ireland. TEL 353-59-9170200, FAX 353-59-9182097, publications@hq.teagasc.ie, http://www.teagasc.ie. Circ: 500 (paid).

TECHNICAL AND COMMERCIAL MESSAGE. see *ENGINEERING*

630 FRA ISSN 0298-3540
LE TECHNICIEN D'AGRICULTURE TROPICALE. Text in French. 1983. irreg.
Published by: (Agence de Cooperation Culturelle et Technique), Editions Maisonneuve et Larose, 15 rue Victor Cousin, Paris, 75005, France. TEL 33-1-4441-4937, FAX 33-1-4325-7741, servedit@wanadoo.fr, http://semioweb.msh-paris.fr/escom/wwwarchives/EditeurEnLigne/ml/ml.html.

TECHNISCHE UNIVERSITAET BERLIN. INSTITUT FUER SOZIALOEKONOMIE DER AGRARENTWICKLUNG. SCHRIFTENREIHE DES FACHBEREICHS. see *AGRICULTURE—Agricultural Economics*

630 634.9 FIN ISSN 0355-0567
TEHO A. Text in Finnish; Summaries in English. 1946. 6/yr. EUR 38 domestic; EUR 50 foreign (effective 2002); includes Teho B. back issues avail. **Document type:** *Journal, Trade.* **Description:** Deals with the rationalization of work related to agriculture, forestry, ergonomics, home economics, consumer education.
Related titles: ♦ Series: Teho B. ISSN 0355-2527.
Indexed: AEA, AbHyg, AnBrAb, DSA, FCA, FPA, ForAb, HerbAb, HortAb, MaizeAb, NemAb, NutrAb, OrnHort, PHN&I, RPP, RRTA, S&F, SeedAb, TriticAb, WAE&RSA.
Published by: TTS Institute (Tyotehoseura)/Work Efficiency Institute, Melkonkatu 16 A, PO Box 28, Helsinki, 00211, Finland. TEL 358-9-29041200, FAX 358-8-6922084, tts@tts.fi, http://www.tts.fi. Ed. Pirkko Kasanen. Circ: 4,647.

630 RUS
TEKHNIKA I OBORUDOVANIE DLYA SELA. Text in Russian. 1998. m. USD 269 in United States (effective 2000).
Indexed: RefZh.
Published by: Izdatel'stvo Delo i Pravo, Ul Yablochkova 5, Moscow, 127254, Russian Federation. TEL 7-095-2104030, FAX 7-095-2103308. Ed. V A Bautin. **Dist. by:** East View Information Services, 3020 Harbor Ln. N., Minneapolis, MN 55447. TEL 763-550-0961, FAX 763-559-2931.

TELHAN PATRIKA/OILSEEDS JOURNAL. see *CHEMISTRY—Organic Chemistry*

TELMA. see *EARTH SCIENCES*

630 COL ISSN 0049-3333
TEMAS DE ORIENTACION AGROPECUARIA; conviertase en un agricultor o ganadero progesista. Text in Spanish. 1966. bi-m. USD 20.
Address: Apartado Aereo 13169, Bogota, CUND, Colombia. Ed. Ruben Ruiz Camacho. Circ: 50,000.

630 FRA ISSN 0338-1811
TEMPE INFORMATIONS. Text in French. 1972. m.
Formerly (until 1972): Tempe Lait Informations (0338-1803)
Related titles: ♦ Supplement to: Action Agricole de Tarn et Garonne. ISSN 0338-182X.
Published by: Cooperative Laiti, 420 av. de Monclar, Montauban, Cedex 82017, France. TEL 63-63-11-15, FAX 63-20-15-65.

630 USA CODEN: TFHSAT
TENNESSEE AGRI SCIENCE. Text in English. 1952. q. free. charts; illus. index. **Document type:** *Academic/Scholarly.* **Description:** Reports on research on agriculture and natural resources conducted by the Tennessee Agricultural Experiment Station.
Formerly (until 1995): Tennessee Farm and Home Science (0040-3229)
Indexed: AEA, AnBrAb, BiolAb, CTFA, ChemAb, CurCont, DSA, FCA, FPA, FS&TA, ForAb, HerbAb, HortAb, IndVet, MaizeAb, NutrAb, PN&I, S&F, SeedAb, SoyAb, VetBull, WeedAb. —CASDDS.
Published by: University of Tennessee at Knoxville, Agricultural Experiment Station, 103 Morgan Hall, Knoxville, TN 37996-4506. TEL 865-974-7121, FAX 865-974-6479, taescomm@utk.edu, http://www.taes.utk.edu/. Pub. B P Reichert. Circ: 4,500.

630 USA ISSN 1062-8983
TENNESSEE FARM BUREAU NEWS. Text in English. 1923. bi-m. adv. illus. **Document type:** *Newsletter, Trade.* **Description:** Farm-consumer-rural resident publication for members of the Tennessee Farm Bureau.
Formerly: F B News (0162-2617)
Published by: Tennessee Farm Bureau Federation, 147 Bear Creek Pike, Columbia, TN 38401. TEL 931-388-7872, FAX 931-388-5818, pread@tfbf.com, http://www.tnfarmbureau.org. Ed. Pettus L Read. Adv. contact Stacey Warner. B&W page USD 4,675, color page USD 5,725; 9.75 x 13.75. Circ: 120,000 (paid).

630 USA ISSN 0040-3245
TENNESSEE FARMER. Text in English. 1954. m. USD 29 (effective 2001). adv. illus. **Document type:** *Newspaper.*
Related titles: Microform ed.: (from PQC).
Published by: Farm Progress Companies, 191 S Gary Ave, Carol Stream, IL 60188. TEL 630-462-2892, http://www.farmprogress.com/. Ed. Wayne Harr TEL 615-595-6116. adv.: B&W page USD 1,515. Circ: 18,000 (paid).

630 ESP ISSN 0212-5684
LA TERRA (BARCELONA); organ d'informacion i debat de la Unio de Pagesos. Text in Catalan. 1975. m. **Document type:** *Trade.* —CINDOC.
Published by: Edicions la Terra S.L., Avinguda Francesc Cambo, 14 3-B, Barcelona, 08003, Spain. TEL 34-93-2680900, FAX 34-93-2684893, laterra@agronet.org, http://www.uniopagesos.es/unio. Ed. Humbert Roma de Asso. Circ: 14,000.

630 ITA ISSN 0040-3768
TERRA E SOLE; agricoltura pratica e meccanica agraria. Text in Italian. 1945. m. adv. bk.rev. bibl.; illus. **Document type:** *Magazine, Trade.* **Description:** Covers agronomics, machinery, and zootechnology.
Indexed: AEA, BioCN&I, FCA, FPA, ForAb, HortAb, IndVet, MaizeAb, OrnHort, PBA, PHN&I, PN&I, PotatoAb, RPP, RevApplEntom, RiceAb, S&F, SoyAb, TriticAb, WAE&RSA, WeedAb.
Published by: Iacico Srl, Via Angelo Poliziano 80, Rome, 00184, Italy. TEL 39-06-4873183, FAX 39-06-4873144, http://www.agravista.com. Ed. Andrea S Silenzi. Adv. contact Vito Marini. Circ: 41,000.

630 ITA ISSN 0040-3776
TERRA E VITA. Text in Italian. 1959. w. (49/yr.). EUR 88 domestic; EUR 300 foreign (effective 2005). adv. bk.rev. charts; illus. index. 112 p./no.; **Document type:** *Magazine, Trade.* **Description:** Features articles written by farmers about farming and the agricultural world.
Incorporates: Raccolto (0033-7269)
Related titles: Online - full text ed.
Indexed: AEA, CBNB, HortAb.
Published by: Il Sole 24 Ore Edagricole, Via Goito 13, Bologna, BO 40126, Italy. TEL 39-051-62267, FAX 39-051-490200, http://www.edagricole.it. Ed. Giorgio Setti. Circ: 33,000.

630 CHE ISSN 1422-3619
TERRE & NATURE. Text in French. 1898. w. CHF 123; CHF 3 newsstand/cover (effective 2000). adv. **Document type:** *Magazine, Consumer.*
Formerly (until 1997): Sillon Romand (1420-4258)
Published by: Edipresse Publications SA, 33 av de la Gare, Lausanne, 1001, Switzerland. TEL 41-21-3494545, FAX 41-21-3494079, terre-redaction@edicom.ch, groupe@edipresse.com, http://www.edicom.ch/terre/present.html. Ed. Bernard Debetaz. adv.: B&W page CHF 5,500, color page CHF 6,490. Circ: 24,460 (controlled).

630 FRA ISSN 1279-2853
TERRE DAUPHINOISE. Text in French. 1977 (vol.32). w. adv. charts; illus.; stat.
Published by: Associations Agricole de l'Isere, 5 rue G. Rivet, B.P. 1064, Grenoble, 38021, France. TEL 76-40-31-32, FAX 76-33-04-82. Ed. M Lalanne Cloute.

630 CAN ISSN 0040-3830
TERRE DE CHEZ NOUS. Text in English. 1929. w. CND 18. adv. bk.rev. —CISTI.
Published by: Union des Producteurs Agricoles, 555 Boul Roland Therrien, Longueuil, PQ J4H 3Y9, Canada. TEL 514-679-0530, FAX 514-679-5436. Ed. Andre Charbonneau. Circ: 44,000.

630 FRA
TERRE DE CHEZ NOUS✶. Text in French. w.
Published by: Societe Comtoise d'Edition et d'Information, 130 bis, Rue de Belfort, BP 939, Besancon, Cedex 25021, France. TEL 81-80-75-77. Ed. M Narbey. Circ: 14,586.

630 CHE
TERRE VALAISANNE. Text in French. 24/yr. **Document type:** *Newspaper, Trade.*
Address: Maison du Paysan, Casa postale 96, Conthey, 1964, Switzerland. TEL 41-27-3454010, FAX 41-27-3454011. Ed. Ariane Alter. Circ: 4,091.

630 FRA ISSN 0750-8093
TERRES D'ARIEGE. Text in French. 1953. 56/yr.
Related titles: ♦ Supplement(s): Gascon Magazine. ISSN 1245-1606.
Published by: Terres d, 32 av. du General de Gaulle, BP 7, Foix, Cedex 09001, France. TEL 61-65-20-00, FAX 61-02-89-60. Ed. Claudes Laborde. Circ: 15,785.

TEXAS AGRICULTURAL STATISTICS. see *AGRICULTURE—Abstracting, Bibliographies, Statistics*

630 USA ISSN 0162-3001
TEXAS AGRICULTURE. WEST TEXAS REGIONAL EDITION. Text in English. 1935. 20/yr. free membership (effective 2005). adv. illus. **Document type:** *Magazine.*
Supersedes in part: Texas Agriculture Weekly; Which was formerly (until 1985): Texas Agriculture (0040-4152)
Related titles: Regional ed(s).: Texas Agriculture. North Texas Regional Edition. ISSN 0162-301X. 1935. free to members.
Published by: Texas Farm Bureau, PO Box 2689, Waco, TX 76702-2689. Ed. Mike Barnett. Pub. Gene Hall. Adv. contact Drew Wenner. Circ: 85,000.

638.1 USA
TEXAS AGRINEWS; the farm and ranch newspaper serving Texas. Text in English. 1981. m. USD 15; free to qualified personnel (effective 1999). adv. back issues avail. **Document type:** *Newspaper.* **Description:** Serves farmers, ranchers, and growers with marketing and agricultural news.
Formerly (until 1993): South Texas AgriNews
Published by: Big River Press, Inc., 1217 N Conway, Box 353, Mission, TX 78572. TEL 956-585-4893, FAX 956-585-2304. Pub. June Brann. Adv. contact Clyde Machen. B&W page USD 1,300. Circ: 9,379 (controlled).

630 USA ISSN 0893-8997
TEXAS F F A MAGAZINE. Text in English. 1928. bi-m. free. **Document type:** *Magazine, Trade.* **Description:** For teenage boys and girls who belong to the Texas Association of Future Farmers of America. Most material pertains to activities in the various FFA chapters, but some feature material is used, particularly during the fall months.
Formerly: Texas Future Farmer (0040-4330)
Published by: Texas F F A Association, 614 E 12th St., Austin, TX 78701. TEL 512-480-8045, FAX 512-472-0555, bshaw@tmail.tea.state.tx.us, http://www.txaged.org. Ed. Tiffany Munson. Circ: 65,500 (paid and free).

630 USA ISSN 0891-5466
TEXAS JOURNAL OF AGRICULTURE AND NATURAL RESOURCES. Text in English. 1987. a. USD 10 (effective 2004). **Document type:** *Journal.*
Indexed: Agr.
Published by: Agriculture Consortium of Texas, c/o Carleton Britton, Department of Range, Wildlife & Fisheries, Texas Tech University, Lubbock, TX 79409-2125. http://www.tarleton.edu/~agcntr/TXJANR/journal.htm. Ed. Carlton M. Britton.

630 USA
TEXAS NEIGHBORS. Text in English. 1985. q. free to members (effective 2005). adv. illus. **Document type:** *Magazine, Consumer.* **Description:** Features items of interest to bureau member families and articles on Texas lifestyles.
Published by: Texas Farm Bureau, P.O. Box 2689, Waco, TX 76702. Ed. Mike Barnett. Pub. Gene Hall. Adv. contact Drew Wenner. B&W page USD 2,860, color page USD 3,610. Circ: 260,000 (controlled).

630 THA ISSN 0049-3589 CODEN: TJASBN
➤ **THAI JOURNAL OF AGRICULTURAL SCIENCE.** Text and summaries in English. 1967. q. THB 600 domestic to non-members; USD 60 foreign to non-members; USD 50 to members (effective 2003). adv. charts; stat.; bibl. Index. 100 p./no.; back issues avail.; reprints avail. **Document type:** *Journal, Academic/Scholarly.* **Description:** Agricultural sciences and related field distribution, scientists, university people interested in tropical agriculture.
Related titles: CD-ROM ed.; Diskette ed.; Online - full text ed.
Indexed: AEA, AIT, AgBio, AgrForAb, AnBrAb, BioCN&I, BiolAb, CIN, CPA, ChemAb, ChemTitl, DSA, ExcerpMed, FCA, FS&TA, ForAb, HelmAb, HerbAb, HortAb, I&DA, IndVet, MaizeAb, NemAb, NutrAb, OrnHort, PBA, PGegResA, PGrRegA, PHN&I, PN&I, PST, PotatoAb, PoultAb, RA&MP, RPP, RRTA, RevApplEntom, RiceAb, S&F, SIA, SeedAb, SoyAb, TriticAb, WAE&RSA, WeedAb, ZooRec. —BLDSC (8813.970000), CASDDS, CISTI, IE, ingenta.
Published by: Agricultural Science Society of Thailand, Kasetsart University, PO Box 1070, Bangkok, 10903, Thailand. TEL 66-2-579-0308 ext 136, FAX 66-2-579-1951 ext 112, agrsns@ku.ac.th, agrsns@nontri.ku.ac.th. Ed., R&P Suranant Subhadrabandhu TEL 66-2-5790308 ext 112. Circ: 2,000.

➤ **THAILAND. NATIONAL STATISTICAL OFFICE. (YEAR) AGRICULTURAL CENSUS.** see *AGRICULTURE—Abstracting, Bibliographies, Statistics*

630 SYR
THAWRAH AL-ZIRAIA/AGRICULTURAL REVOLUTION REVIEW. Text in Arabic. 1965. m. adv. **Document type:** *Government.*
Published by: Ministry of Agrarian Reform, Damascus, Syria. Circ: 7,000.

THESIS ABSTRACTS. see *AGRICULTURE—Abstracting, Bibliographies, Statistics*

630 IND
THOZHIL VANNIGA MUDALEEDU. Text in Tamil. 1993 (Apr.). fortn. INR 200 (effective 2000).
Address: 17 Aziz Mulk First St, Thousand Lights, Chennai, 600 006, India. TEL 91-44-8292979, FAX 91-44-8254745, meenaari@hotmail.com, http://www.intamn.com. Ed. Haridasan V.

630 GBR
THREE COUNTIES FARMING REVIEW. Text in English. 1986. m. free.
Formerly: Five Counties Farming Review
Published by: Community Media Ltd., 32 Waterloo St, Weston-Super-Mar, BS2 31LW, United Kingdom. Ed. David Parker. Circ: 5,500.

630 CHE
THURGAUER BAUER. Text in German. w.
Published by: Thurgauisches Bauernsekretariat, Weinfelden, 8570, Switzerland. TEL 072-224422, FAX 054-218871. Circ: 5,270.

638.1 DNK ISSN 0900-0801
TIDSSKRIFT FOR BIAVL. Text in Danish. 1866. m. DKK 500 (effective 2004). adv. bk.rev. **Document type:** *Newsletter.* **Description:** Discusses technical and political aspects of beekeeping for professionals and hobbyists.
Related titles: CD-ROM ed.: ISSN 1399-0616.
Indexed: ApicAb.
Published by: Danmarks Biavlerforening, Landbocentret, Moellevej 15, Borup, 4140, Denmark. TEL 45-57-561777, FAX 45-57-561703, dbf@biavl.dk, http://www.biavl.dk. Ed. Rolf Tulstrup Theuerkauf. Adv. contact Marianne Svenningsen. color page DKK 3,300; 168 x 248. Circ: 5,500.

630 DNK ISSN 0040-7119
S11
TIDSSKRIFT FOR LANDOEKONOMI. Text in Danish. 1814. 4/yr. DKK 325; DKK 95 per issue (effective 2005). charts; illus. back issues avail. **Document type:** *Journal, Academic/Scholarly.*
Formerly (until 1898): Tidsskrift for Landoekonomie
—CCC.
Published by: Det Kongelige Danske Landhusholdningsselskab/ Royal Danish Agricultural Society, Jacob Gades Alle 12, Vejen, 6600, Denmark. TEL 45-43-411769, FAX 45-43-410210, lhs@1769.dk, http://www.1769.dk.

630 ESP
TIERRA; del agricultor y ganadero. Text in Spanish. 1984. m.
Published by: Union de Pequenos Agricultores/Union of Small Farmers, Avda America, 25 4o, Madrid, 28002, Spain. TEL 1-589-72-18, FAX 1-589-75-54. Ed. Ana Vicandi. Circ: 15,000.

630 CHL ISSN 0717-1609
S475.C5
TIERRA ADENTRO. Text in Spanish. 1995. bi-m. CLP 16,000; USD 70 in the Americas; USD 83 elsewhere. adv. **Document type:** *Academic/Scholarly.* **Description:** Presents accounts, economic studies and practical data of interest to the land and cattle industries.
Formed by the merger of (1980-1995): Investigacion y Progreso Agropecuario Quilamapu (0716-6052); (1982-1995): Investigacion y Progreso Agropecuario Carillanca (0716-5943); (1982-1995): Investigacion y Progreso Agropecuario Remehue (0716-5951); (1980-1995): Investigacion y Progreso Agropecuario La Platina (0716-5331); Which supersedes (1967-1977): Investigacion y Progreso Agricola (0304-5579)
Indexed: FS&TA.
—CISTI.
Published by: (Centro Regional de Investigacion La Platina), Instituto de Investigaciones Agropecuarias, Casilla 439, Correo, 3, Santiago, Chile. TEL 56-2-5417223, FAX 56-2-5417667. Ed. Silvia Altamirano. Circ: 5,000 (controlled).

630 NLD ISSN 1388-509X
TIJDSCHRIFT VOOR DE LEEFOMGEVING. Text in Dutch. 1889. 5/yr. adv. bk.rev. charts; illus. index.
Former titles (until 1997): Heidemtijdschrift (0169-7978); (until 1985): Vereniging Koninklijke Nederlandsche Heide Maatschappij. Tijdschrift (0165-0017)
Indexed: BiolAb.
—BLDSC (8842.450000), CISTI, IE, Infotrieve.
Published by: Vereniging Koninklijke Nederlandsche Heide Maatschappij, Postbus 33, Arnhem, 6800 LE, Netherlands. TEL 31-26-4455146, FAX 31-26-4437827, publ@knhm.nl, http://www.knhm.nl. Ed. P R Bos. Circ: 10,000.

630 GTM
TIKALIA. Text in Spanish. 1982. 2/yr. GTQ 20 domestic; USD 10 foreign (effective 2000). bk.rev.
Published by: Universidad de San Carlos de Guatemala, Facultad de Agronomia, Ciudad Universitaria, Zona 12, Apdo 1545, Guatemala, C A, Guatemala. TEL 502-4769770, FAX 502-4769770, cedia@usac.edu.gt, http://www.usac.edu.gt/ facultades/agronomia/cedia.htm. Ed. David Pinto. Circ: 1,000 (controlled).

630 RUS ISSN 0021-342X
CODEN: ITSAA7
TIMIRYAZEVSKAYA SEL'SKOKHOZYAISTVENNAYA AKADEMIYA. IZVESTIYA. Text in Russian. 1878. 4/yr. USD 85. charts; illus. index.
Indexed: AEA, AgBio, AnBrAb, BIOSIS Prev, BioCN&I, BiolAb, CPA, ChemAb, DSA, FCA, FS&TA, ForAb, HerbAb, HortAb, I&DA, IBSS, IndVet, MaizeAb, NutrAb, OrnHort, PBA, PGegResA, PGrRegA, PHN&I, PN&I, PotatoAb, PoultAb, RA&MP, RPP, RRTA, RefZh, RevApplEntom, S&F, SIA, SeedAb, SoyAb, TriticAb, VITIS, VetBull, WAE&RSA, WeedAb.
—BLDSC (0082.900000), CASDDS, CISTI, East View, Linda Hall.
Published by: Timiryazevskaya Sel'skokhozyaistvennaya Akademiya, Listvennichnaya a-ya 12-a, Moscow, 127550, Russian Federation. Ed. A I Puponin. Circ: 2,400. **US dist. addr.:** East View Information Services, 3020 Harbor Ln. N., Minneapolis, MN 55447. TEL 612-550-0961.

TOBACCO NEWS. see *TOBACCO*

630 USA
TODAY'S F F A. (Future Farmer) Text in English. 1928. a. free to members (effective 2005). **Document type:** *Magazine, Trade.*
Formerly: Florida Future Farmer Magazine
Contact Owner: Florida FFA Association, P.O. Box 141570, Gainesville, FL 32614. TEL 352-378-0060, FAX 352-378-6061, membership@flaffa.org, http://www.flaffa.org. Circ: 13,000 (free).

630 IRL ISSN 0791-4660
TODAY'S FARM. Text in English. 1990. bi-m. EUR 30.50 (effective 2002). adv. **Document type:** *Magazine, Trade.*
Published by: Teagasc, Oak Park, Carlow, Ireland. TEL 353-1-6376000, FAX 353-1-6688023, mmiley@hq.teagasc.ie, http://www.teagasc.ie. adv.: B&W page EUR 2,030, color page EUR 2,665; trim 216 x 299. Circ: 37,000 (paid and controlled).

630 USA ISSN 0739-0092
TODAY'S FARMER. Text in English. 1908. 10/yr. USD 12 (effective 2005). adv. **Document type:** *Magazine, Trade.*
Published by: (Midcontinent Farmers Association Incorporated), M F A, Inc., 201 Ray Young Dr, Columbia, MO 65201. TEL 573-874-5111, FAX 573-976-5430, http://www.mfa-inc.com. Eds. Chuck Lay, Steve Fairchild. Adv. contact Nicole Brink. B&W page USD 3,464, color page USD 4,850; trim 8.5 x 10.78. Circ: 40,000 (paid).

TOHOKU NO NOGYO KISHO/BULLETIN OF THE AGRICULTURAL METEOROLOGY OF TOHOKU DISTRICT. see *METEOROLOGY*

TOKYO NOGYO DAIGAKU AISOTOPU SENTA KENKYU HOKOKU/TOKYO UNIVERSITY OF AGRICULTURE. ISOTOPE CENTER. BULLETIN. see *PHYSICS—Nuclear Physics*

630.5 JPN ISSN 0375-9202
CODEN: TNDNAG
➤ **TOKYO NOGYO DAIGAKU NOGAKU SHUHO/TOKYO UNIVERSITY OF AGRICULTURE. JOURNAL OF AGRICULTURAL SCIENCE.** Text in Japanese. 1937. q. per issue exchange basis only. **Document type:** *Academic/Scholarly.*
Indexed: ChemAb, FCA, FS&TA, INIS AtomInd, RefZh, RiceAb, SFA, WildRev, ZooRec.
—BLDSC (4923.025000), CASDDS, CISTI, IE, ingenta.
Published by: Tokyo Nogyo Daigaku, 1-1-1 Sakuragaoka, Setagaya-ku, Tokyo, 158-8502, Japan. TEL 81-3-5477-2525, FAX 81-3-5477-2632. Ed. Kazumori Morita.

630 DEU ISSN 0936-8302
TOP AGRAR: AUSGABE B. Text in German. 1972. m. EUR 60 domestic; EUR 73.80 foreign (effective 2003). adv. **Document type:** *Journal, Trade.*
—IE, Infotrieve.
Published by: Landwirtschaftsverlag GmbH, Huelsebrockstr 2, Muenster, 48165, Germany. TEL 49-2501-801-0, FAX 49-2501-801204, service@topagrar.com, zentrale@lv-h.de, http://www.topagrar.com, http://www.lv-h.de. Eds. Heinz Guenter Topueth, Wilhelm Wehland. Adv. contact Peter Wiggers.

630 DEU ISSN 0936-8310
TOP AGRAR: AUSGABE R. Text in German. 1972. m. EUR 66 domestic; EUR 80.40 foreign (effective 2003). adv. **Document type:** *Journal, Trade.*
Published by: Landwirtschaftsverlag GmbH, Huelsebrockstr 2, Muenster, 48165, Germany. TEL 49-2501-801-0, FAX 49-2501-801204, service@topagrar.com, zentrale@lv-h.de, http://www.topagrar.com, http://www.lv-h.de. Eds. Heinz Guenter Topueth, Wilhelm Wehland. Adv. contact Peter Wiggers.

630 DEU ISSN 0936-8329
TOP AGRAR: AUSGABE S. Text in German. 1972. m. EUR 66 domestic; EUR 80.40 foreign (effective 2003). adv. **Document type:** *Journal, Trade.*
Published by: Landwirtschaftsverlag GmbH, Huelsebrockstr 2, Muenster, 48165, Germany. TEL 49-2501-801-0, FAX 49-2501-801204, service@topagrar.com, zentrale@lv-h.de, http://www.topagrar.com, http://www.lv-h.de. Eds. Heinz Guenter Topueth, Wilhelm Wehland. Adv. contact Peter Wiggers.

630 DEU ISSN 0342-2399
TOP AGRAR: AUSGABE S - R; das Magazin fuer moderne Landwirtschaft. Text in German. 1972. m. EUR 71.40 domestic; EUR 85.80 foreign; EUR 6.70 newsstand/cover (effective 2003). adv. **Document type:** *Journal, Trade.*
—IE, Infotrieve. **CCC.**
Published by: Landwirtschaftsverlag GmbH, Huelsebrockstr 2, Muenster, 48165, Germany. TEL 49-2501-801-0, FAX 49-2501-801351, service@topagrar.com, zentrale@lv-h.de, http://www.topagrar.com, http://www.lv-h.de. Eds. Heinz Guenter Topueth, Wilhelm Wehland. Adv. contact Peter Wiggers. Circ: 134,000.

630 DEU
TOP AGRAR OESTERREICH. Text in German. m. EUR 38.10 for 6 mos. (effective 2005). **Document type:** *Magazine, Trade.*
Published by: Landwirtschaftsverlag GmbH, Huelsebrockstr 2, Muenster, 48165, Germany. TEL 49-2501-27500, FAX 49-2501-27551, redaktion@lv-topagrar.at, zentrale@lv-h.de, http://www.topagrar.com, http://www.landwirtschaftsverlag.com. Ed. Hans Maad TEL 43-2236-287000. Circ: 14,500 (paid and controlled).

630 CAN ISSN 1488-4313
TOP CROP MANAGER. Text in English. 1984. m. CND 80 domestic; CND 160 foreign; free to qualified personnel (effective 2005). adv. illus. back issues avail. **Document type:** *Magazine, Trade.* **Description:** Focuses on information which guides growers in such areas as weed, insect and disease management, tillage, seeding and planting, fertility, machinery and new technology.
Incorporates: Seed in Canada; Corn In Canada; Beans In Canada
Related titles: ♦ Supplement(s): Potatoes in Canada.
—CISTI.
Published by: Annex Publishing & Printing, Inc., 222 Argyle Ave, Delhi, ON N4B 2Y2, ON N4B 2Y2, Canada. TEL 519-582-2513, 800-265-2827, FAX 519-582-4040, sfredericks@annexweb.com, http://www.topcropmanager.com, http://www.annexweb.com. Ed. Peter Darbishire. Circ: 30,000.

630 658 USA ISSN 1056-0831
TOP PRODUCER. Text in English. 1986. m. (10/yr..). adv. **Document type:** *Trade.*
Formerly: Farm Journal Extra
Related titles: Online - full text ed.: (from Gale Group, LexisNexis, ProQuest Information & Learning).
—CCC.
Published by: Farm Journal Media, 1818 Market St., 31st Fl, Philadelphia, PA 19103-3654. TEL 215-557-8900, 800-523-1538, FAX 215-568-5012, http://www.agweb.com. Ed. Marcia Taylor. Circ: 225,000.

630.7 JPN ISSN 0082-5360
CODEN: JFALAX
TOTTORI UNIVERSITY. FACULTY OF AGRICULTURE. JOURNAL. Text in Multiple languages. 1951. a. per issue exchange basis only. **Document type:** *Academic/Scholarly.*
Indexed: AEA, AgBio, BIOSIS Prev, BioCN&I, BiolAb, FCA, FPA, ForAb, HerbAb, HortAb, I&DA, IndVet, NutrAb, PBA, PoultAb, RefZh, RiceAb, S&F, SFA, SeedAb, TriticAb, VetBull, WAE&RSA, WeedAb, WildRev, ZooRec.
—CASDDS.
Published by: Tottori Daigaku, Nogakubu/Tottori University, Faculty of Agriculture, 4-101 Koyama-Minami, Tottori-shi, 680-0000, Japan. Circ: 750.

630 USA
TOWN & COUNTRY (FONDA). Text in English. 1996. bi-m. adv. back issues avail. **Document type:** *Newsletter.* **Description:** Provides research-based educational information to residents of Fulton and Montgomery Counties, helping residents to help themselves. Topics include financial management, nutrition, health and safety, consumer horticulture, science and technology, and youth development.
Former titles: Changing Horizons; Montgomery County Agricultural News
Published by: Cooperative Extension of Fulton & Montgomery Counties, County Annex Building, PO Box 1500 Park Street, Fonda, NY 12068. TEL 518-853-3471, 518-725-6441, FAX 518-853-4706, 518-725-3233, montgomery@cce.cornell.edu, http://www.ccefm.org. Ed. Karen Kosinski. Circ: 2,000.

630 634.96 AUS ISSN 0814-4540
TOWN AND COUNTRY FARMER. Text in English. 1984. q. AUD 27.50 domestic; AUD 37 in Asia & the Pacific; AUD 43.60 elsewhere (effective 2004). adv. tr.lit. index. back issues avail. **Document type:** *Magazine, Consumer.* **Description:** Covers all aspects of farm management: planning, health and weed control, plus diversifying and alternative farm production activities.

▼ new title ➤ refereed ✶ unverified ♦ full entry avail.

A

Published by: Town and Country Farmer Publications Pty. Ltd., PO Box 798, Benalla, VIC 3672, Australia. TEL 61-3-57641348, FAX 61-3-57641349, tacfarmr@mcmedia.com.au. Eds. Glenn Hurley, Shirley Hurley. Circ: 15,000 (controlled).

630   USA
CODEN: TTCRAV
TRI-OLOGY TECHNICAL REPORT (ONLINE). Text in English. 1962. bi-m. free. **Document type:** *Government.* **Description:** Focuses on pathology, nematology, botany and entomology. **Formerly:** Tri-Ology Technical Report (Print) (0041-2481) **Indexed:** BibAg, BioCN&I, BiolAb, CTFA, HortAb, NemAb, PotatoAb, RPP, RevApplEntom, WeedAb, ZooRec. —BLDSC (9050.675000), CISTI. **Published by:** Department of Agriculture and Consumer Services, Division of Plant Industry, 1911 S W 34th St, Box 147100, Gainesville, FL 32614-7100. TEL 904-372-3505, FAX 904-955-2301. Ed. Wayne N Dixon. R&P Denise Feiber.

630   USA
TRI-STATE NEIGHBOR. Text in English. 1983. bi-w. USD 32.95; free domestic qualified farmers & ranchers (effective 2005). 80 p./no. 4 cols./p.; **Document type:** *Newspaper, Trade.* **Formerly:** The Neighbor **Published by:** Lee Agri-Media, Inc., 4023 State St., Bismark, ND 58803. TEL 701-255-4905, FAX 800-594-8433, ads@tristateneighbor.com, http://www.tristateneighbor.com. Ed. Wendy Sweeter. Circ: 30,000 (paid and free).

630   ESP   ISSN 0210-5616
TRIA; una revista para el campo. Text in Spanish. 1964. fortn. adv. bk.rev. bibl.; illus.; stat. **Published by:** Estructura S.A., Grupo de Estudios Economicos, Gran Via, 32, Madrid, 28013, Spain. TEL 34-91-5386100. Ed. Leandro de le Vega Gil. Circ: 42,000.

TRINIDAD AND TOBAGO. CENTRAL STATISTICAL OFFICE. AGRICULTURAL REPORT. see *AGRICULTURE—Abstracting, Bibliographies, Statistics*

630   LKA   ISSN 1016-1422
S281
TROPICAL AGRICULTURAL RESEARCH. Text in English. 1989. a. **Indexed:** AgBio, AgrForAb, AnBrAb, BioCN&I, CPA, DSA, FCA, FPA, ForAb, HelmAb, HerbAb, HortAb, I&DA, IndVet, MaizeAb, NutrAb, OrnHort, PBA, PGegResA, PGrRegA, PHN&I, PotatoAb, PoultAb, ProtozoAb, RA&MP, RDA, RPP, RRTA, RiceAb, S&F, SIA, SeedAb, SoyAb, TDB, TriticAb, VetBull, WAE&RSA, WeedAb. —BLDSC (9052.900000), IE. **Published by:** University of Peradeniya, Postgraduate Institute of Agriculture, Peradeniya, Sri Lanka. librarian@pdn.ac.lk, http://www.pdn.ac.lk. Ed. Sarath P Nissanka.

631.491   TTO   ISSN 0041-3216
SB111.A2   CODEN: TAGLA2
➤ TROPICAL AGRICULTURE. Text in English. 1924. q. GBP 175 (effective 2001). adv. bk.rev. index. back issues avail. **Document type:** *Academic/Scholarly.* **Description:** Covers all aspects of agriculture in tropical and semi-tropical countries. **Incorporates:** Oil Palm News (0048-1580) **Related titles:** Microfiche ed.: (from BHP); Microfilm ed.: (from PQC). **Indexed:** ASCA, ASFA, ATA, AgBio, Agr, AgrForAb, AnBrAb, B&AI, B&BAb, BAS, BIOSIS Prev, BibAg, BioCN&I, BiolAb, CPA, CTFA, ChemAb, CurCont, DBA, DSA, EIA, EPB, ESPM, EnerInd, EnvAb, FCA, FPA, FS&TA, ForAb, GEOBASE, HerbAb, HortAb, I&DA, ISR, IndVet, MaizeAb, NemAb, NutrAb, OrnHort, PBA, PCI, PGegResA, PGrRegA, PHN&I, PN&I, PollutAb, PotatoAb, PoultAb, RA&MP, RDA, RM&VM, RPP, RRTA, RevApplEntom, RiceAb, S&F, S&MA, SCI, SIA, SPPI, SWRA, SeedAb, SoyAb, TDB, TOSA, TriticAb, VITIS, VetBull, WAE&RSA, WeedAb, ZooRec. —BLDSC (9053.000000), CASDDS, CISTI, IE, Infotrieve, ingenta, Linda Hall. **Published by:** University of the West Indies, Imperial College of Tropical Agriculture, St Augustine, Trinidad & Tobago. TEL 809-645-3640, FAX 809-662-1182, TELEX 24520 UWI WG, trop_agric@hotmail.com. Ed. F A Gumbs.

631.091   LKA   ISSN 0041-3224
TROPICAL AGRICULTURIST; agricultural journal of Sri Lanka. Text in English. 1881. a. LKR 100, USD 15 (effective 1999). adv. bk.rev. charts; illus. index. **Document type:** *Magazine, Academic/Scholarly.* **Description:** Promotes agricultural research in the Tropics. **Related titles:** CD-ROM ed. **Indexed:** AEA, BioCN&I, BiolAb, ChemAb, FCA, HerbAb, HortAb, I&DA, NemAb, NutrAb, PBA, PotatoAb, RPP, RevApplEntom, RiceAb, S&F, SIA, SeedAb, WeedAb. **Published by:** Department of Agriculture, Plant Genetic Resources Centre, Director General of Agriculture, No.1, Sarasavi Mawatha, P.O. Box 59,, Gannoruwa, Peradeniya, Sri Lanka. TEL 94-8-388490, FAX 94-8-388490, TELEX 94-8-388494, pgrc@slt.lk. Ed. S Nagarajah. Circ: 650. **Subscr. to:** Librarian, Central Agricultural Library, Horticultural Research and Development Institute, Gannoruwa, P.O. Box 47, Peradeniya, Sri Lanka. TEL 94-8-388494, FAX 94-8-388490.

338.1   MEX   ISSN 1870-0462
➤ TROPICAL AND SUBTROPICAL AGROECOSYSTEMS. Text in English, Spanish. 2002. 3/yr. free. adv. **Document type:** *Journal, Academic/Scholarly.* **Description:** Devoted to the dissemination of all information contributing to the understanding and development of agroecosystems in tropical and subtropical areas. **Media:** Online - full content. **Published by:** Universidad Autonoma de Yucatan, Facultad de Medicina Veterinaria y Zootecnia, Km 15.5 Carret Xmatkuil, Apdo 4-116, Itzimna, Merida, 97100, Mexico. TEL 52-999-9423200, FAX 52-999-9423205, ccastro@tunku.uady.mx, http://www.uady.mx/sitios/veterina/servicios/journal/journal-inicio.html. Ed., R&P, Adv. contact Carlos A Sandoval-Castro.

631.091   TTO   ISSN 1024-1957
TROPICAL FRUITS NEWSLETTER. Text in English. 199?. q. **Document type:** *Newsletter.* **Description:** Disseminates technical and general information on pre-production, production, harvesting and post-harvesting of tropical fruit. **Indexed:** BioCN&I, HortAb, NutrAb, PHN&I, RevApplEntom, WAE&RSA. —BLDSC (9056.165000). **Published by:** Inter-American Institute for Cooperation on Agriculture, Office at Trinidad, 3 Herbert St, Newtown, Port of Spain, Trinidad & Tobago. TEL 868-628-4403, FAX 868-628-4562, iicatt@iicacarc.org.

631.091   GBR   ISSN 0041-3291
S3   CODEN: TROSAC
➤ TROPICAL SCIENCE. Text in English. 1959. q. USD 650 to institutions; USD 715 combined subscription to institutions print & online eds. (effective 2006). adv. bk.rev. charts; illus.; stat.; abstr. index. back issues avail.; reprints avail. **Document type:** *Journal, Academic/Scholarly.* **Description:** Information within the spheres of science, technology and economics as applied to the development of renewable resources in the tropics and sub-tropics. **Incorporates** (in 1985): Tropical Stored Products Information (0564-3325); Which incorporated: Tropical Storage Abstracts (0305-8964) **Related titles:** Microform ed.: (from PQC); Online - full text ed.: ISSN 1556-9179. USD 650 to institutions (effective 2006). **Indexed:** A&ATA, AEA, AgBio, Agr, AgrForAb, AnBrAb, AnalAb, B&AI, BAS, BIOBASE, BibAg, BioCN&I, BiolAb, CPA, ChemAb, DSA, EIA, EnerInd, ExcerpMed, FCA, FPA, FS&TA, ForAb, HerbAb, HortAb, I&DA, IABS, IPackAb, IndVet, MaizeAb, NemAb, NutrAb, OrnHort, PBA, PGegResA, PGrRegA, PHN&I, PN&I, PST, PlantSci, PotatoAb, PoultAb, RA&MP, RDA, RM&VM, RPP, RevApplEntom, RiceAb, S&F, SIA, SeedAb, SoyAb, TDB, TriticAb, VetBull, WAE&RSA, WeedAb. —BLDSC (9056.600000), CASDDS, CISTI, IE, Infotrieve, ingenta, Linda Hall. **CCC.** **Published by:** John Wiley & Sons Ltd. (Subsidiary of: John Wiley & Sons, Inc.), The Atrium, Southern Gate, Chichester, West Sussex PO19 8SQ, United Kingdom. TEL 44-1243-779777, FAX 44-1243-775878, cs-journals@wiley.co.uk, http://www.whurr.co.uk/whurr/display-journal.asp?sf1=issn&st1=0041-3291&TAG=&CID=, http://www.wiley.co.uk. adv.: page GBP 300. Circ: 157 (paid). Dist. by: Extenza - Turpin, Pegasus Dr, Stratton Business Park, Biggleswade, Beds SG18 8TQ, United Kingdom. TEL 44-1462-672555, FAX 44-1462-480-947, custservturpin@turpinltd.com.

630   IDN   ISSN 0126-0057
S19
TRUBUS; the magazine for the development of agriculture and agribusiness. Text in English. 1969. m. IDR 30,000, USD 19. adv. bk.rev. **Indexed:** EI. **Published by:** Yayasan Sosial Tani Membangun, Jl. Gunung Sahari III-7, Jakarta, Indonesia. TEL 4204402. Ed. Slamet Soeseno. Circ: 50,000.

630   JPN   ISSN 0372-7785
TSURUOKA: YAMAGATA NORIN GAKKAI/YAMAGATA AGRICULTURE AND FORESTRY SOCIETY. JOURNAL. Text in Japanese. 1951. irreg. **Document type:** *Journal, Academic/Scholarly.* **Indexed:** AnBrAb, CPA, FCA, ForAb, HortAb, S&F, SeedAb. **Published by:** Yamagata Norin Gakkai/Yamagata Agriculture and Forestry Society, c/o Yamagata Daigaku Nogakubu, Tsuruoka Campus: Wakaba-machi,, Tsuruoka-shi, Yamagata 997-8555, Japan. TEL 81-235-282805, FAX 81-235-282812.

TURKEY. DEVLET ISTATISTIK ENSTITUSU. CIFTCININ ELINE GECEN FIYATLAR/TURKEY. STATE INSTITUTE OF STATISTICS. PRICES RECEIVED BY FARMERS. see *AGRICULTURE—Abstracting, Bibliographies, Statistics*

TURKEY. DEVLET ISTATISTIK ENSTITUSU. GENEL TARIM SAYIMI/TURKEY. STATE INSTITUTE OF STATISTICS. GENERAL AGRICULTURAL CENSUS. see *AGRICULTURE—Abstracting, Bibliographies, Statistics*

TURKEY. DEVLET ISTATISTIK ENSTITUSU. TARIM ISTATISTIKLERI OZETI/TURKEY. STATE INSTITUTE OF STATISTICS. SUMMARY OF AGRICULTURAL STATISTICS. see *AGRICULTURE—Abstracting, Bibliographies, Statistics*

630   TUR   ISSN 1300-011X
CODEN: TJAFEL
➤ TURKISH JOURNAL OF AGRICULTURE AND FORESTRY/TURK TARIM VE ORMANCILIK DERGISI. Text and summaries in English; Abstracts in Turkish. 1976. 6/yr. USD 150 (effective 2005). **Document type:** *Journal, Academic/Scholarly.* **Formerly** (until 1994): Doga Turkish Journal of Agriculture and Forestry - Doga Turk Tarim ve Ormancilik Dergisi (1010-7649) **Related titles:** Online - full text ed.: ISSN 1303-6173. free (effective 2005) (from EBSCO Publishing). **Indexed:** AEA, AbHyg, AgBio, AgrForAb, BIOSIS Prev, BioCN&I, BioDAb, BiolAb, CIN, CPA, ChemAb, ChemTitl, DSA, EngInd, FCA, FPA, FS&TA, ForAb, GEOBASE, HerbAb, HortAb, I&DA, MaizeAb, NemAb, NutrAb, OrnHort, PBA, PGegResA, PGrRegA, PHN&I, PotatoAb, PoultAb, RA&MP, RDA, RPP, RRTA, RevApplEntom, RiceAb, S&F, SIA, SeedAb, SoyAb, TriticAb, WAE&RSA, WTA, WeedAb. —BLDSC (9072.466500), CASDDS, IE, ingenta, Linda Hall. **Published by:** Scientific and Technical Research Council of Turkey - TUBITAK/Turkiye Bilimsel ve Teknik Arastirma Kurumu, Ataturk Bulvari No. 221, Kavaklidere, Ankara, 06100, Turkey. TEL 90-312-468-5300, FAX 90-312-426-8073, bdym@tubitak.gov.tr, http://journals.tubitak.gov.tr/agriculture/index.php, http://www.tubitak.gov.tr. Ed. Ismail Cakmak.

630   TKM   ISSN 0868-7560
TURKMENISTANYN OBA KHOZHALYGY. Text in Turkmen. m. USD 149 in United States. **Published by:** Ministry of Agriculture, Ul Azadi 63, Ashgabat, 744004, Turkmenistan. TEL 3632-351938. **US dist. addr.:** East View Information Services, 3020 Harbor Ln. N., Minneapolis, MN 55447. TEL 612-550-0961.

630   POL
TYGODNIK ROLNIKOW - OBSERWATOR. Text in Polish. 1990. w. **Published by:** Fundacja Prasowa Solidarnosci, Al Jerozolimskie 125-127, Warsaw, 00017, Poland. TEL 48-22-217419, FAX 48-22-6285727. Ed. Tadeusz Karolak. Circ: 50,000.

TYGODNIK ROLNIKOW - SOLIDARNOSC. see *LABOR UNIONS*

630 658.5   FIN   ISSN 0782-6818
CODEN: TYMEED
TYOTEHOSEURAN METSATIEDOTE. Text in Finnish. 1960. irreg., latest vol.680, 2004. price varies. **Former titles** (until 1986): Tyotehoseuran Metsatiedotus (0358-8955); (until 1980): Metsatiedotus - Tyotehoseura (0355-2500); (until 1976): Tyotehoseuran Metsatiedotus. Tehokortisto (0355-0753) **Indexed:** AgrForAb, FPA, ForAb, I&DA, INIS AtomInd, S&F, WAE&RSA. **Published by:** TTS Institute (Tyotehoseura)/Work Efficiency Institute, Melkonkatu 16 A, PO Box 28, Helsinki, 00211, Finland. TEL 358-9-29041200, FAX 358-8-6922084, tts@tts.fi, http://www.tts.fi/tts/julkaisut/index.html.

630   IND   ISSN 0067-3471
U A S EXTENSION SERIES. Text in English. 1967. irreg., latest vol.14, 1985. reprint service avail. from PQC,ISI. **Document type:** *Academic/Scholarly.* **Related titles:** Microform ed.: (from PQC). **Published by:** University of Agricultural Sciences Bangalore, Communication Centre, Hebbal, Bangalore, Karnataka 560 024, India. Ed. B S Siddaramiah. Circ: 500.

630   IND   ISSN 0067-348X
U A S MISCELLANEOUS SERIES. Text in English. 1965. irreg., latest vol.39, 1988. price varies. reprint service avail. from PQC,ISI. **Document type:** *Academic/Scholarly.* **Related titles:** Microform ed.: (from PQC). **Published by:** University of Agricultural Sciences Bangalore, Communication Centre, Hebbal, Bangalore, Karnataka 560 024, India. Ed. K R Gapanathy. Circ: 500.

630   CHE   ISSN 1420-5025
U F A - REVUE; the magazine of Swiss agriculture. Text in German. 1958. m. adv. bk.rev. 64 p./no. 3 cols./p.; **Document type:** *Magazine, Trade.* **Description:** Provides Switzerland's farmers with timely, pertinent agriculture and management information to help them maximize their profits. **Former titles** (until 1976): Rundschau U F A (1421-4555); (until 1971): U F A - S E G - Rundschau (1421-4547) **Related titles:** French ed.: Revue U F A. ISSN 1420-5106. 1970. **Published by:** Fenaco Landi-Medien, Postfach 344, Winterthur, 8401, Switzerland. TEL 41-52-2642724, FAX 41-52-2132161, info@ufarevue.ch. Ed. Roman Engeler. R&P Hans Peter Kurzen. adv.: B&W page CHF 7,075, color page CHF 8,575; trim 192 x 256. Circ: 94,251.

U K IRRIGATION. see *WATER RESOURCES*

630.8   USA   ISSN 0092-1785
S21.R44   CODEN: XNRCAT
U.S. AGRICULTURAL RESEARCH SERVICE. A R S - N C. (Agricultural Research Service. North Central Region) Text in English. 1972. irreg., latest vol.20, 1975. illus. **Indexed:** BiolAb. —CISTI.

Published by: U.S. Department of Agriculture, Agricultural Research Service, North Central Region, 1815 N University St, Peoria, IL 61604-3999.

630 USA
U S D A NEWS. (U.S. Department of Agriculture) Text in English. m. **Document type:** *Government.*
Related titles: Online - full text ed.
Published by: U.S. Department of Agriculture, Office of Communications, Whitten Bldg, Rm 440 A, 1400 Independence Ave, S W, Washington, DC 20250-1300. ron.hall@usda.gov, http://www.usda.gov/news/pubs/newslett/cover.htm. Ed. Ron Hall.

630 USA ISSN 0065-4612
CODEN: XAAHA4
U.S. DEPARTMENT OF AGRICULTURE. AGRICULTURE HANDBOOK. Text in English. 1949. irreg., latest vol.726, 2004. price varies. **Document type:** *Government.*
Indexed: ABIPC, AEA, Agr, BioCN&I, BiolAb, CPA, CTFA, FCA, FPA, ForAb, HortAb, MaizeAb, NemAb, PBA, PGegResA, ProtozoAb, RM&VM, RPP, RRTA, RevApplEntom, S&F, SeedAb, TOSA, TriticAb, WAE&RSA, WeedAb, ZooRec.
—BLDSC (0760.750000), CISTI.
Published by: U.S. Department of Agriculture, Office of Public Affairs, 14th St & Independence Ave, S W, Washington, DC 20250-1300. TEL 202-720-2791, http://www.nal.usda.gov/ref/USDApubs/agbandbk.htm. **Subscr. to:** U.S. Government Printing Office, Superintendent of Documents, PO Box 371954, Pittsburgh, PA 15250-7954. TEL 202-512-1800, FAX 202-512-2250, orders@gpo.gov, http://www.access.gpo.gov.

630.82 USA ISSN 0065-4639
S21 CODEN: XAAIA7
U.S. DEPARTMENT OF AGRICULTURE. AGRICULTURE INFORMATION BULLETIN. Text in English. 1949. irreg. **Document type:** *Bulletin, Government.*
Related titles: Microfiche ed.: (from PQC).
Indexed: AEA, BioDAb, BiolAb, CTFA, DSA, FPA, ForAb, I&DA, MaizeAb, RRTA, RiceAb, S&F, WAE&RSA.
—CISTI.
Published by: U.S. Department of Agriculture, Office of Public Affairs, 14th St & Independence Ave, S W, Washington, DC 20250-1300. TEL 202-720-2791.

630 USA
U S DEPARTMENT OF AGRICULTURE. AGRICULTURE RESEARCH SERVICE QUARTERLY REPORT. Text in English. q.
Media: Online - full content.
Published by: U.S. Department of Agriculture, Economic Research Service, 1800 M St, N W, Rm 3100, Washington, DC 20036. TEL 202-694-5050, ersinfo@ers.usda.gov, http://www.ers.usda.gov/.

U.S. DEPARTMENT OF AGRICULTURE. ANIMAL AND PLANT HEALTH INSPECTION SERVICE. COOPERATIVE STATE-FEDERAL BRUCELLOSIS ERADICATION PROGRAM: STATISTICAL TABLES. see *AGRICULTURE—Abstracting, Bibliographies, Statistics*

630 351 USA
U.S. DEPARTMENT OF AGRICULTURE. BOARD OF CONTRACT APPEALS. ANNUAL REPORT. Text in English. 1996. a. **Document type:** *Government.*
Related titles: Online - full content ed.
Published by: U.S. Department of Agriculture, Board of Contract Appeals, 2916 S Bldg., Washington, DC 20250-0601. TEL 202-720-7023, FAX 202-720-3059, elaine.hillard@usda.gov, http://www.usda.gov/bca/rpt.html, http://www.usda.gov/bca/index.html.

U.S. DEPARTMENT OF AGRICULTURE. NATIONAL AGRICULTURAL STATISTICS SERVICE. AGRICULTURAL STATISTICS. see *AGRICULTURE—Abstracting, Bibliographies, Statistics*

U.S. DEPARTMENT OF AGRICULTURE. NATIONAL AGRICULTURAL STATISTICS SERVICE. COLD STORAGE. see *AGRICULTURE—Abstracting, Bibliographies, Statistics*

U.S. DEPARTMENT OF AGRICULTURE. NATIONAL AGRICULTURAL STATISTICS SERVICE. FARM NUMBERS AND LAND IN FARMS. see *AGRICULTURE—Abstracting, Bibliographies, Statistics*

U.S. DEPARTMENT OF AGRICULTURE. NATIONAL AGRICULTURAL STATISTICS SERVICE. HONEY. see *AGRICULTURE—Abstracting, Bibliographies, Statistics*

630 USA ISSN 0082-9803
S21
U.S. DEPARTMENT OF AGRICULTURE. REPORT OF THE SECRETARY OF AGRICULTURE. Key Title: Report of the Secretary of Agriculture. Text in English. 1862. a. free. **Document type:** *Government.*
—CISTI.
Published by: U.S. Department of Agriculture, Office of Public Affairs, 14th St & Independence Ave, S W, Washington, DC 20250-1300. TEL 202-720-2791.

630 USA ISSN 0742-9487
HD1491.U5
U.S. DEPARTMENT OF AGRICULTURE. RURAL BUSINESS - COOPERATIVE SERVICE. COOPERATIVE INFORMATION REPORTS. Text in English. 1977. irreg. price varies. **Document type:** *Government.*
Supersedes: U.S. Department of Agriculture. Farmer Cooperative Service. Information (Series) (0082-9765)
Published by: U.S. Department of Agriculture, Rural Business - Cooperative Service, Stop 3250, Washington, DC 20250-3250. TEL 202-720-7558, FAX 202-720-4641.

U.S. DEPARTMENT OF AGRICULTURE. RURAL BUSINESS - COOPERATIVE SERVICE. COOPERATIVE STATISTICS. see *AGRICULTURE—Abstracting, Bibliographies, Statistics*

630 658 USA
U.S. DEPARTMENT OF AGRICULTURE. RURAL BUSINESS - COOPERATIVE SERVICE. SERVICE REPORT. Text in English. irreg. price varies. **Document type:** *Monographic series, Government.* **Description:** Discusses various issues in managing farm cooperatives.
Formerly: U.S. Department of Agriculture. Rural Business - Cooperative Development Service. Service Report.
Published by: U.S. Department of Agriculture, Rural Business - Cooperative Service, Stop 3250, Washington, DC 20250-3250. TEL 202-720-6483, FAX 202-720-4641.

630 USA ISSN 1056-9685
U.S. DEPARTMENT OF AGRICULTURE. RURAL INFORMATION CENTER. PUBLICATION SERIES. Text in English. 1987. irreg. **Document type:** *Monographic series.*
Indexed: Agr.
—CISTI.
Published by: U.S. Department of Agriculture, Rural Information Center, National Agricultural Library, 10301 Baltimore Ave., Rm. 304, Beltsville, MD 20705-2351. TEL 800-633-7701, FAX 301-504-5181, ric@nal.usda.gov, http://www.nal.usda.gov/ric/ricpubs/ricpubs.htm.

630 USA ISSN 0082-9811
S21 CODEN: XATBAD
U.S. DEPARTMENT OF AGRICULTURE. TECHNICAL BULLETIN. Text in English. 1927. irreg., latest no.1911, 2004. price varies. **Document type:** *Bulletin, Government.*
Related titles: Microfiche ed.: (from PMC, PQC).
Indexed: AEA, AnBrAb, BioCN&I, BiolAb, DSA, FCA, FPA, ForAb, HerbAb, HortAb, MaizeAb, NutrAb, PBA, PGegResA, PotatoAb, RDA, RPP, RefZh, RevApplEntom, RiceAb, S&F, SIA, SeedAb, SoyAb, TriticAb, WAE&RSA, WeedAb, ZooRec.
—BLDSC (8641.000000), CASDDS, CISTI.
Published by: U.S. Department of Agriculture, Office of Public Affairs, 14th St & Independence Ave, S W, Washington, DC 20250-1300. TEL 202-720-2791, http://www.nal.usda.gov/ref/USDApubs/tb.htm.

630.58 USA ISSN 0886-7690
S21 CODEN: YAXAA7
U.S. DEPARTMENT OF AGRICULTURE. THE YEARBOOK OF AGRICULTURE. Text in English. 1894. a. price varies. **Document type:** *Government.*
Former titles (until 1980): U.S. Department of Agriculture. Yearbook; (until 1979): U.S. Department of Agriculture. Yearbook of Agriculture (0084-3628)
Related titles: Microfiche ed.: (from PQC).
Indexed: BIOSIS Prev, BiolAb, NutrAb, PBA.
—CISTI.
Published by: U.S. Department of Agriculture, Office of Public Affairs, 14th St & Independence Ave, S W, Washington, DC 20250-1300. TEL 202-720-2791.

630 USA ISSN 0041-7637
U S FARM NEWS✶. Text in English. 1917. bi-m. USD 5. bk.rev. 8 p./no. 3 cols./p.; back issues avail. **Document type:** *Trade.*
Indexed: AltPI.
Published by: U S Farmers Association, W 2561 Sunset Dr, Campbellsport, WI 53010. Ed. Bill Gudex. Circ: 2,500.

U.S. FOREIGN AGRICULTURAL TRADE AND AGRICULTURAL TRADE UPDATES STATISTICAL REPORT. see *AGRICULTURE—Abstracting, Bibliographies, Statistics*

630 PHL
➤ **U S M R & D JOURNAL.** (University of Southern Mindanao Research and Development) Text in English. 1990. 2/yr. PHP 125, USD 25 to individuals; PHP 225, USD 45 to institutions. abstr.; bibl.; charts; illus.; stat. back issues avail. **Document type:** *Journal, Academic/Scholarly.* **Description:** Contains original R&D in the fields of agricultural education and extension, agronomy, animal science, entomology, farming system, horticulture, plant breeding and genetics, plant pathology and soil science.
Former titles: U S M C A Research Journal (0117-0155); (until 1990): U S M Research Journal; (until vol.7, no.2, 1977): M I T Research Journal (0302-7937)
Indexed: FS&TA, IPP.
Published by: University of Southern Mindanao, College of Agriculture, Kabacan, North Cotabato 9407, Philippines. usm@weblingcom, ntangonan@hotmail.com. Ed. Naomi G Tangonan. Circ: 500.

630 DEU ISSN 0303-6340
CODEN: UETIDW
UEBERSICHTEN ZUR TIERERNAEHRUNG. Text in German. 1973. 2/yr. EUR 78; EUR 41 newsstand/cover (effective 2004). bk.rev. back issues avail. **Document type:** *Journal, Academic/Scholarly.*
Indexed: AgBio, AnBrAb, ChemAb, ChemTitl, DSA, FS&TA, HerbAb, IndVet, NutrAb, PBA, PN&I, PoultAb, RM&VM, RRTA, RefZh, SIA, SoyAb, TriticAb, VetBull.
—BLDSC (9079.603000), CASDDS, IE, Infotrieve, ingenta. **CCC.**
Published by: D L G Verlags GmbH, Eschborner Landstr 122, Frankfurt Am Main, 60489, Germany. TEL 49-69-247880, FAX 49-69-24788480, dlg-verlag@dlg-frankfurt.de, http://www.dlg-verlag.de. Ed. J. Kamphues. Circ: 400 (paid).

630 TZA ISSN 0856-0838
UKULIMA WA KISASA/MODERN FARMING; uk. kisasa. Text in Swahili. 1955. bi-m. TZS 200, USD 6; TZS 6 newsstand/cover (effective 2001). adv. charts; illus. back issues avail. **Document type:** *Government.* **Description:** Gives advice on agricultural practic es. Provides forecasts on crop prices along with availability of materials necessary to the industry. Includes coverage of policies affecting the agricultural industry.
Published by: Ministry of Agriculture, Farmers Education & Publicity Section, PO Box 2308, Dar Es Salaam, Tanzania. TEL 255-51-116496, FAX 255-51-122923, TELEX 116496 KI, fepu@twiga.com. Ed., R&P Happiness Mlaki. Adv. contact Jumanne Mnyau. B&W page TZS 160,000, color page TZS 240,000; trim 20.5 x 29. Circ: 35,000.

630 GBR
ULSTER FARMER. Text in English. 1900. w. **Document type:** *Newspaper.*
Published by: Observer Newspapers Ltd., Irish St, Dungannon, N Ireland BT70 1DD, United Kingdom. TEL 22557. Ed. D J Mallon.

631 RWA
UMUHINZI - MWOROZI. Text in Afrikaans. 1975. m. adv.
Published by: (Rwanda. Ministere de l'Agriculture, de l'Elevage et des Forets), O C I R, BP 104, Kigali - Gikondo, Rwanda. Ed. William Mwizerwa. Circ: 1,500.

630 DEU ISSN 0934-4632
UNABHAENGIGE BAUERNSTIMME; eine Zeitung von Baeuerinnen und Bauern. Text in German. 1976. m. EUR 36 (effective 2005). adv. bk.rev. back issues avail. **Document type:** *Newspaper, Trade.*
Published by: (Arbeitsgemeinschaft Baeuerliche Landwirtschaft-Bauernblatt e.V.), Bauernblatt Verlags GmbH, Bahnhofstr 31, Hamm, 59065, Germany. TEL 49-2381-492220, FAX 49-2381-492221, redaktion@bauernstimme.de, verlag@bauernstimme.de, http://www.bauernstimme.de. Ed. Mute Schimpf. Circ: 6,000.

630 FRA ISSN 0244-8459
L'UNION AGRICOLE. Text in French. 1946. w.
Formerly (until 1980): Union Syndicale Agricole (0247-7009)
Published by: Union Syndicale Agricole, Cite de l'Agriculture, B.P. 10, Bois-Guillaume, Cedex 76231, France. TEL 35-60-21-60, FAX 35-60-37-98. Ed. Daniel Cadet. Circ: 12,114.

630 FRA
UNION AGRICOLE DE LA HAUTE-VIENNE. Text in French. w.
Published by: Union Agricole de la, 32 av. du General Leclerc, Limoges, Cedex 87065, France. TEL 55-79-89-60, FAX 55-79-15-99. Ed. Albert Robert. Circ: 7,670.

630 CHE
UNION DES PRODUCTEURS SUISSES. JOURNAL. Text in French. 18/yr.
Published by: Union des Producteurs Suisses, Le Sasselet, Lignieres, 2523, Switzerland. TEL 38511953, FAX 218411621. Ed. Fernand Cuche. Circ: 3,000.

630 CAN ISSN 0041-6878
UNION FARMER. Text in English. 1950. q. CND 25 to individuals; CND 35 to institutions. adv. bk.rev. charts; illus. **Document type:** *Trade.*
—CISTI.
Published by: National Farmers Union, 2717 Wentz Ave, Saskatoon, SK S7K 4B6, Canada. TEL 306-652-9465, FAX 306-664-6226, nfu@sk.sympatico.ca. Ed. Helen Forsey. Adv. contact Joan Lange. Circ: 5,000.

UNION HERALD. see *LABOR UNIONS*

630 FRA
UNION NATIONALE DU COMMERCE DE GROS EN FRUITS ET LEGUMES. BULLETIN. Text in French. bi-m. **Document type:** *Bulletin, Trade.*
Published by: Union Nationale du Commerce de Gros en Fruits et Legumes, 3 rue de la Corderie, Centra 356, Rungis, Cedex 94596, France. TEL 6864354, TELEX 202011.

630 FRA ISSN 1141-0175
UNION PAYSANNE DE LA CORREZE. Text in French. 24/yr.
Published by: Union Paysanne de la, 36 av. du Generale de Gaulle, Tulle, 19000, France. TEL 16-55-26-71-00. Ed. Henri Demontjean. Circ: 8,500.

▼ *new title* ➤ *refereed* ✶ *unverified* ♦ *full entry avail.*

A

630 SWZ ISSN 1021-0873
S338.S9
UNISWA JOURNAL OF AGRICULTURE. Text in English. 1992. a. SZL 30, USD 10. bk.rev. **Document type:** *Academic/Scholarly.* **Description:** Serves as a forum for agricultural development research in the SADCC region. Publishes research papers, case studies, review articles and essays as well as first hand experiences of interest to researchers.
Related titles: Online - full text ed.: (from International Network for the Availability of Scientific Publications, African Journals Online).
—BLDSC (9090.785401).
Published by: University of Swaziland, Faculty of Agriculture, Office of the Dean, Luyengo Campus, Luyengo, Swaziland. TEL 268-83021, FAX 268-83441, TELEX 2087 WD. Ed. Stephen Kayode Subair. Circ: 300.

UNITED STATES SENATE. COMMITTEE ON AGRICULTURE, NUTRITION AND FORESTRY. LEGISLATIVE CALENDAR. see *PUBLIC ADMINISTRATION*

630 VEN ISSN 0041-8285
S211 CODEN: RFAMAM
➤ **UNIVERSIDAD CENTRAL DE VENEZUELA. FACULTAD DE AGRONOMIA. REVISTA.** Text mainly in Spanish; Text occasionally in English, Portuguese; Summaries in English, Portuguese. 1952. q. USD 25; or exchange basis. bibl.; charts; illus.; stat. index. **Document type:** *Academic/Scholarly.* **Description:** Publishes original articles on tropical agriculture, including animal and plant production, food technology and agricultural economics.
Indexed: AEA, ATA, Agrind, BiolAb, CPA, ChemAb, ESPM, FCA, FS&TA, HerbAb, HortAb, IAALC, MBA, NutrAb, OrnHort, PBA, PGrRegA, PHN&I, RPP, RevApplEntom, S&F, SWRA, SeedAb, SoyAb, TriticAb, WeedAb, ZooRec.
—CISTI.
Published by: Universidad Central de Venezuela, Facultad de Agronomia, Apdo. 4579, Maracay, Aragua 2101, Venezuela. TEL 58-43-462212. Ed. Gustavo Trujillo P. Circ: 1,000.

630 VEN ISSN 0376-0030
UNIVERSIDAD CENTRAL DE VENEZUELA. FACULTAD DE AGRONOMIA. REVISTA ALCANCE. Text in Spanish; Summaries in English. 1956. irreg., latest vol.40, 1991. USD 25; or exchange basis. abstr.; bibl.; illus. **Document type:** *Academic/Scholarly.*
Indexed: BibAg, BiolAb, ZooRec.
—CISTI.
Published by: Universidad Central de Venezuela, Facultad de Agronomia, Apdo. 4579, Maracay, Aragua 2101, Venezuela. Ed. Gustavo Trujillo P. Circ: 1,500.

630 URY ISSN 0077-1260
BFMUAW
UNIVERSIDAD DE LA REPUBLICA. FACULTAD DE AGRONOMIA. BOLETIN. Text in Spanish. 1953. irreg. per issue exchange basis. **Document type:** *Bulletin, Academic/Scholarly.*
Indexed: BioCN&I, BiolAb, ChemAb, DSA, ForAb, HortAb, I&DA, WeedAb.
Published by: Universidad de la Republica, Facultad de Agronomia, Av. G Garzon, 780, Montevideo, 12908, Uruguay. Circ: 1,000.

630 ARG ISSN 0370-4661
S15
UNIVERSIDAD NACIONAL DE CUYO. FACULTAD DE CIENCIAS AGRARIAS. REVISTA. Key Title: Revista de la Facultad de Ciencias Agrarias. Universidad Nacional de Cuyo. Text in Spanish. 1949. s-a. **Document type:** *Journal, Academic/Scholarly.*
Indexed: AEA, AgBio, AgrForAb, AnBrAb, BIOSIS Prev, BioCN&I, BiolAb, CPA, FCA, FPA, ForAb, HerbAb, HortAb, I&DA, INIS AtomInd, IndVet, MaizeAb, NemAb, NutrAb, OrnHort, PBA, PGegResA, PGrRegA, PHN&I, PotatoAb, RA&MP, RDA, RPP, S&F, SeedAb, VITIS, VetBull, WAE&RSA, WeedAb.
—CINDOC, CISTI.
Published by: Universidad Nacional de Cuyo, Facultad de Ciencias Agrarias, Almirante Brown, 500, Casilla No. 7, Chacras de Coria, Mendoza, 5528, Argentina. TEL 54-261-4960004, ccea@fca.unc.edu.ar, http://www.fca.uncu.edu.ar/. Ed. Jorge Osvaldo Milone.

630 ARG ISSN 0041-8676
S15
➤ **UNIVERSIDAD NACIONAL DE LA PLATA. FACULTAD DE AGRONOMIA. REVISTA.** Text and summaries in English, Spanish. 1895. s-a. USD 30. adv. bk.rev. bibl.; charts; illus. index. reprints avail. **Document type:** *Academic/Scholarly.* **Description:** Covers general and specific topics related to agriculture and forestry.
Indexed: AgBio, AgrForAb, BioCN&I, BiolAb, CPA, FCA, FPA, ForAb, HerbAb, HortAb, I&DA, MaizeAb, NutrAb, OrnHort, PBA, PGegResA, PGrRegA, PotatoAb, ProtozoAb, RPP, RevApplEntom, S&F, SeedAb, SoyAb, TriticAb, WeedAb, ZooRec.
—BLDSC (7808.800000), CISTI.
Published by: Universidad Nacional de la Plata, Facultad de Agronomia, C.C. 31, Calle 60, Y 119, La Plata, Buenos Aires 1900, Argentina. TEL 54-21-838168, FAX 54-21-233698, infive@isis.unlp.edu.ar. Ed. Edgardo R Montaldi. R&P Daniel Caldiz. Circ: 1,000.

630 BRA ISSN 1413-2591
UNIVERSIDADE DO VALE DO ITAJAI. ALCANCE. Text in Portuguese. 1994. s-a.
Indexed: PSA, SSA, SociolAb, ZooRec.
Published by: Universidade do Vale do Itajai, Central de Atendimento, Santa Catarina, Brazil. TEL 47-261-1300, http://www.univali.br/.

630 BRA ISSN 0084-8646
UNIVERSIDADE FEDERAL DO CEARA. ESCOLA DE AGRONOMIA. DEPARTAMENTO DE FITOTECNIA. RELATORIA TECNICO✱. Text in Portuguese. irreg. free.
Published by: Universidade Federal do Ceara, Escola de Agronomia, Departamento de Fitotecnia, Centro, Caixa Postal 354, Fortaleza, CE 60001-970, Brazil.

630 ITA ISSN 0540-049X
CODEN: AFAGAL
UNIVERSITA CATTOLICA DEL SACRO CUORE. FACOLTA DI AGRARIA. ANNALI. Variant title: Annali della Facolta di Agraria. Text in Italian; Summaries in English, French, Italian. 1955. s-a. adv. abstr. index. **Document type:** *Academic/Scholarly.* **Description:** Publishes original research articles in areas of agronomy, agrarian chemistry and the agrarian industry.
Indexed: AEA, AnBrAb, BiolAb, CIN, CPA, ChemAb, ChemTitl, DSA, ExcerpMed, FCA, FS&TA, HerbAb, HortAb, MLA-IB, NutrAb, PGrRegA, PotatoAb, RRTA, S&F, TriticAb, VITIS, WAE&RSA.
—CASDDS, CISTI. **CCC.**
Published by: (Universita Cattolica del Sacro Cuore, Universita Cattolica del Sacro Cuore, Facolta di Agraria), Vita e Pensiero, Largo Gemelli 1, Milan, 20123, Italy. TEL 39-2-72342370, FAX 39-2-72342974, redazione.vp@mi.unicatt.it. Ed. Carlo Lorenzoni. Circ: 400.

630 ITA ISSN 0365-799X
CODEN: AUNPAE
UNIVERSITA DEGLI STUDI DI NAPOLI. FACOLTA DI SCIENZE AGRARIE. ANNALI. Text in Italian; Summaries in English. 1966. a. charts; illus.; maps; stat. **Document type:** *Academic/Scholarly.* **Description:** Research papers on the agrarian sciences.
Indexed: AEA, AgBio, BioCN&I, CPA, DSA, ForAb, HortAb, I&DA, MaizeAb, NutrAb, PBA, PGegResA, PGrRegA, PHN&I, PotatoAb, RM&VM, RPP, S&F, SFA, SIA, SeedAb, WAE&RSA, WildRev, ZooRec.
—BLDSC (1007.000000), CASDDS, CISTI, Linda Hall.
Published by: Universita degli Studi di Napoli, Facolta di Scienze Agrarie, Portici, NA 80055, Italy. Circ: 500.

630 ITA ISSN 0374-4981
CODEN: AASPAZ
UNIVERSITA DEGLI STUDI DI PERUGIA. FACOLTA DI AGRARIA. ANNALI. Text in Multiple languages. 1942. a.
Indexed: AEA, AgBio, AnBrAb, BIOSIS Prev, BiolAb, CPA, DSA, FCA, FS&TA, ForAb, HerbAb, HortAb, I&DA, NutrAb, PBA, PGegResA, PHN&I, PN&I, PotatoAb, RRTA, RefZh, S&F, TriticAb, VITIS, WAE&RSA.
Published by: Universita degli Studi di Perugia, Facolta di Agraria, Piazza dell'Universita 1, Perugia, 06100, Italy. FAX 39-075-5852067, http://web.unipg.it.

630 634.9 AUT ISSN 0256-4246
UNIVERSITAET FUER BODENKULTUR IN WIEN. DISSERTATIONEN. Text in German. 1972. irreg., latest vol.45, 1996. price varies. **Document type:** *Academic/Scholarly.*
Formerly: Hochschule fuer Bodenkultur in Wien. Dissertationen
Published by: (Universitaet fuer Bodenkultur in Wien), Oesterreichischer Kunst- und Kulturverlag, Postfach 17, Vienna, W 1016, Austria.

630 DEU ISSN 0075-4609
S231 CODEN: ELFLDE
UNIVERSITAET GIESSEN. ERGEBNISSE LANDWIRTSCHAFTLICHER FORSCHUNG. Text in German. 1956. irreg. **Document type:** *Monographic series, Academic/Scholarly.*
Indexed: AgBio, AnBrAb, FCA, HortAb, NutrAb, PN&I, PotatoAb, RPP, RevApplEntom, S&F, TriticAb, WAE&RSA.
—CASDDS.
Published by: Justus-Liebig-Universitaet Giessen, Fachbereich 09 - Agrarwissenschaften, Oekotrophologie und Umweltmanagement, Bismarckstr 24, Giessen, 35390, Germany. TEL 49-641-9937000, FAX 49-641-9939009, claus.m.brodersen@agrar.uni-giessen.de, http://www.uni-giessen.de/fbr09/index.php. Ed. Claus Brodersen. Circ: 1,200.

630 ROM ISSN 1223-494X
UNIVERSITATEA AGRONOMICA ION IONESCU DE LA BRAD. LUCRARI STIINTIFICE. SERIA AGRONOMIE. Text in Romanian. 1957. a.
Formerly: Institutul Agronomic Ion Ionescu de la Brad. Lucrari Stiintifice. Seria Agronomie (0379-8364); Supersedes in part: Institutul Agronomic Ion Ionescu de la Brad. Lucrari Stiintifice. Seria Agronomie-Horticultura (0075-3505)
Indexed: BiolAb, CPA, ChemAb, FCA, HerbAb, HortAb, MaizeAb, PBA, PoultAb, S&F, TOSA, VITIS.
—CISTI.
Published by: Universitatea Agronomica "Ion Ionescu de la Brad", Al. M. Sadoveanu 3, Jassy, Romania.

630 635 ROM ISSN 1454-2382
CODEN: BIAAD4
UNIVERSITATEA DE STIINTE AGRICOLE SI MEDICINA VETERINARA CLUJ-NAPOCA. BULETINUL. SERIA AGRICULTURA SI HORTICULTURA. Text in Romanian; Summaries in English. 1975. a. ROL 35, USD 10. back issues avail.
Former titles (until 1995): Universitatea de Stiinte Agricole Cluj-Napoca. Buletinul. Seria Agricultura si Horticultura (1221-3608); (until 1992): Institutul Agronomic Cluj-Napoca. Buletinul. Seria Agricultura si Horticultura (1220-8450); (until 1990): Institutul Agronomic Cluj-Napoca. Buletinul. Seria Agricultura (0557-465X); Supersedes in part (in 1977): Institutul Agronomic Cluj-Napoca. Buletinul (0378-0554)
Indexed: AEA, BiolAb, FCA, HortAb, MaizeAb, OrnHort, PotatoAb, RevApplEntom, S&F, S&MA, SeedAb, SoyAb, TriticAb, VITIS, WeedAb.
—CASDDS, CISTI.
Published by: Universitatea de Stiinte Agricole si Medicina Veterinara Cluj-Napoca, Str. Manastur 3, Cluj-Napoca, 3400, Romania. Ed. Leon Muntean. Circ: 175.

UNIVERSITATEA DIN CRAIOVA. ANALE. SERIA: BIOLOGIE, AGRONOMIE, HORTICULTURA. see *BIOLOGY*

630 IND ISSN 0067-3455
UNIVERSITY OF AGRICULTURAL SCIENCES, BANGALORE. ANNUAL REPORT. Text in English. 1965. a. INR 50. reprint service avail. from PQC,ISI. **Document type:** *Academic/Scholarly.*
Related titles: Microform ed.: (from PQC).
Indexed: BiolAb, FCA, HerbAb, HortAb.
—CISTI.
Published by: University of Agricultural Sciences Bangalore, Communication Centre, Hebbal, Bangalore, Karnataka 560 024, India. Ed. B S Siddaramiah. Circ: 1,000.

630 IND
UNIVERSITY OF AGRICULTURAL SCIENCES, BANGALORE. COLLABORATIVE SERIES. Text in English. 1968. irreg., latest vol.3, 1976. price varies. reprint service avail. from PQC,ISI. **Document type:** *Academic/Scholarly.*
Published by: University of Agricultural Sciences Bangalore, Communication Centre, Hebbal, Bangalore, Karnataka 560 024, India. Ed. H R Gapanathy.

630 IND
UNIVERSITY OF AGRICULTURAL SCIENCES, BANGALORE. CURRENT RESEARCH. Text in English. 1971. m. USD 30. reprint service avail. from PQC,ISI. **Document type:** *Academic/Scholarly.*
Indexed: AEA, AgrForAb, BioCN&I, BioDAb, BiolAb, CPA, DSA, FCA, FS&TA, FaBeAb, ForAb, HerbAb, HortAb, I&DA, IndVet, MaizeAb, NutrAb, OrnHort, PBA, PGrRegA, PHN&I, PotatoAb, PoultAb, RA&MP, RDA, RPP, RevApplEntom, RiceAb, S&F, S&MA, SAA, SIA, SeedAb, SoyAb, TriticAb, VetBull, WAE&RSA, WeedAb.
Published by: University of Agricultural Sciences Bangalore, Communication Centre, Hebbal, Bangalore, Karnataka 560 024, India. Ed. B S Siddaramiah. Circ: 600.

630 IND
UNIVERSITY OF AGRICULTURAL SCIENCES, BANGALORE. EDUCATIONAL SERIES. Text in English. 1969. irreg., latest vol.9, 1987. price varies. reprint service avail. from PQC,ISI. **Document type:** *Academic/Scholarly.*
Indexed: REE&TA, WAE&RSA.
Published by: University of Agricultural Sciences Bangalore, Communication Centre, Hebbal, Bangalore, Karnataka 560 024, India. Ed. B S Siddaramiah.

630 IND
UNIVERSITY OF AGRICULTURAL SCIENCES, BANGALORE. INFORMATION SERIES. Text in English. irreg., latest vol.8, 1979. price varies. reprint service avail. from PQC,ISI. **Document type:** *Academic/Scholarly.*
Published by: University of Agricultural Sciences Bangalore, Communication Centre, Hebbal, Bangalore, Karnataka 560 024, India.

630 IND
UNIVERSITY OF AGRICULTURAL SCIENCES, BANGALORE. RESEARCH MONOGRAPH SERIES. Text in English. irreg., latest vol.4, 1978. price varies. reprint service avail. from PQC,ISI. **Document type:** *Monographic series, Academic/Scholarly.*
Published by: University of Agricultural Sciences Bangalore, Communication Centre, Hebbal, Bangalore, Karnataka 560 024, India. Ed. B S Siddaramiah.

630 IND
UNIVERSITY OF AGRICULTURAL SCIENCES, BANGALORE. RESEARCH REVIEW SERIES. Text in English. 1977. irreg., latest vol.8, 1988. price varies. reprint service avail. from PQC,ISI. **Document type:** *Academic/Scholarly.*
Published by: University of Agricultural Sciences Bangalore, Communication Centre, Hebbal, Bangalore, Karnataka 560 024, India. Circ: 500.

630 IND
UNIVERSITY OF AGRICULTURAL SCIENCES, BANGALORE. TECHNICAL INFORMATION SERIES. Text in Kannada. 1975. irreg., latest vol.6, 1989. price varies. reprint service avail. from PQC,ISI. **Document type:** *Academic/Scholarly.*
Published by: University of Agricultural Sciences Bangalore, Communication Centre, Hebbal, Bangalore, Karnataka 560 024, India.

630 IND
UNIVERSITY OF AGRICULTURAL SCIENCES, BANGALORE. TECHNICAL SERIES. Text in English. 1973. irreg., latest no.51, 1989. price varies. reprint service avail. from PQC,ISI. **Document type:** *Academic/Scholarly.*
Indexed: AgrForAb, BiolAb, DSA, FCA, HerbAb, HortAb, PotatoAb, RDA, RiceAb, S&MA, WAE&RSA.
Published by: University of Agricultural Sciences Bangalore, Communication Centre, Hebbal, Bangalore, Karnataka 560 024, India.

630 IND
UNIVERSITY OF AGRICULTURAL SCIENCES, BANGALORE. U A S TEXTBOOK SERIES. Text in English. 1979. irreg. reprint service avail. from PQC,ISI. **Document type:** *Academic/Scholarly.*
Published by: University of Agricultural Sciences Bangalore, Communication Centre, Hebbal, Bangalore, Karnataka 560 024, India. Ed. B S Siddaramiah.

630 636.089 TZA
UNIVERSITY OF DAR ES SALAAM. FACULTY OF AGRICULTURE, FORESTRY AND VETERINARY SCIENCE. ANNUAL RECORD OF RESEARCH. Text in English. 1979. a. USD 6. **Document type:** *Academic/Scholarly.*
Published by: Sokoine University of Agriculture, PO Box 3022, Mzumbe-morogoro, Tanzania. Ed. M Mgheni. Circ: 1,000.

630 USA
UNIVERSITY OF GEORGIA, COLLEGE OF AGRICULTURAL AND ENVIRONMENTAL SCIENCES, GEORGIA AGRICULTURAL EXPERIMENT STATIONS. RESEARCH REPORT. Text in English. irreg., latest vol.693, 2002.
Media: Online - full text.
Published by: University of Georgia, College of Agriculture Experiment Stations, Athens, GA 30602. http://extension.caes.uga.edu.

630 USA ISSN 0072-1271
UNIVERSITY OF GEORGIA. COLLEGE OF AGRICULTURE EXPERIMENT STATIONS. BULLETIN. Text in English. irreg. free. **Document type:** *Bulletin, Academic/Scholarly.*
Indexed: ExcerpMed.
—BLDSC (2787.420000), CISTI.
Published by: University of Georgia, College of Agriculture Experiment Stations, Athens, GA 30602. TEL 706-542-2157. Ed. Elinor Ruark. Circ: (controlled).

630 CAN
UNIVERSITY OF MANITOBA. FACULTY OF AGRICULTURAL AND FOOD SCIENCES. ANNUAL PROGRESS REVIEW. Text in English. 1954. a. free. **Document type:** *Academic/Scholarly.*
Former titles: University of Manitoba. Faculty of Agriculture. Annual Progress Review: Agricultural Research, Teaching and Extension (0832-266X); (until 1986): University of Manitoba. Faculty of Agriculture. Annual Progress Report: Agricultural Research, Teaching and Extension (0832-2651); (until 1982): University of Manitoba. Faculty of Agriculture. Annual Progress Report: Agricultural Research and Experimentation (0384-8884); (until 1959): University of Manitoba. Faculty of Agriculture. Progress Report on Agricultural Research (0076-4051)
—BLDSC (1092.834000), CISTI.
Published by: University of Manitoba, Faculty of Agricultural and Food Sciences, Winnipeg, MB R3T 2N2, Canada. TEL 204-474-9295, FAX 204-474-7525, TELEX 44370, c_jorgenson@umanitoba.ca, http://www.umanitoba.ca/afs/. R&P Crystal Jorgenson TEL 204-474-9435. Circ: 1,000; 1,000 (controlled).

630 USA ISSN 1042-2889
CODEN: RBUREB
UNIVERSITY OF NEBRASKA. AGRICULTURAL RESEARCH DIVISION. RESEARCH BULLETIN. Text in English. irreg. **Document type:** *Bulletin, Academic/Scholarly.*
Indexed: Agr.
Published by: University of Nebraska at Lincoln, Agricultural Research Division, Institute of Agriculture and Natural Resources, Lincoln, NE 68583-0918.

630 570 JPN ISSN 1344-848X
S19 CODEN: BSKBAM
UNIVERSITY OF OSAKA PREFECTURE. COLLEGE OF AGRICULTURE. SCIENTIFIC REPORT. Text in Multiple languages. 1951. a. per issue exchange basis. **Document type:** *Academic/Scholarly.*
Former titles (until 1999): University of Osaka Prefecture. Bulletin. Series B: Agriculture and Life Sciences (1342-3266); (until 1997): University of Osaka Prefecture. Series B Agriculture and Life Sciences Bulletin (1342-4548); (until 1993): University of Osaka Prefecture. Bulletin. Series B: Agriculture and Biology (0366-3353); (until 1953): Naniwa University. Bulletin. Series B: Agricultural and Natural Science (0474-7852)
Indexed: Agr, BiolAb, CIN, CPA, ChemAb, ChemTitl, FCA, HortAb, I&DA, IndVet, OrnHort, PBA, PGegResA, PGrRegA, PHN&I, PoultAb, RA&MP, RPP, RRTA, RevApplEntom, RiceAb, S&F, VetBull, WeedAb, ZooRec.
—BLDSC (8195.695000), CASDDS, CISTI.
Published by: University of Osaka Prefecture/Osaka-furitsu Daigaku, 1-1 Gakuen-cho, Sakai-shi, Osaka 593, Japan. TEL 0722-52-1161, FAX 0722-52-6798.

630 PRI ISSN 0163-8238
UNIVERSITY OF PUERTO RICO. AGRICULTURAL EXPERIMENT STATION. BULLETIN. Text and summaries in English, Spanish. 1911. irreg. price varies. back issues avail. **Document type:** *Bulletin, Academic/Scholarly.*
Indexed: BiolAb, RPP.
—CISTI.
Published by: University of Puerto Rico, Agricultural Experiment Station, PO Box 21360, Rio Piedras, 00927, Puerto Rico. TEL 787-767-9705, FAX 787-282-7982. Ed. Wanda I Lugo. Circ: 1,000.

630 PRI ISSN 0041-994X
S181 CODEN: JAUPA8
➤ **UNIVERSITY OF PUERTO RICO. JOURNAL OF AGRICULTURE.** Text and summaries in English, Spanish. 1917. q. USD 25 (effective 2002); or exchange basis. bibl.; illus. back issues avail.; reprint service avail. from PQC,ISI. **Document type:** *Journal, Academic/Scholarly.*
Related titles: Microform ed.: (from PQC).
Indexed: AEA, ASCA, AgBio, Agr, AgrForAb, AnBrAb, BioCN&I, BiolAb, CPA, ChemAb, CurCont, DBA, DSA, FCA, FS&TA, ForAb, HerbAb, HortAb, I&DA, IndVet, MaizeAb, NemAb, NutrAb, OrnHort, PBA, PGegResA, PGrRegA, PHN&I, PN&I, PotatoAb, PoultAb, ProtozoAb, RPP, RevApplEntom, RiceAb, S&F, S&MA, SCI, SFA, SIA, SeedAb, SoyAb, VetBull, WAE&RSA, WeedAb, WildRev, ZooRec.
—BLDSC (4925.000000), CASDDS, CISTI, IDS, IE, Ingenta, Linda Hall.
Published by: University of Puerto Rico, Agricultural Experiment Station, PO Box 21360, Rio Piedras, 00927, Puerto Rico. TEL 787-767-9705, FAX 787-282-7982. Ed. Wanda I Lugo. Circ: 750.

630 PHL
UNIVERSITY OF THE PHILIPPINES AT LOS BANOS. AGRARIAN REFORM INSTITUTE. OCCASIONAL PAPERS. Text in English. 1975. irreg. free. **Document type:** *Academic/Scholarly.*
Published by: University of the Philippines at Los Banos, Institute of Agrarian Studies, Laguna, 4031, Philippines. Ed. Honorio C Batangantang. Circ: 500.

630 JPN ISSN 0370-4246
S19 CODEN: RDNGBM
UNIVERSITY OF THE RYUKYUS. COLLEGE OF AGRICULTURE. SCIENCE BULLETIN/RYUKYU DAIGAKU NOGAKUBU GAKUJUTSU HOKOKU. Text in English, Japanese. 1954. a. free. **Document type:** *Bulletin, Academic/Scholarly.*
Indexed: AgrForAb, BiolAb, ChemAb, ChemTitl, FPA, ForAb, HerbAb, HortAb, IndVet, NutrAb, PBA, SIA, SeedAb, VetBull, WeedAb.
—CASDDS, CISTI, IE, Linda Hall.
Published by: University of the Ryukyus, College of Agriculture/Ryukyu Daigaku Nogakubu, 59 Senbaru, Nakagami-gun, Nishihara-cho, Okinawa-ken 903-0129, Japan. FAX 09889-5-2864. Circ: 400.

630 BIH ISSN 0033-8583
CODEN: RPFUB6
➤ **UNIVERZITET U SARAJEVU. POLJOPRIVREDNI FAKULTET. RADOVI**✱ ; works of the faculty of agriculture university of Sarajevo. Summaries in English, German. 1952. a., latest vol.43, no.47. USD 40 domestic (effective 1999). back issues avail. **Document type:** *Academic/Scholarly.*
Indexed: AnBrAb, ChemAb, DSA, FCA, FS&TA, HerbAb, HortAb, NutrAb, PBA, RASB, RRTA, S&F, SeedAb, WAE&RSA, WeedAb.
—BLDSC (7242.050000), CASDDS, CISTI.
Published by: Univerzitet u Sarajevu, Poljoprivredni Fakultet, Zmaj od Bosne 8, Sarajevo, 71000, Bosnia Herzegovina. TEL 387-653033. Ed. Taib Saric. Circ: 520.

630 IND
UNNAT KRISHI. Text in Hindi. bi-m. INR 12.
Published by: Ministry of Agriculture and Rural Development, Directorate of Extension, Krishi Vistar Bhawan, Dr. K.S. Krishnan Marg, Pusa, New Delhi, 110 012, India. TEL 603568. adv.: page INR 2,000; 210 x 270.

630 IND ISSN 0566-2540
UNNATKRISHI/PROGRESS IN AGRICULTURE. Text in Hindi. 1961. m. INR 5.50. adv. **Document type:** *Government.*
Published by: Ministry of Food & Agriculture, Farm Information Unit Directorate of Extension, R.K. Puram, New Delhi, 110 066, India. Ed. Vidyapati Jha. Circ: 20,000.

630 DEU
UNSER LAND (PASSAU). Text in German. s-a. adv. bk.rev.
Published by: Unser Land Verlags GmbH, Dr.-Hans-Kapfinger-Str 30, Passau, 94032, Germany. TEL 0851-502344, FAX 0851-502256.

THE UPRIGHT OSTRICH. see *BUSINESS AND ECONOMICS—Small Business*

630 AUS
URBAN AGRICULTURE ONLINE. Text in English. 2002 (May 20th). irreg. bk.rev. **Document type:** *Magazine, Academic/Scholarly.*
Media: Online - full content.
Published by: (Urban Agriculture Network (Western Pacific)), Fawer Pty. Ltd., PO Box 85, Mount Gravatt, QLD 4122, Australia. TEL 61-7-3349-1422, FAX 61-7-3343-8287, fawerpl@powerup.com.au. Ed., Pub. Geoff Wilson. R&P Mary Wilson.

UTAH AGRICULTURAL STATISTICS. see *AGRICULTURE—Abstracting, Bibliographies, Statistics*

630 USA ISSN 0042-1502
CODEN: UTSCBA
UTAH SCIENCE. Text in English. 1940. 2/yr. USD 35 for 2 yrs. foreign; free domestic (effective 2005). charts; illus.; stat. Index. reprints avail. **Document type:** *Magazine, Trade.*
Formerly (until 1967): Utah Farm and Home Science (0097-1588)
Indexed: AEA, ASFA, Agr, BiolAb, DSA, EPB, ESPM, FCA, FS&TA, HerbAb, IFP, IndVet, MaizeAb, NutrAb, PBA, PollutAb, RPP, SFA, SWRA, TriticAb, VetBull, WildRev, ZooRec.
—CISTI, Linda Hall.
Published by: Utah Agricultural Experiment Station, Utah State University, 4810 Old Main Hill, AGSC 225, Logan, UT 84322-4810. TEL 435-797-2206, FAX 435-797-3321, lynette@agx.usu.edu, http://www.agx.usu.edu. Ed. Lynette Harris. R&P Lynnette F Harris. Circ: 4,500 (free).

630 IND
UTAMA KHETI BARI✱ . Text in Panjabi. 1970. m. INR 12. adv. charts.
Address: B 1-23-A Hauz Khas, New Delhi, 110 016, India.

630 JPN ISSN 0566-4691
S539.J3 CODEN: UDNGAK
UTSUNOMIYA DAIGAKU NOGAKUBU GAKUJUTSU HOKOKU/UTSUNOMIYA UNIVERSITY. COLLEGE OF AGRICULTURE. BULLETIN. Text in Japanese. 1950. irreg. **Document type:** *Bulletin, Academic/Scholarly.*
Formed by the 1948 merger of: Utsunomiya Koto Norin Gakko Gakujutsu Hokoku, Dai-2-Shu: Norin Keizai; (1934-1948): Utsunomiya Koto Norin Gakko Gakujutsu Hokoku, Dai 1-Shu/Utsunomiya Agricultural College, Section A. Agricultural Sciences and Forestry. Bulletin (0566-4705); Which superseded in part: Utsunomiya Koto Norin Gakko Gakujutsu Hokoku
Indexed: AnBrAb, BIOSIS Prev, BioCN&I, BiolAb, CPA, DSA, ForAb, HerbAb, HortAb, IndVet, NutrAb, OrnHort, PBA, PGegResA, PoultAb, RDA, RRTA, S&F, TriticAb, WAE&RSA, WeedAb.
—CISTI.
Published by: Utsunomiya Daigaku Nogakubu/Utsunomiya University, Faculty of Agriculture, 350 Minemachi, Utsunomiya, Tochigi 321-8505 , Japan. info@env.mine.utsunomiya-u.ac.jp, http://agri.mine.utsunomiya-u.ac.jp/.

630 NOR ISSN 0808-7180
HD2011
UTSYN OVER NORSK LANDBRUK. Text in Norwegian. 1995. a. NOK 195 (effective 2004). **Description:** Status and trends in Norwegian Agriculture.
Supersedes in part (in 1995): N I L F - Rapport (0805-7028)
Related titles: English ed.: Norwegian Agriculture. ISSN 1501-4991.
Published by: Norsk Institutt for Landbruksoekonomisk Forskning (NILF)/Norwegian Agricultural Economics Research Institute (NILF), Schweigaards Gate 33B, Postboks 8024, Dep, Oslo, 0030, Norway. TEL 47-22-367200, FAX 47-22-367299, postmottak@nilf.no, http://www.nilf.no/.

630.2 DEU ISSN 0724-2344
V D L - JOURNAL. (Verband Deutscher Akademiker fur Landwirtschaft, Ernahrung und Landespflege) Text in German. 1950. 10/yr. EUR 52.20 domestic; EUR 58.80 foreign (effective 2003). adv. bk.rev. abstr.; charts; illus.; pat.; stat.; tr.mk. index. **Document type:** *Journal, Academic/Scholarly.*
Former titles: V D L - Nachrichten (0340-7810); Diplomlandwirt (0012-3129)
Related titles: Microfilm ed.

Indexed: RRTA, WAE&RSA.
Published by: (V D L Bundesverband, Berufsverband Agrar, Ernaehrung, Umwelt e.V.), Landwirtschaftsverlag GmbH, Huelsebrockstr 2, Muenster, 48165, Germany. TEL 49-2501-801-0, FAX 49-2501-801204, zentrale@lv-h.de, http://www.lv-h.de. Ed. Dieter Barth. adv.: B&W page EUR 1,568, color page EUR 2,587.20. Circ: 6,238.

VADOSE ZONE JOURNAL. see *ENVIRONMENTAL STUDIES*

630 USA
VALLEY FARMER. Text in English. 1929. w. USD 18 (effective 2001). adv. **Document type:** *Newspaper.* **Description:** Covers farm news and information; lists auctions.
Published by: Valley Tribune, 905 S Henry, Bay City, MI 48706. TEL 517-893-6507. Ed. Mark Schanhals. Pub., Adv. contact David Hebert. Circ: 1,650 (paid).

630 LTU ISSN 1021-4526
VALSTIECIU LAIKRASTIS. Text in Lithuanian. 1940. s-w. USD 140 (effective 2000). adv. **Document type:** *Newspaper, Consumer.* **Description:** Covers all aspects of agriculture, including forestry, social affairs, politics, history, advices, and public opinion. Newspaper is national and is read mostly by countryside people.
Related titles: Microfilm ed.: (from PQC).
Address: Laisves pr 60, Vilnius, 2000, Lithuania. TEL 370-2-421281, valst@takas.lt. Ed., R&P Jonas Svoba TEL 370-2-429942. Adv. contact Ona Baublyte. color 1/4 page USD 1,950, B&W page USD 1,150. Circ: 92,000.

VANUATU. STATISTICS OFFICE. REPORT OF THE AGRICULTURAL CENSUS. see *AGRICULTURE—Abstracting, Bibliographies, Statistics*

VANUATU. STATISTICS OFFICE. REPORT ON SMALL HOLDER AGRICULTURE SURVEY. see *AGRICULTURE—Abstracting, Bibliographies, Statistics*

630 RUS
VASHI SHEST' SOTOK. Text in Russian. 1991. 24/yr. USD 145 in United States. adv.
Address: Ul Varvarka 14, Moscow, 103690, Russian Federation. TEL 7-095-2984789, FAX 7-095-2983830. Adv. contact Sergei Krasichkov. Circ: 120,000. **US dist. addr.:** East View Information Services, 3020 Harbor Ln. N., Minneapolis, MN 55447. TEL 612-550-0961.

630 FRA ISSN 0335-7856
VAUCLUSE AGRICOLE. Text in French. 1978 (no.557). w. adv. charts; illus.; stat.
Published by: Societe des Editions Vaucluse Agricole (Subsidiary of: Site Agroparc), Avignon, Cedex 9 84912, France. TEL 33-4-90843602, FAX 33-4-90840009. Ed. Marie Therese Chevalier. Circ: 7,956.

630 SVK ISSN 0139-6064
VCELAR. Text in Slovak. 1922. m. **Description:** Covers all aspects of bees and bee culture.
Indexed: ApicAb.
Published by: Slovensky Zvaz Vcelarov, Svrcia ul 14, Bratislava, 84208, Slovakia. **Subscr. to:** Slovart G.T.G. s.r.o., Krupinska 4, PO Box 152, Bratislava 85299, Slovakia. TEL 421-2-63839472, FAX 421-2-63839485, http://www.slovart-gtg.sk.

638.1 CZE ISSN 0042-2924
VCELARSTVI. Text in Czech. 1877. m. CZK 30, USD 20.20. adv. bk.rev. illus.
Indexed: ApicAb, BiolAb, ChemAb, ForAb, RASB.
—CISTI.
Published by: Cesky Svaz Vcelary, Kremencova 8, Prague, 11524, Czech Republic. Ed. Miroslav Peroutka. Circ: 52,000. **Subscr. to:** Artia, Ve Smeckach 30, Prague 1 111 27, Czech Republic.

630 GBR ISSN 0960-863X
THE VEGETABLE FARMER. Text in English. 1989. m. GBP 27 domestic; GBP 35 foreign (effective 1999). adv. bk.rev. **Document type:** *Magazine, Trade.* **Description:** Covers the U.K. commercial vegetable-growing industry.
Related titles: E-mail ed.; Online - full content ed.
Published by: A C T Publishing, Lion House, 21 Church Street, Maidstone, kent ME14 1EN, United Kingdom. TEL 44-1622-695656, FAX 44-1622-663733, VEG@actpub.co.uk, info@actpub.co.uk, http://www.actpub.co.uk/mags. Ed. Joseph Champneys. Pub. John Jarrett. Adv. contact Sandy Lynch. B&W page GBP 825, color page GBP 1,320; trim 210 x 297. Circ: 3,400.

630 338.1 DNK ISSN 1600-4760
VEJLEDNING I OEKOLOGISK JORDBRUGSPRODUKTION. Text in Danish. 1999. a., latest 2005. free. **Document type:** *Government.* **Description:** Rules for ecological farming.
Related titles: Online - full text ed.
Published by: Ministeriet for Foedevarer, Landbrug og Fiskeri, Plantedirektoratet/Ministry of Food, Agriculture and Fisheries. Danish Plant Directorate, Skovbrynet 20, Lyngby, 2800, Denmark. TEL 45-45-263600, FAX 45-45-263610, pdir@pdir.dk, http://www.pdir.dk/default.asp?ID=2137.

630 FRA ISSN 0983-3897
VENDEE AGRICOLE. Text in French. 50/yr.
Address: Bd. Reaumur, La Roche-sur-Yon, Cedex 85013, France. TEL 51-36-82-04, FAX 51-36-82-13. Ed. Gilbert Metivier. Circ: 14,000.

VENEZUELA. MINISTERIO DE AGRICULTURA Y CRIA. BOLETIN DE PRECIOS DE PRODUCTOS AGROPECUARIOS. see *AGRICULTURE—Abstracting, Bibliographies, Statistics*

VENEZUELA. MINISTERIO DE AGRICULTURA Y CRIA. DIRECCION DE ECONOMIA Y ESTADISTICA AGROPECUARIA. DIVISION DE ESTADISTICA. PLAN DE TRABAJO. see *AGRICULTURE—Abstracting, Bibliographies, Statistics*

VENEZUELA. MINISTERIO DE AGRICULTURA Y CRIA. DIRECCION DE ECONOMICA Y ESTADISTICA AGROPECUARIA. ANUARIO ESTADISTICO AGROPECUARIO. see *AGRICULTURE—Abstracting, Bibliographies, Statistics*

VENEZUELA. MINISTERIO DE AGRICULTURA Y CRIA. DIRECCION DE PLANIFICACION Y ESTADISTICA. ESTADISTICAS AGROPECUARIAS DE LAS ENTIDADES FEDERALES. see *AGRICULTURE—Abstracting, Bibliographies, Statistics*

630 398 DEU
VEREIN OBERPFAELZISCHES BAUERNMUSEUM. MITTEILUNGEN. Text in German. 1964. a.
Published by: Verein Oberpfaelzisches Bauernmuseum e.V., Regensburgerstr 51, Nabburg, 92507, Germany. TEL 09433-521. Circ: 500.

630 USA ISSN 0083-5706
VERMONT. AGRICULTURAL EXPERIMENT STATION, BURLINGTON. RESEARCH REPORT. Text in English. 1951. irreg., latest vol.59, 1990. free.
Formerly (until 1968): Vermont. Agricultural Experiment Station, Burlington. Miscellaneous Publications Series
Indexed: Agr.
Published by: Vermont Agricultural Experiment Station, University of Vermont, Morrill Hall, Burlington, VT 05405. FAX 802-656-8642. Ed. Larae M Donnellan.

630 USA ISSN 0083-5714
VERMONT. AGRICULTURAL EXPERIMENT STATION, BURLINGTON. STATION BULLETIN SERIES. Text in English. 1887. irreg., latest vol.697, 1989. free. **Document type:** *Bulletin.*
Published by: Vermont Agricultural Experiment Station, University of Vermont, Morrill Hall, Burlington, VT 05405. FAX 802-656-8432. Ed. Larae M Donnellan.

630 USA ISSN 0083-5722
VERMONT. AGRICULTURAL EXPERIMENT STATION, BURLINGTON. STATION PAMPHLET SERIES. Text in English. 1943. irreg., latest vol.43, 1980. free.
Published by: Vermont Agricultural Experiment Station, University of Vermont, Morrill Hall, Burlington, VT 05405. FAX 802-656-8432. Ed. Larae M Donnellan.

630 USA
VERMONT. AGRICULTURAL EXPERIMENT STATION, BURLINGTON. TECHNICAL NOTES. Text in English. 1981. irreg., latest vol.3, 1987. free.
Published by: Vermont Agricultural Experiment Station, University of Vermont, Morrill Hall, Burlington, VT 05405. FAX 802-656-8432. Ed. Larae M Donnellan. Circ: 500.

630 USA
VERMONT SCIENCE NEWSLETTER. Text in English. 1977. 2/yr. free. **Document type:** *Newsletter.*
Published by: Vermont Agricultural Experiment Station, University of Vermont, Morrill Hall, Burlington, VT 05405. FAX 802-656-8432. Ed. Larae M Donnellan.

630 DEU ISSN 0342-6769
DAS VERTRIEBENE LANDVOLK. Text in German. 1957. m. adv. **Document type:** *Newspaper, Trade.*
Formerly: Vertriebene Bauer
Published by: Bauernverband der Vertriebenen e.V., Marktstr 4, Lippstadt, 59555, Germany. TEL 49-2941-58878, FAX 49-2941-79360. Ed. Hanns Kraus. Adv. contact Guenther Fratzscher.

630 BLR
VESTI AKADEMII AGRARNYKH NAVUK. Text in Belorussian. q. USD 129 in United States.
Indexed: AEA, AnBrAb, HortAb, NutrAb, OrnHort, PBA, PGrRegA, PotatoAb, RevApplEntom, WAE&RSA, WeedAb.
Published by: Academy of Agricultural Sciences, Kasintsa 103, ofis 109, Minsk, 220108, Belarus. TEL 0172-2773790. Ed. V S Antonyuk. **US dist. addr.:** East View Information Services, 3020 Harbor Ln. N., Minneapolis, MN 55447. TEL 612-550-0961.

630 KAZ ISSN 0042-4684
CODEN: VSNKBD
VESTNIK SEL'SKOKHOZYAISTVENNOI NAUKI KAZAKHSTANA✶. Text in Russian; Summaries in Kanuri. 1958. m. charts; illus.
Indexed: BiolAb, CIN, ChemAb, ExcerpMed, HerbAb, HortAb, IndVet, MaizeAb, PGrRegA, PN&I, ProtozoAb, RefZh, RevApplEntom, RiceAb, S&F, SeedAb, TriticAb, VetBull, WAE&RSA, ZooRec.
—BLDSC (0034.500000), CASDDS, Linda Hall. **CCC.**
Published by: (Kazakhstan. Ministerstvo Sel'skogo Khozyaistva Rossiiskoi Federatsii RUS), Izdatel'stvo Kainar, Dom Izdatel'stvo, Pr Abaja 143, Almaty, 480124, Kazakstan. Circ: 1,650.

630 AUS ISSN 0819-4599
VICTORIAN FARMER. Text in English. 1968-1992 (vol.196); N.S.. m. AUD 12. adv. **Document type:** *Magazine, Trade.*
Former titles (until Feb. 1987): Victorian Farmer's Federation Newsletter (0819-2057); (until July 1986): V F G A Newsletter (0819-2049); (until 1983): Victorian Farmer (0727-4130); (until 1981): Farmer (Melbourne) (0158-6246); (until 1980): Victoria Farmer (1968) (0042-515X); Incorporates: Victoria Wheat and Woolgrower; Australian Producer
Published by: Victorian Farmers' Federation, Farrer House, 24-28 Collins St, Melbourne, VIC 3000, Australia. TEL 61-3-9207-5555, FAX 61-3-9207-5500, vff@vff.org.au, http://www.vff.org.au. Ed. Lyall Grey. Circ: 20,000.

VIDA APICOLA; revista de apicultura. see *FOOD AND FOOD INDUSTRIES—Bakers And Confectioners*

630 FRA ISSN 1245-124X
VIE AGRICOLE DE LA MEUSE. Text in French. 1945. 50/yr.
Formerly (until 1971): Meuse Agricole (1245-1231)
Published by: Maison de l'Agriculture (Verdun), Places St-Paul, Verdun, 55100, France. TEL 29-83-30-30. Ed. M Lamorlette. Circ: 3,800.

630 FRA
VIE CHARENTAISE. Text in French. 50/yr. adv.
Address: Les Chaumes de Crage, B.P. 1243, Angouleme, Cedex 16006, France. TEL 33-5-45614647, FAX 33-5-45614095. Ed. Gerard Seguin. R&P Alain Lebret. Adv. contact Bernard Martin. Circ: 8,000.

630 FRA ISSN 1163-5479
VIENNE RURALE. Text in French. 50/yr.
Published by: Rurale, 99 av. de la Liberation, Poitiers, Cedex 86035, France. TEL 49-58-55-67. Circ: 10,600.

VINTAGE SPIRIT. see *HISTORY—History Of Europe*

630 332.64 USA ISSN 1064-4067
VIRGINIA AGRICULTURE COMMODITY NEWSLETTER. Text in English. w. free. back issues avail. **Document type:** *Newsletter, Government.* **Description:** Provides livestock, grain, poultry, and egg market prices for the past week to Virginia farmers and agribusinesses.
Published by: Virginia Department of Agriculture & Consumer Services, Virginia Market News Service, 1100 Bank St, Ste 805, Richmond, VA 23219-3638. TEL 804-786-3947, FAX 804-371-7787, mktnews@vdacs.state.va.us, http://www.vdacs.state.va.us/marketnews/. Ed. J P Welch. Circ: 2,400.

630 USA ISSN 0042-6482
VIRGINIA. DEPARTMENT OF AGRICULTURE AND CONSUMER SERVICES. BULLETIN. Text in English. 1900. q. free. illus.; stat. **Document type:** *Bulletin, Government.*
Published by: Department of Agriculture and Consumer Services, PO Box 1163, Richmond, VA 23218. TEL 804-786-2373, FAX 804-371-7679, http://www.state.va.us/vdacs/vdacs.htm. Ed. Kay O'Connell. Circ: 2,300.

917.502 USA
VIRGINIA FARM BUREAU NEWS. Text in English. 1940. 10/yr. membership. adv. **Document type:** *Magazine.* **Description:** Covers agriculture, consumer issues, the federation's insurance and other services.
Published by: Virginia Farm Bureau Federation, 12580 W Creek Pkwy, Box 27552, Richmond, VA 23261. TEL 804-290-1138, FAX 804-290-1096, http://www.fb.com/vfbf, http://www.vafb.com. Ed. Pam Wiley. Adv. contact Cathy Vanderhoff. Circ: 38,000.

630 USA ISSN 0096-6088
S123 CODEN: VPSRA3
VIRGINIA POLYTECHNIC INSTITUTE AND STATE UNIVERSITY. VIRGINIA AGRICULTURAL EXPERIMENT STATION. BULLETIN. Text in English. 1981. irreg. **Document type:** *Bulletin, Academic/Scholarly.* **Description:** Reports of research conducted by the Virginia Agricultural Experiment Station on crops, soils, animal science, agricultural economics, nutrition, agricultural engineering, entomology, and other agricultural fields.
Supersedes (in 1989): Virginia Polytechnic Institute and State University. Research Division. Bulletin; Virginia Polytechnic Institute and State University Research Division. Report (0097-1510)
Media: Online - full text.
Indexed: HerbAb, S&F, ZooRec.

—CASDDS, CISTI, Linda Hall.
Published by: Virginia Polytechnic Institute and State University, Virginia Agricultural Experiment Station, College of Agriculture and Life Sciences, Blacksburg, VA 24061-0402. TEL 540-231-6986, FAX 540-231-4163, http://www.vacs.VT.edu/research/publications/numbered.html. Circ: 1,000.

630 USA CODEN: ISVSE5
VIRGINIA POLYTECHNIC INSTITUTE AND STATE UNIVERSITY. VIRGINIA AGRICULTURAL EXPERIMENT STATION. INFORMATION SERIES. Text in English. 1982. irreg. **Document type:** *Academic/Scholarly.* **Description:** Provides reviews of scientific literature, historical progress reports, and proceedings of significant scientific symposia; presents scientific data in an informal structure.
Formerly: Virginia Polytechnic Institute and State University. College of Agriculture and Life Sciences. Information Series (0742-7425)
Media: Online - full text.
—CISTI, Linda Hall.
Published by: Virginia Polytechnic Institute and State University, Virginia Agricultural Experiment Station, College of Agriculture and Life Sciences, Blacksburg, VA 24061-0402. TEL 540-231-6986, FAX 540-231-4163, http://www.vaes.VT.edu/research/publications/numbered.html. Circ: 1,000.

VISMANDSRAPPORT. see *CONSERVATION*

630 USA ISSN 1529-1669
THE VOICE OF AGRICULTURE. Text in English. 10/yr. free domestic to members. adv. **Document type:** *Magazine, Trade.* **Description:** Focuses on Minnesota Farm Bureau events and activities as well as general agriculture topics.
Formerly (until 2000): The Farmer's Voice (0746-1690)
Published by: Minnesota Farm Bureau, 3080 Eagandale Pl, Eagan, MN 55121-0000. TEL 651-905-2100, FAX 651-905-2159, kharner@fbmn.org, http://www.fbmn.org. Ed. Kristin Harner. adv.: col. inch USD 25. Circ: 35,000 (free).

630 CAN ISSN 0703-8852
VOICE OF THE ESSEX FARMER. Text in English. 1977. s-m. CND 22. adv.
—CISTI.
Published by: Leader Publications Ltd., Main St, P O Box 490, Dresden, ON N0P 1M0, Canada. TEL 519-683-4485, FAX 519-683-4355. Ed. Peter Epp. Circ: 3,925.

630 CAN ISSN 0715-4372
VOICE OF THE HURON FARMER. Text in English. 1981-1988; resumed 199?. s-m. CND 24, USD 52. **Document type:** *Trade.*
—CISTI.
Published by: Leader Publications Ltd., Main St, P O Box 490, Dresden, ON N0P 1M0, Canada. TEL 519-683-4485, FAX 519-683-4355. Ed. Peter Epp. Circ: 4,140.

630 CAN ISSN 0700-723X
VOICE OF THE KENT FARMER. Text in English. 1963. s-m. CND 22. adv.
—CISTI.
Published by: Leader Publications Ltd., Main St, P O Box 490, Dresden, ON N0P 1M0, Canada. TEL 519-683-4485, FAX 519-683-4355. Ed. Peter Epp. Circ: 4,350.

630 CAN ISSN 0703-8860
VOICE OF THE LAMBTON FARMER. Text in English. 1962. s-m. CND 22. adv.
—CISTI.
Published by: Leader Publications Ltd., Main St, P O Box 490, Dresden, ON N0P 1M0, Canada. TEL 519-683-4485, FAX 519-683-4355. Ed. Peter Epp. Circ: 4,775.

630 CAN ISSN 0709-1915
VOICE OF THE MIDDLESEX FARMER. Text in English. 1977. s-m. CND 22. adv.
—CISTI.
Published by: Leader Publications Ltd., Main St, P O Box 490, Dresden, ON N0P 1M0, Canada. TEL 519-683-4485, FAX 519-683-4355. Ed. Peter Epp. Circ: 6,925.

630 FRA ISSN 1141-2356
LA VOIX DE LA TERRE; le journal rural du Lot-et-Garonne. Text in French. s-m. (except m. Jul.-Sept.). adv. charts; illus. 20 p./no. 5 cols./p.; **Document type:** *Newspaper.* **Description:** Covers labor issues for farmers and agricultural workers in the Lot and Garonne region.
Published by: Voix de la Terre, 9 bd. Sylvain-Dumon, Agen, Cedex 47004, France. TEL 33-5-53772950, FAX 33-5-53476916. Ed. Jean Michel Delmas. Pub. Marie France Bonneau. Circ: 7,000.

630 FRA
VOLONTE PAYSANNE DE L'AVERYRON. Text in French. w.
Address: Carrefour de l'Agriculture, Rodez, Cedex 12006, France. Circ: 11,050.

630 FRA ISSN 1163-5487
VOLONTE PAYSANNE DU GERS. Text in French. 1945. 20/yr. adv.
Published by: Chambre d'Agriculture, Maison de l'Agriculture, Route de Mirande, Auch, 32000, France. TEL 33-5-62617777, FAX 33-5-62617707. Ed. Jean Dauzerre. Adv. contact Jean Dauzere. Circ: 18,100.

630 USA
VOOR; journal of popular farm science and rural life. Text in Dutch. 1970. 4/yr. free to qualified personnel.
Related titles: ♦ Regional ed(s).: Furrow. ISSN 0016-3112; ♦ Surco Latinoamericana; ♦ Sulco; ♦ Sillon.
Published by: John Deere Publishing, One John Deere Place, Moline, IL 61265. TEL 309-765-8000. Ed. Jean Claude Hiron. Circ: 50,000.

630 NLD ISSN 0169-345X CODEN: AUWPET
➤ **WAGENINGEN UNIVERSITY PAPERS.** Text in English. 1984. irreg. (2-3/yr), latest vol.3, 2001. price varies. back issues avail. **Document type:** *Monographic series, Academic/Scholarly.* **Description:** Publishes research in plant biology, livestock breeding, agronomic history, and plant protection and propagation.
Formerly (until 2001): Wageningen Agricultural University Papers; Which was formed by the merger of (1918-1984): Landbouwhogeschool Wageningen. Mededelingen (0369-0598); (1968-1984): Landbouwhogeschool Wageningen. Miscellaneous Papers (0083-6990)
Indexed: BiolAb, DSA, FCA, FPA, ForAb, GEOBASE, HerbAb, HortAb, NutrAb, OrnHort, PBA, PGegResA, PHN&I, RA&MP, RPP, RRTA, RevApplEntom, RiceAb, S&F, SFA, SeedAb, WAE&RSA, WildRev, ZooRec.
—CASDDS, CISTI, KNAW.
Published by: (Wageningen University and Research Centre), Backhuys Publishers BV, Postbus 321, Leiden, 2300 AH, Netherlands. TEL 31-71-517-0208, FAX 31-71-517-1856, jos.vandermaesen@algem.pt.wau.nl, backhuys@backhuys.com, http://www.backhuys.com. Ed. L J G van der Maesen. Circ: 200 (controlled).

630 USA ISSN 0043-0129
S1
WALLACES FARMER. Text in English. 1855. 14/yr. USD 23.95 in state Iowa (effective 2005). adv. illus. **Document type:** *Magazine, Trade.*
Related titles: Microform ed.: (from PQC); Online - full text ed.: (from Northern Light Technology, Inc., ProQuest Information & Learning).
Indexed: ABIn, F&GI.
—CISTI, Linda Hall.
Published by: Farm Progress Companies, 191 S Gary Ave, Carol Stream, IL 60188-2095. TEL 630-462-2229, FAX 630-462-2202, info@farmprogress.com, http://www.wallacesfarmer.com, http://www.farmprogress.com/. Ed. Rod Swoboda. adv.: B&W page USD 3,650, color page USD 4,150; trim 8 x 10.75. Circ: 60,000 (paid and controlled).

630 CHE
WALLISER BAUERNBLATT. Text in German. w. **Document type:** *Newspaper, Trade.*
Address: Landwirtschaftszentrum, Visp, 3930, Switzerland. TEL 41-27-9480829. Ed. Peter Gurten. Circ: 2,886.

630 CAN ISSN 1197-3625
WARREN'S FARM & RANCH DIRECTORY. Text in English. 1993. a. free. adv. **Document type:** *Directory.*
Address: P O Box 189, Bethune, SK S0G 0H0, Canada. TEL 306-638-2208, FAX 306-638-3130. Ed., Pub. Kate Warren. Adv. contact Winston Roan. B&W page CND 2,500; trim 10.5 x 8.13. Circ: 170,000.

630 POL CODEN: AWAAEO
WARSAW AGRICULTURAL UNIVERSITY. S G G W. ANNALS. AGRICULTURE. Text mainly in English; Text occasionally in French, German, Russian; Summaries in Polish. 1957. irreg., latest vol.43, 2002. USD 10 per issue. **Document type:** *Bulletin, Academic/Scholarly.*
Former titles: Warsaw Agricultural University. S G G W - A R. Annals. Agriculture (0208-5712); (until 1980): Akademia Rolnicza w Warszawie. Zeszyty Naukowe. Rolnictwo (0511-1692)
Indexed: AEA, AgrAg, AgrLib, AnBrAb, CPA, DSA, FCA, ForAb, HerbAb, HortAb, I&DA, IndVet, MaizeAb, NutrAb, PHN&I, PN&I, PST, PotatoAb, PoultAb, RPP, RefZh, RevApplEntom, S&F, SIA, SeedAb, SoyAb, TriticAb, WAE&RSA, WeedAb.
—CASDDS, CISTI, Linda Hall.
Published by: Szkola Glowna Gospodarstwa Wiejskiego (SGGW)/Warsaw Agricultural University, Ul Nowoursynowska 166, Warsaw, 02787, Poland. TEL 48-22-8439041, FAX 48-22-8471562, jmw_wyd@alpha.sggw.waw.pl, http://www.sggw.waw.pl. Ed. B Gej.

630 GBR ISSN 0955-0283
WARWICKSHIRE FARMER. Text in English. 1973. m. adv.
Published by: County Farmers Publications Ltd., 55 Goldington Rd, Bedford, Beds MK40 3LU, United Kingdom. TEL 44-1234-351401, FAX 44-1234-328614. Ed. S Fisher. Circ: 2,100.

630 USA ISSN 0195-0673
WASHINGTON AGRICULTURAL RECORD. Text in English. 1971. w. USD 65. adv. bk.rev. **Document type:** *Newsletter.*
—CISTI.
Address: PO Box 25001, Georgetown Sta, Washington, DC 20007. TEL 202-333-8190, FAX 202-337-3809. Ed. Matthew S Strachan. Pub. Robert N Pyle. R&P, Adv. contact Robert Pyle. Circ: 500.

WASHINGTON AGRICULTURAL STATISTICS. see *AGRICULTURE—Abstracting, Bibliographies, Statistics*

630 USA ISSN 1070-4442
WASHINGTON STATE GRANGE NEWS; informing Grangers since 1912. Text in English. 1912. m. USD 5.25 (effective 2005). adv. bk.rev. illus.; stat. 20 p./no. 4 cols./p.; **Document type:** *Newspaper, Trade.* **Description:** Informs rural Washington state residents about agricultural trends, legislative news, conservation advances, and the development of cooperatives. Also provides information about the activities of the Grange in Washington.
Formerly (until 1993): Washington Grange News (0043-0587)
Published by: Washington State Grange, PO Box 1186, Olympia, WA 98507-1186. TEL 360-943-9911, FAX 360-357-3548, grangenews@wa-grange.org, http://www.wa-grange.org/grange_newspaper.htm. Ed., Adv. contact Dave Howard. page USD 1,244.64; 10.5 x 15.75. Circ: 45,000 (paid).

WATER & ENERGY INTERNATIONAL. see *WATER RESOURCES*

630 323 USA ISSN 1073-4813
THE WEBSTER AGRICULTURAL LETTER. Text in English. 1981. s-m. USD 397 in North America; USD 477 elsewhere. bk.rev. back issues avail. **Document type:** *Newsletter.*
Formerly (until Jan. 1994): Agricultural Credit Letter (0887-7521)
Published by: Webster Communications Corporation, 3835 N. 9th St., Ste. 401-W, Arlington, VA 22203-1910. TEL 703-525-4512, FAX 703-852-3534, agletter@aol.com, websterj@aol.com. Ed. James C Webster.

WEED SCIENCE SOCIETY OF AMERICA. ABSTRACTS. see *AGRICULTURE—Abstracting, Bibliographies, Statistics*

630 USA
WEEKLY PURCELL AGRICULTURAL COMMODITY MARKET REPORT. Text in English. 2001. w. back issues avail.
Media: Online - full text.
Published by: Virginia Cooperative Extension, 121 Hutcheson Hall, Virginia Tech 0437, Blacksburg, VA 24061-0001. FAX 800-828-1120, http://www.ext.vt.edu/. Ed. Ann A Hertzler.

630 AUS ISSN 0043-194X
WEEKLY TIMES. Text in English. 1869. w. AUD 67.60. adv. bk.rev. illus. **Document type:** *Newspaper.* **Description:** Covers farming, gardening, country life.
Related titles: Microfilm ed.; Online - full text ed.: (from LexisNexis).
Published by: Herald & Weekly Times Ltd., HWT Tower, 40 City Rd, Southbank, VIC 3006, Australia. TEL 61-3-92922000, FAX 61-3-92922697, TELEX 30104. Ed. Hugh Jones. Adv. contact Robert McWaters. Circ: 82,000.

630 GBR ISSN 0040-8050
WELSH FARMER/Y TIR. Text in English, Welsh. 1973 (vol.3). m. GBP 10 domestic; GBP 12 foreign (effective 2000). adv. bk.rev. **Document type:** *Newspaper.* **Description:** Informs the farming community of the latest developments in agriculture.
Former titles: Y Tir and Welsh Farmer; Y Tir
Published by: Farmers' Union of Wales, Gogerddan, Aberystwyth, United Kingdom. TEL 44-1970-820820, FAX 44-1970-820821. Ed. G L Thomas. R&P G.L. Thomas. Adv. contact Lisa Benjy TEL 44-1392-447766. Circ: 15,570 (controlled).

630 GBR ISSN 0955-0291
WEST RIDING FARMER. Text in English. 1957. m. adv.
Published by: County Farmers Publications Ltd., 55 Goldington Rd, Bedford, Beds MK40 3LU, United Kingdom. TEL 44-1234-351401, FAX 44-1234-328614. Ed. A Hepworth. Circ: 3,900.

630 634.9 USA
WEST VIRGINIA. AGRICULTURAL AND FORESTRY EXPERIMENT STATION. ANNUAL REPORT. Text in English. 1980. a. **Document type:** *Corporate.*
Published by: West Virginia University, Agricultural and Forestry Experiment Station, College of Agriculture and Forestry, Morgantown, WV 26506-6108. FAX 304-293-3740. Ed. John Luchok. Circ: 3,000.

630 634.9 USA
WEST VIRGINIA. AGRICULTURAL AND FORESTRY EXPERIMENT STATION. BULLETIN. Text in English. 1888. irreg. free. **Document type:** *Monographic series.*
Indexed: AnBrAb, BiolAb, CurCont, HerbAb, IndVet, NutrAb.
Published by: West Virginia University, Agricultural and Forestry Experiment Station, College of Agriculture and Forestry, Morgantown, WV 26506-6108. TEL 304-293-6368, FAX 304-293-3740.

634.9 USA
WEST VIRGINIA. AGRICULTURAL AND FORESTRY EXPERIMENT STATION. CIRCULAR. Text in English. 1981 (no.119). irreg. charts. **Document type:** *Newsletter.*

▼ new title ➤ refereed ✶ unverified ♦ full entry avail.

A

Indexed: BiolAb, FPA.
Published by: West Virginia University, Agricultural and Forestry Experiment Station, College of Agriculture and Forestry, Morgantown, WV 26506-6108. TEL 304-293-6368, FAX 304-293-3740.

630 634.9 USA
WEST VIRGINIA. AGRICULTURAL AND FORESTRY EXPERIMENT STATION. CURRENT REPORT. Text in English. 1952. irreg., latest vol.75, 1981. free. **Document type:** *Academic/Scholarly.*
Formerly: West Virginia. Agricultural Experiment Station, Morgantown. Current Report (0083-8381)
Indexed: BiolAb, CurCont, FPA, PBA.
—Linda Hall.
Published by: West Virginia University, Agricultural and Forestry Experiment Station, College of Agriculture and Forestry, Morgantown, WV 26506-6108. TEL 304-293-6368, FAX 304-293-3740. Ed. Debbie Fast. Circ: 5,000.

630 338.1 USA ISSN 0025-3545
WEST VIRGINIA. DEPARTMENT OF AGRICULTURE. MARKET BULLETIN. Text in English. 191?. s-m. free. adv. illus.; mkt. **Document type:** *Bulletin, Government.*
Published by: Department of Agriculture, Publications Division, State Capitol, 1900 Kanwha Blvd E, Charleston, WV 25305-0192. TEL 304-348-3708, FAX 304-348-2203. Ed. Howard T Knotts. Circ: 64,000.

630 AUS ISSN 0511-6872
SB950.3.A8
WESTERN AUSTRALIA. AGRICULTURE PROTECTION BOARD. ANNUAL REPORT. Text in English. 1953. a.
Related titles: Online - full text ed.
—BLDSC (1103.400000).
Published by: (Agriculture Protection Board (Western Australia)), Department of Agriculture (Western Australia), 3 Baron-Hay Court, South Perth, W.A. 6151, Australia. TEL 61-8-93683333, enquiries@agric.wa.gov.au, http://www.agric.wa.gov.au/agency/pubns/annualreport/apb2000/index.htm.

630 AUS
S397
WESTERN AUSTRALIA. DEPARTMENT OF AGRICULTURE. ANNUAL REPORT. Text in English. 1940. a. free. **Document type:** *Government.* **Description:** Covers research, extension and regulatory activities of the department.
Former titles: Agriculture Western Australia. Annual Report (1326-4141); (until 1997): Western Australia. Department of Agriculture. Annual Report (0726-9366)
Related titles: Online - full content ed.: 2000.
Indexed: AnBrAb, BiolAb.
—BLDSC (1103.412000), CISTI.
Published by: Department of Agriculture (Western Australia), 3 Baron-Hay Court, South Perth, W.A. 6151, Australia. TEL 61-8-93683333, FAX 61-8-9474-2018, enquiries@agric.wa.gov.au, http://www.agric.wa.gov.au/agency/pubns/annualreport/. Ed. L Jenkins. R&Ps C Harris TEL 61-8-9368-3944, P Sawyer.

630 AUS
WESTERN AUSTRALIA. DEPARTMENT OF AGRICULTURE. BULLETIN. Text in English. 1905. irreg. price varies. **Document type:** *Bulletin, Government.* **Description:** Covers topics relevant to agriculture.
Former titles: Agriculture Western Australia. Bulletin (1326-415X); (until 1995): Western Australia. Department of Agriculture. Bulletin (0729-0012)
Related titles: Online - full content ed.
Indexed: HerbAb.
—BLDSC (2814.502000).
Published by: Department of Agriculture (Western Australia), 3 Baron-Hay Court, South Perth, W.A. 6151, Australia. TEL 61-8-93683333, FAX 61-8-9474-2018, enquiries@agric.wa.gov.au, http://www.agric.wa.gov.au/agency/pubns/bulletin/. R&P C Harris TEL 61-8-9368-3944.

630 AUS
WESTERN AUSTRALIA. DEPARTMENT OF AGRICULTURE. PRIMARY FOCUS. Text in English. 1995. q. AUD 51 domestic for Farmnotes, Primary Focus and Journal of Agriculture; AUD 66 foreign for Farmnotes, Primary Focus and Journal of Agriculture (effective 2001). **Document type:** *Government, Trade.*
Formerly: Agriculture Western Australia. Primary Focus (1441-0109)
—CISTI.
Published by: Department of Agriculture (Western Australia), 3 Baron-Hay Court, South Perth, W.A. 6151, Australia. TEL 61-8-93683333, FAX 61-8-9474-2018, http://www.agric.wa.gov.au/.

630 AUS
WESTERN DISTRICT FARMER. Text in English. 1987. m. AUD 18 (effective 2001). adv. charts; illus. **Document type:** *Newspaper.* **Description:** Provides information on broadacre and intensive farming for farmers within the Western District of Victoria.
Published by: Hamilton Spectator Partnership, PO Box 416, Hamilton, VIC 3300, Australia. TEL 61-3-55721011, FAX 61-3-55723800, http://www.spec.com.au. Ed. Pat Cameron. R&P Richard Beks. Adv. contact Sue Williams. page AUD 140,630; trim 290 x 445. Circ: 24,000.

630 USA ISSN 1525-1217
WESTERN FARM PRESS; timely, reliable information for Western agriculture. Text in English. 1979. 29/yr. USD 36 domestic; USD 179 foreign; free to qualified personnel in CA or AZ (effective 2005). adv. **Document type:** *Magazine, Trade.*
Formerly: California - Arizona Farm Press (0164-5331)
Related titles: Online - full text ed.: (from bigchalk, EBSCO Publishing, Factiva, Florida Center for Library Automation, Gale Group, H.W. Wilson, O C L C Online Computer Library Center, Inc., ProQuest Information & Learning).
Indexed: B&AI.
—CCC.
Published by: Primedia Business Magazines & Media, Inc. (Subsidiary of: Primedia, Inc.), 9800 Metcalf Ave, Overland Park, KS 66212-2216. TEL 913-341-1300, FAX 913-967-1898, gfrey@primedia.com, inquiries@primediabusiness.com, http://westernfarmpress.com/, http://www.primediabusiness.com. Eds. Harry Cline, Hembree Brandon. Pub. Greg Frey TEL 952-851-4613. Adv. contact Mike Lafferre. Circ: 24,000 (paid).

630 CAN ISSN 0043-4094
WESTERN PRODUCER. Text in English. 1923. w. CND 46.01 domestic; USD 75 in United States; CND 250 foreign (effective 2000). adv. bk.rev. charts; mkt.; illus. **Document type:** *Newspaper.* **Description:** News for farms families.
Related titles: Microfilm ed.: (from CML, SOC); Online - full text ed.: (from EBSCO Publishing).
Indexed: CBCARef, CBPI.
—CISTI.
Published by: Western Producer Publications, P O Box 2500, Saskatoon, SK S7K 2C4, Canada. TEL 306-665-3500, FAX 306-665-4961, newsroom@producer.com, http://www.producer.com. Ed., R&P Elaine Shein. Pub. Allan Laughland. Adv. contact Darryl Thompson. Circ: 96,324 (paid).

630 USA
WHATCOM COUNTY FARM REVIEW. Text in English. 1960. m. USD 27 (effective 2000). adv. charts; illus.; stat. back issues avail. **Document type:** *Newspaper.*
Published by: Lewis Publishing Co., 113 Sixth St, Box 153, Lynden, WA 98264. TEL 360-354-4445, FAX 360-398-1731. Ed. Calvin Bratt. Pub. Michael D Lewis. R&P Mike Lewis. Adv. contact Connie Pugh. Circ: 8,000.

630 GBR ISSN 0143-9596
WHAT'S NEW IN FARMING. Text in English. 1977. m. USD 150. adv. **Document type:** *Trade.*
—CISTI. CCC.
Published by: Morgan-Grampian (Farming) Press Ltd. (Subsidiary of: Morgan-Grampian plc), Morgan-Grampian House, 30 Calderwood St, London, SE18 6QH, United Kingdom. TEL 081-855-7777, FAX 081-854-7476. Ed. Donald Taylor. Adv. contact Alistair Fitzpatrick. Circ: 48,000.

630 CAN ISSN 1187-2179
WHO'S WHO IN BRITISH COLUMBIA AGRICULTURE. Text in English. 1978. a. CND 10. adv. **Description:** A listing of personnel in government, academia, farm associations, finance, agribusiness and consulting firms involved in agriculture.
Published by: Country Life Ltd., 10317 158A Street, Surrey, BC V4N 2M5, Canada. TEL 604 951-4444, FAX 604 951-4445. Ed., Pub. Peter Wilding.

631 POL ISSN 0137-3838
WIADOMOSCI ZIELARSKIE. Text in Polish. 1958. m. USD 18. **Document type:** *Magazine, Trade.*
Indexed: AgrLib.
Published by: (Stowarzyszenie Naukowo-Techniczne Inzynierow i Technikow Przemyslu Spozywczego), Hortpress Sp. z o.o., ul Kopernika 34, Warsaw, 00336, Poland. TEL 48-22-8261626. Ed. Urszula Uszynska Nowicka. Circ: 9,600. **Dist. by:** Ars Polona, Krakowskie Przedmiescie 7, Warsaw, Poland. **Co-sponsors:** Zrzeszenie Producentow Roslin Zielarskich; Zjednoczenie Przemyslu Zielarskiego "Herbapol".

630 DEU ISSN 0939-9445
WILDHALTUNG. Text in German. 1990. bi-m. **Document type:** *Journal, Academic/Scholarly.*
Formed by the merger of (1984-1990): Landwirtschaftliche Wildhaltung (0930-3006); Which was formerly (until 1986): Landwirtschaftliche Wildgehege (0176-9723); (1982-1990): Wildtiere in Gehegen (0930-0856); Which was formerly (until 1986): Informationen zur Haltung von Wild (0723-1334)
Indexed: RefZh.
—CCC.
Published by: Bundesverband fuer Landwirtschaftliche Wildhaltung e.V., Godesberger Allee 142-148, Bonn, 53175, Germany. TEL 49-228-8198297, FAX 49-228-376449, s.voell@bauernverband.de, http://www.blw-wildhaltung.de. Circ: 1,200.

630 GBR ISSN 0043-566X
WILTSHIRE FARMER. Text in English. 1962. m. adv.
Published by: County Farmers Publications Ltd., 55 Goldington Rd, Bedford, Beds MK40 3LU, United Kingdom. TEL 44-1234-351401, FAX 44-1234-328614. Ed. T Bawley. Circ: 1,950.

630 AUS
WIMMERA FARMER. Text in English. m. adv. **Document type:** *Newspaper, Consumer.*
Published by: Wimmera Mail-Times Pty, 84-92 Wilson St, Horsham, VIC 3400, Australia. TEL 61-3-53820181, FAX 61-3-53826787, wmt@netconnect.com.au. Circ: 17,000.

630 USA ISSN 0043-6356
WISCONSIN AGRICULTURIST. Text in English. 1849. 15/yr. USD 23.95 (effective 2005). adv. bk.rev. **Document type:** *Magazine, Trade.* **Description:** Emphasizes management information for farmers.
Related titles: Microfilm ed.
—Linda Hall.
Published by: Farm Progress Companies, 191 S Gary Ave, Carol Stream, IL 60188-2095. TEL 630-462-2229, FAX 630-462-2202, info@farmprogress.com, http://www.wisconsinagriculturist.com, http://www.farmprogress.com/. Ed. Fran O'Leary. adv.: B&W page USD 2,150, color page USD 2,650; trim 10.5 x 14.5. Circ: 25,000 (paid and controlled).

630 USA
WISCONSIN STATE FARMER. Text in English. 1956. w. USD 15. adv.
Address: PO Box 152, Waupaca, WI 54981. TEL 715-258-5546, FAX 715-258-8162. Ed. Carla Hagenow. Circ: 30,000.

630 GBR ISSN 0955-0305
WORCESTERSHIRE FARMER & RECORD. Text in English. 1925. m. adv.
Formerly: Worcestershire Record; Incorporates: Worcestershire Grower
—BLDSC (9347.720000).
Published by: County Farmers Publications Ltd., 55 Goldington Rd, Bedford, Beds MK40 3LU, United Kingdom. TEL 44-1234-351401, FAX 44-1234-328614. Ed. P Hudson. Circ: 2,200.

WORKING PAPERS ON WOMEN IN INTERNATIONAL DEVELOPMENT. see *BUSINESS AND ECONOMICS—International Development And Assistance*

630 USA
WORLD AG EXPO. Text in English. m. **Document type:** *Magazine, Trade.*
Published by: (World Ag Expo), DairyBusiness Communications (Subsidiary of: Multi Ag Media LLC), 6437 Collamer Rd, East Syracuse, NY 13057-1031. TEL 800-334-1904, FAX 315-703-7988, dmorneau@dairybusiness.com, http://www.dairybusiness.com.

630 USA
▼ **WORLD AG EXPO V I P PREVIEW.** (Very Important Producers) Text in English. 2004. a. free to qualified personnel. **Document type:** *Magazine, Trade.* **Description:** Provides advance information on the World Ag Expo for the top farmers in California.
Published by: (World Ag Expo), DairyBusiness Communications (Subsidiary of: Multi Ag Media LLC), 6437 Collamer Rd, East Syracuse, NY 13057-1031. TEL 800-334-1904, FAX 315-703-7988, dmorneau@dairybusiness.com, http://www.dairybusiness.com. Circ: 30,000 (controlled).

630 USA ISSN 1052-0279
S21.F6
WORLD AGRICULTURAL PRODUCTION. Text in English. 1979. m. USD 152 domestic; USD 304 foreign (effective 2005). reprint service avail. from CIS. **Document type:** *Government.*
Former titles (until 1987): World Crop Production (1046-3224); (until 1986): Foreign Agriculture Circular. World Crop Production (0271-3691)
Related titles: Microfiche ed.: (from CIS); Online - full text ed.
Indexed: AmStI, DSA, MaizeAb, RASB, RiceAb, SIA, SoyAb, TriticAb, WAE&RSA.
—CISTI.
Published by: U.S. Department of Agriculture, Foreign Agricultural Service, Information Division, Rm 5920 S, Washington, DC 20250-1000. info@fas.usda.gov, http://www.fas.usda.gov. **Subscr. to:** U.S. Department of Commerce, National Technical Information Service, 5285 Port Royal Rd, Springfield, VA 22161. TEL 703-605-6060, 800-363-2068, FAX 703-605-6900, subscriptions@ntis.gov, http://www.ntis.gov/ordering.htm.

630 CHE ISSN 0259-8213
HD9275.A1
WORLD MARKET FOR DAIRY PRODUCTS. Text in English. 1980. a. CHF 25. **Document type:** *Trade.* **Description:** Survey of trade, production, consumption and price trends in fresh milk, milk powders, butter and cheeses.
Related titles: Microfiche ed.: (from CIS); French ed.; Spanish ed.
Indexed: IIS, RASB.
—CISTI.
Published by: General Agreement on Tariffs and Trade, Centre William Rappard, 154 rue de Lausanne, Geneva 21, 1211, Switzerland. TEL 41-22-739-5208, FAX 41-22-739-5458.

WORLD METEOROLOGICAL ORGANIZATION. COMMISSION FOR AGRICULTURAL METEOROLOGY. ABRIDGED FINAL REPORT OF THE (NO.) SESSION. see *METEOROLOGY*

547 660 631 GBR ISSN 1369-2062
WORLDWIDE DIRECTORY OF AGROBIOLOGICALS ON CD-ROM. Text in English. 1990. a. GBP 125, USD 225 (effective 2000). back issues avail. **Document type:** *Trade.* **Description:** Lists more than 2,000 beneficial organisms and biological and other nonsynthetic products for use in agriculture, horticulture, forestry, and gardens. Provides expanded product details and a glossary of 1,750 entries describing pests, weeds, diseases, and crops.
Formerly: World Directory of Agrobiologicals
Media: CD-ROM.
Published by: C P L Scientific Ltd., 43 Kingfisher Ct, Hambridge Rd, Newbury, Berks RG14 5SJ, United Kingdom. TEL 44-1635-574920, FAX 44-1635-529322, press@cplsci.demon.co.uk, http://www.cplpress.com. Eds. J Coombs, K E Hall. Adv. contact K E Hall.

630 USA ISSN 1071-0272
WYOMING AGRICULTURE. Text in English. 1938. m. USD 1 to members (effective 2000). adv. back issues avail. **Document type:** *Newspaper, Trade.* **Description:** Contains news for agriculture producers regarding production, as well as political and regulatory issues in Wyoming. Lists Wyoming Farm Bureau events.
Published by: Wyoming Farm Bureau Federation, 406 S 21st St, Box 1348, Laramie, WY 82070. TEL 307-745-4835, FAX 307-721-7790, snoecker@mwfbi.com. Ed., R&P, Adv. contact Suzy Noecker TEL 307-721-7728. Circ: 8,000 (controlled).

630 TWN ISSN 1015-8367
XIANGJIAN XIAOLU/COUNTRY ROAD; if you eat, you are involved in agriculture. Text in Chinese. 1975. m. TWD 1,000; USD 75 foreign; TWD 100 newsstand/cover (effective 1999). adv. charts; illus. index. **Document type:** *Consumer.* **Description:** Introduces a wide base of consumers to information about agriculture, focused on domestically produced agricultural products, family gardening, recreational agriculture, and the conservation of agricultural resources.
Formerly (until 1989): Nongye Zhoukan - Agri-Week (0379-4040)
Published by: Council of Agriculture, 14 Wenchow St, Taipei, Taiwan. TEL 886-2-362-8148, FAX 886-2-2363-6724, h3628148@ms15.hinet.net, http://www.coa.gov.tw/ch/fst/index/htm. Ed. Shu Lien Yu. Pub. Pi Phong Hong. adv.: B&W page TWD 872.70, color page TWD 1,454.50; trim 210 x 290. Circ: 10,000 (paid). **Dist. in US by:** May Produce Company, 742 East Garvey Ave, C, Monterey, CA 91754. TEL 626-572-3168, 626-572-2888.

XIANGZHEN QIYE, MINYING JINGJI/TOWNSHIP ENTERPRISES AND CIVILIAN MANAGED ECONOMY. see *BUSINESS AND ECONOMICS—Small Business*

630 CHN ISSN 1004-1389
XIBEI NONGYE XUEBAO/ACTA AGRICULTURAE BOREALI - OCCIDENTALIS SINICA. Text in Chinese, English; Abstracts in English. 1992. q. USD 24; USD 32 foreign. illus. 104 p./no.; **Document type:** *Academic/Scholarly.* **Description:** Covers the latest technological developments in agriculture.
Related titles: Online - full text ed.: (from East View Information Services).
Indexed: AEA, AgBio, AnBrAb, BioCN&I, CPA, FCA, FS&TA, HortAb, I&DA, IndVet, MaizeAb, PBA, PGegResA, PGrRegA, PHN&I, PN&I, PotatoAb, PoultAb, RPP, RevApplEntom, RiceAb, S&F, SIA, SeedAb, SoyAb, TriticAb, VetBull, WeedAb, ZooRec.
Published by: Shaanxi Academy of Agricultural Science, Shaanxi Sheng Nongye Kexueyuan Nei, Yangling Zheng, Xianyang, Shaanxi 712100, China. TEL 7088401. Ed. Qikun Wang. **Dist. overseas by:** China International Book Trading Corp, 35 Chegongzhuang Xilu, Haidian District, PO Box 399, Beijing 100044, China.

630 CHN ISSN 1000-2642
CODEN: XNDXEQ
XINAN NONGYE DAXUE XUEBAO/SOUTHWEST AGRICULTURAL UNIVERSITY. JOURNAL. Text in Chinese. 1985. bi-m. **Document type:** *Academic/Scholarly.*
Related titles: Online - full text ed.: (from East View Information Services).
Indexed: AgBio, AgrForAb, AnBrAb, BioCN&I, CPA, FCA, ForAb, HerbAb, HortAb, I&DA, IndVet, MaizeAb, NemAb, NutrAb, OrnHort, PBA, PGegResA, PGrRegA, PHN&I, PN&I, PotatoAb, PoultAb, ProtozoAb, RA&MP, RDA, RPP, RevApplEntom, RiceAb, S&F, SIA, SeedAb, SoyAb, TriticAb, VetBull, WAE&RSA, WeedAb, ZooRec.
—BLDSC (4902.240000).
Published by: Xinan Nongye Daxue, Xuebao Bianjibu, Chongqing, China.

630 330.9 CHN
XINCUN. Text in Chinese. 1981. m. CNY 15 (effective 1989).
Published by: Jilin Renmin Chubanshe, Qikan Bu/Jilin People's Publishing House, Stalin Dajie, P.O. Box 20, Changcun, Jilin, China. TEL 884490. Circ: 55,000.

630 JPN ISSN 0513-4676
CODEN: YDKNA2
YAMAGATA DAIGAKU KIYO (NOGAKU)/YAMAGATA UNIVERSITY. BULLETIN (AGRICULTURAL SCIENCE). Text in Japanese. 1950. a. **Document type:** *Bulletin, Academic/Scholarly.*
—BLDSC (2821.700000).
Published by: Yamagata Daigaku/Yamagata University, Publicatin Committee, Library, Division of Information Processing & Management, 1-4-12, Kojirakawa, Yamagata, Yamagata 990-9585, Japan. TEL 81-23-6285054, FAX 81-23-6285059, http://www.lib.yamagata-u.ac.jp.

630 JPN ISSN 0388-9327
CODEN: YNHODT
YAMAGUCHI-KEN NOGYO SHIKENJO KENKYUHHOKOKU/ YAMAGUCHI AGRICULTURAL EXPERIMENT STATION. BULLETIN. Text in Japanese. 1953. a.
Formerly (until 1962): Yamaguchi-ken Nogyo Shikenjo. Kenkyu Iho/Yamaguchi Agricultural Experiment Station. Preliminary Report Series (0388-9319)
Indexed: BIOSIS Prev, BiolAb.
Published by: Yamaguchi-ken Nogyo Shikenjo/Yamaguchi Agricultural Experiment Station, 1419 Oouchi-mihori, Yamaguchi, Yamaguchi 753-0214, Japan. TEL 81-0839-270211, FAX 81-0839-270214.

630 JPN ISSN 0513-1715
CODEN: YDNGAU
YAMAGUCHI UNIVERSITY. FACULTY OF AGRICULTURE. BULLETIN. Text in Japanese. 1950. a. **Document type:** *Bulletin, Academic/Scholarly.*
Indexed: BioCN&I, BiolAb, FCA, HerbAb, IndVet, PBA, RPP, S&F, VetBull.
—CASDDS, CISTI.
Published by: Yamaguchi Daigaku, Nogakubu/Yamaguchi University, Faculty of Agriculture, 1677-1 Yoshida, Yamaguchi-shi, 753-0841, Japan. Ed. Noriyuki Fujita.

630 570 CHN ISSN 1671-4652
YANGZHOU DAXUE XUEBAO (NONGYE YU SHENGMING KEXUE BAN)/JOURNAL OF YANGZHOU UNIVERSITY (AGRICULTURAL & LIFE SCIENCES EDITION). Text in Chinese. 1980. q. CNY 5 newsstand/cover (effective 2003). **Document type:** *Journal, Academic/Scholarly.*
Former titles (until 2002): Jiangsu Nongye Yanjiu/Jiangsu Agricultural Research; Jiangsu Nongxueyuan Xuebao/Jiangsu Agricultural College. Journal (1000-2049)
Related titles: Online - full text ed.: (from East View Information Services, WanFang Data Corp.).
Indexed: AnBrAb, CPA, FCA, ForAb, HortAb, IndVet, MaizeAb, NutrAb, PBA, PGegResA, PGrRegA, PN&I, PoultAb, RPP, RefZh, RevApplEntom, RiceAb, SeedAb, TriticAb, VetBull, WeedAb.
—BLDSC (4917.509850), IE.
Published by: (Yangzhou University), Jiangsu Nongye Yanjiu, 12 Wenhui East Road, Yangzhou, 225009, China. xuebao@mail.yzu.edu.cn, http://jsnyyj.periodicals.com.cn/default.html. **Dist. outside of China by:** Educational Publications Import and Export Corporation, 15 Xueyuan Road, Haiding District, Beijing, China.

YEARBOOK OF AGRICULTURAL STATISTICS OF BANGLADESH. see *AGRICULTURE—Abstracting, Bibliographies, Statistics*

630 USA
YIELD. Text in English. q. **Document type:** *Journal, Trade.* **Description:** Covers the people, companies, technologies, financing and issues at the forefront of the changes being seen in the ag, food and fiber industries.
Published by: Doane Agricultural Service Co., 11701 Borman Dr, Ste 300, St. Louis, MO 63146-4199. TEL 314-569-2700, FAX 314-569-1083, http://www.agrimarketing.com/yieldsup.php, http://www.doane.com.

630 GBR ISSN 0955-0313
YORK COUNTY FARMER. Text in English. 1960. m. adv.
Formerly: North Riding (No.2) Farmer
Published by: County Farmers Publications Ltd., 55 Goldington Rd, Bedford, Beds MK40 3LU, United Kingdom. TEL 44-1234-351401, FAX 44-1234-328614. Ed. A Hepworth. Circ: 1,650.

630 USA
YOUR ILLINOIS F F A. (Future Farmers of America) Text in English. 1940. 3/yr. free. **Description:** News about the Illinois FFA and affiliated groups for members, alumni and friends.
Published by: Illinois F F A, PO Box 50, Roanoke, IL 61561. TEL 309-923-7413, FAX 309-923-7618. Circ: 17,000 (controlled).

YUANZINENG NONGYE YINGYONG/APPLICATIONS OF ATOMIC ENERGY IN AGRICULTURE. see *ENERGY—Nuclear Energy*

630 CHN ISSN 1004-390X
S471.C6
YUNNAN NONGYE DAXUE XUEBAO/YUNNAN AGRICULTURAL UNIVERSITY. JOURNAL. Text in Chinese. q. CNY 5 newsstand/cover (effective 2002). **Document type:** *Journal, Academic/Scholarly.*
Related titles: Online - full content ed.: (from WanFang Data Corp.); Online - full text ed.: (from East View Information Services).
Indexed: AgBio, AgrForAb, AnBrAb, BioCN&I, CPA, FCA, FS&TA, ForAb, HortAb, I&DA, IndVet, MaizeAb, OrnHort, PBA, PGegResA, PGrRegA, PN&I, PotatoAb, PoultAb, RA&MP, S&F, SeedAb, TriticAb, ZooRec.
—BLDSC (4918.140400), IE, ingenta.
Published by: Yunnan Nongye Daxue/Yunnan Agricultural University, Editorial Department, Kunming, Heilongtan 650201, China. ndxb@ynmail.com, http://ynnydxxb.periodicals.com.cn/default.html. Ed. Hai-ru Chen. **Dist. by:** China International Book Trading Corp, 35 Chegongzhuang Xilu, Haidian District, PO Box 399, Beijing 100044, China. TEL 86-10-68412045, FAX 86-10-68412023, cibtc@mail.cibtc.com.cn, http://www.cibtc.com.cn.

630 DEU ISSN 0946-6614
Z M P AGRARMARKT; Nachrichten fuer Verbraucher und Wirtschaft. Text in German. 4/w. **Document type:** *Bulletin.*
Published by: Zentrale Markt und Preisberichtstelle GmbH, Rochusstr 2, Bonn, 53123, Germany. TEL 49-228-9777173, FAX 49-228-9777179, info@zmp.de, http://www.zmp.de.

338.1 DEU
Z M P MARKTBERICHT. MITTEL- UND OSTEUROPA. AGRARMAERKTE AKTUELL. Text in German. fortn. **Document type:** *Bulletin, Trade.*
Published by: Zentrale Markt und Preisberichtstelle GmbH, Rochusstr 2, Bonn, 53123, Germany. TEL 49-228-9777173, FAX 49-228-9777179, info@zmp.de, http://www.zmp.de.

630 DEU ISSN 0946-6630
Z M P NACHRICHTEN. Text in German. 2/w. **Document type:** *Bulletin.*
Published by: Zentrale Markt und Preisberichtstelle GmbH, Rochusstr 2, Bonn, 53123, Germany. TEL 49-228-9777176, FAX 49-228-9777179, info@zmp.de, http://www.zmp.de.

630 EGY ISSN 1110-0338
ZAGAZIG JOURNAL OF AGRICULTURAL RESEARCH/ MAGALLAT AL-BIHU? AL-ZIRAA'IYYAT KOLIYYAT AL-ZIRAA'AT AL-ZAQAAZIQ. Text in English. 1973. s-a. **Document type:** *Journal, Academic/Scholarly.*
Published by: Zagazig University, Faculty of Agriculture, Banha Branch, Mushtuhur, Zagazig, Egypt. TEL 20-55-323490, 20-55-345452, http://derp.sti.sci.eg/data/0195.htm. Ed. Dr. Hasan A H Rabia.

ZAMBIA. CENTRAL STATISTICAL OFFICE. AGRICULTURAL AND PASTORAL PRODUCTION (COMMERCIAL FARMS). see *AGRICULTURE—Abstracting, Bibliographies, Statistics*

ZAMBIA. CENTRAL STATISTICAL OFFICE. QUARTERLY AGRICULTURAL STATISTICAL BULLETIN. see *AGRICULTURE—Abstracting, Bibliographies, Statistics*

ZAMBIA. MINISTRY OF AGRICULTURE, FOOD AND FISHERIES. ANNUAL AGRICULTURAL STATISTICAL BULLETIN. see *AGRICULTURE—Abstracting, Bibliographies, Statistics*

630 PAK
ZARAAT. Text in English, Sindhi. 1982. q. PKR 50. adv. bk.rev. **Document type:** *Academic/Scholarly.* **Description:** Scientific information about agriculture.
Published by: Sind Agriculture University, Zaraat Publication Committee, Tandojam, Hyderabad, Sind, Pakistan. Ed. Dr. M Y Panhwer. Circ: 1,000.

630 DEU ISSN 0044-2194
HD1401
ZEITSCHRIFT FUER AGRARGESCHICHTE UND AGRARSOZIOLOGIE. Abbreviated title: Z A A. Text in German. 1953. 2/yr. EUR 66 to non-members; EUR 35 newsstand/cover (effective 2004). bk.rev. charts; illus.; stat.; bibl. index. back issues avail. **Document type:** *Journal, Trade.*
Indexed: AmH&L, BAS, BHA, BibCart, DIP, HistAb, IBR, IBZ, PAIS, PCI, RASB, RRTA, WAE&RSA.
—CISTI, IE. **CCC.**
Published by: (Gesellschaft fuer Agrargeschichte und Agrarsoziologie), D L G Verlags GmbH, Eschborner Landstr 122, Frankfurt Am Main, 60489, Germany. TEL 49-69-247880, FAX 49-69-24788480, dlg-verlag@dlg-frankfurt.de, http://www.dlg-verlag.de. Eds. C. Zimmermann, W. Roesener. Circ: 800.

630 RUS
ZEMEL'NYE VESTI. Text in Russian. 1994. 24/yr. USD 145 in United States (effective 2000).
Address: Begovaya ul 17, Moscow, 125284, Russian Federation. TEL 7-095-9452964. **Dist. by:** East View Information Services, 3020 Harbor Ln. N., Minneapolis, MN 55447. TEL 763-550-0961, FAX 763-559-2931.

630 RUS ISSN 0044-3913
S13 CODEN: ZMLDAH
ZEMLEDELIE. Text in Russian. 1939. bi-m. USD 63 foreign (effective 2004). adv. bk.rev. bibl.; charts; illus.; stat. index.

A

A

Indexed: AEA, BiolAb, CIN, ChemAb, ChemTitl, FCA, ForAb, HerbAb, MaizeAb, PBA, PotatoAb, RASB, RPP, RefZh, S&F, S&MA, SeedAb, SoyAb, TriticAb, WAE&RSA, WeedAb. —CASDDS, CINDOC, CISTI, East View, Linda Hall.
Address: Sadovaya-Spasskaya 18, Moscow, 107807, Russian Federation. TEL 7-095-2072110, FAX 7-095-2072870. Ed. Vladilen A Ivanov. Circ: 11,170. **Dist. by:** M K - Periodica, ul Gilyarovskogo 39, Moscow 129110, Russian Federation. TEL 7-095-2845008, FAX 7-095-2813798, info@periodicals.ru, http://www.mkniga.ru.

630 CHE
ZENTRALBLATT LAND- UND MILCHWIRTSCHAFT. Text in German. w.
Address: Weststr 10, Bern 6, 3000, Switzerland. TEL 031-449311, FAX 031-449236, TELEX 912395. Ed. Anton Haas. Circ: 63,524.

630 CHN ISSN 1008-9209
CODEN: ZNDXEE
ZHEJIANG DAXUE XUEBAO (NONGYE YU SHENGMING KEXUE BAN)/ZHEJIANG UNIVERSITY. JOURNAL (AGRICULTURE & LIFE SCIENCE). Text in Chinese. 1956. bi-m. CNY 48 domestic; USD 60 foreign (effective 2000). reprints avail. **Document type:** *Academic/Scholarly.*
Description: Publishes research papers on vegetable culture, horticulture, tea science, agricultural microbiology, crop science, biotechnology, soil science and agricultural engineering.
Formerly: Zhejiang Nongye Daxue Xuebao (1000-2111)
Related titles: CD-ROM ed.; Microfiche ed.; Online - full text ed.: (from East View Information Services).
Indexed: AEA, ASFA, AgBio, AgrForAb, AnBrAb, B&BAb, BioCN&I, CPA, DSA, ESPM, EnvEAb, FCA, FPA, FS&TA, ForAb, HerbAb, HortAb, I&DA, IndVet, MBA, MaizeAb, NemAb, NutrAb, OrnHort, PBA, PGegResA, PGrRegA, PHN&I, PN&I, PollutAb, PotatoAb, PoultAb, ProtozoAb, RA&MP, RDA, RM&VM, RPP, RefZh, RevApplEntom, RiceAb, S&F, SIA, SWRA, SeedAb, SoyAb, TDB, TriticAb, VetBull, WAE&RSA, WeedAb, ZooRec.
—BLDSC (4918.150515), CASDDS.
Published by: Zhejiang Daxue, Huajiachi Campus of Zhejiang University, Hangzhou, Zhejiang 310029, China. TEL 86-571-87952783, jacheng@zjau.edu.cn, xuebao(n)@zju.edu.cn. Ed. Cheng Jia'an. **Dist. overseas by:** China International Book Trading Corp, 35 Chegongzhuang Xilu, Haidian District, PO Box 399, Beijing 100044, China. TEL 86-10-68412045, FAX 86-10-68412023, cibtc@mail.cibtc.com.cn, http://www.cibtc.com.cn/.

630 CHN
ZHEJIANG NONGYE DAXUE XUEBAO/ZHEJIANG AGRICULTURAL UNIVERSITY. JOURNAL. Text in Chinese. 1979. q. CNY 49 domestic; CNY 8 newsstand/cover domestic. **Document type:** *Academic/Scholarly.*
Indexed: AEA, AgBio, AnBrAb, BioCN&I, CPA, EngInd, FCA, FPA, HortAb, I&DA, NutrAb, PBA, PGrRegA, PHN&I, PN&I, RPP, RevApplEntom, RiceAb, S&F, SeedAb.
Published by: Zhejiang Nongye Daxue Chubanshe/Zhejiang Agricultural University Press, Huajiachi, Hangzhou, 310029, China. xuebao@zju.edu.cn. Ed. Jia-an Chen. **Dist. by:** China International Book Trading Corp, 35 Chegongzhuang Xilu, Haidian District, PO Box 399, Beijing 100044, China. TEL 86-10-68412045, FAX 86-10-68412023, cibtc@mail.cibtc.com.cn, http://www.cibtc.com.cn.

630 CHN ISSN 0528-9017
ZHEJIANG NONGYE KEXUE/ZHEJIANG AGRICULTURAL SCIENCE. Text in Chinese. bi-m. **Document type:** *Academic/Scholarly.*
Related titles: Online - full text ed.: (from East View Information Services).
Indexed: AEA, AgBio, AgrForAb, AnBrAb, BioCN&I, CPA, FCA, FS&TA, ForAb, HelmAb, HerbAb, HortAb, I&DA, IndVet, MaizeAb, NemAb, NutrAb, OrnHort, PBA, PGegResA, PGrRegA, PHN&I, PN&I, PotatoAb, PoultAb, ProtozoAb, RA&MP, RASB, RDA, RPP, RevApplEntom, RiceAb, S&F, SIA, SeedAb, SoyAb, TriticAb, WAE&RSA, WeedAb.
Published by: Zhejiang Nongye Kexueyuan/Zhejiang Academy of Agricultural Science, 48 Shiqiao Lu, Hangzhou, Zhejiang 310021, China. TEL 42701. Ed. Zhou Jiefang. **Co-sponsor:** Zhejiang Nongye Daxue.

630 CHN ISSN 1004-1524
ZHEJIANG NONGYE XUEBAO/ACTA AGRICULTURAE ZHEJIANGENSIS. Text in Chinese. 1989. bi-m. CNY 24 domestic (effective 2003). 56 p./no.; **Document type:** *Journal, Academic/Scholarly.*
Related titles: ♦ CD-ROM ed.: Chinese Academic Journals Full-Text Database. Agriculture; Online - full content ed.: (from WanFang Data Corp.); Online - full text ed.: (from East View Information Services).
Indexed: AEA, AgBio, AgrForAb, AnBrAb, BioCN&I, CPA, DSA, FCA, ForAb, HelmAb, HerbAb, HortAb, I&DA, IndVet, MaizeAb, NemAb, NutrAb, OrnHort, PBA, PGegResA, PGrRegA, PHN&I, PN&I, PoultAb, ProtozoAb, RA&MP, RPP, RiceAb, S&F, SIA, SeedAb, SoyAb, TriticAb, VetBull, WAE&RSA, WeedAb.
—BLDSC (0589.200000), IE, ingenta.

Published by: Zhejiang Sheng Nongye Kexueyuan, 198 Shiqiao Lu, Hangzhou, Zhejiang 310021, China. TEL 86-571-86404190, FAX 86-571-86404065, 86-571-86400481, zjnyxb@zaas.org, http://zjnyxb.periodicals.com.cn/default.html. Ed. Jian Ping Chen. **Dist. by:** China International Book Trading Corp, 35 Chegongzhuang Xilu, Haidian District, PO Box 399, Beijing 100044, China. TEL 86-10-68412045, FAX 86-10-68412023, cibtc@mail.cibtc.com.cn, http://www.cibtc.com.cn.

630 CHN ISSN 1000-8047
CODEN: ZHGUEC
➤ **ZHONGGUO GUOSHU/CHINA'S FRUIT TREES.** Text in Chinese. 1959. q. CNY 24 domestic; USD 36 foreign (effective 2001). adv. bk.rev.; video rev. abstr.; charts; illus.; mkt. cum.index. back issues avail. **Document type:** *Academic/Scholarly.* **Description:** Provides forum to exchange experiences of fruit production, report on studies and experiments on fruit trees, advances for research of fruit trees,k spread scientific Technology of fruit trees, supply scientific information abroad.
Related titles: CD-ROM ed.; Fax ed.; Online - full text ed.: (from East View Information Services).
Indexed: AEA, AgBio, AgrForAb, BioCN&I, CPA, FPA, ForAb, HortAb, I&DA, NemAb, OrnHort, PBA, PGegResA, PGrRegA, PHN&I, PN&I, PoultAb, RA&MP, RDA, RM&VM, RPP, RRTA, S&F, SIA, SeedAb, WAE&RSA, WeedAb.
—BLDSC (3180.164000).
Published by: Zhongguo Nongye Kexueyuan, Guoshu Yanjiusuo/Chinese Academy of Agricultural Sciences, Fruit Tree Research Institute, Wenquan, Xingcheng, Liaoning 125100, China. TEL 86-429-5155760, FAX 86-429-5157700. Ed. Wenguang Mi. Adv. contact Weiyi Weng. color page USD 100; trim 175 x 260. Circ: 20,000.

630 951 CHN ISSN 1000-4459
S471.C6
ZHONGGUO NONG-SHI/AGRICULTURAL HISTORY OF CHINA. Text in Chinese. 1982. q. CNY 12, USD 24.
Related titles: Online - full text ed.: (from East View Information Services).
Indexed: AmH&L, HistAb, RASB.
Published by: (Zhongguo Nongye Yichan Yanjiushi/Institute for Chinese Agricultural Heritage), Nongye Chubanshe/China Agricultural Press, 2 Nongzhanguan Beilou, Chaoyang District, Beijing, 100026, China. TEL 5005894. Circ: 2,000. **Dist. in US by:** China Books & Periodicals Inc, 360 Swift Ave., Ste. 48, S San Fran, CA 94080-6220. TEL 415-282-2994. **Co-sponsor:** Zhongguo Nongye Lishi Xuehui/Chinese Society of Agricultural History.

ZHONGGUO NONGCUN JINRONG/CHINA RURAL FINANCE. see *BUSINESS AND ECONOMICS—Banking And Finance*

630 CHN ISSN 1002-381X
➤ **ZHONGGUO NONGJI TUIGUANG/CHINA AGRO-TECHNOLOGY EXTENSION.** Text in Chinese. 1985. bi-m. CNY 21 (effective 1999 & 2000). **Document type:** *Journal, Academic/Scholarly.* **Description:** Introduces and promotes agricultural technologies.
Formerly (until Aug. 1991): Nongji Tuiguang, Agricultural Technology Marketing
Related titles: CD-ROM ed.; Online - full content ed.: (from WanFang Data Corp.); Online - full text ed.: (from East View Information Services).
Published by: (Zhongguo Nongji Tuiguang Xiehui/Chinese Agricultural Technology Extension Association), Zhongguo Nongji Tuiguang, Maizidian 20-hao Lou, Beijing, 100026, China. natesc_qk@agri.gov.cn, http://zgnjtg.periodicals.com.cn/default.html. Circ: 100,000. **Dist. by:** China International Book Trading Corp, 35 Chegongzhuang Xilu, Haidian District, PO Box 399, Beijing 100044, China. TEL 86-10-68412045, FAX 86-10-68412023, http://www.cibtc.com.cn. **Co-sponsor:** Quanguo Nongye Jishu Tuiguang Fuwu Zongxing/National Agricultural Technology Extension & Service Center.

630 CHN ISSN 1007-4333
S19
ZHONGGUO NONGYE DAXUE XUEBAO/CHINA AGRICULTURAL UNIVERSITY. JOURNAL. Text in Chinese. 1996. q. CNY 30 domestic; CNY 5 newsstand/cover domestic. **Document type:** *Academic/Scholarly.* **Description:** Publishes academic papers on agronomy, horticulture, plant protection, soil science and plant nutrition, animal sciences, veterinary medicine, agricultural meteorology, agricultural biology, food science, land resources and applied chemistry.
Formed by the 1995 merger of: Beijing Nongye Daxue Xuebao/Acta Agriculturae Universitatis Pekinensis (0479-8007); (1982-1995): Beijing Nongye Gongcheng Daxue Xuebao (1000-1514)
Related titles: Online - full text ed.: (from East View Information Services).
Indexed: AEA, AgBio, AgrForAb, AnBrAb, B&BAb, BioCN&I, CPA, DSA, ESPM, EntAb, FCA, ForAb, HerbAb, HortAb, I&DA, IndVet, MaizeAb, NemAb, NutrAb, OrnHort, PBA, PGegResA, PGrRegA, PHN&I, PN&I, PotatoAb, PoultAb, ProtozoAb, RA&MP, RDA, RM&VM, RPP, RefZh, RevApplEntom, RiceAb, S&F, SIA, SeedAb, SoyAb, TDB, TriticAb, VetBull, WAE&RSA, WeedAb, ZooRec.
—BLDSC (4729.215500), IE, ingenta.

Published by: Zhongguo Nongye Daxue, 2, Yuanmingyuanxi Road, Haidian District, Beijing, 100094, China. TEL 86-2-62632619. **Dist. by:** China International Book Trading Corp, 35 Chegongzhuang Xilu, Haidian District, PO Box 399, Beijing 100044, China. TEL 86-10-68412045, FAX 86-10-68412023, cibtc@mail.cibtc.com.cn, http://www.cibtc.com.cn.

630 636 CHN ISSN 0578-1752
S471.C6 CODEN: CKNYAR
ZHONGGUO NONGYE KEXUE/CHINESE AGRICULTURAL SCIENCES. Text in Chinese; Abstracts in English. 1960. bi-m. USD 6.72 per issue. **Document type:** *Academic/Scholarly.*
Related titles: Online - full text ed.: (from East View Information Services).
Indexed: AEA, AgBio, AgrForAb, AnBrAb, BioCN&I, CIN, CPA, ChemAb, ChemTitl, DSA, FCA, FS&TA, ForAb, HelmAb, HerbAb, HortAb, I&DA, IndVet, MaizeAb, NemAb, NutrAb, OrnHort, PBA, PGegResA, PGrRegA, PHN&I, PN&I, PotatoAb, PoultAb, ProtozoAb, RA&MP, RDA, RM&VM, RPP, RefZh, RiceAb, S&F, SIA, SeedAb, SoyAb, TriticAb, VetBull, WAE&RSA, WeedAb, ZooRec.
—BLDSC (8169.300000), CASDDS, CISTI, Linda Hall.
Published by: Zhongguo Nongye Kexueyuan/Chinese Academy of Agricultural Sciences, Chinese Society for Horticultural Science, 30 Baishiqiao Lu, Beijing, 100081, China. TEL 8314433, FAX 8315645. Ed. Liu Gengling. Circ: 15,000.

ZHONGGUO NONGYE QIXIANG/CHINESE AGRICULTURAL METEOROLOGY. see *METEOROLOGY*

ZHONGGUO NONGYE WENZHAI - NONGYE GONGCHENG/CHINESE AGRICULTURAL ABSTRACTS - AGRICULTURAL ENGINEERING. see *AGRICULTURE—Abstracting, Bibliographies, Statistics*

630 CHN ISSN 1001-4187
ZHONGGUO TIANCAI/CHINESE BEETS. Text in Chinese. q.
Published by: Zhongguo Nongye Kexueyuan, Tiancai Yanjiusuo/Chinese Academy of Agricultural Sciences, Beet Research Institute, Hulan Xian, Heilongjiang 150501, China. Ed. Cai Bao.

630 CHN ISSN 1002-0551
ZHONGGUO TIANCAI TANGYE/CHINA BEET & SUGAR. Text in Chinese. 1963. bi-m. USD 15 domestic; USD 30 foreign (effective 2001). adv. **Description:** Covers sugar beet, breeding, phyiology, biochemistry, cultivation, plant protection, soil and fertilizer, evaporation and energy economy, crystallization, product storage and distribution, and more.
Formerly (until 1991): Tiancia Tangye - Beet and Sugar (1000-6451)
Related titles: Online - full text ed.: (from East View Information Services).
Published by: (Qinggongye Bu/Ministry of Light Industry, Tiancai Tangye Kexue Yanjiusuo/Sugarbeet and Sugar Institute), Tiancai Tangye Bianjibu, 333 Xuegu Rd, Harbin, Heilongjiang 150086, China. TEL 86-451-668-3245, FAX 86-451-666-2881. Ed. Qin Wenxin. Adv. contact Jiang Ming. B&W page USD 1,000, color page USD 4,000. Circ: 3,000.

638.1 CHN ISSN 0412-4367
ZHONGGUO YANGFENG/APICULTURE OF CHINA. Text in Chinese; Summaries in English. 1957. bi-m. CNY 24 domestic; USD 28, CNY 4 newsstand/cover (effective 2001). adv. bk.rev. index. **Document type:** *Academic/Scholarly.* **Description:** Contains experiment reports on apiculture, bee disease, pollination and honey bee products.
Related titles: CD-ROM ed.; Fax ed.; Online - full text ed.: (from East View Information Services).
Published by: Zhongguo Nongye Kexueyuan, Yangfeng Yanjiusuo/Chinese Academy of Agricultural Sciences, Institute of Apicultural Research, Xiangshan, Beijing, 100093, China. sinoapis@public2.east.net.cn. Ed., Adv. contact Zhensheng Ye. page USD 1,000. Circ: 20,000 (paid).

630 ZWE
ZIMBABWE. AGRICULTURAL DEVELOPMENT AUTHORITY. ANNUAL REPORT AND ACCOUNTS. Text in English. a. adv. **Document type:** *Corporate.*
Formerly: Zimbabwe. Agricultural and Rural Development Authority. Annual Report and Accounts
Published by: Agricultural and Rural Development Authority, Causeway, PO Box CY 1420, Harare, Zimbabwe. TEL 263-4-700095, FAX 263-4-700880, TELEX 22272 ZW, library@arda.samara.co.zw. Ed. L Mhlanga. R&P, Adv. contact L. Mhlanga TEL 263-4-705841.

630 ZWE ISSN 1017-5156
CODEN: ZIAJEO
ZIMBABWE AGRICULTURAL JOURNAL. Text in English. 1903. bi-m. ZWD 2. adv. bk.rev. charts; illus. index. **Document type:** *Academic/Scholarly.*
Formerly: Rhodesia Agricultural Journal (0035-4686)
Indexed: ASFA, AnBrAb, ApicAb, BiolAb, ChemAb, CurCont, ESPM, FCA, FS&TA, HerbAb, HortAb, ISAP, IndVet, NutrAb, PBA, RASB, RPP, RRTA, RevApplEntom, S&F, SFA, TobAb, VetBull, WAE&RSA, WeedAb, ZooRec.
—CISTI, Linda Hall.

Published by: (Zimbabwe. Information Services), Ministry of Lands Agriculture and Rural Resettlement, Research and Specialist Services, Causeway, PO Box 8108, Harare, Zimbabwe. Ed. R J Fenner. Circ: 1,200.

630 ZWE ISSN 0251-1045
S338.Z55 CODEN: ZJARDK
THE ZIMBABWE JOURNAL OF AGRICULTURAL RESEARCH. Text in English. 1963. s-a. ZWD 10, USD 16. bk.rev. charts; illus. cum.index. back issues avail. **Document type:** *Government.*
Former titles (until 1980): Rhodesian Journal of Agricultural Research (0035-4813); (until 1967): Rhodesia, Zambia and Malawi Journal of Agricultural Research (0370-8101)
Indexed: AgrForAb, AnBrAb, BioCN&I, BiolAb, CPA, ChemAb, CurCont, DSA, EIA, EnerInd, ExcerpMed, FCA, FPA, FS&TA, ForAb, HerbAb, HortAb, ISAP, IndVet, MaizeAb, NemAb, NutrAb, OrnHort, PBA, PGegResA, RDA, RPP, RevApplEntom, S&F, SoyAb, TobAb, TriticAb, VetBull, WAE&RSA, WeedAb, ZooRec.
—BLDSC (9513.240000), CISTI, Linda Hall.
Published by: (Zimbabwe. Information Services), Ministry of Lands Agriculture and Rural Resettlement, Research and Specialist Services, Causeway, PO Box 8108, Harare, Zimbabwe. Ed. R J Fenner. Circ: 1,000. **Co-sponsor:** Southern African Centre for Co-operation in Agricultural Research.

630 BHR
AL-ZIRA'A FIL-ALAM AL-ARABI/AGRICULTURE IN THE ARAB WORLD. Text in Arabic. m.
Published by: Falcon Publishing, PO Box 5028, Manama, Bahrain. TEL 253162, FAX 259694, TELEX 8917.

630 CHE
ZUERCHER BAUER. Text in German. w.
Address: Nueschelerstr 35, Zuerich, 8023, Switzerland. TEL 01-2117379, FAX 01-2121723. Ed. Hannes Ringger. Circ: 13,000.

630 CHN ISSN 1001-7283
ZUOWU ZAZHI/CROPS. Text in Chinese. q. **Document type:** *Journal, Academic/Scholarly.*
Related titles: Online - full text ed.: (from East View Information Services).
Published by: Zhongguo Zuowu Xuehui/Chinese Society of Crop Science, Zhongguo Nongye Kexueyuan, 30 Baishiqiao Lu, Beijing, 100081, China. TEL 891731. Ed. Wang Hengli.

630 310 DEU
1 X 1 IHR PARTNER. Text in German. 1967. bi-m. adv. **Document type:** *Magazine, Consumer.*
Published by: Profil Werbe- & Verlagsgesellschaft, Breitenweg 29-33, Bremen, 28195, Germany. TEL 49-421-171700, FAX 49-421-3092296. adv.: B&W page EUR 1,300, color page EUR 2,350. Circ: 5,300.

630 FIN ISSN 1459-4463
4 H PILKE. Text in Finnish. 1945. 8/yr. EUR 30 (effective 2005). adv. bk.rev.; film rev.; play rev. **Document type:** *Magazine, Consumer.*
Formerly (until 2003): Nuorten Sarka (0029-6139)
Published by: Suomen 4H-Liitto/4H Federation in Finland, Karjalankatu 2 A, Helsinki, 00520, Finland. TEL 358-9-75124200, FAX 358-9-75124255, pilke@4h-liitto.fi, 4h-liitto@4h-liitto.fi, http://www.4h-liitto.fi/jasenlehti/. Ed. Seppo Hassinen TEL 358-9-75124230. Circ: 19,500 (controlled).

AGRICULTURE—Abstracting, Bibliographies, Statistics

381.45002 USA
A B C BLUE BOOK: U S AND CANADIAN FARM PUBLICATIONS. Text in English. s-a. looseleaf. USD 25 to members. **Description:** Publishes six-month circulation averages for agricultural periodicals.
Supersedes in part: A B C Blue Book: U S and Canadian Magazines and Farm Publications
Published by: Audit Bureau of Circulations, 900 N Meacham Rd, Schaumburg, IL 60173-4968. TEL 847-605-0909, FAX 847-605-0483, http://www.accessabc.com.

630.21 NLD ISSN 0929-7790
ACTUELE ONTWIKKELING VAN BEDRIJFSRESULTATEN EN INKOMENS. Text in Dutch. 1993. a. price varies. **Document type:** *Government.* **Description:** Provides an analysis of actual income development in Dutch agriculture.
Formed by the merger of (1982-1992): Inkomensontwikkeling in de Agrarische Sector (0921-4119); (1983-1992): Raming van de Bedrijfsuitkomsten van de Glastuinbouw- en Champignonbedrijven (0921-4267); Prognose van Bedrijfsuitkomsten op Akkerbouw- en Veehouderijbedrijven (1381-3463); Which was formerly (1975-1983): Prognose van Bedrijfsuitkomsten op Akkerbouw- en Rundveehouderijbedrijven (0921-4143)
Published by: Landbouw-Economisch Instituut, Burgemeester Patijnlaan 19, The Hague, 2585 BE, Netherlands. TEL 31-70-3358330, 31-70-3358134, FAX 31-70-3615624, informatiecentrum.lei@wur.nl, informatie.lei@wur.nl, http://www.lei.dlo.nl. Ed. Hans van Hoeven. Circ: 600.

AGBIOTECH NEWS AND INFORMATION. see *BIOLOGY—Abstracting, Bibliographies, Statistics*

633.1021 NLD ISSN 0002-1075
AGRARISCH WEEKOVERZICHT. Text in Dutch. 1953. w. **Document type:** *Trade.* **Description:** Offers statistical data on prices of agricultural commodities (dairy, produce, and livestock), fodders, and fodder crops.
Published by: Landbouw-Economisch Instituut, Burgemeester Patijnlaan 19, The Hague, 2585 BE, Netherlands. TEL 31-70-330-8330, FAX 31-70-361-5624, postmaster@lei.nl, http://www.lei.nl. Circ: 3,500. **Subscr. to:** Postbus 29703, The Hague 2502 LS, Netherlands.

630.21 DEU ISSN 0945-7623
AGRARMAERKTE IN ZAHLEN. DEUTSCHLAND. Text in German. a. **Document type:** *Bulletin, Trade.*
Published by: Zentrale Markt und Preisberichtstelle GmbH, Rochusstr 2, Bonn, 53123, Germany. TEL 49-228-9777173, FAX 49-228-9777179, info@zmp.de, http://www.zmp.de.

338.1021 DEU ISSN 0945-764X
AGRARMAERKTE IN ZAHLEN. EUROPAEISCHE UNION. Text in German. 1994. a. **Document type:** *Bulletin, Trade.*
Related titles: CD-ROM ed.
Indexed: WAE&RSA.
Published by: Zentrale Markt und Preisberichtstelle GmbH, Rochusstr 2, Bonn, 53123, Germany. TEL 49-228-9777173, FAX 49-228-9777179, info@zmp.de, http://www.zmp.de.

338.1021 DEU ISSN 0945-7593
AGRARMAERKTE IN ZAHLEN. MITTEL- UND OSTEUROPA. Text in German. 1995. a. **Document type:** *Bulletin, Trade.*
Indexed: WAE&RSA.
Published by: Zentrale Markt und Preisberichtstelle GmbH, Rochusstr 2, Bonn, 53123, Germany. TEL 49-228-9777173, FAX 49-228-9777179, info@zmp.de, http://www.zmp.de.

016.63 USA ISSN 0897-3237
AGRICOLA C R I S. Text in English. 1970. q. **Document type:** *Bibliography.* **Description:** Covers journal articles, monographs, theses, microforms, audiovisuals, software and technical reports.
Media: Magnetic Tape. **Related titles:** CD-ROM ed.; Online - full text ed.: (from National Information Services Corp. (N I S C)).
Published by: (Current Research Information Systems), U.S. National Agricultural Library, 10301 Baltimore Ave, Rm 204, Beltsville, MD 20705-2351. TEL 301-504-6613, FAX 301-504-7098, ag98help@nal.usda.gov, http://www.nal.usda.gov/ag98/.

630.21 TZA ISSN 0251-2440
AGRICULTURAL ABSTRACTS FOR TANZANIA. Text in English. 1978. s-a. USD 28.
Formerly: Abstracting and Indexing Bulletin for Agricultural and Animal Husbandry
Published by: Library Services Board, National Documentation Centre, P O Box 9283, Dar es Salaam, Tanzania. TEL 255-51-150048-9. Ed. D A Sekimang'a. Circ: 200.

016.6313 GBR ISSN 0308-8863
Z5074.E6
AGRICULTURAL ENGINEERING ABSTRACTS. Text in English. 1976. bi-m. USD 1,445 in the Americas to institutions except Canada; GBP 825 elsewhere to institutions; USD 1,550 combined subscription in the Americas to institutions except Canada; print & online eds.; GBP 885 combined subscription elsewhere to institutions print & online eds. (effective 2006). adv. back issues avail. **Document type:** *Abstract/Index.* **Description:** Covers research developments in agricultural engineering and instrumentation.
Related titles: Online - full text ed.: USD 1,225 in the Americas to institutions except Canada; GBP 700 elsewhere to institutions (effective 2006) (from DIMDI, The Dialog Corporation).
—BLDSC (0746.002000). **CCC.**
Published by: CABI Publishing (Subsidiary of: CAB International), CAB International, Wallingford, Oxfordshire OX10 8DE, United Kingdom. TEL 44-1491-832111, FAX 44-1491-833508, cabi@cabi.org, http://www.cabi-publishing.org/. Ed. Liza Conner. adv.: B&W page GBP 50, B&W page USD 80; 170 x 267. Circ: 135. **Subscr. addr. in N America:** CABI Publishing North America, 875 Massachusetts Ave, 7th Fl, Cambridge, MA 02139. TEL 617-395-4056, 800-528-4841, FAX 617-354-6875, cabi-nao@cabi.org.

630.21 IND
AGRICULTURAL PRICES IN INDIA. Text in English, Hindi. 1957. a. INR 275, USD 16.48. **Document type:** *Government.*
Former titles: India. Ministry of Agriculture. Directorate of Economics and Statistics. Bulletin of Agriculture Prices; Agricultural Prices in India; All India Report on Agricultural Census
Published by: Ministry of Agriculture, Directorate of Economics and Statistics, A-2E-3 Kasturba Gandhi Marg Barracks, New Delhi, 110 001, India. TEL 91-11-381523. Ed. Brajesh Kumar Gautam. Circ: 600. **Dist. by:** Controller of Publications, Civil Lines, New Delhi 110 006, India.

630.21 CYP
AGRICULTURAL REGIONS OF CYPRUS. Text in English. 1983. irreg. CYP 2 per issue (effective 1999). **Document type:** *Government.* **Description:** Offers a comparative analysis of the agro-economic regions of Cyprus with such statistics as the availability of resources, land use, cropping patterns, levels of production and productivity.
Published by: Ministry of Finance, Department of Statistics and Research, 13 Andreas Araouzos St, Nicosia, 1444, Cyprus. TEL 357-2-309318, FAX 357-2-374830, cydsr@cytanet.com.cy, http://www.pio.gov.cy/dsr.

630.21 ETH
AGRICULTURAL SAMPLE SURVEY FOR (YEAR). (In 7 series) Text in English. a. ETB 16, USD 2.15. back issues avail. **Document type:** *Government.* **Description:** Presents reports on land utilization, farm management practices, area and major crop production, livestock, poultry, and bee hives.
Related titles: CD-ROM ed.; Diskette ed.
Published by: Central Statistical Authority, PO Box 1143, Addis Ababa, Ethiopia. TEL 251-1-115470, FAX 251-1-550334.

630.21 GRC ISSN 0065-4574
AGRICULTURAL STATISTICS OF GREECE. Key Title: Georgike Statistike tes Ellados. Text in English, Greek. 1961. a., latest 1996. back issues avail. **Document type:** *Government.*
Published by: National Statistical Service of Greece, Statistical Information and Publications Division/Ethniki Statistiki Yperesia tes Ellados, 14-16 Lykourgou St, Athens, 101 66, Greece. TEL 30-1-3289-397, FAX 30-1-3244-708, http://www.statistics.gr, http://www.statistics.gr/Main_eng.asp.

630.21 MYS ISSN 0127-4708
HD2080.6.Z9
➤ **AGRICULTURAL STATISTICS OF SARAWAK.** Text in English. 1971. a., latest 1998. MYR 5. charts; stat. **Document type:** *Government.* **Description:** Contains statistics of agricultural crops and imports and exports of agricultural commodities of the State of Sabah.
Indexed: FCA, HerbAb.
—CISTI.
Published by: Department of Agriculture, Statistics Unit, Kota Kinabalu, Sabah 88632, Malaysia. TEL 60-88-283283, FAX 60-88-239046, doasabah@tm.net.my. Circ: 250 (controlled and free).

636.0021 LUX
HD9425.E8
AGRICULTURAL STATISTICS SERIES NO.2: ANIMAL PRODUCTION. Text in English, French, German. 1975. q. USD 110. charts; stat. **Description:** Statistics on meat, eggs and poultry, milk and milk products.
Formerly: Statistical Office of the European Communities. Animal Production (0250-6580); Formed by the merger of: Statistical Office of the European Communities. Monthly Statistics. Eggs; Statistical Office of the European Communities. Monthly Statistics. Meat; Statistical Office of the European Communities. Monthly Statistics. Milk
Related titles: Microfiche ed.: (from CIS); Online - full text ed.
Indexed: IIS.
—CISTI.
Published by: European Commission, Statistical Office of the European Communities, Rue Alcide de Gasperi, Luxembourg, 2920, Luxembourg. TEL 43011, TELEX COMMEUR LU 3423. **Dist. in the U.S. by:** Unipub, 4611-F Assembly Drive, Lanham, MD 20706-4391. TEL 301-459-0056, 800-274-4888.

338.1021 LUX
AGRICULTURAL STATISTICS SERIES NO.3: EUROPEAN COMMUNITIES INDEX OF AGRICULTURAL PRICES. Text in English. s-a. USD 100. **Description:** Shows trends of monthly community producer price indices for agricultural products and the purchase of the means of agricultural production over the last 13 available months.
Formerly: E C Agricultural Price Indices (0250-5967)
Related titles: Microfiche ed.: (from CIS).
Indexed: IIS.
—CISTI.
Published by: European Commission, Statistical Office of the European Communities, Rue Alcide de Gasperi, Luxembourg, 2920, Luxembourg. **Subscr. in U.S. to:** Bernan Associates, Bernan, 4611-F Assembly Dr., Lanham, MD 20706-4391. TEL 301-459-0056.

016.63 IND ISSN 0002-1733
AGRICULTURE CHECKLIST. Text in English. 1966. bi-m. looseleaf. INR 150, USD 30 (effective 2000). adv. bk.rev. bibl. **Document type:** *Trade.*
Published by: K.K. Roy (Private) Ltd., 55 Gariahat Rd., P O Box 10210, Kolkata, West Bengal 700 019, India. Ed. K K Roy. R&P M Misra TEL 91-33-475-4872. Circ: 1,000.

338.1021 DNK ISSN 0905-5142
AGRICULTURE IN DENMARK. Text in English. 1973. s-a., latest 2004. stat.; charts. **Document type:** *Trade.* **Description:** Provides statistical information on the agricultural situation in Denmark, including summary coverage of topics relating to production, marketing, and economic forecasting.
Formerly (until 1988): Landoekonomisk Oversigt (English Edition) (0905-5207)
Related titles: Online - full text ed.; ♦ Danish ed.: Landoekonomisk Oversigt. ISSN 0107-7163.

A

—CISTI.
Published by: Danske Landboforeninger/Danish Farmers' Association, Axelborg, Vesterbrogade 4A, Copenhagen V, 1620, Denmark. TEL 45-33-394600, FAX 45-33-394606, dl@dansklandbrug.dk, http://www.dansklandbrug.dk/get/17270.html.

630.21 PHL
AGRIDEV WEEKLY BULLETIN. Text in English. w. **Document type:** *Bulletin, Government.* **Description:** Summary of agricultural situations throughout the Philippines. Weather, crop, livestock, poultry and fishery information.
Formerly: Philippines. Department of Agriculture. Bureau of Agricultural Statistics. Weekly Agricultural Situation Report
Published by: Department of Agriculture, Bureau of Agricultural Statistics, BEN-LOR Bldg, Quezon City, 1184, Philippines. FAX 63-2-968-966, da-bas@gaia.psdn.org. Ed. Aurora D Abaya. R&P Romeo S Recide. Circ: 300.

016.63 POL
AGRO-AGEN; bibliographic database. Text and summaries in English. 1992. q. EUR 795, USD 1,000 domestic to institutions; EUR 1,192, USD 1,500 foreign to institutions (effective 2006). adv. bibl. cum.index: 1992-1998. back issues avail. **Document type:** *Abstract/Index.* **Description:** Indexes the contents of Polish journals published in English covering biology, agriculture and environment.
Media: CD-ROM.
Published by: Akademia Rolnicza (Poznan), Biblioteka Glowna, Ul Witosa 45, Poznan, 61693, Poland. TEL 48-61-8487312, FAX 48-61-8487810, zokasprz@au.poznan.pl. Ed. Zofia Kasprzak.

016.63 POL
AGRO-KONF; bibliographic database. Text in English, Polish. 1992. q. PLZ 400 domestic; USD 310 foreign (effective 2000). bibl.; stat. **Document type:** *Abstract/Index.* **Description:** Includes conference materials concerning nature, environmental sciences, and applied sciences.
Media: Online - full text. **Related titles:** CD-ROM ed.
Published by: Akademia Rolnicza (Poznan), Biblioteka Glowna, Ul Witosa 45, Poznan, 61693, Poland. TEL 48-61-8487809, FAX 48-61-8487810, wgolab@owl.au.poznan.pl, http://150.254.174.29. Pub. Wlodzimierz Golab.

016.63 POL
AGRO-LIBREX; bibliographic database. Text in English, Polish. 1992. q. EUR 1,509, USD 1,898 domestic to institutions; EUR 2,264, USD 2,847 foreign to institutions (effective 2006). adv. **Document type:** *Abstract/Index.* **Description:** Indexes the contents of Polish journals and series covering biology, agriculture, forestry, horticulture, animal science, wood, food, nutrition, environmental and veterinary sciences.
Media: CD-ROM.
Published by: Akademia Rolnicza (Poznan), Biblioteka Glowna, Ul Witosa 45, Poznan, 61693, Poland. TEL 48-61-8487312, FAX 48-61-8487810, zokasprz@au.poznan.pl. Eds. Renata Tomaszewska, Zofia Kasprzak.

016.63 USA
AGROBASE. Text in English. m. USD 1,095 single user; USD 1,595 single network user; USD 2,395 up to 5 network users; USD 3,595 up to 10 network users (effective 2000). **Document type:** *Abstract/Index.* **Description:** Combines the comprehensive abstracting and indexing databases on agriculture, agricultural economics, and the world food supply, Agris and Agricola.
Media: Online - full text (from National Information Services Corp. (N I S C)).
Published by: National Information Services Corp. (N I S C), Ste 6, Wyman Towers, 3100 St Paul St, Baltimore, MD 21218. TEL 410-243-0797, FAX 410-243-0982, sales@nisc.com, http://www.nisc.com. **Subscr. to:** National Technical Information Service, Government Research Center, 5285 Port Royal Rd, Springfield, VA 22161. TEL 703-605-6060, 800-363-2068, http://www.ntis.gov.

016.63 GBR
AGROFORESTRY ABSTRACTS (ONLINE EDITION). Text in English. q. USD 490 in the Americas to institutions except Canada; GBP 280 elsewhere to institutions (effective 2006). Index. **Document type:** *Abstract/Index.* **Description:** Covers all aspects of agroforestry. Includes agroforestry components and processes - trees, animals and crops; production, service, conservation, human ecology, and social and economic aspects; development issues; research and methodology.
Media: Online - full text (from DIMDI, The Dialog Corporation). **Related titles:** CD-ROM ed.: Agroforestry Abstracts (CD-ROM Edition).
Published by: (International Council for Research in Agroforestry (ICRAF)), CABI Publishing (Subsidiary of: CAB International), CAB International, Wallingford, Oxfordshire OX10 8DE, United Kingdom. TEL 44-1491-832111, FAX 44-1491-833508, cabi@cabi.org, http://www.cabi-publishing.org/.

016.63 POL ISSN 1427-5805
AKADEMIA ROLNICZA WE WROCLAWIU. ZESZYTY NAUKOWE. BIBLIOGRAFIE. Text in Polish. 1996. irreg. price varies. **Document type:** *Academic/Scholarly.*
Related titles: ◆ Series of: Akademia Rolnicza we Wroclawiu. Zeszyty Naukowe. ISSN 0867-7964.
Published by: Akademia Rolnicza we Wroclawiu/Agricultural University of Wroclaw, Ul Norwida 25, Wroclaw, 50375, Poland. TEL 48-71-3205101, wyd@ozi.ar.wroc.pl. **Subscr. to:** Wydawnictwo Akademii Rolniczej we Wroclawiu, ul Sopocka 23, Wroclaw 50344, Poland.

630.21 USA
ALASKA AGRICULTURAL STATISTICS. Text in English. 1960. a. USD 5 (effective 2000). **Document type:** *Government.*
Former titles: Alaska Agricultural Statistics Service. Agricultural Statistics (0065-5694); (until 1962): Alaska Farm Production (0516-4850)
Indexed: SRI.
Published by: Agricultural Statistics Service, PO Box 799, Palmer, AK 99645. TEL 907-745-4272. Eds. Delon A Brown, David Mueller. **Dist. by:** Agricultural Statistics Board Publications, South Bldg, Rm 5829, U S Department of Agriculture, Washington, DC 20250.

630.21 USA
ALASKA FARM REPORTER. Text in English. m. USD 7 (effective 2000). **Document type:** *Government.*
Published by: Agricultural Statistics Service, PO Box 799, Palmer, AK 99645. TEL 907-745-4272. Ed. David Mueller. **Dist. by:** Agricultural Statistics Board Publications, South Bldg, Rm 5829, U S Department of Agriculture, Washington, DC 20250.

633.1021 USA
ALASKA WEEKLY CROP WEATHER. Text in English. w. (May-Oct.). USD 9 (effective 2000). **Document type:** *Government.*
Former titles: Alaska Agricultural Statistics Service. Crop Weather Report; Alaska Crop and Livestock Reporting Service. Weekly Crop-Weather
Published by: Agricultural Statistics Service, PO Box 799, Palmer, AK 99645. TEL 907-745-4272. Ed. David Mueller. **Dist. by:** Agricultural Statistics Board Publications, South Bldg, Rm 5829, U S Department of Agriculture, Washington, DC 20250.

016.63 USA
AMERICAN SOCIETY OF AGRONOMY. ANNUAL MEETINGS ABSTRACTS (CD-ROM). Text in English. 1950. a. USD 20 (effective 2004). adv. **Document type:** *Abstract/Index.* **Description:** Includes abstracts of volunteer papers as well as invitational papers presented at the society's annual meetings.
Former titles (until 2000): American Society of Agronomy. Annual Meetings Abstracts (Print); (until 1998): Agronomy Abstracts (0375-5495)
Indexed: PBA.
—Linda Hall. **CCC.**
Published by: American Society of Agronomy, Inc., 677 S Segoe Rd, Madison, WI 53711. TEL 608-273-8080, FAX 608-273-2021, headquarters@agronomy.org, http://www.agronomy.org. Circ: 12,500.

016.63 GBR ISSN 0003-3499
SF1
ANIMAL BREEDING ABSTRACTS; a monthly abstract of world literature. Text in English. 1933. m. USD 1,750 in the Americas to institutions except Canada; GBP 1,000 elsewhere to institutions; USD 1,875 combined subscription in the Americas to institutions except Canada; print & online eds.; GBP 1,070 combined subscription elsewhere to institutions print & online eds. (effective 2006). adv. bk.rev. abstr. index. back issues avail.; reprints avail. **Document type:** *Abstract/Index.* **Description:** Covers animal breeding, genetics, reproduction, and production; includes research about immunogenetics, genetic engineering, and fertility improvement.
Related titles: Online - full text ed.: USD 1,490 in the Americas to institutions except Canada; GBP 850 elsewhere to institutions (effective 2006) (from DIMDI, The Dialog Corporation).
Indexed: AgBio, DSA, HelmAb, IndVet, PN&I.
—BLDSC (0903.000000), Linda Hall. **CCC.**
Published by: CABI Publishing (Subsidiary of: CAB International), CAB International, Wallingford, Oxfordshire OX10 8DE, United Kingdom. TEL 44-1491-832111, FAX 44-1491-833508, orders@cabi.org, http://www.cabi-publishing.org/. Eds. M Djuric, Richard J Laight. adv.: B&W page GBP 125, B&W page USD 200; 170 x 267. Circ: 355.

630.21 FRA ISSN 0243-6825
ANNUAIRE DE STATISTIQUE AGRICOLE. Text in French. a. **Document type:** *Government.*
Related titles: Microfiche ed.
Published by: Ministere de l'Agriculture et de la Peche, Service Central des Enquetes et Etudes Statistiques, 251 rue de Vaugirard, Paris, Cedex 15 75732, France. TEL 33-1-49558585, FAX 33-1-49558503, scees75@wanadoo.fr, http://www.agriculture.gouv.fr. Ed. G Raulin.

ANUARIO ESTADISTICO DE EXISTENCIAS, FAENA Y EXPORTACION. see *FOOD AND FOOD INDUSTRIES—Abstracting, Bibliographies, Statistics*

016.63 GBR ISSN 0003-648X
CODEN: APIBAE
APICULTURAL ABSTRACTS. Text in English. 1950. q. GBP 165 (effective 2005). adv. bk.rev. pat.; tr.lit. index. cum.index: 1950-1972; 1973-1983 (microfiche). back issues avail. **Document type:** *Abstract/Index.* **Description:** Gives quick access to the world's literature on bee science and beekeeping.
Related titles: Diskette ed.; Online - full text ed.: (from The Dialog Corporation).
Indexed: RefZh.
—CISTI, Linda Hall. **CCC.**
Published by: International Bee Research Association, 18 North Rd, Cardiff, Wales CF10 3DT, United Kingdom. TEL 44-2920-372409, FAX 44-2920-665522, mail@ibra.org.uk, http://www.ibra.org.uk/aa.html. Ed., Adv. contact Dr. Pamela A Munn. page GBP 145; 115 x 175. Circ: 400.

630.21 ARG
ARGENTINA. INSTITUTO NACIONAL DE ESTADISTICA Y CENSOS. CENSO NACIONAL AGROPECUARIO (YEAR); resultados generales - caracteristicas basicas. Text in Spanish. 1992. irreg. price varies. **Document type:** *Government.* **Description:** Contains information on the principal variables that characterize the structure of the agricultural sector.
Published by: Instituto Nacional de Estadistica y Censos, Avda. Presidente Julio A. Roca, 615 P B, Capital Federal, Buenos Aires 1067, Argentina. TEL 54-114-3499662, FAX 54-114-3499621, ces@indec.mecon.ar, http://www.indec.mecon.ar.

630.21 ARG
ARGENTINA. INSTITUTO NACIONAL DE ESTADISTICA Y CENSOS. ENCUESTA NACIONAL AGROPECUARIA. Text in Spanish. 1993. irreg. price varies. **Document type:** *Government.*
Published by: Instituto Nacional de Estadistica y Censos, Avda. Presidente Julio A. Roca, 615 P B, Capital Federal, Buenos Aires 1067, Argentina. TEL 54-114-3499662, FAX 54-114-3499621, ces@indec.mecon.ar, http://www.indec.mecon.ar.

636.0021 ARG ISSN 0066-7269
ARGENTINA. JUNTA NACIONAL DE CARNES. SINTESIS ESTADISTICA. Text in Spanish. 1934. a. ARS 9,600. index.
Formerly (1956-1969): Argentina Republic. Junta Nacional de Carnes. Resena
Published by: Junta Nacional de Carnes, San Martin, 459, Capital Federal, Buenos Aires 1004, Argentina. Circ: 2,000.

636.0021 ARG
ARGENTINA. SECRETARIA DE AGRICULTURA GANADERIA Y PESCA. SITUACION DEL MERCADO DE CARNES. Text in Spanish. 1992. m.?. **Document type:** *Government.*
Related titles: English ed.: Argentina. Secretariat for Agriculture, Livestock and Fisheries. Market Situation and the Role of Government in the Argentinian Meat Sector.
Published by: Secretaria de Agricultura Ganaderia y Pesca, Avda. Paseo Colon, 922 1o Of 146, Capital Federal, Buenos Aires 1063, Argentina.

637.1021 ARG
ARGENTINA. SECRETARIA DE ESTADO DE AGRICULTURA Y GANADERIA. AREA DE TRABAJO DE LECHERIA. RESENA ESTADISTICA. Text in Spanish. 1964. irreg. free. stat.
Media: Duplicated (not offset). **Related titles:** Cards ed.
Published by: (Argentina. Area de Trabajo de Lecheria), Secretaria de Estado de Agricultura y Ganaderia, Avda. Paseo Colon, 922, Capital Federal, Buenos Aires 1063, Argentina. Circ: 1,000.

016.63461 IDN
ASIAN AND PACIFIC COCONUT COMMUNITY. BIBLIOGRAPHY SERIES. Text in English. irreg. **Document type:** *Bibliography.* **Description:** Lists documents related to coconut wood, small-scale processing of coconuts and coconut-based farming systems.
Published by: Asian and Pacific Coconut Community, 3rd Fl., Lina Bldg., Jl H R Rasuna Said Kav B 7, Kuningan, Jakarta, 12920, Indonesia. TEL 62-21-5221712, FAX 62-21-52217140, TELEX 62209 APCCIA.

630.21 314 ROM ISSN 1454-4520
ASPECTS ON THE EVOLUTION OF AGRICULTURE IN RUMANIA. Text in English, Romanian; Summaries in English, Romanian. 1999. a. ROL 25,000; USD 10 foreign. **Document type:** *Government.* **Description:** Contains statistics for all agriculture.
Published by: Comisia Nationala pentru Statistica/National Commission for Statistics, Bd. Libertatii 16, Sector 5, Bucharest, 70542, Romania. TEL 40-1-3363370, FAX 40-1-3124873, ciu@cus.kappa.ro. R&P Ivan Ungureanu Clementina.

633.021 AUS ISSN 1442-7184
AUSTRALIA. BUREAU OF STATISTICS. AGRICULTURAL COMMODITIES, AUSTRALIA. Text in English. 1998. a. AUD 21 (effective 2003). **Document type:** *Government.*

Published by: Australian Bureau of Statistics, PO Box 10, Belconnen, ACT 2616, Australia. TEL 61-2-6252-5249, FAX 61-2-6252-6778, http://www.abs.gov.au.

630.021 AUS
AUSTRALIA. BUREAU OF STATISTICS. AGRICULTURAL INDUSTRIES, FINANCIAL STATISTICS, AUSTRALIA, PRELIMINARY. Text in English. 1989. a. AUD 17 (effective 2001). **Document type:** *Government.* **Description:** Preliminary financial year estimates of turnover, value added, cash operating surplus and indebtedness of farm businesses classified by 13 agricultural industries.
Former titles: Australia. Bureau of Statistics. Agricultural Industries, Financial Statistics, Australia. Preliminary Estimates (1320-6443); (until 1993): Agricultural Industries, Financial Statistics, Australia. First Preliminary Estimates (1037-8952)
Published by: Australian Bureau of Statistics, PO Box 10, Belconnen, ACT 2616, Australia. TEL 61-2-6252-5249, FAX 61-2-6252-6778, http://www.abs.gov.au.

630.021 AUS ISSN 1322-865X
HD2151
AUSTRALIA. BUREAU OF STATISTICS. AGRICULTURE, AUSTRALIA. Text in English. 1993. a. free. **Document type:** *Government.* **Description:** Covers the structure of the Australian farming sector and included details of land use, crop and horticultural activity, and livestock numbers.
—CISTI.
Published by: Australian Bureau of Statistics, PO Box 10, Belconnen, ACT 2616, Australia. TEL 61-2-6252-5249, FAX 61-2-6252-6778, http://www.abs.gov.au.

630.021 AUS
AUSTRALIA. BUREAU OF STATISTICS. AGSTATS MANUAL. Text in English. 1977. quinquennial. price varies. **Document type:** *Government.*
Published by: Australian Bureau of Statistics, PO Box 10, Belconnen, ACT 2616, Australia. TEL 61-2-6252-5249, FAX 61-2-6252-6778, http://www.abs.gov.au.

630.21 AUS ISSN 0157-7727
AUSTRALIA. BUREAU OF STATISTICS. AUSTRALIAN FARMING IN BRIEF. Text in English. 1977. a. AUD 1.25 for brochure (effective 2002). **Document type:** *Government.* **Description:** Contains condensed information about agriculture and related industries, farm businesses, estimated value of agricultural operations, land use, fertilizer usage, and production of crops, fruit, and livestock products.
Published by: Australian Bureau of Statistics, PO Box 10, Belconnen, ACT 2616, Australia. TEL 61-2-6252-5249, FAX 61-2-6252-6778, http://www.abs.gov.au.

630.21 AUS ISSN 1320-6486
AUSTRALIA. BUREAU OF STATISTICS. AUSTRALIAN WINE AND GRAPE INDUSTRY. Text in English. 1979. a. AUD 24 (effective 2003). **Document type:** *Government.* **Description:** Covers bearing and non-bearing vines, and production of grapes for winemaking and drying purposes.
Formed by the merger of (1979-1993): Viticulture, Australia (0158-9067); (1979-1993): Wine Production, Australia and States (1031-0827)
Published by: Australian Bureau of Statistics, PO Box 10, Belconnen, ACT 2616, Australia. TEL 61-2-6252-5249, FAX 61-2-6252-6778, http://www.abs.gov.au.

630.21 AUS ISSN 1443-8453
AUSTRALIA. BUREAU OF STATISTICS. DIRECTORY OF AGRICULTURAL AND RURAL STATISTICS. Text in English. 1998. triennial. AUD 44 (effective 2002). **Document type:** *Government.*
Formerly (until 2001): Australia. Bureau of Statistics. Directory of Agricultural Statistics
Published by: Australian Bureau of Statistics, PO Box 10, Belconnen, ACT 2616, Australia. TEL 61-2-6252-5249, FAX 61-2-6252-6778, http://www.abs.gov.au.

633.021 AUS
AUSTRALIA. BUREAU OF STATISTICS. HOME PRODUCTION OF SELECTED FOODSTUFFS, AUSTRALIA. Text in English. 1992. irreg. AUD 20 (effective 1998). **Document type:** *Government.* **Description:** Details home production of fruit, vegetables, poultry, eggs, beer, wine and nuts.
Published by: Australian Bureau of Statistics, PO Box 10, Belconnen, ACT 2616, Australia. TEL 61-2-6252-5249, FAX 61-2-6252-6778, http://www.abs.gov.au.

636.021 AUS ISSN 1441-1210
AUSTRALIA. BUREAU OF STATISTICS. LIVESTOCK AND MEAT, AUSTRALIA. Text in English. 1998. m. AUD 18.50 (effective 2003). **Document type:** *Government.*
Published by: Australian Bureau of Statistics, PO Box 10, Belconnen, ACT 2616, Australia. TEL 61-2-6252-5249, FAX 61-2-6252-6778, http://www.abs.gov.au.

636.021 AUS ISSN 0728-4047
AUSTRALIA. BUREAU OF STATISTICS. LIVESTOCK PRODUCTS, AUSTRALIA. Text in English. 1981. q. AUD 22 (effective 2003). **Document type:** *Government.* **Description:** Provides information about livestock slaughterings, meat production, milk intake by factories, receivals of wool by brokers, and exports of meat.
Published by: Australian Bureau of Statistics, PO Box 10, Belconnen, ACT 2616, Australia. TEL 61-2-6252-5249, FAX 61-2-6252-6778.

630.021 AUS ISSN 1328-6900
AUSTRALIA. BUREAU OF STATISTICS. PRINCIPAL AGRICULTURAL COMMODITIES, AUSTRALIA, PRELIMINARY. Text in English. 1981. a. AUD 19 (effective 2003). **Document type:** *Government.* **Description:** Preliminary statistics on area and production of principal cereals for grain; area intended to be sown to barley, oats and wheat for all purposes; livestock numbers, lambing and intended matings.
Former titles: Australia. Bureau of Statistics. Principal Agricultural Commodities, Australia, Preliminary, Agricultural Production and Farmers' Intentions for (Next) Season (1033-4823); Principal Agricultural Commodities, Australia, Preliminary
Published by: Australian Bureau of Statistics, PO Box 10, Belconnen, ACT 2616, Australia. TEL 61-2-6252-5249, FAX 61-2-6252-6778, http://www.abs.gov.au.

636.0021 AUS
AUSTRALIA. BUREAU OF STATISTICS. QUEENSLAND OFFICE. CATTLE BREEDS, QUEENSLAND. Text in English. 1973. irreg., latest 1987. AUD 10. **Description:** Cattle numbers, summary of breeds, breeds by type in local government areas and statistical divisions.
Published by: Australian Bureau of Statistics, Queensland Office, 313 Adelaide St, Brisbane, QLD 4000, Australia. TEL 61-7-3222-6350, FAX 61-7-3222-6283, http://www.abs.gov.au.

636.0021 AUS ISSN 0815-7103
AUSTRALIA. BUREAU OF STATISTICS. SHEEP AND WOOL, AUSTRALIA, PRELIMINARY. Text in English. 1983. a. AUD 10.50. **Document type:** *Government.* **Description:** Contains estimates from the Agricultural Census of sheep numbers, lambing statistics, numbers of sheep shorn and wool produced.
Published by: Australian Bureau of Statistics, PO Box 10, Belconnen, ACT 2616, Australia.

338.1021 AUS ISSN 1031-0797
AUSTRALIA. BUREAU OF STATISTICS. VALUE OF PRINCIPAL AGRICULTURAL COMMODITIES PRODUCED, AUSTRALIA, PRELIMINARY. Text in English. 1965. a. AUD 18.50 (effective 2003). **Document type:** *Government.* **Description:** Provides preliminary estimates of the gross value of production of selected crops, livestock slaughtering and livestock products.
Formerly: Value of Agricultural Commodities Produced, Australia, First Estimates
Published by: Australian Bureau of Statistics, PO Box 10, Belconnen, ACT 2616, Australia. TEL 61-2-6252-5249, FAX 61-2-6252-6778, http://www.abs.gov.au.

016.63 BGD
BANGLADESH AGRICULTURAL SCIENCES ABSTRACTS. Short title: B A S A. Text in English. 1974. biennial. BDT 50, USD 20. **Document type:** *Abstract/Index.*
Indexed: API.
Published by: Bangladesh Agricultural University Old Boys' Association, c/o Dept. of Soil Science, Agricultural University, Mymensingh, Bangladesh. Ed. M Eaqub. Circ: 500.
Co-sponsor: Bangladesh Agricultural Research Council.

630.21 BEL ISSN 1379-4752
BELGIUM. INSTITUT NATIONAL DE STATISTIQUE. AGRICULTURE. STATISTIQUES AGRICOLES. Key Title: Statistiques Agricoles - Institut National de Statistique. Text in French. 1971. q. EUR 32 includes yearly inventory (effective 2002). charts. back issues avail. **Document type:** *Government.* **Description:** Presents a statistical overview of the current state of agricultural economics in Belgium, along with agricultural trends.
Formerly (until 2001): Belgium. Institut National de Statistique. Statistiques Agricoles (0067-5466)
Related titles: ♦ Dutch ed.: Belgium. Nationaal Instituut voor de Statistiek. Landbouw. Landbouwstatistieken. ISSN 1379-4744.
Indexed: PAIS.
—CISTI.
Published by: Institut National de Statistique/Nationaal Instituut voor de Statistiek (Subsidiary of: Ministere des Affaires Economiques), Rue de Louvain 44, Brussels, 1000, Belgium. TEL 32-2-548-6211, FAX 32-2-548-6367, http://www.statbel.fgov.be.

630.21 BEL ISSN 1379-4744
BELGIUM. NATIONAAL INSTITUUT VOOR DE STATISTIEK. LANDBOUW. LANDBOUWSTATISTIEKEN. Key Title: Landbouw. Landbouwstatistieken - Nationaal Instituut voor de Statistiek. Text in Dutch. 1969. q. charts. back issues avail. **Document type:** *Government.* **Description:** Offers a statistical overview of trends and the current state of agriculture in Belgium.
Formerly (until 2001): Belgium. Nationaal Instituut voor de Statistiek. Landbouwstatistieken (0772-7615)
Related titles: ♦ French ed.: Belgium. Institut National de Statistique. Agriculture. Statistiques Agricoles. ISSN 1379-4752.
Published by: Institut National de Statistique/Nationaal Instituut voor de Statistiek (Subsidiary of: Ministere des Affaires Economiques), Rue de Louvain 44, Brussels, 1000, Belgium. TEL 32-2-548-6211, FAX 32-2-548-6367, http://www.statbel.fgov.be.

016.63 016.94 HUN
BIBLIOGRAPHIA HISTORIAE RERUM RUSTICARUM INTERNATIONALIS/INTERNATIONAL BIBLIOGRAPHY OF AGRICULTURAL HISTORY. Text in Hungarian; Index in Hungarian, English. 1964. biennial. USD 40. index. **Document type:** *Bibliography.* **Description:** Provides data on works concerning agricultural history and related fields.
Published by: Magyar Mezogazdasagi Muzeum/Hungarian Agricultural Museum, PO Box 129, Budapest, 1367, Hungary. TEL 36-1-3430573, FAX 36-1-3439120. Eds. Eva Voros, Peter Hajdu. R&P Gyorgy Feher TEL 36-1-3438485. Circ: 500.

016.635 NLD
BIBLIOGRAPHY ON SOILLESS CULTURE. Text in Dutch. 1957. biennial. membership only. **Document type:** *Bibliography.* **Description:** Comprehensive summaries of current literature on soilless culture.
Published by: International Society for Soilless Culture, PO Box 52, Wageningen, 6700 AB, Netherlands. TEL 31-317-413809, FAX 31-317-423457.

016.63 GBR ISSN 0143-1404
CODEN: DWTRDW
BIOCONTROL NEWS AND INFORMATION. Text in English. 1980. q. USD 655 in the Americas to institutions except Canada; GBP 375 elsewhere to institutions; USD 700 combined subscription in the Americas to institutions except Canada; print & online eds.; USD 400 combined subscription elsewhere to institutions print & online eds. (effective 2006). adv. reprints avail. **Document type:** *Abstract/Index.* **Description:** A news, reviews, commentary and abstract journal of current developments in biocontrol.
Related titles: Online - full text ed.: USD 140 in the Americas to individuals; GBP 80 elsewhere to individuals; USD 500 in the Americas to institutions; GBP 285 elsewhere to institutions (effective 2005) (from DIMDI, EBSCO Publishing, The Dialog Corporation).
Indexed: HerbAb, HortAb, NemAb, OrnHort, PBA, PGegResA, RDA, RPP, RevApplEntom, S&F, WAE&RSA, WeedAb, ZooRec.
—BLDSC (2071.100000), CISTI. **CCC.**
Published by: CABI Publishing (Subsidiary of: CAB International), CAB International, Wallingford, Oxfordshire OX10 8DE, United Kingdom. TEL 44-1491-832111, FAX 44-1491-833508, cabi@cabi.org, http://www.cabi-publishing.org/. Ed. Rebecca Murphy. Adv. contact Sarah Harris TEL 44-1491-829310. B&W page GBP 75, B&W page USD 120; 170 x 267. Circ: 270. **Subscr. in N America to:** CABI Publishing North America, 875 Massachusetts Ave, 7th Fl, Cambridge, MA 02139. TEL 617-395-4056, 800-528-4841, FAX 617-354-6875, cabi-nao@cabi.org.

BIOFUELS ABSTRACTS. see *ENERGY—Abstracting, Bibliographies, Statistics*

BIOLOGICAL & AGRICULTURAL INDEX. see *BIOLOGY—Abstracting, Bibliographies, Statistics*

016.63 DEU ISSN 0300-4627
BLATT FUER SORTENWESEN. Text in German. 1968. m. EUR 40.50 (effective 2004). bk.rev. pat. **Document type:** *Journal, Government.*
Indexed: VITIS.
—CISTI.
Published by: (Germany, Federal Republic. Bundessortenamt), Deutscher Landwirtschaftsverlag GmbH, Berliner Str 112A, Berlin, 13189, Germany. TEL 49-30-29397450, FAX 49-30-29397459, dlv.berlin@dlv.de, http://www.dlv.de. Circ: 700 (paid and controlled).

BOTANICAL PESTICIDES ABSTRACTS. see *ENVIRONMENTAL STUDIES—Abstracting, Bibliographies, Statistics*

630.21 BWA
BOTSWANA. CENTRAL STATISTICS OFFICE. AGRICULTURE STATISTICS. Text and summaries in English. 1967. a. charts. back issues avail. **Document type:** *Government.* **Description:** Contains data on livestock and crops production in the country.
Related titles: E-mail ed.; Fax ed.
Published by: Central Statistics Office, c/o Government Statistician, Private Bag 0024, Gaborone, Botswana. TEL 267-31-352200, FAX 267-31-352201, csobots@gov.bw. Ed. G M Charumbira. **Subscr. to:** Government Printer, Private Bag 0081, Gaborone, Botswana. TEL 267-353202, FAX 267-312001, http://www.gov.bw.

630.21 BWA ISSN 1013-574X
BOTSWANA. MINISTRY OF AGRICULTURE. AGRICULTURAL STATISTICS. Text in English. irreg. charts. **Document type:** *Government.*

A

Published by: Ministry of Agriculture, Division of Planning and Statistics, Private Bag 0033, Gaborone, Botswana. TEL 267-328780, FAX 267-328847, TELEX 2752 SACCAR BD. Ed. Henry G Jobeta. R&P Dan B Gomballime. **Subscr. to:** Government Printer, Private Bag 0081, Gaborone, Botswana. TEL 267-353202, FAX 267-312001, http://www.gov.bw. **Co-sponsor:** Central Statistics Office.

630.21 CAN
BRITISH COLUMBIA. MINISTRY OF AGRICULTURE AND FOOD. ANNUAL STATISTICS (YEAR). Text in English, 1911. a. free. **Document type:** *Government.*
Former titles: British Columbia. Ministry of Agriculture and Fisheries. Annual Statistics (1180-4718); (until 1988): British Columbia. Ministry of Agriculture and Food. Agricultural Statistics Profile (0848-4724); (until 1982): British Columbia. Ministry of Agriculture and Food. Agriculture Statistics Yearbook (0706-1471); (until 1973): British Columbia. Department of Agriculture. Agricultural Statistics Report (0407-2049); (until 1928): British Columbia. Department of Agriculture. Agricultural Statistics (0319-8812)
—CISTI, Linda Hall.
Published by: Ministry of Agriculture, Fisheries and Food, Policy and Legislation Statistical Services Unit, Nootka Ct, 808 Douglas St, Sta Provincial Government, P O Box 9120, Victoria, BC V8W 9B4, Canada. TEL 604-387-7169, FAX 604-387-9704, agf_bcbn@galaxy.gov.bc.ca. Circ: 1,000.

016.6365 GBR ISSN 1746-6202
SF481
▼ **BRITISH POULTRY ABSTRACTS.** Text in English. 2005. a. GBP 37.50 per issue (effective 2005); free with subscr. to British Poultry Science. **Document type:** *Journal, Abstract/Index.* **Description:** Publishes abstracts from the World's Poultry Science Association (WPSA) - UK Branch Annual Meeting.
Related titles: Online - full content ed.: ISSN 1746-6210.
Published by: Taylor & Francis Ltd (Subsidiary of: Taylor & Francis Group), 4 Park Sq, Milton Park, Abingdon, OX14 4RN, United Kingdom. TEL 44-1235-828600, FAX 44-1235-829000, info@tandf.co.uk, http://www.tandf.co.uk/journals/titles/17466202.asp. Eds. Barry O Hughs, Murdo G MacLeod.

016.6329 USA ISSN 1524-5799
CODEN: CAFUFC
C A SELECTS. FUNGICIDES. Text in English. s-w. USD 315 to non-members; USD 95 to members (effective 2005). **Document type:** *Abstract/Index.* **Description:** Covers preparation, mechanism of action, and effects of antifungal agents.
Former titles: C A Selects Plus. Fungicides (1084-0052); C A Selects. Fungicides (0160-9068)
Published by: Chemical Abstracts Service (C A S) (Subsidiary of: American Chemical Society), 2540 Olentangy River Rd., Columbus, OH 43210-0012. TEL 614-447-3600, FAX 614-447-3713, help@cas.com, http://www.cas.org, http://caselects.cas.org. **Subscr. to:** PO Box 3012, Columbus, OH 43210. TEL 800-753-4227, FAX 614-447-3751.

016.632954 USA ISSN 1524-5802
CODEN: CAHEF8
C A SELECTS. HERBICIDES. Text in English. s-w. USD 315 to non-members; USD 95 to members (effective 2005). **Document type:** *Abstract/Index.* **Description:** Covers preparation, mechanism of action, and effects of herbicides; plant growth inhibitors and defoliants.
Former titles: C A Selects Plus. Herbicides (1084-0060); C A Selects. Herbicides (0160-9084)
Published by: Chemical Abstracts Service (C A S) (Subsidiary of: American Chemical Society), 2540 Olentangy River Rd., Columbus, OH 43210-0012. TEL 614-447-3600, FAX 614-447-3713, help@cas.com, http://www.cas.org, http://caselects.cas.org. **Subscr. to:** PO Box 3012, Columbus, OH 43210. TEL 800-753-4227, FAX 614-447-3751.

016.6329517 USA ISSN 1524-5810
CODEN: CSINFU
C A SELECTS. INSECTICIDES. Text in English. s-w. USD 315 to non-members; USD 95 to members (effective 2005). **Document type:** *Abstract/Index.* **Description:** Covers preparation, mechanism of action, and effects of insecticides; insect control and repellants.
Former titles: C A Selects Plus. Insecticides (1084-2373); C A Selects. Insecticides (0160-9092)
Published by: Chemical Abstracts Service (C A S) (Subsidiary of: American Chemical Society), 2540 Olentangy River Rd., Columbus, OH 43210-0012. TEL 614-447-3600, FAX 614-447-3713, help@cas.com, http://www.cas.org, http://caselects.cas.org. **Subscr. to:** PO Box 3012, Columbus, OH 43210. TEL 800-753-4227, FAX 614-447-3751.

016.63 USA ISSN 1555-6085
S494.5.B563
C S A AGRICULTURAL & ENVIRONMENTAL BIOTECHNOLOGY ABSTRACTS. Text in English. m. USD 435 (effective 2006). index on CD-ROM. back issues avail. **Document type:** *Abstract/Index.* **Description:** Covers basic research and applications of biotechnology techniques in the food industry, agriculture and the environment.
Media: Online - full text.
Published by: C S A Journal Division (Subsidiary of: Cambridge Information Group), 7200 Wisconsin Ave, Ste 715, Bethesda, MD 20814. TEL 301-961-6798, 800-843-7751, FAX 301-961-6799, journals@csa.com, http://www.csa.com/factsheets/agricultural-set-c.php. Ed. Deborah B Whitman. Pub. Ted Caris.

338.1 USA
CALIFORNIA. AGRICULTURAL STATISTICS SERVICE. AGRICULTURAL STATISTICS REVIEW. SUMMARY. Text in English. a. USD 15; USD 30 foreign (effective 1999). **Document type:** *Government.* **Description:** Summary of over 69 crops, their acreage, production, value, ranking, and major producing counties.
Published by: Agricultural Statistics Service, 1220 N St, Rm 243, Sacramento, CA 95814.

630.21 USA ISSN 0279-2656
S600.62.C2
CALIFORNIA. AGRICULTURAL STATISTICS SERVICE. CROP WEATHER REPORT. Text in English. 1981. w. USD 30; USD 60 foreign (effective 1999). **Document type:** *Government.* **Description:** Covers weather's effect on crops, planting and harvesting, weekly and accumulated precipitation data and temperature by station.
Published by: Agricultural Statistics Service, 1220 N St, Rm 243, Sacramento, CA 95814.

637.1021 USA
CALIFORNIA. AGRICULTURAL STATISTICS SERVICE. DAIRY INDUSTRY STATISTICS. Text in English. a. USD 10; USD 20 foreign (effective 1999). **Document type:** *Government.* **Description:** Provides historic and detailed data on the dairy industry.
Indexed: SRI.
Published by: Agricultural Statistics Service, 1220 N St, Rm 243, Sacramento, CA 95814.

630.21 USA
CALIFORNIA. AGRICULTURAL STATISTICS SERVICE. FIELD CROP REVIEW. Text in English. m. USD 15; USD 30 foreign (effective 1999). **Document type:** *Government.* **Description:** Covers field crops such as grain, cotton, hay, and sugar beet; provides data on acreage, production, value, price, warehouse, and farm labor.
Published by: Agricultural Statistics Service, 1220 N St, Rm 243, Sacramento, CA 95814.

630.21 USA
CALIFORNIA. AGRICULTURAL STATISTICS SERVICE. FRUIT AND NUT REVIEW. Text in English. m. USD 15; USD 30 foreign (effective 1999). **Document type:** *Government.* **Description:** Covers grape, citrus, deciduous, and nut acreage, production, price and utilization.
Published by: Agricultural Statistics Service, 1220 N St, Rm 243, Sacramento, CA 95814. TEL 916-445-6076.

630.21 USA
CALIFORNIA. AGRICULTURAL STATISTICS SERVICE. GRAPE ACREAGE. Text in English. a. USD 10; USD 20 foreign (effective 1999). **Document type:** *Government.* **Description:** Provides information on acreage of grapes by year planted, variety, and county; removal data.
Related titles: Diskette ed.
Published by: Agricultural Statistics Service, 1220 N St, Rm 243, Sacramento, CA 95814.

630.21 USA
CALIFORNIA. AGRICULTURAL STATISTICS SERVICE. GRAPE CRUSH REPORT. Text in English. 2/yr. (diskette a.). USD 20 domestic for print or diskette version; USD 40 foreign for print or diskette version (effective 1999). **Document type:** *Government.* **Description:** Covers tons purchased and crushed, Brix factors, and preliminary and final prices per ton by variety and by district.
Related titles: Diskette ed.
Published by: Agricultural Statistics Service, 1220 N St, Rm 243, Sacramento, CA 95814.

636.0021 USA
CALIFORNIA. AGRICULTURAL STATISTICS SERVICE. LIVESTOCK REVIEW. Text in English. m. USD 15; USD 30 foreign (effective 1999). **Document type:** *Government.* **Description:** Covers livestock inventories, intentions, and values; pasture, slaughter, and on-feed data for cattle and sheep.
Published by: Agricultural Statistics Service, 1220 N St, Rm 243, Sacramento, CA 95814.

636.0021 USA
CALIFORNIA. AGRICULTURAL STATISTICS SERVICE. POULTRY REPORT. Text in English. m. USD 15; USD 30 foreign (effective 1999). **Document type:** *Government.* **Description:** Covers chicken and turkey, settings, hatchings, eggs produced, inventory, value, and cold storage.
Published by: Agricultural Statistics Service, 1220 N St, Rm 243, Sacramento, CA 95814.

630.21 USA
CALIFORNIA. AGRICULTURAL STATISTICS SERVICE. VEGETABLE REVIEW. Text in English. 5/yr. USD 7; USD 14 foreign (effective 1999). **Document type:** *Government.* **Description:** Covers the production and processing of fresh vegetables as well as market value.
Published by: Agricultural Statistics Service, 1220 N St, Rm 243, Sacramento, CA 95814.

630.21 USA
CALIFORNIA. AGRICULTURAL STATISTICS SERVICE. WALNUTS, RAISINS AND PRUNES (PRICE REPORT). Text in English. a. USD 1 (effective 1999). **Document type:** *Government.*
Published by: Agricultural Statistics Service, 1220 N St, Rm 243, Sacramento, CA 95814.

637.1021 USA ISSN 0892-4406
CALIFORNIA DAIRY INFORMATION BULLETIN. Text in English. m. USD 15; USD 30 foreign (effective 1999). **Document type:** *Bulletin, Government.* **Description:** Covers production, utilization, and prices of milk and dairy products.
Formerly: California. Agricultural Statistics Service. Dairy Information Bulletin (0279-2605)
Published by: Agricultural Statistics Service, 1220 N St, Rm 243, Sacramento, CA 95814.

630.21 CAN ISSN 0317-4980
CANADA. GRAIN COMMISSION. CORPORATE SERVICES. CANADIAN GRAIN EXPORTS. Text in English, French. 1936. a. CND 40 domestic; CND 45 foreign (effective 2001). **Document type:** *Government.* **Description:** Compiles Canadian grain export statistics by grain, grade, country of destination, and port of loading.
Former titles: Canada. Grain Commission. Economics and Statistics Division. Canadian Grain Exports; Canada. Board of Grain Commissioners. Canadian Grain Exports.
Related titles: Online - full text ed.: USD 30 (effective 2000).
Published by: Canadian Grain Commission, Corporate Services/Commission Canadienne des Grains, 700 303 Main St, Winnipeg, MB R3C 3G8, Canada. TEL 204-983-1570, FAX 204-983-0248, smudry@cgc.ca, fhodgkinson@cgc.ca, http://www.cgc.ca/. Ed. Tom Askin. R&P Susan Mudry TEL 204-983-2758.

633.1021 CAN ISSN 0832-6215
CANADA. GRAIN COMMISSION. CORPORATE SERVICES. EXPORTS OF CANADIAN GRAIN AND WHEAT FLOUR. Key Title: Exports of Canadian Grain and Wheat Flour. Text in English, French. 1967. m. CND 80 domestic; CND 150 foreign (effective 2001). stat. **Document type:** *Government.* **Description:** Canadian grain export statistics by grain, country of destination and port of loading.
Formerly: Canada. Grain Commission. Economics and Statistics Division. Exports of Canadian Grain and Wheat Flour
Related titles: Online - full content ed.
Published by: Canadian Grain Commission, Corporate Services/Commission Canadienne des Grains, 700 303 Main St, Winnipeg, MB R3C 3G8, Canada. TEL 204-983-1570, fhodgkinson@cgc.ca, smudry@cgc.ca, http://www.cgc.ca/. R&P Susan Mudry TEL 204-983-2758. Circ: 200 (controlled).

633.1021 CAN
CANADA GRAINS COUNCIL. STATISTICAL HANDBOOK. Text in English. 1974. a. CND 54.50 domestic to non-members; CND 59.50 in North America to non-members; CND 64.50 elsewhere to non-members; CND 44.50 domestic to members; CND 49.50 in North America to members; CND 54.50 elsewhere to members (effective 1999). **Document type:** *Bulletin.* **Description:** Production, trade, prices and handlings of Canadian grains.
Related titles: Diskette ed.
Published by: Canada Grains Council, 330 360 Main St, Winnipeg, MB R3C 3Z3, Canada. TEL 204-942-2254, FAX 204-947-0992, dmutch@canadagrainscouncil.ca, http://www.canadagrainscouncil.ca. Circ: 1,500.

630.21 CAN ISSN 1499-3066
CANADA. STATISTICS CANADA. CANADA FOOD STATS. Text in English, French. 2001. s-a.
Media: CD-ROM.
—CISTI.
Published by: Statistics Canada, Agriculture Natural Resources Division, Rm 1500, Main Building, Holland Ave, Ottawa, ON K1A 0T6, Canada.

637.1021 CAN ISSN 0300-0753
CANADA. STATISTICS CANADA. DAIRY REVIEW/CANADA. STATISTIQUE CANADA. REVUE LAITIERE. Text in English, French. 1932. q. CND 119 domestic (effective 1999); USD 119 foreign. **Document type:** *Government.* **Description:** Provides a statistical summary of the dairy situation in Canada and the provinces, including farm sales of milk for fluid and manufacturing purposes.
Incorporates (in Apr. 1995): Production and Inventories of Process Cheese and Instant Skim Milk Powder (0705-551X)
Related titles: Microform ed.: (from MML).
—CISTI.

Published by: Statistics Canada, Operations and Integration Division, Circulation Management, Jean Talon Bldg, 2 C12, Tunney's Pasture, Ottawa, ON K1A 0T6, Canada. TEL 613-951-7277, 800-267-6677, FAX 613-951-1584, http://www.statcan.ca.

338.1021 CAN ISSN 1480-9591
CANADA. STATISTICS CANADA. ECONOMIC OVERVIEW OF FARM INCOMES. Text in English, French. 1998. a. CND 45; USD 54 in United States; USD 63 elsewhere. **Document type:** *Government.* **Description:** Provides a detailed picture of the performance of Canadian farms as revealed by the information compiled from tax returns of unincorporated and incorporated farmers.
Formed by the merger of (1990-1998): Agricultural Financial Statistics (1188-7516); (1992-1998): Economic Overview of Farm Incomes, by Farm Type, Canada (1484-2599)
—CISTI.
Published by: Statistics Canada, Circulation Management, Jean Talon Bldg, 2 C12, Tunney's Pasture, Ottawa, ON K1A 0T6, Canada. TEL 613-951-7277, 800-267-6677, FAX 613-951-1584, http://www.statcan.ca. Circ: 400 (controlled).

338.1021 CAN ISSN 1206-5064
CANADA. STATISTICS CANADA. FARM CASH RECEIPTS. (Catalogue 62-003) Text in English, French. 1996. q. CND 71, USD 85 domestic; USD 99 foreign. **Document type:** *Government.* **Description:** Presents indexes of prices received by farmers from the sale of agricultural products.
Formerly (until 1996): Canada. Statistics Canada. Farm Cash Receipts and Farm Product Price Index (1201-4001); Which was formed by the merger of (1946-1996): Canada. Statistics Canada. Farm Products Price Index (0835-0906); Which was formerly (until 1986): Canada. Statistics Canada. Index Numbers of Farm Prices of Agricultural Products (0380-7541); (1940-1996): Canada. Statistics Canada. Farm Cash Receipts (0703-7945); Which was formerly (until 1964): Canada. Dominion Bureau of Statistics. Farm Finance Section. Agriculture Division. Farm Cash Income (0703-7953); (until 1949): Canada. Dominion Bureau of Statistics. Agriculture Division. Canadian Farm Income (0826-7510); (until 1948): Canada. Dominion Bureau of Statistics. Agricultural Division. Cash Income from the Sale of Farm Products by Provinces and by Months (0703-7961); (until 1941): Canada. Dominion Bureau of Statistics. Agricultural Branch. Farm Cash Income (0826-7502)
Related titles: Online - full text ed.: ISSN 1480-7599.
—CISTI.
Published by: Statistics Canada, Publications Sales and Services, Ottawa, ON K1A 0T6, Canada. TEL 613-951-7277, FAX 613-951-1584.

630.21 CAN ISSN 0575-8548
S133
CANADA. STATISTICS CANADA. FIELD CROP REPORTING SERIES/CANADA. STATISTIQUE CANADA. SERIE DE RAPPORTS SUR LES GRANDES CULTURES. Text in English, French. 1922. irreg. CND 15; USD 15 foreign (effective 1999). **Document type:** *Government.* **Description:** Details farm stocks of grain, crop area, yield and production.
Related titles: Microform ed.: (from MML).
—CISTI.
Published by: Statistics Canada, Operations and Integration Division, Circulation Management, Jean Talon Bldg, 2 C12, Tunney's Pasture, Ottawa, ON K1A 0T6, Canada. TEL 613-951-7277, 800-267-6677, FAX 613-951-1584, http://www.statcan.ca.

636.0021 CAN ISSN 0383-008X
CANADA. STATISTICS CANADA. FRUIT AND VEGETABLE PRODUCTION/CANADA. STATISTIQUE CANADA. PRODUCTIONS DE FRUITS ET LEGUMES. Text in English, French. 1932. s-a. CND 62 domestic; USD 62 foreign (effective 1999). **Document type:** *Government.* **Description:** Provides an overview of the Canadian fruit and vegetable production sector.
Related titles: Microform ed.: (from MML); Online - full text ed.
Published by: Statistics Canada, Operations and Integration Division, Circulation Management, Jean Talon Bldg, 2 C12, Tunney's Pasture, Ottawa, ON K1A 0T6, Canada. TEL 613-951-7277, 800-267-6677, FAX 613-951-1584, http://www.statcan.ca.

338.1021 CAN ISSN 0068-7189
CANADA. STATISTICS CANADA. PRODUCTION OF POULTRY AND EGGS/CANADA. STATISTIQUE CANADA. PRODUCTION DE VOLAILLE ET OEUFS. Text in English, French. 1936. a. CND 38 domestic; USD 38 foreign (effective 1999). **Document type:** *Government.* **Description:** Presents current and historical data on the turkey, chicken, stewing hen and egg industries in Canada.
Formerly: Canada. Statistics Canada. Production of Poultry and Eggs in Canada
Related titles: Microform ed.: (from MML); Online - full text ed.
—CISTI.
Published by: Statistics Canada, Operations and Integration Division, Circulation Management, Jean Talon Bldg, 2 C12, Tunney's Pasture, Ottawa, ON K1A 0T6, Canada. TEL 613-951-7277, 800-267-6677, FAX 613-951-1584, http://www.statcan.ca.

633.1021 CAN ISSN 1201-5679
CANADIAN GRAINS INDUSTRY STATISTICAL HANDBOOK. Text in English. 1974. a. CND 39.50 to members; CND 49.50 to non-members. **Document type:** *Directory.*
Published by: Canada Grains Council, 330 360 Main St, Winnipeg, MB R3C 3Z3, Canada. TEL 204-942-2254, FAX 204-947-0992, dmutch@canadagrainscouncil.ca, http://www.canadagrainscouncil.ca.

630.21 BRA ISSN 0103-6157
CENSO AGROPECUARIO. (Issued in 6 regional eds.) Text in Portuguese. 1940. quinquennial. price varies. **Document type:** *Government.* **Description:** Contains data on farm characteristics, employed persons, livestock, and agricultural production.
Formerly (until 1970): Censo Agricola; Supersedes in part (in 1950): Recenseamento Geral do Brasil
Published by: Fundacao Instituto Brasileiro de Geografia e Estatistica, Centro de Documentacao e Disseminacao de Informacoes, Rua General Canabarro, 706 Andar 2, Maracana, Rio de Janeiro, RJ 20271-201, Brazil. TEL 55-21-264-5424, FAX 55-21-2841959, http://www.ibge.gov.br.

016.63 630.21 USA
(YEAR) CENSUS OF AGRICULTURE. Text in English. irreg., latest 1997. USD 50 (effective 2001); for a 3 CD set. stat. **Document type:** *Government.*
Media: CD-ROM. **Related titles:** Online - full content ed.; ♦ Print ed.: Census of Agriculture. Volume 3: Special Studies. Farm and Ranch Irrigation Survey; ♦ Census of Agriculture. Volume 3: Special Studies. Census of Aquaculture; ♦ Census of Agriculture. Volume 3: Special Studies. Census of Horticultural Specialties; ♦ Census of Agriculture. Volume 2: Subject Series. Ranking of States and Counties; ♦ Census of Agriculture. Volume 2: Subject Series. ZIP Code and Congressional District Tabulations; ♦ Census of Agriculture. Volume 2: Subject Series. Agricultural Atlas of the United States; ♦ Census of Agriculture. Volume 1: Geographic Area Series.
Published by: U.S. Department of Agriculture, National Agricultural Statistics Service, 1400 Independence Ave, S W, Washington, DC 20250-2000. nass@nass.usda.gov, http://www.usda.gov/nass. **Subscr. to:** 5285 Port Royal Rd, Springfield, VA 22161. TEL 703-605-6220, 800-999-6779, FAX 603-605-6900.

630.21 USA
CENSUS OF AGRICULTURE. VOLUME 1: GEOGRAPHIC AREA SERIES. Text in English. irreg. (approx. 54 reports), latest 1997. USD 968 (effective 2001); price varies for individual reports. stat. **Document type:** *Government.* **Description:** Provides statistical information on farming, ranching, and related activities for each State and the counties within.
Related titles: ♦ CD-ROM ed.: (Year) Census of Agriculture; Online - full content ed.
Published by: U.S. Department of Agriculture, National Agricultural Statistics Service, 1400 Independence Ave, S W, Washington, DC 20250-2000. nass@nass.usda.gov, http://www.nass.usda.gov/census/, http://www.usda.gov/nass. **Subscr. to:** U.S. Government Printing Office, Superintendent of Documents, PO Box 371954, Pittsburgh, PA 15250-7954. TEL 202-512-1800, FAX 202-512-2250, orders@gpo.gov, http://www.access.gpo.gov; 5285 Port Royal Rd, Springfield, VA 22161. TEL 703-605-6220, 800-999-6779, FAX 603-605-6900.

630.21 USA
CENSUS OF AGRICULTURE. VOLUME 2: SUBJECT SERIES. AGRICULTURAL ATLAS OF THE UNITED STATES. Text in English. irreg. USD 25 Per Report (effective 2001). stat. **Document type:** *Government.* **Description:** Features a series of maps highlighting agricultural activities and characteristics, such as farm number and size, selected crops harvested, livestock and poultry inventories and number sold, agricultural sales, production expenses, land use, irrigation patterns, fertilizer and chemical use, and machinery and equipment inventories. Covers the United States, States, and counties.
Related titles: ♦ CD-ROM ed.: (Year) Census of Agriculture; Online - full content ed.
Published by: U.S. Department of Agriculture, National Agricultural Statistics Service, 1400 Independence Ave, S W, Washington, DC 20250-2000. nass@nass.usda.gov, http://www.usda.gov/nass. **Subscr. to:** 5285 Port Royal Rd, Springfield, VA 22161. TEL 703-605-6220, 800-999-6779, FAX 603-605-6900.

630.21 USA
CENSUS OF AGRICULTURE. VOLUME 2: SUBJECT SERIES. RANKING OF STATES AND COUNTIES. Text in English. irreg., latest 1997. USD 25 Per Report (effective 2001). stat. **Document type:** *Government.* **Description:** Ranks the leading States and counties for selected items from the 1997 Census of Agriculture. Items ranked include number of farms, value of products sold, inventory of livestock and poultry, and production and acreage of major crops. Most tables show data for 20 leading States and 100 leading counties. Also, most tables include the cumulative percent of the United States total as each leading State or county is ranked.
Related titles: ♦ CD-ROM ed.: (Year) Census of Agriculture; Online - full content ed.

Published by: U.S. Department of Agriculture, National Agricultural Statistics Service, 1400 Independence Ave, S W, Washington, DC 20250-2000. nass@nass.usda.gov, http://www.usda.gov/nass. **Subscr. to:** 5285 Port Royal Rd, Springfield, VA 22161. TEL 703-605-6220, 800-999-6779, FAX 603-605-6900.

630.21 USA
CENSUS OF AGRICULTURE. VOLUME 2: SUBJECT SERIES. ZIP CODE AND CONGRESSIONAL DISTRICT TABULATIONS. Text in English. irreg., latest 1997. price varies. stat. **Document type:** *Government.* **Description:** Presents agricultural statistics by five-digit postal ZIP Code and Congressional district in two separate files, for all farms in all 50 states. Tables show the total market value of products sold and the number of farms by size for land in farms, crop-land harvested, selected crops, and inventory of cattle, calves, hogs, and pigs. Crops vary by state, and tables show number of farms by acres harvested for commodities, such as tobacco, cotton, soybeans for beans, peanuts for nuts, and land in orchards.
Related titles: ♦ CD-ROM ed.: (Year) Census of Agriculture; Online - full content ed.
Published by: U.S. Department of Agriculture, National Agricultural Statistics Service, 1400 Independence Ave, S W, Washington, DC 20250-2000. nass@nass.usda.gov, http://www.usda.gov/nass. **Subscr. to:** 5285 Port Royal Rd, Springfield, VA 22161. TEL 703-605-6220, 800-999-6779, FAX 603-605-6900.

630.21 USA
CENSUS OF AGRICULTURE. VOLUME 3: SPECIAL STUDIES. CENSUS OF AQUACULTURE. Text in English. irreg., latest 1998. USD 20 Per Report (effective 2001). stat. **Document type:** *Government.* **Description:** Provides data on size of operation, methodology, sales by category, losses, irrigation, and other topics. This will be the Nation's first census of aquaculture.
Related titles: ♦ CD-ROM ed.: (Year) Census of Agriculture; Online - full content ed.
Published by: U.S. Department of Agriculture, National Agricultural Statistics Service, 1400 Independence Ave, S W, Washington, DC 20250-2000. nass@nass.usda.gov, http://www.usda.gov/nass. **Subscr. to:** 5285 Port Royal Rd, Springfield, VA 22161. TEL 703-605-6220, 800-999-6779, FAX 603-605-6900.

630.21 USA
CENSUS OF AGRICULTURE. VOLUME 3: SPECIAL STUDIES. CENSUS OF HORTICULTURAL SPECIALTIES. Text in English. irreg., latest 1998. USD 20 Per Report (effective 2001). stat. **Document type:** *Government.*
Related titles: ♦ CD-ROM ed.: (Year) Census of Agriculture; Online - full content ed.
Published by: U.S. Department of Agriculture, National Agricultural Statistics Service, 1400 Independence Ave, S W, Washington, DC 20250-2000. nass@nass.usda.gov, http://www.usda.gov/nass. **Subscr. to:** 5285 Port Royal Rd, Springfield, VA 22161. TEL 703-605-6220, 800-999-6779, FAX 603-605-6900.

630.21 USA
CENSUS OF AGRICULTURE. VOLUME 3: SPECIAL STUDIES. FARM AND RANCH IRRIGATION SURVEY. Text in English. 1840. irreg., latest 1998. USD 25 Per Report (effective 2001). **Document type:** *Government.* **Description:** Displays results from a sample survey of farm and ranch operators who reported using irrigation in the 1997 census. Includes acres irrigated; yields of specified crops; method of distribution; quantity and source of water used; number and depth of wells; pumps used in moving water; energy use; and expenditures for maintenance and investments for each State, 18 water resource areas, and the United States.
Related titles: ♦ CD-ROM ed.: (Year) Census of Agriculture; Online - full content ed.
Published by: U.S. Department of Agriculture, National Agricultural Statistics Service, 1400 Independence Ave, S W, Washington, DC 20250-2000. nass@nass.usda.gov, http://www.usda.gov/nass. **Subscr. to:** 5285 Port Royal Rd, Springfield, VA 22161. TEL 703-605-6220, 800-999-6779, FAX 603-605-6900.

633.1021 CAN ISSN 0820-9030
CEREALS AND OILSEEDS REVIEW. Text in English. 1978. m. CND 138, USD 166 domestic; USD 193 foreign. **Description:** Reports on supply and disposition of the four traditional major wheat exporters.
Formerly (until 1982): Grains and Oilseeds Review (0706-3555); Which was formed by the merger of (1941-1978): Coarse Grains Review (0009-9996); Which was formerly (until 1970): Coarse Grains Quarterly (0829-7517); (until 1949): Canadian Coarse Grains (0829-7509); (1970-1978): Oilseeds Review (0703-251X); (19??-1978): Wheat Review (0043-471X); Which was formerly (until 1950): Monthly Review of the Wheat Situation
Related titles: Online - full text ed.: ISSN 1492-4048.
—CISTI.
Published by: Statistics Canada, Operations and Integration Division, Circulation Management, Jean Talon Bldg, 2 C12, Tunney's Pasture, Ottawa, ON K1A 0T6, Canada. TEL 613-951-7277, 800-267-6677, FAX 613-951-1584, http://www.statcan.ca.

A

016.63 CZE
CESKA ZEMEDELSKA A POTRAVINARSKA BIBLIOGRAFIE. Variant title: Czech Agricultural Bibliography. Text in Czech. 1966. a. USD 50 (effective 2003). **Document type:** *Bibliography.* **Description:** Contains bibliographical citations of journals and serials published in Czech Republic.
Former titles (until 2000): Ceska Zemedelska Bibliografie; (until 1990): Ceskoslovenska Zemedelska Bibliografie (0232-0851)
Media: Online - full content.
Published by: Ceska Akademie Zemedelskych Ved, Ustav Zemedelskych a Potravinarskych Informaci/Czech Academy of Agricultural Sciences, Institute of Agricultural and Food Information, Slezska 7, Prague 2, 120 56, Czech Republic. TEL 420-2-227010355, FAX 420-2-227010116, kaderabkova@uzpi.cz, http://www.agronavigator.cz. Ed. Mrs. Irena Kaderabkova.

630.21 GBR
CHARTERED INSTITUTE OF PUBLIC FINANCE AND ACCOUNTANCY. COUNTY FARMS STATISTICS. ACTUALS. Text in English. a. GBP 55. back issues avail.
Published by: (Statistical Information Service), Chartered Institute of Public Finance and Accountancy, 3 Robert St, London, WC2N 6RL, United Kingdom. TEL 44-20-7543-5800, FAX 44-20-7543-5700, http://www.cipfa.org.uk.

630.21 CHL
CHILE. INSTITUTO NACIONAL DE ESTADISTICAS. ESTADISTICAS AGROPECUARIAS. (In 2 parts: Uso del Suelo; Produccion Fruticola) Text in Spanish. a. CLP 2,000; USD 13.50 in United States; USD 15.90 elsewhere (effective 1999).
Formerly (until 1985): Programa de Mejoramiento de las Estadisticas Agropecuarias
Published by: Instituto Nacional de Estadisticas, Casilla 498, Correo 3, Ave. Bulnes, 418, Santiago, Chile. TEL 56-2-6991441, FAX 56-2-6712169.

636.0021 CHL
CHILE. INSTITUTO NACIONAL DE ESTADISTICAS. ESTADISTICAS PECUARIAS. Text in Spanish. 1985. s-a. CLP 2,000; USD 13.50 in United States; USD 15 elsewhere.
Published by: Instituto Nacional de Estadisticas, Casilla 498, Correo 3, Ave. Bulnes, 418, Santiago, Chile. TEL 56-2-6991441, FAX 56-2-6712169.

633.1021 CHL
CHILE. INSTITUTO NACIONAL DE ESTADISTICAS. INDUSTRIA MOLINERA. TRIGO. Text in Spanish. 1978. q. CLP 1,100; USD 7.50 in United States; USD 8.60 elsewhere.
Published by: Instituto Nacional de Estadisticas, Casilla 498, Correo 3, Ave. Bulnes, 418, Santiago, Chile. TEL 56-2-6991441, FAX 56-2-6712169.

338.1021 631.021 USA
COMMERCIAL FERTILIZERS REPORT. Text in English. biennial. USD 25 (effective 1999). **Description:** Reports historical data on US fertilizer consumption by nutrient back to fiscal year (July-June) 1960. Also includes a detailed breakdown of fertilizer material use by state for the last two fiscal years.
Published by: Fertilizer Institute, 501 Second St, N E, Washington, DC 20002. TEL 202-675-8250, FAX 202-544-8123, http://www.tfi.org.

338.1021 USA
COMMODITY YEARBOOK STATISTICAL UPDATE. Text in English. 3/yr. USD 95 (effective 1999). charts; mkt.; stat. **Document type:** *Trade.*
Formerly: Commodity Yearbook Statistical Abstract Service (0010-3241)
Related titles: Microfiche ed.: (from CIS).
Indexed: SRI.
Published by: Commodity Research Bureau, 330 S. Wells St., Ste. 612, Chicago, IL 60606-7112. TEL 312-454-1801, 800-621-5271, FAX 312-454-0239, info@crbtrader.com, http://www.crbtrader.com. Eds. Chris Lown, Steve Lown. R&P Jennifer Ehrich.

630.21 IRL
COMPENDIUM OF IRISH ECONOMIC AND AGRICULTURE STATISTICS (YEAR). Text in English. a. **Document type:** *Government.*
Published by: Department of Agriculture, Food & Rural Development/An Roinn Talmhaiochta Bia Agus Forbartha Tuaithe, Agriculture House, Kildare St, Dublin, Dublin 2, Ireland. TEL 353-1-607-2000, information@daff.irlgov.ie, http://www.irlgov.ie/daff, http://www.irlgov.ie/daff/.

630.21 NZL ISSN 0545-7769
COMPENDIUM OF NEW ZEALAND FARM PRODUCTION STATISTICS. Text in English. 1955. biennial. NZD 5 (effective 2001). **Document type:** *Trade.*
—CISTI.
Published by: Meat and Wool Boards' Economic Service, P.O. Box 5179, Wellington, New Zealand. FAX 64-4-712-173. Circ: 4,000.

636.0021 HND
CONSUMO PECUARIO NACIONAL. Text in Spanish. a. **Document type:** *Government.*
Published by: Secretaria de Planificacion, Coordinacion y Presupuesto, Direccion General de Estadistica y Censos, Tegucigalpa DC, Honduras.

630.21 NLD ISSN 0921-4305
CONSUMPTIE VAN VOEDINGSMIDDELEN IN NEDERLAND. Text in Dutch. 1983. a. price varies. **Document type:** *Government.*
Published by: Landbouw-Economisch Instituut, Burgemeester Patijnlaan 19, The Hague, 2585 BE, Netherlands. TEL 31-70-330-8330, FAX 31-70-361-5624, postmaster@lei.dlo.nl, http://www.lei.dlo.nl/lei.

630.21 USA ISSN 0010-9754
HD9070.1
COTTON: WORLD STATISTICS. Text in English. 1947. a. USD 125 (effective 2000). charts; stat.
Related titles: CD-ROM ed.; Microfiche ed.: (from CIS); Online - full text ed.
Indexed: IIS, PROMT, TTI, WTA.
—IE, Infotrieve.
Published by: International Cotton Advisory Committee, 1629 K St N W, Ste 702, Washington, DC 20006. TEL 202-463-6660, FAX 202-463-6950, TELEX 408272789, publications@icac.org, http://www.icac.org.

016.631 GBR ISSN 0306-7556
CROP PHYSIOLOGY ABSTRACTS. Text in English. 1975. bi-m. USD 1,810 in the Americas to institutions except Canada; GBP 1,035 elsewhere to institutions; USD 1,935 combined subscription in the Americas to institutions except Canada; print & online eds.; GBP 1,105 combined subscription elsewhere to institutions print & online eds. (effective 2006). adv. back issues avail.; reprints avail. **Document type:** *Abstract/Index.* **Description:** Deals with the physiology of all higher plants of economic importance.
Related titles: Online - full text ed.: USD 1,540 in the Americas to institutions; GBP 880 elsewhere to institutions (effective 2006) (from DIMDI, The Dialog Corporation).
—CCC.
Published by: CABI Publishing (Subsidiary of: CAB International), CAB International, Wallingford, Oxfordshire OX10 8DE, United Kingdom. TEL 44-1491-832111, FAX 44-1491-833508, cabi@cabi.org, http://www.cabi-publishing.org/. Ed. David Simpson. adv.: B&W page GBP 60, B&W page USD 95; 170 x 267. Circ: 75. **Subscr. addr. in N America:** CABI Publishing North America, 875 Massachusetts Ave, 7th Fl, Cambridge, MA 02139. TEL 617-395-4056, 800-528-4841, FAX 617-354-6875, cabi-nao@cabi.org.

633 LUX
CROP PRODUCTION HALF-YEARLY STATISTICS. Text in English. 2/yr. USD 80. **Description:** Contains most recent data on land use, arable crops (areas, yields and production) and fruit and vegetable consumption, weather conditions, supply balance sheet, plant products and fruit.
Former titles: Agricultural Statistics Series No.1: Crop Production; Statistical Office of the European Communities. Crop Production (0378-3588)
Related titles: Microfiche ed.: (from CIS).
Indexed: IIS, RASB.
—CISTI.
Published by: (European Commission, Statistical Office of the European Communities), European Commission, Office for Official Publications of the European Union, 2 Rue Mercier, Luxembourg, L-2985, Luxembourg. **Dist. in U.S. by:** Bernan Associates, Bernan, 4611-F Assembly Dr., Lanham, MD 20706-4391. TEL 301-459-0056, 800-274-4447.

016.63 USA ISSN 0090-0508
Z5071 CODEN: CCASDR
CURRENT CONTENTS: AGRICULTURE, BIOLOGY & ENVIRONMENTAL SCIENCES. Short title: C C: A B & E S. Text in English. 1970. w. Index. **Document type:** *Academic/Scholarly.* **Description:** Tables of contents of the world's leading publications covering biology, biotechnology and applied microbiology.
Formerly: C C A F V (Current Contents, Agricultural, Food and Veterinary Sciences) (0011-3379)
Related titles: CD-ROM ed.: (from Thomson I S I); Diskette ed.; Magnetic Tape ed.; Online - full text ed.
Indexed: AESIS, AnalAb, VITIS.
—BLDSC (3496.126000), CASDDS.
Published by: Thomson I S I (Subsidiary of: Thomson Corporation), 3501 Market St., Philadelphia, PA 19104. TEL 215-386-0100, FAX 215-386-2911, http://www.isinet.com.

630.21 CYP ISSN 0379-0924
CYPRUS. DEPARTMENT OF STATISTICS AND RESEARCH. AGRICULTURAL STATISTICS. Text in English, Greek. a. CYP 5 (effective 1999). **Document type:** *Government.* **Description:** Summarizes accounts of the broad agricultural sector, with data on crop and livestock production, forestry and fishing, employment and land use.
Formerly: Cyprus. Department of Statistics and Research. Agricultural Survey.
Published by: Ministry of Finance, Department of Statistics and Research, 13 Andreas Araouzos St, Nicosia, 1444, Cyprus. TEL 357-2-309318, FAX 357-2-374830, cydsr@cytanet.com.cy, http://www.pio.gov.cy/dsr.

630.21 CYP
CYPRUS. DEPARTMENT OF STATISTICS AND RESEARCH. CENSUS OF AGRICULTURE. Text in English, Greek. irreg. CYP 10 per issue (effective 1999). **Document type:** *Government.* **Description:** Provides information on the structure of agricultural holdings.
Published by: Ministry of Finance, Department of Statistics and Research, 13 Andreas Araouzos St, Nicosia, 1444, Cyprus. TEL 357-2-309301, FAX 357-2-374830, cydsr@cytanet.com.cy, http://www.pio.gov.cy/dsr.

636.0021 CYP
CYPRUS. DEPARTMENT OF STATISTICS AND RESEARCH. CENSUS OF POULTRY. Text in English. 1982. irreg. CYP 0.75 (effective 1998). **Document type:** *Government.* **Description:** Presents number of holders, structure and size of poultry units and number of poultry; covers chickens, pigeons, rabbits and quail.
Published by: Ministry of Finance, Department of Statistics and Research, 13 Andreas Araouzos St, Nicosia, 1444, Cyprus. TEL 357-2-309301, FAX 357-2-374830, cydsr@cytanet.com.cy, http://www.pio.gov.cy/dsr.

637.1021 CAN ISSN 0317-6207
DAIRY FACTS AND FIGURES AT A GLANCE. Text in English. a. CND 5 (effective 2000). **Description:** Collection of tables containing statistical information on the Canadian dairy industry, as well as related international data.
—CISTI.
Published by: Dairy Farmers of Canada, 75 Albert St, Ste 1101, Ottawa, ON K1P 5E7, Canada. FAX 613-236-0905, http://www.dairyfarmers.org, http://www.dairybureau.org.

637.1021 USA ISSN 0098-6690
HD9275.U3
DAIRY MARKET STATISTICS: ANNUAL SUMMARY. Text in English. 1965. a. USD 4. **Document type:** *Government.*
—CISTI.
Published by: U.S. Department of Agriculture, Agricultural Marketing Service, 1400 Independence Ave, S W, Washington, DC 20250.

637.1021 USA
DAIRY MONTHLY IMPORTS. Text in English. m. back issues avail. **Document type:** *Government.*
Related titles: Online - full text ed.
Indexed: AmStI.
Published by: U.S. Department of Agriculture, Foreign Agricultural Service, Information Division, Rm 5920 S, Washington, DC 20250-1000. info@fas.usda.gov, http://ffas.usda.gov/dmi.arc.html.

016.6371 GBR ISSN 0011-5681
DAIRY SCIENCE ABSTRACTS. Text in English. 1939. m. USD 1,810 in the Americas to institutions except Canada; GBP 1,035 elsewhere to institutions; USD 1,935 combined subscription in the Americas to institutions except Canada; print & online eds.; GBP 1,105 combined subscription elsewhere to institutions print & online eds. (effective 2006). adv. bk.rev. abstr.; pat.; stat.; illus. index. back issues avail.; reprints avail. **Document type:** *Abstract/Index.* **Description:** Provides information on all aspects of milk production, secretion, processing, and milk products.
Related titles: Online - full text ed.: USD 1,540 in the Americas to institutions; GBP 880 elsewhere to institutions (effective 2006) (from DIMDI, The Dialog Corporation).
—BLDSC (3516.000000), CISTI, Linda Hall. **CCC.**
Published by: CABI Publishing (Subsidiary of: CAB International), CAB International, Wallingford, Oxfordshire OX10 8DE, United Kingdom. TEL 44-1491-832111, FAX 44-1491-833508, cabi@cabi.org, http://www.cabi-publishing.org/. Ed. Richard J Laight. adv.: B&W page GBP 160, B&W page USD 255; 170 x 267. Circ: 440. **Subscr. in N. America:** CABI Publishing North America, 875 Massachusetts Ave, 7th Fl, Cambridge, MA 02139. TEL 617-395-4056, 800-528-4841, FAX 617-354-6875, cabi-nao@cabi.org.

637.1021 NZL ISSN 0114-975X
➤ **DAIRY STATISTICS.** Text in English. 1970. a. free (effective 2003). stat. 45 p./no. 1 cols./p.; back issues avail. **Document type:** *Academic/Scholarly.* **Description:** Contains statistics on New Zealand dairy industry.
Former titles (until 1990): New Zealand Dairy Board. Livestock Improvement Division. Annual Report (0114-2917); (until 1988): Livestock Improvement Report (0113-2806); Farm Production Report and Summary of Boards Work (0111-1388)
Related titles: Online - full content ed.
Indexed: AnBrAb, DSA.
Published by: Livestock Improvement Corporation Ltd., Cnr. Ruakura & Morrinsville Rds., Private Bag 3016, Hamilton, New Zealand. TEL 64-7-8560700, FAX 64-7-8582741, ghansson@lic.co.nz, http://www.lic.co.nz. Ed. Glenn Hansson. Circ: 2,900.

338.109489 DNK ISSN 0108-5522
HD2001
DENMARK. DANMARKS STATISTIK. LANDBRUG. Text in Danish. 1983. price varies. **Document type:** *Government.*

Formerly (until 1983): Landbrugets Produktions- og Prisforhold (0106-2034); Which superseded in part (1976-1983): Statistiske Efterretninger A (0105-306X); (1976-1983): Statistiske Efterretninger B (0105-3078); Which both superseded in part (1909-1976): Statistiske Efterretninger (0039-0674)
Related titles: ♦ Series of: Denmark. Danmarks Statistik. Statistiske Efterretninger. Indhold. ISSN 1396-8173.
Published by: Danmarks Statistik, Sejroegade 11, Copenhagen Oe, 2100, Denmark. TEL 45-39-173917, FAX 45-39-173939.

630.21   DNK
DENMARK. DANMARKS STATISTIK. LANDBRUGSSTATISTIK. Text in Danish; Notes in English. 1936. a. DKK 191.20 (effective 2000). index. **Document type:** *Government.*
Formerly: Denmark. Danmarks Statistik. Landbrugsstatistik. Herunder Gartneri og Skovbrug (0070-3559)
Indexed: RASB.
Published by: Danmarks Statistik, Sejroegade 11, Copenhagen Oe, 2100, Denmark. TEL 45-39-17-39-17, FAX 45-31-18-48-01.

338.1021   DNK
HD2001
DENMARK. MINISTERIET FOR FOEDEVARER, LANDBRUG OG FISKERI. FOEDEVAREOEKONOMISK INSTITUT. LANDBRUGSREGNSKABSSTATISTIK/AGRICULTURAL ACCOUNTS STATISTICS. Key Title: Landbrugsregnskabsstatistik. Text in Danish, English. 1917. a. price varies.
Formerly (until 2002): Denmark. Statens Jordbrugs- og Fiskerioekonomiske Institut. Serie A: Landbrugsregnskabsstatistik (0107-5675)
—BLDSC (8442.005000), CISTI.
Published by: Ministeriet for Foedevarer, Landbrug og Fiskeri, Foedevareoekonomisk Institut/Ministry of Food, Agriculture and Fisheries, Danish Research Institute of Food Economics, Rolighedsvej 25, Frederiksberg C, 2000, Denmark. TEL 45-35-28-68-00, FAX 45-35-28-68-01, sjfi@sjfi.dk, http://www.sjfi.dk.

338.1021   DNK
SB319.3.D4
DENMARK. MINISTERIET FOR FOEDEVARER, LANDBRUG OG FISKERI. FOEDEVAREOEKONOMISK INSTITUT. SERIE D: GARTNERI-REGNSKABSSTATISTIK/HORTICULTURAL ACCOUNTS STATISTICS. Key Title: Gartneriregnskabsstatistik. Text in Danish; Summaries in English. 1980. a. price varies.
Formerly (until 2002): Denmark. Statens Jordbrugs-Fiskeoekonomisk Institut. Serie D: Gartneri-Regnskabsstatistik (0107-5705)
Indexed: WAE&RSA.
—CISTI.
Published by: Ministeriet for Foedevarer, Landbrug og Fiskeri, Foedevareoekonomisk Institut/Ministry of Food, Agriculture and Fisheries, Danish Research Institute of Food Economics, Rolighedsvej 25, Frederiksberg C, 2000, Denmark. TEL 45-35-28-68-00, FAX 45-35-28-68-01, sjfi@sjfi.dk, http://www.sjfi.dk.

338.1021   GBR
DIRECTORY AND STATISTICS OF AGRICULTURAL CO-OPERATIVES AND OTHER FARMER CONTROLLED BUSINESSES IN THE U K. Text in English. 1970. a. GBP 45 (effective 1999). stat. **Document type:** *Directory.* **Description:** Covers 6700 agricultural, horticultural and fishery co-operatives in the UK. Provides name and address, names of chairman and secretary, telephone and telex numbers, registration number, activities, membership and turnover figures.
Former titles: Directory of Agricultural Co-Operatives in the United Kingdom (1359-9232); Directory of Agricultural, Horticultural and Fishery Co-Operatives in the United Kingdom (0265-7155); Directory of Agricultural Co-Operatives in the United Kingdom (0307-689X)
Published by: Plunkett Foundation, Plunkett Foundation, 23 Hanborough Business Park, Lodge Rd, Long Hanborough, Witney, Oxon OX8 8LH, United Kingdom. TEL 44-1993-883636, FAX 44-1993-883576, info@plunkett.co.uk. Circ: 1,060.

338.1021   BOL
ENCUESTA NACIONAL AGROPECUARIA. RESULTADOS DE LA PRODUCCION AGRICOLA. Text in Spanish. a.
Published by: (Bolivia. Departamento de Estadisticas Agropecuarias), Instituto Nacional de Estadistica, Casilla de Correos 6129, La Paz, Bolivia.

ESTADISTICA MENSUAL DE FAENA Y EXPORTACION. see *FOOD AND FOOD INDUSTRIES—Abstracting, Bibliographies, Statistics*

338.1021   PAN   ISSN 0378-2581
HD9424.P26
ESTADISTICA PANAMENA. SITUACION ECONOMICA. SECCION 312. PRODUCCION PECUARIA. Text in Spanish. 1954. a. PAB 1 domestic (effective 2000). **Document type:** *Bulletin, Government.* **Description:** Presents information on cattle, pigs and chickens, including milk and egg production.

Published by: Direccion de Estadistica y Censo, Contraloria General, Apdo. 5213, Panama City, 5, Panama. FAX 507-210-4801. Circ: 850.

633.1021   PAN   ISSN 0378-2565
SB192.P2
ESTADISTICA PANAMENA. SITUACION ECONOMICA. SECCION 312. SUPERFICIE SEMBRADA Y COSECHA DE ARROZ, MAIZ Y FRIJOL DE BEJUCO. Text in Spanish. 1954. a. PAB 1 domestic (effective 2000). **Document type:** *Bulletin, Government.* **Description:** Presents data on the harvests of rice, corn and beans.
Published by: Direccion de Estadistica y Censo, Contraloria General, Apdo. 5213, Panama City, 5, Panama. FAX 507-210-4801. Circ: 800.

630.21   PAN
SB87.P2
ESTADISTICA PANAMENA. SITUACION ECONOMICA. SECCION 312. SUPERFICIE SEMBRADA Y COSECHA DE CAFE Y CANA DE AZUCAR. Text in Spanish. 1954. a. PAB 0.75 domestic (effective 2000). **Document type:** *Bulletin, Government.* **Description:** Offers data on the harvests of coffee and sugar cane. Includes export amounts and prices.
Formerly: Estadistica Panamena. Situation Economica. Seccion 312. Superficie Sembrada y Cosecha de Cafe, Tabaco y Cana de Azucar (0378-2573)
Published by: Direccion de Estadistica y Censo, Contraloria General, Apdo. 5213, Panama City, 5, Panama. FAX 507-210-4801. Circ: 700.

338.1021   PAN   ISSN 0378-2530
HD1821
ESTADISTICA PANAMENA. SITUACION ECONOMICA. SECCION 351. PRECIOS PAGADOS POR EL PRODUCTOR AGROPECUARIO. Text in Spanish. 1974. a. PAB 0.75 domestic (effective 2000). **Document type:** *Bulletin, Government.* **Description:** Presents prices paid for animal feed, fertilizer, pesticide, farm equipment, construction materials, veterinary care, and rice and corn seed.
Published by: Direccion de Estadistica y Censo, Contraloria General, Apdo. 5213, Panama City, 5, Panama. FAX 507-210-4801. Circ: 700.

338.1021   PAN   ISSN 0378-2611
ESTADISTICA PANAMENA. SITUACION ECONOMICA. SECCION 351. PRECIOS RECIBIDOS POR EL PRODUCTOR AGROPECUARIO. Text in Spanish. 1958. s-a. PAB 2 domestic (effective 2000). **Document type:** *Bulletin, Government.* **Description:** Presents prices received on the sale of agricultural products.
Published by: Direccion de Estadistica y Censo, Contraloria General, Apdo. 5213, Panama City, 5, Panama. FAX 507-210-4801. Circ: 800.

338.1021   PAN   ISSN 0378-2549
ESTADISTICA PANAMENA. SITUACION ECONOMICA. SECCION 351. PRECIOS RECIBIDOS POR EL PRODUCTOR AGROPECUARIO. COMPENDIO. Text in Spanish. 1975. a. PAB 1 domestic (effective 2000). **Document type:** *Bulletin, Government.*
Published by: Direccion de Estadistica y Censo, Contraloria General, Apdo. 5213, Panama City, 5, Panama. FAX 507-210-4801. Circ: 800.

630.21   PAN   ISSN 0378-4991
HD9014.P3
ESTADISTICA PANAMENA. SITUACION ECONOMICA. SECCION 352. HOJA DE BALANCE DE ALIMENTOS. Text in Spanish. 1960. a. PAB 1 domestic (effective 2000). **Document type:** *Bulletin, Government.* **Description:** Offers data on production, foreign commerce, internal resources and their usage, and consumption.
Published by: Direccion de Estadistica y Censo, Contraloria General, Apdo. 5213, Panama City, 5, Panama. FAX 507-210-4801. Circ: 250.

016.636   NLD   ISSN 1382-6077
EUROPEAN ASSOCIATION FOR ANIMAL PRODUCTION. ANNUAL MEETING. BOOK OF ABSTRACTS. Short title: E A A P Book of Abstracts Series. Text in English. 1995. a. EUR 45 (effective 2005). **Document type:** *Proceedings, Abstract/Index.*
Indexed: BIOSIS Prev.
—CISTI.
Published by: (European Association for Animal Production ITA), Wageningen Academic Publishers, PO Box 220, Wageningen, 6700 AE, Netherlands. TEL 31-317-476516, FAX 31-317-453417, EAAP@WageningenAcademic.com, info@wageningenacademic.com, http://www.WageningenAcademic.com/EAAP, http://www.wageningenacademic.com. Ed. Y van der Honing. Pub., R&P Mike Jacobs TEL 31-317-476516. Circ: 1,000 (paid).

630.21   LUX   ISSN 1562-1340
HD1920.5
EUROSTAT STATISTICS IN FOCUS. AGRICULTURE AND FISHERIES. Text in English. 1991. a. **Document type:** *Government.*

Former titles: Eurostat. Statistics in Focus. Agriculture, Forestry and Fisheries (1024-4263); (until 1994): Eurostat. Rapid Reports. Agriculture, Forestry and Fisheries (1017-5776); Which superseded in part: Eurostat. Rapid Reports. Agriculture (1016-0221)
Related titles: ♦ French ed.: Eurostat Statistiques en Bref. Agriculture et Peche. ISSN 1561-8455; ♦ German ed.: Eurostat Statistik Kurz Gefasst. Landwirtschaft und Fischerei. ISSN 1562-1359.
Indexed: AgrForAb, AnBrAb, DSA, FPA, ForAb, HerbAb, HortAb, IIS, MaizeAb, PN&I, PoultAb, RPP, RRTA, S&F, SIA, TriticAb, WAE&RSA.
—BLDSC (8453.536710).
Published by: European Commission, Statistical Office of the European Communities, Rue Alcide de Gasperi, Luxembourg, 2920, Luxembourg. TEL 352-4301-34526, FAX 352-4301-34415, eurostat-infodesk@cec.eu.int, http://www.europa.eu.int/comm/eurostat. **Dist. in the U.S. by:** Unipub. TEL 800-274-4888.

630.21   LUX   ISSN 1562-1359
EUROSTAT STATISTIK KURZ GEFASST. LANDWIRTSCHAFT UND FISCHEREI. Text in German. 1991. m. **Document type:** *Government.*
Former titles: Eurostat. Statistik Kurzgefasst. Land- und Forstwirtschaft, Fischerei (1024-428X); Eurostat. Schnellberichte. Land- und Forstwirtschaft, Fischerei (1017-5784)
Related titles: ♦ English ed.: Eurostat Statistics in Focus. Agriculture and Fisheries. ISSN 1562-1340; ♦ French ed.: Eurostat Statistiques en Bref. Agriculture et Peche. ISSN 1561-8455.
Published by: European Commission, Statistical Office of the European Communities, Rue Alcide de Gasperi, Luxembourg, 2920, Luxembourg. TEL 352-4301-34526, FAX 352-4301-34415, eurostat-infodesk@cec.eu.int, http://www.europa.eu.int/comm/eurostat. **Dist. in the U.S. by:** Unipub. TEL 800-274-4888.

630.21   LUX   ISSN 1561-8455
EUROSTAT STATISTIQUES EN BREF. AGRICULTURE ET PECHE. Text in French. 1991. m. **Document type:** *Government.*
Former titles (until 1999): Eurostat. Statistiques en Bref. Agriculture, Sylviculture et Peche (1024-4271); (until 1994): Eurostat. Statistiques Rapides. Agriculture, Sylviculture et Peche (1017-5768)
Related titles: ♦ English ed.: Eurostat Statistics in Focus. Agriculture and Fisheries. ISSN 1562-1340; ♦ German ed.: Eurostat Statistik Kurz Gefasst. Landwirtschaft und Fischerei. ISSN 1562-1359.
Published by: European Commission, Statistical Office of the European Communities, Rue Alcide de Gasperi, Luxembourg, 2920, Luxembourg. TEL 352-4301-34526, FAX 352-4301-34415, eurostat-infodesk@cec.eu.int, http://www.europa.eu.int/comm/eurostat. **Dist. in the U.S. by:** Unipub. TEL 800-274-4888.

631.3021 338.1021   CAN   ISSN 1201-8325
EXTRACTION SYSTEM OF AGRICULTURAL STATISTICS/SYSTEME D'EXTRACTION DES STATISTIQUES AGRICOLES. Text in English, French. 1993. a.
Media: CD-ROM.
Published by: Statistics Canada, Publications Sales and Services, Ottawa, ON K1A 0T6, Canada. TEL 613-951-8116, infostats@statcan.ca, http://www.statcan.ca/english/Dli/Data/Ftp/esas.htm.

016.6318   IND   ISSN 0014-5564
F A I ABSTRACT SERVICE. Text in English. 1962. m. USD 15. abstr. **Document type:** *Abstract/Index.*
Published by: Fertiliser Association of India, 10 Shaheed Jit Singh Marg, New Delhi, 110 067, India. TEL 91-11-656-7144, FAX 91-11-696-0052. Ed. K P Sundaram. Circ: 2,200.

630.21   ITA   ISSN 1020-8100
HD1421
F A O BULLETIN OF STATISTICS/BOLETIN F A O DE ESTADISTICAS/BULLETIN F A O DE STATISTIQUES. (Food and Agriculture Organization of the United Nations) Text in English, French, Spanish. 1952. q. USD 20 (effective 1999). mkt.; stat. index, cum.index. back issues avail. **Description:** Provides facts and data on world food and agricultural conditions, with an analysis of the factors influencing them.
Former titles (until 2000): F A O Quarterly Bulletin of Statistics (1011-8780); (until 1989): F A O Monthly Bulletin of Statistics (0379-0010); (until 1978): F A O Monthly Bulletin of Agricultural Economics and Statistics (0027-0229)
Related titles: Microfiche ed.: (from CIS); Online - full text ed.
Indexed: B&AI, DSA, HortAb, IIS, KES, NutrAb, PAIS, RASB, RefZh, RiceAb, SIA, WAE&RSA, WBA.
—CISTI, Linda Hall.
Published by: Food and Agriculture Organization of the United Nations, Sales and Marketing Group, Viale delle Terme di Caracalla, Rome, 00100, Italy. TEL 39-06-57054350, FAX 39-06-57053360, fi-publications@fao.org, http://www.fao.org. Circ: 7,800.

▼ *new title*   ➤ *refereed*   ✳ *unverified*   ♦ *full entry avail.*

A

338.1021 GBR
FARM BUSINESS STATISTICS FOR SOUTH EAST ENGLAND. Text in English. 1969. a. GBP 6 per issue (effective 2003). charts; stat. **Document type:** *Monographic series, Academic/Scholarly.*
Published by: (Department of Agricultural Economics), Imperial College of Science, Technology and Medicine, Department of Agricultural Sciences at Wye (Subsidiary of: University of London), Wye, Ashford, Kent TN25 5AH, United Kingdom. TEL 44-20-75942617, FAX 44-20-75942754, http://www.wye.ic.ac.uk. Circ: 800.

338.1021 CAN ISSN 0835-6246
FARMING FACTS. Text in English. 1980. a.
Published by: (Statistics Canada, Agriculture Natural Resources Division), Statistics Canada, Publications Sales and Services, Ottawa, ON K1A 0T6, Canada. TEL 613-951-8116, 800-267-6677, infostats@statcan.ca, http://www.statcan.ca.

637.1021 USA ISSN 0501-4670
FEDERAL MILK ORDER MARKET STATISTICS. Text in English. 1960. m. free. stat. reprint service avail. from CIS. **Document type:** *Government.*
Related titles: Microfiche ed.: (from CIS).
Indexed: AmStI.
—CISTI.
Published by: (Dairy Division), U.S. Department of Agriculture, Agricultural Marketing Service, 1400 Independence Ave, S W, Washington, DC 20250. TEL 202-720-2352. Circ: 800.

631.8021 IND ISSN 0430-327X
FERTILISER ASSOCIATION OF INDIA. FERTILISER STATISTICS. Text in English. 1956. a. USD 25. charts; stat.
—Linda Hall.
Published by: Fertiliser Association of India, 10 Shaheed Jit Singh Marg, New Delhi, 110 067, India. TEL 91-11-656-7144, FAX 91-11-696-0052.

338.1021 631.021 USA
FERTILIZER FINANCIAL FACTS. Text in English. a. USD 425 (effective 1999). film rev.; video rev. **Document type:** *Trade.* **Description:** Provides yearly and quarterly summaries of overall industry economic performance.
Published by: Fertilizer Institute, 501 Second St, N E, Washington, DC 20002. TEL 202-675-8250, FAX 202-544-8123, hvroomen@tfi.org, http://www.tfi.org. R&P Harry L Vroomen.

338.1021 631.021 USA
FERTILIZER INSTITUTE. ANNUAL SUMMARY. Text in English. a. USD 550; includes Fertilizer Record and Production Survey. **Document type:** *Trade.* **Description:** Provides corrected fiscal-year totals for all production categories as reported in the Fertilizer Record.
Published by: Fertilizer Institute, 501 Second St, N E, Washington, DC 20002. TEL 202-544-8123, FAX 202-675-8250, http://www.tfi.org.

338.1021 631.021 USA
FERTILIZER INSTITUTE. MONTHLY EXPORTS AND IMPORTS. Text in English. m. USD 350 to non-members; USD 175 to members. **Document type:** *Trade.*
Published by: Fertilizer Institute, 501 Second St, N E, Washington, DC 20002. TEL 202-675-8250, FAX 202-544-8123, http://www.tfi.org.

338.1021 631.021 USA
FERTILIZER INSTITUTE. PRODUCTION SURVEY. Text in English. s-a. USD 550; includes Fertilizer Record and Annual Summary. **Document type:** *Trade.* **Description:** Summarizes data on all products covered in the Fertilizer Record.
Published by: Fertilizer Institute, 501 Second St, N E, Washington, DC 20002. TEL 202-675-8250, FAX 202-544-8123, http://www.tfi.org.

016.633 GBR ISSN 0015-069X
SB183
FIELD CROP ABSTRACTS; monthly abstract journal on world annual cereal, legume, root, oilseed and fibre crops. Text in English. 1948. m. USD 2,470 in the Americas to institutions except Canada; GBP 1,410 elsewhere to institutions; USD 2,645 combined subscription in the Americas to institutions except Canada; print & online eds.; GBP 1,510 combined subscription elsewhere to institutions print & online eds. (effective 2006). adv. bk.rev. abstr.; bibl. index. back issues avail.; reprints avail. **Document type:** *Abstract/Index.* **Description:** Covers literature on agronomy, field production, crop botany, and physiology of all annual field crops, both temperate and tropical.
Related titles: Online - full text ed.: USD 2,100 in the Americas to institutions; GBP 1,200 elsewhere to institutions (effective 2006) (from DIMDI, The Dialog Corporation).
—BLDSC (3920.000000), CISTI, Linda Hall. **CCC.**
Published by: CABI Publishing (Subsidiary of: CAB International), CAB International, Wallingford, Oxfordshire OX10 8DE, United Kingdom. TEL 44-1491-832111, FAX 44-1491-833508, cabi@cabi.org, http://www.cabi-publishing.org/. Ed. Anton M Doroszenko. adv.: B&W page GBP 85, B&W page USD 135; 170 x 267. Circ: 230. **Subscr. in N America to:** CABI Publishing North America, 875 Massachusetts Ave, 7th Fl, Cambridge, MA 02139. TEL 617-395-4056, 800-528-4841, FAX 617-354-6875, cabi-nao@cabi.org.

631 FIN ISSN 0786-2857
FINLAND. MINISTRY OF AGRICULTURE AND FORESTRY. INFORMATION CENTRE. STATISTICS. MAATILATILASTOLLINEN VUOSIKIRJA/YEARBOOK OF FARM STATISTICS. Text in English, Finnish, Swedish. 1869. a., latest 2004. price varies. stat. **Document type:** *Yearbook, Government.* **Description:** Statistics on farms, agricultural production, population, consumption, foreign trade, etc.
Formerly (until 1988): Suomen Virallinen Tilasto. 3. Maatalous (0355-4554)
Related titles: ♦ Series of: Finland. Tilastokeskus. Maa-, Metsa-ja Kalatalous. ISSN 1456-8268.
Published by: Ministry of Agriculture and Forestry, Information Centre, Liisankatu 8, PO Box 310, Helsinki, 00023, Finland. TEL 358-20-772005, FAX 358-20-7721395, tietopalvelukeskus@mmm.fi, http://tike.mmm.fi/Tilasto/Julkaisut/vuosikirja.htm, http://www.mmm.fi. Ed. Tarja Kortesmaa TEL 358-20-7721372. Circ: 500.

630.21 FIN ISSN 1455-2523
S242.F5
FINLAND. MINISTRY OF AGRICULTURE AND FORESTRY. INFORMATION CENTRE. STATISTICS. TIETOKAPPA. Variant title: Monthly Review of Agricultural Statistics. Text in English, Finnish, Swedish. 1955. m. EUR 45 (effective 2005). charts; stat. **Document type:** *Magazine, Government.* **Description:** Publishes data on agriculture: statistics on dairies and slaughterhouses, yields, use of arable land and number of livestock.
Formerly (until 1997): Finland. National Board of Agriculture. Statistics. Monthly Review of Agricultural Statistics (0786-938X)
Published by: Ministry of Agriculture and Forestry, Information Centre, Liisankatu 8, PO Box 310, Helsinki, 00023, Finland. TEL 358-20-772005, FAX 358-20-7721395, tietopalvelukeskus@mmm.fi, http://www.mmm.fi. Ed. Tarja Kortesmaa TEL 358-20-7721372. Circ: 450.

630.21 FIN ISSN 1456-8268
FINLAND. TILASTOKESKUS. MAA-, METSA- JA KALATALOUS/AGRICULTURE, FORESTRY AND FISHERY. Text in Finnish. 1968. q. EUR 111 (effective 2005). stat. **Document type:** *Government.*
Former titles (until 1999): Finland. Tilastokeskus. Maa- ja Metsatalous (0784-8404); (until 1988): Finland. Tilastokeskus. K T. Kansantalouden Tilinpito (0355-2276)
Related titles: ♦ Series: Metsatilastollinen Vuosikirja. ISSN 0359-968X; ♦ Finland. Ministry of Agriculture and Forestry. Information Centre. Statistics. Maatilatilastollinen vuosikirja. ISSN 0786-2857; ♦ Finland. Tilastokeskus. Maatilatalouden Tulo- ja Verotilasto. ISSN 0784-9966.
Indexed: ASFA.
—CISTI.
Published by: Tilastokeskus/Statistics Finland, Tyopajakatu 13, Statistics Finland, Helsinki, 00022, Finland. TEL 358-9-17341, FAX 358-9-17342750, http://www.stat.fi/.

630.21 634.9021 FIN ISSN 0784-9966
FINLAND. TILASTOKESKUS. MAATILATALOUDEN TULO- JA VEROTILASTO/FINLAND. STATISTIKCENTRALEN. GAARDSBRUKETS INKOMST- OCH SKATTESTATISTIK. Text in Finnish, Swedish. 1989. a., latest 2003. EUR 27 (effective 2005). **Document type:** *Government.*
Related titles: ♦ Series of: Finland. Tilastokeskus. Maa-, Metsa-ja Kalatalous. ISSN 1456-8268.
—CISTI.
Published by: Tilastokeskus/Statistics Finland, Tyopajakatu 13, Statistics Finland, Helsinki, 00022, Finland. TEL 358-9-17341, FAX 358-9-17342750, http://www.stat.fi/.

630.21 634.9021 FIN ISSN 0784-9974
FINLAND. TILASTOKESKUS. MAATILATALOUDEN YRITYS- JA TULOTILASTO/FINLAND. STATISTIKCENTRALEN. GAARDSBRUKETS FOERETAGS- OCH INKOMSTSTATISTIK. Text in English, Finnish, Swedish. 1988. a., latest 2003. EUR 27 (effective 2005). **Document type:** *Government.*
Formerly (1977-1985): Finland. Tilastokeskus. Maatilatalous (0356-2913); Supersedes in part (1968-1988): Finland. Tilastokeskus. Tilastotiedotus KT. Kansantalouden Tilinpito (0355-2276)
—CISTI.
Published by: Tilastokeskus/Statistics Finland, Tyopajakatu 13, Statistics Finland, Helsinki, 00022, Finland. TEL 358-9-17341, FAX 358-9-17342750, http://www.stat.fi/.

630.21 USA
FLORIDA AVOCADO ADMINISTRATIVE COMMITTEE. SHIPMENTS REPORT. Text in English. 1954. w. back issues avail. **Description:** Covers amount of Florida shipments, prices, California shipments, and import shipments.
Published by: Florida Avocado Administrative Committee, 18710 S W 288th St, Homestead, FL 33030. TEL 305-247-0848, FAX 305-245-1315. Circ: 400.

630.21 USA
FLORIDA LIME ADMINISTRATIVE COMMITTEE. SHIPMENTS REPORT. Text in English. 1955. w. back issues avail. **Description:** Covers amount of Florida shipments, prices, Mexican lime totals, import totals, and California shipments.
Published by: Florida Lime Administrative Committee, 18710 S W 288th St, Homestead, FL 33030. TEL 305-247-0848, FAX 305-245-1315. Circ: 400. **Subscr. to:** PO Box 900188, Homestead, FL 33090-0188.

630.21 THA ISSN 1014-3696
FOOD AND AGRICULTURE ORGANIZATION OF THE UNITED NATIONS. ASIA AND THE PACIFIC COMMISSION ON AGRICULTURAL STATISTICS. PERIODIC REPORT. Text in Thai. 1967. irreg. free.
Formerly: Asia and the Far East Commission on Agricultural Statistics. Periodic Report
Published by: Food and Agriculture Organization of the United Nations, Regional Office for Asia and the Pacific, Maliwan Mansion, 39 Phra Atit Rd, Bangkok, 10200, Thailand. TEL 66-2-6974000, FAX 66-2-6974445, http://www.apfcweb.org/Publications/2001-10.pdf.

338.1021 USA
FOREIGN PRODUCTION, SUPPLY AND DISTRIBUTION OF AGRICULTURAL COMMODITIES. Text in English. q. USD 305 in North America; USD 610 elsewhere (effective 2001). **Description:** Covers the production, import and export, and domestic use of grains, rice, dairy, poultry, livestock, oilseeds, cotton, coffee, sugar, and tobacco.
Media: Magnetic Tape.
Published by: (Tripura. Department of Agriculture ZAF), U.S. Department of Commerce, National Technical Information Service, 5285 Port Royal Rd, Springfield, VA 22161. TEL 703-605-6000, info@ntis.gov, http://www.ntis.gov.

016.63 FRA ISSN 1274-1116
FRANCE. MINISTERE DE L'AGRICULTURE ET DE LA PECHE. AGRESTE. CAHIERS. Key Title: Agreste. Les Cahiers. Text in French. 1972. q. **Document type:** *Government.*
Former titles: France. Ministere de l'Agriculture et de la Foret. Agreste. Cahiers (0998-4178); (until 1990): France. Ministere de l'Agriculture. Cahiers de Statistiques Agricoles (0336-9943); France. Ministere de l'Agriculture et du Developpement Rural. Cahiers de Statistiques Agricoles (0336-4178)
Related titles: Microfiche ed.
Indexed: AEA, PN&I, PoultAb, RRTA, WAE&RSA.
Published by: Ministere de l'Agriculture et de la Peche, Service Central des Enquetes et Etudes Statistiques, 251 rue de Vaugirard, Paris, Cedex 15 75732, France. TEL 33-1-49558585, FAX 33-1-49558503, scees75@wanadoo.fr, http://www.agriculture.gouv.fr. **Subscr. to:** BP 88, Castanet Tolosan Cedex 31326, France.

630.21 FRA
FRANCE. MINISTERE DE L'AGRICULTURE ET DE LA PECHE. AGRESTE INFO; la statistique agricole. Text in French. bi-m. back issues avail. **Document type:** *Government.* **Description:** Provides information on new Agreste publications.
Former titles: France. Ministere de l'Agriculture, de la Peche et de l'Alimentation. Agreste Info; France. Ministere de l'Agriculture et de la Foret. Agreste Info (1150-1324)
Published by: Ministere de l'Agriculture et de la Peche, Service Central des Enquetes et Etudes Statistiques, 251 rue de Vaugirard, Paris, Cedex 15 75732, France. TEL 33-1-49558585, FAX 33-1-49558503, http://www.agriculture.gouv.fr. Ed. G Raulin.

016.3381 FRA
S229
FRANCE. MINISTERE DE L'AGRICULTURE ET DE LA PECHE. AGRESTE LE BULLETIN. Text in French. 1962. m. **Document type:** *Bulletin, Government.*
Former titles: France. Ministere de l'Agriculture, de la Peche et de l'Alimentation (1270-265X); (until 1995): France. Ministere de l'Agriculture et de la Peche. Series: Bulletin (1142-3218); France. Ministere de l'Agriculture. Service Central des Enquetes et Etudes Statistiques. Bulletin de Statistique Agricole (0336-9919); Cahiers Mensuels de Statistique Agricole
Related titles: Microfiche ed.
Indexed: RRTA, WAE&RSA.
Published by: Ministere de l'Agriculture et de la Peche, Service Central des Enquetes et Etudes Statistiques, 251 rue de Vaugirard, Paris, Cedex 15 75732, France. TEL 33-1-49558585, FAX 33-1-49558503, http://www.agriculture.gouv.fr.

338.1021 FRA
FRANCE. MINISTERE DE L'AGRICULTURE ET DE LA PECHE. DONNEES CHIFFRES. I A A. Text in French. 1978. irreg. **Document type:** *Government.*
Incorporates: France. Ministere de l'Agriculture et de la Peche. Recolte de Bois et Production de Sciage; Former titles: France. Ministere de l'Agriculture, de la Peche et de l'Alimentation. Donnees Chiffres. I A A; France. Ministere de l'Agriculture et de la Foret. Donnees Chiffres. I A A; Incorporates in part: France. Ministere de l'Agriculture. Series "S". Industries Agricoles et Alimentaires (0243-6647); Former titles: France. Ministere de l'Agriculture. Informations Repides. Statistiques des Entreprises (0243-6167); France. Ministere de l'Agriculture. Informations Rapides Agro-Alimenta
Published by: Ministere de l'Agriculture et de la Peche, Service Central des Enquetes et Etudes Statistiques, 251 rue de Vaugirard, Paris, Cedex 15 75732, France. TEL 33-1-49558585, FAX 33-1-49558503, http://www.agriculture.gouv.fr.

630.21 FRA
HD1941
FRANCE. MINISTERE DE L'AGRICULTURE ET DE LA PECHE. GRAPH-AGRI (REGIONS). Text in French. irreg. **Document type:** *Government.*
Former titles: France. Ministere de l'Agriculture, de la Peche et de l'Alimentation. Conjoncture Graph-Agri (Regions) (1167-4717); (until 1992): France. Ministere de l'Agriculture et de la Foret. Graph-Agri (Regions) (0755-1908)
Published by: Ministere de l'Agriculture et de la Peche, Service Central des Enquetes et Etudes Statistiques, 251 rue de Vaugirard, Paris, Cedex 15 75732, France. TEL 33-1-49558585, FAX 33-1-49558503, http://www.agriculture.gouv.fr.

338.1021 DEU ISSN 0176-7445
GERMANY. STATISTISCHES BUNDESAMT. FACHSERIE 16, LOEHNE UND GEHAELTER, REIHE 1: ARBEITERVERDIENSTE IN DER LANDWIRTSCHAFT. Text in German. a. **Document type:** *Government.*
Supersedes: Germany (Federal Republic, 1949-). Statistisches Bundesamt. Loehne und Gehaelter. Reihe 1: Arbeiterverdienste in der Landwirtschaft
Indexed: RASB.
Published by: Statistisches Bundesamt, Gustav-Stresemann-Ring 11, Wiesbaden, 65180, Germany. TEL 49-611-75-1, FAX 49-611-724000, http://www.statistik-bund.de.

338.1021 DEU ISSN 0072-3894
GERMANY. STATISTISCHES BUNDESAMT. FACHSERIE 17, PREISE, REIHE 1: PREISE UND PREISINDIZES FUER DIE LAND- UND FORSTWIRTSCHAFT. Text in German. m. **Document type:** *Government.*
Indexed: RASB.
Published by: Statistisches Bundesamt, Gustav-Stresemann-Ring 11, Wiesbaden, 65180, Germany. TEL 49-611-75-1, FAX 49-611-724000, http://www.statistik-bund.de.

338.1021 DEU ISSN 0072-3681
GERMANY. STATISTISCHES BUNDESAMT. FACHSERIE 3, LAND- UND FORSTWIRTSCHAFT, FISCHEREI; REIHE 2: BETRIEBS-, ARBEITS- UND EINKOMMENSVERHAELTNISSE. (Consists of several subseries) Text in German. irreg. price varies. **Document type:** *Government.*
Published by: Statistisches Bundesamt, Gustav-Stresemann-Ring 11, Wiesbaden, 65180, Germany. TEL 49-611-75-1, FAX 49-611-724000, http://www.statistik-bund.de.

630.21 DEU
GERMANY. STATISTISCHES BUNDESAMT. FACHSERIE 3, LAND- UND FORSTWIRTSCHAFT, FISCHEREI; REIHE 3: LANDWIRTSCHAFTLICHE BODENNUETZUNG UND PFLANZLICHE ERZEUGUNG. Text in German. 1961. a. **Document type:** *Government.*
Former titles: Germany (Federal Republic, 1949-). Statistisches Bundesamt. Fachserie 3: Land- und Forstwirtschaft, Fischerei; Reihe 3: Bodennuetzung und Pflanzliche Erzeugung; Germany (Federal Republic, 1949-). Statistisches Bundesamt. Fachserie 3, Reihe 3: Pflanzliche Erzeugung; Germany (Federal Republic, 1949-). Statistisches Bundesamt. Fachserie 3, Reihe 3: Gartenbau und Weinwirtschaft
Published by: Statistisches Bundesamt, Gustav-Stresemann-Ring 11, Wiesbaden, 65180, Germany. TEL 49-611-75-1, FAX 49-611-724000, http://www.statistik-bund.de.

636.0021 DEU
GERMANY. STATISTISCHES BUNDESAMT. FACHSERIE 3, LAND- UND FORSTWIRTSCHAFT, FISCHEREI; REIHE 4: VIEHBESTAND UND TIERISCHE ERZEUGUNG. Text in German. a. **Document type:** *Government.*
Formerly: Germany (Federal Republic, 1949-). Statistisches Bundesamt. Fachserie 3, Reihe 4: Tierische Erzeugung
Published by: Statistisches Bundesamt, Gustav-Stresemann-Ring 11, Wiesbaden, 65180, Germany. TEL 49-611-75-1, FAX 49-611-724000, http://www.statistik-bund.de.

016.63 DEU ISSN 0433-860X
GESELLSCHAFT FUER BIBLIOTHEKSWESEN UND DOKUMENTATION DES LANDBAUES. MITTEILUNGEN. Text in German; Abstracts occasionally in English. 1959. irreg. EUR 15, USD 20 per issue (effective 2005). adv. bk.rev. bibl. cum.index: 1958-1973. back issues avail. **Document type:** *Monographic series, Academic/Scholarly.*
Indexed: IBZ.
Published by: Gesellschaft fuer Bibliothekswesen und Dokumentation des Landbaues, c/o Dr. B. Schlindwein, TU Muenchen, Freising, 85350, Germany. TEL 49-8161-714029, FAX 49-8161-715093, schlind@weihenstephan.de, http://hal.weihenstephan.de. Ed., R&P Dr. Birgid B Schlindwein. Circ: 150 (controlled).

633.1 CAN ISSN 0381-3010
GRAIN STATISTICS WEEKLY/STATISTIQUES HEBDOMADAIRES DES GRAINS. Text in English, French. 1942. w. CND 250 domestic (effective 2001). stat. **Document type:** *Government.*
Related titles: Online - full content ed.
—CISTI.
Published by: Canadian Grain Commission, Corporate Services/Commission Canadienne des Grains, 700 303 Main St, Winnipeg, MB R3C 3G8, Canada. TEL 204-983-1570, FAX 204-983-0248, smudry@cgc.ca, http://www.cgc.ca/.

016.633 GBR ISSN 1350-9837
SB183
GRASSLANDS AND FORAGE ABSTRACTS; monthly abstract journal on grassland husbandry and fodder crop production. Text in English. 1931. m. USD 1,455 in the Americas to institutions except Canada; GBP 830 elsewhere to institutions; USD 1,560 combined subscription in the Americas to institutions except Canada; print & online eds.; GBP 890 combined subscription elsewhere to institutions print & online eds. (effective 2006). adv. bk.rev. abstr. index. back issues avail.; reprints avail. **Document type:** *Abstract/Index.* **Description:** Main topics covered include: management, productivity, and economics of grasslands and fodder crops; species and cultivar descriptions; fodder conservation; composition and nutritive value; botany; plant physiology; grassland ecology; and seed production, testing, and storage.
Formerly: Herbage Abstracts (0018-0602)
Related titles: Online - full text ed.: USD 1,235 in the Americas to institutions except Canada; GBP 705 elsewhere to institutions (effective 2006) (from DIMDI, The Dialog Corporation).
—CISTI, Linda Hall. **CCC.**
Published by: CABI Publishing (Subsidiary of: CAB International), CAB International, Wallingford, Oxfordshire OX10 8DE, United Kingdom. TEL 44-1491-832111, FAX 44-1491-833508, cabi@cabi.org, http://www.cabi-publishing.org/. adv.: B&W page GBP 75, B&W page USD 120; 170 x 267. Circ: 225. **Subscr. addr. in N America:** CABI Publishing North America, 875 Massachusetts Ave, 7th Fl, Cambridge, MA 02139. TEL 617-395-4056, 800-528-4841, FAX 617-354-6875, cabi-nao@cabi.org.

636.0021 GRC ISSN 1107-0129
GREECE. NATIONAL STATISTICAL SERVICE. AGRICULTURAL AND LIVESTOCK PRODUCTION (YEAR). Key Title: Paragoge Georgikon kai Ktenotrofikon Proionton Etous (Year). Text in Greek. 1934. a., latest 1998. back issues avail. **Document type:** *Government.*
Published by: National Statistical Service of Greece, Statistical Information and Publications Division/Ethniki Statistiki Yperesia tes Ellados, 14-16 Lykourgou St, Athens, 101 66, Greece. TEL 30-1-3289-397, FAX 30-1-3241-102, http://www.statistics.gr, http://www.statistics.gr/Main_eng.asp.

630.21 GRC
GREECE. NATIONAL STATISTICAL SERVICE. REVISED AGRICULTURAL PRICE INDICES. Text in English, Greek. 1974. irreg., latest 1994. USD 7. back issues avail. **Document type:** *Government.*
Formerly (until 1985): Greece. National Statistical Service. Agricultural Price Indices
Published by: National Statistical Service of Greece, Statistical Information and Publications Division/Ethniki Statistiki Yperesia tes Ellados, 14-16 Lykourgou St, Athens, 101 66, Greece. TEL 30-1-3289-397, FAX 30-1-3241-102.

633.1021 USA ISSN 1183-3777
GREY BOOK✶. Text in English. 1991. m. USD 75 (effective 2000). **Document type:** *Trade.* **Description:** Specializes in export and production data for the United States, Canada and Australia with a special interest in pulses, birdseeds, and oilseeds.
Published by: Stat Publishing, 250 H St, Blaine, WA 98230-4033. TEL 604-535-8505, FAX 604-531-8818, publisher@statpub.com, http://statpub.com/stat. Pub. P B Clancey.

633.1021 GBR ISSN 1350-3057
HOME - GROWN CEREALS AUTHORITY. CEREALS STATISTICS. Text in English. 1975. a.
Published by: Home - Grown Cereals Authority, Caledonia House, 223 Pentonville Rd, London, N1 9HY, United Kingdom. TEL 44-20-75203920, FAX 44-20-75203958, publication@hgca.com, http://www.hgca.com.

630.21 HUN
HD1940.5
HUNGARY. KOZPONTI STATISZTIKAI HIVATAL. MEZOGAZDASAGI ELELMISZERIPARI STATISZTIKAI EVKONYV/HUNGARY. CENTRAL STATISTICAL OFFICE. YEARBOOK OF AGRICULTURAL STATISTICS. Text in Hungarian. 1981. a. HUF 185. stat. **Document type:** *Government.*
Formerly: Hungary. Kozponti Statisztikai Hivatal. Mezogazdasagi Statisztikai Evkonyv (0230-4066)
Published by: Kozponti Statisztikai Hivatal, Marketing Oszta'ly, Keleti Karoly utca 5-7, Budapest, 1024, Hungary. TEL 36-1-345-6000, FAX 36-1-345-6699, http://www.ksh.hu. Circ: 1,600.

630.21 HUN ISSN 0238-7891
HD1940.5
HUNGARY. KOZPONTI STATISZTIKAI HIVATAL. MEZOGAZDASAGI ELELMISZERIPARI STATISZTIKAI ZSEBKONYV. Text in Hungarian. a. HUF 200. stat. **Document type:** *Government.*
Formerly: Hungary. Kozponti Statisztikai Hivatal. Mezogazdasagi Statisztikai Zsebkonyu (0441-4683)
Indexed: RASB.
Published by: Kozponti Statisztikai Hivatal, Marketing Oszta'ly, Keleti Karoly utca 5-7, Budapest, 1024, Hungary. TEL 36-1-345-6000, FAX 36-1-345-6699, http://www.ksh.hu. Circ: 1,500.

016.6364 GBR ISSN 0568-2800
INDEX OF CURRENT RESEARCH ON PIGS. Text in English. 1954. a. USD 300 in the Americas to institutions except Canada; GBP 170 elsewhere to institutions (effective 2006). **Document type:** *Abstract/Index.* **Description:** Contains research projects in progress throughout the world and lists publications from the previous year.
Indexed: AnBrAb, NutrAb.
—CISTI. **CCC.**
Published by: CABI Publishing (Subsidiary of: CAB International), CAB International, Wallingford, Oxfordshire OX10 8DE, United Kingdom. TEL 44-1491-832111, FAX 44-1491-833508, cabi@cabi.org, http://www.cabi-publishing.org/. **Subscr. addr. in N America:** CABI Publishing North America, 875 Massachusetts Ave, 7th Fl, Cambridge, MA 02139. TEL 617-395-4056, 800-528-4841, FAX 617-354-6875, cabi-nao@cabi.org.

338.1021 IND
INDIA. DEPARTMENT OF RURAL DEVELOPMENT. ADMINISTRATIVE INTELLIGENCE DIVISION. SOME SPECIAL PROGRAMMES OF RURAL DEVELOPMENT. STATISTICS. Text in English. a. stat.
Published by: Ministry of Agriculture, Department of Rural Development, New Delhi, 110 001, India.

636.0021 IND ISSN 0536-8502
HD9016.I4
INDIA. MINISTRY OF AGRICULTURE. BULLETIN ON FOOD STATISTICS. Text in English, Hindi. 1972. a. INR 260, USD 93.60. stat. **Document type:** *Government.*
Formerly: Studies in the Economics of Poultry Farming in Punjab
—CISTI.
Published by: Ministry of Agriculture, Department of Agriculture and Cooperation, Directorate of Economics and Statistics, A-2E-3 Kasturba Gandhi Marg Barracks, New Delhi, 110 001, India. TEL 11-381523. Ed. Brajesh Kumar Gautam. Circ: 650.

633.1021 IND
INDIAN DEOILED CAKES EXPORTERS' PERFORMANCE MONITOR. Text in English, French, German, Italian. 1986. m. USD 500. **Description:** Statistics relating to quantity, prices and turnover of each participating deoiled cake exporter in India.
Published by: Commercial Information Services, No. 1 Beena Bldg., 6th Rd., T.P.S. 4, Bandra, Mumbai, Maharashtra 400 050, India. TEL 91-22-6426703. Ed. C Moonjely. Circ: 300.

632.9021 IND
INDIAN FERTILISER STATISTICS. Text in English. 1967. a. free. stat.
Indexed: S&F.
Published by: Ministry of Chemicals and Fertilizers, Economics and Statistics Division, New Delhi, India. Circ: (controlled).

338.176021 PRT ISSN 0871-8997
INDICADORES DA PRODUCAO ANIMAL. Text in Portuguese. 1989. q. **Description:** Provides statistical data on animal husbandry with an emphasis in production.
Formerly (until 1991): Estatisticas da Producao Animal (0871-3278)
Published by: Instituto Nacional de Estatistica, Ave. Antonio Jose de Almeida 2, Lisbon, 1000-043, Portugal. TEL 351-21-8426100, FAX 351-21-8426380, ine@ine.pt, http://www.ine.pt/.

630.21 PRT ISSN 0871-9004
INDICADORES DA PRODUCAO VEGETAL. Text in Portuguese. 1987. q. **Description:** Provides statistical data on vegetable production in Portugal.
Formerly (until 1991): Portugal. Instituto Nacional de Estatisica. Estatisticas da Producao Vegetal (0871-1356)
Published by: Instituto Nacional de Estatistica, Ave. Antonio Jose de Almeida 2, Lisbon, 1000-043, Portugal. TEL 351-21-8426100, FAX 351-21-8426380, ine@ine.pt, http://www.ine.pt/.

016.57 IDN
INDONESIAN BIOLOGICAL AND AGRICULTURAL INDEX/INDEKS BIOLOGI DAN PERTANIAN DE INDONESIA. Text in English, Indonesian. 1969. bi-m. free.
Former titles (until 1980): Index of Biology, Agriculture and Agro Economy (0216-0803); Indonesian Biological and Agricultural Index (0019-3593)
Indexed: B&AI.
Published by: National Library for Agricultural Science, Jalan Ir. Haji Juanda 20, Bogor, Indonesia. Ed. Sulastuti Sophia. Circ: 1,500.

A

016.63   DEU   ISSN 0946-9761
**INFORMATIONSDIENST PRAXISBEZOGENER LITERATUR IM
WEINBAU.** Text in German. 1994. q. EUR 19 domestic; EUR
21 in Europe (effective 2005). **Document type:**
Abstract/Index. **Description:** Abstracts from journals, books,
conference proceedings and reports on all aspects of
technical literature on wine and grapevines in the German
language.
Related titles: Online - full text ed.
Published by: Bundesanstalt fuer Zuechtungsforschung an
Kulturpflanzen, Institut fuer Rebenzuechtung Geilweilerhof,
Siebeldingen, 76833, Germany. TEL 49-6345-41141, FAX
49-6345-919050, doku-vitis@bafz.de, http://www.bafz.de/
siebeldingen. Eds. Martin Klenert, Werner Koeglmeier. Circ:
150 (controlled).

016.631   POL   ISSN 0373-7837
**INSTYTUT HODOWLI I AKLIMATYZACJI ROSLIN.
BIULETYN/INSTITUTE OF PLANT BREEDING AND
ACCLIMATIZATION. BULLETIN.** Text in Polish; Summaries in
English. 1951. q. EUR 98 foreign (effective 2005). bk.rev.
reprints avail. **Document type:** *Academic/Scholarly.*
Description: Contains publications of plant breeding and
genetics, physiology, biochemistry, phytopathology - important
for practical plant breeding and seed production, as well as
publications on the value of collected germ plasm for creation
of new plant genotypes.
Indexed: AEA, AbHyg, AgBio, AgrAg, AgrLib, BioCN&I, BiolAb,
CPA, FCA, HerbAb, HortAb, I&DA, IndVet, MaizeAb, NemAb,
NutrAb, OrnHort, PBA, PGegResA, PGrRegA, PHN&I,
PotatoAb, RA&MP, RM&VM, RPP, RefZh, RevApplEntom,
S&F, SIA, SeedAb, SoyAb, TriticAb, WAE&RSA, WeedAb.
—BLDSC (2099.300000), CISTI, IE, ingenta.
Published by: Instytut Hodowli i Aklimatyzacji Roslin/Plant
Breeding and Acclimatization Institute, Radzikow, Blonie,
05870, Poland. TEL 48-22-7253611, FAX 48-22-7254714,
postbox@ihar.edu.pl, http://www.ihar.edu.pl. Ed. Henryk J
Czembor. R&P Krystyna Weka. Dist. by: Ars Polona,
Krakowskie Przedmiescie 7, Warsaw, Poland. TEL
48-22-9263914, FAX 48-22-9265334,
arspolona@arspolona.com.pl, http://www.arspolona.com.pl.

016.6371   BEL   ISSN 0538-7086
**INTERNATIONAL DAIRY FEDERATION. CATALOGUE OF I D F
PUBLICATIONS/FEDERATION INTERNATIONALE
LAITIERE. CATALOGUE DES PUBLICATIONS.** Text in
English, French. 1973. a. free. bk.rev. **Document type:**
Catalog.
Media: Duplicated (not offset).
Published by: International Dairy Federation/Federation
Internationale de Laiterie, Diamant Building, Bd Auguste
Reyers 80, Brussels, 1030, Belgium. TEL 32-2-7339888, FAX
32-2-7330413. Circ: 3,000.

016.6371   GBR   ISSN 1361-0198
INTERNATIONAL FOOD ABSTRACTS. DAIRY DISK. Text in
English. 1995. bi-m. GBP 355 (effective 2000). **Document
type:** *Abstract/Index.*
Media: CD-ROM.
Published by: Leatherhead Food International Ltd., Randalls Rd,
Leatherhead, Surrey KT22 7RY, United Kingdom. TEL
44-1372-376761, FAX 44-1372-386228, hbennett@lfra.co.uk.

633.1021   GBR
**INTERNATIONAL GRAINS COUNCIL. WORLD GRAIN
STATISTICS (YEAR).** Text in English, French, Russian,
Spanish. 1955. a., latest 2000. GBP 100, USD 160 (effective
2001). charts. **Document type:** *Trade.* **Description:** Compiles
long-term data on production, trade, and prices of wheat,
corn, barley, and other coarse grains.
Former titles: International Wheat Council. World Grain Statistics;
(until 1987): World Wheat Statistics (0512-3844)
—BLDSC (9356.029900), CISTI.
Published by: International Grains Council, One Canada Sq,
Canary Wharf, London, E14 5AE, United Kingdom. TEL
44-20-7513-1122, FAX 44-20-7513-0630, igc-fac@igc.org.uk,
http://www.igc.org.uk.

016.6316   NLD   ISSN 0074-6436
                                       CODEN: BIIIDY
**INTERNATIONAL INSTITUTE FOR LAND RECLAMATION AND
IMPROVEMENT. BIBLIOGRAPHY.** Text in English. 1960.
irreg., latest vol.18, 1984. price varies. **Document type:**
Bibliography.
Indexed: FCA, HerbAb, RRTA, S&F, WAE&RSA.
—CISTI.
Published by: International Institute for Land Reclamation and
Improvement, PO Box 45, Wageningen, 6700 AA,
Netherlands. TEL 31-317-490144, FAX 31-317-417187,
ilri@ilri.nl. Ed. M G Bos. R&P E A Rylhsen.

630.21   USA   ISSN 1041-9268
IOWA CROPS & WEATHER. Text in English. 1976. m.
((Jan.-Mar.); Weekly (Apr.-Nov.)). looseleaf. USD 13 (effective
2003). **Document type:** *Newsletter, Government.*
Description: Covers crop development and how it is affected
by weather conditions in Iowa.
Published by: Iowa Agricultural Statistics, 210 Walnut St, Rm
833, Des Moines, IA 50309. TEL 515-284-4340, FAX
515-284-4342, nass-ia@nass.usda.gov, http://nass.usda.gov/
ia. Ed. Jim Sands. Circ: 1,050.

333.31021   IRL   ISSN 1393-3280
**IRELAND. CENTRAL STATISTICAL OFFICE. AGRICULTURAL
LAND SALES.** Text in English. 1996. q. charts; stat.
Document type: *Government.* **Description:** Documents the
amount and prices of agricultural real estate bought and sold.
Related titles: Online - full text ed.
Published by: Central Statistics Office/Eire, An Phriomh-Oifig
Staidrimh, Skehard Rd., Cork, Ireland. TEL 353-21-4535000,
FAX 353-21-4535555, information@cso.ie,
http://www.cso.ie/releasespublications/
pr_agricultureandfishing.htm.

630.21   IRL   ISSN 1393-2764
**IRELAND. CENTRAL STATISTICS OFFICE. AGRICULTURAL
LABOUR INPUT.** Text in English. 1995. a. charts; stat.
Document type: *Government.*
Related titles: Online - full text ed.
Published by: Central Statistics Office/Eire, An Phriomh-Oifig
Staidrimh, Skehard Rd., Cork, Ireland. TEL 353-21-4535000,
FAX 353-21-4535555, information@cso.ie,
http://www.cso.ie/releasespublications/
pr_agricultureandfishing.htm.

338.1021   IRL   ISSN 1393-5100
**IRELAND. CENTRAL STATISTICS OFFICE. AGRICULTURAL
PRICE INDICES.** Text in English. 1997. m. charts; stat.
Document type: *Government.* **Description:** Monitors the
prices of agricultural inputs.
Formed by the 1997 merger of: Ireland. Central Statistics Office.
Agricultural Input Price Index. (0791-3346); Which was
formerly (until 1987): Ireland. Central Statistics Office.
Agricultural Price Index Numbers; Ireland. Central Statistics
Office. Agricultural Output Price Index (0791-3354); Which was
formerly (until 1987): Ireland. Central Statistics Office.
Agricultural Output Price Index Numbers
Media: Duplicated (not offset). **Related titles:** Online - full text ed.
Published by: Central Statistics Office/Eire, An Phriomh-Oifig
Staidrimh, Skehard Rd., Cork, Ireland. TEL 353-21-4535000,
FAX 353-21-4535555, information@cso.ie,
http://www.cso.ie/releasespublications/
pr_agricultureandfishing.htm.

338.1021   IRL   ISSN 1393-5526
**IRELAND. CENTRAL STATISTICS OFFICE. AGRICULTURAL
PRICE INDICES. PRELIMINARY ESTIMATES.** Text in
English. 1996. a. charts; stat. **Document type:** *Government.*
Description: Presents estimated annual indices for both
agricultural input and output prices.
Formerly (until 1997): Ireland. Central Statistics Office.
Preliminary Estimates of Agricultural Input and Output Price
Indices (1393-399X)
Related titles: Online - full text ed.
Published by: Central Statistics Office/Eire, An Phriomh-Oifig
Staidrimh, Skehard Rd., Cork, Ireland. TEL 353-21-4535000,
FAX 353-21-4535555, information@cso.ie,
http://www.cso.ie/releasespublications/
pr_agricultureandfishing.htm.

338.1021   IRL   ISSN 1393-6867
**IRELAND. CENTRAL STATISTICS OFFICE. AREA, YIELD AND
PRODUCTION OF CROPS.** Text in English. 1995. a. charts;
stat. **Document type:** *Government.*
Formerly (until 1998): Ireland. Central Statistics Office. Estimated
Area, Yield and Production of Crops (1393-2284)
Related titles: Online - full text ed.
Published by: Central Statistics Office/Eire, An Phriomh-Oifig
Staidrimh, Skehard Rd., Cork, Ireland. TEL 353-21-4535000,
FAX 353-21-4535555, information@cso.ie,
http://www.cso.ie/releasespublications/
pr_agricultureandfishing.htm.

633.1021   IRL   ISSN 1393-3825
**IRELAND. CENTRAL STATISTICS OFFICE. CEREALS SUPPLY
BALANCE.** Text in English. 1996. a. charts; stat. **Document
type:** *Government.*
Related titles: Online - full text ed.
Published by: Central Statistics Office/Eire, An Phriomh-Oifig
Staidrimh, Skehard Rd., Cork, Ireland. TEL 353-21-4535000,
FAX 353-21-4535555, information@cso.ie,
http://www.cso.ie/releasespublications/
pr_agricultureandfishing.htm.

338.1021   IRL   ISSN 1393-6689
**IRELAND. CENTRAL STATISTICS OFFICE. CROPS AND
LIVESTOCK SURVEY - FINAL ESTIMATES.** Text in English.
a. charts; stat. **Document type:** *Government.*
Former titles (until 1996): Ireland. Central Statistics Office.
Agricultural Statistics, June. Land Utilisation and Numbers of
Livestock (0791-3524); (until 1986): Ireland. Central Statistics
Office. Agricultural Statistics, June. Final Results; (until 1984):
Ireland. Central Statistics Office. Crops and Pasture; Ireland
Central Central Statistics Office. Crops and Livestock
Numbers. (0075-0549)
Published by: Central Statistics Office/Eire, An Phriomh-Oifig
Staidrimh, Skehard Rd., Cork, Ireland. TEL 353-21-4535000,
FAX 353-21-4535555, information@cso.ie,
http://www.cso.ie/releasespublications/
pr_agricultureandfishing.htm.

338.1021   IRL   ISSN 1393-7278
**IRELAND. CENTRAL STATISTICS OFFICE. CROPS AND
LIVESTOCK SURVEY, JUNE - PROVISIONAL RESULTS.**
Text in English. 1970. a. charts; stat. **Document type:**
Government.
Formerly (until 1997): Ireland. Central Statistics Office.
Agricultural Statistics, June - Provisional Estimates for Certain
Items (0791-3141)
Related titles: Online - full text ed.
Published by: Central Statistics Office/Eire, An Phriomh-Oifig
Staidrimh, Skehard Rd., Cork, Ireland. TEL 353-21-4535000,
FAX 353-21-4535555, information@cso.ie,
http://www.cso.ie/releasespublications/
pr_agricultureandfishing.htm.

636.021   IRL   ISSN 0791-3133
**IRELAND. CENTRAL STATISTICS OFFICE. DECEMBER
LIVESTOCK SURVEY.** Text in English. 1976. a. charts; stat.
Document type: *Government.*
Former titles (until 1989): Ireland Central Statistics Office.
Livestock Enumeration (0791-3125); (until 1984): Ireland
Central Statistics Office. Livestock Numbers (0075-059X)
Media: Duplicated (not offset). **Related titles:** Online - full text ed.
Published by: Central Statistics Office/Eire, An Phriomh-Oifig
Staidrimh, Skehard Rd., Cork, Ireland. TEL 353-21-4535000,
FAX 353-21-4535555, information@cso.ie,
http://www.cso.ie/releasespublications/
pr_agricultureandfishing.htm.

338.1021   IRL   ISSN 1393-5453
**IRELAND. CENTRAL STATISTICS OFFICE. EARNINGS OF
AGRICULTURAL WORKERS.** Text in English. 1995. triennial.
charts; stat. **Document type:** *Government.*
Formerly (until 1997): Ireland. Central Statistics Office. Earnings
of Permanent Agricultural Workers (1393-1598)
Related titles: Online - full text ed.
Published by: Central Statistics Office/Eire, An Phriomh-Oifig
Staidrimh, Skehard Rd., Cork, Ireland. TEL 353-21-4535000,
FAX 353-21-4535555, information@cso.ie,
http://www.cso.ie/releasespublications/pr_earns.htm.

338.1021   IRL
**IRELAND. CENTRAL STATISTICS OFFICE. FARM
STRUCTURES SURVEY.** Text in English. 1993. biennial.
charts; stat. **Document type:** *Government.* **Description:**
Analyzes the structure of Irish farms for the year, classified by
size, type, number of livestock, and work force. Compares
results with previous censuses.
Published by: Central Statistics Office/Eire, An Phriomh-Oifig
Staidrimh, Skehard Rd., Cork, Ireland. TEL 353-21-4535000,
FAX 353-21-4535555, information@cso.ie, http://www.cso.ie.

636.4021   IRL   ISSN 1393-5119
**IRELAND. CENTRAL STATISTICS OFFICE. LIVESTOCK
SLAUGHTERINGS.** Text in English. 1984. m. charts; stat.
Document type: *Government.*
Former titles (until 1997): Ireland. Central Statistics Office. Pig
Slaughterings (1393-2276); (until 1995): Ireland. Central
Statistics Office. Number and Weight of Pigs Slaughtered at
Bacon Factories (0791-3044)
Media: Duplicated (not offset). **Related titles:** Online - full text ed.
Published by: Central Statistics Office/Eire, An Phriomh-Oifig
Staidrimh, Skehard Rd., Cork, Ireland. TEL 353-21-4535000,
FAX 353-21-4535555, information@cso.ie,
http://www.cso.ie/releasespublications/
pr_agricultureandfishing.htm.

636.0021   IRL   ISSN 1393-2667
**IRELAND. CENTRAL STATISTICS OFFICE. MEAT SUPPLY
BALANCE.** Text in English. 1995. a. charts; stat. **Document
type:** *Government.* **Description:** Reconciles the total supplies
of a product with the various uses taking account of changes
in stock levels.
Related titles: Online - full text ed.
Published by: Central Statistics Office/Eire, An Phriomh-Oifig
Staidrimh, Skehard Rd., Cork, Ireland. TEL 353-21-4535000,
FAX 353-21-4535555, information@cso.ie,
http://www.cso.ie/releasespublications/
pr_agricultureandfishing.htm.

637.1021   IRL   ISSN 1393-3310
**IRELAND. CENTRAL STATISTICS OFFICE. MILK AND MILK
PRODUCTS SUPPLY BALANCE.** Text in English. 1996. a.
charts; stat. **Document type:** *Government.*
Related titles: Online - full text ed.
Published by: Central Statistics Office/Eire, An Phriomh-Oifig
Staidrimh, Skehard Rd., Cork, Ireland. TEL 353-21-4535000,
FAX 353-21-4535555, information@cso.ie,
http://www.cso.ie/releasespublications/
pr_agricultureandfishing.htm.

637.1021   IRL   ISSN 1393-516X
IRELAND. CENTRAL STATISTICS OFFICE. MILK STATISTICS.
Key Title: Milk Statistics. Text in English. m. charts; stat.
Document type: *Government.*
Former titles (until 1997): Ireland. Central Statistics Office.
Production of Milk and Milk Products (0791-3036); (until
1987): Ireland. Central Statistics Office. Production of Butter
and Separated Milk Powder
Media: Duplicated (not offset). **Related titles:** Online - full text ed.

Published by: Central Statistics Office/Eire, An Phriomh-Oifig Staidrimh, Skehard Rd., Cork, Ireland. TEL 353-21-4535000, FAX 353-21-4535555, information@cso.ie, http://www.cso.ie/releasespublications/pr_agricultureandfishing.htm.

338.1021 IRL ISSN 1393-6948
IRELAND. CENTRAL STATISTICS OFFICE. OUTPUT, INPUT AND INCOME IN AGRICULTURE. Text in English. 197?. a. charts; stat. **Document type:** *Government.*
Former titles (until 1998): Ireland. Central Statistics Office. Estimated Output, Input and Income in Agriculture (0791-3001); (until 1985): Ireland Central Statistics Office. Estimates of the Quantity and Value of Agricultural Output (0075-0557)
Related titles: Online - full text ed.
Published by: Central Statistics Office/Eire, An Phriomh-Oifig Staidrimh, Skehard Rd., Cork, Ireland. TEL 353-21-4535000, FAX 353-21-4535555, information@cso.ie, http://www.cso.ie/releasespublications/pr_agricultureandfishing.htm.

338.1021 IRL ISSN 1393-5577
IRELAND. CENTRAL STATISTICS OFFICE. OUTPUT, INPUT AND INCOME IN AGRICULTURE. ADVANCE ESTIMATE. Text in English. 1986. a. charts; stat. **Document type:** *Government.*
Formerly (until 1997): Ireland. Central Statistics Office. Advance Estimate of Output, Input and Income in Agriculture (0791-301X)
Related titles: Online - full text ed.
Published by: Central Statistics Office/Eire, An Phriomh-Oifig Staidrimh, Skehard Rd., Cork, Ireland. TEL 353-21-4535000, FAX 353-21-4535555, information@cso.ie, http://www.cso.ie/releasespublications/pr_agricultureandfishing.htm.

338.1021 IRL ISSN 1393-6905
IRELAND. CENTRAL STATISTICS OFFICE. OUTPUT, INPUT AND INCOME IN AGRICULTURE. PRELIMINARY ESTIMATE. Text in English. 1986. a. charts; stat. **Document type:** *Government.*
Formerly (until 1998): Ireland. Central Statistics Office. Preliminary Estimate of Output, Input and Income in Agriculture (0791-3028)
Related titles: Online - full text ed.
Published by: Central Statistics Office/Eire, An Phriomh-Oifig Staidrimh, Skehard Rd., Cork, Ireland. TEL 353-21-4535000, FAX 353-21-4535555, information@cso.ie, http://www.cso.ie/releasespublications/pr_agricultureandfishing.htm.

636.4021 IRL ISSN 1393-709X
IRELAND. CENTRAL STATISTICS OFFICE. PIG SURVEY - JUNE. Text in English. 1998. a. charts; stat. **Document type:** *Government.*
Formed by the merger of (1987-1998): Ireland. Central Statistics Office. Pig Survey - April (0791-3079); Which was formerly (1974-1987): Ireland. Central Statistics Office. Pig Enumeration - April (0791-3060); (1987-1998): Ireland. Central Statistics Office. Pig Survey - August (0791-3095); Which was formerly (1974-1987): Ireland. Central Statistics Office. Pig Enumeration - August (0791-3087)
Related titles: Online - full text ed.
Published by: Central Statistics Office/Eire, An Phriomh-Oifig Staidrimh, Skehard Rd., Cork, Ireland. TEL 353-21-4535000, FAX 353-21-4535555, information@cso.ie, http://www.cso.ie/releasespublications/pr_agricultureandfishing.htm.

636.0021 IRL ISSN 1393-8096
IRELAND. CENTRAL STATISTICS OFFICE. SIZE OF HERD. Text in English. 1976. biennial. charts; stat. **Document type:** *Government.* **Description:** Contains details of the number of agricultural holdings with cattle or pigs, respectively, and the number of cattle and pigs, classified by size of herd.
Formerly (until 1999): Ireland. Central Statistics Office. Distribution of Cattle and Pigs by Size of Herd (0790-7729)
Related titles: Online - full text ed.
Published by: Central Statistics Office/Eire, An Phriomh-Oifig Staidrimh, Skehard Rd., Cork, Ireland. TEL 353-21-4535000, FAX 353-21-4535555, information@cso.ie, http://www.cso.ie/releasespublications/pr_agricultureandfishing.htm.

016.6317 GBR ISSN 0306-7327
S612
IRRIGATION AND DRAINAGE ABSTRACTS. Text in English. 1975. bi-m. USD 1,040 in the Americas to institutions except Canada; GBP 595 elsewhere to institutions; USD 1,110 combined subscription in the Americas to institutions except Canada; print & online eds.; GBP 635 combined subscription elsewhere to institutions print & online eds. (effective 2006). adv. back issues avail. **Document type:** *Abstract/Index.* **Description:** Topics covered include: water management, irrigation of crop plants, soil-water relations, salinity and toxicity problems, environmental aspects, irrigation, drainage, plant water relations, meteorological aspects, and human and animal health.
Related titles: Online - full text ed.: USD 885 in the Americas to institutions except Canada (effective 2005); GBP 505 elsewhere to institutions (effective 2006) (from DIMDI, The Dialog Corporation).
—CCC.
Published by: CABI Publishing (Subsidiary of: CAB International), CAB International, Wallingford, Oxfordshire OX10 8DE, United Kingdom. TEL 44-1491-832111, FAX 44-1491-833508, cabi@cabi.org, http://www.cabi-publishing.org/. Ed. Liza Conner. Adv. contact Sarah Harris TEL 44-1491-829310. B&W page GBP 90, B&W page USD 145; 170 x 267. Circ: 115. **Subscr. in N America to:** CABI Publishing North America, 875 Massachusetts Ave, 7th Fl, Cambridge, MA 02139. TEL 617-395-4056, 800-528-4841, FAX 617-354-6875, cabi-nao@cabi.org.

630.21 ISR ISSN 0334-2573
ISRAEL. CENTRAL BUREAU OF STATISTICS. AGRICULTURAL STATISTICS QUARTERLY. Text in Hebrew, English. q. USD 30. charts; stat. **Document type:** *Government.*
Formerly: Israel. Central Bureau of Statistics. Agricultural Statistics Monthly
Indexed: RASB.
Published by: Central Bureau of Statistics, PO Box 13015, Jerusalem, 91130, Israel. TEL 972-2-6553364, FAX 972-2-6521340.

636.0021 ITA
SF55.I8
ITALY. ISTITUTO NAZIONALE DI STATISTICA. STATISTICHE DELLA CACCIA E DELLA PESCA. Text in Italian. 1960. a. **Document type:** *Government.*
Formerly: Italy. Istituto Nazionale di Statistica. Statistiche della Caccia, Pesca e Cooperazione; Which superseded in part (in 1988): Italy. Istituto Nazionale di Statistica. Statistiche della Zootecnia, della Pesca e della Caccia; Which was formerly: Italy. Istituto Centrale di Statistica. Annuario Statistico della Zootecnia, della Pesca e della Caccia (0390-6426); (until 1975): Italy. Istituto Centrale di Statistica. Annuario di Statistiche Zootecniche (0075-1774); Statistiche delle Macellazione
Indexed: RASB.
—CISTI.
Published by: Istituto Nazionale di Statistica, Via Cesare Balbo 16, Rome, 00184, Italy. FAX 39-06-46735198. Circ: 1,200.

630.21 CIV ISSN 1018-2217
IVORY COAST. MINISTERE DE L'AGRICULTURE. ANNUAIRE DES STATISTIQUES AGRICOLES. Text in French. 1970. a. USD 20. adv. **Document type:** *Directory, Government.*
Formerly (until 1989): Ivory Coast. Ministere de l'Agriculture. Statistiques Agricoles
Published by: Ministere de l'Agriculture et des Ressources Animales, Direction des Statistiques de la Documentation et de l'Informatique, BP V203, Abidjan, Ivory Coast. TEL 225-21-58-63. Ed., Adv. contact Acoupo Asseupi.

630.21 NLD ISSN 0923-0718
JAARSTATISTIEK VAN DE VEEVOEDERS. Text in Dutch. 1971. a. **Document type:** *Government.*
Published by: Landbouw-Economisch Instituut, Burgemeester Patijnlaan 19, The Hague, 2585 BE, Netherlands. TEL 31-70-330-8330, FAX 31-70-361-5624, postmaster@lei.dlo.nl, http://www.lei.dlo.nl/lei.

630.21 JPN
JAPAN BANANA IMPORTERS ASSOCIATION. ANNUAL REPORT OF BANANA STATISTICS. Text in Japanese. a.
Published by: Japan Banana Importers Association/Nihon Banana Yunyu Kumiai, 2-7-9 Hirakawa-cho, Chiyoda-ku, Tokyo, 102-0093, Japan. TEL 03-263-0461.

630.21 JPN
JAPAN BANANA IMPORTERS ASSOCIATION. MONTHLY BULLETIN OF BANANA STATISTICS. Text in Japanese. m.
Published by: Japan Banana Importers Association/Nihon Banana Yunyu Kumiai, 2-7-9 Hirakawa-cho, Chiyoda-ku, Tokyo, 102-0093, Japan. TEL 03-263-0461.

630.21 JPN
JAPAN FRUIT GROWERS COOPERATIVE ASSOCIATION. FRUIT STATISTICS IN JAPAN✶ . Text in Japanese. irreg.
Published by: Japan Fruit Growers Cooperative Association/Nihon Engei Nogyo Kyodokumiai Rengokai, 2-1 Tokai 3-chome, Ota-ku, Tokyo, 143-0001, Japan. TEL 03-257-3336.

JOURNAL OF AGRICULTURAL, BIOLOGICAL, AND ENVIRONMENTAL STATISTICS. see *BIOLOGY—Abstracting, Bibliographies, Statistics*

630.21 USA
KENTUCKY AGRICULTURAL STATISTICS. Text in English. 1948. a. free. illus. **Document type:** *Government.*
Indexed: SRI.
Published by: Department of Agriculture, Kentucky Agricultural Statistics Service, PO Box 1120, Louisville, KY 40201. TEL 502-582-5293, http://www.nass.usda.gov/ky. Ed. Leland E Brown. R&P William Brannen. Circ: 5,000.

630.21 KEN ISSN 0300-2373
KENYA. CENTRAL BUREAU OF STATISTICS. AGRICULTURAL CENSUS (LARGE FARM AREAS). Text in English. irreg. price varies. stat. **Document type:** *Government.*
Published by: Ministry of Finance and Planning, Central Bureau of Statistics, PO Box 30266, Nairobi, Kenya. **Subscr. to:** Government Press, Haile Selaissie Ave., PO Box 30128, Nairobi, Kenya. TEL 254-2-334075.

016.6313 USA
KEY GUIDE TO ELECTRONIC RESOURCES: AGRICULTURE. Text in English. 1995. irreg. USD 39.50 (effective 1999). **Document type:** *Directory.* **Description:** Coverage includes commercial online databases, CD-ROM databases, OPAC-accessible collections, bulletin board systems, and all network-based electronic journals, newsletters and discussion groups related to agriculture.
Related titles: ♦ Series of: The Key Guide Series.
Published by: Information Today, Inc., 143 Old Marlton Pike, Medford, NJ 08055-8750. TEL 609-654-6266, FAX 609-654-4309, custserv@infotoday.com, http://www.infotoday.com. Ed. Wilfred Drew.

016.63 NLD
KONINKLIJK INSTITUUT VOOR DE TROPEN. CRITICAL REVIEWS AND ANNOTATED BIBLIOGRAPHIES. Text in Dutch. irreg. back issues avail. **Document type:** *Bibliography.* **Description:** Covers literature on rural development and tropical agriculture.
Formerly: Koninklijk Instituut voor de Tropen. Annotated Bibliographies Series (0924-9745)
Published by: (Koninklijk Instituut voor de Tropen/Royal Tropical Institute, Information and Documentation), K I T Publishers, Mauritskade 63, PO Box 95001, Amsterdam, 1090 HA, Netherlands. TEL 31-20-568-8272, FAX 31-20-568-8286, kitpress@kit.nl, publishers@kit.nl, http://www.kit.nl. Ed. Paul van den Boorn. Pub. Ron Smit. **Dist. in US & Canada by:** Eiron Inc., PO Box 40072, Washington, DC 20016. TEL 202-966-3240.

630.21 KWT
KUWAIT. CENTRAL STATISTICAL OFFICE. AGRICULTURAL STATISTICS BULLETIN/KUWAIT. AL-IDARAH AL-MARKAZIYYAH LIL-IHSA'. NASHRAH AL-IHSA'AT AL-ZIRA'IYYAH. Text in Arabic, English. 1971. a., latest covers 1995-1996. **Document type:** *Government.*
Published by: Central Statistical Office/Al-Idarah al-Markaziyyah lil-Ihsa', P O Box 26188, Safat, 13122, Kuwait. TEL 965-2428200, FAX 965-2430464.

016.63 NLD ISSN 0168-1850
L E I - DRAAD. Text in Dutch. 1983. bi-m. free. **Document type:** *Bibliography.* **Description:** Includes lists of abstracts of publications, reports and studies of the institute, as well as a list of articles from other publications concerning agriculture.
Indexed: RevApplEntom.
—KNAW.
Published by: Landbouw-Economisch Instituut, Burgemeester Patijnlaan 19, The Hague, 2585 BE, Netherlands. TEL 31-70-330-8330, FAX 31-70-361-5624, informatie@lei.dlo.nl, http://www.lei.nl/lei. Ed. G C de Graaff.

630.21 NLD ISSN 0166-8129
LANDBOUW-ECONOMISCH INSTITUUT. MEDEDELINGEN. Text in Dutch. 1968. irreg., latest vol.591. price varies. back issues avail. **Document type:** *Monographic series, Government.* **Description:** Discusses issues in Dutch agriculture, horticulture, and agricultural economics.
Indexed: AEA, DSA, HortAb, OrnHort, PN&I, PotatoAb, RPP, RRTA, S&F, TriticAb, WAE&RSA, WeedAb.
Published by: Landbouw-Economisch Instituut, Burgemeester Patijnlaan 19, The Hague, 2585 BE, Netherlands. TEL 31-70-330-8330, FAX 31-70-361-5624, informatie@lei.dlo.nl, http://www.lei.nl.

630.21 NLD ISSN 0921-7169
LANDBOUW-ECONOMISCH INSTITUUT. PERIODIEKE RAPPORTAGE. Text in Dutch. 1982. irreg. price varies. back issues avail. **Document type:** *Government.* **Description:** Presents statistical overviews in agriculture, horticulture, and aquaculture.
Indexed: AEA, DSA, HortAb, OrnHort, WAE&RSA.
—BLDSC (6426.320000).
Published by: Landbouw-Economisch Instituut, Burgemeester Patijnlaan 19, The Hague, 2585 BE, Netherlands. TEL 31-70-330-8330, FAX 31-70-361-5624, informatie@lei.dlo.nl, http://www.lei.nl.

333.79 NLD ISSN 1571-3067
LANDBOUW, MILIEU, NATUUR EN ECONOMIE. Text in Dutch. 1993. a. EUR 25 (effective 2005). **Document type:** *Government.*
Formerly (until 2002): Landbouw, Milieu en Economie (0929-0036); Which incorporated (in 1997): Jaarstatistiek van de Kunstmeststoffen (0925-9767); Which was formerly (until 1980): Jaarstatistiek van de Kunstmestindustrie (0921-4321); (1967-1975): Jaarstatistiek van de Kunstmeststoffen (0925-9775)
Indexed: WAE&RSA.

▼ *new title* ➤ *refereed* ✶ *unverified* ♦ *full entry avail.*

A

Published by: Landbouw-Economisch Instituut, Burgemeester Patijnlaan 19, The Hague, 2585 BE, Netherlands. TEL 31-70-3358330, 31-70-3358134, FAX 31-70-3615624, informatie.lei@wur.nl, i, http://www.lei.dlo.nl.

016.63 DNK ISSN 0107-7163
LANDOEKONOMISK OVERSIGT. Text in Danish. 1954. a., latest 2004. stat.; charts. **Document type:** *Yearbook, Trade.* **Description:** Presents statistical information on the agricultural situation in Denmark, with discussion of topics including production, marketing, and economic forecasts.
Related titles: Online - full text ed.; ♦ English ed.: Agriculture in Denmark. ISSN 0905-5142.
Published by: Danske Landboforeninger/Danish Farmers' Association, Axelborg, Vesterbrogade 4A, Copenhagen V, 1620, Denmark. TEL 45-33-394600, FAX 45-33-394606, dl@dansklandbrug.dk, http://www.ddl.dk/get/15500.html, http://www.dansklandbrug.dk.

LEVANTAMENTO SISTEMATICO DA PRODUCAO AGRICOLA/SYSTEMATIC SURVEY OF AGRICULTURAL PRODUCTION. see *AGRICULTURE—Agricultural Economics*

630.21 LBR
LIBERIA. MINISTRY OF AGRICULTURE. PRODUCTION ESTIMATES OF MAJOR CROPS✶. Text in English. a.
Formerly: Liberia. Ministry of Agriculture. National Rice Production Estimates
Published by: Ministry of Agriculture, Monrovia, Liberia. **Co-sponsor:** Ministry of Planning and Economic Affairs.

630.21 LBR
LIBERIA. MINISTRY OF AGRICULTURE. STATISTICAL HANDBOOK✶. Text in English. triennial.
Published by: Ministry of Agriculture, Monrovia, Liberia.

630.21 LBY
LIBYA. CENSUS AND STATISTICS DEPARTMENT. AGRICULTURAL CENSUS. Text in Arabic, English. 1974. decennial. free. **Document type:** *Government.*
Published by: Secretariat of Planning, Census and Statistics Department, P O Box 600, Tripoli, Libya.

630.21 MDG
MADAGASCAR. MINISTERE DE LA PRODUCTION AGRICOLE ET DU PATRIMOINE FONCIER. STATISTIQUES AGRICOLES. ANNUAIRE. Text in French. 1969. a. MGF 25,595. **Description:** Covers a variety of topics concerning agriculture in Madagascar.
Formerly: Malagasy Republic. Ministere de la Production Agricole et la Reforme Agraire. Statistiques Agricoles. Annuaire
Published by: Ministere de la Production Agricole et du Patrimoine Foncier, Service de la Methodologie et du Traitement des Informations Statistiques, BP 7086, Antananarivo, 101, Madagascar. Circ: 100.

630.21 IND ISSN 0304-6184
S280.M26
MADHYA PRADESH. DIRECTORATE OF AGRICULTURE. AGRICULTURAL STATISTICS. Key Title: Agricultural Statistics, Madhya Pradesh. Text in English. a.
Published by: Directorate of Agriculture, Bhopal, Madhya Pradesh, India.

016.63 HUN ISSN 0025-0198
MAGYAR MEZOGAZDASAGI BIBLIOGRAFIA. Text in Hungarian. 1960. q. HUF 2,000 (effective 2000). bibl. index. 164 p./no.; **Document type:** *Bibliography.*
Media: Diskette.
Indexed: RASB.
Published by: Orszagos Mezogazdasagi Konyvtar es Dokumentacios Kozpont, Attila ut 93, Budapest, 1253, Hungary. TEL 36-1-4894900, FAX 36-1-4894949, ebalagh@amon.omgk.hu, http://www.omgk.hu. Eds. Erika Gulacsi Papay, Eszter Balagh.

016.6331 GBR
MAIZE ABSTRACTS ONLINE. Text in English. 1975. w. USD 1,165 in the Americas to institutions except Canada; GBP 665 elsewhere to institutions (effective 2006). back issues avail. **Document type:** *Abstract/Index.* **Description:** Topics covered include: plant breeding and genetics, plant physiology, soil science, pests and diseases, agricultural engineering, crop science, seeds and grains, weeds and weed control, agricultural economics, and nutrition and quality.
Media: Online - full text (from DIMDI, The Dialog Corporation).
Published by: CABI Publishing (Subsidiary of: CAB International), CAB International, Wallingford, Oxfordshire OX10 8DE, United Kingdom. TEL 44-1491-832111, FAX 44-1491-833508, cabi@cabi.org, http://www.cabi-publishing.org/. Ed. Halina J Dawson. **Subscr. addr. in N America:** CABI Publishing North America, 875 Massachusetts Ave, 7th Fl, Cambridge, MA 02139. TEL 617-395-4056, 800-528-4841, FAX 617-354-6875, cabi-nao@cabi.org.

630.21 MWI ISSN 0076-3292
MALAWI. NATIONAL STATISTICAL OFFICE. NATIONAL SAMPLE SURVEY OF AGRICULTURE. Text in English. 1970. irreg. (in 4 vols.), latest 1992-1993. price varies. stat. **Document type:** *Government.*
Incorporates: Malawi. National Statistical Office. Compendium of Agricultural Statistics (0085-3011)
Media: Duplicated (not offset).
Published by: (Malawi. Commissioner for Census and Statistics), National Statistical Office, PO Box 333, Zomba, Malawi. TEL 265-50-522377, FAX 265-50-523130.

630.21 MYS
SB299.P3
MALAYSIA. DEPARTMENT OF STATISTICS. COCOA, COCONUT AND TEA STATISTICS HANDBOOK, MALAYSIA/MALAYSIA. JABATAN PERANGKAAN. BUKU MAKLUMAT PERANGKAAN KOKO, KELAPA DAN TEH, MALAYSIA. Text in English. 1988. irreg., latest 1996. MYR 18. **Document type:** *Government.*
Formerly: Malaysia. Department of Statistics. Handbook of Oil Palm, Cocoa, Coconut and Tea Statistics Malaysia (0127-4694)
Published by: Department of Statistics/Jabatan Perangkaan, Jalan Cenderasari, Kuala Lumpur, 50514, Malaysia. TEL 60-3-294-4264, FAX 60-3-291-4535, jpmeto@po.jaring.my, http://www.statistics.gov.my.

338.1 MYS
MALAYSIA. DEPARTMENT OF STATISTICS. REPORT OF THE PADDY YIELD SURVEY, MALAYSIA/MALAYSIA. JABATAN PERANGKAAN. LAPORAN PENYIASATAN HASIL PADI, MALAYSIA. Text in English, Malay. a. MYR 7. **Document type:** *Government.*
Published by: Department of Statistics/Jabatan Perangkaan, Jalan Cenderasari, Kuala Lumpur, 50514, Malaysia. TEL 60-3-294-4264, FAX 30-3-291-4535, jpmeto@po.jaring.my, http://www.statistics.gov.my.

630.21 CAN
MARKET TRENDS. Text in English. 1986. w. free. back issues avail. **Document type:** *Government.* **Description:** Includes forecast prices of grain, trade statistics for hogs, cattle and grain, and information for farmers.
Published by: Agriculture and Food, B5 Walter Scott Bldg, 3085 Albert St, Regina, SK S4S 0B1, Canada. TEL 306-787-5140, FAX 306-787-0216, lstinson@agr.gov.sk.ca, http://www.agr.gov.sk.ca/saf. Circ: 400.

338.1021 USA
MASSACHUSETTS AGRICULTURE (YEAR) ANNUAL REPORT✶. Text in English. 1972. a. free. illus.; stat.
Formerly: Massachusetts Agricultural Statistics (0092-9794)
Indexed: SRI.
Published by: Department of Food and Agriculture, 251 Causeway St Ste 500, Boston, MA 02114-2151. FAX 617-727-7235. Circ: 1,000. **Co-sponsors:** New England Agricultural Statistics Service; U.S. Department of Agriculture.

630.21 MUS
MAURITIUS. CENTRAL STATISTICAL OFFICE. DIGEST OF AGRICULTURAL STATISTICS. Text in English. 1984. a., latest 1997. MUR 75 per issue (effective 2001). charts. **Document type:** *Government.* **Description:** Provides a general statistical overview of the agricultural economics situation in Mauritius.
Published by: Mauritius. Central Statistical Office, L.I.C. Centre, President John Kennedy St, Port Louis, Mauritius. TEL 230-212-2316, FAX 230-212-4150, cso@intnet.mu, http://statsmauritius.gov.mu. **Subscr. to:** Mauritius. Government Printing Office, Ramtoolah Bldg, Sir S Ramgoolam St, Port Louis, Mauritius. TEL 230-234-5294, 230-242-0234, FAX 230-234-5322.

016.63 DEU ISSN 0026-3788
SF221 CODEN: MILCAD
MILCHWISSENSCHAFT/MILK SCIENCE INTERNATIONAL; journal of nutrition research and food science. Text in English, German. 1945. bi-m. EUR 264; EUR 79 newsstand/cover (effective 2004). adv. bk.rev. abstr.; bibl.; charts; illus.; mkt.; pat. index. back issues avail. **Document type:** *Magazine, Abstract/Index.*
Indexed: AEA, ASCA, AbHyg, AgBio, AgrForAb, AnBrAb, B&BAb, BIOSIS Prev, BioCN&I, BiolAb, ChemAb, ChemTitl, CurCont, CurPA, DBA, DSA, ESPM, ExcerpMed, FS&TA, ISR, IndVet, MBA, MaizeAb, NutrAb, PN&I, RA&MP, RM&VM, RPP, RRTA, RefZh, RiceAb, S&F, SCI, SIA, SoyAb, TDB, VetBull, WAE&RSA.
—BLDSC (5767.000000), CASDDS, CINDOC, CISTI, GNLM, IDS, IE, Infotrieve, ingenta, Linda Hall. **CCC.**
Published by: A V A Verlag Allgaeu GmbH, Porschestr 2, Kempten, 87437, Germany. TEL 49-831-571420, FAX 49-831-79008, info@ava-verlag.de, http://www.ava-verlag.de. adv.: B&W page EUR 1,050, color page EUR 1,665. Circ: 1,305 (paid).

630.21 FRA ISSN 0989-0025
MUTUALITE SOCIALE AGRICOLE. ANNUAIRE STATISTIQUE. Text in French. a.
Published by: Mutualite Sociale Agricole, Les Mercuriales, 40 rue Jean Jaures, Bagnolet, Cedex 93547, France. TEL 33-1-41637777, FAX 33-1-41637266, info@msa.fr, http://www.msa.fr.

016.63 USA
N T I S ALERTS: AGRICULTURE & FOOD. Text in English. 5/yr. USD 224.25 in North America; USD 299 elsewhere (effective 2005). index. back issues avail. **Document type:** *Newsletter, Bibliography.*
Former titles: Abstract Newsletter: Agriculture and Food (0364-7994); Weekly Abstracts Newsletter: Agriculture and Food; Weekly Government Abstracts. Agriculture and Food
Related titles: Microform ed.: (from NTI).
Published by: U.S. Department of Commerce, National Technical Information Service, 5285 Port Royal Rd, Springfield, VA 22161. TEL 703-605-6000, info@ntis.gov, http://www.ntis.gov/product/alerts.htm.

016.63 USA ISSN 1066-257X
Z5073
NATIONAL CENTER FOR AGRICULTURAL UTILIZATION RESEARCH PUBLICATIONS AND PATENTS. Text in English. 1940. a., latest 2002. free (effective 2003). bibl.; pat. back issues avail. **Document type:** *Newsletter, Bibliography.*
Formerly: Northern Regional Research Center Publications and Patents
Published by: (National Center for Agricultural Utilization Research), U.S. Department of Agriculture, Agricultural Research Service, Library, National Center for Agricultural Utilization Research, 1815 N University, Peoria, IL 61604. TEL 309-685-4011, http://www.ars.usda.gov/main/main.htm. Ed., R&P Joyce Blumenshine TEL 309-681-6526. Circ: 200.

630.21 ESP
NEKAZAL ELIKAGAI SEKTOREAREN ESTATISTIKA URTEKARIA E.A.E./ANUARIO ESTADISTICO DEL SECTOR AGROALIMENTARIO C.A.P.V. Text in Basque, Spanish. 1988. a., latest 1997.
Published by: (Basque Region. Industri, Nekazaritza eta Arrantza Saila/Departamento de Industria, Agricultura y Pesca), Eusko Jaurlaritzaren Argitalpen-Zerbitzu Nagusia/Servicio Central de Publicaciones del Gobierno Vasco, Donostia-San Sebastian, 1, Vitoria-gasteiz, Alava 01010, Spain. TEL 34-945-018561, FAX 34-945-018709, hac-sabd@ej-gv.es, http://www.ej-gv.net/publicaciones.

630.21 USA ISSN 0077-8540
HD1775.N6
NEW MEXICO AGRICULTURAL STATISTICS. Text in English. 1962. a. free. **Document type:** *Government.*
Indexed: SRI.
Published by: Department of Agriculture, Agricultural Statistical Service, P O Box 30005, Dept 5600, Las Cruces, NM 88003-0005. **Co-sponsor:** U.S. Department of Agriculture.

630.21 USA ISSN 0276-8798
HD1775.N8
NEW YORK AGRICULTURAL STATISTICS. Text in English. a. free. **Document type:** *Bulletin, Government.*
Related titles: Microfiche ed.: (from CIS).
Indexed: SRI.
—CISTI.
Published by: Department of Agriculture and Markets, 1 Winner s Cir, Albany, NY 12235-0001. FAX 518-453-6564. Circ: 2,800 (controlled).

016.63 AUT ISSN 0028-9744
NIEDEROESTERREICHISCHE LANDES-LANDWIRTSCHAFTSKAMMER. AMTLICHER MARKTBERICHT. Text in German. 1922. w. looseleaf. bk.rev. abstr.; mkt. index, cum.index. **Document type:** *Bulletin, Trade.*
Published by: Niederoesterreichische Landes-Landwirtschaftskammer, Wiener Str 64, St. Poelten, 3100, Austria. TEL 43-2742-2599300, FAX 43-2742-2591009, office@lk-noe.at, http://www.lk-noe.at. Circ: 2,200.

630.21 JPN ISSN 0029-1757
S303
NORIN SUISAN TOKEI GEPPO/MONTHLY STATISTICS ON AGRICULTURE, FORESTRY AND FISHERIES. Text in Japanese. 1956. m. JPY 17,904 (effective 2002).
Incorporates (in 1976): Norin Suisan Tokei Shihyo (0029-1765)
Published by: Association of Agriculture & Forestry Statistics, 3-9-13, Shimo-Meguro, Meguro-ku, Tokyo, 153-0064, Japan. TEL 81-3-3492-2990, FAX 81-3-3492-2971, henshu@aafs.or.jp, http://www.aafs.or.jp/.

630.21 JPN ISSN 0388-5976
NORIN SUISAN TOSHO SHIRYO GEPPO. Text in Japanese. m. JPY 7,176; JPY 7,176.01 newsstand/cover (effective 2002). adv. bk.rev. abstr.; bibl. index. 32 p./no.;
Former titles (until 1979): Norin Tosho Shiryo Geppo (0029-1773); (until 1954): Norinsho Tosho Geppo (0446-5474)
Published by: (Japan. Ministry of Agriculture, Forestry and Fisheries, Japan. Statistics and Information Department), Association of Agriculture & Forestry Statistics, 3-9-13, Shimo-Meguro, Meguro-ku, Tokyo, 153-0064, Japan. TEL 81-3-3492-2990, FAX 81-3-3492-2971, henshu@aafs.or.jp, http://www.aafs.or.jp/index.html. Circ: 1,400.

630.21 JPN ISSN 1342-5757
S19
NORIN TOKEI CHOSA/MONTHLY BULLETIN OF AGRICULTURAL STATISTICS AND RESEARCH. Text in English. 1951. m. JPY 6,672; JPY 6,672 newsstand/cover (effective 2002). stat. **Document type:** *Journal, Government.*
Published by: Association of Agriculture & Forestry Statistics, 3-9-13, Shimo-Meguro, Meguro-ku, Tokyo, 153-0064, Japan. TEL 81-3-3492-2990, FAX 81-3-3492-2971, henshu@aafs.or.jp, http://www.aafs.or.jp/.

630.21   USA   ISSN 0737-1624
S99
NORTH DAKOTA AGRICULTURAL STATISTICS. Text in English. 1956. a. USD 12 (effective 2000). **Document type:** *Government.* **Description:** Provides comprehensive crop, livestock and price statistics, including county estimates.
Formerly: North Dakota Crop and Livestock Statistics (0078-1541)
Related titles: Microfiche ed.: (from CIS).
Indexed: SRI.
—Linda Hall.
Published by: North Dakota Agricultural Statistics Service, PO Box 3166, Fargo, ND 58108. TEL 701-239-5306, FAX 701-239-5613, nass-nd@nass.usda.gov, http://www.usda.gov/nass/. Ed., Pub. Larry W Beard. Circ: 1,800 (paid).

630.21   USA
NORTH DAKOTA GRAIN AND OILSEED TRANSPORTATION STATISTICS. Text in English. 1975. a. free.
Published by: North Dakota State University, Upper Great Plains Transportation Institute, P O Box 5074, Fargo, ND 58105. FAX 701-231-1945. Ed. Kimberly Vachal. Circ: 250.

630.21   NOR   ISSN 0078-1894
HA1501
NORWAY. STATISTISK SENTRALBYRAA. JORDBRUKSSTATISTIKK/STATISTICS NORWAY. AGRICULTURAL STATISTICS. Text in Norwegian, English. 1937. a., latest 2002. back issues avail. **Document type:** *Government.*
Related titles: ♦ Series of: Norges Offisielle Statistikk. ISSN 0300-5585.
—CISTI.
Published by: Statistisk Sentralbyraa/Statistics Norway, Kongensgate 6, Postboks 8131, Dep, Oslo, 0033, Norway. TEL 47-21-090000, FAX 47-21-094973, ssb@ssb.no, http://www.ssb.no/emner/10/04/10/nos_jordbruk/.

016.6331   GBR   ISSN 0309-135X
SF95
NUTRITION ABSTRACTS AND REVIEWS. SERIES B: LIVESTOCK FEEDS AND FEEDING. Text in English. 1931. m. USD 1,635 in the Americas to institutions except Canada; GBP 935 elsewhere to institutions; USD 1,750 combined subscription in the Americas to institutions except Canada; print & online eds.; GBP 1,000 combined subscription elsewhere to institutions print & online eds. (effective 2006). adv. back issues avail.; reprints avail. **Document type:** *Abstract/Index.* **Description:** Covers the analysis, technology, and biochemistry of feeds.
Supersedes in part: Nutrition Abstracts and Reviews (0029-6619)
Related titles: Online - full text ed.: USD 1,390 in the Americas to institutions except Canada; GBP 795 elsewhere to institutions (effective 2006) (from DIMDI, The Dialog Corporation).
Indexed: AgBio, AnBrAb, DSA, HerbAb, IndVet, MaizeAb, NutrAb, PN&I, PoultAb, RM&VM, SoyAb, TriticAb, VetBull.
—CISTI, Linda Hall. **CCC.**
Published by: CABI Publishing (Subsidiary of: CAB International), CAB International, Wallingford, Oxfordshire OX10 8DE, United Kingdom. TEL 44-1491-832111, FAX 44-1491-833508, cabi@cabi.org, http://www.cabi-publishing.org/. adv.: B&W page GBP 200, B&W page USD 315; 170 x 267. Circ: 455. **Subscr. in N America to:** CABI Publishing North America, 875 Massachusetts Ave, 7th Fl, Cambridge, MA 02139. TEL 617-395-4056, 800-528-4841, FAX 617-354-6875, cabi-nao@cabi.org.

630.21   RUS
OSNOVNYE POKAZATELI SEL'SKOGO KHOZYAISTVA ROSSII. Text in Russian. s-a. RUR 286 (effective 2005). **Document type:** *Bulletin, Government.* **Description:** Contains major statistical data on the economic situation of the agriculture in Russia.
Published by: Gosudarstvennyi Komitet Rossiiskoi Federatsii po Statistike/Federal State Statistics Office, ul Myasnitskaya 39, Moscow, 107450, Russian Federation. TEL 7-095-2074902, FAX 7-095-2074087, stat@gks.ru, http://www.gks.ru.

630.21   PAK
PAKISTAN. FOOD AND AGRICULTURE DIVISION. AGRICULTURAL STATISTICS OF PAKISTAN. Text in English. 1952. a. free.
Formerly: Pakistan. Food and Agricultural Division. Yearbook of Agricultural Statistics (0078-8139)
Published by: (Pakistan. Planning Unit), Ministry of Food, Agriculture and Rural Development, Food and Agriculture Division, 210-H-G-6/3, Islamabad, Pakistan.

630.21   BRA   ISSN 0103-6181
SB186.3
PESQUISA DE ESTOQUES. (Issued in 28 regional eds.) Text in Portuguese. 1974. s-a. USD 20 per vol.. **Document type:** *Government.* **Description:** Provides information on existing stocks of cotton, rice, beans, soyabeans, wheat and more, in storage units all over Brazil.
Former titles (until 1987): Pesquisa Especial de Armazenagem; (until 1986): Armazenagem e Estocagem a Seco e a Frio (0101-028X)

Published by: Fundacao Instituto Brasileiro de Geografia e Estatistica, Centro de Documentacao e Disseminacao de Informacoes, Rua General Canabarro, 706 Andar 2, Maracana, Rio de Janeiro, RJ 20271-201, Brazil. TEL 55-21-264-5424, FAX 55-21-2841959, http://www.ibge.gov.br.

016.6329   GBR
PESTICIDE INDEX. Text in English. 1984. irreg., latest vol.3, 1995. GBP 35 (effective 2000). **Document type:** *Trade.* **Description:** Lists the generic and trade names of pesticides in use worldwide. Provides information on the components, activity and marketing companies of crop protection products. Includes marketing company addresses.
Published by: British Crop Protection Council, Bear Farm, Binfield, Bracknell, Berks RG42 5QE, United Kingdom. TEL 44-118-934-2727, FAX 44-118-934-1998, publications@BCPC.org, http://www.bcpc.org. **Co-sponsor:** The Royal Society of Chemistry.

630.21   PHL
PHILIPPINES. DEPARTMENT OF AGRICULTURE. BUREAU OF AGRICULTURAL STATISTICS. DEVELOPMENT INDICATORS IN PHILIPPINE AGRICULTURE. Text in English. a. **Document type:** *Government.* **Description:** For policy-makers and planners: for monitoring and evaluating programs related to agriculture.
Published by: Department of Agriculture, Bureau of Agricultural Statistics, BEN-LOR Bldg, Quezon City, 1184, Philippines. FAX 63-2-968-966. R&P Romeo S Recide. Circ: 500.

636.0021   PHL
PHILIPPINES. DEPARTMENT OF AGRICULTURE. BUREAU OF AGRICULTURAL STATISTICS. LIVESTOCK AND POULTRY PERFORMANCE REPORT. Text in English. a. charts; stat. **Document type:** *Bulletin, Government.* **Description:** Results of the Bureau's surveys on livestock and poultry and the monitoring of animals slaughtered in abbatoirs.
Formerly: Philippines. Department of Agriculture. Bureau of Agricultural Statistics. Livestock, Poultry and Fishery Statistics Bulletin
Media: Duplicated (not offset).
Published by: Department of Agriculture, Bureau of Agricultural Statistics, BEN-LOR Bldg, Quezon City, 1184, Philippines. FAX 63-2-968-966, da-bas@gaia.psdn.org. R&P Romeo S Recide. Circ: 300.

630.21   PHL
PHILIPPINES. DEPARTMENT OF AGRICULTURE. BUREAU OF AGRICULTURAL STATISTICS. RICE AND CORN SITUATION OUTLOOK. Text in English. q. **Document type:** *Government.* **Description:** Rice and corn prospects for the coming quarter; includes area and production forecast of rice and corn.
Formerly: Philippines. Department of Agriculture. Bureau of Agricultural Statistics. Rice and Corn Outlook
Published by: Department of Agriculture, Bureau of Agricultural Statistics, BEN-LOR Bldg, Quezon City, 1184, Philippines. FAX 63-2-968-966, da-bas@gaia.psdn.org. R&P Romeo S Recide. Circ: 700.

630.21   PHL
PHILIPPINES. DEPARTMENT OF AGRICULTURE. BUREAU OF AGRICULTURAL STATISTICS. SELECTED STATISTICS IN AGRICULTURE. Text in English. a. **Document type:** *Government.* **Description:** Statistics on crops, livestock, poultry and fisheries; annual average process of selected commodities.
Published by: Department of Agriculture, Bureau of Agricultural Statistics, BEN-LOR Bldg, Quezon City, 1184, Philippines. FAX 63-2-968-966, da-bas@gaia.psdn.org. R&P Romeo S Recide. Circ: 500.

016.6364   GBR   ISSN 0143-9014
                 CODEN: PNINEZ
PIG NEWS & INFORMATION. Text in English. 1980. q. USD 580 in the Americas to institutions except Canada; GBP 330 elsewhere to institutions; USD 620 combined subscription in the Americas to institutions except Canada; print & online eds.; GBP 355 combined subscription elsewhere to institutions print & online eds. (effective 2006). adv. **Document type:** *Journal, Abstract/Index.* **Description:** Covers the important developments in pig breeding, molecular genetics, pig health, nutrition, housing and management, economics, welfare, reproduction and production.
Related titles: Microfiche ed.; Online - full text ed.: USD 490 in the Americas to institutions except Canada; GBP 280 elsewhere to institutions (effective 2006) (from DIMDI, The Dialog Corporation).
Indexed: AEA, AgBio, AnBrAb, DSA, FS&TA, HelmAb, HerbAb, I&DA, IIS, IndVet, MaizeAb, NutrAb, RDA, S&F, SoyAb, TriticAb, VetBull, WAE&RSA.
—CISTI, IE, Infotrieve. **CCC.**
Published by: CABI Publishing (Subsidiary of: CAB International), CAB International, Wallingford, Oxfordshire OX10 8DE, United Kingdom. TEL 44-1491-832111, FAX 44-1491-833508, cabi@cabi.org, http://www.cabi-publishing.org/. Adv. contact Sarah Harris TEL 44-1491-829310. B&W page GBP 260, B&W page USD 410; 170 x 267. Circ: 650. **Subscr. addr. in N America:** CABI Publishing North America, 875 Massachusetts Ave, 7th Fl, Cambridge, MA 02139. TEL 617-395-4056, 800-528-4841, FAX 617-354-6875, cabi-nao@cabi.org.

016.63152   GBR   ISSN 0032-0803
PLANT BREEDING ABSTRACTS. Text in English. 1930. m. USD 2,730 in the Americas to institutions except Canada; GBP 1,560 elsewhere to institutions; USD 2,925 combined subscription in the Americas to institutions except Canada; print & online eds.; GBP 1,670 combined subscription elsewhere to institutions print & online eds. (effective 2006). adv. bk.rev. abstr. index. reprints avail. **Document type:** *Abstract/Index.* **Description:** Covers world literature on crop breeding and genetics. All species of economic importance are included.
Related titles: Online - full text ed.: USD 2,320 in the Americas to institutions except Canada; GBP 1,325 elsewhere to institutions (effective 2006) (from DIMDI, The Dialog Corporation).
Indexed: RASB.
—BLDSC (6514.000000), CISTI. **CCC.**
Published by: CABI Publishing (Subsidiary of: CAB International), CAB International, Wallingford, Oxfordshire OX10 8DE, United Kingdom. TEL 44-1491-832111, FAX 44-1491-833508, cabi@cabi.org, http://www.cabi-publishing.org/. Adv. contact Sarah Harris TEL 44-1491-829310. B&W page GBP 135, B&W page USD 215; 170 x 267. Circ: 375. **Subscr. addr. in N America:** CABI Publishing North America, 875 Massachusetts Ave, 7th Fl, Cambridge, MA 02139. TEL 617-395-4056, 800-528-4841, FAX 617-354-6875, cabi-nao@cabi.org.

016.63   GBR   ISSN 0305-9154
PLANT GROWTH REGULATOR ABSTRACTS. Text in English. 1975. q. USD 990 in the Americas to institutions except Canada; GBP 565 elsewhere to institutions; USD 1,060 combined subscription in the Americas to institutions except Canada; print & online eds.; GBP 605 combined subscription elsewhere to institutions print & online eds. (effective 2006). adv. back issues avail. **Document type:** *Abstract/Index.* **Description:** Deals with the role of chemicals in plant growth regulation and beneficial modification of plant growth processes.
Related titles: Online - full text ed.: USD 840 in the Americas to institutions except Canada; GBP 480 elsewhere to institutions (effective 2006) (from DIMDI, The Dialog Corporation).
—CCC.
Published by: CABI Publishing (Subsidiary of: CAB International), CAB International, Wallingford, Oxfordshire OX10 8DE, United Kingdom. TEL 44-1491-832111, FAX 44-1491-833508, cabi@cabi.org, http://www.cabi-publishing.org/. Ed. Debbie Cousins. adv.: B&W page GBP 60, B&W page USD 95; 170 x 267. Circ: 115. **Subscr. addr. in N America:** CABI Publishing North America, 875 Massachusetts Ave, 7th Fl, Cambridge, MA 02139. TEL 617-395-4056, 800-528-4841, FAX 617-354-6875, cabi-nao@cabi.org.

630.21   PRT   ISSN 0870-533X
HD2026
PORTUGAL. INSTITUTO NACIONAL DE ESTATISTICA. ESTATISTICAS AGRICOLAS. Text in Portuguese, French. 1943. a. EUR 12 (effective 2005).
Former titles (until 1970): Portugal. Instituto Nacional de Estatistica. Estatisticas Agricolas e Alimentares (0302-5853); (until 1964): Portugal. Instituto Nacional de Estatistica. Estatistica Agricola (0302-4504)
Published by: Instituto Nacional de Estatistica, Ave. Antonio Jose de Almeida 2, Lisbon, 1000-043, Portugal. TEL 351-21-8426100, FAX 351-21-8426380, ine@ine.pt, http://www.ine.pt/. **Orders to:** Imprensa Nacional, Direccao Comercial, rua D. Francisco Manuel de Melo 5, Lisbon 1100, Portugal.

630.21   PRT   ISSN 0871-8032
HD4966.A292
PORTUGAL. INSTITUTO NACIONAL DE ESTATISTICA. INQUERITO AO GANHO DOS TRABALHADORES AGRICOLAS. Text in Portuguese. 1991. s-a. **Description:** Provides statistical data on agricultural workers in Portugal.
Published by: Instituto Nacional de Estatistica, Ave. Antonio Jose de Almeida 2, Lisbon, 1000-043, Portugal. TEL 351-21-8426100, FAX 351-21-8426380, http://www.ine.pt/.

630.21   GBR   ISSN 0957-7505
SB129
POSTHARVEST NEWS AND INFORMATION. Text in English. 1990. bi-m. USD 1,245 in the Americas to institutions except Canada; GBP 710 elsewhere to institutions; USD 1,330 combined subscription in the Americas to institutions except Canada; print & online eds.; GBP 760 combined subscription elsewhere to institutions print & online eds. (effective 2006). adv. **Document type:** *Trade.* **Description:** Covers current research on postharvest technology. Provides timely news items, review articles, and abstracts of interest to researchers, administrators, and planners.
Related titles: Online - full text ed.: USD 1,060 in the Americas to institutions except Canada; GBP 605 elsewhere to institutions (effective 2006).
Indexed: AEA, BioCN&I, CPA, FS&TA, HortAb, OrnHort, PGrRegA, RA&MP, RDA, RPP, RevApplEntom, WAE&RSA.
—BLDSC (6563.922000), CISTI. **CCC.**

A

Published by: CABI Publishing (Subsidiary of: CAB International), CAB International, Wallingford, Oxfordshire OX10 8DE, United Kingdom. TEL 44-1491-832111, FAX 44-1491-833508, cabi@cabi.org, http://www.cabi-publishing.org/. Ed. Alexis Rendell-Dunn. Adv. contact Sarah Harris TEL 44-1491-829310. B&W page GBP 50, B&W page USD 80; 170 x 267. Circ: 150. **Subscr. addr. in N America:** CABI Publishing North America, 875 Massachusetts Ave, 7th Fl, Cambridge, MA 02139. TEL 617-395-4056, 800-528-4841, FAX 617-354-6875, cabi-nao@cabi.org.

016.633491 GBR ISSN 0308-7344
POTATO ABSTRACTS. Text in English. 1976. q. USD 850 in the Americas to institutions except Canada; GBP 485 elsewhere to institutions; USD 910 combined subscription in the Americas to institutions except Canada; print & online eds.; GBP 520 combined subscription elsewhere to institutions print & online eds. (effective 2006). adv. back issues avail. **Document type:** *Abstract/Index.* **Description:** Contains the latest information on potato production, from production of true seeds and seed tubers to storage, marketing and consumption.
Related titles: Online - full text ed.: USD 720 in the Americas to institutions except Canada; GBP 410 elsewhere to institutions (effective 2006) (from DIMDI, The Dialog Corporation).
—CCC.
Published by: CABI Publishing (Subsidiary of: CAB International), CAB International, Wallingford, Oxfordshire OX10 8DE, United Kingdom. TEL 44-1491-832111, FAX 44-1491-833508, cabi@cabi.org, http://www.cabi-publishing.org/. Adv. contact Sarah Harris TEL 44-1491-829310. B&W page GBP 60, B&W page USD 95; 170 x 267. Circ: 135. **Subscr. in N America to:** CABI Publishing North America, 875 Massachusetts Ave, 7th Fl, Cambridge, MA 02139. TEL 617-395-4056, 800-528-4841, FAX 617-354-6875, cabi-nao@cabi.org.

630.21 GBR ISSN 0266-6022
CODEN: PJLREY
POTATO STATISTICS IN GREAT BRITAIN. Text in English. 1984. a. GBP 20. **Document type:** *Bulletin.*
Published by: British Potato Council, Broad Field House, 4 Between Towns Rd, Cowley, Oxford, OX4 3PP, United Kingdom. TEL 44-1865-714455, FAX 44-1865-716418. Ed. M Plass.

016.6365 GBR ISSN 0306-1582
POULTRY ABSTRACTS. Text in English. 1975. m. USD 1,040 in the Americas to institutions except Canada; GBP 595 elsewhere to institutions; USD 1,110 combined subscription in the Americas to institutions except Canada; print & online eds.; GBP 635 combined subscription elsewhere to institutions print & online (effective 2006). adv. back issues avail. **Document type:** *Abstract/Index.*
Related titles: Online - full text ed.: USD 885 in the Americas to institutions except Canada; USD 505 elsewhere to institutions (effective 2006) (from DIMDI, The Dialog Corporation).
—CCC.
Published by: CABI Publishing (Subsidiary of: CAB International), CAB International, Wallingford, Oxfordshire OX10 8DE, United Kingdom. TEL 44-1491-832111, FAX 44-1491-833508, cabi@cabi.org, http://www.cabi-publishing.org/. Ed. Alexandra J Kemp. Adv. contact Sarah Harris TEL 44-1491-829310. B&W page GBP 80, B&W page USD 125; 170 x 267. Circ: 240. **Subscr. addr. in N America:** CABI Publishing North America, 875 Massachusetts Ave, 7th Fl, Cambridge, MA 02139. TEL 617-395-4056, 800-528-4841, FAX 617-354-6875, cabi-nao@cabi.org.

636.5021 USA ISSN 0565-1980
HD1751
POULTRY MARKET STATISTICS. Text in English. a. USD 12. **Document type:** *Government.*
Formerly: U.S. Agricultural Marketing Service. Dairy and Poultry Market Statistics
—CISTI.
Published by: U.S. Department of Agriculture, Agricultural Marketing Service, 1400 Independence Ave, S W, Washington, DC 20250. TEL 202-720-6911.

630.21 PRT ISSN 0871-9152
PRECOS E RENDIMENTOS NA AGRICULTURA. Text in Portuguese. 1991. q.
Published by: Instituto Nacional de Estatistica, Ave. Antonio Jose de Almeida 2, Lisbon, 1000-043, Portugal. TEL 351-21-8426100, FAX 351-21-8426380, ine@ine.pt, http://www.ine.pt/.

338.1021 CAN
PRINCE EDWARD ISLAND. DEPARTMENT OF AGRICULTURE. AGRICULTURAL STATISTICS. Text in English. 1966. a. illus.; stat.
Published by: Department of Agriculture, P O Box 2000, Charlottetown, PE C1A 7N8, Canada. TEL 902-368-4856, FAX 902-368-4857. Circ: 750. **Co-sponsor:** Statistics Canada.

630.21 BRA ISSN 0101-3963
S191
PRODUCAO AGRICOLA MUNICIPAL; culturas temporarias e permanentes. (Also avail. in 28 regional eds.) Text in Portuguese. 1973. a. USD 70 for 4-vol. set; USD 20 for individual regional eds.. **Document type:** *Government.* **Description:** Provides annual estimates on quantity, harvested area, productivity and value of production of 30 permanent and 30 temporary agricultural products.
Formerly (until 1974): Levantamento da Producao Agricola Municipal (0100-543X)
Media: Diskette.
Published by: Fundacao Instituto Brasileiro de Geografia e Estatistica, Centro de Documentacao e Disseminacao de Informacoes, Rua General Canabarro, 706 Andar 2, Maracana, Rio de Janeiro, RJ 20271-201, Brazil. TEL 55-21-264-5424, FAX 55-21-2841959, http://www.ibge.gov.br.

636.0021 BRA ISSN 0101-4234
HD9424.B7
PRODUCAO DA PECUARIA MUNICIPAL. (Avail. in 28 regional reports) Text in Portuguese. 1973. a. USD 70 for 4-vol. set; USD 20 for individual regional reports. **Document type:** *Government.* **Description:** Provides information on livestock and poultry, as well as on amount and value of milk, wool, eggs, honey, and beeswax.
Formerly: Levantamento do Producao Pecuaria (0100-493X)
Published by: Fundacao Instituto Brasileiro de Geografia e Estatistica, Centro de Documentacao e Disseminacao de Informacoes, Rua General Canabarro, 706 Andar 2, Maracana, Rio de Janeiro, RJ 20271-201, Brazil. TEL 55-21-264-5424, FAX 55-21-2841959, http://www.ibge.gov.br.

338.1021 VEN
PRODUCCION AGRICOLA - PERIODO DE INVIERNO. Text in Spanish. 1965. irreg., latest 1976. free.
Published by: (Venezuela. Ministerio de Agricultura y Cria), Direccion de Planificacion y Estadistica (Subsidiary of: Ministerio de Agricultura y Cria), Division de Estadistica, Centro Simon Bolivar, Torre Norte 16o, Caracas, 1010, Venezuela.

338.1021 VEN
PRODUCCION AGRICOLA - PERIODO DE VERANO. Text in Spanish. 1965. irreg., latest 1976. free.
Published by: (Venezuela. Ministerio de Agricultura y Cria), Direccion de Planificacion y Estadistica (Subsidiary of: Ministerio de Agricultura y Cria), Division de Estadistica, Centro Simon Bolivar, Torre Norte 16o, Caracas, 1010, Venezuela.

630.21 PRI
PUERTO RICO. OFICINA DE ESTADISTICAS AGRICOLAS. BOLETIN SEMESTRAL DE ESTADISTICAS AGRICOLAS. Text in Spanish. 1973 (vol.13). s-a. free. **Document type:** *Government.* **Description:** Provides monthly and annual statistics including those on local production, prices, imports, exports, slaughter and the labor force in Puerto Rico.
Formerly (until 1980): Puerto Rico. Oficina de Estadisticas Agricolas. Boletin Mensual de Estadisticas Agricolas
Indexed: PAIS.
Published by: (Puerto Rico. Agricultural Statistics Office USA), Department of Agriculture, P.O. Box 10163, Santurce, 00908, Puerto Rico. Circ: 450.

633.11 CAN
QUALITY OF WESTERN CANADIAN WHEAT EXPORTS/QUALITE DES EXPORTATIONS DE BLE DE L'OUEST CANADIEN. Text in English, French. 1955. s-a. free (effective 2001). stat. **Document type:** *Government.*
Related titles: Online - full content ed.
Published by: Canadian Grain Commission, Corporate Services/Commission Canadienne des Grains, 700 303 Main St, Winnipeg, MB R3C 3G8, Canada. TEL 204-983-1570, contact@cgc.ca, http://www.cgc.ca/.

630.21 NLD ISSN 1385-8335
RAMING VAN DE BEDRIJFSUITKOMSTEN VAN DE BEDRIJVEN MET GROENTEELT IN DE OPEN GROND, FRUIT- EN BLOEMBOLLENT. Text in Dutch. 1984. a. **Document type:** *Government.*
Former titles (until 1992): Raming van de Bedrijfsuitkomsten van de Bedrijven met Groenteteelt in de Open Grond, Fruit- en Bloembollenbedrijven (1385-8327); (until 1989): Raming van de Bedrijfsuitkomsten van de Bedrijven met Groenteteelt in de Open Grond en van Fruitteeltbedrijven (1385-8319); Which was formed by the 1987 merger of: Raming van de Bedrijfsuitkomsten van de Bedrijven met Groenteteelt in de Open Grond (0921-4240); Raming van de Bedrijfsuitkomsten van de Fruitteeltbedrijven (0921-4259)
Published by: Landbouw-Economisch Instituut, Burgemeester Patijnlaan 19, The Hague, 2585 BE, Netherlands. TEL 31-70-330-8330, FAX 31-70-361-5624, postmaster@lei.dlo.nl, http://www.lei.dlo.nl/lei. Eds. A Boers, W A H B Bouwman.

016.3381 RUS
REFERATIVNYI ZHURNAL. EKONOMIKA AGROPROMYSHLENNOGO KOMPLEKSA. Text in Russian. 1960. m. USD 103 foreign (effective 2006). **Document type:** *Journal, Abstract/Index.*
Related titles: CD-ROM ed.; Online - full text ed.
Published by: Vserossiiskii Institut Nauchnoi i Tekhnicheskoi Informatsii (VINITI), Ul Usievicha 20, Moscow, 125190, Russian Federation. TEL 7-095-1526441, FAX 7-095-9430060, dir@viniti.ru, http://www.viniti.ru. **Dist. by:** Informnauka Ltd., Ul Usievicha 20, Moscow 125190, Russian Federation. alfimov@viniti.ru.

016.6316 RUS ISSN 0034-2548
CODEN: RZPAAV
REFERATIVNYI ZHURNAL. POCHVOVEDENIE I AGROKHIMIYA. Text in Russian. 1960. m. USD 307 foreign (effective 2006). **Document type:** *Abstract/Index.*
Related titles: CD-ROM ed.; Online - full text ed.
Indexed: ChemAb.
—CASDDS, East View, Linda Hall.
Published by: Vserossiiskii Institut Nauchnoi i Tekhnicheskoi Informatsii (VINITI), Ul Usievicha 20, Moscow, 125190, Russian Federation. TEL 7-095-1526441, FAX 7-095-9430060, dir@viniti.ru, http://www.viniti.ru. Ed. Yurii Arskii. **Dist. by:** Informnauka Ltd., Ul Usievicha 20, Moscow 125190, Russian Federation. alfimov@viniti.ru.

016.6313 RUS ISSN 0034-2602
REFERATIVNYI ZHURNAL. TRAKTORY I SEL'SKOKHOZYAISTVENNYE MASHINY I ORUDIYA. Text in Russian. 1956. m. USD 345 foreign (effective 2006). **Document type:** *Journal, Abstract/Index.*
Related titles: CD-ROM ed.; Online - full text ed.
Indexed: AEA.
—Linda Hall.
Published by: Vserossiiskii Institut Nauchnoi i Tekhnicheskoi Informatsii (VINITI), Ul Usievicha 20, Moscow, 125190, Russian Federation. TEL 7-095-1526441, FAX 7-095-9430060, dir@viniti.ru, http://www.viniti.ru. **Dist. by:** Informnauka Ltd., Ul Usievicha 20, Moscow 125190, Russian Federation. alfimov@viniti.ru.

630.21 ETH
REPORT ON AVERAGE PRODUCERS' PRICE - AGRICULTURAL PRODUCTS. Text in English. q. ETB 52, USD 7 (effective 1999). back issues avail. **Document type:** *Government.* **Description:** Presents average producers' prices of cereals, pulses, oil seeds, vegetables, fruits, spices, livestock, draft animals, dairy products and eggs, hides and skins, and more.
Related titles: CD-ROM ed.; Diskette ed.
Published by: Central Statistical Authority, PO Box 1143, Addis Ababa, Ethiopia. TEL 251-1-115470, FAX 251-1-550334.

016.6329 GBR ISSN 0957-6762
REVIEW OF AGRICULTURAL ENTOMOLOGY; consisting of abstracts of reviews of current literature on applied entomology throughout the world. Text in English. 1913. m. USD 2,090 in the Americas to institutions except Canada; GBP 1,195 elsewhere to institutions; USD 2,240 combined subscription in the Americas to institutions except Canada; print & online eds.; GBP 1,280 combined subscription elsewhere to institutions print & online eds. (effective 2006). adv. bk.rev. index. back issues avail. **Document type:** *Abstract/Index.* **Description:** Covers literature on insects and other pests of cultivated plants, forest trees and stored products, and beneficial arthropods such as parasites and predators.
Formerly: Review of Applied Entomology. Series A: Agricultural (0305-0076)
Related titles: Online - full text ed.: USD 1,775 in the Americas to institutions except Canada; GBP 1,015 elsewhere to institutions (effective 2006) (from DIMDI, The Dialog Corporation).
Indexed: BioCN&I, FS&TA.
—CISTI, Linda Hall. **CCC.**
Published by: CABI Publishing (Subsidiary of: CAB International), CAB International, Wallingford, Oxfordshire OX10 8DE, United Kingdom. TEL 44-1491-832111, FAX 44-1491-833508, cabi@cabi.org, http://www.cabi-publishing.org/. Adv. contact Sarah Harris TEL 44-1491-829310. B&W page GBP 150, B&W page USD 240; 170 x 267. Circ: 465. **Subscr. addr. in N America:** CABI Publishing North America, 875 Massachusetts Ave, 7th Fl, Cambridge, MA 02139. TEL 617-395-4056, 800-528-4841, FAX 617-354-6875, cabi-nao@cabi.org.

338.1021 DEU ISSN 0344-5267
RHEINLAND AKTUELL; Analysen - Daten - Informationen. Text in German. 1977. 3/yr. free. **Document type:** *Bulletin, Trade.* **Description:** Presents agricultural statistics of the Rhineland area of Nordrhein-Westfalen.
Published by: Landwirtschaftskammer Rheinland, Endenicher Allee 60, Bonn, 53115, Germany. TEL 49-228-703-223, FAX 49-228-703498, TELEX 886685-LWRH-D. Ed. Hans Peter Rehse.

016.631 GBR ISSN 0141-0164
RICE ABSTRACTS. Text in English. 1978. q. USD 910 in the Americas to institutions except Canada; GBP 520 elsewhere to institutions; USD 970 combined subscription in the Americas to institutions except Canada; print & online eds.; GBP 555 combined subscription elsewhere to institutions print & online eds. (effective 2006). adv. back issues avail. **Document type:** *Abstract/Index.* **Description:** Brings you the latest information on rice production, from germination to storage, consumption and marketing.

Related titles: Online - full text ed.: USD 770 in the Americas to institutions except Canada; GBP 440 elsewhere to institutions (effective 2006) (from DIMDI, The Dialog Corporation).
—CCC.
Published by: CABI Publishing (Subsidiary of: CAB International), CAB International, Wallingford, Oxfordshire OX10 8DE, United Kingdom. TEL 44-1491-832111, FAX 44-1491-833508, cabi@cabi.org, http://www.cabi-publishing.org/. Adv. contact Sarah Harris TEL 44-1491-829310. B&W page GBP 60, B&W page USD 95; 170 x 267. Circ: 75. **Subscr. addr. in N America:** CABI Publishing North America, 875 Massachusetts Ave, 7th Fl, Cambridge, MA 02139. TEL 617-395-4056, 800-528-4841, FAX 617-354-6875, cabi-nao@cabi.org.

630.21 CAN ISSN 0702-7389
S161
SASKATCHEWAN AGRICULTURE AND FOOD. AGRICULTURAL STATISTICS. Text in English. 1975. a. free. charts; stat. back issues avail. **Document type:** *Government.*
Related titles: Microfiche ed.
—CISTI.
Published by: Agriculture and Food, B5 Walter Scott Bldg, 3085 Albert St, Regina, SK S4S 0B1, Canada. TEL 888-613-3975 (in US only), FAX 306-721-4626, pad@sk.sympatico.ca, http://www.agr.gov.sk.ca/saf. Circ: 3,000.

016.63 RUS
SEL'SKOKHOZYAISTVENNAYA LITERATURA. Text in Russian. 1948. m. RUR 840, USD 140 (effective 1999). adv. bk.rev. abstr.; bibl. index. **Document type:** *Bibliography.* **Description:** Organ of the National Agricultural Bibliography; covers books, brochures and provides an analytical registry of serial publications and non-periodical collections of papers.
Formerly (until 1992): Sel'skokhozyaistvennaya Literatura S.S.S.R. (0037-1688)
Indexed: AnBrAb, IndVet, NutrAb, VetBull, WeedAb.
—CISTI, East View.
Published by: (Tsentral'naya Nauchnaya Sel'skokhozyaistvennaya Biblioteka), Rossiiskaya Akademiya Sel'skokhozyaistvennykh Nauk/Russian Academy of Agricultural Sciences, c/o Tsentral'naya Nauchnaya Sel'skokhozyaistvennaya Biblioteka, Orlikov per 3, Moscow, 107804, Russian Federation. TEL 7-095-2075398, FAX 7-095-2078972, TELEX 911032, sis@cnshb.msk.ru, http://www.cnshb.ru. Ed. V G Pozdnyakov. Adv. contact L N Pirumova. Circ: 300.

630.21 SYC
SEYCHELLES. PRESIDENT'S OFFICE. STATISTICS DIVISION. AGRICULTURE SURVEY. Text in English. irreg. SCR 60. stat.
Published by: (Seychelles. Statistic Division), President's Office, Department of Finance, Box 206, Victoria, Mahe, Seychelles.

SINTESIS BASICA DE ESTADISTICA VITINICOLA ARGENTINA. see *AGRICULTURE—Crop Production And Soil*

630.21 FRA
SITUATION ET STATISTIQUES MONDIALES DU SECTEUR VITICOLE. Text in English, French. 1980. a. **Description:** Reports on the previous year's acreage devoted to viticultural production, exports, imports, consumption of wine and grapes, inventories.
Formerly: Situation de la Viticulture dans le Monde
Related titles: ♦ Supplement to: Office International de la Vigne et du Vin. Bulletin. ISSN 0029-7127.
Published by: Office International de la Vigne et du Vin, 18 rue d'Aguesseau, Paris, 75008, France. TEL 33-1-44948080, FAX 33-1-42669063, oiv@oiv.int, http://www.oiv.int.

016.6364 USA ISSN 0163-173X
SOCIETY FOR RANGE MANAGEMENT. INTERNATIONAL RANGELAND CONGRESS. ABSTRACTS OF PAPERS. Text in English. 196?. a. USD 5 (effective 1995). back issues avail. **Document type:** *Proceedings.*
Former titles (until 1979): Society for Range Management. Annual Meeting. Abstracts of Papers Presented (0736-1416); (until 1971): American Society for Range Management. Annual Meeting. Abstracts of Papers Presented (0886-5515)
Published by: Society for Range Management, 445 Union Blvd, Ste 230, Lakewood, CO 80228-1259. TEL 303-986-3309, FAX 303-986-3892.

016.6318 GBR ISSN 0038-0792
S590 CODEN: SOFEAT
SOILS AND FERTILIZERS. Variant title: Commonwealth Bureau of Soil Science. Soils and Fertilizers. Imperial Bureau of Soil Science. Soils and Fertilizers. Text in English. 1937. m. USD 2,790 in the Americas to institutions except Canada; GBP 1,595 elsewhere to institutions; USD 2,985 combined subscription in the Americas to institutions except Canada; print & online eds.; GBP 1,705 combined subscription elsewhere to institutions print & online eds. (effective 2006). adv. bk.rev. illus. index. back issues avail.; reprints avail. **Document type:** *Abstract/Index.* **Description:** Aimed at specialists in the land resource and fertilizer sciences.
Related titles: Online - full text ed.: USD 2,370 in the Americas to institutions except Canada; GBP 1,355 elsewhere to institutions (effective 2006) (from DIMDI, The Dialog Corporation).
—BLDSC (8327.000000), CISTI, Linda Hall. **CCC.**
Published by: CABI Publishing (Subsidiary of: CAB International), CAB International, Wallingford, Oxfordshire OX10 8DE, United Kingdom. TEL 44-1491-832111, FAX 44-1491-833508, cabi@cabi.org, http://www.cabi-publishing.org/. Adv. contact Sarah Harris TEL 44-1491-829310. B&W page GBP 175, B&W page USD 275; 170 x 267. Circ: 380. **Subscr. addr. in N America:** CABI Publishing North America, 875 Massachusetts Ave, 7th Fl, Cambridge, MA 02139. TEL 617-395-4056, 800-528-4841, FAX 617-354-6875, cabi-nao@cabi.org.

338.1 FRA ISSN 1608-1056
SOURCE O E C D. AGRICULTURE AND FOOD STATISTICS. Text in English. 2000. irreg. EUR 192, USD 223, GBP 130, JPY 26,200 (effective 2005). **Description:** Provides policy-relevant agricultural statistics and support estimates, quantifying the economics of agriculture.
Incorporates: Agricultural Commodities Outlook Database; Agricultural Policies in Emerging and Transition Economies; Economic Accounts for Agriculture (1016-5886); Producer and Consumer Support Estimates
Media: Online - full text (from Gale Group, IngentaConnect).
—CISTI.
Published by: Organization for Economic Cooperation and Development, 2 Rue Andre Pascal, Paris, 75775 Cedex 16, France. TEL 33-1-45248200, FAX 33-1-45248500, http://www.oecd.org.

338.1021 ZAF
SOUTH AFRICA. DEPARTMENT OF AGRICULTURE. DIRECTORATE OF AGRICULTURAL STATISTICS. ABSTRACT OF AGRICULTURAL STATISTICS/ KORTBEGRIP VAN LANDBOUSTATISTIEKE. Text in Afrikaans, English. 1958. a. free. stat. **Document type:** *Abstract/Index.*
Former titles: South Africa. Department of Agriculture and Fisheries. Division of Economic Services. Abstract of Agricultural Statistics; South Africa. Department of Agricultural Economics and Marketing. Division of Agricultural Marketing Research. Abstract of Agricultural Statistics
Published by: National Department of Agriculture, Directorate of Agricultural Statistics, Private Bag X144, Pretoria, 0001, South Africa. TEL 12-319-7141, secdass@nda.agric.za. Circ: (controlled).

630.21 ZAF
SOUTH AFRICA. STATISTICS SOUTH AFRICA. AGRICULTURAL SURVEY. Text in English. a. ZAR 10 domestic; ZAR 11 foreign (effective 2000). **Document type:** *Government.*
Formerly (until Aug. 1998): South Africa. Central Statistical Service. Agricultural Survey (1021-5867)
Published by: Statistics South Africa/Statistieke Suid-Afrika, Private Bag X44, Pretoria, 0001, South Africa. TEL 27-12-310-8911, FAX 27-12-310-8500, info@statssa.pwv.gov.za, http://www.statssa.gov.za.

630.21 ZAF
SOUTH AFRICA. STATISTICS SOUTH AFRICA. STATISTICAL RELEASE. AGRICULTURAL SURVEY. Text in English. a. **Document type:** *Government.* **Description:** Covers employment, income, current and capital expenditures, assets, and production.
Formerly (until Aug. 1998): South Africa. Central Statistical Service. Statistical Release. Agricultural Survey
Published by: Statistics South Africa/Statistieke Suid-Afrika, Private Bag X44, Pretoria, 0001, South Africa. TEL 27-12-310-8911, FAX 27-12-310-8500, info@statssa.pwv.gov.za, http://www.statssa.gov.za.

016.63 ESP ISSN 0211-9897
SPAIN. MINISTERIO DE AGRICULTURA, PESCA Y ALIMENTACION. BOLETIN MENSUAL DE ESTADISTICA AGRARIA. Text in Spanish. m. charts; illus. index. **Document type:** *Bulletin, Government.*
Indexed: PAIS.
Published by: (Spain. Secretaria General Tecnica), Ministerio de Agricultura Pesca y Alimentacion, Centro de Publicaciones, Paseo Infanta Isabel 1, Madrid, 28014, Spain. TEL 34-91-3475550, FAX 34-91-3475722, mllopisj@mapya.es, http://www.mapya.es. Ed. Porfirio Sanchez Rodriguez. R&P Juan Carlos Palacios Lopez.

630.21 ESP ISSN 1576-4869
S253
SPAIN. MINISTERIO DE AGRICULTURA PESCA Y ALIMENTACION. SECRETARIA GENERAL TECNICA. ANUARIO DE ESTADISTICA AGROALIMENTARIA. Text in Spanish. 1904. a. price varies. charts. **Document type:** *Monographic series, Government.*
Former titles (until 2001): Spain. Ministerio de Agricultura Pesca y Alimentacion. Secretaria General Tecnica. Anuario de Estadistica Agraria (0212-1158); (until 1972): Spain. Ministerio de Agricultura, Pesca y Alimentacion. Anuario Estadistico de Produccion Agricola (0081-3419); (until 1942): Spain. Ministerio de Agricultura. Avance Estadistico
Indexed: RASB.
—BLDSC (1563.499150).
Published by: (Spain. Secretaria General Tecnica), Ministerio de Agricultura Pesca y Alimentacion, Centro de Publicaciones, Paseo Infanta Isabel 1, Madrid, 28014, Spain. TEL 34-91-3475550, FAX 34-91-3475722, mllopisj@mapya.es, http://www.mapya.es. Ed. Porfirio Sanchez Rodriguez. R&P Juan Carlos Palacios Lopez.

630.21 USA
STATISTICAL HIGHLIGHTS OF U.S. AGRICULTURE. Text in English. biennial. **Document type:** *Government.*
Related titles: Online - full content ed.
Published by: U.S. Department of Agriculture, National Agricultural Statistics Service, 1400 Independence Ave, S W, Washington, DC 20250-2000. TEL 800-999-6779, nass@nass.usda.gov, http://www.usda.gov/nass/pubs/stathigh/content.htm, http://www.nass.gov/nass.

338.1021 LUX ISSN 0254-3834
STATISTICAL OFFICE OF THE EUROPEAN COMMUNITIES. AGRICULTURAL PRICES; selected series - chronos data bank. Text in English. q. USD 110. stat. **Description:** Statistics on selling prices of plant products, selling prices of animal products and purchase prices of the means of agricultural production.
Formed by the 1981 merger of: Statistical Office of the European Communities. Selling Prices of Animal Products (0378-6722); Statistical Office of the European Communities. Selling Prices of Vegetables Products (0378-6714)
Related titles: Microfiche ed.: (from CIS).
Indexed: IIS.
—CISTI.
Published by: (European Commission, Statistical Office of the European Communities), European Commission, Office for Official Publications of the European Union, 2 Rue Mercier, Luxembourg, L-2985, Luxembourg. **Dist. in the U.S. by:** Bernan Associates, Bernan, 4611-F Assembly Dr., Lanham, MD 20706-4391. TEL 301-459-0056, 800-274-4447.

630.21 LUX
STATISTICAL OFFICE OF THE EUROPEAN COMMUNITIES. STATISTICAL YEARBOOK. AGRICULTURE. Text in English. 1961. a. USD 25. **Document type:** *Monographic series.*
Formerly: Statistical Office of the European Communities. Statistique Agricole (0081-4946)
Related titles: Microfiche ed.: (from CIS).
Indexed: IIS.
Published by: (European Commission, Statistical Office of the European Communities), European Commission, Office for Official Publications of the European Union, 2 Rue Mercier, Luxembourg, L-2985, Luxembourg. **Dist. in the U.S. by:** Bernan Associates, Bernan, 4611-F Assembly Dr., Lanham, MD 20706-4391. TEL 301-459-0056, 800-274-4447.

636.0021 ITA
STATISTICHE DELLA RAZZA BRUNA. Text in Italian. stat. **Document type:** *Bulletin, Trade.* **Description:** Presents data relative to the consistency of the livestock heritage, Herdbook, and production of the breed in all Italian provinces.
Published by: Associazione Nazionale Allevatori Razza Bruna, Localita Ferlina 204, Bussolengo, VR 37012, Italy. TEL 39-045-6401990, FAX 39-045-7156655, anarb@anarb.it, http://www.anarb.it.

338.1021 AUT
STATISTIK AUSTRIA. ERGEBNISSE DER LANDWIRTSCHAFTLICHEN STATISTIK. Text in German. 1948. a. **Document type:** *Government.* **Description:** Data on livestock, milk, and overall farm production.
Formerly: Austria. Statistisches Zentralamt. Ergebnisse der Landwirtschaftlichen Statistik (0067-2327)
Related titles: ♦ Series of: Beitraege zur Oesterreichischen Statistik. ISSN 0067-2319.
Published by: Statistik Austria, Guglgasse 13, Vienna, W 1110, Austria. TEL 43-1-711280, FAX 43-1-711287728, info@statistik.gv.at, http://www.statistik.at.

630.21 AUT
STATISTIK AUSTRIA. LANDWIRTSCHAFTLICHE MASCHINENZAEHLUNG. Text in German. 1954. irreg. price varies. **Document type:** *Government.* **Description:** Data on stock of agricultural machinery and implements.
Former titles: Austria. Statistisches Zentralamt. Landwirtschaftliche Maschinenzaehlung (0259-7977); Austria. Statistisches Zentralamt. Ergebnisse der Landwirtschaftlichen Maschinenzaehlung
Related titles: ♦ Series of: Beitraege zur Oesterreichischen Statistik. ISSN 0067-2319.
Published by: Statistik Austria, Guglgasse 13, Vienna, W 1110, Austria. TEL 43-1-711280, FAX 43-1-711287728, info@statistik.gv.at, http://www.statistik.at.

630.21 DEU ISSN 0072-1581
HD1951
STATISTISCHES JAHRBUCH UEBER ERNAEHRUNG, LANDWIRTSCHAFT UND FORSTEN DER BUNDESREPUBLIK DEUTSCHLAND. Text in German. 1956. a. EUR 69.95 (effective 2005). **Document type:** *Government.*
Indexed: RASB.
—CCC.

▼ *new title* ➤ *refereed* ✶ *unverified* ♦ *full entry avail.*

A

Published by: Bundesministerium fuer Verbraucherschutz, Ernaehrung und Landwirtschaft, Rochusstr 1, Bonn, 53123, Germany. TEL 49-228-5290, FAX 49-228-5294262, poststelle@bmvel.bund.de, http://www.verbraucherministerium.de.

338.1021 SDN
SUDAN YEARBOOK OF AGRICULTURAL STATISTICS. Text in English. 1974. a.
Supersedes: Bulletin of Agricultural Statistics of the Sudan
Published by: Department of Agricultural Economics, Statistics Division, P O Box 1246, Khartoum, Sudan.

338.1021 SWZ ISSN 0302-4024
SWAZILAND. CENTRAL STATISTICAL OFFICE. CENSUS OF INDIVIDUAL TENURE FARMS. Text in English. 1968. a. free. stat. **Document type:** *Government.*
Media: Duplicated (not offset).
Published by: Central Statistical Office, PO Box 456, Mbabane, Swaziland. TEL 268-43765. Circ: 600.

630.21 SWE ISSN 0082-0199
SWEDEN. STATISTISKA CENTRALBYRAAN. JORDBRUKSSTATISTISK AARSBOK. Text in Swedish; Summaries in English. 1965. a. SEK 280.
Indexed: RASB.
Published by: Statistiska Centralbyraan/Statistics Sweden, Publishing Unit, Orebro, 70189, Sweden. Circ: 1,500.

630.21 SWE ISSN 0082-0288
SWEDEN. STATISTISKA CENTRALBYRAAN. STATISTISKA MEDDELANDEN. SERIE J, JORDBRUK, SKOGSBRUK OCH FISKE. Text in Swedish; Summaries in English. 1963. irreg. SEK 2,100.
Published by: Statistiska Centralbyraan/Statistics Sweden, Publishing Unit, Orebro, 70189, Sweden. Circ: 1,175.

630.21 IND ISSN 0082-1586
TAMIL NADU. DEPARTMENT OF STATISTICS. SEASON AND CROP REPORT. Text in English. 1902. a. INR 5.
Published by: Director of Statistics, Chennai, Tamil Nadu 600 006, India. **Subscr. to:** Government Publication Dpot, 166 Anna Rd., Chennai, Tamil Nadu 600 002, India.

630.21 TZA
TANZANIA. MINISTRY OF AGRICULTURE AND LIVESTOCK DEVELOPMENT. BULLETIN OF CROP STATISTICS. Text in English. 1975. a. **Document type:** *Bulletin, Government.*
Former titles: Tanzania. Ministry of Agriculture. Bulletin of Crop Statistics; Bulletin of Crop and Livestock Statistics
Published by: Ministry of Agriculture and Livestock Development, Planning and Marketing Division, PO Box 9192, Dar Es Salaam, Tanzania. Ed. M S Ravivarma. Circ: 200.

630.21 USA
HD9417.T4
TEXAS AGRICULTURAL STATISTICS. Text in English. 1994. a., latest 1996, for the year 1995. USD 30; free to Texas farmers and ranchers. charts; illus.; mkt.; stat. **Document type:** *Government.* **Description:** Contains crop statistics, livestock statistics, and economic statistics.
Formed by the merger of (1968-1994): Texas Livestock Statistics (0091-1550); (1968-1994): Texas Small Grains Statistics (0091-4673); Texas Crop Statistics
Related titles: Series of: Texas Department of Agriculture. Bulletin.
Published by: Texas Agricultural Statistics Service, PO Box 70, Austin, TX 78767. TEL 512-916-5581, FAX 512-916-5956, nass-tx@nass.usda.gov, http://www.io.com/~tass. Ed. Dennis Findley. Circ: 2,700. **Co-sponsor:** Texas Department of Agriculture.

630.21 THA
THAILAND. NATIONAL STATISTICAL OFFICE. (YEAR) AGRICULTURAL CENSUS. Text in English, Thai. 1950. every 10 yrs. (in 5 vols.). price varies. **Document type:** *Government.* **Description:** Contains data on legal status of holder, land tenure, land use and irrigation, rice, field crop, flower and ornamental plant, permanent crop, para rubber and livestock.
Published by: (Thailand. Statistical Data Bank and Information Dissemination Division), National Statistical Office, Larn Luang Rd, Bangkok, 10100, Thailand. TEL 66-2-282-1535, FAX 66-2-281-3814, binfodsm@nso.go.th, http://www.nso.go.th/. Circ: 3,000.

016.63 IND ISSN 0379-3990
THESIS ABSTRACTS. Text in English. 1975. q. INR 200, USD 60. adv. **Description:** Abstracts of Master's and doctoral theses approved for degrees by the various agricultural universities and National Institutes in India.
Published by: Haryana Agricultural University, Hisar, Haryana 125 004, India. TEL 73721. Ed. R P Bansal. Circ: 500.

630.21 TTO
TRINIDAD AND TOBAGO. CENTRAL STATISTICAL OFFICE. AGRICULTURAL REPORT. Text in English. 1950. a. TTD 15, USD 7.50 (effective 2000). **Document type:** *Government.*
Formerly: Trinidad and Tobago. Central Statistical Office. Quarterly Agricultural Report
Published by: Central Statistical Office, 35-41 Queen St, PO Box 98, Port-of-Spain, Trinidad, Trinidad & Tobago. TEL 868-623-6495, FAX 868-625-3802.

016.636 SCG ISSN 0041-3755
TRZISTE STOKE I STOCHIH PROIZODA✱; konjunkturne informacije. Text in Serbo-Croatian. 1962. s-m. YUN 1,000. stat.
Published by: Zavod za Trzisna Istrazivanja, Belgrade Stock Exchange, Omladinskih Brigada 1, P.O. Box 214, Belgrade, 11070. Ed. Julije Drasinover. Circ: (controlled).

630.21 TUR ISSN 1300-123X
HA1911
TURKEY. DEVLET ISTATISTIK ENSTITUSU. CIFTCININ ELINE GECEN FIYATLAR/TURKEY. STATE INSTITUTE OF STATISTICS. PRICES RECEIVED BY FARMERS. Text in English, Turkish. 1977. a., latest 1993. USD 40 (effective 1996). **Document type:** *Government.*
Related titles: Diskette ed.
Published by: Devlet Istatistik Enstitusu/State Institute of Statistics, Necatibey Caddesi 114, Ankara, 06100, Turkey. TEL 90-312-4185027, FAX 90-312-4710432.

630.21 TUR
TURKEY. DEVLET ISTATISTIK ENSTITUSU. GENEL TARIM SAYIMI/TURKEY. STATE INSTITUTE OF STATISTICS. GENERAL AGRICULTURAL CENSUS. (Consists of: Village Information Survey; Agricultural Holdings Survey) Text in English, Turkish. 1941. irreg., latest 1991. USD 70 for Village Information Survey. **Document type:** *Government.*
Related titles: Diskette ed.
Published by: Devlet Istatistik Enstitusu/State Institute of Statistics, Necatibey Caddesi 114, Ankara, 06100, Turkey. TEL 90-312-4185027, FAX 90-312-4170432, yayin@die.gov.tr, http://www.die.gov.tr. Circ: 1,500.

630.21 TUR ISSN 1300-1213
HA1911
TURKEY. DEVLET ISTATISTIK ENSTITUSU. TARIM ISTATISTIKLERI OZETI/TURKEY. STATE INSTITUTE OF STATISTICS. SUMMARY OF AGRICULTURAL STATISTICS. Text in English, Turkish. 1957. a. USD 45 (effective 1998). **Document type:** *Government.*
Published by: Devlet Istatistik Enstitusu/State Institute of Statistics, Necatibey Caddesi 114, Ankara, 06100, Turkey. TEL 90-312-4185027, FAX 90-312-4170432, yayin@die.gov.tr, http://www.die.gov.tr.

338.1021 TUR ISSN 1300-3577
TURKEY. DEVLET ISTATISTIK ENSTITUSU. TARIMSAL URETIM DEGERI/TURKEY. STATE INSTITUTE OF STATISTICS. VALUE OF AGRICULTURAL PRODUCTION. Text in English, Turkish. a., latest 1989. USD 75 (effective 1996). **Document type:** *Government.* **Description:** Provides statistical information on agricultural and animal production, including market shares and production value.
Related titles: Diskette ed.
Published by: Devlet Istatistik Enstitusu/State Institute of Statistics, Necatibey Caddesi 114, Ankara, 06100, Turkey. TEL 90-312-4185027, FAX 90-312-4170432.

338.1021 TUR ISSN 0082-6936
HA1911
TURKEY. DEVLET ISTATISTIK ENSTITUSU. TARIMSAL YAPI VE URETIM/TURKEY. STATE INSTITUTE OF STATISTICS. AGRICULTURAL STRUCTURE AND PRODUCTION. Text in English, Turkish. 1936. a. USD 65 (effective 1998). **Document type:** *Government.* **Description:** Provides statistical information by province on all aspects of agricultural activity, including area under cultivation, production and yields of vegetable, fruit and tree crops, agricultural machinery, as well as apiculture, livestock and animal production and sericulture.
Published by: Devlet Istatistik Enstitusu/State Institute of Statistics, Necatibey Caddesi 114, Ankara, 06100, Turkey. TEL 90-312-4185027, FAX 90-312-4170432, yayin@die.gov.tr, http://www.die.gov.tr. Circ: 750.

338.1 USA
S53
U S D A - N A S S; Idaho agricultural statistics. Text in English. 1972. a. USD 5 (effective 2000). **Document type:** *Government.*
Formerly (until 2001): Idaho Agricultural Statistics (0094-1271)
Related titles: Microfiche ed.: (from CIS).
Indexed: SRI.
Address: PO Box 1699, Boise, ID 83701. TEL 208-334-1507, 800-727-9540, FAX 208-334-1114, nass.id@nass.usda.gov, http://www.nass.usda.gov/id/homepage.htm. Ed. D G Gerhardt. Circ: 2,500.

630.21 USA
U.S. DEPARTMENT OF AGRICULTURE. ANIMAL AND PLANT HEALTH INSPECTION SERVICE. COOPERATIVE STATE-FEDERAL BOVINE TUBERCULOSIS ERADICATION PROGRAM: STATISTICAL TABLES✱. Text in English. a. free. stat.
Published by: U.S. Animal and Plant Health Inspection Service, U S Department of Agriculture Health Inspection Service, 4700 River Rd, Riverdale, MD 20737-1228. TEL 301-734-5240.

630.21 USA
U.S. DEPARTMENT OF AGRICULTURE. ANIMAL AND PLANT HEALTH INSPECTION SERVICE. COOPERATIVE STATE-FEDERAL BRUCELLOSIS ERADICATION PROGRAM: STATISTICAL TABLES✱. Text in English. a. free. stat.
Published by: U.S. Animal and Plant Health Inspection Service, U S Department of Agriculture Health Inspection Service, 4700 River Rd, Riverdale, MD 20737-1228. TEL 301-734-5240.

630.24 USA
U.S. DEPARTMENT OF AGRICULTURE. NATIONAL AGRICULTURAL STATISTICS SERVICE. AGRICULTURAL CHEMICAL USAGE. Text in English. 3/yr. USD 50 domestic; USD 100 foreign (effective 2000). **Document type:** *Government.*
Related titles: Online - full text ed.
Published by: U.S. Department of Agriculture, National Agricultural Statistics Service, 1400 Independence Ave, S W, Washington, DC 20250-2000. TEL 202-720-4889, FAX 202-690-1311, nass@nass.usda.gov, http://www.usda.gov/nass.

380.141021 USA ISSN 0002-1601
HD9004
U.S. DEPARTMENT OF AGRICULTURE. NATIONAL AGRICULTURAL STATISTICS SERVICE. AGRICULTURAL PRICES. Key Title: Agricultural Prices. Text in English. 1942. m. USD 80 domestic; USD 160 foreign (effective 2000). back issues avail. **Document type:** *Government.* **Description:** Supplies comparative information on prices received by farmers for various commodities and prices paid by farmers for commodities and services, interest, taxes, and farm wage rates.
Related titles: Online - full text ed.: (from The Dialog Corporation).
Indexed: AmStI.
—CISTI.
Published by: U.S. Department of Agriculture, National Agricultural Statistics Service, 1400 Independence Ave, S W, Washington, DC 20250-2000. TEL 202-720-4889, FAX 202-690-1311, nass@nass.usda.gov, http://www.usda.gov/nass.

630.21 USA ISSN 0082-9714
HD1751
U.S. DEPARTMENT OF AGRICULTURE. NATIONAL AGRICULTURAL STATISTICS SERVICE. AGRICULTURAL STATISTICS. Key Title: Agricultural Statistics. Text in English. 1936. a. USD 28 domestic; USD 56 foreign (effective 2000). **Document type:** *Government.*
Related titles: Microfilm ed.: (from BHP); Online - full text ed.
—BLDSC (0755.566000), CISTI.
Published by: U.S. Department of Agriculture, National Agricultural Statistics Service, 1400 Independence Ave, S W, Washington, DC 20250-2000. TEL 202-720-4889, FAX 202-690-1311, nass@nass.usda.gov, http://www.usda.gov/nass.

637.5 USA
U.S. DEPARTMENT OF AGRICULTURE. NATIONAL AGRICULTURAL STATISTICS SERVICE. BROILER HATCHERY. Text in English. w. USD 150 domestic; USD 300 foreign (effective 2000). **Document type:** *Government.*
Related titles: Online - full text ed.
Indexed: AmStI.
Published by: U.S. Department of Agriculture, National Agricultural Statistics Service, 1400 Independence Ave, S W, Washington, DC 20250-2000. TEL 202-720-4889, FAX 202-690-1311, nass@nass.usda.gov, http://www.usda.gov/nass.

636.0021 USA ISSN 0094-3819
U.S. DEPARTMENT OF AGRICULTURE. NATIONAL AGRICULTURAL STATISTICS SERVICE. CATTLE. Key Title: Cattle. Text in English. 1972. 14/yr. (2 Cattle plus 12 Cattle on Feed). USD 45 domestic; USD 90 foreign (effective 2000). stat. back issues avail. **Document type:** *Government.*
Supersedes in part (in 1973): Agricultural Statistics Board Reports: Cattle, Sheep and Goat Inventory (0094-3827)
—CISTI.
Published by: U.S. Department of Agriculture, National Agricultural Statistics Service, 1400 Independence Ave, S W, Washington, DC 20250-2000. TEL 202-720-4889, FAX 202-690-1311, nass@nass.usda.gov, http://www.usda.gov/nass.

636.0021 USA ISSN 0364-202X
U.S. DEPARTMENT OF AGRICULTURE. NATIONAL AGRICULTURAL STATISTICS SERVICE. CATTLE ON FEED. Text in English. 1963. 14/yr. USD 45 includes s-a. Cattle Reports (effective 2000). back issues avail. **Document type:** *Government.* **Description:** Contains the total number of cattle and calves on feed, placements, marketing, and other disappearance; by class, feedlot and by size groups for selected states.
Formerly: U.S. Crop Reporting Board. Cattle and Calves on Feed
Related titles: Online - full text ed.: (from The Dialog Corporation).
Indexed: AmStI.
—CISTI.

Published by: U.S. Department of Agriculture, National Agricultural Statistics Service, 1400 Independence Ave, S W, Washington, DC 20250-2000. TEL 202-720-4333, help@usda.mannlib.cornell.edu, http://www.usda.gov/nass/.

634 USA
U.S. DEPARTMENT OF AGRICULTURE. NATIONAL AGRICULTURAL STATISTICS SERVICE. CHERRY PRODUCTION. Text in English. a. USD 15 domestic; USD 30 foreign (effective 2000). **Document type:** *Government.*
Related titles: Online - full text ed.
Published by: U.S. Department of Agriculture, National Agricultural Statistics Service, 1400 Independence Ave, S W, Washington, DC 20250-2000. TEL 202-720-4889, FAX 202-690-1311, nass@nass.usda.gov, http://www.usda.gov/nass.

636.0021 USA ISSN 1076-3945
CODEN: CHEGED
U.S. DEPARTMENT OF AGRICULTURE. NATIONAL AGRICULTURAL STATISTICS SERVICE. CHICKENS AND EGGS. Text in English. 15/yr. USD 60 domestic; USD 120 foreign (effective 2000). back issues avail. **Document type:** *Government.*
Former titles (until 1994): Agricultural Statistics Board Report: Eggs, Chickens and Turkeys (0093-013X); (until 1969): U.S. Crop Reporting Board. Hatchery Production (0093-0121)
Indexed: AmStI.
—CISTI.
Published by: U.S. Department of Agriculture, National Agricultural Statistics Service, 1400 Independence Ave, S W, Washington, DC 20250-2000. TEL 202-720-4889, FAX 202-690-1311, nass@nass.usda.gov, http://www.usda.gov/nass.

634 USA ISSN 0883-2870
HD9259.C54
U.S. DEPARTMENT OF AGRICULTURE. NATIONAL AGRICULTURAL STATISTICS SERVICE. CITRUS FRUITS. Key Title: Citrus Fruits. Text in English. a. USD 15 per issue domestic; USD 30 per issue foreign (effective 2000). **Document type:** *Government.*
Formerly (until 1975): Citrus Fruits by States (0732-3476)
Related titles: Online - full text ed.
Published by: U.S. Department of Agriculture, National Agricultural Statistics Service, 1400 Independence Ave, S W, Washington, DC 20250-2000. TEL 202-720-4889, FAX 202-690-1311, nass@nass.usda.gov, http://www.usda.gov/nass.

630.21 USA ISSN 0091-1267
U.S. DEPARTMENT OF AGRICULTURE. NATIONAL AGRICULTURAL STATISTICS SERVICE. COLD STORAGE. Key Title: Cold Storage. Text in English. 1945. 13/yr. USD 55 domestic; USD 110 foreign (effective 2000). back issues avail. **Document type:** *Government.* **Description:** Contains the regional and national end-of-month stocks of meats, dairy products, poultry products, fruits, nuts and vegetables in public and private refrigerated warehouses.
Related titles: Online - full text ed.
Indexed: AmStI.
—CISTI.
Published by: U.S. Department of Agriculture, National Agricultural Statistics Service, 1400 Independence Ave, S W, Washington, DC 20250-2000. TEL 202-720-4889, FAX 202-690-1311, nass@nass.usda.gov, http://www.usda.gov/nass.

633 USA ISSN 0093-4313
UNCLASSED
U.S. DEPARTMENT OF AGRICULTURE. NATIONAL AGRICULTURAL STATISTICS SERVICE. COTTON GINNINGS. Key Title: Cotton Ginnings, A10. Text in English. 13/yr. USD 55 domestic; USD 110 foreign (effective 2000). **Document type:** *Government.*
Incorporates (in 1991): Cotton Ginnings, A20 (0093-4321)
Related titles: Online - full text ed.
—CISTI.
Published by: U.S. Department of Agriculture, National Agricultural Statistics Service, 1400 Independence Ave, S W, Washington, DC 20250-2000. TEL 202-720-4889, FAX 202-690-1311, nass@nass.usda.gov, http://www.usda.gov/nass.

664.8 USA ISSN 0196-884X
HD9259.C73
U.S. DEPARTMENT OF AGRICULTURE. NATIONAL AGRICULTURAL STATISTICS SERVICE. CRANBERRIES. Key Title: Cranberries. Text in English. a. USD 15 per issue domestic; USD 30 per issue foreign (effective 2000). **Document type:** *Government.*
Related titles: Online - full text ed.
—CISTI.
Published by: U.S. Department of Agriculture, National Agricultural Statistics Service, 1400 Independence Ave, S W, Washington, DC 20250-2000. TEL 202-720-4889, FAX 202-690-1311, nass@nass.usda.gov, http://www.usda.gov/nass.

630.21 USA ISSN 0363-8561
SB83
U.S. DEPARTMENT OF AGRICULTURE. NATIONAL AGRICULTURAL STATISTICS SERVICE. CROP PRODUCTION. Key Title: Crop Production. Text in English. 17/yr. USD 80 domestic; USD 160 foreign (effective 2000). back issues avail.; reprint service avail. from CIS. **Document type:** *Government.*
Related titles: Microfiche ed.: (from CIS); Online - full text ed.: (from The Dialog Corporation).
Indexed: AmStI, CPA, FCA, HerbAb, I&DA, MaizeAb, PGrRegA, RASB, RiceAb, SeedAb, SoyAb, WeedAb.
—CISTI.
Published by: U.S. Department of Agriculture, National Agricultural Statistics Service, 1400 Independence Ave, S W, Washington, DC 20250-2000. TEL 202-720-4889, FAX 202-690-1311, nass@nass.usda.gov, http://www.usda.gov/nass.

630 USA
U.S. DEPARTMENT OF AGRICULTURE. NATIONAL AGRICULTURAL STATISTICS SERVICE. CROP PROGRESS. Text in English. 36/yr. USD 100 domestic; USD 200 foreign (effective 2000). **Document type:** *Government.*
Related titles: Online - full text ed.
Published by: U.S. Department of Agriculture, National Agricultural Statistics Service, 1400 Independence Ave, S W, Washington, DC 20250-2000. TEL 202-720-4889, FAX 202-690-1311, nass@nass.usda.gov, http://www.usda.gov/nass.

633.021 USA ISSN 0884-2329
HD9001
U.S. DEPARTMENT OF AGRICULTURE. NATIONAL AGRICULTURAL STATISTICS SERVICE. CROP VALUES. Key Title: Crop Values. Text in English. 195?. a. USD 15 domestic; USD 30 foreign (effective 2000). **Document type:** *Government.*
Related titles: Online - full text ed.
—CISTI.
Published by: U.S. Department of Agriculture, National Agricultural Statistics Service, 1400 Independence Ave, S W, Washington, DC 20250-2000. TEL 202-720-4889, 800-999-6779, FAX 202-690-1311, nass@nass.usda.gov, http://www.usda.gov/nass.

637.1021 USA ISSN 0093-1446
U.S. DEPARTMENT OF AGRICULTURE. NATIONAL AGRICULTURAL STATISTICS SERVICE. DAIRY PRODUCTS. Key Title: Dairy Products. Text in English. 1972. 13/yr. USD 55 domestic; USD 110 foreign (effective 2000). stat. back issues avail. **Document type:** *Government.*
Related titles: Online - full text ed.
Indexed: AmStI.
—CISTI.
Published by: U.S. Department of Agriculture, National Agricultural Statistics Service, 1400 Independence Ave, S W, Washington, DC 20250-2000. TEL 202-720-4889, FAX 202-690-1311, nass@nass.usda.gov, http://www.usda.gov/nass.

636.0021 USA ISSN 0145-3904
U.S. DEPARTMENT OF AGRICULTURE. NATIONAL AGRICULTURAL STATISTICS SERVICE. EGG PRODUCTS. Key Title: Egg Products. Text in English. 1954. m. USD 45 domestic; USD 90 foreign (effective 2000). back issues avail. **Document type:** *Government.*
Indexed: AmStI.
Published by: U.S. Department of Agriculture, National Agricultural Statistics Service, 1400 Independence Ave, S W, Washington, DC 20250-2000. TEL 202-720-4889, FAX 202-690-1311, nass@nass.usda.gov, http://www.usda.gov/nass.

331.1193 USA ISSN 0363-8545
U.S. DEPARTMENT OF AGRICULTURE. NATIONAL AGRICULTURAL STATISTICS SERVICE. FARM LABOR. Key Title: Farm Labor. Text in English. 1943. q. USD 30; USD 60 foreign (effective 1999). back issues avail. **Document type:** *Government.* **Description:** Includes regional and national information for self-employed, unpaid, and hired workers in the agriculture field.
Related titles: Online - full text ed.
Published by: U.S. Department of Agriculture, National Agricultural Statistics Service, 1400 Independence Ave, S W, Washington, DC 20250-2000. TEL 202-720-4889, FAX 202-690-1311, nass@nass.usda.gov, http://www.usda.gov/nass. Ed. Steve Logan.

338.1 USA
U.S. DEPARTMENT OF AGRICULTURE. NATIONAL AGRICULTURAL STATISTICS SERVICE. FARM NUMBERS AND LAND IN FARMS. Text in English. a. USD 15 domestic; USD 30 foreign (effective 2000). **Document type:** *Government.*
Related titles: Online - full text ed.
Published by: U.S. Department of Agriculture, National Agricultural Statistics Service, 1400 Independence Ave, S W, Washington, DC 20250-2000. TEL 202-720-4889, FAX 202-690-1311, nass@nass.usda.gov, http://www.usda.gov/nass.

338.1 USA ISSN 0191-0531
S561
U.S. DEPARTMENT OF AGRICULTURE. NATIONAL AGRICULTURAL STATISTICS SERVICE. FARM PRODUCTION EXPENDITURES. Key Title: Farm Production Expenditures. Text in English. a. USD 20 domestic; USD 40 foreign (effective 2000). **Document type:** *Government.*
Related titles: Online - full text ed.
—CISTI.
Published by: U.S. Department of Agriculture, National Agricultural Statistics Service, 1400 Independence Ave, S W, Washington, DC 20250-2000. TEL 202-720-4889, FAX 202-690-1311, nass@nass.usda.gov, http://www.usda.gov/nass.

633 635.9 USA ISSN 0272-6793
SB405
U.S. DEPARTMENT OF AGRICULTURE. NATIONAL AGRICULTURAL STATISTICS SERVICE. FLORICULTURE CROPS. Key Title: Floriculture Crops. Text in English. 1978. a. USD 20 domestic; USD 40 foreign (effective 2000). **Document type:** *Government.*
Related titles: Online - full text ed.
—CISTI.
Published by: U.S. Department of Agriculture, National Agricultural Statistics Service, 1400 Independence Ave, S W, Washington, DC 20250-2000. TEL 202-720-4889, FAX 202-690-1311, nass@nass.usda.gov, http://www.usda.gov/nass.

633.1021 USA
U.S. DEPARTMENT OF AGRICULTURE. NATIONAL AGRICULTURAL STATISTICS SERVICE. GRAIN STOCKS. Key Title: Grain Stocks. Text in English. q. USD 30 domestic; USD 60 foreign (effective 2000). stat. back issues avail. **Document type:** *Government.*
Related titles: Online - full text ed.
Indexed: AmStI.
Published by: U.S. Department of Agriculture, National Agricultural Statistics Service, 1400 Independence Ave, S W, Washington, DC 20250-2000. TEL 202-720-4889, FAX 202-690-1311, nass@nass.usda.gov, http://www.usda.gov/nass.

636.0021 USA ISSN 0565-2189
SF395.8.A1
U.S. DEPARTMENT OF AGRICULTURE. NATIONAL AGRICULTURAL STATISTICS SERVICE. HOGS AND PIGS. Key Title: Hogs and Pigs. Text in English. 1968. q. USD 30 domestic; USD 60 foreign (effective 2000). back issues avail. **Document type:** *Government.*
Related titles: Online - full text ed.
Indexed: AmStI.
—CISTI.
Published by: U.S. Department of Agriculture, National Agricultural Statistics Service, 1400 Independence Ave, S W, Washington, DC 20250-2000. TEL 202-720-4889, FAX 202-690-1311, nass@nass.usda.gov, http://www.usda.gov/nass.

338.17 USA
U.S. DEPARTMENT OF AGRICULTURE. NATIONAL AGRICULTURAL STATISTICS SERVICE. HONEY. Text in English. a. USD 15 domestic; USD 30 foreign (effective 2000). **Document type:** *Government.*
Related titles: Online - full text ed.
Published by: U.S. Department of Agriculture, National Agricultural Statistics Service, 1400 Independence Ave, S W, Washington, DC 20250-2000. TEL 202-720-4889, FAX 202-690-1311, nass@nass.usda.gov, http://www.nass.usda.gov/nass.

633 USA
U.S. DEPARTMENT OF AGRICULTURE. NATIONAL AGRICULTURAL STATISTICS SERVICE. HOP STOCKS. Text in English. s-a. USD 30 domestic; USD 60 foreign (effective 2000). **Document type:** *Government.*
Related titles: Online - full text ed.
Published by: U.S. Department of Agriculture, National Agricultural Statistics Service, 1400 Independence Ave, S W, Washington, DC 20250-2000. TEL 202-720-4889, FAX 202-690-1311, nass@nass.usda.gov, http://www.usda.gov/nass.

636.0021 USA ISSN 0499-0544
U.S. DEPARTMENT OF AGRICULTURE. NATIONAL AGRICULTURAL STATISTICS SERVICE. LIVESTOCK SLAUGHTER. Key Title: Livestock Slaughter. Text in English. 13/yr. USD 60 domestic; USD 120 foreign (effective 2000). back issues avail. **Document type:** *Government.*
Indexed: AmStI.
Published by: U.S. Department of Agriculture, National Agricultural Statistics Service, 1400 Independence Ave, S W, Washington, DC 20250-2000. TEL 202-720-4889, 800-999-6779, FAX 202-690-1311, nass@nass.usda.gov, http://www.usda.gov/nass.

A

636 USA ISSN 0748-0318
HD9414
U.S. DEPARTMENT OF AGRICULTURE. NATIONAL AGRICULTURAL STATISTICS SERVICE. MEAT ANIMALS: PRODUCTION, DISPOSITION AND INCOME. Key Title: Meat Animals: Production, Disposition and Income. Text in English. 1975. a. USD 15 domestic; USD 30 foreign (effective 2000). **Document type:** *Government.*
Formerly (until 1983): Meat Animals (0094-7385)
Related titles: Online - full text ed.
—CISTI.
Published by: U.S. Department of Agriculture, National Agricultural Statistics Service, 1400 Independence Ave, S W, Washington, DC 20250-2000. TEL 202-720-4889, FAX 202-690-1311, nass@nass.usda.gov, http://www.usda.gov/nass.

637.1021 USA ISSN 0026-4202
HD9282.U3
U.S. DEPARTMENT OF AGRICULTURE. NATIONAL AGRICULTURAL STATISTICS SERVICE. MILK PRODUCTION. Key Title: Milk Production. Text in English. m. (plus a. cumulation). USD 45 domestic; USD 90 foreign (effective 2000). back issues avail. **Document type:** *Government.*
Related titles: Online - full text ed.
Indexed: AmStl.
—CISTI.
Published by: U.S. Department of Agriculture, National Agricultural Statistics Service, 1400 Independence Ave, S W, Washington, DC 20250-2000. TEL 202-720-4889, FAX 202-690-1311, nass@nass.usda.gov, http://www.usda.gov/nass.

338.1 USA ISSN 0749-8683
SF405.M6
U.S. DEPARTMENT OF AGRICULTURE. NATIONAL AGRICULTURAL STATISTICS SERVICE. MINK. Key Title: Mink. Text in English. a. USD 15 domestic; USD 30 foreign (effective 2000). **Document type:** *Government.*
Formerly (until 1976): Mink Production (0191-1155)
Related titles: Online - full text ed.
Published by: U.S. Department of Agriculture, National Agricultural Statistics Service, 1400 Independence Ave, S W, Washington, DC 20250-2000. TEL 202-720-4889, FAX 202-690-1311, nass@nass.usda.gov, http://www.usda.gov/nass.

633 USA ISSN 0197-6281
HD9235.M952
U.S. DEPARTMENT OF AGRICULTURE. NATIONAL AGRICULTURAL STATISTICS SERVICE. MUSHROOMS. Key Title: Mushrooms. Text in English. 1966. a. USD 15 domestic; USD 30 foreign (effective 2000). **Document type:** *Government.*
Related titles: Online - full text ed.
—CISTI.
Published by: U.S. Department of Agriculture, National Agricultural Statistics Service, 1400 Independence Ave, S W, Washington, DC 20250-2000. TEL 202-720-4889, FAX 202-690-1311, nass@nass.usda.gov, http://www.usda.gov/nass.

635.6021 USA ISSN 1057-7912
U.S. DEPARTMENT OF AGRICULTURE. NATIONAL AGRICULTURAL STATISTICS SERVICE. NONCITRUS FRUITS AND NUTS. Key Title: Noncitrus Fruits and Nuts. Text in English. s-a. USD 30 domestic; USD 60 foreign (effective 2000). back issues avail. **Document type:** *Government.*
Published by: U.S. Department of Agriculture, National Agricultural Statistics Service, 1400 Independence Ave, S W, Washington, DC 20250-2000. TEL 202-720-4889, FAX 202-690-1311, nass@nass.usda.gov, http://www.usda.gov/nass.

630.21 USA ISSN 0499-0579
U.S. DEPARTMENT OF AGRICULTURE. NATIONAL AGRICULTURAL STATISTICS SERVICE. PEANUT STOCKS AND PROCESSING. Key Title: Peanut Stocks and Processing. Text in English. m. USD 45 domestic; USD 90 foreign (effective 2000). back issues avail. **Document type:** *Government.*
Related titles: Online - full text ed.
Indexed: AmStl.
Published by: U.S. Department of Agriculture, National Agricultural Statistics Service, 1400 Independence Ave, S W, Washington, DC 20250-2000. TEL 202-720-4889, FAX 202-690-1311, nass@nass.usda.gov, http://www.usda.gov/nass. Ed. Herman Ellison.

635.21021 USA
U.S. DEPARTMENT OF AGRICULTURE. NATIONAL AGRICULTURAL STATISTICS SERVICE. POTATOES AND POTATO STOCKS. Text in English. 7/yr. USD 40 domestic; USD 80 foreign (effective 2000). back issues avail. **Document type:** *Government.*
Formerly (until 1995): Agricultural Statistics Board Report: Potatoes
Related titles: Online - full text ed.
Indexed: AmStl.

Published by: U.S. Department of Agriculture, National Agricultural Statistics Service, 1400 Independence Ave, S W, Washington, DC 20250-2000. TEL 202-720-4889, FAX 202-690-1311, nass@nass.usda.gov, http://www.usda.gov/nass.

636.0021 USA ISSN 0364-2682
HD9437.U6
U.S. DEPARTMENT OF AGRICULTURE. NATIONAL AGRICULTURAL STATISTICS SERVICE. POULTRY SLAUGHTER. Key Title: Poultry Slaughter. Text in English. m. USD 50 domestic; USD 100 foreign (effective 2000). back issues avail. **Document type:** *Government.*
Indexed: AmStl.
—CISTI.
Published by: U.S. Department of Agriculture, National Agricultural Statistics Service, 1400 Independence Ave, S W, Washington, DC 20250-2000. TEL 202-720-4889, FAX 202-690-1311, nass@nass.usda.gov, http://www.usda.gov/nass.

631.8 USA ISSN 1083-3714
SB950.2.A1
U.S. DEPARTMENT OF AGRICULTURE. NATIONAL AGRICULTURAL STATISTICS SERVICE. RESTRICTED USE PESTICIDES. Key Title: Restricted Use Pesticides. Text in English. a. USD 15 domestic; USD 30 foreign (effective 2000). **Document type:** *Government.*
Related titles: Online - full text ed.
—CISTI.
Published by: U.S. Department of Agriculture, National Agricultural Statistics Service, 1400 Independence Ave, S W, Washington, DC 20250-2000. TEL 202-720-4889, FAX 202-690-1311, nass@nass.usda.gov, http://www.usda.gov/nass.

633.1021 USA ISSN 1057-7920
U.S. DEPARTMENT OF AGRICULTURE. NATIONAL AGRICULTURAL STATISTICS SERVICE. RICE STOCKS. Key Title: Rice Stocks. Text in English. q. USD 30 domestic; USD 60 foreign (effective 2000). back issues avail. **Document type:** *Government.*
Related titles: Online - full text ed.
Indexed: AmStl.
Published by: U.S. Department of Agriculture, National Agricultural Statistics Service, 1400 Independence Ave, S W, Washington, DC 20250-2000. TEL 202-720-4889, FAX 202-690-1311, nass@nass.usda.gov, http://www.usda.gov/nass.

636.6 USA ISSN 0094-3851
SF375.4.A1
U.S. DEPARTMENT OF AGRICULTURE. NATIONAL AGRICULTURAL STATISTICS SERVICE. SHEEP AND GOATS. Key Title: Sheep and Goats. Text in English. 1972. 3/yr. USD 27 domestic; USD 54 foreign (effective 2000). **Document type:** *Government.*
Supersedes in part (in 1973): Agricultural Statistics Board Reports: Cattle, Sheep and Goat Inventory (0094-3827)
Related titles: Online - full text ed.
—CISTI.
Published by: U.S. Department of Agriculture, National Agricultural Statistics Service, 1400 Independence Ave, S W, Washington, DC 20250-2000. TEL 202-720-4889, FAX 202-690-1311, nass@nass.usda.gov, http://www.usda.gov/nass.

U.S. DEPARTMENT OF AGRICULTURE. NATIONAL AGRICULTURAL STATISTICS SERVICE. TROUT PRODUCTION. see *FISH AND FISHERIES—Abstracting, Bibliographies, Statistics*

636.5 USA
U.S. DEPARTMENT OF AGRICULTURE. NATIONAL AGRICULTURAL STATISTICS SERVICE. TURKEY HATCHERY. Text in English. 12/yr. USD 50 domestic; USD 100 foreign (effective 2000). Supplement avail. **Document type:** *Government.*
Related titles: Online - full text ed.
Indexed: AmStl.
Published by: U.S. Department of Agriculture, National Agricultural Statistics Service, 1400 Independence Ave, S W, Washington, DC 20250-2000. TEL 202-720-4889, FAX 202-690-1311, nass@nass.usda.gov, http://www.usda.gov/nass.

630.21 USA ISSN 0193-6603
U.S. DEPARTMENT OF AGRICULTURE. NATIONAL AGRICULTURAL STATISTICS SERVICE. VEGETABLES. Key Title: Vegetables. Text in English. bi-m. USD 35 domestic; USD 70 foreign (effective 2000). back issues avail. **Document type:** *Government.*
Related titles: Online - full text ed.
—CISTI.
Published by: U.S. Department of Agriculture, National Agricultural Statistics Service, 1400 Independence Ave, S W, Washington, DC 20250-2000. TEL 202-720-4889, FAX 202-690-1311, nass@nass.usda.gov, http://www.usda.gov/nass.

630.21 USA
U.S. DEPARTMENT OF AGRICULTURE. RURAL BUSINESS - COOPERATIVE SERVICE. COOPERATIVE STATISTICS. Text in English. irreg. USD 5 (effective 2000). **Document type:** *Government.* **Description:** Provides the latest statistics on farmer cooperatives in the U.S.
Formerly: Statistics of Farmer Cooperatives (0081-5128)
Published by: U.S. Department of Agriculture, Rural Business - Cooperative Service, Stop 3250, Washington, DC 20250-3250. TEL 202-720-7558, FAX 202-720-4641. Ed. Daniel Campbell.

630.21 USA
HD9002
U.S. FOREIGN AGRICULTURAL TRADE AND AGRICULTURAL TRADE UPDATES STATISTICAL REPORT∗. Text in English. 1971. a. USD 34; included with subscr. to Foreign Agricultural Trade of the United States. **Document type:** *Government.*
Formerly: U.S. Foreign Agricultural Trade Statistical Report (0362-0530)
—CISTI.
Published by: U.S. Department of Agriculture, Economic Research Service, Information Division, 1800 M St, N W, Ste 3, Washington, DC 20036-5828. TEL 800-999-6779. **Dist. by:** ERS-NASS.

338.1021 USA
U.S. FOREIGN AGRICULTURAL TRADE STATISTICAL REPORT. FISCAL YEAR∗. Text in English. a. USD 29. **Document type:** *Government.*
Indexed: RASB.
Published by: U.S. Department of Agriculture, Economic Research Service, Information Division, 1800 M St, N W, Ste 3, Washington, DC 20036-5828. TEL 800-999-6779, http://www.econ.ag.gov/. Ed. Martha R Evans. **Dist. by:** ERS-NASS. TEL 800-999-6779.

UKRAINSKYI REFERATYVNYI ZHURNAL. SERIYA 2. TEHNIKA, PROMYSLOVIST', SIL'S'KE HOSPODARSTVO/UKRAINIAN JOURNAL OF ABSTRACTS. SER. 2. ENGINEERING, INDUSTRY, AGRICULTURE. see *ENGINEERING— Abstracting, Bibliographies, Statistics*

636.0021 USA ISSN 0739-0734
URNER BARRY'S NATIONAL WEEKLY HATCH REPORT. Text in English. 1982. w.
Published by: Urner Barry Publications, Inc., PO Box 389, Toms River, NJ 08754-0389. TEL 732-240-5330, FAX 732-341-0891, mail@urnerbarry.com. Ed. Russell Whitman.

630.21 USA ISSN 0276-0193
S119
UTAH AGRICULTURAL STATISTICS. Text in English. 1971. a. free. **Document type:** *Government.*
Related titles: Microfiche ed.: (from CIS).
Indexed: SRI.
Published by: Department of Agriculture, 350 N Redwood Rd, Box 146500, Salt Lake City, UT 84114-6500. TEL 801-538-7100. R&P Delroy Reiting TEL 801-524-5003. **Co-sponsor:** U.S. Department of Agriculture, Utah Agricultural Statistical Service.

630.21 VUT
VANUATU. STATISTICS OFFICE. REPORT OF THE AGRICULTURAL CENSUS. (Part I: The Results; Part II: Summary of Results) Text in English. irreg., latest 1984. VUV 1,000, USD 15 for Part I; VUV 100, USD 10 for Part II. adv. **Document type:** *Government.*
Published by: Statistics Office, PMB 19, Port Vila, Vanuatu. TEL 678-22110, FAX 678-24583. Ed. Jacob Isaiah. Adv. contact Tali Saurei.

630.21 VUT
VANUATU. STATISTICS OFFICE. REPORT ON SMALL HOLDER AGRICULTURE SURVEY. Text in English. 1989. a. VUV 1,000, USD 15 (effective 1996). adv. **Document type:** *Government.* **Description:** Contains detailed data on cocoa practices, cocoa fermenting, livestock and pastures.
Published by: Statistics Office, PMB 19, Port Vila, Vanuatu. TEL 678-22110, FAX 678-24583. Ed. Jacob Isaiah. Adv. contact Tali Saurei.

338.1021 VEN
VENEZUELA. MINISTERIO DE AGRICULTURA Y CRIA. BOLETIN DE PRECIOS DE PRODUCTOS AGROPECUARIOS. Text in Spanish. 1955. m. free. **Document type:** *Bulletin, Government.*
Published by: (Venezuela. Ministerio de Agricultura y Cria), Direccion de Planificacion y Estadistica (Subsidiary of: Ministerio de Agricultura y Cria), Division de Estadistica, Centro Simon Bolivar, Torre Norte 16o, Caracas, 1010, Venezuela.

630.21 VEN ISSN 0085-7653
VENEZUELA. MINISTERIO DE AGRICULTURA Y CRIA. DIRECCION DE ECONOMIA Y ESTADISTICA AGROPECUARIA. DIVISION DE ESTADISTICA. PLAN DE TRABAJO∗. Text in Spanish. a. **Document type:** *Government.*
Published by: (Venezuela. Direccion de Planificacion y Estadistica), Ministerio de Agricultura y Cria, Centro Simon Bolivar Torre Norte 16o, Caracas, DF 1010, Venezuela.

630.21 VEN ISSN 0083-5366
VENEZUELA. MINISTERIO DE AGRICULTURA Y CRIA. DIRECCION DE ECONOMICA Y ESTADISTICA AGROPECUARIA. ANUARIO ESTADISTICO AGROPECUARIO. Text in Spanish. 1961. a. free. **Document type:** *Government.*
Published by: (Venezuela. Ministerio de Agricultura y Cria), Direccion de Planificacion y Estadistica (Subsidiary of: Ministerio de Agricultura y Cria), Division de Estadistica, Centro Simon Bolivar, Torre Norte 16o, Caracas, 1010, Venezuela.

630.21 VEN
VENEZUELA. MINISTERIO DE AGRICULTURA Y CRIA. DIRECCION DE PLANIFICACION Y ESTADISTICA. ESTADISTICAS AGROPECUARIAS DE LAS ENTIDADES FEDERALES. Text in Spanish. 1962. biennial. free. **Document type:** *Government.*
Published by: (Venezuela. Ministerio de Agricultura y Cria), Direccion de Planificacion y Estadistica (Subsidiary of: Ministerio de Agricultura y Cria), Division de Estadistica, Centro Simon Bolivar, Torre Norte 16o, Caracas, 1010, Venezuela.

630.21 USA ISSN 0095-4330
S125
WASHINGTON AGRICULTURAL STATISTICS. Text in English. 1973. a. free. 140 p./no.; **Document type:** *Government.*
Related titles: Microfiche ed.: (from CIS); Online - full content ed.
Indexed: SRI.
—CISTI.
Published by: U.S. Department of Agriculture, Agricultural Statistics Service (Olympia), PO Box 609, Olympia, WA 98507-0609. TEL 360-902-1940, FAX 360-902-2091, nass-wa@nass.usda.gov, http://www.nass.usda.gov/wa. Circ: 3,000.

636.5 USA
WATT POULTRY STATISTICAL YEARBOOK: INTERNATIONAL EDITION. Text in English. 1937. m. USD 72 (effective 2001). adv. **Document type:** *Trade.* **Description:** Provides an in-depth statistical overview of the international poultry industry.
Published by: Watt Publishing Co., 513 Fifth St, S W, Cullman, AL 35055. TEL 205-734-6800, FAX 205-739-6945, http://www.wattnet.com. Ed. Gary Thornton. Pub. Charles Olentine. adv.: B&W page USD 4,550, color page USD 5,800. Circ: 20,000 (controlled).

016.63258 GBR ISSN 0043-1729
SB611
WEED ABSTRACTS; compiled from world literature. Text in English. 1954. m. USD 1,285 in the Americas to institutions except Canada; GBP 735 elsewhere to institutions; USD 1,375 combined subscription in the Americas to institutions except Canada; print & online eds.; GBP 785 combined subscription elsewhere to institutions print & online eds. (effective 2006). adv. bk.rev. abstr. index. back issues avail. **Document type:** *Abstract/Index.* **Description:** Covers the current literature on weeds, weed control, and allied subjects.
Related titles: Online - full text ed.: USD 1,095 in the Americas to institutions except Canada; GBP 625 elsewhere to institutions (effective 2006) (from DIMDI, The Dialog Corporation).
—CISTI, Linda Hall. **CCC.**
Published by: CABI Publishing (Subsidiary of: CAB International), CAB International, Wallingford, Oxfordshire OX10 8DE, United Kingdom. Ed. Kathryn A Graves. Adv. contact Sarah Harris TEL 44-1491-829310. B&W page GBP 75, B&W page USD 120; 170 x 267. Circ: 265. **Subscr. addr. in N America:** CABI Publishing North America, 875 Massachusetts Ave, 7th Fl, Cambridge, MA 02139. TEL 617-395-4056, 800-528-4841, FAX 617-354-6875, cabi-nao@cabi.org.

016.63 USA ISSN 1542-9075
SB612.A2
WEED SCIENCE SOCIETY OF AMERICA. ABSTRACTS. Text in English. 1956. a. reprint service avail. from PQC,ISI. **Document type:** *Abstract/Index.*
Formerly (until 1967): Weed Society of America. Abstracts (0511-4144)
Indexed: DBA, WeedAb.
Published by: Weed Science Society of America, PO Box 7050, Lawrence, KS 66044-8897. TEL 800-627-0629, FAX 785-843-1274, wssa@allenpress.com, http://www.wssa.net/society.html. Circ: 1,500.

664 636 USA
WEEKLY INSIDERS TURKEY REPORT AND WEEKLY HATCH REPORT. Text in English. 1974. w. USD 190 (effective 2004). adv. back issues avail. **Document type:** *Newsletter, Trade.* **Description:** Contains slaughter figures, consumption patterns, U.S. Storage Stock Estimates and comparative weekly prices.
Supersedes: Weekly Insiders Turkey Letter (0160-4910); Which superseded in part (in 1972): Weekly Insiders Poultry Letter (0276-0274)
Published by: Urner Barry Publications, Inc., PO Box 389, Toms River, NJ 08754-0389. TEL 732-240-5330, FAX 732-341-0891, mail@urnerbarry.com, http://www.urnerbarry.com. Ed. Michael O'Shaughnessy. Circ: 230 (paid).

630.21 GBR ISSN 0262-8325
HD1930.W3
WELSH AGRICULTURAL STATISTICS. Text in English. a. GBP 10 (effective 2000). **Document type:** *Government.*
Supersedes (in 1979): Annual Digest of Welsh Agricultural Statistics
—BLDSC (9294.320000).
Published by: (Great Britain. Publication Unit), National Assembly of Wales, Statistical Directorate, Cathays Park, Cardiff, CF10 3NQ, United Kingdom. TEL 44-2920-825054, FAX 44-2920-825350, stats.pubs@wales.gsi.gov.uk.

016.6331 GBR ISSN 0265-7880
WHEAT, BARLEY AND TRITICALE ABSTRACTS. Text in English. 1975. bi-m. USD 1,655 in the Americas to institutions except Canada; GBP 945 elsewhere to institutions; USD 1,770 combined subscription in the Americas to institutions except Canada; print & online eds.; GBP 1,010 combined subscription elsewhere to institutions print & online eds. (effective 2006). adv. back issues avail. **Document type:** *Abstract/Index.* **Description:** Contains the latest information on production, from germination to storage, consumption and marketing.
Formerly: Triticale Abstracts (0307-7004)
Related titles: Online - full text ed.: USD 1,410 in the Americas to institutions except Canada; GBP 805 elsewhere to institutions (effective 2006) (from DIMDI, The Dialog Corporation).
—CCC.
Published by: CABI Publishing (Subsidiary of: CAB International), CAB International, Wallingford, Oxfordshire OX10 8DE, United Kingdom. TEL 44-1491-832111, FAX 44-1491-833508, cabi@cabi.org, http://www.cabi-publishing.org/. Adv. contact Sarah Harris TEL 44-1491-829310. B&W page GBP 60, B&W page USD 95; 170 x 267. Circ: 60. **Subscr. addr. in N America:** CABI Publishing North America, 875 Massachusetts Ave, 7th Fl, Cambridge, MA 02139. TEL 617-395-4056, 800-528-4841, FAX 617-354-6875, cabi-nao@cabi.org.

016.636 USA ISSN 0510-4130
HD9284.U4
WHO'S WHO IN THE EGG AND POULTRY INDUSTRIES. Text in English. 1929. a. USD 85 (effective 1999). adv. **Document type:** *Trade.* **Description:** Serves as a one step reference to poultry industries in the US and Canada. Lists suppliers and processors to the broiler, egg and turkey industries for business leaders who buy and sell in the poultry industry.
—CISTI.
Published by: Watt Publishing Co., 122 S Wesley Ave, Mt. Morris, IL 61054-1497. TEL 815-734-4171, FAX 815-734-5649, http://www.wattnet.com. Ed. Robert Tuten. Pub. Charles Olentine. Adv. contact Anita Martin. B&W page USD 2,250, color page USD 3,075; trim 10.75 x 8. Circ: 8,000.

630.21 NZL
HD9908.N45
WOOLPRO. Text in English. 1972. a. NZD 25 (effective 2000). stat. **Document type:** *Trade.* **Description:** Summarizes the production, availability, price and export of New Zealand wool.
Former titles (until 1999): New Zealand Wool Group. Statistical Handbook; (until 1997): Wools of New Zealand. Statistical Handbook (1173-3179); (until 1993): New Zealand Wool Board. Statistical Handbook (0110-1242); (until 1977): Statistical Analysis of New Zealand Wool Production and Disposal
Address: Wool House, 10 Brandon St, PO Box 3225, Wellington, 6015, New Zealand. TEL 64-4-472-6888, FAX 64-4-473-7872, rebecca.munson@woolpro.co.nz, http://www.woolpro.co.nz/. Ed. R Munson. Circ: 1,500.

016.3381 GBR ISSN 0043-8219
HD1401
WORLD AGRICULTURAL ECONOMICS AND RURAL SOCIOLOGY ABSTRACTS; abstracts of world literature. Text in English. 1959. m. USD 1,950 in the Americas to institutions except Canada; GBP 1,115 elsewhere to institutions; USD 2,090 combined subscription in the Americas to institutions except Canada; print & online eds.; GBP 1,195 combined subscription elsewhere to institutions print & online eds. (effective 2006). adv. bk.rev. illus. index, cum.index. back issues avail.; reprints avail. **Document type:** *Abstract/Index.*
Supersedes: Digest of Agricultural Economics and Marketing
Related titles: Online - full text ed.: USD 1,665 in the Americas to institutions except Canada; GBP 950 elsewhere to institutions (effective 2006) (from DIMDI, The Dialog Corporation).
—BLDSC (9352.500000), CISTI.
Published by: CABI Publishing (Subsidiary of: CAB International), CAB International, Wallingford, Oxfordshire OX10 8DE, United Kingdom. Ed. Janice Osborn. Adv. contact Sarah Harris TEL 44-1491-829310. B&W page GBP 100, B&W page USD 95; 170 x 267. Circ: 340. **Subscr. addr. in N America:** CABI Publishing North America, 875 Massachusetts Ave, 7th Fl, Cambridge, MA 02139. TEL 617-395-4056, 800-528-4841, FAX 617-354-6875, cabi-nao@cabi.org.

630.21 BGD
YEARBOOK OF AGRICULTURAL STATISTICS OF BANGLADESH. Text in English. 1975. a. BDT 200, USD 35. **Document type:** *Government.* **Description:** Data on major aspects of agriculture such as data on area, production and yield rate of crops.
Former titles: Agricultural Statistics of Bangladesh (0065-4566); Agricultural Yearbook of Bangladesh
Published by: Bureau of Statistics, Secretariat, Dhaka, 2, Bangladesh. Circ: 500.

338.1021 ZMB
ZAMBIA. CENTRAL STATISTICAL OFFICE. AGRICULTURAL AND PASTORAL PRODUCTION (COMMERCIAL AND NON-COMMERCIAL). Text in English. 1966. a. ZMK 3. **Document type:** *Government.*
Supersedes in part: Zambia. Central Statistical Office. Agricultural and Pastoral Production (0080-1305)
Published by: Central Statistical Office, PO Box 31908, Lusaka, Zambia. TEL 260-1-211231.

630.21 ZMB
ZAMBIA. CENTRAL STATISTICAL OFFICE. AGRICULTURAL AND PASTORAL PRODUCTION (COMMERCIAL FARMS). Text in English. a. USD 12. **Document type:** *Government.*
Supersedes in part: Zambia. Central Statistical Office. Agricultural and Pastoral Production (0080-1305)
Published by: Central Statistical Office, PO Box 31908, Lusaka, Zambia. TEL 260-1-211231.

338.1021 ZMB
ZAMBIA. CENTRAL STATISTICAL OFFICE. AGRICULTURAL AND PASTORAL PRODUCTION (NON-COMMERCIAL). Text in English. 1972. a., latest 1977-78. USD 25. **Document type:** *Government.*
Supersedes in part: Zambia. Central Statistical Office. Agricultural and Pastoral Production (0080-1305)
Published by: Central Statistical Office, PO Box 31908, Lusaka, Zambia. TEL 260-1-211231.

630.21 ZMB
ZAMBIA. CENTRAL STATISTICAL OFFICE. QUARTERLY AGRICULTURAL STATISTICAL BULLETIN. Text in English. q. ZMK 5. **Document type:** *Bulletin, Government.*
Published by: Central Statistical Office, PO Box 31908, Lusaka, Zambia. TEL 260-1-211231.

630.21 ZMB
ZAMBIA. MINISTRY OF AGRICULTURE, FOOD AND FISHERIES. ANNUAL AGRICULTURAL STATISTICAL BULLETIN. Text in English. 1964-1976; resumed 1979. q. ZMK 500, USD 25. **Document type:** *Bulletin, Government.*
Former titles: Zambia. Ministry of Agricultural and Water Development. Quarterly Agricultural Statistical Bulletin; Zambia. Ministry of Lands and Agriculture. Quarterly Agricultural Statistical Bulletin; Zambia. Ministry of Rural Development. Quarterly Agricultural Statistical Bulletin
Published by: (Zambia. Statistics Section), Ministry of Agriculture, Food and Fisheries, Ridgeway, PO Box 50197, Lusaka, 15100, Zambia. TEL 228244, TELEX AGRIM ZA 43950. Circ: 500.

016.63 CHN ISSN 1002-5103
ZHONGGUO NONGYE WENZHAI - NONGYE GONGCHENG/CHINESE AGRICULTURAL ABSTRACTS - AGRICULTURAL ENGINEERING. Text in Chinese. 1989. bi-m. USD 30 (effective 1993). **Document type:** *Abstract/Index.* **Description:** Covers significant research literature in agricultural engineering at home and abroad.
Published by: Beijing Nongye Gongcheng Daxue/Beijing Agricultural Engineering University, Qinghua Donglu, Beijing, 100083, China. TEL 2017267. Ed. Lu Zhongxiao. Circ: 1,000.

636.0021 ZWE
ZIMBABWE. CENTRAL STATISTICAL OFFICE. AGRICULTURAL PRODUCTION ON RESETTLEMENT SCHEMES. Text in English. a. ZWD 189.50 in Africa; ZWD 250.20 in Europe; ZWD 316 elsewhere (effective 2000). **Document type:** *Government.*
Published by: Central Statistical Office, Causeway, PO Box 8063, Harare, Zimbabwe. TEL 263-4-706681, FAX 263-4-728529.

636.0021 ZWE
ZIMBABWE. CENTRAL STATISTICAL OFFICE. AGRICULTURE, FORESTRY AND FISHING. Text in English. a. ZWD 49.20 in Africa; ZWD 65.10 in Europe; ZWD 82.20 elsewhere (effective 2000). **Document type:** *Government.*
Published by: Central Statistical Office, Causeway, PO Box 8063, Harare, Zimbabwe. TEL 263-4-706681, FAX 263-4-728529.

636.0021 ZWE
ZIMBABWE. CENTRAL STATISTICAL OFFICE. CENSUS OF REGISTERED POULTRY PRODUCERS. Text in English. a. ZWD 60.40 in Africa; ZWD 77.60 in Europe; ZWD 91.90 elsewhere (effective 2000). **Document type:** *Government.*
Published by: Central Statistical Office, Causeway, PO Box 8063, Harare, Zimbabwe. TEL 263-4-706681, FAX 263-4-728529.

636.0021 ZWE
ZIMBABWE. CENTRAL STATISTICAL OFFICE. COMMUNAL LAND IRRIGATION SCHEMES. Text in English. a. ZWD 82.70 in Africa; ZWD 105.10 in Europe; ZWD 129.40 elsewhere (effective 2000). **Document type:** *Government.*
Published by: Central Statistical Office, Causeway, PO Box 8063, Harare, Zimbabwe. TEL 263-4-706681, FAX 263-4-728529.

636.0021 ZWE
ZIMBABWE. CENTRAL STATISTICAL OFFICE. LARGE SCALE COMMERCIAL FARMS. Text in English. a. ZWD 326.10 in Africa; ZWD 430.40 in Europe; ZWD 543.40 elsewhere (effective 2000). **Document type:** *Government.*
Published by: Central Statistical Office, Causeway, PO Box 8063, Harare, Zimbabwe. TEL 263-4-706681, FAX 263-4-728529.

636.0021 ZWE
ZIMBABWE. CENTRAL STATISTICAL OFFICE. LIVESTOCK ON LARGE SCALE COMMERCIAL FARMS. Text in English. a. ZWD 115.80 in Africa; ZWD 150.10 in Europe; ZWD 187.30 elsewhere (effective 2000). **Document type:** *Government.*
Published by: Central Statistical Office, Causeway, PO Box 8063, Harare, Zimbabwe. TEL 263-4-706681, FAX 263-4-728529.

636.0021 ZWE
ZIMBABWE. CENTRAL STATISTICAL OFFICE. QUARTERLY POULTRY CENSUS. Text in English. 1966. q. ZWD 67 in Africa; ZWD 80 in Europe; ZWD 83 in Asia; ZWD 89 in the Americas. **Document type:** *Government.*
Published by: Central Statistical Office, Causeway, PO Box 8063, Harare, Zimbabwe. Circ: 70.

636.0021 ZWE
ZIMBABWE. CENTRAL STATISTICAL OFFICE. REGISTERED DECIDUOUS FRUIT GROWERS. Text in English. a. ZWD 42 in Africa; ZWD 59.90 in Europe; ZWD 69.30 elsewhere (effective 2000). **Document type:** *Government.*
Published by: Central Statistical Office, Causeway, PO Box 8063, Harare, Zimbabwe. TEL 263-4-706681, FAX 263-4-728529.

636.0021 ZWE
ZIMBABWE. CENTRAL STATISTICAL OFFICE. SMALL SCALE COMMERCIAL FARMS. Text in English. a. ZWD 126.90 in Africa; ZWD 165.20 in Europe; ZWD 206.60 elsewhere (effective 2000). **Document type:** *Government.*
Published by: Central Statistical Office, Causeway, PO Box 8063, Harare, Zimbabwe. TEL 263-4-706681, FAX 263-4-728529.

AGRICULTURE—Agricultural Economics

338.1 AUS
▼ **A B A R E FARM SURVEYS REPORT (YEAR).** (Australian Bureau of Agricultural and Resource Economics) Text in English. 2003. a. AUD 15 (effective 2003).
Media: Online - full content.
Published by: Australian Bureau of Agricultural and Resource Economics, GPO Box 1563, Canberra, ACT 2601, Australia. TEL 61-2-62722000, FAX 61-2-62722001, sales@abare.gov.au, http://www.abareconomics.com. Ed., R&P Andrew Wright TEL 61-2-62722290.

338.1 RUS ISSN 0235-2443
S13
➤ **A P K: EKONOMIKA, UPRAVLENIE.** (Agro-Promyshlennyi Kompleks) Text in Russian; Summaries in English, Russian. 1921. m. USD 199 foreign (effective 2004). **Document type:** *Journal, Trade.* **Description:** Dedicated to experience and problems in the agrarian reform, organization of the management and marketing, economic work in the countryside.
Indexed: RASB, RefZh.
—BLDSC (0007.562000), CISTI, East View.
Published by: Izdatel'stvo Kolos, Sadovaya-Spasskaya 18, Moscow, 107807, Russian Federation. TEL 7-095-2072057, FAX 7-095-9753731. Ed. Marlen M Makeenko. Circ: 50,000.

338.1 AUT
A W I BERICHTE ONLINE. (Agrarwirtschaft) Text in German. 2001. m. **Document type:** *Government.*
Media: Online - full content.
Published by: Bundesanstalt fuer Agrarwirtschaft (Subsidiary of: Bundesministerium fuer Land- und Forstwirtschaft, Umwelt und Wasserwirtschaft), Schweizertalstr 36, Vienna, 1133, Austria. TEL 43-1-8773651-0, FAX 43-1-877365159, office@awi.bmlf.gv.at, http://www.awi.bmlf.gv.at. Ed. Peter Handschur.

AARDAPPELWERELD MAGAZINE. see *BUSINESS AND ECONOMICS—Domestic Commerce*

338.1 NOR ISSN 1650-7541
▼ **ACTA AGRICULTURAE SCANDINAVICA. SECTION C. FOOD ECONOMICS.** Text in English. 2004. q. GBP 173, USD 285 combined subscription to institutions print & online eds. (effective 2006). **Document type:** *Journal, Academic/Scholarly.*
Related titles: Online - full text ed.: ISSN 1651-288X. GBP 164, USD 271 to institutions (effective 2006) (from EBSCO Publishing, Gale Group, IngentaConnect, O C L C Online Computer Library Center, Inc., Swets Information Services).
—BLDSC (0589.015000), IE.
Published by: Taylor & Francis A S (Subsidiary of: Taylor & Francis Group), Biskop Gunnerusgate 14A, PO Box 12 Posthuset, Oslo, 0051, Norway. TEL 47-23-103460, FAX 47-23-103461, journals@tandf.no, http://www.tandf.co.uk/journals/titles/16507541.asp. Ed. Morgens Lund. **Subscr. to:** Taylor & Francis Ltd, Journals Customer Service, Rankine Rd, Basingstoke, Hants RG24 8PR, United Kingdom. TEL 44-1256-813000, FAX 44-1256-330245.

338.43 630.285 SVK ISSN 1335-2571
HD1940.4
➤ **ACTA OECONOMICA ET INFORMATICA**; the scientific journal for economics and informatics in agriculture. Text in Slovak, English; Summaries in English. 1998. s-a. SKK 120; SKK 60 newsstand/cover (effective 2002 - 2003). index. 30 p./no. 2 cols./p.; back issues avail. **Document type:** *Journal, Academic/Scholarly.* **Description:** Covers agricultural economics and the application of information technologies to agriculture.
Indexed: AEA, AnBrAb, DSA, HortAb, I&DA, MaizeAb, NutrAb, PHN&I, PN&I, PotatoAb, RDA, RefZh, S&F, SIA, TriticAb, WAE&RSA.
—CISTI.
Published by: Slovenska Pol'nohospodarska Univerzita v Nitre/Slovak University of Agriculture in Nitra, Tr. A. Hlinku 2, Nitra, 949 76, Slovakia. TEL 421-37-65117514, 421-37-65122514, FAX 421-37-6511560, admin-www@uniag.sk, http://www.uniag.sk. Ed. Vladimir Gozora. Pub. Peter Bielik.

➤ **ACTUELE ONTWIKKELING VAN BEDRIJFSRESULTATEN EN INKOMENS.** see *AGRICULTURE—Abstracting, Bibliographies, Statistics*

333 ITA ISSN 1592-6117
AESTIMUM. Text in English; Summaries in English. 1956. s-a. EUR 36 to individuals print & online eds.; EUR 47 to institutions print & online eds. (effective 2003). charts; illus. back issues avail. **Document type:** *Journal, Academic/Scholarly.* **Description:** Covers the study and management of natural resources in rural and protected areas.
Former titles (until 1987): Centro di Studi di Estimo e di Economia Territoriale. Aestimum (1592-6095); (until 1975): Aestimum (1592-6109)
Related titles: Online - full text ed.: 2000.
Published by: (Centro di Studi di Estimo e di Economia Territoriale), Firenze University Press, Borgo Albizi 28, Florence, 50122, Italy. TEL 39-055-2347658, FAX 39-055-242944, e-press@unifi.it, http://epress.unifi.periodici.it. Ed. E Marone. Circ: 200 (paid).

338.1 FRA ISSN 1161-8051
AFRIQUE. Text in French. 1991. irreg.
Related titles: ♦ Supplement to: Courrier de la Planete. ISSN 1161-8043.
Published by: Solidarites Agro-Alimentaires, 3191 route de Mende, BP 5056, Montpellier, Cedex 1 34033, France. TEL 67-54-47-23, FAX 67-54-25-27.

338.1 USA ISSN 1053-2692
AG EXECUTIVE. Text in English. 1983. m. looseleaf. USD 84 (effective 2005). bk.rev. back issues avail.; reprints avail. **Document type:** *Newsletter, Trade.* **Description:** Covers agricultural finance and management issues.
Published by: Ag Executive, Inc., 115 E Twyman, Bushnell, IL 61422-1320. TEL 309-772-2168, FAX 309-772-2167, ageexecutive@earthlink.net, darrellD@aol.com, info@agexecutive.com, http://www.agexecutive.com/exec.html. Eds., Pubs. Darrell L Dunteman, Darrell L. Dunteman. R&P Darrell L Dunteman. Circ: 3,200 (paid).

AG LENDER. see *BUSINESS AND ECONOMICS—Banking And Finance*

338.1 660.6 USA ISSN 1522-936X
S494.5.B563
➤ **AGBIOFORUM.** Text in English. 1998. q. free (effective 2005). abstr.; charts; bibl.; stat. Index. back issues avail. **Document type:** *Journal, Academic/Scholarly.* **Description:** Publishes articles on the economics and management of agricultural biotechnology. Provides information and new ideas leading to socially responsible and economically efficient decisions in science, public policy and private strategies pertaining to agricultural biotechnology.
Media: Online - full content.
Indexed: Agr, BiolAb, JEL.
Published by: University of Missouri, Columbia, Agriculture & Engineering Department, 200 Mumford Hall, Columbia, MO 65211. TEL 573-882-2831, FAX 573-882-3958, admin@agbioforum.org, http://www.agbioforum.org. Ed. Nicholas Kalaitzandonakes. R&P Leonie A Marks TEL 573-882-4632.

380.141 USA ISSN 1047-4781
HD9001 CODEN: AGEXEZ
AGEXPORTER. Text in English. 1937. m. USD 44 (effective 2001). charts; illus. index. reprint service avail. from CIS,PQC. **Document type:** *Government.* **Description:** Provides information for business firms selling United States farm products overseas, this magazine provides timely information on overseas trade opportunities, including reports on marketing activities and how-to's of agricultural exporting.
Formerly (until 1989): Foreign Agriculture (0015-7163)
Related titles: Microfiche ed.: (from CIS); Microform ed.: (from MIM, PQC); Online - full text ed.: (from bigchalk, Florida Center for Library Automation, Gale Group, H.W. Wilson, Northern Light Technology, Inc., O C L C Online Computer Library Center, Inc., ProQuest Information & Learning).
Indexed: ABIn, ABS&EES, Agr, AmStI, AnBrAb, ApicAb, B&AI, BibAg, BiolAb, DSA, F&GI, HortAb, IUSGP, KES, MEA&I, PAIS, PCI, PROMT, PotatoAb, RASB, RRTA, RefZh, TDB, TTI, WAE&RSA.
—BLDSC (0736.259500), CISTI, IE, Infotrieve, ingenta, Linda Hall.
Published by: U.S. Department of Agriculture, Foreign Agricultural Service, Information Division, Rm 4638 S, Washington, DC 20250-1000. TEL 202-720-9437, FAX 202-720-3229, http://ffas.usda.gov/info/agexporter/agexport.html. Circ: 1,800. **Subscr. to:** U.S. Government Printing Office, Superintendent of Documents.

380.141 GBR ISSN 0002-1024
CODEN: AGEUFR
AGRA EUROPE. Text in English. 1963. w. GBP 2,036 domestic; GBP 2,522 in Europe; GBP 2,698 elsewhere (effective 2005). bk.rev. mkt.; stat. q. index. **Document type:** *Newsletter, Trade.* **Description:** Covers European and world developments affecting the production and marketing of food and agricultural commodities.
Related titles: Online - full text ed.: (from Factiva, Florida Center for Library Automation, Gale Group, Northern Light Technology, Inc.).
Indexed: DSA, HortAb, IndVet, MaizeAb, NutrAb, PN&I, PROMT, PotatoAb, PoultAb, RRTA, SoyAb, TriticAb, VetBull, WAE&RSA.
—BLDSC (0736.800000), CISTI.
Published by: Agra Europe (London) Ltd. (Subsidiary of: T & F Informa plc), 80 Calverley Rd, Tunbridge Wells, Kent TN1 2UN, United Kingdom. TEL 44-1892-533813, FAX 44-1892-544895, marketing@agra-europe.com, http://www.agra-net.com. Ed. Guy Faulkner. **Subscr. to:** PO Box 297044, Ft. Worth, TX 76129.

AGRARFINANZ. see *BUSINESS AND ECONOMICS—Banking And Finance*

AGRARMAERKTE IN ZAHLEN. EUROPAEISCHE UNION. see *AGRICULTURE—Abstracting, Bibliographies, Statistics*

AGRARMAERKTE IN ZAHLEN. MITTEL- UND OSTEUROPA. see *AGRICULTURE—Abstracting, Bibliographies, Statistics*

338.1 RUS
AGRARNAYA ROSSIYA; nauchno-proizvodstvennyi zhurnal. Text in Russian. 1998. bi-m. USD 72 foreign (effective 2004). **Document type:** *Journal.*
Published by: Izdatel'stvo Folium, Dmitrovskoe shosse 58, Moscow, 127238, Russian Federation. TEL 7-095-4825544, 7-095-4825590, agros@folium.ru, info@folium.ru, http://www.folium.ru/ru/journals/agros. **Dist. by:** M K - Periodica, ul Gilyarovskogo 39, Moscow 129110, Russian Federation. TEL 7-095-2845008, FAX 7-095-2813798, info@periodicals.ru, http://www.mkniga.ru.

338.1 CHE ISSN 1023-3938
HD1401
AGRARWIRTSCHAFT UND AGRARSOZIOLOGIE/ECONOMIE ET SOCIOLOGIE RURALES. Text in Multiple languages. 1973. s-a. CHF 25 domestic; CHF 30 foreign (effective 2002).
Formerly (until 1980): Zeitschrift fuer Agrarwirtschaft und Agrarsoziologie (1421-9476)
Indexed: AbHyg, AgBio, DSA, ForAb, HortAb, IndVet, NutrAb, PAIS, PGegResA, PHN&I, PN&I, PotatoAb, PoultAb, RDA, RRTA, S&F, TDB, TriticAb, WAE&RSA.
Published by: Schweizerische Gesellschaft fuer Agrarwirtschaft und Agrarsoziologie/Swiss Society for Agricultural Economics and Rural Sociology, c/o IAW-ETH, Sonneggstr. 33, Zurich, 8092, Switzerland. http://www.sga.unibe.ch/.

338.1 ZAF ISSN 0303-1853
HD1401
➤ **AGREKON (ENGLISH ED).** Text in English. 1962. q. ZAR 75, USD 20 in Africa to non-members; USD 100 elsewhere to non-members (effective 2001). charts; mkt.; stat. cum.index every 5 years. **Document type:** *Academic/Scholarly.* **Description:** Promotes research and discussion on agricultural economic issues related to southern Africa.
Related titles: Online - full text ed.
Indexed: AEA, AgBio, Agr, DSA, FPA, FS&TA, ForAb, HortAb, I&DA, IBSS, ISAP, IndVet, MaizeAb, NutrAb, OrnHort, PBA, PGegResA, PHN&I, PN&I, PoultAb, RDA, RPP, RRTA, S&F, SIA, SeedAb, SoyAb, TDB, TriticAb, VetBull, WAE&RSA, WeedAb.
—BLDSC (0738.700000), IE, ingenta.
Published by: Landbou-Ekonomie Vereniging van Suid-Afrika/Agricultural Economics Association of South Africa, Posbus 12986, Hatfield, Pretoria 0028, South Africa. TEL 27-12-420-3248, FAX 27-12-342-2713, jkirsten@postino.up.ac.za, http://www.journals.co.za/ej/ejour_agrekon.html, http://www.aeasa.org.za. Ed. T I Fenyes. R&P J F Kirsten. Circ: 500 (controlled).

380.141 USA ISSN 0002-1180
AGRI MARKETING; the magazine for professionals selling to the farm market. Text in English. 1962. m. (10/yr.). USD 40 in US & Canada; USD 62 elsewhere (effective 2005). adv. bk.rev. charts; illus.; stat. index. back issues avail.; reprints avail. **Document type:** *Magazine, Trade.*

Related titles: Microfilm ed.; Online - full text ed.: (from Florida Center for Library Automation, Gale Group, H.W. Wilson, O C L C Online Computer Library Center, Inc.); Supplement(s): Marketing Services Guide.
Indexed: ABIn, BPI, F&GI.
—BLDSC (0738.930000), CISTI, IE, ingenta.
Published by: Doane Agricultural Services, 11701 Borman Dr, Ste 300, St. Louis, MO 63146-4193. TEL 314-569-2700, FAX 314-569-1083, info@agrimarketing.com, http://www.agrimarketing.com, http://www.doane.com. Pub. Bill Schurmann. Adv. contact Judy Knoll. B&W page USD 2,410, color page USD 3,500. Circ: 8,449 (controlled).

338.1 USA ISSN 0742-4477
HD1401 CODEN: AGRBEY
➤ **AGRIBUSINESS (NEW YORK)**; an international journal. Text in English. 1984. q. USD 1,299 domestic to institutions; USD 1,339 in Canada & Mexico to institutions; USD 1,373 elsewhere to institutions; USD 1,429 combined subscription domestic to institutions print & online eds.; USD 1,469 combined subscription in Canada & Mexico to institutions print & online eds.; USD 1,503 combined subscription elsewhere to institutions print & online eds. (effective 2006). adv. back issues avail. **Document type:** *Journal, Academic/Scholarly.* **Description:** Serves the nonfarm sectors of the food and fiber system with articles that deal with the business aspects of agricultural production. For agribusiness economists, managers, and engineers, academic and industry market researchers, government analysts,and food quality technologists.
Related titles: Microform ed.: (from PQC); Online - full text ed.: ISSN 1520-6297. USD 1,299 to institutions (effective 2006) (from EBSCO Publishing, ProQuest Information & Learning, Swets Information Services, Wiley InterScience).
Indexed: ABIn, ABS&EES, AgBio, Agr, AnBrAb, B&AI, BAS, DSA, EIA, EnvAb, FPA, FS&TA, HortAb, IndVet, JEL, MaizeAb, NutrAb, PBA, PGegResA, PHN&I, PN&I, PotatoAb, PoultAb, RA&MP, RDA, RPP, RRTA, RefZh, RevApplEntom, RiceAb, SIA, SeedAb, SoyAb, TriticAb, VetBull, WAE&RSA, WeedAb.
—BLDSC (0738.954000), CISTI, IE, Infotrieve, ingenta. **CCC.**
Published by: John Wiley & Sons, Inc., 111 River St, Hoboken, NJ 07030-5774. TEL 201-748-6000, FAX 201-748-5915, uscs-wis@wiley.com, http://www3.interscience.wiley.com/cgi-bin/jhome/35917, http://www.wiley.com. Ed. Ronald W Cotterill. adv.: B&W page GBP 640, color page GBP 1,515; trim 165 x 254. Circ: 1,700. **Subscr. outside of US to:** John Wiley & Sons Ltd., The Atrium, Southern Gate, Chichester, West Sussex PO19 8SQ, United Kingdom. TEL 44-1243-843335, 0800-243407, FAX 44-1243-843232, cs-journals@wiley.co.uk.

338.1 ITA ISSN 0002-1229
AGRICOLTORE TREVISANO✶. Text in Italian. 1945. s-m. membership. adv. bk.rev. illus. **Document type:** *Newspaper.*
Published by: Unione Provinciale Agricoltori di Treviso, Viale Cadorna, 10, Treviso, TV 31100, Italy. Ed. Fulvio Fantini. Circ: 6,500.

338.1 ITA ISSN 1721-7679
AGRICOMMERCIO E GARDEN CENTER. Text in Italian. 1987. m. (11/yr.). EUR 62 domestic; EUR 110 foreign (effective 2005). adv. 48 p./no.; **Document type:** *Magazine, Trade.*
Formerly (until 2002): Agrigiornale del Commercio (0394-5537)
Published by: (Compaq - Associazione Commercianti Produttori Agricoli Confcommercio), Il Sole 24 Ore Edagricole, Via Goito 13, Bologna, BO 40126, Italy. TEL 39-051-62267, FAX 39-051-490200, http://www.edagricole.it. Ed. Giorgio Setti. Circ: 11,500.

338.1 BRA ISSN 0044-6793
HD1875.S3
AGRICULTURA EM SAO PAULO. Text in Portuguese. 1951. s-a. USD 30 (effective 2000). bk.rev. stat. cum.index. **Description:** Covers institutional scientific production; includes technical, scientific and research articles.
Indexed: AEA, AnBrAb, CTFA, ChemAb, DSA, FCA, FS&TA, HerbAb, HortAb, MaizeAb, NutrAb, OrnHort, PAIS, PHN&I, PoultAb, RDA, RRTA, S&F, SIA, SeedAb, SoyAb, TDB, WAE&RSA.
—BLDSC (0741.880000), CISTI, GNLM, IE, ingenta.
Published by: Instituto de Economia Agricola, Av Miguel Stefano, 3900, Saude, Caixa Postal 6802, Sao Paulo, SP 04301-002, Brazil. TEL 55-11-5770244 ext 2354, FAX 55-11-2764062, cct@iea.sp.gov.br, http://www.iea.sp.gov.br. Ed. Cesar Roberto Leite da Silva. Circ: (controlled).

338.1 ESP
AGRICULTURA Y COOPERACION. Text in Spanish. 1983. m. **Document type:** *Trade.* **Description:** Contains reports, interviews, and studies of the agricultural situation in the area of agricultural economics.
Published by: Union Provincial de Cooperativas del Campo de Valencia, Caballeros, 26, Valencia, 46001, Spain. TEL 34-96-394-2301, FAX 34-96-352-8849. Ed., Adv. contact Leonor Juan Sanchiz. Circ: 5,000.

338.1 USA ISSN 1068-2805
HD1773.A2
AGRICULTURAL AND RESOURCE ECONOMICS REVIEW. Text in English. 1972. s-a. USD 25 membership (effective 2005). **Document type:** *Journal, Academic/Scholarly.*
Former titles (until 1992): Northeastern Journal of Agricultural and Resource Economics (0899-367X); (until Oct. 1984): Northeastern Agricultural Economics Council. Journal (0163-5484)
Related titles: Online - full text ed.: (from ProQuest Information & Learning).
Indexed: AEA, AbHyg, AgBio, Agr, AgrForAb, AnBrAb, DSA, ESPM, FCA, FPA, ForAb, H&SSA, HortAb, I&DA, IndVet, JEL, MaizeAb, NutrAb, PHN&I, PoultAb, RDA, RRTA, RefZh, RevApplEntom, RiskAb, S&F, SIA, TriticAb, VetBull, WAE&RSA, WeedAb.
—BLDSC (0743.140000), CISTI, IE, ingenta.
Published by: Northeastern Agricultural and Resource Economics Association, c/o Dr Doug Morris, Secretary, 56 College Rd, 316 James Hall, Durham, NH 03824-3589. arer@arec.umd.edu, http://www.narea.org/journal.htm. Eds. Lori Lynch, Wesley Musser. Circ: 500 (paid).

338.1 IND
AGRICULTURAL BANKER. Text in English. 1978. q. INR 56. adv. bk.rev.
Published by: S.R. Suneja Ed. & Pub., B4/29 Safdarjang Enclave, New Delhi, 110 029, India. Circ: 3,000.

338.1 NPL
AGRICULTURAL CREDIT. Text in English. q.
Published by: (Agricultural Credit Training Institute), Agricultural Development Bank, Ramshah Path, Panchayat Plaza, Kathmandu, Nepal. TEL 216075. Ed. Prem Nath Ojha.

338.1 CAN ISSN 0837-2136
HG2051.C39
AGRICULTURAL CREDIT CORPORATION OF SASKATCHEWAN. ANNUAL REPORT. Text in English. 1973. a. free. **Document type:** *Corporate.*
Formerly: Saskatchewan FarmStart Corporation. Annual Report (0709-325X)
Published by: Agricultural Credit Corporation of Saskatchewan, P O Box 820, Swift Current, SK S9H 4Y7, Canada. TEL 306-778-8455, FAX 306-778-8614. Ed. Margot Trembath. Circ: 500.

338.1 MWI
AGRICULTURAL DEVELOPMENT AND MARKETING CORPORATION. ANNUAL REPORT AND STATEMENT OF ACCOUNTS. Text in English. a. free. stat. **Document type:** *Government.*
Supersedes: Agricultural Development and Marketing Corporation. Annual Report; Agricultural Development Corporation. Balance Sheet and Accounts; Which was formerly: Farmers Marketing Board. Balance Sheet and Accounts
Published by: Agricultural Development and Marketing Corporation (ADMARC), PO Box 5052, Limbe, Malawi. TEL 265-640044.

338.1 USA ISSN 0169-5150
HD1401 CODEN: AGECE6
➤ **AGRICULTURAL ECONOMICS.** Text in Dutch. 1986. bi-m. USD 95 combined subscription in the Americas to individuals; EUR 80 combined subscription in Europe to individuals; GBP 53 combined subscription elsewhere to individuals; USD 632 combined subscription in the Americas to institutions; GBP 351 combined subscription elsewhere to institutions (effective 2006). bk.rev. back issues avail.; reprint service avail. from PSC. **Document type:** *Journal, Academic/Scholarly.* **Description:** Provides a focal point for the publication of work on research, extension and outreach, consulting, advising, entrepreneurship, administration and teaching, in the areas of agricultural economics.
Related titles: Microform ed.: (from PQC); Online - full text ed.: ISSN 1574-0862. USD 600 in the Americas to institutions; GBP 333 elsewhere to institutions (effective 2006) (from Blackwell Synergy, EBSCO Publishing, Gale Group, IngentaConnect, O C L C Online Computer Library Center, Inc., ScienceDirect, Swets Information Services).
Indexed: AEA, ASCA, AgBio, Agr, AgrForAb, B&AI, BAS, BIOBASE, BibAg, BioCN&I, CurCont, DSA, FCA, FPA, FS&TA, ForAb, GEOBASE, HortAb, I&DA, IABS, IndVet, JEL, MaizeAb, NutrAb, OrnHort, PBA, PGegResA, PHN&I, PN&I, PlantSci, PotatoAb, PoultAb, ProtozoAb, RASB, RDA, RRTA, RefZh, RevApplEntom, RiceAb, S&F, SIA, SSCI, SWA, SeedAb, SoyAb, TDB, TOSA, TriticAb, VetBull, WAE&RSA, WTA, WeedAb.
—BLDSC (0745.580000), CISTI, IDS, IE, Infotrieve, ingenta. **CCC.**
Published by: (International Association of Agricultural Economists GBR), Blackwell Publishing, Inc. (Subsidiary of: Blackwell Publishing Ltd.), Commerce Place, 350 Main St, Malden, MA 02148. TEL 781-388-8206, FAX 781-388-8232, iaae-agecon@gwdg.de, subscrip@blackwellpub.com, http://www.blackwellpublishing.com/journal.asp?ref=0169-5150&site=1. Eds. G Norton, S von Cramon-Taubadel. Circ: (controlled).

338.1 CZE ISSN 0139-570X
HD101
➤ **AGRICULTURAL ECONOMICS/ZEMEDELSKA EKONOMIKA.** Text and summaries in English, Czech. 1954. m. USD 214 (effective 2003). adv. bk.rev. abstr.; stat. index. **Document type:** *Academic/Scholarly.* **Description:** Scientific papers and reviews dealing with economics, management, informatics, ecology, social economy and sociology.
Incorporates (in 1993): Sociologie Venkova a Zemedelstvi; Which was formerly: U V T I Z Sbornik - Sociologie Zemedelstvi (0231-5688); U V T I Z Sbornik - Sociologie a Historie Zemedelstvi (0231-5572)
Indexed: AEA, DSA, FCA, FPA, ForAb, HortAb, I&DA, MaizeAb, NutrAb, OrnHort, PHN&I, PN&I, PoultAb, RDA, REE&TA, RRTA, RefZh, S&F, SIA, SeedAb, TriticAb, WAE&RSA.
—BLDSC (9499.550000), CISTI, IE, ingenta.
Published by: Ceska Akademie Zemedelskych Ved, Ustav Zemedelskych a Potravinarskych Informaci/Czech Academy of Agricultural Sciences, Institute of Agricultural and Food Information, Slezska 7, Prague 2, 120 56, Czech Republic. TEL 420-2-227010302, FAX 420-2-227010116, rott@uzpi.cz, http://www.cazv.cz. Ed. Mrs. Alena Rottova. R&P Mr. Jan Rydlo. Circ: 500.

338.1 GRC ISSN 1109-2580
AGRICULTURAL ECONOMICS REVIEW. Text in English. 2000. s-a.
Indexed: JEL.
—BLDSC (0745.835500), IE.
Published by: Greek Association of Agricultural Economists, c/o Prof K Mattas, Dept of Agricultural Economics, Aristotle University of Thessaloniki, PO Box 225, Salonika, 541 24, Greece. TEL 30-2310-998807, FAX 30-2310-998828, mattas@auth.gr.

AGRICULTURAL FINANCE DATABOOK. see *BUSINESS AND ECONOMICS—Banking And Finance*

338.1 USA ISSN 0002-1466
HG2051.U5
➤ **AGRICULTURAL FINANCE REVIEW.** Text in English. 1938. s-a. USD 25 in North America; USD 35 elsewhere (effective 2005). bk.rev. charts; mkt.; stat.; abstr. index. 2 cols./p.; back issues avail. **Document type:** *Journal, Academic/Scholarly.* **Description:** Provides a forum for research teaching and extension publication, and discussion of issues in agricultural finance.
Related titles: Microfiche ed.: (from CIS).
Indexed: AgBio, Agr, DSA, FCA, IBR, IBZ, IUSGP, JEL, PAIS, PN&I, RASB, RRTA, S&F, SRI, SoyAb, TriticAb, WAE&RSA.
—BLDSC (0746.650000), CISTI, IE, ingenta, Linda Hall.
Published by: Cornell University, Department of Applied and Management Economics, 357 Warren Hall, Ithaca, NY 14853-7801. TEL 607-255-4534, FAX 607-255-1589, ell4@cornell.edu, http://www.afr.aem.cornell.edu. Ed. Eddy L LaDue. Circ: 200 (controlled).

338.1 USA
AGRICULTURAL LAW UPDATE. Text in English. 1981. m. USD 75 in North America; USD 95 elsewhere. bk.rev.
Formerly (until 1983): Agricultural Law Newsletter
Published by: American Agricultural Law Association, School of Law, University of Arkansas, Fayetteville, AR 72701. TEL 501-575-7389, FAX 501-575-2053, bbabione@mercury.uark.edu, http://www.aglaw-assn.org. Ed. Linda G McCormick. Circ: 1,000.

380.141 JOR
AGRICULTURAL MARKETING/TASWIQ AL-ZIRAIY. Text in Arabic. 1966. q. adv.
Indexed: PotatoAb.
Published by: Ministry of National Economy, Department of Agricultural Marketing, P O Box 2097, Amman, Jordan. Ed. Fahed Al Azeb.

380.141 BEL
HD9015.E8
AGRICULTURAL MARKETS: PRICES. Text in English. 1962. q. USD 155 (effective 1998).
Formed by the 1981 merger of: Marches Agricoles. Prix: Produits Vegetaux - Agricultural Markets. Prices: Vegetable Products (0378-4436); Marches Agricoles. Prix: Produits Animaux - Agricultural Markets. Prices: Livestock Products (0378-4444); Marches Agricoles. Prix: Notes Explicatif
Indexed: IIS.
—BLDSC (0750.408800).
Published by: European Commission, Rue de la Loi - Wetstraat 200, Brussels, 1049, Belgium. http://europa.eu.int. **Subscr. to:** Bernan Associates, Bernan, 4611-F Assembly Dr., Lanham, MD 20706-4391. TEL 301-459-0056.

338.1 USA
AGRICULTURAL OUTLOOK FORUM. PROCEEDINGS. Variant title: Annual Agricultural Outlook Conference Proceedings. (Conference is held in Feb.) Text in English. 1982. a. USD 25 domestic; USD 50 foreign. **Document type:** *Proceedings, Government.* **Description:** Proceedings of speeches and statements submitted by Annual Agricultural Outlook Conference participants.
Formerly: Outlook (Year) Proceedings
Related titles: Online - full text ed.: (from The Dialog Corporation).

A

A

Indexed: Agr, BibAg.
Published by: U.S. Department of Agriculture, World Agricultural Outlook Board, 14th St and Independence Ave, S W, South Bldg, Rm 5143, Washington, DC 20250-3812. TEL 202-720-5447, 877-891-2208, agforum@oce.usda.gov, http://www.usda.gov/oce/woab/agforum.htm. Ed. Raymond L Bridge. Circ: 700. **Dist. by:** NTIS.

AGRICULTURAL PRICES IN INDIA. see *AGRICULTURE—Abstracting, Bibliographies, Statistics*

338.1 BGD
AGRICULTURAL PRODUCTION LEVELS IN BANGLADESH. Text in English. 1976. a. free. charts; stat.
Published by: Bureau of Statistics, Secretariat, Dhaka, 2, Bangladesh. Ed. A K M Ghulam Rabbani.

338.1 GBR ISSN 1464-5661
AGRICULTURAL RESEARCH AND EXTENSION NETWORK. NEWSLETTER. Text in English. 1979. s-a. bk.rev. back issues avail. **Document type:** *Newsletter.*
Former titles: Agricultural Administration Research Extension Network. Newsletter (0951-1865); Agricultural Administration Network. Newsletter (0260-7883)
Indexed: ARDT, AgrForAb, MaizeAb, RDA, RevApplEntom, SeedAb, WAE&RSA.
Published by: Overseas Development Institute, Portland House, Stag Pl, London, SWIE 5DP, United Kingdom. TEL 44-171-393-1600, FAX 44-171-393-1699, rpeg@odi.org.uk, http://www.oneworld.org/odi/rpeg. Ed. Cate Turton. Circ: 1,000.

338.1 CYP ISSN 0379-0827
HD2057
➤ **AGRICULTURAL RESEARCH INSTITUTE. AGRICULTURAL ECONOMICS REPORT.** Text in English. 1973. irreg., latest vol.40, 2001. free. bibl.; charts; illus.; stat. back issues avail.; reprints avail. **Document type:** *Monographic series, Academic/Scholarly.* **Description:** Contains input-output analytical data on the crop and animal market.
Indexed: DSA, FS&TA, HortAb, PHN&I, RDA, WAE&RSA.
—BLDSC (0745.746000), CISTI.
Published by: Ministry of Agriculture Natural Resources and the Environment, Agricultural Research Institute, PO Box 22016, Nicosia, 1516, Cyprus. TEL 357-22-403107, FAX 357-22-316770, library@arinet.ari.gov.cy, http://www.ari.gov.cy. Ed. A P Mavrogenis. Circ: 400.

338.1 USA ISSN 1011-3363
AGRICULTURAL REVIEW FOR EUROPE. Text in English. 1958. irreg., latest vol.1-6, no.37. price varies.
Former titles: Review of the Agricultural Situation in Europe at the End of (Year) (0085-5618); Agricultural Market Review
Related titles: Microfiche ed.: (from CIS); French ed.: Revue Agricole pour l'Europe. ISSN 1011-159X; Russian ed.: Sel'skohozjstvennyj obzor Evropy. ISSN 1014-5443.
Indexed: DSA, IIS, MaizeAb, PN&I, PotatoAb, PoultAb, RiceAb, TriticAb, WAE&RSA.
—CISTI.
Published by: (United Nations, Economic Commission for Europe (ECE) CHE), United Nations Publications, Rm DC2-853, United Nations Bldg, 2 United Nations Plaza, New York, NY 10017. TEL 212-963-8302, 800-253-9646, FAX 212-963-3489, publications@un.org, http://www.un.org/publications, http://www.un.org/Pubs.

AGRICULTURAL STATISTICS SERIES NO.3: EUROPEAN COMMUNITIES INDEX OF AGRICULTURAL PRICES. see *AGRICULTURE—Abstracting, Bibliographies, Statistics*

338.1 ITA
AGRICULTURAL TAXATION STUDIES. Text in Italian. 1992 (no.4). irreg.
Published by: Food and Agriculture Organization of the United Nations, Sales and Marketing Group, Viale delle Terme di Caracalla, Rome, 00100, Italy. TEL 39-06-57054350, FAX 39-06-57053360.

380.141 USA ISSN 0084-6058
AGRICULTURAL TRADE IN EUROPE. Text in English. 1960. a. USD 11.
Published by: (United Nations, Economic Commission for Europe (ECE) CHE), United Nations Publications, Rm DC2-853, United Nations Bldg, 2 United Nations Plaza, New York, NY 10017. TEL 212-963-8300, 800-253-9646, FAX 212-963-3489, publications@un.org, http:/www.un.org/publications, http://www.un.org/Pubs.

331.21 IND ISSN 0084-6066
AGRICULTURAL WAGES IN INDIA. Text in English, Hindi. 1950. a. INR 115. **Document type:** *Government.*
Published by: Ministry of Agriculture, Department of Agriculture and Cooperation, Directorate of Economics and Statistics, A-2E-3 Kasturba Gandhi Marg Barracks, New Delhi, 110 001, India. TEL 91-11-381523. Ed. Brajesh Kumar Gautam. Circ: 350.

338.1 CAN ISSN 1482-9770
AGRICULTURE & AGRI-FOOD CANADA. FARM INCOME AND ADAPTATION POLICY DIRECTORATE. FARM INCOME, FINANCIAL CONDITIONS AND GOVERNMENT EXPENDITURES. DATA BOOK. Text in English, French. 1988. s-a.
Related titles: Online - full text ed.: ISSN 1488-0040.
—CISTI.
Published by: Agriculture & Agri-Food Canada, Farm Income and Adaptation Policy Directorate, Sir John Carling Bldg, 930 Carling Ave, Ottawa, ON K0A 0C5, Canada. TEL 613-759-7266, 613-759-6610, FAX 613-759-7235, http://www.agr.gc.ca/spb/fiap-dpraa/pub_e.php.

338.1 CAN ISSN 1206-6842
AGRICULTURE DEVELOPMENT FUND - PROJECT. Text in English. a. free. **Document type:** *Government.* **Description:** Covers agriculture and food-related research and development projects.
Published by: Agriculture and Food, Communications Branch, B5 Walter Scott Bldg, 3085 Albert St, Regina, SK S4S 0B1, Canada. TEL 888-613-3975, FAX 306-721-4626, pad@sk.sympatico.ca, http://www.agr.gov.sk.ca/saf. Circ: 1,200.

338.1 310 CAN ISSN 0833-6210
AGRICULTURE ECONOMIC STATISTICS. Text in English. 1957. a.
Former titles (until 1985): Farm Net Income Reference Handbook (0837-5240); (until 1978): Farm Net Income Reference Book (0837-5232); (until 1965): Handbook of Agricultural Statistics. Part II, Farm Income (0837-5224)
—CISTI.
Published by: Statistics Canada, Communications Division, 3rd Fl, R H Coats Bldg, Ottawa, ON K1A 0A6, Canada. TEL 800-263-1136, infostats@statcan.ca, http://www.statcan.ca.

AGRO-CHEMICALS NEWS IN BRIEF. see *AGRICULTURE—Crop Production And Soil*

338.1 FRA ISSN 1152-880X
AGRO-DISTRIBUTION. Text in French. 1990. 10/yr.
Published by: C E P Groupe France Agricole, 8 Cite Paradis, Paris, Cedex 10 75493, France. TEL 33-1-40227900, FAX 33-1-48240315. Ed. Catherine Queheille. Circ: 9,000.

338.1 FRA ISSN 0989-2648
AGRO PERFORMANCES. Text in French. 1987. 6/yr. EUR 38.11 (effective 2005).
Indexed: RefZh.
Published by: S E P C O, Departement de Communication, 83 av. de la Grande Armee, Paris, Cedex 16 75782, France. TEL 40-66-21-71, FAX 1-45-01-82-87, TELEX 642020F, http://www.sepco.fr/05_liens/agro_perf.htm. Adv. contact Geraldine Herve. Circ: 3,500.

338.1 BRA ISSN 0100-4298
HD1871
AGROANALYSIS. Text in Portuguese. 1977-1989; resumed 1994. m. USD 150 (effective 2000). adv. **Document type:** *Academic/Scholarly.* **Description:** Provides a survey of Brazilian agrobusiness and how it is affected by both national and international economic policies.
Indexed: AEA, AgBio, AgrForAb, AnBrAb, DSA, FCA, FPA, FS&TA, ForAb, HerbAb, HortAb, I&DA, IndVet, MaizeAb, NutrAb, PAIS, PBA, PGegResA, PHN&I, PN&I, PoultAb, RDA, RPP, RRTA, RiceAb, S&F, SIA, SeedAb, SoyAb, TDB, TriticAb, VetBull, WAE&RSA, WeedAb.
—BLDSC (0764.552900).
Published by: (Instituto Brasileiro de Economia, Centro de Estudos Agricolas), Fundacao Getulio Vargas, 190 Praia de Botafogo, Rio de Janeiro, RJ 22253-53-900, Brazil. TEL 55-21-559-5623, FAX 55-21-559-5623, assine@fgv.br. Ed. Regis Norberto da Cunta Alimandro. Adv. contact Else Flejlau. Circ: 10,000.

AGROBASE. see *AGRICULTURE—Abstracting, Bibliographies, Statistics*

338.1 RUS
AGROBIZNES. Text in Russian. 2002. bi-m. RUR 2,970 domestic to individuals; RUR 5,082 domestic to corporations (effective 2005). **Document type:** *Magazine, Trade.*
Published by: Independent Media (Moscow), ul Vyborgskaya dom 16, str 1, Moscow, 125212, Russian Federation. TEL 7-095-2323200, FAX 7-095-2329265, agro@imedia.ru, podpiska@imedia.ru, http://www.agro-business.ru, http://www.independent-media.ru. Ed. Nikolai Lychev. Circ: 10,000.

338.1 BGR
▼ **AGROBIZNES/AGROBUSINESS.** Text in Bulgarian. 2003. m. BGL 30 domestic; EUR 30 in Europe; USD 55 elsewhere (effective 2005). **Document type:** *Magazine.* **Description:** Dedicated to Bulgaria's European integration in the agriculture sector and food industry. Aims to assist Bulgarian agricultural companies so that Bulgaria's agriculture sector and food industry could withstand the competition of European Union member states.
Published by: Economedia, ul Ivan Vazov 20, et. 2, Sofia, Bulgaria. TEL 359-2-9376444, FAX 359-2-9376236.

338.1 CHL ISSN 0716-8764
AGROECONOMICO. Text in Spanish. 1984. bi-m. CLP 26,000 domestic; USD 120 foreign (effective 2005). adv. bk.rev. charts; illus.; mkt.; stat. cum.index every 2 years. back issues avail. **Document type:** *Magazine, Trade.* **Description:** Contains technical, economic and market information on agricultural economic and agricultural products.
Formerly (until 1991): Informativo Agro-Economico (0716-0941)
Published by: Fundacion Chile, Departamento Agroindustria, Parque Antonio Rabat, 6165, PO Box 773, Vitacura, Santiago, Chile. TEL 56-2-240-0429, FAX 56-2-241-9387, ptobar@fundch.cl, http://www.agroeconomico.cl, http://www.fundacionchile.cl. Ed. Patricia Tobar. Adv. contact Maria Nieves Sandoval. B&W page CLP 41, color page CLP 47.50; trim 215 x 275. Circ: 3,000 (paid).

338.1 SVK
AGROEKONOMIKA✱. Text in Slovak. 1962. m. USD 18.
Former titles (until 1992): Ekonomika Polnohospodarstva (0323-2670); (until 1976): Ekonomika Zemedelstvi (0013-3124)
Indexed: RASB.
Published by: Ministerstvo Podmospodarstva a Vyzivy, Dobrovicova 12, Bratislava, 80000, Slovakia.

338.1 SCG ISSN 0350-5928
AGROEKONOMIKA. Text in Serbo-Croatian; Summaries in English. 1972. a. adv. bk.rev. back issues avail. **Document type:** *Journal, Academic/Scholarly.* **Description:** Covers theoretical and empirical contributions from the areas of agricultural economics and rural sociology.
Published by: Univerzitet u Novom Sadu, Poljoprivredni Fakultet, Institut za Ekonomiku Poljoprivrede i Sociologiju Sela/University of Novi Sad, Faculty of Agriculture, Institute of Agricultural Economics and Rural Sociology, Trg D Obradovica 8, Novi Sad, 21000. TEL 381-11-450355, FAX 381-11-459761, tica@polj.ns.ac.yu, http://polj.ns.ac.yu/srpski/ins_eko.htm. Ed. Bronislav S Djurdjev. Circ: 1,000.

338.1 USA
AGROINDUSTRY: LATIN AMERICAN INDUSTRIAL REPORT✱. (Avail. for each of 22 Latin American countries) Text in English. 1985. a. USD 435; per country report.
Published by: Aquino Productions, P O Box 15760, Stamford, CT 06901-0760. Ed. Andres C Aquino.

338.43 ESP ISSN 1139-8256
AGRONEGOCIOS; semanario independiente de informacion agricola, ganadera y alimentaria. Text in Spanish. 1999. w. EUR 58 domestic; EUR 94 in Europe; EUR 123 elsewhere (effective 2004). **Document type:** *Magazine, Trade.* **Description:** Includes information about price and markets both national and international.
Related titles: Online - full text ed.: AgroNegocios Online. 2001. EUR 45.08 (effective 2004).
Published by: Eumedia S.A., Claudio Coello 16, 1o, Madrid, 28001, Spain. TEL 34-91-4264430, FAX 34-91-5753297, http://www.eumedia.es. Ed. Jaime Lamo de Espinosa. Adv. contact Julia Dominguez. Circ: 35,000 (paid).

338.1 MEX
AGRONEGOCIOS EN MEXICO. Text in Spanish. 1992. m. MXP 150. **Document type:** *Trade.* **Description:** Covers cattle, finance, forestry, poultry and industry.
Address: 3A Coa. Bahamas 31, Mexico, Col Lomas Estrella, Iztapalapa, Mexico City, DF 09890, Mexico. TEL 656-59-18. Ed. Alfredo Saenz Colin. Pub. Salvador Sosa Fuentes. Circ: 3,000.

AGRONOMY FOR SUSTAINABLE DEVELOPMENT; sciences des productions vegetales et de l'environnement. see *AGRICULTURE—Crop Production And Soil*

380.141 UKR
AHROKOMPAS. Text in Ukrainian. m. USD 15 foreign.
Description: Provides a legal base for agricultural producers.
Published by: Kompaniya Lunivest Marketing, A-ya 400, Kiev, 252150, Ukraine. TEL 380-44-261-5140. Ed. Olga Sidorenko.
US dist. addr.: East View Information Services, 3020 Harbor Ln. N., Minneapolis, MN 55447. TEL 612-550-0961.

338.1 NLD ISSN 0923-7143
AKKERBOUW (THE HAGUE). Text in Dutch; Summaries in English. 1971. quinquennial. price varies. charts; stat. back issues avail. **Document type:** *Government.* **Description:** Presents industrial economic reflections on arable farming over the past five years.
Published by: Landbouw-Economisch Instituut, Burgemeester Patijnlaan 19, The Hague, 2585 BE, Netherlands. TEL 31-70-330-8330, FAX 31-70-361-5624, omcpubl@lei.dlo.nl, http://www.lei.nl. Ed. J H Jager.

338.1 USA ISSN 1065-3775
HF1416.5
AMERICAN FOOD AND AG EXPORTER DIRECTORY. Text in English. 1989. a. USD 120 to libraries (effective 1999).
Description: Lists export firms, agents, brokers, manufacturers, growers, processors, freight forwarders, and others involved in exporting America's agricultural commodities; also lists contact names, addresses, phone and fax numbers.
Formerly: American Agricultural Exporter Directory
—CISTI.

Published by: American Dream Network Inc., PO Box 810391, Boca Raton, FL 33481-0391. TEL 561-447-0810, FAX 561-368-9125. Ed. James E Prevor. Circ: 17,000.

338.1   USA
AMERICAN FOOD AND AG EXPORTER MAGAZINE. Text in English. 1989. q. USD 218; USD 297 in Canada; USD 328 elsewhere (effective 2000). Description: Covers information for importers of America's food and agricultural export products. Includes agricultural news and stories about growers, handlers, services and export businesses.
Formerly (until 1990): American Agricultural Exporter Magazine; Incorporates: California Agricultural Exporter
Published by: American Dream Network Inc., PO Box 810391, Boca Raton, FL 33481-0391. TEL 561-447-0810, FAX 561-368-9125. Ed. James Prevor. Circ: 17,000.

338.1   USA   ISSN 0002-9092
S560   CODEN: AJAEBA
➤ AMERICAN JOURNAL OF AGRICULTURAL ECONOMICS. Text in English. 1919. 5/yr. USD 217 combined subscription in the Americas to institutions & the Caribbean (print & online eds.); GBP 227 combined subscription elsewhere to institutions print & online eds. (effective 2006). adv. bk.rev. bibl.; charts; illus.; stat. index. back issues avail.; reprint service avail. from PSC. Document type: Journal, Academic/Scholarly. Description: Provides a forum for creative and scholarly work in the field. Covers the economics of agriculture, natural resources and the environment, and rural and community development.
Formerly (until 1968): Journal of Farm Economics (1071-1031)
Related titles: Microfiche ed.: (from PMC); Microfilm ed.: (from PMC); Online - full text ed.: ISSN 1467-8276. USD 206 in the Americas to institutions & the Caribbean; GBP 227 elsewhere to institutions (effective 2006) (from Blackwell Synergy, EBSCO Publishing, Florida Center for Library Automation, Gale Group, H.W. Wilson, IngentaConnect, JSTOR (Web-based Journal Archive), Northern Light Technology, Inc., O C L C Online Computer Library Center, Inc., Swets Information Services).
Indexed: ABIn, AEA, APEL, ASCA, ASFA, AbHyg, AgBio, AgeL, Agr, AgrForAb, AnBrAb, ApicAb, B&AI, BAS, BPI, BPIA, BibAg, Biostat, BusI, CIS, CREJ, CTFA, CurCont, DSA, EIA, ESPM, EngInd, EnvAb, EnvEAb, ExcerpMed, FCA, FPA, FS&TA, FamI, ForAb, GEOBASE, HerbAb, HortAb, I&DA, IAOP, IBSS, ILD, ISR, IndVet, JEL, MEA&I, MaizeAb, NutrAb, ORMS, PAIS, PBA, PCI, PGegResA, PHN&I, PN&I, PollutAb, PotatoAb, PoultAb, ProtozoAb, QC&AS, RASB, RDA, REE&TA, RPP, RRTA, RefZh, RevApplEntom, RiceAb, RiskAb, S&F, SCI, SIA, SSCI, SeedAb, SoyAb, T&II, TDB, TriticAb, VITIS, VetBull, WAE&RSA, WTA, WeedAb.
—BLDSC (0820.950000), CISTI, Ei, IDS, IE, Infotrieve, ingenta, Linda Hall. CCC.
Published by: (American Agricultural Economics Association), Blackwell Publishing, Inc. (Subsidiary of: Blackwell Publishing Ltd.), Commerce Place, 350 Main St, Malden, MA 02148. TEL 781-388-8206, FAX 781-388-8232, subscrip@blackwellpub.com, http:// www.blackwellpublishing.com/journals/AJAE. Eds. B Wade Brorsen, Christopher B Barrett, Ian M Sheldon, Stephen K Swallow. adv.: page USD 500. Circ: 7,000.

338.1   MEX   ISSN 0185-6944
ANALISIS DE LA AGRICULTURA SINALOENSE. Text in Spanish. 1963. q. USD 40.
Formerly: Analisis de la Situacion Agricola de Sinaloa (0517-6956)
—CISTI.
Published by: Confederacion de Asociaciones Agricolas del Estado de Sinaloa, Juan Carrasco 787 Nte., Culiacan, SINALOA 80000, Mexico. TEL 31097, FAX 671-30108, TELEX 665822 CAAC ME. Circ: 500.

ANNUAIRE DE STATISTIQUE AGRICOLE. see AGRICULTURE—Abstracting, Bibliographies, Statistics

338.1   ESP   ISSN 0210-637X
ANUARIO HORTOFRUTICOLA ESPANOL. Text in Spanish. 1968. a. adv. Document type: Directory.
Published by: Sucro S.A., Hernan Cortes, 5-1, Valencia, 46004, Spain. TEL 34-6-351-5301, FAX 34-6-352-57-52. Adv. contact Jose Maria Server Martinez. Circ: 5,000.

338.1   USA
APPLIED STATISTICS IN AGRICULTURE; proceedings of the Kansas State University Conference on Applied Statistics in Agriculture. Text in English. a. Description: Discusses statistical issues, problems, and solutions in agricultural research.
Indexed: Agr.
Published by: Kansas State University, Department of Statistics, 101 Dickens Hall, Manhattan, KS 66506-0802. TEL 785-532-6883, FAX 785-532-7736, statinfo@stat.ksu.edu, http://www.ksu.edu/stats/agstat.conference/.

338.1   GBR   ISSN 0305-0920
T1
➤ APPROPRIATE TECHNOLOGY; practical approaches to development. Text in English. 1974. q. GBP 120, USD 240 (effective 2004). adv. bk.rev. illus. index. 58 p./no. 3 cols./p.; Document type: Academic/Scholarly. Description: Focuses on communicating new practical technologies, policies and ideas addressed to the elimination of poverty and hunger.
Incorporates (in 2000): International Agricultural Development (0261-4413); Which was formerly (1980-1981): Third World Agriculture; Formerly: Intermediate Technology Development Group. Bulletin (0538-4028)
Related titles: Online - full text ed.: (from bigchalk, ProQuest Information & Learning).
Indexed: ABIn, AEA, AIT, ARDT, ASCA, AgrForAb, AnBrAb, ApicAb, BrTechI, CLOSS, CurCont, DSA, EIA, EPB, ETA, EnerRev, EngInd, EnvAb, ExcerpMed, FCA, FLUIDEX, FPA, ForAb, GEOBASE, HerbAb, HortAb, I&DA, IBSS, IndVet, JOF, MaizeAb, NutrAb, PHN&I, PotatoAb, PoultAb, RDA, RRTA, Repind, RiceAb, S&F, SPPI, SWA, SoyAb, WAE&RSA, WRCInf, WeedAb.
—BLDSC (1580.700000), CISTI, Ei, IDS, IE, Infotrieve, ingenta, Linda Hall. CCC.
Published by: Research Information Ltd., Grenville Court, Britwell Rd, Burnham, Bucks SL1 8DF, United Kingdom. TEL 44-1628-600499, FAX 44-1628-600488, info@researchinformation.co.uk, http:// www.researchinformation.co.uk/apte.php. Ed. David Dixon. Adv. contact Kumar Patel TEL 44-20-8328-2470. Circ: 2,500.

338.1   GBR   ISSN 0265-556X
ARAB AGRICULTURE. Text in English. 1984. m.
—BLDSC (1583.223890).
Published by: Hilal International (UK) Ltd., Crescent Ct, 102 Victor Rd, Teddington, Midds TW11 8SS, United Kingdom. TEL 44-20-8943-3630, FAX 44-20-8943-3701, post@hilal.co.uk, http://www.hilal.co.uk.

ARAB WORLD AGRIBUSINESS/AL-ZIRA'AH FI-L-ALAM AL-ARABI. see AGRICULTURE

ARUSHA CHAMBER OF COMMERCE AND AGRICULTURE. BULLETIN TO MEMBERS. see BUSINESS AND ECONOMICS—Chamber Of Commerce Publications

338.1   HKG
ASIA - PACIFIC AGRIBUSINESS REPORT. Text in English. 1988. m. USD 240. bk.rev. Document type: Newsletter.
Description: Covers trends and developments in the region's biggest business sector, agribusiness. Includes two special report sections in each issue.
Published by: Asia Letter Group, GPO Box 10874, Hong Kong, Hong Kong. TEL 852-526-2950, FAX 852-526-7131.

333.76   BGD   ISSN 1018-5291
HN655.2.C6   CODEN: AJRDER
ASIA - PACIFIC JOURNAL OF RURAL DEVELOPMENT. Text in English. 1991. s-a. BDT 300; USD 12 in Asia & the Pacific; USD 24 elsewhere. adv. Document type: Academic/Scholarly.
Indexed: AgrForAb, DSA, FPA, ForAb, HortAb, I&DA, IndVet, MaizeAb, NutrAb, PHN&I, PotatoAb, RDA, RiceAb, S&F, SOPODA, TDB, TriticAb, VetBull, WAE&RSA, WeedAb.
Published by: Centre on Integrated Rural Development for Asia and the Pacific, Chameli House, 17 Topkhana Rd, GPO Box 2883, Dhaka, 1000, Bangladesh. Ed. Leelangi Wanasundera. Adv. contact D P Mazumder. page USD 100.

338.1   USA
ASPEN INSTITUTE. RURAL ECONOMIC POLICY PROGRAM. BEST PRACTICE SERIES. Text in English. irreg. price varies. back issues avail. Document type: Monographic series.
Published by: Aspen Institute, Communities Strategies Group, One Dupont Circle N W, Ste 700, Washington, DC 20036. TEL 702-736-5800, FAX 202-736-0790, http:// www.aspeninst.org/rural/. Ed. Kelly Malone.

338.1   USA
ASPEN INSTITUTE. RURAL ECONOMIC POLICY PROGRAM. STRATEGIC OVERVIEW SERIES. Text in English. irreg. USD 10 per vol. back issues avail. Document type: Monographic series. Description: Offers various perspectives on rural economic development.
Published by: Aspen Institute, Communities Strategies Group, One Dupont Circle N W, Ste 700, Washington, DC 20036. TEL 702-736-5800, FAX 202-467-0790, http:// www.aspeninst.org/rural/. Ed. Kelly Malone.

338.1   USA
ASPEN INSTITUTE. RURAL ECONOMIC POLICY PROGRAM. TOOLS FOR PRACTICE SERIES. Text in English. irreg. price varies. back issues avail. Document type: Monographic series. Description: Provides rural communities with advice on best practices.
Published by: Aspen Institute, Communities Strategies Group, One Dupont Circle N W, Ste 700, Washington, DC 20036. TEL 702-736-5800, FAX 202-467-0790, http:// www.aspeninst.org/rural/. Ed. Kelly Malone.

AUSTRALIA. BUREAU OF STATISTICS. VALUE OF PRINCIPAL AGRICULTURAL COMMODITIES PRODUCED, AUSTRALIA, PRELIMINARY. see AGRICULTURE—Abstracting, Bibliographies, Statistics

338.1   AUS   ISSN 1321-7844
HD2151
AUSTRALIAN BUREAU OF AGRICULTURAL AND RESOURCE ECONOMICS. AUSTRALIAN COMMODITIES. Text in English. 1948. q. AUD 150 paper copy; AUD 40 per issue paper copy; AUD 70 online edition; AUD 20 per issue online edition (effective 2003). charts; mkt.; stat. index. Document type: Government. Description: Features short-term outlook for agriculture, forestry and fisheries.
Former titles: Australia. Australian Bureau of Agricultural and Resource Economics. Agriculture and Resources Quarterly (1032-9722); (until Mar. 1989): Australia. Australian Bureau of Agricultural and Resource Economics. Quarterly Review of the Rural Economy; Australia. Bureau of Agricultural Economics. Quarterly Review of the Rural Economy (0156-7446); Supersedes (in 1978): Quarterly Review of Agricultural Economics (0033-5754)
Related titles: Online - full content ed.: (from R M I T Publishing); Online - full text ed.: (from Chadwyck-Healey Inc.).
Indexed: AESIS, ASFA, Agr, AusPAIS, DSA, ESPM, FS&TA, ForAb, GEOBASE, HortAb, I&DA, IBSS, IndVet, JEL, NutrAb, PAIS, PCI, PHN&I, PN&I, PoultAb, RDA, RRTA, S&F, SIA, TTI, TriticAb, VetBull, WAE&RSA, WTA.
—BLDSC (1798.184000), CISTI.
Published by: Australian Bureau of Agricultural and Resource Economics, GPO Box 1563, Canberra, ACT 2601, Australia. TEL 61-2-62722000, FAX 61-2-62722001, sales@abare.gov.au, http://www.abareconomics.com. Ed., R&P Andrew Wright TEL 61-2-62722290.

338.1   AUS
▼ AUSTRALIAN BUREAU OF AGRICULTURAL AND RESOURCE ECONOMICS. AUSTRALIAN CROP REPORT. Text in English. 2003. q. AUD 50; AUD 15 per issue (effective 2003).
Media: Online - full content.
Published by: Australian Bureau of Agricultural and Resource Economics, GPO Box 1563, Canberra, ACT 2601, Australia. TEL 61-2-62722000, FAX 61-2-62722001, sales@abare.gov.au, http://www.abareconomics.com. Ed., R&P Andrew Wright TEL 61-2-62722290.

338.1   AUS
▼ AUSTRALIAN BUREAU OF AGRICULTURAL AND RESOURCE ECONOMICS. CONSULTANCY REPORTS. Text in English. 2003. irreg. free (effective 2003). Document type: Government.
Media: Online - full content.
Published by: Australian Bureau of Agricultural and Resource Economics, GPO Box 1563, Canberra, ACT 2601, Australia. TEL 61-2-62722000, FAX 61-2-62722001, sales@abare.gov.au, http://www.abareconomics.com. Ed., R&P Andrew Wright TEL 61-2-62722290.

338.1   AUS   ISSN 1364-985X
HD1401
➤ THE AUSTRALIAN JOURNAL OF AGRICULTURAL AND RESOURCE ECONOMICS. Text in English. 1997. q. AUD 138 combined subscription in Australia & New Zealand to institutions print & online eds.; USD 334 combined subscription in the Americas to institutions print & online eds.; GBP 216 combined subscription elsewhere to institutions print & online eds. (effective 2006). adv. bk.rev. charts. cum.index every 3 yrs. back issues avail.; reprint service avail. from ISI. Document type: Journal, Academic/Scholarly. Description: Covers economic analysis of Australian agriculture. Includes theoretical and methodological material.
Formed by the merger of (1957-1997): Australian Journal of Agricultural Economics (0004-9395); (1945-1997): Review of Marketing and Agricultural Economics (0034-6616); Which superseded (1937-1945): New South Wales Pastoral Conditions (0047-9926)
Related titles: Online - full text ed.: ISSN 1467-8489. GBP 132 in Australia & New Zealand to institutions; USD 317 in the Americas to institutions; GBP 205 elsewhere to institutions (effective 2006) (from Blackwell Synergy, EBSCO Publishing, Gale Group, IngentaConnect, O C L C Online Computer Library Center, Inc., Swets Information Services).
Indexed: ABIn, AEA, APEL, ASCA, ASFA, AgBio, AgeL, Agr, AgrForAb, AusPAIS, BAS, CREJ, CurCont, DSA, ESPM, EnvEAb, FCA, ForAb, GEOBASE, HerbAb, HortAb, I&DA, IBSS, ISR, IndVet, JEL, NutrAb, OrnHort, PAIS, PBA, PCI, PGegResA, PHN&I, PollutAb, RA&MP, RDA, RPP, RRTA, RiceAb, RiskAb, S&F, SCI, SIA, SSCI, SWRA, SoyAb, TriticAb, VITIS, VetBull, WAE&RSA, WeedAb.
—BLDSC (1801.880000), CISTI, IDS, IE, Infotrieve, ingenta. CCC.
Published by: (Australian Agricultural and Resource Economics Society Inc), Blackwell Publishing Asia (Subsidiary of: Blackwell Publishing Ltd.), 550 Swanston St, Carlton South, VIC 3053, Australia. TEL 61-383591011, FAX 61-383591120, subs@blackwellpublishingasia.com, http:// www.blackwellpublishing.com/journals/AJARE. Eds. Bob Lindner, Dave Pannell, Ross Kingwell. Circ: 1,400.

338.1   DEU   ISSN 0179-5066
B N - BETRIEBSWIRTSCHAFTLICHE NACHRICHTEN FUER DIE LANDWIRTSCHAFT. Text in German. 1940. m.
Published by: Verlag Pflug und Feder GmbH, Koelnstr 202, Sankt Augustin, 53757, Germany. TEL 02241-204085.

A

338.1 PER
BANCO AGRARIO DEL PERU. MEMORIA. Text in Spanish. 1976 (no.45). a.
Published by: Banco Agrario del Peru, c/o Axel Pflucker Otoya, Augusto Wiese 543-547, Lima, Peru.

338.1 BGD ISSN 0070-8143
BANGLADESH. DIRECTORATE OF AGRICULTURAL MARKETING. AGRICULTURAL MARKETING SERIES✶. Text in English. irreg.
Published by: Directorate of Agricultural Marketing, Ministry of Agriculture, Bangladesh Secretariat, Bhaban 4, Dhaka, Bangladesh.

BAY OF PLENTY FARMER. see *AGRICULTURE*

380.141 USA ISSN 1066-0607
BEAN MARKET NEWS. Text in English. 1965. w. (plus a. summary). looseleaf. USD 55; USD 60 in Canada & Mexico; USD 90 elsewhere. back issues avail.; reprint service avail. from CIS. **Document type:** *Government.*
Related titles: Microfiche ed.: (from CIS).
Indexed: AmStl.
—CISTI.
Published by: (Livestock & Seed Division), U.S. Department of Agriculture, Agricultural Marketing Service (Greely), 711 O St., Greely, CO 80631. TEL 970-353-9750, FAX 970-353-9790. **Subscr. to:** U.S.D.A. Agricultural Marketing Service, Livestock & Seed Division, Rm 2613 S, Box 96456, Washington, DC 20090-6456. FAX 202-245-4732.

380.141 NLD
HET BELGISCH A G F ADRESBOEK. (Aardappelen - Groenten - Fruit) Text in Dutch. 1998. a. EUR 20 (effective 2005). **Document type:** *Directory, Trade.* **Description:** Provides a directory of the Belgian fruit and vegetables trade.
Related titles: ♦ Supplement to: Primeur. ISSN 0925-2428.
Published by: Primeur B.V., PO Box 2140, Goes, 4460 MC, Netherlands. TEL 31-113-230621, FAX 31-113-230865, primeur@zeelandnet.nl, info@primeur.tv. Circ: 4,000.

BELGIUM. INSTITUT NATIONAL DE STATISTIQUE. AGRICULTURE. STATISTIQUES AGRICOLES. see *AGRICULTURE—Abstracting, Bibliographies, Statistics*

BELGIUM. NATIONAAL INSTITUUT VOOR DE STATISTIEK. LANDBOUW. LANDBOUWSTATISTIEKEN. see *AGRICULTURE—Abstracting, Bibliographies, Statistics*

338.1 USA
BENTON HARBOR FRUIT & VEGETABLE REPORT. Text in English. 3/w. USD 20. back issues avail. **Document type:** *Newsletter, Government.* **Description:** Provides Benton Harbor fruit market prices, as well as those for the Chicago and Detroit terminal markets.
Published by: U.S. Department of Agriculture (Benton Harbor), 175 Territorial Rd, Ste 201, PO Box 1204, Benton Harbor, MI 49022. TEL 269-925-3270, FAX 269-925-3272.

BILL GARY'S PRICE PERCEPTIONS. see *BUSINESS AND ECONOMICS—Investments*

BOTSWANA. CENTRAL STATISTICS OFFICE. AGRICULTURE STATISTICS. see *AGRICULTURE—Abstracting, Bibliographies, Statistics*

338.121 BWA
BOTSWANA. MINISTRY OF AGRICULTURE. FARM MANAGEMENT SURVEY RESULTS. Text in English. 1980. a. free. bibl.; stat. back issues avail. **Document type:** *Government.*
Formerly: Botswana. Ministry of Commerce and Industry. Farm Management Survey Results
Published by: Ministry of Agriculture, Department of Agricultural Research, Private Bag 003, Gaborone, Botswana. FAX 267-356027, TELEX 2543 VET BD, 2543 VET BD. Ed. Henry G Jobeta. R&P Dan B Gombalume. Circ: 400. **Subscr. to:** Government Printer, Private Bag 0081, Gaborone, Botswana. TEL 267-353202, FAX 267-312001, http://www.gov.bw.

BRITISH POTATO COUNCIL. NEWS. see *AGRICULTURE—Crop Production And Soil*

338.1 USA
BROCK REPORT. Text in English. 1976. w. USD 355 (effective 2000). **Document type:** *Newsletter.*
Incorporates (in 1989): Top Farmer Market Insight (0730-6326)
Published by: Brock & Associates, 2050 W Good Hope Rd, Milwaukee, WI 53209. TEL 414-351-5500, FAX 414-351-3140. Ed. Douglas J Harper. Pub. Richard A Brock.

BUSINESS TIMES. see *BUSINESS AND ECONOMICS*

338.1 BFA ISSN 1021-3236
HC1040.A1
C E D R E S. REVUE ECONOMIQUE ET SOCIALE. Text in French. 1977. q. XOF 40,000.
Indexed: PAIS.
Published by: Centre d'Etudes de Recherche Economique et Social, Universite de Ouagadougou, BP 7021, Ouagadougou, Burkina Faso. TEL 31-19-67, FAX 31-26-86. Ed. Soulama Souleymane. Circ: 500.

363.7 FRA
C E M A G R E F MONTAGNE. ETUDES. Text in French. irreg.
Published by: Centre National de Machinisme Agricole du Genie Rural des Eaux et des Forets, Parc de Tourvoie, B.P. 44, Antony, Cedex 92163, France. TEL 33-4-73382052, FAX 33-4-73387641. Ed. Philippe Coussot.

338.1 FRA
C E M A G R E F PRODUCTION ET ECONOMIE AGRICOLES. ETUDES. Text in French. irreg.
Published by: Centre National de Machinisme Agricole du Genie Rural des Eaux et des Forets, Parc de Tourvoie, B.P. 44, Antony, Cedex 92163, France. TEL 33-4-73382052, FAX 33-4-73387641.

C R B FUTURES PERSPECTIVE - AGRICULTURAL EDITION. see *BUSINESS AND ECONOMICS—Investments*

338.1 FRA ISSN 0755-9208
HN49.C6
CAHIERS D'ECONOMIE ET SOCIOLOGIE RURALES. Text in English, French. 1984. 4/yr. bk.rev. **Document type:** *Academic/Scholarly.* **Description:** Focuses on agriculture and related activities, the way they function from an economic point of view, their social characteristics and their relations with the national and international economy.
Indexed: DSA, ELLIS, FCA, FPA, ForAb, HortAb, I&DA, IndVet, JEL, MaizeAb, NutrAb, OrnHort, PAIS, PBA, PHN&I, PN&I, PotatoAb, PoultAb, RDA, RRTA, RefZh, RevApplEntom, S&F, SociolAb, VITIS, VetBull, WAE&RSA, WeedAb.
—CISTI. **CCC.**
Published by: Institut National de la Recherche Agronomique, Departement d'Economie et de Sociologie Rurales, 63-65 bd. de Brandebourg, Ivry, Cedex 94205, France. TEL 33-1-49596900, FAX 33-1-46704113, seurat@ivry.inra.fr, http://www.dijon.inra.fr/esr/publications/cesr/index.html. Ed. Jean Pierre Amigues. R&P Annick Seurat TEL 33-1-49596972. Circ: 500.

630 VEN ISSN 0798-6270
CALENDARIO AGRICOLA. Text in Spanish. 1970. irreg., latest 1987. free. stat.
Published by: (Venezuela. Ministerio de Agricultura y Cria), Direccion de Planificacion y Estadistica (Subsidiary of: Ministerio de Agricultura y Cria), Division de Estadistica, Centro Simon Bolivar, Torre Norte 16o, Caracas, 1010, Venezuela.

338.1 USA ISSN 0891-9097
HD9007.C2
CALIFORNIA AGRICULTURAL EXPORT DIRECTORY✶. Text in English. 1982. biennial. USD 50 (effective 1999). **Document type:** *Directory.* **Description:** Provides key facts on California companies involved in exporting agricultural products, both fresh and processed. Includes growers, packers, processors, and brokers. Companies are listed alphabetically and by products in details.
Related titles: Diskette ed.: USD 195 (effective 1999).
Published by: (California Department of Food and Agriculture, Agricultural Export Program), Database Publishing Company, 701 E Ball Rd Ste 100, Anaheim, CA 92805-5962. TEL 714-778-6400, FAX 714-778-6811. Ed. Sarah Fraser. R&P Vera Roldan. Circ: 2,800 (controlled).

338.1 USA
CALIFORNIA LETTUCE RESEARCH BOARD. ANNUAL REPORT. Text in English. a. **Description:** Progress reports on research in the production and distribution of iceberg lettuce.
Formerly (until 1997): Iceberg Lettuce Advisory Board. Annual Report
Published by: California Lettuce Research Board, 512 Pajaro St, Salinas, CA 93901. TEL 831-424-3782, FAX 831-424-3785.

338.1 CAN ISSN 1190-8408
HD9014.C2 CODEN: ITPFEB
CANADA. NATIONAL FARM PRODUCTS COUNCIL. ANNUAL REVIEW (YEAR). Text in English, French. 1973. a. free. **Document type:** *Government.* **Description:** Contains review of activities and priorities of the council for the year and includes an overview of the four national poultry and egg agencies.
Former titles (until 1994): Canada. National Farm Products Council. Annual Report (1190-8394); (until 1993): Canada. National Farm Products Marketing Council. Annual Report (0383-414X)
Related titles: E-mail ed.; Online - full text ed.
—CISTI.
Published by: National Farm Products Council, Canada Bldg., 10th Fl., 344 Slater St., Ottawa, ON K1R 7Y3, Canada. TEL 613-995-5553, FAX 613-995-2097, nfpcweb@agr.gc.ca, http://www.nfpc-cnpa.gc.ca. Ed. Lise Corbett. Circ: 2,000.

CANADA. STATISTICS CANADA. ECONOMIC OVERVIEW OF FARM INCOMES. see *AGRICULTURE—Abstracting, Bibliographies, Statistics*

CANADA. STATISTICS CANADA. FARM CASH RECEIPTS. see *AGRICULTURE—Abstracting, Bibliographies, Statistics*

CANADA. STATISTICS CANADA. PRODUCTION OF POULTRY AND EGGS/CANADA. STATISTIQUE CANADA. PRODUCTION DE VOLAILLE ET OEUFS. see *AGRICULTURE—Abstracting, Bibliographies, Statistics*

338.1 CAN ISSN 0317-7483
HD9014.C2
CANADA'S TRADE IN AGRICULTURAL PRODUCTS. Text in English. a. free. **Document type:** *Government.*
Formerly: Canada. Agriculture Canada. Policy Branch. Trade in Agricultural Products (0068-7286)
Published by: Agriculture Canada, Policy Branch, 930 Carling Ave, Ottawa, ON K1A 0C7, Canada. TEL 613-995-5222.

338.1 USA ISSN 0008-3976
➤ **CANADIAN JOURNAL OF AGRICULTURAL ECONOMICS/REVUE CANADIENNE D'ECONOMIE RURALE.** Text in English, French. 1952. q. USD 185 in the Americas; USD 164 in Canada; GBP 109 elsewhere (effective 2006). bk.rev. **Document type:** *Journal, Academic/Scholarly.* **Description:** Provides a forum for scholarship in agricultural economics and farm management including agri-food related topics concerning agribusiness.
Related titles: Microfilm ed.: (from PQC); Online - full text ed.: ISSN 1744-7976. USD 176 in the Americas to institutions; USD 156 in Canada to institutions; GBP 103 elsewhere to institutions (effective 2006) (from Blackwell Synergy, EBSCO Publishing, H.W. Wilson, O C L C Online Computer Library Center, Inc., Swets Information Services); ♦ Supplement(s): Canadian Agricultural Economics and Farm Management Society. Workshop and Annual Meeting Proceedings.
Indexed: ABIn, AEA, APEL, ASCA, ASFA, AbHyg, AgBio, Agr, AgrForAb, AnBrAb, B&AI, BAS, CBCARef, CBPI, CPerI, CurCont, DSA, ESPM, EnvAb, FCA, FPA, FS&TA, FamI, ForAb, HerbAb, HortAb, I&DA, IAOP, IBSS, ISR, IndVet, JEL, MaizeAb, NutrAb, PAIS, PBA, PGegResA, PHN&I, PN&I, PollutAb, PotatoAb, PoultAb, RDA, REE&TA, RRTA, RevApplEntom, RiceAb, RiskAb, S&F, SCI, SFA, SSCI, SeedAb, SoyAb, TOSA, TriticAb, VetBull, WAE&RSA, WeedAb.
—BLDSC (3027.950000), CISTI, IDS, IE, Infotrieve, ingenta, Linda Hall. **CCC.**
Published by: (Canadian Agricultural Economics Society CAN), Blackwell Publishing, Inc. (Subsidiary of: Blackwell Publishing Ltd.), Commerce Place, 350 Main St, Malden, MA 02148. TEL 781-388-8206, FAX 781-388-8232, http://www.blackwellpublishing.com/journal.asp?ref=0008-3976&site=1. Eds. Kevin Chen, Peter Boxall, Scott Jeffrey. Circ: 1,200.

338.1 ISR
CENTER FOR AGRICULTURAL ECONOMIC RESEARCH, REHOVOT. WORKING PAPERS. Text in English. 1969. irreg. **Document type:** *Monographic series.* **Description:** Preliminary reports of research findings in agricultural economics.
Published by: Center for Agricultural Economic Research, P O Box 12, Rehovot, Israel. FAX 972-8-466267.

CENTRAL PLANTATION CROPS RESEARCH INSTITUTE. ANNUAL REPORT. see *AGRICULTURE*

338.1 HKG
CHINA AGRIBUSINESS REPORT. Text in English. 1987. s-m. USD 595. bk.rev. **Description:** Covers China's biggest and most important business sector - agribusiness.
Published by: Asia Letter Group, GPO Box 10874, Hong Kong, Hong Kong. TEL 852-526-2950, FAX 852-526-7131. **Subscr. to:** PO Box 92619, Los Angeles, CA 90009.

338.1 USA ISSN 0886-5558
S1
CHOICES (AMES); the magazine of food, farm and resource issues. Text in English. 1986. q. free (effective 2005). adv. back issues avail. **Document type:** *Bulletin.* **Description:** For people interested in food, farm and resource issues and the policies that affect them.
Media: Online - full text (from Gale Group).
Indexed: AbHyg, AgBio, Agr, AnBrAb, DSA, FCA, ForAb, HerbAb, HortAb, I&DA, IndVet, MASUSE, MaizeAb, NutrAb, PBA, PGegResA, PHN&I, PN&I, PotatoAb, PoultAb, RDA, RPP, RRTA, RevApplEntom, RiceAb, S&F, SIA, SeedAb, SoyAb, TDB, TriticAb, VetBull, WAE&RSA, WeedAb.
—CISTI. **CCC.**
Published by: American Agricultural Economics Association, 415 S Duff, Ste C, Ames, IA 50010-6600. TEL 515-233-3202, FAX 515-233-3101, choices@ag.tamu.edu, info@aaea.org, http://www.choicesmagazine.org/, http://www.aaea.org. adv.: color page USD 1,100. Circ: 6,000.

338.1 CUB ISSN 0138-8584
CIENCIA Y TECNICA EN LA AGRICULTURA. SERIE: ECONOMIA AGROPECUARIA. Abstracts and contents page in English. 1978. 2/yr. USD 14 in the Americas; USD 16 in Europe; USD 17 elsewhere.
Indexed: Agrind.
Published by: Centro de Informacion y Documentacion Agropecuario, Gaveta Postal 4149, Havana, 4, Cuba. **Dist. by:** Ediciones Cubanas, Obispo No. 527, Apdo. 605, Havana, Cuba.

338.1 USA ISSN 0732-7226
HD1775.C6
COLORADO AGRIBUSINESS ROUNDUP. Text in English. 1967. a. USD 5.
Published by: Colorado State University, Department of Agricultural Economics, B 326, Clark, CO 80523. TEL 303-491-6133, FAX 303-491-6441. Ed. J Hugh Winn. Circ: 2,500.

COMMERCIAL FERTILIZERS REPORT. see *AGRICULTURE—Abstracting, Bibliographies, Statistics*

COMMODITIES ONLINE DAILY. see *BUSINESS AND ECONOMICS—Investments*

COMMODITY YEARBOOK STATISTICAL UPDATE. see *AGRICULTURE—Abstracting, Bibliographies, Statistics*

338.1 AUS ISSN 0314-0164
COMPLAN HANDBOOK. Text in English. 1977. a.
Published by: University of New England, Agricultural Business Research Institute, Armidale, NSW 2350, Australia. TEL 067-733555, FAX 067-725376.

338.1 BRA ISSN 0102-2253
HD1871
CONGRESSO BRASILEIRO DE ECONOMIA E SOCIOLOGIA RURAL. ANAIS. Text in Portuguese. 1962. a. USD 90. bk.rev. **Document type:** *Proceedings.*
Formerly: Sociedade Brasileira de Economistas Rurais. Anais da Reuniao
Published by: Sociedade Brasileira de Economia e Sociologia Rural, Edificio Brasilia Radio Center, Av. W-3 Norte - Quadra 702, Salas 1049-1050, Brasilia, DF 70710900, Brazil. TEL 55-61-3283144, FAX 55-61-3283144, sober@tba.com.br, http://www.ufv.br/der/sober/index.htm. Ed., R&P Danilo Rolim Dias de Aguiar. Circ: 1,000.

338.1 USA ISSN 0093-6553
SB369.2.F6
COST OF PICKING AND HAULING FLORIDA CITRUS FRUITS. Text in English. a. stat.
Published by: (Food and Resource Economics Department), University of Florida, Institute of Food and Agricultural Sciences, PO Box 110240, Gainesville, FL 32611-0240. TEL 904-392-6015.

388 NLD
COSUN IN BUSINESS. Text in English. 1967. m. free. illus. **Document type:** *Trade.* **Description:** Reports on the role of Cosun in agricultural economics and food production.
Supersedes (in 199?): Cosun Magazine
Indexed: AEA, FCA, RPP, SeedAb.
—BLDSC.
Published by: Cosun, Postbus 3411, Breda, 4800 MG, Netherlands. TEL 31-76-530-3222, FAX 31-76-530-3303, hmcosun@cosun.com, http://www.cosun.com/indexgb.html. Ed. W H Dijkstra.

338.7 IND ISSN 0304-6907
HD9086.I4
COTTON CORPORATION OF INDIA. ANNUAL REPORT. Key Title: Annual Report - Cotton Corporation of India. Text in English. a. **Document type:** *Corporate.*
Published by: Cotton Corporation of India, Air India Bldg., 12th Fl., Nariman Point, Mumbai, Maharashtra 400 021, India.

338.1 FRA ISSN 1161-8043
COURRIER DE LA PLANETE; developpement, environnement - les defits d'un monde solidaire. Text in French, Albanian. 1981. bi-m. adv. bk.rev. charts; illus.; stat. index. back issues avail. **Document type:** *Newspaper.*
Formerly (until 1991): Lettre de Solagral (0293-3055)
Related titles: ♦ Supplement(s): Afrique. ISSN 1161-8051.
Published by: Solidarites Agro-Alimentaires, 3191 route de Mende, BP 5056, Montpellier, Cedex 1 34033, France. TEL 67-54-47-23, FAX 67-54-25-27. Ed. Francois Lerin. R&P Sarah Mongruel. Circ: 3,000.

332.71 FRA ISSN 1243-9193
CREDIT AGRICOLE PARIS. Text in French. 1968. bi-m. adv. bk.rev. illus.; stat.
Formerly (until 1993): Administrateur du Credit Agriculture (0988-9183)
Published by: (Federation Nationale du Credit Agricole), F N C A, 48 rue la Boetie, Paris, 75008, France. TEL 01495343030, FAX 49-53-44-81, TELEX FENAGRI 650 718. Circ: 27,000.

368.121 USA
CROP INSURANCE INSIDER. Text in English. 1984. q. looseleaf. membership. charts; illus.; stat.; tr.lit. **Document type:** *Newsletter, Trade.* **Description:** Covers crop insurance.
Formed by the merger of: American Association of Crop Insurers. Washington Update; American Association of Crop Insurers. Agent Newsletter
Published by: American Association of Crop Insurers, 1 Massachusetts Ave, N W, 800, Washington, DC 20001-1431. TEL 202-789-4100, 800-746-4726, aac@erols.com, http://www.erols.com. Ed. Michael R McLeod. R&P Bonnie Goff. Circ: 4,500.

338.10715 BOL
CUADERNOS C I P C A (SERIE POPULAR). Text in Spanish. 1974. irreg. price varies. **Description:** Presents study and teaching methods.
Published by: Centro de Investigacion y Promocion del Campesinado, Casilla 5854, La Paz, Bolivia.

338.1 COL ISSN 0122-1450
HD1881
➤ **CUADERNOS DE DESARROLLO RURAL.** Text in Spanish, Portuguese, English, French. 1979. s-a. USD 40 (effective 2003). abstr.; bibl. reprints avail. **Document type:** *Academic/Scholarly.*
Formerly (until 1993): Cuadernos de Agroindustria y Economia Rural (0120-3606)
Published by: (Instituto de Estudios Rurales), Pontificia Universidad Javeriana, Facultad de Estudios Ambientales y Rurales, Transversal 4 No. 42-00, Piso 8, Edificio Jose Rafael Arboleda, Bogota, CUND, Colombia. TEL 57-1-3208320, rdavila@javeriana.edu.co. Ed., Pub., R&P Ricardo Davila.

338.1 CUB
CUBA. CENTRO DE INFORMACION Y DOCUMENTACION AGROPECUARIO. BOLETIN DE RESENAS. SERIE: ECONOMIA AGROPECUARIA. Abstracts in English. 1986. irreg. per issue exchange basis.
Indexed: Agrind.
Published by: Centro de Informacion y Documentacion Agropecuario, Gaveta Postal 4149, Havana, 4, Cuba. **Dist. by:** Ediciones Cubanas, Obispo No. 461, Apdo. 605, Havana, Cuba.

338.1 BRA ISSN 0100-9605
DADOS SOBRE A SITUACAO DA AGROPECUARIA MUNICIPAL NO ESTADO DO PARANA. Text in Portuguese. 1977. a.
Published by: Associacao de Credito e Assistencia Rural, Centro, Caixa Postal 900, Belo Horizonte, MG 30161-970, Brazil.

338.1 338.3 DNK ISSN 1398-554X
HD2001
DENMARK. MINISTERIET FOR FOEDEVARER, LANDBRUG OG FISKERI. FOEDEVAREMINISTERIETS AARSRAPPORT; politik, produktion og forbrug. Text in Danish, English. 1982. a. DKK 95 (effective 1999). Supplement avail. **Document type:** *Government.* **Description:** Annual report from the ministry, describing the economic and political development regarding agriculture and fisheries in Denmark, the EU and internationally.
Former titles (until 1998): Jordbrug og Fiskeri (1395-9948); (until 1995): Jordbrug (0108-884X)
Related titles: Online - full content ed.: ISSN 1398-5558.
Published by: Ministeriet for Foedevarer, Landbrug og Fiskeri, Departmentet/Ministry of Food, Agriculture and Fisheries, Holbergsgade 2, Copenhagen K, 1057, Denmark. TEL 45-33-92-33-01, FAX 45-33-14-50-42, TELEX 27157 MINAG DK, fvm@fvm.dk, http://www.fvm.dk. Circ: 2,000. **Dist. by:** Statens Information, Publikationsafdelingen, PO Box 1103, Copenhagen K 1109, Denmark. TEL 45-33-37-92-28.

338.1060489 DNK
HD2001
DENMARK. MINISTERIET FOR FOEDEVARER, LANDBRUG OG FISKERI. FOEDEVAREOEKONOMISK INSTITUT. AARSBERETNING/DANISH INSTITUTE OF AGRICULTURAL AND FISHERIES ECONOMICS. ANNUAL REPORT. Text in Danish; Summaries in English. 1979. a. DKK 50 (effective 1998). **Document type:** *Journal, Government.*
Former titles (until 2002): Denmark. Statens Jordbrugs- og Fiskerioekonomiske Institut. Aarsberetning (1395-511X); (until 1995): Denmark. Statens Jordbrugsoekonomiske Institut. Aarsberetning (0108-7479); (until 1983): Denmark. Jordbrugsoekonomisk Institut. Aarsberetning (0106-4967)
Indexed: WAE&RSA.
—CISTI.
Published by: Ministeriet for Foedevarer, Landbrug og Fiskeri, Foedevareoekonomisk Institut/Ministry of Food, Agriculture and Fisheries, Danish Research Institute of Food Economics, Rolighedsvej 25, Frederiksberg C, 2000, Denmark. TEL 45-35-28-68-00, FAX 45-35-28-68-01, sjfi@sjfi.dk, http://www.sjfi.dk.

DENMARK. MINISTERIET FOR FOEDEVARER, LANDBRUG OG FISKERI. FOEDEVAREOEKONOMISK INSTITUT. LANDBRUGSREGNSKABSSTATISTIK/AGRICULTURAL ACCOUNTS STATISTICS. see *AGRICULTURE—Abstracting, Bibliographies, Statistics*

338.109489 DNK ISSN 1602-1665
HD2001
DENMARK. MINISTERIET FOR FOEDEVARER, LANDBRUG OG FISKERI. FOEDEVAREOEKONOMISK INSTITUT. RAPPORT/DENMARK. INSTITUTE OF AGRICULTURAL AND FISHERIES ECONOMICS. REPORT. Text in Danish, English. 1981. irreg. (5-7/yr.). price varies. **Document type:** *Monographic series.*
Former titles (until 2002): Denmark. Statens Jordbrugs- og Fiskerioekonomiske Institut. Rapport (1395-5705); (until 1995): Denmark. Statens Jordbrugsoekonomiske Institut. Rapport (0108-7398); (until 1983): Denmark. Jordbrugsoekonomisk Institut. Rapport (0107-5357)

Indexed: AEA, AgBio, AnBrAb, DSA, FCA, ForAb, HortAb, I&DA, IndVet, OrnHort, PGrRegA, PN&I, PotatoAb, PoultAb, RDA, RPP, RevApplEntom, SIA, TriticAb, VetBull, WAE&RSA, WeedAb.
—BLDSC (7269.250000), CISTI, IE.
Published by: Ministeriet for Foedevarer, Landbrug og Fiskeri, Foedevareoekonomisk Institut/Ministry of Food, Agriculture and Fisheries, Danish Research Institute of Food Economics, Rolighedsvej 25, Frederiksberg C, 2000, Denmark. TEL 45-35-28-68-00, FAX 45-35-28-68-01, sjfi@sjfi.dk, http://www.sjfi.dk.

338.1 DNK
HD2001
DENMARK. MINISTERIET FOR FOEDEVARER, LANDBRUG OG FISKERI. FOEDEVAREOEKONOMISK INSTITUT. SERIE B: OEKONOMIEN I LANDBRUGETS DRIFTSGRENE/ ECONOMICS OF AGRICULTURAL ENTERPRISES. Key Title: Oekonomien i Landbrugets Driftsgrene. Text in Danish, English. 1969. a. DKK 60 (effective 1998).
Former titles (until 2002): Denmark. Statens Jordbrugsoekonomiske Institut. Serie B: Oekonomien i Landbrugets Driftsgrene (0107-5683); (until 1982): Regnskabsresultater fra Danske Landbrug i Aaret (Year) (0106-519X)
—BLDSC (8442.010000), CISTI.
Published by: Ministeriet for Foedevarer, Landbrug og Fiskeri, Foedevareoekonomisk Institut/Ministry of Food, Agriculture and Fisheries, Danish Research Institute of Food Economics, Rolighedsvej 25, Frederiksberg C, 2000, Denmark. TEL 45-35-28-68-00, FAX 45-35-28-68-01, sjfi@sjfi.dk, http://www.sjfi.dk.

338.1309489 DNK ISSN 1600-311X
DENMARK. MINISTERIET FOR FOEDEVARER, LANDBRUG OG FISKERI. FOEDEVAREOEKONOMISK INSTITUT. SERIE C: LANDBRUGETS PRISFORHOLD/AGRICULTURAL PRICE STATISTICS. Key Title: Landbrugets Prisforhold. Text in Danish, English. 1967. a. price varies.
Formerly (until 2002): Denmark. Statens Jordbrugs- og Fiskerioekonomiske Institut. Serie C: Landbrugets Prisforhold (0107-5691)
Indexed: HortAb, TriticAb, WAE&RSA.
—CISTI.
Published by: Ministeriet for Foedevarer, Landbrug og Fiskeri, Foedevareoekonomisk Institut/Ministry of Food, Agriculture and Fisheries, Danish Research Institute of Food Economics, Rolighedsvej 25, Frederiksberg C, 2000, Denmark. TEL 45-35-28-68-00, FAX 45-35-28-68-01, sjfi@sjfi.dk, http://www.sjfi.dk.

DENMARK. MINISTERIET FOR FOEDEVARER, LANDBRUG OG FISKERI. FOEDEVAREOEKONOMISK INSTITUT. SERIE D: GARTNERI-REGNSKABSSTATISTIK/HORTICULTURAL ACCOUNTS STATISTICS. see *AGRICULTURE—Abstracting, Bibliographies, Statistics*

338.1 FRA ISSN 1287-8375
LA DEPECHE LE PETIT MEUNIER; l'hebdomadaire de l'economie agricole. Text in French. 199?. w. FRF 698; FRF 1,028 in the European Union; FRF 1,188 elsewhere. adv. illus.; stat.
Formed by the merger of (1946-199?): Depeche Commerciale et Agricole (0011-8931); (1934-199?): Le Petit Meunier (0031-6261)
Published by: Societe d'Edition de la Presse Agricole et Alimentaire Specialisee, 84 bd. de Sebastopol, Paris, 75003, France. Ed. Laurent Estebe. Circ: 15,000.

338.1 NLD ISSN 0926-5589
➤ **DEVELOPMENTS IN AGRICULTURAL ECONOMICS.** Text in Dutch. 1983. irreg., latest vol.11, 2003. price varies. back issues avail. **Document type:** *Monographic series, Academic/Scholarly.*
Indexed: Agr.
—BLDSC (3579.061150), CISTI. **CCC.**
Published by: Elsevier BV (Subsidiary of: Elsevier Science & Technology), Radarweg 29, Amsterdam, 1043 NX, Netherlands. TEL 31-20-4853911, FAX 31-20-4852457, nlinfo-f@elsevier.nl, http://www.elsevier.com/inca/tree/?key=B1DIAE, http://www.elsevier.nl.

➤ **DIRECTORY AND STATISTICS OF AGRICULTURAL CO-OPERATIVES AND OTHER FARMER CONTROLLED BUSINESSES IN THE U K.** see *AGRICULTURE—Abstracting, Bibliographies, Statistics*

630.029 CAN ISSN 0708-3017
DIRECTORY OF ALBERTA'S AGRICULTURAL PROCESSING INDUSTRY. Text in English. 1975. a. free. charts; illus. **Document type:** *Directory, Government.*
Formerly: Agricultural Processing and Manufacturing Guide (0708-3025)
Published by: Agriculture, Food & Rural Development, Agri-Food Development Branch, 7000 113 St, 3rd Fl, Rm 304, Edmonton, AB T6H 5T6, Canada. TEL 780-427-7325, FAX 780-422-3655, pelleti@agric.gov.ab.ca. Ed., R&P Allan Pelletier. Circ: 3,000.

A

A

338.1 USA ISSN 0093-5271
DOANE'S AGRICULTURAL REPORT. Text in English. 1938. w. (50/yr.). USD 129 (effective 2005). bk.rev. **Document type:** *Newsletter, Trade.* **Description:** Covers farm marketing and management.
—CISTI.
Published by: Doane Agricultural Services, 11701 Borman Dr, Ste 300, St. Louis, MO 63146-4193. TEL 314-569-2700, FAX 314-569-1083, http://www.doane.com/dar.php. Pub. Dan Manternach. Circ: 25,000.

338.1 UKR ISSN 0235-6368
DOM, SAD, GOROD. Text in Ukrainian. m.
—East View.
Published by: Izdatel'stvo Niva, Ul Pavlovskaya 11-g, Kiev, Ukraine. TEL 380-44-216-0540. **US dist. addr.:** East View Information Services, 3020 Harbor Ln. N., Minneapolis, MN 55447. TEL 612-550-0961.

E U FOOD LAW. see *LAW—International Law*

338.1 UGA ISSN 0377-7103
HD1401
EASTERN AFRICA JOURNAL OF RURAL DEVELOPMENT. Text in English. 1968. a. USD 25 in Uganda to individuals; USD 30 to individuals Kenya and Tanzania; USD 50 in Africa to individuals; USD 75 elsewhere to individuals; USD 100 to institutions (effective 2004). adv. bk.rev. bibl.; charts; stat. reprint service avail. from PQC.
Formerly (until 1973): East Africa Journal of Rural Development (0012-8333)
Related titles: Microform ed.: (from PQC).
Indexed: FCA, JEL, PAIS, PLESA, SSI.
Published by: Makerere University, Department of Agricultural Economics, PO Box 7062, Kampala, Uganda. TEL 256-41-531152, FAX 256-41-531641, agecon@infocom.co.ug, http://www.makerere.ac.ug/agriculture/. Ed. Barnabas Kiiza. Circ: 800. **Co-sponsor:** Eastern Africa Economic Society.

338.1 ITA ISSN 1126-1668
ECONOMIA AGRO - ALIMENTARE. Text in Italian. 1996. q. EUR 51 domestic; EUR 74 foreign (effective 2003). **Document type:** *Journal, Academic/Scholarly.*
Published by: Franco Angeli Edizioni, Viale Monza 106, Milan, 20127, Italy. TEL 39-02-2837141, FAX 39-02-26144793, redazioni@francoangeli.it, http://www.francoangeli.it.

338.1 COL ISSN 0046-1148
HD9199.A1
ECONOMIA CAFETERA. Text in Spanish. 1966. m. free. charts; stat. **Document type:** *Bulletin.* **Description:** Provides Colombian coffee statistics.
Published by: (Estudios y Proyectos Basicos Cafeteros), Federacion Nacional de Cafeteros de Colombia, Calle 73, 8-13 Piso 10 B, Bogota, DE, Colombia. TEL 57-1-3451088, FAX 57-1-2171021, TELEX 44655. Circ: 8,000 (controlled).

338.1 GBR ISSN 0262-9135
ECONOMIC REPORT ON SCOTTISH AGRICULTURE. Text in English. 1981. a. price varies. **Document type:** *Government.*
Incorporates: Scottish Agricultural Economics; Some Studies of Current Economic Conditions in Scottish Farming (0080-7966); Agricultural Statistics, Scotland (0065-4582)
Indexed: AnBrAb, DSA, FPA, NutrAb, WAE&RSA.
—BLDSC (3654.449000), Linda Hall.
Published by: Scottish Office, Agriculture and Fisheries Department, Pentland House, 47 Robb's Loan, Edinburgh, EH14 1TY, United Kingdom.

338.1 KEN
➤ **ECONOMIC REVIEW OF AGRICULTURAL PRODUCTION AND MARKETING (YEAR).** Text in English. 1963. a. USD 2 per issue. back issues avail. **Document type:** *Government.* **Description:** Provides a review over a period of one year of the agricultural activities of Kenya, from production to marketing. Also reviews government policy concerning food and agriculture.
Formerly: Economic Review of Agriculture
Indexed: RRTA, WAE&RSA.
Published by: (Kenya. Livestock Development & Marketing), Ministry of Agriculture, Development Planning Division, PO Box 14733, Nairobi, Kenya. TEL 254-2-442240, TELEX 22766. Ed. Protus Sigei. Circ: 1,500.

338.1 FRA ISSN 0070-8798
ECONOMIE ET FINANCES AGRICOLES/AGRICULTURAL ECONOMICS AND FINANCE. Text in French. 1971. 10/yr. bk.rev. Supplement avail.
Indexed: FS&TA, MaizeAb, PAIS, SoyAb, TriticAb, WAE&RSA.
Published by: Caisse Nationale du Credit Agricole, 91-93 bd. Pasteur, Paris, 75015, France. Ed. Jacques Lenormand. Circ: 8,000.

338.1 330.9 FRA ISSN 0013-0559
➤ **ECONOMIE RURALE**; agricultures - alimentation - territoires. Text in French. 1949. bi-m. EUR 120 in Europe; EUR 130 elsewhere (effective 2002). adv. bk.rev. bibl.; charts. index. **Document type:** *Trade.* **Description:** Academic journal dealing with French and European agricultural policy, geography, trade, agricultural development, and methodology.
Indexed: AgBio, AgrForAb, AnBrAb, DIP, DSA, ExcerpMed, FPA, ForAb, HerbAb, HortAb, I&DA, IBR, IBZ, ILD, JEL, NutrAb, PAIS, PBA, PGegResA, PHN&I, PN&I, PotatoAb, RDA, REE&TA, RRTA, RiceAb, S&F, SIA, SeedAb, SoyAb, TriticAb, WAE&RSA, WeedAb.
—BLDSC (3658.400000), CISTI, IE, Infotrieve, ingenta.
Published by: Societe Francaise d'Economie Rurale, 16 rue Claude Bernard, Paris, Cedex 5 75231, France. TEL 33-1-47074786, FAX 33-1-44081842, sfer@inapg.inra.fr, http://www.inra.fr. Ed. Luis Pascal Mahe. Circ: 1,000 (paid).

338.1 FRA ISSN 0068-4899
ECONOMIES ET SOCIETES. SERIE AG. PROGRES ET AGRICULTURE. Text in French. 1962. irreg.
Indexed: WAE&RSA.
—IE.
Published by: Les Presses de l'I S M E A, BP 22, Paris, Cedex 13 75622, France. TEL 33-1-55489076, FAX 33-1-55489071, http://www.ismea.org. Ed. Gerard de Bernis. Circ: 1,600.

338.1 UKR
EKONOMIKA APK. Text in Ukrainian. 1994. m. USD 130 in the Americas (effective 2000).
Published by: Ministerstvo Sel'skogo Khozyaistva Ukrainy, Ul. Khreshchatik, 24, Kiev, Ukraine. TEL 261-34-71.

338.1 SCG ISSN 0352-3462
EKONOMIKA POLJOPRIVREDA. Text in Serbian; Summaries in English. 1954. q. YUN 85,000; USD 140 foreign (effective 1999). adv. bk.rev.
Former titles (until 1979): Ekonomika Proizvodnje Hrane (0352-3454); (until 1977): Ekonomika Poljoprivrede (0013-306X)
Indexed: RRTA, WAE&RSA.
—CISTI.
Published by: Savez Poljoprivrednih Inzenjera i Tehnicara Jugoslavije/Association of Agricultural Engineers and Technicians of Yugoslavia, Kneza Milosa 9-1, Belgrade, 11000. TEL 381-3244317, FAX 381-3244317. Ed. Viden Randelovic. R&P Dragustin Nedeljkovic. Circ: 1,100.

338.1 RUS
EKONOMIKA SEL'SKOGO KHOZYAISTVA ROSSII. Text in Russian; Summaries in English, Russian. 1993. m. USD 126 (effective 1999). adv. bk.rev. bibl.; charts; illus.; stat.
Formerly (until 1994): Ekonomika Sel'skogo Khozyaistva (0013-3094)
Indexed: AEA, CDSP, ChemAb, DSA, MaizeAb, RRTA, RefZh, TriticAb, WAE&RSA.
—CCC.
Published by: Izdatel'stvo Kolos, Sadovaya-Spasskaya 18, Moscow, 107807, Russian Federation. TEL 7-095-2071662. Ed. Marlen M Makeenko. Circ: 50,000. **Dist. by:** M K - Periodica, ul Gilyarovskogo 39, Moscow 129110, Russian Federation. TEL 7-095-2845008, FAX 7-095-2813798, info@periodicals.ru, http://www.mkniga.ru.

338.1 FRA ISSN 0396-0102
ELEVEUR DE FRANCE. Text in French. 6/yr.
Published by: Societe Neolait Codislait, BP 1, Yffiniac, 22120, France. TEL 96-72-61-81. Ed. Jean Jacques Bree. Circ: 40,000.

630 VEN ISSN 0798-6351
ENCUESTA AGROPECUARIA. Text in Spanish. 1969. a. free. stat.
Published by: (Venezuela. Ministerio de Agricultura y Cria), Direccion de Planificacion y Estadistica (Subsidiary of: Ministerio de Agricultura y Cria), Division de Estadistica, Centro Simon Bolivar, Torre Norte 16o, Caracas, 1010, Venezuela.

ENCUESTA NACIONAL AGROPECUARIA. RESULTADOS DE LA PRODUCCION AGRICOLA. see *AGRICULTURE—Abstracting, Bibliographies, Statistics*

338.1 COL
ENSAYOS SOBRE ECONOMIA CAFETERA. Text in Spanish. 1987. s-a.
Indexed: PAIS.
Published by: Federacion Nacional de Cafeteros de Colombia, Calle 73, 8-13 Piso 10 B, Bogota, DE, Colombia.

ESTADISTICA PANAMENA. SITUACION ECONOMICA. SECCION 312. PRODUCCION PECUARIA. see *AGRICULTURE—Abstracting, Bibliographies, Statistics*

ESTADISTICA PANAMENA. SITUACION ECONOMICA. SECCION 351. PRECIOS PAGADOS POR EL PRODUCTOR AGROPECUARIO. see *AGRICULTURE—Abstracting, Bibliographies, Statistics*

ESTADISTICA PANAMENA. SITUACION ECONOMICA. SECCION 351. PRECIOS RECIBIDOS POR EL PRODUCTOR AGROPECUARIO. see *AGRICULTURE—Abstracting, Bibliographies, Statistics*

ESTADISTICA PANAMENA. SITUACION ECONOMICA. SECCION 351. PRECIOS RECIBIDOS POR EL PRODUCTOR AGROPECUARIO. COMPENDIO. see *AGRICULTURE—Abstracting, Bibliographies, Statistics*

ETUDES RURALES; revue trimestrielle d'histoire, geographie, sociologie et economie des campagnes. see *SOCIOLOGY*

338.1 GBR ISSN 1360-4392
EUROPEAN POTATO MARKETS MONTHLY. Text in English. 1995. m. GBP 426 domestic; GBP 443 in Europe; GBP 527 elsewhere (effective 2005). **Document type:** *Newsletter, Trade.* **Description:** Comprehensive report with prices, trade and production statistics, policy, market reports and outlook across Europe.
—CISTI.
Published by: Agra Europe (London) Ltd. (Subsidiary of: T & F Informa plc), 80 Calverley Rd, Tunbridge Wells, Kent TN1 2UN, United Kingdom. TEL 44-1892-533813, FAX 44-1892-544895, marketing@agra-net.com, http://www.agra-net.com.

338.1 GBR ISSN 0165-1587
HD1916 CODEN: ERAEDA
➤ **EUROPEAN REVIEW OF AGRICULTURAL ECONOMICS.** Text in English. 1973. q. GBP 210, USD 389, EUR 315 to institutions; GBP 53, USD 98, EUR 80 in developing nations to institutions; GBP 221, USD 409, EUR 332 combined subscription to institutions print & online eds. (effective 2006). adv. bk.rev. cum.index. back issues avail.; reprint service avail. from PSC. **Document type:** *Journal, Academic/Scholarly.* **Description:** Focuses on the discussion and dissemination of theoretical and applied agricultural economics research in Europe and for stimulating ideas relating to the economic problems of agriculture in Europe and other parts of the world.
Related titles: Online - full text ed.: ISSN 1464-3618. GBP 199, USD 368, EUR 299 to institutions (effective 2006) (from EBSCO Publishing, Gale Group, HighWire Press, IngentaConnect, O C L C Online Computer Library Center, Inc., Oxford University Press Online Journals, ProQuest Information & Learning, Swets Information Services).
Indexed: ABIn, ASCA, AbHyg, AgBio, Agr, Agrind, AnBrAb, BAS, Biostat, CREJ, CurCont, DSA, ESPM, FS&TA, Faml, ForAb, HerbAb, HortAb, I&DA, IBSS, ILD, ISR, IndVet, JEL, MaizeAb, NutrAb, OrnHort, PCI, PHN&I, PN&I, PollutAb, PotatoAb, PoultAb, RDA, RM&VM, RRTA, RevApplEntom, RiskAb, S&F, SCI, SIA, SOPODA, SSCI, SoyAb, TriticAb, VetBull, WAE&RSA.
—BLDSC (3829.940000), CISTI, IDS, IE, Infotrieve, ingenta. CCC.
Published by: Oxford University Press, Great Clarendon St, Oxford, OX2 6DP, United Kingdom. TEL 44-1865-556767, FAX 44-1865-556646, jnl.orders@oup.co.uk, http://erae.oxfordjournals.org/, http://www.oxfordjournals.org/. Ed. Dr. Alison Burrell. Pub. Martin Green. R&P Fiona Bennett. Adv. contact Helen Pearson. B&W page GBP 250, B&W page USD 420; 110 x 195. Circ: 550.

338.1 USA ISSN 1010-1365
CODEN: ASBFDF
F A O AGRICULTURAL SERVICES BULLETIN. (Food and Agriculture Organization) Text in English. 1968. irreg., latest vol.140. USD 18 (effective 2001). **Document type:** *Monographic series.* **Description:** This publication describes the sugar industry with particular regard to the production of various categories of sugar and alcohol, processing and utilization of by-products, and the manufacture of pulp and paper. with the diminishing demand for and cost of sugar, diversification towards value-added products can offer opportunities for improving the economics of sugar production.
Formerly: Agricultural Services Bulletin (0378-2182)
Related titles: French ed.: Bulletin des Services Agricoles. ISSN 1014-4218; Spanish ed.: Boletin de Servicios Agricolas. ISSN 1014-4226.
Indexed: BioDAb, FS&TA, HortAb, NutrAb, PGegResA, PHN&I, PoultAb, RDA, RRTA, RevApplEntom, RiceAb, S&F, SIA, TriticAb, WAE&RSA.
—BLDSC (3865.591500), CASDDS, CISTI, IE, ingenta, Linda Hall.
Published by: Food and Agriculture Organization of the United Nations, c/o Bernan Associates, 4611 F Assembly Dr, Lanham, MD 20706-4391. TEL 301-459-7666, FAX 301-459-0056. Circ: 2,000.

338.1 USA ISSN 0259-2495
F A O FERTILIZER AND PLANT NUTRITION BULLETIN. (Food and Agriculture Organization) Text in English. irreg., latest vol.12, 1995. price varies. **Document type:** *Monographic series.*
Formerly (until 1981): F A O Fertilizer Bulletin (0254-5764)
Related titles: Spanish ed.: Boletin F A O, Fertilizantes y Nutricion Vegetal. ISSN 1014-4072; French ed.: Bulletin F A O d'Engrais et Nutrition Vegetale. ISSN 0259-6180.
Indexed: AgrForAb, S&F, WeedAb.
Published by: Food and Agriculture Organization of the United Nations, c/o Bernan Associates, 4611 F Assembly Dr, Lanham, MD 20706-4391. TEL 301-459-7666, FAX 301-459-0056.

338.1 ITA ISSN 1011-5366
F A O INVESTMENT CENTRE TECHNICAL PAPER. (Food and Agriculture Organization) Text in English. 1985. irreg.
Related titles: French ed.: F A O Document Technique du Centre d'Investissement. ISSN 0259-627X; Spanish ed.: F A O Documento Tecnico del Centro de Inversiones. ISSN 1014-3084.

Indexed: S&F, WAE&RSA.
—CISTI.
Published by: Food and Agriculture Organization of the United Nations, Sales and Marketing Group, Viale delle Terme di Caracalla, Rome, 00100, Italy. TEL 39-06-57054350, FAX 39-06-57053360.

338.1　　　　　USA　　　　　ISSN 1014-7640
HD1421
F A O YEARBOOK. PRODUCTION. Text in English, French, Spanish. 1958. a. USD 45 (effective 2000).
Former titles (until 1987): F A O Production Yearbook (0071-7118); (until 1976): Food and Agriculture Organization of the United Nations. Production Yearbook (0378-0775); (until 1958): Yearbook of Food and Agricultural Statistics. Volume I, Production (0256-7393); Supersedes in part (in 1948): Yearbook of Food and Agricultural Statistics (0378-3898); Which was formerly (1905-1945): International Yearbook of Agricultural Statistics (1010-903X)
Related titles: Microfiche ed.: (from CIS).
Indexed: AEA, DSA, FS&TA, HortAb, IIS, NutrAb, RASB, S&F, SIA, WAE&RSA.
—CISTI.
Published by: Food and Agriculture Organization of the United Nations, c/o Bernan Associates, 4611 F Assembly Dr, Lanham, MD 20706-4391. TEL 301-459-7666, FAX 301-459-0056.

380.141　　　　　USA　　　　　ISSN 1014-7632
HD9000.4
F A O YEARBOOK, TRADE. Text in English, French, Spanish. 1947. a. USD 45 (effective 2000). charts; stat.
Former titles: Food and Agriculture Organization of the United Nations. Trade Yearbook (0071-7126); Yearbook of Food and Agricultural Statistics (0378-3898)
Related titles: Microfiche ed.: (from CIS).
Indexed: AEA, AnBrAb, DSA, HortAb, IIS, S&F, SIA, WAE&RSA.
—CISTI.
Published by: Food and Agriculture Organization of the United Nations, c/o Bernan Associates, 4611 F Assembly Dr, Lanham, MD 20706-4391. TEL 301-459-7666, FAX 301-459-0056.

338.1　　　　　USA
F C A BULLETIN. (Farm Credit Administration) Text in English. 1986. m. free. Document type: Government. Description: Presents news and information on regulatory matters and legislation pertaining to the activities of the Farm Credit Administration, which examines and regulates Farm Credit System institutions.
Published by: Farm Credit Administration, Office of Congressional & Public Affairs, 1501 Farm Credit Dr., Mclean, VA 22102-5090. TEL 703-883-4056, FAX 703-883-4066. Ed. Christine Quinn. Circ: 3,000.

338.1　　　　　USA　　　　　ISSN 1076-3856
F M R A NEWS. Text in English. 1937. bi-m. USD 24 domestic; USD 32 foreign (effective 2005). adv. bk.rev.; software rev.; video rev.; Website rev. 16 p./no.; back issues avail.
Document type: Newsletter, Trade. Description: Contains articles of interest to agricultural consultants, farm managers, rural appraisers, and other agricultural professionals.
Related titles: Online - full content ed.
Published by: American Society of Farm Managers and Rural Appraisers, 950 S Cherry St, Ste 508, Denver, CO 80246-2664. TEL 303-758-3513, FAX 303-758-0190, asfmra@agri-associations.org, http://www.asfmra.org/fjournals.htm. Ed. Cheryl Cooley. adv.: page USD 2,000. Circ: 2,700 (controlled).

336.2　　　　　USA　　　　　ISSN 1077-0461
FARM AND RANCH TAX LETTER. Key Title: Ag Executive's Farm and Ranch Tax Letter. Text in English. 1993. m. USD 35 (effective 2005). back issues avail. Document type: Newsletter, Trade. Description: Provides new tax law information and timely tips on how to utilize tax law changes to your benefit. Written for the producer, not the accountant or lawyer, by practicing agricultural tax experts.
Published by: Ag Executive, Inc., 115 E Twyman, Bushnell, IL 61422-1320. TEL 309-772-2168, FAX 309-772-2167, darrellld@aol.com, info@agexecutive.com, http://www.agexecutive.com. Ed., Pub., R&P Darrell L Dunteman. Circ: 3,200 (paid).

FARM BUSINESS ACCOUNTS. SUMMARY OF RESULTS (YEAR). see BUSINESS AND ECONOMICS—Accounting

338.1　　　　　USA
FARM BUSINESS MANAGEMENT ANALYSIS REPORT; annual report for North East and East Central Minnesota. Text in English. 1955. a. USD 5 (effective 2000). charts. index. Document type: Academic/Scholarly. Description: Record summary of active farmers enrolled in farm business management education programs.
Formerly: Farm Business Management
Published by: Central Lakes College, PO Box 99, Staples, MN 56479-0099. TEL 218-894-5164, http://www.mgt.org. R&P DelRay D Lecy. Circ: 1,200.

338.1　　　　　USA
FARM BUSINESS MANAGEMENT UPDATE. Text in English. 1995. q. back issues avail.

Media: Online - full text.
Published by: Virginia Cooperative Extension, 121 Hutcheson Hall, Virginia Tech 0437, Blacksburg, VA 24061-0001. FAX 800-828-1120, http://www.ext.vt.edu/.

FARM BUSINESS STATISTICS FOR SOUTH EAST ENGLAND. see AGRICULTURE—Abstracting, Bibliographies, Statistics

338.1　　　　　GBR
FARM BUSINESS SURVEY IN WALES. Text in English. 1981. a.
—BLDSC (3871.920000).
Published by: University of Wales, Old College, King St, Aberystwyth, Ceredigion, Wales SY23 2AX, United Kingdom. TEL 44-1970-623111, http://www.aber.ac.uk.

332.71　　　　　USA　　　　　ISSN 0883-329X
FARM CREDIT ADMINISTRATION. ANNUAL REPORT. Key Title: Annual Report of the Farm Credit Administration and the Cooperative Farm Credit System. Text in English. 1933. a. free. Document type: Government. Description: Provides statistical information on and analysis of the yearly activities of the FCA and the financial condition of the Farm Credit System institutions, which are examined and regulated by the FCA.
Former titles (until 1984): U.S. Farm Credit Administration. Annual Report of the Farm Credit Administration and the Cooperative Farm Credit System; U.S. Farm Credit Administration. Annual Report of the Farm Credit Administration on the Work of the Cooperative Farm Credit System (0083-0542)
Published by: Farm Credit Administration, Office of Congressional & Public Affairs, 1501 Farm Credit Dr., Mclean, VA 22102-5090. TEL 703-883-4056, FAX 703-883-4066. Ed. Christine Quinn. Circ: 5,000.

338.1　　　　　USA
FARM INCOME. Text in English. a. free. Document type: Government.
Published by: Agricultural Statistics Service, 2 W Edenton St, PO Box 27767, Raleigh, NC 27611. TEL 919-856-4394. Ed. Becky Meadows. Circ: 1,500.

336.225　　　　　USA　　　　　ISSN 1053-6086
KF6369.8.F3
FARM INCOME TAX MANUAL. Text in English. 1954. base vol. plus a. updates. looseleaf. USD 175 base vol(s). (effective 2005). Supplement avail. Document type: Trade. Description: Discusses personal exemptions, personal deducations, credits, sale of capital assets, involuntary conversions, farm partnerships and all other aspects of farm taxes.
Indexed: ATI.
Published by: Michie Company (Subsidiary of: LexisNexis North America), 701 E Water St, Charlottesville, VA 22902-5389. TEL 434-972-7600, 800-446-3410, FAX 434-972-7677, http://www.michie.com. Ed. Charles Davenport.

338.1　　　　　THA　　　　　ISSN 0430-084X
S562.A75
FARM MANAGEMENT NOTES FOR ASIA AND THE FAR EAST. Text in Thai. 1965. biennial. free.
Published by: (Commission on Farm Management for Asia and the Far East), Food and Agriculture Organization of the United Nations, Regional Office for Asia and the Pacific, Maliwan Mansion, 39 Phra Atit Rd, Bangkok, 10200, Thailand. Circ: 300.

338.1　　　　　GBR
FARM MANAGEMENT POCKETBOOK. Text in English. a. GBP 12 per issue (effective 2003). Document type: Monographic series, Academic/Scholarly.
Indexed: AEA, DSA, PoultAb, WAE&RSA.
—BLDSC (3880.530000).
Published by: (Department of Agricultural Economics), Imperial College of Science, Technology and Medicine, Department of Agricultural Sciences at Wye (Subsidiary of: University of London), Wye, Ashford, Kent TN25 5AH, United Kingdom. TEL 44-20-75942617, FAX 44-20-75942754, http://www.wye.ic.ac.uk.

338.1　　　　　CAN　　　　　ISSN 1201-9313
FARM OPERATIONS COST GUIDE. Text in English. a. CND 5 (effective 2004).
Formerly (until 1995): Farm Machinery Costs as a Guide to Custom Rates (0709-6216)
—CISTI.
Published by: Alberta Agriculture, Food & Rural Development, Farm Business Management Branch, 7000 113 St, Edmonton, AB T6H 5T6, Canada. TEL 780-427-0391, 800-292-5697, FAX 780-422-8835.

FARM TAX BRIEF; practical guidance on effective tax planning and the law relating to agricultural land. see BUSINESS AND ECONOMICS—Public Finance, Taxation

338.1　　　　　USA
FARM TAX SAVER. Text in English. 1975. m. USD 50. back issues avail. Document type: Newsletter. Description: Informs on new and existing tax laws of interest to farmers and agriculturists.
Published by: Farm Progress Companies, 191 S Gary Ave, Carol Stream, IL 60188. TEL 708-690-5600, FAX 708-462-2869. Ed. Trenna Grabowski. Pub. Allan Johnson. Circ: 3,200.

338.1　　　　　GBR
FARMING IN THE EAST MIDLANDS. FINANCIAL RESULTS. Text in English. 1948. a. Document type: Bulletin.
—BLDSC (3895.730000).
Published by: University of Nottingham, Rural Business Research Unit, Sutton Bonington Campus, Loughborough, Leics LE12 5RD, United Kingdom. TEL 44-115-951-6070, FAX 44-115-951-6089, sazmfs@szni.nottingham.ac.uk. Ed. Martin Seabrook. Circ: 600.

FEED INDUSTRY REVIEW; a structural and financial analysis of the UK and European animal feed industries. see AGRICULTURE—Feed, Flour And Grain

338.1　　　　　MDA
FERMER/FARMER. Text in Russian. w. Document type: Newspaper, Consumer. Description: Contains useful advice of specialists on problems of farming, novelties of agricultural science and engineering, farming calendars and national Moldovian cuisine.
Published by: Nezavisimaya Moldova, Ul Pushkin 22, Chisinau, 2012, Moldova. TEL 373-2-233605, FAX 373-2-233141, tis@nemo.moldova.su, http://www.mldnet.com/nezmold/index.html. Ed. Yurii Hudoley.

FERTILIZER FINANCIAL FACTS. see AGRICULTURE—Abstracting, Bibliographies, Statistics

FERTILIZER INSTITUTE. ANNUAL SUMMARY. see AGRICULTURE—Abstracting, Bibliographies, Statistics

FERTILIZER INSTITUTE. MONTHLY EXPORTS AND IMPORTS. see AGRICULTURE—Abstracting, Bibliographies, Statistics

338.021 630.021　　　　　USA
FERTILIZER INSTITUTE. PRODUCTION COST SURVEYS; ammonia, phosphate rock, phosphate fertilizer. Text in English. a. USD 425; includes Fertilizer Financial Facts. Document type: Trade. Description: Focuses on average annual cost elements involved in manufacturing key fertilizer products.
Published by: Fertilizer Institute, 501 Second St, N E, Washington, DC 20002. TEL 202-675-8250, FAX 202-544-8123, http://www.tfi.org.

FERTILIZER INSTITUTE. PRODUCTION SURVEY. see AGRICULTURE—Abstracting, Bibliographies, Statistics

631.8　　　　　USA
FERTILIZER RECORD. Text in English. m. USD 550 (effective 1999); includes Production Survey and Annual Summary. film rev.; video rev. Document type: Trade. Description: Monthly production inventory package.
Published by: Fertilizer Institute, 501 Second St, N E, Washington, DC 20002. TEL 202-675-8250, FAX 202-544-8123, hvroomen@tfi.org, http://www.tfi.org. R&P Harry L Vroomen. Circ: 700.

338.1　　　　　USA　　　　　ISSN 0083-0976
FOOD AND AGRICULTURAL EXPORT DIRECTORY. Text in English. 1972. biennial. free. adv. bk.rev. Document type: Directory, Government.
Published by: U.S. Department of Agriculture, Foreign Agricultural Service, Information Division, Rm 5920 S, Washington, DC 20250-1000. TEL 202-720-7937. Circ: 10,000 (controlled).

338.1　　　　　USA　　　　　ISSN 0739-6791
THE FOOD AND FIBER LETTER. Text in English. 1981. w. USD 445 domestic; USD 495 foreign (effective 2005). adv. back issues avail. Document type: Newsletter, Trade. Description: Covers agricultural policy and economics including congressional actions, taxes, transportaion and international developments.
Related titles: Online - full text ed.
—CISTI.
Published by: Informa Economics, Inc., 6862 Elm St, Ste 350, Mclean, VA 22101. TEL 703-734-8787, FAX 703-893-1065, barry.jenkins@informaecon.com, http://www.informaecon.com. Ed., R&P Barry Jenkins.

338.1　　　　　PHL
FOOD BALANCE SHEET OF THE PHILIPPINES. Text in English. a., latest 1993. USD 22 in Asia; USD 28 in Australia & New Zealand; USD 32 in US & Canada; USD 36 in Europe; USD 42 in Latin America; USD 45 elsewhere. stat. Document type: Government. Description: Provides quantitative information on the national food supply situation. Shows trends in food production, changing patterns, flows, and the net supply of food in the country.
Former titles: Philippine Food Balance Sheet; Philippines. National Economic and Development Authority. Food Balance Series
Media: Duplicated (not offset).
Indexed: IIS.
Published by: National Statistical Coordination Board, c/o National Statistical Information Center, Midland-Buendia Bldg, 403 Sen. Gil Puyat Ave., Makati City, Philippines. TEL 63-2-890-9405, FAX 63-2-890-9408, nscb_nsic@mozcom.com.

A

338.1 USA ISSN 1047-0441
HD1751
FOOD COST REVIEW. Text in English. 1983. a. **Document type:** *Government.*
Formerly: Developments in Farm to Retail Price Spreads for Food Products (0741-0174)
—CISTI.
Published by: U.S. Department of Agriculture, Economic Research Service, c/o Debbie Haugan, 1800 M St, N W, Rm 3100, Washington, DC 20036. TEL 202-694-5050.

338.1 ITA
FOOD OUTLOOK. Text in English. 1995. 5/yr. illus.
Media: Online - full content.
Indexed: IIS.
Published by: Food and Agriculture Organization of the United Nations, Global Information and Early Warning System on Food and Agriculture, Viale delle Terme di Caracalla, Rome, Italy. http://www.fao.org/giews.

338.1 GBR ISSN 0306-9192
HD9000.1
➤ **FOOD POLICY.** Text in English. 1976. 6/yr. EUR 225 in Europe to individuals; JPY 29,700 in Japan to individuals; USD 252 to individuals except Europe and Japan; EUR 864 in Europe to institutions; JPY 114,600 in Japan to institutions; USD 966 to institutions except Europe and Japan (effective 2006). adv. bk.rev. index. back issues avail. **Document type:** *Journal, Academic/Scholarly.* **Description:** Focuses on the politics, economics and planning aspects of food, agriculture and nutrition. International in scope.
Related titles: Microform ed.: (from PQC); Online - full text ed.: (from EBSCO Publishing, Gale Group, IngentaConnect, ScienceDirect, Swets Information Services).
Indexed: APEL, ARDT, ASCA, ASD, ASFA, AgBio, Agr, AgrForAb, AnBrAb, B&AI, BAS, BibAg, CREJ, CurCont, DSA, EI, EIA, EPB, ESPM, EnerInd, EnvAb, FCA, FS&TA, FamI, ForAb, FutSurv, GEOBASE, H&SSA, HerbAb, HortAb, IBSS, ISR, IndVet, JEL, KES, MaizeAb, NutrAb, PAIS, PBA, PGegResA, PHN&I, PN&I, PotatoAb, PoultAb, RASB, RDA, REE&TA, RI-1, RI-2, RM&VM, RefZh, RevApplEntom, RiceAb, S&F, S&MA, SCI, SIA, SSCI, SeedAb, SoyAb, TDB, TOSA, TriticAb, VetBull, WAE&RSA, WeedAb.
—BLDSC (3981.780000), CIS, CISTI, IDS, IE, Infotrieve, ingenta. **CCC.**
Published by: Pergamon (Subsidiary of: Elsevier Science & Technology), The Boulevard, Langford Ln, East Park, Kidlington, Oxford OX5 1GB, United Kingdom. TEL 44-1865-843000, FAX 44-1865-843010, foodpolicy@ic.ac.uk, http://www.elsevier.com/locate/foodpol. Eds. A Dorward, J Kydd. **Subscr. to:** Elsevier BV, PO Box 211, Amsterdam 1000 AE, Netherlands. nlinfo-f@elsevier.nl, http://www.elsevier.nl.

➤ **FOREIGN PRODUCTION, SUPPLY AND DISTRIBUTION OF AGRICULTURAL COMMODITIES.** see *AGRICULTURE—Abstracting, Bibliographies, Statistics*

➤ **FRANCE. CAISSE NATIONALE DU CREDIT AGRICOLE. RAPPORT SUR LE CREDIT AGRICOLE MUTUEL.** see *BUSINESS AND ECONOMICS—Banking And Finance*

338.1 FRA
FRANCE. MINISTERE DE L'AGRICULTURE ET DE LA PECHE. AGRESTE ANIMAUX HEBDO. Text in French. 1974. w. **Document type:** *Government.*
Formerly: France. Ministere de l'Agriculture, de la Peche et de l'Alimentation. Conjoncture Animaux Hebdo; Incorporates: France. Ministere de l'Agriculture. Situation Agricole en France. Note de Conjoncture Production Bovine (0243-6280); France. Ministere de l'Agriculture. Situation Agricole en France. Note de Conjoncture Production Porcine (0243-6175)
Published by: Ministere de l'Agriculture et de la Peche, Service Central des Enquetes et Etudes Statistiques, 251 rue de Vaugirard, Paris, Cedex 15 75732, France. TEL 33-1-49558585, FAX 33-1-49558503, http://www.agriculture.gouv.fr.

338.1 FRA ISSN 1624-9011
HD1941
FRANCE. MINISTERE DE L'AGRICULTURE ET DE LA PECHE. AGRESTE. CHIFFRES ET DONNEES. AGRICULTURE. Text in French. 1975. irreg. **Document type:** *Government.*
Former titles (until 2000): France. Ministere de l'Agriculture et de la Peche. Donnees Chiffres Agriculture (1263-0594); (until 198?): France. Ministere de l'Agriculture, de la Peche et de l'Alimentation. Donnees Chiffres Agriculture; France. Ministere de l'Agriculture et de la Foret. Donnees Chiffres Agriculture; Incorporates: France. Ministere de l'Agriculture. Series "S". Production Animales (0243-6566); France. Ministere de l'Agriculture. Series "S". Departements d'Outre-Mer (0243-6574)
Published by: Ministere de l'Agriculture et de la Peche, Service Central des Enquetes et Etudes Statistiques, 251 rue de Vaugirard, Paris, Cedex 15 75732, France. TEL 33-1-49558585, FAX 33-1-49558503, http://www.agriculture.gouv.fr.

338.1 FRA
FRANCE. MINISTERE DE L'AGRICULTURE ET DE LA PECHE. AGRESTE CONJONCTURE. Text in French. 1979. m. **Document type:** *Government.*
Former titles: France. Ministere de l'Agriculture, de la Peche et de l'Alimentation. Conjoncture (1274-1086); (until 1995): France. Ministere de l'Agriculture et de la Foret. Conjoncture Generale (0998-416X); (until 1990): France. Ministere de l'Agriculture. Situation Agricole en France. Conjoncture Generale (0222-5220)
Published by: Ministere de l'Agriculture et de la Peche, Service Central des Enquetes et Etudes Statistiques, 251 rue de Vaugirard, Paris, Cedex 15 75732, France. TEL 33-1-49558585, FAX 33-1-49558503, http://www.agriculture.gouv.fr.

FRANCE. MINISTERE DE L'AGRICULTURE ET DE LA PECHE. AGRESTE LE BULLETIN. see *AGRICULTURE—Abstracting, Bibliographies, Statistics*

338.1 FRA ISSN 1283-4858
HD9323.1
FRANCE. MINISTERE DE L'AGRICULTURE ET DE LA PECHE. AGRESTE PRIMEUR. Text in French. 1974. irreg. **Document type:** *Government.*
Former titles: France. Ministere de l'Agriculture, de la Peche et de l'Alimentation. Agreste Primeur; France. Ministere de l'Agriculture et de la Foret. Donnees; Incorporates in part: France. Ministere de l'Agriculture. Series "S". Industries Agricoles et Alimentaires (0243-6647); France. Ministere de l'Agriculture. Note de Conjoncture Production Vegetale (0243-6248)
Published by: Ministere de l'Agriculture et de la Peche, Service Central des Enquetes et Etudes Statistiques, 251 rue de Vaugirard, Paris, Cedex 15 75732, France. TEL 33-1-49558585, FAX 33-1-49558503, http://www.agriculture.gouv.fr.

FRANCE. MINISTERE DE L'AGRICULTURE ET DE LA PECHE. CONJONCTURE COMMERCE EXTERIEUR AGRO-ALIMENTAIRE. see *BUSINESS AND ECONOMICS—International Commerce*

338.1 FRA
FRANCE. MINISTERE DE L'AGRICULTURE ET DE LA PECHE. CONJONCTURE FRUITS. Text in French. 1977. 7/yr. (m. May-Nov.). **Document type:** *Government.*
Former titles: France. Ministere de l'Agriculture, de la Peche et de l'Alimentation. Conjoncture Fruits; France. Ministere de l'Agriculture et de la Foret. Conjoncture Fruits; Incorporates in part: France. Ministere de l'Agriculture. Note de Conjoncture Production Vegetale (0243-6248); Formerly: France. Ministere de l'Agriculture. Informations Rapides. Fruits (0243-6108)
Published by: Ministere de l'Agriculture et de la Peche, Service Central des Enquetes et Etudes Statistiques, 251 rue de Vaugirard, Paris, Cedex 15 75732, France. TEL 33-1-49558585, FAX 33-1-49558503, http://www.agriculture.gouv.fr.

338.1 FRA
FRANCE. MINISTERE DE L'AGRICULTURE ET DE LA PECHE. CONJONCTURE GRANDES CULTURES. Text in French. 1975. m. **Document type:** *Government.* **Description:** Contains statistics on agricultural production in France.
Former titles: France. Ministere de l'Agriculture, de la Peche et de l'Alimentation. Conjoncture Grandes Cultures; France. Ministere de l'Agriculture et de la Foret. Conjoncture Grandes Cultures; Incorporates in part: France. Ministere de l'Agriculture. Note de Conjoncture Production Vegetale (0243-6248)
Published by: Ministere de l'Agriculture et de la Peche, Service Central des Enquetes et Etudes Statistiques, 251 rue de Vaugirard, Paris, Cedex 15 75732, France. TEL 33-1-49558585, FAX 33-1-49558503, http://www.agriculture.gouv.fr.

338.1 FRA
FRANCE. MINISTERE DE L'AGRICULTURE ET DE LA PECHE. CONJONCTURE LEGUMES. Text in French. 1977. m. **Document type:** *Government.*
Former titles: France. Ministere de l'Agriculture, de la Peche et de l'Alimentation. Conjoncture Legumes; France. Ministere de l'Agriculture et de la Foret. Conjoncture Legumes; Incorporates in part: France. Ministere de l'Agriculture. Note de Conjoncture Production Vegetale (0243-6248); Formerly: France. Ministere de l'Agriculture. Informations Rapides. Legumes (0243-6140)
Published by: Ministere de l'Agriculture et de la Peche, Service Central des Enquetes et Etudes Statistiques, 251 rue de Vaugirard, Paris, Cedex 15 75732, France. TEL 33-1-49558585, FAX 33-1-45558503, http://www.agriculture.gouv.fr.

338.1 FRA
FRANCE. MINISTERE DE L'AGRICULTURE ET DE LA PECHE. CONJONCTURE PRODUCTIONS ANIMALES. Text in French. 1977. irreg. **Document type:** *Government.*
Former titles: France. Ministere de l'Agriculture, de la Peche et de l'Alimentation. Conjoncture Productions Animales; France. Ministere de l'Agriculture et de la Foret. Conjoncture Productions Animales; France. Ministere de l'Agriculture. Informations Rapides. Production Animale (0223-4912)
Published by: Ministere de l'Agriculture et de la Peche, Service Central des Enquetes et Etudes Statistiques, 251 rue de Vaugirard, Paris, Cedex 15 75732, France. TEL 33-1-49558585, FAX 33-1-49558503, http://www.agriculture.gouv.fr.

338.1 FRA
FRANCE. MINISTERE DE L'AGRICULTURE ET DE LA PECHE. CONJONCTURE VITICULTURE. Text in French. 1978. 5/yr. (m. July-Nov.). **Document type:** *Government.*
Former titles: France. Ministere de l'Agriculture, de la Peche et de l'Alimentation. Conjoncture Viticulture; France. Ministere de l'Agriculture et de la Foret. Conjoncture Viticulture; France. Ministere de l'Agriculture. Informations Rapides. Viticulture
Published by: Ministere de l'Agriculture et de la Peche, Service Central des Enquetes et Etudes Statistiques, 251 rue de Vaugirard, Paris, Cedex 15 75732, France. TEL 33-1-49558585, FAX 33-1-49558503, http://www.agriculture.gouv.fr.

338.1 FRA
HD1941
FRANCE. MINISTERE DE L'AGRICULTURE ET DE LA PECHE. GRAPH-AGRI; annuaire de graphiques agricoles. Text in French. 1979. a. **Document type:** *Government.*
Formerly: France. Ministere de l'Agriculture, de la Peche et de l'Alimentation. Conjoncture Graph-Agri (0242-2085)
—CISTI.
Published by: Ministere de l'Agriculture et de la Peche, Service Central des Enquetes et Etudes Statistiques, 251 rue de Vaugirard, Paris, Cedex 15 75732, France. TEL 33-1-49558585, FAX 33-1-49558503, http://www.agriculture.gouv.fr.

338.1 USA
FRESH FRUIT AND VEGETABLE MARKET NEWS: WEEKLY SUMMARY, SHIPMENTS - ARRIVALS. Text in English. w. USD 8; USD 16 foreign.
Formerly: Fresh Fruit and Vegetable Market News: Weekly Summary, Shipments, Unloads (0094-4858)
Published by: (Fruit and Vegetable Division), U.S. Department of Agriculture, Agricultural Marketing Division, Washington, DC 20250. TEL 202-720-2175.

338.1 USA
FRUIT AND VEGETABLE TRUCK RATE AND COST SUMMARY. Text in English. 1975. a. looseleaf. USD 10. back issues avail. **Document type:** *Newsletter, Government.* **Description:** Presents lists of price ranges for, and the cost components and availability of, truck transportation for hauling produce, for all areas of the United States.
Former titles: Fruit and Vegetable Truck Rate; Fruit and Vegetable Truck Rate and Cost Summary
Published by: Federal-State Market News Service (Sacramento), 630 Sansome St, Rm 727, San Francisco, CA 94111. TEL 415-705-1300, FAX 415-705-1301.

634 USA
FRUIT AND VEGETABLE TRUCK RATE REPORT. Text in English. 1978. w. USD 96 domestic; USD 132 foreign. Supplement avail.; back issues avail.; reprint service avail. from CIS. **Document type:** *Government.* **Description:** Provides information on rates for shipping loads of selected produce items to various U.S. cities. Also includes a section on the volume of shipments in the U.S., as compared to the previous week and the previous year.
Related titles: Microfiche ed.: (from CIS).
Indexed: AmStI.
Published by: (U.S. Department of Agriculture), Federal-State Market News Service (Sacramento), 630 Sansome St, Rm 727, San Francisco, CA 94111. TEL 415-705-1300, FAX 415-705-1301. Circ: 120.

338.1 GMB ISSN 0301-8423
GAMBIA. PRODUCE MARKETING BOARD. ANNUAL REPORT. Text in English. 1971. a. free. illus. **Document type:** *Bulletin, Government.*
Formerly: Gambia. Oilseeds Marketing Board. Report
Published by: Produce Marketing Board, Marina Foreshore, PO Box 284, Banjul, Gambia.

GERMANY. STATISTISCHES BUNDESAMT. FACHSERIE 16, LOEHNE UND GEHAELTER, REIHE 1: ARBEITERVERDIENSTE IN DER LANDWIRTSCHAFT. see *AGRICULTURE—Abstracting, Bibliographies, Statistics*

GERMANY. STATISTISCHES BUNDESAMT. FACHSERIE 17, PREISE, REIHE 1: PREISE UND PREISINDIZES FUER DIE LAND- UND FORSTWIRTSCHAFT. see *AGRICULTURE—Abstracting, Bibliographies, Statistics*

GERMANY. STATISTISCHES BUNDESAMT. FACHSERIE 3, LAND- UND FORSTWIRTSCHAFT, FISCHEREI; REIHE 2: BETRIEBS-, ARBEITS- UND EINKOMMENSVERHAELTNISSE. see *AGRICULTURE—Abstracting, Bibliographies, Statistics*

338.1 USA ISSN 1081-6526
HD9000.1
GIANNINI FOUNDATION INFORMATION SERIES. Text in English. 1964. irreg., latest 1997, no.97-1. free. **Document type:** *Monographic series.*

Formerly: Information Series on Agricultural Economics (0073-7887)
Indexed: Agr, PHN&I.
—BLDSC (4169.270000), CISTI.
Published by: University of California at Berkeley, Giannini Foundation of Agricultural Economics, 207 Giannini Hall, Ste 3310, Berkeley, CA 94720-3310. TEL 530-642-7121. Ed. Peter Berck. R&P Robert Sams TEL 530-754-8539.

338.1 USA ISSN 0575-4208
GIANNINI FOUNDATION MONOGRAPH. Text in English. 1961 (no.10). irreg., latest vol.43, 1997. free. back issues avail. **Document type:** *Monographic series, Academic/Scholarly.*
Indexed: HortAb, RefZh, S&F, TriticAb, WAE&RSA.
—BLDSC (4169.300000).
Published by: University of California at Berkeley, Giannini Foundation of Agricultural Economics, 207 Giannini Hall, Ste 3310, Berkeley, CA 94720-3310. TEL 530-642-7121. Ed. Peter Berck. R&P Robert Sams TEL 530-754-8539.

338.1 USA ISSN 0899-3068
HD1775.C2
GIANNINI FOUNDATION RESEARCH REPORT. Text in English. 1930. irreg., latest vol.345, 1998. free. **Document type:** *Monographic series, Academic/Scholarly.*
Former titles (until 1987): Giannini Research Report (0894-8240); (until 1986): Giannini Foundation of Agricultural Economics. Research Report (0072-4459)
Indexed: Agr, FCA, FS&TA, PHN&I, RefZh, WAE&RSA.
—BLDSC (4169.500000), CISTI.
Published by: University of California at Berkeley, Giannini Foundation of Agricultural Economics, 207 Giannini Hall, Ste 3310, Berkeley, CA 94720-3310. TEL 510-642-7121. Ed. Peter Berck. R&P Robert Sams TEL 530-754-8539.

338.1 CAN ISSN 0834-2660
GLOBAL LINK. Text in English, French. 1979. 3/yr. bk.rev. **Document type:** *Newsletter.*
Formerly (until 1986): Thought for Food (0715-7320)
—CISTI.
Published by: Canadian Hunger Foundation, 323 Chapel St, Ottawa, ON K1N 7Z2, Canada. TEL 613-237-0180, FAX 613-237-5969. Ed. Ariella Hostetter. Circ: 10,000.

338.1 ESP ISSN 0211-867X
GONDOLA; revista tecnica del comercio, distribucion y consumo. Text in Spanish. 1980. m.
Published by: Editorial de Medios Tecnicos de Expresion S.A., Estrella San Roma, Comercio, 4, Madrid, 28007, Spain. TEL 1-433-67-50, FAX 1-433-88-74. Ed. Javier Perez Serna.

338.1 GBR
GOOD PRACTICE IN RURAL DEVELOPMENT. Text in English. 1997. irreg. **Document type:** *Monographic series.*
—BLDSC (4201.351750).
Published by: Stationery Office Bookstore, 21 S. Gyle Crescent, Edinburgh, United Kingdom. TEL 44-131-479-3141, FAX 44-131-479-3142.

631 HRV ISSN 0350-3100
S13
GOSPODARSKI LIST. Text in Croatian. 1842. s-m. **Document type:** *Magazine, Trade.*
Former titles (until 1855): Gospodarske Novine (1330-1861); (until 1850): List Druztva Gospodarskoga Horvatsko-Slavonskoga (1330-1853); (until 1849): List Mesecni Horvatsko-Slavonskoga Gospodarskoga Druztva (1330-1772)
Address: Trg Bana J Jelacica 3, Zagreb, 10000, Croatia. TEL 385-1-4816145, FAX 385-1-4816146. Ed. Branko Horvat.

380.141 GBR ISSN 0963-1682
GREEN PAGES; the directory of agriculture in the U.K. Text in English. 1990. a., latest vol.10. GBP 22.50 in United Kingdom; GBP 25 elsewhere (effective 2001). adv. 708 p./no.; **Document type:** *Directory.* **Description:** Lists manufacturers and suppliers of agricultural equipment and supplies.
Related titles: CD-ROM ed.
Published by: Geraldine Flower Publications, 229 Acton Ln, London, W4 5DD, United Kingdom. TEL 44-20-8767-8028, FAX 44-20-8767-8054, enquiries@green-pages.co.uk, http://www.green-pages.co.uk. Ed., R&P, Adv. contact Geraldine Flower. Circ: 20,000 (paid).

338.1 AUT
GRUENER BERICHT. Text in German. 1959. a. free. **Document type:** *Yearbook, Government.*
Formerly: Bericht ueber die Lage der Oesterreichischen Landwirtschaft
Indexed: NutrAb.
Published by: Bundesministerium fuer Land- und Forstwirtschaft, Umwelt und Wasserwirtschaft, Stubenring 1, Vienna, 1012, Austria. TEL 43-1-711006753, FAX 43-1-711005198, http://www.bmlf.gv.at. Circ: 3,100.

338.1 GTM
GUATEMALA. BANCO NACIONAL DE DESARROLLO AGRICOLA. MEMORIA. Abbreviated title: Banadesa. Text in Spanish. 1971. a. stat.
Published by: Banco Nacional de Desarrollo Agricola, 9 Calle No. 9-47, Zona 1, Guatemala City, Guatemala.

338.1 DNK ISSN 0419-9936
HAANDBOG FOR DRIFTSPLANLAEGNING. Variant title: Haandbof i Driftsplanlaegning. Text in Danish. 1963. a., latest 2004. DKK 72 (effective 2005). **Document type:** *Trade.*
Published by: Dansk Landbrugsraadgivning, Landbrugsforlaget/ Danish Agricultural Advisory Service. Publishing, Udkaersvej 15, Skejby, Aarhus N, 8200, Denmark. TEL 45-87-405537, FAX 45-87-405085, forlag@landcentret.dk. Ed. Karen Joergensen.

338.1 DEU ISSN 0723-7383
HANDBUCH DER TIERISCHEN VEREDLUNG. Text in German. 1974. a. EUR 20 (effective 2005). 500 p./no.; back issues avail. **Document type:** *Journal, Trade.*
Published by: Kamlage Verlag GmbH, Iburger Str 112, Osnabrueck, 49082, Germany. TEL 49-541-52371, FAX 49-541-54879, info@kamlage.de, http://www.kamlage.de. Ed., R&P, Adv. contact Barbara Kamlage. Circ: 40,000 (paid).

338.1 POL ISSN 1234-6292
HANDEL ZAGRANICZNY PRODUKTAMI ROLNO-SPOZYWCZYMI; analizy rynkowe. Text in Polish. 1995. s-a. EUR 24 foreign (effective 2005). **Document type:** *Journal, Academic/Scholarly.*
Published by: Instytut Ekonomiki Rolnictwa i Gospodarki Zywnosciowej, ul Swietokrzyska 20, Warsaw, 00002, Poland. TEL 48-22-5054444, ierigz@ierigz.waw.pl, http://www.ierigz.waw.pl. **Dist. by:** Ars Polona, Krakowskie Przedmiescie 7, Warsaw, Poland. TEL 48-22-9263914, FAX 48-22-9265334, arspolona@arspolona.com.pl, http://www.arspolona.com.pl.

HAY & FORAGE GROWER. see *AGRICULTURE—Feed, Flour And Grain*

380.141 USA
HAY MARKET NEWS - NATIONAL. Text in English. w. USD 70; USD 75 in Canada & Mexico; USD 105 elsewhere. **Document type:** *Government.*
Published by: (U.S. Dept. of Agriculture, Agricultural Marketing Service), Market News, 210 Walnut St, Rm 767, Des Moines, IA 50309. Ed. Lisa Whitney.

338.1 USA ISSN 1075-9255
HORIZONS (BLACKSBURG). Text in English. 1931. bi-m. free. stat. **Document type:** *Newsletter.* **Description:** Covers a broad range of topics related to rural and agricultural economies and communities and to the natural resource base of rural and agricultural areas.
Former titles (until 1989): Virginia Agricultural Economics (0042-6466); Virginia Farm Economics
Indexed: EIA, EnerInd.
—Linda Hall.
Published by: Rural Economic Analysis Program, Department of Agricultural and Applied Economics, Virginia Tech, Blacksburg, VA 24061-0401. TEL 540-231-9443, FAX 540-231-7417. Ed., R&P Karen Mundy. Circ: 3,000.

I C A S A NEWS. see *AGRICULTURE—Crop Production And Soil*

I C C O QUARTERLY BULLETIN OF COCOA STATISTICS. see *FOOD AND FOOD INDUSTRIES*

I C C O WORLD COCOA DIRECTORY. see *FOOD AND FOOD INDUSTRIES*

338.1 DEU ISSN 0081-7198
I F O STUDIEN ZUR AGRARWIRTSCHAFT. Text in German. 1967. irreg., latest vol.31, 1995. price varies. **Document type:** *Monographic series.* **Description:** Presents research results of the Department of Agriculture.
Indexed: RRTA, WAE&RSA.
—CISTI, Linda Hall.
Published by: I F O Institut fuer Wirtschaftsforschung, Poschingerstr 5, Munich, 81679, Germany. TEL 49-89-9224-0, FAX 49-89-985369, ifo@ifo.de, http://www.ifo.de. Circ: 400.

338.1 USA ISSN 0886-7372
I F P R I RESEARCH REPORT. Abstracts in English, French, Spanish. 1976. irreg. (approx. 7/yr.). free. bibl.; charts; illus.; stat. back issues avail. **Document type:** *Monographic series, Academic/Scholarly.* **Description:** Research on food policy for developing countries.
Related titles: Microfiche ed.: (from NTI).
Indexed: ARDT, DSA, GEOBASE, NutrAb, RDA, WAE&RSA.
—BLDSC (7762.376000), ingenta.
Published by: International Food Policy Research Institute, 2033 K St, N W, Ste 400, Washington, DC 20006-1002. TEL 202-862-5600, FAX 202-467-4439, TELEX 440054, ispri-info@cgiar.org, http://www.cgair.org/ifpri. Ed. Don Flipincott. Circ: 3,000.

338.1 FRA ISSN 0988-3266
I N R A SCIENCES SOCIALES. Text in French. 1988. bi-m. stat. **Document type:** *Newsletter.* **Description:** Publishes the essentials of the department's research results for professionals in farming, the agro-food industries, teaching, research and technical journalism.
Indexed: AbHyg, AgrForAb, AnBrAb, DSA, ForAb, HortAb, IndVet, MaizeAb, NutrAb, PAIS, PHN&I, PN&I, RRTA, S&F, TriticAb, WAE&RSA.
Published by: Institut National de la Recherche Agronomique, Departement d'Economie et de Sociologie Rurales, 63-65 bd. de Brandebourg, Ivry, Cedex 94205, France. TEL 33-1-49596900, FAX 33-1-46704113, velt3@ivry.inra.fr. Ed. Didier Aubert. Circ: 1,500. **Subscr. to:** I N R A Editions, RD 10, Versailles Cedex 78026, France.

338.1 BGR ISSN 0205-3845
HD2041
IKONOMIKA I UPRAVLENIE NA SELSKOTO STOPANSTVO. Text in Bulgarian; Summaries in English. bi-m. USD 96 foreign (effective 2002). **Document type:** *Journal.* **Description:** Publishes specialized economic reviews on the questions of agriculture, including economics and management.
Indexed: RefZh.
—BLDSC (0086.158000), CISTI.
Published by: Bulgarian Academy of Sciences, Institute of Agricultural Economics, 136 Tsar Boris St., Sofia, 1618, Bulgaria. TEL 359-2-562808, FAX 359-2-562805.

338.1 IND
INDIA. DEPARTMENT OF RURAL DEVELOPMENT. ADMINISTRATIVE INTELLIGENCE DIVISION. PROGRESS REPORT ON SMALL FARMERS DEVELOPMENT AGENCY PROGRAMME. Text in English. a. stat.
Published by: Ministry of Agriculture, Department of Rural Development, New Delhi, 110 001, India.

INDIA. DEPARTMENT OF RURAL DEVELOPMENT. ADMINISTRATIVE INTELLIGENCE DIVISION. SOME SPECIAL PROGRAMMES OF RURAL DEVELOPMENT. STATISTICS. see *AGRICULTURE—Abstracting, Bibliographies, Statistics*

338.1 IND ISSN 0019-5014
HD101
INDIAN JOURNAL OF AGRICULTURAL ECONOMICS. Text in English. 1940. q. USD 125 to institutions (effective 2006). adv. bk.rev. charts; stat. index. Supplement avail. **Document type:** *Academic/Scholarly.* **Description:** Features agricultural and rural development, growth rates in agriculture, dry farming, poverty and income, forestry, livestock, fisheries, and agricultural price policy.
Related titles: Online - full text ed.: (from Northern Light Technology, Inc., ProQuest Information & Learning).
Indexed: AEA, ARDT, ASFA, AgBio, AgrForAb, BAS, CTFA, CurCont, DSA, ESPM, FCA, FPA, FS&TA, ForAb, GEOBASE, HerbAb, HortAb, I&DA, IBSS, ILD, IndVet, JEL, MaizeAb, NutrAb, OrnHort, PAA&I, PBA, PGegResA, PHN&I, PollutAb, PotatoAb, RA&MP, RASB, RDA, RRTA, RiceAb, RiskAb, S&F, SIA, SWRA, SeedAb, SoyAb, TOSA, TriticAb, WAE&RSA, WTA, WeedAb.
—BLDSC (4409.950000), CISTI, IE, Infotrieve, ingenta.
Published by: (Indian Society of Agricultural Economics), Scientific Publishers, 5-A New Pali Rd., Near Hotel Taj Hari Mahal, PO Box 91, Jodhpur, Rajasthan 342 003, India. TEL 91-291-2433323, FAX 91-291-2512580, info@scientificpub.com, http://www.scientificpub.com/bookdetails.php?booktransid=308&bookid=304. Ed. N A Mujumdar. R&P Tara Shukla. Adv. contact Shri G R Shetty. Circ: 1,800.

338.1 CUB ISSN 0138-7480
INFORMACION EXPRESS. SERIE: ECONOMIA Y ORGANIZACION DEL TRABAJO AGROPECUARIO. Text in Spanish. 1977. 2/yr. USD 5 in North America; USD 6 in Europe; USD 9 elsewhere.
Indexed: Agrind.
—CISTI.
Published by: Centro de Informacion y Documentacion Agropecuario, Gaveta Postal 4149, Havana, 4, Cuba. **Dist. by:** Ediciones Cubanas, Obispo No. 527, Apdo. 605, Havana, Cuba.

338.1 BEL ISSN 0073-7895
INFORMATION SERVICE OF THE EUROPEAN COMMUNITIES. NEWSLETTER ON THE COMMON AGRICULTURAL POLICY. Text in English. irreg. (approx. 20/yr.). **Document type:** *Newsletter.*
Published by: Press and Information Service of the European Communities, Rue de la Loi 200, Brussels, 1049, Belgium.

338.1 CMR
INSTITUT PANAFRICAIN POUR LE DEVELOPPEMENT. TRAVAUX MANUSCRITS. Text in French. 1972. irreg. price varies.
Published by: Institut Panafricain pour le Developpement, Centre de Documentation/Pan African Institute for Development, BP 4078, Douala, Cameroon. TEL 237-403770, FAX 237-403068, ipdac@sprynet.com, sgpaidafr@camfido.gn.apc.org. Circ: 200.

338.1 FRA ISSN 0398-8287
INSTITUT TECHNIQUE DE L'AVICULTURE. TENDANCES DES MARCHES. Text in French. 1962. m. looseleaf. EUR 91.89 (effective 2002). bk.rev. back issues avail.
Published by: Institut Technique de l'Aviculture, 28 rue du Rocher, Paris, 75008, France. TEL 33-1-45226240, FAX 33-1-43874613. Circ: 400.

▼ new title ➤ refereed ✶ unverified ♦ full entry avail.

A

338.1 BRA
INSTITUTO DE ECONOMIA AGRICOLA. INFORMACOES ECONOMICAS. Text in Portuguese. 1966. m. USD 65 (effective 2000). charts; stat.
Former titles: Mercados Agricolas; Instituto de Economia Agricola. Informacoes Economicas (0100-4409)
Indexed: AEA, AgBio, AgrForAb, AnBrAb, BioCN&I, CTFA, DSA, FCA, FPA, ForAb, HerbAb, HortAb, I&DA, IndVet, MaizeAb, NutrAb, OrnHort, PBA, PGegResA, PHN&I, PN&I, PotatoAb, PoultAb, RA&MP, RDA, RPP, RRTA, RiceAb, S&F, SIA, SeedAb, SoyAb, TDB, TriticAb, VetBull, WAE&RSA, WeedAb.
—BLDSC (4481.130000), CISTI, IE, ingenta.
Published by: Instituto de Economia Agricola, Av Miguel Stefano, 3900, Saude, Caixa Postal 6802, Sao Paulo, SP 04301-002, Brazil. TEL 55-11-5770244 ext 2354, FAX 55-11-2764062, TELEX 011-56730, cct@iea.sp.gov.br, http://www.iea.sp.gov.br. Ed. Regina Junko Yoshii. Circ: (controlled).

338.1 CHE ISSN 0074-2856
INTERNATIONAL CONFEDERATION FOR AGRICULTURAL CREDIT. ASSEMBLY AND CONGRESS REPORTS✶. Text in English. 1951. irreg. (7th Congress, St. Louis, U.S.A.), latest 1973. **Document type:** *Proceedings.*
Published by: International Confederation for Agricultural Credit, Birmendorferstr 67, Zuerich, 8004, Switzerland. Circ: 500.

338.13 GBR ISSN 0074-2902
HD1405
INTERNATIONAL CONFERENCE OF AGRICULTURAL ECONOMISTS. PROCEEDINGS. Text in English. 1929. triennial. GBP 55.95. adv. **Document type:** *Proceedings, Academic/Scholarly.*
Indexed: WAE&RSA.
Published by: (International Association of Agricultural Economists), Dartmouth Publishing Co. Ltd., Gower House, Croft Rd, Aldershot, Hants GU11 3HR, United Kingdom. Ed. John Irwin. R&P Margaret O'Reilley. Adv. contact Jason Aldous.

338.1 USA ISSN 1096-7508
HD9000.1
➤ **INTERNATIONAL FOOD AND AGRIBUSINESS MANAGEMENT REVIEW.** Text in English. 1998. q. USD 125 membership for individuals in academia, industry and industry; USD 500 membership; USD 60 membership students (effective 2004). back issues avail. **Document type:** *Journal, Trade.* **Description:** Provides a forum for research results, new ideas, new applications of knowledge, and discussions of important topics that enhance the efficiency and effectiveness of the worldwide food and agribusiness system.
Related titles: Online - full text ed.: (from EBSCO Publishing, Gale Group, IngentaConnect, ScienceDirect, Swets Information Services).
Indexed: Agr.
—BLDSC (4540.290000), CISTI, IE, Infotrieve, ingenta.
Published by: International Food and Agribusiness Management Association, 333 Blocker Building, 2124 TAMU, College Station, TX 77843-2124. TEL 979-845-2118, FAX 979-862-1487, iama@tamu.edu, http://www.ifama.org/nonmember/OpenIFAMR/OpenIFAMR.htm.

338.1 GBR
INTERNATIONAL GRAINS COUNCIL. GRAIN MARKET REPORT. Text in English, French, Russian, Spanish. 1972. m. (11/yr.). GBP 300, USD 480 (effective 2001). charts; stat. **Document type:** *Trade.* **Description:** Contains comprehensive facts and figures on the current world market situation for wheat and coarse grains. Supplemented by analyses on matters of topical interest.
Formerly: International Wheat Council. Grain Market Report
Related titles: French ed.; Russian ed.; Spanish ed.
Indexed: IIS, MaizeAb, RRTA, RiceAb, TriticAb, WAE&RSA.
—BLDSC (4208.410370).
Published by: International Grains Council, One Canada Sq, Canary Wharf, London, E14 5AE, United Kingdom. TEL 44-20-7513-1122, FAX 44-20-7513-0630, publications@igc.org.uk, igc-fac@igc.org.uk, http://www.igc.org.uk.

338.1 GBR
➤ **INTERNATIONAL INSTITUTE FOR ENVIRONMENT AND DEVELOPMENT. SUSTAINABLE AGRICULTURE PROGRAMME. HIDDEN HARVEST RESEARCH SERIES.** Text in English. 1993. a., latest vol.5. GBP 13 per vol. (effective 2001). back issues avail. **Document type:** *Monographic series, Academic/Scholarly.* **Description:** The series aims to investigate through local level valuation, the importance of wild plant and animal reserves in agricultural systems and to rural livelihoods.
Formerly: International Institute for Environment and Development. Sustainable Agriculture Programme. Research Series. (1358-3875)
—BLDSC (7769.986800).
Published by: (Sustainable Agriculture Programme), International Institute for Environment and Development, 3 Endsleigh St, London, WC1H ODD, United Kingdom. TEL 44-20-73882117, FAX 44-20-73882826, sustag@iied.org, http://www.iied.org. Ed. Irene Guijt.

338.1 GBR ISSN 1473-5903
▼ ➤ **INTERNATIONAL JOURNAL OF AGRICULTURAL SUSTAINABILITY.** Text in English. 2003. 3/yr. GBP 145, USD 270, EUR 220 to institutions (effective 2005). **Document type:** *Journal, Academic/Scholarly.* **Description:** Dedicated to advancing the understanding of sustainability in agricultural and food systems.
Announced as: International Journal of Sustainable Agriculture
Related titles: Online - full text ed.: (from EBSCO Publishing, Gale Group, Swets Information Services).
Indexed: FCA.
—BLDSC (4541.606000). **CCC.**
Published by: Channel View Publications (Subsidiary of: Multilingual Matters Ltd.), Frankfurt Lodge, Clevedon Hall, Victoria Rd., Clevedon, BS21 7HH, United Kingdom. TEL 44-1275-876519, FAX 44-1275-871673, info@multilingual-matters.com, http://www.channelviewpublications.com. Ed. Dr. Jules Pretty. R&P Ms. Marjukka Grover. Adv. contact Ms. Kathryn King. **Dist. by:** Portland Press Ltd., Commerce Way, Colchester CO2 8HP, United Kingdom. TEL 44-1206-796351, FAX 44-1206-799331, sales@portland-services.com.

338.1 GBR ISSN 1744-7550
▼ ➤ **INTERNATIONAL JOURNAL OF POSTHARVEST TECHNOLOGY AND INNOVATION.** Text in English. 2005. 4/yr. USD 450; USD 545 combined subscription print & online eds. (effective 2005). **Document type:** *Journal, Academic/Scholarly.* **Description:** Offers a scientific forum for dissemination of innovative research findings and industry best practices on postharvest handling techniques, agro-processing and marketing of food and biological products of plant and animal origin.
Related titles: Online - full text ed.: ISSN 1744-7569. USD 450 (effective 2005).
Published by: Inderscience Publishers, IEL Editorial Office, PO Box 735, Olney, Bucks MK46 5WB, United Kingdom. TEL 44-1234-240519, FAX 44-1234-240515, ijpti@inderscience.com, info@inderscience.com, http://www.inderscience.com/ijpti. Ed. Linus Opara.

➤ **INTERNATIONAL MEAT REVIEW.** see *AGRICULTURE—Poultry And Livestock*

338 USA
INTERNATIONAL NETWORK ON PARTICIPATORY IRRIGATION MANAGEMENT. NEWSLETTER. Text in English. irreg., latest vol.11. back issues avail. **Document type:** *Newsletter.* **Description:** Focuses on irrigation management in developing countries.
Media: Online - full content.
Published by: International Network on Participatory Irrigation Management, 600 Pennsylvania Ave SE, 340, Washington, DC 20003. TEL 202-546-7005, FAX 202-318-0215, http://www.inpim.org.

338.1 USA ISSN 1080-2193
IOWA AG REVIEW. Text in English; Summaries in English. 1994. q. free (effective 2003). mkt. back issues avail. **Document type:** *Newsletter, Academic/Scholarly.*
Related titles: Online - full text ed.
—CISTI.
Published by: Iowa State University, Center for Agricultural and Rural Development, 578 Heady Hall, Ames, IA 50011-1070. TEL 515-294-1183, FAX 515-294-6336, card-iaagrev@iastate.edu, card@iastate.edu, http://www.card.iastate.edu/iowa_ag_review/home.html, htttp://www.card.iastate.edu. Ed., R&P Sandra Clarke. Pub. Bruce Babcock.

IRELAND. CENTRAL STATISTICAL OFFICE. AGRICULTURAL LAND SALES. see *AGRICULTURE—Abstracting, Bibliographies, Statistics*

IRELAND. CENTRAL STATISTICS OFFICE. AGRICULTURAL LABOUR INPUT. see *AGRICULTURE—Abstracting, Bibliographies, Statistics*

IRELAND. CENTRAL STATISTICS OFFICE. AGRICULTURAL PRICE INDICES. see *AGRICULTURE—Abstracting, Bibliographies, Statistics*

IRELAND. CENTRAL STATISTICS OFFICE. AGRICULTURAL PRICE INDICES. PRELIMINARY ESTIMATES. see *AGRICULTURE—Abstracting, Bibliographies, Statistics*

IRELAND. CENTRAL STATISTICS OFFICE. CROPS AND LIVESTOCK SURVEY - FINAL ESTIMATES. see *AGRICULTURE—Abstracting, Bibliographies, Statistics*

IRELAND. CENTRAL STATISTICS OFFICE. CROPS AND LIVESTOCK SURVEY, JUNE - PROVISIONAL RESULTS. see *AGRICULTURE—Abstracting, Bibliographies, Statistics*

IRELAND. CENTRAL STATISTICS OFFICE. EARNINGS OF AGRICULTURAL WORKERS. see *AGRICULTURE—Abstracting, Bibliographies, Statistics*

IRELAND. CENTRAL STATISTICS OFFICE. FARM STRUCTURES SURVEY. see *AGRICULTURE—Abstracting, Bibliographies, Statistics*

IRELAND. CENTRAL STATISTICS OFFICE. OUTPUT, INPUT AND INCOME IN AGRICULTURE. see *AGRICULTURE—Abstracting, Bibliographies, Statistics*

IRELAND. CENTRAL STATISTICS OFFICE. OUTPUT, INPUT AND INCOME IN AGRICULTURE. ADVANCE ESTIMATE. see *AGRICULTURE—Abstracting, Bibliographies, Statistics*

IRELAND. CENTRAL STATISTICS OFFICE. OUTPUT, INPUT AND INCOME IN AGRICULTURE. PRELIMINARY ESTIMATE. see *AGRICULTURE—Abstracting, Bibliographies, Statistics*

IRELAND. DEPARTMENT OF AGRICULTURE AND FOOD. ANNUAL REPORT. see *BUSINESS AND ECONOMICS—Economic Situation And Conditions*

IRELAND. DEPARTMENT OF AGRICULTURE AND FOOD. ANNUAL REVIEW AND OUTLOOK; for agriculture and the food industry. see *BUSINESS AND ECONOMICS—Economic Situation And Conditions*

IRELAND. DEPARTMENT OF AGRICULTURE AND FOOD. SCHEMES AND SERVICES (YEAR). see *BUSINESS AND ECONOMICS—Economic Situation And Conditions*

J D JOURNAL. (John Deere) see *AGRICULTURE—Agricultural Equipment*

JAPAN. HOKURIKU NATIONAL AGRICULTURAL EXPERIMENT STATION. BULLETIN. see *AGRICULTURE—Crop Production And Soil*

338.1 GBR ISSN 1471-0358
S494.5.I5
JOURNAL OF AGRARIAN CHANGE. Text in English. 2001. q. EUR 72 combined subscription in Europe to individuals print & online eds.; USD 81 combined subscription in the Americas to individuals & Caribbean, print & online eds.; GBP 48 combined subscription elsewhere to individuals print & online eds.; USD 491 combined subscription in the Americas to institutions & Caribbean, print & online eds.; USD 207 combined subscription in Canada to institutions print & online eds.; GBP 292 combined subscription elsewhere to institutions print & online eds.; EUR 36 combined subscription in Europe to students print & online eds.; USD 40 combined subscription in the Americas to students & Caribbean, print & online eds.; GBP 24 combined subscription elsewhere to students print & online eds. (effective 2006). **Document type:** *Journal.* **Description:** Discusses the social relations and dynamics of production, property, and power in agrarian formations and their processes of change, both historical and contemporary.
Related titles: Online - full text ed.: ISSN 1471-0366. USD 465 in the Americas to institutions & Caribbean; USD 197 in Canada to institutions; GBP 277 elsewhere to institutions (effective 2006); (from Blackwell Synergy, EBSCO Publishing, Gale Group, IngentaConnect, O C L C Online Computer Library Center, Inc., Swets Information Services).
Indexed: ABIn, AgrForAb, GEOBASE, I&DA, PHN&I, PSA, RDA, S&F, SociolAb, WAE&RSA.
—BLDSC (4919.997950), IE, Infotrieve. **CCC.**
Published by: Blackwell Publishing Ltd., 9600 Garsington Rd, Oxford, OX4 2ZG, United Kingdom. TEL 44-1865-776868, FAX 44-1865-714591, customerservices@oxon.blackwellpublishing.com, http://www.blackwellpublishing.com/journals/JAC.

338.1 USA ISSN 0738-8950
HD1401
JOURNAL OF AGRIBUSINESS. Text in English. 1983. s-a. USD 20 domestic to individuals; USD 50 elsewhere to individuals; USD 40 domestic to institutions (effective 2004). **Document type:** *Journal, Academic/Scholarly.* **Description:** Covers agribusiness, economic development, environmental issues related to agriculture, and other topics included under the umbrella of agricultural economics.
Indexed: AgBio, Agr, AgrForAb, AnBrAb, DSA, ForAb, HortAb, MaizeAb, NemAb, NutrAb, PBA, PGegResA, PHN&I, PN&I, RDA, SeedAb, SoyAb, TriticAb, WAE&RSA.
—BLDSC (4919.999300), CISTI, IE, ingenta.
Published by: University of Georgia, Department of Agricultural & Applied Economics, Conner Hall, Athens, GA 30602-7509. TEL 706-542-2481, FAX 706-542-0739, jab@agecon.uga.edu, http://www.agecon.uga.edu/~jab/. Ed. Chung L Huang TEL 706-542-0747.

338.1 USA ISSN 1074-0708
HD1401 CODEN: JAIAE9
➤ **JOURNAL OF AGRICULTURAL AND APPLIED ECONOMICS.** Text in English. 1969. 3/yr. USD 30 domestic to individuals; USD 35 foreign to individuals; USD 50 domestic to libraries; USD 70 foreign to libraries; USD 30 newsstand/cover domestic; USD 35 newsstand/cover foreign (effective 2004). reprint service avail. from PQC. **Document type:** *Journal, Academic/Scholarly.* **Description:** Provides a forum for creative and scholarly work in agricultural economics and related areas. Contributions on methodology and applications in business, research, and teaching phases of agricultural and applied economics are equally encouraged.
Formerly (until 1992): Southern Journal of Agricultural Economics (0081-3052)

Related titles: Microform ed.: (from PQC); Online - full text ed.: (from ProQuest Information & Learning).
Indexed: ASFA, AbHyg, Agr, BPIA, BibAg, CTFA, DSA, EIA, ESPM, EnerInd, FCA, FS&TA, HortAb, IndVet, JEL, MaizeAb, NutrAb, PHN&I, PN&I, PoultAb, REE&TA, RRTA, RiceAb, S&F, SoyAb, TriticAb, WAE&RSA, WeedAb.
—BLDSC (4919.999400), CISTI, IE, ingenta.
Published by: Southern Agricultural Economics Association, c/o Michael Dicks, Department of Agricultural Economics, Oklahoma State University, Stillwater, OK 74078-0505. TEL 405-794-6157, FAX 405-794-8210, JAAE@agecon.uga.edu, http://www.agecon.uga.edu/~jaae/jaae.htm. Ed. John B Penson Jr. Circ: 1,100. **Subscr. to:** H.A. Clonts, Bob Nelson, Department of Agricultural Economics, Auburn University, Auburn, AL 36849. TEL 334-844-5621, FAX 334-844-5639, Rnelson@acesag.auburn.edu.

338.1 USA ISSN 1542-0485
➤ **JOURNAL OF AGRICULTURAL & FOOD INDUSTRIAL ORGANIZATION.** Text in English. 2002. s-a. USD 35 to individuals; USD 250 to institutions (effective 2006). **Document type:** *Academic/Scholarly.*
Media: Online - full content.
Indexed: IBSS, JEL.
Published by: (University of Nebraska at Lincoln, Center for Agricultural & Food Industrial Organization), Berkeley Electronic Press, 2809 Telegraph Ave., Ste 202, Berkeley, CA 94705. TEL 510-665-1200, FAX 510-665-1201, info@bepress.com, http://www.bepress.com/jafio. Ed. Azzeddine Azzam.

338.1 USA ISSN 1068-5502
HD1401
➤ **JOURNAL OF AGRICULTURAL & RESOURCE ECONOMICS.** Text in English. 1976. s-a. USD 75 in North America; USD 80 elsewhere (effective 2004). bk.rev. back issues avail.; reprints avail. **Document type:** *Journal, Academic/Scholarly.*
Formerly (until 1992): Western Journal of Agricultural Economics (0162-1912); Which superseded: Western Agricultural Economics Association. Proceedings
Related titles: Online - full text ed.: (from ProQuest Information & Learning).
Indexed: ABIn, AEA, ASCA, ASFA, AgBio, Agr, AgrForAb, AnBrAb, BioCN&I, CurCont, DSA, ESPM, EnvEAb, FCA, FPA, FS&TA, FamI, ForAb, HortAb, I&DA, IndVet, JEL, MaizeAb, NutrAb, PBA, PHN&I, PN&I, PollutAb, PotatoAb, PoultAb, RDA, RPP, RRTA, RevApplEntom, RiskAb, S&F, SSCI, SSI, SeedAb, SoyAb, TriticAb, VetBull, WAE&RSA, WeedAb.
—BLDSC (4920.150000), CISTI, IDS, IE, Infotrieve, ingenta.
Published by: Western Agricultural Economics Association, c/o Dawn D Thilmany, Assoc. Prof., Colorado State University, Dept. of Agricultural and Resource Economics, Fort Collins, CO 80523-1172. TEL 970-491-7220, FAX 970-491-2067, thilmany@lamar.colostate.edu, http://www.waeaonline.org. Ed. Gary Thompson. R&P Dawn D Thilmany. Circ: 1,100.

338.1 GBR ISSN 0021-857X
HD1401 CODEN: JAGEA7
➤ **JOURNAL OF AGRICULTURAL ECONOMICS.** Text in English. 1928. 3/yr. GBP 138 (effective 2005). bk.rev. bibl.; charts. **Document type:** *Journal, Academic/Scholarly.*
Related titles: Online - full text ed.: ISSN 1477-9552 (from EBSCO Publishing, Gale Group, IngentaConnect).
Indexed: AgeL, AgrForAb, ArtHuCI, B&AI, BAS, BPIA, CREJ, CTFA, CurCont, DSA, EnvAb, FS&TA, FamI, ForAb, GEOBASE, HortAb, I&DA, IBSS, ISR, IndVet, JEL, MaizeAb, NutrAb, PAIS, PHN&I, PN&I, PotatoAb, PoultAb, RASB, RDA, RICS, RRTA, RefZh, RevApplEntom, RiceAb, S&F, SCI, SIA, SSCI, SoyAb, TDB, TOSA, TriticAb, VetBull, WAE&RSA, WeedAb.
—BLDSC (4920.700000), IE, Infotrieve, ingenta.
Published by: (Agricultural Economics Society), Imperial College of Science, Technology and Medicine, Department of Agricultural Sciences at Wye (Subsidiary of: University of London), Wye, Ashford, Kent TN25 5AH, United Kingdom. TEL 44-20-75942617, FAX 44-20-75942754, aes@bhm.co.uk, http://www.aes.ac.uk/publications.htm, http://www.wye.ic.ac.uk. Ed. D I Buteman.

630 JPN ISSN 0913-6134
JOURNAL OF COMMUNICATION BETWEEN RURAL COMMUNITIES AND TOWNS/NOSON TO TOSHI O MUSUBU. Text in Japanese. 1951. m. JPY 3,300. adv. **Document type:** *Academic/Scholarly.*
Published by: Agriculture Forestry and Fisheries Ministry Workers Union, 2-1 Kasumigaseki 1-chome, Chiyoda-ku, Tokyo, 100-0013, Japan. TEL 03-3508-1395, FAX 03-5512-7555. Ed. Yasuo Kondo. Circ: 11,000.

JOURNAL OF CROP IMPROVEMENT; innovations in practice, theory & research. see *AGRICULTURE—Crop Production And Soil*

380.141 USA ISSN 0897-4438
HD9000.1 CODEN: JIFMEI
➤ **JOURNAL OF INTERNATIONAL FOOD & AGRIBUSINESS MARKETING.** Text in English. 1989. s-a. USD 360 combined subscription domestic to institutions print & online eds.; USD 486 combined subscription in Canada to institutions print & online eds.; USD 522 combined subscription elsewhere to institutions print & online eds. (effective 2006). adv. bk.rev. back issues avail.; reprint service avail. from HAW. **Document type:** *Journal, Academic/Scholarly.* **Description:** Presents current and insightful information - descriptive and analytical - on the international food and agribusiness marketing theory and practice.
Related titles: Microfiche ed.: (from PQC); Microform ed.; Online - full text ed.: ISSN 1528-6983. free to institutions (effective 2003); free with print subs. (from EBSCO Publishing, O C L C Online Computer Library Center, Inc., Swets Information Services).
Indexed: ASD, AgBio, Agr, AgrForAb, BPI, BibAg, CurCont, DIP, DSA, FS&TA, HortAb, IBR, IBZ, MaizeAb, NutrAb, OrnHort, PBA, PHN&I, PN&I, PotatoAb, PoultAb, RDA, RefZh, RevApplEntom, SIA, SoyAb, TDB, TriticAb, WAE&RSA.
—BLDSC (5007.661500), Haworth, IDS, IE, Infotrieve, ingenta. **CCC.**
Published by: International Business Press (Subsidiary of: Haworth Press, Inc.), 10 Alice St, Binghamton, NY 13904. TEL 607-722-5857, 800-429-6784, FAX 607-771-0012, 800-895-0582, getinfo@haworthpress.com, http://www.haworthpress.com/web/JIFAM. Ed. Erdener Kaynak TEL 717-566-3054. Pub. William Cohen. adv.: B&W page USD 315, color page USD 550; trim 4.375 x 7.125. Circ: 225 (paid).

➤ **JOURNAL OF RURAL COOPERATION.** see *BUSINESS AND ECONOMICS—Cooperatives*

➤ **JOURNAL OF VEGETABLE SCIENCE.** see *AGRICULTURE—Crop Production And Soil*

338.1 DEU
K T B L KALKULATIONSUNTERLAGEN. Text in German. irreg. price varies. **Document type:** *Monographic series, Trade.*
Published by: Kuratorium fuer Technik und Bauwesen in der Landwirtschaft e.V., Bartningstr 49, Darmstadt, 64289, Germany. TEL 49-6151-70010, FAX 49-6151-7001123, ktbl@ktbl.de, http://www.ktbl.de. R&P Harald Kuehner.

338.1 KEN
KENYA. MINISTRY OF AGRICULTURE. DEVELOPMENT PLANNING DIVISION. YIELDS, COSTS, PRICES. Text in English. a. **Document type:** *Government.*
Formerly: Kenya. Central Development and Marketing Unit. Yields, Costs, Prices
Published by: Ministry of Agriculture, Development Planning Division, PO Box 30028, Nairobi, Kenya. TEL 254-2-718870. Ed. Protus Sigei.

338.1 IND ISSN 0023-1029
HD2346.I5
KHADI GRAMODYOG; journal of rural economy. Text in Hindi. 1954. m. INR 60. bk.rev. stat.
Related titles: English ed.
Indexed: AEA, BAS, ILD.
Published by: Khadi and Village Industries Commission, Directorate of Publicity, Gramodaya Irla Rd., Vile Parle (West), Mumbai, Maharashtra 400 056, India. Ed. Kamal Taori. Pub. S R Fulmali.

338.1 JPN
KONNYAKU NEWS. Text in Japanese. 1948. 3/m. JPY 9,000. adv. back issues avail. **Description:** Contains information about price and exchange rate of konnyaku (paste made from the arum root) for the konnyaku industry.
Published by: Konnyaku Shinbunsha, 12-9 Igusa 5-chome, Suginami-ku, Tokyo, 167-0021, Japan. TEL 03-399-0425. Ed. Teiichi Murakami. Circ: 2,000.

338.1 RUS ISSN 1560-0947
KREST'YANSKIE VEDOMOSTI. Text in Russian. 1990. w. adv. bk.rev. **Document type:** *Newspaper.* **Description:** Covers agricultural information.
Related titles: Microfiche ed.: (from EVP).
Indexed: RASB.
Published by: Igor Abakumov Ed. & Pub., Ul Gilyarovskogo 57, Moscow, 129110, Russian Federation. TEL 095-284-0446, FAX 095-284-5673, kb@cnt.ru. Circ: 102,320. **Co-sponsor:** Agroprombank.

333 USA ISSN 0023-7639
HB1 CODEN: LAECAD
➤ **LAND ECONOMICS**; a quarterly journal devoted to the study of economic and social institutions. Text in English. 1925. q. USD 77 combined subscription to individuals print & online eds.; USD 227 combined subscription to institutions print & online eds. (effective 2006). adv. bk.rev. bibl.; illus. Index. back issues avail.; reprint service avail. from PQC,PSC. **Document type:** *Journal, Academic/Scholarly.*
Formerly (until 1948): Journal of Land and Public Utility Economics (1548-9000)
Related titles: Microform ed.: (from PQC); Online - full text ed.: ISSN 1543-8325. USD 216 (effective 2006) (from EBSCO Publishing, Florida Center for Library Automation, Gale Group, H.W. Wilson, IngentaConnect, JSTOR (Web-based Journal Archive), Northern Light Technology, Inc., O C L C Online Computer Library Center, Inc., ProQuest Information & Learning).
Indexed: ABIn, AIAP, APEL, ASCA, AbHyg, AgeL, Agr, AgrForAb, AmH&L, AnBrAb, BAS, BPI, BPIA, BusI, CMCI, CREJ, CurCont, DIP, EI, EIA, EPB, ESPM, EnvAb, EnvInd, ExcerpMed, F&GI, FPA, FamI, ForAb, GEOBASE, HerbAb, HistAb, HortAb, I&DA, IBR, IBSS, IBZ, ILD, IPARL, JEL, LRI, MEA&I, ManagCont, PAA&I, PAIS, PCI, PGegResA, PHN&I, PRA, PollutAb, PotatoAb, RA&MP, RASB, RDA, RICS, RRTA, RefZh, RevApplEntom, RiskAb, S&F, SFA, SPAA, SSCI, SSI, SUSA, T&II, TDB, WAE&RSA, WeedAb.
—BLDSC (5146.800000), CIS, CISTI, IDS, IE, ingenta. **CCC.**
Published by: (University of Wisconsin at Madison), University of Wisconsin Press, Journal Division, 1930 Monroe St, 3rd Fl, Madison, WI 53711-2059. TEL 608-263-0668, FAX 608-263-1173, journals@uwpress.wisc.edu, http://www.wisc.edu/wisconsinpress/journals/journals/le.html. Ed. Daniel Bromley. adv.: page USD 390; trim 7 x 10. Circ: 1,800.

333.31 USA ISSN 0251-1894
HD101
LAND REFORM, LAND SETTLEMENT AND COOPERATIVES. Text in English. 1963. a. USD 20 (effective 2000). bk.rev. bibl.; charts; illus. cum.index. **Document type:** *Government.*
Related titles: Online - full text ed.: ISSN 1564-3077. 1996; Spanish ed.: Reforma Agraria, Colonizacion y Cooperativas. ISSN 0251-1886; French ed.: Reforme Agraire, Colonisation et Cooperatives. ISSN 0251-1878.
Indexed: AgrForAb, BAS, ForAb, GEOBASE, HerbAb, I&DA, IBSS, ILD, PAIS, ProtozoAb, RASB, RDA, RRTA, S&F, SWA, WAE&RSA.
—BLDSC (5146.880000), IE, Infotrieve.
Published by: (Rural Institutions Division), Food and Agriculture Organization of the United Nations, c/o Bernan Associates, 4611 F Assembly Dr, Lanham, MD 20706-4391. TEL 301-459-7666, FAX 301-459-0056. Ed. H Meliczek.

333.31 USA ISSN 0084-0815
HD107
LAND TENURE CENTER. RESEARCH PAPER. Text mainly in English. 1964. irreg., latest no.13, 1999. price varies in N. America and Western Europe; elsewhere free. **Document type:** *Monographic series.* **Description:** Promotes research and education on social structure, rural institutions, resource use and development.
Indexed: ARDT, WAE&RSA.
Published by: University of Wisconsin at Madison, Land Tenure Center, 1357 University Ave, Madison, WI 53715. TEL 608-262-3657, TELEX 3797422, ltc-uw@facstaff.wisc.edu, http://www.wisc.edu/ltc. Ed. Kurt Brown. R&P Jane Dennis.

LANDBOUW-ECONOMISCH INSTITUUT. PERIODIEKE RAPPORTAGE. see *AGRICULTURE—Abstracting, Bibliographies, Statistics*

338.1 DNK ISSN 0902-7300
LANDBRUGETS DRIFTSOEKONOMI. Text in Danish. 1987. a., latest 2003. DKK 66 (effective 2005). **Document type:** *Trade.*
Formed by the merger of (1980-1987): Landboforeningernes Driftsoekonomiske Virksomhed. Regnskabsresultater. (Year) (0107-1300); (1973-1987): Landboforeningernes Driftsoekonomiske Virksomhed (Year) (0106-861X); Which was formed by the merger of (1957-1973): Landbrugets Oekonomi (0906-1843); (19??-1973): Landbrugets Regnskabsresultater (0906-1835); (1968-1973): Beretning om Regnskabsvirksomheden indenfor de Samvirkende Lolland-Falsterske Landboforeninger (0906-1827); (1916-1973): Landbrugsregnskaber fra Jydske Regnskabskredse (0455-2431)
Published by: Dansk landbrugsraadgivning/Danish Agricultural Advisory Service, Udkaersvej 15, Skejby, Aarhus N, 8200, Denmark. TEL 45-87-405000, FAX 45-87-405010, post@landscentret.dk, http://www.lr.dk.

338.1 NOR ISSN 0800-5974
LANDBRUKSOEKONOMISK FORUM; tidsskrift for landbruk, miljoe og samfunn. Text in Norwegian. 1983. q. NOK 290 to individuals; NOK 485 to institutions; NOK 165 to students; NOK 135, USD 24 per issue (effective 2004). **Document type:** *Academic/Scholarly.* **Description:** Covers agriculture in a wide sense, with economic, environmental and social issues.
Indexed: AbHyg, AgBio, AgrForAb, AnBrAb, DSA, FPA, ForAb, HerbAb, HortAb, IndVet, NutrAb, OrnHort, PGegResA, PHN&I, PN&I, PotatoAb, PoultAb, RA&MP, RDA, RRTA, S&F, TriticAb, VetBull, WAE&RSA.
Published by: (Landbruksoekonomisk Forum), Universitetsforlaget AS/Scandinavian University Press (Subsidiary of: Aschehoug & Co.), Sehesteds Gate 3, Postboks 508, Oslo, 0105, Norway. TEL 47-24-147500, FAX 47-24-147501, post@universitetsforlaget.no, http://www.universitetsforlaget.no/tidsskrifter/article.jhtml?articleID=321, http://www.universitetesforlaget.no. Ed. Sjur Spildo Prestegard.

338.1 DEU
LANDFRAUEN TASCHENKALENDER. Text in German. 1987. a.
Document type: *Bulletin, Trade.*
Published by: Landwirtschaftsverlag GmbH, Huelsebrockstr 2, Muenster, 48165, Germany. TEL 49-2501-801-0, FAX 49-2501-801204, zentrale@lv-h.de, http://www.agrarshop.de.

338.1 DEU ISSN 0341-8278
LANDWIRTSCHAFTLICHER TASCHENKALENDER. Text in German. a. **Document type:** *Bulletin, Trade.*
Published by: Landwirtschaftsverlag GmbH, Huelsebrockstr 2, Muenster, 48165, Germany. TEL 49-2501-801-0, FAX 49-2501-801351, zentrale@lv-h.de, http://www.agrarshop.de.

338.1 ESP
LATIENDA - SUPER; revista de los profesionales de la distribucion y fabricacion. Text in Spanish. 1980. m. EUR 75.01 domestic; EUR 126.01 foreign (effective 2005). adv.
Document type: *Trade.*
Formerly (until 200?): Latienda
Published by: Asociacion Madrilena de Empresarios Minoristas de Alimentacion "La Unica", Jorge Juan, 19-2o, Madrid, 28001, Spain. TEL 34-91-5754239, FAX 34-91-5779686, info@launicaasociacion.es, http://www.launicaasociacion.es. Ed. Primitivo Sanz Martin. Adv. contact Emilio Agreda Marchante. Circ: 10,000.

338.1021 BRA ISSN 0103-443X
SB87.B8
LEVANTAMENTO SISTEMATICO DA PRODUCAO AGRICOLA/SYSTEMATIC SURVEY OF AGRICULTURAL PRODUCTION. Text in Portuguese. 1975. m. USD 240. bk.rev. stat. back issues avail. **Document type:** *Government.*
Description: Presents the results of the survey investigating the total cultivated area, the expected production and productivity of 35 agricultural products.
Published by: Fundacao Instituto Brasileiro de Geografia e Estatistica, Centro de Documentacao e Disseminacao de Informacoes, Rua General Canabarro, 706 Andar 2, Maracana, Rio de Janeiro, RJ 20271-201, Brazil. TEL 55-21-264-5424, FAX 55-21-2841959, http://www.ibge.gov.br. Circ: 700.

338.1 NZL ISSN 1170-7607
HD2195.5
LINCOLN UNIVERSITY. AGRIBUSINESS AND ECONOMICS RESEARCH UNIT. DISCUSSION PAPER. Text in English. 1968. irreg. USD 20 per issue (effective 2001); also avail. on exchange basis. back issues avail.; reprints avail. **Document type:** *Academic/Scholarly.*
Formerly: Lincoln College. Agricultural Economics Research Unit. Discussion Paper (0110-7720)
Indexed: AgBio, AnBrAb, DSA, FPA, ForAb, HerbAb, HortAb, I&DA, PHN&I, PN&I, PoultAb, RA&MP, RDA, RRTA, S&F, WAE&RSA.
—CISTI.
Published by: Lincoln University, Agribusiness and Economics Research Unit, P.O. Box 84, Canterbury, New Zealand. TEL 64-3-32528111, FAX 64-3-253841.

338.1 NZL ISSN 1170-7682
HD1407
LINCOLN UNIVERSITY. AGRIBUSINESS AND ECONOMICS RESEARCH UNIT. RESEARCH REPORT. Text in English. 1964. irreg. USD 30 per issue (effective 2001); also avail. on exchange basis. **Document type:** *Academic/Scholarly.*
Former titles (until 1990): Lincoln College. Agribusiness and Economics Research Unit. Research Report (0113-4485); (until 1987): Agricultural Economics Research Unit. Research Report (0069-3790); (until 1968): Agricultural Economics Research Unit. Publication (0069-3847)
Indexed: AbHyg, AgBio, AnBrAb, BibAg, DSA, FPA, ForAb, HortAb, PHN&I, RDA, RRTA, S&F, WAE&RSA.
—BLDSC (7762.452820), CISTI.
Published by: Lincoln University, Agribusiness and Economics Research Unit, P.O. Box 84, Canterbury, New Zealand. TEL 64-3-252811, FAX 64-3-253847.

338.1 USA
LOS ANGELES WHOLESALE FRUIT & VEGETABLE REPORT*. Text in English. d. USD 180. **Document type:** *Government.*
Published by: U.S. Department of Agriculture, Agricultural Marketing Service (Greely), F & V Division, 1320 E. Olympic Blvd., Los Angeles, CA 90021-1946.

338.7 IND ISSN 0304-7245
HD2346.I52
MADHYA PRADESH STATE AGRO-INDUSTRIES DEVELOPMENT CORPORATION LTD. ANNUAL REPORT. Key Title: Annual Report - Madhya Pradesh State Agro-Industries Development Corporation Ltd. Text in English. a.
Published by: Madhya Pradesh State Agro-Industries Development Corporation Ltd., New Market, T. T. Nagar, Bhopal, Madhya Pradesh, India.

MALAYSIA. DEPARTMENT OF STATISTICS. COCOA, COCONUT AND TEA STATISTICS HANDBOOK, MALAYSIA/MALAYSIA. JABATAN PERANGKAAN. BUKU MAKLUMAT PERANGKAAN KOKO, KELAPA DAN TEH, MALAYSIA. see *AGRICULTURE—Abstracting, Bibliographies, Statistics*

MALAYSIA. DEPARTMENT OF STATISTICS. REPORT OF THE PADDY YIELD SURVEY, MALAYSIA/MALAYSIA. JABATAN PERANGKAAN. LAPORAN PENYIASATAN HASIL PADI, MALAYSIA. see *AGRICULTURE—Abstracting, Bibliographies, Statistics*

380.141 USA ISSN 0190-7492
MARKETING CALIFORNIA ORNAMENTAL CROPS. Text in English. 1968. a. looseleaf. USD 10. back issues avail.
Document type: *Newsletter, Government.*
Published by: (U.S. Department of Agriculture), Federal-State Market News Service (Sacramento), 630 Sansome St, Rm 727, San Francisco, CA 94111. TEL 415-556-5587, FAX 415-705-1301.

380.141 USA
MARKETING CALIFORNIA STRAWBERRIES. Text in English. 1950. a. USD 10. **Document type:** *Newsletter, Government.*
Published by: Federal-State Market News Service (Sacramento), 630 Sansome St, Rm 727, San Francisco, CA 94111. TEL 415-705-1300, FAX 415-705-1301.

338.1 NZL ISSN 0112-0603
MASSEY UNIVERSITY. CENTRE FOR APPLIED ECONOMICS AND POLICY STUDIES. AGRICULTURAL POLICY DISCUSSION PAPER. Key Title: Agricultural Policy Discussion Paper. Text in English. 1976. irreg., latest no.17, 2000. price varies. back issues avail. **Document type:** *Academic/Scholarly.*
Former titles: Massey University. Centre for Agricultural Policy Studies. Agricultural Policy Discussion Paper; (until 1982): Massey University. Department of Agricultural Economics and Farm Management. Technical Discussion Paper
Indexed: DSA, WAE&RSA.
Published by: Massey University, Centre for Applied Economics and Policy Studies, Palmerston North, New Zealand. TEL 64-6-3505799, FAX 64-6-3505660, J.Fisher@massey.ac.nz, http://econ.massey.ac.nz/caps, http://econ.massey.ac.nz/caps/. Ed. Allan N Rae.

338.1 NZL ISSN 0110-5558
MASSEY UNIVERSITY. CENTRE FOR APPLIED ECONOMICS AND POLICY STUDIES. AGRICULTURAL POLICY PAPER. Key Title: Agricultural Policy Paper. Text in English. 1976. irreg., latest vol.21, 1997. price varies. **Document type:** *Academic/Scholarly.*
Formerly: Massey University. Centre for Agricultural Policy Studies. Agricultural Policy Paper
Indexed: NutrAb, WAE&RSA.
—CISTI.
Published by: Massey University, Centre for Applied Economics and Policy Studies, Palmerston North, New Zealand. TEL 64-6-3505799, FAX 64-6-3505660, J.Fisher@massey.ac.nz, http://econ.massey.ac.nz/caps/. Ed. Allan N Rae. Circ: 200.

338.1 NZL ISSN 0111-6339
MASSEY UNIVERSITY. CENTRE FOR APPLIED ECONOMICS AND POLICY STUDIES. AGRICULTURAL POLICY PROCEEDINGS. Key Title: Agricultural Policy Proceedings. Text in English. 1976. irreg., latest vol.19, 1997. price varies.
Document type: *Proceedings.*
Formerly: Massey University. Centre for Agricultural Policy Studies. Agricultural Policy Proceedings
Indexed: PoultAb, SoyAb.
—CISTI.
Published by: Massey University, Centre for Applied Economics and Policy Studies, Palmerston North, New Zealand. TEL 64-6-3505799, FAX 64-6-3505660, J.Fisher@massey.ac.nz, http://econ.massey.ac.nz/caps/. Ed. Allan N Rae. Circ: 200.

MASSEY UNIVERSITY. CENTRE FOR APPLIED ECONOMICS AND POLICY STUDIES. DISCUSSION PAPER IN NATURAL RESOURCE AND ENVIRONMENTAL ECONOMICS. see *BUSINESS AND ECONOMICS—Economic Situation And Conditions*

MAT OG INDUSTRI; status og utvikling i Norsk naerings-og nytelsesmiddelindustri. see *FOOD AND FOOD INDUSTRIES*

338.1 NZL
MEAT AND WOOL BOARDS' ECONOMIC SERVICE. AUTUMN FARM REVENUE AND PRODUCTION REPORT. Text in English. a. (end of May). NZD 135 domestic; NZD 140 foreign (effective 2001). **Description:** Covers a summary of the farming year ending June. The report is presented in 2 sections, section 1 containing the national overview and section 2 regional reports from the five New Zealand reporting regions. The paper covers seasonal conditions, stock health, stock numbers, stock sales, wool production, meat production, farm revenue and general comments.
Published by: Meat and Wool Boards' Economic Service, P.O. Box 5179, Wellington, New Zealand. TEL 64-4-472-2178, FAX 64-4-4712173, info@nzmeat-wool.co.nz, http://www.nzmeat-wool.co.nz.

338.1 NZL
MEAT AND WOOL BOARDS' ECONOMIC SERVICE. DOMESTIC MEAT CONSUMPTION CALENDAR YEAR. Text in English. q. NZD 225 (effective 2001). **Description:** Contains data of the red meat, poultry and pig meat consumption in New Zealand.
Published by: Meat and Wool Boards' Economic Service, P.O. Box 5179, Wellington, New Zealand. TEL 64-4-472-2178, FAX 64-4-4712173, info@nzmeat-wool.co.nz, http://www.nzmeat-wool.co.nz.

338.1 NZL
MEAT AND WOOL BOARDS' ECONOMIC SERVICE. EXPORT BEEF & VEAL PRODUCTION OUTLOOK BY COMBINED REGIONS. Text in English. a. (end of Sep.). NZD 200 domestic; NZD 205 foreign (effective 2001). **Description:** Covers beef and dairy cattle numbers, dairy beef retention and beef production by region.
Published by: Meat and Wool Boards' Economic Service, P.O. Box 5179, Wellington, New Zealand. TEL 64-4-472-2178, FAX 64-4-4712173, info@nzmeat-wool.co.nz, http://www.nzmeat-wool.co.nz.

338.1 NZL
MEAT AND WOOL BOARDS' ECONOMIC SERVICE. EXPORT LAMB AND MUTTON PRODUCTION OUTLOOK. Text in English. a. (end of Sep.). NZD 200 domestic; NZD 205 foreign (effective 2001). **Description:** Details regional production estimates including sheep numbers, ewes mated, lambs tailed, export lamb and mutton production, sensitivity of the estimates, inter-regional stock flows, export production and regional comments.
Published by: Meat and Wool Boards' Economic Service, P.O. Box 5179, Wellington, New Zealand. TEL 64-4-472-2178, FAX 64-4-4712173, info@nzmeat-wool.co.nz, http://www.nzmeat-wool.co.nz.

338.1 NZL
MEAT AND WOOL BOARDS' ECONOMIC SERVICE. EXPORT MEAT PRODUCTION ESTIMATES. Text in English. q. NZD 400 domestic; NZD 410 foreign (effective 2001). **Description:** Covers island and national estimates for export lamb, mutton and beef production, containing comments on stock numbers and lambing, current season production. The end of the year quarter provides an outlook for the following season.
Published by: Meat and Wool Boards' Economic Service, P.O. Box 5179, Wellington, New Zealand. TEL 64-4-472-2178, FAX 64-4-4712173, info@nzmeat-wool.co.nz, http://www.nzmeat-wool.co.nz.

338.1 NZL
MEAT AND WOOL BOARDS' ECONOMIC SERVICE. FARM SECTOR EXCHANGE RATES, PRODUCTION AND FINANCIAL TRENDS. Text in English. a. (Mid Jun.). NZD 225 domestic; NZD 230 foreign (effective 2001). **Description:** Provides a brief overview of the farming season to date, the changes of inflation and industrial factors, interest and exchanges rates, export prices and volumes.
Published by: Meat and Wool Boards' Economic Service, P.O. Box 5179, Wellington, New Zealand. TEL 64-4-472-2178, FAX 64-4-4712173, info@nzmeat-wool.co.nz, http://www.nzmeat-wool.co.nz.

338.1 NZL
MEAT AND WOOL BOARDS' ECONOMIC SERVICE. MOVEMENTS IN SHEEP & BEEF INPUT PRICES. Text in English. a. (1st week of Mar.). NZD 100 domestic; NZD 105 foreign (effective 2001). **Description:** Contains a survey of inputs used on sheep and beef farms as recorded over 12 month period January to January.
Published by: Meat and Wool Boards' Economic Service, P.O. Box 5179, Wellington, New Zealand. TEL 64-4-472-2178, FAX 64-4-4712173, info@nzmeat-wool.co.nz, http://www.nzmeat-wool.co.nz.

338.1 NZL
MEAT AND WOOL BOARDS' ECONOMIC SERVICE. N Z SHEEP AND BEEF FARM SURVEY. (New Zealand) Text in English. a. (Mid. Nov.). NZD 85 domestic; NZD 90 foreign (effective 2001). **Description:** Presents data by farm class and region on a per farm, hectare and stock unit basis. The content includes physical performance data, stock reconciliation, fertilizer usage and financial account analysis that covers revenue, expenditure, balance sheet structure and flow of funds analysis.
Published by: Meat and Wool Boards' Economic Service, P.O. Box 5179, Wellington, New Zealand. TEL 64-4-472-2178, FAX 64-4-4712173, info@nzmeat-wool.co.nz, http://www.nzmeat-wool.co.nz.

338.1 NZL
MEAT AND WOOL BOARDS' ECONOMIC SERVICE. NEW ZEALAND WOOL PRODUCTION ESTIMATES. Text in English. a. (end of Sep.). NZD 200 domestic; NZD 205 foreign (effective 2001). **Description:** Contains region estimates for the current season. Seasonal conditions affecting feed and stock condition and shearing patterns are commented on. Stock numbers and wool production are provided together with estimates of auction and private sales and wool production by segment. The wool price outlook for the season as affected by market influences, price relativities stocks, New Zealand price outlook and export lamb and sheep prices are commented on.
Published by: Meat and Wool Boards' Economic Service, P.O. Box 5179, Wellington, New Zealand. TEL 64-4-472-2178, FAX 64-4-4712173, info@nzmeat-wool.co.nz, http://www.nzmeat-wool.co.nz.

338.1 NZL
MEAT AND WOOL BOARDS' ECONOMIC SERVICE. ONE OFF GENERAL PAPERS. Text in English. irreg. NZD 50 domestic; NZD 55 foreign (effective 2001). **Description:** Covers specific agricultural topics.
Published by: Meat and Wool Boards' Economic Service, P.O. Box 5179, Wellington, New Zealand. TEL 64-4-472-2178, FAX 64-4-4712173, info@nzmeat-wool.co.nz, http://www.nzmeat-wool.co.nz.

338.1 NZL
MEAT AND WOOL BOARDS' ECONOMIC SERVICE. QUARTERLY PRODUCTION REPORT. Text in English. q. NZD 180 domestic; NZD 190 foreign (effective 2001). **Description:** Highlights the estimated livestock numbers, export meat production, wool production, farm revenue and expenditure and farm profit before tax.
Published by: Meat and Wool Boards' Economic Service, P.O. Box 5179, Wellington, New Zealand. TEL 64-4-472-2178, FAX 64-4-4712173, info@nzmeat-wool.co.nz, http://www.nzmeat-wool.co.nz.

338.1 NZL
MEAT AND WOOL BOARDS' ECONOMIC SERVICE. SHEEP AND BEEF INDUSTRY MID-SEASON REVIEW. Text in English. a. (Mid. Dec.). NZD 225 domestic; NZD 230 foreign (effective 2001). **Description:** Covers the key farming points for the year to date. Further analysis details revised estimates for the current season of stock numbers as at 30th of June, stock performance, production volumes, prices received, prices paid and farm gate terms of exchange, sheep and beef farm revenue and expenditure, financing farm operations and an outlook for the following season.
Published by: Meat and Wool Boards' Economic Service, P.O. Box 5179, Wellington, New Zealand. TEL 64-4-472-2178, FAX 64-4-4712173, info@nzmeat-wool.co.nz, http://www.nzmeat-wool.co.nz.

338.1 NZL
MEAT AND WOOL BOARDS' ECONOMIC SERVICE. STOCK NUMBER SURVEY AS AT 30 JUNE. Text in English. a. (Late Jul.). NZD 175 domestic; NZD 180 foreign (effective 2001). **Description:** Details ewes in lamb at 30th June, sheep numbers and cattle numbers. The lamb crop outlook for the season is estimated. Trends in stock numbers are also covered.
Published by: Meat and Wool Boards' Economic Service, P.O. Box 5179, Wellington, New Zealand. TEL 64-4-472-2178, FAX 64-4-4712173, info@nzmeat-wool.co.nz, http://www.nzmeat-wool.co.nz.

338.1 BGR
MEKHANIZATSIA NA ZEMEDELIETO. Text in Bulgarian. 10/yr. USD 80 (effective 2002).
Published by: Bulgarian Academy of Sciences, Institute of Agricultural Economics, 136 Tsar Boris St., Sofia, 1618, Bulgaria. TEL 359-2-562808, FAX 359-2-562805. **Dist. by:** Sofia Books, ul Silivria 16, Sofia 1404, Bulgaria. TEL 359-2-9586257, info@sofiabooks-bg.com, http://www.sofiabooks-bg.com.

338.1 USA ISSN 0065-4442
HD1407
➤ **MICHIGAN STATE UNIVERSITY. AGRICULTURAL ECONOMICS REPORT.** Text in English. 1965. irreg. (approx. 5/yr.). free. **Document type:** *Bulletin, Academic/Scholarly.* **Description:** Focuses on farm management and the economics of agriculture for researchers in the field.
Media: Duplicated (not offset).
Indexed: Agr, DSA, RRTA, SoyAb, WAE&RSA.
—BLDSC (0745.760900).
Published by: Michigan State University, Department of Agricultural Economics, Reference Rm, East Lansing, MI 48824-1039. TEL 517-355-6650, FAX 517-432-1800, agecon@mainlib3.lib.msu.edu. Circ: 60 (controlled).

338.1 USA ISSN 1074-357X
MID-SOUTH FARMER. Text in English. 1994. m. USD 23.95 in state (effective 2005). adv. **Document type:** *Magazine, Trade.*
Published by: Farm Progress Companies, 191 S Gary Ave, Carol Stream, IL 60188-2095. TEL 630-462-2229, FAX 630-462-2202, info@farmprogress.com, http://www.midsouthfarmer.com, http://www.farmprogress.com/. Ed. Carroll Smith. Adv. contact Don Tourte. B&W page USD 2,250, color page USD 2,750; trim 10.5 x 14.5. Circ: 24,000 (paid).

MIDWEST DAIRYBUSINESS. see *AGRICULTURE—Dairying And Dairy Products*

338.1 USA
HD101
MINNESOTA APPLIED ECONOMIST. Text in English. 1914. q. free (effective 2004). charts; illus. back issues avail. **Document type:** *Newsletter.* **Description:** Reports information flowing from the research and educational efforts of the Department of Applied Economics.
Formerly: Minnesota Agricultural Economist (0885-4874)
Indexed: AgBio, Agr, DSA, I&DA, MaizeAb, NutrAb, PAIS, PN&I, PoultAb, S&F, SoyAb, TriticAb, WAE&RSA.
—CISTI.
Published by: University of Minnesota, Department of Applied Economics, 1994 Buford Ave., St. Paul, MN 55108. TEL 612-625-1705, FAX 612-625-6245, http://agecon.lib.umn.edu. Ed. Robert P King. Circ: 4,000 (controlled).

633.5 USA ISSN 0027-0318
HD9093.U4
MONTHLY COTTON LINTERS REVIEW✶. Text in English. 1930. m. free. stat. reprint service avail. from CIS.
Media: Duplicated (not offset). **Related titles:** Microfiche ed.: 1930 (from CIS).
Indexed: AmStI.
Published by: U.S. Agricultural Marketing Service, Cotton Division, 302 Annex Bldg, 12th and C Sts, S W, Washington, DC 20250.

338.1 BEL ISSN 0773-4123
MUSEE ROYAL DE L'AFRIQUE CENTRALE. ANNALES - SCIENCES ECONOMIQUES. SERIE IN 8/KONINKLIJK MUSEUM VOOR MIDDEN-AFRIKA. ANNALEN - ECONOMISCHE WETENSCHAPPEN. REEKS IN 8. Text in French. 1947. irreg., latest vol.23, 1993. price varies. charts; illus. back issues avail. **Document type:** *Monographic series.*
Supersedes (in 1964): Musee Royal du Congo Belge. Annales - Sciences Historiques et Economiques (0773-4115)
Indexed: FPA, ForAb.
Published by: Musee Royal de l'Afrique Centrale/Koninklijk Museum voor Midden-Afrika, Steenweg op Leuven 13, Tervuren, 3080, Belgium. TEL 32-2-7695299, FAX 32-2-767-0242.

338.1 KOR
N A F NEWS. Text in Korean. 1989. q.
Published by: National Agricultural Cooperative Federation, 75, 1-Ka, Chungjeong-Ro, Jung-Ku, Seoul, Korea, S. FAX 02-737-7815, TELEX NACOF-K27421.

338.1 USA
HD1401
N C STATE ECONOMIST. (North Carolina) Text in English. 1952. bi-m. free. charts; illus. **Document type:** *Newsletter.*
Former titles: Tar Heel Economist (0039-9612); Tarheel Farm Economist
Published by: North Carolina State University, North Carolina Cooperative Extension Service, PO Box 8109, Raleigh, NC 27695. TEL 919-515-4553, FAX 919-515-6268. Ed. Charles Safley. R&P Luana Smith TEL 919-515-9670. Circ: 9,500.

N I L F - RAPPORT. (Norsk Institutt for Landbruksoekonomisk Forskning) see *AGRICULTURE*

380.141 USA ISSN 1555-2861
NATIONAL HONEY REPORT. Text in English. m. USD 36 domestic; USD 72 foreign (effective 2000). **Document type:** *Government.* **Description:** Covers bee culture.
Former titles (until 2000): National Honey Market News; Honey Market News (0364-2054)
Related titles: Online - full text ed.: ISSN 1555-2853.
Indexed: AmStI.
Published by: (Honey Market News), U.S. Department of Agriculture, Agricultural Marketing Service (Yakima), 21 N 1st Ave, Ste 224, Yakima, Yakima, WA 98902-2663. TEL 509-575-2494, FAX 509-457-7132. Ed. Linda Verstrate.

NATIONAL INSTITUTE OF ANIMAL AGRICULTURE. ANNUAL MEETING PROCEEDINGS. see *AGRICULTURE—Poultry And Livestock*

NATIONAL LAMB SUMMARY. see *AGRICULTURE—Poultry And Livestock*

380.141 FRA ISSN 0753-2415
NEGOCE AGRICULTURE. Text in French. 1886. bi-m. adv. charts; illus. **Document type:** *Trade.* **Description:** Covers agricultural chemistry.
Incorporates: Grains (0046-6263); Formerly: Engrais
Indexed: ChemAb.
Published by: Secograins, 272 Bourse du Commerce, Paris, Cedex 1 75040, France. TEL 33-1-44769040, FAX 33-1-44769031. Ed. Pierre Neuviale. Circ: 4,000.

338.1 ESP
NEKAZAL SEKTOREAREN EKONOMI KONTUAK/CUENTAS ECONOMICAS DEL SECTOR AGRARIO. Text in Basque, English. 1986. a., latest 1989. **Document type:** *Government.*
Published by: (Basque Region. Nekazaritza eta Arrantza Saila/Departamento de Agricultura y Pesca), Eusko Jaurlaritzaren Argitalpen-Zerbitzu Nagusia/Servicio Central de Publicaciones del Gobierno Vasco, Donostia-San Sebastian, 1, Vitoria-gasteiz, Alava 01010, Spain. TEL 34-945-018561, FAX 34-945-018709, hac-sabd@ej-gv.es, http://www.ej-gv.net/publicaciones. Circ: 1,500.

338.1 USA
NEW MEXICO STATE UNIVERSITY. AGRICULTURAL EXPERIMENT STATION. BULLETIN. Text in English. irreg. (5-10/yr.), latest vol.766, 1992. **Document type:** *Bulletin.*
Indexed: AnBrAb, FCA, HerbAb, RRTA, S&F, SFA, WAE&RSA, WildRev.
Published by: New Mexico State University, Agricultural Experiment Station, Drawer 3AI, Las Cruces, NM 88003-0003. TEL 505-646-2701. Ed. Terry Canup.

338.1 AUS ISSN 0310-186X
NEW SOUTH WALES. DEPARTMENT OF AGRICULTURE. COMMODITY BULLETIN. Text in English. 1972. 4/yr. **Document type:** *Bulletin.* **Description:** Applied economic analysis of descriptive material relevant to all segments of the domestic and export sectors of Australian agricultural and fishing industries.
—CISTI.
Published by: Department of Agriculture, Locked Bag 21, Orange, NSW 2800, Australia. TEL 61-63-913433.

338.1 310 NZL
NEW ZEALAND. STATISTICS NEW ZEALAND. FARM EXPENSES PRICE INDEX. Text in English. q. stat. **Document type:** *Government.*
Published by: Statistics New Zealand/Te Tari Tatau, PO Box 2922, Wellington, New Zealand. TEL 64-4-495-4600, FAX 64-4-473-2626, info@stats.govt.nz, http://www.stats.govt.nz.

338.1 JPN ISSN 0387-3234
NOGYO KEIZAI KENKYU/JOURNAL OF RURAL ECONOMICS. Text in Japanese. 1925. q. JPY 5,000. bk.rev.
Indexed: AEA, APEL, AbHyg, AgBio, AnBrAb, DSA, FCA, ForAb, HerbAb, HistAb, HortAb, I&DA, IndVet, MaizeAb, NutrAb, OrnHort, PBA, PGegResA, PHN&I, PN&I, PotatoAb, PoultAb, RDA, RRTA, RiceAb, S&F, SIA, SoyAb, TDB, TriticAb, VetBull, WAE&RSA.
—CCC.
Published by: (Nihon Nogyo Keizai Gakkai/Agricultural Economic Society of Japan), Iwanami Shoten, Publishers, 2-5-5 Hitotsubashi, Chiyoda-ku, Tokyo, 101-0003, Japan. TEL 81-3-3265-4111, FAX 81-3-239-9618, TELEX 39495, http://edpex104.bcasj.or.jp/aesj/publ/index.htm. **Dist. overseas by:** Japan Publications Trading Co., Ltd., Book Export II Dept, PO Box 5030, Tokyo International, Tokyo 101-3191, Japan. TEL 81-3-32923753, FAX 81-3-32920410, infoserials@jptco.co.jp, http://www.jptco.co.jp.

338.1 JPN ISSN 0387-3242
HD2091
NOGYO SOGO KENKYU. Variant title: Quarterly Journal of Agricultural Economy. Text in Japanese. 1947. q. bk.rev. **Document type:** *Government.*
Indexed: AmH&L, ExcerpMed, ForAb, HistAb, IAOP, IBSS, RASB.
Published by: Norinsuisan-sho, Norim Suisam Seisaku Kemkyujo/Ministry of Agriculture, Forestry and Fisheries - Policy Reserach Institute, 2-1 Nishigahara 2-chome, Kita-ku, Tokyo, 114-0024, Japan. FAX 81-3-3910-3946, www@nriae.affrc.go.jp, www@primaff.affrc.go.jp. Ed. Kazuo Nonaka.

338.1 JPN ISSN 0029-0912
NOGYO TO KEIZAI/AGRICULTURE AND ECONOMY. Text in Japanese. 1934. m.
Published by: Fumin Kyokai, Shuppan-bu/Better Farming Association, Publishing Division, c/o Mainichi Shinbunsha, Dojima, Kita-ku, Osaka-shi, 530-0003, Japan. Ed. Masamitsu Duchi.

338.1 CHN ISSN 1003-7470
HD2096
NONGCUN JINGJI/RURAL ECONOMY. Text in Chinese. 1983. m. CNY 9 (effective 1994). adv. bk.rev. **Document type:** *Academic/Scholarly.*
Related titles: Online - full text ed.: (from East View Information Services).
—BLDSC (8052.434050).
Published by: Sichuan Shehui Kexueyuan, Nongcun Jingji Yanjiusuo/Sichuan Academy of Social Sciences, Rural Economy Research Institute, Shehui Kexueyuan, Qingyang Gong, Chengdu, Sichuan 610072, China. TEL 769347-353. Ed. Guo Zhongzhen. **Co-sponsor:** Sichuan Agricultural Economy Society.

338.1 CHN ISSN 1002-5596
NONGYE HEZUO JINGJI JINGYING GUANLI/MANAGEMENT AND ADMINISTRATION IN RURAL ECONOMY. Text in Chinese. m. CNY 19.20.
Formerly (until 1991): Nongye Jingying Guanli yu Kuaiji Yanjiu
Related titles: Online - full text ed.: (from East View Information Services).
Published by: Nongye Bu, Hezuo Jingji Jingying Guanli Zongzhan, 11 Nongzhanguan Nanli, Beijing, 100026, China. TEL 5005773. Ed. Huian Li.

338.1 CHN ISSN 1671-3427
NONGYE JINGJI DAOKAN/GUIDE TO AGRICULTURAL ECONOMICS. Text in Chinese. 1978. m. CNY 180 (effective 2004). 208 p./no.; **Document type:** *Journal, Academic/Scholarly.*
Former titles (until 2001): Nongye Jingjixue/Agricultural Economics (1009-7538); (until 2000): Nongye Jingji (1001-3059)
Indexed: RASB, RiceAb.

A

Published by: Zhongguo Renmin Daxue, Shubao Zilio Zhongxin/Renmin University of China, Information Center for Social Server, Dongcheng-qu, 3, Zhangzizhong Lu, Beijing, 100007, China. TEL 86-10-64039458, FAX 86-10-64015080, kyes@163.net, http://www.confucius.cn.net/bkdetail.asp?fzt=F2. **Dist. in US by:** China International Book Trading Corp, 35 Chegongzhuang Xilu, Haidian District, PO Box 399, Beijing 100044, China. TEL 86-10-68412045, FAX 86-10-68412023, cibtc@mail.cibtc.com.cn, http://www.cibtc.com.cn.

338.1 CHN ISSN 1000-6389
HD1401
NONGYE JINGJI WENTI/ISSUES IN AGRICULTURAL ECONOMY. Text in Chinese. 1980. m. CNY 5.50 newsstand/cover (effective 2004). back issues avail. **Document type:** *Journal, Academic/Scholarly.*
Related titles: Online - full content ed.: (from WanFang Data Corp.); Online - full text ed.: (from East View Information Services).
—BLDSC (4584.067200), IE.
Published by: (Zhongguo Nongye Jingji Xuehui), Nongye Jingji Wenti, 12, Zhongguancun Nan Dajie, Beijing, 100081, China. TEL 86-10-68918705, FAX 86-10-68919791, nyjjwt@mail.caas.net.cn, http://nyjjwt.periodicals.net.cn/default.html. Ed. Xigang Zhu. **Dist. in US by:** China Books & Periodicals Inc, 360 Swift Ave., Ste. 48, S San Fran, CA 94080-6220. TEL 415-282-2994; **Dist. by:** China International Book Trading Corp, 35 Chegongzhuang Xilu, Haidian District, PO Box 399, Beijing 100044, China. TEL 86-10-68412045, FAX 86-10-68412023, cibtc@mail.cibtc.com.cn, http://www.cibtc.com.cn.

338.1 CHN ISSN 1000-6370
➤ **NONGYE JISHU JINGJI/JOURNAL OF AGROTECHNICAL ECONOMICS.** Text in Chinese. 1982. 6/yr. USD 24 (effective 2002). adv. bk.rev. **Document type:** *Academic/Scholarly.* **Description:** Contains research articles, reports, notes and reviews on all aspects of agricultural economics and technologies.
Related titles: Online - full text ed.: (from East View Information Services).
Indexed: RASB.
Published by: Zhongguo Nongye Jishu Jingji Yanjiuhui/Chinese Society for Agricultural Technology Economics, 12 Zhongguancun Nan Lu, Beijing, 100081, China. TEL 86-10-6217-6213, FAX 86-10-6218-7545, TELEX 222720 CAAS CN, iae@iaecon.com, http://www.iaecn.com. Ed. Xigang Zhu. Pub. Yuqin Li. Circ: 3,000. **Dist. in U.S. by:** China Books & Periodicals Inc, 360 Swift Ave., Ste. 48, S San Fran, CA 94080-6220. TEL 415-282-2994. **Co-sponsor:** Zhongguo Nongye Kexueyuan Nongye Jingji Yanjiusuo - C A A S, Institute of Agricultural Economics.

333 NOR ISSN 0801-2334
NORGES LANDBRUKSHOEGSKOLE. INSTITUTT FOR JORDSKIFTE OG AREALPLANLEGGING. MELDING/AGRICULTURAL UNIVERSITY OF NORWAY. DEPARTMENT OF LAND USE PLANNING. SERIE. Text in Norwegian. 1956. irreg. (2-4/yr.). price varies.
Formerly: Norges Landbrukshoegskole. Institutt for Jordskifte og Eiendomsutforming. Melding (0065-0242)
Indexed: BiolAb, NutrAb, SeedAb.
Published by: Norges Landbrukshoegskole, Institutt for Jordskifte og Arealplanlegging/Agricultural University of Norway, Postboks 29, Aas-nlh, N-1432, Norway.

338.1 JPN
NORIM SUISAN SEISAKU KEMKYU. Text in Japanese. 2001. q. bk.rev. **Document type:** *Government.*
Published by: Norinsuisan-sho, Norim Suisam Seisaku Kemkyujo/Ministry of Agriculture, Forestry and Fisheries - Policy Reserach Institute, 2-1 Nishigahara 2-chome, Kita-ku, Tokyo, 114-0024, Japan. TEL 81-3-3910-3946, FAX 81-3-3910-3946, www@primaff.affrc.go.jp, http://www.primaff.affrc.go.jp.

338.1 NOR ISSN 0333-2500
S249
NORSK INSTITUTT FOR LANDBRUKSOEKONOMISK FORSKNING. DRIFTSGRANSKINGER I JORD- OG SKOGBRUK. Text in Norwegian; Summaries in English. 1912. a. NOK 195 (effective 2004). **Document type:** *Government.* **Description:** Provides information on financial conditions in agriculture for farmers, the public administration, advisers and others.
Formerly (until 1972): Norges Landbruksoekonomiske Institutt. Driftsgranskinger i Jordbruket (0078-1223)
Indexed: AgrForAb, PotatoAb.
—BLDSC (3625.300000).
Published by: Norsk Institutt for Landbruksoekonomisk Forskning (NILF)/Norwegian Agricultural Economics Research Institute (NILF), Schweigaards Gate 33B, Postboks 8024, Dep, Oslo, 0030, Norway. TEL 47-22-367200, FAX 47-22-367299, postmottak@nilf.no, http://www.nilf.no/. Ed. Lars Johan Rustad. Circ: 2,900.

NORSK INSTITUTT FOR LANDBRUKSOEKONOMISK FORSKNING. NOTAT. see *AGRICULTURE*

639.2 AUS
NORTHERN TERRITORY. DEPARTMENT OF PRIMARY INDUSTRY AND FISHERIES. AGNOTE. Text in English. irreg. free. back issues avail. **Document type:** *Monographic series, Government.*
Former titles: Northern Territory. Department of Industries and Development. Agnote; Northern Territory. Department of Primary Production. Agnote (0157-8243)
Indexed: AEA, AbHyg, AgrForAb, AnBrAb, BioCN&I, CPA, FCA, FPA, ForAb, HelmAb, HerbAb, HortAb, I&DA, IndVet, NutrAb, OrnHort, PBA, PHN&I, PN&I, PoultAb, ProtozoAb, RA&MP, RM&VM, RPP, RRTA, RiceAb, S&F, SeedAb, TDB, VetBull, WAE&RSA, WeedAb.
—CISTI.
Published by: Australia. Department of Primary Industry and Fisheries, PO Box 990, Darwin, N.T. 0801, Australia. TEL 61-889-992202, FAX 61-889-992307, hassan.bajhau@nt.gov.au, http://www.dpif.nt.gov.au/dpif/pubcat. Ed. H Bajhau. R&P Hassan Bajhau.

338.1 DEU
OIL WORLD ANNUAL. Text in German. 1987. a. EUR 69.70 domestic to subscribers of Oil World Weekly/Monthly; EUR 72.70 in Europe to subscribers of Oil World Weekly/Monthly; EUR 83.70 elsewhere to subscribers of Oil World Weekly/Monthly; EUR 90.40 domestic; EUR 93.40 in Europe; EUR 104.40 elsewhere (effective 2005). **Document type:** *Journal, Trade.*
Published by: I S T A Mielke GmbH, Langenberg 25, Hamburg, 21077, Germany. TEL 49-40-761050-0, FAX 49-40-7607048, info@oilworld.de, http://www.oil-world.com. Ed., R&P Thomas Mielke.

664.3 DEU
OIL WORLD MONTHLY. Text in English. 2001. m. EUR 352.20 domestic; EUR 354.20 in Europe; EUR 364.20 elsewhere (effective 2005). **Document type:** *Journal, Trade.* **Description:** Covers world supply and demand statistics with breakdown by major countries for the major oilseeds, the respective oils and oilmeals plus palm oil and fish meal.
Related titles: E-mail ed.
Published by: I S T A Mielke GmbH, Langenberg 25, Hamburg, 21077, Germany. TEL 49-40-761050-0, FAX 49-40-7607048, info@oilworld.de, http://www.oil-world.com.

664.3 DEU ISSN 0029-8700
OIL WORLD WEEKLY; the weekly forecasting and information service for oilseeds, oilmeals, oils and fats. Text in English. 1958. w. looseleaf. EUR 498 domestic; EUR 528.60 Europe, Turkey & Cyprus; EUR 552.60 elsewhere (effective 2005). adv. index. **Document type:** *Journal, Trade.*
Related titles: E-mail ed.
—CISTI. **CCC.**
Published by: I S T A Mielke GmbH, Langenberg 25, Hamburg, 21077, Germany. TEL 49-40-761050-0, FAX 49-40-7607048, info@oilworld.de, http://www.oil-world.com. Ed. Thomas Mielke.

338.1 DEU ISSN 0078-6888
OSTEUROPASTUDIEN DER HOCHSCHULEN DES LANDES HESSEN. REIHE 1. GIESSENER ABHANDLUNGEN ZUR AGRAR- UND WIRTSCHAFTSFORSCHUNG DES EUROPAEISCHEN OSTENS. Variant title: Giessener Abhandlungen zur Agrar- und Wirtschaftsforschung des Europaeischen Ostens. Text in German. 1957. irreg., latest vol.223, 2002. price varies. **Document type:** *Monographic series, Academic/Scholarly.*
Indexed: BiolAb, MaizeAb, PoultAb, RDA, RiceAb, SoyAb, WAE&RSA.
Published by: (Universitaet Giessen, Zentrum fuer Kontinentale Agrar- und Wirtschaftsforschung), Duncker und Humblot GmbH, Carl-Heinrich-Becker-Weg 9, Berlin, 12165, Germany. TEL 49-30-7900060, FAX 49-30-79000631, info@duncker-humblot.de, http://www.duncker-humblot.de. Circ: 400.

OXFORD DEVELOPMENT STUDIES. see *BUSINESS AND ECONOMICS—International Development And Assistance*

338.1 FRA ISSN 1637-4975
PAYSAN VIGNERON. Text in French. 1978. 12/yr. **Document type:** *Journal, Trade.*
Former titles (until 2002): Paysan Francais (0997-7759); (until 1988): Revue le Paysan (0184-9638); Which was formed by the merger of (1977-1978): Revue le Paysan (Armagnac, Libournais) (0154-4586); (1925-1978): Revue le Paysan (Edition Charentes) (0154-4578); Which was formerly (until 1972): Paysan (0996-3359)
Published by: Paysan Francais, 10 rue de Bellefonds, Cognac, Cedex 16106, France. TEL 33-5-45352817, FAX 33-5-45352258. Eds. C Mousnier, L Ducom. Circ: 17,165.

338.1 USA ISSN 0740-2562
HD9235.P32
PEANUT INDUSTRY GUIDE. Text in English. 1981. biennial. USD 65; USD 80 foreign (effective 2000). adv. **Document type:** *Trade.*
Formerly (until 1983): Peanut Buyers Guide (0278-6028)
Published by: (National Peanut Council), SpecComm International, Inc., 5808 Faringdon Pl., # 200, Raleigh, NC 27609-3930. TEL 919-872-5040, FAX 919-876-6531, TELEX 440497 NPC DC. Ed. Kim Cutchins. Circ: 1,575.

338.1 USA
PEANUT NEWS. Text in English. m. USD 75.
Published by: (National Peanut Council), Lettercom, Inc., 310 Swann Ave, Alexandria, VA 22314. TEL 703-683-3105. Ed. C Edward Ashdown. Circ: 650. **Subscr. to:** 1500 King St, Ste 301, Alexandria, VA 22314.

338.1 USA
PEANUT REPORT. Text in English. w. USD 8; USD 16 foreign. reprint service avail. from CIS.
Formerly (until 1982): Peanut Market News, Weekly Report
Related titles: Microfiche ed.: (from CIS).
Indexed: AmStI.
Published by: (Fruit and Vegetable Division), U.S. Department of Agriculture, Agricultural Marketing Division, Washington, DC 20250. TEL 202-720-2175.

338.1 BRA
PERNAMBUCO. SECRETARIA DA AGRICULTURA. PLANO ANUAL DE TRABALHO. Text in Portuguese. a.
Formerly: Brazil. Departamento de Agricultura e Abastecimento. Plano Anual de Trabalho do D A A
Published by: Secretaria da Agricultura, Recife, BA, Brazil.

PHILIPPINE JOURNAL OF DEVELOPMENT. see *BUSINESS AND ECONOMICS—Public Finance, Taxation*

333.31 PHL
PHILIPPINES. DEPARTMENT OF AGRARIAN REFORM. PLANNING SERVICE. ANNUAL REPORT. Text in English. 1973. a. **Document type:** *Government.*
Published by: Department of Agrarian Reform, Planning Service, Manila, Philippines.

PLANT PROTECTION QUARTERLY. see *AGRICULTURE—Crop Production And Soil*

PLENTY BULLETIN. see *BUSINESS AND ECONOMICS—International Development And Assistance*

PLOSHTI, DOBIVI I PROIZVODSTVO NA ZEMEDELSKITE KULTURI. see *STATISTICS*

338.1 CAN ISSN 1487-5101
A PORTRAIT OF THE CANADIAN AGRI-FOOD SYSTEM. Text in English. 1997. irreg. **Description:** Compares Canada's macro-economic performance indicators with those of its main economic peers.
Related titles: Online - full text ed.: ISSN 1495-5431.
Published by: Agriculture and Agri-Food Canada, Economic and Policy Analysis Directorate, 960 Carling Ave, Bldg 74, Ottawa, PQ K1A OC6, Canada. TEL 613-759-1746, FAX 613-759-7090, http://www.agr.gc.ca/spb/rad-dra/publications/portrait/portrait_e.php.

338.1 GBR ISSN 0968-0136
PRACTICAL FARM IDEAS. Text in English. 1992. q. GBP 12.95; GBP 18 foreign. bk.rev. illus.; pat. back issues avail. **Document type:** *Trade.* **Description:** Contains farm workshop innovations which enhance a farmer's income.
Published by: Mido Publications Ltd., PO Box 1, Whitland, Carmarthen, United Kingdom. TEL 44-1994-448315, FAX 44-1994-448636, mike@farmideas.co.uk, http://www.farmideas.co.uk. Ed., Pub., R&P Mike Donovan. Circ: 5,000 (paid).

338.1 ITA ISSN 0478-1805
PREVIDENZA SOCIALE NELL'AGRICOLTURA* . Text in Italian. 1950. bi-m. bibl.; stat.
Address: Via Ciro il Grande 21, Rome, RM 00100, Italy.

338.1 USA
PRICES OF AGRICULTURAL PRODUCTS AND SELECTED INPUTS IN EUROPE AND NORTH AMERICA. Text in English. 1950. biennial. USD 36 (effective 1997).
Related titles: Microfiche ed.: (from CIS).
Indexed: IIS.
Published by: (United Nations, Economic Commission for Europe (ECE) CHE), United Nations Publications, Rm DC2-853, United Nations Bldg, 2 United Nations Plaza, New York, NY 10017. TEL 212-963-8302, 800-253-9646, FAX 212-963-3489, publications@un.org, http://www.un.org/publications, http://www.un.org/Pubs.

630 NLD ISSN 0925-2428
PRIMEUR. Text in Dutch, French. 1986. s-m. EUR 47.50 domestic; EUR 47.50 in Belgium; EUR 63 in France; EUR 75 in Europe (effective 2005). adv. back issues avail. **Document type:** *Journal, Trade.* **Description:** Reports on topics in agricultural economics.
Related titles: ♦ Supplement(s): Het Belgisch A G F Adresboek.
Published by: Primeur B.V., PO Box 2140, Goes, 4460 MC, Netherlands. TEL 31-113-230621, FAX 31-113-230865, primeur@zeelandnet.nl, info@primeur.tv, http://www.primeur.tv. adv.: B&W page EUR 715, color page EUR 1,255; 185 x 270. Circ: 4,000 (paid).

PRO-FARM. see *AGRICULTURE—Crop Production And Soil*

PRODUCCION AGRICOLA - PERIODO DE INVIERNO. see *AGRICULTURE—Abstracting, Bibliographies, Statistics*

PRODUCCION AGRICOLA - PERIODO DE VERANO. see *AGRICULTURE—Abstracting, Bibliographies, Statistics*

338.1 ZMB
PRODUCTIVE FARMING. Text in English. 1973. ZMK 36,000 domestic; ZMK 90,000 in Africa; ZMK 132,000 in Europe; ZMK 150,000 in North America. adv. bk.rev. index. back issues avail. **Document type:** *Trade.* **Description:** Covers all aspects of commercial agriculture in Zambia.
Published by: Zambia National Farmers Union, Taz House Cha Cha Cha Rd., PO Box 30395, Lusaka, Zambia. TEL 260-1-222797, FAX 260-1-222736, TELEX ZA 40164. Ed. George Gray. Adv. contact E Hara. Circ: 1,850.

338.1 DNK ISSN 0108-5883
PRODUKTION. Text in Danish. 1960. 12/yr. USD 150. adv. **Document type:** *Trade.* **Description:** Features articles on grain, feeds, fertilizers, seeds, and plant protection, as well as on farm management in general.
Published by: Dansk Landbrugs Grovvareselskab a.m.b.a., Axelborg, Copenhagen V, 1503, Denmark. TEL 45-33-69-87-00, FAX 45-33-69-87-87. Ed. Peder Maltha. Circ: 58,000 (controlled).

338.1 DNK ISSN 1604-1712
PRODUKTIONSOEKONOMI, KVAEG. Text in Danish. 1974. a. **Document type:** *Trade.*
Former titles (until 2002): Poduktionsoekonomi. Kvaeghold (0908-6390); (until 1993): Kvaegholdsoekonomi (0900-3967)
Published by: Dansk landbrugsraadgivning/Danish Agricultural Advisory Service, Udkaersvej 15, Skejby, Aarhus N, 8200, Denmark. TEL 45-87-405000, FAX 45-87-405010, post@landscentret.dk, http://www.lr.dk.

338.1 DNK ISSN 0908-6404
PRODUKTIONSOEKONOMI, PLANTEAVL. Text in Danish. 1994. a.
Formerly (1987-1989): Planteoekonomi (0903-2029)
Published by: Dansk landbrugsraadgivning/Danish Agricultural Advisory Service, Udkaersvej 15, Skejby, Aarhus N, 8200, Denmark. TEL 45-87-405000, FAX 45-87-405010, post@landscentret.dk, http://www.lr.dk.

338.1 636.4 DNK ISSN 1603-4791
PRODUKTIONSOEKONOMI, SVIN. Text in Danish. 1974. a., latest 2004. **Document type:** *Trade.*
Former titles (until 2002): Produktionsoekonomi. Svinehold (0908-6382); (until 1993): Svineholdsoekonomi (0900-5056)
Published by: Dansk landbrugsraadgivning/Danish Agricultural Advisory Service, Udkaersvej 15, Skejby, Aarhus N, 8200, Denmark. TEL 45-87-405000, FAX 45-87-405010, post@landscentret.dk, http://www.lr.dk.

338.1 AUS ISSN 0312-889X
PROFESSIONAL FARM MANAGEMENT GUIDEBOOK. Text in English. 1967. irreg. (approx. 1/yr.). AUD 3.
Published by: University of New England, Agricultural Business Research Institute, Armidale, NSW 2350, Australia. Circ: 4,000.

338.1 332.63 GBR ISSN 0048-5888
PUBLIC LEDGER. Text in English. 1760. w. GBP 477 domestic; GBP 502 in Europe; GBP 527 elsewhere (effective 2005); includes Daily Online Prices. adv. stat. **Document type:** *Journal, Trade.* **Description:** Contains news analysis and prices for over 700 commodities.
Incorporates (1979-2004): World Commodity Markets Monthly (1473-4389); Which was formerly (until 2001): World Commodity Report (0966-467X); Financial Times World Commodity Report
Indexed: KES, RASB.
Published by: Agra Europe (London) Ltd. (Subsidiary of: T & F Informa plc), 80 Calverley Rd, Tunbridge Wells, Kent TN1 2UN, United Kingdom. TEL 44-1892-533813, FAX 44-1892-544895, marketing@agra-net.com, http://www.public-ledger.com/, http://www.agra-net.com.

338.1 ITA
Q A. (Questione Agraria) Text in Italian. 1981. 4/yr. EUR 52 domestic; EUR 89 foreign (effective 2003).
Indexed: AEA, AgBio, DSA, I&DA, MaizeAb, RDA, SoyAb, TriticAb, WAE&RSA.
Published by: Franco Angeli Edizioni, Viale Monza 106, Milan, 20127, Italy. TEL 39-02-2837141, FAX 39-02-26144793, redazioni@francoangeli.it, http://www.francoangeli.it.

338.1 ESP ISSN 0213-0319
QUADERNS AGRARIS. Text in Spanish. 1980. a. free to qualified personnel.
Indexed: IECT.
—CINDOC.
Published by: Institucion Catalana d'Estudis Agraris, Carme, 47, Barcelona, 08001, Spain. TEL 93-318 55 16. Ed. Juanta de Govern.

332.71 TWN ISSN 0033-5665
QUARTERLY JOURNAL OF TAIWAN LAND CREDIT✶. Text in Chinese. 1964. q. bk.rev. charts; mkt.; stat.
Indexed: RASB.
Published by: Land Bank of Taiwan, Credit Investigation & Research Department, 46 Kuan Chien Rd, Taipei, Taiwan. TEL 02-3613020, FAX 02-3115782. Ed. Lu Nien Tsing. Circ: 500 (controlled).

338.1 USA
QUARTERLY SURVEY OF AGRICULTURAL CREDIT CONDITIONS. Text in English. 1976. q. free. **Description:** Presents quarterly data and comments on agricultural conditions in the Eleventh District.
Related titles: Microfiche ed.: (from CIS); Online - full text ed.
Indexed: AmStI.
Published by: Federal Reserve Bank of Dallas, PO Box 655906, Dallas, TX 75265-5906. TEL 214-922-5254, FAX 214-922-5268, Kay.Champagne@dal.frb.org, http://www.dallasfed.org. Ed. Kay Champagne.

338.1 AUS ISSN 0155-221X
QUEENSLAND. DEPARTMENT OF PRIMARY INDUSTRIES. BULLETIN. Text in English. 1976. irreg. **Document type:** *Monographic series.*
Indexed: ESPM.
Published by: Queensland, Department of Primary Industries, 80 Ann St., GPO Box 46, Brisbane, QLD 4001, Australia. TEL 61-7-34046999, FAX 61-7-34046900, callweb@dpi.qld.gov.au, http://www.dpi.qld.gov.au.

380.141 DNK
RAADSNYT. Text in Danish. w. free to qualified personnel. adv. **Document type:** *Newsletter.*
Formerly (until 1982): Landsbrugsraadets Meddelelser
Published by: Landbrugsraadet, Axeltorv 3, Copenhagen V, 1609, Denmark. FAX 33-145072. Circ: 685.

338.1 ESP ISSN 0213-5140
RED CONTABLE AGRARIA NACIONAL. Text in Spanish. irreg., latest 1996. price varies. charts; stat. **Document type:** *Monographic series, Government.*
Published by: (Spain. Secretaria General Tecnica), Ministerio de Agricultura Pesca y Alimentacion, Centro de Publicaciones, Paseo Infanta Isabel 1, Madrid, 28014, Spain. TEL 34-91-3475550, FAX 34-91-3475722, mllopisj@mapya.es, http://www.mapya.es. R&P Juan Carlos Palacios Lopez.

REFERATIVNYI ZHURNAL. EKONOMIKA AGROPROMYSHLENNOGO KOMPLEKSA. see *AGRICULTURE—Abstracting, Bibliographies, Statistics*

338.1060489 DNK ISSN 1398-1951
REGNSKABSSTATISTIK FOR OEKOLOGISK JORDBRUG/ACCOUNT STATISTICS OF ORGANIC FARMING. Text in Danish, English. 1998. a. DKK 40. charts; stat. **Document type:** *Journal, Government.* **Description:** Contains yearly statistics of organic farming in Denmark.
—CISTI.
Published by: Ministeriet for Foedevarer, Landbrug og Fiskeri, Foedevareoekonomisk Institut/Ministry of Food, Agriculture and Fisheries, Danish Research Institute of Food Economics, Rolighedsvej 25, Frederiksberg C, 2000, Denmark. TEL 45-35-28-68-00, FAX 45-35-28-68-01, sjfi@sjfi.dk, http://www.sjfi.dk.

380.141 IND
REPORT ON THE MARKETING OF TOBACCO IN ANDHRA PRADESH. Text in English. a. INR 9.90. charts; stat.
Published by: Directorate of Marketing, Hyderabad, Andhra Pradesh, India.

RESOURCES (WASHINGTON). see *CONSERVATION*

338.1 USA ISSN 1058-7195
HD1401
➤ **REVIEW OF AGRICULTURAL ECONOMICS.** Text in English. 1979. q. USD 162 combined subscription in the Americas to institutions & Caribbean (print & online eds.); GBP 162 combined subscription elsewhere to institutions print & online eds. (effective 2006). adv. index. back issues avail. **Document type:** *Journal, Academic/Scholarly.* **Description:** Provides a forum for exchange of ideas and empirical findings in agricultural economics, particularly in the areas of extension education, applied economic and policy analysis, and decision support analysis.
Former titles (until 1991): North Central Journal of Agricultural Economics (0191-9016); Ohio State University Agricultural Economics; Purdue University Agricultural Economics
Related titles: Online - full text ed.: ISSN 1467-9353. USD 154 in the Americas to institutions & Caribbean; GBP 154 elsewhere to institutions (effective 2006) (from Blackwell Synergy, EBSCO Publishing, Gale Group, IngentaConnect, JSTOR (Web-based Journal Archive), O C L C Online Computer Library Center, Inc., Swets Information Services).
Indexed: ABIn, AEA, ASFA, AbHyg, AgBio, Agr, AgrForAb, AnBrAb, BibAg, Biostat, CurCont, DSA, EPB, ESPM, FS&TA, ForAb, HortAb, I&DA, JEL, MaizeAb, NutrAb, ORMS, OrnHort, PBA, PHN&I, PN&I, PollutAb, PotatoAb, PoultAb, QC&AS, RDA, RRTA, RevApplEntom, S&F, SSCI, SeedAb, SoyAb, TriticAb, WAE&RSA, WeedAb.
—BLDSC (7786.769600), IE, Infotrieve. **CCC.**
Published by: (American Agricultural Economics Association), Blackwell Publishing, Inc. (Subsidiary of: Blackwell Publishing Ltd.), Commerce Place, 350 Main St, Malden, MA 02148. TEL 781-388-8206, FAX 781-388-8232, subscrip@blackwellpub.com, http://www.blackwellpublishing.com/journals/RAE. Eds. Daniel Pick, Katherine R Smith, Susan E Offutt. adv.: page USD 500. Circ: 4,200.

➤ **REVIEW OF REGIONAL STUDIES**; the official journal of the Southern regional science association. see *HOUSING AND URBAN PLANNING*

338.1 NIC
REVISTA DE ECONOMIA AGRICOLA. Text in Spanish. q. USD 9 domestic; USD 15 in Central America; USD 18 in North America; USD 22 in Europe; USD 24 elsewhere.
Published by: Universidad Nacional Autonoma de Nicaragua, Departamento de Economia Agricola, Correo Central, ZONA, 5, Apdo 763, Managua, Nicaragua. TEL 505-2-23311.

338.1 BRA ISSN 0103-2003
REVISTA DE ECONOMIA E SOCIOLOGIA RURAL. Text in Portuguese; Abstracts in English, Portuguese. 1962. q. USD 80. bibl. **Document type:** *Academic/Scholarly.*
Formerly (until 1988): Revista de Economia Rural
Related titles: Online - full text ed.: free (effective 2005).
Indexed: HAPI, SociolAb.
Published by: Sociedade Brasileira de Economia e Sociologia Rural, Edificio Brasilia Radio Center, Av. W-3 Norte - Quadra 702, Salas 1049-1050, Brasilia, DF 70710900, Brazil. TEL 55-61-3283144, FAX 55-61-3283144, sober@tba.com.br, http://www.ufv.br/der/sober/index.htm. Ed. Wilson da Cruz Vieira.

338.1 ESP ISSN 1575-1198
REVISTA ESPANOLA DE ESTUDIOS AGROSOCIALES Y PESQUEROS. Text in Spanish, English, French. 1998. q. EUR 48.08 domestic; EUR 66.11 foreign; EUR 33.06 to students (effective 2002). bk.rev. Index. **Document type:** *Journal, Government.* **Description:** Analyzes the procedures and politics of the agrarian sector.
Formed by the merger of (1976-1998): Agricultura y Sociedad (0211-8394); (1942-1998): Revista Espanola de Economia Agraria (1135-6138); Which was formerly (until 1994): Revista de Estudios Agro-Sociales (0034-8155); (until 1952): Instituto de Estudios Agro-Sociales. Anales (0210-072X); (until 1950): Surco (1132-6301)
Indexed: AEA, AgBio, AgrForAb, AnBrAb, DSA, FCA, FPA, ForAb, HortAb, I&DA, OrnHort, PAIS, PBA, PHN&I, PN&I, RDA, RRTA, RefZh, S&F, SeedAb, TriticAb, WAE&RSA.
—BLDSC (7853.982000), CINDOC, IE, ingenta.
Published by: Ministerio de Agricultura Pesca y Alimentacion, Centro de Publicaciones, Paseo Infanta Isabel 1, Madrid, 28014, Spain. TEL 34-91-3475550, FAX 34-91-3475722, mllopisj@mapya.es, http://www.mapya.es. R&P Juan Carlos Palacios Lopez. Circ: 2,500 (controlled).

RHEINLAND AKTUELL; Analysen - Daten - Informationen. see *AGRICULTURE—Abstracting, Bibliographies, Statistics*

338.1 ITA ISSN 0035-6190
HD1401
RIVISTA DI ECONOMIA AGRARIA. Text in Italian; Summaries in English. 1946. q. EUR 57 domestic to individuals; EUR 74 domestic to institutions; EUR 94 foreign (effective 2003). adv. bk.rev. index, cum.index: 1954-1964. back issues avail. **Document type:** *Journal, Academic/Scholarly.*
Indexed: CurCont, DSA, FPA, FS&TA, ForAb, HortAb, I&DA, IBSS, ILD, IndVet, MaizeAb, NutrAb, PAIS, PHN&I, PN&I, RASB, RDA, RRTA, RiceAb, S&F, SIA, TOSA, TriticAb, VetBull, WAE&RSA.
—BLDSC (7985.200000), CISTI, IE, Infotrieve, ingenta.
Published by: (Societa Italiana di Economia Agraria/Italian Society of Agrarian Economy), Istituto Nazionale di Economia Agraria/National Institute of Agrarian Economy, Via Barberini, 36, Rome, 00187, Italy. TEL 39-6-478561, FAX 39-6-478562, inea@inea.it, http://www.inea.it. Circ: 1,600.

338.1 ISR
RIV'ON KUTNA. Text in Hebrew. 1986. q. ILS 125.
Published by: Heshev, P O Box 40021, Tel Aviv, 61400, Israel. FAX 266233. Circ: 150.

338.1 POL ISSN 0080-3715
ROCZNIKI NAUK ROLNICZYCH. SERIA G. EKONOMIKA ROLNICTWA. Text in Polish; Summaries in English, Polish. 1903. irreg., latest vol.88, 1999. price varies. bibl.; charts. **Document type:** *Academic/Scholarly.*
Indexed: AgrLib, RASB.
—CISTI.
Published by: (Polska Akademia Nauk, Komitet Organizacji Produkcji Rolnej i Wyzywienia Kraju), Wydawnictwo Naukowe P W N SA/Polish Scientific Publishers P W N, ul Miodowa 10, Warsaw, 00251, Poland. TEL 48-22-6954181, FAX 48-22-6954288, ksiegarnia@pwn.pl, http://en.pwn.pl. Circ: 430.

A

352.14 CAN ISSN 0036-0007
JS1721.S3
THE RURAL COUNCILLOR. Text in English. 1966. m. (except Jan. & Aug.). CND 30 to non-members (effective 2000). adv. bk.rev. back issues avail. **Document type:** *Newsletter.* **Description:** Provides information to local rural governments in Saskatchewan.
Published by: Saskatchewan Association of Rural Municipalities, c/o Leeann Minogue, Ed, 2075 Hamilton St, Regina, SK S4P 2E1, Canada. TEL 306-757-3577, FAX 306-565-2141, sarm.mg@sk.sympatico.ca, http://www.quantumlynx.com/sarm. R&P Arita Paul TEL 306-757-3579. Adv. contact Paula Mossing. Circ: 3,500.

338.1 USA ISSN 0886-8611
HC501
RURAL DEVELOPMENT NEWS. Text in English. 1974. 4/yr. free. bk.rev. 12 p./no. 3 cols./p.; back issues avail. **Document type:** *Newsletter.* **Description:** Provides information on research projects, publications, conferences and extension services of interest to readers in the 12 state North Central region.
Formerly: North Central Regional Center for Rural Development. Research Report
Related titles: Online - full text ed.
Indexed: Agr, EnvAb.
Published by: North Central Regional Center for Rural Development, 108 Curtiss Hall, Iowa State University, Ames, IA 50011. TEL 515-294-7648, FAX 515-294-3180, jstewart@iastate.edu, http://www.ag.iastate.edu/centers/rdev/rdn.html. Ed. Julie Stewart. Circ: 4,500.

338.1 IND ISSN 0036-0058
HN681
➤ **RURAL INDIA.** Text in English, Hindi. 1938. m. INR 250 domestic; USD 55 foreign (effective 2001). adv. bk.rev. illus.; mkt.; stat. index. 24 p./no.; **Document type:** *Journal, Academic/Scholarly.* **Description:** Devoted to issues relating to Indian agricultural development and management.
Related titles: E-mail ed.
Indexed: BAS, RRTA, WAE&RSA.
Published by: Surendra Vikram Vaid, Ed. & Pub., Babai House, Gopal Ganj, Orai, Uttar Pradesh 285 001, India. TEL 91-5162-53444, FAX 91-5162-51074, Ed., R&P Surendra Vikram Vaid. Pub. Yogeshwari Vaid. Adv. contact Ashok Vikram Vaid. page INR 1,000; trim 8 x 5.5. Circ: 1,800.

332.7 USA
RURAL UPDATE. Text in English. 1993. irreg. (approx. m.). free. back issues avail. **Description:** Reports on news, innovations, and resources for small-town and rural community economic development.
Media: Online - full text.
Published by: Aspen Institute, Communities Strategies Group, One Dupont Circle N W, Ste 700, Washington, DC 20036. TEL 702-736-5800, FAX 202-467-0790, http://www.aspeninst.org/rural/. Ed. Kelly Malone.

SAMSPEL; om levande naturresurser. see *AGRICULTURE*

338.1 USA
SAN FRANCISCO FRESH FRUIT AND VEGETABLE WHOLESALE MARKET PRICES. Text in English. 1932. a. USD 10. **Document type:** *Newsletter, Government.*
Published by: (U.S. Department of Agriculture), Federal-State Market News Service (Sacramento), 630 Sansome St, Rm 727, San Francisco, CA 94111. TEL 415-705-1300, FAX 415-705-1301.

338.1 USA
SAN FRANCISCO WHOLESALE FRUIT AND VEGETABLE REPORT. Text in English. 1932. d. USD 180; USD 360 foreign. back issues avail. **Document type:** *Government.* **Description:** Presents lists of price ranges, offerings, and status of the produce market; region-by-region market briefs on produce exportation in California.
Published by: (U.S. Department of Agriculture), Federal-State Market News Service (Sacramento), 630 Sansome St, Rm 727, San Francisco, CA 94111. TEL 415-705-1300, FAX 415-705-1301. Circ: 280.

SCANDINAVIAN INSTITUTE OF AFRICAN STUDIES. RURAL DEVELOPMENT. see *ANTHROPOLOGY*

SCHWEIZER LANDTECHNIK. see *AGRICULTURE*

SHEEP & GOAT RESEARCH JOURNAL. see *AGRICULTURE—Poultry And Livestock*

338.1 USA
SITUATION & OUTLOOK REPORT. AGRICULTURAL INCOME & FINANCE. Text in English. 1961. 3/yr. USD 30 (effective 2001). reprint service avail. from CIS. **Document type:** *Government.* **Description:** Looks at farm income, profitability, government payments, production expenses, debts and assets, and other areas of farm finance.
Former titles: U.S. Department of Agriculture. Agricultural Finance Outlook and Situation; U.S. Department of Agriculture. Agricultural Income and Finance Outlook and Situation; (until 1980): Agricultural Finance Outlook (0501-9117)
Related titles: Microfiche ed.: (from CIS); Online - full text ed.: (from The Dialog Corporation).
Indexed: AmStl, MaizeAb, WAE&RSA.
—CISTI.
Published by: U.S. Department of Agriculture, Economic Research Service, 1800 M St. NW, Washington, DC 20036-5831. TEL 202-694-5050, http://www.ers.usda.gov/publications/so/view.asp?f=economics/ais-bb/. **Dist. by:** ERS-NASS, 5285 Port Royal Rd, Springfield, VA 22161.

338.1 USA
SITUATION & OUTLOOK REPORT. COTTON AND WOOL OUTLOOK. Text in English. 1995. 10/yr. **Document type:** *Government.* **Description:** Provides information and statistics on domestic and world cotton and wool production, consumption, export sales, use, and prices, including data on raw fibers and textiles.
Media: Online - full text (from The Dialog Corporation). **Related titles:** ♦ Supplement(s): Situation & Outlook Report. Cotton and Wool Yearbook.
Published by: U.S. Department of Agriculture, Economic Research Service, 1800 M St. NW, Washington, DC 20036-5831. http://www.ers.usda.gov/publications/so/view.asp?f=field/cws-bb/.

338.1 USA
SITUATION & OUTLOOK REPORT. COTTON AND WOOL YEARBOOK. Text in English. 1995. a. USD 21 (effective 2001). **Document type:** *Government.* **Description:** Examines domestic and world cotton production, consumption, export sales, use, and prices, as well as the outlook for domestic and world wool. This report is a supplement to Cotton and Wool Outlook.
Related titles: Online - full content ed.; ♦ Supplement to: Situation & Outlook Report. Cotton and Wool Outlook.
Indexed: WAE&RSA.
Published by: U.S. Department of Agriculture, Economic Research Service, 1800 M St. NW, Washington, DC 20036-5831. ersinfo@ers.usda.gov, http://www.ers.usda.gov/publications/so/view.asp?f=field/cws-bby/. **Dist. by:** ERS-NASS, 5285 Port Royal Rd, Springfield, VA 22161.

SITUATION & OUTLOOK REPORT. LIVESTOCK, DAIRY AND POULTRY. see *AGRICULTURE—Poultry And Livestock*

338.1 USA
HD9001
SITUATION & OUTLOOK REPORT. OUTLOOK FOR U.S. AGRICULTURAL TRADE. Text in English. q. USD 10 (effective 2001). back issues avail.; reprint service avail. from CIS. **Document type:** *Government.* **Description:** Offers the latest value and volume forecasts for U.S. farm exports, by commodity and region, as well as the agricultural trade balance, and projected in ports.
Formerly: Outlook for U.S. Agricultural Exports (0148-9526)
Related titles: Microfiche ed.: (from CIS); Online - full text ed.
Indexed: AmStl.
—CISTI.
Published by: U.S. Department of Agriculture, Economic Research Service, 1800 M St. NW, Washington, DC 20036-5831. TEL 202-694-5050, http://www.ers.usda.gov/publications/so/view.asp?f=trade/aes-bb/. **Subscr. to:** U.S. Government Printing Office, Superintendent of Documents, PO Box 371954, Pittsburgh, PA 15250-7954. TEL 202-512-1800, FAX 202-512-2250, orders@gpo.gov, http://www.access.gpo.gov. **Dist. by:** ERS-NASS, 5285 Port Royal Rd, Springfield, VA 22161. **Co-sponsor:** U.S. Foreign Agricultural Service.

338.1 USA ISSN 0896-0240
HD9101
SITUATION & OUTLOOK REPORT. SUGAR & SWEETENER. Text in English. 1975. 3/yr. USD 11 (effective 2001). back issues avail.; reprint service avail. from CIS. **Document type:** *Government.* **Description:** Examines world and U.S production, consumption, supply and use, trade, stocks, and prices for beet and cane sugar, and high fructose corn syrup.
Former titles (until 1986): U.S. Department of Agriculture. Outlook and Situation Report. Sugar and Sweetener (8755-8548); U.S. Department of Agriculture. Sugar and Sweetener Outlook and Situation (0362-9511); U.S. Department of Agriculture. Economics Management Staff. Sugar and Sweetener Report; Which was formed by merger of: U.S. Department of Agriculture. Economic Research Service. Sugar and Sweetener Situation (0360-0521); U.S. Agricultural Marketing Service. Sugar Market News
Related titles: Microfiche ed.: (from CIS); Online - full text ed.: (from Gale Group, The Dialog Corporation).
Indexed: AmStl, PotatoAb, SIA, WAE&RSA.
—CISTI.
Published by: U.S. Department of Agriculture, Economic Research Service, 1800 M St. NW, Washington, DC 20036-5831. TEL 202-694-5050, shaley@con.ag.gov, http://www.ers.usda.gov/publications/so/view.asp?f=specialty/sss-bb/. **Subscr. to:** U.S. Government Printing Office, Superintendent of Documents, PO Box 371954, Pittsburgh, PA 15250-7954. TEL 202-512-1800, FAX 202-512-2250, orders@gpo.gov, http://www.access.gpo.gov. **Dist. by:** ERS-NASS, 5285 Port Royal Rd, Springfield, VA 22161. TEL 800-999-6779.

338.1 USA
SITUATION & OUTLOOK REPORT. U.S. AGRICULTURAL TRADE UPDATE. Text in English. m. USD 62 (effective 2001). **Document type:** *Government.* **Description:** Covers the monthly farm trade balance, U.S. farm imports and exports by quantity and value, and leading exports and exporters.
Related titles: Online - full content ed.
Published by: U.S. Department of Agriculture, Economic Research Service, 1800 M St. NW, Washington, DC 20036-5831. ersinfo@ers.usda.gov, http://www.ers.usda.gov/publications/so/view.asp?f=trade/fau-bb/. **Dist. by:** ERS-NASS, 5285 Port Royal Rd, Springfield, VA 22161. TEL 800-999-6779, 202-694-5050.

338.1 FRA ISSN 1683-2302
SOURCE O C D E. AGRICULTURE ET ALIMENTATION. (Organisation de Cooperation et de Developpement Economiques) Text in French. irreg. EUR 700, USD 805, GBP 462, JPY 94,500 (effective 2005).
Related titles: Online - full text ed.: ISSN 1684-2952. EUR 488, USD 561, GBP 324, JPY 65,900 (effective 2005) (from EBSCO Publishing, Gale Group, IngentaConnect, Swets Information Services); ♦ English ed.: Source O E C D. Agriculture & Food. ISSN 1608-0149.
Published by: Organization for Economic Cooperation and Development, 2 Rue Andre Pascal, Paris, 75775 Cedex 16, France. TEL 33-1-45248200, FAX 33-1-45248500, http://www.oecd.org. **Dist. by:** Extenza - Turpin, Pegasus Dr, Stratton Business Park, Biggleswade, Beds SG18 8TQ, United Kingdom. TEL 44-1462-687552, FAX 44-1462-480947, subscriptions@extenza-turpin.com; O E C D Turpin North America, PO Box 194, Downingtown, PA 19335-0194. TEL 610-524-5361, 800-456-6323, FAX 610-524-5417, journalscustomer@turpinna.com.

338.1 FRA ISSN 1608-0149
SOURCE O E C D. AGRICULTURE & FOOD. Text in English. irreg. EUR 700, USD 805, GBP 462, JPY 94,500 (effective 2005). stat. **Document type:** *Government.*
Related titles: Online - full content ed.: ISSN 1681-5319. EUR 488, USD 561, GBP 324, JPY 65,900 (effective 2005); Online - full text ed.: 2000 (from Gale Group, IngentaConnect, Swets Information Services); ♦ French ed.: Source O C D E. Agriculture et Alimentation. ISSN 1683-2302.
Published by: Organization for Economic Cooperation and Development, 2 Rue Andre Pascal, Paris, 75775 Cedex 16, France. TEL 33-1-45248200, FAX 33-1-45248500, http://www.oecd.org. **Dist. by:** Extenza - Turpin, Pegasus Dr, Stratton Business Park, Biggleswade, Beds SG18 8TQ, United Kingdom. TEL 44-1462-687552, FAX 44-1462-480947, subscriptions@extenza-turpin.com; O E C D Turpin North America, PO Box 194, Downingtown, PA 19335-0194. TEL 610-524-5361, 800-456-6323, FAX 610-524-5417, journalscustomer@turpinna.com.

338.1 ZAF
SOUTH AFRICA. DEPARTMENT OF AGRICULTURE. DIRECTORATE OF AGRICULTURAL STATISTICS. TRENDS IN THE AGRICULTURAL SECTOR. Text in English. 1968. s-a. free. stat. **Document type:** *Government.*
Former titles: South Africa. Department of Agriculture and Fisheries. Division of Economic Services. Trends in the Agricultural Sector; South Africa. Department of Agricultural Economics and Marketing. Division of Agricultural Marketing and Research. Trends in the Agricultural Sector
Published by: National Department of Agriculture, Directorate of Agricultural Statistics, Private Bag X144, Pretoria, 0001, South Africa. TEL 12-319-7141, secdass@nda.agric.za. Circ: (controlled).

338.1 GBR ISSN 0958-9732
S562.G6
SPECIAL STUDIES IN AGRICULTURAL ECONOMICS. Text in English. 1970. irreg., latest vol.103, 1988. **Document type:** *Monographic series.* **Description:** Reports on the results of economic research on crops and livestock.
Formerly: Agricultural Enterprise Studies in England and Wales
Indexed: AnBrAb, DSA, PN&I, TriticAb, WAE&RSA.
—BLDSC (8404.453000), ingenta.
Published by: University of Reading, Department of Agricultural and Food Economics, 4 Earley Gate, Whiteknights Rd, PO Box 237, Reading, Berks RG6 2AR, United Kingdom. TEL 44-1734-875123, FAX 44-1734-756467, TELEX 847813-RULIB-G.

338.1 NLD ISSN 1011-0054
SPORE. Text in English. 1986. bi-m. free to qualified personnel.
Related titles: French ed.: ISSN 1011-0046; Portuguese ed.: Esporo. ISSN 1019-9381. 1993.
Indexed: ESPM, HortAb, RDA, WAE&RSA.
—BLDSC (8419.320000).
Published by: Technical Centre for Agricultural and Rural Cooperation, Postbus 380, Wageningen, 6700 AJ, Netherlands. TEL 31-317-467100, FAX 31-317-460067, cta@cta.nl, http://www.agricta.org/index.htm, http://www.cta.nl.

STATISTICAL OFFICE OF THE EUROPEAN COMMUNITIES. AGRICULTURAL PRICES; selected series - chronos data bank. see *AGRICULTURE—Abstracting, Bibliographies, Statistics*

STATISTIK AUSTRIA. ERGEBNISSE DER LANDWIRTSCHAFTLICHEN STATISTIK. see *AGRICULTURE—Abstracting, Bibliographies, Statistics*

338.1   HUN   ISSN 1418-2106
HD1407
STUDIES IN AGRICULTURAL ECONOMICS. Text in English. 1962. irreg. per issue exchange basis. **Document type:** *Bulletin.*
Former titles (until 1997): Research Institute for Agricultural Economics. Bulletin (0541-9417); Hungarian Academy of Sciences. Research Institute for Agricultural Economics. Bulletin
Indexed: MaizeAb, RRTA, WAE&RSA.
—CISTI.
Published by: Agrargazdasagi Kutato es Informatikai Intezet/Research and Information Institute for Agricultural Economics, Zsil utca 3-5, PO Box 5, Budapest, 1355, Hungary. TEL 217-10-11, FAX 361-217-7037, TELEX 22-6923. Ed. Sandor Meszaros.

SUDAN YEARBOOK OF AGRICULTURAL STATISTICS. see *AGRICULTURE—Abstracting, Bibliographies, Statistics*

SURVEY OF HOUSEHOLD ECONOMIC ACTIVITIES (YEAR). see *BUSINESS AND ECONOMICS—Economic Situation And Conditions*

633   GBR   ISSN 0309-2968
SUTTON BRIDGE ANNUAL REVIEW. Text in English. 1970. a. **Document type:** *Trade.*
Address: Sutton Bridge, Spalding, Lincs PE12 9YB, United Kingdom. TEL 44-1406-351998. Ed. A C Cunnington.

SWAZILAND. CENTRAL STATISTICAL OFFICE. CENSUS OF INDIVIDUAL TENURE FARMS. see *AGRICULTURE— Abstracting, Bibliographies, Statistics*

SZABAD FOLDMUVES. see *AGRICULTURE*

338.1   DEU   ISSN 0177-6673
TECHNISCHE UNIVERSITAET BERLIN. INSTITUT FUER SOZIALOEKONOMIE DER AGRARENTWICKLUNG. SCHRIFTENREIHE DES FACHBEREICHS. Text in German. 1960. irreg. (5-8/yr.) free. **Description:** Reports on the activities of the institute's faculty; research programs of study, proceedings, and papers focused on the problem of agricultural development in developing countries.
Formerly: Technische Universitaet Berlin. Institut fuer Sozialoekonomie der Agrarentwicklung. Jahresbericht (0170-8376); Incorporates: Technische Universitaet Berlin. Institut fuer Sozialoekonomie der Agrarentwicklung. Annual Report (Abridged Edition) (0170-8309); (until 1976): Technische Universitaet. Institut fuer Sozialoekonomie der Agrarentwicklung. Taetigkeitsbericht (0067-6039)
Media: Duplicated (not offset).
Indexed: ARDT.
Published by: Technische Universitaet Berlin, Fachbereich Internationale Agrarentwicklung, Hellriegelstr 6, Berlin, 14195, Germany. TEL 030-314-71312, FAX 030-314-23222, TELEX 184262-TUBLN-D. Circ: 150.

338.1   NLD   ISSN 0921-481X
TIJDSCHRIFT VOOR SOCIAAL WETENSCHAPPELIJK ONDERZOEK VAN DE LANDBOUW. Short title: T S L. Text in Dutch, English. 1986. q. USD 35 to individuals; USD 50 to institutions. bk.rev. index. back issues avail.
Indexed: AEA, AgBio, DSA, ForAb, HortAb, IndVet, NutrAb, OrnHort, PHN&I, PN&I, PoultAb, RDA, RRTA, S&F, VetBull, WAE&RSA.
—BLDSC (8844.460000), IE, ingenta, KNAW.
Published by: Landbouw-Economisch Instituut, Postbus 29703, The Hague, 2502 LS, Netherlands. TEL 31-70-3614161, FAX 31-70-361-5624, postmaster@lei.dlo.nl, http://www.lei.dlo.nl/lei. Ed. Guido van Huylenbroeck. Circ: 350.

338.41   USA   ISSN 0193-6514
TOBACCO MARKET REVIEW; flue-cured. Text in English. 194?. a. USD 3 per issue (effective 2005).
Formerly (until 1974): Flue-cured Tobacco Market Review (0498-1782)
—CISTI.
Published by: U.S. Department of Agriculture, Agricultural Marketing Service, 1400 Independence Ave, S W, Washington, DC 20250. TEL 202-720-8317, FAX 202-690-0031, http://www.ams.usda.gov.

TURF NEWS. see *AGRICULTURE—Crop Production And Soil*

TURKEY. DEVLET ISTATISTIK ENSTITUSU. TARIMSAL URETIM DEGERI/TURKEY. STATE INSTITUTE OF STATISTICS. VALUE OF AGRICULTURAL PRODUCTION. see *AGRICULTURE—Abstracting, Bibliographies, Statistics*

TURKEY. DEVLET ISTATISTIK ENSTITUSU. TARIMSAL YAPI VE URETIM/TURKEY. STATE INSTITUTE OF STATISTICS. AGRICULTURAL STRUCTURE AND PRODUCTION. see *AGRICULTURE—Abstracting, Bibliographies, Statistics*

338.1   CAN   ISSN 0715-6650
TWO THIRDS. Text in English. 1982. q. CND 3. **Document type:** *Newsletter.*
Indexed: HRIR.
Published by: Canadian Hunger Foundation, 323 Chapel St, Ottawa, ON K1N 7Z2, Canada. TEL 613-237-0180, FAX 613-237-5969. Ed. Tom Taylor. Circ: 1,100.

338.1   USA   ISSN 0083-0445
U.S. DEPARTMENT OF AGRICULTURE. AGRICULTURAL ECONOMIC REPORTS. Text in English. 1961. irreg. price varies. **Document type:** *Government.*
Reports 1-233 (1916-1972) issued as: U.S. Department of Agriculture. Economic Research Service. Agricultural Economics Report
Indexed: AgBio, CTFA, DSA, FCA, MaizeAb, NutrAb, PHN&I, PN&I, PoultAb, RRTA, RevApplEntom, S&F, SoyAb, TOSA, TriticAb, WAE&RSA, WeedAb.
—CISTI.
Published by: U.S. Department of Agriculture, Economic Research Service, c/o Debbie Haugan, 1800 M St, N W, Rm 3100, Washington, DC 20036. TEL 202-694-5050. **Dist. by:** ERS-NASS. TEL 800-999-6799.

338.14   USA   ISSN 0082-9781
HD1751   CODEN: XAGMAF
U.S. DEPARTMENT OF AGRICULTURE. MARKETING RESEARCH REPORT. Text in English. 1952. irreg. **Document type:** *Government.*
Related titles: Microfiche ed.: (from PQC).
Indexed: RRTA, WAE&RSA.
—CASDDS, CISTI.
Published by: U.S. Department of Agriculture, Office of Public Affairs, 14th St & Independence Ave, S W, Washington, DC 20250-1300. TEL 202-720-2791.

U.S. DEPARTMENT OF AGRICULTURE. NATIONAL AGRICULTURAL STATISTICS SERVICE. AGRICULTURAL PRICES. see *AGRICULTURE—Abstracting, Bibliographies, Statistics*

U.S. DEPARTMENT OF AGRICULTURE. NATIONAL AGRICULTURAL STATISTICS SERVICE. CROP VALUES. see *AGRICULTURE—Abstracting, Bibliographies, Statistics*

U.S. DEPARTMENT OF AGRICULTURE. NATIONAL AGRICULTURAL STATISTICS SERVICE. FARM PRODUCTION EXPENDITURES. see *AGRICULTURE— Abstracting, Bibliographies, Statistics*

338.1   USA   ISSN 0082-979X
S21   CODEN: XAPRA7
U.S. DEPARTMENT OF AGRICULTURE. PRODUCTION RESEARCH REPORTS. Text in English. 1956. irreg., latest vol.179, 1980. price varies. **Document type:** *Government.*
Related titles: Microfiche ed.: (from PQC).
Indexed: Agr, BiolAb.
—CASDDS, CISTI.
Published by: U.S. Department of Agriculture, Office of Public Affairs, 14th St & Independence Ave, S W, Washington, DC 20250-1300. TEL 202-720-2791.

338.1   USA   ISSN 0742-9509
U.S. DEPARTMENT OF AGRICULTURE. RURAL BUSINESS - COOPERATIVE SERVICE. RESEARCH REPORTS. Text in English. irreg. price varies. charts; stat. **Document type:** *Monographic series, Government.* **Description:** Presents the results of U.S.D.A. Cooperative Service studies.
Published by: U.S. Department of Agriculture, Rural Business - Cooperative Service, Stop 3250, Washington, DC 20250-3250. TEL 202-720-7558, FAX 202-720-4641.

U.S. FOREIGN AGRICULTURAL TRADE STATISTICAL REPORT. FISCAL YEAR. see *AGRICULTURE—Abstracting, Bibliographies, Statistics*

338.1   MYS   ISSN 0304-8349
HD1471.M34
UNITED PLANTING ASSOCIATION OF MALAYSIA. ANNUAL REPORT. Text in English. 1968. a. MYR 10. **Document type:** *Corporate.*
Published by: United Planting Association of Malaysia, PO Box 10272, Kuala Lumpur, 50708, Malaysia. TEL 603-2485622, FAX 603-2415449. Circ: 1,100.

380.141   USA   ISSN 0093-4429
UNITED STATES: COTTON QUALITY REPORTS FOR GINNINGS∗. Text in English. 1928. m. free. stat. reprint service avail. from CIS.
Media: Duplicated (not offset). **Related titles:** Microfiche ed.: 1928 (from CIS).
Indexed: AmStI, TTI.
Published by: U.S. Agricultural Marketing Service, Cotton Division, 302 Annex Bldg, 12th and C Sts, S W, Washington, DC 20250. TEL 202-447-3193.

338.1   ITA
UNIVERSITA DEGLI STUDI DI TRIESTE. ISTITUTO DI RICERCHE ECONOMICO AGRARIE. PUBBLICAZIONE. Text in Italian. 1971. irreg.

Published by: Universita degli Studi di Trieste, Istituto di Ricerche Economico-Agrarie, Trieste, TS, Italy.

338.1   USA   ISSN 0886-4845
UNIVERSITY OF FLORIDA. FOOD AND RESOURCE ECONOMICS DEPARTMENT. ECONOMIC INFORMATION REPORT. Key Title: Economic Information Report. Text in English. 1969. irreg., latest vol.123, 1979. free.
Former titles: University of Florida. Food and Resource Economics Department. Economics Report; University of Florida. Institute of Food and Agricultural Sciences. Agricultural Economics Series
Indexed: Agr.
—Linda Hall.
Published by: University of Florida, Institute of Food and Agricultural Sciences, PO Box 110240, Gainesville, FL 32611-0240. TEL 904-392-1733. Ed. Richard Bellock. Circ: 2,500.

338.1   USA   ISSN 0073-5213
UNIVERSITY OF ILLINOIS AT URBANA-CHAMPAIGN. DEPARTMENT OF AGRICULTURAL ECONOMICS. AGRICULTURAL FINANCE PROGRAM REPORT. Text in English. 1970. irreg., latest 1970. price varies.
Published by: University of Illinois at Urbana-Champaign, Department of Agricultural Economics, 326 Mumford Hall, MC-710, 1301 W Gregory Dr, Urbana, IL 61801. TEL 217-333-7425.

338.1   USA
HD1511.U6
UNIVERSITY OF ILLINOIS AT URBANA-CHAMPAIGN. DEPARTMENT OF AGRICULTURAL ECONOMICS. LEASE SHARES AND FARM RETURNS. Text in English. 1961. a. USD 3. stat.
Formerly: University of Illinois at Urbana-Champaign. Department of Agricultural Economics. Landlord and Tenant Shares (0160-3027)
Published by: University of Illinois at Urbana-Champaign, Department of Agricultural Economics, 326 Mumford Hall, MC-710, 1301 W Gregory Dr, Urbana, IL 61801. TEL 217-333-2638. Ed. John T Scott. Circ: (controlled).

338.1   GBR
UNIVERSITY OF MANCHESTER. SCHOOL OF ECONOMIC STUDIES. FARM BUSINESS UNIT. BULLETIN. Text in English. irreg., latest vol.231, 1995. GBP 10.50 (effective 2000). **Document type:** *Bulletin.*
Formerly (until 1995): University of Manchester. Faculty of Economic and Social Studies. Department of Agricultural Economics. Bulletin
Indexed: DSA.
—BLDSC (2789.171000).
Published by: (Farm Business Unit), University of Manchester, School of Economic Studies, Oxford Rd, Manchester, Lancs M13 9PL, United Kingdom.

338.1   GBR   ISSN 0557-6911
UNIVERSITY OF READING. DEPARTMENT OF AGRICULTURAL AND FOOD ECONOMICS. FARM BUSINESS DATA. Text in English. 1974. a. GBP 10 (effective 1999). bibl.; charts; stat. **Document type:** *Bulletin.* **Description:** Explores business ratios for account analysis, research reports and forward planning.
Published by: University of Reading, Department of Agricultural and Food Economics, 4 Earley Gate, Whiteknights Rd, PO Box 237, Reading, Berks RG6 2AR, United Kingdom. TEL 44-1734-875123, FAX 44-1734-756467, aesadept@uk.ac.reading. Ed. David Ansell.

338.1   GBR
UNIVERSITY OF READING. DEPARTMENT OF AGRICULTURAL AND FOOD ECONOMICS. OCCASIONAL PAPERS. Text in English. 1993. irreg., latest vol.3, 1994. GBP 8. **Document type:** *Monographic series.*
—BLDSC.
Published by: University of Reading, Department of Agricultural and Food Economics, 4 Earley Gate, Whiteknights Rd, PO Box 237, Reading, Berks RG6 2AR, United Kingdom. TEL 44-1734-875123, FAX 44-1734-756467.

338.1   AUS   ISSN 0817-8771
UNIVERSITY OF SYDNEY. DEPARTMENT OF AGRICULTURAL ECONOMICS. RESEARCH REPORT. Text in English. 1957. irreg., latest no.14, 1996. price varies. **Document type:** *Academic/Scholarly.* **Description:** Contains results of detailed analyses of problems in both agricultural and applied economics.
Formerly: University of Sydney. Department of Agricultural Economics. Mimeographed Report. (0082-0555)
Media: Duplicated (not offset).
Published by: University of Sydney, Department of Agricultural Economics, R D Watt Bldg, Syndey, NSW 2006, Australia. TEL 61-2-9351-2574, FAX 61-2-9351-4953, agec.agric@agec.usyd.edu.au, http://www.usyd.edu.au/su/agec. Circ: 400.

333   USA   ISSN 0084-0807
UNIVERSITY OF WISCONSIN, MADISON. LAND TENURE CENTER. REPRINT. Some issues in Spanish. 1965-1987; resumed 1999 (Jan.-Mar., no.151). irreg. free.

A

Published by: University of Wisconsin at Madison, Land Tenure Center, 1357 University Ave, Madison, WI 53715. TEL 608-262-3657. Ed. Jane B Knowles.

URNER BARRY'S NATIONAL WEEKLY HATCH REPORT. see *AGRICULTURE—Abstracting, Bibliographies, Statistics*

380.141 URY ISSN 0797-3357
URUGUAY. MINISTERIO DE AGRICULTURA Y PESCA. PRECIOS DE PRODUCTOS E INSUMOS AGROPECUARIOS. Text in Spanish. 1974. m. adv.
Published by: Ministerio de Agricultura y Pesca, Direccion de Investigaciones Economicas Agropecuarias, Rincon 22, Montevideo, Uruguay.

UTSYN OVER NORSK LANDBRUK. see *AGRICULTURE*

338.1 ESP
VALENCIA - FRUITS; semanario europeo de informacion economica. Text in Spanish. 1962. w. adv. **Document type:** *Newspaper.*
Published by: Sucro S.A., Hernan Cortes, 5-1, Valencia, 46004, Spain. TEL 34-6-3510295, FAX 34-6-352-57-52. Ed. Amparo Vallier Pino. Adv. contact Jose Maria Server Martinez.

338.1 USA ISSN 1064-4075
VIRGINIA FRUIT AND VEGETABLE BULLETIN. Text in English. s-w. back issues avail. **Document type:** *Government.* **Description:** Provides fruit and vegetable market prices since the last issue, to Virginia farmers and agribusinesses.
Published by: Virginia Department of Agriculture & Consumer Services, Virginia Market News Service, 1100 Bank St, Ste 805, Richmond, VA 23219-3638. TEL 804-786-3947, FAX 804-371-7787, mktnews@vdacs.state.va.us, http://www.vdacs.state.va.us/marketnews/. Ed. J P Welch. Circ: 500.

338.1 USA
HD1775.O5
VISIONS (STILLWATER). Text in English. 1927. 2/yr. free. charts; illus.; mkt.; stat. index. reprint service avail. from PQC. **Document type:** *Magazine, Government.* **Description:** Covers current agricultural issues, including policy analysis, market strategies and production alternatives, as well as related concerns such as rural development, environmental quality and natural resources.
Formerly (until 2000): Oklahoma Current Farm Economics (0030-1701)
Related titles: Microfilm ed.: (from PQC).
Indexed: Agr, CurCont, DSA, FCA, HerbAb, MaizeAb, PN&I, S&F, SoyAb, TriticAb, WAE&RSA.
Published by: Department of Agricultural Economics, Oklahoma Agricultural Experiment Station, Oklahoma State University, 139 Agriculture Hall, Stillwater, OK 74078. TEL 405-744-6161, FAX 405-744-8210. Ed. Harry Mapp. Circ: 1,600. **Co-sponsor:** Oklahoma State University, Division of Agricultural Sciences and Natural Resources.

333 AUS ISSN 1320-3878
WALIS NEWS. (Western Australian Land Information Service) Text in English. irreg.
Published by: Western Australian Land Information Services, PO Box 2222, Midland, W.A. 6056, Australia. TEL 61-8-9273-7046, FAX 61-8-9273-7691, mark@walis.wa.gov.au, http://waliswww.walis.wa.gov.au/working_with_walis/news.

338.1 POL
WARSAW AGRICULTURAL UNIVERSITY. S G G W. ANNALS. AGRICULTURAL ECONOMICS AND RURAL SOCIOLOGY. Text mainly in English; Text occasionally in French, German, Russian; Summaries in Polish. 1957. irreg., latest vol.33, 1998. USD 10 per issue (effective 2003). **Document type:** *Bulletin, Academic/Scholarly.*
Formerly: Warsaw Agricultural University. S G G W - A R. Annals. Agricultural Economics and Rural Sociology (0208-5720)
Indexed: AgrAg, AgrLib, FPA.
—CISTI.
Published by: Szkola Glowna Gospodarstwa Wiejskiego (SGGW)/Warsaw Agricultural University, Ul Nowoursynowska 166, Warsaw, 02787, Poland. TEL 48-22-8439041, FAX 48-22-8471562, jmw_wyd@alpha.sggw.waw.pl, http://www.sggw.waw.pl. Ed. M Adamowicz.

338.1 USA
WEEKLY COTTON TRADE REPORT. Text in English. 192?. w. looseleaf. USD 100. charts; illus.; stat. back issues avail. **Description:** Weekly economic analysis of the futures and cash cotton markets. Includes commentary on the week's events.
Published by: New York Cotton Exchange, 4 World Trade Center, New York, NY 10048. TEL 212-938-7909. Ed. Tim Barry. Circ: 250.

WEEKLY INSIDERS DAIRY & EGG LETTER. see *AGRICULTURE—Dairying And Dairy Products*

380.141 USA ISSN 0043-1850
WEEKLY MARKET BULLETIN. Text in English. 1918. w. USD 22 (effective 2001). adv. 4 p./no.; back issues avail. **Document type:** *Newsletter.* **Description:** Provides news and information for New Hampshire farmers and rural residents.
Published by: Department of Agriculture, Markets & Food, PO Box 2042, Concord, NH 03302-2042. TEL 603-271-3551, FAX 603-271-1109, http://www.ste.nh.us/agric/aghome.html. Ed., R&P, Adv. contact Stephen H Taylor. Circ: 8,200 (paid).

WEEKLY NATIONAL HAY, FEED AND SEED WEEKLY SUMMARY. see *AGRICULTURE—Feed, Flour And Grain*

WELSH AGRICULTURAL STATISTICS. see *AGRICULTURE—Abstracting, Bibliographies, Statistics*

338.1 USA
WESTERN CITRUS REPORT*. Text in English. s-w. USD 132. **Document type:** *Government.*
Published by: (U.S. Department of Agriculture, Agricultural Marketing Service (Los Angeles)), U.S. Department of Agriculture, Agricultural Marketing Service (Greely), F & V Division, 1320 E. Olympic Blvd., Los Angeles, CA 90021-1946.

380.141 USA
WESTERN FRUIT AND VEGETABLE. Text in English. d. USD 20 domestic; USD 40 foreign (effective 2000). **Document type:** *Government.* **Description:** California fruit shipping point prices, volume, market situation and selected wholesale markets.
Formerly: California Fruit Report
Published by: (California. Department of Food and Agriculture), Federal-State Market News Service (Sacramento), 1220 N St., Rm. A-247, Box 942871, Sacramento, CA 94271. TEL 916-654-0298, FAX 916-654-1046.

338.1 USA
WESTERN POTATO AND ONION REPORT. Text in English. d. USD 180. **Document type:** *Government.*
Published by: U.S. Department of Agriculture, Agricultural Marketing Service (Idaho Falls), 1820 E 17th St, Ste 130, Idaho Falls, ID 83404. TEL 208-526-0740, FAX 208-526-9433.

338.1 POL ISSN 1230-0659
WIES I PANSTWO. Text in Polish. 1990. q.
Indexed: AgrLib, RASB.
Published by: Spoldzielnia Wydawnictwo Ludowe, Ul Grzybowska 4, PO Box 71, Warsaw, 00950, Poland. TEL 48-22-208741. Ed. Ryszard Miazek.

338.1 POL ISSN 0137-1673
➤ **WIES I ROLNICTWO.** (English version avail. on request) Text in Polish; Summaries in English. 1973. q. PLZ 40 domestic; PLZ 80 foreign (effective 2003). adv. bk.rev. abstr.; bibl. **Document type:** *Academic/Scholarly.* **Description:** Presents the changes in the rural community and agriculture in Poland and other Central and Eastern European countries in the period of transformation of the political and economic system, and in a perspective of an accession to the European Union.
Indexed: AgrLib, RASB.
Published by: Polska Akademia Nauk, Instytut Rozwoju Wsi i Rolnictwa, Ul Nowy Swiat 72, Warsaw, 00330, Poland. TEL 48-22-8269436, FAX 48-22-8266371, irwir@irwirpan.waw.pl, http://www.irwirpan.waw.pl. Ed., Adv. contact Marek Klodzinski. Circ: 460. **Dist. by:** RUCH S.A., ul Jana Kazimierza 31/33, Warsaw 00958, Poland.

338.1 USA
WOOD PRODUCTS: INTERNATIONAL TRADE AND FOREIGN MARKETS. Text in English. 1985. 5/yr. USD 21. charts; stat. reprint service avail. from CIS. **Document type:** *Government.*
Related titles: Microfiche ed.: (from CIS).
Indexed: AmStI.
Published by: U.S. Department of Agriculture, Foreign Agricultural Service, Information Division, Rm 5920 S, Washington, DC 20250-1000. TEL 202-720-7937. Circ: 360. **Subscr. to:** U.S. Government Printing Office, Superintendent of Documents, PO Box 371954, Pittsburgh, PA 15250-7954. TEL 202-512-1800, FAX 202-512-2250, orders@gpo.gov, http:// www.access.gpo.gov.

WORLD AGRICULTURAL ECONOMICS AND RURAL SOCIOLOGY ABSTRACTS; abstracts of world literature. see *AGRICULTURE—Abstracting, Bibliographies, Statistics*

338.1 USA ISSN 0277-3139
HD9001
WORLD AGRICULTURAL SUPPLY AND DEMAND ESTIMATES. Text in English. 1977. m. USD 38 (effective 2001). stat. reprint service avail. from CIS. **Document type:** *Government.* **Description:** Provides monthly forecasts of production, domestic use, stocks, and exports for major crops of the U.S. and the world, as well as for U.S. livestock and refined sugar production.
Formerly: Agricultural Supply and Demand Estimates (0162-5586)
Related titles: Microfiche ed.: (from CIS); Online - full text ed.: ISSN 1554-9089 (from The Dialog Corporation).
Indexed: AmStI, TTI.
Published by: U.S. Department of Agriculture, World Agricultural Outlook Board, 14th St and Independence Ave, S W, South Bldg, Rm 5143, Washington, DC 20250-3812. TEL 202-720-5447, http://usda.mannlib.cornell.edu/usda. Ed. Raymond L Bridge. Circ: 1,300. **Dist. by:** U.S. Government Printing Office, Superintendent of Documents, PO Box 371954, Pittsburgh, PA 15250-7954. TEL 202-512-1800, FAX 202-512-2250, orders@gpo.gov, http://www.access.gpo.gov.

WORLD FOOD AID NEEDS AND AVAILABILITIES. FOOD SECURITY ASSESSMENT. see *BUSINESS AND ECONOMICS—International Development And Assistance*

THE YELLOW SHEET (TOMS RIVER). see *AGRICULTURE—Poultry And Livestock*

338.1 POL ISSN 0044-1600
HD1995.7
➤ **ZAGADNIENIA EKONOMIKI ROLNEJ.** Text in Polish; Summaries in English. 1953. q. PLZ 80 domestic; USD 30 foreign (effective 2003). adv. bk.rev. abstr.; bibl.; charts; maps; stat. index. 180 p./no.; back issues avail. **Document type:** *Journal, Academic/Scholarly.* **Description:** Covers agricultural economics, food economy, agricultural and rural policies, and rural sociology. Intended for research workers and students.
Related titles: E-mail ed.; Fax ed.; English ed.: Economics of Polish Agriculture. Selected Papers. 1997.
Indexed: AgrAg, AgrLib, RASB, RRTA, WAE&RSA.
—CISTI.
Published by: Instytut Ekonomiki Rolnictwa i Gospodarki Zywnosciowej, ul Swietokrzyska 20, Warsaw, 00002, Poland. TEL 48-22-8266117, FAX 48-22-8271960, ierigz@ierigz.waw.pl, http://www.ierigz.waw.pl. Ed., Pub., Adv. contact Wojciech Jozwiak TEL 48-22-8265802. Circ: 400 (controlled). **Dist. by:** RUCH, ul Jana Kazimierza 31/33, Warsaw 01248, Poland. TEL 48-22-5328732, FAX 48-22-5328724, prenumerata@okdp.ruch.com.pl, http://www.ruch.pol.pl. **Co-sponsor:** Ministerstwo Rolnictwa i Gospodarki Zywnosciowej.

➤ **ZAMBIA. CENTRAL STATISTICAL OFFICE. AGRICULTURAL AND PASTORAL PRODUCTION (COMMERCIAL AND NON-COMMERCIAL).** see *AGRICULTURE—Abstracting, Bibliographies, Statistics*

➤ **ZAMBIA. CENTRAL STATISTICAL OFFICE. AGRICULTURAL AND PASTORAL PRODUCTION (NON-COMMERCIAL).** see *AGRICULTURE—Abstracting, Bibliographies, Statistics*

338.1 CHN ISSN 1006-4583
ZHONGGUO NONGCUN GUANCHA/CHINA RURAL SURVEY. Text in Chinese. 1988. bi-m. USD 48 (effective 2000). adv. **Document type:** *Academic/Scholarly.*
Formerly (until 1995): Nongcun Jingji yu Shehui - Rural Economy and Society (1002-8889)
Related titles: Online - full text ed.: (from East View Information Services).
Indexed: AgBio, AnBrAb, DSA, HortAb, MaizeAb, PBA, PHN&I, PN&I, RDA, RiceAb, S&F, SoyAb, TDB, TriticAb, WAE&RSA, WeedAb.
Published by: Zhongguo Shehui Kexueyuan, Nongcun Fazhan Yanjiusuo/Chinese Academy of Social Sciences, Institute of Rural Development, 5 Jianguomennei Dajie, Beijing, China. Ed. Jiyuan Chen. R&P Jingsong Chen. Adv. contact Jinsong Chen.

338.1 CHN ISSN 1002-8870
HN740.Z9
ZHONGGUO NONGCUN JINGJI/CHINESE RURAL ECONOMY. Text in Chinese. m. USD 96 (effective 2000). adv. **Document type:** *Academic/Scholarly.*
Related titles: Online - full text ed.: (from East View Information Services).
Indexed: AEA, AgrForAb, AnBrAb, DSA, FS&TA, ForAb, HerbAb, HortAb, I&DA, MaizeAb, NutrAb, PHN&I, PN&I, PoultAb, RASB, RDA, RRTA, RiceAb, S&F, SeedAb, TDB, TriticAb, WAE&RSA.
—BLDSC (3181.075000), IE, ingenta.
Published by: Zhongguo Shehui Kexueyuan, Nongcun Fazhan Yanjiusuo/Chinese Academy of Social Sciences, Institute of Rural Development, 5 Jianguomennei Dajie, Beijing, China. TEL 86-10-6513-7744. Ed. Jiyuan Chen. Adv. contact Jinsong Chen. **Dist. in US by:** China Books & Periodicals Inc, 360 Swift Ave., Ste. 48, S San Fran, CA 94080-6220. TEL 415-282-2994, FAX 415-282-0994.

AGRICULTURE—Agricultural Equipment

631.3 AUS ISSN 1036-4242
A F D J. (Australian Farmers' Dealers' Journal) Text in English. 1984. 4/yr. AUD 33 domestic; AUD 77 foreign (effective 2000). adv. bk.rev. tr.lit. **Description:** Covers Australian farm machinery market.
Formerly (until 1990): Australian Farm Dealers Journal (0818-2183)
Published by: Norley Pty. Ltd., PO Box 341, Beaconsfield, VIC 3807, Australia. TEL 61-3-95789122, FAX 61-3-9707-1733, norley@werple.net.au, norley@mira.net, http:// www.infoweb.com.au/agmachinery/., http://www.afdj.com.au. Ed. Peter Levy. Adv. contact Garry Kennedy. B&W page USD 1,595, color page USD 2,255; trim 210 x 270. Circ: 18,500.

631.3 JPN ISSN 0084-5841
S671 CODEN: AMAADL
A M A - AGRICULTURAL MECHANIZATION IN ASIA, AFRICA AND LATIN AMERICA. Text in English. 1971. q. JPY 6,000, USD 56 (effective 2003). adv. bk.rev.; film rev. bibl.; charts; illus.; stat. 90 p./no.; back issues avail. **Document type:** *Journal, Academic/Scholarly.* **Description:** Covers agricultural equipment and mechanical engineering.

Former titles: A M A - Agricultural Mechanization in Southeast Asia; A M A - Agricultural Mechanization in Asia
Indexed: AEA, AIT, AgBio, AgrForAb, AnBrAb, CPA, CTFA, DSA, Englnd, FCA, FPA, FS&TA, HerbAb, HortAb, I&DA, IAOP, MaizeAb, NemAb, NutrAb, OrnHort, PBA, PGegResA, PHN&I, PotatoAb, PoultAb, RA&MP, RDA, RPP, RRTA, RefZh, RevApplEntom, RiceAb, S&F, S&MA, SIA, SeedAb, SoyAb, TDB, TriticAb, WAE&RSA, WeedAb.
—BLDSC (0750.421000), CISTI, Ei, IE, Infotrieve, ingenta, Linda Hall.
Published by: Shin-Norinsha Co. Ltd., 7 Kanda-Nishiki-cho 2-chome, Chiyoda-ku, Tokyo, 101-0054, Japan. TEL 81-3-3291-3674, FAX 81-3-3291-5717, ama@shin-norin.co.jp, shinnorin@blue.ocn.ne.jp. Ed. Yoshisuke Kishida. Adv. contact K Ikeda. Circ: 15,000 (controlled).

631.3 USA ISSN 1535-9409
AG EQUIPMENT POWER. Text in English. 1977. m. USD 12 (effective 2005). adv. back issues avail. **Document type:** *Magazine, Trade.* **Description:** Contains new and used machinery guide and news of interest for growers in Northwestern agriculture.
Formed by the merger of (1988-1993): Fruit Country; Agri-Equipment and Chemical; Which was formerly: Agri-Equipment Today (0192-9526)
Published by: Clintron Publishers, Inc., PO Box 30998, Spokane, WA 99223. TEL 509-458-3924, 800-869-7923, FAX 509-458-3947, info@agpowermag.com, http://www.agpowermag.com. Ed., Pub., R&P, Adv. contact Clint Withers. Circ: 11,000 (controlled).

631.3 USA
▼ **AGEQUIPMENT MANUFACTURER.** Text in English. 2005 (Fall). q. **Document type:** *Magazine, Trade.* **Description:** Targets managers and supervisors of manufacturing companies. Covers business and production operations in such areas as legal concerns, component and production machinery selection, financial issues, marketing, personnel, technology, sales and customer relations.
Published by: Scissortail Productions, Llc. (Subsidiary of: T & F Informa plc), 2302 W 1st St, Cedar Falls, IA 50613-2282. TEL 319-277-3599, FAX 319-277-3783, agrausa@cfu.net, http://www.agra-usa.com/.

631.3 DEU
AGRARGEWERBLICHE WIRTSCHAFT. Text in German. fortn. **Document type:** *Trade.*
Published by: V d A W Beratungs- und Servicegesellschaft mbH, Wollgrasweg 31, Stuttgart, 70599, Germany. TEL 0711-167790, FAX 0711-451093.

631.3 ESP ISSN 1130-5754
AGRICOLA XXI; revista de la mecanizacion agricola. Text in Spanish. bi-m. free.
Formerly (until 1990): Maquinaria Agricola XXI (0214-3143)
Published by: Reed Business Information SA (Subsidiary of: Reed Business Information International), Zancoeta 9, Bilbao, 48013, Spain. TEL 34-944-285600, FAX 34-944-425116, rbi@rbi.es, http://www.rbi.es. Circ: 20,000.

AGRICULTURAL ENGINEERING. see *AGRICULTURE—Crop Production And Soil*

AGRICULTURAL ENGINEERING ABSTRACTS. see *AGRICULTURE—Abstracting, Bibliographies, Statistics*

631.3 ZAF ISSN 0379-6604
➤ **AGRICULTURAL ENGINEERING IN SOUTH AFRICA.** Text and summaries in Afrikaans, English. 1967. biennial. ZAR 160, USD 30 (effective 1999 & 2000). adv. back issues avail. **Document type:** *Academic/Scholarly.* **Description:** Features scientific and semi-scientific papers on applied engineering in South African agriculture. Covers agricultural equipment, irrigation, soil and water engineering, animal housing, processing.
Indexed: AEA, ISAP.
Published by: South African Institute of Agricultural Engineers, PO Box 912 719, Silverton, Pretoria 0127, South Africa. TEL 27-12-8424000, FAX 27-12-8424317, saili@ing1.agric.za. Ed. F B Reinders. R&P F.B. Reinders TEL 27-12-842-4000. Circ: 300 (controlled).

631.3 ZAF
AGRICULTURAL MACHINERY DEALERS' GUIDE. Text in English. 1963. bi-m. ZAR 409.72. **Document type:** *Trade.* **Description:** Reports trade and retail prices of used agricultural machinery in South Africa.
Formerly: Agricultural Machinery Dealers' Digest (0378-5246)
Published by: Mead & McGrouther (Pty) Ltd., PO Box 1240, Randburg, Gauteng 2125, South Africa. TEL 27-11-789-3213, FAX 27-11-789-5218. adv.: B&W page ZAR 550, color page ZAR 900. Circ: 464.

AKADEMIA ROLNICZA WE WROCLAWIU. ZESZYTY NAUKOWE. GEODEZJA I URZADZENIA ROLNE. see *GEOGRAPHY*

631.3 621 POL ISSN 0867-3756
AKADEMIA ROLNICZA WE WROCLAWIU. ZESZYTY NAUKOWE. MECHANIZACJA ROLNICTWA. Text in Polish; Summaries in English. 1990. irreg. price varies. **Document type:** *Academic/Scholarly.*
Related titles: ♦ Series of: Akademia Rolnicza we Wroclawiu. Zeszyty Naukowe. ISSN 0867-7964.
Indexed: AgrLib.
—CISTI.
Published by: Akademia Rolnicza we Wroclawiu/Agricultural University of Wroclaw, Ul Norwida 25, Wroclaw, 50375, Poland. TEL 48-71-3205101, wyd@ozi.ar.wroc.pl. Circ: 270. **Subscr. to:** Wydawnictwo Akademii Rolniczej we Wroclawiu, ul Sopocka 23, Wroclaw 50344, Poland.

631.3 CAN
ALBERTA FARMLIFE. Text in English. 1959. s-w. CND 60 (effective 1999). adv. bk.rev.
Former titles: Giant Farm Life; Giant
Published by: M. Joan Brees, 5438 11th St N E, Calgary, AB T2E 7E9, Canada. TEL 403-274-4002, FAX 403-274-4116, farmlife@cadvision.com. Ed. M Joan Brees. Pub. Bruce Tunnicliffe. Adv. contact Garry Harris. Circ: 69,987.

631.3 USA
AMERICAN SOCIETY OF AGRICULTURAL ENGINEERS. TRANSACTIONS. IRRIGATION ENGINEERING. Variant title: Transactions of the A S A E. Irrigation Engineering. Text in English. 1985. s-a. USD 55 domestic to non-members; USD 60 foreign to non-members; USD 35 domestic to members; USD 40 foreign to members (effective 2001). **Document type:** *Trade.* **Description:** Includes over 30 technical articles on drip, surface, sprinkler, trickle, and other irrigation methods and practices.
Published by: American Society of Agricultural Engineers, 2950 Niles Rd, St. Joseph, MI 49085-9659. TEL 269-429-0300, FAX 269-429-3852, hq@asae.org, http://asae.org/., http://www.asae.org. Ed. Pamela Devore Hansen. R&P Sandy Rutter.

631.3 USA ISSN 1042-7392
ANTIQUE POWER; the tractor collector's magazine. Text in English. 1988. bi-m. USD 26.95 domestic; USD 39.95 foreign; USD 5.95 newsstand/cover (effective 2005). adv. illus. back issues avail. **Document type:** *Magazine, Consumer.* **Description:** Devoted to the interests of antique tractor enthusiasts. Covers all makes of antique tractors. Contains historical research, recollections of their use, restoration tips, show information, toys, literature.
Published by: Antique Power Inc., PO Box 838, Yellow Springs, OH 45387. antique@antiquepower.com, http://www.antiquepower.com. Ed., Pub., R&P Patrick W Ertel. Adv. contact Jamie L Hamilton. Circ: 42,000 (paid). **Subscr. to:** Box 500, Missouri City, TX 77459.

631.3 IND
AUTOMOBILE, TRACTOR, SCOOTER REPORT. Text in English. 1967. w. looseleaf. INR 715, USD 85 (effective 1999). bk.rev. index. **Document type:** *Newsletter.* **Description:** Covers news about automobile and related industry in India.
Formerly: Automobile and Tractor (0045-1053)
Published by: International Press Cutting Service, PO Box 121, Allahabad, Uttar Pradesh 211 001, India. TEL 91-532-622392. Ed. Nandi Khanna. Circ: 1,200.

THE BELT PULLEY. see *HOBBIES*

BIOPRODUCTS CANADA. see *BUSINESS AND ECONOMICS—Trade And Industrial Directories*

631.3087 USA
BREAKING NEW GROUND; cultivating independence for farmers and ranchers with disabilities. Text in English. 1982. a. free. illus. back issues avail. **Document type:** *Newsletter.* **Description:** Discusses issues relevant to farmers and ranchers with physical disabilities.
Related titles: Audio cassette/tape ed.; Diskette ed.
Published by: Breaking New Ground Resource Center, Purdue University, 1146 Agricultural and Biological Engineering Bldg, West Lafayette, IN 47907-1146. TEL 765-494-5088, 800-825-4264, FAX 765-496-1356, bng@ecn.purdue.edu, http://abe.www.ecn.purdue.edu/ABE/Extension/BNG/index, http://www.agrability.org. Ed. Bill Field. Circ: 11,000.

631.3 FRA ISSN 1272-4661
C E M A G R E F. GESTION DES MILIEUX AQUATIQUES. ETUDES. Text in French. 1990. irreg. **Document type:** *Monographic series.*
Formerly (until 1995): C E M A G R E F. Ressources en Eau. Etudes (1158-9914)
Published by: Centre National de Machinisme Agricole du Genie Rural des Eaux et des Forets, Parc de Tourvoie, B.P. 44, Antony, Cedex 92163, France. TEL 33-01-40966121, FAX 33-01-40966036, info@cemagref.fr, http://www.antony.cemagref.fr/.

361.3 FRA ISSN 0992-4302
C E M A G R E F. GROUPEMENT DE BORDEAUX. ETUDE. Text in French. irreg. **Document type:** *Monographic series.*
Published by: Centre National de Machinisme Agricole du Genie Rural des Eaux et des Forets, 50, Ave de Verdun Gazinet, Cestas, Cedex 33612, France. TEL 33-05-5789-0800, FAX 33-05-5789-0801, info@bordeaux.cemagref.fr, http://www.bordeaux.cemagref.fr/.

631.3 CAN ISSN 1492-9058
S671 CODEN: CBEAAH
➤ **CANADIAN BIOSYSTEMS ENGINEERING.** Text in English, French. 1959. a., latest vol.43, 2001. CND 50 domestic; USD 50 foreign (effective 2005). 200 p./no. 2 cols./p.; back issues avail. **Document type:** *Journal, Academic/Scholarly.*
Formerly (until 2001): Canadian Agricultural Engineering (0045-432X)
Related titles: Microfilm ed.: (from PQC).
Indexed: AEA, ASCA, AgBio, Agr, AnBrAb, BiolAb, BrCerAb, C&ISA, CBCARef, CPA, CerAb, CorrAb, CurCont, DSA, E&CAJ, EMA, Englnd, ExcerpMed, FCA, FS&TA, ForAb, HerbAb, HortAb, I&DA, IAA, IAOP, ISMEC, IndVet, M&TEA, MBF, METADEX, MaizeAb, NutrAb, OrnHort, PGegResA, PHN&I, PN&I, PotatoAb, PoultAb, RA&MP, RPP, RefZh, RevApplEntom, RiceAb, S&F, SCI, SIA, SeedAb, SolStAb, SoyAb, TriticAb, VITIS, VetBull, WAA, WAE&RSA, WeedAb.
—BLDSC (3017.625100), CASDDS, CISTI, Ei, IDS, IE, ingenta, Linda Hall. **CCC.**
Published by: Canadian Society of Agricultural Engineering, , R P O University, P O Box 381, Saskatoon, SK S7N 4J8, Canada. TEL 306-966-5319, FAX 306-966-5334, norum@engr.usask.ca, http://www.csae-scgr.ca., http://www.engr.usask.ca/societies/csae/. Ed., Pub. Donald I Norum. Circ: 200. **Outside Canada subscr. to:** ASAE, 2950, Niles, MI 49085-9659.

631.3 636 USA
CENTRAL OREGON RANCHER. Text in English. 1953. m. USD 18 (effective 1995). adv. **Document type:** *Consumer.*
Address: 9263 S Copley Rd, Box 1, Powell Butte, OR 97753-0001. TEL 503-548-8700. Ed. Rod S Johnson. Adv. contact Scott Johnson. Circ: 13,200.

631.3 CUB ISSN 0138-8681
CIENCIA Y TECNICA EN LA AGRICULTURA. SERIE: MECANIZACION DE LA AGRICULTURA. Abstracts and contents page in English. 1978. s-a. USD 14 in North America; USD 16 in Europe; USD 17 elsewhere.
Indexed: Agrind, RiceAb.
—CISTI.
Published by: Centro de Informacion y Documentacion Agropecuario, Gaveta Postal 4149, Havana, 4, Cuba. **Dist. by:** Ediciones Cubanas, Obispo No. 527, Apdo. 605, Havana, Cuba.

CIENCIAS DEL SUELO, RIEGO Y MECANIZACION. see *AGRICULTURE—Crop Production And Soil*

631.3 CUB ISSN 1016-9512
CUBA. CENTRO DE INFORMACION Y DOCUMENTACION AGROPECUARIO. BOLETIN DE RESENAS. SERIE: MECANIZACION DE LA AGRICULTURA. Abstracts in English. 1974. irreg. per issue exchange basis.
Formerly: Cuba. Centro de Informacion y Divulgacion Agropecuario. Boletin de Resenas. Serie: Mecanizacion
Indexed: Agrind.
Published by: Centro de Informacion y Documentacion Agropecuario, Gaveta Postal 4149, Havana, 4, Cuba. **Dist. by:** Ediciones Cubanas, Obispo No. 461, Apdo. 605, Havana, Cuba.

631.3 USA
▼ **THE DEALER BOOK.** Text in English. 2004. q. adv. **Document type:** *Magazine, Trade.* **Description:** Links manufacturers with dealers offering "inside" information and news critical to making informed business decisions.
Published by: Heartland Ag-Business Group, Inc., 1003 Central Ave, Fort Dodge, IA 50501. TEL 800-673-4763, aginfo@agdeal.com, http://www.agdeal.com. Adv. contact Bailey Johnson. B&W page USD 1,000, color page USD 1,665; trim 7.75 x 10.75.

631.3 BRA ISSN 0012-3374
DIRIGENTE RURAL. Text in Portuguese. 1961. m. USD 70. adv. bk.rev. abstr.; bibl.; charts; illus.
Published by: Editora Visao Ltda., Rua Alvaro de Carvalho, 354, Centro, Sao Paulo, SP 01050-070, Brazil. TEL 256-5011, FAX 258-1919. Ed. Hamilton Lucas de Oliveira. Circ: 61,000.

631.3 CAN ISSN 1488-4305
DRAINAGE CONTRACTOR. Text in English. 1974. a. CND 8 domestic; CND 16 foreign (effective 2005). adv. illus. back issues avail. **Document type:** *Magazine, Trade.* **Description:** Covers agricultural land drainage.
Supersedes in part: Agri-Book Magazine (0705-3878)
—CISTI.
Published by: Annex Publishing & Printing, Inc., 222 Argyle Ave, Delhi, ON N4B 2Y2, ON N4B 2Y2, Canada. TEL 519-582-2513, 800-265-2827, FAX 519-582-4040, sfredericks@annexweb.com, http://www.drainagecontractor.com, http://www.annexweb.com. Circ: 8,400.

631.1 DEU
EILBOTE; das Magazin fuer das Landmaschinenwesen. Text in German. 1952. w. adv. bk.rev. **Document type:** *Newspaper, Trade.* **Description:** Covers all aspects of the agricultural machinery trade.

A

Published by: Eilbote Boomgaarden Verlag GmbH, Winsener Landstr 7, Winsen, 21423, Germany. TEL 49-4171-78350, FAX 49-4171-783535, anzeigen@eilbote-online.de, http://www.eilbote-online.de. Ed. Juergen Boomgaarden. Pubs. Juergen Boomgaarden, Renate Boomgaarden. Adv. contact Dagmar Michel. B&W page EUR 2,538, color page EUR 3,198; trim 210 x 297. Circ: 7,066 (controlled).

631.3 621.9 USA
EQUIPMENT MANUFACTURERS INSTITUTE. FIRST OF THE WEEK NEWSLETTER. Text in English. irreg. membership. **Document type:** *Newsletter.* **Description:** Contains news for equipment manufacturerers.
Formerly: Farm and Industrial Equipment Institute. First of the Week Newsletter
Published by: Equipment Manufacturers Institute, 111 E. Wisconsin Ave., Ste. 1000, Milwaukee, WI 53202-4806. TEL 312-321-1470.

631.3 621.9 USA
EQUIPMENT MANUFACTURERS INSTITUTE. RETAIL SALES REPORTS. Text in English. m. USD 100 (effective 1999). **Description:** Contains news for equipment manufacturerers.
Formerly: Farm and Industrial Equipment Institute. Retail Sales Reports
Published by: Equipment Manufacturers Institute, 111 E. Wisconsin Ave., Ste. 1000, Milwaukee, WI 53202-4806. TEL 312-321-1470.

631.3 621.9 USA
EQUIPMENT MANUFACTURERS INSTITUTE. STATE OF THE INDUSTRY. Text in English. s-a. USD 25 (effective 1999). **Description:** Contains news for equipment manufacturerers.
Formerly: Farm and Industrial Equipment Institute. State of the Industry
Published by: Equipment Manufacturers Institute, 111 E. Wisconsin Ave., Ste. 1000, Milwaukee, WI 53202-4806. TEL 312-321-1470.

EUROEQUIPOS & OBRAS. see *MACHINERY*

631.3 USA
F E W A MEMBERSHIP DIRECTORY. Text in English. 1945. a. USD 50 (effective 2000). **Document type:** *Directory.* **Description:** Source for manufacturers or vendors looking for wholesalers of agricultural equipment and related products in North America.
Published by: Farm Equipment Wholesalers Association, PO Box 1347, Iowa City, IA 52244. TEL 319-354-5156, FAX 319-354-5157, info@fewa.org, http://www.fewa.org. Pub. Patricia Collins.

631.3 USA
F E W A TIPS. Text in English. 1946. m. membership. adv. **Document type:** *Newsletter.*
Published by: Farm Equipment Wholesalers Association, PO Box 1347, Iowa City, IA 52244. TEL 319-354-5156, FAX 319-354-5157, info@fewa.org, http://www.fewa.org. Ed., Pub., R&P, Adv. contact Patricia A Collins.

631.3 664.1 GBR
F.O. LICHT'S BUYER'S GUIDE FOR THE SUGAR AND ALLIED INDUSTRIES. Text in English, German. a. GBP 42 in Europe; USD 75 in United States (effective 2000). **Document type:** *Directory, Trade.*
Formerly: F.O. Licht's Guide to Equipment Products and Services for the Sugar and Allied Industries
Published by: F.O. Licht GmbH, 80 Calverley Rd, Tunbridge Wells, Kent TN1 2UN, United Kingdom. TEL 44-1892-533813, FAX 44-1892-544895, marketing@fo-licht.com. Ed. Christoph Berg. Adv. contact Helen Walker.

631.3 GBR
FARM AND HORTICULTURAL EQUIPMENT COLLECTOR. Text in English. bi-m. GBP 12.50; GBP 15.50 in Europe; GBP 17.50 elsewhere. adv. **Document type:** *Consumer.* **Description:** Contains historical information for collectors and restorers of all farm and horticultural related machinery and implements.
Published by: Kelsey Publishing Ltd., Cudham Tithe Barn, Berry's Hill, Cudham, Kent TN16 3AG, United Kingdom. TEL 44-1959-541444, FAX 44-1959-541400, info@kelsey.co.uk, http://www.kelsey.co.uk/fhec.

631.3 USA ISSN 1522-3523
FARM COLLECTOR. Text in English. 1998. m. USD 29.95 domestic; USD 46.75 in Canada; USD 82.75 elsewhere (effective 2003). adv. **Document type:** *Magazine, Trade.*
Related titles: Online - full text ed.: (from Gale Group).
Published by: Ogden Publications, 1503 S W 42nd St, Topeka, KS 66609-1265. TEL 785-274-4300, 800-678-5779, FAX 785-274-4305, editor@farmcollector.com, http:// www.farmcollector.com, http://www.ogdenpubs.com.

631.3 USA ISSN 0014-7958
FARM EQUIPMENT. Text in English. 1969. 7/yr. USD 48 domestic; USD 70 in Canada & Mexico; USD 99 elsewhere; free to qualified personnel (effective 2005). adv. illus. index. **Document type:** *Magazine, Trade.* **Description:** Provides business management information to owners and managers of farm equipment dealerships.
Formerly: Agricultural Equipment Dealer
—CCC.
Published by: Cygnus Business Media, Inc., 1233 Janesville Ave, Fort Atkinson, WI 53538-0803. TEL 800-547-7377, FAX 920-563-1699, http://www.farm-equipment.com, http://www.cygnusb2b.com. Ed. Noel Amerpohl. Pub. Dan Newman. Circ: 11,656 (controlled).

631.3 USA
FARM EQUIPMENT CATALOG. Text in English. 1989. a. USD 19 domestic; USD 26 in Canada; USD 33 elsewhere. adv. **Document type:** *Catalog.* **Description:** Lists farm equipment in ten categories for upper class 1A farm operations in the US.
Published by: Cygnus Business Media, Inc., 1233 Janesville Ave, Fort Atkinson, WI 53538-0803. TEL 920-563-6388, FAX 920-563-1699. Circ: 85,000.

631.3 CAN ISSN 0014-8032
FARM LIGHT & POWER. Text in English. 1959. a. CND 10. adv. charts; illus. **Document type:** *Trade.*
Published by: Farm Light & Power Publications Ltd., 2114 Robinson St, Ste 203, Regina, SK S4T 2P7, Canada. TEL 306-525-3305, FAX 306-757-1810, flp@sk.sympatico.ca. Ed., Pub. Tom Bradley. Adv. contact Adrian Lozinsky. Circ: 70,000.

631.3 CAN
FARM MACHINERY CUSTOM AND RENTAL RATE GUIDE. Text in English. 1975. a. free. **Document type:** *Government.*
Published by: Agriculture and Food, B5 Walter Scott Bldg, 3085 Albert St, Regina, SK S4S 0B1, Canada. TEL 888-613-3975 (in US only), FAX 306-721-4626, pad@sk.sympatico.ca, pdc@agr.gov.sk.ca, http://www.agr.gov.sk.ca/saf. Circ: 12,000.

631.3 USA ISSN 0163-4518
FARM SHOW MAGAZINE. Text in English. 1977. bi-m. USD 19.95 (effective 2005). **Document type:** *Magazine, Trade.* **Description:** Focuses exclusively on new products of interest to high volume farmers and ranchers throughout the U.S. Name, address and phone listed with each new product report so interested readers can contact the company direct for more information.
—CISTI.
Published by: Farm Show Publishing Inc., PO Box 1029, Lakeville, MN 55044. TEL 952-469-5572, 800-834-9665, FAX 952-469-5575, editor@farmshow.com, http:// www.farmshow.com. Ed., Pub. Mark Newhall. Circ: 160,000 (paid).

631.3 NZL ISSN 1174-2720
FARM TRADER. Text in English. m. NZD 4.50 newsstand/cover. adv. **Document type:** *Magazine, Trade.* **Description:** Filled with the latest deals on tractors, farm equipment and machinery from across New Zealand.
Published by: A C P New Zealand, 17B Hargreaves St, College Hill, Pasonby, Auckland, 1036, New Zealand. TEL 64-9-3735408, FAX 64-9-3089498.

631.3 USA
FASTLINE: DAKOTA EDITION. Text in English. 1993. m. USD 10 (effective 2000). **Document type:** *Trade.* **Description:** Designed for the farming industry.
Published by: Fastline Publications, Inc., 4900 Fox Run Rd, Buckner, KY 40010. TEL 502-222-0146, FAX 502-222-0615, info@fastlinepub.com, http://www.fastlinepublications.com. Ed., Pub., R&P William G Howard. Circ: 22,000.

631.3 USA
FASTLINE: ILLINOIS EDITION. Text in English. 1988. m. USD 10 (effective 2000). **Document type:** *Catalog.* **Description:** Designed for the farming industry.
Formerly: Farmers Fastline: Illinois Edition
Published by: Fastline Publications, Inc., 4900 Fox Run Rd, Buckner, KY 40010. TEL 800-626-6409, FAX 502-222-0615, info@fastlinepub.com, http://www.fastlinepublications.com. Ed., Pub., R&P William G Howard. Circ: 22,000.

631.3 USA
FASTLINE: INDIANA EDITION. Text in English. 1981. m. USD 10 (effective 2000). adv. **Document type:** *Trade.* **Description:** Designed for the farming industry.
Former titles: Farmers Fastline: Indiana Edition; Indiana Farmers Fastline
Published by: Fastline Publications, Inc., 4900 Fox Run Rd, Buckner, KY 40010. TEL 800-626-6409, FAX 502-222-0615, info@fastlinepub.com, http://www.fastlinepublications.com. Ed., Pub., R&P William G Howard. Circ: 22,000.

631.3 USA
FASTLINE: IOWA EDITION. Text in English. 1988. m. USD 10 (effective 2000). **Document type:** *Trade.* **Description:** Designed for the farming industry.
Former titles: Farmers Fastline: Iowa Edition; Iowa Farmers Fastline
Published by: Fastline Publications, Inc., 4900 Fox Run Rd, Buckner, KY 40010. TEL 800-626-6409, FAX 502-222-0615, http://www.fastlinepublications.com. Ed., Pub., R&P William G Howard. Circ: 22,000.

631.3 USA
FASTLINE: KANSAS EDITION. Text in English. 1991. m. USD 10 (effective 2000). **Document type:** *Trade.* **Description:** Designed for the farming industry.
Formerly: Farmers Fastline: Kansas Edition
Published by: Fastline Publications, Inc., 4900 Fox Run Rd, Buckner, KY 40010. TEL 800-626-6409, FAX 502-222-0615, info@fastlinepub.com, http://www.fastlinepublications.com. Circ: 22,000.

631.3 USA
FASTLINE: KENTUCKY EDITION. Text in English. 1987. m. USD 10 (effective 2000). **Document type:** *Trade.* **Description:** Design for the farming industry.
Former titles: Farmers Fastline: Kentucky Edition; Kentucky Farmers Fastline
Published by: Fastline Publications, Inc., 4900 Fox Run Rd, Buckner, KY 40010. TEL 800-626-6409, FAX 502-222-0615, info@fastlinepub.com, http://www.fastlinepublications.com. Ed., Pub., R&P William G Howard. Circ: 22,000.

631.3 USA
FASTLINE: MID-ATLANTIC EDITION. Text in English. 1990. m. USD 10 (effective 2000). **Document type:** *Trade.* **Description:** Designed for the farming industry.
Formerly: Farmers Fastline: North Carolina Edition
Published by: Fastline Publications, Inc., 4900 Fox Run Rd, Buckner, KY 40010. TEL 800-626-6409, FAX 502-222-0615, info@fastlinepub.com, http://www.fastlinepublications.com. Ed., Pub., R&P William G Howard. Circ: 22,000.

631.3 USA
FASTLINE: MID-WEST EDITION. Text in English. 1996. m. USD 10 (effective 2000). adv. **Document type:** *Magazine, Trade.* **Description:** Equipment buyers guide for the turcking industry.
Related titles: Online - full text ed.
Published by: Fastline Publications, Inc., 4900 Fox Run Rd, Buckner, KY 40010. TEL 800-626-6409, FAX 502-222-0615, info@fastlinepub.com, http://www.truckersfastline.com, http://www.fastlinepublications.com. Ed., Pub., R&P William G Howard. adv.: B&W page USD 630, color 1/2 page USD 870; trim 7.5 x 10.75. Circ: 22,000 (paid and controlled).

631.3 USA
FASTLINE: MIDSOUTH EDITION. Text in English. 1992. m. USD 10 (effective 2000). adv. **Document type:** *Trade.* **Description:** Equipment buying guide for the farming industry.
Formerly: Farmers Fastline: Arkansas Edition
Related titles: Online - full text ed.
Published by: Fastline Publications, Inc., 4900 Fox Run Rd, Buckner, KY 40010. TEL 800-626-6409, FAX 502-222-0615, info@fastlinepub.com, http://www.farmersfastline.com, http://www.fastlinepublications.com. Ed., Pub., R&P William G Howard. adv.: B&W page USD 630, color page USD 870; trim 7.5 x 10.75. Circ: 22,000 (paid and controlled).

631.3 USA
FASTLINE: MINNESOTA EDITION. Text in English. 1988. m. USD 10 (effective 2000). **Document type:** *Trade.* **Description:** Design for the farming industry.
Former titles: Farmers Fastline: Minnesota Edition; Midwest Farm Exchange - Minnesota
Published by: Fastline Publications, Inc., 4900 Fox Run Rd, Buckner, KY 40010. TEL 800-626-6409, FAX 502-222-0615, info@fastlinepub.com, http://www.fastlinepublications.com. Ed., Pub., R&P William G Howard. Circ: 22,000.

631.3 USA
FASTLINE: MISSOURI EDITION. Text in English. 1989. m. USD 10 (effective 2000). **Document type:** *Trade.* **Description:** Designed for the farming industry.
Formerly: Farmers Fastline: Missouri Edition
Published by: Fastline Publications, Inc., 4900 Fox Run Rd, Buckner, KY 40010. TEL 800-626-6409, FAX 502-222-0615, info@fastlinepub.com, http://www.fastlinepublications.com. Ed., Pub., R&P William G Howard. Circ: 22,000.

631.3 USA
FASTLINE: NEBRASKA EDITION. Text in English. 1991. m. USD 10 (effective 2000). **Document type:** *Trade.* **Description:** Designed for the farming industry.
Formerly: Farmers Fastline: Nebraska Edition
Published by: Fastline Publications, Inc., 4900 Fox Run Rd, Buckner, KY 40010. TEL 800-626-6409, FAX 502-222-0615, info@fastlinepub.com, http://www.fastlinepublications.com. Ed., Pub., R&P William G Howard. Circ: 22,000.

631.3 USA
FASTLINE: NORTHEAST EDITION. Text in English. 1996. m. USD 10 (effective 2000). **Document type:** *Trade.* **Description:** Designed for the farming industry.
Published by: Fastline Publications, Inc., 4900 Fox Run Rd, Buckner, KY 40010. TEL 800-626-6409, FAX 502-222-0615, info@fastlinepub.com, http://www.fastlinepublications.com. Ed., Pub., R&P William G Howard. Circ: 22,000.

631.3 USA
FASTLINE: NORTHLAND EDITION. Text in English. 1997. m. USD 10 (effective 2000). adv. **Document type:** *Magazine, Trade.* **Description:** Equipment buying guide for the trucking industry.
Related titles: Online - full text ed.

Published by: Fastline Publications, Inc., 4900 Fox Run Rd, Buckner, KY 40010. TEL 800-626-6409, FAX 502-222-0615, info@fastlinepub.com, http://www.truckersfastline.com, http://www.fastlinepublications.com. Ed., Pub., R&P William G Howard. adv.: B&W page USD 630, color page USD 870; trim 7.5 x 10.75. Circ: 22,000 (paid and controlled).

631.3 USA
FASTLINE: NORTHWEST FARM EDITION. Text in English. m. USD 10 (effective 2000). adv. **Document type:** *Magazine, Trade.* **Description:** Equipment buying guide for the farming industry.
Related titles: Online - full text ed.
Published by: Fastline Publications, Inc., 4900 Fox Run Rd, Buckner, KY 40010. TEL 800-626-6409, FAX 502-222-0615, info@fastlinepub.com, http://www.farmersfastline.com, http://www.fastlinepublications.com. Ed., Pub., R&P William G Howard. adv.: B&W page USD 630, color page USD 870; trim 7.5 x 10.75. Circ: 22,000 (paid and controlled).

631.3 USA
FASTLINE: OHIO EDITION. Text in English. 1981. m. USD 10 (effective 2000). adv. **Document type:** *Trade.* **Description:** Designed for the farming industry.
Former titles: Farmers Fastline: Ohio Edition; Ohio Farmers Fastline
Published by: Fastline Publications, Inc., 4900 Fox Run Rd, Buckner, KY 40010. TEL 800-626-6409, FAX 502-222-0615, info@fastlinepub.com, http://www.fastlinepublications.com. Circ: 22,000.

631.3 USA
FASTLINE: OKLAHOMA EDITION. Text in English. 1992. m. USD 10 (effective 2000). **Document type:** *Trade.* **Description:** Designed for the farming industry.
Published by: Fastline Publications, Inc., 4900 Fox Run Rd, Buckner, KY 40010. TEL 800-626-6409, FAX 502-222-0615, info@fastlinepub.com, http://www.fastlinepublications.com. Ed. William G Howard. Circ: 22,000.

631.3 USA
FASTLINE: ROCKY MOUNTAIN EDITION. Text in English. 1995. m. USD 10 (effective 2000). **Document type:** *Trade.* **Description:** Designed for the farming industry.
Published by: Fastline Publications, Inc., 4900 Fox Run Rd, Buckner, KY 40010. TEL 800-626-6409, FAX 502-222-0615, info@fastlinepub.com, http://www.fastlinepublications.com. Ed., Pub., R&P William G Howard. Circ: 22,000.

631.3 USA
FASTLINE: SOUTHEAST EDITION. Text in English. 1990. m. USD 10 (effective 2000). **Document type:** *Trade.* **Description:** Designed for the farming industry.
Formerly: Farmers Fastline: Georgia Edition
Published by: Fastline Publications, Inc., 4900 Fox Run Rd, Buckner, KY 40010. TEL 800-626-6409, FAX 502-222-0615, info@fastlinepub.com, http://www.fastlinepublications.com. Ed., Pub., R&P William G Howard. Circ: 22,000.

631.3 USA
FASTLINE: SOUTHWEST EDITION. Text in English. 1997. m. USD 10 (effective 2000). **Document type:** *Trade.* **Description:** Designed for the farming industry.
Published by: Fastline Publications, Inc., 4900 Fox Run Rd, Buckner, KY 40010. TEL 800-626-6409, FAX 502-222-0615, info@fastlinepub.com, http://www.fastlinepublications.com. Ed., Pub., R&P William G Howard. Circ: 22,000.

631.3 USA
FASTLINE: TENNESSEE (FARM EDITION). Text in English. 1990. m. USD 10 (effective 2000). **Document type:** *Trade.* **Description:** Designed for the farming industry.
Formerly: Farmers Fastline: Tennessee Edition
Published by: Fastline Publications, Inc., 4900 Fox Run Rd, Buckner, KY 40010. TEL 800-626-6409, FAX 502-222-0615, info@fastlinepub.com, http://www.fastlinepublications.com. Circ: 22,000.

631.3 USA
FASTLINE: TEXAS EDITION. Text in English. 1993. m. USD 10 (effective 2000). adv. illus. **Document type:** *Trade.* **Description:** Buyer's guide to farm equipment.
Formerly: Farmers Fastline: Texas Edition
Published by: Fastline Publications, Inc., 4900 Fox Run Rd, Buckner, KY 40010. TEL 800-626-6409, FAX 502-222-0615, info@fastlinepub.com, http://www.fastlinepublications.com. Ed., Pub., R&P William G Howard. adv.: B&W page USD 630, color page USD 870; trim 10.75 x 7.5. Circ: 22,000.

631.3 USA
FASTLINE: TRI-STATE EDITION. Text in English. 1995. m. USD 10 (effective 2000). adv. **Document type:** *Magazine, Trade.* **Description:** Equipment buyers guide for the trucking industry.
Related titles: Online - full text ed.
Published by: Fastline Publications, Inc., 4900 Fox Run Rd, Buckner, KY 40010. TEL 800-626-6409, FAX 502-222-0615, info@fastlinepub.com, http://www.truckersfastline.com, http://www.fastlinepublications.com. Ed., Pub., R&P William G Howard. adv.: B&W page USD 630, color page USD 870; trim 7.5 x 10.75. Circ: 22,000.

631.3 FRA
FICHES TECHNIQUES R T D APPLICATIONS AGRICOLES. (Revue Technique Diesel) Text in French. irreg. looseleaf. price varies. charts; illus.
Published by: Editions Techniques pour l'Automobile et l'Industrie (ETAI), 20-22 rue de la Saussiere, Boulogne Billancourt, 92100, France.

631.3 DEU ISSN 0931-6264
FORSCHUNGSBERICHT AGRARTECHNIK. Text in German. irreg. **Document type:** *Monographic series, Trade.*
Published by: Max-Eyth-Gesellschaft Agrartechnik im V D I, Graf-Recke-Str 84, Duesseldorf, 40239, Germany. TEL 49-211-62140, meg@vdi.de.

631.3 IND
HANDBOOK OF INDIAN PUMPS FOR IRRIGATION; salient features and performances. Text in English. 1988. a. INR 300, USD 60.
Published by: Indian Society of Agricultural Engineers, Satya Mansion, Flat nos. 305-306 Community Centre, Ranjit Nagar, New Delhi, 100 008, India. TEL 11-5709003.

631.3 USA ISSN 1047-725X
HOT LINE FARM EQUIPMENT GUIDE. Text in English. 1981. a. (plus m. updates). USD 69.95 (effective 2000). adv. **Document type:** *Journal, Trade.* **Description:** Informs customers about fluctuating farm equipment prices.
Formerly: Farm Equipment Guide
Published by: Heartland Ag-Business Group, Inc., 1003 Central Ave, Fort Dodge, IA 50501. TEL 515-574-2161, 800-673-4763, FAX 515-574-2181. Ed., Pub., R&P, Adv. contact Sandra J Simonson. Circ: 15,000.

631.3 USA ISSN 0019-2953
S671
IMPLEMENT & TRACTOR; agricultural machinery & technology. Text in English. 1886. bi-m. USD 36 in North America; USD 95 elsewhere (effective 2005). adv. bk.rev. charts; illus.; mkt.; pat.; stat.; tr.lit. index. back issues avail. **Document type:** *Magazine, Trade.* **Description:** Published for persons in the farm, turf/lawn and industrial equipment industry in the areas of retail sales and service, marketing, engineering, financing, manufacturing and servicing and general management.
Related titles: Online - full text ed.: (from Florida Center for Library Automation, Gale Group, Northern Light Technology, Inc.).
Indexed: AEA, BusI, F&GI, LRI, PROMT, RASB, RefZh, SRI, T&II.
—CISTI.
Published by: Scissortail Productions, Llc. (Subsidiary of: T & F Informa plc), 2302 W 1st St, Cedar Falls, IA 50613-2282. TEL 319-277-3599, FAX 319-277-3783, mshepherd@cfu.net, agrausa@cfu.net, http://www.ag-equipment.com, http://www.agra-usa.com/. Ed., Pub. Mary Shepherd. Adv. contact Steve Karr. B&W page USD 2,200, color page USD 2,700. Circ: 7,300 (controlled).

631.3 CUB ISSN 0138-7332
INFORMACION EXPRESS. SERIE: MECANIZACION AGROPECUARIA. Text in Spanish. 1977. 3/yr. USD 6 in North America; USD 9 in South America; USD 10 in Europe; USD 14 elsewhere.
Indexed: Agrind.
—CISTI.
Published by: Centro de Informacion y Documentacion Agropecuario, Gaveta Postal 4149, Havana, 4, Cuba. **Dist. by:** Ediciones Cubanas, Obispo No. 527, Apdo. 605, Havana, Cuba.

631.3 ISR
INSTITUTE OF AGRICULTURAL ENGINEERING, BET DAGAN. SCIENTIFIC ACTIVITIES. Text in English. 1971. triennial. USD 25 (effective 1996). illus. **Document type:** *Academic/Scholarly.*
Indexed: BiolAb.
Published by: (Institute of Agricultural Engineering), Agricultural Research Organization, Volcani Center, P O Box 6, Bet Dagan, 50250, Israel. TEL 972-3-9683111, FAX 972-3-993998, TELEX 381476. Circ: 300.

631.3 GBR ISSN 0965-867X
INSTITUTION OF AGRICULTURAL ENGINEERS. MEMBERS' HANDBOOK & BUYERS' GUIDE✶. Text in English. 1951. a. adv. illus. reprint service avail. from PQC.
Former titles (until 198?): Green Book (0017-3932); (until 1971): British Tractors and Farm Machinery (0521-1824)
Published by: Institution of Agricultural Engineers, West End Rd, Silsoe, Bedford, Beds MK45 4DU, United Kingdom. TEL 44-1525-861096, FAX 44-1525-861660, secretary@iagre.org, http://www.iagre.org. Circ: 4,000.

631.3 NER ISSN 0534-4794
INTER-AFRICAN CONFERENCE OF THE MECHANISATION OF AGRICULTURE MEETING✶. Text in English. 1955. irreg.
Published by: (Commission for Technical Co-Operation in Africa South of the Sahara), Maison de l'Afrique, BP 878, Niamey, Niger.

INTERNATIONAL DIRECTORY OF AGRICULTURAL MACHINERY AND IMPLEMENTS IMPORTERS. see *BUSINESS AND ECONOMICS—Trade And Industrial Directories*

INTERNATIONAL GRAINS COUNCIL. REPORT FOR FISCAL YEAR. see *AGRICULTURE—Feed, Flour And Grain*

631.3 USA
INTERNATIONAL SILO ASSOCIATION. NEWSLETTER✶. Text in English. bi-m. **Document type:** *Newsletter, Trade.*
Published by: International Silo Association, 332 Brookview Dr., Luxemburg, WI 54217-1079. cropstorage@cs.com, http://www.silo.org.

631.3 NLD ISSN 0168-6291
TC801 CODEN: IDRSEG
➤ **IRRIGATION AND DRAINAGE SYSTEMS.** Text in English. 1986. q. EUR 392, USD 393, GBP 258 combined subscription to institutions print & online eds. (effective 2005). adv. back issues avail.; reprint service avail. from PSC. **Document type:** *Journal, Academic/Scholarly.* **Description:** Publishes general research and review articles on all aspects of irrigation, including water supply, drainage systems and design, efficiency and management, as well as public health and disease prevention issues.
Related titles: Microform ed.: (from PQC); Online - full text ed.: ISSN 1573-0654 (from EBSCO Publishing, Gale Group, IngentaConnect, Kluwer Online, O C L C Online Computer Library Center, Inc., Springer LINK, Swets Information Services).
Indexed: AEA, ASFA, Agr, AgrForAb, BibLing, BiolAb, BrCerAb, C&ISA, CPA, CerAb, CivEngAb, CorrAb, DSA, E&CAJ, EMA, EPB, ESPM, EngInd, EnvEAb, FCA, FLUIDEX, ForAb, GEOBASE, HerbAb, HortAb, I&DA, IAA, ICEA, M&TEA, MBF, METADEX, MaizeAb, PollutAb, ProtozoAb, RA&MP, RDA, RefZh, RiceAb, S&F, SFA, SWRA, TDB, TriticAb, WAA, WAE&RSA, WeedAb, WildRev.
—BLDSC (4580.948000), CISTI, Ei, IE, Infotrieve, ingenta, Linda Hall. **CCC.**
Published by: Springer-Verlag Dordrecht (Subsidiary of: Springer Science+Business Media), Van Godewijckstraat 30, Dordrecht, 3311 GX, Netherlands. TEL 31-78-6576050, FAX 31-78-6576474, http://springerlink.metapress.com/openurl.asp?genre=journal&issn=0168-6291, http://www.springeronline.com. Ed. Marinus G Bos.

631.84029 USA ISSN 0277-6529
HD1720
IRRIGATION ASSOCIATION. MEMBERSHIP DIRECTORY AND BUYERS' GUIDE. Text in English. a. USD 25 to non-members (effective 1997). adv. **Document type:** *Directory.* **Description:** Features a listing of irrigation companies that are members of the association.
Published by: Irrigation Association, 8260 Willow Oaks Corp Dr, Ste 120, Fairfax, VA 22031-4513. TEL 703-573-3551, FAX 703-573-1913, http://www.irrigation.org. Circ: 2,000.

IRRIGATION BUSINESS & TECHNOLOGY. see *AGRICULTURE—Crop Production And Soil*

631.3 USA
J D JOURNAL. (John Deere) Text in English. 1972. 3/yr. **Description:** Company-wide employee magazine to tie various units and divisions together and keep J.D. people informed of company goals, policies, accomplishments and trends.
Published by: John Deere Publishing, One John Deere Place, Moline, IL 61265. TEL 309-765-4974. Ed. John Gerstner. Circ: 76,000.

631.3 620 JPN ISSN 0386-5126
JAPAN. MINISTRY OF AGRICULTURE, FORESTRY AND FISHERIES. NATIONAL RESEARCH INSTITUTE OF AGRICULTURAL ENGINEERING. ABSTRACTS FROM RESEARCH REPORTS. Text in Japanese. 1974. a. free. **Document type:** *Government.*
Published by: Nougyou Kougaku Kenkyuujo/National Institute for Rural Engineering, 2-1-6 Kannondai, Tsukuba-shi, Ibaraki-ken 305-8609, Japan. TEL 81-298-38-7505. Ed. Hiroshi Sato.

631.3 620 JPN ISSN 0287-0029
TC1
JAPAN. MINISTRY OF AGRICULTURE, FORESTRY AND FISHERIES. NATIONAL RESEARCH INSTITUTE OF AGRICULTURAL ENGINEERING. TECHNICAL REPORT. Text in Japanese. irreg. free. **Document type:** *Government.*
Published by: Nougyou Kougaku Kenkyuujo/National Institute for Rural Engineering, 2-1-6 Kannondai, Tsukuba-shi, Ibaraki-ken 305-8609, Japan. TEL 81-298-38-7505. Ed. Hiroshi Sato.

JARMUVEK, EPITOIPARI ES MEZOGAZDASAGI GEPEK; motorok, vasuti jarmuvek, kozuti jarmuvek, hajok, mezogazdasagi gepek, epitoipari gepek, repulogepek. see *ENGINEERING—Mechanical Engineering*

631.3 DEU
K T B L ARBEITSBLAETTER BAUWESEN UND TIERHALTUNG. Text in German. irreg. price varies. **Document type:** *Monographic series, Trade.*
Formerly: K T B L Arbeitsblaetter Baulich-Technische Selbsthilfe

A

Published by: Kuratorium fuer Technik und Bauwesen in der Landwirtschaft e.V., Bartningstr 49, Darmstadt, 64289, Germany. TEL 49-6151-70010, FAX 49-6151-7001123, ktbl@ktbl.de, http://www.ktbl.de. R&P Harald Kuehner.

631.3 630 DEU
K T B L ARBEITSBLAETTER LANDTECHNIK UND PFLANZENBAU. Text in German. irreg. price varies. **Document type:** *Monographic series, Trade.*
Published by: Kuratorium fuer Technik und Bauwesen in der Landwirtschaft e.V., Bartningstr 49, Darmstadt, 64289, Germany. TEL 49-6151-70010, FAX 49-6151-7001123, ktbl@ktbl.de, http://www.ktbl.de. R&P Harald Kuehner.

KANKYO KAGAKU KENKYUJO HOKOKU/JOURNAL OF ENVIRONMENTAL SCIENCE LABORATORY. see *ENVIRONMENTAL STUDIES*

KEY GUIDE TO ELECTRONIC RESOURCES: AGRICULTURE. see *AGRICULTURE—Abstracting, Bibliographies, Statistics*

631.3 GBR ISSN 1368-373X
KEY NOTE MARKET REPORT: AGRICULTURAL MACHINERY. Variant title: Agricultural Machinery. Text in English. 1981. irreg., latest 1997, Jan. GBP 340 per issue (effective 2002). **Document type:** *Trade.* **Description:** Provides an overview of a specific UK market segment and includes executive summary, market definition, market size, industry background, competitor analysis, current issues, forecasts, company profiles, and more.
Formerly (until 1997): Key Note Report: Agricultural Machinery (0951-6697)
Related titles: CD-ROM ed.; Online - full text ed.
Published by: Key Note Ltd., Field House, 72 Oldfield Rd, Hampton, Mddx TW12 2HQ, United Kingdom. TEL 44-20-8481-8750, FAX 44-20-8783-0049, info@keynote.co.uk, http://www.keynote.co.uk. Ed. Louis Barfe.

631.3 JPN ISSN 0023-1371
KIKAIKA NOGYO/FARMING MECHANIZATION. Text in Japanese; Contents page in English. 1940. m. JPY 8,500 (effective 2003). adv. bk.rev. bibl.; charts; illus.; stat. index. **Document type:** *Magazine.*
Indexed: FCA, HortAb, MaizeAb, PotatoAb, RefZh, S&MA, SeedAb, SoyAb, TriticAb.
—CISTI.
Published by: Shin-Norinsha Co. Ltd., 7 Kanda-Nishiki-cho 2-chome, Chiyoda-ku, Tokyo, 101-0054, Japan. TEL 81-3-3291-3674, FAX 81-3-3291-5717, sinnorin@blue.ocn.ne.jp. Ed. Yoshisuke Kishida. Adv. contact K Ikeda. Circ: 100,000.

631.3 ESP ISSN 0210-1718
LABOREO; revista de la nueva agricultura espanola. Text in Spanish. 1969. m. EUR 77 domestic; EUR 130 foreign (effective 2005). bk.rev. illus.; stat. **Document type:** *Trade.*
Indexed: IECT.
Published by: Grupo Yebenes Editores, S.L., Orellana 10, Madrid, 28004, Spain. TEL 33-91-3081898, FAX 33-91-3192006, laboreo@infonegocio.com, grupoyebenes@infonegocio.com, http://www.grupoyebenes.com/laboreo/index.htm. Ed. Emilio Velasco Machuca. Adv. contact Francisco Javier Goyoaga. Circ: 25,000.

631.3 NLD ISSN 0023-7795
LANDBOUWMECHANISATIE. Text in Dutch. 1950. m. (11/yr.). EUR 65 Netherlands & Belgium; EUR 90.50 elsewhere (effective 2005). adv. bk.rev. charts; illus.; stat.; tr.lit.; tr.mk. index. **Document type:** *Trade.* **Description:** Covers agricultural equipment, techniques, management, and business matters.
Indexed: AEA, AbHyg, AgBio, CISA, CPA, ChemAb, DSA, ExcerpMed, FCA, FPA, HerbAb, HortAb, IndVet, MaizeAb, NemAb, NutrAb, OrnHort, PHN&I, PN&I, PotatoAb, RPP, RRTA, RevApplEntom, S&F, SIA, SeedAb, TriticAb, WAE&RSA, WeedAb.
—CISTI, IE, Infotrieve.
Published by: AgriMedia BV, Postbus 42, Wageningen, 6700 AA, Netherlands. TEL 31-7-465675, FAX 31-7-465671, landbouwmechanisatie@agripers.nl, http://www.landbouwmechanisatie.nl/. Ed. Gertjan Zevenbergen. Adv. contact Aad Ramp TEL 31-7-465679. B&W page EUR 1,186, color page EUR 2,003; 200 x 254. Circ: 7,384.

631.302 DNK ISSN 0107-461X
LANDBRUGETS MASKINOVERSIGT. Text in Danish. 1972. a. DKK 380 (effective 1999). **Document type:** *Catalog.*
Published by: Landskontoret for Bygninger og Maskiner, Skejby, Udkaersvej 15, Aarhus N, 8200, Denmark. TEL 45-87-40-50-00, FAX 45-87-40-50-10, jjh@lr.dk, http://www.lr.dk. Ed. Jens J Hoy. Circ: 400.

631.3 AUT ISSN 0023-7973
LANDMASCHINEN - HANDWERK - HANDEL. Text in German. 1964. m. EUR 52.50 domestic; EUR 70 foreign (effective 2005). adv. bk.rev. illus.; pat.; stat. **Document type:** *Journal, Trade.*
Published by: (Bundesberufsgruppen des Landmaschinenhandels und Landmaschinenhandwerks Oesterreichs), Verlag Lorenz, Ebendorferstr 10, Vienna, W 1010, Austria. TEL 43-1-40566950, FAX 43-1-4068693, maschinen@verlag-lorenz.at, office@verlag-lorenz.at, http://www.verlag-lorenz.at/land/index.html. Ed., Adv. contact Hannelore Wachter-Sieg. B&W page EUR 1,430, color page EUR 2,695; trim 167 x 254. Circ: 3,500.

631.3 DEU ISSN 0047-3995
LANDMASCHINEN RUNDSCHAU✶ ; Agrartechnik Report. Text in German. 1949. bi-m. adv. bk.rev. charts; illus.; stat.
Published by: Verlag Otto Gengenbach GmbH, Postfach 1345, Niefern-Oeschelbronn, 75220, Germany. Circ: 5,900.

631.3 DEU ISSN 0341-261X
LOHNUNTERNEHMEN IN LAND- UND FORSTWIRTSCHAFT; Zeitschrift fuer Dienstleistungen im landlidren Raum. Text in German. 1945. m. adv. bk.rev. illus. **Document type:** *Trade.*
Published by: Verlag Eduard F. Beckmann KG, Postfach 1120, Lehrte, 31251, Germany. TEL 49-5132-8591-0, FAX 49-5132-859125, lu-info@beckmann-verlag.de. Ed. Heiner Behre. Adv. contact Jan Klaus Beckmann. Circ: 4,000.

631.9 BEL ISSN 1370-7604
LOONWERKER EN LANDBOUWTECHNIEK. Text in Dutch. 1986. m. EUR 38 (effective 2004). adv. back issues avail. **Document type:** *Consumer.* **Description:** Deals with agricultural mechanization.
Formerly (until 1993): Loonwerker (0775-2210)
Published by: Rekad N.V., Geelsweg 47A, Herentals, 2200, Belgium. TEL 32-14-286070, FAX 32-14-214774, info@rekad.be, http://rekad.be. Ed. Jomi Memschoote. Adv. contact Hilde Provoost. Circ: 4,110.

631.3 ITA ISSN 1125-8632
MACCHINE E MOTORI AGRICOLI; rivista mensile di meccanizzazione agricola. Short title: M & M A. Text in Italian. 1941. m. (11/yr.). EUR 62 domestic; EUR 110 foreign (effective 2005). adv. bk.rev. bibl.; charts; mkt.; pat.; stat. index. 80 p./no.; **Document type:** *Magazine, Trade.*
Formerly (until 1994): Macchine e Motori Agricoli - I M A il Trattorista (1125-8640); Which was formed by the merger of (1942-1986): Macchine e Motori Agricoli (0024-8967); (1941-1986): I M A Trattorista (0041-1841)
Related titles: Supplement(s): Repertorio delle Macchine Agricole. 1971.
Indexed: AEA, AbHyg, FCA, FPA, ForAb, HerbAb, HortAb, I&DA, MaizeAb, NemAb, NutrAb, OrnHort, PHN&I, RPP, RRTA, RefZh, RevApplEntom, RiceAb, S&F, SIA, SeedAb, SoyAb, TriticAb, WAE&RSA, WeedAb.
Published by: Il Sole 24 Ore Edagricole, Via Goito 13, Bologna, BO 40126, Italy. TEL 39-051-62267, FAX 39-051-490200, http://www.edagricole.it. Ed. Giorgio Setti. Circ: 7,000.

631.3 SWE ISSN 1652-8506
▼ **MASKIN.** Text in Swedish. 2005. a. price varies. **Document type:** *Yearbook, Trade.*
Published by: L R F Media AB, Gaevlegatan 22, Stockholm, 11392, Sweden. TEL 46-8-58836600, FAX 46-8-58836989, lrfmedia@lrfmedia.lrf.se, http://www.media.lrf.se.

631.3 DNK ISSN 0109-0291
MASKINSTATIONEN OG LANDBRUGSLEDEREN. Text in Danish. 1962. m. DKK 400 (effective 2004). adv. bk.rev. abstr.; charts; illus.; mkt.; stat. **Document type:** *Trade.*
Formerly (until 1973): Maskinstationen (0025-4630); Which incorporated (1942-1972): Landbrugslederen (0907-2349)
Published by: (Landsforeningen Danske Maskinstationer/National Association of Agricultural Contractors), Forlaget Moeller, L P Bechs Vej 29, Risskov, 8240, Denmark. TEL 45-86-177758, FAX 45-86-174680, maskinstationen@post.tele.dk, http://www.m-og-l.dk/. Eds. Anne K Moeller, Soeren Moeller. Adv. contact Joergen Nielsen. B&W page DKK 5,200, color page DKK 8,825; trim 172 x 249. Circ: 4,200 (controlled).
Co-sponsors: Foreningen Landbrugslederen; Foereningen Skaanes Maskinstationer.

630 RUS ISSN 0206-572X
S671
MEKHANIZATSIYA I ELEKTRIFIKATSIYA SEL'SKOGO KHOZYAISTVA. Text in Russian. 1930. m. USD 159.95 (effective 1999). bibl.; illus. index.
Formerly (until 1980): Mekhanizatsiya i Elektrifikatsiya Sotsialisticheskogo Sel'skogo Khozyaistva (0130-8076)
Indexed: AEA, AbHyg, AnBrAb, CPA, DSA, FCA, FPA, FS&TA, HerbAb, HortAb, I&DA, IndVet, MaizeAb, NutrAb, OrnHort, PGegResA, PHN&I, PN&I, PotatoAb, PoultAb, RASB, RPP, RefZh, RevApplEntom, S&F, SIA, SeedAb, SoyAb, TriticAb, VetBull, WAE&RSA, WeedAb.
—BLDSC (0111.915000), CISTI, East View.
Address: Sadovaya-Spasskaya 18, Moscow, 107807, Russian Federation. TEL 7-095-2072127, FAX 7-095-2072870. Ed. Ivan E Chesnokov. Circ: 7,090. **Dist. by:** M K - Periodica, ul Gilyarovskogo 39, Moscow 129110, Russian Federation. TEL 7-095-2845008, FAX 7-095-2813798, info@periodicals.ru, http://www.mkniga.ru; **US dist. addr.:** East View Information Services, 3020 Harbor Ln. N., Minneapolis, MN 55447. TEL 612-550-0961.

631.3 USA ISSN 1074-5017
N A E D A EQUIPMENT DEALER. Text in English. 1857. m. USD 45 domestic to individuals; USD 150 foreign to individuals (effective 2005). adv. bk.rev. charts; illus.; stat.; tr.lit. index. 32 p./no.; back issues avail. **Document type:** *Magazine, Trade.* **Description:** Contains management and merchandising editorial for retail dealers of agriculture, industrial and outdoor power equipment.
Former titles (until 1993): Farm and Power Equipment Dealer (0892-6085); (until 1986): Farm and Power Equipment (0014-7834)
Indexed: F&GI.
—CISTI.
Published by: North American Equipment Dealers Association, 1195 Smizer Mill Rd, Fenton, MO 63026-3480. TEL 636-349-5000, FAX 636-349-5443, naeda@naeda.com, http://www.naeda.com. Ed., Adv. contact Mr. Mike Kraemer. Pub. Paul E Kindinger. B&W page USD 1,495; trim 10.88 x 8.25. Circ: 11,500.

631.3 620 JPN
S671
N I R E. BULLETIN. (National Institute for Rural Engineering) Text in Japanese; Summaries in English. 1963. a. **Document type:** *Bulletin, Government.*
Former titles: Nogyo Kogaku Kenkyujo Hokoku (0915-3306); (until 1989): Nogyo Doboku Shikenjo Hokoku/Japan. Ministry of Agriculture, Forestry and Fisheries. National Research Institute of Agricultural Engineering. Bulletin (0549-5725)
Indexed: INIS AtomInd, RefZh.
—BLDSC (2640.480000).
Published by: Nougyou Kougaku Kenkyuujo/National Institute for Rural Engineering, 2-1-6 Kannondai, Tsukuba-shi, Ibaraki-ken 305-8609, Japan. TEL 81-29-8387513, FAX 81-29-8387609, http://ss.nkk.affrc.go.jp.

631.3 643 NGA ISSN 0794-6414
NIGERIAN STORED PRODUCTS RESEARCH INSTITUTE. ANNUAL REPORT. Text in English. 1956. a. charts; illus.; stat. index. back issues avail. **Document type:** *Government.*
Published by: Federal Ministry of Science & Technology, Nigerian Stored Products Research Institute, PMB 1489, Ilorin, Kwara, Nigeria. Ed. J O Oyeniran. Circ: 3,000.

631.3 JPN ISSN 0285-2543
NOGYO KIKAI GAKKAISHI/JAPANESE SOCIETY OF AGRICULTURAL MACHINERY. JOURNAL. Text in Japanese. 1937. q. JPY 9,000 (effective 2005). **Document type:** *Journal, Academic/Scholarly.*
Indexed: AgBio, AnBrAb, BioCN&I, CPA, DSA, FCA, FPA, ForAb, HerbAb, HortAb, I&DA, IndVet, MaizeAb, NemAb, OrnHort, PBA, PGegResA, PGrRegA, PHN&I, PN&I, PotatoAb, PoultAb, RPP, S&F, SIA, SeedAb, SoyAb, TriticAb, WAE&RSA, WeedAb.
—BLDSC (4809.414000), CISTI, IE. **CCC.**
Published by: Nogyo Kikai Gakkai/Japanese Society of Agricultural Machinery, 1-40-2 Nisshin-cho, Omiya, Saitama 331-8537, Japan. jsam@iam.brain.go.jp, http://www.j-sam.org/index-j.html.

631.3 JPN ISSN 0071-3937
NOGYO KIKAI NENKAN/FARM MACHINERY YEARBOOK. Text in Japanese; Abstracts and contents page in English. 1943. a. JPY 10,300 (effective 2003). adv. stat. 2000 p./no.; back issues avail. **Document type:** *Yearbook.* **Description:** Contains latest comments, statistics and useful addresses pertaining to agricultural mechanization in Japan. Commentaries focus on trends in Japan's agricultural development, in agricultural machinery industry and production, and on results of farm machinery research efforts.
Published by: Shin-Norinsha Co. Ltd., 7 Kanda-Nishiki-cho 2-chome, Chiyoda-ku, Tokyo, 101-0054, Japan. TEL 81-3-3291-3674, FAX 81-3-3291-5717, sinnorin@blue.ocn.ne.jp. Ed. Yoshisuke Kishida. Adv. contact K Ikeda. Circ: 10,000.

631.3 JPN ISSN 0029-0971
NOKI SHINBUN/AGRICULTURAL MACHINERY NEWS, WEEKLY. Text in Japanese; Summaries in English. 1933. w. JPY 15,000 (effective 2003). adv. bk.rev. bibl.; charts; illus.; pat.; stat. 16 p./no.; back issues avail.
Published by: Shin-Norinsha Co. Ltd., 7 Kanda-Nishiki-cho 2-chome, Chiyoda-ku, Tokyo, 101-0054, Japan. TEL 81-3-3291-3674, FAX 81-3-3291-5717, sinnorin@blue.ocn.ne.jp. Ed. Yoshisuke Kishida. Adv. contact K Ikeda. Circ: 50,000.

631.3 CHN ISSN 1002-5294
NONGCUN JIXIEHUA/MECHANIZATION IN RURAL AREAS. Text in Chinese. 1986. bi-m. **Document type:** *Academic/Scholarly.*
Related titles: Online - full text ed.: (from East View Information Services).
Published by: Zhongguo Nongye Jixiehua Kexue Yanjiuyuan/Chinese Institute of Agricultural Mechanization, 1 Bei Shatan, Dewai, Beijing, 100083, China. TEL 2017082. Ed. Liang Qijun.

631.3 CHN ISSN 1002-7203
NONGJI SHIYAN YU TUIGUANG/AGRICULTURAL MACHINERY EXPERIMENT AND POPULARIZATION. Text in Chinese. bi-m. CNY 4 per issue domestic (effective 2000). back issues avail. **Document type:** *Academic/Scholarly.*
Related titles: Online - full content ed.: (from WanFang Data Corp.); Online - full text ed.: (from East View Information Services).
Published by: Nongye Bu, Nongji Shiyan Jianding Zongzhan/Ministry of Agriculture, Appraisal Station of Agricultural Machinery Experiments, Dong 3 huan Nan Lu Shilihe, Beijing, 100021, China. TEL 86-1-67347479. Ed. Kunxiu Yi.

631.3 CHN ISSN 0546-9538
NONGYE JIXIE/AGRICULTURAL MACHINERY. Text in Chinese. m. adv.
Address: 1 Bei Shatan, Dewai, Beijing, 100083, China. TEL 2017082. Circ: 120,000.

631.3 CHN ISSN 1000-1298
➤ **NONGYE JIXIE XUEBAO/CHINESE SOCIETY OF AGRICULTURAL MACHINERY. TRANSACTIONS.** Text in Chinese. 1957. q. USD 6.40 per issue. **Document type:** *Academic/Scholarly.* **Description:** Contains studies and researches on theories, designing and manufacturing, and technologies of agricultural machinery.
Related titles: CD-ROM ed.; Online - full text ed.: (from East View Information Services).
Indexed: AEA, AbHyg, AgBio, AnBrAb, C&ISA, CPA, CTFA, DSA, E&CAJ, Englnd, FCA, FS&TA, ForAb, HerbAb, HortAb, I&DA, IAA, IndVet, MaizeAb, NutrAb, OrnHort, PBA, PHN&I, PN&I, PotatoAb, PoultAb, ProtozoAb, RDA, RPP, RevApplEntom, RiceAb, S&F, SIA, SeedAb, SoyAb, TOSA, TriticAb, WAE&RSA, WeedAb.
—BLDSC (8912.480000), Ei, Linda Hall.
Published by: Zhongguo Nongye Jixie Xuehui/Chinese Society of Agricultural Machinery, 1 Bei Shatan, Dewai, Beijing, 100083, China. TEL 86-10-6201-7131, FAX 86-10-6204-3686. Ed., R&P Bingyuan Feng. Pub. Ruiwen Liu. Circ: 1,500. **Subscr. to:** China International Book Trading Corp, 35 Chegongzhuang Xilu, Haidian District, PO Box 399, Beijing 100044, China. TEL 86-10-68412045, FAX 86-10-68412023, cibtc@mail.cibtc.com.cn, http://www.cibtc.com.cn.

631.3 CHN
NONGYE JIXIE ZAZHI/JOURNAL OF AGRICULTURAL MACHINERY. Text in Chinese. m. adv.
Published by: Zhongguo Nongye Jixiehua Kexue Yanjiuyuan/Chinese Institute of Agricultural Mechanization, 1 Bei Shatan, Dewai, Beijing, 100083, China. TEL 2017082. Ed. Shi Yu Wen. Circ: 120,000.

631.3 USA ISSN 1072-2580
O E M INDUSTRY. (Original Equipment Manufacturer) Text in English. 1993. bi-m. USD 60; USD 68 in Canada & Mexico; USD 99 elsewhere. illus. **Document type:** *Trade.*
—**CCC.**
Published by: Cygnus Business Media, Inc., 1233 Janesville Ave, Fort Atkinson, WI 53538-0803. TEL 920-563-6388, FAX 920-563-1699.

631.3 GBR
O E M NEWS. Text in English. bi-m. GBP 15. adv. **Document type:** *Trade.*
Formerly: O E M Newsletter (0267-307X); Which incorporates: Workshop Equipment News (0260-6887)
Published by: Richard Lee Magazines, 88 Main Rd, Suffolk, Romford, Essex RM2 5JB, United Kingdom. TEL 44-1708-743626, FAX 44-1708-743626. Ed., Adv. contact Richard Lee. Circ: 1,200.

631.3 USA ISSN 1048-3039
O E M OFF-HIGHWAY. (Original Equipment Manufacturer) Text in English. m. free to qualified personnel; USD 25 domestic; USD 50 foreign (effective 2004). adv. **Document type:** *Magazine, Trade.* **Description:** Provides a resource for component and general productivity information to engineering, purchasing, manufacturing, marketing and company management.
Former titles (until 1990): O E M (0893-5890); (until 1987): Farm Equipment O E M (0886-1366)
Related titles: Online - full text ed.: (from Gale Group, ProQuest Information & Learning).
—Linda Hall. **CCC.**
Published by: Cygnus Business Media, Inc., 1233 Janesville Ave, Fort Atkinson, WI 53538-0803. TEL 920-563-6388, FAX 920-563-1707. Eds. Iris Poliski, Leslie Shalabi, Steve Ehle. Pubs. Kathy Marr, Phil Merrick. Adv. contact Phil Merrick. Circ: 16,800 (paid and controlled).

631.3 977 USA ISSN 0896-4955
OLD ABE'S NEWS. Text in English. 1985. q. USD 20 domestic to members; USD 25 in Canada to members; USD 30 elsewhere to members (effective 2000). adv. bibl.; illus.; stat.; tr.lit. 54 p./no. 3 cols./p.; back issues avail. **Document type:** *Newsletter.* **Description:** Includes restoration tips, techniques, articles, people stories, club news, and convention news.
Published by: Crooked Hollow Farm, 400 Carriage Dr, Plain City, OH 43064-2101. TEL 614-873-3896, oldabe@usa.net. Ed., Adv. contact David T Erb TEL 614-873-3896. B&W page USD 140. Circ: 2,000.

631.3 USA ISSN 0897-2540
OLD ALLIS NEWS. Text in English. 1983. q. USD 20 in US & Canada; USD 25 elsewhere (effective 1999). back issues avail. **Document type:** *Newsletter.* **Description:** For the collector and enthusiast of Allis-Chalmers tractors and equipment.
Published by: Nan Jones, Ed. & Pub., 10925 Love Rd, Bellevue, MI 49021. TEL 269-763-9770, FAX 269-763-9770. Circ: 4,000.

631.3 658 USA ISSN 0735-6676
S713
OUTDOOR POWER EQUIPMENT OFFICIAL GUIDE. Text in English. a. membership only (effective 2001). **Document type:** *Catalog, Trade.* **Description:** Provides values and serial number information on used lawn and garden machinery.
Related titles: CD-ROM ed.
Published by: Iron Solutions, LLC, 1195 Smizer Mill Rd., Renton, MO 63026-3480. TEL 636-343-8000.

631.3 USA ISSN 1541-0013
OUTDOOR POWER GUIDE. Text in English. 2002. a. USD 29.95 newsstand/cover (effective 2003). adv.
Published by: Heartland Ag-Business Group, Inc., 1003 Central Ave, Fort Dodge, IA 50501. TEL 800-673-4763, aginfo@agdeal.com, http://www.agdeal.com. Pub. Sandra J Simonson. Adv. contact Bailey Johnson.

PLANT & EQUIPMENT. see *BUSINESS AND ECONOMICS—Production Of Goods And Services*

631.3 634.9 AUS ISSN 0817-6043
POWER EQUIPMENT AUSTRALASIA. Text in English. 1979. bi-m. AUD 50 in Australia; USD 78 worldwide (effective 2004). adv. bk.rev. back issues avail. **Document type:** *Magazine, Trade.*
Formerly (until 1985): Power Equipment Australia (0817-6035)
Published by: Glenvale Publications, 4 Palmer Ct, Mt Waverley, VIC 3149, Australia. TEL 61-3-9544-2233, FAX 61-3-9543-1150, glenvale@glenv.com.au, samc@glenv.com.au, http://www.power-equipment.com.au. Ed., Adv. contact Steve Symmons. B&W page AUD 2,090, color page AUD 2,850. Circ: 7,444.

631.3 AUS ISSN 1030-0325
POWER FARMING. Text in English. 1891. bi-m. AUD 24; AUD 42 foreign (effective 2000). adv. charts; illus.; stat. index. **Document type:** *Magazine, Trade.*
Former titles (until 1982): Power Farming Magazine (0311-1911); (until 1969): Power Farming and Better Farming Digest (0032-5996)
Indexed: AEA, ASI, CTFA, FCA, HerbAb, HortAb, Inspec.
—BLDSC (6576.025200), ingenta.
Published by: Diverse Publishing Co. Pty. Ltd., PO Box 370, North Melbourne, VIC 3051, Australia. TEL 61-3-93296040, FAX 61-3-93281116. Ed. John Howell. Circ: 16,000.

631.3 CAN ISSN 0831-2338
PRAIRIE FARMERS CATALOGUE. Text in English. 1979. a. free. adv.
Published by: Prairie Publishing Co., P O Box 100, Oakville, MB R0H 0Y0, Canada. TEL 204-267-2102, FAX 204-267-2585. Ed. Dale H Crampton. Circ: 150,000.

631.3 745.1 USA ISSN 0896-5617
PRAIRIE GOLD RUSH; quarterly newsletter for all Twin City, Minneapolis and Moline enthusiasts. Text in English. 1980. q. USD 16 domestic; USD 20 foreign (effective 2000). adv. back issues avail. **Document type:** *Newsletter.*
Published by: Prairie Gold Rush (PGR), 17390 S SR S8, Seymour, IN 47274. Ed., Pub. Ken Delap II. Adv. contact Cheryl Delap. Circ: 900.

631.3 HUN ISSN 1786-335X
▼ **PROGRESS IN AGRICULTURAL ENGINEERING SCIENCES.** Text in English. 2004. a. USD 78 per vol. (effective 2006). **Document type:** *Journal, Academic/Scholarly.*
Related titles: Online - full text ed.: ISSN 1787-0321.
Published by: Akademiai Kiado Rt. (Subsidiary of: Wolters Kluwer N.V.), Prielle Kornelia U. 19, Budapest, 1117, Hungary. TEL 36-1-4648282, FAX 36-1-4648221, journals@akkrt.hu, http://www.akkrt.hu.

631.3 PHL
RED MACHINERY GUIDE✶. Text in English. 1960. m. GBP 52.70, USD 80. adv. back issues avail.
Contact Dist.: JetSpeed Media Inc., SM-474 Sta. Mesa, Manila, Philippines. TEL 63-2-531-0346, FAX 63-2-531-0352, jetspeed@iconn.com.ph. Ed. W D A Fuller.

631.3 SWE ISSN 1652-8492
▼ **REDSKAP.** Text in Swedish. 2003. a. price varies. **Document type:** *Yearbook, Trade.*
Published by: L R F Media AB, Gaevlegatan 22, Stockholm, 11392, Sweden. TEL 46-8-58836600, FAX 46-8-58836989, lrfmedia@lrfmedia.lrf.se, http://www.media.lrf.se.

REFERATIVNYI ZHURNAL. TRAKTORY I SEL'SKOKHOZYAISTVENNYE MASHINY I ORUDIYA. see *AGRICULTURE—Abstracting, Bibliographies, Statistics*

631.3 658 USA ISSN 0162-6809
S677
REGIONAL OFFICIAL GUIDES: TRACTORS AND FARM EQUIPMENT. Text in English. 1969. q. membership only (effective 2001). **Document type:** *Trade.* **Description:** Provides evaluations of used machinery, with serial numbers and rental information.
Formerly: Official Guide: Tractors and Farm Equipment
—CISTI.
Published by: Iron Solutions, LLC, 1195 Smizer Mill Rd., Renton, MO 63026-3480. TEL 636-343-8000, http://www.ironsolutions.com.

631.3 DEU
REPORT FUER DIE MITARBEITER IN DEUTSCHLAND. Text in German. 1969. q. bk.rev. **Document type:** *Trade.*
Published by: Deere & Company, Steubenstr 36-42, Mannheim, 68140, Germany. TEL 49-621-8298418, FAX 49-621-8298300, TELEX 63056-DCEOD. Ed. Rainer Mache. Circ: 9,700.

631.3 621.9 USA
REPRESENTATIVE✶. Text in English. m.
Published by: Agricultural and Industrial Manufacturers Representatives Association, 5800 Foxridge Dr., No. 115, Mission, KS 66202-2333. TEL 913-262-4511, FAX 913-262-0174.

630 CZE ISSN 1212-9151
S269.C93
➤ **RESEARCH IN AGRICULTURAL ENGINEERING.** Text and summaries in English; Summaries in Czech, Slovak. 1954. q. USD 64 (effective 2003). adv. bk.rev. **Document type:** *Academic/Scholarly.* **Description:** Contains scientific papers and reviews dealing with agricultural engineering, agricultural technology, agricultural buildings and processing of agricultural products.
Formerly (until 2000): Zemedelska Technika (0044-3883)
Indexed: AEA, AnBrAb, CPA, DSA, FCA, FPA, FS&TA, ForAb, HerbAb, HortAb, I&DA, IndVet, MaizeAb, NutrAb, OrnHort, PBA, PGrRegA, PHN&I, PN&I, PotatoAb, RefZh, RevApplEntom, S&F, SIA, SeedAb, TriticAb, WAE&RSA, WeedAb.
—BLDSC (7714.387200), CINDOC, CISTI.
Published by: Ceska Akademie Zemedelskych Ved, Ustav Zemedelskych a Potravinarskych Informaci/Czech Academy of Agricultural Sciences, Institute of Agricultural and Food Information, Slezska 7, Prague 2, 120 56, Czech Republic. TEL 420-2-227010355, FAX 420-2-227010116, forest@login.cz, http://www.cazv.cz. Ed. Mrs. Radka Chlebeckova. R&P Mr. Jan Rydlo. Circ: 450. **Co-sponsor:** Ceska Akademie Zemedelskych Ved/Czech Academy of Agricultural Sciences.

631.3 FRA ISSN 0223-0135
REVUE TECHNIQUE MACHINISME AGRICOLE. Text in French. 1979. 7/yr. charts; illus. **Description:** Explains how to dismantle, repair and reassemble farm tractors, combine harvesters and related machines.
—**CCC.**
Published by: Editions Techniques pour l'Automobile et l'Industrie (ETAI), 20 rue de la Saussiere, Boulogne-Billancourt, 92100, France. TEL 46-04-81-13, FAX 48-25-56-92. Ed. Christian Rey. Circ: 17,000.

SAVREMENA POLJOPRIVREDNA TEHNIKA/ADVANCED AGRICULTURAL ENGINEERING; Jugoslovenski casopis za poljoprivrednu tehniku. see *AGRICULTURE—Crop Production And Soil*

631.3 FRA
SEDIMAGAZINE. Text in French. 4/yr.
Published by: C D E F G, 6 bd. Jourdan, Paris, 75014, France. TEL 45-89-11-99, FAX 45-88-42-18, TELEX 204 264. Ed. Regis Elies. Circ: 2,500.

631.3 RUS ISSN 0131-7393
S671
SEL'SKII MEKHANIZATOR. Text in Russian. 1958. m. USD 109.95. charts; illus. index.
Indexed: RASB, RefZh.
—East View.
Address: Sadovaya-Spasskaya 18, Moscow, 107807, Russian Federation. TEL 7-095-2072155, FAX 7-095-2072870. Ed. Aleksandr I Kolpakov. Circ: 58,000. **Dist. by:** M K - Periodica, ul Gilyarovskogo 39, Moscow 129110, Russian Federation. TEL 7-095-2845008, FAX 7-095-2813798, info@periodicals.ru, http://www.mkniga.ru; **US dist. addr.:** East View Information Services, 3020 Harbor Ln. N., Minneapolis, MN 55447. TEL 612-550-0961.

631.3 BGR ISSN 0037-1718
CODEN: STFMBL
SELSKOSTOPANSKA TEKHNIKA. Summaries in German, Russian. 1964. bi-m. USD 120 foreign (effective 2002). reprint service avail. from IRC. **Description:** Covers mechanization and automatization in plant and animal breeding.
Indexed: AEA, ChemAb, DSA, ExcerpMed, FCA, HortAb, I&DA, MaizeAb, NutrAb, OrnHort, PHN&I, PN&I, PotatoAb, RPP, RRTA, RefZh, RevApplEntom, RiceAb, S&F, SeedAb, SoyAb, TriticAb, WAE&RSA, WeedAb.
—BLDSC (0163.135000), CASDDS, CISTI.

A

Published by: (Natzionalen Tzentar za Agrarni Nauki/National Center for Agrarian Sciences of Bulgaria), Universitetsko Izdatelstvo Sv. Kliment Okhridski/Publishing House of the Sofia University St. Kliment Ohridski, Akad G Bonchev 6, Sofia, 1113, Bulgaria. Ed. Nikola Gaidarov. Circ: 1,690. **Dist. by:** Hemus, 6 Rouski Blvd., Sofia 1000, Bulgaria; **Dist. by:** Sofia Books, ul Silivria 16, Sofia 1404, Bulgaria. TEL 359-2-9586257, info@sofiabooks-bg.com, http://www.sofiabooks-bg.com.

631.3 JPN ISSN 0371-3385
CODEN: STDZAF
SHIGA-KENRITSU TANKI DAIGAKU GAKUJUTSU ZASSHI/SHIGA PREFECTURAL JUNIOR COLLEGE. SCIENTIFIC REPORTS. Text in Japanese; Summaries in English. 1951. s-a.
Indexed: Agrind, CIN, ChemAb, ChemTitl, JPI.
—CASDDS.
Published by: Shiga-kenritsu Tanki Daigaku/Shiga Prefectural Junior College, Hassaka-cho, Hikone-shi, Shiga-ken 522-0057, Japan. Circ: 1,200.

631.3029 USA
SHORTLINER✶. Text in English. 1951. fortn. qualified personnel only. back issues avail.
Published by: Farm Equipment Manufacturers Association, 1000 Executive Pky. Dr., No. 100, St. Louis, MO 63141-6325. TEL 314-991-0702, FAX 314-991-5732. Ed. Robert Schnell. Circ: 1,000.

631.3 USA
SOUTHERN FARM EQUIPMENT MANUFACTURERS. NEWSLETTER✶. Text in English. q. **Document type:** *Newsletter.*
Published by: Southern Farm Equipment Manufacturers, c/o Marlon H Cohn & Associates, 5000 Royal Marco Way, Apt 334, Marco Island, FL 34145-1897.

SPUDMAN; voice of the potato industry. see *AGRICULTURE—Crop Production And Soil*

631.3 NZL
STRAIGHT FURROW (AUCKLAND). Text in English. w. NZD 122.50 (effective 2005). **Document type:** *Newspaper, Trade.* **Description:** Covers agricultural news and views, as well as featuring livestock, animal health and farm equipment pages.
Formerly: Farm Equipment News
Related titles: Online - full content ed.
Published by: New Zealand Rural Press Ltd., PO Box 4233, Auckland, 1001, New Zealand. straightfurrow@ruralpress.com, http://www.straightfurrow.co.nz, http://www.ruralpress.com/. Ed. Liam Baldwin. Adv. contact Marie Reid TEL 64-9-5241185. Circ: 86,434.

631.3 POL ISSN 1732-1719
▼ **TECHNIKA ROLNICZA, OGRODNICZA, LESNA.** Text in Polish. 2004. m. PLZ 84 domestic (effective 2005). **Document type:** *Magazine, Trade.*
Formed by the merger of (1954-2004): Technika Rolnicza (1230-2228); Which was formerly (until 1991): Mechanizacja Rolnictwa (0461-5220); Which was formed by the merger of (1952-1954): Mechanizator Rolnictwa (0461-5255); (1948-1954): Mechanizacja i Elektryfikacja Rolnictwa (1230-2260); (1954-2004): Przeglad Techniki Rolniczej i Lesnej (0867-8243); Which was formerly (until 1992): Maszyny i Ciagniki Rolnicze i Lesne (0867-6828); (until 1990): Maszyny i Ciagniki Rolnicze (0465-2592); (until 1963): Maszyny Rolnicze (0867-7034)
Indexed: AgrLib.
—BLDSC (8736.632000).
Published by: Hortpress Sp. z o.o., ul Kopernika 34, Warsaw, 00336, Poland. TEL 48-22-8261626, FAX 48-22-8264362, technika.rol@hortpress.com, info@hortpress.com, http://www.hortpress.com.

631.3 RUS ISSN 0131-7105
TEKHNIKA V SEL'SKOM KHOZYAISTVE. Contents page in English, French, German. 1941. bi-m. USD 132 foreign (effective 2004). adv. illus.
Indexed: AEA, AgBio, AnBrAb, DSA, FCA, FPA, HerbAb, HortAb, I&DA, IndVet, MaizeAb, NutrAb, OrnHort, PBA, PHN&I, PN&I, PotatoAb, PoultAb, RASB, RPP, RefZh, RiceAb, S&F, SIA, SeedAb, SoyAb, TriticAb, WAE&RSA, WeedAb.
—BLDSC (0180.330000), CINDOC, East View, Linda Hall.
Address: Ul Krzhizhanovskogo 15, Moscow, 117218, Russian Federation. TEL 7-095-2073762, FAX 7-095-2072870. Ed. Petr S Popov. Circ: 3,650. **Dist. by:** M K - Periodica, ul Gilyarovskogo 39, Moscow 129110, Russian Federation. TEL 7-095-2845008, FAX 7-095-2813798, info@periodicals.ru, http://www.mkniga.ru.

631.3 FRA ISSN 0754-121X
TRACTEURS ET MACHINES AGRICOLES; l'officiel de l'agro-equipement. Abbreviated title: T M A. Text in French. 1925. 8/yr. adv. **Document type:** *Trade.* **Description:** Information for those involved in agriculture. Aimed mainly at professionals interested in management and the latest equipment and technology.
Formerly: Farmes Modernes
Indexed: AEA.
Published by: Societe d'Edition de la Press Agricole (SEPA), BP 107, Deuil la Barre, 95170, France. TEL 34285867, FAX 39842787. Circ: 8,000.

631.3 GBR ISSN 0262-8090
TRACTOR & FARM MACHINERY TRADER. Text in English. m. GBP 30 domestic; GBP 30 foreign. adv. **Document type:** *Trade.*
Incorporates: Outdoor Power Equipment News
Published by: Richard Lee Magazines, 88 Main Rd, Suffolk, Romford, Essex RM2 5JB, United Kingdom. TEL 44-1708-743626, FAX 44-1708-743626. Ed., Adv. contact Richard Lee. Circ: 1,750.

631.3 GBR ISSN 1357-3101
TRACTOR & MACHINERY. Text in English. 1994. m. GBP 26.50 domestic; GBP 33 in Europe; GBP 38 elsewhere; GBP 2.20 newsstand/cover. back issues avail. **Document type:** *Consumer.* **Description:** For all tractor enthusiasts.
Published by: Kelsey Publishing Ltd., Cudham Tithe Barn, Berry's Hill, Cudham, Kent TN16 3AG, United Kingdom. TEL 44-1959-541444, FAX 44-1959-541400, info@kelsey.co.uk, http://www.kelsey.co.uk/tractor. Circ: 13,000.

631.3 SWE ISSN 1652-8484
TRAKTOR. Text in Swedish. 2002. a. price varies. **Document type:** *Yearbook, Trade.*
Published by: L R F Media AB, Gaevlegatan 22, Stockholm, 11392, Sweden. TEL 46-8-58836600, FAX 46-8-58836989, lrfmedia@lrfmedia.lrf.se, http://www.media.lrf.se.

631.372 AUT ISSN 0041-0985
TRAKTOR AKTUELL. Text in German. 1966. 2/yr. adv. charts; illus. **Document type:** *Journal, Trade.*
Published by: Agrar Post Verlag Dr. Bruno Mueller GmbH, Schulstr 64, Langenzersdorf, N 2103, Austria. TEL 43-2244-4647, FAX 43-2244-464723, muellers.buero@nextra.at. Ed. Franz Schachinger. adv.: color page EUR 3,500; trim 180 x 270. Circ: 145,000.

361.3 SWE ISSN 1651-9965
▼ **TRAKTOR POWER.** Text in Swedish. 2003. 6/yr. SEK 298 (effective 2005). adv. **Document type:** *Magazine, Trade.*
Published by: L R F Media AB, Gaevlegatan 22, Stockholm, 11392, Sweden. TEL 46-8-58836600, FAX 46-8-58836989, traktorpower@lrfmedia.lrf.se, lrfmedia@lrfmedia.lrf.se, http://www.traktorpower.se/, http://www.media.lrf.se. Ed. Kenneth Fransson. Adv. contact Ulla Jonsson TEL 46-54-7752521. page SEK 19,000; 210 x 297. Circ: 16,600.

631.3 RUS ISSN 0235-8573
S671
TRAKTORY I SEL'SKOKHOZYAISTVENNYE MASHINY; nauchno-tekhnicheskii i proizvodstvennyi zhurnal. Text in Russian. 1930. m. USD 598 foreign (effective 2004). **Document type:** *Journal, Trade.* **Description:** Covers tests conducted in construction, design, production, exploitation of tractors and farming machinery.
Indexed: AEA, AbHyg, AnBrAb, DSA, FCA, FPA, ForAb, HerbAb, HortAb, I&DA, MaizeAb, NutrAb, OrnHort, PGegResA, PHN&I, PN&I, PotatoAb, PoultAb, RA&MP, RASB, RPP, RefZh, RevApplEntom, S&F, SIA, SeedAb, SoyAb, TriticAb, WAE&RSA, WeedAb.
—East View, Linda Hall.
Published by: Izdatel'stvo Mashinostroenie, Stromynskii per 4, Moscow, 107076, Russian Federation. TEL 7-095-2683858, mashpubl@mashin.ru, http://www.mashin.ru/jurnal/content.php?id=3. Ed. A A Karpov. Circ: 1,000. **Dist. by:** M K - Periodica, ul Gilyarovskogo 39, Moscow 129110, Russian Federation. TEL 7-095-2845008, FAX 7-095-2813798, info@periodicals.ru, http://www.mkniga.ru.

631.3 ITA ISSN 1720-3503
TRATTORI E MACCHINE AGRICOLE. Text in Italian. 1997. 10/yr. EUR 33; EUR 3.50 newsstand/cover (effective 2005). **Document type:** *Magazine, Trade.*
Published by: Vado e Torno Edizioni S.r.l., Via Cassano d'Adda 20, Milan, 20139, Italy. TEL 39-02-55230950, FAX 39-02-55230592, abbonamenti@vadoetorno.com, http://www.vadoetorno.com/abbotrat.html. Ed. Maurizio Cervetto. Pub. Gianni Sacedotti. Adv. contact Ornella Cavalli. Circ: 30,000.

631.3 NLD ISSN 1380-8559
TREKKER & WERKTUIG. Text in Dutch. 1992. m. (11/yr.). EUR 72.50; EUR 77.36 in Belgium; EUR 90.69 elsewhere (effective 2005). adv. illus. **Document type:** *Trade.* **Description:** Covers all aspects of tractors.
Formerly (until 1992): Trekker
Published by: Reed Business Information bv (Subsidiary of: Reed Business), Hanzestraat 1, Doetinchem, 7006 RH, Netherlands. TEL 31-314-349911, FAX 31-314-343839, info@reedbusiness.nl, http://www.trekkerenwerktuig.nl, http://www.reedbusiness.nl. Ed. Ad Bal. adv.: B&W page EUR 1,542, color page EUR 2,353; 200 x 270. Circ: 13,796.

TURF NEWS. see *AGRICULTURE—Crop Production And Soil*

631.3 636 NLD ISSN 1387-3105
VEEHOUDERIJ TECHNIEK; vakblad voor veehouders. Text in Dutch. 1998. bi-m. adv. illus.; maps; stat.; tr.lit. back issues avail. **Document type:** *Trade.* **Description:** Reports on milking equipment, livestock pens, slurry treatment, and computing for livestock farmers.
Published by: AgriMedia BV, Postbus 42, Wageningen, 6700 AA, Netherlands. TEL 31-7-476507, FAX 31-7-426044. Circ: 25,000.

631.3 ZAF
THE VETERAN FARMER/VETERAAN BOER. Text in English, Afrikaans. 1995. q. adv. illus. back issues avail. **Document type:** *Magazine, Consumer.* **Description:** Discusses all types of antique farming machinery.
Published by: Veteran Farmer/Veteraan Boer, Dalpark Ext 6, PO Box 17261, Brakpan, 1541, South Africa. TEL 27-11-915-5518, FAX 27-11-805-1309. Ed. Chris Wilson. Pub. Wilfred Mole. Adv. contact Adelaide Janse van Vuuren TEL 27-11-799-7400.

631.3 ESP ISSN 1133-8938
VIDA RURAL. Text in Spanish; Summaries in Spanish. 1990. 20/yr. EUR 80 domestic; EUR 143 in Europe; EUR 192 elsewhere (effective 2005). adv. **Document type:** *Magazine, Trade.* **Description:** For large farm managers, machinery distributors, agricultural experts and technicians.
Formerly (1990-1993): M T - Maquinas y Tractores Agricolas (0214-9206)
Indexed: IECT.
—CINDOC.
Published by: Eumedia S.A., Claudio Coello 16, 1o, Madrid, 28001, Spain. TEL 34-91-4264430, FAX 34-91-5753297, http://www.eumedia.es/revistas/infor_vr.asp. Ed. Jaime Lamo de Espinosa. Adv. contact Julia Dominguez. page EUR 1,445; trim 23 x 30.5. Circ: 24,000.

631 GBR ISSN 0263-7529
VINTAGE TRACTOR. Text in English. 1980. q. USD 20. adv. bk.rev. illus. **Document type:** *Consumer.*
Incorporates: Fordson and Old Tractor Magazine; Which incorporated: Ford Fergie Farmer; Which was formerly: Small Farmer
Published by: Allan T. Condie Publications, Merrivale, Main St, Carlton, Nuneaton, Warks CV13 0BZ, United Kingdom. TEL 01455-290389. Ed. A T Condie. Circ: 2,000.

631.3 USA ISSN 1044-7768
WESTERN RETAILER. Text in English. 1889. m. USD 12 (effective 2005). adv. charts; illus.; stat. **Document type:** *Magazine, Trade.*
Formerly (until May 1989): Hardware and Farm Equipment (0017-7679)
—Linda Hall.
Published by: Western Retail Implement & Hardware Association, PO Box 419264, Kansas City, MO 64141-6264. TEL 816-561-5323, FAX 816-561-1249, mail@westernassn.com, http://www.southwesternassn.com. Ed., Adv. contact Mike Griffith. Pub. Jeff Flora. Circ: 2,000.

WISCONSIN R E C NEWS. see *GENERAL INTEREST PERIODICALS—United States*

631.3 GBR
WORLD PLOUGHING CONTEST. OFFICIAL HANDBOOK. Text in English, Danish. 1954. a. price varies. adv. index. **Document type:** *Catalog.* **Description:** Devoted to news and information about contests, competitors and champions. Also covers technical, historical and international information about ploughing. Includes list of exhibitions and demonstrations.
Published by: (World Ploughing Organization DNK), Society of Ploughmen, Quarry Farm, Loversall, Doncaster, South Yorkshire DN11 9DH, United Kingdom. TEL 44-1302-852469. Eds. Carl Allesoe, Ken Chappell. R&P, Adv. contact Ken Chappell. Circ: 10,000.

631.3 621.9 USA
9N - 2N - 8N - NAA NEWSLETTER. Text in English. 1986. q. USD 16 domestic; USD 19 in Canada; USD 22 elsewhere (effective 2000). bk.rev. back issues avail. **Document type:** *Newsletter.* **Description:** Aimed at enthusiasts of Ford Model N and other Ford tractors 1939-1980 and related equipment. Includes information on use, history, maintenance, and restoration.
Formerly: 9N - 2N - 8N Newsletter (0896-5641)
Address: PO Box 275, E Corinth, VT 05040-0275. http://www.n-news.com. Eds. Gerard W Rinaldi, Robert Rinaldi Jr. Circ: 7,500 (paid).

AGRICULTURE—Computer Applications

ACTA OECONOMICA ET INFORMATICA; the scientific journal for economics and informatics in agriculture. see *AGRICULTURE—Agricultural Economics*

630.285 NLD ISSN 0925-4455
AGRO INFORMATICA. Text in Dutch. 1987. 5/yr. **Document type:** *Academic/Scholarly.*
Published by: V I A S, Postbus 79, Wageningen, 6700 AB, Netherlands. TEL 31-317-485191, FAX 31-317-483976, http://www.vias.nl. Circ: 400 (paid).

630.285 NLD ISSN 0168-1699
S494.5.D3 CODEN: CEAGE6
➤ **COMPUTERS AND ELECTRONICS IN AGRICULTURE.** Text in Dutch. 1984. 10/yr. EUR 1,238 in Europe to institutions; JPY 164,400 in Japan to institutions; USD 1,385 elsewhere to institutions (effective 2006). abstr.; illus. back issues avail.; reprints avail. **Document type:** *Academic/Scholarly.*
Description: Provides international coverage of advances in the application of computers and electronic instrumentation and control systems to agriculture and related industries.
Incorporates (in 1998): A I Applications (1051-8266); Which superseded (1987-1990): A I Applications in Natural Resource Management (0896-6664)
Related titles: Microform ed.: (from PQC); Online - full text ed.: (from EBSCO Publishing, Gale Group, IngentaConnect, ScienceDirect, Swets Information Services).
Indexed: AEA, ASCA, ASFA, AgBio, Agr, AgrForAb, AnBrAb, BIOBASE, BIOSIS Prev, BibAg, BiolAb, BrCerAb, C&ISA, CMCI, CPA, CerAb, CivEngAb, CompLI, CorrAb, CurCont, DSA, E&CAJ, EMA, EPB, ESPM, Englnd, EntAb, FCA, FPA, FS&TA, ForAb, GEOBASE, HerbAb, HortAb, I&DA, IAA, IABS, ISMEC, IndVet, Inspec, M&TEA, MBF, METADEX, MaizeAb, NutrAb, OrnHort, PBA, PGegResA, PGrRegA, PHN&I, PN&I, PlantSci, PotatoAb, PoultAb, RDA, RPP, RRTA, RevApplEntom, RiceAb, S&F, S&MA, SFA, SIA, SWRA, SeedAb, SolStAb, SoyAb, TDB, TriticAb, VITIS, VetBull, WAA, WAE&RSA, WeedAb, WildRev.
—BLDSC (3394.682000), AskIEEE, CISTI, Ei, IDS, IE, Infotrieve, ingenta, Linda Hall. **CCC.**
Published by: Elsevier BV (Subsidiary of: Elsevier Science & Technology), Radarweg 29, Amsterdam, 1043 NX, Netherlands. TEL 31-20-4853911, FAX 31-20-4852457, nlinfo-f@elsevier.nl, http://www.elsevier.com/locate/compag, http://www.elsevier.nl. Eds. J. W. Hummel, R. E. Plant.

630.285 USA ISSN 1524-7961
FARM SMART; Journal of computerized farm management. Text in English. 1981. q. looseleaf. USD 18; USD 36 foreign (effective 1999). adv. bk.rev.; software rev. charts; illus.; stat. **Document type:** *Newsletter.* **Description:** Presents computer applications (software) for farm management, including accounting, livestock, chop production and financial analysis.
Formerly (until 1984): Friendly Farm Computer Newsletter
Related titles: Online - full text ed.
Published by: Farm Business Software Systems, Inc, 1855 55th Ave, Aledo, IL 61231-8610. TEL 309-582-5628, fbsmail@mcol.net, http://www.fbssystems.com. Ed., Adv. contact Wesley Prosser. Pub., R&P Norman Brown. B&W page USD 112,950, color page USD 185,450; trim 19.88 x 8.38. Circ: 5,000 (paid).

▼ **JOURNAL OF INFORMATION TECHNOLOGY IN AGRICULTURE.** see *COMPUTERS*

630 USA
TECAGRI NEWS. Text in English. 1987. irreg. adv. **Document type:** *Newsletter.* **Description:** For large, innovative farmers and ranchers who use computerized farm management to increase profitability.
Formerly: TechAgra News
Published by: Clark Consulting International, Inc., PO Box 600, Dundee, IL 60118-0600. TEL 847-836-5100, FAX 847-836-5140, ag-pr@agpr.com, http://www.agpr.com/consulting/. Ed., Pub., R&P, Adv. contact Warren Clark. Circ: 90,000 (controlled).

630.285 DEU ISSN 0942-6620
ZEITSCHRIFT FUER AGRARINFORMATIK. Variant title: Agrarinformatik. Text in German. q. EUR 65.40 domestic; EUR 71.40 foreign (effective 2003). adv. **Document type:** *Journal, Trade.*
Indexed: AEA, BioCN&I, DSA, FCA, ForAb, HortAb, IndVet, MaizeAb, NutrAb, OrnHort, PBA, PGegResA, PHN&I, RDA, RPP, RevApplEntom, S&F, TriticAb, VetBull, WAE&RSA, WeedAb.
Published by: (Gesellschaft fuer Informatik in der Land-, Forst- und Ernaehrungswirtschaft), Landwirtschaftsverlag GmbH, Huelsebrockstr 2, Muenster, 48165, Germany. TEL 49-2501-801-0, FAX 49-2501-801204, zentrale@lv-h.de, http://www.lv-h.de. Ed. R A E Mueller. Adv. contact Reinhard Geissel. B&W page EUR 960, color page EUR 1,584. Circ: 1,176 (paid and controlled).

AGRICULTURE—Crop Production And Soil

see also AGRICULTURE—Feed, Flour And Grain ; GARDENING AND HORTICULTURE ; RUBBER ; TOBACCO

630 AUS ISSN 1034-8999
A C I A R POSTHARVEST NEWSLETTER. Text in English. 1984. q.
Formerly (until 1989): A C I A R Grain Storage Newsletter (0813-8249)
Related titles: Online - full text ed.
—CISTI.
Published by: Australian Centre for International Agricultural Research, PO Box 1571, Canberra, ACT 2601, Australia. TEL 61-2-62170500, FAX 61-2-62170501, http://www.aciar.gov.au/projects/postharvest/phnews.htm.

631 USA ISSN 0197-8748
CODEN: PPESD9
A P R E S PROCEEDINGS. (American Peanut Research and Education Society) Text in English. 1969. a. USD 40 domestic to individual members; USD 52.50 in Canada & Mexico to individual members; USD 65 elsewhere to individual members; USD 50 domestic to institutional members; USD 62.50 in Canada & Mexico to institutional members; USD 75 elsewhere to institutional members; USD 10 to students (effective 2003). back issues avail. **Document type:** *Proceedings.* **Description:** Compilation of abstracts of professional papers presented at the annual APRES meeting. Includes report of actions taken on behalf of APRES.
Former titles (until 1979): American Peanut Research and Education Association. Proceedings (0160-6719); (until 1974): American Peanut Research and Education Association. Journal (0587-503X)
Indexed: BioCN&I, BiolAb, CPA, CTFA, ChemAb, FCA, FS&TA, PGrRegA, S&MA, SeedAb, TOSA, WeedAb.
—CASDDS, CISTI, Linda Hall.
Published by: American Peanut Research and Education Society, c/o Dr J Ronald Sholar, 376 Ag Hall, Oklahoma State University, Stillwater, OK 74078. TEL 405-372-3052, FAX 405-624-6718, nickeli@provalue.net, http://www.agr.okstate.edu/apres/pubs.htm, http://www.agr.okstate.edu/apres/welcome.htm. Circ: 750.

631 USA ISSN 8755-1187
S671 CODEN: ASEPER
A S A E STANDARDS. Text in English. 1954. a. USD 259 domestic to non-members; USD 285 foreign to non-members; USD 96 to members; USD 399 combined subscription domestic to non-members print & CD-ROM eds.; USD 425 combined subscription foreign to non-members print & CD-ROM eds.; USD 129 combined subscription to members print & CD-ROM eds. (effective 2004). **Document type:** *Trade.* **Description:** Contains over 210 current ASAE Standards, Engineering Practice and Data. Presents performance criteria for products, materials, and systems.
Supersedes: Agricultural Engineers Yearbook of Standards (0065-4477)
Related titles: CD-ROM ed.: 1998. USD 249 domestic to non-members; USD 259 foreign to non-members; USD 83 foreign to members (effective 2004); Microfilm ed.
Indexed: AEA, DSA, I&DA, PHN&I, PoultAb, S&F, WeedAb.
—CISTI, Ei. **CCC.**
Published by: American Society of Agricultural Engineers, 2950 Niles Rd, St. Joseph, MI 49085-9659. TEL 269-429-0300, FAX 269-429-3852, hq@asae.org, http://www.asae.org. Ed. Scott Cedarquist. R&P Sandy Rutter.

631.091 CUB ISSN 0138-7553
A T A C. Text in Spanish. s-a. CUP 120, USD 12 (effective 1996). charts; illus.
Indexed: AEA, BiolAb, FS&TA, PBA, RRTA, S&F, SIA, WAE&RSA.
—BLDSC (1765.445000), CINDOC.
Published by: Asociacion de Tecnicos Azucareros de Cuba, Calle 19, 9 entre N y O, Vedado, La Habana 10400, Cuba. Ed. Luis Santos Estrada.

AARDAPPELWERELD MAGAZINE. see *BUSINESS AND ECONOMICS—Domestic Commerce*

630 USA ISSN 1076-4968
ACRES U S A; the voice for eco-agriculture. Text in English. 1971. m. USD 24 domestic; USD 29 foreign (effective 2000). adv. bk.rev. charts; illus.; stat. cum.index: 1970-1990. **Document type:** *Trade.*
Indexed: F&GI, NPI.
—CISTI.
Address: PO Box 91299, Austin, TX 78709-1299. TEL 512-892-4400, FAX 512-892-4448, info@acresusa.com, http://www.acresusa.com. Ed., Pub., R&P Fred C Walters. Adv. contact Judy L Behler. Circ: 11,000 (paid).

632.726 GBR ISSN 0001-5024
ACRIDOLOGICAL ABSTRACTS. Text in English. irreg.
Published by: Centre for Overseas Pest Research, College House, Wrights Ln, London, W8 5SP, United Kingdom.

630 POL ISSN 0065-0919
CODEN: AASABP
ACTA AGRARIA ET SILVESTRIA. SERIES AGRARIA. Text in Polish; Summaries in English, Russian. 1961. a. price varies. **Document type:** *Monographic series, Academic/Scholarly.* **Description:** Occurrence and control of diseases and pests of plants. Effect of fertilization and cultivation measures.
Formerly (until 1965): Acta Agraria et Silvestria. Seria Rolnicza (0515-2690)
Indexed: AgrAg, AgrLib, BiolAb, ChemAb, ExcerpMed, FCA, HerbAb, HortAb, PBA, PGrRegA, PotatoAb, S&F, SeedAb, TriticAb, WeedAb.
—CASDDS, CISTI.
Published by: (Polska Akademia Nauk, Oddzial w Krakowie, Komisja Nauk Rolniczych i Lesnych), Polska Akademia Nauk, Oddzial w Krakowie, ul sw Jana 28, Krakow, 31018, Poland. TEL 48-12-4224853, FAX 48-12-4222791.

631 NOR ISSN 0906-4710
SB13 CODEN: AASBEV
➤ **ACTA AGRICULTURAE SCANDINAVICA. SECTION B. SOIL AND PLANT SCIENCE.** Text in English. 1950. q. GBP 173, USD 285 combined subscription to institutions print & online eds. (effective 2006). adv. bibl.; charts; illus. back issues avail.; reprint service avail. from PSC. **Document type:** *Journal, Academic/Scholarly.*
Supersedes in part (in 1992): Acta Agriculturae Scandinavica (0001-5121)
Related titles: Online - full text ed.: ISSN 1651-1913. GBP 164, USD 271 to institutions (effective 2006) (from EBSCO Publishing, Gale Group, IngentaConnect, O C L C Online Computer Library Center, Inc., Swets Information Services); Supplement(s): Acta Agriculturae Scandinavica. Supplementum. Section B. ISSN 1651-9140. 1957.
Indexed: AEA, ASCA, AgBio, AgrForAb, BIOBASE, BIOSIS Prev, BioCN&I, BiolAb, CIN, CPA, ChemAb, ChemTitl, CurCont, DSA, FCA, FPA, FS&TA, ForAb, HerbAb, HortAb, I&DA, IABS, ISR, MaizeAb, NemAb, NutrAb, OrnHort, PBA, PGegResA, PGrRegA, PHN&I, PlantSci, PotatoAb, PoultAb, ProtozoAb, RA&MP, RM&VM, RPP, RefZh, RevApplEntom, RiceAb, S&F, SCI, SIA, SeedAb, SoyAb, TriticAb, WAE&RSA, WeedAb.
—BLDSC (0589.010000), CASDDS, CISTI, IDS, IE, Infotrieve, ingenta, Linda Hall. **CCC.**
Published by: (Kungliga Skogs- och Lantbruksakademien/Royal Swedish Academy of Agriculture and Forestry SWE), Taylor & Francis A S (Subsidiary of: Taylor & Francis Group), Biskop Gunnerusgate 14A, PO Box 12 Posthuset, Oslo, 0051, Norway. TEL 47-23-103460, FAX 47-23-103461, journals@tandf.no, http://www.tandf.co.uk/journals/titles/09064710.asp. Ed. Anna Martensson. Circ: 1,000. **Subscr. to:** Taylor & Francis Ltd, Journals Customer Service, Rankine Rd, Basingstoke, Hants RG24 8PR, United Kingdom. TEL 44-1256-813000, FAX 44-1256-330245. **Co-sponsor:** Nordiska Jordbruksforskares Foerening/Nordic Association of Agricultural Scientists (NJF).

631 580 590 SVN ISSN 1581-9175
➤ **ACTA AGRICULTURAE SLOVENICA.** Text in English, Slovenian. 1957. q. USD 70 foreign (effective 2005). back issues avail. **Document type:** *Journal, Academic/Scholarly.*
Description: Publishes papers on agronomy, horticulture, plant biotechnology, food technology of foods of plant origin, agricultural economics and informatics and on zootechnology (genetics, microbiology, immunology, nutrition, physiology, ecology, ethology, dairy science, economics, animal production, technology and information science).
Former titles (until 2004): University of Ljubljana. Biotechnical Faculty. Research Reports (1408-340X); University E. Kardelja in Ljubljana. Biotechnical Faculty. Research Reports (0459-6404)
Related titles: Online - full text ed.: ISSN 1854-1941. free (effective 2005).
Indexed: AbHyg, AgrForAb, BiolAb, CPA, FCA, FPA, HerbAb, HortAb, I&DA, OrnHort, PGrRegA, RA&MP, RPP, RevApplEntom, S&F, SFA, SIA, SeedAb, TriticAb, VITIS, WeedAb, WildRev, ZooRec.
—BLDSC (9428.470000), CISTI.
Published by: Univerza v Ljubljani, Biotehniska Fakulteta/University of Ljubljana, Biotechnical Faculty, Jamnikarjeva 101, Ljubljana, 1000, Slovenia. TEL 386-1-4231161, FAX 386-1-2565782, dekanat@bf.uni-lj.si, http://aas.bf.uni-lj.si/index-en.htm, http://www.bf.uni-lj.si. Ed. Peter Dovc. Circ: 450.

630 COL ISSN 0120-2812
CODEN: CAGAY
ACTA AGRONOMICA. Text in Spanish; Summaries in English, Spanish. 1951. q. COP 1,200 domestic; USD 50 foreign (effective 2000); or exchange basis. bibl.; charts.
Indexed: AEA, AgBio, AgrForAb, AnBrAb, BioCN&I, BiolAb, CPA, ChemAb, DSA, FCA, FPA, ForAb, HerbAb, HortAb, I&DA, IndVet, MaizeAb, NemAb, NutrAb, OrnHort, PBA, PGegResA, PGrRegA, PHN&I, PN&I, PotatoAb, RA&MP, RDA, RPP, RiceAb, S&F, S&MA, SIA, SeedAb, SoyAb, TriticAb, VetBull, WAE&RSA.
—Linda Hall.
Published by: Universidad Nacional de Colombia, Facultad de Ciencias Agropecuarias Palmira, Apdo. 237, Palmira, Colombia. TEL 57-27-17000, FAX 57-27-17032, biblialm@bacata.usc.unal.edu.co. Ed. Heimar Quintero. Circ: 1,000.

ACTA BOTANICA MALACITANA. see *BIOLOGY—Botany*

633 636 SVK ISSN 1335-258X
➤ **ACTA FYTOTECHNICA ET ZOOTECHNICA**; the scientific journal for phytotechnics and zootechnics. Text in Slovak, English; Summaries in English. 1998. q. SKK 240; SKK 60 newsstand/cover (effective 2002 - 2003). index. 30 p./no. 2 cols./p.; back issues avail. **Document type:** *Journal, Academic/Scholarly.* **Description:** Publishes scientific articles on phytotechnics and zootechnics.
Indexed: AEA, AgBio, AgrForAb, AnBrAb, BioCN&I, CPA, DSA, FCA, ForAb, HerbAb, HortAb, I&DA, IndVet, MaizeAb, NutrAb, OrnHort, PBA, PGegResA, PGrRegA, PHN&I, PN&I, PotatoAb, PoultAb, RPP, RefZh, S&F, SIA, SeedAb, SoyAb, TriticAb, VetBull, WAE&RSA, WeedAb.
—CISTI.

Published by: Slovenska Pol'nohospodarska Univerzita v Nitre/Slovak University of Agriculture in Nitra, Tr. A. Hlinku 2, Nitra, 949 76, Slovakia. TEL 421-37-65117514, 421-37-65122514, FAX 421-37-6511560, admin-www@uniag.sk, http://www.uniag.sk. Ed. Magdalena Lacko-Bartosova. Pub. L'udovit Cagan.

A

➤ **ACTA SCIENTIARUM POLONORUM. FORMATIO CIRCUMIECTUS.** see *ENVIRONMENTAL STUDIES*

➤ **ACTUALIZACION DE LAS INVERSIONES AZUCARERAS.** see *BUSINESS AND ECONOMICS—Investments*

633 UGA ISSN 1021-9730
SB95.A338
➤ **AFRICAN CROP SCIENCE JOURNAL**; a journal of tropical crop science and production. Text in English. 1993. q. USD 60 to individuals; USD 180 to institutions (effective 2004). adv. bk.rev. **Document type:** *Academic/Scholarly.* **Description:** Presents a forum for new research in tropical crop science and agricultural development.
Related titles: Online - full text ed.
Indexed: AEA, AgBio, AgrForAb, BioCN&I, CPA, DSA, FCA, FS&TA, ForAb, HerbAb, HortAb, I&DA, MaizeAb, NemAb, NutrAb, OrnHort, PBA, PGegResA, PGrRegA, PHN&I, PotatoAb, RDA, RPP, RevApplEntom, RiceAb, S&F, SIA, SeedAb, SoyAb, TriticAb, WAE&RSA, WeedAb.
Published by: African Crop Science Society, Faculty of Agriculture and Forestry, Makerere University, PO Box 7062, Kampala, Uganda. TEL 256-41-540464, FAX 256-41-531641, acss@starcom.co.ug, http://www.bioline.org.br/cs. Ed. Adipala Ekwamu. Circ: 300.

632.8 CMR ISSN 0379-6930
SB950.3.A33
AFRICAN JOURNAL OF PLANT PROTECTION/REVUE AFRICAINE DE LA PROTECTION DES VEGETAUX. Text in English, French. 1980. s-a. USD 40 to individuals; USD 100 to institutions (effective 1999). bibl.
Formerly: Inter-African Phyto-Sanitary Bulletin
Indexed: RPP.
Published by: Inter-African Phyto-Sanitary Council, BP 4170, Yaounde, Cameroon.

633 ZAF ISSN 1022-0119
CODEN: AJRSE4
AFRICAN JOURNAL OF RANGE & FORAGE SCIENCE. Text in English. 1966. 3/yr. ZAR 380 domestic to individuals; ZAR 342 in Southern Africa to individuals; USD 145 elsewhere to individuals; ZAR 495 domestic to institutions; ZAR 495 in Southern Africa to institutions; USD 220 elsewhere to institutions (effective 2004). adv. bk.rev. illus.; maps; abstr. cum.index. back issues avail. **Document type:** *Journal, Academic/Scholarly.* **Description:** Studies of range and forage science, grasslands, natural vegetation, planted pastures and animal populations.
Formerly (until 1992): Grassland Society of Southern Africa. Journal (0256-6702); Which superseded (in 1984): Grassland Society of Southern Africa. Proceedings of the Annual Congresses (0072-5560)
Related titles: Online - full text ed.: ISSN 1727-9380 (from EBSCO Publishing, Gale Group, IngentaConnect, International Network for the Availability of Scientific Publications, African Journals Online).
Indexed: AEA, AgrForAb, AnBrAb, B&AI, BIOBASE, BIOSIS Prev, BibAg, BiolAb, CPA, ChemAb, DSA, FCA, ForAb, HerbAb, HortAb, I&DA, IBR, IBZ, ISAP, IndVet, MaizeAb, NutrAb, PGegResA, PHN&I, RA&MP, RDA, RPP, S&F, S&MA, SFA, SeedAb, SoyAb, TriticAb, VetBull, WAE&RSA, WeedAb, WildRev, ZooRec.
—CASDDS, CISTI, Linda Hall.
Published by: (Grassland Society of Southern Africa), National Inquiry Services Centre (Pty) Ltd (Subsidiary of: N I S C USA), PO Box 377, Grahamstown, 6140, South Africa. TEL 27-46-622-9698, FAX 27-46-622-9550, info@nisc.co.za, http://www.nisc.co.za/JournalHome/ajrf/home.htm. Ed. A R Palmer. Pub. C Richard Hurt. adv.: page USD 300; 175 x 245. Circ: 450.

630.24 USA ISSN 1072-7361
HD9660.P3
AG CHEM NEW COMPOUND REVIEW; an annual review covering the latest new product developments in the world's crop production industry. Text in English. 1983. a. USD 350 (effective 1997). **Document type:** *Catalog.* **Description:** Identifies over 250 experimental compounds in some phase of public testing. Updates status of previously listed compounds.
Former titles (until 1992): Ag Chem New Product Review; (until 1988): Agricultural Chemical New Product Development Review
Indexed: RPP, RevApplEntom, WeedAb.
Published by: Ag Chem Information Services, 6705 E 71st St, Indianapolis, IN 46220. TEL 317-845-0681, FAX 317-841-1210. Pub. William L Hoplins.

631.8 USA ISSN 1545-4541
HD9483.U5
AG PROFESSIONAL. Text in English. 1956. 12/yr. free to qualified personnel (effective 2005). adv. charts; illus.; stat. back issues avail.; reprints avail. **Document type:** *Magazine, Trade.* **Description:** Provides a broad base of useful purchasing, marketing and management information to fertilizer and agricultural chemical dealers.
Former titles (until 2003): Ag Retailer Magazine (1072-9267); (until 1993): Solutions (0199-9869); (until 1980): Fertilizer Solutions (0015-0312)
Indexed: Agr, ChemAb, ExcerpMed, Inspec, S&F.
—CISTI, Linda Hall.
Published by: Doane Agricultural Service Co., 11701 Borman Dr, Ste 300, St. Louis, MO 63146-4199. TEL 314-569-2700, FAX 314-569-1083, agretailer@doane.com, http://www.agprofessional.com, http://www.doane.com. Pub. Bill Schurmann. adv.: B&W page USD 2,600, color page USD 7,000. Circ: 22,000 (controlled and free).

631 551.6 DEU ISSN 1615-9225
AGRARMETEOROLOGISCHER MONATSBERICHT FUER BRANDENBURG, SACHSEN-ANHALT, THUERINGEN UND SACHSEN. Text in German. 1998. m. **Document type:** *Bulletin, Trade.*
Formed by the merger of (1991-1998): Agrarmeteorologischer Monatsbericht fuer Sachsen-Anhalt, Thueringen und Sachsen (0942-5713); (1991-1998): Agrarmeteorologischer Monatsbericht fuer Mecklenburg-Vorpommern, Brandenburg und Berlin (0943-0822)
Published by: Deutscher Wetterdienst, Abteilung Agrarmeteorologie, Kaiserleistr 29-35, Offenbach, 63067, Germany. TEL 49-69-80624408, FAX 49-69-80624482, landwirtschaft@dwd.de, http://www.dwd.de.

631 551.6 DEU ISSN 0172-9403
AGRARMETEOROLOGISCHER MONATSBERICHT FUER NORDRHEIN-WESTFALEN. Text in German. 1979. m. **Document type:** *Bulletin, Trade.*
Published by: Deutscher Wetterdienst, Kaiserleistr 29-35, Offenbach, 63067, Germany. TEL 49-69-80620, FAX 49-69-80624484, info@dwd.de, http://www.dwd.de.

631 551.6 DEU ISSN 1615-9217
AGRARMETEOROLOGISCHER WOCHENBERICHT FUER BRANDENBURG, SACHSEN-ANHALT, THUERINGEN UND SACHSEN. Text in German. 1998. w. **Document type:** *Bulletin, Trade.*
Formed by the merger of (1991-1998): Agrarmeteorologischer Wochenbericht fuer Sachsen-Anhalt, Thueringen und Sachsen (0939-7051); (1977-1998): Agrarmeteorologischer Wochenbericht fuer Schleswig-Holstein, Hamburg, Niedersachsen und Bremen (0941-1186); Which was formerly (until 1991): Agrarmeteorologischer Wochenbericht fuer Norddeutschland (0344-0397); (1991-1998): Agrarmeteorologischer Wochenbericht fuer Mecklenburg-Vorpommern, Brandenburg und Berlin (0939-706X)
Published by: Deutscher Wetterdienst, Abteilung Agrarmeteorologie, Kaiserleistr 29-35, Offenbach, 63067, Germany. TEL 49-69-80624408, FAX 49-69-80624482, landwirtschaft@dwd.de, http://www.dwd.de.

631 DEU ISSN 0172-293X
AGRARMETEOROLOGISCHER WOCHENBERICHT FUER NORDRHEIN-WESTFALEN. Text in German. 1979. w. **Document type:** *Bulletin, Trade.*
Published by: Deutscher Wetterdienst, Kaiserleistr 29-35, Offenbach, 63067, Germany. TEL 49-69-80620, FAX 49-69-80624484, info@dwd.de, http://www.dwd.de.

631.8 USA
AGRIBUSINESS FIELDMAN. Text in English. 1972. m. USD 19.95 (effective 2001). adv. bk.rev. **Document type:** *Magazine, Trade.* **Description:** Covers chemicals, equipment developments, new applications and provides financial and legislative advice for agribusinessman.
Published by: Western Agricultural Publishing Co. Inc., 4969 E Clinton Way, Ste 104, Fresno, CA 93727-1549. TEL 559-252-7000, FAX 559-252-7387, westag2@psnw.com. Eds. Marnie Katz, Ranot Bailey. Pub. Jim Baltimore. Circ: 8,058 (paid).

634 USA
AGRIBUSINESS FRESH FRUIT AND RAISIN NEWS. Text in English. m. USD 25; USD 45 foreign (effective 1998). adv. **Document type:** *Newspaper, Trade.*
Published by: Agribusiness Publications, 612 N St, Sanger, CA 93657. TEL 209-875-4585, FAX 209-875-4587. Ed., Pub. John C Stubbs. R&P, Adv. contact John Van Nortwick. B&W page USD 880, color page USD 1,280; trim 14 x 10.75. Circ: 10,000 (controlled).

635 ESP ISSN 0211-2728
AGRICOLA VERGEL; fruticultura, horticultura, floricultura, citricultura, vid, arroz. Text in Spanish. 1980. m. EUR 60.37 domestic; EUR 96.55 foreign (effective 2004). **Document type:** *Journal, Trade.* **Description:** Dedicated to floriculture, fruit culture, and horticulture.
Formed by the merger of (1975-1980): Vergel (0210-8089); (1979-1980): Vergel Aficionados (0210-8097)
Indexed: IECT.
—CINDOC.
Published by: Ediciones y Promociones L.A.V., C/Jose Maria de Haro 51, Valencia, 46022, Spain. TEL 34-96-3720261, FAX 34-96-3710516, http://www.edicioneslav.es. Ed. Francisco Salvador Planes Planes.

AGRICOLTURA (BOLOGNA). see *AGRICULTURE*

631.8 GBR ISSN 0140-0657
AGRICULTURAL & VETERINARY CHEMICALS. Text in English. 1960. bi-m. GBP 25, USD 70 domestic; GBP 35 overseas. adv. bk.rev. charts; illus. **Document type:** *Newsletter.* **Description:** Covers news of interest to research chemists, managers of research stations, and converters and formulators of agricultural and veterinary chemicals.
Formerly (until no.26): Agricultural and Veterinary Chemicals and Agricultural Engineering (0002-1377)
Indexed: ChemAb.
Published by: Chandler Publications Ltd., 187 Drury Ln, London, WC2B 5QD, United Kingdom. Ed., Pub. Jack R.D. Heming. Circ: 2,000.

631.3 SCG ISSN 0354-8457
AGRICULTURAL ENGINEERING✶. Text in English. q. YUN 150; USD 60 foreign. **Description:** Covers agricultural engineering and agricultural equipment.
Published by: Vojvodjansko Drustvo za Poljoprivrednu Tehniku/Voivodina's Society of Agricultural Engineers, c/o Institute for Agricultural Mechanisation, P.O. Box 41, Belgrade-Zemun. FAX 381-21-59989, tesic@uns.ns.ac.yu, vlazic@polj.ms.ac.yu. Ed. Milos Tesic. R&P Veselin Lazic. Circ: 300. **Co-sponsor:** Yugoslav Scientific Society of Agricultural Engineers.

AGRICULTURAL ENGINEERING IN SOUTH AFRICA. see *AGRICULTURE—Agricultural Equipment*

630.72 USA ISSN 0002-161X
S1 CODEN: AGREA5
AGRICULTURAL RESEARCH; solving problems for the growing world. Text in English. 1953. m. USD 50 domestic; USD 70 foreign (effective 2004). illus. index. back issues avail.; reprints avail. **Document type:** *Government.* **Description:** Presents in non-technical language information about government research on food, feed, and natural fiber production and use; human nutrition; renewable energy; natural resource conservation; and other agricultural programs.
Related titles: Microform ed.: (from PQC); Online - full text ed.: (from bigchalk, EBSCO Publishing, Florida Center for Library Automation, Gale Group, Northern Light Technology, Inc., O C L C Online Computer Library Center, Inc., ProQuest Information & Learning).
Indexed: ABIn, AEA, ASFA, AgBio, Agr, AgrForAb, AnBrAb, BioCN&I, BiolAb, BiolDig, BrCerAb, C&ISA, CTFA, CerAb, ChemAb, CivEngAb, CorrAb, CurCont, DBA, DSA, E&CAJ, EMA, EPB, ESPM, EnvAb, ExcerpMed, ForAb, GardL, HelmAb, HerbAb, HortAb, I&DA, IAA, IMI, IndVet, M&TEA, MBF, METADEX, MaizeAb, NutrAb, PBA, PHN&I, PN&I, PROMT, PollutAb, PotatoAb, PoultAb, ProtozoAb, RASB, RPP, RevApplEntom, RiceAb, S&F, SIA, SolStAb, TTI, TriticAb, VITIS, VetBull, WAA, WAE&RSA, WeedAb, WildRev.
—BLDSC (0751.950000), CINDOC, CIS, CISTI, IDS, IE, Infotrieve, ingenta, Linda Hall.
Published by: U.S. Department of Agriculture, Agricultural Research Service, 5601 Sunnyside Ave, Beltsville, MD 20705-5130. TEL 301-504-1660, FAX 301-504-1641, armag@asrr.arsusda.gov, http://www.ars.usda.gov/is/AR. Ed. Robert Sowers. R&P Anita Daniels TEL 301-504-1609. Circ: 39,000. **Subscr. to:** U.S. Government Printing Office, Superintendent of Documents, PO Box 371954, Pittsburgh, PA 15250-7954. TEL 202-512-1800, FAX 202-512-2250, orders@gpo.gov, http://www.access.gpo.gov.

AGRICULTURAL SCIENCE DIGEST. see *AGRICULTURE*

631.587 NLD ISSN 0378-3774
S494.5.W3 CODEN: AWMADF
➤ **AGRICULTURAL WATER MANAGEMENT.** Text in English. 1977. 24/yr. EUR 1,500 in Europe to institutions; JPY 199,400 in Japan to institutions; USD 1,683 elsewhere to institutions (effective 2006). adv. bk.rev. bibl.; illus. Index. back issues avail. **Document type:** *Journal, Academic/Scholarly.* **Description:** Presents scientific papers of international significance to the management of agricultural water resources.
Related titles: Microform ed.: (from PQC); Online - full text ed.: (from EBSCO Publishing, Gale Group, IngentaConnect, ScienceDirect, Swets Information Services).
Indexed: AEA, ASCA, ASFA, Agr, AgrForAb, B&AI, BIOBASE, BIOSIS Prev, BioCN&I, BiolAb, CPA, CTFA, CivEngAb, CurCont, DSA, EIA, EPB, ESPM, EnerInd, EnvAb, EnvEAb, FCA, FLUIDEX, ForAb, GEOBASE, HerbAb, HortAb, I&DA, IABS, IAOP, ISR, Inspec, M&GPA, M&TEA, MaizeAb, OrnHort, PBA, PN&I, PollutAb, PotatoAb, PoultAb, RA&MP, RDA, RPP, RefZh, RevApplEntom, RiceAb, S&F, S&MA, SCI, SIA, SJW, SWRA, SeedAb, SoyAb, TriticAb, VITIS, WAE&RSA, WeedAb.
—BLDSC (0757.540000), CISTI, IDS, IE, Infotrieve, ingenta, Linda Hall. **CCC.**

Published by: Elsevier BV (Subsidiary of: Elsevier Science & Technology), Radarweg 29, Amsterdam, 1043 NX, Netherlands. TEL 31-20-4853911, FAX 31-20-4852457, nlinfo-f@elsevier.nl, http://www.elsevier.com/locate/agwat, http://www.elsevier.nl. Eds. B E Clothier, D. Wichelns, J. Oster.

630 THA ISSN 0257-5035
AGRO-CHEMICALS NEWS IN BRIEF. Text in English. 1978. q. USD 100 (effective 2000). bk.rev. bibl.; charts; illus.; mkt. back issues avail. **Description:** Deals with developments in the agro-chemicals sector including trade, handling, distribution and use of fertilizers and pesticides in Asia and the Pacific. Also covers environmental and safety aspects.
Related titles: Microfiche ed.: (from CIS); ♦ Supplement(s): Agro-Chemicals News in Brief. Special Issue. ISSN 1564-6106.
Indexed: AEA, AgBio, AgrForAb, BioCN&I, HortAb, I&DA, IIS, PGegResA, RDA, RevApplEntom, RiceAb, S&F, TDB, TriticAb, WAE&RSA, WeedAb.
Published by: United Nations Economic and Social Commission for Asia and the Pacific, Fertilizer Advisory, Development and Information Network for Asia and the Pacific, Agriculture and Rural Development Division, United Nations Bldg, Rajadamnern Ave, Bangkok, 10200, Thailand. Circ: 1,000. **Co-sponsors:** FAO; UNIDO.

631.80272 GBR ISSN 0961-4672
AGROCHEMICAL PATENT FAST-ALERT. Text in English. 199?. w. GBP 1,690 (effective 2002). **Document type:** *Bulletin, Trade.* **Description:** Provides fast information on agrochemical and plant biotechnology patent competition and research and development activities.
Related titles: ♦ Online - full text ed.: Agrochemical Patent Fast-Alert Online.
—CCC.
Published by: Current Drugs Ltd., 34-42 Cleveland St, Middlesex House, London, W1P 6LB, United Kingdom. TEL 44-20-75808393, FAX 44-20-75805646, info@current-drugs.com, http://www.current-drugs.com. Ed. Tara Dyson. **Subscr. to:** Current Drugs Ltd., 400 Market St, Ste 700, Philadelphia, PA 19106.

631.80272 GBR
AGROCHEMICAL PATENT FAST-ALERT ONLINE. Text in English. w. **Document type:** *Bulletin, Trade.*
Media: Online - full text. **Related titles:** ♦ Print ed.: Agrochemical Patent Fast-Alert. ISSN 0961-4672.
Published by: Current Drugs Ltd., 34-42 Cleveland St, Middlesex House, London, W1P 6LB, United Kingdom. TEL 44-20-75808393, FAX 44-20-75805646, info@current-drugs.com, http://www.current-drugs.com. Ed. Tara Dyson. **Subscr. to:** Current Drugs Ltd., 400 Market St, Ste 700, Philadelphia, PA 19106. TEL 215-721-9700, FAX 215-721-9287.

632.9 JPN ISSN 0919-5505
SB950.3.J3 CODEN: AGJAEP
AGROCHEMICALS JAPAN. Text in English. 1969. s-a. USD 130 (effective 2001). cum.index every 10 vols. **Description:** Covers the development of pesticides, their uses, pesticide registration and other related matters. Assists readers engaged in pesticide science and industry as well as pest control techniques in improving their professional work.
Formerly (until 1992): Japan Pesticide Information (0368-265X)
Indexed: AEA, AbHyg, BIOSIS Prev, BioCN&I, BiolAb, CBNB, CIN, ChemAb, ChemTitl, DBA, FCA, GEOBASE, HortAb, IndVet, MaizeAb, NemAb, OrnHort, PBA, PHN&I, PotatoAb, RA&MP, RM&VM, RPP, RefZh, RevApplEntom, RiceAb, S&F, SIA, SeedAb, SoyAb, TriticAb, WeedAb.
—BLDSC (0764.586700), CASDDS, CISTI, IE, Infotrieve, ingenta.
Published by: Japan Plant Protection Association/Nihon Shokubutsu Boeki Kyokai, 1-43-11 Komagome, Toshima-ku, Tokyo, 170-8484, Japan. Ed. Toshio Sugahara. **Subscr. to:** Sun Publications Service Ltd., Ishii Bldg 3-37, Kanda-Sakuma-cho, Chiyoda-ku, Tokyo 101-0025, Japan. TEL 81-3-3866-9897, FAX 81-3-3861-7715, sunpub@mvc.biglobe.ne.jp. **Co-sponsor:** Japan Crop Protection Association.

630.24 RUS ISSN 1029-2551
CODEN: KSKHE7
AGROKHIMICHESKII VESTNIK. Text in Russian. 1963. bi-m. USD 118 in United States (effective 2004). bk.rev. bibl. index.
Former titles (until 1997): Khimizatsiya Sel'skogo Khozyaistva (0235-2516); (until 1988): Khimiya v Sel'skom Khozyaistve (0023-1185)
Indexed: BiolAb, ChemAb, ChemTitl, DBA, DSA, FCA, FPA, FS&TA, ForAb, HerbAb, HortAb, I&DA, IndVet, MaizeAb, NutrAb, PGrRegA, PotatoAb, PoultAb, RPP, RefZh, RevApplEntom, S&F, SIA, SeedAb, TriticAb, WeedAb.
—CASDDS, CISTI, East View, Linda Hall. **CCC.**
Published by: Gosudarstvennyi Agropromyshlennyi Komitet, Sadovaya-Spasskaya 18, kom 611, Moscow, 107807, Russian Federation. TEL 7-095-2072410, FAX 7-095-9754372. Ed. Irina I Prokhorova. Circ: 3,000. **US dist. addr.:** East View Information Services, 3020 Harbor Ln. N., Minneapolis, MN 55447. TEL 800-477-1005, FAX 800-800-3839, eastview@eastview.com, http://www.eastview.com.

630 PRT ISSN 0002-1911
S15 CODEN: AGLUAN
AGRONOMIA LUSITANA. Text in Portuguese; Summaries in English, French, Portuguese. 1939-19??; resumed 1988. q. bibl.; charts; illus. index, cum.index: vols.1-20.
Indexed: ASFA, AgBio, AgrForAb, AgrLib, AnBrAb, BibAg, BiolAb, CPA, ChemAb, DSA, ESPM, FCA, FPA, FS&TA, ForAb, HerbAb, HortAb, I&DA, IBR, IBZ, MaizeAb, NemAb, NutrAb, OrnHort, PBA, PGegResA, PGrRegA, PotatoAb, RA&MP, RPP, RRTA, RefZh, RevApplEntom, RiceAb, S&F, SIA, SeedAb, TriticAb, VITIS, WAE&RSA, WatResAb, WeedAb, ZooRec.
—BLDSC (0768.000000), CASDDS, CISTI, Linda Hall. **CCC.**
Published by: Estacao Agronomica Nacional, Quinta de Marques, Oeiras, 2780, Portugal. TEL 351-21-4403500, FAX 351-21-4416011, TELEX 63698 EAN P, ean@mail.telepac.pt. Ed. Fernando Ilharco. Circ: 1,200.

AGRONOMIA MESOAMERICANA; revista agropecuaria. see *AGRICULTURE—Poultry And Livestock*

631.4 VEN ISSN 0002-192X
CODEN: ATMVAK
AGRONOMIA TROPICAL. Text in Spanish; Summaries in English, Spanish. 1951. q. VEB 5,000; VEB 60 in developing nations; or exchange basis. bk.rev. bibl.; charts; illus.; maps. index, cum.index: 1951-1962, 1963-1967, 1968-1990. **Document type:** *Government.*
Related titles: CD-ROM ed.
Indexed: AEA, ATA, AgBio, AgrForAb, BioCN&I, BiolAb, CPA, CTFA, ChemAb, CurCont, ExcerpMed, FCA, FPA, FaBeAb, ForAb, HerbAb, HortAb, I&DA, IndVet, MaizeAb, NutrAb, OrnHort, PBA, PGegResA, PGrRegA, PHN&I, PotatoAb, PoultAb, RA&MP, RDA, RPP, RefZh, RevApplEntom, RiceAb, S&F, SIA, SeedAb, SoyAb, TOSA, TriticAb, VetBull, WAE&RSA, WeedAb, WildRev, ZooRec.
—CASDDS, CINDOC, CISTI.
Published by: Fondo Nacional de Investigaciones Agropecuarias, Apdo. 2103, Maracay, 2105, Venezuela. FAX 58-43-836312. Ed. Aydee Cabrera de Green. Circ: 4,653.

630 FRA ISSN 1774-0746
SB7 CODEN: AGRNDZ
➤ **AGRONOMY FOR SUSTAINABLE DEVELOPMENT**; sciences des productions vegetales et de l'environnement. Text in English, French; Summaries in English, French. 1981. q. EUR 465 combined subscription domestic print & online eds.; EUR 530 combined subscription in the European Union print & online eds.; EUR 554 combined subscription elsewhere print & online eds. (effective 2005). bk.rev. bibl.; illus. index.
Document type: *Academic/Scholarly.* **Description:** Publishes scientific articles on both fundamental and applied approaches to plant production and agrarian systems covering biological, physiological, genetic, ecological and economic aspects.
Formerly (until 2004): Agronomie (0249-5627)
Related titles: Online - full text ed.: Agronomie Online. ISSN 1297-9643. 2000 (from EBSCO Publishing, Swets Information Services).
Indexed: AEA, ASCA, ASFA, AgBio, Agr, AgrForAb, AnBrAb, ApicAb, B&BAb, BIOBASE, BIOSIS Prev, BioCN&I, BiolAb, CPA, Cadscan, CurCont, DBA, DSA, ESPM, ExcerpMed, FCA, FPA, FS&TA, ForAb, GEOBASE, HerbAb, HortAb, I&DA, IABS, LeadAb, MaizeAb, NutrAb, OrnHort, PBA, PGegResA, PGrRegA, PHN&I, PN&I, PlantSci, PotatoAb, PoultAb, RA&MP, RPP, RevApplEntom, RiceAb, S&F, S&MA, SCI, SIA, SSCI, SeedAb, SoyAb, TOSA, TriticAb, VITIS, WAE&RSA, WeedAb, Zincscan.
—BLDSC (0771.476000), CASDDS, CISTI, IDS, IE, Infotrieve, ingenta, Linda Hall. **CCC.**
Published by: (France. Institut National de la Recherche Agronomique (INRA)), E D P Sciences, 17 Ave du Hoggar, Parc d'Activites de Courtaboeuf, BP 112, Cedex A, Les Ulis, F-91944, France. TEL 33-1-69187575, FAX 33-1-69860678, subscribers@edpsciences.org, http://www.edpsciences.org. Ed. Max Rives. Circ: 2,500.

631 NZL
➤ **AGRONOMY NEW ZEALAND.** Text in English. 1971. a. NZD 30, USD 15 (effective 2001). bk.rev. back issues avail.
Document type: *Proceedings, Academic/Scholarly.*
Description: Publishes original research on the agronomy of crops and forages, as well as progress reports, reviews and new techniques.
Former titles (until 2000): Agronomy Society of New Zealand. Proceedings Annual Conference (0110-6589); (until 1973): Agronomy Society of New Zealand. Proceedings
Indexed: AEA, AgBio, AgrForAb, BioCN&I, BiolAb, CPA, FCA, ForAb, HerbAb, HortAb, I&DA, IndVet, MaizeAb, NutrAb, OrnHort, PBA, PGegResA, PHN&I, PotatoAb, RA&MP, RPP, RevApplEntom, S&F, SIA, SeedAb, TriticAb, VetBull, WAE&RSA, WeedAb.
—BLDSC (6840.228500), CISTI. **CCC.**
Published by: Agronomy Society of New Zealand, Private Bag 4704, Christchurch, New Zealand. TEL 64-3-325-6400, FAX 64-3-325-2074, deruiterj@crop.cri.nz. Ed. J G Hampton. R&P B A McKenzie TEL 64-3-325-2811. Circ: 400.

631 NZL ISSN 0111-9184
AGRONOMY SOCIETY OF NEW ZEALAND. SPECIAL PUBLICATION. Text in English. 1982. irreg., latest vol.12. **Document type:** *Monographic series.*
Indexed: AgBio, Agr, CPA, FCA, ForAb, HerbAb, HortAb, OrnHort, PBA, PGegResA, PGrRegA, PHN&I, RPP, S&F, SeedAb, TriticAb, WeedAb.
—BLDSC (8371.850000), CISTI, IE, ingenta. **CCC.**
Published by: Agronomy Society of New Zealand, Private Bag 4704, Christchurch, New Zealand. TEL 64-3-325-6400, FAX 64-3-325-2074, deruiterj@crop.cri.nz. Ed. J G Hampton. R&P B A McKenzie TEL 64-3-325-2811.

631.6 POL ISSN 1230-7394
AKADEMIA ROLNICZA, POZNAN. ROCZNIKI. MELIORACJE I INZYNIERIA SRODOWISKA. Text in Polish; Summaries in English. 1972. irreg. price varies. **Document type:** *Academic/Scholarly.* **Description:** Series on natural and technical basis for land reclamation, irrigation, drainage, hydro-reclamation structures, and environmental engineering.
Former titles: Akademia Rolnicza, Poznan. Roczniki. Melioracje; Akademia Rolnicza, Poznan. Roczniki. Melioracje Wodne (0208-8932)
Indexed: AgrAg, AgrLib, BibAg, ForAb.
Published by: (Akademia Rolnicza im. Augusta Cieszkowskiego w Poznaniu), Wydawnictwo Akademii Rolniczej w Poznaniu, ul Witosa 45, Poznan, 61693, Poland. TEL 48-61-487809, FAX 48-61-487802, wgolab@owl.au.poznan.pl, wydar@au.poznan.pl, http://swan.au.poznan.pl/bib/bghome.html. R&P Elzbieta Zagorska TEL 48-61-487806.

631.587 POL ISSN 0137-1967
CODEN: ZNAMDX
AKADEMIA ROLNICZA WE WROCLAWIU. ZESZYTY NAUKOWE. MELIORACJA. Text in Polish; Summaries in English. 1956. irreg. price varies. **Document type:** *Academic/Scholarly.*
Formerly (until 1973): Wyzsza Szkola Rolnicza we Wroclawiu. Zeszyty Naukowe. Melioracja (0520-9293)
Related titles: ♦ Series of: Akademia Rolnicza we Wroclawiu. Zeszyty Naukowe. ISSN 0867-7964.
Indexed: AgrLib.
—CASDDS, CISTI.
Published by: Akademia Rolnicza we Wroclawiu/Agricultural University of Wroclaw, Ul Norwida 25, Wroclaw, 50375, Poland. TEL 48-71-3205101, wyd@ozi.ar.wroc.pl. Circ: 350. **Subscr. to:** Wydawnictwo Akademii Rolniczej we Wroclawiu, ul Sopocka 23, Wroclaw 50344, Poland.

633 CAN ISSN 0707-8293
ALBERTA AGRICULTURE, FOOD AND RURAL DEVELOPMENT. CROP REPORT. Variant title: Alberta Crop Report. Text in English. 1967. irreg.
—CISTI.
Published by: Alberta Agriculture, Food & Rural Development, J. G. O'Donoghue Bldg., 7000 113 St., Edmonton, AB T6H 5T6, Canada. duke@gov.ab.ca, http://www.agric.gov.ab.ca.

368.121 CAN ISSN 1207-4195
ALBERTA FINANCIAL SERVICES CORPORATION. ANNUAL REPORT. Text in English. 1994. a. **Document type:** *Corporate.*
Formed by the merger of (1970-1994): Alberta Hail and Crop Insurance Corporation. Annual Report (0319-3535); Alberta Agricultural Development Corporation. Annual Report (0380-3120)
—CISTI.
Published by: (Alberta. Publishing Branch), Agriculture, Food and Rural Development, Alberta Financial Services Corporation, Publications Office, 7000 113th St, Main Fl, Edmonton, AB T6H 5T6, Canada. TEL 780-427-0391, 800-292-5697, FAX 780-422-8835, http://www.agric.gov.ab.ca.

631 ISR ISSN 0333-8886
SB354.6.I75
ALON HANOTEA. Text in Hebrew. 1945. m. USD 60. **Document type:** *Bulletin.*
Indexed: AEA, AgrForAb, BioCN&I, BioDAb, CPA, FS&TA, HortAb, I&DA, IHP, NemAb, OrnHort, PBA, PGegResA, PGrRegA, PHN&I, RPP, RevApplEntom, S&F, SIA, SeedAb, WAE&RSA, WeedAb.
Published by: Israel Fruit Growers Association, P O Box 40007, Tel Aviv, 61400, Israel. TEL 972-3-6966267, FAX 972-3-6917625. Ed. J Kovetz. Circ: 5,000.

AMATEUR DE BORDEAUX. see *BEVERAGES*

AMERICAN JOURNAL OF ENOLOGY AND VITICULTURE. see *BEVERAGES*

633.491 USA ISSN 1099-209X
CODEN: APOJAY
➤ **AMERICAN JOURNAL OF POTATO RESEARCH.** Text in English. 1913. bi-m. USD 75 (effective 2005). bk.rev. abstr.; bibl.; charts; illus. index. back issues avail. **Document type:** *Journal, Academic/Scholarly.*
Formerly: American Potato Journal (0003-0589)
Related titles: Microfilm ed.: (from PQC); Online - full text ed.: (from ProQuest Information & Learning).
Indexed: AEA, ASCA, AgBio, Agr, BIOBASE, BIOSIS Prev, BibAg, BioCN&I, BiolAb, CIN, CPA, ChemAb, ChemTitl, CurCont, ExcerpMed, FCA, FS&TA, HerbAb, I&DA, IABS, ISR, MaizeAb, NutrAb, PBA, PGegResA, PGrRegA, PHN&I, PlantSci, PotatoAb, RPP, RefZh, RevApplEntom, S&F, SCI, SeedAb, WAE&RSA, WeedAb.

—BLDSC (0834.353000), CASDDS, CISTI, IDS, IE, Infotrieve, ingenta, Linda Hall.
Published by: Potato Association of America, University of Maine, 5715 Coburn Hall, Rm 6, Orono, ME 04469-5715. TEL 207-581-3042, FAX 207-581-3015, umpotato@maine.edu, http://www.maine.edu/PAA. Ed. John Bamberg. Circ: 1,000 (paid).

A

630 USA ISSN 1075-6302
AMERICAN SOCIETY OF SUGAR CANE TECHNOLOGISTS. JOURNAL. Text in English. 1982. a. USD 10 per issue domestic (effective 2005).
—BLDSC (4693.230000).
Published by: American Society of Sugar Cane Technologists, PO Box 25100, Baton Rouge, LA 70894-5100. TEL 225-578-1392, FAX 225-578-1415, assct@assct.org, http://www.assct.org. Ed. Dr. Jeff Hoy.

633 USA ISSN 0741-9848
CODEN: AMVGA5
AMERICAN VEGETABLE GROWER. Text in English. 1953. m. USD 19.95 domestic; USD 28 in Canada; USD 39 elsewhere (effective 2005). adv. bk.rev. charts; illus.; mkt.; tr.lit.
Document type: *Magazine, Trade.* **Description:** Provides extensive coverage of the vegtable market from the details of growing to the strategies of marketing.
Former titles (until 1983): American Vegetable Grower and Greenhouse Grower (0161-8946); (until 1977): American Vegetable Grower (0003-1461)
Related titles: Microform ed.: (from PQC); Online - full text ed.: (from bigchalk, Northern Light Technology, Inc., ProQuest Information & Learning).
Indexed: ABIn, AEA, B&AI, F&GI, FS&TA, HortAb, S&F.
—CISTI, Linda Hall. **CCC.**
Published by: Meister Media Worldwide, 37733 Euclid Ave, Willoughby, OH 44094-5992. TEL 440-942-2000, FAX 440-942-0662, jwmonahan@meistermedia.com, info@meistermedia.com, http://www.meistermedia.com/vegetables/index.html. Ed. Charlotte Sine. Pub. Joseph Monahan. Adv. contact Jon J Miducki. color page USD 4,748. Circ: 30,000 (paid and controlled).

632.9 POL ISSN 1505-7216
CODEN: AAEPF4
ANNALS OF AGRICULTURAL SCIENCES. SERIES E. PLANT PROTECTION. Text in English; Summaries in Polish. 1970. a. price varies. bibl.; charts; illus. **Document type:** *Academic/Scholarly.*
Formerly (until vol.26, no.1-2, 1998): Roczniki Nauk Rolniczych. Seria E. Ochrona Roslin (0080-3693)
Indexed: AEA, AgrAg, AgrLib, BioCN&I, ChemAb, ChemTitl, FCA, FS&TA, ForAb, HortAb, MaizeAb, NutrAb, OrnHort, PBA, PGegResA, PGrRegA, PHN&I, PotatoAb, RDA, RPP, RevApplEntom, S&F, SIA, SeedAb, SoyAb, TriticAb, WeedAb, ZooRec.
—CASDDS, CISTI.
Published by: Instytut Ochrony Roslin/Institute of Plant Protection, ul Miczurina 20, Poznan, 60318, Poland. TEL 48-61-8649001, FAX 48-61-8676301, http://ior.poznan.pl, http://www.ior.poznan.pl. Ed. Jerzy J Lipa. Circ: 610. **Dist. by:** Osrodek Rozpowszechniania Wydawnictw Naukowych PAN, Palac Kultury i Nauki, Warsaw 00901, Poland. **Co-sponsor:** Polska Akademia Nauk, Komitet Ochrony Roslin/Polish Academy of Sciences, Committee of Plant Protection.

630 IND ISSN 0570-1791
S341 CODEN: ANAZBX
➤ **ANNALS OF ARID ZONE.** Text in English. 1962. q. USD 200 to institutions (effective 2006). adv. bk.rev. bibl.; charts; illus. 90 p./no.; back issues avail. **Document type:** *Journal, Academic/Scholarly.* **Description:** Articles and short communications on the biological, physical and socioeconomic aspects of arid and semi-arid regions.
Indexed: ASCA, AgrForAb, AnBrAb, BiolAb, ChemAb, CurCont, DSA, FCA, FPA, ForAb, HerbAb, HortAb, I&DA, IndVet, MaizeAb, NutrAb, PBA, RPP, RRTA, RevApplEntom, S&F, S&MA, SFA, SSCI, SeedAb, SoyAb, TriticAb, WAE&RSA, WildRev, ZooRec.
—BLDSC (1038.500000), CASDDS, IDS, IE, Infotrieve, ingenta, Linda Hall. **CCC.**
Published by: (Arid Zone Research Association of India), Scientific Publishers, 5-A New Pali Rd., Near Hotel Taj Hari Mahal, PO Box 91, Jodhpur, Rajasthan 342 003, India. TEL 91-291-2433323, FAX 91-291-2512580, info@scientificpub.com, http://www.scientificpub.com/bookdetails.php?booktransid=294&bookid=290. Ed. Vinod Shankar. Circ: 800.

➤ **ANNUAL BOOK OF A S T M STANDARDS. VOLUME 04.08. SOIL AND ROCK (I): D420 - D5779.** see *ENGINEERING—Engineering Mechanics And Materials*

635 ARG ISSN 0066-5207
ANUARIO F.H.I. ARGENTINA: FRUTAS Y HORTALIZAS INDUSTRIALIZADAS Y FRESCAS/F.H.I. ANNUAL: FRESH AND INDUSTRIALIZED FRUITS AND VEGETABLES. Text in Spanish; Summaries in English. 1965. irreg. USD 10. adv. bk.rev.
Published by: Riccardo Luchini, Ed. & Pub., 2455 Canning, Buenos Aires, 1425, Argentina. Circ: 1,500.

APPLIED PLANT SCIENCE/TOEGEPASTE PLANTWETENSKAP. see *BIOLOGY—Botany*

631.4 NLD ISSN 0929-1393
QH541.5.S6 CODEN: ASECFN
➤ **APPLIED SOIL ECOLOGY.** Text in English. 1994. 9/yr. EUR 1,114 in Europe to institutions; JPY 148,100 in Japan to institutions; USD 1,246 elsewhere to institutions (effective 2006). abstr.; bibl.; charts; stat. Index. back issues avail. **Document type:** *Journal, Academic/Scholarly.* **Description:** Publishes original research into the role of soil organisms and their interactions in relation to agricultural productivity, nutrient cycling and other soil processes.
Related titles: Microform ed.: (from PQC); Online - full text ed.: (from EBSCO Publishing, Gale Group, IngentaConnect, ScienceDirect, Swets Information Services); ♦ Series of: Agriculture, Ecosystems & Environment. ISSN 0167-8809.
Indexed: ASCA, AbHyg, AgBio, Agr, AgrForAb, BIOBASE, BIOSIS Prev, BioCN&I, BiolAb, CPA, CurCont, DSA, FCA, ForAb, HelmAb, HerbAb, HortAb, I&DA, ISR, MaizeAb, NemAb, NutrAb, PBA, PGegResA, PGrRegA, PN&I, PotatoAb, PoultAb, ProtozoAb, RA&MP, RDA, RM&VM, RPP, RevApplEntom, RiceAb, S&F, SCI, SIA, SeedAb, SoyAb, TriticAb, WAE&RSA, WeedAb, ZooRec.
—BLDSC (1578.400000), CISTI, IDS, IE, Infotrieve, ingenta. **CCC.**
Published by: Elsevier BV (Subsidiary of: Elsevier Science & Technology), Radarweg 29, Amsterdam, 1043 NX, Netherlands. TEL 31-20-4853911, FAX 31-20-4852457, nlinfo-f@elsevier.nl, http://www.elsevier.com/locate/apsoil, http://www.elsevier.nl. Eds. C A Edwards, D. Atkinson, J P Curry.

630 GBR ISSN 0269-6797
ARABLE FARMING. Text in English. 19??. 17/yr. GBP 38 domestic; GBP 101 foreign (effective 2001). adv. illus. **Document type:** *Magazine, Trade.* **Description:** Geared toward farmers and farm managers in Great Britain who grow cereals, sugarbeets, potatoes and other vegetables.
Former titles (until 1973): Arable farmer and Vegetable Grower (0300-2829); (until 1971): Arable Farmer (0003-7524)
Related titles: Online - full text ed.: (from Florida Center for Library Automation, Gale Group, ProQuest Information & Learning).
Indexed: AEA, FCA, HortAb, RPP, RevApplEntom, S&F, WeedAb.
—BLDSC (1583.460000).
Published by: C M P Information Ltd. (Subsidiary of: United Business Media), Riverbank House, Angel Ln, Tonbridge, Kent TN9 1SE, United Kingdom. TEL 44-1732-377591, FAX 44-1732-377465, enquiries@cmpinformation.com, http://www.cmpinformation.com. Pub. Peter Walker. Adv. contact Keith Nicholson. Circ: 35,674. **Subscr. to:** Marlowe House, 109 Station Rd, Sidcup, Kent DA15 7ET, United Kingdom. TEL 44-20-8309-7000.

630 GBR ISSN 0365-0340
S7 CODEN: AAPBCE
ARCHIV FUER ACKER- UND PFLANZENBAU UND BODENKUNDE/ARCHIVES OF AGRONOMY AND SOIL SCIENCE. Text in German; Summaries in English, German, Russian. 1956. bi-m. GBP 1,504, USD 1,896 combined subscription to institutions (other); print & online eds. (effective 2006). bk.rev. charts; stat. index. reprint service avail. from PSC. **Document type:** *Journal, Academic/Scholarly.* **Description:** Topics covered include plant nutrition, fertilizers, soil tillage, soil biotechnology and ecophysiology, amelioration, irrigation and drainage, plant production on arable and grass land, agroclimatology, landscape formation, and environmental management in rural regions.
Formerly (until 1970): Albrecht-Thaer-Archiv (0002-4929)
Related titles: Online - full text ed.: ISSN 1476-3567. GBP 1,429, USD 1,801 to institutions (effective 2006) (from EBSCO Publishing, Gale Group, IngentaConnect, O C L C Online Computer Library Center, Inc., Swets Information Services).
Indexed: BiolAb, CPA, ChemAb, CurCont, ExcerpMed, FCA, FS&TA, FaBeAb, ForAb, HerbAb, I&DA, MSB, MaizeAb, PBA, PGrRegA, RRTA, S&F, SCI, SeedAb, TriticAb, VITIS, WAE&RSA, WeedAb.
—BLDSC (1630.923000), CASDDS, CISTI, IE, Infotrieve, ingenta, Linda Hall. **CCC.**
Published by: (Akademie der Landwirtschaftswissenschaften CHE), Taylor & Francis Ltd (Subsidiary of: Taylor & Francis Group), 4 Park Sq, Milton Park, Abingdon, OX14 4RN, United Kingdom. TEL 44-1235-828600, FAX 44-1235-829000, info@tandf.co.uk, http://www.tandf.co.uk/journals/titles/03650340.asp. Ed. Dr. Elke Schultz. **Subscr. to:** Journals Customer Service, Rankine Rd, Basingstoke, Hants RG24 8PR, United Kingdom. TEL 44-1256-813000, FAX 44-1256-330245, enquiry@tandf.co.uk.

631.5 IND
AREA AND PRODUCTION OF PRINCIPAL CROPS IN INDIA. SUMMARY TABLES. Text in English, Hindi. 1951. a. INR 427.50, USD 25.65. **Document type:** *Government.*
Formerly: Estimates of Area and Production of Principal Crops in India. Summary Tables (0085-0314)
Published by: Ministry of Agriculture, Department of Agriculture and Cooperation, Directorate of Economics and Statistics, A-2E-3 Kasturba Gandhi Marg Barracks, New Delhi, 110 001, India. TEL 11-381523. Ed. Brajesh Kumar Gautam. Circ: 650.

631.4 USA ISSN 1532-4982
S592.17.A73 CODEN: ALRMCW
➤ **ARID LAND RESEARCH AND MANAGEMENT.** Text in English. q. GBP 288, USD 476 combined subscription to institutions print & online eds. (effective 2006). adv. reprint service avail. from PSC. **Document type:** *Journal, Academic/Scholarly.* **Description:** Source of information for fundamental and applied research on lands affected by aridity, including agricultural, pastoral, and forested ecosystems.
Formerly (until 2000): Arid Soil Research and Rehabilitation (0890-3069)
Related titles: Online - full text ed.: ISSN 1521-0405. GBP 274, USD 452 to institutions (effective 2006) (from EBSCO Publishing, Gale Group, IngentaConnect, O C L C Online Computer Library Center, Inc., Swets Information Services).
Indexed: AEA, ASCA, AgBio, Agr, AgrForAb, AnBrAb, BIOBASE, BIOSIS Prev, BibAg, BioCN&I, BiolAb, CIN, CPA, ChemAb, ChemTitl, CurCont, EPB, ESPM, EngInd, EnvEAb, FCA, FaBeAb, ForAb, GEOBASE, HerbAb, HortAb, I&DA, IABS, MBA, MaizeAb, NemAb, NutrAb, OrnHort, PBA, PGegResA, PGrRegA, PlantSci, PollutAb, RA&MP, RDA, RPP, RRTA, RefZh, RiceAb, S&F, S&MA, SIA, SWRA, SeedAb, SoyAb, TriticAb, WAE&RSA, WeedAb.
—BLDSC (1668.259000), CASDDS, CISTI, Ei, IDS, IE, ingenta, Linda Hall. **CCC.**
Published by: Taylor & Francis Inc. (Subsidiary of: Taylor & Francis Group), 325 Chestnut St, Ste 800, Philadelphia, PA 19016. TEL 215-625-8900, 800-354-1420, FAX 215-625-8914, info@taylorandfrancis.com, http://www.tandf.co.uk/journals/titles/15324982.asp, http://www.taylorandfrancis.com. Ed. J Skujins. **Subscr. addr. in Europe:** Taylor & Francis Ltd, Journals Customer Service, Rankine Rd, Basingstoke, Hants RG24 8PR, United Kingdom. TEL 44-1256-813000, FAX 44-1256-330245, enquiry@tandf.co.uk.

630 USA
S37 CODEN: AKABA7
ARKANSAS. AGRICULTURAL EXPERIMENT STATION. RESEARCH REPORT. Text in English. 1886. irreg. (approx. 5/yr.). **Document type:** *Bulletin, Government.* **Description:** Reports on investigative research in agriculture, forestry and home economics.
Incorporates: Arkansas. Agricultural Experiment Station. Special Reports; Former titles: Arkansas. Agricultural Experiment Station. Research Bulletin; Arkansas. Agricultural Experiment Station. Bulletin (0097-3491)
Related titles: Online - full text ed.
Indexed: AbHyg, AnBrAb, BiolAb, DSA, FCA, FPA, ForAb, HerbAb, HortAb, I&DA, IndVet, NutrAb, PHN&I, RiceAb, S&F, SoyAb, TriticAb, WAE&RSA, WeedAb.
—CASDDS, CISTI.
Published by: Agricultural Experiment Station, Communication Services, 110 Agriculture Bldg, 1 University of Arkansas, Division of Agriculture, Fayetteville, AR 72701-1201. TEL 501-575-5647, FAX 501-575-7531, http://www.uark.edu/depts/agripub/publications/. R&P Eloise Cole. Circ: 1,200 (controlled).

630 USA ISSN 1051-3140
CODEN: AKAMA6
ARKANSAS. AGRICULTURAL EXPERIMENT STATION. RESEARCH SERIES. Text in English. 1949. irreg. (approx. 8/yr.). **Document type:** *Government.* **Description:** Reports on agricultural, food and life sciences research.
Formerly (until 1985): Arkansas Agricultural Experiment Station. Mimeograph Series (0099-5010)
Related titles: Online - full text ed.
Indexed: AEA, AgBio, AnBrAb, BioCN&I, BiolAb, CPA, DSA, FCA, HerbAb, HortAb, I&DA, IndVet, NutrAb, OrnHort, PBA, PGegResA, PGrRegA, PHN&I, PN&I, PoultAb, RM&VM, RPP, RevApplEntom, RiceAb, S&F, SeedAb, SoyAb, TriticAb, VetBull, WAE&RSA, WeedAb.
—BLDSC (7769.714000), CASDDS, CISTI, Linda Hall.
Published by: Agricultural Experiment Station, Communication Services, 110 Agriculture Bldg, 1 University of Arkansas, Division of Agriculture, Fayetteville, AR 72701-1201. TEL 501-575-5647, FAX 501-575-7531, http://www.uark.edu/depts/agripub/publications/. R&P Eloise Cole. Circ: 1,000.

632.8 USA
➤ **ARTHROPOD MANAGEMENT TESTS (ONLINE EDITION).** Text in English. a. USD 43 to individuals; USD 64 to institutions (effective 2004). **Document type:** *Academic/Scholarly.* **Description:** Publishes short reports on preliminary and routine screening tests for management of arthropods.
Media: Online - full content. **Related titles:** CD-ROM ed.: USD 29 to non-members; USD 22 to members; USD 58 to institutions (effective 2004).
Published by: Entomological Society of America, 10001 Derekwood Ln, Ste 100, Lanham, MD 20706-4876. TEL 301-731-4535, FAX 301-731-4538, mem@entsoc.org, esa@entsoc.org, http://www.entsoc.org/pubs. Ed. Kailash N Saxena.

631.8　　　　　　GBR　　　　　ISSN 0968-672X
ASIA F A B. Key Title: AsiaFAB. Asia Fertiliser and Agrochemicals Bulletin. Text in English. 1992. s-a. GBP 270, USD 440, EUR 420 (effective 2005); included with subscription to Fertilizer International. **Document type:** *Magazine, Trade.* **Description:** Aims to reflect the growing importance of the Asia-Pacific region in t he market for fertilizers and agrichemicals. Strives to raise awareness of the unique issues affecting agriculture, associated inputs, technology and marketing in the area.
Indexed: WAE&RSA.
Published by: (C R U Publishing), British Sulphur Publishing (Subsidiary of: C R U Publishing), 31 Mt Pleasant, London, WC1X 0AD, United Kingdom. TEL 44-20-79032147, FAX 44-20-79032172, derek.winterbottom@crugroup.com, http://www.britishsulphur.com/journal_af.htm. Ed. Richard Hands.

ASIAN AND PACIFIC COCONUT COMMUNITY. BIBLIOGRAPHY SERIES. see *AGRICULTURE—Abstracting, Bibliographies, Statistics*

631　　　　　　IDN
ASIAN AND PACIFIC COCONUT COMMUNITY. TECHNICAL MEETINGS. PROCEEDINGS. Text in English. a. price varies. **Document type:** *Proceedings.* **Description:** Contains original papers on coconut production & productivity, coconut based farming systems, and small scale processing of coconut products.
Published by: Asian and Pacific Coconut Community, 3rd Fl., Lina Bldg., Jl H R Rasuna Said Kav B 7, Kuningan, Jakarta, 12920, Indonesia. TEL 62-21-520-5160, FAX 62-21-520-5160.

630　　　　　　NZL　　　　　ISSN 0112-1421
ASPARAGUS RESEARCH NEWSLETTER. Text in English. 1983. every 3 wks.
Indexed: HortAb, PBA, PGrRegA, RPP, S&F, WeedAb.
—BLDSC (1745.780000).
Published by: Massey University, Faculty of Agricultural and Horticultural Sciences, Private Bag 11 222, Palmerston North, New Zealand. TEL 64-6-3569099, FAX 64-6-3502263, http://www.palmerstonnorth.massey.ac.nz.

631　　　　　　IDN
ASSESSMENT OF EXPERIENCES WITH NEW VARIETIES OF COCONUT. Text in English. irreg. USD 10. **Document type:** *Monographic series.* **Description:** Incorporates the findings of the field studies done by national experts from India, Indonesia, Papua New Guinea, Philippines, Sri Lanka, Thailand, Vanuatu and Western Samoa and assess their experience with new high yielding varieties of coconut.
Published by: Asian and Pacific Coconut Community, 3rd Fl., Lina Bldg., Jl H R Rasuna Said Kav B 7, Kuningan, Jakarta, 12920, Indonesia. TEL 62-21-5221712, FAX 62-21-5221714, TELEX 62209 APCCIA.

631.4　　　　　FRA　　　　　ISSN 0295-1347
ASSOCIATION FRANCAISE POUR L'ETUDE DU SOL. LETTRE. Text in French. 1983. q.
Related titles: ♦ Supplement to: Etudes et Gestion des Sols. ISSN 1252-6851.
—CISTI.
Published by: Association Francaise pour l'Etude du Sol, Avenue de la Pomme de Pin, BP 20619, Ardon, 45166 OLIVET cedex, France. TEL 33-02-41225421, FAX 33-02-41731557, rossignol@angers.inra.fr.

632.9　　　　　USA　　　　　ISSN 0066-9431
ASSOCIATION OF AMERICAN PESTICIDE CONTROL OFFICIALS. OFFICIAL PUBLICATION. Text in English. 1964. a. USD 30. **Document type:** *Directory.*
Published by: Association of American Pesticide Control Officials, c/o Philip Gray, Box 1249, Hardwick, VT 05843. TEL 802-472-6956, FAX 802-472-6957. Ed. Ed White. Circ: 200.

631.8　　　　　USA　　　　　ISSN 0094-8764
S641　　　　　　　　　　　　CODEN: OPAAAN
ASSOCIATION OF AMERICAN PLANT FOOD CONTROL OFFICIALS. OFFICIAL PUBLICATION. Text in English. 1947. a. USD 30 (effective 2005). **Document type:** *Bulletin.* **Description:** Contains model legislation, definitions, and enforcement policies for regulation of fertilizers.
Formerly: Association of American Fertilizer Control Officials. Official Publication
—CISTI, Linda Hall.
Published by: Association of American Plant Food Control Officials, Inc., Division of Regulatory Services, University of Kentucky, Lexington, KY 40546. TEL 606-257-2668, FAX 606-257-7351, dterry@ca.uky.edu, http://www.aapfco.org. Ed. D L Terry. Circ: 400 (paid).

631.5　　　　　USA
ASSOCIATION OF OFFICIAL SEED CERTIFYING AGENCIES. REPORT OF ACRES APPLIED FOR CERTIFICATION BY SEED CERTIFYING AGENCIES. Text in English. 1959. a. USD 25. **Description:** Covers the seed varieties and acreage being certified by each state, Canada, and New Zealand.
Former titles: Association of Official Seed Certifying Agencies. Production Publication; International Crop Improvement Association. Production Publication (0538-7043)

Published by: Association of Official Seed Certifying Agencies, PO Box 9812, Mississippi State, MS 39762. TEL 601-325-4567, FAX 601-325-8118. Ed. Vance H Watson. Circ: 500.

ATTENDERINGSBULLETIN BIBLIOTHEEK STARING-GEBOUW: LAND, BODEM, WATER. see *ENVIRONMENTAL STUDIES—Abstracting, Bibliographies, Statistics*

634　　　　　　AUS
AUSTRALASIAN TREE CROPS SOURCEBOOK. Text in English. irreg. price varies.
Media: Online - full text.
Published by: Tree Crops Centre, PO Box 27, Subiaco, W.A. 6008, Australia. TEL 61-8-93881965, FAX 61-8-93881852, treecrop@AOI.com.au, http://www.AOI.com.au/atcros/.

AUSTRALIA. BUREAU OF STATISTICS. AGRICULTURAL COMMODITIES, AUSTRALIA. see *AGRICULTURE— Abstracting, Bibliographies, Statistics*

AUSTRALIA. BUREAU OF STATISTICS. AUSTRALIAN WINE AND GRAPE INDUSTRY. see *AGRICULTURE—Abstracting, Bibliographies, Statistics*

AUSTRALIA. BUREAU OF STATISTICS. HOME PRODUCTION OF SELECTED FOODSTUFFS, AUSTRALIA. see *AGRICULTURE—Abstracting, Bibliographies, Statistics*

633　　　　　　AUS
AUSTRALIA. DEPARTMENT OF PRIMARY INDUSTRIES AND ENERGY. COTTON MARKET NEWS. Text in English. 1972. m. stat.
Former titles: Australia. Department of Primary Industry. Cotton Market News; Australia. Department of Agriculture. Marketing Division. Cotton Market News (0310-2084)
Published by: Department of Primary Industries and Energy, GPO Box 858, Canberra, ACT 2600, Australia.

633　　　　　　AUS
AUSTRALIA. DEPARTMENT OF PRIMARY INDUSTRIES AND ENERGY. RAW COTTON MARKETING ADVISORY COMMITTEE. ANNUAL REPORT. Text in English. 1968. a. free.
Formerly: Australia. Department of Primary Industry. Raw Cotton Marketing Advisory Committee. Annual Report
Published by: Department of Primary Industries and Energy, Crops Division, Edmund Barton Bldg., Broughton St, Barton, ACT 2600, Australia. FAX 61-6-272-5672.

634.8　　　　　AUS　　　　　ISSN 1446-8212
　　　　　　　　　　　　　　CODEN: AGWIEC
AUSTRALIAN & NEW ZEALAND GRAPEGROWER & WINEMAKER. Text in English. 1963. m. (2 issues in Jun.). AUD 69.30 domestic; AUD 96 in New Zealand; AUD 159 elsewhere (effective 2003). adv. bk.rev. mkt.; stat. 88 p./no.; back issues avail. **Document type:** *Journal, Trade.* **Description:** Covers various aspects of viticulture oenology.
Former titles (until 2001): Australian Grapegrower & Winemaker (0727-3606); Australian Grapegrower (0004-9239)
Indexed: FS&TA, VITIS.
—BLDSC (1796.875000), IE, ingenta.
Published by: Ryan Publications Pty. Ltd., PO Box 3013, Norwood, SA 5067, Australia. editor@grapeandwine.com.au, admin@grapeandwine.com.au, http:// www.grapeandwine.com.au. Ed., R&P Sonya Logan. Pub. Hartley Higgins. Adv. contact Graham Robertson. Circ: 6,446 (paid).

633　　　　　　AUS　　　　　ISSN 0157-3039
AUSTRALIAN CANEGROWER. Text in English. 1979. fortn. AUD 90 domestic; AUD 118 foreign (effective 2000). adv. bk.rev. charts; illus.; mkt.; maps; stat.; tr.lit. **Document type:** *Trade.* **Description:** Provides news and information for Australian cane growers.
Indexed: SIA.
Published by: Canegrowers, PO Box 1032, Brisbane, QLD 4001, Australia. TEL 61-7-38646444, FAX 61-7-38646429, canegrowers@canegrowers.com.au. Ed. Ron Davies. R&P Bill Kerr TEL 61-7-3864-6444. Adv. contact Jan Collins. Circ: 8,100.

677.2　　　　　AUS　　　　　ISSN 1443-9778
AUSTRALIAN COTTON OUTLOOK. Text in English. 1997. m. adv. **Document type:** *Newspaper, Trade.* **Description:** Keeps those involved with the cotton industry abreast of industry news, issues and market trends.
Published by: Rural Press Ltd. (Subsidiary of: Agricultural Publishers Pty. Ltd.), 70 Neil St., PO Box 864, Toowoomba, QLD 4350, Australia. TEL 61-7-46384633, FAX 61-7-46385491, http://www.australiancottonoutlook.com.au/, http://www.ruralpress.com/. Ed. Genevieve McCauley. Adv. contact Keith Hinz. Circ: 21,150 (controlled).

631　　　　　　AUS　　　　　ISSN 0159-1290
　　　　　　　　　　　　　　CODEN: AUCOFT
THE AUSTRALIAN COTTONGROWER. Text in English. 1980. bi-m. AUD 33 domestic; USD 50 foreign (effective 2005). adv. bk.rev. back issues avail. **Document type:** *Magazine, Consumer.*

Indexed: AEA, AgBio, BioCN&I, FCA, I&DA, RPP, RevApplEntom, S&F, SeedAb, SoyAb, TTI, TriticAb, WAE&RSA, WeedAb.
Published by: Greenmount Press, PO Box 766, Toowoomba, QLD 4350, Australia. TEL 61-7-46593555, FAX 61-7-46384520, cotton@greenmountpress.com.au, http://www.cottongrower.com.au/. Ed. David Dowling. adv.: B&W page AUD 924, color page AUD 419; trim 21 x 27.5. Circ: 2,500.

630　　　　　　AUS
AUSTRALIAN COTTONGROWER. COTTON YEARBOOK. Text in English. a. incld. with subscr. to Australian Cottongrower. **Document type:** *Yearbook, Trade.*
Published by: Greenmount Press, PO Box 766, Toowoomba, QLD 4350, Australia. TEL 61-7-46593555, FAX 61-7-46384520.

630　　　　　　AUS　　　　　ISSN 0816-1089
　　　　　　　　　　　　　　CODEN: AJEAEL
➤ **AUSTRALIAN JOURNAL OF EXPERIMENTAL AGRICULTURE.** Text in English. 1961. 8/yr. AUD 200 combined subscription in Australia & New Zealand to individuals print & online eds.; USD 200 combined subscription elsewhere to individuals print & online eds.; AUD 1,270 combined subscription in Australasia to institutions print & online eds.; USD 1,135 combined subscription elsewhere to institutions print & online eds. (effective 2004). adv. Index, 144 p./no.; back issues avail.; reprints avail. **Document type:** *Journal, Academic/Scholarly.* **Description:** Publishes original research into applied agriculture, papers in animal production, animal-plant interactions, pasture and fodder crops, field crops, agroforestry, extension methodology and horticulture.
Formerly: Australian Journal of Experimental Agriculture and Animal Husbandry (0045-060X)
Related titles: Microform ed.: (from PQC); Online - full text ed.: AUD 180 in Australia & New Zealand to individuals; USD 160 elsewhere to individuals; AUD 1,140 in Australia & New Zealand to institutions; AUD 1,020 elsewhere to institutions (effective 2004) (from EBSCO Publishing, Gale Group, O C L C Online Computer Library Center, Inc., Swets Information Services).
Indexed: AEA, ASCA, AgBio, Agr, AgrForAb, AnBrAb, ApicAb, B&AI, BIOBASE, BIOSIS Prev, BioCN&I, BiolAb, CIN, CPA, Cadscan, ChemAb, ChemTitl, CurCont, DBA, DSA, ESPM, ExcerpMed, FCA, FPA, FS&TA, FaBeAb, ForAb, GEOBASE, HerbAb, HortAb, I&DA, IABS, ISR, IndVet, LeadAb, MaizeAb, NemAb, NutrAb, OrnHort, PBA, PCI, PGegResA, PGrRegA, PHN&I, PN&I, PotatoAb, PoultAb, ProtozoAb, RA&MP, RDA, RM&VM, RPP, RRTA, RefZh, RevApplEntom, RiceAb, S&F, S&MA, SCI, SIA, SWRA, SeedAb, SoyAb, TOSA, TriticAb, VITIS, VetBull, WAE&RSA, WTA, WeedAb, Zincscan.
—BLDSC (1807.695000), CASDDS, CISTI, IDS, IE, Infotrieve, ingenta, Linda Hall. **CCC.**
Published by: (C S I R O Australia), C S I R O Publishing, 150 Oxford St, PO Box 1139, Collingwood, VIC 3066, Australia. TEL 61-3-96627500, FAX 61-3-96627611, chris.anderson@publish.csiro.au, publishing@csiro.au, http://www.publish.csiro.au/journals/ajea. Circ: 850.
Co-sponsor: Australian Agricultural Council.

➤ **AUSTRALIAN JOURNAL OF GRAPE AND WINE RESEARCH.** see *BEVERAGES*

631.4　　　　　AUS　　　　　ISSN 0004-9573
S590　　　　　　　　　　　　CODEN: ASORAB
➤ **AUSTRALIAN JOURNAL OF SOIL RESEARCH.** Text in English. 1963. bi-m. AUD 160 combined subscription in Australia & New Zealand to individuals print & online eds.; USD 160 combined subscription elsewhere to individuals print & online eds.; AUD 1,070 combined subscription in Australia & New Zealand to institutions print & online eds.; AUD 820 combined subscription elsewhere to institutions print & online eds. (effective 2004); 160. adv. bibl.; charts; illus.; stat. Index. back issues avail. **Document type:** *Journal, Academic/Scholarly.* **Description:** Covers all aspects of soil science: genesis, morphology and classification; physics and hydrology; chemistry and mineralogy; biology and biochemistry; soil fertility and plant nutrition; soil and water management and conservation.
Related titles: Microform ed.: (from PQC); Online - full text ed.: AUD 135, USD 125 to individuals; AUD 960, USD 735 to institutions (effective 2004) (from EBSCO Publishing, Florida Center for Library Automation, Gale Group, O C L C Online Computer Library Center, Inc., Swets Information Services).
Indexed: AEA, AESIS, ARI, ASCA, ASFA, AbHyg, AgBio, Agr, AgrForAb, AnBrAb, B&AI, BIOBASE, BIOSIS Prev, BiolAb, BrCerAb, C&ISA, CIN, CPA, CerAb, ChemAb, ChemTitl, CivEngAb, CorrAb, CurCont, DSA, E&CAJ, EMA, EPB, ESPM, EngInd, EnvAb, EnvEAb, ExcerpMed, FCA, FLUIDEX, FPA, ForAb, GEOBASE, HerbAb, HortAb, I&DA, IAA, IABS, INIS AtomInd, ISR, M&TEA, MBA, MBF, METADEX, MaizeAb, MinerAb, NemAb, OrnHort, PBA, PCI, PN&I, PlantSci, PollutAb, PotatoAb, RPP, RevApplEntom, RiceAb, S&F, SCI, SIA, SPPI, SWRA, SeedAb, SolStAb, SoyAb, TriticAb, VITIS, WAA, WAE&RSA, WeedAb.
—BLDSC (1812.600000), CASDDS, CIS, CISTI, Ei, IDS, IE, Infotrieve, ingenta, Linda Hall. **CCC.**
Published by: (C S I R O Australia), C S I R O Publishing, 150 Oxford St, PO Box 1139, Collingwood, VIC 3066, Australia. TEL 61-3-96627628, FAX 61-3-96627611, publishing@csiro.au, http://www.publish.csiro.au/journals/ajsr/. Circ: 750.

A

634 AUS ISSN 0811-3475
AUSTRALIAN MACADAMIA SOCIETY. NEWS BULLETIN* . Text in English. 1974. bi-m. AUD 150; USD 250 foreign. adv. **Document type:** *Bulletin.* **Description:** Provides research, development and marketing information relating to macadamia nuts.
Related titles: Diskette ed.
Published by: Australian Macadamia Society, Suite 1/113 Dawson St, Lismore, NSW 2480, Australia. TEL 61-266-224933, FAX 61-266-224932, macsoc@nor.com.au, http://www.nor.com.au/agriculture/ans/Macadami.htm. Ed., R&P, Adv. contact Beverly Atkinson. page AUD 320. Circ: 600.

633 AUS ISSN 1327-9289
AUSTRALIAN SUGAR INDUSTRY HANDBOOK. Text in English. 1991. a. AUD 22 domestic; AUD 32 foreign (effective 2000). adv. bk.rev. charts; illus.; mkt.; stat.; tr.lit. **Document type:** *Trade.* **Description:** Provides information for Australian cane growers.
Published by: Canegrowers, PO Box 1032, Brisbane, QLD 4001, Australia. TEL 61-7-38646444, FAX 61-7-38646429, canegrowers@canegrowers.com.au. Ed. Ron Davies. R&P Bill Kerr TEL 61-7-3864-6444. Adv. contact Jan Collins. Circ: 7,000.

634.8 AUS
AUSTRALIAN VIGNERONS. Text in English. 2001. bi-m. AUD 30 (effective 2005). **Document type:** *Magazine, Trade.*
Published by: Rural Press Ltd. (Subsidiary of: Agricultural Publishers Pty. Ltd.), GPO Box 2249, Unley, SA 5000, Australia. vignerons@ruralpress.com, http://www.ruralpress.com/. Ed. Peter Brady. Adv. contact Derna Hower. Circ: 6,000.

AUSTRALIAN VITICULTURE. see *BEVERAGES*

632 AUS ISSN 0310-0405
AUSTRALIAN WEED CONTROL HANDBOOK. Text in English. 1973. irreg. AUD 60. adv.
Published by: Butterworth - Heinemann Australia (Subsidiary of: Elsevier Ltd., Books Division), 22 Salmon St, Port Melbourne, VIC 3207, Australia. TEL 61-3-92457111, FAX 61-3-92457577. Ed. Jonathan Glasspool. R&P Judith Davies. Circ: 3,000.

663.2 634 AUT
TP544 CODEN: MIKLD4
➤ **AUSTRIA. HOEHERE BUNDESLEHRANSTALT UND BUNDESAMT FUER WEIN- UND OBSTBAU. MITTEILUNGEN KLOSTERNEUBURG;** Rebe und Wein, Obstbau und Fruechteverwertung. Text in German; Summaries in English, French. 1951. bi-m. adv. bk.rev. abstr.; illus. index. **Document type:** *Journal, Academic/Scholarly.* **Description:** Viticulture, fruit growing, wine and fruit processing.
Former titles: Austria. Hoehere Bundeslehr- und Versuchsanstalt fuer Wein- und Obstbau. Mitteilungen Klosterneuburg (0007-5922); (until 1977): Austria. Hoehere Bundeslehr- und Versuchsanstalt fuer Wein- und Obstbau. Mitteilungen Rebe und Wein, Obstbau und Fruechteverwertung (1017-2149)
Indexed: AEA, AgBio, BIOSIS Prev, BioCN&I, BiolAb, CPA, ChemAb, DSA, FCA, FPA, FS&TA, ForAb, HortAb, I&DA, MSB, NemAb, NutrAb, OrnHort, PBA, PGegResA, PGrRegA, PHN&I, RA&MP, RM&VM, RPP, RevApplEntom, S&F, SIA, SeedAb, SoyAb, VITIS, WAE&RSA, WeedAb.
—CASDDS, CISTI.
Published by: Hoehere Bundeslehranstalt und Bundesamt fuer Wein- und Obstbau, Wiener Strasse 74, Klosterneuburg, N 3400, Austria. FAX 43-2243-26705, direktion@hblawo.bmlf.gv.at, http://www.hblawo.bmlf.gv.at. Ed. Reinhard Eder.

630 GBR
AUTUMN COMBINABLE CROP POCKET BOOK. Text in English. a. **Document type:** *Bulletin, Academic/Scholarly.*
Published by: N I A B, Huntingdon Rd, Cambridge, CB3 0LE, United Kingdom. TEL 44-1223-276381, FAX 44-1223-342328, info@niab.com, paul.nelson@niab.com, http://www.niab.com. Ed. Paul Nelson TEL 44-1223-342225.

631 FRA ISSN 0300-2942
AVENIR AGRICOLE ET VITICOLE AQUITAIN. Text in French. 1972. 24/yr.
Address: 17 Cours Xavier Arnozan, Bordeaux, Cedex 33082, France. TEL 96-88-00. Ed. Artigue. Circ: 23,500.

635 ESP
AZUCARERA COOPERATIVA "ONESIMO REDONDO". REVISTA. Variant title: Revista A C O R. Text in Spanish. 1971. q. free. adv. illus.; tr.lit.
Published by: (Azucarera Cooperativa "Onesimo Redondo"), Sociedad Cooperativa Azucarera, Paseo Isabel la Catolica, 1, Valladolid, 47001, Spain. TEL 35 04 00, TELEX 26474 SCAZ. Circ: 7,500.

634.772 AUS
B G F BULLETIN. Text in English. 1936. m. AUD 30; AUD 35 foreign (effective 1997). adv. **Document type:** *Bulletin.*
Formerly: Banana Bulletin (0045-1398)
Related titles: Microfilm ed.: (from PQC).
Indexed: BioCN&I, HortAb, PBA, RPP, RevApplEntom.
Published by: Banana Growers Federation Co-operative Ltd., PO Box 31, Murwillumbah, NSW 2484, Australia. TEL 066-722488, FAX 066-724868. Ed. Michael Lines Kelly. Circ: 2,000 (controlled).

631 CHE ISSN 1420-7087
B G S DOKUMENTE. Text in German. 1984. irreg. **Document type:** *Monographic series, Academic/Scholarly.*
Published by: Bodenkundliche Gesellschaft der Schweiz, Geographisches Institut der Universitaet Zurich, Winterthurerstr 190, Zuerich, 8057, Switzerland. TEL 41-1-2575121, FAX 41-1-3625227.

631 USA ISSN 0271-5864
BADGER COMMON'TATER. Text in English. 1948. m. USD 18 domestic; USD 50 foreign (effective 2000). adv. **Document type:** *Trade.* **Description:** News and events of the Wisconsin potato industry and agribusiness in general.
Published by: Wisconsin Potato & Vegetable Growers Association, 700 Fifth Ave, Box 327, Antigo, WI 54409. TEL 715-623-7683, FAX 715-623-3176, wpvga@potatowis.org. Ed., R&P, Adv. contact Tamas Houlihan. Circ: 3,850.

632.8 CHN ISSN 1001-1285
➤ **BAIYI KEJI.** Text in Chinese. 1984. q. USD 8. bk.rev. **Document type:** *Academic/Scholarly.*
Related titles: Online - full text ed.: (from East View Information Services).
Published by: Zhongguo Baiyi Fangzhi Yanjiuhui/Termite Research Institute of China, No 693, Moganshan Lu, Hangzhou, Zhejiang 310011, China. TEL 86-571-8071061, FAX 86-571-5151540. Ed. Shuqing Lin. R&P Weiying Xu. Circ: 1,200.

631 IDN ISSN 0216-0021
BALAI PENELITIAN PERUSAHAAN PERKEBUNAN GULA. PROCEEDINGS PERTEMUAN TEKNIS. Text in Indonesian. irreg.
Published by: Pusat Penelitian Perkebunan Gula Indonesia, Jl Pahlawan 25, Pasuruan, 67126, Indonesia. TEL 62-343-21086, FAX 62-343-21178. Ed. Soeprayitnd Lamadji. Circ: 650.

631.5 BGD ISSN 0070-8151
BANGLADESH. DIRECTORATE OF AGRICULTURE. SEASON AND CROP REPORT* . Text in English. a.
Published by: Ministry of Agriculture, Secretariat, Bhaban 4, Dhaka, Bangladesh.

631.4 BGD ISSN 0253-5440
S590 CODEN: BJSSDJ
BANGLADESH JOURNAL OF SOIL SCIENCE. Text in English. 1971 (vol.7). s-a. BDT 10, USD 1.25. charts; illus.; stat.
Formerly: Pakistan Journal of Soil Science (0030-9893)
Indexed: FCA, HerbAb.
—CASDDS.
Published by: Soil Science Society of Bangladesh, c/o Dept. of Soil Science, University of Dhaka, Ramna, Dhaka, 2, Bangladesh. Ed. A Karim. Circ: 350.

633.18 BGD
BANGLADESH RICE RESEARCH INSTITUTE. ANNUAL REPORT. Text in English. 1976. a. BDT 30. stat.
Published by: Bangladesh Rice Research Institute, Publications and Public Relations Division, Joydebpur, Dhaka, Bangladesh. Ed. Mohammad H R Talukdar. Circ: 1,000.

631 CAN ISSN 1188-8911
BARLEY COUNTRY. Text in English. 1992. q. CND 10 domestic; CND 15 foreign (effective 2000). adv. **Document type:** *Newsletter.*
—CISTI.
Published by: Alberta Barley Commission, Ste 237 2116 27 Ave, N E, Calgary, AB T2E 7A6, Canada. TEL 403-291-9111, FAX 403-291-0190. Ed., Adv. contact Shannon Park. B&W page CND 2,500, color page CND 3,000; trim 17 x 11.38. Circ: 39,400.

630.24 DEU
BAYER AGROCHEM COURIER. Text in German, English, Spanish. 1956. q. **Document type:** *Magazine, Trade.*
Published by: Bayer AG, Corporate Communications, Alfred-Nobel-Str 50, Monheim am Rhein, 40789, Germany. TEL 49-2173-380, http://www.agrocourier.com, http://www.bayer.com. Eds. Bernhard Grupp, Georg Priestel. Circ: 160,000.

630 USA ISSN 0084-7747
SB327
BEAN IMPROVEMENT COOPERATIVE. ANNUAL REPORT. Text in English. 1959. a. USD 22 (effective 2004). bk.rev. **Document type:** *Proceedings, Trade.*
Indexed: Agr, PBA.
—BLDSC (1113.184000), IE, ingenta.
Published by: James D. Kelly, Ed. & Pub., Michigan State University, Department of Crop & Soil Sciences, East Lansing, MI 48824. TEL 517-355-0205, FAX 517-353-3955, kellyj@pilot.msu.edu. Circ: 350.

631 CHN ISSN 1001-5698
BEIFANG GUOSHU* /NORTHERN FRUIT TREES. Text in Chinese. 1978. q. USD 2.50. adv. **Document type:** *Academic/Scholarly.* **Description:** Contains fruit tree experimental studies, and production and management experience.
Related titles: Online - full text ed.: (from East View Information Services).
Published by: Liaoning Sheng Guoshu Yanjiusuo/Liaoning Research Institute of Fruit Trees, Tiedong Jie, Wenquan Lu, Xiongyue Cheng, Gai Xian, Liaoning 115214, China. TEL 0417-742192. **Co-sponsor:** Shenyang University of Agriculture, Department of Horticulture.

632.95 DNK ISSN 1395-5403
BEKAEMPELSESMIDDELFORSKNING FRA MILJOESTYRELSEN. Variant title: Pesticides Research. Text in Danish, English. 1992. irreg., latest vol.82, 2004. price varies. back issues avail. **Document type:** *Monographic series, Government.*
Related titles: Online - full text ed.: ISSN 1399-7327.
Indexed: RA&MP, WeedAb, ZooRec.
Published by: Miljoeministeriet, Miljoestyrelsen/Ministry of the Environment. Danish Environmental Protection Agency, Strandgade 29, Copenhagen K, 1401, Denmark. TEL 45-32-660100, FAX 45-32-660479, mst@mst.dk, http://www.mst.dk.

633.51 USA ISSN 1059-2644
BELTWIDE COTTON CONFERENCES. PROCEEDINGS. Text in English. 1991. a. price varies. **Document type:** *Proceedings, Academic/Scholarly.*
Formed by the merger of (1967-1991): Beltwide Cotton Production Research Conferences. Proceedings (0522-8786); (1985-1991): Beltwide Cotton Production Conference. Proceedings (1052-5351); (1984-1991): Cotton Dust Research Conference. Proceedings (0897-5531)
Indexed: AEA, AgBio, Agr, BioCN&I, CPA, FCA, I&DA, PBA, PGegResA, PGrRegA, RDA, RPP, S&F, SeedAb, TTI, TriticAb, WAE&RSA, WeedAb, ZooRec.
Published by: National Cotton Council of America, Inc., PO Box 820285, Memphis, TN 38182. TEL 901-274-9030, FAX 901-725-0510, drichter@cotton.org, info@cotton.org, http://www.cotton.org/beltwide/proceedings.cfm. R&P Debbie Richter.

BENTON HARBOR FRUIT & VEGETABLE REPORT. see *AGRICULTURE—Agricultural Economics*

631 IDN ISSN 0852-0321
BERITA - PUSAT PENELITIAN PERKEBUNAN GULA INDONESIA/INDONESIAN SUGAR RESEARCH CENTER. NEWS. Text in Indonesian; Summaries in English. irreg. USD 6 per issue.
Indexed: AEA, CPA, FCA, HortAb, I&DA, PBA, PGegResA, PGrRegA, PN&I, RDA, RevApplEntom, S&F, SIA, SeedAb, SoyAb, WAE&RSA, WeedAb.
—BLDSC (1940.010000).
Published by: Pusat Penelitian Perkebunan Gula Indonesia, Jl Pahlawan 25, Pasuruan, 67126, Indonesia. TEL 0343-21086, FAX 0343-21178. Ed. Ir Hermono Budhisantoso. Circ: 650.

630 NLD ISSN 0922-8829
BESCHRIJVENDE RASSENLIJST VOOR SIERGEWASSEN (YEAR); bloemisterijgewassen. Text in Dutch. 1987. biennial (3rd.). **Description:** Descriptive list of recommended varieties of cut flowers and bulbs.
Published by: (Netherlands. Centrum voor Plantenveredelings- en Reproduktieonderzoek, Netherlands. Commissie voor de Samenstelling van de Rassenlijst voor Siergewassen), Roto Smeets de Boer n.v., Postbus 507, Hilversum, 1200 AM, Netherlands. TEL 31-35-258611, FAX 31-43-238978. Ed. J J Bakker. Circ: 3,000.

633.63 SWE ISSN 0345-1410
BETODLAREN. Text in Swedish. 1938. q. **Description:** Information for the beet-grower.
Formerly (until 1964): Sveriges Betodlares Centralfoerenings Tidskrift
Indexed: AEA, CPA, FCA, HerbAb, HortAb, NemAb, PBA, PHN&I, RPP, S&F, SIA, SeedAb, TriticAb, WAE&RSA, WeedAb.
—BLDSC (1942.650000).
Published by: Sveriges Betodlares Centralfoerening, PO Box 75, Alnarp, 23053, Sweden. TEL 46-40-46-40-45, FAX 46-706-45-11-36.

631.8 USA ISSN 0006-0089
S605
BETTER CROPS WITH PLANT FOOD. Text in English. 1923. q. USD 8 to non-members; free to qualified personnel (effective 2005). adv. bibl.; charts; illus.; stat.; tr.lit. reprint service avail. from PQC. **Document type:** *Magazine, Trade.* **Description:** Discusses innovations in the fertilizer industry.
Related titles: Microform ed.: (from PQC).
Indexed: AEA, AgrForAb, AnBrAb, BiolAb, CPA, CTFA, ChemAb, DSA, F&GI, FCA, ForAb, HerbAb, HortAb, I&DA, MaizeAb, NutrAb, OrnHort, PBA, PotatoAb, PoultAb, RA&MP, RPP, RRTA, RiceAb, S&F, S&MA, SIA, SeedAb, SoyAb, TriticAb, WAE&RSA, WeedAb.
—BLDSC (1947.000000), CISTI, Linda Hall.

Published by: Potash & Phosphate Institute, 655 Engineering Dr, Ste 110, Norcross, GA 30092-2843. TEL 770-447-0335, FAX 770-448-0439, ppi@ppi-ppic.org, http://www.ppi-ppic.org. Ed. Don Armstrong. Circ: 15,000 (controlled).

631 BEL
LE BETTERAVIER/BIETPLANTER. Text in French, Dutch. 1967. 11/yr. adv. bk.rev. **Document type:** *Newsletter.*
Related titles: Flemish ed.: Bietplanter.
Indexed: AEA, DSA, FCA, FS&TA, HortAb, PBA, RPP, RevApplEntom, S&F, SIA, SeedAb, TriticAb, WAE&RSA, WeedAb.
Published by: (Institut Royal Belge pour l'Amelioration de la Betterave), Confederation des Betteraviers Belges/Confederatie van de Belgische Bietplanters, Rue du Hazoir, 11, Daussoulx, 5020, Belgium. TEL 32-2-5136898, FAX 32-2-5121988, lebetteravier@cbb.be, secretariat@cbb.be. Ed. Jean Francois Sneessens. Circ: 23,000.

630 FRA ISSN 0405-6701
LE BETTERAVIER FRANCAIS. Text in French. 1946. bi-m. adv. illus.; tr.lit.
Supersedes: Planteurs Betteraves
—CISTI.
Published by: Societe d'Edition et de Documentation Agricole (SEDA), 25 rue de Madrid, Paris, 75008, France. TEL 33-1-44707494, FAX 33-1-44707499. Ed. Jacques Baret. Adv. contact Pierre Tailliardat.

633 IND ISSN 0970-6240
BHARATIYA SUGAR. Text in English. 1975. m.
Formerly (until 1985): Maharashtra Sugar (0970-6496)
Indexed: FCA, HortAb, RPP, SIA.
—BLDSC (1947.605450), IE, ingenta.
Published by: Bharatiya Sugar Research Foundation, c/o J. Shinde, ed, Pune, 411 005, India.

BIBLIOGRAPHY ON SOILLESS CULTURE. see *AGRICULTURE—Abstracting, Bibliographies, Statistics*

631.4 DEU ISSN 0178-4765
BIO NACHRICHTEN. Text in German. 1979. 4/yr. membership. adv. bk.rev. **Document type:** *Newsletter.*
Published by: Biokreis Ostbayern e.V., Theresienstr 36, Passau, 94032, Germany. TEL 0851-31696, FAX 0851-32332. Ed., Adv. contact Wolfgang Denk. Circ: 750.

632.9 GBR ISSN 0958-3157
SB975 CODEN: BSTCE6
➤ **BIOCONTROL SCIENCE AND TECHNOLOGY.** Text in English. 1991. 10/yr. GBP 1,268, USD 2,167 combined subscription to institutions print & online eds. (effective 2006). bk.rev. index. back issues avail.; reprint service avail. from PSC. **Document type:** *Journal, Academic/Scholarly.*
Description: Presents original research and reviews in the fields of biological pest, disease, and weed control, including basic research and applications of new techniques.
Related titles: Microfiche ed.; Online - full text ed.: ISSN 1360-0478. GBP 1,205, USD 2,059 to institutions (effective 2006) (from EBSCO Publishing, Gale Group, IngentaConnect, O C L C Online Computer Library Center, Inc., ProQuest Information & Learning, Swets Information Services).
Indexed: AEA, ASCA, AgBio, Agr, AgrForAb, BCI, BIOBASE, BIOSIS Prev, BibAg, BioCN&I, BiolAb, CPA, CurCont, DBA, DSA, EPB, ESPM, EntAb, FCA, FPA, FS&TA, ForAb, GEOBASE, HelmAb, HerbAb, HortAb, IABS, ISR, IndVet, MBA, MaizeAb, NemAb, OrnHort, PBA, PGegResA, PGrRegA, PHN&I, PlantSci, PotatoAb, ProtozoAb, RA&MP, RDA, RM&VM, RPP, RefZh, RevApplEntom, RiceAb, S&F, SCI, SIA, SeedAb, SoyAb, TDB, TriticAb, VITIS, VetBull, WAE&RSA, WeedAb.
—BLDSC (2071.150000), CISTI, IDS, IE, Infotrieve, ingenta. **CCC.**
Published by: Taylor & Francis Ltd (Subsidiary of: Taylor & Francis Group), 4 Park Sq, Milton Park, Abingdon, OX14 4RN, United Kingdom. TEL 44-1235-828600, FAX 44-1235-829000, info@tandf.co.uk, http://www.tandf.co.uk/journals/titles/09583157.asp. Ed. Mark S Goettel. **Subscr. in N. America to:** Taylor & Francis Inc., Customer Services Dept, 325 Chestnut St, 8th Fl, Philadelphia, PA 19106. TEL 215-625-8900, 800-354-1420, FAX 215-625-8914, customerservice@taylorandfrancis.com; **Subscr. to:** Journals Customer Service, Rankine Rd, Basingstoke, Hants RG24 8PR, United Kingdom. TEL 44-1256-813000, FAX 44-1256-330245, enquiry@tandf.co.uk.

631.4 USA ISSN 0006-2863
S1
BIODYNAMICS; a periodical furthering soil conservation and increased fertility in order to improve nutrition and health. Text in English. 1941. bi-m. free to members (effective 2005). adv. bk.rev. illus. index, cum.index. reprint service avail. from PQC. **Document type:** *Magazine, Trade.* **Description:** Covers topics in soil conservation to ensure the cultivation of nutritious vegetables.
Related titles: Microform ed.: (from PQC).
Indexed: BiolAb, ChemAb, EPB, GardL.
—BLDSC (2072.005000), IE, ingenta, Linda Hall.
Published by: Bio-Dynamic Farming and Gardening Association, Inc, c/o Charles Beedy, PO Box 29135, San Francisco, CA 94129. TEL 415-561-7797, FAX 415-561-7796, http://www.biodynamics.com/join.html. Eds. B Bumbarger, H Grotzke. R&P Charles Beedy. Circ: 1,200.

632.9 USA
BIOLOGICAL CONTROL NEWS. Text in English. irreg. **Document type:** *Newsletter, Academic/Scholarly.*
Description: Dedicated to providing information on the use of beneficial organisms for controlling insect and mite pests of the farm, garden, and home.
Formerly: Midwest Biological Control News
Related titles: Online - full text ed.
Address: c/o Dr. Susan E. Rice Mahr, Ed., Univ. of Wisconsin-Madison, Dept. of Horticulture, Madison, WI 53706. TEL 608-265-4505, FAX 608-262-4743, semahr@facstaff.wisc.edu, http://www.entomology.wisc.edu/mbcn/mbcn.html. Ed. Susan Rice Mahr.

631.8 DEU ISSN 0178-2762
CODEN: BFSOEE
➤ **BIOLOGY AND FERTILITY OF SOILS.** Text in English. 1985. bi-m. EUR 1,168 combined subscription to institutions print & online eds. (effective 2005). back issues avail.; reprint service avail. from ISI,PSC. **Document type:** *Journal, Academic/Scholarly.* **Description:** Covers fundamental and applied aspects of the biology and productivity of soils.
Related titles: Microform ed.: (from PQC); Online - full text ed.: ISSN 1432-0789 (from EBSCO Publishing, Springer LINK, Swets Information Services).
Indexed: AEA, ASCA, ASFA, AgBio, Agr, AgrForAb, BIOBASE, BIOSIS Prev, BibAg, BioCN&I, BiolAb, CIN, CPA, ChemAb, ChemTitl, CurCont, DSA, ESPM, EnvEAb, ExcerpMed, FCA, FPA, FaBeAb, ForAb, GEOBASE, HerbAb, HortAb, I&DA, IABS, ISR, M&GPA, MBA, MaizeAb, NemAb, NutrAb, OrnHort, PBA, PGegResA, PGrRegA, PN&I, PlantSci, PollutAb, PotatoAb, PoultAb, ProtozoAb, RA&MP, RM&VM, RPP, RefZh, RevApplEntom, RiceAb, S&F, SCI, SIA, SWRA, SeedAb, SoyAb, TriticAb, VITIS, WAE&RSA, WeedAb, ZooRec.
—BLDSC (2086.998000), CASDDS, CISTI, IDS, IE, Infotrieve, ingenta, Linda Hall. **CCC.**
Published by: (International Society of Soil Science NLD), Springer-Verlag (Subsidiary of: Springer Science+Business Media), Tiergartenstr 17, Heidelberg, 69121, Germany. TEL 49-6221-3450, FAX 49-6221-345229, http://link.springer.de/link/service/journals/00374/index.htm. Ed. P Nannipieri. Adv. contact Stephan Kroeck TEL 49-30-827875739. **Subscr. in the Americas to:** Springer-Verlag New York, Inc., Journal Fulfillment, PO Box 2485, Secaucus, NJ 07096-2485. TEL 800-777-4643, 201-348-4033, FAX 201-348-4505, journals@springer-ny.com, http://www.springer-ny.com; **Subscr. to:** Springer GmbH Auslieferungsgesellschaft, Haberstr 7, Heidelberg 69126, Germany. TEL 49-6221-345-0, FAX 49-6221-345-4229, subscriptions@springer.de.

630 GBR ISSN 1537-5110
S671 CODEN: JAERA2
➤ **BIOSYSTEMS ENGINEERING.** Text in English. 1956. 12/yr. EUR 1,178 in Europe to institutions; JPY 127,400 in Japan to institutions; USD 1,049 to institutions except Europe and Japan (effective 2006). adv. bk.rev. bibl.; charts; illus. index. reprints avail. **Document type:** *Journal, Academic/Scholarly.* **Description:** Reflects the spectrum of interdisciplinary interests inherent in this field, including tractor and vehicle design, cultivation systems, soil drainage and irrigation, crop production, farm buildings, waste engineering, and livestock feeding.
Formerly (until 2002): Journal of Agricultural Engineering Research (0021-8634)
Related titles: Online - full text ed.: ISSN 1537-5129. USD 1,029 (effective 2002) (from EBSCO Publishing, Gale Group, IngentaConnect, O C L C Online Computer Library Center, Inc., ScienceDirect, Swets Information Services).
Indexed: AEA, ASCA, ASFA, AgBio, Agr, AgrForAb, AnBrAb, B&AI, B&BAb, BioCN&I, BioEngAb, BiolAb, CPA, CurCont, DSA, EIA, ESPM, EnerInd, ExcerpMed, FCA, FPA, FS&TA, ForAb, GeotechAb, HerbAb, HortAb, I&DA, IAOP, ISR, IndVet, MaizeAb, NutrAb, OrnHort, PBA, PGrRegA, PHN&I, PN&I, PollutAb, PotatoAb, PoultAb, ProtozoAb, RA&MP, RDA, RPP, RefZh, RevApplEntom, RiceAb, S&F, SCI, SIA, SWRA, SeedAb, SoyAb, TDB, TriticAb, VetBull, WAE&RSA, WeedAb.
—BLDSC (2089.670500), CISTI, IDS, IE, Infotrieve, ingenta, Linda Hall. **CCC.**
Published by: (British Society for Research in Agricultural Engineering), Academic Press (Subsidiary of: Elsevier Science & Technology), 24-28 Oval Rd, London, NW1 7DX, United Kingdom. TEL 44-20-72674466, FAX 44-20-74822293, apsubs@acad.com, http://www.elsevier.com/locate/BiosystemsEng. Ed. B.D. Witney. R&P Catherine John. Adv. contact Nik Screen. **Subscr. to:** Harcourt Publishers Ltd., Foots Cray High St, Sidcup, Kent DA14 5HP, United Kingdom. TEL 44-20-8300-3322, FAX 44-20-8309-0807.

631 BEL ISSN 1370-6233
S494.5.B563 CODEN: BASEFI
BIOTECHNOLOGIE, AGRONOMIE, SOCIETE ET ENVIRONNEMENT. Text and summaries in English, French. 1932-1995 (vol.30); N.S. 1997. q. EUR 70 domestic; EUR 80 foreign (effective 2004). bk.rev. back issues avail. **Document type:** *Academic/Scholarly.* **Description:** Offers original papers, research notes, review articles, and summaries of recent theses as well as reviews of workshops and conferences in the fields of crop and animal production sciences, forestry, soil and earth sciences, rural engineering, environment, bioindustries, food technologies, economy and sociology.
Formerly (until 1997): Bulletin des Recherches Agronomiques de Gembloux (0435-2033); (until 1965): Institut Agronomique et des Stations de Recherches de Gembloux. Bulletin
Related titles: Online - full text ed.: free (effective 2005).
Indexed: AEA, AEBA, ASFA, AgBio, AgrForAb, Agrind, AnBrAb, BIOSIS Prev, BioEngAb, BiolAb, CIS, CPA, DSA, ESPM, EntAb, FCA, FPA, FS&TA, ForAb, HelmAb, HerbAb, HortAb, I&DA, IndVet, MBA, MaizeAb, NutrAb, OrnHort, PBA, PGegResA, PGrRegA, PHN&I, PN&I, PotatoAb, PoultAb, ProtozoAb, RA&MP, RDA, RM&VM, RPP, RefZh, RevApplEntom, RiceAb, S&F, SIA, SWRA, SeedAb, SoyAb, TriticAb, VITIS, VetBull, WAE&RSA, WeedAb, ZooRec.
—BLDSC (2089.823000), CASDDS, CISTI, IE, ingenta.
Published by: Les Presses Agronomiques de Gembloux, Passage des Deportes 2, Gembloux, 5030, Belgium. pressesagro@fsagx.ac.be, http://www.bib.fsagx.ac.be/library/base/eng/home/, http://www.bib.fsagx.ac.be/presses. Ed. J.P. Baudoin. Pub. Bernard Pochet. R&P J P Baudoin. Circ: 900.

631.8 TUR ISSN 0406-3597
SB599
BITKI KORUMA BULTENI/PLANT PROTECTION BULLETIN. Text in Turkish; Abstracts and contents page in English. 1959. q. free. bibl.; charts; illus. index. **Document type:** *Academic/Scholarly.* **Description:** Publishes original research on plant protection in Turkey.
Indexed: AEA, BioCN&I, BiolAb, CPA, FCA, ForAb, HerbAb, HortAb, MaizeAb, NemAb, NutrAb, OrnHort, PBA, PGegResA, PGrRegA, PHN&I, PotatoAb, RA&MP, RDA, RPP, RefZh, RevApplEntom, RiceAb, SIA, SeedAb, TriticAb, WAE&RSA, WeedAb, ZooRec.
—BLDSC (2096.100000), CISTI.
Published by: (Turkey. Tarim ve Koyisleri Bakanligi/Ministry of Agriculture and Rurla Affairs, General Directorate of Agricultural Research, Turkey. Tarimsal Arastirmalar Genel Mudurlugu), Ankara Zirai Mucadele Arastirma Enstitusu/Ankara Plant Protection Research Institute, Bagdat Caddesi No. 250, P K 49, Yenimahalle - Ankara, 06172, Turkey. TEL 3445993, FAX 3151531. Ed. Baki Tastan. Circ: 1,500.

631 USA ISSN 1081-5228
HD9235.S62
BLUEBOOK UPDATE. Text in English. 1994. q. adv. **Document type:** *Newsletter.*
Related titles: ♦ Supplement to: (Year) Soya & Oilseed Bluebook. ISSN 1099-7970.
Published by: Soyatech, Inc., 1369 State Highway 102., Bar Harbor, ME 04609-7019. TEL 207-288-4969, 800-424-SOYA, FAX 207-288-5264, data@soyatech.com, http://www.soyatech.com. Ed. Keri Hayes. R&P Peter Golbitz. Adv. contact Joy Froding. Circ: 6,000.

631 CHE ISSN 1420-6773
BODENKUNDLICHE GESELLSCHAFT DER SCHWEIZ. BULLETIN. Text in German. 1977. a. **Document type:** *Academic/Scholarly.*
—BLDSC (2411.850000).
Published by: Bodenkundliche Gesellschaft der Schweiz, Geographisches Institut der Universitaet Zurich, Winterthurerstr 190, Zuerich, 8057, Switzerland. TEL 41-1-2575121, FAX 41-1-3625227. Ed. Moritz Mueller.

BOLETIN DE AVISOS. see *AGRICULTURE*

634.63 ESP
BOLETIN DE INFORMACION NOTICIAS DEL OLIVAR. Text in Spanish. 12/yr.
Address: M.S. Torres Acosta 10D, Jaen, 23001, Spain. TEL 53-22-51-62. Ed. Jose Bautista.

633 663.93 GTM ISSN 1010-1527
BOLETIN DE PROMECAFE. Text in Spanish. 1978. q. free. bk.rev. bibl.; stat. **Document type:** *Bulletin.* **Description:** Provides comments and recommendations regarding factors that influence production and marketing of coffee in Central America. Special attention is paid on coffee pests, disease control and crop processing.
Related titles: Microfilm ed.
Indexed: AEA, AgBio, AgrForAb, BioCN&I, CPA, FPA, ForAb, HortAb, I&DA, NemAb, OrnHort, PBA, PGegResA, PHN&I, RDA, RM&VM, RPP, RevApplEntom, S&F, SIA, WAE&RSA, WeedAb.
Published by: Instituto Interamericano de Cooperacion para la Agricultura - O E A, Programa Cooperativa Regional para el Desarrollo Tecnologico y Modernizacion de la Caficultura en Mexico, Centroamerica, Republica Dominicana y Jamaica, Apdo. Postal 1815, Guatemala City, Guatemala. TEL 502-2-222-3347, FAX 502-2-334-7603, iicalyp@gbm.hn. Eds. Edgar L Ibarra, Jose Roberto Hernandez. R&P Jose Roberto Hernandez. Circ: 1,100.

A

635 ESP
BOLETIN DEL REGISTRO DE VARIEDADES. Text in Spanish. 4/yr. **Document type:** *Bulletin.*
Published by: (Spain. Instituto Nacional de Semillas y Plantas de Vivero), Ministerio de Agricultura Pesca y Alimentacion, Centro de Publicaciones, Paseo Infanta Isabel 1, Madrid, 28014, Spain. TEL 34-91-3475548, FAX 34-1-3475722. Ed. Guillermo Artolachipi Esteban. R&P Juan Carlos Palacios Lopez. **Subscr. to:** I.N.S.P.V., Jose Abascal, 56, Madrid 28003, Spain.

630 580 USA
BOLETIN VETIVER✶ . Text in English. 1989. s-a. free. cum.index. **Document type:** *Newsletter.* **Description:** Promotes the use of vetiver grasses in various agricultural, land and engineering applications.
Media: Online - full text. **Related titles:** CD-ROM ed.; Spanish ed.
Published by: Vetiver Network, 3601 14th St N, Arlington, VA 22201-4926. TEL 703-771-1942, FAX 703-771-8260, vetiver@vetiver.org, http://www.vetiver.org/. Eds. Joan Miller, Richard Grimshaw. Circ: 4,000.

630 NOR ISSN 0801-7662
BONDE OG SMAABRUKER. Text in Norwegian. 1928. irreg. NOK 230 (effective 2001). adv. **Document type:** *Trade.*
Published by: Norsk Bonde- og Smaabrukarlag, Qevre Vollgt. 9, Oslo, 0158, Norway. TEL 47-22-42-46-00, FAX 47-22-42-46-01, redaksjonen@smabrukarlaget.no, http://www.smabrukarlaget.no. Ed. Aasne Berre Persen. Adv. contact Magne Egil Rendalen. B&W page NOK 14,500, color page NOK 18,100; 255 x 365.

631.4 USA
BOOKS IN SOILS PLANTS AND THE ENVIRONMENT SERIES. Text in English. 1967. irreg., latest vol.100, 2004. USD 185 per vol. vol.100 (effective 2004). adv. **Document type:** *Monographic series.*
Former titles: Books in Soil and the Environment Series (0081-1890); Soil Science Library
Published by: Marcel Dekker Inc. (Subsidiary of: Taylor & Francis Group), 270 Madison Ave, New York, NY 10016-0602. TEL 212-696-9000, FAX 212-685-4540, journals@dekker.com, http://www.dekker.com. Pub. Russell Dekker. R&P Julia Mulligan. Adv. contact Eridania Perez. **Subscr. to:** 6000 Broken Sound Pkwy NW, Ste. 300, Boca Raton, FL 33487-2713. TEL 800-228-1160.

631 BWA
BOTSWANA. MINISTRY OF AGRICULTURE. DIVISION OF ARABLE CROPS RESEARCH. ANNUAL REPORT. Text in English. 1968. a. free. illus.; maps; stat. back issues avail. **Document type:** *Government.* **Description:** Presents a major thrust in arable crops research, addresses drylands farming problems to increase yield and stabilize yearly production.
Supersedes (1947-1959): Bechuanaland Protectorate. Ministry of Agriculture. Review of Crop Experiments
Indexed: BiolAb.
Published by: Ministry of Agriculture, Division of Arable Crops Research, Private Bag 0033, Gaborone, Botswana. TEL 267-328780, FAX 267-328965, TELEX 2752 SACCAR BD. Ed. Dr. G S Maphanyane. R&P Dan B Gombalume. Circ: 200.

BOTSWANA. MINISTRY OF AGRICULTURE. FARM MANAGEMENT SURVEY RESULTS. see *AGRICULTURE—Agricultural Economics*

633 BRA ISSN 1415-4129
BRAZIL. CENTRO NACIONAL DE PESQUISA DE MILHO E SORGO. BOLETIM DE PESQUISA. Text in Portuguese. 1995. irreg., latest vol.3. bibl.; charts.
Indexed: SeedAb.
Published by: Centro Nacional de Pesquisa de Milho e Sorgo, Km 65 da Rodovia 424, Centro, Caixa Postal 151, Sete Lagoas, MG 35701-970, Brazil. TEL 55-31-37791000, FAX 55-31-37791088, ainfo@cnpms.embrapa.br. Circ: 1,000.

633 BRA ISSN 0101-1251
BRAZIL. CENTRO NACIONAL DE PESQUISA DE MILHO E SORGO. RELATORIO TECNICO ANUAL. Text in Portuguese. 1979. irreg., latest vol.6, 1994. charts. **Document type:** *Academic/Scholarly.*
Published by: Centro Nacional de Pesquisa de Milho e Sorgo, Km 65 da Rodovia 424, Centro, Caixa Postal 151, Sete Lagoas, MG 35701-970, Brazil. TEL 55-31-7735466, FAX 55-31-7739252, ainfo@cnpms.embrapa.br. Circ: 1,500.

630 GBR ISSN 0955-1514
SB950.A2 CODEN: PBCDDQ
BRIGHTON CROP PROTECTION CONFERENCE. WEEDS. Text in English. 1953. biennial (in 2 vols., 1 no./vol.), latest 2001, Nov. GBP 55 per issue (effective 2003). back issues avail. **Document type:** *Proceedings.* **Description:** Focuses on weeds looking at new compounds and weed management strategies.
Former titles (until 1989): British Crop Protection Conference. Proceedings. Weeds (0144-1604); (until 1977): British Weed Control Conference. Proceedings (0571-6144)
Indexed: Agr, BIOSIS Prev.
—BLDSC (2284.023500), CISTI, ingenta.
Published by: British Crop Protection Council, Bear Farm, Binfield, Bracknell, Berks RG42 5QE, United Kingdom. TEL 44-118-934-2727, FAX 44-118-934-1998, publications@bcpc.org, http://www.bcpc.org. Ed. Frances McKim.

630 GBR ISSN 0955-1506
BRIGHTON CROP PROTECTION COUNCIL. PESTS & DISEASES CONFERENCE PROCEEDINGS. Text in English. 1988. irreg., latest 2002.
Indexed: BIOSIS Prev.
—BLDSC (2284.023000), CISTI, IE.
Published by: British Crop Protection Council, Bear Farm, Binfield, Bracknell, Berks RG42 5QE, United Kingdom. TEL 44-118-934-2727, FAX 44-118-934-1998, publications@bcpc.org, http://www.bcpc.org/BCPCConference2002/Index.htm.

631.5 CAN ISSN 1190-8475
BRITISH COLUMBIA. MINISTRY OF AGRICULTURE FISHERIES AND FOOD. BERRY PRODUCTION GUIDE FOR COMMERCIAL GROWERS. Text in English. 1970. a. CND 10. **Document type:** *Government.*
Former titles (until 1998): British Columbia. Ministry of Agriculture Fisheries and Food. Berry Production Guide (0706-4306); (until 1970): Ministry of Agriculture. Berry Production Recommendations (0706-4314)
—CISTI.
Published by: Ministry of Agriculture, Food and Fisheries, Stn Prov Govt, PO Box 9058, Victoria, BC V8W 9E2, Canada. **Orders to:** W A I R, 742 Vanalman Ave, Victoria, BC V8V 1X4, Canada.

631.5 CAN ISSN 1198-2217
BRITISH COLUMBIA. MINISTRY OF AGRICULTURE FISHERIES AND FOOD. FLORICULTURE PRODUCTION GUIDE FOR COMMERCIAL GROWERS. Text in English. a. CND 10. **Document type:** *Government.*
Formerly (until 1995): British Columbia. Ministry of Agriculture Fisheries and Food. Greenhouse Floriculture Production Guide for Commercial Growers (1183-5710); Which Superseded in part (in 1991): British Columbia. Ministry of Agriculture Fisheries and Food. Nursery, Greenhouse Vegetable and Ornamental Production Guide for Commercial Growers (0840-8068); Which was formed by the merger of: British Columbia. Ministry of Agriculture and Food. Greenhouse Vegetable Production Guide (0835-0760); British Columbia. Ministry of Agriculture. Nursery Production Guide (0705-5757)
—CISTI.
Published by: Ministry of Agriculture, Food and Fisheries, Stn Prov Govt, PO Box 9058, Victoria, BC V8W 9E2, Canada. Circ: 1,200. **Orders to:** W A I R, 742 Vanalman Ave, Victoria, BC V8V 1X4, Canada.

631.5 CAN ISSN 1192-9197
BRITISH COLUMBIA. MINISTRY OF AGRICULTURE FISHERIES AND FOOD. GREENHOUSE VEGETABLE PRODUCTION GUIDE FOR COMMERCIAL GROWERS. Text in English. 1972. a. CND 10. **Document type:** *Government.*
Supersedes in part (in 1993): British Columbia. Ministry of Agriculture Fisheries and Food. Nursery, Greenhouse Vegetable and Ornamental Production Guide for Commercial Growers (0840-8068); Which was formed by the merger of: British Columbia. Ministry of Agriculture. Nursery Production Guide (0705-5757); British Columbia. Ministry of Agriculture Fisheries and Food. Greenhouse Vegetable Production Guide (0835-0760)
—CISTI.
Published by: Ministry of Agriculture, Food and Fisheries, Stn Prov Govt, PO Box 9058, Victoria, BC V8W 9E2, Canada. **Orders to:** W A I R, 742 Vanalman Ave, Victoria, BC V8V 1X4, Canada.

631.5 CAN ISSN 1198-001X
BRITISH COLUMBIA. MINISTRY OF AGRICULTURE FISHERIES AND FOOD. MANAGEMENT GUIDE FOR GRAPES. Text in English. a. CND 10. bibl. **Document type:** *Government.*
Former titles: British Columbia. Ministry of Agriculture Fisheries and Food. Grape Production Guide; British Columbia. Ministry of Agriculture and Food. Grape Production Guide; British Columbia. Ministry of Agriculture. Grape Production Guide (0701-9858)
—CISTI.
Published by: Ministry of Agriculture, Food and Fisheries, Stn Prov Govt, PO Box 9058, Victoria, BC V8W 9E2, Canada. Circ: 600. **Orders to:** W A I R, 742 Vanalman Ave, Victoria, BC V8V 1X4, Canada.

631.5 CAN ISSN 0705-470X
BRITISH COLUMBIA. MINISTRY OF AGRICULTURE FISHERIES AND FOOD. TREE FRUIT PRODUCTION GUIDE FOR INTERIOR DISTRICTS. Key Title: Tree-Fruit Production Guide for Interior Districts. Text in English. 1978. a. CND 10. **Document type:** *Government.*
Former titles: British Columbia. Ministry of Agriculture and Food. Tree Fruit; British Columbia. Ministry of Agriculture. Tree Fruit Production Guide for Interior Districts
—CISTI.
Published by: Ministry of Agriculture, Food and Fisheries, Stn Prov Govt, PO Box 9058, Victoria, BC V8W 9E2, Canada. Circ: 3,400. **Orders to:** W A I R, 742 Vanalman Ave, Victoria, BC V8V 1X4, Canada.

631.5 CAN ISSN 0318-3661
BRITISH COLUMBIA. MINISTRY OF AGRICULTURE FISHERIES AND FOOD. VEGETABLE PRODUCTION GUIDE. Key Title: Vegetable Production Guide. Text in English. a. CND 10. **Document type:** *Government.*
Former titles: British Columbia. Ministry of Agriculture and Food. Vegetable Production Guide; British Colombia. Ministry of Agriculture. Vegetable Production REcommendations (0318-367X)
—CISTI.
Published by: Ministry of Agriculture, Food and Fisheries, Stn Prov Govt, PO Box 9058, Victoria, BC V8W 9E2, Canada. Circ: 3,000. **Orders to:** W A I R, 742 Vanalman Ave, Victoria, BC V8V 1X4, Canada.

631 GBR ISSN 1368-406X
CODEN: MBCCDO
BRITISH CROP PROTECTION COUNCIL. SYMPOSIUM PROCEEDINGS. Text in English. 1970. irreg., latest no.80, 2003. GBP 35 per issue for no.80, Sept. 2003; GBP 15 per issue for no.79, Nov. 2002 (effective 2003). **Document type:** *Proceedings.* **Description:** The proceedings reproduce the papers in full from the Symposium where they were presented. They are generally detailed accounts of research. Recent topics have included Biodiversity and Conservation in Agriculture, Microbial Insecticides, Biological Control Introductions, and Slug and Snail Pests in Agricultures.
Formerly (until 1995): British Crop Protection Council. Monograph (0306-3941)
Indexed: Agr, VITIS, ZooRec.
—BLDSC (1871.388000), CASDDS, CISTI, IE, ingenta.
Published by: British Crop Protection Council, Bear Farm, Binfield, Bracknell, Berks RG42 5QE, United Kingdom. TEL 44-118-934-2727, FAX 44-118-934-1998, publications@BCPC.org, http://www.bcpc.org.

631 GBR
BRITISH POTATO COUNCIL. NEWS. Text in English. 7/yr. GBP 25 in Europe; GBP 30 elsewhere. **Document type:** *Newsletter.*
Formerly: Potato News (0963-6641)
—CISTI.
Published by: British Potato Council, Broad Field House, 4 Between Towns Rd, Cowley, Oxford, OX4 3PP, United Kingdom. TEL 44-1865-714455, FAX 44-1865-716418.

630 GBR ISSN 1351-6566
CODEN: MBSREE
BRITISH SOCIETY FOR PLANT GROWTH REGULATION. MONOGRAPHS. Text in English. 1978. s-a. GBP 10, USD 20. back issues avail.
Formerly (until 1990): British Plant Growth Regulator Group. Monographs (0952-6463)
Indexed: Agr, CPA, ChemAb, FCA, HerbAb, HortAb, PGrRegA, PotatoAb, SeedAb, TriticAb.
—CASDDS, CISTI.
Published by: British Society for Plant Growth Regulation, University of Bristol, Department of Agricultural Science, Long Ashton Research Station, Bristol, Avon BS18 9AF, United Kingdom. FAX 0275-394007. Ed. M B Jackson. Circ: 500.

633.63 GBR ISSN 0007-1854
BRITISH SUGAR BEET REVIEW. Text in English. 1927. q. free. adv. bk.rev. charts; illus.; stat.; tr.lit. **Document type:** *Magazine, Trade.*
Indexed: AEA, AgBio, BioCN&I, BiolAb, CPA, ChemAb, CurCont, FCA, HerbAb, HortAb, I&DA, NemAb, NutrAb, PBA, PGegResA, PHN&I, PotatoAb, RPP, RRTA, RefZh, RevApplEntom, S&F, SIA, SeedAb, TriticAb, WAE&RSA, WeedAb.
—BLDSC (2345.000000), IE, ingenta.
Published by: British Sugar plc., Oundle Rd, Peterborough, Cambs PE2 9QU, United Kingdom. TEL 44-1733-422904, FAX 44-1733-422487. Ed., R&P Paul Bee. Circ: 15,000 (controlled).

BUG BULLETIN; integrated pest management for ornamental plants. see *GARDENING AND HORTICULTURE*

BUREAU OF SUGAR EXPERIMENT STATIONS. ANNUAL REPORT. see *FOOD AND FOOD INDUSTRIES*

633.61 AUS ISSN 0810-3240
BUREAU OF SUGAR EXPERIMENT STATIONS. BULLETIN. Abbreviated title: B S E S Bulletin. Text in English. 1933. q. AUD 10. illus.
Formerly (until 1983): Cane Growers Quarterly Bulletin (0008-5553)
Indexed: AEA, ASI, AgrForAb, BioCN&I, BiolAb, CPA, ChemAb, FCA, HerbAb, HortAb, I&DA, PBA, RPP, RefZh, RevApplEntom, S&F, SIA, SeedAb, WAE&RSA, WeedAb.
—BLDSC (2354.119600), IE, ingenta.
Published by: Bureau of Sugar Experiment Stations, PO Box 86, Indooroopilly, QLD 4068, Australia. Circ: 8,000.

BURKINA FASO. DIRECTION DE L'HYDRAULIQUE ET DE L'EQUIPEMENT RURAL. SERVICE I.R.H. RAPPORT D'ACTIVITES. see *WATER RESOURCES*

630 ESP
BUTLLETI D'INFORMACIO AGRARIA. Text in Spanish, Catalan. q.

Published by: Generalitat Valenciana, Conselleria de Agricultura, Pesa y Alimentacion. Secretaria General, C. Amadeo de Saboya, 2, Valencia, 46010, Spain. TEL 34-963-866912, FAX 34-963-866907, http://www.gva.es/agricultura/publica.htm.

633 330   USA
BUYERS GUIDE TO U.S. COTTON. Text in English. 1969. a.
Description: Covers U.S. cotton production, varieties, classifications and exporters.
Published by: Cotton Council International, 1521 New Hampshire Ave, N W, Washington, DC 20036-1205. TEL 202-745-7805, FAX 202-483-4040, http://www.cottonusa.org/CCI/. Ed. Allen A Terhaar. Circ: 4,000.

C A SELECTS. FUNGICIDES. see AGRICULTURE—Abstracting, Bibliographies, Statistics

C A SELECTS. HERBICIDES. see AGRICULTURE—Abstracting, Bibliographies, Statistics

C A SELECTS. INSECTICIDES. see AGRICULTURE—Abstracting, Bibliographies, Statistics

632.9   USA   ISSN 1047-8140
                                  CODEN: CSAYEM
C A SELECTS. PESTICIDE ANALYSIS. Text in English. 1988. s-w. USD 315 to non-members; USD 95 to members (effective 2005). **Document type:** Abstract/Index.
Description: Covers the analysis of pesticides (insecticides, herbicides, and fungicides) including chemical and physical analysis of preparations used for the control of plant and animal pests.
Formerly (until 1989): BIOSIS CAS Selects: Pesticide Analysis
Related titles: Online - full text ed.: USD 305 (effective 2004).
Published by: Chemical Abstracts Service (C A S) (Subsidiary of: American Chemical Society), 2540 Olentangy River Rd., Columbus, OH 43210-0012. TEL 614-447-3600, FAX 614-447-3713, help@cas.com, http://www.cas.org, http://caselects.cas.org.

C M B NEWSLETTER. see BUSINESS AND ECONOMICS—Marketing And Purchasing

633   ESP
C O I HOJA DE INFORMACION. Text in Spanish. 1962. s-m. USD 70 in Europe; USD 120 in the Americas. bk.rev. stat. index. back issues avail.
Related titles: French ed.: C O I Feuille d'Information.
Published by: Consejo Oleicola Internacional/International Olive Oil Council - Conseil Oleicole International, Principe de Vergara, 154, Madrid, 28002, Spain. TEL 34-1-5630071, FAX 34-1-5631263. Ed. Fausto Luchetti. Circ: 480.

630   USA   ISSN 1529-9163
C S A NEWS. Text in English. m. free (effective 2004). adv.
Document type: Newsletter, Academic/Scholarly.
Description: Contains information about the society members and activities. Includes news of recent developments in agronomy-related fields.
Former titles (until 2000): Crop Science, Soil Science, Agronomy News (1523-3154); (until 1999): Agronomy News (0568-3106)
Media: Online - full text.
—CISTI. **CCC.**
Published by: (Crop Science Society of America), American Society of Agronomy, Inc., 677 S Segoe Rd, Madison, WI 53711. TEL 608-273-8080, FAX 608-273-2021, news@agronomy.org, http://www.asa-cssa-sssa.org/news/, http://www.asa-cssa-sssa.org/adv.html. Circ: 12,000 (free).

633.63   NLD   ISSN 0165-9375
C S M INFORMATIE. Text in Dutch. 1946. bi-m. free to qualified persons. charts; illus. **Document type:** Trade. **Description:** Covers news and topics relating to sugar-beet cultivation and processing.
Formerly (until 1973): Centrale Suiker Maatschappij. Voorlichtingsblad (0027-710X)
Indexed: AEA, FCA, NemAb, PBA, RPP, SIA, SeedAb, WAE&RSA.
—BLDSC (3490.293500).
Published by: C S M Suiker BV, Postbus 349, Amsterdam, 1000 AH, Netherlands. TEL 31-20-590-6911, FAX 31-20-590-6395, http://www.csmnv.com. Ed. A Goldhoorn. Circ: 11,000.

CALIFORNIA. AGRICULTURAL STATISTICS SERVICE. CROP WEATHER REPORT. see AGRICULTURE—Abstracting, Bibliographies, Statistics

CALIFORNIA. AGRICULTURAL STATISTICS SERVICE. FIELD CROP REVIEW. see AGRICULTURE—Abstracting, Bibliographies, Statistics

CALIFORNIA. AGRICULTURAL STATISTICS SERVICE. FRUIT AND NUT REVIEW. see AGRICULTURE—Abstracting, Bibliographies, Statistics

CALIFORNIA. AGRICULTURAL STATISTICS SERVICE. GRAPE ACREAGE. see AGRICULTURE—Abstracting, Bibliographies, Statistics

CALIFORNIA. AGRICULTURAL STATISTICS SERVICE. GRAPE CRUSH REPORT. see AGRICULTURE—Abstracting, Bibliographies, Statistics

CALIFORNIA. AGRICULTURAL STATISTICS SERVICE. VEGETABLE REVIEW. see AGRICULTURE—Abstracting, Bibliographies, Statistics

CALIFORNIA. AGRICULTURAL STATISTICS SERVICE. WALNUTS, RAISINS AND PRUNES (PRICE REPORT). see AGRICULTURE—Abstracting, Bibliographies, Statistics

630   USA
CALIFORNIA/ARIZONA/TEXAS COTTON. Text in English. 9/yr. free domestic to qualified personnel (effective 2004). adv.
Document type: Magazine.
Published by: Paul Baltimore, 4969 E. Clinton Way, Ste. 104, Fresno, CA 93727-1549. TEL 559-252-7000, FAX 559-252-2787, westag@psnw.com. Ed. Randy Bailey. Pubs. Jim Baltimore, Paul Baltimore. Adv. contact Sherry Mason. page USD 2,628. Circ: 10,000 (controlled).

634   USA   ISSN 0068-5720
CALIFORNIA MACADAMIA SOCIETY. YEARBOOK. Text in English. 1955. a. USD 17.50 to members. adv. cum.index: 1955-1962, 1963-68, 1959-1974, 1975-1980, 1981-85, 1986-1990. **Document type:** Academic/Scholarly.
Indexed: Agr.
Published by: California Macadamia Society, PO Box 1298, Fallbrook, CA 92088. TEL 619-728-8081. Ed. Jim Russell. Circ: 600.

581.464 634.5   USA   ISSN 1538-201X
CALIFORNIA NUTS. Text in English. 2002. s-m. free domestic to qualified personnel. adv. **Document type:** Magazine, Trade.
Description: Focused on providing profitable production and management strategies for nut growers.
Related titles: Online - full text ed.
Published by: Vance Publishing Corp., 10901 W 84th Terrace, Lexena, KS 66214-1821. TEL 913-438-8700, http://www.californianutsmagazine.com, http://www.vancepublishing.com. **Subscr. to:** Subscr. Service Center, 400 Knightsbridge Pkwy, Lincolnshire, IL 60069-3613.

631   USA
CALIFORNIA PRUNE NEWS∗ . Text in English. irreg. free.
Document type: Newsletter. **Description:** California prune industry information.
Published by: California Prune Board, 3841 N Freeway Blvd Ste 120, Sacramento, CA 95834-1968. TEL 925-734-0150, FAX 925-734-0525. Ed., Pub., R&P Richard Peterson. Circ: 1,400 (controlled).

634   USA   ISSN 0527-3277
CALIFORNIA TOMATO GROWER. Text in English. 1958. m. (9/yr.). USD 30; USD 45 foreign (effective 1999). adv. illus.; stat. **Document type:** Trade.
Published by: California Tomato Growers Association, Inc., 10730 Siskiyou Ln., Stockton, CA 95209-3802. TEL 209-478-1761, FAX 209-478-9460. Ed., R&P John C Welty. Adv. contact Tom Fielding. Circ: 2,200.

632.9   USA
CALIFORNIA WEED SCIENCE SOCIETY. ANNUAL CONFERENCE PROCEEDINGS. Text in English. 1949. a.
Formerly (until 1994): California Weed Conference. Proceedings (0097-1731)
Indexed: Agr.
—BLDSC (1082.270300), CISTI, Linda Hall.
Published by: California Weed Science Society, PO Box 3073, Salinas, CA 93919-3073. TEL 831-442-0883, http://www.cwss.org.

CANADA. INDIAN AND NORTHERN AFFAIRS CANADA. SYNOPSIS OF RESEARCH CONDUCTED UNDER THE NORTHERN CONTAMINANTS PROGRAM. see ENVIRONMENTAL STUDIES—Pollution

CANADA. STATISTICS CANADA. FIELD CROP REPORTING SERIES/CANADA. STATISTIQUE CANADA. SERIE DE RAPPORTS SUR LES GRANDES CULTURES. see AGRICULTURE—Abstracting, Bibliographies, Statistics

CANADA. STATISTICS CANADA. FRUIT AND VEGETABLE PRODUCTION/CANADA. STATISTIQUE CANADA. PRODUCTIONS DE FRUITS ET LEGUMES. see AGRICULTURE—Abstracting, Bibliographies, Statistics

631.4   CAN   ISSN 0008-4271
                                  CODEN: CJSSAR
➤ **CANADIAN JOURNAL OF SOIL SCIENCE.** Text in English, French. 1921. q. CND 84 domestic to individuals; CND 96 combined subscription domestic to individuals print & online eds.; USD 89 foreign to individuals; USD 104 combined subscription foreign to individuals print & onlin eds.; CND 131 domestic to institutions; CND 149 combined subscription domestic to institutions print & online eds.; USD 163 foreign to institutions; USD 186 combined subscription foreign to institutions print & online eds.; USD 36 domestic to members; USD 37 elsewhere to members (effective 2005). bibl.; charts; illus.; stat. index. back issues avail.; reprint service avail. from PQC. **Document type:** Academic/Scholarly. **Description:** Publishes pure and applied research on the use, management, structure and development of soils.
Supersedes in part (in 1956): Canadian Journal of Agricultural Science (0366-6557); Which was formerly (until 1952): Scientific Agriculture (0370-887X)
Related titles: Microform ed.: (from PMC, PQC); Online - full text ed.: (from EBSCO Publishing, O C L C Online Computer Library Center, Inc., Swets Information Services).
Indexed: AEA, APD, ASCA, ASFA, AbHyg, Agr, AgrForAb, B&AI, B&BAb, BIOBASE, BIOSIS Prev, BibAg, BioCN&I, BiolAb, CIN, CPA, ChemAb, ChemTitl, CivEngAb, CurCont, DSA, EPB, ESPM, EnvAb, EnvEAb, EnvInd, ExcerpMed, FCA, FLUIDEX, FPA, FaBeAb, ForAb, GEOBASE, HerbAb, HortAb, I&DA, IABS, ISR, MBA, MaizeAb, NemAb, NutrAb, PBA, PGegResA, PN&I, PlantSci, PollutAb, PotatoAb, PoultAb, RPP, RRTA, RefZh, S&F, SCI, SIA, SWRA, SeedAb, SoyAb, TriticAb, WAE&RSA, WeedAb.
—BLDSC (3035.700000), CASDDS, CIS, CISTI, IDS, IE, Infotrieve, ingenta, Linda Hall. **CCC.**
Published by: Agricultural Institute of Canada, 141 Laurier Ave W, Ste 1112, Ottawa, ON K1P 5J3, Canada. TEL 613-232-9459, FAX 613-594-5190, journals@aic.ca, http://www.nrc.ca/aic-journals/cjss.html, http://www.aic.ca. Ed. M R Carter. Circ: 1,200.

641.3521   CAN
CANADIAN POTATO BUSINESS. Text in English. q. CND 35 domestic; USD 35 foreign (effective 2005). **Document type:** Magazine, Trade.
Published by: Issues Ink, 203-897 Corydon Ave, Winnipeg, MB R3M 0W7, Canada. TEL 204-453-1965, FAX 204-475-5247, info@potatobusiness.ca, http://www.potatobusiness.ca.

630   CAN   ISSN 0835-3255
CANADIAN POTATO PRODUCTION. Text in English, French. 1987. 3/yr.
Related titles: Online - full content ed.: Production Canadienne de Pommes de Terre. ISSN 1705-7043.
—CISTI.
Published by: Statistics Canada, Communications Division, 3rd Fl, R H Coats Bldg, Ottawa, ON K1A 0A6, Canada. TEL 800-263-1136, infostats@statcan.ca, http://www.statcan.ca.

631.5   CAN   ISSN 0068-9610
CANADIAN SEED GROWERS ASSOCIATION. ANNUAL REPORT. Text in English. 1903. a. **Document type:** Corporate.
—BLDSC (1137.000000), CISTI.
Published by: Canadian Seed Growers Association, P O Box 8455, Ottawa, ON K1G 3T1, Canada. TEL 613-236-0497. Circ: 6,000.

633.6   CUB   ISSN 1026-0781
SB229.C9
CANAVERAL. Text in Spanish. 1995. q.
Indexed: AEA, FCA, HortAb, NutrAb, SIA, WeedAb.
—CINDOC, CISTI.
Published by: Ministerio del Azucar, Instituto de Investigaciones de la Cana de Azucar, Ave. Vantroi No. 17203, Boyeros, Havana, Cuba.

631   CAN   ISSN 0715-3651
CANOLA DIGEST. Text in English. 1967. 8/yr. CND 35 (effective 2005). adv. **Document type:** Newsletter, Trade.
—**CCC.**
Published by: Canola Council of Canada/Conseil de Canola du Canada, 400-167 Lombard Ave, Winnipeg, MB R3B 0T6, Canada. TEL 204-982-2100, FAX 204-942-1841, admin@canola-council.org, http://www.canola-council.org/digest.html. Ed. Dave Wilkins. Adv. contact Wendy Miller. Circ: 86,000.

631.5   USA
CARGILL BULLETIN. Text in English. 1925. m. free. charts; stat.
Document type: Bulletin. **Description:** Reviews current domestic and international market conditions and public policy questions involving agriculture and world trade.
Formerly: Cargill Crop Bulletin (0008-641X)
Indexed: RefZh.
—Linda Hall.
Published by: Cargill, Inc., PO Box 5625, Minneapolis, MN 55440-5625. TEL 612-742-6202, FAX 612-475-6208, TELEX 290625 CARGILL MPS. Ed., R&P Wendy Tai. Circ: 8,000.

630   USA   ISSN 1541-2628
CAROLINA - VIRGINIA FARMER. Text in English. 2002. m. USD 23.95 (effective 2005). adv. **Document type:** Magazine, Trade.

A

Formed by the merger of: Carolina Farmer; Virginia Farmer (0746-1186)
Published by: Farm Progress Companies, 191 S Gary Ave, Carol Stream, IL 60188-2095. TEL 630-462-2229, FAX 630-462-2202, info@farmprogress.com, http://www.carolina-virginiafarmer.com/, http://www.farmprogress.com/. Eds. Richard Davis, Sara Wyant. Adv. contact Don Tourte. B&W page USD 1,950, color page USD 2,450; trim 10.5 x 14.5. Circ: 23,000 (paid and controlled).

631   USA   ISSN 1071-6653
CARROT COUNTRY. Text in English. 1993. q. USD 8 domestic; USD 14 in Canada & Mexico; USD 18 elsewhere (effective 2005). adv. back issues avail. **Document type:** *Magazine, Trade.* **Description:** Covers carrot production and marketing.
Published by: Columbia Publishing and Design, 413B N 20th Ave, Yakima, WA 98902. TEL 509-248-2452, 800-900-2452, FAX 509-248-4056, brent@carrotcountry.com, http://www.carrotcountry.com. Ed. Brent Clement. Pub., R&P, Adv. contact Mike J Stoker. B&W page USD 790, color page USD 1,290. Circ: 2,229 (paid and controlled).

634.573   IND   ISSN 0970-2423
THE CASHEW. Text in English, Hindi. 1967. q. INR 200 domestic; INR 600 foreign; INR 50 newsstand/cover domestic; INR 150 newsstand/cover foreign (effective 2001). adv. bk.rev. 40 p./no. 2 cols./p.; back issues avail. **Document type:** *Journal, Government.* **Description:** Articles on cashew cultivation, processing, exports, imports and utilization of by-products.
Formerly (until 1987): Cashew Causerie (0970-1818); Supersedes: Cashew News Teller (0045-5911)
Indexed: AgrForAb, FS&TA, ForAb, HortAb, MBA, PBA, PHN&I, RPP, RevApplEntom, S&F, SeedAb, WAE&RSA.
Published by: (India. Directorate of Cashewnut Development), Ministry of Agriculture, Department of Agriculture and Co-operation, Directorate of Cashewnut, Kera Bhavan, Cochin, Kerala 682 011, India. TEL 91-484-373239, FAX 91-484-373239, cashco@vsnl.com. Ed. Venkatesh N Hubballi. Pub., R&P, Adv. contact P P Balasubramanian. B&W page INR 2,750, color page INR 3,000. Circ: 400.

632.9   USA
CEREAL RUST BULLETIN. Text in English. 1963. irreg. looseleaf. free. **Document type:** *Bulletin, Government.* **Description:** Studies the development of the small-grain cereal rusts in the U.S.
Indexed: FCA, HerbAb, MaizeAb, PBA, RPP, TriticAb.
Published by: (Cereal Disease Laboratory), U.S. Department of Agriculture, Agricultural Research Service (St. Paul), 1551 Lindig St., St. Paul, MN 55108. TEL 612-625-6299, FAX 612-649-5054, davidl@puccini.crl.umn.edu, http://www.crl.umn.edu/. Ed., R&P David L Long. Circ: 500 (controlled).

632   DEU   ISSN 0009-1308
                                                CODEN: CHMPDB
DER CHAMPIGNON; Zeitschrift fuer den Pilzanbau. Text in German. 1961. bi-m. EUR 65 domestic; EUR 75 foreign (effective 2005). adv. bk.rev. charts; illus.; stat. **Document type:** *Magazine, Trade.*
Indexed: AEA, BioDAb, CPA, DSA, FPA, FS&TA, HortAb, I&DA, MaizeAb, NemAb, NutrAb, PBA, PGegResA, PHN&I, PN&I, PoultAb, RA&MP, RPP, RefZh, S&F, SoyAb, WAE&RSA.
—BLDSC (3129.580000).
Published by: Bund Deutscher Champignon- und Kulturpilzanbauer e.V., Godesberger Allee 142-148, Bonn, 53175, Germany. TEL 49-228-8100226, FAX 49-228-8100247, info@der-champignon.de, http://www.der-champignon.de. Ed. Eberhard Peters. Adv. contact Liane Wilden. B&W page EUR 515; trim 185 x 270. Circ: 1,000.

633.72   CHN
CHAYE KEXUE JIANBAO/SCIENTIFIC BULLETIN OF TEA. Text in Chinese. q. CNY 1.50. **Description:** Discusses cultivation and propagation of tea shrubs as well as tea processing. Also includes trade information and scientific research on tea in other countries.
Published by: Fujian Sheng Nongye Kexueyuan/Fujian Academy of Agricultural Science, She Kou, Fu'an, Fujian 355015, China. TEL 05031. Ed. Lin Xinjiong. **Dist. overseas by:** Jiangsu Publications Import & Export Corp., 56 Gao Yun Ling, Nanjing, Jiangsu, China.

630.24   NLD   ISSN 0927-0094
                                                CODEN: CHEAET
➤ **CHEMICALS IN AGRICULTURE.** Text in English. 1988. irreg., latest vol.2, 1991. price varies. back issues avail. **Document type:** *Monographic series, Academic/Scholarly.* **Description:** Discusses research into fertilizers, pesticides, herbicides, and other chemicals used in agriculture.
Indexed: CIN, ChemAb, ChemTitl.
—CASDDS.
Published by: Elsevier BV (Subsidiary of: Elsevier Science & Technology), Radarweg 29, Amsterdam, 1043 NX, Netherlands. TEL 31-20-4853911, FAX 31-20-4852457, nlinfo-f@elsevier.nl, http://www.elsevier.nl.

631   ZWE
CHEMISTRY AND SOIL RESEARCH INSTITUTE. ANNUAL REPORT. Text in English. 1964. a. free. back issues avail.

Published by: (Zimbabwe. Chemistry and Soil Research Institute), Ministry of Lands Agriculture and Rural Resettlement, Research and Specialist Services, Causeway, PO Box 8108, Harare, Zimbabwe. Circ: 300.

631.4   ARG   ISSN 0326-3169
                                                CODEN: CISUDT
➤ **CIENCIA DEL SUELO/ARGENTINE SOCIETY OF SOIL SCIENCE. JOURNAL.** Text in English, Spanish; Summaries in English. 1983. s-a. USD 40 (effective 2002). adv. index. **Document type:** *Academic/Scholarly.* **Description:** Covers original papers from Argentinian and foreign researchers. Includes all areas of soil science; physics, chemistry, biology, biochemistry, fertility, and management.
Related titles: Online - full text ed.: (from EBSCO Publishing).
Indexed: AEA, CIN, ChemAb, ChemTitl, FCA, GEOBASE, HerbAb, HortAb, I&DA, MaizeAb, RPP, RevApplEntom, S&F, SeedAb, SoyAb, TriticAb.
—CASDDS.
Published by: Asociacion Argentina de la Ciencia del Suelo, Pabellon Ingeis - Ciudad Universitaria, Buenos Aires, 1428, Argentina. TEL 54-11-47833021, FAX 54-11-47833024, buschiazzo@agro.unlpam.edu.ar, http://www.suelos.org.ar. Ed. Daniel E Buschiazzo. Adv. contact Graciela Hevia. Circ: 800.
Subscr. to: AACS, c/o Daniel Buschiazzo, Fac. de Agronomia, Univ. de N.L.P,, C.C. 300, Santa Rosa, La Pampa 6300, Argentina.

631   CUB   ISSN 1013-9834
                                                CODEN: CTACEV
CIENCIA Y TECNICA EN LA AGRICULTURA. SERIE: CAFE Y CACAO. Abstracts and contents page in English. 1978. s-a. USD 14 in the Americas; USD 16 in Europe; USD 17 elsewhere.
Indexed: AgrForAb, Agrind, S&F, WeedAb.
Published by: Centro de Informacion y Documentacion Agropecuario, Gaveta Postal 4149, Havana, 4, Cuba. **Dist. by:** Ediciones Cubanas, Obispo No. 527, Apdo. 605, Havana, Cuba.

631   CUB   ISSN 0138-7014
CIENCIA Y TECNICA EN LA AGRICULTURA. SERIE: CANERA. Text in Spanish. 3/yr.
—CISTI.
Published by: Centro de Informacion y Documentacion Agropecuario, Gaveta Postal 4149, Havana, 4, Cuba. **Dist. by:** Ediciones Cubanas, Obispo No. 527, Apdo. 605, Havana, Cuba. **Co-sponsor:** Cuba. Ministerio de Azucar.

634   CUB   ISSN 0138-8835
CIENCIA Y TECNICA EN LA AGRICULTURA. SERIE: CITRICOS Y OTROS FRUTALES. Abstracts and contents page in English. 1978. q. USD 17 in North America; USD 19 in South America; USD 21 in Europe; USD 24 elsewhere.
Formerly: Ciencia y Tecnica en la Agricultura. Serie: Citricos
Indexed: Agrind.
Published by: Centro de Informacion y Documentacion Agropecuario, Gaveta Postal 4149, Havana, 4, Cuba. **Dist. by:** Ediciones Cubanas, Obispo No. 527, Apdo. 605, Havana, Cuba.

631   CUB   ISSN 0138-8630
CIENCIA Y TECNICA EN LA AGRICULTURA. SERIE: HORTALIZAS, PAPAS, GRANOS Y FIBRAS. Abstracts and contents page in English. 1982. s-a. USD 14 in the Americas; USD 16 in Europe; USD 17 elsewhere.
Formerly (until 1983): Ciencia y Tecnica en la Agricultura. Serie: Viandas, Hortalizas y Granos
Indexed: Agrind, MaizeAb.
Published by: Centro de Informacion y Documentacion Agropecuario, Gaveta Postal 4149, Havana, 4, Cuba. **Dist. by:** Ediciones Cubanas, Obispo No. 527, Apdo. 605, Havana, Cuba.

631.8   CUB   ISSN 0138-8932
CIENCIA Y TECNICA EN LA AGRICULTURA. SERIE: PROTECCION DE PLANTAS. Abstracts and contents page in English. 1978. q. USD 17 in North America; USD 19 in South America; USD 21 in Europe; USD 24 elsewhere.
Indexed: Agrind, FCA, HerbAb, SIA, WeedAb.
Published by: Centro de Informacion y Documentacion Agropecuario, Gaveta Postal 4149, Havana, 4, Cuba. **Dist. by:** Ediciones Cubanas, Obispo No. 527, Apdo. 605, Havana, Cuba.

631.587   CUB   ISSN 0138-8487
CIENCIA Y TECNICA EN LA AGRICULTURA. SERIE: RIEGO Y DRENAJE. Abstracts and contents page in English. 1978. s-a. USD 14 in North America; USD 16 in Europe; USD 17 elsewhere.
Indexed: Agrind, FCA, HerbAb, S&F.
Published by: Centro de Informacion y Documentacion Agropecuario, Gaveta Postal 4149, Havana, 4, Cuba. **Dist. by:** Ediciones Cubanas, Obispo No. 527, Apdo. 605, Havana, Cuba.

631.4   CUB   ISSN 0138-8983
CIENCIA Y TECNICA EN LA AGRICULTURA. SERIE: SUELOS Y AGROQUIMICA. Abstracts and contents page in English. 1978. 3/yr. USD 17 in North America; USD 19 in South America; USD 20 in Europe; USD 22 elsewhere.
Indexed: Agrind, FCA, HerbAb, HortAb, RiceAb.

Published by: Centro de Informacion y Documentacion Agropecuario, Gaveta Postal 4149, Havana, 4, Cuba. **Dist. by:** Ediciones Cubanas, Obispo No. 527, Apdo. 605, Havana, Cuba.

630   CUB   ISSN 0138-8886
CIENCIA Y TECNICA EN LA AGRICULTURA. SERIE: VIANDAS TROPICALES. Abstracts and contents page in English. 1983. s-a. USD 14 in North America; USD 16 in Europe; USD 17 elsewhere.
Formerly (until 1983): Ciencia y Tecnica en la Agricultura. Serie: Viandas, Hortalizas y Granos
Indexed: AEA, Agrind, FCA, HerbAb.
Published by: Centro de Informacion y Documentacion Agropecuario, Gaveta Postal 4149, Havana, 4, Cuba. **Dist. by:** Ediciones Cubanas, Obispo No. 527, Apdo. 605, Havana, Cuba.

631   CUB
CIENCIAS DEL SUELO, RIEGO Y MECANIZACION. Text in Spanish. 3/yr. USD 22 in South America; USD 24 in North America; USD 28 elsewhere.
Published by: Ediciones Cubanas, Obispo No. 527, Apdo. 605, Havana, Cuba.

630   BRA   ISSN 0100-0039
SF641   CODEN: CNTFBM
➤ **CIENTIFICA;** revista de agronomia. Text in Portuguese; Summaries in English, Portuguese. 1974. s-a. free (effective 2004). bibl.; charts; stat.; abstr. back issues avail. **Document type:** *Journal, Academic/Scholarly.* **Description:** Agronomy.
Indexed: AEA, ASFA, ATA, AgBio, AgrForAb, Agrind, BIOSIS Prev, BioCN&I, BiolAb, CPA, ESPM, EntAb, FCA, FS&TA, ForAb, HerbAb, HortAb, I&DA, IBR, IBZ, M&GPA, MBA, MaizeAb, NemAb, NutrAb, OrnHort, PBA, PGegResA, PGrRegA, PHN&I, PollutAb, PotatoAb, RA&MP, RDA, RPP, RefZh, RevApplEntom, RiceAb, S&F, S&MA, SIA, SeedAb, SoyAb, TOSA, TriticAb, WAE&RSA, WeedAb, ZooRec.
—BLDSC (3198.207000), CASDDS, CISTI, IE, ingenta, Linda Hall.
Published by: Fundacao Editora U N E S P, Praca da Se 108, Sao Paulo, SP 01001-900, Brazil. TEL 55-11-32427171, cgb@marilia.unesp.br, http://www.unesp.br. Ed. Dr. Robertval Daiton Vieira. Circ: 1,000.

630   FRA   ISSN 0751-6037
CIRCUITS CULTURE. Text in French. 1973. m.
Related titles: Online - full text ed.: (from Factiva).
Indexed: CBNB.
—BLDSC (3198.839400).
Published by: Agri Terroir Communication, 61, Rue du XXe-Corps-Americain, Metz, 57000, France. TEL 33-03-87691818, FAX 33-03-87691814, infocentre@editions-mirabelle.com, http://www.editions-mirabelle.com. Ed. Eric Young. Circ: 5,525.

634.3   USA   ISSN 0009-7578
CITROGRAPH; magazine of the citrus industry. Text in English. 1915. m. USD 29.95 (effective 2004). adv. bk.rev. charts; illus.; stat.; tr.lit. **Document type:** *Magazine, Trade.* **Description:** Gives tips on growing produce.
Formerly (until 1969): California Citrograph (1054-7177)
Indexed: BioCN&I, BiolAb, ChemAb, FS&TA, HortAb, RPP, RevApplEntom.
—CISTI, IE, Infotrieve, Linda Hall.
Published by: Western Agricultural Publishing Co. Inc., 4969 E Clinton Way, Ste 104, Fresno, CA 93727-1549. TEL 209-252-7000, FAX 209-252-7387, westag2@psnw.com. Ed. Randy Bailey. Pubs. Jim Baltimore, Paul Baltimore. Circ: 7,400 (paid and controlled).

634 633   USA   ISSN 0009-7586
                                                CODEN: CVGMAX
CITRUS & VEGETABLE. Text in English. 1938. m. USD 45 domestic; USD 40 in Canada & Mexico; USD 75 elsewhere (effective 2005). adv. bk.rev. illus. **Document type:** *Magazine, Trade.*
Indexed: BiolAb, F&GI, FS&TA, HortAb.
—BLDSC (3267.800000), CISTI, IE, Infotrieve, ingenta.
Published by: Vance Publishing Corp., 400 Knightsbridge Pkwy, Lincolnshire, IL 60069. TEL 847-634-2600, 800-255-5113, FAX 847-634-4379, cvmscott@compuserve.com, http://www.citrusandvegetable.com, http://www.vancepublishing.com. Ed. Scott Emerson. Circ: 12,500 (controlled).

634   USA   ISSN 0412-6300
                                                CODEN: TCECDG
CITRUS ENGINEERING CONFERENCE. TRANSACTIONS. Text in English. 1955. a. USD 20 (effective 2004). back issues avail.
Indexed: Agr, FS&TA.
—BLDSC (9020.360000), CASDDS, IE, ingenta.
Published by: Citrus Engineering Conference, Florida Section, 700 Experiment Station Rd, Lake Alfred, FL 33850. TEL 407-207-5094, floridasection@asme.org. Circ: 350.

641.34304   USA
CITRUS NEWS. Text in English. 1998. irreg. back issues avail. **Document type:** *Newsletter.* **Description:** Covers all aspects of citrus growing and use.
Media: Online - full text.

Address: ctownsen@peganet.com, http://www.ultimatecitrus.com/citrusnews.html. Ed. Chet Townsend.

633.74 GBR ISSN 0045-7256
COCOA GROWERS BULLETIN. Text in English. 1963. s-a. free. bk.rev. abstr.; illus.; stat. index. **Document type:** *Academic/Scholarly.* **Description:** Provides an information service to cocoa growers, plantation staff, extension officers and research workers.
Indexed: AEA, ATA, AgBio, AgrForAb, FS&TA, ForAb, HortAb, PBA, PHN&I, RDA, RPP, RevApplEntom, S&F, WAE&RSA, WeedAb.
—BLDSC (3292.738000).
Published by: Cadbury Ltd., Bournville, Birmingham, W Mids B30 2LU, United Kingdom. Ed. Tony Lass. Circ: 1,500 (controlled).

634 IDN ISSN 0854-235X
COCONUT STATISTICAL YEARBOOK. Text in English. a. USD 50 in Asia; USD 60 elsewhere (effective 2001). **Description:** Presents the latest statistical data on world's coconut industry, including production, volume & value of exports, import destinations, processing capacities and coconut conversion tables.
Indexed: IIS.
Published by: Asian and Pacific Coconut Community, 3rd Fl., Lina Bldg., Jl H R Rasuna Said Kav B 7, Kuningan, Jakarta, 12920, Indonesia. TEL 62-21-5221712, FAX 62-21-5221714, TELEX 62209 APCC IA, apcc@indo.net.id, http://www.idrc.org.sg./pan/apcc.

631 IDN
COCONUT WOOD UTILIZATION; proceedings of the workshop for policy makers. Text in English. a.?. USD 10. **Document type:** *Proceedings.* **Description:** Covers products, sawmills and equipment, marketing prospects in Europe, profitability of coconut wood utilization and its integration with national replanting programs.
Published by: Asian and Pacific Coconut Community, 3rd Fl., Lina Bldg., Jl H R Rasuna Said Kav B 7, Kuningan, Jakarta, 12920, Indonesia. TEL 62-21-510-073, FAX 62-21-520-5160.

COFFEE ANNUAL. see *FOOD AND FOOD INDUSTRIES*

COFFEE INTELLIGENCE. see *FOOD AND FOOD INDUSTRIES*

631 ZWE
COFFEE RESEARCH INSTITUTE. ANNUAL REPORT. COFFEE RESEARCH STATION. Text in English. 1976. a. free. back issues avail. **Document type:** *Yearbook, Government.*
Formerly: Horticulture and Coffee Research Institute. Annual Report. Part 2. Coffee Research Station
Published by: Ministry of Agriculture, Coffee Research Institute, PO Box 61, Chipinga, Zimbabwe. TEL 263-27-2476, FAX 263-27-2951, rsscoffee@mango.zw. Ed. D Kumah. Circ: 300. **Subscr. to:** PO Box 8108, Causeway, Zimbabwe.

633 FRA ISSN 1029-3701
COLLOQUE SCIENTIFIQUE INTERNATIONALE SUR LE CAFE. Text in English. 1966. irreg. **Description:** Provides original technical and scientific information about coffee trees and coffee of importance to scientists and professionals.
—BLDSC (3315.207500), ingenta.
Published by: Association Scientifique Internationale du Cafe, 3 Rue de Copenhague, Paris, 75008, France. TEL 33-1-53421338, FAX 33-1-53421339, asic-office@asic-cafe.org, http://www.asic-cafe.org.

633 FRA
COMMERCE FRANCAIS DE LA POMME DE TERRE. Text in French. 6/yr. adv.
Published by: Secopot, 220 Bourse du Commerce, Paris, Cedex 1 75040, France.

COMMERCIAL FERTILIZERS REPORT. see *AGRICULTURE—Abstracting, Bibliographies, Statistics*

COMMON SENSE PEST CONTROL QUARTERLY. see *GARDENING AND HORTICULTURE*

COMMUNICATIONS IN AGRICULTURAL AND APPLIED BIOLOGICAL SCIENCES. see *BIOLOGY—Biotechnology*

631.4 USA ISSN 0010-3624
S590 CODEN: CSOSA2
➤ **COMMUNICATIONS IN SOIL SCIENCE AND PLANT ANALYSIS.** Text in English. 1970. 20/yr. GBP 1,676, USD 2,766 combined subscription to institutions print & online eds. (effective 2006). adv. reprint service avail. from PSC. **Document type:** *Journal, Academic/Scholarly.* **Description:** Presents recent advances in soil science and crop production, with particular reference to elemental content of soils and plants, and plant nutrition.
Related titles: Microform ed.: (from RPI); Online - full text ed.: ISSN 1532-2416. GBP 1,592, USD 2,628 to institutions (effective 2006) (from EBSCO Publishing, O C L C Online Computer Library Center, Inc., Swets Information Services).
Indexed: AEA, ASCA, ASFA, AbHyg, AgBio, Agr, AgrForAb, AnBrAb, AnalAb, B&AI, BIOBASE, BIOSIS Prev, BibAg, BiolAb, CCI, CIN, CPA, CTFA, ChemAb, ChemTitl, CurCont, DSA, EIA, EPB, ESPM, EnerInd, ExcerpMed, F&GI, FCA, FLUIDEX, FPA, ForAb, GEOBASE, HerbAb, HortAb, I&DA, INIS AtomInd, ISR, MSB, MaizeAb, NemAb, NutrAb, OrnHort, PBA, PGegResA, PGrRegA, PN&I, PlantSci, PotatoAb, PoultAb, RA&MP, RDA, RPP, RRTA, RefZh, RevApplEntom, RiceAb, S&F, S&MA, SCI, SFA, SIA, SWRA, SeedAb, SoyAb, TDB, TTI, TriticAb, VITIS, WAE&RSA, WeedAb.
—BLDSC (3363.420000), CASDDS, CISTI, IDS, IE, Infotrieve, ingenta, Linda Hall. **CCC.**
Published by: Taylor & Francis Inc. (Subsidiary of: Taylor & Francis Group), 325 Chestnut St, Ste 800, Philadelphia, PA 19016. TEL 215-625-8900, 800-354-1420, FAX 215-625-2940, info@taylorandfrancis.com, http://www.tandf.co.uk/journals/titles/00103624.asp, http://www.taylorandfrancis.com. Ed. Dr. Harry A Mills. R&P Elaine Inverso. Adv. contact Mary Drabot. page USD 600. Circ: 500 (paid).

➤ **COMPENDIUM OF NEW ZEALAND FARM PRODUCTION STATISTICS.** see *AGRICULTURE—Abstracting, Bibliographies, Statistics*

631 USA
COMPENDIUM OF PLANT DISEASE SERIES. Text in English. irreg. USD 49 (effective 2003). illus. **Document type:** *Monographic series, Academic/Scholarly.* **Description:** Contains information about hot to prevent, diagnose and control plant disease.
Published by: (American Phytopathological Society), A P S PRESS, 3340 Pilot Knob Rd., St. Paul, MN 55121-2097. TEL 651-454-7250, 800-328-7560, FAX 651-454-0766, aps@scisoc.org, http://www.shopapspress.org, http://www.apsnet.org.

COMPOST SCIENCE & UTILIZATION. see *ENVIRONMENTAL STUDIES—Waste Management*

630 AUS
CONFERENCE OF GRASSLAND SOCIETY OF NSW. PROCEEDINGS; getting the best from your farm. Text in English. 1986. a. AUD 25 domestic; USD 20 foreign (effective 2000). **Document type:** *Proceedings.*
Published by: Grassland Society of New South Wales, c/o Orange Agricultural Institute, Forest Rd, Orange, NSW 2800, Australia. TEL 0263-913-828, FAX 0263-913-899. Ed. David Michalk. Pub. M H Campbell. Circ: 1,200.

CONNECTICUT GREENHOUSE NEWSLETTER. see *GARDENING AND HORTICULTURE*

634 IDN
CORD. Text in English. s-a. USD 20 in Asia & the Pacific; USD 25 elsewhere (effective 2001). **Description:** Devoted to original articles on coconut research and development.
Published by: Asian and Pacific Coconut Community, 3rd Fl., Lina Bldg., Jl H R Rasuna Said Kav B 7, Kuningan, Jakarta, 12920, Indonesia. FAX 0062-21-5205160.

633.34 USA ISSN 1544-1644
SB205.S7
CORN AND SOYBEAN DIGEST. Text in English. 1940. m. (11/yr.). USD 30 domestic; USD 35 foreign; free to qualified personnel (effective 2005). adv. charts; illus.; mkt.; stat.; tr.lit. index. back issues avail. **Document type:** *Magazine, Trade.* **Description:** Covers management decisions dealing with production of soybeans, corn, wheat, cotton.
Formerly (until 2003): Soybean Digest (0038-6014)
Related titles: Online - full text ed.: (from bigchalk, Gale Group, H.W. Wilson, LexisNexis, O C L C Online Computer Library Center, Inc., ProQuest Information & Learning).
Indexed: ABIn, B&AI, BiolAb, ChemAb, F&GI.
—CISTI, Linda Hall. **CCC.**
Published by: Primedia Business Magazines & Media, Inc. (Subsidiary of: Primedia, Inc.), 7900 International Dr, Ste 300, Minneapolis, MN 55425. TEL 952-851-9329, FAX 952-851-4601, glamp@primediabusiness.com, inquiries@primediabusiness.com, http://soybeandigest.com, http://www.primediabusiness.com. Ed. Greg Lamp. Pub. Greg Frey TEL 952-851-4613. adv.: B&W page USD 12,495, color page USD 18,690. Circ: 147,000 (controlled). **Subscr. to:** PO Box 12993, Overland Park, KS 66282-2993. TEL 800-441-0294, FAX 913-967-1331.

633 USA ISSN 0069-9993
CODEN: COANFU
CORN ANNUAL. Text in English. 1970. a. free. **Document type:** *Trade.*
Indexed: SRI.
—Linda Hall.
Published by: Corn Refiners Association, Inc., 1701 Pennsylvania Ave, N W, Ste 950, Washington, DC 20006. TEL 202-331-1634, FAX 202-331-2054, details@corn.org, http://www.corn.org. Ed., R&P Shannon Shoesmith. Circ: 10,000.

633.15 USA
CORN FARMER. Text in English. 1991. q. free to qualified personnel (effective 2001). adv. **Description:** For the Mid-Western farmer raising more than 250 acres of corn.
Published by: Meredith Corp., 1716 Locust St, Des Moines, IA 50309-3023. TEL 515-284-3000, 800-556-9184, FAX 515-284-3657, http://www.meredith.com. Ed. Loren Kruse. adv.: B&W page USD 13,155. Circ: 68,000 (controlled).

631 USA
CORNELL FIELD CROPS AND SOILS HANDBOOK. Text in English. every 10 yrs. USD 7.50 (effective 1999). **Document type:** *Bulletin.*
Published by: Cornell University, Media & Technology Services, 7 Business and Technology Park, Ithaca, NY 14850. TEL 607-255-2080, FAX 607-255-9946, dist_center@cce.cornell.edu, http://www.cce.cornell.edu/publications/catalog.html. R&P Carol Doolittle TEL 607-255-5830.

632.9 USA
➤ **CORNELL RECOMMENDATIONS FOR COMMERCIAL TURFGRASS MANAGEMENT.** Text in English. a. price varies. **Document type:** *Academic/Scholarly.* **Description:** Provides cultural an chemical control methods of diseases, weeds and insects. It offers a guide for commercial growers and serious hobbyists as they develop efficient management practices on the farm and in the garden.
Published by: Cornell University, Media & Technology Services, 7 Business and Technology Park, Ithaca, NY 14850. TEL 607-255-2080, FAX 607-255-9946, dist_center@cce.cornell.edu, http://www.cce.cornell.edu/publications/catalog.html. Ed. Judy Stewart. R&P Carol Doolittle TEL 607-255-5830. Circ: 2,000 (paid).

631 USA
CORNELL RECOMMENDATIONS FOR FIELD CROPS. Text in English. a. price varies. **Document type:** *Bulletin.*
Published by: Cornell University, Media & Technology Services, 7 Business and Technology Park, Ithaca, NY 14850. TEL 607-255-2080, FAX 607-255-9946, dist_center@cce.cornell.edu, http://www.cce.cornell.edu/publications/catalog.html. R&P Carol Doolittle TEL 607-255-5830.

632.9 USA ISSN 0277-1624
CORNELL RECOMMENDATIONS FOR PEST CONTROL FOR COMMERCIAL PRODUCTION AND MAINTENANCE OF TREES & SHRUBS. Text in English. a. price varies. **Document type:** *Bulletin.*
Published by: Cornell University, Media & Technology Services, 7 Business and Technology Park, Ithaca, NY 14850. TEL 607-255-2080, FAX 607-255-9946, dist_center@cce.cornell.edu, http://www.cce.cornell.edu/publications/catalog.html. R&P Carol Doolittle TEL 607-255-5830.

633.63 NLD
COSUN MAGAZINE. Text in Dutch. 1966. 10/yr. free. charts; illus.; mkt.; stat. **Document type:** *Magazine, Trade.* **Description:** Agricultural publication devoted to sugar beet production. Covers crop research, diseases, quality control, marketing prices, and association news.
Former titles: Suiker Unie; (until 1995): Maandblad Suiker Unie (0024-8606)
Published by: Royal Co-operative Cosun U.A., Postbus 3411, Breda, 4800 MG, Netherlands. TEL 31-76-5303222, FAX 31-75-5303300, TELEX 54370, wytze.dijkstra@cosun.com. Ed. W H Dijkstra. Circ: 19,000.

633 330 USA ISSN 0199-1779
COTTON ECONOMIC REVIEW. Text in English. m. USD 50. **Description:** Covers U.S. cotton production, supply and exports.
Indexed: PGrRegA, TTI.
Published by: National Cotton Council of America, Inc., 1918 N Pkwy, Shelby County, Memphis, TN 38112. TEL 901-274-9030, FAX 901-725-0510, http://www.cotton.org/beltwide. Ed. Mark Lange. Circ: 4,000.

633 USA ISSN 0746-8385
COTTON FARMING. Text in English. 1957. 12/yr. USD 40 (effective 2005). **Document type:** *Magazine, Trade.* **Description:** Designed for cotton growers and related industry professionals in the cotton farming, sconsulting, ginning and marketing industries.
Indexed: TTI.
Published by: One Grower Publishing, 5118 Park Ave, Ste 131, Memphis, TN 38117. TEL 901-767-4020, FAX 901-767-4026, thorton@onegrower.com, http://www.cottonfarming.com. Ed. Tommy Horton. Circ: 30,000 (paid and controlled).

633.51 USA ISSN 0194-9772
COTTON GROWER. Text in English. 1965. 14/yr. free to qualified personnel (effective 2005). adv. bk.rev. **Document type:** *Magazine, Trade.* **Description:** Serves the growing and marketing of cotton and others allied to the cotton industry.
Formerly: American Cotton Grower (0044-765X)
Related titles: Online - full text ed.: (from Northern Light Technology, Inc., ProQuest Information & Learning).
Indexed: ABIn, TTI.
—CCC.

Published by: Meister Media Worldwide, 37733 Euclid Ave, Willoughby, OH 44094-5992. TEL 440-942-2000, 800-572-7740, FAX 440-942-0662, cg_circ@meisternet.com, http://www.cottongrower.com. Ed. Frank Giles. Pub., Adv. contact Frank Maxcy. page USD 5,095. Circ: 35,000 (controlled).

633 KEN
COTTON LINT AND SEED MARKETING BOARD. ANNUAL REPORT AND ACCOUNTS. Text in English. a. **Document type:** *Corporate.*
Published by: Cotton Lint and Seed Marketing Board, PO Box 30477, Nairobi, Kenya.

COTTON: WORLD STATISTICS. see *AGRICULTURE—Abstracting, Bibliographies, Statistics*

664.8 USA ISSN 0011-0787
CRANBERRIES; the national cranberry magazine. Text in English. 1936. 11/yr. USD 25 domestic; USD 30 in Canada; USD 35 elsewhere (effective 2005). adv. bk.rev. charts; illus.; stat. 32 p./no. 3 cols./p.; back issues avail. **Document type:** *Magazine, Trade.* **Description:** Contains news, economics, research, horticultural information, marketing, and profiles relating solely to the cranberry industry.
Related titles: CD-ROM ed.
Indexed: ChemAb.
—CISTI.
Address: PO Box 113, Allendale, MI 49401. TEL 616-443-3678, cranberries@comcast.net, http://www.cranberriesmagazine.com. Pub. Greg Brown. adv.: page USD 185. Circ: 1,050 (paid).

633 USA ISSN 0735-2689
QK1 CODEN: CRPSD3
➤ **CRITICAL REVIEWS IN PLANT SCIENCES.** Text in English. 1983. bi-m. USD 1,028, GBP 622 combined subscription to institutions print & online eds. (effective 2006). reprint service avail. from PSC. **Document type:** *Journal, Academic/Scholarly.* **Description:** Presents current reviews on subjects in areas such as shortages in world food supply, energy resources, the role of research in increasing crop productivity; also basic research areas in photosynthesis, nitrogen fixation, gene regulation, and genetic engineering.
Related titles: Online - full text ed.: ISSN 1549-7836. USD 977, GBP 591 to institutions (effective 2006) (from bigchalk, EBSCO Publishing, Gale Group, IngentaConnect, O C L C Online Computer Library Center, Inc., ProQuest Information & Learning, ScienceDirect, Swets Information Services).
Indexed: AEA, AEBA, ASCA, ASFA, AbHyg, AgBio, Agr, AgrForAb, B&BAb, BIOBASE, BIOSIS Prev, BibAg, BioCN&I, BiolDig, C&ISA, CIN, CPA, CTFA, ChemAb, ChemTitl, CurCont, E&CAJ, EPB, ESPM, FCA, FPA, FS&TA, ForAb, GardL, GenetAb, HGA, HerbAb, HortAb, I&DA, IAA, IABS, ISR, MBA, MaizeAb, NutrAb, PBA, PGegResA, PGrRegA, PHN&I, PlantSci, PotatoAb, ProtozoAb, RA&MP, RDA, RPP, RRTA, RevApplEntom, RiceAb, S&F, SCI, SIA, SeedAb, SoyAb, TDB, TriticAb, WAE&RSA, WeedAb.
—BLDSC (3487.480000), CASDDS, CISTI, IDS, IE, Infotrieve, ingenta, Linda Hall. **CCC.**
Published by: Taylor & Francis Inc. (Subsidiary of: Taylor & Francis Group), 325 Chestnut St, Ste 800, Philadelphia, PA 19106. TEL 215-625-8900, 800-354-1420, FAX 215-625-2940, info@taylorandfrancis.com, http://www.tandf.co.uk/journals/titles/07352689.asp, http://www.taylorandfrancis.com. Eds. Dennis Gray, Robert Trigiano. **Subscr. outside N. America to:** Taylor & Francis Ltd, Journals Customer Service, Rankine Rd, Basingstoke, Hants RG24 8PR, United Kingdom. TEL 44-1256-813000, FAX 44-1256-330245, enquiry@tandf.co.uk.

631 ZWE
CROP BREEDING INSTITUTE. ANNUAL REPORT. Text in English. 1975. a. free. back issues avail.
Published by: (Zimbabwe. Information Services), Ministry of Lands Agriculture and Rural Resettlement, Research and Specialist Services, Causeway, PO Box 8108, Harare, Zimbabwe. Circ: 250.

630 IND ISSN 0256-0933
CROP IMPROVEMENT. Text in English. 1974. irreg.
Indexed: AEA, AEBA, ASFA, AgBio, BIOSIS Prev, BioCN&I, BiolAb, CPA, DSA, ESPM, FCA, FPA, GenetAb, HerbAb, HortAb, MaizeAb, NutrAb, OrnHort, PBA, PGegResA, PGrRegA, PHN&I, PotatoAb, RA&MP, RPP, RiceAb, S&F, SIA, SWRA, SeedAb, SoyAb, TriticAb.
—BLDSC (3488.136000), IE, Infotrieve, ingenta.
Published by: Crop Improvement Society of India, c/o Punjab Agricultural University, College of Agriculture, Department of Plant Breeding, Ludhiana, Punjab 141 004, India. TEL 91-161-403006, deacoa@pau.edu, http://www.pau.edu/collegeagri.htm.

630 USA ISSN 1543-7833
➤ **CROP MANAGEMENT.** Text in English. irreg. USD 45 to individuals; USD 750 to institutions (effective 2004). **Document type:** *Journal, Academic/Scholarly.*
Media: Online - full content.
Indexed: FCA.
Published by: Plant Management Network, 3340 Pilot Knob Rd, St Paul, MN 55121-2097. TEL 651-454-7250, 800-328-7590, FAX 651-454-0766, editorialoffice@plantmanagementnetwork.org, http://www.plantmanagementnetwork.org/cm/. Ed. Robert L Kallenbach. R&P Miles Wimer.

➤ **CROP PRODUCTION HALF-YEARLY STATISTICS.** see *AGRICULTURE—Abstracting, Bibliographies, Statistics*

➤ **CROP PROTECTION.** see *ENGINEERING—Chemical Engineering*

630.24 DEU ISSN 0590-1243
CROP PROTECTION COURIER (INTERNATIONAL). Text in German. 1960. 3/yr. free. charts; illus. **Document type:** *Bulletin, Trade.*
—CISTI.
Published by: Bayer AG, Geschaeftsbereich Pflanzenschutz, Kaiser-Wilhelm-Allee, Leverkusen, 51368, Germany. TEL 49-2173-384114, FAX 49-2173-383454. Ed. Bernhard Grupp. Circ: 33,500 (controlled).

631 GBR ISSN 0953-2463
THE CROP PROTECTION DIRECTORY. Text in English. 1988. biennial. GBP 125 (effective 2001). adv. 456 p./no. 2 cols./p.; back issues avail. **Document type:** *Directory.*
Related titles: Diskette ed.; ♦ International ed.: The Crop Protection Directory (International Ed.).
Published by: Elaine Warrell Associates, 2 Lock Chase, London, SE3 9HA, United Kingdom. warrell@dircon.co.uk. Eds. Anne Kirkwood, Elaine Warrell. Pub., Adv. contact Elaine Warrell. B&W page GBP 865, color page GBP 1,058; 185 x 260. **Dist. by:** Agrow Reports, 18/20 Hill Rise, Richmond TW10 6UA, United Kingdom. TEL 44-20-8948-3262, FAX 44-20-8948-6866, alan@pjbmktgn.demon.uk; B C P C Publication Sales, Bear Farm, Binfield, Bracknell RG42 5QE, United Kingdom. TEL 44-118-934-2727, FAX 44-118-934-1998, publications@bcpc.org, http://www.bcpc.org.

630 GBR
THE CROP PROTECTION DIRECTORY (INTERNATIONAL ED.). Text in English. 1997. biennial. GBP 135 per vol. (effective 2001). 350 p./no. 2 cols./p.; back issues avail. **Document type:** *Directory.*
Related titles: Diskette ed.; ♦ International ed. of: The Crop Protection Directory. ISSN 0953-2463.
Published by: Elaine Warrell Associates, 2 Lock Chase, London, SE3 9HA, United Kingdom. warrell@dircon.co.uk. Eds. Anne Kirkwood, Elaine Warrell. Pub., Adv. contact Elaine Warrell. **Dist. by:** B C P C Publication Sales, Bear Farm, Binfield, Bracknell RG42 5QE, United Kingdom. TEL 44-118-934-2727, FAX 44-118-934-1998, publications@bcpc.org, http://www.bcpc.org; Agrow Reports, 18/20 Hill Rise, Richmond TW10 6UA, United Kingdom. TEL 44-20-8948-3262, FAX 44-20-8948-6866, alan@pjbmktgn.demon.uk.

630.24 668.6 USA ISSN 1547-2779
S633 CODEN: FMCHA2
CROP PROTECTION HANDBOOK. Text in English. 1914. a., latest 2004. USD 129 (effective 2005). adv. **Document type:** *Magazine, Trade.*
Formerly (until 2003): Farm Chemicals Handbook (0430-0750); Which superseded: American Fertilizer Handbook
Related titles: CD-ROM ed.
—CASDDS, CISTI. **CCC.**
Published by: Meister Media Worldwide, 37733 Euclid Ave, Willoughby, OH 44094-5992. TEL 440-942-2000, 800-572-7740, FAX 440-942-0662, fchb-circ@meisternet.com, http://www.meisterpro.com. Ed. Richard T Meister. Adv. contact Jon J Miducki. Circ: 12,000.

631 IND ISSN 0970-4884
CODEN: CROREU
➤ **CROP RESEARCH**; an international journal. Text in English. 1988. bi-m. USD 300 to institutions (effective 2006). adv. bk.rev. 150 p./no. 2 cols./p.; back issues avail. **Document type:** *Journal, Academic/Scholarly.* **Description:** Contains original research on crops relating to basic and applied aspects of agriculture botany, crop physiology, entomology, horticulture, soil sciences and vegetable crops.
Indexed: AEA, AgBio, AgrForAb, BIOSIS Prev, BioCN&I, BiolAb, CPA, DSA, FCA, FPA, FS&TA, ForAb, HerbAb, HortAb, I&DA, INIS AtomInd, IndVet, MaizeAb, NemAb, NutrAb, OrnHort, PBA, PGegResA, PGrRegA, PHN&I, PotatoAb, PoultAb, ProtozoAb, RA&MP, RDA, RM&VM, RPP, RevApplEntom, RiceAb, S&F, S&MA, SIA, SeedAb, SoyAb, TDB, TriticAb, VITIS, WAE&RSA, WeedAb.
—BLDSC (3488.472000), IE, ingenta.
Published by: Agricultural Research Information Centre, c/o Systematic Printers, U St., Near Video Market Mohalla Udayapurian, Hisar, Haryana 125001, India. Ed. Dr. Vedpal Singh. Pub. Poonam S Chaudhary. adv.: page INR 2,000, page USD 200. Circ: 2,000. **Dist. by:** Scientific Publishers, 5-A New Pali Rd., Near Hotel Taj Hari Mahal, PO Box 91, Jodhpur, Rajasthan 342 003, India. TEL 91-291-2433323, FAX 91-291-2512580, info@scientificpub.com, http://www.scientificpub.com.

630 USA ISSN 0011-183X
SB183 CODEN: CRPSAY
➤ **CROP SCIENCE**; a journal serving the international community of crop scientists . Text in English. 1961. bi-m. USD 255 domestic to non-members; USD 307 foreign to non-members (effective 2005). adv. charts; illus. index. reprints avail. **Document type:** *Journal, Academic/Scholarly.* **Description:** Reports on recent developments in crop breeding and genetics, crop physiology and biochemistry, ecology, cytology, crop and seed production, statistics, and weed control.
Related titles: Online - full text ed.: ISSN 1435-0653 (from bigchalk, EBSCO Publishing, Florida Center for Library Automation, Gale Group, HighWire Press, Northern Light Technology, Inc., ProQuest Information & Learning).
Indexed: AEA, AEBA, ASCA, ASFA, AgBio, Agr, AgrForAb, ApicAb, B&AI, BIOBASE, BIOSIS Prev, BibAg, BioCN&I, BioEngAb, BiolAb, BiolDig, CIN, CIS, CPA, CTFA, ChemAb, ChemTitl, CurCont, DBA, DSA, EPB, ESPM, EntAb, ExcerpMed, F&GI, FCA, FS&TA, ForAb, GenetAb, HGA, HerbAb, HortAb, I&DA, IABS, INIS AtomInd, ISR, IndVet, MBA, MaizeAb, NemAb, NutrAb, OrnHort, PBA, PGegResA, PGrRegA, PHN&I, PN&I, PlantSci, PotatoAb, RA&MP, RM&VM, RPP, RRTA, RevApplEntom, RiceAb, S&F, S&MA, SCI, SIA, SWRA, SeedAb, SoyAb, THA, TOSA, TTI, TriticAb, VITIS, WAE&RSA, WeedAb.
—BLDSC (3488.500000), CASDDS, CISTI, IDS, IE, Infotrieve, ingenta, Linda Hall. **CCC.**
Published by: Crop Science Society of America, 677 S Segoe Rd, Madison, WI 53711. TEL 608-273-8080, FAX 608-273-2021, publications@agronomy.org, http://crop.scijournals.org, http://www.crops.org. Ed. Craig Roberts. Adv. contact Betsy Ahner. Circ: 5,000 (paid).

630 USA ISSN 0895-9978
CROP SCIENCE SOCIETY OF AMERICA. SPECIAL PUBLICATION. Text in English. 1970. irreg. price varies. **Document type:** *Monographic series.*
Indexed: BIOSIS Prev.
—BLDSC (3490.330000). **CCC.**
Published by: Crop Science Society of America, 677 S Segoe Rd, Madison, WI 53711. TEL 608-273-8080, FAX 608-273-2021, http://www.crops.org.

630.24 668.6 USA ISSN 1535-3923
CODEN: CROPBL
CROPLIFE. Text in English. 1973. m. USD 36 (effective 2001). adv. bk.rev. reprint service avail. from PQC. **Document type:** *Journal, Trade.* **Description:** Serves the fertilizer and pesticide manufacturing retailing and distributing fields including manufacturers, dealers, distributors, formulators, and commercial applicators and those in allied fields.
Incorporates (1997-2003): CyberDealer; Formerly (until Apr. 2001): Farm Chemicals (0092-0053); Which was formed by the merger of (1947-1973): Ag Chem and Commercial Fertilizer (0092-0037); Which was formerly (until 1971): Agricultural Chemicals (0096-6681); (1894-1973): Farm Chemicals and Croplife (0014-7885); Which was formerly (until 1970): Farm Chemicals (0893-1399); (until 1951): American Fertilizer and Allied Chemicals (0097-0964); (until 1950): American Fertilizer (0096-6657)
Related titles: Online - full text ed.: (from Factiva, Northern Light Technology, Inc., ProQuest Information & Learning).
Indexed: ABIn, B&AI, CBNB, CIN, CPA, ChemAb, ChemTitl, DBA, F&GI, IndVet, PROMT, RASB, S&F, VetBull, WeedAb.
—BLDSC (3488.640500), CASDDS, CISTI, IE, ingenta, Linda Hall. **CCC.**
Published by: Meister Media Worldwide, 37733 Euclid Ave, Willoughby, OH 44094-5992. TEL 440-942-2000, FAX 440-975-3447. Eds. Jim Sulecki, Paul Schrimpf. Pub. Bill Miller. Circ: 29,686 (controlled).

630 USA
▼ **CROPLIFE IRON.** Text in English. 2004. bi-m. free to qualified personnel (effective 2005). adv. **Document type:** *Magazine, Trade.*
Published by: Meister Media Worldwide, 37733 Euclid Ave, Willoughby, OH 44094-5992. TEL 440-942-2000, 800-572-7740, FAX 440-942-0662, info@meistermedia.com, http://www.croplife.com/iron/index.html, http://www.meistermedia.com. Pub. Alan Strohmeier. Adv. contact Jim Sulecki. B&W page USD 3,445; trim 14.5 x 10.875. Circ: 17,496.

631 GBR ISSN 1364-6559
CROPS; the practical management journal for arable farmers. Text in English. 1984. fortn. GBP 57 domestic; EUR 160 in Europe; USD 168 in United States; GBP 100 elsewhere (effective 2003). adv. back issues avail. **Document type:** *Trade.* **Description:** Contains specialist technical information and arable management advice from politics to pesticides.
Formerly: Crops Weekly (0266-5174)
Related titles: Online - full text ed.: (from EBSCO Publishing, Gale Group, H.W. Wilson, O C L C Online Computer Library Center, Inc., ProQuest Information & Learning).
Indexed: ABIn, B&AI, CBNB, EnvAb.
—BLDSC (3488.645000), CISTI. **CCC.**

Published by: Reed Business Information Ltd. (Subsidiary of: Reed Business), Quadrant House, The Quadrant, Brighton Rd, Sutton, Surrey SM2 5AS, United Kingdom. TEL 44-20-86523500, FAX 44-20-86528932, http://www.reedbusiness.co.uk/. Ed. Charles Abel TEL 44-20-8652-4923. Adv. contact Vic Bunby TEL 44-20-8652-4030. Circ: 34,500. **Subscr. to:** Quadrant Subscription Services, PO Box 302, Haywards Heath, W Sussex RH16 3YY, United Kingdom. TEL 44-1444-475603, FAX 44-1444-445447, rbi.subscriptions@qss-uk.com.

633.6 CUB ISSN 0590-2916
HD9114.C88 CODEN: CUAZAZ
CUBA AZUCAR. Text in Spanish; Summaries in English, French. 1966. q. USD 20 in North America; USD 24 in Europe (effective 2005). abstr.; charts; bibl.; illus.; stat.
Indexed: AEA, FS&TA, HortAb, NutrAb, RPP, SIA.
—CASDDS, CISTI.
Published by: (Cuba. Ministerio de la Azucarera), Ediciones Cubanas, Obispo No. 527, Apdo. 605, Havana, Cuba. TEL 53-7-338942, FAX 53-7-338943. Ed. Rodolfo Escriva.

631 CUB ISSN 0138-8436
CUBA. CENTRO DE INFORMACION Y DOCUMENTACION AGROPECUARIO. BOLETIN DE RESENAS. SERIE: CAFE Y CACAO. Abstracts in English. 1980. irreg. per issue exchange basis. stat.
Formerly: Cuba. Centro de Informacion y Divulgacion Agropecuario. Boletin de Resenas. Serie: Cafe y Cacao
Indexed: Agrind.
Published by: Centro de Informacion y Documentacion Agropecuario, Gaveta Postal 4149, Havana, 4, Cuba. TEL 301672. **Dist. by:** Ediciones Cubanas, Obispo No. 461, Apdo. 605, Havana, Cuba.

634 CUB ISSN 0138-8339
CUBA. CENTRO DE INFORMACION Y DOCUMENTACION AGROPECUARIO. BOLETIN DE RESENAS. SERIE: CITRICOS. Abstracts in English. 1974. irreg. per issue exchange basis. abstr.; charts; stat.
Formerly: Cuba. Centro de Informacion y Divulgacion Agropecuario. Boletin de Resenas. Serie: Citricos y Otras Frutales
Indexed: Agrind.
Published by: Centro de Informacion y Documentacion Agropecuario, Gaveta Postal 4149, Havana, 4, Cuba. TEL 29-2227. **Dist. by:** Ediciones Cubanas, Obispo No. 461, Apdo. 605, Havana, Cuba.

631 CUB ISSN 0138-8231
CUBA. CENTRO DE INFORMACION Y DOCUMENTACION AGROPECUARIO. BOLETIN DE RESENAS. SERIE: HORTALIZAS, PAPAS, GRANOS Y FIBRAS. Abstracts in English. 1984. irreg. per issue exchange basis.
Supersedes in part: Cuba. Centro de Informacion y Divulgacion Agropecuario. Boletin de Resenas. Serie: Viandas, Hortalizas y Granos
Indexed: Agrind.
Published by: Centro de Informacion y Documentacion Agropecuario, Gaveta Postal 4149, Havana, 4, Cuba. **Dist. by:** Ediciones Cubanas, Obispo No. 461, Apdo. 605, Havana, Cuba.

630 CUB ISSN 0138-8088
CUBA. CENTRO DE INFORMACION Y DOCUMENTACION AGROPECUARIO. BOLETIN DE RESENAS. SERIE: PROTECCION DE PLANTAS. Abstracts in English. 1974. s-a. per issue exchange basis.
Formerly: Cuba. Centro de Informacion y Divulgacion Agropecuario. Boletin de Resenas. Serie: Proteccion de Plantas
Indexed: Agrind.
Published by: Centro de Informacion y Documentacion Agropecuario, Gaveta Postal 4149, Havana, 4, Cuba. TEL 301672, TELEX 051-1007. **Dist. by:** Ediciones Cubanas, Obispo No. 461, Apdo. 605, Havana, Cuba.

631.587 CUB ISSN 0138-788X
CUBA. CENTRO DE INFORMACION Y DOCUMENTACION AGROPECUARIO. BOLETIN DE RESENAS. SERIE: RIEGO Y DRENAJE. Abstracts in English. 1974. irreg. per issue exchange basis.
Formerly: Cuba. Centro de Informacion y Divulgacion Agropecuario. Boletin de Resenas. Serie: Riego y Drenaje
Indexed: Agrind, FCA, HerbAb, HortAb.
—CISTI.
Published by: Centro de Informacion y Documentacion Agropecuario, Gaveta Postal 4149, Havana, 4, Cuba. **Dist. by:** Ediciones Cubanas, Obispo No. 461, Apdo. 605, Havana, Cuba.

631.4 CUB ISSN 0138-7936
CUBA. CENTRO DE INFORMACION Y DOCUMENTACION AGROPECUARIO. BOLETIN DE RESENAS. SERIE: SUELOS Y AGROQUIMICA. Abstracts in English. 1974. irreg. per issue exchange basis.
Formerly: Cuba. Centro de Informacion y Divulgacion Agropecuario. Boletin de Resenas. Serie: Suelos y Agroquimica
Indexed: Agrind.

Published by: Centro de Informacion y Documentacion Agropecuario, Gaveta Postal 4149, Havana, 4, Cuba. **Dist. by:** Ediciones Cubanas, Obispo No. 461, Apdo. 605, Havana, Cuba.

631 CUB ISSN 0253-5777
SB215 CODEN: CEAZDS
CUBA. MINISTERIO DE EDUCACION SUPERIOR. CENTRO AZUCAR. Text in Spanish. 3/yr. USD 20 in the Americas; USD 24 in Europe.
Indexed: AEA, AgBio, CIN, ChemAb, ChemTitl, FPA, I&DA, NutrAb, RDA, RPP, RevApplEntom, S&F, SIA, WAE&RSA.
—BLDSC (3113.170220), CASDDS.
Published by: (Cuba. Ministerio de Educacion Superior), Ediciones Cubanas, Obispo No. 527, Apdo. 605, Havana, Cuba.

631 CUB
CUBA. MINISTERIO DEL AZUCAR. INSTITUTO DE INVESTIGACIONES DE LA CANA DE AZUCAR. BOLETIN. Text in Spanish. 3/yr.
Indexed: I&DA.
Published by: Ministerio del Azucar, Instituto de Investigaciones de la Cana de Azucar, Ave. Vantroi No. 17203, Boyeros, Havana, Cuba.

630 USA ISSN 1064-5594
CUCURBIT GENETICS COOPERATIVE. REPORT. Text in English. 1978. a. free membership (effective 2005).
Indexed: AgBio, CPA, FCA, HortAb, NemAb, PBA, PGegResA, PGrRegA, RA&MP, SIA, SeedAb, TDB.
—BLDSC (7411.360200), IE.
Published by: Cucurbit Genetics Cooperative, 2118 Plant Sciences Bldg, College Park, MD 20742-4452. TEL 301-405-4345, FAX 301-314-9308, http://www.umresearch.umd.edu/CGC?cgcrepts.htm, http://www.umresearch.umd.edu/CGC/.

CULTIVAR; cultiver, gerer, entreprendre. see *AGRICULTURE*

631 CUB ISSN 0258-5936
SB111.A2
➤ **CULTIVOS TROPICALES.** Text in English, Spanish; Summaries in English, Spanish. 1979. q. USD 45 domestic (effective 2000). adv. **Document type:** *Academic/Scholarly.* **Description:** Includes scientific resuls of agricultural reseaches.
Related titles: CD-ROM ed.; Online - full text ed.
Indexed: AEA, ATA, AgBio, AgrForAb, Agrind, AnBrAb, BioCN&I, CPA, FCA, ForAb, HerbAb, HortAb, I&DA, MaizeAb, NutrAb, OrnHort, PBA, PGegResA, PGrRegA, PHN&I, PotatoAb, RA&MP, RDA, RPP, RevApplEntom, RiceAb, S&F, SIA, SeedAb, SoyAb, TriticAb, WAE&RSA, WeedAb.
Published by: Instituto Nacional de Ciencias Agricolas, GAVETA POSTAL, 1, San Jose de las Lajas, La Habana 32700, Cuba. TEL 53-64-63290, FAX 53-64-63867, inca@ceniai.inf.cu, inca@reduniv.edu.cu. Ed. Jose Roberto Martin Triana. Adv. contact Walfredo Torres de la Moral. Circ: 1,000.

633 FRA ISSN 1248-0525
CULTURE LEGUMIERE. Text in French. 1993. bi-m. EUR 44 domestic; EUR 54 foreign (effective 2002).
Published by: Agri Terroir Communication, 61, Rue du XXe-Corps-Americain, Metz, 57000, France. TEL 33-03-87691818, FAX 33-03-87691814, infocentre@editions-mirabelle.com, http://www.editions-mirabelle.com.

CURRENT AGRO-TECHNOLOGY FOR POTATO PRODUCTION. see *AGRICULTURE*

CURRENT PLANT SCIENCE AND BIOTECHNOLOGY IN AGRICULTURE. see *BIOLOGY—Biotechnology*

631.7 BRA
D N O C S - FINS E ATIVIDADES. Text in Portuguese. irreg. illus.
Published by: Departamento Nacional de Obras Contra as Secas, Av Duque de Caxias, 1700, sala 413, Caixa Postal 1441 AG CENTRO, Fortaleza, CE 60035-111, Brazil.

633.34 664.805655 CHN ISSN 1000-9841
DADOU KEXUE/SOYBEAN SCIENCE. Text in Chinese. 1982. q. CNY 3.50 domestic. **Document type:** *Academic/Scholarly.*
Related titles: Online - full text ed.: (from East View Information Services).
Indexed: AgBio, BioCN&I, CPA, DSA, FCA, HortAb, I&DA, MaizeAb, NemAb, NutrAb, PBA, PGegResA, PGrRegA, PHN&I, RA&MP, RPP, RevApplEntom, S&F, SIA, SeedAb, SoyAb, WAE&RSA, WeedAb.
—BLDSC (8361.005550), IE, ingenta.
Published by: Heilongjiang Sheng Nongye Kexueyuan, Xuefu Lu 368, Ha'erbin, 150086, China. Ed. Jingling Wang. **Dist. outside of China by:** China International Book Trading Corp, 35 Chegongzhuang Xilu, Haidian District, PO Box 399, Beijing 100044, China. TEL 86-10-68412045, FAX 86-10-68412023, cibtc@mail.cibtc.com.cn, http://www.cibtc.com.cn.

DAILY SUGAR REPORT. see *FOOD AND FOOD INDUSTRIES—Bakers And Confectioners*

DAIRY AND FIELD CROP DIGEST. see *AGRICULTURE—Dairying And Dairy Products*

631.8 USA ISSN 1043-3104
HD9483.U5 CODEN: DEPREN
DEALER PROGRESS; how smart agribusiness is growing. Text in English. 1970. bi-m. USD 40; USD 80 foreign; free to qualified personnel. adv. **Document type:** *Trade.* **Description:** For the commercial fertilizer and agricultural chemical retail dealer.
Former titles (until 1988): Progress (0895-1616); (until 1987): Fertilizer Progress (0002-1598)
—CISTI.
Published by: Fertilizer Institute, 501 Second St, N E, Washington, DC 20002. TEL 202-544-8123, FAX 202-675-8250, http://www.tfi.org. Circ: 26,000 (controlled).

632.6 DNK ISSN 0374-504X
DENMARK. MINISTERIET FOR FOEDEVARER, LANDBRUG OG FISKERI. AARSBERETNING. Variant title: Danish Pest Infestation Laboratory. Annual Report. Text in English; Summaries in Danish. 1949. a. free (effective 2003).
Related titles: Online - full content ed.: ISSN 1602-4125. 1997.
Indexed: BIOSIS Prev, BiolAb.
—CISTI.
Published by: Ministeriet for Foedevarer, Landbrug og Fiskeri, Statens Skadedyrlaboratorium/Danish Pest Infestation Laboratory, Skovbrynet 14, Kgs. Lyngby, 2800, Denmark. TEL 45-45-878055, FAX 45-45-931155, ssl@ssl.dk, http://www.dpil.dk/frames/publ_frm.htm, http://www.ssl.dk.

363.783409 DNK ISSN 1600-6364
TX571.P4
DENMARK. MINISTERIET FOR FOEDEVARER, LANDBRUG OG FISKERI. FOEDEVAREDIREKTORATET. PESTICIDRESTER I FOEDEVARER/PESTICIDE RESIDUES IN DANISH FOOD; resultater fra den danske pesticidkontrol. Text in Danish, English. 1983. a. DKK 130 (effective 1999). **Document type:** *Government.*
Former titles (until 1999): Pesticidrester i Danske Levnedsmidler (0108-2086); Rapport over Pesticidrester i Danske Levnedsmidler
Related titles: Online - full content ed.: ISSN 1600-6380.
Indexed: ChemAb.
Published by: Ministeriet for Foedevarer, Landbrug og Fiskeri, Foedevaredirektoratet/Ministry of Food, Agriculture and Fisheries. Veterinary and Food Administration, Moerkhoej Bygade 19, Soeborg, 2860, Denmark. TEL 45-33-95-60-00, http://www.ufd.dk, http://www.fdir.dk. Circ: 550.

354.3 DNK ISSN 0909-1378
DENMARK. MINISTERIET FOR FOEDEVARER, LANDBRUG OG FISKERI. PLANTEDIREKTORATET. BERETNING/DANISH PLANT DIRECTORATE. ANNUAL REPORT. Text in Danish; Summaries in English. 1994. a. free. stat. Supplement avail.; back issues avail. **Document type:** *Yearbook, Government.*
Formed by the 1994 merger of: Plantedirektoratets Beretning (0906-6217); Plantedirektoratets Beretning. Foder, Goedning, Voksemedier, EV-Stoetteordninger (0906-6195); Plantedirektoratets Beretning. Frugt og Groent, Plantesundhed, Miljoeforanstaltninger, Kartofler, Forstligt, Formeringsmateriale (0906-6209)
Related titles: Online - full text ed.: Denmark. Ministeriet for Foedevarer, Landbrug og Fiskeri. Plantedirektoratet. Beretning. ISSN 1398-5566. free.
Indexed: FCA, SeedAb.
—CISTI.
Published by: Ministeriet for Foedevarer, Landbrug og Fiskeri, Plantedirektoratet/Ministry of Food, Agriculture and Fisheries. Danish Plant Directorate, Skovbrynet 20, Lyngby, 2800, Denmark. TEL 45-45-263600, FAX 45-45-263610, pdir@pdir.dk, http://www.pdir.dk/Default.asp?ID=2270. Ed. Anne Frederiksen. Circ: 1,250.

632.9 ETH ISSN 0418-761X
DESERT LOCUST CONTROL ORGANIZATION FOR EASTERN AFRICA. ANNUAL REPORT. Text in English. 1962. a. free.
Supersedes: East Africa High Commissions Desert Locust Survey. Report
Indexed: RevApplEntom.
Published by: Desert Locust Control Organization for Eastern Africa, PO Box 4255, Addis Ababa, Ethiopia. TEL 251-1-611475, FAX 251-1-611648, TELEX 21510 DLCO ET.

634.8 DEU ISSN 0943-089X
DAS DEUTSCHE WEINMAGAZIN. Text in German. 1946. s-m. EUR 76.80 domestic; EUR 96 foreign; EUR 3.20 newsstand/cover (effective 2004). adv. bk.rev. **Document type:** *Magazine, Trade.*
Formerly (until 1992): Deutsche Weinbau (0012-0979)
Indexed: BiolAb, ChemAb, ExcerpMed, FS&TA, RRTA, RefZh, VITIS, WAE&RSA.
—BLDSC (3575.571000), IE. **CCC.**
Published by: Fachverlag Dr. Fraund GmbH, Postfach 1329, Friedrichsdorf, 61364, Germany. verlag@fraund.de, http://www.fraund.de. adv.: B&W page EUR 2,754, color page EUR 4,375. Circ: 7,629 (paid and controlled).

630 NLD ISSN 0167-4137
CODEN: DAENDT
➤ **DEVELOPMENTS IN AGRICULTURAL ENGINEERING.** Text in Dutch. 1980. irreg., latest vol.12, 2001. price varies. back issues avail. **Document type:** *Monographic series, Academic/Scholarly.* **Description:** Offers new insight on developments and research in all areas of agricultural engineering.

A

Indexed: Agr, BIOSIS Prev.
—BLDSC (3579.061200), CASDDS, CISTI. **CCC.**
Published by: Elsevier BV (Subsidiary of: Elsevier Science & Technology), Radarweg 29, Amsterdam, 1043 NX, Netherlands. TEL 31-20-4853911, FAX 31-20-4852457, nlinfo-f@elsevier.nl, http://www.elsevier.nl.

630 NLD ISSN 0378-519X
CODEN: DCSCDC

➤ **DEVELOPMENTS IN CROP SCIENCE.** Text in English. 1975. irreg., latest vol.26, 2000. price varies. back issues avail. **Document type:** *Monographic series, Academic/Scholarly.*
Description: Publishes research conducted in various areas of agricultural crop science.
Indexed: Agr, BIOSIS Prev.
—BLDSC (3579.070100), CASDDS, CISTI, IE. **CCC.**
Published by: Elsevier BV (Subsidiary of: Elsevier Science & Technology), Radarweg 29, Amsterdam, 1043 NX, Netherlands. TEL 31-20-4853911, FAX 31-20-4852457, nlinfo-f@elsevier.nl, http://www.elsevier.nl.

631 NLD ISSN 0167-840X
CODEN: DVPSD8

DEVELOPMENTS IN PLANT AND SOIL SCIENCES. Text in Dutch. 1981. irreg., latest vol.101, 2003. price varies. **Document type:** *Monographic series, Academic/Scholarly.*
Indexed: Agr, BIOSIS Prev, CIN, ChemAb, ChemTitl, S&F.
—BLDSC (3579.086080), CASDDS, CISTI, IE, ingenta. **CCC.**
Published by: Springer-Verlag Dordrecht (Subsidiary of: Springer Science+Business Media), Van Godewijckstraat 30, Dordrecht, 3311 GX, Netherlands. TEL 31-78-6576050, FAX 31-78-6576474, http://www.springeronline.com.

631.4 NLD ISSN 0166-0918
CODEN: DSSCDM

DEVELOPMENTS IN SOIL SCIENCE. Text in Dutch. 1972. irreg., latest vol.28, 2002. price varies. back issues avail. **Document type:** *Monographic series, Academic/Scholarly.* **Description:** Reports on geologic research in the soil and earth sciences.
Indexed: BIOSIS Prev, BiolAb.
—BLDSC (3579.090000), CASDDS, CISTI, IE, ingenta. **CCC.**
Published by: Elsevier BV (Subsidiary of: Elsevier Science & Technology), Radarweg 29, Amsterdam, 1043 NX, Netherlands. TEL 31-20-4853911, FAX 31-20-4852457, nlinfo-f@elsevier.nl, http://www.elsevier.nl.

631.4 FRA ISSN 0180-9555
CODEN: DOPEDJ

DOCUMENTS PEDOZOOLOGIQUES. Text in French; Summaries in English. 1979. irreg. free to qualified personnel.
Indexed: BiolAb, ChemAb, ZooRec.
—CASDDS.
Published by: Institut National de la Recherche Agronomique, Laboratoire de Zooecologie du Sol, CEPE, B.P. 5051, Montpellier, Cedex 34033, France. Ed. M B Bouche. Circ: 300.

631 IDN

DOMESTIC MARKETING OF COCONUT PRODUCTS. Text in English. a.?. USD 15. **Document type:** *Monographic series.*
Description: Analyzes the current status of Indonesian marketing of coconut products in relation to its share in the export market.
Published by: Asian and Pacific Coconut Community, 3rd Fl., Lina Bldg., Jl H R Rasuna Said Kav B 7, Kuningan, Jakarta, 12920, Indonesia. TEL 62-21-510-073, FAX 62-21-520-5160.

DROUGHT NETWORK NEWS. see *WATER RESOURCES*

633.491 NLD
CODEN: ACEPDG

E A P R ABSTRACTS OF CONFERENCE PAPERS, POSTERS AND DEMONSTRATIONS. Text in English, French, German. 1961 (first conference in 1960). triennial. **Document type:** *Proceedings, Academic/Scholarly.*
Former titles: E A P R Abstracts of Conference Papers (0376-4729); (until 1975): European Association for Potato Research. Proceedings of the Triennial Conference (0071-2507)
Indexed: FCA, HerbAb.
—BLDSC (0554.589550).
Published by: European Association for Potato Research, Postbus 20, Wageningen, 6700 AA, Netherlands. TEL 31-317-483041, FAX 31-317-484575, http://www.dpw.wageningen-ur.nl/epr/. Circ: 700.

632 GBR ISSN 0250-8052
CODEN: OEPBAO

➤ **E P P O BULLETIN**; a journal of regulatory plant protection. Variant title: Bulletin O E P P. Text in English, French. 1951; N.S. 1971. 3/yr. GBP 392 combined subscription in Europe to institutions print & online eds.; USD 724 combined subscription in the Americas to institutions & Caribbean (print & online eds.); GBP 392 combined subscription elsewhere to institutions print & online eds. (effective 2006). adv. bk.rev. abstr.; bibl.; charts; illus. back issues avail.; reprint service avail. from PSC. **Document type:** *Journal, Academic/Scholarly.* **Description:** Publishes research findings on all aspects of plant pathology.
Former titles: European and Mediterranean Plant Protection Organization. Publications. Series A: Reports of Technical Meetings; European and Mediterranean Plant Protection Organization. Publications. Series C: Reports of Working Parties (0071-240X)
Related titles: Microform ed.: N.S. (from PQC); Online - full text ed.: ISSN 1365-2338. N.S. GBP 372 in Europe to institutions; USD 687 in the Americas to institutions & Caribbean; GBP 409 elsewhere to institutions (effective 2006) (from Blackwell Synergy, EBSCO Publishing, Gale Group, IngentaConnect, O C L C Online Computer Library Center, Inc., Swets Information Services).
Indexed: AEA, AgBio, AgrForAb, BIOSIS Prev, BioCN&I, BioDAb, BiolAb, CPA, DBA, FCA, FPA, FaBeAb, ForAb, GardL, HelmAb, HerbAb, HortAb, MaizeAb, NemAb, OrnHort, PBA, PGegResA, PGrRegA, PHN&I, PotatoAb, RA&MP, RPP, RefZh, RevApplEntom, S&F, SIA, SeedAb, SoyAb, TriticAb, VITIS, WAE&RSA, WeedAb, ZooRec.
—BLDSC (3794.370000), CASDDS, CISTI, IE, Infotrieve, ingenta, Linda Hall. **CCC.**
Published by: (European and Mediterranean Plant Protection Organization), Blackwell Publishing Ltd., 9600 Garsington Rd, Oxford, OX4 2ZG, United Kingdom. TEL 44-1865-776868, FAX 44-1865-714591, customerservices@oxon.blackwellpublishing.com, http://www.blackwellpublishing.com/journals/EPP. Ed. I M Smith. Pub. Sue Hewitt. R&P Sophie Savage. Adv. contact Jenny Applin. Circ: 800.

➤ **EARTH GARDEN.** see *NEW AGE PUBLICATIONS*

➤ **ECONOMIA CAFETERA.** see *AGRICULTURE—Agricultural Economics*

630.24 668.6 ECU

ECUADOR. INSTITUTO NACIONAL DE INVESTIGACIONES AGROPECUARIAS. INFORME TECNICO. Text in Spanish. irreg.
Published by: Instituto Nacional de Investigaciones Agropecuarias, Departamento de Comunicacion, Casilla 2600, Quito, Pichincha, Ecuador.

631.4 EGY ISSN 0302-6701
S590 CODEN: EJSSAF

➤ **EGYPTIAN JOURNAL OF SOIL SCIENCE/AL-MAGALLAT AL-MISRIYYAT LI-'ULUM AL-ARADI.** Text in English; Summaries in English, Arabic. 1961. q. USD 147 (effective 2003). abstr.; bibl.; charts. reprint service avail. from IRC. **Document type:** *Journal, Academic/Scholarly.*
Supersedes (in 1972): Magallat 'Ulum al-Aradi lil-Gumhuriyyat al-'Arabiyyat al-Muttahidah (0449-3176)
Indexed: AEA, AgrForAb, BIOSIS Prev, BiolAb, CIN, CPA, ChemAb, ChemTitl, ExcerpMed, FCA, HerbAb, HortAb, I&DA, MaizeAb, OrnHort, PBA, PGrRegA, PotatoAb, PoultAb, RA&MP, RPP, RiceAb, S&F, SIA, SeedAb, SoyAb, TriticAb, VITIS, WeedAb.
—BLDSC (3664.420000), CASDDS, CISTI, IE, ingenta, Linda Hall.
Published by: (Society of Soil Science, Research Department), National Information and Documentation Centre (NIDOC), Tahrir St., Dokki, Awqaf P.O., Giza, Egypt. TEL 20-2-3371696, FAX 20-2-3371746, http://derp.sti.sci.eg/data/0135.htm. Ed. Dr. Hassan Muhmoud Hamdi. Circ: 1,500.

630.24 ESP ISSN 1579-4377

ELECTRONIC JOURNAL OF ENVIRONMENTAL, AGRICULTURAL AND FOOD CHEMISTRY. Cover title: EJEAFChe. Text in English. 2002. 3/yr. free (effective 2005).
Description: Publishes research results dealing with the chemistry and biochemistry of agriculture and food. The topics included are on food chemistry, environmental science and agronomy, and agricultural chemistry.
Media: Online - full text.
Indexed: AgrForAb, FCA, ForAb, HortAb, PHN&I, PotatoAb, PoultAb, RM&VM, S&F, SIA.
Published by: Universidade de Vigo, Faculty of Science, Ourense, 32004, Spain. TEL 34-988-387060, FAX 34-988-387001, labqf@uvigo.es, http://ejeafche.uvigo.es/about.htm.

630 BRA ISSN 1516-1617

EMBRAPA SEMI-ARIDO. CIRCULAR TECNICA. Text in Portuguese. 1980. irreg. **Document type:** *Monographic series.*
Formerly (until 1999): Centro de Pesquisa Agropecuaria do Tropico Semi-Arido. Circular Tecnica (0100-6169)
Indexed: AgrForAb, CPA, DSA, FCA, FPA, ForAb, HerbAb, HortAb, NutrAb, PBA, PGegResA, PGrRegA, PHN&I, PotatoAb, RPP, S&F, SeedAb.
—BLDSC (3265.124780), CISTI.
Published by: Empresa Brasileira de Pesquisa Agropecuaria, Embrapa Semi-Arido (Subsidiary of: Empresa Brasileira de Pesquisa Agropecuaria), Rodovia BR 428 km 152, Zona Rural, Petrolina, PE 56300-970, Brazil. TEL 55-87-3862-1711, FAX 55-87-3862-1744, sac@cpatsa.empraba.br, http://www.cpatsa.embrapa.br.

630 BRA ISSN 1516-1609

EMBRAPA SEMI-ARIDO. COMUNICADO TECNICO. Text in Portuguese. 1980. irreg. **Document type:** *Monographic series.*
Formerly (until 1999): Centro de Pesquisa Agropecuaria do Tropico Semi-Arido. Comunicado Tecnico (0100-6061)
Indexed: AEA, AgrForAb, CPA, FCA, HortAb, I&DA, IndVet, NemAb, NutrAb, PBA, PHN&I, S&F, SIA, SeedAb, VetBull, WAE&RSA.
—BLDSC (3397.472500), CISTI.
Published by: Empresa Brasileira de Pesquisa Agropecuaria, Embrapa Semi-Arido (Subsidiary of: Empresa Brasileira de Pesquisa Agropecuaria), Rodovia BR 428 km 152, Zona Rural, Petrolina, PE 56300-970, Brazil. TEL 55-87-3862-1711, FAX 55-87-3862-1744, sac@cpatsa.empraba.br, http://www.cpatsa.embrapa.br, http://www.embrapa.br.

630 BRA ISSN 1516-1633

EMBRAPA SEMI-ARIDO. DOCUMENTOS. Text in Portuguese. 1978. irreg. **Document type:** *Monographic series.*
Formerly (until 1999): Centro de Pesquisa Agropecuaria do Tropico Semi-Arido. Documentos (0100-9729)
Indexed: AgrForAb, AnBrAb, CPA, DSA, FCA, FPA, ForAb, HerbAb, HortAb, I&DA, MaizeAb, NutrAb, PBA, RRTA, S&F, WAE&RSA.
—BLDSC (3612.103170), CISTI.
Published by: Empresa Brasileira de Pesquisa Agropecuaria, Embrapa Semi-Arido (Subsidiary of: Empresa Brasileira de Pesquisa Agropecuaria), Rodovia BR 428 km 152, Zona Rural, Petrolina, PE 56300-970, Brazil. TEL 55-87-3862-1711, FAX 55-87-3862-1744, http://www.embrapa.br.

630 BRA ISSN 1516-1625

EMBRAPA SEMI-ARIDO. PESQUISA EM ANDAMENTO. Text in Portuguese. 1980. irreg. **Document type:** *Monographic series.*
Formerly (until 1999): Centro de Pesquisa Agropecuaria do Tropico Semi-Arido. Pesquisa em Andamento (0100-6118)
Indexed: AgrForAb, FCA, HerbAb, HortAb, I&DA, PBA, RPP, S&F.
—BLDSC (6428.238290), CISTI.
Published by: Empresa Brasileira de Pesquisa Agropecuaria, Embrapa Semi-Arido (Subsidiary of: Empresa Brasileira de Pesquisa Agropecuaria), Rodovia BR 428 km 152, Zona Rural, Petrolina, PE 56300-970, Brazil. TEL 55-87-3862-1711, FAX 55-87-3862-1744, sac@cpatsa.empraba.br, http://www.cpatsa.embrapa.br.

633 BRA ISSN 1516-781X

EMBRAPA SOJA. DOCUMENTOS. Text in Portuguese. 1982. irreg.
Formerly (until 1999): Centro Nacional de Pesquisa de Soja. Documentos (0101-5494)
Indexed: AEA, AbHyg, AgBio, AgrForAb, BioCN&I, CPA, DSA, FCA, ForAb, HelmAb, HerbAb, HortAb, I&DA, IndVet, MaizeAb, NemAb, NutrAb, OrnHort, PBA, PGegResA, PHN&I, PotatoAb, ProtozoAb, RDA, RPP, RiceAb, S&F, SIA, SeedAb, SoyAb, TDB, TriticAb, VetBull, WAE&RSA, WeedAb.
—BLDSC (3733.096800), CISTI.
Published by: Empresa Brasileira de Pesquisa Agropecuaria, Embrapa Soja (Subsidiary of: Empresa Brasileira de Pesquisa Agropecuaria), Rodovia Carlos Joao Strass (Londrina/Warta), Acesso Orlando Amaral, Caixa Postal 231, Londrina, PR 86001-970, Brazil. TEL 55-43-371-6000, FAX 55-43-371-6100, sac@cnpso.emprapa.br, http://www.cnpso.emprapa.br, http://www.embrapa.br.

630 BRA ISSN 0103-0205
SB251.B7

EMPRESA BRASILEIRA DE PESQUISA AGROPECUARIA. EMBRAPA ALGODAO. DOCUMENTOS. Text in Portuguese. 1981. irreg.
Indexed: AgBio, BioCN&I, FCA, HortAb, PBA, PGegResA, S&F, WAE&RSA, WeedAb.
—BLDSC (3612.105000).
Published by: Empresa Brasileira de Pesquisa Agropecuaria, Embrapa Algodao (Subsidiary of: Empresa Brasileira de Pesquisa Agropecuaria), Rua Oswaldo Cruz 1.143, Centenario, Campina Grande, PB 58107-720, Brazil. TEL 55-83-3413608, FAX 55-83-322-7751, sac@cnpa.embrapa.br, http://www.cnpa.embrapa.br.

ENSAYOS SOBRE ECONOMIA CAFETERA. see *AGRICULTURE—Agricultural Economics*

631.6 ITA ISSN 0014-1100

EST SESIA. Text in Italian. 1954. q. free. charts; illus.
Description: Focuses on irrigation and land reclamation.
Indexed: RefZh.
Published by: Associazione Irrigazione Est Sesia, Via Negroni, 7, Novara, NO 28100, Italy. Ed. Sergio Baratti. Circ: 10,000.

631 580 ESP ISSN 0365-1800
S15

➤ **ESTACION EXPERIMENTAL DE AULA DEI. ANALES.** Text and summaries in English, Spanish. 1948. a. back issues avail. **Document type:** *Academic/Scholarly.* **Description:** Original research in agriculture and related subjects.
Indexed: BiolAb, CPA, ChemAb, HortAb, IECT, PBA, PGrRegA, S&F, VITIS, ZooRec.
Published by: Estacion Experimental de Aula Dei, Apdo. de Correos 202, C. Montanana 177, Zaragoza, 50081, Spain. TEL 34-76-576511, FAX 34-76-575620. Ed. Ed J Abadia Bayona. Circ: 1,000.

➤ **ESTADISTICA PANAMENA. SITUACION ECONOMICA. SECCION 312. SUPERFICIE SEMBRADA Y COSECHA DE CAFE Y CANA DE AZUCAR.** see *AGRICULTURE—Abstracting, Bibliographies, Statistics*

631.4 FRA ISSN 1252-6851
CODEN: BUFSAS

ETUDES ET GESTION DES SOLS. Text and summaries in English, French. 1963. q. bk.rev. charts. index.
Supersedes in part (in 1993): Science du Sol (0767-2853); Which was formerly (until 1983): Association Francaise pour l'Etude du Sol. Bulletin (0335-1653); Which was formed by the merger of (1963-1973): Science du Sol (0036-8318); And (1957-1973): Association Francaise pour l'Etude du Sol. Bulletin (0519-0800)
Related titles: ♦ Supplement(s): Association Francaise pour l'Etude du Sol. Lettre. ISSN 0295-1347.
Indexed: BiolAb, ChemAb, ExcerpMed, RefZh, S&F.
—CASDDS, CISTI, Linda Hall.
Published by: Association Francaise pour l'Etude du Sol, Avenue de la Pomme de Pin, BP 20619, Ardon, 45166 OLIVET cedex, France. TEL 33-2-38417887, FAX 33-2-38417869, afes@orleans.inra.fr. Ed. M Jamagne. Circ: 1,300 (controlled).

631.53 NLD ISSN 0014-2336
CODEN: EUPHAA

➤ **EUPHYTICA**; international journal on plant breeding. Text in English. 1952. 18/yr. EUR 2,548, USD 2,585, GBP 1,678 combined subscription to institutions print & online eds. (effective 2005). adv. bk.rev. bibl.; charts; illus. index. reprint service avail. from PSC. **Document type:** *Journal, Academic/Scholarly.* **Description:** Publishes original research results, critical reviews and short communications on all aspects of plant breeding research.
Related titles: Microform ed.: (from PQC); Online - full text ed.: ISSN 1573-5060 (from EBSCO Publishing, Gale Group, IngentaConnect, Kluwer Online, O C L C Online Computer Library Center, Inc., Ovid Technologies, Inc., Springer LINK, Swets Information Services).
Indexed: AEBA, ASCA, AgBio, Agr, AgrForAb, ApicAb, B&BAb, BIOBASE, BIOSIS Prev, BibLing, BioEngAb, BiolAb, CIN, CIS, CMCI, CPA, CTFA, ChemAb, ChemTitl, CurCont, DBA, DSA, ESPM, FCA, FPA, FS&TA, ForAb, GenetAb, HGA, HerbAb, HortAb, I&DA, IABS, ISR, MBA, MaizeAb, NemAb, NutrAb, OrnHort, PBA, PGegResA, PGrRegA, PHN&I, PlantSci, PotatoAb, RA&MP, RDA, RPP, RefZh, RevApplEntom, RiceAb, S&F, S&MA, SCI, SIA, SeedAb, SoyAb, TOSA, TriticAb, VITIS, WAE&RSA, WeedAb.
—BLDSC (3828.000000), CASDDS, CISTI, IDS, IE, Infotrieve, ingenta, Linda Hall. **CCC.**
Published by: (Stichting Euphytica), Springer-Verlag Dordrecht (Subsidiary of: Springer Science+Business Media), Van Godewijckstraat 30, Dordrecht, 3311 GX, Netherlands. TEL 31-78-6576050, FAX 31-78-6576474, http://springerlink.metapress.com/openurl.asp?genre=journal&issn=0014-2336, http://www.springeronline.com. Ed. R G F Visser.

631.4 RUS ISSN 1064-2293
S590 CODEN: ESSCEY

➤ **EURASIAN SOIL SCIENCE.** Text in English. 1899. m. USD 3,052 in North America; USD 3,515 elsewhere (effective 2004). adv. bk.rev. abstr.; bibl.; charts; illus. index. **Document type:** *Journal, Academic/Scholarly.* **Description:** Covers current Russian literature on all aspects of the soil sciences, including mineralogy and physical properties of soils, as well as soil melioration, irrigation and drainage, forest and range soils, soil pollution and management. Also includes selected relevant articles from periodicals in related fields such as agricultural engineering.
Incorporates (1964-2000): Agricultural Chemistry (1560-0890); Formerly (until 1992): Soviet Soil Science (0038-5832)
Related titles: ♦ Translation of: Agrokhimiya. ISSN 0002-1881; ♦ Translation of: Pochvovedenie. ISSN 0032-180X.
Indexed: AEA, ASCA, ASFA, AgrForAb, BiolAb, CPA, CivEngAb, CurCont, ESPM, EnvEAb, FCA, FLUIDEX, ForAb, GEOBASE, GeotechAb, I&DA, IBR, ISR, MBA, MaizeAb, PollutAb, PotatoAb, RPP, RevApplEntom, RiceAb, S&F, SCI, SWRA, TriticAb, WeedAb.
—BLDSC (0411.747000), CISTI, IDS, IE, Infotrieve, ingenta, Linda Hall. **CCC.**
Published by: (Rossiiskaya Akademiya Nauk/Russian Academy of Sciences), M A I K Nauka - Interperiodica, Profsoyuznaya ul 90, Moscow, 117997, Russian Federation. TEL 7-095-3347420, FAX 7-095-3360666, compmg@maik.ru, http://www.maik.ru/journals/soilsci.htm. Ed. Gleb V Dobrovol'skii. R&P Vladimir I Vasil'ev. Circ: 500. **Subscr. to:** Interperiodica, PO Box 1831, Birmingham, AL 35201-1831. TEL 205-995-1567, 800-633-4931, FAX 205-995-1588.

➤ **EUROFRUIT MAGAZINE.** see *FOOD AND FOOD INDUSTRIES—Grocery Trade*

633 GBR ISSN 0071-2825

EUROPEAN GRASSLAND FEDERATION. PROCEEDINGS OF THE GENERAL MEETING. Text in English. 1965. irreg. EUR 40 per issue (effective 2005). **Document type:** *Proceedings.*
Published by: European Grassland Federation, The British Grassland Society, University of Reading, PO Box 237, Reading, Berkshire RG6 6AR, United Kingdom. FAX 44-1189-666941, office@britishgrassland.com, http://www.europeangrassland.org/offers.html. Circ: 340.

631 NLD ISSN 1161-0301
CODEN: EJAGET

➤ **EUROPEAN JOURNAL OF AGRONOMY.** Text in Dutch. 1992. 8/yr. EUR 680 in Europe to institutions; JPY 90,500 in Japan to institutions; USD 762 elsewhere to institutions (effective 2006). abstr. back issues avail. **Document type:** *Journal, Academic/Scholarly.* **Description:** Describes experimental and theoretical contributions to crop science in various fields.
Related titles: Online - full text ed.: (from EBSCO Publishing, Gale Group, IngentaConnect, ScienceDirect, Swets Information Services).
Indexed: AEA, ASCA, AgBio, Agr, AgrForAb, AnBrAb, BIOBASE, BIOSIS Prev, BiolAb, CIN, CPA, ChemAb, ChemTitl, CurCont, DSA, FCA, ForAb, GEOBASE, HerbAb, HortAb, I&DA, IABS, M&GPA, MaizeAb, NemAb, NutrAb, OrnHort, PBA, PGegResA, PGrRegA, PHN&I, PN&I, PlantSci, PotatoAb, PoultAb, RA&MP, RDA, RPP, RevApplEntom, RiceAb, S&F, SIA, SeedAb, SoyAb, TriticAb, VITIS, WAE&RSA, WeedAb.
—BLDSC (3829.722150), CASDDS, CISTI, IDS, IE, Infotrieve, ingenta. **CCC.**
Published by: (European Society for Agronomy), Elsevier BV (Subsidiary of: Elsevier Science & Technology), Radarweg 29, Amsterdam, 1043 NX, Netherlands. TEL 31-20-4853911, FAX 31-20-4852457, nlinfo-f@elsevier.nl, http://www.elsevier.com/locate/eja, http://www.elsevier.nl. Ed. F Villalobos.

631.4 GBR ISSN 1351-0754
S590 CODEN: ESOSES

➤ **EUROPEAN JOURNAL OF SOIL SCIENCE.** Text in English. bi-m. GBP 50, GBP 75 combined subscription in Europe to individuals print & online eds.; USD 94 combined subscription in the Americas to individuals & Caribbean (print & online eds.); GBP 56 combined subscription elsewhere to individuals print & online eds.; EUR 431 combined subscription in Europe to institutions print & online eds.; USD 796 combined subscription in the Americas to institutions & Caribbean (print & online eds.); GBP 474 combined subscription elsewhere to institutions print & online eds. (effective 2006). adv. bk.rev. bibl.; charts; illus. index. back issues avail.; reprint service avail. from PSC. **Document type:** *Journal, Academic/Scholarly.* **Description:** Publishes research and up-to-date authoritative and critical reviews over the whole field of soil science and its applications.
Formerly (until 1993): Journal of Soil Science (0022-4588); Supersedes in part (in 1993): Pedologie (0079-0419); (in 1993): Science du Sol (0767-2853); Which was formerly: Association Francaise pour l'Etude du Sol. Bulletin (0335-1653); Which was formed by the merger of (1963-1973): Science du Sol (0036-8318); (1957-1973): Association Francaise pour l'Etude du Sol. Bulletin (0519-0800)
Related titles: Microform ed.: (from PQC); Online - full text ed.: ISSN 1365-2389. GBP 409 in Europe to institutions; USD 756 in the Americas to institutions & Caribbean; GBP 450 elsewhere to institutions (effective 2006) (from Blackwell Synergy, EBSCO Publishing, Gale Group, IngentaConnect, O C L C Online Computer Library Center, Inc., Swets Information Services).
Indexed: AEA, AESIS, AGBP, APD, ASCA, ASFA, AbHyg, Agr, AgrForAb, AnalAb, ApMecR, B&AI, B&BAb, BIOSIS Prev, BiolAb, BrArAb, BrCerAb, C&ISA, CIN, CPA, Cadscan, CerAb, ChemAb, ChemTitl, CivEngAb, CorrAb, CurCont, DSA, E&CAJ, EMA, EPB, ESPM, EngInd, EnvEAb, FCA, FLUIDEX, FPA, ForAb, GEOBASE, GeotechAb, HRIS, HelmAb, HerbAb, HortAb, I&DA, IAA, IABS, ICEA, ISR, LeadAb, M&TEA, MBA, MBF, METADEX, MSCI, MaizeAb, MinerAb, NemAb, PBA, PN&I, PetrolAb, PlantSci, PollutAb, PoultAb, RA&MP, RDA, RPP, RefZh, RevApplEntom, RiceAb, S&F, SCI, SIA, SWRA, SeedAb, SolStAb, TDB, TriticAb, VITIS, WAA, WAE&RSA, WeedAb, Zincscan.
—BLDSC (3829.741700), CASDDS, CISTI, Ei, IDS, IE, Infotrieve, ingenta, Linda Hall. **CCC.**
Published by: (British Society of Soil Science), Blackwell Publishing Ltd., 9600 Garsington Rd, Oxford, OX4 2ZG, United Kingdom. TEL 44-1865-776868, FAX 44-1865-714591, customerservices@oxon.blackwellpublishing.com, http://www.blackwellpublishing.com/journals/EJS. Ed. P Loveland. Pub. Sue Hewitt. R&P Sophie Savage. Adv. contact Jenny Applin. Circ: 2,120. **Co-sponsor:** National Societies of Soil Science in Europe.

632.9 GBR ISSN 1460-6127

EUROPEAN MOSQUITO BULLETIN. Text in English. q.
Former titles (until 1998): British Mosquito Bulletin (0961-8384); (until 1991): British Mosquito Group Newsletter (0269-1299)
Indexed: AbHyg, BioCN&I, ProtozoAb, TDB, ZooRec.
Published by: University of East London, Greengate House, 33-35, Greengate St, London, E13 0BG, United Kingdom. TEL 44-20-8590-7722, FAX 44-20-8849-3694.

630 USA ISSN 0899-3270
SB228 CODEN: ENCCEL

EVALUATION OF NEW CANAL POINT SUGARCANE CLONES. Text in English. a. **Document type:** *Government.*
Formerly (until 198?): Sugarcane Variety Tests in Florida (0193-9521)
Indexed: BIOSIS Prev, BiolAb.
—CISTI.
Published by: United States Department of Agriculture, Agricultural Research Service, Sugarcane Field Stat, Star Rt Box 8, Hwy 441, Canal Point, FL 33438. FAX 561-924-6109, bglaz@saa.ars.usda.gov.

631.8 IND

F A I ANNUAL REVIEW OF FERTILISER PRODUCTION AND CONSUMPTION. Text in English. a. USD 10.
Related titles: ♦ Supplement to: Indian Journal of Fertilisers. ISSN 0973-1822.
Published by: Fertiliser Association of India, 10 Shaheed Jit Singh Marg, New Delhi, 110 067, India. TEL 91-11-656-7144, FAX 91-11-696-0052, fai@vsnl.com.

631.4 USA ISSN 0253-2050
CODEN: FSBUDD

F A O SOILS BULLETIN. Text in English. 1965. irreg., latest vol.76, 1999. price varies. bibl. **Document type:** *Monographic series.*
Formerly (until 1977): Food and Agriculture Organization of the United Nations. Soils Bulletin (0532-0437)
Related titles: French ed.; Spanish ed.
Indexed: AEA, Agr, RDA, RefZh, S&F, WAE&RSA.
—BLDSC (3865.742000), CASDDS, CISTI, Linda Hall.
Published by: Food and Agriculture Organization of the United Nations, c/o Bernan Associates, 4611 F Assembly Dr, Lanham, MD 20706-4391. TEL 301-459-7666, FAX 301-459-0056.

631.8 USA ISSN 1014-7675
HD9483.A1

F A O YEARBOOK. FERTILIZER. Text in English, French, Spanish. 1951. a. USD 36 (effective 2000).
Former titles (until 1987): F A O Fertilizer Yearbook (0251-1525); (until 1979): Annual Fertilizer Review (0084-6546); (until 1970): Fertilizers: An Annual Review of World Production, Consumption and Trade (0071-464X); (until 1959): Annual Review of World Production, Consumption and Trade of Fertilizers (0426-7796)
Related titles: Microfiche ed.: (from CIS).
Indexed: IIS, S&F, WAE&RSA.
—CISTI, Linda Hall.
Published by: Food and Agriculture Organization of the United Nations, c/o Bernan Associates, 4611 F Assembly Dr, Lanham, MD 20706-4391. TEL 301-459-7666, FAX 301-459-0056.

631.85 TWN ISSN 0253-9616
CODEN: FBSEDX

F F T C BOOK SERIES. Text in English. 1978. biennial.
Published by: Food and Fertilizer Technology Center, 5F.14 Wenchow St, Taipei, 10616, Taiwan. TEL 886-2-2362-6239, FAX 886-2-2362-0478, fftc@agnet.org, http://www.fftc.agnet.org/.

631.85 TWN

F F T C NEWSLETTER. Text in English. q. back issues avail.
Media: Online - full text.
Published by: Food and Fertilizer Technology Center, 5F.14 Wenchow St, Taipei, 10616, Taiwan. TEL 886-2-2362-6239, FAX 886-2-2362-0478, fftc@agnet.org, http://www.fftc.agnet.org/library/list/pub/nl.html.

631.85 TWN

F F T C TECHNICAL BULLETIN. Text in English. bi-w. back issues avail. **Document type:** *Bulletin.*
Media: Online - full text.
Published by: Food and Fertilizer Technology Center, 5F.14 Wenchow St, Taipei, 10616, Taiwan. TEL 886-2-2362-6239, FAX 886-2-2362-0478, fftc@agnet.org, http://www.fftc.agnet.org/library/list/pub/tb.html.

F.O. LICHT'S DAILY SUGAR REPORT. see *FOOD AND FOOD INDUSTRIES*

F.O. LICHT'S WORLD SUGAR YEARBOOK. see *FOOD AND FOOD INDUSTRIES*

631 GBR

F O S F A INTERNATIONAL. NEWSLETTER. Text in English. 1985. q. **Document type:** *Trade.*
Published by: Federation of Oils Seeds and Fats Associations Ltd., Nordic Bank House, 20 St Dunstans Hill, London, EC3R 8NQ, United Kingdom. TEL 44-20-7283-5511, FAX 44-20-7623-1310, contact@fosfa.org. Eds. William King, Mr. Stuart Logan. R&P, Adv. contact Miss A Baran. Circ: 1,000.

631.5 ZAF ISSN 0367-3073
CODEN: FSAJA6

F S S A JOURNAL. (Fertilizer Society of South Africa) Text in English. 1968. irreg.
—CISTI, Linda Hall.
Published by: Fertilizer Society of South Africa, P.O. Box 75510, Lynnwood Ridge, 0040, South Africa. TEL 012-3491450, FAX 012-3491463, fssamvsa@mweb.co.za.

631 SVN ISSN 0352-3020

FAGOPYRUM; scientific journal on buckwheat research. Text in English. 1981. irreg., latest vol.19, 2002. USD 80 per vol. (effective 2003).
Formerly (until 1981): Buckwheat Newsletter (0351-7942)
Indexed: BioCN&I, CPA, FCA, PBA, PGegResA, RPP, SeedAb.
—BLDSC (3865.220000).

A

Published by: (International Buckwheat Research Association JPN), Univerza v Ljubljani, Biotehniska Fakulteta/University of Ljubljana, Biotechnical Faculty, Jamnikarjeva 101, Ljubljana, 1000, Slovenia. TEL 386-1-4231161, FAX 386-1-2565782, http://www.bf.uni-lj.si/Fagopyrum/. Ed. Ohni Ohnishi.

630.24 668.6 USA ISSN 1043-8858
FARM CHEMICALS INTERNATIONAL. Text in English. q. USD 23 domestic; USD 43 foreign (effective 2000). adv. **Document type:** *Trade.* **Description:** Serves manufacturers, formulators, mixers, dealers, and commercial applicators of fertilizers and pesticides.
Related titles: Online - full text ed.
Indexed: CBNB, DBA, GardL, S&F.
—BLDSC (3873.100000), CISTI. **CCC.**
Published by: Meister Media Worldwide, 37733 Euclid Ave, Willoughby, OH 44094-5992. TEL 440-942-2000, 800-572-7740, FAX 440-942-0662, fci_circ@meisternet.com, http://meistermedia.com/fci-isaa2004. Ed. Jim Sulecki. Adv. contact Al Sray. Circ: 9,000.

631 USA ISSN 1542-2062
THE FARMER-STOCKMAN. Text in English. 1911. m. USD 23.95 in state; USD 30 out of state (effective 2005). adv. **Document type:** *Magazine, Trade.* **Description:** Covers local crop and livestock production; written for Texas farmers and ranchers.
Formerly (until 2002): Texas Farmer-Stockman (0279-165X)
Published by: Farm Progress Companies, 191 S Gary Ave, Carol Stream, IL 60188-2095. TEL 630-462-2229, FAX 630-462-2202, jtsmith@farmprogress.com, info@farmprogress.com, http://www.thefarmerstockman.com, http://www.farmprogress.com/. Ed. J T Smith. Pub. Jeff M Lapin. adv.: B&W page USD 2,150, color page USD 2,650; trim 10.5 x 14.5. Circ: 35,000 (paid).

631.587 AUS ISSN 0014-844X
FARMERS NEWSLETTER. Text in English. 1948. q. AUD 20 (effective 2000); free to qualified personnel. adv. bk.rev. illus. **Document type:** *Newsletter.*
Related titles: Regional ed(s).: Farmers Newsletter. Large Area Edition; Seasonal ed(s).: Farmers Newsletter. Horticultural Edition.
Indexed: AEA, AgBio, BioCN&I, FCA, HortAb, RPP, RRTA, RevApplEntom, S&F, SoyAb, WAE&RSA, WeedAb.
Published by: Irrigation Research & Extension Committee, c/o C.S.I.R.O., Division of Water Resources, Private Bag, Griffith, NSW 2680, Australia. TEL 61-69-601550, FAX 61-69-601562. Ed., Adv. contact Michael Murray TEL 61-2-6993-5822. Circ: 4,200.

631 IDN
FARMERS RECEPTIVITY TO NEW TECHNOLOGIES IN COCONUT. Text in English. a. USD 10. **Description:** Covers the new technologies in the form of new high yielding varieties, use of organic and inorganic fertilizer, pest and disease control, intercropping and intergrazing in coconut land.
Published by: Asian and Pacific Coconut Community, 3rd Fl., Lina Bldg., Jl H R Rasuna Said Kav B 7, Kuningan, Jakarta, 12920, Indonesia. TEL 62-21-510-073, FAX 62-21-520-5160.

631 USA ISSN 0744-7876
FARMER'S REPORT. Text in English. 1979. w. USD 7.50. adv.
Published by: Rochelle Newspapers Inc., 401 N Main, Rochelle, IL 61068. TEL 815-562-4174. Ed. Ken Wise. Circ: 10,500.

630 USA
THE FARMERS - STOCKMAN. Text in English. 1911. m. USD 21.95 in state (effective 2005). adv. **Document type:** *Magazine.*
Formerly (until 2005): Oklahoma Farmer-Stockman (0145-9392)
Published by: Farm Progress Companies, 191 S Gary Ave, Carol Stream, IL 60188. http://www.farmprogress.com/. Ed. J T Smith. adv.: B&W page USD 3,400, color page USD 3,910; trim 10 x 7. Circ: 23,000 (paid).

630 GBR ISSN 0071-3961
FARMING IN THE EAST MIDLANDS. Text in English. a. free. **Document type:** *Bulletin.*
Formerly: Farm Management Notes
Published by: University of Nottingham, Rural Business Research Unit, Sutton Bonington Campus, Loughborough, Leics LE12 5RD, United Kingdom. TEL 44-115-951-6070, FAX 44-115-951-6089, sazmfs@szni.nottingham.ac.uk. Ed. Martin Seabrook.

FEDERACION NACIONAL DE CAFETEROS DE COLOMBIA. INFORME DE LABORES DE LOS COMITES DEPARTAMENTALES DE CAFETEROS. see *FOOD AND FOOD INDUSTRIES*

631 USA
FEDERAL MARKETING ORDERS FOR AVOCADOS; grown in Florida. Text in English. a. **Description:** Covers grade, size, maturity and pack requirements for avocados grown in Florida, and import regulations.
Published by: Florida Avocado Administrative Committee, 18710 S W 288th St, Homestead, FL 33030. TEL 305-247-0848, FAX 305-245-1315.

FERTILISER ASSOCIATION OF INDIA. FERTILISER STATISTICS. see *AGRICULTURE—Abstracting, Bibliographies, Statistics*

631.8 IND
FERTILISER DIGEST. Text in English. 1962. bi-m. INR 3.
Published by: Fertiliser Corporation of India Ltd., Madhuban, 55 Nehru Place, New Delhi, 110 019, India. Ed. R S Mathur. Circ: 4,000.

631.8 IND ISSN 0970-2156
FERTILISER INDUSTRY ANNUAL REVIEW. Text in English. 1978. a. INR 300, USD 35 (effective 2001). adv. **Document type:** *Trade.* **Description:** Contains an overview of the fertilizer industry with contributions from experts.
Published by: Amalgamated Press, Narang House, 2nd Fl, 41 Ambalal Doshi Marg Fort, Mumbai, Maharashtra 400 001, India. TEL 91-22-2650268, 91-22-2654184, FAX 91-22-264-1275. Ed., Pub. Norman J Da Silva. adv.: B&W page GBP 600; trim 175 x 230. Circ: 5,000 (paid).

631.8 IND ISSN 0257-8034
FERTILISER MARKETING NEWS. Text in English. 1970. m. USD 35. adv. charts; illus.
Indexed: AEA, BioCN&I, CPA, FCA, HortAb, I&DA, MaizeAb, NutrAb, PBA, PGegResA, RDA, RevApplEntom, RiceAb, S&F, SeedAb, SoyAb, TriticAb, WAE&RSA, WeedAb.
Published by: Fertiliser Association of India, 10 Shaheed Jit Singh Marg, New Delhi, 110 067, India. TEL 91-11-656-7144, FAX 91-11-696-0052, fai@vsnl.com. Ed. K P Sundaramr. Circ: 3,000.

631.8 GBR ISSN 0267-7822
CODEN: RUBNAX
FERTILISER REVIEW. Text in English. 1984. a. GBP 5 (effective 2003).
Indexed: S&F, WAE&RSA.
—BLDSC (3909.674000).
Published by: The Fertiliser Manufacturers Association, Great North Rd, Peterborough, PE8 6HJ , United Kingdom. TEL 44-1780-781360, FAX 44-1780-781369, http://www.fma.org.uk.

631.8 GBR ISSN 1475-9810
FERTILIZANTES AMERICA LATINA. Text in Spanish. 1996. a. GBP 56, USD 90 (effective 2005). adv. **Document type:** *Magazine, Trade.* **Description:** Covers the fertilizer, micro-nutrients and agronomic sectors in the Latin America and Caribbean region. Provide accurate information on the regions agricultural, nutrient and agronomic needs, fertilizer markets and fertilizer products manufacturing technology and equipment for local conditions.
Published by: British Sulphur Publishing (Subsidiary of: C R U Publishing), 31 Mt Pleasant, London, WC1X 0AD, United Kingdom. TEL 44-20-79032147, FAX 44-20-79032172, derek.winterbottom@crugroup.com, http://www.britishsulphur.com/journal_fal.htm. Ed. Fausto Montoya. Pub. John French TEL 44-20-79032435. Adv. contact Tina Firman TEL 44-20-79032437.

FERTILIZER FINANCIAL FACTS. see *AGRICULTURE—Abstracting, Bibliographies, Statistics*

631.8 GBR ISSN 0951-1490
FERTILIZER FOCUS. Text in English. 1984. 10/yr. GBP 210, USD 345 (effective 2000). adv. bk.rev. **Document type:** *Trade.*
—BLDSC (3910.150000), IE, ingenta.
Address: FMB House, Hampton Hill, 6 Windmill Rd, Hampton, Mddx TW12 1RH, United Kingdom. TEL 44-20-8979-7866, FAX 44-20-8979-4573, fmb@fmb-group.co.uk, http://www.fmb-group.co.uk. Ed. Mike Smith. Pub., Adv. contact Andrew Osborne. Circ: 2,890 (controlled).

FERTILIZER INSTITUTE. ANNUAL SUMMARY. see *AGRICULTURE—Abstracting, Bibliographies, Statistics*

FERTILIZER INSTITUTE. MONTHLY EXPORTS AND IMPORTS. see *AGRICULTURE—Abstracting, Bibliographies, Statistics*

FERTILIZER INSTITUTE. PRODUCTION COST SURVEYS; ammonia, phosphate rock, phosphate fertilizer. see *AGRICULTURE—Agricultural Economics*

FERTILIZER INSTITUTE. PRODUCTION SURVEY. see *AGRICULTURE—Abstracting, Bibliographies, Statistics*

631.8 GBR ISSN 0015-0304
HD9483.A1 CODEN: FRZIAJ
FERTILIZER INTERNATIONAL. Text in English. 1967. bi-m. GBP 270, USD 440, EUR 420 (effective 2005). adv. abstr.; charts; pat.; stat. reprint service avail. from PQC. **Document type:** *Magazine, Trade.* **Description:** Deals with all aspects of the world market for fertilizers. Includes trade, production and consumption data presented in the context of interrelated trends within the fertilizer sector worldwide.
Incorporates (1962-2000): Phosphorus and Potassium (0031-8426); Formerly: World of N P K S
Related titles: Online - full text ed.: (from Gale Group, Northern Light Technology, Inc.).
Indexed: CBNB, CIN, ChemAb, ChemTitl, EngInd, ExcerpMed, KES, PROMT, RASB, S&F, WAE&RSA.
—BLDSC (3910.300000), CASDDS, CISTI, Ei, IE, Infotrieve, ingenta, Linda Hall. **CCC.**
Published by: British Sulphur Publishing (Subsidiary of: C R U Publishing), 31 Mt Pleasant, London, WC1X 0AD, United Kingdom. TEL 44-20-79032147, FAX 44-20-79032172, derek.winterbottom@crugroup.com, http://www.britishsulphur.com/journal_fi.htm. Ed. Mark Evans. R&P John French TEL 44-20-79032435. Adv. contact Tina Firman TEL 44-20-79032437. Circ: 791.

FERTILIZER RECORD. see *AGRICULTURE—Agricultural Economics*

631.8 GBR
FERTILIZER TECHNOLOGY DATABOOK. Text in English. N.S. 1997. irreg. GBP 150, USD 270. reprint service avail. from PQC. **Document type:** *Directory.* **Description:** Serves as a directory of suppliers of process technology and plant equipment.
Former titles: N P K S Processes and Plant Suppliers. World Directory; World Guide to Fertilizer Processes and Plant Suppliers; World Guide to Fertilizer Processes and Constructors
Published by: British Sulphur Publishing (Subsidiary of: C R U Publishing), 31 Mt Pleasant, London, WC1X 0AD, United Kingdom. TEL 44-20-7837-5600, FAX 44-20-7837-0292, smoore@cruint.tcom.co.uk, derek.winterbottom@crugroup.com. Pub., R&P John French TEL 44-20-79032435.

631.8 GBR ISSN 0951-7472
FERTILIZER WEEK. Text in English. 1987. 50/yr. GBP 835. **Document type:** *Newsletter.*
Published by: C P U International Ltd., 31 Mount Pleasant, London, WC1X 0AD, United Kingdom. TEL 0171-837-5600, FAX 0171-837-0292, TELEX 918918-SULFEX-G. Ed. Stephen Mitchell.

631.5 NLD ISSN 0378-4290
CODEN: FCREDZ
➤ **FIELD CROPS RESEARCH.** Text in Dutch. 1978. 18/yr. EUR 1,980 in Europe to institutions; JPY 262,500 in Japan to institutions; USD 2,216 to institutions except Europe and Japan (effective 2006). abstr. back issues avail.; reprints avail. **Document type:** *Journal, Academic/Scholarly.* **Description:** Publishes research results of international relevance arising from the scientific study of crops and farming systems.
Related titles: Microform ed.: (from PQC); Online - full text ed.: (from EBSCO Publishing, Gale Group, IngentaConnect, ScienceDirect, Swets Information Services).
Indexed: AEA, ASCA, ASFA, AgBio, Agr, AgrForAb, B&AI, BIOBASE, BIOSIS Prev, BioCN&I, BiolAb, CPA, CurCont, DBA, EPB, ESPM, EngInd, EnvAb, FCA, ForAb, GEOBASE, HerbAb, HortAb, I&DA, IABS, ISR, Inspec, MaizeAb, NemAb, NutrAb, OrnHort, PBA, PGegResA, PGrRegA, PHN&I, PlantSci, PotatoAb, PoultAb, RA&MP, RDA, RPP, RefZh, RevApplEntom, RiceAb, S&F, S&MA, SCI, SIA, SWRA, SeedAb, SoyAb, TDB, TOSA, TriticAb, WAE&RSA, WTA, WeedAb.
—BLDSC (3920.057000), CISTI, IDS, IE, Infotrieve, ingenta, Linda Hall. **CCC.**
Published by: Elsevier BV (Subsidiary of: Elsevier Science & Technology), Radarweg 29, Amsterdam, 1043 NX, Netherlands. TEL 31-20-4853911, FAX 31-20-4852457, nlinfo-f@elsevier.nl, http://www.elsevier.com/locate/fcr, http://www.elsevier.nl. Eds. Jill M. Lenne, P H Graham.

➤ **FIJI SUGAR YEAR BOOK.** see *FOOD AND FOOD INDUSTRIES*

➤ **FITOPATOLOGIA VENEZOLANA**; revista de la Sociedad Venezolana de Fitopatologia. see *BIOLOGY—Botany*

631 USA
FLORIDA AVOCADO ADMINISTRATIVE COMMITTEE. ANNUAL REPORT. Text in English. 1954. a. back issues avail. **Description:** Summary of year's events, shipment totals, research, weather, statistics, and financial report.
Published by: Florida Avocado Administrative Committee, 18710 S W 288th St, Homestead, FL 33030. TEL 305-247-0848, FAX 305-245-1315. Circ: 500.

631 USA
FLORIDA AVOCADO ADMINISTRATIVE COMMITTEE. MEETING MINUTES. Text in English. 1954. m. back issues avail. **Description:** Special guest articles and reports from the administrator pertaining to items received in the Committee office.
Published by: Florida Avocado Administrative Committee, 18710 S W 288th St, Homestead, FL 33030. TEL 305-247-0848, FAX 305-245-1315. Circ: 400.

FLORIDA AVOCADO ADMINISTRATIVE COMMITTEE. SHIPMENTS REPORT. see *AGRICULTURE—Abstracting, Bibliographies, Statistics*

631 USA
FLORIDA LIME ADMINISTRATIVE COMMITTEE. ANNUAL REPORT. Text in English. 1955. a. back issues avail. **Description:** Summary of year's events, shipment totals, research, weather, statistics, and financial report.

Published by: Florida Lime Administrative Committee, 18710 S W 288th St, Homestead, FL 33030. TEL 305-247-0848, FAX 305-245-1315. Circ: 500.

631 USA
FLORIDA LIME ADMINISTRATIVE COMMITTEE. MEETING MINUTES. Text in English. 1955. m. back issues avail. **Description:** Special guest articles and reports from the administrator regarding items received in the Committee office.
Published by: Florida Lime Administrative Committee, 18710 S W 288th St, Homestead, FL 33030. TEL 305-247-0848, FAX 305-245-1315. Circ: 400.

FLORIDA LIME ADMINISTRATIVE COMMITTEE. SHIPMENTS REPORT. see *AGRICULTURE—Abstracting, Bibliographies, Statistics*

712 635.98 USA
FLORIDA TURF DIGEST. Text in English. bi-m. **Document type:** *Magazine.*
Published by: (Florida Turfgrass Association), Harvest Publishing, PO Box 9125, Winter Haven, FL 33881. http://www.harvestpublishing.com.

630 DEU ISSN 0015-4733
FLUR UND FURCHE; Landwirtschaftsmagazin. Text in German. 1964. q. free. adv. illus. index. **Document type:** *Trade.*
Related titles: ♦ English ed.: Furrow. ISSN 0016-3112; ♦ Swedish ed.: Faran; ♦ Spanish ed.: Surco Mexicana; ♦ Spanish ed.: Surco Argentina; ♦ Norwegian ed.: Fara; ♦ Spanish ed.: Campo y Mecanica. ISSN 0211-4704; Afrikaans ed.: 1895; Danish ed.: 1895; Dutch ed.: 1895; French ed.: 1895; Italian ed.: 1895; Portuguese ed.: 1895.
Indexed: WeedAb.
Published by: Deere & Company, Steubenstr 36-42, Mannheim, 68140, Germany. FAX 49-621-8298300, TELEX 463056-DCEOD. Ed. Rainer Mache. Circ: 163,500.

631 POL ISSN 1506-1973
S13
➤ **FOLIA UNIVERSITATIS AGRICULTURAE STETINESIS. AGRICULTURA.** Text in Polish; Abstracts in English. 1958. a. price varies. bk.rev. **Document type:** *Academic/Scholarly.*
Former titles: Akademia Rolnicza w Szczecinie. Zeszyty Naukowe. Rolnictwo (0137-1924); (until 1972): Wyzsza Szkola Rolnicza w Szczecinie. Zeszyty Naukowe. Rolnictwo (0137-2106)
Indexed: AEA, AgBio, AgrAg, AgrForAb, AgrLib, CPA, ChemAb, FCA, FPA, FS&TA, ForAb, HerbAb, HortAb, I&DA, MaizeAb, NemAb, NutrAb, OrnHort, PBA, PGegResA, PGrRegA, PHN&I, PN&I, PotatoAb, PoultAb, RA&MP, RPP, RRTA, RefZh, RevApplEntom, S&F, SIA, SeedAb, SoyAb, TriticAb, WAE&RSA, WeedAb.
—BLDSC (3965.898000), Linda Hall.
Published by: Akademia Rolnicza w Szczecinie/Agricultural University of Szczecin, Dzial Wydawnictw, Ul Doktora Judyma 22, Szczecin, 71466, Poland. TEL 48-91-4541639, FAX 48-91-4541642, TELEX 0425494 AR, fizj@demeter.zoo.ar.szczecin.pl. Ed. Wieslaw F Skrzypczak.

632 THA
FOOD AND AGRICULTURE ORGANIZATION OF THE UNITED NATIONS. ASIA AND PACIFIC PLANT PROTECTION COMMISSION. QUARTERLY NEWSLETTER. Text and summaries in English. 1958. q. free. back issues avail. **Document type:** *Newsletter.* **Description:** Disseminates information on plant quarantine and protection in these regions.
Formerly: Food and Agricultural Organization of the United Nations. Plant Protection Committee for Southeast Asia and Pacific Region. Quarterly Newsletter (0428-9749)
Indexed: SoyAb.
Published by: Food and Agriculture Organization of the United Nations, Regional Office for Asia and the Pacific, Maliwan Mansion, 39 Phra Atit Rd, Bangkok, 10200, Thailand. Circ: 500.

631 THA ISSN 1014-3351
FOOD AND AGRICULTURE ORGANIZATION OF THE UNITED NATIONS. ASIA AND PACIFIC PLANT PROTECTION COMMISSION. TECHNICAL DOCUMENT. Text and summaries in English. 1958. irreg. (6-8/yr.). free. **Description:** Aimed at professionals and technical field personnel. Contains agricultural research results.
Formerly: Food and Agricultural Organization of the United Nations. Plant Protection Committee for Southeast Asia and Pacific Region. Technical Document (0428-9765)
Indexed: RPP, RevApplEntom, WeedAb.
Published by: Food and Agriculture Organization of the United Nations, Regional Office for Asia and the Pacific, Maliwan Mansion, 39 Phra Atit Rd, Bangkok, 10200, Thailand. Circ: 500 (controlled).

631.4 USA ISSN 0532-0488
S591 CODEN: WSRRDX
FOOD AND AGRICULTURE ORGANIZATION OF THE UNITED NATIONS. WORLD SOIL RESOURCES REPORTS. Text in English. irreg., latest vol.85, 1999. price varies. **Document type:** *Monographic series.*
Indexed: ForAb, HerbAb, I&DA, RDA, RRTA, S&F, WAE&RSA.
—BLDSC (9360.035000), IE, ingenta, Linda Hall.
Published by: Food and Agriculture Organization of the United Nations, c/o Bernan Associates, 4611 F Assembly Dr, Lanham, MD 20706-4391. TEL 301-459-7666, FAX 301-459-0056.

FOOD BIOTECHNOLOGY. see *BIOLOGY—Biotechnology*

631.4 GBR
FOOD MAGAZINE. Text in English. 1993. q. GBP 18 (effective 1998). **Document type:** *Consumer.*
Supersedes in part (in 1995): Living Earth and the Food Magazine (1367-9848); Which was formed by the merger of (1988-1993): Food Magazine (0953-5047); (1988-1993): Living Earth (0954-1098); Which was formerly (until 1988): Soil Association. Review (0951-2381); (until 1985): Soil Association. Quarterly Review (0307-2576); (until 1975): Soil Association. Journal (0038-0709)
Indexed: FS&TA.
—BLDSC (3980.730000), IE, ingenta.
Published by: Food Commission, 94 White Lion St, London, N1 9PF, United Kingdom. TEL 44-1716-287774. Ed. Charlotte Russell.

338.17318 COL
FORO ARROCERO LATINOAMERICANO: BOLETIN INFORMATIVO DEL F L A R. Text in Spanish. 1995. s-a. free. **Document type:** *Newsletter.* **Description:** Presents information for the irrigated rice sector.
Related titles: ♦ English ed.: Latinoamerican Rice Forum: F L A R Newsletter.
Published by: (Unidad de Comunicaciones), Centro Internacional de Agricultura Tropical/International Center for Tropical Agriculture, Publications Unit, Apartado Aereo 6713, Cali, VALLE, Colombia. TEL 57-2-4450000, FAX 57-2-4450073, http://www.ciat.cgiar.org/.

633.4 CAN ISSN 0384-7322
FRASER'S POTATO NEWSLETTER. Text in English. 1967. w. CND 100, USD 90 (effective 1999). adv. **Document type:** *Newsletter.*
—CISTI.
Published by: Fraser's Potato Newsletter Inc., R.R. 1, Hazelbrook, Charlottetown, PE C1A 7J6, Canada. Ed., Pub. Harry Fraser TEL 902-569-2685. Circ: 2,100.

634 USA
FRESH FRUIT AND VEGETABLE MARKET NEWS. Text in English. 1936. 3/w. free. stat.
Media: Duplicated (not offset).
Published by: Department of Agriculture, PO Box 22159, Honolulu, HI 96822. TEL 808-548-2211. Ed. James Omori. Circ: 1,000.

FRESH FRUIT AND VEGETABLE MARKET NEWS: WEEKLY SUMMARY, SHIPMENTS - ARRIVALS. see *AGRICULTURE—Agricultural Economics*

FRESH PRODUCE JOURNAL. see *FOOD AND FOOD INDUSTRIES*

368.121 USA ISSN 0279-6856
FRIENDLY EXCHANGE. Text in English. 1980. q. USD 20; USD 5 newsstand/cover (effective 2005). adv. **Document type:** *Magazine, Consumer.* **Description:** Offers information on a wide variety of lifestyle topics, including home, health, family, finance, and travel.
Indexed: AgeL.
Published by: (Farmers Insurance Group), C - E Publishing (Subsidiary of: C - E Communications), Aegis Group, 30400 Van Dyke Ave, P O Box 2119, Warren, MI 48093. friendly.exchange@cecom.com, http://www.friendlyexchange.com/ME2/Default.asp. Ed. Dan Grantham. Pub. Rick La Fave. R&P Adele Malott. Adv. contact Tom Krempel. B&W page USD 74,350, color page USD 82,590; trim 10.5 x 7.94. Circ: 6,000,000.

631.5 DNK ISSN 1602-7450
FROEAVLEREN. Text in Danish. 1918. 9/yr. DKK 400 domestic; DKK 500 foreign (effective 2003). adv. charts; illus. index. back issues avail. **Document type:** *Magazine, Trade.*
Formerly (until 2002): Dansk Froeavl (0106-3863); Which incorporated (1946-1973): Dansk Havefroeavl (0106-3855)
Related titles: Online - full text ed.; Ed.: The Seed Grower. ISSN 1602-7469. 2002.
Indexed: AEA, CPA, FCA, HerbAb, HortAb, OrnHort, PBA, PGrRegA, S&F, SeedAb, TriticAb, WAE&RSA, WeedAb.
Published by: Danske Froeavlere/Danish Seed Growers, Axelborg, Vesterbrogade 4 A, 4 sal, Copenhagen V, 1620, Denmark. TEL 45-33-394690, FAX 45-33-394605, froe@froeavl.dk, http://www.froeportalen.dk. Ed., Adv. contact Morten Bak Pedersen TEL 45-33-394691. Circ: 2,500.
Co-sponsor: Dansk Havefroeavlerforening.

FRUCHTHANDEL; internationale Fachzeitschrift fuer den Handel mit Fruechten und Gemuese. see *FOOD AND FOOD INDUSTRIES—Grocery Trade*

634 NLD ISSN 0929-6395
FRUCTUS. Text in Dutch. 1992. q. EUR 25 domestic; EUR 34 foreign (effective 2005). **Document type:** *Newspaper.*
Published by: Stichting Behoud en Bevordering Fruitcultuur, Postbus 83, Doesburg, 6980 AB, Netherlands. TEL 31-65-1268802, fructus.doesburg@wxs.nl, http://www.tolderas.nl/.

630 CHE ISSN 0016-2221
FRUECHTE UND GEMUESE/FRUITS ET LEGUMES. Text in French, German. 1933. fortn. (25/yr.). CHF 87; CHF 150 foreign. adv. bk.rev. mkt.; stat. **Document type:** *Newsletter.* **Description:** Focuses on fruit and vegetable production, processing and marketing.
—CISTI.
Published by: Schweizerischer Obstverband, Baarerstr 88, Zug, 6302, Switzerland. TEL 41-41-7286868, FAX 41-41-7286800, sov@swissfruit.ch. Ed. Elois Von Wyl. Circ: 2,500.
Co-sponsor: Schweizerische Gemuese-Union.

A

634 DNK ISSN 1601-6114
FRUGT & GROENT. Text in Danish. 2002. m. adv. bk.rev. **Document type:** *Journal, Trade.*
Formed by the merger of (1982-2002): Groenne Fag (0108-8920); (1991-2002): Frugt og Baer (0906-1738); Which was formerly (until 1991): Frugtavleren (0106-004X); Which was formed by the merger of (1934-1972): Erhvervsfrugtavleren (0106-0058); (1928-1972): Dansk Frugtavl (0011-6289)
Indexed: AEA, HortAb, PGrRegA, WAE&RSA.
—BLDSC (4042.569000).
Published by: Dansk Erhvervsfrugtavl, Lavsenvaenget 20, Odense V, 5200, Denmark. TEL 45-66-12-63-32, FAX 45-66-12-63-35, frugtogbear@adv.dk. Ed. Evald Burgaard. Adv. contact Anne Lise Mikkelsen. Circ: 1,200.

338.1 USA
HD9241
FRUIT AND TREE NUTS OUTLOOK. Text in English. 1937. 3/yr. USD 30 (effective 1999). back issues avail.; reprint service avail. from CIS. **Document type:** *Government.* **Description:** Provides current intelligence and historical data, and forecasts the effects of changing conditions on the U.S. fruit and tree nuts sector; covers production, consumption, shipments, prices received, etc. for fresh and frozen fruit and juice, apples, grapes, wine, raisins, pears, peaches, nectarines, apricots, plums, cherries, kiwi, olives, strawberries, blueberries, bananas, mangoes, papayas, pineapples, oranges, grapefruit, almonds, walnuts, pecans, pistachios, hazelnuts, macademia nuts.
Former titles (until 2002): Situation & Outlook Report. Fruit & Tree Nuts (1051-7901); (until 1988): U.S. Department of Agriculture. Situation and Outlook Report. Fruit; (until 1986): U.S. Department of Agriculture. Outlook and Situation Report. Fruit (8756-9914)
Related titles: Microfiche ed.: (from CIS); Online - full text ed.: (from Gale Group, The Dialog Corporation).
Indexed: AmStl, RRTA, WAE&RSA.
Published by: U.S. Department of Agriculture, Economic Research Service, 1800 M St. NW, Washington, DC 20036-5831. TEL 202-694-5050, http://www.ers.usda.gov/publications/so/view.asp?f=specialty/fts-bb/. **Subscr. to:** U.S. Government Printing Office, Superintendent of Documents, PO Box 371954, Pittsburgh, PA 15250-7954. TEL 202-512-1800, FAX 202-512-2250, orders@gpo.gov, http://www.access.gpo.gov. **Dist. by:** ERS-NASS, 5285 Port Royal Rd, Springfield, VA 22161.

633 NLD ISSN 1569-2930
FRUIT & VEG TECH. Text in English. 2001. bi-m. EUR 57.24 domestic; EUR 75 foreign (effective 2005). adv.
Incorporates (in 2001): Prophyta (0921-5506); Which was formerly (1947-1987): Zaadbelangen (0165-618X)
Published by: Reed Business Information bv (Subsidiary of: Reed Business), Postbus 4, Doetinchem, 7000 BA, Netherlands. TEL 31-314-349911, FAX 31-314-343991, info@reedbusiness.nl, http://www.productonline.reedbusiness.nl/product.asp?catalog%5Fname=RBI&category%5Fname=&product%5Fid=59L%28Octopus%29, http://www.reedbusiness.nl. Ed. Helen Armstrong. adv.: color page EUR 4,139, B&W page EUR 2,805; bleed 221 x 286.

634 CAN
CODEN: CAFRAW
FRUIT & VEGETABLE MAGAZINE. Text in English. 1929. 9/yr. CND 12.84 domestic; USD 40 foreign (effective 2005). adv.
Formerly: Canadian Fruitgrower (0045-4885)
—CISTI.
Published by: Annex Publishing & Printing, Inc., 222 Argyle Ave, Delhi, ON N4B 2Y2, ON N4B 2Y2, Canada. TEL 519-582-2513, 800-265-2827, FAX 519-582-4040, sfredericks@annexweb.com, http://fruitveggie.hortport.com, http://www.annexweb.com. Circ: 4,000 (controlled).

634 GBR ISSN 0961-0464
FRUIT AND VEGETABLE MARKETS. Text in English. m. GBP 476 domestic; GBP 546 in Europe; GBP 615 elsewhere (effective 2005). **Document type:** *Newsletter, Trade.* **Description:** Presents a pan-European view of fresh and processed fruit and vegetables. Includes crop reports, market and trade news, EU report, legislation and the latest price production and trade statistics.
Formerly: Agrafile: Fruit and Vegetables (0950-4931)
—CISTI.

▼ *new title* ➤ *refereed* ✶ *unverified* ♦ *full entry avail.*

A

Published by: Agra Europe (London) Ltd. (Subsidiary of: T & F Informa plc), 80 Calverley Rd, Tunbridge Wells, Kent TN1 2UN, United Kingdom. TEL 44-1892-533813, FAX 44-1892-544895, marketing@agra-net.com, http://www.agra-net.com.

FRUIT AND VEGETABLE TRUCK RATE AND COST SUMMARY. see *AGRICULTURE—Agricultural Economics*

FRUIT AND VEGETABLE TRUCK RATE REPORT. see *AGRICULTURE—Agricultural Economics*

634 USA ISSN 1533-6840
THE FRUIT GROWERS NEWS. Text in English. 1961. m. USD 11 domestic; USD 50 in Canada & Mexico; USD 100 elsewhere (effective 2005). adv. **Document type:** *Newspaper, Trade.* **Description:** Covers growing and marketing techniques, business management ideas, events, meetings, and developments important to the industry.
Formerly: Great Lakes Fruit Growers News (1090-3194)
—CISTI.
Published by: Great American Publishing Co., 75 Applewood Dr, Ste A, Sparta, MI 49345. Ed. Kim Warren. Pub. Matt McCallum. Adv. contacts Kate Lewis, Brenda Bradford. Circ: 13,250 (paid).

634 USA ISSN 0427-6906
FRUIT NOTES. Text in English. 1968. bi-m. USD 20 (effective 2005).
Indexed: Agr.
Published by: University of Massachusetts, College of Agriculture, Cooperative Extension Service, Draper Hall, 40 Campus Center Way, Amherst, MA 01003-9244. TEL 413-545-4800, FAX 413-545-6555, umextadm@umext.umass.edu, http://www.umass.edu/fruitadvisor/fruitnotes/FruitNotes.htm, http://www.umassextension.org.

FRUIT WORLD INTERNATIONAL; review of the international fruit and vegetable wholesale trade. see *FOOD AND FOOD INDUSTRIES*

634 BEL ISSN 1370-0235
FRUITTEELT NIEUWS. Text in Dutch. 1988. fortn. EUR 38.50 domestic; EUR 71.50 in the European Union; EUR 82.50 elsewhere (effective 2004). adv. 32 p./no.; back issues avail. **Document type:** *Journal, Trade.* **Description:** For fruitgrowers: apples, pears, strawberries, berries, plums.
Formerly (until 1993): Fruitteelt (0775-5678)
Indexed: AEA, BioCN&I, CPA, ForAb, HortAb, I&DA, MaizeAb, NutrAb, OrnHort, PBA, PGegResA, PGrRegA, PHN&I, PotatoAb, RDA, RPP, RevApplEntom, S&F, SeedAb, WAE&RSA, WeedAb.
Address: Brede Akker 13, Sint-Truiden, B-3800, Belgium. TEL 32-11-586960, fruitteeltnieuws@pcfruit.be, http://www.pcfruit.be/nl/fruitteeltnieuws.htm. Ed. Jacqueline Mathijs. Pub. Luc Dirix. R&P, Adv. contact J Mathijs. Circ: 2,700.
Co-sponsors: Koninlijk Opzoekingsstation van Gorsem Sint-Truiden; Nationale Vakgroep Fruit van de Belgische Boerenbond Leuven; Studiekring Guvelingen Sint-Truiden.

631 ESP ISSN 1131-5660
FRUTICULTURA PROFESIONAL. Text in Spanish. 1986. bi-m. (plus 1 monograph). EUR 61.40 domestic; EUR 80.50 foreign (effective 2004). adv. **Document type:** *Trade.*
Indexed: IECT.
—CINDOC. **CCC.**
Published by: Agro Latino S.L., Apdo Correos 400, Castelldefels (Barcelona), 08860, Spain. TEL 34-93-6350850, FAX 34-93-6350851, agrolatino@agrolatino.com. Ed. L Daniel Aradas Llorens.

633.72 CHN ISSN 1005-2291
FUJIAN CHAYE/TEA IN FUJIAN. Text in Chinese. q. CNY 10; CNY 2.50 newsstand/cover. **Description:** Addresses the need of professionals engaged in tea production and research to acquire modern techniques of production and processing and to exchange their experience.
Related titles: Online - full text ed.: (from East View Information Services).
Published by: Fujian Sheng Chaye Xiehui/Fujian Provincial Tea Association, Waimao Zhongxin - Foreign Trade Center, Wusi Lu, Fuzhou, Fujian 350001, China. TEL 86-591-756-5272, http://www.si.net.cn/publica/. Ed. Xinjiong Lin. **Dist. overseas by:** Jiangsu Publications Import & Export Corp., 56 Gao Yun Ling, Nanjing, Jiangsu, China.

634.6 CHN ISSN 1004-6089
FUJIAN GUOSHU/FUJIAN FRUIT TREES. Text in Chinese. 1973. q. CNY 12 (effective 1999). **Document type:** *Academic/Scholarly.* **Description:** Covers the cultivation of subtropical fruit trees and related research.
Related titles: Online - full text ed.: (from East View Information Services).
Published by: Fujian Sheng Nongye Kexueyuan, Guoshu Yanjiusuo/Fujian Academy of Agricultural Science, Pomology Institute, Pudang, Fuzhou Shijiao (Suburb), Fuzhou, Fujian 350013, China. TEL 7596409. Ed. Huang Jinsong. **Dist. overseas by:** Jiangsu Publications Import & Export Corp., 56 Gao Yun Ling, Nanjing, Jiangsu, China.

FUJIAN NONGYE DAXUE XUEBAO/FUJIAN AGRICULTURAL UNIVERSITY. JOURNAL. see *AGRICULTURE*

632.9 USA ISSN 0148-9038
CODEN: FNETDO
FUNGICIDE AND NEMATICIDE TESTS. Text in English. a. USD 28 (effective 2005). index. back issues avail. **Document type:** *Monographic series, Academic/Scholarly.* **Description:** Highlights pest control methods.
Related titles: Online - full text ed.: (from EBSCO Publishing).
Indexed: DBA, FCA, MaizeAb, OrnHort, RPP, S&F.
—CISTI, Linda Hall.
Published by: (American Phytopathological Society), A P S PRESS, 3340 Pilot Knob Rd., St. Paul, MN 55121-2097. TEL 651-454-7250, 800-328-7560, FAX 651-454-0766, aps@scisoc.org, http://www.apsnet.org. Ed. Richard E Baird. Circ: 1,000.

G - MAIL. see *BUSINESS AND ECONOMICS*

630 ITA ISSN 0016-6863
G R - ESTIMO E TERRITORIO; valutare e gestire l'ambiente. (Genio Rurale) Text in Italian. 1937. m. (11/yr.). EUR 62 domestic; EUR 110 foreign (effective 2005). adv. bk.rev. charts; illus. index. 48 p./no.; **Document type:** *Magazine, Trade.* **Description:** Covers rural planning and management.
Indexed: AEA, AbHyg, AgBio, AgrForAb, AnBrAb, ApicAb, BioCN&I, CPA, DSA, FCA, FPA, ForAb, HerbAb, HortAb, I&DA, MaizeAb, NutrAb, OrnHort, PAIS, PBA, PGegResA, PHN&I, PN&I, PoultAb, RDA, RRTA, RevApplEntom, RiceAb, S&F, SoyAb, TriticAb, WAE&RSA, WeedAb.
—CISTI.
Published by: Il Sole 24 Ore Edagricole, Via Goito 13, Bologna, BO 40126, Italy. TEL 39-051-62267, FAX 39-051-490200, http://www.edagricole.it. Ed. Giorgio Setti. Circ: 4,000.

631 ISR
GAN SADEH VAMESHEK. Text in Hebrew. m.
Published by: Israel Vegetable Growers Association, 8 Shaul Hamelech Blvd, Tel Aviv, 64733, Israel. Ed. Yaacov Shlish.

631 636 AUS ISSN 0159-6071
GENETIC RESOURCES COMMUNICATION. Text in English. 1980. irreg. free. **Document type:** *Monographic series.*
Indexed: Agr, AgrForAb, BIOSIS Prev, BiolAb, ForAb, HerbAb, HortAb, NutrAb, PBA, PGegResA, S&F, SeedAb.
—BLDSC (4111.910000), CISTI.
Published by: C S I R O, Tropical Agriculture, Brisbane, St Lucia, QLD 4067, Australia. TEL 61-7-32142200, FAX 61-7-32142288, library@tag.csiro.au, http://www.tag.csiro.au. Ed. Grant McDuling. R&P Marshall Mackay.

631.4 550 NLD ISSN 0016-7061
S590 CODEN: GEDMAB
➤ **GEODERMA.** Text in English, French, German. 1967. 24/yr. EUR 2,291 in Europe to institutions; JPY 304,400 in Japan to institutions; USD 2,562 to institutions except Europe and Japan (effective 2006). adv. bk.rev. abstr.; charts; illus. index. back issues avail.; reprints avail. **Document type:** *Journal, Academic/Scholarly.* **Description:** Publishes interdisciplinary papers from the different fields of pedology, focusing on the occurrence and dynamic characterization in space and time of soils in the field.
Related titles: Microform ed.: (from PQC); Online - full text ed.: (from EBSCO Publishing, Gale Group, IngentaConnect, ScienceDirect, Swets Information Services).
Indexed: AEA, AESIS, ASCA, ASFA, AgrForAb, BIOBASE, BIOSIS Prev, BibInd, BiolAb, CIN, CPA, Cadscan, ChemAb, ChemTitl, CurCont, EEA, EIA, EPB, ESPM, EnerInd, EnvEAb, ExcerpMed, FCA, FLUIDEX, FPA, ForAb, GEOBASE, HerbAb, HortAb, I&DA, IABS, ISR, LeadAb, MaizeAb, NemAb, OrnHort, PBA, PN&I, PollutAb, PotatoAb, RA&MP, RDA, RPP, RefZh, RevApplEntom, RiceAb, S&F, SCI, SIA, SPPI, SWRA, SoyAb, TriticAb, VITIS, WAE&RSA, WeedAb, Zincscan.
—BLDSC (4118.050000), CASDDS, CISTI, IDS, IE, Infotrieve, ingenta, Linda Hall. **CCC.**
Published by: Elsevier BV (Subsidiary of: Elsevier Science & Technology), Radarweg 29, Amsterdam, 1043 NX, Netherlands. TEL 31-20-4853911, FAX 31-20-4852457, nlinfo-f@elsevier.nl, http://www.elsevier.com/locate/geoderma, http://www.elsevier.nl. Eds. H. Insam, Jay C. Bell.

632.9 USA
GEORGIA PEST MANAGEMENT NEWSLETTER. Text in English. 1995. m. free. back issues avail. **Document type:** *Newsletter.* **Description:** Designed for specialists and others interested in pest management news.
Related titles: Online - full text ed.
Published by: (College of Agricultural and Environmental Sciences), University of Georgia, Department of Entomology, BioScience Building, Athens, GA 30602-2603. TEL 706-542-1765, pguillebeau@bugs.ent.uga.edu, http://www.ces.uga.edu/Agriculture/entomology/pestnewsletter/newsarchive.html. Ed. Paul Guillebeau.

GERMINATIONS; newsletter of the Butterbrooke Farm seed co-op. see *GARDENING AND HORTICULTURE*

633.41 ITA ISSN 1128-8299
GIORNALE DEL BIETICOLTORE. Text in Italian. 1930. bi-m. free membership. adv. bk.rev. illus.; stat. **Description:** Covers sugar beet production.
Formerly (until 1952): Beta
Related titles: Online - full text ed.
Published by: Associazione Nazionale Bieticoltori, c/o Avenue Media, Via Riva Reno 61, Bologna, Italy. TEL 39-051-6564337, gdb@anb.it, http://www.anb.it. Circ: 50,000 (free).

631 ITA ISSN 0393-9200
GIORNALE DELLA SOIA. Text in Italian. 1985. 5/yr.
Address: Via Savorgnana, 26, Udine, UD 33100, Italy. TEL 432-26-972, FAX 432-507013. Ed. Enos Costantini. Circ: 20,000.

632.9 USA ISSN 1091-1375
SB951.3
GLOBAL FUNGICIDE DIRECTORY. Text in English. 1996. every 30 mos. USD 125 to institutions commercial; USD 90 to institutions academic. **Document type:** *Directory.* **Description:** Covers all existing and experimental fungicide products and compounds in the global crop protection industry, plus a brief overview of the global market for all fungicide compounds.
Published by: Ag Chem Information Services, 6705 E 71st St, Indianapolis, IN 46220. TEL 317-845-0681, FAX 317-841-1210.

632.9 USA ISSN 1079-3275
SB951.4
GLOBAL HERBICIDE DIRECTORY. Text in English. 1994. every 30 mos. USD 150. **Document type:** *Catalog.* **Description:** Covers all existing and new herbicide product development in the world's crop protection industry, and a brief overview of the global herbicide market in dollar value.
Published by: Ag Chem Information Services, 6705 E 71st St, Indianapolis, IN 46220. TEL 317-845-0681, FAX 317-841-1210. Pub. William L Hopkins.

632.9 USA ISSN 1088-8497
SB951.5
GLOBAL INSECTICIDE DIRECTORY. Text in English. 1996. every 30 mos. USD 125. **Document type:** *Directory.* **Description:** Covers all existing and experimental insecticide products and compounds in the global crop protection industry, plus a brief overview of the global market for all insecticide compounds.
Published by: Ag Chem Information Services, 6705 E 71st St, Indianapolis, IN 46220. TEL 317-845-0681, FAX 317-841-1210.

GLOBAL PESTICIDE CAMPAIGNER. see *ENVIRONMENTAL STUDIES—Toxicology And Environmental Safety*

631.587 DNK
GOEDNINGER M.M. FORTEGNELSE OVER DEKLARATIONER, PRODUCENTER OG IMPORTOERER (YEAR). Text in Danish. 1964. a. free. **Document type:** *Catalog, Government.*
Former titles (until 1997): Producenter og Importoerer af Goedninger og Jordforbedringsmidler (0906-9658); Fortegnelse over Fabrikanter og Importoerer af Goedninger og Jordforbedringsmidler; Fortegnelse over Fabrikanter og Importoerer af Goedninger og Grundforbedringsmidler (0109-5498); Fortegnelse over Fabrikanter og Importoerer af Goedningsstoffer og Grundforbedringsmidler
Published by: Plantedirektoratet, Skovbrynet 20, Lyngby, 2800, Denmark. TEL 45-45-96-66-00, FAX 45-45-96-66-10, mb@plantedir.dk, http://www.plantedir.dk. Ed. M Brink. Circ: 800.

635.9642 AUS
GOLF AND SPORTS TURF. Text in English. 1993. bi-m. AUD 39; AUD 78 foreign. adv. **Document type:** *Trade.*
Published by: Glenvale Publications, 4 Palmer Ct, Mt Waverley, VIC 3149, Australia. TEL 61-3-9544-2233, FAX 61-3-9543-1150, glenvale@glenv.com.au, samc@glenv.com.au. Ed., Adv. contact Dianne Barker. Circ: 5,156.

634 AUS ISSN 1321-0165
GOOD FRUIT & VEGETABLES; informing the Australian grower and the industry. Text in English. 1981. m. AUD 62.35; AUD 5.35 newsstand/cover (effective 2005). adv. bk.rev. **Document type:** *Magazine, Trade.* **Description:** Presents news and technical articles for the fruit and vegetable industries.
Incorporates (1980-1991): Commercial Horticulture (0728-3814)
Indexed: INZP.
Published by: Rural Press Ltd. (Subsidiary of: Agricultural Publishers Pty. Ltd.), 10 Sydenham St., PO Box 254, Moonee Ponds, VIC 3039, Australia. TEL 61-3-92870900, FAX 61-3-93705622, http://www.ruralpress.com/publications/detail.asp?publication_id=134. Ed. John Fitzsimmons. Adv. contact Michael Lamond. Circ: 9,500.

630 GBR ISSN 0956-117X
GRAIN QUALITY AND MALTING CHARACTERISTICS OF WINTER AND SPRING BARLEY VARIETIES. Text in English. 1987. a.
—BLDSC (4208.410730).
Published by: N I A B, Huntingdon Rd, Cambridge, CB3 0LE, United Kingdom. TEL 44-1223-276381, FAX 44-1223-342328, info@niab.com, http://www.niab.com.

630 USA ISSN 0193-5585
HD9034
GRAIN STOCKS. Text in English. 19??. q. **Description:** Contains stocks of all wheat, durum wheat, corn, sorghum, oats, barley, soybeans, flaxseed, canola, rapeseed, rye, sunflower, safflower, mustard seed, by States and U.S. and by position (on-farm or off-farm storage); includes number and capacity of off-farm storage facilities and capacity of on-farm storage facilities.
Former titles (until 1975): Grain Stocks in All Positions (0094-1301); (until 1973): Stocks of Grains in All Positions (0499-0609)
Related titles: E-mail ed.; Fax ed.; Online - full content ed.
—CISTI.
Published by: U.S. Department of Agriculture, National Agricultural Statistics Service, 1400 Independence Ave, S W, Washington, DC 20250-2000. nass@nass.usda.gov, http://www.usda.gov/nass. **Subscr. to:** 5285 Port Royal Rd, Springfield, VA 22161. TEL 703-605-6220, 800-999-6779, FAX 603-605-6900.

631 AUS
GRAINS RESEARCH AND DEVELOPMENT CORPORATION. ANNUAL REPORT. Text in English. a. free. **Document type:** *Government.*
Formed by the merger of: Barley Research Council. Annual Report; Grain Legumes Research Council. Annual Report; Oilseeds Research Council. Annual Report; Wheat Research Council. Annual Report (0819-5854)
—CISTI.
Published by: (Australia. Grains Research and Development Corporation), AusInfo, GPO Box 1920, Canberra Mc, ACT 2610, Australia. TEL 61-2-6295-4512, FAX 61-2-6295-4455.

634.8 USA ISSN 1049-670X
GRAPE GROWER. Text in English. 1969. m. USD 19.95 (effective 2004). adv. **Document type:** *Magazine, Trade.*
Formerly: California and Western States Grape Grower (0092-2145)
Published by: Western Agricultural Publishing Co. Inc., 4969 E Clinton Way, Ste 104, Fresno, CA 93727-1549. TEL 559-252-7000, FAX 559-252-7387, westag2@psnw.com. Ed. Randy Bailey. Pubs. Jim Baltimore, Paul Baltimore. adv.: B&W page USD 2,892. Circ: 11,300 (paid and controlled).

634.8 AUS
GRAPE GROWERS. Text in English. m. AUD 54 (effective 2000). adv. **Document type:** *Trade.* **Description:** Deals with viticulture, vineyard management, and grapegrowing.
Published by: Stock Journal Publishers Pty. Ltd., 123 Greenhill Rd, Unley, SA 5061, Australia. TEL 61-8-8372-5222, FAX 61-8-83725282, grapegrowers@rpl.com.au. Ed. Kate McaAvian. Adv. contacts David Shipp, Shirley O'Brien. Circ: 6,000.

641.348 USA ISSN 1542-2860
GRAPES. Text in English. 2001. 7/yr. free domestic to qualified personnel (effective 2002). adv. **Document type:** *Magazine, Trade.*
Published by: Vance Publishing Corp., 10901 W 84th Terrace, Lexena, KS 66214-1821. TEL 913-438-8700, http://www.grapesmagazine.com/, http://www.vancepublishing.com. Ed. Vicky Boyd TEL 209-571-0414. **Subscr. to:** Subscr. Service Center, 400 Knightsbridge Pkwy, Lincolnshire, IL 60069-3613.

630 USA
GRASS & GRAIN. Text in English. 1955. w. (Tue.). USD 37; USD 1 newsstand/cover (effective 2005). **Document type:** *Newspaper, Trade.*
Published by: Ag Press, Inc., 1531 Yuma, Box 1009, Manhattan, KS 66502. TEL 785-539-7558, FAX 785-539-2679, http://www.grassandgrain.com. Ed. Beth Gains Riffel. Pub. Dean Coughenhour. Adv. contact Frank Buchman. Circ: 15,000 (paid). Wire service: AP.

633.2 JPN
CODEN: NPSGAI
➤ **GRASSLAND SCIENCE/NIPPON SOCHI GAKKAI-SHI.** Text in English, Japanese. 1955. bi-m. JPY 8,000 to individual members; JPY 13,000 to institutional members (effective 2001). adv. bk.rev. **Document type:** *Academic/Scholarly.* **Description:** Aims to develop methods of production and utilization of grass and forage crops, and to advance education and research in grassland management.
Former titles (until vol.41, 1995): Japanese Society of Grassland Science. Journal (0447-5933); (until 1961): Japanese Society of Herbage Crops and Grassland Farming - Nippon Sochi Kenkyukaishi (0447-5941)
Indexed: AEA, AgBio, AgrForAb, AnBrAb, BIOSIS Prev, BiolAb, CIN, CPA, ChemAb, ChemTitl, CurCont, DSA, FCA, FPA, ForAb, HerbAb, HortAb, I&DA, IndVet, MaizeAb, NutrAb, OrnHort, PBA, PGegResA, PGrRegA, PHN&I, PoultAb, RPP, RRTA, RevApplEntom, RiceAb, S&F, S&MA, SIA, SeedAb, SoyAb, TOSA, TriticAb, VetBull, WAE&RSA, WeedAb.
—BLDSC (4213.500000), CASDDS, CISTI, IE, ingenta. **CCC.**
Published by: Japanese Society of Grassland Science, c/o National Institute of Livestock and Grassland Science, 768 Senbonmatsu, Nasu-gun, Nishinasuno-machi, Tochigi-ken 329-2747, Japan. TEL 81-287-36-0111, FAX 81-287-36-6629. Ed. Shunpei Kanou. Pub. Masae Shiyomi. Circ: 1,400. **Subscr. to:** Maruzen Co., Ltd., 3-10 Nihonbashi, 2-Chome, Chuo-ku, Tokyo 103, Japan. **Co-sponsor:** Ministry of Education, Science and Culture.

631.4 GBR ISSN 0072-7164
S599.4.G72 CODEN: GBSEA7
GREAT BRITAIN. SOIL SURVEY OF ENGLAND AND WALES. BULLETIN. Text in English. 1964. irreg., latest vol.15, 1984. price varies. **Document type:** *Government.* **Description:** Soil surveys at varied scales.
—Linda Hall.
Published by: Soil Survey and Land Research Centre, Silsoe Campus, Silsoe, Bedford, MK45 4DT, United Kingdom. TEL 44-1525-60428, FAX 44-1525-61147.

631.4 GBR ISSN 0072-7202
CODEN: SSSWD9
GREAT BRITAIN. SOIL SURVEY OF ENGLAND AND WALES. SPECIAL SURVEYS. Text in English. 1969. irreg., latest vol.15, 1988. price varies. **Document type:** *Government.* **Description:** Soil surveys of problem areas of land.
Indexed: S&F.
—Linda Hall.
Published by: Soil Survey and Land Research Centre, Silsoe Campus, Silsoe, Bedford, MK45 4DT, United Kingdom. TEL 44-1525-863242, FAX 44-1525-863253.

631.4 GBR ISSN 0072-7210
CODEN: SSTMDI
GREAT BRITAIN. SOIL SURVEY OF ENGLAND AND WALES. TECHNICAL MONOGRAPHS. Text in English. 1969. irreg., latest vol.18, 1987. price varies. **Document type:** *Government.*
Indexed: S&F.
—Linda Hall.
Published by: Soil Survey and Land Research Centre, Silsoe Campus, Silsoe, Bedford, MK45 4DT, United Kingdom. TEL 44-1525-863242, FAX 44-1525-863253.

GREEN MARKETS WORLD DIRECTORY OF THE FERTILIZER INDUSTRY. see *BUSINESS AND ECONOMICS—Trade And Industrial Directories*

634.772 GRD
GRENADA BANANA CO-OPERATIVE SOCIETY. ANNUAL REPORT AND FINANCIAL STATEMENTS. Text in English. a. **Document type:** *Corporate.*
Published by: Grenada Banana Co-operative Society, Scott St., St. George's, Grenada.

631.5 631.587 ITA ISSN 1021-268X
GRID; the network magazine. Text in English. 1992. s-a. **Document type:** *Newsletter.*
Related titles: Spanish ed.: ISSN 1021-6650; French ed.: ISSN 1021-6642.
Indexed: AEA, AgrForAb, ForAb, I&DA, RDA, S&F, WAE&RSA, WeedAb.
—BLDSC (4216.540100).
Published by: United Nations Food and Agriculture Organization, Land and Water Development Division - I P T R I D, Vialle delle Terme di Caracalla, Rome, 00100, Italy. FAX 39-06-57056275, iptrid@fao.org, http://www.fao.org/iptrid/pub.htm#GRID. Eds. Arum Kandiah, Geoff Pearce, Nicola Hasnip. **Co-publisher:** H R Wallingford.

GROUND WATER CANADA. see *WATER RESOURCES*

630 AUS ISSN 0046-6476
GROWER. Variant title: The South Australian Grower. Text in English. 1946. m. adv. **Document type:** *Magazine, Trade.* **Description:** Provides market reports, outlooks for domestic and export sales, on-farm stories, detailed reports from the industry, and what's new in products, services and techniques.
Indexed: AEA, PROMT.
Published by: Rural Press Ltd. (Subsidiary of: Agricultural Publishers Pty. Ltd.), GPO Box 2249, Adelaide, SA 5001, Australia. TEL 61-8-83725222, http://www.ruralpress.com/publications/detail.asp?publication_id=194. Ed. Peter Brady. Adv. contact Derna Hower. page AUD 1,200. Circ: 8,500.

633 USA ISSN 0745-1784
THE GROWER. Text in English. 1966. m. USD 40 domestic; USD 55 in Canada & Mexico; USD 90 elsewhere (effective 2005). adv. charts; illus.; stat. back issues avail.; reprints avail. **Document type:** *Magazine, Trade.*
Related titles: Microfilm ed.: (from PQC).
Indexed: GardL.
—CISTI. **CCC.**
Published by: Vance Publishing Corp., 400 Knightsbridge Pkwy, Lincolnshire, IL 60069. TEL 847-634-2600, 800-255-5113, FAX 847-634-4379, http://www.growermagazine.com, http://www.vancepublishing.com. Ed. Vicky Boyd TEL 209-571-0414. Pub. Robb Bertels. adv.: B&W page USD 3,975, color page USD 5,970. Circ: 22,000 (controlled).

634 CAN ISSN 0017-4777
THE GROWER. Text in English. 1879. m. USD 30 domestic; USD 40 foreign. adv. bk.rev. charts; illus.; mkt.; stat. **Document type:** *Trade.* **Description:** Presents information on new products, services, systems, labor, research, market events and upcoming trends. Provides a forum and insight into the broader infrastructure of national and international horticultural industries.
Indexed: AEA, PROMT.
Published by: Ontario Fruit and Vegetable Growers Association, 355 Elmira Rd, 103, Guelph, ON N1K 1S5, Canada. TEL 519-763-8728, FAX 519-763-6604, http://thegrower.org. Ed., R&P Jamie Reaume. Pub. Michael Mazur. Adv. contact Shelley Godding. Circ: 10,000.

631 CAN
GUIDE TO CROP PROTECTION. Text in English. a. free. back issues avail. **Document type:** *Government.* **Description:** Covers weed control, plant disease control, seed treatment, and insect control.
Published by: Agriculture and Food, Communications Branch, B5 Walter Scott Bldg, 3085 Albert St, Regina, SK S4S 0B1, Canada. TEL 888-613-3975, FAX 306-721-4626, pad@sk.sympatico.ca, http://www.agr.gov.sk.ca/saf.

632.9540968 ZAF
GUIDE TO THE USE OF HERBICIDES. Text in English. 1993 (14th ed.). irreg. ZAR 15. **Document type:** *Government.*
Published by: (Tripura. Department of Agriculture), Department of Agricultural Development, Private Bag X144, Pretoria, 0001, South Africa. TEL 27-12-206-2181, FAX 27-21-323-2516. **Affiliate:** Directorate of Livestock Improvement and Agricultural Production Resources.

632.95 ZAF
GUIDE TO THE USE OF PESTICIDES AND FUNGICIDES IN THE REPUBLIC OF SOUTH AFRICA. Text in English. 1961. a., latest vol.36, 1993. price varies. **Document type:** *Government.*
Formerly: Guide to the Use of Insecticides and Fungicides in South Africa
Published by: (Tripura. Department of Agriculture), Department of Agricultural Development, Private Bag X144, Pretoria, 0001, South Africa. TEL 27-12-206-2181, FAX 27-12-323-2516. Circ: 6,000.

633.6 GUY
GUYANA SUGAR CORPORATION. ANNUAL REPORTS AND ACCOUNTS. Text in English. 1976. a. illus. **Document type:** *Corporate.* **Description:** Outlines the activities and achievements of the year. Includes a chairman's statement, directors' report, review of operations and financial-statistical statements.
Published by: Guyana Sugar Corporation Ltd., Church St 22, Georgetown, Guyana. TEL 592-2-62918, FAX 592-2-57274. Circ: 1,000.

630 USA
H O M E VOICE. Text in English. 1994. q. adv. bk.rev. **Document type:** *Newsletter, Trade.*
Published by: Hoosier Organic Marketing Education, 8364 S State Rd 39, Clayton, IN 46118-9178. Ed. Cissy Bowman.

HANDBOOK OF INDIAN PUMPS FOR IRRIGATION; salient features and performances. see *AGRICULTURE—Agricultural Equipment*

630 PNG ISSN 0378-8865
CODEN: HARVDQ
➤ **HARVEST**; a pan-Pacific journal of agricultural extension. Text in English. 1971. 2/yr. PGK 16.92 domestic; PGK 25.10 in Asia & the Pacific; PGK 30.90 elsewhere (effective 2002). adv. bk.rev. abstr.; charts; illus. **Document type:** *Academic/Scholarly.* **Description:** Information on projects, research and new recommendations in agriculture, livestock, soil in Papua New Guinea. For DAL officers, research workers, schools and institutions.
Indexed: HortAb, RPP, RevApplEntom, RiceAb, SPPI, WeedAb.
Published by: Department of Agriculture and Livestock, Publication Section, PO Box 417, Konedobu NCD, Papua New Guinea. TEL 675-320-2886, FAX 675-320-2883, dalit@daltron.com.pg. Ed. Jones Hiaso. Circ: 2,000.

630 IND
HARYANA JOURNAL OF HORTICULTURAL SCIENCES. Text in English. 1972. q.
—BLDSC (4271.120000).
Published by: Horticultural Society of Haryana, Department of Horticulture, CCS Haryana Agriculture University, Hissar, Haryana 125 005, India.

633.6 USA
CODEN: HSEAAL
HAWAII AGRICULTURE RESEARCH CENTER. ANNUAL REPORT. Text in English. 1947. a. per issue exchange basis only.
Former titles: Hawaiian Sugar Planters' Association. Annual Report; Hawaiian Sugar Planters' Association Experiment Station. Annual Report (0073-1366)
Indexed: BiolAb, RevApplEntom, WeedAb.
—CISTI.

▼ new title ➤ refereed ✶ unverified ♦ full entry avail.

Published by: Hawaii Agriculture Research Center, 99 193 Aiea Heights Dr, Ste 300, Aiea, HI 96701-3911. TEL 808-487-5561, FAX 808-486-5020. Ed. Stephanie A Whalen.

631 USA
HAY & FEEDSTUFFS. Text in English. w. USD 70; USD 75 in Canada & Mexico; USD 105 elsewhere. **Document type:** *Government.*
Published by: (Livestock & Seed Division), U.S. Department of Agriculture, Agricultural Marketing Service (Greely), 711 O St., Greely, CO 80631. TEL 303-353-9750, FAX 303-353-9790. **Subscr. to:** U.S.D.A. Agricultural Marketing Service, Livestock & Seed Division, Rm 2613 S, Box 96456, Washington, DC 20090-6456. FAX 202-245-4732.

631 USA
HAY THERE. Text in English. 1972. m. USD 260 membership (effective 2000). adv. **Document type:** *Trade.* **Description:** Covers agricultural marketing concerns for hay producers.
Published by: National Hay Association, 102 Treasure Isle Causeway, Ste. 201, St. Petersburg, FL 33706. TEL 727-367-9702, FAX 727-367-9608. Ed. Donald Kieffer. Circ: 600.

633 SCG ISSN 1018-1806
HELIA; international sunflower journal. Text in English. 199?. s-a. **Document type:** *Journal, Academic/Scholarly.*
Indexed: AgBio, AgrForAb, BioCN&I, CPA, FCA, HortAb, I&DA, MaizeAb, OrnHort, PBA, PGegResA, PGrRegA, PHN&I, RA&MP, S&F, SIA, SeedAb, SoyAb, WeedAb.
—BLDSC (4285.100000), CISTI, IE.
Published by: Institut za Ratarstvo i Povrtarstvo/Institute of Field and Vegetable Crops, Maksima Gorkog 30, Novi Sad, Vojvodina 21000. sabo@ifvcns.ns.ac.yu, http://www.ifvcns.co.yu.

633.491 USA ISSN 0018-1986
HINTS TO POTATO GROWERS. Text in English. 1920. irreg. (2-4/yr.). USD 10 to non-members. charts; stat.
Media: Duplicated (not offset).
Published by: New Jersey State Potato Association, Box 231 Blake Hall, Cook College, Rutgers University, New Brunswick, NJ 08903. Ed. Dr. Melvin Henninger. Circ: 150.

631.8 JPN ISSN 0387-2718
CODEN: HKGKD8
HIRYO KAGAKU/FERTILIZER SCIENCE. Text in Japanese. 1978. a.
—BLDSC (3910.430000).
Published by: Hiryo Kagaku Kenkyujo/Fertilization Research Foundation, Nogyogijyutsukaikan, 6th Fl, 1-26-3 Nishigahara, Kita-ku, Tokyo, 114-0024, Japan. TEL 81-3-3915-7140, FAX 81-3-3949-2029.

630 POL ISSN 1231-918X
HODOWLA ROSLIN I NASIENNICTWO. Text in Polish. 1969. bi-m. EUR 29 foreign (effective 2005).
Former titles (until 1987): Hodowla Roslin (0137-1509); (until 1973): Hodowla Roslin i Nasiennictwo (0137-1517)
Indexed: AgrLib.
Published by: Polska Izba Nasienna, ul Kochanowskiego 7/603, Poznan, 60845, Poland. pin.poznan@post.pl, http://pin.org.pl/hrin. Ed. Karol W Duczmal. **Dist. by:** Ars Polona, Krakowskie Przedmiescie 7, Warsaw, Poland. TEL 48-22-9263914, FAX 48-22-9265334, arspolona@arspolona.com.pl, http://www.arspolona.com.pl.

633.1 581.1 GBR
HOME - GROWN CEREALS AUTHORITY. CEREALS R & D CONFERENCE. PROCEEDINGS. Text in English. 1991. a. **Document type:** *Proceedings.*
Published by: Home - Grown Cereals Authority, Caledonia House, 223 Pentonville Rd, London, N1 9HY, United Kingdom. TEL 44-20-75203920, FAX 44-20-75203958, publication@hgca.com, http://www.hgca.com.

633.1 581.1 GBR ISSN 1368-6739
HOME - GROWN CEREALS AUTHORITY. PROJECT REPORT. Text in English. 198?. irreg. **Document type:** *Monographic series.*
Indexed: FS&TA.
—BLDSC (4303.447800), IE.
Published by: Home - Grown Cereals Authority, Caledonia House, 223 Pentonville Rd, London, N1 9HY, United Kingdom. TEL 44-20-75203920, FAX 44-20-75203958, publication@hgca.com, http://www.hgca.com.

633.1 581.1 GBR ISSN 1367-1812
HOME - GROWN CEREALS AUTHORITY. RESEARCH REVIEW. Text in English. 198?. irreg.
—BLDSC (4303.448000), IE.
Published by: Home - Grown Cereals Authority, Caledonia House, 223 Pentonville Rd, London, N1 9HY, United Kingdom. TEL 44-20-75203920, FAX 44-20-75203958, publication@hgca.com, http://www.hgca.com.

633.82 DEU ISSN 0018-4845
HOPFEN - RUNDSCHAU. Text in German. 1950. m. EUR 35; EUR 4 newsstand/cover (effective 2005). adv. bk.rev. charts; illus.; mkt.; stat.; tr.mk. **Document type:** *Magazine, Trade.* **Description:** Reviews all aspects of hops.
Related titles: Cards ed.
Indexed: FS&TA, HortAb.
—BLDSC (4326.650000).
Published by: Verband Deutscher Hopfenpflanzer e.V., Kellerstr 1, Wolnzach, 85283, Germany. TEL 49-8442-957200, FAX 49-8442-957270, http://www.deutscher-hopfen.de/contentserv/hopfenpflanzerverband.de/index.php?StoryID=2127. Ed. O Weingarten. adv.: B&W page EUR 810, color page EUR 2,325; trim 189 x 255. Circ: 3,500.

633 USA ISSN 0889-0463
HOPS MARKET NEWS. Text in English. m. USD 18 domestic; USD 20 in Canada & Mexico; USD 25 elsewhere (effective 2000). back issues avail.; reprint service avail. from CIS. **Document type:** *Government.* **Description:** Provides information about prices and data for national hops production.
Related titles: Microfiche ed.: (from CIS).
Indexed: AmStI.
Published by: (Livestock & Seed Division), U.S. Department of Agriculture, Agricultural Marketing Service (Portland), 1220 S W Third Ave, Rm 1772, Portland, OR 97204. Ed. Lowell Serfling. **Subscr. to:** U.S.D.A. Agricultural Marketing Service, Livestock & Seed Division, Rm 2613 S, Box 96456, Washington, DC 20090-6456. FAX 202-245-4732.

634 USA
HORT EXPO NORTHWEST. Text in English. 1990. a. free (2001). adv. **Document type:** *Trade.* **Description:** Focuses on the northwest fruit industry with emphasis on trade shows in Oregon and Washington.
Published by: Columbia Publishing and Design, 413B N 20th Ave, Yakima, WA 98902. TEL 509-248-2452, 800-900-2452, FAX 509-248-4056, ken@freshcut.com, steve@freshcut.com, http://www.freshcut.com/hort. Ed. Ken Hodge. Adv. contact Loven Queen. Circ: 11,000 (controlled).

630 BRA ISSN 0102-0536
HORTICULTURA BRASILEIRA. Text in Portuguese. 1964. s-a.
Formerly (until 1981): Revista de Olericultura (0101-854X)
Related titles: Online - full text ed.: free (effective 2005).
Indexed: AEA, AgBio, AgrForAb, BioCN&I, CPA, FCA, HerbAb, HortAb, I&DA, MaizeAb, NemAb, NutrAb, OrnHort, PBA, PGegResA, PGrRegA, PHN&I, PN&I, PotatoAb, PoultAb, RA&MP, RDA, RPP, RiceAb, S&F, SIA, SeedAb, SoyAb, TDB, WAE&RSA, WeedAb.
—BLDSC (4329.780000).
Published by: Sociedade de Olericultura do Brasil, C. Postal 237, Botucatu, SP 18603-970, Brazil. TEL 55-14-68027172, FAX 55-14-68023438, hortbras@cnph.embrapa.br, sob@fca.unesp.br, http://www.horticiencia.com.br/hortbras.

HORTICULTURE NEWS. see *GARDENING AND HORTICULTURE*

631 ZWE
HORTICULTURE RESEARCH INSTITUTE. ANNUAL REPORT. PART 1. HORTICULTURAL RESEARCH CENTRE. Text in English. 1976. a. free. **Document type:** *Government.*
Formerly: Horticulture and Coffee Research Institute. Annual Report. Part 1. Horticultural Research Centre
Published by: Ministry of Agriculture, Horticulture Research Institute, PO Box 3748, Marondera, Zimbabwe. Ed. J E Jackson. Circ: 300. **Subscr. to:** Causeway, PO Box 8108, Harare, Zimbabwe.

635 GBR ISSN 0963-3235
HORTICULTURE RESEARCH INTERNATIONAL. ANNUAL REPORT. Text in English. 1991. a., latest 2001/2002. GBP 15 (effective 2003). **Document type:** *Academic/Scholarly.* **Description:** Provides information to producers of horticultural and other plant-based products.
Former titles: B S H R Institute of Horticultural Research. Annual Report (0953-2455); A F R C Institute of Horticultural Research Annual Report; (until 1989): East Malling Research Station. Annual Report (0306-6398)
Indexed: ApicAb, BiolAb, FCA, HerbAb, HortAb, RPP, RevApplEntom, WeedAb.
—CISTI. **CCC.**
Published by: Horticulture Research International, Wellesbourne, Warwick, CV35 9EF, United Kingdom. TEL 44-1789-470382, FAX 44-1789-470552, enquiry.hri@hri.ac.uk, http://www.hri.ac.uk. Circ: 3,000.

631 CAN ISSN 0319-6038
HURON SOIL AND CROP NEWS. Text in English. 1956. a. adv.
Former titles (until 1964): Huron County Soil and Crop News (0319-602X); (until 1961): Huron Soil and Crop News (0319-6011)
Published by: Exeter Times-Advocate, 424 Main St, Exeter, ON, Canada. TEL 519-235-1331. Ed. Ross Haugh. Circ: 7,000.

630 THA ISSN 1015-8650
I B S R A M PROCEEDINGS. (International Board for Soil Research and Management) Text in English. 198?. irreg.
—BLDSC (4360.164300).
Published by: International Board for Soil Research and Management, PO Box 9-109, Bangkok, 10900, Thailand. TEL 66-2-5797590, FAX 66-2-5611230, oibsram@nontri.ku.ac.th, http://uia.org/uiademo/org/f0299.htm.

631.0285 USA ISSN 1084-3736
I C A S A NEWS. Text in English. 1991. a. free. adv. bk.rev. back issues avail. **Document type:** *Newsletter, Trade.* **Description:** Updates on applications, reports on advances in technology and information on program status.
Former titles (until 1995): I B S N A T Views (1076-3112); (until 1993): Agrotechnology Transfer (0883-8631)
Related titles: Online - full text ed.
—CISTI.
Published by: International Consortium for Agricultural Systems Applications (ICASA), 2440 Campus Rd., Box 527, Honolulu, HI 96822. TEL 808-956-7531, FAX 808-956-2711, icasa@icasa.net, http://www.icasa.net. Ed. Gordon Y Tsuji. Adv. contact Agnes Shimamura. Circ: 100.

I C C O COCOA NEWSLETTER. see *FOOD AND FOOD INDUSTRIES*

631 IND ISSN 1017-9933
I C R I S A T REPORT. (International Crops Research Institute for the Semi-Arid Tropics) Text in English. 1991. a.
Formed by the merger of (1980-1990): I C R I S A T Annual Report (0257-2478); (1979-1990): I C R I S A T Research Highlights (0257-2532)
—BLDSC (4362.068930), CISTI, Linda Hall.
Published by: International Crops Research Institute for the Semi-Arid Tropics, Patancheru, Andhra Pradesh 502 324, India. TEL 91-40-23296161, FAX 91-40-23241239, icrisat@cgiar.org, http://www.icrisat.org.

631.8 FRA
I F A TECHNICAL CONFERENCE. PROCEEDINGS. Text in French. biennial. **Document type:** *Proceedings.*
Formerly: I S M A Technical Conference. Proceedings
Published by: International Fertilizer Industry Association, 28 rue Marbeuf, Paris, 75008, France. TEL 33-1-53930500, FAX 33-1-53930547, TELEX 640481F, publications@fertilizer.org, http://www.fertilizer.org.

631.8 USA ISSN 0149-3434
I F D C REPORT. (International Fertilizer Development Center) Text in English. 1976. q.
—BLDSC (4363.279900), CISTI.
Published by: International Fertilizer Development Center, PO Box 2040, Muscle Shoals, AL 35662. TEL 256-381-6600, FAX 256-381-7408, general@ifdc.org, http://www.ifdc.org.

633.2 GBR ISSN 1463-6255
I G E R ANNUAL REPORT & ACCOUNTS. (Institute of Grassland and Environmental Research) Text in English. a.
Published by: Institute of Grassland and Environmental Research, North Wyke Research Station, Okehampton, Devon EX20 2SB, United Kingdom.

633.2 GBR ISSN 1368-5503
I G E R INNOVATIONS. Text in English. 1997. a., latest vol.6, 2002. price varies. **Document type:** *Yearbook, Academic/Scholarly.*
Related titles: Online - full content ed.
Indexed: AgBio, CPA, FCA, HerbAb, I&DA, MaizeAb, PBA, PN&I, RefZh, S&F, SoyAb, TriticAb.
—CISTI, Linda Hall.
Published by: Institute of Grassland and Environmental Research, Aberystwyth Research Centre, Plas Gogerddan, Aberystwyth, Ceredigion, Wales SY23 3EB, United Kingdom. TEL 44-1970-823000, FAX 44-1970-828357, igerlib.igerlib-wpbs@bbsrc.ac.uk, http://www.iger.bbsrc.ac.uk/igerweb/IGER_Innovations/geninfo.html, http://www.iger.bbsrc.ac.uk/igerweb/library/pubs-list.html. Ed., R&P Dr. T Gordon.

633.2 GBR ISSN 1358-5991
I G E R TECHNICAL REVIEW. Text in English. 1994. irreg., latest 1998. price varies. back issues avail. **Document type:** *Monographic series, Academic/Scholarly.*
—BLDSC (4363.396500).
Published by: Institute of Grassland and Environmental Research, Aberystwyth Research Centre, Plas Gogerddan, Aberystwyth, Ceredigion, Wales SY23 3EB, United Kingdom. TEL 44-1970-823000, FAX 44-1970-828357, http://www.iger.bbsrc.ac.uk/igerweb/, http://www.iger.bbsrc.ac.uk/igerweb/library/pubs-list.html.

631 NLD
I L E I A READINGS IN SUSTAINABLE AGRICULTURE. (Centre for Information on Low-External-Input and Sustainable Agriculture) Text in English. irreg., latest vol.4. price varies. illus. back issues avail. **Document type:** *Monographic series, Trade.* **Description:** Discusses specific topics in environmentally sustainable agriculture and their applications in detail.
Published by: Center for and Information on Low-External-Input and Sustainable Agriculture, Kastanjelaan 5, PO Box 64, Leusden, 3830 AB, Netherlands. TEL 31-33-432-6011, FAX 31-33-495-1779, ileia@ileia.nl, http://www.ileia.org.

631 CHE
I P I BULLETIN. Text mainly in English; Text occasionally in Spanish, Portuguese. 1974. irreg., latest vol.15, 1996. price varies. **Document type:** *Bulletin, Trade.*
Indexed: BiolAb, FCA, HerbAb, HortAb, I&DA, S&F.

Published by: International Potash Institute, PO Box 1609, Basel, 4001, Switzerland. TEL 41-61-2612922, FAX 41-61-2612925, ipi@iprolink.ch, http://www.ipipotash.org.

631 CHE ISSN 0379-0495
CODEN: IRTOD9
I P I RESEARCH TOPICS. Text in English. 1976. irreg., latest vol.21, 1997. price varies. **Document type:** *Monographic series, Academic/Scholarly.*
Indexed: BiolAb, FCA, HerbAb, S&F.
—CASDDS, CISTI, Linda Hall.
Published by: International Potash Institute, PO Box 1609, Basel, 4001, Switzerland. TEL 41-61-2612922, FAX 41-61-2612925, ipi@iprolink.ch, http://www.ipipotash.org.

632.9 USA ISSN 0738-968X
I P M PRACTITIONER; monitoring the field of pest management. (Integrated Pest Management) Text in English. 1979. m. USD 35 to individuals; USD 60 to institutions (effective 2005). adv. bk.rev. index. back issues avail. **Document type:** *Newsletter, Trade.* **Description:** Covers integrated pest management programs, methods, products and research.
Indexed: AEA, Agr, AgrForAb, BioCN&I, CPA, FCA, FPA, ForAb, GardL, HerbAb, HortAb, IndVet, MaizeAb, NemAb, NutrAb, OrnHort, PBA, PGrRegA, PHN&I, PotatoAb, PoultAb, RA&MP, RM&VM, RPP, RevApplEntom, S&F, SeedAb, TriticAb, WAE&RSA, WeedAb.
—BLDSC (4567.390000).
Published by: Bio Integral Resource Center, PO Box 7414, Berkeley, CA 94707. TEL 510-524-2567, FAX 510-524-1758. Ed., R&P William Quarles. Circ: 5,000.

626.8 ITA ISSN 1020-7376
I P T R I D ISSUES PAPER. (International Programme for Technology and Research in Irrigation and Drainage) Text in English. 1999. irreg., latest vol.3, 2001. price varies. **Document type:** *Monographic series, Academic/Scholarly.* **Description:** Aims to create awareness among the interested public and the professional community of irrigation and drainage issues, particularly of the positive benefits of irrigated agriculture.
—BLDSC (4567.482500).
Published by: Food and Agriculture Organization of the United Nations, International Programme for Technology and Research in Irrigation and Drainage, Viale delle Terme di Caracalla, Rome, 00100, Italy. iptrid@fao.org, http://www.fao.org/iptrid/publications.html#papers.

635 NLD
I S O S C PROCEEDINGS. Variant title: International Congress on Soilless Culture. Proceedings. Text in English. 1969. quadrennial. back issues avail. **Document type:** *Proceedings.*
Published by: International Society for Soilless Culture, PO Box 52, Wageningen, 6700 AB, Netherlands. TEL 31-317-413809, FAX 31-317-423457.

631 ESP ISSN 1130-6017
➤ **I T E A PRODUCCION VEGETAL.** Text in Spanish; Summaries in English. 1986. 3/yr. adv. **Document type:** *Academic/Scholarly.*
Supersedes in part (in 1990): Informacion Tecnica Economica Agraria (0212-2731)
Indexed: AgBio, AgrForAb, CPA, FCA, FPA, FS&TA, ForAb, HerbAb, HortAb, I&DA, IECT, MaizeAb, NemAb, OrnHort, PBA, PGegResA, PGrRegA, PHN&I, PotatoAb, RA&MP, RDA, RPP, RevApplEntom, RiceAb, S&F, SIA, SeedAb, TriticAb, WAE&RSA, WeedAb.
—BLDSC (4588.572800), CINDOC.
Published by: Asociacion Interprofesional para el Desarrollo Agrario, Montanana, 177, Apartado 727, Zaragoza, 50080, Spain. TEL 34-976-576336, FAX 34-976-575501, alberti@mizar.csic.es. R&P Leonardo Plana. Adv. contact Mercedes Furrez. Circ: 600.

631 AUT
➤ **I W G O NEWSLETTER.** Text in English. 1980. s-a. EUR 20 (effective 2001). abstr. 40 p./no. 1 cols./p.; back issues avail.; reprints avail. **Document type:** *Newsletter, Academic/Scholarly.*
Published by: International Working Group on Ostrinia Nubilalis, Spargelfeldstrasse 191, Vienna, 1226, Austria. TEL 43-1-732162002, FAX 43-1-732162108, http://www.infoland.at/iwgo. Ed. Harald Berger.

633.6 DOM ISSN 1013-980X
HD9114.D6
INAZUCAR. Text in Spanish. bi-m. DOP 3. illus.; stat.
Published by: Instituto Azucarero Dominicano, Centro de los Heroes, Apdo de Correos 667, Santo Domingo, Dominican Republic. Ed. Quirilio Vilorio Sanchez.

631 ITA
INCONTRI AGRICOOP. Text in Italian. 1994. bi-m. illus. back issues avail. **Document type:** *Trade.*
Published by: Agricoop S.c.ar.l., Via Piane, 65-66, Moresco, AP 63010, Italy. TEL 39-734-222911, FAX 39-734-222921, info@agricoop.it, http://www.agricoop.it.

631 IND
INDIA. CARDAMOM BOARD. ANNUAL REPORT. Text in English. a.
Published by: Spices Board, K.C. Ave., St. Vincent Cross Rd., Ernakulam, P O Box 1909, Kochi, Kerala 682 018, India. TEL 353837, FAX 484-364429.

633.83 IND
INDIA. SPICES BOARD. ANNUAL REPORT. Text in English. a. **Document type:** *Corporate.*
Published by: Ministry of Commerce, Spices Board, N.H. Bypass, Palarivattom P.O., P O Box 2277, Cochin, Kerala 682 025, India. TEL 91-484-333610, FAX 91-484-331429, hochn@giasmd01.vsnl.net.in, http://www.indianspices.com.

631.8 IND
INDIAN FERTILISER INDUSTRY DESKBOOK. Text in English. 1976. biennial. INR 175, USD 55 (effective 2000). adv. bk.rev. abstr.; charts; illus. **Document type:** *Trade.*
Related titles: Microform ed.: (from PQC).
Published by: Technical Press Publications, Eucharistic Congress Bldg. No.1, 5/1 Convent St, Colaba, Mumbai, Maharashtra 400 039, India. TEL 91-22-2021446, FAX 91-22-2871499. Ed., Pub. J P de Sousa. adv.: B&W page INR 1,750, color page INR 2,250; trim 18 x 23. Circ: 6,400.

INDIAN FERTILISER STATISTICS. see *AGRICULTURE—Abstracting, Bibliographies, Statistics*

633 IND ISSN 0073-649X
SB229.I4
INDIAN INSTITUTE OF SUGARCANE RESEARCH, LUCKNOW. ANNUAL REPORT. Text in English. 1954. a. per issue exchange basis.
Indexed: RPP.
—CISTI.
Published by: Indian Institute of Sugarcane Research, Lucknow, Uttar Pradesh 2, India.

630.24 668.6 IND ISSN 0367-8229
CODEN: IJACBO
INDIAN JOURNAL OF AGRICULTURAL CHEMISTRY. Text in English. 1968. 3/yr. USD 450 to institutions (effective 2006). adv. bk.rev. back issues avail. **Description:** Publishes all academic and experimental research or review papers dealing with agricultural chemistry, soil science, crop physiology and growth, pesticides, environmental pollution.
Indexed: B&AI, BiolAb, CIN, CPA, ChemAb, ChemTitl, ExcerpMed, FCA, HerbAb, HortAb, I&DA, S&F, SeedAb, TOSA, TriticAb, WeedAb.
—CASDDS, CISTI, Linda Hall.
Published by: Scientific Publishers, 5-A New Pali Rd., Near Hotel Taj Hari Mahal, PO Box 91, Jodhpur, Rajasthan 342 003, India. TEL 91-291-2433323, FAX 91-291-2512580, info@scientificpub.com, http://www.scientificpub.com/bookdetails.php?booktransid=307&bookid=303. Ed. Samarendra Kumar De. adv.: page USD 125. Circ: 475.
Co-sponsor: Indian Council of Agricultural Research.

631.8 IND ISSN 0973-1822
S631 CODEN: FENEAQ
INDIAN JOURNAL OF FERTILISERS. Text in English. 1956. m. USD 80 (effective 2003). adv. bk.rev. abstr.; bibl.; charts; illus.; pat. index. **Document type:** *Academic/Scholarly.* **Description:** Features academic and practical research on the productivity and safety of fertilizers in India.
Formerly: Fertiliser News (0015-0266); Incorporates: Fertiliser Association of India. Annual Review of Fertiliser. Consumption and Production (0430-3288)
Related titles: ♦ Supplement(s): F A I Annual Review of Fertiliser Production and Consumption.
Indexed: AEA, AgBio, AgrForAb, BioCN&I, CPA, ChemAb, DSA, ExcerpMed, FCA, FPA, FS&TA, ForAb, HerbAb, HortAb, I&DA, MaizeAb, NutrAb, OrnHort, PBA, PGegResA, PGrRegA, PHN&I, PotatoAb, PoultAb, RA&MP, RDA, RPP, RRTA, RevApplEntom, RiceAb, S&F, SIA, SeedAb, SoyAb, TDB, TOSA, TriticAb, WAE&RSA, WeedAb.
—BLDSC (3909.620000), CASDDS, IE, ingenta, Linda Hall.
Published by: (Fertiliser Association of India), Scientific Publishers, 5-A New Pali Rd., Near Hotel Taj Hari Mahal, PO Box 91, Jodhpur, Rajasthan 342 003, India. TEL 91-291-2433323, FAX 91-291-2512580, info@scientificpub.com, http://www.scientificpub.com. Ed. K P Sundaram. Circ: 4,600.

630 635 IND ISSN 0253-4355
CODEN: IPLPDQ
INDIAN JOURNAL OF PLANT PROTECTION. Text in English. 1973. s-a.
Indexed: AEA, AgBio, AgrForAb, BIOSIS Prev, BioCN&I, BiolAb, CPA, FCA, FPA, ForAb, HerbAb, HortAb, MaizeAb, NemAb, OrnHort, PBA, PGegResA, PGrRegA, PHN&I, PotatoAb, RA&MP, RDA, RM&VM, RPP, RiceAb, S&F, SIA, SeedAb, SoyAb, TriticAb, VITIS, WAE&RSA, WeedAb, ZooRec.
—BLDSC (4420.152000), CISTI, IE, ingenta, Linda Hall. **CCC.**
Published by: Plant Protection Association of India, Rajendranaga, Hyderabad, India.

630 IND ISSN 0970-6380
INDIAN JOURNAL OF PULSES RESEARCH. Text in English. 1988. s-a.
Indexed: AgBio, AgrForAb, BioCN&I, CPA, FCA, HerbAb, HortAb, I&DA, NemAb, NutrAb, OrnHort, PBA, PGegResA, PGrRegA, PHN&I, RDA, RPP, RiceAb, S&F, SeedAb, SoyAb, TriticAb, WAE&RSA, WeedAb.
—BLDSC (4420.500000), IE, ingenta, Linda Hall.
Published by: Indian Society of Pulses Research and Development, Uttar Pradesh, Kanpur, 208024, India.

631.4 IND ISSN 0970-3349
➤ **INDIAN JOURNAL OF SOIL CONSERVATION.** (Indian J. Soil. Cons.) Text in English. 1973. 3/yr., latest vol.29, no.1. USD 35 (effective 2003). adv. bk.rev. 85 p./no. 2 cols./p.; reprints avail. **Document type:** *Journal, Academic/Scholarly.* **Description:** Includes information on soil conservation, hydrology and erosion processes, sustainable resource management, farming systems, agroforestry, forests and pastures, land degradation, socio-economics, watershed development and environment protection.
Formerly (until 1978): Soil Conservation Digest (0377-5402)
Indexed: AEA, AgrForAb, CPA, DSA, FCA, FPA, ForAb, HerbAb, HortAb, I&DA, MaizeAb, NutrAb, OrnHort, PBA, PGegResA, PGrRegA, PotatoAb, RA&MP, RDA, RPP, RiceAb, S&F, SIA, SeedAb, SoyAb, TriticAb, WAE&RSA, WeedAb.
Published by: Indian Association of Soil and Water Conservationists, 218 Kaulagarh Rd., Dehra Dun, Uttaranchal 248 195, India. TEL 91-135-755386, FAX 91-135-754213, TELEX 585-237SCRI-IN, cswcrti@icar.delhi.nic.in. Ed. S K Dhyani. Pub. O P S Khola. R&P J S Samra. adv.: page INR 1,000. Circ: 1,100 (paid).

630 635 IND ISSN 0253-8040
CODEN: IJWSAB
INDIAN JOURNAL OF WEED SCIENCE. Text in English. 1969. s-a.
Indexed: AEA, AgrForAb, BioCN&I, CPA, FCA, FPA, ForAb, HerbAb, HortAb, I&DA, MaizeAb, OrnHort, PBA, PGegResA, PHN&I, PotatoAb, RA&MP, RDA, RPP, RiceAb, S&F, SIA, SeedAb, SoyAb, TriticAb, WAE&RSA, WeedAb.
—Linda Hall.
Published by: Indian Society of Weed Science, Andhra Pradesh Agricultural University, Rajendranagar, Hyderabad, India.

635.21 IND ISSN 0970-8235
➤ **INDIAN POTATO ASSOCIATION. JOURNAL.** Text and summaries in English. 1974. q. INR 400, USD 40 (effective 2001). adv. bk.rev. 100 p./no.; back issues avail. **Document type:** *Journal, Academic/Scholarly.* **Description:** Disseminates the research work, development and technology on potato production to researchers, growers and potato industry.
Indexed: AEA, AgBio, AgrForAb, BIOSIS Prev, BioCN&I, BiolAb, CPA, FCA, FPA, ForAb, HerbAb, HortAb, I&DA, MaizeAb, NemAb, NutrAb, PBA, PGegResA, PGrRegA, PHN&I, PotatoAb, PoultAb, RA&MP, RDA, RPP, RevApplEntom, RiceAb, S&F, SIA, SeedAb, SoyAb, TriticAb, WAE&RSA, WeedAb.
—CISTI.
Published by: Indian Potato Association, Central Potato Research Institute, Simla, Himachal Pradesh 171 001, India. TEL 91-177-225073, FAX 91-177-224460, khurana@cpri.hp.nic.in. Ed., Adv. contact S M Paul Khurana. Circ: 750 (paid).

630 635 IND
INDIAN SOCIETY OF WEED SCIENCE. ANNUAL REPORT. Text in English. a.
Published by: Indian Society of Weed Science, Andhra Pradesh Agricultural University, Rajendranagar, Hyderabad, India.

INDIAN SPICES. see *BUSINESS AND ECONOMICS—International Commerce*

633 IND ISSN 0019-6428
CODEN: ISUGAS
INDIAN SUGAR; complete sugar journal. Text in English. 1950. m. INR 120. adv. bk.rev. charts; stat. index.
Indexed: AEA, AgBio, AgrForAb, BioCN&I, CPA, ChemAb, DSA, FCA, FS&TA, HerbAb, HortAb, I&DA, MaizeAb, NemAb, NutrAb, PBA, PGegResA, PGrRegA, PHN&I, PotatoAb, RA&MP, RDA, RM&VM, RPP, RevApplEntom, RiceAb, S&F, SIA, SeedAb, SoyAb, TDB, TriticAb, WAE&RSA, WeedAb.
—BLDSC (4429.800000), CASDDS, CISTI, IE, ingenta.
Published by: Indian Sugar Mills Association, Sugar House, 39 Nehru Place, New Delhi, 110 019, India. TEL 6416601. Ed. S L Jain. Circ: 1,100.

INDICADORES DA PRODUCAO VEGETAL. see *AGRICULTURE—Abstracting, Bibliographies, Statistics*

630 IDN ISSN 1411-982X
➤ **INDONESIAN JOURNAL OF AGRICULTURAL SCIENCES.** Text in English; Abstracts in English, Indonesian. 1985. s-a. IDR 13,000 domestic; USD 12 foreign (effective 2002). abstr. index. **Document type:** *Journal, Academic/Scholarly.* **Description:** Publishes primary research articles on crops. The purpose is to disseminate agricultural research results to users, namely researchers, extentionists, and educators in Indonesia as well as abroad.
Former titles: Indonesian Agricultural Sciences; (until 1999): Indonesian Journal of Crop Science (0216-8170)
Related titles: Online - full text ed.
Indexed: AEA, Agr, AgrForAb, BioCN&I, CPA, FCA, ForAb, HerbAb, HortAb, I&DA, MaizeAb, PBA, PGegResA, PHN&I, PotatoAb, PoultAb, RA&MP, RDA, RPP, RevApplEntom, RiceAb, S&F, SeedAb, SoyAb, WAE&RSA.
—CISTI.

Published by: Agency for Agricultural Research & Development, Jl Ir H Juanda 20, Bogor, 16122, Indonesia. TEL 62-251-321746, FAX 62-251-326561, pustaka@bogor.net, http://pustaka.bogor.net. Ed. I Putu Kompiang. Circ: 1,000.

631 NLD ISSN 0926-6690
CODEN: ICRDEW

➤ **INDUSTRIAL CROPS AND PRODUCTS.** Text in English. 1992. 6/yr. EUR 844 in Europe to institutions; JPY 112,000 in Japan to institutions; USD 944 to institutions except Europe and Japan (effective 2006). bk.rev. abstr. back issues avail. **Document type:** *Journal, Academic/Scholarly.* **Description:** Covers advances in the development, production, harvesting, storage and processing of nonfood crops for industrial uses, including applications of pharmaceuticals, lubricants, fuels, fibers, essential oils, biologically active materials, and uses for industrial crop by-products.
Related titles: Microform ed.: (from PQC); Online - full text ed.: (from EBSCO Publishing, Gale Group, IngentaConnect, ScienceDirect, Swets Information Services).
Indexed: AEA, ASCA, AgBio, Agr, AgrForAb, BIOBASE, CIN, CPA, ChemAb, ChemTitl, CurCont, EnvAb, FCA, FLUIDEX, FPA, FS&TA, ForAb, GEOBASE, HerbAb, HortAb, I&DA, IABS, IndVet, Inspec, MaizeAb, NemAb, NutrAb, OrnHort, PBA, PGegResA, PGrRegA, PHN&I, PlantSci, PotatoAb, RA&MP, RDA, RPP, RevApplEntom, RiceAb, S&F, SIA, SeedAb, SoyAb, TriticAb, WAE&RSA, WTA, WeedAb.
—BLDSC (4448.357000), CASDDS, CISTI, IDS, IE, Infotrieve, ingenta. **CCC.**
Published by: (Association for the Advancement of Industrial Crops), Elsevier BV (Subsidiary of: Elsevier Science & Technology), Radarweg 29, Amsterdam, 1043 NX, Netherlands. TEL 31-20-4853911, FAX 31-20-4852457, nlinfo-f@elsevier.nl, http://www.elsevier.com/locate/indcrop, http://www.elsevier.nl. Eds. E. de Jong, F S Nakayama.

631 CUB ISSN 0138-7634
INFORMACION EXPRESS. SERIE: CAFE Y CACAO. Text in Spanish. 1977. 3/yr. USD 6 in North America; USD 9 in South America; USD 10 in Europe; USD 14 elsewhere. stat.
Indexed: Agrind.
—CISTI.
Published by: Centro de Informacion y Documentacion Agropecuario, Gaveta Postal 4149, Havana, 4, Cuba. TEL 301672. **Dist. by:** Ediciones Cubanas, Obispo No. 527, Apdo. 605, Havana, Cuba.

631 CUB ISSN 0138-743X
INFORMACION EXPRESS. SERIE: CITRICOS Y OTROS FRUTALES. Text in Spanish. 1977. 3/yr. CUP 0.90 domestic; USD 6 in North America; USD 9 in South America; USD 10 in Europe; USD 14 elsewhere. stat.
Indexed: Agrind.
—CISTI.
Published by: Centro de Informacion y Documentacion Agropecuario, Gaveta Postal 4149, Havana, 4, Cuba. TEL 301672. **Dist. by:** Ediciones Cubanas, Obispo No. 527, Apdo. 605, Havana, Cuba.

631 CUB ISSN 0138-7286
INFORMACION EXPRESS. SERIE: PROTECCION DE PLANTAS. Text in Spanish. 1977. 4/yr. CUP 1.20 domestic; USD 9 in North America; USD 11 in South America; USD 13 in Europe; USD 18 elsewhere.
Indexed: Agrind.
—CISTI.
Published by: Centro de Informacion y Documentacion Agropecuario, Gaveta Postal 4149, Havana, 4, Cuba. TEL 3016272. **Dist. by:** Ediciones Cubanas, Obispo No. 527, Apdo. 605, Havana, Cuba.

631 CUB
INFORMACION EXPRESS. SERIE: RIEGO Y DRENAJE. Text in Spanish. 1978. 3/yr. USD 6 in North America; USD 9 in South America; USD 10 in Europe; USD 14 elsewhere.
Indexed: Agrind.
Published by: Centro de Informacion y Documentacion Agropecuario, Gaveta Postal 4149, Havana, 4, Cuba. **Dist. by:** Ediciones Cubanas, Obispo No. 527, Apdo. 605, Havana, Cuba.

631 CUB ISSN 0138-7030
INFORMACION EXPRESS. SERIE: SUELOS Y AGROQUIMICA. Text in Spanish. 1977. 4/yr. USD 9 in North America; USD 11 in South America; USD 13 in Europe; USD 18 elsewhere.
Indexed: Agrind.
—CISTI.
Published by: Centro de Informacion y Documentacion Agropecuario, Gaveta Postal 4149, Havana, 4, Cuba. **Dist. by:** Ediciones Cubanas, Obispo No. 527, Apdo. 605, Havana, Cuba.

631 CUB ISSN 0138-7138
INFORMACION EXPRESS. SERIE: TABACO. Text in Spanish. 1977. 2/yr. CUP 0.60 domestic; USD 5 in North America; USD 6 in Europe; USD 9 elsewhere. stat.
Indexed: Agrind.
—CISTI.
Published by: Centro de Informacion y Documentacion Agropecuario, Gaveta Postal 4149, Havana, 4, Cuba. **Dist. by:** Ediciones Cubanas, Obispo No. 527, Apdo. 605, Havana, Cuba.

631 CUB ISSN 0138-7189
INFORMACION EXPRESS. SERIE: VIANDAS, HORTALIZAS Y GRANOS. Text in Spanish. 1977. 5/yr. USD 10 in North America; USD 14 in South America; USD 15 in Europe; USD 21 elsewhere.
Indexed: Agrind.
—CISTI.
Published by: Centro de Informacion y Documentacion Agropecuario, Gaveta Postal 4149, Havana, 4, Cuba. **Dist. by:** Ediciones Cubanas, Obispo No. 527, Apdo. 605, Havana, Cuba.

630 664 FRA ISSN 1242-1626
INGENIEURS DE LA VIE. Text in French. 1945. q. adv. bk.rev. charts; illus.; stat. **Document type:** *Bulletin.*
Formerly: Cahiers des Ingenieurs Agronomes (0035-2179)
Indexed: ExcerpMed.
—CISTI.
Published by: Amicale des Anciens de l'Agro, 5 quai Voltaire, Paris, 75007, France. FAX 33-1-42614850, g.darret@ingeniewsdelagro.org. Ed. Georges Darret. Adv. contact C Renou. Circ: 5,000.

INSTITUT PHYTOPATHOLOGIQUE BENAKI. ANNALES. NOUVELLE SERIE. see *AGRICULTURE*

633 664 FRA ISSN 1250-6893
INSTITUT TECHNIQUE FRANCAIS DE LA BETTERAVE INDUSTRIELLE. COMPTE RENDU DES TRAVAUX EFFECTUES. Text in French. 1954. a.
Formerly (until 1993): Institut Technique Francais de la Betterave Industrielle. Publications (0373-305X)
—CISTI.
Published by: Institut Technique Francais de la Betterave Industrielle/French Technical Industrial Sugarbeet Institute, 45 rue de Naples, Paris, 75008, France. TEL 33-1-42931338, itb@itbfr.org, http://www.institut-betterave.asso.fr.

633 ZAF
INSTITUTE FOR TROPICAL AND SUBTROPICAL CROPS. BULLETIN. Text in English. 1994 (no.426). irreg. illus. **Document type:** *Bulletin, Trade.*
Published by: Agricultural Research Council, Institute for Tropical and Subtropical Crops, PO Box 8783, Pretoria, 0001, South Africa. http://www.arc.agric.za/institutes/itsc/main/history.htm.

631 GBR
INSTITUTE OF ARABLE CROPS RESEARCH. ANNUAL REPORT. Text in English. 1903. a., latest 2001-2002. free. index. **Document type:** *Corporate.*
Formerly (until 2002): Institute of Arable Crops Research. Report (0955-9051); Supersedes (in 1988): Rothamsted Experimental Station Report (0262-1215); Which was formerly: Long Ashton Research Station Report (0954-4968); (until 1985): Long Ashton Research Station Annual Report (0368-7708)
Indexed: BiolAb, CTFA, FCA, FaBeAb, HerbAb, HortAb, MaizeAb, OrnHort, RPP, RevApplEntom, RiceAb, VITIS, WeedAb.
—BLDSC (1302.580000), CISTI, Linda Hall.
Published by: Institute of Arable Crops Research - Rothamsted Research, Rothamsted, Harpenden, Herts AL5 2JQ, United Kingdom. TEL 44-1582-763133, FAX 44-1582-760981, susannah.bolton@bbsrc.ac.uk, http://www.rothamsted.bbsrc.ac.uk/. Ed. S E Allsopp. Circ: 3,000.

633 ISR
INSTITUTE OF FIELD AND GARDEN CROPS. SCIENTIFIC ACTIVITIES. Text in English. triennial. USD 25 (effective 1996). **Document type:** *Government.*
Indexed: BiolAb.
Published by: (Institute of Field and Garden Crops), Agricultural Research Organization, Volcani Center, P O Box 6, Bet Dagan, 50250, Israel. TEL 972-3-980205, FAX 972-3-993998.

633.2 GBR ISSN 1460-3144
S542.G72
INSTITUTE OF GRASSLAND AND ENVIRONMENTAL RESEARCH (UK). ANNUAL REPORT. Text in English. 1965. a., latest 2002. free. back issues avail. **Document type:** *Yearbook, Corporate.*
Former titles (until 1990): Institute for Grassland and Animal Production, England (Berkshire) (0953-7295); Animal and Grassland Research Institute, Hurley, England (Berkshire) Technical Reports; Grassland Research Institute, Hurley, England (Berkshire) Technical Reports (0072-5552)
Media: Online - full content.
Indexed: AnBrAb, BiolAb, FCA, HerbAb, S&F, WeedAb.
—CISTI, Linda Hall.
Published by: Institute of Grassland and Environmental Research, Aberystwyth Research Centre, Plas Gogerddan, Aberystwyth, Ceredigion, Wales SY23 3EB, United Kingdom. TEL 44-1970-823000, FAX 44-1970-828357, igerlib.igerlib-wpbs@bbsrc.ac.uk, http://www.iger.bbsrc.ac.uk/igerweb/Annual_Report/ar.html, http://www.iger.bbsrc.ac.uk/igerweb/library/pubs-list.html. Ed., R&P Dr. T Gordon.

633.2 GBR
INSTITUTE OF GRASSLAND AND ENVIRONMENTAL RESEARCH (UK). TECHNICAL ADVISORY REPORT. Text in English. 1996. irreg., latest no.2, 1999. price varies. back issues avail. **Document type:** *Monographic series, Academic/Scholarly.*
Published by: Institute of Grassland and Environmental Research, Aberystwyth Research Centre, Plas Gogerddan, Aberystwyth, Ceredigion, Wales SY23 3EB, United Kingdom. TEL 44-1970-823000, FAX 44-1970-828357, igerlib.igerlib-wpbs@bbsrc.ac.uk, http://www.iger.bbsrc.ac.uk/igerweb/, http://www.iger.bbsrc.ac.uk/igerweb/library/pubs-list.html.

630 ISR
INSTITUTE OF PLANT PROTECTION. SCIENTIFIC ACTIVITIES. Text in English. triennial. USD 25 (effective 1996). **Document type:** *Government.*
Published by: (Institute of Plant Protection), Agricultural Research Organization, Volcani Center, P O Box 6, Bet Dagan, 50250, Israel. TEL 972-3-9683216, FAX 972-3-993998. Ed. V R Priel. Circ: 200.

631.4 ISR
INSTITUTE OF SOIL, WATER & ENVIRONMENTAL SCIENCES. SCIENTIFIC ACTIVITIES. Text in English. triennial. USD 25 (effective 1998). **Document type:** *Government.*
Formerly: Institute of Soils and Water. Scientific Activities
Published by: (Institute of Soil, Water & Environmental Sciences), Agricultural Research Organization, Volcani Center, P O Box 6, Bet Dagan, 50250, Israel. TEL 972-3-9683216, FAX 972-3-993998.

633.491 ROM ISSN 1016-4839
INSTITUTUL DE CERCETARE SI PRODUCTIE PENTRU CULTURA SI INDUSTRIALIZAREA SFECLEI DE ZAHAR SI A SUBSTANTELOR DULCI-FUNDULEA. LUCRARI STIINTIFICE. SFECLA SI ZAHAR. Text in Romanian; Summaries in English, French, German, Russian. 1969. a. ROL 615.
Former titles: Institutul de Cercetari si Productie a Cartofului, Brasov. Anale. Lucrari Stiintifice; Institutul de Cercetari pentru Cultura Cartofului si Sfeclei de Zahar, Brasov. Anale. Cartoful (0074-0373)
Indexed: BiolAb, FCA, HerbAb, PBA, SIA.
Published by: Institutul de Cercetare si Productie pentru Cultura si Industrializarea Sfeclei de Zahar si a Substantelor Dulci-Fundulea, Judetul Calarasi, Fundulea, 8264, Romania.

633.41 ROM
INSTITUTUL DE CERCETARI PENTRU CEREALE SI PLANTE TEHNICE. LABORATOR SFECLA DE ZAHAR. ANALE. LUCRARI STIINTIFICE. Text in Romanian; Summaries in English, German, Russian. 1968. a. ROL 15,000. **Document type:** *Academic/Scholarly.*
Formerly: Institutul de Cercetari pentru Cultura Cartofului si Sfeclei de Zahar, Brasov. Anale. Sflecla de Zahar (0074-0381)
Indexed: AEA, BiolAb, ForAb, HerbAb, I&DA, PBA, PGrRegA, RPP, RevApplEntom, RiceAb, SeedAb, SoyAb, TriticAb, WeedAb.
Published by: Institutul de Cercetari pentru Cereale si Plante Tehnice, Fundulea-Calarasi, 8264, Romania. Ed. Aurel Florentin Badiu.

632.9 NLD ISSN 0074-0446
SB599
INSTITUUT VOOR PLANTEZIEKTENKUNDIG ONDERZOEK. JAARVERSLAG/RESEARCH INSTITUTE FOR PLANT PROTECTION. ANNUAL REPORT. Text in Dutch, English. 1950. a. price varies. adv. **Document type:** *Proceedings, Academic/Scholarly.*
Indexed: RPP.
—CISTI.
Published by: Instituut voor Plantenziektenkundig Onderzoek, PO Box 9060, Wageningen, 6700 GW, Netherlands. FAX 31-83-701-0113, TELEX 65888 INTAS. Ed. Monique Le Brun. R&P R Straathof. Adv. contact J C Schoenmaker.

INSTYTUT HODOWLI I AKLIMATYZACJI ROSLIN. BIULETYN/INSTITUTE OF PLANT BREEDING AND ACCLIMATIZATION. BULLETIN. see *AGRICULTURE—Abstracting, Bibliographies, Statistics*

630 ITA ISSN 1020-4555
INTEGRATED CROP MANAGEMENT. Text in English. 1996. irreg. **Document type:** *Academic/Scholarly.*
Indexed: HerbAb, HortAb, MaizeAb, SoyAb, WAE&RSA.
—CISTI.
Published by: Food and Agriculture Organization of the United Nations, Via delle Terme di Caracalla, Rome, RM 00100, Italy. TEL 39-06-5705-1, FAX 39-06-5705-3152, FAO-HQ@fao.org, http://www.fao.org.

630 571.4 POL ISSN 0236-8722
CODEN: INAGEX

➤ **INTERNATIONAL AGROPHYSICS**; a quarterly journal on physics in environmental and food sciences. Text in English. 1985-1989 (vol.5); resumed 1992. q. PLZ 100 domestic; EUR 120 foreign (effective 2005). adv. bk.rev. abstr. 50 p./no. 2 cols./p.; reprints avail. **Document type:** *Journal, Academic/Scholarly.* **Description:** Focusses on physical properties and processes effecting plant production.
Indexed: AEA, AgBio, AgrAg, AgrForAb, AgrLib, CPA, ChemAb, DSA, FCA, FLUIDEX, FPA, ForAb, GEOBASE, HerbAb, HortAb, I&DA, MaizeAb, NutrAb, OrnHort, PBA, PGegResA, PHN&I, PN&I, PotatoAb, PoultAb, RA&MP, RiceAb, S&F, SIA, SeedAb, SoyAb, TriticAb, WeedAb.

—BLDSC (4535.654000), CASDDS, CISTI, IE, ingenta, Linda Hall. **CCC.**
Published by: Polska Akademia Nauk, Instytut Agrofizyki/Polish Academy of Sciences, Institute of Agrophysics, ul Doswiadczalna 4, PO Box 201, Lublin, 20290, Poland. TEL 48-81-7445061, FAX 48-81-7445067, editor@demeter.ipan.lublin.pl, http://www.ipan.lublin.pl/?curr_sub=4&sub_op=true&lang=pl&minor_sub=0&panel=0. Ed. Jan Glinski. Adv. contact Ewa Sikora. page USD 25. **Dist. by:** Ars Polona, Krakowskie Przedmiescie 7, Warsaw, Poland. TEL 48-22-9263914, FAX 48-22-9265334, arspolona@arspolona.com.pl, http://www.arspolona.com.pl.

631.8 GBR
INTERNATIONAL CONFERENCE ON FERTILIZERS. PROCEEDINGS. Text in English. 1985 (8th ed.). irreg. GBP 95. **Document type:** *Proceedings.*
Published by: British Sulphur Publishing (Subsidiary of: C R U Publishing), 31 Mt Pleasant, London, WC1X 0AD, United Kingdom. TEL 44-20-7837-5600, FAX 44-20-7837-0292, smoore@cruint.tcom.co.uk, derek.winterbottom@crugroup.com, http://www.cru.co.uk, http://www.britishsulphur.com/. Pub., R&P John French TEL 44-20-79032435.

631.8 GBR ISSN 1466-1314
S631
INTERNATIONAL FERTILISER SOCIETY. PROCEEDINGS. Text in English. 1947. irreg. GBP 12.50 per issue (effective 2003). back issues avail. **Document type:** *Proceedings, Academic/Scholarly.* **Description:** Reports on manufacture and applications of various types of fertilizers.
Formerly (until 1998): Fertiliser Society. Proceedings (0369-9277)
Indexed: AEA, AgBio, Agr, CPA, FCA, HerbAb, HortAb, I&DA, MaizeAb, NutrAb, PBA, PGegResA, PGrRegA, PN&I, RRTA, RiceAb, S&F, SIA, SeedAb, SoyAb, TriticAb, WAE&RSA.
—BLDSC (6732.105000), IE, ingenta, Linda Hall.
Published by: International Fertiliser Society, PO Box 4, Strensall, York YO32 5YS, United Kingdom. TEL 44-1904-492700, FAX 44-1904-492700, secretary@fertiliser-society.org, http://www.fertiliser-society.org/pubchoice.html.

631.8 CHE ISSN 1012-103X
INTERNATIONAL FERTILIZER CORRESPONDENT. Text in English. 1960. 3/yr. free. **Document type:** *Newsletter, Trade.* **Description:** Provides short informations on achievements in the fields of fertilizers and crop fertilization.
Related titles: Online - full text ed.
Published by: International Potash Institute, PO Box 1609, Basel, 4001, Switzerland. TEL 41-61-2612922, FAX 41-61-2612925, ipi@iprolink.ch, http://www.ipipotash.org.

633 RUS ISSN 0074-6185
INTERNATIONAL GRASSLAND CONGRESS. PROCEEDINGS. Text in Russian. 1927. irreg., latest 1974, 12th, Moscow. USD 50. **Document type:** *Proceedings.*
Indexed: FCA, HerbAb, WeedAb.
—CCC.
Published by: International Grassland Congress, All-Union Research Forage Institute, c/o Dr V G Iglovikov, Ed, Lugovaya, Moskovskaya Oblast' 141740, Russian Federation.

633.6 BEL
INTERNATIONAL INSTITUTE FOR BEET RESEARCH. CONGRESS PROCEEDINGS. Short title: I I R B Congress Proceedings. Text and summaries in English, French, German. 1958 (21st). a., latest 2002. EUR 65 per issue (effective 2005). adv. back issues avail. **Document type:** *Proceedings.*
Former titles: International Institute for Beet Research. Journal; International Institute for Sugar Beet Research. Reports of the Winter Congress (0074-6460)
Indexed: FS&TA, WeedAb.
—BLDSC (3415.592000).
Published by: International Institute for Beet Research, Av de Tervuren 195, Brussels, 1150, Belgium. TEL 32-2-737-7091, FAX 32-2-737-7099, iirb@arcadis.be, http://www.iirb.org. R&P Ralph Beckers. Circ: 710.

631.6 NLD ISSN 0165-1803
S605 CODEN: AILRAS
INTERNATIONAL INSTITUTE FOR LAND RECLAMATION AND IMPROVEMENT. ANNUAL REPORT. Text in English. 1960. a. free. adv. charts; illus.; stat. **Document type:** *Corporate.* **Description:** Collects and disseminates research on land and water management throughout the world. Also covers consultancy, training, as well as activities and publications of the Institute.
Indexed: AEA, ASD, FCA, HerbAb, I&DA, RASB, S&F, WeedAb.
—BLDSC (1311.500000), CISTI.
Published by: International Institute for Land Reclamation and Improvement, PO Box 45, Wageningen, 6700 AA, Netherlands. TEL 31-317-490144, FAX 31-317-417187, TELEX 45888 INTAS NL, ilri@ilri.nl, http://www.ilri.nl. Ed. M G Bos. R&P E A Rylhsen. Adv. contact E.A. Rylhsen.

INTERNATIONAL INSTITUTE FOR LAND RECLAMATION AND IMPROVEMENT. BIBLIOGRAPHY. see *AGRICULTURE—Abstracting, Bibliographies, Statistics*

631.6 NLD ISSN 0074-6452
CODEN: PILIAU
INTERNATIONAL INSTITUTE FOR LAND RECLAMATION AND IMPROVEMENT. PUBLICATION. Text in English. 1958. irreg., latest vol.55, 1994. price varies. back issues avail. **Document type:** *Monographic series, Government.* **Description:** Publishes research studies dealing with topics and issues in land and water use, including agricultural development, irrigation, water quality, and related concerns. Also publishes specialized computer programs for applications in the field.
Indexed: FPA, ForAb, I&DA, S&F.
—CISTI.
Published by: International Institute for Land Reclamation and Improvement, PO Box 45, Wageningen, 6700 AA, Netherlands. TEL 31-317-490144, FAX 31-317-417187, ilri@ilri.nl. Ed. M G Bos. R&P E A Rylhsen.

630 USA ISSN 1553-8362
▼ **INTERNATIONAL JOURNAL OF FRUIT SCIENCE.** Text in English. 2005. q. USD 200 combined subscription domestic to institutions print & online eds.; USD 270 combined subscription in Canada to institutions print & online eds.; USD 290 combined subscription elsewhere to institutions print & online eds. (effective 2006). reprint service avail. from HAW. **Document type:** *Journal, Academic/Scholarly.*
Formed by the merger of (1996-2005): Journal of Tree Fruit Production (1055-1387); (1992-2005): Small Fruits Review (1522-8851); Which was formerly (until 2000): Journal of Small Fruit & Viticulture (1052-0015)
Related titles: Online - full content ed.: ISSN 1553-8621; Online - full text ed.: (from EBSCO Publishing).
—Haworth.
Published by: Food Products Press (Subsidiary of: Haworth Press, Inc.), 10 Alice St, Binghamton, NY 13904-1580. TEL 607-722-5857, 800-429-6784, FAX 607-771-0012, 800-895-0582, getinfo@haworthpress.com, http://www.haworthpress.com/. Ed. Amarjit Basra TEL 316-755-7732.

632.9 GBR ISSN 0967-0874
SB950.A1 CODEN: IPEMEH
➤ **INTERNATIONAL JOURNAL OF PEST MANAGEMENT.** Text in English. 1971 (vol.17). q. GBP 467, USD 771 combined subscription to institutions print & online eds. (effective 2006). adv. bk.rev. charts; illus.; stat. index. reprint service avail. from PSC. **Document type:** *Journal, Academic/Scholarly.* **Description:** Covers all spheres of pre- and postharvest pest management, vector-borne diseases and public health, and the relationship of pest management to the wider aspects of farming systems and rural developments.
Former titles: Tropical Pest Management (0143-6147); P A N S (0030-7793)
Related titles: Online - full text ed.: ISSN 1366-5863. GBP 444, USD 732 to institutions (effective 2006) (from EBSCO Publishing, Gale Group, IngentaConnect, O C L C Online Computer Library Center, Inc., Swets Information Services).
Indexed: ASCA, ASFA, AgBio, Agr, AgrForAb, ApicAb, B&BAb, BIOSIS Prev, BibAg, BioCN&I, BioDAb, BiolAb, CIN, CPA, CTFA, ChemAb, ChemTitl, CurCont, DBA, EPB, ESPM, EntAb, FCA, FPA, FS&TA, ForAb, GEOBASE, HelmAb, HerbAb, HortAb, I&DA, IndVet, MBA, MaizeAb, NemAb, NutrAb, OrnHort, PBA, PGegResA, PGrRegA, PHN&I, PN&I, PotatoAb, PoultAb, ProtozoAb, RA&MP, RDA, RPP, RevApplEntom, RiceAb, S&F, S&MA, SIA, SPPI, SeedAb, SoyAb, TOSA, TriticAb, VITIS, VetBull, WAE&RSA, WTA, WeedAb, ZooRec.
—BLDSC (4542.452800), CASDDS, CISTI, IDS, IE, Infotrieve, ingenta, Linda Hall. **CCC.**
Published by: Taylor & Francis Ltd (Subsidiary of: Taylor & Francis Group), 4 Park Sq, Milton Park, Abingdon, OX14 4RN, United Kingdom. TEL 44-1235-828600, FAX 44-1235-829000, info@tandf.co.uk, http://www.tandf.co.uk/journals/titles/09670874.asp. Ed. Mark A Jervis. Circ: 3,000. **Subscr. in N. America to:** Taylor & Francis Inc., Customer Services Dept, 325 Chestnut St, 8th Fl, Philadelphia, PA 19106. TEL 215-625-8900, 800-354-1420, FAX 215-625-8914, customerservice@taylorandfrancis.com; **Subscr. to:** Journals Customer Service, Rankine Rd, Basingstoke, Hants RG24 8PR, United Kingdom. TEL 44-1256-813000, FAX 44-1256-330245, enquiry@tandf.co.uk.

668.65029 GBR ISSN 1351-346X
SB951
INTERNATIONAL PESTICIDE DIRECTORY. Text in English. 1981. a. GBP 75, USD 132 (effective 2001); free with subscription to International Pest Control. adv. **Document type:** *Directory.* **Description:** Directory on trade named pesticides, their active ingredients and the companies that manufacture and market them.
Related titles: CD-ROM ed.: 2001; Online - full content ed.
Indexed: RPP, WeedAb.
—BLDSC (4544.911500), CISTI.
Published by: Research Information Ltd., Grenville Court, Britwell Rd, Burnham, Bucks SL1 8DF, United Kingdom. TEL 44-1628-600499, FAX 44-1628-600488, info@researchinformation.co.uk, http://www.researchinformation.co.uk/ipdi.html. Ed. Bob Yorke. Pub. Kumar Patel TEL 44-20-8328-2470. Adv. contact Ras Patel. B&W page GBP 960. Circ: 6,400.

631.8 CHE
CODEN: PCIIDA
INTERNATIONAL POTASH INSTITUTE. CONGRESS PROCEEDINGS. Text in English. irreg. (Sri Lanka), latest 1994. price varies. **Document type:** *Proceedings, Trade.*
Formerly: International Potash Institute. Congress Report (0074-7505)
—CASDDS.
Published by: International Potash Institute, PO Box 1609, Basel, 4001, Switzerland. TEL 41-61-2612922, FAX 41-61-2612925, ipi@iprolink.ch, http://www.ipipotash.org.

631.8 CHE
CODEN: PCPIA8
INTERNATIONAL POTASH INSTITUTE. PROCEEDINGS OF COLLOQUIOM, CONGRESSES, WORKSHOPS, SEMINARS. Text in English. 1963. irreg., latest vol.24, 1995. price varies. **Document type:** *Proceedings, Trade.*
Formerly: International Potash Institute. Colloquium. Proceedings (0074-7491)
Indexed: BiolAb, CIN, ChemAb, ChemTitl.
—CASDDS.
Published by: International Potash Institute, PO Box 1609, Basel, 4001, Switzerland. TEL 41-61-2612922, FAX 41-61-2612925, ipi@iprolink.ch, http://www.ipipotash.org.

381 USA
INTERNATIONAL RICE INDUSTRY GUIDE. Text in English. a. USD 30 domestic; USD 45 foreign (effective 2001). charts; illus.; maps. **Document type:** *Directory, Trade.*
Published by: SpecComm International, Inc., 5808 Faringdon Pl., # 200, Raleigh, NC 27609-3930. TEL 919-872-5040, FAX 919-876-6531. Ed. Mary Ann Rood. Pub., R&P, Adv. contact Mary Evans.

INTERNATIONAL SILO ASSOCIATION. NEWSLETTER. see *AGRICULTURE—Agricultural Equipment*

631 633.1 IND ISSN 1023-487X
INTERNATIONAL SORGHUM AND MILLETS NEWSLETTER. Text in English. a.
Formerly (until 1994): Sorghum Newsletter (0584-1321)
Indexed: AgBio, Agr, BioCN&I, CPA, FCA, HerbAb, HortAb, I&DA, MaizeAb, NemAb, PBA, PGegResA, PGrRegA, PHN&I, PoultAb, S&F, SIA, SeedAb, TDB, TriticAb, WAE&RSA, WeedAb.
—BLDSC (4549.594000), CISTI, Linda Hall.
Published by: International Crops Research Institute for the Semi-Arid Tropics, Patancheru, Andhra Pradesh 502 324, India. TEL 91-40-23296161, FAX 91-40-23241239, icrisat@cgiar.org, http://www.icrisat.org.

631.5 BEL
S5
INTERNATIONAL SYMPOSIUM ON CROP PROTECTION. PROCEEDINGS. Text and summaries in English, French, German. 1948. a. **Document type:** *Proceedings.*
Supersedes: International Symposium on Crop Protection. Communications (0074-8803)
Related titles: ♦ Issued with: Communications in Agricultural and Applied Biological Sciences. ISSN 1379-1176.
Indexed: B&AI, ChemAb, HerbAb.
Published by: Universiteit Gent, Faculteit van de Landbouwkundige en Toegepaste Biologische Wetenschappen, Coupure Links 653, Gent, 9000, Belgium. TEL 32-9-2646158, FAX 32-9-2646239. Ed. P De Clercq.

631.4 NLD
INTERNATIONAL UNION OF SOIL SCIENCES. BULLETIN. Text in English. 1952. s-a. free to members (effective 2001). adv. bk.rev. 140 p./no.; back issues avail. **Document type:** *Bulletin, Academic/Scholarly.* **Description:** Provides Union news and reports of events and activities, both nationally and internationally. Includes announcements of meetings, conferences and symposia.
Formerly: International Society of Soil Science. Bulletin (0374-0447)
Indexed: S&F.
—CISTI.
Published by: International Union of Soil Sciences, c/o Dr. Alfred E. Hartemink, ICSU World Data Centre for Soils, PO Box 353, Wageningen, 6700 AJ, Netherlands. TEL 31-317-471711, FAX 31-317-471700, Alfred.Hartemink@wur.nl. Ed., R&P Winfried Blum. Adv. contact Peter Luescher. Circ: 7,000. **Subscr. to:** Dr. P. Luescher, Forschungsanstalt W S L, Zuercherstr 111, Birmensdorf Zh 8903, Switzerland.

IOWA CROPS & WEATHER. see *AGRICULTURE—Abstracting, Bibliographies, Statistics*

631 USA
IOWA SEED NEWS. Text in English. 1947. q. membership. **Document type:** *Newsletter.*
Formerly: Seed News
Published by: Iowa Crop Improvement Association, Iowa State University, 2023 Agronomy Hall, Ames, IA 50011. TEL 515-294-6921, FAX 515-294-1897. Ed. Eileen M Feilmeier.

634 571.2 IRL
IRELAND. DEPARTMENT OF AGRICULTURE AND FOOD. CEREAL VARIETIES RECOMMENDED LIST (YEAR). Text in English. a. **Document type:** *Government.*

A

Published by: Department of Agriculture/An Roinn Talmaiochta agus Bia, Agriculture House, Kildare St, Dublin, 2, Ireland. TEL 353-1-607-2000, information@daff.irlgov.ie, http://www.irlgov.ie/daff.

634 571.2 IRL
IRELAND. DEPARTMENT OF AGRICULTURE AND FOOD. HERBAGE VARIETIES RECOMMENDED LIST (YEAR). Text in English. a. **Document type:** *Government.*
Published by: Department of Agriculture, Food & Rural Development/An Roinn Talmhaiochta Bia Agus Forbartha Tuaithe, Agriculture House, Kildare St, Dublin, Dublin 2, Ireland. TEL 353-1-607-2000, information@daff.irlgov.ie, http://www.irlgov.ie/daff/.

634 571.2 IRL
IRELAND. DEPARTMENT OF AGRICULTURE AND FOOD. POTATO VARIETY EVALUATION RESULTS; and recommended list. Text in English. a. **Document type:** *Government.*
Published by: Department of Agriculture, Food & Rural Development/An Roinn Talmhaiochta Bia Agus Forbartha Tuaithe, Agriculture House, Kildare St, Dublin, Dublin 2, Ireland. TEL 353-1-607-2000, information@daff.irlgov.ie, http://www.irlgov.ie/daff/.

634 571.2 IRL
IRELAND. DEPARTMENT OF AGRICULTURE AND FOOD. ROOT FODDER CROP, PULSE AND OILSEED VARIETIES RECOMMENDED LIST (YEAR). Text in English. a. **Document type:** *Government.*
Published by: Department of Agriculture/An Roinn Talmaiochta agus Bia, Agriculture House, Kildare St, Dublin, 2, Ireland. TEL 353-1-607-2000, information@daff.irlgov.ie, http://www.irlgov.ie/daff.

631.5 USA ISSN 0160-7499
S612.2 CODEN: TCPADV
IRRIGATION ASSOCIATION. TECHNICAL CONFERENCE PROCEEDINGS. Key Title: Technical Conference Proceedings - Irrigation Association. Text in English. 1977. a. USD 15 (effective 1996). **Document type:** *Proceedings.*
Formerly: Sprinkler Irrigation Association. Technical Conference Proceedings
Indexed: Agr, BiolAb.
—CASDDS, Linda Hall.
Published by: Irrigation Association, 8260 Willow Oaks Corp Dr, Ste 120, Fairfax, VA 22031-4513. TEL 703-573-3551, FAX 703-573-1913, http://www.irrigation.org. Circ: 2,000.

631.587 USA
IRRIGATION BUSINESS & TECHNOLOGY. Text in English. bi-m. USD 15 domestic to non-members; USD 25 foreign to non-members; free to members. adv. **Document type:** *Journal, Trade.* **Description:** Features association and industry developments, new products, and people in the news. Includes special calendar issues.
Formerly: Irrigation News
Indexed: BibAg.
Published by: Irrigation Association, 8260 Willow Oaks Corp Dr, Ste 120, Fairfax, VA 22031-4513. TEL 703-573-3551, FAX 703-573-1913, http://www.irrigation.org. Circ: 12,500.

630 631 ITA ISSN 0304-0615
ISTITUTO SPERIMENTALE AGRONOMICO. ANNALI. Text in Italian. 1970. a. per issue exchange basis. back issues avail. **Document type:** *Proceedings, Corporate.*
Indexed: AEA, FCA, HerbAb, RefZh, S&F, TriticAb, VITIS.
—CISTI.
Published by: Istituto Sperimentale Agronomico, Via Celso Ulpiani, 5, Bari, BA 70126, Italy. TEL 39-80-5475011, FAX 39-80-5475023. Ed. Dr. V Rizzo. Circ: 1,000.

635 JPN ISSN 0388-4449
IWATE HORTICULTURE EXPERIMENT STATION. BULLETIN. Summaries in English. 1971. irreg., latest vol.6, 1985. **Document type:** *Bulletin.*
Published by: Iwate Horticulture Experiment Station, 20-1 Narita, Kitakami-shi, Iwate-ken 024-0003, Japan. TEL 0197-68-2331. Ed. Akiharu Itoh. Circ: 500.

633.61 JAM
JAMAICAN ASSOCIATION OF SUGAR TECHNOLOGISTS. PROCEEDINGS. Text in English. 1937. a. membership. **Document type:** *Proceedings, Trade.*
Indexed: SIA.
Published by: Jamaican Association of Sugar Technologists, c/o Sugar Industry Research Institute, Kendal Rd, Mandeville, WI, Jamaica. TEL 876-962-2241, FAX 876-962-1288, sirijam@cwjamaica.com. Ed. Dr. Maureen Wilson. Circ: 500.

JAPAN BANANA IMPORTERS ASSOCIATION. ANNUAL REPORT OF BANANA STATISTICS. see *AGRICULTURE—Abstracting, Bibliographies, Statistics*

JAPAN BANANA IMPORTERS ASSOCIATION. MONTHLY BULLETIN OF BANANA STATISTICS. see *AGRICULTURE—Abstracting, Bibliographies, Statistics*

JAPAN FRUIT GROWERS COOPERATIVE ASSOCIATION. FRUIT STATISTICS IN JAPAN. see *AGRICULTURE—Abstracting, Bibliographies, Statistics*

630 JPN ISSN 0439-3600
CODEN: HNGSAG
JAPAN. HOKURIKU NATIONAL AGRICULTURAL EXPERIMENT STATION. BULLETIN. Text in Japanese; Summaries in English. 1960. a. **Description:** Agricultural research in field crops, environment, farm management and land utilization.
Indexed: AEA, BIOSIS Prev, BiolAb, CPA, FCA, HortAb, I&DA, NutrAb, PBA, PHN&I, RPP, RiceAb, S&F, SeedAb, SoyAb, TriticAb, WAE&RSA.
—CASDDS.
Published by: Hokuriku National Agricultural Experiment Station/Hokuriku Kokuritsu Nogyo Shikenjo, Inada, Joetsu-shi, Niigata-ken 943-0154, Japan. TEL 0255-23-4131, FAX 0255-24-8578. Ed. Akira Nakane. Circ: 950.

633 JPN
CODEN: TKKADS
➤ **JAPANESE SOCIETY OF SUGAR BEET TECHNOLOGISTS. PROCEEDINGS.** Text in Japanese; Summaries in English. 1963. a. **Document type:** *Proceedings, Academic/Scholarly.* **Description:** Covers research in all fields related to sugar beet technology. Audience includes universities, agricultural experiment stations, and sugar beet companies.
Former titles: Sugar Beet Research Association. Proceedings (0912-1048); (until 1974): Bulletin of Sugar Beet Research. Supplement (0068-4090)
Indexed: AEA, AgBio, CPA, FCA, FS&TA, HortAb, MaizeAb, NemAb, PBA, PGegResA, PGrRegA, PHN&I, PotatoAb, RDA, RPP, RefZh, RevApplEntom, RiceAb, S&F, SIA, SeedAb, WAE&RSA, WeedAb.
—BLDSC (6742.499000), CASDDS, CISTI.
Published by: Sugar Crop Development Fund, Upland Agriculture Research Center, Hakua Bldg, 4-1 Akasaka -2, Minato-ku, Tokyo, 107-0052, Japan. TEL 81-3-3584-7661, FAX 81-3-3584-7663, scdf_scdf_tokyo@pop02.odn.ne.jp. Ed. Tetsuo Masutani. Circ: 450.

633.6 BRA
JORNALCANA; a melhor noticia do setor. Text in Portuguese. m. BRL 5 newsstand/cover. adv. illus. **Document type:** *Trade.* **Description:** Presents information on the sugar industry in Brazil.
Published by: Apoio e Vendas Comunicacoes Ltda., Rua Martinico Prado, 361, Villa Tiberio, Ribeirao Preto, SP 14050-050, Brazil. TEL 016-6354010, FAX 016-6107266, jornalcana@netsite.com.br, http://www.jornalcana.com.br. Circ: 12,000.

631.8 USA ISSN 0021-8561
S583 CODEN: JAFCAU
➤ **JOURNAL OF AGRICULTURAL AND FOOD CHEMISTRY.** Text in English. 1953. bi-w. USD 1,263 in North America to institutions; USD 1,443 elsewhere to institutions; USD 227 in North America to members; USD 407 elsewhere to members; USD 170 in North America to students; USD 350 elsewhere to students (effective 2006). adv. bibl.; charts; illus. index. back issues avail.; reprints avail. **Document type:** *Journal, Academic/Scholarly.* **Description:** Contains documentation of significant advances in the science of agriculture and food chemistry.
Related titles: Microfiche ed.: USD 907 in North America to institutions; USD 952 elsewhere to institutions (effective 2002); Microfilm ed.: USD 907 in North America to institutions; USD 927 elsewhere to institutions (effective 2002); Online - full text ed.: ISSN 1520-5118. USD 85 (effective 2006) (from EBSCO Publishing, Swets Information Services).
Indexed: AEA, AEBA, ASCA, ASFA, AbHyg, AgBio, Agr, AgrForAb, AnBrAb, AnalAb, ApicAb, B&AI, B&BAb, BBCI, BIOSIS Prev, BibAg, BioCN&I, BioEngAb, BiolAb, CBTA, CCI, CPA, CTFA, ChemAb, ChemoAb, ChromAb, CurCR, CurCont, DBA, DSA, DokArb, EIA, EPB, ESPM, EnvAb, ExcerpMed, FCA, FPA, FS&TA, ForAb, H&SSA, HelmAb, HerbAb, HortAb, I&DA, ISR, IndChem, IndMed, IndVet, Inpharma, MEDLINE, MSB, MaizeAb, NemAb, NutrAb, OceAb, OrnHort, PBA, PE&ON, PGegResA, PGrRegA, PHN&I, PN&I, PollutAb, PotatoAb, PoultAb, ProtozoAb, RA&MP, RCI, RM&VM, RPP, Reac, RefZh, RevApplEntom, RiceAb, S&F, S&MA, SCI, SFA, SIA, SeedAb, SoyAb, TDB, TOSA, Telegen, TriticAb, VITIS, VetBull, WeedAb.
—BLDSC (4920.000000), CASDDS, CINDOC, CISTI, GNLM, IDS, IE, Infotrieve, ingenta, Linda Hall. **CCC.**
Published by: American Chemical Society, 1155 16th St, N W, Washington, DC 20036. TEL 202-872-4614, 800-227-5558, FAX 202-776-8264, service@acs.org, http://pubs.acs.org/jafc, http://www.acs.org. Ed. James N Seiber. adv.: page USD 1,940. Circ: 4,300 (paid). **Subscr. to:** Member & Subscriber Services, PO Box 3337, Columbus, OH 43210. TEL 614-447-3776, 800-333-9511, FAX 614-447-3671.

630 DEU ISSN 0931-2250
SB4 CODEN: ZAPFAR
➤ **JOURNAL OF AGRONOMY AND CROP SCIENCE/ ZEITSCHRIFT FUER ACKER- UND PFLANZENBAU.** Text in English, German. 1853. 6/yr., latest vol.188, no.6, 2002. EUR 96 combined subscription in Europe to individuals print & online eds.; USD 108 combined subscription in the Americas to individuals & Caribbean, print & online eds.; GBP 64 combined subscription elsewhere to individuals print & online eds.; GBP 687 combined subscription in Europe to institutions print & online eds.; USD 1,268 combined subscription in the Americas to institutions & Caribbean, print & online eds.; GBP 755 combined subscription elsewhere to institutions print & online eds. (effective 2006). bk.rev. bibl.; illus.; stat. index. back issues avail. **Document type:** *Journal, Academic/Scholarly.* **Description:** Publishes original papers in the fields of general and special plant production.
Former titles (until 1986): Zeitschrift fuer Acker- und Pflanzenbau (0044-2151); (until 1949): Journal fuer Landwirtschaft (0368-2943)
Related titles: ♦ Online - full text ed.: Journal of Agronomy and Crop Science Online. ISSN 1439-037X.
Indexed: AEA, ASCA, AgBio, Agr, AgrForAb, BIOBASE, BIOSIS Prev, BioCN&I, BiolAb, CIN, CPA, CTFA, ChemAb, ChemTitl, CurCont, DBA, EPB, ExcerpMed, FCA, FS&TA, FaBeAb, ForAb, GEOBASE, HerbAb, HortAb, I&DA, IABS, ISR, MaizeAb, NemAb, NutrAb, OrnHort, PBA, PGegResA, PGrRegA, PHN&I, PlantSci, PotatoAb, RA&MP, RDA, RPP, RefZh, RevApplEntom, RiceAb, S&F, S&MA, SCI, SIA, SeedAb, SoyAb, TOSA, TriticAb, WAE&RSA, WeedAb.
—BLDSC (4926.300000), CASDDS, CISTI, IDS, IE, Infotrieve, ingenta. **CCC.**
Published by: Blackwell Verlag GmbH (Subsidiary of: Blackwell Publishing Ltd.), Kurfuerstendamm 57, Berlin, 10707, Germany. TEL 49-30-32790634, FAX 49-30-32790610, verlag@blackwell.de, http://www.blackwellpublishing.com/journals/JACS, http://www.blackwell.de. Ed. J M Greef. Circ: 450.

630 DEU ISSN 1439-037X
SB4
➤ **JOURNAL OF AGRONOMY AND CROP SCIENCE ONLINE.** Text in English, German. 8/yr. GBP 687 in Europe to institutions; USD 1,268 in the Americas to institutions & Caribbean; GBP 717 elsewhere to institutions (effective 2006). **Document type:** *Academic/Scholarly.*
Media: Online - full text (from Blackwell Synergy, EBSCO Publishing, Gale Group, IngentaConnect, O C L C Online Computer Library Center, Inc., Swets Information Services). **Related titles:** ♦ Print ed.: Journal of Agronomy and Crop Science. ISSN 0931-2250.
Published by: Blackwell Verlag GmbH (Subsidiary of: Blackwell Publishing Ltd.), Kurfuerstendamm 57, Berlin, 10707, Germany. TEL 49-30-32790634, FAX 49-30-32790610, abo@blackwis.de, http://www.blackwell-science.com/~cgilib/jnlpage.bin?Journal=XJACS&File=XJACS&Page=aims, http://www.blackwell.de.

➤ **JOURNAL OF ASIA PACIFIC ENTOMOLOGY.** see *BIOLOGY—Entomology*

634 USA
➤ **JOURNAL OF CITRICULTURE.** Text in English. 1997-1998; resumed 2004 (Spring). s-a. USD 36 to individuals; USD 48 to institutions; USD 60 to libraries. adv. bk.rev. reprints avail. **Document type:** *Academic/Scholarly.* **Description:** Provides worldwide applied research information to citrus growers, citrus extension workers, applied citrus researchers and all others involved with the commercial citrus industry.
—Haworth.
Published by: Haworth Press, Inc., 10 Alice St, Binghamton, NY 13904-1580. TEL 607-722-5857, 800-429-6784, FAX 607-722-1424, 800-895-0582, getinfo@haworthpress.com, http://www.haworthpressinc.com/store/product.asp?sku=J168, http://www.haworthpress.com. Ed. Robert J McNeil. Pub. William Cohen. R&P Ruth Ann Heath TEL 607-722-5857 ext 316. Adv. contact Rebecca Miller-Baum TEL 607-722-5857 ext 337. B&W page USD 300; trim 7.13 x 4.38.

677.21 USA ISSN 1523-6919
➤ **JOURNAL OF COTTON SCIENCE.** Text in English. 1997. q. back issues avail. **Document type:** *Journal, Academic/Scholarly.*
Related titles: Online - full text ed.: ISSN 1524-3303. free (effective 2005).
Indexed: AEA, AgBio, BioCN&I, CPA, FCA, FS&TA, HerbAb, I&DA, PBA, PHN&I, RPP, RevApplEntom, S&F, SeedAb, TTI, WAE&RSA, WeedAb.
Published by: National Cotton Council of America, 1521 New Hampshire Ave, N W, Washington, DC 20036. TEL 202-745-7805, FAX 202-483-4040, awrona@cotton.org, http://www.jcotsci.org/. Ed. Anne Wrona.

630   USA   ISSN 1542-7528
                                   CODEN: JCPRF8
JOURNAL OF CROP IMPROVEMENT; innovations in practice, theory & research. Text in English. 1998. 3/yr. USD 300 combined subscription domestic to institutions print & online eds.; USD 405 combined subscription in Canada to institutions print & online eds.; USD 435 combined subscription elsewhere to institutions print & online eds. (effective 2006). adv. back issues avail.; reprint service avail. from HAW. **Document type:** *Journal, Academic/Scholarly*. **Description:** Provides an international forum for both scientists and practitioners to discuss the latest advancements in basic and applied aspects of crop production.
Formerly (until 2004): Journal of Crop Production (1092-678X)
Related titles: Microform ed.; Online - full text ed.: ISSN 1542-7536. 2002 (June). free to institutions (effective 2003); free with print subs. (from EBSCO Publishing, O C L C Online Computer Library Center, Inc., Swets Information Services).
Indexed: AEA, AEBA, APEL, ASFA, AgBio, Agr, AgrForAb, AnBrAb, B&BAb, BIOBASE, BioCN&I, CPA, DSA, ESPM, FCA, FS&TA, ForAb, GenetAb, HGA, HerbAb, HortAb, I&DA, MaizeAb, NemAb, NutrAb, OrnHort, PBA, PGegResA, PGrRegA, PHN&I, PollutAb, PotatoAb, PoultAb, RA&MP, RDA, RPP, RefZh, RiceAb, RiskAb, S&F, SIA, SWRA, SeedAb, SoyAb, TDB, TriticAb, WAE&RSA, WeedAb.
—BLDSC (4965.652000), Haworth, IE, ingenta. **CCC.**
Published by: Food Products Press (Subsidiary of: Haworth Press, Inc.), 10 Alice St, Binghamton, NY 13904-1580. TEL 607-722-5857, 800-429-6784, FAX 607-771-0012, 800-895-0582, getinfo@haworthpress.com, http://www.haworthpress.com/web/JCRIP/. Ed. Amarjit Basra TEL 316-755-7732. Pub. William Cohen. R&P Ruth Ann Heath TEL 607-722-5857 ext 316. Adv. contact Rebecca Miller-Baum TEL 607-722-5857 ext 337. B&W page USD 315, color page USD 550; trim 4.375 x 7.125. Circ: 97 (paid).

JOURNAL OF ENVIRONMENTAL QUALITY. see *ENVIRONMENTAL STUDIES*

633.53   USA   ISSN 1537-7881
SB255   CODEN: JIHOAU
➤ **JOURNAL OF INDUSTRIAL HEMP**; production, processing and products. Abbreviated title: J I H. Text in English. 1994 (Spr.). s-a. USD 315 combined subscription domestic to institutions print & online eds.; USD 425.25 combined subscription in Canada to institutions print & online eds.; USD 456.75 combined subscription elsewhere to institutions print & online eds. (effective 2006). adv. 120 p./no. 1 cols./p.; reprint service avail. from HAW. **Document type:** *Journal, Academic/Scholarly*. **Description:** Offers practical information for farmers and business people as well as the latest research results for scientists interested in the industrial uses of cannabis. It is a resource for agronomists, environmental scientists, natural fiber and food advocates, hemp businesses, enthusiasts and libraries.
Formerly (until 2002): International Hemp Association. Journal (1381-091X)
Related titles: Online - full text ed.: ISSN 1537-789X. 2002. free to institutions (effective 2003); free with print subs. (from EBSCO Publishing, O C L C Online Computer Library Center, Inc., Swets Information Services).
Indexed: AbHyg, AgBio, BioCN&I, BrCerAb, C&ISA, CerAb, CorrAb, E&CAJ, EMA, FCA, HerbAb, HortAb, IAA, IBR, IBZ, M&TEA, MBF, METADEX, PBA, PGegResA, PHN&I, RA&MP, RefZh, SeedAb, SoyAb, WAA, WAE&RSA.
—BLDSC (5006.150000), CISTI, Haworth, Linda Hall. **CCC.**
Published by: Haworth Press, Inc., 10 Alice St, Binghamton, NY 13904-1580. TEL 607-722-5857, 800-429-6784, FAX 607-722-1424, getinfo@haworthpress.com, http://www.haworthpress.com/web/JIH. Ed. Hayo M G van der Werf. Pub. William Cohen. R&P Ruth Ann Heath TEL 607-722-5857 ext 316. Adv. contact Rebecca Miller-Baum TEL 607-722-5857 ext 337. B&W page USD 315, color page USD 550; trim 4.375 x 7.125.

➤ **JOURNAL OF NEMATOLOGY.** see *BIOLOGY—Zoology*

630   USA   ISSN 1522-886X
➤ **JOURNAL OF NEW SEEDS**; innovations in production, biotechnology, quality and marketing. Abbreviated title: J N S. Text in English. 1999. q. USD 265 combined subscription domestic to institutions print & online eds.; USD 357.75 combined subscription in Canada to institutions print & online eds.; USD 384.25 combined subscription elsewhere to institutions print & online eds. (effective 2006). adv. 120 p./no. 1 cols./p.; back issues avail.; reprint service avail. from HAW. **Document type:** *Journal, Academic/Scholarly*. **Description:** Covers the international range of research and development taking place in the entire field of seed development, from seed production, performance and supply to the many seed protection and policy issues that surround the explosive technology now fueling the development of new seeds.
Related titles: Microfiche ed.; Microfilm ed.; Online - full text ed.: ISSN 1522-9025. free to institutions (effective 2003); free with print subs. (from EBSCO Publishing, O C L C Online Computer Library Center, Inc., Swets Information Services).
Indexed: AEBA, AgBio, Agr, B&BAb, BIOBASE, BIOSIS Prev, BioEngAb, BiolAb, BiolDig, CPA, ESPM, FCA, FS&TA, ForAb, GenetAb, HerbAb, HortAb, MaizeAb, NutrAb, OrnHort, PBA, PGegResA, PGrRegA, PHN&I, PotatoAb, RDA, RPP, RefZh, RiceAb, S&F, SIA, SeedAb, SoyAb, TriticAb, WAE&RSA, WeedAb.
—BLDSC (5022.805000), Haworth, IE, ingenta. **CCC.**

Published by: Food Products Press (Subsidiary of: Haworth Press, Inc.), 10 Alice St, Binghamton, NY 13904-1580. TEL 607-722-5857, 800-429-6784, FAX 607-771-0012, 800-895-0582, getinfo@haworthpress.com, http://www.haworthpress.com/web/JNS. Ed. Amarjit Basra TEL 316-755-7732. Pub. William Cohen. R&P Ruth Ann Heath TEL 607-722-5857 ext 316. Adv. contact Rebecca Miller-Baum TEL 607-722-5857 ext 337. B&W page USD 315, color page USD 550; trim 4.375 x 7.125. Circ: 103 (paid).

630 570   IND   ISSN 0379-5489
S589.5   CODEN: JNABDS
JOURNAL OF NUCLEAR AGRICULTURE AND BIOLOGY. Text in English. 1972. q. INR 200, USD 65 (effective 1991). adv. bk.rev. back issues avail. **Document type:** *Academic/Scholarly*.
Formerly: I S N A Newsletter
Indexed: AnBrAb, BioCN&I, BiolAb, CPA, ChemAb, ChemTitl, CurCont, DSA, ExcerpMed, FCA, ForAb, HerbAb, HortAb, I&DA, INIS AtomInd, IndVet, MaizeAb, NutrAb, OrnHort, PBA, PGrRegA, PHN&I, RPP, RevApplEntom, RiceAb, S&F, SIA, SeedAb, SoyAb, TriticAb, VetBull, WeedAb.
—BLDSC (5022.848000), CASDDS, CISTI, IE, ingenta, Linda Hall.
Published by: Indian Society for Nuclear Techniques in Agriculture and Biology, Nuclear Research Laboratory, Indian Agricultural Research Institute, New Delhi, 110 012, India. Ed. M S Chatrath. R&P M.S. Chatrath. Adv. contact M S Sachdey. Circ: 400 (controlled).

JOURNAL OF PESTICIDE SCIENCE. see *ENGINEERING— Chemical Engineering*

JOURNAL OF PESTICIDE SCIENCE (INTERNATIONAL EDITION). see *ENGINEERING—Chemical Engineering*

631.5   IND   ISSN 0304-5242
SB111.A2   CODEN: JPCRDW
➤ **JOURNAL OF PLANTATION CROPS.** Text in English. 1972. 3/yr. USD 50 (effective 2003). adv. bk.rev. abstr.; bibl. 80 p./no. 2 cols./p.; back issues avail.; reprints avail. **Document type:** *Journal, Academic/Scholarly*. **Description:** Contains a range of articles on plantation crops, besides innumerable, multidisciplinary research papers, review articles, short scientific reports and book reviews.
Indexed: AEA, ATA, AgBio, AgrForAb, BioCN&I, BiolAb, CIN, CPA, ChemAb, ChemTitl, CurCont, FCA, FS&TA, ForAb, HerbAb, HortAb, I&DA, MaizeAb, NemAb, NutrAb, OrnHort, PBA, PGegResA, PGrRegA, PHN&I, RA&MP, RDA, RPP, RRTA, RevApplEntom, S&F, SeedAb, TOSA, WAE&RSA, WeedAb, ZooRec.
—BLDSC (5040.540000), CASDDS, CISTI, IE, ingenta, Linda Hall.
Published by: Indian Society for Plantation Crops, Central Plantation Crops Research Institute, Kasaragod, Kerala 671 124, India. TEL 91-499-4232996, FAX 91-499-4232322, ispcjpc@yahoo.com, http://www.spcindia.org. Ed. George V Thomas. Pub. K V Kasturi Bai. Circ: 800.

631.5   IND   ISSN 0378-2409
                                  CODEN: JRCRDC
JOURNAL OF ROOT CROPS. Text in English. 1975. s-a. INR 200, USD 70 (effective 1992). **Document type:** *Academic/Scholarly*.
Indexed: AEA, AgBio, BioCN&I, BiolAb, CPA, ChemAb, ExcerpMed, FCA, FS&TA, HerbAb, HortAb, I&DA, NemAb, NutrAb, OrnHort, PBA, PGegResA, PGrRegA, PHN&I, PotatoAb, PoultAb, RDA, RPP, RevApplEntom, RiceAb, S&F, SIA, SeedAb, WAE&RSA, WeedAb.
—CASDDS.
Published by: Indian Society for Root Crops, c/o Central Tuber Crops Research Institute, Thiruvananthapuram, Kerala 695 017, India. TEL 91-471-448551, FAX 91-471-448431, TELEX 0435-247 ROOT IN. Ed. M S Palaniswami. Pub. Santha V Pillai. Circ: 300.

631.7   USA   ISSN 0022-4561
S622   CODEN: JSWCA3
➤ **JOURNAL OF SOIL AND WATER CONSERVATION.** Text in English. 1946. bi-m. USD 75 in US & Canada; USD 105 elsewhere (effective 2005). adv. bk.rev.; film rev. abstr.; bibl.; charts; illus.; maps; tr.lit. index, cum.index: vols.1-20; vols.21-25; vols.26-30. back issues avail.; reprint service avail. from PQC,ISI. **Document type:** *Journal, Academic/Scholarly*.
Related titles: Microform ed.: (from PQC); Online - full text ed.: (from bigchalk, Florida Center for Library Automation, Gale Group, O C L C Online Computer Library Center, Inc., ProQuest Information & Learning).
Indexed: AEA, APD, ASFA, AbHyg, Agr, AgrForAb, AnBrAb, B&AI, BIOBASE, BibAg, BiolAb, BiolDig, CADCAM, CPA, ChemAb, CivEngAb, CurCont, DSA, EIA, EPB, ESPM, EngInd, EnvAb, EnvInd, ExcerpMed, F&GI, FCA, FLUIDEX, FPA, ForAb, GEOBASE, GSI, HerbAb, HortAb, I&DA, IABS, IAOP, ISR, M&GPA, M&TEA, MaizeAb, NemAb, NutrAb, OrnHort, PGegResA, PN&I, PlantSci, PollutAb, PoultAb, RDA, REE&TA, RPP, RRTA, RevApplEntom, RiceAb, S&F, S&MA, SCI, SFA, SWRA, SeedAb, SoyAb, TDB, TriticAb, UAA, WAE&RSA, WeedAb, WildRev, ZooRec.
—BLDSC (5064.940000), CINDOC, CIS, CISTI, Ei, IDS, IE, Infotrieve, ingenta, Linda Hall.

Published by: Soil and Water Conservation Society, 945 SW Ankeny Rd., Ankeny, IA 50021-9764. TEL 515-289-2331, 800-843-7645, FAX 515-289-1227, sueb@swcs.org, http://www.swcs.org/. Ed. Deb Happe. Adv. contacts Deb Happe, Suzi Case. Circ: 8,000 (paid).

631.4   DEU   ISSN 1439-0108
JOURNAL OF SOILS AND SEDIMENTS; protection, risk assessment and remediation. Text in English. 2001. q. EUR 270, USD 298, GBP 180 combined subscription to institutions print & online eds. (effective 2005). adv. **Document type:** *Journal, Academic/Scholarly*. **Description:** Contains research on effects caused by the disturbance and contamination of soils and sediments.
Related titles: Online - full text ed.: ISSN 1614-7480. EUR 108 (effective 2002) (from EBSCO Publishing, Kluwer Online, Springer LINK).
Indexed: ASFA, AgBio, AgrForAb, BioCN&I, BiolAb, CPA, ESPM, EnvEAb, FCA, FPA, ForAb, GEOBASE, HerbAb, HortAb, I&DA, IndVet, NemAb, NutrAb, OceAb, PBA, PGrRegA, PHN&I, PN&I, PollutAb, PoultAb, ProtozoAb, RA&MP, RPP, S&F, SWRA, SeedAb, TDB, ToxAb, TriticAb, VetBull, WAE&RSA, WeedAb.
—BLDSC (5065.057000), IE.
Published by: Ecomed Verlagsgesellschaft AG & Co. KG, Justus-von-Liebig-Str 1, Landsberg, 86899, Germany. TEL 49-8191-125-0, FAX 49-8191-125492, info@ecomed.de, http://www.ecomed.de/journals/jss/welcome.htm. Eds. Thomas Knacker, Werner Koerdel, Willie Peijnenburg. Adv. contact Almut Heinrich. page EUR 1,470; trim 216 x 289. **Subscr. to:** Springer-Verlag Dordrecht, Journals Department, PO Box 322, Dordrecht, Netherlands. TEL 31-78-6576392, FAX 31-78-6576474.

634   USA   ISSN 1548-1689
➤ **JOURNAL OF VEGETABLE SCIENCE.** Abbreviated title: J V C P. Text in English. 1993. q. USD 250 combined subscription domestic to institutions print & online eds.; USD 337.50 combined subscription in Canada to institutions print & online eds.; USD 362.50 combined subscription elsewhere to institutions print & online eds. (effective 2006). adv. bk.rev. 120 p./no. 1 cols./p.; back issues avail.; reprint service avail. from HAW. **Document type:** *Journal, Academic/Scholarly*. **Description:** Aimed at professionals who labor with the problems of vegetable crop management - from land preparation to seeding and consumption. Articles cover the wide spectrum of the vegetable industry, including field-related problems like harvesting, shipping and final consumption; and scientific input about vegetables.
Formerly (until 2005, vol 10, #2): Journal of Vegetable Crop Production (1049-6467)
Related titles: Microfilm ed.: (from PQC); Microform ed.; Online - full content ed.: ISSN 1548-1697. free to institutions (effective 2003); free with print subs.; Online - full text ed.: (from EBSCO Publishing, O C L C Online Computer Library Center, Inc., Swets Information Services).
Indexed: AEA, AgBio, Agr, AgrForAb, BioCN&I, BiolDig, CPA, FCA, FPA, FS&TA, ForAb, HerbAb, HortAb, I&DA, MaizeAb, NutrAb, OrnHort, PBA, PGegResA, PGrRegA, PHN&I, PotatoAb, RA&MP, RDA, RPP, RevApplEntom, S&F, SeedAb, TriticAb, WAE&RSA, WeedAb.
—BLDSC (5072.276000), Haworth, IE, Infotrieve, ingenta. **CCC.**
Published by: Food Products Press (Subsidiary of: Haworth Press, Inc.), 10 Alice St, Binghamton, NY 13904-1580. TEL 607-722-5857, 800-429-6784, FAX 607-771-0012, 800-895-0582, getinfo@haworthpress.com, http://www.haworthpress.com/web/JVCP. Ed. Vincent M Russo. Pub. William Cohen. R&P Ruth Ann Heath TEL 607-722-5857 ext 316. Adv. contact Rebecca Miller-Baum TEL 607-722-5857 ext 337. B&W page USD 315, color page USD 550; trim 4.375 x 7.125. Circ: 154 (paid).

634.8 663.2   GBR   ISSN 0957-1264
➤ **JOURNAL OF WINE RESEARCH.** Text in English. 1990. 3/yr. GBP 567, USD 934 combined subscription to institutions print & online eds. (effective 2006). adv. bk.rev. index. back issues avail.; reprint service avail. from PSC. **Document type:** *Journal, Academic/Scholarly*. **Description:** Publishes the results of recent research an all aspects of viticulture, oenology, and the wine trade.
Related titles: Microfiche ed.; Online - full text ed.: ISSN 1469-9672. GBP 541, USD 891 to institutions (effective 2006) (from EBSCO Publishing, Gale Group, IngentaConnect, Northern Light Technology, Inc., O C L C Online Computer Library Center, Inc., ProQuest Information & Learning, Swets Information Services).
Indexed: AgBio, BIOSIS Prev, BioCN&I, BiolAb, BrArAb, CPA, DIP, FPA, FS&TA, ForAb, H&TI, HortAb, IBZ, NumL, NutrAb, OrnHort, PBA, PGegResA, PHN&I, RDA, RPP, RevApplEntom, SIA, SeedAb, VITIS, WAE&RSA.
—BLDSC (5072.632200), IE, Infotrieve, ingenta. **CCC.**
Published by: (Institute of Masters of Wine), Routledge (Subsidiary of: Taylor & Francis Group), 4 Park Sq, Milton Park, Abingdon, Oxon OX14 4RN, United Kingdom. TEL 44-1235-828600, FAX 44-1235-829000, info@routledge.co.uk, http://www.tandf.co.uk/journals/titles/09571264.asp, http://www.routledge.co.uk. Ed. Tim Unwin. **Subscr. to:** Taylor & Francis Ltd, Journals Customer Service, Rankine Rd, Basingstoke, Hants RG24 8PR, United Kingdom. TEL 44-1256-813000, FAX 44-1256-330245.

▼ *new title*   ➤ *refereed*   ✳ *unverified*   ◆ *full entry avail.*

A

634 SCG ISSN 0350-2155
CODEN: JUVODH

➤ **JUGOSLOVENSKO VOCARSTVO/JOURNAL OF YUGOSLAV POMOLOGY.** Text in Serbian; Summaries in English. 1967. q. YUN 100 domestic; USD 30 foreign (effective 2003 - 2004). adv. bk.rev. abstr.; charts; illus.; stat.; bibl. back issues avail. **Document type:** *Journal, Academic/Scholarly.* **Description:** Presents articles on fruit crops, breeding, cultivar trials, plant protection, food technology, cultural practices, and soil management.
Indexed: AEA, AgBio, AgrForAb, BioCN&I, CPA, ChemAb, ForAb, HortAb, I&DA, OrnHort, PBA, PGegResA, PGrRegA, PHN&I, RA&MP, RPP, RefZh, RevApplEntom, S&F, SIA, SeedAb, WAE&RSA, WeedAb.
—CASDDS.
Published by: Jugoslovensko Naucno Vocarsko Drustvo/Yugoslav Scientific Pomological Society, Kralja Petra I/9, Cacak, 32000. TEL 381-32-227550, FAX 381-32-221391, jugvocca@yu1.net. Eds. Mihailo Nikolic, Radoslav Cerovic. Circ: 500.

➤ **K T B L ARBEITSBLAETTER LANDTECHNIK UND PFLANZENBAU.** see *AGRICULTURE—Agricultural Equipment*

634.8 DEU ISSN 0173-6981
K T B L ARBEITSBLAETTER WEINBAU. Text in German. irreg. price varies. **Document type:** *Monographic series, Trade.*
Published by: Kuratorium fuer Technik und Bauwesen in der Landwirtschaft e.V., Bartningstr 49, Darmstadt, 64289, Germany. TEL 49-6151-70010, FAX 49-6151-7001123, ktbl@ktbl.de, http://www.ktbl.de. R&P Harald Kuehner.

631.4 RUS ISSN 0022-9148
CODEN: KAOVA7
KARTOFEL' I OVOSHCHI; nauchno-proizvodstvennyi i popularnyi. Text in Russian. 1956. 8/yr. RUR 400 (effective 2001). bk.rev. **Description:** Focuses on potato and vegetable production and agriculture. Includes information on new products and technology and market news.
Indexed: AEA, AgBio, AgrForAb, BioCN&I, BiolAb, CPA, ChemAb, FCA, FS&TA, ForAb, HerbAb, HortAb, I&DA, MaizeAb, NemAb, NutrAb, OrnHort, PBA, PGegResA, PGrRegA, PHN&I, PotatoAb, RA&MP, RASB, RPP, RefZh, RevApplEntom, S&F, SIA, SeedAb, SoyAb, WAE&RSA, WeedAb.
—CISTI, East View.
Address: Sadovaya-Spasskaya 18, kom 702, Moscow, 107996, Russian Federation. TEL 7-095-2071711, FAX 7-095-2072870. Ed. Svetlana I Sanina. Circ: 17,400. **US dist. addr.:** East View Information Services, 3020 Harbor Ln. N., Minneapolis, MN 55447. TEL 612-550-0961.

633.491 DEU ISSN 0022-9156
DER KARTOFFELBAU. Text in German. 1949. 10/yr. EUR 6 newsstand/cover (effective 2005). adv. bk.rev. charts; illus.; stat. **Document type:** *Magazine, Trade.* **Description:** News about potatoes.
Indexed: AEA, AgBio, CPA, FCA, FS&TA, HerbAb, HortAb, I&DA, MaizeAb, NemAb, NutrAb, PBA, PGegResA, PGrRegA, PHN&I, PotatoAb, RPP, RevApplEntom, S&F, SIA, SeedAb, TriticAb, WAE&RSA, WeedAb.
—BLDSC (5086.450000), CISTI, IE, Infotrieve, ingenta.
Published by: (Vorstand der Foerderungsgemeinschaft der Kartoffelwirtschaft e.V.), Verlag Th. Mann, Nordring 10, Gelsenkirchen, 45894, Germany. TEL 49-209-93040, FAX 49-209-9304185, info@th-mann.de, http://www.th-mann.de. Eds. Guenter Weiss, Dr. Heinz Peter Puetz. Adv. contact Richard Heineke. B&W page EUR 1,560, color page EUR 27,300; trim 186 x 270. Circ: 5,505 (controlled).

KENYA COFFEE; monthly bulletin. see *FOOD AND FOOD INDUSTRIES*

631 KEN
KENYA. NAFAKA NEWS. Text in English. q. **Document type:** *Newsletter.*
Former titles: Kenya. National Cereals and Produce Board. Report; Kenya. Maize and Produce Board. Report; Kenya. Wheat Board. Report
Published by: National Cereals and Produce Board, PO Box 30586, Nairobi, Kenya. TEL 254-2-536028. Ed. Justice Kemei.

631.587 KEN ISSN 0075-5915
KENYA. NATIONAL IRRIGATION BOARD. REPORTS AND ACCOUNTS. Text in English. 1967. irreg., latest 1973. free to recognized institutions. **Document type:** *Government.*
Published by: National Irrigation Board, Lenana Rd., PO Box 30372, Nairobi, Kenya.

631 GBR ISSN 1471-938X
KEY NOTE MARKET REPORT: AGROCHEMICALS & FERTILISERS. Variant title: Agrochemicals & Fertilizers. Text in English. 1993. irreg., latest 2000, June. GBP 340 per issue (effective 2002). **Document type:** *Trade.* **Description:** Provides an overview of a specific UK market segment and includes executive summary, market definition, market size, industry background, competitor analysis, current issues, forecasts, company profiles, and more.
Formerly (until 1993): Key Note Report: Agrochemicals and Fertilizers (1352-657X)
Related titles: CD-ROM ed.; Online - full text ed.
Published by: Key Note Ltd., Field House, 72 Oldfield Rd, Hampton, Mddx TW12 2HQ, United Kingdom. TEL 44-20-8481-8750, FAX 44-20-8783-0049, info@keynote.co.uk, http://www.keynote.co.uk. Ed. Simon Howitt.

631.8 IND ISSN 0023-1010
KHAD PATRIKA. Text in Hindi. 1960. m. INR 75 (effective 1999).
Published by: Fertiliser Association of India, Near Jawaharlal Nehru University, New Delhi, 110 067, India. Ed. R K Tewatia. Circ: 2,600.

633.51 RUS ISSN 0023-1231
SB245 CODEN: KHLOAK
KHLOPKOVODSTVO. Text in Russian. 1922. m. USD 11.40. adv. bk.rev. charts; illus.; stat. index.
Indexed: BiolAb, CTFA, ChemAb, FCA, HerbAb, PGrRegA, RASB, RPP, SeedAb, WTA, WeedAb.
—CASDDS.
Published by: Izdatel'stvo Kolos, Sadovaya-Spasskaya 18, Moscow, 107807, Russian Federation. TEL 7-095-2072125. Ed. I D Blinov. Circ: 13,500. **Co-sponsor:** Ministerstvo Sel'skogo Khozyaistva Rossiiskoi Federatsii.

632 JPN ISSN 0368-623X
CODEN: KNBKAY
KITA NIHON BYOGAICHU KENKYUKAIHO/SOCIETY OF PLANT PROTECTION OF NORTH JAPAN. ANNUAL REPORT. Text in Japanese; Summaries in English, Japanese. 1950. a., latest vol.51, 2000. membership. adv. cum.index 1950-1959; 1960-1969. back issues avail. **Document type:** *Academic/Scholarly.*
Indexed: BioCN&I, ChemAb, FCA, HortAb, OrnHort, PBA, PotatoAb, RPP, RevApplEntom, RiceAb, SeedAb, SoyAb, TriticAb, WeedAb.
—CASDDS. **CCC.**
Published by: Kita Nihon Byogaichu Kenkyukai/Society of Plant Protection of North Japan, c/o National Agricultural Research Center for Tohoku Region, 3 Shimofurumichi, Yotsuya, Omagari-shi, Akita-ken 014-0102, Japan. TEL 81-187-661221, FAX 81-187-662639, kaoruz@affrc.go.jp; akikuchi@affrc.go.jp, etoshima@affrc.go.jp, http://njp.ac.affrc.go.jp/index.html. Ed. Kaoru Zenbayashi. Pub. Tadaoki Inaba. adv.: B&W page JPY 30,000.

632.9 NLD
KNIPSELKRANT BIOLOGISCHE LANDBOUW. Text in Dutch. 1996. m. mkt.; stat. back issues avail. **Document type:** *Newspaper, Trade.* **Description:** Reproduces articles on organic farming from newspapers.
Published by: Publiciteitscentrum Biologische Landbouw/Publicitycentre Organic Agriculture, Postbus 656, Wageningen, 6700 AR, Netherlands. TEL 31-317-415515, FAX 31-317-426589, info@biologisch.nl, http://www.biologisch.nl.

632 JPN ISSN 0023-2521
KOBE PLANT PROTECTION AND PLANT QUARANTINE INFORMATION✶ /KOBE SHOKUBUTSU BOEKI JOHO. Text in Japanese. 1954. m. USD 1. charts; illus.; stat. index.
Published by: Kobe Plant Protection Station/Kobe-shi Shokubutsu Boekisho, 1-1 Hatoba-cho, Chuo-ku, Kobe-shi, Hyogo-ken 650-0042, Japan. Circ: 1,500.

630.24 668.6 NLD ISSN 0169-7625
KOERIER AGRO CHEMIE. Text in Dutch. 1959. irreg. (2-3/yr.). free. charts; illus. **Description:** Covers chemical research in pesticides and treatment of diseases in various domestic crops by the Bayer Company in the Netherlands.
Former titles (until 1978): Agro Chemie-Koerier (0166-2252); Agro Chemie-Koerier Voor Plantenziektenbestrijding
Published by: Bayer Nederland B.V., Postbus 80, Mijdrecht, 3640 AB, Netherlands. TEL 02979-80666, FAX 02979-84165. Circ: 25,000.

631 DNK ISSN 0905-8478
KONGELIGE VETERINAER- OG LANDBOHOEJSKOLE. INSTITUT FOR JORDBRUGSVIDENSKAB. FORSKNINGSRAPPORT/RESEARCH REPORT. Text in Danish. 1989. irreg. free.
Formerly (until 1990): Denmark. Kgl. Veterinaer- og Landbohoejskole. Institut for Planteteknik og Planteernaering. Meddelelser (0105-2543)
—BLDSC (7761.153000).
Published by: Kongelige Veterinaer- og Landbohoejskole, Institut for Jordbrugsvidenskab/Royal Veterinary and Agricultural University. Department of Agricultural Sciences, Thorvaldsensvej 40, Frederiksberg C, 1871, Denmark. TEL 45-35-28-34-96, FAX 45-35-28-34-60.

634.9209489 DNK ISSN 1397-9523
KONGELIGE VETERINAER- OG LANDBOHOEJSKOLE. INSTITUT FOR OEKONOMI, SKOV OG LANDSKAB. FORESTY DISCUSSION PAPER. Text in English. 1996. irreg. **Document type:** *Monographic series.*
Indexed: ForAb, HortAb, RDA, WAE&RSA.
Published by: Kongelige Veterinaer- og Landbohoejskole, Institut for Oekonomi, Skov og Landskab/Royal Veterinary and Agricultural University. Department of Economics and Natural Resources, Rolighedsvej 23, Frederiksberg C, 1958, Denmark. TEL 45-35-28-22-15, FAX 45-35-28-26-71.

632 JPN ISSN 0912-1404
KONGETSU NO NOGYO/AGRICULTURAL CHEMICALS MONTHLY. Text in Japanese. 1957. m. JPY 9,840 (effective 2005). bk.rev. charts; illus. 120 p./no.; **Document type:** *Magazine, Trade.* **Description:** Examines pesticides and their uses.
Formerly (until 1986): Kongetsu no Nogyo (0023-334X)
Indexed: ChemAb, RefZh.
Published by: Chemical Daily Co. Ltd., 16-8, Nihonbashi-Hamacho 3-Chome, Chuo-ku, Tokyo, 103-8485, Japan. TEL 81-3-36637931, FAX 81-3-36632330, http://www.chemicaldaily.co.jp/books/nougyo/index_ng.html. Ed. Isao Imanaka. Circ: 40,000.

KOREAN JOURNAL OF APPLIED ENTOMOLOGY. see *BIOLOGY—Entomology*

KOREAN JOURNAL OF BREEDING. see *AGRICULTURE—Poultry And Livestock*

633.2 DEU ISSN 0023-4427
CODEN: KFFUAS
KRAFTFUTTER/FEED MAGAZINE; Zeitschrift fuer die Futtermittel- und Getreidewirtschaft. Text in English, German. 1953. 10/yr. EUR 140; EUR 12.50 newsstand/cover (effective 2004). adv. bk.rev. charts; illus.; stat. index. **Document type:** *Magazine, Trade.*
Incorporates (1987-199?): Feed Magazine (0937-9134); Which was formerly (until 1989): Feed Magazine International (0933-9744)
Indexed: AEA, AgBio, AnBrAb, BioDAb, CIN, ChemAb, ChemTitl, DBA, DSA, ExcerpMed, HerbAb, HortAb, IndVet, MaizeAb, NutrAb, PBA, PHN&I, PN&I, PoultAb, ProtozoAb, RA&MP, RM&VM, RPP, RefZh, RiceAb, S&F, SIA, SoyAb, TriticAb, VetBull, WAE&RSA.
—CASDDS, IE, Infotrieve. **CCC.**
Published by: Deutscher Fachverlag GmbH, Mainzer Landstr 251, Frankfurt Am Main, 60326, Germany. TEL 49-69-759501, FAX 49-69-75952999, agrar@dfv.de, info@dfv.de, http://www.agrimanager.de/freieressorts/mediadaten/kraftfutter/kraftfutter.html, http://www.dfv.de. adv.: B&W page EUR 1,475, color page EUR 2,530. Circ: 2,226 (paid and controlled).

634 IND
KRISHI CHAYANIKA. Text in Hindi. 1979. q. INR 60, USD 20 (effective 2000). adv. bk.rev. charts; illus. index. back issues avail. **Document type:** *Government.* **Description:** Contains a digest of the specialized knowledge on agricultural research conducted in India and abroad.
Published by: Indian Council of Agricultural Research, Krishi Anusandhan Bhavan, Pusa, New Delhi, 110 012, India. Ed. Ashok Singh. Adv. contact S K Joshi. Circ: 3,000.

633.15 RUS ISSN 0233-7770
KUKURUZA I SORGO. Text in Russian. 1956. bi-m. USD 128 foreign (effective 2005). adv. bk.rev. bibl. index. **Document type:** *Magazine, Trade.* **Description:** Designed for production and research personnel and anyone who is interested in growing and production of corn and sorghum.
Formerly: Kukuruza (0023-5040)
Indexed: AEA, AgBio, BiolAb, CPA, ChemAb, DSA, FCA, ForAb, HerbAb, HortAb, I&DA, MaizeAb, NutrAb, PBA, PGegResA, PHN&I, PotatoAb, PoultAb, RASB, RPP, RefZh, RevApplEntom, RiceAb, S&F, SeedAb, SoyAb, TriticAb, WAE&RSA, WeedAb.
—BLDSC (0094.100000), CISTI, East View. **CCC.**
Published by: Redaktsiya Zhurnala Kukuruza i Sorgo, Sadovaya-Spasskaya 18, a/ya 6, Moscow, 107807, Russian Federation. TEL 7-095-2072381, FAX 7-095-9172178. Ed., Adv. contact Ekaterina A Safonova. Circ: 1,420. **US dist. addr.:** East View Information Services, 3020 Harbor Ln. N., Minneapolis, MN 55447. TEL 800-477-1005, FAX 800-800-3839, eastview@eastview.com, http://www.eastview.com.

630.24 DEU ISSN 0948-762X
KURIER BAYER. Text in German. 1956. 2/yr. free. charts; illus. **Document type:** *Bulletin, Trade.*
Former titles (until 1994): Pflanzenschutz Kurier (0722-0510); (until 1968): Bayer Pflanzenschutz Kurier (0722-0472)
Published by: Bayer AG, Geschaeftsbereich Pflanzenschutz, Kaiser-Wilhelm-Allee, Leverkusen, 51368, Germany. Ed. Bernhard Grupp. Circ: 168,000 (controlled).

631 NLD ISSN 1569-8424
L E I S A. (Low External Input & Sustainable Agriculture) Text in English. 1984. q. USD 25 in developing nations; USD 40 elsewhere (effective 2001). bk.rev.; Website rev. illus. 36 p./no. 3 cols./p.; back issues avail. **Document type:** *Magazine.* **Description:** Discusses techniques and programs in environmentally sustainable agriculture. Developed by and for small farmers.
Formerly (until 1997): I L E I A Newsletter (0920-8771)
Related titles: Online - full content ed.; Spanish ed.: I L E I A Boletin.
Indexed: AEA, ASFA, AbHyg, AgBio, AgrForAb, AnBrAb, BioCN&I, CPA, DSA, ESPM, FCA, FPA, ForAb, HerbAb, HortAb, I&DA, IndVet, MaizeAb, NutrAb, PBA, PGegResA, PotatoAb, RA&MP, RDA, RM&VM, RPP, RRTA, RiceAb, S&F, SIA, SeedAb, SoyAb, TDB, TriticAb, VetBull, WAE&RSA, WeedAb.
—BLDSC (5182.193000), IE.

Published by: Center for and Information on Low-External-Input and Sustainable Agriculture, Kastanjelaan 5, PO Box 64, Leusden, 3830 AB, Netherlands. TEL 31-33-432-6011, FAX 31-33-495-1779, ileia@ileia.nl, http://www.ileia.org, http://www.oneworld.org/ileia.

634.8 DEU ISSN 1439-6432
L W PFAELZER BAUER - DER LANDBOTE; Wochenblatt fuer Landwirtschaft und Weinbau. Text in German. 2000. w. adv. bk.rev. **Document type:** *Newspaper, Trade.*
Formed by the merger of (1949-2000): Pfaelzer Bauer (0031-6660); (1946-2000): Der Landbote (0342-7072)
Published by: (Bauern- und Winzenverband Rheinland-Pfalz Sued e.V.), Fachverlag Dr. Fraund GmbH, An der Brunnenstube 33-35, Mainz, 55120, Germany. TEL 49-6131-62050, FAX 49-6131-620544, verlag@fraund.de, http://www.fraund.de. Ed. Cornelius Mohr. Adv. contact Hennig Leibert. B&W page EUR 2,486, color page EUR 4,202. Circ: 9,135 (paid).

632.9 USA
THE LABEL NEWSLETTER. Text in English. 1989. m. back issues avail. **Document type:** *Newsletter.* **Description:** Aims to disseminate pesticide-related information and encourage the multiplier effect by extending communication channels to clientele.
Media: Online - full text.
Published by: University of Nebraska at Lincoln, Institute of Agriculture and Natural Resources, 114 C B A, Lincoln, NE 68588-0406. eevprcomm@unlvm.unl.edu, http://ianrwww.unl.edu/ianr/pat/thelabel/thelabel.htm. Eds. Clyde Ogg, Larry Schulz.

630 627 NLD ISSN 0023-7604
TC1
LAND AND WATER INTERNATIONAL; a Netherlands review on international hydraulic and agricultural engineering. Text in English; Summaries in English, French, German, Spanish. 1966. q. USD 12. adv. charts; illus. cum.index.
Indexed: EIP, FLUIDEX.
—BLDSC (5146.780000), CISTI.
Published by: Netherlands Engineering Consultants, PO Box 90413, The Hague, 2509, Netherlands. TEL 31-70-3143636, FAX 31-70-3284862, info@nedeco.nl, http://www.nedeco.nl/activities/promotion/lwi/default.asp. Circ: 4,000 (controlled).

631 DEU ISSN 0458-6859
CODEN: LVOEAC
LANDBAUFORSCHUNG VOELKENRODE; wissenschaftliche Mitteilungen der Bundesforschungsanstalt fuer Landwirtschaft (FAL). Text in German; Summaries in English. 1950. q. EUR 32 (effective 2005). index. back issues avail. **Document type:** *Journal, Academic/Scholarly.*
Indexed: AEA, ASCA, AbHyg, AgBio, AnBrAb, CIN, CPA, ChemAb, ChemTitl, CurCont, DSA, FCA, FPA, FaBeAb, ForAb, HerbAb, HortAb, I&DA, IBR, IBZ, IndVet, MaizeAb, NutrAb, OrnHort, PBA, PGegResA, PGrRegA, PHN&I, PN&I, PotatoAb, PoultAb, RA&MP, RDA, RM&VM, RPP, RRTA, RefZh, RevApplEntom, S&F, S&MA, SIA, SSCI, SeedAb, SoyAb, TDB, TOSA, TriticAb, VITIS, VetBull, WAE&RSA, WeedAb.
—BLDSC (5147.000000), CASDDS, CINDOC, CISTI, IDS, IE, ingenta. **CCC.**
Published by: Bundesforschungsanstalt fuer Landwirtschaft (FAL), Bundesallee 50, Braunschweig, 38116, Germany. TEL 49-531-5961001, FAX 49-531-5961099, landbauforschung@fal.de, info@fal.de, http://www.fal.de/index.htm?page=/de/publikationen/default.htm. Ed. Folkhard Isermeyer. Circ: 900.

631.587 USA ISSN 0745-3795
SB472.53
LANDSCAPE & IRRIGATION. Text in English. 1977. m. free to qualified personnel (effective 2005). adv. bk.rev. charts; stat.; tr.lit. index. back issues avail. **Document type:** *Magazine, Trade.*
Incorporates: Landscape Design (1070-3853); (in 1985): Western Landscape News; Former titles: Landscape West and Irrigation News (0191-8745); Landscape West
Related titles: Online - full text ed.: (from Florida Center for Library Automation, Gale Group).
Indexed: GardL.
—**CCC.**
Published by: Adams Business Media, 420 S Palm Canyon Dr, 2nd Fl, Palm Springs, CA 92262. TEL 760-318-7000, FAX 760-323-4877, http://www.greenmediaonline.com/li/, http://www.abm.net. Eds. Jerry Roache, Vanessa Rangel, Joe Treadwell. Pub. Steve Brackett. adv.: color page USD 6,075. Circ: 65,000 (controlled).

630 DEU ISSN 0023-8082
TJ1480
LANDTECHNIK (MUENSTER); Fachzeitschrift fuer Agrartechnik und laendliches Bauen. Text in German; Summaries in English, German. 1946. bi-m. EUR 121.80 domestic; EUR 124.80 foreign (effective 2003). adv. bk.rev. charts; illus. index. **Document type:** *Journal, Trade.*
Incorporates (1951-1990): Grundlagen der Landtechnik (0017-4920); (1950-1974): Landarbeit (0023-771X)
Indexed: AEA, AgBio, AgrForAb, AnBrAb, CPA, DSA, ExcerpMed, FCA, FPA, ForAb, HerbAb, HortAb, I&DA, IndVet, MaizeAb, NemAb, NutrAb, PBA, PHN&I, PN&I, PotatoAb, PoultAb, RA&MP, RPP, RiceAb, S&F, SIA, SeedAb, SoyAb, TriticAb, VetBull, WAE&RSA, WeedAb.
—BLDSC (5153.200000), CISTI, IE, Infotrieve, ingenta, Linda Hall. **CCC.**
Published by: (Verein Deutscher Ingenieure e.V.), Landwirtschaftsverlag GmbH, Huelsebrockstr 2, Muenster, 48165, Germany. TEL 49-2501-801-0, FAX 49-2501-801204, zentrale@lv-h.de, http://www.lv-h.de. Ed. R Metzner. adv.: B&W page EUR 960, color page EUR 1,584. Circ: 1,725.

631.5 NLD ISSN 1567-1844
LANDWERK. Text in Dutch. 1961. 6/yr. EUR 40 domestic to individuals; EUR 55 foreign to individuals; EUR 55 to institutions; EUR 31 to students (effective 2005). adv. bk.rev. bibl.; charts; illus. **Document type:** *Journal, Trade.*
Former titles (until 2000): Tijdschrift Landinrichting (0922-6419); (until 1988): Cultuurtechnisch Tijdschrift (0045-9267)
—IE.
Address: PO Box 618, Wageningen, 6700 AP, Netherlands. TEL 31-317-422966, FAX 31-317-46867, info@landwerk.nl, http://www.landwerk.nl. Ed. Geert van Duinhoven. Pub. Rob Janmaat. Circ: 1,600.

338.17318 COL
LATINOAMERICAN RICE FORUM: F L A R NEWSLETTER. Text in English. s-a.
Related titles: ♦ Spanish ed.: Foro Arrocero Latinoamericano: Boletin Informativo del F L A R.
Published by: Centro Internacional de Agricultura Tropical/International Center for Tropical Agriculture, Publications Unit, Apartado Aereo 6713, Cali, VALLE, Colombia.

630 IND ISSN 0250-5371
CODEN: LRESDD
LEGUME RESEARCH; journal of legume physiology, genetics, breeding, bacterial activity, product quality and technological aspects of cultivation, processing and evaluation. Text in English. 1978. q. USD 70 foreign (effective 2006). bk.rev. **Document type:** *Journal, Academic/Scholarly.* **Description:** It is designed to highlight the fundamental and applied aspects of Legume physiology, genetic, breeding, bacterial activity, production quality and technological aspects of cultivation, processing and evaluation.
Indexed: AEA, AgBio, AgrForAb, BioCN&I, BiolAb, CPA, ChemAb, FCA, FPA, FS&TA, ForAb, HerbAb, HortAb, I&DA, NemAb, NutrAb, OrnHort, PBA, PGegResA, PGrRegA, PHN&I, RA&MP, RDA, RM&VM, RPP, RevApplEntom, RiceAb, S&F, SIA, SeedAb, SoyAb, TOSA, TriticAb, WAE&RSA, WeedAb.
—CASDDS, CISTI, Linda Hall.
Published by: Agricultural Research Communication Centre, 1130 Sadar Bazar, Post Office Marg, Karnal, Haryana 132 001, India. TEL 91-184-255080, http://www.scientificpub.com/bookdetails.php?booktransid=482&bookid=478. Ed. V P Singh. Circ: 3,000. **Subscr. to:** Scientific Publishers. journals@scientificpub.com, http://www.scientificpub.com.

631 ESP ISSN 0457-6039
LEVANTE AGRICOLA; revista internacional de citricos. Text in Spanish. 1962. q. (plus special issue). EUR 53.09 domestic; EUR 66.88 foreign (effective 2004). adv. abstr.; illus.; charts; stat. **Description:** Publishes articles relating to the specialty of citriculture, or the production of citrus fruits.
Indexed: IECT.
—CINDOC.
Published by: Ediciones y Promociones L.A.V., C/Jose Maria de Haro 51, Valencia, 46022, Spain. TEL 34-96-3720261, FAX 34-96-3710516, http://www.edicioneslav.es. Ed. Francisco Salvador Planes Planes.

630 CHN ISSN 1003-6202
LIANGSHI YU SILIAO GONGYE/CEREAL & FEED INDUSTRY. Text in Chinese. 1978. bi-m. CNY 5 newsstand/cover (effective 2005). **Document type:** *Journal, Academic/Scholarly.*
Related titles: Online - full text ed.: (from East View Information Services, WanFang Data Corp.).
—BLDSC (5186.245742).
Address: 3 South Zhuodaoquan Rd., Wuhan, 430079, China. TEL 86-27-87406138, FAX 86-27-87803774, lsyslgy@public.wh.hb.cn, http://lsyslgy.periodicals.net.cn/. Ed. Hang Wang. **Dist. by:** China International Book Trading Corp, 35 Chegongzhuang Xilu, Haidian District, PO Box 399, Beijing 100044, China. TEL 86-10-68412045, FAX 86-10-68412023, cibtc@mail.cibtc.com.cn, http://www.cibtc.com.cn.

LIBERIA. MINISTRY OF AGRICULTURE. PRODUCTION ESTIMATES OF MAJOR CROPS. see *AGRICULTURE—Abstracting, Bibliographies, Statistics*

631 ZAF
LINK; information bulletin for the sugar industry. Text in English. 1992. q. free. Website rev. illus. **Document type:** *Newsletter.*
Indexed: PerIslam.
Published by: South African Sugar Association Experiment Station, Private Bag X02, Mount Edgecombe, 4300, South Africa. TEL 27-31-593205, FAX 27-31-595406, sasex@sugar.org.za, http://www.sugar.co.za. Circ: 3,000.

631 NLD ISSN 0169-0396
LISSE. LABORATORIUM VOOR BLOEMBOLLENONDERZOEK. JAARVERSLAG. Text in Dutch; Summaries in English. 1953. a. **Document type:** *Corporate.*
Indexed: BiolAb.
—BLDSC (4610.300000).
Published by: Laboratorium voor Bloembollenonderzoek, Vennestraat 22, Postbus 85, Lisse, 2160 AB, Netherlands. TEL 31-252-462121, FAX 31-252-417762, info.ppo@wur.nl, http://www.ppo.dlo.nl/ppo/index.htm. Ed. M J Zwart. Circ: 2,000.

631.4 GBR ISSN 1360-1741
S605.5
LIVING EARTH. Text in English. 1993. q. GBP 18 (effective 2002). adv. bk.rev. charts; stat. 36 p./no.; back issues avail. **Document type:** *Magazine, Consumer.* **Description:** Supports organic food and sustainable farming.
Supersedes in part (in 1995): Living Earth and the Food Magazine (1367-9848); Which was formed by the merger of (1988-1993): Food Magazine (0953-5047); (19??-1993): Living Earth (0954-1098); Which was formerly (until 1988): Soil Association. Review (0951-2381); (until 1985): Soil Association. Quarterly Review (0307-2576); (until 1975): Soil Association. Journal (0038-0709)
Indexed: EPB, S&F.
—BLDSC (5282.610000), IE, ingenta.
Published by: Soil Association, 40-56 Victoria St, Bristol, BS1 6BY, United Kingdom. TEL 44-117-929-0661, FAX 44-117-925-2504, info@soilassoc.org, http://www.soilassociation.org. Ed., R&P Elizabeth Winkler TEL 44-117-914-2434. Adv. contact Martin Trowell TEL 44-117-914-2446. Circ: 20,000.

632.9 MLI ISSN 0459-6803
LOCUSTA. Text in English, French. 1954. irreg.
Published by: Organisation Internationale Contre le Criquet Migrateur Africain/International African Migratory Locust Organization, BP 136, Bamako, Mali.

LOS ANGELES WHOLESALE FRUIT & VEGETABLE REPORT. see *AGRICULTURE—Agricultural Economics*

634.8 HUN ISSN 0866-6083
TP559.H9 CODEN: BORGBB
MAGYAR SZOLO- ES BORGAZDASAG/HUNGARIAN JOURNAL OF VITICULTURE AND ENOLOGY. Text in Hungarian; Abstracts and contents page in English. 1991. bi-m. HUF 2,100, USD 20. adv. bk.rev. **Document type:** *Corporate.* **Description:** Covers research, production, management, economics, and news of the association.
Formed by the merger of (1953-1990): Borgazdasag (0006-7741); Which was formerly (until 1954): Borgazdasagi Ertesito (0200-2892); (1971-1990): Szolo-bor Inform (0133-5286); (1981-1990): Szolotermesztes es Boraszat (0230-2241); Which was formerly: Szolotermesztes (0139-4660)
Indexed: FS&TA, HortAb, NutrAb, PBA, VITIS, WAE&RSA.
—CASDDS.
Published by: Wine Producer's Council, Galantai utca 18, Budapest, 1126, Hungary. TEL 36-1-252-4772, FAX 36-1-252-6758. Ed. Eva Herpay. **Subscr. to:** Kultura, PO Box 149, Budapest 1389, Hungary.

630 USA ISSN 1070-1494
S69 CODEN: MLSBBX
MAINE AGRICULTURAL AND FOREST EXPERIMENT STATION. BULLETIN. Text in English. irreg., latest vol.848. **Document type:** *Bulletin.*
Former titles (until 1993): Maine Agricultural Experiment Station. Bulletin (0734-9548); (until 1983): Maine Life Sciences and Agricultural Experiment Station. Bulletin (0099-4448)
Indexed: BioCN&I, FPA, ForAb, RPP, RevApplEntom, S&F, TriticAb, WeedAb.
—BLDSC (2789.152900), CASDDS, CISTI, Linda Hall.
Published by: Maine Agricultural and Forest Experiment Station, University of Maine, 5782 Winslow Hall, Rm 1, Orono, ME 04469-5782. TEL 207-581-3211, maes2@maine.edu, http://www.umaine.edu/mafes/publicat.htm.

630 USA
MAINE POTATO NEWS. Text in English. m. free (effective 2005). **Document type:** *Newspaper, Trade.* **Description:** Official voice of the Maine potato industry.
Published by: Maine Potato Board, 744 Main St, Rm 1, Presque Isle, ME 04769. TEL 207-769-5061, FAX 207-764-4148, mainepotatoes@mainepotatoes.com, http://www.mainepotatoes.com. Circ: 6,000 (free).

633 DEU ISSN 0341-5155
MAIS; Zeitschrift ueber Forschung, Produktionstechnik, Verwertung und Oekonomik. Text in German. 1973. 4/yr. EUR 22.80 domestic; EUR 27.20 foreign; EUR 5.80 newsstand/cover (effective 2005). adv. **Document type:** *Magazine, Trade.*
Indexed: AEA, AgBio, AnBrAb, BioCN&I, CPA, DSA, FCA, HerbAb, HortAb, I&DA, IndVet, MaizeAb, NemAb, NutrAb, PBA, PGegResA, PGrRegA, PHN&I, PN&I, PotatoAb, PoultAb, RM&VM, RPP, RefZh, RevApplEntom, S&F, SeedAb, SoyAb, TriticAb, VetBull, WAE&RSA, WeedAb.
—**CCC.**

A

Published by: (Deutsches Maiskomitee e.V.), Verlag Th. Mann, Nordring 10, Gelsenkirchen, 45894, Germany. TEL 49-209-93040, FAX 49-209-9304185, info@th-mann.de, http://www.th-mann.de. Ed. Dr. Helmut Messner. Adv. contact Richard Heineke. B&W page EUR 1,644, color page EUR 2,880; trim 186 x 270. Circ: 6,305 (paid and controlled).

MANITOBA CROP INSURANCE CORPORATION. ANNUAL REPORT. see *INSURANCE*

630 DNK
MARK. Text in Danish. 1990. m. DKK 504 (effective 2003). adv. **Document type:** *Journal, Trade.*
Formerly (until 2003): Landsbladet Mark (0905-6793)
Published by: Dansk Landbrugs Medier, Vester Farimagsgade 6, Copenhagen V, 1606, Denmark. TEL 46-33-394700. Circ: 10,000.

631 MAR ISSN 0851-1667
MAROC FRUITS. Text in French. 1958. w. adv.
Address: 22 rue Al Messaoudi, Casablanca 02, Morocco. Ed. Ahmed Mansour Nejjai.

630 RUS ISSN 0207-2165
MASLICHNYE KUL'TURY. Text in Russian. 1981. bi-m.
Indexed: FCA, SeedAb, SoyAb, TOSA.
Published by: Izdatel'stvo Kolos, Sadovaya-Spasskaya 18, Moscow, 107807, Russian Federation. TEL 7-095-2072125. Ed. E A Glazunov. Circ: 2,000.

633.1 ITA ISSN 0025-6153
CODEN: MYDCAH
➤ **MAYDICA**; a journal devoted to maize and allied species. Text in English. 1956. q. EUR 180 (effective 2005). adv. bk.rev. charts; illus. index. back issues avail. **Document type:** *Magazine, Trade.* **Description:** Publishes original papers in the field of genetics, molecular biology, biochemistry, physiology, breeding and agronomy of corn and allied species.
Indexed: ASCA, ASFA, AgBio, B&BAb, BIOBASE, BioCN&I, BiolAb, CPA, ChemAb, CurCont, FCA, GenetAb, HGA, HerbAb, HortAb, I&DA, IABS, ISR, MaizeAb, NutrAb, PBA, PGegResA, PGrRegA, PHN&I, PlantSci, RM&VM, RPP, RefZh, RevApplEntom, RiceAb, S&F, S&MA, SCI, SIA, SeedAb, SoyAb, TriticAb, WeedAb.
—BLDSC (5413.340000), CASDDS, CISTI, IDS, IE, Infotrieve, ingenta.
Published by: Istituto Sperimentale per la Cerealicoltura, Sezione di Bergamo, Via Stezzano, 24, Bergamo, BG 24126, Italy. TEL 39-035-313132, FAX 39-035-316054, http://www.cerealicoltura.it. Circ: 1,000.

615.32 633.88 SCG ISSN 0354-5830
➤ **MEDICINAL PLANT REPORT**; proizvodnja i plasman lekovitog, zacinskog i aromaticnog bilja. Text in English, German, Serbian; Summaries in English. 1994. a., latest 2004. USD 10 per issue foreign (effective 2005). adv. **Document type:** *Journal, Academic/Scholarly.* **Description:** Covers medicinal-aromatic plants and spices breeding, production, processing and marketing.
Published by: Drustvo za Lekovito Bilje, Novi Sad/Society for Medicinal and Aromatic Plants, Novi Sad, c/o Prof Milan Martinov, Faculty of Engineering, Novi Sad, Vojvodina 21000. TEL 381-21-350122, FAX 381-21-350592, mmartog@uns.ns.ac.yu. Eds. Milan Martinov, Dusan Adamovic. R&P Dusan Adamovic.

631 IDN
MEETING OF COCONUT PRODUCTS EXPORTERS (YEAR). PROCEEDINGS. Text in English. a. price varies. **Document type:** *Proceedings.* **Description:** Contains assessments of the market situation during the year as well as outlook for the following year with data on production, export of coconuts and other oilseeds, oils and fats.
Published by: Asian and Pacific Coconut Community, 3rd Fl., Lina Bldg., Jl H R Rasuna Said Kav B 7, Kuningan, Jakarta, 12920, Indonesia. TEL 62-21-510-073, FAX 62-21-520-5160.

631.8 USA
METHYL BROMIDES ALTERNATIVES NEWSLETTER. Text in English. 1995. q. **Document type:** *Newsletter, Government.* **Description:** Focuses on odorless gas used in agriculture as a soil pesticide.
Related titles: Online - full text ed.
Published by: U.S. Department of Agriculture, Bldg 005, Rm 237, 10300 Baltimore Ave, Bettsville, MD 20705. TEL 301-504-5321, FAX 301-504-5987, mebrinfo@ars-grin.gov, http://www.ars.usda.gov/is/np/mba/mebrhp.htm. Ed. Kenneth W Vick.

632.9 ITA ISSN 1014-2193
MIGRANT PEST NEWSLETTER. Text in English. 1961. a. free. **Document type:** *Newsletter, Trade.*
Former titles: Locust Newsletter (1014-2207); Desert Locust Newsletter (0417-0946)
Related titles: French ed.: Bulletin d'Information sur les Acridiens. ISSN 1014-2215.
Published by: Food and Agriculture Organization of the United Nations, Sales and Marketing Group, Viale delle Terme di Caracalla, Rome, 00100, Italy. TEL 39-06-57054350, FAX 39-06-57053360, publications-sales@fao.org.

631 IDN
MONOGRAPHS ON COCONUT INDUSTRY. Text in English. a.?. price varies. **Document type:** *Monographic series.* **Description:** Studies the coconut industry in member countries. Deals with the current state of development of the crop as an economic resource, development plans, economic aspects and a range of other topics.
Published by: Asian and Pacific Coconut Community, 3rd Fl., Lina Bldg., Jl H R Rasuna Said Kav B 7, Kuningan, Jakarta, 12920, Indonesia. TEL 62-21-510-073, FAX 62-21-520-5160, TELEX 62863 APCCIA.

631.4 USA ISSN 0147-6874
S590 CODEN: MUSBDU
➤ **MOSCOW STATE UNIVERSITY SOIL SCIENCE BULLETIN.** Text in English. 1974. q. USD 1,875 per vol. in US & Canada; USD 2,155 per vol. elsewhere (effective 2006). charts; illus.; abstr.; maps. index. back issues avail. **Document type:** *Bulletin, Academic/Scholarly.* **Description:** Covers soil genesis, soil chemistry, soil reclamation and physics, plant productivity, soil biology, and ecology.
Related titles: ♦ Translation of: Moskovskii Gosudarstvennyi Universitet. Vestnik. Seriya 16: Biologiya. ISSN 0137-0952.
Indexed: AEA, AgrForAb, BiolAb, CPA, EPB, ExcerpMed, FCA, ForAb, HerbAb, HortAb, I&DA, MaizeAb, NemAb, PotatoAb, RiceAb, S&F, TriticAb, WAE&RSA, WeedAb.
—BLDSC (0416.245000), CISTI, IE, ingenta, Linda Hall. **CCC.**
Published by: (Moskovskii Gosudarstvennyi Universitet im. M.V. Lomonosova/M.V. Lomonosov Moscow State University RUS), Allerton Press, Inc., 18 W 27th St, New York, NY 10001. TEL 646-424-9686, FAX 646-424-9695, journals@allertonpress.com, http://www.allertonpress.com/journals/mus.htm. Ed. Sergei A Shoba.

➤ **MOSKOVSKII GOSUDARSTVENNYI UNIVERSITET. VESTNIK. SERIYA 16: BIOLOGIYA.** see *BIOLOGY*

631.5 RUS ISSN 0137-0944
S599.45.A1 CODEN: VMUPDN
MOSKOVSKII GOSUDARSTVENNYI UNIVERSITET. VESTNIK. SERIYA 17: POCHVOVEDENIE. Text in Russian. 1950. q. USD 59 foreign (effective 2005). **Document type:** *Journal, Academic/Scholarly.*
Supersded in part (in 1976): Moskovskii Universitet. Vestnik. Seriya 6: Biologiya, Pochvovedenie (0579-9422); Which superseded in part (in 1959): Moskovskii Universitet. Vestnik. Seriya Biologii Pochvovedeniya, Geologii, Geografii (0541-0770); Which superseded in part (in 1956): Moskovskii Universitet. Vestnik. Seria Fiziko-matematicheskikh i Estestvennykh Nauk (0463-5434)
Related titles: ♦ English Translation: Moscow State University Biological Sciences Bulletin. ISSN 0096-3925.
Indexed: BAS, BIOSIS Prev, BiolAb, FLP, NumL, RefZh, WAE&RSA.
—CISTI, Linda Hall. **CCC.**
Published by: (Moskovskii Gosudarstvennyi Universitet im. M.V. Lomonosova, Institut Pochvovedeniya/M.V. Lomonosov Moscow State University, Institute of Soil Science), Izdatel'stvo Moskovskogo Gosudarstvennogo Universiteta im. M. V. Lomonosova/Publishing House of Moscow State University, B Nikitskaya 5/7, Moscow, 103009, Russian Federation. TEL 7-095-2295091, FAX 7-095-2036671, kd_mgu@rambler.ru, http://www.msu.ru/depts/MSUPubl. **Dist. by:** M K - Periodica, ul Gilyarovskogo 39, Moscow 129110, Russian Federation. TEL 7-095-2845008, FAX 7-095-2813798, info@periodicals.ru, http://www.mkniga.ru.

631 USA ISSN 0541-3869
MUSHROOM NEWS. Text in English. 1955. m. USD 275 domestic; USD 455 foreign (effective 2005). adv. bk.rev. index. back issues avail. **Document type:** *Journal, Trade.* **Description:** Covers information on mushroom growing and the US mushroom industry.
Related titles: Special ed(s).: News Flash.
—BLDSC (5990.160000), CISTI, IE, ingenta.
Published by: American Mushroom Institute, One Massachusetts Ave, N W, Ste 800, Washington, DC 20001-1401. TEL 202-842-4344, FAX 202-408-7763, http://www.americanmushroom.org/mnews.htm. Pub. Bill Barber. Circ: 1,000.

MUSHROOM RESEARCH. see *BIOLOGY—Botany*

631 AUT ISSN 1011-260X
MUTATION BREEDING NEWSLETTER. Text in English. 1972. irreg. free. **Document type:** *Newsletter, Academic/Scholarly.*
Indexed: CTFA, FCA, OrnHort, PBA, PGrRegA, RefZh, RiceAb, S&MA, SeedAb, SoyAb, TOSA, TriticAb.
—BLDSC (5991.898000).
Published by: International Atomic Energy Agency/Agence Internationale de l'Energie Atomique, Division of Conference and Document Services, Wagramer Str 5, Postfach 100, Vienna, W 1400, Austria. TEL 43-1-2600-0, FAX 43-1-2600-7, sales.publications@iaea.org, http://www.iaea.org. Circ: 1,300.
Co-sponsor: Food and Agriculture Organization of the United Nations.

631 AUT ISSN 1011-2618
MUTATION BREEDING REVIEW. Text in English. 1982. irreg. free. **Document type:** *Monographic series, Academic/Scholarly.*
Indexed: RefZh.
—BLDSC (5991.899000).
Published by: International Atomic Energy Agency/Agence Internationale de l'Energie Atomique, Division of Conference and Document Services, Wagramer Str 5, Postfach 100, Vienna, W 1400, Austria. TEL 43-1-2600-0, FAX 43-1-2600-7, sales.publications@iaea.org, http://www.iaea.org. Circ: 500.
Co-sponsor: Food and Agriculture Organization of the United Nations.

MYCORRHIZA. see *BIOLOGY—Botany*

632.9 PHL
N C P C ANNUAL REPORT. Text in English. 1969. a. free.
Formerly: University of the Philippines at Los Banos. Rodent Research Center. Annual Report
Indexed: BiolAb.
Published by: National Crop Protection Center, College, Laguna, 3720, Philippines. Eds. Aurora M Baltazar, Pablo P Ocampo. Circ: 2,000.

NABOR CARRILLO LECTURE SERIES. PROCEEDINGS. see *ENGINEERING—Civil Engineering*

630 DEU ISSN 0027-7479
SB950.A1 CODEN: NDPBA6
NACHRICHTENBLATT DES DEUTSCHEN PFLANZENSCHUTZDIENSTES. Text in German; Summaries in English, German. 1949. m. EUR 119 domestic; EUR 124.20 foreign; EUR 10 newsstand/cover (effective 2004). adv. bk.rev. illus. index. **Document type:** *Newsletter, Trade.*
Incorporates (1947-1991): Nachrichtenblatt fuer den Pflanzenschutzdienst in der DDR (0323-5912); Formerly (until 1950): Nachrichtenblatt der Biologischen Zentralanstalt Braunschweig (0342-9369)
Indexed: AEA, AbHyg, AgBio, AgrForAb, BioCN&I, BiolAb, CIN, CPA, ChemAb, ChemTitl, DBA, ExcerpMed, FCA, FPA, ForAb, HerbAb, HortAb, I&DA, MSB, MaizeAb, NemAb, NutrAb, OrnHort, PBA, PGegResA, PGrRegA, PHN&I, PotatoAb, PoultAb, RA&MP, RM&VM, RPP, RefZh, RevApplEntom, S&F, SIA, SeedAb, TriticAb, VITIS, WAE&RSA, WeedAb, ZooRec.
—BLDSC (6007.500000), CASDDS, CISTI, IE, Infotrieve, ingenta. **CCC.**
Published by: (Biologische Bundesanstalt fuer Land- und Forstwirtschaft), Verlag Eugen Ulmer GmbH, Wollgrasweg 41, Stuttgart, 70599, Germany. TEL 49-711-4507-0, FAX 49-711-4507-120, info@ulmer.de, http://www.ulmer.de. Ed. S Redlhammer. Adv. contact Dieter Boger. B&W page EUR 820; trim 185 x 260. Circ: 950 (paid and controlled).

638.1 GBR
NATIONAL INSTITUTE OF AGRICULTURAL BOTANY. ANNUAL REPORT AND ACCOUNTS. Text in English. 1919. a. free. **Document type:** *Corporate.*
Formerly: National Institute of Agricultural Botany. Annual Report of the Council and Accounts (0077-4782)
Indexed: BiolAb, FCA, HerbAb, SeedAb, WeedAb.
—CISTI.
Published by: N I A B, Huntingdon Rd, Cambridge, CB3 0LE, United Kingdom. TEL 44-1223-276381, FAX 44-1223-277602, paul.nelson@niab.com, http://www.niab.com. Ed. Paul Nelson TEL 44-1223-342225. Circ: 7,000.

631 USA
NATIONAL POTATO COUNCIL. POTATO STATISTICAL YEARBOOK. Text in English. a. USD 25 (effective 1999).
Formerly (until 199?): National Potato Council. Yearbook
Published by: National Potato Council, 1300 L St, N W, Ste 910, Washington, DC 20005-4107. TEL 303-773-9295, FAX 303-773-9296. Ed. Kristen Damazio.

630.24 661 USA ISSN 1536-8815
NEBRASKA AGRI-BUSINESS DIGEST. Text in English. 1944. q. USD 10 to members; USD 20 to non-members (effective 2004). adv. **Document type:** *Magazine, Trade.* **Description:** News and feature cover advertising, nutrition, management, research, new products, government regulations, appointments, dealer news, and new literature.
Former titles: The Fertilizer & Ag-Chemical Digest (1067-1986); (until 1981): Nebraska Fertilizer and Ag-Chemical Digest (0199-672X)
Published by: Nebraska Agri-Business Association, Inc., 1335 H St, Ste 100, Lincoln, NE 68508-3784. TEL 402-476-1528, FAX 402-476-1259, info@na-ba.com, http://www.na-ba.com. Ed., R&P Robert L Anderson. Adv. contact Rebecca Barker. Circ: 1,000 (paid and free).

630 580 ITA ISSN 0391-9749
➤ **NEMATOLOGIA MEDITERRANEA.** Text in English, French, Italian, Spanish; Summaries in English. 1973. s-a. EUR 77.47 (effective 2004). bk.rev. bibl.; charts; illus. index. back issues avail. **Document type:** *Journal, Academic/Scholarly.*
Indexed: AEA, AgBio, AgrForAb, BioCN&I, CPA, CTFA, FCA, FPA, ForAb, HelmAb, HerbAb, HortAb, MaizeAb, NemAb, OrnHort, PBA, PGegResA, PotatoAb, RA&MP, RPP, RefZh, RevApplEntom, RiceAb, S&F, SIA, SeedAb, SoyAb, TriticAb, WAE&RSA, WeedAb, ZooRec.
—BLDSC (6075.497000), IE, ingenta.

Published by: (Istituto di Nematologia Agraria), Edizioni E T S, Piazza Carrara 16-19, Pisa, Italy. TEL 39-050-29544, FAX 39-050-20158, f.elia@area.ba.cnr.it, info@edizioniets.it, http://www.ba.cnr.it/~nemafe01/nemmed.html, http://www.edizioniets.it. Ed. C E Taylor. Pub., R&P F Lamberti. Circ: 300 (controlled).

363.78 USA ISSN 0198-7267
CODEN: PMNADO

NEW JERSEY MOSQUITO CONTROL ASSOCIATION. PROCEEDINGS. Variant title: Annual Mosquito Review. Text in English. 1914. a. USD 10. index. cum.index: 1914-1916. back issues avail. **Document type:** *Proceedings.*
Formerly (until 1974): New Jersey Mosquito Extermination Association. Proceedings (0096-5596)
Related titles: ♦ Supplement(s): New Jersey Mosquito Control Association. Proceedings. Supplement. ISSN 0190-9614.
Indexed: AbHyg, BioCN&I, BiolAb, ForAb, IndVet, RevApplEntom, TDB, VetBull, WeedAb, ZooRec.
—BLDSC (6841.748000), CISTI, Linda Hall.
Published by: New Jersey Mosquito Control Association, Inc., c/o Mrs Linda L Dickson, Dist Mgr, Box 388, Oxford, NJ 07863-0388. TEL 908-453-3585, FAX 908-453-2662, mosquito@nac.net. Ed. George Hamilton. Circ: 1,500.

363.78 USA ISSN 0190-9614

NEW JERSEY MOSQUITO CONTROL ASSOCIATION. PROCEEDINGS. SUPPLEMENT. Text in English. 1971. a.
Formerly (until 1974): New Jersey Mosquito Extermination Association. Proceedings. Supplement (0731-3969)
Related titles: ♦ Supplement to: New Jersey Mosquito Control Association. Proceedings. ISSN 0198-7267.
—Linda Hall.
Published by: New Jersey Mosquito Control Association, Inc., c/o Mrs Linda L Dickson, Dist Mgr, Box 388, Oxford, NJ 07863-0388. TEL 908-453-3585, FAX 908-453-2662, mosquito@nac.net.

632.9 NZL

NEW ZEALAND AGRICHEMICAL MANUAL. Text in English. 1984. a., latest 2000, Sep. USD 99 (effective 2001). adv. **Document type:** *Directory, Trade.* **Description:** Listings of all agrichemicals used in New Zealand, their properties, active ingredients and how to use them safely and without harm to the environment.
Former titles: New Zealand Agrichemical and Plant Protection Manual (0114-4022); (until 1990): New Zealand Agricultural Manual (0112-2290)
Published by: W H A M Chemsafe Limited, P.O. Box 11-092, Wellington, New Zealand. TEL 64-4-4739243, FAX 64-4-4734530, info@wham.co.nz, http://www.spraybible.com. Ed., R&P Trevor Walton. Pub. Angela Fussell. Adv. contact Angie Fussell. Circ: 5,000 (paid).

634.8 NZL ISSN 1175-6322

NEW ZEALAND GRAPEGROWER. Text in English. 2000. q. NZD 20; NZD 5 newsstand/cover (effective 2005). **Description:** Contains articles on growing techniques, technology and equipment, and stories that profile the different approaches to growing grapes.
Published by: New Zealand Rural Press Ltd., PO Box 4233, Auckland, 1001, New Zealand. hortnews@ruralpress.com, http://www.ruralpress.com/. Ed. Roger Bourne TEL 64-9-3769788. Adv. contact Ros Sellers TEL 64-7-8278648. Circ: 3,000.

631 NZL ISSN 1171-7033

NEW ZEALAND GROWING TODAY. Text in English. bi-m. NZD 52; NZD 4.95 newsstand/cover (effective 2002). adv. **Document type:** *Magazine, Consumer.* **Description:** Covers horticultural research, with emphasis on developing a wide range of crops (new and traditional) for New Zealand's conditions. Provides link between research and commercial growing.
Formerly (until 1992): Growing Today (0112-1588)
Indexed: INZP.
Published by: I N L Magazines Ltd., Wellesley St, PO Box 6341, Auckland, New Zealand. TEL 64-9-3531010, FAX 64-9-3531020, editor@growing-today.co.nz. Ed. Glenys Christian. adv.: B&W page NZD 1,205, color page NZD 2,016; trim 210 x 275. Circ: 14,202 (paid). **Dist. by:** Gordon & Gotch, 2 Carr Rd, Mt Roskill, PO Box 3207, Auckland, New Zealand. TEL 64-9-6253018, gordongotch@gordongotch.co.nz.

631 NZL ISSN 0113-8723

NEW ZEALAND KIWIFRUIT. Text in English. 1983. bi-m. NZD 58.72 (effective 1999). adv. **Document type:** *Trade.*
Indexed: INZP.
Published by: Kiwifruit New Zealand, P.O. Box 9906, Auckland, New Zealand. TEL 64-9-3677500, FAX 64-9-3670220, jacquie@iconz.co.nz. Ed., R&P Jacquie Webby TEL 64-7-5431338. Adv. contact Malcolm Alan. Circ: 3,000.

630 NZL ISSN 1175-9003

NEW ZEALAND PLANT PROTECTION. Text in English. 1948. a., latest 2002, 55th Conference. cum.index vols.1-50. **Document type:** *Proceedings, Academic/Scholarly.* **Description:** Provides a record of the papers presented at the Conference.
Former titles (until 1999): New Zealand Plant Protection Conference. Proceedings (1172-0719); (until 1991): New Zealand Weed and Pest Control Conference. Proceedings (0370-2804); (until 1963): New Zealand Weed Control Conference. Proceedings (0370-0968); (until 1951): The Annual National Weeds Conference. Proceedings
Related titles: Online - full text ed.: 1994.
—BLDSC (6096.690000), CISTI, IE, ingenta. **CCC.**
Published by: New Zealand Plant Protection Society, c/o Sue Zydenbos, Editor, Old West Coast Rd, Halkett, R.D.1, Christchurch, New Zealand. http://www.hortnet.co.nz/publications/nzpps/proceeds.htm. Ed. Sue Zydenbos TEL 64-25-316389.

631.4 NZL ISSN 0545-7904
S599.75.A1

NEW ZEALAND SOIL NEWS. Text in English. 1953. bi-m. membership. bk.rev. 40 p./no.; **Document type:** *Newsletter.* **Description:** Covers all aspects of soil science.
—**CCC.**
Published by: New Zealand Society of Soil Science, c/o Soil Science Group, PO Box 52, Lincoln University, Canterbury, 8150, New Zealand. TEL 64-3-3252811, FAX 64-3-3253607, Campbell@lincoln.ac.nz, http://www.rsnz.govt.nz/clan/nzsss/. Ed. A S Campbell. R&P, Adv. contact A.S. Campbell. Circ: 550.

NEWS FROM APROVECHO. see *ENERGY*

634 USA

NEWSLINK (SHERMAN OAKS). Text in English. bi-w. free domestic to members. **Document type:** *Newsletter, Consumer.*
Formerly: Sunkist Report
Published by: Sunkist Growers, Inc., 14130 Riverside Dr., Sherman Oaks, CA 91423. TEL 818-986-4800, FAX 818-379-7511, http://www.sunkist.com. Ed. Claire Smith. Circ: 6,000 (free).

631 JPN ISSN 0011-1848
CODEN: NISAAJ

➤ **NIHON SAKUMOTSU GAKKAI KIJI/CROP SCIENCE SOCIETY OF JAPAN. PROCEEDINGS/JAPANESE JOURNAL OF CROP SCIENCE.** Text in Japanese; Abstracts in English. 1927. q. JPY 6,000; JPY 4,000 to students (effective 2001). adv. bk.rev. 150 p./no.; reprints avail. **Document type:** *Journal, Academic/Scholarly.*
Related titles: Online - full text ed.: ISSN 1349-0990. 2003. free (effective 2005) (from J-Stage).
Indexed: AEA, ASCA, AgBio, AgrForAb, BIOBASE, BioCN&I, BiolAb, CPA, CTFA, ChemAb, CurCont, ExcerpMed, FCA, FS&TA, FaBeAb, HelmAb, HerbAb, HortAb, I&DA, IABS, INIS AtomInd, MaizeAb, NutrAb, OrnHort, PBA, PGegResA, PGrRegA, PHN&I, PlantSci, PotatoAb, PoultAb, RA&MP, RPP, RevApplEntom, RiceAb, S&F, SIA, SeedAb, SoyAb, TOSA, TriticAb, WAE&RSA, WeedAb.
—BLDSC (4651.480000), CASDDS, CISTI, IDS, IE, ingenta, Linda Hall. **CCC.**
Published by: Crop Science Society of Japan, c/o Graduate School of Agriculture, Tohoku University, 1-1 Tsutsumidori Amemiya-cho, Aoba, Sendai 981-8555, Japan. TEL 81-22-717-8638, FAX 81-22-717-8637, http://www.jstage.jst.go.jp/browse/jcs, http://wwwsoc.nii.ac.jp/cssj/index-e.html. Ed. Toshiro Kuroda. Pub. S Akita. R&P Y Gotoh. Adv. contact Atsushi Ogawa TEL 81-18-872-1630. page JPY 40,000. Circ: 2,000. **Subscr. to:** Kyoritsu Publishing Co. Ltd., 2-22-4 Shinkawa, Chuo-ku, Tokyo 104-0033, Japan. TEL 81-3-3551-9891, FAX 81-3-3553-2047.

631.5 JPN ISSN 0029-0610
S591.55.J3 CODEN: NIDHAX

NIPPON DOJO HIRYOGAKU ZASSHI/JAPANESE JOURNAL OF SOIL SCIENCE AND PLANT NUTRITION. Text in Japanese. 1927. bi-m. JPY 10,000 membership (effective 2004); subscr. incld. with membership. adv. bk.rev. abstr.; charts; illus. **Document type:** *Journal, Academic/Scholarly.*
Formerly (until 1934): Dojo Hiryogaku Zasshi/Society of the Science of Soil and Manure of Japan. Journal (0911-9973)
Indexed: AEA, AgBio, AgrForAb, AnBrAb, BioCN&I, CIN, CPA, ChemAb, ChemTitl, ESPM, FCA, FPA, ForAb, HerbAb, HortAb, I&DA, INIS AtomInd, MaizeAb, NutrAb, OrnHort, PBA, PGrRegA, PHN&I, PN&I, PotatoAb, PoultAb, RA&MP, RDA, RPP, RevApplEntom, RiceAb, S&F, SIA, SWRA, SeedAb, SoyAb, TriticAb, WAE&RSA, WeedAb.
—CASDDS, CISTI, Linda Hall. **CCC.**
Published by: Nippon Dojo Hiryo Gakkai/Japanese Society of Soil Science and Plant Nutrition, 6-26-10-202 Hongo, Bunkyoku, Tokyo, 113-0033, Japan. TEL 81-3-38152085, FAX 81-3-38156018. Ed. Satoshi Matsumoto. Circ: 3,300.

NIPPON NOGEIKAGAKU KAISHI/AGRICULTURAL CHEMICAL SOCIETY OF JAPAN. JOURNAL/JAPAN SOCIETY FOR BIOSCIENCE, BIOTECHNOLOGY, AND AGROCHEMISTRY. JOURNAL. see *BIOLOGY—Biotechnology*

631.8 GBR ISSN 1462-2378
TP245.N8 CODEN: NIMEF6

➤ **NITROGEN & METHANOL.** Text in English. 1959. bi-m. GBP 410, USD 665, EUR 635 (effective 2005). adv. bk.rev. charts; illus.; mkt.; stat. index. reprint service avail. from PQC. **Document type:** *Journal, Academic/Scholarly.* **Description:** Deals with all aspects of the nitrogen fertilizer and methanol industries. Aims to provide analysis of economic and technical developments in nitrogen fertilizers, intermediates and raw materials.
Formerly: Nitrogen (0029-0777)
Related titles: Microform ed.: (from PQC); Online - full text ed.: (from Gale Group).
Indexed: AEA, CBNB, CIN, ChemAb, ChemTitl, EngInd, PGrRegA, PROMT, S&F, WAE&RSA.
—BLDSC (6113.700500), CASDDS, CISTI, Ei, IE, Infotrieve, ingenta, Linda Hall. **CCC.**
Published by: British Sulphur Publishing (Subsidiary of: C R U Publishing), 31 Mt Pleasant, London, WC1X 0AD, United Kingdom. TEL 44-20-79032147, FAX 44-20-79032172, derek.winterbottom@crugroup.com, http://www.britishsulphur.com/journal_nm.htm. Ed. Richard Hands. Pub., R&P John French TEL 44-20-79032435. Adv. contact Tina Firman TEL 44-20-79032437. Circ: 597.

630 JPN ISSN 0029-0882

NOGYO FUMIN/AGRICULTURE AND BETTER FARMING. Text in Japanese. 1929. m. JPY 1,560. adv. abstr.; charts; illus.; stat. index.
Media: Duplicated (not offset).
Published by: Fumin Kyokai, Shuppan-bu/Better Farming Association, Publishing Division, c/o Mainichi Shinbunsha, Dojima, Kita-ku, Osaka-shi, 530-0003, Japan. Ed. Yasuji Miyata. Circ: 190,000.

631.5233 USA ISSN 1554-0502

THE NON-GMO REPORT. (non genetically modified) Text in English. 2001 (Mar.). m. USD 59 to individuals; USD 115 to institutions (effective 2005). adv.
Formerly (until 2005): The Non-GMO Source (1545-6560)
Related titles: Online - full text ed.: ISSN 1555-7154.
Published by: Writing Solutions, Inc., P. O. Box 436, Fairfield, IA 52556. TEL 641-472-1491, 800-854-0586, FAX 641-472-1487, http://www.non-gmosource.com. Ed. Ken Roseboro.

632.9 CHN ISSN 1002-5480
CODEN: NKYGEH

NONGYAO KEXUE YU GUANLI/PESTICIDE SCIENCE AND MANAGEMENT. Text in Chinese. 1989. q. USD 80. **Document type:** *Academic/Scholarly.* **Description:** Covers the policies and regulations of pesticide, use of pesticide, product analytical methods, and pesticide toxicology.
Related titles: Online - full text ed.: (from East View Information Services).
Indexed: CIN, ChemAb, ChemTitl, MSB.
—BLDSC (6428.449000), CASDDS.
Published by: Nongye Bu, Nongyao Jiandingsuo/Ministry of Agriculture, Institute for the Control of Agrochemicals, Liangmaqiao, Beijing, 100026, China. TEL 10-5025929. Ed. Jing Zhiyuan.

633.491 USA

NORTH AMERICAN POTATO VARIETY INVENTORY. Text in English. irreg. USD 5 per issue in US & Canada; USD 8.50 per issue elsewhere. illus.; stat. **Document type:** *Trade.* **Description:** Offers information on varieties of potatoes developed in North America, along with official name, year of release, breeder, agency, and parentage.
Published by: Potato Association of America, University of Maine, 5715 Coburn Hall, Rm 6, Orono, ME 04469-5715. TEL 207-581-3042, FAX 207-581-3015, http://www.ume.maine.edu/PAA.

630.24 668.6 USA ISSN 0065-4418

NORTH CAROLINA AGRICULTURAL CHEMICALS MANUAL. Text in English. 1948. a. USD 18. index. **Document type:** *Bulletin, Academic/Scholarly.*
Published by: North Carolina State University, College of Agriculture and Life Sciences, PO Box 7603, Raleigh, NC 27695. TEL 919-513-3112, FAX 919-513-3112, LA_Jackson@ncsu.edu, http://ipmwww.ncsu.edu/agchem/agchem.html. Circ: 5,000.

712 631 635 USA

NORTH CAROLINA TURFGRASS. Text in English. bi-m. **Document type:** *Magazine.*
Published by: (Turfgrass Council of North Carolina), Harvest Publishing, PO Box 9125, Winter Haven, FL 33881. http://www.harvestpublishing.com.

632.5 USA ISSN 1062-421X

NORTH CENTRAL WEED SCIENCE SOCIETY. RESEARCH REPORT. Text in English. 1948. a.
Formerly (until 1989): North Central Weed Control Conference. Research Report (0099-9547)
—Linda Hall.
Published by: North Central Weed Science Society, Inc., 1508 W University, Champaign, IL 61821-3133. TEL 217-352-4212, FAX 217-352-4241, http://www.ncwss.org.

NORTH DAKOTA GRAIN AND OILSEED TRANSPORTATION STATISTICS. see *AGRICULTURE—Abstracting, Bibliographies, Statistics*

630   ESP
NOTES AGRARIES SETMANALS. Text in Catalan. bi-m. back issues avail.
Media: Online - full text.
Published by: Generalitat Valenciana, Conselleria de Agricultura, Pesa y Alimentacion. Secretaria General, C. Amadeo de Saboya, 2, Valencia, 46010, Spain. TEL 34-963-866912, FAX 34-963-866907, http://www.gva.es/agricultura/elcamp.htm, http://www.gva.es/agricultura/publica.htm.

631   COL
NOTICIAS COMALFI. Text in Spanish. 3/yr. **Document type:** *Academic/Scholarly.*
Published by: Sociedad Colombiana de Control de Malezas y Fisiologia Vegetal, Ciudad Universitaria, Bloque C Modulo 3 Nivel 8, DF, Carrera 50, 27-70, Bogota, CUND, Colombia. TEL 57-1-221-9643. Ed. Jaime Soriano.

632.9   ITA   ISSN 0468-9291
                      CODEN: NOMPA8
NOTIZIARIO SULLA PROTEZIONE DELLE PIANTE. Text in English, Italian; Summaries in English. 1952. a. adv. bk.rev. **Document type:** *Proceedings.*
Formerly (until 1993): Notiziario sulle Malattie delle Piante
Indexed: BiolAb, DBA, DSA, PHN&I, RevApplEntom, TriticAb.
—CASDDS.
Published by: Associazione Italiana per la Protezione delle Piante, c/o Diproval - Sezione di Fitoiatria, Universita degli Studi, Via Filippo Re8, Bologna, MI 40126, Italy. TEL 39-051-2091352, FAX 39-051-2091363, brunelli@agrsci.unibo.it. Ed. Giorgio Domenichini. Circ: 80,000.

634   CAN   ISSN 0078-2386
NOVA SCOTIA FRUIT GROWERS ASSOCIATION. ANNUAL REPORT AND PROCEEDINGS. Text in English. 1874. a. CND 15 to members. adv. **Document type:** *Proceedings, Corporate.*
Indexed: ChemAb, HortAb.
Published by: Nova Scotia Fruit Growers Association, Kentville Agricultural Centre, 32 Main St, Kentville, NS B4N 1J5, Canada. TEL 902-678-1093, FAX 902-678-1567, nsfga@fox.nstn.ca, http://fox.nstn.ca/~nsfga/. Circ: 300.

631   HUN   ISSN 0546-8191
                      CODEN: NOVEAK
➤ **NOVENYTERMELES∗ /PLANT PRODUCTION.** Text in Hungarian; Summaries in English, German, Russian. 1951. bi-m. HUF 708. **Document type:** *Journal, Academic/Scholarly.*
Indexed: AEA, ASCA, AgBio, CIN, CPA, ChemAb, ChemTitl, CurCont, FCA, FS&TA, ForAb, HerbAb, HortAb, I&DA, MaizeAb, NutrAb, PBA, PGegResA, PGrRegA, PHN&I, PotatoAb, RM&VM, RPP, RevApplEntom, RiceAb, S&F, SIA, SeedAb, SoyAb, TriticAb, VetBull, WAE&RSA, WeedAb.
—BLDSC (6180.300000), CASDDS, CISTI, IE, ingenta.
Published by: Agroinform Kiado es Nyomda Kft., Sobieski u 17, Budapest 2, 1096, Hungary. TEL 36-1-215-7533. Ed. Ivan Bocsa.

630.24   JPN   ISSN 0369-4658
NOYAKU KENSASHO HOKOKU/AGRICULTURAL CHEMICALS INSPECTION STATION. BULLETIN. Text in Japanese. 1950. irreg. **Document type:** *Journal, Government.*
Indexed: BioCN&I, RPP, WeedAb.
—CISTI.
Published by: Noyaku Kensasho/Agricultural Chemicals Inspection Station, 2-772, Suzuki-cho, Kodaira-shi, Tokyo, 187-0011, Japan. TEL 81-42-3832151, FAX 81-42-3853361, http://www.acis.go.jp/index.htm.

633   USA
LA NUEVA ERA; en la agricultura. Text in Spanish. 1997. s-a. USD 25 (effective 1999). adv. **Document type:** *Trade.* **Description:** For Mexican growers of major row crops - cotton, corn, wheat and sorghum. Helps growers boost productivity and efficiency and offers vital information on the latest production techniques.
Indexed: RASB.
Published by: Meister Media Worldwide, 37733 Euclid Ave, Willoughby, OH 44094-5992. TEL 440-942-2000, FAX 440-942-0662, pdh.circ@meisternet.com, http://www.meisterpro.com. Ed. Jim Moore. Pub., Adv. contact Jess Ennis. B&W page USD 1,985, color page USD 2,465; trim 8 x 10.75. Circ: 8,700 (controlled).

631.8   NLD   ISSN 1385-1314
S631   CODEN: NCAGFC
➤ **NUTRIENT CYCLING IN AGROECOSYSTEMS.** Text in English. 1980. 9/yr. EUR 1,378, USD 1,408, GBP 908 combined subscription to institutions print & online eds. (effective 2005). adv. bk.rev. back issues avail.; reprint service avail. from PSC. **Document type:** *Journal, Academic/Scholarly.* **Description:** Covers aspects of carbon and nutrient cycling as well as management, their effect in ecological, agronomic, environmental and economic terms. Also deals with subjects in agronomic, agro-forestry and fallow systems or system components such as plants and the fertility, chemistry or microbiology of soils, as well as with system inputs and losses.
Formerly (until vol.48, 1997): Fertilizer Research (0167-1731)
Related titles: Microform ed.: (from PQC); Online - full text ed.: ISSN 1573-0867 (from EBSCO Publishing, Gale Group, IngentaConnect, Kluwer Online, O C L C Online Computer Library Center, Inc., Ovid Technologies, Inc., Springer LINK, Swets Information Services).
Indexed: AEA, AESIS, ASCA, Agr, AgrForAb, AnBrAb, BIOBASE, BIOSIS Prev, BibLing, BiolAb, CPA, CTFA, ChemAb, CurCont, DSA, ESPM, FCA, FaBeAb, ForAb, GEOBASE, HerbAb, HortAb, I&DA, IABS, ISR, MaizeAb, NemAb, NutrAb, OnHort, PBA, PGegResA, PN&I, PollutAb, PotatoAb, PoultAb, RDA, RPP, RefZh, RiceAb, S&F, S&MA, SCI, SIA, SWRA, SeedAb, SoyAb, TOSA, TriticAb, VITIS, WAE&RSA, WeedAb.
—BLDSC (6187.690000), CASDDS, CISTI, IDS, IE, Infotrieve, ingenta, Linda Hall. **CCC.**
Published by: Springer-Verlag Dordrecht (Subsidiary of: Springer Science+Business Media), Van Godewijckstraat 30, Dordrecht, 3311 GX, Netherlands. TEL 31-78-6576050, FAX 31-78-6576474, http://springerlink.metapress.com/openurl.asp?genre=journal&issn=1385-1314, http://www.springeronline.com. Eds. Arvin R Mosier, Paul L G Vlek.

➤ **NUTSHELL (ETTERS).** see *GARDENING AND HORTICULTURE*

➤ **O A N DIRECTORY & BUYER'S GUIDE.** see *BUSINESS AND ECONOMICS—Trade And Industrial Directories*

634   DEU   ISSN 1615-5246
                      CODEN: INOGAV
OBST-, GEMUSE- UND KARTOFFELVERARBEITUNG. Text in German. 1914. m. EUR 104 domestic; EUR 111 foreign (effective 2005). **Document type:** *Journal, Trade.*
Formerly (until 1999): Die Industrielle Obst- und Gemueseverwertung (0367-939X)
Indexed: DSA, FS&TA, PST.
—BLDSC (6208.025000), CASDDS (6208.025000).
Published by: Agrimedia GmbH, Spithal 4, Bergen-Dumme, 29468, Germany. TEL 49-5845-9881-0, FAX 49-5845-988111, mail@agrimedia.com, http://www.agrimedia.com. Ed. Petra Becker. Pub. Uwe Hils.

OBST - WEIN - GARTEN. see *GARDENING AND HORTICULTURE*

OFFICE INTERNATIONAL DE LA VIGNE ET DU VIN. BULLETIN; revue internationale. see *BEVERAGES*

631   USA   ISSN 1087-6626
OHIO ECOLOGICAL FOOD AND FARM ASSOCIATION NEWS. Text in English. 1979. bi-m. USD 15. adv. bk.rev. illus.; stat. **Document type:** *Newsletter.* **Description:** Covers news and information on alternative food systems.
Media: Duplicated (not offset).
Published by: Ohio Ecological Food and Farm Association, PO Box 82234, Columbus, OH 43202. TEL 614-267-3663, FAX 614-267-4763, oeffa@iwaynet.net. Ed. Holly Harman Fackler. Circ: 1,200.

631   GBR   ISSN 1361-8822
OILSEEDS VARIETY HANDBOOK. Text in English. a. GBP 10 per vol. (effective 2003). charts. **Document type:** *Bulletin, Trade.*
Formerly (until 1995): N I A B Recommended Varieties of Oilseed Crops (1354-1382); Which superseded in part (in 1993): N I A B Farmers Leaflet (0305-1277)
Indexed: FCA, HerbAb, PBA.
—BLDSC (6252.610500).
Published by: N I A B, Huntingdon Rd, Cambridge, CB3 0LE, United Kingdom. TEL 44-1223-276381, FAX 44-1223-342328, TELEX 817455-NIAB-G, info@niab.com, paul.nelson@niab.com, http://www.niab.com. Ed. Paul Nelson TEL 44-1223-342225.

630   USA
HD9490.A1
OILSEEDS: WORLD MARKETS AND TRADE. Text in English. 1974. m. stat. **Document type:** *Government.*
Former titles (until 1993): World Oilseed Situation and Outlook (1076-4976); (until 1990): World Oilseed Situation and Market Highlights (1076-4992); (until 1986): Foreign Agriculture Circular. Oilseeds and Products (0145-0921)
Related titles: Online - full content ed.
Published by: U.S. Department of Agriculture, Foreign Agricultural Service, Cotton, Oilseeds, Tobacco & Seeds Division, 1400 Independence Ave. SW, Stop 1051, Washington, DC 20250-1051. TEL 202-720-7037, FAX 202-720-0965, info@fas.usda.gov, http://www.fas.usda.gov.

OLEAGINEUX CORPS GRAS LIPIDES. see *CHEMISTRY—Organic Chemistry*

633   ESP   ISSN 0255-996X
OLIVAE. Text in Spanish. 1984. 5/yr. USD 31 in Europe; USD 40 in the Americas. adv. bk.rev. charts; illus.; stat.
Related titles: French ed.: ISSN 0255-9978; Italian ed.: ISSN 0255-9986; English ed.: ISSN 0255-9994.
Indexed: AEA, BioCN&I, CPA, FCA, HerbAb, HortAb, NutrAb, PBA, PGrRegA, RPP, RevApplEntom, S&F, SeedAb, SoyAb, WAE&RSA, WeedAb.
Published by: Consejo Oleicola Internacional/International Olive Oil Council - Conseil Oleicole International, Principe de Vergara, 154, Madrid, 28002, Spain. TEL 34-1-5630071, FAX 34-1-5631263. Ed. Fausto Luchetti. Circ: 4,000.

634   ITA   ISSN 1127-0713
OLIVO E OLIO. Text in Italian. 1988. m. (10/yr.). EUR 62 domestic; EUR 110 foreign (effective 2005). adv. 80 p./no.; **Document type:** *Magazine, Trade.*
Indexed: AgrForAb, ForAb, HortAb, I&DA, NutrAb, PBA, PHN&I, RPP, S&F, SoyAb, WAE&RSA, WeedAb.
Published by: Il Sole 24 Ore Edagricole, Via Goito 13, Bologna, BO 40126, Italy. TEL 39-051-62267, FAX 39-051-490200, http://www.edagricole.it. Ed. Giorgio Setti. Circ: 7,000.

631   USA   ISSN 0892-578X
ONION WORLD; The voice of the onion industry. Text in English. 1985. 8/yr. USD 15 domestic; USD 27 in Canada & Mexico; USD 45 elsewhere (effective 2005). adv. back issues avail. **Document type:** *Magazine, Trade.* **Description:** Covers onion research, production, and marketing.
Published by: Columbia Publishing and Design, 413B N 20th Ave, Yakima, WA 98902. TEL 509-248-2452, 800-900-2452, FAX 509-248-4056, dbrent@columbiapublication.com, oweditorial@freshcut.com, http://www.onionworld.net. Ed. D Brent. Pub., R&P Mike J Stoker. adv.: B&W page USD 1,390, color page USD 2,090. Circ: 5,300 (paid and controlled).

633   CAN   ISSN 0008-7297
ONTARIO CORN PRODUCER. Text in English. 1983. 12/yr. adv. illus. **Document type:** *Trade.* **Description:** Publishes feature articles about and for corn producers, including but not limited to biographies andnews.
Formerly (until 1985): Cash Crop Farming (1193-7440)
—CISTI.
Published by: Ontario Corn Producers' Association, 90 Woodlawn Rd, W, Guelph, ON N1H 1B2, Canada. TEL 519-837-1660, FAX 519-837-1674. Ed. Terry Boland. R&P, Adv. contact Don Carruthers TEL 519-927-5234. B&W page CND 2,400, color page CND 3,395; trim 10.88 x 8.38. Circ: 21,901.

634.8 663.1   CAN   ISSN 0380-6057
ONTARIO GRAPE GROWER. Text in English. 1968. s-a. free. back issues avail. **Document type:** *Newsletter.*
—CISTI.
Published by: Ontario Grape Growers' Marketing Board, P O Box 100, Vineland, ON L0R 2E0, Canada. TEL 905-688-0990, FAX 905-688-3211. Ed. Brian Leyden. Circ: 8,000 (controlled).

635.9344   NZL   ISSN 1173-3802
THE ORCHARDIST. Text in English. 1928. m. (except Jan.). NZD 81 domestic; NZD 135 in Australia & the Pacific; NZD 145 elsewhere (effective 2001). adv. bk.rev. index. back issues avail. **Document type:** *Trade.* **Description:** Provides news and practical growing information to all New Zealand fruitgrowers. Includes previously unpublished research findings that may be of use to growers and also acts as a communication device for the scientific community.
Formerly (until 1995): Orchardist of New Zealand (0110-6260)
Indexed: AEA, AbHyg, AgBio, BioCN&I, BiolAb, CPA, DSA, FS&TA, ForAb, GardL, HortAb, INZP, IndVet, MaizeAb, NutrAb, PBA, PGegResA, PGrRegA, PHN&I, RDA, RPP, RevApplEntom, S&F, VetBull, WAE&RSA, WeedAb.
—CISTI. **CCC.**
Published by: New Zealand Fruitgrowers Federation, P.O. Box 2175, Wellington, New Zealand. TEL 64-4-4726559, FAX 64-4-4726409, hans@pims.co.nz, http://www.fruitgrowers.org.nz. Ed., R&P Hans Kuiper TEL 64-4-494-9976. Adv. contact Jackie Enright. Circ: 4,800.

ORCHIDEEEN. see *BIOLOGY—Botany*

OREGON WHEAT. see *AGRICULTURE—Feed, Flour And Grain*

ORGANIC GROWER. see *GARDENING AND HORTICULTURE*

635 631.4   NZL   ISSN 1175-5970
ORGANIC N Z. Text in English. 1941. bi-m. membership. adv. bk.rev. **Document type:** *Magazine, Trade.* **Description:** Covers organic agriculture and holistic health issues.
Former titles (until 2001): Soil & Health Journal (0038-0687); Compost Journal
Indexed: INZP.
—CCC.
Published by: Soil & Health Association of New Zealand, P O Box 36-170, Northcote NorthShore City, New Zealand. TEL 64-9-4194536, FAX 64-9-4194556, soil@health.pl.net, http://www.organicnz.pl.net/. Ed. Allan Baddock. Adv. contact Annie Wilson. Circ: 5,000.

633 GBR
ORGANIC VEGETABLE HANDBOOK. Text in English. a. GBP 10 per vol. (effective 2003). **Document type:** *Bulletin, Trade.* **Description:** Discusses which crops are best suited to organic production and describes each one.
Indexed: HortAb, PotatoAb.
Published by: N I A B, Huntingdon Rd, Cambridge, CB3 0LE, United Kingdom. TEL 44-1223-276381, FAX 44-1223-342328, TELEX 817455-NIAB-G, info@niab.com, paul.nelson@niab.com, http://www.niab.com. Ed. Paul Nelson TEL 44-1223-342225.

THE ORGANIC WAY. see *GARDENING AND HORTICULTURE*

630 ESP ISSN 1697-5561
▼ **ORIGEN.** Text in Spanish. 2004. bi-m. EUR 40 domestic; EUR 61 in Europe; EUR 76 elsewhere (effective 2004). **Document type:** *Magazine, Trade.*
Published by: Eumedia S.A., Claudio Coello 16, 1o, Madrid, 28001, Spain. TEL 34-91-4264430, FAX 34-91-5753297, http://www.eumedia.es.

630 570 IND ISSN 0474-7615
CODEN: ORYZAS
ORYZA. Text in English. 1962. q. INR 100, USD 30 to individual members; INR 300, USD 50 to institutional members (effective 2000). bk.rev. back issues avail. **Document type:** *Abstract/Index.* **Description:** Publishes peer reviewed original research articles on all aspects of rice research covering basic and applied work on crop improvement, crop management, crop protection and environmental security.
Related titles: Diskette ed.
Indexed: AEA, AgBio, AgrForAb, BioCN&I, CPA, FCA, HerbAb, HortAb, I&DA, NemAb, NutrAb, PBA, PGegResA, PGrRegA, PHN&I, PotatoAb, RPP, RevApplEntom, RiceAb, S&F, SIA, SeedAb, SoyAb, TriticAb, WAE&RSA, WeedAb.
—BLDSC (6296.750000), CISTI, IE, ingenta.
Published by: Association of Rice Research Workers, Central Rice Research Institute, c/o Editor-in-Chief, Cuttack, Orissa 753 006, India. TEL 91-671-643761, FAX 91-671-641744, TELEX 91-671-676220, crri@x400.nicgw.nic.in. Ed. P. Nayak. Pub. R.C. Dani.

632.9 GBR ISSN 1743-1026
SB950.9 CODEN: PEOUEN
OUTLOOKS ON PEST MANAGEMENT. Text in English. 1989. bi-m. GBP 505, USD 998 (effective 2004). **Document type:** *Journal, Academic/Scholarly.* **Description:** Covers the management of weeds, pests and diseases through chemistry, biology and biotechnology.
Formerly (until 2004): Pesticide Outlook (0956-1250)
Related titles: Online - full text ed.: ISSN 1465-8933. GBP 455, USD 725 to individuals (effective 2003) (from EBSCO Publishing, O C L C Online Computer Library Center, Inc., Swets Information Services).
Indexed: AEA, AbHyg, AgBio, AgrForAb, AnBrAb, BIOBASE, BioCN&I, CBNB, CPA, ChemAb, ChemTitl, FCA, FPA, ForAb, HelmAb, HerbAb, HortAb, I&DA, IndVet, MaizeAb, NemAb, NutrAb, OrnHort, PBA, PGegResA, PHN&I, PotatoAb, ProtozoAb, RA&MP, RDA, RM&VM, RPP, RefZh, RevApplEntom, RiceAb, S&F, SIA, SeedAb, SoyAb, TDB, TriticAb, VetBull, WAE&RSA, WeedAb, WildRev.
—BLDSC (6314.581000), CASDDS, CISTI, IE, Infotrieve, ingenta. **CCC.**
Published by: Research Information Ltd, Grenville Court, Britwell Rd, Burnham, Bucks SL1 8DF, United Kingdom. TEL 44-1628-600499, FAX 44-1628-600488, info@researchinformation.co.uk, http://www.researchinformation.co.uk/pest.php. Ed. Len Copping TEL 44-1799-521369.

633.007 DNK ISSN 0900-5293
OVERSIGT OVER LANDSFORSOEGENE; forsoeg og undersoegelser i de landoekonomiske foreninger. Text in Danish. 1971. a. DKK 125 (effective 2005). cum index: 1919-2003. **Document type:** *Trade.* **Description:** Contains computerized results of field experiments commented on by specialists in crop husbandry.
Related titles: Online - full text ed.; ♦ Includes: Tabelbilag til Landsforsoegene. ISSN 0908-0813.
Indexed: FCA, PBA, PotatoAb, TriticAb.
Published by: Landsudvalget for Planteavl/Danish Agricultural Advisory Committee, Udkaersvej 15, Skejby, Aarhus N, 8200, Denmark. TEL 45-87-405000, FAX 45-87-404010, http://www.lr.dk/planteavl/diverse/lp_oversigten.htm. Ed. Carl Aage Pedersen. Circ: 20,000.

633.491 USA
P A A INSIDER. Text in English. m. USD 5 (effective 2001). **Document type:** *Newsletter, Trade.* **Description:** Reports on news from the Potato Association of America.
Related titles: E-mail ed.: free (effective 2001).
—BLDSC (6327.467000).
Published by: Potato Association of America, University of Maine, 5715 Coburn Hall, Rm 6, Orono, ME 04469-5715. TEL 207-581-3042, FAX 207-581-3015, umpotato@maine.edu, http://potato.tamu.edu/variety/paa.htm, http://www.ume.maine.edu/PAA. Ed. John R Walsh.

631.587 DEU ISSN 1611-2490
▼ ➤ **PADDY AND WATER ENVIRONMENT.** Text in English. 2003. q. EUR 198 combined subscription to institutions print & online eds. (effective 2005). **Document type:** *Journal, Academic/Scholarly.* **Description:** Aims to advance the science and technology of water and environment related disciplines in paddy-farming.
Related titles: Online - full text ed.: ISSN 1611-2504 (from EBSCO Publishing, Springer LINK, Swets Information Services).
Indexed: ASFA, ESPM, EnvEAb, PollutAb, SWRA.
—CCC.
Published by: Springer-Verlag (Subsidiary of: Springer Science+Business Media), Tiergartenstr 17, Heidelberg, 69121, Germany. TEL 49-6221-3450, FAX 49-6221-345229, orders@springer.de, http://www.springer.de. Ed. Yohei Sato. Adv. contact Stephan Kroeck TEL 49-30-827875739. **Subscr. to:** Springer GmbH Auslieferungsgesellschaft, Haberstr 7, Heidelberg 69126, Germany. TEL 49-6221-345-0, FAX 49-6221-345-4229, subscriptions@springer.de; Springer-Verlag New York, Inc.. TEL 800-777-4643, journals@springer-ny.com.

631.5 PAK ISSN 0078-7930
PAKISTAN CENTRAL COTTON COMMITTEE. AGRICULTURAL SURVEY REPORT. Text in English. 1960 (no.2). irreg.
Published by: Pakistan Central Cotton Committee, c/o Secretary, Moulvi Tamizuddin Khan Rd., Karachi 1, Pakistan. TEL 524104-6.

633.51 PAK ISSN 0027-0334
HD9086.P3
PAKISTAN CENTRAL COTTON COMMITTEE. MONTHLY COTTON REVIEW. Text in English. 1968. m. free.
Published by: Pakistan Central Cotton Committee, c/o Secretary, Moulvi Tamizuddin Khan Rd., Karachi 1, Pakistan. TEL 524104-6.

631.5 PAK ISSN 0078-7949
PAKISTAN CENTRAL COTTON COMMITTEE. TECHNOLOGICAL BULLETIN. SERIES A. Text in English. 1960. irreg.
Published by: Pakistan Central Cotton Committee, c/o Secretary, Moulvi Tamizuddin Khan Rd., Karachi 1, Pakistan. TEL 524104-6.

631.5 PAK ISSN 0078-7957
PAKISTAN CENTRAL COTTON COMMITTEE. TECHNOLOGICAL BULLETIN. SERIES B. Text in English. 1959. irreg.
Published by: Pakistan Central Cotton Committee, c/o Secretary, Moulvi Tamizuddin Khan Rd., Karachi 1, Pakistan. TEL 524104-6.

632 PAK ISSN 1015-3055
➤ **PAKISTAN JOURNAL OF WEED SCIENCE RESEARCH.** Text in English. 1988. 4/yr. USD 50 (effective 2005). adv. **Document type:** *Journal, Academic/Scholarly.*
Indexed: FCA.
Published by: Weed Science Society of Pakistan, Dept. of Weed Science, NWFP Agricultural University, Peshawar, 25130, Pakistan. TEL 92-91-9216542, FAX 92-91-9216520, kbmarwat@psh.paknet.com.pk. Ed., R&P Khan Bahadar Marwat. Adv. contact Gul Hassan. page USD 50. Circ: 1,000 (paid and controlled).

634 USA ISSN 0031-3610
PEACH - TIMES. Text in English. 1956. q. USD 40 to members (effective 2002). adv. illus.; stat. 8 p./no.; **Document type:** *Newsletter.* **Description:** For peach growers, packers, horticulturalists; topics include council activities, orchard operation, peach horticulture, research, marketing. Also covers industry politics and lobbying.
Published by: National Peach Council, 12 Nicklaus Ln, Ste 101, Columbia, SC 29229. TEL 803-788-7101, charleswalker@worldnet.att.net. Ed., R&P, Adv. contact Charles Walker. Circ: 2,400.

633.368 USA ISSN 0031-3653
THE PEANUT FARMER. Text in English. 1965. 7/yr. USD 25 domestic; USD 80 foreign; free to qualified personnel (effective 2005). adv. charts; illus.; mkt.; pat.; tr.mk. back issues avail. **Document type:** *Magazine, Trade.* **Description:** For commercial growers of peanuts and related agribusiness.
—CISTI.
Published by: SpecComm International, Inc., 5808 Fairingdon Pl., Ste 200, Raleigh, NC 27609. TEL 919-872-5040, FAX 919-876-6531, merans@peanutfarmer.com, http://www.peanutfarmer.com. Pub. Mary Evans. adv.: B&W page USD 5,125. Circ: 20,000 (controlled).

633.368 USA ISSN 1042-9379
HD9235.P32
THE PEANUT GROWER. Text in English. 1989. m. (Jan.-July). USD 40 (effective 2005). adv. **Document type:** *Magazine, Trade.* **Description:** Covers peanut production practices, marketing, legislation, research and news important to peanut growers.
Published by: One Grower Publishing, 5118 Park Ave, Ste 131, Memphis, TN 38117. TEL 901-767-4020, FAX 901-767-4026, http://www.peanutgrower.com. Circ: 17,700.

PEANUT INDUSTRY GUIDE. see *AGRICULTURE—Agricultural Economics*

PEANUT NEWS. see *AGRICULTURE—Agricultural Economics*

PEANUT REPORT. see *AGRICULTURE—Agricultural Economics*

633.368 USA ISSN 0095-3679
SB351.P3 CODEN: PNTSBY
➤ **PEANUT SCIENCE.** Text in English. 1974. s-a. USD 40 domestic; USD 52.50 in Canada & Mexico; USD 65 elsewhere (effective 2005). illus. back issues avail. **Document type:** *Academic/Scholarly.* **Description:** Presents current research results.
Indexed: Agr, BIOSIS Prev, BibAg, BiolAb, CIN, ChemAb, ChemTitl, FCA, FS&TA, HerbAb, PHN&I, RPP, S&F, SeedAb, TOSA, WeedAb.
—BLDSC (6413.810000), CASDDS, CISTI, IE, ingenta, Linda Hall.
Published by: American Peanut Research and Education Society, c/o Dr J Ronald Sholar, 376 Ag Hall, Oklahoma State University, Stillwater, OK 74078. TEL 405-372-3052, FAX 405-624-6718, http://www.agr.okstate.edu/apres/welcome.htm. Ed., R&P H T Stalker TEL 919-515-3287. Circ: 600.

641.345 USA ISSN 1044-9639
THE PECAN GROWER. Text in English. 1989. q. USD 10 domestic; USD 25 foreign; USD 3 newsstand/cover (effective 2000). adv. charts; illus.; stat. **Document type:** *Trade.* **Description:** Analyzes trends pecan production and the marketplace. Projects the future for pecans.
Published by: Georgia Pecan Growers Association, 4807 Woodland Dr, Tifton, GA 31794-9389. TEL 912-382-2187. Ed., Pub., Adv. contact Jane Crocker. Circ: 3,300.

634.52 USA
PECAN SOUTH. Text in English. 1984. m. USD 18 domestic; USD 30 foreign (effective 2005). adv. bk.rev. charts; illus. index. back issues avail. **Document type:** *Magazine, Trade.*
Formerly (until 1993): Pecan South Including Pecan Quarterly (8750-5797); Incorporates: Pecan Press (0892-2942); Which was formerly: Texas Pecan Press; Formed by the merger of (1974-1984): Pecan South (0192-0863); (1967-1984): Pecan Quarterly (0048-3117)
Related titles: Microfilm ed.: (from PQC).
Indexed: Agr, HortAb.
Published by: Texas Pecan Growers Association, Inc., P.O. Drawer CC, College Sta., TX 77841. TEL 409-846-3285, FAX 409-846-1752, info@tpga.org, http://www.tpga.org. Adv. contact Scott Jennings. page USD 700. Circ: 4,900.

631.4 DEU ISSN 0031-4056
QL110 CODEN: PDBLAM
➤ **PEDOBIOLOGIA.** Text in English. 1961. 6/yr. EUR 214 in Europe to individuals; JPY 27,000 in Japan to individuals; USD 210 to individuals except Europe and Japan; EUR 430 to institutions; EUR 492 in Europe to institutions; JPY 65,600 in Japan to institutions; USD 553 to institutions except Europe and Japan (effective 2006). adv. bk.rev. bibl.; charts; illus. index. reprint service avail. from ISI. **Document type:** *Journal, Academic/Scholarly.* **Description:** Covers fundamental and applied aspects of soil biology.
Related titles: Online - full text ed.: (from bigchalk, EBSCO Publishing, Gale Group, IngentaConnect, O C L C Online Computer Library Center, Inc., ProQuest Information & Learning, ScienceDirect, Swets Information Services).
Indexed: ASCA, ASFA, AgBio, AgrForAb, ApEcolAb, BIOBASE, BIOSIS Prev, BioCN&I, BiolAb, CPA, ChemAb, ChemTitl, CurCont, ESPM, EntAb, EnvAb, EnvInd, ExcerpMed, FCA, FPA, ForAb, GEOBASE, HelmAb, HerbAb, HortAb, I&DA, IABS, IBR, ISR, M&GPA, MBA, MaizeAb, NemAb, NutrAb, PBA, PGegResA, PN&I, PotatoAb, PoultAb, ProtozoAb, RPP, RevApplEntom, RiceAb, S&F, SCI, SIA, SeedAb, SoyAb, TriticAb, VITIS, WeedAb, ZooRec.
—BLDSC (6417.750000), CASDDS, CISTI, IDS, IE, Infotrieve, ingenta, Linda Hall. **CCC.**
Published by: Elsevier GmbH (Subsidiary of: Elsevier BV), Karlstr 45, Munich, 80333, Germany. TEL 49-89-53830, FAX 49-89-5383939, info@elsevier.de, http://www.elsevier.com/locate/pedobi, http://www.elsevier.de. Eds. Juergen Schauermann, Matthias Rillig, Stefan Scheu. adv.: B&W page EUR 400, color page EUR 1,345; trim 170 x 240. Circ: 450 (paid and controlled).

631.4 JPN ISSN 0031-4064
CODEN: PDRJAS
➤ **PEDOLOGIST/PEDOROJISUTO.** Text in English, Japanese. 1957. s-a. JPY 5,000. adv. bk.rev. abstr.; bibl.; charts. index. **Document type:** *Academic/Scholarly.* **Description:** Covers soil science, soil survey and classification.
Indexed: CIN, ChemAb, ChemTitl, FCA, ForAb, HerbAb, HortAb, I&DA, RefZh, RiceAb, S&F, WAE&RSA.
—CASDDS. **CCC.**
Published by: Japanese Society of Pedology/Nippon Pedorogi Gakkai, c/o National Institute of Agro-Environmental Sciences, 3-1-1 Kannondai, Tsukuba-shi, Ibaraki-ken 305-0856, Japan. TEL 81-298-38-8275, FAX 81-298-38-8199. Ed. Nobufumi Miyauchi. Circ: 700 (controlled).

A

338.1 USA ISSN 0079-046X
PENNSYLVANIA. AGRICULTURAL STATISTICS SERVICE. CROP AND LIVESTOCK ANNUAL SUMMARY. Variant title: Pennsylvania. Agricultural Statistics Service. Crop and Livestock Annual Bulletin. Text in English. a. USD 5.
Document type: *Government.*
Formerly: Pennsylvania Crop Reporting Service. C.R.S. (0079-0478); Incorporates: Pennsylvania's Machinery Custom Rates
Published by: Agricultural Statistics Service, 2301 N Cameron St, Harrisburg, PA 17110-9408. TEL 717-787-3904. Circ: 5,000. **Dist. by:** Agricultural Statistics Board Publications, South Bldg, Rm 5829, U S Department of Agriculture, Washington, DC 20250.

631 USA
PEOPLE, FOOD & LAND. Text in English. 1974. a. USD 15; includes monthly bulletin. bk.rev.
Published by: People, Food & Land Foundation, 35751 Oak Spring Dr, Tollhouse, CA 93677. TEL 209-855-3710. Ed. George Ballis. Circ: 1,150.

PESQUISA DE ESTOQUES. see *AGRICULTURE—Abstracting, Bibliographies, Statistics*

632.9 NCL ISSN 1017-6276
PEST ADVISORY LEAFLET. Text in English. 1976. irreg., latest vol.24, 1991. **Document type:** *Monographic series.*
Formerly (until 1989): Advisory Leaflet
Related titles: French ed.: Commission de Pacifique Sud. Fiche Technique. ISSN 1017-6284.
Indexed: BioCN&I, RPP.
—BLDSC (6428.270000).
Published by: Secretariat of the Pacific Community, PO Box D5, Noumea, Cedex 98848, New Caledonia. TEL 687-262000, FAX 687-263818, spc@spc.int, http://www.spc.int.

632.9 USA ISSN 0031-6121
TX325 CODEN: PCONAI
PEST CONTROL. Text in English. 1933. m. USD 45 domestic; USD 69 in Canada & Mexico; USD 105 elsewhere; USD 7 newsstand/cover domestic; USD 10 newsstand/cover in Canada & Mexico; USD 21 newsstand/cover elsewhere (effective 2005). bk.rev. charts; illus.; stat.; tr.lit. Index. back issues avail.; reprints avail. **Document type:** *Magazine, Trade.* **Description:** Emphasis is on continued technological and educational advancement in pest detection, treatment and control methods.
Related titles: Microform ed.: (from PQC); Online - full text ed.: (from bigchalk, EBSCO Publishing, Gale Group, Northern Light Technology, Inc., ProQuest Information & Learning).
Indexed: ABIn, AbHyg, B&AI, BiolAb, CBNB, ChemAb, DBA, EIA, ExcerpMed, F&GI, FPA, HelmAb, IndVet, NutrAb, PHN&I, RM&VM, RRTA, RefZh, RevApplEntom, SAA, SFA, WAE&RSA, WildRev, ZooRec.
—BLDSC (6428.300000), CASDDS, CISTI, IE, Infotrieve, ingenta, Linda Hall. **CCC.**
Published by: Advanstar Communications, Inc., 100 W Monroe St, Ste 1100, Chicago, IL 60603-1905. TEL 312-553-8900, FAX 312-553-8926, info@advanstar.com, http://pestcontrolmag.com, http://www.advanstar.com. Ed. Lisa Shaheen. Circ: 21,000 (controlled).

632.9 GBR ISSN 1362-0452
PEST MANAGEMENT FOCUS. Text in English. 10/yr. GBP 60, USD 105 to individuals; GBP 165, USD 289 to institutions (effective 2001). **Document type:** *Academic/Scholarly.*
Description: Reports on international crop protection developments.
Formerly: Research Trends in Pest Management
Published by: Research Information Ltd., Grenville Court, Britwell Rd, Burnham, Bucks SL1 8DF, United Kingdom. TEL 44-1628-600499, FAX 44-1628-600488, info@researchinformation.co.uk, http://www.researchinformation.co.uk/pema.html. Eds. Kumar Patel TEL 44-20-8328-2470, Richard Wood. Pub. Kumar Patel TEL 44-20-8328-2470.

632.9 USA
PEST MANAGEMENT RECOMMENDATIONS FOR COMMERCIAL TREE-FRUIT PRODUCTION. Text in English. 1950. a. price varies. **Document type:** *Bulletin.*
Former titles (until 1990): Cornell Recommendations for Commercial Tree-Fruit Production; Tree-Fruit Production Recommendations (0070-0118)
Published by: (New York State College of Agriculture and Life Sciences), Cornell University, Media & Technology Services, 7 Business and Technology Park, Ithaca, NY 14850. TEL 607-255-2080, FAX 607-255-9946, dist_center@cce.cornell.edu, http://www.cce.cornell.edu/publications/catalog.html. R&P Carol Doolittle TEL 607-255-5830. Circ: 4,000.

631 USA
PEST MANAGEMENT RECOMMENDATIONS FOR COMMERCIAL VEGETABLE AND POTATO PRODUCTION. Text in English. a. price varies. **Document type:** *Bulletin.*
Formerly (until 1990): Cornell Recommendations for Commercial Potato Production; Incorporates (in 1990): Cornell Recommendations for Commercial Vegetable Production; Which was formerly: Vegetable Production Recommendations
Published by: Cornell University, Media & Technology Services, 7 Business and Technology Park, Ithaca, NY 14850. TEL 607-255-2080, FAX 607-255-9946, dist_center@cce.cornell.edu, http://www.cce.cornell.edu/publications/catalog.html. R&P Carol Doolittle TEL 607-255-5830.

632.9 USA
PEST MANAGEMENT RECOMMENDATIONS FOR SMALL FRUIT CROPS. Text in English. a. price varies. adv. **Document type:** *Bulletin.*
Formerly (until 1990): Small Fruit Pest Control and Culture Guide
Published by: Cornell University, Media Services, 7 8 Business and Technology Park, Ithaca, NY 14850. TEL 607-255-2080, FAX 607-255-9946, dist_cent@cce.cornell.edu. Ed. Mike Powers. R&P, Adv. contact Carol Doolittle.

632.9 CAN
PEST MANAGEMENT RESEARCH REPORT. Text mainly in English; Text occasionally in French. 1962. a. free (effective 2005). **Document type:** *Government.*
Formerly: Canada. Expert Committee on Pesticide Use in Agriculture. Pesticide Research Report (0068-7898)
—CISTI. **CCC.**
Published by: Canadian Agri-Food Research Council, Expert Committee on Integrated Pest Management, Building 60, Heritage House, Central Experimental Farm, Ottawa, ON K1A 0C6, Canada. TEL 613-234-2325, http://www.carc-crac.ca/english/ECIPM/ecipm_1.htm. Circ: 800.

632.9 GBR ISSN 1526-498X
SB950.9 CODEN: PMSCFC
➤ **PEST MANAGEMENT SCIENCE.** Text in English. 1970. m. USD 1,755 to institutions; USD 1,931 combined subscription to institutions print & online eds. (effective 2006). adv. charts; illus. index. back issues avail.; reprint service avail. from ISI. **Document type:** *Journal, Academic/Scholarly.* **Description:** Covers the research, development and effect of products designed for pest control and crop protection.
Formerly: Pesticide Science (0031-613X)
Related titles: Microform ed.: (from PQC); Online - full text ed.: ISSN 1526-4998. USD 1,755 to institutions (effective 2006) (from EBSCO Publishing, Gale Group, IngentaConnect, Swets Information Services, Wiley InterScience).
Indexed: AEA, AESIS, ASCA, ASFA, AbHyg, AgBio, Agr, AgrForAb, AnBrAb, AnalAb, ApicAb, B&AI, BIOBASE, BIOSIS Prev, BibAg, BioCN&I, BiolAb, CCI, CMCI, CPA, CRFR, CSNB, CTFA, ChemAb, ChemTitl, ChemoAb, CurCont, DBA, DSA, EPB, ESPM, EntAb, EnvAb, EnvEAb, ExcerpMed, FCA, FPA, FS&TA, ForAb, GEOBASE, HelmAb, HerbAb, HortAb, I&DA, IABS, ISR, IndMed, IndVet, LHB, M&TEA, MBA, MSB, MaizeAb, NemAb, NutrAb, OrnHort, PBA, PGegResA, PGrRegA, PHN&I, PN&I, PollutAb, PotatoAb, PoultAb, ProtozoAb, RA&MP, RCI, RM&VM, RPP, RevApplEntom, RiceAb, S&F, SCI, SFA, SIA, SWRA, SeedAb, SoyAb, TDB, TriticAb, VITIS, VetBull, WAE&RSA, WRCInf, WeedAb, WildRev, ZooRec.
—BLDSC (6428.332000), CASDDS, CISTI, IDS, IE, Infotrieve, ingenta, Linda Hall. **CCC.**
Published by: (Society of Chemical Industry), John Wiley & Sons Ltd. (Subsidiary of: John Wiley & Sons, Inc.), The Atrium, Southern Gate, Chichester, West Sussex PO19 8SQ, United Kingdom. TEL 44-1243-779777, FAX 44-1243-775878, customer@wiley.co.uk, http://www.interscience.wiley.com/pestmanagementscience, http://www.wiley.co.uk. Ed. G T Brooks. adv.: B&W page GBP 650, color page GBP 1,550; trim 210 x 297. Circ: 706. **Subscr. in the Americas to:** John Wiley & Sons, Inc., 111 River St, Hoboken, NJ 07030-5774. TEL 201-748-6645, 800-225-5945, subinfo@wiley.com.

631.8 BRA ISSN 0103-7277
➤ **PESTICIDAS;** revista de toxicologia e meio ambiente. Text in Portuguese, English, Spanish; Summaries in Portuguese, English. 1991. a., latest vol.11, 2002. Index. back issues avail. **Document type:** *Journal, Academic/Scholarly.* **Description:** Publishes original scientific and technical research papers and reviews in the field of pesticides, ecotoxicology and the environment.
Indexed: ASFA, ESPM, EntAb, FCA, PollutAb, ToxAb, WRCInf.
Published by: Universidade Federal do Parana, Centro de Pesquisa e Processamento de Alimentos, Centro Politecnico da UFPR, Caixa Postal 19083, Curitiba, Parana 81531-990, Brazil. TEL 55-41-3613374, FAX 55-41-2661647, ceppa@engquim.ufpr.br, http://www.engquim.ufpr.br/ceppa/index.html. R&P Elayne M Schlogel. **Dist. by:** Universidade Federal do Parana, Biblioteca Central da U F P R, Rua General Carneiro 370, Curitiba, Parana 81531-990, Brazil. TEL 55-41-3605290, FAX 55-41-2627784, inter@ufpr.br, http://www.sibi.ufpr.br/inter/intensis.html.

631.8 USA ISSN 0048-3575
SB951 CODEN: PCBPBS
➤ **PESTICIDE BIOCHEMISTRY AND PHYSIOLOGY.** Text in English. 1971. 9/yr. EUR 667 in Europe to individuals; JPY 69,600 in Japan to individuals; USD 506 to individuals except Europe and Japan; EUR 1,515 in Europe to institutions; JPY 158,100 in Japan to institutions; USD 1,150 to institutions except Europe and Japan; EUR 107 in Europe to students; JPY 11,100 in Japan to students; USD 93 to students except Europe and Japan (effective 2006). adv. index. back issues avail. **Document type:** *Journal, Academic/Scholarly.*
Description: Discusses the modes of action of plant protection agents such as insecticides, fungicides, herbicides, and similar compounds including nonlethal pest control agents, biosynthesis of pheromones, hormones, and plant resistance agents.
Related titles: Online - full text ed.: ISSN 1095-9939. USD 1,172 (effective 2002) (from EBSCO Publishing, Gale Group, IngentaConnect, O C L C Online Computer Library Center, Inc., ScienceDirect, Swets Information Services).
Indexed: ASCA, ASFA, AbHyg, AgBio, Agr, AgrForAb, AnBrAb, B&AI, B&BAb, BBCI, BIOBASE, BIOSIS Prev, BibAg, BioCN&I, BioDAb, BiolAb, CPA, CRFR, CTFA, ChemAb, ChemTitl, CurCont, DBA, DSA, EIA, EPB, ESPM, EnerInd, EntAb, ExcerpMed, FCA, FPA, ForAb, HelmAb, HerbAb, HortAb, I&DA, IABS, ISR, IndVet, Inpharma, MEDLINE, MaizeAb, NemAb, NutrAb, OrnHort, PBA, PE&ON, PGegResA, PGrRegA, PHN&I, PotatoAb, PoultAb, ProtozoAb, RA&MP, RM&VM, RPP, Reac, RefZh, RevApplEntom, RiceAb, S&F, SCI, SFA, SIA, SWRA, SeedAb, SoyAb, TDB, ToxAb, TriticAb, VetBull, WeedAb, WildRev, ZooRec.
—BLDSC (6428.370000), CASDDS, CINDOC, CISTI, IDS, IE, Infotrieve, ingenta, Linda Hall. **CCC.**
Published by: Academic Press (Subsidiary of: Elsevier Science & Technology), 525 B St, Ste 1900, San Diego, CA 92101-4495. TEL 619-231-6616, 800-894-3434, FAX 619-699-6422, apsubs@acad.com, http://www.elsevier.com/locate/pest, http://www.academicpress.com. Ed. Fumio Matsumura.

➤ **PESTICIDE INDEX.** see *AGRICULTURE—Abstracting, Bibliographies, Statistics*

➤ **PESTICIDE LITIGATION MANUAL.** see *ENVIRONMENTAL STUDIES—Toxicology And Environmental Safety*

631.8 IND ISSN 0970-6763
PESTICIDE RESEARCH JOURNAL. Text in English. s-a. USD 100 to institutions (effective 2006). **Document type:** *Journal, Academic/Scholarly.*
Indexed: AEA, AgBio, AgrForAb, BIOSIS Prev, BioCN&I, BiolAb, CPA, DSA, FCA, FPA, FS&TA, ForAb, HerbAb, HortAb, I&DA, MaizeAb, NemAb, NutrAb, PBA, PGegResA, PGrRegA, PHN&I, PotatoAb, RA&MP, RDA, RM&VM, RPP, RiceAb, S&F, SIA, SeedAb, SoyAb, TDB, TriticAb, WAE&RSA, WeedAb.
—BLDSC (6428.423750), IE, ingenta.
Published by: Scientific Publishers, 5-A New Pali Rd., Near Hotel Taj Hari Mahal, PO Box 91, Jodhpur, Rajasthan 342 003, India. TEL 91-291-2433323, FAX 91-291-2512580, journals@scientificpub.com, http://www.scientificpub.com/bookdetails.php?booktransid=467&bookid=463.

630.24 GBR
PESTICIDE USAGE SURVEY REPORTS ON AGRICULTURE AND HORTICULTURE. Text in English. 1965. a. back issues avail. **Document type:** *Bulletin.*
Published by: M A F F Publications, London, SE99 7TP, United Kingdom. TEL 44-1645-556000.

363.73 USA ISSN 0896-7253
PESTICIDES AND YOU. Text in English. 1981. q. USD 25 to individuals; USD 100 to institutions. abstr.; illus. cum.index 1981-1989. back issues avail. **Document type:** *Newsletter.*
Indexed: EnvAb.
Published by: Beyond Pesticides - National Coalition against the Misuse of Pesticides, 701 E St, SE, Ste 200, Washington, DC 20003. TEL 202-543-5450. Ed. Jay Feldman. Circ: 4,500.

632.9 PAK
PESTICIDES BULLETIN. Text in English. 1988. q. USD 3 per issue.
Published by: Press Corporation of Pakistan, P O Box 3138, Karachi, 75400, Pakistan. TEL 21-455-3703, FAX 21-7736198. Ed. Saeed Hafeez. Circ: 3,000.

571.959 USA ISSN 1520-9350
SB950.9
PESTICIDES, PEOPLE AND NATURE. Text in English. 1999. q. USD 72 to individuals; USD 180 to institutions (effective 2005). **Document type:** *Journal, Academic/Scholarly.*
Description: Seeks to communicate a better understanding of the environment, especially with respect to the impact of pesticides and other toxic chemicals.
—BLDSC (6428.773400), IE, ingenta. **CCC.**
Published by: (Rachel Carson Council), Begell House Inc., 145 Madison Ave, New York, NY 10016-6717. TEL 212-725-1999, FAX 212-213-8368, orders@begellhouse.com, http://www.begellhouse.com/ppn/ppn.html, http://www.begellhouse.com/index.html. Ed. David J McGarvey.

630.24 SCG CODEN: PSTIE8
PESTICIDI I FITOMEDICINA; casopis za pitanja proizvodnje, prometa i primene pesticida. Text in Serbo-Croatian. q.?. **Document type:** *Journal, Academic/Scholarly.* **Description:** Covers production, distribution and application of pesticides.
Formerly (until 2004): Pesticidi (0352-9029)
Indexed: AbHyg, AgBio, BioCN&I, CIN, ChemAb, ChemTitl, FCA, HortAb, MaizeAb, PBA, PotatoAb, RPP, RevApplEntom, S&F, SoyAb, TriticAb, WeedAb.
—BLDSC (6428.777000), CASDDS.
Published by: (Drustvo za Zastitu Bilja Srbije/Plant Protection Society of Serbia), Privredni Pregled, Marsala Birjuzova 3-5, Belgrade, 11000. TEL 381-11-635636, FAX 381-11-629137. Ed. Nesko Neskovic.

631.8 IND ISSN 0970-3012
PESTOLOGY. Text in English. 1977. m. **Document type:** *Journal, Consumer.*
Published by: Scientia Publications Private Ltd., Flat No.48, Bldg. No-3, 1st Fl, Patrakar Co-operative Society, Madhusudan Kalekar Marg, Gandhi Nagar, Bandra (E), Mumbai, 400 059, India. TEL 91-212-6441924, FAX 91-212-4144001, http://www.indiaagronet.com/tomato/exhibition/Publication/pestology/productmain.htm.

632.9 POL ISSN 0208-8703 CODEN: PSTYDL
➤ **PESTYCYDY/PESTICIDES.** Text in English; Summaries in Polish. 1955. q. PLZ 104 domestic; USD 104 foreign (effective 2004). 80 p./no. 1 cols./p.; back issues avail. **Document type:** *Journal, Academic/Scholarly.*
Indexed: AgrAg, AgrLib, BioCN&I, FCA, FS&TA, HortAb, PHN&I, RM&VM, RefZh, S&F, SIA, TriticAb, WeedAb.
—BLDSC (6428.803000), IE, ingenta.
Published by: Instytut Przemyslu Organicznego/Institute of Industrial Organic Chemistry, Ul Annopol 6, Warsaw, 03236, Poland. TEL 48-22-8111231, FAX 48-22-8110799, ipo@ipo.waw.pl. Ed., Pub. Jan Legocki. R&P, Adv. contact Wanda Karas. Circ: 150.

630.24 DEU ISSN 0340-1723 CODEN: PNBYAT
PFLANZENSCHUTZ-NACHRICHTEN BAYER. Text in German. 1948. 3/yr. free. **Document type:** *Journal, Academic/Scholarly.* **Description:** Concentrates on the physico-chemical, technical, biological and biochemical characteristics of active substances produced by Bayer.
Formerly (until 1962): Hoefchen-Briefe (0340-2223)
Related titles: ♦ English ed.: Pflanzenschutz-Nachrichten. ISSN 0079-1342; English ed.: ISSN 0170-0405.
Indexed: AEA, AbHyg, AgBio, AnBrAb, AnalAb, BioCN&I, BiolAb, CIN, CPA, ChemAb, ChemTitl, DSA, ExcerpMed, FCA, FS&TA, ForAb, HerbAb, HortAb, I&DA, IndVet, MaizeAb, NutrAb, PBA, PHN&I, PotatoAb, PoultAb, RDA, RPP, RevApplEntom, RiceAb, S&F, SIA, SeedAb, SoyAb, TDB, TriticAb, VITIS, WAE&RSA, WeedAb.
—CASDDS, CISTI. **CCC.**
Published by: Bayer AG, Geschaeftsbereich Pflanzenschutz, Kaiser-Wilhelm-Allee, Leverkusen, 51368, Germany. TEL 49-2173-384114, FAX 49-2173-383454, http://www.bayer-agro.de. Ed. Maria Esters.

354.599 PHL ISSN 0115-0340
PHILIPPINE COCONUT AUTHORITY. AGRICULTURAL RESEARCH ANNUAL REPORT. Text in English. 1974. a. illus.; stat. **Document type:** *Government.*
Formerly: Philippine Coconut Authority. Agricultural Research Department. Annual Report
Published by: Philippine Coconut Authority, Agricultural Research and Development Branch, Diliman, Quezon City Mm, 1128, Philippines. Circ: 200.

630 PHL ISSN 0048-3826
S17
PHILIPPINE JOURNAL OF PLANT INDUSTRY. Text in English. 1908. q. PHP 300, USD 20.
Formerly: Philippine Journal of Agriculture
Indexed: BAS, BiolAb, ChemAb, FCA, HerbAb, PBA, RiceAb.
—CISTI.
Published by: Bureau of Plant Industry, 692 San Andres St, Malate, Manila, 1004, Philippines. TEL 632-521-76-48, FAX 632-521-76-50. Ed. Nerius I Roperod.

PHILIPPINES. DEPARTMENT OF AGRICULTURE. BUREAU OF AGRICULTURAL STATISTICS. RICE AND CORN SITUATION OUTLOOK. see *AGRICULTURE—Abstracting, Bibliographies, Statistics*

632.9 ESP ISSN 1131-8988
➤ **PHYTOMA ESPANA**; revista de proteccion vegetal. Text in Spanish. 1988. m. EUR 75 domestic; EUR 95 foreign (effective 2005). adv. index. back issues avail. **Document type:** *Journal, Academic/Scholarly.* **Description:** Presents research and development in vegetable protection in Spain.
Related titles: Online - full text ed.
Indexed: CBNB, IECT.
—CINDOC.
Address: C San Jacinto 1-3, Valencia, 46008, Spain. TEL 34-96-3826511, FAX 34-96-3826515, http://www.phytoma.com/revistaphytoma.asp. Circ: 7,000.

630 FRA ISSN 1164-6993 CODEN: PYTOAU
PHYTOMA, LA DEFENSE DES VEGETAUX. Text in French. 1948. m. adv. bk.rev.
Formed by the merger of (1948-1990): Phytoma (0048-4091); (1946-1990): Defense des Vegetaux (0011-7579)
Related titles: Online - full text ed.
Indexed: AEA, AbHyg, AgBio, AgrForAb, BioCN&I, BiolAb, CBNB, CPA, CTFA, ChemAb, DBA, ExcerpMed, FCA, FPA, FS&TA, ForAb, HelmAb, HerbAb, HortAb, I&DA, IndVet, MaizeAb, NemAb, OrnHort, PBA, PGegResA, PGrRegA, PHN&I, PN&I, PotatoAb, RA&MP, RM&VM, RPP, RRTA, RevApplEntom, RiceAb, S&F, SIA, SeedAb, SoyAb, TriticAb, VITIS, VetBull, WAE&RSA, WeedAb.
—BLDSC (6491.000000), CASDDS, CISTI, IE, ingenta. **CCC.**
Published by: Ruralia, 1 rue Gambetta, Boulogne-Billancourt, 92100, France. TEL 33-1-42615142, FAX 33-1-49279190. Ed. Marianne Decoin. R&P J M Mutschler. Adv. contact Marie Francoise Delannoy. Circ: 9,000.

631 ISR ISSN 0334-2123 CODEN: PHPRA2
➤ **PHYTOPARASITICA: ISRAEL JOURNAL OF PLANT PROTECTION SCIENCES.** Text in English. 1973. q. GBP 124 (effective 2000). index. **Document type:** *Proceedings, Academic/Scholarly.*
Indexed: ASCA, ASFA, AgBio, AgrForAb, BIOBASE, BIOSIS Prev, BioCN&I, BioDAb, BiolAb, CIN, CPA, CTFA, ChemAb, ChemTitl, CurCont, DBA, DSA, ESPM, EntAb, ExcerpMed, FCA, FPA, ForAb, HerbAb, HortAb, IABS, ISR, MBA, MaizeAb, NemAb, OrnHort, PBA, PGegResA, PGrRegA, PHN&I, PlantSci, PotatoAb, PoultAb, RA&MP, RDA, RM&VM, RPP, RefZh, RevApplEntom, RiceAb, S&F, SCI, SIA, SeedAb, SoyAb, TriticAb, VITIS, WAE&RSA, WeedAb, ZooRec.
—BLDSC (6494.550000), CASDDS, IDS, IE, Infotrieve, ingenta, Linda Hall.
Published by: Priel Publishers, P O Box 2385, Rehovot, 76123, Israel. TEL 972-8-9365757, FAX 972-8-9365858, apriel@netvision.net.il, http://www.phytoparasitica.org. Ed., Pub. Vivian R Priel.

➤ **PHYTOPATHOLOGIA POLONICA.** see *BIOLOGY—Botany*

632 ITA ISSN 0393-8131
PHYTOPHAGA. Text in Italian; Summaries in English. 1955. a. exchange only. **Description:** Covers problems related to insects and mites in Mediterranean agriculture and how they are investigated and resolved through biology, ecology, relationships between parasites and natural enemies, biological control, integrated control, taxonomy of some important groups useful for biological control. Also addresses the side effects of pesticides.
Formerly (until 1983): Universita degli Studi di Palermo. Istituto di Entomologia Agraria. Bollettino (0078-8619)
Indexed: ASFA, AgrForAb, BioCN&I, ESPM, EntAb, ForAb, HortAb, MaizeAb, OrnHort, PHN&I, PollutAb, RPP, RevApplEntom, VITIS.
Published by: Universita degli Studi di Palermo, Istituto di Entomologia Agraria, Viale delle Scienze, Palermo, PA 90128, Italy. TEL 39-91-423130, FAX 39-91-423410, ragusa@unipa.it.

630 POL ISSN 1231-0778
PIECZARKI. Text in Polish. 1975. q. PLZ 40 domestic (effective 2005). **Document type:** *Magazine, Trade.*
Formerly (until 1976): Biuletyn Produkcji Pieczarek (1231-0905)
Indexed: AgrLib.
Published by: Hortpress Sp. z o.o., ul Kopernika 34, Warsaw, 00336, Poland. TEL 48-22-8261626, FAX 48-22-8264362, pieczarki@hortpress.com, info@hortpress.com, http://www.hortpress.com.

631 NLD
PLANT ANALYSIS PROCEDURES. Text in English. 1995. irreg., latest 2004. looseleaf. price varies. **Document type:** *Academic/Scholarly.* **Description:** Covers manual and automated digestion and determination methods, and procedures for agricultural chemists.
Formerly (until 2004): Plant Analysis Manual
Published by: Springer-Verlag Dordrecht (Subsidiary of: Springer Science+Business Media), Van Godewijckstraat 30, Dordrecht, 3311 GX, Netherlands. TEL 31-78-6576050, FAX 31-78-6576474, http://www.springeronline.com.

PLANT BREEDING/ZEITSCHRIFT FUER PFLANZENZUECHTUNG. see *BIOLOGY—Botany*

PLANT BREEDING ONLINE. see *BIOLOGY—Botany*

631 USA ISSN 0730-2207
SB123 CODEN: PBREE3
PLANT BREEDING REVIEWS. Text in English. 1983. a., latest vol.22, 2002. price varies. cum.index 1982-1986. **Document type:** *Monographic series, Academic/Scholarly.*
Indexed: AgBio, Agr, BIOSIS Prev, CIN, CPA, ChemAb, ChemTitl, FCA, FS&TA, HerbAb, HortAb, MaizeAb, OrnHort, PBA, PGegResA, PHN&I, PotatoAb, RPP, RiceAb, S&F, SeedAb, SoyAb, TriticAb.
—BLDSC (6514.140000), CASDDS, CISTI, IE, Infotrieve, ingenta.
Published by: (American Society for Horticultural Science), John Wiley & Sons, Inc., 111 River St, Hoboken, NJ 07030-5774. TEL 201-748-6000, 800-825-7550, FAX 201-748-5915, uscs-wis@wiley.com, http://www.wiley.com. Ed. Jules Janick. Circ: 1,200. **Co-sponsors:** National Council of Plant Breeders; Society of American Foresters; Crop Science Society of America.

631 GBR
PLANT BREEDING SERIES. Text in English. 1995. irreg. **Document type:** *Monographic series.*
—BLDSC (160000).
Published by: Chapman & Hall Ltd. (Subsidiary of: International Thomson Publishing Group), Journals Department, 2-6 Boundary Row, London, SE1 8HN, United Kingdom. TEL 44-20-78560066, FAX 44-20-7522-9623. Ed. P D S Caligari.

632 USA ISSN 0191-2917 CODEN: PLDIDE
➤ **PLANT DISEASE**; an international journal of applied plant pathology. Text in English. 1917. m. USD 102 combined subscription domestic to members print & online eds.; USD 118 combined subscription in Canada to members print & online eds.; USD 126 combined subscription elsewhere to members print & online eds. (effective 2005). adv. bk.rev. bibl.; charts; illus.; stat. index. back issues avail.; reprint service avail. from PQC. **Document type:** *Journal, Academic/Scholarly.* **Description:** Reports on plant diseases with news about new products and equipment.
Formerly (until vol.63, Dec. 1979): Plant Disease Reporter (0032-0811)
Related titles: Microform ed.: USD 550 domestic; USD 611 foreign (effective 2001) (from MIM, PMC, PQC); Online - full content ed.; Online - full text ed.: (from EBSCO Publishing, ProQuest Information & Learning).
Indexed: ABIPC, AEA, ASFA, AgBio, Agr, AgrForAb, B&AI, BIOSIS Prev, BibAg, BioCN&I, BioDAb, BioEngAb, BiolAb, BiolDig, CPA, CTFA, ChemAb, ChemTitl, CurCont, DBA, ESPM, EngInd, ExcerpMed, FCA, FPA, FS&TA, FaBeAb, ForAb, HGA, HerbAb, HortAb, I&DA, IABS, ISR, IUSGP, IndVet, MBA, MaizeAb, NemAb, OrnHort, PBA, PGegResA, PGrRegA, PHN&I, PlantSci, PotatoAb, PoultAb, RA&MP, RDA, RM&VM, RPP, RRTA, RefZh, RevApplEntom, RiceAb, S&F, S&MA, SCI, SIA, SPPI, SeedAb, SoyAb, TDB, TOSA, TriticAb, VITIS, VirolAbstr, WAE&RSA, WeedAb.
—BLDSC (6514.943000), CASDDS, CISTI, IDS, IE, Infotrieve, ingenta, Linda Hall. **CCC.**
Published by: American Phytopathological Society, 3340 Pilot Knob, St. Paul, MN 55121-2097. TEL 651-454-7250, 800-328-7560, FAX 651-454-0766, aps@scisoc.org, http://www.apsnet.org/pd. Ed. Alan Biggs. Adv. contact Rhonda Wilke. Circ: 3,700.

➤ **PLANT FOODS FOR HUMAN NUTRITION.** see *NUTRITION AND DIETETICS*

633 GBR ISSN 1479-2621
SB123.3 CODEN: PVSEEC
➤ **PLANT GENETIC RESOURCES**; characterisation and utilisation. Text in English. 1922. 3/yr. USD 370 in the Americas to institutions except Canada; GBP 210 elsewhere to institutions; USD 395 combined subscription in the Americas to institutions except Canada; print & online eds.; GBP 225 combined subscription elsewhere to institutions print & online eds. (effective 2006). adv. bk.rev. illus. index. **Document type:** *Journal, Academic/Scholarly.* **Description:** Provides an international venue for research papers and scholarly reviews on varieties, seeds, agro-ecology, and the improved deployment of plant genetic resources. Emphasizes practical applications, new methods, and progress in flora biotechnology.
Former titles (until 2001): Plant Varieties and Seeds (0952-3863); (until vol.17, no.3): National Institute of Agricultural Botany. Journal (0077-4790)
Related titles: Online - full text ed.: ISSN 1479-263X. USD 315 in the Americas to institutions except Canada; GBP 180 elsewhere to institutions (effective 2006) (from EBSCO Publishing, Gale Group, IngentaConnect, Ovid Technologies, Inc., Swets Information Services).
Indexed: AEA, ASCA, AgBio, Agr, BIOBASE, BIOSIS Prev, BiolAb, CPA, ChemAb, CurCont, FCA, FS&TA, ForAb, HerbAb, HortAb, IABS, MaizeAb, NutrAb, OrnHort, PBA, PGegResA, PGrRegA, PHN&I, PlantSci, PotatoAb, RA&MP, RASB, RPP, RefZh, RevApplEntom, RiceAb, S&F, SIA, SeedAb, SoyAb, TriticAb, WAE&RSA, WeedAb.
—BLDSC (6517.720000), CASDDS, CISTI, IE, ingenta, Linda Hall. **CCC.**
Published by: (N I A B), CABI Publishing (Subsidiary of: CAB International), CAB International, Wallingford, Oxfordshire OX10 8DE, United Kingdom. TEL 44-1491-832111, FAX 44-1491-833508, cabi@cabi.org, http://www.cabi-publishing.org/. Ed. Robert Koebner. adv.: B&W page GBP 190, B&W page USD 900; 170 x 225. Circ: 1,000.

631 TWN ISSN 0577-750X
CODEN: PLPBBH

➤ **PLANT PROTECTION BULLETIN/CHUNG HUA CHU WU PAO HU HSUEH HUI HUI KAN.** Text in Chinese, English; Summaries in Chinese, English. 1959. q. TWD 1,200 domestic; USD 70 foreign (effective 2003). adv. back issues avail. **Document type:** *Bulletin, Academic/Scholarly.* **Description:** Covers plant pathology, economic pests, weed science, pollutants, environment stresses and pesticide related researches.
Indexed: AgBio, AgrForAb, BIOSIS Prev, BioCN&I, BiolAb, CPA, FCA, FPA, FS&TA, ForAb, HerbAb, HortAb, I&DA, MaizeAb, NemAb, NutrAb, OrnHort, PBA, PGegResA, PHN&I, PotatoAb, RA&MP, RDA, RPP, RRTA, RevApplEntom, RiceAb, S&F, SIA, SeedAb, SoyAb, TDB, TriticAb, VITIS, WAE&RSA, WeedAb, ZooRec.
—BLDSC (6523.080000), CASDDS, CISTI, IE, ingenta.
Published by: Plant Protection Society of the Republic of China, 11 Kuang Ming Rd, Wufeng, Taichung, 413, Taiwan. TEL 886-4-23302101, FAX 886-4-23324050, ccho@wufeng.tari.gov.tw, jwliao@tactri.gov.tw, http://www.pps.org.tw. Ed., R&P ChyiChen Ho TEL 886-4-23302301 ext 631. Circ: 500.

631 AUS ISSN 0815-2195
CODEN: PPQUE8

➤ **PLANT PROTECTION QUARTERLY.** Text in English. 1981. q. AUD 55 domestic to individuals; AUD 65 in Asia & the Pacific to individuals; AUD 69 elsewhere to individuals; AUD 88 domestic to institutions; AUD 98 in Asia & the Pacific to institutions; AUD 102 elsewhere to institutions (effective 2003). adv. bk.rev.; software rev. cum.index: 1985-1995. back issues avail.; reprints avail. **Document type:** *Journal, Academic/Scholarly.* **Description:** Covers all aspects of the protection of economic plants and desirable vegetations from weeds, pests and diseases.
Formerly (until 1985): Australian Weeds (0725-0150)
Indexed: AEA, AgBio, Agr, AgrForAb, BIOSIS Prev, BioCN&I, BiolAb, CIN, CPA, ChemAb, ChemTitl, DBA, DSA, FCA, ForAb, HerbAb, HortAb, I&DA, IndVet, MaizeAb, NutrAb, OrnHort, PBA, PGegResA, PGrRegA, PHN&I, PN&I, PotatoAb, PoultAb, RA&MP, RPP, RRTA, RevApplEntom, RiceAb, S&F, SIA, SeedAb, SoyAb, TriticAb, VITIS, WAE&RSA, WeedAb, ZooRec.
—BLDSC (6523.280000), CASDDS, CISTI, IE, ingenta.
Address: PO Box 42, Meredith, VIC 3333, Australia. TEL 61-3-52861533, FAX 61-3-52861533, richardson@weedinfo.com.au, http://www.weedinfo.com.au/ppq_frame.htm. Ed., R&P R G Richardson. Adv. contact F J Richardson. Circ: 500 (paid).

632.9 ZWE

PLANT PROTECTION RESEARCH INSTITUTE. ANNUAL REPORT. Text in English. a. free. back issues avail.
Indexed: BiolAb.
Published by: (Zimbabwe. Information Services), Ministry of Lands Agriculture and Rural Resettlement, Research and Specialist Services, Causeway, PO Box 8108, Harare, Zimbabwe. Circ: 250.

630 CZE ISSN 1212-2580
CODEN: SUSRD8

➤ **PLANT PROTECTION SCIENCE.** Text and summaries in English; Summaries in Czech, Slovak. 1965. q. USD 85 (effective 2005). bk.rev. back issues avail. **Document type:** *Journal, Academic/Scholarly.* **Description:** Contains scientific papers and reviews dealing with diseases and pests of plants, weeds and plant protection.
Former titles (until 1997): Ochrana Rostlin (0862-8645); (until 1989): U V T I Z Sbornik - Ochrana Rostlin (0036-5394); (until 1976): Sbornik U V T I - Ochrana Rostlin (0590-5141)
Indexed: AEA, AgBio, AgrForAb, ApicAb, BIOSIS Prev, BibAg, BioCN&I, BiolAb, CPA, FCA, FPA, FS&TA, ForAb, HerbAb, HortAb, MaizeAb, NemAb, OrnHort, PBA, PGegResA, PGrRegA, PHN&I, PotatoAb, RA&MP, RM&VM, RPP, RefZh, RevApplEntom, RiceAb, S&F, SIA, SeedAb, SoyAb, TriticAb, VITIS, WAE&RSA, WeedAb, ZooRec.
—BLDSC (6523.301000), CISTI, IE, ingenta.
Published by: Ceska Akademie Zemedelskych Ved, Ustav Zemedelskych a Potravinarskych Informaci/Czech Academy of Agricultural Sciences, Institute of Agricultural and Food Information, Slezska 7, Prague 2, 120 56, Czech Republic. TEL 420-2-227010203, FAX 420-2-227010116, braun@uzpi.cz, http://www.cazv.cz. Ed. Mrs. Marcela Braunova. R&P Mr. Jan Rydlo. Circ: 350. **Co-sponsor:** Ceska Akademie Zemedelskych Ved/Czech Academy of Agricultural Sciences.

➤ **PLANT RESOURCES OF SOUTH-EAST ASIA.** see *BIOLOGY—Botany*

631 GBR ISSN 0048-4342

PLANT VARIETIES AND SEEDS GAZETTE. Text in English. 1965. m. GBP 35 domestic; GBP 43.50 foreign. stat. back issues avail. **Document type:** *Government.*
—CISTI. **CCC.**
Published by: (Great Britain. Ministry of Agriculture, Fisheries and Food), Sovereign Press, c/o Alan Justice, The Stationery Office, 11 Steedman St, London, SE17 3AF, United Kingdom. TEL 44-20-7740-4035, FAX 44-20-7740-4111. Circ: 330.

632.9 CHE ISSN 0257-9030

PLANT VARIETY PROTECTION; gazette and newsletter of UPOV. Text in English. 1975. irreg. (3-4/yr.). free. bk.rev. charts. index. **Document type:** *Newsletter, Trade.* **Description:** Events on plant variety protection legislation and events of general interest in the UPOV member states.
Published by: International Union for the Protection of New Varieties of Plants (UPOV), 34 Chemin des Colombettes, Geneva 20, 1211, Switzerland. TEL 41-22-338-9111, FAX 41-22-733-0336, upov.mail@wipo.int, http://www.upov.int. Circ: 1,500.

632.9 DNK ISSN 0108-4887

PLANTEBESKYTTELSEMIDLER. Text in Danish. 1977. a.
Published by: Ministeriet for Foedevarer, Landbrug og Fiskeri, Danmarks Jordbrugsforskning/Ministry of Food, Agriculture and Fisheries. Danish Institute of Agricultural Sciences, PO Box 50, Tjele, 8830, Denmark. TEL 45-8999-1900, FAX 45-8999-1919.

631.6 RUS ISSN 0032-180X
S590 CODEN: PVDEAZ

POCHVOVEDENIE. Text in Russian; Abstracts and contents page in English. 1899. m. RUR 930 for 6 mos. domestic (effective 2004). bk.rev. bibl.; charts; illus.; stat. index. **Document type:** *Journal, Academic/Scholarly.* **Description:** Covers all aspects of the soil sciences, including mineralogy and physical properties of soils, as well as soil melioration, irrigation and drainage, forest and range soils, soil pollution and management. Also includes selected relevant articles from periodicals in related fields such as agricultural engineering.
Related titles: Microfiche ed.: (from IDC); ♦ English Translation: Eurasian Soil Science. ISSN 1064-2293.
Indexed: AEA, AgrForAb, BIOSIS Prev, BiolAb, CIN, CPA, ChemAb, ChemTitl, DSA, EngInd, ExcerpMed, FCA, ForAb, HerbAb, HortAb, I&DA, MaizeAb, NemAb, NutrAb, PBA, PGegResA, PN&I, PotatoAb, PoultAb, RDA, RPP, RRTA, RefZh, RevApplEntom, RiceAb, S&F, SIA, SeedAb, SoyAb, TriticAb, VITIS, WAE&RSA, WeedAb, ZooRec.
—BLDSC (0131.000000), CASDDS, CISTI, East View, Ei, KNAW, Linda Hall. **CCC.**
Published by: (Rossiiskaya Akademiya Nauk/Russian Academy of Sciences), Izdatel'stvo Nauka, Profsoyuznaya ul 90, Moscow, 117864, Russian Federation. TEL 7-095-3347151, FAX 7-095-4202220, secret@naukaran.ru, http://www.maik.rssi.ru/cgi-bin/list.pl?page=pochved, http://www.naukaran.ru. Circ: 4,635.

631.4 BGR ISSN 0861-9425
CODEN: PAEKEH

POCHVOZNANIE, AGROKHIMIA I EKOLOGIA. Text in Bulgarian; Summaries in Bulgarian, English, Russian. 1966. bi-m. BGL 1.40 per issue; USD 110 foreign (effective 2002). reprint service avail. from IRC. **Document type:** *Journal.* **Description:** Covers soil science, agrochemistry and ecology.
Formerly (until 1992): Pochvoznanie i Agrokhimiia (0554-341X)
Indexed: AEA, AgBio, BioCN&I, BiolAb, CPA, ChemAb, FCA, FPA, FS&TA, ForAb, HerbAb, HortAb, I&DA, INIS AtomInd, MaizeAb, OrnHort, PBA, PGrRegA, PHN&I, PotatoAb, RA&MP, RPP, RefZh, RiceAb, S&F, SIA, SeedAb, SoyAb, TOSA, TriticAb, VITIS, WAE&RSA, WeedAb.
—CASDDS, CISTI, Linda Hall.
Published by: National Centre for Agrarian Sciences, 125 Tsarigradsko Shosse Blvd., Sofia, 1113, Bulgaria. TEL 359-2-709127. Ed. Petko Ivanov. Circ: 1,228. **Dist. by:** Hemus, 6 Rouski Blvd., Sofia 1000, Bulgaria; **Dist. by:** Sofia Books, ul Silivria 16, Sofia 1404, Bulgaria. TEL 359-2-9586257, info@sofiabooks-bg.com, http://www.sofiabooks-bg.com.

631.4 POL ISSN 0079-2985
S590 CODEN: PJSOBN

POLISH JOURNAL OF SOIL SCIENCE. Text in English; Summaries in Polish, Russian. 1968. s-a. PLZ 40 foreign (effective 2003). bibl.; charts; illus. **Document type:** *Journal, Academic/Scholarly.* **Description:** Theoretical and practical works on soil physics, chemistry and fertilizing.
Indexed: AEA, ASFA, AgrAg, AgrForAb, AgrLib, BiolAb, CIN, CPA, ChemAb, ChemTitl, ESPM, ExcerpMed, FCA, FPA, ForAb, GEOBASE, HerbAb, HortAb, I&DA, MBA, MaizeAb, OrnHort, PGegResA, PGrRegA, PN&I, PollutAb, PotatoAb, RPP, RefZh, S&F, SWRA, TriticAb, WeedAb.
—CASDDS, CISTI, Linda Hall.
Published by: (Polska Akademia Nauk, Komitet Gleboznawstwa i Chemii Rolnej/Polish Academy of Sciences, Committee of Soil Science and Agricultural Chemistry), Uniwersytet Marii Curie-Sklodowskiej, Instytut Nauk o Ziemi, ul Akademicka 19, Lublin, 20033, Poland. TEL 48-81-5375026, geograf@biotop.umcs.lublin.pl, http://biotop.umcs.lublin.pl/~binoz/innaukoz.htm.

633.491 FRA ISSN 0032-4159

LA POMME DE TERRE FRANCAISE. Text in French. 1938. bi-m. adv. bk.rev. charts; illus.; stat. index.
Indexed: BiolAb, FCA, FS&TA, HerbAb, PBA, PotatoAb, RRTA, S&F, WAE&RSA.
—CISTI.
Published by: Editions du Billon, 5 Cite Riverin, Paris, 75010, France. TEL 33-1-42408990, FAX 33-1-42-408991, edb@wanadoo.fr. Ed. Dorothee Bourget. Pub. Sylvain Cousin. Adv. contact Regie Helium. Circ: 6,800.

POMONA. see *GARDENING AND HORTICULTURE*

630 POL ISSN 1508-6143

PORADNIK PLANTATORA BURAKA CUKROWEGO. Text in Polish. 1998. q. PLZ 24 domestic (effective 2005). **Document type:** *Magazine, Trade.*
Published by: Hortpress Sp. z o.o., ul Kopernika 34, Warsaw, 00336, Poland. TEL 48-22-8261626, FAX 48-22-8264362, ppbc@hortpress.com, info@hortpress.com, http://www.hortpress.com.

POSTHARVEST NEWS AND INFORMATION. see *AGRICULTURE—Abstracting, Bibliographies, Statistics*

630 SWE ISSN 1651-3061

POTATIS & GROENSAKER. Text in Swedish. 1983. q. SEK 585 domestic; SEK 665 in Europe; SEK 705 elsewhere (effective 2004). adv. **Document type:** *Journal, Trade.*
Former titles (until 2002): Potatisodlaren (1401-9450); (until 1987): S P O R Potatispedlaren (0281-0646)
Published by: Groena Naeringens Riksorganisation, Klara Oestra Kyrkogatan 12, Stockholm, 10533, Sweden. TEL 46-8-7875300, FAX 46-8-7875310, info@gro.se, http://www.gro.se. Ed. Susanne Baerveldt TEL 46-35-211634. Circ: 2,100.

658.8 634 USA ISSN 0886-4780

POTATO COUNTRY. Text in English. 1973. 9/yr. USD 15 domestic; USD 30 in Canada & Mexico; USD 45 elsewhere (effective 2005). adv. back issues avail. **Document type:** *Magazine, Trade.* **Description:** Covers potato research, production, and marketing.
Formerly (until 1985): Ag-Marketer (0193-7901)
Published by: Columbia Publishing and Design, 413B N 20th Ave, Yakima, WA 98902. TEL 509-248-2452, 800-900-2452, FAX 509-248-4056, dbret@columbiapublication.com, pseditorial@freshcut.com, http://www.potatocountry.com, http://www.freshcut.com/columbiapub/home.htm. Ed. D Brent. Pub., R&P, Adv. contact Mike J Stoker. B&W page USD 1,390, color page USD 2,090. Circ: 6,883 (paid and controlled).

635 USA ISSN 0146-499X

POTATO GROWER OF IDAHO. Text in English. 1972. m. USD 15.95 (effective 2005). adv. illus. back issues avail.; reprints avail. **Document type:** *Magazine, Trade.*
—CISTI.
Published by: Harris Publishing, Inc. (Idaho Falls), 360 B St, Idaho Falls, ID 83402-3547. TEL 208-524-7000, FAX 208-522-5241, gary@potatogrower.com, bobby@harrispublishing.com, http://www.potatogrower.com, http://www.harrispublishing.com. Ed. David Fairbourn. Pub. Jason Harris. Adv. contact Richard Holley. B&W page USD 2,797, color page USD 4,279. Circ: 12,000 (controlled); 500 (paid); 1,000 (free).

631 CAN

POTATO NEWSLETTER. Text in English, French. 1979. bi-m. looseleaf. free. back issues avail. **Document type:** *Newsletter, Government.* **Description:** Covers cost of production, market reports, producer's budgeting, extension specialists.
Related titles: Diskette ed.; Online - full text ed.
Published by: Department of Agriculture, Plant Industry Branch, P O Box 6000, Fredericton, NB E3B 5H1, Canada. TEL 506-457-7244, FAX 506-457-7267, mmacdonald@gov.nb.ca. Ed. Robert P Hinds. Circ: 1,000 (controlled).

633.4 NLD ISSN 0014-3065
CODEN: PORHBW

➤ **POTATO RESEARCH.** Text in English, French, German. 1958. q. EUR 125 (effective 2002). bk.rev. included in 4th issue. 100 p./no. 1 cols./p.; back issues avail. **Document type:** *Journal, Academic/Scholarly.*
Formerly: European Potato Journal
Indexed: AEA, ASCA, AgBio, Agr, BIOBASE, BioCN&I, BioDAb, BiolAb, CIN, CPA, ChemAb, ChemTitl, CurCont, DBA, ExcerpMed, FCA, FS&TA, HerbAb, HortAb, I&DA, IABS, ISR, NemAb, PBA, PGegResA, PGrRegA, PHN&I, PlantSci, PotatoAb, RDA, RPP, RevApplEntom, S&F, SCI, SIA, SeedAb, TriticAb, WAE&RSA, WeedAb.
—BLDSC (6565.450000), CASDDS, CISTI, IDS, IE, Infotrieve, ingenta.
Published by: European Association for Potato Research, Postbus 20, Wageningen, 6700 AA, Netherlands. TEL 31-317-483041, FAX 31-317-484575, http://www.agro.wau.nl/eapr. Ed. P C Struik. Circ: 1,000.

➤ **POTATO STATISTICS IN GREAT BRITAIN.** see *AGRICULTURE—Abstracting, Bibliographies, Statistics*

635.21 USA ISSN 1057-7882

POTATO STOCKS. Text in English. 1984. m. **Document type:** *Trade.* **Description:** Contains the grower, processor, and the local dealer potato storage stocks in fall producing areas.
Published by: (United States. Agricultural Statistics Board, United States. Crop Reporting Board), U.S. Government Printing Office, 732 N Capitol St NW, Washington, DC 20401. TEL 202-512-1530, 888-293-6498, FAX 202-512-1262, gpoaccess@gpo.gov, http://jan.mannlib.cornell.edu/reports/nassr/field/ppo-bb/, http://www.gpo.gov. **Subscr. to:** U.S. Government Printing Office, Superintendent of Documents.

631 GBR
POTATOES VARIETY HANDBOOK. Text in English. a. GBP 15 per vol. (effective 2003). charts. **Document type:** *Bulletin, Trade.* **Description:** Provides detailed information on cultivating potato crops.
Indexed: FCA.
Published by: N I A B, Huntingdon Rd, Cambridge, CB3 0LE, United Kingdom. TEL 44-1223-276381, FAX 44-1223-342328, TELEX 817455-NIAB-G, info@niab.com, paul.nelson@niab.com, http://www.niab.com. Ed. Paul Nelson TEL 44-1223-342225.

632 DEU ISSN 0032-6801
DER PRAKTISCHE SCHAEDLINGSBEKAEMPFER. Text in German. 1949. m. adv. bk.rev. charts; illus.; stat. index. **Document type:** *Trade.*
Indexed: DBA, RefZh, ZooRec.
—BLDSC (6601.140000), IE, Infotrieve, ingenta.
Published by: (Deutscher Schaedlingsbekaempfer-Verband), Verlag Eduard F. Beckmann KG, Postfach 1120, Lehrte, 31251, Germany. TEL 49-5132-8591-0, FAX 49-5132-859125, dps-info@beckmann-verlag.de. Ed. Heiner Behre. Circ: 1,700.

PRIMEUR. see *AGRICULTURE—Agricultural Economics*

631 RUS ISSN 0207-2173
PRIUSADEBNOE KHOZYAISTVO. Text in Russian. 1981. m. USD 120 in North America.
—BLDSC (0133.100200), East View.
Published by: Sel'skaya Nov', Sadovaya-Spasskaya 20, GSP-6, Moscow, 107807, Russian Federation. TEL 7-095-9301039, FAX 7-095-9754976. Ed. A I Rebel'skii. Circ: 25,000. **Dist. by:** M K - Periodica, ul Gilyarovskogo 39, Moscow 129110, Russian Federation. TEL 7-095-2845008, FAX 7-095-2813798, info@periodicals.ru, http://www.mkniga.ru; **US dist. addr.:** East View Information Services, 3020 Harbor Ln. N., Minneapolis, MN 55447. TEL 612-550-0961.

338.1 CAN ISSN 0830-1654
PRO-FARM. Text in English. 1974. 4/yr. CND 150 to institutions; CND 75 to libraries; CND 25 to students (effective 2003). adv. bk.rev. illus.; tr.lit. **Description:** Informs members of policy developments in the western Canadian grain industry.
Former titles (until 1985): Palliser Wheatgrower; Palliser Wheat Growers Association. Newsletter (0704-1349)
—CISTI.
Published by: Western Canadian Wheat Growers Association, 2216 Lorne St, Regina, SK S4P 2M7, Canada. TEL 306-586-5866, FAX 306-586-2707, wcwga@wcwga.ca, http://www.wcwga.ca/PRO_Farm/index.shtml. Ed. Alanna Koch. R&P, Adv. contact Chris Dodd. page CND 1,850. Circ: 7,000.

PRODUCTIVE FARMING. see *AGRICULTURE—Agricultural Economics*

635 USA
PRODUCTORES DE HORTALIZAS. Text in Spanish. 1992. m. USD 70 (effective 2000). adv. **Document type:** *Trade.* **Description:** Emphasizes proven production methods that can be adopted by Mexican commercial vegetable growers.. The focus is on technical advances covering all aspects of vegetable production.
Published by: Meister Media Worldwide, 37733 Euclid Ave, Willoughby, OH 44094-5992. TEL 440-942-2000, FAX 440-975-3447, pdh_circ@meisternet.com. Ed. Jim Moore. adv.: B&W page USD 1,350, color page USD 1,750; trim 10.75 x 8. Circ: 10,000.

635 BEL ISSN 0777-9844
PROEFTUIN NIEUWS. Text in Dutch. 1990. fortn. EUR 75 domestic; EUR 150 foreign (effective 2003). adv. charts; illus.; mkt.; stat.; tr.lit. 40 p./no. 3 cols./p.; back issues avail. **Document type:** *Bulletin.* **Description:** Presents technical, scientific, marketing and price information for greenhouses, nurseries, and open air vegetable growers.
Indexed: AEA, BioCN&I, HortAb, I&DA, OrnHort, PBA, PHN&I, RPP, RevApplEntom, S&F, SeedAb, WAE&RSA.
—BLDSC (6857.006000).
Published by: V.Z.W. Proeftuinnieuws, Binnenweg 6, St-Katelijne-Waver, 2860, Belgium. TEL 32-15-552771, FAX 32-15-553061, ptn@pstdrc.be. Ed. L. Peeters. R&P L Peeters. Adv. contact P. De Wit TEL 32-16-244747. Circ: 3,500 (controlled).

631 GBR ISSN 1467-6702
PROFESSIONAL AGRONOMY; the magazine for crop professionals. Text in English. 1994. bi-m. GBP 30. adv. charts; illus.; pat.; stat.; tr.lit. back issues avail. **Document type:** *Trade.* **Description:** Covers issues that concern crop protection professionals; news and reviews of core research and what is coming through the pipeline.
Formerly (until 1998): The Advisor (1462-172X)
Published by: Carter Spencer Publishing Ltd., The Old Coach House, Southern Rd, Thame, Oxon OX9 2ED, United Kingdom. TEL 44-1844-260960, FAX 44-1844-260267. Ed. Nick Carter. Pub., R&P, Adv. contact David Spencer. page GBP 1,550; trim 210 x 297. Circ: 3,500 (controlled).

632.9 AUS
PROFESSIONAL PEST MANAGER. Text in English. 1996. bi-m. AUD 37.40 (effective 2000). **Document type:** *Trade.*
Published by: Richard Milne Pty. Ltd., PO Box 163, Drummoyne, NSW 1470, Australia. TEL 61-2-97139822, FAX 61-2-97139266, milnepublications@attglobal.net. Circ: 3,250 (controlled).

634.8 FRA ISSN 0369-8173
PROGRES AGRICOLE ET VITICOLE. Text in French. 1884. bi-m. adv. bk.rev.
Indexed: AEA, AgBio, BioCN&I, CPA, HortAb, I&DA, NemAb, NutrAb, OrnHort, PBA, PGegResA, PGrRegA, PHN&I, RDA, RM&VM, RPP, RevApplEntom, S&F, SIA, VITIS, WAE&RSA, WeedAb.
—Linda Hall. **CCC.**
Published by: Societe du Progres Agricole et Viticole, 1 bis rue de Verdun, Montpellier, 34000, France. Circ: 18,000.

PROGRESS IN PESTICIDE BIOCHEMISTRY AND TOXICOLOGY. see *ENGINEERING—Chemical Engineering*

630.24 668.6 MEX
PRONTUARIO AGROQUIMICO. Text in Spanish. 1984. a.
Published by: Ediciones P L M S.A. de C.V., San Bernardino 17, Col del Valle, Mexico City, DF 03100, Mexico. TEL 52-5-6841311. Ed. Dr. Emilio Rosenstein. Circ: 40,000.

630 POL ISSN 0079-7154
PRZEGLAD NAUKOWEJ LITERATURY ROLNICZEJ I LESNEJ; gleboznawstwo, chemia rolna, ogolna uprawa roli i roslin i siedliska lesne. Text in Polish. 1955. a. price varies.
Published by: Polskie Towarzystwo Gleboznawcze, Ul Wisniowa 61, Warsaw, 02520, Poland. Ed. W Trzcinski. Circ: 1,210. **Dist. by:** Ars Polona, Krakowskie Przedmiescie 7, Warsaw, Poland.

630 CAN ISSN 1701-9125
PULSEPOINT. Text in English. 1985. q. **Document type:** *Magazine, Trade.*
Former titles (until 2001): Saskatchewan Pulse Grower (1206-9582); (until 1997): Pulse Newsletter (1201-3862); (until 1990): Pulse Crop Newsletter (1205-2655)
—CISTI.
Published by: (Saskatchewan Pulse Growers), Sunrise Publishing Ltd., 2213 B Hanselman Ct, Saskatoon, SK S7L 6A8, Canada. TEL 306-244-5668, 800-247-5743, FAX 306-244-5679, news@sunrisepublish.com, http://www.sunrisepublish.com.

631 IDN ISSN 0216-9967
PUSAT PENELITIAN PERKEBUNAN GULA INDONESIA. ANNUAL REPORT/INDONESIAN SUGAR RESEARCH CENTER. ANNUAL REPORT. Text in Indonesian. a. USD 15.
Published by: Pusat Penelitian Perkebunan Gula Indonesia, Jl Pahlawan 25, Pasuruan, 67126, Indonesia. TEL 0343-21086, FAX 0343-21178. Ed. H Untung Murdiyatmo. Circ: 650.

631 IDN ISSN 0125-9997
PUSAT PENELITIAN PERKEBUNAN GULA INDONESIA. BULLETIN/INDONESIAN SUGAR RESEARCH CENTER. BULLETIN. Text in Indonesian; Summaries in English. irreg. USD 6 per issue.
Indexed: AgBio, BioCN&I, CPA, FCA, HortAb, PBA, RPP, RevApplEntom, S&F.
Published by: Pusat Penelitian Perkebunan Gula Indonesia, Jl Pahlawan 25, Pasuruan, 67126, Indonesia. TEL 0343-21086, FAX 0343-21178. Circ: 650.

633.1 AUS ISSN 1322-9397
QUALITY OF AUSTRALIAN CANOLA. Text in English. 1993. a., latest vol.6, 1998. charts; illus.; maps; stat. back issues avail. **Document type:** *Bulletin.* **Description:** Covers seed quality in canola trials grown in Australia each year.
Indexed: FCA, PBA.
Published by: (Canola Association of Australia), Agricultural Research Institute, Private Mail Bag, Wagga Wagga, NSW 2650, Australia. TEL 61-2-69381818, FAX 61-2-69381809, mailerr@agric.nsw.gov.au. Ed. R J Mailer. Circ: 500.

634 AUS ISSN 0312-8989
QUANDONG. Text in English. q. AUD 54 combined subscription includes WANATCA Yearbook (effective 2001). adv. bk.rev.
—BLDSC (7168.186000).
Published by: West Australian Nut & Tree Crop Association (Inc.), PO Box 565, Subiaco, W.A. 6008, Australia. TEL 61-8-93881965, FAX 61-8-93881852, wanatca@AOI.com.au, http://www.aoi.com.au/wanatca/. Circ: 600.

632.9 NCL ISSN 1017-6268
QUARANTINE ADVISORY LEAFLET. Text in French. 1984. irreg., latest vol.21, 1988. **Document type:** *Monographic series.*
Published by: Secretariat of the Pacific Community, PO Box D5, Noumea, Cedex 98848, New Caledonia. TEL 687-262000, FAX 687-263817, spc@spc.int, http://www.spc.int.

631 DEU ISSN 0724-4606
RAPS; Fachzeitschrift fuer Oel- und Eiweisspflanzen. Text in German. 1983. 4/yr. EUR 5.80 newsstand/cover (effective 2005). adv. back issues avail. **Document type:** *Magazine, Trade.*
Indexed: RefZh.
—IE, Infotrieve.
Published by: Verlag Th. Mann, Nordring 10, Gelsenkirchen, 45894, Germany. TEL 49-209-93040, FAX 49-209-9304185, info@th-mann.de, http://www.th-mann.de. Eds. Guenter Weiss, Dr. Heinz Peter Puetz. Adv. contact Richard Heineke. B&W page EUR 2,160, color page EUR 3,690; trim 186 x 270. Circ: 18,597 (paid and controlled).

634.9 NLD ISSN 0924-929X
RASSENLIJST VOOR BOMEN. Text in Dutch. 1990. a. **Description:** Recommendations for improved strains and varieties of trees for commercial production.
Published by: (Netherlands. Centrum voor Plantenveredelings- en Reproduktieonderzoek), Roto Smeets de Boer n.v., Postbus 507, Hilversum, 1200 AM, Netherlands. TEL 31-35-258611, FAX 31-35-238978.

631 NLD ISSN 0169-6750
RASSENLIJST VOOR FRUITGEWASSEN. Text in Dutch. 1933. quinquennial. **Description:** Descriptive list of recommended strains and varieties of fruit for commercial cultivation.
Published by: (Netherlands. Centrum voor Plantenveredelings- en Reproduktieonderzoek), Roto Smeets de Boer n.v., Postbus 507, Hilversum, 1200 AM, Netherlands. TEL 31-35-258611, FAX 31-35-238978.

630 NLD ISSN 0169-6319
RASSENLIJST VOOR GROENTEGEWASSEN: GLASGROENTEN. Text in Dutch. 1983 (vol.32). a.
Published by: (Netherlands. Centrum voor Plantenveredelings- en Reproduktieonderzoek), Roto Smeets de Boer n.v., Postbus 507, Hilversum, 1200 AM, Netherlands. TEL 31-35-258611, FAX 31-35-238978.

631 NLD ISSN 0169-636X
RASSENLIJST VOOR GROENTEGEWASSEN: VOLLEGRONDSGROENTEN. Text in Dutch. 1943. a., latest vol.37, 1992. **Description:** Descriptive list of recommended varieties of vegetables.
Published by: (Netherlands. Centrum voor Plantenveredelings- en Reproduktieonderzoek), Roto Smeets de Boer n.v., Postbus 507, Hilversum, 1200 AM, Netherlands. TEL 31-35-258611, FAX 31-35-238978.

631 NLD
RASSENLIJST VOOR LANDBOUWGEWASSEN. Short title: Landbouwgewassen. Text in Dutch. 1924. a. **Document type:** *Magazine, Consumer.* **Description:** Descriptive list of recommended strains and varieties of field crops.
Former titles: Beschrijvende Rassenlijst voor Landbouwgewassen (0168-7484); (until 1941): Beschrijvende Rassenlijst
Published by: (Netherlands. Centrum voor Plantenveredelings- en Reproduktieonderzoek), Roto Smeets de Boer n.v., Postbus 507, Hilversum, 1200 AM, Netherlands. TEL 31-35-258611, FAX 31-35-238978. Ed. J E Parleviet.

633 BGR ISSN 0568-465X
RASTENIEVUDNI NAUKI. Text in Bulgarian; Summaries in English, Russian. 1964. 10/yr. USD 130 foreign (effective 2002). **Document type:** *Journal, Trade.* **Description:** Covers questions of selection, seed-production, new sorts, and new technologies in plant-growing.
Indexed: FCA.
—BLDSC (0140.266000), CISTI, IE, ingenta, Linda Hall.
Published by: National Center for Agrarian Sciences, Tsarigradsko shosse Blvd. 125, bl. 1, entry 1, room 215, Sofia, 1113, Bulgaria. TEL 359-2-709127. **Dist. by:** Sofia Books, ul Silivria 16, Sofia 1404, Bulgaria. TEL 359-2-9586257, info@sofiabooks-bg.com, http://www.sofiabooks-bg.com.

REBE UND WEIN. see *BEVERAGES*

RECOMMENDATIONS ON THE SAFE USE OF PESTICIDES IN SHIPS. see *ENVIRONMENTAL STUDIES—Toxicology And Environmental Safety*

REFERATIVNYI ZHURNAL. POCHVOVEDENIE I AGROKHIMIYA. see *AGRICULTURE—Abstracting, Bibliographies, Statistics*

628.4458 IDN
REGIONAL WORKSHOP ON WASTE HEAT RECOVERY TECHNOLOGY IN COCONUT PROCESSING. Text in English. a.?. USD 10. **Document type:** *Proceedings.* **Description:** Contains reports and technical papers that deal with the basis of the technology, financial and economic appraisal of application of waste heat technology in coconut processing and the transfer strategy for the process.
Published by: Asian and Pacific Coconut Community, 3rd Fl., Lina Bldg., Jl H R Rasuna Said Kav B 7, Kuningan, Jakarta, 12920, Indonesia. TEL 62-21-510-073, FAX 62-21-520-5160.

631.8 IND ISSN 0257-3245
RESEARCH AND DEVELOPMENT REPORTER. Text in English. 1984. s-a. INR 10. **Document type:** *Academic/Scholarly.*
Indexed: HortAb, PotatoAb, RDA, RPP, SIA, WAE&RSA, WeedAb.
—BLDSC (7714.796150), Linda Hall.
Published by: Rajasthan Fertilizers Trading Corporation, 18-9 Trikuta Nagar, Jammu, Jammu & Kashmir 180 004, India. TEL 531124. Ed. R S Sharma. Circ: 500.

▼ new title ➤ refereed ✶ unverified ♦ full entry avail.

A

631 NLD
CODEN: IBJAA6
RESEARCH INSTITUTE FOR AGROBIOLOGY AND SOIL FERTILITY. ANNUAL REPORT. Variant title: Jaarverslag A B - D L O. Text and summaries in Dutch. 1916. a. free. back issues avail. **Document type:** *Corporate.* **Description:** Covers research done in the various departments of the Institute, as well as information on organization, events, activities, tests and more.
Formerly: Instituut voor Bodemvruchtbaarheid. Jaarverslag (0434-6785)
Indexed: AEA, BioCN&I, BiolAb, CPA, DSA, FCA, HerbAb, HortAb, I&DA, RPP, RevApplEntom, S&F, WAE&RSA, WeedAb.
Published by: Research Institute for Agrobiology and Soil Fertility, Postbus 14, Wageningen, 6700 AA, Netherlands. TEL 31-317-475700, FAX 31-317-423110, postmaster@ab.dlo.nl. Ed. H Terburg. Circ: 1,500 (controlled).

630 IND ISSN 0972-3226
➤ **RESEARCH ON CROPS**; an international journal. Text in English. 2000. 3/yr. INR 1,000 domestic; USD 300 foreign (effective 2003). adv. bk.rev. abstr. 150 p./no. 2 cols./p.; back issues avail. **Document type:** *Journal, Academic/Scholarly.* **Description:** Publishes articles describing basic and applied aspects of research on crops including horticultural, vegetable, medicinal, spices, cereals, flower etc crops.
Indexed: AEA, AgBio, AgrForAb, BioCN&I, CPA, DSA, FCA, ForAb, HerbAb, HortAb, I&DA, MaizeAb, NemAb, NutrAb, OrnHort, PBA, PGegResA, PGrRegA, PHN&I, PotatoAb, PoultAb, RA&MP, RDA, RM&VM, RPP, RiceAb, S&F, SIA, SeedAb, SoyAb, TriticAb, WAE&RSA, WeedAb.
—BLDSC (7737.380000), IE.
Published by: Gaurav Society of Agricultural Research Information Centre, c/o Systematic Printers, Near Video Market, Udayapuria St, Hisar, Haryana 125 001, India. TEL 91-1662-230467, aricmd@hotmail.com, mdgsaric@yahoo.com, http://www.cropresearch.org. Ed. Dr. Ved Pal Singh. Pub., Adv. contact Mrs. Poonam S Chaudhary TEL 91-1662-244049. page INR 2,000, page USD 200; 6 x 8. Circ: 1,100 (paid and controlled).

630 USA ISSN 1076-3333
S671 CODEN: RSOUE7
RESOURCE (NILES); engineering & technology for a sustainable world. Text in English. 1994. m. (10/yr.). USD 75 domestic to non-members; USD 100 foreign to non-members; USD 24 domestic to members; USD 44 foreign to members (effective 2005). adv. bk.rev. bibl.; charts; illus.; tr.lit. index. reprints avail. **Document type:** *Magazine, Trade.* **Description:** Focuses on trends in technology. Broad interest articles and continuing departments spotlight engineering progress in agriculture, food, biotechnology, aquaculture, forestry, machinery, and soil and water.
Formed by the merger of (1920-1994): Agricultural Engineering (0002-1458); (1983-1994): Within A S A E (0741-0387)
Related titles: Microfilm ed.: (from PQC); Online - full text ed.: (from Florida Center for Library Automation, Gale Group, O C L C Online Computer Library Center, Inc., ProQuest Information & Learning).
Indexed: AEA, AgBio, AnBrAb, B&AI, BioDAb, BiolAb, CADCAM, CPA, ChemAb, DSA, EPB, ESPM, EngInd, EnvAb, EnvEAb, ExcerpMed, F&GI, FCA, FPA, ForAb, GeotechAb, HerbAb, HortAb, I&DA, Inspec, MaizeAb, NutrAb, PHN&I, PN&I, PollutAb, PoultAb, RASB, RPP, RefZh, S&F, SSCI, SoyAb, TriticAb, WAE&RSA, WRCInf, WeedAb, WildRev.
—CIS, CISTI, Ei, IDS, IE, Infotrieve, Linda Hall. **CCC.**
Published by: American Society of Agricultural Engineers, 2950 Niles Rd, St. Joseph, MI 49085-9659. TEL 269-429-0300, FAX 269-429-3852, hq@asae.org, http://www.asae.org. Ed. Suzanne Howard. Pub. Donna M. Hull. R&P Sandy Rutter. Adv. contact Pam Bakken. Circ: 10,000 (paid).

631 FRA ISSN 0996-858X
REUSSIR CEREALES - GRANDES CULTURES. Text in French. 1987. 11/yr. adv. **Document type:** *Newspaper.* **Description:** Technical and economical informations about crop production.
Published by: Editions Reussir, 19 quai de Juillet, CP 700, Caen, Cedex 9 1414, France. TEL 33-2-31357700, FAX 33-2-31357718, m.jourdan@reussir.tm.fr. Ed. Marie Hombeline Vincent. Pub., R&P Marc Jourdan. Adv. contact Jean Pierre Dumas. Circ: 86,000.

634 FRA ISSN 1761-5348
REUSSIR, FRUITS ET LEGUMES. Text in French. 1983. m. (except July-Aug. combined). FRF 285; FRF 365 in Europe; FRF 440 elsewhere; (effective 1998). adv. **Document type:** *Journal, Trade.*
Former titles (until 1998): Fruits et Legumes (0754-0698); Reussir (1261-8160)
Published by: Groupe Reussir, 51 rue Albert Camus, Box 20131, Agen, 47004, France. TEL 33-5-53778370, FAX 33-5-53778371. Circ: 8,500.

634.8 FRA ISSN 1261-0208
REUSSIR VIGNE. Text in French. 1994. 10/yr. adv. **Description:** Technical and economical information about wine production.
Published by: Editions Reussir, 19 quai de Juillet, CP 700, Caen, Cedex 9 1414, France. TEL 33-2-31357700, FAX 33-2-31357718, m.jourdan@reussir.tm.fr. Ed. Marie Annick Carre. Pub. Henri Lefebvre. R&P Marc Jourdan. Adv. contact Jean Pierre Dumas. Circ: 30,000.

633 ARG ISSN 0327-151X
CODEN: RAMAEF
REVISTA AGROPECUARIO DE MANFREDI Y MARCOS JUAREZ. Abbreviated title: R A M. Text mainly in Spanish; Text occasionally in English; Abstracts in English, Spanish. 1985. s-a. ARS 6, USD 8. bibl.; charts; illus. **Document type:** *Academic/Scholarly.*
Formerly (until 1987): Revista Agronomica de Manfredi (0326-7296)
Indexed: FCA.
—CISTI.
Published by: Estacion Experimental Agropecuaria Manfredi, Manfredi, Cordoba 5988, Argentina. TEL 54-51-57293053, FAX 54-51-57293061. Ed. Carlos Alberto Villata. Circ: 1,200.

631.4 BRA ISSN 0100-0683
CODEN: RBCSDP
REVISTA BRASILEIRA DE CIENCIA DO SOLO. Text in Portuguese. 1977. 3/yr. BRL 100 domestic; USD 100 foreign (effective 2001). back issues avail.
Related titles: Online - full text ed.: free (effective 2005) (from SciELO).
Indexed: AEA, AgBio, AgrForAb, CPA, ChemAb, ChemTitl, CurCont, FCA, FPA, ForAb, HerbAb, HortAb, I&DA, INIS AtomInd, MaizeAb, NemAb, OrnHort, PBA, PN&I, PotatoAb, PoultAb, RDA, RPP, RiceAb, S&F, SIA, SeedAb, SoyAb, TDB, TriticAb, WAE&RSA, WeedAb.
—BLDSC (7844.104900), CISTI, IE, ingenta.
Published by: Sociedade Brasileira de Ciencia do Solo/Soil Sciences Brazilian Society, Caixa Postal 231, Vicosa, MG 36570-000, Brazil. TEL 55-31-8992471, sbcs@solos.ufu.br, http://www.scielo.br/. Ed. Antonio C Moniz.

634 BRA ISSN 0100-2945
CODEN: RBFRD3
REVISTA BRASILEIRA DE FRUTICULTURA. Text in Portuguese. 1978. 3/yr. BRL 84 (effective 2004). **Document type:** *Journal, Trade.*
Related titles: Online - full text ed.: free (effective 2005).
Indexed: AgBio, AgrForAb, BioCN&I, CPA, FCA, FPA, ForAb, HortAb, I&DA, MaizeAb, NemAb, OrnHort, PBA, PGegResA, PGrRegA, PHN&I, PN&I, RPP, RRTA, S&F, SIA, SeedAb, SoyAb, WAE&RSA, WeedAb.
Published by: Sociedade Brasileira de Fruticultura, Via de Acesso Prof Paulo Donato Castellane s/n, Jaboticabal, SP 14884-900, Brazil. TEL 55-16-32092692.

631 BRA ISSN 0101-3122
REVISTA BRASILEIRA DE SEMENTES. Text in Multiple languages. 1979. 3/yr. BRL 50,000, USD 15. adv. back issues avail. **Document type:** *Journal, Academic/Scholarly.* **Description:** Covers the field of agriculture and related areas.
Related titles: Online - full text ed.: 2003. free (effective 2005).
Indexed: AEA, AgBio, AgrForAb, BioCN&I, CPA, FCA, FPA, ForAb, HerbAb, HortAb, I&DA, MaizeAb, OrnHort, PBA, PGegResA, PGrRegA, PHN&I, PotatoAb, PoultAb, RA&MP, RDA, RM&VM, RPP, RiceAb, S&F, SIA, SeedAb, SoyAb, TOSA, TriticAb, WAE&RSA, WeedAb.
—CISTI.
Published by: Associacao Brasileira de Tecnologia de Sementes/Brazilian Association of Seed Technology, A Norte (P Piloto), PO Box 02372, Brasilia, DF 70849-970, Brazil. TEL 61-347-6324, FAX 61-274-3212, TELEX 61-1622, http://www.scielo.br/scielo.php/script_sci_serial/pid_0101-3122/lng_en/nrm_iso. Ed. Mirian T S Eira. Circ: 2,000.

631 CUB ISSN 1607-6273
REVISTA CUBANA DEL ARROZ. Text in Spanish. 1999. m.
Media: Online - full text.
Published by: Instituto de Investigaciones del Arroz, Autopista Novia del Mediodia Km. 16.5, Bauta, Havana, Cuba. TEL 53-78-6803550, liarroz@auta.esihabana.cu. Ed. Alfredo Gutierrez Yanis.

630 CHL ISSN 0717-635X
REVISTA DE LA CIENCIA DEL SUELO Y NUTRICION VEGETAL/JOURNAL OF SOIL SCIENCE AND PLANT NUTRITION. Text in English, Spanish. 2001. s-a. CLP 7,000 domestic; USD 45 foreign (effective 2003).
Indexed: AEA, CPA, FCA, ForAb, HerbAb, HortAb, I&DA, PBA, S&F.
Published by: Sociedad Chilena de la Ciencia del Suelo, c/o Universidad Austral de Chile, Casilla 567, Valdivia, Chile. aellies@uach.cl.

631 CUB ISSN 1010-2752
REVISTA DE PROTECCION VEGETAL. Text in Spanish. 3/yr. USD 20 in the Americas; USD 24 in Europe.
Indexed: AEA, AgBio, AgrForAb, BioCN&I, CPA, FCA, FPA, ForAb, HelmAb, HerbAb, HortAb, MaizeAb, NemAb, NutrAb, OrnHort, PBA, PGegResA, PGrRegA, PHN&I, PotatoAb, RA&MP, RPP, RevApplEntom, RiceAb, S&F, SIA, SeedAb, SoyAb, WeedAb.
Published by: (Instituto de Ciencias Agropecuarias de La Habana, Centro Nacional de Semillas Agropecuaria), Ediciones Cubanas, Obispo No. 527, Apdo. 605, Havana, Cuba. TEL 32-5556-60.

631 MEX ISSN 0185-3309
➤ **REVISTA MEXICANA DE FITOPATOLOGIA.** Text and summaries in English, Spanish. 1981. 2/yr. USD 60 to individuals; USD 100 to institutions (effective 2002). adv. bk.rev. abstr.; charts; illus. back issues avail. **Document type:** *Journal, Academic/Scholarly.* **Description:** Publishes original research articles dealing with fundamental and applied aspects of plant pathology.
Indexed: AgBio, AgrForAb, BIOSIS Prev, BioCN&I, BiolAb, CPA, FCA, FPA, ForAb, HerbAb, HortAb, MaizeAb, NemAb, OrnHort, PBA, PGegResA, PHN&I, PotatoAb, RA&MP, RDA, RM&VM, RPP, RiceAb, S&F, SeedAb, TriticAb, WAE&RSA, WeedAb.
—CISTI.
Published by: Sociedad Mexicana de Fitopatologia, c/o CIMMYT Int., Norman E Borlaug, Km. 12 e 800 y 900 Valle del Yaqui, Apdo. 140, Cd. Obregon, Sonora, CP 85000, Mexico. TEL 52-64-141940, FAX 52-64-145898, g.fuentes@cgiar.org, http://members.tripod.com/~sociedad/sociedad.htm. Ed. Guillermo Fuentes-Davila. Adv. contact Javier Ireta-Moreno. B&W page USD 1,000. Circ: 700.

630 MUS ISSN 0370-3576
CODEN: RASMA9
➤ **REVUE AGRICOLE ET SUCRIERE DE MAURICE/ AGRICULTURAL AND SUGAR REVIEW OF MAURITIUS.** Text in English, French. 1922. 3/yr. MUR 300 domestic; USD 18 foreign (effective 2000). adv. **Document type:** *Proceedings, Academic/Scholarly.*
Indexed: AEA, AgBio, AnBrAb, BioCN&I, BiolAb, CPA, CTFA, ExcerpMed, FCA, FS&TA, ForAb, HerbAb, HortAb, I&DA, IndVet, MaizeAb, OrnHort, PBA, PGrRegA, PLESA, PotatoAb, PoultAb, RDA, RPP, RevApplEntom, S&F, SIA, VetBull, WAE&RSA, WeedAb.
—BLDSC (7883.100000), CASDDS, IE, ingenta.
Published by: Societe de Technologie Agricole et Sucriere de l'Ile Maurice, c/o M.S.I.R.I., Reduit, Mauritius. TEL 230-4541061, FAX 230-4541971. Eds. Clency Barbe, Guy McIntyre. Circ: 600.

➤ **REVUE D'OENOLOGUES ET DES TECHNIQUES VITI-VINICOLES ET OENOLOGIQUES.** see *BEVERAGES*

634.8 FRA ISSN 0395-899X
CODEN: RFOEE4
REVUE FRANCAISE D'OENOLOGIE. Text in French; Summaries in English, Spanish. 1959. bi-m. adv. bk.rev. illus.; tr.lit. **Document type:** *Trade.*
Related titles: Online - full text ed.; ♦ Supplement(s): Union Francaise des Oenologues. Annuaire. ISSN 1161-3580.
Indexed: ChemAb, ChemTitl, RefZh, VITIS.
—BLDSC (7904.211000), CASDDS, IE, ingenta.
Address: Maison des Agriculteurs, Mas de Saporta, Lattes, 34970, France. TEL 33-4-67586906, FAX 33-4-67586891. Ed. Dominique Traxel. Adv. contact Magali Dumas. Circ: 13,000.

634.8 634.9 CHE ISSN 0375-1430
CODEN: RVAHA
REVUE SUISSE DE VITICULTURE, ARBORICULTURE ET HORTICULTURE. Text in French; Summaries in English, German, Italian. 1969. bi-m. CHF 46 (effective 2001). adv. bk.rev. illus.; stat. **Document type:** *Journal, Academic/Scholarly.*
Formerly: Revue Suisse de Viticulture et Arboriculture (0035-4171); Supersedes in part (in 1969): Agriculture Romande (0515-7412)
Indexed: AEA, AgBio, AgrForAb, BioCN&I, BiolAb, CPA, ChemAb, DBA, ExcerpMed, FCA, FPA, FS&TA, ForAb, HerbAb, HortAb, I&DA, OrnHort, PBA, PGegResA, PHN&I, RA&MP, RPP, RefZh, RevApplEntom, S&F, SIA, SeedAb, VITIS, WAE&RSA, WeedAb.
—BLDSC (7953.397500), CASDDS, IE, Infotrieve, ingenta, Linda Hall.
Published by: Association par la Mise en valeur des Travaux de la Recherche Agronomique, Case Postale 516, Nyon 1, 1260, Switzerland. TEL 41-22-3634151, FAX 41-22-3634155. Ed. Andre Maillard. Adv. contact Paul Magnin TEL 41-22-7366913. B&W page CHF 1,312; trim 250 x 180. Circ: 5,000.

633.18 PHL ISSN 0117-0090
Z5074.R5
RICE LITERATURE UPDATE. Text in English. 1989. 2/yr. USD 38.
Published by: International Rice Research Institute, DAPO Box 7777, Metro Manila, Philippines. TEL 63-2-845-0563, FAX 63-2-845-0606, irri@cgiar.org, http://www.cgiar.org/irri/.

631 GBR
RICE MARKET CIRCULAR. Text in English. m.
Published by: London Rice Brokers' Association, Prince Rupert House, 9-10 College Hill, London, EC4, United Kingdom.

631 USA ISSN 1092-5813
RICE WORLD. Text in English. 1981. m. USD 19 (effective 2001). adv. bk.rev. **Document type:** *Trade.*
Formerly: Rice World and Soybean News (0738-5943)
Related titles: Microform ed.
Address: PO Box 340, Helena, AK 72342. TEL 870-338-9181, riceworld@aol.com, dailywor@ipa.net, http://www.thericeworld.com. Ed. Gary Burton. Pub. Clark Smith. Circ: 3,000.

631   ESP   ISSN 0213-3660
RIEGOS Y DRENAJES XXI; revista de la tecnologia del riego drenajes, suelos, fertilizantes, invernaderos y agricultura intensiva. Text in Spanish. 1985. bi-m. EUR 73.20 domestic; EUR 89.21 foreign (effective 2003). adv. illus. **Document type:** *Trade.* **Description:** Covers irrigation technologies, draining, soil, fertilization, greenhouses and intensive agricultural techniques.
Indexed: IECT.
—CINDOC.
Published by: Reed Business Information SA (Subsidiary of: Reed Business Information International), Zancoeta 9, Bilbao, 48013, Spain. TEL 34-944-285600, FAX 34-944-425116, rbi@rbi.es, http://www.rbi.es. Ed. Marcel Lleal. Pub. Manuel Masip. Adv. contact Eduardo Lazaro. Circ: 3,000.

631.4   ITA   ISSN 0035-6034
CODEN: RAGOAN
RIVISTA DI AGRONOMIA. Text in Italian; Summaries in English. 1967. q. EUR 60 in the European Union; EUR 70 elsewhere (effective 2005). bk.rev. index. **Document type:** *Magazine, Trade.* **Description:** Contains concise descriptions of technical and analytical procedures, instruments and equipments to solve problems inherent in agricultural research.
Indexed: AEA, AgBio, AgrForAb, BiolAb, CPA, ChemAb, DSA, ExcerpMed, FCA, ForAb, HerbAb, HortAb, I&DA, MaizeAb, NutrAb, OrnHort, PBA, PGegResA, PGrRegA, PotatoAb, RPP, RevApplEntom, RiceAb, S&F, SeedAb, SoyAb, TriticAb, WAE&RSA, WeedAb.
—BLDSC (7980.400000), CASDDS, CISTI, Linda Hall.
Published by: (Societa Italiana di Agronomia), Forum Societa Editrice Universitaria Udinese, Via Larga 38, Udine, UD 33100, Italy. TEL 39-0432-2600, FAX 39-0432-296756, forum@forumeditrice.it, http://www.forumeditrice.it. Circ: 1,100.

634   ITA   ISSN 0392-954X
RIVISTA DI FRUTTICOLTURA E DI ORTOFLORICOLTURA. Text in Italian; Summaries in English. 1937. m. (11/yr.). EUR 62 domestic; EUR 110 foreign (effective 2005). adv. bk.rev. charts; illus. index. 96 p./no.; **Document type:** *Magazine, Trade.* **Description:** For industrial producers of fruits, vegetables, grapes and flowers.
Former titles (until 1982): Frutticoltura (0016-2310); (until 1954): Rivista di Frutticoltura (0370-5013)
Indexed: AEA, AgBio, AgrForAb, BioCN&I, BiolAb, CPA, ChemAb, DSA, FCA, FPA, FS&TA, ForAb, HortAb, I&DA, NemAb, NutrAb, OrnHort, PBA, PGegResA, PGrRegA, PHN&I, PotatoAb, RA&MP, RM&VM, RPP, RRTA, RefZh, RevApplEntom, S&F, SIA, SeedAb, TriticAb, VITIS, WAE&RSA, WeedAb.
—CISTI.
Published by: Il Sole 24 Ore Edagricole, Via Goito 13, Bologna, BO 40126, Italy. TEL 39-051-62267, FAX 39-051-490200, http://www.edagricole.it. Ed. Giorgio Setti. Circ: 16,500.

630   ITA   ISSN 0304-0593
RIVISTA DI INGEGNERIA AGRARIA. Text in Italian. 1970. q. EUR 51.56 domestic; USD 60.94 foreign (effective 2005). bk.rev. charts; illus.; stat. index. **Document type:** *Journal, Trade.* **Description:** For technicians, researchers and designers of farm machinery.
Indexed: AEA, AbHyg, AnBrAb, BioCN&I, DSA, FCA, FPA, FS&TA, ForAb, HerbAb, HortAb, I&DA, IndVet, MaizeAb, NutrAb, OrnHort, PBA, PHN&I, PN&I, PotatoAb, RPP, RevApplEntom, RiceAb, S&F, SIA, SeedAb, SoyAb, TDB, TriticAb, WAE&RSA, WeedAb.
—BLDSC (7987.010000), IE, ingenta.
Published by: (Associazione Italiana di Ingegneria Agraria), Edizioni E T S, Piazza Carrara 16-19, Pisa, Italy. TEL 39-050-29544, FAX 39-050-20158, info@edizioniets.it, http://www.edizioniets.it. Ed. Adriano Guarnieri. Circ: 1,300.

634.8 663.2   ITA   ISSN 0370-7865
CODEN: RVENAL
RIVISTA DI VITICOLTURA E DI ENOLOGIA. Text in Italian. 1948. q. EUR 51.65 domestic; EUR 72.30 foreign (effective 2002).
Indexed: AgBio, BioCN&I, CPA, ChemAb, ChemTitl, FPA, FS&TA, HortAb, I&DA, NutrAb, OrnHort, PBA, PGegResA, PGrRegA, PHN&I, RPP, RefZh, RevApplEntom, S&F, SIA, SeedAb, VITIS, WAE&RSA.
—BLDSC (7993.600000), CASDDS, CISTI, IE, ingenta.
Address: Via XXVIII Aprile, 26, Conegliano Veneto, TV 31015, Italy. TEL 39-438-456711, FAX 39-438-64779, isvdir@mgdnet.com, http://www.inea.it/isv.html.

631.4   POL   ISSN 0080-3642
S590   CODEN: ROGLAA
ROCZNIKI GLEBOZNAWCZE. Text mainly in Polish; Text occasionally in English; Summaries in English, Russian. 1950. q. USD 40. **Description:** Publishes original papers in soil science, chemistry, mineralogy, soil biology, water supply.
Indexed: AgrAg, AgrForAb, AgrLib, FCA, HerbAb, HortAb, I&DA, PotatoAb, RevApplEntom, S&F, WeedAb.
—CASDDS, CISTI.
Published by: Polskie Towarzystwo Gleboznawcze, Ul Wisniowa 61, Warsaw, 02520, Poland. Ed. Wladyslaw Trzcinski. Circ: 1,470. **Dist. by:** Ars Polona, Krakowskie Przedmiescie 7, Warsaw, Poland.

633 635   POL   ISSN 0080-3650
SB13   CODEN: RNRAAP
ROCZNIKI NAUK ROLNICZYCH. SERIA A. PRODUKCJA ROSLINNA. Text in Polish; Summaries in English, Polish, Russian. 1903. irreg., latest vol.114, no.4, 1999. price varies. bibl.; charts. **Document type:** *Academic/Scholarly.*
Indexed: AgrAg, AgrLib, BiolAb, CPA, ChemAb, ExcerpMed, FCA, FS&TA, HerbAb, HortAb, I&DA, MaizeAb, NutrAb, OrnHort, PBA, PGrRegA, PHN&I, PotatoAb, RA&MP, RPP, RevApplEntom, S&F, SIA, SeedAb, TriticAb, WAE&RSA, WeedAb.
—CASDDS, CISTI.
Published by: (Polska Akademia Nauk, Komitet Uprawy Roslin), Wydawnictwo Naukowe P W N SA/Polish Scientific Publishers P W N, ul Miodowa 10, Warsaw, 00251, Poland. TEL 48-22-6954181, FAX 48-22-6954288, ksiegarnia@pwn.pl, http://en.pwn.pl. Circ: 750.

631.4   USA   ISSN 1063-2565
CODEN: SSAPAV
S S S A SPECIAL PUBLICATION. Text in English. 1967. irreg., latest vol.59, 2002. price varies. adv. **Document type:** *Monographic series.*
Formerly (until 1979): S S S A Special Publication Series (0081-1904)
Indexed: AEA, AbAn, Agr, BIOSIS Prev, BibAg, BiolAb, CIN, ChemAb, ChemTitl, MaizeAb, S&F, WeedAb.
—BLDSC (8425.260000), CASDDS, CISTI, Ei, IE, ingenta. **CCC.**
Published by: Soil Science Society of America, 677 S Segoe Rd, Madison, WI 53711. TEL 608-273-8095, FAX 608-273-2021, http://www.soils.org/. Ed. Jerry Bigham. R&P David Kral. Adv. contact Keith R Schlesinger.

SAFETY NEWS. see *WATER RESOURCES*

633.63   RUS   ISSN 1560-4160
SAKHARNAYA PROMYSHLENNOST. Text in Russian. 1956. m. USD 99.95. bk.rev. bibl.; stat. index.
Former titles (until 1992): Sakharnaya Svekla Proizvodstvo i Pererabotka (0235-2583); (until 1988): Sakharnaya Svekla (0036-3359)
Indexed: AEA, AgBio, BioCN&I, BiolAb, CPA, ChemAb, DSA, FCA, FS&TA, HerbAb, HortAb, I&DA, MaizeAb, NemAb, NutrAb, PBA, PGegResA, PGrRegA, PHN&I, PotatoAb, RASB, RDA, RPP, RefZh, RevApplEntom, S&F, SIA, SeedAb, TriticAb, WAE&RSA, WeedAb.
—CISTI, East View, Linda Hall.
Published by: Beta, Sadovaya-Spasskaya 18, Moscow, 107807, Russian Federation. TEL 7-095-2076408, FAX 7-095-2072290. Ed. Valentina G Zharkova. Circ: 9,000. **Dist. by:** M K - Periodica, ul Gilyarovskogo 39, Moscow 129110, Russian Federation. TEL 7-095-2845008, FAX 7-095-2813798, info@periodicals.ru, http://www.mkniga.ru; **US dist. addr.:** East View Information Services, 3020 Harbor Ln. N., Minneapolis, MN 55447. TEL 612-550-0961.

633   JPN   ISSN 1346-8480
SAKUMOTSU KENKYUUJO KENKYUU HOUKOKU/NATIONAL INSTITUTE OF CROP SCIENCE. BULLETIN. Text in Japanese. 2001. irreg.
Indexed: AgBio, CPA, FCA, HerbAb, HortAb, NemAb, PBA, PGegResA, PHN&I, RPP, S&F, SeedAb, SoyAb, TriticAb.
—BLDSC (2640.105000).
Published by: Nougyou Gijutsu Kenkyuu Kikou Sakumotsu Kenkyuujo/National Agricultural Research Organization, National Institute of Crop Science, Tsukuba, Ibaraki, Kannondai 305-8518, Japan.

SAN FRANCISCO FRESH FRUIT AND VEGETABLE WHOLESALE MARKET PRICES. see *AGRICULTURE—Agricultural Economics*

SAN FRANCISCO WHOLESALE FRUIT AND VEGETABLE REPORT. see *AGRICULTURE—Agricultural Economics*

631.3   SCG   ISSN 0350-2953
SAVREMENA POLJOPRIVREDNA TEHNIKA∗ /ADVANCED AGRICULTURAL ENGINEERING; Jugoslovenski casopis za poljoprivrednu tehniku. Text in Serbian; Summaries in English. 1975. q. YUN 250 domestic; USD 100 foreign. adv. bk.rev. **Document type:** *Proceedings.* **Description:** Covers agricultural engineering and agricultural equipment.
Published by: Vojvodjansko Drustvo za Poljoprivrednu Tehniku/Voivodina's Society of Agricultural Engineers, c/o Institute for Agricultural Mechanisation, P.O. Box 41, Belgrade-Zemun. FAX 381-21-59989, vlazic@polj.ns.ac.yu, tesic@uns.ns.ac.yu. Ed., R&P Veselin Lazic. Circ: 400.
Co-sponsor: Yugoslav Scientific Society of Agricultural Engineers.

630   CAN
SEED.AB.CA; your source for seed. Text in English. s-a. CND 8 (effective 2004). adv. **Document type:** *Magazine, Trade.*
Published by: Issues Ink, 203-897 Corydon Ave, Winnipeg, MB R3M 0W7, Canada. TEL 204-453-1965, FAX 204-475-5247, issues@issuesink.com, http://www.issuesink.com/seed.html. Circ: 70,000.

631   FRA   ISSN 1140-5066
SEED AND AG'CHEM BUSINESS. Text in French. 1983. 2/yr. adv. **Description:** Covers the agrichemical and fertilizer industry.
Formed by the merger of: Seed Business; Ag'Chem Business
Published by: Groupe Liaisons S.A. (Subsidiary of: Wolters Kluwer BV), 1 Avenue Edouard Belin, Rueil Malmaison, Cedex 92856, France. TEL 33-1-41299999, FAX 33-1-41299836. Ed. Blandine Cailliez. Adv. contact Martine Pinel. Circ: 10,000.

631   IND   ISSN 0379-5594
CODEN: SEREDM
SEED RESEARCH. Text in English. 1973. s-a. USD 15 to individuals; USD 50 to institutions. bk.rev. **Document type:** *Academic/Scholarly.* **Description:** Aims to promote the research and development of seed science and technology.
Indexed: AEA, AgBio, AgrForAb, BIOSIS Prev, BioCN&I, BiolAb, CPA, CTFA, ChemAb, FCA, FPA, ForAb, HerbAb, HortAb, I&DA, MaizeAb, NutrAb, OrnHort, PBA, PGegResA, PGrRegA, PHN&I, PotatoAb, RA&MP, RDA, RM&VM, RPP, RevApplEntom, RiceAb, S&F, S&MA, SIA, SeedAb, SoyAb, TOSA, TriticAb, WAE&RSA, WeedAb.
—BLDSC (8218.130000), CASDDS, IE, ingenta, Linda Hall.
Published by: Indian Society of Seed Technology, Indian Agricultural Research Institute, Division of Seed Science & Technology, New Delhi, 110 012, India. TEL 91-11-5784869, FAX 91-11-5752006, TELEX 3177161 IARI IN, Ed. K.Kant. Circ: 700.

631   GBR   ISSN 0960-2585
SB113.2   CODEN: SESREX
➤ **SEED SCIENCE RESEARCH.** Text in English. 1991. q. USD 605 in the Americas to institutions except Canada; GBP 345 elsewhere to institutions; USD 650 combined subscription in the Americas to institutions except Canada; print & online eds.; GBP 295 combined subscription elsewhere to institutions print & online eds. (effective 2006). adv. back issues avail. **Document type:** *Journal, Academic/Scholarly.* **Description:** Provides a medium for the publication of papers in the field of fundamental scientific research on seeds. The emphasis is on the physiology, biochemistry and molecular biology of seeds, covering seed and embryo development, maturation, dormancy, germination, viability, longevity, vigor, reserve mobilization, and the early stages of establishment.
Related titles: Online - full text ed.: ISSN 1475-2735. USD 515 in the Americas to institutions except Canada; GBP 295 elsewhere to institutions (effective 2006) (from EBSCO Publishing, Gale Group, IngentaConnect, Ovid Technologies, Inc., Swets Information Services).
Indexed: AEA, ASCA, AgBio, Agr, AgrForAb, BIOBASE, BIOSIS Prev, BiolAb, CPA, ChemAb, ChemTitl, CurCont, FCA, FS&TA, ForAb, HerbAb, HortAb, I&DA, IABS, ISR, IndVet, MaizeAb, OrnHort, PBA, PGegResA, PGrRegA, PHN&I, PlantSci, RA&MP, RPP, RiceAb, S&F, SCI, SIA, SeedAb, SoyAb, TriticAb, WeedAb.
—BLDSC (8218.155000), CASDDS, CISTI, IDS, IE, Infotrieve, ingenta. **CCC.**
Published by: CABI Publishing (Subsidiary of: CAB International), CAB International, Wallingford, Oxfordshire OX10 8DE, United Kingdom. TEL 44-1491-832111, FAX 44-1491-833508, cabi@cabi.org, http://www.cabi-publishing.org/. Ed. M Cohn. Pub. Liz Bennett TEL 44-1491-829288. Adv. contact Sarah Harris TEL 44-1491-829310. B&W page GBP 190, B&W page USD 300; 170 x 225. Circ: 104. **Subscr. addr. in N America:** CABI Publishing North America, 875 Massachusetts Ave, 7th Fl, Cambridge, MA 02139. TEL 617-395-4056, 800-528-4841, FAX 617-354-6875, cabi-nao@cabi.org.

631.5   CAN   ISSN 0049-0040
SEED SCOOP. Text in English. 1955. 3/yr. **Document type:** *Bulletin.*
Related titles: French ed.: Actualite Semence. ISSN 0715-4844.
—CISTI.
Published by: Canadian Seed Growers Association, P O Box 8455, Ottawa, ON K1G 3T1, Canada. TEL 613-236-0497. Circ: 10,500.

631   USA
THE SEED TECHNOLOGIST NEWSLETTER. Spine title: A O S A and S C S T. Text in English. 1994 (vol.68). 3/yr. (plus a. proceedings). USD 35. bk.rev. **Document type:** *Newsletter.* **Description:** Contains membership news and testing information, along with testing research proposals.
Formerly (until 1997): Seed Technologist News
Published by: Society of Commercial Seed Technologists, c/o Andy Evans, Sec -Treas, Ohio State University, 202 Kottman Hall, 2021 Coffey Rd, Columbus, OH 43210. TEL 614-292-8242, http://www.zianet.com/aosa/index.html. Ed., R&P Diane Mesa. Circ: 575. **Co-sponsor:** Association of Official Seed Analysts.

630   CHE
SEED TESTING INTERNATIONAL. Text in English. 1959. 2/yr. free. back issues avail. **Document type:** *Magazine, Academic/Scholarly.* **Description:** Includes seed testing results, reports and announcements of meetings, committees, courses and seminars and association news.
Formerly (until 2003): I S T A News Bulletin (0256-6478)
Indexed: HortAb, PBA, SeedAb.

▼ *new title*   ➤ *refereed*   ∗ *unverified*   ◆ *full entry avail.*

A

Published by: International Seed Testing Association, Zuerichstr 50, PO Box 308, Bassersdorf, 8303, Switzerland. TEL 41-1-8386000, FAX 41-1-8386001, ista.office@ista.ch, http://www.seedtest.org. Ed. M. Muschick.

631.5 USA ISSN 0080-8504
SEED TRADE BUYER'S GUIDE. Text in English. 1917. a. USD 35. adv. **Document type:** *Trade.* **Description:** Contains a compilation of revised state-by-state seed laws, as well as company and supplier listings.
Related titles: Microform ed.: (from PQC); ♦ Supplement to: Seed World. ISSN 0037-0797.
Published by: Scranton Gillette Communications, Inc., 380 E Northwest Hwy, Ste 200, Des Plaines, IL 60016-2282. TEL 847-391-1000, FAX 847-390-0408. Ed. Mindy Haff. Circ: 5,000.

631.5 USA ISSN 0037-0797
CODEN: SWORAX
SEED WORLD. Text in English. 1915. m. USD 30 (effective 2005). adv. illus.; mkt. reprint service avail. from PQC. **Document type:** *Magazine, Trade.* **Description:** Articles on the latest developments in the production and marketing of crop, vegetable, and fruit seeds, with an ad index, industry announcements and legislative updates.
Incorporates: Florist and Nursery Exchange (0015-4407)
Related titles: Microform ed.: (from PQC); Online - full text ed.: (from Gale Group); ♦ Supplement(s): Seed Trade Buyer's Guide. ISSN 0080-8504.
Indexed: Agr, BiolAb, ChemAb, F&GI, FCA, GardL, HerbAb, MaizeAb, RevApplEntom, S&F, SeedAb, WeedAb.
—CISTI, IE, Infotrieve, Linda Hall. **CCC.**
Published by: Scranton Gillette Communications, Inc., 380 E Northwest Hwy, Ste 200, Des Plaines, IL 60016-2282. TEL 847-391-1000, FAX 847-390-0408, http://www.seedworld.com, http://www.sgcpubs.com/seedworld.html. Ed. Angela Dansby. Pub. Edward Gillette. adv.: B&W page USD 1,050, color page USD 1,745. Circ: 5,142 (paid).

SELEKTSIYA I NASINNYTSTVO; mizhvidomchyi tematychnyi naukovyi zbirnyk. see *BIOLOGY—Botany*

631.5 RUS ISSN 0037-1459
SELEKTSIYA I SEMENOVODSTVO. Text in Russian. 1929. q. USD 80 (effective 2005). adv. bk.rev. bibl. index. **Document type:** *Academic/Scholarly.* **Description:** Covers selection, seed growing, seed testing, problems of related sciences.
Indexed: AEA, BiolAb, ChemAb, FCA, HerbAb, HortAb, I&DA, MaizeAb, PBA, PotatoAb, RPP, RefZh, RiceAb, SeedAb, SoyAb, TriticAb, WeedAb.
—CISTI, East View, Linda Hall.
Address: Sadovaya-Spasskaya 18, Moscow, 107996, Russian Federation. TEL 7-095-9232771, FAX 7-095-2072870. Ed. Lidiya A Tumakova. R&P V A Katkov. Adv. contact V.A. Katkov. B&W page USD 500. Circ: 500. **Dist. by:** M K - Periodica, ul Gilyarovskogo 39, Moscow 129110, Russian Federation. TEL 7-095-2845008, FAX 7-095-2813798, info@periodicals.ru, http://www.mkniga.ru. **Co-sponsor:** Rossiiskaya Akademiya Sel'skokhozyaistvennykh Nauk/Russian Academy of Agricultural Sciences.

631.8 IND
SELF - RELIANCE. Text in English. 1981. q. **Document type:** *Government.* **Description:** Publicizes and highlights the company's achievements, expertise and experience in the field of fertilizers, chemicals and other allied industries. The articles are contributed mainly by engineers and scientists engaged in various fields of activities.
Published by: Projects & Development India Ltd, CIFT Bldgs, PO Sindri, Dhanbad, Bihar 828 122, India. TEL 91-326-51258, FAX 91-326-51272, TELEX 06201-201 PDIL IN, 06201-202 PDIL IN, pdil.sindri@smy.sprintrpg.ems.vsnl.net.in, pdil.sindri@smy.sprintrpg.cms.vsnl.net.in. Circ: 1,500.

630 RUS ISSN 0582-5164
SEL'SKAYA NOV'. Text in Russian. 1966. m. USD 99.95. illus.
Indexed: PBA, RASB.
—East View, Linda Hall.
Published by: Izdatel'stvo Sel'skaya Nov', Sadovaya-Spasskaya 20, Moscow, 107807, Russian Federation. TEL 7-095-9301039, FAX 7-095-9754976. Ed. A I Rebel'skii. Circ: 238,600. **Dist. by:** M K - Periodica, ul Gilyarovskogo 39, Moscow 129110, Russian Federation. TEL 7-095-2845008, FAX 7-095-2813798, info@periodicals.ru, http://www.mkniga.ru; **US dist. addr.:** East View Information Services, 3020 Harbor Ln. N., Minneapolis, MN 55447. TEL 612-550-0961.

634.8 ESP ISSN 0037-184X
CODEN: SEVIAH
SEMANA VITIVINICOLA; al servicio de la vid y el vino. Text in Spanish. 1945. w. (48/yr.). bk.rev. abstr.; bibl.; illus.; stat.; tr.lit. index. **Document type:** *Trade.*
Indexed: ChemAb, FS&TA, IECT, VITIS.
—BLDSC (8237.820000), CASDDS, CINDOC.
Address: Apartado de Correos 642, Valencia, 46080, Spain. TEL 34-6-3749500, FAX 34-6-3749561, semanavi@sevi.net, http://www.sevi.net. Ed. Salvador Estala Alfonso. Pub. Fernando Manjon Estela. Circ: 14,000.

631.5 ITA ISSN 0037-1890
CODEN: SEELBA
SEMENTI ELETTE. Short title: S E. Text in Italian. 1955. 5/yr. EUR 52 domestic; EUR 75 foreign (effective 2005). adv. bk.rev. charts; illus. index. 64 p./no.; **Document type:** *Magazine, Trade.* **Description:** Deals with seed problems of any field, horticultural or garden crop.
Indexed: AEA, AbHyg, AgBio, AnBrAb, BioCN&I, CPA, ChemAb, FCA, FaBeAb, ForAb, HerbAb, HortAb, MaizeAb, NemAb, NutrAb, OrnHort, PBA, PGegResA, PGrRegA, PHN&I, PotatoAb, RA&MP, RPP, RRTA, RevApplEntom, RiceAb, S&F, SIA, SeedAb, SoyAb, TriticAb, WAE&RSA, WeedAb.
—BLDSC (8237.850000), CISTI, IE, ingenta.
Published by: Il Sole 24 Ore Edagricole, Via Goito 13, Bologna, BO 40126, Italy. TEL 39-051-62267, FAX 39-051-490200, http://www.edagricole.it. Ed. Giorgio Setti. Circ: 1,900.

632 JPN ISSN 0037-4091
CODEN: SHBOAO
SHOKUBUTSU BOEKI/PLANT PROTECTION. Text in Japanese. 1947. m. JPY 8,060.
Indexed: CTFA, FCA, ForAb, PHN&I, ProtozoAb, SeedAb, ZooRec.
—BLDSC (6523.000000).
Published by: Japan Plant Protection Association/Nihon Shokubutsu Boeki Kyokai, 1-43-11 Komagome, Toshima-ku, Tokyo, 170-8484, Japan. TEL 03-3866-9897, FAX 03-3861-7715. Ed. Takeo Endo. **Subscr. to:** Sun Publications, Ishi Bldg, 3-37, Sakuma-cho, Tokyo 101-0025, Japan.

631.4 CHN ISSN 1000-288X
SHUITU BAOCHI TONGBAO/BULLETIN OF SOIL AND WATER CONSERVATION. Text in Chinese; Abstracts in Chinese, English. 1981. bi-m. CNY 48 (effective 2004). **Document type:** *Bulletin, Academic/Scholarly.* **Description:** Covers the latest research on soil and water conservation.
Related titles: CD-ROM ed.; Online - full content ed.: (from WanFang Data Corp.); Online - full text ed.: (from East View Information Services).
Published by: (Zhongguo Kexueyuan, Shuili Bu, Shuitu Baochi Yanjiusuo), Kexue Chubanshe/Science Press, 16 Donghuang Cheng Genbei Jie, Beijing, 100717, China. bulletin@ms.iswc.ac.cn, http://stbctb.periodicals.net.cn/default.html, http://www.sciencep.com/. Ed. Jun Liang Tian. **Dist. overseas by:** China International Book Trading Corp, 35 Chegongzhuang Xilu, Haidian District, PO Box 399, Beijing 100044, China. TEL 86-10-68412045, FAX 86-10-68412023, cibtc@mail.cibtc.com.cn, http://www.cibtc.com.cn.

631.4 CHN ISSN 1009-2242
SHUITU BAOCHI XUEBAO/JOURNAL OF SOIL AND WATER CONSERVATION. Text in Chinese. 1987. bi-m. CNY 90 (effective 2004). bk.rev. **Document type:** *Journal, Academic/Scholarly.* **Description:** Covers new theoretical and applied research achievements of soil and water conservation.
Former titles (until 2000): Turang Qinshi yu Shuitu Baochi Xuebao/Journal of Soil Erosion and Soil and Water Conservation (1007-2209); (until vol.9, no.4, 1995): Shuitu Baochi Xuebao/Journal of Soil and Water Conservation
Related titles: CD-ROM ed.; Online - full text ed.: (from WanFang Data Corp.); (from East View Information Services).
Indexed: ASCA, FCA, S&F, SeedAb.
Published by: Zhongguo Kexueyuan, Shuili Bu, Shuitu Baochi Yanjiusuo, 26, Xinong Lu, Xi'an, Shaanxi 712100, China. TEL 86-29-87012707, journal@ms.iswc.ac.cn, http://trqsystbcxb.periodicals.net.cn/default.html, http://www.iswc.ac.cn/. **Dist. by:** China International Book Trading Corp, 35 Chegongzhuang Xilu, Haidian District, PO Box 399, Beijing 100044, China. TEL 86-10-68412045, FAX 86-10-68412023, cibtc@mail.cibtc.com.cn, http://www.cibtc.com.cn.

631.4 CHN ISSN 1005-3409
S622
SHUITU BAOCHI YANJIU/RESEARCH OF SOIL AND WATER CONSERVATION. Text in Chinese; Abstracts in Chinese, English. 1994. q. CNY 20; USD 50 foreign. **Document type:** *Academic/Scholarly.*
Related titles: Online - full text ed.: (from East View Information Services).
Published by: Zhongguo Kexueyuan, Xibei Shuitu Baochi Yanjiusuo/Chinese Academy of Sciences, Xibei Institute of Soil and Water Conservation, Yangling-qu, Xi'an, Shaanxi 712100, China. TEL 86-910-7012705, FAX 86-910-7012210, Libinfo@ms.iswc.ac.cn. Ed. Li Rui. R&P Wang Jingwu. **Co-sponsor:** Shuili Bu - Ministry of Water Resources.

634.8021 ARG ISSN 1514-3104
SINTESIS BASICA DE ESTADISTICA VITINICOLA ARGENTINA. Text in Spanish. 1998. a. ARS 10 (effective 2002).
Related titles: Online - full text ed.: ISSN 1514-3198.
Published by: Instituto Nacional de Vitivinicultura, San Martin 340, Mendoza, 5500, Argentina. TEL 54-261-5216690, FAX 54-261-5216604, http://www.inv.gov.ar/. Ed. Alberto Manzano.

630 USA
SITUATION & OUTLOOK REPORT. OIL CROPS OUTLOOK. Text in English. 1995. 11/yr. **Document type:** *Government.* **Description:** Examines U.S. and world soybean, oilseed and vegetable oil production, supply, prices, and trade; includes U.S. cottonseed, peanuts, sunflowerseed, other special oilseeds, tropical oils, corn oil, and animal fats.
Media: Online - full text (from Gale Group, The Dialog Corporation). **Related titles:** ♦ Supplement(s): Situation & Outlook Report. Oil Crops Yearbook.
Indexed: WAE&RSA.
Published by: U.S. Department of Agriculture, Economic Research Service, 1800 M St. NW, Washington, DC 20036-5831. ersinfo@ers.usda.gov, http://www.ers.usda.gov/publications/so/view.asp?f=field/ocs-bb/.

630 USA
SITUATION & OUTLOOK REPORT. OIL CROPS YEARBOOK. Text in English. 1995. a. USD 21 (effective 2001). **Document type:** *Yearbook, Government.* **Description:** Examines U.S. and world soybean, oilseed, and vegetable oil production, prices, supplies, utilization and trade; includes data on U.S. cotton-seed, peanuts, sunflowerseed, other special oilseeds, tropical oils, corn oil, and animal fats.
Related titles: Online - full content ed.; ♦ Supplement to: Situation & Outlook Report. Oil Crops Outlook.
Published by: U.S. Department of Agriculture, Economic Research Service, 1800 M St. NW, Washington, DC 20036-5831. ersinfo@ers.usda.gov, http://www.ers.usda.gov/publications/so/view.asp?f=field/ocs-bby/. **Dist. by:** ERS-NASS, 5285 Port Royal Rd, Springfield, VA 22161. TEL 800-999-6779.

630 USA
SITUATION & OUTLOOK REPORT. RICE OUTLOOK. Text in English. 1995. m. **Document type:** *Government.* **Description:** Examines U.S. rough, milled, long-grain, and medium/short-grain rice: supply, disappearance, price, acreage, yield, production, stocks, byproducts, brewers' prices, exports, and world rice markets.
Media: Online - full text (from Gale Group, The Dialog Corporation). **Related titles:** ♦ Supplement(s): Situation & Outlook Report. Rice Yearbook.
Published by: U.S. Department of Agriculture, Economic Research Service, 1800 M St. NW, Washington, DC 20036-5831. ersinfo@ers.usda.gov, http://www.ers.usda.gov/publications/so/view.asp?f=field/rcs-bb/.

633 USA
SITUATION & OUTLOOK REPORT. RICE YEARBOOK. Text in English. 1995. a. USD 21 (effective 2001). **Document type:** *Yearbook, Government.* **Description:** Examines U.S. rough, milled, long-grain, and medium/short grain rice: supply, disappearance, price, acreage, yield, production, stocks, byproducts, brewers' prices, exports, and world rice markets.
Related titles: Online - full content ed.; ♦ Supplement to: Situation & Outlook Report. Rice Outlook.
Published by: U.S. Department of Agriculture, Economic Research Service, 1800 M St. NW, Washington, DC 20036-5831. ersinfo@ers.usda.gov, http://www.ers.usda.gov/publications/so/view.asp?f=field/rcs-bby/. **Dist. by:** ERS-NASS, 5285 Port Royal Rd, Springfield, VA 22161. TEL 800-999-6779.

633.71 USA ISSN 0893-8946
HD9131
SITUATION & OUTLOOK REPORT. TOBACCO. Text in English. 1937. 3/yr. USD 11 (effective 2001). bk.rev. charts; mkt.; stat. index. back issues avail.; reprint service avail. from CIS. **Document type:** *Government.* **Description:** Examines burley and flue-cured tobacco production, consumption, supply, use, trade, prices and more, including consumption and trade of tobacco products (cigars, cigarettes, snuff, etc.).
Former titles (until 1986): U.S. Department of Agriculture. Outlook and Situation Report. Tobacco (0889-7948); (until 1981): U.S. Department of Agriculture. Tobacco Situation (0040-8344)
Related titles: Microfiche ed.: (from CIS); Online - full text ed.: (from Gale Group, The Dialog Corporation); ♦ Supplement(s): Situation & Outlook Report. Tobacco Yearbook; Situation & Outlook Yearbook. Tobacco.
Indexed: AmStI, TobAb, WAE&RSA.
—CISTI.
Published by: U.S. Department of Agriculture, Economic Research Service, 1800 M St. NW, Washington, DC 20036-5831. TEL 202-694-5050, http://www.ers.usda.gov/publications/so/view.asp?f=specialty/tbs-bb/. Circ: 3,000. **Subscr. to:** U.S. Government Printing Office, Superintendent of Documents, PO Box 371954, Pittsburgh, PA 15250-7954. TEL 202-512-1800, FAX 202-512-2250, orders@gpo.gov, http://www.access.gpo.gov. **Dist. by:** ERS-NASS, 5285 Port Royal Rd, Springfield, VA 22161. TEL 800-999-6779.

635 USA ISSN 1049-3352
HD9220.U5 CODEN: VSSRES
SITUATION & OUTLOOK REPORT. VEGETABLES & SPECIALTIES. Text in English. 1955. 3/yr. USD 15 (effective 2001). mkt.; stat. back issues avail.; reprint service avail. from CIS. **Document type:** *Government.* **Description:** Examines U.S. production of vegetables and specialty crops including consumption, supply, use, value, trade, prices, processing and more.
Former titles (until 1986): U.S. Department of Agriculture. Situation and Outlook Report. Vegetables (0893-8938); (until 1986): U.S. Department of Agriculture. Outlook and Situation Report. Vegetable (0893-892X); (until 1983): U.S. Department of Agriculture. Vegetable Outlook and Situation (0277-9900); (until 1980): U.S. Department of Agriculture. Vegetable Situation (0042-3084)
Related titles: Microfiche ed.: (from CIS); Online - full text ed.: (from Gale Group, The Dialog Corporation).

Indexed: AmStl, PHN&I, PotatoAb, RASB, WAE&RSA.
—CISTI.
Published by: U.S. Department of Agriculture, Economic Research Service, 1800 M St. NW, Washington, DC 20036-5831. http://www.ers.usda.gov/publications/so/view.asp?f=/specialty/vgs-bb/. **Subscr. to:** U.S. Government Printing Office, Superintendent of Documents, PO Box 371954, Pittsburgh, PA 15250-7954. TEL 202-512-1800, FAX 202-512-2250, orders@gpo.gov, http://www.access.gpo.gov. **Dist. by:** ERS-NASS, 5285 Port Royal Rd, Springfield, VA 22161. TEL 800-999-6779.

630 USA
SITUATION & OUTLOOK REPORT. WHEAT OUTLOOK. Text in English. 1995. 11/yr. USD 21 (effective 2001). **Document type:** *Government.* **Description:** Examines supply, use, demand, price and trade for all U.S. wheat and for individual wheat classes. Includes supply and demand prospects in major importing and exporting countries.
Media: Online - full text (from Gale Group, The Dialog Corporation). **Related titles:** ♦ Supplement(s): Situation & Outlook Report. Wheat Yearbook.
Published by: U.S. Department of Agriculture, Economic Research Service, 1800 M St. NW, Washington, DC 20036-5831. ersinfo@ers.usda.gov, http://www.ers.usda.gov/publications/so/view.asp?f=field/whs-bb/.

630 USA
SITUATION & OUTLOOK REPORT. WHEAT YEARBOOK. Text in English. a. USD 21 (effective 2001). **Document type:** *Yearbook, Government.* **Description:** Examines supply, use, demand, price, and trade for all U.S. wheat and for individual wheat classes. Includes supply and demand prospects in major importing and exporting countries.
Related titles: Online - full content ed.; ♦ Supplement to: Situation & Outlook Report. Wheat Outlook.
Indexed: WAE&RSA.
Published by: U.S. Department of Agriculture, Economic Research Service, 1800 M St. NW, Washington, DC 20036-5831. ersinfo@ers.usda.gov, http://www.ers.usda.gov/publications/so/view.asp?f=field/whs-bby/. **Dist. by:** ERS-NASS, 5285 Port Royal Rd, Springfield, VA 22161. TEL 800-999-6779.

633.6 CUB ISSN 0049-0849
TP375 CODEN: SDCAAR
SOBRE LOS DERIVADOS DE LA CANA DE AZUCAR. Text in Spanish; Summaries in English. 1967. 3/yr. USD 26 in South America; USD 28 in North America; USD 34 elsewhere. charts; illus.
Indexed: ABIPC, BiolAb, CIN, ChemAb, ChemTitl, FS&TA, HortAb, SIA.
—CINDOC.
Published by: (Instituto Cubano de Investigaciones de los Derivados de la Cana de Azucar), Ediciones Cubanas, Obispo No. 527, Apdo. 605, Havana, Cuba. Eds. Gladys Blanco Carracedo, Rainerio Garcia Carmenates. Circ: 1,500 (controlled).

630 COL ISSN 0120-0682
CODEN: RECODY
SOCIEDAD COLOMBIANA DE CONTROL DE MALEZAS Y FISIOLOGIA VEGETAL. REVISTA. Key Title: Revista COMALFI. Text in Spanish; Summaries in English. 1974. 3/yr. COP 10,000 to individuals; USD 20 foreign to individuals; COP 5,000 to students; USD 15 foreign to students. adv. bk.rev. charts; illus.; stat. **Document type:** *Academic/Scholarly.* **Description:** Covers articles on tropical weeds, vegetation and plant physiology. Includes original results of research done in the field of the science of tropical weeds as well as in vegetation.
Indexed: ChemAb, WeedAb.
Published by: Sociedad Colombiana de Control de Malezas y Fisiologia Vegetal, Ciudad Universitaria, Bloque C Modulo 3 Nivel 8, DF, Carrera 50, 27-70, Bogota, CUND, Colombia. TEL 57-1-221-9643, FAX 57-1-2217458. Ed. Jaime Soriano. Circ: 1,000.

631.4 USA ISSN 0096-4522
S590 CODEN: SCSFAD
➤ **SOIL AND CROP SCIENCE SOCIETY OF FLORIDA. ANNUAL PROCEEDINGS.** Text in English. a. **Document type:** *Academic/Scholarly.*
Indexed: AEA, ASCA, AbHyg, AgBio, Agr, BIOSIS Prev, BibAg, BiolAb, CPA, ChemAb, CurCont, DSA, ExcerpMed, FCA, ForAb, HerbAb, HortAb, I&DA, MaizeAb, NemAb, NutrAb, OrnHort, PBA, PGrRegA, PN&I, PotatoAb, PoultAb, RPP, RiceAb, S&F, S&MA, SIA, SSCI, SeedAb, SoyAb, TDB, TOSA, TriticAb, WAE&RSA, WeedAb.
—BLDSC (6818.800000), CASDDS, CISTI, IDS, IE, ingenta.
Published by: (Soil and Crop Science Society of Florida), University of Florida, Institute of Food and Agricultural Sciences, 106 Newell Hall, Gainesville, FL 32611-0510. Ed. B L McNeal.

➤ **SOIL & ENVIRONMENT.** see *ENVIRONMENTAL STUDIES*

➤ **SOIL & SEDIMENT CONTAMINATION**; an international journal. see *ENVIRONMENTAL STUDIES—Pollution*

631.4 USA
SOIL - PLANT ANALYST. Text in English. 1983. q. looseleaf. USD 40. adv. back issues avail. **Document type:** *Newsletter.* **Description:** For operators of soil and plant analysis laboratories. Covers methods for analyzing nutrients in soils, plants, animal wastes, and water. Explores the use of diagnostic techniques that improve nutrient management in crop production and the environment.
Published by: Soil and Plant Analysis Council, Georgia University Sta, Box 2007, Athens, GA 30612-0007. TEL 706-546-0425, FAX 706-548-4891. Ed. J Benton Jones. adv.: page USD 1,200. Circ: 350.

631.4 USA ISSN 0038-075X
S590 CODEN: SOSCAK
➤ **SOIL SCIENCE**; an interdisciplinary approach to soils research. Text in English. 1916. m. USD 212 domestic to individuals; USD 291 foreign to individuals; USD 412 domestic to institutions; USD 492 foreign to institutions (effective 2006). adv. bk.rev. bibl.; charts; illus.; stat. reprints avail. **Document type:** *Journal, Academic/Scholarly.* **Description:** Research articles of interest to soil testing bureaus, soil scientists, agronomists and environmentalists.
Related titles: Microfilm ed.: (from WWS); Online - full text ed.: ISSN 1538-9243. USD 396.50 domestic academic site license; USD 463.50 foreign academic site license; USD 442.25 domestic corporate site license; USD 509.25 foreign corporate site license (effective 2002) (from EBSCO Publishing, H.W. Wilson, O C L C Online Computer Library Center, Inc., Ovid Technologies, Inc., Swets Information Services).
Indexed: ABIPC, AEA, AESIS, ASCA, ASFA, AbHyg, AgBio, Agr, AgrForAb, ApicAb, B&AI, BIOBASE, BIOSIS Prev, BibAg, BiolAb, CIN, CPA, ChemAb, ChemTitl, CivEngAb, CurCont, DBA, EPB, ESPM, EngInd, EnvAb, EnvEAb, ExcerpMed, F&GI, FCA, FLUIDEX, FPA, ForAb, GEOBASE, GeotechAb, HerbAb, HortAb, I&DA, IABS, IBR, INIS AtomInd, ISR, M&TEA, MaizeAb, NemAb, OrnHort, PBA, PN&I, PetrolAb, PlantSci, PollutAb, PoultAb, RPP, RefZh, RevApplEntom, RiceAb, S&F, SCI, SWRA, SeedAb, SoyAb, TriticAb, VITIS, WAE&RSA, WRCInf, WeedAb.
—BLDSC (8324.000000), CASDDS, CISTI, Ei, IDS, IE, Infotrieve, ingenta, Linda Hall. **CCC.**
Published by: (Rutgers, the State University of New Jersey), Lippincott Williams & Wilkins (Subsidiary of: Wolters Kluwer N.V.), 530 Walnut St, Philadelphia, PA 19106-3621. TEL 215-521-8300, FAX 215-521-8902, soilscience@aesop.rutgers.edu, http://www.soilsci.com, http://www.lww.com, http://lww.custhelp.com/. Ed. Dr. Robert L. Tate III. Pub. Michael Hargrett. Adv. contacts Carol Miranda, Ray Thibodeau. B&W page USD 695, color page USD 1,505. Circ: 1,372 (paid).

➤ **SOIL SCIENCE ALERT**; an alerting service covering current articles in Elsevier soil science journals. see *EARTH SCIENCES—Abstracting, Bibliographies, Statistics*

631.4 JPN ISSN 0038-0768
CODEN: SSPNAW
➤ **SOIL SCIENCE AND PLANT NUTRITION.** Text in English. 1955. q. USD 100. **Document type:** *Academic/Scholarly.*
Indexed: AEA, ASCA, ASFA, AgBio, AgrForAb, AnBrAb, BIOBASE, BIOSIS Prev, BioCN&I, BiolAb, CIN, CPA, ChemAb, ChemTitl, CurCont, EIA, EPB, ESPM, EnerInd, ExcerpMed, FCA, FPA, ForAb, HerbAb, HortAb, I&DA, IABS, INIS AtomInd, ISR, MaizeAb, NemAb, NutrAb, OrnHort, PBA, PGegResA, PGrRegA, PHN&I, PN&I, PlantSci, PollutAb, PotatoAb, PoultAb, RA&MP, RPP, RefZh, RevApplEntom, RiceAb, S&F, S&MA, SCI, SIA, SeedAb, SoyAb, TriticAb, WAE&RSA, WeedAb.
—BLDSC (8324.100000), CASDDS, CISTI, IDS, IE, Infotrieve, ingenta, Linda Hall.
Published by: (Japan Society of Soil Science and Plant Nutrition), Business Center for Academic Societies Japan/Nihon Gakkai Jimu Senta, 5-16-19 Honkomagome, Bunkyo-ku, Tokyo, 113-0021, Japan. TEL 81-3-5814-5811, FAX 81-3-5814-5822.

631.4 USA ISSN 1047-4986
CODEN: SABSEP
SOIL SCIENCE SOCIETY OF AMERICA BOOK SERIES. Text in English. 1989. irreg. **Document type:** *Monographic series.*
Indexed: BIOSIS Prev.
—BLDSC (8324.280000), CASDDS, IE, ingenta. **CCC.**
Published by: Soil Science Society of America, 677 S Segoe Rd, Madison, WI 53711. TEL 608-273-8080, FAX 608-273-2021. R&P David Kral.

631.4 USA ISSN 0361-5995
S590.S64 CODEN: SSSJD4
➤ **SOIL SCIENCE SOCIETY OF AMERICA. JOURNAL.** Text in English. 1936. bi-m. USD 247 domestic; USD 277 foreign (effective 2005). adv. bk.rev. bibl.; charts; illus. index. 2 cols./p.; reprints avail. **Document type:** *Journal, Academic/Scholarly.* **Description:** Contains papers on new developments in soil physics, mineralogy, chemistry, microbiology, fertility and plant nutrition, soil genesis and classification, soil and water management, forest and range soils, and fertilizer use and technology.
Formerly (until 1976): Soil Science Society of America. Proceedings (0038-0776)
Related titles: CD-ROM ed.; Microform ed.: (from PMC); Online - full content ed.; Online - full text ed.: ISSN 1435-0661 (from bigchalk, EBSCO Publishing, HighWire Press, ProQuest Information & Learning).
Indexed: ABIPC, AEA, AESIS, ASCA, ASFA, AbHyg, Agr, AgrForAb, AnalAb, B&AI, B&BAb, BIOBASE, BIOSIS Prev, BibAg, BioDAb, BiolAb, BrCerAb, C&ISA, CCI, CIN, CPA, CTFA, CerAb, ChemAb, ChemTitl, CivEngAb, CorrAb, CurCont, DBA, DSA, E&CAJ, EIA, EMA, EPB, ESPM, EnerInd, EngInd, EnvAb, EnvEAb, EnvInd, ExcerpMed, FCA, FLUIDEX, FPA, ForAb, GEOBASE, GSI, GeotechAb, HerbAb, HortAb, I&DA, IAA, IABS, INIS AtomInd, ISR, M&TEA, MBA, MBF, METADEX, MSB, MSCI, MaizeAb, OrnHort, PBA, PGegResA, PGrRegA, PN&I, PetrolAb, PlantSci, PollutAb, PotatoAb, PoultAb, RA&MP, RPP, RefZh, RevApplEntom, RiceAb, S&F, S&MA, SCI, SIA, SWRA, SeedAb, SolStAb, SoyAb, TriticAb, WAA, WAE&RSA, WRCInf, WeedAb.
—BLDSC (8324.300000), CASDDS, CINDOC, CISTI, Ei, IDS, IE, Infotrieve, ingenta, Linda Hall. **CCC.**
Published by: Soil Science Society of America, 677 S Segoe Rd, Madison, WI 53711. TEL 608-273-8095, FAX 608-273-2021, journals@agronomy.org, http://soil.scijournals.org, http://www.soils.org/. Eds. Richard L Mulvaney, Warren A Dick. R&P David Kral. Adv. contact Keith R Schlesinger. B&W page USD 1,190, color page USD 2,915. Circ: 5,600 (paid).

631.4 LKA ISSN 1015-0803
SOIL SCIENCE SOCIETY OF SRI LANKA. JOURNAL. Text in English. 1970. a. LKR 100, USD 5 (effective 1999). adv. bk.rev. **Document type:** *Academic/Scholarly.*
Formerly: Soil Science Society of Ceylon. Journal
Indexed: SLSI.
Published by: Soil Science Society of Sri Lanka, c/o Faculty of Agriculture, University of Sri Lanka, Peradeniya, Sri Lanka. Ed. Deepthi Nanayakkara. R&P D Kumaragamage. Adv. contact Gamini Desilva. Circ: 150.

631.5 USA ISSN 0584-0554
S592.14
SOIL SURVEY HORIZONS. Text in English. 1975. q. bk.rev. back issues avail. **Description:** Expresses ideas, problems, and philosophies concerning the study of soils in the field.
Indexed: AEA, Agr, BibAg, FCA, HortAb, MaizeAb, S&F, SoyAb, WeedAb.
—BLDSC (8324.790000), CISTI, IE, ingenta. **CCC.**
Published by: Soil Science Society of America, 677 S Segoe Rd, Madison, WI 53711. TEL 608-273-8080, FAX 608-273-2021, http://www.soils.org/. Ed. Gerald Miller. R&P David Kral. Circ: 1,200.

631.4 GBR ISSN 0951-3485
SOIL SURVEY RECORD. Text in English. 1970. irreg., latest vol.115, 1990. price varies. **Document type:** *Government.* **Description:** Information about land use and soil content of selected 100 square kilometer areas of England and Wales.
Supersedes: Great Britain. Soil Survey of England and Wales. Records (0072-7180)
Indexed: S&F.
—Linda Hall.
Published by: Soil Survey and Land Research Centre, Silsoe Campus, Silsoe, Bedford, MK45 4DT, United Kingdom. TEL 44-1525-863242, FAX 44-1525-863253.

631.4 NLD ISSN 0936-2568
CODEN: ILSAEN
SOIL TECHNOLOGY SERIES. Text and summaries in English. 1989. a. price varies. back issues avail. **Document type:** *Proceedings.*
Indexed: Agr, CurCont.
—CISTI.
Published by: Elsevier BV (Subsidiary of: Elsevier Science & Technology), Radarweg 29, Amsterdam, 1043 NX, Netherlands. TEL 31-20-4853911, FAX 31-20-4852457, nlinfo-f@elsevier.nl, http://www.elsevier.nl. Circ: 1,000.

631.4 GBR ISSN 0266-0032
CODEN: SUMAEU
➤ **SOIL USE AND MANAGEMENT.** Text in English. 1985. q. USD 245 in the Americas to individuals; GBP 140 elsewhere to individuals; USD 410 in the Americas to institutions; GBP 235 elsewhere to institutions; USD 265 combined subscription in the Americas to individuals print & online; GBP 150 combined subscription elsewhere to individuals print & online; USD 440 combined subscription in the Americas to institutions print & online; GBP 250 combined subscription elsewhere to institutions print & online (effective 2005). adv. bk.rev. charts; illus. back issues avail. **Document type:** *Academic/Scholarly.* **Description:** Provides an international forum for those applying scientific principles to understand and solve important soil problems as they affect crop production and environmental issues.
Related titles: Online - full text ed.: ISSN 1475-2743. USD 140 in the Americas to individuals; GBP 80 elsewhere to individuals; USD 350 in the Americas to institutions; GBP 200 elsewhere to institutions (effective 2005) (from EBSCO Publishing, Gale Group, IngentaConnect, Swets Information Services).

▼ *new title* ➤ *refereed* ✶ *unverified* ♦ *full entry avail.*

Indexed: AEA, ASCA, Agr, AgrForAb, AnBrAb, BIOBASE, BIOSIS Prev, BibAg, BioCN&I, BiolAb, BrCerAb, C&ISA, CPA, CerAb, CivEngAb, CorrAb, CurCont, DSA, E&CAJ, EMA, EPB, ESPM, EngInd, EnvEAb, FCA, FLUIDEX, FPA, FaBeAb, ForAb, GEOBASE, HerbAb, HortAb, I&DA, IAA, IABS, ISR, M&TEA, MBF, METADEX, MaizeAb, NutrAb, OrnHort, PGrRegA, PN&I, PlantSci, PollutAb, PotatoAb, PoultAb, ProtozoAb, RA&MP, RDA, RPP, RiceAb, RiskAb, S&F, SCI, SIA, SWRA, SeedAb, SolStAb, SoyAb, TriticAb, VetBull, WAA, WAE&RSA, WRCInf, WeedAb.
—BLDSC (8326.150000), CASDDS, CISTI, Ei, IDS, IE, Infotrieve, ingenta, Linda Hall. **CCC.**
Published by: (British Society of Soil Science), CABI Publishing (Subsidiary of: CAB International), CAB International, Wallingford, Oxfordshire OX10 8DE, United Kingdom. TEL 44-1491-832111, FAX 44-1491-833508, cabi@cabi.org, http://www.cabi-publishing.org/JOURNALS/SUM/Index.asp. Ed. Dr. D B Davies. Pub. David Smith TEL 44-1491-829325. Adv. contact Sarah Harris TEL 44-1491-829310. B&W page GBP 125, B&W page USD 200; 170 x 240. **Subscr. addr. in N America:** CABI Publishing North America, 875 Massachusetts Ave, 7th Fl, Cambridge, MA 02139. TEL 617-395-4056, 800-528-4841, FAX 617-354-6875, cabi-nao@cabi.org.

➤ **SOILS AND GROUNDWATER CLEANUP.** see *ENVIRONMENTAL STUDIES—Waste Management*

631.4 AUS ISSN 0812-017X
SOILS NEWS. Text in English. 195?. q. bk.rev. **Description:** Published to inform members about decisions by the council, the activities of the different branches, and events of interest.
Published by: Australian Society of Soil Science, Federal Council, c/o CSIRO Division of Soils, Private Mail Bag 2, Glen Osmond, SA 5064, Australia. TEL 61-8-274-9311, FAX 61-8-338-1636, TELEX AA 82406. Ed. Clive Kirkby. Circ: 700.

631 AUT ISSN 1011-2650
SOILS NEWSLETTER. Text in English. 1978. s-a. free. **Document type:** *Newsletter, Trade.*
Published by: International Atomic Energy Agency/Agence Internationale de l'Energie Atomique, Division of Conference and Document Services, Wagramer Str 5, Postfach 100, Vienna, W 1400, Austria. TEL 43-1-2600-0, FAX 43-1-2600-7, sales.publications@iaea.org, http://www.iaea.org. Circ: 1,500. **Co-sponsor:** Food and Agriculture Organization of the United Nations.

631.4 NGA ISSN 0038-1209
S590 CODEN: SOLAAD
SOLS AFRICAINS/AFRICAN SOILS. Text in English, French. 1951. 3/yr. price varies. charts; illus.; tr.lit. cum.index every 2 yrs. back issues avail. **Document type:** *Academic/Scholarly.*
Indexed: BiolAb, ChemAb, GeotechAb.
Published by: Organization of African Unity, Inter-African Bureau for Soils/Organisation de l'Unite Africaine, NPA Bldg. 4th Fl., 26-28 Marina, PMB 2359, Lagos, Nigeria. TEL 234-1-2633430, FAX 234-1-2636093, TELEX 28786 TECOAU NG, oaustrc.lagos@rcl.dircon.co.uk. Ed. Johnson Ekpere. Circ: 2,000.

SOUTH AFRICAN JOURNAL FOR ENOLOGY AND VITICULTURE. see *BEVERAGES*

631 ZAF ISSN 0257-1862
CODEN: SAJSEV
➤ **SOUTH AFRICAN JOURNAL OF PLANT AND SOIL.** Text in English. 1983. q. ZAR 190 to institutions; USD 72 foreign (effective 2000). adv. **Document type:** *Academic/Scholarly.*
Indexed: AEA, ASFA, AbAn, AgBio, Agr, AgrForAb, BIOSIS Prev, BioCN&I, BiolAb, CIN, CPA, CTFA, ChemAb, ChemTitl, DBA, ESPM, EntAb, FCA, FS&TA, ForAb, GEOBASE, HerbAb, HortAb, I&DA, INIS AtomInd, ISAP, M&TEA, MaizeAb, NemAb, NutrAb, OrnHort, PBA, PGegResA, PGrRegA, PHN&I, PollutAb, PotatoAb, RA&MP, RDA, RPP, RefZh, RevApplEntom, S&F, S&MA, SIA, SWRA, SeedAb, SoyAb, TriticAb, VITIS, WAE&RSA, WeedAb.
—BLDSC (8339.710000), CASDDS, IE, ingenta.
Published by: (South African Society for Crop Production), South African Bureau for Scientific Publications, PO Box 11663, Pretoria, Hatfield 0028, South Africa. TEL 27-12-322-6404, FAX 27-12-320-7803, bspman@icon.co.za, http://www.safest.org.za/bsp. Ed., Adv. contact J B J van Rensburg. Circ: 1,060. **Co-sponsors:** Southern African Weed Science Society; Soil Science Society of Southern Africa.

631 ZAF ISSN 0375-2682
SOUTH AFRICAN SUGAR ASSOCIATION EXPERIMENT STATION. ANNUAL REPORT. Text in English. a., latest 2000. ZAR 20 (effective 1999). illus. **Document type:** *Corporate.* **Description:** Includes information on sugarcane breeding, pest and disease control, soil research, biotechnology, farm planning, irrigation, extension, and agronomy research and crop modelling.
—BLDSC (1245.800000).
Published by: South African Sugar Association Experiment Station, Private Bag X02, Mount Edgecombe, 4300, South Africa. TEL 27-31-593205, FAX 27-31-595406, sasex@sugar.org.za, http://www.sugar.co.za. Circ: 3,200.

631 ZAF
SOUTH AFRICAN SUGAR ASSOCIATION EXPERIMENT STATION. BULLETIN. Text in English. irreg. ZAR 30 (effective 2001). charts; illus. back issues avail. **Document type:** *Bulletin.* **Description:** Includes information on breeding, pest and disease control, irrigation and soil conservation.
Published by: South African Sugar Association Experiment Station, Private Bag X02, Mount Edgecombe, 4300, South Africa. TEL 27-31-593205, FAX 27-31-595406, sasex@sugar.org.za, http://www.sugar.co.za. Circ: 3,000.

632.954 ZAF
SOUTH AFRICAN SUGAR ASSOCIATION EXPERIMENT STATION. HERBICIDE GUIDE. Text in English. q. looseleaf. ZAR 20 (effective 2001). **Description:** Deals with weed control in sugar cane.
Published by: South African Sugar Association Experiment Station, Private Bag X02, Mount Edgecombe, 4300, South Africa. TEL 27-31-593205, FAX 27-31-595406, sasex@sugar.org.za, http://www.sugar.co.za. Circ: 3,200.

SOUTH AFRICAN SUGAR JOURNAL. see *FOOD AND FOOD INDUSTRIES*

631 ZAF ISSN 0373-045X
CODEN: PSATAA
➤ **SOUTH AFRICAN SUGAR TECHNOLOGISTS' ASSOCIATION. PROCEEDINGS.** Variant title: S A S T A Proceedings. Text in English. 1927. a., latest vol.76, 2002. ZAR 100 (effective 2003). illus. **Document type:** *Proceedings, Academic/Scholarly.* **Description:** Contains information on sugarcane agriculture, breeding, pests, diseases, manufacturing, milling, soil research, biotechnology, irrigation, agronomy, and extension.
Related titles: CD-ROM ed.
Indexed: AEA, CIN, CPA, ChemAb, ChemTitl, FCA, FS&TA, I&DA, MaizeAb, PBA, PGrRegA, PHN&I, RPP, RevApplEntom, S&F, SIA, WAE&RSA, WeedAb.
—BLDSC (6840.560000), CASDDS, CISTI.
Published by: South African Sugar Technologists' Association, Private Bag X02, Mount Edgecombe, 4300, South Africa. TEL 27-31-593205, FAX 27-31-595406, TELEX 6-23020, sasta@sugar.org.za, http://www.sasta.co.za. Circ: 700.

633.368 USA ISSN 0038-3694
SOUTHEASTERN PEANUT FARMER. Text in English. 1962. 6/yr. USD 20 (effective 2005). adv. 32 p./no.; **Document type:** *Magazine, Trade.* **Description:** News articles on the legislative, financial, and policy issues affecting this agricultural industry in this region of the country.
Published by: Georgia Peanut Commission, PO Box 967, Tifton, GA 31793-0967. TEL 229-386-3470, FAX 229-386-3501, sepf@gapeanuts.com, info@gapeanuts.com, http://www.gapeanuts.com/sepf.asp. Pub. Don Koehler. Adv. contact Joan S. Underwood. B&W page USD 3,225, color page USD 3,925; trim 8.5 x 11. Circ: 8,063 (paid). **Co-sponsors:** Alabama Peanut Producers Association; Florida Peanut Producers Association.

630.24 USA ISSN 0362-4463
SB610.2 CODEN: SWSPBE
SOUTHERN WEED SCIENCE SOCIETY. PROCEEDINGS. Text in English. a. price varies. **Document type:** *Proceedings, Academic/Scholarly.*
Indexed: Agr, BiolAb, DBA, HortAb, S&F, WeedAb.
—BLDSC (6841.945000), CASDDS, CISTI, IE, ingenta, Linda Hall.
Published by: Southern Weed Science Society, c/o Robert A Schmidt, 1508 W University, Champaign, IL 61821-3133. TEL 217-352-4212, FAX 217-352-4241, http://www.weedscience.msstate.edu/swss/.

633 664 USA
THE SOY CONNECTION. Text in English. 190?. 3/yr.
Published by: United Soybean Board, 16640 Chesterfield Grove Rd, Ste 130, Chesterfield, MO 63005. TEL 800-989-8721, http://www.unitedsoybean.org. Ed. adfsadf adfsadf.

633 664 USA ISSN 1099-7970
HD9235.S62
(YEAR) SOYA & OILSEED BLUEBOOK. Text in English. a. USD 70 domestic; USD 85 elsewhere (effective 2000); includes q. Bluebook Update. adv. charts; mkt.; stat. back issues avail. **Document type:** *Directory.* **Description:** Lists key players in the global oilseed processing industry. Includes company information, product listings, and reference material for the soybean, corn, cottonseed, canola, rapeseed, sunflower, palm and palm kernel industries.
Former titles (until 1999): Soya Bluebook Plus (1081-3063); (until 1996): Soya Bluebook (0275-4509); (until 1980): Soybean Digest Blue Book (0081-3222)
Related titles: Microfilm ed.; ♦ Supplement(s): Bluebook Update. ISSN 1081-5228.
Indexed: SRI.
—CISTI, Linda Hall.
Published by: Soyatech, Inc., 1369 State Highway 102., Bar Harbor, ME 04609-7019. TEL 207-288-4969, 800-424-SOYA, FAX 207-288-5264, data@soyatech.com, http://www.soyatech.com. Ed. Keri Hayes. Pub., R&P Peter Golbitz. Adv. contact Joy Froding. B&W page USD 2,175, color page USD 2,850; trim 10.88 x 8.25. Circ: 2,500.

583.74 USA
SOYBEAN SOUTH. Text in English. 6/yr. USD 40 (effective 2005). **Document type:** *Magazine, Trade.* **Description:** Targets soybean growers in southern U.S. states.
Published by: One Grower Publishing, 5118 Park Ave, Ste 131, Memphis, TN 38117. TEL 901-767-4020, FAX 901-767-4026.

633 ESP
SPAIN. DIRECCION GENERAL DE LA PRODUCCION AGRARIA. CAMPANA ALGODONERA. Text in Spanish. irreg.
Published by: Ministerio de Agricultura, Direccion General de la Produccion Agraria, Madrid, Spain.

632.9 ESP ISSN 0213-6910
SPAIN. MINISTERIO DE AGRICULTURA, PESCA Y ALIMENTACION. BOLETIN DE SANIDAD VEGETAL: PLAGAS. Text in Spanish. 1975. q. **Document type:** *Bulletin, Academic/Scholarly.*
Formerly (until 1985): Spain. Ministerio de Agricultura, Pesca y Alimentacion. Servicio de Defensa Contra Plagas e Inspeccion Fitopatologica. Boletin (0210-8038)
Indexed: AgBio, AgrForAb, BioCN&I, BioDAb, DBA, FCA, FPA, FS&TA, ForAb, HerbAb, HortAb, IECT, MaizeAb, NemAb, NutrAb, OrnHort, PBA, PGegResA, PHN&I, PotatoAb, RA&MP, RM&VM, RPP, RefZh, RevApplEntom, RiceAb, S&F, SIA, SeedAb, SoyAb, TriticAb, WAE&RSA, WeedAb, ZooRec.
—CINDOC, CISTI.
Published by: (Spain. Subdireccion General de Sanidad Vegetal), Ministerio de Agricultura Pesca y Alimentacion, Centro de Publicaciones, Paseo Infanta Isabel 1, Madrid, 28014, Spain. TEL 34-91-3475550, FAX 34-91-3475722, mllopisj@mapya.es, http://www.mapya.es. Ed. Ramon Vazquez Hombrados. R&P Juan Carlos Palacios Lopez.

633 CAN ISSN 0828-3737
SPECIALTY CROP REPORT. Text in English. 1982. a. free. back issues avail. **Document type:** *Government.* **Description:** Reports the production of lentils, beans, peas, mustard, sunflowers, caraway seed, buckwheat, triticale and fava beans grown in Saskatchewan.
—CISTI.
Published by: Agriculture and Food, B5 Walter Scott Bldg, 3085 Albert St, Regina, SK S4S 0B1, Canada. TEL 888-613-3975 (in US only), FAX 306-721-4626, pad@sk.sympatico.ca, http://www.agr.gov.sk.ca/saf. Circ: 3,000.

SPORTSTURF. see *SPORTS AND GAMES—Ball Games*

630 GBR
SPRING COMBINABLE CROP POCKET BOOK. Text in English. a. GBP 15 per vol. (effective 2003). **Document type:** *Bulletin, Academic/Scholarly.*
Published by: N I A B, Huntingdon Rd, Cambridge, CB3 0LE, United Kingdom. TEL 44-1223-276381, FAX 44-1223-342328, info@niab.com, paul.nelson@niab.com, http://www.niab.com. Ed. Paul Nelson TEL 44-1223-342225.

631 USA ISSN 0739-022X
SPUDLETTER. Text in English. irreg. **Document type:** *Newsletter.*
Published by: National Potato Council, 1300 L St, N W, Ste 910, Washington, DC 20005-4107. TEL 303-773-9295, FAX 303-773-9296. Ed. Carol Reseigh. Circ: 10,500.

633.491 631.3 USA ISSN 0038-8661
SB211.P8
SPUDMAN; voice of the potato industry. Text in English. 1963. 8/yr. USD 35; free to qualified personnel (effective 2004). adv. bk.rev. back issues avail. **Document type:** *Magazine, Trade.* **Description:** For growers and decision-makers involved with the growing, shipping, packing, buying and processing of potatoes.
—CISTI, Linda Hall.
Published by: Great American Publishing Co., 75 Applewood Dr, Ste A, Sparta, MI 49345. http://www.spudman.com. Ed. Kim Warren. Pub. Matt McCallum. Adv. contact Brenda Bradford. B&W page USD 2,526, color page USD 3,880; trim 8.5 x 11. Circ: 15,500 (paid and controlled).

633.51 USA ISSN 0279-3148
STAPLREVIEW. Text in English. 1921. m. USD 1. adv. charts; stat. reprint service avail. from CIS.
Formerly: Staple Cotton Review (0038-9838)
Related titles: Microfiche ed.: (from CIS).
Indexed: AmStI, TTI.
—Linda Hall.
Published by: Staple Cotton Cooperative Association, 210 214 W Market St, Greenwood, MS 38930. TEL 601-453-6231. Ed. R L Clarke.

STOCK JOURNAL. see *AGRICULTURE—Poultry And Livestock*

631 BEL ISSN 0770-9404
CODEN: SUBEAH
LA SUCRERIE BELGE. Text in English, French. 1872. a. free. adv. **Document type:** *Bulletin.*
Indexed: AEA, ChemAb, ExcerpMed, FCA, FS&TA, HerbAb, HortAb, NutrAb, PHN&I, RefZh, S&F, SIA, WAE&RSA.
—BLDSC (8506.000000), CISTI.

Published by: Societe Generale des Fabricants de Sucre de Belgique, Av Tervuren 182, Brussels, 1150, Belgium. TEL 32-2-7758069, FAX 32-2-7758075, TELEX 24523 RAFT B, info@subel.be. Ed. Marc Rosiers. Adv. contact Christine Sneppe. Circ: 1,500. **Co-sponsor:** Societe Technique et Chimique de Sucrerie de Belgique.

630 SDN ISSN 0562-5068
SUDAN COTTON REVIEW. Text in English. 1958. a.
Published by: Cotton Public Corporation, P O Box 1672, Khartoum, Sudan.

SUGAR MILLING RESEARCH INSTITUTE. ANNUAL REPORT. see *FOOD AND FOOD INDUSTRIES*

SUGAR TECH; an international journal of sugar crops and related industries. see *FOOD AND FOOD INDUSTRIES*

633.63 USA ISSN 0039-4750
SUGARBEET GROWER. Text in English. 1963. bi-m. USD 12 domestic; USD 18 foreign (effective 2005). adv. illus.
Document type: *Magazine, Trade.*
Published by: Sugar Publications, 503 Broadway, Fargo, ND 58102. TEL 701-476-2111, FAX 701-476-2182, http://www.sugarpub.com. Ed., R&P Don Lilleboe. Adv. contacts Don Lilleboe, Todd Phelps. Circ: 12,800 (controlled).

631.5 USA ISSN 0192-8988
THE SUNFLOWER (BISMARCK). Text in English. 1979 (vol.5). 6/yr. USD 9 domestic; USD 36 foreign (effective 2005). adv. **Document type:** *Magazine, Consumer.* **Description:** Aimed at sunflower producers and those involved in the sunflower industry. Includes production techniques, marketing updates, legislative and industry related news.
—CISTI.
Published by: National Sunflower Association, 4023 State St, Bismarck, ND 58503. TEL 701-328-5100, FAX 701-328-5101, klngrtner@sunflowernsa.com, klngrtner@sunflowerusa.com, http://www.sunflowernsa.com. Ed. Larry Kleingartner. Adv. contact Lerrene Kroh TEL 701-328-5107. B&W page USD 1,470. Circ: 29,345 (paid and controlled).

631.5 SWE ISSN 0346-2099
SVENSK FROETIDNING. Text in Swedish. 1932. m. (10/yr.). SEK 300 (effective 1998). adv. **Document type:** *Academic/Scholarly.*
Indexed: AEA, FCA, HerbAb, MaizeAb, PBA, RPP, RevApplEntom, SeedAb, WAE&RSA, WeedAb.
Published by: Sveriges Froe- och Oljevoextodlana, Fack 96, Alnarp, 23053, Sweden. FAX 46-40-41-55-04. Ed. Gunilla Larsson. Adv. contact Jeannette R Fredriksson. Circ: 10,000.

631.5 SWE ISSN 0039-6990
CODEN: SUTTAG
SVERIGES UTSAEDESFOERENINGS TIDSKRIFT/SWEDISH SEED ASSOCIATION. JOURNAL; organ foer svensk vaextforaedling. Text in English, Swedish; Summaries in English. 1891. q. SEK 80 (effective 2002). adv. bk.rev. bibl.; charts; illus. index. **Document type:** *Trade.*
Formerly (until 1894): Allmaenna Svenska Utsaedesfoereningens Tidskrift
Indexed: AgBio, BioCN&I, BiolAb, CPA, ChemAb, DSA, FCA, ForAb, HerbAb, HortAb, I&DA, MaizeAb, NemAb, NutrAb, OrnHort, PBA, PGegResA, PHN&I, PotatoAb, RPP, RevApplEntom, S&F, SIA, SeedAb, SoyAb, TriticAb, WAE&RSA, WeedAb.
—CASDDS, CISTI.
Published by: Sveriges Utsaedesfoerening/Swedish Seed Association, Svalov, 26881, Sweden. TEL 46-418-667-000, FAX 46-418-66-71-00, ylva.myllenberg@swseed.se. Ed. R von Bothmer. Circ: 1,300.

630 POL ISSN 0082-1276
CODEN: STNRDA
SZCZECINSKIE TOWARZYSTWO NAUKOWE. WYDZIAL NAUK PRZYRODNICZO-ROLNICZYCH. PRACE. Text in Polish; Summaries in English, German, Russian. 1959. irreg. price varies.
Indexed: BiolAb.
Published by: (Wydzial Nauk Przyrodniczo-Rolniczych), Szczecinskie Towarzystwo Naukowe, ul Wojska Polskiego 96, Szczecin, 71481, Poland. wtarc@univ.szczecin.pl. **Dist. by:** Ars Polona, Krakowskie Przedmiescie 7, Warsaw, Poland.

661.8 USA
T F I ACTION. (The Fertilizer Institute) Text in English. 1968. m. membership. **Description:** Informs members of the institute's activities.
Published by: Fertilizer Institute, 501 Second St, N E, Washington, DC 20002. TEL 202-675-8250, FAX 202-544-8123, kmathers@tfi.org, http://www.tfi.org. Ed., R&P Kathy Mathers. Circ: 3,000 (controlled).

633.007 DNK ISSN 0908-0813
TABELBILAG TIL LANDSFORSOEGENE; forsoeg i de landoekonomiske foreninger. Text in Danish. 1971. a. DKK 205 (effective 1999). charts. **Document type:** *Trade.*
Description: Contains results of field experiments collected and calculated in experimental series, conducted by local agricultural advisors and members of the farmers union.
Related titles: ♦ Issued with: Oversigt over Landsforsoegene. ISSN 0900-5293.

Published by: Landsudvalget for Planteavl/Danish Agricultural Advisory Committee, Udkaersvej 15, Skejby, Aarhus N, 8200, Denmark. TEL 45-87-405000, FAX 45-87-404010, http://www.lr.dk. Ed. Carl Aage Pedersen. Circ: 800.

631 570 540 620 TWN ISSN 0255-5581
SB215.T33
➤ **TAIWAN SUGAR RESEARCH INSTITUTE. ANNUAL REPORT/TAI-WAN TANG YEH YEN CHIU SO NIEN PAO.** Text in English. 1967. a., latest 2000. free. adv. abstr.; bibl.; charts; illus.; maps; stat. back issues avail. **Document type:** *Proceedings, Academic/Scholarly.* **Description:** Annual report on the progress and achievements of research on sugar cane breeding, cultivation, pest control, sugar manufacturing, by-products utilization, and improvement of Phalaenopsis orchids.
Indexed: AEA, AnBrAb, BioCN&I, BiolAb, DSA, ExcerpMed, FCA, HerbAb, HortAb, I&DA, MaizeAb, NutrAb, OrnHort, PBA, PHN&I, PotatoAb, RM&VM, RPP, RevApplEntom, S&F, SIA, SoyAb, TriticAb, WeedAb.
—BLDSC (1464.600000), ingenta.
Published by: Taiwan Sugar Research Institute, 54 Sheng Chan Rd, Tainan, Taiwan. TEL 886-6-2671911, FAX 886-6-2685425, TSC02@taisugar.com.tw. Ed., Adv. contact Long-Hue Wang. R&P Long Hue Wang. Circ: 850 (controlled).

631.587 JPN ISSN 0915-6550
TAMEIKE NO SHIZEN/NATURE OF IRRIGATION POND. Text in Japanese. 1983. 2/yr. membership.
Published by: Temeike no Shizen Kenkyukai/Nature Study of Irrigation Pond Society, Japan, c/o Mr Murakami, Nagoyashi Kogai Kenkyujo, 1-14 Chudocho, Minami-ku, Nagoya-shi, Aichi-ken 457-0000, Japan.

TAMIL NADU. DEPARTMENT OF STATISTICS. SEASON AND CROP REPORT. see *AGRICULTURE—Abstracting, Bibliographies, Statistics*

TANZANIA. MINISTRY OF AGRICULTURE AND LIVESTOCK DEVELOPMENT. BULLETIN OF CROP STATISTICS. see *AGRICULTURE—Abstracting, Bibliographies, Statistics*

631 TZA
TANZANIA. NATIONAL AGRICULTURAL RESEARCH PROGRAMME. PROJECT REPORT. Text in English. a. **Document type:** *Government.*
Formerly: Tanzania. National Agricultural Research Programme. Summary of Programmes
Published by: Ministry of Agriculture, Crop Development Division, PO Box 9071, Dar Es Salaam, Tanzania.

631.5 DEU ISSN 0082-1799
TASCHENBUCH DER PFLANZENARZTES. Text in German. 1951. a. **Document type:** *Bulletin, Trade.*
Published by: Landwirtschaftsverlag GmbH, Huelsebrockstr 2, Muenster, 48165, Germany. TEL 49-2501-801-0, FAX 49-2501-801351, zentrale@lv-h.de, http://www.agrarshop.de. Ed. E Meyer.

TEA RESEARCH ASSOCIATION. MEMORANDUM. see *BEVERAGES*

TEA RESEARCH ASSOCIATION. OCCASIONAL SCIENTIFIC PAPERS. see *BEVERAGES*

TEA RESEARCH ASSOCIATION. TOCKLAI EXPERIMENTAL STATION. SCIENTIFIC ANNUAL REPORT. see *BEVERAGES*

630 MEX
TECNICA EN AGRICULTURA Y GANADERIA. Text in Spanish. 1970. bi-m. adv.
Published by: (Asociacion Mexicana de Periodistas), Publicaciones y Promociones Impresas, Melchor Ocampo 156 1 Piso, A.P. 30-526, Mexico City 4, DF, Mexico. Circ: 5,000.

633.5 RUS ISSN 0235-2559
CODEN: TABKA8
TEKHNICHESKIE KUL'TURY. Text in Russian. 1988. q. USD 43 (effective 1997).
Formed by the merger of (1924-1988): Len i Konoplya (0024-418X); (1937-1988): Tabak (0039-873X)
Indexed: AEA, BiolAb, ChemAb, FCA, HerbAb, PBA, PHN&I, RASB, SeedAb.
—CASDDS, CISTI.
Address: Sadovaya-Spasskaya 18, Moscow, 107807, Russian Federation. TEL 7-095-2071655.

630 MDG ISSN 0563-1637
HD2135.M26
TERRE MALGACHE/TANY MALAGASY. Text in French. 1967. irreg., latest vol.20, 1980. MGF 2,000. charts; illus.; stat.
Indexed: CCA.
—CISTI.
Published by: Universite de Madagascar, Etablissement d'Enseignement Superieur des Sciences Agronomiques, BP 175, Antananarivo, Madagascar. Circ: 1,500.

634.8 FRA
TERRES DE BOURGOGNE. Text in French. 50/yr. **Document type:** *Magazine, Trade.*
Related titles: Online - full text ed.; Regional ed(s).: Terres de Bourgogne (Edition Cote d'Or). ISSN 1145-1572; Terres de Bourgogne (Edition Nievre). ISSN 1145-1564; Terres de Bourgogne (Edition Yonne). ISSN 1146-2140.
Address: 4 Rue de Bastogne ZAE Cap Nord, Saint Apollinaire, 21850, France. TEL 33-3-80789040, FAX 33-3-80700802, terres.bourgogne@reussir.tm.fr, http://www.terres-de-bourgogne.com. Ed. Jean Luc Berthome. Circ: 20,000.

631.8 THA ISSN 0085-7246
THAILAND. DIVISION OF AGRICULTURAL CHEMISTRY. REPORT ON FERTILIZER EXPERIMENTS AND SOIL FERTILITY RESEARCH*. Text in English. 1966. irreg.
Published by: Ministry of Agriculture, Division of Agricultural Chemistry, Rajadamnern Ave, Bangkok 9, Thailand.

AL-TIKNULUJIA AL-MULA'IMAH/MIDDLE EAST APPROPRIATE TECHNOLOGY NEWS. see *TECHNOLOGY: COMPREHENSIVE WORKS*

634 ESP
TODO CITRUS. Text in Spanish. 3/yr. EUR 33.90 domestic; EUR 40 foreign (effective 2004). illus. **Document type:** *Trade.*
—CINDOC.
Published by: Agro Latino S.L., Apdo Correos 400, Castelldefels (Barcelona), 08860, Spain. TEL 34-93-6350850, FAX 34-93-6350851, agrolatino@agrolatino.com.

630.24 668.6 JPN ISSN 0040-8719
S19 CODEN: TJARAJ
TOHOKU JOURNAL OF AGRICULTURAL RESEARCH. Text in English. 1950. q. per issue exchange basis only (effective 2005). charts; illus. **Document type:** *Academic/Scholarly.*
Indexed: ASFA, AgBio, AnBrAb, BIOSIS Prev, BiolAb, CPA, ChemAb, ChemTitl, DSA, ESPM, FCA, FPA, FS&TA, ForAb, HerbAb, HortAb, INIS AtomInd, IndVet, NutrAb, PBA, PollutAb, PoultAb, RA&MP, RPP, RefZh, RiceAb, S&F, SFA, SIA, SeedAb, TriticAb, VITIS, VetBull, WeedAb, WildRev, ZooRec.
—BLDSC (8860.000000), CASDDS, CISTI, IE, ingenta, Linda Hall. **CCC.**
Published by: Tohoku Daigaku, Nogakubu/Tohoku University, Faculty of Agriculture, 1-1 Tsutsumi-dori Amamiya-cho, Sendai-shi, Miyagi-ken 981, Japan. Circ: 1,000.

620.24 668.6 JPN ISSN 0563-8313
TOKYO UNIVERSITY OF AGRICULTURE AND TECHNOLOGY. ANNUAL REPORT/TOKYO NOKO DAIGAKU NENPO. Text in Japanese; Summaries in English. 1949. biennial. per issue exchange basis. bk.rev. **Document type:** *Academic/Scholarly.*
Indexed: TTI.
—BLDSC (1471.750000), CISTI.
Published by: Tokyo University of Agriculture and Technology/Tokyo Noko Daigaku, Fuchu-shi, Japan. TEL 81-42-367-5570, FAX 81-42-367-5571. Circ: 2,000.

633 USA ISSN 1093-3980
THE TOMATO MAGAZINE. Text in English. 1997. 6/yr. USD 10 domestic; USD 18 in Canada & Mexico; USD 25 elsewhere (effective 2005). adv. **Document type:** *Magazine, Trade.*
Description: Focuses on the tomato industry with emphasis on fresh and greenhouse tomatoes.
Published by: Columbia Publishing and Design, 413B N 20th Ave, Yakima, WA 98902. TEL 509-248-2452, 800-900-2452, FAX 509-248-4056, brent@columbiapublications.com, tmeditorial@freshcut.com, http://www.tomatomagzine.com, http://www.freshcut.com/columbiapub/home.htm. Ed. Brent Clement. Pub., Adv. contact Mike J Stoker. B&W page USD 1,390, color page USD 2,090. Circ: 6,800 (paid and controlled).

634 USA
TREE FRUIT. Text in English. bi-m. USD 19.95 (effective 1999). **Document type:** *Trade.* **Description:** Covers improving production practices, economics of production and marketing, on-farm feature stories, and research and legislative developments.
Published by: Western Agricultural Publishing Co. Inc., 4969 E Clinton Way, Ste 104, Fresno, CA 93727-1549. TEL 559-252-7000, FAX 559-252-7387, westag2@psnw.com. Ed. Mark Arcamonte. adv.: B&W page USD 1,676, color page USD 2,406; trim 10.88 x 8.38. Circ: 7,600.

631 MWI
TREE NUT AUTHORITY. REPORT. Text in English. 1970. a. stat. **Document type:** *Corporate.*
Supersedes: Tung Board. Annual Report
Published by: Tree Nut Authority, PO Box 930, Blantyre, Malawi. TEL 265-671182.

634.3 USA ISSN 0041-2570
TRIANGLE (LAKELAND). Text in English. 1950. w. (except July). membership. charts; stat.; mkt. **Document type:** *Newsletter.*
Description: Gives tips to keep Florida Citrus Mutual grower members up to date on issues that affect the way they operate their business.
Related titles: Online - full text ed.
Indexed: ChemAb.
Published by: Florida Citrus Mutual, PO Box 89, Lakeland, FL 33802. TEL 239-682-1111, FAX 239-682-1074, http://www.fl-citrus-mutual.com. Ed. Wendy Bourland. Circ: 6,786 (paid).

▼ new title ➤ refereed ✶ unverified ♦ full entry avail.

A

633.2 AUS ISSN 0049-4763
SB202.A8 CODEN: TRGRB4

➤ **TROPICAL GRASSLANDS.** Text in English. 1967. 4/yr. AUD 150 domestic; USD 100 foreign; AUD 75 membership (effective 2002). adv. bk.rev. charts. index. **Document type:** *Journal, Academic/Scholarly.* **Description:** Publishes the results of research and development in the evaluation, management and utilization of pastures and fodder crops in tropical and sub-tropical agriculture, descriptions of farming systems and review articles.
Related titles: Microfilm ed.: (from PQC).
Indexed: ASCA, ATA, AgBio, Agr, AgrForAb, AnBrAb, BIOBASE, BIOSIS Prev, BioCN&I, BiolAb, CPA, CurCont, DSA, FCA, ForAb, HerbAb, HortAb, I&DA, IABS, ISR, IndVet, MaizeAb, NemAb, NutrAb, OrnHort, PBA, PGegResA, PHN&I, PN&I, PlantSci, RDA, RPP, RRTA, RefZh, RiceAb, S&F, S&MA, SCI, SIA, SPPI, SeedAb, SoyAb, TriticAb, VetBull, WAE&RSA, WeedAb.
—BLDSC (9056.200000), IDS, IE, Infotrieve, ingenta.
Published by: Tropical Grassland Society of Australia Inc., 306 Carmody Rd, St Lucia, QLD 4067, Australia. TEL 61-73-3770209, FAX 61-73-3713946, secretary@tropicalgrasslands.asn.au, http://www.tropicalgrasslands.asn.au. Ed., R&P Lyle Winks. Circ: 626.

632.9 TZA ISSN 0082-6642
TROPICAL PESTICIDES RESEARCH INSTITUTE. ANNUAL REPORT. Text in English. 1957. a. available on exchange basis.
Indexed: BiolAb, HortAb, RPP, RevApplEntom.
Published by: Tropical Pesticides Research Institute, PO Box 3024, Arusha, Tanzania.

630.13 BEL ISSN 0771-3312
CODEN: TRPIEP

➤ **TROPICULTURA.** Text in English, French, Spanish; Contents page in English. 1983. q. free (effective 2004). bk.rev. **Document type:** *Journal, Academic/Scholarly.* **Description:** Dedicated to the problems of agriculture in developing countries. It publishes original articles, research and synthesis notes, book and thesis summaries as well as reviews of films and videos relative to all aspects of rural development: plant and animal production, veterinary science, forestry science, soilscience, rural engineering, environmental sciences, bio-industry, agro-food science, sociology and economy.
Indexed: AEA, AgBio, AgrForAb, AnBrAb, BIOSIS Prev, BioCN&I, BiolAb, CIS, CPA, DSA, FCA, FPA, ForAb, HelmAb, HerbAb, HortAb, I&DA, IndVet, MaizeAb, NemAb, NutrAb, OrnHort, PBA, PGegResA, PGrRegA, PHN&I, PN&I, PotatoAb, PoultAb, ProtozoAb, RA&MP, RDA, RPP, RevApplEntom, RiceAb, S&F, SFA, SIA, SeedAb, SoyAb, TDB, TriticAb, VetBull, WAE&RSA, WeedAb, WildRev.
—BLDSC (9057.040000), IE, ingenta.
Published by: (Belgium Administration for Cooperation and Development), A G C D - A B O S, 1A, Square du Bastion, B-1050, Brussels, 1050, Belgium. TEL 32-2-5501961, FAX 32-2-5147277, ghare.tropicultura@belgacom.net, mjdesmet.tropicultura@belgacom.net, http://www.bib.fsagx.ac.be/tropicultura/. Ed. Guy Mergeai. R&P Marie-Josee Desmet TEL 32-2-519-0476. Circ: 2,500 (paid and controlled).

➤ **TURANG/SOIL.** see *EARTH SCIENCES*

631.8 CHN ISSN 1002-0616
TURANG FEILIAO/SOIL FERTILIZER. Text in Chinese. bi-m.
Related titles: Online - full text ed.: (from East View Information Services).
Indexed: CPA, FCA, HerbAb, HortAb, I&DA, MaizeAb, PBA, PGrRegA, S&F, SeedAb, SoyAb, TriticAb.
Published by: (Turang Feiliao Yanjiusuo), Zhongguo Nongye Kexueyuan/Chinese Academy of Agricultural Sciences, Chinese Society for Horticultural Science, 30 Baishiqiao Lu, Beijing, 100081, China. TEL 896531. Ed. Lin Bao.

TURANGXUE JINZHAN/PROGRESS IN SOIL SCIENCE. see *EARTH SCIENCES*

635.9642 USA ISSN 0899-417X
TURF NEWS. Text in English. 1977. bi-m. membership. adv. bk.rev. back issues avail. **Document type:** *Magazine, Trade.* **Description:** Sent to turfgrass sod farm operations, suppliers, educators, students, and industry associates. Topic include seed, equipment, business, marketing, and agronomics for turfgrass sod farmers.
Published by: Turfgrass Producers International, 2 E. Main St., East Dundee, IL 60118-1322. TEL 847-705-9898, FAX 847-705-8347, info@turfgrasssod.org, http://www.turfgrasssod.org. Ed. Bob O'Quinn. R&P Douglas Fender. Adv. contact Terri Berkowitz. B&W page USD 1,080; trim 10.88 x 8.13. Circ: 1,450 (paid).

631.587 GBR
U.K. IRRIGATION ASSOCIATION QUARTERLY. Text in English. 1981. q. membership. adv. bk.rev. **Document type:** *Newsletter.* **Description:** Keeps members of the UKIA informed about developments in irrigation.
Published by: U.K. Irrigation Association, c/o Silsoe College, Cranfield University, Silsoe, Bedford, MK45 4DT, United Kingdom. TEL 44-1525-861503, FAX 44-1525-861660, secretray@ukia.org, http://www.ukia.org. Adv. contact Rachel Mulvanerty.

U.S. DEPARTMENT OF AGRICULTURE. ANIMAL AND PLANT HEALTH INSPECTION SERVICE. COOPERATIVE STATE-FEDERAL BOVINE TUBERCULOSIS ERADICATION PROGRAM: STATISTICAL TABLES. see *AGRICULTURE—Abstracting, Bibliographies, Statistics*

U.S. DEPARTMENT OF AGRICULTURE. NATIONAL AGRICULTURAL STATISTICS SERVICE. AGRICULTURAL CHEMICAL USAGE. see *AGRICULTURE—Abstracting, Bibliographies, Statistics*

U.S. DEPARTMENT OF AGRICULTURE. NATIONAL AGRICULTURAL STATISTICS SERVICE. CHERRY PRODUCTION. see *AGRICULTURE—Abstracting, Bibliographies, Statistics*

U.S. DEPARTMENT OF AGRICULTURE. NATIONAL AGRICULTURAL STATISTICS SERVICE. CITRUS FRUITS. see *AGRICULTURE—Abstracting, Bibliographies, Statistics*

U.S. DEPARTMENT OF AGRICULTURE. NATIONAL AGRICULTURAL STATISTICS SERVICE. COTTON GINNINGS. see *AGRICULTURE—Abstracting, Bibliographies, Statistics*

U.S. DEPARTMENT OF AGRICULTURE. NATIONAL AGRICULTURAL STATISTICS SERVICE. CRANBERRIES. see *AGRICULTURE—Abstracting, Bibliographies, Statistics*

U.S. DEPARTMENT OF AGRICULTURE. NATIONAL AGRICULTURAL STATISTICS SERVICE. CROP PRODUCTION. see *AGRICULTURE—Abstracting, Bibliographies, Statistics*

U.S. DEPARTMENT OF AGRICULTURE. NATIONAL AGRICULTURAL STATISTICS SERVICE. CROP PROGRESS. see *AGRICULTURE—Abstracting, Bibliographies, Statistics*

U.S. DEPARTMENT OF AGRICULTURE. NATIONAL AGRICULTURAL STATISTICS SERVICE. CROP VALUES. see *AGRICULTURE—Abstracting, Bibliographies, Statistics*

U.S. DEPARTMENT OF AGRICULTURE. NATIONAL AGRICULTURAL STATISTICS SERVICE. HOP STOCKS. see *AGRICULTURE—Abstracting, Bibliographies, Statistics*

U.S. DEPARTMENT OF AGRICULTURE. NATIONAL AGRICULTURAL STATISTICS SERVICE. MUSHROOMS. see *AGRICULTURE—Abstracting, Bibliographies, Statistics*

U.S. DEPARTMENT OF AGRICULTURE. NATIONAL AGRICULTURAL STATISTICS SERVICE. NONCITRUS FRUITS AND NUTS. see *AGRICULTURE—Abstracting, Bibliographies, Statistics*

U.S. DEPARTMENT OF AGRICULTURE. NATIONAL AGRICULTURAL STATISTICS SERVICE. PEANUT STOCKS AND PROCESSING. see *AGRICULTURE—Abstracting, Bibliographies, Statistics*

U.S. DEPARTMENT OF AGRICULTURE. NATIONAL AGRICULTURAL STATISTICS SERVICE. POTATOES AND POTATO STOCKS. see *AGRICULTURE—Abstracting, Bibliographies, Statistics*

U.S. DEPARTMENT OF AGRICULTURE. NATIONAL AGRICULTURAL STATISTICS SERVICE. RESTRICTED USE PESTICIDES. see *AGRICULTURE—Abstracting, Bibliographies, Statistics*

U.S. DEPARTMENT OF AGRICULTURE. NATIONAL AGRICULTURAL STATISTICS SERVICE. VEGETABLES. see *AGRICULTURE—Abstracting, Bibliographies, Statistics*

631.8 USA
U.S. ENVIRONMENTAL PROTECTION AGENCY. OFFICE OF PESTICIDE PROGRAMS. CBI REVIEW. Text in English. bi-m.
Indexed: PAIS.
Published by: U.S. Environmental Protection Agency, Ariel Rios Bldg, 1200 Pennsylvania Av N W, Washington, DC 20460.

632.9 USA ISSN 0083-0518
U.S. ENVIRONMENTAL PROTECTION AGENCY. PESTICIDES ENFORCEMENT DIVISION. NOTICES OF JUDGMENT UNDER FEDERAL INSECTICIDE, FUNGICIDE, AND RODENTICIDE ACT. Variant title: Pesticide Enforcement. Text in English. irreg. free. **Document type:** *Government.*
Published by: U.S. Environmental Protection Agency, 401 M St, S W, Washington, DC 20460. **Subscr. to:** National Technical Information Service, Government Research Center, 5285 Port Royal Rd, Springfield, VA 22161. TEL 703-605-6060, 800-363-2068, http://www.ntis.gov.

631.4 USA ISSN 0083-3304
U.S. NATURAL RESOURCES CONSERVATION SERVICE. NATIONAL ENGINEERING HANDBOOK SECTIONS. Text in English. irreg. **Document type:** *Government.*
Related titles: Microfiche ed.
Published by: U.S. Natural Resources Conservation Service, PO Box 2890, Washington, DC 20013. TEL 202-720-2472, FAX 202-720-4593. **Subscr. to:** National Technical Information Service, Government Research Center, 5285 Port Royal Rd, Springfield, VA 22161. TEL 703-605-6060, 800-363-2068, http://www.ntis.gov.

631.4 USA ISSN 0083-3320
S599.A1 CODEN: SSIRA9
U.S. NATURAL RESOURCES CONSERVATION SERVICE. SOIL SURVEY INVESTIGATION REPORTS. Text in English. 1967. irreg. **Document type:** *Monographic series, Government.* **Description:** Presents soil characterization data and discusses the chemical, physical, and morphological aspects of important soils for a given region.
—CISTI.
Published by: U.S. Natural Resources Conservation Service, PO Box 2890, Washington, DC 20013. TEL 202-720-2472, FAX 202-720-4593. **Subscr. to:** National Technical Information Service, Government Research Center, 5285 Port Royal Rd, Springfield, VA 22161. TEL 703-605-6060, 800-363-2068, http://www.ntis.gov; U.S. National Soil Survey Center, Midwest NTC, Federal Bldg, Rm 152, 100 Centennial Mall N, Lincoln, NE 68508-3866. TEL 402-437-5363, FAX 402-437-5336.

631.4 USA ISSN 0083-3339
U.S. NATURAL RESOURCES CONSERVATION SERVICE. TECHNICAL PUBLICATIONS. Text in English. irreg. price varies. **Document type:** *Monographic series, Government.*
Published by: U.S. Natural Resources Conservation Service, PO Box 2890, Washington, DC 20013. TEL 202-720-2472, FAX 202-720-4593. **Subscr. to:** National Technical Information Service, Government Research Center, 5285 Port Royal Rd, Springfield, VA 22161. TEL 703-605-6060, 800-363-2068, http://www.ntis.gov.

634.8 FRA ISSN 0242-6706
UNION GIRONDINE DES VINS DE BORDEAUX. Text in French. 11/yr.
Published by: Federation des Syndicats des Grands Vins de Bordeaux, 1 Cours du 30 Juillet, Bordeaux, 33000, France. TEL 33-5-56002298, FAX 33-5-56485379. Ed. Michel Dando. Pub. Daniel Fournier. Circ: 8,100.

631 PER
UNIVERSIDAD NACIONAL DE AGRARIA. TALLER DE ESTUDIOS ANDINOS. SERIE COSTA CENTRAL. Text in Spanish. 1978. irreg.
Published by: (Taller de Estudios Andinos), Universidad Nacional Agraria, Aptdo. 456, Lima, Peru.

630 ROM
➤ **UNIVERSITATEA DE STIINTE AGRONOMICE SI MEDICINA VETERINARA. LUCRARI STIINTIFICE. SERIA A, AGRONOMIE.** Text in Romanian; Summaries in English. 1957. a. per issue exchange basis only. back issues avail. **Document type:** *Academic/Scholarly.*
Former titles: Universitatea de Stiinte Agronomice. Lucrari Stiintifice. Seria A, Agronomie (1222-5339); (until 1993): Institutul Agronomic Nicolae Balcescu. Lucrari Stiintifice. Seria A, Agronomie (0521-3401); (until 1964): Institutul Agronomic Nicolae Balcescu. Lucrari Stiintifice. Seria A, Pedologie, Ingrasaminte, Chimie Agricola, Amelioratii Agricole (1220-1995); Which superseded in part (in 1960): Institutul Agronomic Nicolae Balcescu. Anuarul Lucrarirol Stiintifice (1220-1987)
Indexed: FCA, TriticAb.
—CISTI.
Published by: Universitatea de Stiinte Agronomice si Medicina Veterinara, Bd. Marasti 59, Sector 1, Bucharest, 71331, Romania. TEL 40-1-2223700, FAX 40-1-2232693.

631.6 631.587 ROM
UNIVERSITATEA DE STIINTE AGRONOMICE SI MEDICINA VETERINARA. LUCRARI STIINTIFICE. SERIA E, IMBUNATATIRI FUNCIARE. Text in Romanian; Summaries in English. 1973. a. per issue exchange basis only. **Document type:** *Academic/Scholarly.*
Former titles: Universitatea de Stiinte Agronomice. Lucrari Stiintifice. Seria E, Imbunatatiri Funciare; (until 1992): Institutul Agronomic Nicolae Balcescu. Lucrari Stiintifice. Seria E, Imbunatatiri Funciare (1015-2172)
Published by: Universitatea de Stiinte Agronomice si Medicina Veterinara, Bd. Marasti 59, Sector 1, Bucharest, 71331, Romania. TEL 40-1-2242576, FAX 40-1-2232693.

632 BEL ISSN 0435-950X
UNIVERSITEIT GENT. CENTRUM VOOR ONKRUIDONDERZOEK. MEDEDELING. Text in Dutch, English; Summaries in English. 1965. s-a. free to research institutions (effective 2005). **Document type:** *Newspaper, Academic/Scholarly.*
Indexed: FCA, HerbAb, HortAb, MaizeAb, OrnHort, PBA, PotatoAb, S&F, TriticAb, WeedAb.
—CISTI.

Published by: Universiteit Gent, Centrum voor Onkruidonderzoek, Coupure Links 653, Gent, 9000, Belgium. FAX 32-9-264-6224, robert.bulcke@rug.ac.be. Circ: 250.

631   USA   ISSN 0096-8498
UNIVERSITY OF GEORGIA. AGRICULTURAL EXPERIMENT STATIONS. SOUTHERN COOPERATIVE SERIES BULLETIN. Text in English. irreg., latest 1983.
Indexed: HortAb.
—CISTI, Linda Hall.
Published by: University of Georgia, Agricultural Experiment Stations, Athens, GA 30602. Ed. Kathleen Sheridan.

631.4   CAN   ISSN 0085-1329
UNIVERSITY OF GUELPH. DEPARTMENT OF LAND RESOURCE SCIENCE. PROGRESS REPORT. Text in English. 1954. a. free. bibl.; charts; illus. **Document type:** *Academic/Scholarly.* **Description:** Provides details of personnel and programs within the department, as well as brief articles on current research activities.
Media: Duplicated (not offset).
Published by: University of Guelph, Department of Land Resource Science, Guelph, ON N1G 2W1, Canada. TEL 519-824-4120, FAX 519-824-5730, http://www.uoguelph.ca. Ed. T McGonigle. R&P T J Gillespie. Circ: 1,500.

630   CZE   ISSN 1212-0731
UNIVERSITY OF SOUTH BOHEMIA IN CESKE BUDEJOVICE. FACULTY OF AGRICULTURE. COLLECTION OF SCIENTIFIC PAPERS. SERIES FOR CROP SCIENCES. Text in Czech; Abstracts in English. 1984. s-a. **Document type:** *Journal, Academic/Scholarly.*
Former titles (until 1999): Jihoceske Univerzity v Ceskych Budejovicich. Zemedelske Fakulty. Rada Fytotechnicka. Sbornik (1210-6259); (until 1992): Vysoka Skola Zemedelska v Praze. Agronomicke Fakulty v Ceskych Budejovicich. Rada Fytotechnicka. Sbornik (0862-0377); (until 1986): Provozne Ekonomicka Fakulta v Ceskych Budejovicich. Rada Fytotechnicka. Sbornik (0231-9179)
Indexed: AEA, AgBio, AgrForAb, AnBrAb, BIOSIS Prev, BioCN&I, BiolAb, CPA, DSA, FCA, FPA, ForAb, HerbAb, HortAb, I&DA, MaizeAb, NutrAb, OrnHort, PBA, PGegResA, PotatoAb, RA&MP, RPP, S&F, SIA, SeedAb, TriticAb, WAE&RSA, WeedAb.
—CISTI.
Published by: Jihoceska Univerzita v Ceskych Budejovicich , Zemedelska Fakulta/University of South Bohemia in Ceske Budejovice, Faculty of Agriculture, Studentska 13, Ceske Budejovice, 370 05, Czech Republic. wolkova@zf.jcu.cz, http://www.zf.jcu.cz. Ed. Petr Hartvich. Circ: 220.

633   TTO
UNIVERSITY OF THE WEST INDIES. ANNUAL REPORT ON COCOA RESEARCH. Text in English. 1930. a. free. bibl.; illus. **Document type:** *Academic/Scholarly.*
Indexed: BiolAb.
Published by: University of the West Indies, Office of Publication, St. Augustine, Trinidad & Tobago. TEL 868-6628788. Ed. Frances Bekele. Circ: 200.

630.24   SWE   ISSN 0346-4997
VAEXTSKYDDSKURIREN. Text in Swedish. 1960. s-a. free. charts; illus.
Published by: Bayer (Sverige) AB Agro-Kemi, Fack 50113, Malmo, 20211, Sweden. Ed. Gunnar Holma. Circ: 40,000 (controlled).

631   USA   ISSN 0889-4787
VALLEY POTATO GROWER. Text in English. 1946. 9/yr. free (effective 2005). adv. **Document type:** *Magazine, Trade.* **Description:** For potato farmers thoughout the US and the world. Covers current events, innovations, industry problems and solutions, marketing and production information, research results, safety and governmental issues, and pest-weed control.
Published by: Red River Valley Potato Growers Association, 420 Business Hwy 2, E. Grand Forks, MN 56721. TEL 218-773-3633, FAX 218-773-6227, communication@nppga.org, http://www.nppga.org. Ed. Todd Phelps. adv.: B&W page USD 1,720, color page USD 2,670; trim 10.88 x 8.5. Circ: 11,773 (paid and controlled).

635   USA
VEGETABLE. Text in English. 1991. bi-m. USD 19.95 (effective 1999). **Description:** Covers improving production practices, economics of production and marketing, on-farm feature stories, and research and legislative developments.
Published by: Western Agricultural Publishing Co. Inc., 4969 E Clinton Way, Ste 104, Fresno, CA 93727-1549. TEL 559-252-7000, FAX 559-252-7387, westag2@psnw.com. Ed. Marnie Katz. adv.: B&W page USD 1,100, color page USD 1,600; trim 10.88 x 8.38. Circ: 6,200.

635   POL   ISSN 1506-9427
                                 CODEN: BIWAA9
➤ **VEGETABLE CROPS RESEARCH BULLETIN.** Text in English; Summaries in English, Polish. 1953. s-a. PLZ 35 domestic; USD 15 foreign (effective 2003). bk.rev. charts; illus.; bibl. cum.index. back issues avail.; reprints avail.
Document type: *Journal, Academic/Scholarly.* **Description:** Examines various aspects of vegetable crop research and developments such as crop and soil cultivation, plant breeding, plant protection, weed science, plant nutrition, storage.
Formerly (until 1998): Biuletyn Warzywniczy (0509-6839)
Indexed: AEA, AbHyg, AgBio, AgrAg, AgrForAb, AgrLib, BioCN&I, BiolAb, CPA, FCA, FPA, FS&TA, ForAb, HerbAb, HortAb, I&DA, MaizeAb, NemAb, NutrAb, OrnHort, PBA, PGegResA, PGrRegA, PHN&I, PotatoAb, RA&MP, RPP, RevApplEntom, S&F, SIA, SeedAb, SoyAb, TriticAb, WAE&RSA, WeedAb.
—BLDSC (9152.042000), CASDDS, CISTI, Linda Hall.
Published by: Instytut Warzywnictwa/Research Institute of Vegetable Crops, Ul. Konstytucji 3 Maja 1-3, Skierniewice, 96100, Poland. TEL 48-468-333434, FAX 48-468-333186, bulletin@inwarz.skierniewice.pl, inwarz@inwarz.skierniewice.pl, http://www.inwarz.skierniewice.pl. Eds. Adam Dobrzanski, Franciszek Adamicki. Pub. Adam Dobrzanski. Circ: 400.
Co-sponsor: Komitet Badan Naukowych/Committee of Scientific Research.

635   USA   ISSN 1533-6824
                                 CODEN: GLVNEL
THE VEGETABLE GROWERS NEWS. Text in English. 1966. m. USD 11 (effective 2005). **Document type:** *Newspaper, Trade.* **Description:** Covers growing and marketing techniques, business management ideas, events, meetings and developments for vegetable and potato growers, bedding plant and greenhouse operators and farm and roadside market operators.
Formerly: Great Lakes Vegetable Growers News (1049-8494)
Published by: Great American Publishing Co., 75 Applewood Dr, Ste A, Sparta, MI 49345. TEL 616-887-9008, gap@i2k.net, http://www.vegetablegrowersnews.com. Ed. Karen Gentry. Pub. Matt McCallum. R&P Lee Dean. Adv. contact Brenda Bradford. Circ: 12,000.

631   GBR   ISSN 1361-2069
VEGETABLE VARIETY HANDBOOK. Text in English. 1961. a. GBP 15 per vol. (effective 2003). **Document type:** *Bulletin, Trade.* **Description:** Describes 14 different vegetable crops and offers tips on growing and cultivating them.
Formerly (until 1995): Vegetable Growers Leaflet (0470-1321)
Indexed: HortAb, MaizeAb, PBA.
—BLDSC (9152.272000), CISTI.
Published by: N I A B, Huntingdon Rd, Cambridge, CB3 0LE, United Kingdom. TEL 44-1223-276381, FAX 44-1223-342328, TELEX 817455-NIAB-G, info@niab.com, http://www.niab.com. Ed. Paul Nelson TEL 44-1223-342225.

632.9   DNK   ISSN 0907-4066
VEJLEDNING I PLANTEVAERN. Text in Danish. 1992. a., latest 2004. DKK 109 (effective 2005). **Document type:** *Trade.*
Formed by the merger of (1984-1992): Plantevaern i Landbruget (0109-3312); 1987-1992): Vejledning i Plantebeskyttelse i Landbrugs- og Specialafgoeder (0905-4359)
Published by: (Denmark. Landskontoret for Uddannelse), Dansk Landbrugsraadgivning, Landbrugsforlaget/Danish Agricultural Advisory Service. Publishing, Udkaersvej 15, Skejby, Aarhus N, 8200, Denmark. TEL 45-87-405537, FAX 45-87-405085, forlag@landcentret.dk, http://www.lr.dk/uddannelse. Circ: 8,000.

632.9   USA   ISSN 0507-6773
                                 CODEN: PVPCBM
VERTEBRATE PEST CONFERENCE. PROCEEDINGS. Text in English. 1962. biennial, latest 20th Vertebrate Pest Conferenc. USD 25 per issue (effective 2004). 375 p./no. 2 cols./p.; back issues avail. **Document type:** *Proceedings, Academic/Scholarly.*
Indexed: Agr, BiolAb, DBA, SFA, WildRev, ZooRec.
—BLDSC (6849.815000), CASDDS, CISTI, Linda Hall.
Published by: Vertebrate Pest Council, c/o TP Salmon, University of California, Dept. Wildlife, Fish & Conservation Biology, 1 Shields Ave, Davis, CA 95616-8751. TEL 530-752-8751, FAX 530-752-4154, http://www.vpconference.org/. Ed. A Charles Crabb. R&P Terrell P Salmon TEL 530-752-8751. Circ: 1,000.

VESITALOUS; Finnish journal of water economy, hydraulic and agricultural engineering. see *WATER RESOURCES*

631   CUB
VIANDAS TROPICALES. BOLETIN DE RESENAS. Text in Spanish. 1974. irreg. per issue exchange basis. bibl.; charts; stat. **Description:** Covers recent advances in science and technology while examining the various tendencies and developments in these areas.
Supersedes in part: Cuba. Centro de Informacion y Divulgacion Agropecuario. Boletin de Resenas. Serie: Viandas, Hortalizas y Granos; Which was formerly: Cuba. Centro de Informacion y Documentacion Agropecuario. Boletin de Resenas. Serie: Viandas, Hortalizas y Granos

Published by: (Instituto Nacional de Investigaciones en Viandas Tropicales), Centro de Informacion y Documentacion Agropecuario, Gaveta Postal 4149, Havana, 4, Cuba. **Dist. by:** Ediciones Cubanas, Obispo No. 461, Apdo. 605, Havana, Cuba.

634.8   FRA   ISSN 1145-5799
VIGNE. Text in French. 11/yr.
Indexed: VITIS.
Published by: C E P Groupe France Agricole, 8 Cite Paradis, Paris, Cedex 10 75493, France. TEL 33-1-40227900, FAX 33-1-48240315. Ed. Cesar Compadre. Circ: 30,000.

634.8   FRA   ISSN 0049-643X
VIGNERON CHAMPENOIS; organe de la vigne et du vin de champagne. Text in French. 1873. m. (11/yr.). adv. stat.
Document type: *Bulletin.*
Indexed: VITIS.
Published by: Association Viticole Champenoise, 5 rue Henri-Martin, BP 135, Epernay, Cedex 51204, France. TEL 33-3-26511930, FAX 33-3-26511957. Ed. D Moncomble. Adv. contact Xavier Rinville. Circ: 5,500.

634.8   FRA   ISSN 0995-7944
VIGNERON DES COTES DU RHONE ET DU SUD EST. Text in French. 1946. 24/yr. **Document type:** *Newspaper.*
Address: 6 rue des Trois Faulons, Avignon, 84000, France. TEL 90-27-24-24, FAX 90-85-26-83. Eds. F Fabre, Sylvie Reboul. Circ: 10,000.

634.8   FRA
VIGNES LANGEUDOC-ROUSILLON. Text in French. m. **Document type:** *Newspaper.*
Formerly: Vignes Provence Languedoc-Rousillon
Address: BP 249, Saint Jean de Vedas, Cedex 34434, France. TEL 33-04-67070371, FAX 33-04-67070371. Ed. M Ponce Andre. Circ: 21,000.

634.8 663.2   ITA   ISSN 0390-0479
SB387   CODEN: VIGNDL
VIGNEVINI. Short title: V V. Text in Italian. 1974. m. (10/yr.). EUR 62 domestic; EUR 110 foreign (effective 2005). adv. 96 p./no.;
Document type: *Magazine, Trade.* **Description:** Covers wine and vineyards.
Indexed: AEA, AgBio, BioCN&I, CIN, CPA, ChemAb, ChemTitl, FCA, FPA, FS&TA, ForAb, HortAb, I&DA, NemAb, NutrAb, OrnHort, PBA, PGegResA, PGrRegA, PHN&I, RA&MP, RPP, RevApplEntom, S&F, SIA, SeedAb, TriticAb, VITIS, WAE&RSA, WeedAb.
—BLDSC (9236.110000), CASDDS, CISTI, IE, ingenta.
Published by: Il Sole 24 Ore Edagricole, Via Goito 13, Bologna, BO 40126, Italy. TEL 39-051-62267, FAX 39-051-490200, http://www.edagricole.it. Ed. Giovanna Villani. Circ: 8,000.

631 663   USA   ISSN 1047-4951
TP544   CODEN: VWMAE9
VINEYARD AND WINERY MANAGEMENT; the bottom line resource for grower and vintner. Text in English. 1975. bi-m. USD 37 domestic; USD 47 in Canada & Mexico; USD 57 elsewhere (effective 2004). adv. bk.rev. **Document type:** *Magazine, Trade.* **Description:** Offers information and advice for today's wine and vineyard industries with detailed management techniques for winegrowers.
Formerly: Eastern Grape Grower and Winery News (0194-5254)
Indexed: VITIS.
—CISTI.
Published by: Vineyard & Winery Services, Inc., PO Box 231, Watkins Glen, NY 14891. TEL 607-535-7133, 800-535-5670, FAX 607-535-2998, http://www.vwm-online.com. Pubs. Hope Merletti, J William Moffett. Circ: 4,500.

VINS D'ALSACE; revue viticole et vinicole mensuelle. see *BEVERAGES*

634 635   USA   ISSN 1064-4083
VIRGINIA FRUIT AND VEGETABLE MARKET INFORMATION. Text in English. m. back issues avail. **Document type:** *Government.* **Description:** Provides fruit and vegetable crop and market conditions for Virginia and competing areas, to Virginia farmers and agribusinesses only.
Published by: Department of Agriculture and Consumer Services, 1100 Bank St, Ste 805, Richmond, VA 23219-3638. TEL 804-786-3947, FAX 804-371-7787. Ed. J P Welch. Circ: 500.

712 631 635   USA
VIRGINIA TURFGRASS JOURNAL. Text in English. bi-m. **Document type:** *Magazine.*
Published by: (Virginia Turfgrass Council), Harvest Publishing, PO Box 9125, Winter Haven, FL 33881. http://www.harvestpublishing.com.

634.8   FRA   ISSN 0757-4673
VITI. Text in French. m. EUR 53 domestic; EUR 63 foreign (effective 2002). adv.
Formerly (until 1982): Vititechnique (0399-3558)
Published by: Agri Terroir Communication, 61, Rue du XXe-Corps-Americain, Metz, 57000, France. TEL 33-03-87691818, FAX 33-03-87691814, infocentre@editions-mirabelle.com, http://www.editions-mirabelle.com. Circ: 32,513.

▼ *new title*   ➤ *refereed*   ✳ *unverified*   ◆ *full entry avail.*

634.8 FRA ISSN 0244-4860
VITI VINICOLE. Text in French. w.
Address: B.P. 57, Mauguio, Cedex 34140, France. TEL 67-29-36-29, FAX 67-29-59-20, TELEX 485 807. Ed. Alain Gosse. Circ: 19,683.

634.8 ESP ISSN 1131-5679
VITICULTURA ENOLOGIA PROFESIONAL. Text in Spanish. 1989. bi-m. EUR 45.20 domestic; EUR 59.65 foreign (effective 2004). adv. **Document type:** *Trade.*
Indexed: IECT, VITIS.
—CINDOC.
Published by: Agro Latino S.L., Apdo Correos 400, Castelldefels (Barcelona), 08860, Spain. TEL 34-93-6350850, FAX 34-93-6350851, agrolatino@agrolatino.com. Pub. Daniel Aradas Llorens.

634.8 FRA ISSN 1151-1109
VITICULTURE EN VAL DE LOIRE. Text in French. 8/yr.
Address: 11 impasse Ambroise Croizat, BP 136, Saint-Pierre-des-Corps, Cedex 37701, France. TEL 47-44-21-85, FAX 47-32-02-55. Ed. M Aubard. Circ: 3,200.

634.8 USA
VITICULTURE NOTES. Text in English. 1998. bi-m. back issues avail.
Media: Online - full text.
Published by: Virginia Cooperative Extension, 121 Hutcheson Hall, Virginia Tech 0437, Blacksburg, VA 24061-0001. FAX 800-828-1120, http://www.ext.vt.edu/.

634.8 581.3 DEU ISSN 0042-7500
CODEN: VITIAY
➤ **VITIS;** journal of grapevine research. Text in English. 1956. q. EUR 48; EUR 12 newsstand/cover (effective 2005). bk.rev. abstr.; bibl.; charts; illus. index. 50 p./no. 2 cols./p.; **Document type:** *Journal, Abstract/Index.*
Related titles: ♦ Supplement(s): Vitis - Viticulture and Oenology Abstracts (Online Edition).
Indexed: AEA, ASCA, AgBio, AgrForAb, B&BAb, BCI, BIOBASE, BioCN&I, BiolAb, CIN, CPA, ChemAb, ChemTitl, CurCont, DSA, ExcerpMed, FPA, FS&TA, ForAb, GenetAb, HGA, HortAb, I&DA, IABS, IBZ, ISR, NemAb, OrnHort, PBA, PGegResA, PGrRegA, PHN&I, PlantSci, RASB, RPP, RRTA, RefZh, RevApplEntom, S&F, SCI, SIA, SeedAb, VITIS, WeedAb.
—BLDSC (9244.120000), CASDDS, CISTI, IDS, IE, ingenta, Linda Hall. **CCC.**
Published by: Bundesanstalt fuer Zuechtungsforschung an Kulturpflanzen, Institut fuer Rebenzuechtung Geilweilerhof, Siebeldingen, 76833, Germany. TEL 49-6345-41141, FAX 49-6345-919050, vitis@bafz.de, doku-vitis@bafz.de, http://www.bafz.de/siebeldingen. Eds. H Duering, Martin Klenert, Werner Koeglmeier. Circ: 700.

634.8 581.3 DEU
VITIS - VITICULTURE AND OENOLOGY ABSTRACTS (ONLINE EDITION). Variant title: Vitis - V E A. Text in German, English. 1984. 4/yr. free (effective 2005). index. **Document type:** *Abstract/Index.* **Description:** Abstracts from journals, books, conference proceedings and reports on all aspects of vine and grapevine science and technology.
Formerly (until 2003): Vitis - Viticulture and Oenology Abstracts (Print Edition) (0175-8292)
Media: Online - full content. **Related titles:** ♦ Supplement to: Vitis. ISSN 0042-7500.
—BLDSC (9244.120100), CISTI, Linda Hall. **CCC.**
Published by: Bundesanstalt fuer Zuechtungsforschung an Kulturpflanzen, Institut fuer Rebenzuechtung Geilweilerhof, Siebeldingen, 76833, Germany. TEL 49-6345-410, FAX 49-6345-919050, doku-vitis@bafz.de, http://vitis-vea.zadi.de, http://www.bafz.de/siebeldingen. Eds. Martin Klenert, Werner Koeglmeier. Circ: 700.

630 RUS ISSN 0372-3283
S13 CODEN: TVZKA3
VSESOYUZNYI NAUCHNO-ISSLEDOVATEL'SKII INSTITUT ZERNOVOGO KHOZYAISTVA. TRUDY✱. Text in Russian. 1964. irreg. price varies. bibl.; illus.
Indexed: ChemAb.
—CASDDS.
Published by: (Vsesoyuznyi Nauchno-Issledovatel'skii Institut Zernovogo Khozyaistva), Rossiiskaya Akademiya Sel'skokhozyaistvennykh Nauk/Russian Academy of Agricultural Sciences, c/o Tsentral'naya Nauchnaya Sel'skokhozyaistvennaya Biblioteka, Orlikov per 3, Moscow, 107804, Russian Federation. Circ: 3,500.

632 635 USA
W S S A NEWSLETTER. Text in English. 1970. 4/yr. adv. charts; illus. **Document type:** *Newsletter.*
Formerly: Weeds Today (0886-7712)
Media: Online - full text.
Indexed: FCA, HerbAb, S&F, WeedAb.
Published by: Weed Science Society of America, PO Box 7050, Lawrence, KS 66044-8897. TEL 800-627-0629, FAX 785-843-1274, wssa@allenpress.com, http://www.wssa.net/society.html. Circ: 2,500 (controlled).

631.6 POL
CODEN: AWARD6
WARSAW AGRICULTURAL UNIVERSITY. S G G W. ANNALS. LAND RECLAMATION. Text mainly in English; Text occasionally in French, German, Russian; Summaries in Polish. 1957. irreg., latest vol.32, 2001. USD 10 per issue (effective 2003). **Document type:** *Bulletin, Academic/Scholarly.*
Former titles: Warsaw Agricultural University. S G G W - A R. Annals. Land Reclamation (0208-5771); (until 1980): Akademia Rolnicza, Warsaw. Zeszyty Naukowe. Melioracje Rolne (0373-0034)
Indexed: ChemAb, RefZh.
—CASDDS, CISTI, Linda Hall.
Published by: Szkola Glowna Gospodarstwa Wiejskiego (SGGW)/Warsaw Agricultural University, Ul Nowoursynowska 166, Warsaw, 02787, Poland. TEL 48-22-8439041, FAX 48-22-8471562, jmw_wyd@alpha.sggw.waw.pl, http://www.sggw.waw.pl. Ed. C Somorowski.

WASEDA SEIBUTSU/WASEDA BIOLOGY. see *BIOLOGY*

632.9 570 AUS ISSN 1444-6162
CODEN: WBMEAH
➤ **WEED BIOLOGY AND MANAGEMENT.** Text in English. q. USD 186 combined subscription in the Americas to individuals print & online eds.; EUR 171 combined subscription in Europe to individuals print & online eds.; GBP 114 combined subscription elsewhere to individuals print & online eds.; USD 335 combined subscription in the Americas to institutions print & online eds.; GBP 207 combined subscription elsewhere to institutions print & online eds. (effective 2006). back issues avail. **Document type:** *Journal, Academic/Scholarly.* **Description:** Contains original research, review articles, technical reports and short communications in all aspects of weed science.
Related titles: Online - full text ed.: ISSN 1445-6664. USD 318 in the Americas to institutions; GBP 197 elsewhere to institutions (effective 2006) (from Blackwell Synergy, EBSCO Publishing, Gale Group, IngentaConnect, O C L C Online Computer Library Center, Inc., Swets Information Services).
Indexed: AgBio, Agr, BIOBASE, BIOSIS Prev, BioCN&I, BiolAb, CPA, FCA, HerbAb, HortAb, I&DA, MaizeAb, OrnHort, PBA, PGegResA, PGrRegA, RA&MP, RDA, RM&VM, RiceAb, S&F, SIA, SeedAb, SoyAb, TTI, TriticAb, WAE&RSA, WeedAb.
—BLDSC (9284.302000), CISTI, IE, Infotrieve, ingenta. **CCC.**
Published by: (Weed Science Society of Japan JPN), Blackwell Publishing Asia (Subsidiary of: Blackwell Publishing Ltd.), 550 Swanston St, Carlton South, VIC 3053, Australia. TEL 61-383591011, FAX 61-383591120, subs@blackwellpublishingasia.com, http://www.blackwellpublishing.com/journals/WBM. Ed. Kazuyuki Itoh.

632.9 USA ISSN 0741-9856
WEED CONTROL MANUAL. Text in English. a. USD 54 (effective 2000). adv. **Document type:** *Trade.*
Formerly: Weed Control Manual and Herbicide Guide (0511-411X)
—CCC.
Published by: Meister Media Worldwide, 37733 Euclid Ave, Willoughby, OH 44094-5992. TEL 440-572-7742, FAX 440-942-0662, wcm_circ@meisternet.com. Ed. Stella Naegely. Pub., Adv. contact Jess Ennis. Circ: 8,000.

632.9 GBR ISSN 0043-1737
SB611 CODEN: WEREAT
➤ **WEED RESEARCH.** Text in English, French, German. 1961. bi-m. GBP 465 combined subscription in Europe to institutions print & online eds.; USD 860 combined subscription in the Americas to institutions & Caribbean (print & online eds.); GBP 512 combined subscription elsewhere to institutions print & online eds. (effective 2006). adv. bibl.; charts; illus. index. back issues avail.; reprint service avail. from ISI. **Document type:** *Journal, Academic/Scholarly.* **Description:** Concerned with the study of weeds, their management and control, and related topics.
Related titles: Microform ed.: (from PQC); Online - full text ed.: Weed Research Online. ISSN 1365-3180. 1999. GBP 442 in Europe to institutions; USD 819 in the Americas to institutions & Caribbean; GBP 486 elsewhere to institutions (effective 2006) (from Blackwell Synergy, EBSCO Publishing, Gale Group, IngentaConnect, O C L C Online Computer Library Center, Inc., Swets Information Services).
Indexed: AEA, ASCA, ASFA, AgBio, Agr, AgrForAb, B&AI, BIOBASE, BIOSIS Prev, BioCN&I, BiolAb, CPA, ChemAb, CurCont, DBA, EPB, ExcerpMed, FCA, FaBeAb, ForAb, GEOBASE, HerbAb, HortAb, I&DA, IABS, ISR, MaizeAb, NemAb, NutrAb, OrnHort, PBA, PGegResA, PGrRegA, PN&I, PlantSci, PotatoAb, PoultAb, RA&MP, RPP, RRTA, RefZh, RevApplEntom, RiceAb, S&F, S&MA, SCI, SIA, SeedAb, SoyAb, TOSA, TriticAb, VITIS, WAE&RSA, WeedAb.
—BLDSC (9284.400000), CASDDS, CISTI, IDS, IE, Infotrieve, ingenta, Linda Hall. **CCC.**
Published by: (European Weed Research Society), Blackwell Publishing Ltd., 9600 Garsington Rd, Oxford, OX4 2ZG, United Kingdom. TEL 44-1865-776868, FAX 44-1865-714591, customerservices@oxon.blackwellpublishing.com, http://www.blackwellpublishing.com/journals/WRE. Ed. Cathy Knott. Pub. Elaine Stott. R&P Sophie Savage. Adv. contact Jenny Applin. Circ: 1,455.

632 USA ISSN 0043-1745
SB611 CODEN: WEESA6
➤ **WEED SCIENCE.** Text in English. 1951. bi-m. abstr.; bibl.; charts; illus. index. reprint service avail. from PQC,ISI. **Document type:** *Journal, Academic/Scholarly.* **Description:** Covers the science of weeds and other topics related to this science.
Formerly (until 1967): Weeds (0096-719X)
Related titles: Microform ed.: (from PMC, PQC); Online - full text ed.: ISSN 1550-2759 (from BioOne, C S A, O C L C Online Computer Library Center, Inc.).
Indexed: AEA, ASCA, ASFA, AgBio, Agr, AgrForAb, B&AI, BIOBASE, BIOSIS Prev, BibAg, BioCN&I, BiolAb, CIN, CPA, CTFA, ChemAb, ChemTitl, CurCont, DBA, EPB, ESPM, ExcerpMed, F&GI, FCA, ForAb, GEOBASE, HerbAb, HortAb, I&DA, IABS, ISR, IndVet, MaizeAb, NemAb, OrnHort, PBA, PGegResA, PGrRegA, PlantSci, PotatoAb, PoultAb, RA&MP, RM&VM, RPP, RefZh, RevApplEntom, RiceAb, S&F, S&MA, SCI, SIA, SWRA, SeedAb, SoyAb, TOSA, TriticAb, VITIS, VetBull, WAE&RSA, WeedAb.
—BLDSC (9284.450000), CASDDS, CISTI, IDS, IE, Infotrieve, ingenta, Linda Hall.
Published by: Weed Science Society of America, PO Box 7050, Lawrence, KS 66044-8897. TEL 800-627-0629, FAX 785-843-1274, wssa@allenpress.com, http://www.wssa.net, http://www.wssa.net/society.html. Ed. Robert L Zindahl. Circ: 3,000.

630 635 IND
WEED SCIENCE NEWSLETTER. Text in English. q.
Published by: Indian Society of Weed Science, Andhra Pradesh Agricultural University, Rajendranagar, Hyderabad, India.

632.9 USA ISSN 0890-037X
SB612.A2 CODEN: WETEE9
➤ **WEED TECHNOLOGY.** Text in English. 1987. q. **Document type:** *Academic/Scholarly.*
Related titles: Online - full text ed.: ISSN 1550-2740 (from BioOne, C S A, O C L C Online Computer Library Center, Inc.).
Indexed: AEA, ASFA, AgBio, Agr, AgrForAb, BIOBASE, BIOSIS Prev, BioCN&I, BiolAb, CIN, CPA, ChemAb, CurCont, DBA, EPB, ESPM, FCA, ForAb, GEOBASE, HerbAb, HortAb, I&DA, IABS, IndVet, MaizeAb, NemAb, NutrAb, OrnHort, PBA, PGegResA, PGrRegA, PHN&I, PlantSci, PotatoAb, RA&MP, RM&VM, RPP, RRTA, RefZh, RevApplEntom, RiceAb, S&F, SIA, SWRA, SeedAb, SoyAb, TriticAb, VITIS, WAE&RSA, WeedAb.
—BLDSC (9284.485000), CASDDS, CISTI, IDS, IE, Infotrieve, ingenta, Linda Hall.
Published by: Weed Science Society of America, PO Box 7050, Lawrence, KS 66044-8897. TEL 800-627-0629, FAX 785-843-1274, wssa@allenpress.com, http://www.wssa.net/society.html. Ed. Chester L Foy.

➤ **WEED WORLD.** see *DRUG ABUSE AND ALCOHOLISM*

634.653 USA
THE WEEKLY NEWSLINE. Text in English. 1980. w. looseleaf. USD 125 domestic; USD 165 foreign (effective 2000). adv. charts; mkt.; stat. back issues avail. **Document type:** *Newsletter.* **Description:** Provides market information and industry news for avocado growers.
Published by: California Avocado Society, Inc., 1457 Winter Haven Rd, Fallbrook, CA 92028-4606. TEL 760-728-6416, FAX 760-728-4133, jmccorm@tfb.com. Ed., R&P James McCormack. Adv. contact Eric Lunquist. Circ: 1,500 (controlled).

633 USA ISSN 0043-1974
QC983
WEEKLY WEATHER AND CROP BULLETIN. Text in English. 1872. w. USD 60 domestic (effective 2004). illus. Index. back issues avail.; reprint service avail. from CIS. **Document type:** *Bulletin, Government.*
Formerly (until 1924): Weekly Weather Chronicle
Related titles: Online - full content ed.
Indexed: AmStI, IUSGP.
—CISTI.
Published by: (U.S. Dept. of Agriculture, U.S. National Oceanic and Atmospheric Administration), The Joint Agricultural Weather Facility, USDA S Bldg, Rm 4443B, Washington, DC 20250. wwcb@jawfsrv.wwb.noaa.gov., http://www.usda.gov/oce/waob/jawf/wwcb.html.

631.4 GBR ISSN 0083-7938
WELSH SOILS DISCUSSION GROUP. REPORT. Text in English. 1960. a. price varies.
Indexed: ChemAb, S&F.
—CISTI.
Published by: Welsh Soils Discussion Group, c/o Dr. D.A. Jenkins, Dept. of Biochemistry and Soil Science, University College of North, Bangor, Gwynedd, Wales LL57 2UW, United Kingdom. Circ: 250.

WER UND WAS - OBST-, GEMUESE-, KARTOFFEL- UND NAEHRMITTEL-INDUSTRIE. see *BUSINESS AND ECONOMICS—Trade And Industrial Directories*

633.18 CIV
WEST AFRICA RICE DEVELOPMENT ASSOCIATION. ANNUAL REPORT. Text in French, English. a. **Document type:** *Corporate.*
Published by: West Africa Rice Development Association, 01 BP 2551, Bouake, Ivory Coast. TEL 225-31634514, FAX 225-31634714, warda@cgiar.org.

634 641.345 AUS ISSN 0810-6681
WEST AUSTRALIAN NUT AND TREE CROP ASSOCIATION YEARBOOK. Short title: W A N A T C A Yearbook. Text in English. 1975. a. AUD 50 combined subscription includes Quandong (effective 1999).
Formerly (until 1980): West Australian Nutgrowing Society Yearbook (0312-8997)
Indexed: AgBio, AgrForAb, BIOSIS Prev, BiolAb, CPA, FPA, ForAb, HerbAb, HortAb, I&DA, NutrAb, OrnHort, PBA, PGegResA, PGrRegA, PHN&I, RA&MP, RDA, RPP, S&F, TDB, WAE&RSA.
Published by: West Australian Nut & Tree Crop Association (Inc.), PO Box 565, Subiaco, W.A. 6008, Australia. TEL 61-8-93881965, FAX 61-8-93881852, wanatca@AOI.com.au, http://www.AOI.com.au/wanatca. Circ: 500.

630 363.7 AUS
WESTERN AUSTRALIA. DEPARTMENT OF AGRICULTURE. RESOURCE MANAGEMENT TECHNICAL REPORTS. Text in English. irreg.
Published by: (Department of Agriculture (Western Australia), Natural Resource Sciences Unit USA), Department of Agriculture (Western Australia), 3 Baron-Hay Court, South Perth, W.A. 6151, Australia. TEL 61-8-93683333, enquiries@agric.wa.gov.au, http://www.agric.wa.gov.au/environment/links/RMtechreports/.

WESTERN CITRUS REPORT. see *AGRICULTURE—Agricultural Economics*

634 USA ISSN 0164-6001
WESTERN FRUIT GROWER. Text in English. 1954. m. USD 19.95 domestic; USD 28 in Canada; USD 39 elsewhere (effective 2005). adv. bk.rev. illus.; mkt.; stat. reprint service avail. from PQC. **Document type:** *Trade.*
Related titles: Online - full text ed.: (from Northern Light Technology, Inc., ProQuest Information & Learning).
Indexed: ABIn.
—CISTI. **CCC.**
Published by: Meister Media Worldwide, 37733 Euclid Ave, Willoughby, OH 44094-5992. TEL 440-942-2000, 800-572-7740, FAX 440-942-0662, afg.edit@meistermedia.com, http://www.americanfruitgrower.com/index.html, http://www.meistermedia.com. Ed. Brian Sparks. Pub. Bill Miller. Adv. contact Jon J Miducki. Circ: 26,000.

630 658 USA ISSN 0043-3799
WESTERN GROWER AND SHIPPER; the business magazine of the Western produce industry. Short title: W G & S. Text in English. 1929. m. USD 18 domestic; USD 36 foreign (effective 2005). adv. charts; illus. **Document type:** *Magazine, Trade.*
Related titles: Online - full text ed.: (from The Dialog Corporation).
—Linda Hall.
Published by: Western Growers Association, PO Box 2130, Newport Beach, CA 92658. TEL 949-863-1000, FAX 949-863-9028, champguys@aol.com, tchelling@wga.com, http://www.wga.com. Ed. Tim Linden. Pub. Heather Flower. Adv. contact Tom Fielding. Circ: 6,000 (controlled).

WESTERN POTATO AND ONION REPORT. see *AGRICULTURE—Agricultural Economics*

634.11 USA ISSN 0043-4701
WHEAT LIFE. Text in English. 1956. m. (11/yr.). USD 50 (effective 2005). adv. mkt. **Document type:** *Magazine, Trade.*
—CISTI.
Published by: Washington Association of Wheat Growers, 109 E First Ave, Ritzville, WA 99169-2394. TEL 509-659-0610, FAX 509-659-4302, wheat@wawg.org, http://www.wawg.org. Ed., Pub. David A Andersen. Circ: 13,700 (controlled).

WILD MATTERS. see *CONSUMER EDUCATION AND PROTECTION*

630 USA
➤ **WILEY SERIES IN GEOTECHNICAL ENGINEERING.** Text in English. 1951. irreg., latest 1993. price varies. **Document type:** *Monographic series, Academic/Scholarly.*
Former titles: Series in Geotechnical Engineering; Soil Engineering Series
Published by: John Wiley & Sons, Inc., 111 River St, Hoboken, NJ 07030-5774. TEL 201-748-6000, 800-825-7550, FAX 201-748-5915, uscs-wis@wiley.com, http://www.wiley.com. Eds. Robert V Whitman, T William Lambe.

634.8 AUS ISSN 0726-9498
WINE INDUSTRY NEWSLETTER. Text in English. 1981. q.
Related titles: Online - full text ed.
Published by: Department of Agriculture (Western Australia), 3 Baron-Hay Court, South Perth, W.A. 6151, Australia. TEL 61-8-93683333, enquiries@agric.wa.gov.au, http://www.agric.wa.gov.au/programs/hort/viticulture/newsletter/.

WINES AND VINES; the authoritative voice of the grape and wine industry. see *BEVERAGES*

634.8 AUT ISSN 0043-5953
DER WINZER; das Fachblatt des oesterreichischen Weinbaues. Text in German. 1945. m. EUR 75 domestic; EUR 92 foreign (effective 2004). adv. bk.rev. illus. **Document type:** *Magazine, Trade.*
Indexed: VITIS.
Published by: (Bundesverband der Weinbautreibenden Oesterreichs), Oesterreichischer Agrarverlag GmbH, Achauer Str 49a, Leopoldsdorf, N 2333, Austria. TEL 43-2235-4040, FAX 43-2235-404929, j.glatt@pklwk.at, office@agrarverlag.at, http://www.agrarverlag.at/derwinzer/. Ed. Josef Glatt. Adv. contact Romana Hummer. B&W page EUR 3,224, color page EUR 7,878; trim 175 x 260. Circ: 16,700 (paid and controlled).

DIE WINZER ZEITSCHRIFT. see *BEVERAGES*

631.4 DEU ISSN 0049-7711
CODEN: WIFUAB
DAS WIRTSCHAFTSEIGENE FUTTER; Erzeugung-Konservierung-Verwertung. Text in German; Summaries in English, French, German. 1955. 3/yr. EUR 78 (effective 2003). adv. bk.rev. charts; illus. back issues avail. **Document type:** *Journal, Trade.*
Indexed: BIOSIS Prev, BiolAb, ChemAb, DSA, ExcerpMed, FCA, HerbAb, MaizeAb, NutrAb, PBA, PHN&I, PotatoAb, PoultAb, S&F, SeedAb, SoyAb, TriticAb, WeedAb.
—BLDSC (9325.553000), CASDDS. **CCC.**
Published by: (Deutsche Landwirtschafts-Gesellschaft e.V.), D L G Verlags GmbH, Eschborner Landstr 122, Frankfurt Am Main, 60489, Germany. TEL 49-69-247880, FAX 49-69-24788480, dlg-verlag@dlg-frankfurt.de, http://www.dlg-verlag.de. Ed. Dr. Staudacher. Circ: 800.

WOOLPRO. see *AGRICULTURE—Abstracting, Bibliographies, Statistics*

632.9 NLD ISSN 1572-4379
➤ **WORLD CROP PESTS.** Text in English. 1985. irreg., latest 1997, vol 7B. price varies. back issues avail. **Document type:** *Monographic series, Academic/Scholarly.* **Description:** Publishes research in a wide variety of agricultural crop pests.
Indexed: ZooRec.
—BLDSC (9353.980000), ingenta.
Published by: Elsevier BV (Subsidiary of: Elsevier Science & Technology), Radarweg 29, Amsterdam, 1043 NX, Netherlands. TEL 31-20-4853911, FAX 31-20-4852457, nlinfo-f@elsevier.nl, http://www.elsevier.nl. Ed. Dr. Maurice W. Sabelis.

661 GBR
WORLD DIRECTORY OF FERTILIZER MANUFACTURERS. Text in English. irreg., latest vol.10, 1998. GBP 260, USD 400 (effective 1998). **Document type:** *Directory.* **Description:** Contains company information on almost 800 fertilizer producers worldwide. Each entry contains full contact details; a brief description of the company; a list of the products manufactured; names of key personnel; ownership & subsidiary details; plant locations and capacities.
Published by: British Sulphur Publishing (Subsidiary of: C R U Publishing), 31 Mt Pleasant, London, WC1X 0AD, United Kingdom. TEL 44-20-7837-5600, FAX 44-20-7837-0292, smoore@cruint.tcom.co.uk, derek.winterbottom@crugroup.com, http://www.cru.co.uk, http://www.britishsulphur.com/. Pub., R&P John French TEL 44-20-79032435.

661 GBR
WORLD DIRECTORY OF FERTILIZER PRODUCTS. Text in English. irreg., latest vol.10, 1998. GBP 260, USD 400 (effective 1998). **Document type:** *Directory.* **Description:** Provides product and company information on more than 1,100 companies worldwide. Includes sections on producers, trading and marketing organizations, raw material suppliers and state purchasing organizations.
Published by: British Sulphur Publishing (Subsidiary of: C R U Publishing), 31 Mt Pleasant, London, WC1X 0AD, United Kingdom. TEL 44-20-7837-5600, FAX 44-20-7837-0292, smoore@cruint.tcom.co.uk, derek.winterbottom@crugroup.com, http://www.cru.co.uk, http://www.britishsulphur.com/. Pub., R&P John French TEL 44-20-79032435.

631.8 GBR ISSN 0512-2953
WORLD FERTILIZER PLANT LIST AND ATLAS. Text in English. 1964. irreg., latest vol.11, 1997. GBP 260, USD 400. **Document type:** *Directory.* **Description:** Contains listings and an atlas of the world's fertilizer plants. Each listing entry includes plant location, owner, annual capacity, products manufactured and expansion plans.
Published by: British Sulphur Publishing (Subsidiary of: C R U Publishing), 31 Mt Pleasant, London, WC1X 0AD, United Kingdom. TEL 44-20-7837-5600, FAX 44-20-7837-0292, smoore@cruint.tcom.co.uk, derek.winterbottom@crugroup.com, http://www.cru.co.uk, http://www.britishsulphur.com/. Pub., R&P John French TEL 44-20-79032435.

631 GBR ISSN 0142-5757
WORLD SUGAR JOURNAL✱. Text in English. 1978. m. USD 280. adv. bk.rev.
—CISTI.
Published by: NG Osman & Assoc. Ltd., Sugerama, 1 Murdoch Rd, Wokingham, Berks RG40 2DL, United Kingdom. Ed. N G Osman.

633.6 664.1 JPN ISSN 0049-8149
WORLD SUGAR NEWS/KAIGAI SATO JOHO. Text in Japanese. 1962. bi-m. membership. stat.
Published by: Japan Sugar Refiners' Association/Seito Kogyokai, 5-7 Sanban-cho, Chiyoda-ku, Tokyo, 102-0075, Japan. Circ: 600.

632 IND ISSN 0971-7552
WORLD WEEDS. Text in English. 1994. q. USD 80 (effective 2005). **Document type:** *Journal, Academic/Scholarly.* **Description:** Contains information on common weeds and parasitic flowering plants.
—BLDSC (9360.179070).
Published by: International Book Distributors, 9/3, Rajpur Rd., First Fl, Dehra Dun, Uttar Pradesh 248 001, India. ibdbooks@sancharnet.in. Eds. Dhan Singh, Y P S Pundir. Pub. R.P. Singh.

634.8 ZAF ISSN 0043-9657
WYNBOER; a magazine for wine-lovers, wine-growers and those interested in good living - tydskrif vir wynliefhebbers, wynboere en almal geinteresseerd in wellewendheid. Text in Afrikaans, English. 1931. m. ZAR 130. adv. bk.rev. illus.; mkt.; stat. index. **Document type:** *Trade.*
Indexed: FS&TA, ISAP, VITIS.
Published by: Kooperatieve Wijnbouwers Vereniging van S.A. Bpk. (KWV), Main St, PO Box 528, Suider-Paarl, KwaZulu-Natal 7624, South Africa. TEL 27-21-8073304, FAX 27-21-8631562, ridderd@kwv.co.za. Ed. Henry C K Hopkins. R&P Henry C.K. Hopkins. Adv. contact Sue Smith. Circ: 7,663.

632.9 JPN ISSN 0049-8335
YOKOHAMA PLANT PROTECTION NEWS/YOKOHAMA SHOKUBUTSU BOEKI NYUSU. Text in Japanese. 1953. s-m. looseleaf. free. charts; illus.; stat. index.
Published by: Yokohama Plant Protection Station/Norin-sho Yokohama Shokubutsu Boekisho, 5-57 Kita-Nakadori, Naka-ku, Yokohama-shi, Kanagawa-ken 231-0003, Japan. TEL 81-45-211-7164, FAX 81-45-211-0890. Ed. Toshiro Kabayashi. Circ: 2,000.

633 DEU ISSN 0344-9378
Z M P BILANZ GEMUESE. Text in German. a. **Document type:** *Bulletin, Trade.*
Which was formerly: Agrarmaerkte in der Bundesrepublik. Obst und Gemuese (0400-7638); Agrarmaerkte in der Bundesrepublik (0515-6823)
Related titles: CD-ROM ed.
Published by: Zentrale Markt und Preisberichtstelle GmbH, Rochusstr 2, Bonn, 53123, Germany. TEL 49-228-9777173, info@zmp.com, http://www.zmp.de.

633 DEU ISSN 0170-8422
Z M P BILANZ KARTOFFELN. Text in German. a. **Document type:** *Bulletin, Trade.*
Supersedes in part: Agrarmaerkte Bundesrepublik Deutschland, EWG und Weltmarkt. Getreide, Futtermittel und Kartoffeln (0572-3191); Which was formerly: Agrarmaerkte in der Bundesrepublik und im Ausland. Getreide, Futtermittel und Kartoffeln (0343-9542); Agrarmaerkte in der Bundesrepublik. Getreide, Futtermittel und Kartoffeln (0343-9488); Which supersedes in part: Agrarmaerkte in der Bundesrepublik (0515-6823)
Related titles: CD-ROM ed.
Published by: Zentrale Markt und Preisberichtstelle GmbH, Rochusstr 2, Bonn, 53123, Germany. TEL 49-228-9777173, info@zmp.de, http://www.zmp.de.

633 DEU ISSN 0344-9394
Z M P BILANZ OBST. Text in German. a. **Document type:** *Bulletin, Trade.*
Which was formerly: Agrarmaerkte in der Bundesrepublik. Obst und Gemuese (0400-7638); Agrarmaerkte in der Bundesrepublik (0515-6823)
Related titles: CD-ROM ed.
Published by: Zentrale Markt und Preisberichtstelle GmbH, Rochusstr 2, Bonn, 53123, Germany. TEL 49-228-9777173, info@zmp.de, http://www.zmp.de.

633 DEU
Z M P MARKTBERICHT. DER MARKT OBST UND GEMUESE. Text in German. m. **Document type:** *Bulletin, Trade.*
Published by: Zentrale Markt und Preisberichtstelle GmbH, Rochusstr 2, Bonn, 53123, Germany. TEL 49-228-9777173, FAX 49-228-9777179, info@zmp.de, http://www.zmp.de.

633 DEU ISSN 0946-6576
Z M P MARKTBERICHT. FRUEHKARTOFFELN. Text in German. 1994. 30/yr. **Document type:** *Bulletin, Trade.*
Published by: Zentrale Markt und Preisberichtstelle GmbH, Rochusstr 2, Bonn, 53123, Germany. TEL 49-228-9777173, FAX 49-228-9777179, info@zmp.de, http://www.zmp.de.

633 DEU
Z M P MARKTBERICHT. KARTOFFELN. Text in German. w.
Document type: *Bulletin, Trade.*
Published by: Zentrale Markt und Preisberichtstelle GmbH, Rochusstr 2, Bonn, 53123, Germany. TEL 49-228-9777173, FAX 49-228-9777179, info@zmp.de, http://www.zmp.de.

633 DEU
Z M P MARKTBERICHT. OBST UND GEMUESE - SUEDWEST. Text in German. w. **Document type:** *Bulletin, Trade.*
Published by: Zentrale Markt und Preisberichtstelle GmbH, Rochusstr 2, Bonn, 53123, Germany. TEL 49-228-9777173, FAX 49-228-9777179, info@zmp.de, http://www.zmp.de.

630 CHN ISSN 1005-3956
ZAJIAO SHUIDAO/JOURNAL OF HYBRID RICE. Text in Chinese. 1986. bi-m. **Document type:** *Journal, Academic/Scholarly.*
Related titles: Online - full text ed.: (from East View Information Services, WanFang Data Corp.).
—BLDSC (4340.370000).
Address: Mapoling, Shangsha, 410125, China. TEL 86-731-4690835, FAX 86-731-4691877, jhybrice@public.cs.hn.cn, http://zjsd.periodicals.net.cn/. Ed. Long-Ping Yuan.

631 ZMB
ZAMBIA. DEPARTMENT OF AGRICULTURE. RESEARCH AND SPECIALIST SERVICES. ANNUAL REPORT. Text in English. a. free. **Document type:** *Government.*
Published by: Department of Agriculture, Research Branch, Principal Research Officer, Mount Makulu Research Sta., Private Bag 7, Chilanga, Zambia. Circ: 2,000.

631.4 ZMB
ZAMBIA. MINISTRY OF AGRICULTURE AND WATER DEVELOPMENT. LAND USE BRANCH. SOIL SURVEY REPORT. Text in English. 1967. irreg. per issue exchange basis. **Document type:** *Government.*
Formerly: Zambia. Ministry of Lands and Agriculture. Land Use Branch. Soil Survey Report
Published by: Ministry of Agriculture and Water Development, Land Use Branch, c/o Soil Survey Unit, Mount Makulu Research Station, Private Bag 7, Chilanga, Zambia. TEL 260-1-278087. Circ: (controlled). **Co-sponsor:** Norwegian Agency for International Development.

632 RUS ISSN 1026-8634
CODEN: ZSRSBX
ZASHCHITA I KARANTIN RASTENII. Text in Russian. 1932. m. USD 119.95 foreign (effective 2000). index.
Formerly (until 1996): Zashchita Rastenii (0044-1864)
Indexed: AEA, ApicAb, BioCN&I, BioDAb, BiolAb, CTFA, ChemAb, DBA, FCA, ForAb, HerbAb, HortAb, MaizeAb, OrnHort, PBA, PGegResA, PGrRegA, PHN&I, PotatoAb, RM&VM, RPP, RefZh, RevApplEntom, RiceAb, S&F, SeedAb, TriticAb, WeedAb, ZooRec.
—BLDSC (0070.915000), CASDDS, CISTI. **CCC.**
Published by: Izdatel'stvo Kolos, Sadovaya-Spasskaya 18, Moscow, 107807, Russian Federation. TEL 7-095-207213, FAX 7-095-2071015. Ed. V E Savzdarg. Circ: 64,000.

633 RUS
ZASHCHITA RASTENII. Text in Russian. m. **Document type:** *Newspaper, Trade.*
Published by: Agrorus', Mosfil'movskaya ul, 52, Moscow, 119590, Russian Federation. TEL 7-095-9379812, FAX 7-095-2326825, agrorus@agrorus.com, http://www.agrorus.com. Circ: 40,000.

631.587 DEU ISSN 0049-8602
S612 CODEN: ZBEWDX
ZEITSCHRIFT FUER BEWAESSERUNGSWIRTSCHAFT/ JOURNAL OF APPLIED IRRIGATION SCIENCE. Text and summaries in English, German. 1966. s-a. EUR 82 to non-members; EUR 46 newsstand/cover (effective 2004). adv. bk.rev. bibl.; illus. index. back issues avail. **Document type:** *Journal, Trade.*
Related titles: Online - full text ed.
Indexed: AEA, CPA, FCA, HerbAb, HortAb, I&DA, IBR, IBZ, MaizeAb, PotatoAb, RDA, S&F, SIA, SeedAb, TriticAb, WAE&RSA.
—CCC.
Published by: D L G Verlags GmbH, Eschborner Landstr 122, Frankfurt Am Main, 60489, Germany. TEL 49-69-247880, FAX 49-69-24788480, dlg-verlag@dlg-frankfurt.de, http://www.wiz.uni-kassel.de/kww/zfb/zfb_i.html, http://www.dlg-verlag.de. Ed. Dr. Peter Wolff. Circ: 400.

633 RUS ISSN 0235-2532
CODEN: ZRKZAB
ZERNOVYE KUL'TURY. Text in Russian. 1963. q. USD 80 foreign (effective 2004). index.
Formerly (until 1988): Zernovoe Khozyaistvo (0372-9893)
Related titles: Microfiche ed.: (from EVP).
Indexed: FCA, RefZh, TriticAb.
—CASDDS, CISTI, East View.
Address: Sadovaya-Spasskaya 18, Moscow, 107807, Russian Federation. Ed. Viktor V Kasatkin. **Dist. by:** M K - Periodica, ul Gilyarovskogo 39, Moscow 129110, Russian Federation. TEL 7-095-2845008, FAX 7-095-2813798, info@periodicals.ru, http://www.mkniga.ru.

632.9 CHN ISSN 1004-7255
ZHIBAO JISHU YU TUIGUANG. Text in Chinese. 1981. q. adv.
Document type: *Academic/Scholarly.*
Formerly (until 1993): Bingchong Cebao (1002-4948)
Related titles: Online - full text ed.: (from East View Information Services).
Published by: Quanguo Zhiwu Baohu Zongzhan/National Plant Protection Station, 11 Nongzhanguan Nanli, Beijing, 100026, China. TEL 5003579, FAX 01-5025146, TELEX 210086 CPPGS CN. Ed. Feng Guichun.

333.74 CHN ISSN 1000-6311
QH541.5.P7 CODEN: ZHCAEY
ZHONGGUO CAODI/GRASSLAND OF CHINA. Text in Chinese. 1979. bi-m. CNY 3, USD 1.40 per issue (effective 2003).
Document type: *Journal, Academic/Scholarly.*
Related titles: Online - full text ed.: (from East View Information Services).
—BLDSC (4213.430000), CISTI.
Published by: Zhongguo Nongye Kexueyuan, Caoyuan Yanjiusuo, 120, Wulanchaibu Dong Lu, Huhehaote, 010010, China. TEL 86-471-4926880, FAX 86-471-4961330, Cgi@puplic.hh.nm.cn, http://zgcd.periodicals.com.cn/default.html. **Dist. by:** China International Book Trading Corp, 35 Chegongzhuang Xilu, Haidian District, PO Box 399, Beijing 100044, China. TEL 86-10-68412045, FAX 86-10-68412023, cibtc@mail.cibtc.com.cn, http://www.cibtc.com.cn.

633 CHN
ZHONGGUO MALINGSHU/CHINESE POTATO JOURNAL. Text in Chinese. 1987. bi-m. CNY 5 per issue (effective 2003).
Document type: *Journal, Academic/Scholarly.*
Formerly: Malingshu Zazhi/Journal of Potatoes (1001-0092)
Related titles: Online - full text ed.: (from East View Information Services).
—BLDSC (3181.048705), IE.
Published by: Dongbei Nongye Daxue, Editorial Dept. of Chinese Potato Journal, Xiangfang-qu, Harbin, 150030, China. TEL 86-451-5390739, 86-451-5390370, potatobjb@neau.edu.cn, http://zgmls.periodicals.net.cn/default.html.

633 CHN ISSN 1000-6346
CODEN: ZSHUEQ
ZHONGGUO SHUCAI/CHINESE VEGETABLES. Text in Chinese. 1981. bi-m. USD 18 (effective 1994). adv. **Document type:** *Academic/Scholarly.*
Indexed: AEA, AgBio, BioCN&I, CPA, FCA, FPA, FS&TA, ForAb, HerbAb, HortAb, I&DA, MaizeAb, NemAb, OrnHort, PBA, PGegResA, PGrRegA, PHN&I, PotatoAb, PoultAb, RA&MP, RDA, RPP, RiceAb, S&F, SIA, SeedAb, SoyAb, WAE&RSA, WeedAb.
Published by: (Shucai Huahui Yanjiusuo), Zhongguo Nongye Kexueyuan/Chinese Academy of Agricultural Sciences, Chinese Society for Horticultural Science, 30 Baishiqiao Lu, Beijing, 100081, China. TEL 8314433, FAX 8316374. Ed. Li Shude. Adv. contact Mo Qing. color page USD 3,000.

631.4 CHN ISSN 1000-0941
ZHONGGUO SHUITU BAOCHI. Text in Chinese. m.
Related titles: Online - full text ed.: (from East View Information Services).
Published by: Shuili Bu, Huang He Shuili Weiyuanhui, 11 Jinshui Lu, Zhengzhou, Henan 450003, China. TEL 22971. Ed. Hao Zhifeng.

630 636 CHN ISSN 1007-8347
ZHONGZHI YU YANGZHI. Abbreviated title: Planting and Breeding. Text in Chinese. s-m. CNY 108 (effective 2004).
Document type: *Journal, Academic/Scholarly.*
Formerly (until 1997): Yangzhiye Xinxi (1005-4464)
Published by: Zhongguo Renmin Daxue, Shubao Zilio Zhongxin/Renmin University of China, Information Center for Social Server, Dongcheng-qu, 3, Zhangzizhong Lu, Beijing, 100007, China. TEL 86-10-64039458, FAX 86-10-64015080, kyes@163.net, http://www.confucius.cn.net/bkdetail.asp?fzt=X3. **Dist. in the US by:** China Publications Service, PO Box 49614, Chicago, IL 60649. TEL 312-288-3291, FAX 312-288-8570; **Dist. by:** China International Book Trading Corp, 35 Chegongzhuang Xilu, Haidian District, PO Box 399, Beijing 100044, China. TEL 86-10-68412045, FAX 86-10-68412023, cibtc@mail.cibtc.com.cn, http://www.cibtc.com.cn.

633 CHN ISSN 1000-8071
ZHONGZI SHIJIE/WORLD OF SEEDS. Text in Chinese. m.
Published by: Heilongjiang Sheng Zhongzi Xiehui, 43, Wenchang Jie, Harbin, Heilongjiang 150001, China. TEL 224517. Ed. Guan Xun.

631 ZWE
ZIMBABWE. COFFEE RESEARCH INSTITUTE. ANNUAL REPORT. PART 2. NYANGA EXPERIMENTAL STATION. Text in English. 1976. a. free. **Document type:** *Government.*
Formerly: Horticultural and Coffee Research Institute. Annual Report. Part 3. Rhodes Experimental Station
Published by: Ministry of Agriculture, Coffee Research Institute, Marondera, PO Box 3748, Marondera, Zimbabwe. Circ: 300.

633.51 ZWE
ZIMBABWE. COTTON RESEARCH INSTITUTE. ANNUAL REPORT. Text in English. 1969. a. free. back issues avail.
Document type: *Government.*
Indexed: FCA, HerbAb.
Published by: (Zimbabwe. Information Services), Ministry of Lands, Agriculture and Rural Resettlement, Research and Specialist Services, PO Box 8108, Causeway, Zimbabwe. Circ: 300 (controlled).

631 ZWE
ZIMBABWE. MINISTRY OF AGRICULTURE. SEED SERVICES. ANNUAL REPORT. Text in English. a. free. back issues avail.
Document type: *Government.*
Indexed: BiolAb.
Published by: (Zimbabwe. Information Services), Ministry of Lands Agriculture and Rural Resettlement, Research and Specialist Services, Causeway, PO Box 8108, Harare, Zimbabwe. Circ: 250.

633.6 DEU ISSN 0044-5398
DIE ZUCKERRUEBE. Text in German. 1952. bi-m. EUR 6 newsstand/cover (effective 2005). adv. charts; illus. **Document type:** *Magazine, Trade.*
Indexed: FCA, HerbAb, S&F, SIA.
Published by: Verlag Th. Mann, Nordring 10, Gelsenkirchen, 45894, Germany. TEL 49-209-93040, FAX 49-209-9304185, info@th-mann.de, http://www.th-mann.de. Eds. Gunter Weiss, Dr. Heinz Peter Puetz. Adv. contact Richard Heineke. B&W page EUR 2,388, color page EUR 4,383; trim 186 x 270. Circ: 16,453 (paid and controlled).

637 DEU ISSN 1431-6714
DIE ZUCKERRUEBEN ZEITUNG. Text in German. 1965. 6/yr. adv. 5 cols./p.; **Document type:** *Newspaper, Trade.*
Formerly: Deutsche Zuckerruebenzeitung
Published by: Verband Sueddeutscher Zueckerruebenanbauer e.V., Simon-Breu-Str 52, Wuerzburg, 97074, Germany. TEL 49-931-796950, FAX 49-931-7969520, vsz@vsz.de, http://www.vsz.de. Ed. Henning Wiedenroth. Adv. contact Doris Ofenhitzer TEL 49-9324-99867. Circ: 35,000.

633 CHN ISSN 1000-6435
SB123.3
ZUOWU PINZHONG ZIYUAN/CROP GENETIC RESOURCES. Text in Chinese. 1982. q. CNY 10 (effective 2000); USD 10 foreign. adv. **Document type:** *Academic/Scholarly.*
Formerly: Zhongguo Zhongye/China Seeds
Related titles: Online - full text ed.: (from East View Information Services).
Indexed: AgBio, FCA, FS&TA, HortAb, MaizeAb, NemAb, PBA, PGegResA, PHN&I, PotatoAb, RPP, RevApplEntom, RiceAb, SeedAb, SoyAb, TriticAb, WeedAb.
Published by: (Zuowu Pinzhong Ziyuan Yanjiusuo), Zhongguo Nongye Kexueyuan/Chinese Academy of Agricultural Sciences, Chinese Society for Horticultural Science, 30 Baishiqiao Lu, Beijing, 100081, China. TEL 86-10-6218-6657, FAX 86-10-6218-6629. Eds. Chen Lijuan, Liu Genquan.

633 CHN ISSN 0496-3490
CODEN: TSHPA9
➤ **ZUOWU XUEBAO/ACTA AGRONOMICA SINICA.** Text in Chinese; Summaries in English. 1975. bi-m. CNY 156 (effective 2004). adv. **Document type:** *Journal, Academic/Scholarly.* **Description:** Publishes research in all areas of crop science.
Related titles: Online - full text ed.: (from East View Information Services, WanFang Data Corp.).
Indexed: AEA, AgBio, CPA, CTFA, FCA, FS&TA, HerbAb, HortAb, I&DA, MaizeAb, NemAb, NutrAb, PBA, PGegResA, PGrRegA, PHN&I, RA&MP, RPP, RefZh, RevApplEntom, RiceAb, S&F, S&MA, SeedAb, SoyAb, TriticAb, WAE&RSA, WeedAb.
—BLDSC (0590.400000), CISTI, IE, ingenta, Linda Hall.
Published by: (Zhongguo Zuowu Xuehui/Chinese Society of Crop Science), Kexue Chubanshe/Science Press, 16 Donghuang Cheng Genbei Jie, Beijing, 100717, China. TEL 86-1-4010642, FAX 86-1-4019810, xbzw@chinajournal.net.cn, http://zuowxb.periodicals.net.cn/default.html, http://www.sciencep.com/. Ed. Qiaosheng Zhuang. Circ: 11,000. **Dist. overseas by:** China International Book Trading Corp, 35 Chegongzhuang Xilu, Haidian District, PO Box 399, Beijing 100044, China. TEL 86-10-68412045, FAX 86-10-68412023, cibtc@mail.cibtc.com.cn, http://www.cibtc.com.cn.

AGRICULTURE—Dairying And Dairy Products

see also AGRICULTURE—Poultry And Livestock

637.05 AUS
A D C REPORT. Text in English. 1999. bi-m. **Document type:** *Trade.*
Media: Online - full text.
Published by: Dairy Australia, Level 5, IBM Tower, 60 City Rd, Southbank, VIC 3006, Australia. TEL 61-3-96943777, FAX 61-3-96943733, http://www.dairyaustralia.com.au.

637 CAN ISSN 1184-0684
ADVANCES IN DAIRY TECHNOLOGY. Variant title: Western Canadian Dairy Seminar. Proceedings. Text in English. 1989. a.
Indexed: Agr.
—BLDSC (0704.240300), CISTI.

Published by: (Western Canadian Dairy Seminar), University of Alberta, Faculty of Extension, 8303-112 St, Edmonton, AB T6G 2J7, Canada. TEL 780-492-3109, extinfo@ualberta.ca, http://www.extension.ualberta.ca.

637   USA
AGRI-MARK MONTHLY. Text in English. 1980. m. in house only. **Document type:** Newsletter. **Description:** Newsletter on Northeast dairying published for the members of the Agri-Mark dairy cooperative. Covers national and regional dairy industry events, legislation, and pricing.
Published by: Agri-Mark, Inc., 100 Milk St, Office Park, Methuen, MA 01844. Ed. Douglas Dimento. Circ: 4,500.

637   USA
AGRIBUSINESS DAIRYMAN. Text in English. 1983. m. USD 36 domestic; USD 60 foreign; USD 4.50 newsstand/cover. adv. back issues avail. **Document type:** Trade. **Description:** Focuses monthly on different editorial subjects. Coves all the major dairy fairs and expositions.
Published by: Agribusiness Publications, 612 N St, Sanger, CA 93657. TEL 209-875-4585, FAX 209-875-4587. Ed., Pub. John C Stubbs. R&P, Adv. contact John Van Nortwick. B&W page USD 1,270, color page USD 1,930; trim 10.75 x 8.25. Circ: 10,000 (controlled).

637.1   USA   ISSN 0065-7263
AMERICAN ASSOCIATION OF MEDICAL MILK COMMISSIONS. METHODS AND STANDARDS FOR THE PRODUCTION OF CERTIFIED MILK✶. Text in English. 1909. a. free.
Published by: American Association of Medical Milk Commissions, Inc., c/o Hopping, 1475 Midland Rd Apt 7, Southern Pines, NC 28387-2100.

637   FRA   ISSN 1163-9849
ANNUAIRE DES INDUSTRIES LAITIERES. Text in French. 1950. a. EUR 155 (effective 2004). 412 p./no.; **Document type:** Directory, Trade.
Former titles (until 1991): Annuaire du Lait (1154-4538); (until 1990): Annuaire National du Lait (0084-6538)
Published by: Editions Comindus, 1 Rue Descombes, Paris, 75017, France. TEL 31-1-43807916, FAX 31-1-40539192, http://www.editionscomindus.fr.

ARCHIVOS DE ZOOTECNIA. see AGRICULTURE—Poultry And Livestock

ARGENTINA. SECRETARIA DE ESTADO DE AGRICULTURA Y GANADERIA. AREA DE TRABAJO DE LECHERIA. RESENA ESTADISTICA. see AGRICULTURE—Abstracting, Bibliographies, Statistics

637.1 664.028   ESP
ARTE HELADERO. Text in Spanish. 6/yr.
Address: CARMEN, 4 y 6, Sant Cugat Del Valles, Barcelona 08190, Spain. TEL 3-675-08-11, FAX 3-675-38-61. Ed. Ignacio Corbero. Circ: 6,000.

637   AUS   ISSN 0814-4494
AUSTRALIAN DAIRY FARMER. Text in English. 1984. bi-m. adv. bk.rev. **Document type:** Magazine, Trade. **Description:** Provides information to enable dairyfarmers throughout Australia to improve their productivity and profitability and improve their lifestyle.
Published by: (Australian Dairy Industry Council), Rural Press Ltd. (Subsidiary of: Agricultural Publishers Pty. Ltd.), 10 Sydenham St., PO Box 254, Moonee Ponds, VIC 3039, Australia. TEL 61-3-92870900, FAX 61-3-93705622, http://adf.farmonline.com.au/home.asp, http:// www.ruralpress.com/. Ed. Alastair Dowie. Adv. contact Peter Roach. Circ: 15,835.

637   AUS   ISSN 0157-7964
AUSTRALIAN DAIRY FOODS; Production - Processing - Packaging - Marketing. Text in English. 1941. bi-m. AUD 85 domestic; AUD 105 in New Zealand; AUD 135 elsewhere (effective 2000). adv. **Document type:** Journal, Trade. **Description:** Covers all aspects of the Australian dairy industry and market.
Formerly (until 1979): Australian Institute of Dairy Factory Managers and Secretaries. Butter Fats and Solids (0045-0553)
Indexed: FS&TA.
—BLDSC (1798.280000).
Published by: (Dairy Industry Association of Australia), Indigo Arch Pty. Ltd., PO Box 351, North Melbourne, VIC 3051, Australia. TEL 61-3-95761275, FAX 61-3-95761276. Ed., R&P Chris Greenwood. Adv. contact David Fallick. Circ: 2,500.

636.2142   AUS
THE AUSTRALIAN HOLSTEIN JOURNAL. Text in English. 1906. m. AUD 60; AUD 65 foreign (effective 1996). adv. illus. back issues avail. **Document type:** Trade. **Description:** Contains dairy industry information.
Former titles (until 1994): Australian Holstein Dairyman (1038-8923); (until 1992): Australian Holstein-Friesian Dairyman (1035-0004); Supersedes in part (in 1989): Dairyman (0311-9653); Which was formerly: Australian Dairy Journal; Livestock Bulletin (0024-5186)
Indexed: F&GI.

Published by: (Holstein Friesian Association of Australia), Australian Holstein Journal, PO Box 6759, Shepparton, VIC 3632, Australia. TEL 61-58-315205, FAX 61-58-311747. Ed. Jackie Ekers. Adv. contact June Clark. B&W page AUD 500, color page AUD 700. Circ: 3,500. **Subscr. to:** HFAA, Private Bag 14, Flemington, VIC 3031, Australia. TEL 61-3-93761811, FAX 61-3-9372-1394.

637   AUS   ISSN 0004-9433
                              CODEN: AJDTAZ
➤ **AUSTRALIAN JOURNAL OF DAIRY TECHNOLOGY.** Text in English. 1945. 3/yr. (Apr., Jul. & Oct.). AUD 100 domestic; AUD 120 foreign (effective 2005). adv. bk.rev. charts; illus., abstr. cum.index every 10 yrs. **Document type:** Journal, Academic/Scholarly. **Description:** Includes full technical and scientific papers on issues of importance to the industry's productive future and helps ensure that the results of research projects are made widely known.
Related titles: CD-ROM ed.; Magnetic Tape ed.; Microfilm ed.: (from PMC, PQC); Online - full text ed.: (from Northern Light Technology, Inc., ProQuest Information & Learning, The Dialog Corporation).
Indexed: ABIn, ASCA, AbHyg, AgBio, Agr, AnBrAb, BIOSIS Prev, BioDAb, BiolAb, CIN, ChemAb, ChemTitl, CurCont, CurPA, DSA, ExcerpMed, FS&TA, ISR, IndVet, MSB, NutrAb, PCI, PotatoAb, RM&VM, RPP, RRTA, RefZh, SCI, SIA, SoyAb, TDB, VetBull, WAE&RSA.
—BLDSC (1807.000000), CASDDS, CINDOC, CISTI, IDS, IE, Infotrieve, ingenta, Linda Hall.
Published by: Dairy Industry Association of Australia, c/o Ms Kristine Manser, Private Bag 16, 671 Sneydes Rd., Werribee, VIC 3030, Australia. TEL 61-3-97313393, FAX 61-3-97313206, diaa@dairy.com.au, http://www.diaa.asn.au. Circ: 1,700 (paid and controlled).

637   AUS   ISSN 1034-9561
AUSTRALIAN MYCOTOXIN NEWSLETTER. Text in English. 1990. q. free. bk.rev. illus. back issues avail. **Document type:** Academic/Scholarly.
Related titles: Online - full text ed.
Published by: Australian Centre for International Agricultural Research, PO Box 1571, Canberra, ACT 2601, Australia. TEL 61-2-62170500, FAX 61-2-62170501, http://www.aciar.gov.au. Eds. A Holicing, J C Eyles, J I Pitt. R&P.G I Johnson. Circ: 1,800.

636.2142   GBR   ISSN 0005-2442
AYRSHIRE CATTLE SOCIETY'S JOURNAL. Text in English. 1929. s-a. GBP 30 to non-members (effective 2000). adv. bk.rev. illus.; mkt. **Document type:** Journal, Trade. **Description:** Relates to all activities of Ayrshire dairy cow, including genetic improvement, promotion, show and sales.
Indexed: DSA.
—CISTI.
Published by: Ayrshire Cattle Society of Great Britain & Ireland, 1 Racecourse Rd, Ayr, Scotland KA7 2DE, United Kingdom. TEL 44-1292-267123, FAX 44-1292-611973, society@ayrshirescs.org, http://www.ayrshirescs.org/. Ed. Stuart Thomson. Adv. contact Elaine Cuthbertson. Circ: 4,000.

637   GBR
AYRSHIRE DAIRYMAN. Text in English. 1985. s-a. GBP 10 (effective 2000). back issues avail. **Document type:** Newsletter, Trade. **Description:** Presents farm features, show and sales reports, and other dairy-related information for dairy farmers, advisors, and colleges.
Published by: Ayrshire Cattle Society of Great Britain & Ireland, 1 Racecourse Rd, Ayr, Scotland KA7 2DE, United Kingdom. TEL 44-1292-267123, FAX 44-1292-611973, society@ayrshirescs.org, http://www.ayrshirescs.org/. Ed. Stuart Thompson. Circ: 2,600.

637   USA   ISSN 0005-2450
AYRSHIRE DIGEST. Text in English. 1912. bi-m. USD 20 in US & Canada; USD 22 elsewhere (effective 2005). adv. bk.rev. illus.; stat. back issues avail. **Document type:** Magazine, Trade. **Description:** Covers issues relating to the Ayrshire breed.
—CISTI.
Published by: Ayrshire Breeders' Association, 1224 Alton Creek Rd, Ste B, Columbus, OH 43228. TEL 614-335-0020, FAX 614-315-0023, info@usayrshire.com, http:// www.usayrshire.com/digest.htm. Eds. Andrew Stevens, Erica Davis. Pub., R&P, Adv. contact Seth Johnson TEL 614-575-4620. B&W page USD 275, color page USD 475. Circ: 1,500.

637   GBR
THE AYRSHIRE JOURNAL. Text in English. 1928. s-a. GBP 10 (effective 2000). **Document type:** Journal, Trade. **Description:** Covers information about the Ayrshire breed of dairy cow.
Published by: Ayrshire Cattle Society of Great Britain & Ireland, 1 Racecourse Rd, Ayr, Scotland KA7 2DE, United Kingdom. TEL 44-1292-267123, FAX 44-1292-611973, society@ayrshirescs.org, http://www.ayrshirescs.org/. Circ: 2,500.

630   BRA   ISSN 0005-4275
BALDE BRANCO. Text in Portuguese. 1964. m. BRL 10,200. adv. bk.rev. illus.

Published by: Cooperativa Central de Laticinios do Estado de Sao Paulo, Rua Gomes Cardim, 532, Bras, Sao Paulo, SP 03050-000, Brazil. Ed. Luiza Roxo Pimentel. Circ: 30,000 (controlled).

636 637   DNK   ISSN 0906-009X
BOVILOGISK; tidsskrift om kvaegbrug. Text in Danish. 1987. m. DKK 595 domestic; DKK 775 in Europe; DKK 979 elsewhere (effective 2005). adv. **Document type:** Magazine, Trade. **Description:** Covers subjects of interest to dairy farmers.
Formerly (until 1990): Bovilogisk Tidsskrift Kvaeget (0902-431X)
Related titles: Online - full text ed.
Published by: Dansk Agrar Forlag A-S (Subsidiary of: FagbladsGruppen A/S), Birk Centerpark 36, Herning, 7400, Denmark. TEL 45-76-207970, FAX 45-96-265296, bovilogisk@agrar.dk, post@agrar.dk, http://www.bovilogisk.dk, http://www.agrar.dk. Eds. Louise Lindegaard Weinrich, Niels Damgaard Hansen. adv.: page DKK 8,900; 270 x 184. Circ: 1,600.

637   AUS   ISSN 0815-9777
BRITISH ALPINE BREEDERS GROUP OF AUSTRALIA. NEWSLETTER. Text in English. 1972. q. AUD 6. adv. bk.rev. back issues avail. **Document type:** Newsletter.
Published by: British Alpine Breeders Group of Australia, RMB 8680, Bannockburn, VIC 3331, Australia. Ed. P C Keays. Circ: 50.

637   GBR   ISSN 0955-3614
BRITISH HOLSTEIN SOCIETY JOURNAL. Text in English. 1975. 5/yr. GBP 18 domestic; GBP 25 foreign. adv. **Document type:** Trade. **Description:** Contains news and information on the society and its activities of interest to members. Publishes articles related to the breeding of Holstein cattle, along with their management and feeding. Announces awards.
Published by: British Holstein Society, Foley House, 28 Worcester Rd, Malvern, Worcs WR14 4YY, United Kingdom. TEL 44-1684-565477, FAX 44-1684-893290. Ed., R&P, Adv. contact Martin Hall. Circ: 3,500.

637   USA   ISSN 0007-2516
BROWN SWISS BULLETIN. Text in English. 1922. m. USD 20 domestic; USD 35 foreign (effective 2005). adv. back issues avail. **Document type:** Magazine, Trade. **Description:** Contains stories and information on Brown Swiss breed, breeders, meetings, shows and sales reports.
—CISTI, Linda Hall.
Published by: (Brown Swiss Cattle Breeders Association of U.S.A.), Purebred Publishing, Inc., 7616 Slate Ridge Blvd, Reynoldsburg, OH 43068. TEL 614-864-2409, FAX 614-864-5614, info@usguernsey.com, bpayne@usguernsey.com, http://www.usguernsey.com. Ed. Adam Barbee. adv.: B&W page USD 315, color page USD 495; 8 x 11. Circ: 1,417 (paid); 200 (free).

BROWSE. see AGRICULTURE—Poultry And Livestock

637   NLD   ISSN 0927-6769
C M ACTUEEL. Text in Dutch. 1945. bi-w. charts; illus. back issues avail. **Document type:** Newsletter. **Description:** Covers dairy farming, milk production, milk quality, and milk production economics and the market for dairy products.
Formerly (until 1991): Melk (0025-8962)
Indexed: KES.
Published by: Campina Melkunie, PO Box 2100, Zaltbommel, 5300 CC, Netherlands. TEL 31-418-571316, FAX 31-418-540116, redactie@campina.com, http:// www.campina.nl. Eds. Gerjan Zeisiak, Wim van Beuzekom. Circ: 15,000.

CALIFORNIA. AGRICULTURAL STATISTICS SERVICE. DAIRY INDUSTRY STATISTICS. see AGRICULTURE—Abstracting, Bibliographies, Statistics

CALIFORNIA DAIRY INFORMATION BULLETIN. see AGRICULTURE—Abstracting, Bibliographies, Statistics

636.2142   USA
A CALL TO CUD. Text in English. a. USD 2 per issue (effective 2000). **Description:** Explores the spiritual nature of cows and animals including humans.
Related titles: Online - full content ed.
Published by: Call to Cud, 87 Richard St, Apt 7, Passaic, NJ 07055. dailycow@aol.com, http://members.aol.com/DailyCow/indexhcom.htm. Ed., Pub. David R Wyder.

CANADA. STATISTICS CANADA. DAIRY REVIEW/CANADA. STATISTIQUE CANADA. REVUE LAITIERE. see AGRICULTURE—Abstracting, Bibliographies, Statistics

636.2142   CAN
CANADIAN BROWN SWISS AND BRAUNVIEH ASSOCIATION NEWSLETTER/CLOCHE. Text in English, French. 1983. q. CND 16; CND 28 foreign. adv. **Document type:** Newsletter. **Description:** Covers the dairy industry, genetics, artificial insemination, embryo transfer, dairy products.
Formerly: Bell
Related titles: Online - full content ed.
Indexed: e-psyche.

Published by: Canadian Brown Swiss and Braunvieh Association, RR#5, Guelph, ON M1H 6J2, Canada. TEL 519-821-2811, FAX 519-763-6582, brownswiss@gencor.ca, http://www.rkde.com/browncow. Circ: 500.

637 CAN ISSN 0382-3229
CANADIAN DAIRY COMMISSION. ANNUAL REPORT. Text in English. 1968. a.
Published by: Canadian Dairy Commission, Bldg 55 NCC Driveway, 950 Carling Ave, Ottawa, ON K1A 0Z2, Canada. TEL 613-792-2000, FAX 613-792-2009, cdc-ccl@agr.gc.ca, http://www.cdc.ca/cdc/.

637 BRA ISSN 0100-7904
CENTRO NACIONAL DE PESQUISA DE GADO DE LEITE. RELATORIO TECNICO. Text in Portuguese. 1978. irreg.
Indexed: DSA.
—BLDSC (7354.106300).
Published by: Empresa Brasileira de Pesquisa Agropecuaria, Centro Nacional de Pesquisa de Gado de Leite (Subsidiary of: Empresa Brasileira de Pesquisa Agropecuaria), Rua Eugenio do Nascimento 610 - Dom Bosco, Juiz de Fora, MG 36038-330, Brazil. TEL 55-32-32494700, FAX 55-32-32494701, sac.hortalicas@embrapa.br, http://www.cnpgl.embrapa.br. Circ: 3,000.

637.1 USA ISSN 0891-1509
CODEN: CHMNE6
CHEESE MARKET NEWS. Text in English. 1981. w. (Fri.). USD 105 domestic; USD 155 in Canada; USD 315 elsewhere (effective 2005). adv. bk.rev. tr.lit.; illus. 16 p./no. 4 cols./p.; back issues avail. **Document type:** *Newspaper, Trade.* **Description:** Provides weekly investigative news reporting and analysis for the cheese, dairy and deli business. Covers consolidations, legislation, market trends and prices, personnel, events and new products.
Supersedes (1981-1986): National Dairy News (0279-2508)
Related titles: Online - full text ed.: (from Gale Group).
—CISTI.
Published by: Quarne Publishing L.L.C., PO Box 620244, Middleton, WI 53562. TEL 608-831-6002, FAX 608-831-1004, squarne@cheesemarketnews.com, chmarknews@aol.com, http://www.cheesemarketnews.com. Ed., R&P Kate Sander TEL 608-288-9090. Pub., Adv. contact Susan K Quarne. B&W page USD 2,900. Circ: 2,200 (paid).

637.3 USA ISSN 0009-2142
CODEN: CHERA8
CHEESE REPORTER. Text in English. 1876. w. (Fri.). USD 95 domestic; USD 140 in Canada & Mexico; USD 180 elsewhere (effective 2005). adv. bk.rev. illus. 16 p./no. 4 cols./p.; **Document type:** *Newspaper, Trade.* **Description:** Surveys key price and production trends, indicators and analysis; legislation and regulatory initiatives affecting the dairy industry; analyzes current events, consumer trends and industry response, industry events and company and personnel transitions.
Indexed: FS&TA, WAE&RSA.
—CISTI.
Published by: Cheese Reporter Publishing Co., Inc., 2810 Crossroads Dr, Ste 3000, Madison, WI 53718. TEL 608-246-8430, FAX 608-246-8431, kthome@cheesereporter.com, http://www.cheesereporter.com. Ed., Pub., R&P Richard Groves. Adv. contact Kevin Thome. col. inch USD 49.70. Circ: 2,150 (paid).

637.4 USA
CHIMES (SUDBURY). Text in English. q. **Document type:** *Newsletter.*
Published by: International Association of Ice Cream Vendors, 100 N. 20th St., Ste. 400, Philadelphia, PA 19103-1462. Ed. Charlene Mayfield. Circ: 250 (paid).

COATES'S HERD BOOK (BEEF). see *AGRICULTURE—Poultry And Livestock*

637 GBR ISSN 0069-4932
COATES'S HERD BOOK (DAIRY). Text in English. 1822. a. GBP 10, USD 20 (effective 2000). **Document type:** *Trade.*
Published by: Shorthorn Society of Great Britain and Ireland, 4th St, National Agricultural Centre, Stoneleigh Park, Kenilworth, Warks CV8 2LG, United Kingdom. TEL 44-2476-696549, FAX 44-2476-696729, mtaggart@shorthorn.freeserve.co.uk, http://www.shorthorn.co.uk. Ed. Martin Taggart. Circ: 700.

CONFECTIONERY PRODUCTION. see *FOOD AND FOOD INDUSTRIES—Bakers And Confectioners*

637 USA
CREAM SEPARATOR AND DAIRY NEWSLETTER. Text in English. bi-m. USD 15. adv. back issues avail. **Document type:** *Newsletter.*
Published by: Cream and Dairy Collector Association, Rte 3, Arcadia, WI 54612. TEL 608-323-7470. Ed. Paul Dettloff Dum. Circ: 250 (paid).

637 FRA ISSN 1141-7730
CREMIER FROMAGER. Text in French. 1989. 9/yr. EUR 60.98. bk.rev.
Published by: E P R I M, 60 bis, rue de l'Hermitage, Pontoise, 95300, France. TEL 30-38-30-77, FAX 30-73-05-97. Ed. Samy Kerkeny. Pub. Jacques Boursier. R&P Yves Roux. Adv. contact Marjorie Leveque. Circ: 6,000.

636.2142 GBR
D A I S Y - THE DAIRY INFORMATION SYSTEM. Text in English. 1994 (no.2). irreg. adv. **Document type:** *Academic/Scholarly.* **Description:** Covers the veterinary and economic aspects of raising dairy cows.
Published by: University of Reading, Department of Agriculture, Earley Gate,, University Of Reading, Reading, Berks RG6 6AT, United Kingdom. Ed. R J Esslemont. Adv. contact R.J. Esslemont.

637.1 USA
D F A LEADER. Text in English. 1968. m. USD 20 (effective 2005). adv. **Document type:** *Magazine.* **Description:** Covers cooperative, legislative developments, dairy industry news, health, economic events and human interest stories.
Formerly: Mid-Am Reporter (0195-5624)
Published by: Dairy Farmers of America, P O Box 909700, Kansas City, MO 64190-9700. jgerke@dfamilk.com, http://www.dfamilk.com. Ed. Jason Gerke. Circ: 22,000.

637 DEU ISSN 1617-2795
CODEN: DMZEAI
D M Z. (Deutsche Molkerei Zeitung) Text in German. 1878. fortn. EUR 318.46; EUR 16 newsstand/cover (effective 2005). adv. back issues avail. **Document type:** *Magazine, Trade.*
Former titles (until 1998): D M Z - Lebensmittelindustrie und Milchwirtschaft (0938-9369); (until 1990): Deutsche Molkerei-Zeitung (0366-9424); (until 1951): Sueddeutsche Molkerei-Zeitung (0370-9396)
Indexed: AEA, AbHyg, AgBio, AnBrAb, DSA, FS&TA, HortAb, IndVet, NutrAb, PBA, PHN&I, PN&I, PST, RM&VM, RRTA, RefZh, SIA, SoyAb, VetBull, WAE&RSA.
—BLDSC (3605.718100), CASDDS, CISTI, IE. **CCC.**
Published by: A V A Verlag Allgaeu GmbH, Porschestr 2, Kempten, 87437, Germany. TEL 49-831-571420, FAX 49-831-79008, info@ava-verlag.de, http://www.ava-verlag.de. Ed. Nadja Sigulla. adv.: B&W page EUR 1,600, color page EUR 2,500. Circ: 3,470.

637 AUS
D R D C NEWS. Text in English. bi-m. **Document type:** *Newsletter.* **Description:** Informs manufacturing researchers and manufacturing companies of DRDC policies and research activities.
Related titles: Online - full text ed.
Published by: Dairy Australia, Level 5, IBM Tower, 60 City Rd, Southbank, VIC 3006, Australia. TEL 61-3-96943777, FAX 61-3-96943733, http://www.biziworks.com.au/biziworks/BiziGen?ownerID=DRDC1&docID=257, http://www.dairyaustralia.com.au.

636.2142 USA
DAILY COW. Text in English. 1988. a. USD 5 (effective 2000). back issues avail. **Description:** All about cows from a human's point of view.
Related titles: Online - full text ed.
Address: 87 Richard St, Apt 7, Passaic, NJ 07055. dailycow@aol.com, http://members.aol.com/dczines/index2.htm. Ed. David R Wyder.

338.1771 USA
DAIRY AND FIELD CROP DIGEST∗ **.** Text in English. 1970. bi-m. **Document type:** *Trade.*
Published by: Regional Cooperative Extension Dairy Program, 56 Main St, Owego, NY 13827. TEL 607-535-7161.

637 641.37 GBR
THE DAIRY COUNCIL. TOPICAL UPDATE. Text in English. irreg.
Formerly: National Dairy Council. Topical Update
—BLDSC (8867.414360).
Published by: The Dairy Council, 5-7 John Princes St, London, W1G 0JN, United Kingdom. TEL 44-20-7499-7822, FAX 44-20-7408-1353, info@dairycouncil.org.uk, http://www.milk.co.uk.

637 IRL ISSN 0790-732X
DAIRY EXECUTIVE. Text in English. 1903. bi-m. adv. stat. **Document type:** *Trade.*
Former titles (until 1986): Irish Agricultural and Creamery Review (0021-1036); (until 1932): Creamery Manager (0790-3332)
Published by: Dairy Executives' Association, 33 Kildare St., Dublin, 2, Ireland. TEL 353-1-6761989, FAX 353-1-6767162. Circ: 2,000.

637 IRL
DAIRY EXECUTIVE. DIRECTORY AND DIARY. Text in English. 1906. a. adv. bk.rev. **Document type:** *Directory.*
Former titles: Irish Creamery Managers' Association. Creamery Directory and Diary; Irish Creamery Managers' Association. Creamery Yearbook and Diary (0075-0751)
Published by: Dairy Executives' Association, 33 Kildare St., Dublin, 2, Ireland. TEL 353-1-6761989, FAX 353-1-6767162. Circ: 2,000.

338.1771 GBR ISSN 1461-9229
DAIRY FACTS AND FIGURES. Text in English. 1956. a. GBP 50 in Europe; GBP 53.50 rest of world (effective 2001). charts; stat. 276 p./no.; **Document type:** *Directory, Trade.* **Description:** Provides marketing and production data for the UK and European Dairy industries.
Formerly (until 1996): United Kingdom Dairy Facts and Figures (0503-3535); Incorporates (in 1996): E C Dairy Facts and Figures; Which superseded: E E C Dairy Facts and Figures
Indexed: DSA.
—BLDSC (3514.620000).
Published by: The Dairy Council, 5-7 John Princes St, London, W1G 0JN, United Kingdom. TEL 44-20-7499-7822, info@dairycouncil.org.uk, http://www.milk.co.uk. Eds. Ian Wakeling, Lynn Pickett.

DAIRY FACTS AND FIGURES AT A GLANCE. see *AGRICULTURE—Abstracting, Bibliographies, Statistics*

637 GBR ISSN 1475-6994
DAIRY FARMER. Text in English. 1929. m. GBP 37; GBP 47 in Europe; USD 89 elsewhere (effective 2000). adv. bk.rev. charts; illus.; mkt.; pat.; tr.lit.; tr.mk. Supplement avail. **Document type:** *Magazine, Trade.* **Description:** Topics of interest to farmers and farm managers who raise dairy cows in Great Britain.
Former titles (until 1984): Dairy Farmer and Dairy-Beef Producer (1475-6986); (until 1963): Dairy Farmer (0011-5576)
Related titles: Online - full text ed.: (from Gale Group, LexisNexis, ProQuest Information & Learning); ♦ Supplement(s): S W Dairy Farmer.
Indexed: ABIn, AEA, DSA, IndVet.
—BLDSC (3514.695000), IE, ingenta.
Published by: C M P Information Ltd. (Subsidiary of: United Business Media), Riverbank House, Angel Ln, Tonbridge, Kent TN9 1SE, United Kingdom. TEL 44-1732-377591, FAX 44-1732-377465, enquiries@cmpinformation.com, http://www.cmpinformation.com. Ed. Peter Hollinshead. Pub. Peter Walker. Adv. contact Roy Jacques. Circ: 25,732. **Subscr. to:** Marlowe House, 109 Station Rd, Sidcup, Kent DA15 7ET, United Kingdom. TEL 44-20-8309-7000.

637 USA ISSN 1055-0607
TX795.A1 CODEN: DAFIEK
DAIRY FIELD; helping processors manage the changing industry. Text in English. 1905. m. USD 85.03 domestic; USD 150.03 foreign; USD 15.03 per issue; free to qualified personnel (effective 2003). adv. illus.; tr.lit. Supplement avail. **Document type:** *Magazine, Trade.* **Description:** Contains articles of interest to executives and department heads in the dairy processing industry.
Former titles (until 1991): Dairy Field Today (1053-9425); (until 1990): Dairy Field (0198-9995); (until 1979): Dairy and Ice Cream Field (0011-555X); (until 1967): Ice Cream Field and Ice Cream Trade Journal (0536-2598); Which was formed by the merger of (1922-1965): Ice Cream Field (0096-2546); (1905-1965): Ice Cream Trade Journal (0096-2031); Incorporated (1917-1968): Ice Cream Review (0096-2023); Which incorporated (in 1967): Manufactured Milk Products Journal (0099-5258); (until 1953): Butter, Cheese and Milk Products Journal (0099-510X); (until 1950): National Butter and Cheese Journal (0099-5320); (until 1936): National Butter Journal (0099-7625); (until 1930): Butter and Cheese Journal (0099-7412); (until 1928): Butter Cheese and Egg Journal (0735-0902)
Related titles: Online - full text ed.: (from bigchalk, EBSCO Publishing, Florida Center for Library Automation, Gale Group, Northern Light Technology, Inc., O C L C Online Computer Library Center, Inc., ProQuest Information & Learning).
Indexed: ABIn, AEA, B&I, BiolAb, ChemAb, CurPA, DSA, FS&TA, NutrAb, RRTA, SIA, WAE&RSA.
—BLDSC (3514.710000), CISTI, Linda Hall.
Published by: Stagnito Communications, Inc. (Subsidiary of: Ascend Media), 155 Pfingsten Rd., Ste. 205, Deerfield, IL 60015. TEL 847-205-5660, FAX 847-205-5680, info@stagnito.com, http://www.dairyfield.com, http://www.stagnito.com. Ed. Cathy Sivak. Pub. Korry Stagnito. Adv. contact Catherine Wynn. B&W page USD 4,600, color page USD 6,300; trim 10.825 x 14.5. Circ: 20,500 (controlled).

DAIRY FOODS; innovative ideas and technologies for dairy processors. see *FOOD AND FOOD INDUSTRIES*

637 IND ISSN 0970-3438
DAIRY GUIDE. Text in English. 1978. q. INR 200. bk.rev. **Document type:** *Trade.*
Published by: C.P. Narang (Pvt.) Ltd., 1700-IV Urban Estate, Gurgaon, 122 001, India. TEL 91-124-320728, FAX 91-124-327400. Ed. Ricky Thaper. adv.: page INR 1,000; trim 190 x 140. Circ: 7,300.

637 CAN ISSN 0011-5606
DAIRY GUIDE. Text in English. 1970. 10/yr. adv. bk.rev. **Document type:** *Trade.*
Related titles: Microfilm ed.
Published by: Farm Business Communications, P O Box 6600, Winnipeg, MB R3C 3A7, Canada. TEL 204-944-5761, FAX 204-942-8463. Ed. Gren Winslon. Adv. contact Tom Mumby. Circ: 18,333.

636.2142 USA ISSN 0011-5614
DAIRY HERD MANAGEMENT; the business magazine for top dairy farmers. Text in English. 1965. m. USD 59.88 domestic; free to qualified personnel (effective 2005). adv. abstr.; charts; illus.; stat. reprint service avail. from PQC. **Document type:** *Magazine, Trade.*
Related titles: Microform ed.: (from PQC); Online - full text ed.: (from Northern Light Technology, Inc., ProQuest Information & Learning).
Indexed: ABIn, B&AI, DSA, F&GI, IndVet.
—CISTI. **CCC.**
Published by: Vance Publishing Corp., 10901 W 84th Terrace, Lexena, KS 66214-1821. TEL 913-438-8700, 800-255-5113, FAX 913-438-0695, rrei@vancepublishing.com, http://www.dairyherd.com, http://www.vancepublishing.com. Eds. Rob Wiley, Tom Quaife. Pub. Bill Newham. Adv. contact Sloise Seaman Wettach. Circ: 71,057 (paid).

338.1771 USA
DAIRY HOT LINE. Text in English. 1997. bi-m. USD 9.95 domestic; USD 14.95 in Canada & Mexico; USD 21.95 elsewhere (effective 2004). adv.
Published by: Heartland Ag-Business Group, Inc., 1003 Central Ave, Fort Dodge, IA 50501. TEL 515-955-1600, 800-673-4763, aginfo@agdeal.com, http://www.agdeal.com. Adv. contact Bailey Johnson. B&W page USD 800, color page USD 1,332; trim 7.75 x 10.75.

637 IND ISSN 0970-9932
DAIRY INDIA YEARBOOK. Text in English. 1983. irreg. USD 295. adv. **Description:** Sourcebook on trade technical and economic aspects of dairying. 7000 specialists and organizations are listed by business name and geographic location.
Indexed: AnBrAb, DSA.
Published by: P.R. Gupta Pub., A-25 Priyadarshini Vihar, New Delhi, 110 092, India. TEL 91-11-2243326, FAX 91-11-2243039, yearbook@giasdl01.vsnl.net.in. Ed. Sharad Gupta. Circ: 2,500 (paid).

637.1 IRL
DAIRY IRELAND. Text in English. bi-m. adv. **Document type:** *Magazine, Trade.*
Published by: Irish Creamery Milk Suppliers Association, John Feely House, 15 Upper Mallow St., Limerick, Ireland. TEL 353-61-314677, FAX 353-61-315737, icmsa@eircom.net, http://www.icmsa.ie. adv.: page EUR 1,905; trim 210 x 297. Circ: 6,000 (controlled).

637 USA
DAIRY: LATIN AMERICAN INDUSTRIAL REPORT✶. (Avail. for each of 22 Latin American countries) Text in English. 1985. a. USD 435; per country report.
Published by: Aquino Productions, P O Box 15760, Stamford, CT 06901-0760. Ed. Andres C Aquino.

637.1 ZAF ISSN 1561-4301
THE DAIRY MAIL. Text in Afrikaans, English. 1964. m. ZAR 180 (effective 2001). adv. charts; illus.; stat. index. 128 p./no.; **Document type:** *Newsletter, Trade.*
Formerly (until 1994): Milk Producer (0026-4199)
Indexed: DSA.
Published by: Milk Producers' Organisation, PO Box 1284, Pretoria, 0001, South Africa. TEL 27-12-8044800, FAX 27-12-8044811. Eds. Hennie Basson, Izak Hofmeyr. Adv. contacts Christine Hugo, Elmarie De Lange. B&W page ZAR 3,135, color page ZAR 3,975; 149 x 210. Circ: 7,800.

637 USA ISSN 0744-1282
DAIRY MARKET NEWS. Text in English. 1919. w. USD 50 domestic; USD 125 out of North America (effective 2001). charts; mkt. 14 p./no. 2 cols./p.; **Document type:** *Newsletter, Government.*
Related titles: Fax ed.; Online - full text ed.
Indexed: AmStI.
Published by: U.S. Department of Agriculture, Agricultural Marketing Division, Washington, DC 20250. TEL 608-224-5080, FAX 608-224-5078, http://www.ams.usda.gov/dairy/mncs/index.htm. Ed. Donald O Nelson. Circ: 1,000.

DAIRY MARKET STATISTICS: ANNUAL SUMMARY. see *AGRICULTURE—Abstracting, Bibliographies, Statistics*

637 GBR ISSN 1475-0686
DAIRY MARKETS. Text in English. w. GBP 842 domestic; GBP 911 in Europe; GBP 1,031 elsewhere; GBP 1,029 combined subscription domestic print & online eds.; GBP 1,098 combined subscription in Europe print & online eds.; GBP 1,218 combined subscription elsewhere print & online eds. (effective 2005). **Document type:** *Newsletter, Trade.* **Description:** Reports the latest figures on European dairy prices and production and the important trade and company news of the week.
Formerly: Dairy Markets Weekly (0957-8625)
Related titles: Fax ed.; Online - full text ed.: (from Gale Group).
Indexed: RefZh.
Published by: Agra Europe (London) Ltd. (Subsidiary of: T & F Informa plc), 80 Calverley Rd, Tunbridge Wells, Kent TN1 2UN, United Kingdom. TEL 44-1892-533813, FAX 44-1892-544895, marketing@agra-net.com, http://www.agra-net.com.

338.1771 AUS
DAIRY MONITOR. Text in English. d. **Document type:** *Trade.*
Media: Online - full content.
Published by: Roy Morgan Research, PO Box 2282 U, Melbourne, VIC 3001, Australia. TEL 61-3-96296888, FAX 61-3-96291250, http://www.roymorgan.com.

DAIRY MONTHLY IMPORTS. see *AGRICULTURE—Abstracting, Bibliographies, Statistics*

637 IRL
DAIRY NEWS. Text in English. 4/yr.
Published by: Bord Bainne, Grattan House, Mount St., Dublin, 2, Ireland. TEL 619599, FAX 612788, TELEX 93615. Ed. Aidan McCarthy.

637.1 USA
DAIRY PIPELINE. Text in English. 1995. m. back issues avail.
Media: Online - full text.
Published by: Virginia Cooperative Extension, 121 Hutcheson Hall, Virginia Tech 0437, Blacksburg, VA 24061-0001. FAX 800-828-1120, http://www.ext.vt.edu/.

330 CAN ISSN 0318-2967
DAIRY POLICY. Text in English, French. a. free. **Description:** Policy statement of Dairy Farmers of Canada, developed by Canadian milk producers as basis for future lobbying activity.
Published by: Dairy Farmers of Canada, 75 Albert St, Ste 1101, Ottawa, ON K1P 5E7, Canada. http://www.dairyfarmers.org, http://www.dairybureau.org.

637 USA
DAIRY PRODUCER. Text in English. 1990. m. USD 17.95. adv. **Document type:** *Trade.* **Description:** Covers dairy practices and marketing. Features successful producers in the Great Lakes, Northeast and West dairy regions.
Related titles: ♦ Supplement to: Kansas Farmer; ♦ Supplement to: Dakota Farmer. ISSN 1069-5397.
Published by: Farm Progress Companies, 191 S Gary Ave, Carol Stream, IL 60188. TEL 708-690-5600, FAX 708-462-2869. Ed. Shannon Linderoth. Pub. Allan Johnson. Circ: 101,248.

637 USA
DAIRY PRODUCER HIGHLIGHTS. Text in English. 1950. a. USD 10. charts; stat. **Document type:** *Directory.* **Description:** Includes statistics on the dairy industry from farm to consumer, covering production, processing and consumption of milk, with information on Federal programs affecting the industry.
Published by: National Milk Producers Federation, 2101 Wilson Blvd, Ste 400, Arlington, VA 22201. TEL 703-243-6111, http://www.nmpf.org. Ed. Chris Nubern. Circ: 5,000.

338.1771 USA ISSN 1051-645X
DAIRY PROFIT WEEKLY. Text in English. w. USD 179 (effective 2005). **Document type:** *Newsletter, Trade.*
Published by: Multi Ag Media LLC, 6437 Collamer Rd., East Syracuse, NY 10357-1031. TEL 800-334-1904, http://www.dairybusiness.com. Pub. Joel Hastings.

637 AUS
DAIRY R & D NEWS. Text in English. bi-m. **Document type:** *Newsletter.* **Description:** Informs dairy farmers, researchers and extension officers of DRDC research activities and directions.
Published by: Dairy Australia, Level 5, IBM Tower, 60 City Rd, Southbank, VIC 3006, Australia. TEL 61-3-96943777, FAX 61-3-96943733, http://www.biziworks.com.au/biziworks/BiziGen?ownerID=DRDC1&docID=258, http://www.dairyaustralia.com.au. **Subscr. to:** NRE Information Centre, 8 Nicholson St, East Melbourne, VIC 3002, Australia. TEL 61-3-96378080, FAX 61-3-96378150.

637 USA
DAIRY ROUNDUP. Text in English. 1973. a. free.
Published by: Kent Feeds Inc., 1600 Oregon St, Muscatine, IA 52761. TEL 319-264-4211.

DAIRY SCIENCE ABSTRACTS. see *AGRICULTURE—Abstracting, Bibliographies, Statistics*

DAIRY STATISTICS. see *AGRICULTURE—Abstracting, Bibliographies, Statistics*

637 USA ISSN 1056-1382
DAIRY TODAY. Text in English. 1985. 10/yr. USD 30; free to qualified personnel (effective 2005). adv. **Document type:** *Magazine, Trade.* **Description:** Contains information on changes in federal regulations, marketing data and insight related to the industry.
Formerly: Dairy Extra
Related titles: Online - full text ed.: (from Gale Group, LexisNexis, ProQuest Information & Learning).
—CCC.
Published by: Farm Journal Media, 1818 Market St., 31st Fl, Philadelphia, PA 19103-3654. TEL 215-557-8900, 800-523-1538, FAX 215-568-5012, dairytoday@farmjournal.com, http://www.diarytoday.com, http://www.agweb.com. Ed. Jim Dickrell. Pub. Allen Moczygemba. Adv. contact Wayne Bollum. Circ: 52,000 (controlled).

637 USA ISSN 0736-4962
DAIRY WORLD. Text in English. 1967. bi-m. USD 6 domestic; USD 20 foreign; USD 1 newsstand/cover (effective 2005). adv. bk.rev. **Document type:** *Magazine.*
Related titles: Microfilm ed.: (from PQC).
Indexed: F&GI.
Published by: Independent Buyers Association Inc., 27 Providence Rd, Millbury, MA 01527. TEL 508-865-2507, FAX 508-865-5891, dairyworldc@ibaprintshop.com. Circ: 42,000 (paid).

637 NZL ISSN 0301-8830
DAIRYFARMING ANNUAL. Text in English. 1948. a. NZD 20 (effective 1999). adv. back issues avail.
Indexed: AgBio, AnBrAb, BiolAb, DSA, FCA, HerbAb, INZP, IndVet, NemAb, NutrAb, PHN&I, RPP, RevApplEntom, S&F, WAE&RSA, WeedAb.
Published by: Massey University, Animal Science Department, Palmerston North, New Zealand. Ed. Gavin Wilson. R&P, Adv. contact Edwina Neilson TEL 64-6-3569099. Circ: 800.

637 NZL ISSN 0114-1473
THE DAIRYMAN. Text in English. 1989. m. NZD 25 (effective 2005). **Document type:** *Newspaper, Trade.* **Description:** Contains industry news alongside practical, financial and property advice.
Published by: New Zealand Rural Press Ltd., PO Box 4233, Auckland, 1001, New Zealand. dairyman@ruralpress.com, http://www.ruralpress.com/. Ed. Susan Topless TEL 64-9-3769786. Adv. contact Liz Storrie TEL 64-7-8382384. Circ: 25,500.

636 USA
DAIRYMEN'S DIGEST. Text in English. m. USD 12 (effective 2005). **Document type:** *Magazine, Trade.*
Contact: Associated Milk Producers, Inc., 315 N. Broadway, New Ulm, MN 56073. TEL 507-354-8295, FAX 507-359-8651, http://www.ampi.com. Ed. Sheryl Doering Meshke.

637 USA ISSN 0745-9033
DAIRYMEN'S DIGEST (NORTH CENTRAL REGION EDITION). Text in English. 1969. m. USD 10 (effective 1998). adv. back issues avail. **Document type:** *Trade.* **Description:** Provides information on dairying issues, including methods, products and manufacturing, and lobbying activities.
Related titles: Microfiche ed.
Published by: North Central A M P I, Inc., PO Box 455, New Ulm, MN 56073. TEL 507-354-8295, FAX 507-359-8608. Ed., R&P, Adv. contact Sheryl Doering Meshke. B&W page USD 81,729; trim 10.75 x 8.25. Circ: 12,000.

637 USA ISSN 0164-6486
DAIRYMEN'S DIGEST: SOUTHERN REGION EDITION✶. Text in English. 1969. m. free. adv. bk.rev. back issues avail.
Published by: Associated Milk Producers, Inc., 3500 William D Tate Ave No.100, PO Box 5040, Grapevine, TX 76051-8734. TEL 817-461-2674. Ed. Raymond Crouch. Circ: 9,400.

637 DNK ISSN 0904-4310
CODEN: JHBLAI
DANISH DAIRY & FOOD INDUSTRY - WORLDWIDE. Text in English. 1976. biennial. free. adv. charts; illus.; stat.; mkt. index.
Formerly (until 1988): Danish Dairy Industry-Worldwide (0105-1210)
Indexed: ChemAb, DSA, FS&TA, NutrAb, RRTA, RefZh, WAE&RSA.
—BLDSC (3519.127000), IE, ingenta.
Published by: Association of Dairy Engineers, The Old Dairy, Landbrugsvj 65, Odense S, 5260, Denmark. TEL 45-66-124025, FAX 45-66-144026, maelk@post9.tele.dk. Ed. K Mark Christensen. Circ: 20,000. **Co-sponsor:** Association of Danish Dairy Managers.

636.2142 DNK ISSN 1395-878X
DANSKE MAELKEPRODUCENTER. Text in Danish. 1994. m. DKK 460; DKK 55 per issue (effective 2004). adv. **Document type:** *Trade.*
Published by: (Landsforeningen af Danske Maelkeproducenter), Boers-Mark A/S, Vestergade 19, Struer, 7600, Denmark. TEL 45-97-841380, FAX 45-97-841370, borsmark@bors-mark.dk, http://borsmark.synkron3-2.dir.dk/sw327.asp, http://www.bors-mark.dk. Ed. Peder Mouritsen. Adv. contact Soeren Andersen. page DKK 10,900; 182 x 265. Circ: 5,092.

637 DEU ISSN 0012-0480
DEUTSCHE MILCHWIRTSCHAFT. Text in German. 1887. fortn. EUR 286.33 domestic; EUR 288.90 foreign; EUR 9 newsstand/cover (effective 2004). adv. bk.rev. bibl.; pat.; stat.; tr.lit. index, cum.index. **Document type:** *Magazine, Trade.*
Formerly (until 1969): Moelkerei- und Kaeserei-Zeitung (0540-6013)
Indexed: AEA, AbHyg, AgBio, BiolAb, DSA, FS&TA, IPackAb, IndVet, NutrAb, PN&I, PST, RRTA, RevApplEntom, S&F, SIA, SoyAb, WAE&RSA.
—BLDSC (3573.030000), IE, ingenta. **CCC.**
Published by: (Zentralverband Deutscher Milchwirtschaftler e.V.), Verlag Th. Mann, Nordring 10, Gelsenkirchen, 45894, Germany. TEL 49-209-93040, FAX 49-209-9304185, info@th-mann.de, http://www.th-mann.de. Ed. Roland Sossna. adv.: B&W page EUR 1,600, color page EUR 2,530; trim 186 x 270. Circ: 4,142 (controlled).

▼ new title ➤ refereed ✶ unverified ♦ full entry avail.

A

DIRECTORIO DE LACTEOS MEXICANOS. see *BUSINESS AND ECONOMICS—Trade And Industrial Directories*

637.1   FRA
E N I L REVUE. Text in French. 1975. 9/yr. adv.
Published by: (Ecoles Nationales d'Industrie Laitiere des Organismes Associes), Promotion Presse Internationale, 7 Cour des Petites-Ecuries, Paris, 75010, France. TEL 33-1-42471205. Circ: 5,000.

637   GBR   ISSN 1364-7407
E U DAIRY MONITOR. (European Union) Text in English. base vol. plus irreg. updates. looseleaf. GBP 347 base vol(s). in Europe basic vol. & first year updates; GBP 353 base vol(s). elsewhere basic vol. & first year updates; GBP 318 renewals domestic for 2005 updates (renewals only); GBP 329 renewals in Europe for 2005 updates (renewals only); GBP 348 renewals elsewhere for 2005 updates (renewals only) (effective 2005). **Document type:** *Newsletter, Trade.* **Description:** Contains complete and consolidated texts of EU dairy legislation in one volume and includes regular updates.
Published by: Agra Europe (London) Ltd. (Subsidiary of: T & F Informa plc), 80 Calverley Rd, Tunbridge Wells, Kent TN1 2UN, United Kingdom. TEL 44-1892-533813, FAX 44-1892-544895, marketing@agra-net.com, http://www.agra-net.com.

637   FRA   ISSN 1143-4376
ECHO DE LA CREMERIE. Text in French. 1989. 4/yr.
Address: 29 rue Violet, Paris, 75015, France. TEL 45-75-05-60, FAX 45-79-98-34. Ed. Jacques Aroud. Circ: 10,000.

637   CAN   ISSN 0226-3947
SF227.C2
ECONOMICS OF MILK PRODUCTION IN ALBERTA. Text in English. a. **Document type:** *Government.*
—CISTI.
Published by: Alberta Agriculture, Production Economics Branch, Food & Rural Development, 7000 113th St, 3rd Fl, Rm 303, Edmonton, AB T6H 5T6, Canada. TEL 403-427-4005, FAX 403-427-5220.

637   EGY   ISSN 0378-2700
                          CODEN: EJDSDB
➤ **EGYPTIAN JOURNAL OF DAIRY SCIENCE.** Text in English; Summaries in Arabic, English. 1973. s-a. USD 45 (effective 2001). adv. bk.rev. abstr. back issues avail. **Document type:** *Academic/Scholarly.* **Description:** Publishes original research findings in the field of dairy science.
Indexed: AgrForAb, AnBrAb, BioDAb, CIN, ChemAb, ChemTitl, CurPA, DSA, ExcerpMed, FPA, FS&TA, HerbAb, HortAb, IndVet, MaizeAb, NutrAb, PotatoAb, PoultAb, RA&MP, RM&VM, RPP, RefZh, RiceAb, SIA, SoyAb, TDB, VetBull, WAE&RSA.
—BLDSC (3664.370000), CASDDS, CISTI, IE, ingenta.
Published by: Egyptian Society of Dairy Science, National Research Centre, Sharia Tahrir, Cairo, Egypt. TEL 20-2-701211, FAX 20-2-3370931. Ed. A. A. Hofi. R&P, Adv. contact Mohamed H. Abd-es-Salam TEL 20-2-5685026. Circ: 1,000.

➤ **EIER-WILD-GEFLUEGEL-MARKT.** see *FOOD AND FOOD INDUSTRIES*

➤ **EMPIRE STATE FARMER.** see *AGRICULTURE*

637   DEU   ISSN 1436-7955
EUROPAEISCHER MOLKEREI- UND KAESEREI-ADRESSKALENDER; Vormerk-, Auskunfts- und Fachanschriftenbuch fuer die gesamte Milchwirtschaft. Text in German. 1976. a. EUR 39 (effective 2003). adv. back issues avail. **Document type:** *Magazine, Trade.*
Former titles (until 1996): European Dairy Directory (1430-7294); (until 1991): Europaeischer Molkerei und Kaeserei Adresskalender (0724-3219)
Published by: A V A Verlag Allgaeu GmbH, Porschestr 2, Kempten, 87437, Germany. TEL 49-831-571420, FAX 49-831-79008, info@ava-verlag.de, http://www.ava-verlag.de.

637   DEU   ISSN 0936-6318
EUROPEAN DAIRY MAGAZINE. Text in English. 1989. bi-m. EUR 52.20; EUR 9.50 newsstand/cover (effective 2005). adv. back issues avail. **Document type:** *Magazine, Trade.*
Indexed: AEA, BioDAb, DSA, FS&TA, IndVet, NutrAb, RA&MP, RDA, RefZh, TriticAb, WAE&RSA.
—BLDSC (3829.688830), CISTI, IE, ingenta. **CCC.**
Published by: Verlag Th. Mann, Nordring 10, Gelsenkirchen, 45894, Germany. TEL 49-209-93040, FAX 49-209-9304185, info@th-mann.de, http://www.th-mann.de. Ed. Roland Sossna. Adv. contact Anke Haremsa. B&W page EUR 2,080, color page EUR 3,010; trim 186 x 270. Circ: 6,083 (paid and controlled).

637   USA   ISSN 0014-7826
FARM AND DAIRY; the auction guide & the rural marketplace. Text in English. 1914. w. (Thu.). USD 28 (effective 2005). adv. bk.rev. bibl.; illus. **Document type:** *Newspaper.* **Description:** Serves as a key to reaching the rural audience in Ohio, western Pennsylvania and the panhandle of West Virginia.

Published by: Lyle Printing and Publishing Co., 185 East State St, Box 38, Salem, OH 44460. TEL 330-337-3419, 800-837-3419, FAX 330-337-9550, scrowell@farmanddairy.com, editorial@farmanddairy.com, http://www.farmanddairy.com. Ed. Susan M Crowell. Pub. Scot M Darling. Adv. contact Scot Darling. B&W page USD 612, color page USD 1,087; trim 11 x 8.5. Circ: 34,290; 33,722 (paid).

637 658   GBR   ISSN 0968-0128
FARMING BUSINESS. Text in English. 1966. bi-m. membership. charts; illus. **Document type:** *Trade.* **Description:** Covers farm management, cattle breeding, and animal health.
Supersedes (in 1992): Better Breeding (0006-0046); Formerly: Better Management (0006-0186)
Indexed: AEA, DSA, HerbAb, HongKongiana, MaizeAb, NutrAb, RRTA, WAE&RSA.
—CISTI.
Published by: Genus Ltd., Westmere Dr, Crewe, Ches CW1 6ZY, United Kingdom. TEL 44-1270-536536, FAX 44-1270-536601. Ed. Jane Craigie. Circ: 40,000 (controlled).

637   USA   ISSN 0745-7553
FARMSHINE. Text in English. 1979. w. USD 12 (effective 2005). adv. **Document type:** *Magazine.* **Description:** Provides news, features, and market reports to dairy farmers in Pennsylvania and surrounding states.
—CISTI.
Published by: Dieter Krieg, Ed. & Pub., State & Main Sts, PO Box 219, Brownstown, PA 17508-0219. TEL 717-656-8050, FAX 717-656-8188, cowsrus1@td.net, http://www.farmshine.com. Ed., Pub., R&P Dieter Krieg. Circ: 13,540.

FEDERAL MILK ORDER MARKET STATISTICS. see *AGRICULTURE—Abstracting, Bibliographies, Statistics*

637   FIN   ISSN 0789-7286
                          CODEN: FJDSAJ
FINNISH JOURNAL OF DAIRY SCIENCE. Text in English, Finnish, German; Summaries in English. 1939. a. adv. back issues avail.
Formerly (until 1990): Meijeritieteellinen Aikakauskirja (0367-2387)
Indexed: BIOSIS Prev, BiolAb, CIN, ChemAb, ChemTitl, DSA, FS&TA, IndVet, VetBull, WAE&RSA.
—BLDSC (3929.180000), CASDDS, CISTI.
Published by: Finnish Society of Dairy Science/Meijeritieteellinen Seura r.y., University of Helsinki, Dept of Food Technology, Dairy Science, PO Box 27, Helsinki, 00014, Finland. TEL 358-9-19158312, tapani.alatossava@helsinki.fi. Ed. Eeva Liisa Ryhanen. Circ: 600.

FOOD NEW ZEALAND. see *FOOD AND FOOD INDUSTRIES*

FOOD PROTECTION TRENDS. see *FOOD AND FOOD INDUSTRIES*

637.1   FRA
FRANCE. MINISTERE DE L'AGRICULTURE ET DE LA PECHE. CONJONCTURE LAIT ET PRODUITS LAITIERS. Text in French. 1977. m. **Document type:** *Government.*
Former titles: France. Ministere de l'Agriculture, de la Peche et de l'Alimentation. Conjoncture Lait et Produits Laitiers; France. Ministere de l'Agriculture et de la Foret. Conjoncture Lait et Produits Laitiers; France. Ministere de l'Agriculture. Conjoncture Lait et Produits Laitiers; France. Ministere de l'Agriculture. Informations Rapides. Lait et Produits Laitiers; France. Ministere de l'Agriculture. Informations Rapides. Statistique Laitiere (0223-4939)
Published by: Ministere de l'Agriculture et de la Peche, Service Central des Enquetes et Etudes Statistiques, 251 rue de Vaugirard, Paris, Cedex 15 75732, France. TEL 33-1-49558585, FAX 33-1-49558503, http://www.agriculture.gouv.fr.

338.1771   DEU   ISSN 1433-7363
G V-FRISCHE-MAGAZIN. (Gemeinschaftsverpflegung) Text in German. 1998. q. **Document type:** *Magazine, Trade.*
Formerly (until 1999): Frische-Magazin (1436-9176)
Published by: Buecker Fachverlag GmbH & Co. KG, Postfach 1363, Bad Breisig, 53492, Germany. TEL 49-2633-45400, FAX 49-2633-97415, redaktion@milch-marketing.de, http://www.milch-marketing.de/bueckerverlag. Eds. Frank Wegerich, Niels Hupperich. Circ: 7,500 (paid and controlled).

GELATO ARTIGIANALE. see *FOOD AND FOOD INDUSTRIES*

637   GBR
GOLD TOP NEWS. Text in English. 3/yr.
Published by: Quality Milk Producers Ltd., The Bury Farm, Pednor Rd, Chesham, Bucks HP5 2JY, United Kingdom, TEL 0494-784572, FAX 0494-791700. Ed. S R Baker. Circ: 1,200.

637 636.2   USA   ISSN 0017-5110
GUERNSEY BREEDERS' JOURNAL. Text in English. 1910. 10/yr. USD 20 domestic (effective 2005). adv. stat.; illus. s-a. index. reprint service avail. from PQC. **Document type:** *Magazine, Trade.*
Related titles: Microform ed.: (from PQC).
—CISTI, Linda Hall.

Published by: American Guernsey Association, 7614 Slate Ridge Blvd, Box 666, Reynoldsburg, OH 43068. TEL 614-864-2409, FAX 614-864-5614, info@usguernsey.com, http://www.usguernsey.com. adv.: B&W page USD 365, color page USD 540. Circ: 1,400.

H R I - BUYERS GUIDE. (Hotels, Restaurants, Institutions) see *FOOD AND FOOD INDUSTRIES*

338.0029   DEU   ISSN 0948-9053
HANDBUCH MILCH. Text in German. 1980. 3 base vols. plus irreg. updates. EUR 99.50 (effective 2003). **Document type:** *Directory, Trade.*
Former titles (until 1992): Behr's Handbuch Milch (0178-3734); (until 1985): B B V Handbuch Milch (0173-8119)
Published by: B. Behr's Verlag GmbH & Co. KG, Averhoffstr. 10, Hamburg, 22085, Germany. TEL 49-40-2270080, FAX 49-40-2201091, info@behrs.de, http://www.behrs.de.

HIGHLIGHTS. see *BIOLOGY—Genetics*

637   USA   ISSN 0018-2885
SF232.A1H63
HOARD'S DAIRYMAN; the national dairy farm magazine. Text in English. 1885. s-m. (20/yr.). USD 16 domestic; USD 40 foreign (effective 2005). adv. charts; illus.; stat. index. reprint service avail. from PQC. **Document type:** *Magazine, Trade.* **Description:** Offers dairy farm news and dairy management information in the US and Canada.
Related titles: Microfilm ed.: (from PQC).
Indexed: B&AI, DSA, F&GI, FS&TA, RRTA, WAE&RSA.
—CISTI, IE, Infotrieve, Linda Hall.
Published by: W.D. Hoard and Sons Co., PO Box 801, Fort Atkinson, WI 53538. TEL 920-563-5551, FAX 920-563-7298, hoards@hoards.com, http://www.hoards.com/. Ed., Pub. W D Knox. adv.: B&W page USD 13,327, color page USD 15,827; trim 10.25 x 14.25. Circ: 63,023 (paid); 18,110 (controlled).

637 664   JPN   ISSN 0285-1806
HOKKAIDO EIYO SYOKURYO GAKKAISHI/HOKKAIDO SOCIETY OF FOOD AND NUTRITION. JOURNAL. Text and summaries in Japanese. 1954. a. JPY 1,300, USD 6.50. adv.
Published by: Hokkaido Society of Food and Nutrition, c/o Department of Biochemistry, Hokkaido University School of Medicine, N-15-W-7, Kita-ku, Sapporo, 060, Japan. Ed. Yoh Imai. Circ: 1,000.

636.234   NLD   ISSN 1380-2879
HOLSTEIN INTERNATIONAL; maandblad voor de moderne Holsteinfokker. Text in Dutch, Spanish. 1994. m. EUR 52 (effective 2005). adv. illus. back issues avail. **Document type:** *Trade.* **Description:** Contains articles of interest to breeders and marketers of top-quality Holstein cattle.
Related titles: English ed.: ISSN 1380-2887; German ed.: ISSN 1380-2895; French ed.
Published by: Holstein International BV, PO Box 80, Stiens, 9050 AB, Netherlands. TEL 31-58-2574345, FAX 31-58-2575732, info@holsteininternational.com, http://www.hi-site.com/nieuwsbrief/nieuws_nl.php. Circ: 10,000.

636.2142   CAN   ISSN 0710-1309
HOLSTEIN JOURNAL. Text mainly in English; Text occasionally in French. 1938. m. CND 30 domestic; CND 70 foreign (effective 2000). adv. bk.rev. charts; illus. index. **Document type:** *Trade.* **Description:** Provides news and information on Holstein dairy cattle breeding.
Formerly: Holstein-Friesian Journal (0018-3687)
—CISTI, Linda Hall.
Published by: Holstein Journal Group Inc., 9120 Leslie St, Unit 105, Richmond, ON L4B 3J9, Canada. TEL 905-886-4222, FAX 905-886-0037, peter@holsteinjournal.com, http://www.holsteinjournal.com. Ed. Bonnie E Cooper. Pub. G Peter English. Adv. contact G. Peter English. Circ: 9,577 (paid).

637   GBR   ISSN 1466-0733
HOLSTEIN JOURNAL. Text in English. 1919. bi-m. GBP 18. adv. bk.rev. illus. **Document type:** *Journal, Trade.* **Description:** Provides information on cattle breeding and genetic improvement with herd, show, sale, research, new product and regional features.
Former titles (until 1998): Holstein Friesian Journal (0954-6219); British Friesian Journal (0007-0726)
Indexed: AnBrAb.
Published by: Holstein UK & Ireland, Scotsbridge House, Scots Hill, Rickmansworth, Herts WD3 3BB, United Kingdom. TEL 44-1923-494600, FAX 44-1923-770003, journal@holstein-uk.org, http://www.holstein-uk.org, http://www.holstein-UK.org. Ed. Simon Gee. Adv. contact Jennifer Alderman. Circ: 14,500 (controlled).

636.2142   USA   ISSN 0199-4239
HOLSTEIN WORLD. Text in English. 1904. m. USD 38.95 domestic; CND 70 in Canada; USD 69.95 elsewhere (effective 2005). adv. bk.rev. charts; illus.; mkt.; stat. index. Supplement avail.; reprint service avail. from PQC. **Document type:** *Magazine.* **Description:** For high-income milk producers who own or manage genetically superior Holstein dairy cattle.
Formerly (until 1979): Holstein-Friesian World (0018-3695)
Related titles: Microfilm ed.: (from PQC).
—CISTI, Linda Hall.

Published by: DairyBusiness Communications (Subsidiary of: Multi Ag Media LLC), 6437 Collamer Rd, East Syracuse, NY 13057-1031. TEL 800-439-3990, FAX 315-703-7988, http://www.holsteinworld.com. Eds. Joel P Hastings, Karen Knnutsen. Pub., R&P Joel P Hastings. adv.: B&W page USD 2,030. Circ: 16,000 (paid).

HOOFS & HORNS. see *AGRICULTURE—Poultry And Livestock*

636.234 USA
HORIZONS (SHAWANO). Text in English. s-a. USD 16 to individuals; USD 40 to institutions (effective 2005). **Document type:** *Newsletter, Trade.* **Description:** Includes educational information for dairy farmers plus update on sires and services provided for their use.
Published by: Cooperative Resources International, PO Box 469, Shawano, WI 54166-0469. TEL 715-526-2141, FAX 715-526-4511, http://cridata.crinet.com/cri. Ed. Terri Dallas.

HUSDJUR. see *AGRICULTURE—Poultry And Livestock*

637 ESP ISSN 0210-0037
I L E. (Industrias Lacteas Espanolas) Text in Spanish. 1978. m. (10/yr.). EUR 10 (effective 2004). adv. bk.rev. reprints avail. **Document type:** *Trade.* **Description:** Covers all areas of the dairy trade.
Indexed: IECT.
—CINDOC.
Published by: Publicaciones Tecnicas Alimentarias S.A., Capitan Haya 35, 4o A, Madrid, 28020, Spain. TEL 34-91-3665207, FAX 34-91-5555173, publitasa@mundivia.es, http://www.publitasa.com. Ed. Alfredo Val. R&P Carlos Ayala. Adv. contact Paloma Delolmo. Circ: 4,000.

570 IND ISSN 0971-5436
INDIAN JOURNAL OF DAIRY & BIOSCIENCES. Text in English. 1990. a.
Indexed: AEA, AbHyg, AgBio, AgrForAb, AnBrAb, DSA, HerbAb, IndVet, MaizeAb, NutrAb, PN&I, RDA, RM&VM, RPP, S&F, SIA, SoyAb, TriticAb, VetBull, WAE&RSA.
—BLDSC (4410.990000), IE.
Published by: National Dairy Research Institute, c/o Dr. B.N.Mathur, Director, NDRI Deemed University, Karnal, 132 001, India. TEL 91-0184-252800, FAX 91-0184-250042, http://karnal.nic.in/res_ndri.asp.

637.1 ITA ISSN 0019-7513
INDUSTRIA DEL LATTE. Text in Multiple languages. 1965. q.
Indexed: AbHyg, AgBio, AnBrAb, DSA, IndVet, NutrAb, RefZh, SIA, SoyAb, TriticAb, WAE&RSA, WeedAb.
Published by: Centro Sperimentale del Latte, Strada per Merlino 3, Zelo Buon Persico, LO 26839, Italy. TEL 39-02-906961, FAX 39-02-906999, http://www.csl.it.

637 ARG ISSN 0046-9181
INDUSTRIA LECHERA. Text in Spanish. 1919. bi-m. ARS 15, USD 5. adv. play rev. bibl.; illus.; stat.
Indexed: ChemAb, DSA, FS&TA.
—CISTI.
Published by: Centro de la Industria Lechera, Medina, 281, Capital Federal, Buenos Aires 1407, Argentina. Circ: 3,000.

637 BRA ISSN 0100-3674
CODEN: RILCAY
INSTITUTO DE LATICINIOS CANDIDO TOSTES. REVISTA. Text in Portuguese. 1946. bi-m.
Formerly (until 1957): Felctiano (0102-2237)
Indexed: AEA, AgBio, DSA, FS&TA, HortAb, IndVet, NutrAb, RDA, RPP, SoyAb, VetBull, WAE&RSA.
—CASDDS.
Published by: Instituto de Laticinios Candido Tostes, Centro, Caixa Postal 183, Juiz De Fora, MG 36001-970, Brazil. TEL 55-32-2243116, FAX 55-32-2243113. Ed. Geraldo Magela Carozzi de Miranda.

637.1 USA ISSN 0074-1671
INTERNATIONAL ASSOCIATION OF MILK CONTROL AGENCIES. PROCEEDINGS OF ANNUAL MEETINGS. Text in English. 1937. a. USD 10 (effective 1999). **Document type:** *Proceedings.*
Published by: International Association of Milk Control Agencies, c/o Charles Huff, New York Dept of Agriculture and Markets, 1 Winners Circle, Albany, NY 12235. TEL 518-457-5731, FAX 518-485-5816. Circ: (controlled).

637 BEL ISSN 0259-8434
SF221 CODEN: BIDFDY
INTERNATIONAL DAIRY FEDERATION. BULLETIN/ FEDERATION INTERNATIONALE DE LAITERIE. BULLETIN. Text in English, French. 1960. m. EUR 405 (effective 2005). index, cum.index. **Document type:** *Bulletin.*
Former titles (until 1985): Federation Internationale de Laiterie. Bulletin Annuel (0250-5118); International Dairy Federation. Annual Bulletin (0074-4484)
Related titles: Supplement(s): International Dairy Federation. Special Issue. ISSN 1025-8515.
Indexed: AEA, AbHyg, AgBio, AnBrAb, BiolAb, CIN, ChemAb, ChemTitl, CurPA, DSA, FS&TA, HerbAb, HortAb, IndVet, MaizeAb, NutrAb, PBA, PHN&I, PN&I, RDA, REE&TA, RM&VM, RPP, RRTA, S&F, SIA, SoyAb, TDB, TriticAb, VetBull, WAE&RSA.
—BLDSC (2587.550000), CASDDS, CISTI, IE, ingenta.
Published by: International Dairy Federation/Federation Internationale de Laiterie, Diamant Building, Bd Auguste Reyers 80, Brussels, 1030, Belgium. TEL 32-2-733-9888, FAX 32-2-733-0413, info@fil-idf.org, http://www.fil-idf.org/content/default.asp?. Circ: 1,500.

INTERNATIONAL DAIRY FEDERATION. CATALOGUE OF I D F PUBLICATIONS/FEDERATION INTERNATIONALE LAITIERE. CATALOGUE DES PUBLICATIONS. see *AGRICULTURE—Abstracting, Bibliographies, Statistics*

637 BEL ISSN 0538-7094
INTERNATIONAL DAIRY FEDERATION. INTERNATIONAL STANDARD/FEDERATION INTERNATIONALE DE LAITERIE. NORME INTERNATIONALE. Text in English. 1955. irreg. price varies.
Indexed: BiolAb, DSA, NutrAb.
Published by: International Dairy Federation/Federation Internationale de Laiterie, Diamant Building, Bd Auguste Reyers 80, Brussels, 1030, Belgium. TEL 32-2-7339888, FAX 32-2-7330413. Circ: 3,000.

637 NLD ISSN 0958-6946
SF221 CODEN: IDAJE6
➤ **INTERNATIONAL DAIRY JOURNAL.** Text in English. 1991. 12/yr. EUR 1,731 in Europe to institutions; JPY 229,800 in Japan to institutions; USD 1,937 elsewhere to institutions; EUR 130 in Europe to qualified personnel; JPY 17,500 in Japan to qualified personnel; USD 147 elsewhere to qualified personnel (effective 2006). adv. back issues avail. **Document type:** *Journal, Academic/Scholarly.* **Description:** Publishes original papers and critical reviews on all aspects of dairy science and technology.
Incorporates (in 1997): Netherlands Milk and Dairy Journal (0028-209X)
Related titles: Microform ed.: (from PQC); Online - full text ed.: (from EBSCO Publishing, Gale Group, IngentaConnect, ScienceDirect, Swets Information Services).
Indexed: AEA, ASCA, AgBio, Agr, AgrForAb, AnBrAb, B&BAb, BIOBASE, BIOSIS Prev, BioEngAb, BiolAb, CIN, ChemAb, ChemTitl, CurCont, DSA, FS&TA, HerbAb, IABS, ISR, IndVet, MBA, MSB, NutrAb, PN&I, RefZh, SCI, SIA, SoyAb, VetBull, WAE&RSA, WeedAb.
—BLDSC (4539.501800), CASDDS, CISTI, IDS, IE, Infotrieve, ingenta, Linda Hall. **CCC.**
Published by: Elsevier BV (Subsidiary of: Elsevier Science & Technology), Radarweg 29, Amsterdam, 1043 NX, Netherlands. TEL 31-20-4853911, FAX 31-20-4852457, nlinfo-f@elsevier.nl, http://www.elsevier.com/locate/idairyj, http://www.elsevier.nl. Ed. P Jelen.

338.476 GBR ISSN 1745-7785
INTERNATIONAL DAIRY TOPICS. Text in English. bi-m. GBP 50, USD 75, EUR 80 (effective 2005). adv. **Document type:** *Magazine, Trade.* **Description:** Technical magazine for professional milk and dairy producers that focuses on the key issues of nutrition, breeding, milking and health.
Published by: Positive Action Publications Ltd., PO Box 4, Driffield, N Humberside YO25 9DJ, United Kingdom. TEL 44-1377-241724, FAX 44-1377-253640, info@positiveaction.co.uk, http://www.positiveaction.co.uk/pap/mags/idt/idtmain.html, http://positiveaction.co.uk.

INTERNATIONAL FOOD ABSTRACTS. DAIRY DISK. see *AGRICULTURE—Abstracting, Bibliographies, Statistics*

636 PAK ISSN 1811-9743
▼ ➤ **INTERNATIONAL JOURNAL OF DAIRY SCIENCE.** Text in English. 2004. q. USD 350 (effective 2005). **Document type:** *Journal, Academic/Scholarly.* **Description:** Publishes original research on all aspects of dairy science including animal husbandry, the physiology, biochemistry and endocrinology of lactation, milk production, composition, preservation, processing and separation, biotechnology and food science, properties of milk proteins and other components, dairy products such as cheese, fermented milks and spreads, relevant studies in bacteriology, enzymology and immunology, the use of milk products in other foods and the development of methods relevant to these subjects.
Related titles: Online - full text ed.: ISSN 1811-9751. free (effective 2005).
Published by: Asian Network for Scientific Information, 308-Lasani Town, Sargodha Rd, Faislabad, 38090, Pakistan. TEL 92-41-2001145, FAX 92-41-731433, http://www.ansinet.org/c4p.php?j_id=ijds, http://www.ansinet.net.

637 GBR ISSN 1364-727X
SF221 CODEN: IJDTFQ
➤ **INTERNATIONAL JOURNAL OF DAIRY TECHNOLOGY.** Text in English. 1947. q. GBP 248 combined subscription in Europe to institutions print & online eds.; USD 460 combined subscription in the Americas to institutions & Caribbean (print & online eds.); GBP 274 combined subscription elsewhere to institutions print & online eds. (effective 2006). adv. bk.rev. bibl.; charts; illus.; stat. index. back issues avail. **Document type:** *Journal, Academic/Scholarly.* **Description:** Contains information and expertise concerning the dairy industry.
Formerly (until 1997): Society of Dairy Technology. Journal (0037-9840)
Related titles: ♦ Online - full text ed.: International Journal of Dairy Technology Online. ISSN 1471-0307.
Indexed: AEA, ASCA, AbHyg, AgBio, Agr, AgrForAb, AnBrAb, B&BAb, BIOBASE, BIOSIS Prev, BioCN&I, BiolAb, ChemAb, CurCont, DSA, ESPM, ExcerpMed, FS&TA, ForAb, HortAb, IPackAb, ISR, IndVet, NutrAb, PST, RDA, RRTA, RefZh, SCI, SIA, SSCI, SoyAb, TriticAb, VetBull, WAE&RSA.
—BLDSC (4542.182500), CASDDS, CINDOC, CISTI, IDS, IE, Infotrieve, ingenta, Linda Hall. **CCC.**
Published by: (Society of Dairy Technology), Blackwell Publishing Ltd., 9600 Garsington Rd, Oxford, OX4 2ZG, United Kingdom. TEL 44-1865-776868, FAX 44-1865-714591, editor@sdt.org, customerservices@oxon.blackwellpublishing.com, http://www.blackwellpublishing.com/journals/IDT. Ed. Dr. Hugh Pinnock TEL 44-1869-345838. Circ: 1,400.

➤ **IRELAND. CENTRAL STATISTICS OFFICE. MILK AND MILK PRODUCTS SUPPLY BALANCE.** see *AGRICULTURE—Abstracting, Bibliographies, Statistics*

➤ **IRELAND. CENTRAL STATISTICS OFFICE. MILK STATISTICS.** see *AGRICULTURE—Abstracting, Bibliographies, Statistics*

636 IRL
IRISH GRASSLAND ASSOCIATION. JOURNAL. Text in English. 1962. a. **Document type:** *Journal.*
Formerly (until vol.35, 2001): Irish Grassland and Animal Protection Association. Journal (0332-0588)
—BLDSC (4571.522000).
Published by: Irish Grassland Association, Borris-in-Ossary, Co. Laois, Ireland. info@irishgrassland.com, http://www.irishgrassland.com.

637.1 DEU ISSN 1432-6132
JAHRBUCH DER EUROPAEISCHEN MILCHWIRTSCHAFT. Text in German. 1950. a. EUR 89 (effective 2005). adv. **Document type:** *Directory, Trade.* **Description:** Reports on dairy farming in Germany and Europe.
Former titles (until 1994): Jahrbuch der Milchwirtschaft (0721-4332); (until 197?): Zentralverband Deutscher Molkereifachleute und Milchwirtschaftler. Verbands-Jahrbuch (0514-3357)
Published by: (Zentralverband Deutscher Milchwirtschaftler e.V.), Verlag Th. Mann, Nordring 10, Gelsenkirchen, 45894, Germany. TEL 49-209-93040, FAX 49-209-9304185, info@th-mann.de, http://www.th-mann.de. Ed. Roland Sossna. adv.: B&W page EUR 1,000, color page EUR 1,615; trim 81 x 122. Circ: 4,500.

636.2142 GBR ISSN 0446-7310
JERSEY AT HOME. Text in English. 1951. s-a. GBP 21, USD 34 membership (effective 2005). adv. bk.rev. stat.; tr.lit. **Document type:** *Magazine, Trade.* **Description:** Official publication of the R.J.A.H.S. covering activities of the society, Jersey cattle, agriculture, and country issues on the island of Jersey.
—CISTI.
Published by: Royal Jersey Agricultural and Horticultural Society, W J C B Center, La Route de la Trinite, Jersey, Channel Islands JE3 5JP, United Kingdom. TEL 44-1534-866555, society@royaljersey.co.uk, http://www.royaljersey.co.uk/. Ed. J W Godfrey. Circ: 2,000 (controlled).

JOURNAL OF ANIMAL SCIENCE AND TECHNOLOGY. see *AGRICULTURE—Poultry And Livestock*

637 GBR ISSN 0022-0299
CODEN: JDRSAN
➤ **JOURNAL OF DAIRY RESEARCH.** Text in English. 1929. q. GBP 340 to institutions; USD 550 in North America to institutions; GBP 370 combined subscription to institutions print & online eds.; USD 598 combined subscription in North America to institutions print & online eds. (effective 2006). adv. bibl.; charts; illus. index. back issues avail.; reprint service avail. from PQC. **Document type:** *Journal, Academic/Scholarly.* **Description:** Research on all aspects of milk production and preservation, and fundamental effects of processing. Includes the composition of milk for several animal species.
Related titles: Microform ed.: (from PQC); Online - full text ed.: ISSN 1469-7629. GBP 312 to institutions; USD 506 in North America to institutions (effective 2006) (from EBSCO Publishing, O C L C Online Computer Library Center, Inc., Swets Information Services).
Indexed: AEA, ASCA, AbHyg, AgBio, Agr, AnBrAb, AnalAb, B&AI, B&BAb, BIOBASE, BIOSIS Prev, BibAg, BiolAb, CIN, CTA, ChemAb, ChemTitl, ChemoAb, CurCont, CurPA, DBA, DSA, ESPM, ExcerpMed, FCA, FS&TA, FoVS&M, HelmAb, HerbAb, HortAb, IABS, ISR, IndMed, IndVet, MEDLINE, MaizeAb, NRN, NutrAb, PN&I, PoultAb, RASB, RM&VM, RPP, RefZh, SCI, SIA, SoyAb, TriticAb, VetBull, WAE&RSA.
—BLDSC (4966.000000), CASDDS, CINDOC, CISTI, GNLM, IDS, IE, Infotrieve, ingenta, Linda Hall. **CCC.**
Published by: (Institute of Food Research), Cambridge University Press, The Edinburgh Bldg, Shaftesbury Rd, Cambridge, CB2 2RU, United Kingdom. TEL 44-1223-312393, FAX 44-1223-315052, jdr@hri.sari.ac.uk, information@cambridge.org, http://uk.cambridge.org/journals/dar. Eds. D G Chamberlain, Eric Needs. R&P Linda Nicol TEL 44-1223-325757. Adv. contact Rebecca Curtis TEL 44-1223-325757. Circ: 750. **Co-sponsor:** Hannah Research Institute.

637 USA ISSN 0022-0302
CODEN: JDSCAE
➤ **JOURNAL OF DAIRY SCIENCE.** Text in English. 1917. m. USD 450 in North America; USD 500 elsewhere (effective 2005). adv. abstr.; bibl.; charts; illus. index. back issues avail.; reprints avail. **Document type:** *Journal, Academic/Scholarly.* **Description:** Provides current technical and scientific information for all segments of the dairy industry.
Related titles: Microform ed.: (from PMC, PQC); Online - full text ed.: ISSN 1525-3198 (from EBSCO Publishing, ProQuest Information & Learning).
Indexed: AEA, ASCA, AbHyg, AgBio, Agr, AgrForAb, AnBrAb, AnalAb, B&AI, BIOSIS Prev, BibAg, BioCN&I, BiolAb, CIN, ChemAb, ChemTitl, CurCont, CurPA, DBA, DSA, DentInd, EnvAb, ExcerpMed, FCA, FPA, FS&TA, FoVS&M, GenetAb, HGA, HelmAb, HerbAb, HortAb, I&DA, ISR, IndMed, IndVet, MBA, MEDLINE, MaizeAb, NutrAb, PBA, PHN&I, PN&I, PotatoAb, ProtozoAb, RM&VM, RPP, RRTA, RefZh, RiceAb, S&F, SCI, SIA, SSCI, SoyAb, TOSA, Telegen, TriticAb, VetBull, WAE&RSA, WeedAb.
—BLDSC (4967.000000), CASDDS, CINDOC, CISTI, GNLM, IDS, IE, Infotrieve, ingenta, Linda Hall. **CCC.**
Published by: American Dairy Science Association, 1111 N Dunlap Ave, Savoy, IL 61874. TEL 217-356-3182, FAX 217-398-4119, adsa@assochq.org, http://jds.fass.org/, http://www.adsa.org. Eds. Jean Rice, Stephen C Nickerson. Circ: 5,062 (paid and free). **Subscr. to:** Allen Press Inc., PO Box 1897, Lawrence, KS 66044. TEL 785-843-1235, FAX 785-843-1274, orders@allenpress.com, http://www.allenpress.com.

338.1771 PAK ISSN 1728-9750
THE JOURNAL OF DAIRY SCIENCES. Text in English. 1985. m. GBP 300 (effective 2005). **Document type:** *Journal, Academic/Scholarly.* **Description:** Study of dairy sciences.
Published by: (Dairy Association), International Press, P O Box 17700, Karachi, 75300, Pakistan. TEL 92-21-4947486, FAX 92-21-4989257, light_68@hotmail.com. Ed. Dr. H R Siddiqui.

637 IND ISSN 0971-4456
CODEN: JFHSEP
JOURNAL OF DAIRYING, FOODS & HOME SCIENCES. Text in English. 1982. q. USD 81.98 (effective 2005). **Document type:** *Academic/Scholarly.* **Description:** Features original research articles on all aspects of dairying, foods and home sciences by eminent research workers.
Formerly (until 1992): Asian Journal of Dairy Research (0253-6595)
Indexed: AEA, AnBrAb, BioDAb, BiolAb, ChemAb, DSA, FCA, FS&TA, HortAb, IndVet, MaizeAb, NutrAb, PBA, PGrRegA, PHN&I, PN&I, PST, PotatoAb, RDA, RPP, RiceAb, S&F, SIA, SoyAb, TDB, TriticAb, WAE&RSA.
—BLDSC (4967.101000), CASDDS, CISTI.
Published by: Journal of Dairying Foods & Home Sciences, 307, Sector 8, Urban Estate, Karnal, Haryana 132 001, India. TEL 91-184-283307. Ed. V D Mudgal. Pub., Adv. contact O N Mathur. **Subscr. to:** Scientific Publishers, 5-A New Pali Rd., Near Hotel Taj Hari Mahal, PO Box 91, Jodhpur, Rajasthan 342 003, India. info@scientificpub.com, http://www.scientificpub.com.

JOURNAL OF FOOD PROTECTION. see *FOOD AND FOOD INDUSTRIES*

637.1 SWE ISSN 1651-4408
KAERNFULLT FRAAN SVENSK MJOELK. Text in Swedish. 1995. 23/yr. **Document type:** *Newsletter.*
Formerly (until 1998): Kaernfullt fraan Mejerierna (1401-8713)
Related titles: Online - full text ed.
Published by: Svensk Mjoelk AB/Swedish Dairy Association, Torsgatan 14, Stockholm, 10546, Sweden. TEL 46-771-191900, FAX 46-8-218363, info@svenskmjolk.se, http://www.svenskmjolk.se/press/IE/Karnfullt.asp. Ed. Claes Henriksson. Circ: 23,300.

338.1771 DEU ISSN 0940-208X
KAESE-THEKE; Verkaufspraxis fuer das Fachpersonal in Bedienungsabteilungen. Variant title: Kaesetheke. Text in German. 1991. q. EUR 17.90; EUR 2.50 newsstand/cover (effective 2005). adv. **Document type:** *Magazine, Trade.*
Published by: Buecker Fachverlag GmbH & Co. KG, Postfach 1363, Bad Breisig, 53492, Germany. TEL 49-2633-45400, FAX 49-2633-97415, redaktion@milch-marketing.de, http://www.milch-marketing.de. Ed. Elke Hoffmann. Pub. Juergen Buecker. Adv. contact Michaela Weber. page EUR 4,810; trim 185 x 250. Circ: 11,963 (controlled).

KANSAS FOOD DEALERS BULLETIN. see *FOOD AND FOOD INDUSTRIES—Grocery Trade*

637 658 GBR ISSN 1365-4543
KEY NOTE MARKET REPORT: MILK & DAIRY PRODUCTS. Variant title: Milk & Dairy Products. Text in English. 1987. irreg., latest 2001, Feb. GBP 340 per issue (effective 2002). **Document type:** *Trade.* **Description:** Provides and overview of a specific UK market segment and includes executive summary, market definition, market size, industry background, competitor analysis, current issues, forecasts, company profiles, and more.
Formerly (until 1996): Key Note Report: Milk and Dairy Products (0954-4275)
Related titles: CD-ROM ed.; Online - full text ed.
Published by: Key Note Ltd., Field House, 72 Oldfield Rd, Hampton, Mddx TW12 2HQ, United Kingdom. TEL 44-20-8481-8750, FAX 44-20-8783-0049, info@keynote.co.uk, http://www.keynote.co.uk. Ed. Jenny Baxter.

637 338.1 THA ISSN 0023-1053
KHAO SETTHAKIT KAN-KASET/AGRICULTURAL ECONOMIC NEWS. Text in Thai. 1955. m. free.
Published by: (Thailand. Ministry of Agriculture and Cooperatives, Thailand. Office of Agricultural Economics), Chuan Pim Partnership Ltd., 469 Phra Su Maen Rd, Bangkok, Thailand. Ed. Nipont Dilokkunanant. Circ: 120,000.

637 DEU ISSN 0023-1347
SF227.G3 CODEN: KMWFAF
KIELER MILCHWIRTSCHAFTLICHE FORSCHUNGSBERICHTE. Text in German. 1949. 4/yr. EUR 69; EUR 20 newsstand/cover (effective 2004). adv. bk.rev. **Document type:** *Journal, Trade.*
Indexed: AEA, ASCA, AbHyg, AgBio, AnBrAb, BiolAb, ChemAb, ChemTitl, CurCont, DSA, ExcerpMed, FS&TA, IndVet, Inspec, NutrAb, PHN&I, PN&I, RM&VM, RefZh, S&F, SIA, SoyAb, VetBull, WAE&RSA.
—BLDSC (5095.025000), CASDDS, IDS, IE, ingenta, Linda Hall. **CCC.**
Published by: (Germany. Bundesanstalt fuer Milchforschung), Verlag Th. Mann, Nordring 10, Gelsenkirchen, 45894, Germany. TEL 49-209-93040, FAX 49-209-9304185, info@th-mann.de, http://www.th-mann.de. Ed. Dr. E Schlimme. Adv. contact Heike Turowski. B&W page EUR 440, color page EUR 1,040; trim 126 x 190. Circ: 828 (controlled).

KVAEG. see *AGRICULTURE—Poultry And Livestock*

LACTEOS Y CARNICOS MEXICANOS. see *FOOD AND FOOD INDUSTRIES*

LACTIC ACID BACTERIA. see *BIOLOGY—Microbiology*

637 ITA ISSN 0392-6060
IL LATTE; rivista tecnica per l'industria lattiero-caseariа. Text in Italian. 1927. m. EUR 47 domestic; EUR 90 in Europe; EUR 105 elsewhere (effective 2005). adv. bk.rev. abstr.; bibl.; charts; illus.; stat. index. **Description:** Information concerning plants, production techniques and methods of analysis used in the dairy and cheese industry.
Indexed: AbHyg, AnBrAb, ChemAb, CurCont, DSA, FS&TA, HerbAb, HortAb, IndVet, MaizeAb, NutrAb, PHN&I, PN&I, RDA, RM&VM, RPP, RRTA, SIA, VetBull, WAE&RSA.
—BLDSC (5160.400000), IE, ingenta.
Published by: Tecniche Nuove SpA, Via Eritrea 21, Milan, MI 201, Italy. TEL 39-02-390901, FAX 39-02-7570364, latte@tecnichenuove.com, info@tecnichenuove.com, http://www.tecnichenuove.com/epages/tecnichenuove.storefront/4309d7a9010431202740c0a80105058c/Product/View/LT&2D3. Ed. Roberto Tognella. Circ: 7,076.

637 USA ISSN 1073-3019
LECHERO LATINO. Text in English. 1987. q. USD 20; USD 25 foreign (effective 2000). adv. back issues avail. **Document type:** *Trade.* **Description:** For larger, progressive dairymen in Mexico, Colombia, Brazil, Argentina, Uruguay and Chile.
Supersedes (in 1990): Lechero Latinoamericano; Which was formerly: Holstein Latinoamericano
Published by: DairyBusiness Communications (Subsidiary of: Multi Ag Media LLC), 6437 Collamer Rd., East Syracuse, NY 13057-1031. TEL 315-703-7979, 800-334-1904, FAX 315-703-7988, http://www.dairybusiness.com. Ed. Hugo Varela Alvarez. Adv. contact Sal Gomez. B&W page USD 2,300, color page USD 3,080; trim 10.88 x 8.13. Circ: 15,500 (controlled).

LOUISIANA CATTLEMAN. see *AGRICULTURE—Poultry And Livestock*

637 FIN ISSN 0782-2383
M T. MEJERITIDSKRIFT FOER FINLANDS SVENSKBYGD. Text in Swedish. 1939. 4/yr. adv. bk.rev. **Document type:** *Magazine, Trade.*
Formerly (until 1980): Mejeritidskrift foer Finlands Svenskbygd (0355-0532)
Related titles: ♦ Issued with: L o A. ISSN 0355-0680.
Indexed: DSA, FS&TA, WAE&RSA.
Published by: Svenska Lantbruksproducenternas Centralfoerbund/Central Union of Swedish-Speaking Agricultural Producers in Finland, Fredriksgatan 61 A 34, Helsinki, 00100, Finland. TEL 358-9-5860460, FAX 358-9-6941358, http://www.slc.fi.

637 DNK ISSN 0024-9645
MAELKERITIDENDE. Text in Danish; Text occasionally in English. 1888. bi-w. DKK 1,038 domestic; DKK 954 foreign (effective 2005). adv. **Document type:** *Newsletter, Trade.* **Description:** Focuses on the latest developments within dairy production, processing and related fields.
Indexed: DSA, FS&TA, NutrAb, RM&VM, WAE&RSA.
—CCC.
Published by: (Foreningen af Mejeriledere og Funktionaerer/Danish Dairy Managers Association), Dansk Mejeriingenioer Forening/Danish Dairy Engineers Association, Det Gamle Mejeri, Landbrugsvej 65, Odense S, 5620, Denmark. TEL 45-66-124025, FAX 45-66-144026, info@maelkeritidende.dk, dmf@maelkeritidende.dk, http://www.maelkeritidende.dk. Ed., Adv. contact K. Mark Christensen. page DKK 11,200; trim 188 x 278. Circ: 2,000 (controlled). **Co-publisher:** Foreningen af Mejeriledere og Funktionaerer/Danish Dairy Managers Association.

MARKET LEADERS IN THE WORLD DAIRY INDUSTRY. see *FOOD AND FOOD INDUSTRIES—Grocery Trade*

637 AUS
MARKET REVIEW. Text in English. bi-m. **Document type:** *Bulletin, Trade.* **Description:** Dedicated to the Australian dairy market and dairy production.
Media: Online - full content.
Published by: Dairy Australia, Level 5, IBM Tower, 60 City Rd, Southbank, VIC 3006, Australia. TEL 61-3-96943777, FAX 61-3-96943733, http://www.dairyaustralia.com.au.

637 USA
MARSCHALL ITALIAN & SPECIALITY CHEESE SEMINAR. PROCEEDINGS. Text in English. irreg.
—BLDSC (6847.263900).
Published by: Rhodia, Inc, 2802 Walton Commons West, Madison, WI 53718. TEL 608-231-1888, FAX 608-231-2443.

637 NOR ISSN 0025-8776
MEIERIPOSTEN. Text in Norwegian; Summaries in English. 1914. 11/yr. NOK 360 domestic; NOK 480 foreign (effective 2000). adv. bk.rev. back issues avail. **Document type:** *Journal, Trade.* **Description:** Focuses on developments in technology, techniques and economics in the dairy and ice cream industries as well as related food industries both locally and abroad.
Indexed: AEA, AgBio, AnBrAb, ChemAb, DSA, FS&TA, IndVet, NutrAb, PST, PotatoAb, RRTA, SIA, VetBull, WAE&RSA.
—BLDSC (5536.350000).
Published by: Norske Mejerifolks Landsforening/Norwegian Association of Dairy Managers, Postboks 398, Sentrum, Oslo, 0103, Norway. TEL 47-22-42-25-20, FAX 47-22-41-38-01, meieriposten.nml@oslo.online.no. Ed., R&P Steinar Husby. Adv. contact Randi Smith. B&W page NOK 4,200, color page NOK 8,040; trim 185 x 260. Circ: 2,168.

637 DNK ISSN 0107-7635
MEJERISTEN. Text in Danish. 1932. 10/yr. adv.
Published by: Dansk Mejeristforbund, Rosenvangsalle 235, Hojbjerg, 8270, Denmark. Circ: 3,100.

637.1 BEL ISSN 1376-7232
MELKVEEBEDRIJF. Text in Dutch. 2000. 10/yr. EUR 42 (effective 2004). **Document type:** *Magazine, Trade.*
Published by: Rekad N.V., Geelsweg 47A, Herentals, 2200, Belgium. TEL 32-14-286070, FAX 32-14-214774, info@rekad.be, http://rekad.be.

637 MEX
MEXICO HOLSTEIN. Text in Spanish. 1969. m. **Document type:** *Trade.*
Published by: (Mexican Holstein Breeders Association), Editorial Ano Dos Mil, S.A., Indianapolis 70, Mexico City, DF 03810, Mexico. TEL 52-5-255-1833. adv.: B&W page USD 780, color page USD 1,115; trim 10.63 x 8.25. Circ: 6,500.

637 USA
MICHIGAN DAIRY LINE. Text in English. 1987. q. free. **Document type:** *Newsletter.*
Published by: Michigan Dairy Council, 2163 Jolly Rd, Okemos, MI 48864-3961. TEL 517-349-8480, FAX 517-349-6218. Ed. Kimberley Stapelfeldt. Circ: 5,000.

631.12 USA ISSN 0026-2315
MICHIGAN MILK MESSENGER. Text in English. 1919. m. USD 5 to non-members; free to members (effective 2005). adv. illus.; mkt.; stat. **Document type:** *Magazine, Trade.* **Description:** News of the Michigan dairy industry. Reports on meetings, markets, and association developments.
Published by: Michigan Milk Producers Association, 41310 Bridge St, PO Box 8002, Novi, MI 48375-8002. TEL 248-474-6672, FAX 248-474-0924, http://www.mimilk.com. Ed. Mindy Pratt. Circ: 4,500 (paid and controlled).

637 USA ISSN 1087-7096
MIDWEST DAIRYBUSINESS. Text in English. 1996. m. USD 38.95 (effective 2005); free to qualified personnel. adv. reprints avail. **Document type:** *Magazine, Trade.* **Description:** Provides Midwestern milk producers with business and management information to enhance profitability.
Published by: DairyBusiness Communications (Subsidiary of: Multi Ag Media LLC), 6437 Collamer Rd., East Syracuse, NY 13057-1031. FAX 315-703-7988, dmorneau@dairybusiness.com, http://www.dairybusiness.com/midwest/. Ed. Dave Natzke. adv.: B&W page USD 3,215, color page USD 4,300; trim 10.875 x 8.125. Circ: 26,500 (controlled).

MILCH - FETTWAREN - EIER - HANDEL. see *FOOD AND FOOD INDUSTRIES*

637.1 DEU ISSN 0176-5124
MILCH-MARKETING. Text in German. 1984. m. EUR 60 domestic; EUR 83 foreign; EUR 4 newsstand/cover (effective 2005). adv. back issues avail. **Document type:** *Magazine, Trade.*
Indexed: DSA, NutrAb, RRTA, RiceAb, WAE&RSA.
Published by: Buecker Fachverlag GmbH & Co. KG, Postfach 1363, Bad Breisig, 53492, Germany. TEL 49-2633-45400, FAX 49-2633-97415, redaktion@milch-marketing.de, http://www.milch-marketing.de. Ed. Stephan Camphausen. adv.: page EUR 4,810; trim 185 x 250. Circ: 8,580 (paid and controlled).

637 DEU ISSN 0343-0200
DIE MILCHPRAXIS UND RINDERMAST. Text in German. 1964. 4/yr. EUR 5.80 newsstand/cover (effective 2005). adv. bk.rev. charts; illus. **Document type:** *Magazine, Trade.*
Formerly: Milch-Praxis (0026-3753)
Indexed: AEA, AnBrAb, DSA, HelmAb, HerbAb, IndVet, MaizeAb, NutrAb, PHN&I, RefZh, S&F, SIA, SoyAb, TriticAb, VetBull, WAE&RSA, WeedAb.
—BLDSC (5766.450000), IE, ingenta. **CCC.**
Published by: Verlag Th. Mann, Nordring 10, Gelsenkirchen, 45894, Germany. TEL 49-209-93040, FAX 49-209-9304185, info@th-mann.de, http://www.th-mann.de. Eds. Guenter Weiss, Dr. Heinz Peter Puetz. Adv. contact Richard Heineke. B&W page EUR 2,130, color page EUR 3,360; trim 186 x 270. Circ: 23,785 (paid and controlled).

637.1 DEU ISSN 0933-0682
MILCHSTRASSE; die Kundenzeitschrift fuer Kaese, Butter und Milchfrischprodukte. Text in German. 1987. bi-m. **Document type:** *Magazine, Trade.*
Published by: Buecker Fachverlag GmbH & Co. KG, Postfach 1363, Bad Breisig, 53492, Germany. TEL 49-2633-45400, FAX 49-2633-97415, bueckerverlag@t-online.de, redaktion@milch-marketing.de, http://www.milch-marketing.de.

631 658.8 GBR ISSN 0309-0809
MILK BULLETIN. Text in English. 1954. m. GBP 9.25. adv. charts; mkt.; stat. **Document type:** *Bulletin.*
Formerly: S.M.M.B. Bulletin (0036-1666)
Indexed: DSA.
Published by: Scottish Milk Marketing Board, Underwood Rd, Paisley, Renfrewshire PA3 1TJ, United Kingdom. FAX 041-889-1225. Circ: 3,200 (controlled).

637.1 USA ISSN 0740-9222
HD9275.U8
MILK FACTS. Text in English. 1938. a. USD 35 (effective 1997 & 1998). adv. **Document type:** *Trade.* **Description:** Reference data on the production and consumption of dairy products, and on the economics of the dairy industry.
Published by: Milk Industry Foundation, 1250 H St, N W, Washington, DC 20005. FAX 202-331-7820. Ed., R&P, Adv. contact Susan Kjellqvist.

637 GBR
HD9282.G69 CODEN: MIINAV
MILK INDUSTRY INTERNATIONAL; the journal for manufacturers, processors and retailers. Text in English. 1920. m. GBP 60 in United Kingdom; GBP 75 rest of world (effective 2001). adv. bk.rev. charts; illus.; stat. **Document type:** *Trade.*
Formerly (until 1995): Milk Industry (0026-4172)
Related titles: Microform ed.: (from PQC).
Indexed: AEA, CurCont, CurPA, DSA, FS&TA, IPackAb, PST, RRTA, RefZh, WAE&RSA.
—BLDSC (5770.000000), CISTI.
Published by: National Dairymen's Association, 19 Cornwall Terr, London, NW1 4QP, United Kingdom. TEL 0171-935-4562, FAX 0171-486-7244. Ed. Elizabeth Grindlay. Adv. contact Nigel Stephens. Circ: 5,100.

338.1771 658 USA
MILK MARKET ADMINISTRATOR'S BULLETIN. Text in English. m. free (effective 2005). **Document type:** *Newsletter, Government.*
Formerly (until 2005): Market Administrator's Bulletin
Published by: U.S. Department of Agriculture, Milk Market Administrator, 1325 Industrial Pkwy N, Brunswick, OH 44212. TEL 330-225-4758, FAX 330-220-6675, http://www.fmmaclev.com. Ed. William Pollock. Circ: 4,000 (free).

637.1 GBR ISSN 0950-3730
MILK PRODUCTS. Text in English. 10/yr. GBP 568 domestic; GBP 607 in Europe; GBP 666 elsewhere (effective 2005). charts; stat. **Document type:** *Newsletter, Trade.* **Description:** Regular report containing the latest European and international statistics on trade, production and prices for milk, butter and cheese.
Published by: Agra Europe (London) Ltd. (Subsidiary of: T & F Informa plc), 80 Calverley Rd, Tunbridge Wells, Kent TN1 2UN, United Kingdom. TEL 44-1892-533813, FAX 44-1892-544895, marketing@agra-net.com, http://www.agra-net.com.

636.2142 USA
MINNESOTA DAIRY PLANTS. Text in English. 1910. biennial. free. **Document type:** *Government.*
Published by: Department of Agriculture, Dairy and Food Inspection Division, 90 W Plato Blvd, St Paul, MN 55107. TEL 651-297-2132, 651-296-1592. Ed. Sandra Dunn. Circ: 400.

637.1 HRV ISSN 0351-9104
MLJEKARSKI LIST. Text in Croatian. 1962. m. EUR 20 foreign (effective 2005). **Document type:** *Journal, Academic/Scholarly.*
Published by: Hrvatska Mljekarska Udruga/Croatian Dairy Society, Ilica 31-III, Zagreb, 10000, Croatia. TEL 385-1-4812410, hmu@zg.htnet.hr, http://www.hmu.hr/Djelatnost_HMU_files/Mljekarski_list.htm. Circ: 43,000.

637 HRV ISSN 0026-704X
CODEN: MLJEAU
MLJEKARSTVO; list za unapredenje mljekarstva. Text in Croatian; Summaries in English. 1950. m. EUR 48 foreign (effective 2005). adv. bk.rev. charts; illus.; tr.lit. index. back issues avail. **Document type:** *Journal, Academic/Scholarly.* **Description:** Covers topics in the field of milk and milk products technology.
Related titles: Fax ed.
Indexed: AEA, AnBrAb, CIN, ChemAb, ChemTitl, DSA, FS&TA, HerbAb, HortAb, IndVet, MaizeAb, NutrAb, PBA, PN&I, RM&VM, RPP, RRTA, SIA, SoyAb, TriticAb, VetBull, WAE&RSA.
—BLDSC (5879.740000), CASDDS, IE, ingenta.
Published by: Hrvatska Mljekarska Udruga/Croatian Dairy Society, Ilica 31-III, Zagreb, 10000, Croatia. hmu@zg.htnet.hr, http://www.hmu.hr/Djelatnost_HMU_files/Mljekarstvo.htm. Ed. Ljubica Tratnik. R&P Vera Volaric. Circ: 600. **Co-sponsor:** Ministarstvo Znanosti i Tehnologije Republike Hrvatske.

637 DEU ISSN 0043-2512
DIE MOLKEREI-ZEITUNG WELT DER MILCH; Fachzeitschrift fuer die europaeische Milch- und Nahrungsmittelindustrie. Text in German. 1946. fortn. adv. illus. **Document type:** *Journal, Trade.*
Indexed: AEA, AnBrAb, DSA, FS&TA, HortAb, IndVet, NutrAb, RRTA, SIA, WAE&RSA.
—BLDSC (5901.200000), IE, ingenta.
Published by: Wemcard Medien, Friedrich-Ebert-Str 2, Sibbesse, 31079, Germany. TEL 49-5065-90890, FAX 49-5065-908966, info@wemcard.de, http://www.wemcard.de. adv.: color page EUR 1,500; trim 190 x 245. Circ: 2,600 (paid).

637 RUS ISSN 1019-8946
CODEN: MOPRAI
➤ **MOLOCHNAYA PROMYSHLENNOST'.** Text in Russian. 1988. 8/yr. USD 100. bk.rev. bibl.; illus. index. **Document type:** *Academic/Scholarly.*
Supersedes in part (in 1992): Molochnaya i Myasnaya Promyshlennost' (0235-2575); Formed by the merger of (1934-1988): Molochnaya Promyshlennost' (0026-9026); (1940-1988): Myasnaya Industriya S.S.S.R. (0027-5492)
Related titles: Microfiche ed.: (from EVP).
Indexed: AgBio, BiolAb, ChemAb, DSA, FS&TA, NutrAb, PST, RASB, RRTA, RefZh, SIA, SoyAb, WAE&RSA.
—BLDSC (0116.000000), CASDDS, CINDOC, CISTI, East View, Linda Hall.
Address: Sadovaya-Spasskaya 18, Moscow, 107807, Russian Federation. TEL 7-095-2072050, FAX 7-095-2072870, noreditor@rosnet.rosmailcom. Ed. Tat'yana A Kuznetsova. **US dist. addr.:** East View Information Services, 3020 Harbor Ln. N., Minneapolis, MN 55447. TEL 612-550-0961.

➤ **MONTHLY PRICE REVIEW.** see *FOOD AND FOOD INDUSTRIES*

➤ **THE MOOSLETTER.** see *HOBBIES*

➤ **NAS CHOV**; casopis pro zivocisnou vyrobu. see *AGRICULTURE—Poultry And Livestock*

636.2142 USA ISSN 0077-3255
NATIONAL ASSOCIATION OF ANIMAL BREEDERS. ANNUAL PROCEEDINGS. Text in English. 1952. a. USD 8.25 domestic; USD 12 foreign (effective 2000). **Document type:** *Proceedings.*
Published by: National Association of Animal Breeders, PO Box 1033, Columbia, MO 65205. TEL 573-445-4406, FAX 573-446-2279, naab-css@naab-css.org, http://www.naab-css.org. Ed. Gordon A Doak.

NATIONAL DAIRY COUNCIL. QUARTERLY REVIEW. see *NUTRITION AND DIETETICS*

637 IND ISSN 0301-8407
NATIONAL DAIRY RESEARCH INSTITUTE. ANNUAL REPORT. Text in English. 1923. a. free. **Document type:** *Academic/Scholarly.*
Indexed: AnBrAb, BiolAb, DSA, FCA, FS&TA, HerbAb.
Published by: Indian Council of Agricultural Research, National Dairy Research Institute, Karnal, Haryana 132 001, India. TEL 91-184-252800, TELEX 0396-204-NDRI, ndri@x400.nicgw.nic.in. Ed. O S Tomer. Circ: 1,500.

637.1 USA ISSN 0271-9967
CODEN: AMNCDO
NATIONAL MASTITIS COUNCIL. ANNUAL MEETING PROCEEDINGS. Text in English. 1962. a. USD 19.95 to members; USD 24.95 to non-members (effective 2005). **Document type:** *Proceedings, Academic/Scholarly.*
Indexed: Agr.
—BLDSC (1087.853500), CISTI, IE, ingenta.
Published by: National Mastitis Council, 421 S 9 Mound Rd, Verona, WI 53593. TEL 608-848-4615, FAX 608-848-4671, anne@nmconline.org, nmc@nmconline.org, http://www.nmconline.org. Ed. Anne Saemen.

637.1 USA
NATIONAL MASTITIS COUNCIL. REGIONAL MEETING PROCEEDINGS. Text in English. a. USD 24.95 to members; USD 29.95 to non-members (effective 2002).
Related titles: CD-ROM ed.: USD 29.95 to members; USD 34.95 to non-members (effective 2002).
Published by: National Mastitis Council, 421 S 9 Mound Rd, Verona, WI 53593. TEL 608-848-4615, FAX 608-848-4671, nmc@nmconline.org, http://www.nmconline.org.

635.2142 UKR
➤ **NATSIONAL'NA AKADEMIYA NAUK UKRAINY. INSTYTUT TVARYNNYTSTVA. NAUKOVO-TEKHNICHNYI BIULETEN'**; mizhvidomchyi temetichnyi naukovyi zbirnik. Text in Ukrainian; Summaries in English, Russian. 1971. s-a. UAK 8 per issue (effective 2003). 150 p./no.; back issues avail. **Document type:** *Journal, Academic/Scholarly.* **Description:** Presents results of research in the fields of dairy and beef cattle breeding, nutrition, feeding and housing, for animal scientists.
Formerly: Molochno-m'yasne Skotarstvo (0544-7453)
Indexed: AnBrAb.
Published by: Natsional'na Akademiya Nauk Ukrainy, Instytut Tvarynnytstva, P-v Kulinichi, Kharkov, 312120, Ukraine. TEL 380-572-953181, FAX 380-572-953066. Ed. G M Kuznetsov. R&P V S Linnik. Circ: 200 (paid).

➤ **NAUTA/CATTLE.** see *AGRICULTURE—Poultry And Livestock*

637 USA ISSN 0279-8611
NEW YORK HOLSTEIN NEWS. Text in English. 1946. m. USD 25 domestic; USD 35 in Canada & Mexico; USD 55 elsewhere (effective 2005). adv. index. back issues avail.; reprint service avail. from PQC. **Document type:** *Magazine, Trade.* **Description:** Provides milk production records, cattle show results, and merchandising information for member herds throughout in New York State.
Formerly: New York Holstein Friesian News (0028-727X)
Published by: New York Holstein Association, 957 Mitchell St., Ithaca, NY 14851. TEL 607-273-7591, FAX 607-273-7612, nyhadame@clarityconnect.com, http://www.nyholsteins.com/ny_holstein_news.htm. Ed. Jason Pullis. Pub. William Fought. Circ: 3,500 (controlled).

637 USA ISSN 0732-9121
SF232.N7
NEW YORK STATE DAIRY STATISTICS. Text in English. a. free. **Document type:** *Bulletin, Government.*
Former titles: New York Dairy Statistics; New York Crop Reporting Service. Statistics Relative to the Dairy Industry in New York State (0077-8974)
Published by: (Division of Dairy Industry Services), Department of Agriculture and Markets, 1 Winner s Cir, Albany, NY 12235-0001. Circ: 1,800.

637 NZL ISSN 0111-915X
NEW ZEALAND DAIRY EXPORTER. Text in English. 1925. m. NZD 35 domestic; NZD 110 foreign (effective 2001). adv. bk.rev. index. **Document type:** *Trade.* **Description:** Spans the industry with stories on dairy farm production, research, manufacturing, and marketing.
Indexed: DSA, INZP.
—CISTI. **CCC.**
Published by: New Zealand Dairy Exporter Ltd., PO Box 299, Wellington, New Zealand. TEL 64-4-990300, FAX 64-4-4990330, enquiries@dairymag.co.nz. Ed. Lance McEldowney. Adv. contact Corrie Cook TEL 64-9-837-5367. Circ: 22,352.

338.1771 USA
NEWS FOR DAIRY CO-OPS. Text in English. 1916. bi-w. free domestic to members; USD 50 domestic to non-members (effective 2005). **Document type:** *Newsletter, Trade.*
Published by: National Milk Producers Federation, 2101 Wilson Blvd, Ste 400, Arlington, VA 22201. TEL 703-243-6111, FAX 703-841-9328, cgalen@nmpf.org, http://www.nmpf.org. Ed. Christopher Galen. Circ: 3,000 (controlled and free).

637 DEU ISSN 0724-3227
NORDDEUTSCHER MOLKEREI- UND KAESEREI-ADRESSKALENDER; Milchwirtschaft zum Nachschlagen. Text in German. 1936. a. EUR 30.68 (effective 2002). back issues avail. **Document type:** *Directory, Trade.*
Published by: V V GmbH - Volkswirtschaftlicher Verlag, Kederbacherstr 50, Munich, 81377, Germany. TEL 49-89-7141013, FAX 49-89-7141013, vv-verlag@t-online.de.

A

A

353.9 USA ISSN 0091-9446
HD9282.U5
NORTH DAKOTA. MILK STABILIZATION BOARD. ANNUAL REPORT OF ADMINISTRATIVE ACTIVITIES. Text in English. 1968. a.
Published by: North Dakota Milk Stabilization Board, 206 1/2 N 6th St, Rm 5, Bismarck, ND 58501. TEL 701-224-2988. Circ: 300.

636 USA
NORTHEAST DAIRY BUSINESS. Text in English. m. USD 38.95 domestic; free domestic to qualified personnel (effective 2005). **Document type:** *Magazine, Trade.*
Published by: Multi Ag Media LLC, 6437 Collamer Rd., East Syracuse, NY 13052-1031. http://www.dairybusiness.com. Ed. Eleanor Jacobs.

637 JPN ISSN 0910-7878
NYUGIKYO SHIRYO/JAPAN DAIRY TECHNICAL ASSOCIATION. BULLETIN. Text in Japanese. 1951. bi-m. back issues avail.
Formerly (until 1967): Gikyo Shiryo - Japan Dairy Products Technical Association. Bulletin (0910-786X)
Published by: Nihon Nyugyo Gijutsu Kyokai, 14-19 Kudan-Kita 1-chome, Chiyoda-ku, Tokyo, 102-0073, Japan. TEL 03-264-1921. Circ: 750.

636.2142 AUT
OESTERREICHISCHE MILCH- UND LEBENSMITTELWIRTSCHAFT. Text in German. 1946. s-m. **Document type:** *Trade.*
Formerly: Oesterreichische Milchwirtschaft (0369-786X)
Indexed: DSA, FS&TA, NutrAb, PN&I, RRTA, SoyAb, WAE&RSA.
Published by: (Milchwirtschaftsfonds), Oesterreichischer Agrarverlag GmbH, Achauer Str 49a, Leopoldsdorf, N 2333, Austria. TEL 43-2243-333006, FAX 43-2243-3330056, redaktion3@agrarverlag.co.at, http://www.agrarverlag.co.at, http://www.agrarverlag.at. Ed. Wilhelm Sadofsky. Circ: 2,000.

636.2142 USA ISSN 0899-4862
OHIO NEWS. Variant title: Holstein News. Text in English. 1925. bi-m. USD 15; free to members (effective 2005). adv. bk.rev. 60 p./no.; **Document type:** *Magazine, Trade.*
Formerly: Ohio Holstein News (0199-7580)
—Linda Hall.
Published by: Ohio Holstein Association, Inc., 1375 Heyl Rd, Box 479, Wooster, OH 44691. TEL 330-264-9088, FAX 330-263-1653, oholstein@bright.net. Ed., R&P, Adv. contact Esther Welch. B&W page USD 190, color page USD 540. Circ: 2,400 (paid and free).

637 CAN ISSN 1192-800X
ONTARIO DAIRY FARMER MAGAZINE. Text in English. 6/yr. **Document type:** *Trade.* **Description:** Dairy farming business news for Ontario.
Former titles: Dairy Farmer Quarterly Magazine (1182-8900); Ontario Dairy Farmer (0832-5162)
—CISTI.
Published by: Bowes Publishers Ltd., PO Box 7400, London, ON N5Y 4X3, Canada. TEL 519-473-0010, FAX 519-473-2256. Ed. Paul Mahon. Pub. Mervyn J Hawkins.

637 CAN ISSN 0030-3038
ONTARIO MILK PRODUCER. Text and summaries in English, French. 1925. m. CND 25.68; CND 36 foreign. adv. mkt.
—CISTI, Linda Hall.
Published by: Ontario Milk Marketing Board, 6780 Campobello Rd, Mississauga, ON L5N 2L8, Canada. TEL 905-821-8970, FAX 905-821-3160. Ed. Bill Dimmick. Adv. contact Bob Mercer. Circ: 14,000.

P L M. (Production Laitiere Moderne) see *AGRICULTURE—Poultry And Livestock*

637 ITA
PARMIGIANO-REGGIANO. Text in Italian. 1971. s-a. free. adv.
Published by: Consorzio Formaggio Parmigiano-Reggiano, Via Kennedy, 18, Reggio Emilia, RE 42100, Italy. Ed. Luigi Verrini. Circ: 13,000.

PASTICCERIA INTERNAZIONALE. see *FOOD AND FOOD INDUSTRIES—Bakers And Confectioners*

637 CUB ISSN 0258-5987
PASTOS Y FORRAJES. Text in Spanish; Summaries in English, Spanish. 1978. 3/yr. USD 18 in the Americas; USD 20 in Europe. **Description:** Provides articles and research for professionals in the field of agriculture.
Indexed: AEA, AgrForAb, CPA, DSA, FCA, ForAb, HerbAb, HortAb, NutrAb, OrnHort, PBA, PGegResA, PGrRegA, PN&I, RDA, RPP, RevApplEntom, RiceAb, S&F, SIA, SeedAb, WAE&RSA, WeedAb.
Published by: (Estacion Experimental de Pastos y Forrajes "Indio Hatuey"), Ediciones Cubanas, Obispo No. 527, Apdo. 605, Havana, Cuba. TEL 32-5556-60.

637.1 SWE ISSN 1403-9842
PEJLING FRAAN SVENSK MJOELK. Text in Swedish. 1997. 4/yr. SEK 200 (effective 2001). adv. **Document type:** *Magazine, Trade.*
Formerly (until 1998): Pejling fraan Mejerierna (1403-0357)
Published by: Svensk Mjoelk AB/Swedish Dairy Association, Torsgatan 14, Stockholm, 10546, Sweden. TEL 46-771-191900, FAX 46-8-218363, info@svenskmjolk.se, http://www.svenskmjolk.se. Ed. Magnus Jansson. Adv. contact Lena Hultman. B&W page SEK 10,200, color page SEK 14,900; trim 220 x 246. Circ: 4,000.

POTRAVINARSKE AKTUALITY. MLEKARENSKY PRUMYSL. see *FOOD AND FOOD INDUSTRIES*

637.1 SCG ISSN 0353-6564
➤ **PREHRAMBENA INDUSTRIJA;** casopis za proizvodnju, tehnologiju, bioinzenjerstvo i marketing. Text in Serbian. 1990. a. USD 20 (effective 2004). **Document type:** *Journal, Academic/Scholarly.*
Indexed: RefZh.
Published by: Univerzitet u Novom Sadu, Tehnoloski Fakultet, Zavod za Tehnologiju Zita i Brasna/University in Novy Sad, Institut for Cereal and Flour Technology, Bul Cara Lazara 1, Novi Sad, 21000. TEL 381-21-350133, FAX 381-21-450413, nscereal@eunet.yu. Ed., R&P, Adv. contact Marijana Caric. Circ: 300 (paid and controlled).

637.1 GBR ISSN 0141-223X
PRESERVED MILK. Text in English. 1964. 10/yr. GBP 590 domestic; GBP 623 in Europe; GBP 696 elsewhere (effective 2005). back issues avail. **Document type:** *Newsletter, Trade.* **Description:** Regular report containing the latest European and international statistics on trade, production and prices for skim and whole milk powder, casein, whey and condensed milk.
Published by: Agra Europe (London) Ltd. (Subsidiary of: T & F Informa plc), 80 Calverley Rd, Tunbridge Wells, Kent TN1 2UN, United Kingdom. TEL 44-1892-533813, FAX 44-1892-544895, marketing@agra-net.com, http://www.agra-net.com. Ed. Guy Faulkner.

636.2142 FRA ISSN 1161-2665
LA PRIM HOLSTEIN. Text in French. 1946. q. adv. stat.
Former titles (until 1990): Francaise Frisonne (0240-0154); Francaise Frisonne Pied Noire (0046-4872)
Published by: Unite Nationale de Selection et de Promotion de la Race Bovine Prim Holstein, Le Montsoreau, St. Sylvain d'Anjou, 49480, France. FAX 33-2-41432396. Ed. Jacques Boully. Circ: 15,000.

637 FRA
PROCESS ALIMENTAIRE; le mensuel des techniques laitieres et alimentaires. Text in French. 1945. m. EUR 110 domestic; EUR 163 foreign (effective 2004). adv. bibl.; illus.; tr.lit. index. **Document type:** *Magazine, Trade.* **Description:** Deals with the dairy industry and the various branches technically or economically connected to it.
Former titles: Process Magazine (0998-6650); (until 1989): Technique Laitiere et Marketing (0295-6268); (until 1985): Technique Laitiere (0040-1242)
Indexed: AEA, BiolAb, DSA, FS&TA, HortAb, IndVet, NutrAb, PN&I, PoultAb, RM&VM, RRTA, RefZh, SIA, TriticAb, WAE&RSA.
—BLDSC (6849.983150), IE, ingenta.
Published by: Editions du Boisbaudry, 13 Square du Chene Germain, Cesson Sevigne, 355773, France. TEL 33-2-99322121, http://www.editionsduboisbaudry.com. Ed. Francois Morel. Circ: 9,900.

637 CAN ISSN 0228-1686
PRODUCTEUR DE LAIT QUEBECOIS. Text in French. 1980. m. CND 15. back issues avail. **Document type:** *Trade.*
Indexed: AEA, AgBio, AnBrAb, DSA, FCA, HelmAb, IndVet, MaizeAb, NutrAb, RRTA, S&F, SoyAb, VetBull, WAE&RSA.
—BLDSC (6853.060550), CISTI, IE, ingenta.
Published by: Federation des Producteurs de Lait du Quebec, 555 bd Roland Therrien, Longueuil, PQ J4H 3Y9, Canada. TEL 514-679-0530, FAX 514-679-5436. Ed. Hugues Belzile. Circ: 18,000.

637 AUS ISSN 0033-6106
QUEENSLAND DAIRYFARMER. Text in English. 1946. m. AUD 50; AUD 55 foreign. adv. bk.rev. illus. **Document type:** *Newspaper.* **Description:** Latest developments in Queensland and Australian dairy industry and tropical dairy farming techniques.
Published by: Queensland Dairyfarmers Organization, Brisbane, PO Box 61, Brisbane Roma Street, QLD 4003, Australia. TEL 07-3236-2955, FAX 07-3236-2956, http://www.dairypage.com.au. Ed., R&P Anne Chamberlain TEL 61-7-38930359. Adv. contact Morris Lake. Circ: 2,500.

637 JPN ISSN 0388-001X
CODEN: JCDSDH
RAKUNO GAKUEN DAIGAKU KIYO. SHIZEN KAGAKU HEN/RAKUNO GAKUEN UNIVERSITY. JOURNAL: NATURAL SCIENCE. Text mainly in Japanese; Text occasionally in English, German; Summaries in English. 1961. a. per issue exchange basis (effective 2003). abstr. **Document type:** *Academic/Scholarly.*
Supersedes in part: College of Dairy Agriculture, Hokkaido. Journal (0069-570X)
Indexed: AEA, AgBio, Agrind, AnBrAb, BIOSIS Prev, BioCN&I, BiolAb, CIN, CPA, ChemAb, ChemTitl, CurCont, DSA, FCA, ForAb, HelmAb, HerbAb, HortAb, I&DA, IndVet, JPI, MaizeAb, NutrAb, PBA, PGegResA, PGrRegA, PHN&I, PN&I, PotatoAb, PoultAb, ProtozoAb, RM&VM, RPP, RefZh, RevApplEntom, S&F, SFA, SIA, SoyAb, TriticAb, VetBull, WAE&RSA, WildRev, ZooRec.
—BLDSC (4845.600000), CASDDS, CISTI.
Published by: Rakuno Gakuen Daigaku/Rakuno Gakuen University, 582-1 Bunkyodai Midori-cho, Ebetsu-shi, Hokkaido 069, Japan. Ed. Kazuo Horiuchi. Circ: 1,000.

637 USA
RECAP OF MILK RECEIPTS AND UTILIZATION IN MONTANA. Text in English. s-a. free. **Document type:** *Government.*
Formerly: Report of Milk Utilization in Montana (0080-1267)
Published by: Milk Control Bureau, 301 N lRoberts St, Rm 236, P O Box 202001, Helena, MT 59620-2001. TEL 406-444-2875, FAX 406-444-1432. Ed. Marlys Koontz. Circ: 560.

637.1 FRA ISSN 0995-6492
REUSSIR LAIT - ELEVAGE. Text in French. 1979. 11/yr. adv. **Document type:** *Newspaper.* **Description:** Technical and economical information about milk production.
Former titles (until 1989): Revue Laitiere Elevage (0992-6070); (until 1986): Revue Laitiere Francaise. Elevage (0756-2667); (until 1983): Reussir (0240-1541)
Published by: Editions Reussir, 19 quai de Juillet, CP 700, Caen, Cedex 9 1414, France. TEL 33-2-31357700, FAX 33-2-31357718, TELEX 632 322 F, m.jourdan@reussir.tm.fr. Eds. Marc Jourdan, Annick Conte. Pub., R&P Marc Jourdan. Adv. contact Jean Pierre Dumas. Circ: 69,000.

637.1 ARG ISSN 0327-5418
REVISTA ARGENTINA DE LACTOLOGIA. Text in Spanish. 1988. s-a. **Document type:** *Academic/Scholarly.*
Indexed: AgBio, DSA, FS&TA, NutrAb, WAE&RSA.
—BLDSC (7841.260000).
Published by: (Instituto de Lactologia Industrial), Universidad Nacional del Litoral Santa Fe, Facultad de Ingenieria Quimica, Santiago Del Estero, 2829, Santa Fe, 3000, Argentina. TEL 54-42-530302, FAX 54-42-571162, azalazar@fiqus.unl.edu.ar, http://www.unl.edu.ar/. Ed. Carlos A Zalazar. **Co-sponsor:** Centro Regional de Investigacion y Desarrollo de Santa Fe.

REVISTA BRASILEIRA DE ZOOTECNIA/BRAZILIAN JOURNAL OF ANIMAL SCIENCE. see *VETERINARY SCIENCE*

637 FRA ISSN 0035-3590
SF221 CODEN: RLAFA9
REVUE LAITIERE FRANCAISE. Text in French. 1876. 10/yr. adv. bk.rev. bibl.; charts; illus.; stat. index. **Document type:** *Newspaper.* **Description:** Focuses on the dairy industry: process, research, companies, economy, milk products and their market.
Incorporating: Industrie Laitiere
Indexed: DSA, FS&TA, HerbAb, IndVet, NutrAb, PGegResA, PN&I, PoultAb, RDA, RefZh, SIA, WAE&RSA.
Published by: (Societe des Editions Laitieres Francaises), Editions Reussir, 19 quai de Juillet, CP 700, Caen, Cedex 9 1414, France. TEL 33-2-31357700, FAX 33-2-31357718, m.jourdan@reussir.tm.fr. Eds. Marc Jourdan, Rita Lemoine. Pub. Marc Jourdan. Adv. contact Jean Pierre Dumas. Circ: 4,000.

637 ITA ISSN 0392-3827
CODEN: RILAAS
RIVISTA DEL LATTE. Text in Italian. 1946. q. EUR 65 (effective 2005). adv. **Document type:** *Magazine, Trade.*
Indexed: DSA, FS&TA.
—CASDDS.
Published by: (Associazione Licenziati Istituto Sperimentale di Caseificio), Promedia Publishing, Via Battista De Rolandi 15, Milan, 20156, Italy. TEL 39-02-324434, FAX 39-02-39257667, info@promediapublishing.it, http://www.promediapublishing.it. Ed. Elio Ligugnana. Circ: 1,000.

637.1 GBR
S W DAIRY FARMER. Text in English. a. GBP 22, USD 33; includes Dairy Farmer magazine. adv. bk.rev. back issues avail. **Document type:** *Trade.* **Description:** Covers all aspects of dairy farming.
Related titles: ♦ Supplement to: Dairy Farmer. ISSN 1475-6994.
Published by: Morgan-Grampian (Farming) Press Ltd. (Subsidiary of: Morgan-Grampian plc), Morgan-Grampian House, 30 Calderwood St, London, SE18 6QH, United Kingdom. TEL 01473-241122, FAX 01473-240501. Ed. Shirley Macmillan. Adv. contact John M Welford.

SAM. see *AGRICULTURE—Poultry And Livestock*

637 CHE ISSN 0370-9108
SCHWEIZERISCHE MILCHZEITUNG. Text in French, German. 1874. 52/yr. CHF 101 (effective 2003). adv. **Document type:** *Newspaper, Trade.*
Related titles: Supplement(s): Schweizerische Milchwirtschafteiche Forschung. ISSN 0255-9056.
Indexed: DSA, FS&TA, IndVet, NutrAb, RRTA.
—BLDSC (8118.800000).

Published by: Publi-Lactis AG, Gurtengasse 6, Bern, 3001, Switzerland. TEL 41-31-3122431, FAX 41-31-3122185, cliengme@milchzeitung.ch, info@milchzeitung.ch, http://www.milchzeitung.ch. Ed., R&P Claude Liengme. Adv. contact Kurt Flueckiger. B&W page CHF 4,752, color page CHF 5,802. Circ: 5,300.

637 ITA ISSN 0390-6361
CODEN: SLCAAF
➤ **SCIENZA E TECNICA LATTIERO-CASEARIA**; journal of the Italian Dairy Science Association. Text in English, Italian; Summaries in English. 1949. bi-m. EUR 78 domestic (effective 2003). bk.rev. abstr.; bibl.; charts; illus. cum.index. 80 p./no.; back issues avail. **Document type:** *Journal, Academic/Scholarly.* **Description:** Contributes to the diffusion of the studies and techniques related to the production, preservation, transportation and utilization of milk and its by-products.
Former titles (until 1960): Scienza e Tecnica del Latte (0390-007X); (until 1957): Bollettino dell"Associazione Italiana Tecnici del Latte (0390-637X); (until 1953): Scienza e Tecnica Lattiero-Casearia (0036-889X)
Indexed: AEA, AbHyg, AgBio, AgrForAb, AnBrAb, ChemAb, ChemTitl, DSA, FS&TA, IndVet, MaizeAb, NutrAb, RM&VM, RPP, RRTA, SIA, SoyAb, VetBull, WAE&RSA.
—BLDSC (8205.135000), CISTI, IE, ingenta.
Published by: Associazione Italiana Tecnici del Latte/Italian Dairy Science Association, Via Torelli 17, Parma, 43100, Italy. TEL 39-0521-902621, FAX 39-0521-902611, stlc@unipr.it. Ed. Primo Mariani. Circ: 1,700.

637 636 JPN ISSN 1341-691X
S18 CODEN: HDSKDJ
SEIBUTSU SEISANGAKU KENKYU/HIROSHIMA UNIVERSITY. FACULTY OF APPLIED BIOLOGICAL SCIENCE. JOURNAL. Text in English, Japanese. 1955. s-a. free. **Document type:** *Academic/Scholarly.*
Former titles (until 1992): Hiroshima Daigaku Seibutsu Seisan Gakubu Kiyo (0387-7647); (until 1978): Hiroshima Daigaku Suichikusan Gakubu Kiyo (0440-8756)
Indexed: AEA, ASFA, AgBio, AnBrAb, BIOSIS Prev, BioCN&I, BiolAb, DSA, ESPM, FS&TA, HortAb, I&DA, IndVet, NutrAb, PGrRegA, PHN&I, PN&I, RDA, RM&VM, RPP, RefZh, RiceAb, S&F, SFA, VetBull, WAE&RSA, WildRev, ZooRec.
—BLDSC (4743.410000), CISTI, Linda Hall.
Published by: Hiroshima University, Faculty of Applied Biological Science, 4-4 Kagamiyama 1-chome, Higashi-hiroshima, 739-8528, Japan. Circ: 1,000.

637 JPN ISSN 1340-2773
CODEN: SBRRE7
SNOW BRAND R & D REPORTS/YUKIJIRUSHI NYUGYO KENKYU HOKOKU. Text in Japanese; Summaries in English, Japanese. 1950. irreg. (approx. a.). free. **Document type:** *Academic/Scholarly.*
Formerly: Snow Brand Milk Products Company. Research Laboratory. Reports - Yukijirushi Nyugyo Kenkyujo Hokoku (0082-4763)
Indexed: AgBio, AnBrAb, CIN, ChemAb, ChemTitl, DSA, FS&TA, NutrAb, SoyAb, TriticAb.
—BLDSC (8313.992000), CASDDS.
Published by: Snow Brand Milk Products Co. Ltd./Yukijirushi Nyugyo K.K., R&D Planning Department, 1-1-2 Minami-Dai, Kawagoe-shi, Saitama-ken 350-1165, Japan. TEL 0492-42-8111, FAX 0492-46-5649. Ed., R&P Masayoshi Fukushima. Pub. Kazuo Ido. Circ: 400.

354.68 ZAF
SOUTH AFRICA. MILK BOARD. ANNUAL REPORT. Text in Afrikaans, English. 1946. a. free. **Document type:** *Government.*
Former titles (until 1995): South Africa. Dairy Board. Annual Report; South Africa. Dairy Control Board. Annual Report; South Africa. Milk Board. Annual Report
Published by: Milk Board/Melkraad, PO Box 1284, Pretoria, 0001, South Africa. TEL 27-12-8044800, FAX 21-12-8044811. Ed. J Hanekom. Circ: 1,000.

637 USA
SOUTHERN DAIRY✶. Text in English. 1992. bi-m. free. **Document type:** *Newspaper.*
Published by: Rural Press U S A, 1101 Spring Forest Rd, Ste 101, Raleigh, NC 27615. TEL 919-676-3276, 800-477-1737, FAX 919-676-9803. Ed. Amy Leslie. Pub. Jeff Tennant. adv.: B&W page USD 1,954. Circ: 16,000.

637 DEU ISSN 0724-3235
SUEDDEUTSCHER MOLKEREI- UND KAESEREI-ADRESSKALENDER; Milchwirtschaft zum Nachschlagen. Text in German. 1924. a. EUR 30.68 (effective 2002). back issues avail. **Document type:** *Directory, Trade.*
Published by: V V GmbH - Volkswirtschaftlicher Verlag, Kederbacherstr 50, Munich, 81377, Germany. TEL 49-89-7141013, FAX 49-89-7141013, vv-verlag@t-online.de.

SUIZO CARNE Y LECHE. see *AGRICULTURE—Poultry And Livestock*

SVERIGES LANTBRUKSUNIVERSITET. INSTITUTIONEN FOER HUSDJURSGENETIK - RAPPORT/SWEDISH UNIVERSITY OF AGRICULTURAL SCIENCES. DEPARTMENT OF ANIMAL BREEDING AND GENETICS - PUBLICATION. see *AGRICULTURE—Poultry And Livestock*

636.2142 USA ISSN 0190-4531
TECHNICAL CONFERENCE ON ARTIFICIAL INSEMINATION AND REPRODUCTION. PROCEEDINGS. Text in English. 1966. biennial. USD 18 domestic; USD 27 foreign (effective 2000). **Document type:** *Proceedings, Academic/Scholarly.*
Indexed: AnBrAb.
—BLDSC (6849.669000), CISTI.
Published by: National Association of Animal Breeders, PO Box 1033, Columbia, MO 65205. TEL 573-445-4406, FAX 573-446-2279, naab-css@naab-css.org, http://www.naab-css.org. Ed. Jere R. Mitchell.

637.1 FRA ISSN 1167-8550
TELEX LAITERIE -BOISSONS. Text in French. 11/yr. **Document type:** *Trade.*
Published by: Groupe Alain Thirion, 58 rue d'Alsace, Epinal, 88000, France. TEL 33-3-29291226, FAX 33-3-29354154. Ed. Alain Thirion. R&P Nathalie Berthier. Circ: 10,000.

637 JPN ISSN 0289-3096
TOCHIGI PREFECTURAL DAIRY EXPERIMENTAL INSTITUTE. BULLETIN. Text in Japanese. a. free. adv. back issues avail. **Document type:** *Bulletin.*
Published by: Tochigi Prefectural Dairy Experimental Institute, 298 Senbonmatsu, Nasu-gun, Nishinasuno-machi, Tochigi-ken 329-2747, Japan. Ed. Michihiro Sogama. Adv. contact Michihiro Sugama. Circ: 300.

636.234 USA
TRI-STATE DAIRY NUTRITION CONFERENCE. PROCEEDINGS. Text in English. a. USD 20 (effective 2004). back issues avail.
Indexed: Agr.
Published by: Tri-State Dairy Nutrition Conference, 214 Animal Science Bldg, 2029 Fyffe Rd, Columbus, OH 43210-1095. TEL 614-688-3143, http://www.ag.ohio-state.edu/~tristatedairy/proceeding.htm.

U.S. DEPARTMENT OF AGRICULTURE. NATIONAL AGRICULTURAL STATISTICS SERVICE. DAIRY PRODUCTS. see *AGRICULTURE—Abstracting, Bibliographies, Statistics*

U.S. DEPARTMENT OF AGRICULTURE. NATIONAL AGRICULTURAL STATISTICS SERVICE. MILK PRODUCTION. see *AGRICULTURE—Abstracting, Bibliographies, Statistics*

636.2142 DNK ISSN 1397-3010
UGENYT FRA MEJERIFORENINGEN. Text in Danish. 1973. w. DKK 375; DKK 325 foreign (effective 1999). bk.rev. **Document type:** *Trade.* **Description:** Information from the Danish Dairy Board for member dairy companies.
Formerly (until 1997): Mejeribrugets Uge-Nyt (0302-833X)
Published by: Mejeriforeningen/Danish Dairy Board, Frederiks Alle 22, Aarhus C, 8000, Denmark. TEL 45-87-31-20-00, FAX 45-87-31-20-01, ddb@mejeri.dk-. Eds. Eivind Hougaard, Henning Mortensen. Circ: 3,800.

UNITED CAPRINE NEWS. see *AGRICULTURE—Poultry And Livestock*

637.1 GBR
UNITED NEWS. Text in English. 1963. m. free. adv. bk.rev. **Document type:** *Magazine, Trade.* **Description:** Provides assistance on all aspects of dairy management in order to increase the efficient production of high quality raw milk.
Formerly (until 1995): Topics
Published by: (United Dairy Farmers Ltd.), Greer Publications, 5B Edgewater Business Park, Belfast Harbour Estate, Belfast, BT3 9JQ, United Kingdom. TEL 44-28-9078-3200, FAX 44-28-9078-3210, http://www.ulsterbusiness.com/greer. Ed. Kathy Jensen. Adv. contact Caroline McLean. Circ: 4,100.

636.2142 USA ISSN 0270-4153
WEEKLY INSIDERS DAIRY & EGG LETTER. Text in English. 1974. w. USD 190 (effective 2004). adv. stat. back issues avail. **Document type:** *Newsletter.* **Description:** Covers the storage stocks of whole, liquid and dried eggs, slaughter and consumption figures and retail selling prices as well as critical data on butter, margarine and cheese.
Published by: Urner Barry Publications, Inc., PO Box 389, Toms River, NJ 08754-0389. TEL 732-240-5330, FAX 732-341-0891, mail@urnerbarry.com, http://www.urnerbarry.com. Ed. Randy Pesciotta. Adv. contact Katie Hopkins. Circ: 100 (paid).

637 USA ISSN 1528-4360
SF232.W47
WESTERN DAIRY BUSINESS. Text in English. 1922. m. USD 38.95; free (effective 2005). adv. bk.rev. illus.; mkt.; stat. index. back issues avail.; reprints avail. **Document type:** *Magazine, Trade.* **Description:** For the large herd dairy farmer. Emphasizes news about dairy farmers and dairy farming, and related dairy industries. Covers state and national legislation, scientific and technical advances in milk production and marketing, feeding, and breeding.
Former titles (until 2000): Western Dairyman (1079-0578); (until 1995): The Dairyman (0011-572X)
—CISTI.
Published by: DairyBusiness Communications (Subsidiary of: Multi Ag Media LLC), 6437 Collamer Rd, East Syracuse, NY 13057-1031. TEL 315-703-7979, 800-439-3990, FAX 315-703-7988, mbise@dairybusiness.com, http://www.dairybusiness.com. Ed. Todd Fitchette. Pub. Joel Hastings. adv.: B&W page USD 3,215, color page USD 4,300; trim 10.88 x 8.13. Circ: 17,500 (paid and controlled).

637 CAN ISSN 1194-9511
WESTERN DAIRY FARMER QUARTERLY MAGAZINE. Text in English. 1991. q. CND 16 Western Canada; CND 25 Eastern and Central Canada; CND 30 in United States; CND 35 elsewhere (effective 2000). adv. **Document type:** *Trade.*
Published by: Bowes Publishers Ltd., 4504 61 Ave Leduc, Leduc, AB T4E 3Z1, Canada. TEL 403-986-2271, FAX 403-986-6397, wdfarmer@ccinet.ab.ca. Ed. Ken Nelson. Pub., Adv. contact Neil Sutcliffe. B&W page CND 971, color page CND 1,390; trim 10.75 x 8.13. Circ: 6,982.

637.1 664 GBR
THE WORLD MARKET FOR DAIRY PRODUCTS. Text in English. a., latest 2002, Feb. GBP 5,050 domestic; EUR 7,900 in Europe; USD 7,900 elsewhere (effective 2003). **Document type:** *Trade.*
Formerly: Dairy Products: A World Survey
Published by: Euromonitor, 60-61 Britton St, London, EC1 5UX, United Kingdom. TEL 44-20-7251-8024, FAX 44-20-7608-3149, info@euromonitor.com, http://www.euromonitor.com.

637 DEU
Z M P BILANZ DAIRY REVIEW. Text in German. a. **Document type:** *Bulletin, Trade.*
Published by: Zentrale Markt und Preisberichtstelle GmbH, Rochusstr 2, Bonn, 53123, Germany. TEL 49-228-9777173, FAX 49-228-9777179, info@zmp.de, http://www.zmp.de.

637.1 DEU ISSN 0344-9386
Z M P BILANZ MILCH. Text in German. a. **Document type:** *Bulletin, Trade.*
Former titles (until 1977): Agrarmaerkte Bundesrepublik Deutschland, EWG und Weltmarkt. Milch und Milcherzeugnisse (0343-9593); Agrarmaerkte in der Bundesrepublik und im Ausland. Milch, Butter, Kaese, Eier (0343-9577); Agrarmaerkte in der Bundesrepublik. Milch, Butter, Kaese, Eier (0400-762X); Which supersedes in part: Agrarmaerkte in der Bundesrepublik (0515-6823)
Related titles: CD-ROM ed.
Published by: Zentrale Markt und Preisberichtstelle GmbH, Rochusstr 2, Bonn, 53123, Germany. TEL 49-228-9777173, FAX 49-228-9777179, info@zmp.de, http://www.zmp.de.

637.1 DEU
Z M P MARKTBERICHT. EUROPAMARKT DAUERMILCH. Text in German. 10/yr. **Document type:** *Bulletin, Trade.*
Published by: Zentrale Markt und Preisberichtstelle GmbH, Rochusstr 2, Bonn, 53123, Germany. TEL 49-228-9777173, FAX 49-228-9777179, info@zmp.de, http://www.zmp.de.

637.1 DEU ISSN 0946-6517
Z M P MARKTBERICHT. EUROPAMARKT MILCH - BUTTER - KAESE. Text in German. 10/yr. **Document type:** *Bulletin, Trade.*
Published by: Zentrale Markt und Preisberichtstelle GmbH, Rochusstr 2, Bonn, 53123, Germany. TEL 49-228-9777173, FAX 49-228-9777179, info@zmp.de, http://www.zmp.de.

637.1 DEU
Z M P MARKTBERICHT. MILCH. Text in German. w. **Document type:** *Bulletin, Trade.*
Published by: Zentrale Markt und Preisberichtstelle GmbH, Rochusstr 2, Bonn, 53123, Germany. TEL 49-228-9777173, FAX 49-228-9777179, info@zmp.de, http://www.zmp.de.

637.1 DEU
Z M P MARKTBERICHT. MILCHWIRTSCHAFTLICHE VORSCHAU. Text in German. m. **Document type:** *Bulletin, Trade.*
Published by: Zentrale Markt und Preisberichtstelle GmbH, Rochusstr 2, Bonn, 53123, Germany. TEL 49-228-9777173, FAX 49-228-9777179, info@zmp.de, http://www.zmp.de.

637 NLD
ZELFKAZER. Text in Dutch. 1947. m.
Published by: Centraal Orgaan Zuivelcontrole, Afdeelingeeling Boerenkaas, PO Box 250, Leusden, 3830 EG, Netherlands. FAX 033-940674, TELEX 79386. Circ: 1,700.

637 CHN ISSN 1001-2230
ZHONGGUO RUPIN GONGYE/CHINA DAIRY INDUSTRY. Text in Chinese. bi-m. CNY 180; USD 270 foreign. **Description:** Covers dairy production, processing, equipment and technologies, research and development of various dairy products.
Related titles: Online - full text ed.: (from East View Information Services).
Indexed: AgBio, AnBrAb, DSA, FS&TA, HelmAb, HortAb, IndVet, MaizeAb, NutrAb, PHN&I, PoultAb, RA&MP, RM&VM, RiceAb, SIA, SoyAb, TDB, VetBull, WAE&RSA.

▼ new title ➤ refereed ✶ unverified ♦ full entry avail.

—BLDSC (3180.128700), IE, ingenta.
Published by: Heilongjiang Rupin Gongye Jishu Kaifa Zhongxin/Heilongjiang Dairy Industry Technical Development Center, 337 Xuefu Rd, Harbin, Heilongjiang 150069, China. TEL 86-451-6662740, FAX 86-451-6664742, srpzx@ems.hls.tc.edu.cn. Ed. Peng Liu. R&P Ya Xian Li TEL 86-451-662740. **Co-sponsor:** China Dairy Industry Association.

637 NLD ISSN 0044-5436
ZUIVELNIEUWS. Text in Dutch. 1968. w. adv. bk.rev. charts. **Document type:** *Newsletter, Trade.*
Formerly: Kaas
Published by: GemZu, Patrijsweg 58, Rijswijk (ZH), 2289 EX, Netherlands. TEL 31-70-3369450, FAX 31-70-3369454. Ed. M P J Poot. Circ: 950.

637 NLD ISSN 0165-8573
ZUIVELZICHT. Text in Dutch. 1906. 20/yr. EUR 89.75 domestic; EUR 111.95 foreign; EUR 50.70 to students (effective 2005). adv. bk.rev.
Indexed: DSA, FS&TA, KES, WAE&RSA.
—IE, Infotrieve.
Published by: (Dutch Dairy Association), Koninklijke BDU Uitgeverij BV, Postbus 67, Barneveld, 3770 AB, Netherlands. TEL 31-342-494264, FAX 31-342-494299, zuivelzicht@wxs.nl, http://www.zuivelzicht.nl. Ed. Tiny Brouwers. Adv. contact Hielke van der Werf TEL 31-342-494270. Circ: 3,500.

AGRICULTURE—Feed, Flour And Grain

A F I A SAFETYGRAM. see *AGRICULTURE—Poultry And Livestock*

633.2 AUS ISSN 1328-6544
A L F A LOTFEEDING. Text in English. 1995. bi-m. AUD 28.10 (effective 2005). adv. **Document type:** *Magazine, Trade.* **Description:** Covers the feeding, stock management, technology, design and equipment used in modern lotfeeding operations across Australia.
Published by: (Australian Lot Feeders' Association), Rural Press Ltd. (Subsidiary of: Agricultural Publishers Pty. Ltd.), 10 Sydenham St., PO Box 254, Moonee Ponds, VIC 3039, Australia. TEL 61-3-92870900, FAX 61-3-93705622, http://www.lotfeeding.com.au, http://www.ruralpress.com/. Ed. Jon Condon TEL 61-7-38268200. Adv. contact Donna Clarke. B&W page AUD 1,610, color page AUD 2,110; trim 200 x 275. Circ: 11,000 (paid).

AGRARISCH WEEKOVERZICHT. see *AGRICULTURE—Abstracting, Bibliographies, Statistics*

ALASKA WEEKLY CROP WEATHER. see *AGRICULTURE—Abstracting, Bibliographies, Statistics*

933 936 USA ISSN 1075-0487
ALIMENTOS BALANCEADOS PARA ANIMALES. Text in Spanish, English. 1994. bi-m. USD 42 domestic; USD 48 in Canada; USD 54 elsewhere (effective 2005). adv. **Document type:** *Magazine, Trade.* **Description:** For professionals in the Latin American poultry and livestock feed industry. Covers the latest international developments in feed technology, including advances in equipment, ingredients, and services. Provides market data on more than 20 countries.
Published by: Watt Publishing Co., 122 S Wesley Ave, Mt. Morris, IL 61054-1497. TEL 815-734-4171, FAX 815-734-5649, gill@wattmm.com, http://www.wattnet.com. Ed. Clayton Gill. Pub., R&P Clay Schreiber. adv.: B&W page USD 3,045, color page USD 3,785. Circ: 8,000 (controlled).

AMERICAN FEED INDUSTRY ASSOCIATION. ANNUAL AND SEMIANNUAL MEETINGS OF THE NUTRITION COUNCIL. PROCEEDINGS. see *AGRICULTURE—Poultry And Livestock*

AMERICAN FEED INDUSTRY ASSOCIATION. PRODUCTION SCHOOL PROCEEDINGS. see *AGRICULTURE—Poultry And Livestock*

633.2 NLD ISSN 0377-8401
CODEN: AFSTDH
➤ **ANIMAL FEED SCIENCE AND TECHNOLOGY.** Text in English. 1976. 28/yr. EUR 2,290 in Europe to institutions; JPY 304,500 in Japan to institutions; USD 2,561 elsewhere to institutions (effective 2006). adv. bk.rev. illus.; bibl. index. **Document type:** *Journal, Academic/Scholarly.* **Description:** Publishes scientific papers dealing with the production, composition and nutritive value of feeds for animals.
Related titles: Microform ed.: (from PQC); Online - full text ed.: (from EBSCO Publishing, Gale Group, IngentaConnect, ScienceDirect, Swets Information Services).
Indexed: ASCA, AbHyg, AgBio, Agr, AgrForAb, AnBrAb, BIOBASE, BIOSIS Prev, BioDAb, BiolAb, CIN, CPA, ChemAb, ChemTitl, CurCont, DSA, FCA, FPA, FS&TA, ForAb, HerbAb, HortAb, ISR, IndVet, Inspec, MEDLINE, MaizeAb, NutrAb, PBA, PGegResA, PHN&I, PN&I, PotatoAb, PoultAb, ProtozoAb, RA&MP, RM&VM, RPP, RefZh, RiceAb, S&F, S&MA, SCI, SFA, SIA, SeedAb, SoyAb, TDB, TOSA, TriticAb, VetBull, WAE&RSA, WeedAb, WildRev.
—BLDSC (0903.550000), CASDDS, CISTI, IDS, IE, Infotrieve, ingenta, Linda Hall. **CCC.**
Published by: Elsevier BV (Subsidiary of: Elsevier Science & Technology), Radarweg 29, Amsterdam, 1043 NX, Netherlands. TEL 31-20-4853911, FAX 31-20-4852457, nlinfo-f@elsevier.nl, http://www.elsevier.com/locate/anifeedsci, http://www.elsevier.nl. Eds. P H Robinson, P Uden, W J Wiseman.

664.72 FRA ISSN 0295-7868
ANNUAIRE DE LA MEUNERIE FRANCAISE. Text in French. a. EUR 78 (effective 2005). **Document type:** *Directory, Trade.*
Published by: Agence Generale de Publication, 32 Rue de la Bienfaisance, Paris, 75008, France. TEL 33-1-40268124, FAX 33-1-40263440, agp-gerverau@wanadoo.fr. Adv. contact Martine Tissier.

633.2 FRA ISSN 0752-7535
ANNUAIRE DE L'ALIMENTATION ANIMALE. Text in French. a. FRF 535 domestic; FRF 585 foreign. adv.
Related titles: English ed.: European Feed Directory.
Published by: (Groupe pour la Croissance et la Developpement International des Industries de l'Agro-Alimentaire, du Commerce et de l'Habitat), Gedeon Marketing Eurl, BP 16, Telgruc-sur-Mer, 29560, France. TEL 33-2-98273766, FAX 33-2-98273765. Ed., Pub., Adv. contact Jacques Fitamant. Circ: 2,500 (controlled).

ARCHIVOS DE ZOOTECNIA. see *AGRICULTURE—Poultry And Livestock*

633.18 COL ISSN 0120-2634
ARROZ EN LAS AMERICAS. Text in Spanish. 1979. s-a. free to qualified personnel. **Document type:** *Newsletter.* **Description:** Provides progress reports from rice researchers and developers in tropical countries, interchange of technical notes, and other news.
Indexed: AgBio, FCA, PBA, RiceAb, WAE&RSA, WeedAb.
Published by: (Unidad de Comunicaciones), Centro Internacional de Agricultura Tropical/International Center for Tropical Agriculture, Publications Unit, Apartado Aereo 6713, Cali, VALLE, Colombia. TEL 57-2-4450000, FAX 57-2-4450073, ciat@cgnet.com, http://www.ciat.cgair.org/. Ed. Luis R Sanint. Circ: 1,000 (controlled).

633.2 USA
ASSOCIATION OF AMERICAN FEED CONTROL OFFICIALS. OFFICIAL PUBLICATION. Text in English. 1942. a. USD 25 (effective 1997 & 1998). adv. back issues avail. **Document type:** *Trade.*
Published by: (Association of American Feed Control Officials, Inc.), American Feed Control Officials, c/o Georgia Dept of Agriculture, Capitol Sq, Atlanta, GA 30334. TEL 404-656-3637, FAX 404-656-9380. Ed., Pub., R&P, Adv. contact Paul Bachman TEL 612-297-7176. Circ: 2,500.

633.1 USA
ASSOCIATION OF OPERATIVE MILLERS. BULLETIN. Text in English. 1918. m. looseleaf. membership only. index. back issues avail. **Document type:** *Bulletin, Trade.*
Indexed: FS&TA.
—BLDSC (2401.900000).
Published by: Association of Operative Millers, 5001 College Blvd., Ste. 104, Leawood, KS 66211-1618. TEL 913-338-3377, FAX 913-338-3553. Ed. Harvey McCray. Circ: 1,800.

338.0029 USA ISSN 1549-8158
HD9057.A1
BAKING, SNACK DIRECTORY & BUYERS GUIDE. Text in English. a. USD 195 (effective 2000). **Document type:** *Directory.*
Formerly (until 1990): Baking Directory - Buyers Guide
Published by: Sosland Publishing Company, 4800 Main St, Ste 100, Kansas City, MO 64112-2513. TEL 816-756-1000, FAX 816-756-0494, bakesnack@sosland.com. Ed. Laurie Gorton.

633.1 DEU
BESCHREIBENDE SORTENLISTE GETREIDE, MAIS, OELFRUECHTE, LEGUMINOSEN UND HACKFRUECHTE. Text in German. a. **Document type:** *Directory, Government.*
Published by: (Germany, Federal Republic. Bundessortenamt), Landbuch Verlagsgesellschaft mbH, Kabelkamp 6, Hannover, 30179, Germany. TEL 49-511-67806-0, 49-511-67806-0, info@landbuch.de, http://www.landbuch.de. Circ: 6,000.

633.1 DEU
BESCHREIBENDE SORTENLISTE KARTOFFELN. Text in German. a. **Document type:** *Directory, Government.*
Published by: (Germany, Federal Republic. Bundessortenamt), Landbuch Verlagsgesellschaft mbH, Kabelkamp 6, Hannover, 30179, Germany. TEL 49-511-67806-0, FAX 49-511-67806220, info@landbuch.de, http://www.landbuch.de. Circ: 2,500.

633.2 POL ISSN 1231-8337
BIULETYN NAUKOWY PRZEMYSLU PASZOWEGO/BULLETIN SCIENTIFIC OF FEED INDUSTRY. Text in Polish. 1962. q.
Former titles (until 1994): Biuletyn Informacyjny Przemyslu Paszowego (0137-1568); (until 1966): Centrane Laboratorium Przemyslu Paszowego. Biuletyn Informacyjny (1230-4735)
Indexed: AEA, AgrLib, AnBrAb, DSA, HortAb, IndVet, NutrAb, PHN&I, PN&I, PotatoAb, PoultAb, RM&VM, SeedAb, SoyAb, TriticAb, VetBull.
—BLDSC (2105.429000).
Published by: Centralne Laboratorium Przemyslu Paszowego, Branzowy Osrodek Informacji Naukowej Technicznej i Ekonomicznej, Ul Chmielna 2, Lublin, 20079, Poland. TEL 48-81-24716, FAX 48-81-22564. Ed. Jadwiga Najda.

633.1 GBR
BOTANICAL DESCRIPTIONS OF CEREAL VARIETIES. Text in English. a. looseleaf. GBP 28 per vol. (effective 2003). charts; illus. **Document type:** *Bulletin, Trade.* **Description:** Provides highly detailed botanical descriptions of varieties of wheat, barley, oats, triticale, rye, and durum produced in the UK.
Published by: N I A B, Huntingdon Rd, Cambridge, CB3 0LE, United Kingdom. TEL 44-1223-276381, FAX 44-1223-342328, TELEX 817455-NIAB-G, info@niab.com, paul.nelson@niab.com, http://www.niab.com. Ed. Paul Nelson TEL 44-1223-342225.

BOVILOGISK; tidsskrift om kvaegbrug. see *AGRICULTURE—Dairying And Dairy Products*

BULLETIN OF GRAIN TECHNOLOGY. see *AGRICULTURE*

633 658.8 GBR ISSN 1473-1045
BUSINESS RATIO REPORT. COMPOUND ANIMAL FEEDSTUFFS. Text in English. 1980. a. GBP 275 (effective 2001). charts; stat. **Document type:** *Trade.*
Former titles (until 2001): Business Ratio. Compound Animal Feedstuffs (1469-7319); (until 2000): Business Ratio Plus. Compound Animal Feedstuffs (1359-4729); (until 1995): Business Ratio Plus: The Compound Animal Feedstuffs Industry (1357-7034); (until 1994): Business Ratio Report. Compound Animal Feedstuffs (0261-7692)
Published by: The Prospect Shop Ltd., Field House, 72 Oldfield Rd, Hampton, Middx TW12 2HQ, United Kingdom. TEL 44-20-8461-8730, 44-20-8481-8720, FAX 44-20-8783-1940, info@theprospectshop.co.uk.

641.33 MEX
C I M M Y T ECONOMICS WORKING PAPER. Text in English. 1978. irreg., latest no.01-02. USD 3 (effective 2002); free in developing nations. **Document type:** *Monographic series.* **Description:** Covers research in Asia, Africa, and Latin America on production economics, maize and wheat production trends, impacts of maize and wheat research, genetic diversity of maize and wheat, research resource allocation.
Indexed: PBA, PGegResA, RiceAb, S&F, SeedAb, TriticAb, WAE&RSA.
Published by: Centro International de Mejoramiento de Maiz y Trigo/International Maize and Wheat Improvement Center, Apartado Postal 6-641, Mexico City, DF 06600, Mexico. kcassaday@cgiar.org, http://www.cimmyt.org. R&P K Cassaday. Circ: 750.

CANADA. GRAIN COMMISSION. CORPORATE SERVICES. CANADIAN GRAIN EXPORTS. see *AGRICULTURE—Abstracting, Bibliographies, Statistics*

CANADA. GRAIN COMMISSION. CORPORATE SERVICES. EXPORTS OF CANADIAN GRAIN AND WHEAT FLOUR. see *AGRICULTURE—Abstracting, Bibliographies, Statistics*

CANADA GRAINS COUNCIL. STATISTICAL HANDBOOK. see *AGRICULTURE—Abstracting, Bibliographies, Statistics*

354.54097105 CAN ISSN 1701-0861
CANADIAN GRAIN COMMISSION. PERFORMANCE REPORT. Text in English. 2001. a. **Document type:** *Government.*
Media: Online - full content. **Related titles:** Print ed.: ISSN 1701-0853; French ed.: Commission Canadienne des Grains. Rapport sur le Rendement. ISSN 1701-087X.
Published by: Canadian Grain Commission, Corporate Services/Commission Canadienne des Grains, 600-303 Main St., Winnipeg, MB R3C 3G8, Canada. TEL 204-983-2770, 800-853-6705, FAX 204-983-2751, contact@cgc.ca, http://www.cgc.ca/.

CANADIAN GRAINS INDUSTRY STATISTICAL HANDBOOK. see *AGRICULTURE—Abstracting, Bibliographies, Statistics*

633 664 ITA
CEREAL POLICIES REVIEW. Text in Italian. 1991. a.
Indexed: TriticAb, WAE&RSA.
Published by: Food and Agriculture Organization of the United Nations, Sales and Marketing Group, Viale delle Terme di Caracalla, Rome, 00100, Italy. TEL 39-06-57054350, FAX 39-06-57053360.

633.1 HUN ISSN 0133-3720
CODEN: CRCMCL
CEREAL RESEARCH COMMUNICATIONS. Text and summaries in English. 1973. q. HUF 10,000 domestic; USD 100 foreign (effective 2005). adv. bk.rev. 130 p./no. 1 cols./p.; back issues avail. **Document type:** *Journal, Academic/Scholarly.* **Description:** Covers breedings, genetics quality, physiology, pathology of cereal and oil crops. It is useful for research workers, university teachers and students.

Indexed: ASCA, AgBio, AgrForAb, BIOBASE, BIOSIS Prev, BiolAb, CIN, CPA, ChemAb, ChemTitl, CurCont, FCA, FS&TA, HerbAb, HortAb, I&DA, IABS, MaizeAb, NutrAb, PBA, PGegResA, PGrRegA, PHN&I, PlantSci, PotatoAb, RA&MP, RM&VM, RPP, RefZh, RevApplEntom, RiceAb, S&F, SIA, SeedAb, SoyAb, TriticAb, WeedAb.
—BLDSC (3120.008000), CASDDS, CISTI, IDS, IE, ingenta.
Published by: Gabonatermesztesi Kutato Kozhasznu Tarsasag/Cereal Research Non-Profit Company, PF 391, Szeged, 6701, Hungary. TEL 36-62-435235, FAX 36-62-420101, crc@gk-szeged.hu, http://www.gk-szeged.hu. Ed., R&P, Adv. contact Zoltan Kertesz. Pub. J Matuz. Circ: 540 (paid and controlled).

CEREALS AND OILSEEDS REVIEW. see *AGRICULTURE—Abstracting, Bibliographies, Statistics*

CHILE. INSTITUTO NACIONAL DE ESTADISTICAS. INDUSTRIA MOLINERA. TRIGO. see *AGRICULTURE—Abstracting, Bibliographies, Statistics*

664.7 USA
CHINA FEED, GRAIN AND OILSEED. Text in Chinese. s-a. adv. **Document type:** *Trade.* **Description:** Provides technical information in modern simplified Chinese to feed manufacturers, flour millers, and oil seed processors.
Published by: Watt Publishing Co., 122 S Wesley Ave, Mt. Morris, IL 61054-1497. TEL 815-734-4171, FAX 815-734-5649, http://www.wattnet.com. adv.: B&W page USD 6,640, color page USD 7,940. Circ: 6,000.

633.1 CHN ISSN 1005-4111
CHINESE RICE RESEARCH NEWSLETTER/ZHONGGUO SHUIDAO YANJIU TONGBAO. Text in English. 1990. q. USD 20 (effective 2002). **Document type:** *Newsletter, Academic/Scholarly.* **Description:** Provides information on Chinese rice in such areas as genetics, breeding methods, yield potential, grain quality, nutrition, farm machinery, and soils and fertilizer management.
Indexed: AEA, AgBio, BioCN&I, CPA, FCA, HortAb, I&DA, MaizeAb, NemAb, NutrAb, PBA, PGegResA, PGrRegA, PHN&I, PN&I, RPP, RevApplEntom, RiceAb, S&F, SeedAb, TriticAb, WAE&RSA, WeedAb.
—BLDSC (3181.072000).
Published by: Zhongguo Shuidao Yanjiusuo/China National Rice Research Institute, 359 Tiyuchang Lu, Hangzhou, Zhejiang 310006, China. TEL 86-571-63370480, FAX 86-571-63371745, sinorice@public.fy.hz.zj.cn, cjrs@fy.hz.zj.cn, http://www.cnrri.org. Ed. Xiyuan Liao. R&P Nantian Li.

633.18 CUB ISSN 0138-8789
CIENCIA Y TECNICA EN LA AGRICULTURA. SERIE: ARROZ. Abstracts and contents page in English. 1978. s-a. USD 14 in North America; USD 16 in Europe; USD 17 elsewhere.
Indexed: Agrind, FCA, HerbAb, RiceAb.
Published by: Centro de Informacion y Documentacion Agropecuario, Gaveta Postal 4149, Havana, 4, Cuba. **Dist. by:** Ediciones Cubanas, Obispo No. 527, Apdo. 605, Havana, Cuba.

633.2 CUB ISSN 0138-8533
CIENCIA Y TECNICA EN LA AGRICULTURA. SERIE: PASTOS Y FORRAJES. Text in Spanish; Abstracts and contents page in English. 1978. 2/yr. USD 14 in North America; USD 16 in Europe; USD 17 elsewhere.
Indexed: Agrind, DSA, FCA, HerbAb, HortAb, NutrAb, S&F, SeedAb, SoyAb.
Published by: Centro de Informacion y Documentacion Agropecuario, Gaveta Postal 4149, Havana, 4, Cuba. **Dist. by:** Ediciones Cubanas, Obispo No. 527, Apdo. 605, Havana, Cuba.

CIENCIA Y TECNICA EN LA AGRICULTURA. SERIE: VIANDAS TROPICALES. see *AGRICULTURE—Crop Production And Soil*

636.1 USA ISSN 0010-3101
COMMERCIAL REVIEW. Text in English. 1890. 3/m. USD 40 domestic; USD 45 foreign (effective 2005). adv. illus. 8 p./no. 2 cols./p.; **Document type:** *Magazine, Trade.* **Description:** Emphasizes on news coverage of the grain, feed, seed, fertilizer and garden supply milling industries of the Pacific Coast slopes. Covers export markets, domestic markets and crop estimates.
Formerly: Oregon Feed, Seed and Suppliers Association. Commercial Review
Published by: (Oregon Feed and Grain Association), Commercial Review, Inc., 2380 N W Roosevelt St, Portland, OR 97210-2323. TEL 503-226-2758, FAX 503-244-0947, 503-224-0947, haysmgmt@pipeline.com. Ed., Pub., Adv. contact Dennis Hays. B&W page USD 320, color page USD 495. Circ: 1,050 (paid and free).

633.18 CUB ISSN 0138-838X
CUBA. CENTRO DE INFORMACION Y DOCUMENTACION AGROPECUARIO. BOLETIN DE RESENAS. SERIE: ARROZ. Abstracts in English. 1974. irreg. per issue exchange basis. abstr.; stat.
Formerly: Cuba. Centro de Informacion y Divulgacion Agropecuario. Boletin de Resenas. Serie: Arroz
Indexed: Agrind.
Published by: Centro de Informacion y Documentacion Agropecuario, Gaveta Postal 4149, Havana, 4, Cuba. TEL 301672. **Dist. by:** Ediciones Cubanas, Obispo No. 461, Apdo. 605, Havana, Cuba.

633.2 CUB ISSN 0138-7839
CUBA. CENTRO DE INFORMACION Y DOCUMENTACION AGROPECUARIO. BOLETIN DE RESENAS. SERIE: PASTOS Y FORRAJES. Text in Spanish; Abstracts in English. 1974. irreg. CUP 1,000; or exchange basis. charts; illus.; stat.
Formerly: Cuba. Centro de Informacion y Divulgacion Agropecuario. Boletin de Resenas. Serie: Pastos
Indexed: Agrind.
—CISTI.
Published by: Centro de Informacion y Documentacion Agropecuario, Gaveta Postal 4149, Havana, 4, Cuba. TEL 29-2227. **Dist. by:** Ediciones Cubanas, Obispo No. 461, Apdo. 605, Havana, Cuba.

633.2 USA
DIRECT-FED MICROBIAL, ENZYME & FORAGE ADDITIVE COMPENDIUM. Text in English. 1992. biennial. USD 125 (effective 2001). adv.
Published by: Miller Publishing Co., 12400 Whitewater Dr., Ste. 160, Minnetonka, MN 55343-2524. TEL 952-931-0211, FAX 952-938-1832. Ed., R&P Sarah Muirhead TEL 952-930-4346. Adv. contact Gary Ashbacher TEL 952-930-4349. B&W page USD 2,095, color page USD 3,495; trim 11 x 8.25. Circ: 1,200.

633.1 USA
DURAM WHEAT REPORT. Text in English. q. USD 8; USD 9 in Canada & Mexico; USD 11 elsewhere. **Document type:** *Government.*
Published by: (Livestock & Seed Division), U.S. Department of Agriculture, Agricultural Marketing Service (Greely), 711 O St., Greely, CO 80631. TEL 303-353-9750, FAX 303-353-9790. **Subscr. to:** U.S.D.A. Agricultural Marketing Service, Livestock & Seed Division, Rm 2613 S, Box 96456, Washington, DC 20090-6456. FAX 202-245-4732.

633.11 USA
DURUM KERNELS. Text in English. s-a. USD 50; USD 90 for 2 yrs.; USD 130 for 3 yrs. (effective 2000). **Document type:** *Newsletter.*
Published by: U S Durum Growers Association, 4023 State St, Bismark, ND 58503. TEL 701-222-2204, http://www.durumgrowers.com/.

633.1 USA
DURUM WHEAT REPORT. Text in English. q. USD 8; USD 9 in Canada & Mexico; USD 11 elsewhere. reprint service avail. from CIS. **Document type:** *Government.* **Description:** Presents national information about the prices and supply of durum wheat.
Related titles: Microfiche ed.: (from CIS).
Indexed: AmStI.
Published by: (Livestock & Seed Division), U.S. Department of Agriculture, Agricultural Marketing Service (St. Paul), 208 New Livestock Exchange Bldg., South St. Paul, MN 55675. Circ: 90. **Subscr. to:** U.S.D.A. Agricultural Marketing Service, Livestock & Seed Division, Rm 2613 S, Box 96456, Washington, DC 20090-6456. FAX 202-245-4732.

338.1 DEU ISSN 0014-0228
ERNAEHRUNGSDIENST; unabhaengige Handels- und Boersenzeitung. Variant title: Agrarzeitung Ernaehrungsdienst. Text in German. 1946. 2/w. EUR 383; EUR 4.50 newsstand/cover (effective 2003). adv. bk.rev. charts; stat. **Document type:** *Newspaper, Trade.*
Related titles: Online - full text ed.
Indexed: CBNB, RRTA, WAE&RSA.
Published by: Deutscher Fachverlag GmbH, Mainzer Landstr 251, Frankfurt Am Main, 60326, Germany. TEL 49-69-759501, FAX 49-69-75952999, agrar@dfv.de, info@dfv.de, http://www.agrimanager.de, http://www.dfv.de. adv.: B&W page EUR 5,685, color page EUR 7,014. Circ: 5,066.

ESTADISTICA PANAMENA. SITUACION ECONOMICA. SECCION 312. SUPERFICIE SEMBRADA Y COSECHA DE ARROZ, MAIZ Y FRIJOL DE BEJUCO. see *AGRICULTURE—Abstracting, Bibliographies, Statistics*

EUROPEAN ASSOCIATION FOR ANIMAL PRODUCTION. ANNUAL MEETING. BOOK OF ABSTRACTS. see *AGRICULTURE—Abstracting, Bibliographies, Statistics*

EUROPEAN ASSOCIATION FOR ANIMAL PRODUCTION. SCIENTIFIC SERIES. see *AGRICULTURE—Poultry And Livestock*

338.1 630 GBR
FARM BUSINESS DATA (YEAR). Text in English. 2000. a. GBP 12 (effective 2000). **Description:** Contains statistics comparing various farms of the same size based on data collected by investigational officer from agricultural holdings in Central Southern England and the South West Midlands.
Indexed: DSA, WAE&RSA.
—BLDSC (3871.920000).
Published by: University of Reading, Department of Agricultural and Food Economics, 4 Earley Gate, Whiteknights Rd, PO Box 237, Reading, Berks RG6 2AR, United Kingdom. TEL 44-118-987-5123, FAX 44-118-975-6467, aesadept@reading.ac.uk, http://www.rdg.ac.uk/AcaDepts/ae. Ed. Mr. Rod Vaughan.

633.1 USA ISSN 0071-450X
FEED ADDITIVE COMPENDIUM. Text in English. 1963. a. (plus monthly updates), latest 2004. USD 260 domestic; USD 275 foreign; USD 200 to institutions colleges (effective 2005). adv. Supplement avail.; reprint service avail. from PQC.
Related titles: ♦ Supplement to: Feedstuffs. ISSN 0014-9624.
—CISTI. **CCC.**
Published by: Miller Publishing Co., 12400 Whitewater Dr., Ste. 160, Minnetonka, MN 55343-2524. TEL 952-931-0211, FAX 952-938-1832, http://www.feedstuffs.com/ME2/dirsect.asp?sid=9E937630D3A44C80B1F1AD3D6080D22F&nm=Other+Products. Ed., R&P Sarah Muirhead TEL 952-930-4346. Adv. contact Gary Ashbacher TEL 952-930-4349. B&W page USD 3,350, color page USD 4,825. Circ: 2,900.

633.2 USA ISSN 0886-5884
FEED AND FEEDING DIGEST. Text in English. 1972 (vol.24). m. membership. **Document type:** *Trade.*
Published by: National Grain and Feed Association, 1250 Eye St N W, Ste 1003, Washington, DC 20005. TEL 202-289-0873, FAX 202-289-5388, ngfa@ngfa.org, http://www.ngfa.org. Circ: 2,800.

633.2 631.3 USA ISSN 1055-3223
FEED & GRAIN. Text in English. 1969. 7/yr. USD 48 domestic; USD 68 in Canada & Mexico; USD 99 elsewhere (effective 2005). adv. illus. index. 82 p./no. 3 cols./p.; **Document type:** *Magazine, Trade.* **Description:** Provides owners and operators of feed and allied grain-handling and processing industries with business management, industry and equipment information.
Former titles (until 1991): Feed and Grain Times (0163-4119); Feed - Grain Equipment Times (0014-9551)
Related titles: Online - full text ed.: (from Gale Group, ProQuest Information & Learning).
Indexed: NutrAb.
—**CCC.**
Published by: Cygnus Business Media, Inc., 1233 Janesville Ave, Fort Atkinson, WI 53538-0803. TEL 920-563-6388, 920-563-1698, 800-547-7377, FAX 920-563-1699, arlette.sambs@cygnuspub.com, rich.reiff@cygnuspub.com, http://www.feedandgrain.com, http://www.cygnusb2b.com/index.cfm. Ed. Jean Van Dyke. Pub., Adv. contact Vicki Roth. B&W page USD 4,925, color page USD 6,025; trim 7.8 x 10.75. Circ: 16,500 (controlled).

636 USA ISSN 0014-9543
FEED BULLETIN. Text in English. d. USD 750 (effective 2001). adv. mkt.; stat. back issues avail.; reprints avail. **Document type:** *Bulletin.* **Description:** Daily comparative price guides and editorial market update.
Media: Duplicated (not offset). **Related titles:** E-mail ed.; Online - full content ed.
Published by: Jacobsen Publishing Co., 1123 W. Washington Blvd., Chicago, IL 60607-2057. TEL 312-726-6600, FAX 312-726-6654, info@by-products.com, http://www.by-proudcts.com. Ed. John Ferris. R&P Bill Ferris.

633.2 GBR ISSN 0950-771X
FEED COMPOUNDER. Text in English. 1980. m. (Jun.-Jul. comb.). GBP 56 in United Kingdom; GBP 66 in Europe; GBP 86 elsewhere (effective 2000). adv. bk.rev. stat. back issues avail. **Document type:** *Trade.* **Description:** Provides technical journal for manufacturers of animal feedingstuffs covering nutrition, animal health, mill machinery, economics, legislation.
Indexed: AbHyg, AgBio, AnBrAb, DSA, FS&TA, HerbAb, HortAb, IndVet, MaizeAb, NutrAb, PBA, PHN&I, PN&I, PoultAb, RM&VM, RPP, SIA, SoyAb, TriticAb, VetBull, WAE&RSA.
—BLDSC (3902.118000), IE, ingenta. **CCC.**
Published by: H G M Publications, HGM House, Nether End, Baslow, Bakewell, Derbys DE45 1SR, United Kingdom. TEL 44-1246-584000, 44-1246-584002, FAX 44-1246-584005, mail@hgmpubs.com, http://www.hgmpubs.com. Ed. Andrew D Mounsey. Pub. Howard Mounsey. Adv. contact Simon P Mounsey. Circ: 2,850.

633.2 USA
FEED CONTROL COMMENT. Text in English. m. membership only. **Document type:** *Newsletter.* **Description:** Provides current information on happenings in the area of regulatory compliance and nutrition. Reports news of FDA, USDA and feed control matters nationwide.
Published by: American Feed Industry Association, 1501 Wilson Blvd, Ste 1100, Arlington, VA 22209. TEL 703-524-0810, FAX 703-524-1921, http://www.afia.org.

630 GBR ISSN 0965-2558
FEED FACTS QUARTERLY. Text in English. q. GBP 70 in United Kingdom; GBP 80 rest of Europe; GBP 90 elsewhere (effective 2000). adv. bk.rev. charts; illus.; stat.; tr.lit. **Document type:** *Trade.* **Description:** Provides reports and analysis of British and European Community feed production and ration formulation data.
Formerly (until 1990): Digest of Feed Facts and Figures

A

▼ new title ➤ refereed ✶ unverified ♦ full entry avail.

—CCC.
Published by: H G M Publications, HGM House, Nether End, Baslow, Bakewell, Derbys DE45 1SR, United Kingdom. TEL 44-1246-584000, 44-1246-584002, FAX 44-1246-584005, mail@hgmpubs.com, http://www.hgmpubs.com. Ed., Adv. contact Simon P Mounsey. Pub. Howard Mounsey. Circ: 1,200.

633.2 USA
FEED FOR THOUGHT. Text in English. q. membership.
Document type: *Newsletter.*
Related titles: Online - full text ed.
Published by: (American Feed Industry Association Aquaculture Committee), American Feed Industry Association, 1501 Wilson Blvd, Ste 1100, Arlington, VA 22209. TEL 703-524-0810, FAX 703-524-1921, http://www.afia.org.

633.2 GBR
FEED INDUSTRY REVIEW; a structural and financial analysis of the UK and European animal feed industries. Text in English. 1988. triennial. GBP 195 (effective 2000). adv. **Document type:** *Trade.* **Description:** Supplies an extensive structural and financial analysis of the UK and European compound animal feeding stuffs industries. Aimed at senior personnel in the industry and to suppliers and advisors to the industry.
Indexed: e-psyche.
Published by: H G M Publications, HGM House, Nether End, Baslow, Bakewell, Derbys DE45 1SR, United Kingdom. TEL 44-1246-584000, 44-1246-584002, FAX 44-1246-584005, mail@hgmpubs.com, http://www.hgmpubs.com. Ed. Roger W Dean. Adv. contact Simon P Mounsey. B&W page GBP 435, color page GBP 870; trim 210 x 297. Circ: 400.

636 USA ISSN 0274-5771
CODEN: FEINEW
FEED INTERNATIONAL. Text in English. m. free to qualified personnel (effective 2004). adv. **Document type:** *Trade.* **Description:** For the feed industry in Europe, Asia, Middle East, and Africa. Disseminates clear and concise articles on animal nutrition, feed processing technology, and marketing.
Related titles: Online - full text ed.: (from EBSCO Publishing).
Indexed: AEA, AbHyg, AgBio, AnBrAb, DSA, HortAb, IndVet, MaizeAb, NutrAb, PBA, PN&I, PoultAb, RA&MP, RDA, RM&VM, RPP, RiceAb, SFA, SIA, SoyAb, TriticAb, VetBull, WAE&RSA.
—BLDSC (3902.122700). **CCC.**
Published by: Watt Publishing Co., 122 S Wesley Ave, Mt. Morris, IL 61054-1497. TEL 815-734-4171, FAX 815-734-5649, http://www.wattnet.com. Ed. Clayton Gill. Pub. Clay Schreiber. Adv. contact Laura Orsted. B&W page USD 4,450, color page USD 6,050; trim 10.75 x 8. Circ: 20,605 (controlled).

633 340 GBR ISSN 0969-0735
KD2376.F4
FEED LEGISLATION. Text in English. 1993. triennial. GBP 47, USD 88 (effective 2000). charts; illus. **Document type:** *Trade.* **Description:** Provides comprehensive guide to UK and European legislation concerning the manufacture, storage and distribution of feedstuffs for livestock.
—CCC.
Published by: H G M Publications, HGM House, Nether End, Baslow, Bakewell, Derbys DE45 1SR, United Kingdom. TEL 44-1246-584000, 44-1246-584002, FAX 44-1246-584005, mail@hgmpubs.com, http://www.hgmpubs.com. Ed. David Williams. Adv. contact Simon P Mounsey. Circ: 600 (controlled).

636 USA ISSN 0014-956X
CODEN: FEMAA9
FEED MANAGEMENT; the magazine for manufacturers of animal feed in North America. Text in English. 1950. m. USD 50 domestic; USD 70 in Canada; USD 100 elsewhere; free to qualified personnel (effective 2005). adv. charts; illus.; stat.; tr.lit. index. reprints avail. **Document type:** *Magazine, Trade.* **Description:** Provides feed industry professionals with accurate and timely information about the efficient, profitable, and safe production and distribution of livestock and poultry feed.
Incorporates: Feed Age
Related titles: Microfiche ed.: (from PQC).
Indexed: BiolAb, ExcerpMed, F&GI, SFA, WildRev.
—CISTI, Linda Hall. **CCC.**
Published by: Watt Publishing Co., 122 S Wesley Ave, Mt. Morris, IL 61054-1497. TEL 815-734-4171, FAX 815-734-5649, http://wattnet.com. Ed. Clayton Gill. Pub., R&P Clay Schreiber. Adv. contact Nancy Wagner. B&W page USD 4,100, color page USD 5,710; trim 10.75 x 8. Circ: 20,182 (controlled).

633.2 NLD ISSN 0928-124X
CODEN: FEMIF4
FEED MIX. Text in Dutch. bi-m. adv. **Document type:** *Trade.*
Indexed: AgBio, Agr, AgrForAb, AnBrAb, DSA, HelmAb, HortAb, IndVet, MaizeAb, NutrAb, PBA, PN&I, PotatoAb, PoultAb, RA&MP, RM&VM, RPP, RefZh, SIA, SoyAb, VetBull, WAE&RSA, WeedAb.
—BLDSC (3902.123800), CASDDS, CISTI, IE, ingenta. **CCC.**
Published by: Reed Business Information bv (Subsidiary of: Reed Business), Hanzestraat 1, Doetinchem, 7006 RH, Netherlands. TEL 31-314-349911, FAX 31-314-343839, info@reedbusiness.nl, http://www.reedbusiness.nl. Ed. Naheeda Kahn. Adv. contact Miguel Mendes de Leon TEL 31-314-349584. Circ: 7,000.

633.11 NLD
FEED TECH. Text in Dutch. 1997. 8/yr. USD 95. adv.
Description: Focuses on worldwide developments in feed milling technology and animal feed including ingredients, pet food, aquaculture, and nutrition.
Published by: Reed Business Information bv (Subsidiary of: Reed Business), Hanzestraat 1, Doetinchem, 7006 RH, Netherlands. TEL 31-314-349911, FAX 31-314-343839, info@reedbusiness.nl, http://www.reedbusiness.nl. Eds. Naheeda Kahn, Roger Gilbert. Adv. contact Miguel Mendes de Leon TEL 31-314-349584. Circ: 12,000.

636 338.1 JPN ISSN 0014-9586
FEED TRADE. Text in Japanese. 1965. 6/yr. JPY 3,000; USD 200 foreign. illus.
Published by: Japan Feed Trade Association/Shiryo Yushutsunyu Kyogikai, c/o Koizumi Bldg, 4-3-13 Ginza, 4-3-13 Ginza, Chuo-ku, Tokyo, 104-0061, Japan. TEL 03-3563-6441, FAX 03-3567-2297. Ed. Morio Morisaki. Circ: 2,000.

633.2 USA
FEEDGRAM. Text in English. m. membership only. **Description:** Provides current news on industry developments and the association's activities. Features legislative, regulatory and feed control updates; committee news, membership items, meeting reports, and USDA briefs.
Published by: American Feed Industry Association, 1501 Wilson Blvd, Ste 1100, Arlington, VA 22209. TEL 703-524-0810, FAX 703-524-1921, http://www.afia.org.

633.1 636 USA ISSN 0014-9624
HD9052.U5 CODEN: FDSTAL
FEEDSTUFFS; the weekly newspaper for agribusiness. Text in English. 1929. w. USD 144 domestic; USD 150 in Canada; USD 210 in the Americas; USD 280 in Europe & Middle East; USD 280 elsewhere (effective 2005). adv. bk.rev. charts; illus.; mkt.; stat.; tr.lit. reprints avail. **Document type:** *Newspaper, Trade.*
Related titles: Microform ed.: (from PQC); Online - full text ed.: (from EBSCO Publishing, Florida Center for Library Automation, Gale Group, O C L C Online Computer Library Center, Inc.); ♦ Supplement(s): Feed Additive Compendium. ISSN 0071-450X; Direct-fed Microbial, Enzyme, & Forage Additive Compendium. USD 125 per issue domestic; USD 165 per issue foreign (effective 2002).
Indexed: AEA, AbHyg, AgBio, Agr, AnBrAb, B&I, BioDAb, BiolAb, BusI, ChemAb, DBA, DSA, F&GI, FCA, HerbAb, HlthInd, IndVet, LRI, MaizeAb, ManagCont, NutrAb, PBA, PHN&I, PN&I, PROMT, PoultAb, RASB, RDA, RM&VM, RPP, RRTA, S&F, S&MA, SIA, SeedAb, SoyAb, T&II, TOSA, TriticAb, VetBull, WAE&RSA.
—BLDSC (3902.200000), CASDDS, CISTI. **CCC.**
Published by: Miller Publishing Co., 12400 Whitewater Dr., Ste. 160, Minnetonka, MN 55343-2524. TEL 952-931-0211, FAX 952-938-1832, http://www.feedstuffs.com. Ed., Pub. Sarah Muirhead TEL 952-930-4346. adv.: B&W page USD 3,880; trim 10 x 14.5. Circ: 15,650.

FOOD SCIENCE CATALOG. see *FOOD AND FOOD INDUSTRIES*

633.2 USA
▼ **FOOD SENTRY.** Text in English. 2003. q. **Document type:** *Magazine, Trade.*
Published by: Ridley Feed Operations, 424 N Riverfront Dr, PO Box 8500, Mankato, MN 56002-8500. TEL 507-388-9400, FAX 507-388-9415, http://www.ridleyinc.com/.

630 CAN ISSN 0383-3356
FORAGE CROP RECOMMENDATIONS. Text in English. 1972. biennial. free. back issues avail. **Document type:** *Government.* **Description:** Forage crops, grasses and legumes recommended for Saskatchewan's farmers, seeding rates, herbicides used in grasses and legumes.
—CISTI.
Published by: Agriculture and Food, B5 Walter Scott Bldg, 3085 Albert St, Regina, SK S4S 0B1, Canada. TEL 888-613-3975 (in US only), FAX 306-721-4626, pdc@agr.gov.sk.ca, pad@sk.sympatico.ca, http://www.agr.gov.sk.ca/saf. Circ: 4,000.

G - MAIL. see *BUSINESS AND ECONOMICS*

633 HUN ISSN 0133-0918
TS2120 CODEN: GABODG
GABONAIPAR✱. Text in Hungarian. 1962. q. USD 18.
Document type: *Trade.*
Formerly (until 1975): Malomipar es Termenyforgalom (0464-7920)
Indexed: ChemAb, FS&TA.
—CASDDS.
Published by: Magyar Elelmezesipari Tudomanyos Egyesulet, P.F. 5, Budapest, 1361, Hungary.

664.75 DEU
TX761 CODEN: GEMBAN
GETREIDETECHNOLOGIE; Zeitschrift fuer Getreide, Mehl, Brot, Feine Backwaren, Backmittel, Teigwaren, Cerealien. Text in German. 1972. bi-m. EUR 239 domestic; EUR 249 foreign (effective 2005). adv. bk.rev. charts; illus. index. **Document type:** *Journal, Trade.*
Formerly (until 2004): Getreide, Mehl und Brot (0367-4177); Which was formed by the merger of (1951-1972): Brot und Gebaeck (0007-2419); (1931-1972): Getreide und Mehl (0046-5879); Which was formerly (until 1941): Muehlenlaboratorium (0369-2590)
Indexed: BiolAb, CIN, ChemAb, ChemTitl, ExcerpMed, FCA, FS&TA, HerbAb, MaizeAb, RefZh, S&F.
—BLDSC (4165.212500), CASDDS, CISTI, IE, Infotrieve, ingenta, Linda Hall. **CCC.**
Published by: (Arbeitsgemeinschaft Getreideforschung), BackMedia Verlagsgesellschaft mbH, Universitaetsstr 74a, Bochum, 44789, Germany. TEL 49-234-901990, FAX 49-234-9019919, http://www.agfdt.de/ns/gmb.htm, http://www.backmedia.info. Ed. Wilfried Seibel. Circ: 3,000.

633 PHL
GINTONG BUTIL/GOLDEN GRAINS. Text in English, Tagalog. 1973. m. free. illus.
Published by: National Food Authority, E. Rodriguez Sr. Ave, Quezon City, Philippines. FAX 7121364. Ed. Rebecca C Olarte. Circ: 10,000 (controlled).

658.8 USA ISSN 1047-4978
CODEN: GFEMER
GRAIN & FEED MARKETING. Text in English. 1982. q. free to qualified personnel (effective 2005). adv. **Document type:** *Magazine, Trade.*
Indexed: BPIA.
Published by: Marketing Communications Corporations, PO Box 174, Freeport, IL 61032. TEL 815-232-5176, FAX 815-232-1363. Ed., Pub. Floyd Roberts. Circ: 12,029 (free).

633.2 338.1 GBR ISSN 1466-3872
GRAIN & FEED MILLING TECHNOLOGY. Text in English. 1891. bi-m. GBP 102; GBP 120 foreign (effective 2000). adv. bk.rev. back issues avail. **Document type:** *Trade.* **Description:** International magazine for senior executives concerned with grain, flour and feed production worldwide. Subjects covered include technological developments, commodity and market trends.
—CISTI.
Published by: Turret R A I plc, Armstrong House, 38 Market Sq, Uxbridge, Middx UB8 1TG, United Kingdom. FAX 44-1895-454647, agrifood@aol.com. Ed. Peter Bell. Pub. Andrew West. R&P Peter de Lacey. adv.: B&W page GBP 1,476, color page GBP 2,288; trim 178 x 254. Circ: 11,000 (paid).

664.72029 USA ISSN 1098-4615
TS2120
GRAIN & MILLING ANNUAL. Text in English. 1995. a. USD 95 (effective 2000). adv. stat. **Document type:** *Directory.*
Former titles: North American Grain & Milling Annual (1082-1740); Which was formed by the merger of (1987-1995): Milling Directory - Buyer's Guide (1045-9030); (1987-1995): Grain Guide - North American Yearbook (1049-4073); Which superseded: Grain Directory - Buyer's Guide
Published by: Sosland Publishing Company, 4800 Main St, Ste 100, Kansas City, MO 64112-2513. TEL 816-756-1000, FAX 816-756-0494, worldgrain@sosland.com. Ed. Stormy Wylie. Circ: 9,200.

631.3 CAN ISSN 0410-7470
GRAIN ELEVATORS IN CANADA/SILOS A GRAIN DU CANADA. Text in English, French. 1911. a. (plus m. updates). CND 120 (effective 2001). stat. **Document type:** *Government.*
Related titles: Online - full content ed.
Published by: Canadian Grain Commission, Corporate Services/Commission Canadienne des Grains, 700 303 Main St, Winnipeg, MB R3C 3G8, Canada. TEL 204-983-3309, fhodgkinson@cgc.ca, http://www.cgc.ca/.

338.1 USA ISSN 0274-7138
GRAIN JOURNAL. Text in English. 1972. bi-m. USD 40 (effective 2005). adv. back issues avail. **Document type:** *Magazine, Trade.* **Description:** Contains useful and innovative news to the grain handling, merchandising and feed industries.
Published by: Country Journal Publishing Company, 3065 Pershing Ct, Decatur, IL 62526-1564. TEL 217-877-9660, 800-728-7511, FAX 217-877-6647, ed@grainnet.com, http://www.grainnet.com. Pub. Mark Avery. Adv. contact Deb Coontz. Circ: 12,000 (controlled).

338.1 CAN ISSN 0383-4417
HD9044.C3
GRAIN MATTERS. Text in English. 1976. bi-m. free. back issues avail. **Document type:** *Newsletter.*
Related titles: French ed.
—CISTI.
Published by: Canadian Wheat Board, 423 Main St, Winnipeg, MB R3B 1B3, Canada. TEL 204-983-3421, FAX 204-983-4678, TELEX 07-57801, http://www.cwb.ca. Ed., R&P Brian Stacey. Circ: 118,000.

GRAIN STATISTICS WEEKLY/STATISTIQUES HEBDOMADAIRES DES GRAINS. see *AGRICULTURE—Abstracting, Bibliographies, Statistics*

633 USA
GRAIN STOCKS REPORT. Text in English. w. USD 65 domestic; USD 70 in Canada & Mexico; USD 105 elsewhere (effective 2000). back issues avail.; reprint service avail. from CIS.
Document type: *Government.*
Related titles: Microfiche ed.: (from CIS).
Indexed: AmStI.
Published by: (Livestock & Seed Division), U.S. Department of Agriculture, Agricultural Marketing Service (Portland), 1220 S W Third Ave, Rm 1772, Portland, OR 97204. Ed. Lowell Serfling. **Subscr. to:** U.S.D.A. Agricultural Marketing Service, Livestock & Seed Division, Rm 2613 S, Box 96456, Washington, DC 20090-6456. FAX 202-245-4732.

GRAIN TRANSPORTATION SITUATION. see *TRANSPORTATION*

GRAIN: WORLD MARKETS AND TRADE. see *BUSINESS AND ECONOMICS—Trade And Industrial Directories*

633.1 CAN ISSN 0229-8090
GRAINEWS; cattleman's corner. Text in English. 1975. 16/yr. CND 29.50. adv. illus. index. **Document type:** *Newspaper, Trade.* **Description:** Agricultural newspaper for farm families. Provides information on grain and oilseed production and marketing, financial management, machinery management, livestock production and marketing. Includes cartoons, jokes, and articles on everyday life.
—CISTI.
Published by: United Grain Growers Ltd., 201 Portage Ave, P O Box 6600, Winnipeg, MB R3C 3A7, Canada. TEL 800-665-0502, FAX 204-944-5416, http://www.fbc.unitedgrain.ca. Ed., R&P Andy Sirski. Pub. Palmer Anderson. Adv. contact Tom Mumby. Circ: 52,000 (paid).

633 AUS
GRAINLINE. Text in English. 1967. biennial. free. adv. **Document type:** *Newsletter.*
Former titles: Bulk Grain (1032-5824); (until 1988): Bulk Wheat Year Book (0813-3735)
—CISTI.
Published by: GrainCorp Operations Ltd., Level 10, 51 Druitt St, Sydney, NSW 2000, Australia. TEL 61-2-9325-9100, FAX 61-2-93259180, www.graincorp.com.au. Ed., Pub., R&P Melanie Vere. Circ: 8,500.

633.1 GBR ISSN 1467-6672
GRASSES AND HERBAGE LEGUMES VARIETY LEAFLET. Variant title: N I A B Descriptive List of Grasses and Herbage Legumes. Text in English. a. GBP 10 per vol. (effective 2003). **Document type:** *Bulletin, Trade.* **Description:** Discusses ways in which to plant and cultivate grasses and legumes.
Formerly (until 1998): N I A B Recommended List of Grasses and Herbage Legumes (1356-4978); Which superseded in part (in 1993): N I A B Farmers Leaflet (0305-1277)
Indexed: PBA.
Published by: N I A B, Huntingdon Rd, Cambridge, CB3 0LE, United Kingdom. TEL 44-1223-276381, FAX 44-1223-342328, TELEX 817455-NIAB-G, info@niab.com, paul.nelson@niab.com, http://www.niab.com. Ed. Paul Nelson TEL 44-1223-342225.

GREY BOOK. see *AGRICULTURE—Abstracting, Bibliographies, Statistics*

GROVVARELEDEREN. see *BUSINESS AND ECONOMICS—Domestic Commerce*

636.085 GBR
HANDBOOK OF FEED ADDITIVES. Text in English. 1982. a. GBP 49 in United Kingdom; GBP 51 in Europe; GBP 54 elsewhere (effective 2000). adv. **Document type:** *Directory.* **Description:** Provides compendium of data sheets for additives available for use in livestock feeds and drinking waters. Products included are: medicines, zootechnicals, enzymes and micro-organisms, acidifiers, antioxidants, mould inhibitors and pigmenters.
Formerly (until 1998): Handbook of Medicinal Feed Additives (0957-2368)
—CISTI. **CCC.**
Published by: H G M Publications, HGM House, Nether End, Baslow, Bakewell, Derbys DE45 1SR, United Kingdom. TEL 44-1246-584000, 44-1246-584002, FAX 44-1246-584005, mail@hgmpubs.com, http://www.hgmpubs.com. Ed. Andrew D Mounsey. Pub. Howard Mounsey. Adv. contact Simon P Mounsey. Circ: 3,000.

633 USA ISSN 0891-5946
HAY & FORAGE GROWER. Text in English. 1986. q. USD 25 domestic; USD 55 foreign; free to qualified personnel (effective 2005). back issues avail. **Document type:** *Magazine, Trade.*
Related titles: Online - full text ed.: (from EBSCO Publishing, LexisNexis).
—**CCC.**
Published by: Primedia Business Magazines & Media, Inc. (Subsidiary of: Primedia, Inc.), 7900 International Dr, Ste 300, Minneapolis, MN 55425. TEL 952-851-9329, FAX 952-851-4601, inquiries@primediabusiness.com, http://www.hayandforage.com, http://www.primediabusiness.com. Ed. Neil Tietz. Pub. Ron Sorensen. Adv. contact Cindy Kramer. Circ: 60,000 (paid). **Subscr. to:** PO Box 12993, Overland Park, KS 66282-2993. TEL 800-441-0294, FAX 913-967-1331.

HOME - GROWN CEREALS AUTHORITY. CEREALS STATISTICS. see *AGRICULTURE—Abstracting, Bibliographies, Statistics*

633.1 338.1 GBR ISSN 0951-0958
HOME - GROWN CEREALS AUTHORITY. PROGRESS REPORTS ON RESEARCH AND DEVELOPMENT. Text in English. 1968. irreg. **Document type:** *Monographic series.*
Published by: Home - Grown Cereals Authority, Caledonia House, 223 Pentonville Rd, London, N1 9HY, United Kingdom. TEL 44-20-75203920, FAX 44-20-75203958, publication@hgca.com, http://www.hgca.com.

633 PHL
SB191.R5
I R R I CORPORATE REPORTS. Text in English. 1974. a. price varies. adv. **Document type:** *Corporate.*
Formerly: I R R I Research Highlights (0115-1142)
Indexed: FCA, HerbAb, RPP, RevApplEntom.
—CISTI.
Published by: International Rice Research Institute, DAPO Box 7777, Metro Manila, Philippines. TEL 63-2-845-0563, FAX 63-2-891-1292, 63-2-845-0606, irri@cgiar.org, e.hettel@cgiar.org, http://www.cgiar.org/irri/. Adv. contact E P Hettel.

633 PHL ISSN 0117-0880
SB191.R5
I R R I PROGRAM REPORT. Text in English. 1963. a. price varies. back issues avail.
Formerly: I R R I Annual Report (0074-7793)
Indexed: ATA, BibAg, BiolAb, FCA, HerbAb, PBA, RPP, RevApplEntom, WAE&RSA, WeedAb, ZooRec.
Published by: International Rice Research Institute, DAPO Box 7777, Metro Manila, Philippines. TEL 63-2-845-0563, FAX 63-2-845-0606, irri@cgiar.org, http://www.cgiar.org/irri/.

338.1 USA ISSN 0897-5019
IDAHO GRAIN. Text in English. bi-m. USD 50. adv. back issues avail. **Document type:** *Trade.* **Description:** Provides information growers need to keep aware of the issues that can and do affect their farming operations.
Formerly: Idaho Wheat
Published by: Idaho Grain Producers Association, 821 W. State St., Boise, ID 83702-5832. TEL 208-345-0706. Ed. Steve C Johnson. Circ: 20,000. **Co-sponsor:** Idaho Wheat Commission, Idaho Barley Commission.

INDIAN DEOILED CAKES EXPORTERS' PERFORMANCE MONITOR. see *AGRICULTURE—Abstracting, Bibliographies, Statistics*

INDUSTRIES DES CEREALES. see *FOOD AND FOOD INDUSTRIES*

633.18 CUB ISSN 0138-7731
INFORMACION EXPRESS. SERIE: ARROZ. Text in Spanish. 1977. 3/yr. CUP 0.90 domestic; USD 6 in North America; USD 9 in South America; USD 10 in Europe; USD 14 elsewhere. stat.
Indexed: Agrind.
—CISTI.
Published by: Centro de Informacion y Documentacion Agropecuario, Gaveta Postal 4149, Havana, 4, Cuba. TEL 301672. **Dist. by:** Ediciones Cubanas, Obispo No. 527, Apdo. 605, Havana, Cuba.

633.2 CUB ISSN 0138-6786
INFORMACION EXPRESS. SERIE: PASTOS Y FORRAJES. Text in Spanish. 1977. 4/yr. USD 9 in North America; USD 11 in South America; USD 13 in Europe; USD 18 elsewhere.
Indexed: Agrind.
—CISTI.
Published by: Centro de Informacion y Documentacion Agropecuario, Gaveta Postal 4149, Havana, 4, Cuba. **Dist. by:** Ediciones Cubanas, Obispo No. 527, Apdo. 605, Havana, Cuba.

INTERNATIONAL GRAINS COUNCIL. GRAIN MARKET REPORT. see *AGRICULTURE—Agricultural Economics*

338.1 GBR
INTERNATIONAL GRAINS COUNCIL. REPORT FOR FISCAL YEAR. Text in English, French, Spanish, Russian. 1949. a., latest 2000. GBP 30, USD 50 to non-members (effective 2000). charts; stat. **Document type:** *Proceedings.* **Description:** Provides a detailed review of the activities of the IGC and FAC and its committees.
Formerly: International Wheat Council. Report for Fiscal Year; Which formed by the 1986 merger of: Review of the World Wheat Situation; Which was formerly: International Wheat Council. Review of the World Grains Situation (0539-1318); And: International Wheat Council Annual Report; Which was formerly: International Wheat Council. Report for Crop Year (0539-1296)
Related titles: French ed.; Russian ed.; Spanish ed.
—BLDSC (7524.059900).
Published by: International Grains Council, One Canada Sq, Canary Wharf, London, E14 5AE, United Kingdom. TEL 44-20-7513-1122, FAX 44-20-7513-0630, igc-fac@igc.org.uk, http://www.igc.org.uk.

A

633 338.1 GBR
INTERNATIONAL GRAINS COUNCIL. WHEAT AND COARSE GRAIN SHIPMENTS. Text in English. a., latest 1999. GBP 75, USD 120 (effective 2000). charts; stat. **Document type:** *Trade.* **Description:** Covers commercial and noncommercial shipments of wheat and coarse grains by origin and destination.
Formerly: International Wheat Council. Record of Coarse Grains Shipments
Published by: International Grains Council, One Canada Sq, Canary Wharf, London, E14 5AE, United Kingdom. TEL 44-20-7513-1122, FAX 44-20-7513-0630, igc-fac@igc.org.uk, http://www.igc.org.uk.

INTERNATIONAL GRAINS COUNCIL. WORLD GRAIN STATISTICS (YEAR). see *AGRICULTURE—Abstracting, Bibliographies, Statistics*

633 GBR ISSN 1464-0147
INTERNATIONAL MILLING DIRECTORY. Variant title: International Milling Directory and Buyers' Guide. Text in English. 1991. a. GBP 89; GBP 95 foreign. **Document type:** *Directory, Trade.* **Description:** Comprehensive reference source for the flour and feed milling industries worldwide. Contains extensive analysis of commodity supply and demand trends, articles on milling science and technology, legislation, trade policy, and statistical data.
Formerly (until 1995): Milling European Directory and Buyers' Guide (Year)
Published by: Turret R A I plc, Armstrong House, 38 Market Sq, Uxbridge, Middx UB8 1TG, United Kingdom. TEL 44-1895-454545, FAX 44-1895-454647. Ed., Pub. Susan Fraser.

633 PHL
INTERNATIONAL RICE RESEARCH NOTES. Text in English. 1976. 2/yr. USD 24 (effective 2001). **Document type:** *Newsletter.*
Formerly: International Rice Research Newsletter (0115-0944)
Indexed: AEA, AgBio, AgrForAb, BIOSIS Prev, BioCN&I, BiolAb, CPA, FCA, FPA, HerbAb, I&DA, IPP, MaizeAb, NutrAb, PBA, PGegResA, PGrRegA, PotatoAb, PoultAb, RPP, RevApplEntom, RiceAb, S&F, S&MA, SeedAb, TriticAb, WAE&RSA, WeedAb.
—BLDSC (4548.190000), CISTI, IE, ingenta, Linda Hall.
Published by: International Rice Research Institute, DAPO Box 7777, Metro Manila, Philippines. TEL 63-2-845-0563, FAX 63-2-845-0606, irri@cgiar.org, http://www.cgiar.org/irri/.

INTERNATIONAL SORGHUM AND MILLETS NEWSLETTER. see *AGRICULTURE—Crop Production And Soil*

IRELAND. CENTRAL STATISTICS OFFICE. CEREALS SUPPLY BALANCE. see *AGRICULTURE—Abstracting, Bibliographies, Statistics*

JOURNAL OF ANIMAL SCIENCE AND TECHNOLOGY. see *AGRICULTURE—Poultry And Livestock*

633.1 GBR ISSN 0733-5210
CODEN: JCSCDA
➤ **JOURNAL OF CEREAL SCIENCE.** Text in English. 1983. 6/yr. EUR 178 in Europe to individuals; JPY 19,100 in Japan to individuals; USD 179 elsewhere to individuals; EUR 744 in Europe to institutions; JPY 80,300 in Japan to institutions; USD 660 elsewhere to institutions (effective 2006). adv. reprints avail. **Document type:** *Journal, Academic/Scholarly.* **Description:** Provides an international forum for the publication of original research papers covering all aspects of cereal science related to the functional and nutritional quality of cereal grains and their products.
Related titles: Online - full text ed.: ISSN 1095-9963. USD 698 (effective 2002) (from EBSCO Publishing, Gale Group, IngentaConnect, O C L C Online Computer Library Center, Inc., ScienceDirect, Swets Information Services).
Indexed: AEA, ASCA, AgBio, Agr, AnalAb, BIOBASE, BIOSIS Prev, BibAg, BiolAb, CIN, CPA, ChemAb, ChemTitl, CurCont, DSA, Englnd, FCA, FS&TA, HortAb, I&DA, ISR, MEDLINE, MaizeAb, NutrAb, PBA, PGegResA, PGrRegA, PHN&I, PN&I, PotatoAb, PoultAb, RA&MP, RPP, RefZh, RiceAb, S&F, S&MA, SCI, SIA, SeedAb, SoyAb, TriticAb, WeedAb.
—BLDSC (4955.105000), CASDDS, CISTI, Ei, IDS, IE, Infotrieve, ingenta, Linda Hall. **CCC.**
Published by: Academic Press (Subsidiary of: Elsevier Science & Technology), 24-28 Oval Rd, London, NW1 7DX, United Kingdom. TEL 44-20-7267-4466, FAX 44-20-7482-2293, apsubs@acad.com, http://www.elsevier.com/locate/jcs. Ed. B. A. Stone.

▼ new title ➤ refereed ✶ unverified ♦ full entry avail.

A

664.7 USA ISSN 1544-0478
TS1300
▼ ➤ **JOURNAL OF NATURAL FIBERS.** Text in English. 2004 (Spr.). q. USD 400 combined subscription domestic to institutions print & online eds.; USD 540 combined subscription in Canada to institutions print & online eds.; USD 580 combined subscription elsewhere to institutions print & online eds. (effective 2006). reprint service avail. from HAW.
Document type: *Journal, Academic/Scholarly.* **Description:** Presents new achievements in basic research and the development of multi-purpose applications that further the economical and ecological production of hard fibers, protein fibers, seed, bast, leaf, and cellulosic fibers.
Related titles: Online - full text ed.: ISSN 1544-046X (from EBSCO Publishing, O C L C Online Computer Library Center, Inc., Swets Information Services).
Indexed: C&ISA, E&CAJ, IAA, Inspec, TTI.
—Haworth.
Published by: Food Products Press (Subsidiary of: Haworth Press, Inc.), 10 Alice St, Binghamton, NY 13904-1580. TEL 607-722-5857, 800-429-6784, FAX 607-771-0012, 800-895-0582, getinfo@haworthpress.com, http://www.haworthpress.com/web/JNF. Ed. Ryszard Kozlowski. Pub. William Cohen. R&P Ruth Ann Heath TEL 607-722-5857 ext 316. Adv. contact Rebecca Miller-Baum TEL 607-722-5857 ext 337.

633 338.1 USA
KANSAS CITY BOARD OF TRADE REVIEW. Text in English. 1916. d. USD 120; USD 75 for 6 mos. (effective 2000).
Document type: *Newsletter.* **Description:** Contains commentary on KCBT futures trading, futures prices and open interest, Kansas City Spot Basis, nominal ranges for corn, sorghum and soybeans, Kansas City truck bids, regional truck bids, gulf grain bids.
Formerly: Kansas City Grain Market Review (0738-7296)
Published by: Kansas City Board of Trade, 4800 Main St, Ste 303, Kansas City, MO 64112. TEL 816-753-7500, FAX 816-531-0627, kcbt@kcbt.com, http://www.kcbt.com. Ed. Deborah J Bollman.

633 USA
KANSAS CORN PERFORMANCE TESTS. Text in English. 1939. a. free. stat.
Published by: Kansas State University, Agricultural Experiment Station, Manhattan, KS 66506. TEL 913-532-7251. Ed. Kraig Roozeboom. Circ: 7,500.

633 USA
KANSAS SORGHUM PERFORMANCE TESTS. GRAIN & FORAGE. Text in English. 1958. a. free. stat.
Formerly: Kansas Grain Sorghum Performance Tests
Published by: Kansas State University, Agricultural Experiment Station, Manhattan, KS 66506. TEL 913-532-7251. Ed. Kraig Roozeboom. Circ: 12,000.

633 USA
KANSAS STATE UNIVERSITY. FOOD AND FEED GRAIN INSTITUTE. TECHNICAL ASSISTANCE IN GRAIN STORAGE, PROCESSING AND MARKETING, AND AGRIBUSINESS DEVELOPMENT. (In 4 subseries: Technical Assistance Reports (US ISSN 0453-2481); Manuals; Special Reports; Research Reports) Text in English. 1968. irreg.
Formerly (until 1974): Kansas State University. Food and Feed Grain Institute. Technical Assistance in Food Grain Drying, Storage, Handling and Transportation (0071-7150)
Related titles: Microform ed.
Published by: Kansas State University, Food and Feed Grain Institute, Shellenberger Hall, Manhattan, KS 66506. TEL 913-532-6161. Circ: 150. **Co-sponsor:** U.S. Agency for International Development.

633 GBR ISSN 1367-3432
KEY NOTE MARKET REPORT: ANIMAL FEEDSTUFFS. Variant title: Animal Feedstuffs. Animal Feedstuffs Market Report. Text in English. 1995. irreg., latest 2001, Oct. GBP 340 per issue (effective 2002). mkt.; stat. **Document type:** *Trade.*
Description: Provides an overview of a specific UK market segment and includes executive summary, market definition, market size, industry background, competitor analysis, current issues, forecasts, company profiles, and more.
Formerly: Key Note Report: Animal Feedstuffs
Related titles: CD-ROM ed.; Online - full text ed.
Published by: Key Note Ltd., Field House, 72 Oldfield Rd, Hampton, Mddx TW12 2HQ, United Kingdom. TEL 44-20-8481-8750, FAX 44-20-8783-0049, info@keynote.co.uk, http://www.keynote.co.uk. Ed. Emily Pattullo.

633.1 664.752 RUS ISSN 0235-2508
S13 CODEN: KHLEES
KHLEBOPRODUCTY. Text in Russian; Summaries in English. 1927. m. USD 259.95 (effective 1999). adv. charts; pat.; illus. index. 2 cols./p.; back issues avail. **Document type:** *Magazine, Corporate.* **Description:** Includes research and praxis in the elevator, mill, groats, bakery, pasta and confectionery industries.
Former titles (until 1988): Khlebopekarnaya i Konditerskaya Promyshlennost' (0023-1215); Zakupki Sel'skokhozyaistvennykh Produktov; Mukomolno-elevatornaya i Kombikormovaya Promyshlennost' (0131-2413)
Related titles: Microfiche ed.: (from EVP).
Indexed: BiolAb, CIN, ChemAb, ChemTitl, DSA, FS&TA, RASB, RefZh, RiceAb, SIA, TriticAb.
—BLDSC (0394.810000), CASDDS, CISTI, East View, IE, Linda Hall.
Address: 1-i Shchipovskii per 20, Moscow, 113093, Russian Federation. TEL 7-095-959-6649, FAX 7-095-959-6649, khleboprod@natre-net.ru. Ed., Pub. Alexci Dushkin. R&P, Adv. contact Boris Grazhdankin. B&W page USD 600, color page USD 900; trim 20.3 x 27.9. Circ: 2,000.

633.1 USA ISSN 0885-5811
KING'S GULF GRAIN GUIDE. Text in English. 1985. w. USD 687. back issues avail.
Published by: King Publishing Co., PO Box 52210, Knoxville, TN 37950. TEL 615-584-6294.

633 RUS ISSN 0235-2605
KOMBIKORMOVAYA PROMYSHLENNOST'. Text in Russian. 1972. 8/yr. USD 96 foreign (effective 2003). adv.
Indexed: FS&TA, RefZh.
—CISTI, East View.
Address: Sadovaya-Spasskaya 18, Moscow, 107807, Russian Federation. TEL 7-095-2071645, FAX 7-095-9755452. Ed. Nataliya V Olevskaya. adv.: B&W page USD 800, color page USD 2,000. Circ: 1,800. **Dist. by:** M K - Periodica, ul Gilyarovskogo 39, Moscow 129110, Russian Federation. TEL 7-095-2845008, FAX 7-095-2813798, info@periodicals.ru, http://www.mkniga.ru; **US dist. addr.:** East View Information Services, 3020 Harbor Ln. N., Minneapolis, MN 55447. TEL 612-550-0961.

633 RUS
KORMOPROIZVODSTVO. Text in Russian. 1966. q. USD 160 foreign (effective 2003).
Former titles: Kormovye Kul'tury (0235-2540); (until 1988): Kormoproizvodstvo (0206-538X)
Indexed: AEA, AgrForAb, AnBrAb, CPA, DSA, FCA, FPA, ForAb, HerbAb, HortAb, I&DA, IndVet, MaizeAb, NutrAb, PBA, PGegResA, PGrRegA, PHN&I, PN&I, PotatoAb, PoultAb, RA&MP, RASB, RPP, RefZh, RevApplEntom, S&F, SIA, SeedAb, SoyAb, TriticAb, VetBull, WAE&RSA, WeedAb.
—CISTI.
Address: Sadovaya-Spasskaya 18, Moscow, 103045, Russian Federation. TEL 7-095-2072110. Ed. Gennadii M Chemodanov. Circ: 5,270. **Dist. by:** M K - Periodica, ul Gilyarovskogo 39, Moscow 129110, Russian Federation. TEL 7-095-2845008, FAX 7-095-2813798, info@periodicals.ru, http://www.mkniga.ru; **US dist. addr.:** East View Information Services, 3020 Harbor Ln. N., Minneapolis, MN 55447. TEL 612-550-0961.

636 HRV ISSN 0023-4850
CODEN: KRMIA9
KRMIVA✶; mjesecnik za pitanje ishrane stoke i proizvodnje stocne hrane. Text in Croatian; Summaries in English. 1959. m. adv. bk.rev.
Indexed: AEA, AgBio, AnBrAb, CPA, ChemAb, DSA, FCA, FS&TA, HelmAb, HerbAb, HortAb, IndVet, MaizeAb, NutrAb, PBA, PHN&I, PN&I, PoultAb, ProtozoAb, RA&MP, RDA, RM&VM, RPP, S&F, SIA, SeedAb, SoyAb, TriticAb, VetBull, WAE&RSA.
—BLDSC (5118.400000), CASDDS, IE, ingenta.
Published by: Hrvatsko Agronomsko Drustvo, Berislaviceva 6, Zagreb, 1000, Croatia. Ed. Hrvoje Zlatic. Circ: 1,000.

633.18 BRA ISSN 0023-9143
CODEN: LARRAL
LAVOURA ARROZEIRA. Text in Portuguese. 1947. bi-m. USD 50. adv. bk.rev. charts; illus.; mkt.; stat. index.
Indexed: AEA, ATA, AgBio, CPA, ChemAb, FCA, HerbAb, I&DA, IAALC, MaizeAb, NutrAb, PAIS, PBA, PGrRegA, PHN&I, RPP, RevApplEntom, RiceAb, S&F, SeedAb, SoyAb, TriticAb, WAE&RSA, WeedAb.
—CASDDS, CISTI.
Published by: Instituto Rio Grandense do Arroz, Missoes Av. 342, Porto Alegre, RGS 90230100, Brazil. TEL 051-226-51-44, FAX 051-226-15-67. Ed. Maria da Graca Coelho de Souza. Circ: 19,200.

633 636 338.1 USA
LIVESTOCK & GRAIN MARKET NEWS BRANCH. WEEKLY SUMMARY. Text in English. 1953. w. USD 85; USD 90 in Canada & Mexico; USD 120 elsewhere (effective 1999). stat. reprint service avail. from CIS. **Document type:** *Government.*
Former titles: Grain and Feed Weekly Summary and Statistics; Grain and Feed Market News; Which was formed by the 1982 merger of: Grain Market News (0364-099X); Feed Market News (0364-2046); Which superseded in part: Grain Market News and Feed Market News (0017-3061)
Related titles: Microfiche ed.: (from CIS).
Indexed: AmStI.
—CISTI.
Published by: U.S. Department Of Agriculture, Livestock & Grain Market News Branch, 1428 S. Pioneer Way, Moses Lake, WA 98837. TEL 509-675-3611, http://www.ams.usda.gov/lsg/mncs/pdf%5Fweekly/compweekly.htm.

633.2 USA
MARYLAND AND MID-ATLANTIC NUTRITION CONFERENCE FOR FEED MANUFACTURERS. PROCEEDINGS. Text in English. 1961. a.
Formerly (until 2003): Maryland Nutrition Conference for Feed Manufacturers. Proceedings (0542-8386)
Indexed: Agr.
—BLDSC (6847.264000).
Published by: (Mid-Atlantic Nutrition Conference), University of Maryland, c/o Maryland Feed Industry Council, College Park, MD 20742. TEL 301-405-1000, http://www.inform.umd.edu/MNC/index.html, http://www.inform.umd.edu/EdRes/ReadingRoom/Newsletters/EthnoMusicology/Digest. Ed. Nick Zimmermann. **Co-publisher:** Mid-Atlantic Nutrition Conference.

633.1 CAN ISSN 0831-9421
LE MEUNIER; au service du producteur agricole. Text in English. 1965. 3/yr. CND 10 (effective 1999). adv. **Document type:** *Trade.*
Formerly (until 1986): Meunier Quebecois (0831-9413)
—CISTI.
Published by: Association Quebecoise des Industris de Nutrition Animale et Cerealiere (AQINAC), 2323 boul Versant Nord, local 115, Ste Foy, PQ G1N 4P4, Canada. TEL 418-688-9227, FAX 418-688-3575. Ed., R&P, Adv. contact Andre J Pilon. B&W page CND 995, color page CND 1,620. Circ: 16,000.

MILLING & BAKING NEWS. see *FOOD AND FOOD INDUSTRIES—Bakers And Confectioners*

664.7 USA
MILLING JOURNAL. Text in English. 1993. q. USD 40 (effective 2000). adv. **Document type:** *Trade.* **Description:** Provides technical and equipment information for the milling industry.
Published by: Country Journal Publishing Company, 3065 Pershing Ct, Decatur, IL 62526-1564. TEL 217-877-9660, FAX 217-877-6647. Ed. Ed Zdrojewski. Pub. Mark Avery. Adv. contact Deb Coontz. B&W page USD 475; trim 11 x 8.5. Circ: 1,700.

621.453 664.72 DNK ISSN 0026-8852
MOELLEN. Text in Danish. 1884. 5/yr. DKK 200 membership (effective 2000). adv. bk.rev. **Document type:** *Catalog.*
Description: Features articles on the history and preservation of wind and water mills, and the milling of flour and grain.
Formerly (until 1895): Tidsskrift for Skandinavisk Moelleindustri (0909-3222)
Published by: Dansk Moellerforening, Eranthisvej 20, Odense C, 5000, Denmark. TEL 45-66-12-30-67. Ed. Otto Rasmussen. adv.: B&W page DKK 700. Circ: 800.

664.7 ITA ISSN 0026-9018
MOLINI D'ITALIA; rassegna mensile dei cereali e derivati. Text in Italian. 1950. m. adv. charts; illus.; stat. index.
Indexed: ChemAb.
—Linda Hall.
Published by: (Associazione degli Industriali Mugnai e Pastai d'Italia), Avenue Media, Via Riva Reno 61, Bologna, 40122, Italy. TEL 39-051-6564311, FAX 39-051-6564350, http://www.avenuemedia.it. Ed. Luigi Costato. Circ: 3,000.

664.7 DEU
TS2120
MUEHLE UND MISCHFUTTER; Fachzeitschrift fuer Getreideverarbeitung und Mischfutter-Herstellung, Verfahrenstechnik im Schuettgut-, Lebensmittel- und Non-Food-Bereich. Text in German. 1863. fortn. EUR 217 domestic; EUR 235.80 foreign; EUR 8.30 newsstand/cover (effective 2005). adv. bk.rev. charts; illus.; pat.; stat.; tr.lit. index. **Document type:** *Magazine, Trade.*
Former titles: Muehle und Mischfuttertechnik (0027-2949); (until 1965): Muehle (0369-2582)
Indexed: AEA, AbHyg, AnBrAb, BioCN&I, CISA, DSA, FCA, FS&TA, FaBeAb, HortAb, IndVet, MaizeAb, NutrAb, PBA, PHN&I, PN&I, PotatoAb, PoultAb, ProtozoAb, RA&MP, RDA, RM&VM, RPP, RevApplEntom, S&F, SIA, SeedAb, SoyAb, TDB, TOSA, TriticAb, VetBull, WAE&RSA.
—CISTI. **CCC.**
Published by: Verlag Moritz Schaefer GmbH & Co. KG, Postfach 2254, Detmold, 32712, Germany. TEL 49-5231-92430, FAX 49-5231-924343, info@vms-detmold.de, http://www.muehle-online.de. Ed. K. Klaus Kunis. Adv. contact Silke Friedrichs. B&W page EUR 920, color page EUR 1,740; trim 190 x 270. Circ: 3,200 (paid and controlled).

633 USA
N C P A NEWSLETTER. Text in English. fortn. membership.
Document type: *Newsletter.*
Published by: National Cottonseed Products Association, PO Box 172267, Memphis, TN 38187-2267. TEL 901-682-0800, FAX 901-682-2856. Ed. Ben Morgan.

665 USA ISSN 0077-4022
NATIONAL COTTONSEED PRODUCTS ASSOCIATION. TRADING RULES. Text in English. 1897. a. USD 10 to non-members. **Document type:** *Trade.*
Published by: National Cottonseed Products Association, PO Box 172267, Memphis, TN 38187-2267. TEL 901-682-0800, FAX 901-682-2856, TELEX WUI 650-274-5680. Ed. Ben Morgan. Circ: 1,000.

633 USA
NATIONAL OILSEED PROCESSORS ASSOCIATION. YEARBOOK AND TRADING RULES. Text in English. 1936. a. USD 50 (effective 2001). **Document type:** *Directory.*

Former titles: National Oilseed Processors Association. Yearbook; (until Aug. 1989): National Soybean Processors Association. Yearbook (0077-5789)
Published by: National Oilseed Processors Association, 1255 23rd St N W, Ste 220, Washington, DC 20037. TEL 202-452-8040, FAX 202-835-0400. Circ: 2,500.

665 USA ISSN 0030-1442
CODEN: OMGAAW
OIL MILL GAZETTEER. Text in English. 1895. m. USD 20 domestic; USD 37 foreign (effective 2005). adv. charts; stat. 32 p./no.; back issues avail.; reprints avail. **Document type:** *Magazine, Trade.* **Description:** Contains information on oilseed processing.
Indexed: ChemAb, FS&TA, NutrAb, TOSA.
—BLDSC (6252.110000), Linda Hall.
Published by: (Oil Mill Superintendents Association), International Oil Mill Superintendents Association, 1835 Edinburgh St, Prattville, AL 36066. TEL 334-491-1754, FAX 334-491-3109, gazetteer@iomsa.org, general@iomsa.org, http://www.iomsa.org/features.asp. Ed. Hersh Austin. Circ: 1,400 (paid). **Co-sponsor:** Tri-State Oil Mill Superintendents Association.

633.11 338.1 USA ISSN 0897-5051
OREGON WHEAT. Text in English. 1954. bi-m. USD 15 to non-members (effective 2005). adv. **Document type:** *Magazine, Trade.*
Formerly (until 1971): Wheat West
Published by: Oregon Wheat Growers League, 115 S E 8th St, Pendleton, OR 97801. tdennee@owgl.org, http://www.owgl.org. Ed. Tammy Dennee. Circ: 5,500 (controlled).

633 USA
PACIFIC NORTHWEST GRAIN MARKET NEWS. Text in English. w. USD 65 domestic; USD 70 in Canada & Mexico; USD 100 elsewhere (effective 2000). back issues avail. **Document type:** *Government.* **Description:** Provides grain data and prices on a regional basis.
Published by: (Livestock & Seed Division), U.S. Department of Agriculture, Agricultural Marketing Service (Portland), 1220 S W Third Ave, Rm 1772, Portland, OR 97204. Ed. Lowell Serfling. **Subscr. to:** U.S.D.A. Agricultural Marketing Service, Livestock & Seed Division, Rm 2613 S, Box 96456, Washington, DC 20090-6456. FAX 202-245-4732.

PANORAMA PANADERO. see *FOOD AND FOOD INDUSTRIES—Bakers And Confectioners*

633 USA ISSN 0740-2996
SB114.U7
PENNSYLVANIA. DEPARTMENT OF AGRICULTURE. SEED REPORT. Text in English. 1927. a. free. **Document type:** *Government.*
Published by: (Bureau of Plant Industry), Department of Agriculture, 2301 N Cameron St, Harrisburg, PA 17110-9408. TEL 717-787-4843, FAX 717-787-2387. Ed. Joe D Garvey. Circ: 550.

633.1 NGA ISSN 1595-2304
PHACTION; the newsletter of the global post-harvest forum. Text in English. 1999. s-a. **Document type:** *Newsletter, Academic/Scholarly.* **Description:** Provides information on tools and trends that support decision makers dealing with postharvest agricultural research and development policies.
Published by: International Institute of Tropical Agriculture, PMB 5320, Ibadan, Oyo, Nigeria. TEL 234-2-241-2626, FAX 234-2-241-2221, iita@cgiar.org, http://www.cgiar.org/iita. Eds. J van S Graver TEL 61-2-6251-5557, S Ferris TEL 256-41-223460.

PROFESSIONAL AGRONOMY; the magazine for crop professionals. see *AGRICULTURE—Crop Production And Soil*

664.7 POL ISSN 0033-2461
SB189
PRZEGLAD ZBOZOWO - MLYNARSKI. Text in Polish. 1946. m. PLZ 180; PLZ 15 per issue (effective 2004). adv. bk.rev. abstr.; bibl.; charts; illus.; pat.; stat. index. 56 p./no.; **Document type:** *Trade.*
Related titles: Supplement(s): Centralne Laboratorium Technologii Przetworstwa i Przechowalnictwa Zboz w Warszawie. Biuletyn. ISSN 0365-9348. 1968.
Indexed: AgrLib, ChemAb, FS&TA, NutrAb, RASB.
Published by: Wydawnictwo SIGMA - N O T Sp. z o.o., ul Ratuszowa 11, PO Box 1004, Warsaw, 00950, Poland. TEL 48-22-8180918, FAX 48-22-6192187, informacja@sigma-not.pl, http://www.sigma-not.pl. Ed. Roman Jurga. adv.: B&W page PLZ 1,500, color page PLZ 3,300. Circ: 800.

QUALITY OF AUSTRALIAN CANOLA. see *AGRICULTURE—Crop Production And Soil*

633.1 CAN ISSN 0836-1657
QUALITY OF WESTERN CANADIAN CANOLA/QUALITE DU CANOLA DE L'OUEST CANADIEN. Text in English, French. 1990. a. free (effective 2001). charts; stat. **Document type:** *Government.*
Related titles: Online - full content ed.: 1996.
—CISTI.
Published by: Canadian Grain Commission, Grain Research Laboratory/Laboratoire de Recherches sur les Grains, 600 303 Main St, Winnipeg, MB R3C 3G8, Canada. TEL 204-984-0506, FAX 204-983-2751, contact@cgc.ca, http://www.cgc.ca.

633.11 CAN ISSN 0849-3855
QUALITY OF WESTERN CANADIAN WHEAT/QUALITE DU BLE DE L'OUEST CANADIEN. Text in English, French. 1996. a. free (effective 2001). charts; stat. **Document type:** *Bulletin, Government.*
Media: Online - full content.
—CISTI.
Published by: Canadian Grain Commission, Grain Research Laboratory/Laboratoire de Recherches sur les Grains, 600 303 Main St, Winnipeg, MB R3C 3G8, Canada. TEL 204-984-0506, FAX 204-983-2751, contact@cgc.ca.

633.1 AUS ISSN 1321-1986
QUEENSLAND GRAINGROWER. Text in English. 1959. w. AUD 50. adv. back issues avail.
Published by: (Queensland Graingrowers' Association), Western Publishers Pty. Ltd., 10 Joseph St, PO Box 188, Toowoomba, QLD 4350, Australia. TEL 076-32444, FAX 076-382118. Ed. Stephen Darracott. Circ: 10,000.

633.1 AUS ISSN 1448-6040
QUEENSLAND GRAINS OUTLOOK. Text in English. 1985. m. **Document type:** *Newspaper, Trade.*
Former titles (until 2001): Queensland Farmer and Grazier Grains; (until 2000): Queensland Farmer and Grazier (1321-2125); Queensland Farmer (Southern and Western Edition) (0817-9387); Which incorporated (1985-19??): Western Grazier (0817-9395)
Published by: Rural Press Ltd. (Subsidiary of: Agricultural Publishers Pty. Ltd.), 70 Neil St., PO Box 864, Toowoomba, QLD 4350, Australia. TEL 61-7-46383222, FAX 61-7-46382118, http://www.ruralpress.com/. Adv. contact Keith Hinz. Circ: 19,300.

633.1 BRA ISSN 0101-9708
REUNIAO GERAL DE CULTURA DO ARROZ. ANAIS. Text in Portuguese. 1976. biennial. charts; stat. **Description:** Covers Brazilian rice cultivation, includes the technology used, the various forms of cultivation, and discusses the various events held for organizations involved with rice cultivation.
Indexed: FCA, HerbAb, WeedAb.
Published by: Centro de Pesquisa Agropecuaria de Terras Baixas de Clima Temperado, Centro, Caixa Postal 403, Pelotas, RS 96001-970, Brazil. TEL 532-758100, FAX 532-758221, cpact@sede.embrapa.br. Circ: 600.

633 ESP ISSN 0210-1270
➤ **REVISTA DE PASTOS.** Text in Spanish, English. 1971. s-a. EUR 30 domestic; EUR 35 in Europe; EUR 40 elsewhere (effective 2003 - 2004). bk.rev. **Document type:** *Journal, Academic/Scholarly.* **Description:** Presents papers on pasture and animal production, including a review in each issue.
Indexed: AEA, AgrForAb, AnBrAb, CPA, DSA, ForAb, HerbAb, HortAb, I&DA, IECT, NemAb, NutrAb, PBA, PGegResA, RPP, S&F, SIA, SeedAb, TriticAb, WAE&RSA, WeedAb.
—CINDOC.
Published by: Sociedad Espanola para el Estudio de los Pastos, Apartado 10, La Coruna, 15080, Spain. TEL 34-981-647902, FAX 34-981-673656, juan.pineiro.andion@xunta.es, http://www.seepastos.es. Ed., R&P Juan Pineiro Andion. Circ: 400.

636 FRA ISSN 0242-6595
CODEN: REAADG
REVUE DE L'ALIMENTATION ANIMALE; mensuel des industries de la nutrition animale. Text in French. 1950. m. (10/yr.). FRF 690; FRF 770 foreign (effective 1997). adv. index. back issues avail. **Document type:** *Directory, Trade.* **Description:** Covers strategy, buying, formulating, processing and marketing feed for any kind of animals.
Formerly (until 1981): Industries de l'Alimentation Animale (0046-9300)
Indexed: ChemAb, NutrAb, RefZh.
—CASDDS, CISTI.
Published by: Gedeon Marketing Eurl, BP 16, Telgruc-sur-Mer, 29560, France. TEL 33-2-98273766, FAX 33-2-98273765. Ed., Pub., Adv. contact Jacques Fitamant. Circ: 3,000 (controlled).

633.1 USA ISSN 1096-2581
RICE FARMING. Text in English. 1967. 6/yr. USD 40; free to qualified personnel (effective 2005). adv. charts; illus.; tr.lit. **Document type:** *Magazine, Trade.*
Formerly: Rice Farming and Rice Industry News (0194-0929)
Published by: One Grower Publishing, 5118 Park Ave, Ste 131, Memphis, TN 38117. TEL 901-767-4020, FAX 901-767-4026, http://www.ricefarming.com. Ed. Carroll Smith. adv.: B&W page USD 2,460, color page USD 3,455. Circ: 13,000.

633.1 USA ISSN 0364-8087
RICE MARKET NEWS. Text in English. w. USD 80; USD 85 in Canada & Mexico; USD 110 elsewhere; USD 130 by fax. back issues avail.; reprint service avail. from CIS. **Document type:** *Government.*
Related titles: Fax ed.; Microfiche ed.: (from CIS).
Indexed: AmStI.
Published by: (Livestock & Seed Division), U.S. Department of Agriculture, Agricultural Marketing Service (Little Rock), PO Box 391, Little Rock, AR 72203. Ed. Steve Cheney. **Subscr. to:** U.S.D.A. Agricultural Marketing Service, Livestock & Seed Division, Rm 2613 S, Box 96456, Washington, DC 20090-6456. FAX 202-245-4732.

633.2 ZAF
S A GRAAN/S A GRAIN; mondstuk van Graan Suid-Afrika/mouthpiece of Grain South Africa. (South Africa) Text in Afrikaans, English. 2000. m. ZAR 1.14 newsstand/cover domestic (effective 2005).
Published by: SA Graan Grain, Postbus 88, Bothaville, 9600, South Africa. nampo@mweb.co.za. Ed. Jurgen van Onselen.

633.1 CHE
SCHWEIZER HANDELS-BOERSE. Text in German. 1919. w. CHF 138; CHF 180 foreign.
Published by: Schweizerische Handelsboerse, Bahnhofquai 7, Postfach 7075, Zuerich, 8023, Switzerland. TEL 01-2112870, FAX 01-2112872. Circ: 2,600.

664.7 CHE
SCHWEIZERISCHER MUEHLEN - ANZEIGER; Fachblatt fuer die Muehlenindustrie. Text in German. 1890. s-m. CHF 103; CHF 170 foreign. **Document type:** *Trade.*
Published by: Schweizerische Handelsboerse, Bahnhofquai 7, Postfach 7075, Zuerich, 8023, Switzerland. TEL 01-2112870, FAX 01-2112872. Circ: 800.

SEED.AB.CA; your source for seed. see *AGRICULTURE—Crop Production And Soil*

633 FRA ISSN 0395-8930
SEMENCES ET PROGRES. Text in French. 1974. q. adv. **Document type:** *Newspaper.*
Indexed: RefZh.
Address: 44 rue du Louvre, Paris, 75001, France. TEL 33-1-42363960, FAX 33-1-42361617. Ed., R&P Francois Haquin. Adv. contact Marie-Jose Dunais. Circ: 9,000 (paid).

633.2 CHN ISSN 1001-0084
SILIAO BOLAN/FEED PANORAMA. Text in Chinese; Abstracts in English. 1988. bi-m. USD 30.
Related titles: Online - full text ed.: (from East View Information Services).
Published by: Dongbei Nongxueyuan/Northeast Institute of Agriculture, Xiangfang-qu, Harbin, Heilongjiang 150030, China. TEL 0451-5665886, FAX 0451-5665886. Ed. Wang Qinggao. Circ: 5,000.

338.1 USA
SITUATION & OUTLOOK REPORT. FEED OUTLOOK. Text in English. 1995. 11/yr. **Document type:** *Government.* **Description:** Examines prospective production, supply, use, prices, demand, and trade for corn, sorghum, barley, oats, and hay.
Media: Online - full text (from Gale Group, The Dialog Corporation). **Related titles:** ♦ Supplement(s): Situation & Outlook Report. Feed Yearbook.
Published by: U.S. Department of Agriculture, Economic Research Service, 1800 M St. NW, Washington, DC 20036-5831. ersinfo@ers.usda.gov, http://www.ers.usda.gov/publications/so/view.asp?f=field/fds-bb/.

338.1 USA
SITUATION & OUTLOOK REPORT. FEED YEARBOOK. Text in English. 1995. a. USD 21 (effective 2001). **Description:** Examines production, supply, use, demand, and trade for corn, sorghum, barley, oats, and hay.
Related titles: Online - full content ed.; ♦ Supplement to: Situation & Outlook Report. Feed Outlook.
Indexed: WAE&RSA.
Published by: U.S. Department of Agriculture, Economic Research Service, 1800 M St. NW, Washington, DC 20036-5831. ersinfo@ers.usda.gov, http://www.ers.usda.gov/publications/so/view.asp?f=field/fds-bby/. **Dist. by:** ERS-NASS, 5285 Port Royal Rd, Springfield, VA 22161. TEL 800-999-6779.

664.7 ITA ISSN 0040-1862
TS2120 CODEN: TEMOAZ
TECNICA MOLITORIA. Text in Italian; Summaries in English. 1950. m. EUR 40 domestic; EUR 73 in Europe; EUR 105 elsewhere (effective 2005). adv. bk.rev. abstr.; bibl.; charts; illus.; pat. index. **Document type:** *Magazine, Trade.* **Description:** Covers pasta making, wheat milling, feed mills, silos and cereal chemistry. Includes technical and scientific articles by Italian and foreign experts. Supplies descriptions of machines.
Indexed: AEA, AbHyg, AgBio, AgrForAb, CPA, ChemAb, DSA, FCA, FS&TA, HerbAb, HortAb, IndVet, MaizeAb, NutrAb, PBA, PGegResA, PHN&I, PN&I, PoultAb, RM&VM, RPP, RRTA, RefZh, RevApplEntom, RiceAb, SIA, SeedAb, SoyAb, TriticAb, VetBull, WAE&RSA.
—BLDSC (8762.510000), CASDDS, IE, ingenta, Linda Hall. CCC.

A

Published by: Chiriotti Editori S p A, Viale Rimembranza 60, Pinerolo, TO 10064, Italy. TEL 39-0121-393127, FAX 39-0121-794480, info@chiriottieditori.it, http://www.tecnicamolitoria.com, http://www.chiriottieditori.com. Ed., R&P Mrs. Chiara Chiriotti. Pub. Mr. Giovanni Chiriotti. Adv. contact Mr. Giuseppe Chiriotti. Circ: 4,000.

633.2 636.2   AUS   ISSN 1034-6147
TODAY'S FEED LOTTING. Text in English. 1988. q. AUD 50. **Document type:** *Consumer, Trade.*
Incorporates (1987-1996): Prime Beef (1030-1992)
Published by: Peter Buffey Media Pty. Ltd., PO Box 6337, Toowoomba West, QLD 4350, Australia. TEL 61-746333262, FAX 61-746333285. Ed., R&P Peter Buffey. Adv. contact Lyn Buffey. B&W page AUD 720, color page AUD 980. Circ: 1,700.

U.S. DEPARTMENT OF AGRICULTURE. NATIONAL AGRICULTURAL STATISTICS SERVICE. GRAIN STOCKS.
see *AGRICULTURE—Abstracting, Bibliographies, Statistics*

U.S. DEPARTMENT OF AGRICULTURE. NATIONAL AGRICULTURAL STATISTICS SERVICE. RICE STOCKS.
see *AGRICULTURE—Abstracting, Bibliographies, Statistics*

V W D - GETREIDE, FUTTERMITTEL, OELE. see *BUSINESS AND ECONOMICS—Investments*

633   CAN   ISSN 0382-3601
VARIETIES OF GRAIN CROPS FOR SASKATCHEWAN. Text in English. 1972. a. free. back issues avail. **Document type:** *Government.*
Related titles: Microfiche ed.
—CISTI.
Published by: Agriculture and Food, B5 Walter Scott Bldg, 3085 Albert St, Regina, SK S4S 0B1, Canada. TEL 888-613-3975 (in US only), FAX 306-721-4626, pad@sk.sympatico.ca, pdc@agr.gov.sk.ca, http://www.agr.gov.sk.ca/saf. Circ: 100,000.

663.2   USA   ISSN 1065-5948
VIRGINIA HAY CLEARING HOUSE. Text in English. m. back issues avail. **Document type:** *Government.* **Description:** Serves as a clearing house between buyers and sellers of Virginia hay. Lists buyers, sellers and descriptions of hay.
Published by: Department of Agriculture and Consumer Services, 1100 Bank St, Ste 805, Richmond, VA 23219-3638. TEL 804-786-3947, FAX 804-371-7787. Ed. J P Welch. Circ: 800.

633.2   USA
WASHINGTON FEEDLINE. Text in English. irreg. (3-5/yr.). membership. **Description:** Provides designated recipients of member companies with news of legislation important to the feed industry. Gives accounts of actions taken in response to specific bills and alerts members to the potential effect of certain legislative proposals.
Published by: American Feed Industry Association, 1501 Wilson Blvd, Ste 1100, Arlington, VA 22209. TEL 703-524-0810, FAX 703-524-1921, http://www.afia.org.

633.2   USA
WAYN-E-GRAM MAGAZINE. Text in English. 1966. q. adv. **Document type:** *Newsletter.* **Description:** For dealers who market Wayne feed products.
Published by: Continental Grain Company, Wayne Feed Division, 8500, Mankato, MN 56002-8500. TEL 312-930-1050, FAX 312-466-6614. Ed. Barbara K Becker. Adv. contact Meg Arbetman. Circ: 2,500 (controlled).

633.2 338.1   USA
WEEKLY NATIONAL HAY, FEED AND SEED WEEKLY SUMMARY. Text in English. w. USD 85 domestic; USD 90 in Canada & Mexico; USD 115 elsewhere (effective 2001). charts; illus.; mkt.; maps; stat. back issues avail. **Document type:** *Government.*
Former titles: Weekly National Feed and Seed Summary; (until 1998): California Alfalfa Hay Report
Media: Fax. **Related titles:** Fax ed.; Online - full text ed.
Published by: U.S. Department Of Agriculture, Livestock & Grain Market News Branch, 1428 S. Pioneer Way, Moses Lake, WA 98837. TEL 509-675-3611. Circ: 300.

WHEAT, BARLEY AND TRITICALE ABSTRACTS. see *AGRICULTURE—Abstracting, Bibliographies, Statistics*

633.1   USA   ISSN 0745-8991
HD9030.1   CODEN: WOGREJ
WORLD GRAIN. Text in English. m. USD 36; free to qualified personnel (effective 2005). adv. **Document type:** *Magazine, Trade.*
Related titles: Online - full text ed.
Indexed: FS&TA.
—BLDSC (9356.029700), CISTI, IE, ingenta, Linda Hall.
Published by: Sosland Publishing Company, 4800 Main St, Ste 100, Kansas City, MO 64112-2513. TEL 816-756-1000, FAX 816-756-0494, worldgrain@sosland.com, http://www.world-grain.com/, http://www.sosland.com. Ed. Arvin Donely. Pub. Mark Cornwell. Circ: 10,900 (paid and free).

633.1   GBR   ISSN 1745-2899
HD9030
▼ **WORLD GRAIN MARKETS REPORT.** Text in English. 2005 (Jan.). 24/yr. Please contact publisher for subscr. prices.. **Document type:** *Bulletin, Trade.* **Description:** Offers detailed and concise coverage of the latest grain market news, trade statistics, analysis and world production estimates for the international grains industry.
Incorporates (1986-2005): Grain & Oilseeds (1356-9155); Which was formerly (until 1994): Agrafile: Grain and Oilseeds (0950-494X)
Related titles: Online - full text ed.: World Grain Markets Report Online.
Published by: Agra Europe (London) Ltd. (Subsidiary of: T & F Informa plc), 80 Calverley Rd, Tunbridge Wells, Kent TN1 2UN, United Kingdom. TEL 44-1892-533813, FAX 44-1892-544895, marketing@agra-net.com, http://www.agra-net.com.

633.1   CHN   ISSN 1001-6899
CODEN: WLGXEG
WUHAN LIANGSHI GONGYE XUEYUAN XUEBAO/WUHAN FOOD INDUSTRY COLLEGE. JOURNAL. Text in English. 1982. q. CNY 10, USD 10. adv. **Document type:** *Academic/Scholarly.* **Description:** Publishes academic papers on food technology, grain lipid engineering, animal breeding, grain and oil processing machinery, economics, management and computer application.
Indexed: FS&TA.
Published by: Wuhan Liangshi Gongye Xueyuan, 129 Shundao St, Wuhan, Hubei 430022, China. TEL 027-5866971, FAX 027-5834951. Eds. Fu Lumin, Xu Xianghua. Adv. contact Xu Xianghua. page USD 250. Circ: 6,000 (paid).

633.2   DEU   ISSN 0941-9098
Z M P BILANZ GETREIDE, OELSAATEN, FUTTERMITTEL. Text in German. 1975. a. adv. **Document type:** *Bulletin, Trade.*
Formerly: Z M P Bilanz Getreide-Futtermittel (0170-7809)
Related titles: CD-ROM ed.
Published by: Zentrale Markt und Preisberichtstelle GmbH, Rochusstr 2, Bonn, 53123, Germany. TEL 49-228-9777173, FAX 49-228-9777179, info@zmp.de, http://www.zmp.de.

633.1   DEU
Z M P MARKTBERICHT. GETREIDE - OELSAATEN - FUTTERMITTEL. Text in German. w. **Document type:** *Bulletin, Trade.*
Published by: Zentrale Markt und Preisberichtstelle GmbH, Rochusstr 2, Bonn, 53123, Germany. TEL 49-228-9777173, FAX 49-228-9777179, info@zmp.de, http://www.zmp.de.

633.1   DEU
Z M P MARKTBERICHT. OELSAATEN SPEZIALINFO. Text in German. w. **Document type:** *Bulletin, Trade.*
Published by: Zentrale Markt und Preisberichtstelle GmbH, Rochusstr 2, Bonn, 53123, Germany. TEL 49-228-9777173, FAX 49-228-9777179, info@zmp.de, http://www.zmp.de.

338.1   DEU
Z V INFORMATIONEN. Text in German. m. back issues avail. **Document type:** *Journal, Trade.*
Published by: Zentralverband des Deutschen Getreide-, Futter- und Duengemittelhandels e.V., Beueler Bahnhofsplatz 18, Bonn, 53196, Germany. TEL 49-228-975850, FAX 49-228-9758530. Circ: 1,500.

641.3318   CHN   ISSN 1006-8082
➤ **ZHONGGUO DAOMI/CHINA RICE.** Text in Chinese. 1994. bi-m. USD 30 (effective 2002). **Document type:** *Bulletin, Academic/Scholarly.* **Description:** Provides information on Chinese rice in such areas as rice research, production, grain processing and trade.
Related titles: Online - full text ed.: (from East View Information Services)
Indexed: AEA, AgBio, CPA, FCA, FS&TA, HortAb, I&DA, MaizeAb, NutrAb, PBA, PGegResA, PGrRegA, PHN&I, PN&I, PotatoAb, RDA, RPP, RevApplEntom, RiceAb, S&F, SeedAb, TriticAb, WAE&RSA, WeedAb.
Published by: Zhongguo Shuidao Yanjiusuo/China National Rice Research Institute, 359 Tiyuchang Lu, Hangzhou, Zhejiang 310006, China. TEL 86-571-63370271, FAX 86-571-63371745, sinorice@public.fy.hz.zj.cn, http://www.cnrri.org. Ed. Hongfa Cai. R&P Pan Qianlin. Adv. contact Wang Nuoxing.

633.1   CHN   ISSN 1001-7216
➤ **ZHONGGUO SHUIDAO KEXUE/CHINESE JOURNAL OF RICE SCIENCE.** Text in Chinese, English. 1986. q. USD 40 (effective 2002). adv. **Document type:** *Academic/Scholarly.* **Description:** Publishes original papers on rice research, including experiment reports, short communications, reviews, research notes, etc.
Related titles: Online - full text ed.: (from East View Information Services).
Indexed: AEA, ASFA, AgBio, BioCN&I, CPA, EntAb, FCA, HerbAb, HortAb, I&DA, MaizeAb, NemAb, NutrAb, PBA, PGegResA, PGrRegA, PHN&I, PN&I, RA&MP, RPP, RevApplEntom, RiceAb, S&F, SIA, SeedAb, SoyAb, TriticAb, WeedAb.
—BLDSC (3180.674500).

Published by: Zhongguo Shuidao Yanjiusuo/China National Rice Research Institute, 359 Tiyuchang Lu, Hangzhou, Zhejiang 310006, China. sinorice@public.fy.hz.zj.cn, cjrs@fy.hz.zj.cn, http://www.cnrri.org. Ed. Shaokai Min. R&P, Adv. contact Li Jian.

633   SCG   ISSN 0351-0999
CODEN: ZIHLDU
➤ **ZITO HLEB**; casopis za tehnologiju zita i brasna. Text in Serbo-Croatian; Abstracts in English. 1974. bi-m. EUR 100 (effective 2005). adv. bk.rev. **Document type:** *Journal, Academic/Scholarly.*
Indexed: CIN, ChemAb, ChemTitl, FS&TA, RefZh.
—CASDDS.
Published by: Univerzitet u Novom Sadu, Tehnoloski Fakultet, Zavod za Tehnologiju Zita i Brasna/University in Novy Sad, Institut for Cereal and Flour Technology, Bul Cara Lazara 1, Novi Sad, 21000. TEL 381-21-350133, FAX 381-21-450413, nscereal@eunet.yu. Ed., R&P, Adv. contact Marija Saric. Circ: 550 (controlled).

AGRICULTURE—Poultry And Livestock

see also AGRICULTURE—Dairying And Dairy Products ; LEATHER AND FUR INDUSTRIES ; VETERINARY SCIENCE

636   CUB
A C P A. Text in Spanish. s-a. USD 18 in South America; USD 20 in North America; USD 22 elsewhere.
Published by: (Asociacion Cubana de Produccion Animal), Ediciones Cubanas, Obispo No. 527, Apdo. 605, Havana, Cuba.

636   USA
A F I A SAFETYGRAM. Text in English. m. USD 65 to non-members; USD 32.50 to members. **Description:** Features the latest in safety practices, prevention, and regulations.
Published by: American Feed Industry Association, 1501 Wilson Blvd, Ste 1100, Arlington, VA 22209. TEL 703-524-0810, FAX 703-524-1921, http://www.afia.org.

636.0832   USA
A I F NEWSLETTER. Text in English. 1987. m. looseleaf. USD 25. back issues avail. **Document type:** *Newsletter.* **Description:** Serves as an information source for what is happening in the animal rights movement and activist groups' activities. Also provides updates on achievements in animal agriculture research and education, new educational materials, and future products and materials to benefit producers and the industry.
Published by: Animal Industry Foundation, 1501 Wilson Blvd, Ste 1100, Arlington, VA 22209. TEL 703-524-0810, FAX 703-524-1921, aif@aif.org, http://www.aif.org. Ed. Steve Kopperud. R&P Kay Johnson. Circ: 3,500.

A L F A LOTFEEDING. see *AGRICULTURE—Feed, Flour And Grain*

636   ETH
A L P A N NETWORK PAPER. (African Livestock Policy Analysis Network) Text in English. 1985. 2/yr. **Description:** Information network for policy makers, analysts and implementors involved in livestock research and development in Africa.
Published by: International Livestock Centre for Africa, PO Box 5689, Addis Ababa, Ethiopia. TEL 251-1-613115, FAX 251-1-611892, ILCA@CGNET.COM, ilca@cgnet.com.

636   ETH
A L P A N NEWSLETTER. (African Livestock Policy Analysis Network) Text in English. 1985. 2/yr. **Document type:** *Newsletter.* **Description:** Provides information on developments in the livestock field and introduces Network Papers authored by ALPAN members.
Published by: International Livestock Centre for Africa, PO Box 5689, Addis Ababa, Ethiopia. TEL 251-1-613215, FAX 251-1-611892, ilca@cgnet.com.

636.6   USA
A P A NEWS AND VIEWS. Text in English. q. USD 10 domestic membership; USD 25 foreign membership (effective 2000). **Document type:** *Newsletter.* **Description:** Covers purebred poultry as a hobby and exhibition poultry.
Former titles: Fancy Feather. A P A News and Views; (until 1987): American Poultry Association. News and Views
Published by: American Poultry Association, 2209, Mango, FL 33550-2209. Ed. Lorna F Rhodes.

A T L; lantbrukets affaerstidning. (Annonsblad till Tidskrift foer Landtmaen) see *AGRICULTURE*

636 346.066   USA
AAMPLIFIER. Text in English. s-m. USD 50 to non-members (effective 2001). back issues avail. **Document type:** *Newsletter.* **Description:** Provides information for the meat industry on trends, education and developments. Includes news for members and an update.

Published by: American Association of Meat Processors, PO Box 269, Elizabethtown, PA 17022. TEL 717-367-1168, FAX 717-367-9096, aamp@aamp.com, http://www.aamp.com. Ed. Stephen F Krut. Circ: 2,200.

636.2 GBR
ABERDEEN - ANGUS HERD BOOK. Text in English. 1884. a. GBP 30. back issues avail. **Document type:** *Trade.*
Published by: Aberdeen-Angus Cattle Society, Pedigree House, 6 King's Pl, Perth, Scotland PH2 8AD, United Kingdom. TEL 44-1738-622477, FAX 44-1738-636436, info@aberdeen-angus.co.uk. Ed. Ron McHattie. Circ: 350.

636.2 GBR ISSN 0001-317X
ABERDEEN - ANGUS REVIEW. Text in English. 1919. a. GBP 7. adv. illus.; mkt. **Document type:** *Journal, Trade.*
—CISTI.
Published by: Aberdeen-Angus Cattle Society, Pedigree House, 6 King's Pl, Perth, Scotland PH2 8AD, United Kingdom. TEL 44-1738-622477, FAX 44-1738-636436, info@aberdeen-angus.co.uk. Ed. Robert Anderson. Circ: 2,600.

636 POL ISSN 0065-0935
SF1 CODEN: AASZBW
ACTA AGRARIA ET SILVESTRIA. SERIES ZOOTECHNICA. Text in Polish; Summaries in English, Russian. 1961. a. price varies. bibl.; charts. **Document type:** *Monographic series, Academic/Scholarly.* **Description:** Experimental studies on farm animal breeding, physiology, animal hygiene and environment as well as animal reproduction.
Formerly (until 1965): Acta Agraria et Silvestria. Seria Zootechniczna (0376-1568)
Indexed: AEA, AgrAg, AgrLib, AnBrAb, BiolAb, ChemAb, ExcerpMed, FCA, HerbAb, I&DA, IndVet, MaizeAb, NutrAb, PN&I, PoultAb, S&F, TriticAb, VetBull, ZooRec.
—CASDDS, KNAW.
Published by: (Polska Akademia Nauk, Oddzial w Krakowie, Komisja Nauk Rolniczych i Lesnych), Polska Akademia Nauk, Oddzial w Krakowie, ul sw Jana 28, Krakow, 31018, Poland. TEL 48-12-4224853, FAX 48-12-4222791.

636 HUN ISSN 1418-1789
ACTA AGRARIA KAPOSVARIENSIS. Text in Hungarian. 1987. s-a. **Document type:** *Journal, Academic/Scholarly.*
Former titles (until 1997): Pannon Agrartudomanyi Egyetem. Allattenyesztesi Kar. Szaktanacsok (0866-1596); (until 1989): Agrartudomanyi Egyetem. Allattenyesztesi Kar. Szaktanacsok (0238-244X)
Indexed: AEA, AbHyg, AgBio, AnBrAb, DSA, FCA, FPA, ForAb, HelmAb, HortAb, IndVet, MaizeAb, NutrAb, PN&I, PoultAb, ProtozoAb, RM&VM, RRTA, S&F, SeedAb, SoyAb, TriticAb, VetBull, WAE&RSA, WeedAb.
—BLDSC (0588.660000).
Published by: Kaposvari Egyetem, Allattudomanyi Kar/University of Kaposvar, Faculty of Animal Science, 40 Guba Sandor St, Kaposvar, 7400, Hungary. TEL 36-82-314155, FAX 36-82-320175, alpar@mail.atk.u-kaposvar.hu, http://www.atk.u-kaposvar.hu/szeregys/gyakorlat/kuttema.htm.

636 NOR ISSN 0906-4702
SF1 CODEN: ASSAEI
➤ **ACTA AGRICULTURAE SCANDINAVICA. SECTION A. ANIMAL SCIENCE.** Text in English. 1950. q. GBP 173, USD 285 combined subscription to institutions print & online eds. (effective 2006). adv. bibl.; charts; illus. back issues avail.; reprint service avail. from PSC. **Document type:** *Academic/Scholarly.*
Supersedes in part (in 1992): Acta Agriculturae Scandinavica (0001-5121)
Related titles: Online - full text ed.: ISSN 1651-1972. GBP 164, USD 271 to institutions (effective 2006) (from EBSCO Publishing, Gale Group, IngentaConnect, O C L C Online Computer Library Center, Inc., Swets Information Services); Supplement(s): Acta Agriculturae Scandinavica. Supplementum. Section B. ISSN 1651-9140. 1957.
Indexed: AEA, ASCA, AgBio, AnBrAb, BIOSIS Prev, BioCN&I, BioDAb, BiolAb, CIN, CPA, Cadscan, ChemAb, ChemTitl, CurCont, DSA, EnvAb, EnvInd, ExcerpMed, FCA, FS&TA, HerbAb, HortAb, ISR, IndVet, LeadAb, NutrAb, PBA, PN&I, PoultAb, ProtozoAb, RA&MP, REE&TA, RM&VM, RPP, RRTA, S&F, SCI, SFA, SIA, SeedAb, SoyAb, TriticAb, VetBull, WAE&RSA, WildRev, Zincscan, ZooRec.
—BLDSC (0589.005000), CASDDS, CISTI, IDS, IE, Infotrieve, ingenta, Linda Hall. **CCC.**
Published by: (Kungliga Skogs- och Lantbruksakademien/Royal Swedish Academy of Agriculture and Forestry SWE), Taylor & Francis A S (Subsidiary of: Taylor & Francis Group), Biskop Gunnerusgate 14A, PO Box 12 Posthuset, Oslo, 0051, Norway. TEL 47-23-103460, FAX 47-23-103461, journals@tandf.no, http://www.tandf.co.uk/journals/titles/09064702.asp. Ed. Odd Vangen. Circ: 1,000. **Subscr. to:** Taylor & Francis Ltd, Journals Customer Service, Rankine Rd, Basingstoke, Hants RG24 8PR, United Kingdom. TEL 44-1256-813000, FAX 44-1256-330245. **Co-sponsor:** Scandinavian Association of Agricultural Scientists.

➤ **ACTA FYTOTECHNICA ET ZOOTECHNICA**; the scientific journal for phytotechnics and zootechnics. see *AGRICULTURE—Crop Production And Soil*

636 GBR ISSN 0885-2405
ADVANCES IN MEAT RESEARCH SERIES. Text in English. 1985. irreg., latest vol.7, 1991. price varies. **Document type:** *Monographic series.*
Indexed: Agr, CIN, ChemAb, ChemTitl.
—BLDSC (0709.373000), CISTI. **CCC.**
Published by: Pergamon (Subsidiary of: Elsevier Science & Technology), The Boulevard, Langford Ln, East Park, Kidlington, Oxford OX5 1GB, United Kingdom. TEL 44-1865-843000, FAX 44-1865-843010. Eds. A M Pearson, T R Dutson. **Subscr. to:** Elsevier BV, PO Box 211, Amsterdam 1000 AE, Netherlands. TEL 31-20-485-3757, FAX 31-20-485-3432, nlinfo-f@elsevier.nl, http://www.elsevier.nl.

636.4 CAN ISSN 1489-1395
ADVANCES IN PORK PRODUCTION. Text in English. 1990. a. CND 30 (effective 2004). back issues avail.
Indexed: Agr.
—CISTI. **CCC.**
Published by: (University of Alberta, Department of Agricultural, Food and Nutritional Science, Banff Pork Seminar, University of Alberta, Department of Animal Science), University of Alberta, Faculty of Extension, 8303-112 St, Edmonton, AB T6G 2J7, Canada. extinfo@ualberta.ca, http://www.extension.ualberta.ca.

636.2 NGA ISSN 1596-4019
SF55.N5
AFRICAN JOURNAL OF LIVESTOCK EXTENSION. Text in English. 2002. a. back issues avail. **Document type:** *Journal, Academic/Scholarly.* **Description:** Aims to bring to the fore the role and significance of livestock in maintaining rural, peri-urban and urban households, vis-a-vis its impact on poverty alleviation, household nutritional status, economic coping strategy and provision of employment.
Related titles: Online - full text ed.: (from International Network for the Availability of Scientific Publications, African Journals Online).
Published by: University of Ibadan, Faculty of Agriculture and Forestry, Ibadan, Nigeria. ajlex@fastmail.com, https://www.ajol.info/journal_index.php?jid=2&ab=ajlex. Ed. L.A. Akinbile.

636 ETH ISSN 1013-7750
➤ **AFRICAN LIVESTOCK RESEARCH.** Text in English, French. 1978-1989 (no.35); N.S. 1992. q. USD 75 to individuals; USD 120 to institutions. **Document type:** *Academic/Scholarly.* **Description:** Disseminates the results of strategic, basic and applied research that relates to livestock and mixed crop-livestock systems in Africa.
Supersedes: I L C A Bulletin (0255-0008); Bulletin du C I P E A (0255-0016)
Related titles: Microfiche ed.: N.S.
Indexed: AEA, AgrForAb, AnBrAb, FCA, HerbAb, MaizeAb, PLESA, RDA, S&F, S&MA, SoyAb, TriticAb, WAE&RSA.
—CISTI.
Published by: International Livestock Centre for Africa, PO Box 5689, Addis Ababa, Ethiopia. ILCA@CGNET.COM, ilca@cgnet.com. Ed. Michael Smalley. Circ: 3,431.

636.2 ZAF ISSN 0515-6203
AFRIKANER BEESJOERNAAL. Text in Afrikaans, English. 1953. q. adv.
Published by: (Afrikaner Cattle Breeders' Association), Dreyer Printers & Publishers, 21 Krause St, PO Box 286, Bloemfontein, 9300, South Africa.

AGRICULTURA; revista agropecuaria. see *AGRICULTURE*

AGRICULTURAL RESEARCH; solving problems for the growing world. see *AGRICULTURE—Crop Production And Soil*

AGRICULTURAL SCIENCE DIGEST. see *AGRICULTURE*

AGRICULTURAL STATISTICS SERIES NO.2: ANIMAL PRODUCTION. see *AGRICULTURE—Abstracting, Bibliographies, Statistics*

636 CRI ISSN 1021-7444
S476.A1
➤ **AGRONOMIA MESOAMERICANA**; revista agropecuaria. Text in Spanish. 1990. a. USD 11 per issue domestic; USD 13 per issue foreign (effective 2004). **Document type:** *Academic/Scholarly.*
Indexed: AEA, AgBio, AgrForAb, AnBrAb, BioCN&I, CPA, DSA, FCA, FPA, FS&TA, ForAb, HerbAb, HortAb, I&DA, IndVet, JEL, MaizeAb, NemAb, NutrAb, OrnHort, PBA, PGegResA, PGrRegA, PHN&I, PotatoAb, PoultAb, RA&MP, RDA, RPP, RefZh, RevApplEntom, RiceAb, S&F, SIA, SeedAb, SoyAb, VetBull, WAE&RSA, WeedAb, ZooRec.
—BLDSC (0768.250000), IE, ingenta.
Published by: (Programa Cooperativo Centroamericano de Mejoramiento de Cultivos y Animales (PCCMCA)), Universidad de Costa Rica, Estacion Experimental Fabio Baudrit Moreno, Apdo. Postal 183, Alajuela, 4050, Costa Rica. TEL 506-433-9111, FAX 506-433-7100, pccmca@sol.racsa.co.cr, pccmca@cariari.ucr.ac.cr. Ed. Rodolfo Araya V. R&P Rodolfo Araya V.

636 POL ISSN 0137-1770
AKADEMIA ROLNICZA, POZNAN. ROCZNIKI. ZOOTECHNIKA. Text in Polish; Summaries in English. 1967. irreg. price varies. **Document type:** *Academic/Scholarly.* **Description:** Features works on animal breeding, such as: cattle, pigs, horses, sheep; also articles on animal feeding and fodder; also on fishing.
Indexed: AgrAg, AgrLib, BibAg, SoyAb, ZooRec.
Published by: (Akademia Rolnicza im. Augusta Cieszkowskiego w Poznaniu), Wydawnictwo Akademii Rolniczej w Poznaniu, ul Witosa 45, Poznan, 61693, Poland. TEL 48-61-487809, FAX 48-61-487802, wgolab@owl.au.poznan.pl, wydar@au.poznan.pl, http://sawn.au.poznan.pl/bib/bghome.html. R&P Elzbieta Zagorska TEL 48-61-487806.

636 POL
AKADEMIA ROLNICZA WE WROCLAWIU. ZESZYTY NAUKOWE. ZOOTECHNIKA. Text in Polish; Summaries in English. 1956. irreg. price varies. **Document type:** *Academic/Scholarly.*
Formerly (until 1973): Wyzsza Szkola Rolnicza we Wroclawiu. Zeszyty Naukowe. Zootechnika (0520-9323)
Related titles: ♦ Series of: Akademia Rolnicza we Wroclawiu. Zeszyty Naukowe. ISSN 0867-7964.
Indexed: AgrLib, ZooRec.
—CASDDS, CISTI.
Published by: Akademia Rolnicza we Wroclawiu/Agricultural University of Wroclaw, Ul Norwida 25, Wroclaw, 50375, Poland. TEL 48-71-3205101, wyd@ozi.ar.wroc.pl. Circ: 320. **Subscr. to:** Wydawnictwo Akademii Rolniczej we Wroclawiu, ul Sopocka 23, Wroclaw 50344, Poland.

636.2 USA ISSN 0516-3889
ALABAMA CATTLEMAN. Text in English. 1958. m. USD 30 (effective 2005). adv. **Document type:** *Magazine, Trade.*
Published by: Alabama Cattleman's Association, 201 S Bainbridge St, PO Box 2499, Montgomery, AL 36102-2499. TEL 334-265-1867, FAX 334-834-5326, mag@bamabeef.org, http://www.bamabeef.org. Ed., Pub. William E Powell. Adv. contact Layne Lunn. Circ: 12,500 (controlled).

636.2 CAN ISSN 1187-0761
ALBERTA BEEF. Text in English. 1976. m. CND 20; USD 35 foreign. adv. bk.rev. **Document type:** *Trade.* **Description:** Targets Alberta's commercial beef producers.
Former titles (until 1991): World of Beef (0848-8142); World of Beef and Feedlot Management; World of Beef and Stockmans Record; World of Beef
Published by: Creative Motion Publishing, 202 2915 19th St, N E, Calgary, AB T2E 7A2, Canada. TEL 403-250-1090, FAX 403-291-9546. Ed. Cindy McCreath. Adv. contact Lee Gunderson. Circ: 14,000.

ALIMENTOS BALANCEADOS PARA ANIMALES. see *AGRICULTURE—Feed, Flour And Grain*

636 HUN ISSN 0230-1814
CODEN: ATAKDW
ALLATTENYESZTES ES TAKARMANYOZAS/HUNGARIAN JOURNAL OF ANIMAL PRODUCTION. Text in Hungarian. 1951. bi-m. HUF 2,800. bk.rev. **Document type:** *Newsletter.* **Description:** Covers research and development in animal production and nutrition in Hungary.
Formerly (until 1980): Allattenyesztes - Animal Breeding (0365-4052)
Indexed: AEA, AgBio, AgrForAb, AnBrAb, CIN, ChemAb, ChemTitl, DSA, FCA, HelmAb, HerbAb, HortAb, IndVet, MaizeAb, NutrAb, PBA, PGegResA, PN&I, PoultAb, ProtozoAb, RA&MP, RM&VM, RPP, RRTA, S&F, SIA, SoyAb, TriticAb, VetBull, WAE&RSA, WeedAb.
—CASDDS, CISTI.
Published by: (Hungary. Ministry of Agriculture and Rural Development), Allattenyesztesi es Takarmanyozasi Kutato-Intezet, Herceghalom, 2053, Hungary. TEL 36-1-23-319133, FAX 36-1-23-319133, TELEX 226664, atk@atk.iif.hu. Ed. Janos Gundel. Circ: 1,000.

636 FRA
ALLIANCE PASTORALE. BULLETIN. Text in French. 1932. m. adv. **Document type:** *Bulletin.*
Published by: Syndicat de l'Alliance Pastorale, Montmorillon, 86500, France. TEL 33-5-49833030, FAX 33-5-49833050, ap@alliancepastorale.fr. Ed. Nicolas Decazes. Adv. contact Micheline Marlaud.

636.296 AUS ISSN 1328-8318
ALPACAS AUSTRALIA. Text in English. 1992. q. **Document type:** *Journal, Consumer.*
Published by: Australian Alpaca Association, Inc., Ste 1, 818 Whitehouse Rd, Box Hill, VIC, Australia.

636.587 USA ISSN 0065-745X
SF489.B2
AMERICAN BANTAM ASSOCIATION. YEARBOOK. Text in English. 1917. a. USD 15 (effective 2000). adv. **Document type:** *Yearbook.*
Published by: American Bantam Association, PO Box 127, Augusta, NJ 07822. Ed. Eleanor Vinhage. Circ: 3,000.

A

636.2 USA
AMERICAN CATTLEMEN. Text in English. 1998. bi-m. USD 9.95 domestic; USD 14.95 in Canada & Mexico; USD 21.95 elsewhere (effective 2004). adv. **Document type:** *Trade.*
Published by: Heartland Ag-Business Group, Inc., 1003 Central Ave, Fort Dodge, IA 50501. TEL 515-955-1600, 800-673-4763, aginfo@agdeal.com, http://www.agdeal.com. Adv. contact Bailey Johnson. B&W page USD 800, color page USD 1,332; trim 7.75 x 10.75. Circ: 90,000.

664.9 USA ISSN 1042-5233
AMERICAN CATTLEWOMAN. Text in English. 1972. bi-m. USD 25. bk.rev. **Document type:** *Newsletter.* **Description:** Profiles women in the cattle industry.
Former titles: American National CattleWomen Newsletter (0744-4389); American National CowBelles Newsletter
Published by: American National CattleWomen, Inc., PO Box 3881, Englewood, CO 80155. TEL 303-694-0313, FAX 303-694-2390. Ed., Pub., R&P Patricia Sherwood. Circ: 7,000.

636.2 USA
AMERICAN DEXTER CATTLE ASSOCIATION. BULLETIN. Text in English. bi-m. USD 10 (effective 2000). **Document type:** *Bulletin.*
Published by: American Dexter Cattle Association, 4150 Merino Ave., Watertown, MN 55388-8320. TEL 660-463-7704.

636.2 USA ISSN 0065-8081
AMERICAN DEXTER CATTLE ASSOCIATION. HERD BOOK. Text in English. 1920. a. USD 10 (effective 2000). cum.index: 1960-1987. **Document type:** *Newsletter.*
Published by: American Dexter Cattle Association, 4150 Merino Ave., Watertown, MN 55388-8320. TEL 660-463-7704. Ed. Richard Henry.

AMERICAN FARRIER'S ASSOCIATION NEWSLETTER. see *SPORTS AND GAMES—Horses And Horsemanship*

AMERICAN FARRIERS JOURNAL. see *SPORTS AND GAMES—Horses And Horsemanship*

636 USA ISSN 1057-6649
CODEN: PMACEN
AMERICAN FEED INDUSTRY ASSOCIATION. ANNUAL AND SEMIANNUAL MEETINGS OF THE NUTRITION COUNCIL. PROCEEDINGS. Text in English. 1944. a. USD 100 to non-members; USD 150 to members (effective 2005). back issues avail. **Document type:** *Proceedings.* **Description:** Presentations given during the national and regional production schools. Subjects vary widely. Covers truck operations, workers' compensation, energy management, OSHA regulations, FDA updates, safety, pelleting, etc.
Formerly: American Feed Manufacturers Association. Annual Meeting of the Nutrition Council. Proceedings
Indexed: BiolAb.
Published by: (Nutrition Council), American Feed Industry Association, 1501 Wilson Blvd, Ste 1100, Arlington, VA 22209. TEL 703-524-0810, FAX 703-524-1921, http://www.afia.org. Circ: 1,500.

636 USA
AMERICAN FEED INDUSTRY ASSOCIATION. PRODUCTION SCHOOL PROCEEDINGS. Text in English. a. USD 50 to non-members; USD 25 to members. **Document type:** *Proceedings.*
Published by: (Production School), American Feed Industry Association, 1501 Wilson Blvd, Ste 1100, Arlington, VA 22209. TEL 703-524-0810, FAX 703-524-1921, http://www.afia.org.

636.3 USA
AMERICAN GOAT SOCIETY BUYERS GUIDE✶. Text in English. a. looseleaf. free. **Document type:** *Directory, Trade.*
Published by: American Goat Society, Inc., 735 Oakridge Ln., Pipe Creek, TX 78063-5658. TEL 518-875-6708. Circ: 600.

636.39 USA ISSN 0065-8456
AMERICAN GOAT SOCIETY. YEAR BOOK✶. Text in English. 1935. a. membership. adv. index. **Document type:** *Bulletin.*
Published by: American Goat Society, Inc., 735 Oakridge Ln., Pipe Creek, TX 78063-5658. TEL 518-875-6708. Ed. Sandra Mason. Circ: 450.

636.3 USA
AMERICAN POLYPAY SHEEP NEWS. Text in English. m. USD 50 membership (effective 2005). **Document type:** *Newsletter, Trade.* **Description:** Covers all areas of interest concerning the polypay sheep - sales, production, health; inquiries and their breeders.
Published by: American Polypay Sheep Association, 15603 173rd Ave, Milo, IA 50166. TEL 641-942-6402, FAX 641-942-6502, info@polppay.org, http://www.polypay.org. Circ: 250.

636.3 USA
AMERICAN RAMBOUILLET SHEEP BREEDERS ASSOCIATION. NEWSLETTER. Text in English. q. **Document type:** *Newsletter.*
Published by: American Rambouillet Sheep Breeders Association, 1610 S. Fm 3261., Levelland, TX 79336-9230. TEL 915-949-4414.

636 USA ISSN 0886-4357
AMERICAN RED ANGUS. Text in English. 1954. 10/yr. USD 25 domestic; USD 40 in Canada; USD 50 elsewhere (effective 2005). adv. charts; illus.; stat. **Document type:** *Magazine, Trade.*
Published by: Red Angus Association of America, 4201 N Interstate 35, Denton, TX 76207. TEL 940-387-3502, FAX 940-383-4036, info@redangus.org, http://www.redangus.org/. Adv. contact Kevin LeMaster. Circ: 9,000 (controlled).

636 USA
AMERICAN SOCIETY OF ANIMAL SCIENCE. TRIENNIAL SYMPOSIUM. PROCEEDINGS. Text in English. triennial. **Document type:** *Proceedings, Academic/Scholarly.*
Formerly (until 2002): Animal Reproduction Symposium. Proceedings (0570-1244)
Published by: American Society of Animal Science, 1111 N Dunlap Ave, Savoy, IL 61874. TEL 217-356-9050, FAX 217-938-4119, asas@assochq.org, http://www.asas.org.

636 USA ISSN 0569-7832
CODEN: PMWSA7
AMERICAN SOCIETY OF ANIMAL SCIENCE. WESTERN SECTION PROCEEDINGS. Text in English. 1949. a., latest vol.52, 2001. price varies. **Document type:** *Proceedings, Academic/Scholarly.*
Indexed: Agr, FS&TA.
—BLDSC (6631.870000), IE, ingenta, Linda Hall.
Published by: American Society of Animal Science, 1111 N Dunlap Ave, Savoy, IL 61874. TEL 217-356-9050, FAX 217-938-4119, asas@assochq.org, http://www.asas.org/westernsection. R&P G S Lewis. Circ: 600.

AMERICAN STANDARD CHINCHILLA RABBIT ASSOCIATION. NEWSLETTER. see *PETS*

636 ESP ISSN 1577-8568
ANAPORC. Text in Spanish. 1981. m. adv. bk.rev.
Related titles: Online - full text ed.: ISSN 1577-8576. 1999.
Published by: Prodive S.A., C Joaquin Costa 15, Madrid, 28002, Spain. TEL 34-91-5636002, FAX 34-91-5640940, javier.marcos@revista-anaporc.com, http://www.revista-anaporc.com. Ed. Santiago Martin Rillo.

636.39 ZAF ISSN 0003-3464
ANGORA GOAT & MOHAIR JOURNAL/ANGORABOK- EN SYBOKHAARBLAD. Text in Afrikaans, English. 1959. s-a. ZAR 50 (effective 2001). adv. bk.rev. mkt.; stat.; tr.lit. **Description:** Covers mohair and Angora goats, as well as agricultural concerns.
Indexed: AnBrAb, ISAP.
Published by: S.A. Mohair Grower's Association, PO Box 50, Jansenville, Eastern Cape 6265, South Africa. TEL 27-49-8360140, FAX 27-49-8360140. Ed., Adv. contact J. Englebrecht. Pub. J Englebrecht. R&P J Engelbrecht TEL 27-41-4871386. B&W page ZAR 175, color page ZAR 500. Circ: 2,500. **Co-sponsors:** Angora Goat Stud Breeders' Association of S.A.; Mohair Board.

636.39 USA
ANGORA GOAT EXCHANGE. Text in English. bi-m. USD 9. **Description:** For angora goat raisers.
Address: 2458 Morrice Rd, Owosso, MI 48867.

636.2 USA
ANGUS; the magazine. Text in English. 1987. m. USD 15 (effective 2005). adv. **Document type:** *Magazine, Trade.* **Description:** Keeps members of the Western State Angus Association abreast of trends and changes in the Angus industry in the West and beyond.
Published by: James Danekas & Associates, Inc., 3222 Ramos Cir., Ste 8, PO Box 613, Sacramento, CA 95827. TEL 916-362-2697, FAX 916-362-4015, http://www.cwo.com/~jdainc. Ed. James A Danekas. Circ: 4,600.

636.2 USA
ANGUS BEEF BULLETIN. Text in English. 1982. 4/yr. adv. **Document type:** *Trade.*
Published by: American Angus Association, 3201 Frederick Ave, St. Joseph, MO 64506-2997. TEL 816-383-5270. Ed., R&P Shauna Hermel. Pub. Richard Spader. Adv. contact Cheryl Oxley. page USD 1,095. Circ: 63,000 (controlled).

636.2 NZL ISSN 0300-3345
ANGUS HERD BOOK OF NEW ZEALAND. Text in English. 1919. a. NZD 40 to members (effective 2000). **Document type:** *Trade.* **Description:** Lists pedigree Angus cattle registered in New Zealand.
Published by: New Zealand Angus Association Inc., P.O. Box 503, 52 Kimbotton Rd, Felding, New Zealand. TEL 64-6-3234484, FAX 64-6-3233878. Ed. Christine Bristol. Circ: 700.

636.2 USA ISSN 0194-9543
ANGUS JOURNAL. Text in English. 1979. m. USD 50 domestic; USD 80 in Canada; USD 125 elsewhere (effective 2005). adv. bk.rev. illus.; mkt. **Document type:** *Journal, Trade.* **Description:** Official publication for the American Angus Association. Features and pictures on breeding Angus cattle, ranching, herd management. Includes information on association activities, registration and research.
Supersedes (as of vol.60, 1979): Aberdeen-Angus Journal (0001-3161)
Related titles: Microform ed.: (from PQC); Online - full text ed.: ISSN 1552-3276.
—CISTI, Linda Hall.
Published by: American Angus Association, 3201 Frederick Ave, St. Joseph, MO 64506-2997. TEL 816-383-5200, 800-821-5478, FAX 816-233-6575, journal@ngus.org, journal@angusjournal.com, http://www.angusjournal.com. Ed., R&P Shauna Hermel. Adv. contact Cheryl Oxley. page USD 775. Circ: 17,500 (paid).

636.2 USA ISSN 0402-4265
ANGUS TOPICS. Text in English. 1955. m. USD 12; USD 24 foreign. adv. **Document type:** *Trade.* **Description:** Provides informative articles and sale opportunities relative to breeding and raising registered Angus cattle.
Published by: Angus Topics, Inc., PO Box 397, Carmi, IL 62821. TEL 618-382-8553, FAX 618-382-3436. Ed., R&P Judy M Bingman. Adv. contact E R Bingman. Circ: 10,000.

ANIMAL BIOTECHNOLOGY. see *BIOLOGY—Biotechnology*

636 USA
ANIMAL FINDERS' GUIDE. Text in English. 1984. 18/yr. USD 25 domestic; USD 55 foreign (effective 2001). adv. bk.rev. **Document type:** *Trade.* **Description:** Devoted to the exotic animal owner.
Address: PO Box 99, Prairie Creek, IN 47869. TEL 812-898-2678, FAX 812-898-2013, animalfinder@thnet.com, http://www.animalfindersguide.com. Ed., Pub., R&P Patrick D Hoctor. Adv. contact Sharon K Hoctor. page USD 190. Circ: 4,000 (paid).

636 GBR ISSN 0266-8629
ANIMAL HEALTH. Text in English. 1972. a. **Document type:** *Government.*
Formerly: Report on the Animal Health Services in Great Britain (0432-4501)
—BLDSC (0903.590000).
Published by: Ministry of Agriculture Fisheries and Food, HS Stationery Office, Flat 2, St Clements House, 2-16 Colegate, Norwich, NR3 1BQ, United Kingdom. **Co-sponsors:** Department of Agriculture for Welsh; Department of Agriculture and Fisheries for Scotland.

636 636.089 GRC
ANIMAL HUSBANDRY AND BREEDING. Text in Greek. 1986. q. back issues avail. **Document type:** *Academic/Scholarly.* **Description:** Covers livestock production and provides marketing information on new methods, technology and techniques, breeders, scientists and traders.
Published by: Agrotechnical Publications S.A., 24-26 Favierou St, Athens, 104 38, Greece. TEL 30-1-5222-054, FAX 30-1-5246-628, TELEX 222264 STIM GR. Ed. Costas Colotouros. Circ: 8,000.

636.0852 CAN
ANIMAL NUTRITION ASSOCIATION OF CANADA. EASTERN NUTRITION CONFERENCE. PROCEEDINGS. Text in English; Abstracts in English, French. 1996. a. CND 40 to non-members; CND 30 to members. back issues avail. **Document type:** *Proceedings.* **Description:** Discusses animal nutrition research.
Formerly: Canadian Feed Industry Association. Eastern Nutrition Conference. Proceedings (1203-8881)
—BLDSC (3646.763000).
Published by: Animal Nutrition Association of Canada, 325 Dalhousie St, Ste 625, Ottawa, ON K1N 7G2, Canada. TEL 613-241-6421, FAX 613-241-7970, info@anac-anac.ca, cfia@cfia-aciaa.ca. Ed. Tracey McGrath.

636 AUS
ANIMAL PRODUCTION IN AUSTRALIA (CD-ROM EDITION). Text in English. biennial. free to members. **Document type:** *Proceedings, Academic/Scholarly.*
Media: CD-ROM.
Published by: The Australian Society of Animal Production Inc., PO Box 61, Toowong, QLD 4066, Australia. asap@adelaide.edu.au, http://www.asap.asn.au.

636 NLD ISSN 0378-4320
QP251 CODEN: ANRSDV
➤ **ANIMAL REPRODUCTION SCIENCE.** Text in Dutch. 1977. 24/yr. EUR 1,838 in Europe to institutions; JPY 243,900 in Japan to institutions; USD 2,056 to institutions except Europe and Japan (effective 2006). back issues avail. **Document type:** *Journal, Academic/Scholarly.* **Description:** Publishes scientific papers dealing with the study of reproduction of all animals which could be regarded as being useful to man.
Related titles: Microform ed.: (from PQC); Online - full text ed.: (from EBSCO Publishing, Gale Group, IngentaConnect, ScienceDirect, Swets Information Services).
Indexed: AEA, AEBA, ASCA, ASFA, AbHyg, AgBio, Agr, AgrForAb, AnBrAb, B&BAb, BIOBASE, BIOSIS Prev, BibRep, BiolAb, CIN, ChemAb, ChemTitl, CurCont, DBA, DSA, ExcerpMed, FPA, FoVS&M, ForAb, HelmAb, IABS, ISR, IndMed, IndVet, MEDLINE, MaizeAb, NutrAb, PN&I, PoultAb, ProtozoAb, RA&MP, RM&VM, RefZh, SCI, SFA, SIA, SoyAb, VetBull, WeedAb, WildRev, ZooRec.
—BLDSC (0905.076000), CASDDS, CISTI, IDS, IE, Infotrieve, ingenta, Linda Hall. **CCC.**

Published by: Elsevier BV (Subsidiary of: Elsevier Science & Technology), Radarweg 29, Amsterdam, 1043 NX, Netherlands. TEL 31-20-4853911, FAX 31-20-4852457, nlinfo-f@elsevier.nl, http://www.elsevier.com/locate/anireprosci, http://www.elsevier.nl. Eds. J E Kinder, K L Macmillan.

636 JPN ISSN 0017-7520
ANIMAL REPRODUCTION TECHNIQUES/HANSHOKU GIJUTSU. Text in Japanese. 1950. q. JPY 1,000, USD 15. adv. bk.rev.
Published by: Hokkaido Artificial Insemination Technician Association/Hokkaido Kachiku Jinko Juseishi Kyokai, c/o Hokunoren, Nishi-1-chome, Kita-4-jo, Sapporo, 060, Japan. Ed. Michiro Wakabayashi. Circ: 2,000.

ANIMAL RESEARCH. see *BIOLOGY—Zoology*

636 GBR ISSN 1357-7298
SF1 CODEN: ANIPA8
➤ **ANIMAL SCIENCE.** Text in English. 1944. bi-m. USD 620 in the Americas to institutions except Canada; GBP 325 elsewhere to institutions; USD 665 combined subscription in the Americas to institutions except Canada; print & online eds.; GBP 350 combined subscription elsewhere to institutions print & online eds. (effective 2006). bibl.; charts; illus.; stat. Index. back issues avail. **Document type:** *Journal, Academic/Scholarly.* **Description:** Papers deal with genetics, nutrition, husbandry, physiology, biochemical variation and the interrelationships of the animal environment.
Former titles (until 1995): Animal Production (0003-3561); (until 1959): British Society of Animal Production. Proceedings (0369-8521)
Related titles: Online - full text ed.: USD 610 in the Americas to institutions except Canada; GBP 320 elsewhere to institutions (effective 2006) (from EBSCO Publishing).
Indexed: AEA, ASCA, ASFA, AgBio, Agr, AgrForAb, AnBrAb, B&AI, BIOSIS Prev, BiolAb, CIN, ChemAb, ChemTitl, CurCont, DBA, DSA, ECI, FCA, FPA, FS&TA, FoVS&M, HelmAb, HerbAb, HortAb, IIS, ISR, IndVet, MaizeAb, NutrAb, PBA, PHN&I, PN&I, PoultAb, ProtozoAb, RA&MP, RASB, RRTA, RefZh, RiceAb, S&F, SCI, SFA, SIA, SeedAb, SoyAb, TriticAb, VetBull, WAE&RSA, WildRev, ZooRec.
—BLDSC (0905.101800), CASDDS, CISTI, IDS, IE, Infotrieve, ingenta, Linda Hall. **CCC.**
Published by: (British Society of Animal Science), CABI Publishing (Subsidiary of: CAB International), CAB International, Wallingford, Oxfordshire OX10 8DE, United Kingdom. TEL 44-1491-832111, FAX 44-1491-833508, publishing@cabi.org, http://www.bsas.org.uk/publs/anisci.htm, http://www.cabi-publishing.org/. Circ: 2,150 (paid).

636 AUS ISSN 1344-3941
CODEN: ASCJFY
➤ **ANIMAL SCIENCE JOURNAL.** Text in English. 1924. bi-m. USD 397 combined subscription in the Americas to individuals & Caribbean, print & online eds.; EUR 368 combined subscription in Europe to individuals print & online eds.; GBP 245 combined subscription elsewhere to individuals print & online eds.; USD 576 combined subscription in the Americas to institutions & Caribbean, print & online eds.; GBP 355 combined subscription elsewhere to institutions print & online eds. (effective 2006). adv. bk.rev. charts; abstr. 100 p./no.; back issues avail.; reprints avail. **Document type:** *Journal, Academic/Scholarly.* **Description:** Publishes original articles (full papers and rapid communications) and review articles in all fields of animal and poultry science: Genetics and breeding, genetic engineering, reproduction, embryo manipulation, nutrition, feeds and feeding, physiology, anatomy, environment and behavior, animal products (milk, meat, eggs and their by-products) and their processing, and livestock economics.
Former titles (until 1999): Animal Science and Technology (0918-2365); (until 1991): Japanese Journal of Zootechnical Science (0021-5309)
Related titles: Online - full text ed.: ISSN 1740-0929. USD 576 in the Americas to institutions; GBP 355 elsewhere to institutions (effective 2006) (from Blackwell Synergy, EBSCO Publishing, Gale Group, IngentaConnect, O C L C Online Computer Library Center, Inc., Swets Information Services); ♦ Japanese ed.: Nihon Chikusan Gakkaiho.
Indexed: AEA, AEBA, ASFA, AbHyg, AgBio, AgrForAb, AnBrAb, B&BAb, BIOSIS Prev, BiolAb, CIN, ChemAb, ChemTitl, DSA, ESPM, FS&TA, ForAb, HerbAb, HortAb, IndVet, MaizeAb, NutrAb, PBA, PHN&I, PN&I, PotatoAb, PoultAb, ProtozoAb, RM&VM, RPP, RefZh, RevApplEntom, RiceAb, S&F, SFA, SIA, SoyAb, TDB, TriticAb, VetBull, WAE&RSA, WildRev, ZooRec.
—BLDSC (0905.106270), CASDDS, CISTI, IE. **CCC.**
Published by: (Japanese Society of Animal Science/Nihon Chikusan Gakkai JPN), Blackwell Publishing Asia (Subsidiary of: Blackwell Publishing Ltd.), 550 Swanston St, Carlton South, VIC 3053, Australia. TEL 61-383591011, FAX 61-383591120, subs@blackwellpublishingasia.com, http://www.blackwellpublishing.com/journals/ASJ. Ed. Hiroshi Tomogane. Circ: 3,000.

636 POL ISSN 0860-4037
CODEN: ANPREJ
➤ **ANIMAL SCIENCE PAPERS AND REPORTS.** Text in English; Summaries in Polish. 1986. q. PLZ 8 (effective 1999). **Document type:** *Academic/Scholarly.*
Indexed: ASFA, AgBio, AgrAg, AgrLib, AnBrAb, B&BAb, BIOSIS Prev, BiolAb, CIN, ChemAb, ChemTitl, DSA, FS&TA, GenetAb, HelmAb, HerbAb, IndVet, NutrAb, PN&I, PoultAb, RefZh, S&F, SeedAb, VetBull, WAE&RSA.
—BLDSC (0905.106600), CASDDS, CISTI.
Published by: Polska Akademia Nauk, Instytut Genetyki i Hodowli Zwierzat, Mrokow, Jastrzebiec, 05-551, Poland. TEL 48-22-756711, FAX 48-22-7561699. Ed. Jerzy Piotrowski. Circ: 250.

636 FRA ISSN 1161-9635
ANNUAIRE DES INDUSTRIES AVICOLES. Text in French. 1956. a. EUR 120 (effective 2004). 312 p./no.; **Document type:** *Directory, Trade.*
Formerly (until 1991): Annuaire National de l'Aviculture (0066-3328)
Published by: Editions Comindus, 1 Rue Descombes, Paris, 75017, France. TEL 31-1-43807916, FAX 31-1-40539192, http://www.editionscomindus.fr.

636 FRA ISSN 1166-1011
ANNUAIRE DES INDUSTRIES CHARCUTIERES. Text in French. a. EUR 155 (effective 2004). 544 p./no.; **Document type:** *Directory, Trade.*
Former titles (until 1991): Annuaire de la Charcuterie (1154-452X); (until 1990): Annuaire Officiel de la Charcuterie (0293-9967)
Published by: Editions Comindus, 1 Rue Descombes, Paris, 75017, France. TEL 31-1-43807916, FAX 31-1-40539192, http://www.editionscomindus.fr.

636.5 BRA
ANUARIO AVICOLA & SUINICOLA. Text in Portuguese. 1912. a. USD 80. adv. bk.rev.
Former titles (until 1989): Anuario Avicola e Anuario Suincola; Anuario Agricola e Avicola
Published by: Gessulli Editores Ltda., Praca Sergipe, 154, Caixa Postal 198, Porto Feliz, SP 18540-000, Brazil. TEL 55-152-623133, FAX 55-152-623919. Ed. Osvaldo Penha Gessulli. Circ: 15,000.

APIS; the international journal bulletin for specialty livestock and pet-animal product development. see *VETERINARY SCIENCE*

636 ESP
APLAUSOS. Text in Spanish. 52/yr.
Address: Avda Baron de Carcer, 48, Valencia, 46001, Spain. TEL 6-351-81-76, FAX 6-351-48-80. Circ: 16,908.

636.5 DEU ISSN 0003-9098
CODEN: AGEFAB
➤ **ARCHIV FUER GEFLUEGELKUNDE/ARCHIVES DE SCIENCE AVICOLE/ARCHIVES OF POULTRY SCIENCE.** Text in German; Summaries in English, French, Russian. 1927. bi-m. EUR 471.60; EUR 79 newsstand/cover (effective 2004). adv. bk.rev. charts; illus.; stat. index. **Document type:** *Journal, Academic/Scholarly.* **Description:** Contains articles on poultry science, breeding economics and techniques.
Related titles: Microfilm ed.: (from PMC); Online - full text ed.: ISSN 1612-9199.
Indexed: AEA, ASCA, AbHyg, AgBio, AgrForAb, AnBrAb, BIOSIS Prev, BiolAb, CIN, ChemAb, ChemTitl, CurCont, DBA, DSA, FS&TA, HortAb, ISR, IndVet, MaizeAb, NutrAb, PBA, PN&I, PoultAb, ProtozoAb, RA&MP, RM&VM, RefZh, RiceAb, S&F, SCI, SIA, SoyAb, TriticAb, VetBull, WAE&RSA.
—BLDSC (1610.950000), CASDDS, CISTI, IDS, IE, Infotrieve, ingenta. **CCC.**
Published by: (Deutsche Vereinigung fuer Gefluegelwissenschaft e.V.), Verlag Eugen Ulmer GmbH, Wollgrasweg 41, Stuttgart, 70599, Germany. TEL 49-711-4507-0, FAX 49-711-4507-120, info@ulmer.de, http://www.archiv-fuer-gefluegelkunde.de, http://www.ulmer.de. Eds. M Grashorn, S Gerken. R&P Gerd Friedrich. Adv. contact Sigrid Holdschik. B&W page EUR 516; trim 185 x 260. Circ: 600.

636 DEU ISSN 0003-9438
SF105 CODEN: ARTZAJ
➤ **ARCHIV FUER TIERZUCHT/ARCHIVES OF ANIMAL BREEDING.** Text in German; Summaries in English, German, Russian. 1958. 6/yr. EUR 118; EUR 19.70 newsstand/cover (effective 2004). bk.rev. charts; stat. index. **Document type:** *Journal, Academic/Scholarly.* **Description:** Publishes original contributions as well as short communications presenting methods and results to the fundamentals of biological farm animals and animal breeding aspects of horse, cattle, pig sheep goat, poultry and other small agricultural use animals.
Indexed: AEA, ASCA, AgBio, AgrForAb, AnBrAb, BIOSIS Prev, BiolAb, ChemAb, CurCont, DSA, FS&TA, ForAb, HelmAb, HerbAb, IndVet, MaizeAb, NutrAb, PBA, PGegResA, PN&I, PoultAb, ProtozoAb, RM&VM, RRTA, SCI, SoyAb, TriticAb, VetBull, WAE&RSA.
—BLDSC (1625.010000), CASDDS, CISTI, IDS, IE, ingenta. **CCC.**
Published by: Forschungsinstitut fuer die Biologie Landwirtschaftlicher Nutztiere, Wilhelm-Stahl-Allee 2, Dummerstorf, 18196, Germany. TEL 49-38208-685, FAX 49-38208-68602, fbn@fbn-dummerstorf.de, http://www.fbn-dummerstorf.de/fbn/literatur/Archiv/archteng.htm. Ed. E Ritter.

➤ **ARCHIVES OF ANIMAL NUTRITION.** see *VETERINARY SCIENCE*

637 ESP ISSN 0004-0592
SF1 CODEN: AZOTAW
➤ **ARCHIVOS DE ZOOTECNIA.** Text and summaries in English, French, Spanish, Portuguese. 1952. q. EUR 45 domestic; EUR 85 foreign (effective 2005). bk.rev. abstr.; bibl.; charts; illus. index, cum.index: 1952-1999. back issues avail. **Document type:** *Journal, Academic/Scholarly.* **Description:** Publishes experimental and research work on forage and pasture production, animal feeding, genetics, ethnology and reproduction and the optimization of systems in animal production. Its main emphasis is on the Mediterranean regions.
Related titles: Online - full content ed.: free (effective 2005).
Indexed: AEA, ASFA, AgBio, AgrForAb, AnBrAb, BIOSIS Prev, BibAg, BiolAb, CIN, ChemAb, ChemTitl, DSA, ESPM, ExcerpMed, FCA, FPA, FS&TA, FaBeAb, ForAb, HelmAb, HerbAb, HortAb, IECT, IndVet, MaizeAb, NutrAb, PBA, PGegResA, PN&I, PoultAb, RDA, RRTA, RevApplEntom, S&F, SFA, SIA, SoyAb, TriticAb, VetBull, WAE&RSA, WeedAb, WildRev, ZooRec.
—BLDSC (1658.000000), CASDDS, CINDOC, CISTI, IE, ingenta, Linda Hall. **CCC.**
Published by: (Universidad de Cordoba, Facultad de Veterinaria), Universidad de Cordoba, Servicio de Publicaciones, Ave. Menendez Pidal, s-n, Cordoba, 14071, Spain. TEL 34-957-218125, FAX 34-957-218196, pa1gocag@lucano.uco.es, publicaciones@uco.es, http://www.uco.es/organiza/servicios/publica/az/az.htm. Ed. Dr. A G Gomez-Castro. Circ: 600.

636 VEN ISSN 1022-1301
➤ **ARCHIVOS LATINOAMERICANOS DE PRODUCCION ANIMAL/LATIN-AMERICAN ARCHIVES OF ANIMAL PRODUCTION.** Text in Spanish, English, Portuguese; Abstracts in English. 1993. 3/yr. USD 40 in Latin America to individuals; USD 50 in US & Canada to individuals; USD 60 elsewhere to individuals; USD 100 to institutions (effective 2002 - 2003). adv. Index. back issues avail. **Document type:** *Journal, Academic/Scholarly.* **Description:** The journal publishes high quality original research on all aspects of animal science.
Related titles: E-mail ed.; Online - full text ed.: free (effective 2005).
Indexed: AgBio, AgrForAb, AnBrAb, CPA, DSA, ForAb, HerbAb, I&DA, IndVet, MaizeAb, NutrAb, PBA, PN&I, PotatoAb, PoultAb, RDA, RiceAb, S&F, SIA, SoyAb, TriticAb, VetBull, WAE&RSA.
Published by: Asociacion Latinoamericana de Produccion Animal, Av 20. No60-63 Edif Piacoa 9, Maracaibo, ZU 4001, Venezuela. archivos-alpa@cantv.net, http://www.alpa.org.ve/ojs/index.php. Ed. Paul F Randel. Pub., R&P, Adv. contact Omar Araujo-Febres. Circ: 1,500 (paid); 220 (free).

636.2 ARG
ARGENTINA. JUNTA NACIONAL DE CARNES. BOLETIN DIARO DE INFORMACIONES. Text in Spanish. d. ARS 40,000.
Published by: Junta Nacional de Carnes, San Martin, 459, Capital Federal, Buenos Aires 1004, Argentina.

636.2 ARG
ARGENTINA. JUNTA NACIONAL DE CARNES. BOLETIN SEMANAL SOBRE GANADOS, CARNES Y SUBPRODUCTOS. Text in Spanish. w. ARS 25,000.
Published by: Junta Nacional de Carnes, San Martin, 459, Capital Federal, Buenos Aires 1004, Argentina.

636 382 ARG
ARGENTINA. JUNTA NACIONAL DE CARNES. EXPORTACIONES DE PRODUCTOS GANADEROS. Text in Spanish. 1968. m. ARS 8,700. stat.
Published by: Junta Nacional de Carnes, San Martin, 459, Capital Federal, Buenos Aires 1004, Argentina. Circ: 300.

ARGENTINA. JUNTA NACIONAL DE CARNES. SINTESIS ESTADISTICA. see *AGRICULTURE—Abstracting, Bibliographies, Statistics*

338.1 ARG
ARGENTINA. MERCADO NACIONAL DE HACIENDA. ANUARIO. Text in Spanish. a. illus.; stat.
Formerly: Argentine Republic. Mercado Nacional de Hacienda. Memoria (0570-8621)
Published by: Mercado Nacional de Hacienda, Tellier 2406, Buenos Aires, 1440, Argentina.

ARGENTINA. SECRETARIA DE AGRICULTURA GANADERIA Y PESCA. SITUACION DEL MERCADO DE CARNES. see *AGRICULTURE—Abstracting, Bibliographies, Statistics*

636 USA
ARIZONA CATALOG. Text in English. m. USD 14.95 (effective 2004). **Document type:** *Magazine, Trade.*
Published by: American Livestock Publications, Inc., 2231 Rio Grande, N.W., Albuquerque, NM 87104. TEL 505-243-9515, http://www.aaalivestock.com. Ed., Pub. Charles Stocks. Circ: 10,000 (paid).

636.2 USA ISSN 8750-8281
ARIZONA CATTLELOG. Text in English. 1945. m. USD 9. adv. back issues avail. **Document type:** *Trade.* **Description:** Covers all aspects of cattle production.

A

▼ new title ➤ refereed ✶ unverified ♦ full entry avail.

Published by: (Arizona Cattlemen's Association), Charles R. Stocks Co., 9436 Rio Grande Blvd N W, Albuquerque, NM 87114. TEL 505-243-9515, FAX 505-243-9598. R&P Sandy Eastlake. Circ: 1,800.

636.2 USA ISSN 0004-1750
ARKANSAS CATTLE BUSINESS. Text in English. 1965. m. USD 35 membership (effective 2005). adv. bk.rev. **Document type:** *Magazine, Trade.* **Description:** Contains articles and features of interest to cattle ranchers in Arkansas.
Published by: Arkansas Cattlemen's Association, 310 Executive Ct, Little Rock, AR 72205-4550. TEL 501-224-2114, FAX 501-224-5377, info@arbeef.org. Ed. Claude "Tubby" Smith. Adv. contact Amy Boder. B&W page USD 675, color page USD 1,075. Circ: 17,000 (paid and free).

636 660.6 KOR ISSN 1011-2367
CODEN: AJASEL
➤ **ASIAN - AUSTRALASIAN JOURNAL OF ANIMAL SCIENCES.** Variant title: A J A S. Text in English. 1988. 12/yr., latest vol.14, 2001. USD 70 to individuals; USD 120 to institutions; USD 50 to individuals to member countries in AAAP area; USD 70 to institutions to member countries in AAAP area (effective 2005). adv. bk.rev. **Document type:** *Journal, Academic/Scholarly.* **Description:** Disseminates research on the zoology of domestic farm animals, including diseases and environmental issues.
Indexed: AEA, ASCA, AbHyg, AgBio, Agr, AgrForAb, AnBrAb, BIOSIS Prev, BibAg, BiolAb, CIN, CPA, ChemAb, ChemTitl, CurCont, DSA, FCA, FPA, FS&TA, FoVS&M, ForAb, HelmAb, HerbAb, HortAb, I&DA, IndVet, MaizeAb, NutrAb, OrnHort, PBA, PGegResA, PHN&I, PN&I, PoultAb, ProtozoAb, RA&MP, RDA, RM&VM, RPP, RRTA, RevApplEntom, RiceAb, S&F, SIA, SSCI, SeedAb, SoyAb, TDB, TriticAb, VetBull, WAE&RSA, WeedAb.
—BLDSC (1742.389000), CASDDS, CISTI, IDS, IE, ingenta.
Published by: Asian - Australasian Association of Animal Production Societies, Rm 708 Sammo Sporex, 1638-32 Sillimbon-dong, Gawanak-gu, Seoul, 151-730, Korea, S. TEL 82-2-8886558, FAX 82-2-8886559, ajas@ajas.info, http://www.ajas.info/, http://www.ajas.snu.ac.kr. Ed. Dr. J K Ha. Circ: 1,000. **Co-publisher:** Korean Society of Animal Science and Technology.

636.4 ARG ISSN 0004-4741
ASOCIACION ARGENTINA CRIADORES DE CERDOS. REVISTA. Text in Spanish. 1922. 3/yr. per issue exchange basis. adv. bk.rev. mkt.; stat.
Published by: Asociacion Argentina Criadores de Cerdos, Florida, 520, Capital Federal, Buenos Aires 1005, Argentina. Ed. Carlos M Vieites. Circ: 5,000.

636 VEN
ASOCIACION LATINOAMERICANA DE PRODUCCION ANIMAL. MEMORIA. Text in Spanish; Summaries in English, Portuguese, Spanish. 1966. a. USD 15. abstr. cum.index: vols. 1-10. back issues avail.
Indexed: AnBrAb, BiolAb, DSA, NutrAb, RRTA, WAE&RSA.
Published by: Asociacion Latinoamericana de Produccion Animal, Av 20. No60-63 Edif Piacoa 9, Maracaibo, ZU 4001, Venezuela. Ed. Claudio F Chicco. Circ: 1,500.

636.2 CAN ISSN 1184-0021
ATLANTIC BEEF. Text in English. 1990. 5/yr. CND 14 domestic; CND 18 foreign; CND 3.50 newsstand/cover (effective 2005). adv. bk.rev. **Document type:** *Consumer.* **Description:** For and about beef producers in the four provinces of Atlantic Canada. Presents latest information from research stations, for show results and for a sharing of breeding and production tips, and just plain news about what their beef farming neighbors are doing.
Published by: D v L Publishing, P O Box 1509, Liverpool, NS B0T 1K0, Canada. TEL 902-354-5411, 877-354-3764, dvl@atcon.com, http://www.countrymagazines.com. Ed., Pub. Dirk van Loon. R&P, Adv. contact Brook Gray. Circ: 4,000.

AUSTRALIA. BUREAU OF STATISTICS. LIVESTOCK AND MEAT, AUSTRALIA. see *AGRICULTURE—Abstracting, Bibliographies, Statistics*

AUSTRALIA. BUREAU OF STATISTICS. LIVESTOCK PRODUCTS, AUSTRALIA. see *AGRICULTURE—Abstracting, Bibliographies, Statistics*

AUSTRALIA. BUREAU OF STATISTICS. QUEENSLAND OFFICE. CATTLE BREEDS, QUEENSLAND. see *AGRICULTURE—Abstracting, Bibliographies, Statistics*

AUSTRALIA. BUREAU OF STATISTICS. SHEEP AND WOOL, AUSTRALIA, PRELIMINARY. see *AGRICULTURE—Abstracting, Bibliographies, Statistics*

636 AUS
AUSTRALIAN CATTLE & SHEEP INDUSTRY OVERVIEW. Text in English. 1991. m. AUD 200 domestic; AUD 450 foreign (effective 2001). 16 p./no.; back issues avail. **Document type:** *Trade.* **Description:** Offers an overview of the Australian cattle and sheep market: trends, developments, and influences.
Former titles (until 2000): Australian Meat and Livestock Review (1329-2986); (until 1997): Meat and Livestock Review
Published by: Meat and Livestock Australia Ltd., Market Intelligence Unit, Locked Bag 991, North Sydney, NSW 2059, Australia. TEL 61-2-9463-9333, 61-2-9463-9163, FAX 61-2-9463-9393, 61-2-9954-0752, kstanford@mla.com.au, http://www.mla.com.au. Ed. Peter Weeks. Circ: 1,500.

636.39 AUS ISSN 0045-0472
AUSTRALIAN GOAT WORLD. Text in English. 1945. bi-m. AUD 18 (effective 1999). **Document type:** *Newsletter.*
Published by: Dairy Goat Society of Australia Ltd., PO Box 189, Kiama, NSW 2533, Australia. Ed., Pub. R Heston. Circ: 900.

636 AUS ISSN 0814-7663
AUSTRALIAN HEREFORD QUARTERLY. Text in English. 1961. q. AUD 35 domestic; AUD 80 foreign (effective 2001). adv. bk.rev. 144 p./no.; **Document type:** *Trade.*
Former titles: Australian Hereford Annual (0067-1886); Hereford Quarterly (0311-2144)
Published by: Australian Hereford Society Ltd., PO Box 1014, Spring Hill, QLD 4004, Australia. TEL 61-7-32362166, FAX 61-7-32362177, hereford@hereford.com.au, http://www.hereford.com.au. Ed., R&P, Adv. contact Tony Lamberth. Circ: 8,000.

636.2 AUS
AUSTRALIAN POLL DORSET JOURNAL. Text in English. 1970. 3/yr. AUD 20 (effective 1999). adv. bk.rev.
Published by: (Australian Poll Dorset Association Inc.), Weston Studstock Advertising Pty. Ltd., GPO Box 75 B, Melbourne, VIC 3001, Australia. TEL 61-3-98176711. Ed. D Story. Circ: 1,500.

636.4 AUS
THE AUSTRALIAN PORK NEWSPAPER. Text in English. 198?. m. AUD 24. adv. bk.rev. **Document type:** *Newspaper.* **Description:** Covers industry news, research, products.
Formerly (until 1997): Pork Producer
Published by: Collins Media, PO Box 387, Cleveland, QLD 4163, Australia. TEL 61-7-32861833, FAX 61-7-38212637, media@powerup.com.au. Ed. Ron Collins. Adv. contact Margaret Darvall. B&W page AUD 840, color page AUD 1,150; 250 x 400. Circ: 3,180.

636 AUS ISSN 1034-6260
AUSTRALIAN POULTRY SCIENCE SYMPOSIUM. Text in English. 1989. a. back issues avail. **Document type:** *Proceedings.* **Description:** Covers nutrition, disease control and production of poultry. Includes research, education, industry and government services.
Formerly (until 1989): Poultry Husbandry Research Foundation Symposium
Indexed: FS&TA.
—BLDSC (6842.496400).
Published by: University of Sydney, Poultry Research Foundation, Editorial Office, Sydney, NSW 2006, Australia. TEL 61-2-46550658, FAX 61-2-46550693, wmuir@camden.usyd.edu.au, http://www.vetsci.usyd.edu.au/foundations/prf.shtml. Ed., R&P Rae Pym TEL 61-7-33652604. Circ: 200.

636.4 AUS
AUSTRALIAN PUREBRED PIG HERD BOOK. Text in English. 1911. a. AUD 5 (effective 1999). adv. **Document type:** *Directory.*
Formerly (until 1990): Australian Stud Pig Herd Book
Published by: Australian Pig Breeders' Association, PO Box 189, Kiama, NSW 2533, Australia. FAX 61-242-323350. Ed. Mrs. C Brown. Circ: 200.

636 ESP ISSN 0005-1896
AVANCES EN ALIMENTACION Y MEJORA ANIMAL. Text in Spanish. 1960. bi-m. USD 50 foreign (effective 1999). adv. bk.rev. bibl.; charts; illus.; mkt.; pat.; stat. index.
Incorporates (1976-198?): Suplemento Ganado Porcino (0213-4470); Formerly (until 1962): Avances en Alimenacion Animal (1135-5557)
Indexed: AnBrAb, BIOSIS Prev, BiolAb, ChemAb, DSA, FaBeAb, HerbAb, IECT, IndVet, NutrAb, PN&I, PotatoAb, PoultAb, S&F, SIA, SoyAb, TriticAb, VetBull, WAE&RSA.
—CINDOC.
Address: Juan Vigon, 32o D., Madrid, 28003, Spain. Ed. Amalio de Juana Sardon. Circ: 2,000.

636 CHL ISSN 0378-4509
CODEN: APANDD
AVANCES EN PRODUCCION ANIMAL. Text in Spanish; Summaries in English. 1976. s-a. CLP 200, USD 4. bk.rev. charts; illus.; abstr. index, cum.index. **Document type:** *Newspaper.*
Indexed: AgBio, AgrForAb, AnBrAb, BiolAb, CPA, ChemAb, DSA, FS&TA, ForAb, HerbAb, I&DA, IndVet, MaizeAb, NutrAb, PN&I, PoultAb, S&F, SeedAb, SoyAb, TriticAb, VetBull.
—CASDDS, CISTI.
Published by: Universidad de Chile, Facultad de Ciencias Agrarias, Veterinarias y Forestales, Casilla 1004, Santiago, Chile. TEL 56-2-5417703, FAX 56-2-5417055. Ed. Mario Silva G. R&P Alberto Mansilla. Circ: 1,000.

AVIAN AND POULTRY BIOLOGY REVIEWS. see *BIOLOGY—Zoology*

636.5 COL
AVICULTURA COLOMBIANA. Text in Spanish. 1980. m. adv.
Address: Apartado Aereo 24215, Bogota, CUND, Colombia. Circ: 10,000.

636.5 BRA ISSN 0009-0905
AVICULTURA INDUSTRIAL. Text in Portuguese. 1912. m. USD 90 (effective 2000). adv. illus. index. **Document type:** *Trade.*
Formerly: Chacaras e Quintais - Agricultura e Pecuaria
Published by: Gessulli Editores Ltda., Praca Sergipe, 154, Caixa Postal 198, Porto Feliz, SP 18540-000, Brazil. TEL 55-152-623133, FAX 55-152-623919, gessulli@gessulli.com.br, http://www.gessulli.com.br. Ed. Osvaldo Penha Gessulli. adv.: color page USD 3,600; 290 x 215. Circ: 20,000.

636.5 USA ISSN 0736-2056
AVICULTURA PROFESIONAL✶. Text in Spanish. 1983. q. free to qualified personnel. adv. bk.rev. **Description:** Source of current technology for the Latin American poultry industry.
Published by: Avicultura Profesional, Inc., 184 Hickory Poin Dr, Athens, GA 30605. TEL 706-549-4092, FAX 706-543-1854. Ed. Nick Dale. Circ: 7,500 (controlled).

636.5 NLD
AVICULTURA PROFESSIONAL. Text in Dutch. 10/yr. USD 68 (effective 2000). adv. **Document type:** *Trade.* **Description:** Addresses the specific needs of the commercial poultry sector in Latin America.
Published by: Reed Business Information bv (Subsidiary of: Reed Business), Hanzestraat 1, Doetinchem, 7006 RH, Netherlands. TEL 31-314-349911, FAX 31-314-343839, info@reedbusiness.nl, http://www.reedbusiness.nl. Ed. Soledad Urrutia. Adv. contact Tomas Domic. Circ: 10,000.

636.4 DNK ISSN 0907-0567
AVLS-INFORMATION. Text in Danish. 1989. q.
Published by: Avlscentret Mulstrup, Boers-Mark, c/o Gitte Boersing, Sparsborgvej 12, Struer, 7600, Denmark. TEL 45-97-84-13-80, FAX 45-97-84-13-70. adv.: B&W page DKK 6,200, color page DKK 11,420. Circ: 4,000.

630 USA ISSN 1088-4122
THE BAGPIPE. Text in English. 1983. q. USD 16 domestic; USD 28 foreign (effective 2001). adv. 50 p./no. 3 cols./p.; **Document type:** *Magazine, Trade.* **Description:** Highland cattle information.
Published by: American Highland Cattle Association, 200 Livestock Exchange Bldg, 4701 Marion St, Denver, CO 80216-2134. TEL 303-292-9102, FAX 303-292-9171, ahea@envisionnet.net, http://www.highlandcattle.org. Pub. Chris Hawkins. R&P, Adv. contact Ginnah Moses. Circ: 1,400.

636 BGD ISSN 0379-430X
BANGLADESH JOURNAL OF ANIMAL SCIENCE. Text in English. 1968. s-a. BDT 100 to individuals; USD 10 foreign to individuals; BDT 200 to institutions; USD 15 foreign to institutions (effective 1999). adv. bk.rev. charts; stat. **Document type:** *Academic/Scholarly.* **Description:** Contains scholarly articles covering topics in animal husbandry.
Formerly: Animal Science Journal of Pakistan (0003-3588)
Indexed: AnBrAb, BiolAb, ChemAb.
—BLDSC (1861.640000), CISTI.
Published by: Bangladesh Husbandry Association, Bangladesh Agricultural University, Department of Animal Nutrition, Mymensingh, 2202, Bangladesh. TEL 880-91-55695, FAX 880-91-55810. Ed., Pub., R&P, Adv. contact Abidur Reza. page BDT 7,500. Circ: 1,000.

338.1 USA
BANTAM STANDARD. Text in English. irreg. USD 30 (effective 2000). **Document type:** *Directory.* **Description:** Descriptions of Bantam chickens with complete variety listings.
Published by: American Bantam Association, PO Box 127, Augusta, NJ 07822.

636.5 HUN ISSN 0133-011X
BAROMFITENYESZTES ES FELDOLGOZAS✶. Text in Hungarian; Contents page in English, German, Russian. 1952. q. USD 20. charts; illus.; stat. **Document type:** *Academic/Scholarly.*
Formerly (until 1977): Baromfiipar (0005-6049); Which superseded in part (in 1954): Hus-, Baromfi- es Hutoipar (0200-2795)
Indexed: AnBrAb, FS&TA, NutrAb, PoultAb, RRTA, WAE&RSA.
Published by: Magyar Elelmezesipari Tudomanyos Egyesulet, P.F. 5, Budapest, 1361, Hungary. Ed. Karoly Csomos. **Subscr. to:** Kultura, PO Box 149, Budapest 1389, Hungary.

636.2 USA ISSN 0005-7738
CODEN: SDMEAL
BEEF. Text in English. 1964. 13/yr. USD 35 domestic; USD 45 foreign; free to qualified personnel (effective 2004). adv. illus. **Document type:** *Magazine, Trade.* **Description:** Focuses on beef cattle industry.
Related titles: Online - full text ed.: (from bigchalk, EBSCO Publishing, Gale Group, H.W. Wilson, O C L C Online Computer Library Center, Inc., ProQuest Information & Learning).
Indexed: ABIn, B&AI, F&GI.
—CCC.

Published by: Primedia Business Magazines & Media, Inc. (Subsidiary of: Primedia, Inc.), 9800 Metcalf Ave, Overland Park, KS 66212-2216. TEL 913-341-1300, FAX 913-967-1898, beef@intertec.com, inquiries@primediabusiness.com, http://www.beef-mag.com, http://www.primediabusiness.com. Ed. Joe Roybal TEL 952-851-4710. adv.: color page USD 12,595. Circ: 100,000 (controlled). **Subscr. to:** PO Box 12993, Overland Park, KS 66282-2993. TEL 800-441-0294, FAX 913-967-1331.

636.2 USA
BEEF BULLETIN✶ . Text in English. q.
Published by: Illinois Beef Council, 2060 W Iles Ave, No B, Springfield, IL 62704-4174. TEL 217-787-4280. Ed. Patricia Merna Petska.

636.085 USA ISSN 0744-253X
BEEF BUSINESS BULLETIN. Text in English. 1977. 26/yr. free membership (effective 2005). adv. stat. **Document type:** *Bulletin, Trade.* **Description:** Focuses on the cattle industry.
Formerly: N C A Weekly Bulletin; Supersedes: N L F A Feed-Lines (0047-8938)
Related titles: Online - full text ed.
—CISTI.
Published by: National Cattlemen's Beef Association, PO Box 3469, Englewood, CO 80155-3469. TEL 303-694-0305, FAX 303-770-6921, http://www.beefusa.org. Ed., R&P Curt Olson. Adv. contact Jill DeLucero. Circ: 32,000 (controlled).

636.2 AUS ISSN 1324-5309
BEEF IMPROVEMENT NEWS. Text in English. 1988. bi-m. AUD 55 (effective 2001). adv. bk.rev. charts; illus.; mkt.; maps; stat.; tr.lit. 36 p./no.; back issues avail. **Document type:** *Magazine, Consumer.* **Description:** Provides technical, commercial and marketing information for progressive beef producers and service providers to the beef industry.
—BLDSC (6658.600000).
Published by: (Beef Improvement Association of Australia), Livestock Publications, 5 B Lion St, Hawthorn, VIC 3122, Australia. TEL 61-3-9818-8600, FAX 61-3-9818-8611, optimal@magestic.net.au, optimalads@magestic.net.au, http://www.meataustralia.com. Ed. Andrew Gerdiner. Pub. Athol Economou. R&P Joe Edwards. Adv. contact Tom Joiner. color page AUD 2,190; 240 x 340. Circ: 32,000 (paid).

636.2 CAN ISSN 0846-0043
BEEF IN B C. Text in English. 1986. 7/yr. CND 24. adv. bk.rev.
Address: 10145 Durango Rd 4, Kamloops, BC V2C 6T4, Canada. TEL 604-573-3611, FAX 604-573-5155. Ed. A L Leach. Circ: 3,200.

636.2 USA
BEEF PRODUCER. Text in English. m.
Related titles: ♦ Supplement to: Kansas Farmer.
Published by: Farm Progress Companies, 191 S Gary Ave, Carol Stream, IL 60188. http://www.farmprogress.com/. Ed. Mick Kreidler TEL 515-278-7784.

636.2 USA
BEEF ROUNDUP. Text in English. 1973. a. free. **Description:** Focuses on the cattle breeding industry.
Published by: Kent Feeds Inc., 1600 Oregon St, Muscatine, IA 52761. TEL 319-264-4211.

636.2 USA
BEEF TIMES. Text in English. 1993. m. USD 15 (effective 2003). adv. charts; illus.; mkt. 48 p./no.; **Document type:** *Newspaper, Trade.* **Description:** Conveys current information to beef producers on economic, political, and technical trends in the industry.
Related titles: Online - full text ed.
Published by: Lee Publications, Inc (Subsidiary of: Lee Enterprises, Inc.), 311 Main Ave., W, Twin Falls, ID 83301. TEL 208-735-3256, FAX 208-734-9667, janet.goffin@lee.net, http://www.agweekly.com/home/beeftimes/. Ed. Carol Ryan Dumas. Pub., Adv. contact Brian Kroshus TEL 208-735-3254. Circ: 19,500.

636 USA ISSN 1056-1390
BEEF TODAY. Text in English. 1985. 10/yr. free domestic to qualified personnel (effective 2005). adv. **Document type:** *Magazine, Trade.* **Description:** Focuses on the cattle breeding industry.
Formerly (until 1987): Beef Extra
Related titles: Online - full text ed.: (from ProQuest Information & Learning).
Published by: Farm Journal Media, 1818 Market St., 31st Fl, Philadelphia, PA 19103-3654. TEL 215-557-8900, 800-523-1538, FAX 215-568-5012, scornett@farmjournalmedia.com, scornett@farmjournal.com, http://www.farmjournalmedia.com. Ed. Steve Cornett. Pub. Allen Moczygemba. Circ: 22,000 (controlled).

636 USA ISSN 0747-010X
BEEFALO NICKEL. Text in English. 1979. bi-m. USD 15; USD 25 foreign (effective 1997). adv. **Document type:** *Trade.* **Description:** Information on all aspects of Beefalo cattle breeding.
Formerly (until 1984): Beefalo Journal (0199-3542)
Published by: (American Beefalo World Registry), Olvis Publishing Co., PO Box 178, Lexington, OK 73051. TEL 405-527-9252, FAX 405-527-9266. Ed. Mike Edwards. Adv. contact O L Edwards. Circ: 1,500 (paid).

636.2 USA ISSN 0194-4282
BEEFMASTER COWMAN. Text in English. 1979. m. USD 25 domestic (effective 2005). 64 p./no.; **Document type:** *Magazine, Trade.* **Description:** Focuses on the Beefmaster cattle breeding industry.
Formerly: Beefmaster Bull-Etin
Published by: (Beefmaster Breeders United), Gulf Coast Publishing, 11201 Morning Court, San Antonio, TX 78213. TEL 210-344-8300, FAX 210-344-8300, editor@beefmastercowman.com, info@BeefmasterCowman.com. Pub. E C Larkin Jr. Circ: 4,400 (paid).

636.4 USA ISSN 1087-643X
SF393.C5
BERKSHIRE NEWS, CHESTER WHITE JOURNAL, POLAND CHINA ADVANTAGE, SPOTTED NEWS. Text in English. 1994. bi-m. USD 10. adv. illus.; stat. **Document type:** *Trade.* **Description:** Contains tips on raising hogs.
Former titles (until 1996): Chester White Journal, Poland China Advantage, Spotted News (1082-6920); (until 1995): Chester White Journal and Spotted News (1075-0177); Which was formed by the merger of (1910-1994): Chester White Journal (0009-3386); (1961-1994): Spotted News (0038-8432); (1984-1994): Purebred Picture (8750-1880); Which was formed by the merger of: Poland China World (0032-2466); American Landrace - Berkshire News; Which was formed by the merger of (1953-1982): American Landrace (0002-970X); (1935-1982): Berkshire News (0005-9196)
—CISTI, Linda Hall.
Published by: Poland China Record Association, PO Box 9758, Peoria, IL 61612-9758. TEL 309-691-6301, FAX 309-691-0168. Ed. Daniel Parrish. Circ: 2,500. **Co-sponsors:** Chester White Swine Record Association; Spotted Swine Association.

636 ITA
BIANCO NERO. Text in Italian. 11/yr.
Published by: National Association of Frisian Cattle Farmers and Breeders, Via Bergamo, 292, Cremona, CR 26100, Italy. TEL 372-412-521, FAX 372-296-70, TELEX 316608 ANAFI I. Ed. Bruno Biseo. Circ: 11,000.

636 USA ISSN 1056-2400
BISON WORLD. Text in English. 1975. q. USD 125 (effective 2001). adv. bk.rev. **Document type:** *Trade.* **Description:** Contains articles for people involved in the bison industry.
Published by: National Bison Association, 1400 W. 122nd Ave., Ste. 106, Denver, CO 80234-3440. TEL 303-292-2833, FAX 303-292-2564, info@bisoncentral.com, http://www.bisoncentral.com. Ed., R&P Sam Albrecht. Adv. contact Orana Wood. B&W page USD 595, color page USD 685. Circ: 3,000.

677.3 636.3 USA
BLACK SHEEP NEWSLETTER. Text in English. 1974. q. USD 14 domestic; USD 18 foreign (effective 2005). adv. bk.rev. back issues avail. **Document type:** *Newsletter, Trade.* **Description:** For growers, spinners and textile artists interested in colored and white sheep wool and other animal fibers.
Published by: Black Sheep Press, 25455 N.W. Dixie Mtn. Rd., Scappose, OR 97056. TEL 503-621-3063, FAX 604-731-2653, bsnewsltr@aol.com, http://www.blacksheeppress.com. Ed., R&P, Adv. contact Peggy Lundquist. Pubs. Peggy Lundquist, Rich Lundquist. page USD 215. Circ: 2,500.

636.3 GBR
BLACK WELSH MOUNTAIN SHEEP BREEDERS' ASSOCIATION. ANNUAL FLOCK BOOK. Text in English. 1922. a. GBP 20 (effective 2000). **Document type:** *Directory.* **Description:** Lists breeders with details of their flocks.
Published by: Black Welsh Mountain Sheep Breeders' Association, Touchstone, 3 Quarry Cottages, Bourton On The Hill, Moreton-in-marsh, Glos GL56 9AJ, United Kingdom. TEL 44-1386-701538. R&P David Parker. Circ: 400.

636.3 GBR
BLACKFACE SHEEP BREEDERS' ASSOCIATION JOURNAL. Text in English. 1948. a. GBP 12. adv. bk.rev. **Document type:** *Trade.*
Media: Duplicated (not offset).
Published by: Blackface Sheep Breeders' Association, c/o A.M. Fenton, 26 York Pl, Perth, Perthshire PH2 8EH, United Kingdom. TEL 44-1738-623780, FAX 44-1738-621206. Circ: 200.

BLOODSTOCK BREEDERS' REVIEW. see *SPORTS AND GAMES—Horses And Horsemanship*

636 BRA ISSN 0067-9615
CODEN: BOIPAQ
BOLETIM DE INDUSTRIA ANIMAL. Text in Portuguese; Summaries in English. 1929. s-a. USD 41. adv. bk.rev. index. back issues avail. **Document type:** *Bulletin.*
Formerly (until 1940): Revista de Industria Animal (0370-5382)
Indexed: AEA, ATA, AgBio, AgrForAb, AnBrAb, BiolAb, CPA, DSA, FCA, FS&TA, ForAb, HelmAb, HerbAb, HortAb, IndVet, MaizeAb, NutrAb, PBA, PGegResA, PGrRegA, PHN&I, PN&I, PoultAb, ProtozoAb, RDA, RM&VM, RRTA, RevApplEntom, S&F, SIA, SeedAb, SoyAb, TOSA, TriticAb, VetBull, WeedAb.
—BLDSC (2153.500000), CASDDS, CISTI.
Published by: Instituto de Zootecnia, Rua Heitor Penteado 56, Nova Odessa, SP 13460-000, Brazil. TEL 55-19-34669400, http://www.iz.sp.gov.br. Ed. Valdinei Tadeu Paulino. R&P Mario Augusto Brajao. Circ: 1,200.

BOLETIN DE PRENSA. see *AGRICULTURE*

636 ESP ISSN 0213-8980
BOLETIN VERDE; informacion agraria y lactea. Text in Spanish. 1972. q. free.
Indexed: DSA, IndVet.
Published by: Nestle - Espana, Ave. PAISES CATALANES, 25 54, Esplugues De Llobregat, Barcelona 08950, Spain. TEL 34-93-3717100. Ed. Jose Pablo Semur Decha.

636.587 USA ISSN 0068-0117
BOOK OF BANTAMS. Text in English. 1963. irreg. USD 8.50 (effective 2000). **Document type:** *Directory.*
Published by: American Bantam Association, PO Box 127, Augusta, NJ 07822. Ed. George Fitterer. Circ: 10,000.

636 ZAF
BORDER AGRICULTURAL SHOW PRIZE LIST. Text in Afrikaans, English. a. adv.
Published by: Border Agricultural Society, Komani St, PO Box 159, Queenstown, South Africa. Circ: 7,000.

636.3 GBR
BORDER LEICESTER FLOCK BOOK. Text in English. 1896. a. GBP 15 to non-members (effective 2001). back issues avail. **Document type:** *Directory.*
Published by: Society of Border Leicester Sheep Breeders, Greenend, St Boswells, Melrose, Roxburghshire TD6 9ES, United Kingdom. TEL 44-1835-823759. Ed. Nesta D Todd. Circ: 400.

636.0021 BWA
BOTSWANA. MINISTRY OF AGRICULTURE. LIVESTOCK MANAGEMENT SURVEY RESULTS. Text in English. 1983. a. free. **Document type:** *Government.*
Published by: Ministry of Agriculture, Department of Agricultural Research, Private Bag 003, Gaborone, Botswana. FAX 267-356027, TELEX 2543 VET BD. Ed. Henry G Jobeta. R&P Dan B Gombalume. **Subscr. to:** Government Printer, Private Bag 0081, Gaborone, Botswana. TEL 267-353202, FAX 267-312001, http://www.gov.bw. **Co-sponsor:** Central Statistics Office.

636.2 FRA ISSN 0985-150X
BOVINS LIMOUSINS. Text in French. 1964. 5/yr. FRF 250 (effective 2000). adv.
Published by: France Limousin Selection, UPRA, Lanaud, Boisseuil, 87220, France. TEL 33-5-55064631, FAX 33-5-55064630, http://www.limousine.org. Ed., R&P Dominique Favier. Pub. Jean Noel Bonnet. Adv. contact Marie Christine Decorgnol. Circ: 3,500.

636.2 USA ISSN 0192-6764
BRAHMAN JOURNAL. Text in English. 1970. m. USD 15. adv. bk.rev. **Document type:** *Trade.* **Description:** Concerns the breeding and maintainance of Brahman cattle.
—CISTI.
Published by: (American Brahman Breeders Association), Sagebrush Publishing Co., Inc., PO Box 220, Eddy, TX 76524. TEL 254-859-5507, FAX 254-859-5451. Ed., R&P, Adv. contact Joe Brockett TEL 817-859-5507. Circ: 3,900 (paid).

636 AUS
BRAHMAN NEWS. Text in English. 1972. q. AUD 27.50 domestic; AUD 50 foreign (effective 2001). adv. **Document type:** *Magazine, Trade.*
Related titles: Online - full content ed.
Published by: Australian Brahman Breeders' Association Ltd., PO Box 796, Rockhampton, QLD 4700, Australia. TEL 61-79-277799, FAX 61-79-225805, paulad@brahman.com.au, http://www.brahman.com.au. Ed., Pub. John Croaker. Adv. contact Paula Driscoll. Circ: 2,500.

636.2 USA ISSN 0006-9132
BRANGUS JOURNAL. Text in English. 1952. m. USD 20; USD 40 in Canada & Mexico; USD 75 elsewhere (effective 1999 - 2000). adv. charts; illus. **Document type:** *Trade.* **Description:** Covers news about the beef cattle industry and how it affects Brangus breeders.
—CISTI.
Published by: (International Brangus Breeders Association), Brangus Publications, Inc., 5750 Epsilon, San Antonio, TX 78249. TEL 210-696-4343. Ed. Lea Weinheimer. Circ: 3,000.

636 USA
BREEDERS DIGEST. Text in English. 1930. bi-m. USD 10 (effective 2005). **Document type:** *Magazine, Trade.*
Formerly: Berkshire News/Chester White Journal/Poland Chinaadvantage/Spotted News

A

Published by: CPS Swine Co., PO Box 9758, Peoria, IL 61612-0151. TEL 309-691-0151, FAX 309-691-0168, cpspeoria@mindspring.com, http://www.cpsswine.com/breedersdigest/breedersdigest.htm. Ed. Jack Wall. Circ: 2,600 (paid).

636.2 USA
BREEDERS JOURNAL. Text in English. q. free. adv. **Document type:** *Trade.*
Published by: American Breeders Service, 2016 Simsbury Court, Fort Collins, CO 80524-1979. TEL 303-482-8918, FAX 303-482-8916. Ed. Kathleen Bee. Adv. contact Ed Peck. Circ: 126,000.

636.2 GBR
BRITISH CATTLE BREEDERS CLUB. ANNUAL CONFERENCE PAPERS. Text in English. a., latest 2001. **Document type:** *Proceedings.*
Formerly: The British Cattle Breeders Club. Digest (no.)
—BLDSC (1082.43845).
Published by: British Cattle Breeders Club, c/o SDHBS, Westpoint, Clyst St Mary's, Exeter, EX5 1DJ, United Kingdom. TEL 44-1392-447494, FAX 44-1392-447495, bcbc@sdhbs.org.uk.

636.39 GBR ISSN 0068-2039
BRITISH GOAT SOCIETY. HERD BOOK. Text in English. 1886. a. GBP 15. **Document type:** *Directory.* **Description:** Contains details of all milk-producing goats registered in the previous year in England.
—CISTI.
Published by: British Goat Society, 34 Fore St, Bovey Tracey, Newton Abbot, Devon TQ13 9AD, United Kingdom. TEL 44-1626-833168.

636.39 GBR ISSN 0953-8070
BRITISH GOAT SOCIETY. MONTHLY JOURNAL. Text in English. 1879. m. (11/yr.). GBP 15. adv. illus. **Document type:** *Trade.* **Description:** Contains articles on goatkeeping, reports of society meetings, letters, announcements, show results, and milk yields.
—CISTI, IE.
Published by: British Goat Society, 34 Fore St, Bovey Tracey, Newton Abbot, Devon TQ13 9AD, United Kingdom. TEL 44-1626-833168.

636.39 GBR ISSN 0068-2047
BRITISH GOAT SOCIETY. YEAR BOOK. Text in English. 1921. a. GBP 7. **Document type:** *Trade.* **Description:** Contains review articles on a wide range of subjects concerning goat keeping.
Indexed: AnBrAb.
Published by: British Goat Society, 34 Fore St, Bovey Tracey, Newton Abbot, Devon TQ13 9AD, United Kingdom. TEL 44-1626-833168.

▼ **BRITISH POULTRY ABSTRACTS.** see *AGRICULTURE—Abstracting, Bibliographies, Statistics*

636.5 GBR ISSN 0007-1668
CODEN: BPOSA4
➤ **BRITISH POULTRY SCIENCE.** Text in English. 1960. bi-m. GBP 204, USD 367 combined subscription to institutions print & online eds. (effective 2006). adv. bk.rev. charts; illus.; mkt. index. back issues avail.; reprint service avail. from PSC. **Document type:** *Journal, Academic/Scholarly.*
Related titles: Microfiche ed.; Online - full text ed.: ISSN 1466-1799. GBP 194, USD 349 to institutions (effective 2006) (from EBSCO Publishing, Gale Group, IngentaConnect, Northern Light Technology, Inc., O C L C Online Computer Library Center, Inc., ProQuest Information & Learning, Swets Information Services).
Indexed: AEA, ASCA, AbHyg, AgBio, Agr, AgrForAb, AnBrAb, BIOSIS Prev, BioCN&I, BiolAb, CIN, ChemAb, ChemTitl, CurCont, CurPA, DBA, DSA, FCA, FPA, FS&TA, FoVS&M, HelmAb, HerbAb, HortAb, ISR, IndMed, IndVet, MEDLINE, MaizeAb, NutrAb, PBA, PHN&I, PN&I, PoultAb, ProtozoAb, RA&MP, RDA, RM&VM, RPP, RRTA, RiceAb, SCI, SFA, SIA, SoyAb, TOSA, TriticAb, VetBull, WAE&RSA, WildRev, ZooRec.
—BLDSC (2339.300000), CASDDS, CISTI, GNLM, IDS, IE, Infotrieve, ingenta, Linda Hall. **CCC.**
Published by: Taylor & Francis Ltd (Subsidiary of: Taylor & Francis Group), 4 Park Sq, Milton Park, Abingdon, OX14 4RN, United Kingdom. TEL 44-1235-828600, FAX 44-1235-829000, info@tandf.co.uk, http://www.tandf.co.uk/journals/titles/00071668.asp. Eds. Barry O Hughs, Murdo G MacLeod. **Subscr. in N America to:** Taylor & Francis Inc., Customer Services Dept, 325 Chestnut St, 8th Fl, Philadelphia, PA 19106. TEL 215-625-8900, 800-354-1420, FAX 215-625-8914, customerservice@taylorandfrancis.com; **Subscr. to:** Journals Customer Service, Rankine Rd, Basingstoke, Hants RG24 8PR, United Kingdom. TEL 44-1256-813000, FAX 44-1256-330245, enquiry@tandf.co.uk.

636.9322 GBR ISSN 0068-2411
BRITISH RABBIT COUNCIL YEAR BOOK. Text in English. 1961. a. GBP 8 to members (effective 2000).
Formerly (until 1969): British Rabbits
Published by: British Rabbit Council, 7 Kirk Gate, Newark, Notts NG24 1AD, United Kingdom. TEL 44-1636-676042, FAX 44-1636-611683. Ed. J Jalland. Circ: 5,000.

636.2 GBR ISSN 0263-967X
CODEN: BOPUDB
BRITISH SOCIETY OF ANIMAL SCIENCE. OCCASIONAL PUBLICATION. Text in English. 1978. irreg., latest vol.19, 1995.
Indexed: Agr, DBA.
—CASDDS.
Published by: British Society of Animal Science, PO Box 3, Penicuik, Midlothian, Scotland EH26 0RZ, United Kingdom. TEL 44-131-4454508, FAX 44-131-5353120, bsas@ed.sac.ac.uk, http://www.bsas.org.uk/.

636.5 AUS ISSN 1322-8064
THE BRITISH WHITE BULLETIN. Text in English. a. **Document type:** *Bulletin.*
Published by: British White Society, 239 Redbank Rd, Wauchope, NSW 2446, Australia. TEL 02-65851349. Ed., Pub. John Old.

637 636.39 CAN
BROWSE. Text in English. 1952. bi-m. CND 20. adv. back issues avail. **Document type:** *Newsletter.*
Published by: Ontario Goat Breeders' Association, P O Box 2776, Sta A, Sudbury, ON P3A 5J3, Canada. TEL 705-866-2770. Ed. Pat Marcotte. Adv. contact Manon Whitman. Circ: 300.

636.293 THA ISSN 0857-1554
BUFFALO JOURNAL; an international journal of buffalo science. Text in English. 1985. 3/yr. USD 190; USD 80 newsstand/cover (effective 2003). back issues avail. **Document type:** *Journal, Academic/Scholarly.* **Description:** Publishes research paper, reviews and comments on buffalo anatomy, breeding, diseases, genetics, management, nutrition, physiology, reproduction, and socio-economic problem.
Indexed: AgBio, AgrForAb, AnBrAb, DSA, FPA, FS&TA, ForAb, HelmAb, HerbAb, IndVet, MaizeAb, NutrAb, PBA, PHN&I, PN&I, PoultAb, RDA, RM&VM, RevApplEntom, RiceAb, SIA, SoyAb, TriticAb, VetBull, WAE&RSA.
—BLDSC (2357.595000), IE, ingenta.
Published by: Thai Buffalo Association, Research Centre for Bioscience in Animal Production, Faculty of Veterinary Science, Henri Dunant St, Bangkok, 10330, Thailand. TEL 662-2518936, 662-2189238, FAX 662-2189736, kmaneewa@netserv.chula.ac.th. Ed. M Kamonpatana.

636.089 KEN ISSN 0378-9721
CODEN: BAHADH
BULLETIN OF ANIMAL HEALTH AND PRODUCTION IN AFRICA/BULLETIN DES SANTE ET PRODUCTION ANIMALES EN AFRIQUE. Text and summaries in English, French. 1953. q. USD 15; USD 20 foreign. abstr.; bibl.; charts; illus. index. back issues avail. **Document type:** *Academic/Scholarly.* **Description:** Publishes articles on original research relevant to animal health and production activities that may lead to improvement of the livestock industry in Africa and better utilization of her animal resources.
Formerly: Bulletin of Epizootic Diseases of Africa (0525-1443)
Related titles: Supplement(s): Weekly Information Leaflets.
Indexed: AEA, AgBio, Agr, AgrForAb, AnBrAb, BioCN&I, BiolAb, CurCont, DSA, FPA, ForAb, HelmAb, HerbAb, HortAb, IndVet, MEDLINE, MaizeAb, NutrAb, OrnHort, PN&I, PoultAb, ProtozoAb, RA&MP, RDA, RM&VM, RevApplEntom, SFA, SIA, SoyAb, TDB, TriticAb, VetBull, WAE&RSA, WildRev, ZooRec.
—CASDDS, CISTI, GNLM.
Published by: Organization of African Unity, Inter-African Bureau of Animal Resources/Organisation de l'Unite Africaine, Bureau Interafricain des Resources Animales, PO Box 30786, Nairobi, Kenya. TEL 254-2-338544, FAX 254-2-332046, TELEX 22983. Ed. W N Masiga.

636 DEU ISSN 0722-4540
BUNDESVERBAND DER TIERZUCHT- UND BESAMUNGSTECHNIKER. INFORMATIONSBLATT. Text in German. 1970. q. **Document type:** *Journal, Academic/Scholarly.*
Indexed: RefZh.
Published by: Bundesverband der Tierzucht- und Besamungstechniker e.V., Postfach 1204, Neustadt, 91402, Germany. TEL 49-9161-9729, FAX 49-9161-61807.

636 330.9 GBR ISSN 1470-6857
BUSINESS RATIO. MEAT PROCESSORS. Text in English. 1975. a. GBP 275 (effective 2001). charts; stat. **Document type:** *Trade.* **Description:** Analyses and compares the financial performances of leading companies. Provides industry performance summaries, trends, and forecasts.
Former titles (until 2000): Business Ratio Plus: Meat Processors (1354-540X); (until 1994): Business Ratio Report: Meat Processors (0267-6699); Which supersedes in part (in 1985): Business Ratio Report: Meat and Poultry Processors (0261-9032)
Published by: The Prospect Shop Ltd., Field House, 72 Oldfield Rd, Hampton, Middx TW12 2HQ, United Kingdom. TEL 44-20-8461-8730, 44-20-8481-8720, FAX 44-20-8783-1940, info@theprospectshop.co.uk.

636 330.9 GBR ISSN 1470-6865
BUSINESS RATIO. MEAT WHOLESALERS. Text in English. 1975. a. GBP 275 (effective 2001). charts; stat. **Document type:** *Trade.* **Description:** Analyses and compares the financial performance of leading companies. Provides industry performance summaries, trends, and forecasts.
Former titles (until 2000): Business Ratio Plus: Meat Wholesalers (1354-3431); (until 1994): Business Ratio Report: Meat Wholesalers (0261-9040)
Published by: The Prospect Shop Ltd., Field House, 72 Oldfield Rd, Hampton, Middx TW12 2HQ, United Kingdom. TEL 44-20-8461-8730, 44-20-8481-8720, FAX 44-20-8783-1940, info@theprospectshop.co.uk.

636 658 GBR ISSN 1470-692X
BUSINESS RATIO: POULTRY PROCESSORS. Text in English. 1975. a. GBP 275 (effective 2001). charts; stat. **Document type:** *Trade.*
Former titles (until 2000): Business Ratio Plus: Poultry Processors (1354-3423); (until 1994): Business Ratio Report. Poultry Processors (0267-730X); Which supersedes in part (in 1985): Business Ratio Report. Meat and Poultry Processors (0261-9032)
Published by: The Prospect Shop Ltd., Field House, 72 Oldfield Rd, Hampton, Middx TW12 2HQ, United Kingdom. TEL 44-20-8461-8730, 44-20-8481-8720, FAX 44-20-8783-1940, info@theprospectshop.co.uk.

636 NOR ISSN 0807-5069
BUSKAP. Text in Norwegian. 1949. 8/yr. NOK 500 (effective 2001). adv. 56 p./no.; **Document type:** *Magazine, Trade.*
Formerly (until 1996): Buskap og Avdraatt (0007-7194); Incorporates (1962-1964): Avslaget for Norsk Roedt FE - Medlemsblad (0806-2781)
Related titles: Online - full content ed.
Indexed: AEA, AnBrAb, DSA, FCA, HerbAb, IndVet, NutrAb, PN&I, VetBull, WAE&RSA.
—BLDSC (2934.964900). **CCC.**
Published by: (N R F Norwegian Cattle), Geno, Hamar, 2326, Norway. TEL 47-62-52-06-00, FAX 47-62-52-06-10, buskap@geno.no, http://www.buskap.no. Ed. Jan Erik Kjaer. Pub. Mari Bjoerke. Adv. contact Aksel Karlsen. color page NOK 17,000, B&W page NOK 13,600; 185 x 260. Circ: 26,000.

636 BFA
C E B V. Text in French. 1974 (no.7). irreg.
Published by: Communaute Economique du Betail et de la Viande, Secretariat, Ouagadougou, Burkina Faso.

CALIFORNIA. AGRICULTURAL STATISTICS SERVICE. LIVESTOCK REVIEW. see *AGRICULTURE—Abstracting, Bibliographies, Statistics*

CALIFORNIA. AGRICULTURAL STATISTICS SERVICE. POULTRY REPORT. see *AGRICULTURE—Abstracting, Bibliographies, Statistics*

636.2 USA ISSN 0008-0942
CALIFORNIA CATTLEMAN. Text in English. 1917. m. USD 20 to non-members; free to members (effective 2005). adv. illus. **Document type:** *Magazine, Consumer.* **Description:** Aims to keep the commercial beef industry abreast of issues, technology, activities, politics, market and trends within the Western commercial beef and ranching industry.
Indexed: CalPI.
—CISTI.
Published by: (California Cattlemen's Association), Cornerpost Publications, 29802 Road 44, Visalia, CA 93291. TEL 559-651-3083, FAX 559-651-3086, staff@calcattlemen.org, http://www.m3cattlemarketing.com/ccm.html. Adv. contact Matt MacFarlane. color page USD 1,050. Circ: 4,836 (controlled).

636 USA
CALIFORNIA WOOL GROWERS NEWSLETTER. Text in English. m. membership. adv. **Document type:** *Newsletter.*
Formerly: California Wool Growers Association. Bi-Weekly Newsletter
Published by: California Wool Growers Association, 1225 H St, Ste 101, Sacramento, CA 95814. TEL 916-444-8122. Ed. Jay B Wilson. R&P Jay Wilson. Circ: 1,000.

636.5 CAN ISSN 1182-638X
CANADA. AGRICULTURE CANADA. HATCHERY REVIEW. Text in English. 1960. q. free. **Document type:** *Government.* **Description:** Coverage of hatchery operations in Canada, by province and month, with comparative figures.
Formerly: Canada. Agriculture Canada. Hatchery Outlook
Published by: Agriculture Canada, Sir John Carling Bldg, 930 Carling Ave, Ottawa, ON K1A 0C7, Canada. TEL 819-994-0246, FAX 819-953-0969.

636 CAN ISSN 0068-7324
CANADA. AGRICULTURE CANADA. LIVESTOCK MARKET REVIEW. Text in English. a. free. **Document type:** *Government.* **Description:** Annual market situation commentary, numbers of animals marketed, average prices, preliminary imports and exports on a monthly and annual comparison base.
Published by: (Canada. Red Meat Division), Agriculture Canada, Sir John Carling Bldg, 930 Carling Ave, Ottawa, ON K1A 0C7, Canada. TEL 819-994-0246, FAX 819-953-0969.

636 CAN ISSN 0705-9981
CANADA LIVESTOCK MEAT TRADE REPORT. Text in English. 1949. w. free. Supplement avail. **Document type:** *Government.* **Description:** Comprehensive summary of livestock prices, numbers, slaughterings, carcass weights and movements at various locations within the provinces of Canada.
Formerly (until 1973): Live Stock and Meat Trade Report (0706-0009)
—CISTI.
Published by: (Canada. Red Meat Division), Agriculture Canada, Sir John Carling Bldg, 930 Carling Ave, Ottawa, ON K1A 0C7, Canada. TEL 819-994-0246, FAX 819-953-0969.

CANADA. NATIONAL FARM PRODUCTS COUNCIL. ANNUAL REVIEW (YEAR). see *AGRICULTURE—Agricultural Economics*

636.5 CAN
CANADA POULTRYMAN BUYERS' GUIDE. Text in English. 1997. a. free with subscr. to Canadian Poultry Magazine. adv. tr.lit. back issues avail. **Document type:** *Directory, Trade.* **Description:** Offers a list of all businesses that supply or service the Canadian poultry industry.
Related titles: Online - full text ed.
Published by: Annex Publishing & Printing, Inc., 222 Argyle Ave, Delhi, ON N4B 2Y2, ON N4B 2Y2, Canada. TEL 519-582-2513, 800-265-2827, FAX 519-582-4040, sfredericks@annexweb.com, http://www.annexweb.com. Ed. Jim Knisley. Pub., Adv. contact Tim Muise. R&P Susan Fredericks. page CND 1,393; trim 10.88 x 8.13. Circ: 9,000.

636.5 CAN ISSN 0068-8134
CANADA WHO'S WHO OF THE POULTRY INDUSTRY. Text in English. 1952. a. free with subscr. to Canadian Poultry Magazine. adv. illus.; stat. index. **Document type:** *Directory, Trade.*
—CISTI.
Published by: Annex Publishing & Printing, Inc., 222 Argyle Ave, Delhi, ON N4B 2Y2, ON N4B 2Y2, Canada. TEL 519-582-2513, 800-265-2827, FAX 519-582-4040, sfredericks@annexweb.com, http://www.annexweb.com. Ed. Jim Knisley. Pub. Susan Fredericks. Adv. contact Tim Muise. B&W page CND 1,393, color page CND 2,216; trim 10.88 x 8.25. Circ: 5,800 (paid).

636.5 CAN
CANADA'S POULTRY AND EGG INDUSTRY. Text in English. 2002. a. **Document type:** *Government.* **Description:** Provides information about the performance of Canada(UNKNOWN CHARACTER)s poultry and egg industry. It covers broiler hatching eggs, chicken, turkey, and food eggs, and provides information such as total production, farm cash receipts, exports, per-capita consumption, and industry contacts.
Related titles: Online - full content ed.; French ed.
Published by: National Farm Products Council, Canada Bldg., 10th Fl., 344 Slater St., Ottawa, ON K1R 7Y3, Canada. TEL 613-995-6752, FAX 613-995-2097, nfpcweb@agr.gc.ca, http://www.nfpc-cnpa.gc.ca.

636.2 CAN ISSN 0008-2961
CANADIAN AYRSHIRE REVIEW. Text in English, French. 1920. m. CND 32.10 domestic; USD 25 in United States; USD 30 elsewhere. adv. back issues avail. **Document type:** *Trade.*
Indexed: RefZh.
—CISTI, Linda Hall.
Published by: Ayrshire Breeders' Association of Canada, P O Box 188, Ste Anne De Bellevue, PQ H9X 3V9, Canada. TEL 514-398-7970, FAX 514-398-7972. Ed., R&P, Adv. contact Linda Ness. Circ: 1,700.

CANADIAN BROWN SWISS AND BRAUNVIEH ASSOCIATION NEWSLETTER/CLOCHE. see *AGRICULTURE—Dairying And Dairy Products*

636.2 CAN ISSN 0843-9613
CANADIAN CATTLE BUYER; business news of the cattle and beef packing industry. Text in English. fortn. charts. **Document type:** *Newsletter.*
—CISTI.
Published by: Ministry of Agriculture, Food and Rural Affairs (Toronto), Policy Analysis Branch, Legislative Bldg, Queen s Park, Toronto, ON M7A 2B2, Canada. TEL 416-326-3246, FAX 416-326-9892. Ed. Lorrie Mackinnon.

636.3 CAN ISSN 0829-075X
HD9904.C2
CANADIAN CO-OPERATIVE WOOL GROWERS MAGAZINE. Text in English. 1958. a. CND 3 to non-members. adv. **Document type:** *Trade.*
Former titles: Canadian Wool Grower; Canadian Wool Grower and Sheep Breeder (0045-5598)
—CISTI.
Published by: Canadian Cooperative Wool Growers Ltd., P O Box 130, Carleton Place, ON K7C 3P3, Canada. FAX 613-257-8896, ccwghq@wool.ca, http://www.wool.ca. Ed. Eric Bjergso. Circ: 15,000.

636.2 CAN ISSN 0831-3008
CANADIAN GUERNSEY JOURNAL. Text in English. 1927. 4/yr. CND 35 domestic; CND 50 foreign (effective 2000). adv. bk.rev. **Document type:** *Trade.*
Formerly: Canadian Guernsey Breeders' Journal (0045-4907)
—CISTI, Linda Hall.
Published by: Canadian Guernsey Association, 368 Woolwich St, Guelph, ON N1H 3W6, Canada. TEL 519-836-2141, FAX 519-824-9250. Ed. V M Macdonald. Circ: 1,000.

636.2 CAN ISSN 0008-3739
CANADIAN HEREFORD DIGEST. Text mainly in English; Text occasionally in French. 1956. 9/yr. CND 32.10, USD 30 domestic; CND 60 foreign (effective 1999). adv.
—CISTI.
Published by: Gilmore Publications (1980) Ltd., 5160 Skyline Way N E, Calgary, AB T2E 6V1, Canada. TEL 403-274-1734, FAX 403-275-4999. Ed., Pub. Kurt Gilmore. Adv. contact Janice McCurdie. Circ: 2,700.

636.2 CAN ISSN 0008-3909
CANADIAN JERSEY BREEDER. Text in English; Section in French. 1946. 10/yr. CND 25. adv. charts; illus. index.
—CISTI, Linda Hall.
Published by: Jersey Cattle Association of Canada, 350 Speedvale Ave W, Unit 9, Guelph, ON N1H 7M7, Canada. TEL 519-821-9150, FAX 519-821-2723. Ed. Betty Clements. Circ: 1,800.

636 CAN ISSN 0382-6406
CANADIAN JERSEY HERD RECORD. Text in English. 1978 (vol.38). irreg., latest 1986.
Formerly: Jersey Cattle Association of Canada. Record (0382-6414)
—CISTI.
Published by: Jersey Cattle Association of Canada, 350 Speedvale Ave W, Unit 9, Guelph, ON N1H 7M7, Canada. TEL 519-821-1020, FAX 519-821-2723.

636 CAN ISSN 0008-3984
CODEN: CNJNAT
➤ **CANADIAN JOURNAL OF ANIMAL SCIENCE.** Text in English, French. 1921. q. CND 80 domestic to individuals; CND 91 combined subscription domestic to individuals print & online eds.; CND 85 foreign to individuals; CND 99 combined subscription foreign to individuals print & online eds.; CND 125 domestic to institutions; CND 142 combined subscription domestic to institutions print & online eds.; CND 155 foreign to institutions; CND 177 combined subscription foreign to institutions print & online eds. (effective 2004). adv. bibl.; charts; illus.; stat. index. back issues avail. **Document type:** *Journal, Academic/Scholarly.* **Description:** Research on all aspects of farm animals and their products.
Supersedes in part (in 1956): Canadian Journal of Agricultural Science (0366-6557); Which was formerly (until 1952): Scientific Agriculture (0370-887X)
Related titles: Microform ed.: (from PMC, PQC); Online - full text ed.: (from EBSCO Publishing, O C L C Online Computer Library Center, Inc., Swets Information Services).
Indexed: AEA, ASCA, ASFA, AbHyg, AgBio, Agr, AnBrAb, B&AI, BIOSIS Prev, BibAg, BioDAb, BiolAb, BiolDig, CIN, Cadscan, ChemAb, ChemTitl, CurCont, DBA, DSA, EPB, EnvAb, FCA, FS&TA, FoVS&M, HerbAb, HortAb, ISR, IndVet, LeadAb, MaizeAb, NutrAb, PBA, PHN&I, PN&I, PotatoAb, PoultAb, ProtozoAb, RA&MP, RDA, RM&VM, RefZh, RevApplEntom, S&F, S&MA, SCI, SFA, SIA, SSCI, SeedAb, SoyAb, TDB, TriticAb, VetBull, WAE&RSA, WeedAb, WildRev, Zincscan, ZooRec.
—BLDSC (3028.500000), CASDDS, CIS, CISTI, IDS, IE, Infotrieve, ingenta, Linda Hall. **CCC.**
Published by: (Canadian Society of Animal Science), Agricultural Institute of Canada, 141 Laurier Ave W, Ste 1112, Ottawa, ON K1P 5J3, Canada. TEL 613-232-9459, FAX 613-594-5190, journals@aic.ca, http://pubs.nrc-cnrc.gc.ca/aic-journals/cjas.html, http://www.aic.ca. Ed. M A Price TEL 780-492-3235. R&P, Adv. contact T Fenton. Circ: 1,300.

636 CAN ISSN 0008-4344
CANADIAN LACOMBE BREEDERS ASSOCIATION. NEWSLETTER. Text in English. 1958. irreg. (3-4/yr.). mkt. **Document type:** *Newsletter.*
Formerly: Lacombe News
Media: Duplicated (not offset).
Published by: Dr. H.T. Fredeen, Ed. & Pub., 2320 41 Ave N E, Calgary, AB T2E 6W8, Canada. Circ: 300.

636.5 CAN ISSN 1703-2911
CANADIAN POULTRY MAGAZINE. Text in English, French. 1912. m. CND 25.68 domestic; USD 60 foreign (effective 2005). adv. charts; illus.; stat. back issues avail. **Document type:** *Magazine, Trade.* **Description:** Provides information on poultry and the poultry industry, designed primarily for Canadian commercial poultry producers.
Formerly (until 2002): Canada Poultryman (0008-2732)
—CISTI. **CCC.**
Published by: Annex Publishing & Printing, Inc., 222 Argyle Ave, Delhi, ON N4B 2Y2, ON N4B 2Y2, Canada. TEL 519-582-2513, 800-265-2827, FAX 519-582-4040, sfredericks@annexweb.com, http://www.canadianpoultrymag.com, http://www.annexweb.com. Ed. Marilyn White. Circ: 8,387.

636.4 CAN ISSN 0045-5423
CANADIAN SWINE✶. Text in English. 1939. q. CND 12. adv. bk.rev. **Description:** Information on the Canadian purebred swine industry.
—CISTI.
Published by: Canadian Swine Breeders' Association, 2417 Holly La, Ottawa, ON K1V 7P2, Canada. TEL 613-731-5531. Ed. Karen Sample. Circ: 3,000.

636 346.066 USA
CAPITOL LINE-UP. Text in English. s-m. USD 50 to non-members (effective 2001); includes A A M P Lifier; free to members. **Document type:** *Newsletter.* **Description:** Updates on regulatory and legislative matters.
Published by: American Association of Meat Processors, PO Box 269, Elizabethtown, PA 17022. TEL 717-367-1168, FAX 717-367-9096, aamp@aamp.com, http://www.aamp.com. Ed. Bernard Shire. Circ: 2,300.

630 ESP ISSN 0214-249X
CARNE; revista profesional. Text in Spanish. 1943. m. (10/yr.).
Published by: Federacion Madrilena de las Industrias de Carnes, Canos del Peral, 1, Madrid, 28013, Spain. TEL 1-274-13-24, FAX 1-542-77-85. Ed. Eugenio Cano Hernandez. Circ: 10,000.

636 ESP ISSN 0210-5543
CARNICA 2000; revista de las industrias carnicas espanolas. Text in Spanish. 1973. m. (10/yr.). EUR 10 newsstand/cover (effective 2004). adv. bk.rev. reprints avail. **Document type:** *Trade.* **Description:** Covers all topics of the meat trade, from production to consumption.
Indexed: IECT.
—CINDOC.
Published by: Publicaciones Tecnicas Alimentarias S.A., Capitan Haya 35, 4o A, Madrid, 28020, Spain. TEL 34-91-3665207, FAX 34-91-5555173, publitasa@mundivia.es, http://www.publitasa.com. Ed. Alfredo Val. R&P Carlos Ayala. Adv. contact Paloma Delolmo. Circ: 6,500.

636.2 USA ISSN 1058-0484
CASCADE CATTLEMAN. Text in English. 1988. m. USD 12 (effective 2005). adv. 4 cols./p.; back issues avail. **Document type:** *Magazine, Trade.*
Published by: Pioneer Newspaper, 1301 Esplanade, Klamath Fall, OR 97601. TEL 541-885-4460, FAX 541-885-4447, cascade.magazines@heraldandnews.com, http://www.cascadecattleman.com. adv.: B&W page USD 475, color page USD 695. Circ: 5,500 (paid).

636.2 USA ISSN 0897-2737
CATTLE BUSINESS IN MISSISSIPPI. Text in English. 1958. 10/yr. USD 4; free to members (effective 2005). adv. bk.rev. illus.; stat. reprints avail. **Document type:** *Magazine, Trade.*
Formerly: Cattle Business
Published by: Mississippi Cattlemen's Association, 680 Monroe St, Ste A, Jackson, MS 39202-3422. TEL 601-354-8951, FAX 601-355-7128, cbmag@bellsouth.net, http://www.mscattleman.org. adv.: B&W page USD 605, color page USD 1,005. Circ: 5,000.

636.2 USA ISSN 1083-8392
CATTLE BUYERS WEEKLY; marketing and business news for the beef industry. Text in English. 1987. w. USD 169 (effective 2003). **Document type:** *Newsletter, Trade.* **Description:** Provides detailed news and information on the North American meat and livestock industry.
Related titles: Online - full text ed.
Address: PO Box 2533, Petaluma, CA 94953-2533. TEL 707-765-1725, FAX 707-765-6069, info@cattlebuyersweekly.com, http://www.cattlebuyersweekly.com. Ed., Pub. Steve Kay.

636 USA ISSN 0411-289X
CATTLE GUARD. Text in English. 1954. m. USD 20 (effective 2005). adv. **Document type:** *Magazine, Trade.* **Description:** Features stories about Colorado cattlemen; regular columns from association president, association executive vice president, Colorado Cattle Women's president, and Colorado State University; stories on the cattle industry economics, trends, and business management; and reports on association conventions, meetings, and policy statements.
Published by: Colorado Cattlemen's Association, 8833 Ralston Rd, Arvada, CO 80002-2239. TEL 303-431-6422, FAX 303-431-6446, terry@coloradocattle.org, http://www.coloradocattle.org. Eds. Lauren Whittemore, Pat Ptolemy. Pub., Adv. contact Pat Ptolemy. page USD 900. Circ: 13,000.

636.2089 GBR ISSN 0969-1251
CATTLE PRACTICE. Text in English. 1993. q. GBP 100 domestic membership; GBP 110 foreign membership incl. Ireland; GBP 20 domestic to students; GBP 30 foreign to students incl. Ireland (effective 2005). **Document type:** *Journal, Trade.* **Description:** Provides copies of papers given at the meeting throughout the year in addition to other specific papers of interest to members.
Indexed: AEA, AbHyg, AgBio, AnBrAb, BioCN&I, DSA, FoVS&M, HelmAb, HerbAb, IndVet, MaizeAb, NutrAb, PBA, PN&I, PotatoAb, PoultAb, ProtozoAb, RM&VM, SoyAb, TriticAb, VetBull, WAE&RSA.
—BLDSC (3093.296200), IE.
Published by: British Cattle Veterinary Association, The Green, Frampton-On-Severn, Glos GL2 7EP, United Kingdom. TEL 44-1452-740816, FAX 44-1452-741117, office@cattlevet.co.uk, http://www.bcva.org.uk/member/cattle.asp.

A

▼ new title ➤ refereed ✶ unverified ♦ full entry avail.

A

636.2 AUS ISSN 0313-9158
CATTLEMAN. Text in English. m. USD 12. adv.
Published by: Western Publishers Pty. Ltd., 10 Joseph St, PO Box 188, Toowoomba, QLD 4350, Australia. TEL 076-324444, FAX 076-382118. Ed. Stephen Darracott. Circ: 5,200.

636.2 USA ISSN 0008-8552
SF17
CATTLEMAN. Text in English. 1914. m. USD 25 domestic; USD 40 foreign (effective 2001). adv. illus.; stat. index. reprint service avail. from PQC. **Document type:** *Trade.*
Related titles: Microfilm ed.: (from PQC); Online - full text ed.: (from ProQuest Information & Learning).
—CISTI.
Published by: Texas and Southwestern Cattle Raisers Association Inc., 1301 W Seventh St, Fort Worth, TX 76102. TEL 817-332-7155, http://www.thecattlemanmagazine.com. Ed. Lionel Chambers. Circ: 1,564; 15,294 (paid).

636 ZWE
CATTLEMAN OF THE YEAR. Text in English. a. adv. illus. **Document type:** *Trade.*
Related titles: ♦ Supplement to: The Farmer. ISSN 1011-0488.
Published by: Modern Farming Publications, Agriculture House, Moffat St., PO Box 1622, Harare, Zimbabwe. TEL 263-4-753278, FAX 263-4-750754. Ed. Felicity Wood. Adv. contact Michael Rook. B&W page ZWD 9,911, color page ZWD 11,946; bleed 216 x 280.

636.2 CAN ISSN 0008-3143
CATTLEMEN; the beef magazine. Text in English. 1938. m. CND 24. adv. charts; illus.; mkt.; pat.; stat. **Document type:** *Trade.*
Formerly (until 1969): Canadian Cattlemen (0319-504X)
Related titles: Microform ed.: (from PQC).
—CISTI. **CCC.**
Published by: Farm Business Communications, P O Box 6600, Winnipeg, MB R3C 3A7, Canada. TEL 204-944-5761, FAX 204-942-8463. Ed. Gren Winslow. Adv. contact Tom Mumby. Circ: 28,700.

636.2 MEX
CEBU. Text in Spanish. 1976. m. USD 20. adv.
Published by: (Asociacion Mexicana de Criadores de Cebu), Editorial Ano Dos Mil, S.A., Indianapolis 70, Mexico City, DF 03810, Mexico. Ed. Juan Francisco Gonzalez Inigo. Circ: 7,500.

CENTRAL OREGON RANCHER. see *AGRICULTURE—Agricultural Equipment*

636.9322 USA ISSN 0009-1294
CHAMPAGNE NEWS★. Text in English. m. USD 3. adv. charts; stat.
Media: Duplicated (not offset).
Published by: (Champagne d'Argent Rabbit Federation), Wayne Cleer, Ed. & Pub., 1704 Heisel, Pekin, IL 61554. Circ: 385.

636 FRA ISSN 0395-8183
CHAROLAIS. Text in French. 1966. q. EUR 30 domestic; EUR 35 in Europe; EUR 40 elsewhere (effective 2002). adv. **Document type:** *Bulletin.*
Indexed: RefZh.
—CISTI.
Published by: Herd Book Charolais, 8 rue de Lourdes, BP 222, Nevers, Cedex 58002, France. TEL 33-03-86597700, FAX 33-03-86597719. Ed. Albert Merlet. Pub., Adv. contact Cecile Lamirault TEL 33-03-86597700. Circ: 8,250.

636.2 CAN ISSN 0824-1767
CHAROLAIS BANNER; official publication of the Canadian purebred Charolais cattle industry. Text in English. 1966. 10/yr. CND 32.10, USD 35 (effective 1999). adv. illus. **Document type:** *Trade.*
Formerly: Canadian Charolais Banner (0008-5499)
—CISTI.
Published by: Charolais Banner Ltd., 200, 1933 8th Ave, Regina, SK S4R 1E9, Canada. TEL 306-546-3940, FAX 306-546-3942, banner@charolaisbanner.com, http://www.charolaisbanner.com. Ed. Candace By. Pub., Adv. contact Helge By. Circ: 2,100.

636.2 CAN ISSN 0828-7600
CHAROLAIS CONNECTION; official publication of the Canadian commercial Charolais industry. Text in English. 1984. 2/yr. included with Charolais Banner. adv. charts; illus.; stat.; tr.lit. back issues avail.
—CISTI.
Published by: Charolais Banner Ltd., 200, 1933 8th Ave, Regina, SK S4R 1E9, Canada. TEL 306-546-3940, FAX 306-546-3942. Ed. Candace By. Pub., Adv. contact Helge By. Circ: 18,000.

636 USA ISSN 0191-5444
CHAROLAIS JOURNAL. Text in English. 1977. m. USD 30 domestic; USD 50 foreign (effective 2000). adv. **Document type:** *Trade.*
—CISTI.
Published by: Charolais Publications, Inc., PO Box 20247, Kansas City, MO 64195. TEL 816-464-5977, FAX 816-464-5759, chjourn@sound.net. Ed. Julie Olson TEL 816-464-5977. R&Ps David Hobbs, Julie Olson TEL 816-464-5977. Adv. contact David Hobbs. Circ: 5,500.

636.39 FRA ISSN 0045-6608
LA CHEVRE; revue des eleveurs de chevres. Text in French. 1958. 6/yr. adv. **Description:** Technical and economical information about goat breeding.
Indexed: AEA, AgBio, AgrForAb, AnBrAb, DSA, ForAb, HelmAb, HerbAb, IndVet, NutrAb, PoultAb, ProtozoAb, RDA, RRTA, S&F, VetBull, WAE&RSA.
Published by: (Societe de Presse et d'Edition Ovine et Caprine (S.P.E.O.C.)), Editions Reussir, 19 quai de Juillet, CP 700, Caen, Cedex 9 1414, France. TEL 33-2-31357700, FAX 33-2-31357718, m.jourdan@reussir.tm.fr. Eds. Marc Jourdan, Jean-Claude Le Jaouen. Pub. Claude Allo. R&P Marc Jourdan. Adv. contact Jean Pierre Dumas. Circ: 45,000 (controlled). **Co-sponsor:** Institut Technique de l'Elevage Ovin et Caprin.

CHICAGO DAILY HIDE AND TALLOW BULLETIN; the first daily hide market service established in America. see *LEATHER AND FUR INDUSTRIES*

338.1 USA
CHICKEN DISEASES. Text in English. 1980. a. USD 6 (effective 2000).
Published by: American Bantam Association, PO Box 127, Augusta, NJ 07822. Ed. F P Jeffrey.

636 JPN ISSN 0009-3874
CHIKUSAN NO KENKYU/ANIMAL HUSBANDRY. Text in Japanese. 1947. m. JPY 16,000. adv. bk.rev. index. **Document type:** *Academic/Scholarly.*
Indexed: B&AI, DSA, FS&TA, RRTA, WAE&RSA.
Published by: Yokendo Co. Ltd., 30-15 Hongo 5-chome, Bunkyo-ku, Tokyo, 113-0033, Japan. TEL 03-3814-0911, FAX 03-3812-2615. Ed. Kiyoshi Oikawa. Circ: 20,000.

CHILE. INSTITUTO NACIONAL DE ESTADISTICAS. ESTADISTICAS PECUARIAS. see *AGRICULTURE—Abstracting, Bibliographies, Statistics*

636 CZE ISSN 0323-1534
CHOVATEL. Text in Czech. 1966. m. USD 21.10.
Formerly: Drobne Hospodarske Zvirectvo
Indexed: AnBrAb.
Published by: Cesky Svaz Chovatelu, Makova 3, Prague, 18253, Czech Republic. Ed. Hana Zvolska. **Subscr. to:** Artia, Ve Smeckach 30, Prague 1 111 27, Czech Republic.

636.4 CUB ISSN 0138-8738
CODEN: CAGPDY
CIENCIA Y TECNICA EN LA AGRICULTURA. SERIE: GANADO PORCINO. Abstracts and contents page in English. 1978. 4/yr. USD 17 in North America; USD 19 in South America; USD 21 in Europe; USD 24 elsewhere.
Indexed: Agrind, AnBrAb, NutrAb, PN&I.
Published by: Centro de Informacion y Documentacion Agropecuario, Gaveta Postal 4149, Havana, 4, Cuba. **Dist. by:** Ediciones Cubanas, Obispo No. 527, Apdo. 605, Havana, Cuba.

636 USA
CLYDESDALE NEWS. Text in English. 1970. a. USD 15 (effective 2001). back issues avail. **Document type:** *Trade.*
Published by: Clydesdale Breeders of the U.S.A., 17346 Kelley Rd, Pecatonica, IL 61063. TEL 815-247-8780, FAX 815-247-8337, secretary@clydesusa.com, clydesusa@aol.com, http://www.clydesusa.com. Circ: 1,500.

636.2 GBR ISSN 0069-4924
COATES'S HERD BOOK (BEEF). Text in English. 1882. a. GBP 10 to members. adv. **Document type:** *Trade.*
Published by: Shorthorn Society of Great Britain and Ireland, 4th St, National Agricultural Centre, Stoneleigh Park, Kenilworth, Warks CV8 2LG, United Kingdom. TEL 44-2476-696549, FAX 44-2476-696729, mtaggart@shorthorn.freeserve.co.uk, http://www.shorthorn.co.uk. Ed. Martin Taggart. Circ: 800.

COLORADO AGRIBUSINESS ROUNDUP. see *AGRICULTURE—Agricultural Economics*

636.2 ITA
CONOSCERE I TORI. Text in Italian. s-a. **Document type:** *Magazine, Trade.* **Description:** Presents production and morphology evaluations of sires. Indexes are calculated using the Blup Animal Model procedure.
Published by: Associazione Nazionale Allevatori Razza Bruna, Localita Ferlina 204, Bussolengo, VR 37012, Italy. TEL 39-045-6701990, FAX 39-045-7156655, anarb@anarb.it, http://www.anarb.it.

CONSUMO PECUARIO NACIONAL. see *AGRICULTURE—Abstracting, Bibliographies, Statistics*

636 USA ISSN 0885-7687
CORNELL NUTRITION CONFERENCE FOR FEED MANUFACTURERS. PROCEEDINGS. Text in English. 1947. a. USD 15 in US & Canada; USD 25 elsewhere (effective 2005).
Related titles: CD-ROM ed.: USD 15 in US & Canada; USD 25 elsewhere (effective 2005).
Published by: Cornell Nutrition Conference, New York State College of Agriculture and Life Sciences, Department of Animal Science, Cornell University, Ithaca, NY 14853. TEL 607-255-4478, FAX 607-255-1335. **Co-sponsor:** American Feed Manufacturers' Association.

630 640 GBR
COUNTRY SMALLHOLDING; organic living at its best. Text in English. 1975. m. GBP 20.95; GBP 24.95 foreign; GBP 2.10 newsstand/cover (effective 1999). adv. bk.rev. stat.; tr.lit.; illus. index. back issues avail. **Document type:** *Consumer.* **Description:** Covers information on homesteading, particularly livestock and poultry keeping on a small scale. Also directed toward organic gardeners and growers.
Former titles (until 1999): Country Garden and Smallholding (1358-216X); (until 1995): Country Garden (1353-2790); (until 1994): Home Farm (0264-8873); (until 1982): Practical Self Sufficiency (0309-510X); Which incoporated: Self-Reliance Newsletter
Published by: Broad Leys Publishing Co., Buriton House, Station Rd, Newport, Saffron Walden, Essex CB11 3PL, United Kingdom. TEL 44-1799-540922, FAX 44-1799-541367, cgs@broadleys.com, http://www3.mistral.co.uk/cgs. Ed. Helen Sears. Pub., R&P David Thear. Adv. contact Jan Ayres. B&W page GBP 350, color page GBP 500; trim 210 x 298. Circ: 21,000 (paid). **Dist. by:** Warners Group Publications Plc, The Maltings, West St, Bourne, Lincs PE10 9PH, United Kingdom. TEL 44-1778-393652, FAX 44-1778-393668, tomb@warnersgroup.co.uk.

636.2 USA ISSN 0279-8204
COW COUNTRY. Text in English. 1950. q. USD 20 to non-members; free to members (effective 2005). adv. back issues avail. **Document type:** *Magazine, Trade.* **Description:** Discusses cattle breeding.
Published by: Wyoming Stock Growers Association, 113 E 20th, Cheyenne, Laramie, WY 82001. TEL 307-638-3942, FAX 307-634-1210, http://www.wysga.org. Ed. Kosha Olsen. Circ: 1,600 (paid).

636 382 USA
COW NEWS & BULL VIEWS. Text in English. 1987. bi-m. looseleaf. USD 5 (effective 1998). adv. **Document type:** *Newsletter.* **Description:** News and information on recording, registering and promoting American Breed cattle which are approximately 1/2 Brahman, 1/4 Charolais, 1/8 Bison, 1/16 Hereford, 1/16 Shorthorn.
Formerly: News and Views (Portales)
Published by: American Breed International Association, Inc., 1530 S Ave E, Portales, NM 88130. TEL 505-359-1496. Ed. Jewell Jones Swisher. Circ: 500.

636 USA
COWBOY'S DIGEST. Text in English. 1974. bi-m. USD 18 (effective 2005). **Document type:** *Newspaper, Trade.*
Formerly: Kalispell Livestock Weekly News
Published by: Jeanne Benson Ed. & Pub., 2443 N. Frontage Rd., Billings, MT 59103. TEL 406-628-6456, FAX 406-628-6445, http://www.cowboysdigest.com. Pub. Jeanne Benson. Circ: 1,500 (paid).

636.2 USA
COWBOYS DIGEST. Text in English. 1974. bi-m. USD 15. adv. **Document type:** *Newspaper.*
Address: PO Box 1196, Kalispell, MT 59903. TEL 406-752-7525, FAX 406-752-7520. Ed., Pub., R&P, Adv. contact Jeanne Carpenter. Circ: 2,000.

636.5 CUB
CUBA. CENTRO DE INFORMACION Y DOCUMENTACION AGROPECUARIO. BOLETIN DE RESENAS. SERIE: AVICULTURA. Text in Spanish. 1974. irreg. per issue exchange basis.
Formerly: Cuba. Centro de Informacion y Divulgacion Agropecuario. Boletin de Resenas. Serie: Avicultura
Published by: Centro de Informacion y Documentacion Agropecuario, Gaveta Postal 4149, Havana, 4, Cuba.

636.4 CUB ISSN 1011-968X
CUBA. CENTRO DE INFORMACION Y DOCUMENTACION AGROPECUARIO. BOLETIN DE RESENAS. SERIE: GANADO PORCINO. Text in Spanish; Abstracts in English. 1974. irreg. per issue exchange basis.
Formerly: Cuba. Centro de Informacion y Divulgacion Agropecuario. Boletin de Resenas. Serie: Ganado Porcino
Indexed: Agrind.
Published by: Centro de Informacion y Documentacion Agropecuario, Gaveta Postal 4149, Havana, 4, Cuba. **Dist. by:** Ediciones Cubanas, Obispo No. 461, Apdo. 605, Havana, Cuba.

636.9322 ESP ISSN 0210-1912
CUNICULTURA. Text in Spanish. 1976. bi-m., latest vol.26, 2001. EUR 38.46 domestic; EUR 55 foreign (effective 2004). adv. bk.rev. illus.; stat.; abstr.; bibl.; mkt. index. back issues avail. **Document type:** *Trade.* **Description:** For rabbit growers.
Published by: Real Escuela de Avicultura, Plana del Paraiso 14, Arenys De Mar, Barcelona 08350, Spain. TEL 34-93-7921137, FAX 34-93-7921537, avinet@avicultura.com, http://www.avicultura.com. Ed., Pub. Jose A Castello. Adv. contact Luis Carrasco. Circ: 2,950.

636.9322 FRA ISSN 0152-3058
CUNICULTURE; la revue de l'eleveur de lapins. Text in French. 1974. bi-m. EUR 49.50 in Europe (effective 2001).
Indexed: AEA, AgBio, AnBrAb, DSA, HelmAb, IndVet, NutrAb, ProtozoAb, RM&VM, TriticAb, VetBull, WAE&RSA.
—BLDSC (3492.481400), IE.
Published by: Association Francaise de Cuniculture, BP 50, Lempdes, 63370, France. TEL 33-4-73920152, FAX 33-4-73928680, asfrcuni@easynet.fr, http://www.rabbit-science.com. Ed. Francois Lebas.

CYPRUS. DEPARTMENT OF STATISTICS AND RESEARCH. CENSUS OF POULTRY. see *AGRICULTURE—Abstracting, Bibliographies, Statistics*

636 CZE ISSN 1212-1819
CODEN: ZIVYAY
➤ **CZECH JOURNAL OF ANIMAL SCIENCE.** Text and summaries in English; Summaries in Czech, Slovak. 1956. m. USD 214 (effective 2003). bk.rev. bibl.; charts. **Document type:** *Academic/Scholarly.* **Description:** Contains scientific papers and reviews dealing with genetics and breeding, physiology, reproduction, nutrition and feeds, technology, ethology and economics of cattle, pig, sheep, poultry, fish and other farm animals.
Formerly (until 1997): Zivocisna Vyroba (0044-4847)
Indexed: AEA, ASCA, AbHyg, AgBio, AnBrAb, BiolAb, CIN, ChemAb, ChemTitl, CurCont, DSA, FS&TA, HelmAb, HerbAb, HortAb, IndVet, MaizeAb, NutrAb, PHN&I, PN&I, PoultAb, ProtozoAb, RA&MP, RM&VM, RRTA, RefZh, RevApplEntom, S&F, SIA, SSCI, SoyAb, TriticAb, VetBull, WAE&RSA.
—BLDSC (3507.371450), CASDDS, CISTI, IDS, IE, ingenta, Linda Hall.
Published by: Ceska Akademie Zemedelskych Ved, Ustav Zemedelskych a Potravinarskych Informaci/Czech Academy of Agricultural Sciences, Institute of Agricultural and Food Information, Slezska 7, Prague 2, 120 56, Czech Republic. TEL 420-2-227010352, FAX 420-2-227010116, edit@uzpi.cz, http://www.cazv.cz. Ed. Mrs. Zdenka Radosova. R&P Mr. Jan Rydlo. Circ: 600. **Co-sponsor:** Ceska Akademie Zemedelskych Ved/Czech Academy of Agricultural Sciences.

636.5 636.4 DEU ISSN 0948-4221
CODEN: DDGSE8
D G S INTERN. (Deutsche Gefluegelwirtschaft und Schweineproduktion) Text in German. 1948. w. EUR 164.20 domestic; EUR 182.20 foreign (effective 2004). adv. bk.rev. charts; illus.; stat. index. **Document type:** *Magazine, Trade.*
Supersedes in part (in 1995): D G S (0340-3858); Which was formerly: Deutsche Gefluegelwirtschaft (0012-0162)
Indexed: RRTA, WAE&RSA.
Published by: (Zentralverband der Deutschen Gefluegelwirtschaft), Verlag Eugen Ulmer GmbH, Wollgrasweg 41, Stuttgart, 70599, Germany. TEL 49-711-4507-0, FAX 49-711-4507-120, info@ulmer.de, http://www.ulmer.de. Ed. Cordula Moebius. R&P Gerd Friedrich. Adv. contact Annelie Purwing. B&W page EUR 2,613.60, color page EUR 3,753.60; trim 185 x 270. Circ: 4,800 (paid and controlled).

636.5 DEU ISSN 0947-5664
D G S MAGAZIN; Fachinformationen fuer die Gefluegelwirtschaft und Schweineproduktion. (Deutsche Gefluegelwirtschaft und Schweineproduktion) Text in German. 1948. m. EUR 84.80 domestic; EUR 91.80 foreign; EUR 6.50 newsstand/cover (effective 2005). adv. **Document type:** *Magazine, Trade.*
Supersedes in part (in 1995): D G S (0340-3858); Which was formerly: Deutsche Gefluegelwirtschaft (0012-0162)
Published by: (Zentralverband der Deutschen Gefluegelwirtschaft e.V.), Verlag Eugen Ulmer GmbH, Wollgrasweg 41, Stuttgart, 70599, Germany. TEL 49-711-45070, FAX 49-711-4507120, info@ulmer.de, http://www.ulmer.de/Artikel.dll?MID=472. Ed. Cordula Moebius. adv.: B&W page EUR 2,689.20, color page EUR 3,829.20; trim 185 x 270. Circ: 5,412 (paid).

636.39 USA ISSN 0011-5592
DAIRY GOAT JOURNAL. Text in English. 1916. bi-m. USD 21 domestic; USD 28 foreign (effective 2005). adv. bk.rev. illus. **Document type:** *Magazine, Trade.* **Description:** Provides current information on the dairy goat, including milking and cheese-making techniques.
Indexed: BiolAb.
—CISTI, IE, Infotrieve, Linda Hall.
Published by: Countryside Publications, Ltd., 145 Industrial Dr, Medford, WI 54451. TEL 715-785-7979, FAX 715-785-7414, http://www.dairygoatjournal.com. Ed. Jennifer Stultz. Pub. Dave Belanger. Adv. contact Alicia Komanec. Circ: 7,000 (paid).

636.39 AUS ISSN 0815-9769
DAIRY GOAT SOCIETY OF AUSTRALIA. VICTORIAN BRANCH NEWSLETTER. Text in English. 1978. q. AUD 20 domestic; AUD 20 foreign (effective 2002). adv. bk.rev. 10 p./no.; back issues avail. **Document type:** *Newsletter.* **Description:** Contains animal husbandry (goat) information. Contains local issues as affecting goats and their management.
Published by: Dairy Goat Society of Australia, Victorian Branch, 119 Mc Glones Rd, Drouin, VIC 3818, Australia. TEL 61-3-5625-2995, FAX 61-3-5625-3532. Ed., Adv. contact R Patton. R&P G Keays. B&W page AUD 25. Circ: 400. **Subsc. to:** c/o G. Keays, RMB 8680, Bannockburn, VIC 3331, Australia.

DAIRY INDIA YEARBOOK. see *AGRICULTURE—Dairying And Dairy Products*

636.4 DNK ISSN 1601-8400
DANAVL MAGASINET. Text in Danish. 1996. irreg. (3/4 yr.) back issues avail. **Document type:** *Bulletin, Trade.*
Formerly (until 2001): DanAvl Dokumenterer (1396-7800)
Related titles: Online - full text ed.
Published by: Landsudvalget for Svin, Afdelingen for Avl og Opformering, Udkjaervej 15, Skejby, Aarhus N, 8200, Denmark. http://www.danskeslagterier.dk/view.asp?ID=1996, http://www.danavl.dk.

636 CHN
DANGDAI XUMU/MODERN ANIMAL HUSBANDRY. Text in Chinese. q.
Published by: Beijing Shi Xumu Ju/Beijing Bureau of Animal Husbandry, Dewai, 75 Bingjiaokou, Beijing, 100088, China. TEL 2014549. Ed. Yu Shuangmuo.

636.4 DNK ISSN 0906-9488
DANSK AVLSNYT; magasin for aktive svineproducenter. Text in Danish. 1989. 10/yr. DKK 390; DKK 55 per issue (effective 2004). adv. **Document type:** *Journal, Trade.* **Description:** News for pig farmers.
Formerly (until 1991): Kollund Avls-Nyt (0906-947X)
Published by: Boers-Mark A/S, Vestergade 19, Struer, 7600, Denmark. TEL 45-97-841380, FAX 45-97-841370, borsmark@bors-mark.dk, http://borsmark.synkron3-2.dir.dk/sw325.asp, http://www.bors-mark.dk. Ed. Hagbard Nielsen. adv.: page DKK 10,900; 182 x 265. Circ: 5,555.

636.5 DNK ISSN 0045-9607
DANSK ERHVERVSFJERKRAE. Text in Danish. 1879. m. DKK 1,350 to institutional members (effective 2005). adv. bk.rev. charts; illus. index. **Document type:** *Magazine, Trade.*
Supersedes in part (in 1971): Tidsskrift for Fjerkraeavl (0040-7046); Which incorporates (1964-1965): Erhvervsfjerkrae (0425-1954)
Address: Oester Finderupsvej 2, Finderup, Skjern, 6900, Denmark. TEL 45-97-361050, FAX 45-97-361250, dedk@post16.tele.dk, http://www.erhvervsfjer.landbrug.dk. Ed. L Yding Soerensen. Adv. contact Joergen Nyberg Larsen TEL 45-33-394000. Circ: 1,400.

636.2 DNK ISSN 1397-3592
DANSK KOEDKVAEG; magasinet for aktive koedkvaegsprodukter. Text in Danish. 1996. q. DKK 195 (effective 2004).
Incorporates (197?-1996): Simmentaleren (1602-6543)
Published by: Boers-Mark A/S, Vestergade 19, Struer, 7600, Denmark. TEL 45-97-841380, FAX 45-97-841370, borsmark@bors-mark.dk, http://www.bors-mark.dk. Ed. Hagbard Nielsen.

636.2 DNK ISSN 1602-0634
DANSK LANDBRUGSRAADGIVNING. DANSK KVAEG. AARSRAPPORT. Text in Danish. 1972. a. **Document type:** *Trade.*
Former titles (until 2002): Landsudvalget for Kvaeg. Aarsrapport (1396-2833); (until 1996): Landsudvalget for Kvaeg. Aarsberetning (0900-1794)
Related titles: ♦ Series of: Dansk Landbrugsraadgivning. Dansk Kvaeg. Rapport. ISSN 1602-3846.
Published by: Dansk Landbrugsraadgivning, Dansk Kvaeg/Danish Agricultural Advisory Service. Danish Cattle Husbandry, Udkaersvej 15, Skejby, Aarhus N, 8200, Denmark. TEL 45-87-405000, FAX 45-87-405010.

636.0021 DNK ISSN 0909-5799
DANSK LANDBRUGSRAADGIVNING. DANSK KVAEG. AARSSTATISTIK, AVL. Text in Danish. 1983. a. stat. **Document type:** *Trade.*
Former titles (until 1994): Landskontoret for Kvaeg. Aarsstatistik (0902-2252); (until 1986): Landskontoret for Kvaeg. Aarsberetning (0990-2244)
Related titles: ♦ Series of: Dansk Landbrugsraadgivning. Dansk Kvaeg. Rapport. ISSN 1602-3846.
Published by: Dansk Landbrugsraadgivning, Dansk Kvaeg/Danish Agricultural Advisory Service. Danish Cattle Husbandry, Udkaersvej 15, Skejby, Aarhus N, 8200, Denmark. TEL 45-87-405000, FAX 45-87-405010.

636.2 DNK ISSN 1601-9644
DANSK LANDBRUGSRAADGIVNING. DANSK KVAEG. KOEDKVAEG. Text in Danish. 1991. a. **Document type:** *Trade.*
Formerly (until 2002): Landsudvalget for Kvaeg. Koedkvaegavlen (0907-4783)
Related titles: ♦ Series of: Dansk Landbrugsraadgivning. Dansk Kvaeg. Rapport. ISSN 1602-3846.
Published by: Dansk Landbrugsraadgivning, Dansk Kvaeg/Danish Agricultural Advisory Service. Danish Cattle Husbandry, Udkaersvej 15, Skejby, Aarhus N, 8200, Denmark. TEL 45-87-405000, FAX 45-87-405010.

636.2 DNK ISSN 1602-3846
DANSK LANDBRUGSRAADGIVNING. DANSK KVAEG. RAPPORT. Text in Danish. 1991. irreg., latest vol.109, 2004. price varies. back issues avail. **Document type:** *Monographic series, Trade.*

Formerly (until 2002): Landsudvalget for Kvaeg. Rapport (0906-1398)
Related titles: ♦ Series: Dansk Landbrugsraadgivning. Dansk Kvaeg. Koedkvaeg. ISSN 1601-9644; ♦ Dansk Landbrugsraadgivning. Dansk Kvaeg. Aarsrapport. ISSN 1602-0634; ♦ Dansk Landbrugsraadgivning. Dansk Kvaeg. Aarsstatistik, Avl. ISSN 0909-5799.
Published by: Dansk Landbrugsraadgivning, Dansk Kvaeg/Danish Agricultural Advisory Service. Danish Cattle Husbandry, Udkaersvej 15, Skejby, Aarhus N, 8200, Denmark. TEL 45-87-405000, FAX 45-87-405010, http://www.lr.dk/kvaeg/system/visrapportserie.asp.

636.2 DNK ISSN 1603-9491
DANSK LANDBRUGSRAADGIVNING. DANSK KVAEG. RAPPORT, DANSK KVAEG. Text in Danish. 1992. a.
Formerly (until 2002): Landsudvalget for Kvaeg. Aarsrapport (0907-5305)
Published by: Dansk Landbrugsraadgivning, Dansk Kvaeg/Danish Agricultural Advisory Service. Danish Cattle Husbandry, Udkaersvej 15, Skejby, Aarhus N, 8200, Denmark. TEL 45-87-405000, FAX 45-87-405010.

636.5 DNK ISSN 0907-9718
DET DANSKE FJERKRAERAAD. BERETNING. Text in Danish. 1975. a. **Document type:** *Trade.*
Former titles (until 1992): Landsudvalget for Fjerkraeavlen. Beretning (0415-3669); (until 1975): Landsudvalget for Fjerkrae. Beretning (0901-1315)
Published by: Det Danske Fjerkraeraad, Trommesalen 5, Copenhagen V, 1614, Denmark. TEL 45-33-254100, FAX 45-33-251121, fjerkraeraad@poultry.dk, danskfjerkrae.dk.

636.3 GBR
DARTMOOR SHEEP BREEDERS' ASSOCIATION. ANNUAL FLOCK BOOK. Text in English. 1909. a. GBP 10.
Published by: Dartmoor Sheep Breeders' Association, Aish Park House 3a, Fore St, South Brent, Devon TQ10 9BQ, United Kingdom. TEL 03647-3657. Ed. J A Hanney.

636.2 GBR ISSN 0070-2986
DAVY'S DEVON HERD BOOK. Text in English. 1851. a. GBP 15 (effective 2000). **Description:** Carries the registrations of cattle for the Devon breed in the UK.
Published by: Devon Cattle Breeders' Society, Wisteria Cottage, Iddesleigh, Winkleigh, Devon EX19 8BG, United Kingdom. TEL 44-1837-810942, FAX 44-1837-810942. Ed., Pub., R&P, Adv. contact A J Lane. Circ: 85.

636 NZL ISSN 0110-7992
THE DEER FARMER. Text in English. 1979. 11/yr. (plus a cumulation). NZD 89.95 domestic; AUD 117 in Australia; CND 135 in Canada; USD 95 elsewhere (effective 2002). adv. bk.rev. **Document type:** *Trade.*
Indexed: INZP.
Published by: Deer Farmer Publications Ltd., P.O. Box 11092, Wellington, New Zealand. TEL 64-4-4739243, FAX 64-4-4734530, info@wham.co.nz, http://www.deerfarmer.co.nz. Eds. Angela Fussell, Trevor Walton. Pub., R&P Trevor Walton. Adv. contact Angela Fussell. Circ: 4,000.

DEERFARMERS' DIGEST. see *AGRICULTURE*

351.823 636 DNK ISSN 1398-201X
SF83.D43
DENMARK. MINISTERIET FOR FOEDEVARER, LANDBRUG OG FISKERI. DANMARKS JORDBRUGSFORSKNING. AARSBERETNING/DENMARK. DANISH INSTITUTE OF ANIMAL SCIENCE. ANNUAL REPORT. Text in Danish. 1996. a. free. **Document type:** *Government.*
Formed by the merger of (1974-1996): Denmark. Statens Husdyrbrugsforsoeg. Aarsrapport (0106-8547); (1992-1996): Denmark. Landbrugsministeriet. Statens Planteavlsforsoeg. Aarsberetning (1398-1927)
Indexed: DSA, IndVet, NutrAb, PoultAb.
—CISTI.
Published by: Ministeriet for Foedevarer, Landbrug og Fiskeri, Danmarks Jordbrugsforskning/Ministry of Food, Agriculture and Fisheries. Danish Institute of Agricultural Sciences, PO Box 50, Tjele, 8830, Denmark. TEL 45-8999-1900, FAX 45-8999-1919.

636 DNK ISSN 1397-9892
DENMARK. MINISTERIET FOR FOEDEVARER, LANDBRUG OG FISKERI. RAPPORT. HUSDYRBRUG. Text in Multiple languages. 1998. irreg., latest vol.48, 2003. price varies. back issues avail. **Document type:** *Monographic series, Academic/Scholarly.* **Description:** Primarily contains research results and trial statements aimed at Danish conditions.
Indexed: AEA, AgBio, AnBrAb, DSA, HelmAb, HerbAb, IndVet, MaizeAb, NutrAb, PBA, PN&I, PoultAb, S&F, SIA, TriticAb, VetBull, WAE&RSA.
—BLDSC (3605.611000), CISTI.
Published by: Ministeriet for Foedevarer, Landbrug og Fiskeri, Danmarks Jordbrugsforskning/Ministry of Food, Agriculture and Fisheries. Danish Institute of Agricultural Sciences, PO Box 50, Tjele, 8830, Denmark. TEL 45-89-991900, FAX 45-89-991919, djf@agrsci.dk, http://www.agrsci.dk/djfpublikation/default.htm.

636 DNK ISSN 0105-6883
CODEN: BSHUDX

DENMARK. STATENS HUSDYRBRUGSFORSOEG. BERETNING/DENMARK. DANISH INSTITUTE OF ANIMAL SCIENCE. REPORT. Text in Danish; Summaries in English. 1883. irreg. price varies. **Document type:** *Government.*
Former titles (until 1975): Denmark. Forsoegslaboratoriet. Beretning (0005-8904); (until 1915): Denmark. Den Kongelige Veterinaer- og Landbohoejskoles Laboratorium for Landoekonomiske Forsoeg. Beretning (0105-2314)
Indexed: AEA, AnBrAb, DSA, FCA, FS&TA, HerbAb, IndVet, NutrAb, RRTA, SIA, SoyAb, TriticAb, VetBull, WAE&RSA.
—CISTI.
Published by: Ministeriet for Foedevarer, Landbrug og Fiskeri, Danmarks Jordbrugsforskning/Ministry of Food, Agriculture and Fisheries. Danish Institute of Agricultural Sciences, PO Box 50, Tjele, 8830, Denmark. TEL 45-8999-1900, FAX 45-8999-1919. Circ: 1,300.

636 DNK ISSN 0908-021X

DENMARK. STATENS HUSDYRBRUGSFORSOEG. FORSKNINGSRAPPORT/DENMARK. DANISH INSTITUTE OF ANIMAL SCIENCE. RESEARCH REPORT. Text in Danish. 1993. irreg. price varies. back issues avail. **Document type:** *Trade.*
Indexed: AEA, AnBrAb, DSA, MaizeAb, NutrAb, PN&I, TriticAb.
—CISTI.
Published by: Ministeriet for Foedevarer, Landbrug og Fiskeri, Danmarks Jordbrugsforskning/Ministry of Food, Agriculture and Fisheries. Danish Institute of Agricultural Sciences, PO Box 50, Tjele, 8830, Denmark. TEL 45-8999-1900, FAX 45-8999-1919.

636.5 DEU ISSN 0863-3576

DEUTSCHE GEFLUEGEL ZEITUNG. Text in German. 1952. fortn. EUR 50 (effective 2002). adv. **Document type:** *Magazine, Trade.*
Former titles (until 1990): Garten und Kleintierzucht. Ausgabe B: Rassegefluegelzuechter (0433-1818); (until 1962): Deutsche Gefluegel-Zeitung (0415-567X)
Published by: Deutscher Bauernverlag GmbH, Wilhelmsaue 37, Berlin, 10713, Germany. TEL 49-30-464060, FAX 49-30-46406205, gefluegelzeitung@bauernverlag.de, info@bauernverlag.de, http://www.gefluegelzeitung.de, http://www.bauernverlag.de. Ed. Elke Thomas. adv.: B&W page EUR 1,608, color page EUR 2,573. Circ: 18,600 (paid and controlled).

636.3 DEU ISSN 0720-0862

DEUTSCHE SCHAFZUCHT. Text in German. 1908. 2/m. EUR 81 domestic; EUR 90.20 foreign; EUR 4 newsstand/cover (effective 2004). adv. illus.; mkt.; stat. **Document type:** *Magazine, Trade.*
Formerly (until 1980): Deutsche Schaefereizeitung (0012-0677)
—CCC.
Published by: (Vereinigung Deutscher Landesschafzuchtverbaender), Verlag Eugen Ulmer GmbH, Wollgrasweg 41, Stuttgart, 70599, Germany. TEL 49-711-45070, FAX 49-711-4507120, info@ulmer.de, http://www.ulmer.de. Ed. Guenther Dierichs. R&P Gerd Friedrich. Adv. contact Annelie Purwing. B&W page EUR 2,570.40, color page EUR 3,710.40; trim 185 x 270. Circ: 8,561 (paid and controlled).

636.3 GBR

DORSET DOWN FLOCK BOOK. Text in English. 1906. a. adv. **Document type:** *Yearbook.*
Published by: Dorset Down Sheep Breeders' Association, c/o June Pither, Greenway Farm, Bishop's Lydeard, Taunton, Somers, United Kingdom. TEL 44-1823-432301, FAX 44-1823-432301, sheepieju@virgin.net. Pub., Adv. contact June Pither. R&P June Pither Sec. Circ: 150.

636.3 GBR

DORSET HORN AND POLL DORSET SHEEP BREEDERS' ASSOCIATION. FLOCK BOOK. Text in English. a. GBP 30.
Published by: Dorset Horn and Poll Dorset Sheep Breeders' Association, Dorset, Agriculture House, Acland Rd, Dorchester, Dorset DT1 1EF, United Kingdom. TEL 44-1305-262126. Circ: 350.

636 USA ISSN 0012-5865

THE DRAFT HORSE JOURNAL. Text in English. 1964. q. USD 27 domestic; USD 32 in Canada; USD 37 elsewhere (effective 2005). adv. bk.rev. illus. Index. back issues avail.; reprints avail. **Document type:** *Magazine, Trade.* **Description:** Covers trade news of the draft horse industry, including all draft horse breeds and draft mules.
Published by: Draft Horse Journal, PO Box 670, Waverly, IA 50677. TEL 319-352-4046, FAX 319-352-2232, drafthorse@webiowaplus.net, http://www.drafthorsejournal.com, http://www.horseshoes.com. R&P Lynn Telleen. adv.: B&W page USD 560, color page USD 950. Circ: 21,100 (paid and controlled).

636 USA ISSN 1097-9131

DROVERS. Text in English. 1873. m. USD 59.88; free to qualified personnel (effective 2005). adv. illus. **Document type:** *Magazine, Trade.*
Formerly (until 1999): Drovers Journal (0012-6454)
—CCC.
Published by: Vance Publishing Corp., 10901 W 84th Terrace, Lexena, KS 66214-1821. TEL 913-438-8700, 800-255-5113, FAX 913-438-0695, ghenderson@drovers.com, http://www.drovers.com, http://www.vancepublishing.com. Eds. Greg Henderson, Tom Quaife. Pub. Bill Newham. Adv. contact Stan Erwine. Circ: 98,968 (controlled).

636.21 IRL ISSN 1393-2152

DRYSTOCK FARMER. Text in English. 1995. q. EUR 25 (effective 2002). adv. **Document type:** *Magazine, Trade.*
Published by: Irish Cattle and Sheep Farmers' Association, Unit 9, Lyster House, Portlaoise, Co. Laois, Ireland. TEL 353-502-62120, FAX 353-502-62121, info@icsaireland.com, http://www.icsaireland.com. adv.: color page EUR 1,906; trim 210 x 297. Circ: 5,000 (controlled).

636.5 637.5 USA ISSN 0896-2804

EGG INDUSTRY; covering egg production, processing & marketing. Text in English. 1895. m. USD 48 domestic; USD 54 in Canada; USD 60 elsewhere; free to qualified personnel (effective 2005). adv. illus.; mkt. reprint service avail. from PQC. **Document type:** *Magazine, Trade.* **Description:** Addresses the news and technology needs of those engaged in the production, processing, and marketing of eggs worldwide. For industry managers to assist them in keeping in tune with the latest news, technology developments and marketing trends.
Formerly (until Oct. 1987): Poultry Tribune (0032-5805)
Related titles: Microfilm ed.: (from PQC).
Indexed: BiolAb, CurPA.
—CISTI, Linda Hall. **CCC.**
Published by: Watt Publishing Co., 122 S Wesley Ave, Mt. Morris, IL 61054-1497. TEL 815-734-4171, FAX 815-734-5649, http://www.wattnet.com. Pub. Clay Schreiber. adv.: page USD 2,425. Circ: 2,000 (controlled).

637.5 USA

EGG PRODUCTION TESTS: UNITED STATES AND CANADA✶. Text in English. 1959. a. free.
Published by: U.S. Animal and Plant Health Inspection Service, U S Department of Agriculture Health Inspection Service, 4700 River Rd, Riverdale, MD 20737-1228. TEL 301-734-5240. Ed. R D Schar. Circ: 15,000.

636 EGY ISSN 0302-4520
CODEN: EGAPBW

EGYPTIAN JOURNAL OF ANIMAL PRODUCTION. Text in English; Summaries in Arabic, English. 1961. s-a. EGP 24 domestic to individuals; USD 24 foreign to individuals; EGP 48 domestic to institutions; USD 48 foreign to institutions (effective 1999). charts; illus.; stat. reprint service avail. from IRC. **Document type:** *Journal, Academic/Scholarly.*
Former titles (until 1971): United Arab Republic Journal of Animal Production (0302-4512); (until 1969): Journal of Animal Production of the United Arab Republic (0449-2161)
Indexed: AnBrAb, BiolAb, ChemAb, DSA, FCA, FS&TA, HerbAb, IndVet, NutrAb, PoultAb, RevApplEntom, S&MA, SIA, SoyAb, TriticAb, VetBull.
—CASDDS, CISTI, Linda Hall.
Published by: (National Information and Documentation Centre (NIDOC), Egyptian Society of Animal Production), Cairo University, Faculty of Agriculture, Gameaat El-Qahera Str, Giza, Egypt. TEL 20-2-5701235, 20-2-5724107, http://derp.sti.sci.eg/data/0199.htm. Circ: 1,000.

EGYPTIAN JOURNAL OF RABBIT SCIENCE. see *BIOLOGY—Zoology*

636 EGY ISSN 1110-5623

EGYPTIAN POULTRY SCIENCE. Text in English. 1981. q. EGP 15 to individuals; EGP 30 to institutions (effective 2003). **Document type:** *Journal, Academic/Scholarly.*
Indexed: AgBio, AnBrAb, DSA, HelmAb, IndVet, PoultAb, RM&VM, TriticAb.
Published by: The Egyptian Poultry Science Association, Faculty of Agriculture, Alexandria University, 22 El-Gaish Str., Al-Shatby, Alexandria, Egypt. TEL 20-3-5976594, 20-3-5975405, http://derp.sti.sci.eg/data/0239.htm. Ed. Dr. Muhammad Abdel-Munaem Kasba.

636 JPN ISSN 0286-4754

EIYO SEIRI KENKYUKAIHO/JAPANESE SOCIETY FOR ANIMAL NUTRITION AND METABOLISM. PROCEEDINGS. Text in Japanese. 1956. s-a. JPY 3,000 (effective 2000). adv. **Document type:** *Academic/Scholarly.*
—CCC.
Published by: Kachiku Eiyo Seiri Kenkyukai/Japanese Society for Animal Nutrition and Metabolism, Miyazaki University, Faculty of Agriculture, Animal Science Division, Miyazaki, 889-2192, Japan. TEL 81-985-58-7201, FAX 81-985-58-7201; a0c301u@cc.miyazaki-u.ac.jp. Ed. Ryoj Onodera.

636.9322 FRA ISSN 0220-5149

L'ELEVEUR DE LAPINS. Text in French. 1978. 4/yr. EUR 38 domestic; EUR 90 foreign (effective 2004). adv.
Published by: Editions du Boisbaudry, 13 Square du Chene Germain, Cesson Sevigne, 355773, France. TEL 33-2-99322121, http://www.editionsduboisbaudry.com. Circ: 3,000.

636 FRA ISSN 1634-8273

L'ELEVEUR LAITIER. Text in French. 11/yr. FRF 459 (effective 2000).
Former titles (until 2002): Revue de l'Eleveur Laitier (1266-5975); (until 1995): Revue de l'Eleveur (1254-2768)
Indexed: RefZh.
Published by: C E P Groupe France Agricole, 8 Cite Paradis, Paris, Cedex 10 75493, France. TEL 33-1-40227900, FAX 33-1-48240315. Ed. Bruno Patenotre. Circ: 40,000.

636 FRA ISSN 0046-1822

ELEVEUR MAINE ANJOU. Text in French. 1952. q. free. bk.rev.
Published by: U P R A Maine Anjou, 36-38 rue de Razilly, BP 52, Chateau Gontier, 53200, France. Ed. E Labit.

636.2 BRA ISSN 1516-9308

EMBRAPA GADO DE CORTE. COMUNICADO TECNICO. Text in Portuguese. 1979. irreg.
Formerly (until 1998): Centro Nacional de Pesquisa de Gado de Corte. Comunicado Tecnico (0100-7807)
Indexed: AEA, AnBrAb, BioCN&I, DSA, HerbAb, IndVet, NutrAb, PBA, RDA, RM&VM, RPP, S&F, SeedAb, VetBull, WAE&RSA.
—BLDSC (3397.463000).
Published by: Empresa Brasileira de Pesquisa Agropecuaria, Centro Nacional de Pesquisa de Gado de Corte (Subsidiary of: Empresa Brasileira de Pesquisa Agropecuaria), Rodovia BR 262 km 4, Campo Grande, 79002-970, Brazil. TEL 55-67-3682000, FAX 55-67-3682150, sac@cnpgc.embrapa.br, http://www.cnpgc.embrapa.br.

636.2 BRA ISSN 1517-3747

EMBRAPA GADO DE CORTE. DOCUMENTOS. Text in Portuguese. 1981. irreg., latest documentos 126. charts. **Document type:** *Monographic series, Government.*
Formerly: Centro Nacional de Pesquisa de Gado de Corte. Documentos (0100-9443)
Related titles: Online - full text ed.
Indexed: AnBrAb, DSA, ForAb, HerbAb, IndVet, NutrAb, ProtozoAb, RDA, S&F, WAE&RSA, WeedAb.
—BLDSC (3612.103100).
Published by: Empresa Brasileira de Pesquisa Agropecuaria, Centro Nacional de Pesquisa de Gado de Corte (Subsidiary of: Empresa Brasileira de Pesquisa Agropecuaria), Rodovia BR 262 km 4, Campo Grande, 79002-970, Brazil. TEL 55-67-3682000, FAX 55-67-3682150, sac@cnpgc.embrapa.br, http://www.embrapa.br/english/publications/index.htm, http://www.cnpgc.embrapa.br.

636 USA

EMU TODAY & TOMORROW. Text in English. m. USD 25 domestic; USD 50 foreign (effective 2005). adv. **Document type:** *Magazine, Trade.*
Published by: Schatz Publishing Group, 11950 W. Highland Ave., Blackwell, OK 74631-6511. TEL 580-628-2933, FAX 580-628-2011, http://www.emutoday.com. Ed. Sheree Lewis. adv.: B&W page USD 5,455, color page USD 6,730.

636.5 SLV

ENCUESTA AVICOLA✶. Text in Spanish. irreg. exchange. stat.
Published by: (El Salvador. Direccion General de Economia Agropecuaria), Ministerio de Agricultura y Ganaderia, c/o OSPA 31, Avda. del Sur, 627, San Salvador, El Salvador. TEL 23-2598. Ed. Rene Aguilar Giron.

636.2 GBR ISSN 0071-0571

ENGLISH GUERNSEY HERD BOOK. Text in English. 1885. a. GBP 15. index. **Description:** Details cattle breeding.
Published by: English Guernsey Cattle Society, Bury Farm, Pednor Rd, Chesham, Bucks HP5 2LA, United Kingdom.

EQUATOR; newsletter on scientific co-operation in tropical animal health. see *VETERINARY SCIENCE*

ETHNOZOOTECHNIE. see *BIOLOGY—Zoology*

ETHNOZOOTECHNIE. HORS-SERIE. see *BIOLOGY—Zoology*

ETHOLOGY. see *BIOLOGY—Zoology*

ETHOLOGY ONLINE. see *BIOLOGY—Zoology*

EUROPEAN ASSOCIATION FOR ANIMAL PRODUCTION. ANNUAL MEETING. BOOK OF ABSTRACTS. see *AGRICULTURE—Abstracting, Bibliographies, Statistics*

636 NLD ISSN 0071-2477
SF1 CODEN: EAAPAN

➤ **EUROPEAN ASSOCIATION FOR ANIMAL PRODUCTION. SCIENTIFIC SERIES.** Text in English; Text occasionally in French, Multiple languages. 1950. irreg., latest vol.116, 2005. price varies. back issues avail. **Document type:** *Monographic series, Academic/Scholarly.*
Indexed: BIOSIS Prev, BiolAb, ChemAb, FS&TA.
—BLDSC (7059.750000), CISTI, IE, ingenta. **CCC.**
Published by: (European Association for Animal Production), Wageningen Academic Publishers, PO Box 220, Wageningen, 6700 AE, Netherlands. TEL 31-317-476516, FAX 31-317-453417, EAAP@wageningenacademic.com, info@wageningenacademic.com, http://www.wageningenacademic.com. Pub., R&P Mike Jacobs TEL 31-317-476516. Circ: 1,000.

636 NLD ISSN 1570-7318
EUROPEAN ASSOCIATION FOR ANIMAL PRODUCTION. TECHNICAL SERIES. Text in English; Text occasionally in French. 2001. irreg., latest vol.5, 2004. price varies. back issues avail. **Document type:** *Monographic series, Academic/Scholarly.*
Published by: Wageningen Academic Publishers, PO Box 220, Wageningen, 6700 AE, Netherlands. TEL 31-317-476516, FAX 31-317-453417, EAAP@WageningenAcademic.com, info@wageningenacademic.com, http://www.wageningenacademic.com/eaap. Pub., R&P Mike Jacobs TEL 31-317-476516.

636 USA ISSN 0254-6019
CODEN: FAPPDA
F A O ANIMAL PRODUCTION AND HEALTH PAPERS. (Food and Agriculture Organization) Text in English. irreg., latest vol.144, 1999. price varies. **Document type:** *Monographic series.*
Formerly: F A O Animal Production and Health Series (1010-9021)
Related titles: Spanish ed.: Estudio F A O, Produccion y Sanidad Animal. ISSN 1014-1200; French ed.: Etude F A O, Production et Sante Animales. ISSN 1014-1197.
Indexed: AEA, AbHyg, AgBio, AgrForAb, AnBrAb, BIOSIS Prev, BioCN&I, DSA, FPA, FS&TA, ForAb, HelmAb, HerbAb, HortAb, IndVet, NutrAb, OrnHort, PBA, PGegResA, PN&I, PoultAb, ProtozoAb, RA&MP, RDA, RPP, RevApplEntom, RiceAb, S&F, SFA, SIA, SeedAb, VetBull, WAE&RSA.
—BLDSC (3865.593800), CISTI, IE, ingenta, Linda Hall.
Published by: Food and Agriculture Organization of the United Nations, c/o Bernan Associates, 4611 F Assembly Dr, Lanham, MD 20706-4391. TEL 301-459-7666, FAX 301-459-0056.

636 ESP
F A S A G A - ANDALUCIA; la revista del campo andaluz. Text in Spanish. 1985. m. free.
Published by: Federacion del Agricultores y Ganaderos de Andalucia, Edif Jerez 74, planta 2, Jerez De La Frontera, Cadiz 11405, Spain. TEL 34-956-307900, TELEX 75083 ASAJ E. Ed. Cristobal Cantos Ruiz.

636.3 SWE ISSN 1650-2426
FAARSKOETSEL. Text in Swedish. 1921. 8/yr. SEK 510 to members (effective 2004). adv. bk.rev. abstr.; charts; illus.; mkt.; stat.; tr.lit. index. **Document type:** *Journal, Trade.*
Former titles (until 1997): Sveriges Lammgaardar (1402-5922); (until 1997): Faarskoetsel (0014-8598); (until 1961): Svenska Faaravelsfoereningens Tidskrift; (until 1928): Svenska Faaravelsfoereningens Maanadsblad
Indexed: AnBrAb, DSA, IndVet, SoyAb, VetBull, WAE&RSA.
Published by: Svenska Faaravelsfoerbundet/Swedish Sheep Breeders Association, Brogaarden, Jalla, Uppsala, 75594, Sweden. info@faravelsforbundet.com, http://www.faravelsforbundet.com/medlem/farskotsel.asp. Ed. Annika Forsgren Piuva. Circ: 5,983.

636.9322 DNK ISSN 0900-288X
FAELLESUDVALGET TIL KANINAVLENS FREMME. BERETNING. Text in Danish. 1965. biennial. DKK 45. illus.
Published by: Faellesudvalget til Kaninavlens Fremme, Birkevaenget 74, Vejen, 6600, Denmark.

635.5 GBR ISSN 0262-3846
FANCY FOWL. Text in English. 1981. m. USD 52 (effective 2001). adv. bk.rev. **Document type:** *Trade.* **Description:** For those interested in breeding, conserving and exhibiting poultry, including waterfowl and pigeons.
Published by: T P Publications, Barn Acre House, Saxtead Green, Woodbridge, Suffolk IP13 9QJ, United Kingdom. TEL 44-1728-685832, FAX 44-1728-685842, todaymagazines@lineone.net. Ed. Liz Fairbrother. Adv. contact Greg Davis. Circ: 3,000.

636.4 CAN ISSN 1486-5947
FARM AND COUNTRY - PORK; serving Canada's leading hog farmers. Text in English. 1970. q. CND 12; CND 15.50 foreign. adv. illus. **Document type:** *Trade.*
Former titles (until 1998): Pork Producer (1197-1363); (until 1993): Hog Marketplace Quarterly (0380-3651); (until 1975): Market Place Quarterly
—CISTI.
Published by: Agricultural Publishing Co., 1 Yonge St Ste 1504, Toronto, ON M5E 1E5, Canada. TEL 416-364-5324, FAX 416-364-5857, agpub@inforamp.net, http://www.agpub.on.ca. Ed. John M Muggeridge. Adv. contact David Cowl. Circ: 10,442.

FARM ANIMAL VOICE; better lives for animals and us. see *ANIMAL WELFARE*

636 GBR ISSN 0144-6169
FARM ANIMAL WELFARE CO-ORDINATING EXECUTIVE. NEWSLETTER. Text in English. 1979. a. free. **Document type:** *Newsletter.*
Published by: Farm Animal Welfare Co-ordinating Executive, c/o Miss D. Hayman, Springhill House, 280 London Rd, Charlton Kings, Cheltenham, Glos GL52 6HS, United Kingdom. Ed. Robin Corbett. Circ: 3,000.

FARM SCIENTIST. see *VETERINARY SCIENCE*

636 CAN ISSN 0380-352X
FEATHER FANCIER. Text in English. 1945. m. CND 21.40 domestic; USD 20 foreign (effective 2000). adv. bk.rev.
Description: Devoted to the improvement of standard-bred poultry, pigeons, waterfowl, pheasants and other avian species.
—CISTI.
Published by: Jim Gryner, Ed. & Pub., 4094 Ross St, R R 5, Forest, ON N0N 1J0, Canada. TEL 519-899-2364, FAX 519-899-2364, ffancier@xcelco.on.ca, http://www.farmshow.net/feather. Pub. Jim Gryner. Adv. contact Linda Gryner. Circ: 2,500 (paid).

FEED CONTROL COMMENT. see *AGRICULTURE—Feed, Flour And Grain*

636.2 USA ISSN 1083-5385
FEED LOT. Text in English. 1993. 6/yr. USD 15; USD 30 foreign. adv. **Document type:** *Trade.* **Description:** For large feedlots and their related cow and calf operations and large 500 plus cow - calf, stocker operations, and backgrounding operations. Covers all phases of production from breeding, genetics, animal health, nutrition, equipment design, research through finishing fat cattle.
Published by: Feed Lot Magazine, 116 E Long, Box 850, Dighton, KS 67839-0850. TEL 620-397-2838, 800-798-9515, FAX 620-397-2839, feedlot@st-tel.net, http://www.feedlotmagazine.com. Ed., Pub., R&P Robert Strong. Adv. contact Greg Strong. B&W page USD 2,386, color page USD 2,880; trim 10.75 x 8. Circ: 9,042 (controlled).

636 AUS ISSN 1441-6557
FEEDBACK; meat and livestock industry journal. Text in English. 1999. 10/yr. AUD 60; USD 100 foreign. bk.rev. charts; illus.; mkt.; stat. back issues avail. **Document type:** *Newsletter, Trade.* **Description:** Presents news and industry developments of benefit to cattle, sheep, and goat producers, including research and development, and market analysis.
Published by: Meat and Livestock Australia Ltd., Level 1, 165 Walker St., North Sydney, NSW 2089, Australia. TEL 61-2-9463-9333, FAX 61-2-9463-9393, feedback@mla.com.au, http://www.mia.com.au, http://www.mla.com.au. Ed. Lucy Hall. Circ: 6,000.

FEEDGRAM. see *AGRICULTURE—Feed, Flour And Grain*

636.4 JPN ISSN 0289-7237
FEEDING. Text in Japanese. m. JPY 1,400 per issue. **Document type:** *Trade.* **Description:** Covers nutrition, marketing, and technical information of farm management for farmers, manufacturers and distributors.
Published by: Chikusan Publishing Co. Ltd. (Subsidiary of: Midori Group), Ikebukuro Nishiguchi Sky Bldg, 2-14-4 Ikebukuro, Toshima-ku, Tokyo, 171-0014, Japan. TEL 03-3590-9454. Circ: 15,000.

FEEDSTUFFS; the weekly newspaper for agribusiness. see *AGRICULTURE—Feed, Flour And Grain*

636.5 FRA ISSN 1260-5646
FILIERES AVICOLE. Text in French. 1962. m. (11/yr.). EUR 82 domestic; EUR 95 foreign (effective 2004). adv. illus.
Document type: *Magazine, Trade.*
Formerly (until 1994): Aviculteur (0150-939X)
—CCC.
Published by: Editions du Boisbaudry, 13 Square du Chene Germain, Cesson Sevigne, 355773, France. TEL 33-2-99322121, http://www.editionsduboisbaudry.com. Circ: 9,000.

FINANCIAL SURVEY. MEAT, EGG & POULTRY INDUSTRY; company data for success. see *BUSINESS AND ECONOMICS—Trade And Industrial Directories*

636.3 USA
FINNSHEEP SHORT TALES✳. Text in English. 1980. s-a. **Document type:** *Newsletter, Trade.*
Published by: Finnsheep Breeders Association, 107 Morning Glory Ln, Aurora, NC 27806-9466. TEL 317-297-3670. Ed. Claire H Carter.

636.5 SWE ISSN 0015-3338
FJAEDERFAE. Text in Swedish. 1908. m. SEK 400 (effective 2001). adv. bk.rev. illus.; stat. **Document type:** *Newspaper, Trade.*
Published by: (S F S - Svenska Aegg), Pig Poultry Press AB, Domkyrkoesplanaden 3A, Vaesteraas, 72213, Sweden. TEL 46-21-126402, FAX 46-21-126407, journalistgruppen@secher.pp.se. Ed., R&P Sven Secher. Adv. contact Roger Mattsson TEL 46-21-38-16-90. Circ: 1,900.

636.5 NOR ISSN 0015-3354
FJOERFE. Text in Norwegian. 1884. m. NOK 300 (effective 1997). adv. bk.rev. charts; illus.; mkt.; stat.
—CCC.
Published by: Norsk Fjoerfelag, Postboks 73, Aas, 1430, Norway. TEL 64-943366, FAX 64-943370. Ed. Dagfinn Valland. Circ: 1,912.

636.2 AUT
FLECKVIEHZUCHT IN OESTERREICH. Text in German. q. EUR 14.40 domestic; EUR 18.10 foreign (effective 2005).
Document type: *Magazine, Trade.*
Published by: (Arbeitsgemeinschaft Oesterreichischer Fleckviehzuechter), Leopold Stocker Verlag, Hofgasse 5, Graz, St 8011, Austria. TEL 43-316-821636, FAX 43-316-835612, stocker-verlag@stocker-verlag.com, http://www.stocker-verlag.com.

636.3 AUS ISSN 0314-7312
FLEECE AND FLOCK; a guide for hand spinners, weavers and coloured sheep breeders. Text in English. 1974. a. membership. back issues avail. **Document type:** *Catalog.*
Published by: South Australian Coloured Sheep Owners' Society Inc., PO Box 110, Fullarton, SA 5063, Australia. Ed. Verle Wood. Circ: 250.

636.2 DEU ISSN 0946-2902
FLEISCHRINDER JOURNAL. Text in German. 1994. q. EUR 26.60 domestic; EUR 28.80 foreign; EUR 7 newsstand/cover (effective 2003). adv. **Document type:** *Journal, Trade.*
Published by: Landwirtschaftsverlag GmbH, Huelsebrockstr 2, Muenster, 48165, Germany. TEL 49-2501-801-0, FAX 49-2501-801204, frjservice@landwirtschaftsverlag.com, zentrale@lv-h.de, http://www.landwirtschaftsverlag.com/frj/, http://www.lv-h.de. adv.: B&W page EUR 1,178, color page EUR 2,003. Circ: 12,487.

636.3 GBR
FLOCK BOOK OF DEVON CORNWALL LONGWOOL SHEEP. Text in English. 1977. a. GBP 10.
Published by: Devon and Cornwall Longwool Flockbook Association, Cherbourne, West Ln, Dolton, Winkleigh, Devon EX19 8QU, United Kingdom. Circ: 100.

636.3 GBR
FLOCK BOOK OF OXFORD DOWN SHEEP. Text in English. 1889. a. GBP 7 domestic; GBP 8.50 foreign (effective 1999). adv. **Document type:** *Directory.*
Published by: Oxford Down Sheep Breeder's Association, Bishops Gorse, Lighthorne, Warcs CV35 0BB, United Kingdom. TEL 44-1423-770736, john.brigg@virgin.net. Ed. Jeffrey Stephenson. Adv. contact Ann Knott. Circ: 150.

636.2 USA ISSN 0015-3958
FLORIDA CATTLEMAN AND LIVESTOCK JOURNAL. Text in English. 1936. m. free membership (effective 2005). adv. bk.rev. illus. **Document type:** *Magazine, Trade.*
—CISTI.
Published by: Florida Cattlemen's Association, 800 Shakerag Rd., Kissimmee, Osceola, FL 34744. TEL 407-846-8025, FAX 407-933-8209, fcmfca@aol.com, http://floridacattlemen.org. R&P Jim Handley. Adv. contact Barbara Starcher. B&W page USD 595, color page USD 895; trim 11 x 8.25. Circ: 5,000 (paid and free).

636 POL ISSN 1506-1698
SF1
➤ **FOLIA UNIVERSITATIS AGRICULTURAE STETINENSIS. ZOOTECHNICA.** (Includes: Teratologica Scripta) Text in Polish; Abstracts in English. 1966. a. price varies. bk.rev. **Document type:** *Journal, Academic/Scholarly.*
Former titles: Akademia Rolnicza w Szczecinie. Zeszyty Naukowe. Zootechnika (0137-1940); (until 1973): Wyzsza Szkola Rolnicza w Szczecinie. Zeszyty Naukowe. Zootechnika (0137-2122)
Indexed: AbHyg, AgBio, AgrLib, AnBrAb, CPA, ChemAb, DSA, FCA, HelmAb, HortAb, IndVet, MaizeAb, NutrAb, OrnHort, PN&I, PotatoAb, PoultAb, ProtozoAb, RA&MP, RRTA, RefZh, RevApplEntom, S&F, SIA, SoyAb, TriticAb, VetBull.
—BLDSC (3965.899500).
Published by: Akademia Rolnicza w Szczecinie/Agricultural University of Szczecin, Dzial Wydawnictw, Ul Doktora Judyma 22, Szczecin, 71466, Poland. TEL 48-91-4541639, FAX 48-91-4541642, TELEX 0425494 AR, fizj@demeter.zoo.ar.szczecin.pl, http://www.ar.szczecin.pl/pliki/index2.html. Ed. Wieslaw F Skrzypczak.

➤ **FRANCE. MINISTERE DE L'AGRICULTURE ET DE LA PECHE. AGRESTE ANIMAUX HEBDO.** see *AGRICULTURE—Agricultural Economics*

636 ESP ISSN 0211-3767
FRISONA ESPANOLA. Text in Spanish. 1981. bi-m. adv.
Document type: *Trade.* **Description:** Technical coverage of the Holstein Freisian breed.
Indexed: IECT.
—CINDOC.
Published by: Confederacion de Asociaciones de Frisona Espanola, APDO DE CORREOS, 31, Valdemoro, Madrid 28340, Spain. TEL 34-1-8952412, FAX 34-1-8951471. Ed. Domnino Garrote Manso. Adv. contact Baldomero Fernandez.

GAITED HORSE INTERNATIONAL MAGAZINE. see *SPORTS AND GAMES—Horses And Horsemanship*

636 GBR ISSN 0950-7701
GALLOWAY HERD BOOK. Text in English. 1878. a. GBP 8 (effective 2001). **Document type:** *Trade.*

A

Published by: Galloway Cattle Society, 15 New Market St, Castle Douglas, Kirkcudbrightshire DG7 1HY, United Kingdom. Ed. A J McDonald.

636.2 GBR ISSN 0430-9928
GALLOWAY JOURNAL. Text in English. a. free (effective 2001). adv. **Document type:** *Journal, Trade.*
Published by: Galloway Cattle Society, 15 New Market St, Castle Douglas, Kirkcudbrightshire DG7 1HY, United Kingdom. Ed. A J McDonald. Circ: 2,000.

333.72 USA ISSN 1087-1276
GAME BIRD AND CONSERVATIONISTS GAZETTE. Text in English. 1952. m. USD 20 (effective 1999). adv. bk.rev. charts; illus.; tr.lit. index. back issues avail. **Document type:** *Trade.*
Former titles: Game Birds Breeders and Conservationists Gazette (1074-2077); Game Bird Breeders, Aviculturists, Zoologists, and Conservationists Gazette (0164-3711)
Indexed: SFA, WildRev.
Published by: Allen Publishing Co., PO Box 171227, Salt Lake City, UT 84117. TEL 801-575-1111. Ed., R&P George Allen. Adv. contact Jim Wilson. Circ: 18,000.

636.2 MEX
GANADERO/RANCHER. Text in English, Spanish. 1975. bi-m. MXP 150, USD 72. adv. **Document type:** *Consumer.*
Description: Covers the livestock industry in Mexico and other countries.
Published by: Editorial Ocampo S.A. de C.V., ZARAGOZA 11, San Juan Tepepan, Mexico City, DF 16020, Mexico. TEL 525-590-1445. Ed. Jorge Ruben Ocampo Trujillo. Adv. contact Ana Cristina Miranda. B&W page USD 835, color page USD 1,170. Circ: 7,000. **Subscr. to:** ESTAFETAS 5, Col Postal, Mexico City, DF 03410, Mexico.

636.4 MEX
GANADO PORCINO. Text in Spanish. 1978. s-a. adv.
Indexed: IECT, NutrAb.
Address: Vivero de la Floresta No. 116 Tlanepantla, Mexico City, Mexico. Ed. J Filberto Ruiz Valerio. Circ: 20,000.

636.2 USA ISSN 1084-5100
GELBVIEH WORLD. Text in English. 1987. m. USD 25; USD 50 foreign (effective 1998). adv. charts; illus.; mkt.; maps; tr.lit. back issues avail. **Document type:** *Trade.* **Description:** Designed to educate association members and promote the Gelbvieh breed of cattle in North America.
Published by: American Gelbvieh Association, 10900 Dover St, Westminster, CO 80021. TEL 303-465-2333, FAX 303-465-2339, aga@www.gewlbvieh.org, http://www.gelbvieh.org/~aga. Ed., Adv. contact Troy Applehans. R&P Tom Brink. page USD 578; trim 11 x 8.5. Circ: 3,900 (paid).

GENETIC RESOURCES COMMUNICATION. see *AGRICULTURE—Crop Production And Soil*

636.2 USA
GEORGIA CATTLEMAN. Text in English. 1972. m. USD 20 to non-members; USD 15 to members. adv.
Published by: Georgia Cattlemen's Association, PO Box 24510, Macon, GA 31212. TEL 912-474-6560. Ed. Glenn Smith. Circ: 6,700.

636 USA
GEORGIA LIVESTOCK. Text in English. w. USD 40; USD 45 in Canada & Mexico; USD 75 elsewhere. back issues avail. **Document type:** *Government.*
Published by: (Livestock & Seed Division), U.S. Department of Agriculture, Agricultural Marketing Service (Greely), 711 O St., Greely, CO 80631. Ed. Ernie Morgan. **Subscr. to:** U.S.D.A. Agricultural Marketing Service, Livestock & Seed Division, Rm 2613 S, Box 96456, Washington, DC 20090-6456. FAX 202-245-4732.

GERMANY. STATISTISCHES BUNDESAMT. FACHSERIE 3, LAND- UND FORSTWIRTSCHAFT, FISCHEREI; REIHE 4: VIEHBESTAND UND TIERISCHE ERZEUGUNG. see *AGRICULTURE—Abstracting, Bibliographies, Statistics*

591.63 636.63 FRA ISSN 1261-3436
GIBIER ET CHASSE. Text in French. m. EUR 50 (effective 2004). **Document type:** *Journal.* **Description:** Techniques for husbandry of game animals.
Published by: Gibier et Chasse Eurl, Ferme Aurelie, Le Pouget, Saint Cere, 46400, France. TEL 33-5-65106656, FAX 33-5-65106540, revue-gibier-et-chasse2@wanadoo.fr, http://www.revue-gibier-et-chasse.fr, http://www.revuegibieretchasse.fr. Ed., Pub. Yves Mercier.

636.39 NZL ISSN 1174-0434
THE GOAT FARMER. Text in English. 1986. bi-m. NZD 55 domestic; AUD 50 in Australia; USD 34 in United States; GBP 24 in United Kingdom; NZD 80 in Asia (effective 2001). adv. bk.rev. 40 p./no.; back issues avail. **Document type:** *Trade.* **Description:** Covers goat health and management, fibre market news and prices, goat meat news and markets (including boer breed information), processing news.
Former titles: Premier Fiber News (0113-9746); (until 1987): Fibre News (0113-972X); New Zealand Mohair News (0112-997X); (until 1986): N.Z. Mohair Journal (0112-0492); (until 1982): Mohair Producers Association of New Zealand. Newsletter and Information Booklet
Related titles: Online - full text ed.
Indexed: INZP.
Published by: Capricorn Publications Ltd., P.O. Box 641, 130 Maunu Rd, Whangarei, New Zealand. TEL 64-9-438-0335, FAX 64-9-438-0493, geoff@caprine.co.nz, http://www.caprine.co.nz. Ed., R&P Geoff Minchin. Adv. contact Ed Heath. B&W page USD 500, color page USD 700; trim 190 x 273. Circ: 6,000 (paid).

GOAT VETERINARY SOCIETY JOURNAL. see *VETERINARY SCIENCE*

636.952 USA ISSN 0017-1506
GOBBLES. Text in English. 1947. m. USD 35 (effective 2004). adv. 16 p./no.; **Document type:** *Magazine, Trade.*
Description: Reaches an audience involved in all aspects of the turkey industry: hatchery, grower, processor and breedman. Covers research and current industry events.
Published by: Minnesota Turkey Growers Association, 108 Marty Dr., Buffalo, MN 55313. TEL 763-682-2171, FAX 763-682-5546, lara@minnesotaturkeys.com, http://www.minnesotaturkeys.com. Ed., R&P, Adv. contact Lara Durben. B&W page USD 450, color page USD 1,230. Circ: 1,000 (paid).

636 664.9 POL ISSN 0367-4916
CODEN: GOMIAC
GOSPODARKA MIESNA. Text in Polish. 1949. m. PLZ 192.45 domestic; EUR 97 foreign (effective 2005). adv. 80 p./no.; **Document type:** *Magazine, Trade.*
Indexed: AgrLib, ChemAb, FS&TA, NutrAb.
—CASDDS.
Published by: Wydawnictwo SIGMA - N O T Sp. z o.o., ul Ratuszowa 11, PO Box 1004, Warsaw, 00950, Poland. TEL 48-22-8180918, FAX 48-22-6192187, gospodarkamiesna@sigma-not.pl, informacja@sigma-not.pl, http://www.sigma-not.pl/?url=/tytul/GospodarkaMiesna. Ed. Malgorzata Witek. adv.: B&W page PLZ 1,800, color page PLZ 3,500. Circ: 2,500. **Dist. by:** Ars Polona, Krakowskie Przedmiescie 7, Warsaw, Poland. TEL 48-22-9263914, FAX 48-22-9265334, arspolona@arspolona.com.pl, http://www.arspolona.com.pl.

GREECE. NATIONAL STATISTICAL SERVICE. AGRICULTURAL AND LIVESTOCK PRODUCTION (YEAR). see *AGRICULTURE—Abstracting, Bibliographies, Statistics*

636.4 SWE ISSN 1402-8085
GRIS/PIG. Text in Swedish. 1997. m. SEK 180; SEK 400 foreign. adv. index. **Document type:** *Newspaper.*
Indexed: AnBrAb, PN&I.
Published by: Keka Konsult AB, Fack 6479, Kumla, 69293, Sweden. TEL 46-19-57-60-90, FAX 46-19-58-00-50, gris@agrar.se. Ed. Lars Gunnar Lannhard. Circ: 5,000.

636.2 GBR
GUERNSEY BREEDERS' JOURNAL. Text in English. s-a. GBP 1 per issue.
Related titles: Microform ed.: (from PQC).
Published by: English Guernsey Cattle Society, Bury Farm, Pednor Rd, Chesham, Bucks HP5 2LA, United Kingdom.

GUERNSEY BREEDERS' JOURNAL. see *AGRICULTURE—Dairying And Dairy Products*

636.2 USA ISSN 0017-5552
GULF COAST CATTLEMAN. Text in English. 1935. m. free to cattlemen; USD 15 (effective 2005). adv. 54 p./no.; **Document type:** *Magazine, Trade.* **Description:** Covers the production of commercial beef cattle in the Gulf Coast states.
Formerly (until 1948): Coastal Cattleman
—Linda Hall.
Published by: Gulf Coast Publishing, 11201 Morning Court, San Antonio, TX 78213. TEL 210-344-8300, FAX 210-344-8300, editor@gulfcoastcattleman.com, info@GulfCoastCattleman.com. Pub. E C Larkin Jr. Adv. contact David Neason. Circ: 15,800 (paid and free).

636 CHN ISSN 1002-6746
GUOWAI XUMU KEJI/FOREIGN ANIMAL HUSBANDRY SCIENCE AND TECHNOLOGY. Text in Chinese. 1974. bi-m. CNY 18 (effective 1997). **Document type:** *Academic/Scholarly.*
Related titles: Online - full text ed.: (from East View Information Services).
Published by: Zhongguo Nongye Kexueyuan, Xumu Yanjiusuo/Chinese Academy of Agricultural Sciences, Institute of Animal Husbandry, Yuanmingyuan Lu, Haidian-qu, Beijing, 100094, China. TEL 86-10-6258-1177, FAX 86-10-6258-2594. Ed. Nianfan Guo.

636 GBR
GWLAD; important information from the Agriculture amd Rural Affairs Depratment. Text in English. m. **Document type:** *Trade.*
Related titles: Online - full text ed.; Welsh ed.
—BLDSC (4233.330450).
Published by: Welsh Assembly Government, Agricultural and Rural Affairs Department, 1st Floor, Crown Buildings, Cathays Park, Cardiff, CF1 3NQ, United Kingdom. TEL 44-29-20-826801, FAX 44-29-20-823327, gwlad@stratamatrix.co.uk, http://www.gwlad-cymru.com/, http://www.wales.gov.uk/subiagriculture/index.htm. Eds. Dylan Iorwerth, Roy Hancock.

H R I - BUYERS GUIDE. (Hotels, Restaurants, Institutions) see *FOOD AND FOOD INDUSTRIES*

636.2 DNK ISSN 0900-8012
HAANDBOG FOR KVAEGHOLD. Variant title: Haandbog i Kvaeghold. Text in Danish. 1958. a., latest 2004. DKK 72 (effective 2005). adv. **Document type:** *Trade.*
Published by: (Denmark. Landskontoret for Uddannelse), Dansk Landbrugsraadgivning, Landbrugsforlaget/Danish Agricultural Advisory Service. Publishing, Udkaersvej 15, Skejby, Aarhus N, 8200, Denmark. TEL 45-87-405537, FAX 45-87-405085, forlag@landcentret.dk, http://www.lr.dk/uddannelse.

636.4 DNK ISSN 0900-8977
HAANDBOG FOR SVINEHOLD. Variant title: Haandbog i Svinehold. Text in Danish. 1971. a., latest 2005. prive varies. **Document type:** *Trade.*
Published by: (Landsudvalget for Svin/National Committee for Pig Breeding and Production), Dansk Landbrugsraadgivning, Landbrugsforlaget/Danish Agricultural Advisory Service. Publishing, Udkaersvej 15, Skejby, Aarhus N, 8200, Denmark. TEL 45-87-405537, FAX 45-87-405085, forlag@landcentret.dk. Ed. Else Vils.

HAESTMAGASINET. see *SPORTS AND GAMES—Horses And Horsemanship*

HANDBOOK OF FEED ADDITIVES. see *AGRICULTURE—Feed, Flour And Grain*

HANDBUCH DER TIERISCHEN VEREDLUNG. see *AGRICULTURE—Agricultural Economics*

636.5 USA ISSN 0082-9722
HATCHERIES AND DEALERS PARTICIPATING IN THE NATIONAL POULTRY IMPROVEMENT PLAN✱. Text in English. 1937. a. free.
Formerly: U.S. Department of Agriculture. Animal Science Research Branch. Hatcheries and Dealers Participating in the National Improvement Plan
Published by: (Animal Physiology and Genetics Institute), U.S. Animal and Plant Health Inspection Service, U S Department of Agriculture Health Inspection Service, 4700 River Rd, Riverdale, MD 20737-1228. TEL 301-734-5240. Ed. R D Schar. Circ: 6,500.

636 USA
HEALTHY ANIMALS. Text in English. q. **Document type:** *Bulletin.*
Media: Online - full text.
Published by: U.S. Department of Agriculture, Agricultural Research Service, Whitten Bldg, 14th and Independence Ave, S W, Washington, DC 20250-9410. TEL 202-720-2600, http://www.ars.usda.gov/is/np/ha/index.html, http://www.ars.usda.gov/main/main.htm.

636 CHN ISSN 1005-2739
HEILONGJIANG DONGWU FANZHI ZAZHI/HEILONGJIANG JOURNAL OF ANIMAL BREEDING. Text in Chinese. 1993. q. CNY 3.50 newsstand/cover domestic (effective 2000). **Document type:** *Academic/Scholarly.*
Related titles: Online - full content ed.: (from WanFang Data Corp.); Online - full text ed.: (from East View Information Services).
Published by: Heilongjiang-sheng Jiachu Fanzhiyu Zhidaozhan, Haping Lu, Ha'erbin, 150060, China. TEL 86-451-6693074. Ed. Neng-bin Tan.

636.2 GBR ISSN 0073-1943
HERD BOOK OF HEREFORD CATTLE. Text in English. 1846. a. GBP 30 (effective 2001). **Document type:** *Trade.*
Description: Records all pedigree Hereford cattle born in the UK.
Published by: Hereford Cattle Society, Hereford House, Hereford, 3 Offa St, Hereford, HR1 2LL, United Kingdom. TEL 44-1432-272057, FAX 44-1432-350608, postroom@herefordcattle.org, http://www.herefordcattle.org. Ed. David Prothero.

636.2 GBR ISSN 0073-1951
HEREFORD BREED JOURNAL. Text in English. 1932. a. GBP 20 for 3 yrs. domestic; GBP 25 for 3 yrs. foreign (effective 2001). **Document type:** *Trade.* **Description:** Contains current information on pedigree Hereford cattle in the UK and worldwide.
Published by: Hereford Cattle Society, Hereford House, Hereford, 3 Offa St, Hereford, HR1 2LL, United Kingdom. TEL 44-1432-272057, FAX 44-1432-350608, postroom@herefordcattle.org, http://www.herefordcattle.org.

636.2   USA   ISSN 1085-9896
HEREFORD WORLD. Text in English. 1995. m. (11/yr.). USD 40 (effective 2005). adv. bk.rev. illus. **Document type:** *Magazine, Trade.* **Description:** Contains news, information, and acts as a marketing medium for breeders of Hereford cattle, horned and polled.
Formed by the merger of (1947-1995): Polled Hereford World (0162-7953); (1910-1995): American Hereford Journal (0002-872X)
—CISTI, Linda Hall.
Published by: (American Polled Hereford Association), Hereford Publications, Inc., PO Box 014059, Kansas City, MO 64101-0059. TEL 816-842-3757, hworld@hereford.org, http://www.hereford.org. Ed. Angie Denton. Circ: 10,000 (paid).

636.1 798   DNK
HEST. Text in Danish. 1991. 10/yr. DKK 340 (effective 2003). adv. **Document type:** *Journal, Trade.*
Formerly (until 2003): Landsbladet Hest (0906-6616)
Published by: Dansk Landbrugs Medier, Vester Farimagsgade 6, Copenhagen V, 1606, Denmark. TEL 46-33-394700. Circ: 6,263.

636.4   USA
HOG PRODUCER. Text in English. 10/yr. adv. **Document type:** *Trade.*
Related titles: ♦ Supplement to: Kansas Farmer.
Published by: Farm Progress Companies, 191 S Gary Ave, Carol Stream, IL 60188. TEL 630-462-2892, FAX 630-462-2885. Eds. JoAnn Alumbaugh, Tim Sickman TEL 502-266-9556. Circ: 115,287.

636   USA   ISSN 1056-1374
HOGS TODAY. Text in English. 1985. m. (10/yr..). **Document type:** *Trade.*
Formerly: Hog Extra
Published by: Farm Journal Media, 1818 Market St., 31st Fl, Philadelphia, PA 19103-3654. TEL 215-557-8900, 800-523-1538, FAX 215-568-5012, http://www.agweb.com. Ed. Dean Houghton. Circ: 121,697.

636.2142   AUS   ISSN 1321-0173
HOOFS & HORNS. Variant title: H & H. Text in English. 1994. q. AUD 29 domestic; AUD 70 in Asia & the Pacific; AUD 85 elsewhere (effective 2005). illus. **Document type:** *Magazine, Consumer.* **Description:** Contains information about horses and cows for children.
Published by: Outback Publishing Co., Ste 302, 115 Military Rd, PO Box 1078, Neutral Bay, NSW 2089, Australia. TEL 61-2-99088050, FAX 61-2-99088070, http:// www.outbackmag.com.au/home.asp?pageid= 614053A946F7E94D. Ed. Sophie Herron. Pub. Paul Myers.

HORSE CONNECTION. see *SPORTS AND GAMES—Horses And Horsemanship*

637.1   SWE   ISSN 0046-8339
HUSDJUR. Text in Swedish. 1948. 11/yr. SEK 495; SEK 48 per issue (effective 2004). adv. bk.rev. 76 p./no.; **Document type:** *Magazine, Trade.*
Former titles (until 1968): Svensk Husdjursskoetsel; (until 1958): Ladugaarden
Related titles: Online - full text ed.
Indexed: AnBrAb, DSA, IndVet, NutrAb, PN&I, WAE&RSA.
Published by: Svensk Mjoelk AB/Swedish Dairy Association, Haallsta, Eskilstuna, 63184, Sweden. TEL 46-16-163556, FAX 46-16-21125, husdjur@svenskmjolk.se, info@svenskmjolk.se, http://www.husdjur.se, http://www.svenskmjolk.se. Ed., Pub. Britt-Marie Jafner TEL 46-16-163457. Adv. contact Marie Louise Ankersten TEL 46-16-163516. B&W page SEK 25,200, color page SEK 30,000; 370 x 270. Circ: 18,900.

636.4   DNK   ISSN 0906-0995
HYOLOGISK; tidsskrift for svineproducenter. Text in Danish. 1979. m. DKK 595 domestic; DKK 775 in Europe; DKK 979 elsewhere (effective 2005). adv. **Document type:** *Magazine, Trade.*
Formerly (until 1990): Hyologisk Tidsskrift Svinet (0106-1933)
Related titles: Online - full text ed.
Published by: Dansk Agrar Forlag A-S (Subsidiary of: FagbladsGruppen A/S), Birk Centerpark 36, Herning, 7400, Denmark. TEL 45-76-207970, FAX 45-96-265296, hyologisk@agrar.dk, post@agrar.dk, http://www.hyologisk.dk, http://www.agrar.dk. Eds. Anja Pernille Jacobsen, Niels Damgaard Hansen. adv.: page DKK 11,200; 270 x 184. Circ: 3,300.

636.006   ETH   ISSN 1014-9015
SF83.A35
I L C A ANNUAL REPORT AND PROGRAMME HIGHLIGHTS. Text in English. a. charts; illus. **Description:** Highlights ILCA's research at the head-quarters and its field research programmes in Ethiopia, Niger, Nigeria, Mali, and Kenya, as well as work on livestock economics and politics, trypanotolerance, forage agronomy, small ruminants, soils and plant nutrition, and support services.
Formerly: I L C A Annual Report (0255-0040)
Related titles: French ed.
Indexed: SeedAb.
—BLDSC (4364.102500), CISTI.

Published by: International Livestock Centre for Africa, PO Box 5689, Addis Ababa, Ethiopia. TEL 251-1-613215, FAX 251-1-611892, ilca@cgnet.com.

636   ETH   ISSN 0255-0024
I L C A NEWSLETTER. Text in English. 1982. q. **Document type:** *Newsletter.* **Description:** Describes ILCA's research and collaboration with agricultural research services, along with news of workshops and conferences, all in the context of African livestock research and development.
Related titles: French ed.: ISSN 0255-0032.
Indexed: FS&TA.
—CISTI.
Published by: International Livestock Centre for Africa, PO Box 5689, Addis Ababa, Ethiopia. TEL 251-1-613215, FAX 251-1-611892, ilca@cgnet.com.

636   ETH
I L C A PROCEEDINGS. Text in English. 1980. irreg. **Document type:** *Proceedings.*
Published by: International Livestock Centre for Africa, PO Box 5689, Addis Ababa, Ethiopia. TEL 251-1-613215, FAX 251-1-611892, ilca@cgnet.com.

636   ETH   ISSN 0257-8409
I L C A RESEARCH REPORT. Text in English. 1982. irreg., latest vol.16, 1987.
Formerly: International Livestock Centre for Africa. Research Report
Related titles: French ed.
—CISTI,
Published by: International Livestock Centre for Africa, PO Box 5689, Addis Ababa, Ethiopia. TEL 251-1-613215, FAX 251-1-611892, TELEX 21207 ILCA ET, ilca@cgnet.com.

636   ESP   ISSN 1130-6009
► I T E A PRODUCCION ANIMAL. Text in Spanish; Summaries in English. 1970. 3/yr. adv. **Document type:** *Academic/Scholarly.*
Supersedes in part (in 1990): Informacion Tecnica Economica Agraria (0212-2731)
Indexed: AEA, AgBio, AgrForAb, AnBrAb, BioCN&I, CPA, DSA, FCA, ForAb, HelmAb, HerbAb, HortAb, I&DA, IECT, IndVet, MaizeAb, NemAb, NutrAb, PBA, PGegResA, PGrRegA, PHN&I, PN&I, PotatoAb, PoultAb, ProtozoAb, RA&MP, RDA, RPP, RRTA, S&F, SIA, SeedAb, SoyAb, TriticAb, VetBull, WAE&RSA, WeedAb.
—BLDSC (4588.572700), CINDOC.
Published by: Asociacion Interprofesional para el Desarrollo Agrario, Montanana, 177, Apartado 727, Zaragoza, 50080, Spain. TEL 34-976-576336, FAX 34-976-575501, alberti@mizar.csic.es. R&P Leonardo Plana. Adv. contact Mercedes Ferruz. Circ: 600.

► IDAHO FARMER - STOCKMAN. see *AGRICULTURE*

636.3 677.31   USA
IDAHO WOOL GROWERS BULLETIN. Text in English. 1928. m. USD 20 (effective 2005). adv. charts; illus.; mkt.; stat.; tr.lit. back issues avail. **Document type:** *Bulletin, Trade.*
Related titles: CD-ROM ed.; Diskette ed.
Published by: Idaho Wool Growers Association, 802 W Bannock, Ste 205, Box 2596, Boise, ID 83701. TEL 208-344-2271, FAX 208-336-9447, info@idahowool.org, http://www.idahowool.org. Ed., R&P, Adv. contact Trudi Gebauer. Pub. Mike Guerry. page USD 285; trim 7.5 x 9.7. Circ: 800.

636.2   USA
ILLINOIS BEEF. Text in English. 1987. bi-m. USD 45. adv. **Description:** Contains association news, information and educational articles about the beef industry.
Published by: Illinois Beef Association, 2060 W Iles Ave, No B, Springfield, IL 62704-4174. TEL 217-787-4280, FAX 217-793-3605, ilbeef@al.com. Ed. Maralee M Johnson. Circ: 3,757.

INDEX OF CURRENT RESEARCH ON PIGS. see *AGRICULTURE—Abstracting, Bibliographies, Statistics*

INDIA. MINISTRY OF AGRICULTURE. BULLETIN ON FOOD STATISTICS. see *AGRICULTURE—Abstracting, Bibliographies, Statistics*

636.084   IND   ISSN 0970-3209
                                        CODEN: IJNUEA
► INDIAN JOURNAL OF ANIMAL NUTRITION. Text in English. 1984. q. INR 700 domestic; USD 70 foreign (effective 2001). adv. bk.rev. 100 p./no. 1 cols./p.; back issues avail. **Document type:** *Journal, Academic/Scholarly.* **Description:** Contains animal nutrition research in ruminants, poultry and other monogastric animals.
Indexed: AgrForAb, AnBrAb, BIOSIS Prev, BiolAb, DSA, FPA, FS&TA, ForAb, HerbAb, HortAb, IndVet, MaizeAb, NutrAb, OrnHort, PBA, PGegResA, PHN&I, PN&I, PoultAb, ProtozoAb, RA&MP, RDA, RM&VM, RevApplEntom, RiceAb, S&F, S&MA, SIA, SeedAb, SoyAb, TOSA, TriticAb, VetBull, WAE&RSA, WeedAb.
—Linda Hall.

Published by: Animal Nutrition Society of India, National Dairy Research Institute, Karnal, Haryana 132 001, India. TEL 91-184-259057, FAX 91-184-250042, TELEX 0396-204 NDRI IN, pps@ndri.hry.nic.in. Ed. K K Singhal. Adv. contact Aruna Chhabra. B&W page INR 1,500. Circ: 700.

636   IND   ISSN 0970-1524
INDIAN JOURNAL OF ANIMAL PRODUCTION AND MANAGEMENT. Text in English. 1970. q. INR 300, USD 50 (effective 2000). adv. bk.rev. bibl.; charts; stat. **Document type:** *Academic/Scholarly.*
Formerly (until 1985): Indian Journal of Animal Production
Indexed: AgBio, AgrForAb, AnBrAb, DSA, ForAb, HerbAb, HortAb, IndVet, MaizeAb, NutrAb, PHN&I, PN&I, PoultAb, RDA, RM&VM, RiceAb, SIA, SoyAb, TDB, TriticAb, VetBull, WAE&RSA.
—BLDSC (4410.192200), IE, ingenta.
Published by: Indian Society of Animal Production and Management, Dept. of Livestock Production & Management, Agricultural University, Hisar, Haryana 125 004, India. Ed. C K Aggarwal. Circ: 450. Dist. by: H P C Publishers Distributors Pvt. Ltd., 4805 Bharat Ram Rd, 24 Darya Ganj, New Delhi 110 002, India. TEL 91-11-325-4402, FAX 91-11-686-3511.

636   IND   ISSN 0970-2997
INDIAN JOURNAL OF ANIMAL REPRODUCTION. Text in English. 1981. m. USD 100 to institutions (effective 2006). adv. back issues avail. **Document type:** *Journal.*
Indexed: AgBio, AnBrAb, DSA, HortAb, IndVet, NutrAb, PN&I, PoultAb, RA&MP, RM&VM, SIA, VetBull.
Published by: (Indian Society for the Study of Animal Reproduction), Scientific Publishers, 5-A New Pali Rd., Near Hotel Taj Hari Mahal, PO Box 91, Jodhpur, Rajasthan 342 003, India. TEL 91-291-2433323, FAX 91-291-2512580, info@scientificpub.com, http://www.scientificpub.com/ bookdetails.php?booktransid=443&bookid=439.

636   IND   ISSN 0367-6722
SF1   CODEN: IALRBR
INDIAN JOURNAL OF ANIMAL RESEARCH; half-yearly research journal of animal, food, dairying and zoological sciences. Text in English. 1967. s-a. INR 300 domestic; USD 40 foreign (effective 2004). **Document type:** *Academic/Scholarly.* **Description:** Publishes results of original research work on various aspects of Animal sciences, viz., animal breeding, physiology, nutrition, diseases, production, fisheries and zoological sciences.
Formerly (until 1971): Indian Journal of Science and Industry. Section B. Animal Sciences (0367-830X); **Supersedes in part** (in 1970): Indian Journal of Science and Industry (0019-5618)
Indexed: AEA, AgBio, AgrForAb, AnBrAb, BiolAb, ChemAb, DSA, FS&TA, ForAb, HelmAb, HerbAb, HortAb, IndVet, MaizeAb, NutrAb, PGegResA, PHN&I, PN&I, PoultAb, ProtozoAb, RA&MP, RDA, RM&VM, RevApplEntom, RiceAb, S&F, SAA, SIA, TDB, TriticAb, VetBull, WAE&RSA, WeedAb.
—CASDDS, CISTI, Linda Hall.
Published by: Agricultural Research Communication Centre, 1130 Sadar Bazar, Post Office Marg, Karnal, Haryana 132 001, India. TEL 91-184-255080. Ed. Dr. D D Sharma. Adv. contact R D Goel.

636.5   IND   ISSN 0019-5529
                                        CODEN: IJPOAW
INDIAN JOURNAL OF POULTRY SCIENCE. Text in English. 1966. 3/yr. USD 75 to institutions (effective 2006). adv. bk.rev. bibl.; charts; stat.
Incorporates (1982-1984): Avian Research (0970-1273); Which was formerly (1913-1981): Indian Poultry Gazette (0019-6142)
Indexed: AEA, AgBio, AgrForAb, AnBrAb, BIOSIS Prev, BioCN&I, BiolAb, ChemAb, DBA, DSA, FS&TA, HelmAb, HortAb, IndVet, MaizeAb, NutrAb, PHN&I, PoultAb, ProtozoAb, RA&MP, RDA, RM&VM, RRTA, RevApplEntom, RiceAb, SIA, SoyAb, TDB, TriticAb, VetBull, WAE&RSA, WeedAb.
—BLDSC (4420.190000), CASDDS, CISTI, IE, Infotrieve, ingenta, Linda Hall.
Published by: (Indian Poultry Science Association), Scientific Publishers, 5-A New Pali Rd., Near Hotel Taj Hari Mahal, PO Box 91, Jodhpur, Rajasthan 342 003, India. TEL 91-291-2433323, FAX 91-291-2512580, info@scientificpub.com, http://www.scientificpub.com/ bookdetails.php?booktransid=447&bookid=443. Ed. P N Verman. Circ: 500.

636.5   IND   ISSN 0970-9738
INDIAN POULTRY INDUSTRY YEARBOOK. Text in English. 1974. a. USD 250. bk.rev. **Description:** Sourcebook on trade, technical and economic aspects of poultry. Lists 7,000 specialists and organizations by business and geographic locations.
Indexed: AnBrAb, NutrAb.
Published by: S.P. Gupta Pub., A-25 Priyadarshini Vihar, Patparganj Rd., New Delhi, 110 092, India. TEL 91-11-224-3326, FAX 91-11-2243039. Ed. Sharad Gupta. adv.: B&W page USD 800; trim 15 x 20. Circ: 2,500 (paid).

636.5   IND   ISSN 0019-6150
                                        CODEN: IPRWD9
INDIAN POULTRY REVIEW. Text in English. 1969. m. looseleaf. USD 70 (effective 1995). adv. bk.rev. abstr.; illus.
Indexed: ChemAb, ISA.
—BLDSC (4427.850000), CASDDS.

Published by: Indian Poultry Lovers Association, 57-B Townshend Rd., Kolkata, West Bengal 700 025, India. TEL 4750838. Ed. G N Ghosh. Circ: 18,000.

636.2 USA
INDIANA BEEF. Text in English. 1981. bi-m. free. adv. **Document type:** *Magazine, Trade.* **Description:** Includes articles on management, marketing and beef industry activities for beef cattle feeders, producers and supporters.
Published by: Indiana Beef Cattle Association, 8770 Guion Rd, Ste A, Indianapolis, IN 46268-3043. TEL 317-872-2333, FAX 317-872-2364, sbradway@indianabeef.org, http://www.indianabeef.org/Indiana%20Beef%20mag.htm. Ed., Adv. contact Debbie Shoufler. Circ: 7,600.

636.2 ITA
INDICE GENETICO VACCHE. Text in Italian. s-a. **Document type:** *Magazine, Trade.* **Description:** Catalog presents the cow genetic index of the best living Italian Brown cows, calculated using the Blup Animal Model procedure.
Published by: Associazione Nazionale Allevatori Razza Bruna, Localita Ferlina 204, Bussolengo, VR 37012, Italy. TEL 39-045-6701990, FAX 39-045-7156655, anarb@anarb.it, http://www.anarb.it.

636.5 USA ISSN 0019-7467
INDUSTRIA AVICOLA. Text in Spanish, English. 1952. m. USD 72 domestic; USD 78 in Canada; USD 84 elsewhere; free to qualified personnel (effective 2005); dist. only in Pan-American countries. adv. charts; illus.; stat. back issues avail.; reprints avail. **Document type:** *Magazine, Trade.* **Description:** For the commercial poultry industry in Latin America; covers all aspects of growing, processing and marketing of poultry and eggs.
Related titles: Online - full text ed.: (from EBSCO Publishing); ♦ Regional ed(s).: Poultry International. ISSN 0032-5767.
—IE. **CCC.**
Published by: Watt Publishing Co., 122 S Wesley Ave, Mt. Morris, IL 61054-1497. TEL 815-734-4171, FAX 815-734-5649, wright@wattmm.com, http://www.wattnet.com. Ed. Chris Wright. Pub. Charles Olentine. adv.: B&W page USD 3,750, color page USD 7,470; trim 10.75 x 8. Circ: 15,000 (controlled).

636.4 USA ISSN 0279-7771
INDUSTRIA PORCINA. Text in Spanish. 1981. q. USD 25; USD 45 foreign (effective 1997). adv. **Document type:** *Trade.* **Description:** For distribution to swine industry leaders in Latin American countries.
Related titles: Special ed(s).: Industria Porcina. Annual Buyers Guide.
—IE.
Published by: Watt Publishing Co., 122 S Wesley Ave, Mt. Morris, IL 61054-1497. TEL 815-734-4171, FAX 815-734-5649. Ed. Peter Best. Pub., R&P Clay Schreiber. Adv. contact Donna Carlson. B&W page USD 2,800, color page USD 3,910; trim 10.75 x 8. Circ: 8,842 (controlled).

636.4 DNK ISSN 1602-4168
INFO SVIN. Text in Danish. 1996. irreg. free. **Document type:** *Trade.*
Media: Online - full content.
Published by: Landsudvalget for Svin/National Committee for Pig Breeding and Production, Axelborg, Axeltorv 3, Copenhagen V, 1609, Denmark. TEL 45-33-116050, FAX 45-33-116814, lu@danskeslagterier.dk, http://www.infosvin.dk, http://www.danskeslagterier.dk.

636 ESP
INFORMACION AGROPECUARIA. Text in Spanish. 1975. w. free.
Published by: Consorcio para el Fomento de la Riqueza Ganadera, Diputacion y Caja de Ahorros, Delegacion Agricultura J. de C.L., Delegacion Territorial de Agricultura, G. y M. Santa Catalina, 15, Segovia, 40003, Spain. TEL 34-911-431414.

636 CUB ISSN 0138-7685
INFORMACION EXPRESS. SERIE: APICULTURA. Text in Spanish. 1977. 2/yr. USD 5 in Europe; USD 9 elsewhere.
Indexed: Agrind.
—CISTI.
Published by: Centro de Informacion y Documentacion Agropecuario, Gaveta Postal 4149, Havana, 4, Cuba. **Dist. by:** Ediciones Cubanas, Obispo No. 527, Apdo. 605, Havana, Cuba.

636 CUB ISSN 0138-7383
INFORMACION EXPRESS. SERIE: AVICULTURA. Text in Spanish. 1977. 3/yr. USD 10 in North America; USD 14 in South America; USD 15 in Europe; USD 21 elsewhere. charts; illus.; stat.
Indexed: Agrind, ChemAb.
—CISTI.
Published by: Centro de Informacion y Documentacion Agropecuario, Gaveta Postal 4149, Havana, 4, Cuba. TEL 301672. **Dist. by:** Ediciones Cubanas, Obispo No. 527, Apdo. 605, Havana, Cuba.

636 CUB ISSN 0138-7537
INFORMACION EXPRESS. SERIE: GANADO EQUINO. Text in Spanish. 1977. a. USD 3 in North America; USD 4 in Europe; USD 5 elsewhere.
Indexed: Agrind.
—CISTI.
Published by: Centro de Informacion y Documentacion Agropecuario, Gaveta Postal 4149, Havana, 4, Cuba. **Dist. by:** Ediciones Cubanas, Obispo No. 527, Apdo. 605, Havana, Cuba.

636 CUB ISSN 0138-7588
INFORMACION EXPRESS. SERIE: GANADO PORCINO. Text in Spanish. 1977. 4/yr. USD 9 in North America; USD 11 in South America; USD 13 in Europe; USD 18 elsewhere.
Indexed: Agrind.
—CISTI.
Published by: Centro de Informacion y Documentacion Agropecuario, Gaveta Postal 4149, Havana, 4, Cuba. **Dist. by:** Ediciones Cubanas, Obispo No. 527, Apdo. 605, Havana, Cuba.

636 CUB ISSN 0138-7081
INFORMACION EXPRESS. SERIE: RUMIANTES. Text in Spanish. 1977. 4/yr. USD 9 in North America; USD 11 in South America; USD 13 in Europe; USD 18 elsewhere.
Indexed: Agrind.
—CISTI.
Published by: Centro de Informacion y Documentacion Agropecuario, Gaveta Postal 4149, Havana, 4, Cuba. **Dist. by:** Ediciones Cubanas, Obispo No. 527, Apdo. 605, Havana, Cuba.

636 ITA ISSN 0020-0778
INFORMATORE ZOOTECNICO. Short title: I Z. Text in Italian. 1953. 22/yr. EUR 68 domestic; EUR 200 foreign (effective 2005). adv. bk.rev. charts; illus. index. 80 p./no.; **Document type:** *Magazine, Trade.* **Description:** Provides up-to-date information on animal husbandry. Includes articles on breeding and reproduction methods.
Indexed: NutrAb.
Published by: Il Sole 24 Ore Edagricole, Via Goito 13, Bologna, BO 40126, Italy. TEL 39-051-62267, FAX 39-051-490200, http://www.edagricole.it. Ed. Giorgio Setti. Circ: 40,000.

636 RWA
INSTITUT DES SCIENCES AGRONOMIQUES DU RWANDA. DEPARTEMENT DES PRODUCTIONS ANIMALES. COMPTE RENDU DES TRAVAUX. Text in French. a.
Published by: Institut des Sciences Agronomiques, Departement des Productions Vegetales, BP 138, Butare, Rwanda.

INSTITUT TECHNIQUE DE L'AVICULTURE. TENDANCES DES MARCHES. see *AGRICULTURE—Agricultural Economics*

636.2 636.5 USA
INTERNATIONAL CONFERENCE ON LIVESTOCK IN THE TROPICS. Text in English, Spanish. 1967. a. USD 10. **Document type:** *Proceedings.*
Former titles: International Conference on Livestock and Poultry in the Tropics (Proceedings); Livestock and Poultry in Latin America. Annual Conference (0085-2805)
Published by: University of Florida, Animal Science Department, 125 Tropical Animal Science, 459 Shealy Dr, Box 110910, Gainesville, FL 32611-0910. TEL 904-392-2186, FAX 904-3922-7652, TELEX 568757. Eds. J H Conrad, V Carbia. Circ: 500. **Co-sponsor:** Institute of Food and Agricultural Sciences, Florida Cooperative Extension Service.

636 GBR ISSN 0959-9363
INTERNATIONAL HATCHERY PRACTICE. Text in English. 1985. 8/yr. GBP 50, USD 75, EUR 80 (effective 2005). adv. bk.rev. reprints avail. **Document type:** *Magazine, Trade.* **Description:** Technical publication for poultry breeders and hatcheries worldwide.
Indexed: IndVet, NutrAb, PoultAb, ProtozoAb, RM&VM, RefZh.
—BLDSC (4540.702000).
Published by: Positive Action Publications Ltd., PO Box 4, Driffield, N Humberside YO25 9DJ, United Kingdom. TEL 44-1377-241724, FAX 44-1377-253640, http://www.positiveaction.co.uk/pap/mags/ihp/ihpmain.html, http://positiveaction.co.uk. Ed., Pub. Nigel Horrox. Adv. contact Geoff Hall. B&W page GBP 1,782, color page GBP 2,306. Circ: 13,500.

636.0832 660.6 IND ISSN 0970-2857
CODEN: IASCEK
➤ **INTERNATIONAL JOURNAL OF ANIMAL SCIENCES.** Text in English. 1986. s-a. USD 100. adv. bk.rev. bibl.; charts; illus. **Document type:** *Academic/Scholarly.* **Description:** Publishes research and review articles in the field of animal health, animal biology, animal production, dairy science and biotechnology.
Formerly (until 1987): Farm Animals
Indexed: AgBio, AgrForAb, AnBrAb, BiolAb, ChemAb, DBA, DSA, FPA, ForAb, HelmAb, HerbAb, HortAb, IndVet, MaizeAb, NutrAb, PN&I, PoultAb, ProtozoAb, RA&MP, RDA, RM&VM, RevApplEntom, RiceAb, SIA, TriticAb, VetBull, WAE&RSA, ZooRec.
—BLDSC (4542.082000), IE, Infotrieve, ingenta. **CCC.**
Published by: Nitasha Publications, 921, Sector 14, Sonipat, Haryana 131 001, India. TEL 91-1662-32703. Ed., Pub., R&P, Adv. contact Sadhana Jindal.

636 CHE ISSN 0259-8183
HD9433.A1
INTERNATIONAL MARKETS FOR MEAT. Text in English. 1981. a. CHF 25. **Document type:** *Trade.* **Description:** Reports on main trends in international trade of bovine meat.
Former titles (until 1985): Arrangement Regarding Bovine Meat (1014-031X); World Market for Bovine Meat (1011-4645)
Related titles: Microfiche ed.: (from CIS); French ed.: Marches Internationaux de la Viande. ISSN 0259-8191; Spanish ed.: Mercados Internacionales de la Carne. ISSN 0259-8205.
Indexed: IIS.
Published by: General Agreement on Tariffs and Trade, Centre William Rappard, 154 rue de Lausanne, Geneva 21, 1211, Switzerland. TEL 41-22-739-5208, FAX 41-22-739-5458.

636 USA
INTERNATIONAL MEAT REVIEW. Text in English. bi-w. USD 50 domestic; USD 60 in Canada & Mexico; USD 80 elsewhere. **Document type:** *Government.*
Published by: U.S. Department Of Agriculture, Livestock & Grain Market News Branch, 1428 S. Pioneer Way, Moses Lake, WA 98837. TEL 509-675-3611, http://www.ams.usda.gov/lsg/mncs/pdf%5Fweekly/compweekly.htm.

636 ESP ISSN 0074-6959
INTERNATIONAL MEETING OF ANIMAL NUTRITION EXPERTS. PROCEEDINGS. Text in English, French, Italian, Spanish. 1958. irreg. USD 8. bk.rev. cum.index every 6 yrs. **Document type:** *Proceedings.*
Published by: Ritena, PO Box 466, Barcelona, 08080, Spain. FAX 34-3-2370771. Ed. J Amich Gali. Circ: 1,200.

636.4 GBR ISSN 0963-5866
INTERNATIONAL PIG TOPICS; the techical publication for progressive breeders and pig producers. Text in English. 1985. 8/yr. GBP 50, USD 75, EUR 80 (effective 2005). adv. bk.rev. reprints avail. **Document type:** *Magazine, Trade.* **Description:** Technical publication for progressive pig producers around the world.
Indexed: AnBrAb, FS&TA, IndVet, NutrAb, PN&I, RM&VM, RefZh, WAE&RSA.
—BLDSC (4544.935200).
Published by: Positive Action Publications Ltd., PO Box 4, Driffield, N Humberside YO25 9DJ, United Kingdom. TEL 44-1377-241724, FAX 44-1377-253640, info@positiveaction.co.uk, http://www.positiveaction.co.uk/pap/mags/ipt/iptmain.html, http://positiveaction.co.uk. Ed., Pub. Nigel Horrox. Adv. contacts Colin Foster, Geoff Hall. B&W page GBP 1,614, color page GBP 2,114. Circ: 18,500.

636.5 USA
INTERNATIONAL POULTRY EXPOSITION GUIDE. Text in English. 1984. a. USD 5 (effective 1999). adv. back issues avail. **Document type:** *Trade.* **Description:** Provides a preview of products being exhibited at the International Poultry Exposition of the US Poultry and Egg Association.
Formerly: International Poultry Trade Show Guide (1044-551X)
—**CCC.**
Published by: Watt Publishing Co., 122 S Wesley Ave, Mt. Morris, IL 61054-1497. TEL 815-734-4171, FAX 815-734-5649, http://www.wattnet.com. Ed. Lisa Thornton. Pub. Charles Olentine. Adv. contact Anita Martin. B&W page USD 3,255, color page USD 4,380; trim 10.75 x 8. Circ: 24,000.

636 GBR
INTERNATIONAL POULTRY PRODUCTION. Text in English. 1993. 8/yr. GBP 50, USD 75, EUR 80 (effective 2005). adv. bk.rev. **Document type:** *Magazine, Trade.* **Description:** Technical publication for poultry meat and egg producers and processors worldwide.
Indexed: IndVet, NutrAb, PoultAb, ProtozoAb, RefZh, SoyAb, WAE&RSA.
Published by: Positive Action Publications Ltd., PO Box 4, Driffield, N Humberside YO25 9DJ, United Kingdom. TEL 44-1377-241724, FAX 44-1377-253640, info@positiveaction.co.uk, http://www.positiveaction.co.uk/pap/mags/ipp/ippmain.html, http://positiveaction.co.uk. Ed., Pub., R&P, Adv. contact Nigel Horrox. B&W page GBP 2,090, color page GBP 2,612. Circ: 18,000.

636 USA ISSN 0279-4608
IOWA CATTLEMAN. Text in English. 1972. 10/yr. USD 40 to members (effective 2000). adv. **Document type:** *Trade.* **Description:** Covers developments in beef production with information and services to members of the Iowa Cattlemen's Association.
Published by: Iowa Cattlemen's Association, PO Box 1490, Ames, IA 50014-1490. TEL 515-296-2266, FAX 515-296-2261, carol@iabeef.org. Ed., R&P, Adv. contact Christa Hartsook. Pub. Joel Brinkmeyer. page USD 780; trim 7.0625 x 10.1875. Circ: 14,000.

636.4 USA
IOWA PORK PRODUCER. Text in English. 1970. m. membership. adv. bk.rev. **Document type:** *Magazine, Trade.* **Description:** Presents information on swine production, marketing, and animal health, as well as state and national legislative issues of importance to the swine industry in Iowa.

Published by: Iowa Pork Producers Association, PO Box 71009, Clive, IA 50325-0009. TEL 515-225-7675, 800-372-7675, FAX 515-225-0563, info@iowapork.org, http://www.iowapork.org. Ed., Pub. Peter H Theodore. Adv. contact Mary Lea Hampton. B&W page USD 1,400, color page USD 2,150; trim 10.75 x 8. Circ: 19,837.

636.4 664.9 USA ISSN 1043-9676
IOWA PORK TODAY. Text in English. 1987. m. USD 16 (effective 1999). adv. **Document type:** *Newspaper, Trade.* **Description:** Covers the pork industry in Iowa. Contains production, and animal and herd health information.
Published by: Cedar Rapids Gazette, PO Box 5279, Cedar, IA 52406. TEL 319-398-8461, IFT@FYIowa.infi.net. Ed., R&P Lori Leonard. Pub. Stephen Dewitt. Adv. contact Terry Reilly. Circ: 25,000.

IRELAND. CENTRAL STATISTICS OFFICE. DECEMBER LIVESTOCK SURVEY. see *AGRICULTURE—Abstracting, Bibliographies, Statistics*

IRELAND. CENTRAL STATISTICS OFFICE. LIVESTOCK SLAUGHTERINGS. see *AGRICULTURE—Abstracting, Bibliographies, Statistics*

IRELAND. CENTRAL STATISTICS OFFICE. MEAT SUPPLY BALANCE. see *AGRICULTURE—Abstracting, Bibliographies, Statistics*

IRELAND. CENTRAL STATISTICS OFFICE. PIG SURVEY - JUNE. see *AGRICULTURE—Abstracting, Bibliographies, Statistics*

IRELAND. CENTRAL STATISTICS OFFICE. SIZE OF HERD. see *AGRICULTURE—Abstracting, Bibliographies, Statistics*

IRISH GRASSLAND ASSOCIATION. JOURNAL. see *AGRICULTURE—Dairying And Dairy Products*

633.2 636 ITA
CODEN: ZNAND2
➤ **ITALIAN JOURNAL OF ANIMAL SCIENCE.** Text and summaries in English, Italian. 1975. q. EUR 60 domestic; EUR 75 foreign (effective 2005). adv. bk.rev. index. **Document type:** *Journal, Academic/Scholarly.* **Description:** For livestock breeders and feed producers.
Former titles (until 2003): Zootecnica e Nutrizione Animale (0390-0487); Alimentazione Animale (0002-5429)
Indexed: ASFA, AgBio, AgrForAb, AnBrAb, BiolAb, ChemAb, CurCont, DSA, ESPM, FCA, HerbAb, IndVet, MaizeAb, NutrAb, PBA, PGegResA, PN&I, PotatoAb, PoultAb, RA&MP, RM&VM, RRTA, SIA, SoyAb, TriticAb, VetBull, WAE&RSA.
—BLDSC (4588.339600), CASDDS, CISTI, IE, Linda Hall.
Published by: (Associazione Scientifica di Produzione Animale/Scientific Association of Animal Production), Avenue Media, Via Riva Reno 61, Bologna, 40122, Italy. TEL 39-051-6564311, FAX 39-051-6564350, avenuemedia@avenuemedia.it, http://www.aspajournal.it, http://www.avenuemedia.it. Circ: 4,500.

➤ **ITALY. ISTITUTO NAZIONALE DI STATISTICA. STATISTICHE DELLA CACCIA E DELLA PESCA.** see *AGRICULTURE—Abstracting, Bibliographies, Statistics*

636 JPN ISSN 0289-4238
JAPAN. IBARAKI NATIONAL INSTITUTE OF ANIMAL INDUSTRY. ANNUAL REPORT/NIPPON IBARAKI CHIKUSAN SHIKENJO NENPO. Text in Japanese. a. **Document type:** *Government.*
Formerly: Japan. Chiba National Institute of Animal Industry. Annual Report
Indexed: AEA.
Published by: Ibaraki National Institute of Animal Industry/Ibaraki Chikusan Shikenjo, Tsukuba Norindanchi, P.O. Box 5, Ibaraki, 305, Japan.

636 JPN ISSN 0077-488X
CODEN: CSKKAQ
JAPAN. IBARAKI NATIONAL INSTITUTE OF ANIMAL INDUSTRY. BULLETIN/NIPPON IBARAKI CHIKUSAN SHIKENJO. CHIKUSAN SHIKENJO KENKYU HOKOKU. Text in Japanese; Summaries in English. 1963. irreg. abstr.; charts; illus. **Document type:** *Bulletin, Government.* **Description:** Presents summaries of articles published on animal industry research.
Formerly: Japan. Chiba National Institute of Animal Industry. Bulletin
Indexed: AEA, AnBrAb, BibAg, BiolAb, CIN, ChemAb, ChemTitl, DSA, FCA, FS&TA, HerbAb, IndVet, NutrAb, PBA, PN&I, PoultAb, RefZh, SoyAb, VetBull, WAE&RSA.
—CASDDS, CISTI.
Published by: Ibaraki National Institute of Animal Industry/Ibaraki Chikusan Shikenjo, Tsukuba Norindanchi, P.O. Box 5, Ibaraki, 305, Japan. Circ: 1,100.

636.2 GBR ISSN 0021-5929
THE JERSEY. Text in English. 1971 (no.107). a. GBP 10 (effective 2000). adv. back issues avail. **Document type:** *Trade.* **Description:** Keeps persons interested up to date with all matters pertaining to Jersey cattle within the UK.
Formerly: Jersey Cow
Indexed: DSA.
Published by: Jersey Cattle Society of the United Kingdom, Scotsbridge House, Scots Hill, Rickmansworth, Hertfordshire WD3 3BB, United Kingdom. TEL 44-1923-695282, FAX 44-1923-695303, jcsoffice@jerseycattle.org, http://www.jerseycattle.org/. Ed., R&P Chris Barnes TEL 44-1923-695203. Circ: 1,000 (controlled).

JERSEY AT HOME. see *AGRICULTURE—Dairying And Dairy Products*

636 GBR
JERSEY HERD BOOK AND MEMBERS DIRECTORY. Text in English. 1958. a. GBP 25 (effective 2000). **Document type:** *Directory.*
Former titles: Combined Jersey Herd Book, Directory and Elite Register of the U.K.; Jersey Herd Book and Directory of the U.K. (0075-3629); Jersey Herd Book of the U.K.
Media: Microfiche.
Published by: Jersey Cattle Society of the United Kingdom, Scotsbridge House, Scots Hill, Rickmansworth, Hertfordshire WD3 3BB, United Kingdom. TEL 44-1923-695282, FAX 44-1923-695303. R&P Chris Barnes TEL 44-1923-695203.

636.2 USA ISSN 0021-5953
JERSEY JOURNAL. Text in English. 1953. m. USD 25 (effective 2005). adv. bk.rev. illus. **Document type:** *Magazine, Trade.* **Description:** Contains news and advertising of interest to Jersey cattle owners. Reflects policies and positions of the AJCA Board of Directors.
Related titles: Online - full text ed.: (from Newsbank, Inc.).
—CISTI, Linda Hall.
Published by: American Jersey Cattle Association, 6486 E Main St, Reynoldsburg, OH 43068-2362. TEL 614-861-3636, FAX 614-861-8040, info@usjersey.com, http://www.usjersey.com. Ed. Kimberly A Billman. adv.: page USD 535. Circ: 3,250 (paid).

636 DNK ISSN 1397-6362
JORDBRUGSFORSKNING/DENMARK. DANISH INSTITUTE OF ANIMAL SCIENCE. SCIENTIFIC REPORT. Text in Danish. 1997. 10/yr. DKK 200 (effective 2002). back issues avail. **Description:** Results of research in Danish agriculture and animal husbandry.
Formed by the merger of (1993-1997): Denmark. Statens Planteavlsforsoeg In-fo (0908-6242); (1991-1997): Denmark. Statens Husdyrbrugsforsoeg. Husdyrsforskning (0908-0368); Which was formerly (1974-1991): Denmark. Statens Husdyrbrugsforsoeg. Meddelelse (0106-8857)
Indexed: AbHyg, AgBio, AnBrAb, DSA, FCA, ForAb, HortAb, IndVet, NutrAb, OrnHort, PHN&I, PN&I, PoultAb, RM&VM, RPP, S&F, TriticAb, WAE&RSA, WeedAb.
—CISTI.
Published by: Ministeriet for Foedevarer, Landbrug og Fiskeri, Danmarks Jordbrugsforskning/Ministry of Food, Agriculture and Fisheries. Danish Institute of Agricultural Sciences, PO Box 50, Tjele, 8830, Denmark. TEL 45-8999-1900, FAX 45-8999-1919, http://www.agrsci.dk/djfpublikation/default.htm.

636 POL ISSN 1230-1388
CODEN: JFESEA
➤ **JOURNAL OF ANIMAL AND FEED SCIENCES.** Text in English; Summaries in English, Polish. 1903; N.S. 1992. q. (in 1 vol., 4 nos./vol.). PLZ 150 domestic; USD 100 foreign (effective 2003 - 2004). bk.rev. bibl.; charts; illus. 200 p./no. 1 cols./p.; reprints avail. **Document type:** *Journal, Academic/Scholarly.* **Description:** Publishes original papers on basic and applied research in the field of animal breeding and genetics, physiology of nutrition, animal feeding, feed technology and food preservation.
Formerly (until 1992): Roczniki Nauk Rolniczych. Seria B - Zootechniczna (0080-3669)
Indexed: AEA, AgBio, AgrAg, AgrForAb, AgrLib, AnBrAb, BIOSIS Prev, BiolAb, ChemAb, CurCont, DSA, FCA, FPA, FS&TA, HelmAb, HerbAb, HortAb, IndVet, MaizeAb, NutrAb, PBA, PN&I, PotatoAb, PoultAb, ProtozoAb, RDA, RM&VM, RiceAb, S&F, SIA, SeedAb, SoyAb, TriticAb, VetBull, WAE&RSA, WeedAb.
—BLDSC (4935.375000), CASDDS, CISTI, IDS, IE, ingenta.
Published by: Polska Akademia Nauk, Instytut Fizjologii i Zywienia Zwierzat im. Jana Kielanowskiego/Polish Academy of Science, Kielanowski Institute of Animal Physiology and Nutrition, Jablonna, 05110, Poland. TEL 48-22-7824175, FAX 48-22-7742038, infizyz@atos.warman.com.pl, http://www.ifzz.pl/beta/jafs/1a.htm. Circ: 250. **Dist. by:** D H N P A N, Twarda 51/55, Warsaw 00818, Poland. TEL 48-22-6549411, FAX 48-22-6549411, ksiegarnia@dhn.pl.

636 DEU ISSN 0931-2668
SF1 CODEN: JABAE8
➤ **JOURNAL OF ANIMAL BREEDING AND GENETICS/ ZEITSCHRIFT FUER TIERZUECHTUNG UND ZUECHTUNGSBIOLOGIE.** Text in English; Summaries in English, French, German, Spanish. 1924. bi-m. EUR 308, GBP 205 combined subscription in Europe to individuals print & online eds.; USD 380 combined subscription in the Americas to individuals & Caribbean, print & online eds.; GBP 226 combined subscription elsewhere to individuals print & online eds.; GBP 642 combined subscription in Europe to institutions print & online eds.; USD 1,166 combined subscription in the Americas to institutions & Caribbean, print & online eds.; GBP 706 combined subscription elsewhere to institutions print & online eds. (effective 2006). bk.rev. illus.; stat. index. back issues avail.; reprint service avail. from ISI. **Document type:** *Journal, Academic/Scholarly.* **Description:** Reports on the progress of research in animal production, quantitative genetics, biology, and evolution of domestic animals.
Formerly (until 1987): Zeitschrift fuer Tierzuechtung und Zuechtungsbiologie (0044-3581)
Related titles: ♦ Online - full text ed.: Journal of Animal Breeding and Genetics Online. ISSN 1439-0388.
Indexed: AEA, AEBA, ASCA, ASFA, AgBio, Agr, AnBrAb, B&BAb, BIOSIS Prev, BiolAb, ChemAb, CurCont, DBA, DSA, ESPM, FS&TA, FoVS&M, GenetAb, HGA, ISR, IndVet, M&GPA, MEDLINE, NutrAb, PBA, PHN&I, PN&I, PoultAb, RRTA, RefZh, RevApplEntom, S&F, SAA, SCI, SFA, SIA, SoyAb, VetBull, WAE&RSA, WildRev, ZooRec.
—BLDSC (4935.450000), CASDDS, CISTI, IDS, IE, Infotrieve, ingenta. **CCC.**
Published by: Blackwell Verlag GmbH (Subsidiary of: Blackwell Publishing Ltd.), Kurfuerstendamm 57, Berlin, 10707, Germany. TEL 49-30-32790634, FAX 49-30-32790610, verlag@blackwell.de, http://www.blackwellpublishing.com/journals/JBG, http://www.blackwell.de. Ed. Georg Erhardt. Circ: 400 (paid and controlled).

636 DEU ISSN 1439-0388
JOURNAL OF ANIMAL BREEDING AND GENETICS ONLINE. Text in English; Summaries in English, French, German. bi-m. GBP 610 in Europe to institutions; USD 1,127 in the Americas to institutions & Caribbean; GBP 671 elsewhere to institutions (effective 2006). **Document type:** *Academic/Scholarly.*
Media: Online - full text (from Blackwell Synergy, EBSCO Publishing, Gale Group, IngentaConnect, O C L C Online Computer Library Center, Inc., Swets Information Services).
Related titles: ♦ Print ed.: Journal of Animal Breeding and Genetics. ISSN 0931-2668.
Published by: Blackwell Verlag GmbH (Subsidiary of: Blackwell Publishing Ltd.), Kurfuerstendamm 57, Berlin, 10707, Germany. TEL 49-30-32790665, FAX 49-30-32790610, abo@blackwis.de, http://www.blackwell-science.com/~cgilib/jnlpage.bin?Journal=XJABG&File=XJABG&Page=aims, http://www.blackwell.de.

636 USA ISSN 0021-8812
SF1 CODEN: JANSAG
➤ **JOURNAL OF ANIMAL SCIENCE**; leading source of new knowledge and perspectives in animal science. Text in English. 1942. m. (1 vol./yr.). USD 160 to members; USD 450 in North America to institutions; USD 500 elsewhere to institutions (effective 2005). bk.rev. bibl.; charts; illus.; stat. cum.index 1942-1998. back issues avail.; reprints avail. **Document type:** *Journal, Academic/Scholarly.* **Description:** Covers many subjects within animal science as they relate to agriculturally important species: applied science, breeding and genetics, environment and behavior, growth and developmental biology, meat science, nonruminant and ruminant nutrition, pharmacology and toxicology, physiology and endocrinology, forage and rangeland utilization, contemporary issues in animal science, molecular genetic markers, and pedagogical issues.
Related titles: CD-ROM ed.: USD 100 to non-members; USD 40 to members (effective 2001); Microform ed.: (from PMC, PQC); Online - full text ed.: ISSN 1525-3163. USD 110 (effective 2005) (from bigchalk, EBSCO Publishing, Northern Light Technology, Inc., O C L C Online Computer Library Center, Inc., ProQuest Information & Learning).
Indexed: AEA, ASCA, ASFA, AgBio, Agr, AgrForAb, AnBrAb, B&AI, BIOSIS Prev, BiolAb, CIN, CIS, CPA, ChemAb, ChemTitl, CurCont, CurPA, DBA, DSA, EPB, ExcerpMed, F&GI, FCA, FPA, FS&TA, FoVS&M, ForAb, GenetAb, HGA, HelmAb, HerbAb, HortAb, I&DA, ISR, IndMed, IndVet, MEDLINE, MaizeAb, NRN, NutrAb, OrnHort, PBA, PGegResA, PGrRegA, PHN&I, PN&I, PotatoAb, PoultAb, ProtozoAb, RA&MP, RDA, RM&VM, RPP, RRTA, RefZh, RiceAb, S&F, S&MA, SCI, SFA, SIA, SSCI, SoyAb, TOSA, TriticAb, VetBull, WAE&RSA, WeedAb, WildRev, ZooRec.
—BLDSC (4937.000000), CASDDS, CINDOC, CISTI, GNLM, IDS, IE, Infotrieve, ingenta, Linda Hall.
Published by: American Society of Animal Science, 1111 N Dunlap Ave, Savoy, IL 61874. TEL 217-356-5090, FAX 217-938-4119, johne@assochq.org, http://jas.fass.org, http://www.asas.org. Ed. John Edwards. R&P Leon Jeter. Adv. contact Amy Kemp. Circ: 5,000.

636 KOR
SF1 CODEN: HGCHAG
JOURNAL OF ANIMAL SCIENCE AND TECHNOLOGY. Text mainly in Korean; Summaries in English. 1958. bi-m. USD 40; effective Jan. 1991. adv. bk.rev. **Document type:** *Academic/Scholarly.*
Formerly (until 2000): Han'guk Ch'uksan Hakhoe Chi / Korean Journal of Animal Sciences (0367-5807)
Indexed: AEA, AgBio, AgrForAb, AnBrAb, BIOSIS Prev, BioCN&I, BiolAb, CPA, ChemAb, DSA, FCA, FPA, FS&TA, ForAb, HerbAb, HortAb, I&DA, IndVet, MaizeAb, NutrAb, PBA, PN&I, PST, PoultAb, ProtozoAb, RA&MP, RDA, RPP, RiceAb, S&F, S&MA, SIA, SeedAb, SoyAb, TDB, TriticAb, VetBull, WAE&RSA, WeedAb.
—BLDSC (4937.170000), CASDDS, CISTI. **CCC.**
Published by: Korean Society of Animal Sciences, Korean Society of Animal Sciences and Technology, The Korea Science and Technology Center, Room 909, 635-4, Yeogsam-dong, Kangnam-ku, Seoul, 135-703, Korea, S. TEL 82-2-562-0377, FAX 82-2-562-0379, ksas1956@ksas1956.or.kr. Ed. Chung Soo Chung. Circ: 1,500.

JOURNAL OF APPLIED ANIMAL WELFARE SCIENCE. see *ANIMAL WELFARE*

636.5 USA ISSN 1056-6171
SF481 CODEN: JAPRFS
➤ **THE JOURNAL OF APPLIED POULTRY RESEARCH.** Abbreviated title: J A P R. Text in English. 1992. q. USD 100 to institutions (effective 2005). bk.rev. back issues avail. **Document type:** *Academic/Scholarly.* **Description:** Provides practical, reliable and timely information to those whose livelihood is derived from the commercial production of poultry and those whose research benefits this sector.
Related titles: Online - full text ed.: ISSN 1537-0437 (from ProQuest Information & Learning).
Indexed: AEA, AbHyg, AgBio, Agr, AnBrAb, BioCN&I, CurCont, DSA, FS&TA, FoVS&M, HerbAb, I&DA, IndVet, MaizeAb, NutrAb, PBA, PHN&I, PN&I, PoultAb, ProtozoAb, RM&VM, RevApplEntom, S&F, SIA, SoyAb, TriticAb, VetBull, WAE&RSA, WeedAb.
—BLDSC (4946.670000), CASDDS, CISTI, IDS, IE, Infotrieve, ingenta. **CCC.**
Published by: (Poultry Science Association Inc.), Applied Poultry Science, Inc., Circulation Department, Box 80286, Athens, GA 30608. TEL 706-354-3954, FAX 706-354-3455, ewalker@negia.net, http://www.poultryscience.org/japr/japr.html, http://www.allenpress.com. Ed. Henry Wilson.

636 JPN ISSN 1346-7395
➤ **JOURNAL OF POULTRY SCIENCE.** Text in English. 2001. q. JPY 5,000 domestic membership; JPY 8,000 foreign membership (effective 2005). adv. bibl. back issues avail. **Document type:** *Journal, Academic/Scholarly.*
Supersedes in part: Nippon Kakin Gakkaishi (0029-0254)
Related titles: Online - full content ed.: ISSN 1349-0486. 2002. free (effective 2005); Online - full text ed.: (from J-Stage).
Indexed: AgBio, AnBrAb, BIOSIS Prev, BiolAb, DSA, IndVet, PoultAb, ProtozoAb, RA&MP, SIA, SoyAb, TriticAb.
—CISTI, Linda Hall.
Published by: Nihon Kakin Gakkai/Japan Poultry Science Association, c/o National Institute of Livestock and Grassland Science, Tsukuba Norin-danchi, PO Box 5, Ibaraki, 305-0901, Japan. jpsa@affrc.go.jp, http://wwwsoc.nii.ac.jp/jpsa/. Ed. K Shimada. R&P, Adv. contact M. Naito TEL 81-298-38-8622.

636.4 FRA ISSN 0767-9874
JOURNEES DE LA RECHERCHE PORCINE EN FRANCE. Text in French. 1969. a.
Indexed: AEA, AgBio, AnBrAb, DSA, HelmAb, IndVet, MaizeAb, NutrAb, PN&I, PotatoAb, RM&VM, RiceAb, S&F, SIA, SoyAb, TriticAb, VetBull, WAE&RSA.
—BLDSC (5073.518000), IE, ingenta.
Published by: Institut Technique du Porc, 149 Rue de Bercy, Paris, 75595 Cedex 12, France. TEL 33-1-40045375, FAX 33-1-40045377, http://www.itp.asso.fr.

636.2 DNK ISSN 0109-3800
KALVEPRODUCENTEN. Text in Danish. 1983. bi-m. membership. adv. illus.
Published by: Landsforeningen af Danske Slagtekalveproducenter, c/o Eilif Bigum, Gislum, Binderupvej 17, Aars, 9600, Denmark. Circ: 200.

636.9322 DEU ISSN 0941-0848
KANINCHEN. Text in German. 1960. m. EUR 32.50 (effective 2003). adv. **Document type:** *Magazine, Trade.*
Former titles (until 1992): Unsere Kleintiere (0863-3592); (until 1990): Garten und Kleintierzucht. Ausgabe D: Kleintierzuechter (0433-1834); (until 1962): Der Kleintierzuechter (0323-6730)
Published by: Deutscher Bauernverlag GmbH, Wilhelmsaue 37, Berlin, 10713, Germany. TEL 49-30-464060, FAX 49-30-46406205, kaninchen@bauernverlag.de, info@bauernverlag.de, http://www.kaninchenzeitung.de, http://www.bauernverlag.de. Ed. Gisela Becker. adv.: B&W page EUR 1,158, color page EUR 1,876. Circ: 10,400 (controlled).

KANSAS CITY BOARD OF TRADE REVIEW. see *AGRICULTURE—Feed, Flour And Grain*

636 USA ISSN 0022-8826
KANSAS STOCKMAN. Text in English. 1916. 10/yr. USD 100 membership (effective 2005). adv. bk.rev. charts; illus.; stat. **Document type:** *Magazine, Trade.*
Published by: Kansas Livestock Association, 6031 SW 37th St, Topeka, KS 66614-5128. kla@kla.org, http://www.kansasstockman.com. Ed., R&P Todd Domer. Adv. contact Tammy Houk. Circ: 8,000.

636 NAM
KARAKUL. Text in English. 1958. a. adv.
Published by: Board of Karakul Breeders Society of South Africa, Head Office, PO Box128, Windhoek, 9100, Namibia. Ed. B Von Kunow. Circ: 2,000.

636.3 GBR
KERRY HILL FLOCK BOOK SOCIETY. FLOCK BOOK. Text in English. a.
Published by: Kerry Hill Flock Book Society, Broadheath, Kerry Hill Flock Book Society, Bramleys, Presteigne, Powys LD8 2HG, United Kingdom. TEL 44-1544-267353, FAX 44-1544-267353.

636 USA ISSN 0889-2857
KETCH PEN. Text in English. 1983. m. USD 100 to members (effective 2005). adv. **Document type:** *Magazine, Trade.*
Published by: Washington Cattlemen's Association, 1301 N Dollarway, P O Box 96, Ellensburg, WA 98926. TEL 509-925-9871, FAX 509-925-3004, wacattle@elltel.net, http://www.washingtoncattlemen.org. Ed. Amy Cziske. Circ: 2,000 (paid).

KOETTBRANSCHEN. see *FOOD AND FOOD INDUSTRIES*

636.4 DNK ISSN 1603-8401
KONGRES FOR SVINEPRODUCENTER. Text in Danish. 1998. irreg., latest 2004. back issues avail. **Document type:** *Proceedings, Trade.*
Published by: Landsudvalget for Svin/National Committee for Pig Breeding and Production, Axelborg, Axeltorv 3, Copenhagen V, 1609, Denmark. TEL 45-33-116050, FAX 45-33-116814, lu@danskeslagterier.dk, http://www.danskeslagterier.dk.

636 631 634.9 635 KOR ISSN 0250-3360
S494 CODEN: KJBRDU
➤ **KOREAN JOURNAL OF BREEDING.** Text in Korean, English; Abstracts in English. 1969. 4/yr. KRW 30,000, USD 50 (effective 2001). adv. back issues avail. **Document type:** *Academic/Scholarly.*
Related titles: CD-ROM ed.
Indexed: BiolAb, FCA, INIS AtomInd, PBA.
—BLDSC (5113.523000), CASDDS, CISTI.
Published by: Korean Breeding Society, School of Plant Sciences, Seoul National University, Suwon, 441-744, Korea, S. TEL 82-331-290-2307, FAX 82-331-292-0804, heejkoh@alliant.snu.ac.kr, http://aginfo.snu.ac.kr/breeding. Ed. Yeong-Ho Lee. R&P Seok Dong Kim. Circ: 700.

636 RUS ISSN 0023-4885
KROLIKOVODSTVO I ZVEROVODSTVO. Text in Russian. 1910. bi-m. USD 99.95. bk.rev. index.
Indexed: AEA, AnBrAb, BiolAb, ChemAb, HelmAb, HerbAb, IndVet, MaizeAb, NutrAb, ProtozoAb, RASB, RM&VM, RefZh, SoyAb, TriticAb, VetBull.
—CISTI, East View.
Published by: Izdatel'stvo Kolos, Sadovaya-Spasskaya 18, Moscow, 107807, Russian Federation. TEL 7-095-2072125, FAX 7-095-2072870. Ed. A T Erin. Circ: 38,400. **US dist. addr.:** East View Information Services, 3020 Harbor Ln. N., Minneapolis, MN 55447. TEL 612-550-0961.

636.2 637 DNK
KVAEG. Text in Danish. 1990. m. DKK 504 (effective 2003). adv. **Document type:** *Journal, Trade.*
Formerly (until 2003): Landsbladet Kvaeg (0905-6785)
Published by: Dansk Landbrugs Medier, Vester Farimagsgade 6, Copenhagen V, 1606, Denmark. TEL 46-33-394700. Circ: 8,076.

636.2 CAN
KYLOE CRY. Text in English. a. membership. **Document type:** *Newsletter, Trade.*
Published by: Canadian Highland Cattle Society, 307 Spicer, Knowlton, PQ J0E 1V0, Canada. TEL 450-243-1150, FAX 450-243-1150, highland@chcs.ca, http://www.chcs.ca. Ed., Pub., R&P Margaret Badger TEL 450-243-5543. Circ: 500.

636 ESP
LABRANZA; publicacion de formacion e informacion para el agricultor y ganadero. Text in Spanish. 1982. bi-m.
Address: Pollo Martin, 34 1oC, Salamanca, 37005, Spain. TEL 923-25-64-80. Ed. Jorge Avenas Rodriguez. Circ: 25,000.

636 SWE ISSN 0023-7159
LADUGAARDSFOERMANNEN. Text in Swedish. 1929. 6/yr. **Document type:** *Trade.*
Published by: Ladugaardsfoermannens Riksfoerfund, c/o Haakan Loefvgren, Backgatan 9, Gnesta, 64635, Sweden. TEL 46-158-26136, ladugardsformannen@telia.com. Ed. Lennart Rosen.

636.3 USA
LAMB & WOOL. Text in English. m. USD 20 (effective 2005); free to members. 8 p./no. 3 cols./p.; back issues avail. **Document type:** *Newsletter, Trade.* **Description:** Contains educational material on lamb, sheep, and wool production.
Published by: Iowa Sheep Industry Association, 5771 230th St., Sibley, IA 51249. iasheep@iowatelecom.net, http://www.iowasheep.com/about.html. Circ: 250 (controlled); 389 (free); 639 (paid and controlled).

LANDBAUFORSCHUNG VOELKENRODE; wissenschaftliche Mitteilungen der Bundesforschungsanstalt fuer Landwirtschaft (FAL). see *AGRICULTURE—Crop Production And Soil*

636.4 DNK ISSN 0904-3640
LANDSUDVALGET FOR SVIN. AARSBERETNING/NATIONAL COMMITTEE FOR PIG BREEDING, HEALTH AND PRODUCTION. ANNUAL REPORT. Text in Danish. 1973. a. free. illus. back issues avail. **Document type:** *Corporate.*
Formerly (until 1988): Svineavl og -Produktion i Danmark (0106-7338)
Related titles: English ed.: National Committee for Pig Breeding and Production. Annual Report. ISSN 0906-1452. 1983.
Indexed: PN&I.
—CISTI.
Published by: Landsudvalget for Svin/National Committee for Pig Breeding and Production, Axelborg, Axeltorv 3, Copenhagen V, 1609, Denmark. TEL 45-33-116050, FAX 45-33-116814, lu@danskeslagterier.dk, http://www.danskeslagterier.dk. Ed. Hans-Henrik E Jensen. Circ: 30,000.

636.4 DNK ISSN 1395-3192
LANDSUDVALGET FOR SVIN. AFDELINGEN FOR AVL OG OPFORMERING. AARSBERETNING. Text in Danish. 1991. a. **Document type:** *Trade.*
Related titles: Online - full text ed.
Published by: Landsudvalget for Svin, Afdelingen for Avl og Opformering, Udkjaervej 15, Skejby, Aarhus N, 8200, Denmark. http://www.danavl.dk.

636 USA
LEAN TRIMMINGS. Text in English. 1980. w. looseleaf. membership. adv. back issues avail. **Document type:** *Newsletter.* **Description:** Covers regulatory stipulations, news, technology and other developments in the meat industry.
Formerly: W S M A Bulletin
Published by: National Meat Association, 1970 Broadway, Ste 825, Oakland, CA 94612. TEL 510-763-1533, FAX 510-763-6186, nma@hooked.net, http://www.nmaonline.org. Ed., Pub., R&P, Adv. contact Jeremy Russell. Circ: 1,400 (controlled).

LEBENSMITTEL- UND BIOTECHNOLOGIE; die oesterreichische Fachzeitschrift fuer Lebensmittelindustrie und -forschung. see *FOOD AND FOOD INDUSTRIES*

636.3 GBR
LEICESTER LONGWOOL SHEEPBREEDERS' ASSOCIATION. FLOCK BOOK. Text in English. biennial. GBP 5 to institutional members; GBP 15 to members.
Published by: Leicester Longwool Sheepbreeders' Association, St House Farm, Loftus, Saltburn, Saltburn-by-the-sea, Cleveland TS13 4UX, United Kingdom. TEL 0287-640541.

338.1 636.088 FIN ISSN 1236-1895
LIHATALOUS. Text in Finnish. 1942. 8/yr. EUR 74 domestic; EUR 92 foreign (effective 2005). adv. 52 p./no.; back issues avail. **Document type:** *Magazine, Trade.* **Description:** Deals with issues conserning cattle production, processing and marketing.
Former titles (until 1993): Lihantuottaja (0355-046X); (until 1971): Osuusteurastamo (0472-2116)
Related titles: E-mail ed.
Published by: Lihateollisuuden Tutkimuskeskus/Finnish Meat Research Institute, PO Box 56, Haemeenlinna, 13101, Finland. raila.aaltonen@ltk.fi, http://www.htk.fi/ltk/lehti/, http://www.ltk.fi. Ed., R&P Raila Aaltonen TEL 358-3-5705330. Adv. contact Maritta Humala TEL 358-9-657022. B&W page EUR 1,000, color page EUR 1,650; 200 x 257. Circ: 6,000 (controlled).

636.2 CAN ISSN 0381-5552
LIMOUSIN LEADER. Text in English. m. CND 25. adv. **Document type:** *Trade.* **Description:** Edited for breeders of Limousin cattle. Works with farmers and ranchers to take the Limousin story to purebred breeders and commercial cattlemen.
Published by: Bollum Marketing Inc., 1935 32nd Ave, N E, Ste 253, Calgary, AB T2E 7C8, Canada. TEL 403-291-6770. Ed., Pub., R&P, Adv. contact Randy Bollum.

636.2 USA ISSN 8750-2127
LIMOUSIN WORLD. Text in English. 1983. m. USD 22 (effective 1997). adv. reprints avail. **Description:** Features news and educational material of interest and use to Limousin cattle breeders.
Published by: Limousin World, Inc., PO Box 850870, Yukon, OK 73085. FAX 405-350-0054. Ed. Kyle Haleysch. Pub. Dan Wedman. Adv. contact Lisa Garza. Circ: 10,000.

636.242 DNK ISSN 0900-050X
LIMOUSINE NYT. Text in Danish. 1979. 6/yr. membership. adv. 24 p./no. 3 cols./p.

Published by: Dansk Limousine Forening, Udkaersvej 15, Aarhus N, 8200, Denmark. TEL 45-87-40-50-00, FAX 45-87-40-50-10, http://www.lro.dk/limousin/LimoNyt.htm. Ed. Bodil Falkenberg TEL 45-97-53-83-89. Circ: 1,600.

636.3 GBR
LINCOLN LONGWOOL SHEEP BREEDERS' ASSOCIATION. ANNUAL FLOCK BOOK. Text in English. a. GBP 28 (effective 2000). **Document type:** *Bulletin.*
Published by: Lincoln Longwool Sheep Breeders' Association, Lincolnshire Show Ground, Grange-De-Lings, Lincoln, LN2 2NA, United Kingdom. TEL 44-1522-511395, FAX 44-1522-520345. Circ: 120.

636 GBR
LINCOLN RED CATTLE SOCIETY ANNUAL HERD BOOK. Text in English. 1896. a. GBP 40 (effective 1999). adv. **Document type:** *Bulletin.* **Description:** Examines Lincoln Red Cattle registration, rules, and regulations as they pertain to the Pedigree Cattle Society.
Published by: Lincoln Red Cattle Society, Lincolnshire Show Ground, Grange-De-Lings, Lincoln, LN2 2NA, United Kingdom. TEL 44-1522-511395, FAX 44-1522-520345, lrcs@farmersweekly.net. Circ: 120.

636.2 USA
LINE RIDER. Text in English. 1965. bi-m. membership. adv. illus. **Document type:** *Bulletin.*
Formerly: Idaho Cattleman
Published by: Idaho Cattle Association, PO Box 15397, Boise, ID 83715. TEL 208-343-1615, FAX 208-344-6695. Ed. Cathy Josling. R&P Sara Braasch. Adv. contact David Britton. Circ: 1,400 (paid).

636 FRA ISSN 0981-4183
LINEAIRES. Text in French. 11/yr. **Document type:** *Magazine, Trade.*
Published by: Editions du Boisbaudry, 13 Square du Chene Germain, Cesson Sevigne, 355773, France. TEL 33-2-99322121, http://www.editionsduboisbaudry.com. Circ: 15,000.

LIVESTOCK & GRAIN MARKET NEWS BRANCH. WEEKLY SUMMARY. see *AGRICULTURE—Feed, Flour And Grain*

636 GBR ISSN 1356-9139
LIVESTOCK AND MEAT. Text in English. 1986. m. GBP 530 domestic; GBP 559 in Europe; GBP 615 elsewhere (effective 2005). **Document type:** *Newsletter, Trade.* **Description:** Concise report on the European livestock and meat market including legislative changes, policy updates and statistics on price, consumption, slaughtering, livestock numbers and trade volumes.
Formerly: Agrafile: Livestock and Meat (0950-4958)
Published by: Agra Europe (London) Ltd. (Subsidiary of: T & F Informa plc), 80 Calverley Rd, Tunbridge Wells, Kent TN1 2UN, United Kingdom. TEL 44-1892-533813, FAX 44-1892-544895, marketing@agra-net.com, http://www.agra-net.com.

636 GBR
LIVESTOCK CROP POCKET BOOK. Text in English. a. **Document type:** *Bulletin, Academic/Scholarly.*
Published by: N I A B, Huntingdon Rd, Cambridge, CB3 0LE, United Kingdom. TEL 44-1223-276381, TELEX 817455-NIAB-G, info@niab.com, paul.nelson@niab.com, http://www.niab.com.

636 USA
LIVESTOCK: LATIN AMERICAN INDUSTRIAL REPORT✶. (Avail. for each of 22 Latin American countries) Text in English. 1985. a. USD 435; per country report.
Published by: Aquino Productions, P O Box 15760, Stamford, CT 06901-0760. Ed. Andres C Aquino.

636 658.8 USA ISSN 0024-5208
LIVESTOCK MARKET DIGEST. Text in English. 1953. w. USD 20 (effective 2005). adv. charts; mkt. **Document type:** *Newspaper.*
Indexed: BPIA.
Published by: Livestock Market Digest, Inc, PO Box 7458, Albuquerque, NM 87194. chuck@aaalivestock.com, http://aaalivestock.com. Ed. Emil Reutzel Jr. Circ: 45,000.

636 677.3 USA
LIVESTOCK, MEAT AND WOOL MARKET NEWS. Text in English. w. USD 70; USD 75 in Canada & Mexico; USD 105 elsewhere. reprint service avail. from CIS. **Document type:** *Government.*
Related titles: Microfiche ed.: (from CIS).
Indexed: AmStI.
Published by: U.S. Department Of Agriculture, Agricultural Marketing Service (Washington), Livestock & Seed Division, South Bldg, Rm 2623, Box 96456, Washington, DC 20090-6456. TEL 202-720-6231, FAX 202-690-3732. Ed. Kim R Harmon. **Subscr. to:** U.S.D.A. Agricultural Marketing Service, Livestock & Seed Division, Rm 2613 S, Box 96456, Washington, DC 20090-6456. TEL 202-245-4732, FAX 202-245-4732.

636 COL
➤ **LIVESTOCK RESEARCH FOR RURAL DEVELOPMENT (ONLINE EDITION);** the international journal for research into sustainable developing world agriculture. Text in English, Spanish. 1989. q. free (effective 2005). back issues avail. **Document type:** *Journal, Academic/Scholarly.*
Formerly: Livestock Research for Rural Development (Print Edition) (0121-3784)
Media: Online - full text.
Indexed: AEA, ASFA, AgBio, AgrForAb, AnBrAb, CPA, DSA, ESPM, FCA, FPA, ForAb, HelmAb, HerbAb, HortAb, IndVet, MaizeAb, NutrAb, OrnHort, PBA, PGegResA, PHN&I, PN&I, PollutAb, PoultAb, ProtozoAb, RDA, RM&VM, RiceAb, S&F, SIA, SeedAb, SoyAb, TDB, TriticAb, VetBull, WAE&RSA.
—BLDSC (5282.410000).
Published by: Centro para la Investigacion en Sistemas Sostenibles de Produccion Agropecuaria, Tejares San Fernando, Carrera 35a Oeste, 3-66, Apartado Aereo 20591, Cali, Valle, Colombia. TEL 57-2-8930931, FAX 57-2-8935535, lrrd@cipav.org.co, http://www.cipav.org.co/lrrd/. Ed. Thomas R Preston.

636 USA
LIVESTOCK ROUNDUP. Text in English. bi-w. free to qualified personnel (effective 2005). **Document type:** *Newspaper.*
Contact Owner: Lee Agri-Media, Inc., PO Box 239, Tekamah, Burt, NE 68061. TEL 402-374-2226, FAX 402-374-2739, jue.zink@lee.net, http://www.livestockroundup.net.

636 NLD ISSN 1871-1413
CODEN: LPSCDL
➤ **LIVESTOCK SCIENCE.** Text in English. 1974. 21/yr. EUR 1,557 in Europe to institutions; JPY 206,300 in Japan to institutions; USD 1,740 elsewhere to institutions; EUR 108 in Europe to qualified personnel; JPY 14,400 in Japan to qualified personnel; USD 120 elsewhere to qualified personnel (effective 2006). adv. bk.rev. abstr.; bibl.; illus. index. back issues avail. **Document type:** *Journal, Academic/Scholarly.* **Description:** Publishes original research papers and comprehensive reviews in the field of livestock production.
Formerly (until 2005): Livestock Production Science (0301-6226)
Related titles: Microform ed.: (from PQC); Online - full text ed.: (from EBSCO Publishing, Gale Group, IngentaConnect, ScienceDirect, Swets Information Services).
Indexed: AEA, ASCA, AbHyg, AgBio, Agr, AgrForAb, AnBrAb, BIOBASE, BIOSIS Prev, BiolAb, CurCont, DBA, DSA, FCA, FPA, FS&TA, FoVS&M, HelmAb, HerbAb, HortAb, ISR, IndVet, MEDLINE, MaizeAb, NutrAb, PBA, PHN&I, PN&I, PoultAb, ProtozoAb, RA&MP, RDA, RM&VM, RPP, RRTA, RefZh, RiceAb, S&F, SCI, SFA, SIA, SSCI, SoyAb, TDB, TriticAb, VetBull, WAE&RSA, WTA, WeedAb, WildRev.
—BLDSC (5282.350000), CASDDS, CISTI, IDS, IE, Infotrieve, ingenta, Linda Hall. **CCC.**
Published by: (European Association for Animal Production), Elsevier BV (Subsidiary of: Elsevier Science & Technology), Radarweg 29, Amsterdam, 1043 NX, Netherlands. TEL 31-20-4853911, FAX 31-20-4852457, nlinfo-f@elsevier.nl, http://www.elsevier.com/wps/find/journaldescription.cws_home/706547/description#description, http://www.elsevier.nl. Ed. J Boyazoglu.

636.2 USA
LIVESTOCK UPDATE. Text in English. 1995. m. back issues avail.
Media: Online - full text.
Published by: Virginia Cooperative Extension, 121 Hutcheson Hall, Virginia Tech 0437, Blacksburg, VA 24061-0001. FAX 800-828-1120, http://www.ext.vt.edu/.

636 USA ISSN 0162-5047
LIVESTOCK WEEKLY. Text in English. 1949. w. USD 25 (effective 2000). adv. illus. **Document type:** *Newspaper.*
Formerly: West Texas Livestock Weekly (0049-724X)
Published by: Southwest Publishers, Inc., PO Box 3306, San Angelo, TX 76902. TEL 325-949-4611, FAX 325-949-4614. Ed. Steve Kelton. Pub. Robert S Frank. Adv. contact Paula Rankin. Circ: 18,000 (paid).

636.2142 USA
LOUISIANA CATTLEMAN. Text in English. 1967. m. USD 25 to members. adv. **Document type:** *Trade.* **Description:** Provides information on current activities, research and programs related to the cattle industry both nationally and locally.
Formerly: Louisiana Cattleman - Louisiana Dairyman
Published by: Louisiana Cattlemen's Association, 4921 I 10 Frontage Rd, Port Allen, LA 70767. TEL 504-343-3491, FAX 504-336-0002. Ed. Sharon Lytle Hoffeld. Adv. contact Bob Felknor. B&W page USD 490, color page USD 1,150; trim 10 x 7.25. Circ: 5,500.

636.7 USA ISSN 0146-9436
M A S K C KOMONDOR NEWS. Text in English. 1973. bi-m. USD 22; USD 25 foreign (effective 1996). adv. bk.rev. back issues avail. **Document type:** *Newsletter.* **Description:** Reports on the Hungarian Komondor, a rare and endangered breed of livestock guard dog.
Published by: Middle Atlantic States Komondor Club, Inc., 102 Russell Rd, Princeton, NJ 08540. TEL 609-924-0199. Ed. Gail Sheddy. Adv. contact Joy C Levy. Circ: 350.

636 AUS
M L A ANNUAL REPORT; laying the foundations. Text in English. a. AUD 15 (effective 2000). **Document type:** *Corporate.*
Formerly (until 1999): A M L C Annual Report
Published by: Meat and Livestock Australia Ltd., Level 1, 165 Walker St., North Sydney, NSW 2089, Australia. TEL 61-2-9463-9333, FAX 61-2-9463-9393, http://www.mla.com.au. Ed., Pub. Lucy Hull. Circ: 9,000.

636.40099 AUS ISSN 1324-9177
MANIPULATING PIG PRODUCTION. Text in English. 1987. biennial. **Document type:** *Proceedings, Trade.*
—BLDSC (5360.324000), IE.
Published by: Australasian Pig Science Association (Inc.), APSA Memberships: Dr Bruce Mullan, Animal Research and Development Services, Agriculture Western Australia, Locked Bag No. 4,, Bentley Delivery Centre, W.A. 6983, Australia. TEL 61-3-94596720, FAX 61-3-94598887, mail@parexcellence.com.au, http://www.apsa.asn.au/.

636 363.728 USA
MANURE MATTERS. Text in English. m. **Document type:** *Newsletter, Academic/Scholarly.*
Published by: Livestock Environmental Issues Committee, c/o Chris Henry, 217 LW Chase Hall, University of Nebraska, Lincoln, NE 68583. TEL 402-472-6529, chenry1@unl.edu, http://manure.unl.edu/.

636 363.728 CAN
MANURE MATTERS. Text in English. 2002 (Dec.). q. CND 25 (effective 2004). **Document type:** *Journal, Trade.*
Published by: Issues Ink, 203-897 Corydon Ave, Winnipeg, MB R3M 0W7, Canada. TEL 204-453-1965, FAX 204-475-5247, issues@issuesink.com, http://www.issuesink.com. Circ: 10,000.

636 USA
MARCHIGIANA NEWS. Text in English. 1984. bi-m. USD 10 (effective 2000). adv. back issues avail. **Document type:** *Newsletter.* **Description:** For Marchigiana cattle breeders - information on the breed, upcoming events, latest happenings.
Published by: American International Marchigiana Society, Marky Cattle Association, Box 198, Walton, KS 67151-0198. TEL 316-837-3303. Ed., Pub., Adv. contact Martie Knudsen.

636.008 338.4 GBR ISSN 0140-6388
MEAT AND LIVESTOCK COMMISSION. ECONOMICS SERVICES. MEAT DEMAND TRENDS. Text in English. 1976. 4/yr. GBP 135 domestic; GBP 155 foreign (effective 2001 - 2002). charts; illus.; mkt.; stat. 40 p./no. 1 cols./p.; back issues avail. **Document type:** *Trade.* **Description:** Provides analysis and articles on all aspects of consumption and demand for meat and meat products in Europe.
Formerly (until 1993): Meat and Livestock Commission. Economic Information Service. Meat Demand Trends
Indexed: AbHyg, AgBio, FS&TA, IndVet, PN&I, PoultAb, VetBull, WAE&RSA.
—BLDSC (5413.690100).
Published by: (Economic Services), Meat and Livestock Commission, Winterhill House, Snowdon Dr, PO Box 44, Milton Keynes, Bucks MK6 1AX, United Kingdom. TEL 44-1908-844396, FAX 44-1908-609221, vikki_gatt@mlc.org.uk. Ed. Sue Fisher. R&P Jenny Spencer TEL 44-1908-844330. Adv. contact Vikki Gatt.

636 GBR ISSN 0263-2217
MEAT AND LIVESTOCK COMMISSION. INTERNATIONAL MEAT MARKET REVIEW. Text in English. 1968. s-a. GBP 89; GBP 100 foreign (effective 2001 - 2002). charts; stat. 88 p./no. 1 cols./p.; back issues avail. **Document type:** *Trade.*
Formerly: Meat and Livestock Commission, Bucks, England. International Market Survey (0047-634X)
Indexed: PoultAb, WAE&RSA.
Published by: Meat and Livestock Commission, Winterhill House, Snowdon Dr, PO Box 44, Milton Keynes, Bucks MK6 1AX, United Kingdom. TEL 44-1908-844396, FAX 44-1908-609221. Ed., R&P Jenny Spencer TEL 44-1908-844330. Adv. contact Vikki Gatt. Circ: 1,000.

636 USA ISSN 0738-6745
HD9413
MEAT & POULTRY DIRECTORY. Text in English. 1984. a. USD 125 (effective 2005). adv. **Document type:** *Directory, Trade.* **Description:** Contains 8,000 listings of meat and poultry producers, processors, brokers, distributors, renderers, and slaughterers.
Published by: Urner Barry Publications, Inc., PO Box 389, Toms River, NJ 08754-0389. TEL 800-932-0617, mail@urnerbarry.com, http://www.urnerbarry.com. Ed. Joe Soja. Adv. contact Danielle Klem. Circ: 2,000 (paid).

354.59 USA
MEAT AND POULTRY INSPECTION REGULATIONS; meat inspection, poultry inspection, rabbit inspection, voluntary inspection and certificate service of meat and poultry, humane slaughter of livestock. Text in English. 1990. base vol. plus m. updates. looseleaf. USD 297 (effective 2001); USD 290 foreign (effective 1995). **Document type:** *Government.* **Description:** Publishes the regulations for slaughter and processing of livestock and poultry, as well as certain voluntary services for more humane slaughter.

A

Published by: U.S. Department of Agriculture, Food Safety and Inspection Service, Rm 1140, South Bldg, 14th and Independence Ave, SW, Washington, DC 20250. TEL 202-720-2109, FAX 202-690-3023, http://www.fsis.usda.gov. **Subscr. to:** U.S. Government Printing Office, Superintendent of Documents, PO Box 371954, Pittsburgh, PA 15250-7954. TEL 202-512-1800, FAX 202-512-2250, orders@gpo.gov, http://www.access.gpo.gov.

636 338.1 NZL ISSN 0112-739X
HD9436.N48
MEAT AND WOOL BOARDS' ECONOMIC SERVICE. ANNUAL REVIEW OF THE NEW ZEALAND SHEEP & BEEF INDUSTRY; review of physical and economic conditions in sheepfarming in New Zealand. Text in English. 1952. a. NZD 150 (effective 2001); or on exchange basis. **Document type:** *Trade.*
Formerly: Meat and Wool Boards' Economic Service. Annual Review of the Sheep Industry (0078-0138)
Indexed: AnBrAb, WAE&RSA.
Published by: Meat and Wool Boards' Economic Service, P.O. Box 5179, Wellington, New Zealand. TEL 64-4-472-2178, FAX 64-4-4712173, info@nzmeat-wool.co.nz, http://www.nzmeat-wool.co.nz. Circ: 2,500.

636.3 NZL
MEAT AND WOOL BOARDS' ECONOMIC SERVICE. GOAT INDUSTRY LIVESTOCK PRODUCTION AND RETURNS INFORMATION. Text in English. a. (Nov.). NZD 70 domestic; NZD 75 foreign (effective 2001). **Description:** Includes item series of goat numbers, herd size and region statistic, farm types with goat herds and physical and financial data for sheep and beef farms with goats. Slaughtering and production patterns over time are recorded on an island and New Zealand basis. Farm gate returns for goat products are noted together with FOB receipts and export volumes.
Published by: Meat and Wool Boards' Economic Service, P.O. Box 5179, Wellington, New Zealand. TEL 64-4-472-2178, FAX 64-4-4712173, info@nzmeat-wool.co.nz, http://www.nzmeat-wool.co.nz.

636.3 NZL
MEAT AND WOOL BOARDS' ECONOMIC SERVICE. LAMB CROP. Text in English. a. (Mid. Nov.). NZD 175 domestic; NZD 180 foreign (effective 2001). **Description:** Covers the total number of ewes mated, lambing percentage, by region and island and a forecast of the export lamb slaughter for the current year. General comments of the overall lambing, lamb thrift, drafting, schedule comments are recorded. Regional production area reports are included.
Published by: Meat and Wool Boards' Economic Service, P.O. Box 5179, Wellington, New Zealand. TEL 64-4-472-2178, FAX 64-4-4712173, info@nzmeat-wool.co.nz, http://www.nzmeat-wool.co.nz.

636 NZL
MEAT AND WOOL BOARDS' ECONOMIC SERVICE. STOCK AND WEATHER. Text in English. bi-m. NZD 135 domestic; NZD 150 foreign (effective 2001). **Description:** Contains regional reports cover weather, feed, stock condition, health and performance and stock values.
Published by: Meat and Wool Boards' Economic Service, P.O. Box 5179, Wellington, New Zealand. TEL 64-4-472-2178, FAX 64-4-4712173, info@nzmeat-wool.co.nz, http://www.nzmeat-wool.co.nz.

636 USA
MEAT GOAT MONTHLY NEWS. Text in English. 1994. m. USD 27 domestic; USD 47 in Canada & Mexico (effective 2005). **Document type:** *Magazine, Trade.*
Formerly: Boer Trader & Meat Goat News
Contact: Scott Campbell, P.O. Box 2678, San Angelo, TX 76902. TEL 915-655-4434, FAX 915-658-8250, info@ranchmagazine.com, http://www.ranchmagazine.com. Ed. Gary Cutrer. Pub. Scott Campbell. Circ: 2,500 (paid and free).

636 NLD ISSN 0924-7068
MEAT INTERNATIONAL. Text in English. 1991. 10/yr. USD 115 (effective 2000). adv. illus. **Document type:** *Trade.* **Description:** Covers all aspects of the international meat industry.
—BLDSC (5413.735500), IE, ingenta.
Published by: Reed Business Information bv (Subsidiary of: Reed Business), Hanzestraat 1, Doetinchem, 7006 RH, Netherlands. TEL 31-314-349911, FAX 31-314-343839, info@reedbusiness.nl, http://www.reedbusiness.nl. Adv. contact Ramon Portocarrero. B&W page USD 4,595; trim 276 x 204. Circ: 21,000.

636 330.9 USA ISSN 0889-3608
MEAT SHEET. Text in English. 1974. d. looseleaf. USD 400 (effective 2000). adv. back issues avail. **Document type:** *Newsletter.* **Description:** Gives prices of wholesale beef, pork, and poultry cuts used by meat packers, processors, and retailers.
Address: PO Box 124, Westmont, IL 60559-0124. TEL 630-963-2252, FAX 630-963-2980, meatsheet@aol.com. Ed. Deborah A Ash. Pub. Tiffany M Albanos. Adv. contact William Albanos. Circ: 2,000.

636 AUS ISSN 1442-9128
MEAT THE MARKET. Text in English. 1999. w. looseleaf. AUD 150 domestic to non-members; AUD 850 foreign to non-members; AUD 220 domestic to non-members with Market Statistics; AUD 1,100 foreign to non-members with Market Statistics; AUD 110 domestic to non-members Market Statistics only; AUD 400 foreign to non-members Market Statistics only (effective 2000); free to members. mkt.; stat.; tr.lit. back issues avail. **Document type:** *Newsletter, Trade.* **Description:** Provides weekly market analysis.
Related titles: Fax ed.: AUD 270 domestic to non-members; AUD 1,200 foreign to non-members; AUD 130 to members; AUD 380 domestic to non-members with Market Statistics; AUD 1,600 foreign to non-members with Market Statistics; AUD 190 to members with Market Statistics; AUD 180 domestic to non-members Market Statistics only; AUD 600 foreign to non-members Market Statistics only; AUD 60 to members Market Statistics only (effective 2000); Online - full content ed.
—CISTI.
Published by: Meat & Livestock Australia Ltd., Locked Bag 991, North Sydney, NSW, Australia. TEL 61-2-9463-9163, FAX 61-2-9954-0752, http://www.mla.coa.au. Ed. Peter Weeks. Circ: 1,800.

636.2 MEX ISSN 0047-7036
MEXICO GANADERO✶. Text in Spanish. 1957. m. MXP 150. adv. bk.rev.
Published by: Confederacion Nacional Ganadera, Calz.Mariano Escobedo No. 714, Col. Anzures, Mexico, D.F., 11590, Mexico. TEL 52-5-2542952, FAX 52-5-2541953, http://www.cng.com.mx/. Circ: 25,000.

636.2 USA
MIDWEST GALLOWAY NEWS. Text in English. 1994. q. illus. **Document type:** *Newsletter, Trade.* **Description:** Contains news of interest to breeders and keepers of Galloway cattle.
Address: N4265 County Rd H, Elkhorn, WI 53121. TEL 414-723-3276, kallimon@elknet.net, http://www.galloway-world.org/agba/midwest.htm. Ed., Pub. Zoe Siperly.

636.2 ITA
LE MIGLIORI PRODUZIONI. Text in Italian. a.?. **Document type:** *Magazine, Trade.* **Description:** Presents the data relative to the cows and herds which obtained the best productions during the year.
Published by: Associazione Nazionale Allevatori Razza Bruna, Localita Ferlina 204, Bussolengo, VR 37012, Italy. TEL 39-045-6701990, FAX 39-045-7156655, anarb@anarb.it, http://www.anarb.it.

MILCH - FETTWAREN - EIER - HANDEL. see *FOOD AND FOOD INDUSTRIES*

636.2 DEU ISSN 0941-1348
MILCHRIND; Journal fuer Zuechtung, Biotechnologie und Leistungspruefung. Text in German. 1977. q. EUR 26.60 domestic; EUR 28.80 foreign; EUR 7 newsstand/cover (effective 2003). adv. **Document type:** *Journal, Trade.*
Formerly: Deutsche Schwarzbunte
Published by: (Deutscher Holstein Verband e.V.), Landwirtschaftsverlag GmbH, Huelsebrockstr 2, Muenster, 48165, Germany. TEL 49-2501-801-0, FAX 49-2501-801-204, mrservice@landwirtschaftsverlag.com, zentrale@lv-h.de, http://www.lv-h.de. Ed. Christine Topf. Adv. contact Paul Pankoke. B&W page EUR 3,452, color page EUR 5,870. Circ: 38,200 (paid and controlled).

636.234 USA ISSN 1073-9394
SF199.S56
MILKING SHORTHORN JOURNAL. Text in English. 1919. bi-m. USD 20 domestic; USD 30 foreign (effective 2005). adv. bk.rev. charts; illus. **Document type:** *Magazine, Trade.* **Description:** Discusses cattle breeding, society programs, articles relating to dairying, production achievements and state association news.
Former titles (until 1992): Journal of the Milking Shorthorn and Illawarra Breeds (0145-8264); (until 1975): Milking Shorthorn Journal (0026-4229)
—CISTI, Linda Hall.
Published by: American Milking Shorthorn Society, 800 Pleasant St, Beloit, WI 53511-5456. TEL 608-365-3332, FAX 608-365-6644, milkshorthorns@tds.net, http://www.milkingshorthorn.com. adv.: B&W page USD 265. Circ: 740.

636 USA ISSN 1058-7063
MINIATURE DONKEY TALK. Text in English. 1987. bi-m. USD 32; USD 5 newsstand/cover; USD 55 foreign (effective 2000). adv. bk.rev. illus. back issues avail. **Document type:** *Trade.* **Description:** Covers health, management, veterinary, and training topics.
Published by: Pheasant Meadow Farm, Inc., 1338 Hughes Shop Rd, Westminster, MD 21158. TEL 410-875-0118, FAX 410-857-9145, minidonk@qis.net, http://www.qis.net/~minidonk/donktext.htm. Ed., Pub., R&P Bonnie Gross. Adv. contact Mike Gross. B&W page USD 220, color page USD 350; trim 6.75 x 9.5. Circ: 5,700 (paid).

636.2 USA ISSN 0192-3056
MISSOURI BEEF CATTLEMAN. Text in English. 1971. m. USD 50 membership (effective 2005). adv. **Document type:** *Magazine, Trade.*
Published by: Missouri Cattlemen's Association, 2306 Bluff Creek Dr, #100, Columbia, MO 65201. TEL 573-499-9162, FAX 573-499-9167, mobeef@tfsnet., http://www.mocattle.org. Ed., Pub. Andy Atzenweiler. Adv. contact Larry Atzenweiler. B&W page USD 830, color page USD 1,160; trim 10.88 x 8.5. Circ: 6,200 (controlled).

MISSOURI. DEPARTMENT OF AGRICULTURE. WEEKLY MARKET SUMMARY. see *AGRICULTURE*

630 RUS ISSN 0026-9034
MOLOCHNOE I MYASNOE SKOTOVODSTVO. Text in Russian. 1956. bi-m. USD 112 foreign (effective 2003). bk.rev. bibl.; illus.; stat. index.
Indexed: AnBrAb, ChemAb, DSA, FS&TA, NutrAb, RefZh.
—CISTI, East View.
Address: Sadovaya-Spasskaya 18, Moscow, 107807, Russian Federation. TEL 7-095-2071946, FAX 7-095-2072870. Ed. Vadim V Korzhenevskii. Circ: 4,000. **Dist. by:** M K - Periodica, ul Gilyarovskogo 39, Moscow 129110, Russian Federation. TEL 7-095-2845008, FAX 7-095-2813798, info@periodicals.ru, http://www.mkniga.ru; **US dist. addr.:** East View Information Services, 3020 Harbor Ln. N., Minneapolis, MN 55447. TEL 612-550-0961.

636 ESP ISSN 1577-3167
MONOGRAFIAS I N I A. GANADERA. Text in Spanish. 1973. irreg. price varies. **Document type:** *Monographic series, Government.*
Supersedes in part (in 1998): Instituto Nacional de Investigaciones Agrarias. Coleccion Monografias (0210-3354)
Indexed: AnBrAb, IECT.
—CINDOC, CISTI.
Published by: (Spain. Instituto Nacional de Investigacion y Tecnologia Agraria y Alimentaria), Ministerio de Agricultura Pesca y Alimentacion, Centro de Publicaciones, Paseo Infanta Isabel 1, Madrid, 28014, Spain. TEL 34-91-3475550, FAX 34-91-3475722, mllopisj@mapya.es, http://www.mapya.es.

636 USA
MONTANA FARMER - STOCKMAN. Text in English. 1913. 14/yr. USD 21.95 in state; USD 30 out of state (effective 2001). adv. bk.rev. stat. **Document type:** *Trade.*
Former titles: Montana Farmer (1073-1458); (until 1993): Montana Farmer - Stockman (1041-1674)
Published by: Farm Progress Companies, 191 S Gary Ave, Carol Stream, IL 60188. TEL 630-462-2892, FAX 630-462-2885, swyant@farmprogress.com, http://www.farmprogress.com/. Ed. Lisa Schmidt TEL 406-287-2271. Adv. contact Don Tourte. B&W page USD 3,000, color page USD 8,400. Circ: 16,458 (paid).

636 USA ISSN 0047-7990
MONTANA STOCKGROWER. Text in English. 1910. 2/yr. free membership (effective 2005). adv. bk.rev. **Document type:** *Magazine, Trade.* **Description:** Contains market information, industry issues and regulatory information, and general background of Montana's beef cattle industry.
Published by: Montana Stockgrowers Association, 420 N California St, Helena, MT 59601. TEL 406-442-3420, FAX 406-449-5105, msga@mtbeef.org, msgahelena@aol.com, http://www.mtbeef.org. Ed. Kelli Butenko. adv.: B&W page USD 400, color page USD 800; trim 11 x 8.5. Circ: 1,900 (controlled).

636.3 USA ISSN 0027-0024
CODEN: MWOGA
MONTANA WOOL GROWER. Text in English. 1928. 4/yr. USD 50 (effective 2005). adv. stat.; tr.lit. index. **Document type:** *Magazine, Trade.* **Description:** Provides information relating to the sheep industry, especially in Montana.
Indexed: BiolAb.
Published by: Montana Wool Growers Association, PO Box 1693, Helena, MT 59624. TEL 406-442-1330, FAX 406-449-8606, woolymwga@aol.com, http://www.mtsheep.org. Pub., Adv. contact Robert N. Gilbert. Circ: 1,400 (paid and free).

MONTHLY PRICE REVIEW. see *FOOD AND FOOD INDUSTRIES*

THE MOOSLETTER. see *HOBBIES*

636 USA
MULES AND MORE. Text in English. 1990. m. USD 18 domestic; USD 30 foreign (effective 2000). adv. bk.rev. **Document type:** *Trade.* **Description:** Carries mule show results, training, calendar of events, sales for mule wagon and harness enthusiasts.
Address: PO Box 460, Bland, MO 65014. TEL 573-646-3934, FAX 573-646-3407, mules@socket.net, http://www.mulesandmore.com. Ed., Pub., R&P Sue Cole. Adv. contact Liz Maddison. Circ: 7,600 (paid).

636 ESP ISSN 0214-9192
MUNDO GANADERO. Text in Spanish; Summaries in Spanish. 1990. 11/yr. EUR 65 domestic; EUR 97 in Europe; EUR 111 elsewhere (effective 2005). adv. bibl. **Document type:** *Magazine, Trade.* **Description:** For stock breeders, distributors of zoo sanitary products, veterinarians, and agricultural experts. Includes national and international news concerning livestock.

Indexed: AEA, AgBio, AnBrAb, BioCN&I, DSA, FCA, HelmAb, HerbAb, HortAb, IECT, IndVet, MaizeAb, NutrAb, PN&I, PoultAb, ProtozoAb, RDA, RM&VM, S&F, SIA, SoyAb, VetBull, WAE&RSA.
—BLDSC (5983.853000), CINDOC.
Published by: Eumedia S.A., Claudio Coello 16, 1o, Madrid, 28001, Spain. TEL 34-91-4264430, FAX 34-91-5753297, http://www.eumedia.es/revistas/infor_mg.asp. Ed. Dr. Carlos Buxade Carbo. Adv. contact Julia Dominguez. page EUR 985; trim 23 x 30.5. Circ: 14,500.

MYASNAYA INDUSTRIYA. see *FOOD AND FOOD INDUSTRIES*

637.5 GBR ISSN 1461-1295
N F U NATIONAL WEEKLY EGG MARKET INTELLIGENCE REPORT. Text in English. 1990. w. GBP 45 (effective 1999). adv. mkt.; stat. back issues avail. **Document type:** *Trade.* **Description:** Weekly price information and industry news.
Media: Fax. **Related titles:** Fax ed.
Published by: National Farmers Union, Agriculture House, 164 Shaftesbury Ave, London, WC2H 8HL, United Kingdom. TEL 44-20-73317200, FAX 44-20-73317401, NFU@nfuonline.com, http://www.nfu.org.uk/. Ed. Paul Cooper. R&P, Adv. contact John Smith. Circ: 5,000 (paid).

636.3 AUS ISSN 1033-3029
N.S.W. FARMERS NEWS. (New South Wales) Text in English. 1969 (vol.18). m. membership only. adv. charts; illus. **Document type:** *Newsletter, Trade.* **Description:** Focuses on agriculture, including sheep, cattle, pigs, goats, grains, horticulture and agricultural economics.
Formerly (until Jan. 1990): Livestock and Grain Producers; Incorporates: Muster (0027-4925); United Farmer
Published by: N.S.W. Farmers Association, GPO Box 1068, Sydney, NSW 2001, Australia. TEL 61-2-92511700, FAX 61-2-92315249. Ed., R&P, Adv. contact Donna Gersbach. B&W page AUD 36. Circ: 20,000.

636.2142 CZE ISSN 0027-8068
NAS CHOV; casopis pro zivocisnou vyrobu. Text in Czech; Summaries in English, German, Russian. 1940. m. CZK 48, USD 25.20.
Incorporates: Chov Hospodarskych Zvierat (0323-1488)
Indexed: AnBrAb, DSA, NutrAb.
—CISTI.
Published by: Strategie, spol. s r.o., Nas Chov, Elisky Peskove 13, Prague 5, 150 00, Czech Republic. Ed. Jiri Matous. **Subscr. to:** Artia, Ve Smeckach 30, Prague 1 111 27, Czech Republic.

NATIONAL ASSOCIATION OF ANIMAL BREEDERS. ANNUAL PROCEEDINGS. see *AGRICULTURE—Dairying And Dairy Products*

636 USA
NATIONAL CARLOT MEAT TRADE REPORT. Text in English. d. USD 290; USD 315 in Canada & Mexico; USD 460 elsewhere. **Document type:** *Government.* **Description:** Contains carcass information and data on livestock species.
Published by: (Livestock & Seed Division), U.S. Department of Agriculture, Agricultural Marketing Service (Greely), 711 O St., Greely, CO 80631. Ed. Mike Erwin. **Subscr. to:** U.S.D.A. Agricultural Marketing Service, Livestock & Seed Division, Rm 2613 S, Box 96456, Washington, DC 20090-6456. FAX 202-245-4732.

636 USA ISSN 0885-7679
NATIONAL CATTLEMEN. Text in English. 1985. 8/yr. free to members (effective 2005). adv. **Document type:** *Magazine, Trade.*
Published by: National Cattlemen's Beef Association, 9110 E Nichols Ave, Ste 300, Centennial, CO 80112-3450. TEL 303-694-0305, http://www.beefusa.org. Ed., R&P Curt Olson. Adv. contact Jill DeLucero. color page USD 3,565. Circ: 38,000 (paid and controlled).

636.9322 USA
NATIONAL FEDERATION OF FLEMISH GIANT RABBIT BREEDERS. QUARTERLY NEWSLETTER. Text in English. q. USD 10 to members. **Document type:** *Newsletter.*
Published by: National Federation of Flemish Giant Rabbit Breeders, 233 Aultman Ave, N W, Canton, OH 44708. TEL 330-477-1382. Ed., Pub. Roger E Dent. Circ: 500.

636 USA
NATIONAL HEREFORD HOG ANNUAL NEWSLETTER. Text in English. 1942. a. looseleaf. free. adv. back issues avail. **Document type:** *Newsletter, Academic/Scholarly.*
Published by: National Hereford Hog Record Association, 22405 480 Ave, Flandreau, SD 57028. TEL 605-997-2116, FAX 605-997-2116. Ed. Ruby Schrecengost. Circ: 300.

636.4 USA ISSN 0027-9447
CODEN: NAHFAP
NATIONAL HOG FARMER. Text in English. 1956. m. USD 115 domestic; USD 127 in Canada; USD 139 elsewhere (effective 2005). adv. bk.rev. illus. back issues avail.; reprints avail. **Document type:** *Magazine, Trade.* **Description:** Focuses on swine; covers the entire pork production industry, from on-farm hog production to the marketing, processing and retailing of pork.
Related titles: Online - full text ed.: (from bigchalk, EBSCO Publishing, Gale Group, H.W. Wilson, LexisNexis, O C L C Online Computer Library Center, Inc., ProQuest Information & Learning).
Indexed: ABIn, B&AI, F&GI.
—CISTI. **CCC.**
Published by: Primedia Business Magazines & Media, Inc. (Subsidiary of: Primedia, Inc.), 7900 International Dr, Ste 300, Minneapolis, MN 55425. TEL 952-851-9329, FAX 952-851-4601, nhf@primediabusiness.com, inquiries@primediabusiness.com, http://nationalhogfarmer.com, http://www.primediabusiness.com. Ed. Dale Miller. Pub. Ron Sorensen. Circ: 35,000 (controlled). **Subscr. to:** PO Box 12993, Overland Park, KS 66282-2993. TEL 800-441-0294, FAX 913-967-1331.

636.3 USA
NATIONAL INSTITUTE OF ANIMAL AGRICULTURE. ANNUAL MEETING PROCEEDINGS. Text in English. a.
—BLDSC (1087.836900).
Published by: National Institute of Animal Agriculture, 1910 Lyda Drive, Bowling Green, KY 42104. TEL 502-782-9798, FAX 502-782-0188, sheep2goat@aol.com, http://www.lcionline.org.

636.3 USA
NATIONAL LAMB SUMMARY. Text in English. w. USD 70; USD 75 in Canada & Mexico; USD 105 elsewhere. **Document type:** *Government.*
Published by: U.S. Department Of Agriculture, Livestock & Grain Market News Branch, 201 Walnut St, Rm 767, Des Moines, IA 50309-2106. http://www.ams.usda.gov/lsg/mncs/pdf%5Fweekly/compweekly.htm.

636.5 USA
NATIONAL POULTRY NEWS. Text in English. 1980. q. USD 10; USD 2 newsstand/cover (effective 2003). adv. back issues avail. **Document type:** *Newspaper, Consumer.* **Description:** Promotes poultry, exotic fowl and exotic animals.
Formerly (until 1988): Hen House Herald
Address: 207 13th Ave., Brookings, SD 57006-2519. TEL 864-855-0140, nationalpoultrynews@yahoo.com, frizzlebird@yahoo.com, http://www.nationalpoultrynews.com, http://www.webcom.com/777/npn.html. Ed., Pub., R&P, Adv. contact Glenda L Heywood.

630 677.3 USA ISSN 1066-0593
NATIONAL WOOL MARKET REVIEW. Variant title: Wool Market News. Text in English. 33/yr. USD 40; USD 45 in Canada & Mexico; USD 75 elsewhere. back issues avail.; reprint service avail. from CIS. **Document type:** *Government.*
Related titles: Microfiche ed.: (from CIS).
Indexed: AmStI.
Published by: (Livestock & Seed Division), U.S. Department of Agriculture, Agricultural Marketing Service (Greely), 711 O St., Greely, CO 80631. TEL 970-353-9750, FAX 970-353-9790. **Subscr. to:** U.S.D.A. Agricultural Marketing Service, Livestock & Seed Division, Rm 2613 S, Box 96456, Washington, DC 20090-6456. FAX 202-245-4732.

636.2142 FIN ISSN 1238-268X
NAUTA/CATTLE. Text in Finnish; Summaries in Swedish. 1971. 5/yr. EUR 49 (effective 2005). adv. bk.rev. charts; illus.; stat. **Document type:** *Magazine, Trade.* **Description:** Covers cattle breeding and care.
Formerly (until 1995): Nautakarja (0028-131X); Which was formed by the merger of (1927-1971): Finlands Ayrshireboskap (1235-242X); (1927-1971): Suomen Ayrshirekarja (1235-2411); (1947-1971): Suomen Karja (0371-4128); Which incorporated (1947-1963): Finsk Boskap (1235-2403)
Published by: Suomen Kotielainjalostusosuuskunta/Finnish Animal Breeding Association - FABA, PO Box 40, Vantaa, 01301, Finland. TEL 358-20-7472020, FAX 358-20-7472021, toimitus@faba.fi, http://www.faba.fi/lehdet/nauta/. Ed. Anita Lampinen. adv.: B&W page EUR 1,450, color page EUR 2,300; 185 x 265. Circ: 13,000.

636 ESP ISSN 0214-6401
NAVARRA AGRARIA; revista tecnica de agricultura, ganaderia y montes. Text in Spanish. 1985. bi-m. EUR 15.93 Sat. (effective 2004). **Document type:** *Journal, Government.*
Indexed: IECT.
—CINDOC.
Published by: (Gobierno de Navarra, Departamento de Agricultura, Ganaderia y Montes), Gobierno de Navarra, Fondo de Publicaciones, Navas de Tolosa 21, Pamplona, Navarra 31002, Spain. TEL 34-9848-427121, FAX 34-9848-427123, fondo.publicaciones@cfnavarra.es, http://www.navarra.es. Circ: 165,000.

636.2 USA ISSN 1062-8274
NEBRASKA CATTLEMAN. Text in English. 1944. m. USD 50 (effective 2005). adv. **Document type:** *Magazine, Trade.* **Description:** Covers production and marketing of beef cattle, legislative action affecting the industry, and activities sponsored by the organization.
Published by: Nebraska Cattlemen, Inc., 134 S 13th St, Ste 900, Lincoln, NE 68508-1917. TEL 402-475-2333, FAX 402-475-0822, http://www.nebraskacattleman.com. Ed. Mike Fitzgerald. Adv. contact Steve Ditmer. Circ: 9,040.

636 340 USA
NEBRASKA LIVESTOCK BRAND BOOK. Text in English. 1908. quadrennial. USD 40.20.
Published by: Nebraska Brand Committee, PO Box 1, Alliance, NE 69301. TEL 308-763-2930, FAX 308-763-2934. Circ: 500.

636.2 USA ISSN 0047-9489
THE NEVADA RANCHER. Text in English. 1971. m. USD 15.98 (effective 2005). adv. bk.rev. illus. back issues avail. **Document type:** *Magazine, Trade.* **Description:** Provides for the agricultural community of Nevada and neighboring states.
Related titles: Microfilm ed.: (from LIB).
Published by: Emigrant Trails Publishing, Inc., 1475 Cornell Ave., Ste 500, Lovelock, NV 89419-0620. TEL 775-273-7245, FAX 775-273-0500, therancher@nevadarancher.com, rminer@nevadarancher.com, http://www.nevadarancher.com. Pub., Adv. contact Gwen Carter. B&W page USD 752. Circ: 3,500 (paid).

636.2 USA
NEW MEXICO STOCKMAN. Text in English. 1935. m. USD 15.95; USD 2 newsstand/cover (effective 2005). adv. bk.rev. **Document type:** *Magazine, Trade.*
Published by: (New Mexico Cattle Growers Association), Charles R. Stocks Co., 9436 Rio Grande Blvd N W, Albuquerque, NM 87114. TEL 505-243-9515, FAX 505-998-6236, chuck@aaalivestock.com, http://www.aaalivestock.com. Ed., Pub. Charles Stocks. Circ: 10,799 (paid). **Co-sponsors:** New Mexico Wool Growers; New Mexico Horse Council.

636.2 NZL ISSN 1170-2915
THE NEW ZEALAND ANGUS CATTLEMAN. Text in English. 1990. a. NZD 50 to members (effective 2000). adv. **Document type:** *Trade.* **Description:** Covers beef industry in general.
Published by: New Zealand Angus Association Inc., P.O. Box 503, 52 Kimbotton Rd, Felding, New Zealand. TEL 64-6-3234484, FAX 64-6-3233878. Ed. Christine Bristol. adv.: B&W page NZD 695, color page NZD 895.

636 NZL ISSN 0111-3976
NEW ZEALAND SOCIETY OF ANIMAL PRODUCTION. OCCASIONAL PUBLICATION. Text in English. 1972. irreg. price varies. **Document type:** *Academic/Scholarly.*
Indexed: AgBio, AnBrAb, DSA.
Published by: New Zealand Society of Animal Production, c/o AgResearch Ruakura, Private Bag 3123, Hamilton, New Zealand. TEL 64-7-8569150, FAX 64-7-8569150, nzsap.animal@xtra.co.nz, http://nzsap.org.nz.

636 NZL ISSN 0370-2731
CODEN: PZAPAD
NEW ZEALAND SOCIETY OF ANIMAL PRODUCTION. PROCEEDINGS. Text in English. 1941. a. price varies. **Document type:** *Proceedings, Academic/Scholarly.*
Related titles: CD-ROM ed.
Indexed: AEA, AbHyg, AgBio, AnBrAb, BIOSIS Prev, BioCN&I, BiolAb, DSA, FCA, FS&TA, ForAb, HelmAb, HerbAb, HortAb, I&DA, IndVet, MaizeAb, NutrAb, PBA, PHN&I, PN&I, PoultAb, RA&MP, RDA, RM&VM, RPP, S&F, SFA, SIA, SoyAb, TDB, TriticAb, VetBull, WAE&RSA, WeedAb, WildRev, ZooRec.
—BLDSC (6774.300000), CASDDS, IE, ingenta, Linda Hall. **CCC.**
Published by: New Zealand Society of Animal Production, c/o AgResearch Ruakura, Private Bag 3123, Hamilton, New Zealand. TEL 64-7-8569150, FAX 64-7-8569150, nzsap.animal@xtra.co.nz, http://nzsap.org.nz/sap6.html. Circ: 1,000.

636 CAN ISSN 0228-1023
NIAGARA FARMERS' MONTHLY. Text in English. 1972. 11/yr. USD 15. **Description:** Covers the Niagara peninsula; editorial content provides information on new and up-to-date methods in poultry, beef, pork, fruit farming, local interest stories, and information on new machinery.
—CISTI.
Address: 131 College St, P O Box 52, Smithville, ON L0R 2A0, Canada. TEL 416-957-3751, FAX 416-957-0088. Ed. Ivan G Carruthers. Circ: 15,200.

636 NGA ISSN 0189-0514
CODEN: JAPRDQ
JOURNAL OF ANIMAL PRODUCTION RESEARCH. Abbreviated title: N A P R I Journal. Text in English. 1981. s-a. USD 90 per issue (effective 2003). adv. bk.rev. cum.index. back issues avail.; reprints avail. **Document type:** *Journal, Academic/Scholarly.*
Indexed: Agr, PoultAb.
Published by: National Animal Production Research Institute, Ahmadu Bello University, PMB 1096, Zaria, Kaduna, Nigeria. napri@inet-global.com. Ed. L O Eduvie. Circ: 1,000.

636 NGA ISSN 0331-2062
CODEN: NJAPDI
➤ **NIGERIAN JOURNAL OF ANIMAL PRODUCTION.** Text in English. 1974. s-a. NGN 5,050 domestic to individuals; USD 105 foreign to individuals; NGN 1,000 to students (effective 2003). adv. bk.rev. 100 p./no. 2 cols./p.; back issues avail. **Document type:** *Journal, Academic/Scholarly.*
Indexed: AgrForAb, AnBrAb, DSA, ForAb, HerbAb, IndVet, MaizeAb, NutrAb, PoultAb, ProtozoAb, RM&VM, SeedAb, SoyAb, VetBull, WAE&RSA.

A

Published by: Nigerian Society for Animal Production, c/o University of Agriculture, Department of Animal Nutrition, PMB 2240, Abeokuta, Ogun, Nigeria. TEL 234-39245171, FAX 234-39243045, oduguwa2002@yahoo.com, http://www.nsap.net. Eds. J A Agunbiade, O O Oduguwa. Circ: 500 (paid).

636 JPN
NIHON CHIKUSAN GAKKAIHO. Text in Japanese. 1924. q.
Related titles: ♦ English ed.: Animal Science Journal. ISSN 1344-3941.
Published by: Japanese Society of Animal Science/Nihon Chikusan Gakkai, 201 Nagatani Corporas, Ikenohata 2-9-4, Taito-ku, Tokyo, 110-0008, Japan. TEL 81-3-3828-8409, FAX 81-3-3828-7649, editasj@siren.ocn.ne.jp, http://wwwsoc.nacsis.ac.jp/jszs/index.html.

636.4 JPN ISSN 0913-882X
NIHON YOTON GAKKAISHI/JAPANESE JOURNAL OF SWINE SCIENCE. Text in Japanese. 1964. q. **Document type:** *Journal, Academic/Scholarly.*
Formerly (until 1986): Nihon Yoton Kenkyukaishi/Japanese Journal of Swine Science (0388-8460)
Indexed: AgBio, AnBrAb, DSA, HortAb, IndVet, MaizeAb, PN&I, S&F, SIA, SoyAb, WAE&RSA.
—BLDSC (4658.866000).
Published by: Nihon Yoton Gakkai/Japanese Society of Swine Science, Tokyo University of Agriculture, Department of Animal Science, 1737 Funako Atsugi-shi, Kanagawa, 243-0034, Japan. TEL 81-46-2706584, FAX 81-46-2706585, sukemori@nodai.ac.jp, http://youton.ac.affrc.go.jp/gakkaisi.html.

636.2 FRA ISSN 1621-7500
NORMANDE. Text in French. 1947. q. adv. **Document type:** *Bulletin.*
Formerly (until 2000): U P R A Normande Informations (0399-2918)
Indexed: RefZh.
Published by: U P R A Normande Informations, 14 rue Alexandre Fleming, B.P. 106, Herouville-Saint-clair, 14204, France. TEL 31-2-31440203, FAX 31-2-31440250, http://www.lanormande.com/en/contact.php. Ed. Arnaud Marie. Adv. contact N Durouchoux. Circ: 6,500.

636.3 GBR
NORTH COUNTRY CHEVIOT SHEEP SOCIETY. FLOCK BOOK. Text in English. 1946. a. GBP 5 domestic; GBP 7.50 foreign (effective 2000). **Document type:** *Trade.*
Published by: North Country Cheviot Sheep Society, 16 St Vincent Rd, Tain, Ross-shire IV19 1JR, United Kingdom. TEL 44-1862-894014, FAX 44-1862-894014, wm@nc-cheviot.co.uk, http://www.nc-cheviot.co.uk. Ed., R&P W Morrison. Pub. Lewis Recordings. Circ: 500.

636 USA ISSN 1062-4287
THE NORTH DAKOTA STOCKMAN. Text in English. 1953. m. USD 50 (effective 2005). adv. bk.rev. **Document type:** *Magazine, Trade.* **Description:** Provides news and information of interest to state and county cattlemen, feeders and livestock leaders.
Formerly (until 1976): Bar North (0404-8997)
Published by: North Dakota Stockmen's Association, 407 S Second St, Bismarck, ND 58504. TEL 701-223-2522, FAX 701-223-2587, stockman@ndstockmen.org, ndsa@ndstockmen.org, http://www.ndstockmen.org. Ed. Julie Ellingson. Circ: 3,500 (paid).

NORTHEAST DAIRY BUSINESS. see *AGRICULTURE—Dairying And Dairy Products*

636 ESP ISSN 0210-5659
NUESTRA CABANA; revista de la nueva ganaderia espanola. Text in Spanish. 1972. m. EUR 70.99 domestic; EUR 92.82 foreign (effective 2004). adv. bk.rev. illus.; stat. **Description:** Contains information on new products and technology for the feeding, health, sanitation, commercialization and management of livestock.
Indexed: IECT.
—CINDOC.
Published by: Tecnipublicaciones Espana, S.L., Avda de Manoteras 44, 3a Planta, Madrid, 28050, Spain. TEL 34-91-2972000, FAX 34-91-2972154, tp@tecnipublicaciones.com, http://www.tecnipublicaciones.com. adv.: B&W page EUR 569, color page EUR 812; bleed 210 x 285. Circ: 11,000.

636.2 DNK ISSN 1601-8621
NYHEDSBREV; Dansk kvaeg. Text in Danish. 1997. bi-w. DKK 375 (effective 2005). adv. back issues avail. **Document type:** *Newsletter, Trade.*
Former titles (until 2002): Producentorientering (1397-4319); (until 1997): Mejeribrugets Producentorientering (0909-7635)
Related titles: Online - full text ed.
Published by: Dansk Landbrugsraadgivning, Dansk Kvaeg/Danish Agricultural Advisory Service. Danish Cattle Husbandry, Udkaersvej 15, Skejby, Aarhus N, 8200, Denmark. TEL 45-87-405000, FAX 45-87-405010, http://www.lr.dk/kvaeg/system/visnyhedDK.asp. Ed. Lars Winther.

636 AUT
OESTERREICHISCHE FLEISCHER-ZEITUNG. Text in German. fortn. EUR 75 domestic; EUR 110 foreign (effective 2005). adv. bk.rev. **Document type:** *Newspaper, Trade.*
Formerly: Viehhandel (0049-6308)
Published by: (Bundesinnung der Fleischer), Oesterreichischer Wirtschaftsverlag GmbH (Subsidiary of: Sueddeutscher Verlag GmbH), Wiedner Hauptstr 120-124, Vienna, W 1051, Austria. TEL 43-1-546640, FAX 43-1-54664406, office@wirtschaftsverlag.at, http://www.wirtschaftsverlag.at. Ed., Adv. contact Johannes Rottensteiner. B&W page EUR 2,300, color page EUR 3,200; trim 275 x 400. Circ: 2,000 (paid and controlled).

636.2 USA ISSN 0048-1556
OHIO JERSEY NEWS. Text in English. 1936. m. USD 5. adv.
Published by: Ohio Jersey Breeders Association Inc., PO Box 532, Prospect, OH 43342. TEL 614-262-1452. Ed. A Bud Baird. Circ: 1,200.

OHIO NEWS. see *AGRICULTURE—Dairying And Dairy Products*

636 JPN ISSN 0915-4728
OKAYAMA-KEN SOGO CHIKUSAN SENTA KENKYU HOHKOKU/OKAYAMA PREFECTURAL CENTER FOR ANIMAL HUSBANDRY AND RESEARCH. BULLETIN. Text in Japanese; Summaries in English, Japanese. 1990. a. **Document type:** *Bulletin.*
—BLDSC (2668.447000).
Published by: Okayama-ken Sogo Chikusan Senta/Okayama Prefectural Center for Animal Husbandry and Research, 2272, Kita, kume-gun, Asahi-cho, Okayama-ken 709-34, Japan. TEL 086727-3321. Ed. Seigo Amano. Pub. Mitsuo Akagi.

636.2 USA ISSN 0030-1698
OKLAHOMA COWMAN. Text in English. 1958. m. USD 50 membership (effective 2005). adv. bk.rev. illus. **Document type:** *Magazine, Trade.* **Description:** Provides cattle breeding tips.
Published by: Oklahoma Cattlemen's Association, 2500 Exchange Ave, Oklahoma City, OK 73108. TEL 405-235-4391, FAX 405-235-3608, http://www.okcattlemen.org. Ed., Adv. contact A J Smith. B&W page USD 700. Circ: 4,694 (paid).

636.2 NLD ISSN 0030-2775
ONS VEE✱; maandblad voor de veehouderij. Text in Dutch. 1967 (vol.18). m. adv. illus.
Address: Past. van Akenstraat 8, Roosendaal, Netherlands.

636 CAN
ONTARIO BEEF. Text in English. 1963. 5/yr. membership. adv. back issues avail. **Document type:** *Newsletter, Trade.* **Description:** Provides information to Ontario beef cattle producers, cow-calf, backgrounder, feed lot and seed stock operators.
Formerly (until 1994): Breeder & Feeder (0712-5291)
Published by: Ontario Cattlemen's Association, 130 Malcolm Rd, Guelph, ON N1K 1B1, Canada. TEL 519-824-0334, FAX 519-824-9101, ontbeef@cattle.guelph.on.ca, http://www.cattle.guelph.on.ca. Ed., R&P Marilyn Robbins. Adv. contact Cathy Lasby. Circ: 20,931 (controlled).

636 CAN ISSN 1195-5457
ONTARIO BEEF FARMER MAGAZINE. Text in English. 1993. 4/yr. CND 16.05; CND 20 in United States; CND 25 elsewhere. adv.
Published by: Bowes Publishers Ltd., PO Box 7400, London, ON N5Y 4X3, Canada. TEL 519-473-0010, FAX 519-473-2256. Ed. Paul Mahon. Pub. Mervyn J Hawkins. adv.: B&W page CND 1,150, color page CND 1,645; trim 10.75 x 8.13. Circ: 13,499.

636.4 CAN
ONTARIO HOG FARMER MAGAZINE. Text in English. 1988. 6/yr. adv. **Document type:** *Trade.*
Former titles: Ontario Hog Farmer Quarterly (0847-7752); (until 1989): Ontario Hog Farmer (0847-7760)
Published by: Bowes Publishers Ltd., PO Box 7400, London, ON N5Y 4X3, Canada. TEL 519-473-0010, FAX 519-473-2256. Ed. Paul Mahon. Pub. Mervyn J Hawkins. Circ: 8,498.

636.3 CAN ISSN 0844-5303
ONTARIO SHEEP NEWS. Text in English. 1987. bi-m. CND 12.84 (effective 1999). adv. **Document type:** *Trade.*
—CISTI.
Address: 130 Malcolm Rd, Guelph, ON N1K 1B1, Canada. TEL 519-836-0043, FAX 519-824-9101. Ed., R&P, Adv. contact Jennifer Rock. B&W page CND 300; trim 11 x 8.5. Circ: 5,800.

636.2 USA
OREGON BEEF PRODUCER. Text in English. 1952. m. USD 50 to members (effective 2005). adv. bk.rev. **Document type:** *Magazine, Trade.*
Formerly: Oregon Cattleman (0471-9174)
Published by: Oregon Cattlemen's Association, 3415 Commercial St, S E, Ste E, Salem, OR 97302. TEL 503-274-2333, FAX 503-229-5232, glens@orcattle.com, wrangler@teleport.com, http://www.orcattle.com. adv.: B&W page USD 465, color page USD 740. Circ: 2,500.

636 ESP ISSN 1130-4863
OVIS. Text in Spanish. 1989. bi-m. **Document type:** *Trade.*
Related titles: CD-ROM ed.: Aula Veterinaria.
Indexed: IECT.
—CINDOC.
Published by: Luzan 5 S.A. de Ediciones, Pasaje Virgen de la Alegria 14, Madrid, 28027, Spain. TEL 34-91-4051595, FAX 34-91-4034907, luzan@luzan5.es, http://www.luzan5.es.

636 RUS
OVTSY, KOZY, SHERSTYANOE DELO. Text in Russian. bi-m. USD 85 in United States.
Indexed: RefZh.
Published by: Ovtsy Kozy Sherstyanoe Delo, Ul Pasechnaya 4, Moscow, 127550, Russian Federation. TEL 7-095-9760690. **US dist. addr.:** East View Information Services, 3020 Harbor Ln. N., Minneapolis, MN 55447. TEL 612-550-0961.

636.3 GBR
OXFORD DOWN SHEEP BREEDER'S ASSOCIATION MAGAZINE. Text in English. 3/yr. GBP 10 (effective 1999). adv. **Document type:** *Newsletter.*
Published by: Oxford Down Sheep Breeder's Association, Bishops Gorse, Lighthorne, Warcs CV35 0BB, United Kingdom. TEL 44-1423-770736, john.brigg@virgin.net. Ed. Jeffrey Stephenson. Adv. contact Ann Knott. color page GBP 130. Circ: 350 (paid).

636.2142 FRA ISSN 1143-5852
P L M. (Production Laitiere Moderne) Text in French. m. (11/yr.). EUR 65 domestic; EUR 118 foreign (effective 2004). adv. illus. **Document type:** *Magazine, Trade.*
Formerly: Eleveur de Bovins - P L M
Indexed: AEA, AnBrAb, DSA, IndVet, MaizeAb, NutrAb, WAE&RSA.
Published by: Editions du Boisbaudry, 13 Square du Chene Germain, Cesson Sevigne, 355773, France. TEL 33-2-99322121, http://www.editionsduboisbaudry.com. Circ: 26,000.

636 USA ISSN 1098-8483
PACIFIC NORTHWEST ANIMAL NUTRITION CONFERENCE. PROCEEDINGS. Text in English. 1966. a. USD 20 (effective 2004). back issues avail.
Indexed: Agr.
Published by: Pacific Northwest Animal Nutrition Conference, c/o Dennis Hays, 2380 NW Roosevelt St., Portland, OR 97210. TEL 530-226-2758, FAX 530-224-0947, haysmgmt@pipeline.com, http://www.pnwanc.org/past.html.

636 PAK ISSN 0083-8292
PAKISTAN. DIRECTORATE OF LIVESTOCK FARMS. REPORT. Text in English. 1962. a.
Published by: Directorate of Livestock Farms, 16 Cooper Rd., Lahore, Pakistan. Circ: 100.

636 PAK
PAKISTAN JOURNAL OF ANIMAL SCIENCES. Text in English. q. PKR 10, USD 1.25. adv. bibl.; charts.
Published by: Society for the Advancement of Animal Sciences, c/o Veterinary Research Institute, Ghazi Rd., Lahore 13, Pakistan.

636.2 MEX ISSN 0304-2502
PASTIZALES. Text in Spanish; Summaries in English. 1970. s-a. free. bibl.; charts; illus. back issues avail. **Document type:** *Bulletin.* **Description:** Provides results of research in range management, cattle production and other topics.
—CISTI.
Published by: Instituto Nacional de Investigaciones Forestales, Agricolas y Pecuarias, Campo Experimental "La Campana", Apdo. Postal 1204, Chihuahua, Mexico. TEL 52-14-810769, FAX 52-14-810257. Eds. Esteban Gutierrez Ronquillo, Raul Escobar Tolentino. Circ: 1,500.

636.5 USA
PEAFOWL REPORT. Text in English. 1991. bi-m. USD 20 domestic; USD 35 in Canada; USD 45 elsewhere. **Document type:** *Newsletter.* **Description:** Provides current news and information on the raising and care of peafowl (peacocks and peahens).
Formerly: Wacky World of Peafowl Report (1056-6759)
Published by: Iowa Peacock Farm Publications, Peacocks UR, Minden, IA 51553. TEL 712-483-2473, FAX 712-483-2155, http://www.peafowl.com. Eds. Debra Buck, Dennis Fett. R&P Dennis Fett. Circ: 1,000 (paid).

636 USA ISSN 1092-9614
PERFORMANCE HORSE. Text in English. 199?. m. USD 24.95 domestic; USD 60 in Canada & Mexico; USD 110 elsewhere (effective 2005). adv. **Document type:** *Magazine, Trade.* **Description:** Devoted solely to the dynamic world of reining, cutting and working cowhorses.
Published by: My Little Salesman, 2895 Chad Dr, Eugene, OR 97408. TEL 800-493-2295, FAX 541-342-3307, http://www.performancehorse.com, http://www.mlsinc.com.

PHILIPPINES. DEPARTMENT OF AGRICULTURE. BUREAU OF AGRICULTURAL STATISTICS. LIVESTOCK AND POULTRY PERFORMANCE REPORT. see *AGRICULTURE—Abstracting, Bibliographies, Statistics*

636.5 PAK
PIA-SHAVER/POULTRY. Text in English, Urdu. 1971. m. USD 2 per issue.
Published by: Press Corporation of Pakistan, P O Box 3138, Karachi, 75400, Pakistan. TEL 21-455-3703, FAX 21-7736198. Ed. Saeed Hafeez. Circ: 3,000.

636.4 GBR ISSN 0031-9759
PIG FARMING. Text in English. 1954. m. GBP 28; GBP 38 in Europe; USD 74 elsewhere (effective 2000). adv. bk.rev. charts; illus.; tr.lit. **Document type:** *Magazine, Trade.* **Description:** News and articles of interest to farmers and farm managers in Great Britain and Northern Ireland who raise sows or pigs.
Related titles: Online - full text ed.: (from Florida Center for Library Automation, Gale Group, LexisNexis, ProQuest Information & Learning).
Indexed: ABIn, AEA, DBA, DSA, ExcerpMed, IndVet.
—BLDSC (6500.000000), CISTI.
Published by: C M P Information Ltd. (Subsidiary of: United Business Media), Riverbank House, Angel Ln, Tonbridge, Kent TN9 1SE, United Kingdom. TEL 44-1732-364422, FAX 44-1732-377675, enquiries@cmpinformation.com, http://www.cmpinformation.com. Ed., R&P Roger Abbott. Adv. contact Jason Davies. Circ: 9,000. **Subscr. to:** Marlowe House, 109 Station Rd, Sidcup, Kent DA15 7ET, United Kingdom. TEL 44-20-8309-7000.

636.4 USA
PIG INTERNATIONAL; covering the pig industry in Europe, Asia-Pacific, North America and Africa. Text in English. 1971. m. USD 48 domestic; USD 84 foreign (effective 2005). adv. Supplement avail. **Document type:** *Magazine, Trade.* **Description:** Features all aspects of pig production and marketing for pig businessmen in Europe, Asia, Africa, and North America.
Former titles: Pig International. Europe, Africa and Asia - Pacific (0191-8834); Pig International. Europe, Asia, Africa, Latin America and Oceania Edition
Indexed: DBA, IndVet, NutrAb, PN&I.
—BLDSC (6500.027000), IE, ingenta. **CCC.**
Published by: Watt Publishing Co., 122 S Wesley Ave, Mt. Morris, IL 61054-1497. TEL 815-734-4171, FAX 815-734-5649. Ed. Peter Best. Pub. Clay Schreiber. Adv. contact Nancy Wagner. B&W page USD 4,200, color page USD 5,710; trim 10.75 x 8. Circ: 20,000 (controlled).

THE PIG JOURNAL. see *VETERINARY SCIENCE*

636.4 JPN ISSN 0915-9622
PIG MAGAZINE/YOTONKAI. Text in Japanese. m. JPY 800 per issue. **Document type:** *Trade.* **Description:** Covers pig breeding, fattening, and pig farm management for pig farmers, researchers, students and government.
Published by: Chikusan Publishing Co. Ltd. (Subsidiary of: Midori Group), Ikebukuro Nishiguchi Sky Bldg, 2-14-4 Ikebukuro, Toshima-ku, Tokyo, 171-0014, Japan. TEL 03-3590-9454. Circ: 32,000.

PIG NEWS & INFORMATION. see *AGRICULTURE—Abstracting, Bibliographies, Statistics*

636 NLD ISSN 1387-3946
PIG PROGRESS; international magazine on pig keeping. Variant title: Worldwide Pig Progress. Text in English. 1984. 10/yr. EUR 142 (effective 2005). adv. **Document type:** *Trade.* **Description:** Covers breeding techniques, diet and health care, housing and pigsty equipment.
Formerly (until 1997): Pigs (0168-9533)
Indexed: FS&TA, IndVet, PN&I, SoyAb.
—CISTI, Infotrieve.
Published by: Reed Business Information bv (Subsidiary of: Reed Business), Hanzestraat 1, Doetinchem, 7006 RH, Netherlands. TEL 31-314-349550, FAX 31-314-340515, info@reedbusiness.nl, http://www.reedbusiness.nl. Ed. Anabel Evans TEL 31-314-349145. Pub. Michel Veen. Adv. contact Miguel Mendes de Leon TEL 31-314-349584. Circ: 15,028.

636 GBR ISSN 0966-3592
PIG WORLD. Text in English. 1987. m. GBP 20; GBP 30 foreign. adv. **Document type:** *Trade.* **Description:** All aspects of indoor and outdoor pig husbandry in the UK and other EC countries.
Indexed: DSA, NutrAb, WAE&RSA.
Address: Benniworth, PO Box 181, Lincoln, Lincs LN3 6LE, United Kingdom. FAX 44-1507-313798. Ed. S Walton. Circ: 8,000 (paid).

636 GBR
PIGPLAN MANAGEMENT SERVICES. QUARTERLY DATA SHEET. Text in English. q. GBP 6.50 per issue. **Document type:** *Bulletin.*
Formerly (until 1992): Pig Improvement Services. Quarterly Data Sheet
Published by: Meat and Livestock Commission, Winterhill House, Snowdon Dr, PO Box 44, Milton Keynes, Bucks MK6 1AX, United Kingdom. TEL 44-1908-844396, FAX 44-1908-609221. R&P Jenny Spencer TEL 44-1908-844330. Adv. contact Vikki Gatt.

636.5 BEL ISSN 0771-3908
PLUIMVEE. Text in Dutch. 1965. m. adv. illus. reprints avail. **Document type:** *Journal, Trade.*
Address: Opworp 13, Lummen, 3560, Belgium. TEL 32-13-521715, FAX 32-13-521955, info@pluimvee.be, http://www.pluimvee.be. Ed., Pub., R&P, Adv. contact Clem Reynders. Circ: 3,000.

636.5 NLD ISSN 0166-8250
PLUIMVEEHOUDERIJ. Text in Dutch. 1923. 50/yr. EUR 95 (effective 2005). adv. bk.rev. charts; illus.; mkt. **Document type:** *Trade.* **Description:** Trade news for the entire poultry industry.
Formerly (until 1971): Bedrijfspluimveehouder (0005-7649)
Indexed: KES.
Published by: (Nederlandse Organisatie van Pluimveehouders/ Dutch Organization of Poultry-Keepers), Reed Business Information bv (Subsidiary of: Reed Business), Hanzestraat 1, Doetinchem, 7006 RH, Netherlands. TEL 31-314-349911, FAX 31-314-343839, info@reedbusiness.nl, http:// www.pluimveehouderij.nl/Home.asp, http:// www.reedbusiness.nl. Ed. Wim Wisman. Adv. contact Cor van Nek. B&W page EUR 1,712, color page EUR 2,597; trim 285 x 215. Circ: 6,140.

THE POINTING DOG JOURNAL. see *SPORTS AND GAMES—Outdoor Life*

636.4 664.9 FRA ISSN 0296-9076
PORC MAGAZINE. Text in French. 1968. m. (11/yr.). EUR 78 domestic; EUR 93 foreign (effective 2004). adv. illus. **Document type:** *Magazine, Trade.*
Formerly (until 1985): Eleveurs de Porcs (0395-8353)
Indexed: DSA, IndVet, RevApplEntom, VetBull, WAE&RSA.
—BLDSC (6554.050000), IE, ingenta.
Published by: Editions du Boisbaudry, 13 Square du Chene Germain, Cesson Sevigne, 355773, France. TEL 33-2-99322121, http://www.editionsduboisbaudry.com. Circ: 13,500.

636.4 USA ISSN 0745-3787
PORK; the business monthly for pork producers. Text in English. 1981. m. USD 29.94; USD 6.95 newsstand/cover (effective 2005). adv. charts; illus.; mkt.; stat.; tr.lit. index. reprint service avail. from PQC. **Document type:** *Magazine, Trade.* **Description:** Provides livestock managers with news of the latest developments in the pork industry, with related veterinary advances.
Incorporates (1964-1992): Hog Farm Management (0018-3180); Formerly (until 198?): Pork Producers Reference (0279-6813)
Related titles: Microform ed.: (from PQC).
Indexed: AEA, AgBio, AnBrAb, B&AI, DSA, F&GI, IndVet, NutrAb, PN&I, RDA, S&F, VetBull, WAE&RSA.
—CISTI. **CCC.**
Published by: Vance Publishing Corp., 10901 W 84th Terrace, Lexena, KS 66214-1821. TEL 913-438-8700, FAX 913-438-0695, http://www.porkmag.com, http:// www.vancepublishing.com. Ed. Marlys Miller. Circ: 26,769 (controlled).

636.4 330 USA
▼ **PORK BUSINESS JOURNAL.** Text in English. 2003. bi-m. **Document type:** *Magazine, Trade.*
Published by: Farm Journal Media, 1818 Market St., 31st Fl, Philadelphia, PA 19103-3654. TEL 215-557-8900, 800-523-1538, FAX 215-568-5012, http://www.agweb.com.

636 AUS ISSN 1032-3759
SF391
PORK JOURNAL. Text in English. 1978. bi-m. AUD 52 includes Newsletter (effective 2000). adv. back issues avail. **Document type:** *Trade.* **Description:** News and management hints for pig farmers.
Incorporates: Pig Farmer (0031-9740); Formerly: Australian Pork Journal (0156-5907)
Published by: Richard Milne Pty. Ltd., PO Box 163, Drummoyne, NSW 1470, Australia. TEL 61-2-97139822, FAX 61-2-97139266, milnepublications@ibm.net, milnepublications@attglobal.net. Ed., R&P Brian McErlane. Adv. contact Pauline Holyoake. Circ: 3,272.

636.4 USA
PORK PRODUCER NEWS. Text in English. 1973. q. free.
Formerly (until 197?): Pork Roundup
Published by: (Advertising Department), Kent Feeds Inc., 1600 Oregon St, Muscatine, IA 52761. TEL 319-264-4211.

636.4 CAN
PORK REPORT. Text in English. w. free. adv. **Document type:** *Newsletter.* **Description:** Include information on the production and marketing of pork and related matters.
Published by: S P I Marketing Group, 502 45th St W, 2nd Fl, Saskatoon, SK S7L 6H2, Canada. TEL 306-653-3014, 800-667-2003, FAX 306-244-2918, spi@sk.sympatio.ca, http://agri-infolink.com/spi. Ed., R&P Rob Brown. Circ: 2,100 (controlled).

636.4 USA
PORK REPORT. Text in English. 1982. 4/yr. free (effective 2005). adv. **Document type:** *Magazine, Trade.*
Published by: National Pork Producers Council, 1776 NW 114th St, Clive, IA 50325-7073. TEL 515-223-2600, FAX 515-223-2646, porkreport@porkboard.com, porkreport@nppc.org, http://www.porkboard.com. Pub. Jan Jorgensen. adv.: B&W page USD 3,400, color page USD 4,500; trim 10.88 x 8.25. Circ: 109,000 (controlled).

636.5 USA ISSN 1096-3057
POULTRY (CHICAGO). Text in English. 1994 (Apr.). 6/yr. USD 80 domestic; USD 100 in Canada; USD 120 elsewhere (effective 2004).
Formerly (until 1997): Poultry Marketing & Technology (1079-2155)
Related titles: Online - full text ed.
Indexed: Agr.
Published by: Marketing and Technology Group, Inc., 1415 N Dayton St, Chicago, IL 60622. TEL 312-266-3311, FAX 312-266-3363, http://web.meatingplace.com/MagInfoM/ InfoPoultry.asp, http://www.meatingplace.com. Pub. Mark Lefens. Circ: 10,179.

636.5 USA ISSN 0032-5716
POULTRY AND EGG MARKETING; the bi-monthly news magazine of the poultry marketing industry. Text in English. 1921. 6/yr. USD 12; free to qualified personnel. adv. charts; illus.; stat. **Document type:** *Newspaper.*
Formerly: Poultry and Eggs Weekly
—CISTI.
Published by: Poultry and Egg News, 345 Green St, N W, PO Box 1338, Gainesville, GA 30503. FAX 770-532-4894, editorial@poultryandeggnews.com. Ed. Christopher Hill. Pub., R&P Randall Smallwood. Adv. contact Charles McEachern. B&W page USD 1,425, color page USD 1,825; trim 13.25 x 11. Circ: 10,400.

636 AUS ISSN 1032-3767
POULTRY DIGEST. Text in English. 1985. bi-m. AUD 33 (effective 2000). adv. back issues avail. **Document type:** *Trade.* **Description:** Information for egg and broiler farmers.
Formerly: Australian Poultry Digest (0815-9297)
Indexed: PoultAb.
Published by: Richard Milne Pty. Ltd., PO Box 163, Drummoyne, NSW 1470, Australia. TEL 61-2-97139822, FAX 61-2-97139266, milnepublications@ibm.net, milnepublications@attglobal.net. Ed., R&P Brian McErlane. Adv. contact Pauline Holyoake. Circ: 2,241.

636 GBR ISSN 1354-2591
POULTRY FORUM. Text in English. 6/yr. adv. **Document type:** *Trade.*
Published by: National Farmers Union, Agriculture House, 164 Shaftesbury Ave, London, WC2H 8HL, United Kingdom. TEL 44-20-73317200, FAX 44-20-73317401, NFU@nfuonline.com, http://www.nfu.org.uk/. Adv. contact John Smith. Circ: 4,500.

636.5 IND ISSN 0032-5740
POULTRY GUIDE. Text in English. 1964. bi-m. INR 300. bk.rev. charts; illus.; mkt.; stat.; tr.lit. **Document type:** *Trade.* **Description:** Provides technical and other useful information for efficient and profitable production in the trade.
Related titles: Hindi ed.
Indexed: FS&TA, NutrAb.
—BLDSC (6570.250000).
Published by: C.P. Narang (Pvt.) Ltd., 1700-IV Urban Estate, Gurgaon, 122 001, India. TEL 91-124-320728, FAX 91-124-327400. Ed. Ricky Thaper. adv.: page INR 1,000; trim 190 x 140. Circ: 7,000.

636.5 USA ISSN 0032-5767
CODEN: POINE8
POULTRY INTERNATIONAL. Text in English. 1962. 14/yr. USD 78 domestic; USD 90 in Canada; USD 102 elsewhere (effective 2005). adv. charts; stat. **Document type:** *Magazine, Trade.* **Description:** International commercial focus on production, processing and marketing of eggs, broilers and turkeys. Provides the latest technological innovations in production and processing as well as addressing the marketing and management issues crossing geographical segments of the industry.
Related titles: Online - full text ed.: (from EBSCO Publishing); ♦ Regional ed(s).: Industria Avicola. ISSN 0019-7467.
Indexed: AEA, AnBrAb, DBA, FS&TA, IndVet, MaizeAb, NutrAb, PoultAb, ProtozoAb, RM&VM, TriticAb.
—BLDSC (6570.310000), CISTI, IE, Infotrieve, ingenta. **CCC.**
Published by: Watt Publishing Co., 122 S Wesley Ave, Mt. Morris, IL 61054-1497. TEL 815-734-4171, FAX 815-734-5649, langman@wattmm.com, http://www.wattnet.com. Eds. David Martin, Jackie Linden. Pub. Charles Olentine. Adv. contact Barb Burke. B&W page USD 4,500, color page USD 6,025; trim 8 x 10.75. Circ: 23,000.

636.5 USA
POULTRY INTERNATIONAL: CHINA EDITION. Text in Chinese. s-a. USD 30. adv. **Document type:** *Trade.* **Description:** Provides articles on the latest technology and management from Europe, America, and other regions of Asia to assist the Chinese in the development of their infrastructure and poultry husbandry.

▼ *new title* ➤ *refereed* ✶ *unverified* ♦ *full entry avail.*

A

Published by: Watt Publishing Co., 122 S Wesley Ave, Mt. Morris, IL 61054-1497. TEL 815-734-4171, FAX 815-734-5649, http://www.wattnet.com. Ed. David Martin. Pub. Charles Olentine. adv.: B&W page USD 3,500, color page USD 4,500. Circ: 10,000.

636.5 338.1 CAN ISSN 0032-5775
POULTRY MARKET REVIEW. Text in English. 1950. a. free. **Document type:** *Government.* **Description:** Provides annual poultry market statistics, number of birds slaughtered, hatched, set, table eggs graded, processed egg production, imports, exports and interprovincial movement on a monthly, provincial and annual basis.
—CISTI.
Published by: Agriculture Canada, Poultry Development Division, Sir John Carling Bldg., 930 Carling Ave, Ottawa, ON K1A 0C7, Canada. TEL 819-994-0246, FAX 819-953-0969. Circ: 2,000.

POULTRY MARKET STATISTICS. see *AGRICULTURE—Abstracting, Bibliographies, Statistics*

636.5 LBN
POULTRY MIDDLE EAST & NORTH AFRICA. Text in Arabic. 1979. 6/yr. LBP 25,000, USD 15 (effective 1998). adv. **Document type:** *Trade.*
Indexed: SIA.
Published by: Middle East Agriculture Publishers (M E A P), Zalka, Cite Moussa, Block A, 1170, P O Box 90, Beirut, Lebanon. TEL 961-1-896478, FAX 961-1-897259. Ed. Ghassan Sayegh. Pub. Antoine Sayegh. Adv. contact Mary Beyrouty. Circ: 22,000.

636.5 USA ISSN 0032-5783
POULTRY PRESS. Text in English. 1914. m. USD 21 (effective 2005). adv. bk.rev. illus. **Document type:** *Magazine, Trade.* **Description:** Devoted to poultry, including waterfowl, and the bantam industry. Covers news and views of industry; interested in reports of exhibitions and shows throughout the country.
Address: PO Box 542, Connersville, IN 47331-0542. TEL 765-827-0932, FAX 765-827-4186, poultryp@si-net.com. Ed., R&P William F Wulff. Adv. contact William Wulff. Circ: 5,500 (paid).

636.2 USA
POULTRY ROUNDUP. Text in English. 1973. a. free.
Published by: Kent Feeds Inc., 1600 Oregon St, Muscatine, IA 52761. TEL 319-264-4211.

636.5 USA ISSN 0032-5791
SF481 CODEN: POSCAL
➤ **POULTRY SCIENCE.** Text in English. 1908. m. USD 50 combined subscription to members print & online eds.; USD 425 combined subscription to institutions print & online eds. (effective 2005). adv. bk.rev. bibl.; illus.; abstr. index. back issues avail.; reprint service avail. from PQC. **Document type:** *Journal, Academic/Scholarly.*
Related titles: Microform ed.: (from PQC); Online - full text ed.: (from ProQuest Information & Learning).
Indexed: AEA, ASCA, AbHyg, AgBio, Agr, AgrForAb, AnBrAb, B&AI, BIOSIS Prev, BibAg, BioCN&I, BiolAb, CIN, CPA, ChemAb, ChemTitl, CurCont, CurPA, DBA, DSA, DentInd, ExcerpMed, FCA, FS&TA, FoVS&M, HelmAb, HerbAb, HortAb, I&DA, ISR, IndMed, IndVet, MEDLINE, MaizeAb, NutrAb, PBA, PHN&I, PN&I, PST, PoultAb, ProtozoAb, RA&MP, RM&VM, RPP, RRTA, RiceAb, S&F, SCI, SFA, SIA, SeedAb, SoyAb, TDB, TOSA, TriticAb, VetBull, WAE&RSA, WeedAb, WildRev, ZooRec.
—BLDSC (6571.000000), CASDDS, CISTI, GNLM, IE, Infotrieve, ingenta, Linda Hall. **CCC.**
Published by: Poultry Science Association Inc., 1111 N Dunlap Ave, Savoy, IL 61874. TEL 217-356-5285, FAX 217-398-4119, psa@assochq.org, http://www.poultryscience.org/ps/institutionip.htm. Ed. Susan Pollock. Circ: 3,500 (paid).

636.5 GBR ISSN 0306-7610
➤ **POULTRY SCIENCE SYMPOSIUM SERIES.** Text in English. 1965. irreg., latest vol.25, 1999. USD 130 per vol. vol.25 (effective 2004); price varies. **Document type:** *Academic/Scholarly.*
Indexed: Agr.
—BLDSC (6571.060000), CISTI.
Published by: Oxford University Press, Great Clarendon St, Oxford, OX2 6DP, United Kingdom. TEL 44-1865-556767, FAX 44-1865-556646, enquiry@oup.co.uk, http://www.oup-usa.org/catalogs/general/series/Poultry_Science_Symposium_Series.html, http://www.oup.co.uk/.

636.5 USA ISSN 0885-3371
SF481
POULTRY TIMES. Text in English. 1954. bi-w. USD 12 domestic; USD 28 in Canada; USD 36 elsewhere (effective 2005). adv. illus. **Document type:** *Magazine, Trade.*
Formed by the merger of: Poultryman (0278-5595); Southeastern Poultry Times (0038-3708); Texas Poultry and Egg News (0040-4608); Incorporates: Georgia Poultry Times
—CISTI.
Published by: Poultry and Egg News, 345 Green St, N W, PO Box 1338, Gainesville, GA 30503. TEL 770-536-2476, FAX 770-532-4894, chull@poultryandeggnews.com, editorial@poultryandeggnews.com, http:www.poultryandeggnews.com. Ed., Pub. Christopher Hill. Adv. contact Cindy Wellborn. B&W page USD 3,000, color page USD 3,475; trim 11 x 13.25. Circ: 10,000 (paid).

636.592 016 USA ISSN 1529-1677
HD9437.A1
POULTRY U S A. Text in English. 2000. bi-m. free to qualified personnel. adv. charts; illus.; stat.; tr.lit. **Document type:** *Magazine, Trade.* **Description:** An international turkey magazine dedicated to supporting every phase of the turkey industry by providing information for decision-makers on breeding, production, management, processing, and marketing.
Formed by the merger of (1968-2000): Turkey World (0041-4271); (1957-2000): Broiler Industry (0007-2176); Which incorporated: Poultry Processing and Marketing; Which was formerly (until 1977): Broiler Business; (until 1975): Poultry Meat (0048-4970)
Indexed: IndVet, WAE&RSA.
—CISTI, Linda Hall. **CCC.**
Published by: Watt Publishing Co., 122 S Wesley Ave, Mt. Morris, IL 61054-1497. TEL 815-734-4171, FAX 815-734-5649, http://www.wattnet.com. Eds. Bernard E Heffernan, Gary Thornton. Pub. Charles Olentine. adv.: page USD 5,120; trim 10.75 x 8. Circ: 20,000 (controlled).

636.5 GBR ISSN 0032-5813
POULTRY WORLD. Text in English. 1874. m. GBP 28.80; EUR 46 in Europe; USD 86.40 in United States; GBP 52 elsewhere (effective 2003). adv. charts; illus.; stat. reprints avail. **Document type:** *Trade.* **Description:** Covers all poultry interests from breeding to marketing, from hobby poultry keeping to large scale production and processing.
Related titles: Online - full text ed.: (from EBSCO Publishing, Gale Group, H.W. Wilson, O C L C Online Computer Library Center, Inc., ProQuest Information & Learning).
Indexed: ABIn, AEA, B&AI.
—BLDSC (6571.150000), CISTI. **CCC.**
Published by: Reed Business Information Ltd. (Subsidiary of: Reed Business), Quadrant House, The Quadrant, Brighton Rd, Sutton, Surrey SM2 5AS, United Kingdom. TEL 44-20-86523500, FAX 44-20-86528932, http://www.reedbusiness.co.uk/. Ed. John Farrant TEL 44-20-8652-4020. Pub. Roger Williams. Adv. contact Chris Joslin TEL 44-20-8652-4025. Circ: 6,236. **Subscr. to:** Quadrant Subscription Services, Rockwood House, 9-17 Perrymount Rd, Haywards Heath, W. Sussex RH16 3DH, United Kingdom. TEL 44-20-8652-3500, FAX 44-20-8652-8932, rbi.subscriptions@qss-uk.com.

636 USA
PRAIRIE FARMER. Text in English. 1841. m. USD 23.95 in state (effective 2005). adv. **Document type:** *Magazine, Trade.*
Published by: Farm Progress Companies, 191 S Gary Ave, Carol Stream, IL 60188-2095. TEL 630-462-2229, FAX 630-462-2202, swyany@farmprogress.com, info@farmprogress.com, http://www.prairiefarmer.com/, http://www.farmprogress.com/. Eds. Cherry Brieser-Stout, Sara Wyant. adv.: B&W page USD 3,550, color page USD 4,050; trim 10.5 x 14.5. Circ: 40,000 (paid and controlled).

636 NLD ISSN 0928-2076
PRAKTIJKONDERZOEK. Key Title: P P Uitgave. Text in Dutch. 1990. 4/yr. includes Jaarverslag. **Document type:** *Corporate.*
Former titles: Praktijkonderzoek Pluimveehouderij; Praktijkonderzoek voor de Pluimveehouderij (0924-9087)
Indexed: VetBull.
Published by: Praktijkonderzoek Pluimveehouderij, Postbus 31, Beekbergen, 7360 AA, Netherlands. TEL 31-55-5066500, FAX 31-55-5064858. Ed. F G Vink. Circ: 550.

PRODUCAO DA PECUARIA MUNICIPAL. see *AGRICULTURE—Abstracting, Bibliographies, Statistics*

PRODUKTIONSOEKONOMI, SVIN. see *AGRICULTURE—Agricultural Economics*

636 ITA ISSN 0033-0000
PRODUZIONE ANIMALE. Text in English, French, German, Italian. 1962. q. adv. abstr.; charts; illus. index.
Indexed: AnBrAb, BiolAb, ChemAb, DSA, NutrAb.
—CISTI.
Published by: Istituto della Produzione Animale, Facolta di Agraria, Portici, NA 80055, Italy. Ed. Manlio Bettini. Circ: 500.

636 ITA ISSN 1825-3199
PROFESSIONE ALLEVATORE. Text in Italian. 1971. m. (11/yr.). EUR 52 domestic; EUR 100 foreign (effective 2005). adv. **Document type:** *Magazine, Trade.*
Published by: Point Veterinaire Italie Srl (Subsidiary of: Wolters Kluwer N.V.), Via Medardo Rosso 11, Milan, 20159, Italy. TEL 39-02-6085231, FAX 39-02-6682866, info@pointvet.it, http://www.pointvet.it. Ed. Dr. J P Dagneauz. Circ: 32,000.

636.9322 636.5 ITA ISSN 1825-3245
PROFESSIONE AVICUNICOLTORE. Text in Italian. 2001. m. (11/yr.). EUR 27 domestic; EUR 50 foreign (effective 2005). **Document type:** *Magazine, Trade.*
Published by: Point Veterinaire Italie Srl (Subsidiary of: Wolters Kluwer N.V.), Via Medardo Rosso 11, Milan, 20159, Italy. TEL 39-02-6085231, FAX 39-02-6682866, info@pointvet.it, http://www.pointvet.it.

636.4 ITA ISSN 1593-571X
PROFESSIONE SUINICOLTORE. Text in Italian. 2001. m. (11/yr.). EUR 47 domestic; EUR 90 foreign (effective 2005). **Document type:** *Magazine, Trade.*
Published by: Point Veterinaire Italie Srl (Subsidiary of: Wolters Kluwer N.V.), Via Medardo Rosso 11, Milan, 20159, Italy. TEL 39-02-6085231, FAX 39-02-6682866, info@pointvet.it, http://www.pointvet.it.

636.5 RUS ISSN 0033-3239
PTITSEVODSTVO/POULTRY. Text in Russian. 1951. bi-m. USD 95. bk.rev. illus. index.
Indexed: AEA, AnBrAb, BiolAb, ChemAb, DSA, HelmAb, IndVet, NutrAb, PoultAb, RASB, RM&VM, RefZh, SoyAb, TriticAb, VetBull, WAE&RSA.
—BLDSC (0135.000000), CISTI, East View.
Address: Sadovaya-Spasskaya 18, kom 706, Moscow, 107807, Russian Federation. TEL 7-095-2071660, FAX 7-095-2072870. Ed. Mikhail G Petrash. **Dist. by:** M K - Periodica, ul Gilyarovskogo 39, Moscow 129110, Russian Federation. TEL 7-095-2845008, FAX 7-095-2813798, info@periodicals.ru, http://www.mkniga.ru; **US dist. addr.:** East View Information Services, 3020 Harbor Ln. N., Minneapolis, MN 55447. TEL 612-550-0961.

636.2 DEU
R U W REPORT. Text in German. 1969. 4/yr. free. adv. bk.rev.; film rev.; play rev. bibl.; illus.; stat. **Document type:** *Newsletter, Trade.*
Formerly (until 1993): Mitteilungen aus der Rheinischen Rinderzucht (0026-6868)
Published by: Rinder-Union-West, Schiffahrter Damm 235a, Muenster, 48147, Germany. TEL 49-251-92880, FAX 49-251-9288219, info@ruweg.de, http://www.ruweg.de. Ed. Stefan Rensing. Adv. contact Ida Laukemper. B&W page EUR 1,300; trim 191 x 260. Circ: 20,000 (controlled).

636.9322 USA ISSN 0894-7791
SF451
RABBIT GAZETTE. Text in English. 1979. bi-m. USD 12.
Formerly: Rabbits (0277-3171)
—CISTI.
Published by: R G Publishing, 1725 S W Blvd, Kansas City, KS 66103. TEL 913-722-2229. Ed. Charlie Clarke. Circ: 2,400.

636.9322 CAN ISSN 0033-7242
RABBITS IN CANADA. Text in English. 1970. bi-m. USD 9. bk.rev. stat.
—CISTI.
Published by: Clay Publishing Co. Ltd., One Oak St, Bewdley, ON K0L 1E0, Canada. TEL 416-797-2281. Ed. Charlotte F Clay. Circ: 1,000.

636.5 DNK ISSN 0909-1904
RACEFJERKRAE. Text in Danish. 1971. m. DKK 260. adv. **Document type:** *Trade.*
Formerly (until 1994): Tidsskrift for Racefjerkraeavl (0106-438X); Which supersedes in part (1879-1971): Tidsskrift for Fjerkraeavl (0040-7046); Which incorporates (1964-1965): Erhvervsfjerkrae (0425-1954)
Published by: Danmarks Fjerkraeavlerforening for Raceavl, Noerreportcentret, PO Box 1327, Holstebro, 7500, Denmark. TEL 45-97-405844, FAX 45-97-407944, dffr@racefjerkrae.dk, http://www.racefjerkrae.dk. Ed. Willy Littau. Circ: 5,500.

636 USA ISSN 1084-5402
SF371
RANCH & RURAL LIVING MAGAZINE. Text in English. 1920. m. USD 27 domestic; USD 47 foreign (effective 2005); includes Breeder Directory, Wool & Mohair Warehouse Directory. adv. illus.; maps; mkt.; stat. back issues avail. **Document type:** *Magazine, Trade.* **Description:** Serves ranchers and livestock producers involved with sheep, goat, and cattle, as well as the wool and mohair industries. Features stories about farming, rural life, regional history, political changes, and tales of the Old West.
Former titles (until 1991): Ranch Magazine (0145-8515); (until 1971): Sheep and Goat Raiser (0037-3397)
Related titles: Microfilm ed.; Online - full text ed.: (from ProQuest Information & Learning).
Indexed: SFA, WildRev.
—Linda Hall.
Published by: (Texas Sheep and Goat Raisers Association), Scott Campbell, Ed.&Pub., PO Box 2678, San Angelo, TX 76902. TEL 325-655-4434, FAX 325-658-8250, info@ranchmagazine.com. Pub. Scott Campbell. Adv. contact Jennifer Schroeder. B&W page USD 500; trim 13 x 10.5. Circ: 11,500 (paid).

RANCH DOG TRAINER. see *PETS*

636.4 USA ISSN 0190-0528
SF85 CODEN: RNGLE7
RANGELANDS. Text in English. 1974. bi-m. USD 45 domestic to individuals; USD 65 foreign to individuals; USD 120 domestic to institutions; USD 140 foreign to institutions (effective 2005). adv. bk.rev. bibl. reprint service avail. from PQC. **Document type:** *Magazine, Trade.* **Description:** Offers non-technical advice for land users and land managers.
Former titles (until 1979): Rangeman's Journal (0095-6236); (until 1974): Rangeman's News
Related titles: Microfiche ed.: (from PQC); Microfilm ed.: (from PQC); Online - full text ed.: ISSN 1551-501X (from BioOne, C S A).
Indexed: AEA, Agr, AgrForAb, AnBrAb, BioCN&I, CPA, ForAb, GEOBASE, HerbAb, HortAb, I&DA, IndVet, NutrAb, PBA, PGegResA, PoultAb, RDA, RRTA, RevApplEntom, S&F, SFA, SeedAb, TDB, VetBull, WAE&RSA, WeedAb, WildRev, ZooRec.
—BLDSC (7254.417300), CISTI, IE, ingenta. **CCC.**
Published by: Society for Range Management, 445 Union Blvd, Ste 230, Lakewood, CO 80228-1259. TEL 303-986-3309, srmden@ix.netcom.com, http://www.rangelands.org/srm.shtml. Ed. Gary Frasier. Adv. contact Patty Rich. Circ: 5,100.

636 NOR ISSN 0333-256X
➤ **RANGIFER**; research, management and husbandry of reindeer and other northern ungulates. Text in English. 1981. 2/yr. NOK 200 in Scandinavia; NOK 240 in Europe; NOK 280 elsewhere; NOK 150 to students (effective 2005). bk.rev. back issues avail. **Document type:** *Journal, Academic/Scholarly.* **Description:** Publishes articles on any arctic species of ungulates but primarily on reindeer, cariboou and muskox, reindeer management and husbandry.
Related titles: ♦ Supplement(s): Rangifer. Special Issue. ISSN 0801-6399.
Indexed: AgBio, AnBrAb, BIOSIS Prev, BiolAb, CPA, DSA, FPA, ForAb, HelmAb, HerbAb, HortAb, IndVet, KWIWR, NutrAb, OrnHort, RM&VM, RPP, RRTA, RevApplEntom, S&F, SFA, VetBull, WAE&RSA, WildRev, ZooRec.
—BLDSC (7254.425300), IE, ingenta. **CCC.**
Published by: Nordisk Organ for Reinforskning (NOR)/Nordic Council for Reindeer Husbandry Research, c/o University of Tromsoe, Senter for Samiske Studier, Tromsoe, 9037, Norway. TEL 47-77-646906, FAX 47-77-645510, nor.rangifer@sami.uit.no, http://www.rangifer.no, http://www.sami.uit.no. Ed. Rolf Egil Haugerud.

636 NOR ISSN 0808-2359
RANGIFER. REPORT. Text in Multiple languages. 1995. irreg., latest vol.5, 2001. price varies. abstr. back issues avail. **Document type:** *Proceedings, Academic/Scholarly.*
Indexed: AnBrAb, BIOSIS Prev, BiolAb, DSA, HelmAb, IndVet, NutrAb, ProtozoAb, VetBull, WildRev, ZooRec.
Published by: Nordisk Organ for Reinforskning (NOR)/Nordic Council for Reindeer Husbandry Research, c/o University of Tromsoe, Senter for Samiske Studier, Tromsoe, 9037, Norway. TEL 47-77-646906, FAX 47-77-645510, nor.rangifer@veths.no, nor.rangifer@sami.uit.no, http://www.rangifer.no, http://www.sami.uit.no. Ed. Rolf Egil Haugerud.

636 NOR ISSN 0801-6399
➤ **RANGIFER. SPECIAL ISSUE**; research, management and husbandry of reindeer and other northern ungulates. Text in English. 1982. irreg., latest vol.12, 2000. price varies. back issues avail. **Document type:** *Proceedings, Academic/Scholarly.*
Related titles: ♦ Supplement to: Rangifer. ISSN 0333-256X.
Indexed: WildRev.
—BLDSC (7254.425400).
Published by: Nordisk Organ for Reinforskning (NOR)/Nordic Council for Reindeer Husbandry Research, c/o University of Tromsoe, Senter for Samiske Studier, Tromsoe, 9037, Norway. TEL 47-77-646906, FAX 47-77-645510, nor.rangifer@veths.no, nor.rangifer@sami.uit.no, http://www.rangifer.no, http://www.sami.uit.no. Ed. Rolf Egil Haugerud.

➤ **RARE BREEDS JOURNAL.** see *PETS*

636 ITA ISSN 0300-3477
RAZZA BOVINA PIEMONTESE. Text in Italian, English. 1970. q. free. illus. index. **Document type:** *Newspaper.* **Description:** Contains information on the results of genetic selection, development and promotion of the Piedmontese breed worldwide.
Published by: Associazione Nazionale Allevatori Bovini di Razza Piemontese, Via Valeggio, 22, Turin, TO 10128, Italy. TEL 39-173-750791, FAX 39-173-750915. Ed. Vittorio Faroppa. Circ: 4,000 (controlled).

636.089 ITA
LA RAZZA BRUNA. Text in Italian. 1961. bi-m. EUR 18 domestic; EUR 26 foreign (effective 2005). adv. **Document type:** *Magazine, Trade.* **Description:** Presents general, technical, and economical information for breeders, especially for the Bruna breeders.
Published by: Associazione Nazionale Allevatori Razza Bruna, Localita Ferlina 204, Bussolengo, VR 37012, Italy. TEL 39-045-6701990, FAX 39-045-7156655, anarb@anarb.it, http://www.anarb.it. Ed. Giuseppe Perotti. Adv. contact Paola Fassini. Circ: 10,000.

636 GBR ISSN 0269-5642
RECENT ADVANCES IN ANIMAL NUTRITION. Text in English. 1977. a. GBP 60 (effective 2005).
—BLDSC (7303.761000), CISTI, IE. **CCC.**
Published by: Nottingham University Press, Manor Farm, Church Lane, Thrumpton, Nottingham, NG11 0AX, United Kingdom. TEL 44-115-9831011, FAX 44-115-9831003, http://nup.com/acatalog/recent_advances_in_animal_nutrition.html. Eds. J Wiseman, P C Garnsworthy.

636 USA ISSN 0034-1614
RECORD STOCKMAN. Text in English. 1889. w. (Wed.). USD 45 (effective 2005). adv. bk.rev. illus.; mkt. **Document type:** *Newspaper.*
Published by: R S Livestock Publishers, 4800 Wadsworth, Ste 320, PO Box 1209, Wheat Ridge, CO 80034-1209. TEL 303-425-5777, FAX 303-431-7545, stockman@recordstockman.com, http://www.recordstockman.com. Ed. Dan Green. Pub. Harry Green Jr. Adv. contact Ann Meyers. Circ: 18,500.

636.2 USA
RED POLL BEEF JOURNAL. Text in English. 1937. s-a. USD 20 (effective 2005). adv. illus.; mkt. **Document type:** *Journal.*
Formerly: Red Poll News (0034-2033)
Published by: American Red Poll Association, PO Box 147, Bethany, MO 64424-0147. TEL 660-425-7318, FAX 660-425-8374. Ed. Ken Harwell. Circ: 1,000 (paid).

636.2 GBR
RED POLL HERD BOOK. Text in English. 1874. a. looseleaf. GBP 20 (effective 2003). adv. back issues avail. **Document type:** *Directory, Trade.*
Published by: Red Poll Cattle Society, 52 Border Cottage Lane, Wickham Market, Woodbridge, Suffolk 1P13 0EZ, United Kingdom. TEL 44-1394-380643, 44-1728-747230, FAX 44-1394-610058, 44-1728-748226. Ed., R&P Mrs. Terina J Booker. Circ: 230 (controlled).

636 ITA ISSN 0370-4327
QL461 CODEN: REDIAI
REDIA. Text in Italian. 1903. a.
Indexed: AgBio, AgrForAb, BIOSIS Prev, BioCN&I, BiolAb, FCA, FPA, ForAb, HerbAb, HortAb, MaizeAb, NemAb, NutrAb, PBA, PHN&I, RA&MP, RPP, RefZh, S&F, SeedAb, SoyAb, VITIS, WeedAb, ZooRec.
—CISTI, Linda Hall.
Published by: Istituto Sperimentale per la Zoologia Agraria/Experimental Institute for Agricultural Zoology, Via Lanciola 12/a, Cascine del Riccio, Florence, 50125, Italy. TEL 39-055-24921, FAX 39-055-209177, isza@fi.flashnet.it, http://www.inea.it/isza/sede/default.htm.

REFERATIVNYI ZHURNAL. BIOLOGIYA SEL'SKOKHOZYAISTVENNYKH ZHIVOTNYKH. see *BIOLOGY—Abstracting, Bibliographies, Statistics*

REFERATIVNYI ZHURNAL. GENETIKA I SELEKTSIYA SEL'SKOKHOZYAISTVENNYKH ZHIVOTNYKH. see *BIOLOGY—Abstracting, Bibliographies, Statistics*

636.2 ITA
REGOLAMENTI DEL LIBRO GENEALOGICO DELLA RAZZA BRUNA. Text in Italian. **Document type:** *Magazine, Trade.* **Description:** Contains Italian Brown breed Herdbook rules, technical rules, and regulations for shows.
Published by: Associazione Nazionale Allevatori Razza Bruna, Localita Ferlina 204, Bussolengo, VR 37012, Italy. TEL 39-045-6701990, FAX 39-045-7156655, anarb@anarb.it, http://www.anarb.it.

THE RETRIEVER JOURNAL. see *SPORTS AND GAMES—Outdoor Life*

636.5 FRA ISSN 1261-4319
REUSSIR AVICULTURE. Text in French. 1994. 10/yr. adv. **Description:** Technical and economical information about poultry and egg production.
Published by: Editions Reussir, 19 quai de Juillet, CP 700, Caen, Cedex 9 1414, France. TEL 33-2-31357700, FAX 33-2-31357718, m.jourdan@reussir.tm.fr. Eds. Marc Jourdan, Pascal Le Douarin. Pub., R&P Marc Jourdan. Adv. contact Jean Pierre Dumas. Circ: 10,000.

636.2 FRA ISSN 1260-1799
REUSSIR BOVINS - VIANDE. Text in French. 1994. 11/yr. adv. **Description:** Technical and economical information about beef production.
Published by: Editions Reussir, 19 quai de Juillet, CP 700, Caen, Cedex 9 1414, France. TEL 33-2-31357700, FAX 33-2-31357718, m.jourdan@reussir.tm.fr. Eds. Marc Jourdan, Francois d'Alteroche. Pub., R&P Marc Jourdan. Adv. contact Jean Pierre Dumas. Circ: 35,000.

636 FRA ISSN 1638-4830
REUSSIR PATRE. Text in French. 1953. 10/yr. FRF 290 domestic; FRF 415 foreign (effective 2000); FRF 45 newsstand/cover. adv. charts; illus.; stat. **Description:** Technical and economic information about sheep breeding.
Formerly (until 2002): Patre (0475-9141)
Indexed: AnBrAb.
—CISTI.
Published by: (Societe de Presse et d'Edition Ovine et Caprine (S.P.E.O.C.)), Editions Reussir, 19 quai de Juillet, CP 700, Caen, Cedex 9 1414, France. TEL 33-2-31357700, FAX 33-2-31357718, m.jourdan@reussir.tm.fr. Eds. Marc Jourdan, Jean-Claude Le Jaouen. Pub. Claude Allo. R&P Marc Jourdan. Adv. contact Jean Pierre Dumas. Circ: 5,300 (controlled). **Co-sponsor:** Institut Technique de l'Elevage Ovin et Caprin.

636.4 FRA ISSN 1261-4327
REUSSIR PORCS. Text in French. 1994. 11/yr. adv. **Description:** Technical and economical information about pig production.
Published by: Editions Reussir, 19 quai de Juillet, CP 700, Caen, Cedex 9 1414, France. TEL 33-2-31357700, FAX 33-2-31357718, m.jourdan@reussir.tm.fr. Eds. Marc Jourdan, Claudine Gerard. Pub., R&P Marc Jourdan. Adv. contact Jean Pierre Dumas. Circ: 14,000.

636.5 BRA ISSN 1516-635X
REVISTA BRASILEIRA DE CIENCIA AVICOLA/BRAZILIAN JOURNAL OF POULTRY SCIENCE. Text in Multiple languages. 1999. 3/yr. USD 30 (effective 2004). **Document type:** *Journal, Trade.*
Related titles: Online - full text ed.: free (effective 2005).
Indexed: AgBio, AnBrAb, IndVet, MaizeAb, PoultAb, ProtozoAb, RM&VM, SIA, SoyAb, TriticAb, WAE&RSA.
Published by: Fundacao APINCO de Ciencia e Tecnologia Avicolas, Av Andrade Neves 2501, castelo, Campinas, SP 13070-002, Brazil. TEL 55-19-32436555, FAX 55-19-32438542.

REVISTA COLOMBIANA DE CIENCIAS PECUARIAS. see *VETERINARY SCIENCE*

636.5 CUB ISSN 0138-6352
REVISTA CUBANA DE CIENCIA AVICOLA. Text in Spanish; Summaries in English, Spanish. 2/yr. USD 16 in South America; USD 20 in North America (effective 2000). adv. bk.rev. abstr.; bibl.; charts; illus. cum.index: 1972-1979. back issues avail. **Document type:** *Academic/Scholarly.*
Related titles: Diskette ed.
Indexed: AEA, AgBio, AgrForAb, AnBrAb, BioCN&I, BiolAb, ChemAb, DSA, FPA, HelmAb, HortAb, IndMed, IndVet, NutrAb, PotatoAb, PoultAb, ProtozoAb, RA&MP, RM&VM, RevApplEntom, RiceAb, SIA, SoyAb, VetBull, WAE&RSA, WeedAb.
Published by: (Biblioteca), Instituto de Investigaciones Avicolas, GAVETA POSTAL, 1, Santiago de las Vegas, Ciudad de La Habana 17200, Cuba. iiacan@ceniai.inf.cu. Ed. Elena Trujillo Gil. Pub. Ramon Elias Laurent. Adv. contact Alberto Ramirez Moreno. **Dist. by:** Empresa Ediciones Cubanas, Apdo. 605, Ciudad De La Habana 1, Cuba.

636 CUB ISSN 0258-6010
REVISTA DE PRODUCCION ANIMAL. Text in Spanish. 1985. 3/yr. USD 20 in the Americas; USD 24 in Europe.
Published by: (Cuba. Ministerio de Educacion Superior), Ediciones Cubanas, Obispo No. 527, Apdo. 605, Havana, Cuba.

636 VEN
REVISTA PECUARIA/RANCHING REVIEW. Text in Spanish. 1938. bi-m.
Published by: Federation Nacional de Ganaderos de Venezuela, Edf. Casa de Italia, Piso 7, Ofc. 16-19, Ave. La Industria San Bernardino, Caracas, 101, Venezuela. Ed. Adolfo Alvarez Perera.

636.5 FRA ISSN 0048-7902
REVUE AVICOLE. Text in French. 1891. 6/yr. adv. bk.rev. illus.; stat. **Description:** Concerned with the breeding of poultry, rabbits, and pigeons.
Published by: Societe Centrale d'Aviculture de France, 34 rue de Lille, Paris, 75007, France. TEL 33-1-42612644. Ed. Jean Claude Periquet.

REVUE DE L'ALIMENTATION ANIMALE; mensuel des industries de la nutrition animale. see *AGRICULTURE—Feed, Flour And Grain*

REVUE D'ELEVAGE ET DE MEDECINE VETERINAIRE DES PAYS TROPICAUX. see *VETERINARY SCIENCE*

636 DEU ISSN 0724-1208
RHEINISCHE FRIEDRICH-WILHELMS-UNIVERSITAET. INSTITUT FUER TIERZUCHTWISSENSCHAFT. ARBEITEN. Text in German. irreg. price varies. **Document type:** *Monographic series, Academic/Scholarly.*
Formerly (until 1981): Rheinische Friedrich-Wilhelms-Universitaet. Institut fuer Tierzucht und Tierfuetterung. Arbeiten (0374-5368)
Published by: Rheinische Friedrich-Wilhelms-Universitaet, Institut fuer Tierzuchtwissenschaft, Endenicher Allee 15, Bonn, 53115, Germany. TEL 49-228-739328, FAX 49-228-732284, itz@uni-bonn.de, http://www.itz.uni-bonn.de.

636 DEU
RIND IM BILD. Text in German. 1922. q. EUR 25.50 (effective 2001). adv. bk.rev. abstr.; charts; illus.; mkt.; stat. **Document type:** *Magazine, Trade.*

Former titles: Bullen (0942-282X); (until 1992): Angler Rinderzucht (0171-7383); (until 1977): Angler Tierzucht (0003-3227)
Published by: (Rinderzucht Schleswig-Holstein eG), Rind im Bild Selbstverlag, Rendsburger Str 178, Neumuenster, 24537, Germany. TEL 49-4321-905300, FAX 49-4321-905395, rsheg@rsheg.de. Ed. H. Ruediger Wolf. adv.: color page EUR 1,280. **Co-sponsor:** Landeskontrollverband Schleswig-Holstein e.V.

636.2 DEU ISSN 0948-9118
RINDERZUCHT BRAUNVIEH. Variant title: Braunvieh. Text in German. 1995. q. EUR 18.40 to members; EUR 22 to non-members; EUR 5.60 newsstand/cover (effective 2004). adv. **Document type:** *Magazine, Trade.*
Related titles: Online - full text ed.
Published by: Deutscher Landwirtschaftsverlag GmbH, Lothstr 29, Munich, 80797, Germany. TEL 49-89-127051, FAX 49-89-12705335, redbraun@dlv.de, dlv.muenchen@dlv.de, http://www.rinderzucht-braunvieh.de, http://www.dlv.de. Ed. Johannes Urban. Adv. contact Henning Stemmler. B&W page EUR 2,419, color page EUR 3,780; trim 188 x 270. Circ: 14,850 (paid and controlled).

636.2 DEU ISSN 0948-7247
RINDERZUCHT FLECKVIEH. Variant title: Fleckvieh. Text in German. 19??. q. EUR 20.20 to non-members; EUR 18 to members; EUR 5.70 newsstand/cover (effective 2004). adv. **Document type:** *Magazine, Trade.*
Related titles: Online - full text ed.
Published by: Deutscher Landwirtschaftsverlag GmbH, Lothstr 29, Munich, 80797, Germany. TEL 49-89-127051, FAX 49-89-12705335, redfleck@dlv.de, dlv.muenchen@dlv.de, http://www.rinderzucht-fleckvieh.de, http://www.dlv.de. Ed. Johannes Urban. Adv. contact Henning Stemmler. B&W page EUR 3,175, color page EUR 4,774; trim 188 x 270. Circ: 18,262 (paid and controlled).

636.5 ITA ISSN 0005-2213
RIVISTA DI AVICOLTURA. Short title: A V. Text in Italian. 1931. bi-m. EUR 52 domestic; EUR 75 foreign (effective 2005). adv. bk.rev. bibl.; charts; illus.; mkt.; stat.; tr.lit.; tr.mk. index. 48 p./no.; **Document type:** *Magazine, Trade.* **Description:** Shows the problems of Italian poultry breeding in a worldwide context.
Indexed: AEA, AgBio, AnBrAb, BioCN&I, DSA, IndVet, MaizeAb, NutrAb, PBA, PN&I, PotatoAb, PoultAb, ProtozoAb, RM&VM, RPP, RevApplEntom, S&F, SoyAb, TriticAb, VetBull, WAE&RSA.
—BLDSC (7981.620000), IE, ingenta.
Published by: Il Sole 24 Ore Edagricole, Via Goito 13, Bologna, BO 40126, Italy. TEL 39-051-62267, FAX 39-051-490200, http://www.edagricole.it. Ed. Giorgio Setti. Circ: 3,900.

636.9322 ITA ISSN 0010-5929
RIVISTA DI CONIGLICOLTURA. Short title: C N. Text in Italian. 1963; N.S.. bi-m. EUR 52 domestic; EUR 75 foreign (effective 2005). adv. bk.rev. charts; illus. index. 48 p./no.; **Document type:** *Magazine, Trade.* **Description:** For breeders of rabbits and fur animals.
Indexed: AEA, AgBio, AnBrAb, DSA, IndVet, NutrAb, PBA, PN&I, PoultAb, ProtozoAb, RA&MP, RDA, RM&VM, TriticAb, VetBull, WAE&RSA.
—BLDSC (7984.200000), IE, ingenta.
Published by: Il Sole 24 Ore Edagricole, Via Goito 13, Bologna, BO 40126, Italy. TEL 39-051-62267, FAX 39-051-490200, http://www.edagricole.it. Ed. Giorgio Setti. Circ: 2,600.

636.4 ITA ISSN 0035-662X
RIVISTA DI SUINICOLTURA; rivista tecnico-economica per gli allevatori di suini. Short title: S N. Text in Italian. 1959. m. EUR 62 domestic; EUR 110 foreign (effective 2005). adv. 80 p./no.; **Document type:** *Magazine, Trade.* **Description:** Deals with all economic problems of pig breeding, feeding, processing and marketing.
Formerly (until 1976): Suinicoltura (1124-6995)
Indexed: AEA, AbHyg, AgBio, AnBrAb, BioCN&I, DSA, HelmAb, HerbAb, HortAb, IndVet, MaizeAb, NutrAb, PN&I, PoultAb, ProtozoAb, RA&MP, RDA, RM&VM, RevApplEntom, S&F, SIA, SoyAb, TriticAb, VetBull, WAE&RSA.
—BLDSC (7993.220000), IE, ingenta.
Published by: Il Sole 24 Ore Edagricole, Via Goito 13, Bologna, BO 40126, Italy. TEL 39-051-62267, FAX 39-051-490200, http://www.edagricole.it. Ed. Giorgio Setti. Circ: 4,800.

636.3 GBR
ROMNEY SHEEP BREEDERS' SOCIETY. HANDBOOK. Text in English. 1895. a. free. adv. **Document type:** *Trade.*
Formerly: Romney Sheep Breeders' Society. Flock Book (0305-5965)
Published by: Romney Sheep Breeders' Society, 2 Woodland Close, W Malling, Kent ME19 GRR, United Kingdom. TEL 44-1497-363839, FAX 44-1497-363839, alan.t.west@btinternet.com. R&P Alan West TEL 44-1732-845637. Circ: 2,000.

ROULEI YANJIU/MEAT RESEARCH. see *FOOD AND FOOD INDUSTRIES*

636 USA ISSN 0889-2970
RURAL HERITAGE; in support of farming and logging with horses, mules and oxen since 1976. Text in English. 1976. bi-m. USD 28 domestic; USD 35 in Canada; USD 40 elsewhere (effective 2005). bk.rev.; video rev. illus.; mkt. 100 p./no.; back issues avail.; reprints avail. **Document type:** *Journal, Trade.* **Description:** For farmers, loggers, and others who use draft animal power.
Formerly: Evener (0164-6613)
Related titles: Online - full content ed.: 1997.
Indexed: Agr.
Address: 281 Dean Ridge Ln, Gainesboro, TN 38562-5039. TEL 931-268-0655, editor@ruralheritage.com, http://www.ruralheritage.com. Ed., R&P, Adv. contact Gail Damerow. Pub. Allan Damerow. Circ: 4,500 (paid).

636.085 USA ISSN 0036-0104
RURAL ROUNDUP. Text in English. 1950. a. free. charts; illus.
Published by: Kent Feeds Inc., 1600 Oregon St, Muscatine, IA 52761. TEL 319-264-4211.

RWANDA. MINISTERE DE L'AGRICULTURE ET DE L'ELEVAGE. RAPPORT ANNUEL. see *AGRICULTURE*

636.3 AUS
S A C S O S NEWSLETTER. Text in English. 1974. m. AUD 15. back issues avail. **Document type:** *Newsletter.* **Description:** For breeders of colored sheep and users of natural colored wool.
Published by: South Australian Coloured Sheep Owners' Society Inc., PO Box 110, Fullarton, SA 5063, Australia. Ed. Verle Wood.

636.2 ZAF
S A HOLSTEIN JOURNAL/S A HOLSTEIN JOERNAAL. Text and summaries in Afrikaans, English. 1912. 3/yr. ZAR 20 domestic; ZAR 73 foreign (effective 2000). adv. illus.; stat. **Document type:** *Trade.* **Description:** Contains Holstein and other dairy related articles concerning the breed. Articles art mostly based on being informative and useful (educational) to the dairy breeder & farmer. Feedback is given on shows, sales (holstein), overseas tour groups to international dairy events and other breed activities.
Former titles (until 1999): S A Holstein Friesland Journal (1018-6492); (until 1991): South African Friesland Journal (0036-0724)
Indexed: DSA, ISAP.
—CISTI.
Published by: S. A. Holstein, PO Box 544, Bloemfontein, 9300, South Africa. TEL 27-51-4479123, FAX 27-51-4304224, info@saholstein.co.za, http://www.saholstein.co.za. Ed., R&P, Adv. contact Andra Welthagen. B&W page ZAR 1,069, color page ZAR 1,336; trim 210 x 297. Circ: 1,500 (paid).

636.2 ZAF ISSN 1561-3305
S A HOLSTEINER. (selected articles avail. by fax) Text in Afrikaans, English. 1991. s-a. ZAR 2.50 domestic; ZAR 30 foreign (effective 2000). adv. illus. back issues avail. **Document type:** *Trade.* **Description:** Offers members, who represent highly specialized breeds of holstein cattle, informative and useful news and articles on dairy-related issues; alerts readers to important events.
Former titles (until 1999): S A Holstein Frieslander (1025-0522); (until 1995): S A Holstein Friesland Mini Journal (1018-6506)
Indexed: ISAP.
Published by: S. A. Holstein, PO Box 544, Bloemfontein, 9300, South Africa. TEL 27-51-4479123, FAX 27-51-4304224, info@saholstein.co.za, http://www.saholstein.co.za. Ed., R&P, Adv. contact Andra Welthagen. B&W page ZAR 2,020, color page ZAR 2,316; trim 210 x 145. Circ: 10,000 (paid).

S A MEAT - VLEIS. see *FOOD AND FOOD INDUSTRIES*

636.4 DNK ISSN 1604-5874
S P F-SUNDHEDSREGLER FOR S P F-BESAETNINGER. (Specific Pathogene Free) Text in Danish. 2001. a. **Document type:** *Trade.* **Description:** Covers health rules in hog farming in Denmark.
Formerly (until 2003): S P F-Sundhedsregler for Roede og Blaa Besaetninger (1603-2764)
Published by: Danske Slagterier, SPF-Sundhedsstyringen, Drejervej 7, Vejen, 6600, Denmark. TEL 45-76-964600, FAX 45-76-964700, post@spfsus.dk, http://www.spf.dk/sw/default3.asp?layout=3, http://www.spfsus.dk.

636.4 DEU ISSN 0944-307X
S U S - SCHWEINEZUCHT UND SCHWEINEMAST. Text in German. 1953. 6/yr. EUR 37.20 domestic; EUR 43.20 foreign; EUR 6.50 newsstand/cover (effective 2003). adv. bk.rev. bibl.; charts; illus. index. **Document type:** *Magazine, Trade.*
Formerly (until 1992): Schweinezucht und Schweinemast (0036-7176)
Indexed: AnBrAb, DSA, FS&TA, IndVet, NutrAb, VetBull.
—CCC.
Published by: (Zentralverband der Deutschen Schweineproduktion e.V.), Landwirtschaftsverlag GmbH, Huelsebrockstr 2, Muenster, 48165, Germany. TEL 49-2501-801-0, FAX 49-2501-801204, susservice@landwirtschaftsverlag.com, zentrale@lv-h.de, http://www.lv-h.de. Ed. Heinrich Niggemeyer. Adv. contact Paul Pankoke. B&W page EUR 2,375, color page EUR 3,920. Circ: 15,498.

636 USA
SALT AND TRACE MINERALS NEWSLETTER. Text in English. 1966. s-a. free (effective 2000). **Document type:** *Newsletter.*
Formerly: Agricultural Digest (0568-2622)
Published by: Salt Institute, 700 N Fairfax St, Ste 600, Alexandria, VA 22314-2040. TEL 703-549-4648, FAX 703-548-2194, info@saltinstitute.org, http://www.saltinstitute.org. Ed. Andrew Briscoe. Circ: 2,500.

636.2142 ESP
SAM. Text in Spanish. 1952. q. free.
Published by: Cooperativa Lechera S A M, Barrio de San Antonio s-n, Renedo De Pielagos, Cantabria 39470, Spain. TEL 42-57-03-43, FAX 42-57-07-86. Ed. Juan Ignacio de Sebastian Palomares. Circ: 12,000.

636.2 USA ISSN 0036-455X
SANTA GERTRUDIS JOURNAL★ . Text in English. 1959. m. USD 15. adv. illus.; stat. index. reprints avail. **Document type:** *Trade.*
Address: 1965 Summer Ln, Roanoke, TX 76262-9130. Circ: 3,600.

636.3 NOR ISSN 0036-5009
SAU OG GEIT. Text in Norwegian. 1947. bi-m. NOK 330 (effective 1998). adv. bk.rev. illus. **Description:** Provides articles and information on animal husbandry, particularly that of sheep and goat breeding.
Indexed: AnBrAb, NutrAb.
—CCC.
Published by: Norsk Sau- og Geitalslag/Norwegian Sheep and Goatbreeders Association, Postboks 2323, Solli, Oslo, 0201, Norway. TEL 47-02-444288, FAX 47-2-43-16-60. Ed. Arne Maurtvedt. Circ: 21,000.

636.3 NLD ISSN 0165-3156
HET SCHAAP. Text in Dutch. 1956. 10/yr. EUR 57 (effective 2005). adv. bk.rev. charts; illus.; stat. **Document type:** *Trade.* **Description:** Publishes specialist trade news about sheep farming in the Netherlands.
Published by: (Nederlands Texels Schapenstamboek en Noord Hollands Schapenstamboek/Studbook Organisations for Sheepbreeding in the Netherlands), Reed Business Information bv (Subsidiary of: Reed Business), Hanzestraat 1, Doetinchem, 7006 RH, Netherlands. TEL 31-314-349911, FAX 31-314-343839, info@reedbusiness.nl, http://www.productonline.reedbusiness.nl/product.asp?catalog%5Fname=RBI&category%5Fname=&product%5Fid=063%28Octopus%29, http://www.reedbusiness.nl. Ed. Wim Wisman. adv.: B&W page EUR 1,154, color page EUR 1,983; trim 215 x 285. Circ: 9,300.

636.3 AUT
SCHAFE UND ZIEGEN AKTUELL. Text in German. 1991. q. EUR 14.10 domestic; EUR 17.90 foreign; EUR 4.60 newsstand/cover (effective 2005). adv. **Document type:** *Magazine, Trade.*
Formerly: Schafe Aktuell
Published by: Leopold Stocker Verlag, Hofgasse 5, Graz, St 8011, Austria. TEL 43-316-821636, FAX 43-316-835612, stocker-verlag@stocker-verlag.com, http://www.stocker-verlag.com/landwirtschaftliche-Zeitschriften-38-10/Schafe-und-Ziegen-aktuell.html. Ed. Ferdinand Ringdorfer. Adv. contact Manuela Jantscher. B&W page EUR 953, color page EUR 1,868; trim 190 x 260. Circ: 7,000.

636 CHE
SCHWEIZER FLECKVIEH. Text in French, German. 8/yr. **Document type:** *Trade.*
Formerly: Simmentaler Fleckvieh (0258-6509)
Indexed: AEA, AgBio, AnBrAb, DSA, IndVet, NutrAb, VetBull, WAE&RSA.
Published by: Schweizerische Fleckviehzuchtverband, Zollikofen, 3052, Switzerland. TEL 031-9106111, FAX 031-9106199. Ed. Niklaus Flueckiger. Circ: 14,500.

636.5 CHE ISSN 1420-9217
SCHWEIZERISCHE GEFLUEGELZEITUNG. Text in German. 1939. m. CHF 39. adv. bk.rev. charts; illus. **Document type:** *Newspaper.*
Former titles: Geflugel und Kleinvieh (0016-5832); Gefluegelhof
Published by: Verlag Schweizerische Gefluegelzeitung, Burgerweg 24, Zollikofen, 3052, Switzerland. TEL 41-31-9110127, FAX 41-31-9116460, sgz@pop.agri.ch. Ed. H R Meier. R&P, Adv. contact Manuel Strasser. Circ: 1,300.

636 CHE
SCHWEIZERISCHE VIEHAENDLER ZEITUNG. Text in French, German, Italian. q.
Address: Postfach 53, Oberegg, 9413, Switzerland. TEL 01-2563209. Ed. A Schuler. Circ: 1,779.

636.4 USA ISSN 1079-7963
SEEDSTOCK EDGE. Text in English. 1994. 9/yr. USD 25 domestic; USD 50 foreign (effective 2005). adv. illus.; mkt. **Document type:** *Magazine, Trade.* **Description:** Includes swine-based articles, specializing in genetics and the sale of breeding stock.
Formed by the 1994 merger of: Duroc News (0012-7299); American Hampshire Herdsman (0002-8681)
—CISTI, Linda Hall.

Published by: National Swine Registry, 1769 U S Hwy 52 W, PO Box 2417, West Lafayette, IN 47996-2417. TEL 765-463-3594, FAX 765-497-2959, nsr@nationalswine.com, http://www.nationalswine.com/. Ed. Darrell Anderson. adv.: page USD 350. Circ: 6,500 (paid).

SEIBUTSU SEISANGAKU KENKYU/HIROSHIMA UNIVERSITY. FACULTY OF APPLIED BIOLOGICAL SCIENCE. JOURNAL. see *AGRICULTURE—Dairying And Dairy Products*

338.1 637.5 ESP ISSN 0210-0541
SELECCIONES AVICOLAS. Text in Spanish. 1959. m. EUR 49.04 domestic; EUR 80 foreign (effective 2004). adv. bk.rev. abstr.; illus.; stat.; bibl.; mkt. index. back issues avail. **Document type:** *Trade.* **Description:** Serves the poultry industry in Spain and Latin American countries.
Published by: Real Escuela de Avicultura, Plana del Paraiso 14, Arenys De Mar, Barcelona 08350, Spain. TEL 34-93-7921137, FAX 34-93-7921537, avinet@avicultura.com, http://www.avicultura.com. Ed., Pub. Jose A Castello. Adv. contact Luis Carrasco. Circ: 3,100.

636 FRA
SELECTIONS AVICOLES; aviculture, colombiculture, cuniculture. Text in French. 1962. m. (10/yr.). adv.
Published by: Editions H. Artese, B.P. 245, Agen, Cedex 47006, France. TEL 53-66-51-13, FAX 53-66-67-33. Circ: 16,000.

636.5 CAN ISSN 0315-6915
SHAVER FOCUS. Text in English. 1964. 2/yr. free. charts; illus. **Document type:** *Newsletter.* **Description:** Contains technical information relating to the production of eggs and meat chickens. Includes nutrition, disease control, breeding and genetics, management and husbandry, economics, processing and marketing.
—CISTI.
Published by: Shaver Poultry Breeding Farms, Ltd., P O Box 400, Cambridge, ON N1R 5V9, Canada. TEL 519-621-5191, FAX 519-621-9407, TELEX 069-59337, info@shaverpoultry.com. Ed. Dr. Peter Hunton. Circ: 5,000.

636.3 USA
SHEEP & GOAT RESEARCH JOURNAL. Text in English. 1984. 3/yr. USD 40; USD 55 foreign (effective 2000). abstr.; charts; stat. back issues avail. **Document type:** *Academic/Scholarly.* **Description:** Reports on research on the keeping of sheep and goats in agriculture.
Indexed: Agr, AnBrAb, DSA, FS&TA, IndVet, MaizeAb, NutrAb, RevApplEntom, SoyAb, TriticAb, VetBull, WAE&RSA, WeedAb.
—ingenta.
Published by: National Institute of Animal Agriculture, 1910 Lyda Drive, Bowling Green, KY 42104. TEL 502-782-9798, FAX 502-782-0188, lci@premiernet.net, sheep2goat@aol.com, http://www.lcionline.org. Ed. Maurice Shelton. Pub. Glenn N Slack. **Subscr. to:** PO Box 51267, Bowling Green, KY 42102-5567.

636.3 ETH
SHEEP AND GOATS IN HUMID WEST AFRICA. Text in English. irreg.
Published by: International Livestock Centre for Africa, PO Box 5689, Addis Ababa, Ethiopia.

636.3 USA ISSN 0037-3400
SHEEP BREEDER AND SHEEPMAN. Text in English. 1880. m. USD 18. adv. bk.rev. charts.
—CISTI, Linda Hall.
Published by: Mead Livestock Services, PO Box 796, Columbia, MO 65205. TEL 314-442-8257. Ed. Larry E Mead. Circ: 10,000.

636.3 GBR ISSN 0141-2434
THE SHEEP FARMER. Text in English. 1974. m. GBP 20 domestic; GBP 30 foreign (effective 2000). adv. bk.rev. **Document type:** *Trade.* **Description:** Studies all aspects of the production and marketing of sheep and wool.
Published by: National Sheep Association, c/o John Kendall, Ed, 28 Newport St, London, W1X 4JY, United Kingdom. TEL 44-20-7624-5731, FAX 44-20-7624-6645. Ed. John Kendall. Adv. contact Mandy Burgess. Circ: 11,000.

636.3 677.3 USA ISSN 0279-9200
SHEEP MAGAZINE; the magazine for entrepreneurial flockmasters. Text in English. 1979. m. USD 21 (effective 2005). adv. bk.rev. illus. back issues avail. **Document type:** *Magazine, Trade.* **Description:** Contains information of interest to owners of sheep, wool producers, lamb producers, and those involved in wool crafts industries.
Published by: Countryside Publications, Ltd., 145 Industrial Dr, Medford, WI 54451. TEL 715-785-7979, FAX 715-785-7414, http://www.sheepmagazine.com. Ed. Nathan Griffith. Pub. Dave Belanger. Adv. contact Alicia Komanec. page USD 649; trim 8.5 x 11. Circ: 7,500 (paid).

636.3 USA ISSN 8750-7897
THE SHEPHERD; a guide for sheep and farm life. Text in English. 1956. m. USD 25 (effective 2005). adv. bk.rev. illus. index. 52 p./no. 3 cols./p.; back issues avail. **Document type:** *Magazine, Trade.* **Description:** Devoted to all aspects of the sheep industry. Produced on a sheep farm by a staff having over 100 years experience in sheep raising and farm life.
—IE.
Published by: Sheep and Farm Life, Inc., 5696 Johnston Rd, New Washington, OH 44854. TEL 419-492-2364, FAX 419-947-1302, shepmag@bright.net. Ed. Guy Flora. R&P Pat Flora. Circ: 4,800 (paid).

636 USA ISSN 0149-9319
SHORTHORN COUNTRY. Text in English. 1976. m. (except Jun.). USD 24 (effective 2004). adv. back issues avail. **Document type:** *Magazine, Trade.* **Description:** Presents articles on management and the beef industry for producers of Shorthorn beef cattle.
—CISTI.
Published by: Durham Management Co., 8288 Hascall St, Omaha, NE 68124-3234. TEL 402-393-7051, FAX 402-393-7080, http://www.beefshorthornusa.com. Eds. Arin Strasburg, Debbie Hostert. Pub. Don Cagwin. adv.: page USD 540. Circ: 3,000 (paid).

636.234 GBR ISSN 0141-4895
SHORTHORN JOURNAL. Text in English. 1932. s-a. GBP 6, USD 10 (effective 2000). adv. bk.rev. illus. **Document type:** *Trade.*
Formerly (until 1978): Dairy Shorthorn Journal (0011-569X)
Published by: Shorthorn Society of Great Britain and Ireland, 4th St, National Agricultural Centre, Stoneleigh Park, Kenilworth, Warks CV8 2LG, United Kingdom. TEL 44-2476-696549, FAX 44-2476-696729, mtaggart@shorthorn.freeserve.co.uk, http://www.shorthorn.co.uk. Ed. Martin Taggart. Circ: 1,000.

636.2 CAN ISSN 0037-427X
SF199.S56
SHORTHORN NEWS. Text in English. 1940. 8/yr. CND 20. adv. illus.
—CISTI.
Published by: Progress Typesetting, P O Box 63, Quappelle, SK S0G 4A0, Canada. TEL 306-699-7110, FAX 306-699-7111. Ed. Craig Andrew. Circ: 11,800.

636.4 FIN ISSN 0037-5101
SIKA/PIG. Text in Finnish; Summaries in Swedish. 1910. 5/yr. EUR 49 (effective 2005). adv. illus.; stat. **Document type:** *Magazine, Trade.*
Published by: Suomen Kotielainjalostusosuuskunta/Finnish Animal Breeding Association - FABA, PO Box 40, Vantaa, 01301, Finland. TEL 358-20-7472020, FAX 358-20-7472021, toimitus@faba.fi, http://www.faba.fi. Ed. Jouko Syvaerjaervi. adv.: B&W page EUR 1,240, color page EUR 2,080; 210 x 297. Circ: 5,000.

636.2 630 AUS
SIMBEEF. Text in English. 1974. 4/yr. AUD 30 (effective 2000). adv. charts; illus.; tr.lit. **Document type:** *Newsletter, Trade.* **Description:** Covers news relating to Australian Simmental, Simbeef and Simbrah cattle.
Formerly (until 1995): Simmental News (0815-6077)
Indexed: AnBrAb, DSA, IndVet.
Published by: Australian Simmental Breeders Association Ltd., GPO Box 5219, Sydney, NSW 2001, Australia. TEL 61-2-97646111, FAX 61-2-97646100, speers@simmental.com.au. Ed. P Speers. Circ: 2,000.

636.2 ZAF
SIMMBULLETIN. Text in Afrikaans, English. 1986. irreg., latest 1994. **Document type:** *Bulletin.*
Formerly (until 1993): Kliente Bulletin - Clients Bulletin
Published by: Simmentaler Cattle Breeders' Society of S.A./Simmentaler Beestelersgenootskap van S.A., PO Box 3868, Bloemfontein, 9300, South Africa. TEL 27-51-477696, FAX 27-51-471529.

636 GBR
SIMMENTAL ANNUAL REVIEW. Text in English. 1972. a. GBP 20 (effective 2001). adv. **Document type:** *Bulletin.*
Published by: British Simmental Cattle Society, National Agricultural Centre, Stoneleigh Park, Kenilworth, Warks CV8 2LR, United Kingdom. TEL 44-2476-696513, FAX 44-2476-696724, information@britishsimmental.co.uk, http://www.britishsimmental.co.uk. Ed., Adv. contact Roger Trewhella. Circ: 2,750.

636 USA ISSN 0192-3072
SIMMENTAL SHIELD. Text in English. 1972. m. USD 18. adv. back issues avail.; reprints avail.
Published by: (American Simmental Association), Shield Publishing Co. Inc., PO Box 71, Lindsborg, KS 67456-0071. Circ: 7,000.

636.2 ZAF
SIMMENTALER JOURNAL. Text in Afrikaans, English. 1976. a. USD 30. adv. **Document type:** *Trade.*
Published by: Simmentaler Cattle Breeders' Society of S.A./Simmentaler Beestelersgenootskap van S.A., PO Box 3868, Bloemfontein, 9300, South Africa. TEL 27-51-477696, FAX 27-51-471529. Ed. C P Massmann. Circ: 1,200 (controlled).

636.2 DNK ISSN 1602-6314
SIMMENTALEREN. Text in Danish. 1996. q. DKK 650 membership (effective 2004). adv. **Document type:** *Trade.*
Supersedes in part (in 2000): Dansk Koedkvaeg (1397-3592)
Published by: Simmentalerforeningen for Danmark/Danish Simmental Society, c/o Verner Olesen, Nyhavevej 1 A, Kappendrup, Langeskov, 5550, Denmark. TEL 45-65-972840, FAX 45-65-972880. Ed. Laurits Schytz TEL 45-75-873144. Adv. contact Soeren Grunnel TEL 45-75-332019.

636.5 MEX
SINTESIS-AVICOLA. Text in Spanish. m. MXP 940.
Published by: Editorial Ano Dos Mil, S.A., Indianapolis 70, Mexico City, DF 03810, Mexico. Ed. Juan Francisco Gonzalez Inigo.

636.4 MEX
SINTESIS-PORCINA. Text in Spanish. m. MXP 940.
Published by: Editorial Ano Dos Mil, S.A., Indianapolis 70, Mexico City, DF 03810, Mexico. Ed. J Mario Montanez.

338.1 USA
HD9411
SITUATION & OUTLOOK REPORT. LIVESTOCK, DAIRY AND POULTRY. Text in English. 1937. m. USD 72 (effective 2001). charts; mkt.; stat. index. reprint service avail. from CIS. **Document type:** *Government.* **Description:** Contains timely livestock, dairy and poultry information focusing on current production, price, and trade statistics for each of the sectors.
Formerly (until 1998): Livestock, Dairy and Poultry Monthly; (until 1996): Livestock, Dairy and Poultry Situation & Outlook (1076-2183); Incorporates (1994-1996): Hog Outlook (1080-9627); (1994-1996): Cattle and Sheep Outlook (1080-0719); (1994-1996): Poultry Outlook (1080-0700); Formed by the 1994 merger of: Livestock and Poultry Update (1048-1605); Situation and Outlook Report. Dairy (1050-9151); Which was formerly (until 1986): Outlook and Situation Report. Dairy (0889-9835); (until 1984): Dairy Outlook and Situation (0734-9505); (until 1981): Dairy Situation (0011-5703); Situation and Outlook Report. Livestock and Poultry (1054-0849); Which was formerly (until 1986): Livestock and Poultry Outlook and Situation; Livestock and Poultry Situation; Livestock and Meat Outlook and Situation (0278-923X); Livestock and Meat Situation (0024-516X); Poultry and Egg Outlook and Situation (0277-0814); Poultry and Egg Situation (0032-5708)
Related titles: Microfiche ed.: (from CIS); Online - full text ed.: (from Gale Group, The Dialog Corporation); ♦ Supplement(s): Aquaculture Outlook.
Indexed: AmStI, PN&I, RASB.
—CISTI.
Published by: U.S. Department of Agriculture, Economic Research Service, c/o Debbie Haugan, 1800 M St, N W, Rm 3100, Washington, DC 20036. TEL 202-694-5050, http://www.ers.usda.gov/publications/so/view.asp?f=livestock/ldp-mbb/. **Dist. by:** ERS-NASS.

636.3 NLD ISSN 0921-4488
CODEN: SRUREW
➤ **SMALL RUMINANT RESEARCH.** Text in English; Summaries in French, German, Spanish. 1980-1984; N.S. 1988. 18/yr. EUR 1,714 in Europe to institutions; JPY 227,500 in Japan to institutions; USD 1,917 elsewhere to institutions (effective 2006). bk.rev. reprints avail. **Document type:** *Academic/Scholarly.* **Description:** Covers nutrition, physiology, anatomy, genetics, microbiology, ethology, product technology, socio-economics, management, veterinary medicine and husbandry engineering.
Formerly (until 1984): International Goat and Sheep Research (0197-7393)
Related titles: Microform ed.: N.S. (from PQC); Online - full text ed.: (from EBSCO Publishing, Gale Group, IngentaConnect, ScienceDirect, Swets Information Services).
Indexed: AEA, ASCA, AgBio, Agr, AgrForAb, AnBrAb, BIOBASE, BIOSIS Prev, BibAg, BiolAb, ChemAb, CurCont, DBA, DSA, FPA, FS&TA, FoVS&M, ForAb, HelmAb, HerbAb, HortAb, IndVet, MEDLINE, MaizeAb, NutrAb, OrnHort, PBA, PGegResA, PHN&I, PN&I, PoultAb, ProtozoAb, RA&MP, RDA, RM&VM, RPP, RRTA, RevApplEntom, RiceAb, SIA, SoyAb, TDB, TriticAb, VetBull, WAE&RSA, WeedAb, WildRev.
—BLDSC (8310.140000), CASDDS, CISTI, IDS, IE, Infotrieve, ingenta, Linda Hall. **CCC.**
Published by: (International Goat Association), Elsevier BV (Subsidiary of: Elsevier Science & Technology), Radarweg 29, Amsterdam, 1043 NX, Netherlands. TEL 31-20-4853911, FAX 31-20-4852457, nlinfo-f@elsevier.nl, http://www.elsevier.com/locate/smallrumres, http://www.elsevier.nl. Ed. J Boyazoglu. Circ: 500.

636 KEN
SMALL RUMINANT RESEARCH NETWORK NEWSLETTER. Text in English. 1984. 3/yr. free. bk.rev. **Document type:** *Newsletter.*
Formerly: Small Ruminant and Camel Group Newsletter
Published by: International Livestock Center for Africa, PO Box 46847, Nairobi, Kenya. FAX 254-2-631481, TELEX 25747 ILCA KE. Ed. S H B Lebbie. Circ: 1,400.

630 ARG ISSN 0037-8631
S15
SOCIEDAD RURAL ARGENTINA. ANALES. Text in Spanish. 1866. 10/yr. ARS 22,000. adv.
Related titles: ♦ Supplement(s): Sociedad Rural Argentina. Memoria. ISSN 0081-0630.
Indexed: BiolAb, ChemAb, IBR.
—CISTI.

Published by: Sociedad Rural Argentina, Florida, 460, Capital Federal, Buenos Aires 1005, Argentina. Circ: 15,000.

338.1 ARG ISSN 0081-0630
SOCIEDAD RURAL ARGENTINA. MEMORIA. Text in Spanish. 1887. a. free.
Related titles: ♦ Supplement to: Sociedad Rural Argentina. Anales. ISSN 0037-8631.
—CISTI.
Published by: Sociedad Rural Argentina, Florida, 460, Capital Federal, Buenos Aires 1005, Argentina. Circ: 15,000.

SOCIETE D'ETHNOZOOTECHNIE. LETTRE. see *BIOLOGY—Zoology*

SOCIETY FOR RANGE MANAGEMENT. INTERNATIONAL RANGELAND CONGRESS. ABSTRACTS OF PAPERS. see *AGRICULTURE—Abstracting, Bibliographies, Statistics*

636 ZAF ISSN 0375-1589
CODEN: SAJAC9
➤ **SOUTH AFRICAN JOURNAL OF ANIMAL SCIENCE.** Text in English. 1971. 3/yr. ZAR 250 domestic; USD 100 foreign (effective 2004). adv. **Document type:** *Academic/Scholarly.* **Description:** Publishes original contributions in animal science research.
Incorporates: South African Society of Animal Production. Proceedings. Handelinge (0081-2536); And (1958-1981): Agroanimalia (0302-7104); Which superseded in part (in 1969): Suid-Afrikaanse Tydskrif vir Landbouwetenskap/South African Journal of Agricultural Science (0585-8860)
Related titles: Online - full text ed.: free (effective 2005) (from EBSCO Publishing, International Network for the Availability of Scientific Publications, African Journals Online).
Indexed: AEA, ASCA, ASFA, AgBio, Agr, AgrForAb, AnBrAb, BIOSIS Prev, BiolAb, CIN, ChemAb, ChemTitl, CurCont, DBA, DSA, FCA, FPA, FS&TA, FoVS&M, HerbAb, HortAb, INIS AtomInd, ISAP, IndVet, MaizeAb, NutrAb, PBA, PHN&I, PN&I, PoultAb, RA&MP, RDA, RM&VM, RRTA, RefZh, S&F, S&MA, SFA, SIA, SoyAb, TriticAb, VetBull, WAE&RSA, WildRev, ZooRec.
—BLDSC (8338.650000), CASDDS, CISTI, IDS, IE, Infotrieve, ingenta, Linda Hall.
Published by: (South African Society of Animal Science), South African Bureau for Scientific Publications, PO Box 11663, Pretoria, Hatfield 0028, South Africa. TEL 27-12-322-6404, FAX 27-12-320-7803, bspman@icon.co.za, http://www.inasp.info/ajol/journals/sajas/about.html, http://www.safest.org.za/bsp. Ed., Adv. contact J G van der Walt. Circ: 700.

636.5 ZAF ISSN 0257-201X
SOUTH AFRICAN POULTRY BULLETIN. Text in Afrikaans, English. 1906. m. ZAR 250 domestic; ZAR 430 foreign. adv. bk.rev. back issues avail. **Document type:** *Trade.*
Indexed: AEA, AbHyg, AgBio, AnBrAb, BioCN&I, HerbAb, ISAP, IndVet, MaizeAb, NutrAb, PBA, PHN&I, PoultAb, ProtozoAb, RDA, RM&VM, RPP, S&F, SoyAb, VetBull, WAE&RSA.
Published by: (South African Poultry Association), Promass (Pty) Ltd., PO Box 1192, Honeydew, Gauteng 2040, South Africa. TEL 27-11-7952051, FAX 27-11-7953180, sapa@pixie.co.za. Ed. Zach Coetzee. adv.: B&W page ZAR 1,050; trim 210 x 300. Circ: 2,250.

636 USA ISSN 0038-3384
SOUTH DAKOTA STOCKGROWER. Text in English. 1930. bi-m. USD 35; USD 5 per issue (effective 2004). adv. illus. **Document type:** *Magazine, Trade.*
—Linda Hall.
Published by: South Dakota Stock Growers Association, 426 St Joesph St, Rapid City, SD 57701. TEL 605-342-0429, FAX 605-342-0463, carriesdsga@mcleodusa.net. Circ: 1,800 (controlled).

636.2 USA
SOUTHERN CATTLE✶. Text in English. 1992. q. free. **Document type:** *Newspaper.*
Published by: Rural Press U S A, 1101 Spring Forest Rd, Ste 101, Raleigh, NC 27615. TEL 919-676-3276, 800-477-1737, FAX 919-676-9803. Ed. Amy Leslie. Pub. Jeff Tennant. adv.: B&W page USD 1,954. Circ: 15,000.

636.4 USA
SOUTHERN HOGS✶. Text in English. 1992. m. free. **Document type:** *Newspaper.*
Published by: Rural Press U S A, 1101 Spring Forest Rd, Ste 101, Raleigh, NC 27615. TEL 919-676-3276, 800-477-1737, FAX 919-676-9803. Ed. Amy Leslie. Pub. Jeff Tennant. adv.: B&W page USD 1,954. Circ: 15,000.

636 USA
SOUTHERN LIVESTOCK REVIEW. Text in English. 1995. m. USD 18 subscr - mailed; free newsstand/cover (effective 2005). **Document type:** *Newspaper, Trade.*
Formerly: Mid-South Livestock Review
Published by: Don Dowdle, Ed. & Publisher, PO Box 423, Somerville, TN 38068. TEL 901-465-4042, FAX 901-465-5493, slreview@bellsouth.net, http://www.southernlivestockrev.com. Ed., Pub. Don Dowdle. Circ: 13,500 (free).

636.5 USA
SOUTHERN POULTRY✶. Text in English. 1992. q. free. **Document type:** *Newspaper.*
Published by: Rural Press U S A, 1101 Spring Forest Rd, Ste 101, Raleigh, NC 27615. TEL 919-676-3276, FAX 919-676-9803. Ed. Amy Leslie. Pub. Jeff Tennant. Circ: 12,000.

636 USA ISSN 1050-9526
SOUTHWEST STOCKMAN. Text in English. w. USD 30. adv. **Document type:** *Newspaper.*
Published by: R S Livestock Publishers, 4800 Wadsworth, Ste 320, PO Box 1209, Wheat Ridge, CO 80034-1209. TEL 303-425-5777, FAX 303-431-7545. Ed. Dan Green. Pub. Harry Green Jr. Adv. contact Ann Meyers. Circ: 16,000.

636 ESP ISSN 1695-971X
S542.S69 CODEN: IAPAEX
SPANISH JOURNAL OF AGRICULTURAL RESEARCH. Text in Multiple languages. 2002. 3/yr. Price varies. charts. **Document type:** *Monographic series, Academic/Scholarly.*
Formed by the merger of (1986-2002): Investigacion Agraria. Produccion y Sanidad Animales (0213-5035); Which was formerly (1981-1985): Spain. Instituto Nacional de Investigaciones Agrarias. Anales. Series: Ganaderia (0211-4674); (1986-2002): Investigacion Agraria. Produccion y Protection Vegetales (0213-5000); Which was formerly (until 1985): Spain. Instituto Nacional de Investigaciones Agrarias. Anales. Serie: Agricola (0211-4682); Which was formed by the merger of (1971-1980): Spain. Instituto Nacional de Investigaciones Agrarias. Anales. Serie: Proteccion Vegetal (0210-2501); Which was formerly (until 1969): Boletin de Patologia Vegetal y Entomologia Agricola (0366-2381); (1926-1927): Estacion de Patologia Vegetal. Boletin (0210-3273); (1971-1980): Spain. Instituto Nacional de Investigaciones Agrarias. Anales. Serie: Produccion Vegetal (0376-1851); Which superseded in part (1952-1971): Spain. Instituto Nacional de Investigaciones Agronomicas. Anales (0020-4129)
Indexed: AEA, AgBio, AgrForAb, AnBrAb, BIOSIS Prev, BioCN&I, BiolAb, CPA, ChemAb, DSA, FCA, FS&TA, ForAb, HelmAb, HerbAb, HortAb, I&DA, IECT, IndVet, MaizeAb, NutrAb, OrnHort, PBA, PGegResA, PGrRegA, PN&I, PoultAb, RA&MP, RDA, RevApplEntom, S&F, SIA, SeedAb, SoyAb, TriticAb, VetBull, WAE&RSA, WeedAb.
—CASDDS, CINDOC, CISTI. **CCC.**
Published by: (Spain. Instituto Nacional de Investigacion y Tecnologia Agraria y Alimentaria), Ministerio de Agricultura Pesca y Alimentacion, Centro de Publicaciones, Paseo Infanta Isabel 1, Madrid, 28014, Spain. TEL 34-91-3475550, FAX 34-91-3475722, mllopisj@mapya.es, http://www.mapya.es. Ed. Antonio Lopez Sebastian. R&P Carmen Montejo. Circ: 1,500.

636.3 USA ISSN 0038-6626
SPEAKING OF "COLUMBIAS". Text in English. 1960. m. membership. adv.
Published by: Columbia Sheep Breeders Association of America, PO Box 272, Upper Sandusky, OH 43351. TEL 419-482-2608. Ed. Richard L Gerber. Circ: 3,000.

636.4 POL ISSN 0239-5096
STAN HODOWLI I WYNIKI OCENY SWIN/REPORT ON PIG BREEDING IN POLAND. Text in Polish. 1982. a., latest vol.22, 2004. **Document type:** *Journal, Academic/Scholarly.*
Indexed: AgrLib.
—BLDSC (8430.238500).
Published by: Instytut Zootechniki/Institute of Animal Production, ul Sarego 2, Krakow, 31047, Poland. TEL 48-12-2588111, FAX 48-12-2588150, izooinfo@izoo.krakow.pl, http://www.izoo.krakow.pl.

STATISTICHE DELLA RAZZA BRUNA. see *AGRICULTURE—Abstracting, Bibliographies, Statistics*

636 NLD ISSN 0926-485X
STICHTING PRAKTIJKONDERZOEK PLUIMVEEHOUDERIJ. JAARVERSLAG. Text in Dutch. 1977. a. **Document type:** *Corporate.*
Supersedes (in 1991): Stichting Pluimveeteeltproefbedrijven. Jaarverslag (0927-0442)
Published by: Stichting Praktijkonderzoek Pluimveehouderij, Postbus 31, Beekbergen, 7360 AA, Netherlands. TEL 31-55-506-6500, FAX 31-55-506-4858.

636 AUS ISSN 1321-1919
STOCK JOURNAL. Text in English. 1904. w. (Thu.). AUD 140.40; AUD 3 newsstand/cover (effective 2005). adv. bk.rev. abstr.; stat. **Document type:** *Newspaper, Consumer.* **Description:** Deals with agriculture and rural affairs.
Formerly: Adelaide Stock and Station Journal
Published by: Rural Press Ltd. (Subsidiary of: Agricultural Publishers Pty. Ltd.), GPO Box 2249, Adelaide, SA 5001, Australia. TEL 61-8-83725222, http://sj.farmonline.com.au/home.asp, http://www.ruralpress.com/. Ed. Will Rayner. Adv. contact David Shipp. Circ: 15,589.

636 CAN ISSN 0820-4683
STOCKGROWER DIGEST. Text in English. 1972. m. CND 2, USD 3. adv. illus.
Former titles (until 1987): Saskatchewan Stockgrower Magazine (0820-4675); (until 1984): Saskatchewan Stockgrower (0315-6117)
—CISTI.
Published by: Maple Creek News Ltd., P O Box 1360, Maple Creek, SK S0N 1N0, Canada. TEL 306-667-2133. Ed. Jack Migowsky. Circ: 6,000.

636 USA ISSN 0899-1057
STOCKMAN - GRASS FARMER✶. Text in English. 1945. m. USD 15. adv. illus. **Document type:** *Magazine, Trade.* **Description:** Devoted to the art and science of turning grass into beef, lamb, or milk.
Former titles: Stockman Farmer (0192-7140); Mid-South Stockman Farmer; Mississippi Valley Stockman-Farmer (0026-6434)
Published by: Mid-South Stockman-Farmer, PO Box 2300, Ridgeland, MS 39158-2300. sgf@stockmangrassfarmer.com, http://www.stockmangrassfarmer.com. Ed. H Allan Nation. Circ: 10,632.

636.3 GBR
SUFFOLK SHEEP SOCIETY FLOCK BOOK. Text in English. 1887. a. GBP 18. **Document type:** *Trade.* **Description:** Pedigrees of registered Suffolk sheep.
Published by: Suffolk Sheep Society, Sheep Centre, Malvern, Worcs WR13 6PH, United Kingdom. Ed. Penny Lawrence. Circ: 1,400.

SUFFOLK STUD BOOK. see *SPORTS AND GAMES—Horses And Horsemanship*

636.4 BRA ISSN 0100-9125
SUINOCULTURA INDUSTRIAL. Text in Portuguese. 1979. bi-m. USD 60 (effective 2000). adv. illus. index. **Document type:** *Trade.*
Published by: Gessulli Editores Ltda., Praca Sergipe, 154, Caixa Postal 198, Porto Feliz, SP 18540-000, Brazil. TEL 55-152-623133, FAX 55-152-623919, gessulli@gessulli.com.br, http://www.gessulli.com.br. Ed. Osvaldo Penha Gessulli. adv.: page USD 3,600; 290 x 215. Circ: 13,000.

636.2142 MEX ISSN 1025-2568
SUIZO CARNE Y LECHE. Text in English, Spanish. 1989. bi-m. MXP 150, USD 72 (effective 1995). adv. **Document type:** *Consumer.* **Description:** Covers Brown Swiss and Braunvieh cattle.
Published by: Editorial Ocampo S.A. de C.V., ZARAGOZA 11, San Juan Tepepan, Mexico City, DF 16020, Mexico. TEL 525-590-1445. Ed. Ruben Ocampo Trujillo. Adv. contact Ana Cristina Miranda. B&W page USD 835, color page USD 1,170. Circ: 3,000.

636.5 FIN ISSN 1238-9889
SUOMEN SIIPIKARJA. Text in Finnish. 1995. q. adv. charts; illus.; stat. index. **Document type:** *Magazine, Trade.* **Description:** Concerned with egg production, poultry breeding and pullet rearing.
Formed by the merger of (1919-1995): Siipikarja (0037-5098); (1957-1995): Kanatalous (0356-2743); (1989-1995): L S K - Uutiset; (1992-1995): Isa-Info
Published by: Suomen Siipikarjaliitto ry/Finland's Poultry Association - Finlands Fjaederfaefoerbund, Keskuskatu 21, Jokioinen, 31600, Finland. TEL 358-3-4384737, FAX 358-3-4384738, http://www.siipi.net/siipikarjaliitto/index.html. Ed. Ilkka Raukola. adv.: B&W page EUR 900, color page EUR 1,558; trim 277 x 190. Circ: 3,000.

SURINAAMSE LANDBOUW/SURINAM AGRICULTURE. see *AGRICULTURE*

636.4 SWE ISSN 1650-5077
SVENSK GRIS MED KNORR. Text in Swedish. 1962. m. SEK 450 (effective 2001). adv. illus.; stat. **Document type:** *Journal, Trade.*
Formerly (until 2001): Svinskotsel (0346-2471)
Published by: Pig Poultry Press AB, Domkyrkoesplanaden 3A, Vaesteraas, 72213, Sweden. TEL 46-21-126402, FAX 46-21-126407, journalistgruppen@secher.pp.se. Ed., R&P Sven Secher. Adv. contact Roger Mattsson TEL 46-21-38-16-90.

636.294 SWE ISSN 1101-198X
SVENSK HJORTAVEL. Text in Swedish. 1971. bi-m. SEK 300 to members (effective 1993).
Published by: Riksfoerbundet foer Svensk Hjortavel, c/o E Johansson, Hjortaroed, Tyringe, 28200, Sweden.

636.082 SWE ISSN 1401-7520
SF41.R37 CODEN: RSLSDJ
SVERIGES LANTBRUKSUNIVERSITET. INSTITUTIONEN FOER HUSDJURSGENETIK - RAPPORT/SWEDISH UNIVERSITY OF AGRICULTURAL SCIENCES. DEPARTMENT OF ANIMAL BREEDING AND GENETICS - PUBLICATION. (Was not published in yr. 2000) Text in English, Swedish; Summaries in English. 1972. irreg., latest vol.128, 1997. free. **Document type:** *Academic/Scholarly.*
Former titles (until 1996): Sveriges Lantbruksuniversitet. Institutionen foer Husdjursfoeraedling och Sjukdomsgenetik (0347-9706); (until 1978): Lantbrukshoegskolan. Institutionen foer Husdjursfoeraedling - Rapport (0346-6752)
—BLDSC (7113.220000), CISTI.

Published by: Sveriges Lantbruksuniversitet, Institutionen foer Husdjursgenetik/Swedish University of Agricultural Sciences, Department of Animal Breeding and Genetics, PO Box 7023, Uppsala, 75007, Sweden. TEL 46-18-671941, FAX 46-18-672848.

636.4 DNK
SVIN. Text in Danish. 1990. m. DKK 504. adv. **Document type:** *Journal, Trade.*
Formerly (until 2003): Landsbladet Svin (0905-6777)
Published by: Dansk Landbrugs Medier, Vester Farimagsgade 6, Copenhagen V, 1606, Denmark. TEL 46-33-394700. Circ: 5,670.

636.4 NOR ISSN 1503-0237
SVIN; tidsskrift for svineavlsproduksjon. Text in Norwegian. 1965. 10/yr. NOK 580 to non-members; NOK 480 to members (effective 2005). adv. **Document type:** *Magazine, Trade.*
Formerly (until 2001): Svineavlsnytt (0332-7566)
Published by: Norsvin, Norsvinsenteret, Postboks 504, Hamar, 2304, Norway. TEL 47-62-510100, FAX 47-62-510101, svineavlsnytt@norsvin.no, http://www.norsvin.no/nors/ForsideVis.ListeSvin. Ed. Tore Maelumsaeter TEL 47-62-510107. Adv. contact Geir Berntsen TEL 47-62-941033. Circ: 4,341.

636.4 RUS ISSN 0039-713X
CODEN: SVINAI
SVINOVODSTVO. Text in Russian. 1930. bi-m. USD 104 (effective 2004). bk.rev. illus. index.
Indexed: AEA, AgBio, AnBrAb, BiolAb, ChemAb, DSA, HelmAb, HerbAb, HortAb, IndVet, MaizeAb, NutrAb, PHN&I, PN&I, PotatoAb, PoultAb, RA&MP, RASB, RM&VM, RPP, RefZh, RevApplEntom, S&F, SIA, SoyAb, TriticAb, VetBull, WAE&RSA.
—CASDDS, CISTI, East View. **CCC.**
Address: Sadovaya-Spasskaya 18, Moscow, 107807, Russian Federation. TEL 7-095-9751533, FAX 7-095-2072870. Ed. Kim D Baev. Circ: 5,700. **Dist. by:** M K - Periodica, ul Gilyarovskogo 39, Moscow 129110, Russian Federation. TEL 7-095-2845008, FAX 7-095-2813798, info@periodicals.ru, http://www.mkniga.ru.

636 635 IND
SWARAJYA SANDESH. Text in Hindi. 1964. w. INR 120; INR 3 newsstand/cover. 5 cols./p.; **Description:** Covers rural development, poultry, animal husbandry, horticulture, and co-operatives.
Published by: R.K. Sharma Ed. & Pub., 2-8 Ansari Rd., Daryaganj, New Delhi, 110 002, India. TEL 91-11-23266178. Circ: 51,030.

636.5 USA ISSN 0082-8661
TABLES ON HATCHERY AND FLOCK PARTICIPATION IN THE NATIONAL POULTRY IMPROVEMENT PLAN✶ . Text in English. 1937. a. free.
Incorporates: U.S. Agricultural Research Service. Animal Science Research Division. Tables on Hatchery and Flock Participation in the National Turkey Improvement Plan (0082-867X)
Published by: U.S. Animal and Plant Health Inspection Service, U S Department of Agriculture Health Inspection Service, 4700 River Rd, Riverdale, MD 20737-1228. TEL 301-734-5240. Ed. R D Scher. Circ: 4,000.

636.4 USA ISSN 0082-1608
TAMWORTH ANNUAL. Text in English. 1965. irreg. bk.rev.
Published by: Tamworth Swine Association, 414 Van Deman St, Washington Court House, OH 43160. Ed. Robert Highfield. Circ: 1,500.

636.4 FRA ISSN 0181-6764
TECHNI-PORC. Text in French. 1969. bi-m. EUR 45 domestic; EUR 53 foreign (effective 2002). **Description:** Provides information on domestic and foreign hog production, technical and economic performances, nutrition, selection and quality control.
Formerly (until 1977): Institut Technique du Porc. Bulletin (0395-7292)
Indexed: AEA, AgBio, AnBrAb, DSA, FCA, HortAb, IndVet, NutrAb, PN&I, PoultAb, RDA, RefZh, S&F, SoyAb, TDB, TriticAb, VetBull, WAE&RSA.
—BLDSC (8736.980000), IE, ingenta.
Published by: Institut Technique du Porc, 149 Rue de Bercy, Paris, 75595 Cedex 12, France. TEL 33-1-40045375, FAX 33-1-40045377, http://www.itp.asso.fr.

TECHNICAL CONFERENCE ON ARTIFICIAL INSEMINATION AND REPRODUCTION. PROCEEDINGS. see *AGRICULTURE—Dairying And Dairy Products*

TECNICA EN AGRICULTURA Y GANADERIA. see *AGRICULTURE—Crop Production And Soil*

636.2 MEX ISSN 0040-1889
CODEN: TPMXA3
TECNICA PECUARIA EN MEXICO. Text in Spanish; Summaries in English. 1963. s-a. MXP 80, USD 4. bibl.; charts; illus.; stat.
Related titles: Online - full text ed.: (from EBSCO Publishing).
Indexed: AgrForAb, AnBrAb, BioCN&I, BiolAb, ChemAb, DSA, FCA, HelmAb, HerbAb, IndVet, MaizeAb, NutrAb, PN&I, PoultAb, ProtozoAb, RDA, RM&VM, RRTA, RevApplEntom, S&F, SAA, SIA, SeedAb, VetBull, WAE&RSA, WeedAb.
—BLDSC (8762.530000), CASDDS, CISTI, IE, ingenta.
Published by: Instituto Nacional de Investigaciones Pecuarias, Departamento de Divulgacion Tecnica, KM 15.5 Carretera Mexico-Toluca, Cuajimalpa, Apartado Postal 41 652, Mexico City, DF 05000, Mexico. Circ: 2,000. **Co-sponsor:** Secretaria de Agricultura y Recursos Hidraulicos.

636.6 GBR
TEESWATER SHEEP BREEDERS' ASSOCIATION. ANNUAL FLOCK BOOK. Text in English. 1949. a. GBP 10 all breeders (effective 2000). adv. **Document type:** *Directory.* **Description:** Records pedigree registered lambs and breeders' names and addresses.
Published by: Teeswater Sheep Breeders' Association, 1 The Mount, Leyburn, N Yorks DL8 5JA, United Kingdom. TEL 44-1969-623432. Ed., R&P, Adv. contact David Ward. Circ: 140 (controlled).

636 USA
TEXAS BRANGUS. Text in English. m.
Published by: Texas Brangus Breeders Association, 328, Seguin, TX 78156-0328. TEL 409-846-5733.

636.2 USA ISSN 0744-4761
TEXAS HEREFORD. Text in English. 1951. m. USD 15 (effective 2001). adv. **Document type:** *Trade.* **Description:** Contains information for members and others interested in Hereford cattle. Informs readers of news, sales, shows, and other events.
Published by: Texas Hereford Association, 4609 Airport Freeway, Fort Worth, TX 76117. TEL 817-831-3161, FAX 817-831-3162. Ed., Pub., R&P, Adv. contact Jack Chastain. Circ: 2,200 (paid).

636.309489 DNK ISSN 0906-1746
TIDSSKRIFT FOR DANSK FAAREAVL. Text in Danish. 1936. 10/yr. DKK 350 (effective 2004). adv. charts; illus.; mkt.; stat. **Document type:** *Newsletter, Trade.*
Formerly (until 1991): Tidsskrift for Faareavl (0040-7038)
Indexed: AnBrAb, DSA.
Published by: Landsforeningen Dansk Faareavl, Nygade 56, Skjern, 6900, Denmark. TEL 45-96-801255, FAX 45-97-353006, http://www.sheep.dk. Ed., Adv. contact Peter Busch. Circ: 2,500.

636.9322 DNK ISSN 0900-3401
TIDSSKRIFT FOR KANINAVL. Text in Danish. 1895. 11/yr. DKK 375 (effective 2004).
Published by: Danmarks Kaninavlerforening, c/o Kaj Mikkelsen, Fasanvej 13, Roende, 6410, Denmark. TEL 45-86-379303, FAX 45-86-379373, http://www.kaniner.dk. Ed. Ela Noergard TEL 45-97-865858.

TODAY'S FEED LOTTING. see *AGRICULTURE—Feed, Flour And Grain*

636 USA
TRI-STATE LIVESTOCK NEWS. Text in English. 1963. w. (Sat.). USD 47; USD 1.50 newsstand/cover (effective 2005). **Document type:** *Newspaper, Trade.* **Description:** Agricultural news serving cattle, sheep and horse producers and crop producers in South Dakota, North Dakota, Montana, Wyoming and Nebraska.
Published by: Country Media, Inc., 1615 First Ave., Scottsbluff, NE 69361. TEL 308-635-1892, editor@tlsn.com, http://www.tsln.com. Ed. Larry Gram. Pub. Helen Merriman. Adv. contact Sabrina Harmon. Circ: 11,000 (paid).

TROPICAL ANIMAL HEALTH AND PRODUCTION. see *VETERINARY SCIENCE*

TRZISTE STOKE I STOCHIH PROIZODA; konjunkturne informacije. see *AGRICULTURE—Abstracting, Bibliographies, Statistics*

TURKISH JOURNAL OF VETERINARY AND ANIMAL SCIENCES/DOGA TURK VETERINERLIK VE HAYVANCILIK DERGISI. see *VETERINARY SCIENCE*

636 AUS
U G A GRAZIER. Text in English. m. AUD 18. adv. back issues avail. **Document type:** *Newspaper.* **Description:** Provides news and information for Queensland graziers.
Published by: United Graziers Association of Queensland, PO Box 167, Brisbane Roma Street, QLD 4003, Australia. Ed., Adv. contact Mark Phelps. page AUD 900. Circ: 3,000.

636 USA
U.S. BELTIE NEWS✶ . Text in English. 1980. m. USD 25 to members. **Document type:** *Newsletter.* **Description:** Covers cattle breeds.
Published by: Belted Galloway Society, Inc., PO Box 56, Holly Springs, MS 38635-0056. TEL 601-333-4453. Ed. Jane Faul.

338.1 USA ISSN 1522-0567
U S D A BROILER MARKET NEWS REPORT. Text in English. 3/w. (Mon., Wed. & Fri.). USD 160 domestic; USD 180 in Canada & Mexico; USD 235 elsewhere (effective 2000). back issues avail. **Document type:** *Government.*
Supersedes in part: U S D A Poultry Market News Report; Which was formerly: U S D A Poultry Report; Poultry Report
Related titles: Fax ed.: USD 370 domestic (effective 2001).
Published by: U S D A, Agricultural Marketing Service, Poultry Programs, Market News Branch, 210 Walnut St, Rm 951, Des Moines, IA 50309-2103. TEL 515-284-4471, FAX 515-284-4468, http://www.ams.usda.gov/marketnews.htm. Ed., R&P Mary L Adkins.

636 USA ISSN 1520-6114
U S D A EGG & POULTRY WEEKLY REVIEW. Text in English. w. USD 150 domestic (effective until Aug. 2000). back issues avail. **Document type:** *Government.*
Former titles: U S D A Poultry and Egg Weekly Review; Poultry and Egg Weekly Review
Media: Fax.
Published by: U S D A, Agricultural Marketing Service, Poultry Programs, Market News Branch, 210 Walnut St, Rm 951, Des Moines, IA 50309-2103. TEL 515-284-4471, FAX 515-284-4468, http://www.ams.usda.gov/marketnews.htm. R&P Mary L Adkins.

637.5 USA ISSN 1520-6122
U S D A EGG MARKET NEWS REPORT. Text in English. s-w. USD 125 domestic; USD 140 in Canada & Mexico; USD 175 elsewhere (effective 2000). back issues avail. **Document type:** *Government.*
Formerly: Egg Report
Related titles: Fax ed.: USD 310 domestic (effective 2000).
Published by: U S D A, Agricultural Marketing Service, Poultry Programs, Market News Branch, 210 Walnut St, Rm 951, Des Moines, IA 50309-2103. TEL 515-284-4471, FAX 515-284-4468, http://www.ams.usda.gov/marketnews.htm. Ed. Mary L Adkins.

636.5 USA
U S D A POULTRY MARKET NEWS. ANNUAL SUMMARY. (Also avail. on Zip Disk) Text in English. a. USD 15 in North America; USD 20 elsewhere (effective 2000). **Document type:** *Government.*
Formerly: Poultry Market News. Annual Summary
Related titles: Diskette ed.
Published by: U S D A, Agricultural Marketing Service, Poultry Programs, Market News Branch, 210 Walnut St, Rm 951, Des Moines, IA 50309-2103. TEL 515-284-4471, FAX 515-284-4468, http://www.ams.usda.gov/marketnews.htm. R&P Mary L Adkins.

636.5 USA ISSN 0891-8309
U S D A POULTRY MARKET NEWS. MONTHLY SUMMARY. Text in English. m. USD 115 domestic; USD 125 in Canada; USD 150 elsewhere (effective 2000). reprint service avail. from CIS. **Document type:** *Government.*
Former titles: Poultry Market News. Monthly Summary; Cold Storage Report Monthly Summary; Cold Storage Report Monthly
Related titles: Diskette ed.; Fax ed.: USD 250 domestic (effective 2000); Microfiche ed.: (from CIS).
Indexed: AmStI.
Published by: U S D A, Agricultural Marketing Service, Poultry Programs, Market News Branch, 210 Walnut St, Rm 951, Des Moines, IA 50309-2103. TEL 515-284-4471, FAX 515-284-4468, http://www.ams.usda.gov/marketnews.htm. Ed. Mary L Adkins.

636.592 USA ISSN 1522-0575
U S D A TURKEY MARKET NEWS REPORT. Text in English. 3/w. (Mon., Wed. & Fri.). USD 125 domestic; USD 140 in Canada & Mexico; USD 175 elsewhere (effective 2000). **Document type:** *Government.*
Supersedes in part: U S D A Poultry Market News Report; Which was formerly: U S D A Poultry Report; Poultry Report
Related titles: Fax ed.: USD 250 domestic (effective 2000).
Published by: U S D A, Agricultural Marketing Service, Poultry Programs, Market News Branch, 210 Walnut St, Rm 951, Des Moines, IA 50309-2103. TEL 515-284-4471, FAX 515-284-4468, http://www.ams.usda.gov/marketnews.htm.

U.S. DEPARTMENT OF AGRICULTURE. NATIONAL AGRICULTURAL STATISTICS SERVICE. BROILER HATCHERY. see *AGRICULTURE—Abstracting, Bibliographies, Statistics*

U.S. DEPARTMENT OF AGRICULTURE. NATIONAL AGRICULTURAL STATISTICS SERVICE. CATTLE. see *AGRICULTURE—Abstracting, Bibliographies, Statistics*

U.S. DEPARTMENT OF AGRICULTURE. NATIONAL AGRICULTURAL STATISTICS SERVICE. CATTLE ON FEED. see *AGRICULTURE—Abstracting, Bibliographies, Statistics*

U.S. DEPARTMENT OF AGRICULTURE. NATIONAL AGRICULTURAL STATISTICS SERVICE. CHICKENS AND EGGS. see *AGRICULTURE—Abstracting, Bibliographies, Statistics*

U.S. DEPARTMENT OF AGRICULTURE. NATIONAL AGRICULTURAL STATISTICS SERVICE. EGG PRODUCTS. see *AGRICULTURE—Abstracting, Bibliographies, Statistics*

U.S. DEPARTMENT OF AGRICULTURE. NATIONAL AGRICULTURAL STATISTICS SERVICE. HOGS AND PIGS. see *AGRICULTURE—Abstracting, Bibliographies, Statistics*

A

U.S. DEPARTMENT OF AGRICULTURE. NATIONAL AGRICULTURAL STATISTICS SERVICE. LIVESTOCK SLAUGHTER. see *AGRICULTURE—Abstracting, Bibliographies, Statistics*

U.S. DEPARTMENT OF AGRICULTURE. NATIONAL AGRICULTURAL STATISTICS SERVICE. MEAT ANIMALS: PRODUCTION, DISPOSITION AND INCOME. see *AGRICULTURE—Abstracting, Bibliographies, Statistics*

U.S. DEPARTMENT OF AGRICULTURE. NATIONAL AGRICULTURAL STATISTICS SERVICE. MINK. see *AGRICULTURE—Abstracting, Bibliographies, Statistics*

U.S. DEPARTMENT OF AGRICULTURE. NATIONAL AGRICULTURAL STATISTICS SERVICE. POULTRY SLAUGHTER. see *AGRICULTURE—Abstracting, Bibliographies, Statistics*

U.S. DEPARTMENT OF AGRICULTURE. NATIONAL AGRICULTURAL STATISTICS SERVICE. SHEEP AND GOATS. see *AGRICULTURE—Abstracting, Bibliographies, Statistics*

U.S. DEPARTMENT OF AGRICULTURE. NATIONAL AGRICULTURAL STATISTICS SERVICE. TURKEY HATCHERY. see *AGRICULTURE—Abstracting, Bibliographies, Statistics*

636.5 ITA ISSN 1593-1005
UNAVICOLTURA. Text in Italian. 1965. s-a. adv. bk.rev. abstr.; charts; illus.; stat. back issues avail. **Description:** Intended for those in the poultry industry.
Former titles (until 1986): U N A Notizie di Avicoltura (0391-8793); U N A Informazione Avicole
Published by: Unione Nazionale dell'Avicoltura - Servizi s.r.l., Via Vibio Mariano 58, Rome, RM 00189, Italy. TEL 39-06-3325841, FAX 39-06-33252427, http://www.unavicoltura.it. Ed. Rino Celadon. Adv. contact Rita Pasquarelli. Circ: 9,800.

636.39 USA ISSN 0164-9353
UNITED CAPRINE NEWS✱. Text in English. m. USD 17; USD 25 foreign (effective 1998). adv. **Document type:** *Newspaper, Trade.*
Published by: Jeff Klein, Ed. & Pub., P O Box 328, Crowley, TX 76036-0328. TEL 817-579-5211, FAX 817-579-2606. R&P, Adv. contact Jeff Klein.

636 ROM
CODEN: LSIVDF
UNIVERSITATEA AGRONOMICA ION IONESCU DE LA BRAD. LUCRARI STIINTIFICE. SERIA ZOOTECHNIE - MEDICINA VETERINARIA. Text in Romanian. 1957. a.
Formerly: Institutul Agronomic Ion Ionescu de la Brad. Lucrari Stiintifice. Seria Zootechnie - Medicina Veterinaria (0075-3513)
Indexed: AnBrAb, BiolAb, HelmAb, IndVet, NutrAb, PN&I, PoultAb, RM&VM, RevApplEntom, VITIS, VetBull.
—CASDDS, CISTI.
Published by: Universitatea Agronomica "Ion Ionescu de la Brad", Al. M. Sadoveanu 3, Jassy, Romania.

636 636.089 ROM ISSN 1454-2390
CODEN: BIAVDX
UNIVERSITATEA DE STIINTE AGRICOLE SI MEDICINA VETERINARA CLUJ-NAPOCA. BULETINUL. SERIA ZOOTEHNIE SI MEDICINA VETERINARA. Text in Romanian; Summaries in English, French. 1975. a. back issues avail.
Former titles (until 1995): Universitatea de Stiinte Agricole Cluj-Napoca. Buletinul. Seria Zootehnie si Medicina Veterinara (1221-3594); (until 1992): Institutul Agronomic Cluj-Napoca. Buletinul. Seria Zootehnie si Medicina Veterinara (0557-4668); Supersedes in part (in 1977): Institutul Agronomic Cluj-Napoca. Buletinul (0378-0554)
Indexed: AnBrAb, BioDAb, BiolAb, DSA, FS&TA, HelmAb, IndVet, NutrAb, PN&I, PoultAb, ProtozoAb, RevApplEntom, SFA, SoyAb, VetBull, WildRev, ZooRec.
—CASDDS, CISTI.
Published by: Universitatea de Stiinte Agricole si Medicina Veterinara Cluj-Napoca, Str. Manastur 3, Cluj-Napoca, 3400, Romania. Ed. Alexandru Salontai. Circ: 500.

636 ROM
UNIVERSITATEA DE STIINTE AGRONOMICE SI MEDICINA VETERINARA. LUCRARI STIINTIFICE. SERIA D, ZOOTEHNIE. Text in Romanian; Summaries in English. 1960. a. per issue exchange basis only. **Document type:** *Academic/Scholarly.*
Former titles: Universitatea de Stiinte Agronomice. Lucrari Stiintifice. Seria D, Zootehnie; (until 1992): Institutul Agronomic Nicolae Balcescu. Lucrari Stiintifice. Seria D, Zootehnie (0374-8898); Which supersedes in part (in 1970): Institutul Agronomic Nicolae Balcescu. Lucrari Stiintifice. Seria C, Zootehnie si Medicina Veterinara (0524-8108); Which supersedes in part: Institutul Agronomic Nicolae Balcescu. Anuarul Lucrarilor Stiintifice (1120-1987)
Indexed: AnBrAb, DSA, NutrAb, PoultAb.
—CISTI.
Published by: Universitatea de Stiinte Agronomice si Medicina Veterinara, Bd. Marasti 59, Sector 1, Bucharest, 71331, Romania. TEL 40-1-2242576, FAX 40-1-2232693.

636 CZE ISSN 1212-558X
UNIVERSITY OF SOUTH BOHEMIA IN CESKE BUDEJOVICE. FACULTY OF AGRICULTURE. COLLECTION OF SCIENTIFIC PAPERS. SERIES FOR ANIMAL SCIENCES. Text in Czech; Abstracts in English. 1984. s-a. **Document type:** *Journal, Academic/Scholarly.*
Former titles (until 1999): Jihoceske Univerzity v Ceskych Budejovicich. Zemedelske Fakulty. Rada Zootechnicka. Sbornik (1210-6240); (until 1992): Agronomicke Fakulty v Ceskych Budejovicich. Rada Zootechnicka. Sbornik (0862-0369); (until 1986): Provozne Ekonomicka Fakulta v Ceskych Budejovicich. Zootechnicka Rada. Sbornik (0231-9098)
Indexed: AEA, AgBio, AnBrAb, BIOSIS Prev, BiolAb, DSA, FCA, HerbAb, HortAb, IndVet, MaizeAb, NutrAb, PN&I, PoultAb, RRTA, SIA, VetBull, WAE&RSA.
—CISTI.
Published by: Jihoceska Univerzita v Ceskych Budejovicich , Zemedelska Fakulta/University of South Bohemia in Ceske Budejovice, Faculty of Agriculture, Studentska 13, Ceske Budejovice, 370 05, Czech Republic. wolkova@zf.jcu.cz, http://www.zf.jcu.cz. Ed. Petr Hartvich.

URNER BARRY'S NATIONAL WEEKLY HATCH REPORT. see *AGRICULTURE—Abstracting, Bibliographies, Statistics*

338.19 664 USA ISSN 0273-9992
URNER BARRY'S PRICE-CURRENT. Text in English. 1858. d. (Mon.-Fri.). USD 444 domestic; USD 498 in Canada; USD 631 elsewhere (effective 2005). adv. mkt.; stat. **Document type:** *Newsletter, Trade.* **Description:** Covers the poultry and egg industries.
Formerly (until 1980): Producers' Price-Current (0032-9711)
Related titles: Online - full text ed.: USD 120 per month (effective 1999).
Published by: Urner Barry Publications, Inc., PO Box 389, Toms River, NJ 08754-0389. TEL 732-240-5330, FAX 732-341-0891, mail@urnerbarry.com, http://shop.urnerbarry.com/Merchant2/merchant.mv?Screen=CTGY&Store_Code=ubp&Category_Code=Price-Current, http://www.urnerbarry.com. Adv. contact Janice Brown. Circ: 3,000 (paid).

338.19 664 USA ISSN 0273-5016
URNER BARRY'S PRICE CURRENT (WEST COAST EDITION). Text in English. 1974. s-w. USD 444, USD 498, USD 631 (effective 2005). adv. back issues avail. **Document type:** *Newspaper, Newsletter, Trade.*
Formerly: Producer's Price Current (West Coast Edition) (0270-420X)
Published by: Urner Barry Publications, Inc., PO Box 389, Toms River, NJ 08754-0389. TEL 732-240-5330, FAX 732-341-0891, mail@urnerbarry.com, http://www.urnerbarry.com. Adv. contact Janice Brown. Circ: 150 (paid).

636.2 DEU ISSN 0722-3668
V F Z. (Vieh und Fleisch Handelszeitung) Text in German. 1900. w. EUR 32.80 for 6 mos. (effective 2005). adv. bk.rev. abstr.; tr.lit. **Document type:** *Newspaper, Trade.*
Incorporates (1968-1980): Vieh und Fleisch (0722-3404); Which was formerly (until 1969): Deutscher Vieh- und Fleischhandelsbund. Verbands-Mitteilungen (0722-3617); Formerly (until 1968): Allgemeine Viehhandels-Zeitung (0722-365X)
Published by: Deutsche Viehhandelsgesellschaft mbH, Fachverlag Vieh und Fleisch, Adenauerallee 176, Bonn, 53113, Germany. TEL 49-228-2807946, FAX 49-228-218908, vfz@dvfb.org, webmaster@dvfb.org, http://www.dvfb.org. Circ: 5,000.

V W D - VIEH UND FLEISCH. see *BUSINESS AND ECONOMICS—Investments*

636.2 ITA
LA VALUTAZIONE MORFOLOGICA DELLA RAZZA BRUNA. Text in Italian. **Document type:** *Magazine, Trade.* **Description:** Displays the methods used in the morphology evaluation of the Italian Brown breed.
Published by: Associazione Nazionale Allevatori Razza Bruna, Localita Ferlina 204, Bussolengo, VR 37012, Italy. TEL 39-045-6701990, FAX 39-045-7156655, anarb@anarb.it, http://www.anarb.it.

636.4 NLD ISSN 0166-5952
VARKENS; vakblad voor devarkenshouderij. Text in Dutch. 1937. 13/yr. USD 107 (effective 2001). adv. **Document type:** *Trade.*
Former titles: Maandblad Varkens; (until 1987): Mandblad voor de Varkensfokkerij en -Mesterij (0923-0122); (until 1982): Varkensfokkerij-Mesterij (0923-0157); (until 1976): Varkensfokkerij (0923-0149); (until 1975): Maandblad voor de Varkensfokkerij (0024-8649)
Indexed: RefZh.
—BLDSC (9146.670000).
Published by: Nederlands Varkensstamboek, Postbus 43, Beuningen ((Gld)), 6640 AA, Netherlands. TEL 31-24-6779999, FAX 31-24-6779800, info@varkens.nl. Ed. Marga te Velde. Adv. contact Theo van Rossum TEL 0314-355756. Circ: 17,550.

636.4 BEL ISSN 0777-5091
VARKENSBEDRIJF. Text in Dutch. 1989. m. EUR 41 (effective 2004). adv. bk.rev. back issues avail. **Document type:** *Trade.* **Description:** For professionals who breed pigs.
Published by: Rekad N.V., Geelsweg 47A, Herentals, 2200, Belgium. TEL 32-14-286070, FAX 32-14-214774, info@rekad.be, http://rekad.be. Ed. Jomi Memschoote. Adv. contact Hilde Provoost. B&W page EUR 1,060. Circ: 7,550.

636.4 NLD ISSN 0169-0167
VARKENSHOUDERIJ. Text in Dutch. 1972. bi-w. EUR 167.63 (effective 2005). adv. bk.rev. charts; illus. **Document type:** *Trade.* **Description:** Covers all aspects of pig husbandry: management, health care, housing and feeding.
Related titles: ◆ Supplement to: Boerderij. ISSN 0006-5617.
Published by: Reed Business Information bv (Subsidiary of: Reed Business), Hanzestraat 1, Doetinchem, 7006 RH, Netherlands. TEL 31-314-349911, FAX 31-314-343839, info@reedbusiness.nl, http://www.zibb.nl/landbouw, http://www.reedbusiness.nl. adv.: B&W page EUR 2,058, color page EUR 3,183; trim 215 x 285. Circ: 8,148.

636.2 NLD ISSN 0168-6585
VEEHOUDEN NU; kritisch voorlichtingsblad voor veehouderij en veredelingslandbouw. Text in Dutch. 1951. bi-m. adv. bk.rev. **Document type:** *Bulletin.*
Formerly: Veevoeding (0042-3041)
Published by: Agrio, Postbus 58, Wehl, 7030 AB, Netherlands. TEL 31-314-684448, FAX 31-314-682008. Ed. E Voortman. Adv. contact E. Voortman. Circ: 20,000.

636 NLD ISSN 0169-0213
VEEHOUDERIJ. Text in Dutch. 1972. bi-w. EUR 167.63 (effective 2005). adv. bk.rev. charts; illus. **Document type:** *Trade.* **Description:** Information on all aspects of dairy farming: breeding policy, health care of cattle, stall accomodation, milk production and mechanization of labor.
Related titles: ◆ Supplement to: Boerderij. ISSN 0006-5617.
Published by: Reed Business Information bv (Subsidiary of: Reed Business), Hanzestraat 1, Doetinchem, 7006 RH, Netherlands. TEL 31-314-349911, FAX 31-314-343839, info@reedbusiness.nl, http://www.zibb.nl/landbouw, http://www.reedbusiness.nl. adv.: B&W page EUR 3,095, color page EUR 4,221; trim 215 x 285. Circ: 24,580.

VEEHOUDERIJ TECHNIEK; vakblad voor veehouders. see *AGRICULTURE—Agricultural Equipment*

636 NLD ISSN 0168-7565
VEETEELT. Text in Dutch. 1949. fortn. EUR 52 domestic; EUR 104 foreign; EUR 33 domestic to students; EUR 5.50 newsstand/cover (effective 2005). adv. bk.rev. charts; illus. **Document type:** *Trade.*
Former titles (until 1984): Friese Veefokkerij (0016-139X); (until 1971): Friesch Rundvee-Stamboek. Mededelingen (0016-1381); Incorporates (19??-1984): Informatie en Advies (0921-173X); (1957-1984): Het Veebedrijf (0167-0921); (1983-1984): Bedrijfsvoorlichting Veehouderij (0169-569X)
Related titles: CD-ROM ed.; E-mail ed.; Fax ed.
Indexed: RefZh.
—CISTI.
Published by: CR Delta, PO Box 454, Arnhem, 6800 AL, Netherlands. TEL 31-26-3898800, FAX 31-26-3898839, veeteelt@veeteelt.nl, http://www.veeteelt.nl. Ed. Bert De Lange. R&P, Adv. contact Willem Gemmink. Circ: 49,455; 45,685 (paid).

639 VEN
VENEZUELA. MINISTERIO DE AGRICULTURA Y CRIA. DIVISION DE ESTADISTICA. ENCUESTA AVICOLA NACIONAL. Text in Spanish. 1962. a. free. illus. **Document type:** *Government.*
Published by: Ministerio de Agricultura y Cria, Direccion de Planificacion y Estadistica, Centro Simon Bolicar, Torre Norte 16o, Caracas, 1010, Venezuela.

639 VEN
VENEZUELA. MINISTERIO DE AGRICULTURA Y CRIA. DIVISION DE ESTADISTICA. ENCUESTA DE GANADO PORCINO. Text in Spanish. a. **Document type:** *Government.*
Published by: Ministerio de Agricultura y Cria, Direccion de Planificacion y Estadistica, Centro Simon Bolivar Torre Norte 16o, Caracas, DF 1010, Venezuela.

VETERINARIA E ZOOTECNIA. see *VETERINARY SCIENCE*

636 FRA ISSN 0241-0389
➤ **VIANDES ET PRODUITS CARNES.** Text in French. 1979. bi-m. **Document type:** *Bulletin, Academic/Scholarly.* **Description:** A technical review for meat processors and traders, technical schools and advisory services.
Indexed: FS&TA.
—BLDSC (9232.040000), CISTI, IE, ingenta.
Published by: Association pour le Developpement de l'Institut de la Viande, 2 rue Chappe, Clermont-Ferrand, Cedex 2 63039, France. TEL 33-4-73985380, FAX 33-4-73985388, adiv@adiv.fr. Ed., R&P, Adv. contact Xavier Vigneron. Pub. Michel Saudan. Circ: 550.

636.4 AUS ISSN 1440-8171
VIC-PIG. Text in English. 1998. q.
Related titles: Online - full text ed.: ISSN 1440-818X. 1998.

Published by: Victorian Institute of Animal Science (Subsidiary of: Department of Primary Industries), Sneydes Rd, Private Bag 7, Werribee, VIC 3030, Australia. mailto:customer.service@dpi.vic.gov.au, http://www.nre.vic.gov.au/web/root/domino/cm_da/nrecfa.nsf/67dfe622a27a81634a256a1d002b4401/d5ca5bb6e02bd7cbca256c9f001a75b2?OpenDocument.

636.2   USA
VIRGINIA CATTLEMAN; the monthly voice of Virginia's cattle industry. Text in English. m. USD 25 to members (effective 2001). adv. **Document type:** *Newspaper, Trade.*
Published by: Virginia Cattlemen's Association, PO Box 9, Daleville, VA 24083. TEL 540-992-0009, FAX 540-992-1009, vca@vacattlemen.org, http://www.vacattlemen.org. Ed. Reginald B Reynolds. Adv. contact Frances Metcalf. page USD 490; 13 x 10. Circ: 10,000. **Co-sponsor:** National Cattlemen's Beef Association.

636.39   USA   ISSN 0042-8078
VOICE OF A G S* . Text in English. 1936. q. membership. adv. **Document type:** *Bulletin.*
Published by: American Goat Society, Inc., 735 Oakridge Ln., Pipe Creek, TX 78063-5658. TEL 518-875-6708. Ed. Penny Tyler. Circ: 600.

636   SVK   ISSN 1335-3691
SF55.S56   CODEN: VPVZB9
➤ **VYSKUMNY USTAV ZIVOCISNEJ VYROBY V NITRE. VEDECKE PRACE/JOURNAL OF FARM ANIMAL SCIENCE.** Text in Slovak; Abstracts and contents page in English. 1961. a. SKK 800, USD 16 (effective 2003). adv. **Document type:** *Journal, Academic/Scholarly.* **Description:** Provides scientific papers on all aspects of animal production in Slovak Republic.
Indexed: BiolAb, CIN, ChemAb, ChemTitl.
—CASDDS.
Published by: Vyskumny Ustav Zivocisnej Vyroby v Nitre/Research Institute of Animal Production at Nitra, Hlohovska 2, Nitra, 94992, Slovakia. TEL 421-37-7783094, FAX 421-37-6546361, hetenyi@vuzv.sk, http://www.uvtip.sk/slovak/rezort/vuzv. Ed. Ladislav Hetenyi. R&P Maria Kovalcikova. Adv. contact Vojtech Brestensky TEL 421-37-6546369. Circ: 350.

636   NLD   ISSN 1574-1125
W A A P BOOK OF THE YEAR. Text in English. a. EUR 99 (effective 2005). **Document type:** *Journal, Academic/Scholarly.*
Published by: (World Association for Animal Production ITA), Wageningen Academic Publishers, PO Box 220, Wageningen, 6700 AE, Netherlands. TEL 31-317-476516, FAX 31-317-453417, info@wageningenacademic.com, http://www.wageningenacademic.com.

W K C NEWS BULLETIN. see *PETS*

636   POL
CODEN: AAASEQ
WARSAW AGRICULTURAL UNIVERSITY. S G G W. ANNALS. ANIMAL SCIENCE. Text mainly in English; Text occasionally in French, German, Russian; Summaries in Polish. 1957. irreg., latest vol.39, 2002. USD 6 per issue. **Document type:** *Bulletin, Academic/Scholarly.*
Former titles: Warsaw Agricultural University. S G G W - A R. Annals. Animal Science (0208-5739); (until 1980): Akademia Rolnicza, Warsaw. Zeszyty Naukowe. Zootechnika; Szkola Glowna Gospodarstwa Wiejskiego. Zeszyty Naukowe. Zootechnika (0509-7134)
Indexed: AEA, AgBio, AgrForAb, AgrLib, AnBrAb, BioCN&I, CIN, CPA, ChemAb, ChemTitl, DSA, FCA, FS&TA, ForAb, HelmAb, HerbAb, HortAb, IndVet, MaizeAb, NemAb, NutrAb, PBA, PN&I, PoultAb, RA&MP, RefZh, S&F, SIA, SoyAb, TriticAb, VetBull, WAE&RSA, ZooRec.
—CASDDS, CISTI, Linda Hall.
Published by: Szkola Glowna Gospodarstwa Wiejskiego (SGGW)/Warsaw Agricultural University, Ul Nowoursynowska 166, Warsaw, 02787, Poland. TEL 48-22-8439041, FAX 48-22-8471562, jmw_wyd@alpha.sggw.waw.pl, http://www.sggw.waw.pl. Ed. W Empel. **Dist. by:** Ars Polona, Krakowskie Przedmiescie 7, Warsaw, Poland. TEL 48-22-9263914, FAX 48-22-9265334, arspolona@arspolona.com.pl, http://www.arspolona.com.pl.

636   USA
WASHINGTON FARMER-STOCKMAN. Text in English. m. USD 21.95 in state; USD 30 out of state; USD 75 foreign (effective 2001). **Document type:** *Newsletter.*
Formed by the merger of part of (1992-1996): Inland Farmer (1073-144X); Which was formerly (until 1993): Inland Farmer-Stockman (1062-290X); and part of (1992-1996): Pacific Farmer (1071-6548); Which was formerly (until 1993): Pacific-Farmer Stockman (1062-256X); Inland Farmer-Stockman & Pacific Farmer-Stockman were formed by merger of part of (1971-1992): Oregon Farmer-Stockman (1041-2719); and part of (1971-1992): Washington Farmer-Stockman (1041-2727); Which both superseded: Western Farmer and Agricultural Age
Published by: Farm Progress Companies, 191 S Gary Ave, Carol Stream, IL 60188. TEL 630-690-5600, FAX 630-462-2869, info@farmprogress.com, http://www.farmprogress.com/. Ed. Len Richardson TEL 925-687-1662.

WASHINGTON FEEDLINE. see *AGRICULTURE—Feed, Flour And Grain*

636   AUS   ISSN 1441-7634
WASTELINE (ONLINE EDITION); news from the livestock environmental management services team. Text in English. 1998. **Document type:** *Newsletter.*
Media: Online - full text. **Related titles:** ◆ Print ed.: Wasteline (Print Edition). ISSN 1441-7626.
Published by: Department of Primary Industries, Australian Seafood Extension and Advisory Service, PO Box 102, Toowoomba, QLD 4350, Australia. TEL 61-7-4688-1096, FAX 61-7-4688-1192, http://www.dpi.qld.gov.au/newsletters/wasteline/1/. Ed. Sarah Connors.

363   AUS   ISSN 1441-7626
WASTELINE (PRINT EDITION). Text in English. irreg. **Document type:** *Government.*
Related titles: ◆ Online - full text ed.: Wasteline (Online Edition). ISSN 1441-7634.
Published by: Department of Primary Industries, Australian Seafood Extension and Advisory Service, PO Box 102, Toowoomba, QLD 4350, Australia. TEL 61-7-4688-1096, FAX 61-7-4688-1192.

WATT POULTRY STATISTICAL YEARBOOK: INTERNATIONAL EDITION. see *AGRICULTURE—Abstracting, Bibliographies, Statistics*

WEEKLY INSIDERS DAIRY & EGG LETTER. see *AGRICULTURE—Dairying And Dairy Products*

WEEKLY INSIDERS POULTRY REPORT. see *FOOD AND FOOD INDUSTRIES*

WEEKLY INSIDERS TURKEY REPORT AND WEEKLY HATCH REPORT. see *AGRICULTURE—Abstracting, Bibliographies, Statistics*

636   USA   ISSN 0043-1842
WEEKLY LIVESTOCK REPORTER. Text in English. 1897. w. USD 18; USD 1 newsstand/cover (effective 2005). adv. bk.rev. 5 cols./p.; back issues avail. **Document type:** *Newspaper, Trade.* **Description:** For commercial cowmen, purebred breeders and buyers, feedlot operators and agribusiness people.
Incorporates: Texas Livestock Journal; Formerly: Daily Livestock Reporter
Published by: Livestock Service, Inc., 120 N Rayner St, Box 7655, Fort Worth, TX 76111-0655. TEL 817-831-3147, FAX 817-831-3117, service@weeklylivestock.com, http://www.weeklylivestock.com. Ed., Pub. Phil Stoll. Adv. contact Donna Hamby. B&W page USD 875, color page USD 1,275; trim 10.25 x 13.5. Circ: 10,000 (paid).

636.2   GBR
WELSH BLACK CATTLE SOCIETY HERD BOOK. Text in English. 1904. a. GBP 15 per issue (effective 2005). video rev. illus.; mkt.; stat. back issues avail. **Document type:** *Directory, Trade.*
Published by: Welsh Black Cattle Society, 13 Bangor St, Caernarfon, Gwynedd LL55 1AP, United Kingdom. TEL 44-1286-672391, FAX 44-1286-672022, info@welshblackcattlesociety.org, http://www.welshblackcattlesociety.org/shop.htm. Ed. S Evelyn Jones. Circ: 1,000.

636.2   GBR
WELSH BLACK CATTLE SOCIETY JOURNAL. Text in English, Welsh. 1976. a. GBP 7.50 per issue (effective 2005). adv. **Document type:** *Journal, Trade.*
Published by: Welsh Black Cattle Society, 13 Bangor St, Caernarfon, Gwynedd LL55 1AP, United Kingdom. TEL 44-1286-672391, FAX 44-1286-672022, info@welshblackcattlesociety.org, http://www.welshblackcattlesociety.org/shop.htm. Ed. S Evelyn Jones. Circ: 1,000.

636 639.2   DEU   ISSN 1619-3288
WER UND WAS - FLEISCH-, FISCH-, FEINKOST-INDUSTRIE. Text in German. 1976. biennial. EUR 369.50 (effective 2003). **Document type:** *Directory, Trade.*
Formerly (until 2000): Wer und Was in der Deutschen Fleisch-, Fisch-, und Feinkost-Industrie (0170-7353)
Published by: B. Behr's Verlag GmbH & Co. KG, Averhoffstr. 10, Hamburg, 22085, Germany. TEL 49-40-2270080, FAX 49-40-2201091, info@behrs.de, http://www.behrs.de. Adv. contact Frau Nuesslein.

637   AUS   ISSN 0729-3445
WESTERN AUSTRALIAN EGG MARKETING BOARD. NEWSLETTER. Text in English. 1949. m. free. adv. stat.
Published by: Western Australian Egg Marketing Board, 43-45 McGregor Rd., Palmyra, Australia. Circ: 500.

636.2   USA   ISSN 1074-0031
WESTERN BEEF PRODUCER. Text in English. 1993. 16/yr. adv. **Document type:** *Trade.*

Published by: Western Farmer-Stockman Magazines (Subsidiary of: Cowles Publishing Co.), PO Box 2160, Spokane, WA 99210-1615. TEL 509-459-5361, FAX 509-459-5102. Pub. E W Ramsey Pub Dir. Adv. contact Richard C Brantley. Circ: 34,404 (controlled).

636   USA   ISSN 1542-2054
THE WESTERN FARMER - STOCKMAN. Text in English. 1998. m. USD 23.95 (effective 2005). adv. bk.rev. charts; illus. **Document type:** *Magazine, Trade.*
Formed by the 1998 merger of: Wyoming Farmer-Stockman; Which was formerly: Wyoming Stockman-Farmer (0043-9800); (1993-1998): Utah Farmer (1071-653X); Which was formerly: Utah Farmer-Stockman (1041-1666); Nevada Farmer
Published by: Farm Progress Companies, 191 S Gary Ave, Carol Stream, IL 60188-2095. TEL 630-462-2229, FAX 630-462-2202, info@farmprogress.com, http://www.westernfarmerstockman.com, http://www.farmprogress.com/. adv.: B&W page USD 1,850, color page USD 2,350; trim 10.5 x 14.5. Circ: 30,000 (paid).

636.4   CAN   ISSN 0225-3488
WESTERN HOG JOURNAL. Text in English. 1972. q. free to hog producers. adv. bk.rev. charts; illus.; stat. **Document type:** *Trade.*
Formerly (until vol. 8, 1979): Alberta Hog Journal (0315-3800) —CISTI.
Published by: Alberta Pork, 10319 Princess Elizabeth Ave, Edmonton, AB T5G 0Y5, Canada. TEL 780-474-8288, FAX 780-479-5128, TELEX 03-73367, whj@albertapork.com, http://www.albertapork.com. Adv. contact James Shaw. Circ: 7,500 (controlled).

636   USA   ISSN 0094-6710
WESTERN LIVESTOCK JOURNAL WEEKLY. Text in English. w. (Mon.). USD 35 (effective 2005). adv. illus. **Document type:** *Newspaper.* —CISTI.
Published by: Crow Publications, Inc. (Denver), 650 S Lipan, Denver, CO 80223. TEL 303-722-7600, FAX 303-722-0155, editorial@wlj.net, http://www.wlj.net. Pub. Pete Crow. Circ: 24,000 (paid).

636   USA
WESTERN LIVESTOCK REPORTER. Text in English. 1940. w. (Wed.). USD 29 (effective 2004). adv. **Document type:** *Newspaper, Trade.* **Description:** Provides in-depth national, state, and local news for livestock producers, cattlemen, and sheep growers in the Northwest.
Published by: Western Livestock Reporter, Inc., PO Box 30758, Billings, MT 59107. TEL 406-259-5406, FAX 406-259-6888, winclass@imt.net, http://www.cattleplus.com. Ed. Jamie Lane. Pub. Patrick K. Goggins. Circ: 12,000 (paid). Wire service: AP.

636.5   USA
WESTERN POULTRY DISEASE CONFERENCE. PROCEEDINGS. Text in English. 1970. a. back issues avail.
Formerly (until 1983): Western Poultry Disease Conference and Poultry Health Symposium. Proceedings (0094-8780)
Indexed: Agr.
—BLDSC (6849.883000), CISTI.
Published by: Western Poultry Disease Conference, c/o Dr. Joan Jeffrey, UCD-VMTRC, 18830 Rd. 112, Tulare, CA 93274. Ed. Dr. David D. Frame.

WHO'S WHO IN THE EGG AND POULTRY INDUSTRIES. see *AGRICULTURE—Abstracting, Bibliographies, Statistics*

636.5   USA
WHO'S WHO INTERNATIONAL IN THE EGG & POULTRY INDUSTRY. Text in English. 1970. a. USD 15. adv. **Document type:** *Directory, Trade.* **Description:** Buyer's guide of suppliers of poultry equipment, services, and supplies. Gives addresses, phone and fax information for companies serving the worldwide industry.
Published by: Watt Publishing Co., 122 S Wesley Ave, Mt. Morris, IL 61054-1497. TEL 815-734-4171, FAX 815-734-5649, http://www.wattnet.com. Ed. David Martin. Pub. Charles Olentine. Adv. contact Anita Martin. B&W page USD 4,250, color page USD 5,800; trim 10.75 x 8. Circ: 23,632.

631.5   BEL
WILD & GEVOGELTE/VOLAILLE ET GIBIER. Text in Dutch, French. 1993. q. adv. back issues avail. **Document type:** *Proceedings, Trade.* **Description:** Includes general information for small game and poultry businesses.
Published by: Federation on Wild & Gevogelte, Gentsesteenweg 393, Brussels, 1080, Belgium. TEL 32-2-4666831, FAX 32-2-4666831, hendrina.nyenhof@euronet.be. Ed., R&P, Adv. contact Raf Deseure. Circ: 2,500 (controlled).

636   USA
WINGS & HOOVES. Text in English. 1989. m. USD 18 domestic; USD 30 in Canada & Mexico; USD 45 elsewhere (effective 2001). adv. bk.rev. mkt. **Document type:** *Newsletter.* **Description:** Looks at the exotic animal marketplace, carries regular market prices and provides husbandry information. Devoted to profitable agriculture and livestock.
Published by: J. Haid, Ed. & Pub., Rt 1, Box 32, Forestburg, TX 76239-9706. TEL 940-964-2314, FAX 940-964-2314, wingsandhooves@nortexinfo.net. R&P J Haid. Adv. contact J. Haid. Circ: 5,000.

▼ *new title*   ➤ *refereed*   * *unverified*   ◆ *full entry avail.*

A

636.3 677.3 NZL ISSN 0043-7875
WOOL TECHNOLOGY AND SHEEP BREEDING. Text in English. 1954. q. NZD 100 to individuals; NZD 140 to libraries (effective 2001). adv. bk.rev. **Document type:** *Academic/Scholarly.* **Description:** Contains articles about on-farm production, handling, transport, early-stage processing and marketing of wool, and all aspects of sheep breeding and husbandry.
Indexed: AEA, ASCA, AgBio, AnBrAb, BiolAb, CPA, ChemAb, CurCont, DSA, HelmAb, HerbAb, HortAb, I&DA, IndVet, NutrAb, PBA, RDA, RM&VM, RRTA, RevApplEntom, S&F, SIA, SSCI, SeedAb, TTI, TriticAb, VetBull, WAE&RSA, WTA, WeedAb.
—BLDSC (9347.480000), CISTI, IE, Infotrieve, ingenta.
Published by: Wool Research Organisation of New Zealand Inc., Private Bag 4749, Christchurch, New Zealand. TEL 64-3-325-2421, FAX 64-3-3242717, cottle@wronz.org.nz, http://www.wronz.org.nz. Ed. David J Cottle. R&P, Adv. contact Errol Wood. Circ: 510.

THE WORKING BORDER COLLIE. see *PETS*

636.737 AUS ISSN 0312-3480
WORKING KELPIE COUNCIL. NATIONAL STUD BOOK. Text in English. 1967. irreg. (2-3/yr.). AUD 7.50 to non-members (effective 1999). back issues avail. **Description:** Provides pedigree details of Australian Kelper sheepdogs.
Related titles: Diskette ed.
Published by: Working Kelpie Council, PO Box 306, Castle Hill, NSW 2154, Australia. TEL 61-2-8999224, FAX 61-2-9894-2140, wkc@hartingdale.com.au, http://www.hartingdale.com.au/wkc/index.htm. Ed. B M Cooper. Circ: 620 (controlled).

636 ITA ISSN 1014-6954
SF1 CODEN: WARVAI
WORLD ANIMAL REVIEW (MULTILINGUAL EDITION). Text in Multiple languages. 1972. q. USD 18 (effective 1999). **Description:** Brings into focus the various aspects of animal production, animal health and animal products. Designed for those concerned with livestock and their related food by-products industries.
Formed by the 199? merger of: World Animal Review (English Edition) (0049-8025); Revue Mondiale de Zootechnie (0252-0176); Revista Mundial de Zootecnia (0252-0184)
Indexed: AEA, ASCA, AgrForAb, AnBrAb, ApicAb, BiolAb, CurCont, DSA, FCA, FS&TA, FoVS&M, ForAb, HelmAb, HerbAb, HortAb, IndVet, NutrAb, PN&I, PoultAb, RASB, RDA, RRTA, RevApplEntom, SIA, SPPI, SoyAb, VetBull, WAE&RSA.
—CASDDS, CISTI, IE, Linda Hall.
Published by: Food and Agriculture Organization of the United Nations, Sales and Marketing Group, Viale delle Terme di Caracalla, Rome, 00100, Italy. TEL 39-06-57054350, FAX 39-06-57053360.

WORLD BUIATRICS CONGRESS. see *VETERINARY SCIENCE*

636 ITA ISSN 0084-1552
WORLD CONFERENCE ON ANIMAL PRODUCTION. PROCEEDINGS. (Proceedings published by organizing committee) Text in English, French, German, Spanish. 1963. irreg., latest 1973, 3rd, Melbourne. **Document type:** *Proceedings.*
Published by: World Association for Animal Production, Via G Tomassetti 3, 1A, Rome, 00161, Italy. TEL 39-06-44202639, FAX 39-06-86329263, waap@waap.it, http://www.waap.it.

636.5 NLD ISSN 1388-3119
SF481 CODEN: MWPOEZ
WORLD POULTRY; production - processing - marketing. Text in Dutch. 1990. m. EUR 185 (effective 2005). adv. illus. **Document type:** *Journal, Trade.* **Description:** Covers breeding techniques, feeding and veterinary care of poultry.
Formerly (until 1997): Misset World Poultry (0926-924X); Which was formed by the merger of (1984-1990): Poultry (0169-4405); (1936-1990): World Poultry (0960-1694); Which was formerly (until 1984): World Poultry Industry (0260-387X); (until 1980): Poultry Industry (0032-5759)
Indexed: AEA, AbHyg, AgBio, AnBrAb, BioCN&I, DSA, FS&TA, HelmAb, HerbAb, HortAb, IndVet, MaizeAb, NutrAb, PBA, PGegResA, PHN&I, PN&I, PoultAb, ProtozoAb, RA&MP, RDA, RM&VM, RPP, RefZh, RevApplEntom, RiceAb, S&F, SIA, TDB, TriticAb, VetBull, WAE&RSA.
—BLDSC (9358.144000), CISTI, IE, ingenta, Linda Hall.
Published by: Reed Business Information bv (Subsidiary of: Reed Business), Hanzestraat 1, Doetinchem, 7006 RH, Netherlands. TEL 31-314-349550, FAX 31-314-340515, info@reedbusiness.nl, http://www.reedbusiness.nl. Ed. Wiebe van der Sluis TEL 31-314-349260. Pub. Michel Veen. Adv. contact Miguel Mendes de Leon TEL 31-314-349584. Circ: 24,722.

636.5 GBR ISSN 1740-049X
▼ **WORLD POULTRYMEAT.** Text in English. 2003. 24/m. GBP 633 worldwide (effective 2005). stat. **Document type:** *Newsletter, Trade.* **Description:** Provides expert news, comment, analysis and statistics on poultrymeat markets and updates on political and regulatory developments affecting the industry.
Related titles: Online - full content ed.
Published by: Agra Europe (London) Ltd. (Subsidiary of: T & F Informa plc), 80 Calverley Rd, Tunbridge Wells, Kent TN1 2UN, United Kingdom. TEL 44-1892-533813, FAX 44-1892-544895, marketing@agra-net.com, http://www.agra-net.com.

WORLD RABBIT SCIENCE. see *BIOLOGY—Zoology*

636.5 NLD
WORLD'S POULTRY SCIENCE ASSOCIATION. PROCEEDINGS OF WORLD'S POULTRY CONGRESS. (Proceedings published and distributed by host country.) Text in Dutch. quadrennial. adv. bk.rev. **Document type:** *Proceedings.*
Formerly: World's Poultry Science Association. Report of the Proceedings of International Congress (0084-2532)
Indexed: CurCont.
Published by: World's Poultry Science Association, c/o Dr Piet Simons, Sec, Centre for Applied Research "Het Spelderholt", PO Box 31, Beekbergen, 7360 AA, Netherlands. TEL 31-55-506-4858.

636.5 GBR ISSN 0043-9339
SF481 CODEN: WPSJAO
➤ **WORLD'S POULTRY SCIENCE JOURNAL.** Text in Dutch. 1944. q. USD 230 in the Americas to institutions except Canada; GBP 130 elsewhere to institutions; USD 245 combined subscription in the Americas to institutions except Canada; print & online eds.; GBP 140 combined subscription elsewhere to institutions print & online eds. (effective 2006). bk.rev. bibl.; charts; illus.; stat. back issues avail.; reprints avail. **Document type:** *Journal, Academic/Scholarly.* **Description:** Provides an international forum for the exchange and dissemination of information on poultry science including research, education and industry organization.
Related titles: Microform ed.: (from PQC); Online - full text ed.: ISSN 1743-4777. USD 195 in the Americas to institutions except Canada; GBP 110 elsewhere to institutions (effective 2006) (from EBSCO Publishing, Gale Group, IngentaConnect, Ovid Technologies, Inc., Swets Information Services).
Indexed: AEA, ASCA, AgBio, Agr, AnBrAb, B&AI, BioCN&I, BiolAb, ChemAb, CurCont, CurPA, DBA, DSA, FS&TA, HelmAb, HortAb, I&DA, ISR, IndVet, MEDLINE, MaizeAb, NutrAb, PBA, PN&I, PoultAb, ProtozoAb, RA&MP, RDA, RM&VM, RPP, RRTA, RiceAb, S&F, SCI, SFA, SIA, SoyAb, TriticAb, VetBull, WAE&RSA, WeedAb, WildRev.
—BLDSC (9364.000000), CASDDS, CISTI, GNLM, IE, Infotrieve, ingenta, Linda Hall. **CCC.**
Published by: (World's Poultry Science Association NLD), CABI Publishing (Subsidiary of: CAB International), CAB International, Wallingford, Oxfordshire OX10 8DE, United Kingdom. TEL 44-1491-832111, FAX 44-1491-833508, cabi@cabi.org, http://www.cabi-publishing.org/. Ed. D G Martin. Pub. Katy Christomanou TEL 44-1491-829187.

➤ **XUMU SHOUYI XUEBAO/ACTA VETERINARIA ET ZOOTECHNICA SINICA.** see *VETERINARY SCIENCE*

636 USA ISSN 1066-8195
THE YELLOW SHEET (TOMS RIVER). Text in English. 1892. d. (Mon-Fri). USD 482 (effective 2004). adv. back issues avail.; reprints avail. **Document type:** *Newsletter.* **Description:** Provides eight pages of unbiased meat quotes to help pinpoint the latest trading levels of beef, pork, lamb, veal, meat by-products, carcasses and boxed cuts.
Related titles: Fax ed.; Online - full text ed.
Published by: Urner Barry Publications, Inc., PO Box 389, Toms River, NJ 08754-0389. TEL 732-240-5330, FAX 732-341-0891, salesl@urnerbarry.com, mail@urnerbarry.com, http://www.urnerbarry.com. Ed. Joseph Muldowney. Adv. contact Katie Hopkins. Circ: 1,500 (paid).

637.5 DEU
Z M P BILANZ EIER UND GEFLUEGEL. Text in German. a. **Document type:** *Bulletin, Trade.*
Related titles: CD-ROM ed.
Published by: Zentrale Markt und Preisberichtstelle GmbH, Rochusstr 2, Bonn, 53123, Germany. TEL 49-228-9777173, FAX 49-228-9777179, info@zmp.com, http://www.zmp.de.

636.2 DEU
Z M P BILANZ VIEH UND FLEISCH. Text in German. a. **Document type:** *Bulletin, Trade.*
Related titles: CD-ROM ed.
Published by: Zentrale Markt und Preisberichtstelle GmbH, Rochusstr 2, Bonn, 53123, Germany. TEL 49-228-9777173, FAX 49-228-9777179, info@zmp.de, http://www.zmp.de.

636.5 DEU
Z M P MARKTBERICHT. GEFLUEGEL. Text in German. w. **Document type:** *Bulletin, Trade.*
Published by: Zentrale Markt und Preisberichtstelle GmbH, Rochusstr 2, Bonn, 53123, Germany. TEL 49-228-9777173, FAX 49-228-9777179, info@zmp.de, http://www.zmp.de.

637.5 DEU
Z M P MARKTBERICHT. MARKTJOURNAL EIER. Text in German. m. **Document type:** *Bulletin, Trade.*
Published by: Zentrale Markt und Preisberichtstelle GmbH, Rochusstr 2, Bonn, 53123, Germany. TEL 49-228-9777173, FAX 49-228-9777179, info@zmp.de, http://www.zmp.de.

636.2 DEU ISSN 0946-6509
Z M P MARKTBERICHT. VIEH UND FLEISCH. Text in German. 1994. w. **Document type:** *Bulletin, Trade.*
Published by: Zentrale Markt und Preisberichtstelle GmbH, Rochusstr 2, Bonn, 53123, Germany. TEL 49-228-9777173, FAX 49-228-9777179, info@zmp.de, http://www.zmp.de.

ZHIVOTNOVOD DLYA VSEKH. see *VETERINARY SCIENCE*

636 BGR ISSN 0514-7441
SF1 CODEN: ZHVNAS
ZHIVOTNOVUDNI NAUKI. Summaries in English, German, Russian. 1964. 6/yr. BGL 1.50 per issue; USD 132 foreign (effective 2002). bk.rev. bibl.; illus. reprint service avail. from IRC. **Document type:** *Journal.*
Indexed: AEA, AgBio, AgrForAb, AnBrAb, BIOSIS Prev, BioCN&I, BiolAb, CPA, ChemAb, DSA, FCA, FPA, FS&TA, ForAb, HelmAb, HerbAb, HortAb, I&DA, INIS AtomInd, IndVet, MaizeAb, NutrAb, PBA, PGrRegA, PHN&I, PN&I, PotatoAb, PoultAb, ProtozoAb, RA&MP, RM&VM, RPP, RefZh, RevApplEntom, S&F, SIA, SeedAb, SoyAb, TriticAb, VetBull, WAE&RSA, WeedAb, ZooRec.
—BLDSC (0058.010000), CASDDS.
Published by: (Natzionalen Tzentar za Agrarni Nauki/National Center for Agrarian Sciences of Bulgaria), Universitetsko Izdatelstvo Sv. Kliment Okhridski/Publishing House of the Sofia University St. Kliment Okhridski, Akad G Bonchev 6, Sofia, 1113, Bulgaria. Ed. Zahari Zahariev. Circ: 1,000. **Dist. by:** Hemus, 6 Rouski Blvd., Sofia 1000, Bulgaria; **Dist. by:** Sofia Books, ul Silivria 16, Sofia 1404, Bulgaria. TEL 359-2-9586257, info@sofiabooks-bg.com, http://www.sofiabooks-bg.com.

ZHONGGUO NONGYE KEXUE/CHINESE AGRICULTURAL SCIENCES. see *AGRICULTURE*

636.0855 CHN ISSN 1004-3314
ZHONGGUO SILIAO/CHINA FEED. Text in Chinese. 1990. s-m. adv.
Related titles: Online - full text ed.: (from East View Information Services).
Published by: Zhongguo Siliao Gongye Xiehui, 33 Dongdan Santiao, Beijing, 100005, China. TEL 86-10-5136541. **Dist. overseas by:** China International Book Trading Corp, 35 Chegongzhuang Xilu, Haidian District, PO Box 399, Beijing 100044, China.

636 CHN ISSN 0258-7033
CODEN: ZXZADM
ZHONGGUO XUMU ZAZHI/CHINESE JOURNAL OF ANIMAL SCIENCE. Text in Chinese. 1963. bi-m. USD 0.70 per issue.
Related titles: Online - full text ed.: (from East View Information Services).
Indexed: AEA, AgBio, AgrForAb, AnBrAb, ChemAb, DSA, ForAb, HerbAb, HortAb, IndVet, MaizeAb, NutrAb, PBA, PN&I, PoultAb, RA&MP, RM&VM, RiceAb, SIA, SoyAb, TOSA, TriticAb, VetBull, WAE&RSA.
—BLDSC (3180.292000), CASDDS, CISTI, IE, ingenta, Linda Hall.
Published by: Zhongguo Xumu Shouyi Xuehui/Chinese Society of Animal Husbandry and Veterinary Science, 33 Nong Feng Li, Dongdaqiao, Chaoyang-qu, Beijing, 100020, China. TEL 86-1-65066533. Ed. Feng Yanglian.

ZHONGZHI YU YANGZHI. see *AGRICULTURE—Crop Production And Soil*

ZIMBABWE. CENTRAL STATISTICAL OFFICE. QUARTERLY POULTRY CENSUS. see *AGRICULTURE—Abstracting, Bibliographies, Statistics*

636 ZWE
ZIMBABWE. MINISTRY OF AGRICULTURE. DIVISION OF LIVESTOCK AND PASTURES. ANNUAL REPORT. Text in English. 1973. a. free. back issues avail. **Document type:** *Government.*
Indexed: AnBrAb.
Published by: (Zimbabwe. Information Services), Ministry of Lands Agriculture and Rural Resettlement, Research and Specialist Services, Causeway, PO Box 8108, Harare, Zimbabwe. Circ: 800.

636 BRA ISSN 0044-5320
ZOOTECNIA. Text in Portuguese; Summaries in English. 1961. q. USD 43.
Indexed: ATA, DSA, HerbAb, NutrAb.
—CISTI.
Published by: Instituto de Zootecnia, Rua Heitor Penteado 56, Nova Odessa, SP 13460-000, Brazil. TEL 55-19-34669400, http://www.iz.sp.gov.br. Ed. Valdinei Tadeu Paulino. R&P Mario Augusto Brajao.

636 CUB
ZOOTECNIA DE CUBA. Text in Spanish. 1991. 4/yr. USD 30 in South America; USD 32 in North America; USD 36 elsewhere. **Description:** Contains articles on the results of scientific and technical research about the species of greatest economic importance to Cuban agriculture.
Indexed: AnBrAb, DSA, IndVet.

Published by: Centro de Informacion y Documentacion Agropecuario, Gaveta Postal 4149, Havana, 4, Cuba. TEL 29-2227. Ed. Juan Manuel Castro Morejon. Circ: 2,000. **Subscr. to:** Dpto. de Ediciones y Extension Agropecuarias, Comercializacion y Dist., Omoa-Este No. 12-B entre Pila y Matadero, Cerro, Ciudad de La Habana, Cuba. **International dist. by:** Ediciones Cubanas, Obispo No. 527, Apdo. 605, Havana, Cuba.

636 VEN ISSN 0798-7269
ZOOTECNIA TROPICAL. Text in English, Spanish. 1982. s-a. per issue exchange basis. bibl.; charts; illus. **Document type:** *Government.*
Related titles: Online - full text ed.: free (effective 2005).
Indexed: AgrForAb, AnBrAb, CPA, DSA, FCA, ForAb, HelmAb, HerbAb, HortAb, I&DA, IndVet, MaizeAb, NutrAb, PBA, PGegResA, PN&I, PoultAb, ProtozoAb, RDA, S&F, SIA, SeedAb, VetBull, WAE&RSA, WeedAb.
Published by: Fondo Nacional de Investigaciones Agropecuarias, Apdo. 2103, Maracay, 2105, Venezuela. FAX 58-43-836312. Ed. Alberto Valle. Circ: 600.

636 RUS ISSN 0235-2478
CODEN: CRYSEF
ZOOTEKHNIYA. Text in Russian. 1928. m. USD 180 foreign (effective 2004). adv. bk.rev. illus. index.
Formerly: Zhivotnovodstvo (0044-4480)
Indexed: AEA, AgBio, AnBrAb, BiolAb, ChemAb, DSA, FCA, FS&TA, HerbAb, IndVet, MaizeAb, NutrAb, PHN&I, PN&I, PotatoAb, PoultAb, RASB, RefZh, S&MA, SoyAb, TriticAb, VetBull, WAE&RSA.
—CASDDS, CISTI, East View, Linda Hall.
Address: Sadovaya-Spasskaya 18, Moscow, 107807, Russian Federation. TEL 7-095-2072080, FAX 7-095-2072080. Ed. Andrei T Mysik. adv.: page USD 500; trim 285 x 205. Circ: 7,200. **Dist. by:** M K - Periodica, ul Gilyarovskogo 39, Moscow 129110, Russian Federation. TEL 7-095-2845008, FAX 7-095-2813798, info@periodicals.ru, http://www.mkniga.ru.

636 DEU
ZUCHTWAHL UND BESAMUNG. Text in German. 1955. 2/yr. adv. back issues avail. **Document type:** *Journal, Trade.*
Indexed: AEA, AnBrAb, DSA, IndVet, NutrAb, PN&I.
Published by: Besamungsverein Neustadt an der Aisch e.V., Karl Eibl Str 17-27, Neustadt an der Aisch, 91413, Germany. TEL 49-9161-7870, FAX 49-9161-787250, info@bvn-online.de, http://www.bvn-online.de. Ed. W Breuer. Circ: 25,000.

636 DEU ISSN 0044-5401
CODEN: ZUECAZ
➤ **ZUECHTUNGSKUNDE.** Summaries in English, French, Russian. 1926. bi-m. EUR 474 domestic; EUR 473.90 foreign; EUR 86 per issue (effective 2005). adv. bk.rev. abstr.; bibl.; charts; illus. **Document type:** *Journal, Academic/Scholarly.* **Description:** Contains technical information aimed at animal breeders, breeding advisers and directors, scientists and students.
Indexed: AEA, AbHyg, AgBio, AnBrAb, BIOSIS Prev, BiolAb, ChemAb, CurCont, DIP, DSA, FS&TA, HerbAb, HortAb, IBR, ISR, IndVet, MaizeAb, NutrAb, PN&I, PoultAb, ProtozoAb, RA&MP, RRTA, SCI, SIA, SoyAb, TriticAb, VetBull, WAE&RSA.
—BLDSC (9537.000000), CASDDS, CISTI, IDS, IE, ingenta, Linda Hall. **CCC.**
Published by: (Deutsche Gesellschaft fuer Zuechtungskunde e.V.), Verlag Eugen Ulmer GmbH, Wollgrasweg 41, Stuttgart, 70599, Germany. TEL 49-711-45070, FAX 49-711-4507120, info@ulmer.de, http://www.zuechtungskunde.de, http://www.ulmer.de. Ed. F Schmitten. R&P Gerd Friedrich. Adv. contact Sigrid Holdschik. B&W page EUR 580; trim 140 x 216. Circ: 622 (paid and controlled).

AIR TRANSPORT

see TRANSPORTATION—Air Transport

AIRLINE INFLIGHT AND HOTEL INROOM

see TRAVEL AND TOURISM—Airline Inflight And Hotel Inroom

ALLERGOLOGY AND IMMUNOLOGY

see MEDICAL SCIENCES—Allergology And Immunology

ALTERNATIVE MEDICINE

see also MEDICAL SCIENCES

➤ **A A M TERRA NUOVA**; rivista ecoalternativa. (Agricoltura Alimentazione Medicina) see *ENVIRONMENTAL STUDIES*

615.5 GBR ISSN 0966-7164
A Q. (Aromatherapy Quarterly) Text in English. 1983. q.
Indexed: CINAHL.
—**CCC.**
Published by: Aromatherapy Quarterly, Inc., 5 Ranelagh, London, SW13 OBY, United Kingdom. FAX 44-0181-3921691. **Subscr. to:** Box 421, Inverness, CA 94937-0421 .

615.3 AUS
ACCESS (MORISSET). Text in English. q. free to members. **Document type:** *Newsletter, Trade.* **Description:** Provides information on the activities of the Board, as well as events and industry trends.
—BLDSC (0570.820123).
Published by: National Herbalists Association of Australia, 13 Breillat St., Annandale, NSW 2038, Australia. TEL 61-2-95558885, FAX 61-2-95558884, nhaa@nhaa.org.au, http://www.nhaa.org.au/access.html. Ed. Anne Cowper.

615.822 USA
ACUPRESSURE NEWS. Text in English, French, German, Italian. 1987. a., latest vol.16. USD 2.50 (effective 2001). tr.mk. 8 p./no. 3 cols./p.; back issues avail.; reprints avail. **Document type:** *Newsletter.* **Description:** Jin Shin Do Bodymind Acupressure combines gentle yet deep finger pressure on specific acu-points with body focusing techniques, to help physical and emotional tension and armoring.
Published by: Jin Shin Do Foundation, Acupressure Workshop, 1084 G San Miguel Canyon Rd, Watsonville, CA 95076. TEL 831-763-7702, FAX 831-763-1551, http://www.jinshindo.org. Ed. Iona Marsaa Teeguarden. Circ: 6,000 (paid and controlled).

615.892 615.845 USA ISSN 0360-1293
RM184 CODEN: AEREDS
➤ **ACUPUNCTURE AND ELECTRO-THERAPEUTICS RESEARCH**; the international journal. Text in English. 1976. q. USD 250 domestic; USD 280 foreign (effective 2005). bk.rev. abstr.; bibl.; charts; illus.; stat. index. back issues avail. **Document type:** *Journal, Academic/Scholarly.* **Description:** Covers developments in basic and clinical research in acupuncture, electro-therapeutics and related fields. Fosters efforts to understand and improve these treatments and their use in diagnosis, prognosis, treatment and prevention of diseases in both Western and Oriental medicine.
Related titles: Microform ed.; Online - full text ed.: (from EBSCO Publishing).
Indexed: AMED, ASCA, B&BAb, BIOSIS Prev, BiolAb, BrCerAb, C&ISA, CINAHL, CerAb, ChemAb, CorrAb, CurCont, DentInd, E&CAJ, EMA, EngInd, ExcerpMed, IAA, IndMed, Inpharma, M&TEA, MBF, MEDLINE, METADEX, NSCI, PsycholAb, Reac, SCI, SolStAb, WAA.
—BLDSC (0677.930000), CASDDS, CISTI, Ei, GNLM, IDS, IE, Infotrieve, ingenta, KNAW, Linda Hall. **CCC.**
Published by: (International College of Acupuncture and Electro-Therapeutics), Cognizant Communication Corporation, 3 Hartsdale Rd, Elmsford, NY 10523-3701. TEL 914-592-7720, FAX 914-592-8981, cogcomm@aol.com, http://www.cognizantcommunication.com. Ed. Dr. Yoshiaki Omura. Pub., R&P Robert N Miranda. Adv. contact Lori Miranda. Circ: 1,000.

615.5 FRA ISSN 1633-3454
ACUPUNCTURE & MOXIBUSTION. Text in French. 2002. m. adv. bibl.; illus. **Document type:** *Magazine, Trade.*
Formed by the merger of (1973-2002): Revue Francaise de Medecine Traditionelle Chinoise (0758-2633); Which was formerly (until 1982): Mensuel du Medecin Acupuncteur (0301-6366); (1968-2002): Meridiens (0580-5872)
Indexed: AMED.
—BLDSC (7904.201000), IE. **CCC.**
Published by: Nguyen Van Nghi Ed. & Pub., 27 bd. d'Athenes, Marseille, 13001, France. acudoc@wanadoo.fr.

615.5 GBR ISSN 0964-5284
CODEN: ACMEFP
➤ **ACUPUNCTURE IN MEDICINE.** Text in English. 1981. s-a. GBP 20 in Europe to non-members; GBP 25 elsewhere to non-members (effective 2001). adv. bk.rev. cum.index. 2 cols./p.; back issues avail. **Document type:** *Journal, Academic/Scholarly.* **Description:** Aimed at medical practitioners. Publishes the results of controlled trials, reviews, audits, case histories and speculative discussion concerning acupuncture and related techniques.
Related titles: Online - full text ed.: USD 82 to institutions (effective 2002) (from EBSCO Publishing).
Indexed: AMED, CINAHL, ExcerpMed, RefZh.
—BLDSC (0677.935000), GNLM, IE, Infotrieve, ingenta. **CCC.**
Published by: British Medical Acupuncture Society, 12 Marbury House, Higher Whitley, Warrington, Ches WA4 4QW, United Kingdom. TEL 44-1925-730727, FAX 44-1925-730492, editor@medical-acupuncture.org.uk, admin@medical-acupuncture.org.uk, http://www.medical-acupuncture.co.uk/aimintro.htm. Eds. Dr. Jacqueline Filshie, Dr. Mike Cummings. R&P Dr. Mike Cummings. Adv. contact Julian Price. page GBP 225. Circ: 5,000.

610.95 615.892 NLD ISSN 1382-6883
➤ **ADVANCED TRADITIONAL CHINESE MEDICINE SERIES.** Text mainly in English; Text occasionally in Chinese. 1996. irreg., latest vol.8, 1998. price varies. back issues avail. **Document type:** *Monographic series, Academic/Scholarly.* **Description:** Publishes studies on the theory and practice of traditional Chinese medicine, including discussions of herbs, techniques, and clinical applications. Volumes include glossary of terminology in Pinyin and Chinese characters.
Indexed: IndMed.
—**CCC.**
Published by: I O S Press, Nieuwe Hemweg 6B, Amsterdam, 1013 BG, Netherlands. TEL 31-20-6883355, FAX 31-20-6203419, order@iospress.nl, http://www.iospress.nl. **Subscr. to:** I O S Press, Inc, 4502 Rachael Manor Dr., Fairfax, VA 22032-3631. iosbooks@iospress.com.

➤ **ADVANCES IN MIND - BODY MEDICINE.** see *MEDICAL SCIENCES*

615.5 DEU ISSN 1614-8339
AERZTEZEITSCHRIFT FUER NATURHEILVERFAHREN UND REGULATIONSMEDIZIN. Text mainly in German; Summaries in English, French. 1959. m. EUR 49.90; EUR 37.60 to students; EUR 6.10 newsstand/cover (effective 2005). adv. bk.rev. charts; illus. index, cum.index. back issues avail. **Document type:** *Magazine, Trade.*
Former titles (until 2003): Aerztezeitschrift fuer Naturheilverfahren (0720-6003); (until 1981): Physikalische Medizin und Rehabilitation (0031-9287)
Indexed: ExcerpMed, RefZh.
—GNLM. **CCC.**
Published by: (Zentralverband der Aerzte fuer Naturheilverfahren und Regulationsmedizin e.V.), Medizinisch Literarische Verlagsgesellschaft mbH, Postfach 1151-1152, Uelzen, 29501, Germany. TEL 49-581-808151, FAX 49-581-808158, mlverlag@mlverlag.de, http://www.zaen.org/index.php?content=zeitschrift, http://www.mlverlag.de. Ed. Jens Meyer-Wegener. adv.: B&W page EUR 1,590, color page EUR 2,920; trim 175 x 240. Circ: 12,200 (paid and controlled).

615.5 USA
AESCLEPIAN CHRONICLES. Text in English. 1995. m. back issues avail. **Document type:** *Newsletter.* **Description:** Promotes the role of holistic health practice and integral philosophy.
Related titles: Online - full text ed.
Published by: Synergistic Health Center, 1506 E Franklin St, Ste 104, Chapel Hill, NC 27514. TEL 919-932-7266, http://www.forthrt.com/~chronicl/homepage.html.

615.892 DEU ISSN 1614-6891
CODEN: AKUPE
AKUPUNKTUR & TRADITIONELLE CHINESISCHE MEDIZIN. Variant title: Akupunktur. Text in German. 1973. q. EUR 25.10; EUR 18.40 domestic to students; EUR 7.20 newsstand/cover (effective 2003). adv. bk.rev. back issues avail. **Document type:** *Magazine, Academic/Scholarly.* **Description:** Publishes articles on scientific research in acupuncture and includes lists of courses and events.
Former titles (until 2003): AKU (0940-6646); (until 1991): Akupunktur: Theorie und Praxis (0340-3130)
Indexed: CINAHL, ExcerpMed.
—**CCC.**
Published by: Medizinisch Literarische Verlagsgesellschaft mbH, Postfach 1151-1152, Uelzen, 29501, Germany. TEL 49-581-808151, FAX 49-581-808158, mlverlag@mlverlag.de, http://www.mlverlag.de. Ed., Pub. Dr. Thomas Weinschuetz. adv.: B&W page EUR 840, color page EUR 1,630. Circ: 6,000 (paid).

615.892 POL ISSN 1425-8838
AKUPUNKTURA POLSKA. Text in Polish, English. 1996. q. EUR 37 foreign (effective 2005). **Document type:** *Journal, Academic/Scholarly.*
Published by: Polskie Towarzystwo Akupunktury, Redakcja - Akupunktura Polska, Instytut - Centrum Zdrowia Matki Polski, ul Rzgowska 281/289, Lodz, 93338, Poland. TEL 48-42-2711398, FAX 48-42-2711357, http://www.akupunktura.org/polskaakupunktura/index.php. Ed. Piotr Wozniak. **Dist. by:** Ars Polona, Krakowskie Przedmiescie 7, Warsaw, Poland. TEL 48-22-9263914, FAX 48-22-9265334, arspolona@arspolona.com.pl, http://www.arspolona.com.pl.

615.892 DEU
AKUPUNKTURMAGAZIN. Text in German. 4/yr. **Document type:** *Magazine, Consumer.*
Published by: Publimed Medizin und Medien GmbH, Paul-Heyse-Str 31a, Munich, 80336, Germany. TEL 49-89-51616171, FAX 49-89-51616199, akumag@publimed.de, schreiber@publimed.de, http://www.publimed.de/akupunktur_magazin/.

A

615.5 USA ISSN 1076-2809
R733 CODEN: ACTHFZ
➤ **ALTERNATIVE & COMPLEMENTARY THERAPIES**; a bimonthly publication for health care practitioners. Text in English. 1995. bi-m. USD 425 domestic to institutions; USD 550 foreign to institutions; USD 509 combined subscription domestic to institutions print & online eds.; USD 630 combined subscription foreign to institutions print & online eds. (effective 2006). adv. back issues avail.; reprint service avail. from PSC. **Document type:** *Journal, Academic/Scholarly.* **Description:** Covers latest trends in the field of alternative medicine. Topics covered include a variety of nontraditional holistic health specialties.
Related titles: Online - full text ed.: USD 379 to institutions (effective 2006) (from EBSCO Publishing, Gale Group, O C L C Online Computer Library Center, Inc., Swets Information Services).
Indexed: AMED, CINAHL, ExcerpMed, IPA, e-psyche.
—BLDSC (0803.581470), CISTI, GNLM, IE, Infotrieve, ingenta. **CCC.**
Published by: Mary Ann Liebert, Inc. Publishers, 140 Huguenot St 3rd Fl, New Rochelle, NY 10801-5215. TEL 914-740-2100, FAX 914-740-2101, 800-654-3237, info@liebertpub.com, http://www.liebertpub.com/act.

615.5 USA ISSN 1096-942X
ALTERNATIVE MEDICINE ALERT. Text in English. 1997. m. USD 299; USD 50 newsstand/cover (effective 2006). **Document type:** *Newsletter, Trade.* **Description:** Dedicated to providing clinically sound information on alternative medicine to medical professionals.
Related titles: Online - full text ed.: (from EBSCO Publishing, Gale Group).
—CCC.
Published by: Thomson American Health Consultants, Inc. (Subsidiary of: Thomson Corporation, Healthcare Information Group), 3525 Piedmont Rd, N E, Bldg 6, Ste 400, Atlanta, GA 30305. TEL 404-262-5511, 800-688-2421, FAX 404-262-7837, 800-284-3291, customerservice@ahcpub.com, http://www.ahcpub.com. Pub. Brenda L Mooney TEL 404-262-5403.

615.5 USA
ALTERNATIVE MEDICINE MAGAZINE. Text in English. 1994. 9/yr. USD 24.95 domestic; USD 45 foreign (effective 2003). adv. bk.rev. illus. **Document type:** *Magazine, Consumer.* **Description:** Offers feature articles, departments, and digest summaries of information from doctor's journals, research, conferences and newsletters, covering the entire field of alternative medicine.
Formerly: Alternative Medicine Digest (1081-4000)
Related titles: Online - full text ed.
Indexed: CINAHL.
Published by: Alternative Medicine, 951 Front St., Novato, CA 94945-3236. TEL 800-515-4325, info@alternativemedicine.com, http://www.alternativemedicine.com. Ed. Susan Clare Ellis. Pub. Burton Goldberg. R&P Tom Klaber TEL 415-789-1415. Adv. contact Harold Abend. Circ: 170,000.

615.5 USA
➤ **ALTERNATIVE MEDICINE RESEARCH REPORT.** Text in English. m. USD 259 (effective 2005). **Document type:** *Newsletter, Academic/Scholarly.* **Description:** Designed to help physicians keep up with all the clinical research as well as the reimbursement and legislative developments surrounding complementary and alternative medicine.
Published by: National Health Information, LLC, PO Box 15429, Atlanta, GA 30333. TEL 404-607-9500, FAX 404-607-0095, nhi@nhionline.net, http://www.nhionline.net.

615.5 USA ISSN 1089-5159
R733 CODEN: ALMRFP
➤ **ALTERNATIVE MEDICINE REVIEW**; a journal of clinical therapeutics. Text in English. 1996. bi-m. USD 95 domestic; USD 150 foreign (effective 2004). bk.rev. abstr. **Document type:** *Journal, Academic/Scholarly.* **Description:** Dedicated to providing accurate, timely and clinically relevant original articles, abstracts, and literature reviews to the practicing preventive health-care professional.
Related titles: Online - full text ed.: (from EBSCO Publishing, Florida Center for Library Automation, Gale Group).
Indexed: AMED, CINAHL, ExcerpMed, IDIS, IndMed, MEDLINE, RA&MP.
—BLDSC (0803.588880), CISTI, GNLM, IE, Infotrieve, ingenta. **CCC.**
Published by: Thorne Research Inc., PO Box 25, Dover, ID 83825. TEL 208-263-1337, FAX 208-265-2488, altmedrev@thorne.com, sales@s1.thorne.com, http://www.thorne.com/alternative/alter_main.html. Ed. Kathleen A Head. Pub. A F Czap.

615.5 USA
ALTERNATIVE MEDICINE SOURCEBOOK. Text in English. 1999 (June). irreg., latest 2002, 2nd edition. USD 78 per vol. (effective 2004). charts. Index. **Description:** Contains basic information for the layperson about non-traditional therapies, including acupuncture, homeopathy, herbal remedies, mega-vitamin regimes, and more, along with current research data.
Published by: Omnigraphics, Inc., 615 Griswold St, Detroit, MI 48226. TEL 313-961-1340, 800-234-1340, FAX 313-961-1383, 800-875-1340, info@omnigraphics.com, http://www.omnigraphics.com. Ed. Allan R Cook.

615.5 USA ISSN 1078-6791
R733 CODEN: ATHMF7
➤ **ALTERNATIVE THERAPIES IN HEALTH AND MEDICINE.** Text in English. 1995. bi-m. USD 68 domestic to individuals; USD 107 foreign to individuals; USD 177 domestic to institutions; USD 272 foreign to institutions; USD 15 newsstand/cover domestic; USD 20 newsstand/cover foreign (effective 2005). adv. back issues avail. **Document type:** *Journal, Academic/Scholarly.* **Description:** Explores the integration of alternative therapies with conventional medical practices.
Related titles: Online - full text ed.: (from bigchalk, EBSCO Publishing, ProQuest Information & Learning).
Indexed: AMED, AbHyg, AgrForAb, BiolDig, CINAHL, CurCont, ExcerpMed, FPA, ForAb, GSI, HelmAb, HortAb, IDIS, INI, IPA, IndMed, Inpharma, MEDLINE, NRN, NutrAb, OrnHort, PE&ON, RA&MP, RDA, Reac, SIA, SoyAb, TDB, WeedAb.
—BLDSC (0803.661500), CISTI, GNLM, IDS, IE, Infotrieve, ingenta. **CCC.**
Published by: InnoVision Communications, 169 Saxony Rd., Ste. 103, Encinitas, CA 92024-6779. FAX 866-828-2962, alternative.therapies@innerdoorway.com, info@invcom.com, http://www.alternative-therapies.com. Pub. Ram Capoor. Adv. contact Kathi Magee. Circ: 12,000 (paid).

615.5 USA ISSN 1522-3396
ALTERNATIVE THERAPIES IN WOMEN'S HEALTH. Text in English. 1998. m. USD 349; USD 58 newsstand/cover (effective 2006). **Document type:** *Newsletter, Academic/Scholarly.* **Description:** Investigates the effectiveness of alternative therapies for women's health problems and potential uses within conventional medical practice, and analyzes the latest scientific research regarding botanicals and complementary therapies.
Related titles: Online - full text ed.: (from EBSCO Publishing, Gale Group).
Indexed: CINAHL.
—BLDSC (0803.661750). **CCC.**
Published by: Thomson American Health Consultants, Inc. (Subsidiary of: Thomson Corporation, Healthcare Information Group), 3525 Piedmont Rd, N E, Bldg 6, Ste 400, Atlanta, GA 30305. TEL 404-262-5511, 800-688-2421, FAX 404-262-7837, 800-284-3291, customerservice@ahcpub.com, http://www.ahcpub.com/ahc_root_html/products/newsletters/atwh.html.

THE AMERICAN JOURNAL OF CHINESE MEDICINE. see *MEDICAL SCIENCES—Abstracting, Bibliographies, Statistics*

615.53 IND ISSN 0257-7941
R605
ANCIENT SCIENCE OF LIFE. Text in English. 1981. q. INR 140, USD 37 (effective 2001). adv. bk.rev. 85 p./no. 2 cols./p.; back issues avail.; reprints avail. **Document type:** *Journal, Academic/Scholarly.* **Description:** Publishes research papers on Ayurveda, the Indian system of medicine, and allied disciplines. Also acts as an interdisciplinary medium on all aspects of medical health care.
Indexed: AMED, FPA, ForAb, HortAb, RM&VM.
—BLDSC (0900.325500), IE, ingenta.
Published by: International Institute of Ayurveda, Ramanathapuram, P O Box 7102, Coimbatore, Tamil Nadu 641 045, India. TEL 313188, FAX 314953, ayurveda@vsnl.com, http://www.avpayurveda.org. Ed. S Vijayan. Pubs. Dr. G Gangadharan, Suresh Kunar. R&P P R Krishna Kumar. adv.: B&W page INR 2,500; 165 x 220. Circ: 2,000.

▼ **ANNALS OF TRADITIONAL CHINESE MEDICINE.** see *MEDICAL SCIENCES*

615.535 USA
AROMATHERAPY JOURNAL. Text in English. q. USD 7.95 newsstand/cover domestic; USD 8.95 newsstand/cover in Canada. **Document type:** *Magazine, Consumer.*
Formerly: Scentsitivity (1523-4711)
Related titles: Online - full text ed.: (from EBSCO Publishing).
Published by: The National Association for Holistic Aromatherapy, 4509 Interlake Ave. N., Ste. 233, Seattle, WA 98103-6773. TEL 206-547-2164, FAX 206-547-2680, info@naha.org, http://www.naha.org/journal.html.

615.5 AUS
AROMATHERAPY TODAY. Text in English. q. AUD 41.80 domestic; AUD 50 in New Zealand; GBP 18 in United Kingdom; GBP 20 in Europe; USD 40 in US & Canada; AUD 60 elsewhere (effective 2001). 52 p./no.; **Document type:** *Magazine, Consumer.* **Description:** Covers all aspects of aromatherapy; each issue includes an extensive profile on a specific essential oil as well as regular features such as research reports, calendars of international and Australian aromatherapy conferences, and items of general interest about aromatherapy.
—BLDSC (1684.346000).
Published by: Aromatherapy Today Publications Pty Ltd., PO Box 211, Kellyville, NSW 2155, Australia. TEL 61-2-98949933, FAX 61-2-98940199, jkerr@aromatherapytoday.com, http://www.aromatherapytoday.com/. Pub. John Kerr.

AROMATIC NEWS; news from the Aromatic News Project. see *BIOLOGY—Botany*

615.5 IND ISSN 0970-4086
ARYAVIDYAN. Text in English. 1987. q. USD 15 (effective 2003).
Published by: Arya Vaidya Sala, Vaidyaratnam P. S. Varier's Arya Vaidya Sala, Kottakkal, Kerala 676 503, India. TEL 91-493-742216, FAX 91-493-742210, mail@aryavaidyasala.com, http://www.aryavaidyasala.com. **Subscr. to:** Scientific Publishers, 5-A New Pali Rd., Near Hotel Taj Hari Mahal, PO Box 91, Jodhpur, Rajasthan 342 003, India.

ATKINS: A PASSION FOR HEALTHY LIVING. see *NUTRITION AND DIETETICS*

615.3 AUS ISSN 1033-8330
➤ **AUSTRALIAN JOURNAL OF MEDICAL HERBALISM.** Text in English. 1989. q. free to members. adv. bk.rev. abstr. Index. **Document type:** *Journal, Academic/Scholarly.* **Description:** Publishes material on all aspects of medical herbalism with emphasis on phytochemistry, pharmacology and clinical applications of medicinal plants.
Indexed: AMED, AbHyg, AgrForAb, CINAHL, FPA, ForAb, HortAb, NutrAb, OrnHort, PGegResA, ProtozoAb, RA&MP, RM&VM, SeedAb, TDB, WAE&RSA, WeedAb.
—BLDSC (1810.230000), IE, ingenta.
Published by: National Herbalists Association of Australia, 13 Breillat St., Annandale, NSW 2038, Australia. TEL 61-2-95558885, FAX 61-2-95558884, nhaa@nhaa.org.au, http://www.nhaa.org.au. Ed., R&P, Adv. contact Anne Cowper. page AUD 250. Circ: 1,600.

615.88 AUS ISSN 1326-3390
➤ **AUSTRALIAN TRADITIONAL-MEDICINE SOCIETY. JOURNAL.** Text in English. q. USD 187 membership for accredited member; USD 110 membership for associated member; USD 77 membership for student member (effective 2005). adv. bk.rev. 60 p./no. 2 cols./p.; **Document type:** *Journal, Academic/Scholarly.* **Description:** Presents articles on all aspects of the principles and practice of alternative medicine including Western herbal medicine.
Formerly (until 1995): A T O M S Journal (1324-647X)
Related titles: Online - full text ed.: (from EBSCO Publishing).
Indexed: AMED, AbHyg, AgrForAb, CINAHL, DSA, HortAb, NutrAb, ProtozoAb, RA&MP, RM&VM.
—BLDSC (4707.607000).
Published by: Australian Traditional-Medicine Society Ltd., PO Box 1027, Meadowbank, NSW 2114, Australia. TEL 61-2-98096800, FAX 61-2-98097570, journal@atms.com.au, http://www.atms.com.au. Ed., R&P, Adv. contact Raymond Khoury TEL 61-2-98091652. Circ: 10,000.

613 363.7 USA
AWARENESS MAGAZINE. Text in English. bi-m. USD 18 domestic; USD 36 foreign (effective 2000). **Document type:** *Magazine, Consumer.* **Description:** Devoted to improving your life and the life of our planet.
Related titles: Online - full text ed.
Published by: Awareness Publishing Group, Inc., 7441 Garden Grove Blvd Ste C, Garden Grove, CA 92841-4209. TEL 714-894-5133, 800-758-3223, FAX 714-890-1664, awarenessmag@earthlink.net, http://www.awarenessmag.com.

615.5 IND ISSN 0970-7158
➤ **AYURVEDA EDUCATION SERIES/AYURVEDA SHIKSHAN MALA.** Text in English, Marathi. 1978. irreg., latest vol.65, 1997. price varies. charts. back issues avail. **Document type:** *Monographic series, Academic/Scholarly.*
Related titles: CD-ROM ed.
Address: 36 Kothrud, Pune, Maharashtra 411 029, India. TEL 91-20-5463132, FAX 91-20-5383933, drph_k@yahoo.com. Ed. Dr. P H Kulkarni.

615.53 IND
AYURVEDA SAUKHYAM SERIES. Text in English, Sanskrit. 1980. irreg. price varies. index. **Document type:** *Monographic series.* **Description:** Includes fundamental principles of Ayurveda, anatomy, physiology, hygiene, various aspects of public health, and the treatment of diseases.
Published by: Concept Publishing Company, A 15-16 Commercial Block, Mohan Garden, New Delhi, 110 059, India. TEL 91-11-564-8039, FAX 91-11-564-8053.

615.5 GBR ISSN 1472-6882
CODEN: BCAMCV
➤ **B M C COMPLEMENTARY AND ALTERNATIVE MEDICINE.** (BioMed Central) Text in English. 2001. irreg. free (effective 2006). **Document type:** *Journal, Academic/Scholarly.* **Description:** Publishes original research articles in all aspects of complementary and alternative healthcare interventions.
Media: Online - full content (from EBSCO Publishing, National Library of Medicine).
Indexed: ExcerpMed, MEDLINE.
—Infotrieve. **CCC.**

Published by: BioMed Central Ltd. (Subsidiary of: Current Science Ltd), Middlesex House, 34-42 Cleveland St, London, W1T 4LB, United Kingdom. TEL 44-20-76319131, FAX 44-20-76319923, info@biomedcentral.com, http://www.biomedcentral.com/bmccomplementalternmed/. Ed. Fiona Godlee.

615.5 CHN ISSN 0476-0247
BEIJING ZHONGYI/BEIJING TRADITIONAL CHINESE MEDICINE. Text in Chinese. bi-m.
Indexed: HortAb.
Published by: (Beijing Zhongyi Xuehui), Beijing Zhongyi Zazhishe, A-7 Dongdan Santiao, Beijing, 100005, China. TEL 6127766.

615.5 USA
BETTER HEALTH MAGAZINE. Text in English. bi-m. free domestic CT residents; USD 15 elsewhere (effective 2005). **Document type:** *Magazine, Bibliography.*
Published by: Hospital of St. Raphael, 1450 Chapel St., New Haven, CT 06511. TEL 203-789-3972, FAX 203-789-4053. Ed. Cynthia Wolfe-Boynton. Adv. contact Meredith Long. Circ: 148,000 (controlled and free).

615.5 IND
BIKALPA CHIKITSA SAMBAD. Text in English. quadrennial.
Indexed: AMED.
Published by: Medical College of Alternative Medicines, 3 Canal St, Kolkata, 700 041, India.

BOTTOM LINE / HEALTH. see *PHYSICAL FITNESS AND HYGIENE*

615.892 GBR ISSN 0260-5996
BRITISH ACUPUNCTURE ASSOCIATION. NEWSLETTER✶. Text in English. 1965. 2/yr. **Document type:** *Newsletter.*
Formerly (until 1976): Acupuncture Association. Newsletter (0307-4994)
Published by: British Acupuncture Association & Register, 34 Alderney St, London, SW1V 4EW, United Kingdom.

615.5 GBR ISSN 0959-6879
➤ **BRITISH JOURNAL OF PHYTOTHERAPY.** Text in English. 1990. s-a. GBP 27.50 to individuals; GBP 38 to institutions. adv. bk.rev. **Document type:** *Academic/Scholarly.*
Related titles: Online - full text ed.: (from EBSCO Publishing).
Indexed: AMED, RefZh.
—BLDSC (2319.300000), GNLM, IE, ingenta.
Published by: College of Phytotherapy, Bucksteep Manor, Bodle St, Hailsham, E Sussex BN27 4RJ, United Kingdom. TEL 44-1323-834800, FAX 44-1323-834801, medherb@pavilion.co.uk, http://www.blazeweb.com/phytotherapy. Ed., Adv. contact Douglas Schar. R&P Pamela Bull. Circ: 600.

615.5 580 IND ISSN 0253-6889
CODEN: BMERDZ
BULLETIN OF MEDICO-ETHNO-BOTANICAL RESEARCH. Text in English; Summaries in Hindi. 1980. q. INR 60. adv. bk.rev. bibl.; charts; illus. **Description:** Covers folk medicine, pharmacognosy, and phytochemistry. Examines the correlation between ancient insights and modern scientific thought.
Indexed: HortAb.
—CASDDS, CISTI.
Published by: Central Council for Research in Ayurveda and Siddha, Jawahar Lal Nehru Bhartiya Chikitsa Avum Homeopathy Anusandhan Bhavan, No.61-65, Institutional Area, Opp. 'D' Block, Janakpuri, New Delhi, 110 001, India. http://www.ccras.org/. Ed. Dr. V N Pandey. Circ: 300.

615.5 USA ISSN 1090-1965
➤ **CALIFORNIA JOURNAL OF ORIENTAL MEDICINE.** Text in English. q. USD 60 (effective 2002). adv. **Document type:** *Academic/Scholarly.*
Related titles: Online - full text ed.: (from EBSCO Publishing).
Indexed: CINAHL.
Published by: California State Oriental Medical Association, 160637, Sacramento, CA 95816-0637. TEL 800-477-4564, office@csomaonline.org, http://www.csomaonline.org. Ed. Lorenzo Puertas.

615.321 CAN ISSN 0848-9629
➤ **CANADIAN JOURNAL OF HERBALISM.** Text in English. 1979. q. CND 45 to individual members; CND 107 to corporations (effective 2005). adv. bk.rev. reprints avail. **Document type:** *Journal, Consumer.* **Description:** Covers herbal medicine, complementary health care. Includes botanical and pharmacological profiles on specific plants, therapeutics and updates on legislation and quality control as well as environmental issues relating to health.
Formerly (until 1988): Ontario Herbalists Association. Journal
Published by: Ontario Herbalists Association, R.R. #1, Port Burwell, ON N0J 1T0, Canada. TEL 877-OHA-HERB (877-642-4372), cjh@herbalists.on.ca, info@herbalists.on.ca, http://www.herbalists.on.ca. Ed. Mr. John Redden. Adv. contact Mr. Mark McEwan. Circ: 2,500.

➤ **CANNABIS CULTURE**; marijuana & hemp around the world. see *LIFESTYLE*

▼ ➤ **CANNABIS KULTUR**; das Marijuana Magazin. see *LIFESTYLE*

➤ **CARE MAGAZINE**; South Carolina's premier waiting room publication. see *MEDICAL SCIENCES*

615.5 IND ISSN 0255-8726
CENTRAL COUNCIL FOR RESEARCH IN UNANI MEDICINE. ANNUAL REPORT✶. Text in English. 1978. a. **Document type:** *Government.*
Published by: Ministry of Health & Family Welfare, Central Council for Research in Unani Medicine, Nirman Bhavan, Maulana Azad Rd., New Delhi, 110 110, India.

615.5 CAN
CHECKUP. Text in English. bi-m. CND 20 (effective 2005). **Document type:** *Magazine, Consumer.* **Description:** Dedicated to producing informative articles about health and wellness that will guide us in our search for a healthy lifestyle and optimal health.
Address: 202, 1324-11 Ave S W, Calgary, AB, Canada. TEL 403-209-4061, FAX 403-209-4060, info@checkupmagazine.ca, http://www.checkupmagazine.ca.

615.5 THA
CHEEWAJIT. Text in Thai. bi-m. THB 50 newsstand/cover (effective 2002). adv. **Document type:** *Magazine, Consumer.* **Description:** Promotes a holistic health approach to self care, prevention, rehabilitation and treatment.
Related titles: Online - full text ed.
Published by: Amarin Printing & Publishing Public Co. Ltd., 7/9-18 Arun Amarin Rd., Bangkoknoi, Bangkok, 10700, Thailand. TEL 66-2-434-0286, FAX 66-2-434-8699, info@amarin.co.th, http://www.cheewajit.com, http://www.amarin.co.th.

615.5 DEU ISSN 0930-2786
CODEN: CHMEFE
➤ **CHINESISCHE MEDIZIN**; theoretische Grundlagen, Diagnostik, Akupunktur, Arzneimittel, Taiji, Qigong. Text in German. 1986. q. EUR 100.93 to institutions (effective 2005). adv. abstr. back issues avail. **Document type:** *Journal, Academic/Scholarly.*
Related titles: Online - full text ed.
Indexed: ExcerpMed.
—BLDSC (3181.122970), CISTI, GNLM, IE. **CCC.**
Published by: (Societas Medicinae), Urban und Vogel Medien und Medizin Verlagsgesellschaft mbH (Subsidiary of: Springer Science+Business Media), Neumarkter Str 43, Munich, 81673, Germany. TEL 49-89-4372-1411, FAX 49-89-4372-1410, verlag@urban-vogel.de, http://www.urban-vogel.de. Eds. C H Hempen, E Stueder-Wobmann. R&P Oliver Renn. Adv. contact Sibylle Schurr TEL 49-89-43721353. B&W page EUR 960, color page EUR 1,800. Circ: 1,900 (paid and controlled).
Subscr. to: Springer GmbH Auslieferungsgesellschaft, Haberstr 7, Heidelberg 69126, Germany. TEL 49-6221-345-0, FAX 49-6221-345-4229, subscriptions@springer.de, http://link.springer.de.

➤ **CHOJUGAKU KENKYU/RESEARCH OF LONGEVITY SCIENCE.** see *GERONTOLOGY AND GERIATRICS*

615.5 JPN ISSN 0389-4843
CHUI RINSHO/CLINICAL JOURNAL OF TRADITIONAL CHINESE MEDICINE. Text in Japanese. 1980. q. JPY 1,600 per issue.
Published by: Toyo Gakujutsu Shuppansha, 1-5 Miyakubo 3-chome, Ichikawa-shi, Chiba-ken 272-0822, Japan.

615.880901 USA
COLLEGE OF MAHARISHI VEDIC MEDICINE NEWS. Text in English. 1999. bi-m. bk.rev. back issues avail. **Document type:** *Newsletter, Academic/Scholarly.* **Description:** Includes case histories of patients treated with Maharishi Vedic Medicine, as well as news of the faculty and students.
Formerly: Vedic Medicine News
Media: Online - full text.
Published by: Maharishi University of Management, College of Maharishi Vedic Medicine, 1000 N Fourth St, Fairfield, IA 52557. TEL 515-472-1194, 800-831-6523, FAX 515-472-1297, cshaw@mum.edu, http://www.mum.edu/CMVM/news.html. Ed. Craig Shaw.

700 535.84 GBR ISSN 1351-1696
COLOURAMA; world's premier colour magazine & directory. Text in English. 1970. a. GBP 3.80 per issue domestic; GBP 4.50 per issue in Europe; GBP 5.50 per issue elsewhere (effective 2003). adv. bk.rev. 32 p./no. 2 cols./p.; back issues avail. **Document type:** *Directory.* **Description:** Concerns the power of color and vibrational healing, and related topics in complementary medicine.
Formerly (until 1993): Colour Circle
Published by: International Association of Colour, 46 Cottenham Rd, Histon, Cambs CB4 9ES, United Kingdom. TEL 44-1223-563403, FAX 44-1223-237113, info@iac-colour.co.uk.uk, http://www.iac-colour.co.uk/colouramamagazine.htm. Ed., R&P, Adv. contact Michael Grevis. B&W page GBP 150, color page GBP 450; trim 210 x 297. Circ: 1,000.

615.5 DEU ISSN 0949-2402
CO'MED; Das Fachmagazin fuer Complementaer-Medizin. Variant title: Complementaer-Medizin. Text in German. 1995. m. EUR 75 (effective 2004). adv. **Document type:** *Magazine, Trade.*
Published by: CO'MED Verlagsgesellschaft mbH, Schlossgasse 4, Hochheim, 65239, Germany. TEL 49-6145-93380, FAX 49-6145-933833, verlag@comedverlag.com, http://www.comedverlag.de/fachmagazin.php. Ed. Nadja Schmidt. Adv. contact Sibylle Bohl. B&W page EUR 2,150, color page EUR 2,825; trim 210 x 297. Circ: 13,953 (paid and controlled).

COMMON GROUND HAWAII. see *PSYCHOLOGY*

COMPENDIUM OF SELF-CARE PRODUCTS. see *PHARMACY AND PHARMACOLOGY*

615.5 USA ISSN 1549-084X
▼ **COMPLEMENTARY AND ALTERNATIVE MEDICINE.** Text in English. 2004 (Oct.). irreg. price varies. **Document type:** *Monographic series.*
Published by: Praeger Publishers (Subsidiary of: Greenwood Publishing Group Inc.), 88 Post Rd W, Box 5007, Westport, CT 06881-5007. TEL 203-226-3571, info@greenwood.com, http://www.greenwood.com.

615.5 USA ISSN 1533-2101
R733 CODEN: AHPRFC
➤ **COMPLEMENTARY HEALTH PRACTICE REVIEW.** Text in English. 1995. 3/yr. USD 317, GBP 205 to institutions; USD 330, GBP 213 combined subscription to institutions print & online eds. (effective 2006). adv. bk.rev.; software rev.; video rev.; Website rev. abstr.; bibl.; illus. 80 p./no.; back issues avail. **Document type:** *Journal, Academic/Scholarly.* **Description:** Serves as a forum for alternative health care practitioners and traditional health care professionals who incorporate alternative methods into their practices (e.g. homeopathy, meditation, hypnotherapy, acupressure and acupuncture, chiropractic medicine, art therapy, and related disciplines and procedures). Includes news from NIH - OAM, and a calendar.
Formerly (until 2000): Alternative Health Practitioner (1076-1675)
Related titles: Online - full text ed.: ISSN 1552-3845. USD 314, GBP 203 to institutions (effective 2006) (from EBSCO Publishing, O C L C Online Computer Library Center, Inc., Sage Publications, Inc., Swets Information Services).
Indexed: AMED, CINAHL, SOPODA.
—BLDSC (3364.203660), CISTI, IE, ingenta. **CCC.**
Published by: Sage Science Press (US) (Subsidiary of: Sage Publications, Inc.), 2455 Teller Rd, Thousand Oaks, CA 91320. TEL 805-499-0721, FAX 805-499-0871, info@sagepub.com, http://www.sagepub.com/journal.aspx?pid=356. Ed. Susan Gaylord. adv.: B&W page USD 495, color page USD 810; trim 7 x 10. Circ: 1,648 (paid). **Overseas subscr. to:** Sage Publications Ltd., 1 Oliver's Yard, 55 City Rd, London EC1 1SP, United Kingdom. TEL 44-20-73740645, FAX 44-20-73748741, subscription@sagepub.co.uk.

610 USA ISSN 1531-538X
COMPLEMENTARY THERAPIES IN CHRONIC CARE. Text in English. 2000. m. USD 329 (effective 2003). **Document type:** *Newsletter, Trade.* **Description:** Contains case studies and advice on which alternative therapies may work with existing conventional medical treatments.
Related titles: Online - full text ed.: (from Gale Group).
Published by: Thomson American Health Consultants, Inc. (Subsidiary of: Thomson Corporation, Healthcare Information Group), 3525 Piedmont Rd, N E, Bldg 6, Ste 400, Atlanta, GA 30305. TEL 404-262-5511, 800-688-2421, FAX 404-262-7837, 800-284-3291, customerservice@ahcpub.com, http://www.ahcpub.com/ahc_root_html/products/newsletters/ctcc.html.

COMPLEMENTARY THERAPIES IN CLINICAL PRACTICE. see *MEDICAL SCIENCES—Nurses And Nursing*

COMPLEMENTARY THERAPIES IN MEDICINE. see *MEDICAL SCIENCES—Chiropractic, Homeopathy, Osteopathy*

615.892 DNK ISSN 1602-1851
DANSK MEDICINSK SELSKAB FOR AKUPUNKTUR. Text in Danish. 1986. q. illus. back issues avail. **Document type:** *Academic/Scholarly.*
Formerly (until 1999): Akupunktur (0903-7675)
Related titles: Online - full text ed.
Address: c/o Ruth Kirkeby, Nellikevej 1, Soenderborg, 6400, Denmark. TEL 45-74-433718, FAX 45-73623050, kirkeby@dadlnet.dk, http://www.akupunkturdoktor.dk/bladet.asp, http://www.akupunkturdoktor.org. Ed. Vibeke Halasi.

615.5 IND ISSN 0970-3381
➤ **DEERGHAYU INTERNATIONAL.** Text in English. 1984. q. INR 200; USD 10 foreign (effective 2001). adv. bk.rev. abstr. 32 p./no. 2 cols./p.; back issues avail.; reprints avail. **Document type:** *Journal, Academic/Scholarly.* **Description:** Contains case reports, research results and reviews on Indian medicine.

Published by: Ayurveda Education Series, 36 Kothrud, Pune, Maharashtra 411 029, India. TEL 91-20-5463132, FAX 91-20-5383933, roveda_99@yahoo.com. Ed. Dr. P H Kulkarni. Adv. contact Pavan Kulkarni. B&W page INR 2,000, color page INR 3,000; trim 267 x 203.

615.5 USA
DINSHAH HEALTH SOCIETY NEWSLETTER. Text in English. 1976. q. USD 3 (effective 2000). back issues avail. **Document type:** *Newsletter.* **Description:** Covers general health topics, including unorthodox methods of healing (primarily chromopathy).
Published by: Dinshah Health Society, PO Box 707, Malaga, NJ 08328. TEL 856-692-4686, http://www.wj.net/dinshah. Ed. Darius Dinshah. Circ: 4,075.

DIRECTION; a journal on the Alexander Technique. see *PHYSICAL FITNESS AND HYGIENE*

615.5 POL ISSN 1230-9370
DOMOWY DOKTOR; miesiecznik medycyny naturalnej. Text in Polish. 1993. m. PLZ 2.60 newsstand/cover. back issues avail. **Description:** Covers natural medicine.
Published by: Faktor Sp. z o.o., Ul Ksiecia Wladyslawa Opolskiego 3 a, Kety, 32650, Poland. TEL 48-33-453888. Ed. Jozej Gaweda. Circ: 17,500.

615.53 USA ISSN 1069-6253
THE DOOR OPENER; Connecticut's holistic health and metaphysical networking magazine. Text in English. 1986. q. USD 12; USD 3 newsstand/cover (effective 2000). adv. back issues avail. **Document type:** *Consumer.* **Description:** Includes articles, calendar of events, and lists of resources covering holistic health and metaphysics in Connecticut.
Published by: An Open Door, 70 Valley Falls Rd., Vernon, CT 06066. TEL 860-875-4101, FAX 860-875-4101, anopendoor@aol.com, http://www.anopendoor.com. Ed., Pub., Adv. contact Jon Roe. R&P John Roe. page USD 290; trim 11 x 8.5. Circ: 2,300 (paid).

615.8 USA ISSN 1085-0880
DR. ANDREW WEIL'S SELF HEALING; creating natural health for your body and mind. Text in English. 1995. m. USD 19.95 (effective 2004). adv. bk.rev. index. back issues avail. **Document type:** *Newsletter, Consumer.* **Description:** Covers natural health and well-being.
Related titles: Online - full text ed.
Published by: Martha Stewart Living Omnimedia LLC, PO Box 2057, Marion, OH 43305-2057. TEL 800-523-3296, FAX 617-926-5021, drwn@kable.com, http://www.drweilselfhealing.com. Circ: 380,000 (paid).

615.5 GBR ISSN 1368-9797
DR. ATKINS' HEALTH REVELATIONS. Text in English. 1996. m. USD 39.95 in United States. back issues avail. **Document type:** *Newsletter, Consumer.* **Description:** Focuses on special diet to combat major diseases.
—CCC.
Published by: (Atkins Center for Complementary Medicine USA), Agora Ireland Publishing & Services, 11th Fl, Centre Point, 103 New Oxford St, London, WC1A 1QQ, United Kingdom. TEL 44-20-7447-4018, FAX 44-20-7447-4041. Circ: 6,000.

615 610 GBR ISSN 1362-6035
EQUILIBRIUM. Text in English. 1995. q. **Description:** Aims to serve as an educational resource with information on various treatments, therapies, products and views on health. Includes articles on homeopathy, essential oils and extracts, physiotherapy, immunology, choosing a doctor etc.
Published by: Equilibrium Health Resources Ltd., c/o Julia Bard, Ed., Clarendon Centre, 16 Clarendon Rd, Hornsey, London, N8 0DJ, United Kingdom. TEL 44-20-7241-2960, FAX 44-20-7241-2960, equilibr@dircon.co.uk.

ESALEN CATALOG. see *PSYCHOLOGY*

615.5 USA
ESOTERIC SCHOOL OF SHAMANISM AND MAGIC TIPS E-ZINE. Text in English. w.
Media: Online - full text.
Published by: Esoteric School of Shamanism and Magic Tips TEL 970-323-8643, http://www.shamanschool.com/. Ed. Stephanie Yeh.

ETHNOBOTANY. see *BIOLOGY—Botany*

615.5 AUT ISSN 1609-4557
➤ **EUROPEAN JOURNAL OF ACUPUNCTURE.** Text in English. 2000. q. USD 75 domestic; USD 115 foreign; USD 35 newsstand/cover (effective 2001). adv. back issues avail. **Document type:** *Journal, Academic/Scholarly.* **Description:** Improves communication and understanding in international acupuncture research and applications.
Related titles: Online - full text ed.: ISSN 1609-4565.
Indexed: ExcerpMed.
Published by: V I C E R Publishing, PO Box 14, Vienna, A-1097, Austria. TEL 43-676-9568085, FAX 43-676-9568086, vicer@vicer.org, http://www.vicer.org. Ed., R&P Roland Hofbauer. adv.: B&W page USD 1,700, color page USD 2,200. Circ: 1,000 (paid and controlled).

➤ **EUROPEAN JOURNAL OF HERBAL MEDICINE.** see *PHARMACY AND PHARMACOLOGY*

610.95 GBR ISSN 1351-6647
EUROPEAN JOURNAL OF ORIENTAL MEDICINE. Text in English. 1977; N.S. 1993. s-a. GBP 20 domestic; GBP 21 in Europe; GBP 26 elsewhere. adv. bk.rev. back issues avail. **Document type:** *Academic/Scholarly.* **Description:** Stimulates debate and scholarship in Chinese medicine and other traditions of Oriental medicine.
Former titles (until 1993): British Journal of Acupuncture (0143-4977); (until 1979): British Acupuncture Association. Journal (0142-2340)
Related titles: Online - full text ed.: (from EBSCO Publishing).
Indexed: AMED, ExcerpMed.
—BLDSC (3829.733260), GNLM, IE, ingenta.
Address: 19 Trinity Rd, London, N2 8JJ, United Kingdom. Circ: 700.

615.5 USA ISSN 1741-427X
▼ ➤ **EVIDENCE - BASED COMPLEMENTARY AND ALTERNATIVE MEDICINE.** Abbreviated title: e C A M. Text in English. 2004. 3/yr. USD 153, GBP 291, EUR 230 to institutions (effective 2006). **Document type:** *Journal, Academic/Scholarly.* **Description:** Seeks to apply scientific rigor to the study of complementary and alternative medicine.
Related titles: Online - full text ed.: ISSN 1741-4288. free (effective 2005) (from EBSCO Publishing, Gale Group, HighWire Press, IngentaConnect, National Library of Medicine, O C L C Online Computer Library Center, Inc., Swets Information Services).
—IE. **CCC.**
Published by: Oxford University Press (Subsidiary of: Oxford University Press), 198 Madison Ave, New York, NY 10016. TEL 800-334-4249, jnlorders@oup-usa.org, http://ecam.oxfordjournals.org/, http://www.us.oup.com.

615.5 IRN ISSN 1684-0240
FASLNAMAH-I GIYAHAN-I DARUYI/JOURNAL OF MEDICINAL PLANTS. Text in Persian, Modern; Abstracts in English. 2002. q. **Document type:** *Journal, Academic/Scholarly.* **Description:** Contains original work and reviews in the field of research and teaching in herbal medicine.
Published by: Institute of Medicinal Plants, No: 97, Bozorgmehr Ave., Ghods Ave., Enghelab St., PO Box 13145-1446, Tehran, Iran. TEL 98-21-6462179, FAX 98-21-6465554, contact@imp.ac.ir, http://www.imp.ac.ir/Publications/Journal/Journal.asp. Ed. Dr. Shafiei M.

FITOTERAPIA. see *BIOLOGY—Botany*

FOCUS ON ALTERNATIVE AND COMPLEMENTARY THERAPIES; an evidence based approach. see *PHARMACY AND PHARMACOLOGY*

615.5 TUR ISSN 1300-5618
FORMSANTE. Text in Turkish. 1994. m. adv. **Document type:** *Magazine, Consumer.*
Related titles: Online - full text ed.
Published by: D B R - Dogan Burda Rizzoli Dergi Yayyncylyk ve Pazarlama A.S., Hurriyet Medya Towers, Gunesli - Istanbul, 34212, Turkey. TEL 90-212-4103111, FAX 90-212-4103112, formsante@dbr.com.tr, abone@dbr.com.tr, http://www.formsante.com.tr, http://www.dbr.com.tr.

615.8 CHE ISSN 1424-7364
CODEN: FKKNFH
➤ **FORSCHENDE KOMPLEMENTAERMEDIZIN UND KLASSISCHE NATURHEILKUNDE/RESEARCH IN COMPLEMENTARY AND NATURAL CLASSICAL MEDICINE.** Text in English, German. 1994. bi-m. CHF 254 in Europe; CHF 274.40 elsewhere; CHF 304 combined subscription in Europe print & online eds.; CHF 324.40 combined subscription elsewhere print & online eds. (effective 2006). adv. back issues avail. **Document type:** *Journal, Academic/Scholarly.* **Description:** Establishes a bridge of communication between complementary medicine and university research medicine on a scientific level.
Formerly (until 2000): Forschende Komplementaermedizin (1021-7096)
Related titles: Online - full text ed.: ISSN 1421-9999. CHF 212 (effective 2006) (from EBSCO Publishing, O C L C Online Computer Library Center, Inc., Swets Information Services).
Indexed: AMED, CurCont, ExcerpMed, HortAb, INI, IndMed, Inpharma, MEDLINE, PE&ON, RA&MP, Reac.
—BLDSC (4008.991200), GNLM, IDS, IE, Infotrieve, ingenta, KNAW. **CCC.**
Published by: S. Karger AG, Allschwilerstr 10, Basel, 4009, Switzerland. TEL 41-61-3061111, FAX 41-61-3061234, karger@karger.ch, http://www.karger.com/FKM, http://www.karger.ch. Ed. H. Walach. adv.: page EUR 2,100; trim 180 x 242. Circ: 4,000 (paid and controlled).

➤ **FOUR CORNERS.** see *NEW AGE PUBLICATIONS*

615.5 USA
FREE SPIRIT JOURNAL. Text in English. q. USD 20; USD 30 foreign. adv. **Document type:** *Bulletin.* **Description:** Features articles by and for alternative practitioners who use various aspects of clearing technology and operate independently.
Related titles: Online - full text ed.
Address: PO Box 4326, San Rafael, CA 94913-4326. TEL 415-492-0728, 800-799-3733, FAX 415-499-8441, http://www.freezone.org/f_spirit.htm. Ed. Hank Levin.

615.5 CHN ISSN 1000-338X
FUJIAN ZHONGYI YAO/FUJIAN JOURNAL OF TRADITIONAL CHINESE MEDICINE. Text in Chinese. 1956-1966; resumed 1981. bi-m. USD 1.20 per issue. adv. bk.rev.
Related titles: CD-ROM ed.; Online - full text ed.: (from East View Information Services).
Indexed: ExtraMED, PBA.
—GNLM.
Published by: Fujian Zhongyi Xueyuan/Fujian Institute of Traditional Chinese Medicine, 282 Wusi Lu, Fuzhou, Fujian 350003, China. TEL 0591-7841296, FAX 0591-7842524. Ed. Yu Changrong. Circ: 16,000. **Dist. overseas by:** China International Book Trading Corp. 35 Chegongzhuang Xilu, Haidian District, PO Box 399, Beijing 100044, China. **Co-sponsor:** Zhonghua Quanguo Zhongyi Xuehui Fujian Fenhui.

615.5 JPN
FUKUOKA ISHI KANPO KENKYUKAI KAIHO/FUKUOKA MEDICAL ASSOCIATION FOR KAMPO MEDICINE. Text in Japanese. 1980. m.
Published by: Fukuoka Ishi Kanpo Kenkyukai, 6-1 Wakahisa 2-chome, Minami-ku, Fukuoka-shi, 815-0042, Japan.

FUNCTIONAL FOODS AND NUTRACEUTICALS; the magazine for the global supply market. see *NUTRITION AND DIETETICS*

GERSON HEALING NEWSLETTER. see *MEDICAL SCIENCES*

GINSENG REVIEW. see *PHARMACY AND PHARMACOLOGY*

615.89 ITA ISSN 1120-3560
GIORNALE ITALIANO DI RIFLESSOTERAPIA ED AGOPUNTURA. Text in Italian. 1989. s-a.
Indexed: ExcerpMed.
Published by: Societa Italiana di Riflessoterapia Agopuntura Auricoloterapia, C.so Galileo Ferraris 164, Torino, 10134, Italy. TEL 011-3042857, FAX 011-3045623, info@agopuntura-siraa.it, http://www.siraa.it/home.html.

GREATLIFE. see *NUTRITION AND DIETETICS*

615.5 USA
THE GREY FOX. Text in English. m. adv. **Document type:** *Newsletter.* **Description:** Covers alternative medicine in a simple and straightforward fashion with an emphasis on providing practical information that can be applied to making positive changes in everyone's lifestyle.
Media: Online - full text.
Published by: TGFox, Inc. marc@cide.com, http://www.tgfox.com. Ed. Ronald L Breazeale.

615.5 CHN
GUANGXI ZHONGYI YAO/GUANGXI TRADITIONAL CHINESE MEDICINE. Text in Chinese. bi-m.
Published by: Guangxi Zhongyi Xueyuan/Guangxi Institute of Traditional Chinese Medicine, 21 Mingxiu Donglu, Nanning, Guangxi 530001, China. TEL 32101. Ed. Ban Qiuwen.
Co-sponsor: Zhonghua Quanguo Zhongyi Xuehui, Guangxi Fenhui.

GUOWAI YIXUE (ZHONGYI ZHONGYAO FENCE)/FOREIGN MEDICAL SCIENCES (TRADITIONAL CHINESE MEDICINE). see *MEDICAL SCIENCES*

GUOYI LUNTAN/FORUM ON TRADITIONAL CHINESE MEDICINE. see *PHARMACY AND PHARMACOLOGY*

615.5 USA
H L Q THREE RIVERS RESOURCE GUIDE FOR HOLISTIC LIVING. Text in English. 1980. a. USD 7; USD 9 foreign (effective 1997). adv. bk.rev. index. **Document type:** *Directory, Consumer.* **Description:** Focuses on personal health, social responsibility, global awareness, and self sufficiency.
Former titles: Three Rivers Wellness Directory (1060-006X); Former titles: H L Q Wellness Calendar; H L Q Magazine; Holistic Learning Quarterly
Published by: H L Q Associates, PO Box 86054, Pittsburgh, PA 15221-0054. TEL 412-242-9355, hlq@trfn.clpgh.org, http://trfn.clpgh.org/hlq. Ed. Allen Goodman. Pub. Priscilla Brown. Adv. contact Marlene Linden. Circ: 10,000 (paid).

H S R: HEALTH SUPPLEMENT RETAILER. see *NUTRITION AND DIETETICS*

HANF!; das Cannabis-Magazin. see *LIFESTYLE*

HANFBLATT; das Magazin fuer Hanfkultur. see *LIFESTYLE*

HEADS. see *LIFESTYLE*

HEALING LIFESTYLES & SPAS. see *MEDICAL SCIENCES—Physical Medicine And Rehabilitation*

615.5 AUS
HEALTH & HEALING; journal of complementary medicine. Text in English. 1981. q. AUD 24.80 domestic; AUD 45.80 foreign (effective 2001). adv. bk.rev. abstr. 60 p./no.; back issues avail. **Document type:** *Journal, Consumer.*
Formerly: Australasian Health and Healing (0812-3896)
Published by: Trim-Keg Party Ltd, 29 Terrace St, PO Box 1424, Kingscliff, NSW 2487, Australia. TEL 61-2-6674-2407, FAX 61-2-6674-3633. Ed., R&P, Adv. contact Maurice Finkel. Circ: 12,000 (paid).

615.5 USA ISSN 0895-9986
HEALTH CONSCIOUSNESS; the international holistic magazine. Text in English. 1980. bi-m. USD 28 (effective 2004). adv. bk.rev. illus. back issues avail. **Document type:** *Magazine, Consumer.* **Description:** Contains health news for both the lay and professional reader. Includes viewpoints from pioneers in alternative medicine.
Formerly: Kup's Komments
Indexed: AMED.
—BLDSC (4274.959800), IE, ingenta.
Published by: Dr. Roy B. Kupsinel, Ed. & Pub., Shangri La Ln, Box 550, Oviedo, FL 32765. TEL 407-365-6681, FAX 407-365-1834. Circ: 2,500.

HEALTHOLOGY. see *PHYSICAL FITNESS AND HYGIENE*

HEALTHY OPTIONS. see *PHYSICAL FITNESS AND HYGIENE*

615.5 CHN ISSN 1002-2619
➤ **HEBEI ZHONGYI/HEBEI JOURNAL OF TRADITIONAL CHINESE MEDICINE.** Text in Chinese. 1979. bi-m. CNY 3.20 per issue. adv. bk.rev. **Document type:** *Academic/Scholarly.*
Related titles: Online - full text ed.: (from East View Information Services).
—BLDSC (4282.215736).
Published by: Hebei Yixue Kexueyuan, Qingbao Yanjiusuo/Hebei Academy of Medical Sciences, Medical Information Institute, 241 Qingyuanjie, Shijiazhuang, Hebei 050021, China. TEL 86-311-5813579, hezhong_yi@163.net. Ed. Wanzhen Sun. Circ: 500. **Dist. by:** China International Book Trading Corp, 35 Chegongzhuang Xilu, Haidian District, PO Box 399, Beijing 100044, China. TEL 86-10-68412045, FAX 86-10-68412023, cibtc@mail.cibtc.com.cn, http://www.cibtc.com.cn.

615.853 DEU ISSN 0343-768X
HEILBAD UND KURORT. Text in German. 1949. 10/yr. EUR 2.70 newsstand/cover (effective 2003). adv. **Document type:** *Magazine, Consumer.*
Published by: Floettmann Verlag GmbH, Berliner Str 63, Guetersloh, 33330, Germany. TEL 49-5241-86080, http://www.floettmann.de. adv.: B&W page EUR 655, color page EUR 1,020. Circ: 2,900 (paid and controlled).

615.5 ISL
HEILSUHRINGURINN; timarit um hollefni og heilsuraekt. Text in Icelandic. 1978. s-a. ISK 1,000 (effective 2001). back issues avail. **Description:** Deals with issues in alternative medicine, orthomolecular medicine and natural hygiene.
Related titles: Magnetic Tape ed.
Address: Sidumula 27, Reykjavik, 108, Iceland. TEL 354-568-9933. Circ: 2,000.

HERBALGRAM; the journal of the American Botanical Council & the Herb Research Foundation. see *BIOLOGY—Botany*

615.5 AUT ISSN 1609-4573
CODEN: HCMEAT
➤ **HERBALS AND COMPLEMENTARY MEDICINE.** Text in English. 2000. q. USD 75 domestic; USD 115 foreign; USD 35 newsstand/cover (effective 2001). adv. back issues avail.; reprints avail. **Document type:** *Journal, Academic/Scholarly.* **Description:** Publishes articles, case reports, reviews, and letters that improve communications in understanding herbal effects and all parts of complementary medicine.
Related titles: Online - full text ed.: ISSN 1609-4581.
Indexed: ExcerpMed.
Published by: V I C E R Publishing, PO Box 14, Vienna, A-1097, Austria. TEL 43-676-9568085, FAX 43-676-9568086, vicer@vicer.org, http://www.vicer.org. Ed., R&P Roland Hofbauer. adv.: B&W page USD 1,700, color page USD 2,200. Circ: 1,000 (paid and controlled).

581.63 AUS ISSN 0729-560X
➤ **HERBOLOGY.** Text in English. 1979. q. AUD 27.50 domestic; AUD 30 foreign (effective 2003). adv. bk.rev. charts. 56 p./no. 2 cols./p.; back issues avail. **Document type:** *Magazine, Academic/Scholarly.* **Description:** Educates people in the use, taking and growing of herbs.
Published by: Australian Herb Society, c/o All Rare Herbs, PO Box 91, Mapleton, QLD 4560, Australia. TEL 61-7-54469243, FAX 61-7-54469277, aherbsoc@hotmail.com.au, http://www.maleny.net.au/sunweb/groups/aherbsoc.html. Ed., R&P, Adv. contact Denise Patterson. B&W page AUD 82.50; trim 4.5 x 6.5. Circ: 600.

615.5 USA ISSN 1086-1955
RM666.H33
HERBS FOR HEALTH. Text in English. 1996. bi-m. USD 19.95 domestic; USD 29.95 foreign (effective 2005). adv. illus. back issues avail. **Document type:** *Magazine, Consumer.* **Description:** Focuses on remedial and nutritional benefits of nature's herbs and spices.
Published by: Ogden Publications, 1503 S W 42nd St, Topeka, KS 66609-1265. TEL 785-274-4300, 800-678-5779, FAX 785-284-4316, http://www.ogdenpubs.com. Ed. Kathryn Compton. Pub. Bryan Welch. adv.: color page USD 3,800; trim 8 x 10.5.

615.535 USA
HERBS TO YOUR HEALTH. Text in English. m. free. **Document type:** *Newsletter.* **Description:** Presents information about herbs, vitamins, and other healthful botanicals.
Media: E-mail.
Address: shirbell@vcn.com. Ed. Shirley Bell.

HIGH TIMES; the magazine of the counter-culture. see *LIFESTYLE*

HOLISTIC HEALTH DIRECTORY. see *NEW AGE PUBLICATIONS*

HOLISTIC HEALTH SOURCEBOOK. see *NEW AGE PUBLICATIONS*

615.5 USA ISSN 0886-1676
HOMOEOPATHY TODAY. Text in English. 1980. m. (11/yr.). USD 45 in US & Canada membership; USD 65 elsewhere membership (effective 2002). **Document type:** *Magazine, Consumer.* **Description:** Contains practical information and news about homoeopathic medicine, including self-care, informative cases and cures, homeopathic animal care, book reviews, conference reviews, the latest research in the field, a calendar of events, and more.
Published by: National Center for Homoeopathy, 801 N Fairfax St, Ste 306, Alexandria, VA 22314. TEL 877-624-0613, 703-548-7790, FAX 703-548-7792, http://www.homeopathic.org/.

615.892 JPN ISSN 0287-6760
IDO NO NIPPON/JOURNAL OF JAPANESE ACUPUNCTURE & MOXIBUSTION. Text in Japanese. 1938. m. JPY 450 per issue.
Indexed: RefZh.
Published by: Ido no Nipponsha, 1-45 Oppama-Hon-cho, Yokosuka-shi, Kanagawa-ken 237-0068, Japan.

INDIAN INSTITUTE OF HISTORY OF MEDICINE. BULLETIN. see *MEDICAL SCIENCES*

615.5 IND ISSN 0972-5938
INDIAN JOURNAL OF TRADITIONAL KNOWLEDGE. Text in English. 2002. q. USD 150 to institutions (effective 2006). **Document type:** *Journal, Academic/Scholarly.* **Description:** Provides articles about the observation and experimental investigation of the biological activities of the materials from plants, animals and minerals, used in the traditional health-care systems.
Published by: Scientific Publishers, 5-A New Pali Rd., Near Hotel Taj Hari Mahal, PO Box 91, Jodhpur, Rajasthan 342 003, India. TEL 91-291-2433323, FAX 91-291-2512580, journals@scientificpub.com, http://www.scientificpub.com/bookdetails.php?booktransid=476&bookid=472.

615.5 IND
INDIAN JOURNAL OF UNANI MEDICINE∗ ; devoted to interdisciplinary research in Unani medicine and allied sciences. Text in English. 1991. s-a. **Document type:** *Academic/Scholarly.*
Published by: Ministry of Health & Family Welfare, Central Council for Research in Unani Medicine, Nirman Bhavan, Maulana Azad Rd., New Delhi, 110 110, India. Ed. Hakim Ummul Fazal.

615.5 IND ISSN 0971-314X
INDIAN MEDICINE/INDIYAN MEDISIN. Text in English, Telugu. 1971 (vol.20). m. INR 50. adv. bk.rev. charts. **Description:** Covers alternative medicine with special emphasis on Ayurveda.
Published by: Indian Medicine Industries, Dubagunta Nivas, Vijayawada, Andhra Pradesh 520 002, India. Ed. Dr. D L Narayana. Circ: 2,000.

615.85 USA
CODEN: IJIMGV
➤ **INTEGRATIVE MEDICINE**; a clinician's journal. Text in English. 1999. bi-m. USD 66 domestic to individuals; USD 106 foreign to individuals; USD 171 domestic to institutions; USD 221 foreign to institutions; USD 12 newsstand/cover (effective 2005). adv. bk.rev. charts; illus.; abstr. 56 p./no. 2 cols./p.; back issues avail. **Document type:** *Journal, Academic/Scholarly.* **Description:** Covers clinical aspects of natural and integrative medicine for the healthcare professional.
Former titles (until 2003): The International Journal of Integrative Medicine (1522-6255); (until 1998): American Journal of Natural Medicine (1521-4702)
Indexed: CINAHL, ExcerpMed, IDIS.
—CCC.

Published by: InnoVision Communications, 169 Saxony Rd., Ste. 103, Encinitas, CA 92024-6779. FAX 866-828-2962, info@invcom.com.

615.5 USA ISSN 1522-5062
INTEGRATIVE MEDICINE CONSULT. Text in English. 1998. m. **Document type:** *Newspaper, Trade.* **Description:** Contains impartial, up-to-date, science-based information about alternative therapies and botanical medicines.
Media: Online - full content.
Indexed: IPA.
Published by: Integrative Medicine Communications, 1600 Riveredge Pkwy Ste 100, Atlanta, GA 30328. TEL 770-980-0888, FAX 770-955-2326, http://www.onemedicine.com/.

INTEGRATIVE NURSING. see *MEDICAL SCIENCES—Nurses And Nursing*

INTERNATIONAL COLLATION OF TRADITIONAL AND FOLK MEDICINE. see *MEDICAL SCIENCES*

615.5 301 USA
INTERNATIONAL CONFERENCE ON THE STUDY OF SHAMANISM AND ALTERNATIVE MODES OF HEALING. PROCEEDINGS. Text in English. 1984. a. USD 23.95 (effective 2003). back issues avail. **Document type:** *Proceedings, Academic/Scholarly.* **Description:** Essays and discussion of interdisciplinary approaches to alternative healing and forms of shamanism.
Published by: Independent Scholars of Asia, Inc., 2321 Russell St, No 3C, Berkeley, CA 94705-1959. TEL 510-849-3791, FAX 510-849-3791, riheinze@juno.com, http://www.hypersphere.com/isa. Ed., Pub. Ruth-Inge Heinze. R&P Ruth Inge Heinze. Circ: 100 (paid).

615.5 616.97 GBR ISSN 1357-9452
➤ **INTERNATIONAL JOURNAL OF ALTERNATIVE & COMPLEMENTARY MEDICINE.** Text in English. 1983. m. GBP 31.50 domestic to individuals; GBP 37 in Europe to individuals; GBP 45 elsewhere to individuals; GBP 24.50 domestic to students; GBP 29 in Europe to students; GBP 37.50 elsewhere to students (effective 2001). adv. video rev.; bk.rev. illus.; stat.; tr.lit. back issues avail. **Document type:** *Journal, Academic/Scholarly.* **Description:** Contains news, articles, research, features, debate, treatment, masterclasses, case histories, comment, services, etc. Aimed at alternative and complementary practitioners, doctors, nurses.
Former titles (until 1991): Journal of Alternative & Complementary Medicine (0959-9886); (until 1987): Journal of Alternative Medicine (0950-5466)
Published by: Reasonhold Limited, 9 Rickett St, London, SW6 1RU, United Kingdom. TEL 44-20-7385-0012, FAX 44-20-7385-4566. Ed., R&P Graeme Millar. Pub. Satpal Dulay. Adv. contact Julia March. B&W page GBP 575, color page GBP 850; trim 182 x 272. Circ: 5,000 (paid).

615.537 GBR ISSN 0962-4562
➤ **INTERNATIONAL JOURNAL OF AROMATHERAPY.** Text in English. 1988. 4/yr. EUR 61 in Europe to individuals; JPY 6,600 in Japan to individuals; USD 55 to individuals except Europe and Japan; EUR 201 in Europe to institutions; JPY 21,700 in Japan to institutions; USD 180 to institutions except Europe and Japan (effective 2006). **Document type:** *Journal, Academic/Scholarly.* **Description:** Covers the pursuit of health and well-being, whether mental, emotional or physical, through aromatherapy treatment.
Related titles: Online - full text ed.: (from EBSCO Publishing, ScienceDirect, Swets Information Services).
Indexed: AMED, AbHyg, AgrForAb, DSA, ExcerpMed, FPA, ForAb, HortAb, OrnHort, PHN&I, RA&MP, RM&VM, SeedAb, TDB.
—BLDSC (4542.104400), IE, ingenta.
Published by: Churchill Livingstone (Subsidiary of: Elsevier Health Sciences), Robert Stevenson House, 1-3, Baxter's Pl, Leith Walk, Edinburgh, Midlothian EH1 3AF, United Kingdom. TEL 44-131-5562424, FAX 44-131-5581278, journals@harcourt.com, http://www.elsevier.com/locate/issn/09624562, http://www.harcourt-international.com/. Ed. Bob Harris. **Subscr. to:** Harcourt Publishers Ltd., Foots Cray High St, Sidcup, Kent DA14 5HP, United Kingdom. TEL 44-20-83085700, FAX 44-20-83090807.

615.5 USA ISSN 1047-1979
RM184
➤ **INTERNATIONAL JOURNAL OF CLINICAL ACUPUNCTURE.** Text in English. 1990. q. USD 140 domestic to individuals; USD 190 foreign to individuals; USD 380 domestic to institutions; USD 435 foreign to institutions (effective 2006). abstr.; charts; illus. back issues avail. **Document type:** *Journal, Academic/Scholarly.* **Description:** Emphasizes clinical results in acupuncture.
Indexed: AMED.
—BLDSC (4542.169500), GNLM, IE, Infotrieve, ingenta. **CCC.**
Published by: Allerton Press, Inc., 18 W 27th St, New York, NY 10001. TEL 646-424-9686, FAX 646-424-9695, journals@allertonpress.com, http://www.allertonpress.com/journals/acup.htm. Ed. Dr. Daiyi Tang.

▼ *new title* ➤ *refereed* ∗ *unverified* ♦ *full entry avail.*

615.5 USA ISSN 1540-2584
➤ **THE INTERNET JOURNAL OF ALTERNATIVE MEDICINE.** Text in English. 2002. s-a. free to individuals; USD 500 to institutions (effective 2005). adv. **Document type:** *Journal, Academic/Scholarly.*
Media: Online - full content.
Published by: Internet Scientific Publications, L.L.C., 23 Rippling Creek Dr, Sugar Land, TX 77479. TEL 832-443-1193, FAX 281-240-1533, skoutoub@bastyr.edu, wenker@ispub.com, http://www.ispub.com/ostia/index.php?xmlFilePath=journals/ijam/front.xml. Ed. Dr. Samer Koutoubi.

615.5 JPN ISSN 1348-7922
▼ **JAPANESE JOURNAL OF COMPLEMENTARY AND ALTERNATIVE MEDICINE.** Text in Japanese. 2004. m.
Related titles: Online - full content ed.: ISSN 1348-7930. free (effective 2005); Online - full text ed.: (from J-Stage).
Published by: Japanese Society for Complementary and Alternative Medicine, Shin-Bilu #203, 1-36 Takaoka-cho, Kanazawa, Ishikawa 920-0864, Japan. TEL 81-76-2653900, FAX 81-76-2653901, cam@med.kanazawa-u.ac.jp, http://www.jcam-net.jp/shoseki/kaishi.html, http://www.jcam-net.jp/index.html.

615.5 CHN ISSN 1001-9537
CODEN: CIYCD5
JIANGSU ZHONGYI/JIANGSU TRADITIONAL CHINESE MEDICINE. Text in Chinese. 1956. m. adv. bk.rev. **Document type:** *Academic/Scholarly.* **Description:** Covers Chinese herbal medicine, acupuncture, massage, qigong, and health care issues.
Published by: Jiangsu Sheng Weisheng Ting/Jiangsu Provincial Bureau of Public Health, 42 Zhongyang Lu, Nanjing, Jiangsu 210008, China. TEL 643684. Ed. Zhang Huaqiang. Adv. contact Yabo Huang. B&W page CNY 2,500, color page CNY 5,000. Circ: 100,000. **Dist. overseas by:** China International Book Trading Corp, 35 Chegongzhuang Xilu, Haidian District, PO Box 399, Beijing 100044, China.

615.5 CHN
JILIN ZHONGYIYAO/JILIN TRADITIONAL CHINESE MEDICINE. Text in Chinese. bi-m.
Published by: Changchun Zhongyiyuan/Changchun Institute of Traditional Chinese Medicine, 15 Gongnong Dalu, Changchun, Jilin 130021, China. Ed. Gao Guangzhen.

615.8 615.5 USA ISSN 1075-5535
R733 CODEN: JACPFP
➤ **JOURNAL OF ALTERNATIVE & COMPLEMENTARY MEDICINE;** research on paradigm, practice, and policy. Text in English. 1993. 10/yr. USD 443 domestic to institutions; USD 527 foreign to institutions; USD 519 combined subscription domestic to institutions print & online eds.; USD 608 combined subscription foreign to institutions print & online eds. (effective 2006). Supplement avail.; back issues avail.; reprint service avail. from PSC. **Document type:** *Journal, Academic/Scholarly.* **Description:** Acts as an interdisciplinary source for research in alternative medical therapies. The primary goal is the establishment of rigorous research methodologies.
Related titles: Online - full text ed.: ISSN 1557-7708. USD 395 to institutions (effective 2006) (from EBSCO Publishing, Gale Group, O C L C Online Computer Library Center, Inc., Swets Information Services).
Indexed: AMED, AbHyg, AgrForAb, BioCN&I, CINAHL, CPA, CurCont, DSA, ExcerpMed, FCA, FPA, ForAb, HerbAb, HortAb, INI, IPA, ISR, IndMed, Inpharma, MEDLINE, NRN, NutrAb, OrnHort, PE&ON, PGegResA, PHN&I, ProtozoAb, RA&MP, RDA, RILM, RM&VM, Reac, RiceAb, SCI, SIA, SoyAb, TDB, WAE&RSA, WeedAb.
—BLDSC (4927.202300), CISTI, GNLM, IDS, IE, Infotrieve, ingenta. **CCC.**
Published by: Mary Ann Liebert, Inc. Publishers, 140 Huguenot St 3rd Fl, New Rochelle, NY 10801-5215. TEL 914-740-2100, FAX 914-740-2101, 800-654-3237, info@liebertpub.com, http://www.liebertpub.com/acm. Ed. Kim A Jobst.

615.535 610 USA ISSN 1538-7496
➤ **JOURNAL OF AMERICAN HERBALISTS GUILD.** Text in English. 2000. s-a. USD 45 to non-members; free to members (effective 2005).
Indexed: CINAHL.
—BLDSC (4686.352000), IE.
Published by: The American Herbalists Guild, 1931 Gaddis Rd, Canton, GA 30115. TEL 770-751-6021, FAX 770-751-7472, ahgoffice@earthlink.net, http://www.americanherbalistsguild.com/GUILDMEM.HTM.

615.535 GBR ISSN 1028-6020
JOURNAL OF ASIAN NATURAL PRODUCTS RESEARCH. Text in English. 2000. 8/yr. GBP 860, USD 1,109 combined subscription to institutions print & online eds. (effective 2006). reprint service avail. from PSC. **Document type:** *Journal, Academic/Scholarly.* **Description:** Presents scientific articles from the field of natural product research on Asian ethnic medicine.
Related titles: Online - full text ed.: ISSN 1477-2213. GBP 817, USD 1,054 to institutions (effective 2006) (from EBSCO Publishing, Gale Group, IngentaConnect, O C L C Online Computer Library Center, Inc., Swets Information Services).
Indexed: ASFA, AgBio, AgrForAb, B&BAb, BBCI, CCI, CPA, CurCR, ExcerpMed, FPA, ForAb, HortAb, IndChem, MEDLINE, PBA, PGegResA, PGrRegA, RA&MP, RCI, RM&VM, RPP, SeedAb, SoyAb.
—BLDSC (4947.244000), IE, Infotrieve. **CCC.**
Published by: Taylor & Francis Ltd (Subsidiary of: Taylor & Francis Group), 4 Park Sq, Milton Park, Abingdon, OX14 4RN, United Kingdom. TEL 44-1235-828600, FAX 44-1235-829000, info@tandf.co.uk, http://www.tandf.co.uk/journals/titles/10286020.asp. Ed. Xiao Tian Liang. **Subscr. in N America to:** Taylor & Francis Inc., Customer Services Dept, 325 Chestnut St, 8th Fl, Philadelphia, PA 19106. TEL 215-625-8900, 800-354-1420, FAX 215-625-8914, customerservice@taylorandfrancis.com; **Subscr. to:** Journals Customer Service, Rankine Rd, Basingstoke, Hants RG24 8PR, United Kingdom. TEL 44-1256-813000, FAX 44-1256-330245, enquiry@tandf.co.uk.

JOURNAL OF BODYWORK AND MOVEMENT THERAPIES. see *MEDICAL SCIENCES—Physical Medicine And Rehabilitation*

▼ **JOURNAL OF CANCER INTEGRATIVE MEDICINE.** see *MEDICAL SCIENCES—Oncology*

615.5 GBR ISSN 0143-8042
CODEN: JCMOBE
JOURNAL OF CHINESE MEDICINE. Text in English. 1979. 3/yr. GBP 30 domestic to individuals; GBP 33 in Europe to individuals; GBP 36 elsewhere to individuals (effective 2003). adv. bk.rev. 50 p./no. 2 cols./p.; back issues avail. **Document type:** *Journal, Academic/Scholarly.* **Description:** Covers the entire field of traditional Chinese medicine.
Related titles: CD-ROM ed.: 1998. GBP 141 per issue (effective 2003).
Indexed: AMED, CINAHL, ExcerpMed, RefZh.
—BLDSC (4958.110000), IE, ingenta.
Address: 22 Cromwell Rd, Hove, E Sussex BN3 3EB, United Kingdom. TEL 44-1273-777760, FAX 44-1273-7485888, info@jcm.co.uk, http://www.jcm.co.uk. Ed., R&P Peter Deadman. Circ: 2,000. **Dist. in US by:** Eastland Press, 1240 Activity Dr, Ste D, Vista, CA 92083. TEL 800-453-3278, orders@eastlandpress.com.

615.5 610 USA ISSN 1553-3840
▼ ➤ **JOURNAL OF COMPLEMENTARY & INTEGRATIVE MEDICINE.** Text in English. 2004. 3/yr. USD 35 to individuals; USD 225 to institutions (effective 2006). **Document type:** *Journal, Academic/Scholarly.*
Media: Online - full content.
Published by: Berkeley Electronic Press, 2809 Telegraph Ave., Ste 202, Berkeley, CA 94705. TEL 510-665-1200, FAX 510-665-1201, info@bepress.com, http://www.bepress.com/jcim. Ed. Ed Lui.

➤ **JOURNAL OF DANCE MEDICINE & SCIENCE.** see *MEDICAL SCIENCES—Physical Medicine And Rehabilitation*

➤ **JOURNAL OF HERBAL PHARMACOTHERAPY;** innovations in clinical & applied evidence-based herbal medicinals. see *MEDICAL SCIENCES—Internal Medicine*

➤ **JOURNAL OF INTERPROFESSIONAL CARE.** see *MEDICAL SCIENCES*

615.5 316.532 GBR ISSN 1368-3497
JOURNAL OF NATURAL MEDICINE. Text in English. 1993. q. GBP 19.50 in Europe; GBP 25.50 elsewhere; free to members (effective 2003). adv. bk.rev. **Document type:** *Journal, Academic/Scholarly.* **Description:** Contains articles related to natural forms of medicine, as well as, news case histories, practitioner profiles and a Materia Medica.
Formerly (until 1997): Vis Medicatrix Natrae (1355-4417)
—BLDSC (5021.210000), IE, ingenta.
Published by: General Council and Register of Consultant Herbalists, 32 King Edward Rd, Swansea, SA1 4LL, United Kingdom. office@irch.org, http://www.irch.org/, http://www.irch.org/forms_journal.htm. Ed., R&P I H James. Adv. contact M James.

633.88 IND ISSN 0972-5547
JOURNAL OF NATURAL REMEDIES; dedicated to medicinal plant research. Text in English. 2001. 2/yr. INR 250 domestic; USD 25 foreign (effective 2005). **Document type:** *Journal, Academic/Scholarly.* **Description:** Its principal subject matter is the immunomodulatory effect of the bark of the plant Albizzia Lebbeck.
Indexed: AbHyg, AgrForAb, ESPM, ExcerpMed, FPA, ForAb, H&SSA, HelmAb, HortAb, OrnHort, PBA, PGegResA, PHN&I, PoultAb, RA&MP, RM&VM, RiskAb, SIA, SeedAb, TDB, WeedAb.
—BLDSC (5021.225200), IE.
Published by: Natural Remedies Private Ltd., Plot No. 5B, Veerasandra Industrial Area, 19th K.M. Stone, Hosur Rd, Bangalore, Karnataka 561 229, India. TEL 91-80-7832265, FAX 91-80-7834369, jnr@naturalremedy.com, http://www.jnronline.com.

615.535 USA ISSN 1047-7837
➤ **JOURNAL OF NATUROPATHIC MEDICINE.** Text in English. 1990. q. adv. bk.rev. **Document type:** *Journal, Academic/Scholarly.*
Related titles: Online - full text ed.: (from EBSCO Publishing).
Indexed: AMED.
—BLDSC (5021.308000), ingenta.
Published by: American Association of Naturopathic Physicians, 601 Valley St, Ste 105, Seattle, WA 98409-4229. TEL 206-298-0126, FAX 206-209-0129, 74602.3715@compuserve.com, http://www.healthy.net/library/journals/naturopathic/. Eds. Emily Kane, Lauri Aesoph. Adv. contact Cathleen Rapp TEL 408-687-0453. Circ: 3,500.

615.5 IND ISSN 0254-3478
R605
JOURNAL OF RESEARCH IN AYURVEDA AND SIDDHA. Text in English; Summaries in Hindi. 1966. q. INR 60, USD 4. adv. bk.rev. abstr.; bibl.; charts; illus.; stat. index. **Description:** Covers work on fundamental anthropological and behavioral details referred to in clinical and literary studies of medicinal systems.
Formerly (until 1980): Journal of Research in Indian Medicine (0022-4286)
Media: Duplicated (not offset).
Indexed: BiolAb, ChemAb.
—BLDSC (5052.003000), CISTI, GNLM.
Published by: Central Council for Research in Ayurveda and Siddha, Jawahar Lal Nehru Bhartiya Chikitsa Avum Homeopathy Anusandhan Bhavan, No.61-65, Institutional Area, Opp. 'D' Block, Janakpuri, New Delhi, 110 001, India. TEL 91-011-25614970, FAX 91-011-25528748, ccras@ndf.vsnl.net.in, http://www.ccras.org/. Ed. Dr. V N Pandey. Circ: 300.

615.5 200 USA ISSN 1079-8390
➤ **JOURNAL OF SPIRITUAL BODYWORK.** Text in English. 1995. q. USD 25; USD 30 foreign (effective 1999). bk.rev. index. back issues avail. **Document type:** *Academic/Scholarly.* **Description:** Provides information about different kinds of spiritual healing (including massage) to laymen, clergymen, and members of licensed professions concerned with the healing arts.
Media: Online - full text.
—CCC.
Published by: (Church for Spiritual Healing and Health), Spiritual Massage Healing Ministry, 6907 Sherman St, Philadelphia, PA 19119. TEL 215-842-0265, FAX 215-842-2388, aschatz@unix.temple.edu, http://www.healingandlaw.com. Ed., Pub., R&P Albert Schatz. Circ: 290 (paid).

615.5 JPN ISSN 0288-2485
KANPO IGAKU/CHINESE MEDICINE. Text in Japanese. 1977. m. JPY 450 per issue.
Published by: Kanpo Igakusha/Kanpo Medicine Publications, 12-7 Niban-cho, Chiyoda-ku, Tokyo, 102-0084, Japan.

615.5 JPN ISSN 0385-6526
KANPO KENKYU/STUDY ON CHINESE MEDICINE. Text in Japanese. 1975. m. JPY 400 per issue.
Published by: Gekkan Kanpo Kenkyu, 5-23 Nakatsu 2-chome, Kita-ku, Osaka-shi, 531-0071, Japan.

615.5 JPN ISSN 0451-307X
KANPO NO RINSHO/JOURNAL OF KAMPO MEDICINE. Text in Japanese. 1954. m. JPY 850 per issue (effective 1999). adv. **Description:** Looks to contribute to the development of East-Asian medicine.
—CCC.
Published by: Toa Igaku Kyokai/Association of East Asian Medicine, 1-5 Misaki-cho 2-chome, Chiyoda-ku, Tokyo, 101-0061, Japan. TEL 03-3264-8410, FAX 03-3265-5995. Ed. Isao Tuchiya. R&P, Adv. contact Toa Igaku Kyokai. Circ: 1,600.

615.5 JPN ISSN 0914-6407
KANPO TO MEN'EKI ARERUGI★ /KAMPO AND IMMUNO-ALLERGY. Text in Japanese; Summaries in English, Japanese. 1988. a. JPY 4,500.
Published by: Medikaru Toribyun/Medical Tribune Inc., Nibancho TS Bldig, 2-1 Nibancho, Chiyoda-ku, Tokyo, 102-0084, Japan. TEL 86-3-32397210, FAX 86-3-32397243, www.google.com, http://www.medical-tribune.co.jp/.

615.5 JPN ISSN 0912-9545
KANSAI SHINKYU TANKI DAIGAKU NENPO/KANSAI COLLEGE OF ACUPUNCTURE MEDICINE. ANNUAL REPORT. Text in English, Japanese. 1985. a.
Published by: Kansai Shinkyu Tanki Daigaku, 990 Ogai-To, Sennan-gun, Kumatori-cho, Osaka-fu 590-0432, Japan.

615.5 JPN ISSN 0912-0718
KATSU/JAPAN INSTITUTE OF TRADITIONAL MEDICINE. NEWS. Text in Japanese. 1959. m. JPY 400 per issue.
Published by: Nihon Kanpo Igaku Kenkyujo, 2-20 Nihonbashi 2-chome, Chuo-ku, Tokyo, 103-0027, Japan.

615.5 JPN
➤ **KEIRAKU CHIRYO/JAPANESE SOCIETY OF ACUPUNCTURE. JOURNAL.** Text in Japanese. 1965. q. JPY 7,000. adv. bk.rev. **Document type:** *Academic/Scholarly.*
Published by: Keiraku Chiryo Gakkai, 14-9 Jinnan 1-chome, Shibuya-ku, Tokyo, 150-0041, Japan. TEL 81-3-3461-2426, FAX 81-3-3770-1675. Ed., Pub., R&P, Adv. contact Okabe Somei.

➤ **KRAUT UND RUEBEN**; biologisches Gaertnern und naturgemaesses Leben. see *GARDENING AND HORTICULTURE*

➤ **L O H A S JOURNAL.** see *BUSINESS AND ECONOMICS*

615.88 POL ISSN 1233-9253
LEKARZ DOMOWY MEDYCYNY LUDOWEJ; miesiecznik lekarski. Text in Polish. 1995. bi-m. PLZ 2.50 newsstand/cover. back issues avail. **Description:** Covers folk herbal medicine.
Published by: Faktor Sp. z o.o., Ul Ksiecia Wladyslawa Opolskiego 3 a, Kety, 32650, Poland. TEL 48-33-453888. Ed. Jozef Gaweda. Circ: 8,000.

615.5 615.328 CHN ISSN 1000-1719
R97.7.C5 CODEN: LZZAEJ
LIAONING ZHONGYI ZAZHI/LIAONING JOURNAL OF TRADITIONAL CHINESE MEDICINE. Text in Chinese. 1979. m. USD 0.70 per issue.
Related titles: Online - full text ed.: (from East View Information Services).
Indexed: DentInd, IndMed.
—BLDSC (5186.247500).
Published by: Liaoning Zhongyi Xueyuan/Liaoning College of Traditional Chinese Medicine, 79 Congshan Donglu, Shenyang, Liaoning 110032a, China. **Dist. outside China by:** China International Book Trading Corp, 35 Chegongzhuang Xilu, Haidian District, PO Box 399, Beijing 100044, China. **Co-sponsor:** Zhonghua Quanguo Zhongyi Xuehui Liaoning Fenhui.

615.5 USA ISSN 1524-198X
LIFE EXTENSION; the ultimate source for new health and medical findings from around the world. Text in English. m. USD 40 domestic; USD 47 in Canada; USD 60 elsewhere; USD 3.95, CND 4.95 newsstand/cover (effective 2003). adv. illus. **Document type:** *Magazine, Consumer.* **Description:** Provides information and articles on the latest in health and medical findings.
Related titles: Online - full text ed.: (from EBSCO Publishing).
Indexed: CINAHL.
Published by: Life Extension Foundation, PO Box 229120, Hollywood, FL 33022. TEL 954-766-8433, 800-678-8989, FAX 954-761-9199, generalquestions@lifeextension.com, http://www.lef.org/magazine/mag_all.html.

615.535 CAN
LIFESTYLE AND WELLNESS. Text in English. q. CND 10.70 domestic; USD 15 in United States; CND 2.50 newsstand/cover (effective 2000). **Document type:** *Magazine, Consumer.*
Address: 2813 Victoria Park Ave, Scarborough, ON M1W 1A1, Canada. TEL 416-492-6598, sheilam@spirit.ca, http://www.starpages.com/lifestyle-wellness.

613 USA
LILIPOH; a quarterly guide to health, nutrition and the environment. Text in English. q. USD 24 domestic; USD 28 foreign (effective 2002). adv. **Document type:** *Consumer.* **Description:** Offers hope and courage in dealing with illnes as a phenomenon reflective of the soul and spirit as well as the body.
Indexed: AltPI.
Published by: Lilipoh Inc, Box 649, Nyack, NY 10960. TEL 914-268-2627, FAX 914-268-2764, info@lilipoh.com, http://lilipoh.com. Pub. Christine Murphy.

LONGEVITY REPORT. see *MEDICAL SCIENCES*

615 USA ISSN 1092-8774
➤ **M I S A H A NEWSLETTER.** Text in English. 1993. q. USD 20 domestic; USD 25 foreign (effective 2001). bibl. 24 p./no.; back issues avail. **Document type:** *Newsletter, Academic/Scholarly.*
Related titles: Online - full text ed.
Published by: Monterrey Institute for the Study of Alternative Healing Arts, 3855 Via Nona Marie, Ste 102-C, Carmel, CA 93923. TEL 831-622-7975, FAX 831-625-9617, misaha@aol.com, http://www.whps.com/misaha. Ed. Savely Savva. Circ: 400.

➤ **MACROBIOTICS TODAY.** see *NUTRITION AND DIETETICS*

651.89 CAN
A MAGAZINE OF PEOPLE AND POSSIBILITIES. Text in English. 1990. 5/yr. free. **Description:** Seeks to connect people and explore possibilities in a rich exchange of vital information about health, ecology, personal growth, professional development, creativity, and wellness.
Formerly (until 1995): In Touch (Calgary) (1188-3944)
Related titles: Online - full text ed.
Published by: Rebecca Ryan Resources, #611, 7620 Elbow Dr S W, Calgary, AB T2V 1K2, Canada. TEL 403-245-6815, hayv@intouchmag.com, http://www.intouchmag.com. Ed. Veronica M Hay.

615.5 GBR
MASSAGE AND HEALTH REVIEW. Text in English. 1991. 3/yr. AUD 21 (effective 2001). **Document type:** *Newsletter.*
Indexed: AMED.
Published by: Massage Therapy Institute of Great Britain, P.O. Box 2726, London, NW2 3NR, United Kingdom. TEL 44-20-8208-1607, FAX 44-20-8208-1639. Ed. Safia Shah. Circ: 450.

615.822 USA ISSN 0895-0814
RM721
MASSAGE THERAPY JOURNAL. Text in English. 1946. q. USD 25 in US & Canada; USD 70 elsewhere; USD 6.50 newsstand/cover (effective 2005). adv. bk.rev.; music rev.; video rev. tr.lit. 176 p./no.; back issues avail.; reprints avail. **Document type:** *Journal, Trade.* **Description:** Feature articles and columns cover techniques, research, successful practices, business advice and industry news relating to massage therapy.
Formerly (until 1962): Massage Journal
Indexed: CINAHL, EEA.
Published by: American Massage Therapy Association, 500 Davis St., Ste. 900, Evanston, IL 60201-4464. TEL 847-864-0123, FAX 847-864-1178, mschwanz@amtamassage.org, http://www.amtamassage.org. Ed. Michael Schwanz. R&P Joseph Schlesinger TEL 847-864-0123 ext 133. Adv. contact Christina Rompon TEL 847-869-5127 ext 113. color page USD 3,096; 7.125 x 9.875. Circ: 61,000 (paid).

615.5 FRA ISSN 0760-811X
MEDECINES NOUVELLES. Text in French. 1985. q. **Document type:** *Monographic series.* **Description:** Informs on the new medical therapies.
Formerly: Cahiers Pratiques de Medecine (1243-7042)
Published by: Societe J A G, BP 002, Blangy-le-Chateau, 14130, France. TEL 33-2-31648505. Ed. Annie Cristinacce. Pub. Jean Jacques Rocca Cristinacce. Circ: 33,000.

MEDICINA NATURALE. see *MEDICAL SCIENCES—Chiropractic, Homeopathy, Osteopathy*

615.53 GBR ISSN 1027-4502
MEDICINAL AND AROMATIC PLANTS. Text in English. 1997. irreg. price varies. **Document type:** *Monographic series, Academic/Scholarly.*
—CCC.
Published by: Taylor & Francis Ltd (Subsidiary of: Taylor & Francis Group), 4 Park Sq, Milton Park, Abingdon, OX14 4RN, United Kingdom. TEL 44-1235-828600, FAX 44-1235-829000, info@tandf.co.uk, http://www.tandf.co.uk/journals.

615.892 BGR ISSN 1311-2759
MEDITSINSKI PREGLED. AKUPUNKTURA/MEDICAL REVIEW. ACUPUNCTURE. Text in Bulgarian. 1999. 3/yr. BGL 12 domestic; USD 35 foreign (effective 2005). 48 p./no. 1 cols./p.; **Document type:** *Journal, Academic/Scholarly.* **Description:** Publishes original articles in the field of acupuncture and acupressure, traditional chinese medicine.
Indexed: RefZh.
Published by: Meditsinski Universitet - Sofia, Tsentralna Meditsinska Biblioteka, Tsentur za Informatsiia po Meditsina/Medical University - Sofia, Central Medical Library, Medical Information Center, 1 Sv Georgi Sofiiski ul, Sofia, 1431, Bulgaria. TEL 359-2-9522342, FAX 359-2-9522393, pslavova@medun.acad.bg, http://www.medun.acad.bg/cmb_htm/cmb1_home_bg.htm. Ed. E Iliev. R&P, Adv. contact Lydia Tacheva.

615.5 JPN ISSN 0912-2419
➤ **MEIJI SHINKYU IGAKU/MEIJI UNIVERSITY OF ORIENTAL MEDICINE. BULLETIN.** Text in Japanese; Abstracts in English. 1986. s-a. dist. to libraries of medical schools & researchers of acupuncture only. 150 p./no.; **Document type:** *Journal, Academic/Scholarly.*
Published by: Meiji Shinkyu Daigaku/Meiji University of Oriental Medicine, Funai-gun, Hiyoshicho, Kyoto 629-0392, Japan. TEL 81-771-72-1181, FAX 81-771-72-0326, kiyou_edit@muom_meiji-u.ac.jp. Ed. Kenji Kawakita. Pub. Kinya Kuriyama. Circ: 350.

615.892 USA
MERIDIANS (COLUMBIA); redefining health. Text in English. q. USD 20 domestic; USD 30 foreign (effective 2000). bk.rev. illus. **Document type:** *Consumer.* **Description:** Contains detailed articles and information regarding acupuncture and related health care issues.
Formerly (until 1992): Journal of Traditional Acupuncture (0270-661X)
Related titles: Online - full text ed.: (from EBSCO Publishing).
Indexed: AMED.
—BLDSC (5680.789880), ingenta.
Published by: Traditional Acupuncture Institute, 7750 Montpelier Rd, Laurel, MD 20723-6010. TEL 301-596-6006. Ed. Mary Ellen Zorbaugh. R&P John Wilson TEL 410-997-4888. Circ: 2,000.

MOJE ZDROWIE; domowy poradnik medyczny. see *PUBLIC HEALTH AND SAFETY*

615.5 IND ISSN 0971-684X
➤ **N A M A H**; a journal of Sri Aurobindo International Institute for Integral Health and Research. (New Approaches to Medicine And Health) Text in English. 1993. q. looseleaf. INR 150 domestic; USD 25 foreign; INR 60 newsstand/cover domestic; USD 8 newsstand/cover foreign (effective 2003). bk.rev.; Website rev. abstr.; charts; illus. 50 p./no.; back issues avail.; reprints avail. **Document type:** *Journal, Academic/Scholarly.* **Description:** Reports on developments in new approaches in medicine and general health care.
Published by: Sri Aurobindo Society, Academy of the Future, Beach Office - EDP Section, 1 Rue Rangapillai St, Pondicherry, Tamil Nadu 605 001, India. TEL 91-413-2336396, FAX 91-413-2334447, namah@sriaurobindosociety.org.in, http://www.sriaurobindosociety.org.in. Eds. Dr. Alok Pandey, Dr. Soumitra Basu. Pub. Pradeep Narang. R&P A R Ganguly.

➤ **N C A H F NEWSLETTER**; quality in the health marketplace. (National Council Against Health Fraud) see *PUBLIC HEALTH AND SAFETY*

362 USA ISSN 1081-5678
N H O NEWSLINE. Text in English. 1984. s-m. membership only. **Document type:** *Newsletter.* **Description:** Provides brief updates of regulatory and educational news and information of relevance to hospice administrators.
Former titles (until 1991): N H O Hospice News; N H O President's Letter
Published by: National Hospice Organization, 1700 Diagonal Rd, Ste 3000, Arlington, VA 222314. TEL 703-243-5900, FAX 703-525-5762, http://www.nho.org. Ed. Larry Beresford. Circ: 2,800 (controlled).

N O H A NEWS. see *NUTRITION AND DIETETICS*

615.5 JPN ISSN 0911-9760
NAGAKURA KANPO DAIJESUTO/NAGAKURA KANPO DIGEST. Text in Japanese. 1970. a.
Published by: Nagakura Seiyaku K.K./Nagakura Pharmaceutical Co., Ltd., 7-16 Shoten-Shita 1-chome, Nishinari-ku, Osaka-shi, 557-0012, Japan.

NAMESTE. see *HUMANITIES: COMPREHENSIVE WORKS*

615.5 DEU ISSN 1433-9935
NATUR UND GESUNDHEIT; aktuelle Informationen aus der Naturheilkunde. Text in German. 1997. m. (14/yr.). EUR 102 (effective 2005). adv. back issues avail. **Document type:** *Newsletter, Consumer.* **Description:** Contains information on natural healing, alternative medicine, therapies and remedies.
Related titles: Online - full text ed.
Published by: F I D Verlag GmbH, Koblenzer Str 99, Bonn, 53177, Germany. TEL 49-228-9550333, FAX 49-228-82055756, info@fid-verlag.de, http://www.fid-verlag.de/natur_und_gesundheit.php. Ed. Ingeborg Gernaj. Pub. Helmut Graf. R&P, Adv. contact Susanne Kolle. **Subscr. to:** Leser-Service, Postfach 1327, Neckarsulm 74150, Germany. TEL 49-7132-959205, FAX 49-7132-959209.

NATURAL BEAUTY & HEALTH. see *PHYSICAL FITNESS AND HYGIENE*

613 GBR
NATURAL HEALTH. Text in English. q. **Document type:** *Magazine, Consumer.* **Description:** Contains information and advice on how to lead a healthy and happy life.
Published by: Ultima Publishing Ltd., 46 Oxford St, London, W1N 9FJ, United Kingdom. TEL 44-20-7436-6800, FAX 44-20-7636-6886, info@ultimapublishing.com, http://www.ultimapublishing.com.

613.7 USA ISSN 1067-9588
AP2
NATURAL HEALTH. Text in English. 1971. 10/yr. USD 14.97 domestic; USD 26.97 foreign; USD 4.95 newsstand/cover domestic; CND 5.95 newsstand/cover in Canada (effective 2005). adv. bk.rev. back issues avail.; reprint service avail. from PQC. **Document type:** *Magazine, Consumer.* **Description:** Guide to mind, body, and spirit self-care.
Former titles (until Nov. 1992): EastWest Natural Health (1061-4664); (until Jan. 1992): EastWest (0888-1375); (until 1986): East West Journal (0191-3700); (until 1978): EastWest (0149-0362); (until 1977): East West Journal (0149-7839)
Related titles: Microform ed.: (from PQC); Online - full text ed.: (from America Online, Inc., EBSCO Publishing, Gale Group, O C L C Online Computer Library Center, Inc.).
Indexed: AMED, AltPI, CHNI, NPI, PerIslam.
—BLDSC (6037.930000), IE, ingenta.
Published by: A M I - Weider Publications (Subsidiary of: American Media, Inc.), 415 Madison Ave., 14th Fl, New York, NY 10017. TEL 212-339-1900, FAX 212-696-5374, http://www.naturalhealthmag.com. Eds. Elizabeth Tuner, Hillary Dowdle. Pub. Randy Frank Leeds. adv.: B&W page USD 12,540, color page USD 15,135. Circ: 250,000 (paid).

NATURAL HEALTH & WELL-BEING; complementary therapies for you & yours. see *PHYSICAL FITNESS AND HYGIENE*

A

613.7 USA
NATURAL HEALTH HOLLYWOOD. Text in English. 2001 (Oct.). a. USD 4.95 newsstand/cover; USD 5.95 newsstand/cover in Canada (effective 2001). **Document type:** *Magazine, Consumer.* **Description:** Contains celebrity choices and recommendations on natural health and beauty products and lifestyles.
Published by: A M I - Weider Publications (Subsidiary of: American Media, Inc.), 415 Madison Ave., 14th Fl, New York, NY 10017. TEL 818-884-6800, 800-998-0731, FAX 818-716-5626.

NATURAL HEALTH PRODUCTS CANADA B2B INDUSTRY GUIDE. see *BUSINESS AND ECONOMICS—Trade And Industrial Directories*

NATURAL HEALTH REVIEW. see *PHYSICAL FITNESS AND HYGIENE*

NATURAL PARENT. see *CHILDREN AND YOUTH—About*

NATURAL PHARMACY. see *PHARMACY AND PHARMACOLOGY*

615.5 USA ISSN 1082-0531
THE NATURAL WAY; For Better Health. Text in English. 1995. bi-m. USD 18; USD 3.50 newsstand/cover; USD 24 foreign (effective 1999). adv. bk.rev.; software rev.; video rev. back issues avail. **Document type:** *Consumer.* **Description:** Promotes natural methods of living, healing towards better health.
Related titles: E-mail ed.; Fax ed.; Online - full text ed.: (from EBSCO Publishing).
Published by: The Publishing Group, 1 Bridge St Ste 125, Irvington, NY 10533. TEL 914-591-2011, FAX 914-591-2017, NatWay@aol.com. Ed., R&P Cathy Raymond. Pub. Warren Tabatch. Adv. contact Arthur Maxwell. B&W page USD 3,829, color page USD 5,208; trim 10.88 x 8.13. Circ: 150,000 (paid).

613.7 USA ISSN 1080-6180
NATURALLY WELL. Variant title: Dr. Marcus Laux's Naturally Well. Text in English. 199?. m. USD 39.95 (effective 2004). **Document type:** *Newsletter, Consumer.* **Description:** Offers detailed health solutions, including natural therapies, dietary and lifestyle factors that can contribute to longevity and overall well-being.
Formerly (until 1995): Malibu Natural Health Letter (1079-8803)
Published by: Phillips Health, LLC (Subsidiary of: Phillips International, Inc.), 7811 Montrose Rd, Potomac, MD 20854. TEL 301-340-2100, 800-777-5005, information@phillips.com, http://www.drmarcuslaux.com/c/newsletter.asp?cookie%5Ftest=1, http://www.phillips.com/health/. Ed. Dr. Marcus Laux.

615.5 DEU ISSN 0720-826X
DER NATURARZT; Ihr Ratgeber fuer ein gesundes Leben. Text in German. 1979. m. EUR 37.20 domestic; EUR 43.50 foreign; EUR 3.50 newsstand/cover (effective 2003). adv. bk.rev. charts; illus. index. **Document type:** *Magazine, Consumer.*
Formed by the merger of (1954-1979): Gewinne Dein Leben Neu (0431-820X); (1861-1979): Der Naturarzt. Bundeausgabe (0340-3041); Which superseded in part: Der Naturarzt (0028-081X)
Published by: Access Marketing GmbH, Alt Falkenstein 37a, Koenigstein, 61462, Germany. TEL 49-6174-92630, FAX 49-6174-926328, info@naturarzt-access.de, http://www.naturarzt-access.de. Pub., Adv. contact Gisela Grein. B&W page EUR 2,807, color page EUR 3,880. Circ: 69,800 (paid and controlled).

615.5 AUS ISSN 0815-7006
NATURE AND HEALTH. Text in English. 1977. bi-m. (7/yr.). AUD 44 domestic; AUD 55 in New Zealand; AUD 66 in Asia; AUD 88 elsewhere (effective 2005). adv. bk.rev. **Document type:** *Magazine, Consumer.* **Description:** Covers diverse health care topics: natural health, self-improvement body care, relationships, organic gardening, natural beauty and fitness, oriental herbs, whole foods, science, social change, and spirituality.
Former titles (until 1984): Nature and Health Australia (0815-6999); (until 1980): Nature and Health Quarterly (0158-9911)
Published by: Yaffa Publishing Group Pty Ltd., 17-21 Bellevue St, Surry Hills, NSW 2010, Australia. TEL 61-2-92812333, FAX 61-2-92812750, yaffa@yaffa.com.au, http://www.yaffa.com.au. Ed. Pamela Allardice. Pub. Tracy Yaffa. Adv. contact Margaret Forbes. B&W page AUD 2,080, color page AUD 3,200; trim 210 x 273.

615.5 DEU ISSN 0177-6754
➤ **NATURHEILPRAXIS MIT NATURMEDIZIN**; Fachzeitschrift fuer Naturheilkunde, Erfahrungsheilkunde und biologische Heilverfahren. Text in German. 1947. m. EUR 88.80 domestic; EUR 103.20 foreign; EUR 7.90 newsstand/cover (effective 2003). adv. bk.rev. illus. index. **Document type:** *Journal, Academic/Scholarly.*
Former titles (until 1984): N. Naturheilpraxis (0177-6746); (until 1983): Naturheilpraxis (0028-0941)
—GNLM. **CCC.**
Published by: Richard Pflaum Verlag GmbH und Co. KG, Lazarettstr 4, Munich, 80636, Germany. TEL 49-89-126070, FAX 49-89-12607202, unterstoeger@naturheilpraxis.de, info@pflaum.de, http://www.naturheilpraxis.de, http://www.pflaum.de. Ed. K F Liebau. Adv. contact Christine Keller TEL 49-89-12607210. B&W page EUR 1,925, color page EUR 3,155; trim 185 x 256. Circ: 16,403.

615.5 USA ISSN 0028-100X
NATUROPATH✶. Text in English. 1961. m. USD 7.50. adv. bk.rev. stat.; tr.lit.
Published by: Naturopath Publishing Co., 141 N Steelhammer Dr, Silverton, OR 97381-1821. TEL 206-695-0213. Ed. Robert W Noble. Circ: 3,600.

NEW AGE JOURNAL SOURCEBOOK. see *NEW AGE PUBLICATIONS*

613 USA
NEW VISIONS MAGAZINE. Text in English. 1988. m. USD 20 (effective 2005). adv. bk.rev.; music rev. 54 p./no. 2 cols./p.; back issues avail.; reprints avail. **Document type:** *Magazine, Consumer.*
Related titles: Online - full content ed.
Published by: New Visions Magazine, Inc., PO Box 409, Hilltown, PA 18927. TEL 215-453-7371, FAX 215-453-7320, nvm@bellatlantic.net, http://www.newvisionsmagazine.com. Pub. Barry Joshua Detwiler. adv.: page USD 480; 7 x 9. Circ: 52,000 (free).

615.5 158 USA
NEXUS (BOULDER); Colorado's holistic journal. Text in English. 1980. bi-m. USD 21. adv. bk.rev. illus. **Document type:** *Newspaper.* **Description:** Publishes news and commentary pertaining to all aspects of holistic and alternative health care and related issues.
Address: 1680 Sixth St, Ste 6, Boulder, CO 80302. TEL 303-442-6662, FAX 303-442-7596, nexuspub@aol.com, http://www.nexuspub.com. Ed., Pub. Ravi Dykema. R&P, Adv. contact Margo Hayden. Circ: 54,000 (controlled).

NIGERIAN JOURNAL OF NATURAL PRODUCTS AND MEDICINE. see *PHARMACY AND PHARMACOLOGY*

NUTRITION FORUM. see *NUTRITION AND DIETETICS*

ONKRUID; voor aarde, lichaam en geest. see *NEW AGE PUBLICATIONS*

ORGANICA; a magazine of arts & activism. see *LITERATURE*

615.5 JPN
ORIENTAL MEDICINE. Text in Japanese. m. JPY 1,408 per issue. **Document type:** *Trade.* **Description:** Covers kampo medicine, acupuncture, moxibustion, manipulative therapeutics for physicians, herbal pharmacists, and manufacturers.
Published by: Midori - Shobo Co. Ltd. (Subsidiary of: Midori Group), Ikebukuro Nishiguchi Sky Bldg, 2-14-4 Ikebukuro, Toshima-ku, Tokyo, 171-0014, Japan. TEL 03-35990-4441, FAX 03-3590-4446. Ed. Toshikazo Nakamura. Circ: 18,000.

DE ORTHOMOLECULAIRE KOERIER; Nederlands - Vlaams tijdschrift voor nutritionele geneeskunde. see *NUTRITION AND DIETETICS*

615.321 USA ISSN 1099-9566
RS164
P D R FOR HERBAL MEDICINES. (Physicians' Desk Reference) Text in English. 1998. irreg., latest 3rd Ed. USD 59.95 newsstand/cover (effective 2005). **Document type:** *Trade.* **Description:** Covers scientific findings on efficacy, safety and potential interactions, including clinical trials, case reports, and meta-analysis results.
—**CCC.**
Published by: Thomson P D R, Five Paragon Dr., Montvale, NJ 07645-1742. TEL 201-358-7200, 800-232-7379, http://www.pdr.net/.

THE PANIC RELIEF NEWS. see *PSYCHOLOGY*

615.5 DEU
PARA; Zeitschrift fuer alternative Heilkunde und spirituelles Leben. Text in German. bi-m. EUR 26 domestic; EUR 30 foreign (effective 2004). adv. **Document type:** *Magazine, Consumer.*
Published by: Mediengruppe Koenig, Aeussere Zeulenrodaer Str 11, Greiz, 07973 , Germany. TEL 49-3661-674213, FAX 49-3661-674214, verlag-koenig@t-online.de, http://www.die-para.de, http://www.mediengruppe-koenig.de. Adv. contact Uwe Hilke. B&W page EUR 1,170, color page EUR 1,555; trim 185 x 265.

615.5 USA
PATHOS NET (ONLINE). Text in English. 1999. bi-m. free. **Document type:** *Consumer.* **Description:** Covers alternative methods of health and healing.
Formerly: Pathos Magazine (Print Edition)
Media: Online - full text.
Published by: Alexander Publishing, Inc. TEL 406-676-4825, FAX 406-676-4824, jbedell@pathosnet.com, http://www.pathosnet.com. Ed. Jerri Bedell.

615.8 ZAF ISSN 1022-2170
PATHWAYS TO HEALTH. Text in English. 1993. m. ZAR 91 (effective 1999). adv. **Document type:** *Consumer.* **Description:** To discuss issues, concepts and trends related to the various "pathways to health" so that our readers can make informed and educated decisions as to the path they want to follow.
Published by: F A S Publications, PO Box 41632, Craighall, Gauteng 2024, South Africa. FAX 27-11-7876316, sophie@fas.co.za. Ed. Monica Fairall. Pub. Ian Hughes. R&P Sophie MacKensie TEL 27-11-7893740. Adv. contact Theresa de Jongh. page ZAR 8,380; trim 275 x 210. Circ: 20,000.

615.5 IND ISSN 0972-3293
PHYTOMEDICA. Text in English. 1978. s-a. USD 70 to institutions (effective 2006). **Document type:** *Journal, Academic/Scholarly.*
Formerly: Indian Journal of Indigenous Medicines (0971-5452)
Indexed: ASFA, ESPM, ExcerpMed.
—BLDSC (6491.400000).
Published by: Society for Phytomedica, Indian Herbs House, Sharda Nagar, Saharanpur, 247 001, India. http://www.scientificpub.com/bookdetails.php?booktransid=461&bookid=457. Ed. S. Misra. **Subscr. to:** Scientific Publishers, 5-A New Pali Rd., Near Hotel Taj Hari Mahal, PO Box 91, Jodhpur, Rajasthan 342 003, India. journals@scientificpub.com, http://www.scientificpub.com.

POSITIVE HEALTH; integrated medicine for the 21st century. see *PHYSICAL FITNESS AND HYGIENE*

POSTEPY FITOTERAPII. see *PHARMACY AND PHARMACOLOGY*

POTPOURRI FROM HERBAL ACRES. see *GARDENING AND HORTICULTURE*

615.5 POL ISSN 1231-6652
PRZEPISY MEDYCYNY LUDOWEJ; miesiecznik zdrowia. Text in Polish. 1994. bi-m. PLZ 2.50 newsstand/cover. back issues avail. **Description:** Covers folk medicine.
Published by: Gawenda Sp. z o.o., Ul Kiecia Wladyslawa Opolskiego 3 a, Kety, 32650, Poland. TEL 48-33-453888. Ed. Jozef Gaweda. Circ: 22,500.

615.5 158 AUT ISSN 1605-4652
PULSAR; Zeitschrift fuer Gesundheit, Therapie und Innere Entwicklung. Text in German. 1989. m. EUR 28 domestic; EUR 38 in Europe; EUR 68 elsewhere (effective 2005). adv. bk.rev. illus. 68 p./no. 4 cols./p.; **Document type:** *Newspaper, Consumer.*
Related titles: Online - full text ed.: ISSN 1605-1300.
Published by: Bach Verlag KEG, Wutschdorf 89, St. Ulrich, 8072, Austria. TEL 43-3135-809020, FAX 43-3135-809023, zeitschrift@pulsar.at, http://www.pulsar.at. Ed. Marlis Bach. Pub., Adv. contact Kurt Bach. B&W page EUR 1,200; trim 192 x 250. Circ: 18,000 (paid).

615.5 USA
RADIANCE TECHNIQUE JOURNAL. Text in English. 1980. s-a. membership. adv. bk.rev. back issues avail. **Document type:** *Newsletter.* **Description:** Features alumni sharing news of their use of The Radiance Technique; includes the latest articles on the subject. Also includes information on peace projects in the U.S. and abroad.
Former titles: T R T and R P A I Journal; Radiance Technique Newsletter; Radiance Technique Journal (1040-5836); Reiki Journal
Published by: The Radiance Technique International Association, Inc., PO Box 40570, St. Petersburg, FL 33743-0570. TEL 727-343-8212, TRTPeace@aol.com, http://www.trtia.org. R&P Shoshana Shay. Circ: 2,000 (paid).

615.89 NZL ISSN 1174-3530
RAINBOW NEWS; the spirit of aotearoa. Text in English. 1990. bi-m. NZD 21; NZD 4.20 newsstand/cover (effective 2001). music rev.; bk.rev. back issues avail. **Document type:** *Magazine, Consumer.* **Description:** Covers holistic health, lifestyle, native, workshops, retreats, and events.
Formerly (until 1997): Rainbow Network (0114-328X)
Published by: Healthy Options Ltd., 100 Grage Rd, PO Box 13209, Tauranga, New Zealand. http://www.healthyoptions.co.nz. Ed., R&P, Adv. contact Toni Bourget. Pub. Janice-Ann Priest. Circ: 14,000.

615.5 DEU
REIKI MAGAZIN. Text in German. 1997. q. EUR 23 domestic; CHF 44 in Switzerland; EUR 32 elsewhere (effective 2005). adv. **Document type:** *Magazine, Consumer.*
Published by: Juergen Kindler Verlag, Gaudystr 12, Berlin, 10437, Germany. TEL 49-30-44046935, FAX 49-30-44046936, verlag@reiki-magazin.de, http://www.reiki-magazin.de. Ed. Juergen Kindler. adv.: page EUR 800; trim 200 x 280.

615.851 USA ISSN 1539-6533
REIKI NEWS MAGAZINE. Text in English. 2002. q. USD 15 domestic; USD 18 in Canada; USD 22 elsewhere; USD 6 newsstand/cover (effective 2004). adv. **Document type:** *Magazine, Consumer.* **Description:** Provides a source of information, inspiration and practical advice about the practice of Reiki.
Related titles: Online - full text ed.

Published by: International Center for Reiki Training, 21421 Hilltop St, #28, Southfield, MI 48034. TEL 248-948-8112, 800-332-8112, FAX 248-948-9534, center@reiki.org, http://www.reikinm.com, http://www.reiki.org. Ed. William Lee Rand. Adv. contact Corey Hogan Bippes TEL 509-999-3016. B&W page USD 825, color page USD 1,320; 7.5 x 9.875. Circ: 20,000 (paid).

615.5 DEU ISSN 1435-1218
REPORT NATURHEILKUNDE. Text in German. 1997. m.
Document type: *Magazine, Consumer.*
Published by: Verlagsgesellschaft Tischler GmbH, Kaunstr 34, Berlin, 14163, Germany. TEL 49-30-8011018, FAX 49-30-8016661, media-service@firmengruppe-tischler.de.

615.5 FRA ISSN 0337-6877
➤ **REVUE FRANCAISE D'ACUPUNCTURE.** Text in French; Summaries in English. 1975. q. EUR 60 foreign (effective 2003). adv. bk.rev.; music rev. cum.index: 1975-1977; 1978-1991; 1982-1984; 1985-1988; 1989-1993. back issues avail. **Document type:** *Academic/Scholarly.* **Description:** Covers techniques in acupuncture medicine.
Related titles: Diskette ed.
Indexed: RefZh.
—GNLM.
Published by: Association Francaise d'Acupuncture, Tour CIT, 3 rue de l'Arrivee, Paris, Cedex 15 75749, France. TEL 33-1-43202626, FAX 33-1-43205446, afa-qibo@imginet.fr, http://members.aol.com:/lishishen/acupuncture. Ed. Gilles Andres. Adv. contact Isabelle Regne.

615.535 613.7 ITA ISSN 1128-4366
SALUTE NATURALE; la nuova via del vivere bene. Variant title: Riza Salute Naturale. Text in Italian. 1999. m. EUR 31 (effective 2005). adv. **Document type:** *Magazine, Consumer.* **Description:** Contains information about natural and holistic medicine.
Published by: Edizioni Riza, Via Luigi Anelli 1, Milan, 20122, Italy. TEL 39-02-5845961, info@riza.it, http://www.riza.it. Ed. Rosalba Pagano. Pub. Liliana Tieger. Circ: 150,000.

615.5 RUS
SAMOLECHENIE. Text in Russian. bi-m. **Document type:** *Journal.*
Published by: NauchTekhLitIzdat, Alymov per, dom 17, str 2, Moscow, 107258, Russian Federation. TEL 7-095-2690004, FAX 7-095-3239010, pribor@tgizdat.ru, http://www.tgizdat.ru/mag/samolech.

615.5 CHE ISSN 1015-0684
CODEN: SZGCA3
SCHWEIZERISCHE ZEITSCHRIFT FUER GANZHEITSMEDIZIN/ JOURNAL SUISSE DE MEDECINE GLOBALE/JOURNAL SUISSE DE MEDECINE HOLISTIQUE. Text in Multiple languages. 1989. 8/yr. CHF 74 domestic; EUR 67 in Europe; CHF 15 newsstand/cover (effective 2005). **Document type:** *Journal, Academic/Scholarly.*
Indexed: AMED, ExcerpMed.
—BLDSC (8122.053000).
Published by: Dr. Becker Media Consulting - Verlag fuer GanzheitsMedizin, Peter Merian-Str 58, Basel, 4002, Switzerland. TEL 41-61-2729009, FAX 41-61-2729008, becker@ganzheitsmedizin.ch, http://www.ganzheitsmedizin.ch. Ed. Stefan Becker. Circ: 8,500 (paid and controlled).

615.5 USA ISSN 1095-0656
R733
➤ **THE SCIENTIFIC REVIEW OF ALTERNATIVE MEDICINE AND ABERRANT MEDICAL PRACTICES.** Text in English. 1997. q. USD 60 domestic to individuals; USD 70 foreign to individuals; USD 100 to institutions (effective 2004). bk.rev. back issues avail. **Document type:** *Journal, Academic/Scholarly.* **Description:** Evaluates the claims of alternative medicine.
Formerly (until 2001): The Scientific Review of Alternative Medicine
Indexed: CINAHL, ExcerpMed.
—BLDSC (8203.914500), IE, ingenta.
Published by: Prometheus Books Inc., 59 John Glenn Dr., Amherst, NY 14228-2197. TEL 716-691-0133, 800-421-0351, FAX 716-691-0137, mfrench@prometheusmail.com. Ed. Dr. Wallace Sampson. Pub. Paul Kurtz.

202.2 HUN ISSN 1216-7827
BL2370.S5
➤ **SHAMAN**; journal of the International Society for Shamanistic Research. Text in English. 1993. s-a. USD 40 to individuals; USD 50 to institutions (effective 2001). adv. bk.rev. abstr.; bibl.; charts; maps. 96 p./no.; back issues avail. **Document type:** *Journal, Academic/Scholarly.* **Description:** An international periodical for the shamanistic studies and as such publishes original articles on shamanism and neighboring fields. In addtion, the journal publishes brief accounts of work in progress, abstracts of dissertations and annoucements of coming events.
Related titles: Online - full content ed.
Indexed: AICP, IBSS.
Published by: Molnar & Kelemen Oriental Publishers, PO Box 1195, Szeged, 6701, Hungary. TEL 36-1-3169947, FAX 36-1-3150461, customtr@elender.hu, http://www.folkscene.hu, http://www.arts.u-szeged.hu/journal/shaman.html. Ed. Mihaly Hoppal. Pub., R&P, Adv. contact Adam Molnar.

615.5 615.328 CHN ISSN 0559-7269
SHANGHAI ZHONGYIYAO ZAZHI/REVISTA DE MEDICINA TRADICIONAL CHINA DE SHANGHAI/REVUE DE MEDECINE TRADITIONNELLE CHINOISE/SHANGHAI JOURNAL OF TRADITIONAL CHINESE MEDICINE. Text in Chinese. m. CNY 48, USD 22.80 per issue (effective 2003). **Document type:** *Academic/Scholarly.*
Related titles: Print ed.: (from WanFang Data Corp.).
Address: 600, Zhongshan North 2nd Street, Shanghai, 200032, China. TEL 86-21-54231274, FAX 86-21-64172934, shzzs@msproxy.shutcm.edu.cn, http://shzyyzz.periodicals.com.cn/default.html. Ed. Bangxian Zhu. **Dist. by:** China International Book Trading Corp, 35 Chegongzhuang Xilu, Haidian District, PO Box 399, Beijing 100044, China. TEL 86-10-68412045, FAX 86-10-68412023, cibtc@mail.cibtc.com.cn, http://www.cibtc.com.cn.

615.5 CHN ISSN 1000-7156
SHANXI ZHONGYI/SHANXI JOURNAL OF TRADITIONAL CHINESE MEDICINE. Text in Chinese. 1985. bi-m. CNY 3.50 newsstand/cover (effective 2001). 64 p./no.; **Document type:** *Academic/Scholarly.* **Description:** Covers the latest development, trends, theories and applications of traditional Chinese medicine.
Related titles: Online - full text ed.: (from East View Information Services).
Published by: (Shanxi Sheng Weisheng Ting), Shanxi Zhongyi Bianjibu, 23 Donghua Men, Taiyuan, Shanxi 030013, China. TEL 86-351-4173499. Ed. Bingyi Qi.

615.5 USA
SHARE GUIDE; the holistic health magazine. Text in English. 1989. bi-m. (on-line ed. w.). USD 14 domestic; USD 22 foreign (effective 2001). adv. bk.rev.; music rev.; software rev.; video rev. tr.lit. 116 p./no.; back issues avail. **Document type:** *Magazine, Consumer.* **Description:** A holistic health magazine focusing on alternative medicine, personal growth, and environmental awareness.
Related titles: CD-ROM ed.; Online - full text ed.: 1995.
Published by: The Share Guide, 453 Benicia Dr, Santa Rosa, CA 95409-3003. TEL 707-538-0558, 877-488-4938, FAX 707-538-0552, share@shareguide.com, http://www.shareguide.com. Ed., R&P Janice Hughes. Pubs. Dennis Hughes, Janice Hughes. Adv. contact Dennis Hughes. B&W page USD 899, color page USD 1,500; trim 11 x 8.5. Circ: 30,000.

SHIZHEN GUOYI GUOYAO/LISHIZHEN MEDICINE AND MATERIA MEDICA RESEARCH. see *PHARMACY AND PHARMACOLOGY*

615.5 CHN ISSN 1000-3649
SICHUAN ZHONGYI/SICHUAN JOURNAL OF TRADITIONAL CHINESE MEDICINE. Text in Chinese. m.
Related titles: Online - full text ed.: (from East View Information Services).
Published by: Zhonghua Quanguo ZhongYi Xuehui, Sichuan Fenhui/Chinese National Society for Traditional Chinese Medicine, Sichuan Branch, 80, Wenmiao Xijie, Chengdu, Sichuan 610041, China. TEL 26595. Ed. Jin Jiajun.

SPIRIT & DESTINY; for women who want the best possible future. see *WOMEN'S INTERESTS*

615.852 USA ISSN 1080-3262
SPIRITUAL MASSAGE MINISTRY NEWSLETTER. Text in English. 1995. q. looseleaf. USD 25; USD 30 foreign (effective 1999). bk.rev. index. back issues avail. **Document type:** *Newsletter.* **Description:** Provides information about different types of spiritual healing to laymen, clergymen, and other professionals concerned with health and the healing arts.
Media: Online - full text.
Published by: Church for Spiritual Healing and Health, Spiritual Massage Healing Ministry, 6907 Sherman St, Philadelphia, PA 19119. TEL 215-842-0265, FAX 215-842-2388, aschatz@unix.temple.edu, http://ww.healingandlaw.com. Ed., Pub., R&P Rev. Albert Schatz. Circ: 300.

615.535 299 USA ISSN 1520-5444
SPIRITUALITY & HEALTH; the soul body connection. Text in English. 1998. bi-m. USD 24.95 domestic; USD 29.95 in Canada; USD 34.95 elsewhere; USD 4.95 newsstand/cover domestic; USD 6.75 newsstand/cover in Canada (effective 2004). adv. bk.rev.; film rev.; music rev.; video rev. 72 p./no.; **Document type:** *Magazine, Consumer.* **Description:** Chronicles the spiritual renaissance of the 21st century and the connection between spirituality and personal well-being in its broadest sense. Explores all aspects of personal growth including spiritual beliefs, music, media and the arts, and provides practical resources for individual exploration and practice.
Published by: Spirituality and Health Publishing, Inc., 74 Trinity Place, New York, NY 10006-2088. TEL 212-602-0705, FAX 212-602-0726, editor@spiritualityhealth.com, http://www.spiritualityhealth.com. Ed. Robert Owens Scott. Pub., Adv. contact Peter D Wild TEL 212-602-0772. R&P Betsy Robinson TEL 212-602-0706. page USD 3,500; 8.5 x 11. Circ: 70,000 (paid); 10,000 (controlled). **Dist. by:** Ingram Periodicals, PO Box 7000, La Vergne, TN 37086-7000.

615.535 299 GBR ISSN 1743-1867
▼ **SPIRITUALITY AND HEALTH INTERNATIONAL.** Text in English. 2004. q. USD 280 to institutions; USD 308 combined subscription to institutions print & online eds. (effective 2006). **Document type:** *Journal, Academic/Scholarly.*
Related titles: Online - full text ed.: ISSN 1557-0665. USD 280 (effective 2006).
—CCC.
Published by: John Wiley & Sons Ltd. (Subsidiary of: John Wiley & Sons, Inc.), The Atrium, Southern Gate, Chichester, West Sussex PO19 8SQ, United Kingdom. TEL 44-1243-779777, FAX 44-1243-775878, cs-journals@wiley.co.uk, http://www.wiley.co.uk.

615.5 SWE ISSN 1104-5477
SVENSK TIDSKRIFT FOER MEDICINSK AKUPUNKTUR. Text in Swedish. 1993. q. SEK 200; SEK 55 newsstand/cover (effective 2000 & 2001). **Document type:** *Trade.*
Published by: (Legitimerade Sjukskoeterskors Akupunkturfoerening), Via Media, PO Box 640, Landskrona, 26125, Sweden. TEL 46-418-10780, FAX 46-418-12394, viamedia@nornemark.com, http://www.nornemark.com/viamedia. Ed. Katarina Johansson. Circ: 2,100 (paid).
Co-sponsor: Svensk Laekarefoerening foer Akupunktur.

TAI CHI & ALTERNATIVE HEALTH. see *ASIAN STUDIES*

615.5 USA ISSN 1548-2030
▼ **TAKE-CARE CONNECTIONS**; holistic & natural strategies for bettering self & surroundings. Text in English. 2003 (Jun.). 10/yr. USD 15 (effective 2004).
Published by: Take-Care Communications, LLC, P. O. Box 5610, Hillsborough, NJ 08844. TEL 908-874-0237, http://www.takecareconnections.com. Ed. Sheila Cohill. Pubs. Ken Schneider, Sheila Cohill. Adv. contact Ken Schneider.

615.537 ITA
TERAPIE NATURALI E ERBE. Text in Italian. 1984. m. USD 70. adv. **Document type:** *Magazine, Consumer.*
Former titles: Erbe e Terapie Naturali; Erbe Secondo Natura
Published by: Stampa Natura Solidarieta SpA, Via Antonio Bazzini, 40, Milan, MI 20131, Italy. TEL 39-02-26680654, FAX 39-02-26680664. Circ: 40,000.

TIJDSCHRIFT VOOR CREATIEVE THERAPIE. see *PSYCHOLOGY*

615.82 NLD ISSN 0928-0065
➤ **TIJDSCHRIFT VOOR INTEGRALE GENEESKUNDE.** Text in Dutch; Summaries in Dutch, English. 1984. bi-m. EUR 50; EUR 30 to students (effective 2005). adv. bk.rev. back issues avail. **Document type:** *Academic/Scholarly.* **Description:** Publishes studies of fundamental and applied research relating to complementary medicine, alternative medicine, homeopathy, health policy and developments in diagnosis and other branches of the medical sciences.
Formerly (until 1992): Nederlands Tijdschrift voor Integrale Geneeskunde (0169-0701)
—IE, Infotrieve.
Published by: Stichting Tijdschrift voor Integrale Geneeskunde, Postbus 133, Harderwijk, 3840 AC, Netherlands. TEL 31-341-414231, http://www.tigweb.nl/tig/info/. Ed. B Wiegant.

615.5 USA ISSN 1525-4283
TOWNSEND LETTER FOR DOCTORS & PATIENTS. Text in English. 1983. 10/yr. USD 57 in state in Washington state; USD 54 out of state; USD 79 in Canada & Mexico; USD 117 rest of world; USD 38 in state to students in Wahington state; USD 36 out of state to students; USD 66 in Canada & Mexico to students (effective 2004). adv. bk.rev. **Document type:** *Consumer.*
Formerly (until 1995): Townsend Letter for Doctors (1059-5864)
Related titles: Online - full text ed.: (from EBSCO Publishing, Florida Center for Library Automation, Gale Group, O C L C Online Computer Library Center, Inc.).
Indexed: AMED.
—BLDSC (8873.005110), IE, ingenta.
Address: 911 Tyler St, Port Townsend, WA 98368-6541. TEL 360-385-6021, FAX 360-385-0699, editorial@townsendletter.com, info@townsendletter.com, http://www.townsendletter.com Eds. Irene Alleger, Dr. Jonathan Collin. Pub. Dr. Jonathan Collin. R&P, Adv. contact Barbara Smith. Circ: 6,000 (paid).

TRAGER NEWSLETTER. see *MEDICAL SCIENCES—Physical Medicine And Rehabilitation*

610 CAN
TURFSEER'S ALTERNATIVE HEALTH AND BUSINESS OPPORTUNITIES NEWSLETTER. Text in English. bi-m. **Document type:** *Newsletter.* **Description:** Focuses on drug-free natural healing and alternative medicine using natural remedies.
Media: Online - full text.
Address: Canada. Turfseer@aol.com, http://hartley.on.ca/turfseer. Pub. Lewis Papier.

613.7 613.2 CAN ISSN 1180-0291
VITALITY MAGAZINE; Toronto's monthly wellness journal. Text in English. 1989. m. (10/yr.). CND 30 domestic; CND 35 in United States; CND 40 elsewhere. adv. **Document type:** *Consumer.* **Description:** Covers holistic health, nutritional medicine, self development, news and reviews of events and services in Toronto.
Address: 356 Dupont St, Toronto, ON M5R 1V9, Canada. TEL 416-964-0528. Ed. Julia Woodford. Adv. contact Jody Hatt. Circ: 44,000 (controlled).

615.5 USA
VOICE OF NAPRAPATHY. Text in English. 1955. irreg., latest vol.82, 1988. back issues avail. **Description:** A forum for practitioners of naprapathy, a system of manipulation administered by the hands.
Published by: American Naprapathic Association, 5321 N Central Ave, Chicago, IL 60630. TEL 312-685-6020. Ed. Ray Webster. Circ: 5,000. **Subscr. to:** 5913 W Montrose Ave, Chicago, IL 60634. **Co-sponsor:** Illinois Naprapathic Association.

WEED WORLD. see *DRUG ABUSE AND ALCOHOLISM*

615.5 GBR ISSN 1352-1241
WHAT DOCTORS DON'T TELL YOU✶. Text in English. 1989. m. USD 47, GBP 27 (effective 2004). bk.rev. abstr. back issues avail. **Document type:** *Academic/Scholarly.* **Description:** Criticizes conventional medicine and shows its failings through scientific evidence.
Indexed: AMED.
—BLDSC (9309.679050), IE, ingenta.
Address: 2 salisbury Rd, London, SW19 4EZ, United Kingdom. TEL 44-870-4449886, FAX 44-870-4449887, cs@wddty,co,uk, http://www.wddty.co.uk. Ed. Lynne McTaggart. Pub. Bryan Hubbard.

WHOLENESS. see *RELIGIONS AND THEOLOGY*

615.5 615.328 CHN ISSN 0256-7415
XINZHONGYI/NEW JOURNAL OF TRADITIONAL CHINESE MEDICINE. Text in Chinese. 1969. m. CNY 42 (effective 1999). **Document type:** *Academic/Scholarly.* **Description:** Covers theory and clinical practice of traditional Chinese medicine.
Related titles: Online - full text ed.: (from East View Information Services).
—BLDSC (6084.322000).
Published by: Guangzhou Zhongyiyao Daxue/Guangzhou University of Traditional Chinese Medicine, 12, Jichang Lu, Guangzhou, Guangdong 510405, China. TEL 86-20-86591233, FAX 86-20-86594735, xbgutcm@ihw.com.cn. Ed. Li Renxian. adv.: B&W page USD 5,000. Circ: 80,000. **Dist. overseas by:** China International Book Trading Corp, 35 Chegongzhuang Xilu, Haidian District, PO Box 399, Beijing 100044, China.

615.53 CAN ISSN 1488-0253
YOUR LIFE - YOUR CHOICE. Text in English. 1997. s-m. free. adv. back issues avail. **Document type:** *Newsletter.* **Description:** Discusses the choices available with alternative medicine.
Media: Online - full text. **Related titles:** E-mail ed.
Address: 188 Gammage St, London, ON N5Y 2B3, Canada. TEL 519-645-7797, yourlife@life-choices.com, http://www.life-choices.com. Ed., Pub., R&P Brigitte Synesael. Circ: 3,000.

615.5 615.328 CHN ISSN 0255-2914
R97.7.C5
YUNNAN ZHONGYI ZAZHI/YUNNAN JOURNAL OF TRADITIONAL CHINESE MEDICINE. Text in Chinese. 1980. bi-m. USD 0.80 per issue. adv. **Document type:** *Academic/Scholarly.* **Description:** Covers scientific researches, theories and clinical practices in traditional Chinese medicine, medical materials, acupuncture, and moxibustion.
Related titles: CD-ROM ed.
Indexed: ExtraMED.
Published by: Yunnan Sheng Zhongyi Zhongyao Yanjiusuo/Yunnan Research Institute of Traditional Chinese Medicine and Material Medica, Lianhua Chi, Kunming, Yunnan 650223, China. TEL 5154494. Ed. Zhang Zhen. Adv. contact Zhao Hua. **Dist. overseas by:** China International Book Trading Corp, 35 Chegongzhuang Xilu, Haidian District, PO Box 399, Beijing 100044, China.

615.5 DEU ISSN 0044-3182
ZEITSCHRIFT FUER NATURHEILKUNDE. Text in German. 1949. m. EUR 27.61; EUR 2.30 newsstand/cover (effective 2005). adv. bk.rev. **Document type:** *Magazine, Consumer.*
Published by: Berufsverband der Heilpraktiker Nordrhein-Westfalen e.V., Kasernenstr 26, Solingen, 42651, Germany. TEL 49-212-47285, FAX 49-212-42711, redaktion@verlag-zfn.de, http://www.verlag-zfn.de/html/zfn.html. Circ: 5,800.

615.892 DEU ISSN 1430-4783
ZEITSCHRIFT FUER QIGONG YANGSHENG. Text in German. 1993. a. EUR 14.40 newsstand/cover (effective 2003). **Document type:** *Magazine, Consumer.*
Published by: Medizinisch Literarische Verlagsgesellschaft mbH, Postfach 1151-1152, Uelzen, 29501, Germany. TEL 49-581-808151, FAX 49-581-808158, mlverlag@mlverlag.de, http://www.mlverlag.de.

615.5 615.328 CHN ISSN 0411-8421
ZHEJIANG ZHONGYI ZAZHI/ZHEJIANG JOURNAL OF TRADITIONAL CHINESE MEDICINE. Text in Chinese. 1956. m. CNY 3.50 per issue domestic (effective 2000). back issues avail. **Document type:** *Academic/Scholarly.*
Related titles: CD-ROM ed.; Online - full text ed.: (from East View Information Services).
Indexed: ExtraMED.
Published by: Zhejiang-sheng Zhongyiyao Yanjiuyuan/Zhejiang Academy of Traditional Chinese Medicine, Tianmushan Lu 26 Hao, Hangzhou, Zhejiang 310007, China. TEL 86-571-8842882, FAX 86-571-8845196. Ed. Yi Cheng Chen. **Dist. overseas by:** China International Book Trading Corp, 35 Chegongzhuang Xilu, Haidian District, PO Box 399, Beijing 100044, China.

615.892 CHN ISSN 1000-0607
ZHENCI YANJIU/ACUPUNCTURE RESEARCH. Text in Chinese. 1976. q. CNY 32 (effective 2004). **Document type:** *Journal, Academic/Scholarly.*
Formerly (until 1979): Zhenci Mazui (1000-7814)
Related titles: Online - full text ed.: (from East View Information Services).
Indexed: MEDLINE.
—BLDSC (0677.953000), IE, Infotrieve, ingenta.
Published by: Zhongguo Zhongyi Yanjiuyuan/Chinese Academy of Traditional Chinese Medicine, 18 Bei Xincang, Beijing, 100700, China. TEL 86-10-84034459, FAX 86-10-64013968, wangshaorong@263.net, cintcm@mail.cintcm.ac.cn, http://www.cintcm.com/magazine/FMS/lanmu/zhenciyanjiu/zhenciyanjiu_jianjie.htm, http://www.cintcm.ac.cn/. **Dist. by:** China International Book Trading Corp, 35 Chegongzhuang Xilu, Haidian District, PO Box 399, Beijing 100044, China. TEL 86-10-68412045, FAX 86-10-68412023, cibtc@mail.cibtc.com.cn, http://www.cibtc.com.cn.

ZHONGCAOYAO/CHINESE TRADITIONAL AND HERBAL DRUGS. see *MEDICAL SCIENCES*

615.5 CHN ISSN 1007-5798
ZHONGGUO MINJIAN LIAOFA/CHINA'S NATUROPATHY. Text in Chinese. 1993. m. USD 30; CNY 4.80, USD 2.50 newsstand/cover (effective 2001). **Document type:** *Academic/Scholarly.*
Related titles: Online - full content ed.: (from WanFang Data Corp.); Online - full text ed.: (from East View Information Services).
Published by: Zhongguo Zhongyiyao Chubanshe, Zhaoyang Qu, 7, Dongxing Lu, Beijing, 100027, China. **Dist. by:** China International Book Trading Corp, 35 Chegongzhuang Xilu, Haidian District, PO Box 399, Beijing 100044, China. TEL 86-10-68412045, FAX 86-10-68412023, cibtc@mail.cibtc.com.cn, http://www.cibtc.com.cn.

615.5 CHN ISSN 1672-3651
▼ **ZHONGGUO TIANRAN YAOWU/CHINESE JOURNAL OF NATRUAL MEDICINES.** Text in Chinese. 2003. bi-m. CNY 90 (effective 2005). **Document type:** *Journal, Academic/Scholarly.*
Related titles: Online - full text ed.
—BLDSC (9512.818000).
Address: 24, Tongjia Xiang, Nanjing, 210009, China. TEL 81-25-83271565, FAX 81-25-83271229, zgtryw@sohu.com, http://zgtryw.periodicals.net.cn/. Ed. Guo-Jun Xu. **Dist. by:** China International Book Trading Corp, 35 Chegongzhuang Xilu, Haidian District, PO Box 399, Beijing 100044, China. TEL 86-10-68412045, FAX 86-10-68412023, cibtc@mail.cibtc.com.cn, http://www.cibtc.com.cn.

615.892 CHN
ZHONGGUO ZHENJIU/CHINESE ACUPUNCTURE AND MOXIBUSTION. Text in Chinese; Abstracts in English. 1981. m. USD 32.40 (effective 2001); USD 2.70 newsstand/cover.
Published by: (China Academy of Traditional Chinese Medicine), Zhongguo Zhenjiu Zazhishe, Dongzhimennei, Beijing, 100700, China. TEL 86-1-84014607. **Dist. by:** China International Book Trading Corp, 35 Chegongzhuang Xilu, Haidian District, PO Box 399, Beijing 100044, China. TEL 86-10-68412045, FAX 86-10-68412023, cibtc@mail.cibtc.com.cn, http://www.cibtc.com.cn. **Co-sponsor:** Chinese Society of Acupuncture and Moxibustion.

ZHONGGUO ZHONGYAO ZAZHI/CHINA JOURNAL OF CHINESE MATERIA MEDICA. see *PHARMACY AND PHARMACOLOGY*

ZHONGHUA YANGSHENG BAOJIAN/CHINESE BREATH EXERCISE. see *PHYSICAL FITNESS AND HYGIENE*

615.5 CHN ISSN 1003-305X
R812
ZHONGYI JIAOYU/EDUCATION OF TRADITIONAL CHINESE MEDICINE. Text in Chinese. 1982. bi-m. CNY 30 (effective 2004). **Document type:** *Journal, Academic/Scholarly.* **Description:** Covers all aspects of education of traditional Chinese medicine.
Related titles: Online - full text ed.: (from East View Information Services, WanFang Data Corp.).
Published by: Beijing Zhongyiyao Daxue/Beijing University of Chinese Medicine, 11 Bei San Huan Dong Lu, Chao Yang District, Beijing, 100029, China. TEL 86-10-64286602, bucmpo@public.bta.net.cn, http://zyjy.periodicals.net.cn/default.html, http://www.bjucmp.edu.cn/. **Dist. overseas by:** China International Book Trading Corp, 35 Chegongzhuang Xilu, Haidian District, PO Box 399, Beijing 100044, China.

615.5 615.328 CHN ISSN 1001-1668
ZHONGYI ZAZHI. Text in Chinese. 1955. m. CNY 91.60 (effective 2004).
Formerly (until 1978): Xin Yiyaoxue Zazhi (0376-656X)
Related titles: ♦ Spanish ed.: Revista de la Medicina Tradicional China. ISSN 1130-4405; English ed.: Journal of Traditional Chinese Medicine. ISSN 0255-2922. 1981.
Indexed: IndMed, RefZh.
—CISTI, Linda Hall.
Published by: Zhongguo Zhongyi Yanjiuyuan/Chinese Academy of Traditional Chinese Medicine, 18 Bei Xincang, Beijing, 100700, China. TEL 86-10-64035632, FAX 86-10-86472013, jtcm@public3.bta.net.cn, http://www.jtcm.net.cn/, http://www.cintcm.ac.cn/. **Dist. by:** China International Book Trading Corp, 35 Chegongzhuang Xilu, Haidian District, PO Box 399, Beijing 100044, China. TEL 86-10-68412045, FAX 86-10-68412023, cibtc@mail.cibtc.com.cn, http://www.cibtc.com.cn.

ZHONGYI ZHENGGU/JOURNAL OF TRADITIONAL CHINESE ORTHOPEDICS AND TRAUMATOLOGY. see *MEDICAL SCIENCES—Orthopedics And Traumatology*

ZHONGYIYAO XINXI/INFORMATION ON TRADITIONAL CHINESE MEDICINE. see *MEDICAL SCIENCES*

ALTERNATIVE MEDICINE—Abstracting, Bibliographies, Statistics

615.5 GBR
A M E D. (Allied and Complementary Medicine Database) Text in English. base vol. plus m. updates. price varies per Online Service Provider. index. **Document type:** *Abstract/Index.* **Description:** Covers the fields of allied and complementary medicine with references to articles from 400 journals. Coverage is strongly European with the majority of titles in English. Includes coverage of complementary medicine, physiotherapy, occupational therapy, rehabilitation and podiatry.
Media: Online - full content (from Data-Star, SilverPlatter Information, Inc.). **Related titles:** CD-ROM ed.
Published by: British Library, Health Care Information Service, British Library, Boston Spa, Wetherby, W Yorks LS23 7BQ, United Kingdom. TEL 44-1937-546520, les.wilkinson@bl.uk, http://www.bl.uk/collections/health/amed.html.

016.613 USA
ALT-HEALTH WATCH; alternative health & wellness. Text in English. bi-m. **Document type:** *Abstract/Index.* **Description:** Focuses on the many perspectives of complementary, holistic and integrated approaches to healthcare and wellness. Offers a resource of nearly 50,000 articles.
Media: Online - full text.
Published by: EBSCO Publishing (Subsidiary of: EBSCO Industries, Inc.), 10 Estes St, PO Box 682, Ipswich, MA 01938-0682. TEL 978-356-6500, 800-653-2726, FAX 978-356-6565, ep@epnet.com, http://www.epnet.com. **Subscr. to:** Subscription Services, PO Box 1943, Birmingham, AL 35201-1943. TEL 205-991-6600, FAX 205-995-1518.

016.615 CHN ISSN 1003-3521
➤ **ZHONGGUO YAOXUE WENZHAI/CHINESE PHARMACEUTICAL ABSTRACTS.** Text in Chinese. 1982. m. USD 250. adv. **Document type:** *Abstract/Index.* **Description:** Published on the basis of the Traditional Chinese Medicines (TCMs) Contemporary Literature Database, as well as abstracts in modern drugs in China. Covers 420 current domestic medical journals.
Published by: Guojia Yiyao Guanli-ju, Keji Qingbao Yanjiusuo/State Pharmaceutical Administration of China, Science and Technology Information Research Institute, A-38 Beilishilu, Beijing, 100810, China. TEL 86-10-6831-3344, FAX 86-10-6831-1978. Ed. Fengwen Guo.

➤ **ZHONGGUO YIXUE WENZHAI (ZHONGYI)/CHINA MEDICAL ABSTRACTS (TRADITIONAL MEDICINE SCIENCE).** see *MEDICAL SCIENCES—Abstracting, Bibliographies, Statistics*

ANAESTHESIOLOGY

see MEDICAL SCIENCES—Anaesthesiology

ANALYTICAL CHEMISTRY

see CHEMISTRY—Analytical Chemistry

ANIMAL WELFARE

see also PETS

➤ **A I F NEWSLETTER.** see *AGRICULTURE—Poultry And Livestock*

636.0832 636.089 AUS ISSN 1039-9089
A N Z C C A R T NEWS. Variant title: Anzccart News. Text in English. 1988. q. free. bk.rev.; Website rev. 20 p./no.; back issues avail.; reprints avail. **Document type:** *Newsletter, Academic/Scholarly.*
Formerly (until 1993): A C C A R T News
Indexed: AbHyg, AgBio, AnBrAb, HelmAb, IndVet, PN&I, PoultAb, ProtozoAb, RM&VM.
Published by: Australian and New Zealand Council for the Care of Animals in Research and Teaching Limited, Dept. of Environmental Biology, University of Adelaide, Adelaide, SA 5005, Australia. TEL 61-8-8303-7586, FAX 61-8-8303-7587, anzccart@adelaide.edu.au, http://www.adelaide.edu.au/anzccart/. Ed. Dr. Robert Baker. Circ: 6,000.

636.0832 USA ISSN 1554-6624
▼ **A S P C A ACTION.** (American Society for the Prevention of Cruelty to Animals) Text in English. 2005 (Spr.). q.
Published by: American Society for the Prevention of Cruelty to Animals, 424 E 92nd St, New York, NY 10128. TEL 212-876-7700, information@aspca.org, http://www.aspca.org.

179.3 USA ISSN 1521-6381
A S P C A ANIMAL WATCH. Text in English. 1947. q. USD 20 to members. bk.rev. illus.; stat. 52 p./no.; back issues avail. **Document type:** *Magazine, Consumer.* **Description:** Animal welfare issues and features on care of companion animals, as well as wild animals.
Formerly (until 1992): A S P C A Report; Supersedes (in 1981): A S P C A Bulletin; Which superseded (in 1977): Animal Protection (0003-357X)
Published by: American Society for the Prevention of Cruelty to Animals, 345 Park Ave South 9th Fl, New York, NY 10010-1707. TEL 212-876-7700, FAX 212-410-0087, editor@aspca.org, http://www.aspca.org/calendar/watch.htm. Ed. Marion S Lane. Pub. Larry Hawk. Circ: 330,000.

179.3 179.4 USA ISSN 0274-7774
HV4701
THE A V MAGAZINE. Text in English. 1892. q. USD 20 to members (effective 1999). bk.rev. charts; illus. back issues avail.; reprints avail. **Document type:** *Consumer.* **Description:** Seeks to end experiments using animals and promote humane research by awarding grants for work not involving animals.
Formerly: A-V (0001-2831)
Published by: American Anti-Vivisection Society, Noble Plaza, Ste 204, 801 Old York Rd, Jenkintown, PA 19046. TEL 215-887-0816, FAX 215-887-2088, aavsonline@aol.com, http://www.aavs.org/. Ed. Tina Nelson. Circ: 11,000.

636.0832 USA ISSN 1082-9644
A W I C RESOURCE SERIES. (Animal Welfare Information Center) Text in English. 1995. irreg. **Document type:** *Monographic series.*
Indexed: AnBrAb, IndVet, PoultAb, VetBull.
—BLDSC (1840.618300).
Published by: U.S. Department of Agriculture, National Agricultural Library, Animal Welfare Information Center, 10301 Baltimore Blvd, 4th Fl, Beltsville, MD 20705-2351. TEL 301-504-6212, FAX 301-504-7125, awic@nal.usda.gov, http://www.nal.usda.gov/awic/pubs/awicdocs.htm.

179.3 179.4 USA ISSN 1071-1384
A W I QUARTERLY. Text in English. 1951. q. USD 25 (effective 2005); free to qualified personnel. bk.rev. illus. reprints avail. **Document type:** *Newsletter.* **Description:** Reports on current animal welfare issues, including treatment of captive animals in laboratories, commercial trade, factory farms, and traplines, laws and treaties affecting animals.
Former titles (until 1992): Animal Welfare Institute Quarterly (0743-0841); (until 1981): Animal Welfare Institute Information Report (0003-3596)
Indexed: Agr.
Published by: Animal Welfare Institute, PO Box 3650, Washington, DC 20007. TEL 202-337-2332, FAX 202-338-9478, awi@awionline.org, http://www.awionline.org, Ed. Christine Stevens. Circ: 4,000 (paid); 15,000 (controlled).

179.3 USA
ACTION ALERT (NEW YORK). Text in English. 1973. irreg. USD 15 membership (effective 2004). bk.rev. back issues avail. **Document type:** *Newsletter.* **Description:** Fashion column encourages and assists people in pursuing their fashion goals with clothing not involving suffering, confinement or death of animals.
Published by: Beauty Without Cruelty U S A, 175 W 12th St, Ste 16G, New York, NY 10011-8275. TEL 212-989-8073, FAX 212-989-8073, beautywocruelty@aol.com. Ed., Pub., R&P Ethel Thurston. Circ: 7,000 (paid and controlled).

179.3 179.4 AUS
ACTION MAGAZINE; the animal's voice. Text in English. 1980. s-a. AUD 20 domestic; AUD 40 foreign (effective 2000). adv. bk.rev.; video rev. back issues avail. **Document type:** *Consumer.*
Former titles: Action (Elwood); (until 1993): Animal Liberation; (until 1985): Outcry (Glen Iris) (0725-9700)
Published by: Action, PO Box 15, Elwood, VIC 3184, Australia. TEL 61-3-9531-4367, FAX 61-3-9531-4257, amag@netspace.net.au. Ed., Pub., R&P Patty Mark. Circ: 3,000.

636.0832 USA ISSN 1072-2068
HV4701
ACT'IONLINE. Variant title: Action Line (Darien). Text in English. 1977. q. USD 25 (effective 2001). adv. bk.rev. illus. Index. reprints avail. **Document type:** *Newsletter.* **Description:** Works to protect animals from cruelty, abuse and institutionalized exploitation.
Former titles: Friends of Animals Reports; Animals (New York); Actionline
Published by: Friends of Animals, Inc., 777 Post Rd, Ste 205, Darien, CT 06820-4721. TEL 203-656-1522, FAX 203-656-0267, contact@friendsofanimals.org, http://www.friendsofanimals.org. Ed., R&P Priscilla Feral. Circ: 200,000.

179.3 USA ISSN 1040-2225
ADVOCATE (ENGLEWOOD). Text in English. 1952. q. USD 15 (effective 1999). adv. illus.; stat. reprints avail. **Document type:** *Consumer.* **Description:** Informs readers of the Association's progress in protecting animals.
Former titles (until 1983): National Animal Protection Newsletter; Animal Protection News; Which was formed by the merger of: National Humane Review (0027-948X); Animal Shelter Shoptalk (0027-9471); National Humane Newsletter; National Humane Shoptalk (0027-9498); American Humane Association Annual Report; American Humane Association. National Humane Report (0065-8596)
Indexed: Agr.
Published by: American Humane Association, Animal Protection Division, 63 Inverness Dr E, Englewood, CO 80112-5117. TEL 303-792-9900, FAX 303-792-5333, http://www.amerhumane.org. Ed. Roxanne Hawn. Adv. contact Roxanne Ayala. Circ: 35,000.

179.3 179.4 GBR
ADVOCATES FOR ANIMALS. ANNUAL PICTORIAL REVIEW. Text in English. 1912. a., latest 2001. free. adv. bk.rev. back issues avail. **Document type:** *Bulletin.*
Formerly (until 1990): Scottish Society for Prevention of Vivisection. Annual Pictorial Review (0080-8210)
Published by: Advocates for Animals, 10 Queensferry St, Edinburgh, EH2 4PG, United Kingdom. TEL 44-131-225-6039, FAX 44-131-220-6377, advocates.animals@virgin.net, http://www.advocatesforanimals.org.uk. Ed., Pub., R&P, Adv. contact Les Ward. Circ: 10,000.

333.72 USA
ALIVE (MILWAUKEE). Text in English. q. USD 35 to members. charts; illus.; maps. **Description:** Covers animal research, conservation, and news and events of the society.
Published by: Zoological Society of Milwaukee County, 10005 W Bluemound Rd, Milwaukee, WI 53226-4383. TEL 414-258-2333, FAX 414-258-6311. Ed. Patricia Harrigan Mills.

179.3 USA
HV4702
ALLANIMALS. Text in English. 1954. q. USD 25 membership (effective 2005). illus. **Document type:** *Magazine, Consumer.* **Description:** Contains helpful advice on caring for animals and suggestions for helping animals in need.
Former titles (until 1999): H S U S News (1059-1621); Humane Society News; Humane Society of the United States. News (0018-733X)
Indexed: WildRev.
Published by: (Humane Society of the United States), Time, Inc (Subsidiary of: Time Warner, Inc.), Time & Life Bldg,, Rockefeller Center, 29th Fl, 1271 Ave of the Americas, New York, NY 10020-1393. TEL 212-522-1212, http://www.hsus.org/press_and_publications/humane_society_magazines_and_newsletters/all_animals, http://www.timeinc.com. Circ: 450,000.

ALTEX. see *MEDICAL SCIENCES—Experimental Medicine, Laboratory Technique*

179.3 GBR ISSN 1354-7437
ANIMAL ACTION. Text in English. 1975. bi-m. GBP 5.40; GBP 6.90 foreign; GBP 1.30 newsstand/cover (effective 2001). adv. illus. reprints avail. **Document type:** *Consumer.* **Description:** Covers all aspects of animal welfare and the work of the Royal Society for young people.
Former titles (until 1994): Animal World (0968-2147); (until 1981): Animal Ways
Published by: Royal Society for the Prevention of Cruelty to Animals, Wilberforce Way, Oakhurst Business Park, Southwater, Horsham, W Sussex RH13 7WN, United Kingdom. TEL 44-707-5335-999, 0870-010-1181, FAX 44-1403-241048, publications@rspca.org.uk, http://www.rspca.org.uk. Ed. Michaela Miller. Adv. contact Tom Glenister TEL 44-20-7389-0808. B&W page GBP 600, color page GBP 950; trim 210 x 297. Circ: 75,000. **Dist. by:** Comag, Tavistock Works, Tavistock Rd, W Drayton, Middx UB7 7QX, United Kingdom. TEL 44-1895-433800.

179.3 USA ISSN 1045-9979
ANIMAL ACTIVIST ALERT. Text in English. 1983. q. free to members. illus. back issues avail. **Document type:** *Newsletter.* **Description:** Provides information on how readers can act (write letters, make calls) on behalf of animals in emergency situations.
Published by: Humane Society of the United States, 2100 L St, N W, Washington, DC 20037. TEL 202-452-1100, http://www.hsus.org/pubs.html. Ed. Ann Stockho. Circ: 10,000.

179.3 ZAF ISSN 0379-654X
ANIMAL ANTI-CRUELTY LEAGUE. CHAIRMAN'S REPORT. Text in English. 1972. a. ZAR 10 (effective 1999). **Document type:** *Corporate.*
Published by: Animal Anti-Cruelty League, PO Box 7, Rosettenville, 2130, South Africa. TEL 27-11-435-0672, FAX 27-11-435-0693, aaclnbod@lafrica.com, http://www.satis.co.za/aacl. Ed. Tony Guia.

179.4 179.3 GBR
ANIMAL CONCERN. ANNUAL REPORT; for the total abolition of animal exploitation. Text in English. a. GBP 10 (effective 2005). adv. **Document type:** *Newsletter, Consumer.* **Description:** Advocates the total abolition of live animal research and the promotion of animal rights.
Formerly: Scottish Anti-Vivisection Society. Annual Report
Published by: Animal Concern Ltd., PO Box 5178, Dumbarton, G82 5YJ, United Kingdom. TEL 44-1389-841639, FAX 44-1389-841639, animals@jfrobins.force9.co.uk, http://www.animalconcern.com/. Ed., Pub., R&P, Adv. contact John F Robins.

179.4 179.3 GBR
ANIMAL CONCERN NEWS; campaigning for the exploited. Text in English. 1981. q. GBP 10 waged; GBP 5 unwaged; GBP 2 under 16; GBP 100 lifetime (effective 2005); (free on newstands). adv. bk.rev. **Document type:** *Newsletter, Consumer.* **Description:** Reports on the welfare of animals in zoos, parks, and laboratories and the action the organization is taking on their behalf. Advises the public on action they should take.
Former titles (until 1988): S A V S News; Scottish Anti-Vivisection Society. Newsletter (0261-2089)
Related titles: Online - full text ed.
Published by: Animal Concern Ltd., PO Box 5178, Dumbarton, G82 5YJ, United Kingdom. TEL 44-1389-841639, FAX 44-1389-841639, animals@jfrobins.force9.co.uk, http://www.animalconcern.com/. Ed., Pub., R&P, Adv. contact John F Robins. Circ: 400.

179.4 GBR
ANIMAL CONCERN NEWS UPDATE. Text in English. 1994. q. GBP 10; GBP 5 unwaged; GBP 2 under 16; GBP 100 lifetime (effective 2000). illus. **Document type:** *Bulletin, Consumer.* **Description:** Alerts persons concerned with animal welfare to important events and political action steps they can take.
Published by: Animal Concern Ltd., PO Box 5178, Dumbarton, G82 5YJ, United Kingdom. TEL 44-1389-841639, FAX 44-1389-841639, animals@jfrobins.force9.co.uk. R&P John F Robins.

179.3 CAN ISSN 1204-6639
ANIMAL DEFENCE LEAGUE OF CANADA. BULLETIN. Text in English. 1957. 2/yr. free. bk.rev. **Document type:** *Bulletin.* **Description:** Promotes animal rights/welfare, increases public awareness of oppression of animals, and how to prevent or alleviate animal exploitation, cruelty and suffering.
Formerly (until 1992): Animal Defence League of Canada. News Bulletin (0044-829X)
Published by: Animal Defence League of Canada, Sta C, P O Box 3880, Ottawa, ON K1Y 4M5, Canada. http://www.ncf.ca/animal-defence. Circ: 2,500.

636.032 GBR ISSN 0961-9518
ANIMAL DEFENDERS INTERNATIONAL. Text in English. 1986. q. GBP 17 domestic; GBP 30 foreign. adv. **Document type:** *Magazine, Consumer.* **Description:** Details the activities of the organization, an animal welfare and conservation group specializing in animal rescues and anti-circus campaigning.
Supersedes in part (in 1990): Campaigner and Animal's Defender (0954-321X); Which was formed by the merger of (19??-1986): Campaigner (Ruislip); (1879-1986): Animals Defender and Anti-vivisection News (0954-7797); Which was formerly (until 1983): Animals Defender
Published by: National Anti-Vivisection Society, 261 Goldhawk Rd, London, W12 8EU, United Kingdom. TEL 44-20-88469777, FAX 44-20-88469712, info@navs.org.uk, http://www.navs.org.uk. Ed., R&P Jan Creamer. Adv. contact Mandy Mills.

636.0832 AUS ISSN 1445-9701
ANIMAL HEALTH SURVEILLANCE QUARTERLY REPORTS. Text in English. q. **Description:** Provides a topical summary of animal health matters for the quarter.
Media: Online - full content.
Published by: Animal Health Australia, Suite 15, 26-28 Napier Close, Deakin, ACT 2600, Australia. TEL 61-2-62325522, FAX 61-2-62325511, aahc@aahc.com.au, http://www.aahc.com.au/status/ahsquarterly/.

636.0832 PAK ISSN 1728-9505
ANIMAL HUSBANDRY. PROCEEDINGS. Text in English. 1984. m. GBP 300 (effective 2005). **Document type:** *Proceedings, Academic/Scholarly.*
Published by: (Animal Husbandry Association), International Press, P O Box 17700, Karachi, 75300, Pakistan. TEL 92-21-4947486, FAX 92-21-4989257, light_68@hotmail.com. Ed. Dr. M A Niazi.

179.3 USA
➤ **ANIMAL ISSUES.** Text in English. 1969. q. USD 35 (effective 2002); includes membership. adv. bk.rev. illus. reprints avail. **Document type:** *Academic/Scholarly.* **Description:** Covers animal-related issues on the plight of wild and domesticated animals.
Formerly: Mainstream (Sacramento) (0891-088X)
Published by: Animal Protection Institute, PO Box 22505, Sacramento, CA 95822. TEL 916-447-3085, 800-348-7387, FAX 916-447-3070, onlineapi@aol.com, info@api4animals.org, http://www.api4animals.org. Ed., R&P Gil Lamont. Pub. Alan Berger. Adv. contact Barbara Tugaeff. Circ: 50,000 (controlled).

179.3 USA ISSN 1088-8802
K1
ANIMAL LAW. Text in English. 1995. a. USD 15 to individuals; USD 25 to institutions (effective 2005). bk.rev. illus. reprints avail. **Document type:** *Journal, Academic/Scholarly.* **Description:** Aims to broadcast animal issues to the legal community by covering topics such as animals as property, bioethics and animal experimentation, federal animal protection statutes, and animal rights versus animal sacrifice.
Related titles: Online - full text ed.: (from LexisNexis).
Indexed: CLI, FamI, LRI.
Published by: Lewis & Clark College, Northwestern School of Law, 10015 S W Terwilliger Blvd, Portland, OR 97219. TEL 503-768-6758, 800-444-4111, FAX 503-768-7055, animalaw@lclark.edu, lclr@lclark.edu, http://www.lclark.edu/org/animalaw/. Ed. Liz Pifke.

ANIMAL LAW REPORT. see *LAW*

344.049 340 USA
ANIMAL LEGAL REPORTS SERVICES. REPORT FOR ANIMAL WELFARE AND LAW ENFORCEMENT PROFESSIONALS. Text in English. q. USD 72.45 Animal Welfare and Law Enforcement Professionals (effective 2005). **Document type:** *Newsletter, Corporate.* **Description:** Reports on animal cases nationwide. Edited by lawyers and veterinarians.
Published by: Animal Legal Reports Services, Llc., P O Box 2249, Davidson, NC 28036-2249. TEL 704-664-3892, 800-630-2577, FAX 704-664-6412, info@animallegalreports.com, http://www.animallegalreports.com/reports/alrs_sample3.pdf. Ed. Adam P Karp.

344.049 340 USA
ANIMAL LEGAL REPORTS SERVICES. REPORT FOR LEGAL PROFESSIONALS. Text in English. q. USD 82.95 Legal Professionals (effective 2005). **Document type:** *Newsletter, Corporate.* **Description:** Reports on animal cases nationwide. Edited by lawyers and veterinarians.
Published by: Animal Legal Reports Services, Llc., P O Box 2249, Davidson, NC 28036-2249. TEL 704-664-3892, 800-630-2577, FAX 704-664-6412, info@animallegalreports.com, http://www.animallegalreports.com/reports/alrs_sample1.pdf. Ed. Nancy O'Brien.

344.049 636.0832 340 USA
▼ **ANIMAL LEGAL REPORTS SERVICES. REPORT FOR VETERINARY PROFESSIONALS.** Text in English. 2005. q. USD 82.95 Veterinary Professionals (effective 2005). **Document type:** *Newsletter, Corporate.* **Description:** Reports on animal cases nationwide. Edited by lawyers and veterinarians.
Published by: Animal Legal Reports Services, Llc., P O Box 2249, Davidson, NC 28036-2249. TEL 704-664-3892, 800-630-2577, FAX 704-664-6412, info@animallegalreports.com, http://www.animallegalreports.com/reports/alrs_sample2.pdf. Ed. Gregory M Dennis.

179.3 GBR ISSN 0964-4628
ANIMAL LIFE. Text in English. 1971. q. GBP 6 domestic; GBP 7 foreign; GBP 17.50 domestic membership (effective 2001). adv. charts; illus. 32 p./no.; **Document type:** *Magazine, Consumer.* **Description:** Covers all aspects of animal welfare and cruelty.
Formerly (until 1990): R S P C A Today (0048-8720)
Published by: Royal Society for the Prevention of Cruelty to Animals, Wilberforce Way, Oakhurst Business Park, Southwater, Horsham, W Sussex RH13 7WN, United Kingdom. TEL 44-707-5335-999, 0870-010-1181, FAX 0870-753-0048, publications@rspca.org.uk, http://www.rspca.org.uk. Ed. Amanda Bailey. R&P Michaela Miller. Adv. contact Terry Lock TEL 44-1372-276233. page GBP 2,000; trim 210 x 297. Circ: 60,000.

636.0832 USA
ANIMAL LIFE. Text in English. 1997. s-a.
Media: Online - full content.
Address: Willard Straught Hall, Cornell University, Box 39, Ithaca, NY 14853. http://www.envirolink.org:80/arrs/AnimalLife. Ed. Peter Wilson.

636.0832 IND ISSN 0972-2963
ANIMAL NUTRITION AND FEED TECHNOLOGY. Text in English. 2001. s-a. **Description:** Publishes articles in all areas of animal nutrition and feed technology i.e., biochemical and physiological basis of protein, energy, mineral and vitamin metabolism, nutritional effects and performance criteria, nutritional quality, safety and toxicity of feedstuffs, aspects of practical animal feeding, production, processing and preservation of feedstuffs covering farm, pet and aquatic animals.
Indexed: AgrForAb, AnBrAb, DSA, FCA, FPA, ForAb, HerbAb, IndVet, MaizeAb, NutrAb, PoultAb, ProtozoAb, RDA, RM&VM, RiceAb, S&F, SIA, SoyAb, TriticAb, VetBull, WAE&RSA.
—BLDSC (0905.009500).
Published by: Animal Nutrition Association, General Secretary, IVRI, Izatnagar, 243 122, India. TEL 91-581-442313, FAX 91-581-447284, anft@ivri.up.nic.in. Ed. Dr. K Sharma.

636.0832 USA ISSN 1071-0035
ANIMAL PEOPLE. Text in English. 1992. 10/yr. USD 24; USD 2 newsstand/cover (effective 2000). adv. bk.rev. **Document type:** *Newspaper.* **Description:** Covers hard news and informed opinion pertaining to all aspects of animal protection, including conservation of endangered species, animal control and rescue, animal rights, etc.
Address: PO Box 960, Clinton, WA 98236-0960. TEL 360-579-2505, FAX 360-579-2575, anmlpepl@whidbey.com, http://www.animalpeoplenews.org/. Ed. Merritt Clifton. Pub. Kim Bartlett. adv.: B&W page USD 1,155. Circ: 15,000.

179.3 USA
HV4762.A56
ANIMAL SHELTERING; the community animal care, control, and protection resource. Text in English. 1978. bi-m. USD 8 (effective 1998 & 1999). adv. bk.rev. illus. reprints avail. **Document type:** *Trade.* **Description:** Covers animal control and sheltering.
Formerly (until 1996): Shelter Sense (0734-3078)
Indexed: WildRev.
Published by: Humane Society of the United States, 2100 L St, N W, Washington, DC 20037. TEL 202-452-1100, FAX 202-258-3081, asm@ix.netcom.com, http://www.hsus.org/pubs.html. Ed. Geoffrey L Handy. Circ: 3,000.

636.0832 GBR ISSN 0962-7286
CODEN: ANWEEF
➤ **ANIMAL WELFARE.** Text in English. 1992. q. GBP 40, USD 80 to individual members; GBP 50, USD 100 to individuals non-members; GBP 50, USD 100 to institutional members; GBP 70, USD 140 to institutions non-members (effective 2005). Website rev.; bk.rev.; software rev.; video rev. illus.; abstr.; bibl.; charts. Index. 1 cols./p.; back issues avail.; reprints avail. **Document type:** *Journal, Academic/Scholarly.* **Description:** Publishes research on the well-being of wild and domesticated animals.
Indexed: AEA, ASCA, AgBio, Agr, AnBeAb, AnBrAb, BIOSIS Prev, BiolAb, ChemAb, CurCont, DIP, DSA, EngInd, ExcerpMed, FS&TA, FoVS&M, IAB, ISR, IndVet, NutrAb, PN&I, PoultAb, PsycInfo, PsycholAb, S&F, SCI, SSCI, VetBull, WAE&RSA, WildRev, ZooRec, e-psyche.
—BLDSC (0905.132000), IDS, IE, Infotrieve, ingenta. **CCC.**
Published by: Universities Federation for Animal Welfare, The Old School, Brewhouse Hill, Wheathampstead, St Albans, Herts AL4 8AN, United Kingdom. TEL 44-1582-831818, FAX 44-1582-831414, journal@ufaw.org.uk, ufaw@ufaw.org.uk, http://www.ufaw.org.uk/journal/Animal%20welfare.htm. Ed. James Kirkwood.

179.3 USA ISSN 1522-7553
HV4764
ANIMAL WELFARE INFORMATION CENTER BULLETIN. Variant title: A W I C Bulletin. Text in English. 1990. q. free. **Document type:** *Bulletin, Government.* **Description:** Publishes articles on animal-welfare issues, along with other information of use to persons conducting biomedical research. Lists funding opportunities for related research.
Formerly: Animal Welfare Information Center Newsletter (1050-561X)
Related titles: Online - full text ed.
Indexed: Agr, ChemAb, DSA, ExcerpMed, IndVet, PN&I.
—BLDSC (0905.135500).
Published by: (U.S. Department of Agriculture), U.S. Department of Agriculture, National Agricultural Library, Animal Welfare Information Center, 10301 Baltimore Blvd, 4th Fl, Beltsville, MD 20705-2351. TEL 301-504-6212, FAX 301-504-7125, tallen@nal.usda.gov, awic@nal.usda.gov, http://netvet.wustl.edu/awic.htm, http://www.nal.usda.gov/awic. Ed., R&P Tim Allen TEL 301-504-5174. Circ: 6,200.

179.3 USA
ANIMALIFE. Text in English. 1989. s-a. USD 1.50 per issue; USD 2.50 per issue foreign. adv. illus. **Document type:** *Newsletter.* **Description:** Forum for discussion, information, and education about animal rights and liberation issues.
Related titles: Online - full text ed.
Published by: Cornell Students for the Ethical Treatment of Animals, Cornell University, Willard Straight Hall, Box 39, Ithaca, NY 14853. bp26@cornell.edu, http://www.envirolink.org/arrs/AnimaLife. Ed. Brin O'Connell. Circ: 2,000.

179.3 179.4 USA
ANIMALS' ADVOCATE. Text in English. 1982. 4/yr. looseleaf. USD 15 membership (effective 2005). bk.rev. back issues avail. **Document type:** *Newsletter, Consumer.*
Formerly: Animal Legal Defense Fund. Newsletter
Published by: Animal Legal Defense Fund, 127 Fourth St, Petaluma, CA 94952-3005. TEL 707-769-7771, FAX 707-769-0785, info@aldf.org, http://www.aldf.org. Ed. Barry Bergman. Circ: 110,000 (paid).

179.3 GBR ISSN 0254-3923
HV4701
ANIMALS INTERNATIONAL. Text in English. 1974. 2/yr. GBP 12.50, USD 20. bk.rev. illus.; stat. reprints avail. **Document type:** *Newsletter.*
Formerly: Animalia; Which supersedes: W F P A News (0049-8068)
Indexed: Agr.
Published by: World Society for the Protection of Animals, 2 Langley Ln, London, SW8 1TJ, United Kingdom. TEL 44-171-793-0540, FAX 44-171-793-0208, wspa@wspa.org.uk, http://www.way.net.wspa/. Ed. Jonathan Pearce. Circ: 35,000.

179.2 AUS ISSN 1320-2464
ANIMALS TODAY. Text in English. 1993. 3/yr. AUD 25 domestic; AUD 40 foreign (effective 2001). adv. bk.rev. illus. 32 p./no. 3 cols./p.; back issues avail.; reprints avail. **Document type:** *Bulletin, Consumer.* **Description:** Focuses on the plight of exploited animals in society and reports on what is being done to help them.
Related titles: Online - full text ed.: (from EBSCO Publishing).
Indexed: MASUSE.
Published by: Australian and New Zealand Federation of Animal Societies Inc., PO Box 1023, Collingwood, VIC 3066, Australia. TEL 61-3-93296333, FAX 61-3-93296441, enquiries@animalsaustralia.org, http://www.animalsaustralia.org. Eds. Dominique Thiriet, Glenys Oogjes, Lisa Curtin. R&P, Adv. contact Glenys Oogjes. Circ: 3,000.

179.3 CAN ISSN 0700-8392
ANIMALS' VOICE. Text in English. 1957. q. CND 20. adv. bk.rev. **Document type:** *Consumer.* **Description:** Includes O S P C A news, discussions on animal welfare and pet care solutions.
Published by: Ontario S P C A, 16640 Yonge St, Newmarket, ON L3Y 4V8, Canada. TEL 905-898-7122, FAX 905-853-8643, jingham@hockup.net. Ed., R&P Susan Swanek. Adv. contact Roger Leblanc. B&W page USD 850. Circ: 65,000 (controlled).

636.0832 CAN ISSN 1192-4861
ANIMALTALK. Key Title: Animal Talk. Text in English. 1974. 3/yr. adv. bk.rev. **Document type:** *Newsletter, Consumer.* **Description:** Presents news, features, and reviews of the Society and animal welfare, pet care, and animal behavior issues.
Former titles (until 1990): Toronto Humane Society. Society News (0845-5082); (until 1987): Humane Viewpoint (0316-9014)
Indexed: ISAP.
Published by: Toronto Humane Society, 11 River St, Toronto, ON M5A 4C2, Canada. TEL 416-392-2273, FAX 416-392-9978, info@torontohumanesociety.com, http://www.torontohumanesociety.com. Ed., R&P, Adv. contact Amy White. Pub. Johnston Adams. Circ: 50,000.

179.3 FRA ISSN 0986-3354
ANIMAUX MAGAZINE. Text in French. 1982. m. EUR 28 (effective 2005). adv. **Description:** News on animal welfare and on SPA actions, wildlife subjects.
Formerly (until 1982): S.P.A. (0180-6564)
Published by: Societe Protectrice des Animaux, 39 bd. Berthier, Paris, 75017, France. TEL 33-1-43804066, FAX 33-1-47637476, infos@spa.asso.fr, http://www.spa.asso.fr. Ed. Evelyne Stawicki. R&P, Adv. contact Maryline Brisson.

636.0832 POL ISSN 1642-3402
ANNALS OF ANIMAL SCIENCE. Text in English, Polish. 2001. s-a. (in 1 vol., 2 nos./vol.). USD 35 foreign (effective 2005). **Document type:** *Journal, Academic/Scholarly.*
Indexed: AgrAg, HelmAb, SIA.
—BLDSC (1037.900000).

Published by: Instytut Zootechniki/Institute of Animal Production, ul Sarego 2, Krakow, 31047, Poland. TEL 48-12-2588111, FAX 48-12-2588150, annals@izoo.krakow.pl, izooinfo@izoo.krakow.pl, http://www.izoo.krakow.pl. Ed. Ewa Slota.

APIS; the international journal bulletin for specialty livestock and pet-animal product development. see *VETERINARY SCIENCE*

179.3 GBR ISSN 0004-167X
THE ARK (LONDON); Journal of the Catholic Study Circle for Animal Welfare. Text in English. 1937. 3/yr., latest vol.188. GBP 10, USD 25 (effective 2001). bk.rev. illus. 64 p./no. 1 cols./p.; back issues avail. **Document type:** *Journal, Academic/Scholarly.* **Description:** Promotes concern and respect for animals, theology concerning animals and creation.
Indexed: AnBrAb, BrArAb.
—BLDSC (1668.700000).
Published by: Catholic Study Circle for Animal Welfare, c/o Hon Secretary, 39 Onslow Gardens, South Woodford, London, E18 1ND, United Kingdom. TEL 0-1993-703616, djonesark@waihrose.com, http://www.catholic-animals.org. Ed., R&P Deborah Jones TEL 0-1993-703616. Circ: 2,000.

636.0832 USA
ARK ONLINE; the online magazine for people who care about animals. Text in English. irreg. **Description:** Dedicated to people who care about animals. Includes actions you can take on behalf of animals both locally and worldwide.
Media: Online - full text.
Address: bob@arkonline.com, http://www.arkonline.com/. Ed., Pub. Bob Schlesinger.

ASKO; dwumiesiecznik kynologiczny. see *PETS*

AUSTRALASIAN PRIMATOLOGY. see *BIOLOGY—Zoology*

636.0832 DEU ISSN 0936-3815
BERLINER TIERFREUND. Text in German. 1989. 5/yr. EUR 20 membership (effective 2005). bk.rev. back issues avail. **Document type:** *Magazine, Consumer.*
Published by: Tierschutzverein fuer Berlin, Hausvater Weg 39, Berlin, 13057, Germany. TEL 49-30-76888112, FAX 49-30-76888150, info@tierschutz-berlin.de, http://www.tierschutz-berlin.de/main/tierfreund.htm. Ed., R&P, Adv. contact Carola Ruff.

636.0832 USA
BEST FRIENDS; all the good news about animals, wildlife, and the earth. Text in English. 1992. bi-m. USD 25 donation (effective 2004). adv. illus.
Published by: Best Friends Animal Society, 5001 Angel Canyon Dr, Kanab, UT 84741. TEL 435-644-2001, FAX 435-644-2078, info@bestfriends.org, http://www.bestfriends.org. Adv. contact Ashley Tillman TEL 818-762-2001. Circ: 200,000.

179.3 GBR
BLUE CROSS ILLUSTRATED. Text in English. 3/yr. GBP 3. illus. back issues avail. **Description:** Illustrates the many aspects of Blue Cross work and shows supporters how their money is spent. Includes features, news and reviews.
Published by: Blue Cross, 1-5 Hugh St, Victoria, London, SW1 1QQ, United Kingdom. Ed. James Combe. Circ: 9,000.

BUSTARD STUDIES. see *CONSERVATION*

C B S G NEWS. (Conservation Breeding Specialist Group) see *CONSERVATION*

179.3 USA
C H A I LIGHTS. Text in English. 1984. q. USD 18 (effective 1999). bk.rev. 8 p./no. 3 cols./p.; back issues avail. **Document type:** *Newsletter, Trade.* **Description:** Relates problems for animals in Israel and CHAI's effort to help.
Published by: Concern for Helping Animals in Israel, PO Box 3341, Alexandria, VA 22302. TEL 703-370-0333, 866-308-0333, FAX 703-370-1314, chai_us@compuserve.com, http://www.chai-online.org. Ed., R&P Nina Natelson TEL 703-658-9650. Circ: 5,000 (paid).

179.4 CHE
C I V I S: INTERNATIONAL FOUNDATION REPORT; for the abolition of vivisection. Text in English. 1988. q. CHF 20, USD 15. back issues avail.; reprints avail. **Description:** Aims to demonstrate that animal experimentation does not promote human health, and therefore should be abolished.
Published by: (Centro Informazione Vivisezionista Internazionale Scientifica), Fondazione Hans Ruesch, Via Motta 51, PO Box 152, Massagno, 6900, Switzerland. TEL 83-41166. Ed. Hans Ruesch.

636.0832 USA
CALF NEWS; the magazine for cattle feeders. Text in English. 1963. m. USD 33 domestic; USD 38 foreign (effective 2005). adv. **Document type:** *Magazine.*
Formerly: Calf News (0007-7798)
Published by: Calf News Magazine Ltd., 10720 S. Forest Dr., Colorado Springs, CO 80908-3962. TEL 719-495-0303, FAX 719-495-9204, steve@calfnews.com, http://www.calfnews.com. Ed., Pub. Betty Jo Gigot. adv.: B&W page USD 1,695, color page USD 2,689. Circ: 4,300 (controlled).

636.0832 GBR
CAMPAIGNER (LONDON). Text in English. 1879. s-a. GBP 17; GBP 23 foreign (effective 2000). adv. bk.rev. illus. index. **Document type:** *Bulletin.* **Description:** Gives reports on the dangers and futility of using animals in medical research; news on drugs, health and animal experiments.
Supersedes in part (in 1990): Campaigner and Animal's Defender; Which incorporated (in 1986): Campaigner; Formerly: Animals: Defender and Anti-Vivisection News (0954-321X)
Published by: National Anti-Vivisection Society, 261 Goldhawk Rd, London, W12 8EU, United Kingdom. TEL 44-20-8846-9777, FAX 44-20-8846-9712. Ed., R&P, Adv. contact Jan Creamer. Circ: 20,000.

CANINE CONNECTIONS. see *PETS*

CAPRINAE NEWS. see *CONSERVATION*

636.0832 CAN ISSN 0825-1711
CARING FOR ANIMALS. Text in English. 1984. s-a. looseleaf. free. back issues avail. **Document type:** *Newsletter.* **Description:** For members of animal care communities.
Published by: (Experimental Animals Committee), Canadian Federation of Humane Societies, 30 Concourse Gate, Ste 102, Nepean, ON K2E 7V7, Canada. TEL 613-224-8072, FAX 613-723-0252, cfhs@magi.com. Ed. Stephanie Brown. Circ: 2,800.

THE CAT. see *PETS*

CAT NEWS. see *CONSERVATION*

179.3 798 ITA ISSN 1590-413X
CAVALLO MAGAZINE; mensile di natura, politica e cultura. Text in Italian. 1986. m. adv. bk.rev. back issues avail. **Document type:** *Magazine, Consumer.*
Published by: Superprint Srl (Subsidiary of: Monrif Group), Viale Milanofiori Strada 3, Palazzo B11, Assago, MI 20090, Italy. TEL 39-02-575771, FAX 39-02-57577263, http://www.monrifgroup.net/ita/periodici.html. Ed. Mario Palumbo. R&P Roberto Pignoni. Adv. contact Cinzia Romano. Circ: 26,322 (controlled).

636.0832 BEL
CHAINE/KETEN. Text in Dutch, French. 1962. q. **Document type:** *Newsletter.* **Description:** Promotes worldwide education to protect animals from cruelty, and to protect nature and the environment.
Published by: Chaine Bleue Mondiale a.s.b.l., Av de Vise 39, Brussels, 1170, Belgium. TEL 32-2-673-5230, FAX 32-2-672-0947, bwk.cbm@vt4.net, http://www.bwk-cbm.org. Ed. Marleen Elsen Verlodt.

CHELONIAN CONSERVATION BIOLOGY. see *CONSERVATION*

CHIENS SANS LAISSE; magazine de l'education et des sports canins. see *PETS*

CLUMBERS. see *PETS*

179.3 USA ISSN 1526-6230
THE COMPASSIONATE SHOPPER. Text in English. 1973. 3/yr. bk.rev. back issues avail. **Document type:** *Newsletter, Consumer.* **Description:** Informs the public about the massive suffering imposed on animals by the fashion, cosmetic and household product industries. Lists manufacturers and retailers of cruelty-free apparel, cosmetics and household products.
Published by: Beauty Without Cruelty U S A, 175 W 12th St, Ste 16G, New York, NY 10011-8275. TEL 212-989-8073, FAX 212-989-8073, thurston@access1.com, beautywocruelty@aol.com. Pub., R&P Ethel Thurston. Circ: 3,000 (paid); 4,000 (controlled).

179.3 NLD
D A R - GELUIDEN. Text in Dutch. bi-m. adv.
Published by: (Vereniging Dierenambulance Rotterdam), De Groene Lijn, Essendijkweg 1, Poortvliet, 4693 SC, Netherlands. Circ: 4,500.

DEUTSCHER JAGDTERRIERCLUB. NACHRICHTENBLATT. see *PETS*

636.0832 NLD ISSN 0165-3172
DIER. Text in Dutch. 1920. bi-m. adv. bk.rev. illus. **Document type:** *Consumer.*
Formerly (until 1978): Dierenbescherming (0012-2599)
Published by: Nederlandse Vereniging tot Bescherming van Dieren, Postbus 85980, The Hague, 2508 CR, Netherlands. TEL 31-70-314-2700, FAX 31-70-314-2777, info@dierenbeschermg.nl, http://www.dierenbescherming.nl. Ed. J B Dobbe. R&P J.B. Dobbe TEL 31-70-3142730. Circ: 175,000.

179.1 179.3 SWE ISSN 0345-2409
DJURENS RAETT MED DJURFRONT. Text in Swedish. 1906. 4/yr. SEK 100 (effective 2004). adv. bk.rev. 5 cols./p.; **Document type:** *Newspaper.* **Description:** Focuses on issues concerned with anti-vivisection and rights of animals.
Incorporates (1974-1988): Djurfront (0345-2417)
Related titles: Audio cassette/tape ed.
Published by: Foerbundet Djurens Raett/Animal Rights Sweden, PO Box 2005, Aelvsjoe, 12502, Sweden. TEL 46-8-55591400, FAX 46-8-55591450, info@djurensratt.se, http://www.djurensratt.se/dyntext/xlink.asp?id=268. Ed., Adv. contact Ingegerd Erlandsson. Circ: 48,000.

179 SWE ISSN 0281-1545
DJURENS VAERLD. Text in Swedish. 1958-1974; resumed 1981. q. SEK 50 (effective 2004). bk.rev. illus. **Document type:** *Academic/Scholarly.*
Incorporates (1957-1983): Djurexpressen (0012-432X)
Published by: Svenska Djurskyddsfoereningen, PO Box 5867, Stockholm, 10240, Sweden. TEL 46-8-7830368, FAX 46-8-7830369, info@djurskydd.org, http://www.djurskydd.org. Circ: 8,000.

179.3 SWE ISSN 1651-4505
DJURSKYDDET; tidningen foer djurskyddet Sverige. Text in Swedish. 1890. 5/yr. SEK 100 membership (effective 2004). adv. bk.rev. illus. **Document type:** *Magazine, Consumer.*
Former titles (until 2002): Djurtidningen Djurskyddet (1101-4423); (until vol.3, 1989): Djurskyddet; (until vol.4, 1970): Djurvaennernas Tidning Djurskyddet; (until 1938): Djurskyddet (0012-4346)
Published by: Djurskyddet Sverige/Swedish Association for Animal Welfare, Markvardsgatan 10, 4 tr, Stockholm, 11353, Sweden. TEL 46-8-6733511, FAX 46-8-6733666, http://www.djurskyddet.se/medlemsskapmedlemstidning.htm. Ed. John Erik Trollsten.

DODO; journal of the wildlife conservation trusts. see *CONSERVATION*

179.3 636.1 AUS ISSN 1031-6280
DONKEY DIGEST. Text in English. 1972. q. USD 25 (effective 2000). adv. bk.rev. illus. back issues avail. **Document type:** *Bulletin.* **Description:** All aspects of donkey welfare and training.
Published by: Affiliated Donkey Societies of Australia, 5 Doyle Rd., Dagun, QLD 4570, Australia. TEL 61-07-54843749, FAX 61-07-54843771. Ed., R&P, Adv. contact Elaine Bradley. Circ: 600.

179 DNK ISSN 1397-1379
DYRENES RET. Text in Danish. 1977. q. DKK 120 (effective 2004). adv. bk.rev. **Document type:** *Consumer.*
Former titles (until 1995): Dyrenes Ret - Vor Pligt (0906-1290); (until 1990): Komiteen mod Dyreforsoeg, Fonden til Sygdomsbekaempelse uden Dyreforsoeg (0109-3878)
Published by: Landsforeningen Komiteen mod Dyreforsoeg, Valdemarsgade 67, 5 tv, PO Box 59, Charlottenlund, 2920, Denmark. TEL 45-39-404056, dyrenesret@mail.dk, http://www.dyrenesret.dk. Ed. Henning Lobbe. adv.: B&W page DKK 2,300. Circ: 2,000.

363.7 GBR
ENVIRONMENTAL ENRICHMENT REPORTS. Text in English. 1988. irreg., latest vol.4, 1991. GBP 0.50, USD 1.50 per issue (effective 2003). back issues avail. **Document type:** *Monographic series.*
Published by: Universities Federation for Animal Welfare, The Old School, Brewhouse Hill, Wheathampstead, St Albans, Herts AL4 8AN, United Kingdom. TEL 44-1582-831818, FAX 44-1582-831414, journal@ufaw.org.uk, http://www.ufaw.org.uk/.

ERSATZ- UND ERGAENZUNGSMETHODEN ZU TIERVERSUCHEN. see *MEDICAL SCIENCES—Experimental Medicine, Laboratory Technique*

179.3 799.2 DEU ISSN 1612-4642
CODEN: ZEJAAA
➤ **EUROPEAN JOURNAL OF WILDLIFE RESEARCH.** Text in German; Summaries in English, French, German. 1955. q. EUR 270 combined subscription to institutions print & online eds. (effective 2005). adv. bk.rev. illus. index. back issues avail.; reprint service avail. from ISI. **Document type:** *Journal, Academic/Scholarly.*
Formerly (until 2003): Zeitschrift fuer Jagdwissenschaft (0044-2887)
Related titles: Online - full text ed.: ISSN 1439-0574. EUR 243 to institutions (effective 2003) (from EBSCO Publishing, Springer LINK, Swets Information Services).
Indexed: ASCA, AgBio, AnBrAb, ApicAb, BIOBASE, BIOSIS Prev, BiolAb, ChemAb, CurCont, ExcerpMed, FPA, FS&TA, ForAb, HelmAb, HerbAb, HortAb, IBR, IndVet, KWIWR, MaizeAb, NutrAb, PN&I, PoultAb, ProtozoAb, RA&MP, RM&VM, RRTA, RefZh, RevApplEntom, S&F, SFA, VetBull, WAE&RSA, WeedAb, WildRev, ZooRec.
—BLDSC (3829.747345), IDS, IE, Infotrieve, ingenta. **CCC.**
Published by: Springer-Verlag (Subsidiary of: Springer Science+Business Media), Tiergartenstr 17, Heidelberg, 69121, Germany. TEL 49-6221-3450, FAX 49-6221-345229, orders@springer.de, http://www.springer.de. Ed. Walburga Lutz. Adv. contact Stephan Kroeck TEL 49-30-827875739.
Subscr. to: Springer-Verlag New York, Inc., Journal Fulfillment, PO Box 2485, Secaucus, NJ 07096-2485. TEL 201-348-4033, FAX 201-348-4505, journals@springer-ny.com; Springer GmbH Auslieferungsgesellschaft, Haberstr 7, Heidelberg 69126, Germany. TEL 49-6221-345-0, FAX 49-6221-345-4229, subscriptions@springer.de.

A

636.0832 GBR
F A B JOURNAL. Text in English. 1958. q. GBP 20 (effective 1999). adv. bk.rev. charts; illus.; stat. back issues avail.
Document type: *Magazine, Consumer.* **Description:** Contains items of interest to veterinarians and breeders specializing in cats, as well as general-interest articles for cat lovers and owners.
Formerly: F A B Bulletin
Media: Duplicated (not offset).
Published by: Feline Advisory Bureau, Taeselbury, High St, Tisbury, Salisbury, Wilts SP3 6LD, United Kingdom. TEL 44-1747-871872, FAX 44-1747-871873, fab.fab@ukonline.co.uk, http://web.ukonline.co.uk/fab.fab.html. Ed., R&P, Adv. contact Claire Bessant. Circ: 3,500 (paid).

179.3 GBR ISSN 0268-4306
F R A M E NEWS. Text in English. 1979. irreg. (3-4/yr.). GBP 15, USD 25 (effective 2003). illus. **Document type:** *Newsletter.* **Description:** Discusses the organization's efforts to abolish the use of animals in laboratory testing. Reports general news in the area.
Formerly (until 1984): F R A M E Technical News (0143-8352)
Published by: Fund for the Replacement of Animals in Medical Experiments, Russell & Burch House, 96-98 N Sherwood St, Nottingham, NG1 4EE, United Kingdom. TEL 44-115-9584740, FAX 44-115-9503570, atla@frame.org.uk, http://www.frame.org.uk. Ed. Vivienne Hunter.

179.3 636 GBR ISSN 1473-1800
CODEN: WSTWBM
FARM ANIMAL VOICE; better lives for animals and us. Text in English. 1967. q. GBP 21 domestic membership; GBP 26 foreign membership; GBP 10 domestic membership students, senior citizens & unemployed; GBP 30 domestic membership family; GBP 36 foreign membership family (effective 2003). adv. bk.rev. illus. 24 p./no. 2 cols./p.; **Document type:** *Magazine.* **Description:** Covers CIWF's Campaigns to end the factory farming of animals and the cruel live export trade with sections on UK and international investigations, celebrity interviews, other CIWF news, events and diary dates.
Formerly (until 2001): Agscene (1367-1006)
Indexed: IndVet.
Published by: Compassion in World Farming Ltd., Charles House, 5a Charles St, Petersfield, Hants GU32 3EH, United Kingdom. TEL 44-1730-264208, 44-1720-268863, FAX 44-1730-260791, compassion@ciwf.co.uk, http://www.ciwf.co.uk. Ed. Joyce D'Silva. Adv. contact Angie Greenaway TEL 44-1730-237370. Circ: 20,000.

179.3 USA
FARM SANCTUARY NEWS. Text in English. 1986. q. USD 15 membership (effective 2001). **Document type:** *Newsletter.* **Description:** Provides news and updates on animal agriculture issues and campaigns.
Formerly (until 1986): Sanctuary News (0149-9084)
Published by: Farm Sanctuary, Inc., PO Box 150, Watkins Glen, NY 14891-0150. TEL 607-583-2225, FAX 607-583-2041, info@farmsanctuary.org, http://www.farmsanctuary.org. Ed., R&P Lorri Bauston. Circ: 75,000.

FLAMINGO SPECIALIST GROUP NEWSLETTER. see *CONSERVATION*

FRESSNAPF ZEITUNG. see *PETS*

179.3 GBR ISSN 0016-1276
FRIEND OF ANIMALS. Text in English. 1916. q. GBP 2. bk.rev. illus. index. **Document type:** *Newsletter.* **Description:** Contains articles and stories of interest to animal lovers.
Formerly: Little Animal's Friend
Published by: (The Council for Protection of Animals), Humane Education Society, Animals' Convalescent Home, Newgate, Wilmslow, SK9 5LN, United Kingdom. TEL 44-1625-520802. Ed. Arthur Thompson. Circ: 1,500.

179.3 GBR
FRIENDS OF F R A M E. Text in English. m. free (effective 2003). illus. **Document type:** *Newsletter.* **Description:** Covers organization news and events for donors.
Media: Online - full text.
Published by: Fund for the Replacement of Animals in Medical Experiments, Russell & Burch House, 96-98 N Sherwood St, Nottingham, NG1 4EE, United Kingdom. TEL 44-115-9584740, FAX 44-115-9503570, atla@frame.org.uk, http://www.frame.org.uk/Friends_of_FRAME/FoF.htm. Ed. Vivienne P Hunter.

FROGLOG. see *CONSERVATION*

GAJAH. see *CONSERVATION*

GNUSLETTER. see *CONSERVATION*

636.0832 USA
GORILLA GAZETTE. Text in English. a. free to qualified personnel (effective 2005). **Document type:** *Academic/Scholarly.*
—BLDSC (4201.517850).
Address: c/o Beth Armstrong, 510 Diana Blvd, Merrit Island, FL 32953. TEL 321-454-6285, elynn57@aol.com, pete@gorilla-haven.org. Ed. Beth Armstrong. Pub. Jane Dewar.

179.3 USA ISSN 1078-6244
GRRR!; kids bite back. Text in English. 1994. 2/yr. free to members (effective 2005). bk.rev. illus. 16 p./no.; back issues avail.; reprints avail. **Document type:** *Magazine, Consumer.*
Related titles: Online - full text ed.
Published by: People for the Ethical Treatment of Animals, Inc., 501 Front St, Norfolk, VA 23510. TEL 757-622-7382, FAX 757-622-0457, peta@peta.org, http://www.peta.org. Ed. Ingrid Newkirk. R&P Robyn Wesley. Circ: 30,000 (free).

636.0832 NLD ISSN 0922-520X
HART VOOR DIEREN. Text in Dutch. 1988. m. EUR 34.65; EUR 3.15 newsstand/cover (effective 2005). adv. illus. **Document type:** *Magazine, Consumer.* **Description:** Discusses ways in which to care for and nurture pets.
Incorporates (1979-1988): Kat en Hond (0922-5218)
Published by: Vipmedia Publishing en Services, Takkebijsters 57A, Breda, 4817 BL, Netherlands. TEL 31-76-5301717, FAX 31-76-5144531, info@vipmedia.nl, http://www.hartvoordieren.nl/, http://www.vipmedia.nl. Circ: 97,000. **Subscr. in Belgium to:** Vipmedia, Bredabaan 852, Merksem 2170, Belgium; **Subscr. to:** Postbus 7122, Breda 4800 GC, Netherlands. TEL 31-76-5301722, FAX 31-76-5205235.

636.0832 USA
HUMANE NEWS. Text in English. 1970. m. USD 10 (effective 1998). adv. bk.rev. **Document type:** *Newsletter, Consumer.* **Description:** Covers animal rights, legislation and animal welfare.
Published by: Associated Humane Societies, Inc., 124 Evergreen Ave, Newark, NJ 07114. TEL 973-824-7080, FAX 973-824-2720, http://www.petfinder.org/shelters/NJ01.html. Ed., R&P, Adv. contact Roseann Trezza. Circ: 75,000.

179.3 179.4 GBR ISSN 0263-1407
HUMANE SLAUGHTER ASSOCIATION NEWSLETTER. Text in English. 1979. a. GBP 10 (effective 2001). back issues avail. **Document type:** *Newsletter, Corporate.*
Published by: Humane Slaughter Association and Council of Justice to Animals, Old School, Brewhouse Hill, Wheathampstead, St Albans, Herts AL4 8AN, United Kingdom. TEL 44-1582-831919, FAX 44-1582-831414. Circ: 1,000.

179.3 GBR ISSN 0264-8741
HUMANE SLAUGHTER ASSOCIATION REPORT AND ACCOUNTS. Text in English. 1922. a. GBP 10 (effective 2001). back issues avail. **Document type:** *Corporate.*
Published by: Humane Slaughter Association and Council of Justice to Animals, Old School, Brewhouse Hill, Wheathampstead, St Albans, Herts AL4 8AN, United Kingdom. TEL 44-1582-831919, FAX 44-1582-831414, info@hsa.org.uk. Circ: 1,000.

179.3 200 USA
I N R O ADS✶. Text in English. 1986. 3/yr. USD 15; includes membership. bk.rev. **Document type:** *Newsletter, Consumer.* **Description:** Conveys religious attitudes with respect to the treatment of animals by humans.
Former titles: I N R Ads; I N R A Network News
Published by: International Network for Religion and Animals, 2913 Woodstock Ave, Silver Spring, MD 20910. Ed. Rev. Dr Marc A Wessels. Circ: 2,400.

179.3 AUS
IMPACT (SOUTH BRISBANE)✶; a voice for the animals. Text in English. 1980. bi-m. AUD 25 domestic membership; AUD 31 foreign membership. bk.rev. **Document type:** *Newsletter.* **Description:** Covers aspects of cruelty to animals. Includes president's report, thank you's to volunteers and supporters, compassionate shop news, and information on current campaigns.
Former titles (until 1993): QuALM Newsletter Animal Liberation; (until 1983): QuALM (0813-6440)
Published by: Animal Liberation Queensland, PO Box 463, Annerley, QLD 4103, Australia. TEL 61-7-32559572, FAX 61-7-8441658, alibqld@powerup.com.au, http://homepage.powerup.com.au/%7Ealibqld/ALqld.htm. Ed., R&P Jeannie Sheppard. Circ: 1,200.

636.0832 CAN ISSN 0842-6155
IMPACT OF ANIMAL RIGHTS CAMPAIGNS IN CANADA. Text in English. 1988. irreg.
Published by: Library of Parliament, Parliamentary Research Branch, Information Service, Ottawa, ON K1A 0A9, Canada.

179.3 USA
IN DEFENSE OF ANIMALS MAGAZINE. Key Title: I D A Magazine. Text in English. q. **Document type:** *Newsletter.*
Published by: In Defense of Animals, 131 Camino Alto, Ste E, Mill Valley, CA 94941. TEL 415-388-9641, FAX 415-388-0388, ida@idausa.org, http://www.petropolitan.com/petpages/pet961025guestbyline.html. Ed. Laura Moretti. Circ: 70,000.

636.0832 USA ISSN 1546-6736
HV4764
▼ **INFORMATION PLUS REFERENCE SERIES. ANIMAL RIGHTS.** Text in English. 2003. biennial. USD 40 per vol. (effective 2005). **Document type:** *Monographic series, Academic/Scholarly.*
Related titles: Online - full content ed.; ◆ Series of: Information Plus Reference Series.
Published by: Gale Group (Subsidiary of: Thomson Corporation), 27500 Drake Rd, Farmington Hills, MI 48331-3535. TEL 248-699-4253, 800-877-4253, FAX 248-699-8035, http://www.galegroup.com.

636 GBR ISSN 1463-998X
INSTITUTE FOR ANIMAL HEALTH. Variant title: Institute for Animal Health. Report. Text in English. 1988. a.
Formerly (until 1991): Institute for Animal Health. Annual Report (0953-2811)
—BLDSC (4519.430000), CISTI.
Address: Compton, Newbury, Berks, RG20 7NN, United Kingdom. TEL 44-1635-578411, FAX 44-1635-577237, animal.health@bbsrc.ac.uk, http://www.iah.bbsrc.ac.uk.

INTERNATIONAL JOURNAL OF ANIMAL SCIENCES. see *AGRICULTURE—Poultry And Livestock*

179.3 USA ISSN 1051-8827
INTERNATIONAL SOCIETY FOR ANIMAL RIGHTS. REPORT. Text in English. 1959. q. USD 15. bk.rev. **Document type:** *Newsletter.*
Former titles (until Aug. 1983): Society for Animal Rights. Report; N C S A W Report (0027-6340)
Published by: International Society for Animal Rights, Inc., 965 Griffin Pond Rd, Clarks Summit, PA 18411-9214. TEL 717-586-2200, FAX 717-586-9580, isar@aol.com, http://www.isar.com. Ed. Susan Altieri. Circ: 50,000.

INTERNATIONAL UNION FOR CONSERVATION OF NATURE AND NATURAL RESOURCES. SPECIES SURVIVAL COMMISSION - CROCODILE SPECIALIST GROUP NEWSLETTER. see *CONSERVATION*

INTERNATIONAL UNION FOR CONSERVATION OF NATURE AND NATURAL RESOURCES. SPECIES SURVIVAL COMMISSION - DEER SPECIALIST GROUP. NEWSLETTER. see *CONSERVATION*

INTERNATIONAL UNION FOR CONSERVATION OF NATURE AND NATURAL RESOURCES. SPECIES SURVIVAL COMMISSION - HYAENA SPECIALIST GROUP BULLETIN. see *CONSERVATION*

INTERNATIONAL UNION FOR CONSERVATION OF NATURE AND NATURAL RESOURCES. SPECIES SURVIVAL COMMISSION - OTTER SPECIALIST GROUP BULLETIN. see *CONSERVATION*

INTERNATIONAL UNION FOR CONSERVATION OF NATURE AND NATURAL RESOURCES. SPECIES SURVIVAL COMMISSION - SPECIALIST GROUP ON STORKS, IBISES, AND SPOONBILLS NEWSLETTER. see *CONSERVATION*

INTERNATIONAL UNION FOR CONSERVATION OF NATURE AND NATURAL RESOURCES. SPECIES SURVIVAL COMMISSION - VETERINARY SPECIALIST GROUP. NEWSLETTER. see *CONSERVATION*

636.0832 USA ISSN 1088-8705
SF405.5 CODEN: JAAWAV
➤ **JOURNAL OF APPLIED ANIMAL WELFARE SCIENCE.** Short title: J A A W S. Text in English. 1989. q. USD 355 in US & Canada to institutions; USD 385 elsewhere to institutions; USD 375 combined subscription in US & Canada to institutions print & online eds.; USD 405 combined subscription elsewhere to institutions print & online eds. (effective 2006). adv. bk.rev. illus. cum.index. back issues avail.; reprint service avail. from PSC. **Document type:** *Journal, Academic/Scholarly.* **Description:** Publishes reports and articles on methods of experimentation, husbandry and care that demonstrably enhance the welfare of farm, laboratory, companion and wild animals.
Supersedes (in 1995): Humane Innovations and Alternatives (1062-4805); Which was formerly (until 1991): Humane Innovations and Alternatives in Animal Experimentation (0893-9535)
Related titles: Online - full text ed.: ISSN 1532-7604. USD 340 worldwide to institutions (effective 2006) (from EBSCO Publishing, Gale Group, O C L C Online Computer Library Center, Inc., Swets Information Services).
Indexed: AEA, AgBio, Agr, AnBrAb, ChemAb, DSA, ExcerpMed, IAB, IndVet, NutrAb, PN&I, PhilInd, PoultAb, PsycInfo, PsycholAb, RDA, VetBull, WAE&RSA, WildRev, ZooRec, e-psyche.
—BLDSC (4616.316500), IE, Infotrieve, ingenta. **CCC.**
Published by: (American Society for the Prevention of Cruelty to Animals, Psychologists for the Ethical Treatment of Animals), Lawrence Erlbaum Associates, Inc., 10 Industrial Ave, Mahwah, NJ 07430-2262. TEL 201-258-2200, 800-926-6579, FAX 201-236-0072, journals@erlbaum.com, http://www.leaonline.com/loi/jaws. Eds. Kenneth Shapiro, Stephen Zawistowski. adv.: page USD 400; trim 5 x 8.

333.72 USA ISSN 1050-821X
K I N D NEWS JR. EDITION. (Kids in Nature's Defense) Text in English. 1983. 9/yr. (m. during school year). USD 30 domestic; USD 50 foreign (effective 2003). illus. 4 p./no.; **Document type:** *Newspaper, Academic/Scholarly.* **Description:** For schoolchildren in grades 3-4. Teaches children kindness to people, animals, and the Earth.
Formerly: Kind News 1
Published by: National Association for Humane and Environmental Education, PO Box 362, E Haddam, CT 06423-0362. TEL 860-434-8666, FAX 860-434-9579, nahee@nahee.org, http://www.nahee.org. Eds. Cathy Vicenti, Jessica Vanase, Lesia Winiarsky. R&P Lorie Blake TEL 860-434-8666 ext. 10. Circ: 1,222,800 (paid).

363.7 USA ISSN 1069-4544
K I N D NEWS PRIMARY. (Kids in Nature's Defense) Text in English. 1993. 9/yr. (m. during school year). USD 30 domestic; USD 50 foreign (effective 2003). illus. **Document type:** *Newspaper.* **Description:** For kindergarteners and first- and second-graders. Teaches children kindness to people, animals, and the Earth.
Published by: National Association for Humane and Environmental Education, PO Box 362, E Haddam, CT 06423-0362. TEL 860-434-8666, FAX 860-434-9579, nahee@nahee.org, http://www.nahee.org/ kindnews_kindteacher.asp. Ed. Lesia Winiarsky. R&P Lorie Blake TEL 860-434-8666 ext. 10. Circ: 1,222,800 (paid).

363.7 USA ISSN 1050-9542
K I N D NEWS SR. EDITION. (Kids in Nature's Defense) Text in English. 1983. 9/yr. (m. during school year). USD 30 domestic; USD 50 foreign (effective 2003). illus. 4 p./no.; **Document type:** *Newspaper.* **Description:** For schoolchildren in grades 5-6. Teaches children kindness to people, animals, and the Earth.
Formerly: Kind News 2
Published by: National Association for Humane and Environmental Education, PO Box 362, E Haddam, CT 06423-0362. TEL 860-434-8666, FAX 860-434-9579, nahee@nahee.org, http://www.nahee.org. Ed. Bill Derosa. R&P Lorie Blake TEL 860-434-8666 ext. 10. Circ: 1,222,800 (paid).

179.3 DEU
KATZENSCHUTZ KORRESPONDENZ. Text in German. 1976. q. EUR 20 membership (effective 2004). adv. bk.rev. back issues avail. **Document type:** *Newsletter, Consumer.*
Published by: Dortmunder Katzenschutzverein e.V., Postfach 120125, Dortmund, 44291, Germany. Circ: 2,300.

636.0832 USA ISSN 0898-3364
LABORATORY ANIMAL WELFARE. Text in English. 1984. a.
Published by: National Library of Medicine, 8600 Rockville Pike, Bethesda, MD 20209. TEL 301-594-5983, FAX 301-496-4000, http://www.nlm.nih.gov.

LATHAM LETTER. see *SOCIAL SERVICES AND WELFARE*

179.3 636.089 DEU ISSN 0948-4647
LEBENDIGE TIERWELT; tieraerztlicher Ratgeber fuer Tierfreunde. Text in German. 1994. q. EUR 8.60 (effective 2003). adv. bk.rev. back issues avail. **Document type:** *Magazine, Consumer.*
Published by: (Bundesverband Praktischer Tieraerzte e.V.), Schluetersche GmbH und Co. KG, Hans-Boeckler-Allee 7, Hannover, 30173, Germany. TEL 49-511-85500, FAX 49-511-85502405, vertrieb@schluetersche.de, http://www.schluetersche.de. adv.: B&W page EUR 2,928, color page EUR 4,564. Circ: 91,948 (paid and controlled).

636.0832 100 USA
LIVE AND LET LIVE; pro-life - animal rights - libertarian. Text in English. 1992. irreg. USD 1 newsstand/cover (effective 2003). adv. bk.rev. back issues avail. **Document type:** *Newsletter.* **Description:** Seeks to explore and develop a theory and strategy of fetal and animal rights from a libertarian - individualist framework. Provides a forum for libertarian and other animal-rights advocates outside the political, religious and philosophical mainstream of the animal-rights movement.
Published by: James N. Dawson, Ed. & Pub., PO Box 613, Redwood Valley, CA 95470. TEL 707-485-7092. Circ: 100.

179.4 363.7 641.5 GBR
LIVING WITHOUT CRUELTY DIARY (YEAR). Text in English. 1989. a. GBP 5 (effective 1999). **Document type:** *Directory.* **Description:** Provides recipes, news features, and other information for vegetarians and persons concerned with the environment. Contains a directory of environmental organizations.
Published by: Jon Carpenter Publishing, 2 Spendlove Centre, Charlbury, Chipping Norton, Oxon OX7 3PQ, United Kingdom. Ed. Mark Gold. Pub. Jon Carpenter.

179.3 179.4 GBR
LORD DOWDING FUND FOR HUMANE RESEARCH. BULLETIN. Text in English. 1980 (no.14). s-a. per issue contribution. adv. illus. **Document type:** *Bulletin.* **Description:** Gives scientific reports on projects that will replace the use of live animals in medical research.
Published by: National Anti-Vivisection Society, 261 Goldhawk Rd, London, W12 8EU, United Kingdom. TEL 44-20-8846-9777, FAX 44-20-8846-9712. Ed., R&P, Adv. contact Jan Creamer. Circ: 20,000.

179.309 GBR
MOREDUN. ANNUAL REPORT. Text in English. a.
Formerly: Moredum Foundation. Annual Report —BLDSC (1355.939000).
Published by: Moredun Foundation, 408 Gilmeron Rd, Edinburgh, EH17 7JH, United Kingdom. TEL 44-131-664-3262, FAX 44-131-664-8001.

179.4 USA
N A V S ANIMAL ACTION REPORT. Text in English. 1930. q. USD 25 membership (effective 2004); subscr. incld. with membership. adv. bk.rev. illus. back issues avail.; reprints avail. **Document type:** *Newsletter, Consumer.* **Description:** Publishes news and commentary on issues pertaining to vivisection and animal research, and reports the society's activities to foster public awareness and protest the continued existence of these practices.
Former titles: N A V S Bulletin and N A V S Animal Action Report; (until 199?): N A V S Bulletin (0270-8132)
Indexed: Agr, CIJE.
Published by: National Anti-Vivisection Society, 53 W Jackson Blvd, Ste 1552, Chicago, IL 60604-3795. TEL 312-427-6065, FAX 312-427-6524, navs@navs.org, http://www.navs.org. Circ: 30,000.

636.0832 USA
N E A V S UPDATE. Text in English. 1921. q. USD 20 donation. bk.rev. back issues avail. **Document type:** *Newsletter.*
Former titles: N E A V S Members Quarterly (1052-6978); (until 1990): Reverence for Life (0279-0513)
Related titles: Online - full content ed.
Published by: New England Anti-Vivisection Society, 333 Washington St, Ste 850, Boston, MA 02108-5100. TEL 617-523-6020, FAX 617-523-7925, info@ma.neavs.com, http://www.neavs.org. Ed., R&P Melinda B Everett TEL 617-523-6020 ext 17. Circ: 3,000.

179.3 USA
N Y T T S NEWSNOTES. Text in English. 1970. q. USD 20. adv. **Document type:** *Newsletter.* **Description:** Covers the care, breeding and conservation of the turtles and tortoises of the world.
Published by: New York Turtle and Tortoise Society, PO Box 878, Orange, NJ 07051-0878. TEL 212-459-4803, jvanabbema@erols.com, http://www.erols.com/jvanabbema/ nytts.htm. Ed. Jim Van Abbema. Circ: 1,500.

179.3 GBR ISSN 0077-4448
NATIONAL EQUINE (AND SMALLER ANIMALS) DEFENCE LEAGUE. ANNUAL REPORT. Text in English. 1909. a. GBP 3 (effective 2001). back issues avail. **Document type:** *Newsletter, Corporate.*
Published by: National Equine Defence League, National Equine Defence League, Oaktree Farm, Wetheral Shields, Wetheral, Carlisle, CA4 8JA, United Kingdom. TEL 44-1228-560082, FAX 44-1228-560985. Ed. Frank E Tebbutt. R&P Frank Tebbutt. Circ: 3,000.

179.3 USA
NATURAL HORSE. Text in English. 1999. 8/yr. USD 24.95 domestic; USD 32.95 in Canada; USD 49.95 elsewhere; USD 29.95 domestic print & online eds.; USD 37.95 in Canada print & online eds.; USD 55.95 elsewhere print & online eds. (effective 2001). **Description:** Focuses on humane alternatives to traditional horse care.
Address: PO Box 10, Holtwood, PA 17532. TEL 717-284-3720, 800-660-8923, FAX 717-284-3720, publisher@naturalhorse.com. Ed. Randi Peters.

NEW ZEALAND BEEKEEPER. see *BIOLOGY—Entomology*

179.3 USA ISSN 1547-6987
HV4701
NO COMPROMISE; the militant, direct action publication of grassroots animal liberationists & their supporters. Text in English. 1996. q. USD 15 domestic; USD 20 foreign (effective 2004). **Document type:** *Magazine.*
Address: 740A 14th St. #125, San Francisco, CA 94114. TEL 831-425-3007, nc-info@nocompromise.org, http://www.nocompromise.org.

NORTHEAST CANINE COMPANION. see *PETS*

636.0832 363.7 USA
OCEAN ALERT; campaign news on dolphins, whales, and the marine environment. Text in English. 198?. s-a. charts; illus.; maps; stat. **Document type:** *Newsletter.* **Description:** Treats marine mammal issues and includes information on what people can do to help.
Published by: (International Marine Mammal Project), Earth Island Institute, 300 Broadway, Ste 28, San Francisco, CA 94133-3312. TEL 415-788-3666, FAX 415-788-7324, marinemammal@igc.apc.org. R&P Laura Seligsohn. Circ: 10,000.

OCEANS ILLUSTRATED; giving voice to the silent world. see *EARTH SCIENCES—Oceanography*

179.3 FRA ISSN 0297-5785
QL690.F8
L'OISEAU MAGAZINE. Text in French. 1985. q. EUR 18.29 domestic; EUR 24.39 foreign (effective 2004). **Document type:** *Magazine, Consumer.* **Description:** Informs on the birds' integration in the ecosystems, the dangers they encounter and the measures taken to protect them.
Published by: Ligue pour la Protection des Oiseaux, La Corderie Royale, BP 263, Rochefort, 17305 Cedex, France. TEL 33-5-46821234, FAX 33-5-46839586, http://www.lpo.fr. Ed. Yann Hermieu. Pub. Pierre Pellerin.

ORGANIC FARMING; Soil Association's journal for organic horticulture & agriculture. see *AGRICULTURE*

OTTER RAFT. see *CONSERVATION*

179.3 USA ISSN 0030-6789
OUR ANIMALS. Text in English. 1906. q. USD 7.50 domestic; USD 10 in Canada; USD 15 elsewhere (effective 2004). adv. bk.rev. charts; illus. reprints avail. **Document type:** *Consumer.* **Description:** Publishes upbeat stories and articles about the services of the San Francisco S.P.C.A. Also includes pet care tips.
Published by: San Francisco Society for the Prevention of Cruelty to Animals, 2500 16th St, San Francisco, CA 94103. TEL 415-554-3000, FAX 415-552-7041, ouranimals@sfspca.org, http://www.sfspca.org/ourani.html. Ed. Paul M Glassner. Pub., R&P, Adv. contact Paul Glassner. Circ: 40,000.

179.3 USA ISSN 0030-6851
OUR FOURFOOTED FRIENDS. Text in English. 1899. q. membership only. adv. bk.rev. illus. **Document type:** *Magazine, Internal.* **Description:** Focuses on animal welfare and treatment.
Published by: Animal Rescue League of Boston, PO Box 265, Boston, MA 02117. http://www.arlboston.org/. Ed. Arthur G Slade. Circ: 18,000.

179.3 USA
HV4763
P E T A'S ANIMAL TIMES (ENGLISH EDITION). Text in English. 1980. q. USD 16 membership (effective 2005). bk.rev. illus. 23 p./no.; back issues avail.; reprints avail. **Document type:** *Magazine, Consumer.* **Description:** Examines issues of animal abuse and animal rights.
Formerly (until 1994): P E T A News (0899-9708)
Published by: People for the Ethical Treatment of Animals, Inc., 501 Front St, Norfolk, VA 23510. TEL 757-622-7382, FAX 757-622-0457, peta@peta.org, http://www.peta.org/liv/ animaltimes. Ed. Ingrid Newkirk. R&P Robyn Wesley. Circ: 350,000 (paid and controlled).

179.3 DEU ISSN 0947-8507
P E T A'S ANIMAL TIMES (GERMAN EDITION). Text in German. 1994. q. illus.; tr.lit. back issues avail. **Document type:** *Magazine, Consumer.*
Published by: People for the Ethical Treatment of Animals Inc., Postfach 311503, Stuttgart, 70475, Germany. TEL 49-711-8666165, FAX 49-711-8666166, info@peta.de, http://www.peta.de. Ed. Ingrid Newkirk. Circ: 20,000 (paid).

PARADE OF ROYALTY (YEAR). see *PETS*

PENDIK VETERINER MIKROBIYOLOJI DERGISI/JOURNAL OF PENDIK VETERINARY MICROBIOLOGY. see *VETERINARY SCIENCE*

PETSPECTIVES. see *PETS*

173.9 USA
PLASTRON PAPERS. Text in English. 1970. irreg. USD 20 for 4 issues. adv. **Document type:** *Newsletter.* **Description:** Contains scientific and technical articles of interest to professional biologists and serious hobbyists.
Published by: New York Turtle and Tortoise Society, PO Box 878, Orange, NJ 07051-0878. TEL 212-459-4803. Ed. James Van Abbema. Circ: 1,500.

PRIMATE EYE. see *ANTHROPOLOGY*

636.0832 ISR ISSN 0793-0070
PROANIMAL; independent non-profit bulletin for animal welfare and rights in Israel. Text in English. 1992. 2/yr. USD 5 per issue (effective 2000). adv. bk.rev. illus. back issues avail. **Document type:** *Bulletin.* **Description:** Publishes articles, reviews and news relating to animal welfare and animal rights issues in Israel.
Address: P O Box 2039, Rehovot, 76120, Israel. FAX 972-8-9467632. Eds. Karin Zupko, Suzanne Trauffer. Circ: 3,000.

A

179.4 NLD ISSN 1380-4316
PROEFDIERVRIJ. Text in Dutch. 1977. q. bk.rev. back issues avail. **Document type:** *Newsletter.* **Description:** Includes information about animal experimentation with the purpose to inform the public and to change their attitude in favor of animals and against vivisection.
Former titles (until 1994): Proefkonijn (0169-8915); (until 1985): Nederlands Bond tot Bestrijding van de Vivisectie. Berichten (0165-8778); Which was formed by the merger of (1971-1977): Androkles (0169-9989); (1971-1977): Androkles Bulletin (0169-9180); Incorporates (1992-1997): ProefkoneenNieuws (1382-9734); Incorporates (in 1999): Tegenbericht (1381-6438); Which was formerly (until 1995): Raegeermuis (0924-9400); (until 1990): Nieuwsbrief. Anti - Vivisectie - Stichting (0169-2704); (1930-1981): Mededelingen. Anti - Vivisectie - Stichting (0165-8816)
Address: Gevers Deynootweg 61, The Hague, 2586 BJ, Netherlands. TEL 31-70-306-2468, info@proefdiervrij.nl, http://www.proefdiervrij.nl. Ed. Joop van Eijk. Circ: 5,500.

179.3 028.3 SWE ISSN 1651-5528
RAEDDA DJUREN!. Text in Swedish. 1991. q. SEK 60 (effective 2005). **Document type:** *Magazine, Consumer.*
Formerly (until 2002): Ungdom foer Djurens Raett (1104-1412)
Published by: Foerbundet Djurens Raett/Animal Rights Sweden, PO Box 2005, Aelvsjoe, 12502, Sweden. TEL 46-8-55591400, FAX 46-8-55591450, info@djurensratt.se, http://www.djurensratt.se/dyntext/xlink.asp?id=269. Ed. Karin Gunnarsson.

RE-INTRODUCTION NEWS. see *CONSERVATION*

179.3 GBR
ROYAL SOCIETY FOR THE PREVENTION OF CRUELTY TO ANIMALS. ANNUAL REVIEW. Text in English. a. charts; illus. **Document type:** *Corporate.* **Description:** Outlines the activities of the RSPCA over the past year.
Formerly (until 2000): Royal Society for the Prevention of Cruelty to Animals. Annual Report
Published by: Royal Society for the Prevention of Cruelty to Animals, Wilberforce Way, Oakhurst Business Park, Southwater, Horsham, W Sussex RH13 7WN, United Kingdom. TEL 44-707-5335-999, 0870-010-1181, FAX 0870-753-0048, publications@rspca.org.uk, http://www.rspca.org.uk.

ROYAL SOCIETY FOR THE PREVENTION OF CRUELTY TO ANIMALS. TRUSTEES' REPORT AND ACCOUNTS. see *BUSINESS AND ECONOMICS—Accounting*

333.72 NZL ISSN 1174-9369
S A F E MAGAZINE; the voice for all animals. (Save Animals from Exploitation) Key Title: S A F E Series. Text in English. 1983. s-a. NZD 25 domestic; NZD 30 foreign (effective 2001). 34 p./no.; back issues avail. **Description:** Provides current news and information of issues relating to animal rights and the environment.
Formerly (until Oct. 2000): Safeguard (Christchurch) (1171-6320)
Published by: S A F E Inc., P.O. Box 13366, Christchurch, New Zealand. TEL 64-3-3799711, safe@chch.planet.co.nz, safe.ak@ihug.co.nz, http://www.safe.org.nz. Ed. Anthony Terry. Circ: 4,000.

636.0832 CAN
SASKATCHEWAN HUMANITARIAN. Text in English. q. adv. **Document type:** *Newsletter.*
Published by: Saskatchewan Society for Prevention of Cruelty to Animals, P O Box 37, Saskatoon, SK S7K 3K1, Canada. TEL 306-382-7722, FAX 306-384-3425. Ed. Susan McCune. Adv. contact Frances Wach.

SATYA; magazine of vegetarianism, environmentalism, and animal advocacy. see *NUTRITION AND DIETETICS*

636.0832 NZL
SAVE ANIMALS FROM EXPLOITATION. CAMPAIGN REPORT. Text in English. s-a. 8 p./no.; **Description:** Provides a comprehensive insight and focus on particular issues relating to animal rights in New Zealand and how to help.
Published by: S A F E Inc., P.O. Box 13366, Christchurch, New Zealand. TEL 64-3-3799711, safe@chch.planet.co.nz, safe.ak@ihug.co.nz. Ed. Anthony Terry.

179.3 CHE
SCHWEIZER TIERSCHUTZ; du und die Natur. Text in German. 1874. 4/yr. CHF 12.80. adv. bk.rev. **Document type:** *Bulletin.* **Description:** Covers laws and regulations concerning protection of animals, research in behavior and habits, zoology, hunting, etc. Includes association news, reports of events, and new publications.
Formerly: Tierfreund (0040-7313)
Published by: Schweizer Tierschutz STS, Dornacherstr 101, Basel, 4008, Switzerland. TEL 41-61-3611515, FAX 41-61-3611516. Ed. H P Haering. Circ: 60,000.

179.3 USA ISSN 0742-5260
SCIENTISTS CENTER FOR ANIMAL WELFARE. NEWSLETTER. Text in English. 1978. q. USD 40. bk.rev. index. back issues avail. **Document type:** *Newsletter.* **Description:** Directed to scientists, administrators, and regulatory agencies interested in current issues of animal welfare in research, testing, and education.
Published by: Scientists Center for Animal Welfare, 7833 Walker Dr, 340, Greenbelt, MD 20770-3229. TEL 301-345-3500, FAX 301-345-3503, scaw@erols.com. Ed., R&P Lee Krulisch. Circ: 5,000.

636.0832 USA ISSN 1088-8152
THE SHAPE OF ENRICHMENT. Text in English. q. USD 15 (effective 2005). **Document type:** *Journal, Trade.* **Description:** Covers environmental enrichment for animals. Includes feature articles, regular columns, short notes, conference announcements, letters, and other notices.
Published by: The Shape of Enrichment, Inc., 1650 Minden Dr, San Diego, CA 92111-7124. shape@enrichment.org, http://www.enrichment.org/publication.html.

179.3 USA ISSN 1066-4890
SHOPTALK (ENGLEWOOD). Text in English. q. USD 10 (effective 1999). adv. stat. back issues avail. **Document type:** *Trade.* **Description:** Publishes practical information on animal shelter management for the animal care and control professional.
Published by: American Humane Association, Animal Protection Division, 63 Inverness Dr E, Englewood, CO 80112-5117. TEL 303-792-9900, FAX 303-792-5333. Ed. Roxanne Hawn. Adv. contact Roxanne Ayala. Circ: 9,300 (controlled).

SIRENEWS. see *CONSERVATION*

SMALL CARNIVORE CONSERVATION. see *CONSERVATION*

179.3 NLD ISSN 1063-1119
QL85 CODEN: SANIEL
➤ **SOCIETY & ANIMALS**; social scientific studies of the human experience of other animals. Text in English. 1983; N.S. 1993. q. USD 61 in the Americas to individuals; EUR 49 elsewhere to individuals; USD 249 combined subscription in the Americas to institutions print & online eds.; EUR 1,999 combined subscription elsewhere to institutions print & online eds. (effective 2006). adv. bk.rev. illus. cum.index. back issues avail.; reprint service avail. from PSC. **Document type:** *Journal, Academic/Scholarly.* **Description:** Publishes original research studies describing and analyzing the ways in which animals figure in human life, in particular examining applied uses of animals in research, medicine, science and agriculture, animals in the popular culture, including animal symbolism and cultic rituals, wildlife and environmental issues, as well as sociopolitical and legal concerns.
Former titles (until 1993): P S Y E T A Bulletin; (until 1986): P S Y E T A Newsletter
Related titles: Online - full text ed.: ISSN 1568-5306. N.S. USD 224 in the Americas to institutions; EUR 179 elsewhere to institutions (effective 2006) (from EBSCO Publishing, Gale Group, IngentaConnect, Kluwer Online, O C L C Online Computer Library Center, Inc., Springer LINK, Swets Information Services).
Indexed: ASCA, Agr, CJA, CurCont, FoVS&M, IAB, IBSS, PsycInfo, PsycholAb, RefZh, SOPODA, SSA, SSCI, SociolAb, WildRev, ZooRec, e-psyche.
—BLDSC (8319.187500), IDS, IE, Infotrieve, ingenta. **CCC.**
Published by: (Psychologists for the Ethical Treatment of Animals USA), Brill Academic Publishers, PO Box 9000, Leiden, 2300 PA, Netherlands. TEL 31-71-53-53500, FAX 31-71-53-17532, cs@brill.nl, http://www.brill.nl/m_catalogue_sub6_id9005.htm. Ed. Kenneth Shapiro. Circ: 400. **Subscr. in N. America to:** PO Box 605, Herndon, VA 20172. TEL 703-661-1585, 800-337-9255, FAX 703-661-1501, cs@brillusa.com. **Distr. outside N. America by:** c/o Turpin Distribution, Stratton Business Park, Pegasus Drive, Biggleswade, BEDFORDSHIRE SG 18 8TQ, United Kingdom. TEL 44-1767-604-954, FAX 44-1767-601-640, brill@turpin-distribution.com.

156 636.0832 GBR ISSN 1363-464X
SOCIETY FOR COMPANION ANIMAL STUDIES. JOURNAL. Text in English. 1988. q. GBP 15 domestic; GBP 20 foreign (effective 2000). adv. **Document type:** *Newsletter.*
Indexed: IAB, e-psyche.
Published by: Society for Companion Animal Studies, 10b Leny Rd, Callander, FK17 8BA, United Kingdom. TEL 44-1877-330996, FAX 44-1877-330996, http://www.vetweb.co.uk/sites/scas/scashome.htm. Ed., R&P, Adv. contact Anne Docherty. Circ: 600.

T R A F F I C BULLETIN. (Trade Records Analysis of Flora and Fauna in Commerce) see *CONSERVATION*

TAPIR CONSERVATION. see *CONSERVATION*

TENTACLE. see *CONSERVATION*

179.3 179.4 GBR
U A C T A. (United Against Cruelty to Animals) Text in English. 1965. bi-m. GBP 3 to non-members. bk.rev.
Published by: Animals' Vigilantes, James Mason House, 24 Salisbury St, Fordingbridge, Hants SP6 1AF, United Kingdom. TEL 44-425-653663. Ed. Ted Cox. Circ: 10,000.

636.0832 GBR ISSN 0956-1137
U F A W ANIMAL WELFARE RESEARCH REPORT. Text in English. 1988 (no.2). irreg., latest vol.9, 1996. price varies. **Document type:** *Monographic series.*
Indexed: ZooRec.
Published by: Universities Federation for Animal Welfare, The Old School, Brewhouse Hill, Wheathampstead, St Albans, Herts AL4 8AN, United Kingdom. TEL 44-1582-831818, FAX 44-1582-831414, ufaw@ufaw.org.uk, http://www.ufaw.org.uk/.

179.3 GBR ISSN 0263-4600
U F A W ANNUAL REPORT AND ACCOUNTS. Text in English. 1926. a. GBP 10 to individual members; GBP 50, USD 100 to institutional members; GBP 5 to students (effective 2003). bk.rev. **Document type:** *Academic/Scholarly.* **Description:** Discusses animal welfare and scientific research into the needs of animals.
—CISTI.
Published by: Universities Federation for Animal Welfare, The Old School, Brewhouse Hill, Wheathampstead, St Albans, Herts AL4 8AN, United Kingdom. TEL 44-1582-831818, FAX 44-1582-831414, journal@ufaw.org.uk, http://www.ufaw.org.uk/. Circ: 3,000.

636.0832 GBR
U F A W HANDBOOK ON THE CARE AND MANAGEMENT OF LABORATORY ANIMALS. Text in English. 1993 (6th ed.). latest 7th edition, base vol. plus irreg. updates. price varies. **Document type:** *Journal, Trade.* **Description:** Provides guidance on practical animal husbandry, breeding, laboratory procedures and disease control for a wide variety of vertebrates.
Published by: (Universities Federation for Animal Welfare), Blackwell Publishing Ltd., 9600 Garsington Rd, Oxford, OX4 2ZG, United Kingdom. TEL 44-1865-776868, FAX 44-1865-714591, customerservices@oxon.blackwellpublishing.com, http://www.blackwellpublishing.com.

179.3 GBR ISSN 0566-8700
U F A W NEWS-SHEET. Text in English. 1965. a. (free with Annual Report and Accounts). bk.rev. **Document type:** *Newsletter.*
—CISTI.
Published by: Universities Federation for Animal Welfare, The Old School, Brewhouse Hill, Wheathampstead, St Albans, Herts AL4 8AN, United Kingdom. TEL 44-1582-831818, FAX 44-1582-831414, journal@ufaw.org.uk, http://www.ufaw.org.uk/. Circ: 3,000.

THE VEGAN. see *NUTRITION AND DIETETICS*

THE VEGAN NEWS. see *NUTRITION AND DIETETICS*

179.3 FRA
LA VOIX DES BETES; organe officiel d'assistance aux animaux. Text in French. 5/yr. free to qualified personnel. bk.rev. illus. **Document type:** *Magazine, Consumer.*
Published by: Fondation Assistance aux Animaux, 24 Rue Berlioz, Paris, 75116, France. TEL 33-1-40671004, http://www.krabott.free.fr/nfaa/. Ed. Robert Quemy. Pub. Arlette Alessandri. Circ: 11,000; 46,000 (controlled).

333.9 USA
WHALEWATCH. Text in English. q. USD 17 to members. back issues avail. **Description:** Describes the IWC's whale protection and whale advocacy activities for members who have adopted whales.
Published by: International Wildlife Coalition, 70 E Falmouth Hwy, East Falmouth, MA 02536. TEL 508-548-8328. Ed. James Kinney.

WILD ABOUT ANIMALS; the magazine for all pet owners and animal lovers. see *PETS*

333.95416 USA
WILD HORSE AND BURRO DIARY✶. Text in English. 1960. q. membership. bk.rev. back issues avail. **Document type:** *Newsletter.* **Description:** Brings readers in touch with current issues pertaining to the protection of wild horses and burros and their habitat in the United States and worldwide.
Published by: International Society for the Protection of Mustangs and Burros, HC 53 BOX 7C, INTERIOR, JACKSON, SD 57750-9606. TEL 605-433-5600, FAX 602-991-2920, ispmb@gwtc.net, ispmb@qwtc.net. Ed. Karen Sussman. Circ: 2,000.

WILDLIFE AUSTRALIA. see *CONSERVATION*

636.0832 USA
WILDLIFE DAMAGE CONTROL SPECIALISTS NEWSLETTER. Text in English. 1998. bi-m. free. Website rev. 2 p./no. 1 cols./p.; back issues avail. **Document type:** *Trade.* **Description:** Designed to help keep the professional animal damage controller up-to-date on issues relating to animal rights, business policies, new products, new animal control information, etc.
Media: Online - full text.
Published by: Wildlife Damage Control, 340 Cooley St, Springfield, MA 01128. admin@wildlifedamagecontrol.com, http://www.wildlifedamagecontrol.com. Ed. Stephen Vantassel TEL 413-796-9916.

179.3 639.9 GBR
WILDLIFE GUARDIAN. Text in English. 1924. q. free to members (effective 2005). adv. bk.rev.; software rev.; video rev.; Website rev. 24 p./no.; back issues avail. **Document type:** *Magazine, Consumer.* **Description:** Presents news about cruelty to animals through bloodsport activities. Features protection efforts, personal profiles and political comments.
Formerly: Cruel Sports
Published by: League Against Cruel Sports Ltd., Sparling House, 83-87 Union St, London, SE1 1SG, United Kingdom. TEL 44-20-7403-6155, FAX 44-20-7403-4532, guardian@league.uk.com, mail@league.uk.com, http://www.league.uk.com. Eds. Peter Anderson, Susan Kerry Bedell. R&P Susan Kerry Bedell. Adv. contact Maresa Bossano. Circ: 40,000.

179.3 RUS
ZOV. Text in Russian. 1990. bi-m. RUR 36 for 6 mos.. bk.rev. illus. 4 p./no. 5 cols./p.; back issues avail. **Document type:** *Newspaper.* **Description:** Offers a forum to discuss animal welfare issues, publishes poetry/fiction about animals, answers readers questions, toward the goal of educating readers.
Published by: Rossiiskoe Obshchestvo Pokrovitel'stva Zhivotnym/Russian Society for the Protection of Animals, 2-i Neopalimovskii per 3, Moscow, 119121, Russian Federation. TEL 7-095-2471704, FAX 7-095-2464079. Ed. Stanislav Dewitte. Circ: 1,000; 2,000 (paid).

ANTHROPOLOGY

see also ARCHAEOLOGY ; FOLKLORE

301 USA ISSN 0090-9939
GN43.A2
A A A GUIDE (YEAR). Text in English. 1968. a. USD 50 to non-members; USD 35 to members (effective 1999). index. reprints avail. **Document type:** *Trade.* **Description:** Lists academic, museum and research departments of anthropology; faculties and their specialties; student enrollment figures; PhD dissertations in anthropology.
Formerly: Guide to Departments of Anthropology (Year)
Published by: American Anthropological Association, 2200 Wilson Blvd, Ste 600, Arlington, VA 22201. TEL 703-528-1902, FAX 703-528-3546, http://www.aaanet.org. Ed. Julie Legg. R&P Terry Clifford. Circ: 4,000.

305.8 ITA
A E S; materiali, studi e argomenti di etnografia e storia sociale. Text in Italian. 1993. s-a.
Published by: Associazione di Etnografia e Storia Sociale, c/o Diakronia, Via Albini, 4-b, Vigevano, PV 27029, Italy.

A G S QUARTERLY. see *ART*

301 USA ISSN 0738-064X
➤ **A M S STUDIES IN ANTHROPOLOGY.** Text in English. 1983. irreg., latest vol.11, 1993. price varies. back issues avail. **Document type:** *Monographic series, Academic/Scholarly.* **Description:** Monographs of specific ethnographic studies in anthropology.
Published by: (Abrahams Magazine Service), A M S Press, Inc., 63 Flushing Ave., # 417, Brooklyn, NY 11205-1005. TEL 212-777-4700, FAX 212-995-5413.

301 DEU
A P A D BULLETIN. Text in English, French. irreg., latest vol.14, 1998. **Document type:** *Academic/Scholarly.*
—BLDSC (2394.475000).
Published by: (Association Euro-Africaine pour l'Anthropologie du Changement Social et du Developpement), Lit Verlag, Grindelberg 15a, Hamburg, 20144, Germany. lit@lit-verlag.de, http://www.lit-verlag.de. Ed. Brehima Kassibo.

A P U PRESS ALASKANA BOOK SERIES. see *HISTORY—History Of North And South America*

306 GBR
➤ **A S A RESEARCH METHODS IN SOCIAL ANTHROPOLOGY.** Text in English. 1976. irreg. price varies. index. reprint service avail. from ISI. **Document type:** *Monographic series, Academic/Scholarly.*
Formerly: A S A Monographs (0066-9679)
—BLDSC (1738.570000). **CCC.**
Published by: (Association of Social Anthropologists of the Commonwealth USA), Berg Publishers, Angel Court, 1st Fl, 81 St Clements St, Oxford, Berks OX4 1AW, United Kingdom. TEL 44-1865-245104, FAX 44-1865-791165, enquiry@bergpublishers.com, http://www.bergpublishers.com/.

➤ **AARNI.** see *HISTORY—History Of Europe*

➤ **ABHANDLUNGEN ANTHROPOGEOGRAPHIE.** see *GEOGRAPHY*

➤ **ABORIGINAL AND TORRES STRAIT ISLANDER STUDIES UNIT RESEARCH REPORT SERIES.** see *ETHNIC INTERESTS*

➤ **ABORIGINAL HISTORY.** see *HISTORY—History Of Australasia And Other Areas*

➤ **ABSTRACTS IN ANTHROPOLOGY.** see *ANTHROPOLOGY—Abstracting, Bibliographies, Statistics*

305.8 TWN ISSN 0001-3935
ACADEMIA SINICA. INSTITUTE OF ETHNOLOGY. BULLETIN. Key Title: Minzuxue Yanjiusuo Jikan, Zhongyang Yanjiuyuan. Text in Chinese, English. 1956. s-a. TWD 400, USD 40. illus. **Document type:** *Bulletin, Academic/Scholarly.*
Indexed: AICP, AnthLit, BAS, IBSS, PSA, SOPODA, SSA, SociolAb.
Published by: Academia Sinica, Institute of Ethnology/Chung Yang Yen Chiu Yuan, Min Tsu Hsueh Yen Chiu So, Nankang, Taipei, 11529, Taiwan. TEL 886-2-26523302, FAX 866-2-652-3378, Lexis@ms6.hinet.net. Ed. Cheng Kuang Hsu. Circ: 1,500. **Subscr. to:** Lexis Book Co. Ltd., 10F-1 No 138, Sec2, Chin-Shan South Rd, Taipei, Taiwan. TEL 886-2-3219033, FAX 866-2-356-8068.

ACADEMIE POLONAISE DES SCIENCES. CENTRE D'ARCHEOLOGIE MEDITERRANEENNE. TRAVAUX. see *ARCHAEOLOGY*

305.8 HUN ISSN 1216-9803
GN1
ACTA ETHNOGRAPHICA HUNGARICA; an international journal of ethnography. Text in English, French, German, Russian. 1950. q. USD 300 (effective 2006). adv. bk.rev. bibl.; charts; illus.; abstr. index. 120 p./no.; back issues avail. **Document type:** *Journal, Academic/Scholarly.* **Description:** Publishes contributions describing recent scientific advances in ethnography, folklore and cultural and social anthropology.
Formerly (until 1990): Academiae Scientiarum Hungaricae. Acta Ethnografica (0001-5628)
Related titles: Online - full text ed.: ISSN 1588-2586 (from EBSCO Publishing, Swets Information Services).
Indexed: AICP, AnthLit, ArtHuCI, BAS, BHA, BiolAb, CurCont, DIP, GEOBASE, IBR, IBSS, IBZ, IndIslam, L&LBA, MLA, MLA-IB, PCI, RASB, RI-1, RI-2, RILM, SSA, SSCI, SociolAb.
—**CCC.**
Published by: (Magyar Tudomanyos Akademia/Hungarian Academy of Sciences), Akademiai Kiado Rt. (Subsidiary of: Wolters Kluwer N.V.), Prielle Kornelia U. 19, Budapest, 1117, Hungary. TEL 36-1-4648282, FAX 36-1-4648221, journals@akkrt.hu, http://www.akkrt.hu. Ed. Bertalan Andrasfalvy.

305.8 CZE ISSN 0862-1209
GN2
ACTA MUSEI MORAVIAE. SUPPLEMENTUM: FOLIA ETHNOGRAPHICA. Text in Czech, English, German. 1959. a. USD 17 (effective 2000). **Document type:** *Academic/Scholarly.*
Formerly (until 1986): Ethnographica (0425-4570)
Related titles: ◆ Supplement to: Acta Musei Moraviae. Scientiae Sociales. ISSN 0323-0570.
Indexed: AICP, RASB.
Published by: Moravske Zemske Muzeum, Zelny trh 6, Brno, 65937, Czech Republic. TEL 420-5-42321205, FAX 420-5-42212792, mzm@mzm.anet.cz, mzm@mzm.cz, http://www.mzm.cz. Ed. Eva Vecerkova.

305.8 POL ISSN 0208-6042
ACTA UNIVERSITATIS LODZIENSIS: FOLIA ETHNOLOGICA. Text in Polish; Summaries in Multiple languages. irreg. **Document type:** *Academic/Scholarly.* **Description:** Covers all aspects of ethnology.
Formerly (until 1982): Acta Universitatis Lodziensis: Folia Ethnographica
Indexed: RASB.
—KNAW.
Published by: Wydawnictwo Uniwersytetu Lodzkiego/Lodz University Press, ul Jaracza 34, Lodz, 90262, Poland. TEL 331671. **Dist. by:** Ars Polona, Krakowskie Przedmiescie 7, Warsaw, Poland.

305.8 POL
ACTA UNIVERSITATIS WRATISLAVIENSIS. ETHNOLOGICA. Text in Polish; Summaries in English, German. 1993. irreg. price varies. **Document type:** *Academic/Scholarly.*
Published by: (Uniwersytet Wroclawski), Wydawnictwo Uniwersytetu Wroclawskiego Spolka z o.o., Pl Uniwersytecki 9-13, Wroclaw, 50-137, Poland. TEL 48-71-441006, FAX 48-71-402735. Ed. Edward Pietraszek. Circ: 300.

301 POL
ACTA UNIVERSITATIS WRATISLAVIENSIS. STUDIA ANTROPOLOGICZNE. Text in Polish. 1994. irreg. price varies. **Document type:** *Academic/Scholarly.*
Indexed: RASB.
Published by: (Uniwersytet Wroclawski), Wydawnictwo Uniwersytetu Wroclawskiego Spolka z o.o., Pl Uniwersytecki 9-13, Wroclaw, 50-137, Poland. TEL 48-71-441076, FAX 48-71-402735. Ed. Tadeusz Krupinski.

301 ARG ISSN 0567-8560
ACTUALIDAD ANTROPOLOGIA✶. Text in Spanish. 1967. s-a.
Related titles: ◆ Supplement to: Etnia. ISSN 0046-2632.
Indexed: AICP.
Published by: Museo Etnografico Municipal Damasco Arce. Instituto de Investigaciones Antropologicas, San Martin 2862, Buenos Aires, 7400, Argentina.

ADVANCES IN GENDER RESEARCH. see *WOMEN'S STUDIES*

AESTHETIK UND NATURWISSENSCHAFTEN. see *PHILOSOPHY*

AFRICA. see *HISTORY—History Of Africa*

306.4 ITA ISSN 1121-8495
AFRICA E MEDITERRANEO; trimestrale di cultura, politica, economia, societa. Text in Italian. 1992. q. EUR 40 domestic; EUR 75 foreign (effective 2005). bk.rev. abstr. back issues avail. **Document type:** *Magazine, Consumer.* **Description:** Contains information on culture, contemporary art, music,literature, society, and immigration problems of the African and Mediterranean countries.
Indexed: PerIslam.
Published by: Lai-Momo Soc. Coop., Via Gamberi 4, Sasso Marconi, BO 40037, Italy. http://www.africaemediterraneo.it, www.africaemediterraneo.it/rivista/editore.htm. Ed. Sandra Federici. Pub. Giacomo Matti. Circ: 1,500.

AFRICA TERVUREN. see *HISTORY—History Of Africa*

AFRICAN AND ASIAN STUDIES. see *SOCIOLOGY*

301 CMR
THE AFRICAN ANTHROPOLOGIST/ANTHROPOLOGUE AFRICAIN. Text in Multiple languages. 1994. s-a. USD 25 in Africa to individuals; USD 40 elsewhere to individuals; USD 60 in Africa to institutions; USD 70 elsewhere to institutions; USD 15 in Africa to students; USD 20 elsewhere to students (effective 2003). bk.rev. **Description:** Provides a forum for African and Africanist anthropologists to publish research reports, articles, book reviews, news items and other useful information.
Formerly (until 1999): African Anthropology (1024-0969)
Related titles: Online - full text ed.: (from International Network for the Availability of Scientific Publications, African Journals Online).
Indexed: AnthLit.
—BLDSC (0732.313600), IE, ingenta.
Published by: Pan African Anthropolgical Association, BP 1862, Yaounde, Cameroon. icassrt@camnet.cm, http://inasp.info/ajol/journals/aa/about.html.

968 CAN ISSN 0832-8277
AFRICAN OCCASIONAL PAPERS SERIES. Text in English. irreg. price varies. adv. **Document type:** *Monographic series.* **Description:** Provides information on topics relevant to African archaeology and anthropology; most material is taken from edited theses submitted for higher degrees at various African universities.
Indexed: FS&TA, HortAb.
Published by: University of Calgary Press, University of Calgary, Faculty of Education ETD 722, 2500 University Dr N W, Calgary, AB T2N 1N4, Canada. TEL 403-220-7550, FAX 403-282-7269, http://www.ucalgary.ca/ucpress, http://www.uofcpress.com. Ed. Shirley A Onn. R&P Wendy Stephens TEL 403-220-3721. Adv. contact Sharon Boyle. **Subscr. to:** Raincoast Books in Vancouver, 8680 Cambie St, Vancouver, BC V6P 6M9, Canada. TEL 800-663-5714, FAX 800-565-3770.

305.8 GBR ISSN 0002-0184
DT751
➤ **AFRICAN STUDIES.** Text in English. 1923. s-a. GBP 187, USD 307 combined subscription to institutions print & online eds. (effective 2006). adv. bk.rev. charts; illus. index. reprint service avail. from PSC. **Document type:** *Journal, Academic/Scholarly.* **Description:** Scholarly articles on topics relevant to African anthropology, history, politics, linguistics, literature, sociology and related studies.
Formerly (until 1938): Bantu Studies (0256-1751)
Related titles: Online - full text ed.: ISSN 1469-2872. GBP 178, USD 293 to institutions (effective 2006) (from EBSCO Publishing, Gale Group, IngentaConnect, O C L C Online Computer Library Center, Inc., Swets Information Services).
Indexed: AICP, ASD, ASSIA, AbAn, AmH&L, AnthLit, BibLing, CCA, CurCont, HistAb, I&DA, IBR, IBSS, IBZ, IIBP, IPSA, ISAP, IndIslam, MEA&I, MLA, MLA-IB, PCI, PSA, RASB, RDA, S&F, SOPODA, SSCI, SSI, SociolAb, TDB, WAE&RSA.
—BLDSC (0734.000000), IDS, IE, Infotrieve, ingenta. **CCC.**
Published by: Routledge (Subsidiary of: Taylor & Francis Group), 4 Park Sq, Milton Park, Abingdon, Oxon OX14 4RN, United Kingdom. TEL 44-1235-828600, FAX 44-1235-829000, info@routledge.co.uk, http://www.tandf.co.uk/journals/titles/00020184.asp, http://www.routledge.com. Eds. Charles Mather, Clive Glaser, Shireen Hassim. Circ: 600.

➤ **AFRICAN STUDIES.** see *HISTORY—History Of Africa*

301 JPN ISSN 0285-1601
DT1
AFRICAN STUDY MONOGRAPHS. Text and summaries in English, French. 1981. q. free. abstr. back issues avail. **Document type:** *Monographic series.* **Description:** Covers the research on the nature of Africa, and the people and cultures there.
Formerly (unil 1976): Kyoto University African Studies (0454-7985)
Related titles: ◆ Supplement(s): African Study Monographs. Supplementary Issue. ISSN 0286-9667.

Indexed: AICP, ARDT, ASD, AnthLit, BibLing, IBSS, SFA, ZooRec.
—BLDSC (0734.920000), Infotrieve. **CCC.**
Published by: Kyoto University, Center for African Area Studies, 46 Yoshidashimoadachi-cho, Sakyo-ku, Kyoto-shi, 606-8304, Japan. TEL 81-75-753-7800, FAX 81-75-753-7810, asm@jambo.africa.kyoto-u.ac.jp, http://jambo.africa.kyoto-u.ac.jp/welcome.html. Circ: 1,000.

301 JPN ISSN 0286-9667
DT1
AFRICAN STUDY MONOGRAPHS. SUPPLEMENTARY ISSUE. Text in English, French. 1982. irreg. free. back issues avail. **Document type:** *Monographic series.* **Description:** Covers research on the nature of Africa, and the people and cultures there.
Related titles: ♦ Supplement to: African Study Monographs. ISSN 0285-1601.
Indexed: AICP, ASD, AnthLit, IBSS, ZooRec.
—BLDSC (0734.921000).
Published by: Kyoto University, Center for African Area Studies, 46 Yoshidashimoadachi-cho, Sakyo-ku, Kyoto-shi, 606-8304, Japan. TEL 81-75-753-7800, FAX 81-75-753-7810, asm@jambo.africa.kyoto-u.ac.jp, http://jambo.africa.kyoto-u.ac.jp/welcome.html. Circ: 1,000.

301 BEL ISSN 0776-7323
AFRICANA GANDENSIA. Text in Dutch. 1976. irreg. **Document type:** *Academic/Scholarly.*
Indexed: BibLing, CCA, IBSS.
Published by: Universiteit Gent, Seminarie voor Afrikaanse Cultuurgeschiedenis, Sint Pietersplein 4, Ghent, 9000, Belgium.

301 PHL ISSN 0117-6595
➤ **AGHAMTAO.** Text in English. 1978. a. PHP 150, USD 15. bk.rev. **Document type:** *Academic/Scholarly.* **Description:** Publishes anthropological papers by Filipino authors.
Indexed: BAS, IPP.
Published by: Ugnayang Pang-Aghamtao, Inc./Anthropological Association of the Philippines, Rm. 208, Philippine Social Science Center, Commonwealth Ave, Diliman, Quezon City, Philippines. TEL 63-2-922-9621. Circ: 1,000.

305.8 JPN ISSN 0285-4406
DS41
AL-RAFIDAN/JOURNAL OF WESTERN ASIATIC STUDIES. Text in English. 1980. irreg. **Document type:** *Monographic series.*
Indexed: AnthLit.
Published by: Kokushikan University, Institute for Cultural Studies of Ancient Iraq, 4-28-1 Setagaya, Setagaya-ku, Tokyo, 154-8515, Japan. TEL 81-3-54813206, FAX 81-3-54813210, ic@kiss.kokushikan.ac.jp, http://www.kokushikan.ac.jp.

ALASKA HISTORY; a publication of the Alaska Historical Society. see *HISTORY—History Of North And South America*

301 USA ISSN 1544-9793
GN560.U6
ALASKA JOURNAL OF ANTHROPOLOGY. Text in English. 2001. irreg. USD 50 to individuals; USD 150 to institutions; USD 35 to members (effective 2003).
Published by: Alaska Anthropological Association, P. O. Box 241686, Anchorage, AK 99524-1686. TEL 907-336-0092, http://www.alaska.net/~oha/aaa/. Ed. Owen K. Mason.

ALASKA NATIVE LANGUAGE CENTER RESEARCH PAPERS. see *LINGUISTICS*

ALBERTA ARCHAEOLOGICAL REVIEW. see *ARCHAEOLOGY*

301 909.04 CAN ISSN 0831-5671
➤ **ALGONQUIAN CONFERENCE. PAPERS.** Variant title: Papers of the Algonquian Conference/Actes du Congres des Algonquianistes. Text in English, French. 1976. a., latest vol.35. CND 48 per issue domestic; USD 48, EUR 48 per issue elsewhere (effective 2005). bibl. Current cumulative index by author available at website. 1 cols./p.; back issues avail. **Document type:** *Proceedings, Academic/Scholarly.* **Description:** A selection of papers from the annual multi-disciplinary conference, all relating to the Algonquian language family.
Indexed: AmH&L, AnthLit, BibLing, HistAb, LingAb, MLA-IB, PCI.
Published by: Algonquian Conference, University of Manitoba, Linguistics Dept., Winnipeg, MB R3T 5V5, Canada. TEL 204-474-9300, FAX 204-474-7671, acogg@cc.umanitoba.ca, http://www.umanitoba.ca/algonquian. Ed. H C Wolfart. Circ: 300.

➤ **ALT-THUERINGEN.** see *HISTORY—History Of Europe*

301 MEX ISSN 0188-7017
GN17.3.M6 CODEN: ALTEFL
ALTERIDADES. Text in Spanish. 1991. a. abstr. **Document type:** *Academic/Scholarly.*
Related titles: Online - full text ed.
Indexed: Inspec, PAIS, PSA, SSA, SociolAb.
Published by: Universidad Autonoma Metropolitana - Iztapalapa, Division de Ciencias Sociales y Humanidades. Departamento de Antropologia, Ave San Rafael Atlixco # 186, Col Vicentina, Del Iztapalapa, Mexico City, 09340, Mexico. TEL 52-55-7724-4760, antro@xanum.uam.mx, http://www.uam-antropologia.info/alteridades.html, http://www.iztapalapa.uam.mx/. Ed. Antulio Sanchez Garcia. Circ: 1,000.

ALTERNATE ROUTES; a journal of critical social research. see *SOCIAL SCIENCES: COMPREHENSIVE WORKS*

301 PER ISSN 0252-886X
F3429
AMAZONIA PERUANA. Text in Spanish. 1977. s-a. USD 40 in Latin America; USD 50 elsewhere. adv. bk.rev. bibl.; charts; illus. back issues avail. **Document type:** *Academic/Scholarly.*
Indexed: AICP, AnthLit, HAPI, IBR, IBSS, PAIS, WeedAb.
Published by: Centro Amazonico de Antropologia y Aplicacion Practica, Programa de Difusion, Madgalena del Mar, Gonzales Prada, 626, Magdalena Del Mar, Apdo Postal 14 0166, Lima, 17, Peru. FAX 638846. Ed. Jaime Regan. Adv. contact Manuel Cornejo. Circ: 1,000.

301 MEX ISSN 0185-1179
E51
AMERICA INDIGENA. Text in English, Spanish, Portuguese; Summaries in English. 1941. q. USD 75 domestic; USD 80 in Latin America; USD 80 in North America; USD 85 elsewhere (effective 2004). bk.rev. bibl.; charts; illus.; stat. cum.index: 1940-1980, 1980-1990. reprints avail. **Description:** Covers anthropology and history of the Indian culture in Latin America. Explores all the natural, social and human disciplines.
Related titles: ♦ Supplement(s): Anuario Indigenista. ISSN 0304-2596.
Indexed: AICP, AmH&L, AnthLit, BibInd, BibLing, HAPI, HistAb, IBR, IBSS, IBZ, ILD, PCI, RI-1, RI-2, RILM, SOPODA.
—BLDSC (0809.750000), IE, Infotrieve, ingenta.
Published by: Instituto Indigenista Interamericano, Ave de las Fuentes 106, Col. Jardines del Pedregal, Del Alvaro Obregon, Mexico City, DF 01900, Mexico. TEL 52-55-55958410, FAX 52-55-55954324, ininin@data.net.mx, http://www.cdi.gob.mx/conadepi/iii/.

301 USA ISSN 0160-1873
GN3
AMERICAN ANTHROPOLOGICAL ASSOCIATION. ABSTRACTS OF MEETINGS. Text in English. a. USD 15 (effective 1999). reprints avail. **Document type:** *Proceedings, Abstract/Index.* **Description:** Publishes the abstracts of papers to be presented at the annual meeting.
Indexed: AICP.
Published by: American Anthropological Association, 2200 Wilson Blvd, Ste 600, Arlington, VA 22201. TEL 703-528-1902, FAX 703-528-3546, http://www.aaanet.org. Ed. Frederick T Custer. R&P Terry Clifford. adv.: page USD 660; trim 11 x 8.5.

301 USA ISSN 0002-7294
GN1 CODEN: AMATA7
➤ **AMERICAN ANTHROPOLOGIST.** Text in English. 1899. q. USD 213 to non-members & institutions (effective 2006). adv. bk.rev. bibl.; charts; illus. Index. reprints avail. **Document type:** *Journal, Academic/Scholarly.* **Description:** Covers cultural, physical, linguistic and applied anthropology. Includes information on archaeology.
Related titles: Microform ed.: ISSN 0364-9873 (from PQC); Online - full text ed.: (from bigchalk, H.W. Wilson, JSTOR (Web-based Journal Archive), O C L C Online Computer Library Center, Inc., ProQuest Information & Learning).
Indexed: ABS&EES, AICP, ASCA, AbAn, Acal, AgeL, AmH&L, AnthLit, ArtHuCI, B&AI, BAS, BEL&L, BRD, BRI, BibLing, BiolAb, BrArAb, CBRI, CJA, ChLitAb, ChPerI, CommAb, CurCont, DIP, EI, ExcerpMed, FLI, FamI, GSI, HistAb, IBR, IBSS, IBZ, IPSA, IPsyAb, IndIslam, L&LBA, MEA&I, MLA, MLA-IB, MRD, MaizeAb, NumL, PCI, PRA, PSA, PopulInd, PsycInfo, PsycholAb, RASB, RI-1, RI-2, RILM, RefSour, SFSA, SOPODA, SPPI, SRRA, SSA, SSCI, SSI, SWA, SociolAb, TriticAb, WAE&RSA, ZooRec, e-psyche.
—BLDSC (0810.290000), IDS, IE, ingenta, Linda Hall. **CCC.**
Published by: (American Anthropological Association), University of California Press, Journals Division, 2000 Center St, Ste 303, Berkeley, CA 94704-1223. TEL 510-643-7154, FAX 510-642-9917, journals@ucpress.edu, http://www.ucpress.edu/journals/3a/aa. Eds. Frances Macia-Lees, Susan H Lees. adv.: page USD 1,050; 7 x 9.3. Circ: 13,000.

301 USA ISSN 0065-6941
➤ **AMERICAN ANTHROPOLOGIST. SPECIAL PUBLICATION.** Text in English. 1964. q. reprints avail. **Document type:** *Academic/Scholarly.*
Indexed: AnthLit, e-psyche.
—**CCC.**
Published by: American Anthropological Association, 2200 Wilson Blvd, Ste 600, Arlington, VA 22201. TEL 703-528-1902, FAX 703-528-3546, http://www.aaanet.org. R&P Terry Clifford.

305.8 USA
AMERICAN CULTURES SERIES. Text in English. 1988. irreg., latest vol.13, 1997. price varies. illus. back issues avail. **Document type:** *Monographic series, Academic/Scholarly.* **Description:** Studies the variety and diversity of cultural practices from theoretical, historical, and ethnographic perspectives, cuts across the traditional boundaries between the human and social sciences.
Published by: University of Minnesota Press, 111 Third Ave S, Ste 290, Minneapolis, MN 55401-2520. TEL 612-627-1970, FAX 612-627-1980, http://www.upress.umn.edu/byseries/american.html. Eds. George Lipsitz, Nancy Fraser, Stanley Aronowitz. **Dist. by:** c/o Chicago Distribution Center, 11030 S Langley Ave, Chicago, IL 60628; Plymbridge Distributors Ltd, Plymbridge House, Estover Rd, Plymouth, Devon PL6 7PY, United Kingdom. TEL 44-1752-202300, FAX 44-1752-202330, enquiries@plymbridge.com, http://www.plymbridge.com.

305.8 USA ISSN 0094-0496
GN1 CODEN: AMETFW
➤ **AMERICAN ETHNOLOGIST.** Text in English. 1974. q. USD 127 (effective 2006). adv. bk.rev. bibl.; illus. Index. reprints avail. **Document type:** *Journal, Academic/Scholarly.* **Description:** Presents topical papers, review articles, comments and reflections, and reviews in areas such as ecology, economy, social organization, ethnicity, politics, and ideology.
Related titles: Microform ed.: (from PQC); Online - full text ed.: (from H.W. Wilson, JSTOR (Web-based Journal Archive), O C L C Online Computer Library Center, Inc.).
Indexed: AICP, ASCA, AbAn, AnthLit, ArtHuCI, BAS, BRI, BibLing, CBRI, CERDIC, CJA, ChPerI, CommAb, CurCont, EI, FamI, IBR, IBSS, IBZ, IndIslam, LRI, MEA&I, PCI, PRA, PsycInfo, PsycholAb, RASB, RI-1, RI-2, RILM, SPPI, SRRA, SSA, SSCI, SSI, SociolAb, e-psyche.
—BLDSC (0814.200000), IDS, IE, ingenta. **CCC.**
Published by: (American Anthropological Association, American Ethnological Society), University of California Press, Journals Division, 2000 Center St, Ste 303, Berkeley, CA 94704-1223. TEL 510-643-7154, FAX 510-642-9917, journals@ucpress.edu, http://www.ucpress.edu/journals/3a/ae. Ed. Virginia R Dominguez. adv.: page USD 350; 7 x 9.3. Circ: 3,500.

599.9 USA ISSN 0002-9483
GN1 CODEN: AJPNA9
➤ **AMERICAN JOURNAL OF PHYSICAL ANTHROPOLOGY.** Text in English. 1918. 14/yr. (incl. 2 supplements). USD 2,075 domestic to institutions; USD 2,243 in Canada & Mexico to institutions; USD 2,341 elsewhere to institutions; USD 2,283 combined subscription domestic to institutions print & online eds.; USD 2,451 combined subscription in Canada & Mexico to institutions print & online eds.; USD 2,549 combined subscription elsewhere to institutions print & online eds. (effective 2006). adv. bk.rev. bibl.; charts; illus. index. back issues avail.; reprints avail. **Document type:** *Journal, Academic/Scholarly.* **Description:** Publishes information on human evolution and variation, including primate morphology, physiology, genetics, adaptation, growth, development, and behavior past and present.
Related titles: Microform ed.: (from PQC); Online - full text ed.: ISSN 1096-8644. 1996. USD 2,075 to institutions (effective 2006) (from EBSCO Publishing, Swets Information Services, Wiley InterScience); ♦ Supplement(s): Yearbook of Physical Anthropology. ISSN 0096-848X.
Indexed: AICP, ASCA, ASFA, AbAn, AbHyg, AgBio, AmH&L, AnBrAb, AnthLit, ArtHuCI, BAS, BDM&CN, BIOSIS Prev, BMAb, BiolAb, CTD, ChPerI, CurCont, DSA, DentInd, ExcerpMed, FamI, ForAb, HelmAb, IBSS, ISR, IndIslam, IndMed, IndVet, Inpharma, MEA&I, MEDLINE, MaizeAb, NutrAb, PN&I, ProtozoAb, RASB, RDA, RM&VM, RRTA, Reac, RefZh, SCI, SIA, SRRA, SSCI, SSI, SWA, SeedAb, TDB, VetBull, WAE&RSA, WildRev, ZooRec.
—BLDSC (0832.000000), GNLM, IDS, IE, Infotrieve, ingenta, Linda Hall. **CCC.**
Published by: (American Association of Physical Anthropologists), John Wiley & Sons, Inc., 111 River St, Hoboken, NJ 07030-5774. TEL 201-748-6000, FAX 201-748-5915, uscs-wis@wiley.com, http://www3.interscience.wiley.com/cgi-bin/jhome/28130, http://www.wiley.com. Ed. Clark S Larsen. adv.: B&W page GBP 640, color page GBP 1,515; trim 174 x 254. Circ: 2,550. **Subscr. outside the Americas to:** John Wiley & Sons Ltd., The Atrium, Southern Gate, Chichester, West Sussex PO19 8SQ, United Kingdom. TEL 44-1243-843335, 0800-243407, FAX 44-1243-775878, cs-journals@wiley.co.uk.

➤ **AMERICAN JOURNAL OF PRIMATOLOGY.** see *BIOLOGY—Zoology*

301 USA ISSN 0065-9452
GN2 CODEN: APNHAN
➤ **AMERICAN MUSEUM OF NATURAL HISTORY. ANTHROPOLOGICAL PAPERS.** Text in English. 1907. irreg., latest vol.83, 2000. price varies. bibl.; illus.; maps. back issues avail.; reprints avail. **Document type:** *Monographic series, Academic/Scholarly.* **Description:** Professional basic research papers in anthropology.
Indexed: AmH&L, BIOSIS Prev, BiolAb, HistAb, IBSS, RASB, RefZh, SSCI, ZooRec.
—BLDSC (1542.900000), IE, ingenta, Linda Hall.

Published by: American Museum of Natural History Library, Scientific Publications Distribution, Central Park W at 79th St, New York, NY 10024-5192. TEL 212-769-5545, FAX 212-769-5009, scipubs@amnh.org, http://nimidi.amnh.org. Ed. Brenda Jones. Circ: 1,000.

➤ **AMERICAN UNIVERSITY STUDIES. SERIES 11. ANTHROPOLOGY AND SOCIOLOGY.** see *SOCIAL SCIENCES: COMPREHENSIVE WORKS*

301 URY
AMERINDIA; revista de prehistoria y etnologia de America. Text in Spanish. 1962. biennial. bk.rev.
Indexed: AICP, AnthLit, BibLing, IBR, IBSS, MLA.
Published by: Centro de Estudios Arqueologicos y Antropologicos Americanos, Juan Francisco Zubillaga, 1117, Montevideo, 11313, Uruguay.

301 FRA ISSN 1764-7193
AMNIS. Text in English, French, Spanish. 2001. irreg. free (effective 2005). **Document type:** *Journal, Academic/Scholarly.* **Description:** It aims at providing researchers with a tool that contributes to a thorough and diversified reflection on the recent past, present and future of (East and West) European and (North, South and Central) American societies (19th to 21st centuries).
Media: Online - full text. **Related titles:** Print ed.
Published by: Universite de Bretagne Occidentale, 3 rue des Archives, Brest, Cedex 29285, France. TEL 33-2-98016020, FAX 33-2-98016001, http://www.univ-brest.fr/amnis.

301 MEX ISSN 0185-1225
GN560.M6
ANALES DE ANTROPOLOGIA. Text in Spanish. 1964; N.S. 1992. a. MXP 90, USD 8 (effective 2000). bibl. **Document type:** *Academic/Scholarly.*
Indexed: AICP, AmH&L, AnthLit, HAPI, HistAb, RASB.
Published by: Universidad Nacional Autonoma de Mexico, Instituto de Investigaciones Antropologicas, Circuito Exterior, Ciudad Universitaria, Mexico, DF 04510, Mexico. TEL 52-5-6229531, FAX 52-5-6229651. Ed. Luis Alberto Vargas.

ANALES DE ARQUEOLOGIA Y ETNOLOGIA. see *ARCHAEOLOGY*

ANATOMICAL SCIENCE INTERNATIONAL. see *BIOLOGY*

301 ESP ISSN 1138-347X
ANKULEGI; antropologia kultura eta gizartea. Text in Spanish, French, Catalan. 1997. s-a. EUR 24.50 domestic to individuals; EUR 34.20 in Europe to individuals; EUR 50 elsewhere to individuals; EUR 34.10 domestic to institutions; EUR 42.50 in Europe to institutions; EUR 55.70 elsewhere to institutions (effective 2002).
Related titles: Online - full text ed.
—CINDOC.
Published by: Ankulegi Antropologia Elkartea, Apdo. de Correos 20080, Donostia, San Sebastian 20080, Spain. TEL 34-94-3332690, FAX 34-94-4618010, ankulegi@pangea.org, http://www.pangea.org/ankulegi/.

306.44089 BEL ISSN 0254-4296
DT641
ANNALES AEQUATORIA. Text in English, French. 1937-1962; resumed 1980. a., latest vol.23, 2002. EUR 21 domestic; EUR 23.50 in the European Union; EUR 24.12 in Europe non European Union; USD 35 elsewhere (effective 2003). bk.rev. bibl.; charts; maps. cum.index: 1938-1962; 1980-1999. 600 p./no.; back issues avail. **Document type:** *Journal, Academic/Scholarly.* **Description:** Research into Central African cultures, history and languages, with particular emphasis on the Democratic Republic of the Congo.
Supersedes (1938-1962): Aequatoria (0304-257X)
Related titles: Online - full text ed.: (from International Network for the Availability of Scientific Publications, African Journals Online).
Indexed: AICP, ASD, AnthLit, BibLing, IBSS, PLESA, RILM.
Published by: (Centre Aequatoria COD), Missionnaires du Sacre-Coeur/Missionaries of the Sacred Heart, Stationsstraat 48, Lovenjoel, 3360, Belgium. TEL 32-16-464484, FAX 32-16-460198, vinck.aequatoria@belgacom.net, http://www.aequatoria.be/archives_project. Ed. Honore Vinck. Circ: 300. **Dist. by:** Missionnaires du Sacre-Coeur, 305 S Lake St, PO Box 270, Aurora, IL 60507.

301 ROM ISSN 0570-2259
GN1 CODEN: ARNAAG
ANNUAIRE ROUMAIN D'ANTHROPOLOGIE. Text in Multiple languages. 1952. a.
Indexed: AICP, AnthLit, BiolAb, ExcerpMed, RASB, RefZh.
—GNLM, KNAW.
Published by: (Academia Romana), Editura Academiei Romane/Publishing House of the Romanian Academy, Calea 13 Septembrie 13, Sector 5, Bucharest, 76117, Romania. TEL 40-21-4119008, FAX 40-21-4103983, edacad@ear.ro, http://www.ear.ro. Ed. Olga Necrasov. **Dist. by:** Rodipet S.A., Piata Presei Libere 1, sector 1, PO Box 33-57, Bucharest 3, Romania. TEL 40-21-2224126, 40-21-2226407, rodipet@rodipet.ro.

301 USA ISSN 1091-613X
GN325
➤ **ANNUAL EDITIONS: ANTHROPOLOGY.** Variant title: Anthropology. Text in English. 1974. a., latest 2003, 27th ed. USD 20.31 per vol. (effective 2004). illus. **Document type:** *Academic/Scholarly.*
Formerly (until 1981): Annual Editions: Readings in Anthropology (0095-5582)
Published by: McGraw-Hill - Dushkin (Subsidiary of: McGraw-Hill Higher Education), 2460 Kerper Blvd, Dubuque, IA 52001. TEL 800-243-6532, customer.service@mcgraw-hill.com, http://www.dushkin.com/text-data/catalog/0072862270.mhtml. Ed. Elvio Angeloni. Pub. Ian Nielsen. R&P Cheryl Greenleaf.

599.9 USA ISSN 1074-1844
GN49
ANNUAL EDITIONS: PHYSICAL ANTHROPOLOGY. Text in English. 1992. a., latest 2003, 13th ed. USD 20.31 per vol. (effective 2004). **Document type:** *Academic/Scholarly.*
Published by: McGraw-Hill - Dushkin (Subsidiary of: McGraw-Hill Higher Education), 2460 Kerper Blvd, Dubuque, IA 52001. TEL 800-243-6532, customer.service@mcgraw-hill.com, http://www.dushkin.com/text-data/catalog/0072861533.mhtml. Ed. Elvio Angeloni. Pub. Ian Nielsen. R&P Cheryl Greenleaf.

301 USA ISSN 0084-6570
GN1 CODEN: ARAPCW
➤ **ANNUAL REVIEW OF ANTHROPOLOGY.** Text in English. 1959. a., latest vol.33, 2004. USD 170 to institutions print or online ed.; USD 204 combined subscription to institutions print & online eds. (effective 2006). bibl.; charts; illus.; abstr. index, cum.index. back issues avail.; reprint service avail. from PSC. **Document type:** *Academic/Scholarly.* **Description:** Anthropology reviews synthesize and filter the vast amount of primary research to identify principal contributions in the field.
Formerly (until 1971): Biennial Review of Anthropology (0067-8503)
Related titles: Microfilm ed.: (from PQC); Online - full content ed.: ISSN 1545-4290. USD 166 (effective 2005) (from HighWire Press); Online - full text ed.: (from bigchalk, EBSCO Publishing, H.W. Wilson, JSTOR (Web-based Journal Archive), O C L C Online Computer Library Center, Inc., ProQuest Information & Learning, Swets Information Services).
Indexed: AICP, ASCA, AnthLit, BAS, BIOSIS Prev, BibLing, BiolAb, BrArAb, CCA, CJA, ChPerI, ChemAb, CurCont, DIP, GEOBASE, IBR, IBSS, IBZ, IPSA, L&LBA, MRD, NumL, PCI, PSA, PsycInfo, PsycholAb, RASB, RILM, SOPODA, SSA, SSCI, SSI, SociolAb, e-psyche.
—BLDSC (1520.474000), CASDDS, GNLM, IDS, IE, Infotrieve, ingenta. **CCC.**
Published by: Annual Reviews, 4139 El Camino Way, Palo Alto, CA 94303-0139. TEL 650-493-4400, 800-523-8635, FAX 650-424-0910, service@annualreviews.org, http://arjournals.annualreviews.org/loi/anthro, http://www.annualreviews.org. Ed. William Durham. R&P Laura Folkner.

301 CAN ISSN 1481-3440
ANTHROGLOBE JOURNAL. Text in French, English, Portuguese, Spanish. 1996. irreg. illus. back issues avail.; reprints avail. **Document type:** *Academic/Scholarly.* **Description:** Includes multimedia articles with interactive discussion on anthropology.
Media: Online - full text.
Address: turner@sbcba.org, http://anthro-globe.com/. Ed. Allen Turner.

572 100 001.3 USA ISSN 1083-7264
GN33
➤ **ANTHROPOETICS**; the journal of generative anthropolgy. Text in English. 1995. 2/yr. free (effective 2005). back issues avail. **Document type:** *Academic/Scholarly.* **Description:** Deals with the humanities or human sciences that involve theories regarding human origin.
Media: Online - full content.
Indexed: MLA-IB.
Published by: University of California at Los Angeles, c/o Eric Gans, Department of French, Los Angeles, CA 90095-1550. gans@humnet.ucla.edu, anthro@humnet.ucla.edu, http://www.anthropoetics.ucla.edu, http://www.anthropoetics.ucla.edu/anthro.htm. Ed. Eric Lawrence Gans TEL 310-794-8925.

301 HUN ISSN 0003-5440
GN1
➤ **ANTHROPOLOGIAI KOZLEMENYEK**; a Magyar Biologiai Tarsasag embertani szakosztalyanak folyoirata. Text in English, Hungarian; Summaries in English. 1957. s-a. USD 25 per vol.. adv. bk.rev. back issues avail. **Document type:** *Academic/Scholarly.*
Indexed: AICP, BiolAb, CurCont, SSCI.
—GNLM, KNAW.
Published by: (Magyar Biologiai Tarsasag/Hungarian Biological Society), Eotvos Lorand Tudomanyegyetem, Faculty of Science/Eotvos Lorand University, Department of Biological Anthropology, Pazmany Setany 1/A, Budapest, 1117, Hungary. TEL 36-1-3812161, FAX 36-1-3812162. Circ: 400.

301 PER ISSN 0254-9212
F3429
➤ **ANTHROPOLOGICA.** Key Title: Anthropologica del Departamento de Ciencias Sociales. Text in Spanish. 1983. a. USD 30 (effective 2003). **Document type:** *Academic/Scholarly.*
Incorporates: Revista de Debates: Debates en Antropologia; Which supersedes in part: Debates en Antropologia
Indexed: AICP, AbAn, AnthLit.
Published by: (Departamento de Ciencias Sociales), Pontificia Universidad Catolica del Peru, Fondo Editorial, Plaza Francia 1164, Cercado de Lima, Lima, 1, Peru. TEL 51-14-626390, FAX 51-14-611785, editorial@pucp.edu.pe, http://www.pucp.edu.pe. Ed. Alejandro Ortiz Rescaniere.

301 CAN ISSN 0003-5459
CODEN: ATRPBS
➤ **ANTHROPOLOGICA.** Text in English, French. 1959. s-a. CND 80 domestic to individuals; USD 80 foreign to individuals; CND 90 domestic to institutions; USD 90 foreign to institutions; CND 30 to students; CND 45 per issue domestic; USD 45 per issue foreign (effective 2006). adv. bk.rev. charts; illus. index. reprints avail. **Document type:** *Journal, Academic/Scholarly.* **Description:** Presents articles on social-cultural anthropology and related fields. Devoted to social and cultural issues whether they are prehistoric, historic, contemporary, biological, linguistic, applied or theoretical in orientation.
Incorporates (in 1997): Culture (0229-009X)
Related titles: Microfiche ed.: (from MML); Microform ed.: (from MIM, MML, PQC, SWZ); Online - full text ed.: (from Chadwyck-Healey Inc., Micromedia ProQuest).
Indexed: AICP, AbAn, AmH&L, AnthLit, BAS, BibInd, BiolAb, CBCARef, CBPI, DIP, EI, HistAb, IBR, IBZ, L&LBA, MLA-IB, PCI, PSA, PdeR, PsycInfo, PsycholAb, RASB, RILM, SOPODA, SSA, SSCI, SociolAb, e-psyche.
—BLDSC (1542.860000). **CCC.**
Published by: (Canadian Anthropology Society (C A S C A)/Societe Canadienne d'Anthropologie), Wilfrid Laurier University Press, 75 University Ave W, Waterloo, ON N2L 3C5, Canada. TEL 519-884-0710 ext 6124, FAX 519-725-1399, press@wlu.ca, http://www.wlupress.wlu.ca/jrls/anthro.html. Ed. Winnie Lem. Circ: 750 (paid).

301 ESP ISSN 0301-6587
BD450
ANTHROPOLOGICA; revista de psichologia cultural. Text in Spanish; Summaries in English, French, German. 1973. s-a. USD 15 (effective 2001). bk.rev. bibl. **Document type:** *Academic/Scholarly.*
Indexed: AbAn, AnthLit, MLA.
—CINDOC.
Published by: Instituto de Antropologia de Barcelona, Melchor de Palau, 145 T-4, Barcelona, 08014, Spain. TEL 34-93-4900949, FAX 34-93-2610570, bya@wanadoo.es. Ed., Pub. Angel Aguirre Baztan. Circ: 5,000.

301 BEL ISSN 1377-5723
GN4
➤ **ANTHROPOLOGICA ET PRAEHISTORICA**; bulletin de la Societe Royale Belge d'Anthropologie et Prehistoire. Text in English, Flemish, French; Summaries in English, French. 1882. a., latest vol.113, 2002. EUR 49.58 (effective 2003). bk.rev. illus. reprints avail. **Document type:** *Bulletin, Academic/Scholarly.*
Former titles (until 2001): Anthropologie et Prehistoire (0777-6187); (until 1990): Societe Royale Belge d'Anthropologie et de Prehistoire. Bulletin (0304-1425)
Related titles: Supplement(s): Hominid Remains. ISSN 1373-9662. 1988.
Indexed: AICP, AnthLit, BAS, BrArAb, ExcerpMed, PCI, RASB, ZooRec.
—BLDSC (2748.800000).
Published by: Societe Royale Belge d'Anthropologie et de Prehistoire, Rue Vautier 29, Brussels, 1000, Belgium. TEL 32-2-6274385, FAX 32-2-6274113, AnneHauzeur@kbinirsnb.be, http://www.kbinirsnb.be/ap/srbap. Adv. contact Anne Hauzeur. Circ: 350.

➤ **ANTHROPOLOGICAL ABSTRACTS: CULTURAL - SOCIAL ANTHROPOLOGY FROM AUSTRIA, GERMANY, SWITZERLAND.** see *ANTHROPOLOGY—Abstracting, Bibliographies, Statistics*

301 GBR ISSN 0066-4677
GN1
➤ **ANTHROPOLOGICAL FORUM**; an international journal of social and cultural anthropology and comparative sociology. Text in English. 1963. 3/yr. GBP 241, USD 400, AUD 341 combined subscription to institutions print & online eds. (effective 2006). adv. bk.rev. reprint service avail. from PSC. **Document type:** *Journal, Academic/Scholarly.* **Description:** Provides a forum for both established and innovative approaches to anthropological research, and welcomes manuscripts from both experienced researchers and young scholars seeking publication for the first time.
Related titles: Online - full text ed.: ISSN 1469-2902. GBP 229, USD 380, AUD 324 to institutions (effective 2006) (from EBSCO Publishing, Gale Group, IngentaConnect, O C L C Online Computer Library Center, Inc., R M I T Publishing, Swets Information Services).
Indexed: AICP, AnthLit, AusPAIS, BAS, EI, IBSS, PSA, RASB, RILM, SociolAb.

A

—BLDSC (1542.870000), IE, Infotrieve, ingenta. **CCC.**
Published by: (University of Western Australia AUS), Routledge (Subsidiary of: Taylor & Francis Group), 4 Park Sq, Milton Park, Abingdon, Oxon OX14 4RN, United Kingdom. TEL 44-1235-828600, FAX 44-1235-829000, info@routledge.co.uk, http://www.tandf.co.uk/journals/titles/00664677.asp, http://www.routledge.com. Ed. Robert Tonkinson. Circ: 400 (paid). **Subscr. to:** Taylor & Francis Ltd, Journals Customer Service, Rankine Rd, Basingstoke, Hants RG24 8PR, United Kingdom. TEL 44-1256-813000, FAX 44-1256-330245.

➤ **ANTHROPOLOGICAL INDEX ONLINE.** see *ANTHROPOLOGY—Abstracting, Bibliographies, Statistics*

➤ **ANTHROPOLOGICAL INDEX TO CURRENT PERIODICALS IN THE MUSEUM OF MANKIND LIBRARY.** see *ANTHROPOLOGY—Abstracting, Bibliographies, Statistics*

301 CHE ISSN 0960-0604
GN1 CODEN: AJECER
ANTHROPOLOGICAL JOURNAL ON EUROPEAN CULTURES. Text in English. 1990. s-a. GBP 29.95 per issue Vol.11 (2003) (effective 2003). **Document type:** *Academic/Scholarly.*
Indexed: AICP, AnthLit, SOPODA, SSA, SociolAb.
—BLDSC (1542.878000), IE, ingenta.
Published by: Universite de Fribourg, Seminaire d'Ethnologie, 11 Rte des Bonnesfontaines, Fribourg, 1700, Switzerland. TEL 41-37-219207, FAX 41-37-219729. Eds. Christian Giordano, Ina Maria Greverus.

ANTHROPOLOGICAL LINGUISTICS. see *LINGUISTICS*

ANTHROPOLOGICAL LITERATURE; an index to periodical articles and essays. see *ANTHROPOLOGY—Abstracting, Bibliographies, Statistics*

301 SVN ISSN 1408-032X
➤ **ANTHROPOLOGICAL NOTEBOOKS.** Text in English; Summaries in Slovenian. 1995. a., latest vol.9, no.1, 2003. SIT 1,500, EUR 6.26 per vol. (effective 2005). bk.rev. charts; illus.; maps. Index. back issues avail. **Document type:** *Journal, Academic/Scholarly.* **Description:** Covers social and cultural, linguistic and biological anthropology as well as archaeology.
Indexed: IBR, IBSS, IBZ, MLA-IB, SociolAb.
Published by: Drustvo Antropologov Slovenije/Slovene Anthropological Society, Vecna pot 11, Ljubljana, Slovenia. TEL 386-1-4233388, FAX 386-1-2573390, marica.stefancic@uni-lj.si, http://www.drustvo-antropologov.si. Ed. Borut Telban. Pub. Marija Stefancic. Circ: 150 (paid); 20 (controlled). **Co-sponsor:** Ministrstvo za Solstvo, Znanost in Sport/Ministry of Education, Science and Sport of the Republic of Slovenia.

301 USA ISSN 0003-5491
GN1
➤ **ANTHROPOLOGICAL QUARTERLY.** Abbreviated title: A Q. Text in English. 1928. q. USD 46 to individuals; USD 89 to institutions (effective 2004). adv. bk.rev. abstr.; charts; illus. cum.index. reprint service avail. from PQC. **Document type:** *Journal, Academic/Scholarly.* **Description:** Covers all areas of social and cultural anthropology.
Formerly (until 1953): Primitive Man (0887-3925)
Related titles: Microform ed.: (from MIM, PQC); Online - full text ed.: ISSN 1534-1518. 2000 (from bigchalk, Chadwyck-Healey Inc., EBSCO Publishing, H.W. Wilson, Northern Light Technology, Inc., O C L C Online Computer Library Center, Inc., Project MUSE, ProQuest Information & Learning, Swets Information Services).
Indexed: ABS&EES, AICP, ASCA, AbAn, AgeL, AmH&L, AnthLit, ArtHuCI, BAS, CLFP, CPL, CommAb, CurCont, DIP, EI, EIP, ERA, ETA, FamI, IBR, IBSS, IBZ, IMFL, IndIslam, L&LBA, MEA, MEA&I, MLA-IB, PCI, PRA, PSA, PhilInd, RASB, RDA, REE&TA, RHEA, RI-1, RI-2, RILM, SEA, SENA, SFSA, SOMA, SOPODA, SPPI, SRRA, SSA, SSCI, SSI, SWA, SociolAb, TEA, WAE&RSA.
—BLDSC (1544.400000), IDS, IE, Infotrieve, ingenta. **CCC.**
Published by: Institute for Ethnographic Research, George Washington University, 2110 G St, NW, Washington, DC 20052. TEL 202-994-6984, ifer@gwu.edu, http://aq.gwu.edu/. Ed. Roy Richard Grinker. Circ: 913.

301 JPN ISSN 0918-7960
GN1
➤ **ANTHROPOLOGICAL SCIENCE.** Text in English, Japanese. 1884. 3/yr. JPY 8,000 for membership to individuals; JPY 12,000 for membership to institutions (effective 2004). adv. bk.rev. Index. **Document type:** *Journal, Academic/Scholarly.* **Description:** Publishes original and review articles, brief communications, material reports, and book reviews.
Formerly: Anthropological Society of Nippon. Journal (0003-5505)
Related titles: Online - full text ed.: ISSN 1348-8570. free (effective 2005) (from J-Stage); ♦ Japanese ed.: Anthropological Science. Japanese Series. ISSN 1344-3992.
Indexed: AICP, ASCA, AnthLit, ArtHuCI, BAS, BibLing, BiolAb, CurCont, DIP, ExcerpMed, IBR, IBSS, IBZ, SSCI, ZooRec.
—BLDSC (1545.200000), IDS, IE, ingenta. **CCC.**
Published by: Nippon Jinruigaku Gakkai/Anthropological Society of Nippon, c/o Digital Human Research Center, National Institute of Advanced Industrial Science and Techno, 2-41-6 Aomi, Koto-ku, Tokyo, 135-0064, Japan. TEL 81-3-55308314, FAX 81-3-55302066, anthrop@m.aist.go.jp, http://www.nacos.com/asn/as.html, http://wwwsoc.nii.ac.jp/jinrui/index.html. Ed. Gen Suwa TEL 81-5841-2836. Circ: 1,300.

301 JPN ISSN 1344-3992
ANTHROPOLOGICAL SCIENCE. JAPANESE SERIES. Text in Japanese. 1998. s-a. JPY 8,000 membership (effective 2005). **Document type:** *Journal, Academic/Scholarly.*
Related titles: Online - full text ed.: ISSN 1348-8813. 2003 (from J-Stage); ♦ English ed.: Anthropological Science. ISSN 0918-7960.
—BLDSC (1545.210000). **CCC.**
Published by: Nippon Jinruigaku Gakkai/Anthropological Society of Nippon, c/o Digital Human Research Center, National Institute of Advanced Industrial Science and Techno, 2-41-6 Aomi, Koto-ku, Tokyo, 135-0064, Japan. TEL 81-3-55308314, FAX 81-3-55302066, anthrop@m.aist.go.jp, http://wwwsoc.nii.ac.jp/jinrui/as/ashome.html, http://wwwsoc.nii.ac.jp/jinrui/index.html.

301 GBR ISSN 0044-8370
GN1
ANTHROPOLOGICAL SOCIETY OF OXFORD. JOURNAL. Short title: J A S O. Text in English. 1970. 3/yr. GBP 14, USD 28 to individuals; GBP 25, USD 50 to institutions. adv. bk.rev. cum.index every 10 yrs. **Document type:** *Academic/Scholarly.* **Description:** Provides a forum for current research in social anthropology.
Indexed: AICP, AnthLit, EI, IBSS, L&LBA, PCI, RILM, SOPODA, SSA, SociolAb.
—BLDSC (4698.150000).
Published by: Anthropological Society of Oxford, 51 Banbury Rd, Oxford, OX2 6PE, United Kingdom. TEL 44-1865-274682. Ed. Jonathan Webber. Circ: 700.

301 GBR
ANTHROPOLOGICAL SOCIETY OF OXFORD. OCCASIONAL PAPERS SERIES. Text in English. a. price varies. **Document type:** *Academic/Scholarly.*
Indexed: AnthLit.
Published by: Anthropological Society of Oxford, 51 Banbury Rd, Oxford, OX2 6PE, United Kingdom. TEL 44-1865-274682.

301 GBR ISSN 1463-4996
GN33b
➤ **ANTHROPOLOGICAL THEORY.** Text in English. 2001 (Mar). q. GBP 312, USD 545 to institutions; GBP 324, USD 567 combined subscription to institutions print & online (effective 2006). adv. bk.rev. **Document type:** *Journal, Academic/Scholarly.* **Description:** Explicitly addresses fundamental issues of anthropological theory and epistemology and seeks to bring a better understanding of theory to anthropology.
Related titles: Online - full text ed.: ISSN 1741-2641. GBP 308, USD 539 to institutions (effective 2006) (from EBSCO Publishing, O C L C Online Computer Library Center, Inc., Sage Publications, Inc., Swets Information Services).
Indexed: AnthLit, DIP, IBR, IBSS, IBZ, PSA, SSA, SociolAb.
—BLDSC (1545.750000), IE. **CCC.**
Published by: Sage Publications Ltd. (Subsidiary of: Sage Publications, Inc.), 1 Oliver's Yard, 55 City Rd, London, EC1 1SP, United Kingdom. TEL 44-20-73248500, FAX 44-20-73248600, info@sagepub.co.uk, http://www.sagepub.co.uk/journal.aspx?pid=105473. Eds. Joel Robbins, Jonathan Friedman. Adv. contact Jenny Kirby. page GBP 195; trim 114 x 185. Circ: 1,200. **Subscr. in the Americas to:** Sage Publications, Inc., 2455 Teller Rd, Thousand Oaks, CA 91320. TEL 805-499-0721, FAX 805-499-0871, journals@sagepub.com.

301 DEU ISSN 0066-4685
ANTHROPOLOGIE. Text in Czech, German. 1962. irreg., latest vol.37, 1999. price varies. **Document type:** *Monographic series, Academic/Scholarly.*
Indexed: ASCA, ArtHuCI, IndIslam.
Published by: (Moravske Museum, Brno CZE), Dr. Rudolf Habelt GmbH, Am Buchenhang 1, Bonn, 53115, Germany. TEL 49-228-9238322, info@habelt.de, http://www.habelt.de. Ed. J Jelinek.

301 FRA ISSN 0003-5521
GN1 CODEN: ATRPAR
➤ **L'ANTHROPOLOGIE.** Text in French. 1890. 5/yr. EUR 178.26 domestic to individuals; EUR 173 in Europe to individuals; JPY 23,000 in Japan to individuals; USD 235 elsewhere to individuals; EUR 329.09 domestic to institutions; EUR 336 in Europe to institutions; JPY 43,700 in Japan to institutions; USD 457 elsewhere to institutions (effective 2006). bk.rev. abstr.; illus. index. reprint service avail. from ISI. **Document type:** *Academic/Scholarly.* **Description:** Contains original articles from all anthropological sciences.
Related titles: Microfiche ed.: (from BHP); Microform ed.: (from PQC); Online - full text ed.: (from EBSCO Publishing, Gale Group, IngentaConnect, ScienceDirect, Swets Information Services).
Indexed: AICP, AbAn, AnthLit, BAS, BIOSIS Prev, BibInd, BiolAb, BrArAb, CCA, CurCont, ExcerpMed, GEOBASE, IBSS, IndIslam, NumL, RASB, SSCI, ZooRec.
—BLDSC (1546.000000), GNLM, IDS, IE, Infotrieve, ingenta, Linda Hall. **CCC.**
Published by: Elsevier France, Editions Scientifiques et Medicales (Subsidiary of: Elsevier Science & Technology), 23 Rue Linois, Paris, 75724, France. TEL 33-1-71724600, FAX 33-1-71724650, a.dore@elsevier.fr, academic@elsevier-fr.com, http://www.elsevier.com/locate/anthro. Eds. R Verneau, M Boule. Circ: 825.

301 CZE ISSN 0323-1119
ANTHROPOLOGIE/ANTHROPOLOGY; international journal of the science of man. Text in German. 1962. 3/yr. exchange basis. illus.; maps. **Document type:** *Journal, Academic/Scholarly.*
Related titles: English ed.; French ed.
Indexed: AICP, AnthLit, CurCont, IBR, RILM, SSCI.
—BLDSC (1545.800000), GNLM.
Published by: Moravske Zemske Muzeum, Zelny trh 6, Brno, 65937, Czech Republic. TEL 420-5-42321205, FAX 420-5-42212792, anthropologie@mzm.cz, mzm@mzm.cz, http://www.mzm.cz/Anthropologie. Ed. Marta Dockalova. Circ: 500. **Subscr. to:** Karger Libri AG, Petersgraben 15, Basel 11 4000, Switzerland. **Co-sponsor:** Anthropos Institut.

301 CAN ISSN 0702-8997
GN301 CODEN: ANSOFQ
➤ **ANTHROPOLOGIE ET SOCIETES.** Text in French; Summaries in English, French. 1977. 3/yr. CND 50 domestic to individuals; CND 75 foreign to individuals; CND 100 domestic to institutions; CND 135 foreign to institutions; CND 25 domestic to students; CND 50 foreign to students (effective 2005). adv. bk.rev. index, cum.index. 200 p./no. 1 cols./p.; back issues avail. **Document type:** *Journal, Academic/Scholarly.* **Description:** Open to all theoretical perspectives and cultures of the contemporary world or past societies. Devoted to actual debates in and the contemporary practice of the discipline.
Related titles: Online - full text ed.: (from Gale Group).
Indexed: AICP, AbAn, AnthLit, BAS, BHA, CPerI, CurCont, DIP, IBR, IBZ, L&LBA, PAIS, PCI, PSA, PdeR, RILM, SOPODA, SSA, SSCI, SociolAb.
—IE, Infotrieve.
Published by: (Universite Laval, Departement d'Anthropologie), Les Presses de l'Universite Laval (Subsidiary of: Universite Laval), Pavillon Maurice-Pollack, Bureau 3103, Cite Universitaire, Ste-Foy, PQ G1K 7P4, Canada. TEL 418-656-2803, FAX 418-656-3305, presses@pul.ulaval.ca, http://www.fss.ulaval.ca/ant/revuant.html, http://www.ulaval.ca/pul. R&P Francine Saillant. Circ: 800.

301 FRA ISSN 0993-4871
ANTHROPOLOGIE VISUELLE. Text in French. 1988. irreg., latest vol.3, 1992.
Indexed: IBSS.
Published by: Editions de l' Ecole des Hautes Etudes en Sciences Sociales, 131 bd. Saint-Michel, Paris, 75005, France. TEL 33-1-40467080, FAX 33-1-44070889, editions@ehess.fr, http://www.ehess.fr/editions, http://www.ehess.fr/editions/publications.html. **Dist. by:** Centre Interinstitutionnel pour la Diffusion de Publications en Sciences Humaines, 131 bd. Saint-Michel, Paris 75005, France. TEL 33-1-43544715, FAX 33-1-43548073.

301 AUT ISSN 0066-4693
ANTHROPOLOGISCHE GESELLSCHAFT, VIENNA. MITTEILUNGEN. Text in German. 1870. a. price varies. **Document type:** *Proceedings, Academic/Scholarly.*
Indexed: AICP, AnthLit, BAS, BHA, BiolAb, BrArAb, HistAb.
—Linda Hall.
Published by: (Anthropologische Gesellschaft in Wien), Verlag Ferdinand Berger und Soehne GmbH, Wienerstr 80, Horn, N 3580, Austria. TEL 43-2982-4161332, FAX 43-2982-4161382, office@berger.at, http://www.berger.at.

301 AUT
ANTHROPOLOGISCHEN GESELLSCHAFT IN WIEN. MITTEILUNGEN/ANTHROPOLOGICAL SOCIETY IN VIENNA. REPORTS. Text in German. irreg.
Indexed: AnthLit.
Published by: Anthropologische Gesellschaft in Wien, Burgring 7, Vienna, W 1014, Austria. TEL 43-1-52177569, ag@nhm-wien.ac.at, http://www.nhm-wien.ac.at/ag.

ANTHROPOLOGISCHER ANZEIGER. see *ANTHROPOLOGY—Abstracting, Bibliographies, Statistics*

301 IND ISSN 0972-0073
GN1
➤ **THE ANTHROPOLOGIST**; international journal of contemporary and applied studies of man. Text in English. 1999. q. INR 1,500, USD 50 to individuals; INR 2,000, USD 70 to institutions (effective 2004). adv. bk.rev. 80 p./no. 2 cols./p.; back issues avail.; reprints avail. **Document type:** *Journal, Academic/Scholarly.* **Description:** Publishes theoretical and applied articles and debates on current issues in the interdisciplinary field of human science.
Indexed: AICP, AnthLit, SociolAb.
Published by: Kamla-Raj Enterprises, Chawri Bazar, 2273 Gali Bari Paharwali, New Delhi, 110 006, India. TEL 91-124-5360430, FAX 91-124-2218073, kre@touchtelindia.net, http://www.krepublishers.com. Ed., R&P A K Kalla. Adv. contact Ramesh Kumar. B&W page USD 100, color page USD 300; 8 x 5.5. Circ: 200 (paid).

301 USA ISSN 1061-1959
GN1
➤ **ANTHROPOLOGY AND ARCHEOLOGY OF EURASIA**; a journal of translations. Text in English. 1962. q. USD 149 domestic to individuals; USD 207 foreign to individuals; USD 860 domestic to institutions; USD 944 foreign to institutions (effective 2006). adv. illus. index. back issues avail.; reprint service avail. from PSC. **Document type:** *Journal, Academic/Scholarly.*
Formerly (until 1993): Soviet Anthropology and Archeology (0038-528X)
Related titles: Online - full text ed.: 2004 (June) (from EBSCO Publishing, O C L C Online Computer Library Center, Inc., Swets Information Services).
Indexed: AICP, ASCA, AbAn, AgeL, AnthLit, BAS, CurCont, PCI, RILM, SSCI.
—BLDSC (1546.502670), IDS, IE, Infotrieve, ingenta. **CCC.**
Published by: M.E. Sharpe, Inc., 80 Business Park Dr, Armonk, NY 10504. TEL 914-273-1800, 800-541-6563, FAX 914-273-2106, custserv@mesharpe.com, http://www.mesharpe.com/mall/results1.asp?ACR=AAE. Ed. Marjorie M Balzer. Adv. contact Barbara Ladd TEL 914-273-1800 ext 121. page USD 300; 8 x 5.

301.071 USA ISSN 0161-7761
➤ **ANTHROPOLOGY & EDUCATION QUARTERLY.** Text in English. 1970. q. USD 93 (effective 2005 & 2006). adv. bk.rev. illus. Index. back issues avail.; reprint service avail. from PQC. **Document type:** *Journal, Academic/Scholarly.* **Description:** Publishes anthropological research in education, as well as discussions of educational development and the teaching of anthropology.
Former titles (until 1976): Council on Anthropology and Education Quarterly (0098-2881); C A E Newsletter
Related titles: Microform ed.: (from PQC); Online - full text ed.: ISSN 1548-1492 (from bigchalk, H.W. Wilson, JSTOR (Web-based Journal Archive), O C L C Online Computer Library Center, Inc., ProQuest Information & Learning).
Indexed: ABIn, ABS&EES, AICP, ASCA, AnthLit, ArtHuCI, CIJE, CIS, CPE, ChLitAb, ChPerI, CurCont, EAA, ERA, ETA, EduInd, FamI, IBR, IBSS, IBZ, L&LBA, MEA, MEA&I, PsycInfo, PsycholAb, RI-1, RI-2, RILM, SEA, SENA, SOMA, SOPODA, SRRA, SSA, SSCI, SSI, SWA, TEA, e-psyche.
—BLDSC (1546.502700), IE, Infotrieve, ingenta. **CCC.**
Published by: (Council on Anthropology and Education), University of California Press, Journals Division, 2000 Center St, Ste 303, Berkeley, CA 94704-1223. TEL 510-643-7154, FAX 510-642-9917, journals@ucpress.edu, http://www.ucpress.edu/journals/3a/aeq. Ed. Teresa McCarty. adv.: B&W page USD 295; 4.8 x 8. Circ: 1,500.

301 USA
GN1
ANTHROPOLOGY AND HUMANISM. Text in English. 1974. s-a. USD 44 to non-members; free to members; USD 58 to institutions (effective 2006). adv. bk.rev. illus. back issues avail.; reprints avail. **Document type:** *Journal, Academic/Scholarly.* **Description:** Scholarly journal concerned with what it is to be human; contributions from all major fields of anthropology, including physical anthropology, archaeology, linguistics and ethnology.
Formerly (until 1992): Anthropology and Humanism Quarterly (0193-5615)
Related titles: Online - full text ed.: ISSN 1548-1409.
Indexed: AICP, AbAn, AnthLit, EI, IBR, IBSS, IBZ, MEA&I, RILM.
—BLDSC (1546.502720), IE, ingenta. **CCC.**
Published by: (American Anthropological Association, Society for Humanistic Anthropology), University of California Press, Journals Division, 2000 Center St, Ste 303, Berkeley, CA 94704-1223. TEL 510-643-7154, FAX 510-642-9917, journals@ucpress.edu, http://www.ucpress.edu/journals/3a/ahu/shop.htm. Ed. Edith Turner. adv.: page USD 295; 4.8 x 8. Circ: 600.

306.461 GBR ISSN 1364-8470
ANTHROPOLOGY & MEDICINE. Text in English. 1997 (vol.4). 3/yr. GBP 274, USD 456 combined subscription to institutions print & online eds. (effective 2006). reprint service avail. from PSC. **Document type:** *Journal, Academic/Scholarly.* **Description:** Publishes original papers within the broad framework of medical anthropology and now addresses a world-wide audience.
Related titles: Online - full text ed.: ISSN 1469-2910. GBP 260, USD 433 to institutions (effective 2006) (from EBSCO Publishing, Gale Group, IngentaConnect, O C L C Online Computer Library Center, Inc., Swets Information Services).
Indexed: AICP, ASSIA, AnthLit, CINAHL, ExcerpMed, IBSS, IPsyAb, PsycInfo, PsycholAb, SOPODA, SSA, SociolAb, e-psyche.
—BLDSC (1546.502740), IE, Infotrieve, ingenta. **CCC.**
Published by: Routledge (Subsidiary of: Taylor & Francis Group), 4 Park Sq, Milton Park, Abingdon, Oxon OX14 4RN, United Kingdom. TEL 44-1235-828600, FAX 44-1235-829000, info@routledge.co.uk, http://www.tandf.co.uk/journals/titles/13648470.asp, http://www.routledge.com. Ed. Sushrut Jadhav. **Subscr. to:** Taylor & Francis Ltd, Journals Customer Service, Rankine Rd, Basingstoke, Hants RG24 8PR, United Kingdom. TEL 44-1256-813000, FAX 44-1256-330245.

301 GBR ISSN 0967-201X
ANTHROPOLOGY IN ACTION; journal for applied anthropology in policy and practice. Text in English. 1988. 3/yr. EUR 30 to institutions; free to members (effective 2003). **Document type:** *Journal, Academic/Scholarly.*
—BLDSC (1546.502630), IE, ingenta.
Published by: Anthropology In Action, c/o Stella Richards, School of Comparative & Applied Social Sciences, University of Hull, Cottingham Rd, Hull, HU6 7RX, United Kingdom. TEL 44-1482-466213, S.R.Richards@hull.ac.uk, http://www.angelfire.com/rpg/anthropologyinaction/journal.html. Ed. Jonathan Skinner.

301 USA ISSN 1541-6151
GN2
ANTHROPOLOGY NEWS. Text in English. 1947. m. (except June, July and Aug.). USD 100 to non-members; free to members (effective 2005). adv. bibl.; illus. back issues avail.; reprints avail. **Document type:** *Newsletter, Academic/Scholarly.* **Description:** News of interest to anthropologists; association affairs, departments and people, jobs, grants and support, brief research reports, and announcements.
Former titles (until 1999): Anthropology Newsletter (0098-1605); (until 1974): American Anthropological Association. Newsletter (0002-7286)
Related titles: Microfiche ed.; Online - full text ed.: ISSN 1556-3502.
—**CCC.**
Published by: American Anthropological Association, 2200 Wilson Blvd, Ste 600, Arlington, VA 22201. TEL 703-528-1902, FAX 703-528-3546, http://www.aaanet.org/press/an/index.htm. Adv. contact Corey Gerhard. page USD 1,650; trim 15 x 11.5. Circ: 11,500 (paid).

301 USA ISSN 1053-4202
GN502 CODEN: ATCNEI
➤ **ANTHROPOLOGY OF CONSCIOUSNESS.** Text in English. 1985. s-a. USD 63 (effective 2006). bk.rev. back issues avail. **Document type:** *Journal, Academic/Scholarly.* **Description:** Provides an interdisciplinary forum addressing the cross-cultural dimension of human consciousness from empirical, experimental, and theoretical perspectives.
Former titles (until vol.5, 1989): A A S C Quarterly (1045-4330); A A S C Newsletter (0897-2672)
Related titles: Online - full text ed.: ISSN 1556-3537.
Indexed: AbAn, AnthLit, SOPODA, SSA, e-psyche.
—BLDSC (1546.502770), IE. **CCC.**
Published by: (American Anthropological Association, Society for the Anthropology of Consciousness), University of California Press, Journals Division, 2000 Center St, Ste 303, Berkeley, CA 94704-1223. TEL 510-643-7154, FAX 510-642-9917, journals@ucpress.edu, http://sacaaa.org/aocconts.htm, http://www.ucpress.edu/journals. Ed. Grant Jewell Rich. Circ: 250 (paid).

301 USA ISSN 1054-4720
DJK26
THE ANTHROPOLOGY OF EAST EUROPE REVIEW. Text in English. 1981. s-a. free to members (effective 2005). **Document type:** *Journal, Academic/Scholarly.*
Formerly (until 1989): East European Anthropology Group. Newsletter (0748-7207)
—BLDSC (1546.502820).
Published by: East European Anthropology Group, College of Liberal Arts and Sciences DePaul University, 2352 N Clifton Ave Ste 130, Chicago, IL 60614. http://condor.depaul.edu/~rrotenbe/aeer/main.html. Eds. Julie Hemment, Krista Harper.

ANTHROPOLOGY OF FOOD AND NUTRITION. see *FOOD AND FOOD INDUSTRIES*

301 USA ISSN 0883-024X
CODEN: AWORE9
ANTHROPOLOGY OF WORK REVIEW. Text in English. 1983. q. USD 44 (effective 2005 & 2006). adv. **Document type:** *Journal, Academic/Scholarly.* **Description:** Presents articles, reviews and notes from the perspectives of sociocultural, biological, archeological, linguistic, and/or applied anthropology.
Indexed: AnthLit, IBR, IBZ, SOPODA, SSA.
—BLDSC (1546.515000). **CCC.**
Published by: (Society for the Anthropology of Work), University of California Press, Journals Division, 2000 Center St, Ste 303, Berkeley, CA 94704-1223. TEL 510-643-7154, FAX 510-642-9917, journals@ucpress.edu, http://www.ucpress.edu/journals/3a/awr/index.htm. Ed. David Griffith. adv.: page USD 350; 7 x 9.3.

301 IND
ANTHROPOLOGY RESEARCH ASSOCIATION. RESEARCH BULLETIN. Text in English. 1973. q. USD 5. adv. **Document type:** *Bulletin.*
Published by: University of Lucknow, Anthropology Research Association, Department of Anthropology, Badshaw Bagh, Lucknow, Uttar Pradesh, India. Ed. S M Mujtaba. Circ: 200.

301 GBR ISSN 0268-540X
GN1
ANTHROPOLOGY TODAY. Text in English. 1974. bi-m. USD 106 combined subscription in the Americas to institutions & Caribbean (print & online eds.); GBP 63 combined subscription elsewhere to institutions print & online eds. (effective 2006). bk.rev.; film rev. bibl.; illus. back issues avail.; reprint service avail. from PQC,PSC. **Document type:** *Journal, Academic/Scholarly.* **Description:** Aims to provide a forum for the application of anthropological analysis to public and topical issues, while reflecting the breadth of interests within the discipline of anthropology.
Incorporates (in 1985): R A I N: Royal Anthropological Institute News (0307-6776)
Related titles: CD-ROM ed.; Microform ed.: (from PQC); Online - full text ed.: ISSN 1467-8322. USD 101 in the Americas to institutions & Caribbean; GBP 60 elsewhere to institutions (effective 2006) (from Blackwell Synergy, EBSCO Publishing, Gale Group, IngentaConnect, JSTOR (Web-based Journal Archive), O C L C Online Computer Library Center, Inc., Swets Information Services).
Indexed: AICP, AnthLit, BrArAb, IBSS, MASUSE, NumL, PerIslam, RASB, RILM, SOPODA, SSA, SociolAb, WBA, WMB.
—BLDSC (1546.512600), IE, Infotrieve, ingenta. **CCC.**
Published by: (Royal Anthropological Institute), Blackwell Publishing Ltd., 9600 Garsington Rd, Oxford, OX4 2ZG, United Kingdom. TEL 44-1865-776868, FAX 44-1865-714591, at@therai.org.uk, customerservices@oxon.blackwellpublishing.com, http://www.blackwellpublishing.com/journals/ANTH. Ed. Gustaff Houtman. Circ: 3,200.

301 POL
ANTHROPOS. Text in Polish. irreg. **Document type:** *Monographic series, Academic/Scholarly.*
Published by: Wydawnictwo Uniwersytetu Jagiellonskiego/ Jagiellonian University Press, ul Grodzka 26, Krakow, 31044, Poland. TEL 48-12-4312364, FAX 48-12-4301995, wydaw@if.uj.edu.pl, http://www.wuj.pl.

301 VEN ISSN 0254-1629
ANTHROPOS. Text in Spanish. 1980. 2/yr. VEB 60, USD 10. bk.rev.
Indexed: IPB, IndIslam.
Published by: Instituto Superior Salesiano de Filosofia y Educacion, Ave. El Liceo, Apdo 43, Los Teques, Miranda 1201-A, Venezuela.

301 ITA ISSN 0390-1289
ANTHROPOS. Text in Italian. 1979. irreg., latest vol.36, 1999. price varies. adv. **Document type:** *Monographic series, Academic/Scholarly.*
Indexed: RILM.
Published by: Liguori Editore srl, Via Posillipo 394, Naples, 80123, Italy. TEL 39-081-7206111, FAX 39-081-7206244, liguori@liguori.it, http://www.liguori.it, http://www.liguorieditore.com. Ed. Vittorio Lanternari. Pub. Guido Liguori. Adv. contact Maria Liguori.

306.44089 CHE ISSN 0257-9774
GN1
➤ **ANTHROPOS**; revue internationale d'ethnologie et de linguistique. Text in English, French, German. 1906. 2/yr. CHF 180 (effective 2005). bk.rev. abstr.; bibl.; charts; illus. index, cum.index. reprints avail. **Document type:** *Magazine, Academic/Scholarly.* **Description:** Discusses ethnological issues.
Indexed: AICP, AbAn, AnthLit, BAS, BibInd, BibLing, CurCont, DIP, IBR, IBSS, IBZ, L&LBA, MEA&I, MLA, MLA-IB, PSA, PsycholAb, RI-1, RI-2, RILM, SOPODA, SPPI, SSA, SSCI, SSI, SociolAb.
—BLDSC (1546.519300), IDS, IE, Infotrieve, ingenta.
Published by: (Anthropos Institut), Editions Saint-Paul Fribourg, Perolles 42, Fribourg, 1700, Switzerland. TEL 41-26-4264331, FAX 41-26-4264330, info@paulusedition.ch, http://www.anthropos-journal.de, http://www.paulusedition.ch. Ed. Othmar Gaechter. Circ: 1,000.

➤ **ANTHROPOS**; studies in paleontology and geomorphology. see *PALEONTOLOGY*

301 GRC ISSN 1105-2155
➤ **ANTHROPOS: YEARBOOK IN ANTHROPOLOGY.** Text and summaries in English, Greek. 1974. a. price varies. bk.rev. **Document type:** *Monographic series, Academic/Scholarly.* **Description:** Covers physical anthropology, prehistory, and ethnology.
Indexed: AICP, IBSS.
Published by: Anthropological Association of Greece, 5 Dafnomili St, Athens, 114 71, Greece. TEL 30-1-3610-251. Ed., Pub. Aris N Poulianos. R&P Nicholas Poulianos. Circ: 1,000.

➤ **ANTHROPOZOOLOGICA.** see *BIOLOGY—Zoology*

➤ **ANTHROPOZOOLOGICA NUMERO SPECIAL.** see *BIOLOGY—Zoology*

A

A

301 DNK ISSN 0906-3021
➤ **ANTROPOLOGI.** Variant title: Tidsskriftet Antropologi. Text in Danish, Norwegian, Swedish; Summaries in English. 1977. 2/yr. DKK 250 domestic to individuals; DKK 320 to institutions (effective 2005). adv. bk.rev. illus. 150 p./no.; back issues avail. **Document type:** *Journal, Academic/Scholarly.*
Formerly (until 1990): Stofskifte (0108-1012)
Indexed: AnthLit, BHA, IBSS, RILM.
Published by: Foreningen Stofskifte, c/o Institut for Antropologi, Oester Farimagsgade 5, Copenhagen K, 1353, Denmark. TEL 45-35-323472, FAX 45-35-323465, tidsskrift.antropologi@anthro.ku.dk, http://www.tidsskriftetantropologi.dk/, http://www.anthro.ku.dk/roa. Ed. Kennet Pedersen. Adv. contact Kirsten Roenne. Circ: 750.

301 BOL
ANTROPOLOGIA. Text in Spanish. 1979. s-a. looseleaf. BOB 180, USD 8. bk.rev. back issues avail.
Related titles: Microfilm ed.
Indexed: AnthLit.
Published by: Instituto Nacional de Antropologia, Centro de Documentacion Antropologica, Casilla 20898, La Paz, Bolivia.

305.8 ESP ISSN 1131-5814
GN1
ANTROPOLOGIA; ethnographic magazine of anthropological thought and studies. Text in Spanish. 1991. s-a.
Indexed: AnthLit.
—CINDOC.
Published by: Asociacion Madrilena de Antropologia/Madrilena Association of Anthropology, 8, Duke of Osuna, Madrid, 28015, Spain.

301 PER
ANTROPOLOGIA ANDINA. Text in Spanish. 1976. a. USD 10. adv. bk.rev.
Indexed: AICP.
Published by: Centro de Estudios Andinos Cuzco, Apdo Postal 582, Cuzco, Peru. Ed. J Flores Ochoa. Circ: 1,000.

301 ITA ISSN 0392-9035
ANTROPOLOGIA CONTEMPORANEA. Text in Italian. q.
Indexed: AICP, AnthLit.
Published by: Editrice Il Sedicesimo, Via Mannelli, 29, Florence, FI 50136, Italy. TEL 39-055-2476781, FAX 39-055-2478568.

301 MEX ISSN 0185-142X
F1219
ANTROPOLOGIA E HISTORIA; boletin del Instituto Nacional de Antropologia e Historia. Text in Spanish. 1960. q. price varies. illus. 100 p./no.; **Document type:** *Bulletin, Academic/Scholarly.*
Former titles (until 1976): Instituto Nacional de Antropologia e Historia. Boletin (0020-4102); Which superseded (1922-1939): Museo Nacional de Arqueologia, Historia y Etnografia (0188-1817); (1911-1913): Museo Nacional de Arqueologia, Historia y Etnologia. Boletin (0188-1809); (1903-1904): Museo Nacional de Mexico. Boletin (0188-1795)
Indexed: AICP, BHA, HAPI.
Published by: Instituto Nacional de Antropologia e Historia, Frontera 53, Col. Tizapan San Angel, Mexico City, DF 01000, Mexico. TEL 52-55-509714, FAX 52-55-503503, sub_fomento.cncpbs@inah.gob.mx, http://www.inah.gob.mx. Ed. Jorge Gurria Lacroix. Adv. contact Rosa Laura Hernandez Hernandez.

301 ECU ISSN 1018-7537
F3721
ANTROPOLOGIA ECUATORIANA*. Text in Spanish. 1978. irreg. ECS 50 per issue.
Indexed: AICP.
Published by: Casa de la Cultura Ecuatoriana, Casilla 67, Ave. 6de Diciembre, 794, Quito, Ecuador.

301 PRT ISSN 0870-0990
GN1
➤ **ANTROPOLOGIA PORTUGUESA.** Text and summaries in Portuguese, Spanish, French, English. 1983. a., latest vol.17, 2000. EUR 10 to individuals; EUR 14 to institutions; EUR 9 to students (effective 2003). bk.rev. 200 p./no.; back issues avail. **Document type:** *Journal, Academic/Scholarly.* **Description:** Publishes original articles, interviews and reviews in the field of biological, cultural and social anthropology.
Formerly (until 1983): Contribucao para o Estudo da Antropologia Portuguesa (0374-6836)
Indexed: AICP, AnthLit, IBSS, RefZh.
Published by: Universidade de Coimbra, Departamento de Antropologia, Coimbra, 3000, Portugal. TEL 351-239829051, FAX 351-239823491, alsantos@ci.uc.pt, http://www.uc.pt/antrop/publicacoes/antropologia/antropologia.html, http://www.ci.uc.pt/fctuc/antropol.htm. Circ: 1,000.

301 ESP
ANTROPOLOGIA Y PALEOECOLOGIA HUMANA. Text in Spanish. 1979. irreg.
Indexed: AnthLit.
Published by: (Universidad de Granada, Laboratorio de Antropologia GRD), Universidad de Granada, Servicio de Publicaciones, Antiguo Colegio Maximo, Campus de Cartuja, Granada, 18071, Spain. TEL 34-958-243045, FAX 34-958-246116, http://www.ugr.es.

301 MEX ISSN 0186-9787
ANTROPOLOGIA Y TECNICA. Text in Spanish. 198?. s-a.?.
Indexed: AnthLit.
Published by: Universidad Nacional Autonoma de Mexico, Instituto de Investigaciones Antropologicas, Circuito Exterior, Ciudad Universitaria, Mexico, DF 04510, Mexico. TEL 52-5-622-9531, FAX 52-5-622-9651. Ed. Luis M Torres.

301 VEN ISSN 0003-6110
F2229
ANTROPOLOGICA; revista de etnopsicologia y etnopsiquiatria. Text in Spanish; Text occasionally in English. 1956. 2/yr. VEB 200 domestic to individuals; USD 25 foreign to individuals; VEB 250 domestic to institutions; USD 28 foreign to institutions (effective 2005). adv. bk.rev. charts; illus. cum.index: nos.1-62. **Document type:** *Journal.* **Description:** Covers original research in anthropology and related disciplines conducted in Venezuela and adjacent countries (Brasil north of the Amazon, Colombia, Guyana and Lesser Antilles.).
Indexed: AICP, AbAn, AnthLit, HAPI, IBR, IBSS, PCI, RASB, RILM, SSCI.
Published by: (Instituto Caribe de Antropologia y Sociologia), Fundacion la Salle de Ciencias Naturales, Ave. Boyaca-Mariperez, Piso 5, Apdo 1930, Carcacas, 1010A, Venezuela. TEL 58-212-7938437, FAX 58-212-7937493, icas@yahoo.com, http://www.fundacionlasalle.org.ve. Ed. Werner Wilbert. Circ: 500.

301 MEX
ANTROPOLOGICAS. Text in Spanish. 1964; N.S. 1992. s-a. MXP 30. bibl. **Document type:** *Academic/Scholarly.*
Indexed: AICP, AnthLit.
Published by: Universidad Nacional Autonoma de Mexico, Instituto de Investigaciones Antropologicas, Circuito Exterior, Ciudad Universitaria, Mexico, DF 04510, Mexico. TEL 52-5-622-9531, FAX 52-5-622-9651. Ed. Lorenzo S. Ochoa.

301 ESP ISSN 0213-7720
ANTROPOLOGIES. Text in Spanish, Catalan. 1987. irreg. back issues avail.
Related titles: Online - full text ed.
—CINDOC.
Published by: (Universitat de Barcelona, Associacio Antropologies), Universitat de Barcelona, Servei de Publicacions, Gran Via Corts Catalanes 585, Barcelona, 08007, Spain. TEL 34-93-4021100, http://www.publicacions.ub.es.

301 BRA ISSN 0102-4302
GN301
ANUARIO ANTROPOLOGICO. Text in Portuguese. 1976. a. USD 20.
Indexed: AnthLit.
Published by: Edicoes Tempo Brasileiro Ltda, Rua Gago Coutinho, 61, Laranjeiras, ZC-01, Caixa Postal 16099, Rio De Janeiro, RJ 22221-070, Brazil. Ed. Roberto Cardosa de Oliveira.

305.8 MEX
F1219
➤ **ANUARIO DE ESTUDIOS INDIGENAS.** Text in Spanish. 1986. a., latest vol.8, 2000. MXP 18, USD 8 (effective 2002); or exchange basis. back issues avail. **Document type:** *Academic/Scholarly.* **Description:** Regional studies about Chiapas.
Formerly: Centro de Estudios Indigenas. Anuario (0188-4239)
Published by: Instituto de Estudios Indigenas, Centro Universitario, San Cristobal de las Casas, Barrio de Fatima, Chiapas 29264, Mexico. FAX 52-967-6783534, risoch@montebello.unach.mx.

301 ESP ISSN 0210-7732
ANUARIO DE ESUKO-FOLKLORE. Text in Spanish. 1921. a. back issues avail.
Formerly (until 1926): Sociedad de Eusko Folklore. Anuario (0210-7724)
Indexed: AICP, IBSS.
—CINDOC.
Published by: (Fundacion Jose Miguel Barandiaran), Eusko Ikaskuntza/Sociedad de Estudios Vascos, Palacio Miramar, Miraconcha 48, Donostia, San Sebastian 20007, Spain. TEL 34-943-310855, FAX 34-943-213956, ei-sev@sc.ehu.es, http://www.eusko-ikaskuntza.org/. Circ: 500.

305.8 ESP
ANUARIO ETNOLOGICO DE ANDALUCIA. Text in Spanish. a. **Document type:** *Yearbook.*
Indexed: AnthLit.
—CINDOC.
Published by: Consejeria de Cultura y Medio Ambiente, c/o Director of International Programs, c/ San Jose, 3, Seville, 411071, Spain.

301 MEX ISSN 0304-2596
E51
ANUARIO INDIGENISTA/INDIANIST YEARBOOK. Text in Spanish; Summaries in English. 1962. a. included in subscr. to America Indigena. bk.rev. reprints avail. **Document type:** *Academic/Scholarly.* **Description:** Provides news about the Indians and reports on the institution's activities.
Formerly: Boletin Indigenista
Media: Duplicated (not offset). **Related titles:** ♦ Supplement to: America Indigena. ISSN 0185-1179.
Indexed: AICP, AmH&L, AnthLit, HAPI, HistAb, IBSS, ILD, RASB.
—BLDSC (1564.500000).
Published by: Instituto Indigenista Interamericano, Apdo. Postal 20315, Mexico City, DF 01001, Mexico. TEL 525-5680819, FAX 52-5-652-1274. Circ: (controlled).

THE ARABIST; Budapest studies in Arabic. see *LINGUISTICS*

305.8 306.4 HUN ISSN 1215-9239
ARCHAEOLINGUA. Text in Multiple languages. 1990. irreg. **Document type:** *Monographic series.* **Description:** Publishes studies in the prehistory and early history of central and eastern Europe, with special emphasis on the interrelations of the Danube-Alpine-Adriatic region, and within this wider area more specifically on Hungary in its present-day or historical confines.
Indexed: AnthLit.
Published by: The Archaeolingua Foundation, Uri utca 49, Budapest, 1250, Hungary. http://www.archaeolingua.hu. Eds. Sandor Bokonyi, Wolfgang Meid.

ARCHAEOLOGIA AUSTRIACA; Beitraege zur Palaeantologie, Ur- und Fruehgeschichte Oesterreichs. see *ARCHAEOLOGY*

ARCHAEOLOGICAL SOCIETY OF NEW JERSEY. NEWSLETTER. see *ARCHAEOLOGY*

ARCHAEOLOGY IN MONTANA. see *ARCHAEOLOGY*

ARCHAEOLOGY IN OCEANIA. see *ARCHAEOLOGY*

306 POL ISSN 1641-5973
ARCHEUS; studia z bioetyki i antropologii filozoficznej. Text in Polish. 2000. a., latest 2004. EUR 13 per vol. foreign (effective 2005). **Document type:** *Journal, Academic/Scholarly.*
Published by: (Uniwersytet w Bialymstoku), Wydawnictwo Uniwersytetu w Bialymstoku, ul Marii Sklodowskiej-Curie 14, Bialystok, 15097, Poland. TEL 48-85-7457059, FAX 48-85-7457073, ac-dw@uwb.edu.pl. Ed. Maria Nowacka. **Dist. by:** Ars Polona, Krakowskie Przedmiescie 7, Warsaw, Poland. TEL 48-22-9263914, FAX 48-22-9265334, arspolona@arspolona.com.pl, http://www.arspolona.com.pl.

301 ITA
ARCHIVIO DI ETNOGRAFIA. Text in Italian. 1999. s-a. EUR 20.66 domestic; EUR 46.48 foreign (effective 2003). **Document type:** *Academic/Scholarly.*
Published by: Rubbettino Editore, Viale Rosario Rubbettino 10, Soveria Mannelli, CZ 88049, Italy. TEL 39-0968-662034, FAX 39-0968-662055, segreteria@rubettino.it, http://www.rubbettino.it. Ed. Pietro Sassu.

305.8 ITA ISSN 0373-3009
GN1
➤ **ARCHIVIO PER L'ANTROPOLOGIA E LA ETNOLOGIA.** Text in English, French, Italian. 1871. a. reprints avail. **Document type:** *Academic/Scholarly.*
Indexed: AICP, AnthLit.
—Linda Hall.
Published by: Societa Italiana di Antropologia e Etnologia, Palazzo Nonfinito, Via del Proconsolo, 12, Florence, FI 50122, Italy. TEL 39-055-2396449, FAX 39-055-219438, musant@unifi.it. Pub. Cieto Corrain.

301 USA ISSN 0066-6939
G600 CODEN: ARANBP
➤ **ARCTIC ANTHROPOLOGY.** Text in English. 1962. s-a. USD 58 to individuals; USD 176 to institutions (effective 2006). adv. bk.rev. illus. Index. back issues avail.; reprint service avail. from PQC,PSC. **Document type:** *Journal, Academic/Scholarly.* **Description:** Covers arctic and subarctic anthropology, archaeology, ethnology and ethnohistory, linguistics, human biology and related fields, with emphasis on circumpolar anthropology.
Related titles: Microform ed.: (from PQC); Online - full text ed.: (from EBSCO Publishing).
Indexed: ABS&EES, AICP, ASCA, AbAn, AmH&L, AnthLit, ArtHuCI, BAS, BibInd, BibLing, BiolAb, CurCont, FamI, GEOBASE, HistAb, NAA, RASB, RILM, SSCI, SWA.
—BLDSC (1663.070000), IDS, IE, Infotrieve, ingenta. **CCC.**
Published by: (University of Wisconsin at Madison), University of Wisconsin Press, Journal Division, 1930 Monroe St, 3rd Fl, Madison, WI 53711-2059. TEL 608-263-0668, FAX 608-263-1173, journals@uwpress.wisc.edu, http://www.wisc.edu/wisconsinpress/journals/journals/aa.html. Ed. Susan Kaplan. adv.: page USD 370; trim 8.5 x 11. Circ: 500.

➤ **ARCTIQUE.** see *LINGUISTICS*

301 USA ISSN 0271-0641
ARIZONA STATE UNIVERSITY ANTHROPOLOGICAL RESEARCH PAPERS. Text in English. 1969. irreg. (2-5/yr.), latest vol.51, 1998. price varies. **Document type:** *Monographic series.* **Description:** Publishes original research in archaeology, physical anthropology, social and cultural anthropology and linguistics.
Indexed: AnthLit.

Published by: Arizona State University, Department of Anthropology, Box 872402, Tempe, AZ 85287-2402. TEL 480-965-7596, FAX 480-965-7671, gaclark@asu.edu. Ed., R&P G A Clark. Circ: 500 (controlled).

ARKANSAS AMATEUR. see *ARCHAEOLOGY*

301 ESP ISSN 0212-0372
ARXIU D'ETNOGRAFIA DE CATALUNYA. Text in Catalan. 1982. s-a.
Related titles: Online - full text ed.
Indexed: PCI.
—CINDOC.
Published by: Institut Tarragones d'Antropologia, C. Fortuny, 23, Tarragona, Cataluna 43001, Spain. TEL 34-977-222326, itan@tinet.fut.es, http://www.ub.es/filosof/.

ASCLEPIO; archivo iberoamericano de historia de la medicina. see *MEDICAL SCIENCES*

301 GBR ISSN 1444-2213
GN1
➤ **THE ASIA PACIFIC JOURNAL OF ANTHROPOLOGY.** Text in English. 1977. 3/yr. GBP 150, USD 247, AUD 167 combined subscription to institutions print & online eds. (effective 2006). bk.rev. Index. back issues avail.; reprint service avail. from PSC. **Document type:** *Journal, Academic/Scholarly.*
Formerly (until 2000): Canberra Anthropology (0314-9099)
Related titles: Online - full text ed.: ISSN 1740-9314. GBP 143, USD 235, AUD 167 to institutions (effective 2006) (from EBSCO Publishing, Gale Group, IngentaConnect, O C L C Online Computer Library Center, Inc., Swets Information Services).
Indexed: AICP, AnthLit, BAS, EI, IBR, IBSS, IBZ, PCI, SPPI.
—BLDSC (1742.260679).
Published by: (Australian National University, Research School of Pacific and Asian Studies, Department of Anthropology AUS), Routledge (Subsidiary of: Taylor & Francis Group), 4 Park Sq, Milton Park, Abingdon, Oxon OX14 4RN, United Kingdom. TEL 44-1235-828600, FAX 44-1235-829000, journals@routledge.com, http://www.tandf.co.uk/journals/titles/14442213.asp, http://www.routledge.co.uk. Ed. Dr. Kathryn Robinson. R&P Luise Mambly TEL 61-2-61252195. **Subscr. to:** Taylor & Francis Ltd, Journals Customer Service, Rankine Rd, Basingstoke, Hants RG24 8PR, United Kingdom. TEL 44-1256-813000, FAX 44-1256-330245, enquiry@tandf.co.uk.

301 HKG ISSN 1683-478X
GN625
ASIAN ANTHROPOLOGY. Text in English. 2002 (June). a. USD 11.50 (effective 2004). **Description:** Features interesting new anthropological research on Asia to a global audience.
Indexed: ASG, AmH&L, HistAb, IndIslam.
Published by: Chinese University Press, The (Subsidiary of: Chinese University of Hong Kong, The), The Chinese Univ. of Hong Kong,, Sha Tin, New Territories, Hong Kong, Hong Kong. FAX 852-2603-7355, 852-2603-6692, cup@cuhk.edu.hk, http://www.cuhk.edu.hk/ant/asian/, http://www.chineseupress.com.

ASIE ET MONDE INSULINDIEN. see *LINGUISTICS*

301 ESP ISSN 1132-7952
ASMOZ TA JAKITEZ. Text in Multiple languages. 1992. bi-w. price varies. back issues avail. **Document type:** *Monographic series, Academic/Scholarly.*
Related titles: ♦ Spanish ed.: Asmoz Ta Jakitez (Spanish Edition). ISSN 1133-9861; ♦ French ed.: Asmoz Ta Jakitez (French Edition). ISSN 1254-2199.
Published by: Eusko Ikaskuntza/Sociedad de Estudios Vascos, Palacio Miramar, Miraconcha 48, Donostia, San Sebastian 20007, Spain. TEL 34-943-310855, FAX 34-943-213956, ei-sev@sc.ehu.es, http://www.eusko-ikaskuntza.org/.

301 ESP ISSN 1254-2199
ASMOZ TA JAKITEZ (FRENCH EDITION). Text in French. 1995. irreg.
Related titles: ♦ Multiple languages ed.: Asmoz Ta Jakitez. ISSN 1132-7952; ♦ Spanish ed.: Asmoz Ta Jakitez (Spanish Edition). ISSN 1133-9861.
Published by: Eusko Ikaskuntza/Sociedad de Estudios Vascos, Palacio Miramar, Miraconcha 48, Donostia, San Sebastian 20007, Spain. TEL 34-943-310855, FAX 34-943-213956, ei-sev@sc.ehu.es, http://www.eusko-ikaskuntza.org/.

301 ESP ISSN 1133-9861
ASMOZ TA JAKITEZ (SPANISH EDITION). Text in Spanish. 1993. bi-w.
Related titles: ♦ Multiple languages ed.: Asmoz Ta Jakitez. ISSN 1132-7952; ♦ French ed.: Asmoz Ta Jakitez (French Edition). ISSN 1254-2199.
Published by: Eusko Ikaskuntza/Sociedad de Estudios Vascos, Palacio Miramar, Miraconcha 48, Donostia, San Sebastian 20007, Spain. TEL 34-943-310855, FAX 34-943-213956, ei-sev@sc.ehu.es, http://www.eusko-ikaskuntza.org/.

ASSOCIATION FOR ENVIRONMENTAL ARCHAEOLOGY. SYMPOSIA SERIES. see *ARCHAEOLOGY*

306 USA ISSN 0066-9172
ASSOCIATION FOR SOCIAL ANTHROPOLOGY IN OCEANIA. MONOGRAPH SERIES. Text in English. 1970. irreg., latest 2002. price varies. **Document type:** *Monographic series, Academic/Scholarly.*
Indexed: AnthLit.
Published by: (Association for Social Anthropology in Oceania), University of Pittsburgh Press, Eureka Building, 5th Fl, 3400 Forbes Ave, Pittsburgh, PA 15260. TEL 412-383-2456, 800-621-2736, FAX 412-383-2466, 800-621-8471, press@pitt.edu, http://www.pitt.edu/~press/books_by_series/seriesanthroarchae.html. Eds. Andrew Strathern, Niels Aaboe. Pub. Cynthia Miller. R&P Margie Bachman TEL 412-383-2456.

306 USA ISSN 1095-3000
ASSOCIATION FOR SOCIAL ANTHROPOLOGY IN OCEANIA. NEWSLETTER. Text in English. 1967. 3/yr. looseleaf. USD 35 to members; USD 15 to institutions; USD 20 to students (effective 2003). bk.rev. back issues avail. **Document type:** *Newsletter, Academic/Scholarly.*
Published by: Association for Social Anthropology in Oceania, 2499 Kapiolani Blvd 2403, Honolulu, HI 96826. rensel@hawaii.edu, http://www.soc.hawaii.edu/asao/pacific/hawaiki.html. Eds. Karen Brison, Stephen Leavitt. R&P Jan Rensel. Circ: 400.

ASSOCIATION FOR THE STUDY OF PLAY NEWSLETTER. see *PSYCHOLOGY*

301 USA
ASSOCIATION OF SENIOR ANTHROPOLOGISTS. OCCASIONAL PAPERS. Text in English. 1996. irreg.
Indexed: AnthLit.
Published by: (Association of Senior Anthropologists), American Anthropological Association, 2200 Wilson Blvd, Ste 600, Arlington, VA 22201. TEL 703-528-1902, FAX 703-528-3546, http://www.aaanet.org/asa/occpprs.htm. Ed. Molly G. Schuchat.

301 DNK ISSN 1024-3275
ASUNTOS INDIGENAS. Text in Spanish. 1981. q. DKK 375, EUR 50, USD 60 to individuals lincludes El Mundo Indigena; DKK 600, EUR 80, USD 90 to institutions lincludes El Mundo Indigena (effective 2005). cum.index. back issues avail. **Document type:** *Journal, Consumer.* **Description:** Discusses efforts in supporting indigenous peoples worldwide in their struggle against oppression.
Formerly (until 1994): Grupo Internacional de Trabajo sobre Asuntos Indigenas. Boletin (0107-556X)
Related titles: ♦ English ed.: Indigenous Affairs. ISSN 1024-3283.
Indexed: HRIR.
Published by: International Work Group for Indigenous Affairs, Classensgade 11 E, Copenhagen O, 2100, Denmark. TEL 45-35-270500, FAX 45-35-270507, iwgia@igwia.org, http://www.iwgia.org/sw3918.asp. Ed. Alejandro Parellada.

301 FRA ISSN 0993-538X
ATELIER A S E M I. Text in French. 1988. irreg., latest vol.2, 1992.
Published by: Editions de l' Ecole des Hautes Etudes en Sciences Sociales, 131 bd. Saint-Michel, Paris, 75005, France. TEL 33-1-40467080, FAX 33-1-44070889, editions@ehess.fr, http://www.ehess.fr/editions, http://www.ehess.fr/editions/publications.html. **Dist. by:** Centre Interinstitutionnel pour la Diffusion de Publications en Sciences Humaines, 131 bd. Saint-Michel, Paris 75005, France. TEL 33-1-43544715, FAX 33-1-43548073.

301 POL ISSN 0067-0316
ATLAS POLSKICH STROJOW LUDOWYCH. Text in Polish; Summaries in English. 1949. irreg. price varies.
Published by: Polskie Towarzystwo Ludoznawcze, ul Szewska 36, Wroclaw, 50139, Poland. TEL 48-71-444613. Ed. Barbara Bazielich. Circ: 1,500. **Dist. by:** Ars Polona, Krakowskie Przedmiescie 7, Warsaw, Poland. TEL 48-22-8261201, FAX 48-22-8265334.

305.8 AUS ISSN 0729-4352
DU120
AUSTRALIAN ABORIGINAL STUDIES. Text in English. 1963. s-a. AUD 38.50 to non-members; AUD 33 to members; AUD 19.50 newsstand/cover (effective 2004). bk.rev.; film rev. Index. **Document type:** *Journal, Academic/Scholarly.* **Description:** Contains 3 or 4 scholarly articles on aboriginal studies, accompanied by research reports, news and information.
Formerly (until 1983): A I A S Newsletter (0004-9344)
Related titles: Online - full text ed.: (from Florida Center for Library Automation, Gale Group, R M I T Publishing).
Indexed: AICP, AbAn, AnthLit, AusPAIS, BibLing, IBSS, PCI, RASB, RILM.
—CCC.
Published by: (Australian Institute of Aboriginal and Torres Strait Islander Studies), Aboriginal Studies Press, GPO Box 553, Canberra, ACT 2601, Australia. TEL 61-2-62461183, asp@aiatsis.gov.au, http://www.aiatsis.gov.au/rsrch/aas_jrn/journal.htm, http://www.aiatsis.gov.au/asp/index.htm. Ed. Mary Edmunds. Circ: (controlled).

301 AUS ISSN 0810-1906
➤ **AUSTRALIAN / CANADIAN STUDIES**; a multidisciplinary journal for the humanities and social sciences. Text in English. 1983. s-a. AUD 40 domestic to individuals; NZD 40 in New Zealand to individuals; USD 45 elsewhere to individuals; AUD 45 domestic to institutions; NZD 45 in New Zealand to institutions; USD 50 elsewhere to institutions (effective 2003); subscr. incl. membership. bk.rev.; film rev. illus. 150 p./no.; back issues avail. **Document type:** *Journal, Academic/Scholarly.* **Description:** Offers a comparative analysis of Canadian and Australian - New Zealand cultures from multiple disciplinary perspectives.
Related titles: Online - full text ed.: (from R M I T Publishing).
Indexed: CPerI, IBSS, MLA-IB.
Published by: Association for Canadian Studies in Australia and New Zealand, c/o The Editor-Australian Canadian Studies, Department of English, University of Sydney, Sydney, NSW 2006, Australia. TEL 61-2-93517311, FAX 61-2-96652920, acs@english.usyd.edu.au, acsanz@powerup.com.au, http://homepage.powerup.com.au/~acsanz/. Ed., R&P, Adv. contact Sonia Mycak. **Co-sponsor:** Centre for Research Into Textual and Cultural Studies.

301 AUS ISSN 1035-8811
GN1 CODEN: AJANE6
➤ **THE AUSTRALIAN JOURNAL OF ANTHROPOLOGY.** Key Title: T A J A. Text in English. 1931. 3/yr. AUD 60 domestic to individuals; AUD 80 foreign to individuals; AUD 110 domestic to institutions; AUD 145 foreign to institutions (effective 2004). adv. bk.rev. bibl.; charts; illus.; abstr. Index. 125 p./no. 1 cols./p.; back issues avail.; reprints avail. **Document type:** *Journal, Academic/Scholarly.* **Description:** Publishes scholarly papers in anthropology and related disciplines, particularly concerning Australia and neighboring countries, including Asia.
Formerly (until 1990): Mankind (0025-2328)
Related titles: Online - full text ed.: (from bigchalk, Chadwyck-Healey Inc., EBSCO Publishing, Florida Center for Library Automation, Gale Group, H.W. Wilson, Northern Light Technology, Inc., O C L C Online Computer Library Center, Inc., ProQuest Information & Learning, R M I T Publishing).
Indexed: AICP, AbAn, AnthLit, AusPAIS, BAS, BrArAb, CurCont, EI, IBR, IBSS, MLA-IB, PCI, PSA, RASB, RILM, SOPODA, SSA, SSCI, SSI, SociolAb, WBA, WMB.
—IE, Infotrieve. **CCC.**
Published by: Australian Anthropological Society, LPO Box 8099 ANU, Canberra, ACT 2601, Australia. TEL 61-2-61253208, FAX 61-2-61252711, aas.taja@arts.usyd.edu.au, aas@anu.edu.au, http://www.aas.asn.au/TAJA.htm. Ed., R&P, Adv. contact Michael Allen TEL 61-2-9810-5006. B&W page AUD 50; trim 130 x 200. Circ: 450 (paid). **Subscr. to:** c/o Dept. of Anthropology, University of Sydney, Sydney, NSW 2006, Australia. TEL 61-2-90369352, FAX 61-2-96456171.

➤ **THE AUSTRALIAN JOURNAL OF INDIGENOUS EDUCATION.** see *EDUCATION*

301 006.42 GBR ISSN 0962-9483
CODEN: BIANEA
B I C A. (Bulletin of Information on Computing in Anthropology) Text in English. 1984. irreg. **Document type:** *Bulletin.* **Description:** Deals with topics related to the use of computers in anthropology.
Related titles: Online - full text ed.: ISSN 1363-1829. 1996.
Indexed: Inspec.
Published by: University of Kent, Centre for Social Anthropology and Computing, Department of Sociology and Social Anthropology, Eliot College, University of Kent, Canterbury, CT2 7NS, United Kingdom. TEL 44-1227-823360, FAX 44-1227-827289, http://lucy.ukc.ac.uk/bicaweb.

301 DEU ISSN 0005-3856
BAESSLER ARCHIV; Beitraege zur Voelkerkunde. Text in English, German, French. 1952. a. EUR 79.50 (effective 2005). charts; illus.; maps. back issues avail. **Document type:** *Journal, Academic/Scholarly.*
Related titles: Microfiche ed.: (from IDC).
Indexed: AICP, AnthLit, BAS, DIP, EI, IBR, IBSS, IBZ, IndIslam, RASB, RILM.
—CCC.
Published by: (Museum fuer Voelkerkunde, Berlin), Dietrich Reimer Verlag GmbH, Neue Gruenstr 17, Berlin, 10179, Germany. TEL 49-30-2790760, FAX 49-30-27907655, vertrieb-kunstverlage@reimer-verlag.de, http://www.dietrichreimerverlag.de. R&P Beate Behrens.

301 USA
➤ **BALLENA PRESS ANTHROPOLOGICAL PAPERS.** Text in English. 1973. irreg., latest vol.48, 2001. price varies. adv. illus.; maps. **Document type:** *Academic/Scholarly.* **Description:** Information on the Indians of California and the west.
—BLDSC (1861.027300).
Published by: Ballena Press, 823 Valparaiso Ave, Menlo Park, CA 94025. TEL 415-323-9261, FAX 415-883-4280. Eds. Sylvia Brakke Vane, Thomas C Blackburn. Pub., R&P, Adv. contact Sylvia Brakke Vane. Circ: 2,000. **Subscr. to:** PO Box 2510, Novato, CA 94948.

301   **CHE**   ISSN 0067-4478
BASLER BEITRAEGE ZUR ETHNOLOGIE. Text in German; Summaries in French, English. 1965. irreg., latest vol.40, 2001. CHF 55 (effective 2001). **Document type:** *Monographic series, Academic/Scholarly.*
Formerly (until 1966): Basler Beitraege zur Geographie und Ethnologie. Ethnologische Reihe
Indexed: IBR, IBZ, PCI.
Published by: (Museum der Kulturen), Verlag Wepf und Co., Eisengasse 5, Basel, 4001, Switzerland. TEL 41-61-3119576, FAX 41-61-3119585, wepf@dial.eunet.ch, http://www.wepf.ch. Ed. Nigel Stepenson.

305.8   **SCG**   ISSN 0353-9008
DR1228
BASTINA; glasnik. Variant title: Glasnik Bastina. Text in Serbo-Croatian. 1991. irreg.
Published by: Institut za Proucavanje Kulture Srba, Valjevska 2, Kosovska Mitrovica, 38220. Ed. Milenko Jevtovic.

BAUERNHAEUSER AUS MITTELEUROPA; Aufmasse und Publikationen von Gerhard Eitzen. see *ARCHITECTURE*

BEAD FORUM. see *ARCHAEOLOGY*

739.27   **CAN**   ISSN 0843-5499
NK3650
➤ **BEADS.** Text in English. 1989. a. USD 20; USD 30 foreign. bk.rev. illus.; charts. 80 p./no. 2 cols./p.; back issues avail. **Document type:** *Journal, Academic/Scholarly.* **Description:** Fosters serious research on beads of all materials and periods.
Indexed: AICP.
Published by: Society of Bead Researchers, 1600 Liverpool Ct, Ottawa, ON K1A 0M5, Canada. TEL 613-990-4814, FAX 613-952-1756, karlis.karlins@pc.gc.ca, http://www.mindspring.com/~larinc/sbr/journal/journal.htm, http://www.mindspring.com/~larinc/sbr/index/. Ed. Karlis Karklins. Circ: 1,000.

301 398   **DEU**   ISSN 0930-2328
BEITRAEGE ZUR EUROPAEISCHEN ETHNOLOGIE UND FOLKLORE. REIHE A: TEXTE UND UNTERSUCHUNGEN. Text in German. 1987. irreg., latest vol.6, 2003. price varies. **Document type:** *Monographic series, Academic/Scholarly.*
Indexed: MLA-IB.
Published by: Peter Lang GmbH Europaeischer Verlag der Wissenschaften, Eschborner Landstr 42-50, Frankfurt Am Main, 60489, Germany. TEL 49-69-7807050, FAX 49-69-78070550, zentrale.frankfurt@peterlang.com, http://www.peterlang.de. Ed. Leander Petzoldt. **Dist. by:** Verlag Peter Lang AG, Moosstr. 1, Postfach 350, Pieterlen 2542, Switzerland. TEL 41-32-3761717, FAX 41-32-3761727.

301 398   **DEU**   ISSN 0930-2336
BEITRAEGE ZUR EUROPAEISCHEN ETHNOLOGIE UND FOLKLORE. REIHE B: TAGUNGSBERICHTE UND MATERIALIEN. Text in German. 1987. irreg., latest vol.8, 1998. price varies. **Document type:** *Monographic series, Academic/Scholarly.*
Indexed: MLA-IB.
Published by: Peter Lang GmbH Europaeischer Verlag der Wissenschaften, Eschborner Landstr 42-50, Frankfurt Am Main, 60489, Germany. TEL 49-69-7807050, FAX 49-69-78070550, zentrale.frankfurt@peterlang.com, http://www.peterlang.de. Ed. Leander Petzoldt. **Dist. by:** Verlag Peter Lang AG, Moosstr. 1, Postfach 350, Pieterlen 2542, Switzerland. TEL 41-32-3761717, FAX 41-32-3761727.

BEITRAEGE ZUR RHEINISCHEN VOLKSKUNDE. see *FOLKLORE*

301   **DEU**   ISSN 1616-8860
BERLINER ARBEITEN ZUR ERZIEHUNGS- UND KULTURWISSENSCHAFT. Text in German. 2000. irreg., latest vol.11, 2003. price varies. **Document type:** *Monographic series, Academic/Scholarly.*
Published by: Logos Verlag Berlin, Comeniushof, Gubener Str 47, Berlin, 10243, Germany. TEL 49-30-42851090, FAX 49-30-42851092, redaktion@logos-verlag.de, http://www.logos-verlag.de.

BERNICE PAUAHI BISHOP MUSEUM, HONOLULU. SPECIAL PUBLICATIONS. see *SCIENCES: COMPREHENSIVE WORKS*

BIBLIOGRAPHIC GUIDE TO ANTHROPOLOGY AND ARCHAEOLOGY. see *ANTHROPOLOGY—Abstracting, Bibliographies, Statistics*

BIBLIOGRAPHIE ZUR SYMBOLIK, IKONOGRAPHIE UND MYTHOLOGIE. see *ANTHROPOLOGY—Abstracting, Bibliographies, Statistics*

301   **PRY**
BIBLIOTECA PARAGUAYA DE ANTROPOLOGIA. Text in Spanish. 1980. irreg., latest vol.28, 1998. price varies. back issues avail.

Published by: Universidad Catolica Nuestra Senora de la Asuncion, Centro de Estudios Antropologicos, Casilla de Correos 1718, Asuncion, Paraguay. TEL 595-21-446251, FAX 595-21-445245. Circ: 1,000.

305.8   **POL**   ISSN 0067-7655
BIBLIOTEKA ETNOGRAFII POLSKIEJ. Text in Polish; Summaries in English, French, German. 1958. irreg., latest vol.56, 2003. price varies. bibl.; illus.; maps; charts. 455 p./no. 1 cols./p.; **Document type:** *Monographic series, Academic/Scholarly.*
Indexed: IBSS.
Published by: Polska Akademia Nauk, Instytut Archeologii i Etnologii, Al Solidarnosci 105, Warsaw, 00140, Poland. TEL 48-22-6202881, FAX 48-22-6240100, director@iaepan.edu.pl, http://www.iaepan.edu.pl. Ed. Jolanta Kowalska.

301   **NLD**   ISSN 0067-8023
BIBLIOTHECA INDONESICA. Text in English. 1968. irreg., latest 1998, nos. 26-28. price varies. back issues avail. **Document type:** *Monographic series, Academic/Scholarly.* **Description:** Details literature and poetry of numerous cultures in Indonesia. Aimed at anthropologists, linguists, historians and other scholars interested in Southeast Asia.
—KNAW.
Published by: (Koninklijk Instituut voor Taal-, Land- en Volkenkunde), K I T L V Press, PO Box 9515, Leiden, 2300 RA, Netherlands. TEL 31-71-5272372, FAX 31-71-5272638, kitlvpress@rullet.leidenuniv.nl, kitlvpress@kitlv.nl.

306   **KOR**   ISSN 1226-0568
BIGYO MUNHWA YEONGU/CROSS-CULTURAL STUDIES. Text in Multiple languages. 1993. a. **Description:** Compilation of research work and studies in the field of anthropology.
Published by: Seoul Daehaggyo Bigyo Munhwa Yeonguso/Seoul National University, Institute for Cross-Cultural Studies, San 56-1, Shilim-dong, Kwanak-gu, Seoul, 151-742, Korea, S. TEL 82-2-8805476, FAX 82-2-8860976, css@plaza.snu.ac.kr, http://plaza.snu.ac.kr/~css/index_e.htm.

306.44089   **NLD**   ISSN 0006-2294
DS611   **CODEN: BTTVE2**
➤ **BIJDRAGEN TOT DE TAAL-, LAND- EN VOLKENKUNDE/ JOURNAL OF THE HUMANITIES AND SOCIAL SCIENCES OF SOUTHEAST ASIA AND OCEANIA.** Short title: B K I. Text in Dutch, English. 1853. 4/yr. EUR 50 to individuals; EUR 90 to institutions (effective 2005). bk.rev. bibl.; illus. index, cum.index. 150 p./no.; back issues avail.; reprints avail. **Document type:** *Journal, Academic/Scholarly.* **Description:** Focuses on the linguistics, anthropology and history of Southeast Asia, with particular emphasis on Indonesia.
Formerly (until 1948): Bijdragen tot de Taal-, Land- en Volkenkunde van Nederlandsch-Indie (1383-5409)
Indexed: AICP, ASCA, AnthLit, ArtHuCI, BAS, BibInd, BibLing, CurCont, DIP, EI, HistAb, IBR, IBSS, IBZ, IndIslam, L&LBA, MLA, MLA-IB, PCI, PSA, RASB, SOPODA, SSA, SSCI, SociolAb.
—IDS, IE, Infotrieve, KNAW, Linda Hall.
Published by: (Koninklijk Instituut voor Taal-, Land- en Volkenkunde), K I T L V Press, PO Box 9515, Leiden, 2300 RA, Netherlands. TEL 31-71-5272372, FAX 31-71-5272638, kitlvpress@rullet.leidenuniv.nl, kitlvpress@kitlv.nl, http://www.kitlv.nl/periodicals.html. Ed. Dr. B Arps.

➤ **BIOETHICS FORUM.** see *HUMANITIES: COMPREHENSIVE WORKS*

301   **FRA**   ISSN 1279-7863
GN51
BIOMETRIE HUMAINE ET ANTHROPOLOGIE. Text in French; Summaries in English, French. 1932. s-a. adv. bk.rev. bibl.; charts; illus. index. **Document type:** *Proceedings.*
Former titles (until 1997): Cahiers d'Anthropologie et Biometrie Humaine (0758-2714); (until 1983): Societe de Biometrie Humaine. Revue (0183-5688); Biometrie Humaine (0006-3428); Biotypologie
Indexed: AICP, AbHyg, AnthLit, BiolAb, CIS, ChemAb, DSA, ExcerpMed, IBSS, NutrAb, PsycholAb, RDA, RefZh, TDB, ZooRec.
—CISTI, GNLM, Linda Hall.
Published by: Societe de Biometrie Humaine, 28 rue de Charenton, Paris, 75012, France. TEL 33-1-46330596, FAX 33-1-43408785. Ed. E A Cabanis. R&P Ms. Pineau. Adv. contact M Pineau. Circ: 600.

301   **ITA**   ISSN 0392-2529
BIOPSYCHE; rivista di scienze antropologiche. Text in Italian. 1970. q. bk.rev. back issues avail.
Published by: Ispasa Societa Cooperativa, Corso Italia, 104, Catania, CT 95129, Italy. TEL 095-532181.

BIRKA STUDIES. see *ARCHAEOLOGY*

301   **USA**   ISSN 0893-3111
BISHOP MUSEUM BULLETINS IN ANTHROPOLOGY. Text in English. 1922. irreg., latest vol.7, 1997. price varies. reprints avail. **Document type:** *Bulletin.* **Description:** Contains original and analytical materials on anthropology and archaeology of Hawaii and the Pacific Basin.
Supersedes in part (in 1987): Bernice P. Bishop Museum Bulletin (0005-9439)
Indexed: BiolAb.

—CISTI, Linda Hall.
Published by: (Bernice Pauahi Bishop Museum), Bishop Museum Press, 1525 Bernice St, Box 19000 A, Honolulu, HI 96817. TEL 808-847-3511, FAX 808-841-8968. Circ: 300.

BISHOP MUSEUM OCCASIONAL PAPERS. see *SCIENCES: COMPREHENSIVE WORKS*

BISHOP MUSEUM TECHNICAL REPORT. see *SCIENCES: COMPREHENSIVE WORKS*

301 930.1   **VEN**   ISSN 0257-750X
➤ **BOLETIN ANTROPOLOGICO.** Text in Spanish. 1982. q. VEB 7,000 domestic; USD 45 foreign (effective 2004). **Document type:** *Journal, Academic/Scholarly.* **Description:** Created to divulge the activities of researchers at the Museo Arqueologico Gonzalo Rincon Gutierrez and at the Centro de Investigaciones Etnologicas (CIET) of the Universidad de Los Andes as well as the work of other Venezuelan and foreign researchers.
Related titles: Online - full text ed.: 1998. free (effective 2005).
Published by: Universidad de los Andes, Merida, Av 3, Independencia, Merida, 5101, Venezuela. TEL 58-275-401111, FAX 58-275-527704, info@saber.ula.ve, http://www.saber.ula.ve/boletin_antropologico/, http://www.ula.ve.

301   **MEX**   ISSN 0252-841X
E51
BOLETIN DE ANTROPOLOGIA AMERICANA. Text in English, French, Portuguese, Spanish. 1937. s-a. MXP 75 domestic; USD 21 in North America; USD 24.50 in South America; USD 28 in Asia & the Pacific (effective 2005). cum.index: 1937-1980. reprint service avail. from PQC. **Document type:** *Academic/Scholarly.*
Formerly (until 1979): Boletin Bibliografico de Antropologia Americana
Related titles: Microform ed.: (from PQC); Online - full text ed.: (from Gale Group).
Indexed: AICP, AmH&L, AnthLit, BibInd, HAPI, HistAb, IBR, IBSS, IBZ, PCI.
Published by: Instituto Panamericano de Geografia e Historia, Ex-Arzobispado 29, Col Observatorio, Del Miguel Hidalgo, Mexico City, DF 11860, Mexico. TEL 52-55-52775791, FAX 52-55-52716172, info@ipgh.org.mx, http://www.ipgh.org.mx/. Ed. Luis F Bate. **Subscr. to:** IPGH, c/o Depto. de Distribucion y Ventas, Apdo. 18879, Mexico City, DF 11870, Mexico.

930.26   **PER**   ISSN 1029-2004
F3429
BOLETIN DE ARQUEOLOGIA PUCP. (Boletin de Arqueologia Pontificia Univesidad Catolica del Peru) Text in Spanish. 1997. a. USD 30 (effective 2003). back issues avail.
Published by: Pontificia Universidad Catolica del Peru, Fondo Editorial, Ave. Universitaria Cdra. 18, s-n, Urb. Pando, San Miguel, Lima, 32, Peru. TEL 51-14-4602870, FAX 51-14-4600872, feditor@pucp.edu.pe, http://www.pucp.edu.pe/~fedit/index.html.

301   **VEN**   ISSN 0523-9133
F2301
BOLETIN INDIGENISTA VENEZOLANO. Text in Spanish. 1953. s-a.
Indexed: AnthLit.
Published by: Ministerio de Informacion, Direccion de Asuntos Indigenas, Apartado 2059, Caracas, 1020, Venezuela.

306.44089   **ESP**   ISSN 1138-154X
BOLETIN INTERNACIONAL DE LENGUAS Y CULTURAS AMERINDIAS. Text in Spanish. 1995. biennial. **Description:** Serves as organ of expression to the Valencian Institute of Languages and Amerindian Cultures and publishes the series of small studies and discussions on burning problems in amerindian languages: bilingualism, linguistic policy and normalization, writing, disappearance of languages, etc.
Indexed: AnthLit.
Published by: Instituto Valenciano de Lenguas y Culturas Amerindias/Valenciam Institute of Languages and Amerindian Cultures, Avda. Blasco Ibanez, 32, Valencia, 46010, Spain. TEL 34-96-3983063, FAX 34-96-3864778, Julio.Calvo@uv.es.

BORDERLINES (MINNEAPOLIS). see *POLITICAL SCIENCE*

301 570 610   **USA**   ISSN 0006-7806
DS646.3
BORNEO RESEARCH BULLETIN. Text in English. 1969. a., latest vol.32, 2002, Jul. USD 20 (effective 2005). bk.rev. bibl. back issues avail. **Document type:** *Bulletin, Academic/Scholarly.*
Related titles: Online - full text ed.: (from EBSCO Publishing, Gale Group).
Indexed: AICP, AnthLit, BAS, BibLing, DIP, EI, HerbAb, IBR, IBSS, IBZ, L&LBA, RASB, RDA, SOPODA, SSA, SociolAb, WAE&RSA, ZooRec.
Published by: Borneo Research Council, PO Box A, Phillips, ME 04966. TEL 207-639-3939, FAX 207-639-4600, firebird@tdstelme.net, brc@borneoresearchcouncil.org, http://www.borneoresearchcouncil.org. Ed. Clifford Sather. R&P George N Appell. Circ: 325 (paid).

301 USA
BORNEO RESEARCH COUNCIL MONOGRAPH SERIES. Text in English. irreg., latest vol.5, 2001. **Document type:** *Monographic series.* **Description:** Designed to explore and preserve through publication the natural and cultural heritages of Borneo as expressed in its history, biology, ecology, human ecosystems, anthropolgy, archaeology, and the oral literature of the many indigenous societies.
Published by: Borneo Research Council, PO Box A, Phillips, ME 04966.

301 USA
BORNEO RESEARCH COUNCIL PROCEEDINGS SERIES. Text in English. irreg., latest vol.7, 1999. **Document type:** *Proceedings.*
Published by: Borneo Research Council, PO Box A, Phillips, ME 04966.

301 BRA ISSN 0101-0484
BRAZIL. MUSEU DO INDIO. BOLETIM. DOCUMENTACAO. Text in Portuguese. 1976. irreg., latest vol.5, 1996, Dec. free. **Document type:** *Monographic series, Academic/Scholarly.*
Incorporates (1974-1992): Brazil. Museu do Indio. Boletim. Antropologia (0101-0433); (1979-1992): Brazil. Museu do Indio. Boletim. Etno-Historia (0100-7475); (1980-1992): Brazil. Museu do Indio. Boletim. Linguistica (0101-0530)
Published by: Museu do Indio, Biblioteca Marechal Rondon, Rua das Palmeiras, 55, Botafogo, Rio De Janeiro, RJ 22270-070, Brazil. TEL 55-21-2868899, FAX 55-21-2868899, biblioteca@museodomdio.org.br, http:// www.museudoindio.org.br.

BRITISH FORUM FOR ETHNOMUSICOLOGY. NEWSLETTER. see *MUSIC*

305.8 BGR ISSN 1310-5213
GN301
BULGARSKA ETNOLOGIIA. Text in Bulgarian; Summaries in English. 1975. q. USD 48 foreign (effective 2002). illus. reprint service avail. from IRC. **Document type:** *Journal.*
Formerly (until 1995): Bulgarska Etnografiia (0323-9268)
Indexed: AICP, IBSS, RASB.
—KNAW.
Published by: (Bulgarska Akademiya na Naukite/Bulgarian Academy of Sciences, Etnografski Institut s Muzej/Ethnorgaphic Istitute and Museum), Pensoft Publishers, Akad G Bonchev 6, Sofia, 1113, Bulgaria. TEL 359-2-704508, FAX 359-2-704508, pensoft@mbox.infotel.bg, http://www.pensoft.net. Ed. V Hadzhinikolov. Circ: 580.

BULLETIN OF TIBETOLOGY. see *HISTORY—History Of Asia*

301 JPN ISSN 1347-6424
▼ **BUMMMEI/CIVILIZATIONS.** Text in Japanese; Contents page in English. 2003. s-a. **Document type:** *Journal, Academic/Scholarly.*
—BLDSC (3273.971000).
Published by: Toukai Daigaku, Bummei Kenkyuujo/Tokai University, Institute of Civilization Research, 1117, Kitakaname, Hiratsuka, Kanagawa 259-1292, Japan. TEL 81-463-581211 ext 4901 & 4902, FAX 81-463-502055, bunmei@tsc.u-tokai.ac.jp, http://www.bunmei.u-tokai.ac.jp/.

C I H M E C H. (Centro de Investigaciones Humanisticas de Mesoamerica y el Estado de Chiapas) see *ARCHAEOLOGY*

301 FRA ISSN 1275-0336
C N R S ANTHROPOLOGIE. (Centre Nationale de la Recherche Scientifique) Text in French. 1996. irreg. price varies. **Document type:** *Monographic series, Academic/Scholarly.*
Published by: (France. Centre National de la Recherche Scientifique), C N R S Editions, 15 Rue Malebranche, Paris, 75005, France. TEL 33-1-53102700, FAX 33-1-53102727, http://www.cnrseditions.fr.

306.4 305.8 FRA ISSN 1264-0999
C N R S ETHNOLOGIE. (Centre Nationale de la Recherche Scientifique) Text in French. 1994. irreg. price varies. **Document type:** *Monographic series, Academic/Scholarly.*
Related titles: Series: C N R S Ethnologie. Monde Indien et Himalayen. ISSN 1243-146X. 1993; C N R S Ethnologie. Monde Oceanien. ISSN 1243-0560. 1993.
Published by: (France. Centre National de la Recherche Scientifique), C N R S Editions, 15 Rue Malebranche, Paris, 75005, France. TEL 33-1-53102700, FAX 33-1-53102727, http://www.cnrseditions.fr.

301 NLD ISSN 0925-3084
C N W S PUBLICATIONS. Text in Multiple languages. 1991. irreg. **Document type:** *Monographic series.*
Related titles: Supplement(s): C N W S Publications. Special Series. ISSN 1566-600X.
Indexed: AnthLit.
Published by: Research School of Asian, African and Amerindian Studies, P.O. Box 9515, Leiden, 2300 RA, Netherlands. TEL 31-71-5272171, FAX 31-71-5272939, cnws@let.leidenuniv.nl.

301 BRA ISSN 0104-5679
CADERNOS DE CAMPO; revista dos alunos de pos-graduacao em antropologia. Text in Portuguese. 1991. a. USD 9. adv. bk.rev. abstr.; bibl. **Document type:** *Academic/Scholarly.* **Description:** Covers ethnology, urban anthropology, anthropology of peasantry, anthropological theory, Brazilian anthropology. Articles and reviews written by students and teachers.
Published by: Universidade de Sao Paulo, Programa de Pos-Graduacao em Antropologia Social, Dept. de Antropologia - USP, Centro, Caixa Postal 8105, Sao Paulo, SP 01065-970, Brazil. TEL 55-11-8183779, FAX 55-11-8183163. Ed. Piero de Camargo Leirner.

CAESARAUGUSTA. see *ARCHAEOLOGY*

301 FRA ISSN 0068-5046
CAHIERS DE L'HOMME. Text in French. 1961. irreg., latest vol.34, 1998. price varies. **Document type:** *Monographic series, Academic/Scholarly.*
Indexed: IBSS.
Published by: Editions de l' Ecole des Hautes Etudes en Sciences Sociales, 131 bd. Saint-Michel, Paris, 75005, France. TEL 33-1-40467080, FAX 33-1-44070889, editions@ehess.fr, http://www.ehess.fr/editions, http://www.ehess.fr/editions/publications.html. **Dist. by:** Centre Interinstitutionnel pour la Diffusion de Publications en Sciences Humaines, 131 bd. Saint-Michel, Paris 75005, France. TEL 33-1-43544715, FAX 33-1-43548073.

CAHIERS DE PALEOANTHROPOLOGIE. see *PALEONTOLOGY*

CAHIERS DE SOCIOLOGIE ECONOMIQUE ET CULTURELLE. see *SOCIOLOGY*

CAHIERS DES EXPLORATEURS. see *GEOGRAPHY*

305.896 FRA ISSN 0008-0055
DT1
CAHIERS D'ETUDES AFRICAINES. Text in English, French. 1960. q. EUR 30.50 newsstand/cover (effective 2005). adv. bk.rev. charts; illus. reprints avail. **Document type:** *Academic/Scholarly.*
Related titles: Microfiche ed.: (from IDC).
Indexed: ABCPolSci, AICP, ASD, AmH&L, AnthLit, ArtHuCI, BibInd, BibLing, CCA, CurCont, DIP, GEOBASE, HistAb, IBR, IBSS, IPSA, IndIslam, L&LBA, MLA, MLA-IB, PAIS, PCI, PSA, RASB, RDA, SOPODA, SSA, SSCI, SociolAb, WAE&RSA.
—BLDSC (2948.868000), IE, Infotrieve, ingenta. **CCC.**
Published by: Editions de l' Ecole des Hautes Etudes en Sciences Sociales, 131 bd. Saint-Michel, Paris, 75005, France. TEL 33-1-40467080, FAX 33-1-44070889, distrinet@wanadoo.fr, editions@ehess.fr, http://www.ehess.fr/ editions, http://www.ehess.fr/editions/publications.html. Ed. J L Amselle. Circ: 760. **Subscr. to:** EHESS Service Abonnements, 5-7 rue Marcelin-Berthelot, Wissous Cedex F-91322, France. TEL 33-01-55595253, FAX 33-01-55595250. **Dist. by:** Centre Interinstitutionnel pour la Diffusion de Publications en Sciences Humaines, 131 bd. Saint-Michel, Paris 75005, France. TEL 33-1-43544715, FAX 33-1-43548073.

301 USA ISSN 0272-5452
CALIFORNIA ANTHROPOLOGIST. Text in English. 1971. s-a.
Published by: California State University, Anthropology Department, 5151 State University Dr., Los Angeles, CA 90032. TEL 323-343-2440, FAX 323-343-2446, anthro@calstatela.edu, http://www.calstatela.edu/academic/ anthro/calanth.htm.

301 USA
CALIFORNIA SERIES IN PUBLIC ANTHROPOLOGY. Text in English. irreg. price varies. **Document type:** *Monographic series, Academic/Scholarly.*
—BLDSC (3015.286000).
Published by: University of California Press, Book Series, 2120 Berkeley Way, Berkeley, CA 94720. TEL 510-642-4247, FAX 510-643-7127, askucp@ucpress.edu, http://www.ucpress.edu/ books/PANTH.ser.html, http://www.ucpress.edu/books/ series.html.

301 GBR ISSN 0305-7674
GN1
CAMBRIDGE ANTHROPOLOGY. Text in English. 1973. irreg. GBP 21 to individuals; GBP 33 to institutions (effective 2002).
Indexed: AnthLit, IBSS, PCI.
—BLDSC (3015.940500), IE, ingenta.
Published by: University of Cambridge, Department of Social Anthropology, Free School Lane, Cambridge, CB2 3RF, United Kingdom. TEL 44-01223-334599, FAX 44-01223-335993, socanth-admin@lists.cam.ac.uk, http://www.socanth.cam.ac.uk/cambanth.htm.

CAMBRIDGE STUDIES IN BIOLOGICAL AND EVOLUTIONARY ANTHROPOLOGY. see *BIOLOGY*

301 GBR
CAMBRIDGE STUDIES IN CULTURAL SYSTEMS. Text in English. 1977. irreg. price varies. **Document type:** *Monographic series.*
Published by: Cambridge University Press, The Edinburgh Bldg, Shaftesbury Rd, Cambridge, CB2 2RU, United Kingdom. TEL 44-1223-312393, FAX 44-1223-315052, information@cambridge.org, http://www.cup.cam.ac.uk/. Ed. Clifford Geertz. R&P Linda Nicol TEL 44-1223-325757.

306.461 GBR ISSN 1362-7651
CAMBRIDGE STUDIES IN MEDICAL ANTHROPOLOGY. Text in English. 1993. irreg., latest 2003. **Document type:** *Monographic series, Academic/Scholarly.* **Description:** Includes the study of medical institutions and health care in a variety of rich and poor societies, the investigation of the cultural construction of illness, and the analysis of ideas about the body, birth, maturation, ageing and death.
—BLDSC (3015.994800), IE, ingenta.
Published by: Cambridge University Press, The Edinburgh Bldg, Shaftesbury Rd, Cambridge, CB2 2RU, United Kingdom. TEL 44-1223-312393, FAX 44-1223-315052, information@cambridge.org, http://publishing.cambridge.org/ hss/archaeology/csma, http://publishing.cambridge.org/series.

301 GBR ISSN 0955-2405
CAMBRIDGE STUDIES IN ORAL AND LITERATE CULTURE. Text in English. 1981. irreg. price varies. **Document type:** *Monographic series.*
Published by: Cambridge University Press, The Edinburgh Bldg, Shaftesbury Rd, Cambridge, CB2 2RU, United Kingdom. TEL 44-1223-312393, FAX 44-1223-315052, information@cambridge.org, http://www.cup.cam.ac.uk/, http://publishing.cambridge.org/series. Eds. P Burke, R Finnegan. R&P Linda Nicol TEL 44-1223-325757.

306 GBR
CAMBRIDGE STUDIES IN SOCIAL AND CULTURAL ANTHROPOLOGY. Text in English. 1967. irreg. price varies. **Document type:** *Monographic series.* **Description:** Publishes analytical ethnographies, comparative works and contributions to theory.
Formerly: Cambridge Studies in Social Anthropology (0068-6794)
Indexed: AnthLit, MathR.
—BLDSC (3015.995900), ingenta.
Published by: Cambridge University Press, The Edinburgh Bldg, Shaftesbury Rd, Cambridge, CB2 2RU, United Kingdom. TEL 44-1223-312393, FAX 44-1223-315052, information@cambridge.org, http://publishing.cambridge.org/ series/cssa. Ed. Jack Goody. R&P Linda Nicol TEL 44-1223-325757.

301 CAN ISSN 0316-1897
CANADIAN MUSEUM OF CIVILIZATION. MERCURY SERIES. CANADIAN CENTRE FOR FOLK CULTURE STUDIES. PAPER (NO.)/MUSEE CANADIEN DES CIVILISATIONS. COLLECTION MERCURE. CENTRE CANADIEN D'ETUDES SUR LA CULTURE TRADITIONNELLE. DOSSIER. Text in English, French. 1972. irreg. price varies. adv. **Document type:** *Monographic series, Academic/Scholarly.*
Related titles: Microfiche ed.: (from MML); Microform ed.: (from MML); ◆ Series of: Canadian Museum of Civilization. Mercury Series. ISSN 0316-1854.
Indexed: MLA-IB.
Published by: Canadian Museum of Civilization, 100 Laurier St, P O Box 3100, Sta B, Hull, PQ J8X 4H2, Canada. publications@cmcc.muse.digital.ca. Ed. Jean Francois Blanchette. R&P Nicole Chamberland. Adv. contact Pam Coulas.

301 CAN ISSN 1709-5875
CANADIAN MUSEUM OF CIVILIZATION. MERCURY SERIES. ETHNOLOGY PAPER/MUSEE CANADIEN DES CIVILISATIONS. COLLECTION MERCURE. SERVICE CANADIEN D'ETHNOLOGIE. DOSSIER. Text in English, French. 1972. irreg. price varies. adv. **Document type:** *Monographic series, Academic/Scholarly.* **Description:** Designed to permit the rapid dissemination of information pertaining to the disciplines in which the museum is active.
Former titles (until 200?): Canadian Museum of Civilization. Mercury Series. Canadian Ethnology Service. Paper (No.) (0316-1862); (until 1974): Canadian Museum of Civilization. Mercury Series. Ethnology Division Paper (0316-1870)
Related titles: Microfiche ed.: (from MML); ◆ Series of: Canadian Museum of Civilization. Mercury Series. ISSN 0316-1854; Supplement(s): Canadian Ethnology Service. Annual Review. ISSN 0704-206X.
Indexed: AnthLit.
Published by: Canadian Museum of Civilization, 100 Laurier St, P O Box 3100, Sta B, Hull, PQ J8X 4H2, Canada. publications@civilization.ca. Ed. Jean Francois Blanchette. R&P Nicole Chamberland. Adv. contact Pam Coulas.

THE CANADIAN REVIEW OF SOCIOLOGY AND ANTHROPOLOGY/REVUE CANADIENNE DE SOCIOLOGIE ET D'ANTHROPOLOGIE. see *SOCIOLOGY*

301 NLD ISSN 0921-9781
CARIBBEAN SERIES. Text in Dutch, English. 1985. irreg., latest vol.16, 1995. price varies. back issues avail. **Document type:** *Monographic series.*
—KNAW.
Published by: (Koninklijk Instituut voor Taal-, Land- en Volkenkunde), K I T L V Press, PO Box 9515, Leiden, 2300 RA, Netherlands. TEL 31-71-5272372, FAX 31-71-5272638, ktlvpress@rullet.leidenuniv.nl.

CARNEGIE MUSEUM OF NATURAL HISTORY. ANNALS. see *SCIENCES: COMPREHENSIVE WORKS*

CARNEGIE MUSEUM OF NATURAL HISTORY. BULLETIN. see *SCIENCES: COMPREHENSIVE WORKS*

301. USA
CASE STUDIES IN CULTURAL ANTHROPOLOGY✶. Text in English. irreg. price varies.
Published by: Holt, Rinehart and Winston, Inc., c/o Harcourt Brace Jovanovich, 6277 Sea Harbor Dr, Orlando, FL 32887. TEL 407-345-2500.

301 SVN ISSN 0351-4285
CASOPIS ZA KRITIKO ZNANOSTI. Text in Slovenian. 1973. q.
Formerly (until 1978): Casopis za Kritiko Znanosti, Domisliojo in Novo Antropologijo (1318-525X)
Indexed: RILM.
Published by: Univerza v Ljubljani, Beethovnova 9-I, Ljubljana, 1000, Slovenia. TEL 386-61-121-4170, FAX 386-61-222-618, zalozba@kiss.uni-lj.si.

301 GBR ISSN 0069-0880
CASS LIBRARY OF AFRICAN STUDIES. AFRICANA MODERN LIBRARY✶. Text in English. 1967. irreg. price varies. **Document type:** *Academic/Scholarly.*
Published by: Frank Cass Publishers (Subsidiary of: Taylor & Francis Group), Crown House, 47 Chase Side, Southgate, London, N14 5BP, United Kingdom. TEL 44-20-89202100, FAX 44-20-84478548, info@frankcass.com, http://www.frankcass.com. R&P Anna Whiston.

306.44089 FIN ISSN 0355-0141
CASTRENIANUMIN TOIMITTEITA. Text in Multiple languages. 1971. irreg., latest vol.60. price varies. **Document type:** *Academic/Scholarly.*
Indexed: RASB.
Published by: Suomalais-Ugrilainen Seura/Finno-Ugrian Society, Mariankatu 7 A, PO Box 320, Helsinki, 00171, Finland. TEL 358-09-662149, FAX 358-09-632501. Ed. Seppo Suhonen. **Dist. by:** Tiedekirja OY - Vetenskapsbokhandeln, Kirkkokatu 14, Helsinki 00170, Finland.

305.8 HUN ISSN 1218-2532
CATALOGI MUSEI ETHNOGRAPHIAE. Text in Hungarian; Summaries in English, German. 1993. a. HUF 1,000 or exchange basis. **Document type:** *Catalog.*
Published by: Neprajzi Muzeum/Ethnographical Museum, Kossuth Lajos ter 12, Budapest, 1055, Hungary. TEL 36-1-326340, FAX 36-2-692419. Ed. Attila Selmeczi Kovacs.

301 USA
CENTER FOR ANTHROPOLOGICAL STUDIES. A CLASSIC SOUTHWESTERN REPRINT. Text in English. irreg.
Published by: Center for Anthropological Studies, PO Box 14576, Albuquerque, NM 87191-4576. TEL 505-296-6336.

301 USA
CENTER FOR ANTHROPOLOGICAL STUDIES. CONTRIBUTIONS TO ANTHROPOLOGICAL STUDIES. Text in English. 1978. irreg., latest vol.4, 1987. price varies. adv. **Document type:** *Monographic series.*
Published by: Center for Anthropological Studies, PO Box 14576, Albuquerque, NM 87191-4576. TEL 505-296-6336. Ed., R&P, Adv. contact Albert E Ward. Circ: 1,000.

301 USA
CENTER FOR ANTHROPOLOGICAL STUDIES. ETHNOHISTORICAL REPORT SERIES. Text in English. 1980. irreg., latest vol.2, 1987. price varies. **Document type:** *Monographic series.*
Published by: Center for Anthropological Studies, PO Box 14576, Albuquerque, NM 87191-4576. TEL 505-296-6336. Ed. Albert E Ward.

301 USA
CENTER FOR ANTHROPOLOGICAL STUDIES. SPANISH BORDERLANDS RESEARCH. Text in English. 1980. irreg. price varies. **Document type:** *Monographic series.* **Description:** Studies from the Spanish Colonial period in the southern US.
Published by: Center for Anthropological Studies, PO Box 14576, Albuquerque, NM 87191-4576. TEL 505-296-6336. Ed. Albert E Ward.

301 USA ISSN 0577-0963
GN1
CENTRAL STATES ANTHROPOLOGY SOCIETY. BULLETIN. Variant title: C S A S Bulletin. Text in English. 1966. s-a. USD 10 (effective 2005 & 2006). adv. **Document type:** *Journal, Academic/Scholarly.* **Description:** Contains news and information related to the work and scholarship of the Central States Anthropology Society.
Related titles: Online - full text ed.: ISSN 1548-7431.
—CCC.
Published by: (American Anthropological Association), University of California Press, Journals Division, 2000 Center St, Ste 303, Berkeley, CA 94704-1223. TEL 510-643-7154, FAX 510-642-9917, journals@ucpress.edu, http://www.ucpress.edu/journals/3a/csas/index.htm. Ed. James Hopgood. adv.: page USD 350; 7 x 9.3.

305.8 COD
CENTRE D'ETUDES ETHNOLOGIQUES BANDUNDU. PUBLICATIONS. Text in French. 1966. irreg., latest vol.100, 1988. price varies. bibl.; charts. **Description:** Discusses anthropology, arts and handicrafts, folklore, linguistics, nutrition, history of Africa, religion, rites and mythology, sociology and theater, development and human promotion.
Formerly: Centre d'Etudes Ethnologiques. Publications (0577-1331)
Published by: (Centre d'Etudes Ethnologiques COG), C E E B A Publications, BP 246, Bandundu, Congo, Dem. Republic. Ed. Hermann Hochegger. Circ: 700.

305.8 COD
CENTRE D'ETUDES ETHNOLOGIQUES. PUBLICATIONS. SERIE 2: MEMOIRES ET MONOGRAPHIES. Text in French. 1970. irreg., latest vol.103, 1989. bibl.; charts; illus.
Published by: (Centre d'Etudes Ethnologiques COG), C E E B A Publications, BP 246, Bandundu, Congo, Dem. Republic.

306 004 GBR ISSN 1461-7706
CENTRE FOR SOCIAL ANTHROPOLOGY AND COMPUTING. MONOGRAPHS. Variant title: C S A C. Monographs. Text in English. 1991. irreg. **Document type:** *Monographic series.*
—BLDSC (3490.177650).
Published by: University of Kent, Centre for Social Anthropology and Computing, Department of Sociology and Social Anthropology, Eliot College, University of Kent, Canterbury, CT2 7NS, United Kingdom. TEL 44-1227-823360, FAX 44-1227-827289.

301 CHE ISSN 1015-468X
➤ **CENTRE GENEVOIS D'ANTHROPOLOGIE. BULLETIN.** Text in French. 1989. irreg., latest vol.5, 1999. CHF 45 per vol. (effective 2000). bk.rev. bibl.; illus.; stat. back issues avail. **Document type:** *Bulletin, Academic/Scholarly.*
Formed by the 1989 merger of: Musee d'Ethnographie de la Ville de Geneve. Bulletin Annuel (0072-0828); Which was formerly (1958-1968): Musee et Institut d'Ethnographie de la Ville de Geneve. Bulletin Annuel (0435-2920); And (1914-1989): Archives Suisses d'Anthropologie Generale (0066-6653); Which incorporated (1925-1972): Schweizerischen Gesellschaft fuer Anthropologie und Ethnologie. Bulletin (0081-1254)
Indexed: AICP, AnthLit, BrArAb, IBSS, NumL.
Published by: (Centre Genevois d'Anthropologie), Universite de Geneve, Departement d'Anthropologie et d'Ecologie, Case Postale 511, Geneva, 1211, Switzerland. TEL 41-22-702-6967, FAX 41-22-300-0351, info@anthro.unige.ch, http://www.ville-ge.ch/musinfo/ethg/bcga.htm, http://anthropologie.unige.ch. Eds. Alain Gallay, Louis Necker.
Co-sponsor: Musee d'Ethnographie.

305.8 306 MEX
CENTRO DE ESTUDIOS SUPERIORES DE MEXICO Y CENTROAMERICA. ANUARIO. Text in Spanish. a.
Indexed: AnthLit.
Published by: Universidad de Ciencias y Artes del Estado de Chiapas, Centro de Estudios Superiores de Mexico y Centroamerica.ores de Mexico y Centroamerica./University of Sciences and Arts of the Chiapas State, Center of Superior Studies of Mexico and Central America, Diego Dugelay No. 4, San Cristobal of The Houses, Shiapas, Mexico. TEL 967-80367, FAX 967-80367.

301 PRT
CENTRO DE ESTUDOS REGIONAIS. BOLETIM CULTURAL. Text in Portuguese. 1984. s-a. **Document type:** *Bulletin, Consumer.*
Published by: Centro de Estudos Regionais, Largo do Instituto Historico do Minho 20-22, Viana Do Castelo, 4900, Portugal. TEL 828192. Pub. Antonio A Parente Pereira. Circ: 1,000.

301 BRA ISSN 0104-2262
CENTRO DE MEMORIA REGIONAL. CADERNO. Text in Portuguese. 1993. s-a. **Document type:** *Bulletin.*
Published by: Universidade Sao Francisco, Centro de Memoria Regional, Ave. SAO FRANCISCO DE ASSIS, 218, Braganca Paulista, SP 12900-000, Brazil. TEL 55-11-4041500 ext. 218, usfbib@eu.ansp.br. Ed. Marcos Cezar de Freitas.

306 CZE ISSN 0009-0794
DB191
CESKY LID✶ **/CZECH PEOPLE**; narodni casopis. Text in Czech; Summaries in English, French, German. 1892. q. bk.rev. bibl.; illus. index. **Document type:** *Journal, Academic/Scholarly.* **Description:** Includes work on anthropology, ethnology, and folklore.
Indexed: AICP, AmH&L, BHA, BibInd, BibLing, DIP, HistAb, IBR, IBSS, IBZ, MLA, MLA-IB, NumL, RASB, RILM.
Published by: Akademie Ved Ceske Republiky, Ustav pro Etnografii a Folkloristiku, Machova 7, Prague 2, 120 00, Czech Republic. TEL 42-2-24256740, FAX 42-2-250430. Ed. Zdenek Hanzl. Circ: 1,000. **Dist. in Western countries by:** Kubon und Sagner GmbH, Hesst. 39-41, Munich 80798, Germany. TEL 49-89-54218218, 49-89-54218-0, FAX 49-89-54218218.

301 RUS
CHELOVEK: OBRAZ I SUSHCHNOST'. Text in Russian. a.
Published by: Rossiiskaya Akademiya Nauk, Institut Nauchnoi Informatsii po Obshchestvennym Naukam, Nakhimovskii pr-t 51/21, Moscow, 117997, Russian Federation. TEL 7-095-1288930, FAX 7-095-4202261, info@inion.ru, http://www.inion.ru.

306.4 305.8 FRA ISSN 1257-9947
CHEMINS DE L'ETHNOLOGIE. Text in French. 1994. irreg. price varies. **Document type:** *Monographic series, Academic/Scholarly.*
Published by: C N R S Editions, 15 Rue Malebranche, Paris, 75005, France. TEL 33-1-53102700, FAX 33-1-53102727, http://www.cnrseditions.fr.

CHESOPIEAN; a journal of North American archaeology. see *ARCHAEOLOGY*

CHINESE SOCIOLOGY AND ANTHROPOLOGY; a journal of translations. see *SOCIOLOGY*

CHUNGARA (ARICA). see *ARCHAEOLOGY*

301 USA ISSN 0893-0465
HT101 CODEN: CISOEC
➤ **CITY & SOCIETY.** Text in English. 1987-1992 (Dec.); resumed. s-a. USD 58 (effective 2005 & 2006). adv. reprints avail. **Document type:** *Journal, Academic/Scholarly.* **Description:** Presents articles concerned with urban communities and complex societies.
Related titles: Online - full text ed.: ISSN 1548-744X.
Indexed: AICP, AbAn, AmH&L, AnthLit, GEOBASE, HistAb, IBR, IBSS, IBZ, RILM.
—CCC.
Published by: (American Anthropological Association, Society for Urban, National and Transnational/Global Anthropology), University of California Press, Journals Division, 2000 Center St, Ste 303, Berkeley, CA 94704-1223. TEL 510-643-7154, FAX 510-642-9917, journals@ucpress.edu, http://www.ucpress.edu/journals/3a/city/index.htm. Ed. Emily Schultz. adv.: page USD 295; 4.8 x 8. Circ: 1,000.

306 FRA
LE COCHONGLIER. Text in French. 1998. s-a. membership. back issues avail. **Document type:** *Newsletter.* **Description:** Discusses news and topics of interest to the membership of the Association d'Histoire des Societes Rurales.
Published by: Association d'Histoire des Societes Rurales, Maison de la Recherche en Sciences Humaines, Universite de Caen, Esplanade de la Paix, Caen, 14032, France. TEL 33-2-31566229, FAX 32-2-31566560, http://www.uhb.fr/sc_sociales/crhisco/Hsr05.htm. Ed. Pierre Jaillette.

CODEX FILATELICA. see *PHILATELY*

301 SLV ISSN 0256-7202
➤ **COLECCION ANTROPOLOGIA E HISTORIA.** Text in Spanish. 1973. s-a. free. bibl.; charts; illus. **Document type:** *Academic/Scholarly.*
Published by: Ministerio de Educacion, Direccion de Patrimonio Cultural, Edificio A-5, Plan Maestro Centro de Gobierno, Alameda Juan Pablo II, San Salvador, El Salvador. TEL 503-221-4439, FAX 503-221-4419, registro@es.com.sv, http://www.conacyt.gob.sv/cultura. Ed. America Rodriguez. Pub. Gustavo Herodier. R&P Maria Isaura Arauz. Circ: (controlled).

301 ESP
COLECCION BARANDIARAN. Text in Spanish. 1984. irreg. price varies. back issues avail. **Document type:** *Magazine, Academic/Scholarly.*
Related titles: Online - full text ed.
Published by: Eusko Ikaskuntza/Sociedad de Estudios Vascos, Palacio Miramar, Miraconcha 48, Donostia, San Sebastian 20007, Spain. TEL 34-943-310855, FAX 34-943-213956, ei-sev@sc.ehu.es, http://www.barandiaranfundazioa.com/, http://www.eusko-ikaskuntza.org/.

301 ESP
COLECCION DE ETNOGRAFIA LUIS CORTES VAZQUEZ. Text in Spanish. 1991. a.
Published by: Instituto de Estudios Zamoranos "Florian de Ocampo", Plaza de Viariato, s-n, Zamora, 49071, Spain. TEL 34-980-530486, FAX 34-980-514329, iez@helcom.es, http://www.helcom.es/iez/. Ed. Carmen Seisdedos Sanchez.

301 ITA
COLLANA DI STUDI PALEONTOLOGICI. Text in Italian. 1977. irreg. price varies. **Document type:** *Monographic series, Academic/Scholarly.*
Published by: (Istituto di Antropologia e Paleontologia Umana), Giardini Editori e Stampatori (Subsidiary of: Libra Web), Via Giosue Carducci 60, Ghezzano - La Fontina, Pisa 56123, Italy. TEL 39-050-878066, FAX 39-050-878732, giardinieditori@giardinieditori.it, http://www.libraweb.net.

301 DEU
COLLECTANEA INSTITUTI ANTHROPOS. Text in German, English, French. 1967. irreg., latest vol.43, 1999. price varies. illus. **Document type:** *Monographic series, Academic/Scholarly.*

Published by: (Anthropos Institut CHE), Academia Verlag GmbH, Bahnstr 7, Sankt Augustin, 53757, Germany. TEL 49-2241-345210, FAX 49-2241-345316, kontakt@academia-verlag.de, http://www.academia-verlag.de.

301 CAN ISSN 0078-1053
CODEN: CNORE2
COLLECTION NORDICANA. Variant title: Nordicana. Text and summaries in English, French. 1964. irreg. (3-5/yr.). price varies. back issues avail. **Document type:** *Monographic series, Academic/Scholarly.*
Formerly (until no.49 1986): Quebec (City) Universite Laval. Centre d'Etudes Nordiques. Travaux Divers
—CCC.
Published by: Universite Laval, Centre d'Etudes Nordiques, Quebec, PQ G1K 7P4, Canada. TEL 418-656-3340.

301 HRV ISSN 0350-6134
CODEN: COANDS
➤ **COLLEGIUM ANTROPOLOGICUM.** Text in English; Summaries in English, Croatian. 1977. s-a. HRK 50 domestic to individuals; USD 10 foreign to individuals; HRK 100 domestic to institutions; USD 50 foreign to institutions (effective 2005). adv. bk.rev. charts; illus.; stat. back issues avail. **Document type:** *Journal, Academic/Scholarly.*
Indexed: ASCA, AbAn, AgeL, AnthLit, CurCont, IBSS, IndMed, MEDLINE, PerIslam, RILM, SOPODA, SSA, SSCI, SociolAb.
—BLDSC (3311.355000), CASDDS, IDS, IE, Infotrieve, ingenta.
Published by: (Institut za Antropologiju, Zagreb/Institute for Anthropological Research, Zagreb), Hrvatsko Antropolosko Drustvo/Croatian Anthropological Society, Ulica grada Vukovara 72, Zagreb, 10000, Croatia. TEL 385-1-535145, FAX 385-1-536716, croantro@luka.inantro.hr, http://public.srce.hr/antro/eng/colleg.htm, http://luka.inantro.hr/society. Eds. Hubert Maver, Pavao Rudan. R&P Pavao Rudan. Circ: 1,000.
Co-sponsor: School of Biological Anthropology.

301 DEU ISSN 0930-8555
COLONIA ROMANICA. Text in German. 1986. a.
Indexed: AIAP, RILM.
Published by: Greven Verlag Koeln GmbH, Neue Weyerstr 1-3, Cologne, 50676, Germany. greven.verlag@greven.de, http://www.greven-verlag.de.

COMMERCE AND MASS CULTURE. see *COMMUNICATIONS*

COMPARATIVE CIVILIZATIONS REVIEW. see *HISTORY*

301 PER ISSN 1022-1514
COMUNIDADES Y CULTURAS PERUANAS. Text in Spanish. 1973. irreg., latest vol.28, 1998. price varies. back issues avail. **Document type:** *Academic/Scholarly.*
Related titles: Microfiche ed.
Indexed: IBSS, SOPODA.
Published by: Instituto Linguistico de Verano, c/o Branch Editor, Casilla 2492, Lima, 100, Peru. FAX 51-14-605124. Ed., R&P D Koop. **Subscr. to:** E. Iturriaga y Cia., Jiron Ica 441, Ofc. 202-203, Casilla 4640, Lima 100, Peru.

CONFLICT & COMMUNICATION ONLINE. see *LAW*

301 ESP
CONGRESOS DE ESTUDIOS VASCOS. Text in Spanish. 1918-1930; resumed 1983. irreg. price varies. back issues avail. **Document type:** *Monographic series, Academic/Scholarly.*
Published by: Eusko Ikaskuntza/Sociedad de Estudios Vascos, Palacio Miramar, Miraconcha 48, Donostia, San Sebastian 20007, Spain. TEL 34-943-310855, FAX 34-943-213956, ei-sev@sc.ehu.es, http://www.eusko-ikaskuntza.org/.

301 MEX ISSN 0074-0810
CONGRESOS INDIGENISTAS INTERAMERICANOS. ACTAS. Text in Spanish. every 4 yrs., latest 1993, 11th, Managua, Nicaragua. **Document type:** *Proceedings.*
Formerly: Inter-American Conference on Indian Life. Acts - Congresos Indigenistas Interamericanos. Acta
Published by: Instituto Indigenista Interamericano, Apdo. Postal 20315, Mexico City, DF 01001, Mexico. TEL 525-5680819, FAX 52-5-652-1274. Circ: (controlled).

301 351 FRA ISSN 1160-0683
CONSERVATION DU PATRIMOINE. Text in French. 1992. irreg. price varies. **Document type:** *Monographic series, Government.*
Published by: (Ministere de la Culture et de la Communication), C N R S Editions, 15 Rue Malebranche, Paris, 75005, France. TEL 33-1-53102700, FAX 33-1-53102727, http://www.cnrseditions.fr.

306.4 901 ITA
CONSIGLIO NAZIONALE DELLE RICERCHE. PROGETTO FINALIZZATO BENI CULTURALI. NEWS/NATIONAL RESEARCH COUNCIL (ITALY). SPECIAL PROJECT ON CULTURAL HERITAGE. NEWS. Text in Italian, English. irreg., latest vol.3, 2000, Mar. free. **Document type:** *Newsletter, Academic/Scholarly.* **Description:** Discusses news and activities at the Italian Naional Research Council's Special Project on the Safeguard of Cultural Heritage.
Media: Online - full content.
Published by: Consiglio Nazionale delle Ricerche, Progetto Finalizzato Beni Culturali/National Research Council, Special Project on Cultural Heritage, Vialle dell'Universita 11, Rome, 00185, Italy. TEL 39-06-4463745, FAX 39-06-4463883, cnrpfbc@tin.it, http://www.culturalheritage.cnr.it/news/corpo.html. Ed. Angelo Guarino.

CONTEMPORARY ISSUES IN ASIA AND THE PACIFIC. see *ASIAN STUDIES*

▼ **CONTEMPORARY PSYCHOANALYTIC STUDIES.** see *PSYCHOLOGY*

CONTRAVERSIONS: JEWS AND OTHER DIFFERENCES. see *RELIGIONS AND THEOLOGY—Judaic*

305.8 BRN ISSN 0217-2992
GN635.A75
➤ **CONTRIBUTIONS TO SOUTHEAST ASIAN ETHNOGRAPHY.** Text in English. 1982. irreg., latest vol.12, 2004. USD 25 per issue (effective 2005). adv. bibl.; charts; illus.; maps. back issues avail. **Document type:** *Journal, Academic/Scholarly.* **Description:** Covers the study of the peoples of Southeast Asia, their societies and their cultures. The orientation is essentially ethnographic.
Indexed: AICP, AnthLit, BAS, EI.
Address: c/o Dr. Anthony Walker, Faculty of Arts and Social Sciences, Universiti Brunei Darussalam, Gadong, BE1410, Brunei Darussalam. TEL 673-2-661384, anthonywalker@brunet.bn. Eds. Dr. Anthony Walker, Tan Chee Beng. Pub., R&P Dr. Anthony Walker. adv.: page USD 400. Circ: 500.

301 USA ISSN 0890-9377
CONTRIBUTIONS TO THE STUDY OF ANTHROPOLOGY. Text in English. 1987. irreg., latest vol.9, 2003. price varies. **Document type:** *Monographic series, Academic/Scholarly.*
—BLDSC (3461.453400).
Published by: Greenwood Publishing Group Inc. (Subsidiary of: Harcourt International), 88 Post Rd W, PO Box 5007, Westport, CT 06881. TEL 203-226-3571, FAX 203-226-1502, webmaster@greenwood.com, http://www.greenwood.com.

306 USA ISSN 0198-9871
CONTRIBUTIONS TO THE STUDY OF POPULAR CULTURE. Text in English. 1981. irreg., latest vol.78, 2003. price varies. **Document type:** *Monographic series, Academic/Scholarly.*
—BLDSC (3461.454200), IE, ingenta.
Published by: Greenwood Publishing Group Inc. (Subsidiary of: Harcourt International), 88 Post Rd W, PO Box 5007, Westport, CT 06881. TEL 203-226-3571, FAX 203-226-1502, webmaster@greenwood.com, http://www.greenwood.com.

301 305.8 DNK ISSN 1811-0665
CRITICAL ANTHROPOLOGY. Text in English. irreg. DKK 298 per vol. domestic to individuals; USD 49 per vol. elsewhere to individuals (effective 2005). **Document type:** *Journal.* **Description:** Offers new perspectives on social life in marginal, violent, impoverished, and diasporic situations. Works appearing in this series will initiate new and useful dialogue between humanists, anthropologists, policy-makers, and international aid and development agencies.
Published by: Museum Tusculanum Press, c/o University of Copenhagen, Njalsgade 94, Copenhagen S, 2300, Denmark. TEL 45-35-329109, FAX 45-35-329113, mtp@mtp.dk, http://www.mtp.dk. Ed. Mr. Michael Jackson. R&P Mrs. Marianne Alenius.

301 GBR ISSN 0308-275X
GN1
➤ **CRITIQUE OF ANTHROPOLOGY**; a journal for the critical reconstruction of anthropology. Text in English. 1974. q. GBP 372, USD 651 to institutions; GBP 387, USD 678 combined subscription to institutions print & online eds. (effective 2006). adv. bk.rev. back issues avail. **Document type:** *Journal, Academic/Scholarly.* **Description:** Dedicated to the development of anthropology as a discipline that subjects social reality to critical analysis.
Related titles: Online - full text ed.: ISSN 1460-3721. GBP 368, USD 644 to institutions (effective 2006) (from EBSCO Publishing, O C L C Online Computer Library Center, Inc., Sage Publications, Inc., Swets Information Services).
Indexed: AICP, ASCA, ASSIA, AbAn, AltPI, AnthLit, ArtHuCI, CurCont, DIP, ERA, FamI, HRA, IBR, IBSS, IBZ, IBibSS, LeftInd, MEA&I, PCI, PRA, PSA, RASB, RI-1, RI-2, RILM, SFSA, SOPODA, SRRA, SSA, SSCI, SociolAb, V&AA.
—BLDSC (3487.490300), IE, Infotrieve, ingenta. **CCC.**
Published by: Sage Publications Ltd. (Subsidiary of: Sage Publications, Inc.), 1 Oliver's Yard, 55 City Rd, London, EC1 1SP, United Kingdom. TEL 44-20-73248500, FAX 44-20-73248600, info@sagepub.co.uk, http://www.sagepub.co.uk/journal.aspx?pid=105510. Eds. John Gledhill, Steven Nugent. Adv. contact Jenny Kirby. page GBP 195; trim 184 x 114. Circ: 100. **Subscr. in the Americas to:** Sage Publications, Inc., 2455 Teller Rd, Thousand Oaks, CA 91320. TEL 805-499-0721, FAX 805-499-0871, journals@sagepub.com.

305 GBR ISSN 1068-8536
➤ **CROSS-CULTURAL PERSPECTIVES ON WOMEN.** Text in English. 1992. irreg. price varies. **Document type:** *Monographic series, Academic/Scholarly.* **Description:** Takes up a wide range of current debates using comparative data and analysis of both past and contemporary experiences of women.
Indexed: AnthLit, MLA-IB.
—IE.
Published by: Berg Publishers, Angel Court, 1st Fl, 81 St Clements St, Oxford, Berks OX4 1AW, United Kingdom. TEL 44-1865-245104, FAX 44-1865-791165, enquiry@bergpublishers.com, http://www.bergpublishers.com/. Eds. Jackie Waldren, Shirley Ardener.

➤ **CROSS-CULTURAL PSYCHOLOGY BULLETIN.** see *PSYCHOLOGY*

➤ **CROSS-CULTURAL RESEARCH AND METHODOLOGY SERIES.** see *PSYCHOLOGY*

➤ **CROSSROADS OF LANGUAGE, INTERACTION, AND CULTURE.** see *LINGUISTICS*

301 GTM ISSN 0590-160X
CUADERNOS DE ANTROPOLOGIA. Text in Spanish. 1962. q.
Indexed: AICP, AmH&L, HistAb.
Published by: Universidad de San Carlos de Guatemala, Facultad de Humanidades, Departamento de Publicaciones, 9a Avenida 13-39, Guatemala City Zona, Guatemala.

930.1 PER ISSN 1682-458X
CUADERNOS DE ANTROPOLOGIA. Text in Spanish. 2001. a. back issues avail. **Document type:** *Academic/Scholarly.*
Media: Online - full text.
Published by: Universidad Nacional Mayor de San Marcos, Escuela Academico Profesional de Antropologia, Ciudad Universitaria, Ave. Venezuela, S/N, Lima, 1, Peru. TEL 51-1-4520381, rrpp@unmsm.edu.pe, http://www.unmsm.edu.pe/sociales/antropologia/index.htm.

930.1 ESP ISSN 0213-7399
CUADERNOS DE ETNOLOGIA DE GUADALAJARA. Text in Spanish. 1986. q.
Indexed: RILM.
—CINDOC.
Published by: Diputacion Provincial de Guadalajara, Seccion de Administracion Cultural, Moreno, 10, Guadalajara, 19001, Spain. TEL 34-949-887551.

305.8 ESP ISSN 0590-1871
GN585.S7
CUADERNOS DE ETNOLOGIA Y ETNOGRAFIA DE NAVARRA. Text in Spanish. 1969. a. EUR 7.20 (effective 2004). charts; illus. index. back issues avail. **Document type:** *Journal, Government.*
Indexed: AnthLit, BHA, RILM.
—CINDOC.
Published by: (Gobierno de Navarra, Departamento de Educacion y Cultura), Gobierno de Navarra, Fondo de Publicaciones, Navas de Tolosa 21, Pamplona, Navarra 31002, Spain. TEL 34-9848-427121, FAX 34-9848-427123, fondo.publicaciones@cfnavarra.es, http://www.navarra.es.

301 MEX ISSN 0185-1659
GN1
CUICUILCO. Text in Spanish. 1980. s-a. price varies. adv. bk.rev. **Document type:** *Magazine, Academic/Scholarly.*
Indexed: PSA, SSA, SociolAb.
Published by: (Escuela Nacional de Antropologia e Historia), Instituto Nacional de Antropologia e Historia, Frontera 53, Col. Tizapan San Angel, Mexico City, DF 01000, Mexico. TEL 52-55-509714, FAX 52-55-503503, sub_fomento.cncpbs@inah.gob.mx, http://www.inah.gob.mx. Ed. Arturo Arias Fernandez. Adv. contact Rosa Laura Hernandez Hernandez. Circ: 2,000.

CULTURA DE LOS CUIDADOS. see *MEDICAL SCIENCES*

301 PER ISSN 1017-9542
CULTURA PERUANA✶. Text in Spanish. 1941. q.
Published by: Instituto Nacional de Cultura, Departamental Ancash, Oficio Numero 363, Huaras, Peru.

306.4 USA ISSN 0886-7356
GN301
➤ **CULTURAL ANTHROPOLOGY.** Text in English. 1986. q. USD 50 to individuals; USD 87 to institutions (effective 2005 & 2006). adv. illus. reprint service avail. from PQC. **Document type:** *Journal, Academic/Scholarly.* **Description:** Examines the relationship between anthropology and social and cultural history, hermeneutics, phenomenology and all fields of cultural studies. Includes literary criticism and theory.
Related titles: Online - full text ed.: (from bigchalk, H.W. Wilson, JSTOR (Web-based Journal Archive), O C L C Online Computer Library Center, Inc., ProQuest Information & Learning).

▼ new title ➤ refereed ✶ unverified ◆ full entry avail.

Indexed: ABS&EES, AICP, ASCA, ASSIA, AbAn, AmH&L, AnthLit, ArtHuCI, BAS, BrHumI, CJA, ChPerI, CurCont, FamI, ForAb, HistAb, IBR, IBSS, IBZ, L&LBA, PCI, PGegResA, PRA, RASB, RDA, RI-1, RI-2, RILM, RRTA, SOPODA, SSA, SSCI, SSI, SociolAb, WAE&RSA.
—BLDSC (3491.661000), IE, Infotrieve, ingenta. **CCC.**
Published by: (American Anthropological Association, Society for Cultural Anthropology), University of California Press, Journals Division, 2000 Center St, Ste 303, Berkeley, CA 94704-1223. TEL 510-643-7154, FAX 510-642-9917, journals@ucpress.edu, http://www.ucpress.edu/journals/3a/can. Ed. Ann Anagnost. adv.: page USD 295; 4.5 x 7.5. Circ: 2,100.

305.8 USA ISSN 0882-4371
AC5
➤ **CULTURAL CRITIQUE**; an international journal of cultural studies. Text in English. 1985. 3/yr. USD 30 domestic to individuals; USD 35 foreign to individuals; USD 78 domestic to institutions; USD 83 foreign to institutions (effective 2004). adv. bk.rev. illus. Index. 250 p./no.; back issues avail.; reprints avail. **Document type:** *Journal, Academic/Scholarly.* **Description:** Investigates the broad terrain of cultural interpretation currently defined by the conjunction of literary, philosophical, anthropological, and sociological studies of Marxist, feminist, psychoanalytic, and post-structural methods.
Related titles: Microfiche ed.: (from PQC); Online - full text ed.: ISSN 1534-5203 (from EBSCO Publishing, JSTOR (Web-based Journal Archive), O C L C Online Computer Library Center, Inc., Project MUSE, Swets Information Services).
Indexed: ASCA, AltPI, AmH&L, ArtHuCI, BibInd, CurCont, DIP, FLI, HistAb, HumInd, IBR, IBSS, IBZ, IPSA, LeftInd, MLA-IB, PCI, PSA, PerIslam, RASB, RI-1, RI-2, RILM, SOPODA, SSA, SSCI, SociolAb.
—BLDSC (3491.661600), IDS, IE, Infotrieve, ingenta. **CCC.**
Published by: (Society for Cultural Critique), University of Minnesota Press, 111 Third Ave S, Ste 290, Minneapolis, MN 55401-2520. TEL 612-627-1970, FAX 612-627-1980, cultcrit@tc.umm.edu, ump@umn.edu, http://www.upress.umn.edu/journals/cultcrit.html. Eds. Jochen Schulte-Sasse, John Mowitt, Keya Ganguly. R&P Jeff Moen TEL 612-627-1978. Adv. contact Krista Erickson Anderson TEL 612-627-1938. B&W page USD 200. Circ: 700.

➤ **CULTURAL DYNAMICS.** see *PHILOSOPHY*

306.4 128 USA
CULTURAL MEMORY IN THE PRESENT. Text in English. 1998. irreg., latest vol.23, 2000. price varies. back issues avail. **Document type:** *Monographic series, Academic/Scholarly.* **Description:** Examines the intersection between the practice of close reading and theory in the study of culture.
Indexed: MLA-IB.
Published by: Stanford University Press (Subsidiary of: Stanford University), 1450 Page Mill Rd., Palo Alto, CA 94304-1124. TEL 650-723-9434, FAX 650-725-3457, http://www.sup.org/search/index.html. Eds. Hent de Vries, Mieke Bal. **In Europe:** Cambridge University Press, The Edinburgh Bldg, Shaftesbury Rd, Cambridge CB2 2RU, United Kingdom. TEL 44-1223-312393, FAX 44-1223-315052; **In the Americas:** Cambridge University Press Distribution Center, 110 Brookhill Dr., West Nyack, NY 10994-2140. TEL 800-872-7423.

306.4 USA
CULTURAL SITINGS. Text in English. 1994. irreg., latest vol.6, 2000. price varies. back issues avail. **Document type:** *Monographic series, Academic/Scholarly.* **Description:** Discusses major contemporary and historical cultural issues, from multidisciplinary and transnational perspectives. Bridging historical and theoretical concerns, this series develops and examines narratives exploring the gamut of experiences that continuously redefine contemporary cultures.
Published by: Stanford University Press (Subsidiary of: Stanford University), 1450 Page Mill Rd., Palo Alto, CA 94304-1124. TEL 650-723-9434, FAX 650-725-3457, http://www.sup.org/search/index.html. Ed. Elazar Barkan. **Dist. in Europe by:** Cambridge University Press, The Edinburgh Bldg, Shaftesbury Rd, Cambridge CB2 2RU, United Kingdom. TEL 44-1223-312393, FAX 44-1223-315052; **Dist. in N America by:** Cambridge University Press Distribution Center, 110 Brookhill Dr., West Nyack, NY 10994-2140. TEL 800-872-7423.

305.8 USA
CULTURAL STUDIES OF THE AMERICAS. Text in English. 1999. irreg., latest vol.13, 2003. price varies. back issues avail. **Document type:** *Monographic series, Academic/Scholarly.* **Description:** Assesses the relationship between cultural production and social and political processes in the Americas, from both trans- and international perspectives .
Indexed: MLA-IB.
Published by: University of Minnesota Press, 111 Third Ave S, Ste 290, Minneapolis, MN 55401-2520. TEL 612-627-1970, FAX 612-627-1980, http://www.upress.umn.edu/byseries/csa.html, http://www.upress.umn.edu/journals/. Eds. George Yudice, Jean Franco, Juan Flores. **Dist. by:** c/o Chicago Distribution Center, 11030 S Langley Ave, Chicago, IL 60628; Plymbridge Distributors Ltd, Plymbridge House, Estover Rd, Plymouth, Devon PL6 7PY, United Kingdom. TEL 44-1752-202300, FAX 44-1752-202330, enquiries@plymbridge.com, http://www.plymbridge.com.

306 SWE ISSN 0902-7521
GN301
CULTURE & HISTORY. Text in English. 1987. irreg. adv. **Document type:** *Academic/Scholarly.* **Description:** Interdisciplinary journal of historical anthropology, functioning as an international forum for debate in the general field of cultural historical studies.
Indexed: AICP, AmH&L, AnthLit, BibInd, BrArAb, HistAb, NumL, PCI, RI-1, RI-2, SOPODA.
—BLDSC (3491.668590), IE. **CCC.**
Published by: Taylor & Francis A B (Subsidiary of: Taylor & Francis Group), Hollaendargatan 20, PO Box 3255, Stockholm, 10365, Sweden. TEL 46-8-4408040, FAX 46-8-4408050. Ed. Michael Harbsmeier TEL 45-31-42-15-44.

CULTURE & PSYCHOLOGY. see *PSYCHOLOGY*

306.461 NLD ISSN 0167-4447
CODEN: CIHEET
➤ **CULTURE, ILLNESS AND HEALING**; studies in comparative cross-cultural research. Text in English. 1980. irreg., latest vol.16, 1990. price varies. **Document type:** *Monographic series, Academic/Scholarly.*
—**CCC.**
Published by: Springer-Verlag Dordrecht (Subsidiary of: Springer Science+Business Media), Van Godewijckstraat 30, Dordrecht, 3311 GX, Netherlands. TEL 31-78-6576050, FAX 31-78-6576474, http://www.springeronline.com. Eds. Allan Young, Margaret Lock.

306.461 USA ISSN 0165-005X
RC455.4.E8 CODEN: CMPSD2
➤ **CULTURE, MEDICINE AND PSYCHIATRY**; an international journal of comparative cross-cultural research. Text in English. 1977. q. EUR 409, USD 418, GBP 265 combined subscription to institutions print & online eds. (effective 2005). adv. bk.rev. illus. reprint service avail. from PSC. **Document type:** *Journal, Academic/Scholarly.* **Description:** Provides an international and interdisciplinary forum for the discussion of medical and psychiatric anthropology, cross-cultural psychiatry, and related cross-societal clinical and epidemiological studies.
Related titles: Microform ed.: (from PQC); Online - full text ed.: ISSN 1573-076X (from EBSCO Publishing, Gale Group, IngentaConnect, Kluwer Online, O C L C Online Computer Library Center, Inc., Ovid Technologies, Inc., Springer LINK, Swets Information Services).
Indexed: ASCA, AbAn, AgeL, AnthLit, ArtHuCI, BAS, BibInd, BibLing, BiolAb, CurCont, DIP, EI, ExcerpMed, IBR, IBSS, IBZ, INI, IPsyAb, IndMed, MEA&I, MEDLINE, PCI, PhilInd, PsycInfo, PsycholAb, RefZh, SOPODA, SSA, SSCI, SociolAb, e-psyche.
—BLDSC (3491.669100), CISTI, GNLM, IDS, IE, Infotrieve, ingenta. **CCC.**
Published by: Plenum US (Subsidiary of: Springer Science+Business Media), 233 Spring St, New York, NY 10013. TEL 212-460-1500, FAX 212-460-1575, service@springer-ny.com, http://springerlink.metapress.com/openurl.asp?genre=journal&issn=0165-005X, http://www.springeronline.com. Eds. Anne E Becker, Peter J Guarnaccia.

➤ **CULTURES AU ZAIRE ET EN AFRIQUE.** see *SOCIAL SCIENCES: COMPREHENSIVE WORKS*

306.461 DEU ISSN 0344-8622
RC455.4.E8
CURARE; Zeitschrift fuer Ethnomedizin - journal for ethnomedicine. Text in English, French, German. 1978. s-a. EUR 45; EUR 25 to students (effective 2004). back issues avail. **Document type:** *Journal, Academic/Scholarly.* **Description:** Forum of exchange and discussion concerning traditional medical systems, medical aid programs, health planning, and related issues.
Indexed: AICP, AbHyg, AnthLit, DIP, EI, IBR, IBSS, IBZ, RILM, SOPODA, SSA, SociolAb, TDB.
—BLDSC (3493.435000), GNLM, IE, Infotrieve, ingenta. **CCC.**
Published by: (Arbeitsgemeinschaft Ethnomedizin e.V.), V W B - Verlag fuer Wissenschaft und Bildung, Zossener Str 55, Berlin, 10961, Germany. TEL 49-30-2510415, FAX 49-30-2511136, 100615.1565@compuserve.com, http://www.vwb-verlag.com. Circ: 1,000.

301 USA ISSN 0011-3204
GN1 CODEN: CUANAX
➤ **CURRENT ANTHROPOLOGY.** Text in English. 1955. 5/yr., latest vol.44, 2003, Feb. USD 60 combined subscription to individuals print & online eds.; USD 272 combined subscription to institutions print & online eds.; USD 18 per issue to individuals; USD 70 per issue to institutions (effective 2006). adv. bk.rev. charts; illus. cum.index: 1960-1974. reprint service avail. from PQC,ISI,PSC. **Document type:** *Journal, Academic/Scholarly.* **Description:** Contains research articles and commentary throughout social, cultural, and physical anthropology; ethnology; folklore; and more.
Formerly (until 1956): Yearbook of Anthropology (1524-4555)
Related titles: Microform ed.: (from PQC); Online - full text ed.: ISSN 1537-5382. USD 245 to institutions (effective 2006) (from bigchalk, EBSCO Publishing, Florida Center for Library Automation, Gale Group, JSTOR (Web-based Journal Archive), ProQuest Information & Learning).
Indexed: ABS&EES, AICP, APC, ASCA, AbAn, AcaI, AgeL, AmH&L, AnthLit, ArtHuCI, BAS, BIOSIS Prev, BibLing, BiolAb, BrArAb, CTD, CommAb, CurCont, DIP, EI, FamI, HistAb, IBR, IBSS, IBZ, IPSA, IPsyAb, IndIslam, L&LBA, MASUSE, MEA&I, MEDLINE, MLA, MLA-IB, NAA, NumL, PCI, PSA, PsycInfo, PsycholAb, RASB, RI-1, RI-2, RILM, SCI, SOPODA, SPPI, SRRA, SSA, SSCI, SSI, SWA, SociolAb, ZooRec, e-psyche.
—BLDSC (3494.200000), IDS, IE, Infotrieve, ingenta. **CCC.**
Published by: (Wenner-Gren Foundation for Anthropological Research), University of Chicago Press, Journals Division, Journals Division, PO Box 37005, Chicago, IL 60637. TEL 773-753-3347, FAX 773-753-0811, subscriptions@press.uchicago.edu, http://www.journals.uchicago.edu/CA/. Ed. Benjamin S Orlove. Adv. contact Timothy Hill TEL 773-702-8187. page USD 415; trim 8.5 x 11. Circ: 4,000.

➤ **DAGESTANSKII ETNOGRAFICHESKII SBORNIK.** see *ETHNIC INTERESTS*

301 ZAF
DART. Text in English. irreg. membership. **Document type:** *Newsletter, Academic/Scholarly.* **Description:** News and activities of the institute.
Published by: Institute for the Study of Man in Africa, University of the Witwatersrand Medical School, Rm. 2B17, York Rd, Parktown, Johannesburg 2193, South Africa. TEL 27-11-647-2203, FAX 27-11-643-4318, isma@chiron.wits.ac.za. Ed. Kevin Kuykendall.

301 303 940 FRA ISSN 1242-8809
DE L'ALLEMAGNE. Text in French. 1993. irreg. price varies. **Document type:** *Monographic series, Academic/Scholarly.*
Published by: C N R S Editions, 15 Rue Malebranche, Paris, 75005, France. TEL 33-1-53102700, FAX 33-1-53102727, http://www.cnrseditions.fr.

DENVER MUSEUM OF NATURAL HISTORY. PROCEEDINGS. see *BIOLOGY—Zoology*

306 MEX ISSN 1607-050X
➤ **DESACATOS**; revista de antropologia social. Text in Spanish. 1999. 3/yr. USD 50; MXP 100 newsstand/cover (effective 2005). **Document type:** *Journal, Academic/Scholarly.* **Description:** Features papers produced by original research endeavors on a wide variety of subjects in the realm of the social sciences.
Related titles: Online - full text ed.
Published by: Centro de Investigaciones y Estudios Superiores en Antropologia Social, Hidalgo y Matamoros, Col Tlalpan, Mexico, D.F., 14000, Mexico. desacato@ciesas.edu.mx, ciejuare@juarez.ciesas.edu.mx, http://www.ciesas.edu.mx/bibdf/desacatos/home.html. Ed. Jorge Alonso. Pub., R&P Camila Pascal. Adv. contact Gonzalo Maulen TEL 52-55-56550158. Circ: 1,000 (controlled).

301 NLD ISSN 0304-4092
HX550.A56 CODEN: DIAAER
DIALECTICAL ANTHROPOLOGY; an independent international journal in the critical tradition committed to the transformation of our society and the humane union of theory and practice. Text in English. 1975. q. EUR 345, USD 346, GBP 221 combined subscription to institutions print & online eds. (effective 2005). adv. bk.rev. illus. index. back issues avail.; reprint service avail. from PSC. **Document type:** *Journal, Academic/Scholarly.* **Description:** Publishes social critiques of every aspect of contemporary civilization, comparative and historical essays, case studies of crisis and transition, ethnopoetry/poetics, and professional or personal memoirs.
Related titles: Microform ed.: (from PQC); Online - full text ed.: ISSN 1573-0786 (from EBSCO Publishing, Gale Group, IngentaConnect, Kluwer Online, O C L C Online Computer Library Center, Inc., Springer LINK, Swets Information Services).
Indexed: AICP, ASCA, AbAn, AltPI, AnthLit, ArtHuCI, BAS, BibLing, CurCont, IBSS, LeftInd, MEA&I, PRA, PSA, PhilInd, RASB, SOPODA, SRRA, SSA, SSCI, SociolAb.
—BLDSC (3579.704000), IDS, IE, Infotrieve, ingenta. **CCC.**
Published by: Springer-Verlag Dordrecht (Subsidiary of: Springer Science+Business Media), Van Godewijckstraat 30, Dordrecht, 3311 GX, Netherlands. TEL 31-78-6576050, FAX 31-78-6576474, http://springerlink.metapress.com/openurl.asp?genre=journal&issn=0304-4092, http://www.springeronline.com. Ed. Sabine Jell-Bahlsen.

DIALOGO ANDINO. see *SOCIAL SCIENCES: COMPREHENSIVE WORKS*

301 IND
DIBRUGARH UNIVERSITY. DEPARTMENT OF ANTHROPOLOGY. BULLETIN. Text in English. irreg.
Indexed: AnthLit.
Published by: Dibrugarh University, Department of Anthropology, Rajabheta, Dibrugarh, 786 004, India. TEL 0373-70231, FAX 0373-70323.

DIGGING STICK. see *ARCHAEOLOGY*

301 MEX
DIMENSION ANTHROPOLOGICA. Text in Spanish. 1994. 3/yr. price varies. back issues avail. **Document type:** *Magazine, Academic/Scholarly.*

Indexed: AnthLit.
Published by: (Direccion de Linguistica), Instituto Nacional de Antropologia e Historia, Frontera 53, Col. Tizapan San Angel, Mexico City, DF 01000, Mexico. TEL 52-55-509714, FAX 52-55-503503, sub_fomento.cncpbs@inah.gob.mx, http://www.inah.gob.mx. Adv. contact Rosa Laura Hernandez Hernandez.

306.4 150 ITA ISSN 1721-7199
DIPAV QUADERNI; quadrimestrale di psicologia e antropologia culturale. (Dipartimento Psicologia Antropologia Culturale Verona) Text in Italian. 1996. 3/yr. EUR 39 domestic; EUR 56 foreign (effective 2003). **Document type:** *Journal, Academic/Scholarly.*
Formerly (until 1999): Universita degli Studi di Verona. Istituto di Psicologia. Annali (1721-7202)
Published by: (Universita degli Studi di Verona, Dipartimento di Psicologia e Antropologia Culturale), Franco Angeli Edizioni, Viale Monza 106, Milan, 20127, Italy. TEL 39-02-2837141, FAX 39-02-26144793, redazioni@francoangeli.it, http://www.francoangeli.it.

780.89 USA
DISCOURSE IN ETHNOMUSICOLOGY. Text in English. irreg.
Indexed: AnthLit.
Published by: Ethnomusicology Publications Group, Morrison Hall, Indiana University, Bloomington, IN 47405.

305.8 COL ISSN 0120-050X
DIVULGACIONES ETNOLOGICAS. Text in Spanish. 1952. s-a. bk.rev.
Indexed: AICP.
Published by: Universidad del Atlantico, Instituto de Investigacion Etnologica, Carrera 43 No. 50-53, Apartado Aereo 1890, Barranquilla, ATL, Colombia. Circ: 2,000.

301 DEU
DOBRUDSCHABOTE. Text in German. 1976. q. free.
Published by: Landsmannschaft der Dobrudschadeutschen, Oranienstener Weg 8, Limburg, 65549, Germany. Circ: 850.

305.8 FJI ISSN 0257-1668
DOMODOMO. Text in English. 1983. q. FJD 10.80 newsstand/cover (effective 2002).
Indexed: AnthLit.
Published by: Fiji Museum, P.O. Box 17379, Suva, Fiji. http://www.fijimuseum.org.fj.

DONGNAN WENHUA/CULTURE OF SOUTHEAST CHINA. see *ARCHAEOLOGY*

746.9 GBR ISSN 1360-466X
➤ **DRESS, BODY, CULTURE.** Text in English. 1997. irreg. price varies. **Document type:** *Monographic series, Academic/Scholarly.*
Published by: Berg Publishers, Angel Court, 1st Fl, 81 St Clements St, Oxford, Berks OX4 1AW, United Kingdom. TEL 44-1865-245104, FAX 44-1865-791165, enquiry@bergpublishers.com, http://www.bergpublishers.com/uk/category_list_series.asp?Series_ISSN=1360-466X.

➤ **DURKHEIMIAN STUDIES.** see *SOCIOLOGY*

➤ **E I (ONLINE EDITION).** (Excerpta Indonesica) see *ANTHROPOLOGY—Abstracting, Bibliographies, Statistics*

➤ **EARLY MAN NEWS**; newsletter for human palecology. see *ARCHAEOLOGY*

306.4 GBR ISSN 1464-0414
EAST ASIA JOURNAL; studies in material culture. Text in English. 1998. s-a. GBP 30 in Europe to individuals; GBP 45 elsewhere to individuals; GBP 60 in Europe to institutions; GBP 90 elsewhere to institutions. **Document type:** *Academic/Scholarly.* **Description:** Intends to take a interdisciplinary approach to the study of material culture in East Asia, China, Japan and Korea as well as the countries of the Southeast Asian region. Focuses on "objects"—their making, use and history, and the interpretations given to them. Includes material from archaeology, anthropology, history of technology, art and architecture and literary studies.
Indexed: NumL.
Published by: Eastern Art Publishing Group, PO Box 13666, London, SW14 8WF, United Kingdom. TEL 44-20-83921122, FAX 44-20-83921422, ear@eapgroup.ndirect.co.uk, http://www.eapgroup.ndirect.co.uk. Ed. Wang Tao. Pub., R&P Sajid Rizvi.

301 IND ISSN 0012-8686
GN1 CODEN: EAANAH
➤ **EASTERN ANTHROPOLOGIST.** Text in English. 1947. q. (in 57 vols.). USD 350 to institutions (effective 2006). adv. bk.rev. bibl.; charts. Index. 120 p./no. 1 cols./p.; back issues avail. **Document type:** *Journal, Academic/Scholarly.* **Description:** Features Anthropology and other social sciences.
Indexed: AICP, AnthLit, BAS, BiolAb, CurCont, DIP, EI, IBR, IBSS, IPSA, IndIslam, MEA&I, PAA&I, PSA, PerIslam, RDA, RI-1, RI-2, RILM, SSA, SSCI, SociolAb, WAE&RSA.
—IE, Infotrieve.

Published by: Scientific Publishers, 5-A New Pali Rd., Near Hotel Taj Hari Mahal, PO Box 91, Jodhpur, Rajasthan 342 003, India. TEL 91-291-2433323, FAX 91-291-2512580, info@scientificpub.com, http://www.scientificpub.com/bookdetails.php?booktransid=301&bookid=297. adv.: page INR 5,000; 5 x 8. Circ: 1,000.

301 USA ISSN 0070-8232
➤ **EASTERN NEW MEXICO UNIVERSITY. CONTRIBUTIONS IN ANTHROPOLOGY.** Text in English. 1968. irreg., latest vol.13, 1994. price varies. **Document type:** *Academic/Scholarly.* **Description:** Compilations of various Southwestern archaeological projects. Subjects range from laboratory techniques to original site reports and areal syntheses.
Indexed: AbAn.
Published by: Eastern New Mexico University, Department of Anthropology, Station 3, Portales, NM 88130. TEL 505-562-2206, FAX 505-562-2291, phillip.shelley@enmu.edu. Ed., R&P Phillip Shelley. Circ: 750.

301 306 FRA ISSN 1257-9343
EMPREINTES DE L'HOMME. Text in French. 1994. irreg. price varies. **Document type:** *Monographic series, Academic/Scholarly.*
Published by: C N R S Editions, 15 Rue Malebranche, Paris, 75005, France. TEL 33-1-53102700, FAX 33-1-53102727, http://www.cnrseditions.fr.

ENCOUNTERS SERIES. see *LINGUISTICS*

930.1 ESP ISSN 1130-6580
ERES. SERIE DE ANTROPOLOGIA. Text in Spanish. 1989. a. —CINDOC.
Published by: Cabildo Insular de Tenerife, Museo Arqueologico y Etnografico, Apdo. 133, Santa Cruz de Tenerife, Canarias 38080, Spain. TEL 34-901-501901, http://www.cabtfe.es/.

ESPACIO ABIERTO; cuaderno venezolano de sociologia. see *SOCIOLOGY*

306.4 FRA ISSN 1620-8315
ESPRITS LIBRES. Text in French. 2000. q. **Document type:** *Journal, Academic/Scholarly.*
Published by: L' Harmattan, 5 rue de l'Ecole Polytechnique, Paris, 75005, France. TEL 33-1-43257651, FAX 33-1-43258203, http://www.editions-harmattan.fr.

301 GTM
➤ **ESTUDIOS**; revista de antropologia, arqueologia e historia. Text in Spanish. N.S. 1993. q. per issue exchange basis. **Document type:** *Journal, Academic/Scholarly.* **Description:** Presents articles written by Guatemalans that focus on diverse aspects of arqueology, anthropology and history of Central America.
Published by: Universidad de San Carlos de Guatemala, Instituto de Investigaciones Historicas, Antropologicas y Arqueologicas, Ciudad Universitaria, Edif S-1, nivel 3o, Guatemala City Zona, Guatemala. usachist@usac.edu.gt. Ed. Haroldo Rodas Estrada.

599.9 MEX
ESTUDIOS DE ANTROPOLOGIA BIOLOGICA. Text in Spanish. 1982. biennial. MXP 40 per issue (effective 2000). **Description:** Includes lectures and conferences given at the Physical Anthropology Congress "Juan Comas".
Published by: Universidad Nacional Autonoma de Mexico, Instituto de Investigaciones Antropologicas, Circuito Exterior, Ciudad Universitaria, Mexico, DF 04510, Mexico. TEL 52-5-622-9531, FAX 52-5-622-9651. Ed. Luis Alberto Vargas.

ESTUDIOS DE CULTURA MAYA. see *HISTORY—History Of North And South America*

ESTUDIOS DE CULTURA NAHUATL. see *HISTORY—History Of North And South America*

305.8 MEX
ESTUDIOS DE CULTURA OTOPAME/STUDIES OF OTOPAME CULTURE. Text in Spanish. 1998. biennial.
Indexed: AnthLit.
Published by: Instituto de Investigaciones Antropologicas, Ciudad Universitaria, Mexico, 04510, Mexico. TEL 52-56229554, FAX 52-56229651.

ESTUDIOS DE FOLKLORE. see *FOLKLORE*

ESTUDIOS DE HISTORIA NOVOHISPANA. see *HISTORY—History Of North And South America*

306.44089 CRI ISSN 1409-245X
ESTUDIOS DE LINGUISTICA CHIBCHA. Text in Spanish. 1982. a. USD 25.
Related titles: Online - full text ed.: (from Gale Group).
Indexed: AnthLit.
Published by: Universidad de Costa Rica, Departamento de Linguistica/Costa Rica University, Linguistics Department, San Pedro de Montes de Oca, San Jose, Costa Rica.

301 MEX ISSN 1405-1117
GN564.M6
ESTUDIOS DEL HOMBRE. Text in Spanish. a.

Formerly (until 1994): Anuario (Year) Laboratorio de Antropologia
Published by: Universidad de Guadalajara, Departamento de Estudios del Hombre, Apdo. Postal 1-1814, Guadalajara, Jalisco, Mexico. http://www.cucsh.udg.mx/publica/publica.html. Circ: 1,000.

ESTUDIOS ETNOHISTORICOS DEL ECUADOR. see *HISTORY—History Of North And South America*

ESTUDIOS MICHOACANOS. see *HISTORY—History Of North And South America*

ESTUDIOS SOBRE LAS CULTURAS CONTEMPORANEAS; revista de investigacion y analisis de la cultura. see *HUMANITIES: COMPREHENSIVE WORKS*

301 PRT ISSN 0870-4457
ESTUDOS DE ANTROPOLOGIA CULTURAL E SOCIAL. Text in Portuguese. 1965. irreg., latest vol.15. price varies. back issues avail. **Document type:** *Monographic series.*
Formerly: Estudos de Antropologia Cultural (0870-6891)
Indexed: IBSS.
Published by: (Centro de Antropologia Cultural e Social), Instituto de Investigacao Cientifica Tropical, Rua da Junqueira, 30, Lisbon, 1349-007, Portugal. TEL 351-21-3622621, FAX 351-21-3631460, iict@iict.pt. Circ: 1,000. **Subscr. to:** Centro de Documentacao e Informacao, Rua de Jau, 47, Lisbon 1300, Portugal. TEL 351-21-3644846, FAX 351-21-3628218.

305.8 GBR ISSN 1354-3628
➤ **ETHNICITY AND IDENTITY SERIES.** Text in English. 1993. irreg. price varies. **Document type:** *Monographic series, Academic/Scholarly.* **Description:** Aims to bring together the work of leading researchers in social anthropology and related disciplines on the component elements of identity and ethnicity.
Published by: Berg Publishers, Angel Court, 1st Fl, 81 St Clements St, Oxford, Berks OX4 1AW, United Kingdom. TEL 44-1865-245104, FAX 44-1865-791165, enquiry@bergpublishers.com, http://www.bergpublishers.com/uk/category_list_series.asp?Series_ISSN=1354-3628. Ed. Shirley Ardener.

➤ **ETHNOARTS INDEX.** see *ANTHROPOLOGY—Abstracting, Bibliographies, Statistics*

305.8 ESP ISSN 0211-772X
DP48
ETHNOGRAFIA ESPANOLA. Text in Spanish. 1980. a.
Indexed: AnthLit, PCI, RILM.
Published by: Ministerio de Cultura, Direccion General de Bellas Artes y Archivos, Plaza del Rey, 1, Madrid, 28071, Spain.

305.8 DEU
ETHNOGRAPHIC LIBRARY ON CD. Text in English, German. irreg., latest vol.4, 2000. EUR 25.50 per vol. (effective 2003). **Document type:** *Monographic series, Academic/Scholarly.*
Media: CD-ROM.
Published by: Waxmann Verlag GmbH, Steinfurter Str 555, Muenster, 48159, Germany. TEL 49-251-26504-0, FAX 49-251-2650426, info@waxmann.com, http://www.waxmann.com. Eds. Erich Kasten, Michael Duerr.

301 BEL ISSN 0336-1438
GN2
L'ETHNOGRAPHIE. Text in French. 1859. a. price varies. adv. bk.rev. cum.index. back issues avail.; reprints avail. **Document type:** *Monographic series, Academic/Scholarly.*
Formerly (unitl 1913): Societe d'Ethnographie. Bulletin (0184-7058)
Indexed: AICP, AnthLit, BAS, BibInd, DIP, IBR, IBZ, IndIslam.
Published by: (Societe d'Ethnographie de Paris FRA), Peeters Publishers, Bondgenotenlaan 153, Leuven, 3000, Belgium. TEL 32-16-235170, FAX 32-16-228500, http://www.peeters-leuven.be. Eds. Andre-Marcel d'Ans, Robert Lacombe. Circ: 1,000.

305.8 GBR ISSN 1466-1381
GN301
➤ **ETHNOGRAPHY.** Text in English. 2000. q. GBP 320, USD 560 to institutions; GBP 333, USD 583 combined subscription to institutions print & online eds. (effective 2006). adv. **Document type:** *Journal, Academic/Scholarly.* **Description:** Provides a forum for the ethnographic study of social and cultural change. Aims to become a network for dialogical exchange between monadic ethnographers and those from all disciplines interested in ethnography, theory and society.
Related titles: Online - full text ed.: ISSN 1741-2714. GBP 317, USD 554 to institutions (effective 2006) (from C S A, EBSCO Publishing, O C L C Online Computer Library Center, Inc., Sage Publications, Inc., Swets Information Services).
Indexed: AltPI, AnthLit, CJA, DIP, IBR, IBSS, IBZ, MLA-IB, SSA, SociolAb.
—BLDSC (3815.112500), IE. **CCC.**

Published by: Sage Publications Ltd. (Subsidiary of: Sage Publications, Inc.), 1 Oliver's Yard, 55 City Rd, London, EC1 1SP, United Kingdom. TEL 44-20-73248500, FAX 44-20-73248600, info@sagepub.co.uk, http://www.sagepub.co.uk/journal.aspx?pid=105533. Eds. Loic Wacquant, Paul Willis. adv.: page GBP 195. **Subscr. in the Americas to:** Sage Publications, Inc., 2455 Teller Rd, Thousand Oaks, CA 91320. FAX 805-499-0871, journals@sagepub.com, http://www.sagepub.com.

305.8 USA ISSN 0014-1801
E51

➤ **ETHNOHISTORY**; a quarterly journal relating to the past of culture and societies in all areas of the world. Text in English. 1954. q. USD 35 to individuals; USD 105 to institutions; USD 117 combined subscription to institutions print & online eds. (effective 2006). adv. bk.rev. bibl.; charts; illus. back issues avail.; reprint service avail. from PSC. **Document type:** *Journal, Academic/Scholarly.* **Description:** Emphasizes the joint use of documentary materials and ethnographic or archaeological data, as well as the combination of historical and anthropological approaches, in the study of social and cultural processes and history. It publishes articles, review essays, and book reviews by scholars in anthropology, history, archaeology, linguistics, literature and art history, geography, and other disciplines and is read by historians and anthropologists alike.

Related titles: Microform ed.: (from PQC); Online - full text ed.: ISSN 1527-5477. 1999. USD 105 to institutions (effective 2006) (from bigchalk, EBSCO Publishing, Gale Group, IngentaConnect, JSTOR (Web-based Journal Archive), Northern Light Technology, Inc., O C L C Online Computer Library Center, Inc., Project MUSE, ProQuest Information & Learning, Swets Information Services).

Indexed: ABS&EES, AICP, ASCA, AbAn, AmH&L, AmHI, AnthLit, ArtHuCI, BAS, BrArAb, CurCont, FamI, HistAb, HumInd, IBSS, IndIslam, MEA&I, PCI, PRA, PSA, RI-1, RI-2, SOPODA, SSA, SSCI, SSI, SociolAb.

—BLDSC (3815.115000), IDS, IE, Infotrieve, ingenta. **CCC.**

Published by: (University of Wisconsin At Madison, Department of Anthropology), Duke University Press, 905 W Main St, Ste 18 B, Durham, NC 27701. TEL 919-687-3600, FAX 919-688-3524, subscriptions@dukeupress.edu, http://dukeupress.edu/journals/j_titles.php3?user_id=5594026714, http://www.dukeupress.edu. Eds. Neil L Whitehead, William J Neal. R&P Kay Robin Alexander. Adv. contact Mandy Dailey-Berman TEL 919-687-3636. page USD 365; trim 4.3125 x 6.75. Circ: 1,350 (paid).

305.8918 DEU

➤ **ETHNOLOGIA BALKANICA**; journal for Southeast European anthropology. Text in English. 1997. a. EUR 19 to individuals; EUR 23 to institutions; EUR 10 to students (effective 2003). adv. **Document type:** *Journal, Academic/Scholarly.* **Description:** Provides a forum for scholars in the disciplines of ethnology, anthropology and folklore engaged in the study of Southeast European cultures.

Indexed: MLA-IB.

Published by: (International Association for Southeast European Anthropology), Waxmann Verlag GmbH, Steinfurter Str 555, Muenster, 48159, Germany. TEL 49-251-26504-0, FAX 49-251-2650426, ethnologia@waxmann.com, info@waxmann.com, http://www.waxmann.com. Ed. Klaus Roth. Circ: 400 (paid and controlled).

599.97 DNK ISSN 0425-4597

➤ **ETHNOLOGIA EUROPAEA/JOURNAL OF EUROPEAN ETHNOLOGY**; journal of European ethnology. Text in English. 1967. s-a. DKK 225, GBP 23, USD 38 to individuals; DKK 280, GBP 28, USD 47 to institutions; DKK 150 per issue to individuals (effective 2005). **Document type:** *Journal, Academic/Scholarly.*

Indexed: AICP, AnthLit, BHA, DIP, IBR, IBZ, MLA, MLA-IB, PCI.

—BLDSC (3815.118000), IE, Infotrieve, ingenta. **CCC.**

Published by: Museum Tusculanum Press, c/o University of Copenhagen, Njalsgade 94, Copenhagen S, 2300, Denmark. TEL 45-35-329109, FAX 45-35-329113, mtp@mtp.dk, http://www.mtp.dk. Eds. Bjarne Stoklund, Peter Niedermueller. **Dist. by:** International Specialized Book Services Inc., 5804 N E Hassalo St, Portland, OR 97213-3644. TEL 503-287-3093, FAX 503-280-8832, orders@isbs.com.

305.8 FIN ISSN 0355-1776
GN301

ETHNOLOGIA FENNICA/FINNISH STUDIES IN ETHNOLOGY. Text in English, German; Text occasionally in Finnish. 1971. a. price varies. **Document type:** *Academic/Scholarly.*

Indexed: AnthLit, MLA-IB.

Published by: Seurasaarisaatio/Association of Finnish Ethnologists, Tamminiementie 1, Helsinki, 00250, Finland. TEL 358-9-484234, FAX 358-9-485424, http://www.kolumbus.fi/seurasaarisaatio. Circ: 500.

305.8 POL ISSN 0137-4079
GN1

ETHNOLOGIA POLONA. Text in English. 1975. a., latest vol.24, 2003. price varies. bk.rev. bibl.; illus. 136 p./no. 1 cols./p.; **Document type:** *Monographic series, Academic/Scholarly.* **Description:** Provides theoretical articles and results of detailed studies on ethnology of various countries.

Indexed: AICP, AnthLit, DIP, IBR, IBSS, IBZ.

Published by: Polska Akademia Nauk, Instytut Archeologii i Etnologii, Al Solidarnosci 105, Warsaw, 00140, Poland. TEL 48-22-6202881, FAX 48-22-6240100, director@iaepan.edu.pl, http://www.iaepan.edu.pl. Ed. Maria Paradowska. Circ: 300.

305.8 SWE ISSN 0348-9698
GN1

ETHNOLOGIA SCANDINAVICA; a journal for Nordic ethnology. Text in English, German. 1971. a., latest 2002. price varies. bk.rev. cum.index: 1971-1980. back issues avail. **Document type:** *Academic/Scholarly.*

Supersedes (1937-1971): Folk-Liv

Indexed: AIAP, AICP, AnthLit, BHA, DIP, IBR, IBZ, MLA, MLA-IB.

Published by: Lunds Universitet, Etnologiska Institutionen med Folksarkivet/Lund University, Finngatan 8, Lund, 22362, Sweden. TEL 46-222-7560, FAX 46-222-4205, etn@etn.lu.se, http://www.etn.lu.se/ethscand/. Ed. Jonas Frykman.

305.8 FRA ISSN 0046-2616
GN1

ETHNOLOGIE FRANCAISE/FRENCH ETHNOLOGY. Summaries in English, French. 1953. q. EUR 73 domestic to individuals (effective 2005). adv. reprint service avail. from SCH. **Document type:** *Journal, Academic/Scholarly.* **Description:** Concerned with analyzing the social factors which shape our cultures.

Formerly (until 1970): Arts et Traditions Populaires (0571-2211)

Related titles: Microform ed.: 1971 (from PQC).

Indexed: AICP, AnthLit, BHA, BibInd, DIP, IBR, IBSS, IBZ, MLA-IB, RASB, RILM, SociolAb.

—IE, Infotrieve.

Published by: (Societe d'Ethnologie Francaise), Presses Universitaires de France, 6 Avenue Reille, Paris, 75685 Cedex 14, France. TEL 33-1-58103100, FAX 33-1-58103182, revues@puf.com, http://www.culture.gouv.fr/sef, http://www.puf.com. Ed. Anne Monjaret. Circ: 1,500.

ETHNOLOGIES. see *FOLKLORE*

301 DEU

ETHNOLOGISCHES MUSEUM. VEROEFFENTLICHUNGEN. Text in German. irreg. **Document type:** *Monographic series, Academic/Scholarly.*

Formerly (until 1999): Museums fuer Voelkerkunde. Veroeffentlichungen

Indexed: AnthLit.

Published by: Staatliche Museen zu Berlin, Ethnologisches Museum, Arnimallee 27, Berlin-Dahlem, 14195, Germany. TEL 49-30-8301438, FAX 49-30-8301500, md@smb.spk-berlin.de, http://www.smb.spk-berlin.de/mv/i.html.

305.8 IND

ETHNOLOGY; Ethnobotany. Text in English. a., latest vol.12, 2000. USD 60 (effective 2001). **Document type:** *Academic/Scholarly.*

Published by: H P C Publishers Distributors Pvt. Ltd., 4805 Bharat Ram Rd, 24 Darya Ganj, New Delhi, 110 002, India. FAX 91-11-619-3511, hpcpd@nda.vsnl.net.in, hpcpd@hpc.cc, http://www.hpc.cc, http://www.bizdelhi.com/publisher/hpc.

306 USA ISSN 0014-1828
GN1 CODEN: ETNLB6

➤ **ETHNOLOGY**; an international journal of cultural and social anthropology. Text in English. 1962. q. USD 21 to individuals; USD 40 to institutions (effective 2004). adv. charts; illus. Index. back issues avail.; reprint service avail. from PQC. **Document type:** *Journal, Academic/Scholarly.*

Related titles: Microform ed.: (from PQC); Online - full text ed.: (from bigchalk, Chadwyck-Healey Inc., EBSCO Publishing, Florida Center for Library Automation, Gale Group, Northern Light Technology, Inc., O C L C Online Computer Library Center, Inc., ProQuest Information & Learning).

Indexed: ABM, ABS&EES, AICP, ASCA, AbAn, AmH&L, AnthLit, ArtHuCI, BAS, BiolAb, BrArAb, CurCont, DIP, EI, FamI, GEOBASE, HistAb, IBR, IBSS, IBZ, IPSA, ISR, IndIslam, KWIWR, MEA&I, MLA, MLA-IB, PCI, PSA, PerIslam, PoultAb, RI-1, RI-2, RILM, SOPODA, SPPI, SSA, SSCI, SSI, SUSA, SWR&A, SociolAb, WAE&RSA.

—BLDSC (3815.120000), IDS, IE, Infotrieve, ingenta.

Published by: University of Pittsburgh, Department of Anthropology, 3302 WWPH, Pittsburgh, PA 15260. TEL 412-648-7500, FAX 412-648-7535, ethnolog@pitt.edu, http://www.pitt.edu/~ethnolog. Eds. Richard Scaglion, Leonard Plotnicov. R&P Stacy Hoffman. Circ: 2,000 (paid).

305.8 USA

ETHNOLOGY MONOGRAPHS. Text in English. a.

Indexed: AnthLit.

Published by: University of Pittsburgh, Department of Anthropology, 3302 WWPH, Pittsburgh, PA 15260. TEL 412-648-7503, FAX 412-648-7535, ethnolog@pitt.edu, http://www.pitt.edu/~ethnolog.

ETHNOMUSICOLOGIE. see *MUSIC*

ETHNOMUSICOLOGY. see *MUSIC*

ETHNOMUSICOLOGY FORUM. see *MUSIC*

ETHNOMUSICOLOGY ONLINE. see *MUSIC*

780.89 USA ISSN 1054-1624
ML3797.6

ETHNOMUSICOLOGY RESEARCH DIGEST. Text in English. 1989. irreg. back issues avail. **Document type:** *Newsletter, Academic/Scholarly.* **Description:** Features news, articles and queries on professional ethnomusicology.

Media: Online - full text.

Published by: University of Maryland, c/o Maryland Feed Industry Council, College Park, MD 20742. TEL 301-405-1000, http://www.inform.umd.edu/EdRes/ReadingRoom/Newsletters/EthnoMusicology/Digest.

306.4 GBR ISSN 0014-1844
GN1 CODEN: ESEMBP

➤ **ETHNOS**; journal of anthropology. Text in English. 1936. q. GBP 211, USD 346 combined subscription to institutions print & online eds. (effective 2006). adv. bk.rev. bibl.; illus. cum.index every 10 yrs. reprint service avail. from PSC. **Document type:** *Journal, Academic/Scholarly.* **Description:** Presents articles on social and cultural anthropology, ethnography and non-Western archaeology.

Related titles: Online - full text ed.: ISSN 1469-588X. GBP 200, USD 329 to institutions (effective 2006) (from EBSCO Publishing, Gale Group, IngentaConnect, O C L C Online Computer Library Center, Inc., Swets Information Services).

Indexed: AIAP, AICP, ASSIA, AbAn, AmH&L, AnthLit, BAS, BibLing, BiolAb, BiolDig, BrHumI, CCA, CurCont, DIP, EI, HAPI, HistAb, IBR, IBSS, IBZ, IndIslam, L&LBA, MEA&I, PCI, PSA, RI-1, RI-2, RILM, SOPODA, SSA, SSCI, SociolAb.

—BLDSC (3815.200000), IE, Infotrieve, ingenta. **CCC.**

Published by: (Folkens Museum - Etnografiska/National Museum of Ethnography SWE), Routledge (Subsidiary of: Taylor & Francis Group), 4 Park Square, Milton Park, Abingdon, Oxon OX14 4RN, United Kingdom. TEL 44-1235-828600, FAX 44-1235-829000, info@routledge.co.uk, http://www.tandf.co.uk/journals/titles/00141844.asp, http://www.routledge.co.uk. Eds. Don Kulick, Wilhelm Oestberg. R&P Sally Sweet. Circ: 1,000. **Subscr. to:** Taylor & Francis Ltd, Journals Customer Service, Rankine Rd, Basingstoke, Hants RG24 8PR, United Kingdom. TEL 44-1256-813000, FAX 44-1256-330245, enquiry@tandf.co.uk. **Dist. by:** Universitetsforlaget AS, Sehesteds Gate 3, Postboks 508, Oslo 0105, Norway. TEL 47-22-57-54-00, FAX 47-22-57-53-53.

306.44089 BEL ISSN 0299-1098

ETHNOSCIENCES. Text in French. 1985. irreg., latest vol.10, 1995. price varies. back issues avail. **Document type:** *Monographic series, Academic/Scholarly.*

Related titles: ◆ Series of: Bibliotheque de la S E L A F. ISSN 0249-7050.

Published by: (Societe d'Etudes Linguistiques et Anthropologiques de France FRA, Laboratoire de Langues et Civilisations a Tradition Orale), Peeters Publishers, Bondgenotenlaan 153, Leuven, 3000, Belgium. TEL 32-16-235170, FAX 32-16-228500, http://www.peeters-leuven.be.

301 USA ISSN 0091-2131
GN270 CODEN: ETHSAU

➤ **ETHOS.** Text in English. 1973. q. USD 50 to individuals; USD 71 to institutions (effective 2005 & 2006). adv. bk.rev. charts; illus. reprint service avail. from PQC. **Document type:** *Journal, Academic/Scholarly.* **Description:** Research in psychological anthropology and cross-cultural psychology, including studies on cultural cognition, transcultural psychiatry, ethnopsychiatry, socialization, psychoanalytic anthropology and other psychocultural topics.

Related titles: Microform ed.: (from PQC); Online - full text ed.: (from JSTOR (Web-based Journal Archive), ProQuest Information & Learning).

Indexed: AbAn, AnthLit, BibInd, CurCont, FamI, IBR, IBSS, IBZ, IPsyAb, L&LBA, PCI, PsycInfo, PsycholAb, SOPODA, SSA, SSCI, e-psyche.

—BLDSC (3815.300000), IDS, IE, Infotrieve, ingenta. **CCC.**

Published by: (American Anthropological Association, Society for Psychological Anthropology), University of California Press, Journals Division, 2000 Center St, Ste 303, Berkeley, CA 94704-1223. TEL 510-643-7154, FAX 510-642-9917, journals@ucpress.edu, http://www.ucpress.edu/journals/3a/eth. Ed. Sara Harkness. adv.: page USD 220; trim 9 x 6. Circ: 1,100.

301 ARG ISSN 0046-2632

ETNIA✱. Text in Spanish. 1965. s-a. exchange only. bibl.; charts; illus.

Related titles: ◆ Supplement(s): Actualidad Antropologia. ISSN 0567-8560.

Indexed: AICP, AnthLit, MLA-IB.

Published by: Museo Etnografico Municipal Damasco Arce. Instituto de Investigaciones Antropologicas, San Martin 2862, Buenos Aires, 7400, Argentina. Ed. Lic Floreal Palanca.

301 ESP ISSN 1132-0729
DP302.B468

ETNIKER BIZKAIA. Text in Basque, Spanish; Summaries in Basque, English, French, Spanish. 1985. a. bk.rev. back issues avail. **Document type:** *Bulletin.*

Supersedes (1975-1982): Etniker (1132-0737)

Indexed: AICP.

—CINDOC.

Published by: Instituto Labayru, Departamento de Etnografia, C. Aretxabaleta, 1, 1o, Bilbao, 48010, Spain. TEL 34-94-454-1571, FAX 34-94-454-1571, labayru@labayru.org. Ed. Gurutzi Arregi.

305.8 BOL
ETNOFOLK. Text in Spanish. 1992. 3/yr.
Published by: Comite Departamental de Etnografia y Folklore, Oruro, Bolivia. Ed. Alberto Guerra Gutierrez.

301 NLD ISSN 0921-5158
ETNOFOOR. Text in Dutch, English, German. 1988. s-a. EUR 16 to individuals; EUR 25 to institutions; EUR 11.50 to students (effective 2005). adv. bk.rev. charts; illus.; maps. back issues avail. **Document type:** *Academic/Scholarly.* **Description:** Includes information pertaining to all areas of social and cultural anthropology such as cultures, societies, identities and religions of the world.
Indexed: AICP, AnthLit.
Published by: Universiteit van Amsterdam, Department of Anthropology, Oudezijds Achterburgwal 185, Amsterdam, 1012 DK, Netherlands. TEL 31-20-5252614, FAX 31-20-5253010, y.m.vanede@uva.nl. Circ: 500.

301 POL ISSN 0071-1861
GN585.P6
ETNOGRAFIA POLSKA. Text in Polish; Summaries in English. 1958. s-a. EUR 21 foreign (effective 2005). bk.rev. 222 p./no. 1 cols./p.; **Document type:** *Journal, Academic/Scholarly.* **Description:** Dissertations on ethnological research from Polish scholars about Poland and the world.
Indexed: AICP, AmH&L, BHA, DIP, HistAb, IBR, IBSS, IBZ, IndIslam, MLA-IB, NumL, RILM.
Published by: Polska Akademia Nauk, Instytut Archeologii i Etnologii, Al Solidarnosci 105, Warsaw, 00140, Poland. TEL 48-22-6202881, FAX 48-22-6240100, director@iaepan.edu.pl, http://www.iaepan.edu.pl. Ed. Iwona Kabzinska. Circ: 420. **Dist. by:** Ars Polona, Krakowskie Przedmiescie 7, Warsaw, Poland. TEL 48-22-9263914, FAX 48-22-9265334, arspolona@arspolona.com.pl, http://www.arspolona.com.pl.

305.8 RUS ISSN 0869-5415
GN1
ETNOGRAFICHESKOE OBOZRENIE. Text in Russian; Summaries in English, French. 1926. bi-m. RUR 250 for 6 mos. domestic; USD 216 foreign (effective 2004). bk.rev. charts; illus. index, cum.index every 5 yrs. **Document type:** *Journal, Academic/Scholarly.*
Former titles (until 1991): Sovetskaya Etnografiya (0038-5050); (until 1931): Etnografiya (0257-988X)
Related titles: Microform ed.; Online - full text ed.: (from East View Information Services).
Indexed: ABM, AICP, AmH&L, AnthLit, BAS, BHA, BiolAb, EI, HistAb, IBR, IBSS, IndIslam, MLA-IB, RASB, RILM, RefZh, SOPODA.
—East View, KNAW.
Published by: (Rossiiskaya Akademiya Nauk/Russian Academy of Sciences, Institut Etnologii i Antropologii Im. N.N. Miklukho-Maklaya), Izdatel'stvo Nauka, Profsoyuznaya ul 90, Moscow, 117864, Russian Federation. TEL 7-095-3347151, FAX 7-095-4202220, secret@naukaran.ru, http://www.naukaran.ru. **Dist. by:** M K - Periodica, ul Gilyarovskogo 39, Moscow 129110, Russian Federation. TEL 7-095-2845008, FAX 7-095-2813798, info@periodicals.ru, http://www.mkniga.ru.

301 SCG ISSN 0350-0322
DR314.A1
ETNOGRAFSKI MUZEJ U BEOGRADU. GLASNIK. Text in Serbo-Croatian. 1926. a. **Description:** Articles and essays about national culture and museological researches.
Indexed: AnthLit, RASB, RILM.
Published by: Etnografski Muzej u Beogradu, Studentski trg 13, Belgrade.

572 SVN ISSN 0354-0316
GN1
ETNOLOG. NOVA VRSTA. Text in Slovenian; Summaries in English, French, German. 1926. a. USD 25 (effective 1999). adv. bk.rev. **Document type:** *Academic/Scholarly.*
Former titles (until 1991): Slovenski Etnograf (0350-0330); (until 1945): Etnolog (0353-4855)
Indexed: AICP, BHA, MLA, MLA-IB, RASB, RILM.
Published by: Slovenski Etnografski Muzej, Metelkova 2, Ljubljana, 1000, Slovenia. TEL 386-61-1343235, FAX 386-61-1325377, bojana.rogelj@etno-muzej.si. Ed. Bojana Rogelj Skafar. Adv. contact Irma Kmetic. Circ: 1,000.

ETNOLOGIA I ANTROPOLOGIA KULTUROWA. see *FOLKLORE*

301 CUB
ETNOLOGIA Y FOLKLORE. Text in Spanish. 1966. 2/yr.
Indexed: AICP.
Published by: Academia de Ciencias de Cuba, Instituto de Etnologia y Folklore, Havana, Cuba.

301 SWE ISSN 0374-7530
GN301
ETNOLOGISKA STUDIER. Text in English, Swedish. 1935-1941; resumed 1947. irreg., latest vol.45, 2004. price varies. **Document type:** *Monographic series, Academic/Scholarly.*
Indexed: IBSS.
Published by: Vaerldskulturmuseet, Soedra Vaegen 54, PO Box 5303, Goeteborg, 40227, Sweden. TEL 46-31-632730, info@varldskulturmuseet.se, http://www.varldskulturmuseet.se. Circ: 1,600.

306 DNK ISSN 1398-8980
ETNOLOGISKE STUDIER. Text in Danish. 1988. irreg. DKK 450 per vol. domestic to individuals (effective 2004 - 2005). **Document type:** *Monographic series, Academic/Scholarly.* **Description:** Publishes work and research done within all areas of ethnology.
Published by: Museum Tusculanum Press, c/o University of Copenhagen, Njalsgade 94, Copenhagen S, 2300, Denmark. TEL 45-35-329109, FAX 45-35-329113, mtp@mtp.dk, http://www.mtp.dk. Eds. Bjarne Stoklund, Signe Mellemgaard, Thomas Hoejrup. **Dist. by:** International Specialized Book Services Inc., P O Box 1632, Beaverton, OR 97075-3640. TEL 503-287-3093, FAX 503-280-8832, orders@isbs.com.

301 HRV ISSN 0351-1944
DR1523
➤ **ETNOLOSKA TRIBINA.** Text in Croatian, English, German, French. 1970. a. USD 10 (effective 2001). adv. bk.rev. charts; illus. 300 p./no.; back issues avail. **Document type:** *Journal, Academic/Scholarly.* **Description:** Publishes scientific and professional papers covering all areas of ethnology and anthropology.
Indexed: AICP, IBSS, RILM.
Published by: Hrvatsko Etnolosko Drustvo/Croatian Ethnological Society (Subsidiary of: Institut za Etnologiju i Folkloristiku/Institut of Ethnology and Folklore Research), I Lucica 3, Zagreb, 10000, Croatia. TEL 385-1-4553632, FAX 385-1-4553649, grbic@maief.ief.hr. Ed. Jadranka Grbic. R&P Goran Santek. Adv. contact Aleksej Gotthardi Pavlovsky TEL 381-1-6163629. Circ: 500.

305.8 SCG ISSN 0423-5509
GN1
ETNOLOSKI PREGLED/REVUE D'ETHNOLOGIE. Text in Serbo-Croatian. 1962. s-a. illus.
Indexed: AICP, MLA-IB.
Published by: (Etnolosko Drustvo Jugoslavije YUG), Etnografski Muzej u Beogradu, Studentski trg 13, Belgrade. Ed. Milovan Gavazzi.

305.8 ITA ISSN 1122-6234
GN301
ETNOSISTEMI; processi e dinamiche culturali. Text in Italian. 1994. a. USD 50. **Document type:** *Monographic series.*
Indexed: AICP.
Published by: Centro Informazione e Stampa Universitaria, Viale Ippocrate, 97, Rome, RM 00161, Italy. TEL 39-6-491474, FAX 39-6-4450613. Ed. Mariano Pavanello.

301 FRA ISSN 0338-361X
ETUDES CORSES (1973); histoire, linguistique, archeologie, ethnologie, geographie-humaine. Text in French. 1954. s-a. **Document type:** *Journal, Academic/Scholarly.*
Former titles (until 1973): Corse Historique, Archeologique, Litteraire, Scientifique (0338-3628); (until 1961): Revue d'Etudes Corses (0574-1661); (until 1960): Etudes Corses (1954) (0421-5893)
Indexed: BHA.
—BLDSC (3817.242000).
Published by: (Association des Chercheurs en Sciences Humaines, Domaine Corse), Klincksieck, 6 Rue de la Sorbonne, Paris, 75005, France.

301 CIV ISSN 0423-5673
ETUDES EBURNEENNES✶. Text in French. 1951. a. bibl.; illus.
Indexed: AICP.
Published by: Ministry of National Education and Scientific Research, BP V120, Abidjan, Ivory Coast.

301 SEN
ETUDES MAURITANIENNES✶. Text in French. 1948. irreg. **Document type:** *Monographic series.*
Published by: (Centre de Mauritanie), Institut Fondamental d'Afrique Noire/Cheikh Anta Diop, BP 206, Dakar, Senegal.

305.8 MEX ISSN 0378-5726
ETUDES MESOAMERICAINES. Text in French; Summaries in Spanish. 1972 (series 1). s-a. price varies. adv. bk.rev. abstr.; bibl.; charts; illus.; pat.; tr.lit. **Document type:** *Academic/Scholarly.*
Indexed: AnthLit, IBSS.
Published by: (France. Ministere des Affaires Etrangeres FRA), Centre d'Etudes Mexicaines et Centramericaines, Sierra Leona 330, Apdo. 41-879, Mexico City, DF 11000, Mexico. TEL 540-59-21. Ed. Joelle Gaillac. Circ: 750.

301 FRA ISSN 0766-5075
DS798.A2
➤ **ETUDES MONGOLES ET SIBERIENNES.** Text in French, English; Abstracts in French, English. 1970. a., latest vol.34, 2003. price varies. bk.rev. bibl. back issues avail. **Document type:** *Academic/Scholarly.*
Formerly: Etudes Mongoles (0150-3014)
Indexed: AICP, AmH&L, AnthLit, BAS, BibLing, HistAb, IBSS, MLA, MLA-IB.
Published by: Centre d'Etudes Mongoles et Siberiennes, Ecole Pratique des Hautes Etudes, 5e sec, Sorbonne, Annexe EPHE, 29 Rue DEaviel, Paris, 75013, France. TEL 33-1-45882178, cems@ephe.sorbonne.fr. Ed. Marie-Lise Beffa. Circ: 500. **Dist. by:** Oriens, 10 Boulevard Arago, Paris 75013, France. TEL 33-1-45358028, FAX 33-1-43360150, oriens@club-internet.fr, http://www.abebooks.com/home/oriens.

301 NER ISSN 0373-6296
ETUDES NIGERIENNES. Text in French. 1953. irreg. illus. **Document type:** *Academic/Scholarly.*
Published by: Universite de Niamey, Institut de Recherches en Sciences Humaines, BP 318, Niamey, Niger. TEL 227-73-51-41, TELEX 5258 UNINIM.

ETUDES OCEAN INDIEN. see *LINGUISTICS*

ETUDES RWANDAISES. see *HISTORY—History Of Africa*

301 TGO ISSN 0531-2051
DT582.A2
ETUDES TOGOLAISES; revue togolaise des sciences. Text in French. 1965; N.S. 1971. q. illus. reprints avail.
Indexed: CCA.
Published by: Institut National de la Recherche Scientifique, BP 2240, Lome, Togo.

305.8 ITA ISSN 1124-5425
EUROPAEA. Text in Italian. 1995. s-a.
Related titles: Online - full text ed.
Indexed: AnthLit.
Address: Facolta di Lettere e Filosofia, Piazza d'Armi, Cagliari, 09123, Italy. TEL 39-70-2002202, FAX 39-70-2002304, angionig@unica.it, http://www.unica.it/europaea. Ed. Giulio Angioni.

EUROPE DE TRADITION ORALE. see *LINGUISTICS*

301 001.3 DEU ISSN 0943-8254
➤ **EUROPEAN BULLETIN OF HIMALAYAN RESEARCH.** Text in English. 1991. s-a. EUR 20 to individuals; EUR 32 to institutions (effective 2005). illus. **Document type:** *Journal, Academic/Scholarly.* **Description:** Scholarship and information on the state of current research in the Himalaya region.
Published by: Universitaet Heidelberg, Suedasien - Institut, Im Neuenheimer feld 330, Heidelberg, 69120, Germany. TEL 49-6221-548900, FAX 49-6221-544998, info@sai.uni-heidelberg.de, http://www.sai.uni-heidelberg.de/abt/home.

➤ **EUROPEAN MEETINGS IN ETHNOMUSICOLOGY.** see *MUSIC*

306 USA
EUROPEAN PERSPECTIVES: A SERIES IN SOCIAL THOUGHT AND CULTURAL CRITICISM. Text in English. 1991. irreg., latest 1999. price varies. back issues avail. **Document type:** *Monographic series, Academic/Scholarly.* **Description:** Explores ideas and ideologies in European cultures.
Indexed: MLA-IB.
Published by: Columbia University Press, 61 W 62nd St, New York, NY 10023. TEL 212-459-0600, 800-944-8648, FAX 212-459-3678, 800-944-1844, http://www.cc.columbia.edu/cu/cup.

301 USA ISSN 1060-1538
GN281 CODEN: EVANEW
➤ **EVOLUTIONARY ANTHROPOLOGY**; issues, news, and reviews. Text in English. 1992. bi-m. USD 499 domestic to institutions; USD 559 in Canada & Mexico to institutions; USD 610 elsewhere to institutions; USD 549 combined subscription domestic to institutions print & online eds.; USD 609 combined subscription in Canada & Mexico to institutions print & online eds.; USD 660 combined subscription elsewhere to institutions print & online eds. (effective 2006). adv. illus. back issues avail.; reprints avail. **Document type:** *Journal, Academic/Scholarly.* **Description:** Focuses on all aspects of biological anthropology, paleoanthropology, archaeology, as well as social biology, genetics, and ecology.
Related titles: Microform ed.: (from PQC); Online - full text ed.: ISSN 1520-6505. USD 499 to institutions (effective 2006) (from EBSCO Publishing, Swets Information Services, Wiley InterScience).
Indexed: AICP, AbAn, AnthLit, BIOSIS Prev, CurCont, IBSS, SSCI, WildRev, ZooRec.
—BLDSC (3834.390000), GNLM, IDS, IE, Infotrieve, ingenta. **CCC.**
Published by: John Wiley & Sons, Inc., 111 River St, Hoboken, NJ 07030-5774. TEL 201-748-6000, FAX 201-748-5915, uscs-wis@wiley.com, http://www3.interscience.wiley.com/cgi-bin/jhome/38641, http://www.wiley.com. Ed. John Fleagle. adv.: B&W page GBP 640, color page GBP 1,515; trim 210 x 279. **Subscr. to:** John Wiley & Sons Ltd., The Atrium, Southern Gate, Chichester, West Sussex PO19 8SQ, United Kingdom. TEL 44-1243-843335, 0800-243407, FAX 44-1243-843232, cs-journals@wiley.co.uk.

➤ **EVOLUTIONARY MONOGRAPHS.** see *BIOLOGY*

930.1 USA ISSN 0014-4738
GN1
➤ **EXPEDITION.** Text in English. 1930. 3/yr. USD 27 domestic; USD 31 foreign; USD 9.95 newsstand/cover (effective 2004). bk.rev.; film rev. charts; illus. index. 48 p./no.; back issues avail.; reprint service avail. from PQC. **Document type:** *Journal, Academic/Scholarly.* **Description:** Presents articles on current research in archaeology and anthropology to an audience composed of scholars, students, and the lay public.
Formerly (until 1958): University Museum Bulletin (0096-2953)
Related titles: Microform ed.: (from PQC); Online - full text ed.: (from EBSCO Publishing).
Indexed: A&ATA, AIAP, AICP, AbAn, AnthLit, ArtInd, BAS, BHA, MEA&I, NumL, RILM.
—BLDSC (3836.470000), IE, Infotrieve, ingenta.
Published by: University of Pennsylvania Museum, 3260 South St, Philadelphia, PA 19104-6324. TEL 215-898-4000, expedition@sas.upenn.edu, http://www.museum.upenn.edu/new/Zine/expedition.htmlEd., R&P, Adv. contact Beebe Bahrami. Circ: 4,250.

➤ **FACES**; people, places, & cultures. see *CHILDREN AND YOUTH—For*

➤ **FAITH & CULTURES SERIES.** see *RELIGIONS AND THEOLOGY—Roman Catholic*

301 SWE ISSN 0348-971X
DL1
FATABUREN; Nordiska Museets och Skansens aarsbok. Text in Swedish; Summaries in English. 1897. a. SEK 275. cum index: 1884-1903, 1906-1930. **Document type:** *Yearbook, Academic/Scholarly.*
Formerly (until 1905): Meddelanden fraan Nordiska Museet; Which incorporated: Samfundet foer Nordiska Museets Fraemjande. Meddelanden
Indexed: AICP, BHA, DIP, IBR, IBZ, MLA, MLA-IB, NumL.
Published by: Nordiska Museet, PO Box 27820, Stockholm, 11593, Sweden. TEL 46-8-51956000, FAX 46-8-51954580, nordiska@nordiskamuseet.se, http://www.nordiskamuseet.se. Circ: 5,000.

394 NLD ISSN 0920-3508
FEESTELIJK ZAKENDOEN. Text in Dutch. 1986. q. **Document type:** *Trade.*
—IE.
Published by: Reed Business Information bv (Subsidiary of: Reed Business), Hanzestraat 1, Doetinchem, 7006 RH, Netherlands. TEL 31-314-349911, FAX 31-314-343839, info@reedbusiness.nl, http://www.reedbusiness.nl.

FERMENTUM. see *SOCIOLOGY*

306.4 USA ISSN 1525-822X
GN1
FIELD METHODS. Text in English. 1989. q. USD 623, GBP 402 to institutions; USD 648, GBP 419 combined subscription to institutions print & online eds. (effective 2006). back issues avail. **Document type:** *Journal, Academic/Scholarly.* **Description:** Covers articles about the methods used by field investigators from the social and behavioral sciences, the humanities and corporate research for the collection, management, analysis and presentation of data about human thought and-or human behavior in the natural world.
Former titles (until 1998): Cultural Anthropology Methods Journal (1087-822X); (until 1995): C A M: Cultural Anthoropology Methods (1087-8513); (until 1992): C A M Newsletter (1064-8631)
Related titles: Online - full text ed.: ISSN 1552-3969. USD 616, GBP 398 to institutions (effective 2006) (from EBSCO Publishing, O C L C Online Computer Library Center, Inc., Sage Publications, Inc., Swets Information Services).
Indexed: AICP, AnthLit, IBSS, PsycInfo, PsycholAb, SSA, SociolAb, e-psyche.
—BLDSC (3920.343000), IE, Infotrieve, ingenta. **CCC.**
Published by: Sage Publications, Inc., 2455 Teller Rd, Thousand Oaks, CA 91320. TEL 805-499-0721, FAX 805-499-0871, info@sagepub.com, http://www.sagepub.co.uk/journal.aspx?pid=105556, http://www.sagepub.com. Ed. H Russell Bernard. **Subscr. to:** Sage Publications Ltd., 1 Oliver's Yard, 55 City Rd, London EC1 1SP, United Kingdom. TEL 44-20-73740645, FAX 44-20-73748741, subscription@sagepub.co.uk.

301 USA ISSN 0071-4739
GN2 CODEN: FIEAAV
FIELDIANA: ANTHROPOLOGY. Text in English. 1895. irreg. price varies. bibl.; charts; illus. index. back issues avail.; reprint service avail. from PQC. **Document type:** *Monographic series, Academic/Scholarly.* **Description:** Studies, descriptions and catalogues based on Field Museum collections and research in the field.
Indexed: BiolAb, EI, RASB, RefZh.
—Linda Hall.
Published by: Field Museum, Roosevelt Rd at Lake Shore Dr, Chicago, IL 60605-2496. TEL 312-922-9410, FAX 312-427-7269. Circ: 450.

▼ **FIJIAN STUDIES**; a journal of contemporary Fiji. see *SOCIAL SCIENCES: COMPREHENSIVE WORKS*

301 USA
FILMS: THE VISUALIZATION OF ANTHROPOLOGY. Text in English. 1972. irreg. (every 2-3 yrs.), latest 1988. **Document type:** *Catalog.*
Published by: Pennsylvania State University, Audio-Visual Services, University Park, PA 16802. TEL 800-826-0132, FAX 814-863-2574.

301 USA ISSN 0891-1835
FINDING THE SOURCE. Text in English. 1987. irreg. price varies. **Document type:** *Monographic series, Academic/Scholarly.*
Published by: Greenwood Publishing Group Inc. (Subsidiary of: Harcourt International), 88 Post Rd W, PO Box 5007, Westport, CT 06881. TEL 203-226-3571, FAX 203-226-1502, webmaster@greenwood.com, http://www.greenwood.com.

FINISTERRA; revista portuguesa de geografia. see *GEOGRAPHY*

FINNISCH-UGRISCHE FORSCHUNGEN; Zeitschrift fuer Finnisch-Ugrische Sprach- und Volkskunde. see *LINGUISTICS*

FINSKT MUSEUM. see *ARCHAEOLOGY*

301 USA ISSN 0015-3893
GN2 CODEN: FANTA9
➤ **FLORIDA ANTHROPOLOGIST.** Text in English. 1948. q. USD 25 domestic membership; USD 30 foreign membership (effective 2003). bk.rev. charts; illus. cum.index: vols.1-36, vols.37-40. back issues avail. **Document type:** *Journal, Academic/Scholarly.* **Description:** Covers archaeology, ethnology, physical anthropology, cultural anthropology and associated topics with a focus on Florida and surrounding areas in the Southeastern US and Caribbean.
Incorporates: Florida Anthropological Society Publications
Indexed: AICP, AbAn, AmH&L, AnthLit, BiolAb, RASB, RILM.
—Linda Hall.
Published by: Florida Anthropological Society, Inc., PO Box 82255, Tampa, FL 33682-2255. TEL 813-629-8831, rjw100@juno.com, tsimpson@luna.cas.usf.edu, http://web.usf.edu/~fas. Ed., R&P Ryan Wheeler TEL 850-309-0625. Circ: 900 (paid).

305.8 NLD ISSN 0920-1297
FOCAAL; European journal of anthropology. Text in Dutch, English. 1985. s-a. EUR 19.50 to individuals; EUR 50 to institutions (effective 2001). bk.rev. **Description:** Advocates the simultaneity of ethnography, local insights and global vision. Is dedicated to a subtler understanding of the basic questions human groups find themselves faced with, and explores the possible resources they deploy in their search for solutions.
Indexed: AnthLit, IBSS, PSA, SSA, SociolAb.
—BLDSC (3964.179700), IE, ingenta.
Published by: Katholieke Universiteit, Instituut voor Culturele en Sociale Antropologie, University of Nijmegen, P.O. Box 9102, Nijmegen, 6500 HC, Netherlands. TEL 31-24-3616161, FAX 31-24-3564606, Focaal@box.nl, http://www.focaal.box.nl.

305.8 DNK ISSN 0085-0756
FOLK; journal of the Danish Ethnographic Society. Text in English. 1959. a. bk.rev. bibl.; illus. **Document type:** *Yearbook, Academic/Scholarly.* **Description:** Presents articles on social and cultural anthropology to an international audience.
Indexed: AICP, AnthLit, BAS, BHA, IBR, IBSS, IndIslam, NumL, RASB, RILM, SOPODA.
—BLDSC (3974.570000), IE, ingenta. **CCC.**
Published by: Dansk Etnografisk Forening/Danish Ethnographic Society, c/o Institute of Anthropology, University of Copenhagen, Frederiksholms Kanal 4, Copenhagen K, 1220, Denmark. TEL 45-35-323465, FAX 45-35-323472, journal.folk@anthro.ku.dk. Ed. Poul Pedersen. Circ: 1,000.

305.8 GBR ISSN 0430-8778
GR140
FOLK LIFE: JOURNAL OF ETHNOLOGICAL STUDIES. Text in English. 1963. a. USD 30 (effective 1999). adv. bk.rev. illus. index. **Document type:** *Academic/Scholarly.* **Description:** Devoted to the study of traditional ways of life in Great Britain and Ireland.
Indexed: ABM, AICP, ASCA, ArtHuCI, BHA, BrArAb, CurCont, FPA, IBSS, MLA, MLA-IB, NumL, PCI, RILM.
—BLDSC (3974.571500), IDS.
Published by: Society for Folk Life Studies, Museum of English Rural Life, University of Reading, Whiteknights Park, Reading, United Kingdom. TEL 44-118-931-8663, FAX 44-118-975-1264, r.d.brigden@reading.ac.uk. Ed. Roy Brigden. Circ: 500.

301 SWE ISSN 1102-6502
FOLKENS MUSEUM - NATIONAL MUSEUM OF ETHNOGRAPHY. Text in Swedish. 1934. irreg. price varies. **Document type:** *Monographic series, Academic/Scholarly.*
Former titles: Ethnographical Museum of Sweden. Monograph Series (0081-5632); (until 1953): Ethnographical Museum of Sweden. Publication
Published by: Folkens Museum - Etnografiska/National Museum of Ethnography, PO Box 27140, Stockholm, 10252, Sweden. TEL 46-8-51955000, FAX 46-8-51955070, info@etnografiska.se, http://www.etnografiska.se. Ed. Ulla Wagner. Circ: 1,000.

305.8 FIN ISSN 0085-0764
GR200
FOLKLIVSSTUDIER. Text in Swedish; Summaries in English, German. 1945. irreg., latest vol.19, 1993. price varies. back issues avail. **Document type:** *Monographic series, Academic/Scholarly.*
Related titles: ♦ Series of: Svenska Litteratursaellskapet i Finland. Skrifter. ISSN 0039-6842.
Published by: Svenska Litteratursaellskapet i Finland, Riddaregatan 5, Helsinki, 00170, Finland. TEL 358-9-618777, FAX 358-9-61877277, sls@mail.sls.fi, http://www.sls.fi. Ed. Magnus Pettersson. Circ: (controlled).

FOLKLORE FORUM. see *FOLKLORE*

FOLLETOS DE DIVULGACION. see *ARCHAEOLOGY*

FOOD AND FOODWAYS; explorations in the history and culture of human nutrition. see *NUTRITION AND DIETETICS*

FORSCHUNGSBERICHTE ZUR UR- UND FRUEHGESCHICHTE. see *ARCHAEOLOGY*

155.82 DEU ISSN 0429-1530
FORSCHUNGSERGEBNISSE ZUR ETHNOLOGIE UND SOZIALPSYCHOLOGIE. Text in German. 1953. irreg., latest vol.12, 1980. price varies. **Document type:** *Monographic series, Academic/Scholarly.*
Published by: Duncker und Humblot GmbH, Carl-Heinrich-Becker-Weg 9, Berlin, 12165, Germany. TEL 49-30-7900060, FAX 49-30-79000631, info@duncker-humblot.de, http://www.duncker-humblot.de.

FRENCH POLITICS, CULTURE & SOCIETY. see *POLITICAL SCIENCE*

FRONTIERES; les vivants et les morts. see *PSYCHOLOGY*

301 USA ISSN 1052-0449
FRONTIERS OF ANTHROPOLOGY. Text in English. 1989. irreg. (in 2 vols.). USD 50.95 per vol. (effective 2004). **Document type:** *Monographic series.*
Indexed: AnthLit.
—**CCC.**
Published by: Sage Publications, Inc., 2455 Teller Rd, Thousand Oaks, CA 91320. TEL 805-499-0721, FAX 805-499-0871, info@sagepub.com, http://www.sagepub.com.

930.1 ESP ISSN 1132-1717
FUNDAMENTOS DE ANTROPOLOGIA. Text in Spanish. 1992. a.
—CINDOC.
Published by: Centro de Investigaciones Etnologicas "Angel Ganivet", Palacio Condes de Gabia, Plaza Girones, 1, Granada, Andalucia 18009, Spain.

GALA; revista d'arqueologia i antropologia. see *ARCHAEOLOGY*

301 FRA
GALAXIE ANTHROPOLOGIQUE. Text in French. 1992. q.?.
Published by: Association Nouvelles Etudes Anthropologiques, c/o Jean-Marie Brohm, 28 av. Herbillon, St-Mande, 94160, France. TEL 1-43-74-01-02. Ed. Louis Vincent Thomas. **Subscr. to:** 30 rue Duperre, Paris 75009, France.

301 PRT ISSN 0870-0168
GARCIA DE ORTA: SERIE DE ANTROPOBIOLOGIA. Text in English, French, Italian, Portuguese, Spanish. 1982. irreg., latest vol.9, 1996. price varies. back issues avail. **Document type:** *Academic/Scholarly.*
Indexed: AICP, ASD, AnthLit, IBSS.
—GNLM.
Published by: Instituto de Investigacao Cientifica Tropical, Rua da Junqueira, 30, Lisbon, 1349-007, Portugal. TEL 351-21-3622621, FAX 351-21-3631460, iict@iict.pt. Circ: 1,000. **Subscr. to:** Centro de Documentacao e Informacao, Rua de Jau, 47, Lisbon 1300, Portugal. TEL 351-21-3644846, FAX 351-21-3628218.

301 PRT ISSN 0870-6204
GN590
GARCIA DE ORTA: SERIE DE ANTROPOLOGIA. Text in Portuguese. 1973. s-a.
Indexed: AnthLit.
Published by: Instituto de Investigacao Cientifica Tropical, Rua da Junqueira, 86-1, Lisboa, 1300-344, Portugal. TEL 21-3616340, cacsl@iict.pt, http://www.iict.pt.

301 USA
➤ **GENDERS (ONLINE EDITION).** Text in English. s-a. free (effective 2005). **Document type:** *Academic/Scholarly.*
Media: Online - full content (from Northern Light Technology, Inc., SoftLine Information).
Published by: University of Colorado, Campus Box 226, Boulder, CO 80309. http://www.genders.org/. Eds. Ann Kibbey, Carol Siegel, Thomas Foster.

301 USA ISSN 1537-1727
GN1
GENERAL ANTHROPOLOGY. Text in English. s-a. subscr. incld. with membership. video rev. **Document type:** *Bulletin, Academic/Scholarly.*

—CCC.
Published by: American Anthropological Association, General Anthropology Division, 2200 Wilson Blvd, Ste 600, Arlington, VA 22201. TEL 703-528-1902, FAX 703-528-3546, http://www.aaanet.org/gad/bulletin.htm, http://www.aaanet.org/gad/index.htm. Eds. David W McCurdy TEL 612-696-6587, Patricia Rice TEL 304-293-5801.

304.2   GBR   ISSN 0435-3684
G25   CODEN: GAHGAJ
GEOGRAFISKA ANNALER. SERIES B. HUMAN GEOGRAPHY. Text in English. 1965. q. EUR 51 combined subscription in Europe to individuals print & online eds.; USD 57 combined subscription in the Americas to individuals & Caribbean (print & online eds.); GBP 34 combined subscription elsewhere to individuals print & online eds.; USD 324 combined subscription in the Americas to institutions & Caribbean (print & online eds.); GBP 193 combined subscription elsewhere to institutions print & online eds.; EUR 35 combined subscription in Europe to students print & online eds.; USD 39 combined subscription in the Americas to students & Caribbean (print & online eds.); GBP 23 combined subscription elsewhere to students print & online eds. (effective 2006). reprint service avail. from PSC. **Document type:** Journal, Academic/Scholarly.
Supersedes in part (1919-1965): Geografiska Annaler (0016-7231).
Related titles: Online - full text ed.: ISSN 1468-0467. USD 307 in the Americas to institutions; GBP 183 elsewhere to institutions (effective 2006) (from Blackwell Synergy, EBSCO Publishing, Gale Group, IngentaConnect, JSTOR (Web-based Journal Archive), O C L C Online Computer Library Center, Inc., Swets Information Services).
Indexed: AnthLit, BAS, BibCart, BiolAb, DIP, GEOBASE, IBR, IBSS, IBZ, IndIslam, PSA, RASB, RDA, SSCI, SociolAb, WAE&RSA.
—BLDSC (4124.060000), IE, Infotrieve, ingenta, Linda Hall. **CCC.**
Published by: (Svenska Saellskapet foer Antropologi och Geografi (SSAG) SWE), Blackwell Publishing Ltd., 9600 Garsington Rd, Oxford, OX4 2ZG, United Kingdom. TEL 44-1865-776868, FAX 44-1865-714591, customerservices@oxon.blackwellpublishing.com, http://www.blackwellpublishing.com/journals/GEOB. Ed. Eric Clark.

GEOGRAPHICA HELVETICA; Schweizerische Zeitschrift fuer Laender- und Voelkerkunde. see *GEOGRAPHY*

GERMANIA. see *ARCHAEOLOGY*

GLOBAL CHANGE, PEACE & SECURITY. see *POLITICAL SCIENCE—International Relations*

301   SWE   ISSN 0348-4076
GOTHENBURG STUDIES IN SOCIAL ANTHROPOLOGY. Text in English. 1978. irreg., latest vol.15, 1999. price varies; also exchange basis. **Document type:** Monographic series, Academic/Scholarly.
Related titles: ◆ Series of: Acta Universitatis Gothoburgensis. ISSN 0346-7740.
Indexed: AnthLit, IBSS.
Published by: Acta Universitatis Gothoburgensis, Renstroemsgatan 4, P O Box 222, Goeteborg, 40530, Sweden. jan.ahman@ub.gu.se. Ed. Kaj Aarhem.

301   FRA   ISSN 0764-8928
GN1
GRADHIVA; revue d'histoire et d'archives de l'anthropologie. Text in French. 2/yr. EUR 16 per issue (effective 2004). **Document type:** Magazine, Consumer.
Related titles: Microfiche ed.
Indexed: ABM, AICP, CurCont, IBSS.
Published by: (Musee de l'Homme), Editions Jean - Michel Place, 3 rue Lhomond, Paris, 75005, France. TEL 33-1-44320590, FAX 33-1-44320591, place@jmplace.com, http://www.jmplace.com. Ed. Jean Jamin.

GRASSROOTS DEVELOPMENT. see *BUSINESS AND ECONOMICS—International Development And Assistance*

GUIDE TO DEPARTMENTS OF SOCIOLOGY, ANTHROPOLOGY AND ARCHAEOLOGY IN UNIVERSITIES AND MUSEUMS IN CANADA/ANNUAIRE DES DEPARTEMENTS DE SOCIOLOGIE, D'ANTHROPOLOGIE ET D'ARCHEOLOGIE DES UNIVERSITES ET DES MUSEES DU CANADA. see *SOCIOLOGY*

930.1   ESP
GUIZE. Text in Spanish. a.
—CINDOC.
Published by: Asociacion Canaria de Antropologia, Facultad de Geografia e Historia, Campus de Guajara, La Laguna-Tenerife, 38205, Spain. TEL 34-922-317626, FAX 34-922-317626, agalvant@ull.es. Ed. Jose Alberto Galvan Tudela.

GUIZHOU MINZU YANJIU/STUDY OF GUIZHOU NATIONALITIES. see *ASIAN STUDIES*

301   USA   ISSN 1070-4604
DX101
GYPSY LORE SOCIETY. NEWSLETTER. Text in English. 1978. q. USD 35 in US & Canada to non-members; USD 40 elsewhere to non-members; USD 30 in US & Canada to individual members; USD 35 in US & Canada to institutional members; USD 40 elsewhere to institutional members (effective 2003); inclds. Romani Studies. adv. bibl. cum.index: vols.1-12; vols.13-25. 8 p./no. 2 cols./p.; back issues avail. **Document type:** Newsletter, Academic/Scholarly.
Description: Presents a resource on current research in Gypsy studies.
Formerly: Gypsy Lore Society. North American Chapter. Newsletter (0731-4841)
Indexed: AICP, RASB.
—CCC.
Published by: Gypsy Lore Society, 5607 Greenleaf Rd., Cheverly, MD 20785. TEL 301-341-1261, ssalo@capaccess.org, http://www.gypsyloresociety.org. Ed., R&P, Adv. contact Sheila Salo. page USD 45; trim 6.75 x 9. Circ: 300.

HEIMDAL; revue d'heritage Norois. see *HISTORY—History Of Europe*

301   DEU   ISSN 1437-7837
HERODOT; Wissenschaftliche Schriften zur Ethnologie und Anthropologie. Text in German. 1999. irreg., latest vol.7, 2005. price varies. **Document type:** Monographic series, Academic/Scholarly.
Published by: Verlag Dr. Kovac, Arnoldstr 49, Hamburg, 22763, Germany. TEL 49-40-3988800, FAX 49-40-39888055, info@verlagdrkovac.de, http://www.verlagdrkovac.de/9-9.htm.

HESSISCHE BLAETTER FUER VOLKS- UND KULTURFORSCHUNG. see *ETHNIC INTERESTS*

306 306.4   USA   ISSN 0882-4894
GN397.7.U6
➤ **HIGH PLAINS APPLIED ANTHROPOLOGIST.** Text in English. 1981. s-a. USD 40 to individuals; USD 70 to institutions (effective 2003). bk.rev.; film rev. abstr.; bibl.; maps; charts; illus. 100 p./no. 2 cols./p.; back issues avail. **Document type:** Journal, Academic/Scholarly. **Description:** Publishes articles and commentaries, brief communications on a wide range of topics. Focuses on cultural change and adaptation in the modern world. Explores how humans approach, analyze, and develop solutions to cultural, ecological, economic and technological problems.
Related titles: Online - full text ed.
Indexed: AnthLit.
Published by: High Plains Society for Applied Anthropology, P.O. Box 4147, Boulder, CO 80306. TEL 303-492-6719, FAX 303-492-7970, walkerde@colorado.edu, http://www.colorado.edu/AppAnth/HPSfAA/pubs/journal, http://www.hpsfaa.org. Ed. Larry F Van Horn. R&P Deward Walker. Circ: 150 (controlled).

➤ **HIIDENKIVI.** see *HISTORY*

306   FRA   ISSN 1254-728X
➤ **HISTOIRE ET SOCIETES RURALES.** Text in French. 1994. q. bk.rev. abstr.; bibl.; illus. back issues avail. **Document type:** Journal, Academic/Scholarly. **Description:** Publishes research into all facets of rural societies.
Indexed: AmH&L, HistAb.
Published by: Association d'Histoire des Societes Rurales, Maison de la Recherche en Sciences Humaines, Universite de Caen, Esplanade de la Paix, Caen, 14032, France. TEL 33-2-31566229, FAX 32-2-31566560, jmmoriceau@mrsh.unicaen.fr, http://www.unicaen.fr/mrsh/SOCIETE, http://www.uhb.fr/sc_sociales/crhisco/ahsr.htm. Eds. Ghislain Brunel, Jean-Marc Moriceau. Circ: 1,000 (paid and controlled).

➤ **HISTORIA, ANTROPOLOGIA Y FUENTES ORALES.** see *HISTORY*

➤ **HISTORICAL BIOLOGY**; an international journal of paleobiology. see *PALEONTOLOGY*

301   GBR   ISSN 0275-7206
GN1   CODEN: HIAND7
➤ **HISTORY AND ANTHROPOLOGY.** Text in French. q. GBP 611, USD 913 combined subscription to institutions print & online eds. (effective 2006). adv. reprint service avail. from PSC. **Document type:** Journal, Academic/Scholarly.
Description: Addresses the intersection of history and social sciences, focussing on the interchange between anthropologically-informed history, historically-informed anthropology and the history of ethnographic and anthropological representation.
Related titles: Microform ed.; Online - full text ed.: ISSN 1477-2612. 2002. GBP 580, USD 867 to institutions (effective 2006) (from EBSCO Publishing, Gale Group, IngentaConnect, O C L C Online Computer Library Center, Inc., Swets Information Services).
Indexed: AICP, AmH&L, AnthLit, DIP, HistAb, IBR, IBSS, IBZ, PCI, SociolAb.
—BLDSC (4317.778600), IE, Infotrieve. **CCC.**

Published by: Routledge (Subsidiary of: Taylor & Francis Group), 4 Park Sq, Milton Park, Abingdon, Oxon OX14 4RN, United Kingdom. TEL 44-1235-828600, FAX 44-1235-829000, info@routledge.co.uk, http://www.tandf.co.uk/journals/titles/02757206.asp, http://www.routledge.co.uk. Ed. Dr. Paul Sant-Cassia. **Subscr. to:** Taylor & Francis Ltd, Journals Customer Service, Rankine Rd, Basingstoke, Hants RG24 8PR, United Kingdom. TEL 44-1256-813000, FAX 44-1256-330245, enquiry@tandf.co.uk.

301   USA   ISSN 0891-9348
CODEN: HIANE8
HISTORY OF ANTHROPOLOGY (SERIES). Text in English. 1983. irreg. price varies. bibl. index. **Document type:** Monographic series. **Description:** Covers the history and present practice of anthropological inquiry.
Indexed: AnthLit.
—BLDSC (4317.855000).
Published by: (University of Wisconsin at Madison), University of Wisconsin Press, Journal Division, 1930 Monroe St, 3rd Fl, Madison, WI 53711-2059. TEL 608-263-0668, FAX 608-263-1173, http://www.wisc.edu/wisconsinpress/History_of_Anthropology.html.

301   USA   ISSN 0362-9074
HISTORY OF ANTHROPOLOGY NEWSLETTER. Text in English. 1973. s-a. USD 5 to individuals; USD 7 to institutions; USD 3 to students (effective 2005). bk.rev. bibl. **Document type:** Newsletter, Academic/Scholarly.
Indexed: AICP, AnthLit, HistAb, PCI.
Address: c/o George W Stocking, Dept of Anthropology, University of Chicago, 1126 E 59th St, Chicago, IL 60637. TEL 312-702-7702, FAX 312-702-4503, g-stocking@uchicago.edu, http://www.anthropology.uchicago.edu. Circ: 300 (controlled).

301   JPN   ISSN 0918-1725
GF1
HITO TO SHIZEN/HUMANS AND NATURE. Text in Japanese. 1992. a. **Document type:** Academic/Scholarly.
Indexed: AgBio, BIOSIS Prev, BioCN&I, BiolAb, CPA, ForAb, GEOBASE, HortAb, I&DA, PBA, PGegResA, PN&I, RA&MP, RRTA, S&F, SeedAb, WAE&RSA, WeedAb, ZooRec.
—BLDSC (4336.582230).
Published by: Hyogo Kenritsu Hito to Shizen no Hakubutsukan/Museum of Nature and Human Activities, 6-Chome, Yayoigaoka, Sanda, Hyogo 669-1546, Japan. http://www.nat-museum.sanda.hyogo.jp/.

301   NZL   ISSN 1172-2541
HOCKEN LECTURE. Text in English. 1969. a. price varies.
Published by: University of Otago, Hocken Library, PO Box 56, Dunedin, New Zealand. hocken@library.otago.ac.nz. Ed. S R Strachan. Circ: 250.

HOLIDAYS & SEASONAL CELEBRATIONS. GRADES 1-3. see *EDUCATION—Teaching Methods And Curriculum*

HOLIDAYS & SEASONAL CELEBRATIONS. PRESCHOOL - KINDERGARTEN. see *EDUCATION—Teaching Methods And Curriculum*

202.2   USA
HOLIDAYS, FESTIVALS AND CELEBRATIONS OF THE WORLD DICTIONARY; detailing 2,500 observances from all 50 States and more than 100 nations. Text in English. 1997. irreg., latest vol.3, 2001. USD 98 per vol. (effective 2001). bibl.; charts; illus. **Document type:** Directory, Consumer. **Description:** Describes more than 2,500 holidays, festivals, commemorations, holy days, feasts and fasts, and other observances from all parts of the world. Includes 4 extensive indexes and several appendices.
Published by: Omnigraphics, Inc., 615 Griswold St, Detroit, MI 48226. TEL 313-961-1340, 800-234-1340, FAX 313-961-1383, 800-875-1340, info@omnigraphics.com, http://www.omnigraphics.com. Eds. Helene Henderson, Sue Ellen Thompson. Pub. Frederick G Ruffner Jr. R&P Laurie Lanzen Harris.

301   PAN   ISSN 0439-397X
GN1
HOMBRE Y CULTURA. Text in Spanish. 1962; N.S. 1991. s-a. **Document type:** Academic/Scholarly. **Description:** Publishes works in anthropology and archaeology.
Published by: Universidad de Panama, Centro de Investigaciones Antropologicas, Estafeta Universitaria 10826, Panama City, Panama. Ed. Francoise Guionneau Sinclair.

306   FRA   ISSN 0439-4216
GN1
➤ **L'HOMME**; revue francaise d'anthropologie. Text in French. 1961. q. EUR 54 domestic to individuals; EUR 54 foreign to individuals; EUR 78 domestic to institutions; EUR 90 foreign to institutions (effective 2005). adv. bk.rev. illus. index. reprints avail. **Document type:** Journal, Academic/Scholarly.
Indexed: AICP, ASCA, AnthLit, ArtHuCI, BAS, BibInd, BibLing, CurCont, DIP, EI, IBR, IBSS, IBZ, IPSA, IndIslam, MLA-IB, PCI, PSA, RASB, RILM, SOPODA, SSA, SSCI, SociolAb.
—BLDSC (4326.180000), IDS, IE, Infotrieve, ingenta. **CCC.**

A

Published by: (Laboratoire d'Anthropologie Sociale), Editions de l' Ecole des Hautes Etudes en Sciences Sociales, 131 bd. Saint-Michel, Paris, 75005, France. TEL 33-1-40467080, FAX 33-1-44070889, editions@ehess.fr, http://lhomme.revues.org/. Ed. Jean Jamin. Circ: 1,800 (paid and controlled). **Subscr. to:** EHESS Service Abonnements, 5-7 rue Marcelin-Berthelot, Wissous Cedex F-91322, France. TEL 33-01-55595253, FAX 33-01-55595250, abo.services@wanadoo.fr. **Dist. by:** Editions du Seuil, 27 Rue Jacob, Paris 75006, France. TEL 33-1-40465050, FAX 33-1-40464300, contact@seuil.com, http://www.seuil.com.

301 DEU ISSN 0018-442X
GN1 CODEN: HOMOA7
➤ **HOMO**; journal of comparative human biology. Text in English. 1949. 3/yr. EUR 134 in Europe to individuals; JPY 17,200 in Japan to individuals; USD 132 elsewhere to individuals; EUR 418 to institutions; EUR 470 in Europe to institutions; JPY 61,900 in Japan to institutions; USD 514 elsewhere to institutions (effective 2006). adv. bk.rev. abstr.; bibl.; charts; illus. index. reprints avail. **Document type:** *Journal, Academic/Scholarly.* **Description:** Contains research articles in the field of biological anthropology, with a focus on its population historic, ontogenetic and ethological aspects.
Related titles: Online - full text ed.: ISSN 1618-1301. 2001 (from EBSCO Publishing, Gale Group, IngentaConnect, O C L C Online Computer Library Center, Inc., ScienceDirect, Swets Information Services).
Indexed: AICP, AbAn, AnthLit, ArtHuCI, BAS, BIOSIS Prev, BiolAb, CurCont, DIP, FamI, IBR, IBZ, NAA, RASB, SSCI, e-psyche.
—GNLM, IDS, IE, Infotrieve. **CCC.**
Published by: (Australasian Society of Human Biology AUS), Elsevier GmbH, Urban & Fischer Verlag (Subsidiary of: Elsevier Science & Technology), Loebdergraben 14a, Jena, 07743, Germany. TEL 49-3641-626430, FAX 49-3641-626432, marketing.journals@urbanfischer.de, http://www.elsevier.com/locate/jchb, http://www.urbanfischer.de/journals. Eds. Friedrich W. Roesing TEL 49-731-50025230, Maciej Henneberg, Stanley Ulijaszek. R&P Frances Rothwell. Adv. contact Cora Grotzke. B&W page EUR 320, color page EUR 1,265; 170 x 240. Circ: 350 (paid). **Non-German speaking countries subscr. to:** Nature Publishing Group, Brunel Rd, Houndmills, Basingstoke, Hamps RG21 6XS, United Kingdom. TEL 44-1256-302629, FAX 44-1256-476117, subscriptions@nature.com

301 BRA ISSN 0103-7706
AS80.A1
HORIZONTES; review of social ideas, history. Text in Portuguese. 1990. s-a. **Document type:** *Academic/Scholarly.*
Related titles: Online - full text ed.: (from Northern Light Technology, Inc.).
Indexed: IBSS, SSA.
Published by: Universidade de Sao Francisco, Instituto Franciscano de Antropologia, Ave. SAO FRANCISCO DE ASSIS, 218, Braganca Paulista, SP 12900-000, Brazil. TEL 55-11-78448300, FAX 55-11-78441825, alberto@usf.com.br, ijan@usf.com.br. Ed. Alberto de Silva Moreira.

301 BRA ISSN 0104-7183
GN1
HORIZONTES ANTROPOLOGICOS. Text in Multiple languages. 1994. s-a. **Document type:** *Journal, Academic/Scholarly.*
Related titles: Online - full text ed.: free (effective 2005).
Indexed: IBSS, RILM, SociolAb.
Published by: Universidade Federal do Rio Grande do Sul, Instituto de Filosofia e Ciencias Humanas, Av Bento Gocalves 9500, Porto Alegre, RS 91509-900, Brazil. TEL 55-51-33166647, FAX 55-51-33166638.

304.2 USA ISSN 0300-7839
GF1 CODEN: HMECAJ
➤ **HUMAN ECOLOGY (NEW YORK)**; an interdisciplinary journal. Text in English. 1972. 6/yr. EUR 868, USD 888, GBP 548 combined subscription to institutions print & online eds. (effective 2005). adv. bk.rev. illus. Index. back issues avail.; reprint service avail. from PSC. **Document type:** *Journal, Academic/Scholarly.* **Description:** Discusses the quality of the environment and the role of social and cultural factors and population density in the maintenance of ecosystems.
Related titles: Online - full text ed.: ISSN 1572-9915 (from bigchalk, EBSCO Publishing, Florida Center for Library Automation, Gale Group, IngentaConnect, Kluwer Online, O C L C Online Computer Library Center, Inc., Ovid Technologies, Inc., ProQuest Information & Learning, Springer LINK, Swets Information Services).
Indexed: AICP, AbAn, AbHyg, AgBio, Agr, AgrForAb, AnBrAb, AnthLit, ApEcolAb, BAS, BIOSIS Prev, BibLing, BioCN&I, BiolAb, CurCont, DSA, EI, EIA, EPB, ERA, ESPM, EnerInd, EnerRev, EngInd, EnvEAb, ExcerpMed, FCA, FPA, FamI, ForAb, GEOBASE, HerbAb, HortAb, I&DA, IMFL, IndVet, MEA, MEA&I, MaizeAb, NAA, NutrAb, OrnHort, PBA, PCI, PGegResA, PN&I, PRA, PSA, ProtozoAb, PsycholAb, RA&MP, RASB, RDA, RRTA, RefZh, RiceAb, S&F, SFA, SFSA, SIA, SOPODA, SSA, SSCI, SSI, SUSA, SWA, SociolAb, TDB, VetBull, WAE&RSA, WeedAb, WildRev, ZooRec.
—BLDSC (4336.055000), CISTI, Ei, GNLM, IDS, IE, Infotrieve, ingenta, Linda Hall. **CCC.**
Published by: Plenum US (Subsidiary of: Springer Science+Business Media), 233 Spring St, New York, NY 10013. TEL 212-460-1500, FAX 212-460-1575, service@springer-ny.com, http://springerlink.metapress.com/openurl.asp?genre=journal&issn=0300-7839, http://www.springeronline.com. Ed. Daniel G Bates.

➤ **HUMAN ETHOLOGY BULLETIN.** see *PSYCHOLOGY*

599.938 ITA ISSN 0393-9375
GN281
HUMAN EVOLUTION; international journal. Text in English; Summaries in English, French. 1986. q. EUR 110 domestic; EUR 128 foreign (effective 2005). adv. bk.rev. illus. Index. back issues avail.; reprints avail. **Description:** Multi-disciplinary forum on the study of human evolution. Reflects current interests in molecular evolution, genetics, palaeontology and biological variability considered in social, cultural and physical contexts.
Related titles: Online - full text ed.: ISSN 1824-310X.
Indexed: AICP, AnthLit, BAS, CurCont, ExcerpMed, RASB, ZooRec.
—BLDSC (4336.071200), GNLM, IE, Infotrieve, ingenta, Linda Hall.
Published by: (Universita degli Studi di Firenze, Laboratori di Antropologia, International Institute for the Study of Man), Angelo Pontecorboli Editore, Via Carrand 22, Florence, 50133, Italy. TEL 39-055-5520903, FAX 39-055-5528456, angelo@pontecorboli.it, http://www.pontecorboli.it. Ed. A B Chiarelli. Circ: 700.

301 USA ISSN 0018-7240
GN1
HUMAN MOSAIC; a journal of the social sciences. Text in English. 1966. s-a. USD 9 (effective 2005). adv. bk.rev. bibl.; charts; illus. back issues avail.; reprint service avail. from PQC. **Document type:** *Academic/Scholarly.* **Description:** Provides articles in archaeology, linguistics, cultural and physical anthropology, and all social science disciplines.
Formerly: Mosaic (New Orleans)
Related titles: Microform ed.: (from PQC).
Indexed: AbAn, AnthLit, MEA&I, SOPODA, SSA, SociolAb.
Published by: Tulane University, Department of Anthropology, 1021 Audubon St, New Orleans, LA 70118. TEL 504-865-5336, FAX 504-865-5338, hmosaic@tulane.edu, http://www.tulane.edu/~anthro/other/humos/. Circ: 120.

301 USA ISSN 0018-7259
GN1 CODEN: HUORAY
➤ **HUMAN ORGANIZATION.** Text in English. 1941. q. USD 75 in US & Canada to institutions; USD 85 elsewhere to institutions (effective 2005). adv. illus. index, cum.index. back issues avail.; reprints avail. **Document type:** *Journal, Academic/Scholarly.* **Description:** Applies the concepts of social and behavioral science to issues and problems in the contemporary world.
Formerly: Applied Anthropology (0093-2914)
Related titles: Microform ed.; Online - full text ed.: (from EBSCO Publishing, Northern Light Technology, Inc., O C L C Online Computer Library Center, Inc., ProQuest Information & Learning).
Indexed: ABIn, AESIS, AICP, AMHA, ASCA, ASG, AbAn, AbHyg, AcaI, AgeL, AgrForAb, AmH&L, AnBrAb, AnthLit, BAS, CCME, CIJE, CJA, CLFP, CommAb, CurCont, DIP, DSA, EEA, EI, ERA, ETA, FPA, FamI, ForAb, GEOBASE, HRA, HerbAb, HistAb, HortAb, I&DA, IBR, IBSS, IBZ, IPSA, IndVet, MCR, MEA, MEDLINE, MaizeAb, NutrAb, PAA&I, PCI, PGegResA, PN&I, PRA, PSA, PotatoAb, PoultAb, ProtozoAb, PsycInfo, PsycholAb, RA&MP, RDA, REE&TA, RHEA, RILM, RRTA, RevApplEntom, RiceAb, S&F, SEA, SENA, SFSA, SOMA, SOPODA, SPAA, SPPI, SRRA, SSA, SSCI, SSI, SUSA, SWA, SWR&A, SociolAb, TDB, TEA, V&AA, VetBull, WAE&RSA, e-psyche.
—BLDSC (4336.250000), IE, Infotrieve, ingenta, Linda Hall. **CCC.**
Published by: Society for Applied Anthropology, PO Box 2436, Oklahoma City, OK 73101. TEL 405-843-5113, FAX 405-843-8553, info@sfaa.net, http://www.sfaa.net/ho/. Ed. Donald D Stull. Circ: 4,700.

301 IND ISSN 0970-3411
DS430
HUMAN SCIENCE. Text in English. 1954. q. USD 106 (effective 2003). bk.rev. abstr.; bibl.; charts; illus.; stat. index. **Document type:** *Journal.*
Formerly (until 1982): Anthropological Survey of India. Bulletin (0003-5513)
Indexed: AICP, AnthLit, BAS, IBR, RILM.
Published by: (Anthropological Survey of India), Scientific Publishers, 5-A New Pali Rd., Near Hotel Taj Hari Mahal, PO Box 91, Jodhpur, Rajasthan 342 003, India. TEL 91-291-2433323, FAX 91-291-2512580, info@scientificpub.com, http://www.scientificpub.com. Ed. A K Danda. Circ: 1,500.

301 MEX ISSN 0188-6959
HUMANIDADES (MEXICO, D.F.). Text in Spanish. 1990. bi-w. back issues avail. **Document type:** *Academic/Scholarly.*
Related titles: Online - full text ed.: ISSN 1605-4121. 1997.
Published by: Universidad Nacional Autonoma de Mexico, Instituto de Investigaciones Antropologicas, Circuito Exterior, Ciudad Universitaria, Mexico, DF 04510, Mexico. TEL 52-5-622-9531, FAX 52-5-622-9651, http:/swadesh.unam.mx/.

301 260 CHL
HUMANITAS; revista de antropologia y cultura cristiana. Text in Spanish. q. CLP 22,000 domestic; USD 120 in North America; USD 90 in South America; USD 150 elsewhere (effective 2002). back issues avail. **Document type:** *Academic/Scholarly.*
Related titles: Online - full text ed.
Published by: Pontificia Universidad Catolica de Chile, Centro de Extension, Ave Libertador Bernardo O'Higgins 340, Edif. Communicacion, 6o. Piso, Santiago, Chile. TEL 56-2-6866519, FAX 56-2-6353755, humanitas@puc.cl, http://www.puc.cl/humanitas

HYPNOS. see *PHILOSOPHY*

I C S S R JOURNAL OF ABSTRACTS AND REVIEWS: SOCIOLOGY & SOCIAL ANTHROPOLOGY. see *ANTHROPOLOGY—Abstracting, Bibliographies, Statistics*

301 USA ISSN 1059-8316
GN397
I D A WORKING PAPERS. Text in English, French, Spanish. 1976. irreg. bibl.; charts; illus.; stat. back issues avail. **Document type:** *Academic/Scholarly.* **Description:** Presents recent work on specific areas of Third World development, focusing on applications of anthropology to rural change and environment.
Indexed: SFA, WildRev.
Published by: Institute for Development Anthropology, 1936 State Route 12., Binghamton, NY 13901-5515. TEL 607-772-6244, FAX 607-773-8993, devanth@binghamton.edu, http://www.developmentanthropology.org/index.htm.

I P C REPRINTS. see *SOCIOLOGY*

301 ZAF ISSN 0073-893X
I S M A OCCASIONAL PAPERS. Text in English. 1964. irreg., latest 1978. ZAR 3 per issue (effective 2000). **Document type:** *Monographic series.*
Published by: Institute for the Study of Man in Africa, University of the Witwatersrand Medical School, Rm. 2B17, York Rd, Parktown, Johannesburg 2193, South Africa. TEL 27-11-647-2203. Ed. Noam J Pines. Circ: 800.

301 ZAF ISSN 0073-8921
I S M A PAPERS. Text in English. 1961. irreg., latest vol.41, 1987. ZAR 2 per issue (effective 2000). **Document type:** *Monographic series.* **Description:** Promotes the scientific and social study of man and man's ancestors in Africa from an academic perspective.
Published by: Institute for the Study of Man in Africa, University of the Witwatersrand Medical School, Rm. 2B17, York Rd, Parktown, Johannesburg 2193, South Africa. TEL 27-11-647-2203. Ed. Noam J Pines. Circ: 800.

301 AUT
I U A E S COMMISSION ON URGENT ANTHROPOLOGICAL RESEARCH. NEWSLETTER. Text in English. 1976. irreg., latest vol.6, 1984. index.
Published by: (International Committee on Urgent Anthropological Research), Verlag Stiglmayr, Wienerstrasse 141, Foehrenau, 2822, Austria. Ed. Dr. Anna Hohenwart Gerlachstein. Circ: 800.

306.8 DNK ISSN 0108-9927
I W G I A DOCUMENTO. (International Work Group for Indigenous Affairs) Variant title: Documento International Work Group for Indigenous Affairs. Text in Spanish. 1983. irreg. price varies. back issues avail. **Document type:** *Monographic series.*
Related titles: ♦ English ed.: I W G I A Documents. ISSN 0105-4503.
Published by: International Work Group for Indigenous Affairs, Classensgade 11 E, Copenhagen O, 2100, Denmark. TEL 45-35-270500, FAX 45-35-270507, iwgia@igwia.org, http://www.iwgia.org.

305.8 DNK ISSN 0105-4503
I W G I A DOCUMENTS; documentation of oppression of ethnic groups in various countries. Text in English. 1971. irreg. price varies. cum.index. back issues avail. **Document type:** *Monographic series.* **Description:** Each issue deals with one subject or one group or tribe, providing documentation on the human rights situation of indigenous peoples throughout the world.
Related titles: ♦ Spanish ed.: I W G I A Documento. ISSN 0108-9927; ♦ Supplement to: Indigenous Affairs. ISSN 1024-3283.
Indexed: HRIR, RDA, RefugAb, WAE&RSA.
—BLDSC (4589.110500). **CCC.**
Published by: International Work Group for Indigenous Affairs, Classensgade 11 E, Copenhagen O, 2100, Denmark. TEL 45-35-270500, FAX 45-35-270507, iwgia@igwia.org, http://www.iwgia.org.

306 MEX
ICHAN TECOLOTL. Text in Spanish. 2000. m.
Related titles: Online - full text ed.
Published by: Centro de Investigaciones y Estudios Superiores en Antropologia Social, Hidalgo y Matamoros, Col Tlalpan, Mexico, D.F., 14000, Mexico. ciejuare@juarez.ciesas.edu.mx, http://www.ciesas.edu.mx/bibdf/ichan/home.html.

301 NGA
IGBO PHILOSOPHY✶. Text in English. 1971. a. NGN 0.20 per issue.
Published by: Igbo Philosophical Association, Bigard Memorial Seminary, PMB 921, Enugu, Nigeria. Ed. Rev. Fr C E Ohaeri.

ILLINOIS STEWARD. see *CONSERVATION*

301 PHL
DS688.M2
IMMACULATE CONCEPTION COLLEGE. LA SALLE JOURNAL. Text in Tagalog, English. 1974. a. PHP 125 domestic; USD 15 foreign. bk.rev. **Document type:** *Academic/Scholarly.*
Description: Publishes original articles on topics regarding humanities, social science, education, business, and local history.
Formerly (until 1994): Northwestern Mindanao Research Journal (0115-2009)
Indexed: BAS, IPP.
Published by: Immaculate Conception College, La Salle Graduate School Department, Ozamis City, Misamis Occidental 7200, Philippines. TEL 65-521-10-10, FAX 65-521-10-10. Ed. Emma Villaseran. Circ: 300.

IMMIGRANT COMMUNITIES & ETHNIC MINORITIES IN THE UNITED STATES & CANADA. see *POPULATION STUDIES*

INDEPENDENT SCHOLARS OF ASIA NEWSLETTER. see *ETHNIC INTERESTS*

301 IND ISSN 0019-4387
GN1 CODEN: JIASDA
INDIAN ANTHROPOLOGICAL SOCIETY. JOURNAL. Text in English. 1966. 3/yr. looseleaf. INR 250, USD 50. adv. bk.rev. charts; illus.; stat. index. **Document type:** *Academic/Scholarly.*
Description: Publishes articles in all branches of anthropology including medical anthropology.
Indexed: AICP, AnthLit, BAS, BiolAb, ForAb, PSA, RDA, SOPODA, SSA, SociolAb.
Published by: Indian Anthropological Society, 27 Jawaharlal Nehru Marg, Kolkata, West Bengal 700 016, India. Eds. A K Danda, Arabinda Basu. Circ: 700.

301 IND ISSN 0970-0927
INDIAN ANTHROPOLOGISTS. Text in English. 1971. s-a. INR 600, USD 100 (effective 2001). adv. bk.rev. back issues avail. **Document type:** *Journal, Academic/Scholarly.*
Indexed: AICP, AnthLit, BAS.
Published by: (Indian Anthropological Association), Scientific Publishers, 5-A New Pali Rd., Near Hotel Taj Hari Mahal, PO Box 91, Jodhpur, Rajasthan 342 003, India. TEL 91-291-2433323, FAX 91-291-2512580, info@scientificpub.com, http://www.scientificpub.com. Ed. J S Bhandari. Circ: 500.

INDIAN JOURNAL OF PHYSICAL ANTHROPOLOGY AND HUMAN GENETICS. see *BIOLOGY—Genetics*

305.8 DEU ISSN 0341-8642
E51
INDIANA; contributions to ethnology and linguistics, archaeology and physical anthropology of Indian America. Text in English, German, Spanish. 1973. irreg., latest vol.18, 2001. price varies. bk.rev. reprints avail. **Document type:** *Monographic series, Academic/Scholarly.* **Description:** Covers research in the archaeology, ethnology, physical anthropology, and linguistics of the Indian peoples of the Americas.
Indexed: AICP, AnthLit, BibLing, DIP, HAPI, IBR, IBZ.
Published by: (Ibero-Amerikanisches Institut Preussischer Kulturbesitz Berlin), Gebr. Mann Verlag, Neue Gruenstr 17, Berlin, 10179, Germany. TEL 49-30-2790760, FAX 49-30-2790655, vertrieb-kunstverlage@reimer-verlag.de, http://www.gebrmannverlag.de. R&P Elisabeth Roosens.

INDIANA STUDIES. PROFESSIONAL PAPER. see *EARTH SCIENCES*

305.8 USA
INDIANA UNIVERSITY. FOLKLORE INSTITUTE. SPECIAL PUBLICATIONS. Text in English. irreg.
Indexed: AnthLit.
Published by: Indiana University, Folklore Institute, 504 North Fess, Bloomington, IN 47408. TEL 812-335-8048, FAX 812-855-4008, http://www.indiana.edu/~folklore/jfr.html.

306.8 DNK ISSN 1024-3283
GN380
INDIGENOUS AFFAIRS. Text in English. 1968. q. DKK 375 to individuals includes The Indigenous World; EUR 50 to institutions includes The Indigenous World; USD 60 to individuals includes The Indigenous World; DKK 600 to individuals includes The Indigenous World + Documents; EUR 80 to institutions includes The Indigenous World + Documents; USD 90 to individuals includes The Indigenous World + Documents; DKK 600, EUR 80, USD 90 to institutions includes The Indigenous World; DKK 900, EUR 120, USD 140 to institutions includes The Indigenous World + Documents (effective 2005). back issues avail. **Document type:** *Journal.*
Description: Discusses efforts in supporting indigenous peoples worldwide in their struggle against oppression.
Formerly (until Jan. 1994): I W G I A Newsletter (0105-6387)
Related titles: ♦ Spanish ed.: Asuntos Indigenas. ISSN 1024-3275; ♦ Supplement(s): I W G I A Documents. ISSN 0105-4503.
Indexed: AICP, AnthLit, HRIR, IBSS, RDA, RefugAb, WAE&RSA. —BLDSC (4437.083000), IE, Infotrieve. **CCC.**
Published by: International Work Group for Indigenous Affairs, Classensgade 11 E, Copenhagen O, 2100, Denmark. TEL 45-35-27-05-00, FAX 45-35-27-05-07, http://www.iwgia.org/sw161.asp. Ed. Marianne Jensen. Adv. contact Anette Molbech.

INDIGENOUS KNOWLEDGE INDEX. see *ANTHROPOLOGY—Abstracting, Bibliographies, Statistics*

306.8 DNK ISSN 1024-0217
INDIGENOUS WORLD/MUNDO INDIGENA. Text in English. 1987. a. DKK 375, EUR 50, USD 60 to individuals includes Indigenous Affairs; DKK 750, EUR 80 to individuals includes Indigenous Affairs + Documents; USD 120 to individuals includes Indigenous Affairs +Documents; DKK 600, EUR 100, USD 90 to institutions includes Indigenous Affairs; DKK 1,050, EUR 140, USD 160 to institutions includes Indigenous Affairs + Documents (effective 2005). **Document type:** *Yearbook.*
Description: Updated information on the movements and changes in the indigenous organizational landscape worldwide.
Formerly (until 1994): I W G I A Yearbook (0902-6266)
Related titles: ♦ Spanish ed.: El Mundo Indigena. ISSN 1024-4573.
Indexed: IBSS.
—BLDSC (4437.091000).
Published by: International Work Group for Indigenous Affairs, Classensgade 11 E, Copenhagen O, 2100, Denmark. TEL 45-35-270500, FAX 45-35-270507, iwgia@igwia.org, http://www.iwgia.org/sw1780.asp. Ed. Diana Vinding. Circ: 10,000.

599.9 IDN ISSN 0216-7204
GN49
INDONESIAN JOURNAL OF BIOANTHROPOLOGY/BERKALA BIOANTHROPOLOGI INDONESIA. Text and summaries in English, Indonesian. 1980. irreg., latest vol.4, no.3, 1984. IDR 7,500, USD 20. adv. bk.rev. charts; illus.; stat. back issues avail.
—**CCC.**
Published by: (Department of Physical Anthropology), Gadjah Mada University, College of Medicine/Universitas Gadjah Mada, Fakultas Kedokteran, Sekip, Yogyakarta, Indonesia. Ed. Teuku Jacob. Circ: 1,000.

301 COL ISSN 0121-2079
F2269
INFORMES ANTROPOLOGICOS. Text in Spanish. 1985. irreg. per issue exchange basis. **Document type:** *Monographic series, Academic/Scholarly.* **Description:** Publishes preliminary or provisional reports on Colombian anthropology, including archaeology, history and prehistory, sociology, and linguistics.
Indexed: AICP, AnthLit.
Published by: Instituto Colombiano de Cultura, Instituto Colombiano de Antropologia, Calle 8 No. 8-87, Apartado Aereo 407, Bogota, CUND, Colombia. TEL 57-1-333-0548, FAX 57-1-233-0960, scolican@col1.telecom.com.co. Ed. Margarita Reyes. Circ: 1,000.

301 ESP ISSN 0211-5557
INSTITUT CATALA D'ANTROPOLOGIA. QUADERNS. Text in Spanish. 1980. irreg.
Indexed: AnthLit.
Published by: Institut Catala d'Antropologia, Urgell 259, Barcelona, ss3-08036, Spain. TEL 34-93-3212259.

305.8 FRA ISSN 0768-1380
➤ **INSTITUT D'ETHNOLOGIE (MUSEE DE L'HOMME). MEMOIRES.** Text in French. 1925. irreg., latest vol.36. price varies. bibl.; illus.; maps. back issues avail. **Document type:** *Monographic series, Academic/Scholarly.* **Description:** Publishes scholarly monographs on traditional and contemporary cultures and societies, looking into such areas as ethnology, linguistis, ethnogeography, and cultural documents.
Supersedes (in 1969): Institut d'Ethnologie (Musee de l'Homme). Travaux et Memoires (0767-8703)
Published by: (Institut d'Ethnologie), Museum National d'Histoire Naturelle, 57 Rue Cuvier, Paris, 75231 Cedex 05, France. TEL 33-1-40793777, http://www.mnhn.fr/publication/ethno/aethno.html. Ed. Michel Panoff.

301 RUS
INSTITUT ETNOGRAFII. POLEVYE ISSLEDOVANIYA. Text in Russian. 1975. irreg. price varies. illus.
Indexed: AICP, RASB.
Published by: (Rossiiskaya Akademiya Nauk, Institut Etnografii), Izdatel'stvo Nauka, Profsoyuznaya ul 90, Moscow, 117864, Russian Federation. TEL 7-095-3347151, FAX 7-095-4202220, secret@naukaran.ru, http://www.naukaran.ru. **Dist. by:** M K - Periodica, ul Gilyarovskogo 39, Moscow 129110, Russian Federation. TEL 7-095-2845008, FAX 7-095-2813798, info@periodicals.ru, http://www.mkniga.ru.

305.8 USA
INSTITUTE OF MAYA STUDIES. JOURNAL. Text in English. s-a.
Indexed: AnthLit.
Published by: Institute of Maya Studies, 3280 South Miami Ave., Miami, FL 33129. TEL 305-666-0779, http://www.mayastudies.org/.

301 IND ISSN 0541-7562
AS472.M13
INSTITUTE OF TRADITIONAL CULTURES, MADRAS. BULLETIN. Text in English. s-a. **Document type:** *Bulletin.*
Indexed: BAS.
Published by: (Institute of Traditional Cultures of South & South East Asia), University of Madras, c/o Director, Publications Division, Chennai, Tamil Nadu 600 005, India. TEL 91-44-568778, FAX 91-44-566693.

305.898 PER ISSN 1022-0364
INSTITUTO DE ESTUDIOS PERUANOS. DOCUMENTOS DE TRABAJO. SERIE ANTROPOLOGIA. Key Title: Serie Antropologia. Variant title: Documentos de Trabajo. Serie Antropologia. Text in Spanish. 1985. irreg. price varies. back issues avail. **Document type:** *Monographic series, Academic/Scholarly.* **Description:** Publishes new anthropological research into the indigenous and ethnic groups of Peru.
Related titles: ♦ Series of: Instituto de Estudios Peruanos. Documentos de Trabajo. ISSN 1022-0356.
Published by: (Instituto de Estudios Peruanos), I E P Ediciones (Subsidiary of: Instituto de Estudios Peruanos), Horacio Urteaga 694, Jesus Maria, Lima, 11, Peru. TEL 51-14-3326194, FAX 51-14-3326173, libreria@iep.org.pe, http://iep.perucultural.org.pe.

305.898 PER ISSN 1022-0380
INSTITUTO DE ESTUDIOS PERUANOS. DOCUMENTOS DE TRABAJO. SERIE ETNOHISTORIA. Key Title: Serie Etnohistoria. Variant title: Documentos de Trabajo. Serie Etnohistoria. Text in Spanish. 1985. irreg. price varies. back issues avail. **Document type:** *Monographic series, Academic/Scholarly.* **Description:** Publishes new research in the ethnohistory of Peru.
Related titles: ♦ Series of: Instituto de Estudios Peruanos. Documentos de Trabajo. ISSN 1022-0356.
Published by: (Instituto de Estudios Peruanos), I E P Ediciones (Subsidiary of: Instituto de Estudios Peruanos), Horacio Urteaga 694, Jesus Maria, Lima, 11, Peru. TEL 51-14-3326194, FAX 51-14-3326173, libreria@iep.org.pe, http://iep.perucultural.org.pe.

301 PER
INSTITUTO DE ESTUDIOS PERUANOS. MISCELANEA. Text in Spanish. 1981. irreg., latest vol.8, 1995. price varies. back issues avail. **Document type:** *Monographic series, Academic/Scholarly.*
Published by: (Instituto de Estudios Peruanos), I E P Ediciones (Subsidiary of: Instituto de Estudios Peruanos), Horacio Urteaga 694, Jesus Maria, Lima, 11, Peru. TEL 51-14-3326194, FAX 51-14-3326173, libreria@iep.org.pe, http://iep.perucultural.org.pe.

301 PER ISSN 1019-4525
INSTITUTO DE ESTUDIOS PERUANOS. PROYECTO DE ESTUDIOS ETNOLOGICOS DEL VALLE DE CHANCAY. MONOGRAFIA. Text in Spanish. 1968. irreg., latest vol.7, 1983. price varies. back issues avail. **Document type:** *Monographic series, Academic/Scholarly.*
Published by: (Instituto de Estudios Peruanos), I E P Ediciones (Subsidiary of: Instituto de Estudios Peruanos), Horacio Urteaga 694, Jesus Maria, Lima, 11, Peru. TEL 51-14-3326194, FAX 51-14-3326173, libreria@iep.org.pe, http://iep.perucultural.org.pe.

301 BRA ISSN 0104-2300
H8
➤ **INSTITUTO FRANCISCANO DE ANTROPOLOGIA. CADERNOS.** Text in English, Portuguese, Spanish. 1992. 3/yr. BRL 11; USD 10 foreign. illus.; stat. back issues avail. **Document type:** *Academic/Scholarly.* **Description:** Presents an academic revue on anthropological, cultural and religious issues.
Related titles: E-mail ed.
Indexed: SociolAb.

A

Published by: Universidade de Sao Francisco, Instituto Franciscano de Antropologia, Ave. SAO FRANCISCO DE ASSIS, 218, Braganca Paulista, SP 12900-000, Brazil. TEL 55-11-78448300, FAX 55-11-78441825, alberto@usf.com.br, http://www.usf.com. Ed. Alberto da Silva Moreira. R&P Alberto Moreira. Circ: 800.

➤ **INSTITUTO GOIANO DE PRE-HISTORIA E ANTROPOLOGIA. CADERNOS DE PESQUISA.** see *ARCHAEOLOGY*

301 HND
INSTITUTO HONDURENO DE ANTROPOLOGIA E HISTORIA. ESTUDIOS ANTROPOLOGICOS. Text in Spanish. 1978. irreg., latest vol.9. USD 6 in North America; USD 9 in Europe. **Document type:** *Monographic series.*
Published by: Instituto Hondureno de Antropologia e Historia, Departamento de Investigaciones, Apdo. 1518, Tegucigalpa DC, Honduras. TEL 504-223470, FAX 504-222552. Circ: 1,000.

301 MEX ISSN 0076-7611
INSTITUTO NACIONAL DE ANTROPOLOGIA E HISTORIA. COLECCION CIENTIFICA. Text in Spanish. 1967. irreg., latest vol.392.
Formerly: Instituto Nacional de Antropologia e Historia. Series Cientifica
Indexed: AnthLit.
Published by: Instituto Nacional de Antropologia e Historia, Frontera 53, Col. Tizapan San Angel, Mexico City, DF 01000, Mexico. TEL 52-55-509714, FAX 52-55-503503.

301 ARG
INSTITUTO NACIONAL DE ANTROPOLOGIA Y PENSAMIENTO LATINOAMERICANO. CUADERNOS. Text in Spanish. 1960. irreg. bk.rev. bibl. **Document type:** *Academic/Scholarly.*
Former titles (until 1991): Instituto Nacional de Antropologia. Cuadernos (0570-8346); (until 1962): Instituto Nacional de Investigaciones Folkloricas. Cuadernos (0328-9923)
Indexed: AICP.
Published by: Instituto Nacional de Antropologia y Pensamiento Latinoamericano, 3 de Febrero 1378, Buenos Aires, C1426BJN, Argentina. postmaster@bibapl.edu.ar, http://www.buscadordecoracion.com/inapl.htm.

INSTITUTUM CANARIUM YEARBOOK. ALMOGAREN. see *ARCHAEOLOGY*

INTERCULTURE. see *SOCIOLOGY*

INTERNATIONAL ASSOCIATION FOR CROSS-CULTURAL PSYCHOLOGY. INTERNATIONAL CONFERENCE. SELECTED PAPERS. see *PSYCHOLOGY*

306.4 RUS ISSN 1012-6570
INTERNATIONAL ASSOCIATION FOR THE STUDY OF THE CULTURES OF CENTRAL ASIA. INFORMATION BULLETIN. Text in English, Russian. 1982. irreg.
Indexed: AnthLit.
Published by: (International Association for the Study of Cultures of Central Asia, Documentation and Information Centre), Izdatel'stvo Nauka, Profsoyuznaya ul 90, Moscow, 117864, Russian Federation. secret@naukaran.ru, http://www.naukaran.ru. Ed. S. I. Potapenko.

INTERNATIONAL BIBLIOGRAPHY OF THE SOCIAL SCIENCES. ANTHROPOLOGY. see *ANTHROPOLOGY—Abstracting, Bibliographies, Statistics*

301 AUT
GN301
INTERNATIONAL COMMITTEE ON URGENT ANTHROPOLOGICAL RESEARCH. BULLETIN. Text in English, French, German. 1958. a. charts; illus.; stat. back issues avail. **Document type:** *Bulletin, Academic/Scholarly.*
Formerly: International Committee on Urgent Anthropological and Ethnological Research. Bulletin (0538-5865)
Indexed: AICP, ASD, AbAn, AnthLit, BAS, BibLing, CCA, EI, IBSS, RILM.
Published by: International Committee on Urgent Anthropological Research, Burggasse 33/2, Vienna, 1070, Austria. FAX 43-1-5269380, stephanie.wiesbauer@wiesbauer.org. Ed. Stephanie Wiesbauer-Hohenwart. Circ: 600.

INTERNATIONAL CONFERENCE ON THE STUDY OF SHAMANISM AND ALTERNATIVE MODES OF HEALING. PROCEEDINGS. see *ALTERNATIVE MEDICINE*

301 CAN ISSN 0538-6381
F2001
INTERNATIONAL CONGRESS FOR THE STUDY OF PRE-COLUMBIAN CULTURES OF THE LESSER ANTILLES. PROCEEDINGS. Text in English. 1963. irreg., latest vol.9, 1982. price varies. **Document type:** *Proceedings.*
Indexed: AnthLit.
Published by: International Congress for the Study of Pre-Columbian Cultures of the Lesser Antilles, University of Manitoba, Department of Anthropology, Winnipeg, MB, Canada. Ed. Louis Allaire.

INTERNATIONAL CONGRESS OF PRIMATOLOGY. PROCEEDINGS. see *BIOLOGY—Zoology*

INTERNATIONAL DIRECTORY OF PRIMATOLOGY. see *BIOLOGY—Zoology*

INTERNATIONAL DOCUMENTARY. see *MOTION PICTURES*

301 ITA ISSN 0393-9383
INTERNATIONAL JOURNAL OF ANTHROPOLOGY. Text in English. 1986. q. EUR 80 domestic; EUR 100 foreign (effective 2005). adv. bk.rev. illus. index. back issues avail.; reprints avail. **Document type:** *Academic/Scholarly.* **Description:** Covers anthropological topics outside the scope of human evolution such as auxology, nutrition, paleopathology, applied anthropology, and population biology. Also covers all sectors of contemporary physical anthropology.
Related titles: Online - full text ed.: ISSN 1824-3096.
Indexed: AICP, AnthLit, ExcerpMed.
—BLDSC (4542.083000), GNLM, IE, Infotrieve, ingenta.
Published by: (Universita degli Studi di Firenze, Laboratori di Antropologia, European Anthropological Association), Angelo Pontecorboli Editore, Via Carrand 22, Florence, 50133, Italy. TEL 39-055-5520903, FAX 39-055-5528456, angelo@pontecorboli.it, http://www.pontecorboli.it. Ed. Brunetto Chiarelli. Circ: 500.

INTERNATIONAL JOURNAL OF LISTENING. see *HUMANITIES: COMPREHENSIVE WORKS*

301 GBR ISSN 1047-482X
GN70 CODEN: IJOHEA
➤ **INTERNATIONAL JOURNAL OF OSTEOARCHAEOLOGY.** Text in English. 1991. bi-m. USD 995 to institutions; USD 1,095 combined subscription to institutions print & online eds. (effective 2006). adv. bk.rev. back issues avail.; reprint service avail. from PSC. **Document type:** *Journal, Academic/Scholarly.* **Description:** Deals with all aspects of the study of animal and human bones.
Related titles: Microfiche ed.; Microfilm ed.: (from PQC); Online - full content ed.: ISSN 1099-1212. USD 995 to institutions (effective 2006); Online - full text ed.: (from EBSCO Publishing, Swets Information Services, Wiley InterScience).
Indexed: ASCA, AnthLit, ArtHuCI, BrArAb, CurCont, NumL, SSCI, ZooRec.
—BLDSC (4542.440500), GNLM, IDS, IE, Infotrieve, ingenta. **CCC.**
Published by: John Wiley & Sons Ltd. (Subsidiary of: John Wiley & Sons, Inc.), The Atrium, Southern Gate, Chichester, West Sussex PO19 8SQ, United Kingdom. TEL 44-1243-779777, FAX 44-1243-775878, customer@wiley.co.uk, http://www3.interscience.wiley.com/cgi-bin/jhome/5488, http://www.wiley.co.uk. Ed. Terry O'Connor. adv.: B&W page GBP 650, color page GBP 1,550; trim 200 x 260. Circ: 500. **Subscr. in the Americas to:** John Wiley & Sons, Inc., 111 River St, Hoboken, NJ 07030-5774. TEL 201-748-6645, 800-225-5945, subinfo@wiley.com.

301 USA ISSN 0895-9897
INTERNATIONAL MUSEUM OF CULTURES. PUBLICATIONS IN ETHNOGRAPHY. Text in English; Text occasionally in Spanish, Portuguese. 1976. irreg., latest vol.39, 2002. back issues avail. **Document type:** *Monographic series, Academic/Scholarly.*
Formerly: Summer Institute of Linguistics. Museum of Anthropology Publication (0197-3746)
Related titles: Microfiche ed.
Published by: (International Museum of Cultures), S I L International, 7500 W Camp Wisdom Rd, Dallas, TX 75236. TEL 972-708-7404, FAX 972-708-7363, academic_books@sil.org, http://www.sil.org. Ed. Barbara Jean Moore.

301 NLD ISSN 0074-3496
INTERNATIONAL UNION OF ANTHROPOLOGICAL AND ETHNOLOGICAL SCIENCES NEWSLETTER. Text in Dutch. 1981. 3/yr. USD 15 to individuals; USD 50 to institutions; USD 10 to students. adv. **Document type:** *Newsletter, Trade.* **Description:** Covers anthropology, ethnology, archaeology, linguistics, and news of the Union's activities.
Published by: International Union of Anthropological and Ethnological Sciences, c/o Dr. Peter J M Nas, Leiden University, Wassenaarseweg 52, Leiden, 2300 RB, Netherlands. TEL 31-71-527-3992, FAX 31-71-527-3619, http://www.leidenuniv.nl/fsw/iuaes. R&P, Adv. contact Dr. Peter J M Nas. Circ: 300.

305.8 NLD ISSN 0257-6651
INTERNATIONAL UNION OF ANTHROPOLOGICAL AND ETHNOLOGICAL SCIENCES. NEWSLETTER. Text in English. 1968. irreg., latest vol.63, 2004. **Document type:** *Newsletter, Trade.*
Formerly (until 1976): R E. Review of Ethnology (1015-0471)
Indexed: AICP, AnthLit.
Published by: International Union of Anthropological and Ethnological Sciences, c/o Peter Nas, PO Box 9555, Leiden, 2300 RB, Netherlands. TEL 31-71-5273992, FAX 31-71-5273619, nas@fsw.leidenuniv.nl, http://www.leidenuniv.nl/fsw/iuaes/07-iuaes-news.htm, http://www.leidenuniv.nl/fsw/iuaes/index.htm. Ed. Peter Nas.

301 ITA ISSN 1025-4080
INTERNATIONAL UNION OF PREHISTORIC AND PROTOHISTORIC SCIENCES. CONGRESS. BULLETIN. Text in English. 1958. s-a. free. **Document type:** *Proceedings.*
Formerly (until 1994): International Union of Prehistoric and Protohistoric Sciences. Congress Proceedings (0074-9478)
Indexed: AbAn, BrArAb.
Published by: International Union of Prehistoric and Protohistoric Sciences, Via S Marchesi, 12, Forli', FO 47100, Italy. TEL 39-543-35725, FAX 39-543-35805. Ed. Ubaldo Marra.

INTERSECTIONS IN COMMUNICATIONS AND CULTURE; global approaches and transdisciplinary perspectives. see *SOCIOLOGY*

305.8 709 USA ISSN 0897-8573
IOWA STUDIES IN AFRICAN ART. Text in English. 1984. irreg.
Indexed: AnthLit.
Published by: University of Iowa, School of Art and Art History, E-100 Art Building, Iowa City, IA 52242. TEL 319-335-1771, FAX 319-335-1774, http://www.uiowa.edu/~art/premenu.html.

306.44089 IDN ISSN 0304-2189
GN635.I65
IRIAN: BULLETIN OF IRIAN JAYA. Text and summaries in English, Indonesian. 1972. a. IDR 20,000, USD 20. charts. back issues avail. **Document type:** *Bulletin.* **Description:** An anthropological journal focusing specifically on the indigenous cultures of Irian Jaya.
Related titles: Microfiche ed.
Indexed: AICP, BAS, BibLing, EI, IBSS, MLA, MLA-IB.
Published by: University of Cendarawasih, Irian Jaya, PO Box 1800, Jayapura, 99018, Indonesia. FAX 62-967-81302. Ed. Philip Kosho. Circ: 350.

ITALIAN HISTORY & CULTURE; Yearbook of Georgetown University at Villa Le Balze, Fiesole (Florence). see *HISTORY—History Of Europe*

301 GBR ISSN 1369-7900
J A S O OCCASIONAL PAPERS. (Journal of the Anthropological Society of Oxford) Text in English. 1982. irreg.
Indexed: PCI.
—BLDSC (4663.148000).
Published by: Anthropological Society of Oxford, 51 Banbury Rd, Oxford, OX2 6PE, United Kingdom. TEL 44-1865-274682.

301 NZL ISSN 0032-4000
GN2
➤ **J P S.** (Journal of the Polynesian Society) Text in English. 1892. q. free to members. adv. bk.rev. bibl.; charts; illus. index, cum.index: 1892-1991. **Document type:** *Journal, Academic/Scholarly.*
Related titles: Microfilm ed.: (from BHP); Microform ed.: (from PQC); Online - full text ed.
Indexed: AICP, ASCA, AmH&L, AnthLit, ArtHuCI, BibInd, CurCont, DIP, HistAb, IBR, IBSS, IBZ, INZP, MLA-IB, PCI, RASB, RI-1, RI-2, RILM, SPPI, SSCI.
—IDS, IE, Infotrieve. **CCC.**
Published by: Polynesian Society, Inc., c/o Hon. Secretary, Department of Maori Studies, University of Auckland, Private Bag 92019, Auckland, New Zealand. jps@auckland.ac.nz, http://www.arts.auckland.ac.nz/ant/JPS/journal.html, http://www.arts.auckland.ac.nz/ant/JPS/polsoc.html. Circ: 1,000.

➤ **JAHRBUCH FUER OSTDEUTSCHE VOLKSKUNDE.** see *FOLKLORE*

305.8 JPN ISSN 0021-5023
GN1
JAPANESE JOURNAL OF ETHNOLOGY/MINZOKUGAKU KENKYU. Text in Japanese; Summaries in English. 1935. q. free to members. bk.rev. charts; illus. **Document type:** *Academic/Scholarly.*
Indexed: AICP, AnthLit, CurCont, EI, JPI, RASB.
Published by: Japanese Society of Ethnology/Nihon Minzoku Gakkai, c/o Secretariat, 2-1-1-813 Mita, Minato-ku, Tokyo, 108-0073, Japan. TEL 81-3-5232-0920, FAX 81-3-5232-0922, hoya@t3.rim.or.jp, http://wwwsoc.nii.ac.jp/jse/index.html. Ed. Yasumasa Sekine. **Subscr. to:** Maruzen Co., Ltd., 3-10 Nihonbashi, 2-Chome, Chuo-ku, Tokyo 103, Japan. TEL 81-3-3275-8591, FAX 81-3-3275-0657, journal@maruzen.co.jp, http://www.maruzen.co.jp.

301 JPN
JINRUI DOTAI GAKKAI PUROGURAMU YOKOSHU/HUMAN ERGOLOGY SOCIETY. PROGRAM AND PREPRINTS OF THE CONFERENCE. Text in Japanese.
Published by: Jinrui Dotai Gakkai Kaiho/Human Ergology Society, Rodo Kagaku Kenkyujo, 8-14 Sugao 2-chome, Miyamae-ku, Kawasaki-shi, Kanagawa-ken 216-0015, Japan.

301 JPN ISSN 0289-5293
JINRUIGAKU SHUHO/ANTHROPOLOGICAL REPORTS. Text in English, Japanese. 1948. irreg.
Indexed: AnthLit.
Published by: Jinruigaku Shuho Hakkojo/Publishing Office of Anthropological Reports, Shiritsu Daigaku, Igakubu Kaibogaku Kyoshitsu, 4-54 Asahi-Machi 1-chome, Abeno-ku, Osaka-shi, 545-0051, Japan.

306.4 BOL
JISUNU. Text in Spanish. 1974. irreg. BOB 40, USD 2. adv. bibl.; tr.lit.
Published by: (Academia de la Culturas Nativas de Oriente Boliviano), Editorial los Huerfanos, Casilla 2225, Santa Cruz De La Sierra, Bolivia. Circ: 1,000.

301 DNK ISSN 0021-7484
JORDENS FOLK - ETNOGRAFISK REVY. Text in Danish. 1965. q. DKK 180 to individuals; DKK 50 per issue (effective 2001). bk.rev. illus. index. back issues avail. **Document type:** *Journal, Academic/Scholarly.* **Description:** Human culture and etnography worldwide.
Indexed: RILM.
Published by: Dansk Etnografisk Forening/Danish Ethnographic Society, Nationalmuseet, Frederiksholms Kanal 12, Copenhagen K, 1220, Denmark. TEL 45-33-47-32-22, FAX 45-33-47-32-20, arne.kirstejn.olsen@natmus.dk, http://www.jordensfolk.dk. Ed. Jakob Krause-Jensen. Circ: 4,000.

JORNADAS INTERDISCIPLINARIAS RELIGION Y CULTURA. see *ETHNIC INTERESTS*

305.8 FRA ISSN 0399-0346
DT1
JOURNAL DES AFRICANISTES. Text in English, French. 1931. s-a. adv. bk.rev.; music rev.; Website rev. bibl. back issues avail. **Document type:** *Academic/Scholarly.* **Description:** Studies the ethnography, ethnology, sociology, physical anthropology, history, linguistics, archeology and geography of Africa.
Formerly: Societe des Africanistes. Journal (0037-9166)
Indexed: AICP, ASD, AnthLit, BibInd, BibLing, CCA, DIP, IBR, IBSS, IBZ, PCI, RASB, RILM.
Published by: Societe des Africanistes, Musee de l'Homme, Place du Trocadero, Paris, 75116, France. TEL 33-1-47277255, FAX 33-1-47046340, africanistes@wanadoo.fr, http://www.multimania.com/africanistes. Eds. Dominic Casajus, M Piault. R&P, Adv. contact Francoise Leguennec-Coppens. Circ: 1,500.

301 FRA ISSN 1156-0428
JOURNAL DES ANTHROPOLOGUES. Text in English. 1990. irreg.
Published by: Association des Anthropologues, Maison des Sciences de l'Homme, Bur. 331, 54 Bd Raspail, Paris, 75006, France. TEL 1-49542181, afa@msh-paris.fr.

JOURNAL FOR SEMITICS/TYDSKRIF VIR SEMITISTIEK. see *RELIGIONS AND THEOLOGY—Judaic*

306.4 USA ISSN 0891-7124
JOURNAL FOR THE ANTHROPOLOGICAL STUDY OF HUMAN MOVEMENT. Text in English. 1980. s-a. USD 30 to individuals; USD 40 to institutions (effective 2005). back issues avail. **Document type:** *Journal, Academic/Scholarly.* **Description:** Presents current research and stimulates discussion of ideas and issues that arise from a study of human movement within the framework of anthropological inquiry.
Related titles: Online - full text ed.: (from bigchalk, ProQuest Information & Learning).
Indexed: AnthLit, RILM.
Published by: New York University, Department of Dance Education, 35 W. 4th St., Suite 777, New York, NY 10012. TEL 212-996-5424, FAX 212-995-4043, http://www.anthro.uiuc.edu/JASHM/jashm.html.

301 USA ISSN 0270-2495
JOURNAL OF AFRICAN CIVILIZATIONS. Text in English. 1979. a. USD 24.95 (effective 2003). adv. bk.rev. illus. back issues avail. **Document type:** *Academic/Scholarly.* **Description:** Covers recent archaeological and anthropological studies. Explores contributions by African people to the advancement of world civilization.
—BLDSC (4919.988000). **CCC.**
Published by: (Rutgers, the State University of New Jersey), Transaction Publishers, 390 Campus Dr, Somerset, NJ 07830. TEL 888-999-6778, FAX 732-748-9801, trans@transactionpub.com, http://www.transactionpub.com. Ed. Ivan Van Sertima. Pub. Mary Curtis. R&P Marlena Davidian TEL 732-445-2280 ext 100. Adv. contact Alicja Garbie. Circ: 1,500. **Subscr. to:** Transaction Distribution Center, 390 Campus Dr., Somerset, NJ 08873. TEL 732-445-1245, 888-999-6778, FAX 732-748-9801, orders@transactionpub.com.

JOURNAL OF AFRICAN HISTORY. see *HISTORY—History Of Africa*

301 USA ISSN 0278-4165
CC79.E85 CODEN: JAAOA7
➤ **JOURNAL OF ANTHROPOLOGICAL ARCHAEOLOGY.** Text in English. 1982. 4/yr. EUR 96 in Europe to individuals; JPY 10,100 in Japan to individuals; USD 78 to individuals except Europe and Japan; EUR 403 in Europe to institutions; JPY 42,100 in Japan to institutions; USD 304 to institutions except Europe and Japan (effective 2006). illus. back issues avail.; reprints avail. **Document type:** *Journal, Academic/Scholarly.* **Description:** Devoted to the development of theory and methodology for the systematic and rigorous understanding of the organization, operation, and evolution of human societies.
Related titles: Online - full text ed.: ISSN 1090-2686. USD 324 (effective 2002) (from EBSCO Publishing, Gale Group, IngentaConnect, O C L C Online Computer Library Center, Inc., ScienceDirect, Swets Information Services).
Indexed: AICP, ASCA, AbAn, AnthLit, ArtHuCI, BAS, BrArAb, CurCont, HumInd, IBSS, NumL, RASB, SSCI.
—BLDSC (4937.600000), IDS, IE, Infotrieve, ingenta. **CCC.**
Published by: Academic Press (Subsidiary of: Elsevier Science & Technology), 525 B St, Ste 1900, San Diego, CA 92101-4495. TEL 619-231-6616, 800-894-3434, apsubs@acad.com, http://www.elsevier.com/locate/jaa, http://www.academicpress.com. Ed. John M O'Shea.

301 USA ISSN 0091-7710
GN1 CODEN: JAPRCP
➤ **JOURNAL OF ANTHROPOLOGICAL RESEARCH.** Text in English. 1937. q. USD 30 domestic to individuals; USD 36 foreign to individuals; USD 50 domestic to institutions; USD 56 foreign to institutions (effective 2004). bk.rev. bibl.; charts; illus.; stat. index, cum.index: 1945-1964, 1965-1991, 1992-2001. back issues avail.; reprint service avail. from PQC. **Document type:** *Journal, Academic/Scholarly.* **Description:** Provides problem-oriented articles on recent research findings in ethnology, archaeology, biological anthropology, and linguistic anthropology.
Former titles (until 1972): Southwestern Journal of Anthropology (0038-4801); (until 1945): New Mexico Anthropology (0734-7030)
Related titles: Microfilm ed.: (from PQC); Online - full text ed.
Indexed: ABS&EES, AICP, ASCA, AbAn, AmH&L, AnthLit, ArtHuCI, BAS, BibLing, BiolAb, BrArAb, CCA, ChPerI, CommAb, CurCont, DIP, EI, FamI, HistAb, IBR, IBSS, IBZ, L&LBA, LRI, MLA, MLA-IB, NumL, PRA, RASB, RDA, RI-1, RI-2, RILM, SOPODA, SSA, SSCI, SSI, SociolAb, WAE&RSA.
—BLDSC (4937.700000), IDS, IE, Infotrieve, ingenta. **CCC.**
Published by: University of New Mexico, Department of Anthropology, 1 University of New Mexico, MSC01 1040, Albuquerque, NM 87131-0001. TEL 505-277-4524, jar45@unm.edu, http://www.unm.edu/~jar. Ed., R&P Lawrence G Straus TEL 505-277-4544. Circ: 1,200 (paid).

➤ **JOURNAL OF ASIAN AND AFRICAN STUDIES.** see *SOCIOLOGY*

➤ **JOURNAL OF ASIAN CIVILIZATION.** see *ARCHAEOLOGY*

306.8 AUS ISSN 1440-5202
➤ **JOURNAL OF AUSTRALIAN INDIGENOUS ISSUES.** Text in English. 1998. q. AUD 25 domestic to individuals; AUD 45 foreign to individuals; AUD 35 domestic to institutions; AUD 55 foreign to institutions (effective 2001). 32 p./no.; back issues avail. **Document type:** *Journal, Academic/Scholarly.* **Description:** Aims to provide information on areas such as education, health native title, reconciliation, land rights and sovereignty, and to contribute to the understanding of Australian indigenous issues.
Indexed: AusPAIS.
Address: PO Box 100, Kelvin Grove DC, QLD 4059, Australia. TEL 61-7-3864-3608, FAX 61-7-3864-3982, http://www.qut.edu.au/chan/oodgeroo/journal.htm. Ed., Pub., R&P Andrew Gunstone.

➤ **JOURNAL OF BHUTAN STUDIES.** see *HUMANITIES: COMPREHENSIVE WORKS*

301 USA ISSN 0191-3557
E78.C15 CODEN: JGBAEG
➤ **JOURNAL OF CALIFORNIA AND GREAT BASIN ANTHROPOLOGY.** Text in English. 1974. s-a. USD 30 per vol. (effective 2004). adv. bk.rev. bibl.; charts; illus. **Document type:** *Academic/Scholarly.* **Description:** Original manuscripts on the ethnography, ethnohistory, languages, arts, archaeology, and prehistory of the native peoples of Alta and Baja California and the Great Basin.
Formerly (until 1979): Journal of California Anthropology (0361-7181)
Indexed: AICP, AbAn, AmH&L, AnthLit, BibLing, HistAb, L&LBA, SOPODA, SSA, SociolAb.
—BLDSC (4954.740500).
Published by: California State University, Bakersfield, Department of Sociology - Anthropology, 9001 Stockdale Hwy, Bakersfield, CA 93311. TEL 661-664-2368, http://www.csub.edu/Anthropology/. Eds. Jill Gordon, Mark Q Sutton. R&P Mark Q Sutton. Adv. contact Jill Gardner. Circ: 500.

➤ **JOURNAL OF CONTEMPORARY ETHNOGRAPHY**; a journal of ethnographic research. see *SOCIOLOGY*

➤ **JOURNAL OF CROSS-CULTURAL GERONTOLOGY.** see *GERONTOLOGY AND GERIATRICS*

➤ **JOURNAL OF CULTURAL GEOGRAPHY.** see *GEOGRAPHY*

306.4 901 FRA ISSN 1296-2074
➤ **JOURNAL OF CULTURAL HERITAGE.** Text in English. 2000. 4/yr. EUR 135.55 in France to individuals; EUR 138 in Europe to individuals; JPY 18,400 in Japan to individuals; USD 156 to individuals except Europe and Japan; EUR 262.56 in France to institutions; EUR 283 in Europe to institutions; JPY 34,700 in Japan to institutions; USD 357 to institutions except Europe and Japan (effective 2006). illus. back issues avail. **Document type:** *Journal, Academic/Scholarly.* **Description:** Takes a multi-disciplinary approach to examining the safeguarding and exploitation of important human cultural heritage.
Related titles: Online - full text ed.: (from EBSCO Publishing, Gale Group, IngentaConnect, ScienceDirect, Swets Information Services).
Indexed: A&ATA, ArtHuCI, CurCont.
—BLDSC (4965.844200), IE, ingenta. **CCC.**
Published by: (Consiglio Nazionale delle Ricerche, Progetto Finalizzato Beni Culturali/National Research Council, Special Project on Cultural Heritage ITA), Elsevier France, Editions Scientifiques et Medicales (Subsidiary of: Elsevier Science & Technology), 23 Rue Linois, Paris, 75724, France. TEL 33-1-71724600, FAX 33-1-71724650, academic@elsevier.fr, http://www.elsevier.com/locate/culher, http://www.elsevier.fr. Ed. Angelo Guarino.

306 305.896 301 370 USA ISSN 1542-7358
CB245
▼ ➤ **JOURNAL OF CULTURE AND ITS TRANSMISSION IN THE AFRICAN WORLD.** Text in English. 2003 (Jan.). s-a. USD 25; USD 15 per issue (effective 2003). **Document type:** *Journal, Academic/Scholarly.*
Published by: (Medgar Evers College, The DIRECT Center), Fort Valley State University, The African World Studies Institute, 1005 State University Dr., Fort Valley, GA 31030. TEL 478-822-1034, FAX 478-825-6196, abohs@fvsu.edu, http://www.fvsu.edu/AWSI/index.htm. R&P, Adv. contact Sessi S. F. Aboh TEL 478-825-6056. Circ: 200 (paid); 200 (controlled).

304.2 USA ISSN 1528-6509
GF51
JOURNAL OF ECOLOGICAL ANTHROPOLOGY. Text in English. 1997. s-a. USD 30 to individuals; USD 45 to institutions (effective 2002). **Document type:** *Journal, Academic/Scholarly.* **Description:** Provides an interdisciplinary forum for innovative academic exploration of the interface between humans and their sociocultural and biophysical environments.
Formerly (until 2000): Georgia Journal of Ecological Anthropology (1097-2498)
Indexed: AnthLit.
Published by: University of Georgia, Department of Anthropology, 250 Baldwin Hall, Athens, GA 30602-1619. GJEA@arches.uga.edu, http://www.guallart.dac.uga.edu/JEA. Eds. David G. Casagrande, Rebecca K. Zarger.

599.9 577 USA ISSN 0278-0771
GN476.7 CODEN: JOUEE9
➤ **JOURNAL OF ETHNOBIOLOGY.** Abstracts in English, French, Spanish. 1981. s-a. USD 35 in the Americas to individuals except Mexico; USD 25 in Mexico to individuals; USD 45 elsewhere to individuals; USD 80 in North America to institutions; USD 90 elsewhere to institutions; USD 25 in North America to students; USD 35 elsewhere to students (effective 2004); subscr. includes membership. adv. bk.rev. back issues avail. **Document type:** *Journal, Academic/Scholarly.* **Description:** Features articles about the uses of plants and animals by native peoples worldwide, both prehistorically and historically. Covers ethnozoology, paleoethnobotany, paleozoology, and ethnobotany.
Indexed: AICP, AbAn, AnthLit, BAS, BIOSIS Prev, BiolAb, BrArAb, IBSS, NumL, SFA, WildRev, ZooRec.
—BLDSC (4979.602350), CISTI, IE, ingenta. **CCC.**
Published by: Society of Ethnobiology, c/o Margaret Searry, Dept. of Anthropology, University of North Carolina, Chapel Hill, NC 27599-3115. feedback@ethnobiology.org, http://ethnobiology.org/journal/. Ed. Dr. Naomi F Miller. Circ: 400.

301 GBR ISSN 1464-9888
HD72
JOURNAL OF HUMAN DEVELOPMENT; alternative economics in action. Text in English. 2000. 3/yr. GBP 201, USD 334 combined subscription to institutions print & online eds. (effective 2006). reprint service avail. from PSC. **Document type:** *Journal, Academic/Scholarly.* **Description:** Analyses the concept, measurement and/or practice of human development at local, national and global levels.
Related titles: Online - full text ed.: ISSN 1469-9516. GBP 191, USD 317 to institutions (effective 2006) (from EBSCO Publishing, Gale Group, IngentaConnect, O C L C Online Computer Library Center, Inc., Swets Information Services).
Indexed: DIP, IBR, IBSS, IBZ, PSA, SociolAb.
—BLDSC (5003.413650), IE, Infotrieve, ingenta. **CCC.**

A

Published by: (United Nations Development Programme, Human Development Report Office USA), Routledge (Subsidiary of: Taylor & Francis Group), 4 Park Sq, Milton Park, Abingdon, Oxon OX14 4RN, United Kingdom. TEL 44-1235-828600, FAX 44-1235-829000, info@routledge.co.uk, http://www.tandf.co.uk/journals/titles/14649888.asp, http://www.routledge.co.uk. Eds. Khadija Haq, Richard Jully, Sakiko Fukuda-Parr. Subscr. to: Taylor & Francis Ltd, Journals Customer Service, Rankine Rd, Basingstoke, Hants RG24 8PR, United Kingdom. TEL 44-1256-813000, FAX 44-1256-330245.

JOURNAL OF HUMAN ECOLOGY; international, interdisciplinary journal of man-environment relationship. see ENVIRONMENTAL STUDIES

572 970.1   CAN   ISSN 0838-4711
➤ JOURNAL OF INDIGENOUS STUDIES. Text in English. 1989. s-a. CND 20 to individuals; CND 30 to institutions. bk.rev. back issues avail. Document type: Journal, Academic/Scholarly. Description: Provides an open forum for the dissemination of scholarly research, discussion and ideas.
Related titles: Online - full text ed.
Indexed: AnthLit, BibLing, CPerl, RILM.
Published by: Gabriel Dumont Institute of Native Studies and Applied Research, 121 Broadway Ave E, Regina, SK S4N 0Z6, Canada. TEL 306-522-5691, FAX 306-565-0809, ldorion@sk.sympatico, http://www.schoolnet.ca/aboriginal/gabriel/index-e.html. Ed. Karla Williamson. Circ: 200.

301   JPN   ISSN 0388-0508
CB251
➤ JOURNAL OF INTERCULTURAL STUDIES. Text in English, Spanish. 1974. a. JPY 2,500, USD 25 (effective 2003). adv. bk.rev. charts; illus. Document type: Journal, Academic/Scholarly. Description: Explores the cultural anthropological aspects of any culture.
Indexed: BAS, BibLing, MEA&I, RILM.
Published by: Kansai Gaidai University, Intercultural Research Institute, 16-1 Nakamiyahigashi-cho, Hirakata City, Osaka Pref. 573-1001, Japan. TEL 81-72-8052801, FAX 81-72-8052874. Ed. Michihiro Ito. Circ: 800. Subscr. to: Maruzen Co., Ltd., Export Dept., PO Box 5050, Tokyo International 100-3191, Japan. FAX 81-3-3278-9256, journal@maruzen.co.jp, http://www.maruzen.co.jp.

301   USA   ISSN 1085-7052
GN564.L29
➤ JOURNAL OF LATIN AMERICAN ANTHROPOLOGY. Text in English. 1995. s-a. USD 55 to institutions (effective 2005 & 2006). adv. Document type: Journal, Academic/Scholarly. Description: Contains feature articles, research reports, and news briefs concerning Latin American current affairs, activities, academic programs and more.
Related titles: Online - full text ed.: ISSN 1548-7180 (from H.W. Wilson, O C L C Online Computer Library Center, Inc.).
Indexed: AbAn, AnthLit, HAPI, IBR, IBZ, SSA, SSI, SociolAb.
—CCC.
Published by: University of California Press, Journals Division, 2000 Center St, Ste 303, Berkeley, CA 94704-1223. TEL 510-643-7154, FAX 510-642-9917, journals@ucpress.edu, http://www.ucpress.edu/journals/3a/jlat/index.htm. Ed. Jean Rahier. adv.: page USD 295; 4.5 x 7.5.

➤ JOURNAL OF LATIN AMERICAN LORE. see FOLKLORE

306.44089   USA   ISSN 1055-1360
P35   CODEN: JLIAEI
➤ JOURNAL OF LINGUISTIC ANTHROPOLOGY. Text in English. 1991. s-a. USD 48 (effective 2006). adv. bk.rev. illus. reprints avail. Document type: Journal, Academic/Scholarly. Description: Publishes articles on the anthropological study of language, including analysis of discourse, language in society, language and cognition, and language acquisition of socialization.
Indexed: AICP, AbAn, AnthLit, BibLing, CommAb, CurCont, IBR, IBZ, L&LBA, MLA-IB, SOPODA, SSA, SociolAb.
—BLDSC (5010.474900), IE, ingenta. CCC.
Published by: (American Anthropological Association, Society for Linguistic Anthropology), University of California Press, Journals Division, 2000 Center St, Ste 303, Berkeley, CA 94704-1223. TEL 510-643-7154, FAX 510-642-9917, journals@ucpress.edu, http://www.ucpress.edu/journals/3a/jlin. Eds. Elizabeth Keating, Mary Bucholtz. adv.: page USD 295; 4.5 x 7.5. Circ: 900.

➤ JOURNAL OF MATERIAL CULTURE. see SOCIOLOGY

➤ JOURNAL OF MEDITERRANEAN STUDIES; history, culture and society in the Mediterranean world. see HUMANITIES: COMPREHENSIVE WORKS

➤ JOURNAL OF MEMETICS - EVOLUTIONARY MODELS OF INFORMATION TRANSMISSION. see PHILOSOPHY

➤ JOURNAL OF MUNDANE BEHAVIOR. see SOCIOLOGY

305.8   GBR   ISSN 0954-7169
GN301
➤ JOURNAL OF MUSEUM ETHNOGRAPHY. Text in English. 1976. a., latest vol.14, 2002. GBP 20 to individual members; GBP 25 to institutional members (effective Apr. 2002). bk.rev. illus. back issues avail. Document type: Journal, Academic/Scholarly. Description: World ethnography within museum context.
Formerly (until 1989): Museum Ethnographers Group. Newsletter (0260-0366)
Indexed: AICP.
—BLDSC (5021.128000).
Published by: Museum Ethnographers Group, c/o Margret Carey, 2 Frank Dixon Way, London, SE21 7BB, United Kingdom. Ed. Donna Sharp. R&P Margret Carey TEL 44-20-8693-3930. Circ: 200 (paid); 80 (controlled).

306.43 306.44089   NGA   ISSN 1119-2712
GN387
JOURNAL OF NOMADIC STUDIES. Text in English. irreg. USD 19.43 (effective 2002).
Indexed: AnthLit.
Published by: National Commission for Nomadic Education, No. 9 Kashim Ibrahim Road, Kaduna, 2343, Nigeria. TEL 234-62-239175, FAX 234-62-240613, esoffice@ncne.skannet.com. Ed. Gidado Tahir.

301   USA   ISSN 1538-2834
E78.N77   CODEN: NARNAV
➤ JOURNAL OF NORTHWEST ANTHROPOLOGY. Text in English. 1967. s-a. USD 35 to individuals; USD 55 to institutions; USD 25 to students (effective 2004). abstr.; bibl.; charts; illus. back issues avail. Document type: Journal, Academic/Scholarly.
Formerly (until 2002): Northwest Anthropological Research Notes (0029-3296)
Indexed: A&ATA, AICP, AbAn, AmH&L, AnthLit, BibInd, BiolAb, HistAb, RILM.
—CCC.
Published by: South Fork Press, 625 N Garfield, Moscow, ID 83843-3624. TEL 208-882-0413, FAX 208-882-3393, rsprague@moscow.com. Ed., R&P Roderick Sprague. Circ: 300.

➤ JOURNAL OF PHYSIOLOGICAL ANTHROPOLOGY AND APPLIED HUMAN SCIENCE. see BIOLOGY—Physiology

➤ JOURNAL OF RESEARCH IN AYURVEDA AND SIDDHA. see ALTERNATIVE MEDICINE

301   USA   ISSN 0890-1112
➤ JOURNAL OF RITUAL STUDIES. Text in English. 1987. s-a. USD 25 to individuals; USD 45 to institutions; effective Jan. 1993. adv. bk.rev. cum.index: 1987-1992. back issues avail. Document type: Academic/Scholarly. Description: Presents articles, reviews, correspondence, discussion, announcements and notes from scholars treating ritual in any of its various forms.
Related titles: Online - full text ed.: (from EBSCO Publishing, O C L C Online Computer Library Center, Inc., Ovid Technologies, Inc.).
Indexed: AICP, BibInd, IBSS, MLA-IB, NTA, PSA, R&TA, RI-1, RI-2, RILM, SSA, SociolAb.
—BLDSC (5052.102000), IE, Infotrieve, ingenta.
Published by: University of Pittsburgh, Department of Anthropology, 3302 WWPH, Pittsburgh, PA 15260. jors@pitt.edu, http://www.pitt.edu/~strather/journal.htm. Eds. Andrew Strathern, Pamela J Stewart. Circ: 250.

➤ JOURNAL OF SOCIAL ARCHAEOLOGY. see ARCHAEOLOGY

➤ JOURNAL OF THE SOUTHWEST. see HISTORY—History Of North And South America

➤ JOURNAL OF WORLD PREHISTORY. see ARCHAEOLOGY

➤ JUDAICA IBEROAMERICANA. see ETHNIC INTERESTS

➤ JURNAL ANTROPOLOGI DAN SOSIOLOGI. see SOCIOLOGY

305.8 305.896972   TTO   ISSN 1562-5028
➤ KACIKE; journal of Caribbean Amerindian history and anthropology. Text in English, Spanish, French, Portuguese. 1999. s-a. free (effective 2005). Document type: Academic/Scholarly. Description: Publishes papers on any branch of Anthropology, Archaeology and History that pertains to Caribbean Amerindian societies, communities, groups, organizations, individuals, either past or present.
Media: Online - full content.
Published by: Caribbean Amerindian Centrelink http://www.kacike.org/. Ed. Maximilian C Forte.

➤ KALULU; bulletin of Malawian oral literature and cultural studies. see LITERATURE

301   USA   ISSN 1069-0360
KANSAS ANTHROPOLOGICAL ASSOCIATION NEWSLETTER. Text in English. 1955-1979; N.S. 1989. q. looseleaf. USD 22 membership (effective 2004). 8 p./no. 1 cols./p.; back issues avail. Document type: Newsletter. Description: Contains short articles of interest to Kansas and region; includes association news and announcements.
Published by: Kansas Anthropological Association, PO Box 750962, Topeka, KS 66675-0962. http://www.kshs.org/resource/kaa.htm. Ed. Evelyn Reed. R&P Virginia A Wulfkuhle TEL 785-272-8681 ext 268. Circ: 350.

301   USA   ISSN 1069-0379
E78.K16
THE KANSAS ANTHROPOLOGIST. Text in English. 1989. a., latest vol.23, 2002. USD 22 membership (effective 2004); subscr. incld. in membership package. bk.rev. charts; illus.; abstr.; bibl.; maps. 150 p./no. back issues avail. Document type: Journal, Academic/Scholarly. Description: Contains articles about Kansas and Central Plains archaeology, anthropology, and ethnography.
Former titles (until 1989): Kansas Anthropological Association. Journal; (until 1979): Kansas Anthropological Association. Newsletter (0022-8451)
Indexed: AnthLit.
Published by: (Kansas State Historical Society), Kansas Anthropological Association, PO Box 750962, Topeka, KS 66675-0962. vwulfkuhle@kshs.org, http://www.kshs.org/publicat/anthropologist/, http://www.kshs.org/resource/kaa.htm. Ed., R&P Virginia A Wulfkuhle TEL 785-272-8681 ext 268. Circ: 350.

301   FIN   ISSN 0355-1830
DK450.8
KANSATIETEELLINEN ARKISTO. Text in English, Finnish, German, Swedish. 1934. irreg., latest vol.43, 1997. price varies. illus. Document type: Monographic series, Academic/Scholarly.
Indexed: MLA, MLA-IB, RASB.
Published by: Suomen Muinaismuistoyhdistys/Finnish Antiquarian Society, Nervanderinkatu 13, PO Box 213, Helsinki, 00101, Finland. TEL 358-9-40501, FAX 358-9-40509400. Ed. Leena Sammallahti.

301   ESP   ISSN 0214-7939
KOBIE, REVISTA DE BELLAS ARTES Y CIENCIAS: SERIE ANTROPOLOGIA CULTURAL. Key Title: Kobie. Antropologia Cultural. Text in Basque, French, Spanish; Summaries in Basque, English, French, German, Spanish. 1969. a. back issues avail.
Formerly (until 1984): Kobie. Etnografia (0214-7920); Which supersedes in part (in 1984): Kobie (0211-1942)
Indexed: AICP.
—CINDOC.
Published by: Diputacion Foral de Bizkaia, Departamento de Cultura, PO Box 97, Bilbao, 48070, Spain. TEL 34-4-4157217, FAX 34-4-4162981.

301   ESP   ISSN 0214-7971
DP302.B465
KOBIE, REVISTA DE BELLAS ARTES Y CIENCIAS: SERIE PALEOANTROPOLOGIA. Key Title: Kobie. Paleoantropologia. Text in English, French, Spanish; Summaries in Basque, English, French, German. 1969. a. back issues avail.
Supersedes in part (in 1985): Kobie. Paleoantropologia y Ciencias Naturales (0214-7963); Which supersedes in part (in 1984): Kobie (0211-1942)
Indexed: BHA.
—CINDOC.
Published by: Diputacion Foral de Bizkaia, Departamento de Cultura, PO Box 97, Bilbao, 48070, Spain. TEL 34-4-4157217, FAX 34-4-4162981.

➤ KODAI ORIENTO HAKUBUTSUKAN KIYO/BULLETIN OF THE ANCIENT ORIENT MUSEUM. see ARCHAEOLOGY

305.8   DEU   ISSN 0075-6490
KOELNER ETHNOLOGISCHE MITTEILUNGEN. Text in German. 1960. irreg., latest vol.13, 2002. price varies. back issues avail. Document type: Monographic series, Academic/Scholarly.
Published by: Dietrich Reimer Verlag GmbH, Neue Gruenstr 17, Berlin, 10179, Germany. TEL 49-30-27907760, FAX 49-30-27907655, vertrieb-kunstverlage@reimer-verlag.de, http://www.dietrichreimerverlag.de. R&P Beate Behrens.

305.8   JPN   ISSN 0385-180X
GN301
KOKURITSU MINZOKUGAKU HAKUBUTSUKAN KENKYU HOKOKU/NATIONAL MUSEUM OF ETHNOLOGY. BULLETIN. Text in Japanese; Summaries in English. 1974. q.
Indexed: AnthLit.
Published by: Kokuritsu Minzokugaku Hakubutsukan, 10-1 SenriExpo Park, Suita, Osaka, 565-8511, Japan. TEL 81-6-8762151, http://www.minpaku.ac.jp.

KONINKLIJK INSTITUUT VOOR TAAL-, LAND- EN VOLKENKUNDE. BIBLIOGRAPHICAL SERIES. see ANTHROPOLOGY—Abstracting, Bibliographies, Statistics

301 NLD
KONINKLIJK INSTITUUT VOOR TAAL-, LAND- EN VOLKENKUNDE. PROCEEDINGS. Text in English. 1994. irreg., latest vol.2, 1995. back issues avail. **Document type:** *Proceedings.*
Indexed: AnthLit.
Published by: (Koninklijk Instituut voor Taal-, Land- en Volkenkunde), K I T L V Press, PO Box 9515, Leiden, 2300 RA, Netherlands. TEL 31-71-5272372, FAX 31-71-5272638, kitlvpress@rullet.leidenuniv.nl, kitlvpress@kitlv.nl.

301 NLD ISSN 0074-0470
KONINKLIJK INSTITUUT VOOR TAAL-, LAND- EN VOLKENKUNDE. TRANSLATION SERIES. Text in English. 1956. irreg., latest vol.25, 1995. price varies. back issues avail. **Document type:** *Monographic series, Academic/Scholarly.*
Published by: (Koninklijk Instituut voor Taal-, Land- en Volkenkunde), K I T L V Press, PO Box 9515, Leiden, 2300 RA, Netherlands. TEL 31-71-5272372, FAX 31-71-5272638, kitlvpress@rullet.leidenuniv.nl, kitlvpress@kitlv.nl.

306.44089 NLD
KONINKLIJK INSTITUUT VOOR TAAL-, LAND- EN VOLKENKUNDE. VERHANDELINGEN. Text in English. 1938. irreg., latest vol.170, 1995. price varies. **Document type:** *Monographic series, Academic/Scholarly.* **Description:** Scholarly monographs on historical, cultural, social and linguistic aspects of Indonesian cultures in pre-colonial, colonial and modern times.
Indexed: AnthLit, BibLing, RDA.
Published by: (Koninklijk Instituut voor Taal-, Land- en Volkenkunde), K I T L V Press, PO Box 9515, Leiden, 2300 RA, Netherlands. TEL 31-71-5272372, FAX 31-71-5272638, kitlvpress@rullet.leidenuniv.nl, kitlvpress@kitlv.nl.

301 930.1 USA ISSN 0023-4869
GN2
➤ **KROEBER ANTHROPOLOGICAL SOCIETY. PAPERS.** Text in English. 1949. 3/yr. USD 60 domestic; USD 70 foreign (effective 2004). bk.rev. charts; illus. cum.index: 1949-1994. 200 p./no. 1 cols./p.; back issues avail.; reprints avail. **Document type:** *Journal, Academic/Scholarly.* **Description:** The audience for this publication is mainly anthropologists and social scientists.
Indexed: A&ATA, AICP, AmH&L, AnthLit, BAS, HistAb, IBSS, PCI, SPPI.
—BLDSC (5118.450000), IE, ingenta.
Published by: Kroeber Anthropological Society, Dept of Anthropology, Univ of California, Berkeley, CA 94720-3710. kas@qal.berkeley.edu, http://sscl.berkeley.edu/~kas/, http://www.qal.berkeley.edu/~kas/. Ed. Angela Jenks. Circ: 500.

305.8 SWE ISSN 1102-7908
➤ **KULTURELLA PERSPEKTIV**; svensk etnologisk tidskrift. Text in Swedish; Summaries in English. 1992. q. SEK 245 to individuals; SEK 295 to institutions (effective 2003). bk.rev. **Document type:** *Academic/Scholarly.*
Published by: (Carlsson Bokfoerlag), Foereningen Kulturella Perspektiv, Institutionen foer Kultur och Medier, Umeaa University, Umeaa, 90187, Sweden. TEL 46-90-7869667, FAX 46-90-7867845, anncristin.winroth@kultmed.umu.se. Ed., R&P Roger Jacobsson TEL 46-90-7869657. Adv. contact Anncristin Winroth.

301 JPN ISSN 0286-4568
KYOTO DAIGAKU. REICHORUI KENKYUJO NENPO/KYOTO UNIVERSITY. PRIMATE RESEARCH INSTITUTE. ANNUAL REPORTS. Text in Japanese. 1971. a. free. back issues avail. **Document type:** *Academic/Scholarly.*
Indexed: JPI.
Published by: Kyoto University, Primate Research Institute/Kyoto Daigaku Reichorui Kenkyujo, Kanrin, Inuyama-shi, Aichi-ken 484-8506, Japan. TEL 81-568-63-0567, FAX 81-568-63-0085, shomu@pri.kyoto-u.ac.jp, Shomu@smtp.pri.kyoto-u.ac.jp, http://www.pri.kyoto-u.ac.jp/. Circ: 1,000.

L A C I T O DOCUMENTS AFRIQUE. see *LINGUISTICS*

L A C I T O DOCUMENTS ASIE - AUSTRONESIE. see *LINGUISTICS*

L A C I T O DOCUMENTS EURASIE. see *LINGUISTICS*

301 FRA ISSN 0768-3685
LABORATOIRE D'ANTHROPOLOGIE, PREHISTOIRE, PROTOHISTOIRE ET QUATERNAIRE ARMORICAINS. TRAVAUX. Text in French. 1956. irreg. price varies. **Document type:** *Monographic series, Academic/Scholarly.*
Published by: Universite de Rennes I, Faculte des Sciences, 2 Rue du Thabor - CS 46510, Rennes, 35065, France. TEL 33-2-23233636, FAX 33-2-23233600, http://www.univ-rennes1.fr.

599.9 USA
➤ **LAMBDA ALPHA JOURNAL.** Text in English. 1969. s-a. USD 10; USD 20 foreign (effective 1998). bk.rev. **Document type:** *Academic/Scholarly.* **Description:** Publishes articles and papers in all areas of anthropology.
Formerly: Lambda Alpha Journal of Man (0047-3928)
Indexed: AnthLit.
Published by: Lambda Alpha Anthropology Honors Society, Wichita State University, Department of Anthropology, 130 McKinley Hall, Wichita, KS 67260-0052. TEL 316-689-3195, FAX 316-978-3351, pmojan@twsu.edu. Ed. Peer H Moore Jansen. Circ: 175.

➤ **LANGUAGE AND CULTURE.** see *LINGUISTICS*

➤ **LANGUES ET CIVILISATIONS A TRADITION ORALE.** see *LINGUISTICS*

➤ **LANGUES ET CULTURES AFRICAINES.** see *LINGUISTICS*

➤ **LANGUES ET CULTURES DU PACIFIQUE.** see *LINGUISTICS*

➤ **LANGUES ET SOCIETES D'AMERIQUE TRADITIONNELLE.** see *LINGUISTICS*

➤ **LES LANGUES NEO-LATINES.** see *LINGUISTICS*

➤ **LAW & ANTHROPOLOGY**; international yearbook for legal anthropology. see *LAW*

➤ **LAW/TEXT/CULTURE.** see *LAW*

➤ **LIMINA**; a journal of historical and cultural studies. see *HISTORY—History Of Australasia And Other Areas*

➤ **THE LISTENING PROFESSIONAL.** see *HUMANITIES: COMPREHENSIVE WORKS*

➤ **LITERATUR UND ANTHROPOLOGIE.** see *LITERATURE*

➤ **LITHIC TECHNOLOGY.** see *ARCHAEOLOGY*

306 GBR ISSN 1367-5133
LIVERPOOL STUDIES IN EUROPEAN REGIONAL CULTURES. Text in English. 1994. irreg., latest vol.7, 1999. GBP 15 per issue. **Document type:** *Monographic series.*
—BLDSC (5281.194600), IE, ingenta.
Published by: Liverpool University Press, 4 Cambridge St, Liverpool, L69 7ZU, United Kingdom. TEL 44-151-794-2237, FAX 44-151-794-2235, http://www.liverpool-unipress.co.uk/. Eds. Mairead Nic Craith, Ullrich Kockel. Pub. Robin Bloxsidge. Adv. contact Sandra Robinson.

306 GBR ISSN 0077-1074
➤ **LONDON SCHOOL OF ECONOMICS MONOGRAPHS ON SOCIAL ANTHROPOLOGY.** Text in English. 1940. irreg. price varies. reprint service avail. from PQC. **Document type:** *Monographic series, Academic/Scholarly.* **Description:** Covers various aspects of social anthropology, including field studies and studies of anthropological theory.
—BLDSC (5294.100000), ingenta.
Published by: Berg Publishers, Angel Court, 1st Fl, 81 St Clements St, Oxford, Berks OX4 1AW, United Kingdom. TEL 44-1865-245104, FAX 44-1865-791165, athlonepress@btinternet.com, enquiry@bergpublishers.com, http://www.bergpublishers.com/. **Subscr. to:** Transaction Distribution Center, 390 Campus Dr., Somerset, NJ 08873. TEL 732-445-1245, 888-999-6778, FAX 732-748-9801, orders@transactionpub.com, http://www.transactionpub.com.

306.44089 USA
THE LONG RANGER. Text in English. 1995. s-a. USD 25 per vol. (effective 2004). **Document type:** *Newsletter, Academic/Scholarly.* **Description:** Presents international, interdisciplinary information sharing, discussion and debate among biogeneticists, paleoanthropologists, archaeologists, and historical linguists on questions relating to the emerging sunthesis on language origins and ancestral human spoken languages.
Formerly (until 2002): Mother Tongue (1087-0326)
Indexed: AnthLit.
Published by: Association for the Study of Language in Prehistory, c/o Michael Witzel, 1 Bow St, Cambridge, MA 02138. TEL 617-495-3295, FAX 617-496-8571, witzel@fas.harvard.edu, http://www.people.fas.harvard.edu/~witzel/aslip.html.

LORE AND LANGUAGE. see *LINGUISTICS*

301 557 USA
LOUISIANA GEOLOGICAL SURVEY. ANTHROPOLOGICAL STUDIES SERIES. Text in English. 1935. irreg., latest vol.5, 1994. **Document type:** *Academic/Scholarly.*
Published by: Louisiana Geological Survey, 208 Howe-Russell, Louisiana State University, Baton Rouge, LA 70803. TEL 225-578-5320, FAX 225-578-3662, pat@lgs.bri.lsu.edu, http://www.lgs.lsu.edu.

LUD. see *SOCIOLOGY*

LURATHA. see *ANTHROPOLOGY—Abstracting, Bibliographies, Statistics*

MAGAZIN FUER AMERIKANISTIK; Zeitschrift fuer amerikanische Geschichte. see *HISTORY—History Of North And South America*

301 COL ISSN 0120-3045
GN1
MAGUARE. Text in Spanish. 1987. irreg. per issue exchange basis. **Document type:** *Academic/Scholarly.*
Indexed: AnthLit.
Published by: Universidad Nacional de Colombia, Facultad de Ciencias Humanas, Biblioteca Central, Division de Canje, Apartado Aereo 14490, Santafe de Bogota, Colombia. Ed. Gerardo Ardila.

301 IND ISSN 0258-0446
GN855.I4
MAN & ENVIRONMENT. Text in English. 1976. s-a. USD 40 (effective 2005). bk.rev. **Document type:** *Academic/Scholarly.* **Description:** Publishes original research papers, review articles, short research notes and book reviews.
Indexed: AnthLit, BiolAb.
—Linda Hall.
Published by: Indian Society for Prehistoric and Quaternary Studies, c/o Department of Archaeology, Deccan College, Pune, Maharashtra 411 006, India. TEL 91-212-662982, FAX 91-212-660104, asinha@care2.com, http://www.geocities.com/arunsinha2000/eclectic/man_env.html#ISPQS. Ed. V N Misra. Circ: 500.

301 IND
➤ **MAN AND LIFE.** Text in English. 1975. s-a. INR 215, USD 50 (effective 1999). adv. bk.rev. **Document type:** *Academic/Scholarly.*
Indexed: AICP, AnthLit, BAS.
Published by: Institute of Social Research and Applied Anthropology, 727 Lake Town, Kolkata, West Bengal 700 089, India. TEL 91-33-534-5231, FAX 91-33-5214418. Ed. P K Bhowmick. Circ: 600.

305.8 IND ISSN 0025-1569
GN1 CODEN: MANIAJ
➤ **MAN IN INDIA.** Text in English. 1921. q. USD 32 (effective 2000). bk.rev. bibl.; charts; illus. index. back issues avail.; reprints avail. **Document type:** *Academic/Scholarly.* **Description:** Focuses on ethnology, culture and customs.
Indexed: AICP, ASCA, AbAn, AgeL, AmH&L, AnthLit, ArtHuCI, BAS, BiolAb, CurCont, DIP, FPA, Faml, ForAb, HistAb, IBR, IBSS, IBZ, PAA&I, RASB, RDA, RI-1, RI-2, RILM, RRTA, SSCI, WAE&RSA.
—BLDSC (5358.020000), IE, Infotrieve, ingenta.
Address: 18 Church Rd., Ranchi, Bihar 834 001, India. Ed. Surajit Sinha. Circ: 800. **Dist. by:** H P C Publishers Distributors Pvt. Ltd., 4805 Bharat Ram Rd, 24 Darya Ganj, New Delhi 110 002, India. TEL 91-11-325-4401, FAX 91-11-686-3511.

306 BRA ISSN 0104-9313
GN301 CODEN: MANAFY
➤ **MANA**; estudos de antropologia social. Text in Portuguese; Summaries in English, Portuguese. 1995. s-a. USD 23 domestic to individuals; USD 30 foreign to individuals. adv. abstr.; bibl. back issues avail. **Document type:** *Academic/Scholarly.* **Description:** Presents research projects on social and cultural issues. Seeks to acquaint readers with current issues and up-to-date questions carried out by anthropological research.
Related titles: Online - full text ed.: free (effective 2005) (from SciELO).
Indexed: AICP, AbAn, AnthLit, L&LBA, PSA, SOPODA, SSA, SociolAb.
Published by: (Programa de Pos-Graduacao em Antropologia Social), Universidade Federal do Rio de Janeiro, Departamento de Antropologia, Prq Quinta da Boa Vista, S/N, Sao Cristovao, Mangueira, Rio De Janeiro, RJ 20940-040, Brazil. TEL 55-21-568-9642, FAX 55-21-254-6695, ccapa@easynet.com.br, http://www.alternex.com.br/~ppgas/make.html. Ed. Federico Neiburg. R&P Silvia Nogueira. Circ: 600 (paid); 400 (controlled). **Subscr. to:** Contra Capa Libraria Limitada, Rua Barata Ribeiro, 370, Loja 208, Copacabana, Rio De Janeiro, RJ 22040-000, Brazil. TEL 55-21-236-1999, FAX 55-21-256-0526.

306.4 USA ISSN 0025-2344
GN1 CODEN: MKQUA4
➤ **MANKIND QUARTERLY**; an international quarterly journal dealing with both physical and cultural anthropology including related subjects such as psychology, demography, genetics, linguistics and mythology. Text in English. 1960. q. USD 49.50 (effective 2004). adv. bk.rev. charts; illus. index. reprints avail. **Document type:** *Journal, Academic/Scholarly.* **Description:** Articles on anthropology, anthropological linguistics, mythology and religion, psychology, demography and genetics.
Related titles: Online - full text ed.: (from bigchalk, EBSCO Publishing, Northern Light Technology, Inc., ProQuest Information & Learning).
Indexed: AICP, ASCA, ASSIA, AbAn, AmH&L, AnthLit, ArtHuCI, BAS, BibLing, BiolAb, CJA, CurCont, DIP, EI, Faml, HistAb, IBR, IBSS, IBZ, IPSA, L&LBA, MEA&I, MLA, MLA-IB, PAIS, PsycholAb, RASB, RI-1, RI-2, SOPODA, SSA, SSCI, SociolAb, e-psyche.
—BLDSC (5360.900000), IDS, IE, Infotrieve, ingenta.
Published by: Scott - Townsend Publishers, PO Box 34070, N W, Washington, DC 20043. TEL 202-371-2700, FAX 202-371-1523, socecon@aol.com. Ed. Richard Lynn. R&P, Adv. contact James Johnson. Circ: 1,025.

A

301 USA ISSN 0076-4116
MANKIND QUARTERLY MONOGRAPH SERIES. Text in English. 1961. irreg., latest vol.6. price varies. **Document type:** *Monographic series, Academic/Scholarly.* **Description:** Monographs presenting in-depth studies in the areas of anthropology, psychology and evolution.
Indexed: BIOSIS Prev, BiolAb, RASB.
Published by: Council for Social and Economic Studies, PO Box 34070, N W, Washington, DC 20043. TEL 202-371-2700, FAX 202-371-1523, socecon@aol.com.

301 MYS ISSN 0126-8678
GN635.M4
➤ **MANUSIA DAN MASYARAKAT/MAN AND SOCIETY.** Text in English, Malay. 1972. a. USD 15. adv. bk.rev. **Document type:** *Journal, Academic/Scholarly.*
Indexed: BAS, IBSS, RASB.
Published by: (University of Malaya, Anthropology and Sociology Department), University of Malaya/Perpustakaan Universiti Malaya, Lembah Pantai, Kuala Lumpur, 59100, Malaysia. http://www.um.edu.my. Circ: 1,000.

➤ **MANYU YANJIU/JOURNAL OF MANCHU STUDIES.** see *ASIAN STUDIES*

➤ **MARGARET SHAW LECTURES.** see *ARCHAEOLOGY*

➤ **MARGARETOLOGIST.** see *JEWELRY, CLOCKS AND WATCHES*

➤ **MARKA INSTITUTO DE HISTORIA Y ANTROPOLOGIA ANDINA. MEMORIA.** see *HISTORY—History Of North And South America*

301 570 USA ISSN 1546-7805
GF49
MARYLAND ESSAYS IN HUMAN BIODIVERSITY. Abbreviated title: M E H B. Text in English. 2002 (May). s-a. USD 15 (effective 2003).
Related titles: Online - full text ed.: ISSN 1546-7813.
Published by: University of Maryland, Dept. of Anthropology, 1111 Woods Hall, College Park, MD 20742. TEL 301-405-1423, mehb@anth.umd.edu, http://www.bsos.umd.edu/anth/mehb.

MATERIALIZING CULTURE. see *SOCIOLOGY*

306.4 HRV ISSN 1330-2140
DR301
MATICA. Text in Croatian, English. 1951. m. HRK 100 domestic; USD 40 foreign (effective 2001). adv. bk.rev. **Document type:** *Magazine, Consumer.* **Description:** Provides information about the preservation of Croatian culture for emigrants all over the world.
Former titles (until 1993): Nova Matica (0353-8052); Matica (0025-5920)
Related titles: E-mail ed.; Fax ed.
Indexed: RILM.
Published by: Hrvatska Matica Iseljenika/Croatian Heritage Foundation, Trg Stjepana Radica 3, Zagreb, 10000, Croatia. TEL 385-1-611-5116, FAX 385-1-611-1522, TELEX MIH YU 22499, matica@matis.hr, http://www.matis.hr/matica. Ed. Nenad Goll. Pub. Ante Beljo. Circ: 4,000.

305.8 ESP ISSN 1130-6157
F1435
MAYAB. Text in Spanish. 1985. a.
Indexed: AnthLit, HAPI, PCI.
—CINDOC.
Published by: Spanish Society of Mayan Studies, Complutensian University of Madrid, Faculty of Geography and History, Department of History of America, Madrid, 28040, Spain. TEL 34-91-3945785, FAX 34-91-3945808, adresci@eucmax.sim.ucm.es.

MBYA GUARANI. see *ETHNIC INTERESTS*

301 DNK ISSN 0106-1062
E99.E7
MEDDELELSER OM GROENLAND. MAN & SOCIETY. Variant title: Greenland Man and Society. Text in Danish. 1878. irreg., latest vol.28, 2003. price varies. charts; illus. **Document type:** *Academic/Scholarly.*
Supersedes in part (in 1979): Meddelelser om Groenland (0025-6676)
Indexed: BiolAb, ZooRec.
—BLDSC (5487.300000), CISTI, Linda Hall. **CCC.**
Published by: Dansk Polarcenter/Danish Polar Center, Strandgade 100 H, Copenhagen K, 1401, Denmark. TEL 45-32-880100, FAX 45-32-880101, dpc@dpc.dk, http://www.dpc.dk/polarpubs/. Ed. Hans Christian Gulloev.

305.8 NLD ISSN 0169-9156
MEDEDELINGEN VAN HET RIJKSMUSEUM VOOR VOLKENKUNDE (LEIDEN). Text in Dutch. 1947. irreg. **Document type:** *Monographic series.*
Indexed: AnthLit.
Published by: Rijksmuseum voor Volkenkunde/National Museum of Ethnology, Steenstraat 1, P.O. Box 212, Leiden, 2300, Netherlands. TEL 31-71-168800, FAX 31-71-128437.

306.461 USA ISSN 0145-9740
GN296 CODEN: MDANES
➤ **MEDICAL ANTHROPOLOGY;** cross-cultural studies in health and illness. Text in English. 1977. q. GBP 461, USD 608 combined subscription to institutions print & online eds. (effective 2006). cum.index. reprint service avail. from PQC,ISI,PSC. **Document type:** *Journal, Academic/Scholarly.* **Description:** Publishes papers on the relationship between human behavior, social life, and health within an anthropological context.
Related titles: Microform ed.; Online - full text ed.: ISSN 1545-5882. GBP 438, USD 578 to institutions (effective 2006) (from EBSCO Publishing, Gale Group, IngentaConnect, O C L C Online Computer Library Center, Inc., Swets Information Services).
Indexed: AICP, AbAn, AnthLit, BMAb, BibInd, ChPerI, DIP, IBSS, IBZ, IPsyAb, IndMed, MEDLINE, PsycInfo, PsycholAb, SPPI, e-psyche.
—BLDSC (5526.220000), GNLM, IE, Infotrieve, ingenta. **CCC.**
Published by: Taylor & Francis Inc. (Subsidiary of: Taylor & Francis Group), 325 Chestnut St, Ste 800, Philadelphia, PA 19016. TEL 215-625-8900, 800-354-1420, FAX 215-625-8914, info@taylorandfrancis.com, http://www.tandf.co.uk/journals/titles/01459740.asp, http://www.taylorandfrancis.com. Ed. Stacy Leigh Pigg. **Subscr. in Europe to:** Taylor & Francis Ltd, Journals Customer Service, Rankine Rd, Basingstoke, Hants RG24 8PR, United Kingdom. TEL 44-1256-813000, FAX 44-1256-330245, enquiry@tandf.co.uk.

306.461 USA ISSN 0745-5194
GN296 CODEN: MAQUD5
➤ **MEDICAL ANTHROPOLOGY QUARTERLY;** international journal for the cultural and social analysis of health. Text in English. 1970. q. USD 93 (effective 2005 & 2006). adv. bk.rev. illus. reprint service avail. from PQC,ISI. **Document type:** *Journal, Academic/Scholarly.* **Description:** Review articles and brief research reports on health, disease and illness from a biological, cultural, linguistic, and historical perspective.
Former titles: Medical Anthropology Newsletter (0543-2499); Medical Anthropology
Related titles: Online - full text ed.: (from bigchalk, H.W. Wilson, JSTOR (Web-based Journal Archive), O C L C Online Computer Library Center, Inc., ProQuest Information & Learning).
Indexed: AICP, ASCA, AbAn, AgeL, AnthLit, ArtHuCI, BRI, ChPerI, CurCont, EI, FamI, IBR, IBSS, IBZ, INI, IndMed, MEDLINE, SOPODA, SPPI, SSA, SSCI, SSI, SociolAb.
—BLDSC (5526.231000), GNLM, IE, Infotrieve, ingenta. **CCC.**
Published by: (American Anthropological Association, Society for Medical Anthropology), University of California Press, Journals Division, 2000 Center St, Ste 303, Berkeley, CA 94704-1223. TEL 510-643-7154, FAX 510-642-9917, journals@ucpress.edu, http://www.ucpress.edu/journals/3a/maq. Ed. Pamela Erickson. adv.: page USD 295; 4.5 x 7.5. Circ: 2,000.

930.1 ESP ISSN 0214-2600
MELOUSSA. Text in Spanish, Catalan. 1988. a. back issues avail.
—CINDOC.
Published by: Institut Menorqui d'Estudis, C. Nou, 38 3a. Porta, Mao, 07701, Spain. TEL 34-971-351500, FAX 34-971-351642, infoime@cime.es, http://www.webime.org/.

305.8 ARG ISSN 0327-5752
MEMORIA AMERICANA✶ ; cuadernos de etnohistoria. Text in Spanish. 1991. s-a. **Document type:** *Academic/Scholarly.*
Indexed: AICP.
Published by: Universidad de Buenos Aires, Instituto de Ciencias Antropologicas, 25 de Mayo 221, Piso 3, Buenos Aires, 1002, Argentina. TEL 54-114-4322292, 54-114-3347512, ica@filo.uba.ar, http://www.uba.ar/. Ed. Ana Maria Lorandi.

MENTAL HEALTH, RELIGION & CULTURE. see *PSYCHOLOGY*

MESTIZO SPACES/ESPACES MESTISSES. see *SOCIOLOGY*

301 MEX
MEXICO. DEPARTAMENTO DE INVESTIGACION DE LAS TRADICIONES POPULARES. BOLETIN. Text in Spanish. 1975. irreg.
Published by: Departamento de Investigacion de las Tradiciones Populares, Direccion General de Arte Popular, Apdo. Postal 1856, Mexico City, DF, Mexico.

301 DEU ISSN 0720-5988
F1219
MEXICON; aktuelle Informationen und Studien zu Mesoamerika. Text in English, German, Spanish. 1979. bi-m. EUR 25 domestic; EUR 28 in Europe; USD 35 elsewhere (effective 2005). bibl.; charts; illus. cum.index every 5 yrs. back issues avail. **Document type:** *Journal, Academic/Scholarly.* **Description:** Contains up-to-date information on trends and developments in the fields of Mesoamerican archaeology, ethnohistory and linguistics.
Indexed: AICP, AnthLit, IBR, RILM.
—**CCC.**
Published by: Verlag Anton Saurwein, Am Hennigbach 17, Markt Schwaben, 85570, Germany. FAX 49-8121-924930, editor@mexicon.de, publisher@mexicon.de, http://www.mexicon.de. Ed. Gordon Whittaker. Circ: 800.

305.8 MEX ISSN 0187-702X
F1246
MEYIBO. Text in Spanish. 1977. s-a.
Indexed: AnthLit.
Published by: Universidad Autonoma de Baja California, Instituto de Investigaciones Historicas de la UABC/Independent University of Baja California, Institute of Historical Investigations, University Unit, Bldg. 23, Table of Otay, P.O. Box 506, Tijuana, 22500, Mexico. TEL 6-682-1696, FAX 6-682-1033.

301 401 USA
MICHIGAN DISCUSSIONS IN ANTHROPOLOGY. Text in English. **Description:** Focuses on the practical difficulties that linguistic anthropologists face in resolving tensions between micro- and macro-analytic methodologies.
Indexed: AnthLit.
Published by: University of Michigan, Department of Anthropology, 1020 LSA, 500 South State Street, Ann Arbor, MI 481091382. TEL 734-764-7274, FAX 734-763-6077.

301 USA
➤ **MICHIGAN STATE UNIVERSITY. MUSEUM PUBLICATIONS. ANTHROPOLOGICAL SERIES.** Text in English. 1971. irreg. price varies. charts; illus. **Document type:** *Monographic series, Academic/Scholarly.*
Published by: Michigan State University, Museum, MSU Library, East Lansing, MI 48824. TEL 517-355-2370. Circ: 1,500.

301 GUM ISSN 0026-279X
QH198.M48 CODEN: MCNSBU
➤ **MICRONESICA;** a journal of the University of Guam. Text and summaries in English. 1964. s-a. USD 30 domestic to individuals; USD 45 foreign to individuals; USD 50 domestic to institutions; USD 65 foreign to institutions (effective 2005). bk.rev. charts; illus.; maps. index. Supplement avail.; back issues avail. **Document type:** *Journal, Academic/Scholarly.* **Description:** Original research on anthropology, biology and related fields of the tropical Pacific.
Indexed: AICP, ASFA, AbAn, Agr, BIOSIS Prev, BiolAb, ESPM, MLA-IB, SFA, SPPI, WildRev, ZooRec.
—BLDSC (5759.340000), IE, ingenta.
Published by: (University of Guam USA), University of Guam Press, UOG Sta, Mangilao, 96923, Guam. TEL 671-735-2787, 671-735-2171, FAX 671-734-1299, 671-734-2296, 671-734-4582, http://www.uog.edu/up/micronesica/. Ed. Dr. C S Lobban. R&P Dr. C.S. Lobban. Circ: 350.

➤ **MIGRACIJSKE I ETNICKE TEME/MIGRATION AND ETHNIC THEMES.** see *SOCIOLOGY*

➤ **MINSU/FOLKLORE.** see *FOLKLORE*

➤ **MINZU HUABAO/NATIONALITY PICTORIAL.** see *ETHNIC INTERESTS*

➤ **MINZU YANJIU (BEIJING, 1979)/STUDY IN NATIONALITIES.** see *ASIAN STUDIES*

➤ **MITEKUFAT HA-EVEN.** see *ARCHAEOLOGY*

301 URY ISSN 0076-9770
MOANA: ESTUDIOS DE ANTROPOLOGIA OCEANICA. Text in Spanish. 1966. 3/yr. price varies.
Indexed: AnthLit, SPPI.
Published by: Olaf Blixen, Ed. & Pub., P.O. Box 495, Montevideo, Uruguay.

306.0951 895.1 USA ISSN 1520-9857
PL2303
MODERN CHINESE LITERATURE AND CULTURE. Text in English. 1984. s-a. USD 30 in North America to individuals; USD 40 elsewhere to individuals; USD 60 in North America to institutions; USD 70 elsewhere to institutions; USD 20 in North America to students; USD 30 elsewhere to students (effective 2004). adv. **Document type:** *Journal, Academic/Scholarly.* **Description:** Publishes literature of all genres relating to the culture of modern and contemporary China.
Formerly (until 1998): Modern Chinese Literature (8755-8963)
Indexed: MLA-IB.
Published by: Ohio State University, Foreign Language Publications & Services, 311 Ohio Legal Center, 33 W. 11th Ave., Columbus, OH 43201-2013. TEL 614-292-3838, 800-678-6999, FAX 614-688-3355, mclc@osu.edu, flpubs@osu.edu, http://deall.ohio-state.edu/denton.2/mclc.htm, http://nealrc.osu.edu/FLPUBS/. Ed. Kirk A. Denton. adv.: B&W page USD 200.

301 FRA ISSN 0758-4431
GN585.F8
➤ **MONDE ALPIN ET RHODANIEN;** revue regionale d'ethnologie. Text in French. 1973. q. adv. bk.rev. bibl.; illus. **Document type:** *Academic/Scholarly.* **Description:** Publishes in-depth studies and articles on ethnology, history and linguistics of southeast France, as well as Switzerland and Italy.
Indexed: AICP, BHA, RILM.

Published by: Centre Alpin et Rhodanien d'Ethnologie, Musee Dauphinois, 30 rue Maurice Gignoux, Grenoble, Cedex 1 38031, France. TEL 33-4-76851913, FAX 33-4-76876022, abry@icp.grenet.fr. Ed. Christian Abry. R&P Jeanine Collovati. Adv. contact Jeannine Collovati. Circ: 1,500. **Co-sponsor:** Conseil General de l'Isere.

➤ **MONOGRAPHS AND THEORETICAL STUDIES IN SOCIOLOGY AND ANTHROPOLOGY IN HONOUR OF NELS ANDERSON.** see SOCIOLOGY

301   USA
MONOGRAPHS IN DEVELOPMENT ANTHROPOLOGY. Text in English. irreg. bibl.; charts; illus. back issues avail. **Document type:** Monographic series. **Description:** Covers anthropology and development in West Africa, East Africa, North Africa and the Middle East.
Published by: Institute for Development Anthropology, 1936 State Route 12., Binghamton, NY 13901-5515. TEL 607-772-6244, FAX 607-773-8993, devanth@binghamton.edu, http://www.developmentanthropology.org/index.htm. **Subscr. to:** Westview Press, 5500 Central Ave, Boulder, CO 80301. TEL 303-444-3541.

301   USA
MONOGRAPHS IN ECONOMIC ANTHROPOLOGY. Text in English. 1983. irreg., latest 1983. **Document type:** Monographic series.
—BLDSC (5915.419800).
Published by: (Society for Economic Anthropology), University Press of America, 4720 Boston Way, Ste A, Lanham, MD 20706. TEL 301-359-3366. Ed. Sutti Ortiz.

MONTALBAN. see HUMANITIES: COMPREHENSIVE WORKS

301   ALB   ISSN 0253-1607
MONUMENTET✷ /MONUMENTS. Text in Albanian; Summaries in French. 1971. s-a. USD 10.25.
Indexed: BHA.
Published by: Instituti i Monumenteve te Kultures/Institut des Monuments de Culture, Rr Seremedin Seid Toptani 7, Tirana, Albania. Ed. Valter Shtylla.

MORALTHEOLOGIE - ANTHROPOLOGIE - ETHIK. see PHILOSOPHY

305.8   DEU   ISSN 1435-0556
MUENSTERANER SCHRIFTEN ZUR VOLKSKUNDE - EUROPAEISCHEN ETHNOLOGIE. Text in German. 1998. irreg., latest vol.7, 1999. EUR 19.50 per vol. (effective 2003). **Document type:** Monographic series, Academic/Scholarly.
Published by: Waxmann Verlag GmbH, Steinfurter Str 555, Muenster, 48159, Germany. TEL 49-251-26504-0, FAX 49-251-2650426, info@waxmann.com, http://www.waxmann.com. Ed. Ruth-E. Mohrmann.

306.8   DNK   ISSN 1024-4573
EL MUNDO INDIGENA. Text in Spanish. 1990. a. DKK 375, EUR 50, USD 60 to individuals Includes Asuntos Indigenas; DKK 600, EUR 80, USD 90 to institutions Includes Asuntos Indigenas (effective 2005).
Formerly (until 1994): Anuario (1017-7809)
Related titles: ◆ English ed.: Indigenous World. ISSN 1024-0217.
Published by: International Work Group for Indigenous Affairs, Classensgade 11 E, Copenhagen O, 2100, Denmark. TEL 45-35-270500, FAX 45-35-270507, iwgia@igwia.org, http://www.iwgia.org.

972.81   MEX
MUNDO MAYA/MAYA WORLD. Text in English, Spanish. 1992. q. MXP 180, USD 24; MXP 45, USD 6 newsstand/cover (effective 2000). adv. illus.; maps. back issues avail.
Document type: Consumer. **Description:** Presents articles on Mayan civilization, archeology, ecology, culture and some news about the current situation in Campeche, Chiapas, Quintana Roo, Tabasco and Yucatan.
Related titles: Online - full text ed.
Published by: Organization Tips, S.A. de C.V., Av. Tulum por Uxmal 29 Piso 2 SM 5, Cancun, QUINTANA ROO 77500, Mexico. TEL 52-98-844044, FAX 52-98-841868, editor@mayadiscovery.com, http://www.mayadiscovery.com, http://www.mayatips.com.mx. Ed. Abel Minni Pugliese. Pub., R&P Pablo Simon. Adv. contact Patricia Lopez. B&W page USD 3,660, color page USD 5,800; trim 280 x 215. **Dist. by:** LUCIO BLANCO 435, San Juan Tlihuaca, Mexico City, DF 02400, Mexico.

301   ESP   ISSN 1132-2217
QH7   CODEN: MNBEA4
MUNIBE ANTROPOLOGIA - ARKEOLOGIA. Text mainly in Spanish; Text occasionally in English, French. 1949. a. free to members. bk.rev. index. cum.index: 1949-1972, 1973-1977, 1978-1982, 1983-1987, 1988-1992, 1993-1997. Supplement avail.
Formerly (until 1986): Munibe. Antropologia y Arqueologia (0214-767X); Supersedes in part (in 1984): Munibe (0027-3414)
Indexed: AICP, AnthLit, BHA, BiolAb, ChemAb, HistAb, IECT, PCI, ZooRec.
—BLDSC (5983.915005), CINDOC.

Published by: Sociedad de Ciencias Aranzadi/Zientzi Elkartea, Calle del Alto de Zorroaga 11, Donostia, San Sebastian 20014, Spain. TEL 34-943-466142, FAX 34-943-455811, idazkatitza@aranzadi-zientziak.org, http://www.aranzadi-zientziak.org. Circ: 2,500.

301   MCO   ISSN 0544-7631
GN700   CODEN: MAPBA8
MUSEE D'ANTHROPOLOGIE PREHISTORIQUE DE MONACO. BULLETIN. Text in French. 1954. biennial.
Indexed: AnthLit, ZooRec.
Published by: Musee d'Anthropologie Prehistorique, 62, Boulevard du Jardin Exotique, Monaco, 98002, Monaco. TEL 377-93-152980, FAX 377-93-152981.

MUSEE ROYAL DE L'AFRIQUE CENTRALE. ANNALES - SCIENCES HUMAINES. SERIE IN 8/KONINKLIJK MUSEUM VOOR MIDDEN-AFRIKA. ANNALEN - MENSELIJKE WETENSCHAPPEN. SERIE IN 8. see HUMANITIES: COMPREHENSIVE WORKS

301   BEL
MUSEE ROYAL DE L'AFRIQUE CENTRALE. ARCHIVES D'ANTHROPOLOGIE/KONINKLIJK MUSEUM VOOR MIDDEN-AFRIKA. ARCHIEF VOOR ANTROPOLOGIE. Short title: Archives d'Anthropologie. Text in French. 1960. irreg., latest vol.31, 1991. price varies. back issues avail. **Document type:** Monographic series. **Description:** Discussions of anthropological, ethnographic, historical and linguistic subjects pertaining to Central Africa.
Supersedes: Archives d'Ethnographie (0563-1742)
Published by: Musee Royal de l'Afrique Centrale/Koninklijk Museum voor Midden-Afrika, Steenweg op Leuven 13, Tervuren, 3080, Belgium. TEL 32-2-7695299, FAX 32-2-767-0242.

MUSELETTER. see HISTORY

MUSEO CHILENO DE ARTE PRECOLOMBINO. BOLETIN. see ART

301   ARG   ISSN 0376-2149
MUSEO DE LA PLATA. REVISTA. SECCION ANTROPOLOGIA. Text in Spanish. 1936. irreg.
Supersedes in part (in 1936): Museo de La Plata. Revista (0375-1147)
Indexed: ESPM, RefZh.
—CISTI.
Published by: Universidad Nacional de La Plata, Facultad de Ciencias Naturales y Museo, Avenidas 60 y 122, La Plata, Buenos Aires, Argentina. TEL 54-221-4258252, facultad@museo.fcnym.unlp.edu.ar.

301   DOM   ISSN 0252-8614
MUSEO DEL HOMBRE DOMINICANO. BOLETIN. Text in Spanish. 1972. q. USD 25 (effective 2001). bk.rev. **Document type:** Bulletin, Academic/Scholarly.
Indexed: AICP, AnthLit.
Published by: Museo del Hombre Dominicano, Plaza de la Cultura, Calle Pedro Henriquez Urena, Santo Domingo, Dominican Republic. Circ: 1,000.

301   DOM
MUSEO DEL HOMBRE DOMINICANO. PAPELES OCASIONALES. Text in Spanish. 1973. irreg., latest vol.7, 1981. price varies.
Published by: Museo del Hombre Dominicano, Plaza de la Cultura, Calle Pedro Henriquez Urena, Santo Domingo, Dominican Republic.

MUSEO DEL HOMBRE DOMINICANO. SERIE CATALOGOS Y MEMORIAS. see MUSEUMS AND ART GALLERIES

301   DOM
MUSEO DEL HOMBRE DOMINICANO. SERIE INVESTIGACIONES ANTROPOLOGICAS. Text in Spanish. 1975. irreg., latest vol.24, 1982. price varies. charts; illus.
Published by: Museo del Hombre Dominicano, Plaza de la Cultura, Calle Pedro Henriquez Urena, Santo Domingo, Dominican Republic.

MUSEO DEL HOMBRE DOMINICANO. SERIE MESA REDONDA CONFERENCIAS. see MUSEUMS AND ART GALLERIES

301   COL   ISSN 0120-7296
F2269
MUSEO DEL ORO. BOLETIN. Text in Spanish. 1978. 3/yr. COP 3,600, USD 15. bk.rev.
Indexed: AICP, AnthLit, PCI, RASB.
Published by: Banco de la Republica, Biblioteca Luis Angel Arango, Barrio de la Candelaria, Calle 11, 4-14, Bogota, CUND, Colombia. Circ: 2,000.

301   ESP   ISSN 1135-1853
MUSEO NACIONAL DE ANTROPOLOGIA. ANALES. Key Title: Anales del Museo Nacional de Antropoliga Nos-Otros. Text in Spanish. 1935. a.
Formerly (until 1994): Museo del Pueblo Espanol. Anales (1130-6629)
Indexed: RILM.
—CINDOC.

Published by: Ministerio de Educacion, Cultura y Deporte, Centro de Publicaciones, c/o Ciudad Universitaria, S/N, Madrid, 28040, Spain. TEL 34-91-453-9800; FAX 34-91-4539884.

301   PER
MUSEO NACIONAL DE ANTROPOLOGIA Y ARQUEOLOGIA. SERIE: ANTROPOLOGIA FISICA. Text in Spanish. 1976. irreg.
Published by: Museo Nacional de Antropologia y Arqueologia, Plaza Bolivar, Pueblo Libre, Lima, 21, Peru.

MUSEO NACIONAL DE HISTORIA NATURAL. BOLETIN. see SCIENCES: COMPREHENSIVE WORKS

MUSEO NACIONAL DE HISTORIA NATURAL. NOTICIARIO MENSUAL. see SCIENCES: COMPREHENSIVE WORKS

301   BRA   ISSN 0080-3189
GN1
MUSEU NACIONAL. BOLETIM. ANTROPOLOGIA. Text in Portuguese. 1942. irreg., latest vol.61, 2001. bibl.
Supersedes in part (1923-1941): Museu Nacional. Boletim (0100-1507)
Indexed: BiolAb.
—CISTI, Linda Hall.
Published by: Museu Nacional, Quinta da Boa Vista, Sao Cristovao, Rio de Janeiro, RJ 20940-040, Brazil. TEL 55-21-25688262, FAX 55-21-25681352, museu@mn.ufrj.br, http://www.acd.ufjr.br/~museuhp/homep.htm.

301   BRA
MUSEU PARAENSE EMILIO GOELDI. BOLETIM. NOVA SERIE ANTROPOLOGIA. Text mainly in Portuguese; Text occasionally in French, English. 1957; N.S. 1984. s-a. BRL 13 per issue domestic; USD 15 per issue foreign (effective 2000). bibl.; maps. **Description:** Publishes original papers in anthropology.
Formerly (until 1983, no.84): Museu Paraense Emilio Goeldi. Boletim. Nova Serie: Antropologia (0522-7291)
Indexed: AICP, AnthLit, BiolAb, IBSS, RASB, RefZh.
—KNAW.
Published by: Conselho Nacional de Desenvolvimento Cientifico e Tecnologico, Museu Paraense Emilio Goeldi, Comercio, Caixa Postal 399, Belem, PA 66017-970, Brazil. TEL 091-274-2195, FAX 091-274-1811, mgdoc@musu-goeldi.br. Circ: 1,000.

301.074   USA   ISSN 0892-8339
GN35
➤ **MUSEUM ANTHROPOLOGY.** Text in English. 1976. s-a. USD 49 (effective 2005 & 2006). adv. **Document type:** Journal, Academic/Scholarly. **Description:** Contains articles, commentary, review articles, exhibition and book reviews, and research notes relevant to museum anthropology and the study of material culture.
Formerly (until 1986): Council for Museum Anthropology Newsletter (0199-1450)
Related titles: Online - full text ed.: ISSN 1548-1379.
Indexed: AICP, AnthLit.
—CCC.
Published by: (Council for Museum Anthropology), University of California Press, Journals Division, 2000 Center St, Ste 303, Berkeley, CA 94704-1223. TEL 510-643-7154, FAX 510-642-9917, journals@ucpress.edu, http://www.ucpress.edu/journals/3a/mua/index.htm. Ed. Christina Kreps. adv.: page USD 350; 7 x 9.3.

301   GBR   ISSN 0264-1704
➤ **MUSEUM ETHNOGRAPHERS GROUP. OCCASIONAL PAPER.** Text in English. 1982. irreg., latest vol.4, 1995. GBP 10 domestic (effective 2002). **Document type:** Monographic series, Academic/Scholarly.
—BLDSC (6217.888200).
Published by: Museum Ethnographers Group, c/o Margret Carey, 2 Frank Dixon Way, London, SE21 7BB, United Kingdom. R&P Margret Carey TEL 44-20-8693-3930.

301   DEU   ISSN 0067-5962
MUSEUM FUER VOELKERKUNDE, BERLIN. VEROEFFENTLICHUNGEN. NEUE FOLGE. ABTEILUNG: AFRIKA. Text in German. 1960. irreg., latest vol.12, 1992. price varies. **Document type:** Monographic series.
Published by: Staatliche Museen zu Berlin - Preussischer Kulturbesitz, Generalverwaltung, Stauffenbergstr 41, Berlin, 10785, Germany. FAX 030-2662612, TELEX 183160.

301   DEU
MUSEUM FUER VOELKERKUNDE, BERLIN. VEROEFFENTLICHUNGEN. NEUE FOLGE. ABTEILUNG: AMERIKANISCHE NATURVOELKER. Text in German. 1967. irreg., latest vol.8, 1990. price varies. **Document type:** Monographic series.
Published by: Staatliche Museen zu Berlin - Preussischer Kulturbesitz, Generalverwaltung, Stauffenbergstr 41, Berlin, 10785, Germany. FAX 030-2662612.

MUSEUM FUER VOELKERKUNDE, BERLIN. VEROEFFENTLICHUNGEN. NEUE FOLGE. ABTEILUNG: MUSIKETHNOLOGIE. see MUSIC

A

301 DEU ISSN 0067-5989
MUSEUM FUER VOELKERKUNDE, BERLIN. VEROEFFENTLICHUNGEN. NEUE FOLGE. ABTEILUNG: SUEDSEE. Text in German. 1961. irreg., latest vol.12, 1993. price varies. **Document type:** *Monographic series.*
Published by: Staatliche Museen zu Berlin - Preussischer Kulturbesitz, Generalverwaltung, Stauffenbergstr 41, Berlin, 10785, Germany. FAX 030-2662612.

301 DEU ISSN 0072-9469
GN2
➤ **MUSEUM FUER VOELKERKUNDE HAMBURG. MITTEILUNGEN.** Text in German; Text occasionally in English, French. 1971; N.S.. a. price varies. adv. back issues avail. **Document type:** *Newsletter, Academic/Scholarly.*
Indexed: AICP, AnthLit.
Published by: Museum fuer Voelkerkunde Hamburg, Rothenbaumchaussee 64, Hamburg, 20148, Germany. TEL 49-40-428482502, FAX 49-40-428482242, b.schmelz@voelkerkundemuseum.com, http://www.voelkerkundemuseum.com. Eds. Bernd Schmelz, Wulf Koepke. R&P, Adv. contact Bernd Schmelz. Circ: 1,000.

781.01 ITA ISSN 1825-621X
MUSIC & ANTHROPOLOGY; journal of Mediterranean musical anthropology. Text in English. 1996. a. free (effective 2005).
Description: Provides interdisciplinary contents covering different fields of musical scholarship and the domains of social scientific scholarship, such as cultural and social anthropology, but also between music and psychology, folklore, feminist and gender studies and so forth.
Media: Online - full content.
Published by: Universita degli Studi di Bologna, Dipartimento di Musica e Spettacolo, Via Galliera 3-40121, Bologna, Italy. http://www.muspe.unibo.it/period/MA/index.htm. Ed. Tullia Magrini. **Co-sponsor:** International Council for Traditional Music.

301 HUN ISSN 0580-3594
DR25
MUVELTSEG ES HAGYOMANY✱. Text in Hungarian; Summaries in English, French, German, Russian. 1961. irreg. bibl.; illus. **Document type:** *Academic/Scholarly.*
Indexed: AICP, RASB.
Published by: (Neprajzi Intezet), Kossuth Lajos Tudomanyegyetem, PF 37, Debrecen, 4010, Hungary.

301 POL ISSN 0076-0315
GN585.P6
MUZEUM ARCHEOLOGICZNE I ETNOGRAFICZNE, LODZ. PRACE I MATERIALY. SERIA ETNOGRAFICZNA. Text in Polish; Summaries in English, French. 1957. irreg., latest vol.30, 1995. price varies. **Document type:** *Academic/Scholarly.*
Indexed: AICP, AnthLit, IBSS, RASB.
Published by: Muzeum Archeologiczne i Etnograficzne w Lodzi, Pl Wolnosci 14, Lodz, 91415, Poland. TEL 48-42-6328440, FAX 48-42-6329714. Ed. Elzbieta Krolikowska. Circ: 300.

301 POL ISSN 0068-4643
MUZEUM GORNOSLASKIE W BYTOMIU. ROCZNIK. SERIA ETNOGRAFIA. Text in Polish; Summaries in English, German, Russian. 1966. irreg. USD 15.
Published by: Muzeum Gornoslaskie w Bytomiu/The Museum of Upper Silesia, Pl Jana III Sobieskiego 2, Bytom, 41902, Poland. TEL 48-32-28182941, dobosz@us.edu.pl, mgbytom@us.edu.pl.

MYTHIC SOCIETY. QUARTERLY JOURNAL. see *FOLKLORE*

MYTHOS. see *FOLKLORE*

301 USA ISSN 1556-4789
N A P A BULLETIN. Text in English. 1985. a. price varies. adv. **Document type:** *Monographic series, Academic/Scholarly.*
Related titles: Online - full text ed.: ISSN 1556-4797.
Published by: (National Association for the Practice of Anthropology), University of California Press, Journals Division, 2000 Center St, Ste 303, Berkeley, CA 94704-1223. TEL 510-643-7154, FAX 510-642-9917, Tim_Wallace@ncsu.edu, journals@ucpress.edu, http://www.practicinganthropology.org/napabulletin/, http://www.ucpress.edu/journals. Eds. Alayne Unterberger, Tim Wallace. adv.: page USD 295; 4.5 x 7.5. Circ: 2,100.

N K A; journal of contemporary African art. see *ART*

NAMIBIA SCIENTIFIC SOCIETY. NEWSLETTER/NAMIBIA WISSENSCHAFTLICHE GESELLSCHAFT. MITTEILUNGEN. see *SCIENCES: COMPREHENSIVE WORKS*

NAMIBIANA. see *HISTORY—History Of Africa*

301 JPN
NANZAN ANTHROPOLOGICAL INSTITUTE NEWSLETTER. Text in Japanese. 1992. a. free. **Document type:** *Newsletter.*
Published by: Nanzan University, Anthropological Institute, 18 Yamazato-cho, Showa-ku, Nagoya, 466-8673, Japan. TEL 81-52-8323111 ext 580, 581, FAX 81-52-8336157, nuai@ic.nanzan-u.ac.jp, http://www.nanzan-u.ac.jp/JINRUIKEN/index.html.

NAPRSTEK MUSEUM. ANNALS. see *HUMANITIES: COMPREHENSIVE WORKS*

301 CZE ISSN 0231-844X
DS1
➤ **NAPRSTKOVO MUZEUM ASIJSKYCH, AFRICKYCH A AMERICKYCH KULTUR. ANNALS.** Key Title: Annals of the Naprstek Museum. Text in English, French, German, Spanish. 1962-1992; resumed 1997. a. available on exchange basis (effective 2003). bk.rev. illus.; maps. back issues avail. **Document type:** *Academic/Scholarly.* **Description:** Covers Oriental and non-European studies.
Indexed: AICP, ASD, AnthLit.
Published by: (Narodni Muzeum v Praze), Naprstkovo Muzeum Asijskych, Africkych a Americkych Kultur/Naprstek Museum of Asian, African and American Culture, Betlemske nam 1, Prague 1, 110 00, Czech Republic. TEL 420-2-24497522, FAX 420-2-24497501, asiat.npm@aconet.cz, http://www.aconet.cz/npm/. Ed. Alice Kraemerova. Circ: 500 (controlled).

301 UKR ISSN 0130-6936
NK976.U5
NARODNA TVORCHIST' TA ETNOGRAFIYA; naukovo-populyarnyi zhurnal. Text in Ukrainian. 1925. m. bk.rev.; dance rev.; film rev.; play rev. illus. index. **Document type:** *Journal, Academic/Scholarly.*
Indexed: AICP, BHA, IBSS, MLA, MLA-IB, RASB.
Published by: Natsional'na Akademiya Nauk Ukrainy, Instytut Mystetstvoznavstva, Fol'klorystyky ta Etnolohii im. M.T. Ryl's'koho, vul Hrushevs'koho 4, Kyiv, 252001, Ukraine. TEL 380-44-2294522, http://www.gilan.uar.net/nasu/riafe.html. Circ: 5,000.

NARRIA. see *MUSEUMS AND ART GALLERIES*

301 USA ISSN 1556-3618
NATIONAL ASSOCIATION OF STUDENT ANTHROPOLOGISTS. BULLETIN. Text in English. s-a. USD 12 (effective 1999). **Document type:** *Bulletin.*
Related titles: Online - full text ed.: ISSN 1556-3626.
Published by: (National Association of Student Anthropologists), American Anthropological Association, 2200 Wilson Blvd, Ste 600, Arlington, VA 22201. TEL 703-528-1902, FAX 703-528-3546, http://www.anthrosource.net/loi/nasa, http://www.aaanet.org. Ed. Donald D Wesolowski. R&P Terry Clifford.

NATIONAL MUSEUM OF NATURAL HISTORY QUEST. see *SCIENCES: COMPREHENSIVE WORKS*

301 JPN ISSN 0385-3039
GN1 CODEN: BNSADR
NATIONAL SCIENCE MUSEUM. BULLETIN. SERIES D: ANTHROPOLOGY/KOKURITSU KAGAKU HAKUBUTSUKAN KENKYU HOKOKU. D RUI: JINRUIGAKU. Text in English. 1957. a. per issue exchange basis.
Indexed: AICP, ASFA, AnthLit, BIOSIS Prev, BiolAb, ESPM.
Published by: Monbusho, Kokuritsu Kagaku Hakubutsukan/Ministry of Education, Science and Culture, National Science Museum, 7-20 Ueno-Koen, Taito-ku, Tokyo, 110-0007, Japan.

301 TWN
GN17.3.T28
NATIONAL TAIWAN UNIVERSITY. DEPARTMENT OF ANTHROPOLOGY. BULLETIN. Text in Chinese, English. 1953. a. USD 10 (effective 1999). bk.rev. **Document type:** *Bulletin, Academic/Scholarly.*
Formerly (until 1981): National Taiwan University. Department of Archaeology and Anthropology. Bulletin (0077-5843)
Indexed: AICP.
Published by: National Taiwan University, Department of Anthropology, Taipei, Taiwan. TEL 886-2-23630231, FAX 886-2-363-1658. Ed. Hsieh Chester Jih Chang. Circ: 1,000.

304.2 JPN ISSN 1342-0054
NATURE AND HUMAN ACTIVITIES. Text in English. 1996. a. **Description:** Covers science and human-science interaction.
Indexed: GEOBASE.
Published by: Hyogo Kenritsu Hito to Shizen no Hakubutsukan/Museum of Nature and Human Activities, 6-Chome, Yayoigaoka, Sanda, Hyogo 669-1546, Japan. TEL 81-795-592001, FAX 81-795-592007, http://www.nat-museum.sanda.hyogo.jp/.

NATURHISTORISCHES MUSEUM IN WIEN. ANNALEN. SERIE A, MINERALOGIE UND PETROGRAPHIE, GEOLOGIE UND PALAEONTOLOGIE, ANTHROPOLOGIE UND PRAEHISTORIE. see *SCIENCES: COMPREHENSIVE WORKS*

NEIZVEDANNYE MIRY/UNEXPLORED WORLDS. see *ASTRONOMY*

NELEN YUBU. see *RELIGIONS AND THEOLOGY*

301 HUN ISSN 0077-6599
NEPRAJZI ERTESITO/ETHNOGRAPHIC REVIEW. Text in Hungarian; Summaries in English, French, German, Russian. 1900. a. per issue exchange basis. reprints avail. **Document type:** *Bulletin.*
Indexed: AICP, BHA, RASB.
—BLDSC (6075.697000).
Published by: Neprajzi Muzeum/Ethnographical Museum, Kossuth Lajos ter 12, Budapest, 1055, Hungary. TEL 36-1-326340, FAX 36-2-692419. Ed. Zoltan Fejos.

305.8 HUN ISSN 0077-6602
NEPRAJZI TANULMANYOK/ETHNOGRAPHICAL STUDIES. Text in Hungarian. 1968. irreg., latest 2005. price varies. back issues avail. **Document type:** *Monographic series, Academic/Scholarly.*
Published by: (Neprajzi Kutato Csoport), Akademiai Kiado Rt. (Subsidiary of: Wolters Kluwer N.V.), Prielle Kornelia U. 19, Budapest, 1117, Hungary. TEL 36-1-4648282, FAX 36-1-4648221, journals@akkrt.hu, http://www.akkrt.hu.

301 USA ISSN 0077-7897
E78.N4
NEVADA. STATE MUSEUM, CARSON CITY. ANTHROPOLOGICAL PAPERS. Text in English. 1959. irreg., latest vol.23, 1990. price varies.
Indexed: AbAn, AmH&L, SFA.
Published by: (Department of Anthropology), Nevada State Museum, Publications Office, Capitol Complex, Carson City, NV 89710. TEL 702-687-4810.

NEW ENGLAND ANTIQUITIES RESEARCH ASSOCIATION JOURNAL. see *ARCHAEOLOGY*

301 USA ISSN 1092-3977
DA900
➤ **NEW HIBERNIA REVIEW/IRIS EIREANNACH NUA.** Text in English, Irish, Gaelic. 1997. q. USD 40 domestic to individuals; USD 50 foreign to individuals; USD 60 domestic to institutions; USD 70 foreign to institutions (effective 2005). illus. back issues avail. **Document type:** *Journal, Academic/Scholarly.* **Description:** Explores the culture, art, literature, and religion of Ireland and Irish people at home and abroad.
Related titles: Online - full text ed.: ISSN 1534-5815. 2001 (from EBSCO Publishing, O C L C Online Computer Library Center, Inc., Project MUSE, Swets Information Services).
Indexed: AmH&L, HistAb, MLA-IB, RILM.
—BLDSC (6084.235720).
Published by: University of St. Thomas, Center for Irish Studies, 2115 Summit Ave, St. Paul, MN 55105-1096. http://www.stthomas.edu/irishstudies/nhr.htm. Ed. Thomas Dillon Redshaw. Pub. James Rogers.

➤ **NGULAIG**; monograph series. see *ETHNIC INTERESTS*

305.8 ITA
R NI D'AIGURA/NIDO D'AQUILA; rivista etno-antropologica e linguistica-letteraria delle culture delle Alpi Liguri-Marittime. Text in French, Italian, Provencal; Summaries in French, English. 1983. s-a. USD 30 (effective 1998). bk.rev. bibl.; charts; illus.; maps. cum.index. back issues avail. **Document type:** *Academic/Scholarly.* **Description:** Research in the field of ethno-anthropological matters and linguistic and dialectological matters.
Published by: Ni d'Aigura Center for Studies, Via Francesco Domenico Guerrazzi, 14-14, Genoa, GE 16146, Italy. TEL 39-10-3621829. Ed. Pierleone Massajoli. Circ: 1,000.

305.8 USA ISSN 0822-7942
GN387 CODEN: NOPEES
➤ **NOMADIC PEOPLES.** Variant title: International Union of Anthropological and Ethnological Sciences. Commission on Nomadic Peoples. Newsletter. Text in English, French. 1978-1988; resumed 1990. s-a. USD 50 combined subscription to individuals print & online eds.; USD 130 combined subscription to institutions print & online eds. (effective 2005). adv. bk.rev. illus. back issues avail. **Document type:** *Monographic series, Academic/Scholarly.* **Description:** Studies nomadic peoples and their prospects from a multidisciplinary standpoint.
Formerly (until vol.5, 1980): Newsletter of the Commission on Nomadic Peoples, International Union of Anthropological and Ethnological Sciences
Related titles: Online - full text ed.: (from EBSCO Publishing, Florida Center for Library Automation, Gale Group).
Indexed: AICP, ASD, AnthLit, CCME, PSA, PerIslam, RDA, SOPODA, SSA, SociolAb.
—BLDSC (6116.706000), IE, Infotrieve, ingenta. **CCC.**
Published by: (International Union of Anthropological and Ethnological Sciences NLD, Commission on Nomadic Peoples GBR), Berghahn Books Inc., 150 Broadway, Rm 812, New York, NY 10038-4307. journals@berghahnbooks.com, http://www.berghahnbooks.com. Ed. Michael J Casimir. Pub., Adv. contact Marion Berghahn. R&P Chriscita Corbin. B&W page USD 200. Circ: 400. **Subscr. to:** Box 605, Herndon, VA 20172. **Dist. in UK by:** Berghahn Books Ltd, Estover Rd, Plymouth PL6 7PY, United Kingdom. TEL 44-1752-202301, FAX 44-1752-202333.

301 MEX
➤ **NOROESTE DE MEXICO.** Text in Spanish. 1976. irreg., latest vol.11, 1990. USD 6. adv. bk.rev. **Document type:** *Monographic series, Academic/Scholarly.* **Description:** Papers concerning recent studies in archaeology, history, linguistics and social anthropology of northwest Mexico.
Indexed: AICP, AnthLit.

Published by: Centro I N A H Sonora, Apdo. Postal 1664, Hermosillo, SONORA 83080, Mexico. TEL 52-62-131234, FAX 52-62-172580, inahson@rtn.unison.mx. Ed. Raquel Padilla Ramos.

301 NOR ISSN 0802-7285
NORSK ANTROPOLOGISK TIDSSKRIFT. Text in Norwegian; Summaries in English. 1990. q. NOK 404 to individuals; NOK 580 to institutions; NOK 200 to students; NOK 98 per issue (effective 2004). **Document type:** *Journal, Academic/Scholarly.* **Description:** Presents research by Norwegian anthropologists.
Indexed: NAA.
Published by: (Sosialantropologisk Forening), Universitetsforlaget AS/Scandinavian University Press (Subsidiary of: Aschehoug & Co.), Sehesteds Gate 3, Postboks 508, Oslo, 0105, Norway. TEL 47-24-147500, FAX 47-24-147501, post@universitetsforlaget.no, http://www.universitetsforlaget.no/tidsskrifter/article.jhtml?articleID=335, http://www.universitetesforlaget.no. Ed. Signe Howell.

301 USA ISSN 1539-2546
E49
▼ **NORTH AMERICAN DIALOGUE.** Text in English. 2003. s-a. (1-2/yr.). USD 25 membership (effective 2005). **Document type:** *Newsletter, Academic/Scholarly.*
Related titles: Online - full content ed.: ISSN 1556-4819.
—CCC.
Published by: Society for the Anthropology of North America (Subsidiary of: American Anthropological Association), Membership Services, 4350 N. Fairfax Dr., Ste. 640, Arlington, VA 22203-1620. http://sananet.org/journal.html. Ed. Alisse Waterston TEL 914-576-1939.

301 USA ISSN 1068-9982
E78.E2 CODEN: MNOREA
➤ **NORTHEAST ANTHROPOLOGY.** Text in English. 1971. s-a. USD 20 domestic to individuals; USD 25 foreign to individuals; USD 55 domestic to institutions; USD 60 foreign to institutions (effective 2005). adv. bk.rev. bibl.; illus. back issues avail.; reprints avail. **Document type:** *Journal, Academic/Scholarly.* **Description:** Offers research-based articles and book reviews focusing on past and present populations of the northeastern U.S. and adjacent provinces of Canada.
Formerly (until 1993): Man in the Northeast (0191-4138)
Indexed: AICP, AbAn, AmH&L, AnthLit.
Published by: Binghamton University, Department of Anthropology, PO Box 6000, Binghampton, NY 13902-6000. nrthanth@binghamton.edu, http://www.binghamton.edu/nea/. Ed. Dr. Charles Cobb. Circ: 300 (paid).

301 MEX
NOTAS MESOAMERICANAS. Text in English, Spanish. 1950. a. USD 10. adv. **Document type:** *Academic/Scholarly.*
Former titles: Notas Americanas; Mesoamerican Notes
Indexed: AICP, AnthLit, IBSS.
Published by: Universidad de las Americas Puebla, Departamento de Antropologia, Santa Catarina Martir, Apartado Postal 100, San Andres Cholula, PUE 72820, Mexico. TEL 52-22-470000, http://www.udlap.mx/. Ed. Gabriela Urunuela. Circ: 950.

301 MEX ISSN 0185-0636
GN301
➤ **NUEVA ANTROPOLOGIA**; revista de ciencias sociales. Text in Spanish. 1975. 3/yr. MXP 250 domestic; USD 47 foreign (effective 2004). adv. bk.rev. charts; illus.; stat. cum.index every 2 yrs. **Document type:** *Academic/Scholarly.* **Description:** Publishes articles on anthropology and social sciences.
Related titles: Online - full text ed.: (from EBSCO Publishing).
Indexed: AICP, AnthLit, BibInd, HAPI, IBR, IBZ, SOPODA, SSA, SociolAb.
Published by: (Universidad Nacional Autonoma de Mexico, Instituto de Geologia), Nueva Antropologia A.C., Aldama 74, esquina con Berlin, Colonia del Carmen, Coyoacan, DF 04100, Mexico. sgomez@colmex.mx, publigl@geologia.unam.mx. Ed., R&P Silvia Gomez Tagle TEL 52-5-658-5588. Pub. Silvia Gomez Tagle. Adv. contact Celia Tapia. Circ: 1,000.

301 PHL
➤ **NUEVA CACERES REVIEW.** Text in English. 1972. s-a. Exchange basis only. bk.rev. abstr. 35 p./no.; back issues avail. **Document type:** *Journal, Academic/Scholarly.* **Description:** Contains interdisciplinary coverage of the Bicol region of southern Luzon.
Indexed: IPP.
Published by: University of Nueva Caceres, School of Graduate Studies, Jaime Hernandez Ave, Naga City, Camarines Sur 4400, Philippines. TEL 63-811-6100 loc 29, FAX 63-811-1015.

301 613.2 USA ISSN 1537-1735
GN407
➤ **NUTRITIONAL ANTHROPOLOGY.** Text in English. s-a. USD 11 in US & Canada to institutions; USD 26 elsewhere to institutions (effective 2004 - 2005). bk.rev. **Document type:** *Journal, Academic/Scholarly.* **Description:** Publishes notices and reports of domestic and international meetings, curriculum guides, and other information for professionals in academic and applied careers with interests in anthropological study of food and nutrition.
Formerly (until 1998): Communicator (Washington) (1062-1938)
Related titles: Online - full text ed.: ISSN 1548-7172.
—CCC.
Published by: (American Anthropological Association), University of California Press, Journals Division, 2000 Center St, Ste 303, Berkeley, CA 94704-1223. TEL 510-643-7154, FAX 510-642-9917, journals@ucpress.edu, http://www.ucpress.edu/journals/3a/nua/index.htm. Ed. Kristen Borre. R&Ps Darcy Dapra, Marge Dean TEL 510-642-6188.

069 DNK ISSN 0105-8819
NYT FRA NATIONALMUSEET. Text in Danish. 1979. q. DKK 120; DKK 30 per issue (effective 2004). adv. illus. 48 p./no.; **Document type:** *Consumer.* **Description:** Articles about the exhibitions of the National Museum of Denmark and other relevant issues.
Indexed: NAA.
Published by: Nationalmuseet, Frederiksholms Kanal 12, Copenhagen K, 1220, Denmark. TEL 45-33-134411, FAX 45-33-473333, doga@natmus.dk, http://www.natmus.dk/sw1119.asp. Ed. Jette Sandahl. R&P Helle Damsgaard. Adv. contact Helle Damsgard. Circ: 25,000.

301 USA ISSN 0078-3005
➤ **OCCASIONAL PAPERS IN ANTHROPOLOGY.** Text in English. 1968. irreg., latest vol.14, 1992. USD 16. **Document type:** *Monographic series, Academic/Scholarly.*
Indexed: SSCI.
Published by: Pennsylvania State University, Department of Anthropology, 409 Carpenter Bldg, University Park, PA 16802. TEL 814-865-2509, FAX 814-863-1474. Circ: 500.

301 AUS ISSN 0029-8077
DU28 CODEN: OCEADN
➤ **OCEANIA**; devoted to the study of the indigenous peoples of Australia, Melanesia, Micronesia, Indonesia, Polynesia and Insular Southeast Asia. Text in English. 1930. q. AUD 72 domestic to individuals; USD 72 foreign to individuals; AUD 84 domestic to institutions; USD 84 foreign to institutions (effective 2006). bk.rev. illus. Index. back issues avail.; reprint service avail. from PQC. **Document type:** *Journal, Academic/Scholarly.* **Description:** Publishes contributions in the field of social and cultural anthropology in Australia, Melanesia, Polynesia, Micronesia and Southeast Asia.
Related titles: Microform ed.: (from PQC); Online - full text ed.: (from bigchalk, Chadwyck-Healey Inc., EBSCO Publishing, Florida Center for Library Automation, Gale Group, H.W. Wilson, Northern Light Technology, Inc., O C L C Online Computer Library Center, Inc., ProQuest Information & Learning, R M I T Publishing).
Indexed: AICP, ASCA, ASSIA, AbAn, AnthLit, ArtHuCI, AusPAIS, BAS, BibLing, CurCont, DIP, EI, EIA, EnerInd, IBR, IBSS, IBZ, INZP, MLA-IB, PAIS, PCI, RASB, RI-1, RI-2, RILM, SFA, SPPI, SSCI, SSI, WildRev, ZooRec.
—BLDSC (6231.400000), IDS, IE, Infotrieve, ingenta. **CCC.**
Published by: Oceania Publications, University of Sydney (H42), 116 Darlington Rd, Sydney, NSW 2006, Australia. TEL 61-2-93512666, FAX 61-2-93517488, oceania@arts.usyd.edu.au, http://www.arts.usyd.edu.au/publications/oceania/oceania1.htm. Ed. Neil Maclean. Circ: 800.

➤ **OESTERREICHISCHE GESELLSCHAFT FUER UR- UND FRUEHGESCHICHTE. VEROEFFENTLICHUNGEN.** see *ARCHAEOLOGY*

➤ **OESTERREICHISCHE VOLKSKUNDLICHE BIBLIOGRAPHIE.** see *ANTHROPOLOGY—Abstracting, Bibliographies, Statistics*

➤ **OESTERREICHISCHES MUSEUM FUER VOLKSKUNDE. VEROEFFENTLICHUNGEN.** see *FOLKLORE*

➤ **OIDEION**; the performing arts world-wide. see *ART*

301 USA ISSN 0078-432X
E78.O45
OKLAHOMA ANTHROPOLOGICAL SOCIETY. BULLETIN. Text in English. 1952. a. membership.
Indexed: AbAn, AnthLit.
Published by: Oklahoma Anthropological Society, c/o J Peter Thurmond, Sec -Treas, Rte 1, Box 62B, Chevenne, OK 73628. TEL 580-497-2662, dempseydiu@aol.com. Ed. Richard R Drass. R&P J Peter Thurmond. Circ: 475.

301 USA ISSN 0474-0696
OKLAHOMA ANTHROPOLOGICAL SOCIETY. MEMOIR. Text in English. 1964. irreg. price varies.
Indexed: AbAn, AnthLit.
Published by: Oklahoma Anthropological Society, c/o J Peter Thurmond, Sec -Treas, Rte 1, Box 62B, Cheyenne, OK 73628. TEL 580-497-2662. Ed. Don G Wyckoff. R&P J Peter Thurmond. Circ: 350.

301 USA ISSN 0078-4338
OKLAHOMA ANTHROPOLOGICAL SOCIETY. NEWSLETTER. Text in English. 1952. bi-m. membership. bk.rev. **Document type:** *Newsletter.*
Indexed: AbAn, AnthLit.
Published by: Oklahoma Anthropological Society, c/o J Peter Thurmond, Sec -Treas, Rte 1, Box 62B, Cheyenne, OK 73628. TEL 580-487-2662. Ed. Nona J Leatherwood. R&P J Peter Thurmond. Circ: 475.

ORAL HISTORY. see *HISTORY—History Of Europe*

ORALITE - DOCUMENTS. see *LINGUISTICS*

301 IND ISSN 0972-558X
GN301
THE ORIENTAL ANTHROPOLOGISTS. Text in English. 2001. s-a. USD 95 to institutions (effective 2006). **Document type:** *Journal, Academic/Scholarly.*
Published by: (Oriental Institute of Cultural and Social Institute USA), Scientific Publishers, 5-A New Pali Rd., Near Hotel Taj Hari Mahal, PO Box 91, Jodhpur, Rajasthan 342 003, India. TEL 91-291-2433323, FAX 91-291-2512580, info@scientificpub.com, journals@scientificpub.com, http://www.scientificpub.com/bookdetails.php?booktransid=350&bookid=346.

301 NLD ISSN 0167-4099
➤ **OSO**; tijdschrift voor Surinaamse taalkunde, letterkunde, cultuur en geschiedenis. Text in Dutch; Text occasionally in English. 1982. 2/yr. EUR 20 domestic; EUR 23 foreign (effective 2005). adv. bk.rev. bibl.; illus.; maps. index. 144 p./no.; back issues avail. **Document type:** *Academic/Scholarly.* **Description:** Publishes articles on the anthropology, archaeology, linguistics, literature, culture and history of Surinam.
Indexed: BibLing.
—KNAW.
Published by: Stichting Instituut ter Bevordering van de Surinamistiek (Subsidiary of: Journal for Suriname), Culturele Antropologie, Heidelberglaan 2, Utrecht, 3584 CS, Netherlands. TEL 31-30-2531894, FAX 31-30-2534666, http://www.fss.uu.nl/ca/oso.htm. Ed. Wim Hoogbergen.

301 ITA ISSN 1122-2581
OSSIMORI; periodico di antropologia e scienze umane. Text in Italian. 1992. s-a. bk.rev. **Document type:** *Academic/Scholarly.*
Published by: Protagon Editori Toscani, Strada di Ficareto, Siena, SI 53100, Italy. TEL 39-577-55359, FAX 39-577-56117. Ed., R&P Paolo de Simonis. Circ: 1,000.

301 USA ISSN 0742-1184
➤ **OTHER REALITIES**; descriptive, methodological and theoretical texts. Text in English. 1979. irreg., latest vol.9, 1996. price varies. back issues avail. **Document type:** *Monographic series, Academic/Scholarly.*
Indexed: AnthLit.
Published by: (University of California at Los Angeles, Department of Anthropology), Undena Publications, PO Box 97, Malibu, CA 90265. Ed. S J Denning Bolle. **Dist. by:** 3064 Holline Ct, Lancaster, CA 93535.

306.44089 GBR
OXFORD STUDIES IN ANTHROPOLOGICAL LINGUISTICS. Text in English. irreg., latest 2001. price varies.
Indexed: AnthLit, MLA-IB.
Published by: Oxford University Press, Great Clarendon St, Oxford, OX2 6DP, United Kingdom. TEL 44-1865-556767, FAX 44-1865-556646, enquiry@oup.co.uk, http://www.oup-usa.org/catalogs/general/series/Oxford_Studies_in_Anthropological_Linguistics.html, http://www.oup.co.uk/.

301 USA ISSN 0078-740X
PACIFIC ANTHROPOLOGICAL RECORDS. Text in English. 1968. irreg. price varies. reprint service avail. from PQC.
Published by: (Bishop Museum, Department of Anthropology), Bishop Museum Press, 1525 Bernice St, Box 19000 A, Honolulu, HI 96817. TEL 808-848-4135.

301 JPN ISSN 0387-4745
➤ **PACIFIC SOCIETY. JOURNAL/TAIHEIYO GAKKAI SHI.** Text in English, Japanese. 1979. a., latest vol.25, 2002. JPY 5,000 domestic; USD 20 foreign (effective 2002). bk.rev. 60 p./no.; back issues avail. **Document type:** *Journal, Academic/Scholarly.*
Indexed: APEL.
—CCC.
Published by: Pacific Society/Taiheiyo Gakkai, 4-15-29-3f Mita, Minato-ku, Tokyo, 108-0073, Japan. TEL 81-3-5442-2706, FAX 81-3-5442-2716, pacsoc2@ceres.ocn.ne.jp, http://.osaka-gu.ac.jp/gakkai/taihei. Ed., Pub., R&P, Adv. contact Hiroshi Nakajima. Circ: 600.

➤ **PACIFIC STUDIES**; an interdisciplinary journal devoted to the study of the Pacific - its islands and adjacent countries. see *SOCIAL SCIENCES: COMPREHENSIVE WORKS*

301 DEU ISSN 0078-7809
PAIDEUMA; Mitteilungen zur Kulturkunde. Text in English, French, German. 1938. a. EUR 50 (effective 2002). illus. back issues avail.; reprints avail. **Document type:** *Journal, Academic/Scholarly.*
Indexed: AICP, ASD, AmH&L, AmHI, AnthLit, BibLing, CCA, CurCont, DIP, EI, HistAb, IBR, IBSS, IBZ, IndIslam, MLA-IB, PCI.
—CCC.

A

Published by: (Universitaet Frankfurt, Frobenius Institut), W. Kohlhammer GmbH, Hessbruehlstr 69, Stuttgart, 70565, Germany. TEL 49-711-7863-1, FAX 49-711-7863393, info@kohlhammer-katalog.de, http://www.kohlhammer.de. Circ: 860.

301 USA ISSN 1545-0031
▼ **PALEOANTHROPOLOGY.** Text in English. 2003. m. USD 30 to individuals; USD 65 to institutions (effective 2004).
Media: Online - full content.
—CCC.
Published by: University of Pennsylvania Press, 4200 Pine St, Philadelphia, PA 19104-4011. TEL 215-898-6261, FAX 215-898-0404, http://www.pennpress.org/journals/pa, http://www.upenn.edu/pennpress/.

PANTA REI; revista de ciencia y didactica de la historia. see *HISTORY*

301 599.9 EST ISSN 1406-0140
GN1
PAPERS ON ANTHROPOLOGY. Text in English. 1964. irreg. **Document type:** *Monographic series, Academic/Scholarly.*
Formerly (until 1988): Tartuskii Gosudarstvennyi Universitet. Uchenye Zapiski (0207-4575)
Related titles: Online - full text ed.: (from EBSCO Publishing).
Indexed: AbHyg, DSA, RRTA, SIA.
Published by: (Tartu Ulikooli, Centre of Physical Anthropology/University of Tartu), Tartu University Press, Tiigi 78, Tartu, 50410, Estonia. tyk@ut.ee.

301 DEU ISSN 0938-0116
GN1
➤ **PARAGRANA**; internationale Zeitschrift fuer historische Anthropologie. Text in English, French, German. 1992. 2/yr. EUR 36 domestic; EUR 39 foreign; EUR 24.50 newsstand/cover (effective 2005). **Document type:** *Journal, Academic/Scholarly.* **Description:** Covers current efforts in the continuing study of phenomena and structure of mankind following the collapse of a binding abstract anthropological norm.
Indexed: DIP, IBR, IBZ.
Published by: (Freie Universitaet Berlin, Forschungszentrum fuer Historische Anthropologie), Akademie Verlag GmbH (Subsidiary of: Oldenbourg Wissenschaftsverlag GmbH), Palisadenstr 40, Berlin, 10243, Germany. TEL 49-30-4220060, FAX 49-30-42200657, info@akademie-verlag.de, http://www.akademie-verlag.de.

➤ **PENNSYLVANIA ETHNIC STUDIES NEWSLETTER.** see *ETHNIC INTERESTS*

301 USA
PENNSYLVANIA. HISTORICAL AND MUSEUM COMMISSION. ANTHROPOLOGICAL SERIES. Text in English. 1971. irreg., latest vol.7. price varies. **Document type:** *Monographic series, Academic/Scholarly.* **Description:** Scholarly monographs on the subjects of Indian archeology, anthropology and history focused on Pennsylvania.
Published by: Historical and Museum Commission, 300 North Street, Harrisburg, PA 17120. FAX 717-783-9924. R&P Diane B Reed.

305.8 CHL ISSN 0717-1099
F3069
PENTUKUN. Text in Spanish. 1994. s-a. **Description:** Features research, opinions and reports by investigators and indigenous representatives, as well as articles related to indigenous people.
Indexed: AnthLit.
Published by: Universidad de la Frontera, Instituto de Estudios Indigenas/Frontera University, Institute of Indigenous Studies, Casilla 54-D, Temuco, Chile. TEL 56-45-252648, FAX 56-45-252648, iei@werken.ufro.cl.

PEOPLES OF EAST AFRICA. see *HISTORY—History Of Africa*

305.8 USA
PEOPLES OF THE WORLD. (Regional volumes each updated quinquennially) Text in English. 1989. irreg. USD 65 per vol.; USD 315 for 5-vol. set (effective 2003). **Document type:** *Monographic series, Academic/Scholarly.* **Description:** Studies the culture, geographical setting and historical background of the various peoples of the world in regional editions.
Published by: Gale Group (Subsidiary of: Thomson Corporation), 27500 Drake Rd, Farmington Hills, MI 48331-3535. TEL 248-699-8061, 800-877-4253, FAX 248-699-4253, galeord@gale.com, http://www.gale.com.

PERIPHERIE; Zeitschrift fuer Politik und Oekonomie in der dritten Welt. see *BUSINESS AND ECONOMICS—International Development And Assistance*

PERSPECTIVES IN HUMAN BIOLOGY. see *BIOLOGY*

301 PER
PERU INDIGENA. Text in Spanish. 1948-1961; resumed 1967. s-a. USD 40. **Description:** Looks at the socio-economic problems and culture of the native and farmer communities of Peru.
Indexed: AICP.
Published by: Instituto Indigenista Peruano, Avda. Salaverry, Lima, Peru. Ed. David Alvarado.

301 BRA ISSN 0553-8467
F2519.1.R6
PESQUISAS: PUBLICACOES DE ANTROPOLOGIA. Key Title: Pesquisas. Antropologia. Text in Portuguese. 1957. irreg. per issue exchange basis. **Document type:** *Academic/Scholarly.*
Supersedes in part (in 1960): Instituto Anchietano de Pesquisas. Pesquisas (0480-1873)
Indexed: AnthLit.
—CISTI.
Published by: (Universidade do Vale do Rio dos Sinos, Instituto Anchietano de Pesquisas), Unisinos, Av Unisinos, 950, Sao Leopoldo, RS 93022-000, Brazil. TEL 55-51-5908239, FAX 55-51-5908238.

PHILIPPINE SOCIOLOGICAL REVIEW. see *SOCIOLOGY*

PHOINIX. see *HISTORY—History Of North And South America*

IL PICCOLO MISSONARIO. see *RELIGIONS AND THEOLOGY*

PILIPINAS; an interdisciplinary scholarly journal of Philippine studies. see *HISTORY—History Of Asia*

301 USA ISSN 0032-0447
E78.G73 CODEN: PLNAA3
➤ **PLAINS ANTHROPOLOGIST**; a medium for the anthropological interpretation of the US Great Plains. Text in English. 1954. q. USD 35 domestic to individual members; USD 40 foreign to individual members; USD 45 domestic to institutional members; USD 50 foreign to institutional members; USD 20 domestic to students members; USD 25 foreign to students members (effective 2004). adv. bk.rev. bibl.; charts; illus. index. back issues avail.; reprint service avail. from PQC. **Document type:** *Journal, Academic/Scholarly.*
Related titles: Microfilm ed.: 1954 (from PQC); Online - full text ed.: (from Northern Light Technology, Inc., O C L C Online Computer Library Center, Inc., ProQuest Information & Learning).
Indexed: AICP, ASCA, AbAn, AgeL, AmH&L, AnthLit, ArtHuCI, BIOSIS Prev, BibInd, BiolAb, BrArAb, CurCont, HistAb, RI-1, RI-2, RILM, SSCI.
—BLDSC (6507.100000), IE, Infotrieve, ingenta.
Published by: Plains Anthropological Society, 3201 South St, PO Box 152, Lincoln, NE 68506-3266. john-hedden@uiowa.edu. Ed. Linea Sundstrom TEL 414-229-4720. adv.: page USD 100. Circ: 850.

301 USA ISSN 0160-2802
E78.G73
PLAINS ANTHROPOLOGIST. MEMOIR. Text in English. 1964. irreg. **Document type:** *Monographic series.*
Indexed: AnthLit.
Published by: Plains Anthropological Society, 3201 South St, PO Box 152, Lincoln, NE 68506-3266. TEL 319-384-0728, http://www.uiowa.edu/~osa/plainsanth/index.html. Ed. Linea Sundstrom TEL 414-229-4720.

301 USA
PLANET MAGAZINE (SAN FRANCISCO). Text in English. q. USD 20 domestic; USD 28 in Canada & Mexico; USD 40 elsewhere (effective 2005).
Published by: Planet Magazine, 876 Valencia St., Ste B, San Francisco, CA 94110. TEL 415-643-1441, FAX 208-379-1250, info@planet-mag.com, http://www.planet-mag.com.

069 USA ISSN 1092-2814
F788
➤ **PLATEAU JOURNAL**; land and peoples of the Colorado Plateau. Text in English. 1995. s-a. USD 17 domestic to non-members; USD 26 foreign to non-members; USD 9.95 newsstand/cover (effective 2005). 64 p./no.; **Document type:** *Journal, Academic/Scholarly.* **Description:** Explores the historical, natural, scientific and environmental issues that have affected and are still impacting the Colorado Plateau.
Formerly (until 1997): Canon Journal (1081-4523)
Published by: Museum of Northern Arizona, 3101 N Fort Valley Rd, Flagstaff, AZ 86001-8348. TEL 928-774-5211, FAX 928-779-1527, publications@mna.mus.az.us, http://www.musnaz.org/Research/Publications.htm. Ed. Carol Haralson. R&P L Greer Price TEL 520-638-2481. Circ: 7,500 (paid). **Co-sponsor:** Grand Canyon Association.

➤ **POINT SERIES.** see *ASIAN STUDIES*

930.1 ESP ISSN 1130-0728
DE1
POLIS. Text in Spanish. 1989. a. USD 17 foreign (effective 2002). back issues avail.
—CINDOC.
Published by: Universidad de Alcala de Henares, Facultad de Filosofia y Letras, C. Colegios 2, Alcala de Henares, Madrid 28801, Spain. TEL 34-91-8854448, FAX 34-91-8854410, http://www.uah.es/otrosweb/historia/. Ed. Luis A Garcia Moreno.

344.09 USA ISSN 1081-6976
GN492
➤ **POLITICAL AND LEGAL ANTHROPOLOGY REVIEW.** Short title: Po L A R. Text in English. 1993. s-a. USD 46 (effective 2005 & 2006). adv. bk.rev. bibl. **Document type:** *Journal, Academic/Scholarly.* **Description:** Includes articles, correspondence, and syllabi encompassing current theories and research in the intersection of law, political science, anthropology and sociology.
Related titles: Online - full text ed.: ISSN 1555-2934.
Indexed: AnthLit, HistAb.
—CCC.
Published by: (Association for Political and Legal Anthropology), University of California Press, Journals Division, 2000 Center St, Ste 303, Berkeley, CA 94704-1223. TEL 510-643-7154, FAX 510-642-9917, journals@ucpress.edu, http://www.ucpress.edu/journals/3a/pol/index.htm. Ed. Annelise Riles. adv.: page USD 295; 4.5 x 7.5.

301 USA ISSN 1060-2720
GN492
POLITICAL AND LEGAL ANTHROPOLOGY SERIES. Text in English. 1980. irreg., latest vol.21, 1997. USD 39.95; USD 24.95 paperback ed. (effective 2003). **Document type:** *Monographic series.* **Description:** Contains original analyses of political man. Articles cover a wide range of theoretical, conceptual, and methodological approaches to interrelationships among socioeconomic, cultural, and political phenomena.
Formerly (until 1991): Political Anthropology (0732-1228)
Indexed: AmH&L, AnthLit.
—CCC.
Published by: (Association for Political and Legal Anthropology), Transaction Publishers, 390 Campus Dr, Somerset, NJ 07830. TEL 888-999-6778, FAX 732-748-9801, trans@transactionpub.com, http://www.transactionpub.com. Eds. Benno Ndulu, Nicolas van de Walle. Pub. Mary Curtis. R&P Marlena Davidian TEL 732-445-2280 ext 100. Adv. contact Alicja Garbie. **Subscr. to:** Transaction Distribution Center, 390 Campus Dr., Somerset, NJ 08873. TEL 732-445-1245, 888-999-6778, FAX 732-748-9801, orders@transactionpub.com.

305.8 POL ISSN 0866-9597
POLSKA AKADEMIA NAUK. KOMITET NAUK ETNOLOGICZNYCH. PRACE. Text in Polish. 1979. irreg., latest vol.12, 2004. price varies. **Document type:** *Monographic series, Academic/Scholarly.*
Published by: Polska Akademia Nauk, Komitet Nauk Etnologicznych, ul Sw Marcina 78, Uniwersytet im A Mickiewicza, Instytut Etnografii, Poznan, 61803, Poland. TEL 48-61-8294715, etnolo@main.amu.edu.pl. Ed. Aleksander Posern-Zielinski.

POPULAR CULTURE AND EVERYDAY LIFE. see *SOCIOLOGY*

POVOS E CULTURAS. see *POPULATION STUDIES*

301 USA ISSN 0888-4552
PRACTICING ANTHROPOLOGY. Text in English. q. USD 35 domestic; USD 40 foreign (effective 2005). adv. bk.rev. illus. Index. back issues avail.; reprint service avail. from PSC. **Document type:** *Journal, Academic/Scholarly.* **Description:** Source of career information for applied social and behavioral scientists.
Indexed: AICP, AbAn, AnthLit, SRRA.
—CCC.
Published by: Society for Applied Anthropology, PO Box 24083, Oklahoma City, OK 73124-0083. TEL 405-843-5113, info@sfaa.net, http://www.sfaa.net/pa/pa.html. Ed. Alexander Ervin.

306.4 909 USA
PRE-COLUMBIANA; a journal of long-distance contacts. Text in English. **Description:** Covers lengthy human movements and influences before the time of Columbus, especially the controversial question of ancient sea-borne contacts between the Old and New Worlds; of special interest to Explorers Club members.
Indexed: AnthLit.
Published by: University of California at Davis, Division of Textiles and Clothing, 1 Shields Ave., Davis, CA 95616. Ed. Stephen Jett.

301 FRA ISSN 1167-492X
GN848
PREHISTOIRE ANTHROPOLOGIE MEDITERRANEENNES. Text in French. 1987. a.
Formerly (until 1991): Travaux du Laboratoire d'anthropologie et de Prehistoire des Pays de la Mediterranee Occidentale (1148-2141)
Indexed: AnthLit.
Published by: (Universite de Provence, Laboratoire d'anthropologie et de Prehistoire des Pays de la Mediterranee/University of Provence, Laboratory of Anthropology and Prehistory of the Countries of the Werstern Mediterranean), Universite de Provence, U.F.R. Sciences de la Vie, de la Terre et de l'Environnement, Centre Saint-Charles Place Victor Hugo, Marseille, Cedex 3 13331, France. TEL 4-91-106000, FAX 4-91-106006, stg@up.univ-mrs.fr.

A

PREHISTORIC AMERICAN. see *HISTORY—History Of North And South America*

301 599.8 GBR ISSN 0305-8417
PRIMATE EYE. Text in English. 1967. 3/yr. free to members (effective 2005). adv. bk.rev. **Document type:** *Newsletter, Academic/Scholarly.* **Description:** Includes reports of the Captive Care and Conservation Working Parties, abstracts of talks given at PSGB meetings, details of future meetings and news of primate projects amongst other things.
—BLDSC (6612.917000), IE, ingenta.
Published by: Primate Society of Great Britain, Department of Human Sciences, Loughborough University, Loughborough, LE11 3TU, United Kingdom. TEL 44-1509-228228, FAX 44-1509-223941, info@psgb.org, http://www.psgb.org/PrimateEye/index.html. Ed. Bill Sellers. adv.: page GBP 100; 14.5 x 21. Circ: 2,400.

PRIMATE REPORT. see *BIOLOGY—Zoology*

PRIMATES; journal of primatology. see *BIOLOGY—Zoology*

PROGRESS IN DEVELOPMENT STUDIES. see *SOCIOLOGY*

301 POL
GN2 CODEN: PZANA7
➤ **PRZEGLAD ANTROPOLOGICZNY - ANTHROPOLOGICAL REVIEW.** Text in English; Summaries in Polish. 1926. a., latest vol.65, 2002. PLZ 45 (effective 2005). bk.rev. bibl.; illus. 150 p./no. 2 cols./p.; back issues avail.; reprints avail. **Document type:** *Journal, Academic/Scholarly.*
Formerly (until 1999): Przeglad Antropologiczny (0033-2003)
Related titles: E-mail ed.
Indexed: AICP, AnthLit, BiolAb, RASB, ZooRec.
—KNAW.
Published by: Polskie Towarzystwo Antropologiczne/Polish Anthropological Society, Uniwersytet Adama Mickiewicza, Instytut Antropologii, Umultowska 89, Poznan, 61614, Poland. TEL 48-61-8294510, FAX 48-61-8294504, kaszycka@amu.edu.pl, http://main.amu.edu.pl/~anthro/html/pa.html. Ed. Jan Strzalko. R&P Katarzyna Kaszycka. Circ: 500.

➤ **PSYCHOLOGIE ET SOCIETE.** see *SOCIAL SCIENCES: COMPREHENSIVE WORKS*

305.8 USA
PUBLIC WORLDS SERIES. Text in English. 1996. irreg., latest vol.10, 2002. price varies. back issues avail. **Document type:** *Monographic series, Academic/Scholarly.* **Description:** Publishes new research in the field of transnational cultural studies, examining local public problems and comparing them with other contexts of cultural criticism.
—BLDSC (6970.230000), ingenta.
Published by: University of Minnesota Press, 111 Third Ave S, Ste 290, Minneapolis, MN 55401-2520. TEL 612-627-1970, FAX 612-627-1980, http://www.upress.umn.edu/byseries/publicworlds.html. Eds. Benjamin Lee, Dilip Goankar. **Dist. by:** c/o Chicago Distribution Center, 11030 S Langley Ave, Chicago, IL 60628; Plymbridge Distributors Ltd, Plymbridge House, Estover Rd, Plymouth, Devon PL6 7PY, United Kingdom. TEL 44-1752-202300, FAX 44-1752-202330, enquiries@plymbridge.com, http://www.plymbridge.com.

301 ARG ISSN 0327-6627
➤ **PUBLICAR EN ANTROPOLOGIA Y CIENCIAS SOCIALES.** Text in Spanish; Summaries in English, Spanish. 1992. s-a. USD 15; USD 20 foreign. bk.rev. back issues avail. **Document type:** *Academic/Scholarly.* **Description:** Publishes articles in anthropology, archaeology, social sciences and sociology.
Indexed: AnthLit.
Published by: Colegio de Graduados en Antropologia, Puan 470 4o piso, Of. 403, Buenos Aires, 1046, Argentina. TEL 55-114-4320840, FAX 54-114-4320121, colegiod@hotmail.com. Ed., R&P Mauricio Boivin. Circ: 1,000.

301 BOL
PUMAPUNKU. Text in Spanish. N.S. 1991. s-a.?. **Document type:** *Academic/Scholarly.*
Published by: Centro de Investigaciones Antropologicas Tiwanaku, Ave. 6 De Agosto, 2607 (Altos, Casilla de Correos 2325, La Paz, Bolivia. TEL 340107.

PURUSHARTHA. see *HISTORY—History Of Asia*

QINGHAI MINZU XUEYUAN XUEBAO/QINGHAI INSTITUTE OF NATIONALITIES. JOURNAL. see *ASIAN STUDIES*

301 ITA ISSN 1126-9146
QUADERNI DI ANTROPOLOGIA E SEMIOTICA. Text in Italian. 1983. irreg., latest vol.6, 1990. **Document type:** *Journal, Academic/Scholarly.*
Published by: Edizioni Quattroventi, Piazza Rinascimento 4, Urbino, PS 61029, Italy. TEL 39-072-22588, FAX 39-072-2320998, info@edizioniquattroventi.it, http://www.edizioniquattroventi.it. Ed. Maurizio Del Ninno.

301 320 ITA ISSN 0391-7312
QUADERNI TERZO MONDO. Text in Italian. 1973. 2/yr. EUR 60, USD 60 (effective 2004). back issues avail.; reprints avail. **Document type:** *Monographic series.* **Description:** Covers various problems of the Third World in anthropological, sociological, historical and political perspective.
Indexed: SOPODA.
Published by: Centro Studi Terzo Mondo/Center of Study for the World, Via Giovanni Battista Morgagni, 39, Milan, 20129, Italy. Ed. Umberto Melotti. R&P Elena Sala. Circ: 3,000.

QUALITATIVE INQUIRY. see *SOCIAL SCIENCES: COMPREHENSIVE WORKS*

QUEENSLAND ARCHAEOLOGICAL RESEARCH. see *ARCHAEOLOGY*

301 930.1 306 USA ISSN 1040-1385
F3169 CODEN: RNJOFW
➤ **RAPA NUI JOURNAL.** Text in English; Text occasionally in Spanish. 1986. s-a., latest vol.16. USD 40 in US & Canada to individual members; USD 50 elsewhere to individual members; USD 30 in US & Canada to students; USD 40 elsewhere to students; USD 30 in US & Canada to libraries; USD 40 elsewhere to libraries (effective 2003). adv. bk.rev.; tel.rev.; film rev.; music rev.; video rev.; Website rev. illus.; abstr.; bibl.; charts; maps. back issues avail. **Document type:** *Journal, Academic/Scholarly.* **Description:** Source for current Easter Island and East Polynesian scientific studies and events.
Formerly: Rapa Nui Notes (0890-2097)
Indexed: AICP, L&LBA, RefZh, SOPODA.
Published by: Easter Island Foundation, PO Box 6774, Los Osos, CA 93412-6774. TEL 805-528-6279, 805-528-8558, FAX 825-534-9301, rapanuibooks@att.net, http://www.islandheritage.org. Ed., Pub., R&P, Adv. contact Georgia Lee. Circ: 500.

➤ **RASSEGNA DELLE TRADIZIONI POPOLARI;** rivista trimestrale di ricerca scientifica demologica folklorica antropologica. see *FOLKLORE*

301 CAN ISSN 0318-4137
E78.Q3 CODEN: RAQUFS
RECHERCHES AMERINDIENNES AU QUEBEC. Text in French. 1971. 3/yr. CND 50 to individuals; CND 60 to institutions; CND 40 to students (effective 2005). adv. bk.rev. bibl. index. back issues avail. **Document type:** *Academic/Scholarly.* **Description:** Devoted to the ethnology and archeology of the Inuit and American Indian populations. Covers problems they face in lodging, health, territorial rights.
Indexed: AICP, AbAn, AmH&L, AnthLit, BibLing, HistAb, L&LBA, PdeR, RILM, SSA, SociolAb.
—CCC.
Published by: Societe de Recherches Amerindiennes au Quebec, 6742 rue St -Denis, Montreal, PQ H2S 2S2, Canada. TEL 514-277-6178, reamqu@globetrotter.net, http://www.recherches-amerindiennes.qc.ca. Circ: 1,000.

RECHERCHES PHILOSOPHIQUES AFRICAINES. see *PHILOSOPHY*

301 CHN ISSN 1000-3193
GN1
➤ **RENLEIXUE XUEBAO/ACTA ANTHROPOLOGICA SINICA.** Text in Chinese; Summaries in English. 1982. q. CNY 96 (effective 2004). adv. **Document type:** *Academic/Scholarly.* **Description:** Includes theses on paleoanthropology, modern physical anthropology, applied anthropology, paleolithic culture, and articles on natural environments of ancient man.
Related titles: Online - full text ed.: (from East View Information Services, WanFang Data Corp.).
Indexed: AICP, AbAn, AnthLit, ZooRec.
—BLDSC (0595.830000), IE, ingenta.
Published by: (Zhongguo Kexueyuan, Gujizhui Dongwu yu Gurenlie Yanjiusuo/Chinese Academy of Sciences, Institute of Vertebrate Paleontology and Paleoanthropology), Kexue Chubanshe/Science Press, 16 Donghuang Cheng Genbei Jie, Beijing, 100717, China. TEL 86-10-64000246, FAX 86-10-64030255, linyufen@ivpp.ac.cn, http://rlxxb.periodicals.net.cn/default.html, http://www.sciencep.com/. Circ: 11,000. **Dist. by:** China International Book Trading Corp, 35 Chegongzhuang Xilu, Haidian District, PO Box 399, Beijing 100044, China. TEL 86-10-68412045, FAX 86-10-68412023, cibtc@mail.cibtc.com.cn, http://www.cibtc.com.cn.

➤ **RES;** anthropology and aesthetics. see *ARCHAEOLOGY*

301 USA ISSN 0190-1281
GN448 CODEN: REANEM
RESEARCH IN ECONOMIC ANTHROPOLOGY. Text in English. 1978. irreg., latest vol.24, 2005. price varies. back issues avail. **Document type:** *Monographic series, Academic/Scholarly.* **Description:** Aims strengthen the cross-cultural foundation, the focus has been on economic anthropology as an empirical and theoretical component of general anthropology not only or mainly a form of applied anthropology.
Related titles: Online - full text ed.: (from ScienceDirect); Supplement(s): Research in Economic Anthropology. Supplement.
Indexed: AICP, AnthLit, BAS, IBSS, PCI, SOPODA, SSA, SociolAb.
—BLDSC (7738.910000), IE, ingenta. **CCC.**
Published by: J A I Press Inc. (Subsidiary of: Elsevier Science & Technology), 360 Park Ave S, New York, NY 10010-1710. TEL 212-989-5800, FAX 212-633-3990, usinfo-f@elsevier.com, http://www.elsevier.com/wps/find/bookdescription.cws_home/BS_REA/description#description. Eds. C Werner, N Dannhaeusen.

301 USA
RESEARCH IN YORUBA LANGUAGE AND LITERATURE SERIES. Text in English. 1991. s-a. USD 20 per issue to individuals; USD 30 per issue to institutions (effective 2000). **Document type:** *Monographic series.*
Indexed: BibLing.
Published by: Technicians of the Sacred, 1317 N San Fernando Blvd, Ste 310, Burbank, CA 91504.

301 USA
RESOURCES FOR THE STUDY OF ANTHROPOLOGY✶. Text in English. irreg. price varies.
Published by: Houghton Mifflin Co., 222 Berkeley St, Boston, MA 02116. TEL 617-725-5000, FAX 617-227-5409.

301 USA ISSN 1023-3474
HN1
➤ **REVIEW OF HUMAN FACTOR STUDIES.** Text in English. 1995. s-a. USD 40 in North America to individuals; USD 50 elsewhere to individuals; USD 100 in North America to institutions; USD 110 elsewhere to institutions (effective 2004). **Document type:** *Journal, Academic/Scholarly.* **Description:** Covers research of human factor in the development of societies, including issues such as development administration, education, human resource development and management, technology transfer and/or development.
Related titles: Online - full text ed.: (from EBSCO Publishing).
Indexed: SSA, SociolAb.
Published by: International Institute for Human Factor Development, 2484 Bartel Pl, San Diego, CA 92123. TEL 858-541-1622, FAX 619-849-2310, http://www.iihfd.org/updated/linker.php?c=intro_journal&s=intro_side. Ed. Senyo Adjibolosoo.

301 USA ISSN 0093-8157
Z5111 CODEN: REVAEK
➤ **REVIEWS IN ANTHROPOLOGY.** Text in English. 1974. q. USD 533, GBP 401 combined subscription to institutions print & online eds. (effective 2006). bk.rev. illus. reprint service avail. from PQC,PSC. **Document type:** *Journal, Academic/Scholarly.* **Description:** Presents review commentary from the professional literature of anthropology, including the sub-disciplines of human biology, sociocultural anthropology, archaeology and comparative linguistics.
Related titles: Microform ed.: (from PQC); Online - full text ed.: ISSN 1556-3014. USD 506, GBP 381 to institutions (effective 2006) (from EBSCO Publishing, IngentaConnect, O C L C Online Computer Library Center, Inc., Swets Information Services).
Indexed: ABS&EES, AbAn, AnthLit, BRI, CBRI, DIP, FamI, IBR, IBSS, IBZ, PerIslam, RILM.
—BLDSC (7786.980000), IE, Infotrieve, ingenta. **CCC.**
Published by: Taylor & Francis Inc. (Subsidiary of: Taylor & Francis Group), 325 Chestnut St, Ste 800, Philadelphia, PA 19016. TEL 215-625-8900, 800-354-1420, FAX 215-625-8914, info@taylorandfrancis.com, http://www.tandf.co.uk/journals/titles/00938157.asp, http://www.taylorandfrancis.com. Ed. Dr. Lourdes Giordani. **Subsc. outside N. America:** Taylor & Francis Ltd, Journals Customer Service, Rankine Rd, Basingstoke, Hants RG24 8PR, United Kingdom. TEL 44-1256-813000, FAX 44-1256-330245, enquiry@tandf.co.uk.

301 CHL ISSN 0716-3312
F3069
REVISTA CHILENA DE ANTROPOLOGIA. Text in Spanish. 1962. a. USD 25 (effective 1996). bk.rev. **Document type:** *Academic/Scholarly.* **Description:** Devoted to all areas of anthropology.
Former titles (until 1978): Boletin de Prehistoria de Chile; Antropologia
Indexed: AICP, AnthLit, PCI, RASB.
Published by: Universidad de Chile, Departamento de Antropologia, Casilla 10115, Santiago, Chile. FAX 56-2-6787756. Ed. Manuel Dannemann. Circ: 500.

301 CHL
REVISTA CHILENA DE ANTROPOLOGIA VISUAL. Text in Spanish. q. back issues avail. **Document type:** *Academic/Scholarly.*
Media: Online - full text.
Published by: Universidad Academia de Humanismo Cristiano, Compania 2015, Santiago, Chile. TEL 56-2-6954831, sibacweb@academia.cl, http://www.antropologiavisual.cl/REVISTA/, http://www.academia.cl/. Eds. Antonio Astudio, Samuel Linker.

A

301 COL ISSN 0486-6525
GN1
➤ **REVISTA COLOMBIANA DE ANTROPOLOGIA.** Text in Spanish. 1943. a. COP 40,000 domestic; USD 25 foreign (effective 2000). bk.rev. bibl.; illus.; maps. back issues avail. **Document type:** *Academic/Scholarly.* **Description:** Publishes scientific papers in archaeology, anthropology, sociology, ethnohistory, prehistory, linguistics, and ethnobotany.
Formerly (until 1953): Boletin de Arqueologia (0120-9914)
Indexed: AICP, AnthLit, HAPI, IBR, IBSS, RASB, RILM.
—Linda Hall.
Published by: Instituto Colombiano de Antropologia e Historia, Calle 12 No 2-41, Bogota, Colombia. TEL 57-1-5619400, FAX 57-1-5619600, icanhistoria@mincultura.gov.co, http://www.icanh.gov.co. Ed., R&P Maria Victoria Uribe. Circ: 2,000.

301 BRA ISSN 0034-7701
GN1
➤ **REVISTA DE ANTROPOLOGIA.** Text in Portuguese. 1953. s-a. USD 30. bk.rev. **Document type:** *Academic/Scholarly.*
Related titles: Online - full text ed.: free (effective 2005) (from SciELO).
Indexed: AICP, AmH&L, AnthLit, BiolAb, HAPI, IBR, PSA, RASB, RI-1, RI-2, RILM, SOPODA, SSA, SociolAb.
Published by: Universidade de Sao Paulo, Faculdade de Filosofia, Letras e Ciencias Humanas, Cidade Universitaria, Caixa Postal 8105, Sao Paulo, SP 05508-900, Brazil. TEL 55-11-818-3726, FAX 55-11-818-3163. Ed. Paula Montero. Circ: 1,000.

301 PER
REVISTA DE ANTROPOLOGIA. Text in Spanish. 1994. a. PEN 20; USD 15 foreign. **Document type:** *Academic/Scholarly.*
Published by: Universidad Nacional Mayor de San Marcos, Escuela Academico Profesional de Antropologia, Ciudad Universitaria, Ave. Venezuela, S/N, Lima, 1, Peru. TEL 51-1-4520381, rrpp@unmsm.edu.pe, http://www.unmsm.edu.pe/. Ed. Jorge Casanova Velasquez.

301 ECU ISSN 0557-8507
REVISTA DE ANTROPOLOGIA. Text in Spanish. 1973. q. bk.rev. bibl.; charts; illus.
Indexed: AnthLit, RILM.
Published by: Casa de la Cultura Ecuatoriana, Casilla 67, Ave. 6de Diciembre, 794, Quito, Ecuador. Ed. Manuel A Landivar U.

301 ESP ISSN 1131-558X
GN301
REVISTA DE ANTROPOLOGIA SOCIAL. Text in Spanish. 1991. a., latest vol.10, 2001. EUR 18 in the European Union; EUR 25 elsewhere (effective 2004). back issues avail. **Document type:** *Journal, Academic/Scholarly.* **Description:** Presents advanced studies on social anthropology and ethnography in Spain.
Related titles: CD-ROM ed.: EUR 26 to individuals; EUR 34 to institutions (effective 2003).
Indexed: AICP, AmH&L, HistAb, SSA, SociolAb.
—CINDOC.
Published by: (Universidad Complutense de Madrid, Facultad de Ciencias Politicas y Sociologia), Universidad Complutense de Madrid, Servicio de Publicaciones, C Isaac Peral s/n, Ciudad Universitaria, Madrid, 28040, Spain. TEL 34-91-3946934, FAX 34-91-3946978, dptoants@cps.ucm.es, servicio@publicaciones.ucm.es, http://www.ucm.es/publicaciones. Ed. Ricardo Sanmartin Arce.

301 COL ISSN 0124-485X
REVISTA DE ANTROPOLOGIA Y ARQUEOLOGIA. Text in Spanish. 1985. a. COP 8 domestic; USD 16 foreign (effective 2001). adv. bk.rev. Index. back issues avail. **Document type:** *Academic/Scholarly.*
Formerly: Revista de Antropologia (0120-6613)
Indexed: AICP, AnthLit, HistAb, IBSS.
Published by: (Departamento de Antropologia), Universidad de los Andes, Carrera 1a, No. 18 A-70, Apartado Aereo 4976, Santafe de Bogota, CUND, Colombia. TEL 57-1-282-4066, FAX 57-1-284-1890, TELEX 42343 UNAND CO, infeduni@uniandes.edu.co, http://www.edicion.uniandes.edu.co. Eds. Felipe Cardenas Arroyo, Monika Therrien. Circ: 1,000.

305.8 ROM ISSN 0034-8198
GR257
REVISTA DE ETNOGRAFIE SI FOLCLOR. Text in Romanian; Summaries in French. 1956. 6/yr. bk.rev. bibl.; charts; illus.
Indexed: AICP, BibLing, IBSS, MLA, MLA-IB, RASB, RILM.
Published by: (Academia Romana, Institutul de Etnografie si Folclor C. Brailoiu), Editura Academiei Romane/Publishing House of the Romanian Academy, Calea 13 Septembrie 13, Sector 5, Bucharest, 76117, Romania. TEL 40-21-4119008, FAX 40-21-4103983, edacad@ear.ro. Ed. Alex Dobre. Circ: 1,630. **Dist. by:** Rodipet S.A., Piata Presei Libere 1, sector 1, PO Box 33-57, Bucharest 3, Romania. TEL 40-21-2224126, 40-21-2226407, rodipet@rodipet.ro.

REVISTA DE HISTORIA. see *HISTORY*

305.8 ESP ISSN 1132-6581
GN585.S7
REVISTA D'ETNOLOGIA DE CATALUNYA. Text in Catalan. 1992. s-a. bk.rev.
Indexed: AICP, RILM.
—CINDOC.
Published by: Departament de Cultura, Centre de Promocio de la Cultura Popular i Tradicional Catalana, Ptge. de la Banca, 1-3, Barcelona, 08002, Spain. TEL 34-93-5671000, FAX 34-93-5671002. Ed. Antoni Anguela. Pub. Lluis Calvo.

301 ESP ISSN 0556-6533
E51
REVISTA ESPANOLA DE ANTROPOLOGIA AMERICANA. Text in French, English, Spanish. 1952-1961; resumed 1969. a., latest vol.32, 2002. EUR 21 in the European Union; EUR 30 elsewhere (effective 2005). bk.rev. back issues avail. **Document type:** *Journal, Academic/Scholarly.* **Description:** Focuses on american antropology and ethnology.
Supersedes (1952-1961): Seminario de Estudios Americanistas. Trabajos y Conferencias (0541-8658)
Related titles: CD-ROM ed.: ISSN 1695-503X. 2001. EUR 66 to individuals; EUR 90 to institutions (effective 2003); Online - full text ed.
Indexed: AICP, AmH&L, AnthLit, HAPI, HistAb, IBR, PCI, SociolAb.
—CINDOC. **CCC.**
Published by: (Universidad Complutense de Madrid, Facultad de Geografia e Historia), Universidad Complutense de Madrid, Servicio de Publicaciones, C Isaac Peral s/n, Ciudad Universitaria, Madrid, 28040, Spain. TEL 34-91-3946934, FAX 34-91-3946978, reaa@ghis.ucm.es, info@ucm.es, http://www.ucm.es/BUCM/revistasBUC/portal/revistas/revista.php?id=REAA, http://www.ucm.es/publicaciones. Ed. Emma Sanchez Montanes.

301 ESP ISSN 1134-7368
GN49
➤ **REVISTA ESPANOLA DE ANTROPOLOGIA BIOLOGICA.** Text in Spanish. 1980. a. adv. bk.rev. **Document type:** *Academic/Scholarly.* **Description:** Covers topics in physical and biological anthropology.
Formerly (until 1994): Sociedad Espanola de Antropologia Biologica. Boletin (0213-179X)
Indexed: AbAn, AnthLit, IECT.
—CINDOC.
Published by: Sociedad Espanola de Antropologia Biologica, Fac. de Biologia, Dpto. Biologia Animal I, Univ. Complutense, Madrid, 28040, Spain. TEL 34-91-394-4936, FAX 34-91-394-4947, vfuster@eucmax.sim.ucm.es. Ed., Adv. contact Vicente Fuster. Circ: 210.

301 ESP ISSN 0212-7016
DC611.B31
REVISTA INTERNACIONAL DE LOS ESTUDIOS VASCOS. Short title: R I E V. Text in Spanish. 1907. s-a. price varies. bibl. back issues avail. **Document type:** *Monographic series, Academic/Scholarly.*
Formerly (until 1922): Revue Internationale des Etudes Basques (1136-5846)
Indexed: BibInd, RILM.
—CINDOC.
Published by: Eusko Ikaskuntza/Sociedad de Estudios Vascos, Palacio Miramar, Miraconcha 48, Donostia, San Sebastian 20007, Spain. TEL 34-943-310855, FAX 34-943-213956, ei-sev@sc.ehu.es, http://www.eusko-ikaskuntza.org/.

301 PRT ISSN 0870-0206
PC5001
REVISTA LUSITANA. Variant title: Arquivo de Estudos Filologicos e Etnologicos Relativos a Portugal. Text in English, French, Italian, Spanish. 1887; N.S. 1981. irreg. bk.rev. **Document type:** *Academic/Scholarly.* **Description:** Contains articles about anthropology and ethnology.
Indexed: BibInd, RILM.
Published by: (Centro de Tradicoes Populares Portuguesas), Universidade de Lisboa, Centro de Estudos Geograficos, Alameda da Universidade, Lisbon, 1600-214, Portugal. TEL 351-21-7940218, FAX 351-21-7938690, ceg@mail.telepac.pt, http://www.ceg.ul.pt/. Circ: 1,000.

301 MEX ISSN 0188-7467
REVISTA MEXICANA DE ESTUDIOS ANTROPOLOGICOS. Text in Spanish. 1932. a.
Indexed: AnthLit.
Published by: Sociedad Mexicana de Antropologia/Mexican Society of Anthropology, C.A.P. Polanco, P.O. Box 100, Mexico, 11550, Mexico. somedean@yahoo.com.mx.

301 ESP ISSN 1135-691X
REVISTA MURCIANA DE ANTROPOLOGIA. Text in Spanish. 1994. a., latest vol.6, 1999, for the year 2000. back issues avail. **Document type:** *Academic/Scholarly.*
Indexed: DIP, IBR, IBZ.
—CINDOC.
Published by: Universidad de Murcia, Servicio de Publicaciones, Edificio Saavedra Fajardo, C/ Actor Isidoro Maiquez 9, Murcia, 30007, Spain. TEL 34-968-363887, FAX 34-968-363414, servpubl@um.es, http://www.um.es/spumweb. Ed. Antonino Gonzalez Blanco. Circ: 252.

REVUE D'ETHNOLINGUISTIQUE; cahiers du L A C I T O. see *LINGUISTICS*

▼ **LA REVUE LISA**; litterature, histoire des idees, images, societes du monde anglophone. see *PHILOSOPHY*

RHEINISCH-WESTFAELISCHE ZEITSCHRIFT FUER VOLKSKUNDE. see *HISTORY—History Of Europe*

301 SWE ISSN 0035-5267
DL601
➤ **RIG**; kulturhistorisk tidskrift. Text in Swedish; Summaries in English, German. 1918. q. SEK 150 to individuals; SEK 250 to institutions (effective 2004). adv. bk.rev. illus. index, cum.index. **Document type:** *Journal, Academic/Scholarly.*
Indexed: AICP, AmH&L, BHA, HistAb, IBSS, RASB.
Published by: Foereningen foer Svensk Kulturhistoria, Finngatan 8, Lund, 22362, Sweden. TEL 46-46-2227565, FAX 46-46-2229849, birgitta.svensson@etn.lu.se, http://www.etn.lu.se/rig. Ed. Birgitta Svensson. **Co-sponsors:** Lunds Universitet, Etnologiska Institutionen med Folkarkivet/Lund University; Nordiska Museet.

301 ITA ISSN 0085-5723
RIVISTA DI ANTROPOLOGIA. Text in Italian; Summaries in English, French. 1893. a. bk.rev. back issues avail.; reprints avail. **Document type:** *Academic/Scholarly.* **Description:** Publishes memoirs, communications and reports about scientific subjects concerning the anthropological sciences.
Formerly (until vol.15): Societa Romana di Antropologia. Atti
Related titles: Supplement(s): Rivista di Antropologia. Supplement.
Indexed: AICP, AnthLit, PCI, RASB.
—BLDSC (7981.000000), GNLM.
Published by: Istituto Italiano di Antropologia (Subsidiary of: Universita degli Studi di Roma "La Sapienza"), c/o Dipartimento di Biologia Animale e dell'Uomo, Universita di Roma "La Sapienza", Piazzale Aldo Moro 5, Rome, 00185, Italy. TEL 39-06-49912273, FAX 39-06-49912277, http://www.scienzemfn.uniroma1.it. Eds. Pietro Passarello, Gabriella Spedini.

301 ITA
LA RIVOLTA. Text in Italian. s-a. looseleaf.
Published by: Vittorio Baccelli Ed. & Pub., Casella Postale 132, Lucca, LU 55100, Italy. Circ: 3,000.

306.4 USA
ROCK ART FOUNDATION. SPECIAL PUBLICATIONS. Text in English. 1994. irreg.
Indexed: AnthLit.
Published by: Rock Art Foundation, 4833 Fredericsburg Rd, San Antonio, TX 78229. TEL 888-762-5278, FAX 210-525-9909, admin@rockart.org, http://www.rockart.org.

301 AUS ISSN 0813-0426
GN799.P4
➤ **ROCK ART RESEARCH.** Text in English; Summaries in French, German, Spanish. 1984. s-a. AUD 25 domestic; USD 24.70 foreign (effective 2005). adv. bk.rev. abstr.; bibl.; charts; illus.; maps. Index. 80 p./no.; back issues avail. **Document type:** *Journal, Academic/Scholarly.* **Description:** Devoted to developing theory and methodology for a scientific understanding of prehistoric art forms worldwide.
Related titles: Online - full text ed.: (from R M I T Publishing).
Indexed: AICP, AnthLit, IBSS.
—BLDSC (8001.445000), IE, ingenta. **CCC.**
Published by: Australian Rock Art Research Association, PO Box 216, Caulfield South, VIC 3162, Australia. auranet@optusnet.com.au, http://mc2.vicnet.net.au/home/rar1/web/index.html, http://mc2.vicnet.net.au/home/aura/web/index.html. adv.: page AUD 240; 17 x 25. Circ: 1,000 (paid and controlled).

301 USA ISSN 1528-0748
DX101 CODEN: GYLJAC
➤ **ROMANI STUDIES.** Text in English. 1888-1982; N.S. 1991. s-a. USD 30 in US & Canada to individual members Includes Newsletter; USD 35 elsewhere to individual members Includes Newsletter; USD 35 in US & Canada to non-members Includes Newsletter; USD 40 elsewhere to non-members Includes Newsletter (effective 2003). adv. bk.rev. illus. Index. back issues avail. **Document type:** *Journal, Academic/Scholarly.* **Description:** Publishes original research in Gypsy studies, including articles in anthropology, history, linguistics, music and folklore.
Formerly (until 2000): Gypsy Lore Society. Journal (0017-6087)
Related titles: Online - full text ed.: (from EBSCO Publishing).
Indexed: AICP, AmH&L, AnthLit, BibLing, DIP, HistAb, IBR, IBSS, IBZ, IndIslam, L&LBA, MLA-IB, PAIS, PCI, RILM, SOPODA, SSA, SociolAb.
—**CCC.**
Published by: Gypsy Lore Society, 5607 Greenleaf Rd., Cheverly, MD 20785. TEL 301-341-1261, FAX 301-341-1261, ssalo@capaccess.org, http://www.gypsyloresociety.org. Ed. Yaron Matras. R&P, Adv. contact Sheila Salo. page USD 50; trim 4.5 x 7.5. Circ: 300.

301 GBR ISSN 1359-0987
GN2
➤ **ROYAL ANTHROPOLOGICAL INSTITUTE. JOURNAL.** Text in English. 1901; N.S. 1966. q. USD 556 combined subscription in the Americas to institutions & Caribbean (print & online eds.); GBP 331 combined subscription elsewhere to institutions print & online eds. (effective 2006); includes Anthropology Today. adv. bk.rev. charts; illus.; abstr. index. back issues avail.; reprint service avail. from PQC. **Document type:** *Journal, Academic/Scholarly.* **Description:** Covers all areas of anthropology: physical, social, cultural. Includes information on archaeology and linguistics.
Formerly (until 1995): Man (0025-1496); Incorporates (1871-1965): Royal Anthropological Institute of Great Britain and Ireland. Journal (0307-3114); Which was formerly (until 1906): Anthropological Institute of Great Britain and Ireland. Journal (0959-5295); Which was formed by the merger of (1848-1871): Ethnological Society of London. Journal (1368-0374); Which was formerly (until 1869): Ethnological Society of London.Transactions (1368-0366); (until 1861): Ethnological Society of London. Journal (1368-0358); (1863-1871): Journal of Anthropology (1356-0123); Which was formerly (until 1870): Anthropological Review (1368-0382)
Related titles: CD-ROM ed.: N.S.; Microfilm ed.: N.S. (from BHP); Microform ed.: N.S. (from BHP, PQC); Online - full text ed.: ISSN 1467-9655. N.S. USD 528 in the Americas to institutions & Caribbean; GBP 314 elsewhere to institutions (effective 2006) (from bigchalk, Blackwell Synergy, Chadwyck-Healey Inc., EBSCO Publishing, Florida Center for Library Automation, Gale Group, H.W. Wilson, IngentaConnect, JSTOR (Web-based Journal Archive), O C L C Online Computer Library Center, Inc., Swets Information Services).
Indexed: AC&P, AICP, ASCA, AbAn, AgeL, AmH&L, AnthLit, BAS, BRI, BiolAb, BrArAb, BrHumI, CCA, CurCont, DIP, EI, ERA, ETA, ExcerpMed, FamI, HistAb, IBR, IBSS, IBZ, IndIslam, MEA, MEA&I, MLA-IB, PCI, PSA, PhilInd, RASB, RHEA, RI-1, RI-2, RILM, SEA, SENA, SOMA, SSA, SSCI, SSI, SWA, SociolAb, TEA, WBA, WMB.
—BLDSC (4851.900000), IE, Infotrieve, ingenta, Linda Hall. **CCC.**
Published by: (University of Edinburgh, Department of Social Anthropology, Royal Anthropological Institute of Great Britain and Ireland), Blackwell Publishing Ltd., 9600 Garsington Rd, Oxford, OX4 2ZG, United Kingdom. TEL 44-1865-776868, FAX 44-1865-714591, customerservices@oxon.blackwellpublishing.com, http://www.blackwellpublishing.com/journals/JRAI. Ed. Susan Bayly TEL 44-131-4471190. Circ: 3,200.

301 GBR ISSN 0080-4150
GN2
ROYAL ANTHROPOLOGICAL INSTITUTE. OCCASIONAL PAPER. Text in English. 1902. irreg., latest vol.43, 1996. price varies. **Document type:** *Monographic series.*
Published by: Royal Anthropological Institute of Great Britain and Ireland, 50 Fitzroy St, London, W1P 5HS, United Kingdom. TEL 44-20-73870455, FAX 44-20-73888817, admin@therai.org.uk, http://www.therai.org.uk/pubs/occpapers/occ_papers.html.

354.35 NLD ISSN 0922-7911
S481
ROYAL TROPICAL INSTITUTE. BULLETIN. Key Title: Bulletin - Royal Tropical Institute. Text in English. irreg., latest vol.362, 2004. EUR 11.50 per issue (effective 2005). illus. back issues avail. **Document type:** *Bulletin.* **Description:** Publishes basic and applied multidisciplinary research in the fields of rural development, health and development, tropical hygiene, culture, history and anthropology.
Former titles (until 1988): Koninklijk Instituut voor de Tropen. A O Bulletin; Koninklijk Instituut voor de Tropen. Afdeling Plattelandsontwikkeling. Communications and Bulletins; Formed by the merger of (1914-1986): Koninklijk Instituut voor de Tropen. Afdeling Agrarisch Onderzoek. Bulletin; Koninklijk Instituut voor de Tropen. Afdeling Agrarisch Onderzoek. Communication (0370-1670)
Indexed: ForAb, RDA, TDB, WAE&RSA.
—BLDSC (2701.250000), CISTI, IE, ingenta, KNAW.
Published by: (Koninklijk Instituut voor de Tropen/Royal Tropical Institute), K I T Publishers, Mauritskade 63, PO Box 95001, Amsterdam, 1090 HA, Netherlands. TEL 31-20-5688272, FAX 31-20-5688286, publishers@kit.nl, http://www.kit.nl. Pub. Ron Smit.

305.8 ARG ISSN 0325-1217
GN1
➤ **RUNA.** Text in Spanish. 1948. irreg., latest vol.22, 1995. **Document type:** *Academic/Scholarly.*
Indexed: AICP, AnthLit, HAPI, IBR.
Published by: (Instituto de Ciencias Antropologicas), Universidad de Buenos Aires, Facultad de Filosofia y Letras, Museo Etnografico Juan B. Ambrosetti, Moreno, 350, Capital Federal, Buenos Aires 1091, Argentina. TEL 54-114-3317788. Ed. Carlos Herran.

301 USA ISSN 1066-0127
RUSSIA AND HER NEIGHBORS; facts and views on daily life. Text in English. 1985. irreg. USD 25 to individuals; USD 30 to institutions (effective 2002). bk.rev. bibl.; illus. back issues avail. **Document type:** *Newsletter, Consumer.*
Formerly: Station Relay (0887-8935)
Published by: Highgate Road Social Science Research Station, Inc., 32 Highgate Rd., Berkeley, CA 94707. TEL 510-525-3248, FAX 510-525-3313, edunn@well.com, http://www.hrssrs.org. Ed. Eugenia Miller. R&P Ethel Dunn. Circ: 250.

947 305.8 RUS ISSN 0868-586X
GN1
RUSSKIE STAROZHILY ZAKAVKAZIA: MOLOKANE I DUKHOBORTSY/RUSSIAN EARLY SETTLERS OF THE TRANSCAUCASUS: THE MOLOKANS AND DUKHOBORS. Text in Russian; Summaries in English. irreg. USD 15.50 per issue. **Description:** Presents a multidisciplinary study of the sectarians adaptation to the new, natural, ethnic, cultural and linguistic environments.
Indexed: AnthLit.
Published by: Institut Etnologii i Antropologii Im. N.N. Miklukho-Maklaya (Subsidiary of: Rossiiskaya Akademiya Nauk/Russian Academy of Sciences), Leninsky prospect 32-a, Moscow, 117334, Russian Federation. TEL 7-095-9381747, FAX 7-095-9380600, anthpub@iea.msk.su. Ed. V. Kozlov.

301 USA ISSN 1077-5714
S A C C NOTES - TEACHING ANTHROPOLOGY. Text in English. s-a. USD 15 (effective 1999).
Published by: (Society for Teaching Anthropology in Community Colleges), American Anthropological Association, 2200 Wilson Blvd, Ste 600, Arlington, VA 22201. TEL 703-528-1902, FAX 703-528-3546, http://www.aaanet.org. R&P Terry Clifford.

301 USA
S A E JOURNAL. (Society for the Anthropology of Europe) Text in English. s-a.
Published by: (American Anthropological Association, Society for the Anthropology of Europe), American Anthropological Association, 2200 Wilson Blvd, Ste 600, Arlington, VA 22201. TEL 703-528-1902, FAX 703-528-3546, http://www.aaanet.org/pubs/saejournal.htm. Ed. Kelli Ann Costa.

S E M NEWSLETTER. see *MUSIC*

SACRED HOOP MAGAZINE; shamanism and ancient wisdom for today's world. see *ETHNIC INTERESTS*

301 NOR ISSN 0581-4480
SAMISKE SAMLINGER. Text in Norwegian. 1938. irreg., latest 1992. price varies.
Formerly (until 1948): Nordnorske Samlinger (0801-1060)
Published by: Norsk Folkemuseum, Oslo, 0287, Norway. TEL 47-22-12-37-00, FAX 47-22-12-37-77.

305.8 USA ISSN 0080-5890
SAN DIEGO MUSEUM OF MAN. ETHNIC TECHNOLOGY NOTES. Text in English. 1967. irreg., latest vol.24, 1996. price varies. **Document type:** *Monographic series.* **Description:** Contains studies on specific topics in all areas of New World anthropology and archaeology.
Published by: San Diego Museum of Man, 1350 El Prado, Balboa Park, San Diego, CA 92101. TEL 619-239-2001. Ed., R&P Ken Hedges.

301 USA ISSN 0080-5904
SAN DIEGO MUSEUM OF MAN. PAPERS. Text in English. 1929. irreg., latest vol.33, 1995. price varies. index. **Document type:** *Monographic series.* **Description:** Contains in-depth studies in all areas of New World anthropology and archaeology.
Indexed: AnthLit.
—BLDSC (8072.880000).
Published by: San Diego Museum of Man, 1350 El Prado, Balboa Park, San Diego, CA 92101. TEL 619-239-2001. Ed. Ken Hedges.

SAN YUE SAN. see *LITERATURE*

SANAKIRJOJA - LEXICA SOCIETATIS FENNO-UGRICAE. see *LINGUISTICS*

301 ESP ISSN 1131-5350
SANCHO EL SABIO; revista de cultura e investigacion vasca. Text in Spanish. 1957. a.
Formerly (until 1991): Institucion Sancho el Sabio. Boletin (0211-2396)
Indexed: RILM.
—CINDOC.
Published by: Fundacion Sancho el Sabio, Paseo de la Senda No. 2, Victoria - Gasteiz, 01007, Spain. TEL 34-945-147800, FAX 34-945-140091, fs-inv@sancho-sabio.es, http://www.fsancho-sabio.es/.

301 ECU ISSN 0252-8630
SARANCE. Text in Spanish. 1975. 3/yr. per issue exchange basis.
Indexed: AICP, IBR.
Published by: Instituto Otavaleno de Antropologia, Centro de Documentacion, Seccion Canje, Casilla 10-02-1478, Otavalo, Imbabura, Ecuador. TEL 593-6-920321, FAX 593-6-920461. Circ: 500.

305.8 MYS ISSN 0375-3050
SARAWAK MUSEUM JOURNAL. Text in English. 1966. a.
Description: Devoted to the advancement of knowledge in the natural and human sciences. Publishes articles pertaining to the Asian region in general, but particularly to the Borneo and Sarawak.
Indexed: AnthLit, IBSS, IndIslam, RRTA, ZooRec.
—BLDSC (8076.000000), IE, Infotrieve.
Published by: Sarawak Museum, Tun Abang Haji Openg Road, Kuching, Sarawak, 93566, Malaysia. TEL 60-82-244232, FAX 60-82-246680, http://www.museum.sarawak.gov.my.

305.8 MYS
SARAWAK MUSEUM JOURNAL. SPECIAL ISSUE. Text in English. 1974. irreg.
Indexed: AnthLit.
Published by: Sarawak Museum, Tun Abang Haji Openg Road, Kuching, Sarawak, 93566, Malaysia. TEL 60-82-244232, FAX 60-82-246680, http://www.museum.sarawak.gov.my.

301 SWE
SCANDINAVIAN INSTITUTE OF AFRICAN STUDIES. RURAL DEVELOPMENT. Short title: Rural Development Series. Text in Swedish. irreg. back issues avail. **Document type:** *Monographic series, Academic/Scholarly.*
Published by: (Nordiska Afrikainstitutet/Nordic Africa Institute), Almqvist & Wiksell International, P O Box 7634, Stockholm, 10394, Sweden. FAX 46-8-24-25-43, info@city.akademibokhandeln.se, http://www.akademibokhandeln.se.

SCHWEIZER VOLKSKUNDE (DEUTSCH - FRANZOSISCH - ITALIENISCHE AUSGABE)/FOLKLORE SUISSE/FOLKLORE SVIZZERO; folklore Suisse - folclore Svizzero. see *FOLKLORE*

SCHWEIZERISCHES ARCHIV FUER VOLKSKUNDE; halbjahresschrift im auftrag der schweizerischen gesellschaft fuer volkskunde. see *FOLKLORE*

SCOTTISH STUDIES. see *HISTORY—History Of Europe*

305.8 ARG ISSN 0325-6669
F2822
SCRIPTA ETHNOLOGICA. Text in Spanish. 1973. a.
Related titles: Supplement(s): Scripta Ethnologica. Supplementa. ISSN 0326-3347.
Indexed: AnthLit, RILM.
Published by: Centro Argentino de Etnologia Americana/Argentine Center of American Ethnology, Avda. of May 1437, Fl. 1A, Buenos Aires, 1085, Argentina. TEL 54-11-43811821, FAX 54-11-43811821, caea@sinectis.com.ar.

SCRIPTA MEDITERRANEA. see *HISTORY—History Of The Near East*

301 ESP
SEMANA INTERNACIONAL DE ANTROPOLOGIA VASCA. ACTAS✶ . Text in Spanish. irreg.
Published by: Gran Enciclopedia Vasca, 48006 Calzadas de Mallona 8, Bilbao 6, Spain.

301 ITA ISSN 0392-9094
SEMINARIO DI SCIENZE ANTROPOLOGICHE. Text in English, Italian; Summaries in English, French, Italian. 1979. a. adv. bk.rev. back issues avail.
Published by: Centro di Documentazione per le Scienze Antropologiche, Via Del Proconsolo, 12, Florence, FI 50122, Italy. Ed. Quinzio Milanesi. Circ: 1,000. **Co-sponsor:** Societa Italiana di Ecologia Umana.

305.8 JPN ISSN 0387-6004
GN303
SENRI ETHNOLOGICAL STUDIES. Text in Multiple languages. 1979. irreg. price varies. **Document type:** *Monographic series, Academic/Scholarly.*
Indexed: AnthLit, ESPM, RI-1.
Published by: National Museum of Ethnology (Minpaku)/Kokuritsu Minzokugaku Hakubutsukan, 10-1 Senri Expo Park, Suita, Osaka 565-8511, Japan. TEL 81-6-68762151, FAX 81-6-68788353, jcasmail@idc.minpaku.ac.jp, http://www.minpaku.ac.jp/publication/ses/.

301 001.3 BRA ISSN 1415-689X
GN301
➤ **SEXTA FEIRA**; antropologia artes humanidades. Text in Portuguese. 1997. a. USD 10 (effective 2001). adv. illus. back issues avail. **Document type:** *Journal, Academic/Scholarly.* **Description:** Aims to establish a dialog between Anthropology and Humanities, focusing on contemporary issues.
Published by: Editora 34, Rua Hungria 592, Sao Paulo, SP CEP 01455-000, Brazil. TEL 55-11-38166777, FAX 55-11-38166777, editora34@uol.com.br, pletora@ig.com.br. Ed. Alberto Martins. Pub. Aluizio Leite. Adv. contact Satiko Hikiji. B&W page USD 800, color page USD 1,500. Circ: 1,700 (paid); 300 (controlled).

301 JPN ISSN 0387-2483
SHAKAI JINRUIGAKU NENPO. Text in Japanese. 1975. a. JPY 3,800. adv. **Document type:** *Academic/Scholarly.*

A

Published by: (Tokyo-toritsu Daigaku/Tokyo Metropolitan University, Shakai Jinrui Gakkai/Society for Social Anthropology), Kobundo, 1-7-13 Kanda-Surugadai, Chiyoda-ku, Tokyo, 101-0062, Japan. TEL 03-3294-7542. Circ: 2,000.

SHAMAN; journal of the International Society for Shamanistic Research. see *ALTERNATIVE MEDICINE*

305.8 USA ISSN 0887-8897
BL2370.S5
SHAMAN'S DRUM; a journal of experiential Shamanism. Text in English. 1985. q. USD 18 domestic; USD 22 in Canada & Mexico; USD 34 elsewhere (effective 2004). adv. bk.rev.
Document type: *Consumer.* **Description:** Discusses cross-cultural shamanism, Native American healing and ethnic spirituality.
Published by: Cross-Cultural Shamanism Network, Shaman's Drum, 3600 Cedar Flat Rd no A, Williams, OR 97544. TEL 541-846-1313, FAX 541-846-1204. Ed. Timothy White. R&P Roberta Louis. Adv. contact Judy Wells. Circ: 14,000 (paid).

SIGN LANGUAGE STUDIES. see *LINGUISTICS*

SLOVENSKO ETNOLOSKO DRUSTVO. GLASNIK/SLOVENE ETHNOLOGICAL SOCIETY. BULLETIN. see *HISTORY—History Of Europe*

305.6 SVK ISSN 1335-1303
DB661
➤ **SLOVENSKY NARODOPIS/SLOVAK ETHNOLOGY.** Text in Czech, English, German, Slovak; Summaries in English, German. 1953. q. USD 100 foreign (effective 2005). bk.rev. bibl.; charts; illus. index. **Document type:** *Journal, Academic/Scholarly.* **Description:** Publishes papers on all aspects of Slovak folk culture, including minorities and Slovaks abroad. Comparatively studies ethnographic materials of museums and archives. Also includes papers on methods and approaches to cultural anthropology.
Indexed: AICP, BibLing, MLA, MLA-IB, RASB.
Published by: (Slovenska Akademia Vied, Ustav Etnologie), Slovak Academic Press Ltd., Nam Slobody 6, PO Box 57, Bratislava, 81005, Slovakia. sap@sappress.sk, http://www.sappress.sk. Ed. Dusan Ratica.

301 USA ISSN 0081-0223
GN1 CODEN: SMCAAM
SMITHSONIAN CONTRIBUTIONS TO ANTHROPOLOGY. Text in English. 1887. irreg., latest vol.45, 2001. price varies. reprint service avail. from PQC. **Document type:** *Monographic series, Academic/Scholarly.*
Former titles (until 1965): Smithsonian Institution. Bureau of American Ethnology. Bulletin (0082-8882); (until 1903): Smithsonian Institution. Bureau of Ethnology. Bulletin (1066-1697)
Indexed: AnthLit, BIOSIS Prev, BiolAb, EIP, IBSS, RefZh.
—BLDSC (8311.490000), Linda Hall. **CCC.**
Published by: Smithsonian Institution Press, PO Box 37012, Washington, DC 20013-7012. TEL 202-633-3017, schol.press@si.edu, http://www.si.edu/publications/. Circ: 2,100.

301 IND
SNENG KHASI. Text in Khasi. 1977. m. INR 9, USD 9. adv. bk.rev.
Published by: Hipshon Roy Ed. & Pub., Riatsamthiah, Shillong, Meghalaya 793 001, India. Circ: 600.

306.4 USA ISSN 0155-977X
HM1
➤ **SOCIAL ANALYSIS**; international journal of cultural and social practice. Text in English. 1979. 3/yr. USD 45, GBP 30 to individuals; USD 152, GBP 115 combined subscription to institutions print & online eds. (effective 2005). adv. back issues avail. **Document type:** *Journal, Academic/Scholarly.* **Description:** Publishes both works that address philosophical and ontological orientations of understanding, and those which investigate the forces involved in the production of human suffering.
Related titles: Online - full text ed.: (from EBSCO Publishing, Gale Group, R M I T Publishing).
Indexed: AICP, AnthLit, AusPAIS, BAS, EI, IBSS, PSA, SOPODA, SPPI, SSA, SociolAb.
—BLDSC (8318.041600), IE, Infotrieve, ingenta.
Published by: (University of Adelaide, Department of Anthropology AUS), Berghahn Books Inc., 150 Broadway, Rm 812, New York, NY 10038-4307. journals@berghahnbooks.com, http://www.berghahnbooks.com/journals/sa. Adv. contact Kristina Graaff. Circ: 300.

306 GBR ISSN 0964-0282
GN575 CODEN: SNTHE3
➤ **SOCIAL ANTHROPOLOGY.** Text in English. 1992. 3/yr. GBP 104 to institutions; USD 178 in North America to institutions; GBP 114 combined subscription to institutions print & online eds.; USD 192 combined subscription in North America to institutions print & online eds. (effective 2006). adv. bk.rev. back issues avail. **Document type:** *Journal, Academic/Scholarly.* **Description:** Covers all aspects of anthropology and social anthropology.
Related titles: Online - full text ed.: ISSN 1469-8676. GBP 98 to institutions; USD 165 in North America to institutions (effective 2006) (from EBSCO Publishing, O C L C Online Computer Library Center, Inc., Swets Information Services).
Indexed: AICP, ASSIA, AnthLit, BrArAb, IBSS, L&LBA, PsycInfo, PsycholAb, SOPODA, SSA, SociolAb.
—BLDSC (8318.053750), IE, Infotrieve, ingenta. **CCC.**
Published by: (European Association of Social Anthropologists), Cambridge University Press, The Edinburgh Bldg, Shaftesbury Rd, Cambridge, CB2 2RU, United Kingdom. TEL 44-1223-312393, FAX 44-1223-315052, journals@cambridge.org, http://uk.cambridge.org/journals. Ed. Peter Pels. R&P Linda Nicol TEL 44-1223-325757. Adv. contact Rebecca Curtis TEL 44-1223-325757. **Subscr. to:** Cambridge University Press, 100 Brook Hill Dr, West Nyack, NY 10994. TEL 845-353-7500, FAX 845-353-4141, subscriptions_newyork@cambridge.org

301 300 NLD ISSN 1563-1036
SOCIAL JUSTICE; anthropology, peace and human rights. Text in English. s-a.
Formerly: Human Peace
Indexed: AnthLit, PSA, SociolAb.
Published by: International Union of Anthropological and Ethnological Sciences, c/o Dr. Peter J M Nas, Leiden University, Wassenaarseweg 52, Leiden, 2300 RB, Netherlands. http://www.leidenuniv.nl/fsw/iuaes/index.htm. Ed. Robert A Rubinstein.

SOCIAL SCIENCE INFORMATION; information sur les sciences sociales. see *SOCIAL SCIENCES: COMPREHENSIVE WORKS*

SOCIALNO DELO/SOCIAL WORK. see *SOCIAL SERVICES AND WELFARE*

301 ESP ISSN 0213-8670
SOCIEDAD DE ESTUDIOS VASCOS. BOLETIN. Text in Spanish. 1919-1936; resumed 1981. q. back issues avail. **Document type:** *Bulletin, Academic/Scholarly.*
Published by: Eusko Ikaskuntza/Sociedad de Estudios Vascos, Palacio Miramar, Miraconcha 48, Donostia, San Sebastian 20007, Spain. TEL 34-943-310855, FAX 34-943-213956, ei-sev@sc.ehu.es, http://www.eusko-ikaskuntza.org/.

301 ESP
SOCIEDAD DE ESTUDIOS VASCOS. MEMORIA. Text in Spanish. 1918-1934; resumed 1978. biennial. price varies. back issues avail. **Document type:** *Monographic series, Academic/Scholarly.*
Published by: Eusko Ikaskuntza/Sociedad de Estudios Vascos, Palacio Miramar, Miraconcha 48, Donostia, San Sebastian 20007, Spain. TEL 34-943-310855, FAX 34-943-213956, ei-sev@sc.ehu.es, http://www.eusko-ikaskuntza.org/.

301 FRA ISSN 0037-8984
CODEN: BSANA8
SOCIETE D'ANTHROPOLOGIE DE PARIS. BULLETINS & MEMOIRES. Text in French. 1860. 4/yr. FRF 396.90 in Europe (effective 1999). adv. bk.rev. **Document type:** *Academic/Scholarly.*
Indexed: AICP, AnthLit, BIOSIS Prev, BiolAb, ExcerpMed, RASB, SSCI.
—GNLM, IE, Infotrieve, Linda Hall.
Published by: Societe d'Anthropologie de Paris, Musee de l'Homme, 17 place du Trocadero, Paris, 75116, France. TEL 33-1-44057255, FAX 33-1-44057241, jakobi@mnhn.fr, peyre@mnhn.fr. Ed. Pierre Darli. Pub. Alain Froment. R&P Evelyne Peyre. Adv. contact Lucienne Jakobi.

301 FRA ISSN 0037-9174
E51
➤ **SOCIETE DES AMERICANISTES. JOURNAL.** Text in English, French, Portuguese, Spanish. 1896; N.S. 1903. s-a. EUR 41.20 (effective 2002). adv. bk.rev. bibl.; charts; illus.; abstr. cum.index. 500 p./no.; **Document type:** *Academic/Scholarly.*
Related titles: Microfiche ed.: N.S.
Indexed: AICP, AmH&L, AnthLit, BibLing, DIP, HAPI, HistAb, IBR, IBSS, IBZ, PCI, RASB, RI-1, RI-2, RILM, SSCI.
—IE.
Published by: Societe des Americanistes, Musee de l'Homme, 17 place du Trocadero, Paris, 75116, France. TEL 33-01-47046311, jsa@mae.u-paris10.fr. Ed. Dominique Michelet. R&P, Adv. contact Michele Ballinger. Circ: 1,000.

305.8 AUS
SOCIETE DES ETUDES OCEANIENNES. BULLETIN. Text in French.
Indexed: AnthLit.
Published by: Societe des Etudes Oceaniennes, BP 110, Papeete, TAS, Australia. TEL 689-419-603.

SOCIETE DES EXPLORATEURS ET DES VOYAGEURS FRANCAIS. ANNUAIRE GENERAL. see *GEOGRAPHY*

SOCIETE D'ETUDES LINGUISTIQUES ET ANTHROPOLOGIQUES DE FRANCE. APPLICATIONS ET TRANSFERTS. see *LINGUISTICS*

SOCIETE D'ETUDES LINGUISTIQUES ET ANTHROPOLOGIQUES DE FRANCE. NUMERO SPECIAL. see *LINGUISTICS*

301 CHE ISSN 0373-3076
CODEN: BSNGAI
SOCIETE NEUCHATELOISE DE GEOGRAPHIE. BULLETIN. Text in French. a.
Indexed: AnthLit, RefZh.
Published by: Societe Neuchateloise de Geographie, Case Postale 53, Neuchatel, 2006, Switzerland. http://www.unine.ch/geographie/bsng.html, http://www.unine.ch/geographie/sng.html.

301 CHE ISSN 0582-1592
E51 CODEN: BAGNEI
SOCIETE SUISSE DES AMERICANISTES. BULLETIN/ SCHWEIZERISCHE AMERIKANISTEN-GESELLSCHAFT. BULLETIN. Text in English, French, German, Portuguese, Spanish. 1950; N.S. 1980. a. CHF 35 to members. adv. bibl.; charts; illus. **Document type:** *Academic/Scholarly.*
Indexed: AICP, AnthLit, HAPI, RefZh.
—BLDSC (2756.700000).
Published by: Societe Suisse des Americanistes/Schweizerische Amerikanisten-Gesellschaft, 65-67 Boulevard Carl-Vogt, Geneva, 1205, Switzerland. TEL 41-22-4184544, FAX 41-22-4184551. Ed. Gerhard Baer. R&P, Adv. contact Cendrine Hostettler. Circ: 750.

SOCIETY/SOCIETE. see *SOCIOLOGY*

301 USA
SOCIETY FOR APPLIED ANTHROPOLOGY. NEWSLETTER. Text in English. 1990. q. membership. **Document type:** *Newsletter.* **Description:** Includes news and items of current interest for members and others interested in the application of the social and behavioral sciences to contemporary issues.
Published by: Society for Applied Anthropology, PO Box 2436, Oklahoma City, OK 73101. TEL 405-843-5113, FAX 405-843-8553, info@sfaa.net, http://www.sfaa.net/newsletter/newsletter.html. Ed. Michael Whiteford. Circ: 2,600 (paid).

301 150 GBR ISSN 1367-4102
SOCIETY FOR PHYCHOLOGICAL ANTHROPOLOGY. PUBLICATIONS. Text in English. 1992. irreg., latest 2002. price varies. **Document type:** *Monographic series, Academic/Scholarly.*
Indexed: AnthLit.
—ingenta.
Published by: (Society for Psychological Anthropology USA), Cambridge University Press, The Edinburgh Bldg, Shaftesbury Rd, Cambridge, CB2 2RU, United Kingdom. TEL 44-1223-312393, FAX 44-1223-315052, information@cambridge.org, https://booktrade.cambridge.org/series.asp?series=PSPA, http://www.cup.cam.ac.uk/.

301 USA ISSN 1535-5632
GN17.3.E85
SOCIETY FOR THE ANTHROPOLOGY OF EUROPE. JOURNAL. Text in English. 2001. s-a. USD 43 to non-members (effective 2006). bk.rev. **Document type:** *Journal, Academic/Scholarly.* **Description:** Publishes articles based on empirical research relating to the anthropology of Europe and sessions of meetings.
Related titles: Online - full content ed.: ISSN 1556-5823.
—CCC.
Published by: (Society for the Anthropology of Europe), University of California Press, Journals Division, 2000 Center St, Ste 303, Berkeley, CA 94704-1223. TEL 510-643-7154, FAX 510-642-9917, journals@ucpress.edu, http://www.h-net.org/~sae/sae/JSAE.htm, http://www.ucpress.edu/journals. Ed. Lynn Maners.

SOCIETY FOR THE STUDY OF HUMAN BIOLOGY. SYMPOSIUM SERIES. see *BIOLOGY—Physiology*

SOCIOLINGUISTIQUE; systemes de langues et interactions sociales et culturelles. see *LINGUISTICS*

SOCIOLOGICAL OBSERVATIONS. see *SOCIOLOGY*

SOCIOLOGY WORKING PAPERS. see *SOCIOLOGY*

SOJOURN; journal of social issues in Southeast Asia. see *SOCIOLOGY*

SOLOMON ISLANDS MUSEUM ASSOCIATION. JOURNAL. see *MUSEUMS AND ART GALLERIES*

305.8 ZAF ISSN 0379-8860
GN301 CODEN: SAJEEN
➤ **SOUTH AFRICAN JOURNAL OF ETHNOLOGY/SUID-AFRIKAANSE TYDSKRIF VIR ETNOLOGIE.** Text in English; Summaries in Afrikaans, English. 1978. q. ZAR 190 to institutions; USD 72 foreign (effective 2000). adv. index. **Document type:** *Academic/Scholarly.* **Description:** Publishes original articles of research, updates and comments in the fields of anthropology, ethnology and archaeology.
Related titles: Online - full text ed.: (from EBSCO Publishing).
Indexed: AICP, ASD, AbAn, AnthLit, ERA, ETA, IBSS, ISAP, MEA, RHEA, SEA, SENA, SOMA, SWA, TEA.

Published by: (Association of Afrikaans Ethnologists), South African Bureau for Scientific Publications, PO Box 11663, Pretoria, Hatfield 0028, South Africa. TEL 27-12-322-6404, FAX 27-12-320-7803, bspman@icon.co.zaac.za, http://www.safest.org.za/bsp. Ed., Adv. contact F C de Beer. Circ: 350. **Co-publisher:** South African Society fo Cultural Anthropologists.

➤ **SOUTH AFRICAN MUSEUM. ANNALS/SUID-AFRIKAANSE MUSEUM. ANNALE.** see *BIOLOGY*

➤ **SOUTH ASIA**; journal of South Asian studies. see *HISTORY—History Of Asia*

301 576.5 363.7 300 IND ISSN 0257-7348
GN1
➤ **SOUTH ASIAN ANTHROPOLOGIST.** Text in English. 1980. s-a. USD 95 to institutions (effective 2006). bk.rev. abstr.; bibl.; charts; illus.; maps; stat. cum.index: 1980-1993 in vol.15. 70 p./no. 2 cols./p.; back issues avail. **Document type:** *Journal, Academic/Scholarly.* **Description:** Publishes articles on any field of anthropology relevant to South Asia, including biological, genetical, environmental and developmental studies in South Asia.
Indexed: AICP, AgrForAb, AnBrAb, AnthLit, BAS, FPA, ForAb, HortAb, I&DA, IBR, IBSS, IBZ, NutrAb, RDA, RiceAb, S&F, TDB, WAE&RSA.
—BLDSC (8348.621000), IE, ingenta.
Published by: (Sarat Chandra Roy Institute of Anthropological Studies), Serials Publications, 4, B.S.S. Hall, Khyber Pass Market, Civil Lines, Delhi, 110 054, India. TEL 91-11-3811659, FAX 91-11-3812678, serials@satyam.net.in, http://www.scientificpub.com/bookdetails.php?booktransid=468&bookid=464. Ed. P Dash Sharma. Circ: 200 (paid); 100 (controlled). **Subscr. to:** Scientific Publishers, 5-A New Pali Rd., Near Hotel Taj Hari Mahal, PO Box 91, Jodhpur, Rajasthan 342 003, India. journals@scientificpub.com, http://www.scientificpub.com.

301 954 GBR ISSN 1474-6689
DS335
▼ ➤ **SOUTH ASIAN POPULAR CULTURE.** Text in English. 2003 (Apr.). s-a. GBP 156, USD 258 combined subscription to institutions print & online eds. (effective 2006). illus. **Document type:** *Journal, Academic/Scholarly.* **Description:** An interdisciplinary journal for the social sciences and humanities.
Related titles: Online - full text ed.: ISSN 1474-6697. GBP 148, USD 245 to institutions (effective 2006) (from EBSCO Publishing, IngentaConnect, O C L C Online Computer Library Center, Inc., Swets Information Services).
Indexed: IBSS.
—BLDSC (8348.628900), IE. **CCC.**
Published by: Routledge (Subsidiary of: Taylor & Francis Group), 4 Park Sq, Milton Park, Abingdon, Oxon OX14 4RN, United Kingdom. TEL 44-1235-828600, FAX 44-1235-829000, info@routledge.co.uk, http://www.tandf.co.uk/journals/titles/14746689.asp, http://www.routledge.co.uk. Eds. Dr. Gita Rajan, Moti Gokulsing, Dr. Rajinder Kumer Dudrah. **Subscr. to:** Taylor & Francis Ltd, Journals Customer Service, Rankine Rd, Basingstoke, Hants RG24 8PR, United Kingdom. TEL 44-1256-813000, FAX 44-1256-330245, enquiry@tandf.co.uk.

301 USA ISSN 0081-2994
GN2
SOUTHERN ANTHROPOLOGICAL SOCIETY. PROCEEDINGS. Text in English. 1968. a., latest vol.35, 2002. price varies. adv. **Document type:** *Proceedings.*
Indexed: AnthLit.
—BLDSC (8352.700000).
Published by: (Southern Anthropological Society), University of Georgia Press, 330 Research Dr, Athens, GA 30602-4901. TEL 706-369-6163, FAX 706-369-6131, http://www.smcm.edu/sas/proceedings.htm. Ed. Chris Toumey.

301 USA
SOUTHWESTERN ANTHROPOLOGICAL ASSOCIATION NEWSLETTER. Text in English. 1959. q. bk.rev. **Document type:** *Newsletter, Academic/Scholarly.* **Description:** Includes information on association meetings and members.
Published by: Southwestern Anthropological Association, c/o San Jose State University, Dept. of Anthropology, One Washington Square, San Jose, CA 95192-0113. TEL 408-578-1989, swaa@att.net. Ed. Karl L Designs.

SOUTHWESTERN LORE; journal of Colorado archaeology. see *ARCHAEOLOGY*

301 IND
SPECTRA OF ANTHROPOLOGICAL PROGRESS. Text in English. 1978. irreg. INR 25, USD 6.
Indexed: AnthLit, BAS.
Published by: University of Delhi, Department of Anthropology, New Delhi, 110 007, India.

301 SCG ISSN 0374-082X
AS346
SRPSKA AKADEMIJA NAUKA I UMETNOSTI. ETNOGRAFSKI INSTITUT. GLASNIK. Text in Serbo-Croatian; Summaries in English. 1894. irreg. bk.rev. bibl. **Document type:** *Academic/Scholarly.*
Indexed: AICP, AnthLit.
—Linda Hall.
Published by: (Etnografski Institut YUG), Srpska Akademija Nauka i Umetnosti/Serbian Academy of Arts and Sciences, Knez Mihailova 35, Belgrade, 11000. TEL 381-11-3342400, FAX 381-11-182825, SASApres@bib.sanu.ac.yu, http://www.sanu.ac.yu.

301 SCG
SRPSKA AKADEMIJA NAUKA I UMETNOSTI. ETNOGRAFSKI INSTITUT. ZBORNIK RADOVA. Text in Serbo-Croatian; Summaries in French. 1950. irreg.
Indexed: AICP, AnthLit.
Published by: (Etnografski Institut YUG), Srpska Akademija Nauka i Umetnosti/Serbian Academy of Arts and Sciences, Knez Mihailova 35, Belgrade, 11000. TEL 381-11-3342400, FAX 381-11-182825, SASApres@bib.sanu.ac.yu, http://www.sanu.ac.yu.

305.8 SCG ISSN 0081-4067
SRPSKI ETNOGRAFSKI ZBORNIK. NASELJA I POREKLO STANOVNISTVA. Text in Serbo-Croatian; Summaries in English, French, German, Russian. 1902. irreg. Price varies.
Published by: Srpska Akademija Nauka i Umetnosti/Serbian Academy of Arts and Sciences, Knez Mihailova 35, Belgrade, 11000. TEL 381-11-3342400, FAX 381-11-182825, SASApres@bib.sanu.ac.yu, http://www.sanu.ac.yu. Circ: 1,000. **Dist. by:** Prosveta, Terazije 16, Belgrade, Serbia, Yugoslavia.

301 SCG ISSN 0081-4075
SRPSKI ETNOGRAFSKI ZBORNIK. RASPRAVE I GRADJA. Text in Serbo-Croatian; Summaries in English, French, German, Russian. 1934. irreg. price varies.
Published by: Srpska Akademija Nauka i Umetnosti/Serbian Academy of Arts and Sciences, Knez Mihailova 35, Belgrade, 11000. TEL 381-11-3342400, FAX 381-11-182825, SASApres@bib.sanu.ac.yu, http://www.sanu.ac.yu. Circ: 1,000. **Dist. by:** Prosveta, Terazije 16, Belgrade, Serbia, Yugoslavia.

301 SCG ISSN 0081-4083
SRPSKI ETNOGRAFSKI ZBORNIK. SRPSKE NARODNE UMOTVORINE. Text in Serbo-Croatian; Summaries in English, French, German, Russian. 1927. irreg. Price varies.
Published by: Srpska Akademija Nauka i Umetnosti/Serbian Academy of Arts and Sciences, Knez Mihailova 35, Belgrade, 11000. TEL 381-11-3342400, FAX 381-11-182825, SASApres@bib.sanu.ac.yu, http://www.sanu.ac.yu. Circ: 1,000. **Dist. by:** Prosveta, Terazije 16, Belgrade, Serbia, Yugoslavia.

301 SCG ISSN 0081-4091
SRPSKI ETNOGRAFSKI ZBORNIK. ZIVOT I OBICAJI NARODNI. Text in Serbo-Croatian; Summaries in English, French, German, Russian. 1894. irreg. Price varies. reprints avail.
Published by: Srpska Akademija Nauka i Umetnosti/Serbian Academy of Arts and Sciences, Knez Mihailova 35, Belgrade, 11000. TEL 381-11-3342400, FAX 381-11-182825, SASApres@bib.sanu.ac.yu, http://www.sanu.ac.yu. Circ: 1,000. **Dist. by:** Prosveta, Terazije 16, Belgrade, Serbia, Yugoslavia.

STAATLICHES MUSEUM FUER VOELKERKUNDE DRESDEN. ABHANDLUNGEN UND BERICHTE. see *MUSEUMS AND ART GALLERIES*

305.4 USA
STATE UNIVERSITY OF NEW YORK AT ALBANY. INSTITUTE FOR MESOAMERICAN STUDIES. MONOGRAPH SERIES. Text in English. 1977. irreg., latest vol.11, 1999. price varies. back issues avail. **Document type:** *Monographic series, Academic/Scholarly.* **Description:** Examines and discusses topics in mesoamerican cultural anthropology and history.
Published by: State University of New York at Albany, Institute for Mesoamerican Studies, Department of Anthropology, Social Science 263, 1400 Washington Ave, Albany, NY 12222. TEL 518-442-4722, ims@csc.albany.edu, http://www.albany.edu/anthro/imspage.html. Ed. Michael E Smith. **Orders to:** University of Texas Press, Journals Division, PO Box 7819, Austin, TX 78713. TEL 800-252-3206.

301 ITA ISSN 0394-7963
STORIA, ANTROPOLOGIA E SCIENZE DEL LINGUAGGIO. Text in Italian. 1986. 3/yr.
Published by: Bulzoni Editore, Via dei Liburni 14, Rome, 00185, Italy. bulzoni@bulzoni.it, http://www.bulzoni.it.

301 ITA ISSN 0392-6788
STUDI PER L'ECOLOGIA DEL QUATERNARIO. Text in Italian. 1979. a. bk.rev. **Document type:** *Academic/Scholarly.* **Description:** Contains previously unpublished works concerning ecology of the Quaternary era, prehistoric ecology, palaeoethnology, Quaternary geology, human paleontology and anthropology.
Indexed: AnthLit.
Published by: Universita degli Studi di Firenze, Laboratori di Antropologia, Via del Proconsolo, 12, Florence, 50122, Italy. TEL 39-055-214049, FAX 39-055-283358, antropos@unifi.it, http://www.unifi.it/unifi/antrop. Ed. E Borzatti von Loewenstern. Circ: 800.

301 BEL
STUDIA ANTHROPOLOGICA. Text in Dutch. 1987. irreg., latest vol.4, 1999. price varies. back issues avail. **Document type:** *Monographic series, Academic/Scholarly.* **Description:** Examines and analyzes topics of anthropological inquiry.
Published by: Leuven University Press, Blijde Inkomststraat 5, Leuven, 3000, Belgium. TEL 32-16-325345, FAX 32-16-325352, university.press@upers.kuleuven.ac.be, http://www.kuleuven.ac.be/upers.

305.8 SWE ISSN 0491-2705
STUDIA ETHNOGRAPHICA UPSALIENSIA. Text in Swedish. 1956. a. back issues avail. **Document type:** *Academic/Scholarly.*
Indexed: RASB.
Published by: (Uppsala Universitet, Institutionen foer Allmaem och Jaemfoerande Ethnografi), Almqvist & Wiksell International, P O Box 7634, Stockholm, 10394, Sweden. FAX 46-8-24-25-43, info@city.akademibokhandeln.se, http://www.akademibokhandeln.se.

305.8 SWE ISSN 0346-900X
STUDIA ETHNOLOGICA UPSALIENSIA. Text in Swedish. 1976. irreg., latest vol.17, 1996. price varies. back issues avail. **Document type:** *Monographic series, Academic/Scholarly.*
Related titles: ◆ Series of: Acta Universitatis Upsaliensis. ISSN 0346-5462.
Published by: (Uppsala Universitet), Uppsala Universitet, Acta Universitatis Upsaliensis/University Publications from Uppsala, PO Box 256, Uppsala, 75105, Sweden. TEL 46-18-4713922, http://www.ub.uu.se/upu/auu. Ed. Bengt Landgren.

305.8 FIN ISSN 1235-1954
GN585.F53
STUDIA FENNICA. ETHNOLOGICA. Text in Multiple languages. 1933. irreg. **Document type:** *Monographic series, Academic/Scholarly.*
Supersedes in part (in 1992): Studia Fennica (0085-6835)
Indexed: AICP, IBSS, MLA-IB, RASB.
Published by: Suomalaisen Kirjallisuuden Seura/Finnish Literature Society, Hallituskatu 1, PO Box 259, Helsinki, 00171, Finland. TEL 358-9-131231, FAX 358-9-13123220, sks-fl@finlit.fi, http://www/finlit.fi.

301 CHE ISSN 0570-3085
STUDIA INSTITUTI ANTHROPOS. Text in Dutch, English, French, German. 1950. irreg., latest vol.48, 2000. price varies. illus. **Document type:** *Monographic series, Academic/Scholarly.*
Published by: (Anthropos Institut), Academic Press Fribourg, Perolles 42, Fribourg, 1705, Switzerland. TEL 41-26-4264311, FAX 41-26-4264300.

STUDIA MYTHOLOGICA SLAVICA. see *ETHNIC INTERESTS*

301 USA ISSN 0585-5578
STUDIA SUMIRO-HUNGARICA. Text in English, Hungarian. 1968. irreg., latest vol.3, 1974. bibl.; charts; illus.
Published by: Gilgamesh Publishing Co., 6050 Boulevard East, 20-A, W. New York, NJ 07093. Ed. Miklos Erdy. Circ: 2,000.

STUDIEN ZUR INTERKULTURELLEN PHILOSOPHIE/ETUDES DE PHILOSOPHIE INTERCULTURELLE/STUDIES IN INTERCULTURAL PHILOSOPHY. see *PHILOSOPHY*

301 DEU ISSN 0170-3544
➤ **STUDIEN ZUR KULTURKUNDE.** Text in English, German. 1948. irreg., latest vol.119, 2001. price varies. illus.; maps. back issues avail. **Document type:** *Monographic series, Academic/Scholarly.* **Description:** Contains monographic studies on mostly African cultures covering art, law, kinship and literature.
Indexed: PCI, RASB.
Published by: (Universitaet Frankfurt, Frobenius Institut), Ruediger Koeppe Verlag, Wendelinstr 73-75, Cologne, 50933, Germany. TEL 49-221-4911236, FAX 49-221-4994336, info@koeppe.de, http://www.koeppe.de. Eds. Beatrix Heintze, Heinz Kohl.

➤ **STUDIES IN HISTORICAL ARCHAEOETHNOLOGY.** see *HISTORY—History Of Europe*

306.44089 USA ISSN 0733-5776
STUDIES IN MAYAN LINGUISTICS. Text in English. 1975. irreg. price varies. **Document type:** *Monographic series.*
Indexed: AnthLit.
Published by: University of Missouri at Columbia, Department of Anthropology, 107 Swallow Hall, Columbia, MO 65211-1440. TEL 314-882-3573.

STUDIES IN THE SOCIAL AND CULTURAL FOUNDATIONS OF LANGUAGE. see *LINGUISTICS*

306 IND ISSN 0972-639X
▼ **STUDIES OF TRIBES AND TRIBALS.** Text in English. 2003. 2/yr. INR 800, USD 30 to individuals; INR 1,000, USD 40 to institutions (effective 2004). **Document type:** *Journal, Academic/Scholarly.* **Description:** Aims to serve as a forum for original articles on all aspects of tribes and tribal systems.
Indexed: SociolAb.

Published by: Kamla-Raj Enterprises, Chawri Bazar, 2273 Gali Bari Paharwali, New Delhi, 110 006, India. TEL 91-124-5360430, FAX 91-124-2218073, kre@touchtelindia.net, http://www.krepublishers.com. Ed. Veena Bhasin. Pub. Ramesh Kumar. Circ: 125 (paid and controlled).

305.4 USA ISSN 1040-9548
STUDIES ON CULTURE AND SOCIETY. Text in English. 1986. irreg., latest vol.8. price varies. illus. back issues avail. **Document type:** *Monographic series, Academic/Scholarly.* **Description:** Publishes scholarly research on mesoamerican cultural anthropology and history.
—BLDSC (8490.319500).
Published by: State University of New York, Institute for Mesoamerican Studies, Department of Anthropology, Social Science 263, 1400 Washington Ave, Albany, NY 12222. TEL 518-442-4722, ims@albany.edu, ims@csc.albany.edu, http://www.albany.edu/ims/scultsoc.html, http://www.albany.edu/anthro/imspage.html. Ed. Louise Burkhart. R&P Louise Bukhart. **Orders to:** University of Texas Press, Journals Division, PO Box 7819, Austin, TX 78713. TEL 800-252-3206.

301 SDN ISSN 0562-5130
SUDAN SOCIETY/MUJTAMA. Text in Arabic, English. 1962. a.
Indexed: AICP.
Published by: University of Khartoum, Social Studies Society, Faculty of Economic and Social Studies, P O Box 321, Khartoum, Sudan.

305.8 FIN ISSN 0355-0214
SUOMALAIS-UGRILAISEN SEURA. AIKAKAUSKIRJA/SOCIETE FINNO-OUGRIENNE. JOURNAL. Text in English, Finnish, French, German, Russian. 1885. a. EUR 24 to non-members (effective 2005). **Document type:** *Proceedings, Academic/Scholarly.*
Indexed: BibLing, IBSS, MLA-IB, RASB.
Published by: Suomalais-Ugrilainen Seura/Finno-Ugrian Society, Mariankatu 7 A, PO Box 320, Helsinki, 00171, Finland. TEL 358-9-662149, FAX 358-9-6988249, http://www.sgr.fi. Eds. Tapani Salminen, Jussi Ylikoski. Circ: 600. **Dist. by:** Tiedekirja OY - Vetenskapsbokhandeln, Kirkkokatu 14, Helsinki 00170, Finland.

306.44089 FIN ISSN 0359-7679
SUOMALAIS-UGRILAISEN SEURAN KANSATIETEELLISIA JULKAISUJA/TRAVAUX ETHNOGRAPHIQUES DE LA SOCIETE FINNO-OUGRIENNE. Text in Multiple languages. 1899. irreg., latest 2004. price varies. back issues avail. **Document type:** *Monographic series, Academic/Scholarly.*
Formerly (until 1983): Kansatieteellisi Julkaisuja (0356-5777)
Indexed: IBSS.
Published by: Suomalais-Ugrilainen Seura/Finno-Ugrian Society, Mariankatu 7 A, PO Box 320, Helsinki, 00171, Finland. TEL 358-9-662149, FAX 358-9-6988249, ulla-maija.kulonen@helsinki.fi, http://www.sgr.fi/english/ktjulkaisuja_engl.html. **Dist. by:** Tiedekirja OY - Vetenskapsbokhandeln, Kirkkokatu 14, Helsinki 00170, Finland.

306.44089 FIN ISSN 0355-0230
PH1
SUOMALAIS-UGRILAISEN SEURAN TOIMITUKSIA/SOCIETE FINNO-OUGRIENNE. MEMOIRES. Text in Multiple languages. 1890. irreg., latest vol.239. price varies. **Document type:** *Academic/Scholarly.*
Indexed: BibLing, MLA-IB, RASB.
Published by: Suomalais-Ugrilainen Seura/Finno-Ugrian Society, Mariankatu 7 A, PO Box 320, Helsinki, 00171, Finland. TEL 358-09-662149, FAX 358-09-632501. **Dist. by:** Tiedekirja OY - Vetenskapsbokhandeln.

301 FIN ISSN 0355-3930
➤ **SUOMEN ANTROPOLOGI/ANTROPOLOGI I FINLAND/FINNISH ANTHROPOLOGICAL SOCIETY. JOURNAL.** Text in English, Finnish, Swedish. 1976. q. EUR 30; EUR 7.50 per issue (effective 2004). bk.rev. **Document type:** *Journal, Academic/Scholarly.* **Description:** Contains scholarly articles concerning research in anthropology and related fields.
Indexed: AICP, AnthLit, MLA, MLA-IB, RASB, RILM.
Published by: Suomen Antropologinen Seura/Finnish Anthropological Society, University of Helsinki, Dept of Social and Cultural Anthropology, PO Box 59, Helsinki, 00014, Finland. TEL 358-9-19123841, FAX 358-9-19123006, http://www.helsinki.fi/antropologia/suomenantropologi.htm. Eds. Karen Armstrong TEL 358-9-19122803, Timo Kallinen. R&P Karen Armstrong TEL 358-9-19122803. Circ: 600 (paid and controlled).

301 FIN ISSN 0356-0481
SUOMEN ANTROPOLOGISEN SEURA. TOIMITUKSIA/FINNISH ANTHROPOLOGICAL SOCIETY. TRANSACTIONS. Text in English, Finnish. 1977. irreg. price varies. **Document type:** *Monographic series, Abstract/Index.*
Published by: Suomen Antropologinen Seura/Finnish Anthropological Society, University of Helsinki, Dept of Social and Cultural Anthropology, PO Box 59, Helsinki, 00014, Finland. TEL 358-9-19123841, FAX 358-9-19123006. Ed. Timo Kallinen.

305.897 GBR ISSN 1353-0488
SURVIVAL (LONDON, 1993). Text in English. 1983. s-a. GBP 50, USD 100 (effective 2000). bk.rev.; film rev. **Document type:** *Newsletter.* **Description:** Reports on latest issues facing tribal peoples around the world.
Formerly: Survival International News (0265-1327)
Related titles: French ed.; Italian ed.; Spanish ed.
Indexed: AICP, AnthLit, SSI.
Published by: Survival, 11-15 Emerald St, London, WC1N 3QL, United Kingdom. TEL 44-20-7242-1441, FAX 44-20-7242-1771, info@survival-international.org, http://www.survival-international.org. Ed. Jonathan Mazower. Circ: 20,000.

SWEDEN. STATISTISKA CENTRALBYRAAN. STATISTISKA MEDDELANDEN. SERIE KU, KULTUR. see *ANTHROPOLOGY—Abstracting, Bibliographies, Statistics*

SYMBOLS. see *ARCHAEOLOGY*

305.8 FRA ISSN 0294-7080
BL2462.5
SYSTEMES DE PENSEE EN AFRIQUE NOIRE. Text in French. 1975. a.
Indexed: AnthLit.
Published by: Ecole Pratique des Hautes Etudes, 45-47 rue des Ecoles, Paris, 75005, France. http://www.ephe.sorbonne.fr.

301 MEX ISSN 0185-6286
F1219
T R A C E. (Travaux et Recherches dans les Ameriques du Centre) Text in French, Spanish. 1978. s-a. price varies. adv. bk.rev. **Description:** Contains social science articles about Central America and the West Indies.
Former titles (until 1984): Centre d'Etudes Mexicaines et Centramericaines. Bulletin; Mission Archeologique et Ethnologique Francaise au Mexique
Indexed: AICP, AnthLit, IBR.
Published by: (France. Ministere des Affaires Etrangeres FRA), Centre d'Etudes Mexicaines et Centramericaines, Sierra Leona 330, Apdo. 41-879, Mexico City, DF 11000, Mexico. TEL 540-59-21, FAX 540-59-23. Ed. Joelle Gaillac. Circ: 2,000.

301 HUN
TABULA. Text in Hungarian; Summaries in English, Russian. 1956-1994; N.S. 1998. s-a. per issue exchange basis. bk.rev. **Document type:** *Monographic series.*
Supersedes (in 1998): Neprajzi Kozlemenyek (0028-2774)
Indexed: RASB.
Published by: Neprajzi Muzeum/Ethnographical Museum, Kossuth Lajos ter 12, Budapest, 1055, Hungary. TEL 36-1-326340, FAX 36-2-692419, kili@post.nem.hu. Ed. Forrai Ibolya.

306.4 USA ISSN 1541-9207
GN301
TAKING SIDES: CLASHING VIEWS ON CONTROVERSIAL ISSUES IN CULTURAL ANTHROPOLOGY. Text in English. 2002 (Dec.). biennial, latest 2002, 1st ed. USD 22.50 per vol. (effective 2005). **Document type:** *Academic/Scholarly.*
Published by: McGraw-Hill - Dushkin (Subsidiary of: McGraw-Hill Higher Education), 2460 Kerper Blvd, Dubuque, IA 52001. TEL 800-243-6532, customer.service@mcgraw-hill.com, http://www.dushkin.com. Eds. Kirk M. Endicott, Robert L. Welsch.

301 USA CODEN: TEBIDX
TEBIWA. Text in English. 1958. irreg. USD 10. abstr. 10-yr. cum.index in vol. 11. reprint service avail. from PQC. **Document type:** *Monographic series, Academic/Scholarly.*
Former titles: Tebiwa Miscellaneous Papers; (until vol.19): Tebiwa (0040-0823)
Related titles: Microform ed.: (from PQC).
Indexed: AICP, AbAn, AnthLit, BiolAb, SFA, WildRev, ZooRec.
—Linda Hall.
Published by: Idaho Museum of Natural History, Idaho State University, Box 8096, Pocatello, ID 83209. TEL 208-236-2262. Ed. E S Lohse. Circ: 500.

300 FRA ISSN 0181-0545
TECHNOLOGIES IDEOLOGIES PRATIQUES; revue d'anthropologie des connaissances. Text in French. 1971. s-a. EUR 38.50; EUR 31 to students (effective 2003). **Document type:** *Journal, Abstract/Index.*
Published by: (Universite de Provence), Editions Eres, 11 rue des Alouettes, Ramonville Saint-Agne, 31520, France. TEL 33-5-61751576, FAX 33-5-61735289, eres@edition-eres.com, http://www.edition-eres.com. Circ: 600.

301 ESP ISSN 0212-5552
TEMAS DE ANTROPOLOGIA ARAGONESA/ARAGONESE ANTHROPOLOGY. Text in Spanish. 1983. a.
Indexed: AnthLit.
—CINDOC.
Published by: Instituto Aragones de Antropologia, Edificio de Servicios de la Universidad de Zaragoza, Domingo Miral, 4, Comunidad de Aragon, Zaragoza, 50009, Spain. TEL 34-976-761000, iaa@posta.unizar.es.

301 AUS
➤ **TEMPUS.** Variant title: Archaeology and Material Culture Studies in Anthropology. Text in English. 1973; N.S. 1989. irreg., latest vol.6, 1996. price varies. back issues avail.; reprints avail. **Document type:** *Monographic series, Academic/Scholarly.* **Description:** Provides a forum for communicating anthropologically oriented studies in archaeology and material culture.
Supersedes (in 1989): Occasional Papers in Anthropology
Indexed: AICP, ZooRec.
—BLDSC (8790.327550).
Published by: University of Queensland, Anthropology Museum, St. Lucia, QLD 4072, Australia. TEL 61-7-33652674, FAX 61-7-33654696, l.satterthwait@mailbox.uq.edu.au, http://www.ansoc.uq.edu.au/archaeology/tempus.htm. Eds. Jay Hall, Leonn Satterthwait. Circ: 900 (paid).

301 USA
TENNESSEE ANTHROPOLOGICAL ASSOCIATION. MISCELLANEOUS PAPER. Text in English. 1976. irreg. USD 10 domestic membership; USD 20 foreign membership; includes Association Newsletter and Tennessee Anthropologist. **Document type:** *Monographic series.*
Indexed: AbAn.
Published by: Tennessee Anthropological Association, Department of Anthropology, University of Tennessee, Knoxville, TN 37996-0720. TEL 615-974-4408. R&P Charles H Faulkner. Circ: 300.

301 USA ISSN 0196-0377
TENNESSEE ANTHROPOLOGICAL ASSOCIATION. NEWSLETTER. Text in English. 1976. bi-m. USD 10 membership; USD 20 foreign membership; includes Miscellaneous Papers and Teexas Anthropologist. **Document type:** *Newsletter.*
Indexed: AICP, AbAn, AnthLit.
Published by: Tennessee Anthropological Association, Department of Anthropology, University of Tennessee, Knoxville, TN 37996-0720. TEL 615-974-4408. Ed. Charles H Faulkner.

301 ITA ISSN 0040-375X
E51
TERRA AMERIGA. Text in English, French, German, Italian, Portuguese, Spanish. 1965. q. USD 10. adv. bk.rev.; film rev.; rec.rev. charts; illus.; stat.; tr.lit. cum.index every 2 yrs.
Indexed: AnthLit, HAPI.
Published by: Associazione Italiana Studi Americanistici, Villa De Mari-Gruber, Corso Solferino 25, Genoa, GE 16122, Italy. Ed. Ernesto Lunardi. Circ: 2,000.

305.8 301 FRA ISSN 0760-5668
DC34 CODEN: TERRF6
➤ **TERRAIN.** Text in French; Abstracts in English. 1983. s-a. adv. bk.rev. illus. 186 p./no.; **Document type:** *Journal, Academic/Scholarly.* **Description:** Scientific journal focused on the social anthropology of Europe.
Indexed: AICP, IBR, IBSS, IBZ, L&LBA, RASB, RILM, SOPODA, SSA, SociolAb.
—BLDSC (8794.768000), IE, ingenta.
Published by: Ministere de la Culture, Mission du Patrimoine Ethnologique, 65 rue de Richelieu, Paris, 75002, France. TEL 33-01-40158738, FAX 33-01-40158733, christine.langlois@culture.fr, http://www.culture.gouv.fr/mpe. Ed., R&P Christine Langlois TEL 33-01-40158527. Adv. contact Dorine Bertrand TEL 33-01-40158663. **Subscr. to:** Resigssuer revue Terrain.

➤ **TEXAS PAN AMERICAN SERIES.** see *ETHNIC INTERESTS*

301 AUS ISSN 1326-2777
THAI - YUNNAN PROJECT NEWSLETTER. Text in English. 1988. biennial. **Document type:** *Newsletter.*
Related titles: Online - full text ed.
Published by: Australian National University, Research School of Pacific Studies, Department of Geography, Box 4, G.P.O, Canberra, ACT 2601, Australia. TEL 61-62-492478, http://www.nectec.or.th/thai-yunnan/.

THEM DAYS. see *FOLKLORE*

301 AUT ISSN 1024-5804
GN1
THEORETICAL ANTHROPOLOGY. Text in English. 1994. irreg.
Media: Online - full content.
Address: University of Vienna, Universitatsstrabe 7, Vienna, A-1010, Austria. theoretical.anthropology@univie.ac.at, http://www.univie.ac.at/voelkerkunde/theoretical-anthropology/welcome.html.

THRACO-DACICA. see *HISTORY—History Of Europe*

305.8 ROM
TIBISCUS. SERIA ETNOGRAFIE. Text in Romanian; Summaries in German. a.
Published by: Muzeul Banatului, Piata Huniade 1, Timisoara, Romania.

398 301 NOR ISSN 1502-7473
GR220
➤ **TIDSSKRIFT FOR KULTURFORSKNING.** Text in Norwegian. 2002. q. NOK 330 to individuals; NOK 550 to institutions (effective 2003). bk.rev. **Document type:** *Journal, Academic/Scholarly.* **Description:** Scientific journal in folklore/history and ethnology.
Published by: Novus Forlag, Herman Foss Gate 19, Oslo, 0171, Norway. TEL 47-22-717450, FAX 47-22-718107, novus@novus.no, http://www.novus.no. Ed. Inger Johanne Lyngoe.

301 USA ISSN 1545-4703
▼ **TIPITI**; journal of the Society for the Anthropology of Lowland South America. Text in English. 2003 (Fall). s-a. free to members (effective 2003). **Document type:** *Journal, Academic/Scholarly.*
Published by: Society for the Anthropology of Lowland South America, Dept. of Anthropology, SUNY at Buffalo, 380 MFAC, Buffalo, NY 14261. http://www.salsa-tipiti.org. Ed. Jeffrey Ehrenreich.

306.4 MEX ISSN 0185-0989
TLALOCAN; revista de fuentes para el conocimiento de las culturas indigenas de Mexico. Text in English, Spanish. 1942. irreg., latest vol.11, 1989. USD 17. illus.
Related titles: Online - full text ed.: (from EBSCO Publishing).
Indexed: AnthLit, BibInd, BibLing, HAPI, MLA, MLA-IB, RASB.
Published by: Universidad Nacional Autonoma de Mexico, Instituto de Investigaciones Filologicas, Circuito Mario de la Cueva, Zona Cultura, Ciudad Universitaria, Mexico, 04510, Mexico. TEL 52-5-622-7489, FAX 52-5-665-7874. Ed. Karen Dakin. Circ: 2,000.

301 ESP ISSN 0210-1483
TRABAJOS DE ANTROPOLOGIA. Text in Spanish. 1970. irreg. price varies. **Document type:** *Journal, Academic/Scholarly.*
Published by: (Universitat de Barcelona, Facultat de Biologia), Universitat de Barcelona, Servei de Publicacions, Gran Via Corts Catalanes 585, Barcelona, 08007, Spain. TEL 34-93-4021100, http://www.publicacions.ub.es.

301 PRT ISSN 0304-243X
TRABALHOS DE ANTROPOLOGIA E ETNOLOGIA. Text occasionally in English, French, German, Portuguese, Spanish. 1919. 8/yr. (in 2 vols., 4 nos./vol.). adv. bk.rev. illus. **Document type:** *Academic/Scholarly.* **Description:** Covers current research in archaeology, anthropology, sociology, and philosophy. Includes papers mainly on Portuguese and Spanish subjects.
Formerly (until 1947): Sociedade Portuguesa de Antropologia e Etnologia. Trabalhos (0871-8121)
Indexed: AICP, AnthLit, BHA.
Published by: Sociedade Portuguesa de Antropologia e Etnologia, Faculdade de Ciencias, Universidade do Porto, Praca Gomes Teixeira, Porto, 4099-002, Portugal. TEL 351-20-84656, FAX 351-20-26903, vojsoj@sapo.pt. Ed. Vitor Oliveira Jorge. Circ: 500.

305.8 398 GTM ISSN 0564-0571
GR118.G8
TRADICIONES DE GUATEMALA/TRADITIONS OF GUATEMALA. Text in Spanish. 1968. q.
Indexed: AnthLit, RILM.
Published by: Universidad de San Carlos de Guatemala, Centro de Estudios Folkloricos, Avda La Reforma 0-09,, Zona 10, Guatemala City, Guatemala.

301 SVN ISSN 0352-0447
DR381.S64
➤ **TRADITIONES**; zbornik instituta za slovensko narodopisje. Text in Slovenian; Summaries in English, French, German, Italian. 1972. a. SIT 3,300 domestic; USD 16 foreign (effective 2003). bk.rev. illus.; bibl. back issues avail. **Document type:** *Academic/Scholarly.* **Description:** Examines cultural anthropology, ethnology, ethnomusicology and ethnochorology.
Indexed: BHA, MLA, MLA-IB, RASB, RILM.
—KNAW.
Published by: Slovenska Akademija Znanosti in Umetnosti, Razred za Filoloske in Literarne Vede, Novi Trg 3-5, Ljubljana, 1000, Slovenia. TEL 386-1-4706100, FAX 386-1-4253423, maja.godina@zrc-sazu.si, hlp@zrc-sazu.si, http://www.zrc-sazu.si. Ed. Maja Godina-Golija. Pub. Dusan Merhar. Circ: 1,000. **Dist. by:** Biblioteka Slovenske Akademije Znanosti in Umetnosti, Novi Trg 3, Ljubljana 1000, Slovenia. TEL 386-1-4706245.

305.8 AUT ISSN 1560-182X
➤ **TRANS**; Internet journal for cultural studies. Text in German, French, English. 1997. s-a. adv. **Document type:** *Journal, Academic/Scholarly.* **Description:** A platform for discussion of transdiciplinary initiatives in the areas of literature, language, librarians and cultural studies.
Media: Online - full text.
Indexed: MLA-IB, PhilInd.
Published by: Institut zur Erforschung und Forderung Osterreichischer und Internationaler Literaturprozesse/ Research Institute for Austrian and International Literature and Cultural Studies, Postfach 74, Vienna, 1112, Austria. TEL 43-1-7481-63311, FAX 43-1-7481-63315, arlt@adis.at, http://www.inst.at/trans. Ed. Herbert Arlt. R&P, Adv. contact Andrea Rosenauer.

➤ **TRANSCULTURAL PSYCHIATRY.** see *MEDICAL SCIENCES—Psychiatry And Neurology*

301 305.8 FRA ISSN 1281-7066
TRANSDISCIPLINES. Text in French. 1997. irreg. **Document type:** *Monographic series, Academic/Scholarly.*
Published by: L' Harmattan, 5 rue de l'Ecole Polytechnique, Paris, 75005, France. TEL 33-1-43257651, FAX 33-1-43258203, http://www.editions-harmattan.fr.

301 USA ISSN 1051-0559
GN1
➤ **TRANSFORMING ANTHROPOLOGY.** Text in English. 1990. s-a. USD 38 to non-members; USD 46 to institutions (effective 2005 & 2006). adv. bk.rev. back issues avail. **Document type:** *Journal, Academic/Scholarly.* **Description:** Seeks to advance new conceptual and methodological frameworks for understanding all forms of human diversity and commonality.
Related titles: Online - full text ed.: (from bigchalk, ProQuest Information & Learning).
Indexed: AICP, AnthLit, SSA, SociolAb.
—CCC.
Published by: (Association of Black Anthropologists), University of California Press, Journals Division, 2000 Center St, Ste 303, Berkeley, CA 94704-1223. TEL 510-643-7154, FAX 510-642-9917, journals@ucpress.edu, http://www.ucpress.edu/journals/3a/tran/index.htm. Ed. Lee D. Baker. adv.: page USD 350; 7 x 9.3. Circ: 1,200 (paid).

301 USA
TRANSWORLD IDENTITY RESEARCH SERIES. Text in English. 1982. irreg., latest vol.4, 2000. USD 48 part 1; USD 48 part 2; USD 86 combined subscription part 1 & part 2 (effective 2003). **Document type:** *Monographic series.* **Description:** Monographs on integrative processes in global ramification from political and anthropological points of view.
Formerly (until 2001): Transworld Identity Series (0890-1562)
Published by: Eurolingua, PO Box 101, Bloomington, IN 47402-0101.

301 DEU ISSN 0082-6413
TRIBUS; Jahrbuch des Linden-Museums Stuttgart. Text in German; Text occasionally in English, French, Spanish. 1951. a. EUR 15 (effective 2003). bk.rev. 240 p./no.; back issues avail. **Document type:** *Yearbook, Academic/Scholarly.*
Indexed: AICP, AnthLit, BAS, BrArAb, DIP, IBR, IBSS, IBZ, IndIslam, NumL, RASB.
Published by: Linden-Museum Stuttgart-Staatliches Museum fuer Voelkerkunde, Hegelplatz 1, Stuttgart, 70174, Germany. TEL 49-711-2022400, FAX 49-711-2022590, sekretariat@lindenmuseum.de, http://www.lindenmuseum.de. Ed., R&P, Adv. contact Thomas Michel. Circ: 800 (controlled).

301 CHE ISSN 1420-7834
GN301
➤ **TSANTSA**; Zeitschrift der Schweizerischen Ethnologischen Gesellschaft. Text in English, French, German. 1996. a. CHF 35, EUR 24 per issue (effective 2005). illus. **Document type:** *Journal, Academic/Scholarly.*
Indexed: AnthLit.
Published by: (Schweizerische Ethnologische Gesellschaft), Seismo Verlag, Zaehringerstr 26, Zuerich, 8001, Switzerland. TEL 41-1-2611094, FAX 41-1-2511194, info@seismoverlag.ch, http://www.seismoverlag.ch. Circ: 900 (paid). **Dist. by:** Koch, Neff und Oetinger & Co., Postfach 800620, Stuttgart 70506, Germany. TEL 49-711-78992051, FAX 49-711-78991010.

➤ **TURCICA**; revue d'etudes turques: peuples, langues, cultures, etats. see *ASIAN STUDIES*

305.8 TUR ISSN 0082-6898
TURK ETNOGRAFYA DERGISI/TURKISH REVIEW OF ETHNOGRAPHY. Text in Turkish. 1956. a. per issue exchange basis. **Document type:** *Academic/Scholarly.*
Formerly: Turk Tarih-Arkeologya ve Etnografya Dergisi
Published by: Ministry of Culture, General Directorate of Monuments and Museums/Kultur Bakanligi, Anitlar ve Muzeler Genel Mudurlugu, Ulus - Ankara, 06100, Turkey. TEL 90-312-3104960, FAX 90-312-3111417. **Subscr. to:** Kultur Bakanligi, Doner sermaye Isletmeleri Merkez Mudurlugu, Adakale sok. No. 18, Kizilay-ankara, Turkey.

305.8 USA
U MUT MAYA. Text in English. irreg.
Indexed: AnthLit.
Address: P.O. Box 4686, Arcata, CA 95521. TEL 707-822-1515.

301 USA ISSN 1520-4340
U N L V JOURNAL OF ANTHROPOLOGY. (University of Nevada Las Vegas) Text in English. 1990. a. USD 15 membership (effective 2001).
Published by: University of Nevada, Anthropological Society, 4505 S Maryland Parkway, Las Vegas, NV 89154-5012. TEL 702-895-3590, FAX 702-895-4823, http://wnlv.edu/student_orgs/anthro-society/.

301 GTM
U TZ'IB. Text in Spanish. 1991. s-a. **Document type:** *Academic/Scholarly.* **Description:** Publishes research results, educational material and findings related to the archaeology, anthropology and history of Guatemala.
Indexed: AnthLit.
Published by: Asociacion Tikal, Edif. Galerias Reforma Of. 322, Ave. REFORMA, 8-60, Guatemala City Zona, 01009, Guatemala. TEL 311176.

301 DEU
UEBERSEE-MUSEUM BREMEN. VEROEFFENTLICHUNGEN. SERIES ETHNOLOGY. Text in German. irreg. price varies. **Document type:** *Monographic series.*
Formed by the merger of (1976-199?): Uebersee-Museum Bremen. Veroeffentlichungen. Reihe D: Voelkerkundliche Monographien (0341-9274); (1977-199?): Uebersee-Museum Bremen. Veroeffentlichungen. Reihe F: Bremer Afrika-Archiv (0344-4317)
Published by: Uebersee-Museum Bremen, Bahnhofsplatz 13, Bremen, 28195, Germany. TEL 49-421-3619324, FAX 49-421-3619291.

301 PRY ISSN 0378-9896
F2679
UNIVERSIDAD CATOLICA NUESTRA SENORA DE LA ASUNCION. CENTRO DE ESTUDIOS ANTROPOLOGICOS. SUPLEMENTO ANTROPOLOGICO. Text in Spanish. 1965. 2/yr. (in 1 vol.). PYG 18,000, USD 30 (effective 1998). adv. bk.rev. cum.index. **Document type:** *Academic/Scholarly.*
Indexed: AICP, AmH&L, AnthLit, IBR.
Published by: Universidad Catolica Nuestra Senora de la Asuncion, Centro de Estudios Antropologicos, Casilla de Correos 1718, Asuncion, Paraguay. TEL 595-21-446251, FAX 595-21-445245. Ed. Adriano Irala Burgos. Circ: 1,000.

301 COL ISSN 0120-2510
GN2
UNIVERSIDAD DE ANTIOQUIA. DEPARTAMENTO DE ANTROPOLOGIA. BOLETIN DE ANTROPOLOGIA. Text in Spanish. 1954. a. COP 16,000 domestic; USD 15 foreign (effective 2003). bk.rev. bibl. **Document type:** *Bulletin, Academic/Scholarly.* **Description:** Publishes the department's anthropological research related to Colombia and America.
Formerly: Universidad de Antioquia. Instituto de Antropologia. Boletin de Antropologia (0041-8323)
Indexed: AICP, AmH&L, AnthLit, HAPI.
Published by: Universidad de Antioquia, Departamento de Antropologia, Apdo Aereo 1226, Medellin, Colombia. TEL 2630011 ext 5778, FAX 2638282, bolant@antares.udea.edu.co, sbotero@antares.udea.edu.co. Ed. Sofia Botero Paez. Circ: 1,920.

301 URY ISSN 0250-6564
UNIVERSIDAD DE LA REPUBLICA. FACULTAD DE HUMANIDADES Y CIENCIAS. REVISTA. SERIE CIENCIAS ANTROPOLOGICAS. Text in Spanish. N.S. 1979. irreg. per issue exchange basis.
Supersedes in part: Universidad de la Republica. Facultad de Humanidades. Revista
Published by: Universidad de la Republica, Facultad de Humanidades y Ciencias, c/o Seccion Revista, Dr. Tristan Narvaja, 1674, Montevideo, 11205, Uruguay. Ed. Beatriz Martinez Osorio.

305.8 COL ISSN 0121-2346
UNIVERSIDAD DEL NORTE. CENTRO DE ESTUDIOS REGIONALES. DOCUMENTOS. Key Title: Documentos C E R E S. Text in Spanish. 1987. irreg., latest vol.15, 1998. price varies. back issues avail. **Document type:** *Monographic series, Academic/Scholarly.* **Description:** Publishes research in regional cultures, societies, and history.
Published by: Universidad del Norte, Centro de Estudios Regionales, Km 5, Via a Puerto Colombia, Bloque F, 3o piso, Barranquilla, Colombia. TEL 57-957-3509401, 57-957-3509218, 57-957-3509420, FAX 57-957-3509489, ceres@uninorte.edu.co, http://www.uninorte.edu.co/investigacion/ceres.

306.4 COL ISSN 0122-0179
UNIVERSIDAD DEL NORTE. CENTRO DE ESTUDIOS REGIONALES. MONOGRAFIAS. Key Title: Monografias C E R E S. Text in Spanish. 1989. irreg., latest vol.10, 1998. price varies. back issues avail. **Document type:** *Monographic series, Academic/Scholarly.* **Description:** Examines topics in the anthropology and history of northern Colombia and environs.
Published by: Universidad del Norte, Centro de Estudios Regionales, Km 5, Via a Puerto Colombia, Bloque F, 3o piso, Barranquilla, Colombia. TEL 57-957-3509401, 57-957-3509218, 57-957-3509420, FAX 57-957-3509489, ceres@uninorte.edu.co, http://www.uninorte.edu.co/investigacion/ceres.

UNIVERSIDAD NACIONAL AUTONOMA DE MEXICO. CENTRO DE ESTUDIOS MAYAS. CUADERNOS. see *HISTORY—History Of North And South America*

301 PER
UNIVERSIDAD NACIONAL DEL CENTRO DEL PERU. CUADERNOS UNIVERSITARIOS. SERIE: ESTUDIOS ANDINOS DEL CENTRO. Text in Spanish. irreg., latest vol.4, 1978.
Published by: Universidad Nacional del Centro del Peru, c/o Departamento de Publicaciones, Calle Real, 160, Huancayo, Peru.

A

A

305.8 BRA
UNIVERSIDADE DE SAO PAULO. MUSEU PAULISTA. COLECAO. SERIE DE ETNOLOGIA. Text in Portuguese. 1975. a.
Supersedes in part (in 1975): Museu Paulista. Colecao (0080-6382)
Indexed: AnthLit.
Published by: Universidade de Sao Paulo, Museu Paulista, Parque da Independencia, Centro, Caixa Postal 42 503, Sao Paulo, SP 01059-970, Brazil. Ed. Setembrino Petri.

301 BRA ISSN 0101-451X
UNIVERSIDADE FEDERAL DE SANTA CATARINA. MUSEU DE ANTROPOLOGIA. ANAIS. Text in Portuguese. 1968. irreg. free or exchange basis. bk.rev. bibl.; charts; illus.
Indexed: AnthLit, IBR.
Published by: Universidade Federal de Santa Catarina, Museu de Antropologia, Campus Universitario Trindade, Centro, Caixa Postal 476, Florianopolis, SC 88010-970, Brazil. dhn40.hinave@mhs.mar.br, http://www.abc.org.br. Ed. Neusa Maria Bloemer.

UNIVERSITATIS DEBRECENIENSIS DE LUDOVICO KOSSUTH NOMINATAE. INSTITUTI PHILOLOGIAE SLAVICAE. ANNALES. SLAVICA. see *LINGUISTICS*

306 CIV ISSN 1010-674X
UNIVERSITE D'ABIDJAN. ANNALES. SERIE F: ETHNOSOCIOLOGIE. Text in French. 1969. irreg., latest vol.8, 1979. price varies. bk.rev. bibl.; charts; illus.
Indexed: AICP, AnthLit, PAIS.
Published by: Universite Nationale de Cote d'Ivoire, Institut d'Ethnosociologie, 08 BP 865, Abidjan, Ivory Coast. TEL 43-90-00. Circ: 1,000.

305.8 FRA ISSN 0249-5635
➤ **UNIVERSITE DE BORDEAUX II. CAHIERS ETHNOLOGIQUES.** Text in French. 1972. s-a. abstr.; bibl.; illus. cum.index: 1973-1992. **Document type:** *Academic/Scholarly.*
Formerly: Universite de Bordeaux II. Centre d'Etudes et de Recherches Ethnologiques. Cahiers
Related titles: ◆ Supplement(s): Universite de Bordeaux II. Cahiers Ethnologiques. Memoires. ISSN 0985-9837.
Indexed: AICP, AnthLit.
Published by: (Universite de Bordeaux II (Victor Segalen)), Presses Universitaires de Bordeaux, 3 Place de la Victoire, Bordeaux, 33000, France. TEL 33-5-54313314, FAX 33-5-56314694, TELEX UNIBX II 572 237 F. Ed., R&P Christian Meriot. Circ: 250.

305.8 FRA ISSN 0985-9837
UNIVERSITE DE BORDEAUX II. CAHIERS ETHNOLOGIQUES. MEMOIRES. Text in French. 1986.
Related titles: ◆ Supplement to: Universite de Bordeaux II. Cahiers Ethnologiques. ISSN 0249-5635.
Published by: Presses Universitaires de Bordeaux, 3 Place de la Victoire, Bordeaux, 33000, France. TEL 33-5-54313314, FAX 33-5-56314694, TELEX UNIBX II 572 237 F.

301 USA ISSN 0041-9354
F906
➤ **UNIVERSITY OF ALASKA. ANTHROPOLOGICAL PAPERS.** Cover title: Anthropological Papers of the University of Alaska. Text in English. 1952; N.S. 2001. a. USD 20 to individuals; USD 100 to institutions (effective 2005). adv. bk.rev. bibl.; charts; illus. index. back issues avail. **Document type:** *Monographic series, Academic/Scholarly.* **Description:** Consist of original papers on a variety of topics related to arctic or subarctic anthropology.
Indexed: ABS&EES, AICP, AmH&L, AnthLit, SOPODA. —Linda Hall.
Published by: University of Alaska Fairbanks, Department of Anthropology, 310 Eielson Bldg, PO Box 757720, Fairbanks, AK 99775-7720. TEL 907-474-7288, FAX 907-474-7453, fnkre1@uaf.edu, fyanth@uaf.edu, http://www.uaf.edu/anthro/apua.html. Ed., R&P Maribeth Murray TEL 907-474-6751. Circ: 375.

301 USA ISSN 0066-7501
➤ **UNIVERSITY OF ARIZONA. ANTHROPOLOGICAL PAPERS.** Text in English. 1959. irreg., latest vol.67, 2002. price varies. adv. back issues avail. **Document type:** *Monographic series, Academic/Scholarly.* **Description:** Publishes original studies in archaeology and anthropology, with particular emphasis on Arizona, the Southwest, and Mexico.
Indexed: AnthLit.
Published by: University of Arizona Press, 355 S Euclid Ave, Ste 103, Tucson, AZ 85719. TEL 520-621-1441, FAX 520-621-8899, uapress@uapress.arizona.edu, http://www.uapress.arizona.edu/series/Serid14.htm. Ed. Yvonne Reineke. R&P Julie Blackwell. Adv. contact Wayne Koch TEL 520-621-1441. **Co-sponsor:** Arizona State Museum.

301 USA
GN1 CODEN: FJANER
➤ **THE UNIVERSITY OF FLORIDA JOURNAL OF ANTHROPOLOGY.** Text in English. 1976. 3/yr. USD 15 to individuals; USD 19 to institutions. adv. bk.rev. **Document type:** *Academic/Scholarly.*
Formerly (until 2002): Florida Journal of Anthropology (0164-1662)
Related titles: Online - full text ed.
Indexed: AICP, AnthLit, RASB, SSCI.
Published by: University of Florida, Department of Anthropology, 1350 GPA, Gainesville, FL 32611. TEL 904-392-2031, FAX 904-392-6929, rshtul@ufcc.ufl.edu. Ed. Alana A Lynch. Circ: 125 (paid).

301 GHA ISSN 0533-8646
UNIVERSITY OF GHANA. INSTITUTE OF AFRICAN STUDIES. LOCAL STUDIES SERIES. Text in English. irreg., latest vol.5, 1972. price varies. **Document type:** *Monographic series.*
Published by: University of Ghana, Institute of African Studies, PO Box 73, Legon, Ghana.

UNIVERSITY OF HULL. DEPARTMENT OF SOCIOLOGY AND SOCIAL ANTHROPOLOGY. OCCASIONAL PAPERS. see *SOCIOLOGY*

301 USA ISSN 0085-2457
UNC
➤ **UNIVERSITY OF KANSAS. DEPARTMENT OF ANTHROPOLOGY. PUBLICATIONS IN ANTHROPOLOGY.** Key Title: University of Kansas Publications in Anthropology. Text in English. 1969. irreg., latest vol.19, 1991. price varies. **Document type:** *Academic/Scholarly.*
Indexed: AnthLit.
Published by: University of Kansas Libraries, Exchange & Gifts Department, Level 2W Watson Library, Lawrence, KS 66045. TEL 913-864-3746. Ed. John M Janzen. Circ: 1,000.

301 CAN ISSN 0227-0072
UNIVERSITY OF MANITOBA ANTHROPOLOGY PAPERS. Text in English. 1973. irreg., latest vol.32, 1992. price varies. back issues avail. **Document type:** *Academic/Scholarly.*
Published by: (U M A P Committee), University of Manitoba, Department of Anthropology, 432 Fletcher Argue Bldg, Winnipeg, MB R3T 2N2, Canada. TEL 204-474-9423. Ed. David Stymeist. Circ: 100.

301 USA ISSN 0564-8602
➤ **UNIVERSITY OF MEMPHIS. ANTHROPOLOGICAL RESEARCH CENTER. OCCASIONAL PAPERS.** Text in English. 1967. irreg., latest vol.17, 1997. price varies. **Document type:** *Monographic series, Academic/Scholarly.*
Published by: University of Memphis, Anthropological Research Center, 229 Administration Bldg, Memphis, TN 38152. FAX 901-678-2069. Ed., R&P David Dye TEL 901-678-3330. Circ: 200.

301 USA ISSN 0076-8367
GN2
UNIVERSITY OF MICHIGAN. MUSEUM OF ANTHROPOLOGY. ANTHROPOLOGICAL PAPERS. Text in English. 1949. irreg., latest vol.91, 2001. price varies. adv. charts; illus.; maps. back issues avail.; reprints avail. **Document type:** *Monographic series, Academic/Scholarly.*
Related titles: Microform ed.: (from PQC).
Indexed: AnthLit, BiolAb, RASB, RefZh. —BLDSC (1543.000000).
Published by: University of Michigan, Museum of Anthropology, University Museums Bldg, Ann Arbor, MI 48109. TEL 734-764-0485, FAX 734-763-7783, shorv@umich.edu, http://www.umma.lsa.umich.edu. Ed. Sally Mitani TEL 734-998-6921.

301 USA ISSN 0076-8375
UNIVERSITY OF MICHIGAN. MUSEUM OF ANTHROPOLOGY. MEMOIRS. Text in English. 1969. irreg., latest vol.34, 2000. price varies. back issues avail.; reprint service avail. from PQC. **Document type:** *Monographic series, Academic/Scholarly.*
Indexed: AnthLit.
Published by: University of Michigan, Museum of Anthropology, University Museums Bldg, Ann Arbor, MI 48109. TEL 734-764-0482, FAX 734-763-7783, shorv@umich.edu, http://www.umma.lsa.umich.edu. Ed. Sally Horvath TEL 734-764-0482.

301 USA ISSN 0196-8297
UNIVERSITY OF MICHIGAN. MUSEUM OF ANTHROPOLOGY. TECHNICAL REPORTS. Text in English. 1971. irreg., latest vol.26, 1994. price varies. bibl. back issues avail.; reprint service avail. from PQC. **Document type:** *Monographic series, Academic/Scholarly.*
Indexed: BiolAb.
Published by: University of Michigan, Museum of Anthropology, University Museums Bldg, Ann Arbor, MI 48109. TEL 734-764-0482, FAX 734-763-7783, shorv@umich.edu, http://www.umma.lsa.umich.edu. Ed. Sally Horvath TEL 734-764-0482.

301 USA
➤ **UNIVERSITY OF MISSOURI AT COLUMBIA. MUSEUM OF ANTHROPOLOGY. MISCELLANEOUS PUBLICATIONS IN ANTHROPOLOGY.** Text in English. 1972. irreg. price varies. **Document type:** *Monographic series, Academic/Scholarly.*
Published by: University of Missouri at Columbia, Museum of Anthropology, 104 Swallow Hall, Columbia, MO 65211. TEL 573-882-3573.

301 USA ISSN 0362-1235
UNIVERSITY OF MISSOURI AT COLUMBIA. MUSEUM OF ANTHROPOLOGY. MUSEUM BRIEFS. Text in English. 1969. irreg., latest vol.26, 1982. price varies. **Document type:** *Monographic series.*
Published by: University of Missouri at Columbia, Museum of Anthropology, 104 Swallow Hall, Columbia, MO 65211. TEL 573-882-3573.

301 USA
➤ **UNIVERSITY OF MISSOURI MONOGRAPHS IN ANTHROPOLOGY.** Text in English. 1974. irreg., latest vol.10, 1991. price varies. **Document type:** *Monographic series, Academic/Scholarly.*
Published by: University of Missouri at Columbia, Museum of Anthropology, 104 Swallow Hall, Columbia, MO 65211. TEL 573-882-3573.

➤ **UNIVERSITY OF NEBRASKA STATE MUSEUM. MUSEUM NOTES.** see *MUSEUMS AND ART GALLERIES*

301 USA ISSN 0078-6071
➤ **UNIVERSITY OF OREGON ANTHROPOLOGICAL PAPERS.** Text in English. 1971. irreg., latest vol.55, 1998. price varies. **Document type:** *Monographic series, Academic/Scholarly.*
Published by: University of Oregon, Department of Anthropology, 541 346 5115, Eugene, OR 97403-1218. TEL 541-346-5102, FAX 541-346-0668. Ed. C Melvin Aikens. R&P C. Melvin Aikens. Circ: 500. **Co-sponsor:** University of Oregon Museum of Natural History.

➤ **UNIVERSITY OF SOUTH CAROLINA. INSTITUTE OF ARCHEOLOGY AND ANTHROPOLOGY. ANNUAL REPORT.** see *ARCHAEOLOGY*

301 USA ISSN 0083-4947
E51
➤ **UNIVERSITY OF UTAH ANTHROPOLOGICAL PAPERS.** Text in English. 1950. irreg., latest vol.123, 2001. price varies. adv. **Document type:** *Monographic series, Academic/Scholarly.*
Indexed: BiolAb, RefZh.
Published by: University of Utah Press, 1795 E South Campus Dr, 101, Salt Lake City, UT 84112-9402. TEL 801-581-6771, FAX 801-581-3365, info@upress.utah.edu. Ed. Jeff Grathwohl. R&P Glenda Cotter. Adv. contact Marcelyn Ritchie.

301 POL ISSN 0137-1460
UNIWERSYTET IM. ADAMA MICKIEWICZA. ANTROPOLOGIA. Text in Polish; Summaries in English. 1971. irreg., latest vol.20. price varies. **Document type:** *Monographic series, Academic/Scholarly.*
Formerly: Uniwersytet im. Adama Mickiewicza w Poznaniu. Wydzial Biologii i Nauk o Ziemi. Prace. Seria Antropologia
Published by: Wydawnictwo Naukowe Uniwersytetu im. Adama Mickiewicza/Adam Mickiewicz University Press, Nowowiejskiego 55, Poznan, 61-734, Poland. TEL 48-61-527380, FAX 48-61-527701. Pub. Maria Jankowska. R&P Malgorzata Bis.

UNIWERSYTET JAGIELLONSKI. INSTYTUT FILOLOGII WSCHODNIOSLOWIANSKIEJ. KATEDRA LITERATURY I KULTURY ROSYJSKIEJ. PRACE. see *LITERATURE*

305.8 POL ISSN 0083-4327
GN2
UNIWERSYTET JAGIELLONSKI. ZESZYTY NAUKOWE. PRACE ETNOGRAFICZNE. Text in Polish; Summaries in English. 1963. irreg., latest vol.36, 2001. price varies. index. **Document type:** *Monographic series, Academic/Scholarly.*
Indexed: AICP, RASB.
Published by: (Uniwersytet Jagiellonski, Instytut Etnologii), Wydawnictwo Uniwersytetu Jagiellonskiego/Jagiellonian University Press, ul Grodzka 26, Krakow, 31044, Poland. TEL 48-12-4312364, FAX 48-12-4301995, wydaw@if.uj.edu.pl, http://www.wuj.pl. Ed. Jadwiga Klimaszewska. Circ: 600. **Dist. by:** Ars Polona, Krakowskie Przedmiescie 7, Warsaw, Poland. TEL 48-22-9263914, FAX 48-22-9265334, arspolona@arspolona.com.pl, http://www.arspolona.com.pl.

301 ITA
UOMO & CULTURA; rivista di studi antropologici. Text in Italian. 1967. biennial. price varies. bk.rev.
Indexed: AnthLit, IBSS.
Published by: Dario Flaccovio Editore, Via F Oliveri Mandala, Palermo, PA 90146, Italy. TEL 39-091-202533, FAX 39-091-227702, http://www.darioflaccovio.it. Ed. Silvana Miceli.

301 SWE ISSN 0348-5099
UPPSALA STUDIES IN CULTURAL ANTHROPOLOGY. Text in Swedish. 1979. irreg., latest vol.31, 2000. price varies. back issues avail. **Document type:** *Monographic series, Academic/Scholarly.*
Related titles: ◆ Series of: Acta Universitatis Upsaliensis. ISSN 0346-5462.
Indexed: RDA, WAE&RSA. —KNAW.
Published by: (Uppsala Universitet), Uppsala Universitet, Acta Universitatis Upsaliensis/University Publications from Uppsala, PO Box 256, Uppsala, 75105, Sweden. TEL 46-18-4713922, http://www.ub.uu.se/upu/auu. Ed. Bengt Landgren.

301 USA ISSN 0894-6019
HT101
➤ **URBAN ANTHROPOLOGY AND STUDIES OF CULTURAL SYSTEMS AND WORLD ECONOMIC DEVELOPMENT.** Text in English. 1972. q. USD 75 (effective 2002). illus. reprints avail. **Document type:** *Academic/Scholarly.* **Description:** Articles on urban anthropology and the impact of world economic development on the world's cultural systems.
Formerly (until 1984): Urban Anthropology (0363-2024)
Related titles: Online - full text ed.: (from Gale Group).
Indexed: ABS&EES, AICP, AbAn, AbHyg, AmH&L, AnthLit, BAS, CIJE, CurCont, DIP, DSA, ForAb, GEOBASE, IBR, IBSS, IBZ, NutrAb, PCI, PGegResA, PRA, RDA, RILM, RefZh, SOPODA, SRRA, SSA, SSCI, SSI, SUSA, SWA, SociolAb, TDB, WAE&RSA.
—BLDSC (9123.320000), IE, Infotrieve, ingenta. **CCC.**
Published by: Institute for the Study of Man, 1133 13th St, N W, No C 2, Washington, DC 20005. TEL 202-371-2700, FAX 202-371-1523. Circ: 500.

306.4 051 USA
URBAN MOZAIK. Text in English. bi-m. USD 15; USD 3.95 newsstand/cover (effective 1999). **Document type:** *Consumer.* **Description:** Examines life in a modern multicultural society.
Published by: Studio Q International, Inc., 1034 Front St, Ste 218, Lahaina, Maui, HI 96761. multiculturalmagazine.com. Ed. Carolyn Quan.

305.897 GBR
URGENT ACTION BULLETIN. Text in English. 1982. 6/yr. GBP 50, USD 100 (effective 2000). **Document type:** *Bulletin.* **Description:** Launches a letter writing campaign in support of particular tribal communities facing threat.
Related titles: French ed.; Indonesian ed.; Italian ed.; Japanese ed.; Portuguese ed.; Spanish ed.
Indexed: HRIR.
Published by: Survival, 11-15 Emerald St, London, WC1N 3QL, United Kingdom. TEL 44-20-7242-1441, FAX 44-20-7242-1771, info@survival-international.org, http://www.survival-international.org.

301 305.8 FRA ISSN 1167-816X
UTINAM. Text in French. 1992. q. **Document type:** *Journal, Academic/Scholarly.*
Published by: L' Harmattan, 5 rue de l'Ecole Polytechnique, Paris, 75005, France. TEL 33-1-43257651, FAX 33-1-43258203, http://www.editions-harmattan.fr.

301 USA
➤ **VANDERBILT UNIVERSITY PUBLICATIONS IN ANTHROPOLOGY.** Text in English, Spanish. 1972. s-a. price varies. **Document type:** *Monographic series, Academic/Scholarly.* **Description:** Covers the archaeology, ethnology, and ethnohistory of indigenous cultures in Oaxaca and elsewhere in Mexico.
Indexed: AnthLit.
Published by: (Vanderbilt University, Department of Anthropology), Vanderbilt University Publications in Anthropology, PO Box 1532, Sta B, Nashville, TN 37235. TEL 615-322-7522, FAX 615-343-0230, vupa@ctrvax.vanderbilt.edu. Ed., R&P John Monaghan. Circ: 500. **Subscr. to:** Bookmaster Inc., 2541 Ashland Rd, Box 2139, Mansfield, OH 44905. TEL 419-281-1802, FAX 419-281-6883.

301 IND ISSN 0042-2622
➤ **VANYAJATI.** Text in English, Hindi. 1953. q. USD 30 (effective 2003). bk.rev. illus. index. **Document type:** *Academic/Scholarly.* **Description:** Designed for the Indian tribal communities. Promotes their social, cultural and economic progress and safeguards their constitutional rights.
Related titles: Microform ed.
Indexed: AICP, BAS, RASB.
Published by: Bharatiya Adimjati Sevak Sangh, New Link Rd. (Dr. Ambedkar Road), Jhandewalan, New Delhi, 110 055, India. TEL 7525492, FAX 3532003. Ed. J H Chinchalkar. R&P J.H. Chinchalkar. Circ: 1,000. **Subscr. to:** Scientific Publishers, 5-A New Pali Rd., Near Hotel Taj Hari Mahal, PO Box 91, Jodhpur, Rajasthan 342 003, India. info@scientificpub.com, http://www.scientificpub.com.

➤ **VEREIN FUER VOLKSKUNDE IN WIEN. SONDERSCHRIFTEN.** see *FOLKLORE*

301 CRI ISSN 0304-3703
F1545
VINCULOS. Text and summaries in English, Spanish. 1975. 2/yr. USD 20; or exchange basis. charts; illus.
Indexed: AIAP, AICP, AnthLit, HAPI, IBR, IBZ, PCI.
Published by: (Departamento de Antropologia e Historia), Museo Nacional de Costa Rica, Apdo 749, San Jose, 1000, Costa Rica. TEL 506-221-4429, FAX 506-233-7427. Circ: 1,000.

301 USA ISSN 0894-9468
GN347 CODEN: VIANEQ
➤ **VISUAL ANTHROPOLOGY.** Text in English. 1987. 5/yr. GBP 567, USD 936 combined subscription to institutions print & online eds. (effective 2006). bk.rev.; film rev. illus. reprint service avail. from PSC. **Document type:** *Journal, Academic/Scholarly.*
Related titles: Microform ed.; Online - full text ed.: ISSN 1545-5920. GBP 539, USD 889 to institutions (effective 2006) (from EBSCO Publishing, Gale Group, IngentaConnect, O C L C Online Computer Library Center, Inc., Swets Information Services).
Indexed: ABM, AICP, AbAn, AnthLit, DIP, IBR, IBSS, IBZ, PCI, RILM.
—BLDSC (9241.227300), IE, Infotrieve, ingenta. **CCC.**
Published by: (Commission on Visual Anthropology CHE), Taylor & Francis Inc. (Subsidiary of: Taylor & Francis Group), 325 Chestnut St, Ste 800, Philadelphia, PA 19016. TEL 215-625-8900, 800-354-1420, FAX 215-625-8914, info@taylorandfrancis.com, http://www.tandf.co.uk/journals/titles/08949468.asp, http://www.taylorandfrancis.com. Ed. Paul Hockings. **Subscr. outside N. America to:** Taylor & Francis Ltd, Journals Customer Service, Rankine Rd, Basingstoke, Hants RG24 8PR, United Kingdom. TEL 44-1256-813000, FAX 44-1256-330245, enquiry@tandf.co.uk.

301 USA ISSN 1058-7187
GN347
VISUAL ANTHROPOLOGY REVIEW. Text in English. 1970. s-a. USD 30 (effective 2005 & 2006). adv. bk.rev.; film rev. back issues avail. **Document type:** *Journal, Academic/Scholarly.* **Description:** Includes commentary, articles and thematic analyses of visual anthropology topics.
Former titles (until 1991): Society for Visual Anthropology Review (1053-7147); (until 1990): S V A Review (1053-6779); (until 1989): S V A Newsletter (1046-7688); (until 1985): Society for the Anthropology of Visual Communication. Newsletter (1557-2498); (until 1973): P I E F Newsletter (0030-8013)
Related titles: Online - full text ed.: ISSN 1548-7458.
Indexed: AICP, AnthLit, BrArAb, FLI, IBR, IBSS, IBZ.
—BLDSC (9241.227500), IE, ingenta. **CCC.**
Published by: (American Anthropological Association), University of California Press, Journals Division, 2000 Center St, Ste 303, Berkeley, CA 94704-1223. TEL 510-643-7154, FAX 510-642-9917, journals@ucpress.edu, http://www.ucpress.edu/journals/3a/var. Ed. Najwa Adra. adv.: page USD 350; 9.3 x 7.

301 DEU ISSN 0073-0270
VOELKERKUNDLICHE ABHANDLUNGEN. Text in German. 1964. irreg., latest vol.14, 2001. price varies. back issues avail. **Document type:** *Monographic series, Academic/Scholarly.*
Published by: (Niedersaechsisches Landesmuseum, Hannover), Dietrich Reimer Verlag GmbH, Neue Gruenstr 17, Berlin, 10179, Germany. TEL 49-30-2790760, FAX 49-30-27907655, vertrieb-kunstverlage@reimer-verlag.de, http://www.dietrichreimerverlag.de. R&P Beate Behrens. Circ: 500.

301 AUT
VOELKERKUNDLICHE VEROEFFENTLICHUNGEN. Text in German. irreg. price varies. **Document type:** *Monographic series, Academic/Scholarly.*
Published by: (Anthropologische Gesellschaft in Wien), Verlag Ferdinand Berger und Soehne GmbH, Wienerstr 80, Horn, N 3580, Austria. TEL 43-2982-4161332, FAX 43-2982-4161382, office@berger.at, http://www.berger.at. Ed. Paul Spindler.

306 305.42 USA ISSN 1538-2680
VOICES (ARLINGTON); a publication of the association for feminist anthropology. Text in English. a. USD 16 in US & Canada to institutions; USD 26 elsewhere to institutions (effective 2004 - 2005). **Document type:** *Journal, Academic/Scholarly.* **Description:** Provides a review of the year's activities in feminist anthropology.
Related titles: Online - full text ed.: ISSN 1548-7423.
—**CCC.**
Published by: (Association for Feminist Anthropology), University of California Press, Journals Division, 2000 Center St, Ste 303, Berkeley, CA 94704-1223. TEL 510-643-7154, FAX 510-642-9917, journals@ucpress.edu, http://www.ucpress.edu/journals/3a/vo. Ed. Susan B Hyatt. R&Ps Darcy Dapra, Marge Dean TEL 510-642-6188.

VOLKSLIEDSTUDIEN. see *MUSIC*

301 RUS ISSN 0507-2921
VOPROSY ANTROPOLOGII. Text in Russian. 1960. irreg.
Indexed: AnthLit, ZooRec.
Published by: Moskovskii Gosudarstvennyi Universitet im. M. V. Lomonosova, Institut Antropologii/Lomonosov Moscow State University, Institute of Anthropology, Vorobiovy Gory, Moscow, 119899, Russian Federation. TEL 7-095-9391000, FAX 7-095-9390126, mgu@univer.msu.ru, http://www.msu.ru.

301 GUY
F2379
WALTER ROTH MUSEUM OF ANTHROPOLOGY. JOURNAL. Cover title: Archaeology and Anthropology. Text in English. 1978. a. GYD 1,000, USD 20. bk.rev. back issues avail. **Document type:** *Academic/Scholarly.* **Description:** Presents results of archaeological excavations, anthropological research, and historical findings in the region.
Formerly: Walter Roth Museum of Archaeology and Anthropology. Journal (0256-4653)
Indexed: AnthLit, IBSS.
Published by: Walter Roth Museum of Anthropology, Main St 61, PO Box 10187, Georgetown, Guyana. TEL 592-2-58486, wrma@sdnp.org.gy. Ed., R&P Jennifer Wishart. Circ: 100.

301 570 550 940 NOR
➤ **WAY NORTH;** our natural and cultural heritage. Text in English. 1992. a., latest vol.6, 2000. price varies. bibl.; illus.; maps; stat. back issues avail. **Document type:** *Monographic series, Academic/Scholarly.* **Description:** Aims to give foreigners and tourists a basic understanding of Norway's northernmost region.
Published by: Tromsoe Museum, University of Tromsoe, Tromsoe, N-9037, Norway. TEL 47-77-645000, FAX 47-77-645120, shop@imv.uit.no, http://www.imv.uit.no.

➤ **WEIMARER MONOGRAPHIEN ZUR UR- UND FRUEHGESCHICHTE.** see *ARCHAEOLOGY*

➤ **WICAZO SA REVIEW/RED PENCIL REVIEW;** a journal of Native American studies. see *NATIVE AMERICAN STUDIES*

301 AUT
WIENER BEITRAEGE ZUR ETHNOLOGIE UND ANTHROPOLOGIE. Text in German. 1979. irreg., latest vol.5, 1988. price varies. **Document type:** *Monographic series, Academic/Scholarly.*
Published by: Verlag Ferdinand Berger und Soehne GmbH, Wienerstr 80, Horn, N 3580, Austria. TEL 43-2982-41610, FAX 43-2982-4161268, office@berger.at, http://www.berger.at.

305.8 AUT ISSN 1011-4807
WIENER BEITRAEGE ZUR ETHNOLOGIE UND ANTHROPOLOGIE/VIENNA CONTRIBUTIONS TO ETHNOLOGY AND ANTHROPOLOGY. Text in German. 1930. irreg., latest vol.5, 1993. price varies. **Document type:** *Monographic series, Academic/Scholarly.*
Formerly (until 1984): Wiener Beitraege zur Kulturgeschichte und Linguistik (0083-9922)
Indexed: AnthLit.
Published by: Verlag Ferdinand Berger und Soehne GmbH, Wienerstr 80, Horn, N 3580, Austria. TEL 43-2982-4161332, FAX 43-2982-4161382, office@berger.at, http://www.berger.at.

301 AUT ISSN 0084-0068
GN1
WIENER VOELKERKUNDLICHE MITTEILUNGEN. Text in German. 1953. a. adv. bk.rev. **Document type:** *Journal, Academic/Scholarly.*
Indexed: AICP, AnthLit, EI, IBR.
Published by: Oesterreichische Ethnologische Gesellschaft, Rotensterngasse 14-23, Vienna, W 1020, Austria. TEL 43-1-2120271, FAX 43-1-2120271, voelkerkundemuseum@magnet.at, aduchataeu@yahoo.com. Ed., R&P Armand Duchateau. Circ: 500.

XIBEI MINZU YANJIU/NORTHWEST MINORITIES RESEARCH. see *ASIAN STUDIES*

XIZANG YANJIU/TIBETAN STUDIES. see *ASIAN STUDIES*

306.4 AUS ISSN 1326-902X
HN841
➤ **XTEXT.** Text in English. 1996. s-a. AUD 28 domestic to individuals; AUD 45 foreign to individuals; AUD 38 domestic to institutions; AUD 55 foreign to institutions (effective 2002). illus. **Document type:** *Academic/Scholarly.* **Description:** Adresses theoretical and actual issues in cultural identity, ethnicity, racism, sexuality, and feminism not examined in the mainstream media for academics and persons outside the academic community.
Published by: (Centre for Research Into Textual and Cultural Studies), Xtext, School of English, University of NSW, Sydney, NSW 2052, Australia. TEL 61-2-9385-2303, FAX 61-2-9385-1047, Efi_Hatzimanolis@uow.edu.au, http://www.uow.edu.au/critacs/Xtext.html.

301 USA
➤ **YALE UNIVERSITY. DEPARTMENT OF ANTHROPOLOGY. PUBLICATIONS IN ANTHROPOLOGY.** Text in English. 1936. irreg., latest vol.84. price varies. **Document type:** *Monographic series, Academic/Scholarly.*
Published by: Yale University, Department of Anthropology, PO Box 208118, New Haven, CT 06520. FAX 203-432-9816, joyce.gherloxe@yale.edu. Ed., R&P Leopold Pospisil.

301 HND ISSN 0254-7627
F1505
YAXKIN. Text in Spanish. 1975. s-a. USD 14 in North America to individuals; USD 22 in Europe to individuals; USD 18 in North America to institutions; USD 26 in Europe to institutions (effective 1999). adv. bk.rev. illus. index. **Document type:** *Academic/Scholarly.* **Description:** Covers anthropology, history and cultural geography, usually based on field research carried out in Honduras.
Indexed: AICP, AnthLit.
Published by: Instituto Hondureno de Antropologia e Historia, Departamento de Investigaciones, Apdo. 1518, Tegucigalpa DC, Honduras. TEL 504-223470, FAX 504-222552. Ed. Kevin Ruben Avalos. Adv. contact Olga Joya. Circ: 1,000.

306.4
YEAR 'ROUND CHRISTMAS MAGAZINE. Text in English. q. USD 15.95 (effective 2000). adv. **Document type:** *Magazine, Consumer.* **Description:** Contains articles and special features for people who love Christmas.

▼ new title ➤ refereed ✱ unverified ♦ full entry avail.

Published by: Anton Publications, PO Box 606, Downers Grove, IL 60516.

599.9 USA ISSN 0096-848X
CODEN: YANTAE

➤ **YEARBOOK OF PHYSICAL ANTHROPOLOGY.** Text in English. 1945. a., latest 2004. price varies. reprints avail. **Document type:** *Yearbook, Academic/Scholarly.* **Description:** Presents review articles that summarize and evaluate recent literature in topics of current interest to biological anthropologists.
Related titles: Online - full text ed.; ♦ Supplement to: American Journal of Physical Anthropology. ISSN 0002-9483.
Indexed: AICP, ASCA, AbAn, AnthLit, BIOSIS Prev, BiolAb, BrArAb, IBSS, ISR, RASB, SCI, SSCI.
—BLDSC (9415.000000), GNLM, IE, Infotrieve, ingenta, Linda Hall. **CCC.**
Published by: (American Association of Physical Anthropologists), John Wiley & Sons, Inc., 111 River St, Hoboken, NJ 07030-5774. TEL 201-748-6000, FAX 201-748-5915, sara_stinson@qc.edu, uscs-wis@wiley.com, http://www.physanth.org/pubs/, http://www.wiley.com. Ed. Sara Stinson.

➤ **YMER.** see *GEOGRAPHY*

➤ **YUNNAN MINZU XUEYUAN XUEBAO/YUNNAN INSTITUTE OF NATIONALITIES. JOURNAL.** see *ASIAN STUDIES*

305.8 ESP ISSN 1137-439X
GN549.B3
ZAINAK. Text in Spanish. 1982. irreg. price varies. **Document type:** *Monographic series, Academic/Scholarly.*
Which was formerly (until 1997): Sociedad de Estudios Vascos. Cuadernos de Seccion. Antropologia y Etnografia (0213-0297); Supersedes in part (in 1982): Cuadernos de Seccion. Antropologia, Etnografia, Prehistoria, Arqueologia (0212-3207)
Indexed: IBSS, RILM.
—CINDOC.
Published by: Eusko Ikaskuntza/Sociedad de Estudios Vascos, Palacio Miramar, Miraconcha 48, Donostia, San Sebastian 20007, Spain. TEL 34-943-310855, FAX 34-943-213956, ei-sev@sc.ehu.es, http://www.eusko-ikaskuntza.org/.

306.44089 ZMB
ZAMBIA MUSEUMS JOURNAL. Text in English. 1965. irreg., latest vol.7, 1989. ZMK 20, USD 20. adv. bk.rev. illus. **Document type:** *Academic/Scholarly.*
Formerly: Zambia Journal; Supersedes (1959-1964): Northern Rhodesia Journal
Indexed: AICP, AnthLit, PLESA, SFA.
Published by: Livingstone Museum, PO Box 60498, Livingstone, Zambia. TEL 260-1-228807. Ed. F B Musonda. Circ: 2,000. **Co-sponsor:** Zambia. National Museums Board.

301 DEU ISSN 0044-2666
GN1
ZEITSCHRIFT FUER ETHNOLOGIE. Text in German, English, French. 1869. s-a. EUR 72 (effective 2005). bk.rev. abstr.; bibl.; illus.; stat. index. reprints avail. **Document type:** *Journal, Academic/Scholarly.*
Indexed: AICP, AnthLit, BAS, BibInd, BibLing, CCA, DIP, EI, IBR, IBSS, IBZ, IndIslam, PCI, RASB, RILM, SSA, SSCI, SociolAb.
—IE. **CCC.**
Published by: (Deutsche Gesellschaft fuer Voelkerkunde), Dietrich Reimer Verlag GmbH, Neue Gruenstr 17, Berlin, 10179, Germany. TEL 49-30-2790760, FAX 49-30-27907655, vertrieb-kunstverlage@reimer-verlag.de, http://www.dietrichreimerverlag.de. Eds. Claudius Mueller, Ulla Johansen. R&P Beate Behrens. **Co-sponsor:** Berliner Gesellschaft fuer Anthropologie, Ethnologie und Urgeschichte.

ZEITSCHRIFT FUER VOLKSKUNDE. see *FOLKLORE*

ZESZYTY TARNOGORSKIE. see *HISTORY—History Of Europe*

ZHONGGUO ZANGXUE/CHINA TIBETOLOGY. see *ASIAN STUDIES*

ANTHROPOLOGY—Abstracting, Bibliographies, Statistics

016.301 USA ISSN 0001-3455
GN1
ABSTRACTS IN ANTHROPOLOGY. Text in English. 1970. 8/yr. (in 2 vols.). USD 560 domestic to institutions; USD 575 foreign to institutions (effective 2005). adv. abstr.; illus. index. back issues avail.; reprints avail. **Document type:** *Journal, Abstract/Index.* **Description:** Covers the fields of archaeology, physical anthropology, linguistics, and cultural anthropology.
Related titles: Online - full text ed.: ISSN 1557-5136.
—CINDOC. **CCC.**
Published by: Baywood Publishing Co., Inc., 26 Austin Ave, PO Box 337, Amityville, NY 11701-0337. TEL 631-691-1270, 800-638-7819, FAX 631-691-1770, info@baywood.com, http://www.baywood.com/Journals/PreviewJournal.asp?Id=0001-3455. Eds. Jay F Custer, Roger W Moeller. R&P Julie Krempa. Adv. contact Rochelle Grant.

AFRICAN STUDIES. see *HISTORY—Abstracting, Bibliographies, Statistics*

016.301 DEU
GN1
ANTHROPOLOGICAL ABSTRACTS: CULTURAL - SOCIAL ANTHROPOLOGY FROM AUSTRIA, GERMANY, SWITZERLAND. Text in English, German. 1980. a. EUR 25.90 (effective 2003). adv. bk.rev. back issues avail. **Document type:** *Abstract/Index.* **Description:** Provides the service of communicating anthropological materials published in the German language to non-German speaking scholars.
Formerly (until 1997): Abstracts in German Anthropology (0173-2986)
Related titles: Online - full text ed.: 1980-1997; N.S. 2003. EUR 39.50 per vol. (effective 2003).
Indexed: BrArAb, EI.
Published by: (Anthropological Abstracts), Lit Verlag, Grevener Str. 179, Muenster, 48159, Germany. TEL 49-251-235091, FAX 49-251-231972, lit@lit-verlag.de, http://www.anthropology-online.de/Aga/Abstrcts.html, http://www.lit-verlag.de. Ed. Ulrich Oberdiek. Circ: 750.

016.301 GBR
ANTHROPOLOGICAL INDEX ONLINE. Short title: A I O. Text in English. 1995. every 6 wks. GBP 250, USD 450 to institutions (effective 2005). bibl. back issues avail. **Document type:** *Database, Abstract/Index.* **Description:** Contains about 70,000 journal articles published worldwide that cover all aspects of anthropology, archaeology, ethnography and linguistics.
Media: Online - full text. **Related titles:** ♦ Print ed.: Anthropological Index to Current Periodicals in the Museum of Mankind Library.
Published by: Royal Anthropological Institute, 50 Fitzroy St., London, W1P 5HS, United Kingdom. TEL 44-20-73870455, FAX 44-20-73888817, admin@therai.org.uk, http://aio.anthropology.org.uk/aio/AIO.html, http://www.therai.org.uk.

016.301 GBR
➤ **ANTHROPOLOGICAL INDEX TO CURRENT PERIODICALS IN THE MUSEUM OF MANKIND LIBRARY.** Text in English. 1963. a. illus. reprints avail. **Document type:** *Journal, Academic/Scholarly.*
Former titles: Anthropological Index (0960-1651); (until 1977): Royal Anthropological Institute of Great Britain and Ireland. Library. Anthropological Index (0003-5467); Royal Anthropological Institute of Great Britain and Ireland. Library. Index to Current Periodicals Received in the Library
Related titles: ♦ Online - full text ed.: Anthropological Index Online.
—CCC.
Published by: Royal Anthropological Institute, c/o Museum of Mankind, 6 Burlington Gardens, London, W1X 2EX, United Kingdom. TEL 44-207-387-0455, FAX 44-207-383-4235.

016.301 USA ISSN 0190-3373
Z5112
ANTHROPOLOGICAL LITERATURE; an index to periodical articles and essays. Text in English. 1979. q. USD 325 (effective 2005). bk.rev. bibl.; illus. back issues avail.; reprints avail. **Document type:** *Academic/Scholarly.* **Description:** Provides an author and subject index to 10,000 articles in approximately 900 serials and edited works each year. Articles are focused on the fields of archaeology, biological and physical anthropology, cultural and social anthropology and linguistics.
Related titles: CD-ROM ed.: ISSN 1546-2633; Online - full text ed.: (from Research Libraries Group).
Indexed: RASB.
—GNLM.
Published by: Harvard University, Tozzer Library, 21 Divinity Ave, Cambridge, MA 02138. TEL 617-495-1481, FAX 617-496-2741, http://hcl.harvard.edu/tozzer/anthro_lit/al.html. Ed. Emily H Moss. Circ: 600.

016.301 DEU ISSN 0003-5548
GN1
ANTHROPOLOGISCHER ANZEIGER. Text in English, German; Text occasionally in French, Italian. 1924. q. EUR 268 domestic (effective 2005). adv. bk.rev. charts; illus. reprints avail. **Document type:** *Journal, Academic/Scholarly.*
Incorporates (1899-2002): Zeitschrift fuer Morphologie und Anthropologie (0044-314X)
Indexed: AICP, AnthLit, BAS, BHA, BiolAb, DIP, DentInd, ExcerpMed, IBR, IndMed, MEDLINE, RASB.
—BLDSC (1546.500000), GNLM, IE, Infotrieve, ingenta, Linda Hall. **CCC.**
Published by: E. Schweizerbart'sche Verlagsbuchhandlung, Johannesstr 3A, Stuttgart, 70176, Germany. TEL 49-711-3514560, FAX 49-711-35145699, mail@schweizerbart.de, http://www.schweizerbart.de/j/anthropologischer-anzeiger. Eds. G Hauser, H Walter.

016.301 AUS ISSN 1320-1158
AUSTRALIAN INSTITUTE OF ABORIGINAL AND TORRES STRAIT ISLANDER STUDIES. ANNUAL BIBLIOGRAPHY. Text in English. a. AUD 12. **Document type:** *Bibliography.* **Description:** Contains articles, research notes and reviews on all aspects of Australian Aboriginal studies.
Former titles: Australian Institute of Aboriginal Studies. Annual Bibliography (0156-1553); Australian Institute of Aboriginal Studies. Current Bibliography and Partial Accessions List
Published by: Australian Institute of Aboriginal and Torres Strait Islander Studies, PO Box 553, Canberra, ACT 2601, Australia. TEL 06-246-1111, FAX 06-249-7310. Ed. V Chapman.

B A B WORKING PAPER. (Basler Afrika Bibliographen) see *HISTORY—Abstracting, Bibliographies, Statistics*

016.301 USA ISSN 0896-8101
Z5111
BIBLIOGRAPHIC GUIDE TO ANTHROPOLOGY AND ARCHAEOLOGY. Text in English. 1987. a. USD 360 (effective 2005). **Document type:** *Bibliography.* **Description:** Includes comprehensive subject bibliographies providing complete Library of Congress cataloging and ISBN information for each title.
Published by: G.K. Hall & Co. (Subsidiary of: Gale Group), 12 Lunar Dr, Woodbridge, CT 06525. TEL 203-397-2600, 800-444-0799, FAX 203-397-8296, remmel.nunn@gale.com, http://www.galegroup.com/gkhall. **Subscr. to:** Simon & Schuster, PO Box 7500, Riverside, NJ 08075-8075. TEL 800-223-2336.

016.301 DEU ISSN 0067-706X
Z7836
BIBLIOGRAPHIE ZUR SYMBOLIK, IKONOGRAPHIE UND MYTHOLOGIE. Text in German. 1968. a. EUR 26 (effective 2003). adv. bk.rev. bibl. back issues avail. **Document type:** *Bibliography.* **Description:** List of books on symbolics, iconography and mythological studies published worldwide.
Indexed: BHA, RASB.
Published by: Verlag Valentin Koerner GmbH, Postfach 100164, Baden-Baden, 76482, Germany. TEL 49-7221-22423, FAX 49-7221-38697, valentin.koerner@t-online.de, http://www.koernerverlag.de. Eds. Hermann Jung, Peter Eschweiler. Circ: 1,000.

016.301 USA ISSN 0742-6844
BIBLIOGRAPHIES AND INDEXES IN ANTHROPOLOGY. Text in English. 1984. irreg. price varies. **Document type:** *Bibliography.*
—BLDSC (1993.097200).
Published by: Greenwood Publishing Group Inc. (Subsidiary of: Harcourt International), 88 Post Rd W, PO Box 5007, Westport, CT 06881. TEL 203-226-3571, FAX 203-226-1502, bookinfo@greenwood.com, http://www.greenwood.com.

016.301 NLD
Z3273
E I (ONLINE EDITION). (Excerpta Indonesica) Text in English. 1970. 2/yr. free (effective 2005). bk.rev. abstr.; bibl. cum.index every 5 yrs. **Document type:** *Journal, Abstract/Index.* **Description:** Abstracts recently published articles and books in all fields of the social sciences and humanities pertaining to Indonesia.
Formerly (until 2002): E I (Print Edition) (0046-0885)
Media: Online - full content.
Published by: (Koninklijk Instituut voor Taal-, Land- en Volkenkunde, Afdeling Documentatie Modern Indonesie), K I T L V Press, PO Box 9515, Leiden, 2300 RA, Netherlands. TEL 31-71-5272372, FAX 31-71-5272638, kitlvpress@kitlv.nl, http://www.kitlv.nl/periodicals.htm. Eds. E Ebing, R L Robson-McKillop.

016.3058 USA ISSN 0893-0120
N5310.7
ETHNOARTS INDEX. Text in English. 1983. q. USD 70; USD 80 foreign (effective 1999). bk.rev. bibl. back issues avail. **Document type:** *Abstract/Index.* **Description:** Abstracting and indexing publications on the art of the indigenous peoples of Africa, Oceania, and the Americas.
Formerly: Tribal Arts Review (0748-0024)
Indexed: AnthLit.
Published by: Data Arts, PO Box 30789, Seattle, WA 98103. TEL 206-783-9580. Ed. Eugene C Burt. Circ: 100.

016.306 IND
I C S S R JOURNAL OF ABSTRACTS AND REVIEWS: SOCIOLOGY & SOCIAL ANTHROPOLOGY. Text in English. 1972. s-a. INR 150 domestic to individuals; USD 120 elsewhere to individuals; GBP 80 in Europe to individuals; INR 250 domestic to institutions; USD 120 elsewhere to institutions; GBP 80 in Europe to institutions (effective 2001). bk.rev. index. back issues avail. **Document type:** *Journal, Abstract/Index.* **Description:** Selected reviews of publications as well as abstracts of reserach works in the fields of sociology and social anthropology. Includes works in criminology.
Formerly: I C S S R Journal of Abstracts and Reviews (0302-7546)
Indexed: IBR.
Published by: Indian Council of Social Science Research, 35 Ferozshah Rd., New Delhi, 110 001, India. TEL 91-11-6179832, FAX 91-11-6179836, info@icssr.org, http://www.icssr.org. Ed. N Jayaram. Circ: 450.

016.30608 AUS
INDIGENOUS KNOWLEDGE INDEX. Text in English. 1994. a. AUD 150 (effective 1997 & 1998). back issues avail. **Document type:** *Abstract/Index.*

Published by: Noyce Publishing, GPO Box 2222 T, Melbourne, VIC 3001, Australia. noycepublishing@hotmail.com.

016.306   GBR
Z7161
INTERNATIONAL BIBLIOGRAPHY OF THE SOCIAL SCIENCES. ANTHROPOLOGY. Text in English; Prefatory materials in French. 1955. a., latest vol.48, 2002, Oct. GBP 215, USD 300 per vol. (effective Oct. 2003). adv. back issues avail.; reprints avail. **Document type:** Bibliography. **Description:** Covers monographs and the contents of over 2000 journals in the social sciences from a selective bibliography indexed by subject, geographical term, and author.
Formerly: International Bibliography of the Social Sciences. Social and Cultural Anthropology (0085-2074)
Related titles: ♦ CD-ROM ed.: I B S S CD-ROM. ISSN 1544-9289; ♦ Online - full text ed.: International Bibliography of the Social Sciences.
Indexed: RASB.
—BLDSC (4536.840000).
Published by: (British Library of Political and Economic Science), Routledge (Subsidiary of: Taylor & Francis Group), 4 Park Square, Milton Park, Abingdon, Oxon OX14 4RN, United Kingdom. TEL 44-1235-828600, FAX 44-1235-829000, info@routledge.co.uk, http://www.lse.ac.uk/collections/IBSS/access/access_print.htm, http://www.tandf.co.uk. Circ: 2,000.

016.301   NLD   ISSN 0074-0462
KONINKLIJK INSTITUUT VOOR TAAL-, LAND- EN VOLKENKUNDE. BIBLIOGRAPHICAL SERIES. Text mainly in English; Text occasionally in Dutch, French. 1965. irreg., latest vol.21, 1995. price varies. back issues avail. **Document type:** Monographic series, Bibliography.
Published by: (Koninklijk Instituut voor Taal-, Land- en Volkenkunde), K I T L V Press, PO Box 9515, Leiden, 2300 RA, Netherlands. TEL 31-71-5272372, FAX 31-71-5272638, kitlvpress@rullet.leidenuniv.nl, kitlvpress@kitlv.nl.

016.301   BOL
LURATHA. Text in Spanish. 1978. bi-m. looseleaf. BOB 60, USD 5. adv. bk.rev. index. back issues avail.
Published by: Instituto Nacional de Antropologia, Centro de Documentacion Antropologica, Casilla 20898, La Paz, Bolivia.

016.3064 016.9301 016.94   RUS
NOVAYA LITERATURA PO SOTSIAL'NYM I GUMANITARNYM NAUKAM. ISTORIYA. ARKHEOLOGIYA. ETNOLOGIYA; bibliograficheskii ukazatel'. Text in Russian. 1992. m. USD 450 (effective 2004). **Document type:** Bibliography. **Description:** Presents information about Russian and foreign books on history, archeology and ethnology acquired by the INION library.
Formed by the merger of (1947-1992): Novaya Inostrannaya Literatura po Obshchestvennym Naukam. Istoriya - Arkheologiya - Etnografiya (0134-2827); (1947-1992): Novaya Sovetskaya Literatura po Obshchestvennym Naukam. Istoriya - Arkheologiya - Etnografiya (0134-2746)
Indexed: RASB.
Published by: Rossiiskaya Akademiya Nauk, Institut Nauchnoi Informatsii po Obshchestvennym Naukam, Nakhimovskii pr-t 51/21, Moscow, 117997, Russian Federation. TEL 7-095-1288930, FAX 7-095-4202261, info@inion.ru, http://www.inion.ru. Ed. V N Babenko. **US dist. addr.:** East View Information Services, 3020 Harbor Ln. N., Minneapolis, MN 55447. TEL 800-477-1005, FAX 800-800-3839, eastview@eastview.com, http://www.eastview.com.

016.301   AUT   ISSN 0259-0778
OESTERREICHISCHE VOLKSKUNDLICHE BIBLIOGRAPHIE. Text in German. 1966. irreg., latest vol.36, 2002. price varies. **Document type:** Monographic series, Bibliography.
Published by: Verein fuer Volkskunde, Laudongasse 19, Vienna, W 1080, Austria. TEL 43-1-4068905, FAX 43-1-4085342, verein@volkskundemuseum.at, http://www.volkskundemuseum.at. Ed. Klaus Beitl.

016.57 016.61 016.301   RUS   ISSN 0207-1428
REFERATIVNYI ZHURNAL. MORFOLOGIYA CHELOVEKA I ZHIVOTNYKH. ANTROPOLOGIYA. Text in Russian. 1958. m. USD 576 foreign (effective 2006). **Document type:** Abstract/Index.
Related titles: CD-ROM ed.; Online - full text ed.; ♦ Cumulative ed(s).: Referativnyi Zhurnal. Biologiya. Fiziologiya i Morfologiya Cheloveka i Zhivotnykh. ISSN 0869-4079.
—East View.
Published by: Vserossiiskii Institut Nauchnoi i Tekhnicheskoi Informatsii (VINITI), Ul Usievicha 20, Moscow, 125190, Russian Federation. TEL 7-095-1526441, FAX 7-095-9430060, dir@viniti.ru, http://www.viniti.ru. **Dist. by:** Informnauka Ltd., Ul Usievicha 20, Moscow 125190, Russian Federation. alfimov@viniti.ru.

301.021   SWE   ISSN 0282-3519
DL631
SWEDEN. STATISTISKA CENTRALBYRAAN. STATISTISKA MEDDELANDEN. SERIE KU, KULTUR. Text in Swedish; Summaries in English. 1985. irreg. SEK 375 (effective 1992).
Published by: Statistiska Centralbyraan, Publishing Unit, Orebro, 70189, Sweden. TEL 019-176594.

ANTIQUES

see also ART

745.1   USA
A A D A NEWS. Text in English. bi-m. **Document type:** Directory, Trade. **Description:** Describes membership activities. Includes new members list.
Published by: Associated Antique Dealers of America, PO Box 320, Corte Madera, CA 94925. TEL 415-924-2171. Ed. Sonia B Delew.

A M G B A OCTAGON. see TRANSPORTATION—Automobiles

745.1   USA   ISSN 0048-2358
A P M BULLETIN. Text in English. 1972. q. USD 36 membership (effective 1999); includes AAA News and International Antique Airplane Digest. adv. bk.rev. bibl.; illus. **Document type:** Newsletter. **Description:** Covers donations to APM, news, photos, and activities of other aviation museums worldwide.
Published by: (Air Power Museum), Antique Airplane Association, Inc., 22001 Bluegrass Rd, Ottumwa, IA 52501-8569. TEL 515-938-2773. Ed., Pub., R&P, Adv. contact Robert L Taylor. Circ: 5,000.

A P M MONOGRAPH SERIES. (Antique Phonograph Monthly) see MUSIC

A T H S SHOW TIME. see TRANSPORTATION—Trucks And Trucking

629.222 338.476   USA
ACCELERATOR. Text in English. 1974. q. free to members (effective 2005). bk.rev. **Document type:** Newsletter. **Description:** Contains current museum event notices and historic automotive feature articles.
Published by: Auburn Cord Duesenberg Museum, 1600 S Wayne St, PO Box 271, Auburn, IN 46706. TEL 260-925-1444, FAX 260-925-6266, http://www.acdmuseum.org. Ed. Sheryl Prentice. Circ: 1,650.

ACTA UNIVERSITATIS WRATISLAVIENSIS. ANTIQUITAS. see CLASSICAL STUDIES

629.222   USA   ISSN 0044-6092
ACTION ERA VEHICLE. Text in English. 1967 (vol.5). q. USD 25; USD 29 foreign (effective 1999). adv. bk.rev. illus. back issues avail. **Description:** Articles includes anecdotal, humor, historical, technical tips on restoration and mainteneance and club event coverage.
Published by: (Contemporary Historical Vehicle Association), St. Croix Press, Inc., P O Box 4485, Redding, CA 96099-4485. TEL 530-245-0426, 818-893-6531. Ed. Charles R Smith. Circ: 2,000.

745.1 705   FRA   ISSN 0981-1389
ALADIN; le magazine des chineurs. Text in French. 1987. m. EUR 34.35 domestic; EUR 54 in Europe; EUR 69 newsstand/cover elsewhere (effective 2004). adv. **Document type:** Consumer. **Description:** Covers antiques fairs, auctions and collections, art showing and expositions, art news and analysis.
Published by: Editions Aladin, 7 Rue Jean Mermoz, Versailles, 78000, France. TEL 33-1-39248787, FAX 33-1-39248783, info@aladinmag.com, http://www.aladinmag.com. Ed. Jean Stephane Vincent. Pub., Adv. contact Bruno Delaine. Circ: 81,031.

629.222   USA
BL2747.3
AMERICAN AUSTIN BANTAM CLUB NEWS. Text in English. 1961. bi-m. USD 6. adv.
Published by: American Austin-Bantam Club, 516 W Washington, Washington, IA 52353. Ed. James Peterson. Circ: 300.

666   USA   ISSN 0739-6546
AMERICAN CLAY EXCHANGE✳ . Text in English. 1980. 18/yr. USD 21. cum.index: 1980-1985. back issues avail.
Published by: Page One Publications, 800 Murray Dr, El Cajon, CA 92020. Ed. Susan N Cox.

745.1   USA
AMERICANA FLEA MARKET DIRECTORY✳ . Text in English. a. USD 10.95. **Document type:** Directory.
Formerly: Flea Market Directory
Address: 1205 Cranbrook Dr, Saginaw, MI 48603-5440.

745.1   BEL
ANTIEK & CURIOSA; verzamelhobby. Text in Dutch. 1987. m. adv. bk.rev. index. back issues avail. **Document type:** Bulletin. **Description:** News and articles on antiques, collectibles, memorabilia, auctions, flea markets and more.
Published by: P.R.C. Claes, Nielsestraat 181, Boom, 2850, Belgium. TEL 32-3-888-7461. Ed. Marc Claes. Circ: 14,000.

745.1   SWE   ISSN 0282-8200
ANTIK & AUKTION. Variant title: Vaar Konst. Text in Swedish. 1975. 11/yr. SEK 398 (effective 2005). adv. bk.rev. illus. **Document type:** Magazine, Consumer. **Description:** Focuses on antiques, art, auctions, and interior decoration.

Former titles (until 1985): Nya Antik och Auktion (0346-9212); (until 1978): Antik och Auktion
Published by: Allers Foerlag AB, Landskronavaegen 23, Helsingborg, 25185, Sweden. TEL 46-42-173500, FAX 46-42-173682, http://www.allersforlag.se. Ed. Carin Stentorp. Adv. contact Lilimor Werre TEL 46-8-6794681. page SEK 15,000; 190 x 265. Circ: 59,100 (paid).

745.1   DNK   ISSN 1397-8799
ANTIK & AUKTION; specialbladet om samlere, antikviteter og kunst. Text in Danish. 1997. 6/yr. DKK 357; DKK 59.50 per issue (effective 2004). adv. illus. **Document type:** Magazine, Consumer. **Description:** Contains articles and features on antique sales from auctions at home and abroad.
Published by: Aller Press A-S, Vigerslev Alle 18, Valby, 2500, Denmark. TEL 45-36-152000, FAX 45-36-152696, aa@antikogauktion.dk, direktionen@aller.dk, http://www.antikogauktion.dk, http://www.aller.dk. Ed. Jette Oesterlund TEL 45-33-144422. Adv. contact Morten Buch TEL 45-36-152660. color page DKK 15,000; 208 x 280. Circ: 22,000 (paid).

745.1   SWE   ISSN 1400-4747
ANTIKBOERSEN. Text in Swedish. 1989. 11/yr. SEK 398 domestic; SEK 410 in Norway; SEK 495 in Denmark & Finland; SEK 550 in Europe; SEK 650 in the European Union; SEK 630 elsewhere (effective 2005). **Document type:** Magazine, Consumer.
Formerly (until 1993): Kvalitets- och Antikboersen (1100-8202)
Published by: Antikboersens Foerlag AB, Birkagaten 17, Stockholm, 11336, Sweden. TEL 46-8-54547000, FAX 46-8-54547049, http://www.antikborsen.se/. Ed., Pub., Adv. contact Winston Haakansson.

ANTIKE KUNST. see ARCHAEOLOGY

ANTIKE KUNST. BEIHEFTE. see ARCHAEOLOGY

ANTIQUARIAN. see HISTORY—History Of North And South America

070.5 381.45   USA   ISSN 1522-2985
ANTIQUARIAN, SPECIALTY AND USED BOOK SELLERS; a subject guide and directory. Text in English. 1993. irreg., latest vol.2, 1998. USD 85 per vol. (effective 2001). Index. **Document type:** Directory. **Description:** Lists and describes 5,261 active antiquarian book dealers in the US. Each entry includes contact information and other specific information.
Published by: Omnigraphics, Inc., 615 Griswold St, Detroit, MI 48226. http://www.omnigraphics.com. Ed. Karen Ethridge. Pub. Frederick G Ruffner Jr.

745.1   ITA   ISSN 1124-8335
ANTIQUARIATO. Text in Italian. 1978. m. adv. bk.rev. charts; illus. **Document type:** Magazine, Consumer.
Formerly (until 1981): BolaffiArte Antiquariato (0391-3392)
Published by: Editoriale Giorgio Mondadori SpA (Subsidiary of: Cairo Communication SpA), Via Tucidide 56, Torre 3, Milan, 20134, Italy. TEL 39-02-748111, FAX 39-02-70100102, info@cairocommunication.it, http://www.cairocommunication.it. Ed. Daniela Clerici. Circ: 40,000.

ANTIQUE AIRPLANE ASSOCIATION NEWS. see AERONAUTICS AND SPACE FLIGHT

ANTIQUE & CLASSIC. see TRANSPORTATION—Automobiles

ANTIQUE & COLLECTABLES MONTHLY NEWS MAGAZINE. see HOBBIES

745.1   CAN   ISSN 1708-6469
▼ **ANTIQUE & COLLECTIBLES SHOWCASE.** Text in English. 2003. 8/yr. CND 26 domestic; USD 27 in United States (effective 2004). adv. bk.rev. illus. reprints avail. **Document type:** Magazine, Consumer. **Description:** Aimed at antique lovers and collectors. Articles focus on factual and helpful information for seasoned and beginner collectors.
Formed by the merger of (1965-2003): Antique Showcase (0713-6315); Which was formerly (until vol.17, Nov. 1981): Ontario Showcase (0030-3119); (1982-2003): Collectibles Canada (1196-4812); Which superseded in part (in 1993): Insight on Collectables (0836-5873); Which was formerly (until 1987): Insight (0833-4447); (until 1986): Insight on Collectables (0714-8992)
Published by: Trajan Publishing Corp., 103 Lakeshore Rd, Ste 202, St Catharines, ON L2N 2T6, Canada. TEL 905-646-7744, FAX 905-646-0995, office@trajan.com, http://www.antiqueshowcase.net, http://www.trajan.com. Ed. Barbara Sutton Smith. Pub. Paul Fiocca. adv: B&W page CND 549; trim 10.75 x 8.13. Circ: 9,200.

ANTIQUE ANGLER; a quarterly newsletter-history of fishing-collectible tackle, etc. see SPORTS AND GAMES—Outdoor Life

745.1   USA
ANTIQUE APPRAISAL ASSOCIATION OF AMERICA. NEWSLETTER. Text in English. m. **Document type:** Newsletter.

Published by: Antique Appraisal Association of America, 11361 Garden Grove Blvd, Garden Grove, CA 92643. TEL 714-530-7090.

629.222 USA ISSN 0003-5831
TL1
ANTIQUE AUTOMOBILE. Text in English. 1937. bi-m. USD 30 to members (effective 2005). adv. bk.rev. charts; illus. index, cum.index: 1935-1978. back issues avail.; reprint service avail. from PQC. **Document type:** *Magazine, Consumer.*
Description: Focuses on car collecting and collectors.
Related titles: Microform ed.: (from PQC).
Published by: Antique Automobile Club of America, 501 W Governor Rd, Hershey, PA 17033. TEL 717-534-1910, FAX 717-534-9101. Ed. West Peterson. Circ: 40,000 (paid).

745.1 USA ISSN 8750-1481
ANTIQUE BOTTLE AND GLASS COLLECTOR. Text in English. 1984. m. USD 25 domestic; USD 28 in Canada; USD 31 elsewhere (effective 2005). adv. bk.rev.; mkt. back issues avail.; reprints avail. **Document type:** *Consumer.*
Description: Offers feature articles on antique bottles; includes calendar of events.
Published by: Boyertown Publishing, 102 Jefferson St, PO Box 180, East Greenville, PA 18041. TEL 215-679-5849, FAX 215-679-3068, glswrk@enter.net, http://www.glswrk-auction.com/who.htm. Ed., Pub. James Hagenbuch. R&P Jesse Sailer. Adv. contact Janice Hagenbuch. Circ: 4,100 (paid).

629.222 USA ISSN 0164-7237
CODEN: ORIEEP
ANTIQUE CAR TIMES. Text in English. bi-m. USD 15. **Document type:** *Newsletter.* **Description:** Features articles on antique cars.
Address: 13712 Sardis Rd, Mabelvale, AR 72103. TEL 501-455-2006. Pub. Georgia Stinnett.

745.1 GBR ISSN 0003-584X
ANTIQUE COLLECTING. Text in English. 1965. m. (except Aug. & Jan.). GBP 25 in United Kingdom; GBP 30 overseas (effective 2001). adv. bk.rev. illus. index. reprints avail.
Document type: *Consumer.*
Incorporates: Antique Finder (0003-5874)
Indexed: ABM, BHA, DAAI, RILM.
—BLDSC (1550.230000).
Published by: Antique Collectors Club, 5 Church St, Woodbridge, Suffolk IP12 1DS, United Kingdom. FAX 44-1394-384434, http://www.antiquecc.com/. Ed. Susan Wilson. R&P Sarah Smye TEL 44-1394-385501. Adv. contact Jean Johnson. Circ: 20,000.

745.1 USA ISSN 0892-7162
NK4890.C63
ANTIQUE COMB COLLECTOR; ornamental comb news. Text in English. 1985. bi-m. USD 25 membership (effective 2005). adv. bk.rev. illus.; mkt.; pat.; tr.lit. 8 p./no.; back issues avail.
Document type: *Newsletter, Consumer.* **Description:** Research on the current cost, history, dating, manufacturing, materials, design, styles and care of antique head and hair ornaments. Includes member profiles.
Published by: (Antique Comb Collectors Club International), Pet Project, 90 S Highland Ave, Apt 1204, Tarpon Springs, FL 34689-5351. belvagreen@mciworld.com, comber@gte.net, bgreen4206@aol.com, http://www.geocities.com/Heartland/Pointe/5350. Ed., R&P, Adv. contact Belva Green. Pub. Mary Bachman. Circ: 105 (paid and free).

745.1 USA ISSN 1096-8474
ANTIQUE DOLL COLLECTOR. Text in English. 1993. m. USD 39.95; USD 5.95 newsstand/cover domestic; USD 6.95 newsstand/cover in Canada (effective 2005). adv. 76 p./no.; back issues avail. **Document type:** *Magazine, Consumer.*
Description: Covers antique dolls (made prior to 1950), doll accessories and soft toys, with articles on antique dolls, teddy bears, miniatures and doll houses.
Formerly (until 1997): Antique Doll World (1069-5141)
Published by: Puffin Co., LLC, 6 Woodside Ave., Ste. 300, Northport, NY 11768. TEL 631-261-4100, FAX 631-261-9684, antiquedollcoll@aol.com, http://www.antiquedollcollector.com. Ed. Donna C. Kaonis. adv.: B&W page USD 760, color page USD 1,060; trim 8.375 x 10.875. Circ: 7,000 (paid).

745.1 GBR ISSN 1366-9923
ANTIQUE INTERIORS INTERNATIONAL. Text in English. 1986. q. GBP 16; GBP 3.50 newsstand/cover (effective 1999). adv.
Document type: *Consumer.*
Former titles (until 1997): Antique International (0959-6003); Antique (0951-6913)
Published by: Antique Publications Ltd., 162 Packington St, London, N1 8RA, United Kingdom. TEL 44-171-359-6011, FAX 44-171-359-6025.

745.1 USA
ANTIQUE JOURNAL FOR THE NORTHWEST. Text in English. 1993. m. USD 3 newsstand/cover; USD 24 (effective 2003). adv. **Document type:** *Newspaper.* **Description:** Devoted to antiques in Oregon, Washington, Idaho, and Western Canada. Provides lists of shops and in-depth features about antiques and collectibles, people, book reviews, and show news.
Formed by the 1973 merger of: Antique Gazette; Antique Journal for California & Nevada
Published by: Krause Publications, Inc. (Subsidiary of: F & W Publications, Inc.), 700 E State St, Iola, WI 54990-0001. TEL 715-445-2214, 800-258-0929, FAX 715-445-4087, info@krause.com, http://www.krause.com. Ed. Jennifer Edwards TEL 619-593-2931. Pub. Sandra Hood TEL 619-593-2926. Adv. contact Linda O'Connor TEL 619-593-2927. B&W page USD 909, color page USD 1,215; trim 11.5 x 13.5. Circ: 30,000.

745.1 USA
ANTIQUE JOURNAL FOR THE WEST COAST. Text in English. 1993. m. free domestic wherever available; USD 20 (effective 2005). adv. **Document type:** *Newspaper, Consumer.*
Formerly: Antique Journal For California & Nevada
Published by: Krause Publications, Inc. (Subsidiary of: F & W Publications, Inc.), 700 E State St, Iola, WI 54990-0001. TEL 715-445-2214, FAX 715-445-4087, http://www.collect.com. Ed. Kyle Husfloen. Pub. Greg Smith TEL 715-445-2214 ext 461. adv.: B&W page USD 909, color page USD 1,290. Circ: 30,000 (paid and free).

974 745.1 USA ISSN 1070-8421
GA197.3
ANTIQUE MAP PRICE RECORD & HANDBOOK✶. Text in English. 1983. a. USD 31.05. bk.rev. **Description:** Contains reference information, international dealer directory, and compilation of prices from dealer catalogs.
Formerly: Antique Maps, Sea Charts, City Views, Celestial Charts and Battle Plans, Price Record and Handbook for (Year) (0749-4971)
Published by: David C. Jolly, Ed.& Pub., 1310 N Mitchell Ave, Arlington, IL 60004-4650. TEL 617-232-6222.

796.95 USA
ANTIQUE OUTBOARD MOTOR CLUB NEWSLETTER✶. Text in English. 1976 (vol.9). 8/yr. membership. adv. tr.lit. **Document type:** *Newsletter.* **Description:** Provides current information on club and member activities as well as tips, leads on where to find motors, and new ideas.
Related titles: ◆ Supplement to: Antique Outboarder. ISSN 0003-5904.
Published by: Antique Outboard Motor Club, Inc., PO Box 69, Sussex, WI 53089-0069. TEL 612-323-0179. Ed., Adv. contact Mark Lodge. Circ: 1,799.

ANTIQUE OUTBOARDER. see *SPORTS AND GAMES—Boats And Boating*

ANTIQUE RADIO CLASSIFIED. see *COMMUNICATIONS—Radio*

745.1 USA ISSN 0883-833X
ANTIQUE REVIEW; serving the dealers & collectors of midAmerica. Text in English. 1976. m. USD 23; USD 3.95 newsstand/cover (effective 2003). adv. bk.rev. illus. index, cum.index. back issues avail.; reprints avail. **Document type:** *Newspaper, Trade.*
Formerly: Ohio Antique Review (0192-6721)
Published by: Krause Publications, Inc. (Subsidiary of: F & W Publications, Inc.), 700 E State St, Iola, WI 54990-0001. TEL 715-445-2214, 800-258-0929, FAX 715-445-4087, traderpubs@krause.com, info@krause.com, http://www.collect.com, http://www.krause.com. Ed. Linda Kunkel TEL 563-588-2073 ext 131. Pub., Adv. contact Greg Smith. B&W page USD 446, color page USD 696; trim 10.75 x 12.75. Circ: 5,492 (paid and controlled).

745.1 696 697 USA
ANTIQUE STOVE ASSOCIATION QUARTERLY. Text in English. 1983. q. USD 20 to members (effective 1998). adv. back issues avail. **Document type:** *Newsletter.* **Description:** Antique stove restoration, maintenance and technology. Includes historical notes.
Formerly: Stove Parts Needed
Published by: Antique Stove Association, 2617 Riverside Dr, Houston, TX 77004-7610. TEL 713-528-2990, FAX 713-529-2122. Ed. Macy Stern. Circ: 700.

745.1 696 USA
ANTIQUE STOVE ASSOCIATION. YEARBOOK. Text in English. 1984. a. looseleaf. USD 20 to members (effective 1998). back issues avail. **Document type:** *Monographic series.*
Description: Reference book on antique stoves.
Published by: Antique Stove Association, 2617 Riverside Dr, Houston, TX 77004-7610. TEL 713-528-2990, FAX 713-529-2122. Ed. Macy Stern. Circ: 700 (paid).

ANTIQUE TOY WORLD. see *HOBBIES*

745.1 GBR
THE ANTIQUE TRADE CALENDAR. Text in English. 1992. q.
Document type: *Directory, Trade.*
Published by: G P London, 32 Fredericks Place, North Finchley, London, N12 8QE, United Kingdom. TEL 020-8446-3604, FAX 020-8922-8257. Ed. Stephen Browning. Circ: 15,000 (paid).

745.1 USA ISSN 1083-8430
ANTIQUE TRADER BOOKS ANTIQUES & COLLECTIBLES PRICE GUIDE. Text in English. 1984. m. USD 17.95 per issue (effective 2004). **Document type:** *Consumer.* **Description:** Covers all the major collecting categories popular today as well as ever-expanding coverage of emerging market categories.
Formerly (until 199?): The Antique Rrader Antiques & Collectibles Price Guide (0882-6897)
Published by: Krause Publications, Inc. (Subsidiary of: F & W Publications, Inc.), 700 E State St, Iola, WI 54990-0001. TEL 715-445-2214, 800-258-0929, FAX 715-445-4087, info@krause.com, http://www.collect.com, http://www.krause.com. Ed. Kyle Husfloen. Circ: 100,000 (paid).

745.1 USA ISSN 0161-8342
THE ANTIQUE TRADER WEEKLY; America's weekly antiques and collectibles marketplace. Text in English. 1957. w. USD 38; USD 2.99 newsstand/cover (effective 2005). adv. bk.rev. illus. reprints avail. **Document type:** *Newspaper, Trade.*
Formerly: Antique Trader (0003-5912)
Related titles: Online - full text ed.
Published by: Krause Publications, Inc. (Subsidiary of: F & W Publications, Inc.), 700 E State St, Iola, WI 54990-0001. TEL 715-445-2214, 800-258-0929, FAX 715-445-4087, traderpubs@krause.com, info@krause.com, http://www.antiquetrader.com, http://www.krause.com. Ed. Kyle Husfloen. Pub. Greg Smith. adv.: B&W page USD 1,108, color page USD 1,458; trim 10.75 x 12.75. Circ: 28,559 (paid and free).

745.1 USA
ANTIQUES AND ART AROUND FLORIDA. Text in English. 1985. s-a. USD 10 for 2 yrs.. adv. maps. back issues avail.
Document type: *Trade.* **Description:** Includes maps to the Florida antiques, art, and collectibles market; related feature articles; antiques show schedule; and museum schedules.
Related titles: Online - full text ed.
Published by: Antiques and Art Around Publishing, Inc., PO Box 2481, Fort Lauderdale, FL 33303-2481. TEL 954-768-9430, 800-248-9430, FAX 954-768-0621, aarf@shadow.com, http://aarf.com. Ed., Pub., R&P, Adv. contact Joan Bryant. color page USD 1,488, page USD 1,058; trim 8.38 x 5.38. Circ: 60,000 (controlled).

745.1 USA
ANTIQUES & AUCTION NEWS. Text in English. 1969. w. (Fri.). USD 75 (effective 2005). **Document type:** *Newspaper, Consumer.*
Formerly: Joel Slater's Antiques and Auction News
Published by: Engle Printing & Publishing Co., Inc., 1425 W Main St, Mt Joy, PA 17552. TEL 717-653-1833, 800-800-1833, FAX 717-653-6165, antiquesnews@engleonline.com, newsdept@engleonline.com, http://www.engleonline.com. Ed. Denise M Sater. Adv. contact Marty Wilcox. Circ: 38,000 evening (paid and free).

745.1 GBR ISSN 1464-1836
ANTIQUES & COLLECTABLES MAGAZINE. Text in English. 1998. m. EUR 31.20 in United Kingdom; EUR 53 in Europe; EUR 78 rest of world; EUR 2.60 newsstand/cover (effective 2001). adv. back issues avail. **Document type:** *Magazine, Consumer.* **Description:** Contains price guides, and articles on auctions, collectors and collectable items.
Published by: Merricks Media Ltd., Charlotte House, 12 Charlotte St, Bath, BA1 2NE, United Kingdom. TEL 44-1225-786800, FAX 44-1225-786801, info@merricksmedia.co.uk, http://www.antiques-collectables.co.uk, http://www.merricksmedia.co.uk. Ed. George Perrott. Adv. contact Luke Dart TEL 44-1225-786810. B&W page GBP 970. **Dist. by:** Comag, Tavistock Works, Tavistock Rd, W Drayton, Middx UB7 7QX, United Kingdom. TEL 44-1895-444055, FAX 44-1895-433602.

745.1 USA ISSN 0274-6085
ANTIQUES & COLLECTIBLES MAGAZINE. Text in English. 1980. m. USD 20 (effective 2005). adv. bk.rev. **Document type:** *Magazine, Consumer.* **Description:** For dealers and serious collectors.
Indexed: RILM.
Published by: Antiques & Collectibles, Inc., PO Box 33, Westbury, NY 11590. TEL 516-827-4145, FAX 516-827-4149, gtmag@optonline.net. Ed., Pub. Rich Branciforte. adv.: page USD 500. Circ: 5,000 (paid and controlled).

745.1 USA ISSN 1520-4464
ANTIQUES AND COLLECTIBLES NEWSLETTER. Text in English. 1997. w. free. **Document type:** *Newsletter.*
Description: Contains a humorous look at news in the collecting world by a television appraiser.
Media: Online - full text.
Published by: The Mining Company, PO Box 6572, New York, NY 10128-0006. TEL 212-876-3512, FAX 212-876-3512, newsletter@msjudith.net, http://www.msjudith.net. Ed. Judith Katz-Schwartz. Pub. Judith Katz Schwartz.

745.1 790.023 USA ISSN 1084-0818
ANTIQUES & COLLECTING MAGAZINE. Text in English. 1931. m. USD 32 domestic; USD 44 foreign; USD 3.50 newsstand/cover; USD 4.50 newsstand/cover in Canada (effective 2005). adv. bk.rev. illus. 70 p./no. 3 cols./p.; back issues avail.; reprint service avail. from PQC. **Document type:** *Magazine, Consumer.* **Description:** Focuses on the collecting of antiques for dealers and hobbyists.
Former titles (until Oct. 1993): Antiques and Collecting Hobbies (0884-6294); (until 1985): Hobbies, the Magazine for Collectors (0018-2907)

Related titles: Microfilm ed.: (from PQC); Online - full text ed.: (from EBSCO Publishing, H.W. Wilson, Northern Light Technology, Inc., O C L C Online Computer Library Center, Inc., ProQuest Information & Learning).
Indexed: BRI, CBRI, MagInd, MusicInd, PMR, RGAb, RGPR.
Published by: Lightner Publishing Corporation, 1006 S Michigan Ave, Chicago, IL 60605. TEL 312-939-4767, 800-762-7576, FAX 312-939-0053, info@acmagazine.com. Ed. Theresa Nolan. Pub. Dale Graham. R&P, Adv. contact Greg Graham. B&W page USD 639, color page USD 799; trim 10 x 7. Circ: 20,000 (paid).

745.1 USA
ANTIQUES BULLETIN. Text in English. w. **Document type:** *Bulletin.* **Description:** Covers all aspects of the antiques world, including auction and fairs calendars, trades, dealers directories, editorials, sales, and other useful links.
Media: Online - full text.
Address: barry@antiquesbulletin.com, http://www.antiquesbulletin.com.

745.1 GBR
ANTIQUES DIARY: LONDON AND SOUTH EDITION. Text in English. 1983. bi-m. GBP 16 domestic; GBP 19 in Europe; GBP 35 in United States (effective 2005). adv. bk.rev. bibl.; tr.lit. back issues avail. **Document type:** *Magazine, Consumer.* **Description:** Contains a comprehensive guide to antiques and collector's fair and markets in the region, besides information about auctions and antique shops and centers.
Formerly: Antiques Fairs and Markets Diary: London
Related titles: E-mail ed.; Fax ed.; Online - full text ed.
Published by: Antiques Diary, Twyford, PO Box 30, Reading, Berks RG10 8DQ, United Kingdom. TEL 44-118-9402165, FAX 44-118-9404550, antiquesdiary@btinternet.com, http://www.antiquesworld.co.uk/antiquesdiary/index.html. Ed. Jack Fowler. Pub. Peter W Allwright. Adv. contact Penny Rymer. B&W page GBP 143.35, color page GBP 370; trim 143 x 210. Circ: 15,000. **Dist. by:** Lakeside Newsagents, Unit 10, Tideway Industrial Estate, 87 Kirtling St, London SW8 5BP, United Kingdom. TEL 44-20-7720-6680, FAX 44-20-7498-9616.

745.1 GBR
ANTIQUES DIARY: NORTH & MIDLANDS EDITION. Text in English. 1983. bi-m. GBP 16 domestic; GBP 19 in Europe; GBP 35 in United States (effective 2005). adv. bk.rev. bibl.; tr.lit. back issues avail. **Document type:** *Magazine, Consumer.* **Description:** Contains a comprehensive guide to antiques and collector's fair and markets in the region, besides information about auctions and antique shops and centers.
Formerly: Antiques Fairs and Markets Diary: North and Midlands
Related titles: E-mail ed.; Fax ed.; Online - full text ed.
Published by: Antiques Diary, Twyford, PO Box 30, Reading, Berks RG10 8DQ, United Kingdom. TEL 44-118-9402165, FAX 44-118-9404550, antiquesdiary@btinternet.com, http://www.antiquesworld.co.uk/antiquesdiary/index.html. Ed. Jack Fowler. Pub. Peter W Allwright. Adv. contact Penny Rymer. B&W page GBP 143.35, color page GBP 370; trim 148 x 370. Circ: 15,000. **Dist. by:** Lakeside Newsagents, Unit 10, Tideway Industrial Estate, 87 Kirtling St, London SW8 5BP, United Kingdom. TEL 44-20-7720-6680, FAX 44-20-7498-9616.

745.1 USA
THE ANTIQUES DIRECTORY✶ . Text in English. 1991. m. USD 1.50. illus.
Published by: Brimfield Publishing, 1 Carpenter Rd, Monson, MA 01057-1153. TEL 413-267-3813. Ed. Alan J Morin. Circ: 500.

745.1 GBR ISSN 1351-5047
ANTIQUES FAIRS GUIDE. Text in English. 1987. s-a. GBP 1.50 newsstand/cover. adv. **Document type:** *Consumer.* **Description:** Provides news and information on national and international antiques fairs and conventions.
Published by: H P Publishing, 2 Hampton Court Rd, Harborne, Birmingham B17 9AE, United Kingdom. TEL 44-121-681-8000, FAX 44-121-681-8005. **Dist. by:** Seymour Distribution Ltd, 86 Newman St, London W1T 3EX, United Kingdom. FAX 44-207-396-8002, enquiries@seymour.co.uk.

745.1 GBR ISSN 1365-585X
ANTIQUES INFO MAGAZINE; information for the dealer and collector. Text in English. 1996. bi-m. GBP 16.20 in United Kingdom; GBP 23 in Europe; GBP 32 elsewhere (effective 2001). **Document type:** *Consumer.* **Description:** Contains articles and news about antiques, fairs, and auctions.
Address: PO Box 93, Broadstairs, Kent CT10 3YR, United Kingdom. TEL 44-1843-862069, FAX 44-1843-862014, john.ainsley@antiques-info.co.uk, http://www.antiques-info.co.uk. **Dist. by:** Diamond Magazine Distribution, Rye Wharf, Harbour Rd, Rye, E Sussex TN31 7TE, United Kingdom. TEL 44-1797-225229, FAX 44-1797-225657.

745.1 GBR
ANTIQUES LIFESTYLE. Text in English. 1999. m. GBP 26.40; GBP 2.40 newsstand/cover (effective 2000). adv. **Document type:** *Magazine, Consumer.* **Description:** Covers period homes, antiques and British heritage. Aimed at people who want to stylize their homes and lives around British heritage and history.
Published by: Collect It Ltd., Unit 11, Welle Dr, Hogwood Lane Industrial Estate, Finchampstead, Berks RG40 4QZ, United Kingdom. TEL 44-1189-737888, FAX 44-1189-737667, collectit@dial.pipex.com, http://www.thecollectingsite.com. Ed. Nikki Verrico. Pub., R&P Gwyn Jones. Adv. contact Simon McLaren-Tosh.

745.1 GBR
ANTIQUES MAGAZINE. Text in English. 1982. w. GBP 52, USD 140. adv. bk.rev. **Description:** Presents weekly preview of auctions and antiques fairs, sales reports, prices, calendars and news.
Formerly: Antiques Bulletin (1351-1661)
Published by: H.P. Publishing, Two Hampton Ct, Harborne, Birmingham, W Mids B17 2AE, United Kingdom. TEL 021-426-3300, FAX 021-428-1214. Ed. John Hubbard. Circ: 9,800.

745.1 USA ISSN 1544-2659
NK805
ANTIQUES ROADSHOW INSIDER. Text in English. 2001 (Jul.). m. USD 45 domestic; USD 55 in Canada (effective 2006). **Document type:** *Magazine, Consumer.*
Published by: (Antiques Insider LLC), Belvoir Media Group, LLC, 800 Connecticut Ave, Norwalk, CT 06854-1631. TEL 203-857-3100, 800-424-7887, FAX 203-857-3103, customer_service@belvoir.com, http://www.antiquesroadshowinsider.com/, http://www.belvoir.com. Eds. Larry Canale, Timothy H. Cole. Pub. Philip L. Penny.

745.1 GBR ISSN 0306-1051
ANTIQUES TRADE GAZETTE. Text in English. 1971. w. GBP 74 domestic; EUR 200 in Europe euro zone; GBP 140 in Europe non euro zone; USD 230 in United States; GBP 158 elsewhere (effective 2005). adv. bk.rev. **Document type:** *Newsletter, Consumer.* **Description:** For the professional in the art and antiques market. Lists and reports on auctions and shows.
Indexed: RICS.
Published by: Antiques Publishing (Subsidiary of: D M G World Media Ltd.), 115 Shaftsbury Ave, London, WC2H 8AD, United Kingdom. TEL 44-20-74206600, FAX 44-20-74206605, subscriptions@theantiquedealer.co.uk, editorial@antiquestradegazette.co.uk, http://www.antiquestradegazette.com. Circ: 19,348.

745.1 700 GBR
ANTIQUESNEWS; the Internet newspaper for the British antiquities trade. Text in English. 1998. q. bk.rev.; Website rev. illus.; mkt. **Document type:** *Newspaper, Trade.* **Description:** The newspaper of the British antiques and art trade, circulating to dealers and collectors throughout the world.
Incorporates (1963-2004): Antiques Folio; Formerly (until 2001): Antiques & Art Independent (Online Edition); Which incorporated (1997-2001): Antiques & Art Independent (Print Edition) (1460-9185)
Media: Online - full content.
Address: PO Box 1945, Comely Bank, Edinburgh, Midlothian EH4 1AB, United Kingdom. TEL 44-7000-765263, FAX 44-7000-268478, antiquesnews@hotmail.com, http://www.antiquesnews.co.uk. Ed., Pub. Tony Keniston. Adv. contact Malcolm Webster.

745.1 USA ISSN 0888-5451
ANTIQUEWEEK; weekly antique, auction and collectors' newspaper . Text in English. 1968. w. (Mon.). USD 38.95 for Central or Eastern ed.; USD 67.97 combined subscription for Central & Eastern eds. (effective 2005). adv. bk.rev. illus. reprints avail. **Document type:** *Newspaper, Consumer.* **Description:** Contains articles on all areas of antiques and collectibles.
Former titles (until 1986): Antique Week - Tri-State Trader (0746-4118); (until 1983): Tri-State Trader (0041-2503)
Related titles: Online - full text ed.; ♦ Regional ed(s).: AntiqueWeek - Central Edition; ♦ AntiqueWeek - Eastern Edition; Supplement(s): Antique Shop Guide. ISSN 0149-0192.
Published by: D M G World Media, Inc., 27 N Jefferson St, PO Box 90, Knightstown, IN 46148-0120. TEL 765-345-5133, 800-876-5133, FAX 765-345-3398, connie@antiqueweek.com, http://www.antiqueweek.com. Circ: 64,000 (paid).

745.1 USA
ANTIQUEWEEK - CENTRAL EDITION; weekly antique, auction and collectors' newspaper. Text in English. 1968. w. USD 38.95; USD 69.97 combined subscription includes Eastern Ed. (effective 2005). adv. bk.rev. charts; illus.; mkt. back issues avail. **Document type:** *Newspaper, Consumer.*
Related titles: Microfilm ed.; ♦ Regional ed(s).: AntiqueWeek. ISSN 0888-5451; ♦ AntiqueWeek - Eastern Edition.
Published by: D M G World Media, Inc., 27 N Jefferson St, PO Box 90, Knightstown, IN 46148-0120. TEL 765-345-5133, 800-876-5133, FAX 765-345-3398, http://www.antiqueweek.com. Circ: 46,000 (paid).

745.1 USA
ANTIQUEWEEK - EASTERN EDITION; weekly antique, auction & collectors' newspaper. Text in English. 1986. w. USD 38.95; USD 69.97 combined subscription includes Central Ed. (effective 2005). adv. bk.rev. charts; illus.; mkt. back issues avail. **Document type:** *Newspaper, Consumer.*
Related titles: Microfilm ed.; ♦ Regional ed(s).: AntiqueWeek. ISSN 0888-5451; ♦ AntiqueWeek - Central Edition.
Published by: D M G World Media, Inc., 27 N Jefferson St, PO Box 90, Knightstown, IN 46148-0120. TEL 765-345-5133, 800-876-5133, FAX 765-345-3398, http://www.antiqueweek.com. Circ: 24,000 (paid).

745.1 USA
ANTIQUING DIRECTORY AND TRAVELER'S GUIDE✶ . Text in English. 1985. a. USD 8.95. adv. **Document type:** *Directory.* **Description:** Guide to the location and specialties of approximately 2,500 New England and Hudson Valley antiques shops, shows and auctions, flea markets, geographically arranged with maps, indexed to specialties and services; includes 13-month calendar of antiques shows in the Northeast.
Former titles (until 1991): Antiques and Art Directory and Traveler's Guide; (until 1990): Antiques and Art Directory; Antiques Directory
Published by: August Enterprises, c/o Kate Broughton, Ed, 12 Vine St, Amesbury, MA 01913-1111. TEL 617-665-9181, FAX 617-662-4256. Ed. Kate Broughton. Circ: 12,500.

745.1 DEU
ANTIQUITAETEN-ZEITUNG. Text in German. 1972. fortn. EUR 69.60 domestic; EUR 79.20 foreign; EUR 3.20 newsstand/cover (effective 2004). adv. bk.rev. index. back issues avail. **Document type:** *Newspaper, Consumer.*
Indexed: IBZ.
Published by: Weltkunst Verlag GmbH, Nymphenburger Str 84, Munich, 80636, Germany. TEL 49-89-1269900, FAX 49-89-12699011, info@weltkunstverlag.de, http://www.antiquitaetenzeitung.de, http://www.weltkunstverlag.de. Ed. Jonathan Franks. R&P Juergen Kleidt. Adv. contact Constanze Schmachtenberger. B&W page EUR 1,305, color page EUR 1,525; trim 212 x 320. Circ: 12,000.

745.1 FRA ISSN 1164-2483
ANTIQUITES - INFO; le mensuel des professionnels. Text in French. 1991. m. adv. illus.; mkt.; tr.lit. **Document type:** *Trade.* **Description:** Contains information for professional antique dealers, including antique fairs.
Published by: Livet Editions, Chateau de Boisrigaud, Usson, 64490, France. TEL 33-4-73710004, FAX 33-4-73710362, france.antiquites@liveteditions.fr, b.livet@liveteditions.fr. Pub. Jean Claude Livet. R&P Jean-Claude Livet. Adv. contact Isabelle Nurit. Circ: 15,000 (controlled).

APOLLO; the international magazine of the arts. see *ART*

THE APPRAISERS STANDARD; published solely for collectors, auctioneers, dealers, etc. see *ART*

629.288 USA
ARC & SPARK. Text in English. 1966. m. looseleaf. membership. bk.rev. **Document type:** *Newsletter.* **Description:** News, information and history of antique automobiles.
Published by: Kalamazoo Antique Auto Restorers Club, PO Box 532, Oshtemo, MI 49007. TEL 269-624-6757, FAX 269-624-6757, David.Lyon@wmich.edu. Ed. David O Lyon. Circ: 225.

ARCHAEOLOGIA. see *ARCHAEOLOGY*

623.4 USA ISSN 1557-1297
U810
▼ **THE ARMOUR RESEARCH SOCIETY. JOURNAL.** Text in English. 2003. a. USD 16 per issue (effective 2006).
Formerly (until 2005): The Mail Research Society. Journal (1544-4333)
Published by: The Armour Research Society, 4905 W Bromley Dr, McHenry, IL 60050. TEL 815-575-1060, http://www.armourresearchsociety.org/journal.html.

739.7 GBR ISSN 0004-2439
U799
➤ **ARMS AND ARMOUR SOCIETY JOURNAL.** Text in English. 1953. s-a. GBP 15 to members (effective 2000). adv. bk.rev. illus. back issues avail. **Document type:** *Newsletter, Academic/Scholarly.* **Description:** Presents historical research on arms and armor: swords, daggers, guns, and rifles.
Indexed: AmH&L, BHA, BrArAb, HistAb, NumL.
Published by: Arms and Armour Society, c/o Anthony Dove, PO Box 10232, London, SW19 2ZD, United Kingdom. Ed. Christopher Gravett. Adv. contact M J Sarche. Circ: 500 (paid). **Subscr. to:** The Arms and Armour Society, 135 Peterborough Rd, London E10 6EL, United Kingdom.

739.7 USA ISSN 0380-982X
ARMS COLLECTING. Text in English. 1963. q. USD 22 to individuals; CND 24 in Canada to individuals; GBP 15 in United Kingdom to individuals (effective 1999). adv. bk.rev. charts; illus.; pat. index. **Document type:** *Academic/Scholarly.*
Formerly: Canadian Journal of Arms Collecting (0008-3992)
Published by: Museum Restoration Service, PO Box 70, Alexandria Bay, NY 13607. TEL 613-393-2980, FAX 613-393-3378. Ed. S J Gooding. Circ: 2,100.

ARROW (ROCHESTER). see *TRANSPORTATION—Automobiles*

A

745.1 666 USA ISSN 1043-3317
ARS CERAMICA. Text in English. 1983. a. free to members (effective 2005). adv. bk.rev. 10-yr. index. back issues avail. **Document type:** *Magazine, Academic/Scholarly.* **Description:** Contains general articles on ceramics, pottery, glass, and archaeology.
Indexed: BHA.
Published by: Wedgwood Society of New York, 5 Dogwood Ct., Glen Head, NY 11545. TEL 516-626 3427, FAX 516-626-3430, www@wsny.org, http://www.wsny.org/. Ed., Adv. contact Harwood Johnson TEL 610-892-9213. R&P Barnard Starr. page USD 400; trim 11 x 8.5. Circ: 610 (paid).

745.1 751.6 USA ISSN 0195-8208
N6505
ART & ANTIQUES. Text in English. 1978. m. USD 24.95 domestic; USD 54.95 foreign; USD 4.99 newsstand/cover (effective 2005). adv. bk.rev. charts; illus. 120 p./no. 3 cols./p.; back issues avail.; reprints avail. **Document type:** *Magazine, Consumer.* **Description:** Covers fine art, artists, antiques, beautifully crafted furniture, and intriguing collectibles.
Incorporates (1967-Jan. 1994): Antique Monthly (0003-5882); Formerly (until 1980): American Art and Antiques (0148-9100)
Related titles: Online - full text ed.: (from EBSCO Publishing, H.W. Wilson, O C L C Online Computer Library Center, Inc.).
Indexed: ABM, ABS&EES, AIAP, ASIP, AmH&L, ArtInd, BHA, HistAb, PCI, PMR, RILM.
—BLDSC (1733.346500), IE, ingenta.
Published by: Trans World Publishing, Inc., 2100 Powers Ferry Rd, Ste 300, Atlanta, GA 30339. TEL 770-955-5656, FAX 770-952-0669, editor@artandantiques.net, http://www.artandantiques.net. Ed. Barbara Tapp. Pub. Jay Perkins. R&P Denise Buchalter. Adv. contact Bill Besch. Circ: 127,808 (paid).

ART CONNOISSEUR. see *ART*

ARTS, ANTIQUES ET AUCTIONS. see *ART*

745.1 DNK ISSN 1602-3358
AUKTIONSLIV. Text in Danish. 2002. q. free (effective 2005). adv. **Document type:** *Magazine, Consumer.*
Published by: Bruun Rasmussen Kunstauktioner, Bredgade 33, Copenhagen K, 1260, Denmark. TEL 45-33-436911, FAX 45-33-436966, info@bruun-rasmussen.dk, http://www.bruun-rasmussen.dk. Ed. Sebastian Hauge Lerche. Circ: 35,000 (free).

AUKTIONSPREISE IM KUNSTPREIS JAHRBUCH. BAND 1. see *ART*

AUKTIONSPREISE IM KUNSTPREIS JAHRBUCH. BAND 2. see *ART*

AUKTIONSPREISE IM KUNSTPREIS JAHRBUCH. BAND 3. see *ART*

AUSTIN - HEALEY MAGAZINE. see *TRANSPORTATION—Automobiles*

AUTO RESTORER; the how-to guide for vintage car enthusiasts. see *TRANSPORTATION—Automobiles*

629.222 NLD ISSN 1572-2392
HET AUTOMOBIEL; klassieker magazine. Text in Dutch. 1981. m. EUR 45 (effective 2005). adv. illus. **Document type:** *Consumer.* **Description:** Covers old timers and classic cars, their maintenance and renovation, auctions and events, club news and road tests.
Former titles (until 2003): Automobiel Klassiek en Exclusief (1567-181X); (until 2000): Automobiel (0921-2159); Which incorporated (1994-2002): Voiture's Nieuws (1569-0970); Which was formerly (until 2000): Voiture's Oldtimer Krant (1380-5533)
Published by: Wilbers Publishing BV, Postbus 10, Ulft, 7070 AA, Netherlands. TEL 31-315-681326, FAX 31-315-630813, info@hetautomobiel.nl, info@wilberspublishing.nl, http://www.hetautomobiel.nl/, http://www.wilberspublishing.nl. Ed. Oscar Wilbers. Pub. Peter Wilbers. Adv. contact Christina Djermor. Circ: 15,000.

745.1 GBR ISSN 0968-1485
B B C HOMES AND ANTIQUES. Text in English. 1993. m. GBP 29.88; GBP 2.95 newsstand/cover (effective 2003). adv. **Document type:** *Magazine, Consumer.* **Description:** Full of inspirational features based around real homes plus practical advice on everything from paint techniques to furniture renovation.
Indexed: DAAI.
Published by: (British Broadcasting Corp.), B B C Worldwide Ltd., 80 Wood Ln, London, W12 0TT, United Kingdom. TEL 44-20-84331070, FAX 44-20-84332231, homes.and.antiques@bbc.co.uk, bbcworldwide@bbc.co.uk, http://www.bbcmagazines.com/homesandantiques. Ed. Judith Hall. Pub. Marcus Arthur. Circ: 169,374 (paid). **Dist. by:** Frontline, Park House, 117 Park Rd, Peterborough, Cambs PE1 2TS, United Kingdom. TEL 44-1733-555161, FAX 44-1733-562788.

BECKETT HOT TOYS. see *HOBBIES*

629.222 SWE ISSN 1652-5949
BILSPORT RETRO CARS; det baesta fraan 60-, 70- & 80-talen. Text in Swedish. 6/yr. SEK 199, NOK 265 (effective 2004). adv. **Document type:** *Magazine, Consumer.*
Formerly (until 2004): Depaa (1404-8906)
Published by: Foerlags AB Albinsson & Sjoeberg, PO Box 529, Karlskrona, 37123, Sweden. TEL 46-455-335325, FAX 46-455-311715, fabas@fabas.se, http://www.fabas.se. adv.: color page SEK 12,000; 190 x 275.

BLACK BOOK. HISTORICAL USED CAR XPRESS. see *BUSINESS AND ECONOMICS—Trade And Industrial Directories*

745.1 ESP
BOLETIN ANTIQVARIA. Text in Spanish. m. back issues avail.
Media: E-mail.
Published by: Galeria Antiquaria, C. Lagasca No. 28, 2o., Madrid, 28001, Spain. TEL 34-91-5766429, FAX 34-91-5779428, antiqvaria@antiqvaria.com, http://www.antiqvaria.com/.

745.1 ITA ISSN 0006-6745
BOLLETTINO DI LIBRI ANTICHI E MODERNI DI VARIA CULTURA ESAURITI E RARI. Text in Italian. s-a. adv. bk.rev. bibl.
Published by: Alfredo Guida Editore, Via Port'Alba 20/23, Naples, 80134, Italy. TEL 39-081-446377, FAX 39-081-451883, libri@guida.it, http://www.guida.it.

629.222 USA ISSN 1556-0953
BORGWARD - OWNERS' CLUB. NEWSLETTER; open to owners of Borgward products and enthusiasts. Text in English. 1974. q. USD 25 (effective 1999). adv. back issues avail.; reprints avail. **Document type:** *Newsletter.* **Description:** Deals with the preservation and enjoyment of Borgward automobiles and products.
Published by: Borgward - Owners' Club, 77 New Hampshire Ave, Bay Shore, NY 11706. TEL 516-273-0458, leftyny@aol.com. Ed. Dyck Livant. Circ: 100.

BOULAY 300: WORLD AUCTION REPORT. see *ART*

745.1 GBR ISSN 0955-2553
THE BRADFORD ANTIQUARY. Text in English. 1881. irreg. bk.rev.
—BLDSC (2265.930000).
Published by: Bradford Historical and Antiquarian Society, c/o John Allison, Secret., 366 Idle Rd, Eccleshill, Bradford, BD2 2AW, United Kingdom. http://www.bradfordhistorical.fsnet.co.uk/antiquary/index.html, http://www.bradfordhistorical.fsnet.co.uk/society/index.html.

745.1 GBR
BRITISH ANTIQUE DEALERS' ASSOCIATION YEARBOOK. Text in English. 1986. a. GBP 8 (effective 1999). adv. **Document type:** *Directory, Consumer.* **Description:** Illustrated guide to members' shops. Includes information on buying antiques and lists BADA Fair exhibitors.
Formerly: British Antique Dealers' Association Handbook
Published by: (British Antique Dealer's Association), Burlington Magazine Publications Ltd., 14 Dukes Rd, London, WC1H 9AD, United Kingdom. TEL 44-20-7388-1228, FAX 44-20-7581-9083. Ed. Laura Williams. Pub. Kate Trevelyan. R&P Gillian Craig TEL 44-20-7589-6108. Adv. contact Mike Ross. Circ: 6,000.

629.222 USA ISSN 0194-8415
TL215.B84
BUICK BUGLE✶. Text in English. m. membership. **Description:** For car enthusiasts sharing an interest in the restoration and preservation of old Buicks.
Published by: Buick Club of America, PO Box 401927, Hesperia, CA 92340-1927.

745.1 FRA ISSN 1765-0267
BULLETIN DE L'ANTIQUAIRE, DU BROCANTEUR, ET DES GALLERIES D'ART MODERNE ET CONTEMPORAIN. Text in French. 1948. m. (10/yr.). adv.
Formerly (until 2002): Bulletin de l'Antiquaire et du Brocanteur (1765-0259)
Published by: Syndicat National du Commerce de l'Antiquite et de l'Occasion (SNCAO), 18 rue de Provence, Paris, 75009, France. Circ: 5,500.

BULLETIN D'ETUDES ORIENTALES. see *ASIAN STUDIES*

745.1 JPN
DS820.8 CODEN: KNKAAF
BUNKAZAI HOZON SYUHUKU GAKKAISI. Text in English, Japanese; Summaries in English. 1951. a. JPY 8,000 to members. adv. **Document type:** *Newsletter, Academic/Scholarly.* **Description:** Contains articles on conservation of artistic, archaeological and historical objects mainly of Japan, China and Korea.
Formerly (until vol.40, 1996): Kobunkazai no Kagaku - Scientific Papers on Japanese Antiques and Art Crafts (0368-6272)
Indexed: ChemAb, ChemTitl.
—BLDSC (2930.247200), CASDDS. **CCC.**
Published by: Japan Society for the Conservation of Cultural Property, Kokuritsu Bunkazai Kenkyujo, 13-27 Ueno-Koen, Taito-ku, Tokyo, 110-0007, Japan. TEL 81-3-3823-2241, FAX 81-3-3828-2434. Ed. Sadatoshi Miura. Circ: 600.

745.1 GBR ISSN 1470-6946
BUSINESS RATIO. ANTIQUES AND FINE ART DEALERS AND AUCTIONEERS. Text in English. 1986. a. GBP 275 (effective 2001). charts; stat. **Document type:** *Trade.*
Former titles (until 2000): Business Ratio Plus: Antiques & Fine Art Dealers and Auctioneers (1355-6266); (until 1994): Business Ratio Report. Antiques and Fine Art (0269-8994)
Published by: The Prospect Shop Ltd., Field House, 72 Oldfield Rd, Hampton, Middx TW12 2HQ, United Kingdom. TEL 44-20-8461-8730, 44-20-8481-8720, FAX 44-20-8783-1940, info@theprospectshop.co.uk.

C.A.L. - N-X-211 COLLECTORS SOCIETY. NEWSLETTER. see *AERONAUTICS AND SPACE FLIGHT*

745.1 USA
C Q (NEW YORK); connoisseurs quarterly. Text in English. 2000. q. USD 17; USD 5 newsstand/cover (effective 2001). adv.
Published by: The Art & Antiques Dealers League of America, Inc., 1040 Madison Ave, New York, NY 10021. TEL 212-879-7558, http://www.connoisseursquarterly.com. Ed. Pamela Guthman. Pub. Bob Cihi.

796.77 629.222 USA ISSN 1072-3277
CAMARO ENTHUSIAST✶. Text in English. 1984. bi-m. USD 30. adv. bk.rev. charts; illus.; stat. back issues avail. **Document type:** *Consumer.* **Description:** For the collector, restorer, driver and enthusiast of the Chevrolet Camaro car.
Formerly: Camaro Corral (1058-739X)
Published by: United States Camaro Club, Inc., 522 S Hunt Club Blvd, 415, Apopka, FL 32703-8183. TEL 407-880-1967, FAX 407-880-1972. Ed. Ken Moorhead. Circ: 15,000.

CANINE COLLECTABLES COURIER. see *PETS*

745.1 USA
CAPE COD ANTIQUES MONTHLY. Text in English. 1999. m. USD 21.95 (effective 2000). adv. bk.rev. mkt.; maps; stat.; tr.lit. back issues avail. **Document type:** *Newspaper.* **Description:** Contains current news about antique shops, shows and auctions on Cape Cod. Also contains articles about antiques relating to Cape Cod.
Address: 44 Charles St., PO Box 546, Farmingham, NH 03835. TEL 603-755-4568, FAX 603-755-3990. Ed., Pub., R&P, Adv. contact Charles W Wibel. B&W page USD 500; trim 14.75 x 10.

CAR COLLECTOR. see *TRANSPORTATION—Automobiles*

745.1 USA ISSN 0892-9769
CAROUSEL NEWS & TRADER. Text in English. 1985. 10/yr. USD 35 domestic; USD 40 in Canada; USD 50 elsewhere (effective 2001). adv. bk.rev.; video rev. mkt. 32 p./no. 3 cols./p.; back issues avail. **Document type:** *Trade.* **Description:** Covers all aspects of collecting carousel art.
Formerly (until 1987): Carousel Trader (0892-9750)
Published by: Walter Loucks, Ed. & Pub., 87 Park Ave W, 206, Mansfield, OH 44902. TEL 419-529-4999, FAX 419-529-2321, CNSam@aol.com, http://www.carousel.net.trader/. Adv. contact Walter Loucks TEL 419-529-4999. B&W page USD 450, color page USD 1,400; trim 11 x 8.5. Circ: 5,500.

CARS & PARTS; the magazine serving the car hobbyist. see *TRANSPORTATION—Automobiles*

745.1 747 AUS
CARTER'S PRICE GUIDE TO ANTIQUES IN AUSTRALASIA. Text in English. 1985. a. AUD 125 (effective 2005). adv. mkt.; tr.lit. 800 p./no.; back issues avail. **Document type:** *Catalog, Consumer.* **Description:** Guide to prices of antiques and collectibles of every kind.
Formerly: Carter's Price Guide to Antiques in Australia (0815-7065)
Published by: Carter's Price Guide Pty. Ltd., PO Box 7246, Baulkham Hills BC, NSW 2153, Australia. TEL 61-2-88504600, FAX 61-2-88504100, info@carters.com.au, http://www.cartersworld.com. Ed. Alan Carter. Circ: 15,000.

745.1 700 USA ISSN 1535-5500
THE CATALOGUE OF ANTIQUES & FINE ARTS. Text in English. 2000. bi-m. USD 25 domestic; USD 35 in Canada; USD 50 elsewhere (effective 2004). adv. **Document type:** *Magazine, Consumer.*
Published by: Catalogue of Antiques & Fine Art, 125 Walnut St, Watertown, MA 02472. TEL 617-926-0004, 888-922-0004, FAX 617-926-0104, csr@AntiquesandFineArt.com, http://www.antiquesandfineart.com/index.cfm. Ed. Johanna McBrien. Pub. John S Smiroldo. Adv. contact Melinda Martin.

745.1 ITA ISSN 1124-2841
CHARTA; antiquariato, collezionismo, mercato. Text in Italian. 1992. bi-m. EUR 36.20 domestic; EUR 52 foreign (effective 2005). **Document type:** *Magazine, Consumer.* **Description:** Contains information on all sorts of antique paper and cards, old books, postcards, ex libris, posters, calendars and more.

Published by: Nova Charta Sas, Via Olanda 17, Verona, 37135, Italy. TEL 39-045-502226, FAX 39-045-584524, http://www.novacharta.it. Circ: 20,000.

"CHECK THE OIL!" MAGAZINE; the publication devoted exclusively to Petroliana. see *HOBBIES*

629.288 USA
CHRYSLER 300 CLUB NEWS. Text in English. 1970. q. USD 20 (effective 2004). adv. charts; illus.; stat. 40 p./no. 1 cols./p.; back issues avail. **Document type:** *Newsletter, Consumer.* **Description:** Provides technical statistics on automobiles represented by the Club, restoration information, and member stories.
Published by: Chrysler 300 Club International, Inc., 4900 Jonesville Rd, Jonesville, MI 49250. TEL 517-849-2783, http://www.chrysler300club.com. Ed. Andy Maikonis. R&P George Riehl. Circ: 1,000 (paid and free).

745 USA ISSN 0094-1182
NK1127
CIVIL WAR COLLECTORS' DEALER DIRECTORY✶. Text in English. 1974. irreg., latest 1987-88. USD 4.95. adv.
Published by: Essential Electronics, 409 Jesse Lee Ln, Hampstead, NC 28443. Ed. C L Batson. Circ: 1,000.

745.1 USA
CLARK'S FLEA MARKET U S A; a national directory of flea markets & swap meets. Text in English. 1977. q. USD 38; USD 10.50 per issue (effective 2001). adv. **Document type:** *Directory, Consumer.* **Description:** Lists names, locations, days, cost of space, facilities such as restrooms, showers, camping and food concessions, as well as phone numbers.
Published by: Clark Publications, Clark's Flee Market USA, 5469 Inland Cove Ct, Milton, FL 32583. TEL 850-623-0794, FAX 850-626-2088, fleausa@aol.com. Ed., Pub., R&P, Adv. contact Dorothy Clark. B&W page USD 500; 4.75 x 7.5. Circ: 9,000.

629.2 GBR ISSN 0957-2406
CLASSIC AMERICAN; driving the american dream. Text in English. 1988. m. GBP 46 domestic; GBP 57 foreign; GBP 3.25 newsstand/cover. adv. bk.rev. back issues avail. **Document type:** *Consumer.* **Description:** Examines cars and motorcycles from the 50's and 60's, plus other "Americana" collectables.
Incorporates (in 1992): Vee Magazine
Published by: Guardian Media Group plc, Auto Trader House, Bewsey Industrial Estate, Catherine St, Warrington, Ches WA5 5LH, United Kingdom. TEL 44-1925-625182, FAX 44-1925-625149. Ed. Paul Guinness. R&P Tom Ferguson. Adv. contact Michael Higham. Circ: 30,000. **Dist. by:** Comag, Tavistock Works, Tavistock Rd, W Drayton, Middx UB7 7QX, United Kingdom. TEL 44-1895-444055, FAX 44-1895-433602.

CLASSIC & SPORTSCAR. see *TRANSPORTATION—Automobiles*

CLASSIC BIKE. see *SPORTS AND GAMES—Bicycles And Motorcycles*

629.222 USA ISSN 0009-8310
TL7
CLASSIC CAR. Text in English. 1953. q. adv. bk.rev. illus. index, cum.index. **Document type:** *Consumer.* **Description:** Articles on the history and contemporary restoration and preservation of distinctive automobiles produced from 1925 to 1948.
Published by: Classic Car Club of America, Inc., 1645 S River Rd, Ste 7, Des Plaines, IL 60018-2206. TEL 847-390-0443, FAX 847-390-7118. Ed. Beverly Rae Kimes. Pub. Warren Gordon. Circ: 5,000.

CLASSIC CAR MART. see *TRANSPORTATION—Automobiles*

629.222 796.77 GBR ISSN 0959-9738
CLASSIC CAR WEEKLY. Text in English. 1990. w. GBP 57.20; GBP 1.20 newsstand/cover (effective 1999). adv. bk.rev. 36 p./no.; back issues avail. **Document type:** *Newspaper, Consumer.* **Description:** Provides the up-to-date market place for buying and selling classic cars, plus all the latest news from the classic car scene.
Published by: Emap Active Ltd. (Bushfield House) (Subsidiary of: Emap Consumer Media), Bushfield House, Orton Centre, Peterborough, Cambs PE2 5UW, United Kingdom. TEL 44-1733-237111, FAX 44-1733-231137, http://www.classiccarsworld.co.uk. Ed. Geoff Browne. Pub. Grahame Steed. Adv. contact Julie Galvin. B&W page GBP 1,470, color page GBP 1,960; trim 271 x 340. Circ: 26,000 (paid). **Subscr. to:** Tower Publishing Services Ltd., Tower House, Sovereign Park, Market Harborough, Leics LE16 9EF, United Kingdom. TEL 44-1858-435341, FAX 44-1858-434958. **Dist. by:** Frontline, Park House, 117 Park Rd, Peterborough, Cambs PE1 2TS, United Kingdom. TEL 44-1733-555161, FAX 44-1733-562788.

CLASSIC FORD. see *TRANSPORTATION—Automobiles*

CLASSIC RANGES; parts, services, restoration, sales. see *HOBBIES*

CLOCKS; the international magazine for horological collectors & restorers. see *JEWELRY, CLOCKS AND WATCHES*

COASTAL ANTIQUES & ART. see *ART*

COLLECTIBLE AUTOMOBILE. see *TRANSPORTATION—Automobiles*

745.1 GBR ISSN 0963-7451
COLLECTING DOULTON; the international magazine for collectors of Royal Doulton & Beswick both old & new. Text in English. 1987. bi-m. GBP 17.80; USD 26 in North America. adv. **Document type:** *Newsletter, Consumer.* **Description:** Contains articles of interest to persons collecting, buying and selling Royal Doulton and Beswick fine china.
Published by: Francis Joseph, 5 Southbrook News, London, SE12 8LH, United Kingdom. Ed. Frank Salmon. Pub. Francis Joseph. Adv. contact Doug Pinchin.

745 GBR ISSN 0955-0356
THE COLLECTOR. Text in English. 1987. bi-m. GBP 13 domestic; GBP 25 in Europe; GBP 28 in United States; GBP 31 elsewhere (effective 2005). bk.rev. illus.; maps. 40 p./no.; back issues avail. **Document type:** *Magazine, Consumer.* **Description:** Contains information about antiques and collectibles.
Published by: Barrington Publications, 54 Uxbridge Rd, London, W12 8LP, United Kingdom. artefact@artefact.co.uk, http://www.artefact.co.uk/a-cind.htm. Ed. Paul Hooper. Adv. contact Simon Hughes. Circ: 20,000 (controlled).

COLLECTOR CAR MARKET REVIEW. see *TRANSPORTATION—Automobiles*

745.1 USA ISSN 1077-2774
NK1133
➤ **COLLECTOR MAGAZINE & PRICE GUIDE.** Text in English. 1970. m. USD 23.98 domestic; USD 35 in Canada; USD 39 elsewhere; USD 3.95 per issue (effective 2005). adv. illus.; stat. back issues avail.; reprints avail. **Document type:** *Magazine, Consumer.* **Description:** Covers all categories of antiques and collectibles and their current market values.
Formerly (until 1994): Antique Trader Price Guide to Antiques and Collectors' Items (0556-5367)
Published by: Krause Publications, Inc. (Subsidiary of: F & W Publications, Inc.), 700 E State St, Iola, WI 54990-0001. TEL 715-445-2214, 800-258-0929, FAX 715-445-4087, info@krause.com, http://www.collect.com, http://www.krause.com. Ed. Claire Fliess TEL 563-588-2073 ext 143. Pub. Greg Smith. Adv. contact Greg Smith TEL 715-445-2214 ext 461. B&W page USD 671, color page USD 771; trim 8 x 10.75. Circ: 21,374 (paid and free).

745.1 USA
THE COLLECTOR NEWSMAGAZINE. Text in English. q. free. adv. **Document type:** *Consumer.* **Description:** Publishes news on collectibles, antiques and giftware.
Media: Online - full text.
Published by: D R S Internet Publishing Group, 1575 Old Alabama Rd, Ste 207 241, Roswell, GA 30076-2101. TEL 770-667-5098, collector@drspublishing.com, http://www.drspublishing.com/thecollector. Ed., Pub. Diana R Savastano. R&P Caroline North. Adv. contact T Savage.

745.1 USA ISSN 1097-6892
NK1125
COLLECTORS' EYE. Text in English. 1990. bi-m. USD 19.95. adv. bk.rev. **Document type:** *Consumer.* **Description:** For collectors of antique toys, country store memorabilia, carousel art, decorative arts, folk art and other quality collectibles.
Former titles (until 1998): American Collector (Northport) (1092-8502); (until 1996): Inside Collector (1052-861X)
Published by: Collector Media Company, 6 Woodside Ave. Ste. 300, Northport, NY 11768. TEL 516-261-4100, FAX 516-261-9684, http://www.tias.com. adv.: B&W page USD 600, color page USD 900; trim 8.375 x 10.875. Circ: 15,000 (paid).

COLLECTORS GAZETTE. see *GIFTWARE AND TOYS*

745.1 USA ISSN 1533-3000
COLLECTOR'S MART. Text in English. 1976. q. USD 14.95 domestic; USD 23 foreign; USD 4.95 per issue (effective 2005). adv. bk.rev. illus. reprints avail. **Document type:** *Magazine, Consumer.* **Description:** Written for the collector who buys limited-edition plates, prints, dolls, figurines and other collectibles.
Former titles (until 2000): Collector's Mart Magazine (1066-551X); (until 199?): Collectors Mart (0744-9879); (until 198?): Antique and Collectors Mart (0194-5890)
Related titles: Online - full text ed.: (from EBSCO Publishing).
Indexed: ABCT.
Published by: Krause Publications, Inc. (Subsidiary of: F & W Publications, Inc.), 700 E State St, Iola, WI 54990-0001. TEL 715-445-2214, 800-258-0929, FAX 715-445-4087, collectorsmart@krause.com, info@krause.com, http://www.collectorsmart.net, http://www.krause.com. Ed. Mary Sieber TEL 715-445-2214 ext 247. Pub., Adv. contact Greg Smith TEL 715-445-2214 ext 461. B&W page USD 3,470, color page USD 4,580; trim 7.75 x 10.5. Circ: 46,715 (paid and free).

790.023 USA ISSN 0162-1033
COLLECTORS NEWS & THE ANTIQUE REPORTER. Cover title: Collectors News. Text in English. 1959. m. USD 28 domestic; USD 40 foreign (effective 2005). adv. bk.rev. illus. **Document type:** *Consumer.* **Description:** Features everything for some collectors and something for every collector.
Published by: Collectors News Company, PO Box 156, Grundy Center, IA 50638. TEL 319-824-6981, 800-352-8039, FAX 319-824-3414, collect@collectors-news.com, http://collectors-news.com. Ed. Linda Kruger. Pub., R&P Cherie Souhrada. Adv. contact Ronda Jans. Circ: 15,000 (paid).

745.1 737 USA ISSN 0744-5989
NK805
COLLECTORS' SHOWCASE; America's premier entertainment collectors' magazine . Text in English. 1981. bi-m. USD 19.95 domestic; USD 25.95 in Canada & Mexico; USD 35.95 elsewhere (effective 1999). adv. bk.rev. illus. reprints avail. **Document type:** *Consumer.* **Description:** Contains articles for collectors of animation art, characters and entertainment collectibles and memorabilia.
Related titles: Online - full text ed.
Published by: Source Publications, Inc., 5555 E. 71st St., Ste. 8300, Tulsa, OK 74136-6555. TEL 918-491-9088, 888-622-3446, FAX 918-491-9946, bwilkerson@sourcepub.com, http://www.cslive.com. Ed. Brian Walker. Pub., R&P Rick Long. Adv. contact Darcy Case. Circ: 10,000 (paid). **Subscr. to:** PO Box 500, Missouri City, TX 77459-4052.

COMBAT HANDGUNS. see *SPORTS AND GAMES*

745.1 USA ISSN 1544-824X
E186
COMMON-PLACE. Text in English. q. bk.rev.
Related titles: Online - full text ed.
Published by: American Antiquarian Society, 185 Salisbury St, Worcester, MA 01609. TEL 508-755-5221, FAX 508-753-3311, jkeenum@mwa.org, http://www.common-place.org, http://www.americanantiquarian.org. Ed. Jane Kamensky. R&P Trudy Powers. **Co-sponsor:** Gilder Lehrman Institute of American History.

629.222 745.1 USA ISSN 0045-8554
CORMORANT NEWS BULLETIN. Text in English. 1953. m. looseleaf. membership. adv. charts; illus.
Published by: Packard Automobile Classics, 420 S Ludlow St, Dayton, OH 45402. http://www.packardclub.com. Ed. Stuart Blond. Circ: 4,200.

745.1 ITA ISSN 1593-3555
COSE ANTICHE. Text in Italian. 1992. m. (11/yr.). **Document type:** *Consumer.*
Related titles: Online - full text ed.
Published by: Edimarketing, Via Giovanni Pacini 41, Milan, MI 20131, Italy. TEL 39-02-70632759, FAX 39-02-2665522, info@coseantiche.com, http://www.coseantiche.com. Ed. Paola Lazzaretto. Circ: 30,000.

745.1 USA ISSN 1540-059X
COTTON & QUAIL ANTIQUE GAZETTE. Text in English. 1988. m. USD 20 subscr - mailed; USD 3 newsstand/cover (effective 2004). adv. **Document type:** *Newspaper.* **Description:** Antiques and collectibles trade newspaper for the Southeast US.
Formerly: Antique Gazette
Published by: Krause Publications, Inc. (Subsidiary of: F & W Publications, Inc.), 700 E State St, Iola, WI 54990-0001. TEL 715-445-2214, FAX 715-445-4087, traderpubs@krause.com, http://www.collect.com. Ed. Linda Kunkel TEL 563-588-2073 ext 131. Pub. Greg Smith. Adv. contact Greg Smith TEL 715-445-2214 ext 461. B&W page USD 641, color page USD 826. Circ: 26,316 (paid and free).

COUNTRY HOMES & INTERIORS. see *INTERIOR DESIGN AND DECORATION*

745.1 USA
▼ **COUNTRY LIVING COLLECTING.** Text in English. 2005 (aug.). a. USD 3.95 newsstand/cover (effective 2005). adv. **Document type:** *Journal, Academic/Scholarly.* **Description:** Provides information on antique collection, including where to find and how to live with antiques.
Published by: Hearst Corporation, 224 W 57th St, New York, NY 10019. TEL 212-649-3500, FAX 212-649-3303, http://www.hearstcorp.com. adv.: B&W page USD 20,900, color page USD 28,500; bleed 8.25 x 10.25. Circ: 4,000.

745.1 USA
DISCOVER MID-AMERICA. Text in English. 1973. m. USD 25 (effective 2005). **Document type:** *Newspaper, Consumer.* **Description:** Guide to unique shops in the Midwest, with articles pertaining to antiques and collectibles, events, events calendar and historical sites.
Published by: Discovery Publications, Inc., 400 Grand Ave, Kansas City, MO 64106. TEL 816-474-1516, FAX 816-474-1427, busmgr@discoverypub.com, http://www.discoverypub.com. Ed. Kenneth C Weyand. Pub. Bruce Rodgers. Circ: 22,000 (free).

DISCOVERIES (IOLA); magazine for collectible records & CD's. see *MUSIC*

629.2 USA
DIVCO NEWS; the magazine of multi-stop delivery. Text in English. 1991. bi-m. USD 24 per vol. to individual members; USD 36 per vol. to institutional members (effective 2005). illus. 20 p./no. 2 cols./p.; back issues avail. **Document type:** *Magazine, Consumer.* **Description:** Chronicles the history of Divco milk trucks, profiles the people who used to drive them, and discusses efforts to restore these venerable classics.
Published by: Divco Club of America, PO Box 1142, Kingston, WA 98346-1142. TEL 360-598-3938, editor@divco.org, divcoclub@silverlink.net, http://www.divco.org. Eds. Douglas Campbell, Les Bagley.

738 USA ISSN 1065-7789
DOROTHY KAMM'S PORCELAIN COLLECTOR'S COMPANION. Text in English. 1992. bi-m. looseleaf. USD 28 domestic; USD 32 foreign; USD 6 newsstand/cover (effective 2000). adv. bk.rev. illus.; mkt. index. back issues avail. **Document type:** *Newsletter, Consumer.* **Description:** Dedicated to the identification and appraisal of hand-painted porcelain.
Published by: Kamm Cohen Publishing and Advertising, PO Box 7460, Port St. Lucie, FL 37985-7460. TEL 772-465-4008, FAX 772-460-9050, dorothy.kamm@usa.net. Ed., Adv. contact Dorothy Kamm. Pub. Dean Cohen. Circ: 100 (paid).

THE DOUBLE GUN JOURNAL. see *SPORTS AND GAMES—Outdoor Life*

E T CETERA. see *BUSINESS AND ECONOMICS—Office Equipment And Services*

ENJINE!-ENJINE!. see *FIRE PREVENTION*

745.1 ITA ISSN 1590-0266
L'ESPERTO RISPONDE. Text in Italian. 1985. m. back issues avail. **Document type:** *Consumer.* **Description:** Provides advice for experienced and beginner antique collectors. Contains a large selection of Italian antiques, including descriptions and value estimates.
Published by: Edi Marketing s.r.l., Via Pacini, 41, Milan, MI 20131, Italy. TEL 39-02-70632494, FAX 39-02-2665522, Esperto.risponde@edimarketing.it. Ed. Adalberto Guarnerio.

745.1 700 USA ISSN 8756-775X
EVALUATOR★. Text in English. 1979. q. membership. bk.rev. back issues avail.
Published by: International Society of Fine Arts Appraisers, Ltd., 701S Euclid Ave, Oak Park, IL 60304. TEL 312-848-3340. Ed. Elizabeth Carr. Circ: 500.

745.1 630 USA
FARM ANTIQUES NEWS. Text in English. 1991. bi-m. USD 16 (effective 2005). adv. bk.rev. **Document type:** *Newsletter, Consumer.* **Description:** Covers anything old from the farm: collecting and pricing.
Address: 202 N Washington St, Rock Port, MO 64482-1304. TEL 816-736-4528. Eds. Gary Van Hoozer, Gary VanHoozer. Pub. Gary Van Hoozer. Circ: 2,000 (paid).

621 USA ISSN 0745-6824
FINE TOOL JOURNAL. Text in English. 1970. q. USD 29 domestic; USD 54 foreign (effective 2001). bk.rev. **Document type:** *Catalog, Consumer.* **Description:** Covers tools, tool collecting, tool history, and tools for sale.
Published by: Antique & Collectible Tools, Inc., 27 Fickett Rd, Pownal, ME 04069. TEL 207-688-4962, FAX 207-688-4831, ceb@finetoolj.com, http://www.finetoolj.com. Ed., R&P, Adv. contact Clarence Blanchard. Circ: 2,500 (paid).

FLEETLINE. see *TRANSPORTATION*

745.1 GBR ISSN 1476-816X
FOR THE RECORD. Text in English. 1960. bi-m. adv. bk.rev.; rec.rev. illus. index. **Document type:** *Newsletter.*
Formerly: Hillandale News (0018-1846)
Media: Duplicated (not offset).
—BLDSC (3985.469000).
Published by: City of London Phonograph & Gramophone Society, 2 Kirklands Park, Cupar, KY15 4EP, United Kingdom. TEL 44-1334-54390. Ed. Christopher Hamilton. Circ: 600.

745.1 FRA ISSN 1164-7809
FRANCE - ANTIQUITES; pour comprendre et aimer les antiquites. Text in French. 1981. m. illus.; mkt. back issues avail. **Description:** Includes antique furniture, paintings, and other objects, decorations, market prices, exhibits, and calendars of fairs and shows.
Published by: Livet Editions, Chateau de Boisrigaud, Usson, 64490, France. TEL 33-4-73710004, FAX 33-4-73710362, b.livet@liveteditions.fr. Pub. Jean Claude Livet. R&P Jean-Claude Livet. Circ: 25,000 (controlled).

745.1 ESP ISSN 1130-2747
N7101
GALERIA ANTIQUARIA★. Text in Spanish. 12/yr.
Formed by the 1989 merger of: Galeria (1130-2755); Antiquaria (0212-8810)
Indexed: RILM.
—CINDOC.
Address: C. Lagasca No. 28, 2o., Madrid, 28001, Spain. TEL 34-91-5766429, FAX 34-91-5779428, antiqvaria@antiqvaria.com, http://www.antiqvaria.com/. Ed. Manuel Merchan Diaz. Circ: 10,000.

794 USA ISSN 1529-4706
GAME & PUZZLE COLLECTORS QUARTERLY. (GPCQ) Text in English. 2000. q. USD 30 (effective 2000). adv. 24 p./no.; back issues avail. **Document type:** *Newsletter.* **Description:** Covers history, preservation, collecting news and research regarding of games and puzzles.
Published by: Association of Game and Puzzle Collectors, PMB 321, 197M Boston Post Rd W, Marlborough, MA 01752. http://www.agpc.org. Ed. Wayne Wolf.

745.1 ITA ISSN 0016-559X
GAZZETTA ANTIQUARIA. Text in Italian. 1959. s-a. EUR 9.30 domestic (effective 2004). adv. charts; illus.
Published by: (Associazione Antiquari d'Italia), Edizioni Polistampa, Via Santa Maria 27, Florence, FI 50125, Italy. TEL 39-055-2337702, FAX 39-055-229430, info@polistampa.com, http://www.polistampa.com.

355 ESP ISSN 0436-029X
GLADIUS; etudes sur les armes anciennes, l'armement, l'art militaire et la vie culturelle en Orient et Occident. Text in English, French, German, Spanish. 1961. a. EUR 31.25 domestic (effective 2001). bk.rev. bibl.; illus. index, cum.index.
Indexed: BHA, BrArAb, NumL.
—CINDOC.
Published by: Consejo Superior de Investigaciones Cientificas, Instituto de Estudios sobre Armas Antiguas, Ave de la Constitucion, 114, Jaraiz de la Vera, Caceres 10400, Spain. TEL 34-927-170646, FAX 34-927-170645, hoffmeye@teleline.es. Ed. Ada Bruhn Dehoffmeyer. Circ: 500.

745.1 FIN ISSN 1238-5654
GLORIAN ANTIIKKI. Text in Finnish. 1993. 5/yr. EUR 43 (effective 2004). adv. **Document type:** *Magazine, Consumer.* **Description:** Contains articles on antiques, art, collecting and design.
Formerly (until 1995): Antiikki (1236-9810)
Published by: Sanoma Magazines Finland Corporation, Hoylaamotie 1 D, P.O. Box 100, Helsinki, 00040, Finland. TEL 358-9-1201, FAX 358-9-1205171, info@sanomamagazines.fi, http://www.sanomamagazines.fi. adv.: page EUR 3,800. Circ: 33,034 (paid and controlled).

GOLD BOOK CLASSICS & ANTIQUES. see *TRANSPORTATION—Automobiles*

745.1 GBR ISSN 0262-8902
GOSS AND CRESTED CHINA; a monthly catalogue of Goss china. Text in English. 1975. m. GBP 18 domestic; GBP 30 foreign (effective 2000). bk.rev. illus.; mkt.; tr.lit. back issues avail. **Document type:** *Catalog.* **Description:** Provides a illustrated sales catalogue of English W.H. Goss and other crested procelein manufactured in 1865-1935.
—CCC.
Published by: Milestone Publications, 62 Murray Rd, Horndean, Waterlooville, Hants PO8 9JL, United Kingdom. TEL 44-1705-597440, FAX 44-1705-591975, info@gosschinaclub.demon.co.uk. Ed., R&P Nicholas Pine. Adv. contact Patricia Welbourne. Circ: 500 (paid); 500 (controlled).

745.1 GBR
GUIDE TO THE ANTIQUE SHOPS OF BRITAIN (YEAR). Text in English. a. GBP 14.95 (effective 2000). adv. **Document type:** *Directory.*
—BLDSC (4225.236000).
Published by: Antique Collectors Club, 5 Church St, Woodbridge, Suffolk IP12 1DS, United Kingdom. FAX 44-1394-384434. Ed. Carol Adams. R&P Sarah Smye TEL 44-1394-385501. Adv. contact Jean Johnson.

739.7 USA ISSN 1522-9572
GUN-KNIFE SHOW CALENDAR. Text in English. 1979. q. USD 15.95 domestic; USD 23.95 foreign (effective 2005). adv. illus. reprints avail. **Document type:** *Magazine, Trade.* **Description:** Contains chronological listing of gun shows cross-referenced by state and month. Listings are updated quarterly. Intended as a guide for anyone who attends or displays at gun shows.
Formerly: Gun Show Calendar (0896-6001)
Published by: Krause Publications, Inc. (Subsidiary of: F & W Publications, Inc.), 700 E State St, Iola, WI 54990-0001. TEL 715-445-2214, 800-258-0929, FAX 715-445-4087, gunshow@krause.com, info@krause.com, http://www.collect.com, http://www.krause.com. Pub. Hugh McAloon TEL 715-445-2214 ext 240. Adv. contact Bruce Wolberg TEL 715-445-2214 ext 403. B&W page USD 738, color page USD 1,488; trim 8 x 10.875. Circ: 5,758 (paid and free).

623.4 USA ISSN 0894-8119
GUN LIST; the indexed firearms paper. Text in English. 1984. bi-w. USD 37.98 domestic; USD 113.98 in Canada; USD 171.98 elsewhere; USD 5.50 newsstand/cover (effective 2005). adv. illus. Index. reprints avail. **Document type:** *Magazine, Trade.* **Description:** Covers the marketplace for buying and selling collectible firearms.
Published by: Krause Publications, Inc. (Subsidiary of: F & W Publications, Inc.), 700 E State St, Iola, WI 54990-0001. TEL 715-445-2214, 800-258-0929, FAX 715-445-4087, gunlist@krause.com, info@krause.com, http://www.gunlist.net, http://www.krause.com. Pub. Hugh McAloon TEL 715-445-2214 ext 240. Adv. contacts Bruce Wolberg TEL 715-445-2214 ext 403, Bruce Wolberg TEL 715-445-2214 ext 403. B&W page USD 1,665, color page USD 2,265; trim 10.875 x 13. Circ: 81,120 (paid and free).

GUNS OF THE OLD WEST. see *SPORTS AND GAMES—Outdoor Life*

355 GBR ISSN 0262-4915
H B S A NEWSLETTER. Text in English. 1981. q. looseleaf. membership. bk.rev. back issues avail. **Document type:** *Newsletter.*
Formerly: H B S A Occasional Papers
Published by: Historical Breechloading Smallarms Association, PO Box 12778, London, SE1 6XB, United Kingdom. Ed. B Bergman Field.

HALI; the international magazine of antique carpet and textile art. see *ARTS AND HANDICRAFTS*

745.1 700 USA
HAWAII ANTIQUES, ART, & COLLECTIBLES QUARTERLY. Text in English. 1991. q. USD 8. adv. **Document type:** *Newspaper, Consumer.* **Description:** Contains articles and information on events, art, antiques and collectibles for the consumer and dealer.
Published by: Service Publications, Inc. (Honolulu), PO Box 853, Honolulu, HI 96808. TEL 808-591-0049, FAX 808-591-0038. Ed., Pub. Campbell Mansfield. Adv. contact Lorraine Walters. page USD 415; trim 12 x 10.25. Circ: 8,000.

666 USA ISSN 0731-8014
NK5198.A23
HEISEY NEWS. Text in English. 1972. 13/yr. USD 25 membership; USD 3 per issue to non-members (effective 2005). adv. bk.rev. illus.; tr.lit. index, cum.index: 1972-1981, 1982-1992. 28 p./no. 2 cols./p.; back issues avail. **Document type:** *Newsletter, Consumer.* **Description:** Promotes the education and study of A.H. Heisey and Co. glassware produced in Newark, OH, from 1896-1957.
Published by: Heisey Collectors of America, Inc., 169 W Church St, Newark, OH 43055. TEL 740-345-2932, FAX 740-345-9638, editor@heiseymuseum.org, membership@heiseymuseum.org, http://www.heiseymuseum.org, http://www.heiseymuseum.org/hca/. Ed., Adv. contact Angie Hornberger. page USD 240; 7.5 x 9. Circ: 30 (controlled); 1,600 (paid); 100 (free).

HEMMINGS MOTOR NEWS. see *TRANSPORTATION—Automobiles*

629.222 USA ISSN 8755-2272
TL12
HEMMING'S VINTAGE AUTO ALMANAC. Text in English. 1976. biennial. USD 14.95 (effective 2003). adv. illus. **Document type:** *Directory, Consumer.*
Formerly (until 1982): Vintage Auto Almanac (0363-4639)
Published by: Hemmings Publishing (Subsidiary of: American City Business Journals, Inc.), 222 Main St, PO Box 256, Bennington, VT 05201. TEL 802-442-3101, FAX 802-447-1561, hmnmail@hemmings.com, http://www.hemmings.com. Circ: 25,000.

745.1 DEU
HENRY'S AUKTIONEN. Text in German. 1984. m. **Document type:** *Catalog.*
Published by: Henry's Auktionshaus GmbH, An der Fohlenweide 12-14, Mutterstadt, 67112, Germany. TEL 49-6234-80110. Ed. Heinrich Haege. Circ: 100,000.

HISTORIC MORRIS EMPORIUM; fine wares for fine shoppers. see *LEISURE AND RECREATION*

739.7 USA ISSN 0440-9221
HISTORICAL ARMS SERIES. Text in English. 1963. irreg. price varies.
Published by: Museum Restoration Service, PO Box 70, Alexandria Bay, NY 13607. Ed. S James Gooding. Circ: 5,000.

629.22 GBR
HISTORICAL COMMERCIAL NEWS. Text in English. 1962. every 6 wks. GBP 15. adv. bk.rev. bibl.; illus. **Document type:** *Newsletter.* **Description:** Concerns antique automobiles.
Formerly: H C V C Newsletter
Published by: Historic Commercial Vehicle Society, Iden Grange, Cranbrook Rd, Staplehurst, Tonbridge Wells, Kent TN12 0ET, United Kingdom. FAX 580-893227. Circ: 4,250.

739.7 799.202 ZAF ISSN 0018-2451
HISTORICAL FIREARMS SOCIETY OF SOUTH AFRICA. JOURNAL/HISTORIESE VUURWAPENVERENIGING VAN SUID-AFRIKA. TYDSKRIF. Text in English. 1958. s-a. ZAR 45 to members. adv. **Document type:** *Newsletter.* **Description:** Covers antique and historical firearms used in South Africa.
Formerly (until 1962): South African Muzzle Loaders Association. Journal

A

Indexed: ISAP.
Published by: Historical Firearms Society of South Africa, PO Box 145, Newlands, Cape Province 7725, South Africa. TEL 27-21-642294. Ed. B M Berkovitch. Circ: 450.

739.23 666.1 USA
HOBSTAR. Text in English. 1978. m. (10/yr.). USD 35 to members. adv. bk.rev. back issues avail. **Document type:** *Newsletter.* **Description:** Studies American cut and engraved glass of the period of 1850-1920, emphasizing the "brilliant" period, 1880-1920.
Published by: American Cut Glass Association, The Hobstar, 6 Dutchess Terrace, Beacon, NY 12508. TEL 914-831-2566, FAX 914-831-2566, nick444@aol.com, http://www.cutglass.org. Ed. Nicholas J Boonstra. adv.: B&W page USD 150, color page USD 800; trim 7.5 x 10. Circ: 2,100.

HORN & WHISTLE. see *HOBBIES*

791.44 USA ISSN 0898-6959
HORN SPEAKER; the newspaper for the hobbyist of vintage electronics and sound. Text in English. 1972. m. (10/yr.). USD 18.95 (effective 1999). adv. bk.rev. bibl.; illus.; tr.lit. **Document type:** *Newspaper, Consumer.* **Description:** Discusses radios and phonographs for historical and collecting purposes.
Published by: Jim Cranshaw, Ed. & Pub., PO Box 1193, Mabank, TX 75147. TEL 903-848-0304, cranshaw@gte.net, http://home.navisoft.com/horn/ths2.htm. R&P, Adv. contact Jim Cranshaw. Circ: 1,500 (paid).

629.221 790.023 USA ISSN 0018-5213
TL1
HORSELESS CARRIAGE GAZETTE✶ . Text in English. 1937. bi-m. USD 35 domestic; USD 45 foreign (effective 2000). adv. bk.rev. illus. cum.index. **Document type:** *Journal, Consumer.* **Description:** Highlights cars built before January 1st, 1916.
Published by: Horseless Carriage Club of America, 24244 Hamlin St, West Hills, CA 91307-2825. TEL 559-658-8800, http://www.horseless.com. Ed. John C Meyer III. Circ: 5,500.

745.1 USA ISSN 1082-5185
Z1000.5
HUXFORD'S OLD BOOK VALUE GUIDE. Text in English. 1991. a. USD 19.95 domestic; USD 33 foreign (effective 2000). **Document type:** *Catalog.* **Description:** Features scores of actual buyers listed by the type of subject matter they are searching for as well as dealers offering books at listed prices.
Published by: Collector Books (Subsidiary of: Schroeder Publishing Co., Inc.), PO Box 3009, Paducah, KY 42002-3009. Ed. Sharon Huxford.

I F L A SECTION ON PRESERVATION AND CONSERVATION. NEWSLETTER. (International Federation of Library Associations and Institutions) see *LIBRARY AND INFORMATION SCIENCES*

745.1 780 USA
IN THE GROOVE. Text in English. 1976. m. USD 25 domestic membership; USD 24 in Canada membership; USD 37 elsewhere membership (effective 2000). adv. bk.rev.; music rev.; video rev. bibl.; illus.; mkt. back issues avail. **Document type:** *Newsletter.* **Description:** Provides news and articles of interest to collectors of antique phonographs and other mechanical music instruments and their records or discs.
Published by: Michigan Antique Phonograph Society, 60 Central St, Battle Creek, MI 49017. TEL 616-968-1299, pgstewart@aol.com, http://www.lrbcg.com/pogo/maps.html. Eds. Eileen Stewart, Phil Stewart. Pub. Phil Stewart. R&P, Adv. contact Eileen Stewart. B&W page USD 64; trim 8.5 x 11. Circ: 1,050 (paid); 50 (controlled).

INTERNATIONAL ANTIQUE AIRPLANE DIGEST. see *AERONAUTICS AND SPACE FLIGHT*

701.18 USA ISSN 0734-5534
NK9507
INTERNATIONAL CHINESE SNUFF BOTTLE SOCIETY. JOURNAL. Text in English. 1974. q. USD 95 to members. adv. bk.rev. **Document type:** *Academic/Scholarly.*
Published by: International Chinese Snuff Bottle Society, 2601 N Charles St, Baltimore, MD 21218. TEL 410-467-9400, FAX 410-243-3451, ICSBS@worldnet.att.net, http://www.snuffbottle.org. Ed. Berthe H Ford. R&P Berthe Ford. Adv. contact John Ford. B&W page USD 475, color page USD 1,050. Circ: 700.

INTERNATIONAL PRESERVATION NEWS. see *LIBRARY AND INFORMATION SCIENCES*

INTERNATIONAL SOCIETY OF APPRAISERS. MEMBERSHIP DIRECTORY. see *BUSINESS AND ECONOMICS—Trade And Industrial Directories*

INVALUABLE & TRACE MAGAZINE. see *ART*

745.1 796.95 USA
IRON DOG TRACKS. Text in English. 1976. bi-m. membership. back issues avail. **Document type:** *Newsletter.* **Description:** Contains information on summer and winter meetings, shows, parades and competitive events.
Published by: Antique Snowmobile Club of America, c/o Dave Gunther, 32832 Hwy 39, Pequot Lakes, MN 56472. TEL 218-543-4146, 218-543-4146, http://www.ascoa.org. Ed. Dave Gunther.

739.7 952 723 USA ISSN 1043-1640
JAPANESE SWORD SOCIETY OF THE U S BULLETIN. Text in English. 1959. a. USD 30 in North America; USD 40 elsewhere (effective 1999). adv. bk.rev. **Document type:** *Bulletin.*
Published by: Japanese Sword Society of the U.S., Inc., c/o Dr T C Ford, Box 712, Breckenridge, TX 76424. Ed. T C Ford. Circ: 1,100.

739.7 USA
JAPANESE SWORD SOCIETY OF THE U S NEWSLETTER. Text in English. 1969. bi-m. USD 30 in North America; USD 40 elsewhere (effective 1999). **Document type:** *Newsletter.*
Published by: Japanese Sword Society of the U.S., Inc., c/o Dr T C Ford, Box 712, Breckenridge, TX 76424. Ed. T C Ford. Circ: 1,100.

745.1 USA ISSN 0098-9266
N6520
➤ **JOURNAL OF EARLY SOUTHERN DECORATIVE ARTS.** Text in English. 1975. s-a. USD 35 (effective 2005). bk.rev. 150 p./no.; back issues avail. **Document type:** *Journal, Academic/Scholarly.* **Description:** Features articles on Southern decorative arts from 1670 to 1820; includes furniture, paintings, ceramics, textiles and metalwork.
Indexed: AIAP, AmH&L, BHA, HistAb.
Published by: Museum of Early Southern Decorative Arts, PO Box 10310, Winston Salem, NC 27108-0310. TEL 336-721-7360, FAX 336-721-7367, galbert@oldsalem.org, http://www.oldsalem.org/about/esda.htm, http://www.oldsalem.org/about/mesda.htm. Circ: 1,500 (paid).

745.1 USA ISSN 0738-9736
CODEN: ZNWGDN
KANHISTIQUE; Kansas history and antiques. Text in English. 1975. m. USD 18 (effective 1996). adv. bk.rev. **Document type:** *Newspaper.*
Published by: Ellsworth Reporter, 220 N. Douglas Ave., Ellsworth, KS 67439-3208. TEL 913-472-3103, FAX 913-472-3268. Ed. Edna Marie Lee. Pub. Karl K Gaston.

KEEPING PLACE, KEEPING PACE. see *MUSEUMS AND ART GALLERIES*

625.1 USA ISSN 0271-3241
TF347
KEY, LOCK AND LANTERN✶ . Text in English. 1966. q. USD 21. adv. bk.rev. back issues avail. **Description:** Promotes the hobby of antique railroad hardware collecting.
Published by: Key, Lock and Lantern, Inc., 3400 Ridge Rd, Ste 5 266, Rochester, NY 14626-3458. TEL 716-227-6903. Circ: 1,000.

745.1 737 789.56 POL ISSN 1427-3039
KOLEKCJONER LOMZYNSKI. Text in Polish. 1991. a. PLZ 3 newsstand/cover (effective 2000). adv. mkt. 80 p./no. 1 cols./p.; back issues avail. **Document type:** *Bulletin, Trade.* **Description:** Deals with collecting in general prefering the subjects connected with the region of Lomza.
Published by: Polskie Towarzystwo Numizmatyczne, Oddzial w Lomzy, Ul Krzywe Kolo 1, Lomza, 18400, Poland. TEL 48-86-2162937. Ed., R&P, Adv. contact Sylwester Banaskiewicz TEL 48-86-2165567. page PLZ 250. Circ: 1,000.
Co-sponsor: Urzad Wojewodzki w Lomzy.

745.1 USA ISSN 0738-2405
NK1125
KOVEL'S ANTIQUES AND COLLECTIBLES PRICE LIST. Text in English. a. USD 9.95.
Formerly: Kovel's Antiques Price List
Published by: Crown Publishers, Inc., 201 E 50th St, New York, NY 10022. TEL 212-254-1600. Ed. Terry Kovel.

745.1 USA ISSN 0741-6091
NK1125
KOVELS ON ANTIQUES AND COLLECTIBLES; the newsletter for dealers, collectors and investors. Text in English. 1974. m. looseleaf. USD 36 in US & Canada (effective 2005). bk.rev. bibl.; illus.; stat. index. 12 p./no.; back issues avail. **Document type:** *Newsletter, Trade.*
Published by: Antiques, Inc., 49 Richmondville Ave, Westport, CT 06880. TEL 800-829-9158, nsantique@prodigy.net, http://www.kovel.com. Eds. Ralph Kovel, Terry Kovel TEL 216-752-2252. Pub., R&P Terry Kovel TEL 216-752-2252. Circ: 100,000 (paid). **Subscr. to:** PO Box 420235, Palm Coast, FL 32142-0235.

745.1 NLD ISSN 0165-3687
KUNST & ANTIEKREVUE. Text in Dutch. 1975. bi-m. adv. bk.rev.
Formerly: Antiekrevue
Published by: Antiekrevue B.V., Postbus 85994, The Hague, 2508 CR, Netherlands. TEL 31-70-3648800, FAX 31-78-3633322. Ed. Richard Wagner. Circ: 7,000.

LIGHTHOUSE DIGEST. see *ARCHITECTURE*

745.1 USA ISSN 0161-9284
NK1125
THE MAGAZINE ANTIQUES. Text in English. 1922. m. USD 39.95; USD 5 newsstand/cover (effective 2005). adv. bk.rev. illus. cum.index. 176 p./no.; back issues avail.; reprints avail. **Document type:** *Magazine, Consumer.* **Description:** Emphasizes antique furniture, but also covers paintings, architecture, glass, and textiles.
Formerly: Antiques (0003-5939)
Related titles: Microfilm ed.: (from PQC); Online - full text ed.: (from EBSCO Publishing, Gale Group, Northern Light Technology, Inc., O C L C Online Computer Library Center, Inc., ProQuest Information & Learning).
Indexed: ABM, AIAP, ASCA, AmH&L, ArtHuCI, ArtInd, BAS, BHA, BRI, CBRI, CurCont, HistAb, MagInd, PMR, RGAb, RGPR, RILM.
—BLDSC (5332.807000), IE, Infotrieve, ingenta. **CCC.**
Published by: Brant Publications, Inc., 575 Broadway, 5th Fl, New York, NY 10012. TEL 212-941-2800, FAX 212-941-2885. Ed. Allison Ledes. Pub. Sandra Brant. R&P Katryna Glettler. Adv. contact Jennifer Norton. B&W page USD 4,685, color page USD 6,040. Circ: 63,969. **Subscr. to:** PO Box 37009, Boone, IA 50037-0009. **Dist. in UK by:** Comag, Tavistock Works, Tavistock Rd, W Drayton, Middx UB7 7QX, United Kingdom. TEL 44-1895-444055, FAX 44-1895-433602.

745.1 USA ISSN 0147-0639
AP1
MAINE ANTIQUE DIGEST; the worldwide marketplace for Americana. Text in English. 1973. m. USD 43 domestic; USD 55 foreign (effective 2004). adv. bk.rev. charts; illus. 300 p./no.; **Document type:** *Magazine, Trade.* **Description:** Covers the market for art and antiques in Maine and the US in general.
Related titles: Microform ed.: (from PQC).
Published by: Maine Antique Digest, Inc., PO Box 1429, Waldoboro, ME 04572. TEL 207-832-7534, 800-752-8521, FAX 207-832-7341, mad@maine.com, http://www.maineantiquedigest.com. Ed. Samuel C Pennington. R&P Sally Pennington. Adv. contact Alice Greene. page USD 845. Circ: 30,000.

739.7 USA ISSN 0191-3522
NK6900
MAN AT ARMS; the magazine of arms collecting-investing. Text in English. 1979. bi-m. USD 32 domestic; USD 40 foreign (effective 2002). adv. bk.rev. charts; illus. index. back issues avail. **Document type:** *Consumer.* **Description:** Devoted to history of arms and armour; contains articles on gun and sword collecting.
Published by: Stuart C. Mowbray, PO Box 460, Lincoln, RI 02865. TEL 401-726-8011, service@manatarmsbooks.com. Ed. Stuart C Mowbray. Adv. contact Sue Lincoln. Circ: 20,000 (paid).

799.202 USA ISSN 0883-6949
MANNLICHER COLLECTOR. Text in English. 1985. q. USD 20; USD 29 foreign (effective 2000 - 2001). adv. bk.rev. **Document type:** *Newsletter, Academic/Scholarly.*
Published by: Mannlicher Collectors Association, PO Box 7144, Salem, OR 97303. TEL 503-472-7710, FAX 503-472-7710. Ed. Don L Henry. Circ: 650.

MARKETPLACE (GLEN ELLYN). see *TRANSPORTATION—Automobiles*

745.1 USA ISSN 0279-8344
MASSBAY ANTIQUES✶ . Text in English. 1980. m. USD 15. adv. bk.rev. **Description:** For antiques dealers and collectors in the New England area.
Published by: Northshore Weeklies, Inc., PO Box 293, Danvers, MA 01923-0493. FAX 508-685-3782. Ed. Shannon Aaron. Circ: 22,000.

631.3 745.1 USA ISSN 0897-215X
MASSEY COLLECTORS NEWS - WILD HARVEST. Text in English. 1984. bi-m. USD 24 domestic; USD 28 in Canada; USD 32 elsewhere (effective 2000). adv. back issues avail. **Document type:** *Newsletter.* **Description:** For collectors of Massey Harris and MF tractors and equipment.
Published by: Massey Collectors News, PO Box 529, Denver, IA 50622. TEL 319-984-5292, FAX 319-984-6408. Ed., Pub. Keith Oltrogge. Circ: 1,400.

745.1 USA
MERRY-GO-ROUNDUP. Text in English. 1973. q. USD 35; USD 41 foreign. adv. bk.rev. back issues avail. **Document type:** *Consumer.* **Description:** Articles on the history and preservation of carousels and news related to the subject.
Former titles: National Carousel Association. Carousel Archives; National Carousel Association. Carousel Census
Published by: National Carousel Association, c/o Cynthia L Hennig, Ed, 128 Courtshire Ln, Penfield, NY 14526. TEL 716-377-6762, chennig@frontiernet.net. Ed., Adv. contact Cynthia L Hennig. Circ: 1,450.

745.1 USA
MID-AM ANTIQUE APPRAISERS ASSOCIATION. NEWSLETTER. Text in English. a. **Document type:** *Directory.*
Published by: (Mid-Am Antique Appraisers Association), Karen Hall Publishing Co., PO Box 9681, Springfield, MO 65801. TEL 417-865-7269. Ed. Jacqueline Vadeboncoeur.

745.1 USA ISSN 1042-2501
MIDATLANTIC ANTIQUES MAGAZINE; monthly guide to antiques, auctions, art & collectibles. Text in English. 1983. m. USD 18; USD 3 newsstand/cover (effective 1998). adv. bk.rev. back issues avail. **Document type:** *Trade.* **Description:** Provides auctions and antique show reports listing prices; compares regional prices.
Related titles: Microfilm ed.: (from PQC).
Published by: Henderson Newspapers Inc., 304 S Chestnut St, Box 908, Henderson, NC 27536. TEL 252-492-4001, 800-326-3894, FAX 252-430-0125. Ed., R&P Lydia A Stainback. Pub. Richard Bean. Circ: 14,500. **Dist. by:** Ingram Periodicals, 18 Ingram Blvd., La Vergne, TN 37086-3634. TEL 615-793-5000, FAX 615-783-6043.

355.009 USA ISSN 0026-3966
UC463
MILITARY COLLECTOR & HISTORIAN. Text in English. 1951. q. USD 30 to non-members. adv. bk.rev. **Description:** Historical articles on the material, culture, and traditions of members of the U.S. Armed Forces worldwide and of other nations that serve the Western Hemisphere.
Related titles: Microform ed.: (from PQC).
Indexed: AmH&L, HistAb, PCI, RILM.
Published by: Company of Military Historians HQ and Museum, N Main St, Westbrook, CT 06498. TEL 203-399-9460. Ed. Fred Gaede. Circ: 4,200.

745.1 GBR ISSN 0262-1851
MILLER'S ANTIQUES PRICE GUIDE. Text in English. 1980. a. GBP 24.99 (effective 2005). adv. charts; illus.; mkt. **Document type:** *Catalog, Consumer.* **Description:** Contains price values and text descriptions of antiques and collectibles.
—BLDSC (5773.960000).
Published by: Octopus Publishing Group, Mitchell Beazley - Miller's (Subsidiary of: Hachette Livre), 2-4 Heron Quays, London, E14 4JP, United Kingdom. TEL 44-20-75318400, FAX 44-20-75318534, enquiries@mitchell-beazley.co.uk, http://www.mitchell-beazley.co.uk/mbeazley/results.asp?cat=400&ob=sort_date&ds=millers, http://www.mitchell-beazley.co.uk/mbeazley/miller/miller.htm. Ed. Anna Sanderson. R&P Alison Starling. Adv. contact Elizabeth Smith. Circ: 181,000. **Dist. by:** Phaidon Press, Inc., 180 Varick St, 14th Fl, New York, NY 10014. TEL 212-652-5400, FAX 212-652-5410, ussales@phaidon.com.

MILLER'S CLASSIC MOTORCYCLE YEARBOOK (YEAR). see *SPORTS AND GAMES—Bicycles And Motorcycles*

745.1 GBR
MILLER'S COLLECTABLES PRICE GUIDE. Text in English. a. GBP 18.99 per issue (effective 2005). adv. charts; illus.; mkt. 464 p./no.; **Document type:** *Catalog, Consumer.* **Description:** Offers a guide to the values of various antiques and collectible items.
Published by: Octopus Publishing Group, Mitchell Beazley - Miller's (Subsidiary of: Hachette Livre), 2-4 Heron Quays, London, E14 4JP, United Kingdom. TEL 44-20-75318400, FAX 44-20-75318534, enquiries@mitchell-beazley.co.uk, http://www.mitchell-beazley.co.uk/mbeazley/miller/miller.htm. Eds. Anna Sanderson, Madeline Marsh. Adv. contact Elizabeth Smith. Circ: 50,000. **Dist. in US by:** Phaidon Press, Inc., 180 Varick St, 14th Fl, New York, NY 10014. TEL 212-652-5400, FAX 212-652-5410, ussales@phaidon.com.

MILLER'S COLLECTORS CARS YEARBOOK (YEAR). see *TRANSPORTATION—Automobiles*

MINIWORLD; the magazine for the mighty mini. see *TRANSPORTATION—Automobiles*

MINUTIA. see *TRANSPORTATION—Automobiles*

629.222 USA ISSN 1074-3510
MISS INFORMATION'S AUTOMOTIVE CALENDAR OF EVENTS. Text in English. 1985. m. USD 15. adv. **Document type:** *Newsletter.* **Description:** Lists more than 700 shows, swap meets, auctions, and tours of interest to automotive enthusiasts.
Published by: Bobbie'dine Rodda, Ed. & Pub., 1232 Highland Ave, Glendale, CA 91202. TEL 818-887-1646, FAX 818-888-2648. Circ: 4,000.

745.1 799.202 USA ISSN 1550-8188
TS534.7
MODERN GUNS; identification and values. Text in English. 1979. biennial, latest vol.10. USD 14.95 newsstand/cover (effective 2005). **Document type:** *Directory, Consumer.* **Description:** Covers firearms from 1900 to the present and gives their values.
Published by: Collector Books (Subsidiary of: Schroeder Publishing Co., Inc.), PO Box 3009, Paducah, KY 42002-3009. TEL 800-626-5420.

745.1 BEL ISSN 1568-9379
MORE THAN CLASSIC. Text in Dutch. 2000. 6/yr. EUR 26.96 (effective 2003). **Document type:** *Magazine, Consumer.*
Published by: Sanoma Magazines Belgium, Telecomlaan 5-7, Diegem, 1831, Belgium. TEL 32-2-7762211, FAX 32-2-776-2317.

MOTO LEGENDE. see *SPORTS AND GAMES—Bicycles And Motorcycles*

629.222 USA ISSN 1059-5368
MUSTANG & FORDS. Text in English. 1980. m. USD 19.97; USD 4.99 newsstand/cover (effective 2005). adv. illus. **Document type:** *Magazine, Consumer.* **Description:** Contains the latest information and products on all things Ford.
Former titles (until 1991): Hot Rod's Mustang & Fords (1057-655X); (until 199?): Mustang (0894-5179)
Related titles: Microfiche ed.: (from PQC).
—CCC.
Published by: Primedia Consumer Media & Magazine Group, 9036 Brittanyway, Tampa, FL 33619. TEL 813-679-3500, FAX 813-679-3999, http://www.mustangandfords.com, http://www.primedia.com. Ed. Larry Jewett. Pub. Pam King. adv.: B&W page USD 2,760, color page USD 4,415. Circ: 95,000 (paid).

745.1 USA ISSN 0741-2673
MYSTIC LIGHT OF THE ALADDIN KNIGHTS. Text in English. 1973. bi-m. looseleaf. USD 25 (effective 2005). adv. 12 p./no.; **Document type:** *Newsletter.* **Description:** Includes information about Aladdin brand coal-oil lamps, Aladdin electric lamps, and related Aladdin memorabilia.
Published by: J.W. Courter, Ed. & Pub., 3935 Kelley Rd, Kevil, KY 42053-9431. TEL 270-488-2116, FAX 270-488-2055, brtknight@aol.com, http://www.aladdinknights.org. Ed. J W Courter. R&P, Adv. contact J.W. Courter. Circ: 1,900 (paid and controlled).

NASH TIMES. see *TRANSPORTATION—Automobiles*

745.1 USA ISSN 0899-6172
AM303
NATIONAL DIRECTORY OF ART & ANTIQUES BUYERS & SPECIALISTS✶ . Text in English. 1991. biennial. USD 75. **Document type:** *Directory.* **Description:** Contains over 6,000 specialists from over 800 categories of art, antiques and collectables.
Published by: Merit Agencies, Inc., c/o William D Angelo, 6441 Lochridge Rd, Columbia, MD 21044-4032. Ed. Bill D'Angelo. Circ: 1,000.

NEUDIN (YEAR). see *HOBBIES*

745.1 USA ISSN 0897-5795
THE NEW ENGLAND ANTIQUES JOURNAL. Text in English. 1982. m. USD 22.95 domestic; USD 30 in Canada (effective 2001). adv. bk.rev. 100 p./no.; back issues avail. **Document type:** *Trade.* **Description:** For antiques dealers and collectors: educational articles, auction and antiques show reviews, news and commentary.
Related titles: Online - full content ed.; Supplement(s): Living With Antiques.
Published by: Turley Publications, 92 Main St., Ware, MA 01082-1318. TEL 413-967-3505, 800-432-3505, FAX 413-967-6009, visit@antiquesjournal.com, http://www.antiquesjournal.com. Ed., R&P Jamie Mercier. Pub. Pat Turley. Adv. contact Mark Ehrlich. B&W page USD 685; 15.75 x 10. Circ: 20,000.

THE NEW ENGLAND DOLL COLLECTOR. see *HOBBIES*

745.1 USA
NEW HAMPSHIRE ANTIQUES MONTHLY. Text in English. 1995. m. USD 21.95; USD 2 newsstand/cover (effective 2000). adv. bk.rev. tr.lit. back issues avail. **Document type:** *Newspaper.* **Description:** Includes articles relating to various categories of antiques, auction results, show previews and reviews, and shop news.
Related titles: ◆ Supplement(s): The New England Doll Collector.
Address: 67 Cross St., Farmington, NH 03835-3153. TEL 603-755-4568, FAX 603-755-3990. Ed., Pub. Charles Wibel. Adv. contact Sandra Wibel. B&W page USD 550. Circ: 21,000.

745.1 USA ISSN 0738-8365
NEW YORK ANTIQUE ALMANAC. Text in English. 1975. 5/yr. USD 10 domestic; USD 22 in Canada; USD 24 elsewhere (effective 2005). adv. bk.rev. illus.; stat. back issues avail. **Document type:** *Magazine, Trade.* **Description:** Focuses on the current market in art, antiques and collectibles.
Published by: New York Eye Publishing Co., Inc., 200 E 72nd St., PO Box 2400, New York, NY 10021. TEL 212-988-2700, FAX 212-988-5255, nyantique@aol.com. Ed., Pub. Carol Nadel. Adv. contact Enid Vanraalte. col. inch USD 11. Circ: 69,000.

745.1 USA
NEW YORK - PENNSYLVANIA COLLECTOR✶ ; antiques, art & Americana. Text in English. 1976. m. USD 21 in United States; USD 31 in Canada. adv. bk.rev. **Document type:** *Newspaper, Trade.* **Description:** Contains articles on antiques and collectibles, a special series on antique furniture restoration and identification, and calendars of coming shows and auctions.
Published by: Messenger-Wolfe Publications, Inc., 73 Buffalo St, Canandaigua, NY 14424-1001. TEL 716-924-4040, FAX 716-924-7734, WolfePub@frontiernet.net. Ed. George M Ewing Jr. Adv. contact Ros Parrish. Circ: 7,000.

NEW ZEALAND CLASSIC CAR. see *TRANSPORTATION—Automobiles*

629.288 USA
NEWS-FLITE. Text in English. 1977. q. USD 20 (effective 2000). adv. charts; illus.; stat. back issues avail. **Document type:** *Newsletter.* **Description:** Provides technical information, restoration information, and reprinted articles.
Published by: Chrysler 300 Club International, Inc., 4900 Jonesville Rd, Jonesville, MI 49250. TEL 517-849-2783, FAX 517-849-7447. Ed. Andy Maikonis. R&P George Riehl. Circ: 900.

NEWSLETTER - SOTHEBY'S. see *ART*

629.222 388.3 SWE ISSN 1650-8947
NOSTALGIA. Text in Swedish. 1993. m. SEK 455, NOK 570 (effective 2004). adv. 100 p./no. 4 cols./p.; **Document type:** *Magazine, Consumer.*
Formerly (until 1999): Nostalgia Motor Magazine (1103-7334)
Published by: Foerlags AB Albinsson & Sjoeberg, PO Box 529, Karlskrona, 37123, Sweden. TEL 46-455-335325, FAX 46-455-311715, fabas@fabas.se, http://www.fabas.se. Ed. Goeran Ambell. Pub. Stig L Sjoeberg. Adv. contact Susanne Zec. color page SEK 16,500; trim 190 x 275. Circ: 23,900 (controlled).

OLD AUTOS. see *TRANSPORTATION—Automobiles*

OLD CARS; weekly news and marketplace. see *TRANSPORTATION—Automobiles*

629.222 USA ISSN 0194-6404
OLD CARS PRICE GUIDE. Text in English. 1978. bi-m. USD 19.98 domestic; USD 36.98 foreign; USD 4.98 newsstand/cover (effective 2005). adv. bk.rev. charts; stat.; illus. reprints avail. **Document type:** *Magazine, Consumer.* **Description:** Market value news featuring over 130,000 individual prices, vehicle conditions in six grades, list of all American-made automobiles from 1901 to 1986, and identification photos of models.
Related titles: Microform ed.: (from PQC).
Published by: Krause Publications, Inc. (Subsidiary of: F & W Publications, Inc.), 700 E State St, Iola, WI 54990-0001. TEL 715-445-2214, 800-258-0929, FAX 715-445-4087, old_cars_pg@krause.com, info@krause.com, http://www.krause.com/cars/pg/. Eds. Ken Buttolph TEL 715-445-2214 ext 285, Ron Kowalke TEL 715-445-2214 ext 246. Pub. Rick Groth TEL 715-445-2214 ext 430. Adv. contacts Patrick Lacke TEL 715-445-2214 ext 274, Patrick Lacke TEL 715-445-2214 ext 274. B&W page USD 1,438, color page USD 2,531; trim 8 x 10.875. Circ: 70,356 (paid and free).

OLD GLORY MAGAZINE; vintage restoration today. see *TRANSPORTATION*

745.1 USA ISSN 0030-2031
F6
OLD-TIME NEW ENGLAND. Text in English. 1910-1981; resumed 1995. s-a. USD 35 (effective 1998). adv. illus. index. reprint service avail. from PQC. **Description:** Devoted to the buildings, household furnishings, domestic arts, manners and customs, and minor antiquities of New England.
Related titles: Microfiche ed.: (from PQC); Microfilm ed.: (from PQC).
Indexed: AIAP, APC, ArtInd, BHA, CurCont.
Published by: Society for the Preservation of New England Antiquities, 141 Cambridge St, Boston, MA 02114. TEL 617-227-3956, FAX 617-570-9147, http://www.spnea.arg. Ed. Kathryn Grover. Adv. contact Chris Shute. Circ: 5,000.

745.1 USA ISSN 1064-4164
OLD TOY SOLDIER. Text in English. 1976. q. USD 25 domestic; USD 35 in Canada; USD 56 elsewhere (effective 2003). adv. bk.rev. illus. cum.index: vols.1-10, 11-15. back issues avail.; reprints avail. **Document type:** *Academic/Scholarly.* **Description:** Publishes articles and information of interest to collectors of military and civilian toy figures.
Formerly (until 1990): Old Toy Soldier Newsletter (8756-7652)
Published by: O T S N, Inc., PO Box 13324, Pittsburgh, PA 15243-0324. TEL 412-563-3499, FAX 412-344-5273, raytoys@aol.com, http://www.oldtoysoldier.com. Ed. Norman Joplin. Pub., R&P, Adv. contact Ray Haradin. B&W page USD 150. Circ: 1,900 (paid).

745.1 USA ISSN 0164-3398
THE ORIENTALIA JOURNAL. Text in English. bi-m. USD 21 domestic; USD 38 foreign; USD 6.50 newsstand/cover (effective 2001). **Document type:** *Journal, Trade.* **Description:** For collectors and investors of antiques.
Published by: Orientalia Journal, PO Box 94, Little Neck, NY 11363.

745.1 NLD ISSN 0929-1032
ORIGINE; art & antiques & auctions. Text in Dutch. 1993. bi-m. EUR 39.50; EUR 7.95 newsstand/cover (effective 2003). adv. bk.rev.; Website rev. illus. back issues avail. **Document type:** *Consumer.* **Description:** Includes original articles concerning 500 years of art and antiques documented by original private interiors, exhibitions, news, restoration, and interviews.

Incorporates (1999-2002): Veilingtijdschrift (1566-1105); (1999-2002): Kunstblad (1567-858X)
Related titles: ♦ Supplement(s): Veilingtijdschrift. ISSN 1566-1105.
Published by: A.K.J. van der Gulik Ed & Pub, PO Box 5220, Haarlem, 2000 GE, Netherlands. TEL 31-23-5324233, FAX 31-23-5324518, info@artinterim.nl. Adv. contact F Biloen TEL 06-22605906. B&W page EUR 1,500, color page EUR 1,750. Circ: 19,500.

745.1 USA
P A C: PAPER AND ADVERTISING COLLECTOR. Text in English. 1977. m. USD 19.95 subscr - mailed domestic 3rd class; USD 30 domestic 1st class; USD 35 in Canada (effective 2005). Index. **Document type:** *Newspaper, Consumer.*
Published by: (National Association of Paper and Advertising Collectors), Engle Publishing Co., PO Box 500, Mt. Joy, PA 17552-0500. TEL 800-800-1833, http://www.paperandadvertisingcollector.com. Ed. Denise Sater. Circ: 10,000 (paid).

629.222 USA ISSN 0362-9368
TL215.P25
PACKARD CORMORANT. Text in English. 1953. q. membership. charts; illus.; tr.lit.
Formerly: Cormorant (0045-8546)
Published by: Packard Automobile Classics, 420 S Ludlow St, Dayton, OH 45402. http://www.packardclub.com. Ed. Richard M Langworth.

745.1 790.13 USA ISSN 0741-4927
PN4877
PAPER COLLECTOR'S MARKETPLACE. Text in English. 1983. m. USD 19.95 (effective 2000). adv. bk.rev. back issues avail. **Document type:** *Consumer.* **Description:** For collectors of paper memorabilia, including magazines, newspapers, advertising, postcards, posters and more.
Published by: Watson Graphic Designs, 470 Main St, Box 128, Scandinavia, WI 54977. TEL 715-467-2379, FAX 715-467-2243, pcmpaper@gglbbs.com, http://www.pcmpaper.com. Ed. Judy Watson. Pub., R&P, Adv. contact Doug Watson. B&W page USD 120; trim 11 x 8.5. Circ: 4,000.

745 USA
PATINAGRAM. Text in English. 1977. bi-m. membership. bk.rev. **Document type:** *Newsletter.*
Published by: Potomac Antique Tools and Industries Association, Potomac, MD 20744. TEL 301-292-1606. Ed. Dale Bultman. Circ: 370 (controlled).

745.1 USA ISSN 0031-6644
NK8400
PEWTER COLLECTORS' CLUB OF AMERICA. BULLETIN. Text in English. 1934. s-a. looseleaf. free to members (effective 2004). bk.rev. illus. cum.index every 10 nos. **Document type:** *Bulletin.*
Published by: Pewter Collectors' Club of America, c/o Garland Pass, 71 Hurdle Fence Dr, Avon, CT 06001-4103. http://members.aol.com/pewterpcca. Ed. Garland Pass. Circ: 600.

PIERCE-ARROW SERVICE BULLETIN. see *TRANSPORTATION—Automobiles*

629.222 USA ISSN 0032-1737
PLYMOUTH BULLETIN. Text in English. 1959. bi-m. USD 24 domestic; USD 45 foreign (effective 2001). adv. bk.rev. illus. 56 p./no. 2 cols./p.; back issues avail. **Document type:** *Newsletter.* **Description:** Covers automotive history relating to the Plymouth automobile.
Published by: Plymouth Owners Club, Inc., PO Box 416, Cavalier, ND 58220. TEL 701-549-3746, FAX 701-549-3744, http://www.classicalcar.com/clubs/plymouth/home.htm. Ed., Adv. contact Lanny Knutson TEL 204-636-2353. R&P Jim Benjaminson. Circ: 3,850 (paid).

POSTCARD ART - POSTCARD FICTION. see *ART*

PRACTICAL CLASSICS; buying, restoring & enjoying older cars. see *TRANSPORTATION—Automobiles*

PRAIRIE GOLD RUSH; quarterly newsletter for all Twin City, Minneapolis and Moline enthusiasts. see *AGRICULTURE—Agricultural Equipment*

745.1 700 USA
PROFESSIONAL APPRAISERS INFORMATION EXCHANGE. Text in English. 1995. bi-m. adv. software rev.; bk.rev.; Website rev. illus.; stat.; tr.lit. back issues avail. **Document type:** *Newsletter, Trade.* **Description:** Offers a bi-monthly trade publication for personal property appraisers, including articles by and for experts in gems and jewelry, machinery and equipment, fine art, antiques and residential contents, appraisal regulations and trends.
Related titles: Fax ed.
Published by: International Society of Appraisers, 1131 SW 7th St., Ste. 105, Renton, WA 98055-1229. TEL 206-241-0359, FAX 206-240-0436, isa-hq@compuserve.com, isahq@isa-appraisers.org, http://www.isa-appraisers.org. Ed., Adv. contact Alice Coleman. R&P Christian Coleman. page USD 400. Circ: 2,000 (controlled).

745.1 796.6 USA ISSN 0566-778X
UB777.B2 CODEN: BIKE
RE-UNICYCLING THE PAST; collecting antique unicycles. Variant title: Re-Uni. Text in English; Summaries in French, German. 1991. bi-m. looseleaf. USD 18 domestic; USD 23 in Canada; USD 26 elsewhere; USD 2.99 newsstand/cover (effective 2004). adv. bk.rev.; software rev. bibl.; charts; illus.; stat. cum.index: 1991-2000. 45 p./no. 2 cols./p.; back issues avail.; reprints avail. **Document type:** *Magazine, Consumer.* **Description:** Provides a unique source of information and contacts for those interested in collecting and preserving antique unicycles. Focuses primarily on unicycle collections in the United States and Mexico.
Formerly (until 1996): Collecting Unicycles
Media: Large Type. **Related titles:** Braille ed.: Re-Unicycle Braille; CD-ROM ed.: Re-Unicycling on Disc. 1998. USD 15 (effective 2004); Online - full text ed.: ISSN 0566-666X; German ed.: Gegenwartszeit der Unicycle. ISSN 0094-5110; German Translation: Uebersetzung fuer Re-Unicycling; Abridged ed.: Wee-Unicycling. ISSN 0000-023X; Alternate Frequency ed(s).: Weekly Re-Unicycling. w.; International ed.: World of Re-Unicycling; Includes: Unicycling Galore. ISSN 0747-9980; Regional ed(s).: Re-Unicycling Out West. ISSN 0065-9363; Seasonal ed(s).: Re-Unicycling The Summer. ISSN 0192-7655. 1997; Series: A Series of Wheels. ISSN 0192-7647; Special ed(s).: Best of Re-Unicycling; ♦ Supplement(s): Cycling on One. ISSN 0000-0744.
Indexed: SportS.
—BLDSC (5555.123400).
Published by: (Mid-Atlantic Unicycle Association), One Wheel Good, Inc. (Subsidiary of: Consumer Collectibles Inc.), 147 Lake Valley Rd, Morristown, NJ 07960. TEL 908-219-0286, info@reunicycling.com, info@onewheelgood.com, http://www.reunicycling.com, http://www.onewheel.com. Pub., Adv. contact Craig LeMonde. R&P Freddie Mercyx. B&W page USD 280, color page USD 320; trim 7.25 x 10.75. Circ: 210 (paid); 40 (controlled).

745.1 USA
RENNINGER'S ANTIQUE GUIDE; to shows, shops, antique - flea markets and auctions. Text in English. 1975. 25/yr. USD 15 (effective 2001). adv. bk.rev. 28 p./no. 6 cols./p.; **Document type:** *Newspaper, Trade.*
Address: PO Box 495, Lafayette Hill, PA 19444-0495. TEL 610-828-4614, FAX 610-834-1599, http://www.renningers.com. Ed. Harriett Ackerman. Pub., R&P, Adv. contact Herbert Kratchman. B&W page USD 462. Circ: 60,000.

629.222 USA
RESTORATION MAGAZINE (ONLINE EDITION). Text in English. 1983. a. USD 20 domestic membership (effective 2005). **Document type:** *Magazine, Consumer.*
Formerly (until 2003): Restoration Magazine (Print Edition)
Media: Online - full text.
Published by: International Society for Vehicle Preservation, PO 50046, Tucson, AZ 85703-1046. TEL 520-622-2201, FAX 520-749-3161, whaessner@earthlink.net, http://www.aztexcorp.com. Ed., Pub. Walter R. Haessner. Circ: 15,000 (paid).

RETROVISEUR. see *TRANSPORTATION—Automobiles*

RITTENHOUSE; The Journal of the American Scientific Instrument Enterprise. see *INSTRUMENTS*

ROCKIN' RECORDS; buyers - sellers reference book and price guide. see *MUSIC*

ROUGH RIDER. see *TRANSPORTATION—Automobiles*

629.222 ITA ISSN 1121-5321
RUOTECLASSICHE. Text in Italian. 1987. m. EUR 62.40 domestic; EUR 94 foreign (effective 2005). adv. **Document type:** *Magazine, Consumer.* **Description:** Covers antique automobiles, their history, technology, restoration, and culture.
Published by: Editoriale Domus, Via Gianni Mazzocchi 1/3, Rozzano, MI 20089, Italy. TEL 39-02-824721, editorialedomus@edidomus.it, http://www.edidomus.it. Circ: 32,000.

796.77 USA
SACRED OCTAGON. Text in English. 1964. bi-m. USD 35 (effective 2000). adv. bk.rev. illus. **Description:** Contains information of interest to vintage sports car enthusiasts.
Published by: New England M G 'T' Register, 50, W Davenport, NY 13860-0050. FAX 607-432-3342. Ed., R&P Richard L Knudsen. Circ: 5,000 (paid).

745.1 790.132 SWE ISSN 1102-5212
SAMLARBOKEN. Text in Swedish. 1991. a., latest vol.14, 2004. SEK 120 (effective 2004). **Document type:** *Consumer.*
Incorporates (1989-1991): Tallriksboken (0347-3228)
Published by: Tonkin AB, Gjutformsgatan 9, Ljungsbro, 59074, Sweden. TEL 46-13-66647, FAX 46-13-66771, tonkin@tonkin.se, http://www.tonkin.se. Ed. Archie Tonkin.

745.1 NOR ISSN 0805-0759
SAMLER OG ANTIKKBOERSEN. Text in Norwegian. 1994. bi-m. adv. **Document type:** *Magazine, Consumer.* **Description:** Provides articles and features on antiques and auctions as both a profession and a hobby.
Published by: Allers Familie-Journal A-S, Stenersgaten 2, Postboks 1169, Sentrum, Oslo, 0107, Norway. TEL 47-21-30-10-00, FAX 47-21-30-12-05. Circ: 18,001 (paid).

745.1 DEU
SAMMLER MARKT. Text in German. m. EUR 42 domestic; EUR 100 foreign; EUR 3.50 newsstand/cover (effective 2002). adv. **Document type:** *Magazine, Consumer.*
Published by: Der Heisse Draht Verlag GmbH und Co., Drostestr 14-16, Hannover, 30161, Germany. TEL 49-511-390910, FAX 49-511-39091252, zentrale@dhd.de, http://www.dhd.de. Adv. contact Kai Burkhardt. B&W page EUR 1,803, color page EUR 2,161. Circ: 48,000 (paid and controlled).

745.1 USA
HF5482
SCHROEDER'S ANTIQUES PRICE GUIDE. Text in English. 1977. a. USD 12.95 (effective 2000). adv. illus. **Document type:** *Directory, Trade.* **Description:** Offers prices and information on more than 50,000 items.
Formerly (until 1983): Flea Market Trader (0364-023X)
Published by: Collector Books (Subsidiary of: Schroeder Publishing Co., Inc.), PO Box 3009, Paducah, KY 42002-3009. TEL 270-898-6211, 800-626-5420. Ed. Lisa Stroup. Pub. Bill Schroeder. Adv. contact Rick Loyd.

739.23 USA ISSN 0899-6105
NK7100
SILVER. Text in English. 1968. bi-m. USD 40 domestic; USD 50 in Canada; USD 55 elsewhere (effective 2001). adv. bk.rev. index. back issues avail. **Document type:** *Magazine, Academic/Scholarly.* **Description:** Covers all aspects of silver collecting: American, English and other flatware, hollowware and novelties.
Former titles (until 1985): Silver Magazine (0747-4482); Silver-Rama (0037-5357)
Indexed: BHA.
Published by: Silver Magazine Inc., 200576, Cleveland, OH 44120-9576. TEL 858-756-1054, FAX 858-756-9928, silver@silvermag.com, http://www.silvermag.com. Ed., R&P Connie McNally. Pub. William McNally. Adv. contact Amber Bliss. Circ: 3,000 (paid).

SLANT 6 NEWS. see *TRANSPORTATION—Automobiles*

745.1 917.404 USA ISSN 1051-6719
NK1127
SLOAN'S GREEN GUIDE TO ANTIQUING IN NEW ENGLAND. Text in English. 1989. 2/yr. USD 20. adv. **Document type:** *Trade.* **Description:** Lists over 2800 antiques shops, antiquarian booksellers, period restoration specialists, weekend markets in six New England and eastern New York states.
Formerly (until 1992): Sloan's Green Guide to Antiques Dealers (New England) (0898-090X)
Published by: Antique Press, 66 Charles St, 140, Boston, MA 02114. TEL 617-723-3001, 800-552-5632, FAX 617-248-0185. Ed., Adv. contact Susan P Sloan. Circ: 10,000 (paid).

SPECIAL INTEREST AUTOS. see *TRANSPORTATION—Automobiles*

STUDIES IN THE DECORATIVE ARTS. see *ART*

745.1 USA ISSN 1080-451X
STYLE 1900; the quarterly journal of the arts and crafts movement. Text in English. 1986. q. USD 25 domestic; USD 30 in Canada; USD 35 elsewhere; USD 6.95 newsstand/cover domestic; USD 9.95 newsstand/cover in Canada (effective 2002). bk.rev. back issues avail. **Document type:** *Consumer.* **Description:** Devoted to exploring the art, artists, and philosophers within the arts and crafts movement at the turn of the century.
Formerly (until 1995): Arts and Crafts Quarterly (1074-4568)
Related titles: Online - full text ed.: (from Florida Center for Library Automation, Gale Group).
Indexed: AIAP, DAAI.
Address: 333 N Main St, Lambertville, NJ 08530. TEL 609-397-4104, FAX 609-397-9377, style@ragoarts.com, http://www.style1900.com, http://www.ragoarts.com/st1900.html. Ed. David Rago. Pub. Steven Becker. R&P Dave Care. Adv. contact Miriam Assion. Circ: 13,000 (paid).

TABLEAU; fine arts magazine. see *ART*

THUNDERBIRD SCOOP. see *TRANSPORTATION—Automobiles*

TOY CAR COLLECTOR. see *HOBBIES*

TRASTIENDA; revista del mercado de arte y antiguedades. see *ART*

745.1 USA ISSN 0897-814X
TREASURE CHEST; the information source & marketplace for collectors & dealers. Text in English. 1988. m. USD 25 (effective 2005). adv. bk.rev. illus. back issues avail.
Document type: *Magazine, Consumer.* **Description:** Includes information on antiques and collectibles, calendar of events on auctions, shows, flea markets, and recent sales, and features articles.
Published by: Treasure Chest Publishing, Inc., 564 Eddy St, Providence, RI 02903-4960. TEL 401-272-9444, FAX 401-272-9422. Circ: 50,000 (paid and free).

745.1 DEU ISSN 1618-5242
TROEDLER- UND SAMMLER- JOURNAL. Text in German. 1992. m. EUR 45 domestic; EUR 56.40 foreign (effective 2005). adv.
Document type: *Magazine, Consumer.* **Description:** Information about antique collecting, flea markets and fairs.
Former titles (until 2001): Troedler und Sammeln (1432-0908); (until 1995): Troedler- und Magazin Sammeln (0944-3134); Which was formed by the merger of (1979-1992): Troedler- und Antiquitaetenmagazin (0944-3126); (1984-1992): Magazin Sammeln (1010-3686)
Indexed: IBZ.
Published by: Gemi Verlags GmbH, Pfaffenhofener Str 3, Reichertshausen, 85293, Germany. TEL 49-8441-40220, FAX 49-8441-71846, gemi.verlag@t-online.de, http://www.troedlerundsammeln.de, http://www.gemiverlag.de. Ed. Karl Ruisinger. adv.: color page EUR 1,920, B&W page EUR 1,380; trim 210 x 297. Circ: 65,000 (paid and controlled).

TROUVAILLES. see *ART*

THE TRUMPET (NEW YORK). see *ART*

TUCKER TOPICS. see *TRANSPORTATION—Automobiles*

745.1 RUS
TVERSKAYA STARINA. Text in Russian. 1911. q. USD 129 in United States (effective 2000).
Indexed: RASB.
Published by: Redaktsiya Tverskaya Starina, Ul Sovetskaya 54, Tver', Russian Federation. TEL 0822-227105. **Dist. by:** East View Information Services, 3020 Harbor Ln. N., Minneapolis, MN 55447. TEL 763-550-0961, FAX 763-559-2931.

688.72 745.1 USA ISSN 1044-1344
U S TOY COLLECTOR MAGAZINE. Text in English. 1985. m. USD 21 (effective 1998). adv. bk.rev. illus. back issues avail.
Document type: *Consumer.* **Description:** Contains articles about the history of vintage and antique toy cars and construction toys. Provides a photo-advertising medium for antique transportation and construction toys.
Address: PO Box 172, Helena, MT 59624-0172. TEL 406-443-8594. Ed., Pub. Gordon Rice.

745.1 CAN ISSN 0711-0081
THE UPPER CANADIAN; current trends in antiques and collectibles. Text in English. 1980. bi-m. CND 26 domestic; USD 27 in United States; CND 36 overseas; CND 4.50 newsstand/cover (effective 2002). adv. bk.rev. illus.; tr.lit.; mkt. 60 p./no. 4 cols./p.; back issues avail. **Document type:** *Newspaper, Trade.* **Description:** Caters to the business and passion of antiques and collectibles for collectors and dealers, novice and expert alike. Articles, columns, show and auction coverage and commentary encompass a broad range of issues and topics. Emphasis on price reporting and pictorials.
Related titles: Microfiche ed.
Indexed: CBCARef.
Published by: 710198 Ontario Inc., P O Box 653, Smiths Falls, ON K7A 4T6, Canada. TEL 613-283-1168, FAX 613-283-1345, uppercanadian@recorder.ca, http://www.uppercanadian.com. Ed. Larry Thompson. Pub., R&P Bill Dobson TEL 613-283-5270. Adv. contact Jackie Coldrey. B&W page CND 440; trim 15.5 x 10.25. Circ: 7,000.

629.222 USA ISSN 0274-5003
V-8 TIMES✶. Text in English. 1963. bi-m. USD 30 (effective 2000). adv. bk.rev. charts; illus. **Document type:** *Consumer.*
Description: Magazine for members of the Early Ford V-8 Club of America, focusing on 1932-1953 Ford Motor Company vehicles. Historical, technical, how-to-restore, personal stories, and articles.
Published by: Early Ford V-8 Club of America, 4935 E Mountain View Dr, San Diego, CA 92116-1941. TEL 619-283-1938, fordV8club@aol.com, http://www.earlyfordv8.org, http://www.earlyfordV8.org. Ed. Jerry Windle. Adv. contact Kent Jaquith. Circ: 8,000.

V M R STANDARD USED CAR PRICES. see *TRANSPORTATION—Automobiles*

629.222 USA
V V W C A NEWSLETTER. Text in English. 1976. m. USD 20. adv. bk.rev. back issues avail.
Published by: Vintage Volkswagen Club of America, 818 Main St, Portage, PA 15946. TEL 814-736-4343. Ed. Terry Shuler.

739.7 DNK ISSN 0506-337X
U799
VAABENHISTORISK TIDSSKRIFT. Text in Danish. 1968. 7/yr. adv. illus.
Published by: Vaabenhistorisk Selskab/Danish Arms and Armour Society, c/o K. A. Knudsen, Dysseagervej 17 K, Vanloese, 2720, Denmark. TEL 45-38-74-79-97.

739.7 DNK ISSN 0108-707X
U800.A1
VAABENHISTORISKE AARBOEGER. Text in Danish; Summaries in English, German. 1934. a. bk.rev. cum.index: vols.1-10 in vol.10; vols.11-20 in vol.20. **Document type:** *Monographic series, Academic/Scholarly.*
Indexed: NAA, RASB.
Published by: Vaabenhistorisk Selskab/Danish Arms and Armour Society, c/o K. A. Knudsen, Dysseagervej 17 K, Vanloese, 2720, Denmark. TEL 45-38-74-79-97.

629.222 DEU
VETERAN. Text in German. 1975. q. EUR 17; EUR 5 newsstand/cover (effective 2005). adv. bk.rev. **Document type:** *Magazine, Consumer.*
Published by: Citroen Veteranen Club, Bruehler Str 34, Ketsch, 268775, Germany. TEL 49-6202-64948, FAX 49-6202-68898, Hans-Joachim.Bethge@cvc-club.de, http://www.citroen-veteran.privat.t-online.de/DreamHC/Seite1.html, http://www.cvc-club.de. Ed. Helmut Kloos. Adv. contact Klaus Schaefer. Circ: 750.

THE VETERAN FARMER/VETERAAN BOER. see *AGRICULTURE—Agricultural Equipment*

629 796.7 FRA ISSN 0989-0009
VIE DE LA MOTO. Text in French. 1989. s-m. adv. index. back issues avail.
Published by: Elvea - La Vie de l'Auto, BP 88, Fontainebleau, Cedex 77303, France. TEL 33-1-60715555, FAX 33-1-60722237. Circ: 43,000 (controlled).

629.222 796.7 FRA ISSN 0151-2188
LA VIE DE L'AUTO. Text in French. 1976. w. adv. bk.rev. back issues avail. **Document type:** *Newspaper.* **Description:** Covers classic cars as well as old tractors and trucks.
Published by: Elvea - La Vie de l'Auto, BP 88, Fontainebleau, Cedex 77303, France. TEL 33-1-60715555, FAX 33-1-60722237. Adv. contact Naziha Laroussi. Circ: 68,500 (controlled).

VINTAGE AIRPLANE. see *AERONAUTICS AND SPACE FLIGHT*

VINTAGE COMMERCIAL VEHICLES. see *TRANSPORTATION*

629.222 USA ISSN 0042-6350
TL215.F7
VINTAGE FORD✶. Text in English. 1966. bi-m. USD 22 domestic; USD 27 in Canada; USD 28 elsewhere (effective 2000). adv. bk.rev. charts; illus.; stat. **Document type:** *Academic/Scholarly.*
Media: Duplicated (not offset).
Published by: Model T Ford Club of America, PO Box 126, Centerville, IN 47330-0126. TEL 972-783-7531, FAX 972-783-0575, Jay@MTFCA.com, http://www.MTFCA.com. Ed., R&P Jay G Klehfoth. Adv. contact Barbara L Klehfoth. Circ: 8,000.

VINTAGE RACECAR JOURNAL AND MARKET REPORT. see *TRANSPORTATION—Automobiles*

VINTAGE TRACTOR. see *AGRICULTURE—Agricultural Equipment*

VOLKSWORLD. see *TRANSPORTATION—Automobiles*

745.13 DEU ISSN 0043-261X
N3
WELTKUNST; aktuelle Zeitschrift fuer Kunst und Antiquitaeten. Text in German. 1930. 14/yr. EUR 118.30 domestic; EUR 123.20 foreign; EUR 9.80 newsstand/cover (effective 2003). adv. bk.rev. charts; illus. **Document type:** *Magazine, Consumer.* **Description:** Information on art exhibitions, auctions, art fairs and other events.
Indexed: A&ATA, ABM, ArtInd, BAS, BHA, DIP, IBR, IBZ, RASB.
Published by: Weltkunst Verlag GmbH, Nymphenburger Str 84, Munich, 80636, Germany. TEL 49-89-1269900, FAX 49-89-12699011, info@weltkunstverlag.de, http://www.weltkunstverlag.de. Ed. Gloria Ehret. Adv. contact Gertrud Lohner TEL 49-89-12699050. B&W page EUR 1,365, color page EUR 2,030; trim 194 x 266. Circ: 16,000 (paid).

745.1 USA
WEST COAST LOCK COLLECTORS. Text in English. 1978. q. USD 15; USD 17 foreign (effective 1999). adv. **Document type:** *Newsletter, Trade.* **Description:** Reports on the history and research of antique locks, keys, and related items.
Address: 1427 Lincoln Blvd, Santa Monica, CA 90401. TEL 510-846-4022, DoggyJack@aol.com. Ed., Pub. Don Jackson. R&P, Adv. contact Bob Heilemann. Circ: 220 (paid).

745.1 USA ISSN 0199-3356
WEST COAST PEDDLER; oldest journal of antiques, art & collectibles in the Pacific states. Text in English. 1971. m. USD 24 (effective 1998). adv. bk.rev. **Document type:** *Consumer.* **Description:** Directed to West Coast antique collectors of antiques, fine art, and other investment-grade collectibles.
Address: PO Box 5134, Whittier, CA 90607. TEL 562-698-1718, FAX 562-698-1500. Ed., R&P Robert M Dannenbaum. Pubs. Robert M Dannenbaum, Rosalie Dannenbaum. Adv. contact Inez Spaulding. Circ: 19,225 (paid).

WHEELS OF TIME. see *TRANSPORTATION—Trucks And Trucking*

WORLD FINE ART. see *ART*

745.1 AUS ISSN 1443-6027
WORLD OF ANTIQUES AND ART. Text in English. 1966. s-a. AUD 31.50 domestic; AUD 63 in Asia & New Zealand; AUD 76 elsewhere & New Zealand (effective 2004). adv. bk.rev. illus. index. **Document type:** *Magazine, Consumer.*
Former titles (until 1999): Australian Antique Collector (0727-7253); (until 1981): Australasian Antique Collector (0004-8704)
Published by: Antiques & Art in Australia Pty Ltd, Suite 1b, 10 Spring St, PO Box 324, Bondi Junction, NSW 2022, Australia. TEL 61-2-93892919, FAX 61-2-93877487, info@worldaa.com, http://www.antiquesandart.com.au/. Eds. Eva Jaku, John Wade. Pub. Andre Jaku. Circ: 6,000.

745.1 USA ISSN 0194-9349
CODEN: KESRA9
YESTERYEAR; your monthly guide to antiques and collectibles. Text in English. 1975. m. USD 19 (effective 2003). adv. bk.rev. illus. back issues avail.; reprints avail. **Document type:** *Newspaper.*
Published by: Yesteryear Publications, Inc., PO Box 2, Princeton, WI 54968. TEL 920-787-4808, FAX 920-787-7381. Ed. Michael Jacobi. Circ: 6,500 (paid).

YOUR CLASSIC. see *TRANSPORTATION—Automobiles*

9N - 2N - 8N - NAA NEWSLETTER. see *AGRICULTURE—Agricultural Equipment*

78 QUARTERLY. see *MUSIC*

629.222 USA
1932 BUICK REGISTRY. Text in English. 1974. s-a. looseleaf. free. adv. illus.; mkt. back issues avail. **Document type:** *Newsletter, Consumer.* **Description:** For owners of 1925-1935 Buicks. Provides lists of parts for sale, literature, and restoration tips.
Address: 3000 Warren Rd, Indiana, PA 15701. TEL 724-463-3372, FAX 724-463-8604, buick32@adelphia.net. Ed. M G Blair. Circ: 1,600.

ARCHAEOLOGY

see also ANTHROPOLOGY ; ART ; HISTORY ; PALEONTOLOGY

930.1 NOR ISSN 0802-4936
A M S - RAPPORT. Text in Norwegian. 1988. irreg., latest vol.18, 2001. price varies. bibl.; illus.; maps. back issues avail.
Document type: *Monographic series, Academic/Scholarly.*
Description: Presents reports on cultural heritage, excavations, and museum projects.
Formerly (until 1989): Arkeologisk Museum i Stavanger. Oppdragsrapport (0802-2615)
Published by: Arkeologisk museum i Stavanger/Museum of Archaeology, Stavanger, Postboks 478, Stavanger, 4002, Norway. TEL 47-51-846000, FAX 47-51-846199, ams@ark.museum.no, http://www.ark.museum.no.

913 NOR ISSN 0800-0816
A M S - SKRIFTER. Text in English, Norwegian; Summaries in English, German. 1976. irreg., latest vol.17, 2000. price varies. abstr.; bibl.; illus.; maps. 2 cols./p.; back issues avail.
Document type: *Monographic series, Academic/Scholarly.*
Description: Research papers dealing with prehistoric man and his environment, with emphasis on southwest Norway.
Formerly: Arkeologisk Museum i Stavanger. Skrifter
Indexed: AnthLit, NAA.
—CCC.
Published by: Arkeologisk museum i Stavanger/Museum of Archaeology, Stavanger, Postboks 478, Stavanger, 4002, Norway. TEL 47-51-846000, FAX 47-51-846199, ams@ark.museum.no, http://www.ark.museum.no.

913 NOR ISSN 0332-6411
A M S - SMAATRYKK. Text in English, French, German, Norwegian. 1978. irreg., latest vol.72, 2003. price varies. illus.; maps. back issues avail. **Document type:** *Monographic series, Academic/Scholarly.* **Description:** Popular information on archaeology, cultural heritage, and environment in Rogaland, S.W. Norway, along with museum catalogues.
Indexed: NAA.
—CCC.

Published by: Arkeologisk museum i Stavanger/Museum of Archaeology, Stavanger, Postboks 478, Stavanger, 4002, Norway. TEL 47-51-846000, FAX 47-51-846199, ams@ark.museum.no, http://www.ark.museum.no/5_andre_publtilbud/forlag-sett.htm.

930.1 NOR ISSN 0803-5903
A M S - TILVEKST. (Arkeologisk museum i Stavanger) Text in Norwegian. 1991. irreg., latest vol.5, 1994. price varies. bibl. back issues avail. **Document type:** *Catalog, Academic/Scholarly.* **Description:** Catalogue of the museum's acquisitions.
Published by: Arkeologisk museum i Stavanger/Museum of Archaeology, Stavanger, Postboks 478, Stavanger, 4002, Norway. TEL 47-51-846000, FAX 47-51-846199, ams@ark.museum.no, http://www.ark.museum.no.

913 NOR ISSN 0332-6306
A M S - VARIA. Text in Norwegian; Summaries in English. 1978. irreg., latest vol.39, 2002. price varies. abstr.; bibl.; illus.; maps. 2 cols./p.; back issues avail. **Document type:** *Monographic series, Academic/Scholarly.* **Description:** Research papers and reports dealing with prehistoric man and his environment in southwest Norway.
Indexed: NAA.
—CCC.
Published by: Arkeologisk museum i Stavanger/Museum of Archaeology, Stavanger, Postboks 478, Stavanger, 4002, Norway. TEL 47-51-846000, FAX 47-51-846199, ams@ark.museum.no, http://www.ark.museum.no.

A R A M. see *ASIAN STUDIES*

917 USA
A S M INK. Text in English. 1964. m. Membership (effective 2003). bk.rev. **Document type:** *Newsletter, Academic/Scholarly.* **Description:** Provides information for the member of the Society and contains the latest archeological news in Maryland, field and lab projects needing volunteers, upcoming meetings, workshops, and talks, chapter news...legislation and other action affecting archeology and more.
Formerly: Archaeological Society of Maryland. Newsletter
Published by: Archeological Society of Maryland, Inc., PO Box 65001, Baltimore, MD 21209-5001. TEL 410-664-9060, 410-747-1973, ngeasey@netcrafters.net, http://www.smcm.edu/academics/soan/asm/home.htm. Ed. Lois Nutwell. Circ: 360. **Subscr. to:** 716 Country Club Road, Havre de Grace, MD 21078-2104.

930.1 FRA ISSN 0244-8327
DT379.5
ABBAY. Text in French. 1977. irreg. price varies. adv. bk.rev. index.
Indexed: BHA.
Published by: C N R S Editions, 15 Rue Malebranche, Paris, 75005, France. TEL 33-1-53102700, FAX 33-1-53102727, http://www.cnrseditions.fr. Circ: 1,500 (controlled).

ACADEMIA ROMANA. SECTIA DE STIINTE ISTORICE SI ARHEOLOGIE. MEMORIILE. see *HISTORY—History Of Europe*

ACADEMIA SINICA. INSTITUTE OF HISTORY AND PHILOLOGY. BULLETIN. see *HISTORY—History Of Asia*

ACADEMIE DES INSCRIPTIONS ET BELLES-LETTRES. ETUDES ET COMMENTAIRES. see *LINGUISTICS*

913 POL ISSN 0079-3566
➤ **ACADEMIE POLONAISE DES SCIENCES. CENTRE D'ARCHEOLOGIE MEDITERRANEENNE. ETUDES ET TRAVAUX.** Text in English, French, German, Italian. 1966. irreg., latest vol.17, 1995. price varies. illus. **Document type:** *Academic/Scholarly.* **Description:** Covers archaeology of the Mediterranean, particularly Egypt, Syria, Cyprus, Nubia.
Indexed: BHA.
Published by: Polska Akademia Nauk, Zaklad Archeologii Srodziemnomorskiej, Ul Nowy Swiat 72, pok. 33, Warsaw, 00330, Poland. TEL 48-22-8266560, FAX 48-22-8266560. Ed. Maciej Witkowski. Circ: 185. **Dist. by:** Osrodek Rozpowszechniania Wydawnictw Naukowych PAN, Palac Kultury i Nauki, Warsaw 00901, Poland. FAX 48-22-8268670.
Co-sponsor: State Committee for Scientific Research.

930.1 POL ISSN 0554-5927
➤ **ACADEMIE POLONAISE DES SCIENCES. CENTRE D'ARCHEOLOGIE MEDITERRANEENNE. TRAVAUX.** Text in English, French. 1959. irreg., latest vol.33, 1995. price varies. **Document type:** *Monographic series, Academic/Scholarly.* **Description:** Studies in the archaeology, anthropology and ancient art of the Mediterranean.
Published by: Polska Akademia Nauk, Zaklad Archeologii Srodziemnomorskiej, Ul Nowy Swiat 72, pok. 33, Warsaw, 00330, Poland. TEL 48-22-8266560, FAX 48-22-8266560. Ed. Barbara Lichocka. **Dist. by:** Osrodek Rozpowszechniania Wydawnictw Naukowych PAN, Palac Kultury i Nauki, Warsaw 00901, Poland. FAX 48-22-8268670.

➤ **ACCADEMIA NAZIONALE VIRGILIANA DI SCIENZE LETTERE ED ARTI. ATTI E MEMORIE.** see *HISTORY—History Of Europe*

930.1 GBR ISSN 0968-1116
➤ **ACCORDIA RESEARCH PAPERS.** Text in English. 1990. a., latest vol.8. GBP 30 to individuals; GBP 40 to institutions (effective 2002). back issues avail. **Document type:** *Academic/Scholarly.* **Description:** Deals with all aspects of the development of Italy from prehistory to the pre-industrial period, with archaeology and ancient history as the main focus.
Indexed: BHA.
Published by: University of London, Accordia Research Institute, 31-34 Gordon Sq, London, WC1H 0AH, United Kingdom. TEL 44-20-7679-1532, FAX 44-1784-741602, accordiaa@ntlworld.com. R&P John B Wilkins.

930.1 GBR ISSN 1366-0969
➤ **ACCORDIA SPECIALIST STUDIES ON ITALY.** Text in English. 1992. irreg., latest vol.9, 2000. back issues avail. **Document type:** *Monographic series, Academic/Scholarly.* **Description:** Consists of monographs on a variety of topics within Italian archaeology and the history of ancient Italy.
Published by: University of London, Accordia Research Institute, 31-34 Gordon Sq, London, WC1H 0AH, United Kingdom. TEL 44-20-7679-1532, FAX 44-1784-741602, accordiaa@ntlworld.com. Ed. Ruth Whitehouse. R&P John B Wilkins.

➤ **ACHAEMENID HISTORY.** see *HISTORY—History Of The Near East*

913 ITA ISSN 0065-0900
N1.A1
ACTA AD ARCHAEOLOGIAM ET ARTIUM HISTORIAM PERTINENTIA. 1962. irreg., latest vol.11, 1995. price varies. **Document type:** *Monographic series, Academic/Scholarly.*
Indexed: A&ATA, AIAP, BHA.
Published by: (Istituto di Norvegia in Roma), Giorgio Bretschneider, Casella Postale 30011, Rm47, Rome, 00193, Italy. info@bretschneider.it. Ed. J Rasmus Brandt. Circ: 700.

938 ITA ISSN 0333-1512
ACTA AD ARCHAEOLOGIAM ET ARTIUM HISTORIAM PERTINENTIA (MISCELLANEOUS). Text in Italian. 1981. irreg., latest vol.8, 1992. price varies. illus. back issues avail. **Document type:** *Academic/Scholarly.*
Indexed: A&ATA, AIAP, BHA.
Published by: (Istituto di Norvegia in Roma), Giorgio Bretschneider, Casella Postale 30011, Rm47, Rome, 00193, Italy. info@bretschneider.it.

930.1 DNK ISSN 0065-101X
CC1
➤ **ACTA ARCHAEOLOGICA.** Text in English, German. 1930. a., latest vol.76, no.1, 2005. USD 124 combined subscription to institutions in the Americas & the Caribbean for print & online eds.; GBP 74 combined subscription elsewhere to institutions print & online eds.; EUR 56 combined subscription in Europe to students print & online eds.; USD 62 combined subscription to students in the Americas & the Caribbean for print & online eds.; GBP 37 combined subscription elsewhere to students print & online eds. (effective 2006). adv. bk.rev. illus. reprint service avail. from ISI. **Document type:** *Journal, Academic/Scholarly.*
Related titles: Online - full text ed.: ISSN 1600-0390. USD 118 in the Americas to institutions & Caribbean; GBP 70 elsewhere to institutions (effective 2006) (from Blackwell Synergy, EBSCO Publishing, IngentaConnect, Swets Information Services).
Indexed: AIAP, AICP, AbAn, AnthLit, ArtHuCI, BHA, BrArAb, CurCont, IndIslam, NAA, NumL, RASB, SSCI.
—CCC.
Published by: Blackwell Munksgaard (Subsidiary of: Blackwell Publishing Ltd.), Rosenoerns Alle 1, PO Box 227, Copenhagen V, 1502, Denmark. TEL 45-77-333333, FAX 45-77-333377, customerservice@munksgaard.dk, http://www.blackwellpublishing.com/journals/AAR, http://www.blackwellmunksgaard.com. Ed. Klavs Randsborg TEL 45-3532-4111. Circ: 650.

913 HUN ISSN 0001-5210
DB920 CODEN: ACGCBJ
ACTA ARCHAEOLOGICA ACADEMIAE SCIENTIARUM HUNGARICAE. Text mainly in English, German, French; Text occasionally in Italian, Russian. 1951. q. USD 324 (effective 2006). adv. bk.rev. bibl.; charts; illus.; abstr. index. 120 p./no.; **Document type:** *Journal, Academic/Scholarly.* **Description:** Covers studies of the most important excavations, finds and problems of the period from the Paleolithic to the Middle Ages. Includes short papers on individual finds.
Related titles: Online - full text ed.: ISSN 1588-2551 (from EBSCO Publishing, Swets Information Services).
Indexed: AIAP, AICP, ASCA, AnthLit, BHA, BiolAb, BrArAb, CurCont, DIP, IBR, IBZ, NumL, PCI, RASB, SSCI.
—BLDSC (0596.320000), IE, Infotrieve. **CCC.**
Published by: (Magyar Tudomanyos Akademia/Hungarian Academy of Sciences), Akademiai Kiado Rt. (Subsidiary of: Wolters Kluwer N.V.), Prielle Kornelia U. 19, Budapest, 1117, Hungary. TEL 36-1-4648282, FAX 36-1-4648221, journals@akkrt.hu, http://www.akkrt.hu. Ed. Denes Gabler.

913 POL ISSN 0001-5229
DB350
ACTA ARCHAEOLOGICA CARPATHICA. Text in English, German, Polish, Russian; Summaries in English, French, German, Polish. 1958. a. price varies. bk.rev. **Document type:** *Academic/Scholarly.* **Description:** Prehistory and Early Middle Ages of the Carpathian countries, transcarpathian cultural relations, problems of mountain archaeology.
Indexed: AnthLit, BHA, BrArAb, IBR, NumL, RASB.
—KNAW.
Published by: (Polska Akademia Nauk, Oddzial w Krakowie, Komisja Archeologiczna), Polska Akademia Nauk, Oddzial w Krakowie, ul sw Jana 28, Krakow, 31018, Poland. TEL 48-12-224853, FAX 48-12-222791. Ed. Zenon Wozniak.

913 POL ISSN 0065-0986
ACTA ARCHAEOLOGICA LODZIENSIA. Text in Polish; Summaries in English, French. 1937. a., latest vol.47. USD 59 (effective 2000). bk.rev. **Document type:** *Monographic series.*
Indexed: NumL.
—KNAW.
Published by: Lodzkie Towarzystwo Naukowe/Lodz Scientific Society, ul. M. Sklodowskiej-Curie 11, Lodz, 90-505, Poland. TEL 48-42-6361026, FAX 48-42-6361995. Ed. Witold Swietostawski. **Dist. by:** Ars Polona, Krakowskie Przedmiescie 7, Warsaw, Poland.

930.1 BEL ISSN 0776-2984
ACTA ARCHAEOLOGICA LOVANIENSIA - MONOGRAPHIAE. Text in English, French, German. 1962; N.S. 1989. irreg., latest vol.13, 2001. price varies. bk.rev. charts; illus.; maps. back issues avail. **Document type:** *Monographic series, Academic/Scholarly.*
Indexed: AnthLit, BHA, BrArAb, NumL.
Published by: (Katholieke Universiteit Leuven, Afdeling Archeologie en Kunstwetenschap), Leuven University Press, Blijde Inkomststraat 5, Leuven, 3000, Belgium. TEL 32-16-325345, FAX 32-16-325352, university.press@upers.kuleuven.ac.be, http://www.kuleuven.ac.be/upers. Ed. A Provoost. Circ: 450.

913 SWE ISSN 0065-1001
ACTA ARCHAEOLOGICA LUNDENSIA: MONOGRAPHS OF LUNDS UNIVERSITETS HISTORISKA MUSEUM. SERIES IN 4. Text in English, German. 1954. irreg. price varies. bk.rev. back issues avail. **Document type:** *Monographic series, Academic/Scholarly.*
Indexed: AnthLit.
Published by: (Lunds Universitet/Lund University, Historiska Museum), Almqvist & Wiksell International, P O Box 7634, Stockholm, 10394, Sweden. FAX 46-8-24-25-43, info@city.akadmibokhandeln.se, http://www.akademibokhandeln.se.

571 SWE ISSN 0065-0994
ACTA ARCHAEOLOGICA LUNDENSIA: MONOGRAPHS OF LUNDS UNIVERSITETS HISTORISKA MUSEUM. SERIES IN 8. Text in English, German, Swedish. 1957. irreg. price varies. bk.rev. back issues avail. **Document type:** *Monographic series, Academic/Scholarly.*
Indexed: AnthLit, NAA.
Published by: (Lunds Universitet/Lund University, Historiska Museum), Almqvist & Wiksell International, P O Box 7634, Stockholm, 10394, Sweden. FAX 46-8-24-25-43, info@city.akadmibokhandeln.se, http://www.akademibokhandeln.se. Ed. Berta Stjernquist.

913 CHE ISSN 0065-1052
ACTA BERNENSIA: BEITRAEGE ZUR PRAEHISTORISCHEN, KLASSISCHEN UND JUENGEREN ARCHAEOLOGIE. Text in German. 1963. irreg. price varies. **Document type:** *Monographic series, Academic/Scholarly.*
Indexed: BrArAb.
—CCC.
Published by: Staempfli Verlag AG (Subsidiary of: LexisNexis Europe and Africa), Woelflistr 1, Bern, 3001, Switzerland. TEL 41-31-3006666, FAX 41-31-3006688, verlag@staempfli.com, http://www.staempfli.com. Eds. H Mueller Beck, H G Bandi.

913 940 ESP ISSN 0212-2960
ACTA HISTORICA ET ARCHAEOLOGICA MEDIAEVALIA. Text in Spanish. 1980. a. adv. bk.rev. **Document type:** *Journal, Academic/Scholarly.*
Indexed: BHA, IndIslam, RILM.
—CINDOC.
Published by: (Universitat de Barcelona, Departament de Historia Medieval, Paleografia y Diplomatica), Universitat de Barcelona, Servei de Publicacions, Gran Via Corts Catalanes 585, Barcelona, 08007, Spain. TEL 34-93-4021100, http://www.publicacions.ub.es. Eds. Manuel Riu, Salvador Claramunt. Circ: 1,000.

937 DNK ISSN 0904-2067
DE1
➤ **ACTA HYPERBOREA;** Danish studies in classical archaeology. Text in English. 1988. irreg., latest vol.10, 2002. USD 74 per issue elsewhere to individuals (effective 2005). bk.rev. illus. back issues avail. **Document type:** *Monographic series, Academic/Scholarly.* **Description:** Covers, in thematic issues, important aspects of classical archaeology.
Indexed: DIP, IBR, IBZ.
—CCC.

Published by: (Collegium Hyperboreum), Museum Tusculanum Press, c/o University of Copenhagen, Njalsgade 94, Copenhagen S, 2300, Denmark. TEL 45-35-329109, FAX 45-35-329113, mtp@mtp.dk, http://www.mtp.dk. Eds. Marjatta Nielsen, Pia Guldager Bilde, Tobias Fischer-Hansen, Annette Rathje.

➤ **ACTA MUSEI MORAVIAE. SCIENTIAE SOCIALES/ MORAVSKE ZEMSKE MUZEUM. CASOPIS. VEDY SPOLECENSKE.** see *HISTORY—History Of Europe*

913 900 400 SWE ISSN 0347-5123
ACTA REGIAE SOCIETATIS HUMANIORUM LITTERARUM LUNDENSIS. Text in English, French, German, Swedish. 1960. irreg. price varies. **Document type:** *Monographic series, Academic/Scholarly.*
Published by: Almqvist & Wiksell International, P O Box 7634, Stockholm, 10394, Sweden. FAX 46-8-24-25-43, info@city.akademibokhandeln.se, http://www.akademibokhandeln.se. Ed. Berta Stjernquist.

913 CHE
ACTA REI CRETARIAE ROMANAE FAUTORUM. SUPPLEMENTA. Text in Undetermined. 1974. irreg., latest vol.7, 1990. CHF 15. **Document type:** *Monographic series.*
Published by: Rei Cretariae Romanae Fautorum, c/o Katrin Roth-Rubi, Lorrainestr 32, Bern, 3013, Switzerland.

930.107 POL ISSN 0208-6034
DK4088
ACTA UNIVERSITATIS LODZIENSIS: FOLIA ARCHAEOLOGICA. Text in Polish; Summaries in Multiple languages. 1955-1974; N.S. 1980. irreg. **Document type:** *Academic/Scholarly.*
Description: Presents articles concerning studies on settlement, culture, and the environmental background of settlement development. Studies cover prehistoric times and the Middle Ages, mainly in northern Poland.
Supersedes in part: Uniwersytet Lodzki. Zeszyty Naukowe. Seria 1: Nauki Humanistyczno-Spoleczne (0076-0358)
Indexed: AIAP, AICP, AnthLit, BHA.
—KNAW.
Published by: Wydawnictwo Uniwersytetu Lodzkiego/Lodz University Press, ul Jaracza 34, Lodz, 90262, Poland. TEL 336541. **Dist. by:** Ars Polona, Krakowskie Przedmiescie 7, Warsaw, Poland.

913 POL ISSN 0137-6616
DK409
ACTA UNIVERSITATIS NICOLAI COPERNICI. NAUKI HUMANISTYCZNO-SPOLECZNE. ARCHEOLOGIA. Text in Polish. 1968. irreg. price varies. **Document type:** *Academic/Scholarly.*
Formerly (until 1973): Uniwersytet Mikolaja Kopernika w Torun. Nauki Humanistyczno-Spoleczne. Zeszyty Naukowe. Archeologia (0083-4467)
Indexed: AnthLit, BHA, RASB.
Published by: Uniwersytet Mikolaja Kopernika/Nicolaus Copernicus University, Wydawnictwo, ul Gagarina 39, Torun, 87100, Poland. TEL 48-56-14295. **Dist. by:** Osrodek Rozpowszechniania Wydawnictw Naukowych PAN, Palac Kultury i Nauki, Warsaw 00901, Poland.

ACTA UNIVERSITATIS SZEGEDIENSIS. ACTA ANTIQUA ET ARCHAEOLOGICA. see *CLASSICAL STUDIES*

913 POL ISSN 0081-6302
GN705
ACTA UNIVERSITATIS WRATISLAVIENSIS. STUDIA ARCHEOLOGICZNE. Text in Polish; Summaries in English. irreg. price varies. charts; illus. **Document type:** *Academic/Scholarly.*
Formerly (until 1965): Uniwersytet Wroclawski im. Boleslawa Bieruta. Zeszyty Naukowe. Seria A: Nauki Humanistyczne (0520-9234)
Indexed: AnthLit, NumL.
Published by: (Uniwersytet Wroclawski), Wydawnictwo Uniwersytetu Wroclawskiego Spolka z o.o., Pl Uniwersytecki 9-13, Wroclaw, 50-137, Poland. TEL 48-71-441076, FAX 48-71-402735. Ed. Wlodzimierz Wojciechowski. Circ: 300.

903 930.1 SWE ISSN 0349-8808
ADORANTEN. Text in English, German, Swedish, Danish, Norwegian. 1978. a. SEK 100, USD 15 (effective 2003). adv. bk.rev. 104 p./no. 2 cols./p.; back issues avail. **Document type:** *Bulletin.* **Description:** Presents articles and information on pre-historic rock carvings, primarily in Scandinavia.
Indexed: NAA.
Published by: Scandinavian Society for Prehistoric Art, Rock Art Museum Tanum, Underslos, Tanumshede, 45791, Sweden. TEL 45-4587-4350, FAX 46-525-29555, adorant@bigfoot.com, http://www.ssfpa.se. Ed. Gerhard Milstreu. Circ: 1,200.

930.1 SAU ISSN 1319-8947
ADUMATU; a semi-annual archaeological refereed journal on the Arab World. Text in English, Arabic. 2000 (Jan.). 2/yr. SAR 70 domestic to individuals; USD 30 foreign to individuals; SAR 120 domestic to institutions; USD 45 foreign to institutions (effective 2005).
—BLDSC (0696.684930).
Published by: Adumatu Journal, P O Box 10071, Riyadh, 11433, Saudi Arabia. TEL 966-1-4125266, FAX 966-1-4022545, adumatu@suhuf.net.sa, http://www.adumatu.com.

930.1 560 USA ISSN 1567-7982
ADVANCES IN ARCHAEOLOGICAL AND MUSEUM SCIENCE. Text in English. 1992. irreg., latest vol.5, 2001. price varies. back issues avail. **Document type:** *Monographic series.*
Indexed: BrArAb.
Published by: (Society for Archaeological Sciences), Springer-Verlag New York, Inc. (Subsidiary of: Springer Science+Business Media), 233 Spring St, New York, NY 10013. TEL 212-460-1500, FAX 212-460-1575, service@springer-ny.com, http://www.springer-ny.com. Eds. E V Sayre, M J Aitken, R E Taylor, R H Tykot.

913 AUT ISSN 1015-5104
DT57
AEGYPTEN UND LEVANTE/EGYPT AND THE LEVANT. Text in German. 1990. a. EUR 84 (effective 2003). 200 p./no.; **Document type:** *Yearbook, Academic/Scholarly.* **Description:** Covers archaeological research in Egypt and the Levant.
Indexed: DIP, IBR, IBZ.
Published by: (Universitaet Wien, Institut fuer Aegyptologie), Verlag der Oesterreichischen Akademie der Wissenschaften, Postgasse 7/4, Vienna, W 1011, Austria. TEL 43-1-515813402, FAX 43-1-515813400, verlag@oeaw.ac.at, http://verlag.oeaw.ac.at. **Co-sponsor:** Oesterreichisches Archaeologisches Institut Kairo.

AEGYPTIACA COMPLUTENSIA. see *HISTORY—History Of The Near East*

913 CHE ISSN 1017-5474
AEGYPTICA HELVETICA. Text in French. 1974. irreg., latest vol.10. price varies. **Document type:** *Monographic series, Academic/Scholarly.*
Published by: (Universite de Geneve, Faculte des Lettres), Editions Medecine et Hygiene, 78 avenue de la Rosaraie, Case Postale 456, Geneva 4, 1211, Switzerland. TEL 41-22-7029311, FAX 41-22-7029355, abonnements@medhyg.ch, http://www.medhyg.ch. Ed. Robert Hari. Circ: 600. **Co-sponsor:** Universitaet Basel.

932 ITA ISSN 0001-9046
PA3339
AEGYPTUS; rivista italiana di egittologia e di papirologia. Text in English, French, German. 1920. s-a. EUR 104 domestic; EUR 146 foreign (effective 2003). adv. bk.rev. bibl.; charts; illus.; stat. cum.index: vols.1-50 (1920-1970). **Document type:** *Academic/Scholarly.* **Description:** Publishes scientific articles on the study of ancient Egypt; its culture, people, history and other related areas.
Related titles: Online - full text ed.: (from Chadwyck-Healey Inc.).
Indexed: BHA, BibInd, BibLing, DIP, IBR, IBZ, IndIslam, MLA, MLA-IB, NTA, NumL, OTA, RASB.
Published by: (Universita Cattolica del Sacro Cuore), Vita e Pensiero, Largo Gemelli 1, Milan, 20123, Italy. TEL 39-02-72342335, FAX 39-02-72342260, redazione.vp@mi.unicatt.it. Ed. Orsolina Montevecchi. Circ: 800.

930.1 770 GBR ISSN 0140-9220
DA670.E13
AERIAL ARCHAEOLOGY. Text in English; Summaries in English, French, German. 1977. irreg. price varies. bk.rev. **Document type:** *Academic/Scholarly.*
Indexed: BrArAb, NumL.
Published by: Aerial Archaeology Publications, Lansdown, 3 Breton Close, E. Dereham, Norfolk NR19 1JH, United Kingdom. TEL 44-1362-695835. Ed. Derek A Edwards.

930.1 526.982 USA
THE AERIAL ARCHAEOLOGY NEWSLETTER. Text in English. 1996. q. **Document type:** *Newsletter.* **Description:** Contains discussions of archaeological data gathered from aircraft, satellites, or remote sensors on the ground.
Media: Online - full text.
Published by: Aerial Archaeology Newsletter jaybird@nmia.com, http://www.nmia.com/~jaybird/AAnewsletter/. Ed. Tom Baker.

AEVUM ANTIQUUM; Istituto di Filologia Classica e di Papirologia. see *CLASSICAL STUDIES*

930.1 960 USA ISSN 0263-0338
DT13 CODEN: AAREF2
➤ **AFRICAN ARCHAEOLOGICAL REVIEW.** Text in English. 1983-1994; resumed 1996. q. EUR 278, USD 288, GBP 177 combined subscription to institutions print & online eds. (effective 2005). adv. bk.rev. illus. back issues avail.; reprint service avail. from PSC. **Document type:** *Journal, Academic/Scholarly.* **Description:** Publishes articles on all aspects of the archaeology of Africa and neighboring islands, including new field data and discussions of interregional processes, cultural transitions, and Africa's place in world archaeology.
Related titles: Microform ed.: (from PQC); Online - full text ed.: ISSN 1572-9842 (from EBSCO Publishing, Gale Group, IngentaConnect, Kluwer Online, O C L C Online Computer Library Center, Inc., Springer LINK, Swets Information Services).
Indexed: AICP, ASD, AbAn, AnthLit, BibLing, DIP, HumInd, IBR, IBZ, IndIslam, PCI, RASB.
—BLDSC (0732.314000), IE, Infotrieve, ingenta. **CCC.**
Published by: (Society of Africanist Archaeologists), Plenum US (Subsidiary of: Springer Science+Business Media), 233 Spring St, New York, NY 10013. TEL 212-460-1500, FAX 212-460-1575, service@springer-ny.com, http://springerlink.metapress.com/openurl.asp?genre=journal&issn=0263-0338, http://www.springeronline.com. Ed. Fekri A Hassan.

➤ **AFRICAN OCCASIONAL PAPERS SERIES.** see *ANTHROPOLOGY*

➤ **AKADEMIYA NAUK GRUZII. IZVESTIYA. SERIYA ISTORII, ETNOGRAFII I ISTORII ISKUSSTVA.** see *HISTORY—History Of Europe*

935.03 BEL ISSN 1378-5087
AKKADICA. Text in English, Flemish, French. 1977. s-a. bk.rev. **Document type:** *Bulletin, Academic/Scholarly.*
Formerly (until 2000) Semi-monthly: Akkadica (0772-1331)
Related titles: ♦ Supplement to: Akkadica Plus. ISSN 0779-7842.
Indexed: BibInd, BibLing, DIP, IBR, IBZ.
Published by: Fondation Assyriologique Georges Dossin/Assyriological Foundation Georges Dossin, Parc du Cinquantenaire 10, Brussels, 1000, Belgium. TEL 32-2-741-7374, FAX 32-2-734-0713, akkadica@kmkg-mrah.be, http://www.akkadica.org/periodical.htm. Eds. Denyse Homes-Fredericq, Leon De Meyer.

935.03 BEL ISSN 0779-7842
AKKADICA PLUS. Text in English, French, German. 1984. bi-m. price varies. back issues avail. **Document type:** *Monographic series.*
Related titles: ♦ Supplement(s): Akkadica. ISSN 1378-5087.
Published by: Fondation Assyriologique Georges Dossin/Assyriological Foundation Georges Dossin, Parc du Cinquantenaire 10, Brussels, 1000, Belgium. TEL 32-2-741-7373, FAX 32-2-733-7735, akkadica@kmkg-mrah.be, http://www.akkadica.org/akkplus.htm.

930.1 DNK ISSN 1603-2861
AKTUEL ARKAEOLOGI. Text in Danish. 1994. q. DKK 248; DKK 175 to students (effective 2005). back issues avail. **Document type:** *Magazine, Consumer.*
Former titles (until 2003): Arkaeologi for Alle (1600-9304); (until 2000): S D A Nyt (1396-416X)
Published by: (Sammenslutningen af Danske Amatoerarkaeologer/Association of Danish Amateur Archaeologists), Dahls Forlag, Ny Vordingborgvej 37, Kalvehale, 4771, Denmark. TEL 45-55-380095, redaktionen@aktuelarkaeologi.dk, mail@dahlsforlag.dk, http://www.aktuelarkaeologi.dk/. Eds. Joergen Holm, Henrik Dahl.

917 USA
ALABAMA ARCHAEOLOGICAL SOCIETY. SPECIAL PUBLICATION. Text in English. 1974. irreg. reprint service avail. from PQC. **Document type:** *Academic/Scholarly.*
Related titles: Microform ed.: (from PQC).
Published by: Alabama Archaeological Society, 13075 Moundville Archaeological Park, Moundville, AL 35474. TEL 205-371-2266, FAX 205-371-2494. Ed. Bart Hanson. Circ: 500.

913 ITA ISSN 0394-9427
ALBA POMPEIA; rivista semestrale di studi storici artistici e naturalistici per Alba e territori connessi. Text in Italian; Summaries in English, French. 1908. s-a. EUR 19, USD 35 (effective 2002). bk.rev. bibl. cum.index: 1908-1989. 120 p./no.; back issues avail. **Document type:** *Bulletin.*
Indexed: BHA, DIP, IBR, IBZ.
Published by: Comune di Alba, Museo Civico "Federico Eusebio", Via Paruzza, 1-a, Alba, CN 12051, Italy. TEL 39-0173-290092, FAX 39-0173-362075, ch0002@biblioteche.regione.piemonte.it. Ed. Gianfranco Maggi. Circ: 500 (controlled).

301 CAN ISSN 0701-1776
F1076.9
ALBERTA ARCHAEOLOGICAL REVIEW. Text in English. 1977. s-a. CND 15 (effective 2001). adv. bk.rev. **Document type:** *Academic/Scholarly.*
Supersedes: Archaeological Society of Alberta. Newsletter
Indexed: AICP, AmH&L, AnthLit, HistAb.
Published by: Archaeological Society of Alberta, c/o Jim McMurchy, 97 Eton Rd West, Lethbridge, AB T1K 4T9, Canada. TEL 403-329-2524. Ed. M C Wilson. Circ: 400.

913 USA ISSN 0002-4953
ALBUQUERQUE ARCHAEOLOGICAL SOCIETY NEWSLETTER. Text in English. 1966. m. USD 15 to individuals; USD 8 to institutions (effective 2003). bk.rev. bibl.; illus. back issues avail. **Document type:** *Newsletter.* **Description:** Covers current activities of AAS and feature articles of interest.
Media: Duplicated (not offset).
Published by: Albuquerque Archaeological Society, PO Box 4029, Albuquerque, NM 87196. Ed. Joan Fenicle. Circ: 225.

917 USA ISSN 0894-2625
ALEXANDRIA ARCHAEOLOGY VOLUNTEER NEWS. Text in English. 1982. m. USD 20 (effective 2001). bk.rev. illus. 8 p./no.; **Document type:** *Newsletter.* **Description:** Covers the urban archaeology program of Alexandria, VA, including volunteer opportunities, current digs, local seminars and field trips, and local history.
Published by: Friends of Alexandria Archaeology, 105 N Union St, Alexandria, VA 22314. TEL 703-838-4399, FAX 703-838-6491, ruth.reeder@ci.alexandria.va.us, http://www.alexandriaarchaeology.org. Ed. Tim Dennie. R&P Ruth Reeder. Circ: 550. **Subscr. to:** PO Box 21475, Alexandria, VA 22320.

ALLE TIDERS ODSHERRED. see *HISTORY—History Of Europe*

930.1 DEU
ALMANACH. Text in German. 1997. irreg., latest vol.8, 2002. price varies. **Document type:** *Monographic series, Academic/Scholarly.*
Published by: (Archaeologisches Landesmuseum Baden-Wuerttemberg), Konrad Theiss Verlag GmbH, Moenchhaldenstr 28, Stuttgart, 70191, Germany. TEL 49-711-255270, FAX 49-711-2552717, service@theiss.de, http://www.theiss.de.

ALTERTUMSKUNDE DES VORDEREN ORIENTS. see *ASIAN STUDIES*

AMALTHEIA. see *HISTORY—History Of Europe*

930.1 USA ISSN 1551-823X
AMERICAN ANTHROPOLOGICAL ASSOCIATION. ARCHAEOLOGICAL PAPERS. Text in English. 1987. s-a. USD 24 (effective 2006). adv. **Document type:** *Monographic series, Academic/Scholarly.*
Related titles: Online - full text ed.: ISSN 1551-8248.
Indexed: AnthLit.
—CCC.
Published by: (American Anthropological Association), University of California Press, Journals Division, 2000 Center St, Ste 303, Berkeley, CA 94704-1223. TEL 510-643-7154, FAX 510-642-9917, journals@ucpress.edu, http://www.aaanet.org/ad/book.htm, http://www.ucpress.edu/journals. Ed. Jay K. Johnson. adv.: page USD 350; 7 x 9.3.

913 USA ISSN 0002-7316
E51 CODEN: AANTAM
➤ **AMERICAN ANTIQUITY.** Text in English. 1935. q. free to members (effective 2000). adv. bk.rev. charts; illus. index, cum.index. back issues avail.; reprints avail. **Document type:** *Journal, Academic/Scholarly.* **Description:** Publishes original articles on the archaeology of the New World and related topics, along with research reports and commentary.
Related titles: Microform ed.; Online - full text ed.: (from Florida Center for Library Automation, Gale Group, JSTOR (Web-based Journal Archive), Northern Light Technology, Inc.).
Indexed: AICP, ASCA, AbAn, AmH&L, AmHI, AnthLit, ArtHuCI, ArtInd, BHA, BRI, BrArAb, CBRI, CIS, ChemAb, CurCont, HAPI, HistAb, HumInd, IBR, MEA&I, NumL, PCI, RASB, SFA, SSCI, SportS.
—BLDSC (0810.300000), IDS, IE, Infotrieve, ingenta. **CCC.**
Published by: Society for American Archaeology, 900 Second St, N W, 12, Washington, DC 20002-3557. TEL 202-789-8200, FAX 202-789-0284, publications@saa.org, http://www.saa.org/Publications/AmAntiq/amantiq.html. Ed. Timothy Kohler. R&P Elizabeth Foxwell. Adv. contact Rick Peterson. Circ: 6,400.

930.1 USA ISSN 1093-8400
E159.5
➤ **AMERICAN ARCHAEOLOGY;** a quarterly publication of the Archaeological Conservancy. Text in English. 1980. q. USD 25; USD 3.95 newsstand/cover (effective 2005). adv. bk.rev. illus. 48 p./no.; back issues avail.; reprints avail. **Document type:** *Journal, Academic/Scholarly.* **Description:** Devoted to presenting and preserving the rich diversity of archaeology in the Americas. Helps readers understand and appreciate the archaeological wonders available to them.
Formerly (until 1997): Archaeological Conservancy Newsletter
Indexed: AbAn, AnthLit, BHA, BiolDig.
Published by: Archaeological Conservancy, 5301 Central Ave, NE, Ste 902, Albuquerque, NM 87108-1517. TEL 505-266-1540, FAX 505-266-0311, tacinfo@nm.net, http://www.americanarchaeology.com, http://www.americanarchaeology.org. Ed., R&P, Adv. contact Michael Bawaya. Circ: 35,000 (paid).

913 USA ISSN 0740-8358
AMERICAN ARCHEOLOGY. Text in English. 3/yr. free membership (effective 2005). **Document type:** *Journal.*
Indexed: AmH&L, AnthLit.
Published by: The Archeological Conservancy, 5301 Central Ave N E, Ste 902, Albuquerque, NM 87108-1517. TEL 505-266-1540, tacmag@nm.net, http://www.americanarchaeology.com/. Ed. Michael Bawaya TEL 505-266-9668. Adv. contact Marcia Ulibarri TEL 505-344-6018.

913 USA ISSN 0002-9114
CC1
➤ **AMERICAN JOURNAL OF ARCHAEOLOGY.** Text in English. 1885. q. USD 75 domestic to individuals; USD 95 foreign to individuals; USD 250 domestic to institutions; USD 290 foreign to institutions; USD 47 domestic to students; USD 67 foreign to students (effective 2005). adv. bk.rev. charts; illus.; maps; abstr.; bibl. index. back issues avail.; reprints avail. **Document type:** *Journal, Academic/Scholarly.* **Description:** Presents scholarly essays on archaeology of ancient Europe and the Mediterranean from prehistoric times to Late Antiquity.
Formerly (until 1896): American Journal of Archaeology and of the History of the Fine Arts (1540-5079)
Related titles: Microfilm ed.: (from PMC, PQC); Online - full content ed.: free (effective 2004); Online - full text ed.: (from JSTOR (Web-based Journal Archive)).
Indexed: ABS&EES, AIAP, AICP, ASCA, AbAn, AmHI, AnthLit, ArtHuCI, ArtInd, BAS, BHA, BRD, BRI, BibLing, BrArAb, CBRI, ChemAb, CurCont, DIP, HumInd, IBR, IBZ, IndIslam, MEA&I, NTA, NumL, OTA, RASB, RI-1, RI-2, SSCI.
—BLDSC (0821.200000), IE, ingenta. **CCC.**
Published by: Archaeological Institute of America (Boston), c/o Mark Kurtz, 656 Beacon St, Boston, MA 02215-2006. TEL 617-353-9364, FAX 617-353-6550, aia@aia.bu.edu, http://www.ajaonline.org/, http://www.archaeological.org. Ed. R Bruce Hitchner. Adv. contact Michael Mozina. Circ: 3,600.

916 706 USA ISSN 0065-9991
DT57
AMERICAN RESEARCH CENTER IN EGYPT. JOURNAL. Text in English, French, German. 1962. a., latest vol.38, 2001. free to members (effective 2005). bk.rev. **Document type:** *Journal, Academic/Scholarly.*
Indexed: A&ATA, BibLing, NumL, RASB.
—BLDSC (4692.200000), IE.
Published by: (American Research Center in Egypt, Inc.), Eisenbrauns, PO Box 275, Winona Lake, IN 46590-0275. TEL 574-269-2011, FAX 574-269-6788, http://www.arce.org/publications/journal.htm, http://www.eisenbrauns.com. Circ: 800.

913 USA ISSN 0732-6432
➤ **AMERICAN RESEARCH CENTER IN EGYPT. REPORTS.** Text in English. 1980. irreg., latest vol.12, 1990. price varies. bk.rev. bibl.; illus.; charts. back issues avail. **Document type:** *Monographic series, Academic/Scholarly.*
Indexed: MathR.
Published by: (American Research Center in Egypt, Inc.), Eisenbrauns, PO Box 275, Winona Lake, IN 46590-0275. FAX 574-269-6788, http://www.cisenbrauns.com, http://www.eisenbrauns.com. Ed. John L Foster.

938 GRC ISSN 0360-6651
AMERICAN SCHOOL OF CLASSICAL STUDIES AT ATHENS. ANNUAL REPORT. Text in English. 1882. a. **Document type:** *Journal, Academic/Scholarly.*
Published by: American School of Classical Studies at Athens, 54 Souidias St, Athens, 106 76, Greece. TEL 30-210-7236313, FAX 30-210-7250584, ascsa@ascsa.org, http://www.ascsa.edu.gr.

938 GRC ISSN 1105-2554
AMERICAN SCHOOL OF CLASSICAL STUDIES AT ATHENS. NEWSLETTER. Text in English. 1977. irreg. **Document type:** *Newsletter, Academic/Scholarly.*
Published by: American School of Classical Studies at Athens, 54 Souidias St, Athens, 106 76, Greece. TEL 30-210-7236313, FAX 30-210-7250584, ascsa@ascsa.org, http://www.ascsa.edu.gr.

930.1 572 USA ISSN 0066-0027
GN700
➤ **AMERICAN SCHOOL OF PREHISTORIC RESEARCH. BULLETINS.** Text in English. 1936. irreg., latest vol.45, 2001. price varies. **Document type:** *Monographic series, Academic/Scholarly.*
Indexed: BiolAb, MEA&I, RASB.
Published by: Peabody Museum of Archaeology and Ethnology, Harvard University, 11 Divinity Ave, Cambridge, MA 02138. TEL 617-496-9922, FAX 617-495-7535, ddickers@fas.harvard.edu, http://www.peabody.harvard.edu/publications. R&P Donna Dickerson TEL 617-495-3938.

➤ **AMERICAN SCHOOLS OF ORIENTAL RESEARCH. ANNUAL.** see *HISTORY—History Of The Near East*

➤ **AMERICAN SCHOOLS OF ORIENTAL RESEARCH. NEWSLETTER.** see *ASIAN STUDIES*

930.1 NLD ISSN 1543-0529
▼ **AMERICAN SCHOOLS OF PREHISTORIC RESEARCH MONOGRAPH SERIES.** Text in English. 2003. irreg. USD 49.95 per issue (effective 2004).
Published by: Brill Academic Publishers, PO Box 9000, Leiden, 2300 PA, Netherlands. TEL 31-71-53-53-500, FAX 31-71-5317531, cs@brillusa.com, cs@brill.nl, http://www.brill.nl. **Subscr. in N. America to:** PO Box 605, Herndon, VA 20172. TEL 703-661-1585, 800-337-9255, FAX 703-661-1501. **Distr. outside N. America by:** c/o Turpin Distribution, Stratton Business Park, Pegasus Drive, Biggleswade, BEDFORDSHIRE SG 18 8TQ, United Kingdom. TEL 44-1767-604-954, FAX 44-1767-601-640, brill@turpin-distribution.com.

917 USA
AMERICAN SOCIETY FOR CONSERVATION ARCHAEOLOGY. PROCEEDINGS✶. Text in English. 1976. a. USD 10. bk.rev. **Document type:** *Proceedings.*
Indexed: AnthLit.
Published by: American Society for Conservation Archaeology, c/o Joel I Klein, Ed, 118 Old Post Rd N, Croton On Hudson, NY 10520-1934. Circ: 450.

930.1 USA ISSN 0748-5107
AMERICAN SOCIETY FOR CONSERVATION ARCHAEOLOGY REPORT. Text in English. 1974. s-a. USD 20 to individuals; USD 25 to institutions. bk.rev.
Formerly: American Society for Conservation Archaeology Newsletter
Indexed: AnthLit.
Published by: American Society for Conservation Archaeology, A C A Sta 9, Eastern New Mexico University, Portales, NM 88130. FAX 505-562-2578. Ed. John Montgomery. Circ: 450.

913 USA ISSN 0003-1186
AS36.A497
➤ **AMERICAN SOCIETY OF PAPYROLOGISTS. BULLETIN.** Text in English. 1963. q. USD 35 to institutions; USD 40 foreign (effective 2000). bk.rev. back issues avail. **Document type:** *Bulletin, Academic/Scholarly.* **Description:** Publishes a wide variety of articles of relevance to papyrology and related disciplines.
Indexed: A&ATA, ASCA, ArtHuCI, BibInd, BibLing, CurCont, DIP, IBR, IBZ, NTA, PCI, RI-1, RI-2.
—IE.
Published by: American Society of Papyrologists, Dept of Classics ML 226, 410 Blegen Library, University of Cincinnati, Cincinnati, OH 45221-0226. asp@papyrology.org, http://www.papyrology.org. Ed. Traiano Gagos. Circ: 300 (paid).

930.1 NLD ISSN 1385-7347
AMSTERDAM ARCHAEOLOGICAL STUDIES. Text in English. 1996. irreg. price varies.
Indexed: MLA-IB.
Published by: Amsterdam University Press, Prinsengracht 747-751, Amsterdam, 1017 JX, Netherlands. TEL 31-20-420-0050, FAX 31-20-420-3214, info@aup.nl, http://www.aup.nl. **Subscr. to:** University of Chicago, 11030 S Langley, Chicago, IL 60628. TEL 773-568-1550, 800-621-2736, FAX 773-660-2235, 800-621-8476.

AMSTERDAM STUDIES IN CLASSICAL PHILOLOGY. see *LINGUISTICS*

930.1 FRA
AMURRU. Text in French. 1996. irreg. price varies. **Document type:** *Monographic series.*
Published by: Editions Recherche sur les Civilisations - A D P F, Les Patios Saint-Jacques, 6 rue Ferrus, Paris, Cedex 14 75603, France. TEL 33-1-43131100, FAX 33-1-43131125. Ed., Pub. Hina Descat. Circ: 600.

930.1 ARG ISSN 0325-0288
E51
➤ **ANALES DE ARQUEOLOGIA Y ETNOLOGIA.** Text in Spanish. 1940. a. USD 20 (effective 2003). bk.rev. **Document type:** *Academic/Scholarly.*
Former titles (until 1946): Anales del Instituto de Etnologia Americana; (until 1944): Anales del Instituto de Etnografia Americana
Indexed: AICP, AnthLit, HistAb.
Published by: Universidad Nacional de Cuyo, Instituto de Arqueologia y Etnologia, Casilla Correo 345, Mendoza, Argentina. TEL 54-261-4253010, FAX 54-261-4380457. Ed. Joaquin Roberto Barcena. Circ: 500.

➤ **ANATOLIA ANTIQUA/ESKI ANADOLU.** see *ASIAN STUDIES*

939.561 DEU ISSN 1345-7829
ANATOLIAN ARCHAEOLOGICAL STUDIES. Text in English. 2000. a. EUR 30 (effective 2006). **Document type:** *Journal, Academic/Scholarly.*
Formerly (until 2000): Anatoria Kokogaku Kenkyu
Published by: (Japanese Institute of Anatolian Archaeology JPN), Harrassowitz Verlag, Taunusstr 14, Wiesbaden, 65183, Germany. TEL 49-611-5300, FAX 49-611-530560, verlag@harrassowitz.de, http://www.harrassowitz.de. Adv. contact Robert Gietz.

A

939.561 GBR ISSN 1362-3567
DR431
ANATOLIAN ARCHAEOLOGY. (Related title: Anatolian Studies (ISSN 0066-1546)) Text in English. 1996. a. GBP 31.50 (effective 2000); includes subscr. to Anatolian Studies.
Description: Reports on recent British archaeological research in Turkey.
Published by: British Institute of Archaeology at Ankara, 10 Carlton House Ter, London, SW1Y 5AH, United Kingdom. biaa@britac.ac.uk, http://www.biaa.ac.uk/. Ed. Gina Coulthard.

939.561 GBR ISSN 0066-1546
DS56
➤ **ANATOLIAN STUDIES.** Text in English. 1951. a., latest 2003. GBP 25, USD 45 per vol. (effective 2005); includes subscr. to Anatolian Archaeology. index. **Document type:** *Journal, Academic/Scholarly.* **Description:** Contains articles on the archaeology and related subjects of Turkey and surrounding regions.
Related titles: Online - full text ed.
Indexed: A&ATA, AIAP, AnthLit, BHA, BibLing, IBR, IBSS, IBZ, IndIslam, NumL, PCI, RASB.
Published by: British Institute of Archaeology at Ankara, 10 Carlton House Ter, London, SW1Y 5AH, United Kingdom. TEL 44-20-79695204, FAX 44-20-79695401, biaa@britac.ac.uk, http://www.biaa.ac.uk/publications.html#anatstud. Ed. Gina Coulthard. Circ: 900 (paid).

➤ **ANATOLICA**; annuaire internationale pour les civilisations de l'Asie anterieure. see *HISTORY—History Of Asia*

913 USA ISSN 1077-1646
E75
ANCIENT AMERICAN; archaeology of the Americas before Columbus. Text in English. bi-m. USD 24.95 domestic; USD 29.95 foreign; USD 4.95 newsstand/cover domestic; CND 5.50 newsstand/cover in Canada (effective 2002). adv. bk.rev. illus.; maps. 40 p./no.; **Document type:** *Magazine, Consumer.* **Description:** Covers ancient archaeological findings in the Americas. Attempts to describe without bias the "true prehistory of the American continent." Provides a forum for scholars and non-scholars alike to discuss their views on archaeology in the Americas before the arrival of Christopher Columbus.
Address: PO Box 370, Colfax, WI 54730. TEL 715-962-3299, http://www.ancientamerican.com. Ed. Frank Joseph. Pub., Adv. contact Wayne N May.

915.49 LKA ISSN 0258-9257
ANCIENT CEYLON. Text in English. 1971. irreg. price varies. bk.rev. illus.
Indexed: AICP, BAS.
Published by: Archaeological Survey Department, Sir Marcus Fernando Rd., Colombo, 7, Sri Lanka. FAX 0094-1-696250.

ANCIENT MONUMENTS SOCIETY TRANSACTIONS. see *ARCHITECTURE*

930 BEL
➤ **ANCIENT NEAR EAST STUDIES SUPPLEMENTS.** Text in English, French, German. 1964. irreg. price varies. back issues avail. **Document type:** *Monographic series, Academic/Scholarly.*
Supersedes (in 2000): Abr-Nahrain. Supplements (0065-0390)
Related titles: ◆ Supplement to: Ancient Near Eastern Studies. ISSN 1378-4641.
Indexed: MLA.
Published by: (University of Melbourne, Department of Classical and Near Eastern Studies AUS), Peeters Publishers, Bondgenotenlaan 153, Leuven, 3000, Belgium. TEL 32-16-235170, FAX 32-16-228500, http://www.peeters-leuven.be. Ed. Antonio Sagona.

930 BEL ISSN 1378-4641
PJ3001
➤ **ANCIENT NEAR EASTERN STUDIES.** Text in English, French, German. 1959. a., latest vol.39, 2002. EUR 40 (effective 2005). bk.rev. illus.; maps. Index. Supplement avail. **Document type:** *Journal, Academic/Scholarly.* **Description:** Publishes articles on the cultures of the ancient Near East.
Supersedes (in 2000): Abr-Nahrain (0065-0382)
Related titles: Online - full text ed.: (from EBSCO Publishing, Swets Information Services); ◆ Supplement(s): Ancient Near East Studies Supplements.
Indexed: BAS, BibLing, DIP, IBR, IBZ, IndIslam, MLA-IB, NTA, OTA, R&TA, RI-1, RI-2.
—IE.
Published by: (University of Melbourne, Department of Classical and Near Eastern Studies AUS), Peeters Publishers, Bondgenotenlaan 153, Leuven, 3000, Belgium. TEL 32-16-235170, FAX 32-16-228500, http://poj.peeters-leuven.be/content.php?url=journal&journal_code=ANES, http://www.peeters-leuven.be. Eds. Antonio Sagona, R Boucharlat.

➤ **ANCIENT NEPAL.** see *ASIAN STUDIES*

➤ **ANCIENT SOCIETY**; journal of ancient history of the Greek, Hellenistic and Roman world. see *CLASSICAL STUDIES*

930.102 930.1 FRA ISSN 0735-1348
➤ **ANCIENT T L.** Text in English. 1979. 2/yr. EUR 20 to individuals; EUR 30 to institutions (effective 2003); includes a. supplement. adv. bibl.; illus. back issues avail. **Document type:** *Academic/Scholarly.* **Description:** Covers research and information on the application of luminescence and electron spin resonance techniques to dating archaeological and geological materials.
Indexed: BrArAb, NumL.
Address: Laboratoire de Physique Corpusculaire, Aubiere, Cedex 63177, France. TEL 33-4-73405124, FAX 33-4-73264598, anctl@clermont.in2p3.fr. Ed. Didier Miallier. Circ: 100.

➤ **ANCIENT WORLD**; a scholarly journal for the study of antiquity. see *HISTORY*

930.1 USA ISSN 1055-8756
F2229
➤ **ANDEAN PAST.** Text in English. 1987. biennial. USD 40 per vol. (effective 2001). back issues avail. **Document type:** *Academic/Scholarly.* **Description:** Publishes original research on the prehistory and ethnohistory of South America.
Indexed: AICP, AnthLit, IBR, IBZ.
Published by: Cornell University, Latin American Studies Program, 190 Uris Hall, Ithaca, NY 14853. TEL 607-255-2245, FAX 607-255-8919, daniels@maine.maine.edu. Eds. Daniel H Sandweiss, Monica Barnes. Circ: 250 (paid); 50 (controlled).

913 IND
ANDHRA PRADESH, INDIA. DEPARTMENT OF ARCHAEOLOGY AND MUSEUMS. ANNUAL REPORT. Text in English. irreg. price varies.
Published by: Department of Archaeology and Museums, Hyderabad, Andhra Pradesh 500 001, India.

700 913 IND
ANDHRA PRADESH, INDIA. DEPARTMENT OF ARCHAEOLOGY AND MUSEUMS. ARCHAEOLOGICAL SERIES. Text in English. irreg. price varies. **Document type:** *Monographic series.*
Formerly: Andhra Pradesh, India. Department of Archaeology and Museums. Art and Architectural Series
Published by: Department of Archaeology and Museums, Hyderabad, Andhra Pradesh 500 001, India.

913 IND
ANDHRA PRADESH, INDIA. DEPARTMENT OF ARCHAEOLOGY AND MUSEUMS. ARCHAEOLOGICAL SERIES: A.P. JOURNAL OF ARCHAEOLOGY. Text in English. 1978. irreg. price varies.
Indexed: AIAP, AnthLit.
Published by: Department of Archaeology and Museums, Hyderabad, Andhra Pradesh 500 001, India. Circ: 500.

571 954 IND
ANDHRA PRADESH, INDIA. DEPARTMENT OF ARCHAEOLOGY AND MUSEUMS. EPIGRAPHY SERIES. Text in English. 1967. irreg., latest vol.11, 1976. price varies. **Document type:** *Monographic series.*
Formerly: Andhra Pradesh, India. Department of Archaeology. Epigraphy Series (0066-1651)
Published by: Department of Archaeology and Museums, Hyderabad, Andhra Pradesh 500 001, India.

ANDREWS UNIVERSITY SEMINARY STUDIES. see *RELIGIONS AND THEOLOGY*

914 ESP ISSN 0561-3663
ANEJOS DE ARCHIVO ESPANOL DE ARQUEOLOGIA. Text in Spanish. 1951. irreg. illus. **Document type:** *Journal, Academic/Scholarly.*
Indexed: MLA-IB, NumL.
Published by: (Spain. Consejo Superior de Investigaciones Cientificas), Instituto Espanol de Arqueologia (Subsidiary of: Consejo Superior de Investigaciones Cientificas), Departamento de Publicaciones, Vitruvio 8, Madrid, 28006, Spain.

914.2 GBR ISSN 0306-5790
DA740.A5
ANGLESEY ANTIQUARIAN SOCIETY TRANSACTIONS. Text in English, Welsh. 1913. a. GBP 4. bk.rev. charts; illus.
Indexed: BHA, BrArAb, NumL.
Published by: Anglesey Antiquarian Society and Field Club, c/o HoN Secretary, 1 Fronheulog, Tregarth, Bangor, Gwynedd, United Kingdom. Ed. A D Carr. Circ: 1,000.

930.1 GBR ISSN 0266-2442
➤ **ANGLO-ISRAEL ARCHAEOLOGICAL SOCIETY. BULLETIN.** Text in English. 1982. a., latest vol.18, 2001. GBP 15 per issue domestic; GBP 20 per issue foreign (effective 2005). bk.rev. bibl.; maps. Index. back issues avail. **Document type:** *Journal, Academic/Scholarly.*
Related titles: Online - full text ed.: (from EBSCO Publishing).
Indexed: NTA, OTA, RI-1.
—BLDSC (2393.835000).
Published by: A I A S, 126 Albert St, London, NW1 7NE, United Kingdom. TEL 44-20-76911467, FAX 44-20-76911501, nickslope@aias.org.uk, http://www.aiasoc.fsnet.co.uk/aias_bulletingeneral.htm, http://www.aias.org.uk/. Ed. Dr. Shimon Gibson.

930.1 GBR ISSN 0264-5254
ANGLO-SAXON STUDIES IN ARCHAEOLOGY AND HISTORY. Abbreviated title: A S S A H. Text in English. 1979. a. **Document type:** *Academic/Scholarly.*
Indexed: BHA, BrArAb, NAA, NumL, PCI.
—BLDSC (0902.881000), IE, ingenta.
Published by: Oxford University, School of Archaeology, OUSA, Institute of Archaeology, 36 Beaumont St, Oxford, Oxon OX1 2PG, United Kingdom. TEL 44-1865-278240, FAX 44-1865-278254, http://www.ox.ac.uk. Ed. David Griffiths. **Dist. by:** Oxbow Books, Park End Pl, Oxford OX1 1HN, United Kingdom. TEL 44-1865-241249, FAX 44-1865-794449, oxbow@oxbowbooks.com, http://www.oxbowbooks.com.

ANISTORITON; history, archaeology, art history journal. see *HISTORY*

916 ETH ISSN 0066-2127
ANNALES D'ETHIOPIE. Text in French. 1955. triennial, latest vol.18, 2002. price varies. reprints avail. **Document type:** *Monographic series, Academic/Scholarly.*
Published by: Centre Francais d'Etudes Ethiopiennes, PO Box 5554, Addis Ababa, Ethiopia. TEL 251-1-234767, FAX 251-1-234766, cfee@ethionet.et, http://www.cfee-fces.org/code/pres.htm.

913 FRA ISSN 0003-4398
ANNALES DU MIDI; revue de la France Meridionale. Text in French. 1889. q. bk.rev. bibl.; charts; illus. index, cum.index: 1919-1958. back issues avail.
Indexed: AmH&L, BHA, HistAb, IBR, IBZ, MLA, MLA-IB, PCI, RASB, RILM.
—IE, Infotrieve.
Published by: Editions Edouard Privat, 14 rue des Arts, B.P. 828, Toulouse, Cedex 6 31080, France. TEL 33-5-61110320, FAX 33-5-61137441. Ed. Michel Taillefert. **Subscr. to:** Interconnexion Annales du Midi - Service Abonnements, BP 44, Fenouillet 31150, France. TEL 33-5-61371666.

ANNALES DU MUSEUM DU HAVRE. see *MUSEUMS AND ART GALLERIES*

913 ITA
ANNALI BENACENSI; rassegna di studi paletnologici ed archeologici. Text in Italian. 1974. a. USD 28. **Document type:** *Academic/Scholarly.*
Published by: Gruppo Archeologico Cavriana, Museo Archeologico dell'Alto Mantovano, Piazza Castello, 5, Cavriana, MN 46040, Italy. Ed. Adalberto Piccoli.

930.1 ITA ISSN 1127-7130
DE1
ANNALI DI ARCHEOLOGIA E STORIA ANTICA. Text in English, French, Italian. 1979. a., latest vol.5, 1997. back issues avail. **Document type:** *Academic/Scholarly.*
Former titles (until 1993): Sezione di Archeologia e Storia Antica. Annali (1121-8347); (until 1984): Seminario di Studi del Mondo Classico. Sezione di Archeologia e Storia Antica. Annali (0393-070X)
Indexed: DIP, IBR, IBZ, NumL, PCI.
Published by: Universita degli Studi di Napoli, L'Orientale/Dipartimento di Studi del Mondo Classico e del Mediterraneo Antico, Piazza San Domenico Maggiore 12, Palazzo Corigliano, Naples, NA 80134, Italy. Ed. Bruno D'Agostino. **Dist. by:** Herder Editrice e Libreria s.r.l., Piazza di Montecitorio 117-120, Rome 00186, Italy. TEL 39-06-6795304, FAX 39-6-6784751.

930.1 FRA ISSN 1261-8373
ANNUAIRE DES OPERATIONS DE TERRAIN EN MILIEU URBAIN. Text in French. 1986. a.
Published by: Centre National d'Archeologie Urbaine, Logis des Gouverneurs, 25 avenue Andre-Mairaux, Tours, 37000, France. TEL 33-2-47667237, 33-2-47667600, FAX 33-2-47202866, cnau@culture.gouv.fr, http://www.culture.gouv.fr/culture/cnau/fr/publications.html.

917 CAN ISSN 1181-9057
ANNUAL ARCHAEOLOGICAL REPORT ONTARIO. Text in English. 1990. a.
Published by: Ontario Heritage Foundation, 10 Adelaide St, Toronto, ON M5C 1J3, Canada. TEL 416-325-5000.

930.1 USA ISSN 1092-4760
CC1
ANNUAL EDITIONS: ARCHAEOLOGY. Text in English. 1995. a., latest 2004, 7th ed. USD 20.21 per vol. (effective 2004). illus. **Document type:** *Academic/Scholarly.* **Description:** Contains articles from the public press, including Newsweek, Natural History, Archaeology and The Archaeologist at Work.
Published by: McGraw-Hill - Dushkin (Subsidiary of: McGraw-Hill Higher Education), 2460 Kerper Blvd, Dubuque, IA 52001. TEL 800-243-6532, customer.service@mcgraw-hill.com, http://www.dushkin.com/text-data/catalog/0072949600.mhtml. Ed. Linda L Hasten.

913 HUN ISSN 0238-0218
DB920
ANTAEUS; communicationes ex Instituto Archaeologico Academiae Scientiarum Hungaricae. Text in English, German. 1970. a., latest vol.25, 2002. exchange basis. back issues avail. **Document type:** *Yearbook, Academic/Scholarly.*
Description: Discusses recent discoveries in archaeology.
Formerly (until 1986): Ungarische Akademie der Wissenschaften. Archaeologisches Institut. Mitteilungen (0133-6924)
Indexed: AICP, BHA.
Published by: Magyar Tudomanyos Akademia, Regeszeti Intezet/Hungarian Academy of Sciences, Archaeological Institute, Uri utca 49, Budapest, 1250, Hungary. TEL 36-1-3759011, FAX 36-1-2246719, solti@archeo.mta.hu. Ed. Bela Miklos Szoke.

ANTHROPOLOGICA. see *ANTHROPOLOGY*

ANTHROPOLOGICA ET PRAEHISTORICA; bulletin de la Societe Royale Belge d'Anthropologie et Prehistoire. see *ANTHROPOLOGY*

913 GRC ISSN 0253-5092
ANTHROPOLOGIKA. Text in Greek. 1980. 3/yr. USD 150. adv. bk.rev.
Published by: Paratiritis S.A., 15 Al Stavrou St, Thessaloniki, 546 44, Greece. Ed. G Hourmouziades. Circ: 1,500.

ANTHROPOLOGY AND ARCHEOLOGY OF EURASIA; a journal of translations. see *ANTHROPOLOGY*

709 CHE ISSN 0003-5688
N5320
➤ **ANTIKE KUNST.** Text in English, French, German, Italian. 1958. a. CHF 100 membership (effective 2005). illus. index. back issues avail. **Document type:** *Journal, Academic/Scholarly.*
Indexed: AIAP, ArtInd, BHA, DIP, IBR, IBZ, NumL, PCI, RASB, RILM.
—IE, Infotrieve.
Published by: Vereinigung der Freunde Antiker Kunst, c/o Archaeologisches Seminar der Universitaet, Schoenbeinstr 20, Basel, 4056, Switzerland. FAX 41-61-3038676, publisher@antikekunst.ch, http://www.antikekunst.ch. Ed. Kristine Gex. Pub. Doris Woerner. Circ: 1,150.

700 CHE ISSN 0066-4782
ANTIKE KUNST. BEIHEFTE. Text in English, French, German. 1963. irreg., latest vol.18, 1998. price varies. **Document type:** *Monographic series, Academic/Scholarly.*
Indexed: PCI.
Published by: Vereinigung der Freunde Antiker Kunst, c/o Archaeologisches Seminar der Universitaet, Schoenbeinstr 20, Basel, 4056, Switzerland. FAX 41-61-3038676, publisher@antikekunst.ch, http://www.antikekunst.ch. Ed. Kristine Gex. Pub. Doris Woerner. Circ: 550.

905 DEU ISSN 0003-570X
CB311
ANTIKE WELT; Zeitschrift fuer Archaeologie und Kulturgeschichte. Text in German. 1970. 6/yr. EUR 66; EUR 49.20 to students; EUR 12.80 newsstand/cover (effective 2005). adv. bk.rev. 100 p./no.; **Document type:** *Journal, Academic/Scholarly.*
Indexed: A&ATA, AIAP, ArtInd, BHA, BrArAb, DIP, IBR, IBZ, NumL, PCI.
—IE, Infotrieve. **CCC.**
Published by: Verlag Philipp von Zabern GmbH, Philipp-von-Zabern-Platz 1-3, Mainz, 55116, Germany. TEL 49-6131-287470, FAX 49-6131-2874744, zabern@zabern.de, http://www.kunstbuecher-online.de/zabern/antike-welt/index.php, http://www.zabern.de. Ed. Gerhild Klose. Adv. contact Manuela Dressen TEL 49-6131-2874711. page EUR 2,700; trim 175 x 255.

913 GBR ISSN 0003-5815
DA20
➤ **THE ANTIQUARIES JOURNAL.** Text in English. 1921. a. USD 176, GBP 80 (effective 2005). bk.rev. bibl.; illus.; maps. index. reprints avail. **Document type:** *Journal, Academic/Scholarly.*
Description: International journal of record within archaeology, reporting specialist work to the wider readership and larger issues that concern every archaeologist.
Formerly: Society of Antiquaries. Proceedings
Related titles: Microfiche ed.: (from IDC); Microform ed.: (from PQC).
Indexed: A&ATA, AIAP, AICP, API, AbAn, AmH&L, AnthLit, BHA, BRI, BrArAb, BrHumI, CurCont, DIP, HistAb, IBR, IBZ, IndIslam, NAA, NumL, RASB, RILM, SSCI.
—BLDSC (1550.000000), IE, ingenta. **CCC.**
Published by: Society of Antiquaries of London, Burlington House, Piccadilly, London, W1V 0BE, United Kingdom. TEL 44-20-74797080, FAX 44-20-72876967, admin@sal.org.uk, http://www.maney.co.uk/search?fwaction=show&fwid=625, http://www.sal.org.uk. Ed. David Morgan Evans. R&P Kate Owen TEL 44-20-7479-7089. **Subscr. to:** Maney Publishing, Hudson Rd, Leeds, W Yorks LS9 7DL, United Kingdom. TEL 44-113-2497481, FAX 44-113-2486983, subscriptions@maney.co.uk.

➤ **ANTIQUITAS. REIHE 3. ABHANDLUNGEN ZUR VOR- UND FRUEHGESCHICHTE, ZUR KLASSISCHEN UND PROVINZIAL-ROEMISCHEN ARCHAEOLOGIE UND ZUR GESCHICHTE DES ALTERTUMS.** see *HISTORY*

930.1 DEU ISSN 1435-7445
ANTIQUITATES; Archaeologische Forschungsergebnisse. Text in German. 1992. irreg., latest vol.30, 2004. price varies. **Document type:** *Monographic series, Academic/Scholarly.*
Formerly (until 1998): Antiquates (0945-4896)
Published by: Verlag Dr. Kovac, Arnoldstr 49, Hamburg, 22763, Germany. TEL 49-40-3988800, FAX 49-40-39888055, info@verlagdrkovac.de, http://www.verlagdrkovac.de/1-1.htm.

940.1 BEL ISSN 1250-7334
ANTIQUITE TARDIVE; revue internationale d'histoire et d'archeologie. Text in French. 1993. a., latest vol.13, 2005. EUR 65; EUR 75 combined subscription print & online eds. (effective 2006). back issues avail. **Document type:** *Academic/Scholarly.* **Description:** Publishes original multidisciplinary contributions on the arts, history, archaeology, epigraphy, law and philosophy of late antiquity, covering the 4th through 8th centuries.
Indexed: BHA.
Published by: (Association pour l'Antiquite Tardive), Brepols Publishers, Begijnhof 67, Turnhout, 2300, Belgium. TEL 32-14-448030, FAX 32-14-428919, periodicals@brepols.net, http://www.brepols.net.

ANTIQUITES AFRICAINES. see *HISTORY—History Of Africa*

913 GBR ISSN 0003-598X
CC1 CODEN: ATQYAF
➤ **ANTIQUITY**; a periodical review of archaeology. Text in English. 1927. q. GBP 85, USD 155, EUR 130 to institutions; GBP 95, USD 175, EUR 145 combined subscription to institutions print & online (effective 2005). adv. bk.rev. bibl.; charts; illus.; maps. index, cum.index: vols.1-50. reprints avail. **Document type:** *Journal, Academic/Scholarly.* **Description:** Reports on specialist work in archaeology.
Related titles: Microfiche ed.: (from IDC); Microform ed.: (from MIM, PQC); Online - full text ed.: GBP 80, USD 150, EUR 125 to institutions (effective 2005) (from bigchalk, EBSCO Publishing, Florida Center for Library Automation, Gale Group, H.W. Wilson, Northern Light Technology, Inc., O C L C Online Computer Library Center, Inc., ProQuest Information & Learning).
Indexed: A&ATA, AIAP, AICP, ASCA, AbAn, AcaI, AmH&L, AnthLit, ArtHuCI, ArtInd, BAS, BHA, BibLing, BrArAb, BrHumI, CurCont, DIP, GEOBASE, HumInd, IBR, IBSS, IBZ, IndIslam, MEA&I, MLA, MLA-IB, NAA, NTA, NumL, RASB, RI-1, RI-2, RILM, SSCI.
—BLDSC (1551.000000), IDS, IE, Infotrieve, ingenta. **CCC.**
Published by: Antiquity Publications Ltd., Bidder Bldg, 140 Cowley Rd, Cambridge, CB4 4DL, United Kingdom. TEL 44-1223-426164, FAX 44-1223-423353, editor@antiquity.ac.uk, sales@biologists.com, http://www.biologists.com/other/antiquity/antiquity.html. Ed. Martin Carver. R&P, Adv. contact Libby Peachey TEL 44-1223-313223. page GBP 250. **Dist. by:** Portland Press Ltd., Commerce Way, Colchester CO2 8HP, United Kingdom. TEL 44-1206-796351, FAX 44-1206-799331, sales@portland-services.com, http://www.portland-services.com.

930.1 GBR
ANTIQUITY PAPERS. Text in English. irreg. **Document type:** *Academic/Scholarly.*
—BLDSC (1551.150000).
Published by: Antiquity Publications Ltd., Bidder Bldg, 140 Cowley Rd, Cambridge, CB4 4DL, United Kingdom. TEL 44-1223-426164, FAX 44-1223-423353, sales@biologists.com, http://www.biologists.com.

ANZEIGER FUER DIE ALTERTUMSWISSENSCHAFT. see *CLASSICAL STUDIES*

930.1 GTM
APUNTES ARQUEOLOGICOS. Text in Spanish. 1991. s-a.?. **Document type:** *Academic/Scholarly.*
Published by: Universidad de San Carlos de Guatemala, Escuela de Historia, Area de Arqueologia, Ciudad Universitaria, zona 12, Edificio de Rectoria, Of 307, Guatemala City, Guatemala.

913 ITA ISSN 0391-7304
AQUILEIA NOSTRA. Text in Italian. 1930. a. index. back issues avail.
Indexed: BHA, NumL.
Published by: Associazione Nazionale per Aquileia, Casa Bertoli, Via Popone, 6, Aquileia, UD 33051, Italy. TEL 39-431-91113. Ed. Gino Bandelli. Circ: 750.

930.1 DNK ISSN 0905-7196
DS211 CODEN: AAEPE3
➤ **ARABIAN ARCHAEOLOGY AND EPIGRAPHY.** Text in English. 1990. s-a. EUR 264 combined subscription in Europe to individuals print & online eds.; USD 296 combined subscription in the Americas to individuals print & online eds.; GBP 176 combined subscription in Europe to individuals print & online eds.; USD 546 combined subscription in the Americas to institutions & the Caribbean (print & online eds.); GBP 325 combined subscription elsewhere to institutions print & online eds. (effective 2006). adv. charts; illus. back issues avail.; reprint service avail. from PSC. **Document type:** *Journal, Academic/Scholarly.*
Related titles: ◆ Online - full text ed.: Arabian Archaeology and Epigraphy Online. ISSN 1600-0471.
Indexed: ASCA, AnthLit, ArtHuCI, BibLing, CurCont, GEOBASE, L&LBA, PCI, PerIslam, RI-1, RI-2, SOPODA, SSCI.
—BLDSC (1583.322350), IDS, IE. **CCC.**
Published by: Blackwell Munksgaard (Subsidiary of: Blackwell Publishing Ltd.), Rosenoerns Alle 1, PO Box 227, Copenhagen V, 1502, Denmark. TEL 45-77-333333, FAX 45-77-333377, info@mks.blackwellpublishing.com, http://www.blackwellpublishing.com/journals/AAE, http://www.blackwellmunksgaard.com. Ed. Daniel T Potts. Circ: 300.

930.1 DNK ISSN 1600-0471
ARABIAN ARCHAEOLOGY AND EPIGRAPHY ONLINE. Text in English. s-a. USD 519 in the Americas to institutions & Caribbean; GBP 309 elsewhere to institutions (effective 2006). **Document type:** *Academic/Scholarly.*
Media: Online - full text (from Blackwell Synergy, EBSCO Publishing, Gale Group, IngentaConnect, O C L C Online Computer Library Center, Inc., Swets Information Services). **Related titles:** ◆ Print ed.: Arabian Archaeology and Epigraphy. ISSN 0905-7196.
Published by: Blackwell Munksgaard (Subsidiary of: Blackwell Publishing Ltd.), Rosenoerns Alle 1, PO Box 227, Copenhagen V, 1502, Denmark. TEL 45-77-33-3333, FAX 45-77-33-3377, info@mks.blackwellpublishing.com, http://www.blackwellpublishing.com/journal.asp?ref=0905-7196, http://www.blackwellmunksgaard.com. Adv. contact Eric Rozario TEL 45-77-333301.

930.1 TUR ISSN 1017-7663
ARASTIRMA SONUCLARI TOPLANTISI. Text in Turkish; Text occasionally in English, German. 1984. a. per issue exchange basis. **Document type:** *Academic/Scholarly.* **Description:** Publishes papers on archaeological and epigraphical research at sites in Turkey.
Published by: Ministry of Culture, General Directorate of Monuments and Museums/Kultur Bakanligi, Anitlar ve Muzeler Genel Mudurlugu, Ulus - Ankara, 06100, Turkey. TEL 90-312-3104960, FAX 90-312-3111417.

930.1 AUT
▼ **ARBEITEN ZUR ARCHAEOLOGIE.** Text in German. 2003. irreg. price varies. **Document type:** *Monographic series, Academic/Scholarly.*
Published by: Boehlau Verlag GmbH & Co.KG., Sachsenplatz 4-6, Vienna, W 1201, Austria. TEL 43-1-33024270, FAX 43-1-3302432, boehlau@boehlau.at, http://www.boehlau.at.

913 DEU ISSN 0066-5738
N8555
ARBEITSBLAETTER FUER RESTAURATOREN. Text in German. 1968. 2/yr. **Document type:** *Academic/Scholarly.*
Indexed: A&ATA, BHA, RASB, RILM.
Published by: Roemisch-Germanisches Zentralmuseum, Forschungsinstitut fuer Vor- und Fruehgeschichte, Ernst-Ludwig-Platz 2, Mainz, 55116, Germany. TEL 49-6131-9124-0, FAX 49-6131-9124199, rzentral@mainz-online.de.

913 DEU ISSN 0066-5886
ARCHAEO-PHYSIKA. Text in German. 1965. irreg., latest vol.13, 1993. price varies. **Document type:** *Monographic series, Academic/Scholarly.*
Indexed: BrArAb, NAA.
Published by: Rheinland Verlag GmbH, Abtei Brauweiler, Postfach 2140, Pulheim, 50250, Germany. TEL 49-2234-9854265, FAX 49-2234-82503. **Dist. by:** Dr. Rudolf Habelt GmbH, Am Buchenhang 1, Bonn 53115, Germany.

913 520 USA ISSN 0190-9940
E59.A8
ARCHAEOASTRONOMY; the journal of astronomy culture. Text in English. 1977. a. USD 40 per vol. to individuals; USD 70 per vol. to institutions (effective 2006). adv. bk.rev. back issues avail.; reprint service avail. from PSC. **Document type:** *Journal, Academic/Scholarly.*
Formerly (until 1982): Archaeoastronomy Bulletin (0272-5436)
Related titles: Online - full text ed.: (from EBSCO Publishing).
Indexed: AICP, AnthLit, BrArAb, MathR.
—Linda Hall. **CCC.**
Published by: University of Texas Press, Journals Division, 2100 Comal, Austin, TX 78722. FAX 512-232-7178, journals@uts.cc.utexas.edu, http://www.utexas.edu/utpress/journals/jarch.html, http://www.utexas.edu/utpress/journals/journals.html. Ed. John Carlson. adv.: page USD 175; 7 x 9.5. Circ: 500. **Subscr. to:** PO Box 7819, Austin, TX 78713. TEL 800-252-3206, 800-687-6046.

A

913 520 USA ISSN 1062-189X
E59.A8
ARCHAEOASTRONOMY & ETHNOASTRONOMY NEWS. Text in English. q. **Document type:** *Newsletter.*
Media: Online - full content.
Published by: (University of Maryland), Center for Archaeoastronomy (Subsidiary of: University of Maryland), PO Box "X", College Park, MD 20741-3022. TEL 301-864-6637, FAX 301-699-5337. **Co-sponsor:** International Society for Archaeoastronomy, Ethnoastronomy, and Astronomy in Culture (ISAAC).

301 ESP ISSN 1132-6891
CC79.5.A5
ARCHAEOFAUNA. Text in Multiple languages. 1992. a. back issues avail.
Related titles: Online - full text ed.
Indexed: BIOSIS Prev, BiolAb, IECT, ZooRec.
—BLDSC (1594.530000), CINDOC.
Published by: Asociacion Espanola de Arqueozoologia, C. Munoz Seca, 6, Zaragoza, 500080, Spain. TEL 34-976-557039, FAX 34-976-353226, portico@zaragoza.net, http://www.uam.es/otros/paleofau/RevistaArchaeofauna.htm.

913 709 929 745.1 GBR ISSN 0261-3409
➤ **ARCHAEOLOGIA.** Text in English. 1770. irreg., latest 2004. price varies. back issues avail.; reprint service avail. from PQC. **Document type:** *Monographic series, Academic/Scholarly.* **Description:** Articles concerned with antiquarian interests.
Related titles: Microfiche ed.: (from IDC); Microfilm ed.: (from PQC).
Indexed: A&ATA, AIAP, AICP, ArtInd, BHA, BrArAb, BrHumI, IndIslam, NumL, PCI, RASB.
Published by: Society of Antiquaries of London, Burlington House, Piccadilly, London, W1V 0BE, United Kingdom. TEL 44-20-74797080, FAX 44-20-72876967, admin@sal.org.uk, http://www.sal.org.uk. Ed. David Morgan Evans. R&P Kate Owen TEL 44-20-7479-7089. Circ: 2,000.

➤ **ARCHAEOLOGIA AELIANA.** see *HISTORY—History Of Europe*

930.1 AUT ISSN 0003-8008
DB1
ARCHAEOLOGIA AUSTRIACA; Beitraege zur Palaeantologie, Ur- und Fruehgeschichte Oesterreichs. Text in German. 1947. a. bk.rev. bibl.; charts; illus. cum.index. Supplement avail.; back issues avail. **Document type:** *Journal, Academic/Scholarly.*
Indexed: AICP, AnthLit, BHA, BrArAb, ChemAb, DIP, IBR, IBZ, NumL, RASB.
Published by: (Universitaet Wien, Institut fuer Ur- und Fruehgeschichte), Franz Deuticke Verlag GmbH, Hegelgasse 21, Vienna, W 1015, Austria. TEL 43-1-5121544258, FAX 43-1-5121544289, info@deuticke.at, http://www.deuticke.at. Ed. Herwig Friesinger. Circ: 400.

930.1 BGR ISSN 1310-9537
DR62
➤ **ARCHAEOLOGIA BULGARICA.** Text in English, French, German. 1997. 3/yr. EUR 59 (effective 2005). adv. bk.rev. abstr.; illus.; maps. 100 p./no. 2 cols./p.; back issues avail. **Document type:** *Journal, Academic/Scholarly.* **Description:** Provides forum for research in archaeology with an emphasis on Bulgaria and South-Eastern Europe.
Indexed: AnthLit.
—BLDSC (1594.615000).
Published by: NOUS Publishers Ltd., PO Box 1275, Sofia, 1000, Bulgaria. lvagalin@mail.techno-link.com, http://www.techno-link.com/clients/lvagalin/. Ed., Pub. Lyudmil Vagalinski TEL 359-87-405191. Circ: 500 (paid).

571 GBR ISSN 0066-5894
ARCHAEOLOGIA CANTIANA. Text in English. 1858. a. GBP 15 to individuals; GBP 25 to institutions (effective 2000). adv. bk.rev. index, cum.index. reprints avail. **Document type:** *Academic/Scholarly.* **Description:** Covers archeology and history of Kent.
Indexed: AIAP, BHA, BrArAb, NumL, PCI.
—BLDSC (1594.630000).
Published by: Kent Archaeological Society, Lynwood, 102 Lower Vicarage Rd, Kennington, Ashford, Kent TN24 9AP, United Kingdom. Ed. T G Lawson. Circ: 1,750.

913 CZE
ARCHAEOLOGIA HISTORICA. Text in Czech; Summaries in German. 1976. a. CZK 400 domestic (effective 2003). bk.rev. illus. **Document type:** *Academic/Scholarly.*
Indexed: AICP, BHA, RASB.
Published by: Muzejni a Vlastivedna Solecnost, Solnicni 12, Brno, 0200, Czech Republic. mvsbrno@seznam.cz. Ed. Vladimir Nekuda. Circ: 1,500. **Subscr. to:** Buchexport-Import, Kubon u. Sagner, He3sr.39/41, Postfach 340108, Munich 80798, Germany.

930.1 POL ISSN 1425-3534
DK4088
ARCHAEOLOGIA HISTORICA POLONA. Text in Polish. 1995. irreg.
Indexed: AnthLit.
Published by: (Uniwersytet Mikolaja Kopernika, Uniwersyteckie Centrum Archeologii Sredniowiecza i Nowozytnosci), Uniwersytet Mikolaja Kopernika/Nicolaus Copernicus University, Wydawnictwo, ul Gagarina 39, Torun, 87100, Poland. TEL 48-56-14294, http://www.uni.torun.pl/ksiegarnia/rec_745.html, http://www.wydawnictwo.uni.torun.pl.

930.1 SVN
ARCHAEOLOGIA HISTORICA SLOVENICA. Text in Slovenian, English. 1994. irreg., latest vol.3, 2001. price varies. **Document type:** *Monographic series, Academic/Scholarly.* **Description:** Offers a forum for the research publications of the medieval and later periods of Slovene archaeology.
Published by: (Univerza v Ljubljani, Filozofska Fakulteta, Oddelek za Arheologijo/University of Ljubljana, Faculty of Philosophy, Department of Archaeology), Univerza v Ljubljani, Filozofska Fakulteta/University of Ljubljana, Faculty of Philosophy, Askerceva 2, Ljubljana, 1000, Slovenia. TEL 386-1-2411000, http://www.ff.uni-lj.si. Ed. Katarina Predovnik.

930.1 ISL ISSN 1560-8026
➤ **ARCHAEOLOGIA ISLANDICA;** occasional papers on Icelandic archaeology. Text in Multiple languages. 1998. irreg., latest vol.3, 2004. ISK 3,600 (effective 2004). back issues avail. **Document type:** *Academic/Scholarly.*
—BLDSC (1594.658000).
Published by: Fornleifastofnun Islands/Institute of Archaeology, Barugata 3, Reykjavik, 101, Iceland. TEL 354-551-1033, FAX 354-551-1047, fsi@instarch.is, http://www.instarch.is/publishing.htm. Ed. Gavin Lucas.

913 943.8 POL ISSN 0066-5924
GN845.P7
ARCHAEOLOGIA POLONA. Text in English. 1958. a., latest vol.42, 2004. EUR 25 foreign (effective 2005). bk.rev. charts; illus.; maps. 263 p./no. 1 cols./p.; **Document type:** *Journal, Academic/Scholarly.* **Description:** Polish archaeology and material culture.
Indexed: AICP, AnthLit, BHA, DIP, IBR, IBSS, IBZ, NAA, NumL, RASB.
Published by: Polska Akademia Nauk, Instytut Archeologii i Etnologii, Al Solidarnosci 105, Warsaw, 00140, Poland. TEL 48-22-6202881, FAX 48-22-6240100, director@iaepan.edu.pl, http://www.iaepan.edu.pl. Ed. Zbigniew Kobylinski. **Dist. by:** Ars Polona, Krakowskie Przedmiescie 7, Warsaw, Poland. TEL 48-22-9263914, FAX 48-22-9265334, arspolona@arspolona.com.pl, http://www.arspolona.com.pl.

930.1 USA ISSN 0775-3314
ARCHAEOLOGIA TRANSATLANTICA; a series in Mediterranean archaeology. Text in English. 1981. irreg., latest vol.21, 2003. price varies. illus.; maps. back issues avail. **Document type:** *Monographic series, Academic/Scholarly.*
Published by: Brown University, Center for Old World Archaeology and Art, PO Box 1837, Providence, RI 02912. TEL 401-863-2752, r_holloway@brown.edu.

930.1 ZMB ISSN 0570-6068
ARCHAEOLOGIA ZAMBIANA. Text in English. 1971 (no.14). irreg., latest vol.23. adv. **Document type:** *Academic/Scholarly.*
Indexed: AnthLit.
Published by: National Heritage Conservation Commission, PO Box 60124, Livingstone, Zambia. TEL 260-320354, FAX 260-324509. Ed., R&P, Adv. contact Maxwell Zulu TEL 260-320481.

913 HUN ISSN 0003-8032
DB920
ARCHAEOLOGIAI ERTESITO/ARCHAEOLOGICAL BULLETIN. Text mainly in Hungarian; Summaries in English, French, German; Text occasionally in German. 1869. s-a. USD 90 (effective 2006). adv. bk.rev. bibl. index. 168 p./no.; back issues avail.; reprints avail. **Document type:** *Journal, Academic/Scholarly.* **Description:** Deals with the history and archaeological inheritance of the Hungarian people and of the peoples formerly living on the territory of Hungary.
Indexed: AIAP, AICP, AnthLit, BHA, IBR, IBZ, RASB.
Published by: (Magyar Nemzeti Muzeum/Hungarian National Museum), Akademiai Kiado Rt. (Subsidiary of: Wolters Kluwer N.V.), Prielle Kornelia U. 19, Budapest, 1117, Hungary. TEL 36-1-4648282, FAX 36-1-4648221, journals@akkrt.hu, http://www.akkrt.hu. Ed. Tibor Kovacs.

930.26 DEU
ARCHAEOLOGICA PERUANA. Text in German. 1985. irreg. price varies. **Document type:** *Monographic series, Academic/Scholarly.*
Published by: Konrad Theiss Verlag GmbH, Moenchhaldenstr 28, Stuttgart, 70191, Germany. TEL 49-711-255270, FAX 49-711-2552717, service@theiss.de, http://www.theiss.de.

913.031 DEU ISSN 0177-4840
CC5
ARCHAEOLOGICA VENATORIA. MITTEILUNGSBLATT. Text in German. 1981. irreg. (1-2/yr.). membership. bk.rev. back issues avail. **Description:** Reports on the activities of the Institute for Prehistory.
Indexed: BrArAb.
Published by: Archaeologica Venatoria e.V., c/o Institut fuer Urgeschichte, Tuebingen, 72074, Germany. TEL 07071-292416, FAX 07071-294995. Circ: 350.

ARCHAEOLOGICAL COMPLETION REPORT SERIES. see *HISTORY—History Of North And South America*

930.1 GBR ISSN 1380-2038
➤ **ARCHAEOLOGICAL DIALOGUES.** Text in English. 1994. s-a. USD 100 in North America to institutions; GBP 64 elsewhere to institutions; USD 106 combined subscription in North America to institutions print & online eds.; GBP 66 combined subscription elsewhere to institutions print & online eds. (effective 2006). back issues avail.; reprint service avail. from PSC. **Document type:** *Journal, Academic/Scholarly.* **Description:** Promotes theoretically oriented approaches which go beyond traditional archaeological issues and consider historical, social and philosophical perspectives.
Related titles: Online - full text ed.: ISSN 1478-2294. USD 96 in North America to institutions; GBP 60 elsewhere to institutions (effective 2006) (from EBSCO Publishing, O C L C Online Computer Library Center, Inc., Swets Information Services).
Indexed: AnthLit, BrArAb, GEOBASE, NumL.
—BLDSC (1594.715000), IE, Infotrieve.
Published by: (Archaeological Dialogues Foundation NLD), Cambridge University Press, The Edinburgh Bldg, Shaftesbury Rd, Cambridge, CB2 2RU, United Kingdom. TEL 44-1223-312393, FAX 44-1223-315052, journals@cambridge.org, http://titles.cambridge.org/journals/journal_catalogue.asp?historylinks=ALPHA&mnemonic=ARD, http://uk.cambridge.org/journals. Eds. Fokke Gerritsen, Michael Dietler, Peter Van Dommelen. R&P Linda Nicol TEL 44-1223-325757. Adv. contact Rebecca Curtis TEL 44-1223-325757. **Subscr. to:** Cambridge University Press, 100 Brook Hill Dr, West Nyack, NY 10994. TEL 845-353-7500, FAX 845-353-4141, journals_subscriptions@cup.org

220.93 AUS ISSN 1322-6525
ARCHAEOLOGICAL DIGGINGS; a bi-monthly magazine of recent archaeological finds in the Middle East. Text in English. 1985. bi-m. AUD 39.60 domestic; AUD 45 in New Zealand; AUD 60 elsewhere (effective 2003). adv. bk.rev. charts; illus.; maps. 52 p./no.; back issues avail. **Document type:** *Magazine, Consumer.* **Description:** Archaeological news that keeps readers informed on latest discoveries on the lands of the Bible.
Formerly (until 1994): Diggings (1320-4424)
Address: 2 Neridah Ave, Mount Colah, NSW 2079, Australia. TEL 61-2-94773595, FAX 61-2-94871659, diggings@acay.com.au, http://groups.msn.com/ArchaeologicalDiggings/_homepage.msnw?pgmarket=en-au. Ed., Adv. contact David Clotheart. Pub. David Down. R&P D K Down. page AUD 900. Circ: 4,500 (paid). **Subscr. to:** PO Box 341, Hornsby, NSW 1630, Australia.

913 USA ISSN 0066-5975
➤ **ARCHAEOLOGICAL EXPLORATION OF SARDIS. MONOGRAPHS.** Text in English. 1971. irreg., latest vol.11, 2000. **Document type:** *Monographic series, Academic/Scholarly.*
Published by: Harvard University Art Museums, Archaeological Exploration of Sardis, 32 Quincy St, Cambridge, MA 02138. mbarone@fas.harvard.edu. Eds. Andrew Ramage, Katherine Kiefer. R&P Katherine Kiefer.

913 USA
ARCHAEOLOGICAL EXPLORATION OF SARDIS. REPORTS. Text in English. 1975. irreg., latest vol.3, 1986. **Document type:** *Monographic series, Academic/Scholarly.*
Published by: Harvard University Art Museums, Archaeological Exploration of Sardis, 32 Quincy St, Cambridge, MA 02138. mbarone@fas.harvard.edu. Eds. Andrew Ramage, Katherine Kiefer. R&P Katherine Kiefer.

930.1 USA ISSN 1061-8961
CC76
ARCHAEOLOGICAL FIELDWORK OPPORTUNITIES BULLETIN. Text in English. 1975. a. USD 12.25 to members; USD 15 to non-members (effective 2001). **Document type:** *Directory.* **Description:** Comprehensive guide to excavations, field schools and special programs with openings for volunteers, students and staff throughout the world.
Published by: (Archaeological Institute of America), Kendall - Hunt Publishing Co., 4050 Westmark Dr, Dubuque, IA 52002. TEL 319-589-1000, 800-228-0810, FAX 319-5891046, http://www.kendallhunt.com. Ed. Susanna Burns. Circ: 2,500 (paid).

930.1 GBR ISSN 0066-5983
DA20
➤ **ARCHAEOLOGICAL JOURNAL.** Text in English. 1844. a., latest vol.158, 2001. GBP 45 (effective 2003). bk.rev. index, cum.index every 25 yrs. reprints avail. **Document type:** *Academic/Scholarly.*
Indexed: AIAP, AICP, API, AnthLit, ArtInd, BHA, BrArAb, BrHumI, IBR, IndIslam, NumL, PCI, RASB.
—BLDSC (1594.750000), IE, Infotrieve. **CCC.**
Published by: Royal Archaeological Institute, c/o Society of Antiquaries, Burlington House, Picadilly, London, W1J 0BE, United Kingdom. FAX 44-116-2433839, http://www.royalarchaeolinst.org/. Ed., R&P M Gardiner. Circ: 2,100.

913 572   USA   ISSN 0194-3413
ARCHAEOLOGICAL NEWS. Text in English. 1972. a. USD 15 to individuals; USD 17.50 in Canada & Mexico to individuals; USD 19 elsewhere to individuals; USD 22.50 to institutions; USD 25 in Canada & Mexico to institutions; USD 26.50 elsewhere to institutions (effective 1999). adv. bk.rev. bibl.; illus. back issues avail. **Document type:** *Academic/Scholarly.*
Indexed: AIAP, BHA, DIP, IBR.
Published by: University of Georgia, Department of Classics, Park Hall, Athens, GA 30602. TEL 404-542-2187. Ed. Naomi J Norman. R&P, Adv. contact Amanda Mastrovita TEL 706-542-3839. Circ: 317.

913   CAN   ISSN 0563-9239
ARCHAEOLOGICAL NEWSLETTER. Text in English. 1965; N.S. 1981. irreg. looseleaf. free. back issues avail. **Document type:** *Newsletter.* **Description:** Each newsletter is a first-hand, often from-the-field account of a dig or other project conducted by ROM archaeologists and associates.
Related titles: Microfiche ed.: (from MML); Microfilm ed.: N.S. (from MML); Online - full text ed.: N.S.
Indexed: AIAP, AICP, AnthLit, RASB.
Published by: Royal Ontario Museum, Publications Dept, 100 Queen s Park, Toronto, ON M5S 2C6, Canada. TEL 416-586-5726, FAX 416-586-5643, anl@rom.on.ca, ccaroppo@rom.on.ca, http://www.rom.on.ca/pub/an.htm, http://www.rom.on.ca/ebuff/aboutarc.htm. R&P Christine Caroppo. Circ: 500.

930.1   GBR   ISSN 1075-2196
CC76   CODEN: ARPOE4
➤ **ARCHAEOLOGICAL PROSPECTION.** Text in English. 1994. q. USD 805 to institutions; USD 886 combined subscription to institutions print & online eds. (effective 2006). adv. back issues avail.; reprint service avail. from PSC. **Document type:** *Journal, Academic/Scholarly.* **Description:** International coverage of all types of archaeological sites and the full range of underlying geology.
Related titles: Microform ed.: (from PQC); Online - full content ed.: ISSN 1099-0763. USD 805 to institutions (effective 2006); Online - full text ed.: (from EBSCO Publishing, Swets Information Services, Wiley InterScience).
Indexed: AnthLit, BrArAb, NumL.
—BLDSC (1594.795000), IE, Infotrieve, ingenta. **CCC.**
Published by: John Wiley & Sons Ltd. (Subsidiary of: John Wiley & Sons, Inc.), The Atrium, Southern Gate, Chichester, West Sussex PO19 8SQ, United Kingdom. TEL 44-1243-779777, FAX 44-1243-775878, customer@wiley.co.uk, http://www.interscience.wiley.com/jpages/1075-2196/, http://www.wiley.co.uk. Eds. A Aspinall, A M Pollard. adv.: B&W page GBP 650, color page GBP 1,550; trim 200 x 260. Circ: 500. **Subscr. in the Americas to:** John Wiley & Sons, Inc., 111 River St, Hoboken, NJ 07030-5774. TEL 201-748-6645, 800-225-5945, subinfo@wiley.com.

913   GBR   ISSN 0141-8971
ARCHAEOLOGICAL REPORTS (DURHAM). Text in English. 1977. a. GBP 4 (effective 1998). **Document type:** *Academic/Scholarly.* **Description:** Brief reports on archaeological fieldwork undertaken by the universities.
Indexed: NumL, RASB.
Published by: University of Durham, Department of Archaeology, University of Durham, South Rd, Durham, DH1 3LE, United Kingdom. FAX 44-191-374-3719. Ed. S. Lucy. R&P S Lucy. Circ: 200 (controlled).

938   GBR   ISSN 0570-6084
DF10
➤ **ARCHAEOLOGICAL REPORTS (LONDON).** Text in English. 1954. a., latest vol.48, 2001-2002. GBP 55 per issue (effective 2003); current issue is not available online.. illus. index. back issues avail. **Document type:** *Academic/Scholarly.* **Description:** Summarizes recent archaeological work in Greece and other lands touched by Hellenic civilizations.
Related titles: Online - full text ed.: (from JSTOR (Web-based Journal Archive)); ◆ Supplement to: Journal of Hellenic Studies. ISSN 0075-4269.
Indexed: AIAP, BrHumI, IBR, IBZ.
—BLDSC (1594.810000).
Published by: Society for the Promotion of Hellenic Studies, Senate House, Malet St, London, WC1E 7HU, United Kingdom. TEL 44-20-78628730, FAX 44-20-78628731, hellenic@sas.ac.uk, http://www.hellenicsociety.org.uk/.

913   USA
ARCHAEOLOGICAL RESEARCH TOOLS. Text in English. 1981. irreg., latest vol.7, 1992. price varies. **Document type:** *Monographic series, Academic/Scholarly.* **Description:** Describes practical methods, tools, and techniques used in archaeology.
Indexed: AnthLit.
Published by: (Publications Department), University of California at Los Angeles, Cotsen Institute of Archaeology, A222 Fowler Museum, Box 951510, Los Angeles, CA 90095-1510. TEL 310-825-7411, FAX 310-206-4723.

913   GBR   ISSN 0261-4332
➤ **ARCHAEOLOGICAL REVIEW FROM CAMBRIDGE.** Text in English. 1981. s-a. GBP 18 domestic to individuals; GBP 20 in Europe to individuals; GBP 22 elsewhere to individuals; GBP 22 domestic to institutions; GBP 24 in Europe to institutions; GBP 26 elsewhere to institutions (effective 2005). adv. bk.rev. charts. back issues avail. **Document type:** *Journal, Academic/Scholarly.*
Indexed: AICP, AnthLit, BHA, BibInd, BrArAb, NumL.
—BLDSC (1594.920000).
Address: c/o Department of Archaeology, Downing St, Cambridge, CB2 3D2, United Kingdom. TEL 44-1223-333520, FAX 44-1223-333503, dab32@cam.ac.uk, http://www.cam.ac.uk/societies/arc/, http://www.arch.cam.ac.uk/dept/arc. Eds. David A Barrowclough, Mary Chester-Kadwell. Adv. contact Felix Riede. Circ: 250.

917 930.1   USA   ISSN 0739-5612
F96
ARCHAEOLOGICAL SOCIETY OF CONNECTICUT. BULLETIN✶ . Text in English. 1936. a. USD 15 to members (effective 1998). bk.rev.; film rev. abstr.; bibl.; charts; illus. index. back issues avail. **Document type:** *Bulletin.*
Indexed: AbAn, AnthLit.
Published by: Archaeological Society of Connecticut, Archaeological Research Specialists, 11 Silver Ave., Fort Mitchell, KY 41017-2909. TEL 203-237-4777, FAX 203-237-4667. Ed. Lucianne Lavin. R&P Reger Mueller TEL 860-266-7741. Circ: 250.

917 930.1   USA
ARCHAEOLOGICAL SOCIETY OF CONNECTICUT. NEWSLETTER✶ . Text in English. 3/yr. membership. **Document type:** *Newsletter.*
Published by: Archaeological Society of Connecticut, Archaeological Research Specialists, 11 Silver Ave., Fort Mitchell, KY 41017-2909. TEL 203-237-4777, FAX 203-237-4667. Ed. Tom Harris. R&P Roger W Mueller TEL 860-266-7741.

913   USA   ISSN 0003-8067
F161
ARCHAEOLOGICAL SOCIETY OF DELAWARE. BULLETIN. Text in English. 1933. a. USD 10 to individuals; USD 15 to institutions (effective 1999). charts. **Document type:** *Bulletin.*
Related titles: Microform ed.: (from PQC).
Indexed: AbAn, AnthLit.
Published by: Archaeological Society of Delaware, PO Box 12483, Wilmington, DE 19850-2483. TEL 302-831-6590. Ed. Keith R Doms.

917   USA
ARCHAEOLOGICAL SOCIETY OF DELAWARE. MONOGRAPH. Text in English. 1976. irreg. **Document type:** *Monographic series.*
Published by: Archaeological Society of Delaware, PO Box 12483, Wilmington, DE 19850-2483. TEL 302-831-6590. Ed. Keith Doms.

913   JPN   ISSN 0003-8075
DS11
ARCHAEOLOGICAL SOCIETY OF JAPAN. JOURNAL/ KOKOGAKU ZASSHI. Text in Japanese; Summaries in English. 1910. q. JPY 4,000. bk.rev. illus. index. reprints avail.
Indexed: AnthLit, HistAb, RASB, ZooRec.
Published by: Archaeological Society of Japan/Nihon Koko Gakkai, c/o Tokyo National Museum, 13-9 Ueno Park, Daito-ku, Tokyo, 110, Japan. Circ: 2,800.

913   USA   ISSN 0196-8319
E78.N6   CODEN: BASJEW
ARCHAEOLOGICAL SOCIETY OF NEW JERSEY. BULLETIN. Text in English. 1948. a. USD 15 to individual members; USD 20 to institutional members. bibl.; charts; illus. **Document type:** *Bulletin, Academic/Scholarly.* **Description:** Contains articles and reports of historic and prehistoric archaeological sites by a variety of scholars and other professionals.
Indexed: AbAn, AnthLit.
Published by: Archaeological Society of New Jersey, Humanities Bldg, Seton Hall University, South Orange, NJ 07079. Ed., R&P Charles A Bello. Circ: 300.

930.1   USA   ISSN 0195-6337
ARCHAEOLOGICAL SOCIETY OF NEW JERSEY. NEWSLETTER. Text in English. a. USD 15 to individual members; USD 20 to institutional members. **Document type:** *Newsletter.* **Description:** Deals with notes of current interest to society members.
Published by: Archaeological Society of New Jersey, Humanities Bldg, Seton Hall University, South Orange, NJ 07079. R&P Charles A Bello.

917   USA   ISSN 0587-1719
E78.N65
ARCHAEOLOGICAL SOCIETY OF NEW MEXICO. PAPERS. Text in English. 1968. a. USD 25 (effective 1999); includes newsletter. **Document type:** *Academic/Scholarly.* **Description:** Publishes in honor of a noted scholar, on the latest archaeological scholarship in New Mexico and the Southwest.
Indexed: AnthLit.

Published by: Archaeological Society of New Mexico, PO Box 3485, Albuquerque, NM 87190-3485. TEL 505-586-1931. Ed. Meliha Duran. R&P David Kirkpatrick TEL 505-526-5152. Circ: 400.

913   USA
ARCHAEOLOGICAL SOCIETY OF SOUTH CAROLINA. OCCASIONAL PAPERS. Text in English. 1979. irreg. price varies. bk.rev. **Document type:** *Academic/Scholarly.*
Published by: Archaeological Society of South Carolina, Inc., South Carolina Institute of Archeology and Anthropology, University of South Carolina, Columbia, SC 29208. TEL 803-777-8170, FAX 803-254-1338, nrice@sc.edu, http://www.assc.net. Ed. Christopher Gillam. Circ: 500.

930.1   USA
ARCHAEOLOGICAL SOCIETY OF VIRGINIA. SPECIAL PUBLICATIONS. Text in English. irreg.
Indexed: AnthLit.
Published by: Archaeological Society of Virginia, P.O. Box 70395, Richmond, VA 23255-0395. TEL 804-273-9291, FAX 804-273-0885, http://www.archsocva.org/ASVPress.html.

933   ISR
ARCHAEOLOGICAL SURVEY OF ISRAEL. SURVEY MAP SERIES. Text in Hebrew, English. 1972. irreg., latest 2001. price varies. maps. back issues avail. **Document type:** *Academic/Scholarly.* **Description:** Annotated maps pertaining to archaeological sites in Israel.
Published by: Israel Antiquities Authority, P O Box 586, Jerusalem, 91004, Israel. TEL 972-2-620-4622, FAX 972-2-628-9066, harriet@israntique.org.il.

930.1 677   GBR   ISSN 0169-7331
ARCHAEOLOGICAL TEXTILES NEWSLETTER. Text in English, French, German. 1985. 2/yr. GBP 30 for 2 yrs. (effective 2005). **Document type:** *Journal, Academic/Scholarly.*
Address: c/o Dr. J. P. Wild, 30 Prince's Rd., Heaton Moor, Stockport, SK4 3NQ, United Kingdom. TEL 44-161-4322460, mfassjpw@fs1.go.man.ac.uk. Eds. F C Wild, Dr. John Peter Wild TEL 44-161-4322460. Circ: 200 (paid).

913   CHE   ISSN 0255-9005
DQ30
ARCHAEOLOGIE DER SCHWEIZ/ARCHEOLOGIA SVIZZERA/ARCHEOLOGIE SUISSE. Text in French, German, Italian. 1978. q. CHF 45 (effective 2000). adv. charts; illus. **Document type:** *Academic/Scholarly.*
Supersedes (1970-1977): Schweizerische Gesellschaft fuer Ur- und Fruehgeschichte. Mitteilungsblatt; Helvetia Archaeologica (0018-0173).
Indexed: AnthLit, BHA, BrArAb, DIP, IBR, IBZ, NumL, RASB.
Published by: Schweizerische Gesellschaft fuer Ur- und Fruehgeschichte, Petersgraben 9-11, Basel, 4001, Switzerland. TEL 41-61-2613078, FAX 46-61-2613076, sguf@ubaclu.unibas.ch. Ed. Urs Niffeler. Circ: 2,500.

930.1   DEU   ISSN 0935-9141
ARCHAEOLOGIE IM RHEINLAND. Text in German. 1988. a. EUR 25.90 (effective 2003). **Document type:** *Monographic series, Academic/Scholarly.*
Published by: (Landschaftsverband Rheinland), Konrad Theiss Verlag GmbH, Moenchhaldenstr 28, Stuttgart, 70191, Germany. TEL 49-711-255270, FAX 49-711-2552717, service@theiss.de, http://www.theiss.de.

930.1   DEU   ISSN 0948-311X
ARCHAEOLOGIE IN BERLIN UND BRANDENBURG. Text in German. 1995. irreg., latest vol.6, 2003. price varies. **Document type:** *Monographic series, Academic/Scholarly.*
Published by: Konrad Theiss Verlag GmbH, Moenchhaldenstr 28, Stuttgart, 70191, Germany. TEL 49-711-255270, FAX 49-711-2552717, service@theiss.de, http://www.theiss.de.

913   DEU   ISSN 0176-8522
ARCHAEOLOGIE IN DEUTSCHLAND; das Magazin. Text in German. 1984. bi-m. EUR 59.85; EUR 50.85 to students (effective 2004). adv. bk.rev. **Document type:** *Magazine, Trade.*
Indexed: BrArAb, DIP, IBR, IBZ, NumL.
—**CCC.**
Published by: (Verband der Landesarchaeologen in der Bundesrepublik Deutschland), Konrad Theiss Verlag GmbH, Moenchhaldenstr 28, Stuttgart, 70191, Germany. TEL 49-711-2552714, FAX 49-711-2552717, service@theiss.de, http://www.theiss.de. Ed. Mr. Andre Wais. Adv. contact Ms. Gabriele Opelka. B&W page EUR 1,270, color page EUR 2,530. Circ: 12,198 (paid and controlled).

902   DEU   ISSN 1434-3398
ARCHAEOLOGIE IN OSTWESTFALEN. Text in German. 1997. irreg. **Document type:** *Monographic series, Academic/Scholarly.*
Published by: Verlag fuer Regionalgeschichte, Windelsbleicher Str. 13, Guetersloh, 33335, Germany. TEL 49-5209-980266, FAX 49-5209-980277, regionalgeschichte@t-online.de, http://www.regionalgeschichte.de.

930.1   USA   ISSN 1555-8622
▼ **ARCHAEOLOGIES;** journal of the World Archaeological Congress. Text in English. 2005 (Spr.). s-a. USD 40 to individuals; USD 120 to institutions (effective 2005).

Published by: (World Archaeological Congress GBR), AltaMira Press, 1630 N Main St, Ste 367, Walnut Creek, CA 94596. TEL 925-938-7243, FAX 925-933-9720, explore@altamirapress.com, http://www.altamirapress.com/RLA/Journals/Archaeologies/.

931.434 943 DEU ISSN 0724-8954
DD801.B2345
ARCHAEOLOGISCHE AUSGRABUNGEN IN BADEN-WUERTTEMBERG. Text in German. 1974. a. EUR 21.90 per issue (effective 2003). **Document type:** *Journal, Academic/Scholarly.*
Formerly (until 1982): Archaeologische Ausgrabungen (0341-1222)
Indexed: AnthLit, BHA, BrArAb, DIP, IBR, IBZ, NumL.
Published by: (Gesellschaft fuer Vor- und Fruehgeschichte in Wuerttemberg und Hohenzollern), Konrad Theiss Verlag GmbH, Moenchhaldenstr 28, Stuttgart, 70191, Germany. TEL 49-711-255270, FAX 49-711-2552717, service@theiss.de, http://www.theiss.de. Ed. Joerg Biel.

930.1 DEU
ARCHAEOLOGISCHE FORSCHUNGEN. Text in German. 1975. irreg., latest vol.19, 1997. price varies. back issues avail. **Document type:** *Monographic series, Academic/Scholarly.*
Published by: (Deutsches Archaeologisches Institut Berlin), Gebr. Mann Verlag, Neue Gruenstr 17, Berlin, 10179, Germany. TEL 49-30-2790760, FAX 49-30-27907655, vertrieb-kunstverlage@reimer-verlag.de, http://www.gebrmannverlag.de. R&P Elisabeth Roosens.

930.1 DEU ISSN 0178-1154
N5325
➤ **ARCHAEOLOGISCHE GESELLSCHAFT ZU BERLIN. WINCKELMANNSPROGRAMM.** Text in German. 1920. irreg., latest vol.140, 2001. price varies. **Document type:** *Monographic series, Academic/Scholarly.*
Published by: (Archaeologische Gesellschaft zu Berlin), Walter de Gruyter GmbH & Co. KG, Genthiner Str. 13, Berlin, 10785, Germany. TEL 49-30-260050, FAX 49-30-26005251, wdg-info@degruyter.de, http://www.degruyter.de.

913 DEU ISSN 0341-2873
ARCHAEOLOGISCHE INFORMATIONEN; Mitteilungen zur Ur- und Fruehgeschichte. Text in German. 1972. 2/yr. EUR 52 (effective 2005). **Document type:** *Journal, Academic/Scholarly.*
Indexed: AnthLit, BHA, BrArAb, DIP, IBR, IBZ, RASB.
Published by: (Deutsche Gesellschaft fuer Ur- und Fruehgeschichte), Dr. Rudolf Habelt GmbH, Am Buchenhang 1, Bonn, 53115, Germany. TEL 49-228-9238322, info@habelt.de, http://www.habelt.de.

930.1 DEU ISSN 0721-2399
DAS ARCHAEOLOGISCHE JAHR IN BAYERN. Text in German. 1981. a. EUR 29 (effective 2003). **Document type:** *Yearbook, Academic/Scholarly.*
Published by: (Bayerisches Landesamt fuer Denkmalpflege), Konrad Theiss Verlag GmbH, Moenchhaldenstr 28, Stuttgart, 70191, Germany. TEL 49-711-255270, FAX 49-711-2552717, service@theiss.de, http://www.theiss.de.

913.5 DEU ISSN 1434-2758
DS261.A1
ARCHAEOLOGISCHE MITTEILUNGEN AUS IRAN UND TURAN. NEUE FOLGE. Text in German, English, French. 1968. a. EUR 76 (effective 2005). back issues avail. **Document type:** *Monographic series, Academic/Scholarly.* **Description:** Reports on archaeological excavations and research in Iran conducted by the German Archaeological Institute.
Formerly (until 1997): Archaeologische Mitteilungen aus Iran. Neue Folge (0066-6033)
Indexed: A&ATA, AIAP, AnthLit, BHA, BibLing, DIP, IBR, IBZ, PCI, RASB.
—CCC.
Published by: (Deutsches Archaeologisches Institut, Eurasien Abteilung. Aussenstelle Teheran), Dietrich Reimer Verlag GmbH, Neue Gruenstr 17, Berlin, 10179, Germany. TEL 49-30-2790760, FAX 49-30-27907655, vertrieb-kunstverlage@reimer-verlag.de, http://www.dietrichreimerverlag.de. R&P Beate Behrens.

913 DEU ISSN 0170-5776
ARCHAEOLOGISCHE MITTEILUNGEN AUS NORDWESTDEUTSCHLAND. Text in German. 1978. a. **Document type:** *Academic/Scholarly.*
Published by: (Staatliches Museum fuer Naturkunde und Vorgeschichte Oldenburg), Isensee Verlag, Haarenstr 20, Oldenburg, 26122, Germany. TEL 49-441-25388, FAX 49-441-17872, verlag@isensee.de, http://www.isensee.de. Eds. Joerg Eckert, Mamoun Fansa. Circ: 1,200.

902 DEU ISSN 0178-045X
ARCHAEOLOGISCHE NACHRICHTEN AUS BADEN. Text in German. 1968. s-a. **Document type:** *Journal, Academic/Scholarly.*
Published by: Foerderkreis Archaeologie in Baden, Molkestr 74, Karlsruhe, 76133, Germany. info@foerderkreis-archaeologie.de, http://www.foerderkreis-archaeologie.de.

930.1 DEU
ARCHAEOLOGISCHE PARK XANTEN. FUEHRER UND SCHRIFTEN. Text in German. 1977. irreg., latest vol.18, 1998. **Document type:** *Monographic series, Academic/Scholarly.*
Published by: (Archaeologische Park Xanten), Rheinland Verlag GmbH, Abtei Brauweiler, Postfach 2140, Pulheim, 50250, Germany. TEL 49-2234-9854265, FAX 49-2234-82503. **Dist. by:** Dr. Rudolf Habelt GmbH, Am Buchenhang 1, Bonn 53115, Germany. TEL 49-228-232016, FAX 49-228-9238322.
Co-sponsor: Landschaftsverband Rheinland.

930.1 DEU
ARCHAEOLOGISCHE STAATSSAMMLUNG MUENCHEN. MONOGRAPHIEN. Text in German. 1999. irreg., latest vol.2, 2001. price varies. **Document type:** *Monographic series, Academic/Scholarly.*
Published by: Konrad Theiss Verlag GmbH, Moenchhaldenstr 28, Stuttgart, 70191, Germany. TEL 49-711-255270, FAX 49-711-2552717, service@theiss.de, http://www.theiss.de.

930.1 DEU
ARCHAEOLOGISCHE STAATSSAMMLUNG MUENCHEN. MUSEUMSFUEHRER. Text in German. 1999. irreg., latest vol.2, 2001. price varies. **Document type:** *Monographic series, Academic/Scholarly.*
Published by: (Archaeologische Staatssammlung Muenchen), Konrad Theiss Verlag GmbH, Moenchhaldenstr 28, Stuttgart, 70191, Germany. TEL 49-711-255270, FAX 49-711-2552717, service@theiss.de, http://www.theiss.de.

913 DEU ISSN 0003-8105
CC5
ARCHAEOLOGISCHER ANZEIGER. Text in German. 1849. s-a. EUR 38 per vol. (effective 2005). bk.rev. index. **Document type:** *Journal, Academic/Scholarly.*
Related titles: ◆ Supplement to: Deutsches Archaeologisches Institut. Jahrbuch. ISSN 0070-4415.
Indexed: AIAP, AnthLit, ArtInd, BHA, BrArAb, DIP, IBR, IBZ, NumL, RASB.
—IE, Infotrieve. **CCC.**
Published by: (Deutsches Archaeologisches Institut), Verlag Philipp von Zabern GmbH, Philipp-von-Zabern-Platz 1-3, Mainz, 55116, Germany. TEL 49-6131-287470, FAX 49-6131-2874744, zabern@zabern.de, http://www.zabern.de.

913.363 DEU ISSN 0342-734X
DD51
ARCHAEOLOGISCHES KORRESPONDENZBLATT. Text in German. 1971. 4/yr. illus. index. back issues avail. **Document type:** *Academic/Scholarly.*
Indexed: AIAP, BHA, BibInd, BrArAb, DIP, IBR, IBZ, NAA, NumL, PCI, RILM.
—BLDSC (1595.156000), IE, Infotrieve, ingenta.
Published by: Roemisch-Germanisches Zentralmuseum, Forschungsinstitut fuer Vor- und Fruehgeschichte, Ernst-Ludwig-Platz 2, Mainz, 55116, Germany. TEL 49-6131-9124-0, FAX 49-6131-9124199, rzentral@mainz-online.de. Circ: 2,500.

913 DEU ISSN 0948-8359
CC1
➤ **ARCHAEOLOGISCHES NACHRICHTENBLATT.** Text in German. 1956. q. EUR 49.80 domestic; EUR 57 foreign; EUR 22.50 domestic to students; EUR 25.50 foreign to students; EUR 19 newsstand/cover (effective 2005). adv. abstr.; bibl.; charts; illus.; maps. reprints avail. **Document type:** *Journal, Academic/Scholarly.* **Description:** Publishes papers on the organizational, legal, structural and methodological issues concerning the preservation of historical buildings and monuments.
Formerly (until 1995): Ausgrabungen und Funde (0004-8127)
Indexed: AICP, ASCA, AnthLit, ArtHuCI, BHA, BibInd, BrArAb, CurCont, DIP, IBR, IBZ, NumL, RASB, RILM, SSCI.
—IDS.
Published by: Akademie Verlag GmbH (Subsidiary of: Oldenbourg Wissenschaftsverlag GmbH), Palisadenstr 40, Berlin, 10243, Germany. TEL 49-30-4220060, FAX 49-30-42200657, info@akademie-verlag.de, http://www.akademie-verlag.de. adv.: B&W page EUR 880. Circ: 1,000 (paid and controlled).

913 USA ISSN 0003-8113
GN700
➤ **ARCHAEOLOGY.** Text in English. 1948. bi-m. USD 21.95; USD 4.99 per issue (effective 2005). adv. bk.rev. charts; illus.; maps; tr.lit. cum.index: vols.1-10, 11-26, 27-43. back issues avail.; reprints avail. **Document type:** *Journal, Academic/Scholarly.* **Description:** Reports on archaeological news at sites and museums throughout the world.
Related titles: Microform ed.: (from PQC); Online - full text ed.: (from EBSCO Publishing).
Indexed: A&ATA, ABS&EES, AIAP, AICP, AbAn, AmH&L, AmHI, ArtHuCI, ArtInd, BAS, BHA, BRD, BRI, BiolDig, BrArAb, CBRI, CurCont, HistAb, HumInd, IBR, IndIslam, MASUSE, MEA&I, MagInd, NAA, NTA, NumL, OTA, PMR, RASB, RGAb, RGPR, RI-1, RI-2, RILM, RefSour, SPPI, SSCI.
—BLDSC (1595.050000), IE, Infotrieve, ingenta.
Published by: Archaeological Institute of America, 36-36 33d St, Long Island City, NY 11106. TEL 718-472-3050, FAX 718-472-3051, publisher@archaeology.org, peter@archaeology.org, http://www.archaeology.org/, http://www.he.net/~archaeol/. Ed. Peter Young. Adv. contact Lois Segal. B&W page USD 8,730, color page USD 11,775; 7.375 x 10. Circ: 215,000 (paid).

913 ISR
ARCHAEOLOGY. Text in Hebrew. 1986. q.
Indexed: ArtInd, BRD, CurCont, RGAb.
Published by: (Israel Association of Archaeologists), Ariel Publishing, P O Box 3328, Jerusalem, Israel.

913 GBR ISSN 0140-7880
ARCHAEOLOGY ABROAD BULLETIN. Text in English. 1972. 3/yr. GBP 12, USD 30 to individuals; GBP 17, USD 40 to institutions (effective 2000). **Document type:** *Bulletin.* **Description:** Provides information about opportunities for archaeological fieldwork and excavation outside the UK, listing approximately 1,000 sites annually for both volunteers and staff.
Indexed: BrArAb.
Published by: Archaeology Abroad, 31 Gordon St, London, WC1H 0AH, United Kingdom. FAX 44-20-7383-2572, arch.abroad@ucl.ac.uk, http://www.britarch.ac.uk/archabroad. Ed. Norah Rix Maloney. Circ: 600.

930.1 SWE ISSN 0281-5877
ARCHAEOLOGY AND ENVIRONMENT. Text in English. 1983. irreg., latest vol.18, 2005. price varies. back issues avail. **Document type:** *Monographic series, Academic/Scholarly.*
Indexed: AnthLit.
Published by: Umeaa Universitet, Institutionen foer Arkeologi och Samiska Studier, Umea University, Umea, 90187, Sweden. TEL 46-90-7865542, FAX 46-90-137663, http://www.umu.se/archaeology/publikation/ae.

930.1 BGR ISSN 1310-9499
ARCHAEOLOGY IN BULGARIA. Text in Bulgarian, English; Summaries in French. 1997. s-a. BGL 54 domestic; USD 30 foreign; BGL 27 newsstand/cover (effective 2002). illus. **Document type:** *Journal, Academic/Scholarly.* **Description:** Publishes articles and reports on the most recent archaeological discoveries and texts in prehistory, the archaeology of Antiquity and the Middle Ages, numismatics, sphragistics, epigraphy, and anthropology, as well as reviews and commentary on exhibitions, museums, and new books.
Published by: Bulgarian Academy of Sciences, Archeological Institute and Museum, 2 Saborna St, Sofia, 1000, Bulgaria. TEL 359-2-882406, FAX 359-2-882405, http://www.sca.bg/cultural-periodicals/catalog/arcinbul.htm. Ed. Dr. Dimitar Ovcharov.

930.1 USA ISSN 0044-8591
CC21
ARCHAEOLOGY IN MONTANA. Text in English. 1958. 3/yr. USD 10 to individuals; USD 15 to institutions. adv. bk.rev. bibl.; charts; illus.; stat. index, cum.index: 1958-1969.
Media: Duplicated (not offset).
Indexed: AbAn, AmH&L, AnthLit, HistAb.
Published by: Montana Archaeological Society, Dept of Sociology, Montana State Univ, Bozeman, MT 59717. TEL 406-994-0211. Ed. Dr. Leslie B Davis. Circ: 250.

913 NZL ISSN 0113-7832
DU416
ARCHAEOLOGY IN NEW ZEALAND. Text in English. 1957. q., latest vol.46. NZD 70 domestic; NZD 100 foreign (effective 2003). bk.rev. charts; illus.; maps. cum.index: vols.1-30 (1957-1987). **Document type:** *Academic/Scholarly.* **Description:** Provides an outlet for shorter papers on any topic connected with the study of the prehistory and archaeology in New Zealand and the Pacific.
Formerly (until 1988): New Zealand Archaeological Association. Newsletter (0028-7962)
Related titles: Online - full text ed.
Indexed: AICP, AnthLit, INIS AtomInd, INZP, SPPI.
Published by: New Zealand Archaeological Association, PO Box 6337, Dunedin North, New Zealand. TEL 64-3-4772372, FAX 64-3-4775993, ml.campbell@auckland.ac.nz, http://www.nzarchaeology.org. Ed. Mat Campbell TEL 64-9-3737599. R&P Louise Furey. Circ: 500.

930.1 AUS ISSN 0003-8121
DU1
➤ **ARCHAEOLOGY IN OCEANIA.** Text in English. 1966 (April). 3/yr. (Apr., Jul. & Oct.). AUD 71.25 domestic; USD 71.25 foreign (effective 2006). adv. bk.rev. bibl.; charts; illus.; stat. Index. back issues avail.; reprint service avail. from PQC. **Document type:** *Journal, Academic/Scholarly.* **Description:** Contains in-depth articles and research reports, comments on prehistoric and historical archaeology and human biology of Australia and the Pacific region.
Formerly: Archaeology and Physical Anthropology in Oceania (0728-4896)
Related titles: Microfiche ed.; Microfilm ed.; Online - full text ed.: (from EBSCO Publishing, Gale Group).
Indexed: AICP, AbAn, AnthLit, AusPAIS, BAS, BIOSIS Prev, BibInd, BiolAb, IBR, IBSS, IBZ, PCI, RASB, SPPI.
—Linda Hall. **CCC.**

Published by: Oceania Publications, University of Sydney (H42), 116 Darlington Rd, Sydney, NSW 2006, Australia. TEL 61-2-93512666, FAX 61-2-93517488, oceania@arts.usyd.edu.au, http://www.arts.usyd.edu.au/publications/oceania/arch_oceania1.htm. Ed. J Peter White. Circ: 500.

913 IRL ISSN 0790-892X
DA920
ARCHAEOLOGY IRELAND. Text in English. 1987. q. USD 35. adv. bk.rev. illus. reprints avail. **Document type:** *Consumer.*
Indexed: BHA, BibInd, BrArAb, NumL.
—BLDSC (1595.090700), IE, ingenta.
Address: PO Box 69, Bray, Co. Wicklow, Ireland. TEL 353-1-2862649, FAX 353-1-2864215, http://slarti.ucd.ie/pilots/archaeology/.

930.1 GBR ISSN 0962-4201
ARCHAEOLOGY NORTH WEST. Text in English. 1991. s-a. **Document type:** *Bulletin, Academic/Scholarly.* **Description:** Provides a link between numerous archaeological and local history societies in the North West region of Britain and between professional archaeologists and interested laymen.
Indexed: BrArAb, NumL.
—BLDSC (1595.095450).
Published by: Council for British Archaeology North West, c/o U M A U, University of Manchester, Oxford Rd, Manchester, Lancs M13 9PL, United Kingdom. TEL 44-161-275-2317, FAX 44-161-275-2315. Ed. Michael Nevell.

930.1 USA ISSN 1096-9640
ARCHAEOLOGY ODYSSEY. Text in English. 1998. bi-m. USD 29.70 (effective 2005). adv. bk.rev. illus. back issues avail. **Document type:** *Magazine.*
Indexed: ArtInd, BiolDig.
Published by: Biblical Archaeology Society, 4710 41st St, NW, Washington, DC 20016. TEL 202-364-3300, FAX 202-364-2636, odyssey@bib-arch.org, bas@bib-arch.org, http://www.bib-arch.org/bswb_BR/indexBR.html. Ed. Hershel Shanks. R&P Bonnie Mullin. adv.: B&W page USD 1,980, color page USD 2,900. Circ: 70,000 (paid).

917 USA ISSN 0360-1021
E77.8 CODEN: AENAEV
ARCHAEOLOGY OF EASTERN NORTH AMERICA. Text in English. 1973. a. USD 40 (effective 1999). illus. **Document type:** *Academic/Scholarly.*
Indexed: AICP, AbAn, AnthLit, BibInd.
Published by: Eastern States Archeological Federation, PO Box 386, Bethlehem, CT 06751. TEL 203-266-7741. Ed., R&P Arthur Spiess. Circ: 500.

936.2843 GBR ISSN 0963-0937
ARCHAEOLOGY OF YORK SERIES. Text in English. irreg. price varies. back issues avail. **Document type:** *Monographic series, Academic/Scholarly.* **Description:** Reports on archaeological research at prehistoric, Roman, Viking, Saxon, and medieval sites in and around York.
Indexed: BHA, BrArAb, NumL.
—BLDSC (1595.120000), IE, ingenta. **CCC.**
Published by: (York Archaeological Trust), Council for British Archaeology, Bowes Morrell House, 111 Walmgate, York, YO1 9WA, United Kingdom. TEL 44-1904-671417, FAX 44-1904-671384, info@britarch.ac.uk, http://www.britarch.ac.uk. R&P Kathryn Sleight.

936.2843 GBR
ARCHAEOLOGY OF YORK. SUPPLEMENTARY SERIES. Text in English. 2002. irreg. **Document type:** *Monographic series, Academic/Scholarly.*
—BLDSC (1595.130000).
Published by: York Archaeological Trust, Cromwell House, 13 Ogleforth, York, YO1 7FG, United Kingdom. Ed. P V Addyman.

913 700 GBR ISSN 0003-813X
CC75 CODEN: ARCHAG
➤ **ARCHAEOMETRY.** Text in English. 1958. q. USD 263 combined subscription in the Americas to institutions & Caribbean, print & online eds.; GBP 133 combined subscription elsewhere to institutions print & online eds.; EUR 41 combined subscription in Europe to individuals print & online eds.; USD 60 combined subscription in the Americas to individuals & Caribbean, print & online eds.; GBP 27 combined subscription elsewhere to individuals print & online eds. (effective 2006). adv. bk.rev. bibl.; charts; illus. reprint service avail. from ISI,PSC. **Document type:** *Journal, Academic/Scholarly.* **Description:** Discusses the involvement of the physical sciences in archaeology and art history, with state-of-the-art specialist reports covering current research.
Related titles: Online - full text ed.: ISSN 1475-4754. USD 250 in the Americas to institutions & Caribbean; GBP 126 elsewhere to institutions (effective 2006) (from Blackwell Synergy, EBSCO Publishing, Gale Group, IngentaConnect, O C L C Online Computer Library Center, Inc., Swets Information Services).
Indexed: A&ATA, AIAP, AICP, ASCA, AbAn, AnthLit, ArtHuCI, BAS, BHA, BibInd, BrArAb, CIN, CIS, ChemAb, ChemTitl, CurCont, DIP, GEOBASE, IBR, IBZ, Inspec, MEA&I, NumL, PBA, RefZh, SSCI.
—BLDSC (1595.150000), AskIEEE, CASDDS, IDS, IE, Infotrieve, ingenta. **CCC.**

Published by: (University of Oxford, Research Laboratory for Archaeology and the History of Art), Blackwell Publishing Ltd., 9600 Garsington Rd, Oxford, OX4 2ZG, United Kingdom. TEL 44-1865-776868, FAX 44-1865-714591, customerservices@oxon.blackwellpublishing.com, http://www.blackwellpublishing.com/journals/ARCH. Circ: 1,500.

913 551.46 FRA ISSN 0154-1854
ARCHAEONAUTICA. Text in French. 1977. a. price varies. adv. bk.rev. index. **Document type:** *Academic/Scholarly.* **Description:** Reports concerning underwater archaeology. Includes studies on economic history, maritime history, and naval archaeology.
Indexed: BrArAb, NumL, RASB.
Published by: (France. Centre National de la Recherche Scientifique), C N R S Editions, 15 Rue Malebranche, Paris, 75005, France. TEL 33-1-53102700, FAX 33-1-53102727, http://www.cnrseditions.fr. Ed. Bernard Liou. Circ: 1,250 (controlled).

ARCHAEOZOOLOGIA; revue international d'archeozoologie. see *BIOLOGY—Zoology*

937 NLD ISSN 1384-6183
ARCHAIA HELLAS; monographs on ancient Greek History and archaeology. Text in English. 1995. irreg. price varies. **Document type:** *Monographic series, Academic/Scholarly.*
Published by: J.C. Gieben, Entrepotdok 72b, Amsterdam, 1018 AD, Netherlands. TEL 31-20-6234709, FAX 31-20-6275170, http://www.teachtext.net/gieben/. Ed. Sara B Aleshire. **Dist. in N. America by:** John Benjamins Publishing Co., PO Box 27519, Philadelphia, PA 19118-0519. TEL 215-836-1200.

913 GRC ISSN 1105-0969
DF11
ARCHAILOGIKE HETAIREIA EN ATHENAIS. PRAKTIKA. Text in Greek. 1837. a. price varies. illus. back issues avail. **Document type:** *Proceedings.* **Description:** Publishes full-text reports on the excavations being carried out by the Archaeological Society.
Indexed: BHA, NumL.
Published by: Archaeological Society at Athens/Archaiologike Hetaireia en Athenais, 22 Panepistimiou St, Athens, 106 72, Greece. TEL 30-1-3626-043, FAX 30-1-364-4996. Circ: 500.

930.1 GRC
ARCHAIOLOGIA KAI TECHNES. Text in Greek; Summaries in English. 1981. q. USD 40 in Europe; USD 45 in United States; USD 35 foreign to students. bk.rev. cum.index. **Document type:** *Newsletter, Academic/Scholarly.*
Formerly (until 1996): Archaiologia
Indexed: NumL.
Published by: Athinaika Nea SA (Subsidiary of: Lambrakis Foundation), 80 Michalacopoulou St, Athens, 115 28, Greece. TEL 30-211-365-9767, FAX 30-211-365-9798. Circ: 8,000 (paid).

913 GRC ISSN 0570-6211
DF10
ARCHAIOLOGIKE HETAIREIA. TO ERGON KATA TO (YEAR). Key Title: To Ergon tes Archaeologikes Etaireias kata to ... Text in Greek. 1954. a. USD 21 (effective 1998). illus. back issues avail. **Document type:** *Academic/Scholarly.* **Description:** Provides a summary of the Archaeological Society's excavations and scientific work.
Indexed: NumL.
Published by: Archaeological Society at Athens/Archaiologike Hetaireia en Athenais, 22 Panepistimiou St, Athens, 106 72, Greece. TEL 30-1-364-6043, FAX 30-1-364-4996.

913 GRC ISSN 0570-622X
DF10
ARCHAIOLOGIKON DELTION. Text in English, French, German, Greek, Italian. 1915. irreg. (2-3/yr.) (in 2 vols.). price varies. charts; illus. **Document type:** *Government.* **Description:** Publishes studies on Greek archaeology of all periods, and reports of archaeological activities in Greece.
Indexed: AIAP, BHA, NumL.
Published by: Ministry of Culture, Archaeological Receipts Fund (TAP Service), 57 Panepistimiou St, Athens, 105 64, Greece. TEL 30-1-325-3901-6, FAX 30-1-324-2684. **Dist. by:** Wasmuth, Hardenbergstr 9A, Berlin 10623, Germany.

ARCHEION EUVOIKON MELETON/ARCHIVES OF EUBOEAN STUDIES; Braveio Akademias Athenon. see *CLASSICAL STUDIES*

ARCHEION THESSALIKON MELETON/ARCHIVE OF THESSALIAN STUDIES. see *HISTORY—History Of Europe*

913 ITA ISSN 1120-4559
ARCHEO. Text in Italian. 1985. m. EUR 70.80 (effective 2005). adv. illus.; maps. **Document type:** *Magazine, Consumer.* **Description:** Publishes in-depth articles and news releases on notable archaeological excavations, bringing the past alive to present readers.

Published by: R C S Periodici (Subsidiary of: R C S Mediagroup), Via Angelo Rizzoli, 2, Milan, MI 20132, Italy. TEL 39-2-25845413, FAX 39-2-25845444, info@periodici.rcs.it, http://www.rcsmediagroup.it/siti/periodici.php. Circ: 28,053 (paid). **Dist. in UK by:** Seymour Distribution Ltd, 86 Newman St, London W1T 3EX, United Kingdom. FAX 44-207-396-8002, enquiries@seymour.co.uk.

913 ITA ISSN 0392-0038
➤ **ARCHEOGRAFO TRIESTINO**; raccolta di opuscoli e notizie per Trieste e per l'Istria. Text in Italian. 1829. a. bk.rev. abstr. index. **Document type:** *Academic/Scholarly.* **Description:** Contains articles on archaeology, architecture, history, linguistics, numismatics, and art, mainly concerning Trieste and its region.
Indexed: BHA, NumL.
Published by: Societa di Minerva, c/o Biblioteca Civica "Attilio Hortis", Piazza Attilio Hortis, 4, Trieste, TS 34124, Italy. TEL 39-040-301214, FAX 39-040-660245. Ed. Gino Pavan. Circ: 500.

930.1 FRA ISSN 0570-6270
CC3
ARCHEOLOGIA. Text in French. 1964. m. (11/yr.). adv.
Indexed: AIAP, AICP, BrArAb, NumL.
—BLDSC (1595.400000), IE, Infotrieve.
Published by: Editions Faton S.A., 25 rue Berbisey, Dijon, 21000, France. TEL 33-3-80404104. Circ: 55,000.

930.1 POL ISSN 0066-605X
CC15
ARCHEOLOGIA. Text in English, French, German, Polish; Summaries in French, Russian. 1950. a., latest vol.55, 2004. EUR 21 per vol. foreign (effective 2005). bk.rev. abstr.; bibl.; charts; illus. 163 p./no. 2 cols./p.; **Document type:** *Journal, Academic/Scholarly.* **Description:** Archaeological research in Poland and throughout the world.
Indexed: AIAP, AnthLit, BrArAb, DIP, IBR, IBSS, IBZ, NumL, RASB.
Published by: Polska Akademia Nauk, Instytut Archeologii i Etnologii, Al Solidarnosci 105, Warsaw, 00140, Poland. TEL 48-22-6202881, FAX 48-22-6240100, director@iaepan.edu.pl, http://www.iaepan.edu.pl. Ed. Maria Nowicka. **Dist. by:** Ars Polona, Krakowskie Przedmiescie 7, Warsaw, Poland. TEL 48-22-9263914, FAX 48-22-9265334, arspolona@arspolona.com.pl, http://www.arspolona.com.pl.

913 ITA ISSN 0391-8165
DE1
ARCHEOLOGIA CLASSICA. Text in Italian. 1949. a. price varies. bk.rev. charts; illus. index. back issues avail. **Document type:** *Monographic series, Academic/Scholarly.*
Indexed: AIAP, BHA, BrArAb, DIP, IBR, IBZ, MLA, MLA-IB, NumL.
Published by: (Universita degli Studi di Roma, Istituti di Archeologia e Storia dell'Arte Greca e Romana e di Etruscologia e Antichita Italiche), L'Erma di Bretschneider, Via Cassiodoro, 19, PO Box 6192, Rome, RM 00193, Italy. TEL 39-06-6874127, FAX 39-06-6874129, edizioni@lerma.it, http://www.lerma.it. Ed. Giovanni Colonna.

930.1 ITA ISSN 1126-6236
ARCHEOLOGIA DELL'ARCHITETTURA. Text in Italian. 1996. a., latest vol.6, 2001. EUR 25 domestic; EUR 28 foreign (effective 2005). **Document type:** *Journal, Academic/Scholarly.*
Related titles: ◆ Supplement to: Archeologia Medievale. ISSN 0390-0592.
Published by: Edizioni all'Insegna del Giglio s.a.s., Via N Piccinni 32, Florence, FI 50141, Italy. TEL 39-055-451593, FAX 39-055-450030, redazione@edigiglio.it, http://www.edigiglio.it.

930.1 ITA ISSN 1126-1587
DG975.E53
ARCHEOLOGIA DELL'EMILIA ROMAGNA. Text in Italian. 1997. s-a. EUR 29.95 domestic; EUR 34.09 foreign (effective 2002). **Document type:** *Journal, Academic/Scholarly.*
Published by: Edizioni all'Insegna del Giglio s.a.s., Via N Piccinni 32, Florence, FI 50141, Italy. TEL 39-055-451593, FAX 39-055-450030, http://www.edigiglio.it.

930.1 ITA ISSN 0390-0592
ARCHEOLOGIA MEDIEVALE. Text in Italian. a., latest vol.27, 2000. EUR 40 domestic; EUR 47 foreign (effective 2005). **Document type:** *Journal, Academic/Scholarly.*
Related titles: Online - full text ed.: (from Chadwyck-Healey Inc.); ◆ Supplement(s): Archeologia dell'Architettura. ISSN 1126-6236.
Indexed: AIAP, BHA, BrArAb, NumL.
Published by: Edizioni all'Insegna del Giglio s.a.s., Via N Piccinni 32, Florence, FI 50141, Italy. TEL 39-055-451593, FAX 39-055-450030, redazione@edigiglio.it, http://www.edigiglio.it.

913 POL ISSN 0003-8180
ARCHEOLOGIA POLSKI. Text in Polish; Summaries in English, French, German. 1957. s-a. EUR 25 foreign (effective 2005). bk.rev. abstr.; bibl.; charts; illus. index. 158 p./no. 1 cols./p.; **Document type:** *Journal, Academic/Scholarly.* **Description:** Studies on archaeological elements and methodology; discussions, chronicles.
Indexed: AICP, AbAn, BHA, BibInd, BrArAb, DIP, IBR, IBSS, IBZ, NumL, RASB.
—BLDSC (1595.450000).

Published by: Polska Akademia Nauk, Instytut Archeologii i Etnologii, Al Solidarnosci 105, Warsaw, 00140, Poland. TEL 48-22-6202881, FAX 48-22-6240100, director@iaepan.edu.pl, http://www.iaepan.edu.pl. Ed. Maria Dekowna. Circ: 500. **Dist. by:** Ars Polona, Krakowskie Przedmiescie 7, Warsaw, Poland. TEL 48-22-9263914, FAX 48-22-9265334, arspolona@arspolona.com.pl, http://www.arspolona.com.pl.

930.1 ITA
ARCHEOLOGIA POSTMEDIEVALE. Text in Italian. 1997. a., latest vol.4, 2000. EUR 25 domestic; EUR 28 foreign (effective 2005).
Published by: Edizioni all'Insegna del Giglio s.a.s., Via N Piccinni 32, Florence, FI 50141, Italy. TEL 39-055-451593, FAX 39-055-450030, redazione@edigiglio.it, http://www.edigiglio.it.

913 ITA ISSN 0392-9485
ARCHEOLOGIA VIVA. Text in Italian; Summaries in English. 1982. bi-m. EUR 26.40 domestic; EUR 37 foreign (effective 2005). adv. **Document type:** *Magazine, Consumer.*
Indexed: AIAP, NumL.
Published by: Giunti Gruppo Editoriale SpA, Via Bolognese 165, Florence, 50139, Italy. TEL 39-055-5062376, FAX 39-055-5062397, informazioni@giunti.it, http://www.archeologiaviva.it, http://www.giunti.it. Ed. Piero Pruneti. Circ: 17,600.

913 POL ISSN 1426-7055
ARCHEOLOGIA ZYWA. Text in Polish. 1996. q. EUR 10 foreign (effective 2005).
Address: Powazkowska 68/4, Warszawa, 01728, Poland. http://ciuw.warman.net.pl/alf/biskupin/lata/bisk96/archeo.htm. **Dist. by:** Ars Polona, Krakowskie Przedmiescie 7, Warsaw, Poland. TEL 48-22-9263914, FAX 48-22-9265334, arspolona@arspolona.com.pl, http://www.arspolona.com.pl.

930.1 USA ISSN 0570-6300
ARCHEOLOGICAL SOCIETY OF VIRGINIA. NEWSLETTER. Text in English. 8/yr. free membership (effective 2004). **Document type:** *Newsletter.*
Published by: (Archeological Society of Virginia), A S V Press, PO Box 70395, Richmond, VA 23255-0395. TEL 804-273-9291, FAX 804-273-0885, http://www.asv-archeology.org. Ed. Jack Hranicky.

917 USA ISSN 0003-8202
➤ **ARCHEOLOGICAL SOCIETY OF VIRGINIA. QUARTERLY BULLETIN.** Text in English. 1946. q. USD 25 domestic membership; USD 30 foreign membership (effective 2005). bk.rev. 40 p./no. 2 cols./p.; back issues avail. **Document type:** *Journal, Academic/Scholarly.* **Description:** Publishes technical papers on archeology and historical preservation in Virginia and nearby areas, as well as results of recent research, excavation and preservation activities and programs.
Indexed: AbAn, AmH&L, AnthLit, HistAb, IBR.
Published by: (Archeological Society of Virginia), A S V Press, PO Box 70395, Richmond, VA 23255-0395. TEL 804-273-9291, FAX 804-273-0885, trrein@facstaff.wm.edu, http://www.asv-archeology.org. Pub., R&P Harry A Jaeger. Circ: 1,000 (paid).

913.031 CZE ISSN 0323-1267
ARCHEOLOGICKE ROZHLEDY. Summaries in English; Text mainly in Czech; Text occasionally in English, French, German. 1949. q. EUR 12 per issue (effective 2004). bk.rev.; Website rev. charts; illus.; bibl.; abstr. 200 p./no.; back issues avail.; reprints avail. **Document type:** *Journal, Academic/Scholarly.* **Description:** Articles and reports on new research, conferences, university departments and institutes, as well as museum and institutes for the preservation of archeological monuments.
Indexed: AICP, AnthLit, BHA, BrArAb, IBR, NumL, RASB.
Published by: Akademie Ved Ceske Republiky, Archeologicky Ustav, Letenska 4, Prague, 11801, Czech Republic. TEL 420-2-57533369, FAX 420-2-57532288, jiran@arup.cas.cz, http://www.arup.cas.cz. Ed. Martin Jehek. **Dist. in Western countries by:** Suweco CZ SRO, Ceskomoravska 21, Prague 18021, Czech Republic.

930.1 943.7 SVK ISSN 0231-925X
ARCHEOLOGICKE VYSKUMY A NALEZY NA SLOVENSKU. Text in Slovak. 1974. irreg.
Indexed: RASB.
Published by: (Slovenska Akademia Vied/Slovak Academy of Sciences, Archeologicky Ustav), Vydavatel'stvo Slovenskej Akademie Vied Veda/Veda, Publishing House of the Slovak Academy of Sciences, Dubravska cesta 9, Bratislava, 84234, Slovakia. Ed. Bohuslav Chropovsky. Circ: 500.

930.1 FRA ISSN 0758-7708
DC607.7
ARCHEOLOGIE DU MIDI MEDIEVAL. Text in French. 1983. a. EUR 28.97 (effective 2004).
Indexed: AIAP.
Published by: Centre d'Archeologie Medievale du Languedoc, La Cite, 22, rue du Plo, Carcassonne, 11000, France. TEL 33-4-68712117, http://www.societes-savantes-toulouse.asso.fr/samf/caml/caml.htm.

930.1 FRA ISSN 0221-4792
ARCHEOLOGIE EN LANGUEDOC. Text in French. 1978. a.
Indexed: AnthLit.
Published by: Federation Archeologique de l'Herault, 1 Place de la Liberte, Saint-Guilhem-le-Desert, 34150, France. TEL 46-75-77291.

494.41 CHE ISSN 1420-4584
ARCHEOLOGIE FRIBOURGEOISE/FREIBURGER ARCHAEOLOGIE. Text in French, German. 1983. irreg., latest vol.18. price varies. **Document type:** *Monographic series, Academic/Scholarly.*
Published by: Academic Press Fribourg, Perolles 42, Fribourg, 1705, Switzerland. TEL 41-26-4264311, FAX 41-26-4264300, info@paulusedition.ch, http://www.paulusedition.ch/academic_press/.

930.1 NLD ISSN 1384-7538
➤ **ARCHEOLOGIE IN LIMBURG.** Text in Dutch. 1977. q. EUR 12 (effective 2003). bk.rev. charts; illus.; maps. back issues avail. **Document type:** *Academic/Scholarly.* **Description:** Publishes articles on archaeology, with particular emphasis on the Dutch province of Limburg.
Published by: (Sectie Archeologie), Limburgs Geschied- en Oudheidkundig Genootschap, Postbus 83, Maastricht, 6200 AB, Netherlands. TEL 31-43-321-2586, FAX 31-43-321-8572, info@lgog.nl, http://www.lgog.nl. Ed. W Dijkman. Circ: 600.
Co-sponsor: Archeologische Vereniging Limburg.

930.1 BEL ISSN 0778-2837
ARCHEOLOGIE IN VLAANDEREN; Flanders archeological bulletin. Text in Dutch; Text occasionally in English, French; Summaries in English. 1938-1988; N.S. 1991. a. bk.rev. abstr.; bibl.; illus.; maps. **Document type:** *Academic/Scholarly.* **Description:** Publishes excavation reports and studies on archaeology in Flanders (Belgium).
Former titles (until 1991): Archaeologia Belgica (0772-7488); (until 1949): Archeologie (0003-8210)
Related titles: ◆ Supplement(s): Archeologie in Vlaanderen. Monografieen. ISSN 1370-5768.
Indexed: BHA, BrArAb, NumL.
Published by: Instituut voor het Archeologisch Patrimonium, Phoenixgebouw, 1ste verd., Koning Albert-II-laan 19, Bus 5, Brussel, 1210, Belgium. TEL 32-2-553-1650, FAX 32-2-553-1655. Ed. Guy De Boe. Circ: 1,000.

930.1 BEL ISSN 1370-5768
ARCHEOLOGIE IN VLAANDEREN. MONOGRAFIEEN. Text in Dutch. 1994. irreg. price varies. **Document type:** *Monographic series.* **Description:** Publishes in-depth studies on the archaeology of Flanders (Belgium).
Related titles: ◆ Supplement to: Archeologie in Vlaanderen. ISSN 0778-2837.
Published by: Instituut voor het Archeologisch Patrimonium, Doornveld 1, Bus 30, Asse (Zellik), 1731, Belgium. TEL 32-2-4631333, FAX 32-2-4631951.

930.1 FRA ISSN 0153-9337
CC3
ARCHEOLOGIE MEDIEVALE. Text in French. 1971. a.
Indexed: AIAP, PCI.
—BLDSC (1595.730000).
Published by: (France. Centre National de la Recherche Scientifique), Universite de Caen, Centre de Recherches Archeologiques et Historiques Medievales, Esplanade de la Paix, BP 5186, Caen, 14032, France. TEL 33-231-565500, FAX 33-231-565600, http://www.unicaen.fr.

571 913 FRA ISSN 0066-6084
ARCHEOLOGIE MEDITERRANEENNE. Text in French. 1965. irreg. price varies.
Published by: Klincksieck, 6 Rue de la Sorbonne, Paris, 75005, France. TEL 33-1-43544757, FAX 33-1-40517385, http://www.klincksieck.com.

930.1 NLD ISSN 0928-1444
ARCHEOLOGISCHE ROUTES IN NEDERLAND; op zoek naar de geschiedenis in het landschap. Text in Dutch. 1993. q. illus.; maps. **Document type:** *Consumer.* **Description:** Discusses archaeology, history and environmental education in the Netherlands. Provides information for recreational tours, walking and bicycling.
Published by: Rijksdienst voor het Oudheidkundig Bodemonderzoek te Amersfoort, Kerkstraat 1, Amersfoort, 3811 CV, Netherlands. TEL 31-33-4634233, FAX 31-33-4653235, arne.haytsma@archis.nl, http://www.archis.nl/. Ed. A Haytsma.

913 GBR ISSN 1463-1725
CC1 CODEN: GEOFBC
ARCHEOLOGY INTERNATIONAL. Text in English. 1958. a. USD 20 per issue. 64 p./no.; **Document type:** *Bulletin.*
Formerly (until 1998): University of London. Institute of Archaeology. Bulletin (0076-0722)
Indexed: AnthLit, BHA, BrArAb, BrHumI, DIP, IBR, IBZ, IndIslam, NTA, NumL, RASB.
—BLDSC (1595.090200).
Published by: University College London, Institute of Archaeology, University College London, 31-34 Gordon Square, London, WC1H 0PY, United Kingdom. TEL 44-207-679-7495, FAX 44-207-383-2572, http://www.ucl.ac.uk/archaeology. Ed. David R. Harris. Circ: 800.

ARCHIV FUER PAPYRUSFORSCHUNG UND VERWANDTE GEBIETE. see *HISTORY*

930.1 FRA ISSN 0768-3537
ARCHIVES ROYALES DE MARI. Text in French. 1983. irreg. price varies. **Document type:** *Monographic series.*
Related titles: Microfilm ed.
Published by: Editions Recherche sur les Civilisations - A D P F, Les Patios Saint-Jacques, 6 rue Ferrus, Paris, Cedex 14 75603, France. TEL 33-1-43131100, FAX 33-1-43131125. Ed., Pub. Hina Descat. Circ: 600.

ARCHIVIO STORICO TICINESE. see *HISTORY—History Of Europe*

930.1 ESP ISSN 0210-3230
DP44
ARCHIVO DE PREHISTORIA LEVANTINA. Text in Spanish. 1928. a.
Indexed: AnthLit, PCI.
—CINDOC.
Published by: Diputacion Provincial de Valencia, Servicio de Investigacion Prehistorica/Provincial Delegation of Valencia, Service of Investigation, Valencian Community, Valencia, 46003, Spain.

931 ESP ISSN 0066-6742
ARCHIVO ESPANOL DE ARQUEOLOGIA. Text in English, French, German, Italian, Spanish. 1925. s-a. bk.rev. back issues avail.; reprints avail. **Document type:** *Academic/Scholarly.* **Description:** Covers new developments and historical articles of Spanish archaeology.
Supersedes in part (in 1940): Archivo Espanol de Arte y Arqueologia (0210-4180)
Related titles: Online - full text ed.: (from Chadwyck-Healey Inc.).
Indexed: AIAP, AICP, ArtInd, BHA, BrArAb, DIP, IBR, IBZ, IndIslam, MLA-IB, NumL, PCI, RASB, RI-1, RI-2.
—BLDSC (1654.947000), CINDOC.
Published by: (Spain. Consejo Superior de Investigaciones Cientificas), Instituto Espanol de Arqueologia (Subsidiary of: Consejo Superior de Investigaciones Cientificas), Departamento de Publicaciones, Vitruvio 8, Madrid, 28006, Spain. Ed. Luis Caballero. Circ: 850.

ARETHUSA. see *CLASSICAL STUDIES*

930.1 GRC ISSN 1105-0950
DF10
ARHAIOLOGIKE EPHEMERIS. Text mainly in Greek; Text occasionally in English, French, German. 1837. a. bibl. cum.index: vols.1-21 (1837-1874), vols.22-62 (1883-1923), vols.63-133 (1924-1994). back issues avail. **Document type:** *Academic/Scholarly.* **Description:** Publishes excavation reports and papers on various archaeological subjects.
Formerly (until 1909): Ephemeris Arhaiologike (1105-0942)
Indexed: AIAP, AICP, BHA, IBR, NumL.
Published by: Archaeological Society at Athens/Archaiologike Hetaireia en Athenais, 22 Panepistimiou St, Athens, 106 72, Greece. TEL 30-1-364-6043, FAX 30-1-364-4996. Circ: 500.

ARHEOLOGIA MOLDOVEI/ARCHEOLOGIE DE LA MOLDAVIE. see *HISTORY—History Of Europe*

913 HRV ISSN 0350-7165
DB361
ARHEOLOSKI MUZEJ U ZAGREBU. VJESNIK. Text in Croatian; Summaries in English, French, German. 1870. a., latest vol.33, 2000. HRK 120 domestic; HRK 80 foreign (effective 2001). bk.rev. illus. back issues avail. **Document type:** *Journal, Academic/Scholarly.*
Former titles (until 1958): Vjesnik Hrvatskoga Arheoloskoga Drustva (1330-7924); (until 1895): Viestnik Hrvatskoga Arkeologickoga Druztva (1330-7916)
Indexed: AICP, BHA, BibLing.
Published by: Arheoloski Muzej u Zagrebu, Trg N Zrinskog 19, Zagreb, 10000, Croatia. FAX 385-427-724, amz@zg.tel.hr. Ed. Ante Rendic Miocevic. R&P Ivan Mornik TEL 385-427-600. Circ: 700.

930.1 HRV ISSN 0570-8958
GN700
ARHEOLOSKI RADOVI I RASPRAVE. Text in Croatian. 1959. irreg., latest vol.13, 2001. price varies. **Document type:** *Monographic series, Academic/Scholarly.*
Indexed: AnthLit.
Published by: Hrvatska Akademija Znanosti i Umjetnosti, Zavod za Povijesne i Drustvene Znanosti, Odsjek za Arheologiju/Croatian Academy of Sciences and Arts, Institute of Historical and Social Sciences, Division of Arheology, Ante Kovacica 5, Zagreb, 10000, Croatia. TEL 385-1-4698222, FAX 385-1-4856211, bmigotti@hazu.hr, http://www.hazu.hr/O_arh.html.

913 SVN ISSN 0570-8966
➤ **ARHEOLOSKI VESTNIK/ACTA ARCHAEOLOGICA.** Text in English, French, German, Italian, Serbo-Croatian, Slovenian. 1950. a., latest vol.53, 2002. USD 40 (effective 2003). bk.rev. abstr.; charts; illus.; maps. 400 p./no.; back issues avail. **Document type:** *Journal, Academic/Scholarly.* **Description:** Provides studies and articles by Slovene and foreign scientists on prehistory, Roman provincial archaeology, and archaeology of the Migration Period and the early Middle Ages of the eastern Alpine and western Balkan region.
Indexed: AICP, AnthLit, BHA, CurCont, DIP, IBR, IBZ, NumL, RASB.

—KNAW.
Published by: Slovenska Akademija Znanosti in Umetnosti, Znanstvennoraziskovalni Center, Institut za Arheologijo, Novi trg 2, Ljubljana, 1000, Slovenia. TEL 386-1-4706100, FAX 386-1-4257757, http://www.zrc-sazu.si/iza. Ed. Marjeta Sasel Kos. Circ: 700.

913 USA
➤ **ARIZONA ARCHAEOLOGIST.** Text in English. 1965. a. price varies. back issues avail. **Document type:** *Monographic series, Academic/Scholarly.*
Published by: Arizona Archaeological Society, Inc., PO Box 9665, Phoenix, AZ 85068. TEL 520-621-2970. Ed. Alan Ferg.

301 USA ISSN 0518-6617
ARKANSAS AMATEUR. Text in English. 1962. bi-m. looseleaf. USD 18 includes subscr. to Central States Archaeological Journal (effective 2000). adv. bk.rev. charts; illus. back issues avail. **Document type:** *Newsletter.*
Published by: Northwest Arkansas Archaeological Society, Inc., PO Box 1154, Fayetteville, AR 72702. TEL 501-855-1970. Ed., Pub. Larry Swaim. R&P James F Cherry TEL 501-582-5846. Circ: 450 (paid and controlled).

913 USA ISSN 0015-0711
E78.A8
ARKANSAS ARCHEOLOGICAL SOCIETY. FIELD NOTES. Text in English. 1965. bi-m. USD 25 domestic to institutions; USD 30 foreign to institutions (effective 2003); includes Arkansas Archeologist. bk.rev. charts; illus. **Document type:** *Newsletter, Academic/Scholarly.* **Description:** News from surrounding area research and membership information.
Published by: Arkansas Archeological Society, 2475 N Hatch Ave, Fayetteville, AR 72704-5590. TEL 501-575-3556, FAX 501-575-5453. Ed., R&P Hester A Davis. Circ: 750.

917 USA ISSN 0587-3533
ARKANSAS ARCHEOLOGICAL SURVEY. PUBLICATIONS ON ARCHEOLOGY. POPULAR SERIES. Text in English. 1969. irreg., latest vol.3, 1992. price varies. charts; illus. **Document type:** *Monographic series.*
Published by: Arkansas Archeological Survey Publications, 2475 N Hatch Ave, Fayetteville, AR 72704. TEL 501-575-3556, FAX 501-575-5453, mkennedy@comp.uark.edu. Ed. Mary Lynn Kennedy. R&P Hester Davis TEL 501-575-6550.

917 USA ISSN 0277-6308
ARKANSAS ARCHEOLOGICAL SURVEY. PUBLICATIONS ON ARCHEOLOGY. RESEARCH REPORTS. Text in English. 1975. irreg., latest vol.29, 2000. price varies. **Document type:** *Monographic series.*
Published by: Arkansas Archeological Survey Publications, 2475 N Hatch Ave, Fayetteville, AR 72704. TEL 501-575-3556, FAX 501-575-5453, mkennedy@comp.uark.edu. Ed. Mary Lynn Kennedy. R&P Hester Davis TEL 501-575-6550.

917 USA ISSN 0882-5491
E78.A8
ARKANSAS ARCHEOLOGICAL SURVEY. PUBLICATIONS ON ARCHEOLOGY. RESEARCH SERIES. Text in English. 1967. irreg., latest vol.57, 2000. price varies. charts; illus. **Document type:** *Monographic series.*
Indexed: AnthLit.
Published by: Arkansas Archeological Survey Publications, 2475 N Hatch Ave, Fayetteville, AR 72704. TEL 501-575-3556, FAX 501-575-5453, mkennedy@comp.uark.edu. Ed. Mary Lynn Kennedy. R&P Hester Davis TEL 501-575-6550.

913 USA
ARKANSAS ARCHEOLOGICAL SURVEY. PUBLICATIONS ON ARCHEOLOGY. TECHNICAL PAPERS. Text in English. 1981. irreg., latest vol.10, 1999. price varies. **Document type:** *Monographic series.*
Published by: Arkansas Archeological Survey Publications, 2475 N Hatch Ave, Fayetteville, AR 72704. TEL 501-575-3556, FAX 501-575-5453, mkennedy@comp.uark.edu. Ed. Mary Lynn Kennedy. R&P Hester Davis TEL 501-575-6550.

913 USA ISSN 0004-1718
E78.A8
ARKANSAS ARCHEOLOGIST. Text in English. 1960. a. USD 25 domestic to institutions; USD 30 foreign to institutions (effective 2003); includes Arkansas Archeological Society. Field Notes. illus.; maps. **Document type:** *Monographic series.*
Indexed: AmH&L, AnthLit, HistAb.
Published by: Arkansas Archeological Society, 2475 N Hatch Ave, Fayetteville, AR 72704-5590. TEL 501-575-3556. Ed., R&P Hester A Davis. Circ: 750.

930.1 ESP ISSN 0213-8921
ARKEOIKUSKA; arkeologi aldizkaria. Text in Basque, Spanish. 1981. a. **Description:** Presents all archeological activities conducted in the Basque region.
Published by: (Basque Region. Kultura Saila/Departamento de Cultura), Eusko Jaurlaritzaren Argitalpen-Zerbitzu Nagusia/Servicio Central de Publicaciones del Gobierno Vasco, Donostia-San Sebastian, 1, Vitoria-gasteiz, Alava 01010, Spain. TEL 34-945-018561, FAX 34-945-018709, hac-sabd@ej-gv.es, http://www.ej-gv.net/publicaciones. Circ: 2,500.

930.1 NOR ISSN 0332-6500
ARKEOLOGISKE SKRIFTER. Text in Multiple languages. 1974. irreg.
Indexed: AnthLit.
Published by: Universitetet i Bergen, Arkeologisk Institutt, J. Frieles Gate 1, Bergen, 5007, Norway. TEL 47-55-582942, FAX 47-55-583160, post@ark.uib.no, http://www.hf.uib.no/arkeologisk, http://www.hf.uib.no/arkeologisk/.

914 DNK ISSN 0901-0815
ARKEOLOGISKE UDGRAVNINGER I DANMARK. Abbreviated title: Archaeological Excavations in Denmark. Text in Danish. 1985. a. free. back issues avail. **Document type:** *Academic/Scholarly.*
Indexed: NAA.
Published by: Kulturministeriet, Kulturarvsstyrelsen/Danish Ministry of Culture. Cultural Heritage Division, Slotsholmsgade 1, Copenhagen K, 1216, Denmark. TEL 45-72-265253, FAX 45-72-265101, kuas@kuas.dk, http://www.kuas.dk/tjenester/publikationer/emneopdelt/arkaeologi/aud.jsp. **Subscr. to:** Museumstjenesten, Lysgaard, Sjoerupvej 1, Viborg 8800, Denmark. TEL 45-86-667666, FAX 45-86-667611, mtj@museumstjenesten.com, http://www.museumstjenesten.com.

930.1 560 TUR ISSN 1017-7671
ARKEOMETRI SONUCLARI TOPLANTISI. Text and summaries in Turkish; Text occasionally in English. 1985. a. abstr.; bibl.; illus.; maps; stat. **Document type:** *Academic/Scholarly.* **Description:** Publishes reports of archaeometric evaluations of archaeological finds and prehistoric sites and artifacts, including dendrochronological studies in the Mediterranean basin.
Published by: Ministry of Culture, General Directorate of Monuments and Museums/Kultur Bakanligi, Anitlar ve Muzeler Genel Mudurlugu, Ulus - Ankara, 06100, Turkey. TEL 90-312-3104960, FAX 90-312-3111417.

ARKHEOGRAFICHESKII EZHEGODNIK. see *HISTORY*

930.1 RUS
ARKHEOLOGICHESKIE VESTI. Text in Russian. irreg., latest 2000.
Indexed: AnthLit.
Published by: Rossiiskaya Akademiya Nauk, Institut Istorii Material'noi Kultury, Otdel Paleolita, Dvortsovaya Naberezhnaya, 18, Sankt-Peterburg, 191186, Russian Federation. TEL 7-812-3121484.

913 BGR ISSN 0324-1203
CC13.R9 CODEN: ARKHDP
ARKHEOLOGIIA. Text in Bulgarian; Summaries in French, English, German. 1959. q. BGL 8 domestic; USD 10 foreign (effective 2002). bk.rev. bibl.; charts; illus. reprint service avail. from IRC. **Document type:** *Journal.* **Description:** Publishes articles and reports on the most recent archeological discoveries, discussions; archeology of Antiquity and the Middle Ages, numismatics, sphragistics, anthropology.
Indexed: AIAP, AnthLit, DIP, IBR, IBZ, NumL, RASB, SSCI.
—CASDDS.
Published by: (Bulgarska Akademiya na Naukite, Arkheologicheski Institut i Muzei), Universitetsko Izdatelstvo Sv. Kliment Okhridski/Publishing House of the Sofia University St. Kliment Ohridski, Akad G Bonchev 6, Sofia, 1113, Bulgaria. Ed. D Dimitrov. Circ: 1,800. **Dist. by:** Hemus, 6 Rouski Blvd., Sofia 1000, Bulgaria; **Dist. by:** Sofia Books, ul Silivria 16, Sofia 1404, Bulgaria. TEL 359-2-9586257, info@sofiabooks-bg.com, http://www.sofiabooks-bg.com.

930.1 RUS ISSN 0320-9431
ARKHEOLOGIYA I ETNOGRAFIYA UDMURTII. Text in Russian. 1975. irreg.
Indexed: MLA-IB.
Published by: Udmurdskii Institut Istorii Ekonomiki Literatury, Ul Sovetskaya 14, Izhevsk, Udmurt AR 426020, Russian Federation. Circ: 500.

930.1 UKR
ARKHEOLOHICHNYI LITOPYS LIVOBEREZHNOI UKRAINY. Text in Ukrainian. s-a. USD 80 in United States. **Document type:** *Academic/Scholarly.*
Published by: Tsentru Okhorony ta Doslidzhen' Pam'yatok Arkheolohii, Komsomol'skaya ul 37, Poltava, Ukraine. TEL 380-53-22612. **US dist. addr.:** East View Information Services, 3020 Harbor Ln. N., Minneapolis, MN 55447. TEL 612-550-0961.

930.1 UKR ISSN 0235-3490
DK508.3
ARKHEOLOHIYA; respublikanskyi mizhvidomchyi zbirnyk naukovykh prats. Text in Ukrainian; Summaries in Russian, English. 1989. q. USD 72.68 in United States (effective 2002). **Document type:** *Journal, Academic/Scholarly.* **Description:** Covers archaeological discoveries, anthropological description of population in ancient regions; types of culture of the population, technologies of manufacturing the products; antique architecture, etc. Describes great migration of people in various regions of the world,.
Indexed: AnthLit.
Published by: Natsional'na Akademiya Nauk Ukrainy, Instytut Arkheolohii, 40, Vydubetska St., Kyiv, 252014, Ukraine. TEL 380-44-2963581, FAX 380-44-2954713, ira@iarh.kiev.ua. Ed. P P Tolochko. Circ: 74,006.

930.1 ESP
ARQUENAS; investigacion y ciencias de la naturaleza. Text in Spanish. irreg.
Published by: Edita Impresion, Magallanes, 34, Santander, Cantabria 39007, Spain. Ed. Carlos Gonzalez Luque.

913 MEX ISSN 0187-6074
CC13.S66
ARQUEOLOGIA. Text in Spanish. 1987; N.S. 1989. s-a. MXP 210 domestic; USD 76.80 in US & Canada; USD 85.46 in South America and Central America & the Caribbean; USD 89.60 elsewhere (effective 2003). bk.rev. index. **Document type:** *Magazine, Academic/Scholarly.* **Description:** Covers the archaeology of Mesoamerica and northern Mexico.
Indexed: AnthLit.
Published by: (Coordinacion Nacional de Arqueologia), Instituto Nacional de Antropologia e Historia, Frontera 53, Col. Tizapan San Angel, Mexico City, DF 01000, Mexico. TEL 52-55-509714, FAX 52-55-503503, sub_fomento.cncpbs@inah.gob.mx, http://www.inah.gob.mx. Ed. Alba Guadalupe Mastache F. R&P Amanda Rosales Bada. Adv. contact Rosa Laura Hernandez Hernandez. Circ: 2,000.

930.1 ARG ISSN 0327-5159
F2821
ARQUEOLOGIA✶. Text in Spanish. 1991. a.?. **Document type:** *Academic/Scholarly.*
Published by: (Seccion Prehistoria), Universidad de Buenos Aires, Instituto de Ciencias Antropologicas, 25 de Mayo 221, Piso 3, Buenos Aires, 1002, Argentina. TEL 54-114-4322292, 54-114-3347512. Circ: 200.

930.1 PRT ISSN 0870-2306
CC13.P8
ARQUEOLOGIA. Text in Portuguese. 1980. s-a. adv. **Document type:** *Academic/Scholarly.*
Indexed: AnthLit.
Published by: Grupo de Estudos Arqueologicos do Porto, Rua Antonio Cardoso, 175, Porto, 4100, Portugal. geap@portugalmail.pt, http://www.geocities.com/geap1/page2.html. Ed. Vitor Oliveira Jorge. Circ: 1,000.

930.1 PER
ARQUEOLOGIA DE CERRO SECHIN. Text in Spanish. 1992. irreg., latest 1996. **Document type:** *Academic/Scholarly.*
Supersedes (1980-1985): Arqueologia de Sechin
Published by: Pontificia Universidad Catolica del Peru, Direccion Academica de Investigacion, cuadra 18, Ave. Universitaria, San Miguel, Lima 32, Peru. TEL 622540.

301 ESP ISSN 1136-8195
ARQUEOLOGIA ESPACIAL. Text in Spanish. 1984. irreg.
Related titles: ♦ Series: Seminario de Arqueologia y Etnologia Turolense. Revista. ISSN 1136-8187.
—CINDOC.
Published by: Seminario de Arqueologia y Etnologia Turolense, San Vicente de Paul, 1, Teruel, Aragon 44002, Spain. Ed. Francisco Burillo.

918 600 PRT ISSN 0870-8355
ARQUEOLOGIA INDUSTRIAL. Text in Portuguese. 1987. s-a. adv. bk.rev. **Document type:** *Academic/Scholarly.* **Description:** Covers industrial archaeology in Portugal, with emphasis on architecture and economic history.
Published by: Museu da Ciencia e Industria, Edif das Antiguas Moagens Harmonica, Estrada Nacional 108, Porto, 4003-001, Portugal. TEL 351-22-5300797, FAX 351-22-53006283, mcienciaindustria@um.geira.pt, http://www.geira.pt/mcienciaindustria/. Ed. Jose M Lopes Cordeiro. Circ: 500.

930.1 PRT ISSN 0872-2250
ARQUEOLOGIA MEDIEVAL. Text in Portuguese. 1992. a. price varies.
Published by: (Campo Arqueologico de Mertola), Edicoes Afrontamento, Lda., Rua de Costa Cabral, 859, Porto, 4200-225, Portugal. TEL 351-22-5074220, FAX 351-22-5074229, editorial@edicoesafrontamento.pt, http://www.edicoesafrontamento.pt/. Ed. Claudio Torres.

301 ESP ISSN 1134-3184
ARQUEOLOGIA Y TERRITORIO MEDIEVAL. Text in English. 1994. a.
Indexed: IndIslam.
—CINDOC.
Published by: Universidad de Jean, Area de Historia Medieval, Campus Las Lagunillas s-n, Jean, 21071, Spain. TEL 34-95-3212131. Ed. Vicente Salvatierra Cuenca.

930.1 PRT
ARQUEOLOGO PORTUGUES. Text in Portuguese. 1895. irreg.
Indexed: AnthLit.
Published by: Museu Nacional de Arqueologia, Praca I give to Imperio, Lisboa, 1400, Portugal. TEL 351-1-3620000, FAX 351-1-3620016.

A

301 ESP ISSN 0213-8026
ARSE; boletin del centro arqueologico saguntino. Text in Spanish. 1957. a. **Document type:** *Journal, Academic/Scholarly.*
—CINDOC.
Published by: Centro Arqueologico Saguntino, Caballeros 2, Sagunto, Valencia 46500, Spain.

ART AND ARCHAEOLOGY MAGAZINE. see *ART*

913 700 USA ISSN 0004-2986
ART AND ARCHAEOLOGY NEWSLETTER* . Text in English; Text occasionally in Egyptian, Greek, Latin. 1965. q. USD 7. adv. bk.rev. illus. index.
Related titles: Microform ed.: 1965 (from PQC).
Published by: Otto F. Reiss, Ed. & Pub., c/o H L Brill, 5939 Parsons Blvd, Flushing, NY 11365. Circ: 1,800.

ART, ANTIQUITY, AND LAW. see *ART*

ART, ARTIFACT & ARCHITECTURE LAW. see *LAW*

ARTE E ARCHEOLOGIA; studi e documenti. see *ART*

913 AUS ISSN 0044-9075
➤ **ARTEFACT**; Pacific rim archaeology. Text in English. 1965. a. AUD 25 domestic; AUD 35 foreign (effective 2001). adv. bk.rev. illus. back issues avail. **Document type:** *Academic/Scholarly.* **Description:** Covers archaeology, ethnohistory and anthropology of the Pacific region.
Formerly (1965-1966): Archaeological Society of Victoria. Newsletter (0313-5462)
Related titles: Online - full text ed.: (from R M I T Publishing).
Indexed: AbAn, AnthLit, AusPAIS.
—BLDSC (1733.490000), IE, ingenta.
Published by: Archaeological and Anthropological Society of Victoria Inc., GPO 328C, Melbourne, VIC 3001, Australia. TEL 61-3-93446904, FAX 61-3-93476684, mubullen@hotmail.com, http://www.vicnet.net.au/~aasv/aasvhom.htm. Ed. Yolande Kerridge. R&P Dr. M Bullen TEL 61-3-94862957. Circ: 300 (controlled).

➤ **ARTIBUS ASIAE**; journal of Asian art and archaeology for scholars and connoisseurs. see *ART*

➤ **ARTIBUS ASIAE SUPPLEMENTUM.** see *ART*

913 USA ISSN 0004-3680
E78.S7
ARTIFACT. Text in English. 1964. q. USD 25. bk.rev. **Document type:** *Academic/Scholarly.*
Indexed: AbAn, AnthLit.
Published by: El Paso Archaeological Society, Inc., PO Box 4345, El Paso, TX 79914-4345. TEL 915-751-3295. Ed. Carrol Hederick. Circ: 300.

930.1 USA ISSN 1556-9756
BS620.A1
ARTIFAX. Text in English. q. USD 10 domestic; USD 11 in Canada (effective 2001); includes all society publications. **Document type:** *Newsletter.*
Former titles: Institute for Biblical Archaeology. Newsletter (1084-6077); Near East Archaeological Society. Newsletter
Published by: Institute for Biblical Archaeology, 2175 Bicentennial Court, New Brighton, MN 55112. http://www.bibleartifax.com/. Ed. Clyde Billington.

ASIA INSTITUTE. BULLETIN. see *ASIAN STUDIES*

950 USA ISSN 0066-8435
DS514
➤ **ASIAN PERSPECTIVES**; the journal of archaeology for Asia and the Pacific. Text in English. 1957. s-a. USD 60 to institutions print or online ed; USD 84 combined subscription to institutions print and online eds (effective 2004). adv. bk.rev. illus. index. 160 p./no.; back issues avail.; reprint service avail. from PQC,ISI,PSC. **Document type:** *Journal, Academic/Scholarly.* **Description:** Presents papers on prehistory and archaeology of Asia and the Pacific.
Related titles: Microform ed.: (from PQC); Online - full text ed.: ISSN 1535-8283 (from bigchalk, EBSCO Publishing, Florida Center for Library Automation, Gale Group, H.W. Wilson, Northern Light Technology, Inc., O C L C Online Computer Library Center, Inc., Project MUSE, ProQuest Information & Learning, Swets Information Services).
Indexed: AICP, AMB, AbAn, AmH&L, AnthLit, BAS, DIP, GEOBASE, HumInd, IBR, IBSS, IBZ, PerIslam, RASB, RiceAb, SPPI, SSCI, ZooRec.
—BLDSC (1742.710000), IE, Infotrieve, ingenta. **CCC.**
Published by: University of Hawaii Press, Journals Department, 2840 Kolowalu St, Honolulu, HI 96822-1888. TEL 808-956-8833, FAX 808-988-6052, uhpjourn@hawaii.edu, http://muse.jhu.edu/journals/asian_perspectives/, http://www.uhpress.hawaii.edu/. Ed. Miriam T. Stark. R&P Joel Bradshaw TEL 808-956-6790. Adv. contact Carol Abe. page USD 200. Circ: 500.

301 ESP ISSN 0210-4741
DP44
ASOCIACION ESPANOLA DE AMIGOS DE LA ARQUEOLOGIA. BOLETIN. Text in Spanish. 1974. s-a.
Indexed: RILM.
—CINDOC.
Published by: Asociacion Espanola de Amigos de la Arqueologia, Apdo. Postal 14880, Madrid, 28080, Spain.

932 BEL
ASSASIF. Text in German. 1990. irreg. price varies. **Document type:** *Monographic series.*
Published by: Fondation Egyptologique Reine Elisabeth, Parc du Cinquantenaire 10, Brussels, 1000, Belgium. TEL 32-2-7417364.

930.1 GBR ISSN 1365-3881
CC1
➤ **ASSEMBLAGE**; the Sheffield graduate journal of archaeology. Text in English. 1996. a., latest 2001, Summer. bk.rev. illus. Index. reprints avail. **Document type:** *Academic/Scholarly.*
Media: Online - full text.
Indexed: AIAP, BrArAb, NumL.
Published by: University of Sheffield, Graduate School of Archaeology, 2 Mappin St, Sheffield, S Yorks S1 4DT, United Kingdom. TEL 44-114-222-5102, FAX 44-114-272-7347, assemblage@sheffield.ac.uk, http://www.shef.ac.uk/~assem.

304.2 GBR
ASSOCIATION FOR ENVIRONMENTAL ARCHAEOLOGY. SYMPOSIA SERIES. Text in English. a.
Indexed: AnthLit.
Published by: (Association for Environmental Archaeology), Oxbow Books, Park End Pl, Oxford, OX1 1HN, United Kingdom. TEL 44-1865-241249, FAX 44-1865-794449, oxbow@oxbowbooks.com, http://www.oxbowbooks.com.

930.1 FRA ISSN 0987-2205
ASSOCIATION POUR LA PROMOTION DE LA RECHERCHE ARCHEOLOGIQUE EN ALSACE. CAHIERS. Text in French. 198?. irreg. **Document type:** *Monographic series, Academic/Scholarly.*
Published by: Association pour la Promotion de la Recherche Archeologique en Alsace, 1 Place du General de Gaulle, Zimmersheim, 68440, France.

914 720 ITA
ASSOCIAZIONE PER IMOLA STORICO ARTISTICA. ATTI. Text in Italian. 1980. irreg., latest vol.13. price varies. bk.rev. bibl. **Document type:** *Monographic series.*
Supersedes: Realta Regionale. Fonti e Studi
Published by: University Press Bologna, Santerno Edizioni, Via 4 November, 7, Imola, BO 40026, Italy. TEL 39-542-20908, FAX 39-546-55082. Circ: 2,000.

953.57 UAE
AL-ATHAR FI DAWLAT AL-IMARAT AL-ARABIYYAH AL-MUTTAHIDAH/ARCHAEOLOGY IN THE UNITED ARAB EMIRATES. Text in Arabic, English. 1976. irreg. per issue exchange basis. **Description:** Publishes the results of archaeological investigations in the U.A.E.
Indexed: AnthLit.
Published by: Department of Antiquities and Tourism, P O Box 15715, Al-ain, United Arab Emirates. TEL 641595. Ed. Saif Bin Ali Al Darmaki.

930.1 900 USA ISSN 1083-4141
CC1
ATHENA REVIEW; quarterly journal of archaeology, history, and exploration. Text in English. 1995. q. USD 16. adv. bk.rev. illus. Index. reprints avail. **Document type:** *Academic/Scholarly.* **Description:** Contains well-researched articles of both scholarly and general interest concerning recent finds in archaeology.
Related titles: Online - full text ed.
Indexed: AICP.
Published by: Athena Publications, PO Box 10904, Naples, FL 34101. http://www.athenapub.com/. Ed. William Rust. Circ: 2,000 (paid).

913 GRC ISSN 0004-6604
DF10
ATHENS ANNALS OF ARCHAEOLOGY. Text in English, French, German, Greek, Italian. 1968. irreg. (1-3/yr.). price varies. charts; illus. **Document type:** *Academic/Scholarly.* **Description:** Covers archaeological news from Greece.
Indexed: AIAP, BHA.
Published by: Ministry of Culture, Archaeological Receipts Fund (TAP Service), 57 Panepistimiou St, Athens, 105 64, Greece. TEL 30-1-325-3901-6, FAX 30-1-324-2684, TELEX 225932 TAP GR. **Dist. by:** Wasmuth K.G., Hardenbergstr 9A, Berlin 10623, Germany.

930.1 956 GBR
ATHLONE PUBLICATIONS IN EGYPTOLOGY AND ANCIENT NEAR EASTERN STUDIES. Text in English. 1996. irreg. GBP 50 (effective 2000). illus. **Document type:** *Monographic series, Academic/Scholarly.* **Description:** Aims to contribute across a broad front to an understanding of ancient history, the social sciences, art history and allied disciplines.
Published by: Athlone Press Ltd., 1 Park Dr, London, NW11 7SG, United Kingdom. TEL 44-20-8458-0888, FAX 44-20-8201-8115, athlonepress@btinternet.com. Ed. Tristan Palmer. Pub. Brian Southam. R&P Doris Southam.

571 ISR ISSN 0792-8424
DS111.A1
ATIQOT; Jerusalem: excavation reports and studies. Variant title: Atiqwt. Text in English. 1955. irreg., latest vol.40, 2000. price varies. illus. back issues avail. **Document type:** *Journal, Academic/Scholarly.* **Description:** Reports of archaeological excavations in Israel.
Formed by the merger of (1956-1991): Atiqot (Hebrew Series) (0067-0138); (1955-1991): Atiqot (English Series) (0066-488X)
Indexed: AIAP, BHA, BibLing, IHP, NTA, NumL, RASB, ZooRec.
—IE, Infotrieve.
Published by: Israel Antiquities Authority, P O Box 586, Jerusalem, 91004, Israel. TEL 972-2-620-4622, FAX 972-2-628-9066, harriet@israntique.org.il. Ed. Ayala Sussman. Circ: 1,500. **Dist. by:** Eisenbrauns, PO Box 275, Winona Lake, IN 46590-0275.

930.1 DEU
ATLAS ARCHAEOLOGISCHER GELAENDEDENKMAELER. Text in German. irreg., latest vol.2, no.12, 2002. price varies. **Document type:** *Monographic series, Academic/Scholarly.*
Published by: (Baden-Wuerttemberg. Landesdenkmalamt Baden-Wuerttemberg), Konrad Theiss Verlag GmbH, Moenchhaldenstr 28, Stuttgart, 70191, Germany. TEL 49-711-255270, FAX 49-711-2552717, service@theiss.de, http://www.theiss.de.

ATLAS POLSKICH STROJOW LUDOWYCH. see *ANTHROPOLOGY*

930.1 DEU ISSN 1433-6979
AUSGRABUNGEN UND FUNDE IM FREISTAAT THUERINGEN. Text in German. 1996. irreg., latest vol.7, 2003. price varies. **Document type:** *Monographic series, Academic/Scholarly.*
Published by: (Landesamt fuer Archaeologische Denkmalpflege Thueringen), Konrad Theiss Verlag GmbH, Moenchhaldenstr 28, Stuttgart, 70191, Germany. TEL 49-711-2552770, FAX 49-711-2552717, service@theiss.de, http://www.theiss.de.

913 AUS ISSN 1322-9214
DU106
➤ **AUSTRALASIAN HISTORICAL ARCHAEOLOGY.** Text in English. a. AUD 50 for membership to individuals; AUD 60 for membership to institutions (effective 2002); membership incls. journal & newsletter. bk.rev. back issues avail. **Document type:** *Journal, Academic/Scholarly.*
Formerly: Australian Journal of Historical Archaeology (0810-1868); Supersedes (in 1983): Australian Society for Historical Archeology. (Annual Publication); Which was formerly (until 1973): Studies in Historical Archeology
Related titles: Microform ed.
Indexed: AbAn, AmH&L, AnthLit, AusPAIS, HistAb, PCI, RASB.
—BLDSC (8490.640000).
Published by: Australasian Society for Historical Archaeology, University of Sydney, Holme Bldg, PO Box 220, Sydney, NSW 2006, Australia. asha_secretary@yahoo.co.uk. Circ: 400.

930.1 AUS ISSN 1447-0276
➤ **AUSTRALASIAN INSTITUTE FOR MARITIME ARCHAEOLOGY. BULLETIN.** Variant title: A I M A Bulletin. Text in English. s-a. AUD 45 to individual members; AUD 85 to institutional members; AUD 35 to students. **Document type:** *Bulletin, Academic/Scholarly.* **Description:** Covers the international maritime archaeology scene as well as various Australian projects.
Former titles (until 2001): Australian Institute for Maritime Archaeology. Bulletin (0813-2801); (until 1982): Institute of Maritime Archaeology. Bulletin (0810-6991); (until 1981): Australian Maritime Archaeology Newsletter
—BLDSC (2409.316750), IE, ingenta.
Published by: Australasian Institute for Maritime Archaeology, c/o Tim Smith, Locked Bag 5020, Parramatta, NSW 5020, Australia. TEL 61-2-9849-9574, smitht@heritage.nsw.gov.au, http://www.aima.iinet.net.au.

930.102804 AUS
AUSTRALASIAN INSTITUTE FOR MARITIME ARCHAEOLOGY. NEWSLETTER. Text in English. 1983. q. Free. back issues avail. **Document type:** *Newsletter, Academic/Scholarly.* **Description:** Presents news and results from recent research, excavation work and projects at hand.
Formerly: Australian Institute for Maritime Archaeology. Newsletter (0814-1479)
Media: Online - full text.
—BLDSC (6106.372500).
Published by: Australasian Institute for Maritime Archaeology, c/o Tim Smith, Locked Bag 5020, Parramatta, NSW 5020, Australia. TEL 61-2-9849-9574, smitht@heritage.nsw.gov.au, http://www.aima.iinet.net.au/frames_no/publications/newsletters/newsletter.html. Ed. Ms. Lindsey Shaw.

913 AUS
➤ **AUSTRALASIAN SOCIETY FOR HISTORICAL ARCHAEOLOGY. NEWSLETTER.** Text in English. 1970. q. AUD 50 for membership to individuals; AUD 60 for membership to institutions (effective 2002); membership incls. journal & newsletter. back issues avail. **Document type:** *Newsletter, Academic/Scholarly.* **Description:** Promotes the study of historical archaeology both in Australia and overseas.
Formerly: Australian Society for Historical Archaeology. Research Bulletin (0819-4076)
—BLDSC (6108.345000).

Published by: Australasian Society for Historical Archaeology, University of Sydney, Holme Bldg, PO Box 220, Sydney, NSW 2006, Australia. asha_secretary@yahoo.co.uk. Ed. Ross Gam. Circ: 400.

➤ **AUSTRALIAN ABORIGINAL STUDIES.** see *ANTHROPOLOGY*

914.2 AUS ISSN 0312-2417
CODEN: EGABAN

➤ **AUSTRALIAN ARCHAEOLOGY.** Text in English. 1974. 2/yr. AUD 50 to individual members; AUD 100 to institutions; AUD 30 to students & senior citizens (effective 2004). bk.rev. abstr.; illus.; bibl.; maps. cum.index: vols.1-20. 82 p./no.; back issues avail. **Document type:** *Journal, Academic/Scholarly.*
Description: Contains original articles in all fields of archaeology and other subjects relevant to archaeological research and practice in Australia and nearby areas, including prehistoric (Indigenous), historic, maritime and contemporary periods in terms of research and cultural heritage management.
Related titles: Online - full text ed.: (from R M I T Publishing).
Indexed: AICP, AnthLit, AusPAIS, PCI, ZooRec.
—BLDSC (1797.378500), IE, ingenta.
Published by: Australian Archaeological Association Inc., Archaeology A14, University of Sydney, St Lucia, NSW 2006, Australia. TEL 61-2-93517412, mailbag@australianarchaeology.com, http://www.australianarchaeologicalassociation.com.au. Eds. Dr. Donald Pate, Dr. Pam Smith. Circ: 500.

930.1 AUS
AUSTRALIAN NATIONAL UNIVERSITY. DEPARTMENT OF ARCHAEOLOGY AND NATURAL HISTORY. RESEARCH PAPERS✶. Text in English. irreg.
Formerly: Australian National University. Department of Archaeology and Natural History. Occasional Papers in Prehistory
Indexed: AnthLit.
Published by: Australian National University, Department of Archaeology and Natural History, Research School of Pacific and Asian Studies, Canberra, ACT 0200, Australia. TEL 61-2-61253040, FAX 61-2-61254917, geoff.hope@coombs.anu.edu.au, http://rspas.anu.edu.au/anh/.

917 USA ISSN 0749-1816
AWANYU; newsletter of the archeological society of New Mexico. Text in English. 1972. q. USD 25 (effective 1999); includes A S N M Paper. bk.rev. charts; illus. index. back issues avail. **Document type:** *Newsletter.* **Description:** Presents archaeological news of New Mexico and the Southwest, and membership information about he Archaeological Society of New Mexico.
Superseded: A S N M Newsletter
Indexed: AbAn.
Published by: Archaeological Society of New Mexico, PO Box 3485, Albuquerque, NM 87190-3485. TEL 505-281-3579, FAX 505-281-3579, jjbrody@unm.edu. Eds. J J Brody, Jean Brody. R&P J. J Brody. Circ: 325.

913 GBR
DA880.A9
AYRSHIRE MONOGRAPHS. Text in English. 1877; N.S. 1950. s-a. price varies. bibl.; charts; illus. index. back issues avail. **Document type:** *Monographic series.*
Formerly (until 1987): Ayrshire Collections (0302-3176)
Indexed: BrArAb, NumL.
Published by: Ayrshire Archaeological & Natural History Society, c/o Ronald W. Brash, Publication Mgr., 10 Robsland Ave, Ayr, Ayrshire KA7 2RW, United Kingdom. TEL 44-1292-266745. Ed. J Strawhorn. Circ: 900.

930.1 GBR
AYRSHIRE NOTES. Text in English. s-a. GBP 0.50. bibl.; charts; illus. **Document type:** *Monographic series.*
Published by: Ayrshire Archaeological & Natural History Society, c/o Ronald W. Brash, Publication Mgr., 10 Robsland Ave, Ayr, Ayrshire KA7 2RW, United Kingdom. TEL 44-1292-266745. Ed. John Strawhorn.

AZANIA. see *HISTORY—History Of Africa*

930.1 GBR
B A A S BULLETIN. Text in English. 1981 (no.4). s-a. membership. **Document type:** *Newsletter.* **Description:** Lists future group events and news of local archaeology.
Formerly: B A A R G Bulletin (0262-9828)
Published by: Bristol and Avon Archaeological Society, Bristol City Museum, Queen's Rd, Bristol, BS8 1RL, United Kingdom.

930.1 GBR ISSN 0143-3032
B A R. BRITISH SERIES. (British Archaeological Reports) Text in English. 1974. irreg. **Document type:** *Monographic series.*
Formerly (until 1978): British Archaeological Reports (0306-1205)
Indexed: AnthLit.
—BLDSC (1863.185600), IE, ingenta.
Published by: Archaeopress, Gordon House, 276 Banbury Road, Oxford, OX2 7ED, United Kingdom. bar@archaeopress.com.

930.1 GBR ISSN 0143-3067
B A R. INTERNATIONAL SERIES. (British Archaeological Reports) Text in English. 1975. irreg. price varies. **Document type:** *Monographic series.*
Formerly (until 1978): B A R. Supplementary Series (0143-3016)
Indexed: AnthLit, ZooRec.
—BLDSC (1863.187300). **CCC.**
Published by: Archaeopress, Gordon House, 276 Banbury Road, Oxford, OX2 7ED, United Kingdom. bar@archaeopress.com, http://www.archaeopress.com.

913 709 ITA ISSN 1594-7084
GN818.C3
B C S P. (Bollettino del Centro Camuno di Studi Preistorici) Text in Multiple languages. 1965. a. price varies. bk.rev. bibl.; charts; illus. back issues avail.; reprints avail. **Description:** Contains articles, research reports and surveys on recent discoveries throughout the world. Each published in its original language.
Formerly (until 1977): Centro Camuno di Studi Preistorici. Bollettino (0577-2168)
Indexed: AICP, AnthLit, BrArAb, RASB.
Published by: Centro Camuno di Studi Preistorici, Capo di Ponte, BS 25044, Italy. TEL 39-0364-42091, FAX 39-0364-42572, info@ccsp.it, http://www.ccsp.it. Ed. Emmanuel Anati.

913 930 FRA
B E F A R. PUBLICATION. Text in French. 1877. irreg. (1-2/yr.). price varies. bibl. **Document type:** *Monographic series, Academic/Scholarly.*
Related titles: Microfiche ed.: (from BHP).
Published by: (Bibliotheque des Ecoles Francaises d'Athenes et de Rome), De Boccard Edition - Diffusion, 11 rue de Medicis, Paris, 75006, France. TEL 33-1-43260037, FAX 33-1-43548583, http://www.deboccard.com.

949.5 GBR ISSN 1108-3417
B S A NEWSLETTER. Text in English. 1998. s-a. **Document type:** *Newsletter, Academic/Scholarly.*
Published by: British School at Athens, Senate House, Marlet St, London, WC1E 7HU, United Kingdom. TEL 44-20-7862-8732, FAX 44-20-7867-8733, http://www.bsa.gla.ac.uk.

930.1 USA
BACKDIRT. Text in English. biennial. free (effective 2004). illus. **Document type:** *Academic/Scholarly.* **Description:** Backdirt is a biennial newsletter covering the activities of the faculty, research associates, students, and staff of the Institute of Archaeology at UCLA. It includes research articles, faculty profiles, laboratory news, book excerpts, reports on Institute events, and a public lectures calendar.
Related titles: Online - full text ed.
Indexed: AICP.
Published by: (Publications Department), University of California at Los Angeles, Cotsen Institute of Archaeology, A222 Fowler Museum, Box 951510, Los Angeles, CA 90095-1510. TEL 310-825-7411, FAX 310-206-4723, http://www.sscnet.ucla.edu/ioa/backdirt.htm, http://www.sscnet.ucla.edu/ioa/pubs.html.

930.1 DEU ISSN 0939-0022
BAGHDADER FORSCHUNGEN. Text in German. 1979. irreg., latest vol.24, 2000. price varies. bibl.; charts; illus.; maps. **Document type:** *Monographic series, Academic/Scholarly.*
Published by: (Deutsches Archaeologisches Institut, Orientabteilung), Verlag Philipp von Zabern GmbH, Philipp-von-Zabern-Platz 1-3, Mainz, 55116, Germany. TEL 49-6131-287470, FAX 49-6131-223710, zabern@zabern.de, http://www.zabern.de. Adv. contact Manuela Dressen TEL 49-6131-2874711.

913 DEU ISSN 0418-9698
DS69.5
BAGHDADER MITTEILUNGEN. Text in German, English, French. 1960. a., latest vol.30, 1999. bibl.; charts; illus.; maps. back issues avail. **Document type:** *Journal, Academic/Scholarly.*
Indexed: AIAP, BHA, BibLing, DIP, IBR, IBZ.
Published by: (Deutsches Archaeologisches Institut, Orientabteilung), Verlag Philipp von Zabern GmbH, Philipp-von-Zabern-Platz 1-3, Mainz, 55116, Germany. TEL 49-6131-287470, FAX 49-6131-223710, zabern@zabern.de, http://www.zabern.de. Adv. contact Manuela Dressen TEL 49-6131-2874711.

930.1 ESP ISSN 0210-6132
GN836.A73
BAJO ARAGON. PREHISTORIA. Text in Spanish. 1979. a. varies.
Indexed: AnthLit.
—CINDOC.
Published by: Institucion Fernando el Catolico, Plaza de Espana 2, Zaragoza, 50071, Spain. TEL 34-976-288878, FAX 34-976-288869, ifc@dpz.es, http://ifc.dpz.es. R&P Felix Sanchez TEL 34-976-288858. Adv. contact Maria Luz Cortes TEL 34-976-288879.

BANGLADESH LALIT KALA. see *MUSEUMS AND ART GALLERIES*

BAUSTEINE ZUR ETHNO-POLITISCHEN FORSCHUNG. see *ETHNIC INTERESTS*

BAUTENSCHUTZ UND BAUSANIERUNG; Zeitschrift fuer Bauinstandhaltung und Denkmalpflege. see *BUILDING AND CONSTRUCTION*

739.27 CAN ISSN 0829-8726
GN419.B4
➤ **BEAD FORUM.** Text in English. 1981. s-a. USD 20; USD 30 foreign. bibl.; illus. 12 p./no. 1 cols./p.; back issues avail. **Document type:** *Newsletter, Academic/Scholarly.*
Description: Intended to disseminate timely information related to bead research worldwide.
Indexed: AICP.
Published by: Society of Bead Researchers, 1600 Liverpool Ct, Ottawa, ON K1A 0M5, Canada. TEL 613-990-4814, FAX 613-952-1756, karlis.karlins@pc.gc.ca, http://www.mindspring.com/~larinc/sbr/index/. Ed. Michael Pfeiffer. Circ: 400.

➤ **BEADS.** see *ANTHROPOLOGY*

930.1 GBR ISSN 0958-191X
DA670.B29
BEDFORDSHIRE ARCHAEOLOGY. Text in English. 1962. a.
Formerly (until 1983): Bedfordshire Archaeological Journal (0408-7666)
Indexed: AIAP, BrHumI.
—BLDSC (1872.815400), IE, ingenta.
Published by: Bedfordshire Archaeological Council, 6 Neale Way, Wootton, Bedfordshire MK43 9EP, United Kingdom. TEL 44-1234-228072, ColemanS@deed.bedfordshire.gov.uk, http://www.museums.bedfordshire.gov.uk/localgroups/bac.html. Ed. Stephen Coleman.

BEER-SHEVA. see *RELIGIONS AND THEOLOGY—Judaic*

915 CHN ISSN 1001-0483
DS793.H4
BEIFANG WENWU/NORTHERN CULTURAL RELICS. Text in Chinese. 1985. q. USD 22.50. bk.rev.
Related titles: Online - full text ed.: (from East View Information Services).
Published by: (Heilongjiang Wenwu Guanli Weiyuanhui/ Heilongjiang Provincial Cultural Relics Management Committee), Beifang Wenwu Bianjibu/Heilongjiang Provincial Cultural Relics Management Committee, 50 Hongjun Jie, Dangang District, Harbin, Heilongjiang 150001, China. TEL 3635089. Ed. Wu Wenjie. **Dist. in US by:** China Books & Periodicals Inc, 360 Swift Ave., Ste. 48, S San Fran, CA 94080-6220. TEL 415-282-2994.

930.1 DEU ISSN 0067-4893
BEIHEFTE DER BONNER JAHRBUECHER. Text in German. 1950. irreg., latest vol.52, 1998. price varies. **Document type:** *Monographic series, Academic/Scholarly.*
Indexed: BHA.
Published by: (Landschaftsverband Rheinland), Rheinland Verlag GmbH, Abtei Brauweiler, Postfach 2140, Pulheim, 50250, Germany. TEL 49-2234-9854265, FAX 49-2234-82503. **Dist. by:** Dr. Rudolf Habelt GmbH, Am Buchenhang 1, Bonn 53115, Germany. TEL 49-228-232016, FAX 49-228-9238322.
Co-sponsor: Rheinisches Landesmuseum, Verein von Altertumsfreunden in Rheinlande.

930.1 DEU ISSN 0170-9518
CC5
BEITRAEGE ZUR ALLGEMEINEN UND VERGLEICHENDEN ARCHAEOLOGIE. Text in German. 1979. a.
Indexed: AnthLit, DIP, IBR, IBZ, RILM.
Published by: Verlag Philipp von Zabern GmbH, Postfach 4065, Mainz-am-Rhein, 55030, Germany. TEL 49-6131-287470, FAX 49-6131-223710, zabern@zabern.de, http://www.zabern.de.

BEITRAEGE ZUR RHEINISCHEN VOLKSKUNDE. see *FOLKLORE*

BEITRAEGE ZUR TUEBINGER GESCHICHTE. see *HISTORY—History Of Europe*

913 DEU ISSN 0067-5245
BEITRAEGE ZUR UR- UND FRUEHGESCHICHTLICHEN ARCHAEOLOGIE DES MITTELMEERKULTURRAUMES. Text in German. 1965. irreg., latest vol.34, 2000. price varies. **Document type:** *Monographic series, Academic/Scholarly.*
Published by: Dr. Rudolf Habelt GmbH, Am Buchenhang 1, Bonn, 53115, Germany. TEL 49-228-9238322, info@habelt.de, http://www.habelt.de. Ed. H Hauptmann.

914 GBR ISSN 0309-3093
DA670.B4
➤ **BERKSHIRE ARCHAEOLOGICAL JOURNAL**✶. Text in English. 1871. a. GBP 15 domestic; GBP 20 foreign (effective 2000). bibl.; illus. index. **Document type:** *Academic/Scholarly.*
Description: Covers archaeology and history of Berkshire.
Indexed: AIAP, BHA, BrArAb, BrHumI, NumL.
Published by: Berkshire Archaeological Society, c/o Berkshire Archeological Trust Ltd., Reading Museum & Art Gallery, Blagrave, Reading, Berks RG1 1QH, United Kingdom. TEL 44-1235-831463. Ed. C P Petts. Circ: 250.

A

▼ *new title* ➤ *refereed* ✶ *unverified* ♦ *full entry avail.*

913 DEU ISSN 0344-5089
CC79.C5
➤ **BERLINER BEITRAEGE ZUR ARCHAEOMETRIE.** Text in English, German. 1976. a. EUR 40 (effective 2003). adv. bk.rev. 300 p./no. 1 cols./p.; back issues avail. **Document type:** *Journal, Academic/Scholarly.* **Description:** Information about the scientific analysis and conservation of works of art.
Indexed: A&ATA, AnthLit, BHA, BibInd, NumL.
Published by: Staatliche Museen, Preussischer Kulturbesitz, Schlossstr 1A, Berlin, 14059, Germany. TEL 49-30-2662695, FAX 49-30-2662985, publikationen@smb.spk-berlin.de, http://www.smb.spk-berlin.de. Ed., Adv. contact Josef Riederer. Circ: 400.

930 387 BMU ISSN 1013-431X
F1636
➤ **BERMUDA JOURNAL OF ARCHAEOLOGY AND MARITIME HISTORY.** Text in English. 1944. a. USD 6 (effective 2003). adv. charts; illus. index. **Document type:** *Monographic series, Academic/Scholarly.*
Formerly (until 1989): Bermuda Historical Quarterly
Indexed: AnthLit.
Published by: Bermuda Maritime Museum, PO Box MA133, Mangrove Bay, Bermuda. TEL 441-234-1333, FAX 441-234-1735, marmuse@ibl.bm. Ed. Terry Tucker.

914 CHE ISSN 0259-7764
DE1
BERN UNIVERSITAET. SEMINAR FUER KLASSISCHE ARCHAEOLOGIE. HEFTE. Text in French, German, Italian. 1975. a. price varies. illus. back issues avail. **Document type:** *Academic/Scholarly.*
Formerly: Bern Universitaet. Archaeologisches Seminar. Hefte
Related titles: ◆ Supplement(s): Bern Universitaet. Seminar fuer Klassische Archeologie. Beiheft. ISSN 1422-3694.
Published by: Universitaet Bern, Institut fuer Klassische Archaeologie, Laenggassstr 10, Bern, 3012, Switzerland. TEL 41-31-6318991, FAX 41-31-6314905, dwillers@arch.unibe.ch. Ed. Dietrich Willers. Circ: 20.

914 CHE ISSN 1422-3694
BERN UNIVERSITAET. SEMINAR FUER KLASSISCHE ARCHEOLOGIE. BEIHEFT. Text in German. 1985. irreg. price varies. back issues avail. **Document type:** *Monographic series.* **Description:** Examines topics in the archaeology of classical Greece and Rome.
Related titles: ◆ Supplement to: Bern Universitaet. Seminar fuer Klassische Archaeologie. Hefte. ISSN 0259-7764.
Published by: Universitaet Bern, Institut fuer Klassische Archaeologie, Laenggassstr 10, Bern, 3012, Switzerland. TEL 41-31-6318991, FAX 41-31-6314905, dwillers@arch.unibe.ch. Ed. Dietrich Willers.

930.1 LBN ISSN 0067-6195
DS41
➤ **BERYTUS ARCHEOLOGICAL STUDIES.** Text in English, French, German. 1934. a. USD 15 domestic; USD 20 foreign (effective 1999). adv. bk.rev. back issues avail. **Document type:** *Academic/Scholarly.* **Description:** Devoted to historical and archaeological studies on Syria and Lebanon from prehistoric to Islamic times.
Indexed: AICP, BHA, BibLing, GEOBASE, IBR, IndIslam, MEA&I, NumL, OTA, PCI, RASB.
—IE.
Published by: American University of Beirut, Faculty of Arts and Sciences, AUB Post Hall 106, Beirut, Lebanon. FAX 873-1450231, TELEX 20801 LE AMUNOB, hseeden@aub.edu.lb, http://www.aub.edu.lb/. R&P Helga Seeden. Circ: 400.

➤ **BIBBIA E ORIENTE**; rivista per la conoscenza della Bibbia. see *RELIGIONS AND THEOLOGY*

220 913 USA ISSN 1079-6959
BS620.A1
BIBLE AND SPADE✶. Text in English. 1972-1983; resumed 1987. q. USD 35 to individuals; USD 30 to libraries. adv. bk.rev. charts; illus. index. **Document type:** *Newsletter, Consumer.*
Former titles (until 1993): Archaeology and Biblical Research (1071-0507); (until 1983): Bible and Spade (0162-9301)
Indexed: ChrPI.
Published by: Associates for Biblical Research, PO Box 356, Landisville, PA 17538. TEL 717-892-1044, 800-430-0008, FAX 717-892-3049, abrofc@aol.com, http://www.christiananswers.net/abr/abrhome.html. Ed., R&P Bryant G Wood. Adv. contact Gary A Byers. Circ: 800 (paid).

220.93 USA ISSN 0098-9444
BS620.A1
BIBLICAL ARCHAEOLOGY REVIEW. Abbreviated title: B A R. Text in English. 1975. bi-m. USD 14.97 (effective 2005). adv. bk.rev. illus. 96 p./no.; reprints avail. **Document type:** *Journal, Academic/Scholarly.*
Related titles: Online - full text ed.: (from ProQuest Information & Learning).
Indexed: AIAP, AbAn, ArtInd, ChrPI, GSS&RPL, HumInd, IJP, JewAb, MEA&I, NTA, OTA, PerIslam, R&TA, RI-1, RI-2, RILM.
—BLDSC (1947.851000), IE, Infotrieve, ingenta.
Published by: Biblical Archaeology Society, 4710 41st St, NW, Washington, DC 20016. TEL 202-364-3300, 800-221-4644, FAX 202-364-2636, bas@bib-arch.org, http://www.bib-arch.org/bswb_BAR/indexBAR.html. Ed. Hershel Shanks. Pub. Susan Laden. R&P Bonnie Mullin. adv.: color page USD 5,400. Circ: 180,000. **Dist. addr. in Europe:** The Paternoster Press, Kingstown Broadway, PO Box 300, Carlisle, Cumbria CA3 0QS, United Kingdom. TEL 44-1228-512-512, FAX 44-1228-514-949, postmaster@paternoster-publishing.com, http://www.paternoster-pubishing.com.

913 ROM ISSN 0067-7388
BIBLIOTECA DE ARHEOLOGIE. Text in Romanian; Summaries in French. 1957. irreg., latest vol.49, 1988.
Published by: (Institutul de Arheologie), Editura Academiei Romane/Publishing House of the Romanian Academy, Calea 13 Septembrie 13, Sector 5, Bucharest, 76117, Romania. **Dist. by:** Rodipet S.A., Piata Presei Libere 1, sector 1, PO Box 33-57, Bucharest 3, Romania. TEL 40-21-2224126, 40-21-2226407, rodipet@rodipet.ro.

932 BEL ISSN 0067-7817
BIBLIOTHECA AEGYPTIACA. Text in Dutch. 1932. irreg., latest vol.18, 1991. price varies. **Document type:** *Monographic series.*
Published by: Fondation Egyptologique Reine Elisabeth, Parc du Cinquantenaire 10, Brussels, 1000, Belgium. TEL 32-2-7417364.

913 ITA
BIBLIOTHECA ARCHAEOLOGICA. Text in Italian. 1980. irreg., latest vol.26, 1997. price varies. **Document type:** *Monographic series, Academic/Scholarly.*
Published by: L'Erma di Bretschneider, Via Cassiodoro, 19, PO Box 6192, Rome, RM 00193, Italy. TEL 39-06-6874127, FAX 39-06-6874129, edizioni@lerma.it, http://www.lerma.it.

930.1 GRC ISSN 1105-7785
DF11
BIBLIOTHEKE TES EN ATHENAIS ARCHAILOGIKES HETAIREIAS/ARCHAEOLOGICAL SOCIETY AT ATHENS LIBRARY. Text in Greek, English, French, German. 1851. irreg., latest vol.160, 1996. price varies. illus. back issues avail. **Document type:** *Monographic series.* **Description:** Each publication covers a topic concerning the archaeology, art, history, or culture of Greek antiquity.
Published by: Archaeological Society at Athens/Archaiologike Hetaireia en Athenais, 22 Panepistimiou St, Athens, 106 72, Greece. TEL 30-1-364-6043, FAX 60-1-3644-996.

BIBLIOTHEQUE D'ETUDES COPTES. see *RELIGIONS AND THEOLOGY—Eastern Orthodox*

930.1 301 SWE
BIRKA STUDIES. Text in English. 1992. irreg., latest vol.8, 2003. price varies. back issues avail. **Document type:** *Monographic series, Academic/Scholarly.*
Indexed: AnthLit.
Published by: Riksantikvarieaembetet/Central Board of National Antiquities, PO Box 5405, Stockholm, 11484, Sweden. TEL 46-8-51918000, FAX 46-8-6607284, http://www.raa.se/birka_eng/birka_studies.asp. Ed. Bjoern Ambrosiani.

913 GBR ISSN 0140-4202
BIRMINGHAM & WARWICKSHIRE ARCHAEOLOGICAL SOCIETY. TRANSACTIONS. Text in English. 1871. a. GBP 15 to non-members (effective 2000). bk.rev. charts; illus. **Document type:** *Academic/Scholarly.* **Description:** Contains papers on the archaeology of Birmingham and Warwickshire, including excavation reports.
Indexed: AIAP, BHA, BrArAb, NumL.
Published by: Birmingham & Warwickshire Archaeological Society, Birmingham & Midland Institute, Margaret St, Birmingham, Warks B3 3BS, United Kingdom. Ed. D Hooke. R&P Miss S Middleton TEL 44-121-784-1664. Circ: 350 (controlled).

BOLETIN ANTROPOLOGICO. see *ANTHROPOLOGY*

914 ESP ISSN 0213-6090
DP44
➤ **BOLETIN DE ARQUEOLOGIA MEDIEVAL.** Text in Spanish. 1987. a. price varies. bk.rev. **Document type:** *Bulletin, Academic/Scholarly.* **Description:** Covers medieval archaeology, Christian and Islam, preferably relating to Spain.
—CINDOC.
Published by: Asociacion Espanola de Arqueologia Medieval, Breton de los Herreros, 59, 30 Izq., Apartado Postal 50449, Madrid, 28003, Spain. R&P Juan Zozaya. Circ: 613 (controlled).

913 ITA ISSN 1120-2742
DG401
BOLLETTINO DI ARCHEOLOGIA. Text in Italian. 1989. bi-m. EUR 142 domestic; EUR 154 foreign (effective 2004). **Document type:** *Bulletin, Academic/Scholarly.*
Published by: Istituto Poligrafico e Zecca dello Stato, Piazza Verdi 10, Rome, 00198, Italy. TEL 39-06-85082147, editoriale@ipzs.it, http://www.ipzs.it.

901 ESP ISSN 0214-4999
DP302.H8
BOLSKAN; revista de arqueologia oscense. Text in Spanish. 1983. a. EUR 4.55 (effective 2005). back issues avail.
—CINDOC.
Published by: Instituto de Estudios Altoaragoneses, Ave. del Parque, 10, Huesca, 22002, Spain. TEL 34-974-294120, FAX 34-974-294122, iea@iea.es, http://www.iea.es/.

913 DEU ISSN 0344-810X
CC5
BOREAS; Muenstersche Beitraege zur Archaeologie. Text in German. 1978. a. bk.rev. Supplement avail. **Document type:** *Journal, Academic/Scholarly.*
Related titles: ◆ Supplement(s): Boreas. Beiheft. ISSN 0722-768X.
Indexed: AIAP, BHA, BibInd, NumL, SCI.
Published by: (Westfaelische Wilhelms-Universitaet Muenster, Archaeologisches Seminar und Museum), Wasmuth GmbH und Co. KG, Pfalzburger Str 43-44, Berlin, 10717, Germany. TEL 49-30-8630990, FAX 49-30-86309999, info@wasmuth-verlag.de, http://www.wasmuth-verlag.de.

913 DEU ISSN 0722-768X
BOREAS. BEIHEFT. Text in German. 1980. irreg. **Document type:** *Monographic series, Academic/Scholarly.*
Related titles: ◆ Supplement to: Boreas. ISSN 0344-810X.
Published by: (Westfaelische Wilhelms-Universitaet Muenster, Archaeologisches Seminar und Museum), Wasmuth GmbH und Co. KG, Pfalzburger Str 43-44, Berlin, 10717, Germany. TEL 49-30-8630990, FAX 49-30-86309999, info@wasmuth-verlag.de, http://www.wasmuth-verlag.de.

BRACARA AUGUSTA; revista cultural de regionalismo e historia. see *HISTORY—History Of Europe*

930.1 BEL
BRAIVES. Text in French. 1981. irreg., latest vol.5, 1993. price varies. illus.; maps. **Document type:** *Monographic series, Academic/Scholarly.*
Published by: (Universite Catholique de Louvain, Departement d'Etudes Greques, Latines et Orientales, Publications d'Archeologie et d'Histoire de l'Art), Universite Catholique de Louvain, College Erasme, Pl Blaise Pascal 1, Louvain-la-Neuve, 1348, Belgium. TEL 32-10-474882, FAX 32-10-474870, moucharte@arke.ucl.ac.be, moucharte@fltr.ucl.ac.be, http://juppiter.fltr.ucl.ac.be/FLTR/publications/pub_pahal. R&P Ghislaine Moucharte.

914.2 GBR ISSN 0263-1091
BRISTOL AND AVON ARCHAEOLOGY. Text in English. 1982. a. GBP 7. bk.rev. charts; illus. index. **Document type:** *Proceedings.* **Description:** Contains articles relevant to Avon County.
Supersedes: B A R G Review (0144-6576); Formerly (until 1980): B A R G Bulletin
Indexed: BrArAb, NumL.
Published by: Bristol and Avon Archaeological Society, Bristol City Museum, Queen's Rd, Bristol, BS8 1RL, United Kingdom. Ed. R Birchall. Circ: 350.

930.1 942 GBR ISSN 0068-1032
BRISTOL AND GLOUCESTERSHIRE ARCHAEOLOGICAL SOCIETY, BRISTOL, ENGLAND. TRANSACTIONS. Text in English. 1876. a. GBP 10 in United Kingdom membership; GBP 13 foreign membership (effective 2000 - 2001). bk.rev. cum.index every 10 yrs. (vol.79-90 in 1974, vol.91-100 in 1987, vol.101-110 in 1998). **Document type:** *Monographic series, Academic/Scholarly.* **Description:** Covers archaeological and historical research in the city of Bristol and in Gloucestershire.
Indexed: BHA, DIP, IBR, IBZ, NumL.
—BLDSC (8905.700000).
Published by: Bristol and Gloucestershire Archaeological Society, 22 Beaumont Rd, Longlevens, Gloucester, GL2 0EJ, United Kingdom. TEL 44-1452-302610, http://ihr.sas.ac.uk/ihr/bg/. Ed. John Jurica. R&P D J H Smith. Circ: 900.

BRITANNIA MONOGRAPH SERIES. see *CLASSICAL STUDIES*

930.1 GBR
BRITISH ACADEMY MONOGRAPHS IN ARCHAEOLOGY. Text in English. 1991. irreg., latest no.13, 2002. price varies. illus.; maps. back issues avail. **Document type:** *Monographic series.*
—BLDSC (2286.855000).
Published by: (British Academy), Oxford University Press, Great Clarendon St, Oxford, OX2 6DP, United Kingdom. TEL 44-1865-556767, FAX 44-1865-556646, enquiry@oup.co.uk, http://www.oup-usa.org/catalogs/general/series/, http://www.oup.co.uk/.

930.1 940 GBR ISSN 0068-1202
AS122
BRITISH ACADEMY. PROCEEDINGS. Text in English. 1903. irreg., latest vol.125, 2004. price varies. cum.index: vols.1-63. reprints avail. **Document type:** *Proceedings, Academic/Scholarly.*
Indexed: ASCA, AmH&L, AnthLit, ArtHuCI, BAS, BHA, BibLing, BrArAb, CCMJ, HistAb, IPB, MLA-IB, MathR, NTA, NumL, RASB.
—BLDSC (6665.200000), IDS, IE, ingenta. **CCC.**

Published by: Oxford University Press, Great Clarendon St, Oxford, OX2 6DP, United Kingdom. TEL 44-1865-556767, FAX 44-1865-556646, enquiry@oup.co.uk, http://www.oup.co.uk/.

913 709 723 GBR ISSN 0144-0179
BRITISH ARCHAEOLOGICAL ASSOCIATION. CONFERENCE TRANSACTIONS. Text in English. 1980. a., latest vol.26, 2003, Mar. price varies. **Document type:** *Academic/Scholarly.*
Indexed: API, BHA, BrArAb, NumL.
—BLDSC (3410.268000), IE, ingenta. **CCC.**
Published by: (British Archaeological Association), Maney Publishing, Hudson Rd, Leeds, W Yorks LS9 7DL, United Kingdom. TEL 44-113-2497481, FAX 44-113-2486983, maney@maney.co.uk, http://www.maney.co.uk.

571 913 GBR ISSN 0068-1288
DA20
➤ **BRITISH ARCHAEOLOGICAL ASSOCIATION. JOURNAL.** Text in English. 1843. a. USD 78 per vol. in North America to institutions; GBP 45 per vol. elsewhere to institutions (effective 2005). adv. bk.rev. illus.; maps. cum.index every 5 yrs. back issues avail. **Document type:** *Journal, Academic/Scholarly.*
Indexed: AIAP, BHA, BrArAb, DIP, IBR, IBSS, IBZ, NumL.
—BLDSC (4712.600000), IE, ingenta. **CCC.**
Published by: (British Archaeological Association), Maney Publishing, Hudson Rd, Leeds, W Yorks LS9 7DL, United Kingdom. TEL 44-113-2497481, FAX 44-113-2486983, maney@maney.co.uk, http://www.maney.co.uk/search?fwaction=show&fwid=176. Ed. Dr. Martin Henig. Circ: 1,000. **US subscr. addr.:** Maney Publishing North America, 875 Massachusetts Ave, 7th Fl., Cambridge, MA 02139. TEL 866-297-5154, FAX 617-354-6875, maney@maneyusa.com.

930.1 GBR ISSN 1357-4442
BRITISH ARCHAEOLOGY. Abbreviated title: B A. Text in English. bi-m. GBP 23, USD 50 in United Kingdom to non-members; GBP 28 to non-members rest of Europe (effective 2000). adv. bk.rev. illus. **Document type:** *Bulletin, Academic/Scholarly.* **Description:** Combines the latest British archaeological news with a calendar of conferences, volunteer opportunities at excavations, and study tours.
Incorporates (199?-1999): C B A Briefing (1354-702X); Former titles (until 1994): British Archaeological News (0269-1906); Council for British Archaeology. Newsletter and Calendar of Excavations (0309-3204); Which incorporated (in 1981): Current Archaeological Offprints and Reports (0305-5280); Which was formerly: Current and Forthcoming Offprints on Archaeology in Great Britain and Ireland (0526-4375)
Media: Duplicated (not offset).
Indexed: BHA, BrArAb, NumL.
—BLDSC (2289.151400), IE, ingenta. **CCC.**
Published by: Council for British Archaeology, Bowes Morrell House, 111 Walmgate, York, YO1 9WA, United Kingdom. TEL 44-1904-671417, FAX 44-1904-671384, info@britarch.ac.uk, http://www.britarch.ac.uk. Ed., R&P Simon Denison. Circ: 7,000.

700 949.5 GBR ISSN 0068-2454
DF11
➤ **BRITISH SCHOOL AT ATHENS. ANNUAL.** Text in English; Abstracts in English, Greek. 1894. a., latest vol.96, 2001. price varies. illus.; maps. index. back issues avail.; reprint service avail. from PSC. **Document type:** *Journal, Academic/Scholarly.* **Description:** Includes the work of B.S.A. members on cultural, historical, artistic, or geographic aspects of Greece in classical, medieval, and modern times.
Related titles: Microfiche ed.: (from IDC); Microfilm ed.: (from BHP).
Indexed: A&ATA, AIAP, AICP, API, BHA, BibLing, BrArAb, NumL, PCI, RASB.
—BLDSC (1073.675000), IE, ingenta.
Published by: British School at Athens, Senate House, Marlet St, London, WC1E 7HU, United Kingdom. TEL 44-20-7862-8732, FAX 44-20-7867-8733, publications@bsa.ac.uk, http://www.bsa.gla.ac.uk/pubs/index.htm, http://www.gla.ac.uk. Ed. C B Mee. Circ: 938.

949.5 GBR
BRITISH SCHOOL AT ATHENS. STUDIES SERIES. Variant title: British School of Archaeology at Athens. Studies Series. Text in English. 1996. irreg. Price varies. **Document type:** *Monographic series, Academic/Scholarly.* **Description:** Presents research being conducted at Hellenic and Hellenistic archaeological excavations under the auspices of the British School at Athens.
—BLDSC.
Published by: British School at Athens, Senate House, Marlet St, London, WC1E 7HU, United Kingdom. TEL 44-20-7862-8732, FAX 44-20-7867-8733, publications@bsa.ac.uk, http://www.bsa.gla.ac.uk. **Co-publisher:** British School at Athens.

949.5 GBR ISSN 1464-0813
BRITISH SCHOOL AT ATHENS. SUPPLEMENTARY VOLUME. Text in English. 1966. irreg. price varies. illus.; maps. back issues avail. **Document type:** *Monographic series, Academic/Scholarly.* **Description:** Presents research being conducted at Hellenic and Hellenistic archaeological excavations under the auspices of the British School at Athens.
—BLDSC (8547.452500).
Published by: British School at Athens, Senate House, Marlet St, London, WC1E 7HU, United Kingdom. TEL 44-20-7862-8732, FAX 44-20-7867-8733, publications@bsa.ac.uk, http://www.bsa.gla.ac.uk.

930.1 GBR
➤ **BRITISH SCHOOL AT ROME. ARCHAEOLOGICAL MONOGRAPHS.** Text in English. 1991. irreg., latest vol.14, 2004. price varies. illus. index. 2 cols./p.; back issues avail. **Document type:** *Monographic series, Academic/Scholarly.*
Published by: British School at Rome, c/o The British Academy, 10 Carlton House Terr, London, SW1Y 5AH, United Kingdom. TEL 44-20-7969-5202, FAX 44-20-7969-5401, bsr@britac.ac.uk, http://www.bsr.ac.uk/. Pub., R&P Gillian Clark. **Dist. by:** Oxbow Books, Park End Pl, Oxford OX1 1HN, United Kingdom. TEL 44-1865-241249, FAX 44-1865-794449, oxbow@oxbowbooks.com.

913 709 GBR ISSN 0068-2462
DG12
➤ **BRITISH SCHOOL AT ROME. PAPERS.** Text in English; Text occasionally in Italian. 1902. a. GBP 45 (effective 2001). abstr.; illus. 1 cols./p.; back issues avail.; reprints avail. **Document type:** *Journal, Academic/Scholarly.*
Indexed: AIAP, BHA, BrArAb, IBR.
—BLDSC (6370.650000).
Published by: British School at Rome, c/o The British Academy, 10 Carlton House Terr, London, SW1Y 5AH, United Kingdom. TEL 44-20-7969-5202, FAX 44-20-7969-5401, bsr@britac.ac.uk, http://www.bsr.ac.uk/. Ed. Dr. John Patterson. R&P Gillian Clark. **Dist. by:** Oxbow Books, Park End Pl, Oxford OX1 1HN, United Kingdom. TEL 44-1865-241249, FAX 44-1865-794449, oxbow@oxbowbooks.com.

571 BGR ISSN 0068-3620
BULGARSKA AKADEMIIA NA NAUKITE. ARKHEOLOGICHESKI INSTITUT. IZVESTIIA. Text in Bulgarian. 1910. irreg. price varies. reprint service avail. from IRC.
Indexed: AIAP.
Published by: (Bulgarska Akademiya na Naukite/Bulgarian Academy of Sciences, Bulgarska Akademiya na Naukite, Arkheologicheski Institut i Muzei), Universitetsko Izdatelstvo Sv. Kliment Okhridski/Publishing House of the Sofia University St. Kliment Ohridski, Akad G Bonchev 6, Sofia, 1113, Bulgaria. Ed. D Angelov. Circ: 970. **Dist. by:** Hemus, 6 Rouski Blvd., Sofia 1000, Bulgaria.

930 BEL ISSN 0165-9367
DE2
➤ **BULLETIN ANTIEKE BESCHAVING**; annual papers on Mediterranean archaeology. Short title: BABesch. Text in English, French, German, Italian. 1925. a., latest vol.79, 2004. EUR 85 per vol. (effective 2005). adv. bk.rev. illus.; maps. Index. **Document type:** *Journal, Academic/Scholarly.* **Description:** Publishes original research papers and short communications of broad archaeological significance.
Supersedes: Vereniging tot Bevordering der Kennis van de Antieke Beschaving. Bulletin
Related titles: Online - full text ed.: (from EBSCO Publishing, Swets Information Services); Supplement(s): Babesch. Supplementa. ISSN 0926-9312. 1975.
Indexed: AIAP, BHA, DIP, IBR, IBZ.
—IE.
Published by: (Stichting Babesch), Peeters Publishers, Bondgenotenlaan 153, Leuven, 3000, Belgium. TEL 32-16-235170, FAX 32-16-228500, peeters@peeters-leuven.be, http://poj.peeters-leuven.be/content.php?url=journal&journal_code=BAB, http://www.peeters-leuven.be. Ed. M Van Beeck.

930.1 FRA ISSN 1287-7476
BULLETIN BIBLIOGRAPHIQUE D'ARCHEOLOGIE URBAINE. Text in French. 1986. a.
Former titles (until 1997): Centre National d'Archeologie Urbaine. Bulletin Bibliographique (1260-8645); (until 1991): Bibliographie d'Archeologie Urbaine (1260-8637)
Published by: Centre National d'Archeologie Urbaine, Logis des Gouverneurs, 25 avenue Andre-Mairaux, Tours, 37000, France. TEL 33-2-47667237, 33-2-47667600, FAX 33-2-47202866, cnau@culture.gouv.fr, http://www.culture.gouv.fr/culture/cnau/fr/publications.html.

930.1 MAR ISSN 0068-4015
DT311
BULLETIN D'ARCHEOLOGIE MAROCAINE. Text in French, Arabic. 1956. a. abstr.; bibl.; illus.; maps. **Document type:** *Bulletin, Academic/Scholarly.*
Indexed: AICP, AnthLit, BHA, NumL, RASB.
Published by: Institut National des Sciences, de l'Archeologie et du Patrimoine, Av. John Kennedy - Route des Zaers, Rabat-souissi, Morocco. oz_biblio@hotmail.com.

BULLETIN DE CORRESPONDANCE HELLENIQUE. see *CLASSICAL STUDIES*

BULLETIN D'ETUDES ORIENTALES. see *ASIAN STUDIES*

932 EGY ISSN 1110-2489
DT57
BULLETIN D'INFORMATION ARCHEOLOGIQUE. Text in Arabic. 1990. a., latest vol.9 & 10. EGP 30 domestic (effective 2001). back issues avail. **Document type:** *Bulletin.*
Indexed: BHA.
Published by: Institut Francais d'Archeologie Orientale du Caire, Kasr el-Aini, 37 Sharia Sheikh Aly Youssef, Mounira, P O Box 11562, Cairo, Egypt. TEL 20-2-3571622, FAX 20-2-3544635, ventes@ifao.egnet.net, http://www.ifao.egnet.net. **Dist. by:** Boustany's Publishing House, 29 Faggalah St, Cairo 11271, Egypt. TEL 20-2-5915315, FAX 20-2-4177915.

BULLETIN DU MUSEE HONGROIS DES BEAUX-ARTS. see *ART*

913 FRA ISSN 0007-473X
N2
BULLETIN MONUMENTAL. Text in French. 1834. q. EUR 71 (effective 2005). bk.rev. bibl.; illus. cum.index: 1834-1925, 1926-1954, 1955-1975, 1976-1990. reprints avail. **Document type:** *Proceedings.*
Related titles: Microfiche ed.: (from IDC).
Indexed: AIAP, ASCA, ArtHuCI, ArtInd, BHA, BrArAb, CurCont, DIP, IBR, IBZ, PCI, SSCI.
—IE, Infotrieve.
Published by: Societe Francaise d'Archeologie, Musee National des Monuments Francais, Palais de Chaillot, 1 place du Trocadero, Paris, 75116, France. TEL 33-1-47047896, FAX 33-1-44059425, sfa.sfa@wanadoo.fr. Circ: 2,300.

930.1 GBR ISSN 0307-1650
➤ **BULLETIN SUBTERRANEA BRITANNICA.** Text in English. 1975. a. GBP 12 (effective 1999). back issues avail. **Document type:** *Bulletin, Academic/Scholarly.* **Description:** Features the archeology and history of excavating, and the primary and secondary uses of underground space.
Indexed: BrArAb, NumL.
Published by: Croydon Natural History & Scientific Society Ltd., 96a Brighton Rd, South Croydon, Surrey CR2 6AD, United Kingdom. TEL 44-1737-823456. Ed. P W Sowan.

220 200 AUS ISSN 0007-6260
BS620.A1
➤ **BURIED HISTORY.** Text in English. 1964. q. AUD 25 domestic; AUD 30 in New Zealand; AUD 32 (effective 2000). adv. bk.rev. illus. **Document type:** *Academic/Scholarly.* **Description:** Recent discoveries in biblical and Near Eastern archaeology.
Indexed: ChrPI, OTA.
—BLDSC (2931.633000).
Published by: Australian Institute of Archaeology, Science & Technology Centre, Bldg L, 221 Burwood Rd, Burwood, VIC 3125, Australia. TEL 61-3-92446363, director@aiarch.org.au, http://aiarch.org.au/. Circ: 550.

914 949.7 HRV ISSN 0350-6088
DR1637.B89
BUZETSKI ZBORNIK. Text in Croatian. 1976. a. adv.
Indexed: RILM.
Published by: Opcinska Konferencija S.S.R.N. Buzet, Buzet, 51420, Croatia. FAX 053-61-413. Circ: 1,000.

917 USA
C A A SCIENTIFIC PAPERS. (Center for American Archeology) Text in English. 1976. irreg., latest vol.6, 1991. price varies.
Indexed: AnthLit.
Published by: Center for American Archeology Press, 366, Kampsville, IL 62053-0366. TEL 618-653-4688, FAX 618-653-4235, http://www.caa-archeology.org. Ed. Judie O'Gorman.

913 GBR ISSN 0589-9028
C B A ANNUAL REPORT. Text in English. a. GBP 10 to non-members (effective 2000). **Document type:** *Corporate.* **Description:** Contains reports of the C B A and its constituent committees and regional groups and on the annual accounts, membership lists, the annual Beatrice de Cardi Lecture, and presidential addresses.
Indexed: BrArAb, NumL.
—**CCC.**
Published by: Council for British Archaeology, Bowes Morrell House, 111 Walmgate, York, YO1 9WA, United Kingdom. TEL 44-1904-671417, FAX 44-1904-671384, info@britarch.ac.uk, http://www.britarch.ac.uk. Eds. Jane Thorniley-Walker, Mike Heyworth.

930.1 GBR ISSN 0589-9036
CODEN: RRCADF
C B A RESEARCH REPORTS. Text in English. 1955. irreg. price varies. back issues avail. **Document type:** *Monographic series, Academic/Scholarly.* **Description:** Covers archaeological and scholarly research throughout Great Britain.
Indexed: AnthLit, BHA, BrArAb.
—BLDSC (3095.120000), CASDDS, IE, ingenta. **CCC.**
Published by: Council for British Archaeology, Bowes Morrell House, 111 Walmgate, York, YO1 9WA, United Kingdom. TEL 44-1904-671417, FAX 44-1904-671384, cbabooks@dial.pipex.com, info@britarch.ac.uk, http://www.britarch.ac.uk. R&P Jane Thorniley-Walker.

A

930.1 MEX ISSN 0187-652X
C I H M E C H. (Centro de Investigaciones Humanisticas de Mesoamerica y el Estado de Chiapas) Text in Spanish. 1988. s-a. MXP 30 per issue (effective 2000). **Description:** Includes articles, notes and essays on archaeology, anthropology, history and ethnology of Chiapas, Mexico.
Published by: Universidad Nacional Autonoma de Mexico, Centro de Investigaciones Humanisticas de Mesoamerica y el Estado de Chiapas, 28 de Abril No. 11, San Cristobal de las Casas, Chiapas 029200, Mexico. TEL 52-967-82944, FAX 52-967-82997, cihmech@servidor.unam.mx. Ed. Pablo Gonzalez Casanova Henriquez.

930.1 551.46 ISR ISSN 0792-6073
C M S NEWS. (Center for Maritime Studies) Text in English. 1978. s-a. free. bk.rev. **Document type:** *Newsletter.* **Description:** Covers topics in underwater and coastal archaeology, marine resources and geology, maritime history.
Published by: Haifa University, Center for Maritime Studies, Ha-Carmel, Haifa, 31905, Israel. TEL 972-4-8240600, FAX 972-4-8240493, maritime@research.haifa.ac.il, http://research.haifa.ac.il/~webhum/maritime/recanati.htm. Ed. Nira Karmon. Circ: 1,000.

930.1 USA ISSN 1068-4999
E151
C R M (WASHINGTON). (Cultural Resources Management) Text in English. 1978. bi-m. free (effective 2003). back issues avail. **Document type:** *Journal, Academic/Scholarly.*
Formerly (until 1991): C R M Bulletin (0749-1921)
Related titles: ♦ Online - full content ed.: C R M Online.
Indexed: A&ATA, AIAP, RILM.
—BLDSC (3487.493000), IE, ingenta.
Published by: U.S. Department of the Interior, National Parks Service, Culture Resources, 1849 C Street N W Ste. 350NC, Washington, DC 20240. crmmag@nps.gov, http://www.cr.nps.gov/crm/.

930.1 USA
C R M ONLINE. (Cultural Resource Management) Text in English. 1978. irreg. illus.
Media: Online - full content. **Related titles:** ♦ Print ed.: C R M (Washington). ISSN 1068-4999.
Published by: U.S. Department of the Interior, National Parks Service, Culture Resources, 1849 C Street N W Ste. 350NC, Washington, DC 20240. crmmag@nps.gov, http://www.cr.nps.gov/crm. Ed. Ronald M Greenberg.

930.1 PRT ISSN 0870-6425
CADERNOS DE ARQUEOLOGIA. Text in Portuguese. 1984. a. **Document type:** *Monographic series.*
Indexed: AnthLit.
Published by: Museu D. Diogo de Sousa, Rua dos Bombeiros Voluntarios, Braga, 4700-229, Portugal. TEL 351-253273706, FAX 351-253612366, mdds@um.geira.pt, http://www.ipmuseus.pt.

930.1 737 ESP ISSN 0007-9502
CC37
➤ **CAESARAUGUSTA.** Text in Spanish. 1951. s-a. EUR 15.03 per issue (effective 2002). adv. bk.rev. bibl.; charts; illus. index, cum.index. **Document type:** *Academic/Scholarly.*
Indexed: AmH&L, BHA, BrArAb, HistAb, NumL, PCI.
—CINDOC.
Published by: Institucion Fernando el Catolico, Plaza de Espana 2, Zaragoza, 50071, Spain. TEL 34-976-288878, FAX 34-976-288869, ifc@dpz.es, http://ifc.dpz.es. Ed. Miguel Beltran Lloris. R&P Felix Sanchez TEL 34-976-288858. Adv. contact Maria Luz Cortes TEL 34-976-288879. Circ: 1,000.

914 700 FRA ISSN 0575-0385
DC648.6
CAHIERS ALSACIENS D'ARCHEOLOGIE D'ART ET D'HISTOIRE. Text in French. 1909. a., latest vol.45, 2002. bk.rev. illus. 200 p./no.; **Document type:** *Monographic series, Academic/Scholarly.*
Incorporating (1857-1956): Societe pour la Conservation des Monuments Historiques d'Alsace. Bulletin
Indexed: ABM, BHA, RASB, RILM.
Published by: Societe pour la Conservation des Monuments Historiques d'Alsace, 2 Place du Chateau, Strasbourg, 67000, France. TEL 33-3-88525011, FAX http://www.monuments-alsace.com, relations@monuments-alsace.com. Ed. B Schnitzler. Circ: 1,000.

301 FRA ISSN 1166-0732
CAHIERS D'ARCHEOLOGIE AVEYRONNAISE. Text in English. irreg.
Published by: Association pour la Sauvegarde du Patrimoine Archeologique Aveyronnais, Aspaa le Bourg 12630, Montrozier, France. TEL 33-5-6570-7145, FAX 33-5-6570-7775, aspaa@wanadoo.fr, http://www.aspaa.fr/.

913 900 FRA ISSN 0007-9693
CAHIERS D'ARCHEOLOGIE ET D'HISTOIRE DU BERRY. Text in French. 1965. q. bk.rev. bibl.; illus. **Document type:** *Bulletin.*
Indexed: BHA, DIP, IBR, IBZ, NumL.
Published by: Societe d'Archeologie et d'Histoire du Berry, 8 place des 4 Piliers, B.P. 69, Bourges, Cedex 18002, France. Circ: 600.

930.1 FRA
CAHIERS DE KARNAK. Text in English, French; Summaries in Arabic. 1982. irreg. price varies. **Document type:** *Monographic series.*
Published by: Editions Recherche sur les Civilisations - A D P F, Les Patios Saint-Jacques, 6 rue Ferrus, Paris, Cedex 14 75603, France. TEL 33-1-43131100, FAX 33-1-43131125. Ed., Pub. Hina Descat. Circ: 600.

932 666 EGY ISSN 0259-7381
DT62.P72
CAHIERS DE LA CERAMIQUE EGYPTIENNE. Text in Arabic. 1987. irreg., latest vol.6, 2000. EGP 216, EUR 70.20 (effective 2001). back issues avail. **Document type:** *Proceedings, Academic/Scholarly.* **Description:** Publishes studies of Egyptian ceramics from prehistoric, Pharaonic, Classical, medieval and modern times, including technical, economic and cultural aspects.
Indexed: BHA.
Published by: Institut Francais d'Archeologie Orientale du Caire, Kasr el-Aini, 37 Sharia Sheikh Aly Youssef, Mounira, P O Box 11562, Cairo, Egypt. TEL 20-2-3571622, FAX 20-2-3544635, http://www.ifao.egnet.net. **Dist. by:** Boustany's Publishing House, 29 Faggalah St, Cairo 11271, Egypt. TEL 20-2-5915315, FAX 20-2-4177915.

CAHIERS DE LA MEMOIRE. see *HISTORY—History Of Europe*

930.1 FRA ISSN 0291-2694
CAHIERS DE L'EUPHRATE. Text in English, French. 1985. irreg. price varies. **Document type:** *Monographic series.*
Published by: Editions Recherche sur les Civilisations - A D P F, Les Patios Saint-Jacques, 6 rue Ferrus, Paris, Cedex 14 75603, France. TEL 33-1-43131100, FAX 33-1-43131125. Ed., Pub. Hina Descat. Circ: 600.

930.1 FRA
CAHIERS DE TANIS. Text in French. 1988. irreg. price varies. **Document type:** *Monographic series.*
Published by: Editions Recherche sur les Civilisations - A D P F, Les Patios Saint-Jacques, 6 rue Ferrus, Paris, Cedex 14 75603, France. TEL 33-1-43131100, FAX 33-1-43131125. Ed., Pub. Hina Descat. Circ: 600.

913.38 CAN ISSN 0317-5065
CB311
CAHIERS DES ETUDES ANCIENNES. Text in English. 1972. irreg. price varies. illus.
Published by: Universite du Quebec a Trois Rivieres, C P 500, Trois Rivieres, PQ G9A 5H7, Canada. TEL 514-671-3888, FAX 514-671-2121. Ed. Pierre Senay. Circ: 700. **Dist. by:** Exportlivre, C P 305, Saint Lambert, PQ J4P 3P8, Canada.

913 FRA ISSN 0180-9261
CAHIERS DU MEMONTOIS. Text in French. 1978. irreg., latest vol.72, 2003. price varies. bk.rev. charts; illus. back issues avail. **Document type:** *Monographic series.* **Description:** Covers local archeological and historical facts.
Published by: Groupe Archeologique du Memontois, Malain, Pont-de-Pany, 21410, France. TEL 33-0380-751348, FAX 33-0380-751348, malain_gam@hotmail.com. Ed., Pub. Louis Roussel. Circ: 1,000.

930.1 FRA ISSN 0763-6237
CAHIERS ERNEST - BABELON. Text in French. 1982. irreg. price varies. **Document type:** *Monographic series, Academic/Scholarly.*
Published by: C N R S Editions, 15 Rue Malebranche, Paris, 75005, France. TEL 33-1-53102700, FAX 33-1-53102727, http://www.cnrseditions.fr.

CAHIERS LEOPOLD DELISLE; bulletin de la societe parisienne d'histoire et d'archeologie normandes. see *HISTORY*

CAHIERS LORRAINS. see *HISTORY—History Of Europe*

930.009 977.3 708.1 USA
CAHOKIAN. Text in English. 1975. q. membership. bk.rev. illus.; maps. **Document type:** *Newsletter, Academic/Scholarly.* **Description:** For supporters of Cahokia Mound State Historical site.
Published by: Cahokia Mounds Museum Society, 30 Ramey St, Collinsville, IL 62234. TEL 618-344-7316, FAX 618-346-5162, http://www.cahokiamounds.com. Ed., R&P Chris Pallozola.

942 GBR ISSN 0068-659X
CAMBRIDGE AIR SURVEYS. Text in English. 1952. irreg. price varies. **Document type:** *Monographic series.*
Published by: Cambridge University Press, The Edinburgh Bldg, Shaftesbury Rd, Cambridge, CB2 2RU, United Kingdom. TEL 44-1223-312393, FAX 44-1223-315052, information@cambridge.org, http://publishing.cambridge.org/series/cas. R&P Linda Nicol TEL 44-1223-325757.

CAMBRIDGE ANTIQUARIAN SOCIETY. PROCEEDINGS. see *HISTORY—History Of Europe*

930.1 GBR ISSN 0959-7743
CC1
➤ **CAMBRIDGE ARCHAEOLOGICAL JOURNAL.** Text in English. 1991. 3/yr. USD 180 combined subscription in North America to institutions print & online eds.; GBP 108 combined subscription elsewhere to institutions print & online eds. (effective 2006). adv. bk.rev. illus. Index. back issues avail.; reprints avail. **Document type:** *Journal, Academic/Scholarly.* **Description:** Features theoretical and descriptive research articles, ranging widely in time and covering general topics of archaeology.
Related titles: Online - full text ed.: ISSN 1474-0540 (from EBSCO Publishing, O C L C Online Computer Library Center, Inc., Swets Information Services).
Indexed: AIAP, AICP, AnthLit, ArtHuCI, ArtInd, BibInd, BrArAb, BrHumI, CurCont, NumL.
—BLDSC (3015.941330), IDS, IE, Infotrieve, ingenta. **CCC.**
Published by: (University of Cambridge, McDonald Institute for Archaeological Research), Cambridge University Press, The Edinburgh Bldg, Shaftesbury Rd, Cambridge, CB2 2RU, United Kingdom. TEL 44-1223-312393, FAX 44-1223-315052, journals@cambridge.org, http://uk.cambridge.org/journals/caj/. Ed. Chris Scarre. R&P Linda Nicol TEL 44-1223-325757. Adv. contact Rebecca Curtis TEL 44-1223-325757. **Subscr. to:** Cambridge University Press, 100 Brook Hill Dr, West Nyack, NY 10994. TEL 845-353-7500, FAX 845-353-4141, journals_subscriptions@cup.org

930.1 GBR ISSN 1464-2115
CAMBRIDGESHIRE COUNTY COUNCIL. ARCHAEOLOGICAL FIELD UNIT. REPORT. Text in English. irreg. illus.; maps. back issues avail. **Document type:** *Monographic series, Academic/Scholarly.* **Description:** Reports on archaeological excavations in Cambridgeshire, spanning all time periods.
Indexed: BrArAb.
—BLDSC (7394.160000).
Published by: Cambridgeshire County Council, Archaeological Field Unit, Fulbourn Community Centre, Haggis Gap, Fulbourn, Cambs CB1 5HD, United Kingdom. TEL 44-1223-881614, FAX 44-1223-880946, http://www.camcnty.gov.uk.

971.01 CAN ISSN 0705-2006
F1019
➤ **CANADIAN JOURNAL OF ARCHAEOLOGY.** Text in English, French. 1977. a. CND 75 to individuals; CND 100 to institutions; CND 35 to students (effective 2002). adv. bk.rev. illus. reprints avail. **Document type:** *Academic/Scholarly.*
Related titles: Online - full text ed.: (from EBSCO Publishing).
Indexed: AICP, AmH&L, AnthLit, BHA, BrArAb, CBCARef, HistAb, IBSS.
—CCC.
Published by: Canadian Archaeological Association, c/o Butch Amundson, Sec -Treas, Dept of Anthropology and Archeology, University of Saskatchewan, Saskatoon, SK S7N 5B1, Canada. TEL 250-828-9799, FAX 250-828-9864, cjaeditor@canadianarchaeology.com, nicholas@sfu.ca, http://www.canadianarchaeology.com. Ed., R&P George Nicholas. Circ: 500.

917 CAN ISSN 0317-2244
CANADIAN MUSEUM OF CIVILIZATION. MERCURY SERIES. ARCHAEOLOGICAL SURVEY OF CANADA. PAPER (NO.)/MUSEE CANADIEN DES CIVILISATIONS. COLLECTION MERCURE. COMMISSION ARCHAEOLOGIQUE DU CANADA. DOSSIER. Text in English, French. 1972. irreg. price varies. adv. charts; illus. cum.index. **Document type:** *Monographic series, Academic/Scholarly.* **Description:** Designed to permit the rapid dissemination of information pertaining to the disciplines in which the museum is active.
Related titles: Microfiche ed.: (from MML); ♦ Series of: Canadian Museum of Civilization. Mercury Series. ISSN 0316-1854.
Published by: Canadian Museum of Civilization, 100 Laurier St, P O Box 3100, Sta B, Hull, PQ J8X 4H2, Canada. publications@civilization.ca. Ed. Jean Francois Blanchette. R&P Nicole Chamberland. Adv. contact Pam Coulas.

930.1 AUT ISSN 1025-2320
CARNUNTUM JAHRBUCH. Text in German. 1995. a. EUR 25 (effective 2003). **Document type:** *Monographic series, Academic/Scholarly.*
Indexed: DIP, IBR, IBZ.
Published by: Verlag der Oesterreichischen Akademie der Wissenschaften, Postgasse 7/4, Vienna, W 1011, Austria. TEL 43-1-515813402, FAX 43-1-515813400, verlag@oeaw.ac.at, http://www.verlag.oeaw.ac.at.

930.1 560 GBR ISSN 1467-8837
GN783
CAVE ARCHAEOLOGY & PALAEONTOLOGY RESEARCH ARCHIVE. Abbreviated title: C A P R A. Text in English. 1999. s-a. **Description:** Covers topic relating to archaeological and palaeontological deposits found within caves.
Published by: University of Sheffield, Department of Archaeology and Prehistory, Northgate House, West St, Sheffield, S1 4ET, United Kingdom. TEL 44-114-2222910, FAX 44-114-2722563, capra@sheffield.ac.uk, archaeology@sheffield.ac.uk, http://www.shef.ac.uk/uni/academic/A-C/ap/conf/journal.html.

CELESTINESCA. see *LITERATURE*

CENTER FOR ANTHROPOLOGICAL STUDIES. A CLASSIC SOUTHWESTERN REPRINT. see *ANTHROPOLOGY*

CENTER FOR ANTHROPOLOGICAL STUDIES. CONTRIBUTIONS TO ANTHROPOLOGICAL STUDIES. see *ANTHROPOLOGY*

CENTER FOR ANTHROPOLOGICAL STUDIES. ETHNOHISTORICAL REPORT SERIES. see *ANTHROPOLOGY*

CENTER FOR ANTHROPOLOGICAL STUDIES. SPANISH BORDERLANDS RESEARCH. see *ANTHROPOLOGY*

913 USA ISSN 0008-9559
E75
➤ **CENTRAL STATES ARCHAEOLOGICAL JOURNAL.** Text in English. 1954. q. USD 18 (effective 2003). bk.rev. charts; illus.; stat. index, cum.index. back issues avail. **Document type:** *Academic/Scholarly.*
Indexed: AbAn, AnthLit.
Published by: Central States Archaeological Societies, Inc., 646 Knierim Pl., Kirkwood, MO 63122. TEL 314-821-7675. Ed. John Crowley. Pub. Richard A Watts. Circ: 5,000.

930.1 FRA ISSN 1147-5358
CENTRE DE RECHERCHES ARCHEOLOGIQUES. MONOGRAPHIE. (Centre de Recherches Archeologiques) Text in French. 1972. irreg. price varies. **Document type:** *Monographic series, Academic/Scholarly.*
Formerly (until 1989): Centre de Recherches Archeologiques. Notes et Monographies Techniques (0301-553X)
Published by: C N R S Editions, 15 Rue Malebranche, Paris, 75005, France. TEL 33-1-53102700, FAX 33-1-53102727, http://www.cnrseditions.fr.

913 ITA ISSN 1122-3278
CENTRE JEAN BERARD. CAHIERS. Text in Italian. 1974. irreg., latest vol.20, 1998. price varies. **Document type:** *Journal, Academic/Scholarly.*
Published by: (Centre Jean Berard), Casalini Libri, Via Benedetto da Maiano 3, Fiesole, FI 50014, Italy. info@rre.casalini.com, http://www.casalini.it.

CENTRE NATIONAL D'ARCHEOLOGIE ET D'HISTOIRE DU LIVRE. PUBLICATIONS. see *PUBLISHING AND BOOK TRADE*

913.031 709 ITA
CENTRO CAMUNO DI STUDI PREISTORICI. ARCHIVI. Text in Multiple languages. 1968. irreg., latest vol.13, 2001. price varies. bibl. index. **Document type:** *Monographic series.* **Description:** Includes topics concerned with prehistoric art and other manifestations of intellectual life of prehistoric and primitive man.
Published by: Centro Camuno di Studi Preistorici, Capo di Ponte, BS 25044, Italy. TEL 39-0364-42091, FAX 39-0364-42572, info@ccsp.it, http://www.ccsp.it. Ed. Emmanuel Anati.

913.031 709 ITA
CENTRO CAMUNO DI STUDI PREISTORICI. STUDI CAMUNI. Text in Multiple languages. irreg., latest vol.21, 2001. price varies. illus. **Description:** Essays on prehistoric art and archaeology. Includes topics on ancient people, their art, history and evolution.
Published by: Centro Camuno di Studi Preistorici, Capo di Ponte, BS 25044, Italy. TEL 39-0364-42091, FAX 39-0364-42572, info@ccsp.it, http://www.ccsp.it.

CENTRO CAMUNO DI STUDI PREISTORICI. SYMPOSIA. see *ART*

CENTRO DE ESTUDIOS AVANZADOS DE PUERTO RICO Y EL CARIBE. REVISTA. see *HISTORY—History Of North And South America*

CENTRO DE ESTUDOS REGIONAIS. BOLETIM CULTURAL. see *ANTHROPOLOGY*

913 ITA ISSN 0069-2204
CENTRO STUDI PER LA MAGNA GRECIA, NAPLES. PUBBLICAZIONI PROPRIE✶ . Text in Italian. 1959. irreg., latest vol.6, 1969. Price varies.
Published by: Centro Studi per la Magna Grecia, Istituto di Archeologia, Via Porta Di Massa, 1, Naples, NA 80133, Italy.

CERCLE HISTORIQUE ET FOLKLORIQUE DE BRAINE-LE-CHATEAU DE TUBIZE ET DES REGIONS VOISINES. ANNALES. see *HISTORY—History Of Europe*

914 949.3 398 BEL
CERCLE ROYAL D'HISTOIRE ET D'ARCHEOLOGIE D'ATH ET DE LA REGION ET MUSEES ATHOIS. ANNALES. Text in French. 1913. biennial, latest vol.58, 2002. includes Bulletin. **Document type:** *Monographic series.*
Published by: Cercle Royal d'Histoire et d'Archeologie d'Ath et de la Region et Musees Athois, Rue de Bouchain 16, Ath, 7800, Belgium. TEL 32-68-265170, FAX 32-68-265179.

914 949.3 398 BEL ISSN 0775-4671
CERCLE ROYAL D'HISTOIRE ET D'ARCHEOLOGIE D'ATH ET DE LA REGION ET MUSEES ATHOIS. BULLETIN. Text in French. 1967. bi-m. includes Annales. **Document type:** *Bulletin.*
Published by: Cercle Royal d'Histoire et d'Archeologie d'Ath et de la Region et Musees Athois, Rue de Bouchain 16, Ath, 7800, Belgium. TEL 32-68-265170, FAX 32-68-265179.

914 949.3 398 BEL ISSN 0771-5692
CERCLE ROYAL D'HISTOIRE ET D'ARCHEOLOGIE D'ATH ET DE LA REGION ET MUSEES ATHOIS. ETUDES ET DOCUMENTS. Text in French. 1969. a. **Document type:** *Academic/Scholarly.*
Indexed: BHA.
Published by: Cercle Royal d'Histoire et d'Archeologie d'Ath et de la Region et Musees Athois, Rue de Bouchain 16, Ath, 7800, Belgium. TEL 32-68-265170, FAX 32-68-265179, http://www.ath.be/.

930.1 CZE
CESKA AKADEMIE VED. ARCHEOLOGICKY USTAV. SPISY/CZECH ACADEMY OF SCIENCES. ARCHEOLOGICAL INSTITUTE. LETTERS. Text in Czech. 1994. irreg. (1-2/yr). **Document type:** *Academic/Scholarly.*
Published by: Akademie Ved Ceske Republiky, Archeologicky Ustav, Kralovopolska 147, Brno, 61200, Czech Republic. TEL 42-5-41212140, FAX 42-5-41514123, archeo@isibrno.cz, ps@isibrno.cz, http://www.lib.cas.cz/knav/journals/cz/Spisy_Archeologickeho_ustavu_Brno.htm. Ed. Jaroslav Tejral.

930.1 CZE ISSN 1211-1457
CESKA AKADEMIE VED. ARCHEOLOGICKY USTAV. STUDIE. Text in Czech. 1972-1987; resumed 1995. s-a. **Document type:** *Academic/Scholarly.*
Formerly (until 1987): Ceskoslovenska Akademie Ved. Archeologicky Ustav. Studie (0139-5289)
Published by: Akademie Ved Ceske Republiky, Archeologicky Ustav, Kralovopolska 147, Brno, 61200, Czech Republic. TEL 42-5-41514120, FAX 42-5-41514123, archeo@isibrno.cz, ps@isibrno.cz, http://www.lib.cas.cz/knav/journals/cz/Studie_Archeologickeho_ustavu_Brno.htm. Ed. Jaroslav Tejral.

914 CZE ISSN 1211-992X
CESKA ARCHEOLOGICKA SPOLECNOST. ZPRAVY/CZECH ARCHAEOLOGICAL SOCIETY. NEWS. Text in Czech; Summaries in German. 1957. irreg. per issue exchange basis only. adv. illus. **Document type:** *Bulletin.*
Formerly (until 1992): Ceskoslovenska Spolecnost Archeologicka. Zpravy (0231-6404)
Indexed: AICP, AnthLit.
Published by: Ceska Archeologicka Spolecnost, Letenska 4, Prague, 11801, Czech Republic. Ed. Karel Sklenar. Adv. contact Supplement Avail. Circ: 1,000.

930.1 BEL
LES CHERCHEURS DE LA WALLONIE/RESEARCHES OF WALLONIA. Text in French. a. **Document type:** *Bulletin.*
Indexed: AnthLit.
Published by: Societe Royale Belge d'etudes Geologiques et Archeologiques "Les Chercheurs de la Wallonie"/Royal Belgian Society for Geological and Archeological Studies, Thier des Trixhes 179, Flemalle, 4400, Belgium.

930.1 USA ISSN 0009-3300
E77.8
CHESOPIEAN; a journal of North American archaeology. Text in English. 1963. q. USD 15 domestic; USD 16 in Canada; USD 17 elsewhere (effective 2005). bk.rev. charts; illus. cum.index every 5 yrs. **Document type:** *Journal, Academic/Scholarly.*
Indexed: AbAn, AmH&L, AnthLit, HistAb.
Published by: Institute for Human History, PO Box 648, Gloucester, VA 23061-0648. TEL 804-642-2851. Ed. Christine W Dragoo. Circ: 500.

930.1 GBR
CHESTER ANTIQUARY. Text in English. s-a. **Document type:** *Newsletter.*
Published by: Chester Archaeological Society, Honorary Secretary, 27 Grovesnor St, Chester, CH1 2DD, United Kingdom.

930.1 GBR ISSN 0309-359X
CHESTER ARCHAEOLOGICAL SOCIETY. JOURNAL. Text in English. 1850. a. **Document type:** *Journal, Academic/Scholarly.*
Formerly (until 1966): Chester and North Wales Architectural, Archaeological and Historic Society. Journal (0140-4628)
—BLDSC (4729.160000). **CCC.**
Published by: Chester Archaeological Society, Honorary Secretary, 27 Grovesnor St, Chester, CH1 2DD, United Kingdom.

930.1 GBR
CHESTER ARCHAEOLOGY. EXCAVATION AND SURVEY REPORTS. Text in English. 1978. irreg., latest vol.12. price varies. illus. **Document type:** *Monographic series, Academic/Scholarly.* **Description:** Reports on the preliminary and final findings at archaeological excavations taking place in and around Chester, England.
Former titles (until 1994, no.8): Chester City Council. Archaeological Service Excavation and Survey Reports; (until 1991, no.6): Grosvenor Museum Archaeological and Survey Reports
Published by: Chester City Council, Chester Archaeology, 27 Grosvenor St, Chester, Cheshire CH1 2DD, United Kingdom. TEL 44-1244-402029, p.carrington@chestercc.gov.uk, 44-1244-347522, http://www.chestercc.gov.uk/heritage/archaeology/publications.html. Ed., R&P Peter Carrington TEL 44-1244-402028.

930.1 GBR
CHESTER ARCHAEOLOGY. OCCASIONAL PAPERS. Text in English. 1993. irreg., latest vol.4, 1997. price varies. **Document type:** *Academic/Scholarly.* **Description:** Contains conference proceedings and miscellaneous publications on the archaeology of the Chester region of England, especially collections of research papers.
Formerly (until 1994, no.2): Chester City Council. Archaeological Service Occasional Papers
Indexed: BrArAb, NumL.
Published by: Chester City Council, Chester Archaeology, 27 Grosvenor St, Chester, Cheshire CH1 2DD, United Kingdom. TEL 44-1244-402029, p.carrington@chestercc.gov.uk, 44-1244-347522, http://www.chestercc.gov.uk/heritage/archaeology/publications.html. Ed., R&P Peter Carrington TEL 44-1244-402028.

CHICORA FOUNDATION RESEARCH. see *HISTORY—History Of North And South America*

930.1 USA
CHICORA FOUNDATION RESEARCH CONTRIBUTIONS. Text in English. 1984. irreg., latest vol.204, 1996. price varies.
Published by: Chicora Foundation, Inc., 861 Arbutus Dr, Box 8664, Columbia, SC 29202-8664. TEL 803-787-6910, FAX 803-787-6910, chicora@bellsouth.net, http://www.chicora.org. R&P Debi Hacker.

CHICORA FOUNDATION RESEARCH SERIES. see *HISTORY—History Of North And South America*

930.26 HKG ISSN 1027-1503
DS715
CHINA ARCHAEOLOGY AND ART DIGEST. Text in English. 1996. q. USD 250 (effective 2002). adv. bk.rev. abstr.; illus.; maps. 500 p./no. 2 cols./p.; back issues avail. **Description:** Covers the developments in Chinese archaeology and art history.
Indexed: BAS.
Published by: Art Text (HK) Ltd., Hennessy Rd Post Office, PO Box 20746, Wanchai, Hong Kong, Hong Kong. TEL 86-1-6159-0830, FAX 86-1-6159-0830, atext@public3.bta.net.cn. Ed., Pub., R&P Bruce Doar.

913 DEU ISSN 0069-3715
D52
CHIRON. Text in German. 1971. a. EUR 59.90 (effective 2004). back issues avail.; reprint service avail. from SCH. **Document type:** *Yearbook, Academic/Scholarly.*
Indexed: BibLing, DIP, IBR, IBZ, NumL, PCI, PsycholAb, RASB. —BLDSC (3181.129500), IE, Infotrieve, ingenta. **CCC.**
Published by: (Deutsches Archaeologisches Institut, Kommission fuer Alte Geschichte und Epigraphik), Verlag C.H. Beck oHG, Wilhelmstr 9, Munich, 80801, Germany. TEL 49-89-38189338, FAX 49-89-38189398, bestellung@beck.de, http://www.beck.de. Circ: 600.

CHRONIKA TES CHALKIDIKES. see *HISTORY—History Of Europe*

CHRONIQUE D'EGYPTE. see *ASIAN STUDIES*

913 720 CHE
CHRONIQUE MENSUELLE. Text in French. m.
Indexed: PAIS.
Published by: WCC Publications, 150 route de Ferney, P.O. Box 2100, Geneva 2, 1211, Switzerland.

930.1 301 CHL ISSN 0717-7356
CHUNGARA (ARICA). Text in Spanish. 1972. irreg. CLP 13 domestic to individuals; USD 19 foreign to individuals; CLP 17.50 domestic to institutions; USD 25 in Latin America to institutions; USD 40 elsewhere to institutions (effective 2004).
Related titles: Online - full text ed.: ISSN 0716-1182. 2001. free (effective 2005) (from SciELO).
Indexed: AnthLit.
Published by: Universidad de Tarapaca, Facultad de Ciencias Sociales, Departamento de Arqueologia y Museologia, General Velasquez, 1775, Arica, Chile. TEL 56-58-205302, FAX 56-58-232135, http://www.uta.cl/revistas/chungara/index.html. Ed. Calogero Santoro Vargas.

CIMBEBASIA. see *SCIENCES: COMPREHENSIVE WORKS*

A

930.1 942 GBR
➤ **CIRCENCESTER EXCAVATIONS.** Text in English. 1981. irreg., latest vol.5, 1998. price varies. **Document type:** *Monographic series, Academic/Scholarly.* **Description:** Discusses the archaeology of Cirencester (Roman Corinium) and the preservation of the city's and region's historical and archaeological heritage.
Indexed: BrArAb.
Published by: (Cirencester Excavation Committee), Cotswold Archaeological Trust, Headquarters Building, Unit 9, Kemble Business Park, Cirencester, Glos GL7 6BQ, United Kingdom. TEL 44-1285-771022, FAX 44-1285-771033, info@cotswoldarch.org.uk, cots.arch@virgin.net, http://www.cotswoldarch.org.uk/. Circ: 1,000.

913 945 ITA ISSN 0393-4977
CITTANOVA; mensile indipendente per Nocera, il suo agro e un po piu oltre. Text in Italian. 1979. m. adv. bk.rev. back issues avail. **Document type:** *Newspaper.*
Published by: Antonio Pecoraro Ed. & Pub., Via Giovanni Nicotera, 37, Nocera Inferiore, SA 84014, Italy. Circ: 1,000.
Subscr. to: Casella Postale 2, Nocera Inferiore, SA 84014, Italy.

930.1 ESP ISSN 1133-2085
CLASICOS DE LA ARQUEOLOGIA DE HUELVA. Text in Spanish. 1988. a.
—CINDOC.
Published by: Diputacion Provincial de Huelva, Seccion de Arqueologia, Ave. Martin A. Pinzon, 9, Huevla, Andalucia 21003, Spain. TEL 34-959-494762, FAX 34-959-494762, arqueologia@diphuelva.es, http://www.diphuelva.es/. Ed. Jesus Fernando Jurado.

CLASSICAL AND BYZANTINE MONOGRAPHS. see *CLASSICAL STUDIES*

CODEX FILATELICA. see *PHILATELY*

930 GBR ISSN 0264-6013
COLCHESTER ARCHAEOLOGICAL REPORT. Text in English. 1981. irreg. **Document type:** *Monographic series.*
—BLDSC (3295.590000).
Published by: Council for British Archaeology, Bowes Morrell House, 111 Walmgate, York, YO1 9WA, United Kingdom. TEL 44-1904-671417, FAX 44-1904-671384, info@britarch.ac.uk, http://www.britarch.ac.uk.

COLLANA DI STUDI PALEONTOLOGICI. see *ANTHROPOLOGY*

930.1 BEL
➤ **COLLECTION D'ARCHEOLOGIE JOSEPH MERTENS.** Text in French. 1986. irreg., latest vol.12, 1996. price varies. abstr.; charts; illus.; maps. back issues avail. **Document type:** *Monographic series, Academic/Scholarly.* **Description:** Disseminates archaeological research from Belgium and surrounding areas.
Published by: (Universite Catholique de Louvain, Departement d'Etudes Greques, Latines et Orientales), Centre de Recherches d'Archeologie Nationale (Subsidiary of: Universite Catholique de Louvain, Departement d'Etudes Greques, Latines et Orientales), IEPR, 2 av du Marathon, Louvain-la-Neuve, 1348, Belgium. TEL 32-10-474884, FAX 32-10-474039, Brulet@arke.ucl.ac.be, http://zeus.fltr.ucl.ac.be/recherche/publications/pub_cajm.html. Ed. R Brulet.

930.1 CAN ISSN 0821-3801
COLLECTION PALEO-QUEBEC. Text in French, English. 1974. irreg.
Published by: Societe de Recherches Amerindiennes au Quebec, 6742 rue St -Denis, Montreal, PQ H2S 2S2, Canada. TEL 514-277-6178, http://www.recherches-amerindiennes.qc.ca/Collections.html#Paleoquebec.

913 ITA ISSN 0392-0879
COLLEZIONI E MUSEI ARCHEOLOGICI DEL VENETO. Text in Italian. 1973. irreg. price varies. back issues avail. **Document type:** *Academic/Scholarly.*
Published by: Giorgio Bretschneider, Casella Postale 30011, Rm47, Rome, 00193, Italy. info@bretschneider.it. Ed. Gustavo Traversari.

975 917.55 USA ISSN 0069-5971
COLONIAL WILLIAMSBURG ARCHAEOLOGICAL SERIES. Text in English. 1960. irreg., latest vol.10, 1983. price varies. adv. **Document type:** *Academic/Scholarly.*
Published by: Colonial Williamsburg Foundation, PO Box 1776, Williamsburg, VA 23187-1776. TEL 757-220-7342. Ed., Adv. contact Marley R Brown.

913 USA
COLORADO ARCHAEOLOGICAL SOCIETY MEMOIR SERIES. Text in English. irreg., latest vol.5, 1992. price varies. **Document type:** *Academic/Scholarly.*
Published by: Colorado Archaeological Society, Inc., c/o Audrey Marlar, Membership Chairman, 4215 Balsam St., Wheatridge, CO 80033. TEL 303-866-4671.

▼ **COLUMBIA SEMINAR ON ART IN SOCIETY.** see *ART*

938 ITA ISSN 0392-7636
DG803
COMMISSIONE ARCHEOLOGICA COMUNALE DI ROMA. BULLETTINO/ARCHAEOLOGICAL COMMISSION OF ROME. BULLETIN. Text in Italian. 1872. a., latest vol.104, 2003. price varies. illus. back issues avail. **Document type:** *Journal, Academic/Scholarly.*
Indexed: AIAP, BHA, NumL, PCI.
Published by: (Commissione Archeologica Comunale di Roma), L'Erma di Bretschneider, Via Cassiodoro, 19, PO Box 6192, Rome, RM 00193, Italy. TEL 39-06-6874127, FAX 39-06-6874129, edizioni@lerma.it, http://www.lerma.it. Circ: 1,500.

973.1 USA ISSN 1087-9889
E159.5
COMMON GROUND (WASHINGTON, DC); preserving our nation's heritage. Text in English. 1996. q. free (effective 2005). **Document type:** *Journal, Government.* **Description:** Covers information such as working with Native Americans, managing sites in wilderness lands, African American archeology, public outreach, caring for collections, training, publications, and more.
Formerly: Federal Archeology
Related titles: Online - full text ed.: (from H.W. Wilson).
Published by: U.S. Department of the Interior, National Park Service, Archeology and Ethnography Program, 1849 C St. NW, Washington, DC 20240 . TEL 202-354-2272, FAX 202-354-2277, david_Andrews@nps.gov, http://commonground.cr.nps.gov/Index.cfm, http://www.cr.nps.gov. Pubs. David Andrews, Joseph Flanagan. Circ: 12,000.

CONDUIT. see *HISTORY—History Of Europe*

913 720 FRA ISSN 0069-8881
DC30
CONGRES ARCHEOLOGIQUE DE FRANCE. Text in French. 1834. a. cum.index: 1834-1925, 1926-1954, 1955-1975, 1976-1990. **Document type:** *Proceedings.*
Indexed: AIAP, ArtInd, BHA, RASB.
Published by: Societe Francaise d'Archeologie, Musee National des Monuments Francais, Palais de Chaillot, 1 place du Trocadero, Paris, 75116, France. TEL 33-1-47047896, FAX 33-1-44059425, sfa.sfa@wanadoo.fr. Circ: 2,500.

930.1 FRA
DC30
CONGRES NATIONAL DES SOCIETES HISTORIQUES ET SCIENTIFIQUES. ACTES. SECTION D'ARCHEOLOGIE. Text in French. 1957 (congress of 1954). a. price varies. index. **Document type:** *Proceedings.*
Formerly: Congres National des Societes Savantes. Actes. Section d'Archeologie (0071-8416)
Indexed: AIAP.
Published by: Comite des Travaux Historiques et Scientifiques, 1 rue Descartes, Paris, Cedex 5 75231, France. Ed. Martine Francois. Circ: 650.

913 PRT ISSN 0084-9189
CONIMBRIGA. Text in English, French, Portuguese, Spanish. 1959. a. EUR 20 domestic; EUR 26 foreign (effective 2005). bk.rev. **Document type:** *Academic/Scholarly.*
Related titles: ◆ Supplement(s): Fichero Epigrafico. ISSN 0870-2004.
Indexed: BHA.
Published by: Universidade de Coimbra, Instituto de Arqueologia/University of Coimbra, Institute of Archaeology, Palacio de Sub-Ribas, Coimbra, 3000-395, Portugal. TEL 351-239-851600, FAX 351-239-851609, iarq@ci.uc.pt, http://www.uc.pt/iauc/pub/conimbriga.html. Ed. Raquel Vilaca. Circ: 450.

930.1 GBR ISSN 1350-5033
CC135
➤ **CONSERVATION AND MANAGEMENT OF ARCHAEOLOGICAL SITES.** Text in English. 1995. q. GBP 55, USD 95 to individuals; GBP 95, USD 165 to institutions (effective 2005). **Document type:** *Journal, Academic/Scholarly.* **Description:** Reports on new approaches to the long-term preservation and presentation of archeological sites worldwide.
Indexed: A&ATA, AnthLit, BrArAb, NumL.
—BLDSC (3417.967000), IE, ingenta. **CCC.**
Published by: Earthscan / James & James, 8-12 Camden High St, London, NW1 0JH, United Kingdom. TEL 44-20-73878558, FAX 44-20-73878998, orders@earthscan.co.uk, http://www.earthscan.co.uk/defaultCMAS.asp?sp=&v=6, http://www.jxj.com. Ed. Nicholas Stanley-Price. Pub. Edward Milford.

915.4 IND ISSN 0376-7965
N9051
CONSERVATION OF CULTURAL PROPERTY IN INDIA. Text in English. 1966. a. INR 125 domestic to individuals; USD 60 foreign to individuals; INR 1,000 to institutions (effective 1999). adv. bibl. **Document type:** *Academic/Scholarly.* **Description:** Provides professional centre devoted to the cause of conservation and study of cultural property including historic, archaeological, ethnological, artistic, archival and other material in libraries, manuscript repositories and museums.
Indexed: A&ATA.
Published by: Indian Association for the Study of Conservation of Cultural Property, c/o National Museum Institute, Janpath, New Delhi, 110 011, India. TEL 91-11-3016098, FAX 91-11-3019821. Ed. Shri N Harinarayana. Circ: 500.

CONTINUITY AND CHANGE; a journal of social structure, law and demography in past societies. see *POPULATION STUDIES*

913 GBR ISSN 0307-5087
➤ **CONTREBIS.** Text in English. 1974. a. GBP 5 domestic; GBP 8 foreign (effective 2001). bk.rev. bibl.; charts; illus. **Document type:** *Academic/Scholarly.*
Indexed: BrArAb, NumL.
Published by: Lancaster Archaeological and Historical Society, c/o P.J. Hudson, Proctor House, Kirkgate, Settle, N Yorks BD24, United Kingdom. TEL 44-1524-33649, 44-1729-825773, hudson-history@daelnet.co.uk, http://www.users.daelnet.co.uk/hudson-history/index.html. Ed. W T W Potts. Circ: 200.

913 ITA
CONVEGNO DI STUDI SULLA MAGNA GRECIA. ATTI. Text in Italian. 1961. a., latest vol.41, 2001. EUR 103.29 (effective 2001). cum.index: 1961-1995. **Document type:** *Monographic series, Academic/Scholarly.*
Published by: (Centro Studi per la Magna Grecia), Bardi Editore, Via Piave 7, Rome, 00187, Italy. TEL 39-06-4817656, FAX 39-06-48912574, bardied@tin.it, http://www.bardieditore.com. Circ: 500.

938 GRC ISSN 0271-4663
CORINTH NOTES. Text in English. 1977. irreg. price varies. **Document type:** *Monographic series, Academic/Scholarly.*
Published by: American School of Classical Studies at Athens, 54 Souidias St, Athens, 106 76, Greece. TEL 30-210-7236313, FAX 30-210-7250584, ascsa@ascsa.org, http://www.ascsa.edu.gr.

914.2 IRL ISSN 0010-8731
DA990.C78
➤ **CORK HISTORICAL AND ARCHAEOLOGICAL SOCIETY. JOURNAL.** Text in English. 1892. a., latest vol.107, 2002. EUR 25 (effective 2005). bk.rev. charts; illus. index, cum. index: 1892-1940; 1941-1960; 1961-1970; 1971-1985; 1986-1995. 200 p./no. 2 cols./p.; back issues avail. **Document type:** *Journal, Academic/Scholarly.* **Description:** Covers history, archaeology, genealogy, folk-life, folk-culture, and place-names.
Indexed: AmH&L, BHA, BrArAb, DIP, HistAb, IBR, IBZ, MLA-IB, NumL, PCI.
—BLDSC (4732.250000).
Published by: Cork Historical and Archaeological Society, c/o Maura O'Keeffe, Glenmore Cross, Glanmire, Co. Cork, Ireland. TEL 353-21-831322, 353-21-4902166, FAX 353-21-4903102, http://www.ucc.ie/chas/. Ed. Cornelius G Buttimer. Circ: 600.

913 GBR ISSN 0070-024X
➤ **CORNISH ARCHAEOLOGY.** Text in English. 1962. a. GBP 18 (effective 2000). bk.rev. back issues avail. **Document type:** *Academic/Scholarly.*
Indexed: AnthLit, BHA, BrArAb, NumL.
Published by: Cornwall Archaeological Society, c/o Royal Institution of Cornwall, River St, Truro, Cornwall TR1 2SJ, United Kingdom. Ed. P Gathercole. Circ: 700. **Subscr. to:** c/o Miss U. Davey, 8 Dunheved Rd, Saltash, Cornwall PL12 4BW, United Kingdom.

918 ITA
CORPUS ANTIQUITATUM AMERICANENSIUM ITALIA. COLLANA. Text in Italian. 1981. irreg. price varies. **Document type:** *Monographic series, Academic/Scholarly.*
Published by: (Unione Accademica Nazionale), Bonsignori Editore s.r.l., Viale dei Quattro Venti 47, Rome, RM 00152, Italy. TEL 39-06-5881496, FAX 39-06-5882839.

913 ESP
CORPUS DE MOSAICOS ROMANOS DE ESPANA. Text in Spanish. 1978. irreg. price varies. illus.
Published by: Instituto Espanol de Arqueologia (Subsidiary of: Consejo Superior de Investigaciones Cientificas), Departamento de Publicaciones, Vitruvio 8, Madrid, 28006, Spain. TEL 34-91-5855348.

930.1 ITA
CORPUS DELLE ANTICHITA FENICIE E PUNICHE. Text in Italian. 1991. a. price varies. **Document type:** *Monographic series, Academic/Scholarly.* **Description:** Covers archeological research on the Phoenician and Carthaginian civilizations.
Published by: (Unione Accademica Nazionale), Bonsignori Editore s.r.l., Viale dei Quattro Venti 47, Rome, RM 00152, Italy. TEL 39-06-5881496, FAX 39-06-5882839. Ed. Sabatino Moscati.

CORPUS OF MAYA HIEROGLYPHIC INSCRIPTIONS. see *HISTORY—History Of North And South America*

CORPUS VASORUM ANTIQUORUM. ITALIA. see *CLASSICAL STUDIES*

914 ITA ISSN 1724-4560
CORPUS VASORUM ANTIQUORUM ITALIA. COLLANA. Text in Italian. 1926. irreg. price varies. back issues avail. **Document type:** *Monographic series, Academic/Scholarly.*
Published by: (Unione Accademica Nazionale), L'Erma di Bretschneider, Via Cassiodoro, 19, PO Box 6192, Rome, RM 00193, Italy. TEL 39-06-6874127, FAX 39-06-6874129, edizioni@lerma.it, http://www.lerma.it.

CORSI INTERNAZIONALI DI CULTURA SULL'ARTE RAVENNATE E BIZANTINA. ATTI. see *ART*

930.1 ESP ISSN 0213-4640
CC13.C3
COTA ZERO. Text in Catalan. 1985. a.
—CINDOC.
Published by: Eumo Editorial, C. de Viladomat, 86, Barcelona, 08015, Spain. TEL 34-93-3254684, FAX 34-93-4251713, http://ww.eumoeditorial.com/.

930.1 942 GBR
COTSWOLD ARCHAEOLOGICAL TRUST SERIES. Text in English. 1994. irreg., latest 1998. price varies.
Published by: (Corinium Museum), Cotswold Archaeological Trust, Headquarters Building, Unit 9, Kemble Business Park, Cirencester, Glos GL7 6BQ, United Kingdom. TEL 44-1285-771022, FAX 44-1285-771033, info@cotswoldarch.org.uk, cots.arch@virgin.net, http://www.cotswoldarch.org.uk/.

913 941.7 IRL ISSN 0332-0782
COUNTY KILDARE ARCHAEOLOGICAL SOCIETY. JOURNAL. Text in English. 1895. biennial. EUR 15 per issue to non-members; free membership (effective 2005). bk.rev. charts; illus.; maps. back issues avail. **Document type:** *Journal, Academic/Scholarly.*
Indexed: BHA, BrArAb.
Published by: County Kildare Archaeological Society, c/o Belinda Jacob, Digby Bridge, Sallins, Co. Kildare, Ireland. TEL 353-45-897896, ckas@eircom.net, http://kildare.ie/archaeology/journals.htm. Ed., R&P Raymond Gillespie. Circ: 600.

571 913 IRL ISSN 0070-1327
DA990.L89
COUNTY LOUTH ARCHAEOLOGICAL AND HISTORICAL SOCIETY. JOURNAL. Text in English. 1904. a. EUR 13 to non-members; EUR 11 to members (effective 2005). bk.rev.
Formerly (until 1971): County Louth Archaeological Society. Journal (1393-2195)
Indexed: BHA, BrArAb, NumL.
Published by: County Louth Archaeological and Historical Society, 5 Oliver Plunkett Park, Dundalk, Co. Louth, Ireland. info@clahs.com, http://www.clahs.com/journal.htm. Ed. Noel Ross. Circ: 737.

CRETAN STUDIES. see *CLASSICAL STUDIES*

913 707 ITA
CRONACHE DI ARCHEOLOGIA. Text in English, French, German, Italian. 1962. irreg., latest vol.39. price varies. illus. **Document type:** *Monographic series, Academic/Scholarly.*
Formerly: Cronache di Archeologia e di Storia dell'Arte (0011-1767)
Indexed: BHA.
Published by: (Universita degli Studi di Catania, Istituto di Archeologia e Storia dell'Arte), Giorgio Bretschneider, Casella Postale 30011, Rm47, Rome, 00193, Italy. info@bretschneider.it, http://www.bretschneider.it/. Circ: 300.

930.1 ESP ISSN 0210-3710
CUADERNOS DE ARQUEOLOGIA DE DEUSTO. Text in Spanish. 1974. a.
—CINDOC.
Published by: Universidad de Deusto, Facultad de Filosofia y Letras, Departamento de Publicaciones, Ave de las Universidades, 24, Apartado, Bilbao, Vizcaya 48007, Spain. TEL 34-943-413963, FAX 34-943-413087. Ed. Margarita Munoz Salvatierra.

930.1 ESP ISSN 1133-5645
CUADERNOS DE ARQUEOLOGIA MARITIMA. Text in Spanish. 1992. a. **Document type:** *Journal, Academic/Scholarly.*
Indexed: AnthLit.
—CINDOC.
Published by: (Museo Nacional de Arqueologia Maritima y Cent0ro Nacional de Investigaciones Arqueologicas Submarinas), Ministerio de Educacion, Cultura y Deporte, Centro de Publicaciones, c/o Ciudad Universitaria, S/N, Madrid, 28040, Spain. TEL 34-91-453-9800, FAX 34-91-4539884.

913.031 ESP ISSN 0211-3228
CUADERNOS DE PREHISTORIA. Text in Spanish. 1976. a. price varies. **Document type:** *Monographic series, Academic/Scholarly.*
Indexed: PCI.
—CINDOC.
Published by: Editorial Universidad de Granada, Antiguo Colegio Maximo, Campus de Cartuja, Granada, 18071, Spain. TEL 34-958-246220, FAX 34-958-243931, comunicacion@editorialugr.com, http://www.editorialugr.com. Ed. Fernando Molina Gonzalez.

930.1 ESP ISSN 0211-1608
CUADERNOS DE PREHISTORIA Y ARQUEOLOGIA. Text in Spanish. 1974. a.
Indexed: NumL.
—CINDOC.
Published by: Universidad Autonoma de Madrid, Departamento de Preshitoria y Arqueologia, Madrid, 28049, Spain. TEL 34-91-3974600, FAX 34-91-3974435, fernando.quesada@uam.es, http://www.uam.es. Circ: 500.

CUADERNOS DE RESTAURACION. see *ART*

CULTURAL HERITAGE OCCASIONAL REPORTS SERIES. see *HISTORY—History Of Australasia And Other Areas*

CULTURAL HERITAGE RECORDS SERIES. see *HISTORY—History Of Australasia And Other Areas*

913 942.427 GBR
CUMBERLAND AND WESTMORLAND ANTIQUARIAN AND ARCHAEOLOGICAL SOCIETY. EXTRA SERIES. Text in English. 1966 (no.20). irreg. (vols. 30 & 31), latest 2003. price varies. adv. **Document type:** *Monographic series, Academic/Scholarly.*
—BLDSC (3491.770000), ingenta.
Published by: Cumberland and Westmorland Antiquarian and Archaeological Society (Carlisle), 10 Peter St, Carlisle, Cumbria CA3 8QP, United Kingdom. TEL 44-1228-544120, societyinfo@cwaas.org.uk, http://www.cwaas.org.uk/.

CUMBERLAND AND WESTMORLAND ANTIQUARIAN AND ARCHAEOLOGICAL SOCIETY. RECORD SERIES. see *HISTORY—History Of Europe*

913 GBR ISSN 0143-1625
CUMBERLAND AND WESTMORLAND ANTIQUARIAN AND ARCHAEOLOGICAL SOCIETY. RESEARCH SERIES. Text in English. 1979. irreg., latest vol.10, 2000. price varies. adv. **Document type:** *Monographic series, Academic/Scholarly.*
Indexed: BrArAb.
—BLDSC (3491.785000).
Published by: Cumberland and Westmorland Antiquarian and Archaeological Society (Carlisle), 10 Peter St, Carlisle, Cumbria CA3 8QP, United Kingdom. TEL 44-1228-544120, societyinfo@cwaas.org.uk, http://www.cwaas.org.uk/. Eds. B C Jones, W G Wiseman. R&P R Hall TEL 44-1539-773432.

913 GBR
CUMBERLAND AND WESTMORLAND ANTIQUARIAN AND ARCHAEOLOGICAL SOCIETY. TRACT SERIES. Text in English. 1951 (no.14). irreg., latest vol.19, 1973.
Published by: Cumberland and Westmorland Antiquarian and Archaeological Society (Carlisle), 10 Peter St, Carlisle, Cumbria CA3 8QP, United Kingdom. http://www.cwaas.org.uk/.

913 929 GBR ISSN 0309-7986
CUMBERLAND AND WESTMORLAND ANTIQUARIAN AND ARCHAEOLOGICAL SOCIETY. TRANSACTIONS. Text in English. 1866. a. GBP 17 paper ed.; GBP 22 cloth ed. (effective 2001). **Document type:** *Proceedings, Academic/Scholarly.*
Indexed: ApicAb, BHA, BrArAb, BrHumI, NumL.
—BLDSC (8929.240000), IE, ingenta.
Published by: Cumberland and Westmorland Antiquarian and Archaeological Society (Kendal), 2 High Tenterfell, Kendal, Cumbria LA9 4PG, United Kingdom. TEL 44-1539-773542, info@cwaas.org.uk, http://www.cwaas.org.uk. Ed. W G Wiseman. R&P W.G. Wiseman TEL 44-1539-726816. Circ: 800 (paid).

417.7 930.1 NLD ISSN 0929-0052
CUNEIFORM MONOGRAPHS. Text in English. 1992. irreg., latest vol.6, 1996. price varies. back issues avail. **Document type:** *Monographic series.*
Published by: Styx Publications, Postbus 2659, Groningen, 9704 CR, Netherlands. TEL 31-50-717502, FAX 31-50-733325.

913 GBR ISSN 0011-3212
DA90
CURRENT ARCHAEOLOGY; Britain's favorite archaeology magazine. Text in English. 1967. bi-m. GBP 20 domestic; USD 40 in United States; GBP 25 elsewhere (effective 2003). bk.rev. charts; illus.; maps. biennial index. 44 p./no.; back issues avail. **Document type:** *Magazine, Consumer.* **Description:** Presents the latest news of British archaeology on a semipopular level.
Supersedes (in 1965): Archaeological Newsletter
Related titles: Supplement(s): Handbook of British Archaeology. GBP 4.95 per issue non-subscribers; free to subscribers of Current Archaeology (effective 2003).
Indexed: A&ATA, AIAP, AbAn, AnthLit, BHA, BrArAb, BrHumI, NumL, PCI.
—BLDSC (3494.250000), IE, ingenta.
Published by: A.R.L. Selkirk, 9 Nassington Rd, London, NW3 2TX, United Kingdom. TEL 44-20-74357517, FAX 44-20-79162405, subs@archaeology.co.uk, admin@archaeology.co.uk, http://www.archaeology.co.uk. Eds. Andrew Selkirk, Wendy Selkirk. Circ: 18,000.

930.1 560 USA ISSN 8755-898X
E61
➤ **CURRENT RESEARCH IN THE PLEISTOCENE.** Text in English. 1984. a., latest vol.17. USD 20 domestic; USD 25 foreign (effective 2003). bk.rev. bibl.; charts; illus. 180 p./no.; back issues avail. **Document type:** *Academic/Scholarly.* **Description:** Publishes note-length reports on researchon the earliest peopling of the Americas.
Formerly (until 1984): Center for the Study of Early Man. Current Research (0743-426X)
Indexed: AbAn, AnthLit, BrArAb, NumL, ZooRec.
Published by: Center for the Study of the First Americans, Texas A & M University, Dept of Anthropology, College Station, TX 77843-4352. TEL 979-845-4046, FAX 979-845-4070, csfa@tamu.edu, rbonnichsen@tamu.edu, http://www.centerfirstamericans.com. Ed. Brad Lepper. Pub. Robson Bonnichsen. Circ: 600 (paid).

930.1 SWE ISSN 1102-7355
DL621
➤ **CURRENT SWEDISH ARCHAEOLOGY.** Text in English. 1943. a., latest 2002. SEK 150 (effective 2002). back issues avail. **Document type:** *Journal, Academic/Scholarly.*
Former titles (until 1993): Swedish Archaeology (0282-0803); (until 1983): Swedish Archaeological Bibliography (0586-2000)
Indexed: AnthLit, BrArAb, NAA, RASB.
Published by: Svenska Arkeologiska Samfundet/Swedish Archaeological Society, c/o Archaeology, Soedertoerns Hoegskola, Huddinge, 14189, Sweden. TEL 46-8-6084874, FAX 46-8-6084800, http://www.currentswedisharchaeology.org. Eds. Anders Gustafsson, Kerstin Cassel. Circ: 500.

913 937 CYP ISSN 1010-1136
DS54.3
CYPRUS. DEPARTMENT OF ANTIQUITIES. ANNUAL REPORT. Text in English. 1934-1991; resumed 1995. a. CYP 30, USD 6 (effective 1998). **Document type:** *Government.* **Description:** Contains summary accounts of archaeological research and discoveries during the year; also features an illustrated record of conservation works carried out at sites in Cyprus.
Related titles: Greek ed.
Indexed: AICP, AnthLit.
Published by: Cyprus. Department of Antiquities, Ministry of Communications and Works, Nicosia, Cyprus. TEL 357-2-302191, FAX 357-2-303148. Ed. Hadjissavas Yiannis.

913 937 CYP ISSN 0070-2374
DS54.3
CYPRUS. DEPARTMENT OF ANTIQUITIES. REPORT. Text in English. 1934. a. price varies. **Document type:** *Monographic series, Academic/Scholarly.* **Description:** Contains fully illustrated excavation reports and articles by archaeologists on Cypriote archaeology, culture, and art.
Indexed: AnthLit, BHA.
Published by: Cyprus. Department of Antiquities, Ministry of Communications and Works, Nicosia, Cyprus. TEL 357-2-304167, FAX 357-2-303148. Ed. Hadjissavas Yiannis.

930.1 ESP ISSN 0213-3431
CYPSELA. Text in Spanish, Catalan. 1976. a.
—CINDOC.
Published by: Generalitat de Catalunya, Gaspar Casal s-n, Gerona, Cataluna 17010, Spain. http://www.gencat.es/.

913 ROM ISSN 0070-251X
DR211
DACIA: REVUE D'ARCHEOLOGIE ET D'HISTOIRE ANCIENNE. Text in English, French, German, Russian. 1957. a.
Indexed: AICP, AnthLit, BHA, BrArAb, NumL, PCI.
Published by: Editura Academiei Romane/Publishing House of the Romanian Academy, Calea 13 Septembrie 13, Sector 5, Bucharest, 76117, Romania. TEL 40-21-4119008, FAX 40-21-4103983, edacad@ear.ro, http://www.ear.ro. Ed. Petre Alexandrescu. **Dist. by:** Rodipet S.A., Piata Presei Libere 1, sector 1, PO Box 33-57, Bucharest 3, Romania. TEL 40-21-2224126, 40-21-2226407, rodipet@rodipet.ro.

914 TWN ISSN 0496-6724
DALU ZAZHI/CONTINENT MAGAZINE. Text in Chinese. 1950. m. USD 50. adv. **Document type:** *Academic/Scholarly.*
Indexed: AmH&L, HistAb.
Address: 11-6 Foochow St, Taipei, Taiwan. TEL 02-351-3810, FAX 02-392-3820. Ed. Chen Shen Tu. Pub. Chou Yun Shu. R&P Chen Hwa Lee. Adv. contact Chen-Hwa Lee.

930.1 DEU ISSN 0176-2354
DS94.5
DAMASZENER MITTEILUNGEN. Text in Multiple languages. 1983. irreg., latest vol.13, 2002. price varies. **Document type:** *Monographic series, Academic/Scholarly.*
Indexed: AnthLit, DIP, IBR, IBZ.
—CCC.
Published by: Verlag Philipp von Zabern GmbH, Philipp-von-Zabern-Platz 1-3, Mainz, 55116, Germany. TEL 49-6131-287470, FAX 49-6131-2874744, zabern@zabern.de, http://www.zabern.de.

913 GBR ISSN 0954-8874
DEAN ARCHAEOLOGY. Text in English. 1988. a. GBP 4.95 domestic; GBP 10 in United States (effective 2000 - 2001). cum.index: 1988-1997 in vol.10. 48 p./no. 1 cols./p.; back issues avail. **Document type:** *Proceedings, Academic/Scholarly.*
Indexed: BrArAb, NumL.
Published by: Dean Archaeological Group, 5 Park Court, Bathurst Park Rd, Lydney, Glos GL15 5HG, United Kingdom. TEL 44-1594-843548. Ed., R&P Alf Webb. Circ: 500. **US subscr. to:** B.H. Blackwell Ltd., Periodicals Directory, Hythe Bridge St, PO Box 40, Oxford OX1 2EU, United Kingdom.

935 IRN ISSN 0765-104X
DS261
DELEGATION ARCHEOLOGIQUE FRANCAISE EN IRAN. CAHIERS. Key Title: Cahiers de la D A F I. Text in Persian, Modern. 1971. a. price varies. illus. **Document type:** *Academic/Scholarly.*
Indexed: AIAP, AnthLit.
Published by: Institut Francais de Recherche en Iran, Ave. Shahid Nizari, 52 Adib St., P O Box 15815-3495, Tehran, Iran. TEL 98-21-6401192, FAX 98-21-6405501. Ed. Remy Boucharlat. Circ: 500.

930.1 DEU
DENKMALPFLEGE AN ARCHAEOLOGISCHEN STAETTEN. Text in German. 1988. irreg., latest vol.2, 1993. price varies. **Document type:** *Monographic series, Academic/Scholarly.*
Published by: Konrad Theiss Verlag GmbH, Moenchhaldenstr 28, Stuttgart, 70191, Germany. TEL 49-711-255270, FAX 49-711-2552717, service@theiss.de, http://www.theiss.de.

914 DEU ISSN 0720-9835
DENKMALPFLEGE IN NIEDERSACHSEN. BERICHTE. Text in German. 1981. q. EUR 5.50 per issue (effective 2003). adv. bk.rev. charts; illus. index. back issues avail. **Document type:** *Bulletin, Trade.*
Indexed: BHA, DIP, IBR, IBZ.
Published by: (Niedersaechsisches Landesverwaltungsamt, Institut fuer Denkmalpflege), Verlag C.W. Niemeyer, Osterstr 19, Hameln, 31785, Germany. TEL 49-5151-200312, FAX 49-5151-200319, info@niemeyer-buch.de, http://www.niemeyer-buch.de. Ed. Christiane Segers Glocke. adv.: B&W page EUR 948. Circ: 3,100.

930.1 DEU
DENKMALTOPOGRAPHIE BADEN-WUERTTEMBERG. Text in German. 2002. irreg. price varies. **Document type:** *Monographic series, Academic/Scholarly.*
Published by: (Baden-Wuerttemberg. Landesdenkmalamt Baden-Wuerttemberg), Konrad Theiss Verlag GmbH, Moenchhaldenstr 28, Stuttgart, 70191, Germany. TEL 49-711-255270, FAX 49-711-2552717, service@theiss.de, http://www.theiss.de.

930.1 DEU
DENKMALTOPOGRAPHIE BUNDESREPUBLIK DEUTSCHLAND. Text in German. 1982. irreg., latest vol.16, 2003. price varies. **Document type:** *Monographic series, Academic/Scholarly.*
Published by: (Landesamt fuer Denkmalpflege Hessen), Konrad Theiss Verlag GmbH, Moenchhaldenstr 28, Stuttgart, 70191, Germany. TEL 49-711-255270, FAX 49-711-2552717, service@theiss.de, http://www.theiss.de.

900 DNK ISSN 0902-2961
DENMARK. NATIONALMUSEET. PUBLICATIONS: ARCHAEOLOGICAL HISTORICAL SERIES. Text in Danish, English, French, German. 1943. irreg. price varies. back issues avail. **Document type:** *Monographic series, Academic/Scholarly.*
Formerly (until 1969): Denmark. Nationalmuseet. Nationalmuseets Skrifter (0902-2953)
Published by: Nationalmuseet, Frederiksholms Kanal 12, Copenhagen K, 1220, Denmark. TEL 45-33-134411, FAX 45-33-473333, doga@natmus.dk, http://www.natmus.dk.

571 913 GBR ISSN 0070-3788
DA670.D42
➤ **DERBYSHIRE ARCHAEOLOGICAL JOURNAL.** Text in English. 1879. a., latest vol.123, 2003. GBP 15 (effective 2004). bk.rev. **Document type:** *Academic/Scholarly.*
Indexed: BHA, BrArAb, NumL.
—BLDSC (3554.900000), IE, ingenta.
Published by: Derbyshire Archaeological Society, 2 Mill Close, Swanwick, Alfreton, Derby DE55 1AX, United Kingdom. TEL 44-1773-607329, barbarafoster@talk21.com, http://www.nottingham.ac.uk/~aczsjm/das/daj.html. Ed. D V Fowkes. Circ: 650.

930.1 DEU
DEUTSCHE BURGENVEREINIGUNG. VEROEFFENTLICHUNGEN. Text in German. 1993. irreg., latest vol.5, 1996. price varies. **Document type:** *Monographic series, Academic/Scholarly.*
Published by: (Deutsche Burgenvereinigung e.V.), Konrad Theiss Verlag GmbH, Moenchhaldenstr 28, Stuttgart, 70191, Germany. TEL 49-711-255270, FAX 49-711-2552717, service@theiss.de, http://www.theiss.de.

913 DEU
DEUTSCHE ORIENT-GESELLSCHAFT. ABHANDLUNG. Text in German. 1913. irreg., latest vol.23, 1997. price varies. reprints avail. **Document type:** *Monographic series.*
Formerly: Uruk-Warka: Abhandlungen der Deutschen Orient-Gesellschaft (0083-4793)
Published by: Deutsche Orient-Gesellschaft e.V., Huettenweg 7, Berlin, 14195, Germany. dogva@mail.zedat.fu-berlin.de, http://www.orientgesellschaft.de. Ed. Helmut Freydank.

DEUTSCHE ORIENT-GESELLSCHAFT. MITTEILUNGEN. see *HISTORY—History Of The Near East*

DEUTSCHE ORIENT-GESELLSCHAFT. WISSENSCHAFTLICHE VEROEFFENTLICHUNGEN. see *HISTORY—History Of The Near East*

DEUTSCHER PALAESTINA-VEREIN. ZEITSCHRIFT. see *ASIAN STUDIES*

913 DEU ISSN 0342-1295
DE2
DEUTSCHES ARCHAEOLOGISCHES INSTITUT. ATHENISCHE ABTEILUNG. MITTEILUNGEN - ATHENISCHE MITTEILUNGEN. Text in English, German, Greek. 1876. irreg., latest vol.118, 2003. price varies. charts; bibl.; illus.; maps. back issues avail.; reprints avail. **Document type:** *Monographic series, Academic/Scholarly.* **Description:** Covers developments in archaeological research carried out at the German Archaeological Institute in Athens.
Former titles (until 1921): Kaiserlich Deutsches Archaeologisches Institut. Athenische Abteilung. Mitteilungen (1105-1116); (until 1885): Deutsches Archaeologisches Institut in Athen. Mitteilungen (1105-1108)
Indexed: AIAP, ArtInd, BHA, DIP, IBR, IBZ, NumL, PCI.
—CCC.
Published by: (Deutsches Archaeologisches Institut, Abteilung Athen), Verlag Philipp von Zabern GmbH, Philipp-von-Zabern-Platz 1-3, Mainz, 55116, Germany. TEL 49-6131-287470, FAX 49-6131-2874744, zabern@zabern.de, http://www.zabern.de. Circ: 600.

913 DEU ISSN 0070-4415
DE2
➤ **DEUTSCHES ARCHAEOLOGISCHES INSTITUT. JAHRBUCH.** Text in German. 1886. a. EUR 84 (effective 2006). **Document type:** *Journal, Academic/Scholarly.*
Related titles: ◆ Supplement(s): Archaeologischer Anzeiger. ISSN 0003-8105; ◆ Deutsches Archaeologisches Institut. Jahrbuch Ergaenzungshefte. ISSN 0342-3948.
Indexed: AIAP, ArtInd, BrArAb, DIP, IBR, IBZ, NumL, RASB.
Published by: (Deutsches Archaeologisches Institut), Walter de Gruyter GmbH & Co. KG, Genthiner Str. 13, Berlin, 10785, Germany. TEL 49-30-260050, FAX 49-30-26005251, wdg-info@degruyter.de, http://www.degruyter.com/rs/265_434_ENU_h.htm, http://www.degruyter.de.

930 DEU ISSN 0342-3948
➤ **DEUTSCHES ARCHAEOLOGISCHES INSTITUT. JAHRBUCH ERGAENZUNGSHEFTE.** Text in German. 1888. irreg., latest vol.30, 1998. price varies. **Document type:** *Monographic series, Academic/Scholarly.*
Formerly (until 1913): Kaiserlich Deutsches Archaeologisches Institut. Jahrbuch Ergaenzungsheft (0932-4356)
Related titles: ◆ Supplement to: Deutsches Archaeologisches Institut. Jahrbuch. ISSN 0070-4415.
Published by: (Deutsches Archaeologisches Institut), Walter de Gruyter GmbH & Co. KG, Genthiner Str. 13, Berlin, 10785, Germany. TEL 49-30-260050, FAX 49-30-26005251, wdg-info@degruyter.de, http://www.degruyter.de.

930 DEU ISSN 0342-1287
DE2
➤ **DEUTSCHES ARCHAEOLOGISCHES INSTITUT. ROEMISCHE ABTEILUNG. MITTEILUNGEN.** Text in Multiple languages. 19??. a. EUR 72. back issues avail. **Document type:** *Yearbook, Academic/Scholarly.*
Related titles: Online - full text ed.: (from H.W. Wilson, O C L C Online Computer Library Center, Inc.).
Indexed: AIAP, ArtInd, DIP, IBR, IBZ.
—IE.
Published by: (Deutsches Archaeologisches Institut), Verlag Philipp von Zabern GmbH, Philipp-von-Zabern-Platz 1-3, Mainz, 55116, Germany. TEL 49-6131-287470, FAX 49-6131-223710, zabern@zabern.de, http://www.zabern.de.

913 GBR
DEVON ARCHAEOLOGICAL SOCIETY. NEWSLETTER. Text in English. 1982 (no.21). 3/yr. GBP 9 membership; GBP 3 to students. **Document type:** *Newsletter.* **Description:** Covers future events, current excavations, and topics of debate in Devon archaeology.
Indexed: BrArAb.
Published by: Devon Archaeological Society, R.A.M. Museum, Queen St, Exeter, EX4 3RX, United Kingdom. Ed. Robert Wilson North.

913 GBR ISSN 0305-5795
DEVON ARCHAEOLOGICAL SOCIETY. PROCEEDINGS. Text in English. 1929. a. GBP 9 membership; GBP 3 membership to students (effective 2000). **Document type:** *Proceedings.* **Description:** Includes academic reports on archaeological projects, artefacts and standing buildings in Devon.
Indexed: BHA, BrArAb, NumL.
—BLDSC (6689.800000).
Published by: Devon Archaeological Society, R.A.M. Museum, Queen St, Exeter, EX4 3RX, United Kingdom. Circ: 1,000.

913 GBR ISSN 0264-7540
DEVON ARCHAEOLOGY. Text in English. 1983. irreg. GBP 1 to non-members. **Description:** Summary reports on current Devon archaeology.
Indexed: BrArAb, NumL.
Published by: Devon Archaeological Society, R.A.M. Museum, Queen St, Exeter, EX4 3RX, United Kingdom. Circ: 2,000.

930.1 375 USA ISSN 1539-7130
DIG. Text in English. 1999. m. USD 32.97 domestic; USD 44.97 foreign; USD 4.95 per issue domestic (effective 2005). bk.rev.; Website rev. illus.; stat. 36 p./no.; back issues avail.; reprints avail. **Document type:** *Magazine, Consumer.* **Description:** Readers ages 9-14 share in the thrill of archaeological discovery while learning about the cultural, scientific, and architectural accomplishments of different societies through nonfiction articles, colorful graphics, photos, puzzles, games, and hands-on projects.
Formerly (until 2001): Archaeology's Dig (1524-4458)
Related titles: Online - full text ed.: (from EBSCO Publishing, ProQuest Information & Learning).
Published by: (Archaeological Institute of America), Carus Publishing Company, 315 Fifth St, Peru, IL 61354. TEL 603-924-7209, 800-821-0115, FAX 815-224-2256, custsvc@cobblestone.mv.com, http://www.digonsite.com/, http://www.cricketmag.com. Ed. Rosalie Baker. R&P Patricia Silvestro. Circ: 20,000.

913 ZAF ISSN 1013-7521
DIGGING STICK. Text in English. 1984. 3/yr. ZAR 250 in Africa to institutions; ZAR 450, EUR 60 elsewhere to institutions (effective 2003); includes SA Archaeological Bulletin. bk.rev. charts; illus. back issues avail. **Document type:** *Newsletter, Consumer.* **Description:** Popular articles on archaeology-related subjects, with an emphasis on Southern Africa.
Indexed: AICP, ISAP, RASB.
Published by: South African Archaeological Society, PO Box 15700, Vlaeberg, Cape Town 8018, South Africa. TEL 27-21-4813886, FAX 27-21-4813993, archsoc@isiko.org.za. R&P David Morris TEL 27-53-842-0099. Circ: 1,200.

915 BHR
DILMUN. Text in Arabic, English. 1973. 2/yr.
Indexed: AnthLit.
Published by: Bahrain Historical and Archaeological Society, PO Box 5087, Manama, Bahrain. TEL 727895. Ed. Muhammad Khozai. Circ: 2,000.

933 296.155 GBR ISSN 0070-668X
DISCOVERIES IN THE JUDAEAN DESERT OF JORDAN. Text in English. irreg., latest vol.39, 2002. price varies. illus.; maps. **Document type:** *Monographic series.*
Published by: Oxford University Press, Great Clarendon St, Oxford, OX2 6DP, United Kingdom. TEL 44-1865-556767, FAX 44-1865-556646, enquiry@oup.co.uk, http://www.oup-usa.org/catalogs/general/series/Discoveries_in_the_Judaean_Desert.html.

930.1 GBR ISSN 0419-411X
DA750
DISCOVERY AND EXCAVATION IN SCOTLAND. Text in English. a. Free to members only.
Indexed: BrArAb, NumL.
Published by: Council for Scottish Archaeology, c/o National Museums of Scotland, Chambers St, Edinburgh, EH1 1JF, United Kingdom. TEL 44-131-247-4119, FAX 44-131-247-4126, http://www.nms.ac.uk.

DOCUMENTA ET MONUMENTA ORIENTIS ANTIQUI. see *HISTORY—History Of The Near East*

709.0113 936.3 SWE ISSN 1400-6235
DOCUMENTATION AND REGISTRATION OF ROCK ART IN TANUM; No. 1 Aspeberget (1997), No. 2 Fossum (1999). Text in English. 1997. biennial. SEK 150 per issue; USD 24 per issue foreign (effective 2003). 130 p./no. 2 cols./p.; back issues avail. **Document type:** *Magazine, Academic/Scholarly.* **Description:** Presents the result of the Documentation-project on pre-historic rock art and the database HELIOS.
Published by: (Tanums Haellristningsmuseum), Scandinavian Society for Prehistoric Art, Rock Art Museum Tanum, Underslos, Tanumshede, 45791, Sweden. TEL 45-4587-4350, FAX 45-4587-4350, adorant@bigfoot.com, http://www.ssfpa.se. Ed. Gerhard Milstreu.

930.1 ITA
DOCUMENTI E RICERCHE D'ARTE ALESSANDRINA. Text in Italian. 1946. irreg., latest vol.5, 1984. price varies. **Document type:** *Monographic series, Academic/Scholarly.*

Published by: L'Erma di Bretschneider, Via Cassiodoro, 19, PO Box 6192, Rome, RM 00193, Italy. TEL 39-06-6874127, FAX 39-06-6874129, edizioni@lerma.it, http://www.lerma.it. Eds. Antonino Di Vita, Nicola Bonacasa.

930.1 FRA ISSN 0769-010X
DOCUMENTS D'ARCHEOLOGIE FRANCAISE. Text in French. 1985. irreg. **Document type:** *Monographic series.*
Indexed: AnthLit.
—BLDSC (3608.866900).
Published by: Editions de la Maison des Sciences de l'Homme, 54 bd. Raspail, Paris, 75270 cedex 06, France. TEL 33-1-49542030, FAX 33-1-49542133, http://www.msh-paris.fr.

930.1 CHN ISSN 1001-179X
DS793.S644
DONGNAN WENHUA/CULTURE OF SOUTHEAST CHINA. Text in Chinese. 1985. bi-m. CNY 8, USD 6 per issue. adv. bk.rev. **Document type:** *Academic/Scholarly.* **Description:** Covers archaeology, history, religion, technology, architecture, ethnography and folklore.
Related titles: Online - full text ed.: (from East View Information Services).
Published by: Nanjing Bowuguan/Nanjing Museum, 321 Zhongshan Donglu, Nanjing, Jiangsu 210016, China. TEL 025-645349. Ed. Bao Wei Dong. Circ: 3,000.

913 GBR
DORSET NATURAL HISTORY AND ARCHAEOLOGICAL SOCIETY. MONOGRAPH SERIES. Text in English. 1980. irreg., latest vol.14, 1994. price varies. back issues avail. **Document type:** *Monographic series, Academic/Scholarly.*
Indexed: BrArAb, NumL.
—BLDSC (5916.243500).
Published by: Dorset County Museum, Dorchester, Dorset, United Kingdom. TEL 44-1305-262735, FAX 44-1305-257180, dorsetcountymuseum@dor-mus.demon.co.uk, http://www.dorset.museum.clara.net. Ed. Peter Lock. R&P R Depeyer.

DORSET NATURAL HISTORY AND ARCHAEOLOGICAL SOCIETY. PROCEEDINGS. see *SCIENCES: COMPREHENSIVE WORKS*

930.1 FRA ISSN 1141-7137
DOSSIERS D'ARCHEOLOGIE. Text in French. m. (10/yr.).
Former titles (until 1989): Dossiers Histoire et Archeologie (0299-7339); (until 1985): Histoire et Archeologie (0294-6017)
Indexed: AIAP, AnthLit, BHA, PdeR.
Published by: Editions Faton S.A., 25 rue Berbisey, Dijon, 21000, France. TEL 33-1-80404104.

930.1 FRA ISSN 0298-2250
DOSSIERS DE DOCUMENTATION ARCHEOLOGIQUE. Text in French. 1978. irreg. price varies. **Document type:** *Monographic series, Academic/Scholarly.*
Published by: C N R S Editions, 15 Rue Malebranche, Paris, 75005, France. TEL 33-1-53102700, FAX 33-1-53102727, http://www.cnrseditions.fr.

914 947 RUS ISSN 1560-1382
DREVNEISHIE GOSUDARSTVA VOSTOCNOI EVROPY/ANCIENT STATES IN THE TERRITORY OF THE U.S.S.R.; materialy i issledovaniya. Text in Russian; Summaries in English. 1976. a. price varies. bk.rev.
Formerly (until 1994): Drevneishie Gosudarstva na Territorii S.S.S.R.
Indexed: RASB.
Published by: (Rossiiskaya Akademiya Nauk, Institut Istorii/Russian Academy of Sciences, Institute of History), Izdatel'stvo Nauka, Profsoyuznaya ul 90, Moscow, 117864, Russian Federation. TEL 7-095-3347151, FAX 7-095-4202220, secret@naukaran.ru, http://www.naukaran.ru. Circ: 4,250.

913 USA
DUMBARTON OAKS CONFERENCE PROCEEDINGS. Text in English. 1968. irreg., latest 1999. price varies. bibl.; charts; illus. back issues avail. **Document type:** *Proceedings.* **Description:** Contains papers of the annual conference; covers pre-Columbian art and archaeology.
Published by: Dumbarton Oaks, 1703 32nd St, N W, Washington, DC 20007. TEL 202-339-6401, FAX 202-339-6419, publications@doaks.org, DumbartonOaks@doaks.org, http://www.doaks.org/publications.html. Ed. Jeffrey Quilter. Circ: 1,000.

709 USA ISSN 0070-7546
DF503
DUMBARTON OAKS PAPERS. Text in English. 1940. a., latest vol.57, 2003. price varies.
Related titles: Online - full text ed.: (from JSTOR (Web-based Journal Archive)).
Indexed: A&ATA, ABS&EES, AIAP, ArtInd, BHA, DIP, IBR, IBZ, IndIslam, NumL, PCI, RASB, RI-1, RI-2.
—BLDSC (3631.050000). **CCC.**
Published by: (Dumbarton Oaks), J.J. Augustin, Inc., PO Box 311, Locust Valley, NY 11560. TEL 516-676-1510, http://www.doaks.org/Index.html.

940 USA ISSN 0070-7554
DUMBARTON OAKS STUDIES. Text in English. 1950. irreg. price varies.
—BLDSC (3631.054000).
Published by: (Dumbarton Oaks), J.J. Augustin, Inc., PO Box 311, Locust Valley, NY 11560. TEL 516-676-1510.

930.1 CHN ISSN 1000-4106
DS793.T8
DUNHUANG YANJIU/DUNHUANG STUDIES. Text in Chinese. 1983. q. USD 10 (effective 1995 & 1996). bk.rev. **Document type:** *Academic/Scholarly.* **Description:** Presents Chinese and foreign academic essays on the Dunhuang (Tun Huang) frescoes, including archaeological, religious and literary findings about the Dunhuang Caves.
Related titles: Online - full text ed.: (from East View Information Services).
Indexed: RILM.
Published by: Dunhuang Yanjiu Yuan/Dunhuang Research Institute, Dunhuang, Gansu 736200, China. TEL 86-9473-69009, FAX 86-9473-23007. Ed. Duan Wenjie. Circ: 4,000 (paid). **Dist. overseas by:** Jiangsu Publications Import & Export Corp., 56 Gao Yun Ling, Nanjing, Jiangsu, China.

942.8 GBR ISSN 0265-8038
CODEN: ISMCEE
DURHAM ARCHAEOLOGICAL JOURNAL. Text in English. 1862. a. GBP 15 to individuals; GBP 20 to institutions. bk.rev. back issues avail. **Document type:** *Academic/Scholarly.*
Formerly (until 1984): Architectural and Archaeological Society of Durham and Northumberland. Transactions. New Series (0066-6203)
Indexed: API, BHA, BrArAb, BrHumI, NumL, RILM.
—BLDSC (3632.321000).
Published by: Architectural and Archaeological Society of Durham and Northumberland, c/o Department of Archaeology, South Rd, Durham, Co Durham DH1 3LE, United Kingdom. Ed. Anthony Harding. Circ: 450.

930.1 949.2 NLD ISSN 0169-8060
DUTCH ARCHAEOLOGICAL AND HISTORICAL SOCIETY. STUDIES. Key Title: Studies of the Dutch Archaeological and Historical Society. Text in Dutch. 1969. irreg., latest vol.10, 1986. price varies. **Document type:** *Monographic series.*
Published by: (Dutch Archaeological and Historical Society), Brill Academic Publishers, PO Box 9000, Leiden, 2300 PA, Netherlands. TEL 44-1767-604954, 31-71-53-53-500, FAX 44-1767-601640, 31-71-53-17-532, cs@brill.nl, http://www.brill.nl. R&P Elizabeth Venekamp. **Subscr. in N. America to:** PO Box 605, Herndon, VA 20172. TEL 703-661-1585, 800-337-9255, FAX 703-661-1501, cs@brillusa.com. **Distr. outside N. America by:** c/o Turpin Distribution, Stratton Business Park, Pegasus Drive, Biggleswade, BEDFORDSHIRE SG 18 8TQ, United Kingdom. TEL 44-1767-604-954, FAX 44-1767-601-640, brill@turpin-distribution.com.

930.1 NLD ISSN 0924-3550
DUTCH MONOGRAPHS ON ANCIENT HISTORY AND ARCHAEOLOGY. Text in English. 1985. irreg., latest vol.14, 1996. price varies. back issues avail. **Document type:** *Monographic series.* **Description:** Publishes scholarly studies of topics in ancient history and archaeology, with particular focus on the Roman Empire.
Published by: J.C. Gieben, Entrepotdok 72b, Amsterdam, 1018 AD, Netherlands. TEL 31-20-6234709, FAX 31-20-6275170, http://www.teachtext.net/gieben/. Eds. F J A M Meijer, H W Pleket. **Dist. in N. America by:** John Benjamins Publishing Co., PO Box 27519, Philadelphia, PA 19118-0519. TEL 215-836-1200.

667.2 GBR ISSN 0959-0641
DYES IN HISTORY AND ARCHAEOLOGY. Text in English. a., latest vol.19, 2003. GBP 24.50, USD 45 per vol. (effective 2004). back issues avail. **Document type:** *Monographic series.*
Indexed: A&ATA.
—BLDSC (3635.650000), IE.
Published by: Archetype Publications Ltd., 6 Fitzroy Sq, London, W1T 5HJ, United Kingdom. TEL 44-20-73800800, FAX 44-20-73800500, info@archetype.co.uk, http://www.archetype.co.uk. Ed. Jo Kirby.

930.1 DEU ISSN 0174-4224
GN700
EARLY MAN NEWS; newsletter for human palecology. Text in English. 1976. irreg. (approx. 1/yr). bk.rev. back issues avail. **Document type:** *Newsletter, Academic/Scholarly.*
Indexed: AnthLit.
Published by: Archaeologica Venatoria e.V., c/o Institut fuer Urgeschichte, Tuebingen, 72074, Germany. TEL 07071-292416, FAX 07071-294995. Circ: 300.

913 GBR ISSN 0307-2460
➤ **EAST ANGLIAN ARCHAEOLOGY. REPORT.** Text in English. 1975. irreg., latest vol.98, 2002. price varies. **Document type:** *Monographic series, Academic/Scholarly.* **Description:** Reports on archaeological excavations and surveys in region of East Anglia.
Indexed: AIAP, AnthLit, BHA, BrArAb, NumL.
—BLDSC (3645.790000), IE, ingenta.
Published by: Norfolk Field Archaeology Division, Union House, Gressenhall, Dereham, Norfolk NR20 4DR, United Kingdom. TEL 44-1362-860528, FAX 44-1362-860951, http://www.eaareports.org.uk. Ed. Peter Wade-Martins. Circ: 400. **Dist. by:** Essex County Council Archaeology Section, c/o Phil McMichael, Fairfield Court, Fairfield Rd, Braintree, Essex CM7 3YQ, United Kingdom. **Co-sponsor:** Scole Archaeological Committee, Norwich Survey, Suffolk Archaeological Unit, Essex Archaeological Unit, Lincolnshire Archaeological Unit, Fenland Project.

➤ **EAST ASIA JOURNAL**; studies in material culture. see *ANTHROPOLOGY*

913 GBR ISSN 0012-852X
DA670.Y59
EAST RIDING ARCHAEOLOGIST; refers to the east riding or east part of Yorkshire. Text in English. 1968. biennial. GBP 18 per vol.; GBP 15 membership (effective 2001). charts; illus. back issues avail. **Document type:** *Academic/Scholarly.* **Description:** Compendium of recent fieldwork covering more than 50 sites, plus archaeological discoveries and museum.
Indexed: BHA.
Published by: East Riding Archaeological Society, 455 Chanterlands Avenue, Hull, HU5 4AY, United Kingdom. TEL 44-1482-445232. Ed. D H Evans. R&P D.H. Evans TEL 482-217466. Circ: 400.

930.1 956 BEL ISSN 1781-0930
▼ **EASTERN CHRISTIAN ART**; in the Late Antique and Islamic contexts. Text in English. 2004. a. EUR 60 (effective 2005). **Document type:** *Journal, Academic/Scholarly.* **Description:** Devoted to studies in Christian art and archaeology in the Middle East. Its aim is to present studies about the Christian material culture in countries of the Middle East within a broad, interdisciplinary context, including Late Antique, Byzantine, Islamic, and crusader elements.
Related titles: Online - full text ed.: (from EBSCO Publishing).
Published by: Peeters Publishers, Bondgenotenlaan 153, Leuven, 3000, Belgium. TEL 32-16-235170, FAX 32-16-228500, peeters@peeters-leuven.be, http://poj.peeters-leuven.be/content.php?url=journal&journal_code=ECA, http://www.peeters-leuven.be. Ed. Bas Ter Haar Romeny.

EASTERN NEW MEXICO UNIVERSITY. CONTRIBUTIONS IN ANTHROPOLOGY. see *ANTHROPOLOGY*

913 USA
EASTERN STATES ARCHEOLOGICAL FEDERATION. BULLETIN. Text in English. 1941. a. included with AENA subscr.. **Document type:** *Bulletin.*
Published by: Eastern States Archeological Federation, c/o Edmond Dlutowski, Ed, 105 Woodlawn Rd, Butler, PA 16001. R&P Arthur Spiess. Circ: 500.

913 900 FRA ISSN 0223-5099
D113
ECOLE FRANCAISE DE ROME. COLLECTION. Text in French. 1976. irreg. (4-5/yr.). price varies. **Document type:** *Monographic series, Academic/Scholarly.*
Supersedes: Ecole Francaise de Rome. Melanges: Supplement
Indexed: AIAP, DIP, IBR, IBZ, RASB.
—BLDSC (3310.417000), IE, ingenta.
Published by: De Boccard Edition - Diffusion, 11 rue de Medicis, Paris, 75006, France. TEL 33-1-43260037, FAX 33-1-43548583, http://www.deboccard.com.

913 FRA ISSN 0223-5102
D111
ECOLE FRANCAISE DE ROME. MELANGES: ANTIQUITE. (In 3 series: Antiquite, Moyen Age, Italie et Mediterranee) Text in French, German, Italian. 1881. a. (in 2 vols.). price varies. cum.index: vols.1-82 (1881-1975). back issues avail. **Document type:** *Monographic series, Academic/Scholarly.* **Description:** Contains archaeology and chemical studies relating to Italy and western Mediterranean from prehistoric times to the end of the Roman Empire.
Formerly (until 1971): Melanges d'Archeologie et d'Histoire (0223-4874)
Indexed: AIAP, BHA, BibLing, BrArAb, DIP, IBR, IBZ, NumL, PCI.
—IE. **CCC.**
Published by: De Boccard Edition - Diffusion, 11 rue de Medicis, Paris, 75006, France. TEL 33-1-43260037, FAX 33-1-43548583, http://www.deboccard.com.

EDUBBA; studies ancient history. see *CLASSICAL STUDIES*

930.1 EST ISSN 1406-2933
DK503.3
➤ **EESTI ARHEOLOOGIA AJAKIRI/ESTONIAN JOURNAL OF ARCHAEOLOGY/JOURNAL OF ESTONIAN ARCHAEOLOGY.** Text in Estonian, German, Russian; Summaries in English, German, Russian. 1997. s-a. EUR 30 foreign (effective 2005). abstr.; charts; illus.; maps. 80 p./no.; back issues avail. **Document type:** *Journal, Academic/Scholarly.*
Related titles: Online - full content ed.
Published by: Teaduste Akadeemia Kirjastus/Estonian Academy Publishers, Kohtu 6, Tallinn, 10130, Estonia. TEL 372-6-454504, FAX 372-6-466026, niine@kirj.ee, http://www.kirj.ee. Ed. Valter Lang. R&P Asta Tikerpae TEL 373-6-454504. Adv. contact Asta Tikerpae TEL 373-6-454106.

939 GBR
EGYPT EXPLORATION SOCIETY. MONOGRAPHS. Text in English. irreg. price varies. **Document type:** *Monographic series, Academic/Scholarly.*
Published by: Egypt Exploration Society, 3 Doughty Mews, London, WC1N 2PG, United Kingdom. TEL 44-20-72421880, FAX 44-20-74046118, eeslondon@talk21.com, http://www.ees.ac.uk/monographs.htm.

962 932 EGY ISSN 0082-7835
EGYPT. SERVICE DES ANTIQUITES. ANNALES. Text in French. 1900. irreg. price varies. bk.rev. cum.index: vols.1-30, vols.31-40.
Related titles: Microfiche ed.: (from IDC).
Indexed: AICP, BHA, BibLing.
Published by: Service des Antiquites, Museums Sector, c/o Egyptian National Museum, Midan al-Tahrir, Kasr el-Nil, Cairo, Egypt. Ed. Mohammed Mohsen.

932.01 GBR ISSN 0962-2837
DT57 CODEN: REEVEW
EGYPTIAN ARCHAEOLOGY. Text in English. 1991. s-a. GBP 4.95 per issue (effective 2003). adv. bk.rev. illus. cum.index every 5 yrs. reprints avail. **Document type:** *Bulletin.*
Description: Provides articles on current fieldwork in Egypt, Egyptological research, museum collections and exhibitions.
Indexed: IndIslam, NTA.
—BLDSC (3664.231000), IE, ingenta.
Published by: Egypt Exploration Society, 3 Doughty Mews, London, WC1N 2PG, United Kingdom. TEL 44-20-72421880, FAX 44-20-74046118, eeslondon@talk21.com, http://www.ees.ac.uk/bulletin.htm. Ed. Patricia Spencer. Circ: 5,000.

932 BEL
EGYPTIAN PREHISTORY MONOGRAPHS. Text in English. 1995. irreg., latest vol.2, 2000. price varies. illus.; maps. **Document type:** *Monographic series, Academic/Scholarly.* **Description:** Examines and analyzes archaeological research in the prehistory of Egypt.
Published by: Leuven University Press, Blijde Inkomststraat 5, Leuven, 3000, Belgium. TEL 32-16-325345, FAX 32-16-325352, university.press@upers.kuleuven.ac.be, http://www.kuleuven.ac.be/upers.

EGYPTOLOGISCHE UITGAVEN/EGYPTOLOGICAL PUBLICATIONS. see *HISTORY—History Of The Near East*

EIKON; Beitraege zur antiken Bildersprache. see *CLASSICAL STUDIES*

EIRENE; studia Graeca et Latina. see *CLASSICAL STUDIES*

571 USA ISSN 0070-9573
EL PASO ARCHAEOLOGICAL SOCIETY. SPECIAL REPORTS. Text in English. 1963. a. price varies. bk.rev. **Document type:** *Academic/Scholarly.*
Related titles: Microform ed.
Published by: El Paso Archaeological Society, Inc., PO Box 4345, El Paso, TX 79914-4345. TEL 915-751-3295. Ed. Carrol Hedrick. Circ: 300.

913 USA ISSN 0013-4023
EL PASO ARCHAEOLOGY. Text in English. 1968. m. USD 25; includes Artifact & Newsletter. bk.rev. charts; illus. index. **Document type:** *Newsletter.*
Published by: El Paso Archaeological Society, Inc., PO Box 4345, El Paso, TX 79914-4345. TEL 915-751-3295. Ed. Meliha Duran. Circ: 300.

932 BEL
ELKAB. Text in French. 1971. irreg., latest vol.5, 1990. price varies. **Document type:** *Monographic series.*
Published by: (Comite des Fouilles Belges en Egypte), Fondation Egyptologique Reine Elisabeth, Parc du Cinquantenaire 10, Brussels, 1000, Belgium. TEL 32-2-7339610.

930.1 GBR ISSN 0951-1822
DA920
EMANIA; bulletin of the Navan Research Group. Text in English. 1986. s-a. GBP 6 per issue domestic; GBP 8 per issue elsewhere (effective 2005). back issues avail. **Document type:** *Monographic series, Academic/Scholarly.* **Description:** Devoted to research connected with Navan Fort, the ancient Royal Site in County Armagh, Northern Ireland.
Indexed: AnthLit.
Published by: Navan Research Group, Queens University of Belfast, School of Archaeology, Belfast, BT7 INN, United Kingdom. TEL 44-28-90273186, FAX 44-28-90313628. Ed. James Mallory.

341 ESP ISSN 0213-9278
DP44
EMPURIES; revista de prehistoria, arqueologia y etnologia. Text in Spanish. 1939. a. bibl.; illus. **Document type:** *Academic/Scholarly.*
Formerly (until 1982): Ampurias (0212-0909)
Indexed: AICP, AmH&L, AnthLit, BHA, BrArAb, HistAb, NumL, PCI, RASB.
—CINDOC. **CCC.**

Published by: Generalitat de Catalunya, Departament de Cultura/Museu d'Arqueologia de Catalunya, Parque de Montjuich, Ps De Santa Madrona, 39-41, Barcelona, 08038, Spain. TEL 34-3-4232149, FAX 34-3-4254244, biblio@arsweb.com. Circ: (controlled).

930.1 GBR ISSN 1461-4103
CC81
ENVIRONMENTAL ARCHAEOLOGY; the journal of human palaeoecology. Text in English. 1983. a., latest vol.5, 2000. GBP 30 (effective 2001). bk.rev. back issues avail. **Document type:** *Academic/Scholarly.*
Formerly (until 1996): Circaea (0268-425X)
Indexed: AnBrAb, AnthLit, BrArAb, FCA, ForAb, IndVet, NumL, PBA, PGegResA, PHN&I, PN&I, S&F, SeedAb, WAE&RSA, ZooRec.
—BLDSC (3791.383700), IE, ingenta.
Published by: (Association for Environmental Archaeology), Oxbow Books, Park End Pl, Oxford, OX1 1HN, United Kingdom. TEL 44-1865-241249, oxbow@oxbowbooks.com, http://www.oxbowbooks.com. Ed. Glynis Jones. Adv. contact Clare White.

930.1 ROM ISSN 1220-5249
DS211
EPHEMERIS NAPOCENSIS. Text in Romanian; Summaries in English, French, German. 1991. a.
Related titles: Online - full text ed.
Published by: (Academia Romana, Institutul de Istorie si Arheologie Cluj-Napoca), Editura Academiei Romane/Publishing House of the Romanian Academy, Calea 13 Septembrie 13, Sector 5, Bucharest, 76117, Romania. TEL 40-21-4119008, FAX 40-21-4103983, edacad@ear.ro, http://www.ear.ro. Ed. Nicolae Gudea. Dist. by: Rodipet S.A., Piata Presei Libere 1, sector 1, PO Box 33-57, Bucharest 3, Romania. TEL 40-21-2224126, 40-21-2226407, rodipet@rodipet.ro.

913 IND ISSN 0013-9564
EPIGRAPHIA INDICA. Text in English. 1888. irreg. INR 64 per vol. (8 nos./vol.). bk.rev. charts; illus. biennial index.
Indexed: EI, IndIslam.
Published by: Archaeological Survey of India, Old University Office Bldg., Mysore, Karnataka 570 005, India. Ed. K G Krishnan. Circ: 740. **Subscr. to:** Controller of Publications, Civil Lines, New Delhi 110 006, India.

913 411 USA ISSN 1061-5938
CN1
EPIGRAPHIC SOCIETY. OCCASIONAL PAPERS. Short title: E S O P. Text in English. 1974. a. USD 45 domestic; USD 50 foreign (effective 2000). adv. bk.rev. cum.index: vols.1-15 in 1984, vols.1-17 in 1987. back issues avail. **Document type:** *Monographic series, Academic/Scholarly.* **Description:** Contains articles and photographs of discoveries and decipherment of ancient inscriptions in current research.
Formerly (until 1990): Epigraphic Society. Occasional Publications (0192-5148)
Indexed: AnthLit.
Published by: Epigraphic Society, Inc., 97 Village Post Rd, Danvers, MA 01923-2616. TEL 978-774-1275. Eds. Donal Buchanan, Jon Polansky. R&P Donal Buchanan. Circ: 1,100.

913 ITA ISSN 0013-9572
DS417
EPIGRAPHICA; periodico internazionale di epigrafia. Text in Italian. 1939. s-a. bk.rev. illus.
Indexed: BHA, NTA, PCI.
—IE.
Published by: Fratelli Lega Editori, Corso Mazzini 33, Faenza, RA 48018, Italy. TEL 39-0546-21060.

938 417.7 NLD
EPIGRAPHICA BOEOTICA. Text in English. 1991. irreg. price varies. back issues avail. **Document type:** *Monographic series.* **Description:** Publishes scholarly studies of the ancient inscriptions in Boiotia.
Published by: J.C. Gieben, Entrepotdok 72b, Amsterdam, 1018 AD, Netherlands. TEL 31-20-6234709, FAX 31-20-6275170, http://www.teachtext.net/gieben/. Ed. John M Fossey. **Dist. in N. America by:** John Benjamins Publishing Co., PO Box 27519, Philadelphia, PA 19118-0519. TEL 215-836-1200.

913 DEU ISSN 0343-6500
ERDSTALL. Text in German. 1975. a. EUR 12 (effective 2001). adv. back issues avail. **Document type:** *Yearbook, Academic/Scholarly.*
Published by: Arbeitskreis fuer Erdstallforschung, Tulpenweg 11, Roding, 93426, Germany. TEL 49-9461-2831. Ed. Regine Glatthaar. Adv. contact Hannelore Schulz.

902 ESP ISSN 1130-6572
ERES. SERIE DE ARQUEOLOGIA. Text in Spanish. 1990. a.
—CINDOC.
Published by: Cabildo Insular de Tenerife, Museo Arqueologico y Etnografico, Apdo. 133, Santa Cruz de Tenerife, Canarias 38080, Spain. TEL 34-901-501901, http://www.cabtfe.es/.

913 933 ISR ISSN 0071-108X
ERETZ-ISRAEL. ARCHAEOLOGICAL, HISTORICAL AND GEOGRAPHICAL STUDIES. Text in English, Hebrew. 1951. irreg., latest vol.27, 2003. price varies. back issues avail. **Document type:** *Monographic series, Academic/Scholarly.*
Description: Festschrifts on Israeli archaeology, ancient history and geography.
Indexed: BibLing, IHP, IndIslam, OTA, R&TA, RI-1, RI-2.
Published by: Israel Exploration Society, P O Box 7041, Jerusalem, 91070, Israel. TEL 972-2-6257991, FAX 972-2-6247772, ies@vms.huji.ac.il, http://www.hum.huji.ac.il/ies/. Circ: 1,200.

ERETZ MAGAZINE. see *CONSERVATION*

ERFGOED VAN INDUSTRIE EN TECHNIEK. see *TECHNOLOGY: COMPREHENSIVE WORKS*

301 ESP ISSN 1131-7698
ESPACIO, TIEMPO Y FORMA. SERIE I. PREHISTORIA Y ARQUEOLOGIA. Text in Spanish. 1987. a.
Formerly (until 1989): Espacio, Tiempo y Forma. Serie I, Prehistoria (1130-0116); Which was superseded in par (in 1988): Espacio, Tiempo y Forma (0214-4433)
—CINDOC.
Published by: Universidad Nacional de Educacion a Distancia, Bravo Murillo No. 38, Madrid, Spain. TEL 34-91-3986000, FAX 34-91-3986600, http://www.uned.es/.

930.1 940 GBR ISSN 0308-3462
ESSEX ARCHAEOLOGY AND HISTORY. Text in English. 1972. a.
Indexed: BibInd.
—BLDSC (3811.850000).
Published by: Essex Society for Archaeology and History, c/o Ann Turner, 1 Robin Close, Great Bentley, Colchester, CO7 8QH, United Kingdom. http://www.rydalway.demon.co.uk.

914.2 942 GBR ISSN 0014-0961
ESSEX JOURNAL; a review of Essex archaeology and local history. Text in English. 1966. 3/yr. GBP 10. adv. bk.rev. charts; illus. index. back issues avail. **Document type:** *Academic/Scholarly.*
Incorporates: Essex Review
Indexed: BHA.
—BLDSC (3811.980000).
Address: c/o Michael Beale, The Laurels, The St, Great Waltham, Chelmsford, Essex CMJ 1DE, United Kingdom. TEL 44-1245-360344. Circ: 600.

930.1 ESP ISSN 1130-3441
ESTRAT. Text in Spanish, Catalan. 1989. a.
—CINDOC.
Published by: Centre d'Estudis Comarcals D'Igualada. Seccio d'Arqueologia, Baixada de Sant Nicolau 21, Igualada, Barcelona, 08700, Spain.

918 CHL ISSN 0716-0925
ESTUDIOS ATACAMENOS. Text in Spanish. 1973. s-a. per issue exchange basis. **Document type:** *Journal, Academic/Scholarly.* **Description:** Andean archaeology studies in the north of Chile, with emphasis on the Atacama region.
Related titles: Online - full text ed.: ISSN 0718-1043. free (effective 2005).
Indexed: AICP.
Published by: Universidad Catolica del Norte, Instituto de Investigaciones Arqueologicas, R.P. Gustavo le Paige S.J., San Pedro De Atacama, Chile. FAX 241724, TELEX 225097 UNORTE CL. Ed. Agustin Llagostera Martinez. Circ: 1,000.

930.1 ESP ISSN 0425-3507
ESTUDIOS DE ARQUEOLOGIA ALAVESA. Text in Spanish. 1966. a.
—CINDOC.
Published by: Diputacion Foral de Alava, Plaza de la Provincia, s-n, Vitoria-Gasteiz, 01001, Spain. TEL 34-945-181818, FAX 34-945-181754, dfa@alava.net, http://www.alava.net.

ESTUDIOS DE CULTURA MAYA. see *HISTORY—History Of North And South America*

901 ESP ISSN 0212-9515
DP99
ESTUDIOS DE HISTORIA Y ARQUEOLOGIA MEDIEVALES. Text in Spanish. 1981. a. back issues avail.
—CINDOC.
Published by: Universidad de Cadiz, Servicio de Publicaciones, Rectorado Ancha 16, Cadiz, 11001, Spain. TEL 34-956-0150000, http://www.uca.es/.

930.1 ESP ISSN 0213-0246
DP302.M1
ESTUDIOS DE PREHISTORIA Y ARQUEOLOGIA MADRILENAS/STUDIES OF MADRILENIAN PREHISTORY AND ARCHAEOLOGY. Text in Spanish, English. 1982. a.
Indexed: AnthLit.
—CINDOC.
Published by: Concejalia de Cultura, Ayuntamiento, Museo Municipal, Enrique D'Almonte, 1, Madrid, 28004, Spain. TEL 34-91-4096165, FAX 34-91-4096209, mmnicipal@madrid.es.

ETHNOS; journal of anthropology. see ANTHROPOLOGY

ETHNOS. see ETHNIC INTERESTS

LES ETUDES CLASSIQUES. see CLASSICAL STUDIES

ETUDES DE PHILOLOGIE, D'ARCHEOLOGIE ET D'HISTOIRE
ANCIENNE. see LINGUISTICS

930.1   BEL   ISSN 0777-2173
ETUDES ET RECHERCHES ARCHEOLOGIQUES DE
L'UNIVERSITE DE LIEGE. Text in French. 1982. irreg.
Indexed: AnthLit.
Published by: Universite de Liege, Service de Prehistoire, Pl du
20 Aout, 7, Batiment A1, Liege, 4000, Belgium. TEL
32-4-3665341, FAX 32-4-3665551, prehist@ulg.ac.be,
http://www.ulg.ac.be/prehist/.

930.1   MAR   ISSN 0071-2027
ETUDES ET TRAVAUX D'ARCHEOLOGIE MAROCAINE. Text in
French. 1965. irreg., latest vol.9, 1981. bibl.; illus.; maps.
Document type: Monographic series, Academic/Scholarly.
Published by: Institut National des Sciences, de l'Archeologie et
du Patrimoine, Av. John Kennedy - Route des Zaers,
Rabat-souissi, Morocco.

ETUDES OCEAN INDIEN. see LINGUISTICS

930.1   DEU   ISSN 0949-0434
EURASIA ANTIQUA. Text in German, English. 1995. a., latest
vol.6, 2001. Document type: Journal, Academic/Scholarly.
Indexed: AnthLit.
Published by: (Deutsches Archaeologisches Institut,
Eurasienabteilung), Verlag Philipp von Zabern GmbH,
Philipp-von-Zabern-Platz 1-3, Mainz, 55116, Germany. TEL
49-6131-287470, FAX 49-6131-223710, zabern@zabern.de,
http://www.zabern.de. Adv. contact Manuela Dressen TEL
49-6131-2874711.

EUROPA DOKUMENTARO. see HISTORY—History Of Europe

930.1   GBR   ISSN 1461-9571
CC1
➤ EUROPEAN JOURNAL OF ARCHAEOLOGY. Text in English.
1993. 3/yr. GBP 268, USD 469 to institutions; GBP 279, USD
489 combined subscription to institutions print & online eds.
(effective 2006). adv. back issues avail. Document type:
Journal, Academic/Scholarly. Description: Seeks to promote
open debate among archaeologists committed to a new idea
of Europe in which there is more communication across
national frontiers.
Formerly: (until 1998): Journal of European Archaeology
(0965-7665)
Related titles: Online - full text ed.: ISSN 1741-2722. GBP 266,
USD 464 to institutions (effective 2006) (from EBSCO
Publishing, O C L C Online Computer Library Center, Inc.,
Sage Publications, Inc., Swets Information Services).
Indexed: AnthLit, ArtInd, BiblInd, BrArAb, DIP, IBR, IBSS, IBZ,
OTA, SUSA.
—BLDSC (3829.722550), IE, Infotrieve, ingenta. CCC.
Published by: (European Association of Archaeologists), Sage
Publications Ltd. (Subsidiary of: Sage Publications, Inc.), 1
Oliver's Yard, 55 City Rd, London, EC1 1SP, United Kingdom.
TEL 44-20-73248500, FAX 44-20-73248600,
info@sagepub.co.uk, http://www.sagepub.co.uk/journal.aspx?
pid=105535. Ed. Alan Saville. Adv. contact Jenny Kirby. page
GBP 195; trim 178 x 122. Circ: 1,750. Subscr. in the
Americas to: Sage Publications, Inc., 2455 Teller Rd,
Thousand Oaks, CA 91320. TEL 805-499-0721, FAX
805-499-0871, journals@sagepub.com.

➤ EUROPEAN STUDIES JOURNAL. see HISTORY—History Of
Europe

938   GRC   ISSN 0569-7425
EXCAVATIONS AT THE ATHENIAN AGORA. PICTURE BOOK.
Text in English. 1958. irreg., latest vol.23, 1994. price varies.
Document type: Monographic series, Academic/Scholarly.
Published by: American School of Classical Studies at Athens,
54 Souidias St, Athens, 106 76, Greece. TEL
30-210-7236313, FAX 30-210-7250584, ascsa@ascsa.org,
http://www.ascsa.edu.gr.

EXCERITUS; bulletin for practical research into the Roman army.
see CLASSICAL STUDIES

930.1   GBR   ISSN 1367-3971
EXETER ARCHAEOLOGICAL REPORTS. Text in English. 1979.
irreg.
—BLDSC (3836.244000).
Published by: University of Exeter Press, Reed Hall, Streatham
Dr, Exeter, EX4 4QR, United Kingdom. TEL 44-1392-263066,
FAX 44-1392-263064, uep@ex.ac.uk, http://www.ex.ac.uk/uep.

EXPEDITION. see ANTHROPOLOGY

EXPLORING THE ROMAN WORLD. see CLASSICAL STUDIES

913   POL   ISSN 0860-0007
DK4088
FASCICULI ARCHAEOLOGIAE HISTORICAE. Text in English,
French, German, Russian, Polish. 1987. irreg., latest vol.15,
2002. price varies. bk.rev. 55 p./no. 2 cols./p.; Document
type: Monographic series, Academic/Scholarly. Description:
Publishes works of Polish and foreign authors concerning
historical archaeology.
Indexed: AmH&L, DIP, HistAb, IBR, IBSS, IBZ.
Published by: Polska Akademia Nauk, Instytut Archeologii i
Etnologii, Al Solidarnosci 105, Warsaw, 00140, Poland. TEL
48-22-6202881, FAX 48-22-6240100, director@iaepan.edu.pl,
http://www.iaepan.edu.pl. Ed. Tadeusz Poklewski-Koziell.

930.1   ITA   ISSN 0390-6833
FASTI ARCHAEOLOGICI. Text in Multiple languages. 1948. a.
EUR 362 domestic; EUR 439 foreign (effective 2004).
Document type: Journal, Academic/Scholarly.
Published by: (International Association for Classical
Archaeology), Casa Editrice le Lettere, Costa San Giorgio 28,
Florence, FI 50125, Italy. TEL 39-055-2342710, FAX
39-055-2346010, staff@lelettere.it, www.lelettere.it.

930.1   USA
FEDERAL ARCHEOLOGICAL PROGRAMS AND ACTIVITIES:
THE SECRETARY OF THE INTERIOR'S REPORT TO
CONGRESS. Text in English. 1974. a. free. back issues avail.
Document type: Government. Description: Reports on the
archaeological activites of federal agencies. Concerned with
helping preserve America's archaeological and cultural
heritage.
Former titles: U.S. National Park Service. Federal Archeology:
The Current Program; U.S. National Park Service. Annual
Report to Congress on the Federal Archeological Program
Published by: (U.S. National Park Service), U.S. Department of
the Interior, National Parks Service, 1849 C St NW,
Washington, DC 20240. TEL 202-208-6843,
http://www.nps.gov. Circ: 2,000.

FELIX RAVENNA; rivista di antichita ravennati, cristiane e
bizantine. see ART

LA FENICE. see HISTORY

913   PRT   ISSN 0870-2004
FICHERO EPIGRAFICO. Text in Portuguese. 1982. irreg.
Related titles: ♦ Supplement to: Conimbriga. ISSN 0084-9189.
Published by: Universidade de Coimbra, Instituto de
Arqueologia/University of Coimbra, Institute of Archaeology,
Palacio de Sub-Ribas, Coimbra, 3000-395, Portugal. TEL
351-239-851600, FAX 351-239-851609, iarq@ci.uc.pt,
http://www.uc.pt/iauc/pub/fe.html. Ed. Jose d'Encarnacao.

913 709   HRV   ISSN 0352-6712
DR1521   CODEN: RSPZER
FILOZOFSKI FAKULTET - ZADAR. RAZDIO POVIJESNIH
ZNANOSTI. RADOVI. Text in Croatian; Summaries in English.
1963. a. index, cum.index no.1-12. back issues avail.
Document type: Academic/Scholarly.
Indexed: AmH&L, HistAb, RASB.
Published by: Filozofski Fakultet u Zadru, Obala kralja P
Kresimira IV, 2, Zadar, 23000, Croatia. TEL 385-57-436623.
Circ: 800. Co-sponsor: Samoupravna Interesna Zajednica
Znanosti SR Hrvatske.

708.897   FIN   ISSN 0355-1814
DK445
FINSKT MUSEUM. Text in English, German, Swedish. 1894. a.
illus. cum.index: 1894-1943. Document type: Yearbook,
Academic/Scholarly. Description: Publishes contributions in
archaeology, anthropology, art history, and numismatics.
Supersedes in part (in 1910): Suomen Museo (0355-1806);
Which incorporated (1894-1902): Finskt Museum (1235-0087)
Indexed: AICP, AmH&L, AnthLit, BHA, BrArAb, HistAb, IBR, NAA,
NumL, RASB.
Published by: Suomen Muinaismuistoyhdistys/Finnish Antiquarian
Society, Nervanderinkatu 13, PO Box 213, Helsinki, 00101,
Finland. TEL 358-9-40501, FAX 358-9-40509400. Ed.
Marianne Schauman Loenqvist.

930.1   SWE   ISSN 0281-3386
FJOELNIR; medlemstidning foer arkeologiska foereningen Fjoelnir.
Text in Swedish. 1982. q. SEK 75.
Indexed: NAA.
Published by: Fjoelnir, Institutionen foer Arkeologi, Gustavianum,
Uppsala, 75310, Sweden.

FLINTSHIRE HISTORICAL SOCIETY. PUBLICATIONS,
JOURNAL AND RECORD SERIES. see HISTORY—History
Of Europe

FLORIDA ANTHROPOLOGIST. see ANTHROPOLOGY

930.1   USA   ISSN 0888-4277
F313
FLORIDA ARCHAEOLOGY. Text in English. 1986. irreg.
Indexed: AnthLit.
Published by: Florida Bureau of Archaeological Research, 500 S.
Bronough Street, Tallahassee, FL 32399-0250. TEL
850-245-6333, http://dhr.dos.state.fl.us/bar/.

FLORIDA MUSEUM OF NATURAL HISTORY. BULLETIN. see
BIOLOGY

FOERENINGEN SVENSKA ATHENINSTITUTETS VAENNER.
SKRIFTSERIE. see HISTORY—History Of Europe

930.1   HUN   ISSN 0133-2023
DB901.F6
FOLIA ARCHAEOLOGICA. Text in Multiple languages. 1939. a.
Indexed: AIAP, AnthLit, DIP, IBR, IBZ.
Published by: Magyar Nemzeti Muzeum/Hungarian National
Museum, Muzeum krt 14-16, Budapest, 1088, Hungary. TEL
36-1-3382122, FAX 36-1-3177806, hnm@hnm.hu,
http://www.origo.hnm.hu.

913.031 943.8   POL   ISSN 0239-8524
DK4088
FOLIA PRAEHISTORICA POSNANIENSIA. Text in English,
German; Summaries in English. 1985. a., latest vol.6, 1994.
price varies. bk.rev. abstr.; illus. back issues avail. Document
type: Monographic series, Academic/Scholarly.
Indexed: AICP, AnthLit.
Published by: (Uniwersytet im. Adama Mickiewicza w
Poznaniu/Adam Mickiewicz University, Institute of Prehistory),
Wydawnictwo Naukowe Uniwersytetu im. Adama
Mickiewicza/Adam Mickiewicz University Press,
Nowowiejskiego 55, Poznan, 61-734, Poland. TEL
48-61-527380, FAX 48-61-527701. Ed. Jan Zak. Pub. Maria
Jankowska. R&P Malgorzata Bis. Circ: 600.

930.1   URY
FOLLETOS DE DIVULGACION. Text in Spanish. 1969. irreg. adv.
Formerly: Congreso Nacional de Arqueologia. Actas
Published by: Centro de Estudios Arqueologicos, Casilla de
Correos 6436, Montevideo, Uruguay. Ed. Jorge Baeza.

930.1   ESP   ISSN 0210-2366
DP302.C615
FONAMENTS; prehistoria i mon antic als paisos catalans. Text in
Spanish. 1978. a.
Indexed: AnthLit.
—CINDOC.
Published by: Curial Edicions Catalan, C. de Bruc, 144,
Barcelona, Catalunya 08037, Spain. Ed. Miquel Tarradell.

930.1   CZE
FONTES ARCHAEOLOGICAE MORAVICAE. Text in Czech. irreg.
illus.; maps. Document type: Academic/Scholarly.
Description: Catalogs and examines findings from recent
archaeological excavations.
Indexed: AICP.
Published by: Akademie Ved Ceske Republiky, Archeologicky
Ustav, Kralovopolska 147, Brno, 61200, Czech Republic. TEL
42-5-41212140, FAX 42-5-41514123, archeo@isibrno.cz,
ps@isibrno.cz, http://www.lib.cas.cz/knav/journals/eng/
Fontes_Archaeologicae_Moravicae.htm. Ed. Jaroslav Tejral.

930.1   POL   ISSN 0071-6863
➤ FONTES ARCHAEOLOGICI POSNANIENSES/ANNALES
MUSEI ARCHAEOLOGICI POSNANIENSIS. Text in Polish,
English, German. 1950. irreg. price varies. bk.rev. 250 p./no. 2
cols./p.; back issues avail. Document type: Journal,
Academic/Scholarly.
Formerly: Fontes Praehistorici (0867-1184)
Related titles: E-mail ed.; Fax ed.
Indexed: AICP, AnthLit, BHA, BrArAb, RASB.
Published by: Muzeum Archeologiczne, Palac Gorkow, Ul Wodna
27, Poznan, 61781, Poland. TEL 48-61-8526430, FAX
48-61-8525306, lechk@man.poznan.pl, http://
www.muzarp.poznan.pl. Ed. Lech Krzyzaniak. R&P Wojciech
Smigielski TEL 48-61-8528251. Circ: 800.

913   CZE   ISSN 0015-6183
GN705
FONTES ARCHAEOLOGICI PRAGENSES. Text in English,
French, Russian. 1958. irreg. price varies. charts; illus.; stat.
cum.index. reprints avail. Document type:
Academic/Scholarly.
Indexed: RefZh.
Published by: (Historicke Muzeum), Narodni Muzeum, Vaclavske
nam 68, Prague, 11579, Czech Republic. TEL
420-2-24497350, FAX 420-22246047. Ed. Milan Licka. Circ:
700.

914   ITA
FORMA ITALIAE. SERIE I. Text in Italian. 1926. irreg., latest
vol.39, 2000. price varies. Document type: Monographic
series, Academic/Scholarly.
Supersedes in part (in 1977): Forma Italia (0392-0119)
Published by: Casa Editrice Leo S. Olschki, Viuzzo del Pozzetto
8, Florence, 50126, Italy. TEL 39-055-6530684, FAX
39-055-6530214, celso@olschki.it, http://www.olschki.it.

914   ITA
FORMA ITALIAE. SERIE II. DOCUMENTI. Text in Italian. 1926.
irreg., latest vol.2, 1981. price varies. Document type:
Monographic series, Academic/Scholarly.
Supersedes in part (in 1972): Forma Italia (0392-0119)
Published by: Casa Editrice Leo S. Olschki, Viuzzo del Pozzetto
8, Florence, 50126, Italy. TEL 39-055-6530684, FAX
39-055-6530214, celso@olschki.it, http://www.olschki.it. Circ:
1,000.

A

937 ITA
FORMIANUM. Variant title: Convegno di Studi sull'Antico Territorio di Formia. Atti. Text in Italian. 1993. a.
Published by: (Archeoclub d'Italia), Armando Caramanica Editore, Via Appia, 762, Marina Di Minturno, LT 04020, Italy. TEL 39-771-680838.

913 SWE ISSN 0015-7813
DL601
FORNVAENNEN; tidskrift foer Svensk antikvarisk forskning/journal of Swedish antiquarian research. Text mainly in Swedish; Summaries in English. 1906. q. SEK 200 domestic; SEK 250 foreign (effective 2003). bk.rev. charts; illus. back issues avail.; reprints avail. **Document type:** *Journal, Academic/Scholarly.*
Related titles: Online - full content ed.: ISSN 1404-9430. 2000.
Indexed: A&ATA, AICP, AnthLit, BHA, BibLing, BrArAb, IBR, NAA, NumL, PCI.
—KNAW.
Published by: Kungliga Vitterhets Historie och Antikvitets Akademien/Royal Academy of Letters, History and Antiquities, PO Box 5622, Stockholm, 11486, Sweden. TEL 46-8-4404280, FAX 46-8-4404290, kansli@vitterhetsakad.se, http://www.raa.se/kvhaab/fornvann, http://www.vitterhetsakad.se. Ed. G Trotzig. Circ: 2,000.

930.1 DEU ISSN 0178-3262
FORSCHUNGEN UND BERICHTE DER ARCHAEOLOGIE DES MITTELALTERS IN BADEN-WUERTTEMBERG. Text in German. 1972. irreg., latest vol.25, 2002. price varies. **Document type:** *Monographic series, Academic/Scholarly.*
Published by: (Baden-Wuerttemberg. Landesdenkmalamt Baden-Wuerttemberg), Konrad Theiss Verlag GmbH, Moenchhaldenstr 28, Stuttgart, 70191, Germany. TEL 49-711-255270, FAX 49-711-2552717, service@theiss.de, http://www.theiss.de.

930.1 DEU
FORSCHUNGEN UND BERICHTE ZUR BAU- UND KUNSTDENKMALPFLEGE IN BADEN-WUERTTEMBERG. Text in German. irreg., latest vol.9, 2000. price varies. **Document type:** *Monographic series, Academic/Scholarly.*
Published by: (Baden-Wuerttemberg. Landesdenkmalamt Baden-Wuerttemberg), Konrad Theiss Verlag GmbH, Moenchhaldenstr 28, Stuttgart, 70191, Germany. TEL 49-711-255270, FAX 49-711-2552717, service@theiss.de, http://www.theiss.de.

930.1 DEU ISSN 0724-4347
FORSCHUNGEN UND BERICHTE ZUR VOR- UND FRUEHGESCHICHTE IN BADEN-WUERTTEMBERG. Text in German. 1972. irreg., latest vol.94, 2003. price varies. **Document type:** *Monographic series, Academic/Scholarly.*
Published by: (Baden-Wuerttemberg. Landesdenkmalamt Baden-Wuerttemberg), Konrad Theiss Verlag GmbH, Moenchhaldenstr 28, Stuttgart, 70191, Germany. TEL 49-711-255270, FAX 49-711-2552717, service@theiss.de, http://www.theiss.de.

FORSCHUNGEN ZUR KUNSTGESCHICHTE UND CHRISTLICHEN ARCHAEOLOGIE. see *ART*

930.1 AUT
FORSCHUNGSBERICHTE ZUR UR- UND FRUEHGESCHICHTE. Text in German. 1959. biennial. price varies. **Document type:** *Academic/Scholarly.*
Indexed: ZooRec.
Published by: Oesterreichische Gesellschaft fuer Ur- und Fruehgeschichte, Franz-Klein-Gasse 1, Vienna, W 1190, Austria. TEL 43-1-4277-40473, FAX 43-1-4277-9404. Ed. Dr. J W Neugebauer.

913 FRA
FOUILLES DE DELPHES: COLLECTION. Text in French. irreg. price varies. **Document type:** *Monographic series, Academic/Scholarly.*
Indexed: AIAP.
Published by: De Boccard Edition - Diffusion, 11 rue de Medicis, Paris, 75006, France. TEL 33-1-43260037, FAX 33-1-43548583, http://www.deboccard.com.

930.1 FRA
FOUILLES RECENTES A KHIROKITIA. Text in English, French. 1985. irreg. price varies. **Document type:** *Monographic series.*
Published by: Editions Recherche sur les Civilisations - A D P F, Les Patios Saint-Jacques, 6 rue Ferrus, Paris, Cedex 14 75603, France. TEL 33-1-43131100, FAX 33-1-43131125. Ed., Pub. Hina Descat. Circ: 600.

917 970.1 USA ISSN 1070-7549
PS508.I5
FOUR DIRECTIONS; American Indian literary quarterly. Text in English. 1972. q. membership. adv. bk.rev.; film rev. index. **Document type:** *Academic/Scholarly.* **Description:** Seeks to further awareness of the American Indian spirit in all areas among both American Indian and non-Indian audiences.
Formerly (until 1992): Artifacts (Washington)
Published by: (Institute for American Indian Studies), Snowbird Publishing Company, PO Box 729, Tellico Plains, TN 37385. TEL 615-253-3680. Ed. Joanna Meyer. Pub., Adv. contact William H Meyer. Circ: 1,600. **Subscr. to:** Institute for American Indian Studies, 38 Curtis Rd., Box 1260, Washington, CT 06793. TEL 203-868-0518, FAX 203-868-1649.

913 NOR ISSN 0015-9255
FRA HAUG OK HEDNI. Text in Norwegian. 1960. q. NOK 75 (effective 2003). illus.; maps. back issues avail. **Document type:** *Consumer.* **Description:** Presents archaeology, environmental, and cultural heritage studies of southwest Norway.
Indexed: DIP, IBR, IBZ, NAA.
—CCC.
Published by: (Rogalands Arkeologiske Forening), Arkeologisk museum i Stavanger/Museum of Archaeology, Stavanger, Postboks 478, Stavanger, 4002, Norway. TEL 47-51-846000, FAX 47-51-846199, ams@ark.museum.no, http://www.ark.museum.no.

FRA HOLBAECK AMT: HISTORISKE AARBOEGER. see *HISTORY—History Of Europe*

914 FRA ISSN 0399-6662
DC801.S235
FRANCE. CENTRE REGIONAL ARCHEOLOGIQUE D'ALET. DOSSIERS. Text in French. 1973. s-a. adv. bk.rev. back issues avail. **Document type:** *Bulletin.* **Description:** Studies the archaeology of Brittany.
Related titles: Supplement(s): France. Centre Regional Archeologique d'Alet. Dossiers. Numero Special. ISSN 0997-4342. 1978.
Indexed: BHA, BrArAb, NumL.
Published by: Centre Regional Archeologique d'Alet, Rue de Gaspe, BP 60, Saint Malo, Cedex 35413, France. TEL 33-2-99826373. Ed., Pub., R&P, Adv. contact Loic Langouet TEL 33-2-99286070.

913 FRA ISSN 1286-0999
DC2
FRANCE. COMITE DES TRAVAUX HISTORIQUES ET SCIENTIFIQUES. BULLETIN ARCHEOLOGIQUE: MOYEN-AGE, RENAISSANCE, TEMPS MODERNES. (In two fascicules: Antiquites Nationales; Afrique du Nord) Text in French. 1883. a. price varies. cum.index: 1883-1940. reprints avail.
Formerly (until 1997): France. Comite des Travaux Historiques et Scientifiques. Bulletin Archeologique. Fasc. A: Antiquites Nationales (0997-5322); Which superseded in part in 1975: France. Comite des Travaux Historiques et Scientifiques. Bulletin Archeologique (0071-8394)
Indexed: AIAP, BHA, BibLing.
—CCC.
Published by: Ministere de l'Education Nationale, Comite des Travaux Historiques et Scientifiques, 1 rue Descartes, Paris, 75005, France. Circ: 750.

FRAUEN - FORSCHUNG - ARCHAEOLOGIE. see *WOMEN'S STUDIES*

930.1 IRL
FRONTLINE (DUBLIN). Text in English. 1989. q. EUR 19.05 domestic; EUR 40 foreign (effective 2003).
—BLDSC (4042.084000), ingenta.
Published by: Wordwell Books, PO Box 69, Bray, Wicklow, Ireland. TEL 353-1-2765221, FAX 353-1-2765207, http://www.wordwellbooks.com.

930.1 DEU
FUEHRER ZU ARCHAEOLOGISCHEN DENKMAELERN IN BADEN-WUERTTEMBERG. Text in German. irreg., latest vol.23, 2003. price varies. **Document type:** *Monographic series, Academic/Scholarly.*
Published by: (Baden-Wuerttemberg. Landesdenkmalamt Baden-Wuerttemberg), Konrad Theiss Verlag GmbH, Moenchhaldenstr 28, Stuttgart, 70191, Germany. TEL 49-711-255270, FAX 49-711-2552717, service@theiss.de, http://www.theiss.de.

930.1 DEU
FUEHRER ZU ARCHAEOLOGISCHEN DENKMAELERN IN BAYERN. Text in German. irreg., latest vol.3, 2003. price varies. **Document type:** *Monographic series, Academic/Scholarly.*
Published by: (Bayerisches Landesamt fuer Denkmalpflege), Konrad Theiss Verlag GmbH, Moenchhaldenstr 28, Stuttgart, 70191, Germany. TEL 49-711-255270, FAX 49-711-2552717, service@theiss.de, http://www.theiss.de.

709 DEU ISSN 0071-9757
FUEHRER ZU ARCHAEOLOGISCHEN DENKMAELERN IN DEUTSCHLAND. Text in German. 1983. irreg., latest vol.43, 2003. price varies. index. **Document type:** *Monographic series, Academic/Scholarly.*
Published by: (Nordwestdeutscher und West- und Sueddeutscher Verband fuer Altertumsforschung), Konrad Theiss Verlag GmbH, Moenchhaldenstr 28, Stuttgart, 70191, Germany. TEL 49-711-255270, FAX 49-711-2552717, service@theiss.de, http://www.theiss.de.

930.1 DEU
FUEHRER ZUR HESSISCHEN VOR- UND FRUEHGESCHICHTE. Text in German. irreg., latest vol.6, 2002. price varies. **Document type:** *Monographic series, Academic/Scholarly.*
Published by: (Landesamt fuer Denkmalpfege Hessen), Konrad Theiss Verlag GmbH, Moenchhaldenstr 28, Stuttgart, 70191, Germany. TEL 49-711-255270, FAX 49-711-2552717, service@theiss.de, http://www.theiss.de.

069 CHN ISSN 1005-894X
FUJIAN WENBO/FUJIAN RELICS AND MUSEUM. Text in Chinese. 1979. s-a. CNY 10 domestic; USD 10 foreign (effective 2000). **Document type:** *Academic/Scholarly.* **Description:** Presents archaeological findings and research results, culture exchange with foreign countries.
Published by: (Fujian Kaogu Bowuguan Xuehui/Fujian Archaeological Museum Society), Fujian Provincial Museum, Westlike, Fuzhou, 350003, China. TEL 86-591-3726244, FAX 86-591-3726692, Tonyrita@sohu.com. Ed. Chen Rong. **Dist. overseas by:** Jiangsu Publications Import & Export Corp., 56 Gao Yun Ling, Nanjing, Jiangsu, China.

930.1 USA ISSN 1567-8040
➤ **FUNDAMENTAL ISSUES IN ARCHAEOLOGY.** Text in English. 1995. irreg., latest 2002. price varies. **Document type:** *Monographic series, Academic/Scholarly.* **Description:** Examines current critical issues of broad relevance to anthropological archaeology.
Published by: Springer-Verlag New York, Inc. (Subsidiary of: Springer Science+Business Media), 233 Spring St, New York, NY 10013. TEL 212-460-1500, FAX 212-460-1575, service@springer-ny.com, http://www.springer-ny.com. Eds. Gary M Feinman, T Douglas Price.

913 DEU ISSN 0071-9897
FUNDBERICHTE AUS BADEN-WUERTTEMBERG. Text in German. 1974. irreg., latest vol.25, 2002. price varies. bk.rev. **Document type:** *Monographic series, Academic/Scholarly.*
Formed by the 1974 merger of (1892-1971): Fundberichte aus Schwaben (0016-2752); (1925-1967): Badische Fundberichte (0341-0919)
Indexed: AICP, AnthLit, BHA, BrArAb, IBR, NumL, PCI.
—BLDSC (4056.097300). **CCC.**
Published by: (Baden-Wuerttemberg. Landesdenkmalamt Baden-Wuerttemberg), Konrad Theiss Verlag GmbH, Moenchhaldenstr 28, Stuttgart, 70191, Germany. TEL 49-711-255270, FAX 49-711-2552717, service@theiss.de, http://www.theiss.de.

913 DEU ISSN 0071-9889
FUNDBERICHTE AUS HESSEN. Text in German. 1961. irreg., latest vol.35, 2000. price varies. **Document type:** *Monographic series, Academic/Scholarly.*
Indexed: BHA, BrArAb, NumL.
Published by: Dr. Rudolf Habelt GmbH, Am Buchenhang 1, Bonn, 53115, Germany. TEL 49-228-9238322, FAX 49-228-9238323, info@habelt.de, http://www.habelt.de.

914 709 DEU ISSN 0723-8630
DD901.T8
FUNDE UND AUSGRABUNGEN IM BEZIRK TRIER. Text in German. 1969. a. EUR 8 (effective 2003). 150 p./no.; back issues avail. **Document type:** *Journal, Academic/Scholarly.*
Indexed: AnthLit, DIP, IBR, IBZ.
Published by: Rheinisches Landesmuseum Trier, Weimarer Allee 1, Trier, 54290, Germany. TEL 49-651-97740, FAX 49-651-9774222, rlmtrier@t-online.de, http://www.landesmuseum-trier.de. Circ: 2,000.

930.102809 DNK ISSN 0109-1441
FYNBOER OG ARKAEOLOGI. Text in Danish. 1979. 3/yr. free. bk.rev. illus. **Document type:** *Newsletter.*
Published by: Odense Bys Museer/Odense City Museums, Overgade 48, Odense C, 5000, Denmark. TEL 45-66-14-88-14-4601, FAX 45-65-90-86-00. Ed. Jytte Raun. R&P Jette Hougaard. Circ: 800.

FYND. see *MUSEUMS AND ART GALLERIES*

FYNSKE MINDER. see *HISTORY—History Of Europe*

930.1 FRA ISSN 0994-6837
LE G A M INFO. (Groupement Archeologique du Maconnais) Text in French. 1972. s-a. EUR 15; EUR 10 to students (effective 2004). **Document type:** *Bulletin.*
Published by: Groupement Archeologique du Maconnais (GAM), Maison de l'Archeologie, Rue Sennece, Macon, 71000, France. TEL 33-3-8538-9376, frcognot@hotmail.com, http://membres.lycos.fr/GAM71/gaminfo/framegaminfo.htm.

913 PER ISSN 0254-8240
F2229
GACETA ARQUEOLOGICA ANDINA. Text in Spanish. 1982. bi-m. bk.rev. abstr.; bibl.; charts; illus. back issues avail.
Indexed: AnthLit, HAPI, IBR.
Published by: Instituto Andino de Estudios Arqueologicos, Apdo Postal 11279, Lince, Lima 14, Peru.

301 ESP ISSN 1132-2470
GALA; revista d'arqueologia i antropologia. Text in Spanish. 1992. a.

Published by: Museu Arqueologia i Antropologia, Can Xifreda C. Dr. Reig, Sant Feliu De Codines, Barcelona 08182, Spain. Eds. J Rovira, M Garriga.

GALLAECIA. see *HISTORY—History Of Europe*

913 FRA ISSN 0016-4119
DC30
GALLIA; fouilles et monuments archeologiques en France metropolitaine. Text in French. 1943. s-a. price varies. adv. bk.rev. charts; illus. index. **Document type:** *Monographic series, Academic/Scholarly.*
Related titles: ♦ Supplement(s): Gallia. Supplement. ISSN 0072-0119.
Indexed: AIAP, BHA, BrArAb, IBR, NumL, PCI, RASB.
Published by: (France. Centre National de la Recherche Scientifique), C N R S Editions, 15 Rue Malebranche, Paris, 75005, France. TEL 33-1-53102700, FAX 33-1-53102727, http://www.cnrseditions.fr. Circ: 1,500.

913 FRA ISSN 0016-4127
GN811.A1
GALLIA PREHISTOIRE. Text in French. 1958. s-a. price varies. charts; illus. index. **Document type:** *Monographic series, Academic/Scholarly.*
Related titles: ♦ Supplement(s): Gallia Prehistoire. Supplement. ISSN 0072-0100.
Indexed: AIAP, AnthLit, BrArAb, NumL, PCI, RASB.
Published by: (France. Centre National de la Recherche Scientifique), C N R S Editions, 15 Rue Malebranche, Paris, 75005, France. TEL 33-1-53102700, FAX 33-1-53102727, http://www.cnrseditions.fr. Ed. Leroi-Gourhan.

913 FRA ISSN 0072-0100
GALLIA PREHISTOIRE. SUPPLEMENT. Text in French. 1958. irreg. price varies. adv. bk.rev. index.
Related titles: ♦ Supplement to: Gallia Prehistoire. ISSN 0016-4127.
Indexed: PCI.
Published by: (France. Centre National de la Recherche Scientifique), C N R S Editions, 15 Rue Malebranche, Paris, 75005, France. TEL 33-1-53102700, FAX 33-1-53102727, http://www.cnrseditions.fr. Circ: 1,500 (controlled).

913 FRA ISSN 0072-0119
DC30
GALLIA. SUPPLEMENT. Text in French. 1943. irreg. price varies. adv. bk.rev. index. **Document type:** *Academic/Scholarly.*
Related titles: ♦ Supplement to: Gallia. ISSN 0016-4119.
Indexed: AIAP, BHA, PCI.
Published by: (France. Centre National de la Recherche Scientifique), C N R S Editions, 15 Rue Malebranche, Paris, 75005, France. TEL 33-1-53102700, FAX 33-1-53102727, http://www.cnrseditions.fr. Circ: 1,500 (controlled).

GAYA. see *HISTORY—History Of Europe*

GDANSKIE TOWARZYSTWO NAUKOWE. WYDZIAL 1 - NAUK SPOLECZNYCH I HUMANISTYCZNYCH. KOMISJA ARCHEOLOGICZNA. PRACE. see *HISTORY—History Of Europe*

930.1 JPN ISSN 0454-1634
GEKKAN KOKOGAKU JOURNAL/ARCHAEOLOGICAL JOURNAL. Key Title: Kokogaku Janaru. Text in Japanese. 1965. m. JPY 1,400 per issue (effective 1998). **Document type:** *Academic/Scholarly.*
Published by: Nyu Saiensusha/New Science Co., 3-8-14 Takanawa, Minato-ku, Tokyo, 108-0074, Japan. hk-ns@mk1.macnet.or.jp, http://www.macnet.or.jp/co/hk-ns.

GELDERS ERFGOED. see *HISTORY—History Of Europe*

913 709 CHE ISSN 0072-0585
GENAVA; revue d'archeologie et d'histoire de l'art. Text in French. 1923. a. CHF 50. **Document type:** *Academic/Scholarly.*
Indexed: ABM, AIAP, AICP, BHA, DIP, IBR, IBZ, NumL, RILM.
Published by: Musee d'Art et d'Histoire Geneva, Rue Charles Galland 2, Geneva 3, 1211, Switzerland. TEL 41-22-4182600, FAX 41-22-4182601. Ed. Danielle Buyssens.

913 ITA ISSN 0390-2196
CC9 CODEN: GARCDQ
GEO - ARCHEOLOGIA; periodico dell'Associazione Geo-Archeologica Italiana. Text in Italian. 1973. s-a. back issues avail. **Document type:** *Academic/Scholarly.*
Description: Covers the culture of the geological sciences, includes research and study of various topics in these fields.
Indexed: DIP, IBR, IBZ.
Published by: Associazione Geo-Archeologica Italiana, C/o Fondazione Europeo Dragan, Foro Traiano 1-A, Rome, 00187, Italy. Ed. Claudio Saporetti. **Dist. by:** Herder Editrice e Libreria s.r.l., Piazza di Montecitorio 117-120, Rome 00186, Italy. TEL 39-6-67-94-628, FAX 39-6-678-4751, http://www.herder.it.

913 USA ISSN 0883-6353
CC77.5 CODEN: GEOAEY
➤ **GEOARCHAEOLOGY**; an international journal. Text in English. 1986. 8/yr. USD 1,425 domestic to institutions; USD 1,505 in Canada & Mexico to institutions; USD 1,573 elsewhere to institutions; USD 1,568 combined subscription domestic to institutions print & online eds.; USD 1,648 combined subscription in Canada & Mexico to institutions print & online eds.; USD 1,716 combined subscription elsewhere to institutions print & online eds. (effective 2006). bk.rev. back issues avail. **Document type:** *Journal, Academic/Scholarly.*
Description: Publishes original reports on the environmental settings of archaeological sites, materials analysis of artifacts, and process papers describing new techniques and equipment. Serves as an interface between geology and archaeology.
Related titles: Microform ed.: (from PQC); Online - full text ed.: ISSN 1520-6548. USD 1,425 to institutions (effective 2006) (from EBSCO Publishing, Swets Information Services, Wiley InterScience).
Indexed: AbAn, AnthLit, ArtHuCI, BrArAb, CurCont, NumL, RASB. —BLDSC (4116.841000), IE, Infotrieve, ingenta, Linda Hall. **CCC.**
Published by: John Wiley & Sons, Inc., 111 River St, Hoboken, NJ 07030-5774. TEL 201-748-6000, FAX 201-748-5915, uscs-wis@wiley.com, http://www3.interscience.wiley.com/cgi-bin/jhome/36011, http://www.wiley.com. Ed. E A Bettis.
Subscr. outside the Americas to: John Wiley & Sons Ltd., The Atrium, Southern Gate, Chichester, West Sussex PO19 8SQ, United Kingdom. TEL 44-1243-843335, 0800-243407, FAX 44-1243-843232, cs-journals@wiley.co.uk.

➤ **GERION.** see *HISTORY*

930.1 DEU ISSN 0016-8874
DD53
GERMANIA. Text in German, English, French. 1917. a., latest vol.78, 2000. bk.rev. abstr.; bibl.; charts; illus. index, cum.index 1917-1958. back issues avail.; reprints avail. **Document type:** *Journal, Academic/Scholarly.*
Indexed: AIAP, AICP, AnthLit, BHA, BrArAb, DIP, IBR, IBZ, MLA-IB, NumL, PCI, RASB, SSCI.
Published by: (Deutsches Archaeologisches Institut, Roemisch-Germanische Kommission), Verlag Philipp von Zabern GmbH, Philipp-von-Zabern-Platz 1-3, Mainz, 55116, Germany. TEL 49-6131-287470, FAX 49-6131-223710, zabern@zabern.de, http://www.zabern.de. Adv. contact Manuela Dressen TEL 49-6131-2874711.

913 DEU ISSN 0418-9779
GERMANISCHE DENKMAELER DER VOELKERWANDERUNGSZEIT. SERIES B. Text in German. 1958. irreg., latest vol.18, 1999. price varies. **Document type:** *Monographic series, Academic/Scholarly.*
Indexed: RASB.
Published by: (Roemisch-Germanische Kommission des Deutschen Archaeologischen Instituts), Franz Steiner Verlag Stuttgart GmbH, Birkenwaldstr 44, Stuttgart, 70191, Germany. TEL 49-711-25820, FAX 49-711-2582390, franz.steiner.verlag@t-online.de, http://www.steiner-verlag.de. Ed. Kurt Boehner. R&P Sabine Koerner.

913 CHE ISSN 0072-4270
GESELLSCHAFT PRO VINDONISSA. JAHRESBERICHT. Text in German. 1907. a. price varies. **Document type:** *Yearbook, Academic/Scholarly.*
Indexed: BrArAb, NumL.
Published by: Gesellschaft pro Vindonissa, Vindonissa Museum, Brugg Ag, 5200, Switzerland. TEL 41-56-4412184.

708 CHE ISSN 0072-4289
GESELLSCHAFT PRO VINDONISSA. VEROEFFENTLICHUNGEN. Text in German. 1942. irreg., latest vol.17, 2000. price varies. charts; illus.; stat. Supplement avail. **Document type:** *Monographic series, Academic/Scholarly.*
Published by: Gesellschaft pro Vindonissa, Vindonissa Museum, Brugg Ag, 5200, Switzerland. TEL 41-56-4412184.

GIORNALE STORICO DELLA LUNIGIANA E DEL TERRITORIO LUCENSE. see *HISTORY—History Of Europe*

947.8 BLR
GISTARYCHNA-ARKHEALAGICHNY ZBORNIK/HISTORIC-ARCHAEOLOGIC COLLECTION. Text in Belorussian, Russian, English. 1993. irreg. **Document type:** *Monographic series, Academic/Scholarly.* **Description:** Includes materials on both the archaeology of the Stone, Bronze, Iron and Middle Ages of Belarus, and problems of ancient and medieval history of Belarus and its neighbors (Latvia, Lithuania, Poland, Russia, Ukraine).
Published by: (Natsiyanal'naya Akademiya Navuk Belarusi, Instytut Gistoryi/National Academy of Sciences of Belarus, Institute of History), Vydavetstvo Belaruskaya Navuka/Publishing House Belaruskaya Navuka, 18 Academician V F Kuprevich St, Minsk, 220141, Belarus. TEL 375-17-2632327, FAX 375-17-2637618, belnauka@infonet.by, http://www.ac.by/publications/belling/histar14.html.

GOETTINGISCHE GELEHRTE ANZEIGEN. see *LINGUISTICS*

930.1 ZAF ISSN 0304-3460
CODEN: GSSSDZ
GOODWIN SERIES. OCCASIONAL PAPERS. Text in English. 1972. irreg., latest vol.8, 2000. price varies (free to subscribers of SA Archaeological Bulletin). abstr.; bibl.; charts; illus.; maps. back issues avail. **Document type:** *Bulletin, Academic/Scholarly.*
Indexed: AICP, AnthLit, IBSS.
Published by: South African Archaeological Society, PO Box 15700, Vlaeberg, Cape Town 8018, South Africa. TEL 27-21-4813886, FAX 27-21-4813993, archsoc@isiko.org.za. R&P Margaret Avery. Adv. contact Colin Orr. Circ: 1,200.

930.1 390 BEL
GRAAFSCHAP JETTE. JAARBOEK/COMTE DE JETTE. ANNALES. Text in Dutch, French. 1963. q. bk.rev. charts; illus. **Document type:** *Bulletin.*
Formerly: Comte de Jette. Bulletin (0010-4914)
Published by: Cercle d'Histoire, d'Archeologie et de Folklore du Comte de Jette et des Environs, Av de Brouckere 35, Brussels, 1083, Belgium. Ed. F Van Bellingen.

913 AUT ISSN 0376-5253
PA1.A1
GRAEZER BEITRAEGE; Zeitschrift fuer klassische Altertumswissenschaft. Text in English, French, German, Italian. 1973. s-a. EUR 64.70, USD 63 per vol. (effective 2003). adv. bk.rev. back issues avail. **Document type:** *Journal, Academic/Scholarly.*
Indexed: BibLing, DIP, IBR, IBZ, MLA-IB. —BLDSC (4214.340000).
Published by: Verlag Ferdinand Berger und Soehne GmbH, Wienerstr 80, Horn, N 3580, Austria. TEL 43-2982-4161332, FAX 43-2982-2317235, office@berger.at, http://www.berger.at. Circ: 200.

932 666 EGY ISSN 0255-0903
GROUPE INTERNATIONAL D'ETUDE DE LA CERAMIQUE EGYPTIENNE. BULLETIN DE LIAISON. Key Title: Bulletin de Liaison du Groupe International d'Etude de la Ceramique Egyptienne. Text in English, French, German. 1975. a. EGP 22 domestic; EUR 7.60 foreign (effective 2001). back issues avail. **Document type:** *Academic/Scholarly.* **Description:** Recent discoveries in Egypt and news about ceramological studies in Egyptology.
Published by: (Groupe International d'Etude de la Ceramique Egyptienne), Institut Francais d'Archeologie Orientale du Caire, Kasr el-Aini, 37 Sharia Sheikh Aly Youssef, Mounira, P O Box 11562, Cairo, Egypt. TEL 20-2-3571622, FAX 20-2-3544635. Ed. Helen Jacquet Gordon. Circ: 200. **Dist. by:** Boustany's Publishing House, 29 Faggalah St, Cairo 11271, Egypt. TEL 20-2-5915315, FAX 20-2-4177915, boustany@idsc.net.eg.

913 PRT
GRUPO DE INVESTIGACAO ARQUEOLOGICA DO NORTE. TRABALHOS. Text in Portuguese. 1982. irreg.
Published by: Grupo de Investigacao Arqueologica do Norte, Rua Santiago, 237-4450, S. da Hora (Matosinhos), Porto, 4200, Portugal. Circ: 1,000.

918 GTM
GUATEMALA. CONSEJO NACIONAL PARA LA PROTECCION DE LA ANTIGUA GUATEMALA. CARTA INFORMATIVA. Text in Spanish. bi-m.
Related titles: Supplement(s): Guatemala. Consejo Nacional para la Proteccion de la Antigua Guatemala. Memoria de Labores.
Published by: Consejo Nacional para la Proteccion de la Antigua Guatemala, Convento de Capuchinas, La Antigua Guatemala, 03001, Guatemala. Circ: 500.

GUIDE TO DEPARTMENTS OF SOCIOLOGY, ANTHROPOLOGY AND ARCHAEOLOGY IN UNIVERSITIES AND MUSEUMS IN CANADA/ANNUAIRE DES DEPARTEMENTS DE SOCIOLOGIE, D'ANTHROPOLOGIE ET D'ARCHEOLOGIE DES UNIVERSITES ET DES MUSEES DU CANADA. see *SOCIOLOGY*

930.1 USA
GUIDE TO HISTORICAL ARCHAEOLOGICAL LITERATURE. Text in English. 1990. irreg. price varies. **Document type:** *Academic/Scholarly.* **Description:** Bibliographic essays and compiled references on ethnic group experiences in the New World.
Published by: Society for Historical Archaeology, PO Box 30446, Tucson, AZ 85751. TEL 520-886-8006, FAX 520-886-0182, sha_editor@cup.edu, the_sha@mindspring.com, http://www.sha.org.

933 ISR
GUIDES TO ANTIQUITY SITES. Text in English. 1992. irreg., latest 1999. price varies. illus.; maps. back issues avail. **Document type:** *Monographic series.*
Related titles: Hebrew ed.
Published by: Israel Antiquities Authority, P O Box 586, Jerusalem, 91004, Israel. TEL 972-2-620-4622, FAX 972-2-628-9066, harriet@israntique.org.il.

GUNNERIA. see *BIOLOGY*

A

913 DEU ISSN 0072-9183
HABELTS DISSERTATIONSDRUCKE. REIHE KLASSISCHE ARCHAEOLOGIE. Text in German. 1969. irreg., latest vol.27, 1988. price varies. **Document type:** *Monographic series, Academic/Scholarly.*
Published by: Dr. Rudolf Habelt GmbH, Am Buchenhang 1, Bonn, 53115, Germany. TEL 49-228-9238322, FAX 49-228-9238323, info@habelt.de, http://www.habelt.de.

933 ISR ISSN 1565-043X
DS111.A1
HADASHOT ARKHEOLOGIYOT; excavations and surveys in Israel. Text in English. 2000. irreg., latest vol.113, 2001. USD 36 (effective 2001). illus. index. back issues avail. **Document type:** *Academic/Scholarly.* **Description:** Short reports of excavations in Israel.
Formed by the merger of (1961-2000): Hadashot Arkheologiyot (0047-1569); (1982-2000): Excavations and Surveys in Israel (0334-1607)
Indexed: IHP, NumL, RI-1.
Published by: Israel Antiquities Authority, P O Box 586, Jerusalem, 91004, Israel. TEL 972-2-620-4622, FAX 972-2-560-2628, harriet@israntique.org.il. Eds. Ann Roshwalb-Hurowitz, Lily Gershuny. Circ: 1,500. **Dist. by:** Eisenbrauns, PO Box 275, Winona Lake, IN 46590-0275.

HALLAND; aarsbok foer kulturhistoria och hembygdsvaard i Hallands laen. see *HISTORY—History Of Europe*

913 DEU ISSN 0341-3152
HAMBURGER BEITRAEGE ZUR ARCHAEOLOGIE. Text in German, English, French. 1971. irreg., latest vol.20, 1996. price varies. bibl.; charts; illus.; maps. back issues avail. **Document type:** *Monographic series, Academic/Scholarly.*
Indexed: BrArAb, NumL.
Published by: Verlag Philipp von Zabern GmbH, Philipp-von-Zabern-Platz 1-3, Mainz, 55116, Germany. TEL 49-6131-287470, FAX 49-6131-223710, zabern@zabern.de, http://www.zabern.de. Adv. contact Manuela Dressen TEL 49-6131-2874711.

940 GBR
➤ **HAMPSHIRE STUDIES (YEAR).** Text in English. 1885. a., latest vol.55. GBP 10 (effective 2001). charts; illus.; maps. back issues avail. **Document type:** *Journal, Academic/Scholarly.*
Formerly (until 1996): Hampshire Field Club and Archaeological Society. Proceedings (0142-8950); (until 1958): Hampshire Field Club and Archaeological Society. Papers and Proceedings
Indexed: BHA, BrArAb, BrGeoL, NumL.
—BLDSC (6706.600000).
Published by: Hampshire Field Club, c/o Bruce Howard, County Planning Dept., Hampshire County Council, The Castle, Winchester, Hants SO23 8US, United Kingdom. TEL 44-1962-846736, FAX 44-1962-846776, bruce.howard@hants.gov.uk, http://www.fieldclub.hants.org.uk/. Eds. E Roberts, N Stoodley. R&P Bruce Howard. Circ: 500.

➤ **HANDBUCH DER ORIENTALISTIK. 1. ABTEILUNG. DER NAHE UND DER MITTLERE OSTEN/HANDBOOK OF ORIENTAL STUDIES. SECTION 1. THE NEAR AND MIDDLE EAST.** see *ASIAN STUDIES*

➤ **HANDBUCH DER ORIENTALISTIK. 7. ABTEILUNG. KUNST UND ARCHAEOLOGIE/HANDBOOK OF ORIENTAL STUDIES. SECTION 7. ART AND ARCHEOLOGY.** see *ASIAN STUDIES*

936.3 DNK ISSN 0105-1660
HARJA. Text in Danish. 1976-1985; resumed 199?. irreg. (approx. a.). DKK 25. illus.
Published by: Harja Arkaeologisk Forening, c/o Jane Kjaergaard Andresen, Maagebakken 166, Odense Sv, 5250, Denmark. TEL 45-66-17-50-20. Ed. Jane Kjaergaard Anddresen.

HEIMATJAHRBUCH KREIS AHRWEILER. see *LITERATURE*

HELLENIKA. see *CLASSICAL STUDIES*

930.1 FIN ISSN 0783-2842
HELSINKI PAPERS IN ARCHAEOLOGY. Text in English. 1970. s-a. **Document type:** *Monographic series.*
Formerly (until 1983): Moniste - Helsingin Yliopiston Arkeologian Laitos (0355-1881)
Indexed: AnthLit.
Published by: Helsingin Yliopisto, Kulttuurien Tutkimuksen Laitos, Arkeologia/University of Helsinki, Institute for Cultural Studies, Department of Archaeology, P.O. Box 33, Helsinki, 00014, Finland. TEL 358-9-1911, FAX 358-9-19123010, http://www.helsinki.fi. Eds. Christian Carpelan, Timo Jussila.

902 DEU ISSN 0174-2086
HEPHAISTOS (HAMBURG). Text in German. 1979. irreg., latest vol.18, 2000. price varies. **Document type:** *Journal, Academic/Scholarly.*
Indexed: AIAP.
—BLDSC (4295.847000).
Published by: Universitaet Hamburg, Archaeologisches Institut, Johnsallee 35, Hamburg, 20148, Germany. TEL 49-40-428383070, FAX 49-40-428383255, archaeologie.fb09@uni-hamburg.de, http://www.uni-hamburg.de/Wiss/FB/09/archinst.htm. Ed. Christoph Hocker.

930.1 BEL ISSN 0779-6080
HERLEVEND VERLEDEN - ARCHEOLOGISCHE GIDSEN. Text in Dutch. 1993. irreg., latest vol.2, 1994. price varies. back issues avail. **Document type:** *Monographic series.* **Description:** Publishes guides on topics in the archaeology of Flanders (Belgium).
Published by: Instituut voor het Archeologisch Patrimonium, Doornveld 1, Bus 30, Asse (Zellik), 1731, Belgium. TEL 32-2-4631333, FAX 32-2-4631951.

301 GBR ISSN 0440-7342
HERTFORDSHIRE ARCHAEOLOGY. Text in English. 1968. a.
Published by: St Albans and Hertfordshire Architectural and Archaeological Society, BE Moody, 24 Rose Walk, Hertfordshire, St Albans AL4 9AF, United Kingdom. TEL 44-17-2785-3204, http://www.stalbanshistory.org/.

930.1 480 949.5 USA ISSN 0018-098X
DF10
➤ **HESPERIA.** Text in English. 1932. q. USD 70 domestic to individuals; USD 80 foreign to individuals; USD 130 domestic to institutions; USD 140 foreign to institutions (effective 2005). charts; illus. cum.index. Supplement avail.; back issues avail.; reprints avail. **Document type:** *Journal, Academic/Scholarly.* **Description:** Scholarly research on historical, archaeological, literary, and epigraphical topics concerning prehistoric through medieval Greece.
Related titles: Online - full text ed.: ISSN 1553-5622 (from EBSCO Publishing, Gale Group, H.W. Wilson, JSTOR (Web-based Journal Archive), O C L C Online Computer Library Center, Inc., Project MUSE, ProQuest Information & Learning, Swets Information Services); Supplement(s): Hesperia. Supplement. ISSN 1064-1173. 1937.
Indexed: AIAP, AbAn, ArtHuCI, ArtInd, BibLing, CurCont, DIP, IBR, IBZ, IndIslam, MLA-IB, NTA, NumL, PCI, RASB, SSCI.
—BLDSC (4300.860000), IDS, IE, Infotrieve, ingenta. **CCC.**
Published by: American School of Classical Studies at Athens, 6-8 Charlton St, Princeton, NJ 08540-5232. TEL 609-683-0800, FAX 609-924-0578, tc@ascsa.org, ascsa@ascsa.org, http://www.ascsa.edu.gr/publications/hesperia.htm. Ed., R&P Dr. Tracey Cullen TEL 609-683-0800 ext 22. Circ: 1,100.

930.1 DEU ISSN 1610-0190
DD801.H545
HESSEN ARCHAEOLOGIE. Text in German. 2002. a. EUR 24.90 per vol. (effective 2003). **Document type:** *Monographic series, Academic/Scholarly.*
Published by: (Landesamt fuer Denkmalpfege Hessen), Konrad Theiss Verlag GmbH, Moenchhaldenstr 28, Stuttgart, 70191, Germany. TEL 49-711-255270, FAX 49-711-2552717, service@theiss.de, http://www.theiss.de.

HIAKA KHRONIKA. see *HISTORY—History Of Europe*

HIKUIN. see *HISTORY—History Of Europe*

HIMAVANTA; India's only mountaineering monthly. see *SPORTS AND GAMES—Outdoor Life*

HISTOIRE ET ARCHEOLOGIE. see *HISTORY—History Of Europe*

HISTORIC ILLINOIS. see *ARCHITECTURE*

666.3 USA
HISTORIC ILLINOIS POTTERIES CIRCULAR SERIES. Text in English. 1988. irreg.
Published by: Center for American Archeology Press, PO Box 366, Kampsville, IL 62053. TEL 618-653-4688, FAX 618-653-4235, http://www.caa-archeology.org.

913 USA ISSN 0440-9213
E11
➤ **HISTORICAL ARCHAEOLOGY.** Text in English. 1967. q. free to members (effective 2004). adv. bk.rev. illus. Index. back issues avail.; reprints avail. **Document type:** *Journal, Academic/Scholarly.* **Description:** Presents theoretical perspectives, comparative studies and artifact and site analysis.
Related titles: CD-ROM ed.; Online - full text ed.
Indexed: A&ATA, ASCA, AbAn, AmH&L, AnthLit, ArtHuCI, BHA, BrArAb, CurCont, DIP, HistAb, HumInd, IBR, IBSS, IBZ, NumL, PCI, RASB.
—BLDSC (4316.117000), IDS, IE, Infotrieve, ingenta. **CCC.**
Published by: Society for Historical Archaeology, PO Box 30446, Tucson, AZ 85751. TEL 520-886-8006, FAX 520-886-0182, the_sha@mindspring.com, http://www.sha.org. Ed. Ronald L Michael. Circ: 2,500 (paid).

➤ **THE HISTORICAL REVIEW**; a bi-annual journal of history and archaeology. see *HISTORY—History Of Asia*

➤ **HISTORISCHER VEREIN FUER DAS FUERSTENTUM LIECHTENSTEIN. JAHRBUCH.** see *HISTORY—History Of Europe*

913 940 HRV ISSN 0350-6320
DB329
HISTRIA ARCHAEOLOGICA. Text in Croatian; Summaries in English, German, Italian. 1970. a. bibl.; charts; illus. **Document type:** *Academic/Scholarly.*
Indexed: BHA, RASB.
Published by: Arheoloski Muzej Istre Pula, M Balote 3, Pula, 52000, Croatia. TEL 385-52-21603, FAX 385-52-212415, http://www.mdc.hr/pula. Ed. Zeljko Ujcic. Circ: 1,000.

HOMBRE Y CULTURA. see *ANTHROPOLOGY*

930.1 USA
HOUSTON ARCHAEOLOGICAL SOCIETY. JOURNAL. Text in English. 3/yr.
Indexed: AnthLit.
Published by: Houston Archeological Society, P.O. Box 6751, Houston, TX 77265-6751. http://www.houstonarcheology.org/.

915 CHN ISSN 1001-9928
HUAXIA KAOGU/HUAXIA ARCHAEOLOGY. Text in Chinese. 1987. q. USD 3 per issue. adv. bk.rev. **Document type:** *Academic/Scholarly.*
Related titles: Online - full text ed.: (from East View Information Services).
Published by: Henan Sheng Wenwu Yanjiusuo/Henan Cultural Relics Research Institute, No 9 Longhai Bei 3 Jie, Zhengzhou, Henan, 450004, China. TEL 6252066. Ed. Hao Benxing. Circ: 5,000 (controlled).

930.1 ESP ISSN 0211-1187
HUELVA ARQUEOLOGICA. Text in Spanish, Catalan. 1970. irreg. —CINDOC.
Published by: Diputacion Provincial de Huelva, Seccion de Arqueologia, Ave. Martin A. Pinzon, 9, Huevla, Andalucia 21003, Spain. TEL 34-959-494762, FAX 34-959-494762, arqueologia@diphuelva.es, http://www.diphuelva.es/.

HUMAN MOSAIC; a journal of the social sciences. see *ANTHROPOLOGY*

I A. (Industrial Archeology) see *TECHNOLOGY: COMPREHENSIVE WORKS*

933 ISR
I A A REPORTS. Text in English. 1996. irreg., latest vol.16. price varies. charts; illus. back issues avail. **Document type:** *Monographic series, Academic/Scholarly.* **Description:** Reports and monographs on large-scale archaeological excavations in Israel.
Published by: Israel Antiquities Authority, P O Box 586, Jerusalem, 91004, Israel. TEL 972-2-620-4622, FAX 972-2-628-9066, harriet@israntique.org.il.

913 GBR
I A M S JOURNAL. (Institute for Archaeo-Metallurgical Studies) Text in English. 1980. s-a. GBP 5. illus. **Document type:** *Journal, Academic/Scholarly.* **Description:** Reports of I A M S.
Formerly: I A M S Newsletter (0261-068X)
Indexed: CERDIC, IMMAb.
Published by: University College London, Institute of Archaeology, 31-34 Gordon Sq., London, WC1H 0PY, United Kingdom. TEL 44-20-7380-7532, FAX 44-207-383-2572, http://www.ucl.ac.uk/iams/journal.htm. Ed. Thilo Rehren. Circ: 1,000.

913 AUT
I.C. NACHRICHTEN. Text in German. 1969. 2/yr. EUR 60 membership; EUR 15 to students (effective 2005). bk.rev. charts; illus. **Document type:** *Journal, Academic/Scholarly.*
Published by: Institutum Canarium, Hauslabgasse 31/6, Vienna, O 1050, Austria. FAX 43-1-5457744, hjulbrich@institutum-canarium.org, http://www.institutum-canarium.org. Ed. Werner Pichler. Circ: 400.

I C S NEWSLETTER. see *ART*

930.1 USA
I N A QUARTERLY. Text in English. 1979. q. USD 40 to individuals; USD 25 to students (effective 2000). bk.rev. **Document type:** *Newsletter, Academic/Scholarly.*
Formerly (until 1991): I N A Newsletter (0738-4505)
Indexed: BrArAb, NumL.
Published by: Institute of Nautical Archaeology, Drawer HG, College Station, TX 77841-5137. TEL 409-845-6694, FAX 409-847-9260, http://nautarch.tamu.edu. Ed. Christine A Powell. R&P Christine Powell. Circ: 1,350.

ICONOLOGICAL STUDIES IN ROMAN ART. see *ART*

930.1 USA ISSN 0893-2271
IDAHO ARCHAEOLOGIST. Text in English. 1977. s-a. USD 3.50 per issue (effective 2002).
Indexed: AmH&L, AnthLit.

Published by: Boise State University, Department of Anthropology, 1910 University Drive, Boise, ID 83725-1950. TEL 208-426-3023, FAX 208-426-4329, http://anthro.boisestate.edu/publish.html#IDARCH.

930.1 USA
ILLINOIS ARCHAEOLOGICAL SURVEY. BULLETIN SERIES. Text in English. 1968. irreg. **Document type:** *Monographic series.*
Published by: Center for American Archeology Press, PO Box 366, Kampsville, IL 62053. TEL 618-653-4688, FAX 618-653-4235, http://www.caa-archeology.org.

930.1 USA
ILLINOIS ARCHAEOLOGICAL SURVEY. CIRCULAR SERIES. Text in English. 1976. irreg. **Document type:** *Monographic series.*
Published by: Center for American Archeology Press, PO Box 366, Kampsville, IL 62053. TEL 618-653-4688, FAX 618-653-4235, http://www.caa-archeology.org.

930.1 USA
ILLINOIS ARCHAEOLOGICAL SURVEY. MONOGRAPHS. Text in English. 1970. irreg. **Document type:** *Monographic series.*
Published by: Center for American Archeology Press, PO Box 366, Kampsville, IL 62053. TEL 618-653-4688, FAX 618-653-4235, http://www.caa-archeology.org.

930.1 USA
ILLINOIS ARCHAEOLOGICAL SURVEY. SPECIAL PUBLICATIONS. Text in English. 1973. irreg. **Document type:** *Monographic series.*
Published by: Center for American Archeology Press, PO Box 366, Kampsville, IL 62053. TEL 618-653-4688, FAX 618-653-4235, http://www.caa-archeology.org.

930.1 USA ISSN 1050-8244
E78.I3
ILLINOIS ARCHAEOLOGY. Text in English. 1989. s-a. USD 30 to individuals; USD 40 to institutions (effective 2001). adv. bk.rev.
—CCC.
Published by: (University of Illinois, Illinois Archaeology Survey), Center for American Archeology Press, PO Box 366, Kampsville, IL 62053. TEL 618-653-4688, FAX 618-653-4235, http://www.caa-archeology.org. R&P, Adv. contact Robert Warren TEL 217-524-7903. Circ: 200 (paid).

ILLINOIS. STATE MUSEUM. SCIENTIFIC PAPERS SERIES. see *SCIENCES: COMPREHENSIVE WORKS*

917 USA
ILLINOIS VALLEY ARCHAEOLOGICAL PROGRAM RESEARCH PAPERS. Text in English. irreg., latest vol.7. **Document type:** *Monographic series, Academic/Scholarly.*
Published by: Center for American Archeology Press, PO Box 366, Kampsville, IL 62053. TEL 618-653-4688, FAX 618-653-4232, http://www.caa-archeology.org.

IN CONTEXT. see *HISTORY—History Of North And South America*

930.1 398 USA ISSN 0736-265X
INDIAN - ARTIFACT MAGAZINE. Short title: I A M. Text in English. 1982. q. USD 25 domestic; USD 30 foreign; USD 6.50 newsstand/cover (effective 2001). adv. bk.rev. **Document type:** *Consumer.* **Description:** Presents American Indian prehistory, artifacts, tools, life-styles, customs, tribes and archaeology presented in an easy-to-read format.
Indexed: HistAb.
Published by: Indian Artifact Magazine, Inc., 245 Fairview Rd., Turbotville, PA 17772-9599. TEL 570-437-3698, FAX 570-437-3411, iam@uplink.net, iam@csrlink.net, http://www.indian-artifacts.net, http://www.iampub.com. Ed., R&P Gary L Fogelman TEL 570-437-3698. Adv. contact Joanne Fogelman. Circ: 4,000 (paid).

INDIANA; contributions to ethnology and linguistics, archaeology and physical anthropology of Indian America. see *ANTHROPOLOGY*

990 930.1 950 AUS ISSN 0156-1316
➤ **INDO-PACIFIC PREHISTORY ASSOCIATION BULLETIN.** Text in English. 1978. irreg., latest vol.22. AUD 35 (effective 2003). back issues avail. **Document type:** *Journal, Academic/Scholarly.* **Description:** Contains reviews for publication of paper for IPPA conferences.
Indexed: AICP.
—BLDSC (2564.290000).
Published by: Indo-Pacific Prehistory Association, c/o School of Archaeology & Anthropology, Australian National University, Canberra, ACT 0200, Australia. TEL 61-2-61253120, FAX 61-2-6125-2711, ippa@anu.edu.au, http://arts.anu.edu.au/arcworld/ippa/ippa/htm. Ed. Peter Bellwood. Circ: 500.

609 GBR ISSN 0019-7971
T37
INDUSTRIAL ARCHAEOLOGY; the journal of the history of industry and technology. Text in English. 1964. a. GBP 24, USD 48; GBP 26, USD 52 foreign. adv. bk.rev. illus. cum.index: vols.1-16. back issues avail. **Document type:** *Journal, Academic/Scholarly.*
Formerly (until 1966): Journal of Industrial Archaeology (1359-5970).
Indexed: AIAP, BHA, BrArAb, HistAb, MEA&I, NumL, PCI.
Published by: Graphmitre Ltd., 1 West St, Tavistock, Devon PL19 8DS, United Kingdom. Circ: 1,000.

609 GBR ISSN 1354-1455
INDUSTRIAL ARCHAEOLOGY NEWS. Text in English. 1974. q. free with subscription to Industrial Archaeology Review. **Document type:** *Newsletter, Academic/Scholarly.* **Description:** Covers news and issues in the archaeology of commercial and residential buildings built during the Industrial Revolution.
Formerly (until 1994): A I A Bulletin (0309-0051)
Indexed: BrArAb, BrHumI, IBZ, NumL.
Published by: Association for Industrial Archaeology, AIA Office, School of Archaeological Studies, University of Leicester, Leicester, Leics LE1 7RH, United Kingdom. TEL 44-116-2525337, FAX 44-116-2525005. Ed., R&P Peter Stanier. Adv. contact Isabel Wilson.

609 GBR ISSN 0309-0728
T37
➤ **INDUSTRIAL ARCHAEOLOGY REVIEW.** Text in English. 1976. 2/yr. USD 69 in North America to individuals; GBP 38 elsewhere to individuals; USD 172 in North America to institutions; GBP 98 elsewhere to institutions (effective 2005); includes Industrial Archaelogy News. adv. bk.rev. abstr.; illus. Index. back issues avail.; reprints avail. **Document type:** *Journal, Academic/Scholarly.* **Description:** Presents articles on all aspects of industrial archeology. Includes excavation reports.
Related titles: Online - full text ed.: (from EBSCO Publishing).
Indexed: AIAP, API, AbAn, AmH&L, BHA, BrArAb, BrHumI, EngInd, HistAb, IBR, IBSS, IBZ, NumL.
—BLDSC (4445.330000), CISTI, Ei, IE, Infotrieve, ingenta, Linda Hall. **CCC.**
Published by: (Association for Industrial Archaeology), Maney Publishing, Hudson Rd, Leeds, W Yorks LS9 7DL, United Kingdom. TEL 44-113-2497481, FAX 44-113-2486983, AIA@le.ac.uk, maney@maney.co.uk, http://www.maney.co.uk/industrial.html. Ed. David Gwyn. Adv. contact Kirsty Bailey. B&W page GBP 180; 175 x 235. Circ: 500 (paid). **Subscr. in N America to:** Maney Publishing North America, 875 Massachusetts Ave, 7th Fl., Cambridge, MA 02139. TEL 866-297-5154, FAX 617-354-6875, maney@maneyusa.com.

913 POL ISSN 0085-1876
INFORMATOR ARCHEOLOGICZNY. Text in Polish. 1968. a., latest 1998. PLZ 12 per issue domestic (effective 2000).
Published by: Osrodek Dokumentacji Zabytkow, ul Mazowiecka 11, Warsaw, 00052, Poland. TEL 48-22-6212573. Ed. Slawomir Zolkowski.

913 USA
INKSHERDS. Text in English. 1955. 4/yr. bk.rev. **Document type:** *Newsletter.*
Indexed: AbAn.
Published by: Archaeological Society of Delaware, PO Box 12483, Wilmington, DE 19850-2483. TEL 302-831-6590. Ed. Ronald Thomas. Circ: 110.

913 DEU
INSCHRIFTEN GRIECHISCHER STAEDTE AUS KLEINASIEN. Text in German. 1972. irreg., latest vol.60, 2001. price varies. **Document type:** *Monographic series, Academic/Scholarly.*
Published by: (Oesterreichische Akademie der Wissenschaften AUT), Dr. Rudolf Habelt GmbH, Am Buchenhang 1, Bonn, 53115, Germany. TEL 49-228-9238322, FAX 49-228-9238323, info@habelt.de, http://www.habelt.de. **Co-sponsor:** Nordrhein-Westfaelische Akademie der Wissenschaften.

930.1 BEL ISSN 0776-1244
➤ **INSTITUT ARCHEOLOGIQUE DU LUXEMBOURG. ANNALES.** Text in French. 1847. a., latest vol.132, 2002. EUR 25 (effective 2000). adv. illus.; maps; bibl. **Document type:** *Bulletin, Academic/Scholarly.*
Indexed: BHA.
Published by: Institut Archeologique du Luxembourg, Rue des Martyrs 13, Arlon, 6700, Belgium. TEL 32-63-221236, FAX 32-63-228412, info@ial.be, http://www.ial.be. Eds. J-M Triffaux, P Hannick, R Yande.

913 BEL ISSN 0020-2177
➤ **INSTITUT ARCHEOLOGIQUE DU LUXEMBOURG. BULLETINS**; archeologie-art-histoire-folklore. Text in French. 1925. q. EUR 25 (effective 2000). adv. bk.rev. bibl.; illus.; maps. **Document type:** *Bulletin, Academic/Scholarly.*
Indexed: BHA.
Published by: Institut Archeologique du Luxembourg, Rue des Martyrs 13, Arlon, 6700, Belgium. TEL 32-63-221236, FAX 32-63-228412, info@ial.be, http://www.ial.be. Eds. J-M Triffaux, P Hannick, R Yande.

913 709 BEL ISSN 0776-1260
INSTITUT ARCHEOLOGIQUE LIEGEOIS. BULLETIN. Text in French. 1852. a. **Document type:** *Bulletin, Academic/Scholarly.*
Indexed: AIAP, BHA, NumL.
Published by: (Belgium. Ministere de l'Education Nationale et de la Culture Francaise), Institut Archeologique Liegeois, Quai de Maastricht 13, Liege, 4000, Belgium. TEL 32-41-219404, FAX 32-41-219432.

INSTITUT DE PAPYROLOGIE ET D'EGYPTOLOGIE DE LILLE. CAHIERS DE RECHERCHE; habitat et societes urbaines en Egypte et au Sudan. see *HISTORY—History Of Africa*

932 EGY ISSN 0259-3823
INSTITUT FRANCAIS D'ARCHEOLOGIE ORIENTALE DU CAIRE. BIBLIOTHEQUE D'ETUDE. Key Title: Bibliotheque d'Etude - Institut Francais d'Archeologie Orientale. Text mainly in French; Text occasionally in English. 1908. irreg., latest vol.132, 2001. EGP 107, EUR 33.60 (effective 2001). back issues avail. **Document type:** *Monographic series.* **Description:** Scholarly studies of topics relating to the history, archaeology, art and culture of Egypt from Pharaonic times to the present day.
Published by: Institut Francais d'Archeologie Orientale du Caire, Kasr el-Aini, 37 Sharia Sheikh Aly Youssef, Mounira, P O Box 11562, Cairo, Egypt. TEL 20-2-3571622, FAX 20-2-3544635, ventes@ifao.egnet.net, http://www.ifao.egnet.net. **Dist. by:** Boustany's Publishing House, 29 Faggalah St, Cairo 11271, Egypt. TEL 20-2-5915315, FAX 20-2-4177915.

932 EGY
INSTITUT FRANCAIS D'ARCHEOLOGIE ORIENTALE DU CAIRE. BIBLIOTHEQUE GENERALE. Text in French; Text occasionally in Arabic. 1959. irreg., latest vol.21, 2000. EGP 51 domestic; EUR 16.80 foreign (effective 2001). back issues avail. **Document type:** *Monographic series.* **Description:** Publishes archaeological studies, guides, historical and linguistic studies.
Published by: Institut Francais d'Archeologie Orientale du Caire, Kasr el-Aini, 37 Sharia Sheikh Aly Youssef, Mounira, P O Box 11562, Cairo, Egypt. TEL 20-2-3571622, FAX 20-2-3544635, ventes@ifao.egnet.net, http://www.ifao.egnet.net. **Dist. by:** Boustany's Publishing House, 29 Faggalah St, Cairo 11271, Egypt. TEL 20-2-5915315, FAX 20-2-4177915.

932 EGY ISSN 0255-0962
DT57
INSTITUT FRANCAIS D'ARCHEOLOGIE ORIENTALE DU CAIRE. BULLETIN. Key Title: Bulletin de l'Institut Francais d'Archeologie Orientale. Short title: B I F A O. Text in English, French, German. 1901. a. EGP 162, EUR 45.80 (effective 2001). back issues avail. **Document type:** *Bulletin, Academic/Scholarly.* **Description:** Research on Egyptology (history, archaeology, linguistics).
Related titles: Microfiche ed.: (from IDC).
Indexed: BHA, BibLing, DIP, IBR, IBZ.
Published by: Institut Francais d'Archeologie Orientale du Caire, Kasr el-Aini, 37 Sharia Sheikh Aly Youssef, Mounira, P O Box 11562, Cairo, Egypt. TEL 20-2-3571622, FAX 20-2-3544635, http://www.ifao.egnet.net. Circ: 800. **Dist. by:** Boustany's Publishing House, 29 Faggalah St, Cairo 11271, Egypt. TEL 20-2-5915315, FAX 20-2-4177915.

932 EGY ISSN 0768-2964
INSTITUT FRANCAIS D'ARCHEOLOGIE ORIENTALE DU CAIRE. DOCUMENTS DE FOUILLES. Key Title: Documents de Fouilles. Text in French. 1934. irreg., latest vol.39, 2000. EGP 95 domestic; EUR 27.50 foreign (effective 2001). back issues avail. **Document type:** *Monographic series.* **Description:** Publishes reports of archaeological studies conducted in Egypt, including catalogues of ostraca and papyrii.
Published by: Institut Francais d'Archeologie Orientale du Caire, Kasr el-Aini, 37 Sharia Sheikh Aly Youssef, Mounira, P O Box 11562, Cairo, Egypt. TEL 20-2-3571622, FAX 20-2-3544635, ventes@ifao.egnet.net, http://www.ifao.egnet.net. **Dist. by:** Boustany's Publishing House, 29 Faggalah St, Cairo 11271, Egypt. TEL 20-2-5195315, FAX 20-2-4177915.

932 EGY ISSN 0768-4703
INSTITUT FRANCAIS D'ARCHEOLOGIE ORIENTALE DU CAIRE. FOUILLES. Short title: F I F A O. Text in French. 1924. irreg., latest vol.44, 2001. EGP 155 domestic; EUR 45.80 foreign (effective 2001). back issues avail. **Document type:** *Monographic series.* **Description:** Publishes preliminary reports and detailed reports of archaeological excavations conducted in Egypt.
Published by: Institut Francais d'Archeologie Orientale du Caire, Kasr el-Aini, 37 Sharia Sheikh Aly Youssef, Mounira, P O Box 11562, Cairo, Egypt. TEL 20-2-3571622, FAX 20-2-3544635, ventes@ifao.egnet.net, http://www.ifao.egnet.net. **Dist. by:** Boustany's Publishing House, 29 Faggalah St, Cairo 11271, Egypt. TEL 20-2-5915315, FAX 20-2-4177915.

932 EGY ISSN 0257-411X
INSTITUT FRANCAIS D'ARCHEOLOGIE ORIENTALE DU CAIRE. MEMOIRES. Key Title: Memoires Publies par les Membres de l'Institut Francais d'Archeologie Orientale. Text in French. 1902. irreg., latest vol.117, 2000. EGP 288 domestic; EUR 91.50 foreign (effective 2001). back issues avail. **Document type:** *Monographic series.*
Incorporates (1883-1934): Memoires Publies par les Membres de la Mission Archeologique Francaise au Caire (0257-4128)

Published by: Institut Francais d'Archeologie Orientale du Caire, Kasr el-Aini, 37 Sharia Sheikh Aly Youssef, Mounira, P O Box 11562, Cairo, Egypt. TEL 20-2-3571622, FAX 20-2-3544635, ventes@ifao.egnet.net, http://www.ifao.egnet.net. **Dist. by:** Boustany's Publishing House, 29 Faggalah St, Cairo 11271, Egypt. TEL 20-2-5915315, FAX 20-2-4177915.

A

INSTITUTE FOR AMERICAN INDIAN STUDIES. OCCASIONAL PAPER AND BOOKS. see *NATIVE AMERICAN STUDIES*

913 333.79 550 560 USA
INSTITUTE FOR THE STUDY OF EARTH AND MAN NEWSLETTER. Text in English. 1974. a. free. bibl.; illus. **Document type:** *Newsletter.*
Published by: Southern Methodist University, Institute for the Study of Earth and Man, c/o Heroy Science Hall, Dallas, TX 75275-0274. TEL 214-768-2425, FAX 214-768-4289. Ed. Susan J Liepins. Circ: 2,500.

930.1 BRA
INSTITUTO GOIANO DE PRE-HISTORIA E ANTROPOLOGIA. CADERNOS DE PESQUISA. Text in Portuguese. irreg., latest vol.9, 1995. **Document type:** *Monographic series.*
Published by: Universidad Catolica de Goias, Instituto Goiano de Pre-historia e Antropologia, PRACA UNIVERSITARIA, 1440, Goiania, GO 75370-000, Brazil. TEL 55-62-2271221, FAX 55-62-2243617.

INSTITUTO NACIONAL DE ANTROPOLOGIA Y PENSAMIENTO LATINOAMERICANO. CUADERNOS. see *ANTHROPOLOGY*

914 949.8 ROM
INSTITUTUL DE ARHEOLOGIE - CLUJ-NAPOCA. ANUARUL. Text in Romanian. 1980 (vol.23). a. USD 38.
Supersedes in part: Institutul de Istorie si Arheologie - Cluj-Napoca. Anuarul (0065-048X)
Indexed: RASB.
Published by: (Institutul de Arheologie - Cluj-Napoca), Editura Academiei Romane/Publishing House of the Romanian Academy, Calea 13 Septembrie 13, Sector 5, Bucharest, 76117, Romania. TEL 40-21-4119008, FAX 40-21-4103983. Ed. Aurel Radutiu. **Dist. by:** Rodipet S.A., Piata Presei Libere 1, sector 1, PO Box 33-57, Bucharest 3, Romania. TEL 40-21-2224126, 40-21-2226407, rodipet@rodipet.ro.

913 949.8 ROM ISSN 1221-3705
DR201
INSTITUTUL DE ISTORIE "A.D. XENOPOL". ANUARUL. Text in Romanian. 1963. a.
Formerly (until 1990): Institutul de Istorie si Arheologie "A.D. Xenopol" - Iasi. Anuarul (0074-039X)
Related titles: Online - full text ed.
Indexed: AmH&L, BHA, HistAb, IBR, IBZ.
Published by: (Institutul de Istorie "A.D. Xenopol"), Editura Academiei Romane/Publishing House of the Romanian Academy, Calea 13 Septembrie 13, Sector 5, Bucharest, 76117, Romania. TEL 40-21-4119008, FAX 40-21-4103983, edacad@ear.ro, http://www.ear.ro. Ed. Leon Simanschi. **Dist. by:** Rodipet S.A., Piata Presei Libere 1, sector 1, PO Box 33-57, Bucharest 3, Romania. TEL 40-21-2224126, 40-21-2226407, rodipet@rodipet.ro.

930.1 AUT
INSTITUTUM CANARIUM YEARBOOK. ALMOGAREN. Text in English, French, German, Spanish. 1970. a. EUR 60 membership; EUR 15 to students (effective 2005). bk.rev. **Document type:** *Journal, Academic/Scholarly.*
Formerly: Almogaren
Indexed: AICP, AnthLit, BibLing, CCA.
—CINDOC.
Published by: Institutum Canarium, Hauslabgasse 31/6, Vienna, O 1050, Austria. FAX 43-1-5457744, hjulbrich@institutum-canarium.org, http://www.almogaren.org/index_d.html, http://www.institutum-canarium.org. Ed. Hans Joachim Ulbrich. Circ: 500.

930.1 940 ITA ISSN 0538-2270
PA2019.F5
INSTITUTUM ROMANUM FINLANDIAE. ACTA. Text in Italian. 1963. irreg., latest vol.27, 2002. EUR 45 (effective 2003). **Document type:** *Monographic series.*
Incorporates (1981-1989, vol.4): Institutum Romanum Finlandiae. Opuscola
Indexed: BHA.
Published by: (Institutum Romanum Finlandiae), Bardi Editore, Via Piave 7, Rome, 00187, Italy. TEL 39-06-4817656, FAX 39-06-48912574, bardied@tin.it, http://www.bardieditore.com. Circ: 500.

930.1 USA ISSN 1568-2722
➤ **INTERDISCIPLINARY CONTRIBUTIONS TO ARCHAEOLOGY.** Text in English. 1987. irreg., latest 2005. price varies. back issues avail. **Document type:** *Monographic series, Academic/Scholarly.*
Published by: Springer-Verlag New York, Inc. (Subsidiary of: Springer Science+Business Media), 233 Spring St, New York, NY 10013. TEL 212-460-1500, FAX 212-460-1575, service@springer-ny.com, http://www.springer-ny.com. Ed. Michael A Jochim.

571 930 ITA ISSN 0074-1469
INTERNATIONAL ASSOCIATION FOR CLASSICAL ARCHAEOLOGY. PROCEEDINGS OF CONGRESS. (Proceedings published by host country) Text in Italian. irreg., latest 1978, 11th, London. **Document type:** *Proceedings.*
Indexed: NumL.
Published by: International Association for Classical Archaeology, Piazza San Marco, 49, Rome, RM 00186, Italy.

571 GBR ISSN 0074-3429
INTERNATIONAL CONGRESS FOR PAPYROLOGY. PROCEEDINGS. Text in English. triennial (15th Congress 1977, Brussels). **Document type:** *Proceedings.*
Published by: International Association of Papyrologists, c/o Dr. R.A. Coles, Papyrology Rooms, Ashmolean Museum, Oxford, United Kingdom.

INTERNATIONAL JOURNAL OF CULTURAL PROPERTY. see *ART*

930.1 USA ISSN 1092-7697
CC77.H5 CODEN: IJHAFN
➤ **INTERNATIONAL JOURNAL OF HISTORICAL ARCHAEOLOGY.** Text in English. 1997. q. EUR 240, USD 241, GBP 150 combined subscription to institutions print & online eds. (effective 2005). adv. illus.; maps. reprint service avail. from PSC. **Document type:** *Journal, Academic/Scholarly.* **Description:** Publishes theoretical, methodological, site-specific and descriptive articles on all topics of interest to archaeologists working on historical sites.
Related titles: Online - full text ed.: ISSN 1573-7748 (from EBSCO Publishing, Gale Group, IngentaConnect, Kluwer Online, O C L C Online Computer Library Center, Inc., Springer LINK, Swets Information Services).
Indexed: AICP, AbAn, AmH&L, AnthLit, BibLing, BrArAb, GEOBASE, HistAb, IBSS, NumL.
—BLDSC (4542.281500), IE, Infotrieve, ingenta. **CCC.**
Published by: Plenum US (Subsidiary of: Springer Science+Business Media), 233 Spring St, New York, NY 10013. TEL 212-460-1500, FAX 212-460-1575, service@springer-ny.com, http://springerlink.metapress.com/openurl.asp?genre=journal&issn=1092-7697, http://www.springeronline.com. Eds. Charles E Orser Jr., James A Delle.

913 GBR ISSN 1057-2414
CC77
➤ **INTERNATIONAL JOURNAL OF NAUTICAL ARCHAEOLOGY.** Text in English. 1972. s-a. USD 93 combined subscription in the Americas to individuals & Caribbean (print & online eds.); GBP 61 combined subscription elsewhere to individuals print & online eds.; USD 428 combined subscription in the Americas to institutions & Caribbean (print & online eds.); GBP 299 combined subscription elsewhere to institutions print & online eds. (effective 2006). adv. bk.rev. illus. index. reprints avail. **Document type:** *Journal, Academic/Scholarly.* **Description:** Covers all aspects of nautical archaeological research.
Formerly: International Journal of Nautical Archaeology and Underwater Exploration (0305-7445)
Related titles: Online - full text ed.: ISSN 1095-9270. USD 407 in the Americas to institutions & Caribbean; GBP 284 elsewhere to institutions (effective 2006) (from Blackwell Synergy, EBSCO Publishing, Gale Group, IngentaConnect, O C L C Online Computer Library Center, Inc., ScienceDirect, Swets Information Services).
Indexed: ASCA, AbAn, AnthLit, ArtHuCI, BAS, BHA, BibInd, BrArAb, CurCont, DIP, IBR, IBZ, MEA&I, NAA, NumL, RASB, SSCI.
—BLDSC (4542.370000), IDS, IE, Infotrieve. **CCC.**
Published by: (Nautical Archeology Society), Blackwell Publishing Ltd., 9600 Garsington Rd, Oxford, OX4 2ZG, United Kingdom. TEL 44-1865-776868, FAX 44-1865-714591, customerservices@oxon.blackwellpublishing.com, http://www.blackwellpublishing.com/journals/IJNA. Ed. Paula Martin.

➤ **INTERNATIONAL UNION OF PREHISTORIC AND PROTOHISTORIC SCIENCES. CONGRESS. BULLETIN.** see *ANTHROPOLOGY*

930.1 CZE
INTERNATIONALE TAGUNGEN IN MIKULCICE. Text in Czech. a. **Description:** Concentrates on Slavonic archeology.
Published by: Akademie Ved Ceske Republiky, Archeologicky Ustav, Kralovopolska 147, Brno, 61200, Czech Republic. TEL 42-5-41212140, FAX 42-5-41514123, archeo@isibrno.cz, ps@isibrno.cz, http://www.lib.cas.cz/knav/journals/eng/Internationale_Tagungen.htm. Ed. Jaroslav Tejral.

930.1 GBR ISSN 1363-5387
CC1
➤ **INTERNET ARCHAEOLOGY.** Text in English. 1996. s-a. GBP 39.50 to individuals; GBP 100 to institutions (effective 2002). software rev.; bk.rev. illus. reprints avail. **Document type:** *Journal, Academic/Scholarly.* **Description:** Publishes the results of archaeological research, including excavation reports, analyses of large datasets, programs used to analyze data, and applications of information technology.
Media: Online - full text (from EBSCO Publishing).
Indexed: BrArAb, IBSS, NumL, ZooRec.
—**CCC.**
Published by: Council for British Archaeology, Bowes Morrell House, 111 Walmgate, York, YO1 9WA, United Kingdom. TEL 44-1904-671417, FAX 44-1904-671384, info@briarch.ac.uk, http://www.britarch.ac.uk. Ed., R&P Judith Winters.
Institutional distributor: Extenza - Turpin, Pegasus Dr, Stratton Business Park, Biggleswade, Beds SG18 8TQ, United Kingdom. TEL 44-1462-672555, FAX 44-1462-480-947.

931 USA
➤ **INTERPRETING THE PAST.** Text in English. 1990. irreg., latest vol.7, 1994. price varies. back issues avail. **Document type:** *Monographic series, Academic/Scholarly.* **Description:** Examines classical and Near Eastern history and culture by analyzing art objects and other material remains.
Published by: University of California Press, Book Series, 2120 Berkeley Way, Berkeley, CA 94720. TEL 510-642-4247, FAX 510-643-7127, askucp@ucpress.edu, http://www.ucpress.edu/books/IP.ser.html, http://www.ucpress.edu/books/series.html. **Orders to:** California - Princeton Fulfillment Services, 1445 Lower Ferry Rd, Ewing, NJ 08618. TEL 800-777-4726, FAX 800-999-1958, orders@cpfs.pupress.princeton.edu.

917 USA ISSN 0535-5729
E78.I6
IOWA ARCHEOLOGICAL SOCIETY. JOURNAL. Text in English. 1951. a. USD 15 to individual members; USD 20 to institutional members (effective 2001). bk.rev. **Document type:** *Academic/Scholarly.* **Description:** Publishes articles, discussions of current issues, biographies, and abstracts of current research of permanent scientific value to archaeology.
Indexed: AnthLit.
Published by: Iowa Archeological Society, c/o Office of the State Archaeologist, 700 Clinton St Bldg, University of Iowa, Iowa City, IA 52242. TEL 319-384-0732, FAX 319-384-0768. Eds. Coleen Vaughn, Joe Thompson. Circ: 500.

917.7 USA ISSN 0578-655X
E78.I6
IOWA ARCHEOLOGICAL SOCIETY. NEWSLETTER. Text in English. 1951. q. USD 15 to individual members; USD 20 to institutional members (effective 2001). bk.rev. bibl.; charts; illus. **Document type:** *Newsletter.* **Description:** Contains short articles and announcements pertinent to members of the society.
Related titles: Microform ed.
Indexed: AnthLit.
Published by: Iowa Archeological Society, c/o Office of the State Archaeologist, 700 Clinton St Bldg, University of Iowa, Iowa City, IA 52242. TEL 319-384-0732, FAX 319-384-0768. Ed. Michael Heimbaugh. Circ: 500.

571 USA ISSN 0085-2252
IOWA STATE ARCHAEOLOGIST. REPORT. Text in English. 1970. irreg., latest vol.21, 1999. price varies. bibl.; charts; illus. reprint service avail. from PQC. **Document type:** *Academic/Scholarly.*
Published by: Office of State Archaeologist, 700 Clinton St Bldg, Iowa City, IA 52242-1030. TEL 319-384-0732, FAX 319-384-0768, http://www.uiowa.edu/~osa/focus/publications/index.htm. Ed. William Green. Circ: 750.

935 BEL ISSN 0021-0870
DS251
➤ **IRANICA ANTIQUA.** Text in English, French, German. 1961. a., latest vol.40, 2005. EUR 85 (effective 2005). illus.; maps. Index. reprints avail. **Document type:** *Journal, Academic/Scholarly.* **Description:** Publishes studies in the art, archaeology, ancient history and culture of the Iranian region.
Related titles: Online - full text ed.: (from Chadwyck-Healey Inc., EBSCO Publishing); ◆ Supplement(s): Iranica Antiqua Supplementa. ISSN 0169-877X.
Indexed: AIAP, ArtInd, BibLing, DIP, IBR, IBSS, IBZ, IndIslam, NAA, NumL, PCI.
—**CCC.**
Published by: (Universiteit Gent, Seminar for Near Eastern Art and Archaeology), Peeters Publishers, Bondgenotenlaan 153, Leuven, 3000, Belgium. TEL 32-16-235170, FAX 32-16-228500, peeters@peeters-leuven.be, http://poj.peeters-leuven.be/journal.php?code=IA, http://www.peeters-leuven.be. Ed. E Haerinck.

935 BEL ISSN 0169-877X
➤ **IRANICA ANTIQUA SUPPLEMENTA.** Text in English, French, German. 1962. irreg., latest vol.8, 1996. price varies. illus.; maps. back issues avail. **Document type:** *Monographic series, Academic/Scholarly.*
Related titles: ◆ Supplement to: Iranica Antiqua. ISSN 0021-0870.
Published by: (Universiteit Gent/University of Ghent, Universiteit Gent, Seminar for Near Eastern Art and Archaeology), Peeters Publishers, Bondgenotenlaan 153, Leuven, 3000, Belgium. TEL 32-16-235170, FAX 32-16-228500, http://www.peeters-leuven.be. Ed. E Haerinck.

913 GBR ISSN 0021-0889
➤ **IRAQ.** Text in English. 1934. a. GBP 30, USD 55 (effective 2005). charts; illus. index, cum.index: vols.1-50. reprints avail. **Document type:** *Academic/Scholarly.*
Indexed: AIAP, AICP, AnthLit, BibLing, DIP, IBR, IBSS, IBZ, IndIslam, MEA&I, NTA, OTA, RI-1, RI-2.
—IE, Infotrieve.

Published by: British School of Archaeology in Iraq, 10 Carlton House Terrace, London, SW1Y 5AH, United Kingdom. bsai@britac.ac.uk, http://www.britac.ac.uk/institutes/iraq/newjournal.htm. Eds. A R George, D Collon. Circ: 650.

930.1 FIN ISSN 0355-3108
ISKOS. Text in English, Finnish, Swedish. 1976. irreg., latest vol.11, 1997. price varies. **Document type:** *Monographic series, Academic/Scholarly.*
Published by: Suomen Muinaismuistoyhdistys/Finnish Antiquarian Society, Nervanderinkatu 13, PO Box 213, Helsinki, 00101, Finland. TEL 358-9-40501, FAX 358-9-40509400, Torsten.Edgren@NBA.fi. Ed. Torsten Edgren. **Dist. by:** Bookstore Tiedekirja, Kirkkokatu 14, Helsinki 00170, Finland. TEL 358-0-635-177.

HID ISLENZKA FORNLEIFAFELAG. ARBOK. see *HISTORY—History Of Europe*

933 ISR ISSN 0021-2059
DS111.A1 CODEN: IEXJAM
➤ **ISRAEL EXPLORATION JOURNAL.** Text in English. 1951. s-a. USD 56 (effective 2005). bk.rev. charts; illus.; maps. cum.index every 10 yrs. and cumulative 50 yr. index. back issues avail.; reprint service avail. from PQC. **Document type:** *Academic/Scholarly.* **Description:** Includes articles on prehistory, biblical archaeology, ancient history, and archaeology of later periods, preliminary excavation reports, special discoveries and finds.
Related titles: Microform ed.: (from PQC).
Indexed: ASCA, AnthLit, ArtHuCI, ArtInd, BHA, BibLing, ChemAb, CurCont, DIP, IBR, IBSS, IBZ, IHP, IJP, IndIslam, MEA&I, NTA, NumL, OTA, R&TA, RI-1, RI-2, SSCI.
—BLDSC (4583.700000), IDS, IE, Infotrieve, ingenta, Linda Hall.
Published by: Israel Exploration Society, P O Box 7041, Jerusalem, 91070, Israel. TEL 972-2-625-7991, FAX 972-2-624-7772, ies@vms.huji.ac.il, http://www.hum.huji.ac.il/IES/iej.htm, http://www.hum.huji.ac.il/ies/. Eds. Miriam Tadmor, S. Ahituv. Circ: 2,500.

930.1 ISR ISSN 1565-3617
DS111.A1
ISRAEL MUSEUM STUDIES IN ARCHAEOLOGY. Text in English. a.
Published by: Israel Museum, P O Box 71117, Jerusalem, Israel. FAX 972-2-631833, shop@imj.org.il. Ed. Nancy Benovitz.

913 950 DEU ISSN 0341-9142
DS41
ISTANBULER MITTEILUNGEN. Text in German. 1950. a. EUR 63.50 (effective 2005). back issues avail. **Document type:** *Journal, Academic/Scholarly.* **Description:** Explores the pre-history, archaeology, history and art history of Asia Minor up until the Ottomanic period.
Indexed: AIAP, BHA, BibLing, DIP, IBR, IBZ, IndIslam.
Published by: (Deutsches Archaeologisches Institut, Abteilung Istanbul), Ernst Wasmuth Verlag GmbH, Fuerststr 133, Tuebingen, 72072, Germany. TEL 49-7071-975500, FAX 49-7071-9755013, info@wasmuth-verlag.de, http://www.wasmuth-verlag.de. Ed., R&P Sigrid Hauser. Pub. Ernst J Wasmuth. Circ: 500.

ISTANBULER MITTEILUNGEN. BEIHEFTE. see *HISTORY—History Of The Near East*

938 GRC ISSN 0362-8108
ISTHMIA. Text in English. 1971. irreg., latest vol.8, 1999. price varies. **Document type:** *Monographic series, Academic/Scholarly.*
Published by: American School of Classical Studies at Athens, 54 Souidias St, Athens, 106 76, Greece. TEL 30-210-7236313, FAX 30-210-7250584, ascsa@ascsa.org, http://www.ascsa.edu.gr.

571 ITA ISSN 0530-9867
ISTITUTO INTERNAZIONALE DI STUDI LIGURI. COLLEZIONE DI MONOGRAFIE PREISTORICHE E ARCHEOLOGICHE. Text in Italian, French, Spanish. 1946. irreg. price varies. **Document type:** *Monographic series, Academic/Scholarly.* **Description:** Provides research and scholarly articles in prehistoric, Roman and medieval Liguria (a coastal region of northwestern Italy).
Published by: Istituto Internazionale di Studi Liguri/International Institute of Ligurian Studies, Via Romana 39, Bordighera, IM 18012, Italy. TEL 39-0184-263601, FAX 39-0184-266421, iisl@istitutostudi.191.it, http://www.iisl.it. Circ: 1,000.

930.1 700 ITA
ISTITUTO NAZIONALE DI ARCHEOLOGIA E STORIA DELL'ARTE. RIVISTA. Text in Italian. 1929. a. back issues avail.
Indexed: AIAP, BHA.
Published by: Istituto Nazionale di Archeologia e Storia dell'Arte, Piazza San Marco, 49, Rome, RM 00186, Italy. Ed. Paolo Pellegrino. Circ: 800.

913 ESP ISSN 1137-4489
DP302.B465
ISTURITZ. Text in Spanish. 1982. irreg. price varies. **Document type:** *Monographic series, Academic/Scholarly.*
Formerly (until 1997): Sociedad de Estudios Vascos. Cuadernos de Seccion. Prehistoria y Arqueologia (0213-3024); Which superseded in part (in 1982): Cuadernos de Seccion. Antropologia, Etnografia, Prehistoria, Arqueologia (0212-3207)
Published by: Eusko Ikaskuntza/Sociedad de Estudios Vascos, Palacio Miramar, Miraconcha 48, Donostia, San Sebastian 20007, Spain. TEL 34-943-310855, FAX 34-943-213956, ei-sev@sc.ehu.es, http://www.eusko-ikaskuntza.org/.

913 945 ITA ISSN 0392-7601
ITALICA. Text in Italian. 1910. a.
Formerly (until 1981): Escuela Espanola de Historia y Arqueologia en Roma. Cuadernos de Trabajos (0392-0801)
Indexed: BHA, PCI, RILM.
Published by: Consejo Superior de Investigaciones Cientificas, Escuela Espanola de Historia y Arqueologia en Roma, Via Di Villa Albani, 16, Rome, RM 00198, Italy.

913 947 BGR ISSN 0204-403X
IZVESTIYA NA MUZEITE OT IUGOIZTOCHNA BULGARIYA. Text in Bulgarian. 1976. a.
Published by: Dargavno Izdatelstvo Christo G. Danov, Ul Petko Karavelov 17, Plodiv, 4000, Bulgaria. **Dist. by:** Hemus Foreign Trade Co., 6 Rouski blvd, Sofia 1000, Bulgaria.

913 947 BGR ISSN 0204-4072
IZVESTIYA NA MUZEITE OT IUZHNA BULGARIYA. Text in Bulgarian. 1975. a.
Indexed: BSLBiol.
Published by: Dargavno Izdatelstvo Christo G. Danov, Ul Petko Karavelov 17, Plodiv, 4000, Bulgaria. **Dist. by:** Hemus Foreign Trade Co., 6 Rouski blvd, Sofia 1000, Bulgaria.

930.1 SWE ISSN 1650-1519
➤ **J O N A S.** (Journal of Nordic Archeological Science) Text in Multiple languages. 1978. a. price varies. **Document type:** *Journal, Academic/Scholarly.*
Former titles (until 1999): Laborativ Arkeologi (1101-7848); (until 1987): Rapport fraan Stockholms Universitets Arkeologiska Forskningslaboratorium (0281-8922)
Published by: Stockholms Universitet, Arkeologiska Forskningslaboratorium/Stockholm University. Archaeological Research Laboratory, Greens Villa, Stockholms Universitet, Stockholm, 10691, Sweden. TEL 46-8-16-20-00, FAX 46-8-674-73-66, jonas@arklab.su.se, http://www.arklab.su.se. Ed. Kerstin liden.

➤ **J P S.** (Journal of the Polynesian Society) see *ANTHROPOLOGY*

930.1 USA ISSN 1063-4304
➤ **J R A - THE SUPPLEMENTARY SERIES.** (Journal of Roman Archaeology) Text in English, French, Italian, German, Spanish. 1990. irreg. (5-6/yr.). price varies. bk.rev. bibl.; illus. **Document type:** *Monographic series, Academic/Scholarly.* **Description:** Covers the history, culture, and archaeology of the Roman world.
Related titles: ♦ Supplement to: Journal of Roman Archaeology. ISSN 1047-7594.
—BLDSC (5052.118100), IE, ingenta.
Published by: Journal of Roman Archaeology L.L.C., The Editor, JRA, 95 Peleg Rd, Portsmouth, RI 02871. TEL 401-683-1955, FAX 401-683-1975, jra@journalofromanarch.com, http://JournalofRomanArch.com, http://www.JournalofRomanArch.com. Ed. John H Humphrey.

930.1 JPN
JAPANESE ARCHAEOLOGICAL ASSOCIATION. BULLETIN. Text in Japanese. 3/yr. **Document type:** *Bulletin, Academic/Scholarly.*
Published by: Nihon Kokogaku Kyokai/Japanese Archaeological Association, Hirai-ekimae Kyodo Bldg, 4F, 5-15-5 Hirai, Edogawa-ku, Tokyo, 132-0035, Japan. TEL 81-3-3618-6608, FAX 81-3-3618-6625, http://www.avenue.co.jp/~kouko/.

930.1 CHN ISSN 1001-0327
JIANGHAN KAOGU/JIANGHAN ARCHAEOLOGY. Text in Chinese. 1980. q. CNY 24, USD 16 domestic; USD 24 foreign (effective 2005). adv. bk.rev. **Document type:** *Monographic series.* **Description:** Monographic series on archaeology, palaeoanthropology and paleontology.
Related titles: CD-ROM ed.; Online - full text ed.: (from East View Information Services).
Published by: Archaeological Institute of Hubei Province, Tian'e Cun, Donghu Lu, Wuchang-qu, Wuhan, Hubei 430077, China. TEL 86-10-27-86784158. Ed. Tianyuan Li. Pub. Kaogu Jiang. Adv. contact Boda Hao. Circ: 2,000. **Dist. in U.S. by:** China Books & Periodicals Inc, 360 Swift Ave., Ste. 48, S San Fran, CA 94080-6220. TEL 415-282-2994. **Co-sponsor:** Hubei Provincial Museum.

930.1 USA ISSN 1524-4776
➤ **JOURNAL OF CARIBBEAN ARCHAEOLOGY.** Text in English. 2001. a. free (effective 2005). **Document type:** *Journal, Academic/Scholarly.* **Description:** Covers archaeological research in the Caribbean and surrounding area.
Media: Online - full content.
Published by: University of South Carolina, South Carolina Institute of Archaeology and Anthropology, 1321 Pendleton St, Columbia, SC 29208. TEL 803-777-8170, FAX 803-254-1338, http://www.flmnh.ufl.edu/jca/default.htm, http://www.cas.sc.edu/sciaa/.

➤ **JOURNAL DES AFRICANISTES.** see *ANTHROPOLOGY*

930.1 DEU ISSN 1612-1651
GN861
▼ ➤ **JOURNAL OF AFRICAN ARCHAEOLOGY.** Text in English. 2003. s-a. EUR 60 to individuals; EUR 80 to institutions (effective 2005). **Document type:** *Journal, Academic/Scholarly.* **Description:** Publishes papers focusing on all aspects of African archaeology and has no geographical, chronological or thematic limitations.
—BLDSC (4919.987500).
Published by: Africa Magna Verlag, Heddernheimer Landstr 15, Frankfurt am Main, 60439, Germany. african-archaeology@em.uni-frankfurt.de, http://www.african-archaeology.de. Eds. Peter Breunig, Sonja Magnavita.

➤ **JOURNAL OF AFRICAN CIVILIZATIONS.** see *ANTHROPOLOGY*

➤ **JOURNAL OF AFRICAN HISTORY.** see *HISTORY—History Of Africa*

913 USA ISSN 0449-2153
E78.A28
JOURNAL OF ALABAMA ARCHAEOLOGY. Text in English. 1955. s-a. USD 12 to individuals; USD 17 to institutions; includes Stones and Bones Newsletter. bibl.; charts; illus. back issues avail.; reprint service avail. from PQC. **Document type:** *Academic/Scholarly.*
Related titles: Microform ed.: (from PQC); Online - full text ed.: (from ProQuest Information & Learning).
Indexed: AbAn, AmH&L, AnthLit, HistAb.
Published by: Alabama Archaeological Society, 13075 Moundville Archaeological Park, Moundville, AL 35474. TEL 205-371-2266, FAX 205-371-2494. Ed. Eugene M Futato. Circ: 500.

JOURNAL OF ANCIENT TOPOGRAPHY/RIVISTA DI TOPOGRAFIA ANTICA. see *CLASSICAL STUDIES*

JOURNAL OF ANTHROPOLOGICAL ARCHAEOLOGY. see *ANTHROPOLOGY*

930.1 USA ISSN 1072-5369
CC75 CODEN: JAMTEI
➤ **JOURNAL OF ARCHAEOLOGICAL METHOD AND THEORY.** Text in English. 1994. q. EUR 375, USD 378, GBP 235 combined subscription to institutions print & online eds. (effective 2005). adv. reprint service avail. from PSC. **Document type:** *Journal, Academic/Scholarly.* **Description:** Presents original articles that critically assess and integrate research on a specific subject in archaeological method and theory, including topics in the history of archaeology, significant explorations, and relevant case studies.
Related titles: Online - full text ed.: ISSN 1573-7764 (from EBSCO Publishing, Gale Group, IngentaConnect, Kluwer Online, O C L C Online Computer Library Center, Inc., Springer LINK, Swets Information Services).
Indexed: AICP, AnthLit, ArtHuCI, BibInd, BibLing, BrArAb, CurCont, IBSS, NumL.
—BLDSC (4947.177300), IDS, IE, Infotrieve, ingenta. **CCC.**
Published by: Plenum US (Subsidiary of: Springer Science+Business Media), 233 Spring St, New York, NY 10013. TEL 212-460-1500, FAX 212-460-1575, service@springer-ny.com, http://springerlink.metapress.com/openurl.asp?genre=journal&issn=1072-5369, http://www.springeronline.com. Eds. Catherine M Cameron, James M Skibo.

930.1 USA ISSN 1059-0161
CC1 CODEN: JARRE3
➤ **JOURNAL OF ARCHAEOLOGICAL RESEARCH.** Text in English. 1993. q. EUR 395, USD 405, GBP 255 combined subscription to institutions print & online eds. (effective 2005). adv. bk.rev. bibl.; illus.; maps. reprint service avail. from PSC. **Document type:** *Journal, Academic/Scholarly.* **Description:** Presents state of the art research on specific scholarly issues or themes in archaeology, and reviews current discoveries, field work and excavations.
Related titles: Microfilm ed.: (from PQC); Online - full text ed.: ISSN 1573-7756 (from EBSCO Publishing, Gale Group, IngentaConnect, Kluwer Online, O C L C Online Computer Library Center, Inc., Springer LINK, Swets Information Services).
Indexed: AICP, AbAn, AnthLit, ArtHuCI, BibLing, BrArAb, CurCont, GEOBASE, IBSS, NumL.
—BLDSC (4947.177500), IDS, IE, Infotrieve, ingenta. **CCC.**
Published by: Plenum US (Subsidiary of: Springer Science+Business Media), 233 Spring St, New York, NY 10013. TEL 212-460-1500, FAX 212-460-1575, service@springer-ny.com, http://springerlink.metapress.com/openurl.asp?genre=journal&issn=1059-0161, http://www.springeronline.com. Eds. Gary M Feinman, T. Douglas Price.

A

913 GBR ISSN 0305-4403
CC1 CODEN: JASCDU
➤ **JOURNAL OF ARCHAEOLOGICAL SCIENCE.** Text in English. 1974. 12/yr. EUR 1,172 in Europe to institutions; JPY 126,500 in Japan to institutions; USD 1,041 elsewhere to institutions; EUR 134 in Europe to qualified personnel; JPY 14,500 in Japan to qualified personnel; USD 126 elsewhere to qualified personnel (effective 2006). adv. bk.rev. bibl.; illus. index. reprints avail. **Document type:** *Journal, Academic/Scholarly.* **Description:** Directed to archaeologists and scientists with particular interests in advances in the application of the scientific techniques and methodologies to all areas of archeology.
Related titles: Online - full text ed.: ISSN 1095-9238. USD 1,098 (effective 2002) (from EBSCO Publishing, Gale Group, IngentaConnect, O C L C Online Computer Library Center, Inc., ScienceDirect, Swets Information Services).
Indexed: A&ATA, AIAP, AICP, ASCA, AbAn, AnthLit, ArtHuCI, BHA, BIOSIS Prev, BiolAb, BrArAb, CurCont, FS&TA, GEOBASE, MEA&I, NAA, NumL, PCI, RASB, SSCI, WTA, ZooRec.
—BLDSC (4947.178000), IDS, IE, Infotrieve, ingenta. **CCC.**
Published by: (Society for Archaeological Sciences USA), Academic Press (Subsidiary of: Elsevier Science & Technology), Harcourt Pl, 32 Jamestown Rd, London, NW1 7BY, United Kingdom. TEL 44-20-7424-4200, FAX 44-20-7483-2293, apsubs@acad.com, http://www.elsevier.com/locate/jas. Eds. E Klein, J. Grattan, K. W. Butzer. **Subscr. to:** Harcourt Publishers Ltd., Foots Cray High St, Sidcup, Kent DA14 5HP, United Kingdom. TEL 44-208-3085700, FAX 44-20-83090807, http://www.harcourt-international.com/.

913 IND
JOURNAL OF ARCHAEOLOGY IN ANDHRA PRADESH. Text in English. 1979. irreg. price varies. bk.rev. **Document type:** *Academic/Scholarly.*
Published by: Department of Archaeology and Museums, Hyderabad, Andhra Pradesh 500 001, India. Ed. V V Krishna Sastry. Circ: 500.

306.4 PAK
JOURNAL OF ASIAN CIVILIZATION. Text in English. 1978. s-a. PKR 300, USD 30 per issue (effective 2000). bk.rev. back issues avail. **Document type:** *Academic/Scholarly.*
Formerly: Journal of Central Asia (1016-0701)
Indexed: AnthLit, BAS, IBR, PerIslam.
Published by: (International Association for the Study of the Cultures of Central Asia), Quaid-i-Azam University, Taxila Institute of Asian Civilizations, Islamabad, 45320, Pakistan. TEL 92-51-814620, FAX 92-51-251779. Ed. Ahmad Hassan Dani. Circ: 500. **Co-sponsor:** UNESCO.

THE JOURNAL OF CELTIC STUDIES. see *HISTORY—History Of Europe*

930.1 NLD ISSN 1574-0773
▼ **JOURNAL OF CONFLICT ARCHAEOLOGY.** Text in English. 2005. a., latest vol.2, 2006. USD 65 in the Americas to individuals; EUR 52 elsewhere to individuals; USD 195 combined subscription in the Americas to institutions print & online eds.; EUR 156 combined subscription elsewhere to institutions print & online eds. (effective 2006). back issues avail. **Document type:** *Journal, Academic/Scholarly.* **Description:** Covers battlefield and military archaeology.
Related titles: Online - full text ed.: ISSN 1574-0781. USD 176 in the Americas to institutions; EUR 140 elsewhere to institutions (effective 2006).
—IE.
Published by: Brill Academic Publishers, PO Box 9000, Leiden, 2300 PA, Netherlands. TEL 31-71-53-53500, FAX 31-71-53-17532, cs@brill.nl, http://www.brill.nl/m_catalogue_sub6_id22899.htm. Eds. Iain Banks, Tony Pollard. **Subscr. in N. America to:** PO Box 605, Herndon, VA 20172. TEL 703-661-1585, 800-337-9255, FAX 703-661-1501, cs@brillusa.com. **Distr. outside N. America by:** c/o Turpin Distribution, Stratton Business Park, Pegasus Drive, Biggleswade, BEDFORDSHIRE SG 18 8TQ, United Kingdom. TEL 44-1767-604-954, FAX 44-1767-601-640, brill@turpin-distribution.com.

JOURNAL OF CONSERVATION & MUSEUM STUDIES. see *MUSEUMS AND ART GALLERIES*

417.7 935 USA ISSN 0022-0256
PJ3102 CODEN: JCUSAV
➤ **JOURNAL OF CUNEIFORM STUDIES.** Text in English, French, German. 1947. a. USD 45 domestic to individuals; USD 70 foreign to individuals; USD 55 domestic to institutions; USD 80 foreign to institutions (effective 2005). bk.rev. bibl.; illus. index. back issues avail.; reprint service avail. from PQC. **Document type:** *Journal, Academic/Scholarly.* **Description:** Presents technical and general articles on the history and languages of the ancient Mesopotamian and Anatolian literate cultures.
Media: Large Type. **Related titles:** Microform ed.: (from PQC); Online - full text ed.: (from EBSCO Publishing, JSTOR (Web-based Journal Archive), Northern Light Technology, Inc., ProQuest Information & Learning).
Indexed: AnthLit, BibLing, DIP, IBR, IBZ, L&LBA, MLA-IB, MathR, OTA, PCI, R&TA, RASB, RI-1, RI-2, SOPODA.
—IE. **CCC.**
Published by: American Schools of Oriental Research, 825 Houston Mill Rd, Atlanta, GA 30329. TEL 404-727-0807, FAX 404-727-4719, asorpubs@asor.org, http://www.asor.org. Ed. Piotr Michalowski. Circ: 625 (paid).

948.901 DNK ISSN 0108-464X
DL121
JOURNAL OF DANISH ARCHAEOLOGY. Text in English. 1982. a., latest vol.13, 1996. DKK 200; DKK 250 per issue (effective 2006). illus. back issues avail. **Document type:** *Yearbook, Academic/Scholarly.*
Indexed: AnthLit, BHA, BrArAb, IBR, IBZ, NAA, NumL, ZooRec.
—BLDSC (4967.380000). **CCC.**
Published by: Syddansk Universitetsforlag/University Press of Southern Denmark, Campusvej 55, Odense M, 5230, Denmark. TEL 45-66-157999, FAX 45-66-158126, press@forlag.sdu.dk, http://www.universitypress.dk/.

932 GBR ISSN 0307-5133
DT57
➤ **JOURNAL OF EGYPTIAN ARCHAEOLOGY.** Text in English; Text occasionally in French, German. 1914. a. GBP 40 to members (effective 2005). bk.rev. cum.index every 5 yrs. back issues avail.; reprint service avail. from PSC. **Document type:** *Journal, Academic/Scholarly.* **Description:** Contains scholarly articles and reviews of Egyptological books.
Related titles: Microfiche ed.: (from IDC).
Indexed: AIAP, AICP, ASCA, ArtHuCI, ArtInd, BHA, BibLing, CurCont, DIP, IBR, IBZ, IndIslam, MEA&I, OTA, PCI, RASB.
—BLDSC (4973.280000), IE. **CCC.**
Published by: Egypt Exploration Society, 3 Doughty Mews, London, WC1N 2PG, United Kingdom. TEL 44-20-72421880, FAX 44-20-74046118, eeslondon@talk21.com, http://www.ees.ac.uk/publications/jea.htm. Ed. Lisa M Leahy. R&P Patricia Spencer. Circ: 3,500.

➤ **JOURNAL OF EUROPEAN STUDIES.** see *HISTORY—History Of Europe*

913 USA ISSN 0093-4690
CC1
➤ **JOURNAL OF FIELD ARCHAEOLOGY.** Text in English. 1974. q. USD 48 domestic to individuals; USD 54 foreign to individuals; USD 60 domestic to institutions; USD 66 foreign to institutions (effective 2005). adv. bk.rev. charts; illus.; maps; abstr.; bibl. 128 p./no.; back issues avail.; reprints avail. **Document type:** *Journal, Academic/Scholarly.* **Description:** Publishes articles that deal with reports of field excavation and survey the world over, as well as studies of methodological and technical matters, scientific advances in archaeology, and larger interpretive studies.
Related titles: Microfilm ed.: (from PQC); Online - full text ed.: (from JSTOR (Web-based Journal Archive)).
Indexed: A&ATA, ABS&EES, AIAP, AICP, ASCA, AbAn, AmHI, AnthLit, ArtHuCI, ArtInd, BAS, BHA, BrArAb, CurCont, DIP, HumInd, IBR, IBZ, MEA&I, NAA, NumL, OTA, PCI, RASB, RILM, SPPI, SSCI.
—BLDSC (4984.100000), IE, Infotrieve, ingenta.
Published by: Boston University, Journal of Field Archaeology (Subsidiary of: Trustees of Boston University), 675 Commonwealth Ave, Boston, MA 02215. TEL 617-353-2357, FAX 617-353-6800, jfa@bu.edu, http://jfa-www.bu.edu. Ed. Curtis Runnels. R&P, Adv. contact Al B Wesolowsky TEL 617-353-2357. page USD 200; trim 7.0625 x 8.8125. Circ: 1,200 (paid). **Subscr. to:** Boston University, Scholarly Publications, 985 Commonwealth Ave, Boston, MA 02215. TEL 617-353-4106, norwell@bu.edu.

930.1 PRT ISSN 0874-2677
DP44
JOURNAL OF IBERIAN ARCHAEOLOGY. Text in English. 1998. a. membership. **Description:** Deals with a broad range of subjects over a wide time span, from Prehistory to the present, and considers themes such as the role of archaeology as a scientific discipline and as a public service in the countries of the Iberian Peninsula.
Indexed: AnthLit.
Published by: The Association for the Improvement of Cooperation in Iberian Archaeology, R. Anibal Cunha, 39, 3. s. 7, Porto, 4050, Portugal. FAX 351-2-2026903, voisoj@mail.telepac.pt, http://www.utad.pt/actividades/CAP/Portugues/jia.html.

913 IRL ISSN 0268-537X
CODEN: JRREEF
JOURNAL OF IRISH ARCHAEOLOGY. Text in English. 1983. a. bk.rev. back issues avail. **Document type:** *Academic/Scholarly.* **Description:** Review articles on Irish archaeology, excavation reports and papers on Irish archaeology from prehistory to the later middle ages.
Formerly: Irish Archaeological Research Forum
Indexed: AnthLit, BrArAb, NumL.
—BLDSC (5008.080000), ingenta.
Published by: National Museum of Ireland, Irish Antiquities Division, Department of Archaeology, National University of Ireland, Galway, Ireland. TEL 353-91-524411, FAX 353-91-525700, http://www.nuigalway.ie/jia/. Ed. William O'Brien. Circ: 600.

930.1 USA ISSN 1556-4894
▼ ➤ **JOURNAL OF ISLAND AND COASTAL ARCHAEOLOGY.** Text in English. forthcoming 2006. s-a. USD 138, GBP 84 combined subscription to institutions print & online eds. (effective 2006). bk.rev. **Document type:** *Journal, Academic/Scholarly.* **Description:** Provides an international forum for scholars from a variety of disciplines who share a common interest in studying islands, archipelagoes, and coastal regions.
Related titles: Online - full text ed.: ISSN 1556-1828. forthcoming 2006 (Jan.). USD 130, GBP 80 (effective 2006).
Published by: Taylor & Francis Inc. (Subsidiary of: Taylor & Francis Group), 325 Chestnut St, Ste 800, Philadelphia, PA 19016. TEL 215-625-8900, FAX 215-625-8914, info@taylorandfrancis.com, http://www.tandf.co.uk/journals/titles/15564894.asp, http://www.taylorandfrancis.com. Eds. Jon McVey Erlandson, Scott M Fitzpatrick.

930.1 340 POL ISSN 0075-4277
THE JOURNAL OF JURISTIC PAPYROLOGY. Text in English, French, German, Italian. 1946. a., latest vol.31. price on request. bk.rev. **Document type:** *Journal, Academic/Scholarly.*
Related titles: Supplement(s):.
Indexed: FLP, RASB.
—BLDSC (5009.700000).
Published by: Uniwersytet Warszawski, Zaklad Papirologii i Nauk Pomopcniczych Archeologii, Krakowskie Przedmiescie 26/28, Warsaw, 00927, Poland. TEL 48-22-9520388, http://www.papyrology.uw.edu.pl/papyrology/papyri/jjpeng.htm. Circ: 400. **Dist. by:** Ars Polona, Krakowskie Przedmiescie 7, Warsaw, Poland. TEL 48-22-9263914, FAX 48-22-9265334, arspolona@arspolona.com.pl, http://www.arspolona.com.pl.

930.1 USA ISSN 1557-2285
▼ **JOURNAL OF MARITIME ARCHAEOLOGY.** Text in English. forthcoming 2006 (Mar.). s-a. **Document type:** *Journal, Academic/Scholarly.*
Related titles: Online - full text ed.: ISSN 1557-2293. forthcoming 2006 (Mar.).
Published by: Springer Science+Business Media, Inc., 233 Spring St, New York, NY 10013. TEL 212-460-1500, FAX 212-473-6272.

930.1 GBR ISSN 0952-7648
DE1
JOURNAL OF MEDITERRANEAN ARCHAEOLOGY. Text in English. 1988. 2/yr. GBP 35, USD 55 to individuals; GBP 90, USD 148 to institutions; GBP 28, USD 45 to students (effective 2004). adv. bk.rev. **Document type:** *Journal, Academic/Scholarly.* **Description:** Deals with the entire multicultural world of Mediterranean archaeology.
Related titles: Online - full text ed.: ISSN 1743-1700 (from EBSCO Publishing, Swets Information Services).
Indexed: AnthLit, BibInd, DIP, GEOBASE, IBR, IBZ, PCI, RI-1, RI-2.
—BLDSC (5017.582000), IE, Infotrieve, ingenta.
Published by: (University of Michigan, Department of Classical Studies USA, University of Glasgow, Department of Archaeology), Equinox Publishing Ltd., Unit Six, The Village, 101 Amies St, London, SW11 2JW, United Kingdom. jjoyce@equinoxpub.com, http://www.equinoxpub.com/journals/main.asp?ref=13. Eds. A Bernard Knapp, John F Cherry. Adv. contact Val Hall. page GBP 350. **Subscr. to:** Extenza - Turpin, Pegasus Dr, Stratton Business Park, Biggleswade, Beds SG18 8TQ, United Kingdom. TEL 44-1767-604951, FAX 44-1767-601640.

913 USA ISSN 0883-9697
E78.M65 CODEN: JMAAEJ
JOURNAL OF MIDDLE ATLANTIC ARCHAEOLOGY. Text in English. 1985. a. USD 25 (effective 1999). bk.rev. illus. **Document type:** *Academic/Scholarly.* **Description:** Includes reviewed articles, reports, and book notes.
Indexed: AbAn, AnthLit.
—BLDSC (5019.850000), IE, ingenta.
Published by: Archaeological Services, 68 Sunny Ridge Rd, P O Box 386, Bethlehem, CT 06751. TEL 203-266-7741. Ed., Pub., R&P Roger W Moeller. Circ: 300.

913 USA ISSN 0022-2968
DS41 CODEN: JNESBT
➤ **JOURNAL OF NEAR EASTERN STUDIES.** Text in English. 1884. q. USD 55 combined subscription to individuals print & online eds.; USD 196 combined subscription to institutions print & online eds.; USD 18 per issue to individuals; USD 58 per issue to institutions (effective 2006). adv. bk.rev. illus. Index. 80 p./no.; reprint service avail. from PQC,ISI,PSC. **Document type:** *Journal, Academic/Scholarly.* **Description:** Covers a broad scope of examinations into the ancient and medieval civilizations of the area, including archaeology, history, literature, religion, linguistics, and law.
Former titles (until 1941): American Journal of Semitic Languages and Literatures (1062-0516); (until 1895): Hebraica (0160-2810)
Related titles: Microform ed.: (from MIM, PMC, PQC); Online - full text ed.: ISSN 1545-6978. USD 176 to institutions (effective 2006) (from bigchalk, EBSCO Publishing, Florida Center for Library Automation, Gale Group, JSTOR (Web-based Journal Archive), O C L C Online Computer Library Center, Inc., ProQuest Information & Learning, The Dialog Corporation).

Indexed: A&ATA, AFS, ASCA, AbAn, AmH&L, AnthLit, ArtHuCI, BAS, BHA, BRI, BibLing, CurCont, DIP, HumInd, IBR, IBSS, IBZ, IZBG, IndIslam, L&LBA, MEA&I, MLA, MLA-IB, NTA, OTA, PCI, PRA, PerIslam, R&TA, RASB, RI-1, RI-2, SOPODA, SSCI.
—BLDSC (5021.393000), IDS, IE, Infotrieve, ingenta. **CCC.**
Published by: University of Chicago Press, Journals Division, Journals Division, PO Box 37005, Chicago, IL 60637. TEL 773-753-3347, 877-705-1878, FAX 773-753-0811, 877-705-1879, subscriptions@press.uchicago.edu, http://www.journals.uchicago.edu/JNES. Ed. Robert D Biggs. adv.: page USD 475; trim 6.63 x 9.5. Circ: 1,410 (paid).

913 201.42 SWE ISSN 0283-8486
GN799.R4 CODEN: JPRGE7
JOURNAL OF PREHISTORIC RELIGION. Text in English, French, German. 1987. a., latest vol.15, 2001. USD 15 per issue (effective 2003). adv. bk.rev. **Document type:** *Journal, Academic/Scholarly.*
Indexed: AnthLit.
—IE, Infotrieve.
Published by: Paul Aastroems Foerlag, William Gibsons Vaeg 11, Jonsered, 43376, Sweden. TEL 46-31-7956600, FAX 46-31-7956710, paul.astrom@swipnet.se, info@astromeditions.com, http://www.astromeditions.com. Ed., Pub. Paul Aastroem. Circ: 600.

JOURNAL OF QUATERNARY SCIENCE. see *EARTH SCIENCES—Geology*

930.1 USA ISSN 1047-7594
DG11
➤ **JOURNAL OF ROMAN ARCHAEOLOGY.** Variant title: J R A. Text in English, French, Italian, German, Spanish. 1988. a. USD 59.75 per issue to individuals (effective 2004). bk.rev. illus. back issues avail.; reprints avail. **Document type:** *Journal, Academic/Scholarly.* **Description:** Concerned with all aspects of archaeology in every part of the Roman Empire.
Related titles: ◆ Supplement(s): J R A - The Supplementary Series. ISSN 1063-4304.
Indexed: ArtInd, BrArAb, DIP, IBR, IBZ, NTA, NumL, PCI.
—BLDSC (5052.118000), IE.
Published by: Journal of Roman Archaeology L.L.C., The Editor, JRA, 95 Peleg Rd, Portsmouth, RI 02871. TEL 401-683-1955, FAX 401-683-1975, jra@jounralofromanarch.com, jra@journalofromanarch.com, http://JournalofRomanArch.com. Ed., Pub., R&P John H Humphrey. Circ: 1,050.

➤ **JOURNAL OF ROMAN POTTERY STUDIES.** see *CLASSICAL STUDIES*

913 551 AUT
JOURNAL OF SALT HISTORY/JAHRBUCH FUER SALZGESCHICHTE; Annales d'Histoire du Sel. Text in English, French, German, Italian, Spanish. 1993. a. USD 16 to members; USD 21 to non-members (effective 2000). **Document type:** *Bulletin, Academic/Scholarly.*
—BLDSC (5052.147000), ingenta.
Published by: (International Commission for the History of Salt), Berenkamp Verlag, Salvatorgasse 15, Hall In Tirol, T 6060, Austria. TEL 43-5223-57667, FAX 43-5223-576674, sekretariat@berenkamp-verlag.at, http://www.berenkamp-verlag.at. Ed., R&P Rudolf Palme. Pub. Wolfgang Ingenhaeff. Circ: 500. **Subscr. to:** Rudolf Palme, Institut fuer Rechtsgeschichte, Christoph Probst Platz, Innsbruck, T 6020, Austria. TEL 43-512-5078058, FAX 43-512-5072831.

930.1 306 GBR ISSN 1469-6053
CC72.4
➤ **JOURNAL OF SOCIAL ARCHAEOLOGY.** Text in English. 2001 (per Claire Lazzeri, July 24, 2001). 3/yr. GBP 257, USD 449 to institutions; GBP 267, USD 468 combined subscription to institutions print & online eds. (effective 2006). illus.; maps. **Document type:** *Journal, Academic/Scholarly.* **Description:** Devoted to social approaches to archaeology, engaging with and contributing to theoretical developments from other related disciplines across the social sciences, including politics and heritage issues. Explicitly global in outlook, it covers world archaeology with temporal parameters from prehistory to recent periods.
Related titles: Online - full text ed.: ISSN 1741-2951. GBP 254, USD 444 to institutions (effective 2006) (from EBSCO Publishing, O C L C Online Computer Library Center, Inc., Sage Publications, Inc., Swets Information Services).
Indexed: AnthLit, ArtHuCI, CurCont, DIP, IBR, IBSS, IBZ, SWA.
—BLDSC (5064.751200), IE. **CCC.**
Published by: Sage Publications Ltd. (Subsidiary of: Sage Publications, Inc.), 1 Oliver's Yard, 55 City Rd, London, EC1 1SP, United Kingdom. TEL 44-20-73248500, FAX 44-20-73248600, info@sagepub.co.uk, http://www.sagepub.co.uk/journal.aspx?pid=105685. Eds. Chris Gosden, Lynn Meskell. **Subscr. in the Americas to:** Sage Publications, Inc., 2455 Teller Rd, Thousand Oaks, CA 91320. TEL 805-499-0721, FAX 805-499-0871, journals@sagepub.com.

930.1 USA ISSN 0892-7537
GN700 CODEN: JWPREB
➤ **JOURNAL OF WORLD PREHISTORY.** Text in English. 1987. q. EUR 578, USD 588, GBP 375 combined subscription to institutions print & online eds. (effective 2005). adv. back issues avail.; reprint service avail. from PSC. **Document type:** *Journal, Academic/Scholarly.* **Description:** Explores all aspects of prehistoric cultures worldwide, including the beginnings and early development of complex societies.
Related titles: Microfilm ed.: (from PQC); Online - full text ed.: ISSN 1573-7802 (from EBSCO Publishing, Gale Group, IngentaConnect, Kluwer Online, O C L C Online Computer Library Center, Inc., Springer LINK, Swets Information Services).
Indexed: ABS&EES, AICP, ASCA, AbAn, AnthLit, ArtHuCI, BibInd, BibLing, BrArAb, CurCont, GEOBASE, IBSS, NumL, RASB, SSCI.
—BLDSC (5072.685000), IDS, IE, Infotrieve, ingenta. **CCC.**
Published by: Plenum US (Subsidiary of: Springer Science+Business Media), 233 Spring St, New York, NY 10013. TEL 212-460-1500, FAX 212-460-1575, service@springer-ny.com, http://springerlink.metapress.com/openurl.asp?genre=journal&issn=0892-7537, http://www.springeronline.com. Ed. Angela E Close.

933 296.155 ISR ISSN 0075-4501
JUDEAN DESERT STUDIES. Text in English. 1963. irreg., latest 2002. price varies. **Document type:** *Monographic series, Academic/Scholarly.* **Description:** Monographs on Israeli archaeological discoveries and excavations at prehistoric sites.
Published by: Israel Exploration Society, P O Box 7041, Jerusalem, 91070, Israel. TEL 972-2-625-7991, FAX 972-2-624-7772, ies@vms.huji.ac.il, http://www.hum.huji.ac.il/ies/.

JYSK ARKAEOLOGISK SELSKABS SKRIFTER/JUTLAND ARCHAEOLOGICAL SOCIETY PUBLICATIONS/ PUBLICATIONS DE LA SOCIETE ARCHEOLOGIQUE DU JUTLAND. see *HISTORY—History Of Europe*

917 USA ISSN 1047-742X
K A C RESEARCH SERIES. Text in English. 1985. irreg., latest vol.11, 1997.
Formerly: C A A Research Series; Superseded (1982-1984): Northwestern University. Center for American Archeology. Research Series
Published by: (Center for American Archeology, Kampsville Archaeological Center), Center for American Archeology Press, 366, Kampsville, IL 62053-0366. TEL 618-653-4316, FAX 618-653-4235, http://www.caa-archeology.org.

917 USA
K A C TECHNICAL REPORTS. Text in English. 1986. irreg., latest vol.5, 1994. price varies.
Formerly: C A A Technical Reports
Published by: (Center for American Archeology, Kampsville Archaeological Center), Center for American Archeology Press, 366, Kampsville, IL 62053-0366. TEL 618-653-4688.

932 USA
DT57
K M T: A MODERN JOURNAL OF ANCIENT EGYPT. Text in English. 1990. q. USD 35 domestic; USD 38 in Canada; USD 42 elsewhere (effective 2004). adv. bk.rev. illus. 88 p./no.; back issues avail. **Document type:** *Journal, Academic/Scholarly.* **Description:** Presents research on ancient Egyptian civilization.
Formerly (until 2000): K M T (1053-0827)
—BLDSC (5099.800000), IE, ingenta.
Published by: K M T Communications, Inc., PO Box 1475, Sebastopol, CA 95473. greg@egyptology.com, http://www.egyptology.com/kmt/. Ed. Dennis Forbes. Pub., Adv. contact Michael Kuhlmann TEL 707-823-6079. page USD 920;. Circ: 15,000.

KADMOS; Zeitschrift fuer vor- und fruehgriechische Epigraphik. see *CLASSICAL STUDIES*

938 481.7 DEU ISSN 0453-0586
KADMOS. SUPPLEMENT. Text in Greek, German. 1967. irreg., latest vol.3, 1992. price varies. back issues avail. **Document type:** *Monographic series, Academic/Scholarly.*
Related titles: ◆ Supplement to: Kadmos. ISSN 0022-7498.
Published by: Walter de Gruyter GmbH & Co. KG, Genthiner Str. 13, Berlin, 10785, Germany. TEL 49-30-260050, FAX 49-30-26005251, wdg-info@degruyter.de, http://www.degruyter.de.

930.1 ESP ISSN 0211-5840
KALATHOS. Text in Spanish, English. 1981. a.
Indexed: AnthLit, RILM.
—CINDOC.
Published by: Social Faculty of Humanities and Sciences, Seminary of Archeology and Ethnology Turolense, Scholastic City, s/n, Teruel, 44003, Spain. TEL 34-978610325, FAX 34-978608061.

917 USA
KAMPSVILLE SEMINARS IN ARCHEOLOGY. Text in English. 1982. irreg., latest vol.2, 1986. price varies.
Published by: (Center for American Archeology, Northwestern University), Center for American Archeology Press, 366, Kampsville, IL 62053-0366. TEL 618-653-4688, FAX 618-653-4235, http://www.caa-archeology.org. Ed. Jodie O'Gorman.

917 USA
KAMPSVILLE STUDIES IN ARCHEOLOGY AND HISTORY. Text in English. irreg., latest vol.3, 2000. price varies.
Published by: Center for American Archeology Press, 366, Kampsville, IL 62053-0366. TEL 618-653-4688, FAX 618-653-4235, http://www.caa-archeology.org.

KANSAS ANTHROPOLOGICAL ASSOCIATION NEWSLETTER. see *ANTHROPOLOGY*

THE KANSAS ANTHROPOLOGIST. see *ANTHROPOLOGY*

913 CHN ISSN 0453-2899
DS715
➤ **KAOGU/ARCHAEOLOGY.** Text in Chinese; Contents page in English. m. CNY 105.60 (effective 2004). adv. bk.rev. charts; illus. **Document type:** *Journal, Academic/Scholarly.* **Description:** For popular reading. Contains field reports and short sketches of excavations, discussions about major issues in archeology, and comprehensive reports of excavated materials.
Indexed: AICP, RASB.
Published by: Kexue Chubanshe/Science Press, 16 Donghuang Cheng Genbei Jie, Beijing, 100717, China. TEL 86-10-64000246, FAX 86-10-64030255, http://www.sciencep.com/. Eds. Lu Zhaoyin, Xu Pingfang. Circ: 25,000. **Dist. outside China by:** China International Book Trading Corp, 35 Chegongzhuang Xilu, Haidian District, PO Box 399, Beijing 100044, China. TEL 86-10-68412045, FAX 86-10-68412023, cibtc@mail.cibtc.com.cn, http://www.cibtc.com.cn.

913 CHN ISSN 0453-2902
DS715 CODEN: KKHPAO
➤ **KAOGU XUEBAO/ACTA ARCHAEOLOGICA SINICA.** Text in Chinese; Contents page in English. 1936. q. CNY 51.20 (effective 2004). adv. maps; illus.; charts. **Document type:** *Academic/Scholarly.* **Description:** Includes reports on field excavations, articles on archeological theory, research articles on ancient history and on identifying ancient constructions, anthropology and paleontology.
Indexed: AICP, DIP, IBR, IBZ, RASB.
Published by: Kexue Chubanshe/Science Press, 16 Donghuang Cheng Genbei Jie, Beijing, 100717, China. TEL 86-10-64000246, FAX 86-10-64030255, http://www.sciencep.com/. Eds. Huang Zhanyue, Xu Pingfang. Circ: 15,000. **Dist. outside China by:** China International Book Trading Corp, 35 Chegongzhuang Xilu, Haidian District, PO Box 399, Beijing 100044, China. TEL 86-10-68412045, FAX 86-10-68412023, cibtc@mail.cibtc.com.cn, http://www.cibtc.com.cn.

930.1 CHN ISSN 1000-7830
KAOGU YU WENWU/ARCHAEOLOGY AND CULTURAL RELICS. Text in Chinese; Contents page in English. 1980. bi-m. CNY 33, USD 81. charts; illus. **Document type:** *Academic/Scholarly.*
Related titles: Online - full text ed.: (from East View Information Services).
Published by: Shaanxi Sheng Kaogu Yanjiusuo/Shaanxi Institute of Archaeology, No 3 Leyou Lu, Xi'an, Shaanxi 710054, China. FAX 86-29-5526892. Ed. Gong Qiming. Circ: 8,000. **Dist. in U.S. by:** China Books & Periodicals Inc, 360 Swift Ave., Ste. 48, S San Fran, CA 94080-6220. TEL 415-282-2994; **Dist. outside China by:** China International Book Trading Corp, 35 Chegongzhuang Xilu, Haidian District, PO Box 399, Beijing 100044, China. TEL 86-10-68412045, FAX 86-10-68412023, cibtc@mail.cibtc.com.cn, http://www.cibtc.com.cn.

913 BEL ISSN 0453-3429
DT269.C3
➤ **KARTHAGO**; revue d'archeologie mediterraneenne. Text in English, French. 1950. a., latest vol.26, 2001. EUR 85 (effective 2006). adv. bk.rev. Index. back issues avail. **Document type:** *Journal, Academic/Scholarly.* **Description:** Covers archaeology and history of ancient North Africa and the Mediterranean.
Formerly: Karthago. Collection Epigraphique (0075-5184)
Related titles: Online - full text ed.: (from EBSCO Publishing).
Indexed: AIAP, BHA, NumL, PCI, RASB.
Published by: (Universite de Paris IV (Paris-Sorbonne), Centre d'Etudes Archeologiques de la Mediterranee FRA), Peeters Publishers, Bondgenotenlaan 153, Leuven, 3000, Belgium. TEL 32-16-235170, FAX 32-16-228500, peeters@peeters-leuven.be, http://poj.peeters-leuven.be/content.php?url=journal&journal_code=KAR, http://www.peeters-leuven.be. Ed., Pub., Adv. contact Andre Laronde. Circ: 750.

930.1 560   TUR   ISSN 1017-7655
DR431
KAZI SONUCLARI TOPLANTISI. Text in Turkish; Text occasionally in English, German. 1980. a. per issue exchange basis. **Document type:** *Academic/Scholarly.* **Description:** Reports of explorations, excavations, archaeological and palaeontological research undertaken at sites throughout Turkey.
Indexed: AnthLit.
Published by: Ministry of Culture, General Directorate of Monuments and Museums/Kultur Bakanligi, Anitlar ve Muzeler Genel Mudurlugu, Ulus - Ankara, 06100, Turkey. TEL 90-312-3104960, FAX 90-312-3111417.

913   DEU
KEILSCHRIFTTEXTE AUS BOGHAZKOI. Text in German. 1939. irreg., latest vol.43, 2002. price varies. reprints avail.
Document type: *Monographic series, Academic/Scholarly.*
Published by: (Academie der Wissenschaften und der Literatur Mainz), Gebr. Mann Verlag, Neue Gruenstr 17, Berlin, 10179, Germany. TEL 49-30-2790760, FAX 49-30-27907655, vertrieb-kunstverlage@reimer-verlag.de, http://www.gebrmannverlag.de. Ed. Heinrich Otten. R&P Elisabeth Roosens.

914.2   GBR   ISSN 1365-4055
KENT ARCHAEOLOGICAL RESCUE UNIT. SPECIAL SUBJECT SERIES; the discovery of arachaeological sites at Hayes, Kent 1960-1997. Text in English. 1983. irreg., latest vol.13, 2000. GBP 4 (effective 2001). **Document type:** *Monographic series.* **Description:** Series of publications on excavations and research in Kent and southeast London.
Published by: Kent Archaeological Rescue Unit, 5 Harvest Bank Rd, West Wickham, Kent BR4 9DL, United Kingdom. R&P Brian Philp.

913   GBR   ISSN 0023-0014
DA670.K2
KENT ARCHAEOLOGICAL REVIEW. Text in English. 1965. q. GBP 0.50 (effective 2001). adv. bk.rev. charts; illus. cum.index. back issues avail. **Document type:** *Newsletter.* **Description:** Contains excavation reports.
Indexed: BHA, BrArAb, DIP, IBR, IBZ, NumL.
—BLDSC (5089.588000), IE, ingenta.
Published by: Council for Kentish Archaeology, c/o Dover Roman Painted House, New St, Dover, Kent, United Kingdom. TEL 44-1304-203279, FAX 44-181-462-4737. Ed. Roger Manning. Circ: 900.

930.1   GBR
KENT ARCHAEOLOGICAL SOCIETY. NEWSLETTER. Text in English. 1982. q. membership. **Document type:** *Newsletter.* **Description:** Archeology and history of Kent.
Indexed: BrArAb, NumL.
Published by: Kent Archaeological Society, c/o L. Ilott, 567 Red Hill, Wateringbury, Maidstone, Kent ME18 5BE, United Kingdom.

914.2   GBR   ISSN 0141-2264
KENT MONOGRAPH SERIES. Text in English. 1968. irreg., latest vol.8, 1999. GBP 24 (effective 2001). charts; illus. back issues avail. **Document type:** *Monographic series.* **Description:** Series of publications on excavations within Kent since 1965.
—BLDSC (7769.541660).
Published by: Kent Archaeological Rescue Unit, 5 Harvest Bank Rd, West Wickham, Kent BR4 9DL, United Kingdom. Ed., R&P Brian Philp. Circ: 1,000.

930.1   USA
KENT STATE RESEARCH PAPERS IN ARCHAEOLOGY. Text in English. 1981. irreg. reprint service avail. from PQC.
Document type: *Monographic series, Academic/Scholarly.*
Published by: Kent State University Press, 307 Lowry Hall, PO Box 5190, Kent, OH 44242-0001. TEL 330-672-7913, FAX 330-672-3104, sclarki@kent.edu, http://www.kent.edu. Ed. Mark F Seeman. R&P John T Hubbell.

941.5   IRL   ISSN 0085-2503
DA990.K4
KERRY ARCHAEOLOGICAL AND HISTORICAL SOCIETY. JOURNAL. Text in English. 1968. a. free membership (effective 2005). back issues avail.
Indexed: BHA, BibInd, BrArAb, MLA-IB, NumL.
Published by: Kerry Archaeological and Historical Society, Kerry County Library, Moyderwell, Tralee, Co. Kerry, Ireland. TEL 353-66-7121200, FAX 353-66-7129202, kahs@eircom.net, http://www.kerrycountylibrary.com/kahs.asp. Circ: 450.

914.2   IRL   ISSN 0791-2846
KERRY MAGAZINE. Text in English. 1989. a. free membership (effective 2005).
Indexed: BrArAb, NumL.
Published by: Kerry Archaeological and Historical Society, Kerry County Library, Moyderwell, Tralee, Co. Kerry, Ireland. TEL 353-66-7121200, FAX 353-66-7129202, kahs@eircom.net, http://www.kerrycountylibrary.com/kahs.asp. Circ: 500.

THE KIST. see *HISTORY—History Of Europe*

930.1   FRA
KITION-BAMBOULA. Text in French. 1982. irreg. price varies.
Document type: *Monographic series.*

Published by: Editions Recherche sur les Civilisations - A D P F, Les Patios Saint-Jacques, 6 rue Ferrus, Paris, Cedex 14 75603, France. TEL 33-1-43131100, FAX 33-1-43131125. Ed., Pub. Hina Descat. Circ: 600.

913 970.1   USA   ISSN 0023-1940
F786
► **KIVA;** the journal of Southwestern anthropology and history. Text in English. 1935. q. USD 40 domestic to individuals; USD 80 domestic to institutions; USD 60 foreign to individuals; USD 100 foreign to institutions (effective 2004). adv. bk.rev. charts; illus. index, cum.index: vols.1-30, 31-40, 41-50. reprints avail. **Document type:** *Academic/Scholarly.*
Indexed: AICP, AbAn, AmH&L, AnthLit, HistAb, IBR, PCI, RILM.
—BLDSC (5098.345000), IE, Infotrieve, ingenta.
Published by: (Arizona Archaeological and Historical Society), AltaMira Press, 1630 N Main St, Ste 367, Walnut Creek, CA 94596. TEL 925-938-7243, FAX 925-933-9720, http://www.altamirapress.com/RLA/Journals/Kiva/Index.shtml. Ed. Ronald H Towner. Circ: 1,100. **Subscr. to:** 15200 NBN Way, Blue Ridge Summit, PA 17214. TEL 800-273-2223, FAX 800-338-4550.

► **KOBIE, REVISTA DE BELLAS ARTES Y CIENCIAS: SERIE PALEOANTROPOLOGIA.** see *ANTHROPOLOGY*

913   JPN   ISSN 0452-2516
DS815
KODAI/ARCHAEOLOGICAL SOCIETY OF WASEDA UNIVERSITY. JOURNAL. Text in Japanese. 1950. a.
Document type: *Journal, Academic/Scholarly.*
—BLDSC (4699.900000).
Published by: Waseda Daigaku Kokogakkai/Archaeological Society of Waseda University, Waseda University, School of Letters, Arts & Sciences, 1-24-1 Toyama, Shinjuku-ku, Tokyo, 162-8644, Japan.

930.1 301   JPN   ISSN 0388-7219
KODAI ORIENTO HAKUBUTSUKAN KIYO/BULLETIN OF THE ANCIENT ORIENT MUSEUM. Text in Multiple languages. 1979. a.
Indexed: AnthLit.
Published by: Kodai Oriento Hakubutsukan/Ancient Orient Museum, Sunshine City Bldg. 7F, 3-1-4, Higashi-Ikebukuro, Toshima-ku, Tokyo, 170-8630, Japan. TEL 3-3989-3491, FAX 3-3590-3266, http://home.interlink.or.jp/naom/index.html, http://home.interlink.or.jp/~aom/.

913   DEU   ISSN 0947-1553
DD901.C745
KOELNER JAHRBUCH. Text in German. 1955. irreg., latest vol.36, 2005. price varies. reprints avail. **Document type:** *Monographic series, Academic/Scholarly.* **Description:** Discusses the art and archaeological artifacts in the collection of the Roemisch-Germanischen Museum.
Formerly (until 1994): Koelner Jahrbuch fuer Vor- und Fruehgeschichte (0075-6512)
Indexed: AIAP, AnthLit, BHA, BrArAb, DIP, IBR, IBZ, NumL.
—CCC.
Published by: (Roemisch-Germanisches Museum), Gebr. Mann Verlag, Neue Gruenstr 17, Berlin, 10179, Germany. TEL 49-30-2790760, FAX 49-30-27907655, vertrieb-kunstverlage@reimer-verlag.de, http://www.gebrmannverlag.de. R&P Elisabeth Roosens.
Co-sponsor: Archaeologische Gesellschaft, Cologne.

913 930   ITA   ISSN 0392-0887
KOKALOS. Text in Multiple languages. 1964. irreg. price varies.
Document type: *Monographic series, Academic/Scholarly.*
Indexed: BibLing, NumL, RASB.
Published by: (Universita degli Studi di Palermo, Istituto di Storia Antica), Giorgio Bretschneider, Casella Postale 30011, Rm47, Rome, 00193, Italy. TEL 39-06-6879361, FAX 39-06-6864543, info@bretschneider.it, http://www.bretschneider.it/.

930.1   DEU
KOLLOQUIEN ZUR VOR- UND FRUEHGESCHICHTE. Text in German. 1997. irreg., latest vol.7, 2001. price varies.
Document type: *Monographic series, Academic/Scholarly.*
Indexed: RASB.
Published by: (Deutsches Archaeologisches Institut, Roemisch-Germanische Kommission), Dr. Rudolf Habelt GmbH, Am Buchenhang 1, Bonn, 53115, Germany. TEL 49-228-9238322, FAX 49-228-9238323, info@habelt.de, http://www.habelt.de.

KONINKLIJKE KRING VOOR OUDHEIDKUNDE LETTEREN EN KUNST VAN MECHELEN. HANDELINGEN. see *HISTORY—History Of Europe*

930.1 949   NLD   ISSN 0166-0470
KONINKLIJKE NEDERLANDSE OUDHEIDKUNDIGE BOND. BULLETIN. Cover title: Bulletin K N O B. Text in Dutch; Summaries in English. 1899. 6/yr. EUR 40 domestic to individuals; EUR 50 in Europe to individuals; EUR 60 elsewhere to individuals; EUR 70 domestic to institutions; EUR 80 in Europe to institutions; EUR 90 elsewhere to institutions; EUR 12 domestic to students; EUR 22 in Europe to students (effective 2003). adv. bk.rev. bibl. **Document type:** *Bulletin, Academic/Scholarly.*
Indexed: API, BHA, RASB, RILM.
—IE, Infotrieve.

Published by: Koninklijke Nederlandse Oudheidkundige Bond/Royal Netherlands Archeological Society, Mariaplaats 51, Utrecht, 3511 LM, Netherlands. TEL 31-30-2321756, FAX 31-30-2312951, knob@wxs.nl, http://www.knob.nl, http://home.wxs.nl/~knob. Ed. D J de Vries. Circ: 2,500.

930.1 948.5   SWE   ISSN 0345-6498
KONTAKTSTENCIL. Text in Swedish. 1970. s-a.
Indexed: NAA.
Published by: Goeteborgs Universitet, Institutionen foer Arkeologi, Fack 2133, Goeteborg, 40313, Sweden.

KROEBER ANTHROPOLOGICAL SOCIETY. PAPERS. see *ANTHROPOLOGY*

KRONIKA; casopis za Slovensko krajevno zgodovino. see *HISTORY—History Of Europe*

KRONOS; journal of Cape history. see *HISTORY—History Of Africa*

930.1   SWE   ISSN 1100-4800
KULTURMILJOEVAARD; information. Text in Swedish. 1967. s-a. SEK 160 (effective 2004).
Former titles (until 1989): Kulturminnesvaard (0346-9077); (until 1976): Meddelanden fraan Riksantikvarieaembetet
Indexed: NAA.
Published by: Riksantikvarieaembetet/Central Board of National Antiquities, PO Box 5405, Stockholm, 11484, Sweden.

948.901   DNK   ISSN 0454-6245
KUML. Text in Danish; Summaries in English. 1951. a., latest 2003. price varies. illus. **Document type:** *Yearbook, Academic/Scholarly.*
Indexed: AnthLit, BHA, BrArAb, NumL, RASB.
Published by: (Jysk Arkaeologisk Selskab/Jutland Archeological Society), Aarhus Universitetsforlag/Aarhus University Press, Langelandsgade 177, Aarhus N, 8200, Denmark. TEL 45-89425370, FAX 45-89425380, unipress@au.dk, http://www.unipress.dk.

914   DEU   ISSN 0342-0736
DIE KUNDE; Zeitschrift fuer Ur- und Fruehgeschichte. Text in German. 1933. a. bk.rev. bibl. back issues avail. **Document type:** *Academic/Scholarly.* **Description:** Archaeology of Lower Saxony and neighboring regions.
Indexed: AnthLit, BHA, DIP, IBR, IBZ, NAA.
Published by: Niedersaechsischer Landesverein fuer Urgeschichte, Willy-Brandt-Allee 5, Hannover, 30169, Germany. TEL 49-511-9807715, FAX 49-511-9807710. Ed. Guenter Wegner. Circ: 800.

KUNGLIGA VITTERHETS HISTORIE OCH ANTIKVITETS AKADEMIEN. AARSBOK. see *HISTORY—History Of Europe*

KUNGLIGA VITTERHETS HISTORIE OCH ANTIKVITETS AKADEMIEN. ANTIKVARISKT ARKIV. see *ART*

KUNGLIGA VITTERHETS HISTORIE OCH ANTIKVITETS AKADEMIEN. HANDLINGAR. ANTIKVARISKA SERIEN/ROYAL ACADEMY OF LETTERS, HISTORY AND ANTIQUITIES. PROCEEDINGS. ANTIQUARIAN SERIES. see *ART*

KUNGLIGA VITTERHETS HISTORIE OCH ANTIKVITETS AKADEMIEN. KONFERENSER. see *MEETINGS AND CONGRESSES*

913   DEU   ISSN 0075-725X
KUNST UND ALTERTUM AM RHEIN. Text in German. 1956. irreg., latest vol.142, 1997. price varies. **Document type:** *Monographic series, Academic/Scholarly.*
Published by: (Landschaftsverband Rheinland, Rheinisches Landesmuseum), Rheinland Verlag GmbH, Abtei Brauweiler, Postfach 2140, Pulheim, 50250, Germany. TEL 49-2234-9854265, FAX 49-2234-82503. **Dist. by:** Dr. Rudolf Habelt GmbH, Am Buchenhang 1, Bonn 53115, Germany. TEL 49-228-9238322, FAX 49-228-232017. **Co-sponsor:** Rheinisches Landesmuseum Bonn.

KWARTALNIK HISTORII KULTURY MATERIALNEJ. see *HISTORY—History Of Europe*

930.1   ESP   ISSN 0212-8985
DP302.L48
LAIETANIA. Text in Spanish, Catalan. 1981. a.
Indexed: AnthLit.
—CINDOC.
Published by: Museu Comarcal del Maresme, Carrero, 17-19, Mataro, Barcelona, Catalonia, 08301, Spain. TEL 344-93-7961029. Ed. Joseph Antoni Cerda.

930.1   USA   ISSN 1550-0462
▼ **LAND OF GALILEE.** Text in English. 2004. a. USD 75 per issue (effective 2004). **Document type:** *Monographic series.*
Published by: University of Rochester Press, 668 Mt. Hope Ave., Rochester, NY 14620-2731. TEL 585-275-0419, FAX 585-271-8778, http://www.urpress.com. Ed. Timothy Madigan.

930.1 DEU
LANDESDENKMALAMT BADEN-WUERTTEMBERG. ARBEITSHEFTE. Text in German. 1986. irreg., latest vol.12, 2003. price varies. **Document type:** *Monographic series, Academic/Scholarly.*
Published by: (Baden-Wuerttemberg. Landesdenkmalamt Baden-Wuerttemberg), Konrad Theiss Verlag GmbH, Moenchhaldenstr 28, Stuttgart, 70191, Germany. TEL 49-711-255270, FAX 49-711-2552717, service@theiss.de, http://www.theiss.de.

930.1 550 GBR ISSN 1466-2035
➤ **LANDSCAPES.** Text in English. s-a. GBP 25 in Europe to individuals; GBP 45 in North America to individuals; GBP 30 elsewhere to individuals; GBP 45 in Europe to institutions; GBP 70 in North America to institutions; GBP 50 elsewhere to institutions (effective 2003). bk.rev. abstr.; illus.; maps. 130 p./no. 1 cols./p.; back issues avail. **Document type:** *Journal, Academic/Scholarly.* **Description:** Provides a rich and stimulating new forum for the latest thinking about the history, archaeology and significance of cultural landscapes; focuses on the human role in the evolution of landscapes.
—BLDSC (5153.149200).
Published by: Windgather Press, 31 Bishop Rd, Bollington, Macclesfield, Cheshire SKIO 5RD, United Kingdom. richard@windgather.co.uk, http://www.windgather.co.uk. Ed. Dr. Richard Muir. Pub., R&P, Adv. contact Richard Purslow.

930.1 ITA ISSN 1123-6256
L'ARCHEOLOGO SUBACQUEO. Text in Multiple languages. 1995. 3/yr. EUR 27 (effective 2004). **Document type:** *Journal, Academic/Scholarly.* **Description:** Offers information, comments and opinions about the world of subaqueous archeology in Italy and other nations.
Published by: Edipuglia Srl, Via Dalmazia 22-B, Santo Spirito, BA 70050, Italy. TEL 39-080-5333056, FAX 39-080-5333057, http://www.edipuglia.it.

914 ESP ISSN 1130-989X
LAROUCO; revista da historia primitiva, tradicions orais e patrimonio cultural de Galicia. Text in Spanish. 1991. irreg.
Published by: (Grupo Arqueoloxico Larouco), Edicios do Castro, O Castro, s-n, Sada, Coruna 15168, Spain. TEL 34-981-620200, FAX 34-981-623804.

918 USA ISSN 1045-6635
F1219
➤ **LATIN AMERICAN ANTIQUITY.** Text in English, Spanish. 1990. q. free to members (effective 2004). adv. bk.rev. illus. Index. reprints avail. **Document type:** *Journal, Academic/Scholarly.* **Description:** Publishes articles dealing with the archaeology, prehistory, and ethnohistory of Mesoamerica, Central America, South America, and culturally related areas. Promotes communication between English- and Spanish-speaking archaeologists working in Latin America.
Related titles: Online - full text ed.: (from Gale Group, JSTOR (Web-based Journal Archive)).
Indexed: AICP, AbAn, AcaI, AnthLit, ArtHuCI, BRI, BibInd, CBRI, CurCont, HAPI.
—BLDSC (5157.799000), IDS, IE, Infotrieve, ingenta. **CCC.**
Published by: Society for American Archaeology, 900 Second St, N W, 12, Washington, DC 20002-3557. TEL 202-789-8200, FAX 202-789-0284, publications@saa.org, http://www.saa.org/Publications/LatAmAnt/latamant.html. Ed. Katharina Schreiber. Circ: 1,500.

930.1 FRA ISSN 0996-6900
LATTARA. Text in French. 1988. irreg. **Document type:** *Monographic series, Academic/Scholarly.*
Published by: Association pour la Recherche Archeologique en Languedoc Oriental, Caiverac, 30280, France.

913 PRT ISSN 0870-0044
CC13.P67
LEBA; estudos de quaternario, pre-historia e arqueologia. Text in Portuguese. 1978. irreg., latest vol.7. price varies. bk.rev. back issues avail. **Document type:** *Academic/Scholarly.* **Description:** Covers pre-historical studies and archeology.
Indexed: AICP, ASD, AnthLit.
—BLDSC (5179.569000).
Published by: (Centro de Pre-Historia e Arqueologia), Instituto de Investigacao Cientifica Tropical, Rua da Junqueira, 30, Lisbon, 1349-007, Portugal. TEL 351-21-3622621, FAX 351-21-3631460, iict@iict.pt. Circ: 1,000. **Subscr. to:** Centro de Documentacao e Informacao, Rua de Jau, 47, Lisbon 1300, Portugal. TEL 351-21-3644846, FAX 351-21-3628218.

LECTIONES ORIENTALES. see *ASIAN STUDIES*

930.1 GBR
LEICESTER ARCHAEOLOGY MONOGRAPH. Text in English. irreg., latest vol.3, 1995. **Document type:** *Monographic series, Academic/Scholarly.*
Indexed: BrArAb.
—BLDSC (5181.863000).
Published by: University of Leicester, School of Archaeological Studies, Leicester, LE1 7RH, United Kingdom. TEL 44-116-252-2611, FAX 44-116-252-5005, adm3@leicester.ac.uk. Eds. Jane Webster, Nicholas Cooper.

913 940 GBR ISSN 0140-3990
➤ **LEICESTERSHIRE ARCHAEOLOGICAL AND HISTORICAL SOCIETY. TRANSACTIONS.** Text in English. 1866. a. GBP 15 (effective 1999). adv. bk.rev. **Document type:** *Academic/Scholarly.* **Description:** Archaeological and historical articles covering local material and annual notes of work carried out in the field.
Indexed: BHA, BrArAb, NumL.
—BLDSC (8978.350000), IE, ingenta.
Published by: Leicestershire Archaeological and Historical Society, The Guildhall, Guildhall Ln, Leicester, LE1 5FQ, United Kingdom. Circ: 600.

913 956.9 GBR ISSN 0075-8914
DS56
➤ **LEVANT.** Text in English. 1969. a. GBP 35, USD 65 (effective 2001). bk.rev. back issues avail. **Document type:** *Academic/Scholarly.*
Indexed: AICP, AbAn, AnthLit, BHA, DIP, IBR, IBZ, IndIslam, MEA&I, NTA, OTA, R&TA, RASB, RI-1, RI-2.
—BLDSC (5185.460000).
Published by: The Council for British Research in the Levant, CBRL, St. Peter's College, Oxford, OX1 2DL, United Kingdom. TEL 44-1865-431904, cm@cbrluk.demon.co.uk. Ed., R&P Kay Prag. Circ: 800.

930.1 GBR ISSN 0263-7189
DT221
➤ **LIBYAN STUDIES.** Text in English. 1969. a., latest vol.32. GBP 20 (effective 2002). bk.rev. back issues avail. **Document type:** *Academic/Scholarly.*
Indexed: AICP, ASD, BibLing, DIP, IBR, IBSS, IBZ.
—BLDSC (5207.547400), IE, ingenta.
Published by: Society for Libyan Studies, c/o Institute of Archaeology, 31-34 Gordon Sq, London, WC1H 0PY, United Kingdom. http://www.britac.ac.uk/institutes/libya/. Ed. A I Wilson. R&P Shirley Strong. Circ: 350.

➤ **LINCOLNSHIRE HISTORY AND ARCHAEOLOGY.** see *HISTORY—History Of Europe*

➤ **LINCOLNSHIRE PAST AND PRESENT.** see *HISTORY—History Of Europe*

306 USA ISSN 0197-7261
➤ **LITHIC TECHNOLOGY.** Text in English. 1972. 2/yr. USD 25 in US & Canada to individuals; USD 30 elsewhere to individuals; USD 50 in US & Canada to institutions; USD 60 elsewhere to institutions (effective 2005). bk.rev.; film rev. bibl.; charts; illus.; abstr. cum.index. 2 cols./p.; back issues avail. **Document type:** *Journal, Academic/Scholarly.* **Description:** Concerned with dessemination and knowledge about archaeological stone tools.
Formerly (until 1977): Newsletter of Lithic Technology
Indexed: AICP, AnthLit, BrArAb, NumL.
Published by: University of Tulsa, Department of Anthropology, 600 S College, Tulsa, OK 74104-3189. TEL 918-631-3082, FAX 918-631-2540, george-odell@utulsa.edu, http://www.cas.utulsa.edu/anthropology/lithictechnology/. Ed., R&P George Odell. Circ: 400.

930.1 GBR
LIVERPOOL MONOGRAPHS IN ARCHAEOLOGY AND ORIENTAL STUDIES. Text in English. irreg. back issues avail. **Document type:** *Monographic series, Academic/Scholarly.*
Published by: Liverpool University Press, 4 Cambridge St, Liverpool, L69 7ZU, United Kingdom. TEL 44-151-794-2233, FAX 44-151-794-2235, http://www.liverpool-unipress.co.uk/. Pub. Robin Bloxsidge. Adv. contact Sandra Robinson.

913 ALB
LLIRIA. Text in Albanian; Summaries in French. 1971. s-a. USD 7.50; USD 25 foreign. bk.rev. **Document type:** *Academic/Scholarly.* **Description:** Publishes the results of research, scientific activity and excavations in Albania.
Published by: Akademia e Shkencave e RPSSH, Instituti Arkeologjik/Academy of Sciences, Institute of Archaeology, Tirana, Albania. TEL 42-26501. Ed. M Korkuti. Circ: 700.

913 GBR
LONDON AND MIDDLESEX ARCHAEOLOGICAL SOCIETY & SURREY ARCHAEOLOGICAL SOCIETY. JOINT PUBLICATION. Text in English. 1978. irreg. GBP 25 domestic membership; GBP 35 foreign membership (effective 1999). back issues avail. **Document type:** *Academic/Scholarly.*
Published by: Surrey Archaeological Society, Castle Arch, Guildford, Surrey GU1 3SX, United Kingdom. TEL 44-1483-532454, FAX 44-1483-532454, surreyarch@compuserve.com, http://ourworld.compuserve.com/homepages/surreyarch, http://www.surreyarchaeology.org.uk/. Ed. Glenys Crocker.
Co-sponsor: London and Middlesex Archaeological Society.

571 913 GBR ISSN 0076-0501
DA675
LONDON AND MIDDLESEX ARCHAEOLOGICAL SOCIETY. TRANSACTIONS. Text in English. 1855. a. GBP 15 to individual members; GBP 19.50 to institutional members. **Document type:** *Academic/Scholarly.*
Indexed: AIAP, BHA, BrArAb, NumL, RASB.
Published by: London and Middlesex Archaeological Society, Museum Of London, London Wall, London, EC2Y 5HN, United Kingdom. Ed. John Shepherd. Circ: 900.

913 GBR ISSN 0024-5984
DA677.1
LONDON ARCHAEOLOGIST. Text in English. 1968. q. GBP 10, USD 25 (effective 2003). adv. bk.rev. charts; illus. index. 28 p./no. 2 cols./p.; back issues avail. **Document type:** *Academic/Scholarly.* **Description:** Covers recent excavations, archaeological research, synthesis reports, and related historical articles.
Indexed: A&ATA, AIAP, AbAn, BHA, BrArAb, DIP, IBR, IBZ, NumL.
—BLDSC (5292.950000), IE, Infotrieve, ingenta.
Published by: London Archaeologist Association, c/o Institute of Archaeology, 31 Gordon Sq, London, WC1H 0PY, United Kingdom. TEL 44-20-76794749, FAX 44-20-73832572, c.orton@ucl.ac.uk, http://www.londonarchaeologist.org.uk. Ed., R&P Clive Orton. Adv. contact Roy Stephenson. Circ: 1,500 (paid). **Subscr. to:** Shiela Broomfield, 8 Woodview Cresc., Hildenborough, Tonbridge, Kent TN11 9HD, United Kingdom. s.broomfield@dial.pipex.com.

913 USA
LOUISIANA ARCHAEOLOGY✶. Text in English. 1974. a. membership. bk.rev. bibl.; illus. **Document type:** *Academic/Scholarly.*
Indexed: AnthLit, HistAb.
Published by: Louisiana Archaeological Society, c/o David Jeane, 305 Hickory St, Springhill, LA 71075. TEL 318-539-5944. Circ: 300.

930.1 ESP ISSN 0213-2338
DP44
LUCENTUM. Text in Spanish. 1982. a.
—CINDOC. **CCC.**
Published by: (Universidad de Alicante, Departamento de Prehistoria, Arqueologia e Historia Antigua), Universidad de Alicante, Carr. San Vicente del Raspeig s-n, Alicante, 03690, Spain. TEL 34-96-5903400, FAX 34-96-5903464, http://www.ua.es/.

913 SWE ISSN 0458-4767
LUND UNIVERSITET. HISTORISKA MUSEUM. MEDDELANDEN. Text in Swedish. 1930. biennial. back issues avail. **Document type:** *Academic/Scholarly.*
Formerly (until 1975): Lund Universitet. Historiska Museet Samt Mynt-och Medaljkabinettet. Meddelanden
Indexed: AICP, AnthLit, BrArAb.
Published by: (Historiska Museet), Almqvist & Wiksell International, P O Box 7634, Stockholm, 10394, Sweden. FAX 46-8-24-25-43, info@city.akademibokhandeln.se, http://www.akademibokhandeln.se.

938 TUR ISSN 1300-6444
LYKIA. Text in English, German, Turkish. 1994. irreg. back issues avail. **Document type:** *Monographic series, Academic/Scholarly.*
Published by: Akdeniz Universitesi, Fen-Edebiyat Fakultesi Arkeoloji Bolumu, Kampus Antalya, 07058, Turkey. havva@sci.pascal.akdeniz.edu.tr.

913 USA ISSN 1062-1504
M A S NEWSLETTER. Text in English. 1987. irreg. USD 15 to members. **Document type:** *Newsletter.*
Published by: Maine Archaeological Society, Inc., PO Box 982, Augusta, ME 04332-0982. Ed. John Mother.

MACEDONIAN STUDIES. see *HISTORY—History Of Europe*

913 PRT ISSN 0871-066X
DP528
AL MADAN. Text in Portuguese. 1982. a., latest vol.7, 1998. adv. bk.rev. **Document type:** *Academic/Scholarly.* **Description:** Al-Madan is a portuguese magazine in the field of archaeology, heritage and local history. Each number presents studies, interviews, book reviews, and scientific articles, together with a special folder addressing a theme of general interest.
Published by: Centro de Arqueologia de Almada, APDO, 103 (Torcatas, Almada Codex, 2801, Portugal. TEL 351-2766975, FAX 351-2766975, c.arqueo.alm@mail.telepac.pt. Ed. Jorge Raposo. R&P, Adv. contact Elisabete Goncalves TEL 351-1-2766975. Circ: 2,500.

903 DEU ISSN 0418-9736
GN835.A1
➤ **MADRIDER FORSCHUNGEN.** Text in German. 1956. irreg., latest vol.19, 1997. price varies. **Document type:** *Monographic series, Academic/Scholarly.*
Published by: (Deutsches Archaeologisches Institut, Abteilung Madrid ESP), Walter de Gruyter GmbH & Co. KG, Genthiner Str. 13, Berlin, 10785, Germany. TEL 49-30-260050, FAX 49-30-26005251, wdg-info@degruyter.de, http://www.degruyter.de.

913 DEU ISSN 0418-9744
DP44
MADRIDER MITTEILUNGEN. Text in German. 1960. a., latest vol.41, 2001. price varies. bibl.; charts; illus.; maps. back issues avail. **Document type:** *Journal, Academic/Scholarly.*

Indexed: AIAP, BHA, DIP, HistAb, IBR, IBZ, NumL, RASB.
Published by: (Deutsches Archaeologisches Institut, Abteilung Madrid), Verlag Philipp von Zabern GmbH, Philipp-von-Zabern-Platz 1-3, Mainz, 55116, Germany. TEL 49-6131-287470, FAX 49-6131-223710, zabern@zabern.de, http://www.zabern.de. Adv. contact Manuela Dressen TEL 49-6131-2874711.

913 ITA ISSN 0024-9955
MAGNA GRAECIA; rassegna di archeologia storia arte attualita. Text in Italian. 1966. bi-m. adv. bk.rev. charts; illus.; stat.; tr.lit.
Related titles: Microfilm ed.
Published by: Editoriale Magna Graecia, Viale della Repubblica, 293-C, Cosenza, CS 87100, Italy. TEL 0984-71858. Ed. Tanino De Santis. Circ: 2,000.

MAGUARE. see *ANTHROPOLOGY*

913 HUN ISSN 0076-2504
MAGYARORSZAG REGESZETI TOPOGRAFIAJA. Text in Hungarian. 1967. irreg., latest vol.10, 1998. price varies. back issues avail. **Document type:** *Monographic series, Academic/Scholarly.*
Published by: Akademiai Kiado Rt. (Subsidiary of: Wolters Kluwer N.V.), Prielle Kornelia U. 19, Budapest, 1117, Hungary. TEL 36-1-4648282, FAX 36-1-4648221, journals@akkrt.hu, http://www.akkrt.hu.

571 IND ISSN 0076-2520
MAHARAJA SAYAJIRAO UNIVERSITY OF BARODA. DEPARTMENT OF ARCHAEOLOGY AND ANCIENT HISTORY. ARCHAEOLOGY SERIES. Text in English. 1953. irreg. (approx. 1/yr.). price varies. **Document type:** *Academic/Scholarly.*
Published by: Maharaja Sayajirao University of Baroda, Department of Archaeology and Ancient History, Baroda, Gujarat 390 002, India. Ed. K T M Hegde. Circ: 500.

MAIHAUGEN. see *HISTORY—History Of Europe*

930.1 ESP ISSN 0212-078X
MAINAKE. Text in Spanish. 1979. a. EUR 13.22 (effective 2004). maps; illus. 250 p./no.; **Document type:** *Journal, Academic/Scholarly.*
—CINDOC.
Published by: Diputacion Provincial de Malaga, Plaza de la marina, s-n, Malaga, 29015, Spain. TEL 34-952-133500, http://www.dipumalaga.org/.

913 USA ISSN 0542-1292
F21
MAINE ARCHEOLOGICAL SOCIETY BULLETIN. Text in English. 1960. s-a. USD 20 (effective 1999). bk.rev. illus.; maps. **Document type:** *Academic/Scholarly.*
Indexed: AbAn, AnthLit.
Published by: Maine Archaeological Society, Inc., PO Box 982, Augusta, ME 04332-0982. Ed. David Cook. Circ: 350.

MAINZER ZEITSCHRIFT; Mittelrheinisches Jahrbuch fuer Archaeologie, Geschichte und Kunst. see *ART*

935 IRN ISSN 1015-2830
DS261
MAJALLAH-I BASTANSHINASI O TARIKH/IRANIAN JOURNAL OF ARCHAEOLOGY AND HISTORY. Text in Persian, Modern. 1986. s-a. IRR 8,000 per issue domestic; GBP 18 per issue in the Middle East; GBP 20 per issue in Europe; GBP 23 per issue elsewhere (effective 2001). illus.; maps. **Document type:** *Journal, Academic/Scholarly.* **Description:** Publishes articles related to history and archaeology in general, and archaeological and historical topics directly related to Iran in particular.
Published by: Markaz-i Nashr-i Danishgahi/Iran University Press, 85 Park Ave., P O Box 15875-4748, Tehran, Iran. TEL 98-21-8713232, FAX 98-21-8721816, ird@iup-ir.com. Ed. Ahmad H Mudjani. Circ: 2,500.

MAKEDONIKA. see *HISTORY—History Of Europe*

930.1 948.5 SWE ISSN 0349-697X
MALMOEYA. Text in Swedish. 1970. irreg. price varies.
Published by: Malmoe Museer, Stadsantikvariska Avdelingen, Fack 406, Malmo, 20124, Sweden. TEL 46-40-34-44-34, FAX 46-40-34-42-45. Ed. Chatarina Ibman.

930.1 560 USA ISSN 8755-6898
E61
MAMMOTH TRUMPET. Text in English. 1984. q. USD 20 (effective 2003). adv. back issues avail. **Document type:** *Newspaper.* **Description:** News of discoveries and theories relevant to the earliest peopling of the Americas.
Indexed: AnthLit.
Published by: Center for the Study of the First Americans, Texas A & M University, Dept of Anthropology, College Station, TX 77843-4352. TEL 979-845-4046, FAX 979-845-4070, csfa@tamu.edu, rbonnichsen@tamu.edu, http://www.centerfirstamericans.com. Ed. Jim Chandler. Pub. Robson Bonnichsen. adv.: page USD 250; 7.25 x 9.25. Circ: 1,300.

MAN & ENVIRONMENT. see *ANTHROPOLOGY*

913 CAN ISSN 1188-5424
F1062.9
MANITOBA ARCHAEOLOGICAL JOURNAL. Text in English. 1964. 2/yr. CND 20 to individuals; CND 30 to institutions; CND 12 to students (effective 1999). bk.rev. bibl.; charts; illus. **Document type:** *Academic/Scholarly.* **Description:** Contains research articles on archaeology in Manitoba and adjacent areas.
Formerly (until 1991): Manitoba Archaeological Quarterly
Related titles: Supplement(s): Manitoba Archaeological Newsletter. ISSN 0844-5958. 1989.
Indexed: AbAn, AmH&L, AnthLit, HistAb.
—BLDSC (5360.348000).
Published by: Manitoba Archaeological Society, Inc., P O Box 1171, Winnipeg, MB R3C 2Y4, Canada. TEL 204-942-7243, FAX 204-942-3749. Ed. Sharon Thomson. R&P Leo Pettipas. Circ: 200.

930.1 ITA ISSN 1125-3878
DJK66
IL MAR NERO; journal of archaeology and history. Text in Italian. 1994. a. EUR 34 (effective 2000). **Document type:** *Journal, Academic/Scholarly.* **Description:** Reflects the current state of historical research in the countries bordering on the Black Sea. Accommodates studies and research ranging from prehistory to the Ottoman era.
Indexed: AnthLit.
Published by: Edizioni Quasar, Via Ajaccio 43, Rome, RM 00198, Italy. TEL 39-6-84241993, FAX 39-6-85833591, qn@edizioniquasar.it, http://www.edizioniquasar.it. Eds. Petre Alexandrescu, Serban Papacostea. **Co-publisher:** Editions de la Maison des Sciences de l'Homme.

930.1 945 ITA
LE MARCHE ARCHEOLOGIA, STORIA, TERRITORIO. Text in Italian. 1987. s-a.
Published by: Istituto Regionale per la Pre-Protostoria nelle Marche Arcevia - Sassoferrato, Vicolo Lazzarini, 2, Sassoferrato, AN 60041, Italy. TEL 0732-9465. Ed. Perseo Trojani.

930.1 ZAF
MARGARET SHAW LECTURES. Text in English. 1984. biennial. price varies. **Document type:** *Monographic series, Academic/Scholarly.* **Description:** Publishes lectures delivered by invited speakers. Honors Margaret Shaw and her contribution to ethnography of southern Africa.
Published by: South African Museum, PO Box 61, Cape Town, 8000, South Africa. TEL 27-21-4243330, FAX 27-21-4246716, elouw@samuseum.ac.za. R&P E Louw. Circ: 450 (controlled).

MARGARETOLOGIST. see *JEWELRY, CLOCKS AND WATCHES*

913 440 FRA
MARI ANNALES DE RECHERCHES INTERDISCIPLINAIRES. Text in French. 1982. irreg. price varies. **Document type:** *Bulletin.*
Indexed: AnthLit.
Published by: Editions Recherche sur les Civilisations - A D P F, Les Patios Saint-Jacques, 6 rue Ferrus, Paris, Cedex 14 75603, France. TEL 33-1-43131100, FAX 33-1-43131125. Ed., Pub., R&P Hina Descat. Circ: 600.

930.102804 SWE ISSN 1100-9632
MARINARKEOLOGISK TIDSKRIFT; meddelanden fraan Marinarkeologiska Saellskapet. Text in Swedish. 1978. q. SEK 300 to members; SEK 500 to institutions (effective 2003). back issues avail. **Document type:** *Journal, Academic/Scholarly.*
Formerly (until 1989): Meddelanden fraan Marinarkeologiska Saellskapet (0348-6621)
Indexed: NAA.
Published by: Marinarkeologiska Saellskapet, c/o Thomas Bergstrand, Foermansgatan 2 D, Goeteborg, 41757, Sweden. andreas.olsson@gu.se, http://www.marinarkeologi.net. Eds. Anders Bause, Staffan von Arbin. Pub. Andreas Olsson.

930.1 USA ISSN 0148-6012
MARYLAND ARCHEOLOGY. Text in English. 1968. s-a. Membership (effective 2003). back issues avail. **Document type:** *Academic/Scholarly.* **Description:** Reports the latest findings in Maryland archeology.
Indexed: AnthLit.
Published by: Archeological Society of Maryland, Inc., PO Box 65001, Baltimore, MD 21209-5001. TEL 410-664-9060, 410-747-1973, ngeasey@netcrafters.net, http://www.smcm.edu/academics/soan/asm/home.htm. Ed. Dennis C Curry. **Subscr. to:** 716 Country Club Road, Havre de Grace, MD 21078-2104.

930.14372 CZE ISSN 1211-6327
DB2030
MASARYKOVA UNIVERZITA. FILOZOFICKA FAKULTA. SBORNIK PRACI. M: RADA ARCHEOLOGICKA. Text in Multiple languages. 1996. a. price varies. bk.rev. **Document type:** *Academic/Scholarly.* **Description:** Presents studies in archaeology, especially in the Slavonic prehistory of southern Moravia.
Supersedes in part (in 1996): Masarykova Univerzita. Filozoficka Fakulta. Sbornik Praci. E: Rada Archeologicko - Klasicka; Which was formerly: Univerzita J.E. Purkyne. Filozoficka Fakulta. Sbornik Praci. E: Rada Archeologicko - Klasicka (0231-7915)
Published by: Masarykova Univerzita, Filozoficka Fakulta, A Novaka 1, Brno, 66088, Czech Republic. TEL 420-5-41121102, FAX 420-5-41121406, exchange@phil.muni.cz. Ed. Milos Stedron TEL 420-5-41121337.

913 USA ISSN 0148-1886
F66
MASSACHUSETTS ARCHAEOLOGICAL SOCIETY. BULLETIN. Text in English. 1939. s-a. USD 25 domestic to individual members (effective 2005); USD 30 domestic to institutions; USD 35 foreign to institutions (effective 2001). bk.rev. index, cum.index: vols.1-38, vols.39-48 (1978-1987). **Document type:** *Bulletin, Academic/Scholarly.*
Indexed: AbAn, AnthLit.
Published by: Massachusetts Archaeological Society, Inc., Robbins Museum of Archaeology, PO Box 700, Middleborough, MA 02346-0700. TEL 508-947-9005, info@massarchaeology.org, http://www.massarchaeology.org. Ed. Shirley Blancke. R&P Elizabeth Little. Circ: 800.

970.1 USA
MASSACHUSETTS ARCHAEOLOGICAL SOCIETY. NEWSLETTER. Text in English. N.S. 1974. 3/yr. USD 18 domestic membership; USD 20 foreign membership; USD 30 domestic to institutions; USD 35 foreign to institutions (effective 2001). adv. **Document type:** *Newsletter.* **Description:** News, announcements and items of interest to members of the society.
Published by: Massachusetts Archaeological Society, Inc., Robbins Museum of Archaeology, PO Box 700, Middleborough, MA 02346-0700. TEL 508-947-9005. Ed. Thomas E Lux. adv.: page USD 90; 9.25 x 7.25. Circ: 800.

913 ROM ISSN 1220-5222
DR211
MATERIALE SI CERCETARI ARHEOLOGICE. Text in Romanian; Summaries in French, Romanian. 1955-19??; resumed 1992. a.
Indexed: AICP, BHA, NumL.
Published by: (Academia Romana, Comisia Nationala de Arheologie), Editura Academiei Romane/Publishing House of the Romanian Academy, Calea 13 Septembrie 13, Sector 5, Bucharest, 76117, Romania. Ed. Nicolae Conovici. **Dist. by:** Rodipet S.A., Piata Presei Libere 1, sector 1, PO Box 33-57, Bucharest 3, Romania. TEL 40-21-2224126, 40-21-2226407, rodipet@rodipet.ro.

918 PER
MATERIALES PARA LA ARQUEOLOGIA DEL PERU*. Text in Spanish. 1981. irreg.
Published by: Instituto Nacional de Cultura, Proyecto Especial de Irrigacion Jequetepeque-Zana, Casilla 5247, Ancash 390, Lima, Peru.

930.1 DEU ISSN 1430-3442
MATERIALHEFTE ZUR ARCHAEOLOGIE IN BADEN-WUERTTEMBERG. Text in German. 1982. irreg., latest vol.63, 2002. price varies. **Document type:** *Monographic series, Academic/Scholarly.*
Formerly (until 1993): Materialhefte zur Vor- und Fruehgeschichte in Baden-Wuerttemberg (0938-6769)
Published by: (Baden-Wuerttemberg. Landesdenkmalamt Baden-Wuerttemberg), Konrad Theiss Verlag GmbH, Moenchhaldenstr 28, Stuttgart, 70191, Germany. TEL 49-711-255270, FAX 49-711-2552717, service@theiss.de, http://www.theiss.de.

930.1 DEU
MATERIALHEFTE ZUR BAYERISCHEN VORGESCHICHTE. Text in German. 1953. irreg., latest vol.84, 2003. price varies. **Document type:** *Monographic series, Academic/Scholarly.*
Indexed: RASB.
Published by: (Bayerisches Landesamt fuer Denkmalpflege, Abteilung Bodendenkmalpflege), Verlag Michael Lassleben, Lange Gasse 19, Kallmuenz, 93183, Germany. TEL 49-9473-205, FAX 49-9473-8357, druckerei@oberpfalzverlag-lassleben.de, http://www.oberpfalzverlag-lassleben.de.

MATERIALHEFTE ZUR UR- UND FRUEHGESCHICHTE NIEDERSACHSENS. see *HISTORY—History Of Europe*

MATERIALI E DOCUMENTI TICINESI. see *HISTORY—History Of Europe*

MATERIALIEN ZUR ROEMISCH-GERMANISCHEN KERAMIK. see *CERAMICS, GLASS AND POTTERY*

MATERIALS ISSUES IN ART AND ARCHAEOLOGY. see *ART*

930.1 NLD ISSN 0926-4639
MCGILL UNIVERSITY MONOGRAPHS IN CLASSICAL ARCHAEOLOGY AND HISTORY. Key Title: Monographies en Archeologie et Histoire Classiques de l'Universite McGill. Text in Dutch. 1981. irreg., latest vol.16, 1995. price varies. back issues avail. **Document type:** *Monographic series, Academic/Scholarly.*

Related titles: Series of: Boeotia Antiqua.
—BLDSC (5413.445000).
Published by: (McGill University), J.C. Gieben, Entrepotdok 72b, Amsterdam, 1018 AD, Netherlands. TEL 31-20-6234709, FAX 31-20-6275170, http://www.teachtext.net/gieben/. Ed. J M Fossey. **Dist. in N. America by:** John Benjamins Publishing Co., PO Box 27519, Philadelphia, PA 19118-0519. TEL 215-836-1200.

930.1 069 956 SWE ISSN 0585-3214
DE1
MEDELHAVSMUSEET. BULLETIN. Text in English, French, German. 1961. a. price varies. **Document type:** *Bulletin.*
Indexed: BHA, RASB.
Published by: Medelhavsmuseet/Museum of Mediterranean and Near Eastern Antiquities, PO Box 16008, Stockholm, SE-10321, Sweden. TEL 46-8-51-95-53-80, FAX 46-8-51-95-53-70, info@medelhavsmuseet.smvk.se. Ed. Karen Slej. Circ: 800. **Dist. by:** Almqvist & Wiksell International.

913 GBR ISSN 0076-6097
D111
➤ **MEDIEVAL ARCHAEOLOGY.** Text in English. 1957. a. USD 128 per issue in North America to institutions; GBP 69 per issue elsewhere to institutions (effective 2005). adv. bk.rev. illus. reprints avail. **Document type:** *Journal, Academic/Scholarly.*
Related titles: Online - full text ed.: 2005 (from EBSCO Publishing, Gale Group, IngentaConnect, Swets Information Services).
Indexed: A&ATA, AIAP, AbAn, BEL&L, BHA, BrArAb, DIP, HumInd, IBR, IBZ, NumL, PCI, RASB, RILM.
—BLDSC (5534.265000), IE, Infotrieve, ingenta. **CCC.**
Published by: (Society for Medieval Archaeology), Maney Publishing, Hudson Rd, Leeds, W Yorks LS9 7DL, United Kingdom. TEL 44-113-2497481, FAX 44-113-2486983, maney@maney.co.uk, http://www.maney.co.uk/search?fwaction=show&fwid=382. Ed. John Hines. adv.: B&W page GBP 180; 135 x 190. Circ: 1,500. **Subscr. in N America to:** Maney Publishing North America, 875 Massachusetts Ave, 7th Fl., Cambridge, MA 02139. TEL 866-297-5154, FAX 617-354-6875, maney@maneyusa.com.

930.1 AUS ISSN 1030-8482
➤ **MEDITERRANEAN ARCHAEOLOGY.** Text in English, French, German, Italian. 1988. a. AUD 75 (effective 2005). back issues avail. **Document type:** *Journal, Academic/Scholarly.*
Related titles: Supplement(s): Mediterranean Archaeology. Supplement. ISSN 1328-5092. 1990.
Published by: Meditarch, University of Sydney, Holme Bldg., Box 243, Sydney, NSW 2006, Australia. meditarch@archaeology.usyd.edu.au, http://www.arts.usyd.edu.au/publications/meditarch/. Ed. Derek Harrison.

930.1 936 SWE ISSN 0349-456X
MEDUSA. Text in Swedish. 1980. q. SEK 195 domestic to individuals; SEK 250 foreign to individuals; SEK 225 domestic to institutions; SEK 300 foreign to institutions (effective 2004). adv. bk.rev. illus. cum.inex: 1980-1984, 1985-1990, 1991-1994, 1995-1999. back issues avail. **Document type:** *Journal.* **Description:** Contains articles of a popular nature on archaeology and ancient history.
Published by: Foereningen Foer en Svensk Antiktidskrift, Roedabergsbrinken 14, Stockholm, 11330, Sweden. info@tidskriftenmedusa.se, http://www.tidskriftenmedusa.se/index1.htm. Ed. Gunnel Ekroth. adv.: B&W page SEK 2,000. Circ: 1,600.

930.1 GBR
MEGALITHIC MAGAZINE. Text in English. 2001. q. GBP 20 domestic to individuals; GBP 25 foreign to individuals; GBP 32 domestic to institutions; GBP 40 foreign to institutions (effective 2000). bk.rev. **Document type:** *Academic/Scholarly.* **Description:** Aimed at those interested in the archaeology of the monuments of the megalithic age on all continents and in all time periods.
Published by: (Megalithic Society), Artetech Publishing Co., 54 Frome Rd, Bradford-on-Avon, Wilts BA15 ILD, United Kingdom. TEL 44-1225-862482, FAX 44-1225-865601, terrence.meaden@stonehenge-avebury.net, http://www.stonehenge-avebury.net. Ed. G T Meaden. R&P G.T. Meaden.

LES MELANGES DE LA CASA DE VELAZQUEZ/CASA DE VELASQUEZ, MADRID. MISCELLANIES. see *ART*

935 IRN ISSN 1148-6198
MEMOIRES DE LA DELEGATION ARCHEOLOGIQUE FRANCAISE EN IRAN. Text in Persian, Modern. 1900. irreg. price varies. **Document type:** *Academic/Scholarly.*
Supersedes: Delegation Archeologique Francaise en Iran. Memoires (0169-880X)
Published by: Institut Francais de Recherche en Iran, Ave. Shahid Nizari, 52 Adib St., P O Box 15815-3495, Tehran, Iran. TEL 98-21-6401192, FAX 98-21-6405501. Ed. Remy Boucharlat.

913 GRC ISSN 1105-7181
O MENTOR. Text in Greek. 1988. q. illus. back issues avail. **Document type:** *Academic/Scholarly.* **Description:** Contains Archaeological Society news and short articles on subjects of archaeological or antiquarian interest, along with notes on the current state and condition of Greek antiquities.
Formerly (until 1991): Archaiologike Hetaireia en Athenais. Enemerotiko Deltio (1105-1205)
Published by: Archaeological Society at Athens/Archaiologike Hetaireia en Athenais, 22 Panepistimiou St, Athens, 106 72, Greece. TEL 30-1-364-6043, FAX 30-1-364-4996.

930 GBR ISSN 0140-4032
DA670.M54
MERSEYSIDE ARCHAEOLOGICAL SOCIETY. JOURNAL. Text in English. 1977. a. **Document type:** *Journal, Academic/Scholarly.*
—BLDSC (4824.600000).
Published by: University of Liverpool, School of Archaeology Classics and Oriental Studies, Hartley Bldg, Brownlow St, Liverpool, L69 3GS, United Kingdom. TEL 44-151-7945044, FAX 44-151-7945057, http://www.liv.ac.uk.

913 ITA ISSN 0076-6615
MESOPOTAMIA; rivista di archeologia, epigrafia e storia orientale antica. Text in English, Italian. 1966. a., latest vol.33, 1998. EUR 258 domestic; EUR 300 foreign (effective 2004). **Document type:** *Journal, Academic/Scholarly.*
Indexed: AnthLit, BibLing, DIP, IBR, IBSS, IBZ, NumL.
Published by: (Universita degli Studi di Torino, Centro Ricerche Archeologiche e Scavi di Torino), Casa Editrice le Lettere, Costa San Giorgio 28, Florence, FI 50125, Italy. TEL 39-055-2342710, FAX 39-055-2346010, staff@lelettere.it, www.lelettere.it. Ed. Antonio Invernizzi. Circ: 1,000.

930.1 SWE ISSN 0348-7903
META; medeltidsarkeologisk tidskrift. Text in Swedish. 1979. q. SEK 100 to members (effective 1993).
Published by: Medeltidsarkeologiska Foereningen (Meta), Lunds Universitets Historiska Museum, Kraftstorg 1, Lund, 22350, Sweden.

MEXICON; aktuelle Informationen und Studien zu Mesoamerika. see *ANTHROPOLOGY*

977.4 930 USA ISSN 0543-9728
CODEN: MACGAQ
➤ **MICHIGAN ARCHAEOLOGIST.** Text in English. 1957. q. USD 25 to individuals; USD 30 to institutions. bk.rev. back issues avail. **Document type:** *Academic/Scholarly.*
Indexed: AbAn, AmH&L, AnthLit.
Published by: Michigan Archaeological Society, PO Box 359, Saginaw, MI 48606. barbaram@sosmail.mi.us. Ed., R&P Janet Brashler. Circ: 450.

930.1 ISR ISSN 0334-7311
DS111.A1
➤ **MICHMANIM.** Text and summaries in English, Hebrew. 1985. a., latest vol.17, 2003. looseleaf. USD 8 per vol. (effective 2004). reprints avail. **Document type:** *Bulletin, Academic/Scholarly.* **Description:** Publishes articles concerning artifacts in the museum's collections, conferences and archaeological activities in the north of Israel.
Indexed: IHP.
Published by: Reuben and Edith Hecht Museum, Haifa University, Mt. Carmel, Haifa, 31905, Israel. TEL 972-4-8257773, FAX 972-4-8240724, mushecht@research.haifa.ac.il, http://research.haifa.ac.il/~hecht/Michmanim/micgeneral.html, http://www.research.haifa.ac.il. Ed. Benjamin Sass. R&P Ofra Rimon TEL 972-4-8240171. Circ: 300.

973.92605 USA ISSN 0146-1109
E77.8
➤ **MIDCONTINENTAL JOURNAL OF ARCHAEOLOGY.** Cover title: M C J A. Text in English. 1976. s-a. USD 35 to individuals; USD 80 to institutions (effective 2005). adv. bk.rev. charts; illus. Index. back issues avail.; reprint service avail. from PQC. **Document type:** *Journal, Academic/Scholarly.*
Related titles: Online - full text ed.: (from bigchalk, Florida Center for Library Automation, Gale Group, ProQuest Information & Learning).
Indexed: AICP, AbAn, AmH&L, AnthLit, BibInd, BrArAb, HistAb, IBR.
—BLDSC (5761.314900).
Published by: (Midwest Archeological Conference, Inc.), AltaMira Press, 1630 N Main St, Ste 367, Walnut Creek, CA 94596. TEL 925-938-7243, FAX 925-933-9720, mcja@ssc.msu.edu, explore@altamirapress.com, http://www.altamirapress.com/RLA/Journals/MCJA/. Ed. William A Lovis. Circ: 600.

917 CAN ISSN 0047-7222
THE MIDDEN. Text in English. 1969. 5/yr. CND 14.50; CND 17 foreign (effective 1999). bk.rev. index. **Document type:** *Academic/Scholarly.* **Description:** Dedicated to the archeology of British Columbia.
Formerly: Archaeological Society of British Columbia. Newsletter
Indexed: AbAn.
Published by: Archaeological Society of British Columbia, P O Box 520, Sta A, Vancouver, BC V6C 2N3, Canada. TEL 604-822-2567, http://home.istar.ca/~glenchan/asbc.shtml. Ed. Heather Myles. Circ: 350.

913 GBR ISSN 0957-7718
CC1
MINERVA (LONDON); the international review of ancient art & archaeology. Text in English. 1979. bi-m. GBP 21 domestic; GBP 23 in Europe; USD 50 elsewhere (effective 2005). adv. bk.rev. illus. cum.index. 64 p./no.; back issues avail.; reprints avail. **Document type:** *Magazine, Academic/Scholarly.* **Description:** Presents archaeology in the context of art history.
Incorporates: Archaeology Today (0952-1240); Which was formerly: Popular Archaeology (0143-0262)
Indexed: BAS, BHA, BrArAb, BrEdI, NumL, PCI.
—**CCC.**
Published by: Aurora Publications, 14 Old Bond St, London, W1X 3DB, United Kingdom. TEL 44-20-74952590, FAX 44-20-74911595, minerva@minervamagazine.com, http://minervamagazine.com/index.php. Ed., Pub. Jerome M Eisenberg. R&P Sean Kingsley. Adv. contact I Whitelegg TEL 44-20-7495-2590. B&W page GBP 670, color 1/2 page GBP 1,000; trim 184 x 268. Circ: 10,000.

913 ITA
MINIMA EPIGRAPHICA ET PAPYROLOGICA. Text in Italian. 1998. a. price varies. **Document type:** *Monographic series, Academic/Scholarly.*
Published by: L'Erma di Bretschneider, Via Cassiodoro, 19, PO Box 6192, Rome, RM 00193, Italy. TEL 39-06-6874127, FAX 39-06-6874129, edizioni@lerma.it, http://www.lerma.it. Ed. Felice Costabile.

917 USA ISSN 0026-5403
F608
MINNESOTA ARCHAEOLOGIST. Text in English. 1934. 2/yr. USD 20; USD 22 in Canada. bk.rev. illus. back issues avail. **Document type:** *Academic/Scholarly.*
Related titles: Microfilm ed.: (from BHP, PQC).
Indexed: AbAn, AnthLit, BHA.
Published by: Minnesota Archaeological Society, Fort Snelling History Center, St. Paul, MN 55111. TEL 612-726-1171. Ed. Ted Lofstrom. Circ: 400.

930.1 955 IRN
MIRAS-E FARHANGI. Text in Persian, Modern. 1990 (vol.11). m. IRR 800 per issue. **Description:** Serves as a platform for the publications of articles concerning archaeology, ethnology, traditional arts, architecture, museology and the restoration of artifacts.
Published by: Sazman-i Miras-i Farhangi-i Kishvar/Iranian Cultural Heritage Organization, Azadi Ave. Zanjan St., P O Box 13445 719, Tehran, 13345, Iran. TEL 98-21-6013527, FAX 98-21-6013498. Circ: 10,000.

930.1 USA ISSN 0738-775X
E78.M73
MISSISSIPPI ARCHAEOLOGY. Text in English. 1974. s-a. membership. **Description:** Presents information of a basically technical nature on field work, artifact analysis, and archaeological theory, and to serve as the journal of record for archaeological activity in Mississippi.
Indexed: AnthLit.
Published by: (Mississippi Department of Archives), Mississippi Department of Archives and History, P.O. Box 571, Jackson, MS 39205-0571. http://www.mdah.state.ms.us/misc/ma.html.

913 USA ISSN 0743-7641
F468
MISSOURI ARCHAEOLOGICAL SOCIETY. QUARTERLY. Text in English. 1984. q. membership. back issues avail. **Document type:** *Newsletter.*
Formerly (until 1983): Missouri Archaeological Society. Newsletter (0076-955X)
Indexed: AbAn, AnthLit.
Published by: Missouri Archaeological Society, 101 A Museum Support Center, Rock Quarry Rd at Hinkson Creek, Columbia, MO 65211. TEL 573-882-3544, FAX 573-882-9410, galenm@missouri.edu, http://www.missouri.edu/~moarch/. Ed. Michael J O'Brien. Circ: 1,000 (paid). **Subscr. to:** PO Box 958, Columbia, MO 65205.

913 USA ISSN 0076-9576
F468
MISSOURI ARCHAEOLOGIST. Text in English. 1935. a. USD 15 to members (effective 1999). charts; illus. back issues avail. **Document type:** *Monographic series.*
Indexed: AbAn, AmH&L, AnthLit.
Published by: Missouri Archaeological Society, 101 A Museum Support Center, Rock Quarry Rd at Hinkson Creek, Columbia, MO 65211. TEL 573-882-3544, FAX 573-882-9410, galenm@missouri.edu, http://www.missouri.edu/~moarch/. Ed. W Raymond Wood. Circ: 1,000.

930.1 ISR ISSN 0334-3839
MITEKUFAT HA-EVEN. Text in English; Summaries in Hebrew. 1985. a. ILS 30, USD 25. bk.rev. **Document type:** *Academic/Scholarly.*
Indexed: AnthLit, IHP.
Published by: Israel Prehistoric Society, P.O. Box 1502, Jerusalem, 910014, Israel. TEL 972-2-882434, FAX 972-2-825548. Eds. Erella Hovers, Uri Baruch. Circ: 400.

MITTEILUNGEN ZUR CHRISTLICHEN ARCHAEOLOGIE. see *ART*

A

932 709 DEU ISSN 1434-7091
N7852.5
MITTEILUNGEN ZUR SPAETANTIKEN ARCHAEOLOGIE UND BYZANTINISCHEN KUNSTGESCHICHTE. Text in German, English. 1998. a. EUR 32 (effective 2003). adv. **Document type:** *Monographic series, Academic/Scholarly.* **Description:** Contains articles and lectures on the art and culture of the Byzantine epoch and presents summaries and discussions of discoveries in the archaeology of Byzantine and Egyptian art and antiquities.
Published by: (Verein Spaetantike Archaeologie und Byzantinische Kunstgeschichte e.V. Muenchen), Dr. Ludwig Reichert Verlag, Tauernstr 11, Wiesbaden, 65199, Germany. TEL 49-611-461851, FAX 49-611-468613, reichert.verlag@t-online.de, http://www.reichert-verlag.de. Eds. Johannes Deckers, Marcell Restle. R&P Ursula Reichert. Adv. contact L Reichert. Circ: 300. **Distributed by:** Brockhaus Commission, Kreidlerstr 9, Kornwestheim 70806, Germany.

MNEMOSYNE/MNEMOSUNE. see *HISTORY—History Of Europe*

913 200 FRA ISSN 0154-9049
LE MONDE DE LA BIBLE; histoire art archeologie. Text in French. 1977. 6/yr. (Plus 2 extra). EUR 59.30 domestic; EUR 68.45 in the European Union; EUR 75 elsewhere (effective 2005). adv. bk.rev. **Document type:** *Magazine, Consumer.* **Description:** Brings together culture, history of religion, the Bible, the Holy Land and its peoples and the great civilizations of the past.
Formerly (until 1977): Bible et Terre Sainte (0006-0712)
Indexed: BHA, OTA, RASB.
—CCC.
Published by: Bayard Presse, 3 Rue Bayard, Paris, 75393 Cedex 08, France. TEL 33-1-44356060, FAX 33-1-44356161, redactions@bayard-presse.com, http://www.bayardpresse.com. Ed. Jean-Luc Pouthier. Circ: 25,000.

913 ESP ISSN 0544-7941
MONOGRAFIAS ARQUEOLOGICAS✶. Text in Spanish. 1982. irreg.
Related titles: Supplement(s): Anejo de Caesaraugusta. ISSN 0575-0261. 1966.
Published by: Universidad Autonoma de Madrid, Departamento de Preshitoria y Arqueologia, Carretera de Colmenar km 15000, Canto Blanco, Madrid, 28049, Spain.

913 ITA ISSN 0077-0493
MONOGRAFIE DI ARCHEOLOGIA LIBICA. Text in Italian. 1948. irreg. price varies. **Document type:** *Monographic series, Academic/Scholarly.*
Published by: L'Erma di Bretschneider, Via Cassiodoro, 19, PO Box 6192, Rome, RM 00193, Italy. TEL 39-06-6874127, FAX 39-06-6874129, edizioni@lerma.it, http://www.lerma.it.

932 BEL
MONOGRAPHIES REINE ELISABETH. Text in French. 1971. irreg., latest vol.6, 1989. price varies. **Document type:** *Monographic series.*
Published by: Fondation Egyptologique Reine Elisabeth, Parc du Cinquantenaire 10, Brussels, 1000, Belgium. TEL 32-2-7417364.

932 BEL ISSN 0077-1376
MONUMENTA AEGYPTIACA. Text in French. 1968. irreg., latest vol.6, 1994. price varies. **Document type:** *Monographic series.*
Published by: Fondation Egyptologique Reine Elisabeth, Parc du Cinquantenaire 10, Brussels, 1000, Belgium. TEL 32-2-7417364.

913 DEU ISSN 0077-1384
MONUMENTA AMERICANA. Text in German. 1965. irreg., latest vol.5, 1997. price varies. reprints avail. **Document type:** *Monographic series, Academic/Scholarly.*
Published by: (Ibero-Amerikanisches Institut Preussischer Kulturbesitz Berlin), Gebr. Mann Verlag, Neue Gruenstr 17, Berlin, 10179, Germany. TEL 49-30-2790760, FAX 49-30-2797655, vertrieb-kunstverlage@reimer-verlag.de, http://www.gebrmannverlag.de. Ed. Gerdt Kutscher. R&P Elisabeth Roosens.

913 ITA
MONUMENTA ANTIQUA ETRURIAE. Text in Italian. 1993. irreg., latest vol.2, 1997. price varies. **Document type:** *Monographic series, Abstract/Index.*
Published by: L'Erma di Bretschneider, Via Cassiodoro, 19, PO Box 6192, Rome, RM 00193, Italy. TEL 39-06-6874127, FAX 39-06-6874129, edizioni@lerma.it, http://www.lerma.it.

913 USA ISSN 0363-7565
MONUMENTA ARCHAEOLOGICA. Text in English. 1976. irreg., latest vol.18, 1996. **Document type:** *Monographic series, Academic/Scholarly.* **Description:** Publishes reports and analyses of worldwide archaeological data.
Indexed: AnthLit.
—BLDSC (5966.183500).
Published by: (Publications Department), University of California at Los Angeles, Cotsen Institute of Archaeology, A222 Fowler Museum, Box 951510, Los Angeles, CA 90095-1510. TEL 310-825-7411, FAX 310-206-4723. Ed. Brenda Johnson Grau.

913 709 DEU ISSN 0077-1406
MONUMENTA ARTIS ROMANAE. Text in German, English, French. 1959. irreg., latest vol.31, 2001. price varies. bibl.; charts; illus.; maps. back issues avail. **Document type:** *Monographic series, Academic/Scholarly.*
Published by: Verlag Philipp von Zabern GmbH, Philipp-von-Zabern-Platz 1-3, Mainz, 55116, Germany. TEL 49-6131-287470, FAX 49-6131-223710, zabern@zabern.de, http://www.zabern.de. Eds. F Sinn, K S Freyberger. Adv. contact Manuela Dressen TEL 49-6131-2874711.

MOUSEION/REVUE DE LA SOCIETE CANADIENNE DES ETUDES CLASSIQUES; journal of the Classical Association of Canada. see *CLASSICAL STUDIES*

930.1 DEU ISSN 0178-0492
MUENCHNER ARCHAEOLOGISCHE STUDIEN. Text in German. 1970. irreg., latest vol.8. **Document type:** *Monographic series.*
Published by: Wilhelm Fink Verlag, Ohmstr 5, Munich, 80802, Germany. TEL 49-89-348017, FAX 49-89-341378, http://www.fink.de. R&P Marlene Braun.

MUENSTERSCHE BEITRAEGE ZUR ANTIKEN HANDELSGESCHICHTE. see *CLASSICAL STUDIES*

930.1 EST ISSN 1406-3867
MUINASAJA TEADUS/RESEARCH INTO ANCIENT TIMES; interdistsiplinaarseid uurimusi arheoloogias/interdisciplinary studies in archaeology. Text in Estonian. 1991. irreg., latest vol.11, 2002. price varies. **Document type:** *Monographic series, Academic/Scholarly.*
—BLDSC (5981.860000).
Published by: Eesti Teaduste Akadeemia, Ajaloo Instituut/Estonian Academy of Sciences, Institute of History, Ruutli 6, Tallinn, 0001, Estonia. TEL 372-6-446594, FAX 372-6-443714, AI@teleport.ee.

MUNIBE ANTROPOLOGIA - ARKEOLOGIA. see *ANTHROPOLOGY*

MUSE (COLUMBIA). see *ART*

MUSEO ARCHEOLOGICO DI TARQUINIA. MATERIALI. see *MUSEUMS AND ART GALLERIES*

930.1 CHL
MUSEO ARQUEOLOGICO DE LA SERENA. BOLETIN. Text in Spanish. a. **Document type:** *Bulletin.*
Indexed: AnthLit.
Published by: Museo Arqueologico de la Serena, Cordovez esquina Cienfuegos, La Serena, 4 Region de Coquimbo, Chile. http://www.paseosenchile.cl/ingles/museos/arqueoseren.htm.

930.1 ESP ISSN 0212-5544
DP44
MUSEO ARQUEOLOGICO NACIONAL. BOLETIN/BULLETIN OF THE NATIONAL ARCHAEOLOGICAL MUSEUM. Text in Spanish. 1983. s-a. **Document type:** *Journal, Academic/Scholarly.*
Indexed: AnthLit.
—CINDOC.
Published by: (Museo Arqueologico Nacional/National Archaeological Museum), Ministerio de Educacion, Cultura y Deporte, Centro de Publicaciones, c/o Ciudad Universitaria, S/N, Madrid, 28040, Spain. TEL 34-91-453-9800, FAX 34-91-4539884.

913 ESP
MUSEO ARQUEOLOGICO NACIONAL. CATALOGOS CIENTIFICOS. Text in Spanish. 1980. irreg. price varies. **Document type:** *Bulletin.*
Indexed: AnthLit.
Published by: Ministerio de Cultura, Museo Arqueologico Nacional, Serrano, 13, Madrid, 28001, Spain. TEL 5577912, FAX 4316840. Circ: 700.

MUSEO CHILENO DE ARTE PRECOLOMBINO. BOLETIN. see *ART*

MUSEO DEL HOMBRE DOMINICANO. BOLETIN. see *ANTHROPOLOGY*

MUSEO MUNICIPAL DE HISTORIA NATURAL DE SAN RAFAEL. REVISTA. see *SCIENCES: COMPREHENSIVE WORKS*

913 700 BRA ISSN 0103-9709
F2519
➤ **MUSEU DE ARQUEOLOGIA E ETNOLOGIA. REVISTA.** Key Title: Revista do Museu de Arqueologia e Etnologia. Text in Portuguese; Summaries in English; Abstracts in English. 1991. a. USD 15 to individuals; USD 25 domestic to institutions; USD 30 foreign to institutions (effective 2001). bk.rev. bibl.; charts; illus. **Document type:** *Academic/Scholarly.*
Supersedes (1965-1974): Dedalo (0011-7455); (1979-1989): Revista de Prehistoria (0100-7726)
Indexed: AICP, AnthLit, IBR, RASB.
Published by: Universidade de Sao Paulo, Museu de Arqueologia e Etnologia, Av. Prof. Almeida Prado, 1466, Cidade Universitaria, Sao Paulo, SP 05508-900, Brazil. TEL 55-11-8184978, FAX 55-11-8185042, bibmae@edu.usp.br, http://www.mac.usp.br/biblioteca/. Eds. Maria Cristina Mineiro Scatamacchia, Maria Isabel D'Agostino Fleming. Adv. contact Maria Isabel D'Agostino Fleming. Circ: 1,000.

930.1 GBR
THE MUSEUM ARCHAEOLOGIST. Text in English. irreg., latest vol.24, 1998. **Document type:** *Monographic series, Academic/Scholarly.*
Indexed: BrArAb, NumL.
—BLDSC (5987.138100).
Published by: Society of Museum Archaeologists, 14 Ryegate Rd, Colchester, CO1 1YG, United Kingdom. Ed. Philip J Wise.

917 DEU
MUSEUM FUER VOELKERKUNDE, BERLIN. VEROEFFENTLICHUNGEN. NEUE FOLGE. ABTEILUNG: AMERIKANISCHE ARCHAEOLOGIE. Text in German. 1970. irreg., latest vol.9, 1994. price varies. **Document type:** *Monographic series.*
Published by: Staatliche Museen zu Berlin - Preussischer Kulturbesitz, Generalverwaltung, Stauffenbergstr 41, Berlin, 10785, Germany. FAX 030-2662612.

MUSEUM HELVETICUM; Schweizerische Zeitschrift fuer klassische Altertumswissenschaft. see *CLASSICAL STUDIES*

913 ISR ISSN 0082-2620
MUSEUM OF ANTIQUITIES OF TEL-AVIV-YAFO. PUBLICATIONS. Text in English. 1964. irreg. USD 1.
Published by: Museum of Antiquites of Tel-Aviv-Yafo, P O Box 8406, Tel Aviv Jaffa, Israel.

MUZE/MUSEUM. see *MUSEUMS AND ART GALLERIES*

913 622 669 SCG ISSN 0351-7160
MUZEJ RUDARSTVA I METALURGIJE U BORU. ZBORNIK RADOVA/MUSEUM OF MINING AND METALLURGY IN BOR. PROCEEDINGS. Text in Serbo-Croatian; Summaries in English. 1980. biennial. YUN 15,000.
Published by: Muzej Rudarstva i Metalurgije u Boru/Mining and Metallurgy Museum, Mose Pijade 19, Bor, 19210. TEL 381-30-24963, FAX 381-30-22145, office@museumbor.org.yu, http://www.museumbor.org.yu. Ed. Ilija Jankovic. Circ: 1,000.

708.94972 HRV ISSN 0350-9370
MUZEJSKI VJESNIK/MUSEUM NEWS MAGAZINE. Text in Croatian; Summaries in German. 1978. a. free. bk.rev. back issues avail.
Indexed: RASB, RILM.
Published by: North-West Croatian Museums, Muzejsko Drustvo Sjeverozapadne Hrvatske, Varazdin, 42000, Croatia. Ed. Darko Sacic. Circ: 800.

930.1 ROM ISSN 0255-6812
MUZEUL NATIONAL DE ISTORIE A ROMANIEI. CERCETARI ARHEOLOGICE. Key Title: Cercetari Arheologice. Text in Romanian; Summaries in English, French. 1975. a. **Document type:** *Academic/Scholarly.*
Formerly: Muzeul de Istorie al Republici Socialiste Romania. Cercetari Arheologice
Indexed: BHA, NumL.
Published by: Muzeul National de Istorie a Romaniei, Calea Victoriei 12, Bucharest, Romania. TEL 40-1-6149070.

MUZEUL NATIONAL DE ISTORIE A ROMANIEI. CERCETARI NUMISMATICE. see *NUMISMATICS*

913 943.8 POL ISSN 0458-1520
GN845.P7
MUZEUM ARCHEOLOGICZNE I ETNOGRAFICZNE, LODZ. PRACE I MATERIALY. SERIA ARCHEOLOGICZNA. Text in Polish; Summaries in English. 1956. irreg., latest 1997-98, no.40. price varies. **Document type:** *Academic/Scholarly.*
Indexed: AnthLit, BHA, RASB.
Published by: Muzeum Archeologiczne i Etnograficzne w Lodzi, Pl Wolnosci 14, Lodz, 91415, Poland. TEL 48-42-6328440, FAX 48-42-6329714. Ed. Ryszard Grygiel. Circ: 500.

930.1 POL ISSN 0075-7039
MUZEUM ARCHEOLOGICZNE, KRAKOW. MATERIALY ARCHEOLOGICZNE. Text in Polish; Summaries in German. 1959. irreg., latest vol.33, 2002. USD 20 per vol. foreign (effective 2003). adv. 250 p./no. 2 cols./p.; **Document type:** *Yearbook, Academic/Scholarly.* **Description:** Covers prehistory and medieval ages in Poland as well as Mediterranean (Greek, Hellenistic, Roman) and Egyptian archaeology.
Indexed: AICP, AnthLit, RASB.
—BLDSC (5396.724000).
Published by: Muzeum Archeologiczne w Krakowie, Senacka 3, Krakow, 31002, Poland. TEL 48-12-4227100, FAX 48-12-4227761, mak@ma.krakow.pl, http://www.ma.krakow.pl. Ed., R&P Jacek Rydzewski. Adv. contact Anna Tyniec-Kepinska. Circ: 600.

930.1 POL ISSN 0581-1112
MUZEUM ARCHEOLOGICZNE, KRAKOW. ODDZIAL W NOWEJ HUCIE. MATERIALY ARCHEOLOGICZNE NOWEJ HUTY. Text in Polish; Summaries in English. 1968. a., latest vol.23, 2002. USD 20 per vol. foreign (effective 2003). adv. **Document type:** *Academic/Scholarly.* **Description:** Covers prehistory and medieval ages in the territory of Krakow - Nowa Huta.
Indexed: AICP.
Published by: Muzeum Archeologiczne w Krakowie, Senacka 3, Krakow, 31002, Poland. TEL 48-12-4227100, FAX 48-12-4227761, mak@ma.krakow.pl, http://www.ma.krakow.pl. R&P Malgorzata Kaczanowska. Adv. contact Paulina Poleska. Circ: 450.

913 POL ISSN 0068-4635
MUZEUM GORNOSLASKIE W BYTOMIU. ROCZNIK. SERIA ARCHEOLOGIA. Text in Polish; Summaries in German, Russian. 1962. irreg. USD 15. **Document type:** *Proceedings.*
Published by: Muzeum Gornoslaskie w Bytomiu/The Museum of Upper Silesia, Pl Jana III Sobieskiego 2, Bytom, 41902, Poland. TEL 48-32-28182941, dobosz@us.edu.pl, mgbytom@us.edu.pl.

MUZEUM MESTA BLANSKA. SBORNIK. see *HISTORY—History Of Europe*

930.1 USA
N E A R A TRANSIT NEWSLETTER. Text in English. s-a. **Document type:** *Newsletter.*
Published by: New England Antiquities Research Association, 94 Cross Point Rd, Edgecomb, ME 04556. TEL 207-882-8155, FAX 207-882-8162, krosspt@lincoln.midcoast.com, http://www.neara.org. Ed. Roslyn Strong. R&P Suzanne Carlson. Circ: 500.

930.1 USA
N E A S NEWSLETTER✶. Text in English. q. **Document type:** *Newsletter.*
Published by: (Near East Archaeological Society), Berry Publishing Services, 1325 Remmington Rd., Ste. H, Schaumberg, IL 60173-4815. TEL 800-274-9447, FAX 708-869-4825, 76105.3503@compuserve.com. Pub. Bill Berry.

930.1 900 DEU ISSN 1432-0282
NACHRICHTEN AUS DEM MARTIN-VON-WAGNER-MUSEUM. Text in German. 1996. irreg. **Document type:** *Academic/Scholarly.*
Published by: Ergon Verlag, Grombuehlstr 7, Wuerzburg, 97080, Germany. TEL 49-931-280084, FAX 49-931-282872, ergon-verlag@t-online.de, service@ergon-verlag.de. Eds. S Kummer, U Sinn.

930.1 DEU ISSN 0342-1406
NACHRICHTEN AUS NIEDERSACHSENS URGESCHICHTE. Text in German. 1927. irreg., latest vol.71, 2002. price varies. **Document type:** *Monographic series, Academic/Scholarly.*
Related titles: Supplement(s): Nachrichten aus Niedersachsens Urgeschichte. Beiheft. ISSN 1437-2177. 1996.
Indexed: AnthLit, IBR, IBZ.
Published by: (Archaeologische Kommission fuer Niedersachsen), Konrad Theiss Verlag GmbH, Moenchhaldenstr 28, Stuttgart, 70191, Germany. TEL 49-711-255270, FAX 49-711-2552717, service@theiss.de, http://www.theiss.de.

NAPRSTEK MUSEUM. ANNALS. see *HUMANITIES: COMPREHENSIVE WORKS*

930.1 IRL
NATIONAL MUSEUM OF IRELAND. MEDIEVAL DUBLIN EXCAVATIONS. SERIES A. Text in English. 1992. irreg. price varies. illus. **Document type:** *Monographic series.*
Published by: Royal Irish Academy, 19 Dawson St., Dublin, 2, Ireland. TEL 353-1-6762570, FAX 353-1-6762346, publications@ria.ie, http://www.ria.ie. Ed. Patrick Wallace.
Co-sponsor: National Museum of Ireland.

930.1 IRL
NATIONAL MUSEUM OF IRELAND. MEDIEVAL DUBLIN EXCAVATIONS. SERIES B. Text in English. irreg., latest vol.3, 1993. price varies. illus. **Document type:** *Monographic series.*
Published by: Royal Irish Academy, 19 Dawson St., Dublin, 2, Ireland. TEL 353-1-6762570, FAX 353-1-6762346, publications@ria.ie, http://www.ria.ie. Ed. Sean McGrail.
Co-sponsor: National Museum of Ireland.

930.1 IRL
NATIONAL MUSEUM OF IRELAND. MEDIEVAL DUBLIN EXCAVATIONS. SERIES C. Text in English. irreg., latest vol.2, 1996. **Document type:** *Monographic series, Academic/Scholarly.*
Published by: Royal Irish Academy, 19 Dawson St., Dublin, 2, Ireland. TEL 353-1-6762570, FAX 353-1-6762346.
Co-sponsor: National Museum of Ireland.

NATIONAL TAIWAN UNIVERSITY. DEPARTMENT OF ANTHROPOLOGY. BULLETIN. see *ANTHROPOLOGY*

NATUR UND MENSCH. see *BIOLOGY*

NATURAL HISTORY MUSEUM AND INSTITUTE, CHIBA. BULLETIN. HUMANITIES. see *HISTORY—History Of Asia*

913 570 DEU ISSN 0077-6149
NATURHISTORISCHE GESELLSCHAFT NUERNBERG. ABHANDLUNGEN. Text in German. 1851. irreg., latest vol.43, 2000. price varies. **Document type:** *Monographic series, Academic/Scholarly.*
Indexed: BIOSIS Prev, BiolAb.
Published by: Naturhistorische Gesellschaft Nuernberg e.V., Norishalle, Marientorgraben 8, Nuernberg, 90402, Germany. TEL 49-911-227970, FAX 49-911-2447441, nhgnbg@t-online.de, http://www.nhg-nuernberg.de. Circ: 2,500.

913 980 USA ISSN 0077-6297
F2229
NAWPA PACHA. Text in English, French, Spanish. 1963. a. price varies. **Document type:** *Monographic series, Academic/Scholarly.* **Description:** Scholarly journal dealing with Andean archaeology and related topics.
Indexed: AICP, AnthLit, HAPI, IBR.
Published by: Institute of Andean Studies, PO Box 9307, Berkeley, CA 94709. TEL 510-525-7816. Eds. John H Rowe, Patricia J Lyon. Circ: 550 (controlled).

930.1 USA ISSN 0739-0068
DS56
NEAR EAST ARCHAEOLOGICAL SOCIETY. BULLETIN. Text in English. 1971. a., latest vol.47, 2002. USD 25 per vol. domestic; USD 30 per vol. foreign (effective 2003); includes all society publications. adv. bk.rev. charts; illus.; maps. back issues avail. **Document type:** *Bulletin, Academic/Scholarly.*
Indexed: RI-1, RI-2.
Published by: Near East Archaeological Society, Horn Archeological Museum, Andrews University, Berrien Springs, MI 49104. TEL 269-471-3273, FAX 269-471-3619, archpub@anderws.edu, hornmusm@andrews.edu, http://www.neasoc.org. Ed. Paul Ray. Circ: 350.

930.1 USA ISSN 1094-2076
BS620.A1
➤ **NEAR EASTERN ARCHAEOLOGY.** Text in English. 1938. q. USD 35 to individuals; USD 100 to institutions (effective 2005). adv. bk.rev. bibl.; charts; illus. index. back issues avail.; reprint service avail. from PQC. **Document type:** *Journal, Academic/Scholarly.* **Description:** Presents articles that illustrate Old and New Testament scriptures and history, interprets the meaning of archaeological finds, and traces the evolution of Western culture and traditions.
Formerly (until 1998): Biblical Archaeologist (0006-0895)
Related titles: Microform ed.: (from PQC); Online - full text ed.: ISSN 1557-5594 (from bigchalk, EBSCO Publishing, H.W. Wilson, JSTOR (Web-based Journal Archive), O C L C Online Computer Library Center, Inc., Ovid Technologies, Inc., ProQuest Information & Learning).
Indexed: A&ATA, AICP, ASCA, AbAn, AnthLit, ArtHuCI, ArtInd, BHA, CPL, ChrPI, CurCont, DIP, HumInd, IBR, IBSS, IBZ, IJP, MEA&I, MLA, MLA-IB, NTA, NumL, OTA, R&TA, RASB, RI-1, RI-2, RILM, SSCI.
—BLDSC (6067.945150), IE, Infotrieve, ingenta. **CCC.**
Published by: American Schools of Oriental Research, 825 Houston Mill Rd, Atlanta, GA 30329. TEL 404-727-0807, FAX 404-727-4719, asorpubs@asor.org, http://www.asor.org. Ed. Sandra Scham. adv.: B&W page USD 500; trim 11 x 8.5. Circ: 4,500 (paid).

➤ **NEDERLANDS INSTITUUT TE ROME. MEDEDELINGEN.** see *HISTORY—History Of Europe*

930.1 NLD ISSN 0167-9783
NEDERLANDSE OUDHEDEN. Text in English, German. 1955. irreg., latest vol.15, 1993. price varies. abstr.; bibl.; illus.; maps. **Document type:** *Monographic series, Government.* **Description:** Covers archaeology in the Netherlands, from prehistoric times through the post-Medieval period.
Published by: Rijksdienst voor het Oudheidkundig Bodemonderzoek te Amersfoort, Kerkstraat 1, Amersfoort, 3811 CV, Netherlands. TEL 31-33-4634233, FAX 31-33-4653235, arne.haytsma@archis.nl, http://www.archis.nl/. Ed. A Haytsma.

930.14 GBR
NEOLITHIC STUDIES GROUP SEMINAR PAPERS. Text in English. irreg.
—BLDSC (6075.606950).
Published by: (Neolithic Studies Group), Oxbow Books, Park End Pl, Oxford, OX1 1HN, United Kingdom. TEL 44-1865-241249, FAX 44-1865-794449, oxbow@oxbowbooks.com, http://www.oxbowbooks.com.

938 720 NLD
NETHERLANDS INSTITUTE AT ATHENS. PUBLICATIONS. Text in English. 1990. irreg., latest vol.2, 1995. price varies. illus. back issues avail. **Document type:** *Monographic series, Academic/Scholarly.*
Published by: (Netherlands Institute at Athens), J.C. Gieben, Entrepotdok 72b, Amsterdam, 1018 AD, Netherlands. TEL 31-20-6234709, FAX 31-20-6275170, http://www.teachtext.net/gieben/. Ed. J A K E de Waele. **Dist. in N. America by:** John Benjamins Publishing Co., PO Box 27519, Philadelphia, PA 19118-0519. TEL 215-8236-1204, 215-836-1200.

932 962 NLD ISSN 0922-5234
➤ **NETHERLANDS INSTITUTE OF ARCHAEOLOGY AND ARABIC STUDIES IN CAIRO. PUBLICATIONS.** Text in Dutch. 1973. irreg., latest vol.3, 1979. price varies. **Document type:** *Monographic series, Academic/Scholarly.*
Published by: (Netherlands Institute of Archaeology and Arabic Studies in Cairo), Brill Academic Publishers, PO Box 9000, Leiden, 2300 PA, Netherlands. TEL 31-71-53-53-500, FAX 31-71-53-17-532, cs@brill.nl, http://www.brill.nl. R&P Elizabeth Venekamp. **Subscr. in N. America to:** PO Box 605, Herndon, VA 20172. TEL 703-661-1585, 800-337-9255, FAX 703-661-1501, cs@brillusa.com. **Distr. outside N. America by:** c/o Turpin Distribution, Stratton Business Park, Pegasus Drive, Biggleswade, BEDFORDSHIRE SG 18 8TQ, United Kingdom. TEL 44-1767-604-954, FAX 44-1767-601-640, brill@turpin-distribution.com.

930.1 USA ISSN 1041-4479
NEVADA ARCHAEOLOGIST. Text in English. 1972. a.
Indexed: AnthLit.
Published by: Nevada Archaeological Association, P.O. Box 73145, Las Vegas, NV 89170-3145.

NEVADA. STATE MUSEUM, CARSON CITY. ANTHROPOLOGICAL PAPERS. see *ANTHROPOLOGY*

930.1 USA ISSN 0149-2551
F6
➤ **NEW ENGLAND ANTIQUITIES RESEARCH ASSOCIATION JOURNAL.** Text in English. 1966. s-a. USD 25 domestic; USD 30 foreign (effective 2000). bk.rev. charts; illus.; maps. back issues avail. **Document type:** *Academic/Scholarly.* **Description:** Examines an expanding range of associated disciplines and explores their inter-relationships contributing to a clearer understanding of the origins and purposes of American lithic sites.
Formerly: New England Antiquities Research Association Newsletter
Indexed: AbAn, AnthLit.
Published by: New England Antiquities Research Association, 94 Cross Point Rd, Edgecomb, ME 04556. TEL 207-882-8155, FAX 207-882-8162, krosspt@lincoln.midsoast.com, dongil@cyberportal.net. Ed., Pub., R&P Suzanne Carlson. Circ: 400 (paid); 100 (controlled). **Dist. by:** 77 Court St, PO Box 1050, Laconia, NH 03246.

930.1 USA ISSN 0545-1604
F36
NEW HAMPSHIRE ARCHEOLOGICAL SOCIETY NEWSLETTER. Text in English. 1950. q. free with subscription to New Hampshire Archeologist. bk.rev. bibl.; illus. **Document type:** *Newsletter.*
Media: Duplicated (not offset).
Indexed: AnthLit.
Published by: New Hampshire Archeological Society, c/o Phillips Exeter Academy, 20 Main St, MSC 81337, Department of Anthropology, Exeter, NH 03833-2460. TEL 603-778-3452. Ed. V Bunker. Circ: 250.

930.1 USA ISSN 0077-8346
F36
NEW HAMPSHIRE ARCHEOLOGIST. Text in English. 1950. a. USD 15 to individuals; USD 18 to institutions. illus. **Document type:** *Academic/Scholarly.*
Indexed: AnthLit.
Published by: New Hampshire Archeological Society, c/o Phillips Exeter Academy, 20 Main St, MSC 81337, Department of Anthropology, Exeter, NH 03833-2460. TEL 603-772-4311. Ed. V Bunker. Circ: 250.

913 GBR
NEW STUDIES IN ARCHAEOLOGY. Text in English. 1976. irreg. price varies. **Document type:** *Monographic series.*
Indexed: BrArAb, NumL.
Published by: Cambridge University Press, The Edinburgh Bldg, Shaftesbury Rd, Cambridge, CB2 2RU, United Kingdom. TEL 44-1223-312393, FAX 44-1223-315052, information@cambridge.org, http://www.cup.cam.ac.uk/. R&P Linda Nicol TEL 44-1223-325757.

913 USA ISSN 0077-8915
NEW WORLD ARCHAEOLOGICAL FOUNDATION. PAPERS. Text in English. 1959. irreg., latest vol.66. price varies. back issues avail. **Document type:** *Academic/Scholarly.*
Published by: Brigham Young University, New World Archaeological Foundation, 942 SWKT, Provo, UT 84602. TEL 801-422-8966, FAX 801-422-0021, fred_nelson@byu.edu, http://fhss.byu.edu/anthro/nwaf/. Ed., R&P John E Clark TEL 801-422-3822. Circ: 1,000.

913 USA ISSN 1046-2368
F121 CODEN: BJNAE9
NEW YORK STATE ARCHAEOLOGICAL ASSOCIATION. BULLETIN. Key Title: Bulletin - New York State Archaeological Association (1987). Text in English. 1954. 2/yr. USD 9 to individuals; USD 15 to institutions. charts; illus. back issues avail.; reprints avail. **Document type:** *Bulletin, Academic/Scholarly.* **Description:** Publishes papers in the prehistoric and historical archaeology of New York State sites, including Native American and colonial era settlements.

Former titles (until 1987): New York State Archaeological Association. Bulletin and Journal (0730-5710); New York State Archaeological Association. Bulletin (0028-7512)
Indexed: AICP, AbAn, AmH&L, AnthLit, HistAb.
Published by: (New York State Archaeological Association), Rochester Museum and Science Center, 657 East Ave, Rochester, NY 14607. FAX 716-271-5935, http://www.rmsc.org. Ed. Charles F Hayes III. Circ: 750.

NEW ZEALAND HISTORIC PLACES. see *HISTORY—History Of Australasia And Other Areas*

913 NZL ISSN 0110-540X
DU416
➤ **NEW ZEALAND JOURNAL OF ARCHAEOLOGY.** Text in English. 1979. a. NZD 29 domestic; NZD 40 foreign (effective 2003). charts; illus. **Document type:** *Academic/Scholarly.* **Description:** Publishes articles on all aspects of prehistoric and historic archaeology in New Zealand and the Pacific.
Indexed: AICP, AnthLit, INIS AtomInd, SPPI.
—BLDSC (6093.100000).
Published by: New Zealand Archaeological Association, PO Box 6337, Dunedin North, New Zealand. TEL 64-3-4772372, FAX 64-3-4775993, ml.campbell@auckland.ac.nz, http://www.nzarchaeology.org. Ed. Janet Davidson. Circ: 350. **Co-sponsor:** University of Otago.

➤ **NEWCOMEN SOCIETY FOR THE STUDY OF THE HISTORY OF ENGINEERING AND TECHNOLOGY. TRANSACTIONS.** see *ENGINEERING*

➤ **NEWSLETTER EAST ASIAN ART & ARCHAEOLOGY.** see *ART*

930.1 JPN ISSN 1340-8488
DS815
NIHON KOKOGAKU/JAPANESE ARCHAEOLOGICAL ASSOCIATION. JOURNAL. Text in Japanese. 1994. a. **Document type:** *Journal, Academic/Scholarly.*
Published by: Nihon Kokogaku Kyokai/Japanese Archaeological Association, Hirai-ekimae Kyodo Bldg, 4F, 5-15-5 Hirai, Edogawa-ku, Tokyo, 132-0035, Japan. TEL 81-3-3618-6608, FAX 81-3-3618-6625, http://www.avenue.co.jp/~kouko/.

560 JPN ISSN 0402-852X
➤ **NIHON KOKOGAKU NENPO/ARCHAEOLOGIA JAPONICA/JAPANESE ARCHAEOLOGISTS ASSOCIATION. ANNUAL REPORT.** Text in Japanese; Summaries in English. 1948. a. JPY 6,180. **Document type:** *Academic/Scholarly.*
Published by: Nihon Kokogaku Kyokai/Japanese Archaeological Association, Hirai-ekimae Kyodo Bldg, 4F, 5-15-5 Hirai, Edogawa-ku, Tokyo, 132-0035, Japan. TEL 81-3-3618-6608, FAX 81-3-3618-6625, http://www.avenue.co.jp/~kouko/. Circ: 3,850.

913 630 CHN ISSN 1006-2335
NONGYE KAOGU/AGRICULTURAL ARCHAEOLOGY. Text in Chinese. 1981. q. CNY 80 (effective 2004). **Document type:** *Journal, Academic/Scholarly.*
Related titles: Online - full text ed.: (from East View Information Services).
Published by: Jiangxi Sheng Shehui Kexueyuan, 255, Hongdu Bei Dadao, Nanchang, China. TEL 86-791-8516284, FAX 86-791-8515914. **Dist. in US by:** China Books & Periodicals Inc, 360 Swift Ave., Ste. 48, S San Fran, CA 94080-6220. info@chinabooks.com, http://www.chinabooks.com/; **Dist. by:** China International Book Trading Corp, 35 Chegongzhuang Xilu, Haidian District, PO Box 399, Beijing 100044, China. TEL 86-10-68412045, FAX 86-10-68412023, cibtc@mail.cibtc.com.cn, http://www.cibtc.com.cn.

NORSK SJOEFARTSMUSEUM. AARSBERETNING. see *HISTORY—History Of Europe*

913 USA ISSN 0197-6931
E43 CODEN: NAAREU
➤ **NORTH AMERICAN ARCHAEOLOGIST.** Text in English. 1979. q. USD 67 to individuals; USD 274, USD 282 to institutions (effective 2005). adv. bk.rev. illus. back issues avail.; reprints avail. **Document type:** *Journal, Academic/Scholarly.* **Description:** Covers all aspects of prehistoric and historic archaeology from Paleo-Indian studies to industrial sites; also features the results of resource management and contract archaeology.
Related titles: Online - full text ed.: ISSN 1541-3543 (from EBSCO Publishing).
Indexed: AICP, AbAn, AmH&L, AnthLit, ArtHuCI, BHA, BrArAb, CurCont, DIP, HistAb, IBR, IBZ, PCI.
—BLDSC (6147.958000), IDS, IE, Infotrieve, ingenta. **CCC.**
Published by: Baywood Publishing Co., Inc., 26 Austin Ave, PO Box 337, Amityville, NY 11701-0337. TEL 631-691-1270, FAX 631-691-1770, info@baywood.com, http://www.baywood.com/Journals/PreviewJournal.asp?Id=0197-6931. Ed. Roger W Moeller. R&P Julie Krempa. Adv. contact Rochelle Grant.

913 USA
NORTH CAROLINA ARCHAEOLOGICAL SOCIETY. NEWSLETTER. Text in English. 1938. q. USD 10 to individuals; USD 25 to institutions; includes Southern Indian Studies. **Document type:** *Newsletter.* **Description:** North Carolina archaeological news for society members.
Formerly: Archaeological Society of North Carolina. Newsletter
Published by: North Carolina Archaeological Society, 109 E Jones St, Raleigh, NC 27601-2807. TEL 919-733-7342, FAX 919-733-8653. Ed. Mark A Mathis. Circ: 500.

913 USA
E78.S55
NORTH CAROLINA ARCHAEOLOGY. Text in English. 1949. a. USD 10 to individuals; USD 25 to institutions; includes q. Newsletter. bk.rev. bibl.; illus. **Document type:** *Academic/Scholarly.* **Description:** Articles on the archaeology, ethnohistory and ethnography of Southern Indians and other archaeological issues.
Formerly (until 1999): Southern Indian Studies (0085-6525)
Indexed: AbAn, AmH&L, AnthLit, HistAb, PCI.
Published by: North Carolina Archaeological Society, 109 E Jones St, Raleigh, NC 27601-2807. TEL 919-733-7342, FAX 919-733-8653, http://www.arch.dcr.state.nc.us/ncaspubs.htm. Ed. Mark A Mathis. Circ: 500. **Co-publisher:** Research Laboratories of Archaeology.

913 GBR ISSN 0305-4659
NORTHAMPTONSHIRE ARCHAEOLOGY. Text in English. 1966. a. GBP 10 to individuals; GBP 28 to institutions; GBP 8 to students. adv. bk.rev. illus. **Document type:** *Academic/Scholarly.* **Description:** Reports on individual archaeological sites and subjects in the English Midlands region.
Formerly (until 1973): Northamptonshire Federation of Archaeological Societies. Bulletin
Indexed: BHA, BrArAb, IBR, IBZ, NumL.
Published by: Northamptonshire Archaeological Society, Nene College, History Department, Moulton Park, Northampton, NN2 7AL, United Kingdom. TEL 44-1604-735500, liz.musgrave@nene.ac.uk. Eds. E Musgrave, M Tingle. Pub. Alan Sutton. Circ: 500.

930.1 USA ISSN 0048-0738
NORTHEAST HISTORICAL ARCHAEOLOGY. Text in English. a. USD 30 to individuals; USD 50 to institutions (effective 2005).
Indexed: AmH&L, HistAb.
Published by: Council for Northeast Historical Archaeology, University of Massachusetts Boston, Anthropology Department, 100 Morrissey Blvd, Boston, MA 02125. TEL 617-287-6835, FAX 617-287-6857, cneha.journal@umb.edu, http://www.smcm.edu/Academics/soan/cneha/neha.htm.

930.1 398 GBR ISSN 0268-8476
NORTHERN EARTH; journal of the northern earth mysteries group. Text in English. 1979. q. GBP 6.50 domestic; GBP 8.50 in the European Union; GBP 11 elsewhere; GBP 1.70 newsstand/cover (effective 2001). adv. bk.rev. back issues avail. **Document type:** *Journal, Consumer.*
Published by: Northern Earth Mysteries Group, 10 Jubilee St, Mytholmroyd, Hebden Bridge, West Yorkshire, HX7 5NP, United Kingdom. TEL 44-1422-882441, nemg@btinternet.com, http://www.northernearth.co.uk/, http://www.annexe.org.uk. Ed., Pub., R&P John Billingsley. adv.: page GBP 28; trim 6.5 x 18.75. Circ: 450 (paid).

930.1 NOR ISSN 0029-3652
DL421 CODEN: NRACBX
➤ **NORWEGIAN ARCHAEOLOGICAL REVIEW.** Text in English. 1968. s-a. GBP 46, USD 76 combined subscription to institutions print & online eds. (effective 2006). bk.rev. charts; illus. index. back issues avail.; reprint service avail. from ISI,PSC. **Document type:** *Journal, Academic/Scholarly.* **Description:** Focuses on methodological and theoretical aspects of archaeology, especially Scandinavian.
Related titles: Microform ed.: (from PQC); Online - full text ed.: ISSN 1502-7678. 1999. GBP 48, USD 80 to institutions (effective 2006) (from EBSCO Publishing, Gale Group, IngentaConnect, O C L C Online Computer Library Center, Inc., Swets Information Services).
Indexed: AbAn, AnthLit, BHA, BrArAb, ChemAb, DIP, IBR, IBZ, NAA, NumL.
—BLDSC (6152.105000), IE, Infotrieve, ingenta. **CCC.**
Published by: Taylor & Francis A S (Subsidiary of: Taylor & Francis Group), Biskop Gunnerusgate 14A, PO Box 12 Posthuset, Oslo, 0051, Norway. TEL 47-23-103460, FAX 47-23-103461, journals@tandf.no, http://www.tandf.co.uk/journals/titles/00293652.asp. Ed. Hein Bjartmann Bjerck TEL 47-73-590335. Circ: 750. **Subscr. to:** Taylor & Francis Ltd, Journals Customer Service, Rankine Rd, Basingstoke, Hants RG24 8PR, United Kingdom. TEL 44-1256-813000, FAX 44-1256-330245, enquiry@tandf.co.uk.

➤ **NORWEGIAN INSTITUTE AT ATHENS. MONOGRAPHS.** see *CLASSICAL STUDIES*

➤ **NOTAS MESOAMERICANAS.** see *ANTHROPOLOGY*

930.1 GBR ISSN 0143-0297
NOTTINGHAMSHIRE INDUSTRIAL ARCHAEOLOGICAL SOCIETY JOURNAL. Text in English. 1979. 2/yr. looseleaf. GBP 2.50 (effective 2001). bk.rev. illus. 14 p./no.; back issues avail. **Document type:** *Newsletter, Internal.* **Description:** Covers industrial history and archaeology.
Formerly: Nottinghamshire Industrial Archaeological Society. Newsletter
Indexed: BrArAb, NumL.
Published by: Nottinghamshire Industrial Archaeological Society, c/o Howard Rees, Ed., 47 St Marys Close, Attenborough, Beeston, Nottingham, NG9 6AT, United Kingdom. TEL 44-115-9253226. Ed., R&P Howard Rees. Adv. contact Don Morley TEL 44-1623-792061. Circ: 80.

971 CAN
NOVA SCOTIA ARCHAEOLOGY SOCIETY. CURATORIAL REPORT. Text in English. 1984. irreg., latest vol.87, 1999. price varies. illus. back issues avail. **Document type:** *Monographic series, Academic/Scholarly.* **Description:** Reviews archaeological investigations and findings in Nova Scotia.
Published by: Nova Scotia Archaeology Society, PO Box 36090, Halifax, NS B3J 3S9, Canada. http://www.ednet.ca/educ/museum/mnh/shop/crs.htm, http://nsas.ednet.ns.ca.

913 POL ISSN 0860-5777
NOVENSIA. Key Title: Novaensia. Text in Polish; Summaries in English, Russian. 1987. irreg., latest vol.13, 2002. price varies. **Document type:** *Monographic series, Academic/Scholarly.*
Published by: (Uniwersytet Warszawski, Zaklad Archeologii Srodziemnomorskiej), Wydawnictwa Uniwersytetu Warszawskiego, ul Nowy Swiat 4, Warsaw, 00497, Poland. TEL 48-22-5531319, FAX 48-22-5531318, wuw@uw.edu.pl. Ed. Ludwika Press. R&P Jolatna Okonska. Circ: 350. **Dist. by:** Ars Polona, Krakowskie Przedmiescie 7, Warsaw, Poland. TEL 48-22-9263914, FAX 48-22-9265334, arspolona@arspolona.com.pl, http://www.arspolona.com.pl.

932 POL ISSN 0860-7923
➤ **NUBIA**; Dongola. Text in English. 1990. irreg. price varies. illus. **Document type:** *Monographic series, Academic/Scholarly.* **Description:** Presents excavation results of Polish Archaeological Mission at Old Dangola, Sudan.
Published by: Polska Akademia Nauk, Zaklad Archeologii Srodziemnomorskiej, Ul Nowy Swiat 72, pok. 33, Warsaw, 00330, Poland. TEL 48-22-8266560, FAX 48-22-8266560. Ed. Stefan Jakobielski. **Dist. by:** Osrodek Rozpowszechniania Wydawnictw Naukowych PAN, Palac Kultury i Nauki, Warsaw 00901, Poland. FAX 48-22-8268670.

930.1 DEU ISSN 0938-9539
NUERNBERGER BLAETTER ZUR ARCHAEOLOGIE. Text in German. 1984. a. adv. bk.rev. **Document type:** *Academic/Scholarly.*
Published by: Stadt Nuernberg, Bildungszentrum, Rathausplatz 2, Postfach, Nuernberg, 90317, Germany. TEL 49-911-2312461, FAX 49-911-2315497, klaus_dornisch@bz.stadt.nuernberg.de, http://www.nuernberg.de/rer/bz. Ed. Klaus Dornisch. Adv. contact Sonja Bauer Ramorobi.

NUMISMATICA E ANTICHITA CLASSICHE; quaderni ticinesi. see *NUMISMATICS*

914 945 ITA
NUOVO BULLETTINO ARCHEOLOGICO SARDO. Text in Italian. 1984. a. price varies. bk.rev. index. back issues avail. **Document type:** *Monographic series, Academic/Scholarly.*
Published by: Carlo Delfino Editore, Via Rolando 11a, Sassari, SS 07100, Italy. TEL 39-079-262661, FAX 39-079-261926, info@carlodelfinoeditore.it, http://www.carlodelfinoeditore.it. Ed. Giovanni Lilliu. Circ: 1,000.

913 700 DNK ISSN 0085-3208
N9
NY CARLSBERG GLYPTOTEK. MEDDELELSER. Text in Danish; Summaries in English. 1944. a. DKK 160 (effective 2002). **Document type:** *Bulletin, Academic/Scholarly.*
Indexed: AIAP, BHA.
Published by: Ny Carlsberg Glyptotek, Dantes Plads 7, Copenhagen V, 1556, Denmark. TEL 45-33-41-81-41, FAX 45-33-91-20-58, vh@glyptoteket.dk, http://www.glyptoteket.dk. Circ: 1,000.

930.1 USA ISSN 0713-5815
DT13 CODEN: NYAKE7
NYAME AKUMA. Text in English. 1972. s-a. membership. bk.rev. **Document type:** *Bulletin.* **Description:** Contains short reports on research projects as they take place around the continent.
Indexed: AnthLit.
Published by: Society of Africanist Archaeologists, c/o Dr Jeffrey Fleisher, Department of Sociology and Anthropology, Lehigh University, 681 Taylor St, Bethlehem, PA 18015. safa@rice.edu, http://safa.rice.edu/bulletin.cfm. Ed. Dr. Pamela R Willoughby.

NYT FRA NATIONALMUSEET. see *ANTHROPOLOGY*

OBEROESTERREICHISCHER MUSEALVEREIN. GESLLSCHAFT FUER LANDESKUNDE. JAHRBUCH. see *HISTORY—History Of Europe*

930.1 NLD ISSN 0924-0381
OBOLOS. Text in Dutch. 1989. irreg. **Document type:** *Monographic series.*
Published by: Styx Publications, Postbus 2659, Groningen, 9704 CR, Netherlands. TEL 31-50-717502, FAX 31-50-733325.

ODENSE UNIVERSITY CLASSICAL STUDIES. see *CLASSICAL STUDIES*

930.1 AUT
OESTERREICHISCHE GESELLSCHAFT FUER UR- UND FRUEHGESCHICHTE. VEROEFFENTLICHUNGEN. Text in German. irreg. price varies. **Document type:** *Proceedings.*
Published by: Oesterreichische Gesellschaft fuer Ur- und Fruehgeschichte, Franz-Klein-Gasse 1, Vienna, W 1190, Austria. TEL 43-1-4277-40473, FAX 43-1-4277-9404.

OESTERREICHISCHE ZEITSCHRIFT FUER KUNST UND DENKMALPFLEGE. see *ART*

913 AUT ISSN 0078-3579
➤ **OESTERREICHISCHES ARCHAEOLOGISCHES INSTITUT. JAHRESHEFTE.** Text in German. 1877. a. EUR 129 (effective 2003). **Document type:** *Journal, Academic/Scholarly.*
Former titles (until 1946): Wiener Jahreshefte (0259-1464); (until 1940): Oesterreichisches Archaeologisches Institut in Wien. Jahreshefte (0259-1456); (until 1898): Archaeologisch-Epigraphische Mitteilungen aus Oesterreich (0259-1448)
Indexed: AIAP, BHA, DIP, IBR, IBZ, RASB.
Published by: (Oesterreichisches Archaeologisches Institut), Verlag der Oesterreichischen Akademie der Wissenschaften, Postgasse 7/4, Vienna, W 1011, Austria. TEL 43-1-515813402, FAX 43-222-5139541, verlag@oeaw.ac.at, http://verlag.oeaw.ac.at. Circ: 450.

917 USA ISSN 0048-153X
OHIO ARCHAEOLOGIST. Text in English. 1950. q. USD 20 (effective 2000). bk.rev. charts; illus. **Document type:** *Academic/Scholarly.*
Indexed: AbAn, AnthLit.
Published by: Archaeological Society of Ohio, PO Box 61, Plain City, OH 43064-0061. TEL 614-873-5471. Ed. Robert N Converse. R&P Robert Converse. Circ: 3,000.

938 DEU ISSN 0474-1242
➤ **OLYMPISCHE FORSCHUNGEN.** Text in German. 1944. irreg., latest vol.29, 2001. price varies. back issues avail. **Document type:** *Monographic series, Academic/Scholarly.* **Description:** Publishes results of German archaeological research relating to Olympus and Ancient Greece.
Published by: (Deutsches Archaeologisches Institut), Walter de Gruyter GmbH & Co. KG, Genthiner Str. 13, Berlin, 10785, Germany. TEL 49-30-260050, FAX 49-30-26005251, wdg-info@degruyter.de, http://www.degruyter.de.

930.1 GBR
ONE WORLD ARCHAEOLOGY. Text in English. irreg., latest 2002, May. price varies. back issues avail. **Document type:** *Monographic series, Academic/Scholarly.*
Indexed: AnthLit.
Published by: (World Archaeological Congress), Routledge (Subsidiary of: Taylor & Francis Group), 4 Park Square, Milton Park, Abingdon, Oxon OX14 4RN, United Kingdom. TEL 44-1235-828600, FAX 44-1235-829000, info@routledge.co.uk, http://www.tandf.co.uk/journals.

917 CAN ISSN 0048-1742
ONTARIO ARCHAEOLOGICAL SOCIETY. ARCH NOTES. Text in English. bi-m. CND 40 to individuals; CND 60 to institutions (effective 1999); Subscr. includes: Ontario Archaeology. adv. **Document type:** *Newsletter, Academic/Scholarly.* **Description:** Contains news and information of the Society and of interest to members.
Indexed: AnthLit.
Published by: Ontario Archaeological Society, 11099 Bathurst St, Richmond Hill, ON L4C 0N2, Canada. TEL 905-787-9851, FAX 905-787-9852, oas@globalserve.net, http://www.ontarioarchaeology.on.ca. Eds. Alex von Garnet, Frank Dielerman. R&P Ellen Blaubergs. Adv. contact Jo Holden. Circ: 600.

917 CAN ISSN 0078-4672
CODEN: ONAREU
➤ **ONTARIO ARCHAEOLOGY.** Text in English. 1956. 2/yr. CND 40 to individuals; CND 60 to institutions (effective 1999); Includes Arch Notes. adv. back issues avail. **Document type:** *Academic/Scholarly.*
Indexed: AmH&L, AnthLit, HistAb.
Published by: Ontario Archaeological Society, 11099 Bathurst St, Richmond Hill, ON L4C 0N2, Canada. TEL 905-787-9851, FAX 905-787-9852, oas@globalserve.net, http://www.adamsheritage.on.ca/oas/, http://www.ontarioarchaeology.on.ca. Ed. Alexander von Gernet. R&P, Adv. contact Ellen Blaubergs. Circ: 800 (paid).

930.1 SVN
➤ **OPERA INSTITUTI ARCHAEOLOGICI SLOVENIAE.** Text in Slovenian, German, English. 1995. irreg., latest vol.5, 2002. EUR 28.90 (effective 2003). charts; illus.; maps. 300 p./no.; back issues avail. **Document type:** *Monographic series, Academic/Scholarly.*
Published by: Slovenska Akademija Znanosti in Umetnosti, Znanstvenoraziskovalni Center, Institut za Arheologijo, Novi trg 2, Ljubljana, 1000, Slovenia. TEL 386-1-4706100, FAX 386-1-4257757, http://www.zrc-sazu.si/iza.

➤ **OPUSCULA ATHENIENSIA.** see *CLASSICAL STUDIES*

➤ **OPUSCULA ROMANA.** see *HISTORY—History Of Europe*

➤ **ORIENT EXPRESS;** notes et nouvelles d'archeologie orientale. see *ASIAN STUDIES*

935 USA ISSN 0146-678X
PJ2
ORIENTAL INSTITUTE COMMUNICATIONS. Text in English. 1922. irreg., latest vol.28, 2000. price varies. illus. back issues avail. **Document type:** *Academic/Scholarly.* **Description:** Reports the progress and results of institute activities for the general reader, including archaeological expeditions and excavations.
Indexed: AnthLit.
Published by: University of Chicago, Oriental Institute, 1155 E 58th St, Chicago, IL 60637. TEL 773-702-9508, FAX 773-702-9853, t-urban@uchicago.edu, http://www.oi.uchicago.edu. R&P Thomas G Urban.

ORIENTAL INSTITUTE MUSEUM PUBLICATIONS. see *MUSEUMS AND ART GALLERIES*

932 961 USA
ORIENTAL INSTITUTE NUBIAN EXPEDITION. Text in English. 1967. irreg., latest vol.10, 1992. price varies. back issues avail. **Document type:** *Monographic series.* **Description:** Presents information on archaeological materials excavated in Nubia.
Published by: University of Chicago, Oriental Institute, 1155 E 58th St, Chicago, IL 60637. TEL 773-702-9508, FAX 773-702-9853, t-urban@uchicago.edu, http://www.oi.uchicago.edu. R&P Thomas G Urban.

ORIENTALIA. see *ASIAN STUDIES*

930.1 ITA ISSN 0474-6805
ORIGINI; Preistoria e protostoria delle civilta antiche. Text in Italian. 1967. irreg., latest vol.24, 2002. EUR 70 domestic; EUR 80 foreign (effective 2003).
Indexed: AnthLit.
Published by: Bardi Editore, Via Piave 7, Rome, 00187, Italy. TEL 39-06-4817656, FAX 39-06-48912574, bardied@tin.it, http://www.bardieditore.com.

930 CAN ISSN 0702-7974
OTTAWA ARCHAEOLOGIST. Text in English. 1971. 4/yr. CND 17. bk.rev. illus. **Document type:** *Newsletter.* **Description:** Archaeological news for members of the Society.
Formerly (until Feb. 1976): Archaic Notes (0381-8357)
Media: Duplicated (not offset).
Published by: Ontario Archaeological Society, Ottawa Chapter, P O Box 4939, Sta E, Ottawa, ON K1S 5J1, Canada. TEL 613-833-2245, http://www.cyberus.ca/jlpilon/otchh.htm. Ed. Jean Francois Beaulieu. R&P Jean-Francois Beaulieu. Circ: 80.

930.1 NLD
OUDHEIDKUNDIG GENOOTSCHAP NIFTARLAKE. JAARBOEKJE. Text in Dutch. a. price varies. **Document type:** *Academic/Scholarly.*
Published by: (Oudheidkundig Genootschap Niftarlake), Uitgeverij Verloren, PO Box 1741, Hilversum, 1200 BS, Netherlands. TEL 31-35-685-9856, FAX 31-35-683-6557, http://www.verloren.nl.

930.1 GBR
OXBOW LECTURE SERIES. Text in English. 1995. irreg., latest vol.3. price varies. **Document type:** *Academic/Scholarly.*
Indexed: BrArAb, NumL.
Published by: Oxbow Books, Park End Pl, Oxford, OX1 1HN, United Kingdom. TEL 44-1865-241249, FAX 44-1865-794449, oxbow@oxbowbooks.com, http://www.oxbowbooks.com.

930.1 417.7 GBR ISSN 0309-0701
OXFORD EDITIONS OF CUNEIFORM TEXTS. Text in English. 1923. irreg., latest vol.14, 1999. price varies. illus. **Document type:** *Monographic series.*
Formerly: Oxford Editions of Cuneiform Inscriptions
Indexed: CCMJ.
Published by: Oxford University Press, Great Clarendon St, Oxford, OX2 6DP, United Kingdom. TEL 44-1865-556767, FAX 44-1865-556646, enquiry@oup.co.uk, http://www.oup-usa.org/catalogs/general/series/Oxford_Editions_of_Cuneiform_Texts.html, http://www.oup.co.uk/. **Orders in N. America to:** Oxford University Press, 2001 Evans Rd, Cary, NC 27513. jnlorders@oup-usa.org.

913 GBR ISSN 0262-5253
CC1 CODEN: OJARE2
➤ **OXFORD JOURNAL OF ARCHAEOLOGY.** Text in English. 1982. q. EUR 51 combined subscription in Europe to individuals print & online eds.; USD 57 combined subscription in the Americas to individuals & Caribbean, print & online eds.; GBP 34 combined subscription elsewhere to individuals print & online eds.; GBP 333 combined subscription in Europe to institutions print & online eds.; USD 719 combined subscription in the Americas to institutions & Caribbean, print & online eds.; GBP 428 combined subscription elsewhere to institutions print & online eds.; EUR 33 combined subscription in Europe to students print & online eds.; USD 37 combined subscription in the Americas to students & Caribbean, print & online eds.; GBP 22 combined subscription elsewhere to students print & online eds. (effective 2006). adv. illus. reprint service avail. from PSC. **Document type:** *Journal, Academic/Scholarly.*
Related titles: Online - full text ed.: ISSN 1468-0092. GBP 316 in Europe to institutions; USD 684 in the Americas to institutions & Caribbean; GBP 407 elsewhere to institutions (effective 2006) (from Blackwell Synergy, EBSCO Publishing, Gale Group, IngentaConnect, O C L C Online Computer Library Center, Inc., Swets Information Services).
Indexed: A&ATA, AIAP, AnthLit, BHA, BrArAb, GEOBASE, IBSS, L&LBA, NumL, RASB, SOPODA.
—BLDSC (6321.005840), IE, Infotrieve, ingenta. **CCC.**
Published by: Blackwell Publishing Ltd., 9600 Garsington Rd, Oxford, OX4 2ZG, United Kingdom. TEL 44-1865-776868, FAX 44-1865-714591, customerservices@oxon.blackwellpublishing.com, http://www.blackwellpublishing.com/journals/OJOA. Eds. Andrew Sherratt, Helena Hamerow. Circ: 550.

930.1 GBR
OXFORD MONOGRAPHS ON CLASSICAL ARCHAEOLOGY. Text in English. irreg., latest 2003. price varies. illus.; maps. **Document type:** *Monographic series.*
Published by: Oxford University Press, Great Clarendon St, Oxford, OX2 6DP, United Kingdom. TEL 44-1865-556767, FAX 44-1865-556646, enquiry@oup.co.uk, http://www.oup-usa.org/catalogs/general/series/Oxford_Monographs_on_Classical_Archaeology.html.

930.1 GBR
➤ **OXFORD UNIVERSITY. SCHOOL OF ARCHAEOLOGY. MONOGRAPH.** Text in English. 1984. irreg., latest vol.54, 2000. **Document type:** *Monographic series, Academic/Scholarly.*
Formerly (until 2001): Oxford University. Committee for Archaeology. Monograph (1363-0849)
Indexed: BrArAb, NumL.
—BLDSC (6321.026551), IE, ingenta.
Published by: Oxford University, School of Archaeology, OUSA, Institute of Archaeology, 36 Beaumont St, Oxford, Oxon OX1 2PG, United Kingdom. TEL 44-1865-278240, FAX 44-1865-278254, http://www.ox.ac.uk. **Dist. by:** Oxbow Books, Park End Pl, Oxford OX1 1HN, United Kingdom. TEL 44-1865-241249, FAX 44-1865-794449.

913 940 GBR ISSN 0308-5562
OXONIENSIA. Text in English. 1936. a. GBP 12 (effective 2000). bk.rev. bibl.; charts; illus. index. **Document type:** *Academic/Scholarly.*
Indexed: BHA, BrArAb, NumL, PCI.
—BLDSC (6321.045000).
Published by: Oxfordshire Architectural and Historical Society, c/o Kellogg College, Rewley House, 1 Wellington Sq, Oxford, OX1 2JA, United Kingdom. http://www.oahs.org.uk. Ed., R&P Adrienne Rosen. Circ: 720.

930.1 USA
THE P A R I JOURNAL. Text in English. irreg. USD 25 domestic; USD 40 foreign (effective 2002).
Indexed: AnthLit.
Published by: Pre-Columbian Art Research Institute, David Greene & Co., 970 Dewing Ave., Suite 300, Lafayette, CA 94549-4260. david@dgreenecompany.com.

930.1 USA ISSN 0270-6776
P C A S NEWSLETTER. Text in English. 1961. m. USD 10 domestic; USD 14 foreign (effective 2000). **Document type:** *Newsletter.*
Formerly (until Feb. 1978): Smoke Signals
Indexed: AbAn.
Published by: Pacific Coast Archaeological Society, Inc., PO Box 10926, Costa Mesa, CA 92627-0926. http://www.pcas.org. Ed. Judy Dempsey. Circ: 200.

930.1 USA ISSN 0552-7252
E78.C15
PACIFIC COAST ARCHAEOLOGICAL SOCIETY QUARTERLY. Text in English. 1965. q. USD 32 domestic; USD 41 foreign (effective 2000). bibl. **Document type:** *Academic/Scholarly.*
Indexed: AbAn, AmH&L, AnthLit, CalPI, HistAb.
Published by: Pacific Coast Archaeological Society, Inc., PO Box 10926, Costa Mesa, CA 92627-0926. http://www.pcas.org. Circ: 200 (paid).

A

913 500 BEL ISSN 0257-8727
➤ **PACT/RESEAU EUROPEEN DE SCIENCES ET TECHNIQUES APPLIQUEES AU PATRIMOINE CULTUREL. REVUE.** Variant title: European Network of Scientific and Technical Cooperation. Journal. Text mainly in English; Text occasionally in French, Italian. 1977. irreg. (4-5/yr), latest vol.59, 2000. price varies. bk.rev. illus.; maps. back issues avail. **Document type:** *Monographic series, Academic/Scholarly.* **Description:** Promotes the use of science and the development of scientific techniques in the study of cultural heritage. Disseminates research on the use of scientific methods for dating and analyzing archaeological artifacts.
Related titles: CD-ROM ed.
Indexed: AnthLit, BrArAb, ChemAb, NAA, NumL.
—BLDSC (6333.101000).
Published by: Reseau Europeen de Cooperation Scientifique et Technique Appliquee au Patrimoine Culturel/European Network of Scientific and Technical Cooperation for the Cultural Heritage, Av Leopold 28a, Rixensart, 1330, Belgium. TEL 32-10-474882, FAX 32-2-345403, gmoucharte@wanadoo.be, http://bcs.fltr.ucl.ac.be/tocs-in/default.htm. Ed., R&P Ghislaine Moucharte. Circ: 1,000.
Co-sponsor: Council of Europe/Conseil de l'Europe.

930.1 ITA ISSN 0393-0149
PADUSA. Text in Italian; Summaries in English, Italian. 1965. a. EUR 50 domestic to individuals; EUR 100 foreign to individuals; EUR 65 domestic to institutions print & online eds.; EUR 125 foreign to institutions print & online eds. (effective 2003). bk.rev. abstr.; bibl.; charts; illus. back issues avail. **Document type:** *Academic/Scholarly.* **Description:** Deals with topographic and archeological studies in the Central Eastern Polesano Plain, concentrating mostly on the Bronze and Roman ages.
Related titles: Online - full text ed.
Indexed: BHA, NumL.
Published by: (Centro Polesano di Studi Storici, Archeologici ed Etnografici), Istituti Editoriali e Poligrafici Internazionali (Subsidiary of: Libra Web), Via Giosue' Carducci, 60, Ghezzano - La Fontina, PI 56010, Italy. TEL 39-050-878066, FAX 39-050-878732, iepi@iepi.it, http://www.iepi.it. Ed. Paolo Bellintani. Circ: 500.

571 PAK ISSN 0078-7868
DS378
PAKISTAN ARCHAEOLOGY. Text in English. 1964. a. price varies. **Document type:** *Academic/Scholarly.*
Indexed: AIAP, AnthLit, BAS.
Published by: Department of Archaeology and Museums, 27-A Central Union Commercial Area, Shaheed-e-Millat Rd., Karachi 8, Pakistan.

930.1 570 NLD ISSN 0552-9344
CC1 CODEN: PLHIAV
PALAEOHISTORIA; acta et communicationes instituti bioarchaeologici universitatis groninganae. Text in Dutch, English. 1951. a., latest 1995, vol.35-36, for the years 1993-. price varies. back issues avail. **Document type:** *Academic/Scholarly.*
Indexed: AnthLit, BIOSIS Prev, BrArAb, DIP, IBR, IBZ, NumL, RASB, ZooRec.
—BLDSC (6343.460000). **CCC.**
Published by: (Biologisch- Archaeologisch Instituut), A A Balkema (Subsidiary of: Taylor & Francis The Netherlands), PO Box 1675, Rotterdam, 3000 BR, Netherlands. FAX 31-10-413-5947, sales@balkema.nl, http://www.balkema.nl.
Dist. in U.S. by: Ashgate Publishing Co, Old Post Rd, Brookfield, VT 05036. TEL 800-535-9544.

220.9 933 BEL ISSN 0920-7422
➤ **PALAESTINA ANTIQUA.** Text in English, German. 1982. irreg., latest vol.9, 1999. price varies. illus.; maps. back issues avail. **Document type:** *Monographic series, Academic/Scholarly.* **Description:** Scholarly studies of topics in the history and archaeology of ancient Palestine and neighboring areas.
Published by: Peeters Publishers, Bondgenotenlaan 153, Leuven, 3000, Belgium. TEL 32-16-235170, FAX 32-16-228500, http://www.peeters-leuven.be.

➤ **PALEOECOLOGY OF AFRICA**; and the surrounding islands. see *PALEONTOLOGY*

913 956 200 GBR ISSN 0031-0328
DS101 CODEN: FRFSEL
PALESTINE EXPLORATION QUARTERLY. Text in English. 1869. s-a. USD 75 in North America to individuals; GBP 40 elsewhere to individuals; USD 96 in North America to institutions; GBP 52 elsewhere to institutions (effective 2005). adv. bk.rev. illus. index, cum.index every 2 yrs. back issues avail. **Document type:** *Journal, Academic/Scholarly.*
Related titles: Online - full text ed.: ISSN 1743-1301 (from EBSCO Publishing, Gale Group, IngentaConnect, Swets Information Services).
Indexed: AICP, AbAn, ArtInd, BHA, BibLing, IBR, IHP, IndIslam, MEA&I, NTA, NumL, OTA, PCI, R&TA, RASB, RI-1, RI-2, RILM.
—BLDSC (6345.360000), IE, Infotrieve, ingenta. **CCC.**
Published by: (Palestine Exploration Fund), Maney Publishing, Hudson Rd, Leeds, W Yorks LS9 7DL, United Kingdom. TEL 44-113-2497481, FAX 44-113-2486983, maney@maney.co.uk, http://www.maney.co.uk/search?fwaction=show&fwid=194. Ed. J R Bartlett. Circ: 900. **Subscr. in N America to:** Maney Publishing North America, 875 Massachusetts Ave, 7th Fl., Cambridge, MA 02139. TEL 866-297-5154, FAX 617-354-6875, maney@maneyusa.com.

913 CZE ISSN 0031-0506
➤ **PAMATKY ARCHEOLOGICKE/ARCHAEOLOGICAL MONUMENTS.** Text in Czech; Summaries in English, French, German; Text occasionally in English, German. 1854. s-a. EUR 25 per issue (effective 2004). bk.rev. charts; illus.; maps. 200 p./no.; Supplement avail.; reprints avail. **Document type:** *Journal, Academic/Scholarly.* **Description:** Basic studies of evolution in prehistory and middle ages; methodical articles of a general nature; studies dealing with recent research as well as museum collections.
Indexed: AICP, AnthLit, BHA, RASB.
Published by: Akademie Ved Ceske Republiky, Archeologicky Ustav, Letenska 4, Prague, 11801, Czech Republic. TEL 420-2-57533369, FAX 420-2-57532288. Ed. Michal Ernee.
Dist. in Western countries by: Suweco CZ SRO, Ceskomoravska 21, Prague 18021, Czech Republic.

913 CZE
PAMATKY ARCHEOLOGICKE. BIBLIOGRAPHICAL REGISTER. Text in Czech. irreg., latest 1974. **Description:** Basic studies of evolution in the prehistorical and earlier historical era; methodical articles of a general nature; studies dealing with recent research.
Published by: Akademie Ved Ceske Republiky, Archeologicky Ustav, Letenska 4, Prague, 11801, Czech Republic. TEL 420-2-57533369, FAX 420-2-57532288. Ed. Jan Rataj. **Dist. in Western countries by:** Kubon & Sagner Buchexport - Import GmbH, Postfach 321018, Munich 80328, Germany.

930.1 UKR ISSN 0869-3595
DK508.4
PAM'YAT STOLIT'. Text in Ukrainian. bi-m. USD 95 in United States. **Document type:** *Academic/Scholarly.*
Indexed: RASB.
—East View, KNAW.
Published by: Natsional'na Akademiya Nauk Ukrainy, vul Volodymyrs'ka 54, Kyiv, 01601, Ukraine. TEL 380-44-2352239, FAX 380-44-2343243, prez@nas.gov.ua, http://www.nas.gov.ua. **US dist. addr.:** East View Information Services, 3020 Harbor Ln. N., Minneapolis, MN 55447. TEL 763-550-0961, 612-550-0961, FAX 763-559-2931, eastview@eastview.com.

PAMYATNIKI KUL'TURY. NOVYE OTKRYTIYA/MONUMENTS OF CULTURE. NEW DISCOVERIES. see *ART*

PAN AMERICAN INSTITUTE OF GEOGRAPHY AND HISTORY. COMMISSION ON HISTORY. BIBLIOGRAFIAS. see *HISTORY—History Of North And South America*

930.26 POL ISSN 0137-2831
GN845.P7
PANSTWOWE MUZEUM ARCHEOLOGICZNE. MATERIALY STAROZYTNE I WCZESNOSREDNIOWIECZNE. Text in Polish. 1971. irreg. adv. back issues avail. **Document type:** *Academic/Scholarly.*
Formed by the merger of (1949-1971): Panstwowe Muzeum Archeologiczne. Materialy Wczesnosredniowieczne (0465-3580); (1956-1971): Panstwowe Muzeum Archeologiczne. Materialy Starozytne (0543-0739)
Indexed: AICP, AnthLit, BHA.
Published by: (Panstwowe Muzeum Archeologiczne), Wydawnictwa Akcydensowe, Ul Dluga 52, Warsaw, 00241, Poland. TEL 48-22-313221, FAX 48-22-315195. Adv. contact Wojciech Brzezinski.

932 BEL ISSN 0078-9402
PAPYROLOGICA BRUXELLENSIA. Text in French. 1962. irreg., latest vol.30, 1998. **Document type:** *Monographic series.*
Published by: Fondation Egyptologique Reine Elisabeth, Parc du Cinquantenaire 10, Brussels, 1000, Belgium. TEL 32-2-7417364.

913 ITA
PAPYROLOGICA CASTROCTAVIANA. Text in Italian, English, German, Spanish. 1967. irreg., latest vol.12, 1988. price varies. **Document type:** *Academic/Scholarly.* **Description:** Publishes previously unedited papyri and research on related subjects.
Published by: Pontificio Istituto Biblico/Pontifical Biblical Institute, Via della Pilotta 25, Rome, 00187, Italy. TEL 39-06-695261, FAX 39-06-695266151, pibsegr@pib.ur, http://www.pib.urbe.it.

LA PAROLA DEL PASSATO; rivista di studi antichi. see *CLASSICAL STUDIES*

PARTHICA; incontri di cultura sul mondo antico. see *HISTORY—History Of The Near East*

PAS-DE-CALAIS. COMMISSION DEPARTEMENTALE D'HISTOIRE ET D'ARCHEOLOGIE. MEMOIRES. see *HISTORY—History Of Europe*

930.1 GBR ISSN 1364-324X
THE PAST UNCOVERED. Text in English. 1991. 3/yr. free (effective 2003). back issues avail. **Document type:** *Newsletter.* **Description:** Publishes articles on archaeological discoveries, events and news in the Chester region of the United Kingdom.
Formerly (until 1994): Chester Archaeological Service Newsletter
Related titles: Online - full content ed.
—BLDSC (6409.201950).
Published by: Chester City Council, Chester Archaeology, 27 Grosvenor St, Chester, Cheshire CH1 2DD, United Kingdom. TEL 44-1244-402029, g.dunn@chestercc.gov.uk, 44-1244-347522, http://www.chestercc.gov.uk/heritage/archaeology/news.html. Ed., R&P Gillian Dunn TEL 44-1244-402023.

PATMA-BANASIRAKAN ANDES. see *HISTORY—History Of Europe*

930.1 FRA ISSN 1159-7836
PATRIMOINE AU PRESENT. Text in French. 1992. irreg. price varies. **Document type:** *Monographic series, Academic/Scholarly.*
Published by: (Caisse Nationale des Monuments Historiques et des Sites), C N R S Editions, 15 Rue Malebranche, Paris, 75005, France. TEL 33-1-53102700, FAX 33-1-53102727, http://www.cnrseditions.fr.

PAYS BAS-NORMAND. see *HISTORY—History Of Europe*

PAYS LORRAIN. see *HISTORY—History Of Europe*

930.1 USA
➤ **PEABODY MUSEUM BULLETINS.** Text in English. 1976. irreg., latest vol.8, 1999. price varies. bibl.; illus.; maps. **Document type:** *Monographic series, Academic/Scholarly.*
Published by: Peabody Museum of Archaeology and Ethnology, Harvard University, 11 Divinity Ave, Cambridge, MA 02138. TEL 617-496-9922, FAX 617-495-7535, ddickers@fas.harvard.edu, http://www.peabody.harvard.edu/publications. Adv. contact Donna Dickerson TEL 617-495-3938.

930.1 572 USA ISSN 0079-029X
➤ **PEABODY MUSEUM OF ARCHAEOLOGY AND ETHNOLOGY. MEMOIRS.** Text in English. 1896. irreg., latest vol.19. price varies. bibl.; illus.; maps. reprints avail. **Document type:** *Monographic series, Academic/Scholarly.*
Indexed: AnthLit.
Published by: Peabody Museum of Archaeology and Ethnology, Harvard University, 11 Divinity Ave, Cambridge, MA 02138. TEL 617-496-9922, FAX 617-495-7535, ddickers@fas.harvard.edu, http://www.peabody.harvard.edu/publications. Adv. contact Donna Dickerson TEL 617-495-3938.

930.1 USA
➤ **PEABODY MUSEUM OF ARCHAEOLOGY AND ETHNOLOGY. MONOGRAPHS.** Text in English. 1974. irreg., latest vol.9, 2000. price varies. bibl.; illus.; maps. **Document type:** *Monographic series, Academic/Scholarly.*
Indexed: AnthLit.
Published by: Peabody Museum of Archaeology and Ethnology, Harvard University, 11 Divinity Ave, Cambridge, MA 02138. TEL 617-496-9922, FAX 617-495-7535, ddickers@fas.harvard.edu, http://www.peabody.harvard.edu/publications. Adv. contact Donna Dickerson TEL 617-495-3938.

930.1 572 USA ISSN 0079-0303
E51 CODEN: HPAEAQ
➤ **PEABODY MUSEUM OF ARCHAEOLOGY AND ETHNOLOGY. PAPERS.** Text in English. 1891. irreg., latest vol.83, 2001. price varies. **Document type:** *Monographic series, Academic/Scholarly.*
Indexed: AnthLit, BiolAb, RASB.
—Linda Hall.
Published by: Peabody Museum of Archaeology and Ethnology, Harvard University, 11 Divinity Ave, Cambridge, MA 02138. TEL 617-496-9922, FAX 617-495-7535, ddickers@fas.harvard.edu, http://www.peabody.harvard.edu/publications. R&P Donna Dickerson TEL 617-495-3938.

930.1 USA ISSN 0031-4358
E78.P4 CODEN: PEARA8
THE PENNSYLVANIA ARCHAEOLOGIST. Text in English. 1930. s-a.
Indexed: AmH&L, AnthLit, HistAb.
Published by: Society for Pennsylvania Archaeology, Inc., P.O. Box 10287, Pittsburgh, PA 15232-0287. http://www.shol.com/spa20/spahome/SPA.htm.

PERITIA. see *HISTORY—History Of Europe*

PERSICA. see *HISTORY—History Of Asia*

917 USA
PERSPECTIVES IN CALIFORNIA ARCHAEOLOGY. Text in English. 1991. irreg., latest vol.5, 1998. price varies. **Document type:** *Monographic series, Academic/Scholarly.* **Description:** Covers the prehistoric and historic archaeology of California, including theoretical contributions, methodological or technical studies, regional or chronological themes, and interpretation of excavation data.
Published by: (Publications Department), University of California at Los Angeles, Cotsen Institute of Archaeology, A222 Fowler Museum, Box 951510, Los Angeles, CA 90095-1510. TEL 310-825-7411, FAX 310-206-4723. Ed. Jeanne E Arnold.

938 720 NLD ISSN 1380-2240
DF10
PHAROS. Text in English, French. N.S. 1993. a. EUR 30 per issue (effective 1994). back issues avail. **Document type:** *Academic/Scholarly.* **Description:** Publishes reports of Dutch archaeological and other researches in Greece.
Formerly (until 1993): Netherlands Institute at Athens. Newsletter
Published by: (Netherlands Institute at Athens), J.C. Gieben, Entrepotdok 72b, Amsterdam, 1018 AD, Netherlands. TEL 31-20-6234709, FAX 31-20-6275170, http://www.teachtext.net/gieben/. Eds. J J Feije, J J Hekman. **Dist. in N. America by:** John Benjamins Publishing Co., PO Box 27519, Philadelphia, PA 19118-0519. TEL 215-836-1200.

913 956 NLD ISSN 0031-8329
DS56
PHOENIX. Text in Dutch, English. 1955. 3/yr. EUR 34.50 to non-members; EUR 20.25 to members (effective 2004). adv. illus. **Document type:** *Journal, Academic/Scholarly.* **Description:** Focuses on recent discoveries in the Ancient Near East and Egypt.
Indexed: DIP, IBR, IBZ, NTA, PhilInd, RI-1.
—IE, Infotrieve.
Published by: Vooraziatisch-Egyptisch Genootschap "Ex Oriente Lux", Postbus 9515, Leiden, 2300 RA, Netherlands. TEL 31-71-5272016, eol@let.leidenuniv.nl, http://www.let.leidenuniv.nl/eol/. Circ: 1,400.

PHOINIX. see *HISTORY—History Of North And South America*

PIRRADAZISH: BULLETIN OF ACHAEMENIAN STUDIES. see *HISTORY—History Of The Near East*

PLAINS ANTHROPOLOGIST; a medium for the anthropological interpretation of the US Great Plains. see *ANTHROPOLOGY*

PLAINS ANTHROPOLOGIST. MEMOIR. see *ANTHROPOLOGY*

PLATON. see *CLASSICAL STUDIES*

943.8 913 POL ISSN 0079-3256
GN705.P6
POLSKA AKADEMIA NAUK. ODDZIAL W KRAKOWIE. KOMISJA ARCHEOLOGICZNA. PRACE. Text in English, German, Polish; Summaries in English, German, Russian. 1960. irreg., latest vol.28, 1990. price varies. **Document type:** *Monographic series.*
Published by: (Polska Akademia Nauk, Oddzial w Krakowie, Komisja Archeologiczna), Polska Akademia Nauk, Oddzial w Krakowie, ul sw Jana 28, Krakow, 31018, Poland. TEL 48-12-224853, FAX 48-12-222791.

PONTICA. see *HISTORY—History Of Europe*

930.1 SWE ISSN 0281-014X
POPULAER ARKEOLOGI. Text in Swedish. 1983. q. SEK 210 domestic; SEK 300 foreign (effective 2000). adv. bk.rev. **Document type:** *Magazine, Consumer.*
Related titles: Audio cassette/tape ed.
Indexed: NAA.
Published by: F H T Norrgaarde AB, Norrgaarde Hellvi, Laerbro, 62034, Sweden. TEL 46-498-22-80-00, FAX 46-498-22-80-21, popark@mail.com, http://www.popark.com. Ed. Birgitta Gustafson. Circ: 5,000.

930.14 SVN ISSN 1318-6701
➤ **POROCILO O RAZISKOVANJU PALEOLITA NEOLITA IN ENEOLITA V SLOVENIJI.** Text in Slovenian, English. 1962. a., latest vol.29, 2002. abstr.; illus.; maps. back issues avail. **Document type:** *Journal, Academic/Scholarly.*
Formerly (until 1998): Documenta Praehistorica (1408-967X)
Indexed: AnthLit.
—BLDSC (3609.660000).
Published by: (Univerza v Ljubljani, Filozofska Fakulteta, Oddelek za Arheologijo/University of Ljubljana, Faculty of Philosophy, Department of Archaeology), Univerza v Ljubljani, Filozofska Fakulteta/University of Ljubljana, Faculty of Philosophy, Askerceva 2, Ljubljana, 1000, Slovenia. TEL 386-1-2411000, http://www.ff.uni-lj.si/arheologija/neolitik/documenta.html. Ed. Mihael Budja.

➤ **POSITIONS FOR CLASSICISTS & ARCHAEOLOGISTS.** see *OCCUPATIONS AND CAREERS*

913 GBR ISSN 0079-4236
DA90
➤ **POST-MEDIEVAL ARCHAEOLOGY.** Text in English. 1967. s-a. USD 65 in North America to individuals; GBP 35 elsewhere to individuals; USD 192 in North America to institutions; GBP 104 elsewhere to institutions (effective 2005). adv. bk.rev. cum.index: vols. 1-5, 6-10. back issues avail. **Document type:** *Journal, Academic/Scholarly.* **Description:** Devoted to the study of the archaeological evidences of British and Colonial history of the post-medieval period.. Aims to provide a focus for the discussion of new developments and research priorities and also forms a definitive record of activity in the field.
Related titles: Online - full text ed.: 2005.
Indexed: AIAP, AbAn, AmH&L, BHA, BrArAb, HistAb, NumL.
—CCC.
Published by: (Society for Post-Medieval Archaeology), Maney Publishing, Hudson Rd, Leeds, W Yorks LS9 7DL, United Kingdom. TEL 44-113-2497481, FAX 44-113-2486983, maney@maney.co.uk, http://www.maney.co.uk/search?fwaction=show&fwid=202. Eds. Hugo Blake, William Klemperer. Adv. contact Kirsty Bailey. Circ: 650. **Subscr. in N America to:** Maney Publishing North America, 875 Massachusetts Ave, 7th Fl., Cambridge, MA 02139. TEL 866-297-5154, FAX 617-354-6875, maney@maneyusa.com.

913 USA ISSN 0738-8020
POTTERY SOUTHWEST; news, queries & views on archaeological ceramics by Southwesternists. Text in English. 1974. q. USD 4 in North America; USD 5 elsewhere (effective 2000). illus. **Document type:** *Academic/Scholarly.*
Indexed: AbAn, AnthLit.
Published by: Albuquerque Archaeological Society, 6207 Mossman Pl, N E, Albuquerque, NM 87110. Ed. Eric Blinman.

POWER PLACES OF CALIFORNIA. see *EARTH SCIENCES—Geophysics*

913 POL ISSN 0137-3250
➤ **POZNANSKIE TOWARZYSTWO PRZYJACIOL NAUK. KOMISJA ARCHEOLOGICZNA. PRACE.** Text in Polish; Summaries in English, German. 1922. irreg., latest vol.22, 2002. abstr.; bibl.; charts; illus. **Document type:** *Monographic series, Academic/Scholarly.*
Indexed: ChemAb.
Published by: (Poznanskie Towarzystwo Przyjaciol Nauk, Komisja Archeologiczna), Poznanskie Towarzystwo Przyjaciol Nauk/Poznan Society for the Advancement of the Arts and Sciences, ul Sew Mielzynskiego 27-29, Poznan, 61725, Poland. TEL 48-61-8527441, FAX 48-61-8522205, sekretariat@ptpn.poznan.pl, wydawnictwo@ptpn.poznan.pl, http://www.ptpn.poznan.pl. Circ: 420. **Dist. by:** Ars Polona, Krakowskie Przedmiescie 7, Warsaw, Poland. TEL 48-22-9263914, FAX 48-22-9265334, arspolona@arspolona.com.pl, http://www.arspolona.com.pl.

930.1 GBR ISSN 0951-6417
PRACTICAL HANDBOOKS IN ARCHAEOLOGY. Text in English. 1987. irreg., latest vol.15, 2000. **Document type:** *Monographic series, Academic/Scholarly.*
—BLDSC (6594.079000), ingenta. **CCC.**
Published by: Council for British Archaeology, Bowes Morrell House, 111 Walmgate, York, YO1 9WA, United Kingdom. TEL 44-1904-671417, FAX 44-1904-671384, info@britarch.ac.uk, http://www.britarch.ac.uk/pubs/handbooks.html.

913 DEU ISSN 0079-4848
PRAEHISTORISCHE ZEITSCHRIFT. Text in German, French, English. 1909. s-a. EUR 158; EUR 171 combined subscription print & online eds.; EUR 87 newsstand/cover (effective 2006). adv. bk.rev. cum.index: vols.1-55 in 1985. reprint service avail. from SCH. **Document type:** *Journal, Academic/Scholarly.*
Related titles: Online - full text ed.: ISSN 1613-0804. EUR 158 (effective 2006) (from EBSCO Publishing, Swets Information Services).
Indexed: AICP, AnthLit, BHA, BrArAb, DIP, IBR, IBZ, NAA, NumL.
—BLDSC (6598.300000), IE, Infotrieve, ingenta. **CCC.**
Published by: Walter de Gruyter GmbH & Co. KG, Genthiner Str. 13, Berlin, 10785, Germany. TEL 49-30-260050, FAX 49-30-26005251, wdg-info@degruyter.de, http://www.degruyter.de/rs/268_1260_DEU_h.htm. Eds. Bernhard Hansel, Kark Peschel, Karl-Heinz Willroth. Adv. contact Dietlind Makswitat TEL 49-30-260050. page EUR 550; trim 180 x 257. Circ: 500 (paid and controlled).

PREHISTORIC AMERICAN. see *HISTORY—History Of North And South America*

930.1 USA ISSN 1075-4288
PREHISTORIC ANTIQUITIES & ARCHAEOLOGICAL NEWS QUARTERLY. Text in English. 1981. q. USD 16; USD 6 newsstand/cover (effective 1996). bk.rev. back issues avail. **Document type:** *Consumer.* **Description:** Includes calendar of events, sources, books, and articles.
Published by: Prehistoric Antiquities, 7045 E Rte 245, Box 296, North Lewisburg, OH 43060. TEL 513-747-2225. Ed. B Ballinger. adv.: page USD 130; trim 11 x 8.5. Circ: 3,000 (paid).

913 GBR ISSN 0079-497X
DA670.E13
➤ **PREHISTORIC SOCIETY, LONDON. PROCEEDINGS.** Text in English. 1910. a. GBP 30 per issue to individuals; GBP 45 per issue to institutions (effective 2005). adv. bk.rev. back issues avail. **Document type:** *Proceedings, Academic/Scholarly.*
Formerly (until 1935): Prehistoric Society of East Anglia. Proceedings
Indexed: A&ATA, AICP, AbAn, AnthLit, BrArAb, BrHumI, NAA, NumL, PCI, RASB, SSCI.
—BLDSC (6787.760000), IE, ingenta.
Published by: Prehistoric Society, Institute of Archaeology, University College London, 31-34 Gordon Sq, London, WC1H 0PY, United Kingdom. Prehistoric@ucl.ac.uk, http://www.ucl.ac.uk/prehistoric/pps/pps.html. Ed. Julie Gardiner. R&P T Machling. Circ: 2,000.

930.1 CZE ISSN 1211-7250
PREHLED VYZKUMU/SURVEY OF THE FIELD EXCAVATIONS. Text in Czech, English. a. **Description:** Looks at the past year's excavations, findings, and related activities.
Published by: Akademie Ved Ceske Republiky, Archeologicky Ustav, Kralovopolska 147, Brno, 61200, Czech Republic. TEL 42-5-41212140, FAX 42-5-41514123, ps@sisbrno.cz, archeo@isibrno.cz, http://www.lib.cas.cz/knav/journals/contents/Prehled_vyzkumu_9692.htm. Ed. Jaroslav Tejral.

930.1 ITA ISSN 0393-0157
PREISTORIA ALPINA. Text in Multiple languages. 1971. a. **Document type:** *Journal, Academic/Scholarly.*
Indexed: AnthLit, ZooRec.
—BLDSC (6605.983000).
Published by: Museo Tridentino di Scienze Naturali, Via Calepina 14, Trento, TN 38100, Italy. TEL 39-0461-270311, FAX 39-0461.233830, info@mtsn.tn.it, http://www.mtsn.tn.it.

PRESERVATION NOTES. see *ARCHITECTURE*

914 330.1 949.7 BIH ISSN 0350-1159
HD8419.B6
➤ **PRILOZI/CONTRIBUTIONS.** Summaries in English. 1965-1992; resumed 1993-1994; resumed 1999. a. USD 8.50 (effective 1999). bk.rev. back issues avail. **Document type:** *Academic/Scholarly.* **Description:** Contains a collections of articles and text refered on the period from prehistorical to current time in Bosnia and Herzegovina.
Related titles: Microfilm ed.
Indexed: BibLing.
Published by: Institut za Istoriju Sarajevo/Institute of History in Sarajevo, Djure Djakovica 9, Sarajevo, 71000, Bosnia Herzegovina. TEL 387-71-471667, FAX 387-71-471667. Ed. Ibrehim Karebegovie. adv.: page USD 280. Circ: 500.
Co-sponsors: St. Lawrence Univeristy Solidarity Project; Soros Foundation.

➤ **PRINCETON MONOGRAPHS IN ART AND ARCHAEOLOGY.** see *ART*

➤ **PRINCETON UNIVERSITY ART MUSEUM. RECORD.** see *MUSEUMS AND ART GALLERIES*

913 AUT ISSN 0478-3166
PRO AUSTRIA ROMANA; Nachrichtenblatt fuer die Forschungsarbeit ueber die Roemerzeit in Oesterreich. Text in German. 1951. q. bk.rev. bibl.; illus. back issues avail. **Document type:** *Journal, Academic/Scholarly.* **Description:** Contains reports on recent excavations of Roman times in the territory of Austria.
Related titles: Online - full text ed.
Indexed: DIP, IBR, IBZ.
Published by: Oesterreichisches Archaeologisches Institut, Franz Klein-Gasse 1, Vienna, St 1190, Austria. TEL 43-1-427727101, FAX 43-1-42779271, mailbox@oeai.at, http://www.oeai.at. Circ: 450; 300 (paid). **Co-sponsor:** Oesterreichische Gesellschaft fuer Ur- und Fruehgeschichte.

913 RUS ISSN 0135-8316
PROBLEMY ARKHEOLOGII I ETNOGRAFII. Text in Russian. 1977. irreg. **Document type:** *Academic/Scholarly.*
Indexed: RASB.
Published by: Izdatelstvo Sankt-Peterburgskogo Universiteta, Universitetskaya nab 7-9, St Petersburg, 199034, Russian Federation. Circ: 1,185.

PROSPETTIVA; rivista di storia dell'arte antica e moderna. see *ART*

572 ITA ISSN 0079-7022
CC75
PROSPEZIONI ARCHEOLOGICHE/ARCHEOLOGICAL PROSPECTION. Text and summaries in English, Italian. 1966-1977; N.S. 1990. a. adv. bk.rev. back issues avail.
Indexed: AIAP, AnthLit, BHA, BrArAb.
Published by: Fondazione Carlo M. Lerici, Via Vittorio Veneto, 108, Rome, RM 00187, Italy. Eds. L Cavagnaro Vanoni, M Cucarzi. Circ: 400. **Subscr. to:** Edizioni Et, Corso Indipendenza, 12, Milan, MI 20129, Italy.

930.1 CAN
PROVINCIAL MUSEUM OF ALBERTA. ARCHAEOLOGY OCCASIONAL PAPERS. Text in English. 1975. irreg.

Indexed: AnthLit.
Published by: Provincial Museum of Alberta, 12845-102 Ave., Edmonton, AB, Canada. http://www.pma.edmonton.ab.ca/pma.htm.

913 POL ISSN 0079-7138
PRZEGLAD ARCHEOLOGICZNY. Text in English, Polish; Summaries in English, German. 1919. a., latest vol.52, 2004. EUR 25 per vol. foreign (effective 2005). bk.rev. 169 p./no. 2 cols./p.; **Document type:** *Journal, Academic/Scholarly.* **Description:** Papers on material culture in Poland and Europe.
Indexed: AICP, AnthLit, BHA, BrArAb, DIP, IBR, IBSS, IBZ, IndIslam, RASB.
Published by: Polska Akademia Nauk, Instytut Archeologii i Etnologii, Al Solidarnosci 105, Warsaw, 00140, Poland. TEL 48-22-6202881, FAX 48-22-6240100, director@iaepan.edu.pl, http://www.iaepan.edu.pl. Ed. Boguslaw Gediga. Circ: 450. **Dist. by:** Ars Polona, Krakowskie Przedmiescie 7, Warsaw, Poland. TEL 48-22-9263914, FAX 48-22-9265334, arspolona@arspolona.com.pl, http://www.arspolona.com.pl.

930.1 GBR ISSN 1465-5187
CC1
➤ **PUBLIC ARCHAEOLOGY.** Text in English. 1999. q. GBP 60, USD 95 (effective 1999 - 2000). bk.rev. **Document type:** *Journal, Academic/Scholarly.* **Description:** Aims to analyze and report on archaeological and heritage issues which relate to the wider world of politics, ethics, government, social questions, education, management, economics and philosphy.
Indexed: AnthLit, BrHumI.
—BLDSC (6962.790600). **CCC.**
Published by: Earthscan / James & James, 8-12 Camden High St, London, NW1 0JH, United Kingdom. TEL 44-20-7387-8558, FAX 44-20-7387-8998, http://www.jxj.com. Ed. Neal Asherson. Pub. Edward Milford.

➤ **PURABHILEKH - PURATATVA/ARCHIVES - ARCHAEOLOGY.** see *HISTORY—History Of Asia*

930.1 IND ISSN 0970-2105
PURATATTVA. Text in English. 1967. a.
Indexed: AnthLit.
Published by: Indian Archaeological Society, B-17, Qutab Institutional Area, New Delhi, 110016, India. TEL 91-11-6960654, ias_newdelhi@yahoo.co.uk, http://www.ias-del.org/arch/research.htm.

571 ESP ISSN 0079-8215
PYRENAE: CRONICA ARQUEOLOGICA; annual scientific journal. Text in Spanish. 1965. a. EUR 24.04 (effective 2005). bk.rev. **Document type:** *Journal, Academic/Scholarly.*
Indexed: AnthLit, BHA, HistAb, NumL, PCI.
—CINDOC.
Published by: (Universitat de Barcelona, Facultat de Geografia e Historia, Instituto de Arqueologia), Universitat de Barcelona, Servei de Publicacions, Gran Via Corts Catalanes 585, Barcelona, 08007, Spain. TEL 34-93-4021100, http://www.publicacions.ub.es. Ed. Juan Maluquer de Motes. Circ: 600.

913 ISR ISSN 0033-4839
DS111.A1
QADMONIYOT; journal for the antiquities of Eretz-Israel and Biblical lands. Variant title: Qadmoniot. Text in Hebrew; Contents page in English. 1968. s-a. USD 32 (effective 2003). bk.rev. illus. index. back issues avail. **Document type:** *Academic/Scholarly.* **Description:** Includes articles on biblical archaeology, ancient history, history and archaeology of later periods, and preliminary excavation reports.
Supersedes: Israel Exploration Society. Bulletin; Which was formerly (until 1933): Jewish Palestine Exploration Society. Yediot - Bulletin
Indexed: DIP, IBR, IBZ, IHP, NTA, NumL, OTA, R&TA.
Published by: Israel Exploration Society, P O Box 7041, Jerusalem, 91070, Israel. TEL 972-2-6257991, FAX 972-2-6247772, ies@vms.huji.ac.il, http://www.hum.huji.ac.il/ies/. Ed. A Mazar. Circ: 4,000.

933 ISR ISSN 0333-5844
QEDEM. Text in English. 1970. irreg., latest vol.34, 1993. price varies. back issues avail. **Document type:** *Monographic series, Academic/Scholarly.* **Description:** Scholarly studies and excavation reports on the archaeology of Israel, and related topics pertaining to the Middle East, including numismatics, architecture and prehistoric sites.
Published by: Hebrew University of Jerusalem, Institute of Archaeology, Jerusalem, Israel. Ed. Sue Gorodetsky. Circ: 1,550. **Subscr. to:** Israel Exploration Society, P O Box 7041, Jerusalem 91070, Israel. TEL 972-2-257991, FAX 972-2-247772.

QUADERNI DELLA ROCCA. see *HISTORY—History Of Europe*

930.1 ITA ISSN 1593-2664
QUADERNI DI ARCHEOLOGIA. Text in Italian. 1985. a. EUR 25.82 domestic; EUR 30.99 foreign (effective 2003).
Formerly (until 2000): Universita di Messina. Facolta di Lettere e Filosofia. Istituto di Archeologia. Quaderni (1593-2672)
Published by: (Universita degli Studi di Messina, Dipartimento di Scienze dell'Antichita/Sezione Archeologia), Rubbettino Editore, Viale Rosario Rubbettino 10, Soveria Mannelli, CZ 88049, Italy. TEL 39-0968-662034, FAX 39-0968-662055, segreteria@rubbettino.it, http://www.rubbettino.it.

913 ITA ISSN 1723-0667
QUADERNI DI ARCHEOLOGIA DEL MANTOVANO. Text in Italian. 1991. a. price varies. **Document type:** *Monographic series, Academic/Scholarly.* **Description:** Publishes research works related to the province of Mantova, especially the eastern region.
Formerly (until 1998): Gruppo Archeologico Ostigliese. Quaderni (1121-3949)
Published by: Gruppo Archeologico Ostigliese, Via Piave, 5, Ostiglia, MN 46035, Italy. Ed. Mauro Calzolari.

930.1 ITA ISSN 1120-9224
QUADERNI DI ARCHEOLOGIA DEL VENETO. Text in Italian. 1985. a.
Indexed: BrArAb.
Published by: Edizioni Quasar, Via Ajaccio 43, Rome, RM 00198, Italy. TEL 39-6-84241993, FAX 39-6-85833591, qn@edizioniquasar.it, http://www.edizioniquasar.it.

913 ITA ISSN 0079-8258
QUADERNI DI ARCHEOLOGIA DELLA LIBIA. Text in Italian. 1950. irreg. (vol19), latest 2003. price varies. back issues avail.
Indexed: AIAP, BHA.
Published by: L'Erma di Bretschneider, Via Cassiodoro, 19, PO Box 6192, Rome, RM 00193, Italy. TEL 39-06-6874127, FAX 39-06-6874129, edizioni@lerma.it, http://www.lerma.it.

913 526 ITA ISSN 1122-0953
QUADERNI DI TOPOGRAFIA ANTICA. Text in Italian. irreg., latest vol.10, 1988. price varies. **Document type:** *Monographic series, Academic/Scholarly.*
Indexed: AIAP.
Published by: (Universita degli Studi di Roma "La Sapienza"), Casa Editrice Leo S. Olschki, Viuzzo del Pozzetto 8, Florence, 50126, Italy. TEL 39-055-6530684, FAX 39-055-6530214, celso@olschki.it, http://www.olschki.it.

913 ITA ISSN 0079-8282
QUADERNI E GUIDE DI ARCHEOLOGIA. Text in Italian. 1952. irreg., latest 2000. price varies. **Document type:** *Monographic series, Academic/Scholarly.*
Published by: L'Erma di Bretschneider, Via Cassiodoro, 19, PO Box 6192, Rome, RM 00193, Italy. TEL 39-06-6874127, FAX 39-06-6874129, edizioni@lerma.it, http://www.lerma.it.

930.1 ITA ISSN 1122-7133
➤ **QUADERNI FRIULANI DI ARCHEOLOGIA.** Text in Italian. 1991. a. USD 15; USD 20 foreign. bk.rev. **Document type:** *Academic/Scholarly.* **Description:** Covers archaeology in north-east Italy and Alpine region.
Published by: Societa Friulana di Archeologia, c/o Civici Musei, Castello Di Udine, UD 33100, Italy. TEL 39-432-26560, saccavini@udprvx.fisica.univa.it. Ed. Maurizio Buora. Pub. Massimo Lavarone. R&P Andrea Pessina. Circ: 1,100.

913 ESP ISSN 0211-478X
DP402.B2
QUADERNS D'ARQUEOLOGIA I HISTORIA DE LA CIUTAT. Text in Spanish; Text occasionally in Catalan. 1960. irreg. bk.rev. cum.index: nos.1-17 (1960-1977).
Formerly (until 1977): Museo de Historia, Barcelona. Cuadernos de Arqueologia e Historia de la Cuidad. (0067-415X)
Indexed: AmH&L.
Published by: Museo de Historia de la Ciudad de Barcelona, Plaza del Rey, Barcelona, 08002, Spain. TEL 34-93-3151111, FAX 34-93-3150957, museuhistoria@mail.bcn.es, http://www.bcn.es/. Circ: 500.

914 946 ESP ISSN 0211-142X
QUADERNS D'HISTORIA TARRACONENSE. Text in Spanish. 1977. irreg. price varies. **Document type:** *Bulletin.*
—CINDOC.
Published by: Institut d'Estudis Tarraconenses Ramon Berenguer IV, Seccio d'Arqueologia i Historia, Santa Anna, 8, Tarragona, 43003, Spain. TEL 235032. Ed. F Xavier Ricoma.

913.031 DEU ISSN 0375-7471
QE697.A1 CODEN: QURTBJ
QUARTAER; Jahrbuch fuer Erforschung des Eiszeitalters und der Steinzeit. Text in English, French, German. 1946. a. price varies. bk.rev. reprint service avail. from PQC. **Document type:** *Academic/Scholarly.*
Indexed: AICP, AnthLit, BrArAb, IBR, IBZ, NumL, PCI, RASB, ZooRec.
Published by: (Hugo-Obermaier-Gesellschaft), Saarbruecker Druckerei und Verlag GmbH, Halbergstr 3, Saarbruecken, 66121, Germany. TEL 49-681-66501-0, FAX 49-681-6650110. Circ: 2,000.

930.1 301 AUS ISSN 0814-3021
QUEENSLAND ARCHAEOLOGICAL RESEARCH. Text in English. 1984. irreg.
Related titles: Online - full text ed.: (from R M I T Publishing).
Indexed: AnthLit, AusPAIS.
Published by: University of Queensland, Department of Anthropology, Sociology and Geography, Brisbane, QLD 4072, Australia. TEL 61-7-33653236, FAX 61-7-33651544, asoffice@mailbox.uq.edu.au, http://www.ansoc.uq.edu.au. Ed. Jay Hall.

913 930 DEU ISSN 0079-9149
QUELLENSCHRIFTEN ZUR WESTDEUTSCHEN VOR- UND FRUEHGESCHICHTE. Text in German. 1939. irreg., latest vol.10, 1982. price varies. **Document type:** *Monographic series, Academic/Scholarly.*
Published by: Dr. Rudolf Habelt GmbH, Am Buchenhang 1, Bonn, 53115, Germany. TEL 49-228-9238322, FAX 49-228-9238323, info@habelt.de, http://www.habelt.de. Ed. R Stampfuss.

RAPA NUI JOURNAL. see *ANTHROPOLOGY*

930.1 FRA
RAS SHAMRA-OUGARIT. Text in English, French. 1983. irreg. price varies. **Document type:** *Monographic series.*
Published by: Editions Recherche sur les Civilisations - A D P F, Les Patios Saint-Jacques, 6 rue Ferrus, Paris, Cedex 14 75603, France. TEL 33-1-43131100, FAX 33-1-43131125. Ed., Pub. Hina Descat. Circ: 600.

930.1 ITA ISSN 1721-6303
RASSEGNA DI ARCHEOLOGIA CLASSICA E POSTCLASSICA. Text in Italian. 1979. s-a. EUR 13 domestic; EUR 15 foreign (effective 2005). **Document type:** *Journal, Academic/Scholarly.*
Supersedes in part (in 2001): Rassegna di Archeologia (1721-6281)
Published by: Edizioni all'Insegna del Giglio s.a.s., Via N Piccinni 32, Florence, FI 50141, Italy. TEL 39-055-451593, FAX 39-055-450030, redazione@edigiglio.it, http://www.edigiglio.it.

930.1 ITA ISSN 1721-629X
RASSEGNA DI ARCHEOLOGIA PREISTORICA E PROTOISTORICA. Text in Italian. 1979. s-a. EUR 13 domestic; EUR 15 foreign (effective 2005). **Document type:** *Journal, Academic/Scholarly.*
Supersedes in part (in 2001): Rassegna di Archeologia (1721-6281)
Indexed: BHA.
Published by: Edizioni all'Insegna del Giglio s.a.s., Via N Piccinni 32, Florence, FI 50141, Italy. TEL 39-055-451593, FAX 39-055-450030, redazione@edigiglio.it, http://www.edigiglio.it.

RAYDAN; journal of ancient Yemeni antiquities and epigraphy. see *HISTORY—History Of The Near East*

READING THE PAST. see *LINGUISTICS*

913 USA
READINGS IN LONG ISLAND ARCHAEOLOGY AND ETHNOHISTORY SERIES. Text in English. 1977. a. price varies. illus.; bibl.; charts; maps; stat. back issues avail. **Document type:** *Monographic series, Academic/Scholarly.*
Indexed: AICP.
Published by: Suffolk County Archaeological Association, PO Box 1542, Stony Brook, NY 11790-0910. TEL 631-929-8725, FAX 631-929-6967. Ed., R&P Gaynell Stone. Circ: 1,000.

930.1 ESP ISSN 0213-9219
REAL ACADEMIA DE CULTURA VALENCIA. SECCION DE PREHISTORIA Y ARQUEOLOGIA. SERIE ARQUEOLOGICA. Text in Spanish. 1977. irreg.
Formerly (until 1986): Serie Arqueologica (0212-0070)
—CINDOC.
Published by: Real Academia de Cultura Valenciana, C. Avellanes, 26, Valencia, 46003, Spain. TEL 34-96-3916965, secretari@racv.es, http://www.racv.es/.

913 ESP ISSN 1695-5862
REAL SOCIEDAD ARQUEOLOGICA. BUTLLETI ARQUEOLOGIC. Text mainly in Spanish. 1901. a. USD 10. bk.rev. abstr.; illus.
Formerly: Real Sociedad Arqueologica. Boletin Arqueologico (0034-0863)
Indexed: BHA, BibInd, RILM.
Published by: Real Sociedad Arqueologica Tarraconense, Museo Nacional Arqueologico, Tarragona, Spain. Ed. Rodolfo Cortes. Circ: 1,000 (controlled). **Subscr. to:** Apartado 573, Tarragona 43070, Spain.

930.1 ESP ISSN 1135-2663
RECERQUES DEL MUSEU D'ALCOI. Text in Spanish, Catalan, English. 1992. a.
—CINDOC.
Published by: Museu Arqueologic Municipal D'Alcoi Camil Visedo i Molto, Placeta del Carbo, s-n, Alcoi, 03801, Spain. TEL 34-96-5540302, http://www.alcoi.com/guia/museu/.

RECHERCHES AMERINDIENNES AU QUEBEC. see *ANTHROPOLOGY*

914 BEL
RECHERCHES ARCHEOLOGIQUES EN HAINAUT OCCIDENTAL. BILAN. Text in French. 1972. every 5 yrs. **Document type:** *Catalog.*

Published by: Cercle Royal d'Histoire et d'Archeologie d'Ath et de la Region et Musees Athois, Rue de Bouchain 16, Ath, 7800, Belgium. TEL 32-68-265170, FAX 32-68-265179, http://www.ath.be/.

932 892.7 EGY ISSN 1011-1883

RECHERCHES D'ARCHEOLOGIE, DE PHILOLOGIE ET D'HISTOIRE. Text in French. 1930. irreg., latest vol.31, 1986. price varies. back issues avail. **Document type:** *Monographic series.* **Description:** Scholarly studies of topics relating to the history, archaeology and linguistics of Egypt from Pharaonic to modern time, and other parts of the Islamic world.
Published by: Institut Francais d'Archeologie Orientale du Caire, Kasr el-Aini, 37 Sharia Sheikh Aly Youssef, Mounira, P O Box 11562, Cairo, Egypt. TEL 20-2-3571622, FAX 20-2-3544635, mcmichel@fao.egnet.net, bph@ritsec3.com.eg. **Dist. by:** Boustany's Publishing House, 29 Faggalah St, Cairo 11271, Egypt. TEL 20-2-5915315, FAX 20-2-4177915.

914.2 942 GBR ISSN 1461-0795

THE RECORD. Text in English. 2/yr. free. adv. **Document type:** *Newsletter, Government.* **Description:** Provides information on the architecture and archeology of England. Includes 19th century photographs; air photographs of all England; surveys and photographs of historic buildings; archeological data; plans, drawings and surveys.
Former titles: English Heritage. Record; Great Britain. Royal Commission on the Historical Monuments of England. Record; (until 1997): Great Britain. Royal Commission on the Historical Monuments of England. Newsletter (0957-0241)
Indexed: BrArAb, NumL.
Published by: English Heritage, National Monuments Record Centre, Kemble Dr, Swindon, Wilts SN2 2GZ, United Kingdom. TEL 44-1793-414700, FAX 44-1793-414606, info@rcheme.co.uk, http://www.english-heritage.org.uk. Ed., Adv. contact Jon Cannon. R&P Donnie Mackay TEL 44-1793-414626.

915 CHN ISSN 1004-6275
DS715

RELICS FROM SOUTH. Text in Chinese; Summaries in English. 1989. q. CNY 20; USD 12 foreign. adv. bk.rev. **Document type:** *Government.* **Description:** Reports archaeological excarvations and research articles about cultural relics, archaeology and history.
Formerly (until 1992): Jiangxi Cultural Relics (1001-8646)
Related titles: Online - full text ed.: (from East View Information Services).
Published by: Jiangxi Sheng Bowuguan/Jiangxi Provincial Museum, 327 Bayi Dadao, Nanchang, Jiangxi 330003, China. TEL 86-791-6263531. Ed. Peng Shifan. Circ: 2,500 (paid).

RELIGIONS IN THE GRAECO-ROMAN WORLD. see *RELIGIONS AND THEOLOGY*

REPORTS IN MACKINAC HISTORY AND ARCHAEOLOGY. see *HISTORY—History Of North And South America*

301 USA ISSN 0277-1322
N5310.7

➤ **RES**; anthropology and aesthetics. Text in Multiple languages. 1981. s-a. USD 30 in North America to individuals; USD 42 elsewhere to individuals; USD 64 in North America to institutions; USD 74 elsewhere to institutions (effective 2003). adv. illus. back issues avail. **Document type:** *Journal, Academic/Scholarly.* **Description:** Takes a multidisciplinary approach to the comparative study of aesthetic and religious objects from all cultures and all times.
Indexed: AIAP, AICP, AnthLit, ArtInd, BHA, IBSS, IndIslam, RILM.
—BLDSC (7713.847400).
Published by: Peabody Museum of Archaeology and Ethnology, Harvard University, 11 Divinity Ave, Cambridge, MA 02138. TEL 617-496-9922, FAX 617-495-7535, ddickers@fas.harvard.edu, http://www.peabody.harvard.edu/publications/res.htm. Ed. Francesco Pellizzi. R&P, Adv. contact Donna Dickerson TEL 617-495-3938. B&W page USD 500. Circ: 400.

913.031 GBR ISSN 0950-5830

RESCUE NEWS. Text in English. 1972. 3/yr. GBP 15 to individual members; GBP 20 to institutional members; GBP 8 to students (effective 2005). adv. bk.rev. bibl.; illus. **Document type:** *Newspaper, Consumer.* **Description:** Comment and opinion on archaeological issues in Great Britain.
Indexed: BrArAb, NumL.
Published by: Rescue British Archaeological Trust, 15a Bull Plain, Hertford, Herts SG14 1DX, United Kingdom. rescue@rescue-archaeology.freeserve.co.uk, http://www.rescue-archaeology.freeserve.co.uk/rescuenews/rnindex.html. Ed. J Mellor. Circ: 1,500.

RESTAURACION HOY. see *ART*

930.1 USA ISSN 1050-4877

THE REVIEW OF ARCHAEOLOGY. Text in English. 1980. s-a. USD 25 domestic; USD 27 in Canada & Mexico; USD 32 elsewhere (effective 2005). bk.rev. **Document type:** *Journal, Academic/Scholarly.* **Description:** Review of archaeological literature providing a critical evaluation of the many kinds of records that affect the conduct of archaeology and the interpretation of prehistory.
Formerly (until 1989): Quarterly Review of Archaeology (0278-9825)
Indexed: BrArAb, NumL.
Published by: Review of Archaeology, Inc., Box 430, Williamstown, MA 01267-0430. TEL 413-458-2773, FAX 413-458-5044, diane.a.perault@williams.edu, http://www.reviewofarchaeology.com. Ed., R&P Frederick Hadleigh West. Circ: 300 (paid).

REVIEW OF SCOTTISH CULTURE. see *ETHNIC INTERESTS*

901 ESP ISSN 1138-9435
GN836.A6

REVISTA ATLANTICA-MEDITERRANEA DE PREHISTORIA Y ARQUEOLOGIA SOCIAL. Text in Spanish. 1998. a. back issues avail.
—CINDOC.
Published by: Universidad de Cadiz, Servicio de Publicaciones, Rectorado Ancha 16, Cadiz, 11001, Spain. TEL 34-956-0150000, http://minerva.uca.es/publicaciones/seccion.asp?secc=R-AM, http://www.uca.es/.

930.1 ESP ISSN 1131-883X
CC13.C3

REVISTA D'ARQUEOLOGIA DE PONENT. Text in Catalan. 1991. a. EUR 27 (effective 2002). back issues avail.
—CINDOC.
Published by: Universitat de Lleida, Servei de Publicacions, Placa Victor Siurana, 1, Lleida, 25003, Spain. TEL 34-973-702084, FAX 34-973-702148, eip@eip.udl.es, http://www.udl.es/.

913 BRA ISSN 0102-0420

REVISTA DE ARQUEOLOGIA. Text in Portuguese. 1983. s-a. USD 10.
Indexed: AIAP, AICP, AnthLit.
Published by: Museu Paraense Emilio Goeldi, Setor de Difusao Cientifica e Cultural, Comercio, Caixa Postal 339, Belem, PA 66017-970, Brazil.

918 MEX
E61

REVISTA DE ARQUEOLOGIA AMERICANA. Text in English, French, Portuguese, Spanish. 1990. s-a. MXP 100 domestic; USD 26 in North America; USD 29.50 in South America; USD 33 in Asia & the Pacific (effective 2005). reprint service avail. from PQC. **Document type:** *Academic/Scholarly.*
Formerly: Revista de Arqueologia Mexicana (0188-3631)
Related titles: Microfilm ed.: (from PQC); Online - full text ed.: (from Gale Group).
Indexed: AICP, AnthLit, HAPI.
Published by: Instituto Panamericano de Geografia e Historia, Ex-Arzobispado 29, Col Observatorio, Del Miguel Hidalgo, Mexico City, DF 11860, Mexico. TEL 52-55-52775791, FAX 52-55-52716172, info@ipgh.org.mx, http://www.ipgh.org.mx/. Ed. Oscar Fonseca. Circ: 700. **Subscr. to:** IPGH, c/o Depto. de Distribucion y Ventas, Apdo. 18879, Mexico City, DF 11870, Mexico.

REVISTA DE HISTORIA. see *HISTORY*

913 FRA ISSN 0035-0737
CC3

REVUE ARCHEOLOGIQUE. Text in French. 1844. s-a. EUR 69 domestic to individuals; EUR 77 foreign to individuals; EUR 81 domestic to institutions; EUR 97.06 foreign to institutions (effective 2005). bk.rev. charts; illus. index. reprint service avail. from PQC,SCH. **Document type:** *Journal, Academic/Scholarly.* **Description:** Publishes recent studies on the Greco-Roman times, the Bronze Age, and the start of the Middle Ages.
Related titles: Microform ed.: (from PQC).
Indexed: AIAP, AnthLit, ArtInd, BHA, BiolAb, BrArAb, DIP, IBR, IBSS, IBZ, NumL, PCI, RASB, SSCI.
—IE, Infotrieve. **CCC.**
Published by: Presses Universitaires de France, 6 Avenue Reille, Paris, 75685 Cedex 14, France. TEL 33-1-58103100, FAX 33-1-58103182, REVUEARCHEOLOGIQUE@wanadoo.fr, revues@puf.com, http://www.puf.com. Ed. Martine Fourmont.

930.1 FRA ISSN 1154-1342

REVUE ARCHEOLOGIQUE DE BORDEAUX. Text in French. 1873. a.
Former titles (until 1989): Societe Archeologique de Bordeaux (0995-0761); (until 1985): Societe Archeologique de Bordeaux. Bulletin et Memoires (0755-7051); (until 1917): Societe Archeologique de Bordeaux (1155-6471)
Indexed: BHA, NumL, RILM.
Published by: Societe Archeologique de Bordeaux, Hotel des Societes Savantes, 1 place Bardineau, Bordeaux, 33000, France. TEL 33-5-56444818.

913 FRA ISSN 0220-7796

REVUE ARCHEOLOGIQUE DE L'EST ET DU CENTRE EST. SUPPLEMENT. Text in French. 1974. irreg. price varies.
Related titles: ♦ Supplement to: Revue Archeologique de l'Est. ISSN 1266-7706.
Indexed: BHA.
Published by: (France. Centre National de la Recherche Scientifique), C N R S Editions, 15 Rue Malebranche, Paris, 75005, France. TEL 33-1-53102700, FAX 33-1-53102727, http://www.cnrseditions.fr.

914 FRA ISSN 0767-709X
DC609.4

REVUE ARCHEOLOGIQUE DE L'OUEST. Text in French. 1984. a. EUR 27.44 (effective 2002). adv. bk.rev. back issues avail. **Document type:** *Journal, Academic/Scholarly.* **Description:** Studies the archeology of the west of France: Brittany, Normandy and the Loire country.
Related titles: ♦ Supplement(s): Revue Archeologique de l'Ouest. Supplement. ISSN 1166-8261.
Indexed: AnthLit, BHA, BrArAb, NumL, RILM.
Published by: Association R.A.O., c/o Laboratoire d'Archeometrie, Universite de Rennes, Rennes, Cedex 35042, France. TEL 33-2-99286070, FAX 33-2-99286934. Ed., Pub., R&P, Adv. contact Loic Langouet.

914 FRA ISSN 1166-8261

REVUE ARCHEOLOGIQUE DE L'OUEST. SUPPLEMENT. Text in French. 1984. irreg.
Related titles: ♦ Supplement to: Revue Archeologique de l'Ouest. ISSN 0767-709X.
Published by: Association R.A.O., c/o Laboratoire d'Archeometrie, Universite de Rennes, Rennes, Cedex 35042, France.

930.1 FRA ISSN 0752-5656
CODEN: RAPCE2

➤ **REVUE ARCHEOLOGIQUE DE PICARDIE.** Text in French. 1982. q. **Document type:** *Monographic series, Academic/Scholarly.*
Indexed: BHA, BrArAb, NumL.
—BLDSC (7891.121000), IE, ingenta.
Address: 5 rue H. Daussy, Amiens, 80000, France. TEL 33-3-22973345, FAX 33-3-22943342. Ed. Marc Durand.

913 FRA ISSN 0220-6617
DC30

REVUE ARCHEOLOGIQUE DU CENTRE DE LA FRANCE. Text in French. 1961. a. EUR 53.36 in the European Union to individuals (effective 2001). bk.rev. abstr.; bibl.; charts; illus. index, cum.index every 10 yrs.
Formerly: Revue Archeologique du Centre (0035-0753)
Indexed: BHA.
Published by: (Ministere de la Culture et de la Communication), Editions la Simarre, Z.I. No. 2 - rue Joseph-Cugnot, Joue-les-Tours, 37300, France. TEL 33-2-47535366, FAX 33-2-47674505. Ed. Henri Galinie.

REVUE BELGE D'ARCHEOLOGIE ET D'HISTOIRE DE L'ART/BELGISCH TIJDSCHRIFT VOOR OUDHEIDKUNDE EN KUNSTGESHIEDENIS. see *ART*

REVUE BELGE DE NUMISMATIQUE ET DE SIGILLOGRAPHIE. see *NUMISMATICS*

REVUE BIBLIQUE. see *RELIGIONS AND THEOLOGY*

930.1 FRA ISSN 0399-1237
CC78

REVUE D'ARCHEOMETRIE; bulletin de liaison du groupe des methodes pluridisciplinaires contribuant a l'archeologie. Text in French. 1977. a.
Indexed: AnthLit.
—BLDSC (7891.127000), IE, ingenta.
Published by: Groupe des Methodes Pluridisciplinaires Contribuant de l'archeologie/Group of Multi-field Methods Contributing to Archaeology, University of the Small Rock, Avenue Michel Crepeau, La Rochelle, Cedex 1, 17042, France.

REVUE DE COMMINGES. see *HISTORY—History Of Europe*

913 940 FRA ISSN 1161-7721

REVUE DE LA MANCHE. Text in French. 1959. q. adv. bk.rev. bibl.; illus. **Document type:** *Bulletin, Academic/Scholarly.*
Formerly (until 1991): Societe d'Archeologie et d'Histoire de la Manche. Departement de la Manche. Revue (0996-3642)
Indexed: BHA.
Published by: Societe d Archeologie et d Histoire de la Manche, BP 540, Saint Lo, Cedex 50010, France. TEL 33-2-33571517, FAX 33-2-33570486. Circ: 1,500.

913 940 FRA ISSN 0035-1342

➤ **REVUE DE L'AVRANCHIN ET DU PAYS DE GRANVILLE.** Text in French. 1882. q. EUR 25 domestic; EUR 28 foreign (effective 2003). adv. bk.rev. charts; illus. index. **Document type:** *Bulletin, Academic/Scholarly.*
Published by: Societe d'Archeologie, de Litterature, Sciences et Arts d'Avranches, Mortain et Granville, Centre Culturel de l'Abbaye de Moutons, Avranches, (Manche) 50300, France. TEL 33-01-45-89-48-57, FAX 33-01-45-88-48-32, mldugue@aol.com. Ed., Adv. contact Michael Dugue TEL 33-2-33904510. Circ: 360 (paid).

➤ **REVUE DE QUMRAN.** see *RELIGIONS AND THEOLOGY*

▼ new title ➤ refereed ✶ unverified ♦ full entry avail.

A

950 BEL ISSN 0035-1849
PJ1003
➤ **REVUE D'EGYPTOLOGIE.** Text in English, French, German. 1935. a., latest vol.55, 2004. EUR 80 (effective 2006). bk.rev. illus.; maps. cum.index: vols.1-20. **Document type:** *Monographic series, Academic/Scholarly.* **Description:** Publishes research in all areas of study of ancient Egypt.
Related titles: Online - full text ed.: (from EBSCO Publishing); ◆ Supplement(s): Societe Francaise d'Egyptologie. Bulletin. ISSN 0037-9379.
Indexed: BHA, BibLing, DIP, IBR, IBZ, PCI, RASB, RI-1. —IE.
Published by: (Societe Francaise d'Egyptologie FRA), Peeters Publishers, Bondgenotenlaan 153, Leuven, 3000, Belgium. TEL 32-16-235170, FAX 32-16-228500, peeters@peeters-leuven.be, http://poj.peeters-leuven.be/content.php?url=journal&journal_code=RE, http://www.peeters-leuven.be. Ed. D Valdelle.

➤ **REVUE DES ETUDES GRECQUES.** see *CLASSICAL STUDIES*

913 310 FRA ISSN 0398-0022
REVUE DROMOISE. Text in French. 1866. q. adv. bk.rev. index. **Document type:** *Academic/Scholarly.*
Formerly: Bulletin d'Archeologie et de Statistique de la Drome (0037-8992)
Indexed: BHA, BibInd.
Published by: Societe d'Archeologie d Histoire et de Geographie de la, Archives Departementales, 14 rue de la Manutention, Valence, 26000, France. Ed. Philippe Bouchardeau. Adv. contact Joseph Arbod. Circ: 500.

REVUE DU NORD. ARCHEOLOGIE. see *HISTORY—History Of Europe*

913 944 FRA ISSN 0035-3272
REVUE HISTORIQUE ARDENNAISE. Text in French. 1969. a. adv. bk.rev. charts; illus. back issues avail. **Document type:** *Bulletin.*
Formerly: Etudes Ardennaises (0014-1968)
—IE.
Published by: Societe d'Etudes Ardennaises, BP 831, Charleville-Mezieres, Cedex 08011, France. Ed. Odile Jurbert. Circ: 1,275.

REVUE HISTORIQUE DU CENTRE OUEST. see *HISTORY—History Of Europe*

913 940 FRA ISSN 1158-3371
➤ **REVUE HISTORIQUE ET ARCHEOLOGIQUE DU MAINE.** Text in French. 1876. a. EUR 36 (effective 2001). adv. bibl.; charts; illus.; maps; stat. 350 p./no. 1 cols./p.; back issues avail.; reprints avail. **Document type:** *Yearbook, Academic/Scholarly.*
Indexed: AIAP, BHA.
Published by: Societe Historique et Archeologique du Maine, 17 rue de la Reine Berengere, Le Mans, 72000, France. Pub. Juergen Kloetgen. Adv. contact Pierre Polanchet. Circ: 650.

913 943 CHE ISSN 1013-6924
DQ721
REVUE HISTORIQUE VAUDOISE. Text in French. 1893. a. CHF 40 (effective 2003). adv. charts; illus. **Document type:** *Yearbook, Academic/Scholarly.*
Indexed: BHA.
Published by: Societe Vaudoise d'Histoire et d'Archeologie, Rue de la Mouline 32, Chavannes-pres-Renens, 1022, Switzerland. TEL 41-21-3163711, FAX 41-21-3163755, archives.cantonales@acv.vd.ch. Ed. Laurent Droz.

913 DEU ISSN 0557-7853
RHEINISCHE AUSGRABUNGEN. Text in German. 1968. irreg., latest vol.44, 1998. price varies. **Document type:** *Monographic series, Academic/Scholarly.*
Indexed: BrArAb, RASB.
Published by: (Landschaftsverband Rheinland), Rheinland Verlag GmbH, Abtei Brauweiler, Postfach 2140, Pulheim, 50250, Germany. TEL 49-2234-9854265, FAX 49-2234-82503. **Distr. by:** Dr. Rudolf Habelt GmbH, Am Buchenhang 1, Bonn 53115, Germany. TEL 49-228-9238322, FAX 49-228-232017. **Co-sponsor:** Rheinisches Amt fuer Bodendenkmalpflege.

913 DEU
RHEINISCHES LANDESMUSEUM BONN. KATALOGE. Text in German. 1994. irreg., latest vol.9, 1999. price varies. **Document type:** *Monographic series, Academic/Scholarly.*
Published by: (Rheinisches Landesmuseum Bonn), Rheinland Verlag GmbH, Abtei Brauweiler, Postfach 2140, Pulheim, 50250, Germany. TEL 49-2234-9854265, FAX 49-2234-82503. **Dist. by:** Dr. Rudolf Habelt GmbH, Am Buchenhang 1, Bonn 53115, Germany. TEL 49-228-9238322, FAX 49-228-232017.

914 NLD ISSN 0167-5443
DJ51
RIJKSDIENST VOOR HET OUDHEIDKUNDIG BODEMONDERZOEK TE AMERSFOORT. BERICHTEN. Text in Dutch, English, German. 1950. a. abstr.; bibl.; illus.; maps. **Document type:** *Academic/Scholarly.* **Description:** Covers the archaeology and archaeological heritage of the Netherlands from prehistoric times to the post-Medieval period.
Indexed: AnthLit, BHA, BrArAb, NumL, RASB.
Published by: Rijksdienst voor het Oudheidkundig Bodemonderzoek te Amersfoort, Kerkstraat 1, Amersfoort, 3811 CV, Netherlands. TEL 31-33-4634233, FAX 31-33-4653235, arne.haytsma@archis.nl, http://www.archis.nl/. Ed. A Haytsma. Circ: 1,000.

930.1 NLD ISSN 0924-2767
RIJKSDIENST VOOR HET OUDHEIDKUNDIG BODEMONDERZOEK TE AMERSFOORT. JAARVERSLAG. Text in Dutch. 1947. a. free. bibl.; illus. **Document type:** *Corporate.* **Description:** Publishes information on the archaeological activities of the Service, including investigation reports, reports from provincial and regional archaeologists, and from the Department of Nautical Archaeology.
Published by: Rijksdienst voor het Oudheidkundig Bodemonderzoek te Amersfoort, Kerkstraat 1, Amersfoort, 3811 CV, Netherlands. TEL 31-33-4634233, FAX 31-33-4653235, http://www.archis.nl/. Ed. G Scheepstra.

913 975 USA ISSN 0271-6925
RIPLEY P. BULLEN MONOGRAPHS IN ANTHROPOLOGY AND HISTORY. Text in English. 1978. irreg., latest vol.14, 1993. price varies. back issues avail. **Document type:** *Monographic series.*
Published by: (Florida Museum of Natural History), University Press of Florida, 15 NW 15th St, Gainesville, FL 32611. TEL 352-392-1351, 800-226-3822, FAX 352-392-7302, http://www.upf.com. Ed. Jerald T Milanich.

930.1 NOR ISSN 1503-7436
▼ **RISS.** Text in Norwegian. 2003. q. NOK 130 (effective 2004).
Published by: Universitetet i Bergen, Arkeologisk Institutt, J. Frieles Gate 1, Bergen, 5007, Norway. TEL 47-55-582942, FAX 47-55-583160, rissred@start.no, post@ark.uib.no, http://www.hf.uib.no/Arkeologisk/riss.htm, http://www.hf.uib.no/arkeologisk/.

932 BEL
RITES EGYPTIENS. Text in French, German. 1975 (vol.2). irreg., latest vol.8, 1995. price varies. back issues avail. **Document type:** *Monographic series.*
Published by: Fondation Egyptologique Reine Elisabeth, Parc du Cinquantenaire 10, Brussels, 1000, Belgium. TEL 32-2-7417364.

913 709 945 ITA ISSN 1124-3147
RIVISTA ARCHEOLOGICA DELL'ANTICA PROVINCIA E DIOCESI DI COMO; periodico di antichita ed arte. Text in Italian; Summaries in English, French. 1872. a., latest vol.183, 2001. EUR 31 domestic; EUR 56 foreign (effective 2003). adv. bk.rev. illus.; maps. cum.index: 1872-1992. back issues avail.; reprints avail. **Document type:** *Bulletin, Academic/Scholarly.* **Description:** Features archeological research from Como and its surrounding areas. Directed to archeologists.
Former titles (until 1941): Rivista Archeologica dell'Antica Provincia e Diocesi di Como. Antichita ed Arte (1124-3139); (until 1929): Rivista Archeologica della Provincia e Antica Diocesi di Como. Antichita ed Arte (1124-3120); (until 1914): Rivista Archeologica della Provincia e Antica Diocesi di Como. Antichita ed Belle Arti (1124-2434); Rivista Archeologica della Provincia e Antica Diocesi di Como (0080-3235)
Related titles: Video ed.
Indexed: BHA, NumL.
Published by: Societa Archeologica Comense, Piazza Medaglie d Oro, 6, Como, CO 22100, Italy. Ed., Adv. contact Giorgio Luraschi. Circ: 2,000.

RIVISTA DEGLI STUDI ORIENTALI. see *ASIAN STUDIES*

913 ITA ISSN 0392-0895
CC9
RIVISTA DI ARCHEOLOGIA. Text in Italian. 1977. a., latest vol.26, 2002. price varies. back issues avail. **Document type:** *Monographic series, Academic/Scholarly.*
Indexed: AIAP, BHA, PCI.
Published by: Giorgio Bretschneider, Casella Postale 30011, Rm47, Rome, 00193, Italy. TEL 39-06-6879361, FAX 39-06-6864543, info@bretschneider.it, http://www.bretschneider.it/. Ed. Gustavo Traversari.

913 ITA ISSN 0035-6042
BR130
RIVISTA DI ARCHEOLOGIA CRISTIANA. Text in Italian, English, French, German, Latin, Greek. 1924. s-a. EUR 61.98 domestic; EUR 67.14 in Europe; EUR 82.64 elsewhere (effective 2001). bk.rev. bibl.; illus. index.
Indexed: AIAP, BHA, BrArAb, DIP, IBR, IBZ, NTA.
Published by: Pontificio Istituto di Archeologia Cristiana, Pontificia Commissione di Archeologia Sacra, Via Napoleone III, 1, Rome, RM 00185, Italy. TEL 39-06-4465574, FAX 39-06-4469197, piac.editrice@piac.it, http://www.piac.it. Ed. Dr. Philippe Pergola.

572 ITA ISSN 0035-6514
GN700
➤ **RIVISTA DI SCIENZE PREISTORICHE.** Text in Italian; Summaries in English, French. 1946. a. EUR 40 (effective 2004). bk.rev. abstr.; bibl.; illus. index. **Document type:** *Journal, Academic/Scholarly.* **Description:** Contains original studies on prehistorical and protohistorical cultures, prehistoric art, anthropology,and methodology of prehistoric research.
Indexed: AICP, AnthLit, BrArAb, DIP, IBR, IBZ, RASB.
Published by: Istituto Italiano di Preistoria e Protostoria, Via Sant Egidio 21, Florence, FI 50122, Italy. TEL 39-055-2340765, FAX 39-055-5354821, http://www.iipp.it. Ed. Fabio Martini. Circ: 550 (controlled).

913 ITA ISSN 0390-3877
RIVISTA DI STUDI FENICI. Text in English, French, German, Italian, Spanish. 1973. s-a. bk.rev. back issues avail. **Document type:** *Journal, Academic/Scholarly.*
Indexed: BibLing, BrArAb, DIP, IBR, IBZ, NumL.
Published by: (C.N.R. Istituto di Studi Fenici-Punici), Herder Editrice e Libreria s.r.l., Piazza di Montecitorio 117-120, Rome, 00186, Italy. TEL 39-06-6794628, FAX 39-06-6784751, bookcenter@herder.it, http://www.herder.it. Circ: 1,000.

914.5 ITA ISSN 1120-3579
DG70.P7
RIVISTA DI STUDI POMPEIANI. Text in Italian. 1987. irreg., latest vol.7, 1995-96. price varies. bk.rev. **Description:** In two parts, the first of which is dedicated to scholarly articles on various subjects related to Pompeian art. The second details the activities of the Soprintendenza Archeologica di Pompei e Suburbo, and contains the results of the excavations carried out by the Ufficio Scavi.
Indexed: AIAP.
Published by: (Associazione Internazionale "Amici di Pompei"), L'Erma di Bretschneider, Via Cassiodoro, 19, PO Box 6192, Rome, RM 00193, Italy. TEL 39-06-6874127, FAX 39-06-6874129, edizioni@lerma.it, http://www.lerma.it.

RIVISTA INGAUNA E INTEMELIA. see *ART*

RIVISTA STORICA DELL'ANTICHITA. see *HISTORY*

ROCK ART RESEARCH. see *ANTHROPOLOGY*

914 DEU ISSN 0341-9312
ROEMISCH-GERMANISCHEN KOMMISSION. BERICHTE. Text in German. 1910. a., latest vol.57, 1998. bibl.; charts; illus.; maps. back issues avail. **Document type:** *Journal, Academic/Scholarly.*
Indexed: AnthLit, BHA, BrArAb, DIP, IBR, IBZ, NumL, RASB.
Published by: Verlag Philipp von Zabern GmbH, Philipp-von-Zabern-Platz 1-3, Mainz, 55116, Germany. TEL 49-6131-287470, FAX 49-6131-223710, zabern@zabern.de, http://www.zabern.de. Adv. contact Manuela Dressen TEL 49-6131-2874711.

ROMHORISONT. see *HISTORY—History Of Europe*

913 RUS
ROSSIISKAYA AKADEMIYA NAUK. INSTITUT ARKHEOLOGII. KRATKIE SOOBSHCHENIYA. Text in Russian. 1939. irreg. price varies.
Formerly (until 1993): Akademiya Nauk S.S.S.R. Institut Arkheologii. Kratkie Soobshcheniya (0130-2620)
Indexed: AICP, AnthLit, BHA, NumL, RASB.
Published by: (Rossiiskaya Akademiya Nauk/Russian Academy of Sciences, Rossiiskaya Akademiya Nauk, Institut Arkheologii), Izdatel'stvo Nauka, Profsoyuznaya ul 90, Moscow, 117864, Russian Federation. TEL 7-095-3347151, FAX 7-095-4202220, secret@naukaran.ru, http://www.naukaran.ru. Circ: 2,150. **Dist. by:** M K - Periodica, ul Gilyarovskogo 39, Moscow 129110, Russian Federation. TEL 7-095-2845008, FAX 7-095-2813798, info@periodicals.ru, http://www.mkniga.ru.

913 RUS ISSN 0869-6063
DK30
ROSSIISKAYA ARKHEOLOGIYA. Text in Russian; Abstracts and contents page in French. 1957. q. USD 192 foreign (effective 2005). bk.rev. bibl.; illus.; maps. **Document type:** *Journal, Academic/Scholarly.*
Formerly: Sovetskaya Arkheologiya (0038-5034)
Related titles: Microform ed.; Online - full text ed.: (from East View Information Services).
Indexed: AIAP, AICP, AbAn, AmH&L, AnthLit, BiolAb, DIP, IBR, IBSS, IBZ, IndIslam, NumL, RASB, RILM, RefZh.
—East View. **CCC.**
Published by: (Rossiiskaya Akademiya Nauk, Institut Arkheologii), Izdatel'stvo Nauka, Profsoyuznaya ul 90, Moscow, 117864, Russian Federation. TEL 7-095-3347151, FAX 7-095-4202220, secret@naukaran.ru, http://www.naukaran.ru. Circ: 1,957. **Dist. by:** M K - Periodica, ul Gilyarovskogo 39, Moscow 129110, Russian Federation. TEL 7-095-2845008, FAX 7-095-2813798, info@periodicals.ru, http://www.mkniga.ru.

ROTUNDA. see *ART*

930.1 USA
ROUND ROBBINS NEWSLETTER. FRIENDS OF THE ROBBINS MUSEUM. Text in English. 1993. 3/yr. USD 20 to individual members; USD 30 domestic to institutional members; USD 35 foreign to institutional members (effective 2001). **Document type:** *Newsletter.*
Published by: Massachusetts Archaeological Society, Inc., Robbins Museum of Archaeology, PO Box 700, Middleborough, MA 02346-0700. TEL 508-947-9005.

930.1 IRL
ROYAL IRISH ACADEMY. DISCOVERY PROGRAMME. REPORTS. Text in English. irreg., latest vol.2, 1995. **Document type:** *Monographic series, Academic/Scholarly.*
Published by: (Discovery Programme), Royal Irish Academy, 19 Dawson St., Dublin, 2, Ireland. Ed. Fidelma Hagan. R&P Hugh Shiels.

914.2 820 IRL ISSN 0035-8991
DA900
ROYAL IRISH ACADEMY. PROCEEDINGS. SECTION C: ARCHAEOLOGY, CELTIC STUDIES, HISTORY, LINGUISTICS AND LITERATURE. Text in English. 1836. irreg. price varies. charts; illus. index, cum.index. **Document type:** *Proceedings.*
Related titles: Microform ed.: (from PMC).
Indexed: AICP, AmH&L, ArtHuCI, BHA, BrArAb, CurCont, HistAb, IBR, NumL, PCI, RASB.
—BLDSC (6799.058000), IE, Infotrieve, ingenta, KNAW.
Published by: Royal Irish Academy, 19 Dawson St., Dublin, 2, Ireland. TEL 353-1-6762570, FAX 353-1-6762346, publications@ria.ie, http://www.ria.ie. Eds. M O'Dowd, T Barry. Circ: 600.

913 IRL ISSN 0035-9106
DA900
ROYAL SOCIETY OF ANTIQUARIES OF IRELAND. JOURNAL. Text in English. 1849. a., latest vol.131, 2001. bk.rev. illus. index, cum.index: 1849-1930. **Document type:** *Academic/Scholarly.* **Description:** Publishes contributions to knowledge in the fields of Irish archaeology, architecture, history, genealogy, sociology, folklore and many kindred subjects.
Former titles (until 1890): Royal Historical and Archaeological Association of Ireland. Journal (0790-6382); (until 1870): Historical and Archaeological Association of Ireland. Journal (0790-6374); (until 1868): Kilkenny and South-East of Ireland Archaeological Society. Journal (0790-6366); (until 1856): Kilkenny and South-East of Ireland Archaeological Society. Proceedings and Transactions (0790-6358); (until 1854): Kilkenny Archaeological Society. Transactions (0790-634X)
Indexed: AICP, BHA, BrArAb, DIP, IBR, IBZ, MLA-IB, NumL, PCI, RASB.
—BLDSC (4863.800000).
Published by: Royal Society of Antiquaries of Ireland, 63 Merrion Sq., Dublin, 2, Ireland. TEL 353-1-6761749. Ed. Brian Lacey. Circ: 1,200.

930.1 970.01 USA ISSN 1532-7299
E51
THE S A A ARCHAEOLOGICAL RECORD. Text in English. 1983. 5/yr. free domestic to members; USD 10 per issue domestic (effective 2005). adv. **Document type:** *Bulletin, Academic/Scholarly.*
Former titles (until 2000): S A A Bulletin; (until 1990): Society for American Archaeology. Bulletin (0741-5672)
Indexed: RASB.
—BLDSC (2758.260000). **CCC.**
Published by: Society for American Archaeology, 900 Second St, N W, 12, Washington, DC 20002-3557. TEL 202-789-8200, FAX 202-789-0284, saanews@alishaw.ucsb.edu, publications@saa.org, http://www.saa.org/publications/theSAAarchRec/. adv.: page USD 4,950. Circ: 6,100 (controlled).

913 USA ISSN 0899-8922
CODEN: SARTE6
S A S BULLETIN. Text in English. 1977. q. USD 115 (effective 1999). adv. bk.rev. **Document type:** *Newsletter.* **Description:** Contains cooperative and interdisciplinary research between archaeology and the natural and physical sciences.
Formerly (until 1988): S A S Newsletter (0739-0637)
Indexed: AnthLit, BrArAb, NumL.
Published by: Society for Archaeological Sciences, Radiocarbon Laboratory, Dept of Anthropology, University of California, Riverside, CA 92521. TEL 909-787-5524, FAX 909-787-5409, beards@ucrac1.ucr.edu, http://www.wisc.edu/anthropology/sas/sas.htm. Ed. Rob Tykot. R&P R E Taylor. Adv. contact R E Taylor. Circ: 600 (paid).

930.1 DNK ISSN 1604-665X
▼ **S D A NYT (2005).** (Sammenslutningen af Danske Amatoerarkaeologer) Text in Danish. 2005. biennial. free membership. **Document type:** *Newsletter, Trade.*
Supersedes in part (in 2005): Aktuel Arkaeologi (1603-2861)
Related titles: Online - full text ed.: ISSN 1604-9381.
Published by: Sammenslutningen af Danske Amatoerarkaeologer/Association of Danish Amateur Archaeologists, c/o John Petersen, Hesselbaekpark 47, Farum, 3520, Denmark. TEL 45-44-994647, sda-nyt@pc.dk, http://www.arkaeologi-sda.dk/sda-nyt/sda-nyt.asp. Eds. Peter Skjoedt, John Petersen.

SABAZIA. see *HISTORY*

SAGA OCH SED. KUNGLIGA GUSTAV ADOLFS AKADENIENS AARSBOK/ROYAL SWEDISH GUSTAVUS ADOLPHUS ACADEMY. YEARBOOK. see *FOLKLORE*

930.1 ESP ISSN 0210-3729
DP302.V165
SAGUNTUM. Text in Spanish, Catalan. 1962. a.
Formerly (until 1977): Papeles del Laboratorio de Arqueologia de Valencia (0210-4873)
—CINDOC.
Published by: Universitat de Valencia, Departament de Prehistoria i Arqueologia/Universidad de Valencia. Departamento de Prehistoria y Arqueologia, Ave. Blasco Ibanez, 28, Valencia, 46010, Spain. TEL 34-96-3864242, FAX 34-96-3864093, http://www.uv.es/geohist/. Ed. Bernabeu Auban.

SAHARA; prehistory and history of the Sahara. see *HISTORY—History Of Africa*

913 DEU ISSN 0080-5866
DF221.S3
SAMOS. Text in German. 1961. irreg., latest vol.22, 1998. price varies. **Document type:** *Monographic series, Academic/Scholarly.*
Published by: (Deutsches Archaeologisches Institut), Dr. Rudolf Habelt GmbH, Am Buchenhang 1, Bonn, 53115, Germany. TEL 49-228-9238322, FAX 49-228-9238323, info@habelt.de, http://www.habelt.de.

SAN DIEGO MUSEUM OF MAN. ETHNIC TECHNOLOGY NOTES. see *ANTHROPOLOGY*

SAN DIEGO MUSEUM OF MAN. PAPERS. see *ANTHROPOLOGY*

913 CAN ISSN 0227-7514
F1071.9
SASKATCHEWAN ARCHAEOLOGICAL SOCIETY NEWSLETTER. Text in English. 1963. q. CND 30 (effective 2000). bk.rev. cum.index. **Document type:** *Newsletter.*
Formerly: Saskatchewan Archaeology Newsletter (0036-4878)
Media: Duplicated (not offset).
Indexed: AnthLit.
Published by: Saskatchewan Archaeological Society, 1 -1730 Quebec Ave, Saskatoon, SK S7K 1V9, Canada. TEL 306-664-4124. Ed. M Rollans. Circ: 600.

917 CAN ISSN 0227-5872
F1071.9
SASKATCHEWAN ARCHAEOLOGY. Text in English. 1980. a. CND 15 (effective 2000). back issues avail.
Indexed: AnthLit.
Published by: Saskatchewan Archaeological Society, 1 -1730 Quebec Ave, Saskatoon, SK S7K 1V9, Canada. Eds. Tim Jones, Tom Stevenson.

SASKATCHEWAN. DEPARTMENT OF CULTURE AND RECREATION. ANNUAL REPORT. see *ART*

902 ESP ISSN 1133-2166
SAUTUOLA; estelas funerarias medievales de Cantabria. Text in Spanish. 1975. a.
—CINDOC.
Published by: Diputacion Regional de Cantabria, Gomez Orena, 5-3o, Santander, Cantabria 39003, Spain.

SCHOLIA; studies in classical antiquity. see *CLASSICAL STUDIES*

913 CHE ISSN 0252-1881
GN841
SCHWEIZERISCHE GESELLSCHAFT FUER UR- UND FRUEHGESCHICHTE. JAHRBUCH. Text in French, German, Italian. 1908. a. CHF 150 (effective 2000). bk.rev. index. reprints avail. **Document type:** *Academic/Scholarly.*
Indexed: AICP, BHA, BrArAb, DIP, IBR, IBZ, NumL, RASB.
Published by: Schweizerische Gesellschaft fuer Ur- und Fruehgeschichte, Petersgraben 9-11, Basel, 4001, Switzerland. TEL 41-61-2613078, FAX 46-61-2613076, sguf@ubaclu.unibas.ch. Ed. Urs Niffeler.

913 GBR
➤ **SCOTTISH ARCHAEOLOGICAL JOURNAL.** Text in English. 1969. s-a. GBP 45 in Europe to institutions; USD 84 in North America to institutions; GBP 49 elsewhere to institutions (effective 2005). adv. bk.rev. illus.; maps. index, cum.index: vols.1-10. back issues avail. **Document type:** *Journal, Academic/Scholarly.* **Description:** Contains articles regarding Scottish archeology, particularly western Scotland.
Formerly (until 2000): Glasgow Archaeological Journal (0305-8980)
Related titles: Online - full text ed.: (from EBSCO Publishing).
Indexed: AnthLit, BHA, BrArAb, NumL.
—BLDSC (4183.050000).
Published by: (Glasgow Archaeological Society), Edinburgh University Press, 22 George Sq, Edinburgh, Midlothian EH8 9LF, United Kingdom. TEL 44-131-650-6207, FAX 44-131-662-0053, journals@eup.ed.ac.uk, http://www.eup.ed.ac.uk/newweb/journals/archeo/. Ed. Stephen Driscoll. Adv. contact Douglas McNaughton TEL 44-131-6504420. page GBP 200, page USD 400. Circ: 400.

930.1 GBR ISSN 0958-2002
SCOTTISH ARCHAEOLOGICAL NEWS. Text in English. 3/yr. free to members. bk.rev. **Document type:** *Newsletter, Academic/Scholarly.*
Indexed: BrArAb, NumL.
Published by: Council for Scottish Archaeology, c/o National Museums of Scotland, Chambers St, Edinburgh, EH1 1JF, United Kingdom. TEL 44-131-247-4119, FAX 44-131-247-4126, http://www.nms.ac.uk. Ed. Kenneth Aitchison. Circ: 1,000.

917 USA ISSN 0048-9832
E78.O6
SCREENINGS. Text in English. 1951. m. looseleaf. USD 10 to non-members (effective 2001). bk.rev. charts; illus. back issues avail.
Published by: Oregon Archaeological Society, PO Box 13293, Portland, OR 97213. http://www.oregonarchaeological.org. Ed. Harvey Steele. Circ: 1,000.

930.1 NLD
SCRINIUM✶. Text in Dutch. irreg., latest vol.11, 1996. **Document type:** *Monographic series, Academic/Scholarly.*
Published by: Thela Thesis, Prinseneiland 305, Amsterdam, 1013 LP, Netherlands. TEL 31-20-6255429, FAX 31-20-6203395, office@thelathesis.nl. Ed. A Leewis.

SCRIPTA MEDITERRANEA. see *HISTORY—History Of The Near East*

913 SWE ISSN 0439-8912
SCRIPTA MINORE. REGIAE SOCIETATIS HUMANIORUM LITTERARUM LUNDENSIS. Text in English. 1957. a. price varies. back issues avail. **Document type:** *Academic/Scholarly.*
Indexed: NAA.
Published by: Almqvist & Wiksell International, P O Box 7634, Stockholm, 10394, Sweden. FAX 46-8-24-25-43, info@city.akademibokhandeln.se, http://www.akademibokhandeln.se. Ed. Berta Stjernquist.

938 ITA ISSN 0067-0081
DF11
SCUOLA ARCHEOLOGICA DI ATENE E DELLE MISSIONI ITALIANE IN ORIENTE. ANNUARIO. Text in Italian. 1914; N.S. 1938. irreg., latest vol.67, 1989. price varies. back issues avail. **Document type:** *Monographic series, Academic/Scholarly.* **Description:** Annual prospectus of the Italian School of Archaeology at Athens.
Formerly (until 1943): Regia Scuola Archeologia di Atene e delle Missione Italiane in Oriente. Annuario (0394-0039)
Indexed: AIAP, ArtInd, RASB.
Published by: (Scuola Archeologica di Atene e delle Missioni Italiane in Oriente), L'Erma di Bretschneider, Via Cassiodoro, 19, PO Box 6192, Rome, RM 00193, Italy. edizioni@lerma.it, http://www.lerma.it. Circ: 750.

913 ITA ISSN 0067-009X
SCUOLA ARCHEOLOGICA DI ATENE E DELLE MISSIONI ITALIANE IN ORIENTE. MONOGRAFIE. Text in Italian. 1964. irreg., latest vol.6, 1993. price varies. **Document type:** *Monographic series, Academic/Scholarly.*
Published by: (Scuola Archeologica di Atene), L'Erma di Bretschneider, Via Cassiodoro, 19, PO Box 6192, Rome, RM 00193, Italy. edizioni@lerma.it, http://www.lerma.it. R&P Roberto Marcucci. Circ: 750.

387 ISR ISSN 0077-5193
SEFUNIM. Text in English, Hebrew. 1966. irreg., latest vol.8, 1994. USD 10 (effective 1999). adv. bk.rev. **Document type:** *Academic/Scholarly.* **Description:** Publishes scholarly research on maritime archaeology and history conducted by international scholars affiliated with the museum.
Indexed: IHP, NumL.
Published by: Friends of the National Maritime Museum Haifa, 198 Allenby Rd, P O Box 44855, Haifa, 31447, Israel. TEL 972-4-8536622, FAX 972-4-8539286. Ed. Joseph Ringel. Circ: 1,000.

930.1 305.8927 GBR ISSN 0308-8421
DS201
SEMINAR FOR ARABIAN STUDIES. PROCEEDINGS. Text and summaries in English. 1971. a., latest vol.33, 2003. GBP 50 per issue to libraries (effective 2004). bk.rev. **Document type:** *Proceedings.*
Indexed: AnthLit, BibLing, DIP, IBR, IBZ.
—BLDSC (6849.117500).
Published by: (Seminar for Arabian Studies BEL), Archaeopress, Gordon House, 276 Banbury Road, Oxford, OX2 7ED, United Kingdom. TEL 44-1865-311914, bar@archaeopress.com, http://www.archaeopress.com. Circ: 200.

301 ESP ISSN 1136-8187
DP44
SEMINARIO DE ARQUEOLOGIA Y ETNOLOGIA TUROLENSE. REVISTA. Text in Spanish. 1996. a.
Related titles: ◆ Series of: Arqueologia Espacial. ISSN 1136-8195.
Published by: Seminario de Arqueologia y Etnologia Turolense, San Vicente de Paul, 1, Teruel, Aragon 44002, Spain. Ed. Francisco Burillo.

930.1 ESP ISSN 0211-2264
SERVICIO DE INVESTIGACION PREHISTORICA. SERIE DE TRABAJOS VARIOS. Text in Spanish. 1937. q.
Formerly (until 1942): Serie de Treballs Solts - Servei d'Investigacion Prehistorica (0211-2272)

—CINDOC.
Published by: Diputacion Provincial de Valencia, Instituto Alfonso el Magnanimo, C. Quevedo 10, Valencia, 46001, Spain. TEL 34-96-3883733, FAX 34-96-388-3751. Ed. Josep Carles Lainez.

930.1 GBR ISSN 1362-6752
SHEFFIELD ARCHAEOLOGICAL MONOGRAPHS. Text in English. 1990. irreg., latest 2001, Sept. price varies. **Document type:** *Monographic series, Academic/Scholarly.*
Indexed: AnthLit.
—BLDSC (8255.735000).
Published by: (University of Sheffield), Sheffield Academic Press Ltd (Subsidiary of: Continuum International Publishing Group), The Tower Building, 11 York Rd, London, SE1 7NX, United Kingdom. TEL 44-207-922-0880, FAX 44-207-922-0881, jjoyce@continuumbooks.com, info@continuum-books.com, http://www.continuumbooks.com/.

931 CHN
SICHUAN WENWU/RELICS OF SICHUAN. Text in Chinese. bi-m. USD 18.50.
Published by: Sichuan Wenwu Guanli Weiyuanhui/Sichuan Relics Management Commission, 5 Renmin Nanlu Siduan (Sec 4), Chengdu, Sichuan 610041, China. TEL 553110. **Dist. in US by:** China Books & Periodicals Inc, 360 Swift Ave., Ste. 48, S San Fran, CA 94080-6220. TEL 415-282-2994.

913 ITA ISSN 0037-4571
DG865
SICILIA ARCHEOLOGICA; rassegna periodica di studi, notizie e documentazione. Text in Italian. 1968. 3/yr. adv. bk.rev. bibl.; charts; illus. **Document type:** *Journal, Consumer.*
Indexed: NumL.
Published by: L'Erma di Bretschneider, Via Cassiodoro, 19, PO Box 6192, Rome, RM 00193, Italy. TEL 39-06-6874127, FAX 39-06-6874129, edizioni@lerma.it, http://www.lerma.it. Circ: 1,000.

913 930 ITA ISSN 0392-0909
SIKELIKA. SERIE ARCHEOLOGICA. Text in Italian. 1979. irreg., latest vol.4, 1992. price varies. back issues avail. **Document type:** *Academic/Scholarly.*
Published by: (Centro Siciliano di Studi Storico-Archeologici "Biagio Pace"), Giorgio Bretschneider, Casella Postale 30011, Rm47, Rome, 00193, Italy. info@bretschneider.it.

SIKELIKA. SERIE STORICA. see *HISTORY*

913 POL ISSN 0080-9594
SILESIA ANTIQUA. Text in Polish; Summaries in English, French, German. 1959. a. looseleaf. USD 180 foreign (effective 2002). **Document type:** *Academic/Scholarly.* **Description:** Devoted to the actual research and excavations in the area of Upper and Lower Silesia and of Opole region.
Indexed: AICP, BHA, BrArAb, IBR, RASB.
Published by: Muzeum Archeologiczne Wroclaw, Ul Lieszymskiego 9-Ausena, Wroclaw, 50136, Poland. TEL 48-71-3443638, FAX 48-71-3444785, wevk1@poczte.onet.pl. Ed. K. Demidziuk. **Dist. by:** Ars Polona, Krakowskie Przedmiescie 7, Warsaw, Poland.

913.031 SCG ISSN 1450-5193
DR2114
SINGIDUNUM. Text in Serbian; Summaries in English. 1997. irreg. bk.rev. bibl.; illus. **Description:** Explores archaeological topics about Belgrade in ancient times.
Published by: Arheoloski Institut/Institute of Archaeology, Knez Mihailova 35, Belgrade, 11000. TEL 381-11-637191, FAX 381-11-180189, m.popovic@ai.sanu.ac.yu. Ed. Marko Popovic. Circ: 1,000.

930.1 720 FRA ISSN 0489-0280
SITES ET MONUMENTS. Text in French. 1901. q. **Description:** Aims to protect the landscape and historic sites of France.
Indexed: AIAP, BHA.
Published by: Societe pour la Protection des Paysages et de l'Esthetique de la France, 39 av. de la Motte Picquet, Paris, 75007, France. TEL 33-1-47053771, FAX 33-1-45503161. Ed. Pierre Joste. Pub. Paule Albrecht.

SKALK; nyt om gammelt. see *HISTORY—History Of Europe*

930.1 POL ISSN 0520-9250
SLASKIE SPRAWOZDANIA ARCHEOLOGICZNE. Text in Polish. 1958. irreg., latest vol.33, 1993. price varies. charts; illus. **Document type:** *Academic/Scholarly.*
Indexed: BHA, RASB.
Published by: (Uniwersytet Wroclawski, Katedra Archeologii), Wydawnictwo Uniwersytetu Wroclawskiego Spolka z o.o., Pl Uniwersytecki 9-13, Wroclaw, 50-137, Poland. TEL 48-71-441006, FAX 48-71-402735. Circ: 300.

913 POL ISSN 0080-9993
D147
SLAVIA ANTIQUA; rocznik poswiecony starozytnosciom slowianskim. Text in German, Polish, Russian; Summaries in English, French. 1948. a., latest vol.43, 2002. price varies. adv. bk.rev. charts. **Document type:** *Monographic series, Academic/Scholarly.*
Indexed: AICP, AnthLit, BHA, DIP, IBR, IBZ, NumL.
Published by: (Poznanskie Towarzystwo Przyjaciol Nauk, Wydzial Historii i Nauk Spolecznych), Poznanskie Towarzystwo Przyjaciol Nauk/Poznan Society for the Advancement of the Arts and Sciences, ul Sew Mielzynskiego 27-29, Poznan, 61725, Poland. TEL 48-61-8527441, FAX 48-61-8522205, sekretariat@ptpn.poznan.pl, wydawnictwo@ptpn.poznan.pl, http://www.ptpn.poznan.pl. Circ: 500. **Dist. by:** Ars Polona, Krakowskie Przedmiescie 7, Warsaw, Poland. TEL 48-22-9263914, FAX 48-22-9265334, arspolona@arspolona.com.pl, http://www.arspolona.com.pl.

930.1 SVK
SLOVENSKA AKADEMIA VIED V NITRE. ARCHEOLOGICKY USTAV. STUDIJNE ZVESTI. Text in Slovak; Text occasionally in German. 1956. a. **Document type:** *Yearbook.* **Description:** Presents the results of the archaeological activity, analyses, preliminary and partial evaluations, methodology and inventory works.
Published by: Slovenska Akademia Vied, Archeologicky Ustav/Slovak Academy of Sciences, Institute of Archaeology, Akademicka 2, Nitra, 949 21, Slovakia. TEL 421-87-35738, FAX 421-87-35618, bujna@savnr.savba.sk, http://nic.savba.sk/sav/inst/archeo/studijne.htm. Ed. Josef Bujna.

913 SVK ISSN 1335-0102
SLOVENSKA ARCHEOLOGIA/SLOVAK ARCHEOLOGY. Text and summaries in German, Slovak. 1953. s-a. USD 203 (effective 2000). bk.rev. charts; illus. **Document type:** *Academic/Scholarly.* **Description:** Publishes studies and papers on archaeological research results and theoretical questions concerning Central Europe, especially the Carpathian basin. Presents information on the latest archaeological research in Slovakia.
Indexed: AICP, AnthLit, BHA, NumL, RASB.
Published by: (Slovenska Akademia Vied/Slovak Academy of Sciences, Archeologicky Ustav), Slovak Academic Press Ltd., Nam Slobody 6, PO Box 57, Bratislava, 81005, Slovakia. sap@sappress.sk, http://www.sappress.sk. Ed. Bohuslav Chropovsky.

930.1 SVK
SLOVENSKE NARODNE MUZEUM. ZBORNIK. ARCHEOLOGIA. Text in Slovak, German. 1990. irreg., latest vol.10, 2000. bibl.; illus.; maps. back issues avail. **Document type:** *Yearbook, Academic/Scholarly.*
Published by: (Slovenske Narodne Muzeum, Archeologicke Muzeum), Slovenske Narodne Muzeum, Narodne Muzejne Centrum, Vajanskeho nabr 2, Bratislava, 81436, Slovakia. TEL 421-2-52961973, FAX 421-2-52966653, nmc@snm.sk. Ed. Beata Egyhazy Jurovska.

913 ITA ISSN 0392-0321
SOCIETA ISTRIANA DI ARCHEOLOGIA E STORIA PATRIA. ATTI E MEMORIE. Text in Italian. 1884. a.
Published by: Edizioni Lint Trieste, Viale Ortles 54a, Milan, 20139, Italy. TEL 39-02-5220181, FAX 39-02-52201820, lint@lint.it.

913 700 ITA
SOCIETA PER GLI STUDI STORICI, ARCHEOLOGICI ED ARTISTICI DELLA PROVINCIA DI CUNEO. BOLLETTINO. Text in Italian. 1929. s-a. bk.rev.
Indexed: BHA.
Published by: Societa per gli Studi Storici Archeologici ed Artistici della Provincia di Cuneo, c/o Biblioteca Civica, Via Cacciatori delle Alpi, 9, Casella Postale 91, Cuneo, CN 12100, Italy. TEL 0171-634367. Circ: 1,000.

930.1 700 ITA ISSN 1121-9319
SOCIETA PIEMONTESE DI ARCHEOLOGIA E BELLE ARTI. BOLLETTINO. Text in Italian. 1874. a. USD 35 (effective 1999). cum.index: 1874-1990. back issues avail. **Document type:** *Bulletin.* **Description:** Covers archeology from the Stone Age to medieval times, architecture and all types of art of the Piedmont region.
Indexed: AIAP, BHA.
Published by: Societa Piemontese di Archeologia e Belle Arti, Via Giovanni Francesco Napione, 2, Turin, TO 10124, Italy. TEL 39-11-8177178. Ed. Bruno Signorelli. Circ: 600.

SOCIETA SAVONESE DI STORIA PATRIA. ATTI E MEMORIE. see *HISTORY—History Of Europe*

913 ITA ISSN 0394-1663
SOCIETA TIBURTINA DI STORIA E D'ARTE. ATTI E MEMORIE. Text in Italian. 1921. a.
Formerly (until 1929): Societa Tiburtina di Storia e d'Arte. Atti e Memorie (0392-0348)
Indexed: BHA, NumL.
Published by: Societa Tiburtina di Storia e d'Arte, Villa d'Este, Tivoli, RM 00019, Italy.

914 FRA ISSN 1153-2521
SOCIETE ARCHEOLOGIQUE DE TOURAINE. BULLETIN. Text in French. 1868. a. **Document type:** *Bulletin.*
Indexed: BHA, BibInd.
Published by: Societe Archeologique de Touraine, B.P. 1105, Tours, Cedex 37011, France. Pub. Jean Moreau.

913 FRA ISSN 1149-4670
SOCIETE ARCHEOLOGIQUE DE TOURAINE. MEMOIRES. Text in French. 1842. a. adv. charts; illus. **Document type:** *Monographic series.*
Published by: Societe Archeologique de Touraine, B.P. 1105, Tours, Cedex 37011, France. Pub., Adv. contact Jean Moreau.

914 FRA ISSN 0337-579X
SOCIETE ARCHEOLOGIQUE ET HISTORIQUE DE L'ORLEANAIS. BULLETIN. Text in French. 1959. q.
Indexed: RILM.
Published by: Societe Archeologique et Historique de l'Orleanais, Boite Postale 5223, Orleans Cedex 1, 45052, France. contact@saho.fr.st, http://www.saho.fr.st.

914 FRA ISSN 1295-232X
SOCIETE ARCHEOLOGIQUE ET HISTORIQUE DE TARN ET GARONNE. BULLETIN. Text in French. 1869. a. bk.rev. **Document type:** *Bulletin.*
Formerly (until 1997): Societe Archeologique de Tarn-et-Garonne. Bulletin (1153-2661)
Indexed: BHA.
Published by: Societe Archeologique et Historique de Tarn et Garonne, Rue des Soubirous-Bas, Tarn et Garonne, Montauban, France. Ed. Jean Boutonnet. R&P, Adv. contact Jean-Michel Garric. **Co-sponsors:** Conseil General du Tarn et Garonne; Ville de Montauban.

914 FRA ISSN 0182-3876
SOCIETE ARCHEOLOGIQUE ET HISTORIQUE DES HAUTS CANONS DE L'HERAULT. BULLETIN. Text in English. 1978. a.
Indexed: RILM.
Published by: Societe Archeologique et Historique des Hauts Canons de l'Herault, Le Petit Couvent, 20 rue des Asiles, Bedarieux, 34600, France. TEL 33-4-67953386, salvaire.m@wanadoo.fr.

913 944 FRA ISSN 0037-8895
SOCIETE ARCHEOLOGIQUE, HISTORIQUE, LITTERAIRE ET SCIENTIFIQUE DU GERS. BULLETIN TRIMESTRIEL. Text in French. 1900. q. bk.rev. charts; illus. index, cum.index every 10 yrs. **Document type:** *Bulletin.*
Indexed: BHA.
Published by: Societe Archeologique Historique Litteraire & Scientifique du, c/o Andre Dieulafait, Tres., 13 place Saluste-du-Bartas, BP 16, Auch, Cedex 32001, France. TEL 33-5-62630837. Pub., R&P Georges Courtes. Circ: 1,550.

SOCIETE D'ARCHEOLOGIE COPTE. BIBLIOTHEQUE DE MANUSCRITS. see *RELIGIONS AND THEOLOGY—Eastern Orthodox*

SOCIETE D'ARCHEOLOGIE COPTE. BULLETIN. see *RELIGIONS AND THEOLOGY—Eastern Orthodox*

SOCIETE D'ARCHEOLOGIE COPTE. TEXTES ET DOCUMENTS. see *RELIGIONS AND THEOLOGY—Eastern Orthodox*

914 FRA ISSN 1281-2412
SOCIETE D'ARCHEOLOGIE ET D'HISTOIRE DE LA CHARENTE MARITIME. BULLETIN. Text in French. 1966. a. **Document type:** *Bulletin, Academic/Scholarly.*
Former titles (until 1989): Societe d'Archeologie et d'Histoire de la Charente Maritime. Bulletin de Liaison (0753-4825); (until 1976): Societe d'Archeologie et d'Histoire de la Charente Maritime et Section Archeologique de Saintes. Bulletin de Liaison (0753-4817); Which superseded in part (in 1974): Societe d'Archeologie et d'Histoire de la Charente Maritime et Groupe de Recherches Archeologiques de Saintes. Recueil (0753-4809); Which was formerly (until 1973): Societe d'Archeologie et d'Histoire de la Cherente Maritime. Recueil (0753-4795)
Indexed: BHA.
Published by: Societe d Archeologie et d Histoire de la Manche, 9 rue Mauny, Saintes, 17100, France. TEL 33-5-46746775. Ed. Jean Louis Hillairet.

913 FRA ISSN 0037-9158
SOCIETE D'EMULATION DU BOURBONNAIS. BULLETIN; lettres, sciences et arts. Text in French. 1846. q. adv. bk.rev. illus. index. back issues avail.
Indexed: BHA.
Published by: Societe d'Emulation du Bourbonnais, 4 Pl de L Ancien Palais, Moulins, 03000, France. TEL 70-44-39-03.

SOCIETE DES ANTIQUAIRES DE PICARDIE. BULLETIN TRIMESTRIEL. see *HISTORY—History Of Europe*

SOCIETE DES ANTIQUAIRES DE PICARDIE. MEMOIRES. SERIES IN 8. see *HISTORY—History Of Europe*

SOCIETE DES OCEANISTES. JOURNAL. see *SOCIAL SCIENCES: COMPREHENSIVE WORKS*

SOCIETE DES SCIENCES HISTORIQUES ET NATURELLES DE SEMUR EN AUXOIS ET DES FOUILLES D'ALESIA. BULLETIN. see *HISTORY—History Of Europe*

SOCIETE DES SCIENCES NATURELLES ET D'ARCHEOLOGIE DE TOULON ET DU VAR. ANNALES. see *SCIENCES: COMPREHENSIVE WORKS*

913 940 900 CHE ISSN 1017-849X
DQ441
SOCIETE D'HISTOIRE ET D'ARCHAEOLOGIE DE GENEVE. BULLETIN. Text in Multiple languages. 1892. a. CHF 25. index. reprints avail. **Document type:** *Bulletin, Academic/Scholarly.* **Description:** Details of research, events and developments in history and archaeology in relation to the society.
Published by: Societe d'Histoire et d'Archeologie de Geneve, c/o Bibliotheque Publique et Universitaire de Geneve, Promenade des Bastions, Geneva 4, 1211, Switzerland. TEL 41-22-3466666, FAX 41-22-3472391. Circ: 500. **Subscr. to:** Librairie Droz S.A., 11 rue Massot, Geneva 12 1211, Switzerland. FAX 41-22-3472391.

913 FRA ISSN 0081-0967
SOCIETE D'HISTOIRE ET D'ARCHEOLOGIE DE LA GOELE. BULLETIN D'INFORMATION. Text in French. 1968. a., latest vol.31, 2001. EUR 15 (effective 2003). adv. bk.rev. **Document type:** *Academic/Scholarly.*
Published by: Societe d'Histoire et d'Archeologie de la Goele, Mairie, Dammartin-en-Goele, 77230, France. Ed., R&P Michel Golinelli. Circ: 500.

913 944 FRA ISSN 1153-3277
SOCIETE D'HISTOIRE ET D'ARCHEOLOGIE DE VICHY ET DES ENVIRONS. BULLETIN. Text in French. 1937. s-a. bk.rev. bibl.; charts; illus. **Document type:** *Bulletin.*
Indexed: BHA.
Published by: Societe d'Histoire et d'Archeologie de Vichy, Centre Culturel Valery Larbaud, 15 rue M Foch, Vichy, 03200, France. Ed. George Tixier. Circ: 350.

914 CHE
SOCIETE D'HISTOIRE ET D'ARCHEOLOGIE. MEMOIRES ET DOCUMENTS. SERIE IN 4. Text in French. irreg., latest vol.10, 1983. price varies. **Document type:** *Monographic series, Academic/Scholarly.*
Published by: (Societe d'Histoire et d'Archeologie de Geneva), Librairie Droz S.A., 11 rue Massot, Geneva 12, 1211, Switzerland. TEL 41-22-3466666, FAX 41-22-3472391, droz@droz.org, http://www.droz.org.

914 CHE ISSN 1017-8511
SOCIETE D'HISTOIRE ET D'ARCHEOLOGIE. MEMOIRES ET DOCUMENTS. SERIE IN 8. Text in French. 1841. irreg., latest vol.60, 1998. price varies. **Document type:** *Monographic series, Academic/Scholarly.*
Published by: (Societe d'Histoire et d'Archeologie de Geneve), Librairie Droz S.A., 11 rue Massot, Geneva 12, 1211, Switzerland. TEL 41-22-3466666, FAX 41-22-3472391, droz@droz.org, http://www.droz.org.

913 FRA ISSN 0037-9379
DT57
SOCIETE FRANCAISE D'EGYPTOLOGIE. BULLETIN. Text in French. 1949. 3/yr. membership. bk.rev. illus.; maps. back issues avail. **Document type:** *Bulletin, Academic/Scholarly.*
Related titles: ♦ Supplement to: Revue d'Egyptologie. ISSN 0035-1849.
Indexed: BHA, BibLing, RASB.
Published by: Societe Francaise d'Egyptologie, College de France, 11 Place Marcelin-Berthelot, Paris, 75231 Cedex 05, France. TEL 33-1-40469431, sfe@egypt.edu.

SOCIETE GEOLOGIQUE DE NORMANDIE ET DES AMIS DU MUSEUM DU HAVRE. BULLETIN TRIMESTRIEL. see *EARTH SCIENCES—Geology*

LA SOCIETE GUERNESIAISE. REPORT AND TRANSACTIONS. see *HISTORY—History Of Europe*

SOCIETE HISTORIQUE ET ARCHEOLOGIQUE DU PERIGORD. BULLETIN. see *HISTORY—History Of Europe*

930.1 FRA ISSN 0249-7638
GN700
➤ **SOCIETE PREHISTORIQUE FRANCAISE. BULLETIN.** Text in French; Abstracts in English. 1978. q. EUR 50 (effective 2005). bk.rev. bibl.; charts; illus. index, cum.index: 1904-2000. back issues avail. **Document type:** *Bulletin, Academic/Scholarly.* **Description:** Deals with French research from the Palaeolithic to the Iron-Age.
Formed by the 1978 merger of: Societe Prehistorique Francaise. Bulletin - Etudes et Travaux (0583-8789); Societe Prehistorique Francaise. Bulletin - Comptes Rendus des Seances Mensuelles (0373-5451); Which supersedes (in 1964): Societe Prehistorique de France. Bulletin (0037-9514)
Indexed: A&ATA, AICP, AnthLit, BibInd, BiolAb, BrArAb, NumL, PCI, RASB.
—BLDSC (2748.000000), IE, Infotrieve, ingenta.
Published by: Societe Prehistorique Francaise, 22 rue Saint Ambroise, Paris, 75011, France. TEL 33-1-43571697, FAX 33-1-43577395, spf@wanadoo.fr, http://www.prehistoire.org. Ed. Emmanuelle Boulestin. Circ: 2,000.

949.33 BEL
SOCIETE ROYALE D'ARCHEOLOGIE, D'HISTOIRE ET DE FOLKLORE DE NIVELLES ET DU BRABANT WALLON. ANNALES. Text in French. 1879. irreg., latest vol.27, 1994. adv. bk.rev. illus. **Document type:** *Bulletin.*
Formerly: Societe d'Archeologie, d'Histoire et de Folklore de Nivelles et du Brabant Wallon. Annales
Published by: Societe Royale d'Archeologie d'Histoire et de Folklore de Nivelles et du Brabant Wallon, Musee de Nivelles, Rue de Bruxelles 27, Nivelles, 1400, Belgium. TEL 32-67-882280, FAX 32-67-843234, san@san-niv.be, http://www.san-niv.be/publications.html#pubann. Ed. Jean Luc Delattre. Adv. contact J B Dubois. Circ: 500.

SOCIETE SUISSE DES AMERICANISTES. BULLETIN/ SCHWEIZERISCHE AMERIKANISTEN-GESELLSCHAFT. BULLETIN. see *ANTHROPOLOGY*

917 USA
SOCIETY FOR AMERICAN ARCHAEOLOGY. SPECIAL PUBLICATIONS SERIES. Text in English. irreg. **Document type:** *Monographic series, Academic/Scholarly.*
Published by: Society for American Archaeology, 900 Second St, N W, 12, Washington, DC 20002-3557. TEL 202-789-8200, FAX 202-789-0284.

SOCIETY FOR COMMERCIAL ARCHEOLOGY. JOURNAL. see *ARCHITECTURE*

SOCIETY FOR COMMERCIAL ARCHEOLOGY. NEWS. see *ARCHITECTURE*

913 USA ISSN 0037-9735
CC77.H5
SOCIETY FOR HISTORICAL ARCHAEOLOGY NEWSLETTER. Text in English. 1968. q. free to members (effective 2005). tr.lit. **Document type:** *Newsletter.* **Description:** Contains forums on archaeological conservation, urban archaeology, information on society activities, and current research.
Media: Duplicated (not offset).
Indexed: BrArAb, NumL.
—BLDSC (6108.345000). **CCC.**
Published by: Society for Historical Archaeology, 15245 Shady Grove Rd, Ste 130, Rockville, MD 20850. TEL 301-990-2454, FAX 301-990-9771, hq@sha.org, http://www.sha.org. Ed. William B Lees. Circ: 2,500.

913 USA ISSN 0898-0004
➤ **SOCIETY FOR HISTORICAL ARCHAEOLOGY. SPECIAL PUBLICATION SERIES.** Text in English. 1976. irreg., latest vol.7. price varies. illus. back issues avail. **Document type:** *Monographic series, Academic/Scholarly.* **Description:** Each volume presents selected material culture studies from the artifact assemblages recovered from various excavated sites.
Published by: Society for Historical Archaeology, PO Box 30446, Tucson, AZ 85751. TEL 520-886-8006, FAX 520-886-0182, 520-886-0812, the_sha@mindspring.com, http://www.sha.org. Ed., R&P Ronald L Michael.

➤ **SOCIETY FOR INDUSTRIAL ARCHEOLOGY NEWSLETTER.** see *TECHNOLOGY: COMPREHENSIVE WORKS*

913 GBR ISSN 0953-7155
DA20
SOCIETY OF ANTIQUARIES OF LONDON. OCCASIONAL PAPERS. Text in English. irreg.
—BLDSC (6221.235000), ingenta.
Published by: Society of Antiquaries of London, Burlington House, Piccadilly, London, W1V 0BE, United Kingdom. TEL 44-20-74797080, FAX 44-20-72876967.

913 GBR ISSN 0953-7163
SOCIETY OF ANTIQUARIES OF LONDON. RESEARCH COMMITTEE. REPORTS. Text in English. 1913. irreg.
—BLDSC (7589.850000), IE, ingenta.
Published by: Society of Antiquaries of London, Burlington House, Piccadilly, London, W1V 0BE, United Kingdom. TEL 44-20-74797080, FAX 44-20-72876967.

SOCIETY OF ANTIQUARIES OF SCOTLAND. MONOGRAPH SERIES. see *HISTORY—History Of Europe*

SOCIETY OF ANTIQUARIES OF SCOTLAND. PROCEEDINGS. see *HISTORY—History Of Europe*

SOMERSET AND DORSET NOTES AND QUERIES. see *HISTORY—History Of Europe*

913 500.9 GBR ISSN 0081-2056
SOMERSET ARCHAEOLOGY AND NATURAL HISTORY. Text in English. 1849. a., latest vol.141. GBP 20 domestic; GBP 25 foreign (effective 2002). bk.rev. index, cum.index: vols.81-115, 1935-1971. **Document type:** *Proceedings, Academic/Scholarly.*
Formerly: Somersetshire Archaeological and Natural History Society. Proceedings
Indexed: BHA, BrArAb, NumL.
—BLDSC (8327.823000).
Published by: Somerset Archaeological & Natural History Society, Taunton Castle, Taunton, Somers TA1 4AD, United Kingdom. TEL 44-1823-272429, secretary@sanhs.freeserve.co.uk. Ed. Michael McGarvie. Circ: 1,000.

914.5 ITA
SOPRINTENDENZA ARCHEOLOGICA DI POMPEI. CATALOGHI. Text in Italian. 1986. irreg., latest vol.6, 1997. price varies. **Document type:** *Catalog, Trade.*
Published by: (Soprintendenza Archeologica di Pompei), L'Erma di Bretschneider, Via Cassiodoro, 19, PO Box 6192, Rome, RM 00193, Italy. TEL 39-06-6874127, FAX 39-06-6874129, edizioni@lerma.it, http://www.lerma.it.

914.5 ITA
SOPRINTENDENZA ARCHEOLOGICA DI POMPEI. MONOGRAFIE. Text in Italian. 1986. irreg., latest vol.13, 1997. price varies. **Document type:** *Monographic series, Academic/Scholarly.*
Published by: (Soprintendenza Archeologica di Pompei), L'Erma di Bretschneider, Via Cassiodoro, 19, PO Box 6192, Rome, RM 00193, Italy. TEL 39-06-6874127, FAX 39-06-6874129, edizioni@lerma.it, http://www.lerma.it.

930.1 ZAF ISSN 0038-1969
GN865.S5 CODEN: SARBAG
➤ **SOUTH AFRICAN ARCHAEOLOGICAL BULLETIN.** Text in English. 1945. s-a. ZAR 250 in Africa to institutions; ZAR 450, EUR 60 elsewhere to institutions (effective 2003); includes Digging Stick. bk.rev. abstr.; bibl.; charts; illus.; maps. index. back issues avail. **Document type:** *Journal, Academic/Scholarly.*
Incorporates (in 1972): Goodwin Series
Indexed: AICP, AbAn, AnthLit, ArtHuCI, BrArAb, CCA, CurCont, HistAb, IBR, IBSS, ISAP, NumL, RASB.
—BLDSC (8330.900000), IDS, IE, ingenta.
Published by: South African Archaeological Society, PO Box 15700, Vlaeberg, Cape Town 8018, South Africa. TEL 27-21-4813886, FAX 27-21-4813993, archsoc@isiko.org.za. Ed., R&P Margaret Avery. Circ: 1,200.

➤ **SOUTH AFRICAN MUSEUM. ANNALS/SUID-AFRIKAANSE MUSEUM. ANNALE.** see *BIOLOGY*

930.1 NLD
SOUTH ASIAN ARCHAEOLOGY; proceedings of the international conference. Text in English. 1990. biennial.
Indexed: AnthLit.
Published by: (European Association of Southeast Asian Archaeologists), International Institute for Asian Studies, PO Box 9515, Leiden, 2300 RA, Netherlands. TEL 31-71-5272227, FAX 31-71-5274162, iiasnews@rullet.leidenuniv.nl, http://www.iias.nl.

930.1 USA
SOUTH CAROLINA ANTIQUITIES. Text in English. a. membership. **Description:** Publishes papers on the prehistoric and historic archaeology of South Carolina and the Southeastern United States.
Indexed: AnthLit.
Published by: Archaeological Society of South Carolina, Inc., South Carolina Institute of Archeology and Anthropology, University of South Carolina, Columbia, SC 29208. TEL 803-777-8170, FAX 803-254-1338, nrice@sc.edu, http://www.assc.net.

930.1 USA ISSN 0276-5543
F653
SOUTH DAKOTA ARCHAEOLOGY. Text in English. 1977. a. USD 25 domestic; USD 35 foreign (effective 2004). bk.rev. **Document type:** *Journal, Academic/Scholarly.* **Description:** Contains articles of enduring scientific interest to South Dakota and Midwestern archaeology.
Indexed: AnthLit.
Published by: South Dakota Archaeological Society, 2032 South Grange Ave., Sioux Falls, SD 57105.

930.1 USA
SOUTH DAKOTA ARCHEOLOGICAL SOCIETY NEWSLETTER. Text in English. 1970. q. USD 15 domestic to individuals; USD 25 domestic to institutions (effective 2005). bk.rev.; film rev. back issues avail. **Document type:** *Newsletter, Trade.* **Description:** Conveys information about current research of interest to the members.
Indexed: AnthLit.
Address: PO Box 1257, Rapid City, SD 57709-1257. TEL 605-394-1936, FAX 605-394-1941. Ed., R&P Michael R Fosha.

913 USA ISSN 0734-578X
F211 CODEN: SARHE4
➤ **SOUTHEASTERN ARCHAEOLOGY.** Text in English. 1982. 2/yr. free to members (effective 2004). adv. bk.rev. back issues avail. **Document type:** *Journal, Academic/Scholarly.* **Description:** Contains articles, reports and other information pertaining to archaeological and ethnohistorical research in the southeastern region of the United States.
Formerly (until 1982): Bulletin of the Southeastern Archaeological Conference
Related titles: Online - full text ed.: (from EBSCO Publishing, ProQuest Information & Learning).

▼ new title ➤ refereed ✶ unverified ♦ full entry avail.

A

Indexed: AICP, AbAn, AmH&L, AnthLit, GEOBASE, HistAb, MASUSE.
—BLDSC (8352.354000), IE, ingenta, Linda Hall. **CCC.**
Published by: Southeastern Archaeological Conference, c/o Arkansas Archaeological Survey, Blytheville Research Station, 2520 Friday Spur, Blytheville, AR 72315. TEL 870-532-9104, cpayne@arkansas.net, http://www.southeasternarcheology.org. Ed., R&P, Adv. contact Robert C Mainfort TEL 501-575-6560. Circ: 1,100.

930.1   ZAF   ISSN 1019-5785
➤ **SOUTHERN AFRICAN FIELD ARCHAEOLOGY.** Text in English. 1992. a., latest vol.10, 2001. ZAR 50 domestic to individuals; USD 25 foreign to individuals; ZAR 60 domestic to institutions; USD 30 foreign to institutions (effective 2003). adv. bk.rev. 100 p./no.; back issues avail. **Document type:** *Journal, Academic/Scholarly.* **Description:** Publishes current research projects, site reports, rack art panels, rescue excavations, contract notes and reviews.
Indexed: AICP, SFA.
Published by: Albany Museum, Somerset St, Grahamstown, East Cape 6139, South Africa. TEL 27-46-622312, FAX 27-46-622398, l.webley@ru.ac.za. Eds. J N F Binneman, L E Webley.

001.3   ZAF   ISSN 1681-5564
AZ188.S6
➤ **SOUTHERN AFRICAN HUMANITIES.** Text in English, French, German; Summaries in English. 1989. a. price varies. cum.index. back issues avail. **Document type:** *Academic/Scholarly.* **Description:** Contains research articles on archaeology, anthropology, rock art, shipwrecks, cultural and historical studies.
Formerly (until 2000): Natal Museum Journal of Humanities (1015-0935)
Indexed: AICP, DIP, IBR, IBZ, ISAP.
Published by: Natal Museum, Private Bag 9070, Pietermaritzburg, KwaZulu-Natal 3200, South Africa. TEL 37-33-3451404, FAX 27-33-3450561, dbarracl@nmsa.org.za. R&P D Barraclough. Circ: 200.

913   USA
SOUTHERN ILLINOIS UNIVERSITY AT CARBONDALE. CENTER FOR ARCHAEOLOGICAL INVESTIGATIONS. OCCASIONAL PAPER. Text in English. irreg. price varies. adv. **Document type:** *Monographic series, Academic/Scholarly.*
Indexed: AnthLit.
—BLDSC (6221.310000).
Published by: Southern Illinois University at Carbondale, Center for Archaeological Investigations, Carbondale, IL 62901. TEL 618-453-5031, FAX 618-453-3253. Ed. Donna Butler. Adv. contact Carolyn Taylor. Circ: 750.

913   USA
SOUTHERN ILLINOIS UNIVERSITY AT CARBONDALE. CENTER FOR ARCHAEOLOGICAL INVESTIGATIONS. RESEARCH PAPER. Text in English. 1978. irreg. price varies. adv. **Document type:** *Monographic series, Academic/Scholarly.*
Indexed: AnthLit.
Published by: Southern Illinois University at Carbondale, Center for Archaeological Investigations, Carbondale, IL 62901. TEL 618-453-5031, FAX 618-453-3253. Ed. Donna Butler. R&P Donna E Butler. Adv. contact Carolyn Taylor. Circ: 500.

930.1   USA
SOUTHERN ILLINOIS UNIVERSITY AT CARBONDALE. CENTER FOR ARCHAEOLOGICAL INVESTIGATIONS. VISITING SCHOLAR CONFERENCE. Text in English. a.
Indexed: AnthLit.
Published by: Visiting Scholar Committee, Center for Archaeological Investigations, 3479 Faner Hall, Mailcode 4527, Southern Illinois University Carbondale, Carbondale, IL 62901-4527. TEL 618-453-5031, FAX 618-453-8467.

930.1   USA
SOUTHWESTERN FEDERATION OF ARCHAEOLOGICAL SOCIETIES. TRANSACTIONS. Text in English. a.
Indexed: AnthLit.
Published by: Southwestern Federation of Archaeological Societies, c/o Francis Strickney (Sec-Treas), 201 West Solomon St., Midland, TX 79705.

978.8   USA   ISSN 0038-4844
F778
SOUTHWESTERN LORE; journal of Colorado archaeology. Text in English. 1935. q. USD 20 worldwide to individual members; USD 40 worldwide to institutions; USD 8 worldwide to students; USD 23 combined subscription worldwide (effective 2005 - 2006). adv. bk.rev.; film rev.; video rev. bibl.; charts; illus. cum.index: vols.1-20 (1935-1955), vols.21-30 (1955-1965), vols.31-40 (1965-1975), vols.41-50 (1975-1984), vols.51-60 (1985-1994). 40 p./no. 1 cols./p.; back issues avail. **Document type:** *Journal, Academic/Scholarly.* **Description:** Covers any phase of southwestern, Rocky Mountain and high plains archaeology, anthropology, history, and related subjects.
Indexed: AbAn, AmH&L, AnthLit, HistAb.

Published by: Colorado Archaeological Society, Inc., 2077 S Vrain St, Denver, CO 80219-5034. TEL 303-866-4671, FAX 303-866-2711, kevin.black@chs.state.co.us, http://www.coloradoarchaeology.org/swl_contents.htm. Ed. Mr. Kevin D Black. R&P Mr. Terry Murphy TEL 303-814-1432. Adv. contact Mr. Joel Hurmence TEL 970-481-2124. Circ: 850 (paid); 23 (free).

930.1   ESP   ISSN 1133-4525
SPAL. Text in Spanish. 1993. irreg., latest vol.8, 1999. EUR 31.20 per issue (effective 2005). **Document type:** *Journal, Academic/Scholarly.*
Indexed: AnthLit.
—CINDOC.
Published by: Universidad de Sevilla, Secretariado de Publicaciones, Porvenir 27, Sevilla, 41013, Spain. TEL 34-95-4487444, FAX 34-95-4487443, secpub10@us.es, http://www.us.es/publius/inicio.html.

SPIEGEL HISTORIAEL; magazine voor geschiedenis en archeologie. see *HISTORY*

913   POL   ISSN 0081-3834
GN700
SPRAWOZDANIA ARCHEOLOGICZNE. Text in Polish; Summaries in English. 1955. a., latest vol.56, 2004. EUR 25 per vol. foreign (effective 2005). bk.rev. charts; illus.; maps. 250 p./no. 1 cols./p.; **Document type:** *Journal, Academic/Scholarly.* **Description:** Contains articles and reviews on field research in Little Poland and methodological articles.
Indexed: AICP, BHA, BrArAb, DIP, IBR, IBSS, IBZ, NumL, RASB.
Published by: Polska Akademia Nauk, Instytut Archeologii i Etnologii, Al Solidarnosci 105, Warsaw, 00140, Poland. TEL 48-22-6202881, FAX 48-22-6240100, director@iaepan.edu.pl, http://www.iaepan.edu.pl. Ed. Jan Machnik. Circ: 400. **Dist. by:** Ars Polona, Krakowskie Przedmiescie 7, Warsaw, Poland. TEL 48-22-9263914, FAX 48-22-9265334, arspolona@arspolona.com.pl, http://www.arspolona.com.pl.

SRPSKA AKADEMIJA NAUKA I UMETNOSTI. ODELJENJE DRUSTVENIH NAUKA. SPOMENIK. see *SOCIAL SCIENCES: COMPREHENSIVE WORKS*

913   GBR
DA670.S69
➤ **STAFFORDSHIRE ARCHAEOLOGICAL AND HISTORICAL SOCIETY. TRANSACTIONS.** Text in English. 1960. a. GBP 11 to individuals; GBP 15 to institutions. illus. reprint service avail. from PQC. **Document type:** *Proceedings, Academic/Scholarly.*
Formerly: South Staffordshire Archaeological and Historical Society. Transactions (0457-7817)
Related titles: Microfilm ed.: (from PQC).
Indexed: AIAP, BHA, BrArAb, BrHumL, NumL.
—BLDSC (9010.606000).
Published by: Staffordshire Archaeological and Historical Society, William Salt Library, Veterinary Surgeons 34a, Eastgate St, Stafford, ST16 2LZ, United Kingdom. Ed. Dr. N Tringham. Circ: 300.

930.1   GBR   ISSN 0266-4992
STAFFORDSHIRE ARCHAEOLOGICAL STUDIES. Text in English. 1984. a.
Indexed: AnthLit.
—BLDSC (8426.406700).
Published by: Stoke-on-Trent Potteries Museum & Art Gallery, Bethesda St., Hanley, Stoke-On-Trent, ST1 3DW, United Kingdom. TEL 44-1782-202173, museums@stoke.gov.uk.

930.1   USA
➤ **STANFORD JOURNAL OF ARCHAEOLOGY.** Text in English. 2002. irreg. free (effective 2005). **Document type:** *Journal, Academic/Scholarly.*
Media: Online - full text.
Published by: Stanford University, Archaeology Center, Bldg 60, Main Quad, Stanford, CA 94305. http://archaeology.stanford.edu/journal/newdraft/.

913.031   SCG   ISSN 0350-0241
DR311.A1
STARINAR. Text in English, German, French, Serbian. 1884; N.S. 1950. a. bk.rev. bibl.; illus. back issues avail. **Document type:** *Proceedings.*
Indexed: AIAP, AICP, AnthLit, BHA, NumL, RASB.
—KNAW.
Published by: Arheoloski Institut/Institute of Archaeology, Knez Mihailova 35, Belgrade, 11000. TEL 381-11-637191, FAX 381-11-180189, m.vasic@ai.sanu.ac.yu. Ed. Miloje Vasic. Circ: 800.

913   ITA   ISSN 1120-4699
PJ3701
STATE ARCHIVES OF ASSYRIA BULLETIN. Text in English, Italian. 1987. s-a. back issues avail. **Document type:** *Academic/Scholarly.* **Description:** Devoted to philological and historical studies on the documents from the Neo-Assyrian state archives.
Indexed: BibLing, DIP, IBR, IBZ.

Published by: Sargon srl, Via Armistizio, 277, Padua, PD 35142, Italy. TEL 390-6-6795304, FAX 390-6-3225348. Ed. Frederick Mario Fales. Dist. by: Herder Editrice e Libreria s.r.l., Piazza di Montecitorio 117-120, Rome 00186, Italy. TEL 39-06-6794628, FAX 390-6-3225348, 39-6-6784751, http://www.herder.it.

STATNI OKRESNI ARCHIV V OLOMOUCI. ROCENKA. see *HISTORY—History Of Europe*

913   USA
STONES AND BONES NEWSLETTER. Text in English. 1959. m. USD 12 to individuals; USD 17 to institutions; includes Journal of Alabama Archaeology. bk.rev. charts. reprint service avail. from PQC. **Document type:** *Newsletter.*
Published by: Alabama Archaeological Society, 13075 Moundville Archaeological Park, Moundville, AL 35474. TEL 205-371-2266, FAX 205-371-2494. Ed. Mcdonald Brooms. Circ: 500.

913 956.91   ITA   ISSN 0393-0246
STUDI EBLAITI. Text in English, French, German, Italian. 1979. irreg. USD 60. back issues avail. **Document type:** *Academic/Scholarly.*
Indexed: AnthLit, BibLing.
Published by: Universita degli Studi di Roma "La Sapienza", 5 Piazzale Aldo Moro, Rome, 00185, Italy. TEL 39-06-49911, http://www.uniroma1.it. Ed. Paolo Matthiae. Circ: 1,000.

913 900   ITA   ISSN 0585-4911
STUDI GENUENSI. Text in Italian. 1970. a. EUR 14.50 (effective 2004). **Document type:** *Journal, Academic/Scholarly.* **Description:** Contains historical studies of Genoa and Liguria (a northwestern coastal region of Italy).
Indexed: BHA, MLA.
Published by: Istituto Internazionale di Studi Liguri/International Institute of Ligurian Studies, Via Romana 39, Bordighera, IM 18012, Italy. TEL 39-0184-263601, FAX 39-0184-266421, iisl@istitutostudi.191.it, http://www.iisl.it. Circ: 1,000.

930   NLD
STUDIA AMSTELODAMENSIA AD EPIGRAPHICAM, IUS ANTIQUUM ET PAPYROLOGICAM PERTINENTIA. Text in English, French, German. 1972. irreg., latest vol.34, 1995. price varies. back issues avail. **Document type:** *Monographic series.* **Description:** Presents scholarly studies relating to epigraphs, ancient law, and papyrii.
Published by: J.C. Gieben, Entrepotdok 72b, Amsterdam, 1018 AD, Netherlands. TEL 31-20-6234709, FAX 31-20-6275170, http://www.teachtext.net/gieben/. **Dist. in N. America by:** John Benjamins Publishing Co., PO Box 27519, Philadelphia, PA 19118-0519. TEL 215-836-1200.

913   ESP   ISSN 0210-976X
STUDIA ARCHAEOLOGICA. Text in German. 1969. irreg., latest vol.64, 1980. price varies.
Indexed: PCI.
—CINDOC.
Published by: (Universidad de Santiago de Compostela, Seminario de Arqueologia, Universidad de Santiago de Compostela), Universidad de Valladolid, Departamento de Prehistoria y Arqueologia, Antropologia Social y Ciencias Tecnicas Historiograficas, P. Prado de la Magdalena, s-n, Valladolid, 470011, Spain. preyarq@fyl.uva.es, http://www.fyl.uva.es/prehistoria. Ed. Antonio Bellindo Blanco.

913   ITA   ISSN 0081-6299
STUDIA ARCHAEOLOGICA. Text in Italian. 1961. irreg., latest vol.101, 1999. price varies. **Document type:** *Monographic series, Academic/Scholarly.*
Indexed: AnthLit.
Published by: L'Erma di Bretschneider, Via Cassiodoro, 19, PO Box 6192, Rome, RM 00193, Italy. TEL 39-06-6874127, FAX 39-06-6874129, edizioni@lerma.it, http://www.lerma.it.

930.1 948   FIN   ISSN 0786-5066
STUDIA ARCHAEOLOGICA SEPTENTRIONALIA. Text in Multiple languages. 1989. irreg. price varies.
Published by: Pohjois-Suomen Historiallinen Yhdistys, Historian Laitos, PL 1000, Oulun Yliopisto, 90014, Finland. FAX 358-8-553-3315.

930.1   ESP
STUDIA ARQUEOLOGICA. Text in Spanish. irreg., latest vol.89, 1998. price varies. **Document type:** *Monographic series.*
Published by: Universidad de Valladolid, Secretariado de Publicaciones, Juan Mambrilla, 14, Valladolid, 47003, Spain. TEL 983-423000, FAX 34-83-290300.

STUDIA DEMOTICA. see *CLASSICAL STUDIES*

930.1   NLD   ISSN 0081-6396
STUDIA FRANCISCI SCHOLTEN MEMORIAE DICATA. Text in English, French, German. 1952. irreg., latest vol.5, 1982. **Document type:** *Monographic series, Academic/Scholarly.*
Published by: Nederlands Instituut voor het Nabije Oosten/Netherlands Institute for the Near East, Witte Singel 25, Leiden, 2311 BG, Netherlands. FAX 31-71-527-2038. R&P J de Roos TEL 31-71-527-2036.

STUDIA HELLENISTICA. see *CLASSICAL STUDIES*

913 551 POL ISSN 0137-530X
TN903.P7
STUDIA I MATERIALY DO DZIEJOW ZUP SOLNYCH W POLSCE. Text in Polish; Summaries in English. 1965. a., latest vol.20, 1997. PLZ 8, USD 4 (effective 2002). adv. bk.rev. back issues avail. **Description:** History of salt mines in Poland and Europe, geology of salt deposits, machines and tools used in mines. Includes ethnography, history of art and mining cartography.
Published by: Muzeum Zup Krakowskich/Museum of Cracovian Salt Works, Ul Zamkowa 8, Wieliczka, 32020, Poland. TEL 48-12-2783266, FAX 48-12-2783028, podziemne@muzeum.wieliczka.pl, http://www.muzeum.wieliczka.pl. Ed. Antoni Jodlowski. R&P Elzbieta Benarowska Guzik. Adv. contact Elzbieta Bendarowska Guzik. Circ: 400. **Co-sponsor:** Ministerstwo Kultury i Sztuki/Ministry of Culture and National Heritage.

STUDIA PHOENICIA. see *HISTORY—History Of The Near East*

930.1 DEU ISSN 0942-7635
DF221.T8
STUDIA TROICA. Text in German, French, English. 1991. irreg., latest vol.10, 2001. bibl.; charts; illus.; maps. back issues avail. **Document type:** *Journal, Academic/Scholarly.*
Indexed: DIP, IBR, IBZ.
Published by: Verlag Philipp von Zabern GmbH, Philipp-von-Zabern-Platz 1-3, Mainz, 55116, Germany. TEL 49-6131-287470, FAX 49-6131-223710, zabern@zabern.de, http://www.zabern.de. Adv. contact Manuela Dressen TEL 49-6131-2874711.

STUDIEN ZUM ALTAEGYPTISCHEN TOTENBUCH. see *ASIAN STUDIES*

STUDIEN ZUR GESCHICHTE NORDWEST-GRIECHENLANDS. see *CLASSICAL STUDIES*

930.1 GBR ISSN 0952-4975
STUDIES IN ANCIENT CHRONOLOGY. Text in English. 1987. irreg. **Document type:** *Monographic series.*
Indexed: AnthLit.
Published by: University College London, Institute of Archaeology, 31-34 Gordon Sq., London, WC1H 0PY, United Kingdom. TEL 44-20-76797495, FAX 44-20-73832572, http://www.centuries.co.uk/studies.htm, http://www.ucl.ac.uk/archaeology.

STUDIES IN ANCIENT ORIENTAL CIVILIZATION. see *HISTORY—History Of The Near East*

913 USA
STUDIES IN ARCHAEOLOGICAL SCIENCE. Text in English. 1971. irreg., latest vol.14, 1985. reprint service avail. from ISI.
Published by: Academic Press (Subsidiary of: Elsevier Science & Technology), 525 B St, Ste 1900, San Diego, CA 92101-4495. apsubs@acad.com, http://www.academicpress.com. Ed. G W Dimbleby.

STUDIES IN ASIAN ART AND ARCHAEOLOGY. see *ASIAN STUDIES*

STUDIES IN CONSERVATION. see *ART*

930.1 BEL
STUDIES IN EASTERN MEDITERRANEAN ARCHAEOLOGY. Text in English. 1995. irreg., latest vol.3, 2000. price varies. **Document type:** *Monographic series.* **Description:** Reports on excavations in the eastern Mediterranean area, including archaeozoology, ancient history, architecture, archaeometry, palaeobotany and anthropology.
Published by: (Katholieke Universiteit Leuven, Center for Interdisciplinary Archaeological Research), Brepols Publishers, Begijnhof 67, Turnhout, 2300, Belgium. FAX 32-14-42-89-19, publishers@brepols.com, periodicals@brepols.net.

930.1 938 SWE ISSN 0283-8494
STUDIES IN MEDITERRANEAN ARCHAEOLOGY AND LITERATURE. POCKET-BOOK SERIES. Text in Multiple languages. 1974. irreg., latest vol.163, 2003. price varies. back issues avail. **Document type:** *Monographic series, Academic/Scholarly.*
Formerly (until 1987): Studies in Mediterranean Archaeology. Pocket-Book Series (0347-173X)
—BLDSC (8491.108300).
Published by: Paul Aastroems Foerlag, William Gibsons Vaeg 11, Jonsered, 43376, Sweden. TEL 46-31-7956600, FAX 46-31-7956710, info@astromeditions.com, http://www.astromeditions.com.

930.1 SWE ISSN 0081-8232
STUDIES IN MEDITERRANEAN ARCHAEOLOGY. MONOGRAPH SERIES. Text in English, French, German. 1962. irreg., latest vol.130, 2003. price varies. **Document type:** *Monographic series, Academic/Scholarly.*
Indexed: AIAP, AnthLit, NumL, RASB.
Published by: Paul Aastroems Foerlag, William Gibsons Vaeg 11, Jonsered, 43376, Sweden. TEL 46-31-7956600, FAX 46-31-7956710, info@astromeditions.com, http://www.astromeditions.com. Circ: 1,000.

930.1 SWE ISSN 0562-3871
STUDIES IN NORTH-EUROPEAN ARCHEOLOGY. Text in Multiple languages. 1960. irreg., latest vol.9, 1986. price varies. **Document type:** *Monographic series, Academic/Scholarly.*
Related titles: ♦ Series of: Acta Universitatis Stockholmiensis. ISSN 0346-6418.
Published by: Stockholms Universitet, Acta Universitatis Stockholmiensis, c/o Stockholms Universitetsbibliotek, Universitetsvaegen 10, Stockholm, 10691, Sweden. FAX 46-8-157776. **Dist. by:** Almqvist & Wiksell International, P O Box 7634, Stockholm 10394, Sweden. TEL 46-8-6136100, FAX 46-8-242543, info@akademibokhandeln.se, http://www.akademibokhandeln.se.

913 USA ISSN 0585-7023
E51
➤ **STUDIES IN PRE-COLUMBIAN ART AND ARCHAEOLOGY.** Text in English. 1966. irreg., latest vol.33, 1994. price varies. bibl.; charts; illus. back issues avail. **Document type:** *Monographic series, Academic/Scholarly.*
Indexed: AnthLit.
—CCC.
Published by: Dumbarton Oaks, 1703 32nd St, N W, Washington, DC 20007. TEL 202-339-6401, FAX 202-339-6419, publications@doaks.org, DumbartonOaks@doaks.org, http://www.doaks.org/. Ed. Jeffrey Quilter. R&P Glenn Ruby. Circ: 1,000.

913 ROM ISSN 1220-4781
STUDII SI CERCETARI DE ISTORIE VECHE SI ARHEOLOGIE/ETUDES ET RECHERCHES D'HISTOIRE ANCIENNE ET D'ARCHEOLOGIE. Text in Romanian; Summaries in French. 1950. 4/yr. bk.rev. charts; illus. index.
Formerly: Studii si Cercetari de Istorie Veche (0039-4009)
Related titles: Online - full text ed.
Indexed: AICP, AnthLit, BHA, NumL, RASB.
—KNAW.
Published by: (Academia Romana, Institutul de Arheologie Vasile Parvan), Editura Academiei Romane/Publishing House of the Romanian Academy, Calea 13 Septembrie 13, Sector 5, Bucharest, 76117, Romania. TEL 40-21-4119008, FAX 40-21-4103983, edacad@ear.ro, http://www.ear.ro. Ed. Mircea Babes. **Dist. by:** Rodipet S.A., Piata Presei Libere 1, sector 1, PO Box 33-57, Bucharest 3, Romania. TEL 40-21-2224126, 40-21-2226407, rodipet@rodipet.ro.

220 ISR ISSN 0081-8917
STUDIUM BIBLICUM FRANCISCANUM. COLLECTIO MAIOR. Text in English, French, Italian. 1941. irreg., latest vol.39, 1996. price varies. **Document type:** *Monographic series.*
Related titles: Microfiche ed.: (from IDC).
Published by: Franciscan Printing Press, P O Box 14064, Jerusalem, 91140, Israel. TEL 972-2-6286594, FAX 972-2-6284717, fpp@p-ol.com, http://198.62.75.1/www1/ofm/fpp/FPPmain.html. Circ: 1,000.

220 ISR ISSN 0081-8925
STUDIUM BIBLICUM FRANCISCANUM. COLLECTIO MINOR. Text in English, French, Italian. 1961. irreg., latest vol.35, 1997. price varies. **Document type:** *Monographic series.*
Published by: Franciscan Printing Press, P O Box 14064, Jerusalem, 91140, Israel. TEL 972-2-6286594, FAX 972-2-6284717, fpp@p-ol.com, http://198.62.75.1/www1/ofm/fpp/FPPmain.html. Circ: 1,000.

220 ISR ISSN 0081-8933
BS410
STUDIUM BIBLICUM FRANCISCANUM. LIBER ANNUUS. Text in English, French, German, Italian, Latin. 1951. a., latest vol.47, 1997. price varies. bibl. cum.index: 1951-1970. back issues avail. **Document type:** *Academic/Scholarly.*
Related titles: Microfiche ed.: (from IDC).
Indexed: BHA, NTA, NumL, OTA, RI-1, RI-2.
Published by: Franciscan Printing Press, P O Box 14064, Jerusalem, 91140, Israel. TEL 972-2-6286594, FAX 972-2-6284717, fpp@p-ol.com, http://198.62.75.1/www1/ofm/fpp/FPPmain.html. Circ: 1,200.

913 ISR
STUDIUM BIBLICUM FRANCISCANUM. MUSEUM. Text in English, French, Italian. 1976. irreg., latest vol.13, 1996. price varies. **Document type:** *Monographic series.*
Published by: Franciscan Printing Press, P O Box 14064, Jerusalem, 91140, Israel. TEL 972-2-6286594, FAX 972-2-6284717, fpp@p-ol.com, http://198.62.75.1/www1/ofm/fpp/FPPmain.html. Circ: 1,000.

935 BEL
SUBARTU. Text in English. 1995. irreg., latest vol.8, 2001. bibl. **Document type:** *Monographic series.* **Description:** Publishes studies on the archaeology, history, geography, environment, epigraphy and sociology of the Upper Mesopotamian region from prehistory to the present day.
Published by: (European Centre for Upper Mesopotamian Studies), Brepols Publishers, Begijnhof 67, Turnhout, 2300, Belgium. FAX 32-14-42-89-19, publishers@brepols.com, periodicals@brepols.net.

SUECOROMANA; studia artis historiae instituti romani regni Sueciae. see *HISTORY—History Of Europe*

DER SUELCHGAU. see *HISTORY—History Of Europe*

930.1 USA ISSN 1079-2198
SUFFOLK COUNTY ARCHAEOLOGICAL ASSOCIATION. NEWSLETTER. Text in English. 3/yr., latest vol.27, no.2. USD 20 to members (effective 2003). bk.rev. illus. **Document type:** *Newsletter, Academic/Scholarly.* **Description:** Contains news of archaeological excavations, Native Americans and historic sites in Suffolk county.
Published by: Suffolk County Archaeological Association, PO Box 1542, Stony Brook, NY 11790-0910. TEL 631-929-8725, FAX 631-929-6967. R&P Gaynell Stone.

914.2 942 GBR ISSN 0143-4896
SUFFOLK INSTITUTE OF ARCHAEOLOGY AND HISTORY. NEWSLETTER. Text in English. s-a. GBP 12.50; GBP 15 foreign. **Document type:** *Newsletter.*
Indexed: BrArAb, NumL.
Published by: Suffolk Institute of Archaeology and History, c/o B. Seward, HoN Secy, Roots,, Church Ln, Playford, Ipswich, Suffolk IP6 9DS, United Kingdom. TEL 44-1473-624556. Ed. J Middleton Stewart. R&P B Seward.

914.2 942 GBR ISSN 0262-6004
➤ **SUFFOLK INSTITUTE OF ARCHAEOLOGY AND HISTORY. PROCEEDINGS.** Text in English. 1849. a. GBP 12.50 domestic; GBP 15 overseas (effective 2002). bk.rev. **Document type:** *Proceedings, Academic/Scholarly.*
Indexed: BHA, BrArAb, BrHumI, NumL.
—BLDSC (6826.025500), IE, ingenta.
Published by: Suffolk Institute of Archaeology and History, c/o B. Seward, HoN Secy, Roots,, Church Ln, Playford, Ipswich, Suffolk IP6 9DS, United Kingdom. TEL 44-1473-624556. Ed. D Allen. R&P E A Martin. Circ: 851.

930.1 709 FIN ISSN 0355-1822
SUOMEN MUINAISMUISTOYHDISTYKSEN AIKAKAUSKIRJA/FINSKA FORNMINNESFOERENINGENS TIDSKRIFT. Text in English, Finnish, German, Swedish. 1874. irreg., latest vol.104, 1997. price varies. charts; illus. **Document type:** *Monographic series, Academic/Scholarly.* **Description:** Publishes contributions in archaeology, art history, and cultural history.
Indexed: BHA, RASB.
Published by: Suomen Muinaismuistoyhdistys/Finnish Antiquarian Society, Nervanderinkatu 13, PO Box 213, Helsinki, 00101, Finland. TEL 358-9-40501, FAX 358-9-40509400. Ed. Torsten Edgren.

SUPPLEMENTUM EPIGRAPHICUM GRAECUM. see *CLASSICAL STUDIES*

913 GBR ISSN 0309-7803
SURREY ARCHAEOLOGICAL COLLECTIONS. Text in English. 1858. irreg. GBP 25 domestic; GBP 35 foreign. bk.rev. cum.index: vols. 1-71. back issues avail. **Document type:** *Academic/Scholarly.*
Indexed: BHA, BrArAb, NumL.
—BLDSC (8548.340000). **CCC.**
Published by: Surrey Archaeological Society, Castle Arch, Guildford, Surrey GU1 3SX, United Kingdom. TEL 44-1483-532454, FAX 44-1483-532454, surreyarch@compuserve.com, http://ourworld.compuserve.com/homepages/surreyarch, http://www.surreyarchaeology.org.uk/. Eds. G Crocker, P Nicolaysen. R&P Glenys Crocker.

913 GBR ISSN 0585-9980
SURREY ARCHAEOLOGICAL SOCIETY. BULLETIN. Text in English. 1965. 9/yr. membership. adv. **Document type:** *Bulletin.*
—BLDSC (2770.580000).
Published by: Surrey Archaeological Society, Castle Arch, Guildford, Surrey GU1 3SX, United Kingdom. TEL 44-1483-532454, FAX 44-1483-532454, surreyarch@compuserve.com, http://ourworld.compuserve.com/homepages/surreyarch, http://www.surreyarchaeology.org.uk/. Ed. P M Jones. R&P Glenys Crocker. Circ: 850.

913 GBR ISSN 0308-342X
➤ **SURREY ARCHAEOLOGICAL SOCIETY. RESEARCH VOLUMES.** Text in English. 1974. irreg. GBP 10 membership (effective 2003). **Document type:** *Monographic series, Academic/Scholarly.*
Indexed: BHA, BrArAb.
Published by: Surrey Archaeological Society, Castle Arch, Guildford, Surrey GU1 3SX, United Kingdom. TEL 44-1483-532454, FAX 44-1483-532454, surreyarch@compuserve.com, http://www.surreyarchaeology.org.uk/. Ed., R&P Mrs. Audrey Graham.

913 GBR ISSN 1357-7417
DA670.S97
SUSSEX PAST AND PRESENT. Text in English. 1971. 3/yr. membership. bk.rev. bibl. **Document type:** *Newsletter.*
Former titles (until 1994): Past and Present; (until 1993): S A S News (0307-2568)
Related titles: Online - full text ed.
Indexed: AIAP, BrArAb, NumL.

Published by: Sussex Archaeological Society, Sussex, Bull House, 92 High St, Lewes, Sussex BN7 1XH, United Kingdom. TEL 44-1273-486260, FAX 44-1273-486990. Ed. Andy Freeman.

SVENSKA INSTITUTET I ATHEN. SKRIFTER. SERIE 4. see *CLASSICAL STUDIES*

938 GRC ISSN 0081-9921
SVENSKA INSTITUTET I ATHEN. SKRIFTER. SERIE 8/ACTA INSTITUTI ATHENIENSIS REGNI SUECIAE. Text in Multiple languages. 1951. irreg., latest vol.16, 1999. price varies. bk.rev. back issues avail. **Document type:** *Monographic series, Academic/Scholarly.*
Published by: Svenska Institutet i Athen/Swedish Institute at Athens, Mitseon 9, Athens, 11742, Greece. TEL 30-210-9232102, FAX 30-210-9220925, swedinst@sia.gr, http://www.sia.gr/acta.asp. Ed. B Alroth. Circ: 1,000. **Dist. by:** Paul Aastroems Foerlag, William Gibsons Vaeg 11, Jonsered 43376, Sweden. TEL 46-31-7956600, FAX 46-31-7956710, paul.astrom@swipnet.se, http://www.astromeditions.com.

913 ITA ISSN 0081-993X
DG12
SVENSKA INSTITUTET I ROM. SKRIFTER. ACTA SERIES PRIMA. 4:O. Variant title: Acta Instituti Romani Regni Sueciae. Text in Multiple languages. 1932. irreg., latest vol.57, 2001. price varies. bk.rev. **Document type:** *Monographic series, Academic/Scholarly.*
Indexed: AIAP.
Published by: Svenska Institutet i Rom/Swedish Institute at Rome, Via Omero 14, Rome, 00197, Italy. TEL 39-06-3201596, FAX 39-06-3230265, srisv@vatlib.it, http://www.svenska-institutet-rom.org. Ed. Brita Alroth. Circ: 1,000. **Dist. by:** Paul Aastroems Foerlag, William Gibsons Vaeg 11, Jonsered 43376, Sweden. TEL 46-31-7956600, FAX 46-31-7956710, 46-31-7956710, paul.astrom@swipnet.se, http://www.astromeditions.com.

SVENSKA INSTITUTET I ROM. SKRIFTER. SERIES ALTERA IN 8O. see *HISTORY—History Of Europe*

930.1 305.8 USA ISSN 0889-7425
SYMBOLS. Text in English. 1980. s-a. illus. back issues avail. **Document type:** *Newsletter, Academic/Scholarly.*
Indexed: AnthLit.
Published by: Peabody Museum of Archaeology and Ethnology, Harvard University, 11 Divinity Ave, Cambridge, MA 02138. TEL 617-496-9922, FAX 617-495-7535, http://www.peabody.harvard.edu/publications. R&P Catherine Linardos TEL 617-495-2269.

913 700 FRA ISSN 0039-7946
DS94.5
SYRIA; revue d'art oriental et d'archeologie. Text in French. 1920. 4/yr. (2 double nos./yr.). bk.rev. abstr.; illus. index. **Document type:** *Academic/Scholarly.*
Related titles: Microfiche ed.: (from IDC).
Indexed: AIAP, BHA, BibLing, DIP, IBR, IndIslam, MLA-IB, NumL, PCI, RASB, RI-1, RI-2.
—IE.
Published by: (Institut Francais d'Archeologie de Beyrouth), Librairie Orientaliste Paul Geuthner, 12 rue Vavin, Paris, 75006, France. TEL 33-1-46-34-71-30, FAX 33-1-43-29-75-64, TELEX 250 303 PUBLIC PARIS. Eds. E Will, J Caquot.

930.1 NLD ISSN 0922-3312
T M A. Text in Dutch; Text occasionally in English; Summaries in English. 1988. 2/yr. bk.rev. bibl.; illus.; maps; stat. cum.index every 5 yrs. back issues avail. **Document type:** *Academic/Scholarly.* **Description:** Publishes reports, articles, reviews and commentaries on current Dutch and Belgian archaeological research in the Mediterranean region.
Published by: (Stichting ter Ondersteuning van Oudheidkundig Onderzoek), Tijdschrift voor Mediterrane Archeologie, Poststraat 6, Groningen, 9712 ER, Netherlands. TEL 31-50-5250812, tma53@hotmail.com, http://hagen.let.rug.nl/~tma/. Eds. J W Boema, P A J Attema.

T R A C E. (Travaux et Recherches dans les Ameriques du Centre) see *ANTHROPOLOGY*

914 ESP ISSN 0213-2818
TABONA; revista de prehistoria y de arqueologia y filologia clasicas. Text in Spanish. 1972. a. USD 25 to individuals; USD 30 to institutions. adv. **Document type:** *Academic/Scholarly.*
Indexed: AnthLit, IBR.
—CINDOC.
Published by: (Departamento de Prehistoria, Antropologia y Paleoambiente), Universidad de la Laguna, Secretariado de Publicaciones, Campus Central, La Laguna-Tenerife, Canary Islands 38071, Spain. FAX 34-922-258127.

TALOHA. see *MUSEUMS AND ART GALLERIES*

TAXILA INSTITUTE OF ASIAN CIVILIZATIONS. QUAID-I-AZAM UNIVERSITY. PUBLICATIONS. see *HISTORY—History Of Asia*

936.125 GBR ISSN 1360-5550
➤ **TAYSIDE AND FIFE ARCHAEOLOGICAL JOURNAL.** Text in English. 1994. a. GBP 10 (effective 2005). **Document type:** *Journal, Academic/Scholarly.* **Description:** Contains papers on archaeology of Tayside and Fife (north-east region of Scotland), covering all periods from prehistoric to post-medieval/early modern.
Published by: Tayside & Fife Archaeological Committee, c/o SUAT Ltd., 55 South Methven St, Perth, PH1 5NX, United Kingdom. TEL 44-1738-622393, FAX 44-1738-631626, dhall@suat.demon.co.uk, http://www.tafac.freeuk.com/tafaj.htm. Ed. Lisbeth Thoms. R&P Derek Hall. Circ: 500 (paid and controlled).

938 DEU ISSN 1106-661X
TEKMERIA; Beitraege zur Geschichte der griechischen und roemischen Welt. Text in French, German, Greek, English. 1995. irreg., latest vol.7, 2002. price varies. back issues avail. **Document type:** *Monographic series, Academic/Scholarly.*
Published by: Dr. Rudolf Habelt GmbH, Am Buchenhang 1, Bonn, 53115, Germany. TEL 49-228-9238322, info@habelt.de, http://www.habelt.de.

930.1 933 ISR
TEL AVIV UNIVERSITY. INSTITUTE OF ARCHAEOLOGY. MONOGRAPH SERIES. Text in English, Hebrew. 1973. irreg., latest vol.18, 2000. price varies. adv. back issues avail. **Document type:** *Monographic series, Academic/Scholarly.* **Description:** Publishes historical studies and reports of archaeological excavations.
Published by: (The Emery and Claire Yass Publications in Archaelogy, Sonia and Marco Nadler Institute of Archaeology), Tel Aviv University, Institute of Archaeology, Ramat Aviv, P O Box 39040, Tel Aviv, 69978, Israel. TEL 972-3-6407235, archpubs@post.tau.ac.il. Ed. Jak Yakar. R&P Fiona Ben-Dror TEL 972-3-7235. Adv. contact Shirley Gassner.

930.1 933 ISR
TEL AVIV UNIVERSITY. INSTITUTE OF ARCHAEOLOGY. OCCASIONAL PUBLICATIONS. Text in English. 1993. irreg. price varies. adv. **Document type:** *Academic/Scholarly.*
Indexed: NumL.
Published by: (The Emery and Claire Yass Publications in Archaelogy, Sonia and Marco Nadler Institute of Archaeology), Tel Aviv University, Institute of Archaeology, Ramat Aviv, P O Box 39040, Tel Aviv, 69978, Israel. TEL 972-3-6407235, FAX 972-3-6407237, archpubs@post.tau.ac.il. Ed. Jak Yakar. R&P Fiona Ben-Dror TEL 972-3-7235. Adv. contact Shirley Gassner.

TENNESSEE ANTHROPOLOGICAL ASSOCIATION. MISCELLANEOUS PAPER. see *ANTHROPOLOGY*

TENNESSEE ANTHROPOLOGICAL ASSOCIATION. NEWSLETTER. see *ANTHROPOLOGY*

TERRA AMERIGA. see *ANTHROPOLOGY*

913 930 ITA ISSN 0452-2907
TESTIMONIA SICILIAE ANTIQUA. Text in Italian. 1981. irreg., latest 1988. price varies. **Document type:** *Academic/Scholarly.*
Published by: (Istituto Siciliano per la Storia Antica), Giorgio Bretschneider, Casella Postale 30011, Rm47, Rome, 00193, Italy. info@bretschneider.it.

913 976.4 USA ISSN 0082-2930
F381 CODEN: BTASDX
TEXAS ARCHEOLOGICAL SOCIETY. BULLETIN. Text in English. 1929. a. USD 25; includes newsletter. bk.rev. **Document type:** *Bulletin.*
Indexed: AICP, AmH&L, AnthLit.
Published by: Texas Archeological Society, Center for Archeological Research, Univ of Texas at San Antonio, 6900 N Loop 1604 W, San Antonio, TX 78249-0658. TEL 210-458-4393, FAX 210-458-4870, txarch@onr.com, http://www.txarch.org. R&P L Beavers. Circ: 1,200.

917 USA ISSN 0495-2944
CODEN: PNRME9
TEXAS ARCHEOLOGICAL SOCIETY. SPECIAL PUBLICATION. Text in English. 1962. irreg., latest vol.3, 1976. USD 10 per issue. **Document type:** *Monographic series.*
Published by: Texas Archeological Society, Center for Archeological Research, Univ of Texas at San Antonio, 6900 N Loop 1604 W, San Antonio, TX 78249-0658. TEL 210-458-4393, FAX 210-458-4870, txarch@onr.com, http://www.txarch.org. R&P L Beavers.

913 976.4 USA ISSN 0082-2949
CODEN: TTPHE2
TEXAS ARCHEOLOGY. Text in English. 1957. q. membership. bk.rev.
Published by: Texas Archeological Society, Center for Archeological Research, Univ of Texas at San Antonio, 6900 N Loop 1604 W, San Antonio, TX 78249-0658. TEL 210-458-4393, FAX 210-458-4870, txarch@onr.com, http://www.txarch.org. Circ: 1,200.

930.1 DEU
THEISS ARCHAEOLOGIEFUEHRER. Text in German. 2001. irreg., latest vol.4, 2003. price varies. **Document type:** *Monographic series, Academic/Scholarly.*
Published by: Konrad Theiss Verlag GmbH, Moenchhaldenstr 28, Stuttgart, 70191, Germany. TEL 49-711-255270, FAX 49-711-2552717, service@theiss.de, http://www.theiss.de.

938 BEL ISSN 0775-3411
THORIKOS; preliminary reports of the excavations at Thorikos. Text in English, French. 1963. irreg., latest vol.10, 2000, for years 1983-1988. price varies. adv. illus.; maps. back issues avail. **Document type:** *Monographic series, Academic/Scholarly.* **Description:** Publishes reports on the ongoing archaeological excavations at Thorikos, Greece.
Related titles: Supplement(s): Thorikos Guides.
Published by: (Comite des Fouilles Belges en Grece), Peeters Publishers, Bondgenotenlaan 153, Leuven, 3000, Belgium. TEL 32-16-235170, FAX 32-16-228500, http://www.peeters-leuven.be.

942 GBR ISSN 0309-9210
DA670.N89
➤ **THOROTON SOCIETY OF NOTTINGHAMSHIRE. TRANSACTIONS.** Text in English. 1897. a. GBP 20 to members (effective 2001). bk.rev. cum.index: vols. 1-100. 100 p./no. 2 cols./p.; back issues avail. **Document type:** *Academic/Scholarly.*
Indexed: BHA, BrArAb, NumL, PCI.
Published by: Thoroton Society of Nottinghamshire, Nottinghamshire Archives, County House, Castle Meadow Rd, Nottingham, NG2 1AG, United Kingdom. TEL 0-115-9504524, FAX 44-115-9413997, 44-115-9413997, adrian.henstock@nottscc.gov.uk, http://www.thorotonsociety.org.uk. Ed. A Henstock. Circ: 500.

➤ **THRACO-DACICA.** see *HISTORY—History Of Europe*

930.1 SWE ISSN 1404-8280
TIDSPERSPEKTIV. Text in Swedish; Summaries in English. 2000. biennial. price varies. **Document type:** *Journal, Academic/Scholarly.*
Published by: Umeaa Universitet, Institutionen foer Arkeologi och Samiska Studier, Umea University, Umea, 90187, Sweden. TEL 46-90-7865542, FAX 46-90-7867663, http://www.umu.se/arksam/.

930.1 USA ISSN 0163-0695
E78.T4
LA TIERRA. Text in English. 1974. q. USD 30 to non-members; free to members (effective 2004). **Document type:** *Newsletter.*
Indexed: AnthLit.
Published by: Southern Texas Archaelogical Association, P O Box 791032, San Antonio, TX 78279. http://www.staa.org.

930.1 948.5 SWE ISSN 1100-9586
TILLSLAGET. Text in Swedish. 1987. q. SEK 40 to members.
Published by: Umeaa Arkeologifoerening, Institutionen foer Arkeologi, Umea, 90187, Sweden.

913 DEU ISSN 0082-450X
TIRYNS. Text in German. 1912. irreg., latest vol.11, 1990. price varies. bibl.; charts; illus.; maps. back issues avail. **Document type:** *Monographic series, Academic/Scholarly.*
Published by: (Deutsches Archaeologisches Institut, Athens GRC), Verlag Philipp von Zabern GmbH, Philipp-von-Zabern-Platz 1-3, Mainz, 55116, Germany. TEL 49-6131-287470, FAX 49-6131-223710, zabern@zabern.de, http://www.zabern.de. Adv. contact Manuela Dressen TEL 49-6131-2874711.

930.1 909 SWE ISSN 0349-764X
TJUSTBYGDENS KULTURHISTORISKA FOERENING. AARSBOK. Cover title: Tjustbygden. Text in Swedish. 1926. a. SEK 130 to members (effective 2000). adv. **Document type:** *Academic/Scholarly.*
Formerly (until 1977): Tjustbygdens Kulturhistoriska Foerening. Meddelande
Published by: Tjustbygdens Kulturhistoriska Foerening, Kulbackens Museum, Fack 257, Vastervik, 59323, Sweden. TEL 46-490-21177. Ed. Hans Roupe. Circ: 1,200.

913 FRA ISSN 1161-9473
DE1
TOPOI ORIENT OCCIDENT. Text in French. 1979. a. bk.rev. **Document type:** *Academic/Scholarly.*
Formerly (until 1990): Societe des Amis de la Bibliotheque Salomon Reinach. Bulletin de Liaison (0994-3269)
Indexed: NumL.
Published by: Societe des Amis de la Bibliotheque Salomon Reinach, Maison de l'Orient Mediterraneen, 7 rue Raulin, Lyon, 69007, France. FAX 33-4-78-58-32-76. Ed. Marie Francoise Boussac.

TOR (UPPSALA); tidskrift foer arkeologi: journal of archaeology. see *HISTORY—History Of Europe*

913 POL ISSN 0860-147X
TOWARZYSTWO NAUKOWE W TORUNIU. PRACE ARCHEOLOGICZNE. Text in Polish; Summaries in German. 1938. irreg., latest vol.9, 1991. price varies. **Document type:** *Monographic series.*

Formerly (until 1974): Prace Prehistoryczne
Published by: Towarzystwo Naukowe w Toruniu, Ul Wysoka 16, Torun, 81100, Poland. TEL 48-56-23941. Ed. Krystyna Przewozna Armon. Circ: 750.

913   ESP   ISSN 0211-5174
DP302.N265
TRABAJOS DE ARQUEOLOGIA NAVARRA. Text in Spanish. 1979. a. EUR 15 (effective 2004). **Document type:** *Monographic series, Government.*
Indexed: AnthLit, ZooRec.
—CINDOC.
Published by: (Gobierno de Navarra, Departamento de Educacion y Cultura), Gobierno de Navarra, Fondo de Publicaciones, Navas de Tolosa 21, Pamplona, Navarra 31002, Spain. TEL 34-9848-427121, FAX 34-9848-427123, fondo.publicaciones@cfnavarra.es, http://www.navarra.es.

913   ESP   ISSN 0082-5638
GN835.A1   CODEN: TRPREI
TRABAJOS DE PREHISTORIA. NUEVA SERIE. Text in Spanish. 1960-1968; N.S. 1969. s-a. adv. abstr.; bibl.; charts; illus. back issues avail. **Document type:** *Academic/Scholarly.*
Description: Covers prehistoric research in the Iberian peninsula, the Mediterranean, and Western Europe from the Palaeolithic period through the second Iron Age. Debates the current goals and methods of archaeology.
Related titles: Online - full text ed.: (from Chadwyck-Healey Inc.).
Indexed: AnthLit, PCI.
—CINDOC.
Published by: Instituto de Historia, Departamento de Prehistoria (Subsidiary of: Centro Superior de Investigaciones Cientificas, Departamento de Publicaciones), Duque de Medinaceli, 6, Madrid, 28014, Spain. TEL 34-91-4290626, FAX 34-91-3690940, jsanchez@ceh.csic.es, http://www.ih.csic.es/publicaciones/tp/home.htm. Ed. Ignacio Montero Ruiz. adv.: page EUR 115; 160 x 195. Circ: 600.

913 669   GBR   ISSN 0143-1250
NB1842
TRANSACTIONS OF THE MONUMENTAL BRASS SOCIETY. Text in English. 1887. a. GBP 8. bk.rev. cum.index. back issues avail.
Indexed: BHA, BrArAb.
—CCC.
Published by: (Manuscripts Department), Guildhall Library, Aldermanbury, London, EC2P 2EJ, United Kingdom. Ed. S G H Freeth. Circ: 800.

930.1   ESP   ISSN 1130-7781
TRIBUNA D'ARQUEOLOGIA. Text in Catalan. 1983. a.
—CINDOC.
Published by: Generalitat de Catalunya, Departament de Cultura/Direccio General del Patrimoni Cultural, Portaferrissa, 1, Barcelona, 08002, Spain. TEL 34-93-3162740, FAX 34-93-3162741, http://cultura.gencat.es.

913   DEU   ISSN 0082-643X
TRIERER GRABUNGEN UND FORSCHUNGEN. Text in German. 1929. irreg., latest vol.16, 1999. price varies. charts; bibl.; illus.; maps. index. back issues avail. **Document type:** *Monographic series, Academic/Scholarly.*
Indexed: BrArAb.
Published by: (Rheinisches Landesmuseum, Trier), Verlag Philipp von Zabern GmbH, Philipp-von-Zabern-Platz 1-3, Mainz, 55116, Germany. TEL 49-6131-287470, FAX 49-6131-223710, zabern@zabern.de, http://www.zabern.de. Adv. contact Manuela Dressen TEL 49-6131-2874711.

914 709 737   DEU   ISSN 0041-2953
TRIERER ZEITSCHRIFT FUER GESCHICHTE UND KUNST DES TRIERER LANDES UND SEINER NACHBARGEBIETE. Text in German. 1926. a. EUR 44 (effective 2003). bk.rev. 400 p./no.; back issues avail. **Document type:** *Journal, Academic/Scholarly.*
Indexed: BHA, BrArAb, DIP, IBR, IBZ, NumL.
Published by: Rheinisches Landesmuseum Trier, Weimarer Allee 1, Trier, 54290, Germany. TEL 49-651-97740, FAX 49-651-9774222, rlmtrier@t-online.de, http://www.landesmuseum-trier.de. Circ: 750.

930.1   DEU   ISSN 1436-5219
TUEBINGER ARCHAEOLOGISCHE TASCHENBUECHER. Text in German. 1998. irreg., latest vol.3, 2002. EUR 25.50 per vol. (effective 2003). **Document type:** *Monographic series, Academic/Scholarly.* **Description:** Provides a forum for discussions on all aspects of archaeology.
Published by: Waxmann Verlag GmbH, Steinfurter Str 555, Muenster, 48159, Germany. TEL 49-251-26504-0, FAX 49-251-2650426, info@waxmann.com, http://www.waxmann.com. Eds. Manfred Eggert, Ulrich Veit.

930.1   DEU   ISSN 1430-0931
TUEBINGER SCHRIFTEN ZUR UR- UND FRUEHGESCHICHTLICHEN ARCHAEOLOGIE. Text in German. 1996. irreg., latest vol.7, 2002. EUR 39.90 per vol. (effective 2003). **Document type:** *Monographic series, Academic/Scholarly.* **Description:** Presents papers on ancient and early period archaeology throughout the world.

Published by: Waxmann Verlag GmbH, Steinfurter Str 555, Muenster, 48159, Germany. TEL 49-251-26504-0, FAX 49-251-2650426, info@waxmann.com, http://www.waxmann.com. Ed. Manfred Eggert.

930.1   USA
TULANE UNIVERSITY. CENTER FOR ARCHAEOLOGY. ARCHAEOLOGICAL REPORTS. Text in English. irreg. price varies. **Document type:** *Monographic series, Academic/Scholarly.* **Description:** Publishes archaeological research conducted at Tulane University.
Indexed: AnthLit.
Published by: Tulane University, Center for Archaeology, Department of Anthropology, New Orleans, LA 70118. TEL 504-865-5336, FAX 504-865-5338, http://www.tulane.edu/~anthro/.

930.1   TUR   ISSN 0564-5042
TURK ARKEOLOJI DERGISI/TURKISH REVIEW OF ARCHAEOLOGY. Text in Turkish; Text occasionally in English, German. 1956. a. per issue exchange basis. **Document type:** *Academic/Scholarly.* **Description:** Scholarly articles on archaeological projects undertaken in Turkey.
Indexed: AIAP, AnthLit.
Published by: Ministry of Culture, General Directorate of Monuments and Museums/Kultur Bakanligi, Anitlar ve Muzeler Genel Mudurlugu, Ulus - Ankara, 06100, Turkey. TEL 90-312-3104960, FAX 90-312-3111417.

U TZ'IB. see *ANTHROPOLOGY*

913   GBR   ISSN 0082-7355
DA990.U45   CODEN: UJAYAH
ULSTER JOURNAL OF ARCHAEOLOGY. Text in English. 1938. a. GBP 15 (effective 1998). adv. bk.rev. index. **Document type:** *Academic/Scholarly.*
Indexed: BHA, BrArAb, NumL, RASB.
Published by: Ulster Archaeological Society, Archaeology Dept., Queens University, Belfast, Co Antrim BT7 1NN, United Kingdom. Ed. D Simpson. R&P F McCormick. Circ: 550.

930.1   SWE   ISSN 1104-3520
UMEAA UNIVERSITET. INSTITUTIONEN FOER ARKEOLOGI OCH SAMISKA STUDIER. ARKEOLOGISKA STUDIER. Text in Swedish. 1993. irreg., latest vol.4, 1997. price varies. back issues avail. **Document type:** *Monographic series, Academic/Scholarly.*
Published by: Umeaa Universitet, Institutionen foer Arkeologi och Samiska Studier, Umea University, Umea, 90187, Sweden. TEL 46-90-7865542, FAX 46-90-7867663, http://www.umu.se/arksam/.

930.1   SWE   ISSN 1100-7028
UMEAA UNIVERSITET. INSTITUTIONEN FOER ARKEOLOGI OCH SAMISKA STUDIER. STUDIA ARCHAEOLOGICA UNIVERSITATIS UMENSIS. Text in Swedish; Summaries in English. 1989. irreg., latest 2004. price varies. back issues avail. **Document type:** *Monographic series, Academic/Scholarly.*
Published by: Umeaa Universitet, Institutionen foer Arkeologi och Samiska Studier, Umea University, Umea, 90187, Sweden. TEL 46-90-7865542, FAX 46-90-7867663, http://www.umu.se/archaeology/publikation/sauu/index.html, http://www.umu.se/arksam/.

913   USA
CC77.U5
UNDERWATER ARCHAEOLOGY. Text in English. 1987. irreg. price varies. bibl.; charts; illus.; stat. back issues avail. **Document type:** *Monographic series, Academic/Scholarly.* **Description:** Papers dealing with theory, method and legal issues pertaining to underwater archaeology.
Formerly: Society for Historical Archaeology Conference. Underwater Proceedings (1074-3421)
—BLDSC (9090.008400).
Published by: Society for Historical Archaeology, PO Box 30446, Tucson, AZ 85751. TEL 520-886-8006, FAX 520-886-0182, the_sha@mindspring.com, http://www.sha.org. Circ: 350.

913   ESP   ISSN 0067-4184
UNIVERSIDAD DE BARCELONA. INSTITUTO DE ARQUEOLOGIA Y PREHISTORIA. PUBLICACIONES EVENTUALES. Text in Spanish. 1960. irreg., latest vol.26, 1975. price varies. **Document type:** *Journal, Academic/Scholarly.*
Indexed: NumL.
Published by: (Universitat de Barcelona, Institut de Arqueologia y Prehistoria), Universitat de Barcelona, Servei de Publicacions, Gran Via Corts Catalanes 585, Barcelona, 08007, Spain.

UNIVERSIDAD DE MURCIA. ANALES DE PREHISTORIA Y ARQUEOLOGIA. see *HISTORY—History Of Europe*

930.1   ESP   ISSN 1133-1542
UNIVERSIDAD DE NAVARRA. CUADERNOS DE ARQUEOLOGIA. Text in Spanish. 1993. a. EUR 18 domestic; USD 30 foreign (effective 2005).
—CINDOC.
Published by: Ediciones Universidad de Navarra S.A., Pza. Los Sauces, 1-2, Baranain, (Navarra) 31010, Spain. TEL 34-948-256850, http://www.unav.es/historia/cuadernosdearqueologia/.

UNIVERSIDAD NACIONAL AUTONOMA DE MEXICO. CENTRO DE ESTUDIOS MAYAS. CUADERNOS. see *HISTORY—History Of North And South America*

918   BRA
UNIVERSIDADE DE SAO PAULO. MUSEU PAULISTA. COLECAO. SERIE DE ARQUEOLOGIA. Text in Portuguese. 1975. irreg.
Supersedes in part (in 1975): Museu Paulista. Colecao (0080-6382)
Indexed: AnthLit.
Published by: Universidade de Sao Paulo, Museu Paulista, Parque da Independencia, Centro, Caixa Postal 42 503, Sao Paulo, SP 01059-970, Brazil. Ed. Setembrino Petri.

913 800   ITA   ISSN 0076-1818
UNIVERSITA DEGLI STUDI DI MACERATA. FACOLTA DI LETTERE E FILOSOFIA. ANNALI. Text in Italian. 1968. a. price varies. bk.rev. back issues avail.
Indexed: BHA, MLA, MLA-IB.
Published by: Universita degli Studi di Macerata, Facolta di Lettere e Filosofia, Piaggia Universita, 2, Macerata, MC 62100, Italy. TEL 0773-4181. Ed. Giovanni Ferretti. Circ: 500.

UNIVERSITA DEGLI STUDI DI ROMA. SEMINARIO DI ARCHEOLOGIA E STORIA DELL'ARTE GRECA E ROMANA. STUDI MISCELLANEI. see *CLASSICAL STUDIES*

913   DEU
UNIVERSITAET BONN. SEMINAR FUER ORIENTALISCHE KUNSTGESCHICHTE. VEROEFFENTLICHUNGEN. REIHE A. NIMRUZ. Text in German. 1974. irreg. price varies. **Document type:** *Monographic series, Academic/Scholarly.*
Published by: (Universitaet Bonn, Forschungstelle fuer Orientalische Kunstgeschichte), Dr. Rudolf Habelt GmbH, Am Buchenhang 1, Bonn, 53115, Germany. TEL 49-228-9238322, FAX 49-228-9238323, info@habelt.de, http://www.habelt.de. Ed. Klaus Fischer.

930.1   DEU
UNIVERSITAETSFORSCHUNGEN ZUR PRAEHISTORISCHEN ARCHAEOLOGIE. Text in German. 1989. irreg., latest vol.79, 2001. price varies. **Document type:** *Monographic series, Academic/Scholarly.*
Published by: Dr. Rudolf Habelt GmbH, Am Buchenhang 1, Bonn, 53115, Germany. TEL 49-228-9238322, FAX 49-228-9238323, info@habelt.de, http://www.habelt.de.

UNIVERSITE CATHOLIQUE DE LOUVAIN. DEPARTEMENT D'ARCHEOLOGIE ET D'HISTOIRE DE L'ART. DOCUMENTS DE TRAVAIL. see *ART*

930.1 709   BEL
UNIVERSITE CATHOLIQUE DE LOUVAIN. DEPARTEMENT D'ARCHEOLOGIE ET D'HISTOIRE DE L'ART. PUBLICATIONS. (Consists of 6 subseries: Aurifex, Archaeologica Transatlantica, Numismatica Lovaniensia, Braives, Arts Africains, Musicologica Neolovaniensia) Text in English, French. 1972. irreg., latest vol.96, 1997. price varies. charts; illus.; maps. **Document type:** *Monographic series, Academic/Scholarly.*
Published by: (Universite Catholique de Louvain, Departement d'Etudes Greques, Latines et Orientales, Publications d'Archeologie et d'Histoire de l'Art), Universite Catholique de Louvain, College Erasme, Pl Blaise Pascal 1, Louvain-la-Neuve, 1348, Belgium. TEL 32-10-474882, FAX 32-10-474870, moucharte@arke.ucl.ac.be, moucharte@fltr.ucl.ac.be, http://juppiter.fltr.ucl.ac.be/FLTR/publications/pub_pahal. R&P Ghislaine Moucharte. Circ: 1,000.

UNIVERSITE DE MADAGASCAR. MUSEE D'ART ET D'ARCHEOLOGIE. TRAVAUX ET DOCUMENTS. see *ART*

UNIVERSITE LIBRE DE BRUXELLES. FACULTE DE PHILOSOPHIE ET LETTRES. ANNALES D'HISTOIRE DE L'ART ET D'ARCHEOLOGIE. see *ART*

948.101 948   NOR   ISSN 0333-130X
➤ **UNIVERSITETETS OLDSAKSAMLING. AARBOK.** Text in English, Norwegian; Summaries in English, German. 1927. a. NOK 110 (effective 1998). bk.rev. back issues avail. **Document type:** *Academic/Scholarly.* **Description:** Contains articles on prehistoric and medieval subjects, mainly concerned with Scandinavia and Northern Europe.
Indexed: BHA, BrArAb, NAA, RASB.
Published by: Universitetet i Oslo, Oldsaksamlingen/University Museum of National Antiquities, Frederiks Gate 3, Oslo, 0164, Norway. TEL 47-22-85-1921. Ed., R&P Ellen Hoeigaard Hofseth. Circ: 1,000.

930.1   GBR
UNIVERSITY COLLEGE LONDON. PAPERS FROM THE INSTITUTE OF ARCHAEOLOGY. Text in English. 1990. a. GBP 3.50 to individuals; GBP 7 to institutions (effective 2002).
Indexed: AnthLit.
Published by: University College London, Institute of Archaeology, 31-34 Gordon Sq., London, WC1H 0PY, United Kingdom. TEL 44-207-387-7050, FAX 44-207-383-2572, tcrnpia@ucl.ac.uk, http://www.ucl.ac.uk/archaeology/pia.

UNIVERSITY OF ARIZONA. ANTHROPOLOGICAL PAPERS. see *ANTHROPOLOGY*

560 CAN ISSN 0822-2967
UNIVERSITY OF CALGARY. ARCHAEOLOGICAL ASSOCIATION. ARCHAEOLOGICAL CONFERENCE. PROCEEDINGS. Text in English. 1969. a. price varies. **Document type:** *Proceedings, Academic/Scholarly.*
Formerly: University of Calgary. Archaeological Association. Paleo-Environmental Workshop. Proceedings (0068-5437)
Indexed: AnthLit.
Published by: University of Calgary, Archaeological Association, Department of Archaeology, 2920 24th Ave N W, Calgary, AB T2N 1N4, Canada. TEL 403-220-7120. Circ: 150. **Subscr. to:** Archaeological Association, Department of Archaeology, University of Calgary, 2500 University Dr, N W, Calgary, AB T2N 1N4, Canada.

571 USA ISSN 0068-5933
E51
UNIVERSITY OF CALIFORNIA AT BERKELEY. ARCHAEOLOGICAL RESEARCH FACILITY. CONTRIBUTIONS. Text in English. 1965. irreg. price varies. **Document type:** *Academic/Scholarly.*
Related titles: Microform ed.: (from PQC).
Published by: University of California at Berkeley, Archaeological Research Facility, 2251 College Building, Berkeley, CA 94720. TEL 415-642-2212. Circ: 400.

913 USA
UNIVERSITY OF CALIFORNIA AT LOS ANGELES. INSTITUTE OF ARCHAEOLOGY. MONOGRAPH SERIES. Text in English. 1970. irreg., latest vol.39, 1998. price varies. **Document type:** *Monographic series, Academic/Scholarly.* **Description:** Publishes preliminary and final excavation reports, symposia papers and accounts of research in progress in such areas as ethnoarchaeology, archaeometry and paleodemography.
Formerly: University of California at Los Angeles. Institute of Archaeology. Archaeological Survey. Special Monograph Series (0068-6204)
Indexed: AnthLit.
Published by: (Publications Department), University of California at Los Angeles, Cotsen Institute of Archaeology, A222 Fowler Museum, Box 951510, Los Angeles, CA 90095-1510. TEL 310-825-7411, FAX 310-206-4723. Ed. Brenda Johnson Grau.

UNIVERSITY OF CHICAGO ORIENTAL INSTITUTE. PUBLICATIONS. see *HISTORY—History Of The Near East*

913 GBR ISSN 0144-3313
UNIVERSITY OF EDINBURGH. DEPARTMENT OF ARCHAEOLOGY. OCCASIONAL PAPERS. Text in English. 1978. irreg., latest vol.20, 2000. USD 10 per issue paperback 30 pages (effective 2000). back issues avail. **Document type:** *Monographic series, Academic/Scholarly.*
Indexed: BrArAb.
Published by: University of Edinburgh, Department of Archaeology, Old High School, 12 Infirmary St, Edinburgh, EH1 1LT, United Kingdom. http://super3.arcl.ed.ac.uk/arch/publish/occpapers.htm. **Subscr. to:** Oxbow Books, Park End Pl, Oxford OX1 1HN, United Kingdom. **Dist. by:** The David Brown Book Company, PO Box 511, Oakville, CT 06779. TEL 860-945-9329, FAX 860-945-9468, david.brown.bk.co@snet.net.

913 GBR ISSN 0266-1799
UNIVERSITY OF EDINBURGH. DEPARTMENT OF ARCHAEOLOGY. PROJECT PAPERS. Text in English. 1984. irreg., latest vol.14, 1995. price varies. back issues avail. **Document type:** *Monographic series, Academic/Scholarly.*
Published by: University of Edinburgh, Department of Archaeology, Old High School, 12 Infirmary St, Edinburgh, EH1 1LT, United Kingdom. http://.arcl.ed.ac.uk/arch/publish/occpapers.htm, http://super3.arcl.ed.ac.uk/arch/publish/occpapers.htm. **Subscr. to:** Oxbow Books, Park End Pl, Oxford OX1 1HN, United Kingdom.

930.1 GBR
UNIVERSITY OF GLASGOW. DEPARTMENT OF ARCHAEOLOGY. OCCASIONAL PAPER SERIES. Text in English. 1992. irreg., latest vol.4, 1997. GBP 12.50 (effective 2000). **Document type:** *Monographic series.*
Indexed: BrArAb, NumL.
Published by: University of Glasgow, Department of Archaeology, Gregory Bldg, Glasgow, Lanarkshire G12 8QQ, United Kingdom. TEL 44-141-330-3274, FAX 44-141-330-3544, n.docherty@archaeology.arts.gla.ac.uk, l.wilson@archaeology.arts.gla.ac.uk, http://www.gla.ac.uk/acad/archaeology.

913 SWE
UNIVERSITY OF LUND. ARCHEOLOGICAL INSTITUTE. PAPERS. YEARBOOK/MEDDELANDE FRAAN LUNDS UNIVERSITET HISTORISKA MUSEUM. Text in English. a. back issues avail. **Document type:** *Academic/Scholarly.*
Indexed: AnthLit, NAA.
Published by: Almqvist & Wiksell International, P O Box 7634, Stockholm, 10394, Sweden. FAX 46-8-24-25-43, info@city.akademibokhandeln.se, http://www.akademibokhandeln.se.

915 IND ISSN 0076-2202
UNIVERSITY OF MADRAS. ARCHAEOLOGICAL SERIES✶. Text in English. 1967. irreg.
Published by: University of Madras, c/o Director, Publications Division, Chennai, Tamil Nadu 600 005, India. TEL 91-44-568778, FAX 91-44-566693.

UNIVERSITY OF MANITOBA ANTHROPOLOGY PAPERS. see *ANTHROPOLOGY*

UNIVERSITY OF MISSOURI MONOGRAPHS IN ANTHROPOLOGY. see *ANTHROPOLOGY*

930.1 USA
UNIVERSITY OF PITTSBURGH. DEPARTMENT OF ANTHROPOLOGY. MEMOIRS IN LATIN AMERICAN ARCHAEOLOGY. Text in English. irreg. **Document type:** *Monographic series, Academic/Scholarly.*
Indexed: AnthLit.
Published by: University of Pittsburgh, Department of Anthropology, Latin American Archaeology Publications, Pittsburgh, PA 15260. TEL 412-648-7681, FAX 412-648-7535, ethnolog@pitt.edu, http://www.pitt.edu/~ethnolog.

301 USA ISSN 0162-5799
F271
UNIVERSITY OF SOUTH CAROLINA. INSTITUTE OF ARCHEOLOGY AND ANTHROPOLOGY. ANNUAL REPORT. Text in English. 1976. a. free. **Document type:** *Corporate.* **Description:** Summarizes what individuals have done in their divisions for the previous year.
Published by: University of South Carolina, Institute of Archeology and Anthropology, 1321 Pendleton St, Columbia, SC 29208. TEL 803-777-8170, FAX 803-254-1338. Circ: 400.

UNIVERZITA KOMENSKEHO. FILOZOFICKA FAKULTA. ZBORNIK: MUSAICA. see *ART*

913 POL ISSN 0554-8195
UNIWERSYTET IM. ADAMA MICKIEWICZA. ARCHEOLOGIA. Text in Polish; Summaries in German, English. 1966. irreg., latest vol.44, 1996. price varies. **Document type:** *Monographic series, Academic/Scholarly.* **Description:** Contains current research results of the University's archaeologists, such as their Ph.D. works and monographs.
Formerly (until 1975): Uniwersytet im. Adama Mickiewicza w Poznaniu. Wydzial Filozoficzno-Historyczny. Prace. Seria Archeologia (0860-1259)
Published by: (Uniwersytet im. Adama Mickiewicza w Poznaniu/Adam Mickiewicz University), Wydawnictwo Naukowe Uniwersytetu im. Adama Mickiewicza/Adam Mickiewicz University Press, Nowowiejskiego 55, Poznan, 61-734, Poland. TEL 48-61-527380, FAX 48-61-527701. Pub. Maria Jankowska. R&P Malgorzata Bis.

913 POL ISSN 0083-4300
GN705
UNIWERSYTET JAGIELLONSKI. ZESZYTY NAUKOWE. PRACE ARCHEOLOGICZNE. Text in Polish. 1960. irreg. price varies. **Document type:** *Monographic series, Academic/Scholarly.*
Indexed: AICP, BHA.
Published by: (Uniwersytet Jagiellonski, Instytut Archeologii), Wydawnictwo Uniwersytetu Jagiellonskiego/Jagiellonian University Press, ul Grodzka 26, Krakow, 31044, Poland. TEL 48-12-4312364, FAX 48-12-4301995, wydaw@if.uj.edu.pl, http://www.wuj.pl. Ed. Janusz K Kozlowski. Circ: 700. **Dist. by:** Ars Polona, Krakowskie Przedmiescie 7, Warsaw, Poland. TEL 48-22-9263914, FAX 48-22-9265334, arspolona@arspolona.com.pl, http://www.arspolona.com.pl.

930.1 DEU ISSN 0940-7448
URNENFRIEDHOEFE IN NIEDERSACHSEN. Text in German. 1911. irreg., latest vol.16, 2001. **Document type:** *Monographic series, Academic/Scholarly.*
Indexed: RASB.
Published by: Isensee Verlag, Haarenstr 20, Oldenburg, 26122, Germany. TEL 49-441-25388, FAX 49-441-17872, verlag@isensee.de, http://www.isensee.de.

930.1 USA ISSN 1040-6549
E78.U55
➤ **UTAH ARCHAEOLOGY.** Text in English. 1988. a. USD 20 to members (effective 2002). **Document type:** *Journal, Academic/Scholarly.*
Indexed: AnthLit.
Published by: (Utah Statewide Archaeological Society), Utah Division of State History, Utah State Historical Society, 300 South Rio Grande, Salt Lake City, UT 84101-1143. TEL 801-533-3502, FAX 801-533-3503, ushs@history.state.ut.us, http://www.dced.state.ut.us/history/Services/ararchmag.html. **Co-publishers:** Utah Professional Archaeological Council; Mountain West Center for Regional Studies.

930.1 DEU ISSN 1432-6876
V D R BULLETIN. Text in German. 1996. q. **Document type:** *Bulletin, Academic/Scholarly.*
Incorporates (1990-2001): Arbeitsgemeinschaft der Restauratoren Aktuell (0945-344X)
Published by: Verband der Restauratoren e.V., Haus der Kultur, Weberstr. 61, Bonn, 53113, Germany. TEL 49-228-2437366, FAX 49-228-2619669, info@restauratoren.de, http://www.restauratoren.de.

930.1 DEU
V D R - SCHRIFTENREIHE ZUR RESTAURIERUNG UND GRABUNGSTECHNIK. Text in German. irreg., latest vol.7, 2002. price varies. **Document type:** *Monographic series, Academic/Scholarly.*
Published by: (Verband der Restauratoren e.V.), Konrad Theiss Verlag GmbH, Moenchhaldenstr 28, Stuttgart, 70191, Germany. TEL 49-711-255270, FAX 49-711-2552717, service@theiss.de, http://www.theiss.de.

930.1 948.5 SWE ISSN 0347-4402
DL971.V4
VAESTERGOETLANDS FORNMINNESFOERENINGS TIDSKRIFT. Text in Swedish. 1869. biennial. **Document type:** *Journal, Academic/Scholarly.*
Indexed: BHA, NAA.
Published by: Vaestergoetlands Fornminnesfoerening, Skaraborgs Laensmuseum, Fack 253, Skara, 53223, Sweden.

VARIA ANTIQUA. see *ASIAN STUDIES*

VELEIA; revista de prehistoria, historia antigua, arqueologia y filologia clasicas. see *HISTORY*

VEREENIGING TOT BEOFENING VAN GELDERSCHE GESCHIEDENIS, OUDHEIDKUNDE EN RECHT. WERKEN. see *HISTORY—History Of Europe*

281 700 200 ITA ISSN 1121-9696
VETERA CHRISTIANORUM. Text in English, French, German, Italian, Spanish. 1964. 2/yr. EUR 31 domestic; EUR 41.30 foreign (effective 2005). adv. bk.rev. **Document type:** *Journal, Academic/Scholarly.* **Description:** Covers early Christian literature, history of ancient and medieval Christianity, and archaeological documentation.
Indexed: BHA, BibLing, DIP, IBR, MLA-IB, NTA, RI-1.
—BLDSC (9222.800000), IE, Infotrieve, ingenta.
Published by: (Istituto di Letteratura Cristiana Antica), Edipuglia Srl, Via Dalmazia 22-B, Santo Spirito, BA 70050, Italy. TEL 39-080-5333056, FAX 39-080-5333057, http://www.edipuglia.it. Circ: 1,400.

VIBORG STIFTSMUSEUMS RAEKKE. see *HISTORY—History Of Europe*

915 913 ITA ISSN 0393-0300
VICINO ORIENTE. Text in English, French, German, Italian. 1978. a., latest vol.12, 2000. back issues avail. **Document type:** *Academic/Scholarly.*
Indexed: BibLing, DIP, IBR, IBZ.
Published by: Universita degli Studi di Roma "La Sapienza", Archeologiche e Antropologiche dell'Antichita. Sez. Vicino Oriente, Via Palestro, 63, Rome, RM 00185, Italy. TEL 390-6-6795304, FAX 390-6-3225348, TELEX 621427 NATEL. Eds. Alfonso Archi, Mario Liverani. **Dist. by:** Herder Editrice e Libreria s.r.l., Piazza di Montecitorio 117-120, Rome 00186, Italy. TEL 39-06-6794628, FAX 390-6-3225348, 39-6-6784751, bookcenter@herder.it, http://www.herder.it.

913.48 NOR ISSN 0332-608X
DL1
➤ **VIKING;** tidsskrift for norroen arkeologi - journal of Norse archaeology. Text in Norwegian; Summaries in English. 1937. a. NOK 225 (effective 2003). adv. charts; illus. back issues avail. **Document type:** *Yearbook, Academic/Scholarly.*
Indexed: AIAP, BrArAb, NAA, NumL, RASB.
—BLDSC (9236.374000).
Published by: Norsk Arkeologisk Selskap, Huk Aveny 35, Oslo, 0287, Norway. TEL 47-22-438792, FAX 47-22-135286, nas@arkeologi.no, http://www.arkeologi.no. Ed. Egil Mikkelsen. adv.: B&W page NOK 500.

930.1 PRT ISSN 0872-1653
VIPASCA; arqueologia e historia. Text in Multiple languages. 1992. a. adv. **Document type:** *Academic/Scholarly.*
Published by: Camara Municipal de Aljustrel, Unidade Arqueologica de Aljustrel, c/o Biblioteca, Aljustrel, 7600, Portugal. TEL 351-284-600070, FAX 351-284-602055, c.m.aljustral@mail.telepac.pt. Ed. Carlos Ramos. R&P, Adv. contact Arturo Martins. Circ: 1,000.

913.031 666 HRV ISSN 0350-8447
DB401
VJESNIK ZA ARHEOLOGIJU I HISTORIJU DALMATINSKU. Text in Croatian; Summaries in Multiple languages. 1878. irreg. price varies. bk.rev. back issues avail. **Document type:** *Academic/Scholarly.* **Description:** Covers archaeology and history of Dalmatia.
Indexed: BHA, RASB.
Published by: Arheoloski Muzej (Split), Zrinsko Frankopanska 25, PO Box 186, Split, 21000, Croatia. TEL 385-21-344685. Ed. Emilio Marin. Circ: 750.

VLASTIVEDNY VESTNIK MORAVSKY. see *HISTORY—History Of Europe*

930.1 RUS
VOLGOGRADSKII GOSUDARSTVENNYI UNIVERSITET. NIZHNEVOLZHSKII ARKHEOLOGICHESKII VESTNIK. Text in Russian. irreg.
Indexed: AnthLit.

Published by: (Volgogradskii Gosudarstvennyi Universitet), Volgograd University Press, 20, 2nd Prodol'naya St, Volgograd, 400062, Russian Federation. TEL 7-8442-433479.

913 USA
VOLUMES IN HISTORICAL ARCHAEOLOGY. Text in English. 1986. irreg., latest vol.35. USD 10. back issues avail. **Document type:** *Monographic series.* **Description:** Covers research on historical archaeological sites in the U.S.
Published by: University of South Carolina, South Carolina Institute of Archaeology and Anthropology, 1321 Pendleton St, Columbia, SC 29208. TEL 803-777-8170, FAX 803-254-1338, http://www.cas.sc.edu/sciaa/. Ed. Stanley South. **Co-sponsor:** Conference on Historic Site Archaeology.

930.1 DEU ISSN 0176-6570
➤ **VORGESCHICHTLICHE FORSCHUNGEN.** Text in German. 1924. irreg., latest vol.20, 1996. price varies. **Document type:** *Monographic series, Academic/Scholarly.*
Published by: Walter de Gruyter GmbH & Co. KG, Genthiner Str. 13, Berlin, 10785, Germany. TEL 49-30-260050, FAX 49-30-26005251, wdg-info@degruyter.de, http://www.degruyter.de. Ed. Bernhard Haensel.

914 943.7 CZE ISSN 0862-2930
VYZKUMY V CECHACH. Text in Czech. 1963. irreg., latest 1999. EUR 17 per issue (effective 2004). illus.; maps. 350 p./no.; back issues avail. **Document type:** *Catalog, Academic/Scholarly.*
Supersedes: Ceskoslovenska Akademie Ved. Archeologicky Ustav. Zachranne Oddeleni. Bulletin
Published by: Akademie Ved Ceske Republiky, Archeologicky Ustav, Letenska 4, Prague, 11801, Czech Republic. TEL 420-2-57533369, FAX 420-2-57532288. Ed. M Kuna.

930.1 USA ISSN 0738-8063
W A S NEWSLETTER. Text in English. 1971. irreg. USD 16 domestic; USD 20 foreign (effective 2005). adv. bk.rev. 10 p./no.; back issues avail.; reprints avail. **Document type:** *Newsletter, Academic/Scholarly.* **Description:** Dedicated to the study of man and his culture through the three related areas of archaeology, anthropology and art history.
Media: Duplicated (not offset).
Published by: World Archaeological Society, 120 Lakewood Dr, Hollister, MO 65672. TEL 417-334-2377, ronwriterartist@aol.com, http://www.worldarchaeologicalsociety.com. R&P Ron S Miller TEL 417-334-2377. adv.: page USD 75. Circ: 5,000 (controlled and free).

930.1 ESP ISSN 0214-7092
WAD-AL-HAYARA. Text in Spanish. 1974. a.
Related titles: CD-ROM ed.: ISSN 1576-2890. 1998.
—CINDOC.
Published by: Diputacion Provincial de Guadalajara, Seccion de Administracion Cultural, Moreno, 10, Guadalajara, 19001, Spain. TEL 34-949-887551.

930.1 DEU ISSN 0232-265X
WEIMARER MONOGRAPHIEN ZUR UR- UND FRUEHGESCHICHTE. Text in German. 1978. irreg. price varies.
Published by: Museum fuer Ur- und Fruehgeschichte Thueringens, Humboldtstr 11, Weimar, 99423, Germany. Ed. R Feustel.

WELT UND UMWELT DER BIBEL. see *RELIGIONS AND THEOLOGY*

WEN BO/JOURNAL OF MUSEUMS & ARCHAEOLOGY. see *MUSEUMS AND ART GALLERIES*

930.1 CHN ISSN 0511-4772
DS715
WENWU/CULTURAL RELICS. Text in Chinese; Contents page in English. 1950. m. CNY 60 in Hong Kong; USD 72 elsewhere. adv. bk.rev. illus.
Related titles: Online - full text ed.: (from East View Information Services).
Indexed: AICP, HistAb, NumL, RASB.
Published by: Wenwu Chubanshe/Cultural Relics Publishing House, 29 Wusi Dajie, Beijing, 100009, China. TEL 86-10-6401-0698. Ed. Yang Jin. Circ: 15,000.

930.1 333.72 CHN ISSN 1005-1538
CC135
WENWU BAOHU YU KAOGU KEXUE/SCIENCES OF CONSERVATION AND ARCHAEOLOGY. Text in Chinese. 1989. q. **Document type:** *Journal, Academic/Scholarly.*
Related titles: Online - full text ed.: (from East View Information Services, WanFang Data Corp.).
—BLDSC (8165.710000).
Published by: Shanghai Shi Wenwu Guanli Weihui, 1118, Longwu Lu, Shanghai, 200231, China. TEL 86-21-54362886, FAX 86-21-54363740, lab_sh_museum@yahoo.com.cn, http://wwbhykgkx.periodicals.net.cn/.

915 CHN ISSN 1003-6555
WENWU CHUNQIU/STORIES OF RELICS. Text in Chinese. 1989. bi-m. CNY 36, USD 15 (effective 2001). illus. 80 p./no.; back issues avail. **Document type:** *Academic/Scholarly.*
Related titles: Online - full content ed.: (from WanFang Data Corp.); Online - full text ed.: (from East View Information Services).
Published by: Hebei Wenwu Ju, 4 Dong Dajie, Chang'an-qu, Shijiazhuang, Hebei 050011, China. TEL 86-311-604-9827. Ed. Xu Lu Mei. R&P Cai-Hong Cheng.

931 951 CHN ISSN 1000-0194
DS777.55
WENWU TIANDI. Text in Chinese. bi-m. CNY 13.20.
Indexed: RASB.
Published by: Wenhua Bu, Guwenxian Yanjiushi/Ministry of Culture, China Cultural Relics Research Institute, 29 Wusi St, Beijing, 100009, China. TEL 4015577. Ed. Wu Tiemei. **Dist. in US by:** China Books & Periodicals Inc, 360 Swift Ave., Ste. 48, S San Fran, CA 94080-6220; **Dist. outside China by:** China International Book Trading Corp, 35 Chegongzhuang Xilu, Haidian District, PO Box 399, Beijing 100044, China.

930.10966 NGA ISSN 0331-3158
GN865.W45
WEST AFRICAN JOURNAL OF ARCHAEOLOGY. Text in English, French. 1961. a. NGN 6.25. adv. bk.rev. **Document type:** *Academic/Scholarly.*
Formerly (until 1970): West African Archaeological Newsletter (0083-8160)
Indexed: AICP, ASD, AnthLit, BrArAb, CCA, IBSS, RILM, SSCI.
Published by: (University of Ibadan, Department of Archaeology), Ibadan University Press, University of Ibadan, Ibadan, Oyo, Nigeria.

914 943.8 POL ISSN 0043-5082
➤ **WIADOMOSCI ARCHEOLOGICZNE/BULLETIN ARCHEOLOGIQUE POLONAIS.** Text in Polish. 1873. 2/yr. PLZ 20 (effective 1997). adv. bk.rev. illus. cum.index. **Document type:** *Academic/Scholarly.*
Indexed: AICP, AnthLit, BHA, BrArAb, RASB.
Published by: Panstwowe Muzeum Archeologiczne, Ul Dluga 52, Warsaw, 00241, Poland. TEL 48-22-8313221, FAX 48-22-8315195, TELEX 816700. Ed. Jan Jaskanis. Adv. contact Wojciech Brzezinski. Circ: 700. **Subscr. to:** Osrodek Rozpowszechniania Wydawnictw Naukowych PAN.

➤ **WILBOUR MONOGRAPHS.** see *HISTORY*

500.2 GBR
WILTSHIRE ARCHAEOLOGICAL AND NATURAL HISTORY MAGAZINE. Text in English. 1853. a. GBP 23 to individual members; GBP 28 to institutional members (effective 2000). bk.rev. **Document type:** *Newsletter, Academic/Scholarly.*
Formed by the 1982 merger of: Wiltshire Archaeological Magazine (0309-3476); Wiltshire Natural History Magazine (0309-3468); Which was formerly: Wiltshire Archaeological and Natural History Magazine (0084-0335)
Indexed: BHA, BrArAb, NumL, ZooRec.
—BLDSC (9319.100000).
Published by: Wiltshire Archaeological and Natural History Society, 41 Long St, Devizes, Wilts SN10 1NS, United Kingdom. TEL 44-1380-727369, FAX 44-1380-722150. Ed. J H Chandler. R&P P H Robinson. Adv. contact Netty Rawlings. Circ: 1,500.

913 500.2 GBR
WILTSHIRE ARCHAEOLOGICAL AND NATURAL HISTORY SOCIETY. ANNUAL REPORT (YEAR). Text in English. a. **Document type:** *Proceedings.*
Formerly: Wiltshire Archaeological and Natural History Society. Annual Bulletin
Published by: Wiltshire Archaeological and Natural History Society, 41 Long St, Devizes, Wilts SN10 1NS, United Kingdom. TEL 44-1380-727369, FAX 44-1380-722150. Ed. J H Chandler. R&P P H Robinson.

930.1 USA ISSN 0043-6364
E78.W8
➤ **THE WISCONSIN ARCHEOLOGIST.** Text in English. 1901. q. USD 20 to individuals; USD 30 to institutions. bk.rev. bibl.; charts; illus. cum.index. **Document type:** *Academic/Scholarly.* **Description:** Contains original articles dealing with anthropology (ethnology, physical anthropology, archaeology) of the state of Wisconsin and adjoining regions of the U.S. and Canada. Articles of general topical or theoretical interest are also considered.
Related titles: Microfiche ed.: (from BHP).
Indexed: AbAn, AmH&L, AnthLit, HistAb, MMI.
Published by: Wisconsin Archeological Society, PO Box 1292, Milwaukee, WI 53201. TEL 414-229-4273. Ed. David Overstreet. R&P David F Overstreet. Circ: 650 (paid).

930 BIH ISSN 0352-1990
WISSENSCHAFTLICHE MITTEILUNGEN DES BOSNISCH-HERZEGOWINISCHEN LANDESMUSEUMS. ARCHAEOLOGIE. Text in German. 1976. irreg. **Document type:** *Academic/Scholarly.*
Indexed: AICP.
Published by: Zemaljski Muzej Bosne i Hercegovine, Zmaja od Bosne 3, Sarajevo, 71000, Bosnia Herzegovina. TEL 387-71-668025, FAX 387-71-668025. Ed. Vlajko Palavestra.

914.03 GBR ISSN 0084-1226
WOOLHOPE NATURALISTS' FIELD CLUB, HEREFORDSHIRE. TRANSACTIONS. Text in English. 1851. a., latest vol.49. GBP 13 domestic; GBP 15 foreign (effective 2000). 130 p./no.; back issues avail. **Document type:** *Proceedings.*
Indexed: BrArAb, NumL.
—BLDSC (9013.250000).
Published by: Woolhope Club, Chy-An-Whyloryon, Wigmore, Leominster, Herefordshire HR6 9UD, United Kingdom. Ed., R&P J W Tonkin. Circ: 620.

913 GBR ISSN 0143-2389
WORCESTERSHIRE ARCHAEOLOGICAL SOCIETY. TRANSACTIONS. Text in English. 1923. biennial. GBP 15. **Document type:** *Proceedings.*
Related titles: Microform ed.: (from PQC).
Indexed: BHA, BrArAb, BrHumI, NumL.
—BLDSC (9013.300000), IE, ingenta.
Published by: Worcestershire Archaeological Society, 14 Scobell Close, Pershore, Worcs WR10 1QJ, United Kingdom. TEL 44-1386-554886. Ed. Robin Whittaker. Circ: 350. **Subscr. addr.:** c/o Wing Commander F.R. Short, 10 Sabrina Terr, Worcester WR1 3JD, United Kingdom.

913 GBR ISSN 1362-0657
DA670.W89
WORCESTERSHIRE ARCHAEOLOGY SOCIETY. RECORDER. Text in English. 1967. s-a. GBP 2. bk.rev. **Document type:** *Newsletter.*
Former titles (until 1995): Worcestershire Archaeology and Local History Newsletter (0143-4659); Worcestershire Archaeological Newsletter (0512-204X)
Indexed: BrArAb, NumL.
Published by: Worcestershire Archaeological Society, 14 Scobell Close, Pershore, Worcs WR10 1QJ, United Kingdom. TEL 44-1386-554886. Ed., R&P Robin Whittaker. Circ: 400.

913 USA ISSN 1060-2887
WORLD ARCHAEOLOGICAL SOCIETY. SPECIAL PUBLICATION. Text in English. 1971. irreg. price varies. bibl.; illus. **Document type:** *Academic/Scholarly.* **Description:** Contains articles on the related fields of archaeology, anthropology, and art history that are too long for the W.A.S. Newsletter.
Published by: World Archaeological Society, 120 Lakewood Dr, Hollister, MO 65672. TEL 417-334-2377. Ed., R&P Ron S Miller TEL 417-334-2377.

913 GBR ISSN 0043-8243
CC1 CODEN: WOAREN
➤ **WORLD ARCHAEOLOGY.** Text in English. 1969. q. GBP 282, USD 463 combined subscription to institutions print & online eds. (effective 2006). adv. bibl.; charts; illus. index. reprint service avail. from PSC. **Document type:** *Journal, Academic/Scholarly.* **Description:** Provides a broad geographic cover on archaeological topics ranging from monuments, arid environments and public health to crafts and chronology.
Related titles: Microfiche ed.: (from PQC); Online - full text ed.: ISSN 1470-1375. GBP 268, USD 268 to institutions (effective 2006) (from bigchalk, EBSCO Publishing, Gale Group, IngentaConnect, JSTOR (Web-based Journal Archive), O C L C Online Computer Library Center, Inc., Swets Information Services).
Indexed: A&ATA, AIAP, AICP, ASCA, AbAn, AmH&L, AnthLit, ArtHuCI, ArtInd, BAS, BHA, BibLing, BiolDig, BrArAb, BrHumI, CurCont, DIP, GEOBASE, HistAb, HumInd, IBR, IBSS, IBZ, IndIslam, MEA&I, NTA, NumL, PCI, RASB, RI-1, RI-2, RefZh, SSCI.
—BLDSC (9352.912500), IDS, IE, Infotrieve, ingenta. **CCC.**
Published by: Routledge (Subsidiary of: Taylor & Francis Group), 4 Park Sq, Milton Park, Abingdon, Oxon OX14 4RN, United Kingdom. TEL 44-1235-828600, FAX 44-1235-829000, info@routledge.co.uk, http://www.tandf.co.uk/journals/titles/00438243.asp, http://www.routledge.co.uk. R&P Sally Sweet. adv.: page GBP 200; trim 205 x 135. **Subscr. to:** Taylor & Francis Ltd, Journals Customer Service, Rankine Rd, Basingstoke, Hants RG24 8PR, United Kingdom. TEL 44-1256-813000, FAX 44-1256-330245, enquiry@tandf.co.uk.

930.1 DEU
WUERTTEMBERGISCHES LANDESMUSEUM. ARCHAEOLOGISCHE SAMMLUNGEN, FUEHRER UND BESTANDSKATALOGE. Text in German. 1991. irreg. price varies. **Document type:** *Monographic series, Academic/Scholarly.*
Published by: (Wuerttembergisches Landesmuseum), Konrad Theiss Verlag GmbH, Moenchhaldenstr 28, Stuttgart, 70191, Germany. TEL 49-711-255270, FAX 49-711-2552717, service@theiss.de, http://www.theiss.de.

930.1 900 DEU ISSN 1432-0320
WUERZBURGER FORSCHUNGEN ZUR ALTERTUMSKUNDE. Text in German. 1996. irreg., latest vol.2, 1996. **Document type:** *Academic/Scholarly.*
Published by: Ergon Verlag, Grombuehlstr 7, Wuerzburg, 97080, Germany. TEL 49-931-280084, FAX 49-931-282872, ergon-verlag@t-online.de, service@ergon-verlag.de. Eds. S Boehm, U Sinn.

A

913 USA ISSN 0043-9665
➤ **THE WYOMING ARCHAEOLOGIST.** Text in English. 1959. s-a. looseleaf. USD 30 domestic to institutional members; USD 34 in Canada to institutional members (effective 2003). adv. bk.rev. abstr.; bibl.; charts; illus.; maps; stat. back issues avail. **Document type:** *Journal, Academic/Scholarly.* **Description:** Provides a professional and nonprofessional look at anthropology and archaeology, focusing on Wyoming. Includes papers by professionals, graduate students and avocational archaeologists.
Indexed: AmH&L, AnthLit, HistAb.
Published by: Wyoming Archaeological Society, Inc., 1617 Westridge Terr, Casper, WY 82604-3305. TEL 307-234-5424, FAX 307-268-2224, cbuff@caspercollege.edu. Ed. Danny N Walker. R&P, Adv. contact Carolyn Buff TEL 307-268-2212. Circ: 350.

930.1 DEU
XANTENER BERICHTE. GRABUNG, FORSCHUNG, PRAESENTATION. Text in German. 1992. irreg., latest vol.8, 1999. **Document type:** *Monographic series, Academic/Scholarly.*
Published by: (Landschaftsverband Rheinland), Rheinland Verlag GmbH, Abtei Brauweiler, Postfach 2140, Pulheim, 50250, Germany. TEL 49-2234-9854265, FAX 49-2234-82503. **Dist. by:** Dr. Rudolf Habelt GmbH, Am Buchenhang 1, Bonn 53115, Germany. TEL 49-228-9238322, FAX 49-228-232017.
Co-sponsor: Archaeologische Park Xanten.

YAXKIN. see *ANTHROPOLOGY*

571 913 941 GBR ISSN 0084-4276
DA670.Y59
YORKSHIRE ARCHAEOLOGICAL JOURNAL. Text in English. 1869. a. GBP 12 per vol. from vol. 62; GBP 8 per vol. to members YAS (effective 2004). **Document type:** *Journal.*
Formerly (until 1893): Yorkshire Archaeological and Topographical Journal
Indexed: AIAP, BHA, BibInd, BrArAb, NumL, PCI.
—BLDSC (9421.130000), IE, ingenta.
Published by: Yorkshire Archaeological Society, Claremont, 23 Clarendon Rd, Leeds, LS2 9NZ, United Kingdom. TEL 44-113-2457910, FAX 44-113-2441979, j.heron@shef.ac.uk, sales@yas.org.uk, http://www.laplata.co.uk/yas/content/public.html#yaj. Eds. C A Collinson, J M Collinson. R&P Robert Frost TEL 44-1132-457910. Circ: 1,400.

930.1 GBR
YORKSHIRE ARCHAEOLOGICAL SOCIETY. OCCASIONAL PAPER. Text in English. irreg., latest no.3, 2003. price varies. **Document type:** *Monographic series, Academic/Scholarly.*
—BLDSC (9421.131500).
Published by: Yorkshire Archaeological Society, Claremont, 23 Clarendon Rd, Leeds, LS2 9NZ, United Kingdom. TEL 44-113-2457910, FAX 44-113-2441979, sales@yas.org.uk, http://www.laplata.co.uk/yas/content/public.html.

930.1 941 GBR
YORKSHIRE ARCHAEOLOGICAL SOCIETY. REPORT AND ACCOUNTS. Text in English. a. **Document type:** *Corporate.*
Published by: Yorkshire Archaeological Society, Claremont, 23 Clarendon Rd, Leeds, LS2 9NZ, United Kingdom. TEL 44-113-2457910, FAX 44-113-2441979, sales@yas.org.uk, http://www.laplata.co.uk/yas/. R&P Robert Frost TEL 44-1132-457910.

930.1 GBR ISSN 1351-2676
YOUNG ARCHAEOLOGIST. Text in English. 1993. q. GBP 7.50 (effective 2001). bk.rev. back issues avail. **Document type:** *Newsletter.*
Indexed: BrArAb, NumL.
Published by: Council for British Archaeology, Bowes Morrell House, 111 Walmgate, York, YO1 9WA, United Kingdom. TEL 44-1904-671417, FAX 44-1904-671384, info@britarch.ac.uk, http://www.britarch.ac.uk. Adv. contact Lorraine Balhurst. Circ: 1,400 (controlled).

ZALAI GYUJTEMENY; kozlemenyek zala megye kozgyujtemenyeinek kutatasaibol. see *HISTORY—History Of Europe*

ZAPADOCESKE MUZEUM. SBORNIK. HISTORIE. see *HISTORY*

930.1 SCG ISSN 0352-2474
ZBORNIK NARODNOG MUZEJA U BEOGRADU. ARHEOLOGIYA. Text in Multiple languages. 1983. irreg., latest 2002. price varies. **Document type:** *Monographic series, Academic/Scholarly.*
Supersedes in part (in 1981): Zbornik Narodnog Muzeja u Beogradu (0522-8352)
Indexed: AnthLit.
Published by: Narodni Muzej Beograd, Trg. Republike 1a, Beograd. TEL 381-11-624322, FAX 381-11-627721, narodnimuzej@narodnimuzej.org.yu, http://www.narodnimuzej.org.yu.

ZEITSCHRIFT FUER AEGYPTISCHE SPRACHE UND ALTERTUMSKUNDE. see *ASIAN STUDIES*

913 DEU ISSN 0340-0824
D125
ZEITSCHRIFT FUER ARCHAEOLOGIE DES MITTELALTERS. Text in German. 1973. a. **Document type:** *Journal, Academic/Scholarly.*
Indexed: AIAP, BHA, BibInd, BrArAb, DIP, IBR, IBZ, NumL, PCI.
Published by: Rheinland Verlag GmbH, Abtei Brauweiler, Postfach 2140, Pulheim, 50250, Germany. TEL 49-2234-9854265, FAX 49-2234-82503. **Dist. by:** Dr. Rudolf Habelt GmbH, Am Buchenhang 1, Bonn 53115, Germany. TEL 49-228-9238322, FAX 49-228-232017.

913 DEU
ZEITSCHRIFT FUER ARCHAEOLOGIE DES MITTELALTERS. BEIHEFTE. Text in German. 1981. irreg., latest vol.10, 1998. **Document type:** *Monographic series, Academic/Scholarly.*
Indexed: AIAP.
Published by: Rheinland Verlag GmbH, Abtei Brauweiler, Postfach 2140, Pulheim, 50250, Germany. TEL 49-2234-9854265, FAX 49-2234-82503. **Dist. by:** Dr. Rudolf Habelt GmbH, Am Buchenhang 1, Bonn 53115, Germany. TEL 49-228-9238322, FAX 49-228-232017.

913 DEU ISSN 0084-5299
PJ3104
➤ **ZEITSCHRIFT FUER ASSYRIOLOGIE UND VORDERASIATISCHE ARCHAEOLOGIE.** Text in Multiple languages. 1977 (vol.67). 2/yr. EUR 168; EUR 182 combined subscription print & online eds.; EUR 92 newsstand/cover (effective 2006). adv. bk.rev. reprint service avail. from SCH. **Document type:** *Journal, Academic/Scholarly.*
Related titles: Microfiche ed.: (from BHP); Microfilm ed.: (from BHP); Online - full text ed.: ISSN 1613-1150. EUR 168 (effective 2006) (from EBSCO Publishing, Swets Information Services).
Indexed: BibInd, BibLing, DIP, IBR, IBZ, MLA, MLA-IB, OTA, PCI, RASB, RI-1, RI-2.
—IE, Infotrieve. **CCC.**
Published by: Walter de Gruyter GmbH & Co. KG, Genthiner Str. 13, Berlin, 10785, Germany. TEL 49-30-260050, FAX 49-30-26005251, wdg-info@degruyter.de, http://www.degruyter.de/rs/265_420_DEU_h.htm. Ed. Mr. Walther Sallaberger. Adv. contact Dietlind Makswitat TEL 49-30-260050. page EUR 550; trim 112 x 188. Circ: 500 (paid and controlled).

913 DEU ISSN 0084-5388
PA3339
ZEITSCHRIFT FUER PAPYROLOGIE UND EPIGRAPHIK. Text in German. 1967. 4/yr. EUR 90 (effective 2005). **Document type:** *Journal, Academic/Scholarly.*
Indexed: BHA, BibLing, DIP, IBR, IBZ, NTA, NumL, PCI, RASB.
—BLDSC (9475.870000), IE, Infotrieve, ingenta. **CCC.**
Published by: Dr. Rudolf Habelt GmbH, Am Buchenhang 1, Bonn, 53115, Germany. TEL 49-228-9238322, info@habelt.de, http://www.habelt.de.

913 CHE ISSN 0044-3476
DQ30
ZEITSCHRIFT FUER SCHWEIZERISCHE ARCHAEOLOGIE UND KUNSTGESCHICHTE/REVUE SUISSE D'ART ET D'ARCHEOLOGIE. Variant title: Z A K. Text in English, French, German, Italian. 1939. q. CHF 80 (effective 2001). bk.rev. bibl.; charts; illus. index. reprints avail. **Document type:** *Bulletin, Academic/Scholarly.*
Indexed: AIAP, BHA, BibInd, BrArAb, DIP, IBR, NumL, RASB, WBSS.
Published by: Schweizerisches Landesmuseum/Swiss National Museum, Museumstr 2, Postfach 6789, Zuerich, 8023, Switzerland. TEL 41-1-2186511, FAX 41-1-2112949. Ed. Matthias Senn. Circ: 1,750.

ZEITSCHRIFT FUER VOLKSKUNDE. see *FOLKLORE*

913.031 ESP ISSN 0514-7336
CC13.S66
➤ **ZEPHYRUS.** Text in English, French, Spanish, Portuguese; Abstracts in English. 1950. a., latest vol.51, 1998. **Document type:** *Academic/Scholarly.* **Description:** Contains studies on archaeology and prehistory.
Indexed: AnthLit, BHA, DIP, IBR, IBZ, NumL, PCI.
—CINDOC. **CCC.**
Published by: Ediciones Universidad de Salamanca, Apartado 325, Salamanca, 37080, Spain. TEL 34-923-294598, FAX 34-923-262579, http://www3.usal.es/~eus/indexsp.htm. Ed. Maria Soledad Corchon Rodriguez.

➤ **ZESZYTY GLIWICKIE.** see *HISTORY—History Of Europe*

➤ **ZESZYTY TARNOGORSKIE.** see *HISTORY—History Of Europe*

➤ **ZGODOVINSKI CASOPIS/HISTORICAL REVIEW.** see *HISTORY—History Of Europe*

931 CHN
ZHONGGUO WENWU BAO/CHINA'S CULTURAL RELICS NEWS. Text in Chinese. 1987. s-w. CNY 160 (effective 2004). **Document type:** *Newspaper, Academic/Scholarly.*
Address: Zhaoyang-qu, Beixituan, 2, Gaoyuan Jie Jia, Wenbu Dasha, Beijing, 100029, China. TEL 86-10-84625983, FAX 86-10-84625980, http://www.ccrnews.com.cn/guanggao.htm. **Dist. in US by:** China Books & Periodicals Inc, 360 Swift Ave., Ste. 48, S San Fran, CA 94080-6220. TEL 415-282-2994; **Dist. by:** China International Book Trading Corp, 35 Chegongzhuang Xilu, Haidian District, PO Box 399, Beijing 100044, China. TEL 86-10-68412045, FAX 86-10-68412023, cibtc@mail.cibtc.com.cn, http://www.cibtc.com.cn.

931 CHN ISSN 1003-1731
DS715
ZHONGYUAN WENWU/CULTURAL RELICS OF CENTRAL CHINA. Text in Chinese. 1977. q. USD 24 (effective 2001). **Document type:** *Academic/Scholarly.*
Related titles: Online - full text ed.: (from East View Information Services).
Published by: Henan Bowuyuan/Henan Provincial Museum, No. 8 Nongye Rd, Zhengzhou, Henan 450002, China. TEL 86-371-3511063, FAX 86-371-3850860, zywwbm@china.com, museum@public.zz.ha.cn, http://www.chumus.net/. Eds. Wenjun Zhang, Deshui Zhang. **Dist. in US by:** China Books & Periodicals Inc, 360 Swift Ave., Ste. 48, S San Fran, CA 94080-6220. TEL 415-282-2994.

ARCHAEOLOGY—Abstracting, Bibliographies, Statistics

913 011 USA ISSN 0743-4251
F183
ABSTRACTS IN MARYLAND ARCHEOLOGY. Text in English. 1983. a. USD 65. back issues avail. **Document type:** *Abstract/Index.* **Description:** Abstracts of current monographs, papers, and compliance reports on Maryland archeology.
Published by: Council for Maryland Archeology, c/o James G Gibb, 2554 Carrollton Rd, Annapolis, MD 21403. TEL 410-263-1102. Ed. James D Sorenson. Circ: 100 (paid).

L'ANNEE PHILOLOGIQUE; bibliographie critique et analytique de l'antiquite greco-latine. see *CLASSICAL STUDIES—Abstracting, Bibliographies, Statistics*

ANNUAL EGYPTOLOGICAL BIBLIOGRAPHY/BIBLIOGRAPHIE EGYPTOLOGIQUE ANNUELLE/JAEHRLICHE AEGYPTOLOGISCHE BIBLIOGRAPHIE. see *HISTORY—Abstracting, Bibliographies, Statistics*

930.1 USA ISSN 0162-6469
ARCHAEOLOGICAL INSTITUTE OF AMERICA. ABSTRACTS OF THE GENERAL MEETING. Text in English. 1975. a. USD 10 per issue (effective 2003). back issues avail. **Document type:** *Abstract/Index.* **Description:** Abstracts papers presented at their annual meeting.
—BLDSC (0551.844600).
Published by: Archaeological Institute of America (Boston), c/o Mark Kurtz, 656 Beacon St, Boston, MA 02215-2006. TEL 617-353-9361, FAX 617-353-6550, aia@bu.edu. Circ: 1,000.

ART AND ARCHAEOLOGY TECHNICAL ABSTRACTS (ONLINE EDITION); abstracts of the technical literature on archaeology, architecture, and the fine and applied arts. see *ART—Abstracting, Bibliographies, Statistics*

932 BEL
BIBLIOGRAPHIE PAPYROLOGIQUE. Text in French. 1941. q. EUR 25 to members; EUR 30 to non-members; EUR 40 to members print & diskette eds; EUR 50 to non-members print & diskette eds (effective 2005). **Document type:** *Bibliography.*
Related titles: Diskette ed.
Published by: Fondation Egyptologique Reine Elisabeth, Parc du Cinquantenaire 10, Brussels, 1000, Belgium. TEL 32-2-7417364, http://www.ulb.ac.be/philo/cpeg/bp.htm. Eds. Alain Martin, Georges Nachtergael.

016.9301 GBR
Z2026.A67
BRITISH & IRISH ARCHAEOLOGICAL BIBLIOGRAPHY (ONLINE EDITION). Text in English. s-a. free (effective 2005). abstr.; bibl. reprints avail. **Document type:** *Database, Bibliography.* **Description:** Lists information currently being published on the archaeology of Great Britain and Ireland, with information to allow the original article to be traced and consulted.
Media: Online - full content. **Related titles:** Microform ed.: (from PQC).
Indexed: BHA, RASB.
Published by: b i a b - the british & irish archaeological bibliography (Subsidiary of: Council for British Archaeology), British Academy, 10 Carlton House Ter, London, SW1Y 5AH, United Kingdom. TEL 44-20-79695223, FAX 44-20-79695300, info@biab.ac.uk, http://www.biab.ac.uk. Ed., Adv. contact Isabel Holroyd.

962 932 EGY
EGYPTIAN MUSEUM. LIBRARY. CATALOGUE. Text in Arabic. 1966. irreg. price varies. adv. bk.rev. index. **Document type:** *Catalog, Bibliography.* **Description:** Bibliography of books and articles recently acquired by the library.
Formerly: Egyptian National Museum. Library. Catalogue (0068-5275)

Published by: (Egypt. Organisation des Antiquites Egyptiennes), Egyptian Museum, Library, Midan-el-Tahrir, Kasr el-Nil, Cairo, Egypt. TEL 20-2-5757035. Ed. Dia Abou Ghazi.

INDICE HISTORICO ESPANOL. see *HISTORY—Abstracting, Bibliographies, Statistics*

ISTORIYA SIBIRI I DAL'NEGO VOSTOKA; tekushchii ukazatel' literatury. see *HISTORY—Abstracting, Bibliographies, Statistics*

016.948   DNK   ISSN 0105-6492
N A A. (Nordic Archaeological Abstracts) Text in Multiple languages. 1975. a. DKK 250 to individuals paper edition; DKK 150 to students paper edition; DKK 350 combined subscription to individuals paper and online edition; DKK 600 combined subscription to institutions paper and online edition; DKK 160 combined subscription to students paper and online edition (effective 2005). cum.index: 1974-1988. **Document type:** *Abstract/Index.* **Description:** Presents references and abstracts to journals and books covering prehistoric and medieval archaeology in the Nordic countries.
Related titles: Online - full content ed.
Published by: Nordic Archaeological Abstracts, c/o Department of Prehistoric Archaeology, Moesgaard, Hoejbjerg, 8270, Denmark. TEL 45-89-424622, FAX 45-86-272378, http://www.naa.dk. Ed. Birgit Rasmussen. **Subscr. to:** c/o Museumstjenesten, Sjoerupvej 1, Lysgaard, Viborg 8800, Denmark. TEL 45-86-667666, FAX 45-86-667611.

930   USA   ISSN 0028-2812
NESTOR. Text in English. 1957. m. (Sep.-May). looseleaf. USD 7.50 to individuals; USD 10 foreign to individuals; USD 12.50 to institutions; USD 18.50 foreign to institutions. bk.rev. bibl. back issues avail.; reprint service avail. from PQC. **Document type:** *Academic/Scholarly.* **Description:** Bibliography of material relevant to prehistoric archaeology, Homeric society, Indo-European linguistics and related fields, in the eastern Mediterranean area and southeastern Europe.
Related titles: Diskette ed.; Microform ed.: (from PQC).
Indexed: MLA-IB.
Published by: University of Cincinnati, Department of Classics, 2624 Clifton Ave, Cincinnati, OH 45221. TEL 812-855-1421, nestor@ucbeh.san.uc.edu, http://ucaswww.mcm.uc.edu/classics/nestor/nestor.html. Ed. Eric Cline. Circ: 550. **Affiliate:** Comite International Permanent pour les Etudes Myceniennes.

NOVAYA LITERATURA PO SOTSIAL'NYM I GUMANITARNYM NAUKAM. ISTORIYA. ARKHEOLOGIYA. ETNOLOGIYA; bibliograficheskii ukazatel'. see *ANTHROPOLOGY— Abstracting, Bibliographies, Statistics*

016.913   POL   ISSN 0137-4885
DK409
POLISH ARCHAEOLOGICAL ABSTRACTS. Text in English. 1972. a. price varies. abstr.; bibl. **Document type:** *Abstract/Index.* **Description:** Abstracts on all books and articles concerning Polish archaeology published in the last year in Poland.
Indexed: AICP, BrArAb, RASB.
Published by: (Zaklad Archeologii Wielkopolski), Polska Akademia Nauk, Instytut Historii Kultury Materialnej (Poznan), Ul Zwierzyniecka 20, Poznan, 60814, Poland. Ed. Wojciech Dzieduszycki. Circ: 400. **Dist. by:** Ars Polona, Krakowskie Przedmiescie 7, Warsaw, Poland.

ARCHAEOLOGY—Computer Applications

930.1   ITA   ISSN 1120-6861
CC80.4
ARCHEOLOGIA E CALCOLATORI. Text in Italian. a., latest vol.11, 2000. EUR 25 domestic; EUR 28 foreign (effective 2005). **Document type:** *Journal, Academic/Scholarly.*
Indexed: AnthLit.
Published by: Edizioni all'Insegna del Giglio s.a.s., Via N Piccinni 32, Florence, FI 50141, Italy. TEL 39-055-451593, FAX 39-055-450030, redazione@edigiglio.it, http://www.edigiglio.it.

930.1 004   GBR   ISSN 0305-0475
COMPUTER APPLICATIONS IN ARCHAEOLOGY. Text in English. 1974. a. price varies. **Document type:** *Academic/Scholarly.*
Indexed: A&ATA, BrArAb.
Published by: British Archaeological Reports, Oxford, c/o Dr. C.L.N Ruggles, Treas., Dept. of Computing Studies, University of Leicester, Leicester, LE1 7RH, United Kingdom.

720.285 620.00285   NLD
INTERNATIONAL JOURNAL OF I T IN ARCHITECTURE, ENGINEERING AND CONSTRUCTION. Text in English. q. **Document type:** *Journal, Academic/Scholarly.*
Formerly: Computer-Integrated Design and Construction (1092-5902)
Related titles: Online - full text ed.: (from EBSCO Publishing).
Published by: Millpress Science Publishers, PO Box 84118, Rotterdam, 3009 CC, Netherlands. info@millpress.com, http://www.lboro.ac.uk/it-aec/, http://www.millpress.com/. Ed. Chimay Anumba.

ARCHITECTURE

see also BUILDING AND CONSTRUCTION ; ENGINEERING—Civil Engineering ; HOUSING AND URBAN PLANNING ; REAL ESTATE

720   GBR   ISSN 0261-6823
NA1.A1
A A FILES; annals of the Architectural Association School of Architecture. Text in English. 1981. 3/yr. GBP 15 per issue (effective 2004). bk.rev. charts; illus. cum.index: 1980-1991. 88 p./no.; back issues avail.; reprints avail. **Document type:** *Journal, Academic/Scholarly.* **Description:** Contains articles, reviews, and book reviews covering historical and contemporary architecture and related topics.
Formerly: A A Quarterly (0001-0189)
Indexed: AIAP, API, ArtInd, BHA, BldManAb, RICS.
—BLDSC (0537.071500), CISTI, IE, Infotrieve, ingenta, Linda Hall. **CCC.**
Published by: Architectural Association, 36 Bedford Sq, London, WC1B 3ES, United Kingdom. TEL 44-20-7887-4000, FAX 44-20-7414-0782, publications@aaschool.ac.uk, http://www.aaschool.ac.uk/aafiles/. Ed. Mark Rappolt. R&P Kirsten Morphet TEL 44-20-7887-4021. Circ: 2,500.

720   ITA   ISSN 1123-9255
A & C INTERNATIONAL. Variant title: Archi e Colonne International. Text in Italian, English. 1995. q. **Document type:** *Magazine, Trade.*
Published by: Gangemi Editore, Piazza San Pantaleo 4, Rome, Italy. TEL 39-06-6872774, FAX 39-06-68806189, gangemieditorerc@tin.it, http://www.gangemieditore.it.

720   ESP   ISSN 1132-6409
NA1.A1
A + T/MAGAZINE OF ARCHITECTURE & TECHNOLOGY. (Revista de Arquitectura y Technologia) Variant title: A mas T. Text in English, Spanish. 1992. s-a. EUR 40.87 domestic; EUR 48.08 in Europe; EUR 57.10 elsewhere (effective 2002). illus. 160 p./no.; back issues avail. **Document type:** *Monographic series.*
Indexed: AIAP.
—CINDOC.
Published by: A + T Editiones, General Alava 15-2 A, Vitoria-Gasteiz, 01005, Spain. TEL 34-945-13-42-76, FAX 34-945-13-49-01, http://www.aplust.net/index.html. Ed. Javier Mozas. **Dist. by:** Idea Books Amsterdam, Nieuwe Herengracht 11, Amsterdam 1011 RK, Netherlands.

720   JPN   ISSN 0389-9160
NA6.J33
A + U. Variant title: Architecture and Urbanism. Text in Japanese, English; Summaries in English. 1971. m. JPY 30,000 domestic (effective 2005). adv. bk.rev. bibl.; charts; illus. index. reprints avail. **Document type:** *Academic/Scholarly.* **Description:** Features global trends and concepts in architecture from all over the world. Examines the work of the world's foremost architects.
Indexed: AIAP, API, ASCA, ArtHuCI, ArtInd, BHA, CurCont.
—BLDSC (1601.610000), IE, Infotrieve.
Published by: Japan Architects Co., Ltd., 2-31-2 Yushima, Bunkyo-ku, Tokyo, 113-0034, Japan. TEL 81-3-38162532, FAX 81-3-38128229, au@japan-architect.co.jp, ja-business@japan-architect.co.jp, http://www.japan-architect.co.jp/japanese/2maga/au/au_frame.html. Ed., Pub. Nobuyuki Yoshida. Circ: 25,000.

720   DEU
A B I - AUFTRAG, RECHNUNG, ZAHLUNG. (Aktuelle Berichte und Informationen fuer Architekten und Ingenieure) Text in German. 1997. 6/yr. **Document type:** *Journal, Trade.*
Published by: Verlag der Ingenieur GmbH, Rheinstr 129 c, Ettlingen, 76275, Germany. TEL 49-7243-39396, FAX 49-7243-39395, info@ingenieurverlag.de, http://www.ingenieurverlag.de.

720   DEU
A B I - RISIKEN, HAFTUNG, SCHADENERSATZ. (Aktuelle Berichte und Informationen fuer Architekten und Ingenieure) Text in German. 1997. 6/yr. **Document type:** *Journal, Trade.*
Published by: Verlag der Ingenieur GmbH, Rheinstr 129 c, Ettlingen, 76275, Germany. TEL 49-7243-39396, FAX 49-7243-39395, info@ingenieurverlag.de, http://www.ingenieurverlag.de.

720   DEU
A B I T - BUERO HEUTE. Text in German. 1890. 3/yr. EUR 9.90 newsstand/cover (effective 2004). adv. **Document type:** *Magazine, Trade.*
Published by: Verlagsanstalt Alexander Koch GmbH, Fasanenweg 18, Leinfelden-Echterdingen, 70771, Germany. TEL 49-711-75910, FAX 49-711-7591-368, ait-abo@ait.de, http://www.koch-verlag.de. adv.: B&W page EUR 4,599, color page EUR 7,059. Circ: 18,705 (paid and controlled).

720   DEU
A B I - WIRTSCHAFT, RECHT, STEUER. (Aktuelle Berichte und Informationen fuer Architekten und Ingenieure) Text in German. 1977. 6/yr. **Document type:** *Journal, Trade.*

Published by: Verlag der Ingenieur GmbH, Rheinstr 129 c, Ettlingen, 76275, Germany. TEL 49-7243-39396, FAX 49-7243-39395, info@ingenieurverlag.de, http://www.ingenieurverlag.de.

720   USA
A C S A FACULTY DIRECTORY. Text in English. a. USD 14.95 (effective 1999). **Document type:** *Directory.*
Published by: Association of Collegiate Schools of Architecture, Inc., 1735 New York Ave, N W, Washington, DC 20006. TEL 202-785-2324, FAX 202-628-0448. Ed. Ellen S Cathey.

747   FRA   ISSN 0990-977X
A D. (Architectural Digest) Text in French. 1988. m. adv. **Document type:** *Magazine, Consumer.*
Published by: Publications Conde Nast S.A., 56 A rue du Faubourg Saint-Honore, Paris, 75008, France. TEL 33-1-41494149, FAX 33-1-40890430.

720 700   ZAF   ISSN 1015-5597
A D A MAGAZINE. (Art, Design, Architecture) Text in English. 1986. 2/yr. ZAR 70; ZAR 90 foreign. adv. bk.rev. back issues avail. **Document type:** *Consumer.*
Indexed: AIAP.
Published by: ADA Magazine, PO Box 16093, Vlaeberg, Cape Town 8018, South Africa. TEL 27-21-461-9937, FAX 27-21-4619937. Ed. Jennifer Sorrell. adv.: B&W page ZAR 5,988.02, color page ZAR 8,982.03; trim 420 x 297. Circ: 10,000.

747   USA
A D ARCHITECTURE✱. (Architectural Digest) Text in English. 1987. s-a.
Published by: Knapp Communications Corp., Attn: Circulation Dept, 6300 Wilshire Blvd, Los Angeles, CA 90048. TEL 213-965-3700, FAX 213-937-5643, TELEX 901-321-2437.

720   DEU   ISSN 0177-5472
A H F MITTEILUNGEN. Text in German. 1981. q. **Document type:** *Bulletin, Trade.*
Published by: (Arbeitskreis fuer Hausforschung e.V.), Jonas Verlag, Weidenhaeuser Str 88, Marburg, 35037, Germany. TEL 49-6421-25132, FAX 49-6421-210572, jonas@jonas-verlag.de, http://www.jonas-verlag.de.

720   PRY   ISSN 1606-0911
A I A. (Arquitectura, Ingenieria, Artes) Text in Spanish. 1999. m.
Media: Online - full text.
Published by: Ediciones Sudamericanas, S.R.L., Azara 1098 c. Brasil, Edif. Alpha, 2do. Piso, Ofic. 23, Asuncion, Paraguay. TEL 595-21-212733, http://www.aia.com.py/.

720   USA
A I A - D C NEWS. Text in English. m. membership. **Document type:** *Newsletter.*
Formerly: D C - A I A News
Published by: American Institute of Architects, Washington Chapter, 1777 Church St, N W, Washington, DC 20036. TEL 202-667-1798, FAX 202-667-4327. R&P Jane Moya. Circ: 1,500 (controlled).

720   USA
A I A MICHIGAN MONTHLY BULLETIN. Text in English. 1926. m. membership only. bk.rev. **Document type:** *Newsletter.*
Formerly: M S A Monthly Bulletin (0024-8363)
Published by: American Institute of Architects, Michigan Chapter, 553 E Jefferson St, Detroit, MI 48226. TEL 313-965-4100. Ed. Tim Casai. R&P Lynne Merrill Francis. adv.: B&W page USD 750. Circ: 2,000.

720   USA   ISSN 1079-3933
NA11
A I ARCHITECT. Text in English. 1947. m. free to members (effective 2005). adv. bk.rev. charts; illus. **Document type:** *Newspaper.* **Description:** Contains architectural news.
Former titles (until 1994): Memo (Washington, 1947) (0732-4073); A I A Memo (0001-1487)
Indexed: AIAP, API.
Published by: American Institute of Architects, 1735 New York Ave, N W, Washington, DC 20006. TEL 202-626-7465, stubbss@aiamail.aia.org, http://www.aia.org/aiarchitect/, www.aiaonline.com. Circ: 60,000 (controlled).

720   DEU   ISSN 0173-8046
NK1700   CODEN: AITAEL
A I T. (Architektur, Innenarchitektur, Technischer Ausbau) Text in German. 1890. 10/yr. EUR 123.20 domestic; EUR 147.20 foreign (effective 2004). adv. bk.rev. charts; illus.; tr.lit. index. **Document type:** *Magazine, Trade.*
Former titles (until 1979): Architektur und Wohnwelt (0340-3912); Architektur und Wohnform (0003-8792)
Indexed: AIAP.
—BLDSC (0785.457500), IE, Infotrieve. **CCC.**
Published by: Verlagsanstalt Alexander Koch GmbH, Fasanenweg 18, Leinfelden-Echterdingen, 70771, Germany. TEL 49-711-7591-1, FAX 49-711-7591-368, ait-abo@ait-online.de, http://www.koch-verlag.de. Ed. Dietmar Danner. adv.: B&W page EUR 3,720, color page EUR 5,865. Circ: 16,706.

A P T COMMUNIQUE. see *CONSERVATION*

720 BEL
A PLUS ARCHITECTURE. Text in French. 1973. 6/yr. EUR 60 domestic; EUR 90 in Europe; EUR 110 elsewhere; EUR 45 domestic to students; EUR 75 in Europe to students; EUR 95 elsewhere to students (effective 2005). adv. bk.rev. illus.
Document type: *Academic/Scholarly.* **Description:** Periodical for architecture design, urbanism and plastic arts audience.
Formerly: A Plus (1375-5064)
Related titles: Dutch ed.: A Plus Architectuur.
Indexed: API, MagInd.
Published by: Centre d'Information de l'Architecture, de l'Urbanisme et du Design/Informatiecentrum voor Architectuur, Stedebouw en Design, Rue Ravenstein 23, Bruxelles, 1000, Belgium. TEL 32-2-645-7910, FAX 32-2-640-2795, info@a-plus.be, http://www.a-plus.be. Ed. Claud Icasd. Circ: 13,000.

720 ESP ISSN 1130-2046
A Q; arquitectura andalucia oriental. Text in Spanish. 1981. s-a.
Formerly (until 1989): Arquitectura Andalucia Oriental (0213-0998)
—CINDOC.
Published by: Colegio Oficial de Arquitectos de Andalucia Oriental, Plaza de San Agustin, 3, Granada, Andalucia 18001, Spain. TEL 34-958-205262, FAX 34-958-277144, coaaor@aquired.es, http://www.arquited.es/.

720 CHL ISSN 0716-0852
A R Q. (Arquitectura Diseno Urbanismo) Text in Spanish. 1980. 3/yr. CLP 20.50 domestic; USD 85 in the Americas; USD 96 in Europe; USD 120 elsewhere (effective 2004). back issues avail.
Related titles: Online - full text ed.: ISSN 0717-6996. 2001. free (effective 2005) (from SciELO).
Indexed: AIAP, ArtHuCI, CurCont.
Published by: Pontificia Universidad Catolica de Chile, Facultad de Arquitectura, Diseno y Estudios Urbanos, Los Navegantes 1963, Providencia, Santiago de Chile, Chile. TEL 56-2-6865630, FAX 56-2-6865634, arquedic@puc.cl, http://www.scielo.cl/.

720 CAN ISSN 1203-1488
NA746.Q4
A R Q; revue d'architecture. Text mainly in French; Text occasionally in English. 1981. 4/yr. CND 36.81 domestic to individuals; USD 50 in United States to individuals; USD 60 elsewhere to individuals; CND 57 domestic to institutions (effective 2003). adv. bk.rev. back issues avail. **Document type:** *Journal, Trade.*
Formerly: A R Q: Architecture-Quebec (0710-1163)
Indexed: AIAP, PdeR.
—CISTI.
Published by: Art et Architecture Quebec, 86 rue Morin, Ste-Adele, PQ J8B 2P7, Canada. Ed. Pierre Boyer Mercier. Circ: 2,653.

720 GBR ISSN 1359-1355
NA1
➤ **A R Q: ARCHITECTURAL RESEARCH QUARTERLY.** Variant title: Architectural Research Quarterly. Text in English. 1995. q. USD 220 in North America to institutions; GBP 140 elsewhere to institutions; USD 233 combined subscription in North America to institutions print & online eds.; GBP 145 combined subscription elsewhere to institutions print & online eds. (effective 2006). reprint service avail. from PSC. **Document type:** *Journal, Academic/Scholarly.* **Description:** Contains sections on design, history, theory, environmental design, construction, information technology, and practice.
Related titles: Online - full text ed.: ISSN 1474-0516. USD 210 in North America to institutions; GBP 130 elsewhere to institutions (effective 2006) (from EBSCO Publishing, O C L C Online Computer Library Center, Inc., Swets Information Services).
Indexed: AIAP, API, ArtInd.
—IE, Infotrieve. **CCC.**
Published by: Cambridge University Press, The Edinburgh Bldg, Shaftesbury Rd, Cambridge, CB2 2RU, United Kingdom. TEL 44-1223-312393, FAX 44-1223-315052, journals@cambridge.org, http://journals.cambridge.org/journal_arq:ArchitecturalResearchQuarterly, http://uk.cambridge.org/journals. Ed. Richard Weston. **Subscr. addr. in N American:** Cambridge University Press, 100 Brook Hill Dr, West Nyack, NY 10994. TEL 845-353-7500, FAX 845-353-4141, journals_subscriptions@cup.org

720 GBR
A S C. (Architects Standard Catalogue) Text in English. 1911. a. USD 100. adv. **Document type:** *Trade.*
Former titles: A S C Mini-File; Architects Standard Catalogues (0066-6181)
Published by: Data Distribution Publications, Apex House, London Rd, Northfleet, Gravesend, Kent DA11 9JA, United Kingdom. TEL 44-1322-277788, FAX 44-1322-539627. Pub., R&P Paul HOlden. Adv. contact Julie Skeet. Circ: 19,000.

720 GBR ISSN 0956-4241
A S I JOURNAL. Text in English. 1929. 6/yr. GBP 35 (effective 2001). adv. bk.rev. **Document type:** *Trade.* **Description:** Covers architecture, surveying, engineering, environment and construction.
Formerly (until 1988): Portico (0032-4914)
Indexed: API.
—BLDSC (1742.170800).
Published by: Architecture and Surveying Institute, St Mary House, 15 St Mary St, Chippenham, Wilts SN15 3WD, United Kingdom. TEL 44-1249-444505, FAX 44-1249-443602, mail@asi.org.uk. Ed. Tony Marshall. R&P Ian Norris. Adv. contact Linda Porter. page GBP 475; 189 x 275. Circ: 10,000.

712 USA ISSN 0192-5067
SB469
A S L A MEMBERS HANDBOOK. Text in English. a. USD 195 to non-members; USD 25 to members. adv. **Document type:** *Directory.*
Published by: American Society of Landscape Architects, 636 Eye St, N W, Washington, DC 20001-3736. TEL 202-898-2444, FAX 202-898-1185, scahill@asla.org, http://www.asla.org. Circ: 10,000.

721 USA
A U A NEWS. Text in English. 1986. q. USD 85 domestic to individual members; USD 95 foreign to individual members; USD 650 domestic to corporations; USD 700 foreign to corporations (effective 2003). adv. bk.rev. back issues avail. **Document type:** *Newsletter, Trade.*
Published by: American Underground - Construction Association, 3001 Hennepin Ave, S, Ste D202, Minneapolis, MN 55408. TEL 612-825-8933, FAX 612-825-8944, underground@auaonline.org, http://www.auca.org. Ed., R&P Susan Nelson TEL 714-459-7913. Adv. contact Carin Mindel. Circ: 900.

720 ESP ISSN 0213-487X
A V MONOGRAFIAS/A V MONOGRAPHS. Key Title: A & V. Variant title: Monografias de Arquitectura y Vivienda. A y V. Text in English, Spanish. 1985. bi-m. EUR 100 domestic; EUR 125 in Europe; EUR 145 elsewhere (effective 2005). adv. bibl.; illus. 136 p./no.; back issues avail.; reprints avail. **Document type:** *Monographic series.* **Description:** Each issue covers a chosen architect, city or theme. Devotes its attention to the great masters of 20th century architecture: Wright, Le Corbusier, Mies, Aalto and Kahn who already form part of this historical series which alternates its appearance with other issues centered on contemporary figures.
Related titles: Online - full text ed.
Indexed: AIAP, API, RILM.
—CINDOC, IE, Infotrieve.
Published by: Arquitectura Viva S.L., Aniceto Marinas 32, Madrid, 28008, Spain. TEL 34-91-5487317, AV@arquitecturaviva.com, http://www.arquitecturaviva.com, 34-91-5488191. Ed. Luis Fernandez Galiano. Pub. Luis Fernandez Galiano. R&P Lola Gonzalez. Adv. contact Susana Blanco. color page EUR 1,800; trim 297 x 240. Circ: 9,000. **Dist. by:** Asociacion de Revistas Culturales de Espana, Hortaleza, 75, Madrid 28004, Spain. TEL 34-91-3086066, FAX 34-91-3199267, info@arce.es, http://www.arce.es.

711.4 ISL ISSN 1022-9507
➤ **A V S.** Variant title: Arkitektur Verktaekni Skipulag. Text in English, Icelandic. 1989. q. ISK 3,200; USD 80 foreign (effective 2003). adv. bk.rev. illus. back issues avail. **Document type:** *Magazine, Trade.* **Description:** Focuses on architecture, housing, urban planning and related fields.
Formerly (until 1994): Arkitektur og Skipulag (1016-7293)
Indexed: BHA.
Published by: S.A.V. Ltd., Gardastraeti 17, Reykjavik, 101, Iceland. TEL 354-561-6577, FAX 354-561-6571, skipark@skipark.is, http://www.skipark.is. Ed., R&P Gestur Olafsson. Adv. contact Pondis R Hardardottir. Circ: 7,000.

720 694 USA
A W I NEWSBRIEFS. Text in English. 1992 (vol.40, no.8). m. Price Varies. adv. **Document type:** *Newsletter, Trade.* **Description:** Reports association news and informs readers of events of interest, both past and forthcoming.
Published by: Architectural Woodwork Institute, 1952 Isaac Newton Square W, Reston, VA 20190. TEL 703-733-0600, FAX 703-733-0584, http://www.awinet.org.

720 747 ITA ISSN 0001-3218
NK1700
ABITARE; home, town and environmental living . Text in English, Italian. 1961. 11/yr. EUR 55 domestic; EUR 117 in Europe; EUR 247 elsewhere (effective 2005). bk.rev. abstr.; charts; illus. reprints avail. **Document type:** *Magazine, Consumer.* **Description:** Presents a broad spectrum of lifestyles and living environments by reporting on houses, architecture, and places from around the world.
Formerly (until 1962): Casa Novita (1121-581X)
Indexed: AIAP, ArtInd, DAAI, Search.
—BLDSC (0549.430000).
Published by: Editrice Abitare Segesta SpA, Corso Monforte 15, Milan, MI 20122, Italy. TEL 39-02-76090, FAX 39-02-76090301, abitaremag@abitare.it, http://www.abitare.it. Ed. Italo Lupi. Pub. Renato Minetto. Adv. contact Alessandra Fedele.

720 USA
NA2300.C635
ABSTRACT. Text in English. 1977. a. USD 19.95 per issue. **Document type:** *Monographic series, Academic/Scholarly.*
Supersedes (1977-1987): Precis (0887-8781)
Indexed: AIAP.
—BLDSC.
Published by: Columbia University, Graduate School of Architecture, Planning and Preservation, 400 Avery Hall, New York, NY 10027. TEL 212-854-3414. Ed. Scott Marble.

720 FRA ISSN 0084-5876
ACADEMIE D'ARCHITECTURE. ANNUAIRE. Text in French. irreg. free to members.
Published by: Academie d'Architecture, Hotel de Chaulnes, 9 Place des Vosges, Paris, 75004, France. TEL 33-1-48878310, FAX 33-1-48874442.

ACCESS CURRENTS. see *HANDICAPPED—Physically Impaired*

720 370.58 USA
ACCREDITED PROGRAMS IN ARCHITECTURE; and professional degrees conferred on completion of their curricula in architecture. Text in English. 1940. a. free. **Document type:** *Catalog.*
Former titles (until 1974): Accredited Schools of Architecture; (until 1972): List of Accredited Schools of Architecture (0077-3166)
Published by: National Architectural Accrediting Board, Inc., 1735 New York Ave, N W, Washington, DC 20006. TEL 202-783-2007. Ed. John M Maudlin Jeronimo. Circ: 20,000.

ACTA POLYTECHNICA; prace CVUT v Praze. see *ENGINEERING*

720 690 ZAF ISSN 1023-0564
T28.S435
ACTA STRUCTILIA; wetenskaplijke tydskrif. Text in Afrikaans, English. 1993. biennial. USD 40 (effective 2004). bk.rev. back issues avail. **Document type:** *Journal, Academic/Scholarly.*
Published by: University of the Free State, Department of Quantity Surveying/Universiteit van die Vrystaat, PO Box 339, Bloemfontein, 9300, South Africa. TEL 27-51-4013546, FAX 27-51-4013324, beukesa.sci@mail.uovs.ac.za. Ed. J J P Verster.

ACTA UNIVERSITATIS WRATISLAVIENSIS. HISTORIA SZTUKI. see *ART*

391 ITA ISSN 1591-4135
ACTIVA DESIGN MANAGEMENT. Text in Italian. 1991. q. EUR 21 domestic; EUR 62, USD 60 foreign (effective 2001). adv. **Document type:** *Magazine, Trade.*
Former titles (until 1999): Design Management (1592-3517); (until 1992): MA DE Design Management (1120-9712)
Published by: Design Diffusion Edizioni, Via Lucano 3, Milan, 20135, Italy. TEL 39-02-5516109, FAX 39-02-59902431, info@designdiffusion.com, http://www.designdiffusion.com/riviste/activa/activa.html.

ADDIS ABABA UNIVERSITY. COLLEGE OF TECHNOLOGY. LIBRARY BULLETIN. see *LIBRARY AND INFORMATION SCIENCES*

720 693 USA
ADOBE JOURNAL. Text in English. 1989. irreg. USD 17.50. **Description:** Covers natural building materials.
Address: 707 Marble Ave NW, Albuquerque, NM 87102-2066. TEL 505-243-7801. Ed. Michael Moquin. Circ: 1,500 (paid).

720 ISR ISSN 0334-794X
ADRICHALUT. Text in English, Hebrew. irreg. USD 28.
Indexed: IHP.
Published by: Association of Engineers and Architects in Israel, 200 Dizengoff Rd., P O Box 3082, Tel Aviv, Israel. TEL 972-3-5240274, FAX 972-3-5235993.

720 GBR ISSN 1368-1435
➤ **ADVANCES IN ARCHITECTURE.** Text in English. 1997. irreg., latest vol.14, 2002. **Document type:** *Monographic series, Academic/Scholarly.* **Description:** Provides state-of-the-art information on architectural topics with particular reference to advances in raw fields. Consists of contributions from leading researchers in areas of current interest or active research.
—BLDSC (0699.265500), CISTI.
Published by: WIT Press, Ashurst Lodge, Ashurst, Southampton, Hants SO40 7AA, United Kingdom. TEL 44-238-029-3223, FAX 44-238-029-2853, marketing@witpress.com, http://www.witpress.com. Ed. F Escrig. **US dist. addr.:** Computational Mechanics Inc., 25 Bridge St, Billerica, MA 01821-1007. TEL 978-667-5841, FAX 978-667-7582, marketing@compmech.com, http://www.compmech.com/witpress.

➤ **ADVANCES IN ENVIRONMENT, BEHAVIOR AND DESIGN.** see *ENVIRONMENTAL STUDIES*

720 CHE
AKTUELLE WETTBEWERBS SCENE. Text in French, German, Italian. 1972. 5/yr. CHF 169; CHF 180 foreign. adv. **Document type:** *Trade.*
Published by: Verlag fuer Architekturinformation, Roemeralp, Asylstr 108, Zuerich, 8032, Switzerland. TEL 01-3886626, FAX 01-3886616. Ed. Verena Bertogg. Circ: 1,300.

720 USA
ALABAMA COUNCIL A I A DIRECTORY. Text in English. a. USD 45 (effective 2000). adv. charts. index. **Document type:** *Directory, Trade.*
Formerly: Alabama Architects Handbook; Supersedes (in 1972): Alabama Architect (0002-4120)
Published by: American Institute of Architects, Alabama Council, PO Box 237, Montgomery, AL 36101-0237. TEL 334-264-3037, FAX 334-263-6377, aiaalabama@council.com. Ed. Candace Spradley TEL 334-264-3037. Circ: 2,875 (controlled).

ALBUM, LETRAS Y ARTES. see *ART*

720 FRA ISSN 0180-1597
AMENAGEMENT ET MONTAGNE. Text in French. 1976. 6/yr. adv. 72 p./no.; **Document type:** *Magazine.* **Description:** For building professionals in mountainous regions.
Published by: Montagnexpansion S.A., 2 chemin des Pres, BP 135, Meylan, Cedex 38244, France. TEL 33-076-908438, FAX 33-076-908063, info@montagneexpansion.fr, http://www.mountaindatabank.com. Ed., R&P, Adv. contact Michel Drapier TEL 33-076-909966. Circ: 10,000.

AMERICAN ACADEMY IN ROME. MEMOIRS. see *ART*

AMERICAN BUILDER MAGAZINE. see *BUILDING AND CONSTRUCTION*

720 USA ISSN 1055-0674
NA7571
AMERICAN BUNGALOW. Text in English. 1993. q. USD 29.95 domestic; USD 37.95 in Canada; USD 47.95 elsewhere; USD 14 per issue (effective 2005). adv. bk.rev. illus. back issues avail.; reprints avail. **Description:** Aims to preserve and restore American Bungalow.
Related titles: Online - full content ed.
Indexed: AIAP.
Published by: Brinkmann Design Offices, Inc., 123 S Baldwin Ave, Sierra Madre, CA 91024. http://www.ambungalow.com. Ed. Michelle Gringeri Brown. Pub. John Brinkmann. Adv. contact Linda Texeira.

AMERICAN CONTRACTOR. see *BUILDING AND CONSTRUCTION*

728 USA ISSN 1540-7683
NA7205
AMERICAN DREAM HOMES; the nation's premier home plans magazine. Text in English. 2000. s-a. USD 19.95 per issue (effective 2003).
Formerly (until 2002): Street of Dreams (1527-3962)
Related titles: Online - full text ed.: (from EBSCO Publishing).
Published by: Home Planners, LLC (Subsidiary of: Hanley-Wood, LLC), 3275 W Ina Rd, Ste 220, Tucson, AZ 85741-2153. http://www.homeplanners.com.

720 USA
AMERICAN INSTITUTE OF ARCHITECTS. COLORADO ARCHITECT. Text in English. m. USD 60 (effective 2000). adv. **Document type:** *Newsletter.*
Formerly: American Institute of Architects. Field Report
Published by: American Institute of Architects, One Park Central, 1515 Arapahoe St No 110, Denver, CO 80202-1302. TEL 303-446-2266. Ed. Carolyn T Livingston. Adv. contact Kim Jackson. Circ: 1,800.

720 747 690 USA
AMERICAN INSTITUTE OF BUILDING DESIGN NEWSLETTER. Text in English. 1989. 7/yr. Membership (effective 2003). adv. **Document type:** *Newsletter.*
Published by: American Institute of Building Design, 2505 Main St., Ste 209B, Stratford, CT 06615. TEL 800-366-2423, FAX 203-227-3698, bobbi@aibd.org, http://www.aibd.org. R&P Tammy J Crosby. Adv. contact Bobbi Currie.

AMERICA'S BEST-SELLING HOME PLANS. see *BUILDING AND CONSTRUCTION*

720 ESP ISSN 0214-4727
NA5
ANALES DE ARQUITECTURA. Text in Spanish. 1989. a. **Document type:** *Academic/Scholarly.*
Indexed: AIAP, BHA, BibInd.
—CINDOC.
Published by: (Departamento de Teoria de Arquitectura y Proyectos Arquitectonicos), Universidad de Valladolid, Secretariado de Publicaciones, Juan Mambrilla, 14, Valladolid, 47003, Spain. TEL 34-83-294499, FAX 34-83-290300.

720 913 690 GBR ISSN 0951-001X
DA100
ANCIENT MONUMENTS SOCIETY TRANSACTIONS. Text in English. 1924. a. GBP 15 membership (effective 2000). bk.rev. bibl. reprints avail. **Document type:** *Academic/Scholarly.* **Description:** Covers the architectural history and conservation of historic buildings of all ages and types.
Indexed: AIAP, API, ASCA, ArtHuCI, BHA, BrArAb, BrHumI, CurCont, DIP, IBR, IBZ, NumL.
—BLDSC (8899.200000), IDS, IE, ingenta.
Published by: Ancient Monuments Society, Saint Anns Vestry Hall, 2 Church Entry, London, EC4V 5HB, United Kingdom. TEL 44-171-236-3934, FAX 44-171-329-3677. Ed. Charlotte Bradbeer. Circ: 2,000 (paid).

720 ITA ISSN 1125-9205
NA1119.S5
ANNALI DEL BAROCCO IN SICILIA. Text in Italian. 1994. irreg. **Document type:** *Journal, Academic/Scholarly.*
Published by: Gangemi Editore, Piazza San Pantaleo 4, Rome, Italy. TEL 39-06-6872774, FAX 39-06-68806189, gangemieditorerc@tin.it, http://www.gangemieditore.it.

712 CHE ISSN 0003-5424
SB469
ANTHOS; vierteljahres-Zeitschrift fuer Freiraumgestaltung, Gruen und Landschaftsplanung. Text in French, German. 1962. q. CHF 89; CHF 49 to students; CHF 24 newsstand/cover (effective 2004). adv. bk.rev. charts; illus. reprints avail. **Document type:** *Journal, Trade.*
Indexed: AIAP, API, DIP, GardL, IBR, IBZ, RRTA, WAE&RSA.
—BLDSC (1542.450000), IE, Infotrieve, ingenta.
Published by: Bund Schweizer Landschaftsarchitekten und Landschaftsarchitektinnen, Rue du Doubs 32, La Chaux-de-Fonds, 2300, Switzerland. TEL 41-32-9688889, FAX 41-32-9688833, stephanie.perrochet@span.ch, bsla@bsla.ch, http://www.bsla.ch/de/publikationen/anthos.php. Ed. Stephanie Perrochet. Circ: 5,000.

ANTIMOVSKI HAN. see *ART*

720 USA ISSN 1080-9619
NA2543.S6
APPENDX; culture - theory - praxis. Text in English. 1993. a. USD 16.50 to individuals; USD 25 to institutions. bk.rev. **Document type:** *Academic/Scholarly.*
Indexed: AIAP.
Address: PO Box 382806, Cambridge, MA 02238. http://www.appendx.org. Ed. Darell Fields. Adv. contact Milton Curry.

720 JPN ISSN 0003-7117
APPROACH. Text in Japanese; Summaries in English. 1964. q. free. bk.rev. 28 p./no.; back issues avail. **Document type:** *Academic/Scholarly.* **Description:** Covers a wide range of urban, architectural, cultural, and social subjects.
Related titles: Online - full text ed.: (from Northern Light Technology, Inc.).
Indexed: AIAP, API, IUSGP, RefZh.
Published by: Takenaka Corporation, 1-13 Hon-Machi 4-chome, Chuo-ku, Osaka-shi, 541-0053, Japan. TEL 81-6-252-1201, FAX 81-6-271-0398, http://www.takenaka.co.jp/. Ed. Shunichi Hirao. Circ: 10,000 (controlled).

720 DEU
ARBEITSKREIS FUER HAUSFORSCHUNG. BERICHTE ZUR HAUS- UND BAUFORSCHUNG. Text in German. 1991. irreg., latest vol.2, 1991. EUR 30 to non-members (effective 2003). **Document type:** *Monographic series, Academic/Scholarly.*
Published by: (Arbeitskreis fuer Hausforschung e.V.), Jonas Verlag, Weidenhaeuser Str 88, Marburg, 35037, Germany. TEL 49-6421-25132, FAX 49-6421-210572, jonas@jonas-verlag.de, http://www.jonas-verlag.de.

720 DEU ISSN 0172-2727
TH4805
ARBEITSKREIS FUER HAUSFORSCHUNG. JAHRBUCH. Text in German. a. EUR 30 to non-members (effective 2003). **Document type:** *Bulletin, Trade.*
Former titles (until 1975): Arbeitskreis fuer Hausforschung. Bericht ueber die Tagung (0172-2468); (until 1972): Arbeitskreis fuer Deutsche Hausforschung. Bericht ueber die Tagung (0402-8244); Arbeitskreis fuer Deutsche Hausforschung. Niederschrift ueber die Tagung (0172-2719)
Published by: (Arbeitskreis fuer Hausforschung e.V.), Jonas Verlag, Weidenhaeuser Str 88, Marburg, 35037, Germany. TEL 49-6421-25132, FAX 49-6421-210572, jonas@jonas-verlag.de, http://www.jonas-verlag.de.

720 ITA ISSN 0394-2147
NA680
L'ARCA; la rivista internazionale di architettura, design e comunicazione visiva. Text in English, Italian. 11/yr. EUR 87.70 combined subscription (effective 2005); includes L'Arca Plus and L'Arca Online. adv. bk.rev. illus.; maps. 144 p./no.; back issues avail.; reprints avail. **Document type:** *Magazine, Consumer.* **Description:** Each issue devoted to an important project theme in international architecture and design.
Related titles: Online - full text ed.
Indexed: AIAP, API, DAAI.
—BLDSC (1594.457000), IE, Infotrieve, ingenta.
Published by: L' Arca Edizioni SpA, Via Valcava 6, Milan, MI 20155, Italy. TEL 39-02-325246, FAX 39-02-325481, arca@tin.it, http://www.arcadata.it. Ed. Cesare M Casati. R&P, Adv. contact Titi Casati. Circ: 42,800.

720 FRA ISSN 7141-410X
L'ARCA INTERNATIONAL; la revue internationale d'architecture, design et commmunication visuelle. Text in English, French. 1996. m.
Indexed: AIAP.
Published by: Arca International, 31 av. Princesse Grace, Monaco, 98000, France. TEL 33-4-92165151, FAX 33-4-93504978. Ed. Philippe Gardereau. Pub. Cesare M Casati.

720 NLD
ARCAM NIEUWS. Text in Dutch. 1986. 6/yr. bk.rev. illus. back issues avail. **Document type:** *Newsletter, Academic/Scholarly.* **Description:** Provides information on architectural programs of educational institutes, museums, galleries, and other institutes based in or around Amsterdam and on publications about Amsterdam architecture.
Published by: Amsterdam Centre for Architecture, Waterlooplein 213, Amsterdam, 1011 PG, Netherlands. TEL 31-20-620-4878, FAX 31-20-638-5598, arcam@arcam.nl, http://www.arcam.nl. Ed. Marlies Buurman. Circ: 5,000.

724 ITA ISSN 1127-0268
NA4
L'ARCAPLUS. Text in Italian, English. 4/yr. EUR 87.70 combined subscription (effective 2005); includes L'Arca and L'Arca Online. adv. illus.; maps. 96 p./no.; **Document type:** *Magazine, Consumer.* **Description:** Mono-thematic issues devoted to the best projects on the contemporary scene.
Indexed: API.
—BLDSC (1594.462500).
Published by: L' Arca Edizioni SpA, Via Valcava 6, Milan, MI 20155, Italy. TEL 39-02-325246, FAX 39-02-325481, arca@tin.it, http://www.arcadata.it. Ed. Cesare Casati. R&P Titi Casati. Circ: 26,200.

720 DEU
ARCHE; Architektur- und Energiekonzepte. Text in German. a. adv. **Document type:** *Magazine, Trade.*
Published by: Fachschriften Verlag GmbH, Hoehenstr 17, Fellbach, 70736, Germany. TEL 49-711-52061, 49-711-5206-256, info@fachschriften.de, http:// www.fachschriften.de. adv.: B&W page EUR 8,950, color page EUR 14,440. Circ: 236,860 (controlled).

720 CHE ISSN 1422-5417
➤ **ARCHI.** Text in English, Italian; Summaries in English. 1998. bi-m. CHF 120 domestic; CHF 150 foreign; CHF 24 newsstand/cover (effective 1999). adv. **Document type:** *Academic/Scholarly.* **Description:** Contains review of architecture, engineering and urban planning.
Related titles: Online - full text ed.
Indexed: AIAP, DIP, IBR, IBZ.
Published by: Edizioni Casagrande SA, Case Postale 1291, Bellinzona, 6500, Switzerland. TEL 41-91-8256622, FAX 41-91-8251874, casagrande@casagrande-online.ch, http://www.casagrande-online.ch. Ed. Alberto Caruso. Adv. contact Paola Fusaroli. B&W page CHF 800, color page CHF 1,530; trim 132 x 190. Circ: 31,000 (paid).

720 747 FRA ISSN 0294-8567
NA2
ARCHI-CREE. Text in French. bi-m. adv. **Description:** International architecture magazine that covers the development of architecture, including construction techniques, interior systems and decorative finishes, building components and products, and contract furniture.
Formerly: Architecture Interieure
Indexed: AIAP, API, RASB.
—BLDSC (1601.972000), IE, Infotrieve, ingenta.
Published by: S.E.P., 9 Place du General Catroux, Paris, 75017, France. TEL 33-1-142128084, FAX 33-1-146229879. Ed. Florence Michel. Pub. Joelle Letessier. Adv. contact Nathalie Perier. Circ: 12,667 (paid).

720 PAK
ARCHI TIMES; world news of architecture. Text in English. 1986. m. PKR 500; USD 75 in United States. adv. bk.rev. back issues avail. **Description:** Covers issues related to architecture and engineering.
Address: 99 7th Fl. Ghafoor Chambers, Abdullah Haroon Rd., Karachi, 77400, Pakistan. TEL 92-21-7772397, FAX 92-21-7772417. Ed. Syed M Mujtuba Hussain. Pub. Syed Murtuza Hussain. Adv. contact Naveed Shakil. page USD 700. Circ: 7,500.

720 FRA ISSN 0768-5785
ARCHISCOPIE. Text in French. 1974. 9/yr. EUR 43 domestic; EUR 53 foreign; EUR 29 domestic to students; EUR 45 foreign to students (effective 2002).
Former titles (until 1999): Bulletin d'Informations Architecturales (0223-5331); (until 1980): Bulletin d'Informations Inter-Etablissements (0154-9103); (until 1977): I E Inter Etablissements (0335-9425)
Indexed: AIAP.
Published by: Institut Francais d'Architecture, 6 rue de Tournon, Paris, 75006, France. TEL 33-01-46339036, FAX 33-01-46330211, http://www.archi.fr/IFA/.

720 ZAF
ARCHITECHNOLOGY. Text and summaries in English. 1999 (Oct.). 3/yr. ZAR 70 domestic; USD 20 in Africa; USD 50 elsewhere (effective 2002). adv. **Description:** Covers the latest architectural design technologies.

A

Published by: (South African Institute of Architectural Technologists (SAIAT)), Brooke Pattrick Publications, PO Box 422, Bedfordview, Transvaal 2008, South Africa. TEL 27-11-622-4666, FAX 27-11-616-7196, bestbook@brookepattrick.co.za, http://www.brookepattrick.com/architec.html.

720 NLD ISSN 0044-8621
DE ARCHITECT. Text in Dutch. 1970. 16/yr. EUR 184 domestic; EUR 188.50 foreign (effective 2005). adv. bk.rev. **Document type:** *Trade.* **Description:** For architects, interior designers, and city planners: covers architecture, building and construction.
Related titles: Supplement(s): De Architect. Interieur. ISSN 1567-7923.
Indexed: AIAP, ExcerpMed.
—BLDSC (1597.700000), IE, ingenta.
Published by: Sdu Uitgevers bv, Postbus 20025, The Hague, 2500 EA, Netherlands. TEL 31-70-3789911, FAX 31-70-3854321, sdu@sdu.nl, http://www.dearchitect.nl, http://www.sdu.nl/. adv.: B&W page EUR 2,895; trim 220 x 297. Circ: 7,297.

720 AUS ISSN 1037-3640
ARCHITECT (PERTH). Text in English. q. AUD 35; AUD 45 foreign (effective 1999). adv.
Former titles (until 1986): Architect W.A. (1037-3632); (until 1981): Architect (0003-8393)
Indexed: AIAP, API.
Published by: Royal Australian Institute of Architects, Western Australian Chapter, QVI Upper Plaza Level, 250 St George s Tle, Perth, W.A. 6000, Australia. FAX 61-9-3214708. Ed. Romesh Goonewardene. Adv. contact Gary Davidson. Circ: 2,000. **Subscr. to:** Ms. J. Sanders, Ink Press International, 15 Northwood St, West Leederville, W.A. 6007, Australia.

720 690 ZAF ISSN 0003-8407
ARCHITECT & BUILDER. Text in English. 1951. m. ZAR 188; ZAR 245 foreign (effective 1999). adv. bk.rev. bibl.; charts; illus. **Document type:** *Trade.* **Description:** Serves the professionals in the building world, including architects, contractors, and engineers.
Indexed: AIAP, API, ISAP.
Published by: Laurie Wale (Pty) Ltd., PO Box 4591, Cape Town, 8000, South Africa. TEL 27-21-4618029, FAX 27-21-4619265. Ed. Laurie Wale. Circ: 2,500 (paid).

ARCHITECT, BUILDER, CONTRACTOR & DEVELOPER. see *BUILDING AND CONSTRUCTION*

720 AUS ISSN 1329-1254
NA1
ARCHITECT VICTORIA. Text in English. 1967. 10/yr. AUD 85 domestic; AUD 205 foreign (effective 2005). adv. bk.rev. illus.; mkt. **Document type:** *Newsletter.* **Description:** Covers all aspects of concern to architects, including continuing education, current projects, law and finance.
Formerly: Architect (Melbourne) (1036-5028); Incorporates: Practice Newsletter; (in 1991): Elevations; Which was formerly (until 1985): State Electricity Commission. Newsletter
Indexed: AIAP, API, ArtInd.
Published by: Royal Australian Institute of Architects, Victorian Chapter, 1st Fl., 41 Exhibition St., Melbourne, VIC 8003, Australia. TEL 61-3-96548066, FAX 61-3-96503360, vic@raia.com.au, http:www.raia.com.au. adv.: B&W page AUD 1,150, color page AUD 1,610; trim 186 x 220. Circ: 2,500.

720 PRT
ARCHITECTI. Text in Portuguese. 5/yr.
Indexed: AIAP, API.
Published by: Editora Triforia Lda., Avenida Marques de Tomar, 68 4o Esq, Lisbon, 1000, Portugal. TEL 779-912, FAX 793-83-41. Ed. Luiz Trigueiros.

720 IRL
ARCHITECTS. Text in English. a. adv. **Document type:** *Directory, Trade.* **Description:** Contains articles and features of interest to Irish architects, interior designers, and manufacturers of materials, products and services to the architecture industry.
Published by: Commercial Publications Ltd., Idrone Mews, Idrone Ln., Blackrock, Co. Dublin, Ireland. TEL 353-1-2833233, FAX 353-1-2833254.

ARCHITECTS CATALOG. see *BUSINESS AND ECONOMICS—Trade And Industrial Directories*

666.1 USA
ARCHITECTS' GUIDE TO GLASS, METAL & GLAZING. Text in English. 1972. biennial. USD 20 (effective 1999). adv. bk.rev. charts; illus.; stat. back issues avail. **Document type:** *Trade.*
Published by: U S Glass Publications, Inc., PO Box 569, Garrisonville, VA 22463. TEL 540-720-5584, FAX 540-720-5687, http://www.glass.com, http:// www.woglassmag.com. Ed. Debra A Levy. R&Ps Debra Levy, Melissa Light. Adv. contact Janeen Cipriani TEL 540-720-5584 Ext 112. Circ: 27,000 (controlled).

720 USA ISSN 0066-6173
ARCHITECT'S HANDBOOK OF PROFESSIONAL PRACTICE. Text in English. 1917. irreg. USD 200 to non-members; USD 140 to members. Supplement avail. **Document type:** *Academic/Scholarly.*
Published by: (American Institute of Architects), A I A Press, 1735 New York Ave, N W, Washington, DC 20008. TEL 202-626-7575. Ed. David Haviland. R&P Janet Rumbarger TEL 202-626-7536. Circ: 10,000.

720 IND ISSN 0970-6852
ARCHITECTS INDIA. Text in English. 1960. bi-m. USD 20. adv. bk.rev. charts; illus. **Document type:** *Trade.* **Description:** For architects, engineers, builders, contractors and interior designers. Includes news, technical articles and projects connected with the building industry.
Formerly (until 1989): Architects Trade Journal (0304-8594)
Indexed: API.
Published by: Architects Publishing Corp. of India, 51 Sujata, Ground Fl., Rani Sati Marg, Malad East, Mumbai, Maharashtra 400 097, India. TEL 91-22-883-4442. Ed. Santosh Kumar. Circ: 5,000.

720 GBR ISSN 0003-8466
TH1
ARCHITECTS' JOURNAL. Text in English. 1895. w. GBP 88 domestic; GBP 145 foreign; GBP 135 combined subscription domestic print & online; GBP 174 combined subscription foreign print & online (effective 2005). adv. bk.rev. bibl.; charts; illus. index. back issues avail. **Document type:** *Magazine, Trade.* **Description:** Provides architects and other specifiers who work on creating and maintaining buildings with information and building studies and coverage of technical subjects that affect them.
Related titles: Online - full text ed.: GBP 94 domestic; GBP 80 foreign (effective 2005) (from EBSCO Publishing); ♦ Includes: Concrete Quarterly. ISSN 0010-5376; ♦ Supplement(s): Architect's Journal Focus. ISSN 0951-5380.
Indexed: A&ATA, ABM, ADPA, AIAP, API, ArtInd, BioDAb, BldManAb, BrCerAb, BrHumI, BrTechI, C&ISA, CISA, Cadscan, CerAb, CivEngAb, CorrAb, CurCont, E&CAJ, EMA, HECAB, HRIS, IBuildSA, ICEA, LeadAb, M&TEA, MBF, METADEX, RASB, RICS, SoftAbEng, SolStAb, WAA, Zincscan.
—BLDSC (1598.000000), CISTI, IE, Infotrieve, ingenta. **CCC.**
Published by: Emap Construct Ltd. (Subsidiary of: Emap Business Communications Ltd.), 151 Rosebery Ave, London, EC1R 4GB, United Kingdom. TEL 44-20-8956-3101, FAX 44-20-7505-3535, tina@construct.emap.co.uk, http://www.ajplus.co.uk/, http://www.emap.com/construct/. Ed. Isabel Allen. Pub., R&P Graham Harman. Adv. contact Johnathon Stock. Circ: 17,180. **Dist. by:** Seymour Distribution Ltd, 86 Newman St, London W1T 3EX, United Kingdom. FAX 44-207-396-8002, enquiries@seymour.co.uk.

720 690 GBR ISSN 0951-5380
TH 1
ARCHITECT'S JOURNAL FOCUS; products in practice. Key Title: A J Focus. Text in English. 1982. m. adv. charts; illus. back issues avail. **Document type:** *Trade.*
Formerly (until 1987): Products in Practice (0264-1585)
Related titles: ♦ Supplement to: Architects' Journal. ISSN 0003-8466.
Indexed: BrCerAb, BrHumI, BrTechI, C&ISA, CerAb, CorrAb, E&CAJ, EMA, M&TEA, MBF, METADEX, SolStAb, WAA.
—BLDSC (0785.459340), CISTI, IE, Infotrieve.
Published by: Emap Construct Ltd. (Subsidiary of: Emap Business Communications Ltd.), 151 Rosebery Ave, London, EC1R 4GB, United Kingdom. TEL 44-20-7505-6600, FAX 44-20-7505-3535, tinaf@construct.emap.co.uk, http://www.emapconstruct.co.uk. Ed. Jo White. Pub., R&P Graham Harman. Adv. contact Johnathon Stock. Circ: 18,000.

721 USA ISSN 1552-8081
THE ARCHITECTS NEWSPAPER. Text in English. 20/yr. USD 39 domestic; USD 160 foreign; USD 3.95 newsstand/cover (effective 2005). **Document type:** *Magazine, Consumer.*
Related titles: Online - full text ed.
Published by: The Architect's Newspaper, Llc., P O Box 937, New York, NY 10013. TEL 212-966-0630, FAX 212-966-0633, http://www.archpaper.com. Eds. Cathy Lang Ho, William Menking. Pub. Diana Darling.

720 DNK ISSN 0106-3030
NA1211
ARCHITECTURA; arkitekturhistorisk aarsskrift. Text in Danish; Abstracts in English. 1979. a., latest 2004. price varies. illus. back issues avail. **Document type:** *Journal, Academic/Scholarly.*
Indexed: AIAP, API, ArtHuCI, ArtInd, BHA.
Published by: (Selskabet for Arkitekturhistorie), Arkitektens Forlag/Danish Architectural Press, Overgaden oven Vandet 10, Copenhagen K, 1415, Denmark. TEL 45-32-836900, FAX 45-32-836941, red@arkfo.dk, info@arkfo.dk, http://www.arkfo.dk. Ed. Joergen Hegner Christiansen. Circ: 1,000.

720 HUN ISSN 0066-6270
ARCHITECTURA. Text in Hungarian. 1966. irreg. price varies. illus. **Document type:** *Monographic series.* **Description:** Covers famous architects of the 20th Century and their works.
Indexed: ArtHuCI, BHA.
Published by: Magyar Tudomanyos Akademia/Hungarian Academy of Sciences, PO Box 487, Budapest, 1447, Hungary. TEL 36-1-375-0493, FAX 36-1-375-7858. **Co-sponsor:** Magyar Epitomuveszek Szovetsege.

720 DEU ISSN 0044-863X
NA200
ARCHITECTURA; Zeitschrift fuer Geschichte der Baukunst. Text in German, English. 1971. s-a. EUR 28.50 per issue (effective 2005). bk.rev. charts; illus. reprints avail. **Document type:** *Magazine, Trade.*
Indexed: AIAP, ASCA, ArtHuCI, ArtInd, BHA, CurCont, DIP, IBR, IBRH, IBZ, RASB.
—IDS, IE, Infotrieve. **CCC.**
Published by: Deutscher Kunstverlag GmbH, Nymphenburger Str 84, Munich, 80636, Germany. TEL 49-89-1269900, info@deutscherkunstverlag.de, http://www.kunstbuecher-online.de. Ed. Wulf Schirmer. Circ: 2,500.

720 GBR ISSN 0003-8504
NA1
ARCHITECTURAL DESIGN. Text in English. 1930. bi-m. USD 290 to institutions; USD 320 combined subscription to institutions print & online eds. (effective 2006). adv. bk.rev. abstr.; charts; illus.; tr.lit. index. back issues avail.; reprints avail. **Document type:** *Journal, Academic/Scholarly.* **Description:** Features current architectural thinking, criticism and achievements.
Related titles: Online - full text ed.: ISSN 1554-2769. USD 290 (effective 2006) (from EBSCO Publishing, Wiley InterScience).
Indexed: AIAP, API, ArtHuCI, ArtInd, Cadscan, CurCont, DIP, EEA, EIP, IBR, IBZ, LeadAb, PCI, RASB, SSCI, Zincscan.
—BLDSC (1600.000000), CISTI, IDS, IE, Infotrieve, ingenta. **CCC.**
Published by: John Wiley & Sons Ltd. (Subsidiary of: John Wiley & Sons, Inc.), The Atrium, Southern Gate, Chichester, West Sussex PO19 8SQ, United Kingdom. TEL 44-1243-779777, FAX 44-1243-775878, customer@wiley.co.uk, http://www.wiley.co.uk. Circ: 6,500 (paid). **Subscr. in US to:** John Wiley & Sons, Inc., 111 River St, Hoboken, NJ 07030-5774. TEL 201-748-6645, 800-225-5945, subinfo@wiley.com.

728 747 USA ISSN 0747-5179
NA7205
ARCHITECTURAL DESIGNS. Text in English. 1968. q. USD 31.95; USD 5.95 newsstand/cover (effective 2005). adv. **Document type:** *Magazine, Consumer.* **Description:** Each issue features 200 home plans from over 30 architects and building designers.
Formerly (until 1983): 101 Home Plans
Indexed: ArtHuCI.
Published by: Architectural Designs, Inc., 57 Danbury Rd., Wilton, CT 06897-4439. jd1435@aol.com, prez@architecturaldesigns.com, http:// www.architecturaldesigns.com. Ed. Carol B Davis. Pub., R&P Joel Davis. Adv. contact Kathleen Lappano. Circ: 20,000 (paid and controlled).

720 DEU ISSN 0931-3567
ARCHITECTURAL DIGEST. Abbreviated title: A D. Text in German. 1997. bi-m. EUR 43; EUR 5 newsstand/cover (effective 2004). adv. **Document type:** *Magazine, Consumer.*
Published by: Conde Nast Verlag GmbH, Ainmillerstr 8, Munich, 80801, Germany. TEL 49-89-38104-0, FAX 49-89-38104230, leserbriefe@ad-magazin.de, http://www.ad-magazin.de. Ed. Doris Wiedemann. Pub. Bernd Runge. adv.: page EUR 15,290; trim 213 x 277. Circ: 93,479 (paid and controlled).

720 USA ISSN 1531-4596
ARCHITECTURAL DIGEST EN ESPANOL. Text in Esperanto. 2000. m. USD 75 domestic; USD 100 in Canada; MXP 889 in Mexico; USD 150 elsewhere (effective 2001). adv. **Document type:** *Magazine, Consumer.* **Description:** Contains articles and features on the homes of influential men and woman in the fields of entertainment, business, finance, fashion, literature, and the arts.
Related titles: ♦ English ed.: Architectural Digest. ISSN 0003-8520.
Published by: Conde Nast Americas, 1101 Brickell Ave 15th Fl, Miami, FL 33131. TEL 305-371-9393, 800-792-5999, FAX 305-371-9392, architecturaldigest@ideaspublishinggroup.com, http://www.ideaspublishinggroup.com/magazines/ archdigest.html. adv.: page USD 4,000; trim 8.375 x 10.875. Circ: 185,000 (paid and controlled).

720 GBR ISSN 1350-7524
NA972
ARCHITECTURAL HERITAGE SOCIETY OF SCOTLAND. JOURNAL. Text in English. 1972. a., latest vol.13. GBP 27 per issue in Europe; USD 52 per issue in North America; GBP 29 per issue elsewhere (effective 2005). adv. bk.rev. **Document type:** *Academic/Scholarly.* **Description:** Includes articles and essays by leading historians and researchers in Scottish architecture.
Former titles: Architectural Heritage Society of Scotland. Journal and Annual Report; Scottish Georgian Society. Annual Report and Bulletin; (until 1981): Scottish Georgian Society. Annual Report; Which incorporates: Scottish Georgian Society. Bulletin
Related titles: Online - full text ed.: (from EBSCO Publishing).
Indexed: AIAP, API, BHA.
—BLDSC (1600.170000).

Published by: (Architectural Heritage Society of Scotland), Edinburgh University Press, 22 George Sq, Edinburgh, Midlothian EH8 9LF, United Kingdom. TEL 44-131-650-6207, FAX 44-131-662-0053, journals@eup.ed.ac.uk, http://www.eup.ed.ac.uk/newweb/journals/Architectural/. Pub. Vivian C Bone. Adv. contact Douglas McNaughton TEL 44-131-6504420. Circ: 1,000.

720 942 GBR ISSN 0066-622X
NA190
ARCHITECTURAL HISTORY. Text in English. 1958. a. free membership (effective 2005); includes Newsletter. **Document type:** *Academic/Scholarly.*
Indexed: AIAP, API, ASCA, ArtHuCI, ArtInd, BHA, BrArAb, BrHumI, CurCont, IBRH, NumL.
—BLDSC (1600.200000), IE, ingenta.
Published by: Society of Architectural Historians of Great Britain, Brandon Mead, Old Park Ln, Farnham, Surrey GU9 0AJ, United Kingdom. membership@sahgb.org.uk, http://www.sahgb.org.uk/. Circ: 1,150.

720 USA ISSN 0894-0436
TH7700
ARCHITECTURAL LIGHTING. Text in English. 1987. 8/yr. USD 48 domestic; USD 60 in Canada; USD 86 elsewhere; USD 10 newsstand/cover (effective 2004). adv. bk.rev. charts; illus.; tr.lit. index. back issues avail. **Document type:** *Magazine, Trade.* **Description:** Covers practical, problem-solving approaches to architectural lighting for trade professionals.
Related titles: Online - full text ed.: (from Gale Group, ProQuest Information & Learning).
Indexed: ABIn, AIAP, Search.
—IE, Infotrieve. **CCC.**
Published by: V N U Business Publications (Subsidiary of: V N U Business Media), 770 Broadway, New York, NY 10003-9595. TEL 646-654-7604, info@archlighting.com, bmcomm@vnuinc.com, http://www.lightforum.com/architecturallighting/index.jsp, http://www.vnubusinessmedia.com/. Eds. Alice Liao, Christina Trauthwein TEL 646-654-4481. Pub., Adv. contact Suzanne Tron Haber TEL 646-654-5756. Circ: 30,000. **Subscr. to:** PO Box 1061, Skokie, IL 60076-8061.

720 AUS ISSN 1038-4359
ARCHITECTURAL PRODUCT NEWS. Text in English. 1992. bi-m. AUD 38 domestic; AUD 73 in Asia & the Pacific; AUD 105 elsewhere (effective 2004). adv. back issues avail. **Description:** Provides information on the latest building and interior products available in Australia for architects, designers and building specifiers.
Published by: Architecture Media, L3, 4 Princes St, Port Melbourne, VIC 3207, Australia. TEL 61-3-96164760, FAX 61-3-96464918, publisher@archmedia.com.au, http://www.archmedia.com.au. Ed. Ms. Sue Harris. Pub., R&P Ian Close. Adv. contacts Ms. Victoria Hawthorne, Neil Williams. B&W page AUD 3,490, color page AUD 3,920; trim 220 x 292. Circ: 24,655.

720 USA ISSN 1557-4830
▼ **ARCHITECTURAL PRODUCTS.** Text in English. 2003. bi-m. free to qualified personnel (effective 2003). **Document type:** *Magazine, Trade.*
Published by: Construction Business Media LLC, 579 First Bank Dr, Ste 220, Palatine, IL 60067. TEL 847-359-6493, FAX 847-359-6754, info@arch-products.com, http://www.arch-products.com/.

ARCHITECTURAL PSYCHOLOGY NEWSLETTER. see *PSYCHOLOGY*

720 USA ISSN 0003-858X
NA1 CODEN: ACURAV
ARCHITECTURAL RECORD. Text in English. 1891. m. USD 65.95 domestic; USD 79 in Canada & Mexico; USD 199 elsewhere (effective 2005). adv. bk.rev. charts; illus.; tr.lit. index. Supplement avail.; back issues avail.; reprints avail. **Document type:** *Magazine, Trade.* **Description:** Provides an integrated editorial mix of design ideas, trends, news, and business and professional strategies, computer-aided design, building technology, and product reviews.
Related titles: Microfiche ed.: (from IDC); Microfilm ed.: (from PQC); Online - full text ed.: (from EBSCO Publishing, LexisNexis, Northern Light Technology, Inc., ProQuest Information & Learning).
Indexed: ABS&EES, AIAP, API, ASCA, Acal, ArchI, ArtHuCI, ArtInd, ConcrAb, CurCont, DIP, EngInd, IBR, IBRH, IBZ, ICEA, LRI, MASUSE, MEDLINE, MagInd, PCI, PMR, RASB, RGAb, RGPR, RI-1, RI-2, RICS, RILM, SRI, SSCI, Search, SoftAbEng, T&II.
—BLDSC (1600.450000), CISTI, IDS, IE, Infotrieve, ingenta, Linda Hall. **CCC.**
Published by: (American Institute of Architects), McGraw-Hill Companies, Inc., 2 Penn Plaza, New York, NY 10121. TEL 212-907-3070, 212-512-2000, http://www.archrecord.com/. Ed. Robert Ivy. adv.: B&W page USD 10,310, color page USD 12,990; trim 10.88 x 9. Circ: 90,000 (paid).

720 690 GBR ISSN 0003-861X
NA1
ARCHITECTURAL REVIEW. Text in English. 1897. m. GBP 69 domestic; GBP 77 in Europe; GBP 72 in United States; GBP 105 elsewhere (effective 2004). adv. bk.rev. charts; illus. reprints avail. **Document type:** *Magazine, Trade.*
Related titles: Microfiche ed.: (from IDC); Online - full text ed.: (from Florida Center for Library Automation, Gale Group, Northern Light Technology, Inc., O C L C Online Computer Library Center, Inc., ProQuest Information & Learning).
Indexed: A&ATA, ABM, AIAP, API, ASCA, ArchI, ArtHuCI, ArtInd, BAS, BHA, BrHumI, BrTechI, Cadscan, CurCont, DAAI, GardL, LeadAb, RASB, RICS, Search, Zincscan.
—BLDSC (1600.475000), CISTI, IDS, IE, Infotrieve, ingenta, Linda Hall. **CCC.**
Published by: Emap Construct Ltd. (Subsidiary of: Emap Business Communications Ltd.), 151 Rosebery Ave, London, EC1R 4GB, United Kingdom. TEL 44-20-75056701, http://www.arplus.com/. Ed. Peter Davey TEL 44-20-75056725. Pub. Johnathon Stock. Circ: 18,500. **Subscr. in America to:** Fenner, Reed & Jackson, Box 754, Manhasset, NY 11030-0754. **Dist. by:** Seymour Distribution Ltd, 86 Newman St, London W1T 3EX, United Kingdom. FAX 44-207-396-8002, enquiries@seymour.co.uk.

720 AUS ISSN 1323-367X
ARCHITECTURAL REVIEW AUSTRALIA. Cover title: A R. Text in English. 1993. q. AUD 45 domestic; AUD 120 foreign (effective 2004). adv. **Document type:** *Magazine, Trade.* **Description:** Covers contemporary architecture in Australia and significant buildings and projects from overseas.
Formed by the merger of (1989-1990): Architectural Review Australia (1032-951X); (1987-1992): Interior Designers and Decorators Handbook of Australia
Published by: Niche Media Pty Ltd (Subsidiary of: Waivcom Worldwide Ltd.), 165 Fitzroy St, St Kilda, VIC 3182, Australia. TEL 61-3-95255566, FAX 61-3-95255628, subscription@niche.com.au, http://www.niche.com.au. Ed. Andrew Mackenzie. Adv. contact Lee Bennie. page AUD 8,420; trim 230 x 275.

720 AUS ISSN 0003-8628
NA1 CODEN: ASRVA4
➤ **ARCHITECTURAL SCIENCE REVIEW.** Text in English. 1958. q. AUD 49 domestic to individuals; AUD 87.50 foreign to individuals; AUD 90 domestic to institutions; AUD 175 foreign to institutions (effective 2004). adv. bk.rev. bibl.; charts; illus.; stat. Index. back issues avail.; reprints avail. **Document type:** *Journal, Academic/Scholarly.*
Related titles: Microform ed.: (from PQC); Online - full text ed.: (from Gale Group).
Indexed: AIAP, API, ASFA, AusPAIS, BldManAb, BrCerAb, C&ISA, CISA, CerAb, CivEngAb, CorrAb, DIP, E&CAJ, EEA, EIP, EMA, ESPM, EngInd, IAA, IBR, IBZ, IBuildSA, ICEA, M&TEA, MBF, METADEX, RASB, SWRA, SolStAb, WAA.
—BLDSC (1600.490000), CISTI, Ei, IE, Infotrieve, ingenta, Linda Hall. **CCC.**
Published by: University of Sydney, School of Architectural and Design Science, Faculty of Architecture, Sydney, NSW 2006, Australia. TEL 61-2-93516709, FAX 61-2-93513031, asr@arch.usyd.edu.au, asr@arch.su.edu.au, http://www.arch.usyd.edu.au/nwfa/research/publications.html, http://www.usyd.edu.au/. Ed., R&P H J Cowan. adv.: page AUD 300. Circ: 900.

➤ **ARCHITECTURAL TECHNOLOGY.** see *BUILDING AND CONSTRUCTION*

720.5 AUS ISSN 1326-4826
NA1
➤ **ARCHITECTURAL THEORY REVIEW.** Text in English. 1996. s-a. AUD 30 domestic to individuals; AUD 40 foreign to individuals; AUD 55 domestic to institutions; AUD 65 foreign to institutions; AUD 25 domestic to students; AUD 35 foreign to students (effective 2000). adv. bk.rev. illus. back issues avail. **Document type:** *Academic/Scholarly.* **Description:** Provide a forum for the discussion of architectural theory in relation to contemporary and interdisciplinary thinking among architects and academics.
Indexed: AIAP, API.
—BLDSC (1600.790000), IE, ingenta.
Published by: University of Sydney, Department of Architecture, Planning and Allied Arts, Bldg. G04, Sydney, NSW 2006, Australia. TEL 61-2-9351-2771, FAX 61-2-9351-3855, rubbo—a@arch.usyd.edu.au, http://www.usyd.edu.au/. Eds. Adrian Snodgrass, Anna Rubbo. Adv. contact Anna Rubbo. Circ: 150.

721 978 USA ISSN 1097-4741
ARCHITECTURAL WEST. Text in English. 1998. bi-m. USD 12 domestic; USD 60 foreign; USD 3.50 newsstand/cover (effective 2003). adv. bk.rev. charts; illus.; stat.; tr.lit. **Document type:** *Trade.* **Description:** Aimed at building professionals concerned with the design and specification of the building envelope and with current industry-related news from throughout the West.
Published by: Dodson Publications Inc., 546 Court St, Reno, NV 89501-1711. TEL 775-333-1080, FAX 775-333-1081, info@architecturalwest.com, http://www.architecturalwest.com. Ed., Pub., R&P Marc Dodson. adv.: B&W page USD 1,885, color page USD 3,105; trim 10.88 x 8.38. Circ: 19,800 (controlled).

720 USA ISSN 0746-0554
NA1
ARCHITECTURE. Text in English. 1913. m. USD 55 (effective 2004). adv. bk.rev. bibl.; charts; illus.; stat. Index. back issues avail.; reprints avail. **Document type:** *Magazine, Trade.*
Incorporates (1992-1995): Building Renovation (1070-5988); (1920-1995): Progressive Architecture (0033-0752); Incorporates (1983-1986): Architectural Technology (0740-6142); Former titles (1957-1983): A I A Journal (0001-1479); American Institute of Architects. Journal
Related titles: Microform ed.: (from PQC); Online - full text ed.: (from EBSCO Publishing, Florida Center for Library Automation, Gale Group, H.W. Wilson, O C L C Online Computer Library Center, Inc., ProQuest Information & Learning).
Indexed: ABS&EES, AIAP, API, ASCA, AgeL, ArchI, ArtHuCI, ArtInd, BHA, BusI, CurCont, EngInd, GardL, IBRH, LRI, MASUSE, MEDLINE, PCI, RASB, SSCI, Search, T&II.
—BLDSC (1600.937000), CISTI, IDS, IE, ingenta, Linda Hall. **CCC.**
Published by: V N U Business Publications (Subsidiary of: V N U Business Media), 770 Broadway, New York, NY 10003-9595. info@architecturemag.com, http://www.architecturemag.com/, http://www.vnubusinessmedia.com/. Pub. Gary Gyss. adv.: B&W page USD 9,350, color page USD 12,120; trim 8 x 10.75. Circ: 62,000 (controlled); 28,000 (paid).

720 CHE ISSN 0379-8585
NA2542.4
ARCHITECTURE & BEHAVIOUR/ARCHITECTURE ET COMPORTEMENT. Text in English, French. 1980. q. CHF 70 to individuals; CHF 150 to institutions. adv. bk.rev. **Document type:** *Academic/Scholarly.*
Indexed: AIAP, PsycholAb, e-psyche.
Published by: Swiss Federal Institute of Technology, Department of Architecture, Case Postale 555, Lausanne, 1001, Switzerland. FAX 021-6176317. Ed. Kaj Noschis. Circ: 1,000.

720 690 IND ISSN 0003-8652
ARCHITECTURE AND BUILDING INDUSTRY. Text in English. 1969. m. INR 20, USD 7. adv. bk.rev. bibl.; charts; illus. index.
Indexed: AIAP.
Address: 87-88 New Market, Begam Bridge, Meerut, Uttar Pradesh, India. Ed. Balvir Singh.

720 DEU
ARCHITECTURE & COMPETITIONS. Text in German, English. 1939. q. EUR 65; EUR 58 to students; EUR 19.50 newsstand/cover (effective 2003). adv. bk.rev. charts; illus. 72 p./no.; **Document type:** *Magazine, Trade.* **Description:** The international magazine with a topseat focus. Presents a professional thematic forum for architects and planners: theory, trend and competition results.
Former titles: Architektur und Wettbewerbe (0341-2784); Architektur Wettbewerbe (0003-8806)
Indexed: AIAP, API, PsycholAb.
—BLDSC (1602.410000), IE, ingenta.
Published by: Karl Kraemer Verlag, Schulze-Delitzsch-Str 15, Stuttgart, 70565, Germany. TEL 49-711-7849617, FAX 49-711-7849620, info@kraemerverlag.com. Ed. Friedrich Grimm. Pub. Karl Horst Kraemer. R&P, Adv. contact Katharnia Svendsen. B&W page EUR 1,280, color page EUR 1,980; trim 195 x 245. Circ: 3,500.

720 747 NZL
ARCHITECTURE AND DESIGN TRENDS. Text in English. **Document type:** *Consumer.* **Description:** Provides information for professionals involved in specifying products and services for building and design of commercial projects.
Published by: Trends Publishing International Ltd., Private Bag 11-908, Ellerslie, Auckland, New Zealand. TEL 64-9-571-5700, FAX 64-9-571-5701. Ed. Kirsten Khire.

720 DEU ISSN 0944-4718
NA4125
ARCHITECTURE AND DETAIL. Text in German, English, French. 1993. s-a. EUR 30; EUR 15 newsstand/cover (effective 2003). **Document type:** *Magazine, Trade.*
Indexed: API.
Published by: Karl Kraemer Verlag, Schulze-Delitzsch-Str 15, Stuttgart, 70565, Germany. TEL 49-711-784896-0, FAX 49-711-7849620, 101341.3711@compuserve.com, info@kraemerverlag.com. Ed. Ursula Henn. Pub. Karl Horst Kraemer. R&P Gudrun Kraemer.

720 MEX ISSN 1605-5640
ARCHITECTURE AND HUMANITIES. Text in English. 1999. q. bk.rev.
Media: Online - full text. **Related titles:** ♦ Spanish ed.: Arquitectura y Humanidades. ISSN 1605-5632.
Published by: Universidad Nacional Autonoma de Mexico, Facultad de Arquitectura, c/o Arq. Enrique X. de Anda, Circuito Interior de Cd. Universitaria, Deleg. Coyoacan, Mexico City, DF 04510, Mexico. TEL 52-5-6220318, FAX 52-5-6166545, http://www.architecthum.edu.mx/. Ed. Irasema Gallo Ramirez.

720 GBR

ARCHITECTURE AND URBANISM. Variant title: Serial Books. Architecture and Urbanism. Text in English. 1997. s-a. GBP 9.99, USD 14.95 (effective 2001). illus. 64 p./no.; back issues avail. **Document type:** *Monographic series, Academic/Scholarly.* **Description:** Covers issues in contemporary architecture. For general and academic audiences.
Related titles: ♦ Series of: Black Dog Publishing. Serial Books. Design.
Indexed: AIAP, RASB.
Published by: Black Dog Publishing Ltd., 5 Ravenscroft St., London, E2 7JH, United Kingdom. TEL 44-20-7613-1922, FAX 44 20-7613-1944, info@bdp.demon.co.uk. Ed., Pub. Duncan McCorquodale.

720 AUS ISSN 0003-8725
NA1
ARCHITECTURE AUSTRALIA. Text in English. 1904. bi-m. AUD 66 domestic; AUD 105 in Asia & the Pacific; AUD 125 elsewhere (effective 2004). adv. bk.rev. charts; illus. Index. **Document type:** *Magazine, Trade.* **Description:** Features Australian residential, commercial and public architecture, with a blend of news, views and trends.
Formerly: Architecture in Australia
Related titles: Online - full text ed.: ISSN 1442-0945 (from EBSCO Publishing, Florida Center for Library Automation, Gale Group, R M I T Publishing).
Indexed: AIAP, API, AusPAIS, BldManAb, PCI, RASB, WBA, WMB.
—BLDSC (1601.870000), IE, Infotrieve, ingenta.
Published by: (Royal Australian Institute of Architects), Architecture Media, L3, 4 Princes St, Port Melbourne, VIC 3207, Australia. TEL 61-3-96164760, FAX 61-3-96464918, publisher@archmedia.com.au, http://www.archaust.com/aa/, http://www.archmedia.com.au. Eds. Ms. Justine Clarke, Ms. Sue Harris. R&P Ian Close. Adv. contact Ms. Victoria Hawthorne. Circ: 14,363.

720 690 USA ISSN 1099-6346
NA1
ARCHITECTURE BOSTON. Text in English. 1998. bi-m. USD 26 (effective 2005). adv. bk.rev.; Website rev. illus.; tr.lit. 60 p./no.; back issues avail. **Document type:** *Magazine, Trade.* **Description:** Covers practice issues and social concerns of architects and others in the building industry.
Formerly: Boston Society Of Architects Chapterletter
Related titles: Supplement(s):.
Indexed: AIAP.
Published by: Boston Society of Architects, 52 Broad St, Boston, MA 02109-4301. TEL 617-951-1433, FAX 617-951-0845, architectureboston@architects.org, http://www.architects.org. Eds. Elizabeth S Padjen, Richard Fitzgerald. R&P Pamela De Oliveria-Smit. Adv. contact Mark Egan. B&W page USD 2,640, color page USD 3,440; trim 8.5 x 11. Circ: 25,000 (paid and controlled).

720 AUS ISSN 0729-8714
ARCHITECTURE BULLETIN. Text in English. 1944. m. AUD 44. adv. bk.rev. back issues avail. **Document type:** *Newsletter, Academic/Scholarly.* **Description:** Provides information on architectural projects, issues affecting the profession, and news from the NSW Chapter of the RAIA.
Published by: Royal Australian Institute of Architects, New South Wales Chapter, 3 Manning St, Potts Point, NSW 2011, Australia. TEL 61-2-3562955, FAX 61-2-3681164. Ed. Clim Waites. R&P Jim Waites. Adv. contact Tracie Murray. Circ: 3,000.

720 USA ISSN 0738-1131
NA730.C2
ARCHITECTURE CALIFORNIA. Key Title: arcCA. Text in English. 1979. s-a. USD 34 (effective 2005). adv. bk.rev. **Document type:** *Trade.* **Description:** Provides a forum for the exchange of ideas among architects and other disciplines on the issues currently shaping California architecture. Discusses the relationship of the profession to the interests of the public.
Indexed: AIAP.
Published by: American Institute of Architects, California Council, 1303 J St, 200, Sacramento, CA 95814-2916. TEL 916-448-9082, FAX 916-442-5346. Ed. Mike Martin. R&P Erin Wells. Circ: 10,000.

720 FRA ISSN 0003-8695
L'ARCHITECTURE D'AUJOURD'HUI. Text in French, English. 1930. bi-m. EUR 25 per issue (effective 2005). adv. bk.rev. charts; illus.; tr.lit. index. **Document type:** *Magazine, Consumer.*
Formerly: Architecture Francaise (0003-8717)
Indexed: AIAP, API, ASCA, ArtHuCI, ArtInd, BAS, CurCont, DIP, IBR, IBZ, PCI, RASB, SSCI.
—BLDSC (1601.850000), IE, Infotrieve, ingenta. **CCC.**
Published by: Editions Jean - Michel Place, 3 rue Lhomond, Paris, 75005, France. TEL 33-1-44320590, FAX 33-1-44320591, place@jmplace.com, http://www.jmplace.com. Ed. Jean Michel Place. Circ: 19,275.

720 FRA
ARCHITECTURE ET COMMUNICATION. Text in French. 4/yr.
Published by: Maison de l'Architecture, 11 boulevard des Recollets, Toulouse, Cedex 4 31078, France. TEL 61-52-29-71, FAX 61-25-01-44. Ed. Francois Linares. Circ: 4,000.

720 GRC ISSN 0066-6262
ARCHITECTURE IN GREECE/ARCHITECTONIKA THEMATA. Text in Greek; Summaries in English. 1967. a., latest vol.37, 2003. USD 55 (effective 2003). adv. bk.rev. bibl. index. 192 p./no. 3 cols./p.; back issues avail. **Document type:** *Yearbook, Trade.* **Description:** Covers ideas and projects influencing and shaping the human environment in Greece, along with major international trends and development. Includes architectural competitions and student activities.
Indexed: AIAP, API, EIP.
—BLDSC (1601.960000).
Published by: Architecture in Greece Press, PO Box 3545, Athens, 102 10, Greece. TEL 30-210-7225930, FAX 30-210-7213916, http://www.themataarchitects.gr. Ed., Pub., R&P, Adv. contact Orestis B Doumanis. B&W page USD 1,500, color page USD 1,750; trim 21 x 28. Circ: 5,000.

720 USA ISSN 1061-2963
NA2695.U6
ARCHITECTURE IN PERSPECTIVE (NO.). Text in English. 1986. a., latest no.14. USD 45 to non-members; USD 35 to members (effective 2000). **Document type:** *Catalog.* **Description:** Contains a selection of designated entries chosen from the submitted works of illustrators not chosen for the traveling exhibition and an ASAP membership directory.
Published by: American Society of Architectural Perspectivists, 1518 K St NW, Ste 503, Washington, DC 20005. TEL 202-737-4401, FAX 202-638-4833, hq@csap.org, http://www.asap.org. Ed. Gordon Grice. R&P Brian Hutchings.

720 IRL ISSN 1649-5152
ARCHITECTURE IRELAND. Text in English. 1972. 10/yr. EUR 75 domestic; EUR 100 in Europe; EUR 120 elsewhere; EUR 60 domestic to students; EUR 90 in Europe to students; EUR 100 elsewhere to students; EUR 7.26 newsstand/cover (effective 2005). adv. **Document type:** *Magazine, Trade.* **Description:** Covers the latest developments and products of relevance to architects.
Former titles (until 2003): Irish Architect (0790-8342); (until 1987): R I A I Bulletin (0790-2360)
Indexed: AIAP, API.
Published by: (Royal Institute of the Architects of Ireland), Nova Publishing, 8/9 Sandyford Office Park, Sandyford, Dublin, 18, Ireland. TEL 353-1-2958115, FAX 353-1-2959350, http://www.architectureireland.ie/. Circ: 2,500.

720 USA ISSN 1533-4635
NA735.L37
ARCHITECTURE LAS VEGAS. Text in English. 2001. a. USD 4.95 newsstand/cover (effective 2001). adv. **Document type:** *Magazine, Consumer.*
Published by: Las Vegas Life, LLC, 2290 Corporate Cricle Dr., Ste. 250, Henderson, NV 89014. TEL 702-990-2440, FAX 702-990-2444, feedback@lvlife.com, http://www.vegas.com. Ed. Phil Hagen. Pub. Sharon Bates.

720 USA ISSN 0149-9106
NA730.M6
ARCHITECTURE MINNESOTA. Text in English. 1936. bi-m. USD 18; USD 3.50 newsstand/cover (effective 2004). adv. bk.rev. illus.; tr.lit. cum.index. **Document type:** *Magazine.* **Description:** Presents stories of architectural and environmental interest; design and creative living stories covering the upper midwest.
Formerly (until 1974): Northwest Architect (0029-330X)
Indexed: AIAP.
Published by: American Institute of Architects, Minnesota Society, 275 Market St, Ste 54, Minneapolis, MN 55405. TEL 612-338-6763, FAX 612-338-7981, hauschild@aia-mn.org, http://www.aia-mn.org. Ed. Christopher Hudson. Pub. Beverly Hauschild-Baron. Adv. contact Judith Van Dyne. Circ: 9,500 (controlled).

720 NZL ISSN 0113-4566
ARCHITECTURE NEW ZEALAND. Text in English. 1911. bi-m. NZD 34.50. adv. bk.rev. charts; illus. **Document type:** *Trade.* **Description:** Aimed at professional architects. Covers practice, projects, appraisals, and architectural issues in New Zealand.
Former titles (until 1987): New Zealand Architect; New Zealand Institute of Architects Journal (0027-7207)
Indexed: AIAP, API, BHA, INZP.
—BLDSC (1601.978000), IE, ingenta. **CCC.**
Published by: (N Z Institute of Architects), A G M Publishing Ltd., Newmarket, Private Bag 99 915, Auckland, 1031, New Zealand. TEL 64-9-8464068, FAX 64-9-8468742. Ed. Jonathan Mayo. R&P Robin Beckett. Adv. contact Vanessa Mowlen. Circ: 10,000.

720 ISR ISSN 0792-1268
NA1477
ARCHITECTURE OF ISRAEL/ADRICHALUT YISRAELIT. Variant title: A I. Text in English, Hebrew. 1988. q. USD 75 (effective 1998). adv. **Document type:** *Trade.* **Description:** Presents current Israeli architecture, including innovative interpretations of Western architecture and design, within the wider world architecture context.
Indexed: AIAP, API, IHP.
Address: P O Box 302, Herziliya B, Israel. TEL 972-3-6471135, FAX 972-3-6481491, ai@netvision.net.il. Ed. Ami Ran. Adv. contact R Ben Aharon. page USD 2,980. Circ: 13,000.

720 IND ISSN 0970-2369
NA1504
➤ **ARCHITECTURE PLUS DESIGN.** Text in English. 1984. bi-m. INR 430 domestic; INR 1,500, USD 60 foreign; INR 100 newsstand/cover (effective 2000). adv. bk.rev.; video rev. charts; illus.; maps; stat.; tr.lit. back issues avail. **Document type:** *Academic/Scholarly.* **Description:** Architectural projects, building reviews and analyses, articles related to design, architecture, construction, and other related subjects, book reviews, etc. Audience: architects, urban designers and planners, students, builders and professionals.
—BLDSC (1601.075000), IE, ingenta.
Published by: Media Tranasia (India) Pvt. Ltd., K-35 Green Park, New Delhi, 110 016, India. TEL 91-11-6868775, FAX 91-11-686-7641, TELEX 031-73262 MTIL IN, murlim@giasde01.vsnl.net.in. Ed. Suneet Paul. Pub., R&P Xavier Collaco TEL 91-11-6960926. Adv. contact Raju Sarin. B&W page INR 31,000, color page USD 40,000; trim 8.5 x 10.5. Circ: 30,000.

374 USA ISSN 1081-6909
NA2105
ARCHITECTURE SCHOOLS: SPECIAL PROGRAMS. Text in English. 1983. a. USD 12.95 (effective 1999). **Document type:** *Directory.*
Formerly: Off Campus Study Programs: U S and Abroad
Published by: Association of Collegiate Schools of Architecture, Inc., 1735 New York Ave, N W, Washington, DC 20006. TEL 202-785-2324, FAX 202-628-0448. R&P Beth Young. Circ: 500.

▼ **ARCHITECTURE - TECHNOLOGY - CULTURE.** see *LITERATURE*

720 GBR ISSN 0958-6407
ARCHITECTURE TODAY; the independent architectural magazine. Text in English. 1989. 10/yr. GBP 35 domestic; GBP 40 in the European Union; GBP 55 elsewhere (effective 2001). bk.rev. illus.; tr.lit. back issues avail. **Document type:** *Magazine, Trade.* **Description:** Features new buildings and technical information for the practicing architect.
Indexed: AIAP, DAAI.
—BLDSC (1601.994300), IE, ingenta. **CCC.**
Published by: Architecture Today plc., 161 Rosebery Ave, London, EC1R 4QX, United Kingdom. TEL 44-20-8405-5501, FAX 44-20-8405-5521, editorial@archtoday.demon.co.uk. Eds., Pubs. Ian Latham, Mark Swenarton. R&P Ian Latham. Adv. contact Mark Lewis TEL 44-20-7837-0143. Circ: 20,260.
Subscr. to: Reader Service Dept., Garden Hall House, Wellesley Rd, Sutton, Surrey SM2 5BW, United Kingdom.

720 USA
ARCHITECTURE WEEK; the new magazine of design and building. Text in English. w. free; voluntary contributions. adv. **Document type:** *Magazine, Trade.* **Description:** Provides news and features weekly on architecture and construction, digital media, and building culture.
Media: Online - full content.
Published by: Artifice, Inc., PO Box 1588, Eugene, OR 97440. editor@architectureweek.com, http:// www.architectureweek.com/today.html. Ed. Kevin Matthews.

720 USA
ARCHITECTURESOUTH. Text in English. 1996. q.
Media: Online - full text.
Published by: Point Communications, 1111 Battlewood St, Franklin, TN 37069. http://www.specsite.com/W_grfx/ 007.a.html.

720 307.1 POL ISSN 1429-7507
NA1.A1
ARCHITECTUS. Text in Polish; Summaries in English. 1997. s-a. PLZ 18 (effective 2005). **Document type:** *Academic/Scholarly.* **Description:** Covers the theory of architecture, contemporary and historic esthetics, and urban planning.
Published by: (Politechnika Wroclawska/Wroclaw University of Technology, Wydzial Architektury), Oficyna Wydawnicza Politechniki Wroclawskiej, Wybrzeze Wyspianskiego 27, Wroclaw, 50370, Poland. TEL 48-71-3202994, oficwyd@pwr.wroc.pl, http://www.pwr.wroc.pl/~oficwyd/ #OFICYNA. Ed. Ewa Luzyniecka. R&P Halina Dudek. **Dist. by:** Ars Polona, Krakowskie Przedmiescie 7, Warsaw, Poland. TEL 48-22-9263914, FAX 48-22-9265334, arspolona@arspolona.com.pl, http://www.arspolona.com.pl.

720 DEU ISSN 0003-875X
NA3
DER ARCHITEKT. Text in German. 1951. m. EUR 110 domestic; EUR 137 foreign; EUR 10 newsstand/cover (effective 2001). adv. bk.rev. index. **Document type:** *Magazine, Trade.* **Description:** Forum for debate on a variety of architectural topics.
Indexed: AIAP, DIP, IBR, IBZ, PCI, RASB.

A

Published by: (Bund Deutscher Architekten), Verlagsgesellschaft Rudolf Mueller GmbH & Co. KG, Stolberger Str 84, Cologne, 50933, Germany. TEL 49-221-5497-0, FAX 49-221-5497326, der.architekt@rudolf-mueller.de, http://www.rudolf-mueller.de. Circ: 8,795. **Subscr. in the Americas to:** John Wiley & Sons, Inc., 111 River St, Hoboken, NJ 07030-5774. TEL 201-748-6645, FAX 201-748-6088, subinfo@wiley.com; **Subscr. to:** Wiley - V C H Verlag GmbH & Co. KGaA. TEL 49-6201-606147, FAX 49-6201-606117; **Subscr. to:** John Wiley & Sons Ltd., The Atrium, Southern Gate, Chichester, West Sussex PO19 8SQ, United Kingdom. TEL 44-1243-779777, FAX 44-1243-775878, cs-journals@wiley.co.uk.

720 CZE ISSN 0862-7010
NA4.5
ARCHITEKT. Text in Czech, Slovak. 1955. m. CZK 1,200 domestic; CZK 3,660 in Europe; CZK 5,784 elsewhere (effective 2005). adv. bk.rev. **Document type:** *Journal, Trade.*
Formerly (until 1990): Ceskoslovensky Architekt (0009-0697)
Indexed: AIAP.
Published by: Obec Architektu, Mikulandska 6, Prague, 11000, Czech Republic. redakce@architekt.cz, http://www.casopis-architekt.cz, http://www.architekt.cz. Ed. Jiri Horsky. Adv. contact Marie Kubacova. B&W page CZK 59,000; 297 x 210. Circ: 6,000.

720 POL ISSN 1509-1732
ARCHITEKT (WARSZAWA). Text in Polish. 2000. m. EUR 87 foreign (effective 2005). **Document type:** *Journal, Trade.*
Published by: Wydawnictwo Kwiecinski, ul Grojecka 186 lok 613, Warsaw, 02390, Poland. TEL 48-22-8225049, FAX 48-22-8222039, domyjednorodzinne@kwiecinski.pl, http://www.kwiecinski.pl. **Dist. by:** Ars Polona, Krakowskie Przedmiescie 7, Warsaw, Poland. TEL 48-22-9263914, FAX 48-22-9265334, arspolona@arspolona.com.pl, http://www.arspolona.com.pl.

720 DEU ISSN 0724-7699
ARCHITEKTEN- UND INGENIEURHANDBUCH. Text in German. 1977. a. adv. index. back issues avail. **Document type:** *Journal, Trade.*
Formerly (until 1981): Architektenkammer Schleswig-Holstein. Architektenhandbuch (0344-8290)
Published by: (Architekten- und Ingenieurkammer Schleswig-Holstein), Architektur Verlag Nord GmbH, Schlossstr 5-7, Eutin, 23701, Germany. TEL 49-4521-779250, FAX 49-4521-779260.

720 CZE ISSN 0862-7002
ARCHITEKTU. Text in Czech; Summaries in English. 1938. a. CZK 60, USD 30 (effective 2000).
Formerly (until 1990): Architektura C S R (0300-5305)
Indexed: AIAP, API, BHA, RASB.
Published by: Obec Architektu, Mikulandska 6, Prague, 11000, Czech Republic. Ed. Jiri Horsky. Circ: 6,000.

720 AUT ISSN 1606-4550
ARCHITEKTUR; das oesterreichische Fachmagazin. Text in German. 199?. 8/yr. EUR 50.14 domestic; EUR 68.51 foreign (effective 2003). **Document type:** *Magazine, Trade.*
Related titles: Online - full text ed.: ISSN 1605-8054.
Published by: Laser Verlag GmbH, Hochstr 103, Perchtoldsdorf, 2380, Austria. TEL 43-1-8695829, FAX 43-1-8695820, laser@architektur-online.com, http://www.architektur-online.at. Ed., Pub. Silvia Laser. Circ: 7,000 (controlled).

720 AUT ISSN 0570-6602
➤ **ARCHITEKTUR AKTUELL.** Text in German, English. 1967. m. EUR 95 to institutions (effective 2005). adv. bk.rev. abstr. back issues avail.; reprints avail. **Document type:** *Journal, Academic/Scholarly.* **Description:** Offers a comprehensive overview of the most important events in Austrian and international architecture, interior design, urban planning, rural construction and news from the building industry.
Related titles: Online - full text ed.
Indexed: DIP, IBR, IBZ, RASB.
—IE. **CCC.**
Published by: Springer-Verlag Wien (Subsidiary of: Springer Science+Business Media) journals@springer.at, http://www.springer.at. Ed. Matthias Boeckl. R&P Angela Foessl TEL 43-1-3302415517. Adv. contact Michael Katzenberger TEL 43-1-3302415220. B&W page EUR 2,260, color page EUR 3,616; 180 x 260. Circ: 7,500. **Subscr. in the Americas to:** Springer-Verlag New York, Inc., Journal Fulfillment, PO Box 2485, Secaucus, NJ 07096-2485. TEL 800-777-4643, 201-348-4033, FAX 201-348-4505, journals@springer-ny.com, http://www.springer-ny.com.

720 DEU
ARCHITEKTUR OBJEKTE. Text in German. 1993. bi-m. EUR 10 newsstand/cover (effective 2004). adv. **Document type:** *Magazine, Trade.*
Published by: BAUVE AG i.G., Kirchdorfer Str 87, Bad Woerishofen, 86825, Germany. TEL 49-82473800, FAX 49-8247-380100, information@bauve.de, http://www.bauve.de. adv.: B&W page EUR 3,502, color page EUR 4,882. Circ: 7,523 (paid and controlled).

720 AUT ISSN 1026-8413
ARCHITEKTUR & BAU FORUM. Text in German. fortn. EUR 60 domestic; EUR 103 foreign; EUR 35 to students (effective 2005). adv. illus. **Document type:** *Magazine, Trade.* **Description:** Reports on news and trends in architecture.
Related titles: ◆ Supplement(s): Architektur & Bau News. ISSN 1727-480X; ◆ Architektur und Bauforum Newsletter.
Indexed: AIAP, DIP.
—BLDSC (1602.389900), IE.
Published by: Oesterreichischer Wirtschaftsverlag GmbH (Subsidiary of: Sueddeutscher Verlag GmbH), Wiedner Hauptstr 120-124, Vienna, W 1051, Austria. TEL 43-1-546640, FAX 43-1-54664406, architektur@oewv.at, office@wirtschaftsverlag.at, http://www.wirtschaftsverlag.at. Ed. Konrad E O Fischer. Adv. contact Andreas Hofstaetter. color page EUR 3,900; trim 300 x 440. Circ: 8,442 (paid and controlled).

720 AUT ISSN 1727-480X
ARCHITEKTUR & BAU NEWS. Text in German. 1999. fortn. **Document type:** *Journal, Trade.*
Related titles: ◆ Supplement to: Architektur & Bau Forum. ISSN 1026-8413.
—BLDSC (1602.389960).
Published by: Oesterreichischer Wirtschaftsverlag GmbH (Subsidiary of: Sueddeutscher Verlag GmbH), Wiedner Hauptstr 120-124, Vienna, W 1051, Austria. TEL 43-1-546640, FAX 43-1-54664406, office@wirtschaftsverlag.at, http://www.wirtschaftsverlag.at. Ed. Konrad E O Fischer. Circ: 14,400.

720 690 AUT
ARCHITEKTUR UND BAUFORUM NEWSLETTER. Text in German. m. **Document type:** *Newsletter, Trade.*
Related titles: ◆ Supplement to: Architektur & Bau Forum. ISSN 1026-8413.
Published by: Oesterreichischer Wirtschaftsverlag GmbH (Subsidiary of: Sueddeutscher Verlag GmbH), Wiedner Hauptstr 120-124, Vienna, W 1051, Austria. TEL 43-1-54664, FAX 43-1-54664360, office@oewv.at, office@wirtschaftsverlag.at, http://www.oewv.at, http://www.wirtschaftsverlag.at. Ed. Konrad Fischer.

720 747 CHE ISSN 1010-5778
ARCHITEKTUR UND LADENBAU; europaeische Fachzeitschrift fuer modernen Ladenbau, Schaufenster und Auslage. Text in German. 1964. bi-m. CHF 58; CHF 83 foreign. adv. bk.rev. **Document type:** *Trade.* **Description:** Trade news about modern shop-design, window display and architecture.
Former titles (until 1982): Ladenbau (0458-6123); Architektur und Ladenbau
Indexed: AIAP.
Published by: (Fachgruppe Ladenbau), S H Z Fachverlag AG, Alte Landstr 43, Kuesnacht Zh, 8700, Switzerland. TEL 01-9108022, FAX 01-9105155. Ed. Esther Bollmann. Circ: 4,100.

720 CHE
ARCHITEKTUR UND TECHNIK. Text in German. 1977. m. CHF 29; CHF 4 newsstand/cover (effective 2001). adv. bk.rev. **Document type:** *Magazine, Trade.*
Published by: B & L Verlags AG, Steinwiesenstr 3, Schlieren, 8952, Switzerland. TEL 41-1-7333999, FAX 41-1-7333989, info@blverlag.ch, http://www.blverlag.ch. Ed. Manuel Pestalozzi. Circ: 9,000 (paid).

720 DEU ISSN 0171-7928
ARCHITEKTUR UND WOHNEN. Text in German; Summaries in English. 1968. bi-m. EUR 39; EUR 7.50 newsstand/cover (effective 2005). adv. **Document type:** *Magazine, Consumer.*
Incorporates (1980-1997): Ambiente (0174-3139); Formerly (until 1971): Architektur und Kultiviertes Wohnen (0003-8784)
Indexed: AIAP, DIP, IBR, IBZ, RASB.
Published by: Jahreszeiten Verlag GmbH (Subsidiary of: Ganske Verlagsgruppe), Possmoorweg 5, Hamburg, 22301, Germany. TEL 49-40-27170, FAX 49-40-27172056, redaktion@architektur-und-wohnen.de, jahreszeitenverlag@jalag.de, http://www.jalag.de/zundz/archi/index.html. Ed. Barbara Friedrich. Pub. Thomas Ganske. Adv. contact Roberto Sprengel. B&W page EUR 11,700, color page EUR 15,300. Circ: 88,562 (paid and controlled).

720 SVK ISSN 0044-8680
➤ **ARCHITEKTURA & URBANIZMUS/ARCHITECTURE AND TOWN PLANNING;** journal for architecture and town planning theory. Text and summaries in Czech, English, Slovak. 1966. q. USD 88 foreign (effective 2005). adv. bk.rev. charts; illus.; abstr. 80 p./no. 2 cols./p.; **Document type:** *Journal, Academic/Scholarly.* **Description:** Publishes works on the theory of architecture, town planning and theory of creation of life environment. For architects, both in research and projects, constructors, museums and memorial personnels, university teachers students.
Indexed: API, ArtHuCI, CurCont, EIP, RASB.
Published by: (Slovenska Akademia Vied, Ustav Stavebnictva a Architektury/Slovak Academy of Sciences, Institute of Construction and Architecture), Slovak Academic Press Ltd., Nam Slobody 6, PO Box 57, Bratislava, 81005, Slovakia. usardula@savba.sk, sap@sappress.sk, http://www.ustarch.sav.sk/Dpt/Arch/Archjour/archjour.html, http://www.sappress.sk. Eds. Henrieta Moravcikova, M Dulla. Adv. contact Henrieta Moravcikova.

720 POL ISSN 1232-6372
ARCHITEKTURA - MURATOR. Text in Polish; Summaries in English. 1947. m. EUR 75 foreign (effective 2005). bk.rev. abstr.; bibl.; charts; illus. index. **Document type:** *Magazine, Trade.* **Description:** Includes architectural competitions, history of architecture, professional information, design, art, information about real estate.
Formerly (until 1994): Architektura (0003-8814)
Related titles: Online - full text ed.: ISSN 1689-0507.
Indexed: AIAP, API, BHA.
Published by: (Stowarzyszenie Architektow Polskich - SARP), Wydawnictwo Murator Sp. z o.o., ul Kamionkowska 45, Warsaw, 03812, Poland. TEL 48-22-5905000, FAX 48-22-5905444, architektura_info@murator.com.pl, wydawnictwo@murator.com.pl, http://www.architektura-murator.pl, http://www.murator.com.pl. Ed. Ewa Przestaszewska Porebska. Pub. Zygmunt Stepinski. Adv. contact Anna Piela. Circ: 21,000. **Dist. by:** Ars Polona, Krakowskie Przedmiescie 7, Warsaw, Poland. TEL 48-22-9263914, FAX 48-22-9265334, arspolona@arspolona.com.pl, http://www.arspolona.com.pl.

720 ITA ISSN 0003-8822
L'ARCHITETTO. Text in Italian. 1955. m. (10/yr.). adv. **Document type:** *Magazine, Trade.*
Indexed: API.
Published by: Consiglio Nazionale di Architetti, Pianificatori, Paesaggisti e Conservatori, Via di Santa Maria dell'Anima 10, Rome, 00186, Italy. TEL 39-06-6889901, FAX 39-06-6879520, http://www.archiworld.it. Ed. Massimo Gallione. Circ: 75,000.

720 ITA ISSN 0003-8830
NA4
ARCHITETTURA (MILAN); cronache e storia. Text in Multiple languages. 1955. m. adv. bk.rev. charts; illus. index, cum.index: vols.1-54. back issues avail.
Related titles: Online - full text ed.: (from H.W. Wilson, O C L C Online Computer Library Center, Inc.).
Indexed: AIAP, ArtInd, PCI, RASB.
—BLDSC (1602.570000), IE.
Published by: Mancosu Editore, Via Alfredo Fusco 71, Rome, 00136, Italy. TEL 39-06-351921, FAX 39-06-35409791, http://www.mancosueditore.it.

720 ITA
➤ **ARCHITETTURA & ARTE.** Text in Italian. 1998. q. EUR 40 domestic; EUR 60 foreign (effective 2005). adv. bk.rev. back issues avail. **Document type:** *Academic/Scholarly.* **Description:** Covers various aspects of architecture including history as well as problems in today's architecture.
Related titles: Online - full text ed.
Published by: Angelo Pontecorboli Editore, Via Carrand 22, Florence, 50133, Italy. TEL 39-055-5520903, FAX 39-055-5528456, angelo@pontecorboli.it, http://www.pontecorboli.it. Circ: 700.

720 ITA ISSN 1123-2803
ARCHITETTURA. STORIA E DOCUMENTI. Text in Italian. 1975. s-a. **Document type:** *Journal, Academic/Scholarly.*
Published by: Gangemi Editore, Piazza San Pantaleo 4, Rome, Italy. TEL 39-06-6872774, FAX 39-06-68806189, gangemieditorerc@tin.it, http://www.gangemieditore.it.

720 ITA
ARCHITETTURA URBANISTICA: METODI DI PROGRAMMAZIONE E PROGETTI. Text in Italian. 1975. irreg., latest vol.5, 1978. price varies. **Document type:** *Monographic series, Academic/Scholarly.*
Published by: Giardini Editori e Stampatori (Subsidiary of: Libra Web), Via Giosue Carducci 60, Ghezzano - La Fontina, Pisa 56123, Italy. TEL 39-050-878066, FAX 39-050-878732, giardinieditori@giardinieditori.it, http://www.libraweb.net. Ed. Giacomo Donato.

720 CHE ISSN 1010-4089
NA1.A1
ARCHITHESE. Text in German. 1914. bi-m. CHF 159; CHF 124 to students (effective 2003). **Document type:** *Journal, Academic/Scholarly.*
Former titles (until 1980): Werk-Archithese (0257-9359); (until 1977): Archithese (1010-3600)
Indexed: AIAP, API, ArtInd, BHA, DIP, IBR, IBZ, PCI.
—BLDSC (1602.650000), IE, ingenta.
Published by: Verlag Niggli AG, Steinackerstr 8, Sulgen, 8583, Switzerland. TEL 41-71-6449111, FAX 41-71-6449190, info@niggli.ch, http://www.niggli.ch.

720 USA ISSN 1066-6516
NA1
➤ **ARCHITRONIC;** the electronic journal of architecture. Text in English. 1992. 3/yr. bk.rev. illus. reprints avail. **Document type:** *Academic/Scholarly.* **Description:** Explores the new ranges of architectural communication available through digital media. Serves as a platform for both presenting and reviewing research as a journal, and a forum for stimulating dialogue on emerging ideas.
Media: Online - full text.
Indexed: AIAP.
Published by: Kent State University, School of Architecture and Environmental Design, Kent, OH 44242-0001. TEL 330-672-2869, FAX 330-672-3809, robison@saed.kent.edu, http://www.saed.kent.edu/Architronic/. Ed. Elwin C Robison.

▼ new title ➤ refereed ✶ unverified ◆ full entry avail.

720 690 POL ISSN 1506-5928
ARCHIVOLTA; architektura, wnetrza, inwestycje, konstrukcje, technologie, materialy. Text in Polish. 1999. q.
Address: Ul Lubicz 25, pok. 712, Krakow, 31503, Poland. TEL 48-12-6197120, FAX 48-12-6197469, archivolta@archivolta.com.pl, http://www.archivolta.com.pl. Ed. Krystyna Januszkiewicz.

720 ESP
ARCHIVOS DE ARQUITECTURA: ESPANA SIGLO XX. Text in Spanish. s-a. **Document type:** *Monographic series.*
Description: Selects significant works of Spanish contemporary architecture, with a critical and descriptive approach, within the historical and social context in which they were produced.
Published by: Colegio de Arquitectos de Almeria, Martinez Campos, 29, Almeria, 04002, Spain. TEL 34-950-231440, FAX 34-950-262265.

720 DEU ISSN 0587-3452
NA3
ARCHPLUS; Zeitschrift fuer Architektur, Staedtebau und Design. Text in German. 1968. 4/yr. EUR 49 domestic; EUR 57 foreign; EUR 14 newsstand/cover (effective 2005). adv. bk.rev. bibl.; illus. index. **Document type:** *Magazine, Trade.*
Related titles: Online - full text ed.
Indexed: AIAP, DIP, IBR, IBZ.
—IE, Infotrieve.
Published by: ARCH+ Verlag GmbH, Charlottenstr 14, Aachen, 52070, Germany. TEL 49-241-508303, FAX 49-241-54831, aachen@archplus.net, http://www.archplus.net. Eds. Dr. Nikolaus Kuhnert, Sabine Kraft. Adv. contact Gabriele Lauscher-Dreess TEL 49-241-508303. B&W page EUR 2,710, color page EUR 4,555; trim 188 x 269. Circ: 7,733 (paid).

AREA (MILAN, 1990); rivista internazionale di architettura e arti del progetto. see *HOUSING AND URBAN PLANNING*

720 BGR ISSN 0861-4008
TH4
ARH & ART BORSA. Text in Bulgarian, English. 1992. w. BGL 0.20 newsstand/cover (effective 2002). **Document type:** *Newspaper, Academic/Scholarly.* **Description:** Publishes information on practices, achievements and tendencies in Bulgarian and international architecture, including discussion of such issues in contemporary architecture as aesthetics, philosophy and art, and its role in the material and cultural developments at the turn of the 21st century. The newspaper has established and supports the Architect of the Year Prize and the Architecture Student of the Year Prize, awarded annually since 1995.
Published by: (Chamber of Architects, Suiuz na Arkhitektite v Bulgaria/Union of Bulgarian Architects), ARH & ART Association, 8A Hristo Georgiev St, Sofia, 1504, Bulgaria. TEL 359-2-444871, FAX 359-2-467031, http://www.sca.bg/cultural-periodicals/catalog/arh.htm. Ed. Lenko Petkov.

720 ROM ISSN 0300-5356
ARHITECTURA. Text in Romanian; Summaries in English. 1906. q. USD 20 (effective 1995). adv. bk.rev. abstr.; bibl.; illus.; stat. index. **Document type:** *Academic/Scholarly.*
Indexed: AIAP, API, BHA, EEA, RASB.
Published by: Uniunea Arhitectilor din Romania/Union of Romanian Architects, Str. Academiei 18-20, Sector 1, Bucharest, 70109, Romania. TEL 401-6138080 ext. 183, FAX 401-3120956. Ed. Augustin Ioan. Adv. contact Mariana Celac. Circ: 1,000.

720 HRV ISSN 0350-3666
NA4.5
➤ **ARHITEKTURA**; Croatian Architects Association scholar architectural magazine. Text in Croatian; Summaries in English. 1947. a., latest 2002. HRK 120 per vol. domestic; USD 30 per vol. foreign (effective 2004). adv. bk.rev. index. **Document type:** *Magazine, Academic/Scholarly.*
Indexed: AIAP, BHA.
Published by: Udruzenje Hrvatskih Arhitekata, Trg Bana Jelacica 3-1, Zagreb, 10000, Croatia. TEL 385-1-4816151, FAX 385-1-4816197, daz@zg.hinet.hr, http://www.d-a-z.hr. Ed. Krunoslaw Ivanisin. Adv. contact Maja Trinajstic. Circ: 1,000.

711.4 SCG ISSN 0354-6055
ARHITEKTURA I URBANIZAM; casopis za prostorno planiranje, urbanizam i arhitekturu. Text in Serbo-Croatian. 1960. irreg.
Formerly (until 1994): Arhitektura, Urbanizam (0004-1238)
Indexed: AIAP.
Published by: Institut za Arhitekturu i Urbanizam Srbije, Bulevar Revolucije 73-II, Belgrade. Ed. Zoran Manevic.

720 DNK ISSN 1600-3993
ARK.BYG; arkitekt- og byggebladet. Text in Danish. 1963. 11/yr. (10/yr.). DKK 804 domestic; DKK 912 elsewhere (effective 2003). adv. **Document type:** *Trade.* **Description:** Features articles on subjects relevant to Danish architecture and engineering.
Former titles (until 2002): A D A (0908-1690); (until 1993): D P A (0105-6603); Incorporates (1961-1967): Modul (0026-8798)
Published by: (Associerede Danske Arkitekter), Aller Business AS, Marielundsvej 46 D, Herlev, 2730, Denmark. TEL 45-44-858899, FAX 45-44-858887, info@arkbyg.dk, info@allerbusiness.dk, http://www.arkbyg.dk, http://www.allerbusiness.dk. Ed. Flemming Holten Nielsen. Adv. contact Per Bosholdt. B&W page DKK 15,700, color page DKK 21,630; 265 x 176. Circ: 9,000.

720 BGR ISSN 0324-1254
NA 9
ARKHITEKTURA. Text in Bulgarian; Summaries in English. 1954. 6/yr. USD 92 (effective 2002). adv. **Document type:** *Journal.*
Description: Publishes papers on architectural design, architectural theory and practice, criticism.
Indexed: API, RASB.
Published by: Suiuz na Arkhitektite v Bulgaria/Union of Bulgarian Architects, 11 Krakra, Sofia, 1504, Bulgaria. TEL 359-2-876513, FAX 359-2-23569. Ed. Rossen Valkov. Circ: 4,500. **Dist. by:** Foreign Trade Co. "Hemus", 1-B Raiko Dashalov Pl, Sofia 1000, Bulgaria. TEL 359-2-871686, FAX 359-2-9803319. **Co-sponsor:** Ministerstvo na Stroezhite i Arkhitekturata.

720 BLR
ARKHITEKTURA I STROITEL'STVO. Text in Russian. bi-m. USD 115 in United States. **Document type:** *Government.*
Published by: Ministry of Architecture and Building, Masherova pr 23, bld 1, bur 704, Minsk, 220000, Belarus. TEL 375-172-226-6939. **US dist. addr.:** East View Information Services, 3020 Harbor Ln. N., Minneapolis, MN 55447. TEL 612-550-0961.

720 RUS ISSN 0235-7259
TH4
ARKHITEKTURA I STROITEL'STVO ROSSII. Text in Russian. 1960. m. USD 120. charts; illus. index.
Formerly (until 1989): Na Stroikakh Rossii (0027-7312)
Indexed: ChemAb, RASB, RefZh.
—East View.
Address: Myasnitskaya ul 40, str 6, Moscow, 101000, Russian Federation. TEL 7-095-9219383, FAX 7-095-9219296. Ed. Aleksandr M Sidorin. **Dist. by:** M K - Periodica, ul Gilyarovskogo 39, Moscow 129110, Russian Federation. TEL 7-095-2845008, FAX 7-095-2813798, info@periodicals.ru, http://www.mkniga.ru; **US dist. addr.:** East View Information Services, 3020 Harbor Ln. N., Minneapolis, MN 55447. TEL 612-550-0961.

720 BGR
ARKHITEKTURA, TEORIYA, ISTORIYA/ARCHITECTURE, THEORY, HISTORY. Text in Bulgarian. 1987. irreg.
Published by: (Bulgarian Academy of Sciences, Center for Architectural Studies), Universitetsko Izdatelstvo Sv. Kliment Okhridski/Publishing House of the Sofia University St. Kliment Ohridski, 15 Tsar Osvoboditel Blvd., Sofia, 1504, Bulgaria. TEL 359-2-9792914.

ARKHITEKTURA UKRAINY. see *BUILDING AND CONSTRUCTION*

720 DNK ISSN 0004-198X
NA6
➤ **ARKITEKTEN.** Text in Danish. 1957. 15/yr. DKK 1,370 domestic; DKK 1,389 in Scandinavia; DKK 1,439 in Europe; DKK 1,494 in Greenland; DKK 1,784 elsewhere (effective 2005). adv. bk.rev. charts; illus. index. 64 p./no. 4 cols./p.; back issues avail. **Document type:** *Journal, Academic/Scholarly.* **Description:** Professional news for architects, such as new projects, competitions, urban renewal, building conditions, and design.
Formed by the merger of (1898-1957): Arkitekten. Ugehefte (0903-2355); (1927-1957): Arkitekten. Maanedshefte (0903-2347); Both of which superseded in part (1898-1926): Architekten (0903-2339); Which was formerly (until 1901): Akademisk Architektforening. Meddelelser (0903-2320)
Related titles: CD-ROM ed.; Diskette ed.
Indexed: AIAP, API, BHA, RASB.
Published by: Arkitektens Forlag/Danish Architectural Press, Overgaden oven Vandet 10, Copenhagen K, 1415, Denmark. TEL 45-32-836900, FAX 45-32-836941, red@arkfo.dk, info@arkfo.dk, http://www.arkfo.dk. Eds. Joergen Hegner Christiansen, Lars Nevald, Kim Dirckinck Holmfeld. Adv. contact Steffen Petersen. B&W page DKK 20,500, color page DKK 25,000; 208 x 270. Circ: 8,682. **Co-sponsor:** Akademisk Arkitektforening/Architects Association in Denmark.

720 SWE ISSN 0347-058X
ARKITEKTEN. Text in Swedish. 1975. 11/yr. SEK 477 domestic; SEK 800 in Europe; SEK 900 elsewhere; SEK 65 per issue (effective 2005). adv. **Document type:** *Magazine, Trade.*
Incorporates (1970-2002): A T - Arkitekttidningen (0004-2005); Former titles (until vol.4, 1976): Tidning foer Arkitektfoerbundet; (until vol.3, 1976): Arkitekten; (until vol.1-2, 1976): Tidning foer Arkitektfoerbundet
Related titles: Online - full text ed.
Published by: Sveriges Arkitekter/Swedish Association of Architects, Ansgariegatan 5, PO Box 9225, Stockholm, 10273, Sweden. TEL 46-8-50557700, FAX 46-8-50557705, arkitekten@arkitekt.se, kansli@arkitekt.se, http://www.arkitekt.se/arkitekten. Ed., Pub. Per Lander. adv.: B&W page SEK 17,000, color page SEK 24,000; 193 x 247. Circ: 10,000.

720 SWE
ARKITEKTEN (STOCKHOLM, 2002). Text in Swedish. 2002. 11/yr. SEK 477 domestic; SEK 650 in Europe; SEK 750 elsewhere (effective 2003). adv.
Published by: Sveriges Arkitekter/Swedish Association of Architects, Ansgariegatan 5, PO Box 9225, Stockholm, 10273, Sweden. TEL 46-8-50557700, FAX 46-8-50557705, arkitekten@arkitekt.se, http://www.arkitekt.se. Ed., Pub. Per Lander. adv.: B&W page SEK 9,000, color page SEK 13,500; 193 x 121. Circ: 10,000.

720 NOR ISSN 0004-1998
ARKITEKTNYTT. Text in Norwegian. 1951. fortn. (20/yr.). NOK 525 in Norway Includes Norske Arkitektkonkurranser; NOK 610 in Scandinavia Includes Norske Arkitektkonkurranser; NOK 735 in Europe Includes Norske Arkitektkonkurranser; NOK 830 elsewhere Includes Norske Arkitektkonkurranser (effective 2001). adv. bk.rev. bibl.; illus. index. back issues avail. **Document type:** *Magazine, Trade.*
Indexed: BHA.
—CCC.
Published by: Norske Arkitekters Landsforbund/National Association of Norwegian Architects, Josefines Gate 34, Oslo, 0351, Norway. TEL 47-23-33-25-00, FAX 47-23-33-25-50, arkitektnytt@arkitektnytt.no, http://www.arkitektnytt.no. Ed. Bente Sand. Adv. contact Tom Andresen. Circ: 5,000.
Co-sponsors: Norske Interioerarkitekters Landsforening; Norske Landskapsarkitekters Forening.

720 SWE ISSN 0004-2021
NA6.S85
ARKITEKTUR; the Swedish review of architecture. Text in Swedish; Summaries in English. 1901. 8/yr. SEK 580 Sweden, Norway & Iceland; SEK 725 Denmark & Finland; SEK 1,125 in the European Union; SEK 1,125.01 elsewhere (effective 2001). adv. charts; illus. index. back issues avail. **Document type:** *Magazine, Trade.* **Description:** Provides varying and composite pictures of building and environment in Sweden.
Indexed: AIAP, API, BHA, RASB, RILM.
—BLDSC (1673.600000), IE, ingenta.
Published by: Arkitektur Foerlag AB, PO Box 1742, Stockholm, 11187, Sweden. TEL 46-8-679-61-05, FAX 46-8-611-52-70, redaktionen@arkitektur.se, http://www.arkitektur.se. Ed. Olof Hultin. Adv. contact Suzanne Murray. B&W page SEK 15,600, color page SEK 23,700; trim 190 x 270. Circ: 6,600 (controlled).

720.9489 DNK ISSN 0004-2013
NA6
➤ **ARKITEKTUR DK.** Text in Danish, English, German. 1957. 8/yr. DKK 1,200 domestic; DKK 1,105 in Europe excl. tax; DKK 1,235 elsewhere excl. tax (effective 2005). adv. charts; illus. index. 80 p./no. 2 cols./p.; **Document type:** *Journal, Academic/Scholarly.* **Description:** Portraits of new Danish architecture focusing on new houses, city spaces, sports buildings, churces, and museums.
Formerly (until 1972): Arkitektur (0900-3819)
Indexed: AIAP, API, BHA, EIP, RASB.
—BLDSC (1673.612000), IE.
Published by: Arkitektens Forlag/Danish Architectural Press, Overgaden oven Vandet 10, Copenhagen K, 1415, Denmark. TEL 45-32-836900, FAX 45-32-836941, red@arkfo.dk, info@arkfo.dk, http://www.arkfo.dk. Eds. Martin Keiding, Kim Dirckinck Holmfeld. Adv. contact Steffen Petersen. B&W page DKK 17,800, color page DKK 22,300; 208 x 270. Circ: 4,594.

720 FIN ISSN 0783-3660
NA6
ARKKITEHTI/FINNISH ARCHITECTURAL REVIEW/FINSK ARKITEKTURTIDSKRIFT. Text in Finnish, Swedish; Summaries in English. 1903. 6/yr. EUR 82 domestic; EUR 97 In Nordic and Baltic countries; EUR 130 in Europe; EUR 108 elsewhere (effective 2004). adv. bk.rev. bibl.; charts; illus. **Document type:** *Journal, Trade.*
Formerly (until 1921): A R K; Incorporates (1903-1951): Arkitekten (0782-789X)
Related titles: ♦ Supplement(s): Arkkitehtuurikilpailuja. ISSN 0066-7676.
Indexed: AIAP, API, BHA, EIP, RASB.
—IE, Infotrieve.
Published by: Suomen Arkkitehtiliitto/Finnish Association of Architects, Runeberginkatu 5 A, Helsinki, 00100, Finland. TEL 358-9-584448, FAX 358-9-58444222, ark@safa.fi/ark, http://www.ark.fi/, http://www.safa.fi. Ed. Harri Hautajaervi TEL 358-9-58444220. Circ: 5,300.

720 FIN ISSN 0044-8915
ARKKITEHTIUUTISET/ARKITEKTNYTT. Text in Finnish. 1948. 16/yr. EUR 38 domestic; EUR 46 in Scandinavia and Baltic countries; EUR 51 in Europe; EUR 53 elsewhere (effective 2005). adv. bk.rev. illus. **Document type:** *Newsletter, Trade.*
Published by: Suomen Arkkitehtiliitto/Finnish Association of Architects, Runeberginkatu 5 A, Helsinki, 00100, Finland. TEL 358-9-584448, FAX 358-9-58444222, au@safa.fi, safa@safa.fi, http://www.safa.fi. Ed. Tuomo Sirkia. Circ: 4,700.

720 FIN ISSN 0066-7676
ARKKITEHTUURIKILPAILUJA. Text in Finnish. 1967. irreg.
Description: Updates on architectural competitions in Finland.
Related titles: ♦ Supplement to: Arkkitehti. ISSN 0783-3660.
Indexed: AIAP.

Published by: Suomen Arkkitehtiliitto/Finnish Association of Architects, Runeberginkatu 5 A, Helsinki, 00100, Finland. TEL 358-9-584448, FAX 358-9-58444222, http://www.safa.fi. Ed. Pirjo Pekkarinen TEL 358-9-58444215.

720 690   ITA
➤ **ARKOS**; scienza e restauro. Text in Italian. 2000. q. EUR 37; EUR 9 newsstand/cover. adv. **Document type:** *Magazine, Academic/Scholarly.* **Description:** Contains articles and research on architectural restoration.
Published by: U T E T SpA, via Montefeltro 6/a, Milano, MI 20156, Italy. FAX 39-02-38086626, arkos@utetperiodici.it, abonnamenti@utetperiodici.it, http://www.utetperiodici.it/ark/ark, http://www.utet.com. Ed. Adolfo Pasetti. Pub., R&P Corrado Trevisan. Adv. contact Andrea Ferriani. color page EUR 2,066. Circ: 8,000 (paid).

720   ESP   ISSN 1695-2731
ARQUEOLOGIA DE LA ARQUITECTURA. Text in Multiple languages. 2002. a. EUR 40 (effective 2004). **Document type:** *Journal, Academic/Scholarly.*
Published by: Universidad del Pais Vasco, Servicio Editorial, Apartado 1397, Bilbao, 48080, Spain. TEL 34-94-6015126, FAX 34-94-4801314, luxedito@lg.ehu.es, http://www.ehu.es/servicios/se_az/.

711.4   ARG   ISSN 0328-2384
ARQUIS; arquitectura y urbanismo. Text in English, Spanish. 1993. q. USD 92. bk.rev. **Document type:** *Monographic series, Academic/Scholarly.*
Indexed: AIAP, API.
Published by: (Universidad de Palermo, Centro de Investigaciones en Arquitectura), Editorial CP67 S.A., Local 18, Florida, 683, Capital Federal, Buenos Aires 1375, Argentina. TEL 54-114-3146303, FAX 54-114-3147135, info@cp67.com. Ed. Daniel Silberfaden. Pub. Guillermo Raul Kliczkowski.

720   MEX
ARQUITECTONICA. Text in Spanish. 2002. s-a. USD 20 (effective 2002). **Document type:** *Academic/Scholarly.* **Description:** This new publication offers a multidisciplinary approach to the subject of space. It takes into account the architectural-urban, anthropological-philosophical, artistic and historical points of view.
Published by: Universidad Iberoamericana, Prol Paseo de la Reforma 880, Col Lomas de Santa Fe, Mexico City, DF 01210, Mexico. TEL 52-5-2674000. Ed. Gigliola Carozzi Arosio. Circ: 1,000.

720   ESP   ISSN 0214-1124
ARQUITECTOS. Key Title: Boletin Informativo de la Profesion de Arquitectos. Text in Spanish. 1975. 6/yr. **Document type:** *Newsletter.*
Former titles (until 1984): Consejo Superior de los Colegios de Arquitectos. Revista (0214-1116); (until 1983): Q (0214-1108); (until 1980): Consejo Superior de los Colegios de Arquitectos (0210-0673).
Indexed: API, EIP, RILM.
—CINDOC.
Published by: Consejo Superior de los Colegios de Arquitectos de Espana, Paseo Castellana, 12 4o, Madrid, 28046, Spain. TEL 1-435-22-00, FAX 1-575-38-39. Circ: 22,400.

720   ESP   ISSN 0004-2706
NA5
ARQUITECTURA. Text in Spanish; Summaries in English. 1918. bi-m. USD 106. adv. bk.rev. charts; illus.
Indexed: AIAP, API, BHA, BibInd, PCI, RASB, RILM.
—CINDOC, IE, Infotrieve.
Published by: Colegio Oficial de Arquitectos de Madrid, Barquillo, 12, Madrid, 28004, Spain. TEL 521-82-00, FAX 532-54-99. Circ: 8,200.

ARQUITECTURA & CONSTRUCAO. see *INTERIOR DESIGN AND DECORATION*

720   CUB   ISSN 1010-3821
NA5
ARQUITECTURA CUBA. Text in Spanish; Summaries in English, French. s-a. USD 26 in South America; USD 30 elsewhere. bk.rev. illus.
Indexed: AIAP, IBR.
Published by: (Cuba. Centro de Informacion de la Construccion (CIC), Cuba. Departamento Editorial), Ediciones Cubanas, Obispo No. 527, Apdo. 605, Havana, Cuba. TEL 32-5556-60. Circ: 4,500.

720   ESP
ARQUITECTURA TECNICA. Text in Spanish. 3/yr.
Published by: (Official College of Master Builders and Technical Architects), M I L M S.L., Salamanca, 31 3a, Valencia, 46005, Spain. TEL 6-334-07-07. Ed. D M Galarza.

720   ESP   ISSN 0214-1256
NA673
ARQUITECTURA VIVA. Text in Spanish; Summaries in English. 1988. bi-m. EUR 70 domestic; EUR 95 in Europe; EUR 115 elsewhere (effective 2005). adv. bk.rev. software rev. illus. 128 p./no.; **Document type:** *Journal, Trade.* **Description:** Covers the latest in architecture and all other inevitably related cultural and technical fields.

Related titles: Online - full text ed.
Indexed: AIAP, API, RILM.
—CINDOC, IE, Infotrieve. **CCC.**
Published by: Arquitectura Viva S.L., Aniceto Marinas 32, Madrid, 28008, Spain. TEL 34-91-5487317, AV@arquitecturaviva.com, http://www.arquitecturaviva.com, 34-91-5488191. Ed., Pub. Luis Fernandez Galiano. R&P Lola Gonzalez. Adv. contact Susana Blanco. color page EUR 2,200; trim 297 x 240. Circ: 11,000. **Dist. by:** Asociacion de Revistas Culturales de Espana, Hortaleza, 75, Madrid 28004, Spain. TEL 34-91-3086066, FAX 34-91-3199267, info@arce.es, http://www.arce.es.

720   NIC
ARQUITECTURA Y CONSTRUCCION. Text in Spanish. 1996. bi-m.
Published by: Imprimatur Artes Graficas S.A., Apartado Postal 4637, Managua, Nicaragua. TEL 505-2-2660957, FAX 505-2-2668419. Ed. Sergio de Castro Lopes.

720   MEX   ISSN 1605-5632
ARQUITECTURA Y HUMANIDADES. Text in Spanish. 1999. q.
Media: Online - full text. **Related titles:** ◆ English ed.: Architecture and Humanities. ISSN 1605-5640.
Published by: Universidad Nacional Autonoma de Mexico, Facultad de Arquitectura, c/o Arq. Enrique X. de Anda, Circuito Interior de Cd. Universitaria, Deleg. Coyoacan, Mexico City, DF 04510, Mexico. TEL 52-5-6220318, FAX 52-5-6166545, http://www.architecthum.edu.mx. Ed. Irasema Gallo Ramirez.

711.4   CUB
ARQUITECTURA Y URBANISMO. Text in Spanish. q. USD 25 in North America; USD 26 in South America; USD 28 in Europe.
Published by: (Cuba. Ministerio de Educacion Superior), Ediciones Cubanas, Obispo No. 527, Apdo. 605, Havana, Cuba.

720   BRA   ISSN 0102-8979
NA5
ARQUITETURA E URBANISMO. Text in Portuguese. 1984. bi-m. USD 80 (effective 2000). adv. **Document type:** *Directory.*
Indexed: EIP.
Published by: Editora Pini Ltda., Rua Anhaia 964, Bom Retiro, SP 01130-900, Brazil. TEL 55-11-32248811. Ed. Mario Sergio Pini. Adv. contact Luiz Carlos F Oliveira.

721 690   BRA   ISSN 0104-1908
ARQUITETURA Y CONSTRUCAO; a revista para construir ou reformar sua casa. Text in Portuguese. 1988. m. BRL 108 domestic; USD 89.99 foreign (effective 2005). adv. charts; illus. back issues avail. **Document type:** *Magazine, Consumer.* **Description:** Contains information on building or remodeling one's own home.
Related titles: Online - full text ed.
Published by: Editora Abril, S.A., Av. das Nacoes Unidas, 7221, 11 andar Pinheiros, Sao Paulo, SP 05425-902, Brazil. TEL 55-11-50872112, FAX 55-11-50872100, http://arquitetura.abril.com.br/index.shtml, http://www.abril.com.br/. Ed. Elda Muller. adv.: page BRL 30,100. Circ: 117,350.

ARQUITOP; directory of architects in Portugal. see *BUSINESS AND ECONOMICS—Trade And Industrial Directories*

ARREDO URBANO. see *BUILDING AND CONSTRUCTION*

ARREDO URBANO BIS; supplemento tecnico. see *BUILDING AND CONSTRUCTION*

720   ESP   ISSN 1136-5234
ARS SACRA. Text in Spanish. 1997. q. EUR 51.09 domestic; USD 70 foreign (effective 2002).
—CINDOC.
Published by: (Confederacion Espanola de Productos para la Construccion), Comision Episcopal para el Patrimonio Cultural, C. Lope de Vega 18-bajo, Madrid, 28014, Spain. TEL 34-91-4293375, FAX 34-91-4297478, info@arssacra.com, http://www.arssacra.com/. Ed. Esteban Sancho Campo. Circ: 8,000.

ART, ARTIFACT & ARCHITECTURE LAW. see *LAW*

THE ART BOOK. see *ART*

ARTICHOKE. see *INTERIOR DESIGN AND DECORATION*

910   USA   ISSN 1060-2569
ARTISTIC TRAVELER; architecture & travel with art & photography. Text in English. 1991 (Nov.). bi-m. USD 29 (effective 2004). bk.rev. illus. 12 p./no.; back issues avail.; reprints avail. **Document type:** *Newsletter.* **Description:** Guides people interested in the artistic aspect of architecture to exciting visual experiences. Included is a calendar of museum exhibits and news about architectural attractions, awards and important new buildings.
Related titles: E-mail ed.
Published by: S & R Research, PO Box 2038, Vancouver, WA 98668-2038. TEL 360-737-0632, ulr@artistictraveler.com, http://www.artistictraveler.com. Ed., Pub., R&P Richard Hovey.

ARTS ASIATIQUES. see *ART*

ARTS ET INDUSTRIES. see *ENGINEERING*

720 690 747   THA
▼ **ASIA-PACIFIC TROPICAL HOMES.** Text in English. 2003 (Oct./Dec.). q. adv. **Document type:** *Magazine, Consumer.*
Published by: Artasia Press Co., Ltd., 143/1-2 Soi Dumex, Charoen Nakorn Rd 13, Klong Tonsai, Klongsarn, Bangkok, 10600, Thailand. TEL 66-2-8613360, FAX 66-2-8613363, info@tropicalhomes.biz, info@aapress.net, http://www.tropicalhomes.biz/, http://www.aapress.net/.

720 690   HKG
ASIAN ARCHITECT & CONTRACTOR. Text in English. 1972. m. HKD 280, USD 75. adv. **Document type:** *Trade.* **Description:** Covers Asian, Australian, and Pacific construction projects, plant and product news.
Formerly: Asian Architecture and Builder; Incorporates: Asia Pacific Contractor
Indexed: AIAP, HongKongiana.
Published by: Thomson Press Hong Kong Ltd., 202-203 Hollywood Centre, 233 Hollywood Rd, Hong Kong, Hong Kong. TEL 852-2815-9111, FAX 852-2851-1933. Ed. David Robinson. Pub. J S Uberoi. R&P Rajesh Malik. adv.: B&W page HKD 13,000, color page HKD 16,500; trim 210 x 280. Circ: 16,710.

720   USA   ISSN 0848-8525
TH3401
➤ **ASSOCIATION FOR PRESERVATION TECHNOLOGY INTERNATIONAL. BULLETIN.** Short title: A P T Bulletin. Text in English. 1969. q. USD 100 domestic to individuals membership; USD 125 in Canada to individuals membership; USD 145 elsewhere to individuals membership; USD 150 domestic to institutions membership; USD 200 in Canada to institutions membership; USD 220 elsewhere to institutions membership; USD 30 domestic to students membership; USD 40 in Canada to students membership; USD 50 elsewhere to students membership (effective 2005). adv. bk.rev. illus. index. reprints avail. **Document type:** *Bulletin, Academic/Scholarly.* **Description:** Covers research and practical application of the principles of preservation technology to buildings, sites and objects.
Formerly (until 1991): Association for Preservation Technology. Bulletin (0044-9466)
Related titles: Microfiche ed.
Indexed: A&ATA, AIAP, API, AmH&L, ArtInd, GardL, HistAb, PCI.
—BLDSC (1581.770000), CISTI, IE, ingenta. **CCC.**
Published by: Association for Preservation Technology International, 4513 Lincoln Ave, Ste 213, Lisle, IL 60532-1290. TEL 630-968-6400, FAX 888-723-4242, information@apti.org, http://www.apti.org. Ed., R&P, Adv. contact Diana Waite. Circ: 2,000.

720   USA   ISSN 0194-410X
NA2000
ASSOCIATION OF COLLEGIATE SCHOOLS OF ARCHITECTURE. PROCEEDINGS OF THE ANNUAL MEETING. Key Title: Proceedings of the A C S A Annual Meeting. Text in English. 1979. a. USD 30 (effective 1999). **Document type:** *Proceedings.*
Published by: Association of Collegiate Schools of Architecture, Inc., 1735 New York Ave, N W, Washington, DC 20006. TEL 202-785-2324, FAX 202-628-0448. Ed. Beth Young.

ASSOCIAZIONE PER IMOLA STORICO ARTISTICA. ATTI. see *ARCHAEOLOGY*

790   ESP   ISSN 1134-3672
ASTRAGALO; cultura de la arquitectura y la ciudad. Text in Spanish. 1994. q. EUR 17.50 domestic; EUR 22 in Europe; USD 35 elsewhere (effective 2002).
Indexed: AIAP.
—CINDOC.
Published by: Instituto Espanol de Arquiceleste Ediciones, S.A., Fernand VI, 8 - 1o., Madrid, Spain. TEL 34-91-3100459, FAX 34-91-3100459, info@celesteediciones.com, http://www.celesteediciones.com/. Ed. Antonio Fernandez Alba.

720 740   USA
ATHENAEUM ANNOTATIONS. Text in English. 1976. irreg. membership. **Document type:** *Monographic series.*
Published by: Athenaeum of Philadelphia, 219 S Sixth St, Philadelphia, PA 19106-3794. TEL 215-925-2688, FAX 215-925-3755, athena@libertynet.org, http://www.libertynet.org/~athena. Circ: 1,400.

727   ITA
ATLANTE STORICO DELLE CITTA ITALIANE. Text in Italian. 1986. a. price varies. maps. **Document type:** *Academic/Scholarly.* **Description:** Contains historical research on urban architecture.
Published by: (Universita degli Studi di Roma "La Sapienza", Dipartimento di Storia Urbanistica), Bonsignori Editore s.r.l., Viale dei Quattro Venti 47, Rome, RM 00152, Italy. TEL 39-06-5881496, FAX 39-06-5882839. Ed. Enrico Guidoni.

720   HUN   ISSN 1219-0101
NA6.H8
ATRIUM; architecture - interior design - design. Text in Hungarian. 1995. bi-m. HUF 5,940 (effective 2004). adv. **Document type:** *Magazine, Trade.* **Description:** Deals with architecture, interior design, furnishing and design history.

Published by: Sanoma Budapest Kiadoi Rt. (Subsidiary of: Sanoma Magazines Finland Corporation), Bokor Utca 15-19, Budapest, 1037, Hungary. TEL 36-1-4371100, FAX 36-1-2502303, atrium@sanomabp.hu, info@sanomabp.hu, http://www.atrium.hu, http://www.sanoma.hu. Adv. contact Nora Pellikan. page HUF 600,000; trim 230 x 297. Circ: 10,500 (paid and controlled).

720 DEU ISSN 1612-4928
▼ **AUFTRAGSBERATER FUER ARCHITEKTEN UND INGENIEURE.** Text in German. 2003. m. EUR 180 (effective 2004). **Document type:** *Journal, Trade.*
Published by: (Institut fuer Wirtschaftspublizistik), Vogel Verlag und Druck GmbH & Co. KG, Max-Planck-Str 7-9, Wuerzburg, 97064, Germany. TEL 49-931-4180, FAX 49-931-4182100, marliese_bernhardt@vogel-medien.de, http://www.iww.de/ingenieure/auftragsberater/infoindex.php, http://www.vogel-medien.de.

AUSTRALIAN BUILDING NEWS. see *BUILDING AND CONSTRUCTION*

AUSTRALIAN HOME BEAUTIFUL. see *INTERIOR DESIGN AND DECORATION*

AWARD MAGAZINE. see *BUILDING AND CONSTRUCTION*

724 DEU ISSN 1430-9459
NA680
AWARD WINNING ARCHITECTURE INTERNATIONAL YEARBOOK. Variant title: A W A International Yearbook. Text in English. 1996. a. **Document type:** *Trade.*
Published by: Prestel Verlag, Koeniginstr 9, Munich, 80539, Germany. info@prestel.de, http://www.prestel.de. Ed. Frantisek Sedlacek. R&P Karin Kirmaier.

720 ESP ISSN 1133-0821
AZULEJO, DISTRIBUCION, COLOCACION. Text in Spanish. 1992. q.
—CINDOC.
Published by: Publica Editorial, Ecuador, 75, Barcelona, 08029, Spain. TEL 34-93-3215045, FAX 34-93-3221972, publica@publica.es.

AZURE DESIGN, ARCHITECTURE AND ART. see *ART*

AZURE MAGAZINE; design architecture & art. see *INTERIOR DESIGN AND DECORATION*

720 ESP ISSN 1131-6470
B I A. (Boletin Informativo de Arquitectos Tecnicos y Aparejadores) Text in Spanish. 1974. bi-m.
Indexed: RILM.
—CINDOC.
Published by: Colegio Oficial de Aparejadores y Arquitectos Tecnicos/College of Master Builders and Engineering Architects, C/ Maestro Vitoria 3, Madrid, 28013, Spain. TEL 34-91-7014501, http://www.coaatm.es.

B P N. (Building Products News) see *BUILDING AND CONSTRUCTION*

B T H - TAPETENZEITUNG. (Boden - Tapeten - Heimtextilien) see *INTERIOR DESIGN AND DECORATION—Furniture And House Furnishings*

B W P D A CONVENTION PROCEEDINGS. see *FORESTS AND FORESTRY—Lumber And Wood*

728 DEU ISSN 1616-4512
BARRIEREFREI; Lebensraum fuer Menschen. Text in German. 2000. q. EUR 18.50 domestic; EUR 31 foreign; EUR 5 newsstand/cover (effective 2004). adv. 50 p./no. 3 cols./p.; **Document type:** *Magazine, Trade.*
Published by: A T Fachverlag GmbH, Postfach 500180, Stuttgart, 70331, Germany. TEL 49-711-9529510, FAX 49-711-95295199, info@barrierefrei-online.de, at@at-fachverlag.de, http://www.barrierefrei-online.de, http://www.at-fachverlag.de. Ed. Michaela Heel. Pub. Werner Page. Adv. contact Monika Barchet. B&W page EUR 3,144, color page EUR 3,888; trim 185 x 264. Circ: 14,641 (paid and free).

720 GBR ISSN 1352-2507
BARTLETT RESEARCH PAPERS. Text in English. 1993. irreg. **Document type:** *Academic/Scholarly.*
—BLDSC (1863.827600).
Published by: University College London, Bartlett School of Graduate Studies, Philips House, Gower St., London, WC1E 6BT, United Kingdom. TEL 44-0171-387-7050, FAX 44-0171-916-1887. Ed. Bev Nutt.

790 720 ESP ISSN 0213-0653
NA1309.C15
BASA. Text in Spanish. 1982. s-a.
Formerly (until 1982): Publicacion - COAC, Delegacion de Santa Cruz de Tenerife (0212-6486)
Indexed: RILM.
—CINDOC.

Published by: Colegio de Arquitectos de Canarias, Luis Doreste Silva, 2, Las Palmas de Gran Canaria, 35004, Spain. TEL 34-928-248844, FAX 34-928-241706, coac@coac-lpa.com, http://www.coac-lpa.com.

721 ESP ISSN 1130-1902
BAU; revista de arquitectura, urbanismo, arte y diseno. Text in Spanish. 1989. q.
Related titles: Online - full text ed.
—CINDOC.
Published by: Colegio de Arquitectos de Leon, Alcazar de Toledo, 12 1o., Leon, 24001, Spain. TEL 34-987-875900, FAX 34-987-875901, http://www.arquinex.es/bau.htm, http://www.coal.es/.

720 AUT ISSN 1019-2158
BAUART. Text in German. a. **Document type:** *Magazine, Trade.*
Related titles: Online - full text ed.: ISSN 1605-8445.
Published by: BauArt Verein fuer die Foerderung von Architektur, Staedtebau und Kunst, Renngasse 14, Vienna, 1010, Austria. TEL 43-1-5351663, FAX 43-1-5351278, http://www.nextroom.at/nr/kiosk/bauart. Ed. Walter Zschokke.

720 CHE ISSN 0255-3104
BAUEN IN STAHL/CONSTRUIRE EN ACIER/COSTRUIRE IN ACCIAIO. Text in French, German. 1968. q. looseleaf. CHF 25 domestic; CHF 60 foreign (effective 2002). bk.rev. charts; illus. cum.index. back issues avail. **Document type:** *Monographic series, Trade.* **Description:** Descriptions of modern steel buildings and bridges.
Published by: Stahlbau Zentrum Schweiz, Seefeldstr 25, Zuerich, 8034, Switzerland. TEL 41-1-2618980, FAX 41-1-2620962, info@szs.ch, http://www.szs.ch. Ed. Stephan Zingg. Circ: 6,500 (paid).

BAUEN UND SIEDELN. see *HOUSING AND URBAN PLANNING*

720 DEU
BAUERNHAEUSER AUS MITTELEUROPA; Aufmasse und Publikationen von Gerhard Eitzen. Text in German. 1984. irreg. **Document type:** *Monographic series, Academic/Scholarly.*
Published by: Arbeitskreis fuer Hausforschung e.V., Rheinland-Pfaelzisches Freilichtmuseum, Postfach 18, Bad Sobernheim, 55566, Germany. TEL 49-6751-3840, FAX 49-6751-1207, webmaster@freilichtmuseum-badsobernheim.de, http://www.arbeitskreisfuerhausforschung.de.

720 DEU ISSN 1433-5735
NA3 CODEN: WZAWA9
BAUHAUS UNIVERSITAET WEIMAR. THESIS. Text in English, German. 1994. 6/yr. adv. **Document type:** *Journal, Academic/Scholarly.*
Former titles (until 1997): Bauhaus-Universitaet Weimar. Wissenschaftliche Zeitschrift (1433-4593); (until 1996): Hochschule fuer Architektur und Bauwesen Weimar. Wissenschaftliche Schriften (1433-5026); Which was formed by the merger of (1953-1994): Hochschule fuer Architektur und Bauwesen. Wissenschaftliche Zeitschrift. Ausgabe A (0863-0712); (1953-1994): Hochschule fuer Architektur und Bauwesen. Wissenschaftliche Zeitschrift. Ausgabe B (0863-0720); Both of which superseded in part (in 1985): Hochschule fuer Architektur und Bauwesen Weimar. Wissenschaftliche Zeitschrift (0509-9773)
Indexed: AIAP, CIN, ChemAb, RASB, RefZh, ZentMath.
—BLDSC (8820.092200), CASDDS, Linda Hall. **CCC.**
Published by: Bauhaus Universitaet Weimar, Coudraystr 7, Weimar, 99421, Germany. TEL 49-3643-581152, FAX 49-3643-581156, heidemarie.schirmer@uv.uni-weimar.de, http://ewww.uni-weimar.de/uv/programm/thesis.de.html, http://www.uni-weimar.de. Ed., R&P Heidemarie Schirmer TEL 49-3643-581150. Pub. Reiner Bensch. Adv. contact Marita Fein.

720 690 DEU ISSN 0005-674X
NA3
BAUMEISTER; Zeitschrift fuer Architektur. Text in German; Summaries in English. 1902. m. EUR 127.20 domestic to individuals; EUR 134.40 foreign to individuals; EUR 83.40 domestic to students; EUR 90.60 foreign to students; EUR 14 newsstand/cover (effective 2004). adv. bk.rev. bibl.; charts; illus.; mkt.; pat. index. **Document type:** *Magazine, Trade.*
Related titles: Online - full text ed.: (from H.W. Wilson, O C L C Online Computer Library Center, Inc.).
Indexed: AIAP, API, ArtInd, BHA, DIP, EIP, IBR, IBZ.
—BLDSC (1867.600000), IE, Infotrieve, ingenta. **CCC.**
Published by: Callwey Verlag, Streitfeldstr 35, Munich, 81673, Germany. TEL 49-89-4360050, FAX 49-89-436005113, info@baumeister.de, a.hagenkord@callwey.de, http://www.baumeister.de, http://www.callwey.de. Ed. Wolfgang Bachmann. adv.: B&W page EUR 4,866, color page EUR 7,716. Circ: 25,218 (paid and controlled).

BAUPLAN - BAUORGA; internationale technisch-wirtschaftliche Zeitschrift. see *BUILDING AND CONSTRUCTION*

BAUTENSCHUTZ UND BAUSANIERUNG; Zeitschrift fuer Bauinstandhaltung und Denkmalpflege. see *BUILDING AND CONSTRUCTION*

720 DEU ISSN 0005-6855
TH3
BAUWELT. Text in German. 1910. w. EUR 237.60 domestic; EUR 244.80 foreign; EUR 138 to students; EUR 9.50 newsstand/cover (effective 2004). adv. bk.rev. bibl.; charts; illus.; mkt. index. **Document type:** *Magazine, Trade.*
Indexed: AIAP, API, ChemAb, DIP, ExcerpMed, IBR, IBZ, RASB, RILM.
—BLDSC (1871.000000), IE, ingenta, Linda Hall.
Published by: Bauverlag BV GmbH (Subsidiary of: Springer Science+Business Media), Avenwedderstr 55, Guetersloh, 33311, Germany. TEL 49-5241-802119, FAX 49-5241-809582, bauwelt@bauverlag.de, ulrike.mattern@springer-sbm.com, http://www.baunetz.de/arch/bauwelt/, http://www.bauverlag.de. Ed. Felix Zwoch. Adv. contact Andreas Kirchgessner. B&W page EUR 4,450, color page EUR 7,116; trim 203 x 275. Circ: 13,779 (paid).

720 DEU ISSN 0005-688X
DAS BAUZENTRUM. Text in German. 1960. 10/yr. EUR 51 domestic; EUR 82 foreign; EUR 46 to students; EUR 9.20 newsstand/cover (effective 2004). adv. bk.rev. reprints avail. **Document type:** *Magazine, Trade.*
Published by: Verlag das Beispiel GmbH, Spreestr 9, Darmstadt, 64295, Germany. TEL 49-6151-33557, FAX 49-6151-313089, verlag@das-beispiel.de, http://www.verlag-das-beispiel.de/bauzentrum/. Ed. Otto Spies. adv.: B&W page EUR 4,180; trim 190 x 250. Circ: 14,873 (controlled).

720 747 USA ISSN 1046-6312
NA7205
BEAUTIFUL HOMES. Text in English. 1988. a. USD 5.99 per issue (effective 2005). adv. **Document type:** *Magazine, Consumer.* **Description:** Features currently popular floor plans and pictures of single family detached homes of interest to home planners and builders.
Formerly: Beautiful New Home
Published by: Meredith Corp., 1716 Locust St, Des Moines, IA 50309-3023. TEL 515-284-3000, FAX 515-284-3697, shawn.gilliam@meredith.com, http://www.meredith.com. Ed. Linda Kaft. Pub. Bill Reed. Adv. contact Pat Tomlinson. Circ: 450,000 (paid).

BEBYGGELSEHISTORISK TIDSKRIFT. see *HOUSING AND URBAN PLANNING*

BEIJING JIANZHU GONGCHENG XUEYUAN XUEBAO/BEIJING INSTITUTE OF CIVIL ENGINEERING AND ARCHITECTURE. JOURNAL. see *ENGINEERING—Civil Engineering*

720 NLD
BERLAGE CAHIERS. Text in English. 1992. a. price varies. **Document type:** *Monographic series.*
Indexed: AIAP.
Published by: (Berlage Institute Amsterdam), Uitgeverij 010, Watertorenweg 180, Rotterdam, 3063 HA, Netherlands. TEL 31-10-4333509, FAX 31-10-4529825.

720 USA
BEST NEW SMALL HOME DESIGNS. Text in English. 2002. bi-m. USD 3.99 per issue (effective 2004). **Document type:** *Magazine, Consumer.*
Formerly: New Small Home Plans
Published by: The Garlinghouse Company (Subsidiary of: Active Interest Media), 4125 Lafayette Center Dr, Ste 100, Chantilly, VA 20151. TEL 703-547-4154, 800-235-5700, FAX 703-222-9705, info@garlinghouse.com, http://www.garlinghouse.com. Ed. Wolf Schneider. Pub. James D McNair III. Adv. contact Lisa Smith. Circ: 75,000 (paid).

BETTER HOMES AND GARDENS. see *INTERIOR DESIGN AND DECORATION*

728 USA
TH4816
BETTER HOMES AND GARDENS BUILDING & REMODELING. Text in English. 1945. q. USD 4.99 newsstand/cover domestic (effective 2005). adv. illus.; tr.lit. **Document type:** *Magazine, Consumer.* **Description:** Features a variety of imaginative home-improvement projects, from remodeling and decorating to custom building an addition. Gives timely information on planning projects, selecting products, and working with a contractor.
Former titles: Better Homes & Gardens Remodeling Ideas (0731-7409); Better Homes and Gardens Home Improvement Ideas
Published by: Meredith Corp., 1716 Locust St, Des Moines, IA 50309-3023. TEL 515-284-2130, FAX 515-284-3697, http://www.bhg.com, http://www.meredith.com. Eds. Gayle Goodson Butler, Linda Kast. Pub. Stephen B Levinson. Adv. contact Lisa Monago. B&W page USD 31,190, color page USD 44,820; trim 10.5 x 8. Circ: 450,000 (paid).

721 PRT ISSN 0006-2804
BINARIO; revista de arquitectura, construcao e equipamento. Text in Portuguese; Summaries in English. 1958. m. USD 20. adv. bk.rev. charts; illus.; mkt.; tr.lit. s-a. index.
Address: Praca de Londres, 10, Lisbon, 1000, Portugal. Ed. Jose Luis Quintino. Circ: 2,000.

720   ITA
BIOARCHITETTURE. Text in Italian. 1993. irreg., latest vol.3, 1999. price varies. adv. **Document type:** *Monographic series.*
Published by: Liguori Editore srl, Via Posillipo 394, Naples, 80123, Italy. TEL 39-81-7206111, FAX 39-81-7206244, http://www.liguori.it. Eds. Bianca Bottero, Gianni Scudo. Pub. Guido Liguori. Adv. contact Maria Liguori.

720   GBR
BLACK DOG PUBLISHING. SERIAL BOOKS. DESIGN. Variant title: Serial Books. Text in English. 1998. irreg. illus. back issues avail. **Document type:** *Monographic series, Academic/Scholarly.* **Description:** Covers contemporary designers.
Formerly (until 2001): Black Dog Publishing. Serial Books
Related titles: ♦ Series: Architecture and Urbanism.
Published by: Black Dog Publishing Ltd., 5 Ravenscroft St., London, E2 7JH, United Kingdom. TEL 44-20-7613-1922, FAX 44 20-7613-1944, info@bdp.demon.co.uk. Ed. Alex Payne. Pub. Duncan McCorquodale.

711.4   NLD   ISSN 1389-742X
BLAUWE KAMER; tijdschrift voor landschapsontwikkeling en stedebouw. Text in Dutch. 1993. bi-m. EUR 74 to individuals; EUR 104 to institutions; EUR 54 to students (effective 2005). adv. bk.rev. cum.index: 1991-1995. back issues avail. **Description:** Covers landscape architecture and urban planning issues, including environmental changes in urban and rural areas.
Formerly (until 1998): Blauwe Kamer Profiel (0929-1806); Which was formed by the merger of (1991-1993): Blauwe Kamer (0926-1621); (1990-1993): Profiel (0925-5567)
Published by: Stichting Lijn in Landschap, General Foulkesweg 72, Wageningen, 6703 BW, Netherlands. TEL 31-317-425890, FAX 31-317-425886, blauwekamer@gaw.nl, http://www.blauwekamer.nl/. Ed. Bert Bukman. Pub. Harry Harsema. Adv. contact Rita Kleinhesselink TEL 31-314-360500. B&W page EUR 995; trim 240 x 310. Circ: 2,500.

720   GBR   ISSN 0268-4926
NA968
BLUEPRINT (CHELMSFORD); architecture, design & contemporary culture. Text in English. 1983. m. **Document type:** *Journal, Trade.*
Indexed: ABM, AIAP, ArtInd, DAAI.
—BLDSC (2114.197000), IE, Infotrieve, ingenta. **CCC.**
Published by: E T P Ltd., Roseberry House, 41 Springfield Rd, Chelmsford, Essex CM2 6JJ, United Kingdom. TEL 44-1245-491717, FAX 44-1245-491771, hwoulfe@wilmington.co.uk. Ed. Grant Gibson. Pub. David Wright. **Subscr. to:** Blueprint Subscriptions, Galleon, Building 960, Sittingbourne Research Centre, Sittingbourne, Kent ME9 8AG, United Kingdom. **Dist. by:** Comag Specialist Division, Tavistock Works, Tavistock Rd, W Drayton, Mddx UB7 7QX, United Kingdom.

720   IRL
BLUEPRINT HOME PLANS. Text in English. a. adv. **Document type:** *Magazine, Consumer, Trade.*
Published by: Oisin Publications, 4 Iona Dr., Dublin, 9, Ireland. TEL 353-1-8305236, FAX 353-1-8307860, oisinpr@iol.ie. adv.: B&W page EUR 1,500, color page EUR 2,000. Circ: 10,000 (controlled).

720 690   USA   ISSN 0742-0552
NA705
BLUEPRINTS. Text in English. 1981. q. USD 35 to members (effective 1998). **Document type:** *Newsletter, Academic/Scholarly.*
Indexed: AIAP.
Published by: National Building Museum, 401 F St, N W, Washington, DC 20001. TEL 202-272-2448, FAX 202-272-2564, http://www.nbm.org. Ed. Karen Eisenberg. R&P Lisa Knapp. Circ: 3,000.

BOLIGEN. see *HOUSING AND URBAN PLANNING*

BONYTT/DESIGN FOR LIVING; norsk spesialblad for arkitektur boliginnredning. see *INTERIOR DESIGN AND DECORATION*

720   USA
BOSTON SOCIETY OF ARCHITECTS. CHAPTERLETTER. Text in English. 1914. bi-m. USD 55 domestic; USD 75 foreign (effective 2000). bk.rev. illus. **Document type:** *Newsletter, Trade.*
Published by: Boston Society of Architects, 52 Broad St, Boston, MA 02109-4301. TEL 617-951-1433, FAX 617-951-0845, bsarch@architects.org, http://www.architects.org. Ed. Richard Fitzgerald. R&P Stephen C Sattler. Circ: 5,000.

BOUW. see *BUILDING AND CONSTRUCTION*

BOUWRECHT. see *BUILDING AND CONSTRUCTION*

BRITISH ARCHAEOLOGICAL ASSOCIATION. CONFERENCE TRANSACTIONS. see *ARCHAEOLOGY*

BRITISH ARCHAEOLOGICAL ASSOCIATION. JOURNAL. see *ARCHAEOLOGY*

---

720 760   UKR   ISSN 0135-1699
BUDIVNYTSTVO UKRAINY. Text in Ukrainian, Russian. bi-m. USD 175 in the Americas (effective 2000).
—CISTI.
Published by: Goskomitet Ukrainy po Voprosam Gradostroitel'stva i Arkhitektury, Ul. Lesi Ukrainki, 26, Kiev, Ukraine. TEL 226-27-86. **Dist. by:** East View Information Services, 3020 Harbor Ln. N., Minneapolis, MN 55447. TEL 763-550-0961, FAX 763-559-2931.

BUDOWNICTWO, TECHNOLOGIE, ARCHITEKTURA. see *BUILDING AND CONSTRUCTION*

720   DEU
BUILD; das Architekten-Magazin. Text in German. 1988. bi-m. EUR 30; EUR 5 newsstand/cover (effective 2002). adv. bk.rev. back issues avail. **Document type:** *Magazine, Trade.*
Description: Contains articles and features on prominent architects, their work and their profession, mostly written by the architects themselves.
Former titles (until 2001): Das Architekten Magazin (1615-8210); (until 2000): V F A Profil (0940-3124)
Published by: (Vereinigung Freischaffender Architekten), Verlag Mueller & Busmann, Hofaue 63, Wuppertal, 42103, Germany. TEL 49-202-24836-0, FAX 49-202-2483610, mb@mueller-busmann.de, http://www.mueller-busmann.de. Ed. Reiner Kessler. R&P Ralf Broekman TEL 49-202-2483653. Adv. contact Reinold Eisenbart TEL 49-202-2483650. B&W page EUR 3,985, color page EUR 5,920; trim 185 x 260. Circ: 12,000 (paid).

721 690   USA   ISSN 0192-9070
BUILDER INSIDER. Text in English. 1975. m. USD 15; free to qualified personnel (effective 2004). adv. **Document type:** *Magazine, Trade.* **Description:** For builders, architects and remodelers.
Published by: Michael J. Anderson, Ed. & Pub., 3111 Cole Ave, Dallas, TX 75204-1138. TEL 214-871-2913, FAX 214-871-2931, info@builderinsider.com, http://www.builderinsider.com. Adv. contact Michael J Anderson. Circ: 10,000.

720 690   GBR   ISSN 0007-3318
NA1   CODEN: BULDBE
BUILDING; the voice of the industry. Text in English. 1843. w. GBP 110; GBP 2.40 newsstand/cover (effective 2001). adv. bk.rev. charts; illus.; mkt.; stat. s-a. index. 40 p./no. 3 cols./p.; reprint service avail. from PQC. **Document type:** *Magazine, Trade.* **Description:** Reports on all aspects of the building and construction industry.
Formerly (until 1966): Builder (0366-1059)
Related titles: Microform ed.: (from PQC); Online - full text ed.; ♦ Includes: Construction Monitor; ♦ Supplement(s): Homes. ISSN 1740-3421.
Indexed: A&ATA, AHCMS, AIAP, BldManAb, BrCerAb, BrHumI, BrTechI, CISA, CivEngAb, CoppAb, HECAB, IBuildSA, Inspec, M&TEA, RICS, WSCA.
—BLDSC (2359.200000), CISTI, IE, Infotrieve, ingenta, Linda Hall. **CCC.**
Published by: Builder Group plc., 7th Floor, Anchorage House, 2 Clove Crescent, London, London E14 2BE, United Kingdom. TEL 44-20-75604000, FAX 44-20-75604026, http://www.building.co.uk. Ed. Adrian Barrick. Pub. Tony Arnold. Adv. contact Nina Osborne TEL 44-20-7560-4098. Circ: 23,961. **Subscr. to:** Building, Freepost LE6520, Leicester LE87 4DF, United Kingdom. TEL 44-1858-435345. **Dist. by:** M M C Ltd., Octagon House, White Hart Meadows, Ripley, Woking, Surrey GU23 6HR, United Kingdom. TEL 44-1483-211222, FAX 44-1483-224541.

720   ZAF   ISSN 0258-2228
BUILDING. Text in English. 1985. bi-m. ZAR 181 (effective 1998). adv. bk.rev. back issues avail. **Document type:** *Trade.* **Description:** Follows building concepts, structures, and materials used by the building and construction industries in South Africa.
Indexed: ISAP.
Published by: Avonwold Publishing Co. (Pty) Ltd., Avonwold House, 24 Baker St, Rosebank, Johannesburg, 2196, South Africa. TEL 27-11-788-1610, FAX 27-11-880-2732. Ed. Uli Leitich. Circ: 4,881.

BUILDING ACOUSTICS. see *PHYSICS—Sound*

720   GBR   ISSN 0007-3423
BUILDING DESIGN. Text in English. 1970. w. GBP 75, USD 198 (effective 2000). adv. bk.rev. charts; illus.; stat. reprint service avail. from PQC. **Document type:** *Magazine, Trade.*
Related titles: Microform ed.: (from PQC); Online - full text ed.: (from EBSCO Publishing, Factiva, Florida Center for Library Automation, Gale Group, LexisNexis, O C L C Online Computer Library Center, Inc., ProQuest Information & Learning).
Indexed: AIAP, API, BldManAb, DAAI, RICS.
—BLDSC (2359.710000), CISTI. **CCC.**

Published by: C M P Information Ltd. (Subsidiary of: United Business Media), City Reach, 5 Greenwich View Pl, Millharbour, London, E14 9NN, United Kingdom. TEL 44-20-7861-6137, FAX 44-20-7861-6552, enquiries@cmpinformation.com, http://www.cmpinformation.com. Ed. Robert Bevan. Pub. Louise Rogers TEL 44-20-7861-6309. Adv. contact Bob Hemmings TEL 44-1789-766833. Circ: 29,642.

BUILDING RESEARCH JOURNAL. see *BUILDING AND CONSTRUCTION*

720 621.47   USA
BUILDINGS INSIDE & OUT. Text in English. 1991. s-a. looseleaf. free. bk.rev. back issues avail. **Document type:** *Newsletter, Trade.* **Description:** Covers private and public initiatives in research and development of passive solar and climate responsive design strategies. Also includes conferences, workshops, computer tools, publications, and member news.
Published by: Passive Solar Industries Council, 1331 H St, N W, Ste 1000, Washington, DC 20005-4706. TEL 202-628-7400, FAX 202-393-5043, PSICouncil@aol.com, http://www.psic.org. Ed. Will Zachmann. R&P Will Zachman. Circ: 500.

721   GBR   ISSN 0263-7960
HD7333.A3
➤ **BUILT ENVIRONMENT.** Text in English. 1975. q. GBP 95 to individuals; GBP 185 to institutions & libraries (effective 2005). adv. bk.rev. illus. back issues avail.; reprints avail. **Description:** Each issue is devoted to a different theme of current interest to academics, students and practitioners in urban, regional and environmental planning and architecture.
Formerly (until 1978): Built Environment Quarterly (0308-1508)
Related titles: Online - full text ed.
Indexed: AIAP, API, AbHyg, BldManAb, ErgAb, GEOBASE, HRIS, MEA&I, RICS, SUSA, SWA.
—BLDSC (2366.039600), CISTI, IE, Infotrieve, ingenta, Linda Hall. **CCC.**
Published by: Alexandrine Press, 1 The Farthings, Marcham, Oxon OX13 6QD, United Kingdom. TEL 44-1865-391518, FAX 44-1865-391687, alexandrine@rudkinassociates.co.uk. Eds. David Banister, Major Sir Peter Hall. Pub. Ann Rudkin. Circ: 645.

➤ **BULLETIN MONUMENTAL.** see *ARCHAEOLOGY*

➤ **BUNDESVEREINIGUNG DER LANDESENTWICKLUNGSGESELLSCHAFTEN UND HEIMSTAETTEN. MITTEILUNGEN.** see *HOUSING AND URBAN PLANNING*

721   FIN   ISSN 0357-6574
BYGDESERIEN. Text in Swedish. 1979. a.
Published by: Aalands Folkminnesfoerbund, Aalands Museum, Obbergsvaegen 1, Mariehamn, 22101, Finland.

BYGG & TEKNIK. see *BUILDING AND CONSTRUCTION*

720   NOR   ISSN 0007-7518
NA6
BYGGEKUNST; the Norwegian review of architecture. Text in English, Norwegian. 1919. 8/yr. NOK 650 in Norway; NOK 750 in Scandinavia; NOK 830 in Europe; NOK 870 elsewhere; NOK 95 newsstand/cover (effective 2001). adv. bk.rev. charts; illus. index. back issues avail. **Document type:** *Magazine, Trade.*
Indexed: AIAP, API, BHA.
—BLDSC (2939.520000), IE, ingenta. **CCC.**
Published by: Norske Arkitekters Landsforbund/National Association of Norwegian Architects, Josefines Gate 34, Oslo, 0351, Norway. TEL 47-23-33-25-00, FAX 47-23-33-25-50, redaksjon@byggekunst.no, http://www.byggekunst.no. Ed. Bjoern Larsen. Adv. contact Tom Andresen. color page NOK 22,000, B&W page NOK 16,600. Circ: 6,000. **Co-sponsors:** Norske Landskapsarkitekters Forening; Norske Interioerarkitekters Landsforening.

720 690 747   DNK   ISSN 0904-3241
BYGGEPLADS DANMARK. Text in Danish. 1988. q. DKK 210; DKK 65 newsstand/cover (effective 2001). adv. illus. back issues avail.; reprints avail. **Document type:** *Trade.*
Description: Covers recent building projects in Denmark with detailed descriptions and color photos.
Published by: NOVA Kommunikation A-S, Solvang 23, PO Box 146, Allerod, 3450, Denmark. TEL 45-48-17-00-78, FAX 45-48-17-13-65, info@nova-media.dk, http://www.byggeplads.dk. Ed. Joern Henrik Joergensen. Pub., R&P Poul Jacobsen. Adv. contact Steffen Aunoe. B&W page DKK 17,800, color page DKK 20,200; trim 190 x 270. Circ: 10,000.

720 690   SWE   ISSN 0348-6885
BYGGNADSKULTUR. Text in Swedish. 1977. q. SEK 225 (effective 1996).
Indexed: BHA.
Published by: Svenska Foereningen foer Byggnadsvaard, Fack 6442, Stockholm, 11382, Sweden. TEL 46-8-30-37-855, FAX 46-8-30-87-99.

▼ *new title*   ➤ *refereed*   ✳ *unverified*   ♦ *full entry avail.*

A

720 DNK ISSN 1603-5267
BYGNINGSKULTURENS DAG. Text in Danish. 1996. a. back issues avail. **Document type:** *Monographic series, Academic/Scholarly.*
Former titles (until 2003): Bygningskultur og Haandvaerk (1602-6888); (until 2002): Bygningskulturens Dag (1399-9486)
Published by: (Bygningskulturelt Raad), Kulturministeriet, Kulturarvsstyrelsen/Danish Ministry of Culture. Cultural Heritage Division, Slotsholmsgade 1, Copenhagen K, 1216, Denmark. TEL 45-72-265253, FAX 45-72-265101, kuas@kuas.dk, http://www.bygningskulturensdag.dk, http://www.kuas.dk.

720 CHL ISSN 0716-3622
C.A. CIUDAD/ARQUITECTURA. Variant title: Revista Oficial del Colegio de Arquitectos de Chile. Text in Spanish. 1968. q. USD 21 domestic; USD 83 in the Americas; USD 106 elsewhere (effective 2002). adv. **Document type:** *Academic/Scholarly.*
Indexed: AIAP.
Published by: Colegio de Arquitectos de Chile, Av Libertador B O'Higgins 115, Santiago, Chile. TEL 56-2-6391629, FAX 56-2-6398769, secretari@colegio-arquitectos.cl, http://www.revistaca.cl, http://www.coarq.com. Circ: 3,500.

C O D I A. see *ENGINEERING—Civil Engineering*

711.4 BRA ISSN 1413-2095
NA2000
CADERNOS DE ARQUITETURA E URBANISMO. Text in Portuguese. 1993. s-a. **Document type:** *Journal, Academic/Scholarly.*
Indexed: BHA.
Published by: Pontificia Universidade Catolica de Minas Gerais, Av Dom Jose Gaspar, 500, C Eucaristico, Belo Horizonte, MG 30535-610, Brazil. TEL 55-31-33194271, FAX 55-31-33194129, arquitet@pucminas.br. Circ: 1,000.

720 624 BRA ISSN 1676-6679
➤ **CADERNOS DE POS-GRADUACAO EN ARQUITETURA E URBANISMO.** Text in Portuguese; Abstracts in English. 2001. a. free (effective 2005). **Document type:** *Journal, Academic/Scholarly.*
Published by: Universidade Presbiteriana Mackenzie (Subsidiary of: Instituto Presbiteriano Mackenzie), Rua da Consolacao 896, Pr.2, Sao Paulo-SP, SP 01302-907, Brazil. FAX 55-11-32368302, 55-11-32142582, biblio.per@mackenzie.br, http://www.mackenzie.com.br. Ed. Jose Geraldo Simoes Junior.

720 FRA
CAHIERS DE CANTERCEL. Text in French. a. EUR 42.70 for 3 yrs. (effective 2003).
Published by: Edisud, 3120 route d'Avignon - La Calde, Aix-en-Provence, 13090, France. TEL 33-4-42216144, FAX 33-4-42215620, info@edisud.com, http://www.edisud.com. Eds. Daniel Croci, Jean-pierre Campredon. Pub. Mr. C Y Chaudoreille.

720 USA ISSN 1040-4317
CALIFORNIA ARCHITECTURE AND ARCHITECTS. Text in English. 1980. irreg., latest vol.6, 1986. price varies. **Document type:** *Monographic series.*
Published by: Hennessey & Ingalls, Inc., 8321 Campion Dr., Los Angeles, CA 90045. TEL 310-458-9074, FAX 310-394-2928.

728 USA ISSN 1545-7915
NA7100
CALIFORNIA HOME AND DESIGN. Text in English. 1993. bi-m. USD 36; USD 4 newsstand/cover (effective 2003). adv. **Document type:** *Consumer.*
Former titles (until 2001): Northern California Home and Design; (until 1995): San Francisco Gentry
Published by: 18 Media Inc., 618 Santa Cruz Ave, Menlo Park, CA 94025. TEL 650-324-1818, FAX 650-324-1888, info@18media.com, http://www.18media.com. Ed. Elsie M. Floriani. Pub. Sloane Citron. R&P Dot Juby. Adv. contact Richard Acquaviva. color page USD 2,995; trim 10.88 x 8.38. Circ: 64,000.

728 747 ITA ISSN 1125-1352
IL CAMINO. Text in Italian. 1978. q. EUR 8 newsstand/cover (effective 2005). adv. **Document type:** *Magazine, Consumer.*
Published by: Di Baio Editore SpA, Via Luigi Settembrini 11, Milan, MI 20124, Italy. TEL 39-02-674951, FAX 39-02-67495228, http://www.dibaio.com. Ed. Giuseppe Maria Jonghi Lavarini. Circ: 70,000.

720 CAN ISSN 0008-2872
CANADIAN ARCHITECT. Text in English. 1956. m. CND 49.95 domestic; USD 49.95 in United States; USD 93.95 elsewhere (effective 2005). adv. bk.rev. charts; illus.; tr.lit. index. **Document type:** *Magazine, Trade.* **Description:** Highlights innovative trends in building design, products and technology as well as innovative business techniques.
Related titles: Microfiche ed.: (from MML); Microfilm ed.: (from MML); Microform ed.: (from MML); Online - full text ed.: (from EBSCO Publishing, Micromedia ProQuest, Northern Light Technology, Inc., ProQuest Information & Learning).
Indexed: AIAP, API, ArtInd, BHA, CBCABus, CBCARef, CBPI, CPerl, PCI, RASB.
—BLDSC (3017.180000), CISTI, IE, Infotrieve, ingenta. **CCC.**
Published by: Business Information Group, 12 Concorde Pl, Ste 800, Toronto, ON M3C 4J2, Canada. TEL 416-442-5600, 800-668-2374, FAX 416-442-2191, http://www.cdnarchitect.com, http://www.businessinformationgroup.ca. Circ: 10,770.

720 CAN ISSN 1195-8960
CANADIAN ARCHIVAL INVENTORY SERIES, ARCHITECTURAL RECORDS. Text in English. 1993. irreg. **Document type:** *Monographic series.*
Published by: University of Calgary Press, University of Calgary, Faculty of Education ETD 722, 2500 University Dr N W, Calgary, AB T2N 1N4, Canada. ucpmail@ucalgary.ca, http://www.ucalgary.ca/ucpress, http://www.uofcpress.com.

CANADIAN INTERIORS. see *INTERIOR DESIGN AND DECORATION*

720 747 JPN
CASA BRUTUS. Text in Japanese. m. JPY 10,560 (effective 2005). adv. **Document type:** *Magazine, Consumer.* **Description:** Covers interior design to furniture, dinnerware to gardening, remodeling and good dining for upscale Japanese audience.
Published by: Magazine House, Ltd., 3-13-10 Ginza, Chuo-ku, Tokyo, 104-8003, Japan. http://www.brutusonline.com/casa/, http//:www.magazine.co.jp.

CASA CLAUDIA; a revista para morar melhor. see *INTERIOR DESIGN AND DECORATION*

728 ROM
CASA DE VACANTA. Text in Romanian. m. ROL 252,000 (effective 2002). adv. **Document type:** *Magazine, Consumer.*
Published by: Casa Lux, Bd. Nicolae Titulescu nr. 1, bl. A7, sc. 3, etajele 6, Bucharest, Romania. TEL 40-21-2110610, FAX 40-21-2110610, secretariat@casalux.ro, http://www.casalux.ro.

CASA LUX. see *INTERIOR DESIGN AND DECORATION*

720 ITA ISSN 0008-7181
NA4
CASABELLA; rivista internazionale di architettura. Text in English, Italian. 1928. m. (10/yr.). EUR 88.20 (effective 2004). adv. bk.rev. abstr.; charts; illus. cum.index. reprints avail. **Document type:** *Magazine, Consumer.*
Former titles (until 1964): Casabella Continuita (1125-503X); (until 1954): Costruzioni Casabella (1122-3812); (until 1939): Casabella (1125-5021); (until 1932): La Casa Bella (1122-3405)
Indexed: AIAP, API, ArtHuCI, ArtInd, BHA, CurCont, RASB.
—BLDSC (3057.985000), IE, Infotrieve, ingenta. **CCC.**
Published by: Arnoldo Mondadori Editore SpA, Via Mondadori 1, Segrate, 20090, Italy. TEL 39-02-66814363, FAX 39-030-3198412, http://www.mondadori.com. Circ: 46,000.

728 747 ITA ISSN 1591-3341
CASE AL MARE. Text in Italian. 1980. a. price varies. **Document type:** *Catalog, Consumer.*
Published by: Di Baio Editore SpA, Via Luigi Settembrini 11, Milan, MI 20124, Italy. TEL 39-02-674951, FAX 39-02-67495228, http://www.dibaio.com. Ed. Giuseppe Maria Jonghi Lavarini. Circ: 48,000.

728 747 ITA ISSN 1125-1328
CASE DI CAMPAGNA. Text in Italian. 1979. bi-m. EUR 8 newsstand/cover (effective 2005). **Document type:** *Magazine, Consumer.*
Published by: Di Baio Editore SpA, Via Luigi Settembrini 11, Milan, MI 20124, Italy. TEL 39-02-674951, FAX 39-02-67495228, http://www.dibaio.com. Ed. Giuseppe Maria Jonghi Lavarini. Circ: 62,000.

728 747 ITA ISSN 1125-131X
CASE DI MONTAGNA. Text in Italian. 1978. 3/yr. EUR 8 newsstand/cover (effective 2005). adv. **Document type:** *Magazine, Consumer.*
Published by: Di Baio Editore SpA, Via Luigi Settembrini 11, Milan, MI 20124, Italy. TEL 39-02-674951, FAX 39-02-67495228, http://www.dibaio.com. Ed. Giuseppe Maria Jonghi Lavarini. Circ: 48,000.

720 ITA ISSN 0392-3355
CASTELLUM. Text in Italian; Summaries in English. 1965. s-a. back issues avail. **Document type:** *Journal, Academic/Scholarly.*
Indexed: BHA.
Published by: Istituto Italiano dei Castelli, Castel Sant' Angelo, Rome, Italy. http://www.castit.it. Ed. Rosalbino Fasanella. Pub. Flavio Conti. Circ: 2,900.

720 ESP ISSN 1138-2430
CATALOGOS DE ARQUITECTURA. Text in Spanish. 1997. q.
—CINDOC.
Published by: Colegio Oficial de Arquitectos de Murcia, Jara Carrillo, 5, Murcia, 30004, Spain. TEL 34-968-213268, coamu@coamu.es, http://www.coamu.es/.

▼ **CEDAR LIVING.** see *LIFESTYLE*

720 VEN ISSN 0506-600X
➤ **CENTRO DE INVESTIGACIONES HISTORICAS Y ESTETICAS. BOLETIN.** Text in Spanish. 1964. s-a. **Document type:** *Academic/Scholarly.* **Description:** Presents historical research on Latin American architecture.
Indexed: AIAP, AmH&L, BHA, HistAb.
Published by: Universidad Central de Venezuela, Facultad de Arquitectura y Urbanismo, Caracas, Venezuela. FAX 58-2-7526718.

720 ITA
CENTRO INTERNAZIONALE DI STUDI DI ARCHITETTURA "ANDREA PALLADIO" DI VICENZA. ANNALI DI ARCHITETTURA. Text in Italian. 1959. a. bk.rev. **Description:** Emphasizes the study of Palladio and Renaissance architecture, with news on the activities of the center.
Indexed: AIAP, API, BHA.
Address: Basilica Palladiana, Domus Comestabilis, C.P. 835, Vicenza, VI 36100, Italy. Ed. Fernando Marias.

720.9 USA ISSN 1532-5563
NA957
CENTROPA. Text in English. 2001 (January). 3/yr. USD 65 domestic to individuals; USD 75 foreign to individuals; USD 130 domestic to institutions; USD 140 foreign to institutions (effective 2005). **Document type:** *Academic/Scholarly.*
Indexed: AmH&L, ArtInd, HistAb.
Address: 250 Mercer Street, Ste. B-1601, New York, NY 10012. http://www.artworlds.org/centropa.htm.

720 643.7 666 FRA ISSN 1259-0657
CERAMAGAZINE; le magazine des professionnels du carreau et de la pierre naturelle. Text in French. m. adv.
Published by: Edial Editions, 126 rue du Temple, Paris, 75003, France. TEL 33-1-44788778, FAX 33-1-44788779, cm.redaction@edial.fr, http://www.edial.fr. Ed. Nathalie Vaultrin. Adv. contact Frederic Trumeau. Circ: 10,000.

CERCLE HUTOIS DES SCIENCES ET BEAUX-ARTS. ANNALES. see *HISTORY—History Of Europe*

720 745.5 GBR ISSN 0141-559X
CHARLES RENNIE MACKINTOSH SOCIETY NEWSLETTER. Text in English. 1973. 3/yr. GBP 25 to individuals; GBP 45 to libraries; GBP 15 to students (effective 2001). bk.rev. back issues avail. **Document type:** *Newsletter, Academic/Scholarly.* **Description:** Aims to foster interest in and conserve the buildings and artifacts designed by Mackintosh and his contemporaries.
Indexed: AIAP, API, DAAI.
Published by: Charles Rennie Mackintosh Society, Queens Cross, 870 Garscube Rd, Glasgow, G20 7EL, United Kingdom. TEL 44-141-946-6600, FAX 44-141-945-2321, info@crmsociety.com, http://www.crmsociety.com. Eds. Frank A Walker, Stuart Robertson TEL 44-141-945-5500. R&P Stuart Robertson TEL 44-141-945-5500. Circ: 1,500.

728 796.5 635 CZE
CHATAR & CHALUPAR✶ ; casopis pro kutily, chatare a chalupare. Text in Czech. 1969. m. CZK 264 (effective 1998). abstr.; illus. **Document type:** *Magazine, Consumer.*
Formerly (until 1993): Chatar (0323-1437)
Published by: Casopisy pro Volny Cas s.r.o., Saldova 7, Prague 8, 186 00, Czech Republic. TEL 420-2-24142719, FAX 420-2-24142718, pribylova@obchod.economia.cz, casopisy@provolnycas.cz.

726 ITA ISSN 1125-1360
CHIESA OGGI. Text in Italian. 1992. q. **Document type:** *Magazine, Trade.*
Published by: Di Baio Editore SpA, Via Luigi Settembrini 11, Milan, MI 20124, Italy. TEL 39-02-674951, FAX 39-02-67495228, http://www.dibaio.com.

720 CHN
CHINESE ARCHITECTURE/ZHONGGUO JIANZHU. Text in English. q.
Published by: Zhongguo Jianzhu Jishu Fazhan Zhongxin/China Architectural Technology Development Centre, 19 Chegongzhuang Dajie, Beijing, 100044, China. TEL 8317744. Ed. Zhang Long.

720 CHN ISSN 1006-7329
CHONGQING JIANZHU DAXUE XUEBAO/CHONGQING JIANZHU UNIVERSITY. JOURNAL. Text in Chinese. 1957. bi-m.
Formerly (until 1995): Chongqing Jianzhu Gongcheng Xueyuan Xuebao/Chongqing Institute of Architecture and Engineering. Journal (1000-5838)
Related titles: Online - full text ed.: (from East View Information Services, WanFang Data Corp.).
—BLDSC (4729.336000), IE.
Published by: Chongqing Jianzhu Daxue, Shapingba Bei Jie, B-qu, Zonghelou 403, Chongqing, 400045, China. TEL 86-21-65120556, FAX 86-21-65120555, jian@chinajournal.net.cn, http://cqjzdxxb.periodicals.net.cn/default.html.

CHRONIQUE MENSUELLE. see *ARCHAEOLOGY*

726 704.948 GBR ISSN 0262-4966
CHURCHSCAPE; annual review of the Council for the Care of Churches. Text in English. 1981. a. GBP 2.95. adv. bk.rev. bibl.; illus. **Document type:** *Newsletter, Bibliography.*
Indexed: BHA, RILM.
Published by: Council for the Care of Churches, Fielden House, 13 Little College St, London, SW1P 3SH, United Kingdom. TEL 0171-222-3793, FAX 0171-222-3794. Ed., Adv. contact Jonathan Goodchild. Circ: 1,500.

720 ITA
CITTA E CAMPAGNA. Text in Italian. m.
Address: Via Concordia, 20, Rome, RM 00183, Italy. Ed. Mario Ciranna.

724.2 720.9 USA ISSN 1076-2922
NA260
➤ **THE CLASSICIST.** Text in English. 1995. a. USD 39.95 (effective 2003). adv. **Document type:** *Academic/Scholarly.*
Description: Devoted to the theory and practice of architectural and artistic classicism. Contains essays on architectural theory, education, urbanism, and archeology, as well as practical information on building technology and a section on allied arts.
Indexed: AIAP.
Published by: Institute of Classical Architecture and Classical America, 20 W. 44th St., New York, NY 10036-6604. institute@classicist.org, http://www.classicist.org.

➤ **CLAVIS KLEINE KUNSTHISTORISCHE MONOGRAFIEEN.** see *ART*

➤ **CLAVIS KUNSTHISTORISCHE MONOGRAFIEEN.** see *ART*

720 700 USA
CLEMSON UNIVERSITY. COLLEGE OF ARCHITECTURE. JOURNAL; a journal of educational thought. Text in English. 1967. a. USD 6. bk.rev. charts; illus.; stat.
Formerly: Clemson University. College of Architecture. Semester Review (0009-871X)
Indexed: AIAP.
Published by: (Clemson Architectural Foundation), Clemson University, College of Architecture, Clemson, SC 29631. TEL 803-656-3081, FAX 803-656-3896. Ed. L G Craig. Circ: 3,000.

729 DEU ISSN 1434-0984
CLOUD-CUCKOO-LAND/WOLKENKUCKUCKSHEIM - CLOUD-CUCKOO-LAND - VOZDUSHNYI ZAMOK; international journal of architectural theory. Text in English, German, Russian. 1996. s-a. back issues avail. **Document type:** *Journal, Academic/Scholarly.* **Description:** Intends to create a space between heaven and earth, a space where abstract architectural ideas are confronted with practice and plain reality with creative aesthetic approaches.
Media: Online - full text.
Published by: Brandenburg University of Technology Cottbus, c/o LS Theorie der Architektur, BTU, Postfach 101344, Cottbus, 03013, Germany. wolke1@tu-cottbus.de, fuehr@tu-cottbus.de, http://www.cloud-cuckoo.net, http://www.mcgill.ca/wolke. Ed. Eduard Fuehr.

711.1 NLD ISSN 1571-0882
CODESIGN; international journal of cocreation in design and the arts. Text in English. 4/yr. GBP 125, USD 206 combined subscription to institutions print & online eds. (effective 2006). **Document type:** *Journal, Academic/Scholarly.* **Description:** Reports new research and scholarship in principles, procedures and techniques relevant to collaboration in design.
Related titles: Online - full text ed.: ISSN 1745-3755. GBP 119, USD 196 to institutions (effective 2006) (from EBSCO Publishing, IngentaConnect, Swets Information Services).
Indexed: C&ISA, E&CAJ, IAA.
—BLDSC (3292.783015), IE.
Published by: Taylor & Francis The Netherlands (Subsidiary of: Taylor & Francis Group), Schipolweg 107 C, PO Box 447, Leiden, 2316 XC, Netherlands. TEL 31-715-243080, FAX 31-715-234571, infoho@swets.nl, http://www.tandf.co.uk/journals/titles/15710882.asp, http://www.tandf.co.uk/swets.asp. Ed. Stephen A R Scrivener. **Subscr. in N. America to:** Taylor & Francis Inc., Customer Services Dept, 325 Chestnut St, 8th Fl, Philadelphia, PA 19106. TEL 215-625-8900, 800-354-1420, FAX 215-625-8914. **Subscr. in Europe to:** Taylor & Francis Ltd.

720 ESP
COLECCION KORA. Text in Spanish. 1991. irreg., latest vol.9, 1996. price varies. **Document type:** *Monographic series, Academic/Scholarly.*
Published by: Universidad de Sevilla, Secretariado de Publicaciones, Porvenir 27, Sevilla, 41013, Spain. TEL 34-95-4487444, FAX 34-95-4487443, secpub10@us.es, http://www.us.es/publius/inicio.html.

720 ESP
COLEGIO OFICIAL DE DELINEANTES DE VALENCIA. BOLETIN INFORMATIVO. Text in Spanish. q. **Document type:** *Bulletin.*
Published by: Colegio Oficial de Delineantes de Valencia/Valencia College of Draughtsmen, G.V. Marques del Turia 24, 1o 1a, Valencia, 46005, Spain. TEL 34-96-334-1172. Ed. Gonzalo Divar Loyola.

720 ZAF
COLIMPEX ARCHITECT'S EXECUPAD. Text in Afrikaans, English. a. adv.
Published by: Colimpex Africa (Pty) Ltd., PO Box 5838, Johannesburg, 2000, South Africa.

712 USA
➤ **COLLOQUIUM ON THE HISTORY OF LANDSCAPE ARCHITECTURE. PAPERS.** Text in English. 1972. irreg., latest vol.18, 1998. price varies. **Document type:** *Proceedings, Academic/Scholarly.*
—BLDSC (3631.047000).
Published by: Dumbarton Oaks, 1703 32nd St, N W, Washington, DC 20007. TEL 202-339-6401, FAX 202-339-6419, pulbications@doaks.org, http://www.doaks.org/publications.html. Circ: 1,000.

▼ ➤ **COLUMBIA SEMINAR ON ART IN SOCIETY.** see *ART*

720 CAN
COLUMNS. Text in English. 1978. q. free. adv. **Document type:** *Newsletter.*
Formerly: Saskatchewan Association of Architects. Newsletter
Published by: Alberta Association of Architects, 10515 Saskatchewan Dr, Edmonton, AB T6E 4S1, Canada. TEL 403-439-1431. Ed., Adv. contact Margaret Gates. Circ: 190.
Co-sponsors: Manitoba Association of Architects; Saskatchewan Association of Architects.

720 JPN
COMMERCIAL ARCHITECTURE. Text in Japanese. 1956. 12/yr. USD 458 (effective 1999).
Published by: Intercontinental Marketing Corp., I.P.O. Box 5056, Tokyo, 100-3191, Japan. TEL 81-3-3661-7458, tc9w-ball@asahi-net.or.jp.

COMMERCIAL BUILDING. see *BUILDING AND CONSTRUCTION*

729 IRL ISSN 1649-1645
COMMERCIAL INTERIORS OF IRELAND. Text in English. 1997. a. adv. **Document type:** *Magazine, Trade.*
Published by: Pembroke Publishing Ltd., Unit F5, The Bymac Centre, North West Business Park, Dublin, 15, Ireland. TEL 353-1-8224477, FAX 353-1-8224485, pembrokepublishing@eircom.net. adv.: color page EUR 2,153. Circ: 6,000 (controlled).

700 720 USA ISSN 1058-6539
NA2340
COMPETITIONS (LOUISVILLE). Text in English. 1991. q. USD 38 domestic; USD 42 in Canada & Mexico; USD 60 elsewhere; USD 25 to students (effective 2005). back issues avail. **Document type:** *Magazine, Trade.* **Description:** For artists, planners, and architects; provides current information to the potential competition participant.
Related titles: Supplement(s): Competition Hotline.
Indexed: AIAP.
Published by: Competition Project, Inc., PO Box 20445, Louisville, KY 40250. hotline@competitions.org, http://www.competitions.org/subscribe/about.cfm?CFID=1263842&CFTOKEN=694026. Ed., R&P Dr. G Stanley Collyer. Circ: 1,700 (paid and controlled).

720 ESP ISSN 0214-4832
N7
COMPOSICION ARQUITECTONICA; art & architecture. Text in English, Spanish. 1989. 3/yr. USD 75. adv. illus. back issues avail.
Indexed: AIAP, API.
Published by: (Fundacion F. Obregon Eizaguirre, Instituto de Arte y Humanidades), Comercial Atheneum S.A., Rufino Gonzalez, 26, Madrid, 28037, Spain. TEL 34-1-7542062. Ed. Javier Cenicacelaya.

CONGRES ARCHEOLOGIQUE DE FRANCE. see *ARCHAEOLOGY*

CONSERVATION; G C I newsletter. see *ART*

CONSTRUCTION CRITERIA BASE ONLINE. see *BUILDING AND CONSTRUCTION*

CONSTRUCTION HISTORY. see *BUILDING AND CONSTRUCTION*

720 USA
CONTEMPORARY ARCHITECTS✶. Text in English. 1980. quinquennial. USD 160.
Published by: St. James Press, 27500 Drake Rd, Farmington Hills, Detroit, MI 48331-3535. TEL 800-345-6392, http://www.stjames.com. Ed. Muriel Emanuel.

CONTEMPORARY ART CENTRE OF SOUTH AUSTRALIA. BROADSHEET. see *ART*

CONTEMPORARY STONE & TILE DESIGN. see *BUILDING AND CONSTRUCTION*

720 ITA ISSN 0010-809X
NA4
CONTROSPAZIO/COUNTERSPACE; architettura e urbanistica. Text in Italian. 1969-1981; N.S. 1988. bi-m. EUR 31 (effective 2004). bk.rev. bibl.; charts; illus.; tr.lit. **Document type:** *Journal, Academic/Scholarly.*
Indexed: AIAP, API, BHA.
Published by: Gangemi Editore, Piazza San Pantaleo 4, Rome, Italy. TEL 39-06-6872774, FAX 39-06-68806189, gangemieditorerc@tin.it, http://www.gangemieditore.it. Ed. Marcello Fabbri. Circ: 7,000.

CORDELL'S WHO'S WHO IN BUILDING: DEVELOPERS. see *BUILDING AND CONSTRUCTION*

720 USA ISSN 0731-5384
NA1
CORNELL JOURNAL OF ARCHITECTURE. Text in English. 1981. biennial. USD 30. **Document type:** *Academic/Scholarly.*
Indexed: AIAP, API.
Published by: Cornell University, School of Architecture, 143 E Sibley Hall, Ithaca, NY 14853. TEL 607-255-5236, FAX 607-255-0291, http://www.architecture.cornell.edu/. Ed. Stephanie A Goto. R&P Pablo Gare.

728 DEU ISSN 1432-959X
COUNTRY STYLE; das Magazin fuer Wohnkultur und Lebensart. Text in German. 1997. q. EUR 28; EUR 8 newsstand/cover (effective 2003). adv. **Document type:** *Magazine, Consumer.*
Related titles: Online - full text ed.
Published by: Klocke Verlag GmbH, Hoefeweg 40, Bielefeld, 33619, Germany. TEL 49-521-911110, FAX 49-521-9111112, info@country-style.de, http://www.country-style.de, http://www.klocke-verlag.de. Ed., Pub. Martina Klocke. Adv. contact Wolfgang Pohl. B&W page EUR 4,750, color page EUR 8,400; trim 210 x 297. Circ: 54,846 (paid and controlled).
Subscr. to: Leser-Club Merkur, Postfach 1118, Neckarsulm 74148, Germany. TEL 49-7132-959205. **Distr. by:** Special Interest, Waldstr 70, Dietzenbach 63128, Germany. TEL 49-6074-8235-0.

728 USA ISSN 1538-3911
COUNTRY STYLE HOMES, PLANS AND DESIGNS. Text in English. 1991. s-a. USD 8; USD 3.98 newsstand/cover (effective 2000). adv. back issues avail. **Document type:** *Magazine, Consumer.* **Description:** Includes country houses inspired by classic designs of yesteryear; Victorian, Colonial, farmhouses, ranches and other types.
Published by: HomeStyles Publishing & Marketing, Inc., 213 E. 4th St., 4th Fl., St. Paul, MN 55101-1603. TEL 651-602-5000, 888-626-2026, FAX 651-602-5001, http://www.homestyles.com. Ed. Josh Kimball. Pub. Diana Jasan. R&P Roger Heegaard. Adv. contact Shelley Junker. B&W page USD 3,910, color page USD 4,830; trim 8 x 10.75. Circ: 75,900 (paid).

COUNTRYPOLITAN HOMES & PLANS. see *BUILDING AND CONSTRUCTION*

720 GBR ISSN 1473-835X
➤ **COUNTRYSIDE BUILDING.** Text in English. 1984. q. GBP 20 domestic; GBP 35 foreign (effective 2004). adv. bk.rev. abstr.; bibl.; charts; illus.; stat. 44 p./no.; back issues avail. **Document type:** *Journal, Academic/Scholarly.*
Former titles (until 2000): Rural Design and Building (1362-7376); (until 1999): Farm Buildings and Engineering (0265-5373); Which was formed by the 1984 merger of: Farm Building Digest (0014-7877); Farm Buildings Association. Journal
Related titles: E-mail ed.
Indexed: AEA, BrCerAb, IndVet, PN&I, RICS, VetBull.
—CISTI.
Published by: (Rural Design and Building Association), Ghyll House Publishing Ltd., ATSS House, Station Rd. East, Stowmarket, Suffolk IP14 1RQ, United Kingdom. TEL 44-1449-676049, FAX 44-1449-770028, secretary@rdba.org.uk, http://www.rdba.org.uk, http://www.ghyllhouse.co.uk. Ed., R&P Tony Hutchinson. Adv. contacts Chris Hutchinson, Tony Hutchinson. Circ: 20,000.

➤ **COVJEK I PROSTOR.** see *ART*

720 USA ISSN 0277-6863
NA1
CRIT. Text in English. 1976. q. USD 25 in US & Canada to libraries; USD 100 elsewhere to libraries; free to members (effective 2005). adv. bk.rev.; film rev. illus. back issues avail. **Document type:** *Journal, Academic/Scholarly.* **Description:** Student journal providing a collection of art and literature reflecting current concerns, visions and opinions of architecture students in North America.
Formerly (until 1977): Telesis (Washington) (0364-6521)
Related titles: Online - full text ed.
Indexed: AIAP.
—BLDSC (3487.385500).
Published by: American Institute of Architecture Students, 1735 New York Ave, N W, Washington, DC 20006. TEL 202-626-7472, FAX 202-626-7414, aiasnatl@aol.com, http://www.aiasnatl.org/critonline/. Ed. R. Todd Gabbard. Circ: 10,000.

▼ new title ➤ refereed ✶ unverified ♦ full entry avail.

720 ITA ISSN 0392-5803
CODEN: CLNRDG
CRONACHE CASTELLANE. Text in Italian. 1964. q. back issues avail. **Document type:** *Bulletin, Trade.*
Published by: Istituto Italiano dei Castelli, Castel Sant' Angelo, Rome, Italy. http://www.castit.it. Circ: 2,900.

720 ESP ISSN 0212-5633
NA5
EL CROQUIS; de arquitectura y diseno. Text in English, Spanish. 1982. bi-m. EUR 190 domestic; EUR 248 in Europe; EUR 248 in US & Canada; EUR 301 elsewhere (effective 2005). adv. 240 p./no.; back issues avail. **Document type:** *Monographic series.* **Description:** Publishes information on recent works and projects in architecture, design and construction.
Related titles: Online - full text ed.
Indexed: AIAP, API, RILM.
—CINDOC, IE, Infotrieve. **CCC.**
Published by: El Croquis Editorial, Av. Reyes Catolicos 9, El Escorial, Madrid, 28280, Spain. TEL 34-91-8969410, FAX 34-91-8969411, elcroquis@elcroquis.es, http://www.elcroquis.es/default.asp. Ed., R&P Paloma Poveda. Pubs. Fernando Marquez Cecilia, Richard C Levene. Adv. contact Cristina Poveda. color page EUR 3,000. Circ: 30,000.
Dist. by: Asociacion de Revistas Culturales de Espana, Hortaleza, 75, Madrid 28004, Spain. TEL 34-91-3086066, FAX 34-91-3199267, info@arce.es, http://www.arce.es.

CRYSTAL PALACE FOUNDATION NEWS. see *HISTORY—History Of Europe*

720 USA ISSN 1095-4872
NA1
CSA NEWSLETTER. (Center of the Study of Architecture) Text in English. 1994. 3/yr. back issues avail. **Document type:** *Newsletter.*
Related titles: Online - full text ed.
Published by: Center for the Study of Architecture, Box 60, Bryn Mawr, PA 19010-0060. TEL 610-526-7925, FAX 610-526-7926, neiteljo@brynmawr.edu, http://www.csa.brynmawr.edu/web1/newslet.html.

720.972 MEX ISSN 0185-5131
F1219.3.A6
CUADERNOS DE ARQUITECTURA MESOAMERICANA. Text in Spanish. 1984. s-a. MXP 40 per issue (effective 2000). **Description:** Includes articles on Mesoamerican and Prehispanic architecture. Features essays and reviews that promote building restoration.
Indexed: AIAP, AICP, API, AnthLit.
Published by: Universidad Nacional Autonoma de Mexico, Facultad de Arquitectura, c/o Arq. Enrique X. de Anda, Circuito Interior de Cd. Universitaria, Deleg. Coyoacan, Mexico City, DF 04510, Mexico. TEL 52-5-6220318, FAX 52-5-6166545, http://ce-atl.posgrado.unam.mx/.

720.902 MEX ISSN 0185-8572
NA753
CUADERNOS DE ARQUITECTURA VIRREINAL. Text in Spanish. 1985. irreg. (approx. 1/yr.). MXP 50 per issue (effective 2000). **Description:** Includes articles on Mexican architecture based on Spanish viceroyship, XIV to XVIII centuries.
Indexed: AIAP, API, BHA.
Published by: Universidad Nacional Autonoma de Mexico, Facultad de Arquitectura, c/o Arq. Enrique X. de Anda, Circuito Interior de Cd. Universitaria, Deleg. Coyoacan, Mexico City, DF 04510, Mexico. TEL 52-5-6220318, FAX 52-5-6166545, http://ce-atl.posgrado.unam.mx/. Ed. Juan Artigas.

720 690 CHN ISSN 1002-8439
CUNZHEN JIANSHE/TOWN OR VILLAGE DEVELOPMENT. Text in Chinese. bi-m.
Published by: Zhongguo Jianzhu Jishu Fazhan Zhongxin/China Architectural Technology Development Centre, 19 Chegongzhuang Dajie, Beijing, 100044, China. TEL 8992692. Ed. Ka Rucheng.

720 POL
CODEN: CZTEAY
CZASOPISMO TECHNICZNE. SERIA A: ARCHITEKTURA. Text in Polish; Contents page in Multiple languages. 1877; N.S. 1991. irreg. PLZ 20 (effective 2000). bk.rev. charts; illus. index. **Document type:** *Academic/Scholarly.*
Supersedes in part: Czasopismo Techniczne (0011-4561); Which was formerly (until 1883): Dzwignia (1230-2791)
—CASDDS, Linda Hall.
Published by: Politechnika Krakowska, Ul Warszawska 24, Krakow, 31155, Poland. TEL 48-12-6374289, FAX 48-12-6374289. Ed. Elzbieta Nachlik. Adv. contact Ewa Malochleb. Circ: 12,000.

720 DEU ISSN 1611-1370
NA3
D A M - JAHRBUCH. (Deutsches Architektur Museum) Text in German. 1980. a. EUR 39.95 (effective 2004). **Document type:** *Journal, Trade.*
Former titles (until 2002): D A M Architektur Jahrbuch (0942-7481); (until 1992): Jahrbuch fuer Architektur (0720-4590)
Indexed: IBR.
Published by: Prestel Verlag, Koeniginstr 9, Munich, 80539, Germany. TEL 49-89-3817090, FAX 49-89-38170935, info@prestel.de, http://www.prestel.de. Pub. Juergen Tesch. R&P Karin Kirmaier.

720 ESP ISSN 1137-8883
D A U. (Debats d'Arquitectura i Urbanisme) Key Title: DAU. Debats d'Arquitectura i Urbanisme. Text in Spanish, Catalan. 1996. 3/yr.
—CINDOC.
Published by: Colegio de Arquitectos de Cataluna/Col.legi d'Arquitectes de Catalunya, Placa Nova 5, Barcelona, 08002, Spain. TEL 34-93-3067814, FAX 34-93-4120068, quaderns@coac.es, http://quaderns.coac.net.

720 690 DEU ISSN 0721-1902
NA3
D B - DEUTSCHE BAUZEITUNG; Fachzeitschrift fuer Architekten und Bauingenieure. Text in German; Summaries in English. 1867. m. EUR 134.40; EUR 67.80 to students; EUR 12.20 newsstand/cover (effective 2004). adv. bk.rev. charts; illus.; tr.lit. index. **Document type:** *Magazine, Trade.*
Formerly: D B - Deutsche Bauzeitung - Die Bauzeitung (0011-4766)
Related titles: Microfiche ed.: (from IDC).
Indexed: AIAP, API, DIP, EIP, ExcerpMed, IBR, IBZ.
—BLDSC (3563.600000), IE, Infotrieve, ingenta. **CCC.**
Published by: (Bund Deutscher Baumeister, Architekten und Ingenieure e.V.), Konradin Verlag Robert Kohlhammer GmbH, Ernst Mey Str 8, Leinfelden-Echterdingen, 70771, Germany. TEL 49-711-75940, FAX 49-711-7594399, info@konradin.de, http://db.bauzeitung.de, http://www.konradin.de. Ed. Wilfried Dechau. Adv. contact Marianne Hipp. B&W page EUR 7,480, color page EUR 10,450. Circ: 35,510 (paid).

720 690 DEU ISSN 0011-4782
D B Z; Architektur, Entwurf, Detail. (Deutsche Bauzeitschrift) Text in German. 1953. m. EUR 138 domestic; EUR 144 foreign; EUR 66 to students; EUR 14.50 newsstand/cover (effective 2004). adv. charts; illus.; mkt.; stat.; tr.lit. index. **Document type:** *Magazine, Trade.* **Description:** Covers architecture, design and detail.
Indexed: AIAP, DIP, ExcerpMed, IBR, IBZ.
—BLDSC (3563.580000), IE, Infotrieve, ingenta.
Published by: Bauverlag BV GmbH (Subsidiary of: Springer Science+Business Media), Avenwedderstr 55, Guetersloh, 33311, Germany. TEL 49-5241-802119, FAX 49-5241-809582, ulrike.mattern@springer-sbm.com, http://www.bauverlag.de. Ed. Burkhard Froehlich. adv.: B&W page EUR 6,150, color page EUR 9,623; trim 225 x 297. Circ: 22,499 (paid and controlled).

643.5 ITA ISSN 1592-3452
D D B. (Design Diffusion Bagno) Variant title: Design Diffusion Bagno International. Text in Italian. 2001. bi-m. EUR 46 domestic; EUR 124, USD 120 foreign (effective 2001). adv. **Document type:** *Magazine, Trade.*
Published by: Design Diffusion Edizioni, Via Lucano 3, Milan, 20135, Italy. TEL 39-02-5516109, FAX 39-02-59902431, info@designdiffusion.com, http://www.designdiffusion.com/riviste/bagno/bagno.html.

D I B T MITTEILUNGEN. see *BUILDING AND CONSTRUCTION*

720 FRA ISSN 1167-0991
D L R MAGAZINE. (Distributeurs Loueurs Reparateurs) Text in French. 4/yr.
Published by: S.E.D.L., 28 rue Chapsal, Joinville-le-Pont, 94340, France. TEL 43-97-00-41, FAX 42-83-44-00. Ed. Francis Gilberg. Circ: 3,000.

720 FRA ISSN 1145-0835
NA673
D'A - D'ARCHITECTURES; le magazine professionnel de la creation architecturale. Text in French. 1989. 10/yr. adv.
Indexed: API.
Address: 25 rue du Petit Musc, Paris, 75004, France. TEL 33-1-53019700, FAX 33-1-53019719. Eds. Francis Rambert, Francois Lamarre. Adv. contact Herve Nourissat. Circ: 15,314.

720 ITA ISSN 1720-0342
D'A. D'ARCHITETTURA. Text in Italian. 1990. 3/yr. EUR 34 (effective 2005).
Published by: Gruppo Editoriale Motta, Via Branda Castiglioni 7, Milan, MI 20156, Italy. TEL 39-02-300761, FAX 39-02-38010046, http://www.mottaeditore.it.

DAKENRAAD. see *BUILDING AND CONSTRUCTION*

DE-, DIS-, EX-. see *ART*

720 PRI
DEARQUITECTURA. Text in Spanish. 1988. q. free. bk.rev. **Document type:** *Newsletter.*
Formerly: Universidad de Puerto Rico. Escuela de Arquitectura. Boletin Informativo
Published by: Universidad de Puerto Rico, Escuela de Arquitectura, Apdo 21909, San Juan, 00931-1909, Puerto Rico. FAX 787-763-5377. Ed. Humberto Betancourt.

720 ITA
DEMETRA. Text in Italian. 1991. s-a.
Published by: Ordine Architetti, Pianificatori, Paesaggisti e Conservatori della Provincia di Enna, Via L Da Vinci 9/A, Enna, EN 94100, Italy. TEL 39-0935-531590, http://www.en.architworld.it. **Subscr. to:** Cordaro Editore, Via Dei Calderai, 80, Palermo, PA 90133, Italy. TEL 39-91-6176348.

723 FRA ISSN 0998-5956
DEMEURE HISTORIQUE. Text in French. 1966. q. adv. bk.rev.
Published by: Association des Proprietaires de Monuments Historiques Prives, 57 quai de la Tournelle, Paris, 75005, France. TEL 33-01-55426000, FAX 33-01-43293644, http://www.demeure-historique.org. Ed. Denis Picard.

DEMEURES ET CHATEAUX. see *REAL ESTATE*

725 DEU ISSN 0946-4549
DENKMAL!. Text in German. 1994. a. **Document type:** *Bulletin.*
Indexed: DIP, IBR, IBZ.
Published by: (Landesamt fuer Denkmalpflege Schleswig-Holstein), Westholsteinische Verlagsanstalt Boyens und Co., Am Wulf Isebrand Platz, Heide, 25746, Germany. TEL 49-481-6886162, FAX 49-481-6886467.

DIE DENKMALPFLEGE. see *ART*

725.94 DEU ISSN 0933-694X
DENKMALRECHT DER LAENDER UND DES BUNDES. Text in German. 1983. irreg. price varies. **Document type:** *Monographic series, Trade.*
Published by: (Interparlamentarische Arbeitsgemeinschaft), Erich Schmidt Verlag GmbH & Co. (Berlin), Genthiner Str 30G, Berlin, 10785, Germany. TEL 49-30-250085-0, FAX 49-30-25008511, esv@esvmedien.de, http://www.erich-schmidt-verlag.de.

720 DNK ISSN 1395-2080
DENMARK. MILJOEMINISTERIET. SKOV- OG NATURSTYRELSEN. AARSBERETNING OG REGNSKAB. Text in Danish. 1969. a. illus. **Document type:** *Government.*
Former titles (until 1994): Denmark. Miljoeministeriet. Planstyrelsen. Aarsberetning (0906-4257); (until 1988): Denmark. Statens Bygningsfredningsfond. Aarsberetning og Regnskaber (0903-7470); (until 1987): Denmark. Statens Bygningsfredningsfond. Beretning (0109-4254)
Published by: Miljoeministeriet, Skov- og Naturstyrelsen/Ministry of the Environment. Danish Forest & Nature Agency, Haraldsgade 53, Copenhagen OE, 2100, Denmark. TEL 45-39-472000, FAX 45-39-279899, sns@sns.dk, http://www.skovognatur.dk. **Subscr. to:** Miljoeministeriet, Frontlinien, Rentemestervej 8, Copenhagen NV 2400, Denmark. TEL 45-70-120211, frontlinien@frontlinien.dk, http://www.frontlinien.dk.

DESIGN AND ARCHITECTURE. see *INTERIOR DESIGN AND DECORATION*

720 USA ISSN 1544-3930
NA7235.A6
▼ **DESIGN & ARCHITECTURE (ARIZONA EDITION).** Text in English. 2003 (Sep.). 10/yr. USD 33.95 (effective 2004). **Document type:** *Magazine, Trade.* **Description:** Provides information and ideas on interior design, architecture, decoration, furnishing, landscape architecture, renovation, remodeling and the collection of fine art and wine for the top 3% of homeowners in the market; the elite affluent.
Related titles: Regional ed(s).: Design & Architecture (Chicago Edition). 2004.
Published by: U.S. Media LLC, 15029 N. Thompson Peak, Ste B111-614, Scottsdale, AZ 85260. TEL 480-661-8061, FAX 480-452-0554, info@DAmagazine.com, http://www.damagazine.com/.

720 745 GRC ISSN 0074-1191
NK1451
DESIGN + ART IN GREECE/THEMATA CHOROU + TECHNON. Text in Greek; Summaries in English. 1970. a., latest vol.32, 2001. USD 55 (effective 2003). adv. bibl. index. 192 p./no. 3 cols./p.; back issues avail. **Document type:** *Yearbook, Trade.* **Description:** Architecture and furnishings of houses, offices and shops, visual and applied arts, industrial and graphic design, and exhibitions.
Formerly: Design in Greece
Indexed: AIAP, EIP.
—BLDSC (3559.905000).
Published by: Architecture in Greece Press, PO Box 3545, Athens, 102 10, Greece. TEL 30-210-7225930, FAX 30-210-7213916, http://www.themataarchitects.gr. Ed., Pub., R&P, Adv. contact Orestis B Doumanis. B&W page USD 1,500, color page USD 1,750; trim 21 x 28. Circ: 5,000.

DESIGN - BUILD BUSINESS. see *BUILDING AND CONSTRUCTION*

720 USA ISSN 1093-846X
TH435
DESIGN COST DATA; the cost estimating magazine for architects, builders and specifiers. Text in English. 1958. bi-m. USD 89.40 (effective 2005). adv. bk.rev. charts; illus. index. reprint service avail. from PQC. **Document type:** *Magazine, Trade.* **Description:** Information on cost estimating in design and construction.
Former titles: Design Cost and Data (1054-3163); (until 1990): Design Cost and Data for Management of Building Design (0739-3946); (until 1982): Design Cost and Data for Building Design Management; (until 1981): Design Cost and Data for the Construction Industry (0192-0227); (until 1978): Architectural Design, Cost and Data (0003-8512)
Related titles: Microfiche ed.; Online - full text ed.: (from Northern Light Technology, Inc., ProQuest Information & Learning).
—CCC.
Published by: D C & D Technoligies, Inc., 8602 N 40th St, Tampa, FL 33604. TEL 813-989-9300, FAX 813-980-3982, info@dcd.com, http://www.dcd.com/. Pub., Adv. contact Barbara Castelli. B&W page USD 1,800, color page USD 2,875. Circ: 14,500 (controlled).

720 ITA ISSN 1120-9720
DESIGN DIFFUSION NEWS. Abbreviated title: D D N. Text in Italian. 1990. 9/yr. EUR 67 domestic; EUR 124, USD 120 foreign (effective 2001). adv. **Document type:** *Magazine, Trade.*
Published by: Design Diffusion Edizioni, Via Lucano 3, Milan, 20135, Italy. TEL 39-02-5516109, FAX 39-02-59902431, info@designdiffusion.com, http://www.designdiffusion.com/riviste/ddn/ddn.html.

DESIGN INDABA MAGAZINE. see *ART*

745.05 GBR ISSN 1460-6925
➤ **THE DESIGN JOURNAL.** Text in English. 1997. 3/yr. GBP 110 in Europe to non-members; GBP 125 elsewhere to non-members; GBP 85 in Europe to members EAD; GBP 100 elsewhere to members EAD; GBP 47.50 per issue (effective 2006). back issues avail. **Document type:** *Journal, Academic/Scholarly.* **Description:** Provides an international forum for all aspects of design practice, theory management, and education.
Indexed: DAAI, DIP, IBR, IBZ.
—BLDSC (3559.976800), IE, ingenta. **CCC.**
Published by: (European Academy of Design), Ashgate Publishing Ltd (Subsidiary of: Gower Publishing Co. Ltd.), Gower House, Croft Rd, Aldershot, Hants GU11 3HR, United Kingdom. TEL 44-1252-331551, FAX 44-1252-317446, info@ashgate.com, http://www.ashgate.com.

711.05 USA ISSN 1067-9359
NA9000
DESIGN METHODS; theories, research, education and practice. Text in English. 1966. q. USD 44 domestic; USD 59 foreign (effective 2005). bk.rev. illus. 40 p./no. 1 cols./p.; back issues avail. **Document type:** *Journal, Academic/Scholarly.* **Description:** Presents theories and methods of design in architecture, environmental planning, engineering, and product design.
Former titles (until 1991): Design Methods and Theories (0147-1147); (until vol.12, 1978): D M G - D R S Journal: Design Research and Methods (0091-0449); (until 1971): D M G Newsletter
Indexed: AIAP, API, DAAI.
—CISTI, IE.
Published by: Design Methods Institute, PO Box 3, San Luis Obispo, CA 93406-0003. dpggrant1@charter.net, dpgrant38@charter.net. Ed. Donald P Grant. Circ: 1,000.

711.4 USA
DESIGN RESEARCH NEWS. Text in English. q. USD 24; USD 28 foreign (effective 1999). back issues avail. **Document type:** *Newsletter.* **Description:** Reports on current developments in the field of environmental design research.
Published by: Environmental Design Research Association, PO Box 7146, Edmond, OK 73083-7146. TEL 405-330-4863. Ed. Jon Sanford. R&P Janet Singer.

DESIGN SOLUTIONS. see *INTERIOR DESIGN AND DECORATION*

720 600 GBR ISSN 0142-694X
NA2750 CODEN: DSSTD5
➤ **DESIGN STUDIES.** Text in English. 1979. 6/yr. EUR 822 in Europe to institutions; JPY 109,200 in Japan to institutions; USD 921 elsewhere to institutions; EUR 213 in Europe to qualified personnel; JPY 28,100 in Japan to qualified personnel; USD 237 elsewhere to qualified personnel (effective 2006). adv. bk.rev. illus.; abstr. index. back issues avail.; reprints avail. **Document type:** *Academic/Scholarly.* **Description:** Promotes an understanding of the nature, effectiveness and roles of design in industry and in society by comparing applications in such areas as architecture, engineering, planning, and industrial design.
Related titles: Microform ed.: (from PQC); Online - full text ed.: (from EBSCO Publishing, Gale Group, IngentaConnect, ScienceDirect, Swets Information Services).
Indexed: ABCT, ABM, AIA, AIAP, API, ArtInd, B&BAb, BPIA, BrTechI, CADCAM, CurCont, DAAI, EngInd, ErgAb, Inspec, PCI, RASB, SWA, TEA.
—BLDSC (3560.205000), AskIEEE, Ei, IE, Infotrieve, ingenta, Linda Hall. **CCC.**
Published by: Pergamon (Subsidiary of: Elsevier Science & Technology), The Boulevard, Langford Ln, East Park, Kidlington, Oxford OX5 1GB, United Kingdom. TEL 44-1865-843000, FAX 44-1865-843010, http://www.elsevier.com/locate/destud. Ed. Nigel Cross. **Subscr. to:** Elsevier BV, PO Box 211, Amsterdam 1000 AE, Netherlands. nlinfo-f@elsevier.nl, http://www.elsevier.nl.

➤ **DESIGN TIMES**; the art of interiors. see *INTERIOR DESIGN AND DECORATION*

720 690 NZL
DESIGN TRENDS. Text in English. q. NZD 9.95 (effective 1999). adv. back issues avail. **Document type:** *Trade.* **Description:** Aimed at professionals involved in specifing products and services for building and design of commercial projects in multi-dwelling offices and other commercial developments involving good design.
Published by: Trend Publishing International Ltd., 49 Main Hwy., Ellerslie, Auckland, New Zealand. TEL 64-9-571-5700, FAX 64-9-571-5701, reception@trends.co.nz, http://www.trendsbooks.com. Ed. R Hofmann. Pub. D Johnson. R&P Paul Taylor. Adv. contact Leslie Johnson. Circ: 7,500 (paid); 7,500 (controlled). **Subscr. to:** Private Bag, 11-908 Ellerslie, Auckland, New Zealand. TEL 64-9-415-6340, FAX 64-9-415-6448.

DESIGN WEEK. see *ART*

DESIGN WEEK ACTION PACK. see *ART*

720 USA
DESIGNARCHITECTURE.COM. Text in English. d. **Document type:** *Trade.*
Media: Online - full content.
Published by: DesignArchitecture.com, Inc. kristen@designarchitecture.com, http://www.designarchitecture.com/. Ed. Kristen Richards.

720 690 CAN ISSN 1181-7933
DESIGNER'S BEST HOME PLANS. Text in English. 1990. a. CND 3.50 (effective 2000). adv. **Document type:** *Catalog.* **Description:** Features designs from Canadian home designers and the latest in housing innovations. Contains house plans for a range of styles and budgets.
Published by: Giroux Publishing, 102 Ellis St, Penticton, BC V2A 4L5, Canada. TEL 604-493-0942, FAX 604-493-7526, plan@westhomeplanners.com. Ed. Michael A Giroux. Adv. contact Dennis Thatchuk. Circ: 13,500.

DESIGNERS WEST. see *INTERIOR DESIGN AND DECORATION*

DESIGNERS WEST RESOURCE DIRECTORY. see *INTERIOR DESIGN AND DECORATION*

720 747 USA
DESIGNING WITH TILE & STONE✶. Text in English. 1995. q. adv. tr.lit. back issues avail. **Document type:** *Trade.* **Description:** For the professional architect, interior designer and specifier. Contains articles on how to select, design with, install and maintain ceramic and dimensional stone tile for residential and commercial installations both domestic and international.
Published by: Contemporary Dialysis, Inc., 20335 Ventura Blvd, Ste 400, Woodland Hills, CA 91364. TEL 818-704-5555, FAX 818-704-6500. Pub. Jerry Fisher. Adv. contact Steven Fisher. page USD 3,250. Circ: 12,000.

DESIGNMENT. see *INTERIOR DESIGN AND DECORATION*

720 JPN ISSN 0012-4133
NA2640
DETAIL/DITERU; magazine for architects and engineers. Text in Japanese; Summaries in English. 1964. q. USD 16. adv. illus. **Document type:** *Trade.*
Indexed: RASB.
Published by: Shokokusha Publishing Co. Ltd., 25 Saka-Machi, Shinjuku-ku, Tokyo, 160-0002, Japan. TEL 81-3-3359-3231, FAX 81-3-3357-3961. Ed. Takashi Hosoda. Adv. contact Toshio Takahashi. B&W page JPY 200,000, color page JPY 500,000. Circ: 60,000.

720 DEU ISSN 0011-9571
NA2835
DETAIL; Zeitschrift fuer Architektur & Baudetail. Text in German. 1961. 10/yr. EUR 137.50 domestic to individuals; EUR 141.50 in the European Union to individuals; EUR 146.50 elsewhere to individuals; EUR 86.50 domestic to students; EUR 101.50 in the European Union to students; EUR 106.50 elsewhere to students; EUR 14.50 newsstand/cover (effective 2005). adv. bk.rev. abstr.; charts; illus.; stat.; tr.lit. index. back issues avail. **Document type:** *Magazine, Trade.* **Description:** Covers specific construction topics with examples from current developments and projects.
Related titles: English ed.: Detail. English Edition. ISSN 1614-4600. 2004. EUR 85; EUR 65 to students (effective 2005).
Indexed: AIAP, DIP, IBZ, RASB.
—BLDSC (3560.720000), IE, Infotrieve, ingenta. **CCC.**
Published by: Institut fuer Internationale Architektur-Dokumentation GmbH (Subsidiary of: Reed Business Information GmbH), Postfach 330660, Munich, 80066, Germany. TEL 49-89-3816200, FAX 49-89-398670, vertrieb@detail.de, http://www.detail.de. adv.: B&W page EUR 5,040, color page EUR 8,130. Circ: 39,556 (paid and controlled). **Subscr. to:** Vertriebsunion Meynen GmbH, Im Kappelhof 1, Eltville Am Rhein 65343, Germany. TEL 49-6123-9238-0, FAX 49-6123-923839, detailabo@vertriebsunion.de.

720 DEU ISSN 0420-1329
DEUTSCHER BAUKATALOG. Text in German. a. EUR 32.21; EUR 21.99 with subscr. to Detail (effective 2001). **Document type:** *Journal, Trade.*
Related titles: CD-ROM ed.
Published by: Institut fuer Internationale Architektur-Dokumentation GmbH (Subsidiary of: Reed Business Information GmbH), Postfach 330660, Munich, 80066, Germany. TEL 49-89-3816200, FAX 49-89-398670, vertrieb@detail.de, http://www.detail.de/dbk. **Subscr. to:** Vertriebsunion Meynen GmbH, Im Kappelhof 1, Eltville Am Rhein 65343, Germany. TEL 49-6123-9238-0, FAX 49-6123-923839, detailabo@vertriebsunion.de.

720 DEU ISSN 0012-1215
DEUTSCHES ARCHITEKTENBLATT. Text in German. 1969. m. EUR 5 newsstand/cover (effective 2005). adv. bk.rev. **Document type:** *Magazine, Trade.*
Indexed: AIAP, DIP, IBR, IBZ.
Published by: (Bundesarchitektenkammer), Forum-Verlag GmbH, Zeppelinstr 116, Esslingen, 73730, Germany. TEL 49-711-767270, FAX 49-711-76727144, info@forumverlag.de, http://www.architekten-forum.com, http://www.forumverlag.de. Ed. Reinhart Wustlich. Adv. contact Michael Schoeberl. B&W page EUR 7,587, color page EUR 11,753. Circ: 118,403.

727 USA ISSN 1068-3895
➤ **DIMENSIONS (ANN ARBOR).** Text in English. 1987. a. USD 15 (effective 2000). **Document type:** *Academic/Scholarly.*
Indexed: AIAP.
Published by: University of Michigan, College of Architecture and Urban Planning, 2000 Bonisteel Blvd, Ann Arbor, MI 48109-2069. TEL 734-764-1300, http://www.umich.edu/~dimensio/. Ed. David Cabianca. Circ: 1,000.

➤ **DIRECTORY OF ARCHITECTS IN METROPOLITAN WASHINGTON.** see *BUSINESS AND ECONOMICS—Trade And Industrial Directories*

729 ITA ISSN 1123-9247
NA4
DISEGNARE IDEE IMMAGINI. Text in Italian. 1991. s-a. EUR 15.50 (effective 2004). **Document type:** *Journal, Academic/Scholarly.*
Published by: (Universita degli Sudi di Roma "La Sapienza", Facolta di Architettura), Gangemi Editore, Piazza San Pantaleo 4, Rome, Italy. TEL 39-06-6872774, FAX 39-06-68806189, gangemieditorerc@tin.it, http://www.gangemieditore.it. Ed. Mario Docci.

745.2 ITA
DISEGNO INDUSTRIALE. Text in Italian. 1996. irreg., latest vol.2, 1999. price varies. **Document type:** *Monographic series.*
Published by: Liguori Editore srl, Via Posillipo 394, Naples, 80123, Italy. TEL 39-81-7206111, FAX 39-81-7206244, http://www.liguori.it.

DISTINGUISHED HOME PLANS & PRODUCTS - CUSTOM HOME PLANS GUIDE. see *BUILDING AND CONSTRUCTION*

720 ESP ISSN 0214-9249
DOCUMENTOS DE ARQUITECTURA. Text in Spanish. 1987. 3/yr. **Document type:** *Monographic series.*
Indexed: RILM.
—CINDOC.
Published by: Colegio de Arquitectos de Almeria, Martinez Campos, 29, Almeria, 04002, Spain. TEL 34-950-231255, FAX 34-950-262265.

720 ARG ISSN 0326-8640
NA830
➤ **DOCUMENTOS DE ARQUITECTURA NACIONAL Y AMERICANA.** Text in Spanish. 1973. a., latest vol.40. USD 25 per issue (effective 2003). adv. cum.index: 1973-1980. 100 p./no.; **Document type:** *Magazine, Academic/Scholarly.*
Formerly: Documentos de Arquitectura Nacional
Indexed: AIAP.
Published by: Instituto Argentino de Investigaciones de Historia de la Arquitectura y del Urbanismo, Casilla de Correo 120, Sucursal 48B, Buenos Aires, 1448, Argentina. R&P Ramon Gutierrez.

720 USA ISSN 1041-1607
TH2170
DOME (WHEAT RIDGE). Text in English. 1988. q. USD 40 (effective 1997). **Description:** Deals with domes as part of the development of ultra-low-cost housing worldwide.
Published by: Donald R. Hoflin, Ed. & Pub., 4401 Zephyr St, Wheat Ridge, CO 80033.

720 ITA ISSN 0012-5377
N4
DOMUS; architettura arredamento arte. Text in English, Italian. 1928. m. (11/yr.). EUR 93.50 domestic; EUR 125 foreign (effective 2005). bk.rev. illus. reprints avail. **Document type:** *Magazine, Consumer.*
Indexed: AIAP, API, ArtHuCI, ArtInd, BHA, CurCont, DAAI, RASB, RILM.
—BLDSC (3619.210000), IE, Infotrieve.
Published by: Editoriale Domus, Via Gianni Mazzocchi 1/3, Rozzano, MI 20089, Italy. TEL 39-02-824721, editorialedomus@edidomus.it, http://www.edidomus.it. Ed. Maria Bordone. Adv. contact Giovanna Mazzocchi Bordone.

720 ITA ISSN 1122-8938
DOMUS DOSSIER. Text in Italian. 1993. s-a. adv.
Published by: Editoriale Domus, Via Gianni Mazzocchi 1/3, Rozzano, MI 20089, Italy. TEL 39-02-824721, editorialedomus@edidomus.it, http://www.edidomus.it. Pub. Giovanna Mazzocchi Bordone. Adv. contact Giuseppe Bolandrina.

720 TUR
DOMUS M. Text in Turkish. m. **Document type:** *Magazine, Trade.*
Published by: 1 Numara Hearst Yayincilik, Sabah Tesisleri, Tesvikiye Caddesi 123, Tesvikiye, Istanbul, 80200, Turkey. TEL 90-212-3158000, FAX 90-212-3159272, domusm@birnumara.com.tr.

728 NLD
DUTCH ARCHITECTS. Text in Dutch, English. 199?. irreg., latest vol.6, 2004. EUR 59 per issue (effective 2005). illus. **Document type:** *Trade.* **Description:** Showcases recent projects of nearly 150 Dutch architects and interior designers.
Published by: Uitgeverij B I S, Postbus 323, Amsterdam, 1000 AH, Netherlands. TEL 31-20-5247560, FAX 31-20-5247557, info@bispublishers.nl, http://www.bispublishers.nl.

728 747 USA ISSN 1530-5309
TH4805
DWELL. Text in English. 2000. 8/yr. USD 19.95 domestic; USD 29.95 in Canada; USD 35.95 elsewhere (effective 2005). adv. illus. back issues avail.; reprints avail. **Document type:** *Magazine, Consumer.* **Description:** Presents residential architecture inside and out and explores the way a community shapes its houses and houses shape a community.
Indexed: ASIP.
Published by: Dwell LLC, 99 Osgood Pl., San Francisco, CA 94133. TEL 415-743-9990, FAX 415-743-9970, allison@dwellmag.com, http://www.dwellmag.com. Ed. Allison Arieff. Pubs. Lara Hedberg Deam, Michela Abrams. adv.: color page USD 5,000. Circ: 163,000 (paid).

720 GBR ISSN 0307-1634
➤ **E A A REVIEW.** Text in English. 1957. a. free. adv. **Document type:** *Directory, Academic/Scholarly.* **Description:** Covers new buildings and projects in the Edinburgh area. Includes a directory of architectural practices.
Formerly: Edinburgh Architectural Association E A A Yearbook
Published by: Edinburgh Architectural Association, 15 Rutland St, Edinburgh, EH1 2BE, United Kingdom. TEL 44-131-2297545, FAX 44-131-2282188, mail@e-a-a.org.uk, http://www.edarch.demon.co.uk/review.html. Ed. Brian W Henderson. Circ: 2,000 (controlled).

720 USA ISSN 1556-3596
▼ **ECO-STRUCTURE.** Text in English. 2003 (Spring). q. free to qualified personnel (effective 2003). adv. **Document type:** *Magazine, Trade.*
Published by: Spiderweb Publications, Inc., 1415 W. Nc Highway 54., Ste. 105, Durham, NC 27707-5598. TEL 866-638-5624, http://www.eco-structure.com/, http://www.spiderwebinc.com.

720 GBR
ECODESIGN. Text in English. 1991. 3/yr.
—BLDSC (3648.617500), ingenta.
Published by: Ecological Design Association, The British School, Slad Rd, Stroud, Glos GL5 1QW, United Kingdom. http://www.edaweb.org.

712 ITA ISSN 1121-2225
SB469
EDEN; rivista dell'architettura nel paesaggio. Text in Italian, English. 1991. irreg., latest vol.3. price varies. illus. back issues avail. **Document type:** *Magazine, Consumer.* **Description:** Explores contemporary themes in architecture and landscape design.
Published by: Automobilia Srl, Via Alberto Mario 16, Milan, MI 20149, Italy. TEL 39-02-48021671, FAX 39-02-48194968, automobilia@tin.it. Ed., Pub., Adv. contact Bruno Alfieri.

720 ZAF
EDGE (PORT ELIZABETH). Text in English. 1990. a. illus. **Document type:** *Academic/Scholarly.*
Published by: University of Port Elizabeth Architectural Society, Private Bag X6508, Port Elizabeth, 6000, South Africa. Ed. Graig Coulton.

EDILIZIA (TURIN). see *BUILDING AND CONSTRUCTION*

720 GBR
NA1
➤ **EDINBURGH ARCHITECTURE RESEARCH.** Text in English. 1973. a. looseleaf. GBP 12 per issue (effective 2005). charts; illus. **Document type:** *Journal, Academic/Scholarly.* **Description:** Intends to provide graduates, scholars and other researchers the opportunity to exchange ideas and views in the field of social science perception.
Formerly: E A R (0140-5039)
Indexed: AIAP, API, BHA.
—CISTI.
Published by: The University of Edinburgh, Department of Architecture, 20 Chambers St, Edinburgh, EH1 1JZ, United Kingdom. TEL 44-131-6502618, 44-131-6502305, FAX 44-131-6508019, ear@caad.ed.ac.uk, http://www.caad.ed.ac.uk/publications/ear/. Ed. Mrs. Ruxandra-Iulia Stoica. Circ: 250.

720 AUT ISSN 1433-6278
➤ **EDITION ARCHITEKTUR AKTUELL.** Text in German, English. 1997. irreg., latest vol.3, 2001. price varies. **Document type:** *Monographic series, Academic/Scholarly.*
Published by: Springer-Verlag Wien (Subsidiary of: Springer Science+Business Media) TEL 43-1-3302415-0, FAX 43-1-330242665, books@springer.at, http://www.springer.at. Ed. Matthias Boeckl. R&P Angela Foessl TEL 43-1-3302415517. **Subscr. in N. America to:** Springer-Verlag New York, Inc., 233 Spring St, New York, NY 10013. TEL 800-777-4643, FAX 201-348-4505, orders@springer-ny.com.

➤ **EDUCATIONAL FACILITY PLANNER.** see *EDUCATION*

➤ **EKISTICS**; problems and science of human settlements. see *HOUSING AND URBAN PLANNING*

➤ **ELEMENT UND BAU.** see *BUILDING AND CONSTRUCTION*

➤ **ENERGY DESIGN UPDATE**; the monthly newsletter on energy-efficient housing. see *BUILDING AND CONSTRUCTION*

720 DEU
DER ENTWURF. Text in German. 2000. 2/yr. EUR 5 newsstand/cover (effective 2003). adv. **Document type:** *Journal, Trade.*
Published by: Stadtwandel Verlag, Solmsstr. 22, Berlin, 10961, Germany. TEL 49-30-69504812, FAX 49-30-69504813, info@stadtwandel.de, http://www.stadtwandel.de. adv.: B&W page EUR 3,500, color page EUR 3,900. Circ: 20,000 (paid and controlled).

ENVIRONMENT AND ART LETTER; a forum on architecture and the arts for the Parish. see *RELIGIONS AND THEOLOGY—Roman Catholic*

ENVIRONMENT AND PLANNING B: PLANNING & DESIGN. see *HOUSING AND URBAN PLANNING*

711 USA ISSN 1083-9194
BF353
ENVIRONMENTAL AND ARCHITECTURAL PHENOMENOLOGY NEWSLETTER. Text in English. 1990. 3/yr. USD 10 domestic; USD 12 foreign (effective 2001). bk.rev.; film rev. abstr.; bibl.; illus.; maps. cum.index 1990-1996 in vol. 7, no.3. back issues avail. **Document type:** *Newspaper, Trade.* **Description:** Presents research and design, environmental policies and environmental architecture essays.
Published by: Kansas State University, Architecture Department, c/o David Seamon, Seanton 211, Manhattan, KS 66506-2901. TEL 785-532-5953, FAX 785-532-6722, triad@ksu.edu, http://www-personal.ksu.edu/~triad. Ed., R&P David Seamon. Circ: 200 (paid).

711.4 USA
ENVIRONMENTAL DESIGN RESEARCH ASSOCIATION. ANNUAL CONFERENCE PROCEEDINGS. Short title: E D R A. Annual Conference Proceedings. Text in English. 1969. a. USD 50 to non-members; USD 40 to members (effective 1999). adv. back issues avail.; reprints avail. **Document type:** *Proceedings.*
Indexed: PsycholAb, SSI.
—BLDSC (3661.116000).
Published by: Environmental Design Research Association, PO Box 7146, Edmond, OK 73083-7146. TEL 405-330-4863. Adv. contact Janet Singer. Circ: 900.

711.4 GBR ISSN 1352-8564
NA2000
➤ **ENVIRONMENTS BY DESIGN.** Text in English. 1996. s-a. GBP 21 to institutions; GBP 54 to individuals. bk.rev. **Document type:** *Academic/Scholarly.*
—BLDSC (3791.796000).
Published by: (Kingston University, Faculty of Design), Kingston University Press, Eagle Chambers, 16-18 Eden St, Kingston Upon Thames, Surrey KT1 2QJ, United Kingdom. TEL 44-20-85477052, t.eccles@kingston.ac.uk, http://www.kingston.ac.uk/by_design/, http://www.kingston.ac.uk/design/. Ed., R&P Michael Shoul. Circ: 500.

➤ **EPITES- EPITESZETTUDOMANY/ARCHITECTONICS AND ARCHITECTURE.** see *BUILDING AND CONSTRUCTION*

720 COL ISSN 0120-6702
NA5
ESCALA; arquitectura, arte, ingenieria. Text in Spanish. 1962. bi-m. USD 120; USD 155 foreign. adv. bk.rev. back issues avail. **Document type:** *Monographic series, Trade.* **Description:** Each issue covers a topic in Latin American architecture.
Indexed: AIAP.
Address: Calle 30 No. 17-70, Bogota, CUND, Colombia. TEL 57-1-287-8200, FAX 57-1-232-5148, deserna@col-online.com. Ed. David Eduardo Serna Medina. R&P Carlos Fernando Serna Medina. adv.: B&W page USD 1,000, color page USD 1,500; trim 340 x 240. Circ: 16,000.

720 ESP ISSN 0213-3474
ESCUELA TECNICA SUPERIOR DE ARQUITECTURA DA CORUNA. BOLETIN ACADEMICO. Text in Spanish. 1985. 3/yr.
Indexed: IECT.
—CINDOC.
Published by: Escuela Tecnica Superior de Arquitectura, Castro de Elvina, s-n, La Coruna, 15192, Spain.

711.4 FRA ISSN 0014-0481
HT166
ESPACES ET SOCIETES; revue critique internationale de l'amenagement de l'architecture et de l'urbanisation. Text in French. 1970. q. EUR 52 domestic; EUR 61 foreign (effective 2005). adv. bk.rev. charts; stat. **Document type:** *Journal, Academic/Scholarly.*
Indexed: AIAP, IPSA, PAIS.
—BLDSC (3811.330000), IE, Infotrieve. **CCC.**
Published by: Editions Eres, 11 rue des Alouettes, Ramonville Saint-Agne, 31520, France. TEL 33-5-61751576, FAX 33-5-61735289, eres@edition-eres.com, http://www.espacesetsocietes.msh-paris.fr, http://www.edition-eres.com.

ESTUDOS TECNOLOGICOS. see *SCIENCES: COMPREHENSIVE WORKS*

ETUDES URBAINES. see *HOUSING AND URBAN PLANNING*

EXPERIMENTA; revista para la cultura del proyecto. see *ART*

720 ESP ISSN 1133-6137
EXPRESION GRAFICA ARQUITECTONICA. REVISTA. Variant title: E G A. Revista de Expresion Grafica Arquitectonica. Text in Multiple languages. 1993. a.
Published by: Universitat Politecnica de Valencia, Departamento de Expresion Grafica Arquitectonica, Camino de Vera s/n, Valencia, 46022, Spain. TEL 34-96-3877500, FAX 34-96-3877509, depega@upvnet.upv.es, http://www.upv.es.

F M FACILITY MANAGEMENT. see *BUSINESS AND ECONOMICS—Office Equipment And Services*

720 DEU ISSN 0340-2967
TH1000
F UND I-BAU; Bauen mit Systemen. Text in German. 1966. q. EUR 8 newsstand/cover (effective 2001). adv. bk.rev. abstr.; illus.; pat.; stat. index. **Document type:** *Magazine, Trade.*
Formerly: Fertigteilbau und Industrialisiertes Bauen (0015-0231)
Published by: Element-Verlag GmbH, Zeppelinstr 3, Waiblingen, 71332, Germany. TEL 49-7151-51871, FAX 49-7151-563343. Ed. H Schmid. adv.: B&W page EUR 1,755, color 1/2 page EUR 2,783. Circ: 5,400.

F X; design in business and society. see *INTERIOR DESIGN AND DECORATION*

720 677 USA
FABRIC ARCHITECTURE. Text in English. 1989. bi-m. USD 43 domestic; USD 54 in Canada & Mexico; USD 72 elsewhere (effective 2005). adv. bk.rev. **Document type:** *Magazine, Trade.* **Description:** For architects, designers and fabric specifiers. Covers air and tension structures, awnings and canopies, banners, construction fabrics, landscaping and building codes.
Formerly: Fabrics & Architecture (1045-0483)
Indexed: WTA.
—BLDSC (3863.133700).
Published by: Industrial Fabrics Association International, 1801 W County Rd, B, Roseville, MN 55113-4052. TEL 651-222-6933, 800-225-4324, FAX 651-225-6966, generalinfo@ifai.com, http://www.ifai.com. Ed. Bruce Wright. Pub. Mary Hennessy. Adv. contact Sarah Hyland. B&W page USD 2,635, color page USD 3,675; trim 8.25 x 11. Circ: 10,000.

FACILITIES. see *BUILDING AND CONSTRUCTION*

FACILITY MANAGEMENT JOURNAL. see *BUSINESS AND ECONOMICS—Management*

DER FACILITY MANAGER; Gebaeude und Anlagen besser planen, bauen, bewirtschaften. see *BUSINESS AND ECONOMICS—Management*

720 624 SCG ISSN 0354-4605
FACTA UNIVERSITATIS. SERIES ARCHITECTURE AND CIVIL ENGINEERING. Text in English, French, German. 1997. irreg., latest vol.2, no.1, 1999. **Document type:** *Journal, Academic/Scholarly.*
Indexed: RefZh.
Published by: Univerzitet u Nishu/University of Nis, Univerzitetski Trg 2, P.O. Box 123, Nis, 18000. TEL 381-18-547970, FAX 381-18-547950, gane@junis.ni.ac.yu, facta@ni.ac.yu, http://facta.junis.ni.ac.yu/facta/aace/aace.html, http://ni.ac.yu. Ed. Dragan Velickovic.

720 700 USA ISSN 0014-7001
NA4605
FAITH AND FORM; journal of religion, art and architecture. Text in English. 1967. 4/yr. USD 36 domestic; USD 46 foreign (effective 2005). adv. bk.rev. illus. 32 p./no. 3 cols./p.; back issues avail. **Document type:** *Journal, Academic/Scholarly.* **Description:** For architects, artists, clergy, temple and church administrators, liturgists, building committees, musicians and manufacturers engaged in creation and evaluation of religious art and architecture of all denominations.
Indexed: AIAP, ChrPI.
Address: c/o Douglas Hoffman, 1300 E 9th St., Suite 105, Cleveland, OH 44114. TEL 216-861-5589, FAX 216-623-3710, faithnform@aol.com, http://www.faithnform.com. Ed., R&P Michael Crosbie TEL 203-857-0200 ext 210. Pub., Adv. contact Douglas Hoffman. Circ: 37,500.

720 JPN
FASHIRITI MANEJIMENTO/FACILITY MANAGEMENT. Text in Japanese. 1990. a. JPY 1,000.
Published by: (Joho Shinsutemu linkai), Nihon Kenchiku Gakkai/Architectural Institute of Japan, 26-20 Shiba 5-chome, Minato-ku, Tokyo, 108-0014, Japan. TEL 81-3-34562051, FAX 81-3-34562058.

720 CAN ISSN 0229-7094
➤ **FIFTH COLUMN**; Canadian student journal of architecture/revue Canadienne des etudiants en architecture. Text in English, French. 1979. s-a. CND 35 to individuals for 4 issues; CND 50 to libraries for 4 issues; CND 18 to students for 4 issues (effective 2000). adv. bk.rev. illus. **Document type:** *Academic/Scholarly.* **Description:** Promotes the study of architecture in Canada.
Indexed: AIAP, API.
Published by: School of Architecture, 815 Sherbrooke West, Montreal, PQ H3A 2K6, Canada. TEL 514-398-6700, FAX 514-398-7372, 5column@po-box.mcgill.ca, 5column@chaussegros.architecture.mcgill.ca, http://www.mcgill.ca/arch/5column. Ed. Conor Sampson. Circ: 250.

724 ITA
FLARE; architectural lighting magazine. Text in English, Italian. 1989. 3/yr. EUR 23 domestic; EUR 45 foreign (effective 2005). adv. **Document type:** *Magazine, Trade.*
Published by: Editore Lupetti & Co., Via Hayez 12, Milan, MI 20129, Italy. TEL 39-02-202025, FAX 39-02-20404340, redazione@lupettieditore.it, http://www.lupetti.com. Circ: 60,000.

FLOORS. see *INTERIOR DESIGN AND DECORATION*

▼ **FLORIDA HOMES & LIFESTYLES.** see *INTERIOR DESIGN AND DECORATION*

▼ **FLORIDA INSIDEOUT.** see *INTERIOR DESIGN AND DECORATION*

712 GBR ISSN 0963-9004
FOLLIES; the international magazine for follies, grottoes & garden buildings. Text in English. 1988. q. GBP 18 domestic; GBP 21 foreign (effective Mar. 2001). adv. bk.rev. bibl.; illus. 16 p./no. 2 cols./p.; back issues avail. **Document type:** *Newsletter, Academic/Scholarly.* **Description:** Records and monitors architecture in the landscape and manifestations of architectural eccentricity, past and present. Includes news items and academic articles.
Indexed: AIAP.
Published by: Folly Fellowship, 7 Inches Yard, Market St, Newbury, Berks RG14 5DP, United Kingdom. TEL 44-1635-42864, FAX 44-1635-552366, prboogaart@hetnet.nl, architectsuk@cs.com, http://www.heritage.co.uk/follies/. Ed., Adv. contact Pieter Boogaart TEL 31-40-242-3648. B&W page GBP 120; 186 x 261. Circ: 950 (paid); 50 (controlled).

720 GBR ISSN 1474-7669
THE FOLLIES JOURNAL. Text in English. 2001. a. adv. **Document type:** *Journal.* **Description:** Aims to bring together all those with an interest in follies, grottoes, and garden buildings.
Published by: Folly Fellowship, 19 Sandy Walk, Bramhope, Leeds, LS16 9DW, United Kingdom. s.kellerman@leeds.ac.uk, http://www.maney.co.uk/search?fwaction=show&fwid=159. Ed. Susan Kellerman.

FORM; designtidskriften. see *INTERIOR DESIGN AND DECORATION*

FORM; Zeitschrift fuer Gestaltung. see *INTERIOR DESIGN AND DECORATION*

721 USA ISSN 0015-7686
TA455.G9
FORM & FUNCTION. Text in English. 1964. q. free to qualified personnel. illus. index, cum.index: 1970-1995. back issues avail. **Document type:** *Trade.* **Description:** Carries case histories of buildings exhibiting good design and good use of U.S.G. products.
Indexed: ABM, RASB.
—Linda Hall.
Published by: U S G Corporation, 803871, Chicago, IL 60680-3871. TEL 312-606-4181, FAX 312-606-5566. Ed., R&P William D Leavitt. Circ: 120,000 (controlled).

747 720 FIN ISSN 0358-8904
NK1471.F5
FORM FUNCTION FINLAND. Text in English. 1980. q. EUR 36 domestic; EUR 46 in Europe; EUR 49 elsewhere; EUR 9 newsstand/cover (effective 2005). adv. bk.rev. index. back issues avail. **Document type:** *Journal.* **Description:** Promotes Finnish design, art and architecture abroad.
Indexed: ABM, ArtInd, DAAI.
—BLDSC (4008.307000), IE, Infotrieve, ingenta.
Published by: Design Forum Finland/Finnish Society of Crafts and Design, Erottajankatu 7, Helsinki, 00130, Finland. TEL 358-9-6220810, FAX 358-9-62208181, form.function@designforum.fi, info@designforum.fi, http://www.designforum.fi/servlet/dfpage?did=1061. Eds. Anne Stenros, Anne Veinola. Circ: 5,000 (controlled). **Subscr. to:** Academic Bookstore, PL 23, Helsinki 00381, Finland.

720 DEU ISSN 0949-9261
FORMDISKURS; Zeitschrift fuer Design und Theorie. Text in German. 1996. s-a. **Document type:** *Magazine, Trade.*
—IE.
Published by: Verlag Form GmbH, Hanauer Landstr 161, Frankfurt Am Main, 60314, Germany. TEL 49-69-943325-0, FAX 49-69-94332525, form@form.de, http://www.form.de.

FORT; the international journal of fortification and military architecture. see *MILITARY*

720 USA ISSN 0734-4252
➤ **FORUM (CHICAGO, 1979).** Text in English. 1940. s-a. USD 80; USD 80 foreign (effective 1999). bk.rev. back issues avail. **Document type:** *Academic/Scholarly.* **Description:** Serves as the official bulletin for the society's Committee on Preservation.
Indexed: MagInd.
Published by: Society of Architectural Historians, 1365 North Astor St, Chicago, IL 60610-2144. TEL 312-573-1365, FAX 312-573-1141, info@sah.org, http://www.sah.org. Ed. Zeynep Celik. R&P Billie Gibson. adv.: B&W page USD 400. Circ: 3,550.

711.4 USA ISSN 1536-1012
E151
FORUM JOURNAL. Text in English. 1987. q. USD 115 to members. adv. back issues avail. **Document type:** *Academic/Scholarly.* **Description:** Serves as a forum for expressing opinions, encouraging debate, and conveying information of importance to members.
Formerly (until 1999): Historic Preservation Forum (1056-6309); Which was formed by the merger of (1987-1991): Forum Newsletter (0896-8179); (1987-1991): Preservation Forum (0893-9403)
Indexed: AIAP.
—BLDSC (4024.086630), IE, ingenta.
Published by: National Trust for Historic Preservation, 1785 Massachusetts Ave, N W, Washington, DC 20036. TEL 202-588-6296, http://www.nationaltrust.org. R&P Julia Miller TEL 202-588-6180. Adv. contact Donna Leahy TEL 202-588-6053.

FRA KVANGAARD TIL HUMLEKULE; meddelelser fra Havebrugshistorisk Selskab. see *GARDENING AND HORTICULTURE*

FRAME. see *INTERIOR DESIGN AND DECORATION*

720 USA
NA737.W7
FRANK LLOYD WRIGHT QUARTERLY. Text in English. 1990. q. USD 20; USD 40 membership (effective 1999). adv. bk.rev. illus. back issues avail.; reprints avail. **Document type:** *Academic/Scholarly.* **Description:** Contains in-depth articles about Frank Lloyd Wright, his life and work. Includes a national calendar of events.
Supersedes (1978-1982): Frank Lloyd Wright Newsletter (0160-7375)
Indexed: AIAP, API.
Published by: Frank Lloyd Wright Foundation, Taliesin West, Cactus Rd & 114th St, Scottsdale, AZ 85261-4430. TEL 602-860-2700. Ed., R&P Suzette Lucas. Pub. Suzette A Lucas. Circ: 8,000.

FREUNDESKREIS BLAETTER. see *MUSEUMS AND ART GALLERIES*

720 624 CHN ISSN 1004-6135
➤ **FUJIAN JIANZHU/FUJIAN ARCHITECTURE & CONSTRUCTION.** Text in Chinese. 1983. q. CNY 16. **Document type:** *Journal, Academic/Scholarly.*
Related titles: Online - full text ed.: (from East View Information Services).
Published by: Fujian Tumu Jianzhu Xuehui/Fujian Society of Civil Engineering and Architecture, 240 Beida Rd, Fuzhou, Fujian 350001, China. TEL 86-591-7855358. Ed., Pub., R&P Zhaoyi Yuan. Circ: 5,000. **Dist. overseas by:** China Publication Trading Corporation, P.O. Box 782, Beijing, China.

943 AUT ISSN 0429-8926
FUNDBERICHTE AUS OESTERREICH. Text in German. 1934. a. EUR 195 (effective 2003). charts; illus. **Document type:** *Monographic series, Academic/Scholarly.*
Indexed: BHA, BrArAb, NumL.
Published by: (Austria. Bundesdenkmalamt, Austria. Abteilung fuer Bodendenkmale), Verlag Ferdinand Berger und Soehne GmbH, Wienerstr 80, Horn, N 3580, Austria. TEL 43-2982-4161332, FAX 43-2982-4161382, office@berger.at, http://www.berger.at. Ed. Horst Adler.

720 363.6 USA ISSN 1549-9715
NA105
▼ **FUTURE ANTERIOR.** Text in English. 2004 (Spr). s-a. USD 24 domestic; USD 34 foreign (effective 2005). **Document type:** *Journal.*
Published by: Columbia University, Graduate School of Architecture, Planning and Preservation, 400 Avery Hall, New York, NY 10027. TEL 212-854-3510, FAX 212-864-0410, http://www.arch.columbia.edu/futureanterior.

724 JPN ISSN 0913-1639
G A/GUROBARU AKITEKUCHA. (Global Architecture) Text in English, Japanese. 1970. bi-m. JPY 13,998 (effective 2002). illus. back issues avail. **Document type:** *Monographic series.*
Indexed: AIAP, ArtInd.
Published by: A.D.A. Edita Tokyo Co. Ltd., 3-12-14 Sendagaya, Shibuya-ku, Tokyo, 151-0051, Japan. TEL 03-3403-1581, FAX 03-3497-0649, info@ga-ada.co.jp, http://www.ga-ada.co.jp/english.html. Ed. Yukio Futagawa. Circ: 12,000. **US subscr. to:** G A International Co. Ltd., 594 Broadway, 3rd Fl, P O Box 353, New York, NY 10012. TEL 212-274-9683.

720 JPN ISSN 0389-0066
G A DOCUMENT. (Global Architecture) Text in English, Japanese. q. JPY 11,392 (effective 2002).
Indexed: AIAP, ArtInd, PCI.
—BLDSC (4065.060000).
Published by: A.D.A. Edita Tokyo Co. Ltd., 3-12-14 Sendagaya, Shibuya-ku, Tokyo, 151-0051, Japan. TEL 81-3-3403-1581, FAX 81-3-3497-0649, info@ga-ada.co.jp, http://www.ga-ada.co.jp/gade.html.

728 JPN
G A HOUSES. (Global Architecture) Text in Japanese, English. 1977. q., latest vol.47. JPY 11,392 (effective 2002). **Document type:** *Monographic series.* **Description:** Series on international, contemporary, residential architecture. For architects, students of architecture, and art libraries.
Indexed: AIAP, API.
—BLDSC (4065.100000).
Published by: A.D.A. Edita Tokyo Co. Ltd., 3-12-14 Sendagaya, Shibuya-ku, Tokyo, 151-0051, Japan. TEL 81-3-3403-1581, FAX 81-3-3497-0649, Gaint@aol.com. Eds. Wayne Fuji, Yukio Futugawa. **Dist. by:** G A International Co. Ltd., 180 Varick St, 4th Fl, New York, NY 10014. TEL 212-741-6329, 212-741-6283.

720 SWE ISSN 1652-0033
GAARD & TORP SPECIAL. Text in Swedish. 1989. 6/yr. SEK 299 (effective 2005). **Document type:** *Magazine, Consumer.*
Supersedes in part (in 2003): Antikboersen (1400-4747); Which was formerly (until 1993): Kvalitets- och Antikboersen (1100-8202)
Published by: Antikboersens Foerlag AB, Birkagaten 17, Stockholm, 11336, Sweden. TEL 46-8-54547000, FAX 46-8-54547049, http://www.antikborsen.se. Ed. Gunilla von Platen. Circ: 35,000.

GARTEN UND LANDSCHAFT; Zeitschrift fuer Landschaftsarchitektur. see *GARDENING AND HORTICULTURE*

GAZI UNIVERSITESI MUHENDISLIK MIMARLIK FAKULTESI DERGISI. see *ENGINEERING*

GENTSE BIJDRAGEN TOT DE KUNSTGESCHIEDENIS. see *ART*

724 941.27 GBR ISSN 0963-1070
NA966
GEORGIAN GROUP JOURNAL. Text in English. 1937. a. GBP 24 to individuals; GBP 15 to students (effective 2000). bk.rev. back issues avail. **Document type:** *Academic/Scholarly.* **Description:** Promotes public understanding and appreciation of the classical tradition in British architecture, town planning, and decorative art, as well as the restoration and protection of this architectural and artistic heritage.
Indexed: AIAP, API, BHA, BrArAb, NumL, RILM.
Published by: Georgian Group, 6 Fitzroy Sq, London, W1P 6DX, United Kingdom. TEL 44-20-7387-1720, FAX 44-20-7387-1721. Ed. Richard Hewlings. Circ: 3,250.

A

724 941.27 GBR
GEORGIAN GROUP. SYMPOSIUM PROCEEDINGS. Text in English. irreg. (approx. 1-2/yr.). price varies. back issues avail. **Document type:** *Proceedings.* **Description:** Publishes articles and research on Georgian architecture and craftsmanship.
Published by: Georgian Group, 6 Fitzroy Sq, London, W1P 6DX, United Kingdom. TEL 44-20-7387-1720, FAX 44-20-7387-1721.

724 941.27 GBR
GEORGIAN GROUP. TOWN REPORTS. Text in English. 1993. irreg. (approx. 1-2/yr.). GBP 3.20 per issue. illus. back issues avail. **Document type:** *Monographic series.* **Description:** Examines the state of towns in Britain and the effect of historical conservation policies in these areas. Contains photographic surveys.
Published by: Georgian Group, 6 Fitzroy Sq, London, W1P 6DX, United Kingdom. TEL 44-20-7387-1720, FAX 44-20-7387-1721.

720 ITA ISSN 1721-5463
NA685
IL GIORNALE DELL'ARCHITETTURA. Text in Italian. 2002. m. **Document type:** *Magazine, Consumer.*
Published by: Umberto Allemandi & C. Srl, Via Mancini 8, Turin, TO 10131, Italy. TEL 39-011-8193133, FAX 39-011-8193090, http://www.allemandi.com.

720 666.1 DEU ISSN 0949-2720
GLAS; Architektur und Technik. Text in German. 1995. bi-m. EUR 51 domestic; EUR 57 foreign; EUR 9 newsstand/cover (effective 2005). adv. **Document type:** *Magazine, Trade.*
Published by: Konradin Verlag Robert Kohlhammer GmbH, Ernst Mey Str 8, Leinfelden-Echterdingen, 70771, Germany. TEL 49-711-75940, FAX 49-711-7594399, leserservice@glas-online.de, info@konradin.de, http://www.arcguide.info/arcguide/fachzeitschriften/glas.html, http://www.konradin.de. Ed. Juergen Braun. Adv. contact Marianne Hipp. B&W page EUR 2,280; trim 188 x 270.

720 DEU ISSN 0017-0852
TP845
GLASFORUM; Zeitschrift fuer Architektur, Raumgestaltung, Kunst. Text in German. 1951. bi-m. adv. bk.rev. bibl.; illus. index. **Document type:** *Journal, Trade.*
Indexed: API, RefZh.
—BLDSC (4182.500000), IE, ingenta. **CCC.**
Published by: Verlag Karl Hofmann, Postfach 1360, Schorndorf, 73603, Germany. TEL 49-7181-402127, FAX 49-7181-402111, info@hofmann-verlag.de, http://www.hofmann-verlag.de. Ed. Dieter Schempp. Circ: 10,400.

720 GBR ISSN 1476-0517
GLASS AGE. Text in English. 1958. m. GBP 60 domestic; GBP 75 foreign; GBP 5 newsstand/cover (effective 2003). adv. charts; illus.; stat. **Document type:** *Magazine, Trade.* **Description:** Covers the flat glass and glazing industry, from manufacture to installation. Includes informational articles, business news, and lists of products.
Former titles (until 2001): Glass Age & Window Construction; (until 1999): Glass Age (0017-0992)
Related titles: Microform ed.: (from PQC); Online - full text ed.: (from EBSCO Publishing, Gale Group, LexisNexis, O C L C Online Computer Library Center, Inc.).
Indexed: API, BrTechI, M&TEA.
—BLDSC (4190.300000), Linda Hall. **CCC.**
Published by: C M P Information Ltd. (Subsidiary of: United Business Media), City Reach, 5 Greenwich View Pl, Millharbour, London, E14 9NN, United Kingdom. TEL 44-20-7861-6137, FAX 44-20-7861-6552, enquiries@cmpinformation.com, http://www.glassage.com, http://www.cmpinformation.com. Ed. Richard Schwarz. Pub. Bob Andrew. Adv. contact Dave Broxton. Circ: 10,338 (paid and controlled).

GLASS MAGAZINE. see *CERAMICS, GLASS AND POTTERY*

GLOBAL BUILT ENVIRONMENT REVIEW. see *ENVIRONMENTAL STUDIES*

GOTHENBURG STUDIES IN ART AND ARCHITECTURE. see *ART*

GRAFICA Y DISENO. see *ART*

712 GBR ISSN 1742-3716
SB469
GREEN PLACES. Text in English. 1934. 10/yr. GBP 39.20 domestic; GBP 62 elsewhere; GBP 28.80 to students in UK; GBP 53 in USA, Canada & rest of Europe (effective 2004). adv. bk.rev. bibl.; charts; illus.; stat. cum.index. reprints avail. **Document type:** *Journal, Trade.* **Description:** Raises awareness of environmental, social, cultural and economic factors in the planning, development and management of public space.
Former titles (Nov. 2003): Landscape Design (0020-2908); (until 1971): Institute of Landscape Architects. Journal (0954-4003)
Related titles: Online - full text ed.: (from H.W. Wilson, O C L C Online Computer Library Center, Inc.); ♦ Supplement(s): Green Places News. ISSN 1742-3724; ♦ Plant User. ISSN 0959-4361; ♦ Landlines Tech. ISSN 1470-3807.
Indexed: ABM, AIAP, API, ArtInd, GardL, RASB, RICS, RRTA, WAE&RSA.
—BLDSC (4214.942370), IE, Infotrieve, ingenta. **CCC.**
Published by: Landscape Design Trust, 13a West St, Reigate, Surrey RH2 9BL, United Kingdom. TEL 44-1737-225374, FAX 44-1737-224206, info@landscape.co.uk, http://www.landscape.co.uk/gp.html. Eds. Chris Young TEL 44-1737-221116, Diane Millis. Adv. contact Robert Ellis TEL 44-1737-223144. Circ: 6,500.

712 GBR ISSN 1742-3724
SB469.
GREEN PLACES NEWS. Text in English. 1990. m. (11/yr.). GBP 15 in UK & Ireland; GBP 18 in USA, Canada & rest of Europe; GBP 22 elsewhere; GBP 10 to students in UK & Ireland; GBP 1.50 newsstand/cover in UK & Ireland; GBP 2.50 newsstand/cover elsewhere (effective 2003); includes subscr. to Landlines Tech. adv. **Document type:** *Newspaper.* **Description:** Provides a range of issues relating to the wider environment, including contemporary design, community work, garden design, wildlife conservation and much more. Includes news analysis and professional opinion.
Former titles (until 2003): Landlines (1469-0985); (until 1998): Landscape Design Extra (0962-2187)
Related titles: ♦ Supplement to: Green Places. ISSN 1742-3716.
Indexed: AIAP, BibInd.
—BLDSC (4214.942371). **CCC.**
Published by: Landscape Design Trust, 13a West St, Reigate, Surrey RH2 9BL, United Kingdom. TEL 44-1737-225374, FAX 44-1737-224206, info@landscape.co.uk, http://www.landscape.co.uk/ll.html. Ed. Diane Millis. R&P Ken Fieldhouse TEL 44-1737-221116. Adv. contact Robert Ellis TEL 44-1737-223744.

320 701 720 USA ISSN 1526-3819
NA100
➤ **GREY ROOM.** Text in English. 2000. q. USD 68 combined subscription in US & Canada to individuals print & online eds.; USD 88 combined subscription elsewhere to individuals print & online eds.; USD 217 combined subscription in US & Canada to institutions print & online eds.; USD 237 combined subscription elsewhere to institutions print & online eds. (effective 2006). **Document type:** *Journal, Academic/Scholarly.* **Description:** Devoted to the theorization of modern and contemporary architecture, art and media. Investigates each of the fields separately and how they interact.
Related titles: Online - full text ed.: ISSN 1536-0105. USD 61 to individuals; USD 195 to institutions (effective 2006) (from EBSCO Publishing, Gale Group, IngentaConnect, O C L C Online Computer Library Center, Inc., Swets Information Services).
Indexed: AIAP, ArtInd.
—BLDSC (4216.420950), IE, Infotrieve. **CCC.**
Published by: M I T Press, 55 Hayward St, Cambridge, MA 02142-1493. TEL 617-253-5646, FAX 617-258-6779, editors@greyroom.org, journals-info@mit.edu, http://mitpress.mit.edu/greyroom. Eds. Branden W Joseph, Felicity D Scott, Reinhold Martin.

➤ **GROEN;** vakblad voor de groen in stad en landschap. see *GARDENING AND HORTICULTURE*

712 DEU ISSN 1610-4730
GRUENFORUM.LA; Branchenmagazin fuer GaLaBau und Landschaftsarchitektur. Text in German. 1962. m. EUR 78 domestic; EUR 86.40 foreign (effective 2003). adv. bk.rev. illus. reprints avail. **Document type:** *Magazine, Trade.* **Description:** Trade publication for landscape planning and design. Editorial reports give practical information concerning the use of plants and every second issue focuses on a specific topic.
Former titles (until 2002): Landschaftsarchitektur (0323-3162); (until 1972): Deutsche Gartenarchitektur (0417-1861)
Published by: Thalacker Medien, Bernhard Thalacker Verlag GmbH und Co. KG, Postfach 8364, Braunschweig, 38133, Germany. TEL 49-531-380040, FAX 49-531-3800425, info@thalackermedien.de, http://www.thalackermedien.de. Ed. Matthias Hinkelammert TEL 49-531-3800410. Adv. contact Claudia Schombacher. B&W page EUR 1,849.60, color page EUR 3,037.60; trim 186 x 272. Circ: 5,527 (controlled).

DAS GRUNDEIGENTUM; Zeitschrift fuer die gesamte Grundstuecks-, Haus- und Wohnungswirtschaft. see *HOUSING AND URBAN PLANNING*

GUIA DE FORNECEDORES DA CONSTRUCAO. see *BUILDING AND CONSTRUCTION*

720 ITA
GUIDE AL RESTAURO DEI MONUMENTI. Text in Italian. 1990. irreg., latest vol.3, 1999. price varies. **Document type:** *Monographic series.*
Formerly: Guide di Ricerca Storica e Restauro
Published by: Liguori Editore srl, Via Posillipo 394, Naples, 80123, Italy. TEL 39-81-7206111, FAX 39-81-7206244, http://www.liguori.it. Ed. Giovanni Carbonara.

720.7 USA ISSN 1097-2552
NA2103
GUIDE TO ARCHITECTURE SCHOOLS. Text in English. 1947. irreg. (approx. triennial). USD 19.95 (effective 1999). **Document type:** *Directory.*
Formerly: Guide to Architecture Schools in North America (0092-7856)
Published by: Association of Collegiate Schools of Architecture, Inc., 1735 New York Ave, N W, Washington, DC 20006. TEL 202-785-2324, FAX 202-628-0448. Ed. John K Edwardser.

344.73 620 USA ISSN 0091-8245
KF2925.3.A73
GUIDELINES FOR IMPROVING PRACTICE. ARCHITECTS AND ENGINEERS PROFESSIONAL LIABILITY. Text in English. 1971. bi-m. looseleaf. USD 100. **Document type:** *Trade.*
Published by: Victor O. Schinnerer & Co., Two Wisconsin Circle, Chevy Chase, MD 20815. TEL 301-961-9800. Ed. Thomas H Porterfreld Jr. Circ: 10,500.

720 USA ISSN 1089-2141
GUIDELINES LETTER; new directions and techniques in the design professions. Text in English. 1972. m. USD 85 (effective 2005). bk.rev. index. 4 p./no.; **Document type:** *Newsletter, Trade.* **Description:** Focuses on the needs of small office practice. Includes interview excerpts, new services for architects and designers, and state-of-the-profession in the 1990's.
Formerly: Guidelines Architectural Letter
Published by: San Francisco Institute of Architecture, PO Box 2590, Alameda, CA 94501. TEL 510-523-5172, 800-634-7779, FAX 510-523-5175, sfia@aol.com. Ed. Fred Stitt. Circ: 3,000 (controlled).

720 745.5 USA
NK1127
GUILD SOURCEBOOKS: THE ARCHITECT'S SOURCEBOOK - ARCHITECTURAL ARTS & SCULPTURE. Text in English. 1986. a. USD 37.50 (effective 2000). adv. illus. **Document type:** *Directory.* **Description:** Lists and displays hand-crafted work done by artists for designers and architects.
Formerly: Guild: The Architect's Source of Artists and Artisans; Which supersedes in part: Guild: A Sourcebook of Artists and Artisans; Which was formerly (until 1990): Guild: A Sourcebook of American Craft Artists (0885-3975)
Published by: Guild.com, 931 E Main St, Madison, WI 53703. TEL 608-257-2590, FAX 608-257-2490, info@guild.com, http://www.guild.com. Ed. Toni Fountain Sikes. Circ: 10,000.

722 CHN ISSN 1000-7237
GUJIAN YUANLIN JISHU/TRADITIONAL CHINESE ARCHITECTURE AND GARDENS. Text in Chinese. 1983. q. USD 20. **Document type:** *Academic/Scholarly.*
Related titles: Online - full text ed.: (from East View Information Services).
Published by: Beijing Di'er Fangwu Xiushan Gongcheng Gongsi/Beijing No.2 House Remodeling Engineering Company, 129 Di anmen Dongdajie, Beijing, 100009, China. TEL 86-10-6404-1946. Ed. Xu Shu Hui. Circ: 10,000.
Co-sponsor: Beijing Gudai Jianzhu Gongcheng Gongsi - Beijing Ancient Architecture Engineering Company.

H D K MAGAZIN. (Hochschule der Kuenste Berlin) see *ART*

720 CHE ISSN 0017-6419
HABITATION; revue bimestrielle romande. Text in French. 1928. bi-m. CHF 60; CHF 80 foreign; CHF 45 to students. adv. charts; illus. index. **Document type:** *Trade.*
Indexed: AIAP.
Published by: Union Suisse pour l'Amelioration du Logement, Section Romande, 10 rue du Vieux Marche, Nyon, 1260, Switzerland. TEL 41-22-3613610, FAX 41-22-3613617. Ed. Francois-Joseph Z'Graggen. **Co-sponsor:** Federation des Architectes Suisses.

721 AUS ISSN 1832-8229
▼ ➤ **HAECCEITY PAPERS.** Text in English. 2005. 2/yr. USD 78 to individuals; USD 199 to institutions (effective 2005). **Document type:** *Journal, Academic/Scholarly.* **Description:** Delivers a themed collation of essays on a significant, pertinent and contemporary issue in critical architecture theory.
Media: Online - full content.
Published by: Scorched Ink Pty Ltd, 163/19 Tusculum St, Potts Point, NSW 2011, Australia. TEL 61-404-261282, FAX 61-2-93802211, info@haecceityinc.com, http://www.haeccityinc.com. Ed., R&P, Adv. contact Daniel Pavlovits.

720 CHN ISSN 1006-6780
HARBIN JIANZHU DAXUE XUEBAO/HARBIN UNIVERSITY OF ARCHITECTURE AND ENGINEERING. JOURNAL. Text in Chinese. 1959. bi-m. CNY 60 (effective 2004). **Document type:** *Journal, Academic/Scholarly.*
Formerly: Haerbin Jianzhu Gongchng Xueyuan Xuebao (1000-1883)
Related titles: Online - full content ed.; Online - full text ed.: (from East View Information Services).
Indexed: BrCerAb, C&ISA, CerAb, CorrAb, E&CAJ, EMA, IAA, M&TEA, MBF, METADEX, RefZh, WAA.
—Linda Hall.

Published by: Harbin Jianzhu Daxue/Harbin University of Architecture and Engineering, 66 Xi Dazhi St, Harbin, Heilongjiang 150006, China. TEL 86-451-6281155, FAX 86-451-6282276, Jcivil@hope.hit.edu.cn. **Dist. by:** China International Book Trading Corp, 35 Chegongzhuang Xilu, Haidian District, PO Box 399, Beijing 100044, China. TEL 86-10-68412045, FAX 86-10-68412023, cibtc@mail.cibtc.com.cn, http://www.cibtc.com.cn.

711.4   USA   ISSN 1093-4421
NA1.A12
➤ **HARVARD DESIGN MAGAZINE.** Text in English. 1977. 2/yr. USD 35 domestic to individuals; USD 38 in Canada to individuals; USD 50 elsewhere to individuals; USD 75 domestic to institutions; USD 80 in Canada to institutions; USD 90 elsewhere to institutions; USD 28 domestic to students; USD 30 in Canada to students; USD 43 elsewhere to students; USD 18 newsstand/cover (effective 2005). adv. bk.rev. charts; illus. back issues avail. **Document type:** *Journal, Academic/Scholarly.* **Description:** Explores major issues in architecture, landscape and urban design and planning.
Former titles (until 1997): G S D News (0746-3677); (until 1983): H G S D News (0193-6107)
Related titles: Online - full text ed.
Indexed: ABM, AIAP, ArtInd.
Published by: Harvard University, Graduate School of Design, 48 Quincy St, Cambridge, MA 02138. TEL 617-495-7814, FAX 617-496-3391, hdm@gsd.harvard.edu, http://www.gsd.harvard.edu/research/publications/hdm/, http://www.harvard.edu/hdm. Eds. Nancy Levinson, William S Saunders. R&P Jeffrey Gonyeau. adv.: B&W 1/2 page USD 3,000; trim 9 x 12. **Circ: 16,000 (paid)**. **Dist. by:** Eastern News Distributors Inc., 250 W. 55th St., New York, NY 10019. TEL 212-649-4425, FAX 212-265-1024. **Co-publisher:** M I T Press.

➤ **DAS HAUS.** see *INTERIOR DESIGN AND DECORATION*

720   NLD   ISSN 0017-9515
HEEMSCHUT. Text in Dutch. 1911. bi-m. adv. bk.rev. illus.
Indexed: AIAP, API.
—IE, Infotrieve.
Published by: Bond Heemschut, Nieuwezijds Kolk 28, Amsterdam, 1012, Netherlands. TEL 31-20-6225292, FAX 31-20-6240571, info@heemschut.nl, http://www.heemschut.nl. Circ: 7,500.

HEIMATSCHUTZ/SAUVEGARDE. see *CONSERVATION*

720 994   AUS   ISSN 0157-9231
HERITAGE COUNCIL OF NEW SOUTH WALES ANNUAL REPORT. Text in English. 1978. a. **Description:** Informs on the activities of the Heritage Council during the year.
Published by: Heritage Council of New South Wales, Locked Bag 5020, Parramatta, NSW 2124, Australia. TEL 61-2-96356155, FAX 61-2-98499580. R&P Murray Brown TEL 61-2-93912060.

HERITAGE LIVING. see *HISTORY—History Of Australasia And Other Areas*

720 994   AUS   ISSN 1321-1099
HERITAGE N.S.W. Text in English. 1994. q. back issues avail. **Document type:** *Newsletter, Government.* **Description:** Provides information on activities of the Heritage Council, new publications, innovative local projects and upcoming events.
Published by: Heritage Council of New South Wales, Locked Bag 5020, Parramatta, NSW 2124, Australia. TEL 61-2-96356155, FAX 61-2-98914688, heritageoffice@heritage.nsw.gov.au. Ed., R&P Murray Brown TEL 61-2-93912060. Circ: 5,000.

720   ESP   ISSN 1132-189X
HT169.S652
HISTORIA URBANA. Text in Spanish, Catalan. 1992. q.
—CINDOC.
Published by: Universitat Politecnica de Valencia, Departamento de Urbanismo, Camino de Vera, s-n, Valencia, 46022, Spain. TEL 34-963-877280, FAX 34-963-877289, depurb@upvnet.upv.es, http://www.upv.es/.

728.6   GBR
HISTORIC FARM BUILDINGS GROUP. NEWSLETTER AND JOURNAL. Text in English. 1987. a. bk.rev. **Document type:** *Journal, Academic/Scholarly.*
Incorporates: Historic Farm Buildings Group. Newsletter; Formerly (until 2004): Historic Farm Buildings Group. Journal (0952-5513)
Indexed: BrArAb, NumL.
—BLDSC (6108.504000).
Published by: Historic Farm Buildings Group, c/o Museum of English Rural Life, Rural History Centre, University of Reading, Whiteknights, PO Box 229, Reading, Berks RG6 2AG, United Kingdom. TEL 44-118-9318663, FAX 44-118-9751264, jill.betts@btinternet.com. Ed. Gwen Jones.

HISTORIC GUELPH; the royal city. see *HISTORY—History Of North And South America*

HISTORIC HAWAII MAGAZINE. see *HISTORY—History Of North And South America*

720   GBR   ISSN 0260-8707
NA109.G7
HISTORIC HOUSE. Text in English. 1981. q. GBP 40; (foreign $60) (effective 1997). adv. bk.rev. **Document type:** *Consumer.* **Description:** Covers a range of topics from conservation, the arts, environment and heritage to tourism and marketing for historic-home and garden owners in the U.K.
Indexed: AIAP.
Published by: (Historic Houses Association), Hall - McCartney Ltd., Heritage House, 12 Football Close, Box 21, Baldock, Herts SG7 5AH, United Kingdom. TEL 44-1462-896688, FAX 44-1462-896677. Ed. Peter Sinclair. Pub. Michael McCartney. Adv. contact E A Goldthorpe. Circ: 7,000.

069   USA   ISSN 1083-379X
HISTORIC HOUSE NEWS. Text in English. 1989. q. looseleaf. USD 35 (effective 2000). illus. **Document type:** *Newsletter, Trade.* **Description:** Provides information relating to the 19 historic house museums located in New York City Parks. Includes articles on social history of the houses, updates on the museums and their collections, restoration projects and calendar of events at the houses.
Related titles: Online - full text ed.
Published by: Historic House Trust of New York City, The Arsenal, Rm 203, Central Park, New York, NY 10021. TEL 212-360-8282, FAX 212-360-8201, http://www.preserve.org/hht. Ed., R&P Troy Segal. Circ: 1,500.

727 977   USA   ISSN 0164-5293
HISTORIC ILLINOIS. Text in English. 1978. bi-m. USD 10 (effective 2003). bk.rev. cum.index. 16 p./no.; back issues avail. **Document type:** *Magazine, Government.* **Description:** Reports on the efforts to promote the preservation of important buildings and other historic sites in Illinois.
Indexed: AIAP.
Published by: Illinois Historic Preservation Agency, 500 E Madison, Springfield, IL 62701-1507. TEL 217-524-6045, FAX 217-785-7937, info@ihpa.state.il.us, http://www.illinoishistory.gov/. Ed., R&P Cynthia A. Fuener TEL 217-785-7950. Circ: 3,500 (paid).

HISTORIC KANSAS CITY FOUNDATION GAZETTE. see *HISTORY—History Of North And South America*

HISTORIC TRAVELER; the guide to great historic destinations. see *TRAVEL AND TOURISM*

HISTORICAL SOCIETY OF LOUDOUN COUNTY, VIRGINIA. BULLETIN; 1997 Annual. see *HISTORY—History Of North And South America*

HISTORICAL SOCIETY OF SOUTH AUSTRALIA. JOURNAL. see *HISTORY—History Of Australasia And Other Areas*

HISTORICAL SOCIETY OF SOUTH AUSTRALIA NEWSLETTER. see *HISTORY—History Of Australasia And Other Areas*

720   CHE
HOCHPARTERRE. Text in German. 1988. 10/yr. CHF 100; CHF 130 foreign (effective 1997). adv. bk.rev. **Document type:** *Trade.*
Published by: Hochparterre AG, Ausstellungsstr 25, Zuerich, 8005, Switzerland. TEL 41-1-4442888, FAX 41-1-4442889, hochparterre@access.ch, http://www.hochparterre.ch. Ed. Koebi Gantenbein. Adv. contact Susanna Franzoni. B&W page CHF 4,270, color page CHF 6,920; trim 288 x 221. Circ: 13,000.

728   USA   ISSN 0278-2839
TX311
HOME; the remodeling and decorating resource. Text in English. 1955. 10/yr. USD 10 domestic; USD 20 foreign; USD 3.50 newsstand/cover (effective 2005). adv. bk.rev. illus.; tr.lit. reprints avail. **Document type:** *Magazine, Consumer.* **Description:** Emphasizes home design and architecture, including creative yet practical ideas aimed primarily at the average middle-income homeowner.
Former titles (until 1981): Hudson Home Magazine (0194-1089); (until 1980): Hudson Home Guides (0362-6520); Incorporates: Home Building and Remodeling; Home Planning and Design; Home Improvement and Repair (0361-2813); Home Plans and Ideas; Kitchens, Baths and Family Rooms
Related titles: Online - full text ed.: (from America Online, Inc.).
Indexed: PMR, Search.
Published by: Hachette Filipacchi Media U.S., Inc. (Subsidiary of: Hachette Filipacchi Medias S.A.), 1633 Broadway, New York, NY 10019. TEL 212-767-6000, FAX 212-767-4932, homemag@hfnm.com, http://www.homemag.com, http://www.hfmus.com. Ed. Donna Sapolin. Pubs. Anne Triece, John H. Grant. Adv. contact Jack Grant. B&W page USD 66,900, color page USD 82,700; trim 8 x 10.75. Circ: 1,000,000 (paid). **Subscr. to:** PO Box 56318, Boulder, CO 80322-6318. TEL 800-950-7370.

720 690   HKG
HONG KONG ARCHITECTS & DESIGNERS CATALOGUE (YEAR)∗. Text in English. 1976. a. (in 2 vols.). HKD 550 domestic; USD 115.50 foreign. adv. **Document type:** *Catalog.* **Description:** Covers commercial and domestic interiors, building supplies, home and office furnishing, landscaping, catering and hotel equipment.

Published by: Times Publishing Group, Block C 10th Fl. Seaview Estate, 2-8 Watson Rd., Hong Kong, Hong Kong. FAX 852-2508-0255. Ed. Kenneth Ho. Adv. contact Winnie Kwan. color page HKD 6,800; trim 210 x 285. Circ: 11,200.

HOTEL SPEC. see *HOTELS AND RESTAURANTS*

720 690 747   TWN
HOUSE. Text in Chinese. m. **Document type:** *Magazine, Consumer.*
Published by: Moli Meiren Wenhua Shiye Gufen Youxian Gongsi, Sec. 1, no.96, 4th Fl., Nanjing Dong Road, Taipei, Taiwan. TEL 886-02-25414925, 886-02-25712565, FAX 886-02-25411366, http://www.housemag.com.tw/20/index.htm.

HOUSE BEAUTIFUL. see *INTERIOR DESIGN AND DECORATION*

720   USA   ISSN 1532-8716
HOUSE BEAUTIFUL HOUSES & PLANS; building tips - financing - trends - new products. Text in English. 1957. q. USD 4.50 newsstand/cover (effective 2005). adv. illus. back issues avail. **Document type:** *Magazine, Consumer.* **Description:** Features more than 200 profesionally designed house plans in a wide variety of styles.
Published by: Hanley-Wood, LLC (Subsidiary of: J.P. Morgan Chase & Co.), 3275 W Ina Rd, Ste 220, Tucson, AZ 85741. TEL 520-544-8206, FAX 520-544-8224, tjackson@hanleywood.com, http://www.hanleywood.com. Ed. Arlen Feldwick Jones. Pub. Eric Karaffa. adv.: B&W page USD 14,560, color page USD 20,800; trim 10.75 x 8. Circ: 250,000 (paid).

720   AUS   ISSN 1440-3382
NA7100
HOUSES. Text in English. 1989. bi-m. AUD 60 domestic; AUD 100 in Asia & the Pacific; AUD 120 elsewhere; AUD 18 newsstand/cover (effective 2004). adv. **Document type:** *Trade.* **Description:** Reviews a range of individually designed newly built, renovated or converted projects. Beautifully photographed and presented with detailed plans and product lists.
Formerly (until 1997): Architect Designed Houses (1034-4101)
Related titles: Online - full text ed.: (from EBSCO Publishing, Gale Group).
Indexed: WBA, WMB.
Published by: Architecture Media, L3, 4 Princes St, Port Melbourne, VIC 3207, Australia. TEL 61-3-96164760, FAX 61-3-96464918, publisher@archmedia.com.au, http://www.archmedia.com.au. Eds. Ms. Julie Dillon, Ms. Sue Harris. Adv. contacts Ms. Victoria Hawthorne, Neil Williams. color page AUD 3,589. Circ: 3,590.

HOUSING AND PLANNING YEAR BOOK. see *HOUSING AND URBAN PLANNING*

333.7   FRA   ISSN 1019-679X
I C O M O S NOUVELLES/I C O M O S NEWS. Text in French. 1990. q. USD 32. adv. **Document type:** *Newsletter.*
Formerly: Icomos Information (0394-218X)
Indexed: AIAP, BHA.
Published by: International Council on Monuments and Sites/Counseil International des Monuments et des Sites, 49-51 rue de la Federation, Paris, 75015, France. TEL 33-1-4567-6770, FAX 33-1-4566-0622, secretariat@icomos.org, http://www.international.icomos.org. Ed. Pauline Alphen. Adv. contact Henri Verrier.

I.D.; the international design magazine. (International Design) see *INTERIOR DESIGN AND DECORATION*

720   DEU   ISSN 0081-9018
TA663   CODEN: ILILE6
I L. Text in German, English. 1958. irreg. **Document type:** *Journal, Academic/Scholarly.*
Formerly (until 1969): Entwicklungsstaette fuer den Leichtbau. Mitteilung (0423-2534)
Indexed: AIAP.
Published by: (Institut fuer Leichte Flaechentragwerke), Karl Kraemer Verlag, Schulze-Delitzsch-Str 15, Stuttgart, 70565, Germany. TEL 49-711-78496-0, FAX 49-711-7849620, info@kraemerverlag.com.

IDEA. see *INTERIOR DESIGN AND DECORATION*

720   ARG   ISSN 0327-7577
IDEAS (MENDOZA). Text in Spanish. 1991. a.
Published by: Universidad de Mendoza, Facultad de Arquitectura y Urbanismo, Diag. Dag Hammarskjold 750, Mendoza, 5500, Argentina. TEL 54-261-4200948, FAX 54-251-4200584, unimen@um.edu.ar, http://www.um.edu.ar/um. Ed. Gladys Mabel Tourne.

IDRIJSKI RAZGLEDI. see *HISTORY*

IN CONTEXT. see *HISTORY—History Of North And South America*

720   ZMB   ISSN 1015-0862
NA17.Z3
IN SITU. Text in English. q.

A

Indexed: AIAP, API, GasAb.
Published by: Zambia Institute of Architects, PO Box 76105, Ndola, Zambia. **Co-sponsor:** Surveyors Institute of Zambia.

720 620 ITA
INARCASSA. Text in Italian. 1972; N.S. 1996. bi-m. **Document type:** *Magazine, Trade.* **Description:** Informs engineers and architects of foreseen problems both specific and general in their fields.
Published by: Cassa Nazionale di Previdenza e Assistenza per gli Ingegneri e gli Architetti Liberi Professionisti, Via Salaria 229, Rome, Italy. TEL 39-06-852741, FAX 39-06-85274446, http://www.inarcassa.it. Circ: 177,348.

720.29 IND
INDIAN ARCHITECTS DIRECTORY & REFERENCE BOOK. Text in English. 1969. irreg. USD 40. adv. **Document type:** *Directory.* **Description:** Regional listing of architectural firms in India, with a separate listing of government architectural departments. Includes a special section on prize winning architects.
Former titles: Indian Architects Directory (0256-4017); All India Architects Directory (0587-4793)
Published by: Architects Publishing Corp. of India, 51 Sujata, Ground Fl., Rani Sati Marg, Malad East, Mumbai, Maharashtra 400 097, India. TEL 91-22-883-4442. Ed. A K Gupta. Circ: 5,000.

INDUSTRIA & DISENO. see *ART*

L'INDUSTRIA DELLE COSTRUZIONI. see *BUILDING AND CONSTRUCTION*

720 AUS
INFO-LINK ARCHITECTURAL. Text in English. q. AUD 25.41 (effective 2001). adv. **Document type:** *Trade.*
Former titles (until 1998): Info-link Australia; (until 1993): Info-link; (until 1991): Info-link Magazine; (until 1990): Construction info-link
Published by: Reed Business Information Pty Ltd (Subsidiary of: Reed Business Information International), Locked Bag 2999, Chatswood, NSW 2067, Australia. http://www.infolink.com.au. Circ: 33,050.

720 CAN ISSN 1192-2168
INFO-LINK MAGAZINE. Text in English. 1993. q. CND 20; USD 40 in United States. adv. **Document type:** *Trade.* **Description:** Serves the fields of architecture, interior design, building and construction.
Indexed: ABIX.
Published by: I - L Focus Inc., 270 3044 Bloor St W, Toronto, ON M8X 2Y8, Canada. TEL 416-604-7552, FAX 416-604-2545, infolink@infolinkcanada.com, infolink@total.net, http://www.infolinkcanada.com. Ed. Brian Foster. Pub. Barbara Linden Bach. Adv. contact Barbara Lindenbach. Circ: 47,000 (controlled).

720 USA ISSN 1539-4360
NA1
INFORM (LINCOLN); the journal of architecture, design, and material culture. Text in English. 2000. a.
Published by: University of Nebraska at Lincoln, College of Architecture, 232 Architecture Hall West, Lincoln, NE 68588-0107. TEL 402-472-7943, FAX 402-472-3806, info@unlnotes.unl.edu, http://www.unl.edu/archcoll.

720 USA ISSN 1047-8353
NA730.V8
INFORM (RICHMOND); architecture & design in the mid-atlantic. (Includes directory of Virginia architecture firms) Text in English. 1990. 5/yr. (plus a. directory). USD 22 (effective 2005). adv. bk.rev. **Document type:** *Trade.* **Description:** Aimed at design professionals and potential clients of design services, including architecture, product design, graphic design, historic preservation, and decorative arts.
Indexed: AIAP, LibLit.
—Infotrieve.
Published by: American Institute of Architects, Virginia Society, 15 S Fifth St, Richmond, VA 23219. TEL 804-644-3041, FAX 804-644-6714, http://www.aiava.org/inform.htm. Ed., R&P Vernon Mays. Pub. John W Braymer. Adv. contact Jonathan Dabney. B&W page USD 950, color page USD 1,350; 11 x 8.5. Circ: 8,000.

INFORMATION SOURCES IN ARCHITECTURE AND CONSTRUCTION. see *BUILDING AND CONSTRUCTION*

INGEGNERI ARCHITETTI COSTRUTTORI. see *ENGINEERING—Civil Engineering*

INGENIERIA Y ARQUITECTURA. see *ENGINEERING—Civil Engineering*

720 USA ISSN 0020-1472
NA722
INLAND ARCHITECT. Text in English. 1888. q. USD 37 to libraries; USD 85 professionals; USD 21 to students (effective 2004). adv. bk.rev. illus. reprint service avail. from PQC. **Document type:** *Magazine, Trade.*
Related titles: Microform ed.: 1957 (from PQC); Online - full text ed.: (from H.W. Wilson, O C L C Online Computer Library Center, Inc.).
Indexed: AIAP, API, AgeL, ArtInd, Search.
—BLDSC (4514.870000).
Published by: Real Estate News Corp, 3550 W Peterson Ave, Ste 100, Chicago, IL 60659. TEL 773-866-9900, 888-641-3169, FAX 773-866-9881, rencpbulishing@earthlink.net, inquiries@renpublishing.com, http://www.inlandarchitectmag.com, http://www.renpublishing.com. Ed. Margaret Guzek. Pub. Steven Polydoris. Circ: 30,000 (paid).

INSIGHTS INTO SOUTH AUSTRALIAN HISTORY. see *HISTORY—History Of Australasia And Other Areas*

727.6 USA
INSITES (CHICAGO). Text in English. 1994. q. membership. **Document type:** *Newsletter.* **Description:** Information on Chicago architecture, educational programs, exhibitions and tours offered by the foundation.
Formerly: Chicago Architecture Foundation News
Related titles: Online - full text ed.
Published by: Chicago Architecture Foundation, 224 S Michigan Ave, Chicago, IL 60604-2501. TEL 312-922-3432, FAX 312-922-0481, http://www.architecture.org. Ed., R&P Ania Greiner TEL 312-922-3432 ext.227. Circ: 6,000.

720 USA ISSN 1545-6536
▼ **INSPIRED HOUSE.** Variant title: Taunton's Inspired House. Text in English. 2003 (Nov.). bi-m. USD 24.95 in US & Canada; USD 31 elsewhere; USD 4.99 newsstand/cover domestic; USD 5.99 newsstand/cover in Canada (effective 2005). **Document type:** *Magazine, Consumer.* **Description:** Presents practical, stylish home and interior design ideas and tips.
Published by: Taunton Press, Inc., 63 South Main St, PO Box 5506, Newtown, CT 06470-5506. TEL 203-426-8171, 800-477-8727, FAX 203-426-3434, http://www.taunton.com/inspiredhouse/index.asp. Ed. Marc Vassallo. Circ: 180,000 (controlled).

711.4 SCG
INSTITUT ZA ARHITEKTURU I URBANIZAM SRBIJE. ZBORNIK RADOVA. Text in Serbo-Croatian. 1975 (vol.7). a. charts; illus.; tr.lit.
Published by: Institut za Arhitekturu i Urbanizam Srbije, Bulevar Revolucije 73-II, Belgrade. Ed. N Pejovic.

INSTITUTION OF ENGINEERS (INDIA). ARCHITECTURAL ENGINEERING. see *ENGINEERING—Civil Engineering*

INSTITUTUL POLITEHNIC DIN IASI. BULETINUL. SECTIA 6: CONSTRUCTII, ARHITECTURA. see *BUILDING AND CONSTRUCTION*

720 DEU ISSN 0949-2356
INTELLIGENTE ARCHITEKTUR. Text in German. 1994. 6/yr. EUR 39.90 domestic; EUR 49.50 foreign (effective 2004). **Document type:** *Magazine, Trade.*
Indexed: AIAP.
—BLDSC (4531.832111).
Published by: Verlagsanstalt Alexander Koch GmbH, Fasanenweg 18, Leinfelden-Echterdingen, 70771, Germany. TEL 49-711-75910, FAX 49-711-7591-368, ait-abo@ait.de, http://www.koch-verlag.de.

720 792.8 CAN ISSN 0825-8708
INTER - ART ACTUEL. Text in French. 1978. 3/yr. CND 20 domestic to individuals; CND 35 foreign to individuals; CND 35 to institutions (effective 2000); CND 7.95 newsstand/cover. adv. **Document type:** *Abstract/Index.*
Formerly (until 1984): Intervention (0705-1972)
Indexed: ABM.
Published by: Les Editions Intervention, 345 rue du Pont, Quebec, PQ G1K 6M4, Canada. TEL 418-529-9680, FAX 418-529-6933, edinter@total.net, http://www.total.net/~edinter. R&P Richard Martel. adv.: B&W page CND 625; trim 310 x 210. Circ: 1,200.

720 USA ISSN 1044-3843
NA2542.35
INTERCHANGE (POMONA). Text in English. 1987. a., latest vol.8. USD 20 per issue (effective 2001). **Document type:** *Academic/Scholarly.*
Published by: California State Polytechnic University, College of Environmental Design, 3801 W Temple Ave, Pomona, CA 91768. TEL 909-869-2664, FAX 909-869-4355.

INTERNATIONAL DIRECTORY OF DESIGN. see *ART*

720 GBR ISSN 0269-0837
INTERNATIONAL DIRECTORY OF PRACTICES (YEAR). Text in English. a. GBP 45. **Document type:** *Directory.* **Description:** Covers RIBA member practices working internationally or with international offices.
Published by: (Royal Institute of British Architects), R I B A Publications, Finsbury Mission, 39 Moreland St, London, EC1V 8BB, United Kingdom. TEL 44-20-72251-0791, FAX 44-20-7608-2375.

INTERNATIONAL HOME PLANS; from Drummond Designs, Inc. see *HOUSING AND URBAN PLANNING*

720 GBR ISSN 1026-3454
THE INTERNATIONAL JOURNAL OF ARCHITECTURAL MANAGEMENT PRACTICE & RESEARCH. Text in English. **Description:** Encourages best practice in the design management, production management, and facilities management of buildings - bringing building knowledge back into the design process.
—BLDSC (4542.103500).
Published by: S A A M, The Chief Executive, Alverton Grange, Nottinghamshire NG13 9PB, United Kingdom. TEL 44-1949-850053, FAX 44-1949-851559, mpn@archman.com, http://www.archman.com.

INTERNATIONAL JOURNAL OF VENTILATION. see *HEATING, PLUMBING AND REFRIGERATION*

720 USA ISSN 1049-6564
NA1.A1
➤ **INTERSIGHT.** Text in English. 1990. a., latest vol.8, 2005. charts; illus. 125 p./no. 2 cols./p.; back issues avail. **Document type:** *Journal, Academic/Scholarly.*
Indexed: AIAP.
Published by: State University of New York - Buffalo, School of Architecture and Planning, 335 Hayes Hall, 3435 Main St, Buffalo, NY 14214-3087. TEL 716-829-3485 ext 114, FAX 716-829-3256, intersight@ap.buffalo.edu, architecture@ap.buffalo.edu, http://www.ap.buffalo.edu/. Ed. Albert Bitterman.

727.6 FRA ISSN 0075-0018
INVENTAIRE GENERAL DES MONUMENTS ET DES RICHESSES ARTISTIQUES DE LA FRANCE. Text in French. 1969. irreg. price varies.
Published by: (France. Ministere des Affaires Culturelles), Imprimerie Nationale, BP 154, Douai, Cedex 59505, France. TEL 27-93-70-90, FAX 27-93-70-96, TELEX 120 389 F.

720 USA ISSN 0021-0439
NA1
IOWA ARCHITECT. Text in English. 1954. q. USD 25 to individuals; USD 20 to students (effective 2000). adv. bk.rev. charts; illus. **Document type:** *Journal, Trade.* **Description:** Covers architecture, historic renovation art, product development and design throughout the Midwest: Iowa, Missouri, Nebraska, Kansas, Minnesota, Wisconsin, Illinois, Oklahoma.
Indexed: AIAP.
Published by: (American Institute of Architects, Iowa Chapter), Mauck & Associates, 2655 86th St., Urbandale, IA 50322-4309. TEL 515-243-4010, FAX 515-243-6011, info@aiaiowa.org, Http://www.aiaiowa.org. Ed. Steven Strassburg TEL 515-244-7167. Pub. Kent Mauck. Adv. contact Jane Nieland TEL 515-243-6010. Circ: 12,000.

IRISH ARTS REVIEW. see *ART*

728 IRL
IRISH BUILDING MAGAZINE. Text in English. 8/yr. adv. **Document type:** *Magazine, Trade.*
Address: 35a Patrick St., Dun Laoghaire, Co. Dublin, Ireland. TEL 353-1-2806030, FAX 353-1-2846328, irishbuilding@eircom.net. adv.: color page EUR 2,535. Circ: 4,500 (controlled).

720 IRL ISSN 0021-1206
DA900.I6295
IRISH GEORGIAN SOCIETY. BULLETIN. Text in English. 1958. a. USD 15. adv. bk.rev. illus. index. reprint service avail. from PQC. **Document type:** *Bulletin.*
Related titles: Microform ed.: (from PQC).
Indexed: AIAP, API, BHA.
Published by: Irish Georgian Society, 42 Merrion Sq., Dublin, 2, Ireland. TEL 01-767053. Ed. Desmond Guinness. Circ: 3,500.

ISLAMIC ART AND ARCHITECTURE. see *ART*

ITEMS (VAKEDITIE); tijdschrift voor vormgeving. see *ART*

720 700 HRV
IZ STAROG I NOVOG ZAGREBA. Text in Croatian; Summaries in German. 1957. quadrennial. USD 20. adv. charts; illus.
Published by: Muzej Grada Zagreba, Opaticka 20, Zagreb, 41000, Croatia. TEL 274-642, FAX 38-41-428-294. Ed. Zdenko Kuzmic. Circ: 1,000.

IZVESTIYA VYSSHIKH UCHEBNYKH ZAVEDENII. STROITEL'STVO. see *BUILDING AND CONSTRUCTION*

720 JPN ISSN 1342-6478
J A. (Japan Architect) Text in English, Japanese. 1956. q., latest vol.49. JPY 10,000 domestic; USD 100 in North America (effective 2005). adv. bk.rev. charts; illus. back issues avail. **Document type:** *Magazine, Academic/Scholarly.* **Description:** Contains information and detailed data of selected coverage of top-level Japanese architecture, projects, city planning and new trends.
Formerly (until 1991): Japan Architect (0448-8512)

Related titles: International ed.: Shinkenchiku Jutaku Tokushu. 1985. JPY 24,000 domestic; JPY 28,800 foreign (effective 2001).
Indexed: AIAP, API, ASCA, ArtHuCI, ArtInd, BAS, CurCont, RASB, Search.
—BLDSC (4648.050000), IE.
Published by: Shinkenchiku-sha Co. Ltd./Japan Architect Co., Ltd., 2-31-2 Yushima, Bunkyo-ku, Tokyo, 113-0034, Japan. TEL 81-3-38117101, FAX 81-3-38128229, ja@japan-architect.co.jp, http://www.japan-architect.co.jp/japanese/2maga/ja/ja_frame.html. Ed. Yutaka Shikata. Pub. Nobuyuki Yoshida. R&P Ryugo Maru TEL 81-3-3816-2532. Adv. contact Yukinobu Takizawa TEL 81-3-38117109. color page JPY 400,000, B&W page JPY 300,000. Circ: 18,000 (paid).

725 727 NLD ISSN 0925-7845
JAARBOEK MONUMENTENZORG. Text in Dutch. 1990. a. price varies. bibl.; illus.; tr.lit. back issues avail. **Description:** Discusses the care of historic and historic monuments.
Indexed: AIAP, BHA.
Published by: Waanders Uitgevers, Postbus 1129, Zwolle, 8001 BC, Netherlands. TEL 31-38-4673400, FAX 31-38-4673401, info@waanders.nl, http://www.waanders.nl.

720 CHN ISSN 0577-7429
JIANZHU/CONSTRUCTION & ARCHITECTURE. Text in Chinese. 1954. m. CNY 3.80 newsstand/cover; CNY 7.60 newsstand/cover foreign. adv.
Related titles: Online - full text ed.: (from East View Information Services).
Published by: (Jianshe Bu/Ministry of Construction), Zhonghua Renmin Gonghe Guojianbu, Baiwanzhuang, Beijing, 100835, China. TEL 86-10-68342146. Ed. Shun Qinghua. **Dist. outside China by:** China International Book Trading Corp, 35 Chegongzhuang Xilu, Haidian District, PO Box 399, Beijing 100044, China.

JIANZHU JINGJI. see *BUSINESS AND ECONOMICS*

JIANZHU JISHU/ARCHITECTURAL TECHNOLOGY. see *BUILDING AND CONSTRUCTION*

720 690 CHN ISSN 1006-2661
JIANZHU JISHU JI SHEJI/ARCHITECTURE TECHNOLOGY & DESIGN. Text in Chinese. 1994. m. **Document type:** *Journal, Academic/Scholarly.*
Related titles: Online - full text ed.: (from WanFang Data Corp.).
Published by: Zhongguo Jianzhu Jishu Yanjiuyuan, Xicheng-qu, 19, Chegongzhuang Dajie, Beijing, 100044, China. TEL 86-10-68393613, FAX 86-10-68348832, http://jzjsjsj.periodicals.net.cn/default.html.

JIANZHU JIXIE/CONSTRUCTION MACHINERY. see *MACHINERY*

720 CHN ISSN 0529-1399
NA1545
JIANZHU XUEBAO/ARCHITECTURAL JOURNAL. Text in Chinese. 1954. m. CNY 184 (effective 2001). 64 p./no.
Indexed: API.
—BLDSC (1600.310000), Linda Hall.
Published by: Zhongguo Jianzhu Xuehui/China Architectural Society (Subsidiary of: Zhongguo Kexue Jishu Xuehui/Chinese Association of Science and Technology), No.9 Sanlihe Road, Beijing, 100-835, China. TEL 86-10-68393632, FAX 86-10-68393428, jzxb@chinaasc.org; aj@aj.org.cn. Ed. Zhou Chang. Adv. contact Siwen Zhang TEL 86-10-68393591. Circ: 400,000. **Dist. by:** China International Book Trading Corp, 35 Chegongzhuang Xilu, Haidian District, PO Box 399, Beijing 100044, China. TEL 86-10-68412045, FAX 86-10-68412023, cibtc@mail.cibtc.com.cn, http://www.cibtc.com.cn.

JORD OG VIDEN; information, politik og debat for jordbrugsakademikere. see *AGRICULTURE*

720 PRT ISSN 0870-1504
JORNAL ARQUITECTOS. Text in Portuguese. 1981. 10/yr.
Published by: Associacao dos Arquitectos Portugueses/Portuguese Association of Architects, Trav Carvalho, 21-25, Lisbon, 1249-003, Portugal. TEL 351-21-3241100, FAX 351-21-3241170, geral@oasrs.org, http://www.oasrs.org. Ed. Michel Toussaint. Adv. contact Maria Delurdes Melo. Circ: 6,200.

720 USA ISSN 0738-0895
HT166 CODEN: JAPRER
➤ **JOURNAL OF ARCHITECTURAL AND PLANNING RESEARCH.** Text in English. 1984. q. USD 74 domestic to individuals; USD 106 foreign to individuals; USD 109 domestic to institutions; USD 187 foreign to institutions (effective 2001). bk.rev.; software rev. abstr.; bibl.; illus. 96 p./no.; back issues avail.; reprints avail. **Document type:** *Journal, Academic/Scholarly.* **Description:** Reports on both recent research findings and innovative practices. Provides a link between theory and practice for researchers and practicing professionals.
Supersedes: Journal of Architectural Research
Related titles: Online - full text ed.: (from H.W. Wilson, O C L C Online Computer Library Center, Inc.).
Indexed: ABS&EES, AIAP, API, AbAn, AgeL, ArtHuCI, ArtInd, BrCerAb, C&ISA, CerAb, CivEngAb, CorrAb, CurCont, E&CAJ, EMA, EPB, EnerRev, EngInd, FamI, GEOBASE, IAA, IBSS, Inspec, M&TEA, MBF, METADEX, PAIS, PRA, PsycInfo, PsycholAb, SOPODA, SSCI, SUSA, SolStAb, WAA, e-psyche.
—BLDSC (4947.179600), AskIEEE, CISTI, Ei, IDS, IE, Infotrieve, ingenta, Linda Hall. **CCC.**
Published by: Locke Science Publishing Company, Inc., 28 E Jackson Bldg., 10th Floor L221, Chicago, IL 60604. lockescience@juno.com, http://archone.tamu.edu/Press/japr2.html. Ed. Andrew D Seidel.

720 GBR ISSN 1355-6207
NA109.G7
➤ **JOURNAL OF ARCHITECTURAL CONSERVATION;** historic buildings, monuments, places and landscapes. Text in English. 1995. 3/yr. GBP 45 to individuals; GBP 89.60 to institutions (effective 2003). adv. bk.rev. illus. available with November 2001 issue. back issues avail. **Document type:** *Journal, Academic/Scholarly.* **Description:** Brings the results of research and innovative practice in the conservation of historic buildings, monuments, places, gardens, and landscapes to an international readership.
Indexed: A&ATA, AIAP, API, ArtInd, BrArAb, BrHumI, M&TEA, RICS.
—BLDSC (4947.179800), CISTI, IE, ingenta.
Published by: Donhead Publishing Ltd., Lower Coombe, Donhead St Mary, Shaftesbury, Dorset SP7 9LY, United Kingdom. TEL 44-1747-828422, FAX 44-1747-828522, jac@donhead.com, http://www.donhead.com. Ed. David Watt. Pub., R&P Jill Pearce. Adv. contact Dorothy Newberry. B&W page GBP 200; trim 145 x 225. Circ: 550.

720.71 USA ISSN 1046-4883
NA1 CODEN: JAEDEW
➤ **JOURNAL OF ARCHITECTURAL EDUCATION.** Text in English. 1947. q. USD 58 combined subscription in the Americas to individuals print & online eds.; EUR 56 combined subscription in Europe to individuals print & online eds.; GBP 37 combined subscription elsewhere to individuals print & online eds.; USD 273 combined subscription in the Americas to institutions print & online eds.; GBP 174 combined subscription elsewhere to institutions print & online eds.; USD 25 combined subscription in the Americas to students print & online eds.; EUR 24 combined subscription in Europe to students print & online eds.; GBP 16 combined subscription elsewhere to students print & online eds. (effective 2006). adv. bk.rev. illus. Index. reprint service avail. from PQC. **Document type:** *Academic/Scholarly.* **Description:** Publishes articles on a wide range of topics including history, theory, practice and design.
Former titles (until 1983): J A E (0149-2993); (until 1974): Journal of Architectural Education (0047-2239)
Related titles: Microform ed.: (from PQC); Online - full text ed.: ISSN 1531-314X. USD 259 in the Americas to institutions; GBP 166 elsewhere to institutions (effective 2006); (from EBSCO Publishing, Gale Group, IngentaConnect, O C L C Online Computer Library Center, Inc., Swets Information Services).
Indexed: AIAP, API, ASCA, AgeL, ArchI, ArtHuCI, ArtInd, CADCAM, CIJE, CPE, CurCont, DIP, EEA, EIA, EnerInd, IBR, IBZ.
—BLDSC (4947.180000), CISTI, IDS, IE, Infotrieve, ingenta. **CCC.**
Published by: (Association of Collegiate Schools of Architecture, Inc.), Blackwell Publishing, Inc. (Subsidiary of: Blackwell Publishing Ltd.), Commerce Place, 350 Main St, Malden, MA 02148. TEL 781-388-8206, 800-835-6770, FAX 781-388-8232, http://www.blackwellpublishing.com/journal.asp?ref=1046-4883.

721 624 USA ISSN 1076-0431
TA630 CODEN: JAEIED
➤ **JOURNAL OF ARCHITECTURAL ENGINEERING.** Text in English. 1994. q. USD 228 domestic to institutions; USD 253 combined subscription domestic to institutions print & online eds.; USD 244 foreign to institutions; USD 269 combined subscription foreign to institutions print & online eds. (effective 2005). bk.rev. back issues avail. **Document type:** *Magazine, Academic/Scholarly.* **Description:** Provides a multidisciplinary forum to disseminate practice-based information on the engineering and technical issues concerned with all aspects of building design.
Related titles: CD-ROM ed.: USD 40 to members for CD and online eds.; USD 181 to institutions for CD and online eds. (effective 2001); Online - full text ed.: USD 34 to members; USD 51 to individuals; USD 154 to institutions (effective 2001) (from EBSCO Publishing, Swets Information Services).
Indexed: AS&TI, BrCerAb, C&ISA, CerAb, CivEngAb, CorrAb, E&CAJ, EEA, EMA, ESPM, EngInd, H&SSA, HRIS, IAA, IBR, IBZ, ICEA, M&TEA, MBF, METADEX, SolStAb, WAA.
—BLDSC (4947.182000), CISTI, IE, Infotrieve, ingenta, Linda Hall. **CCC.**
Published by: (Architectural Engineering Division), American Society of Civil Engineers, 1801 Alexander Bell Dr, Reston, VA 20191-4400. TEL 703-295-6300, 800-548-2723, FAX 703-295-6222, http://www.pubs.asce.org/journals/ae.html, http://www.asce.org. Ed. Bijan Mohraz. **Subscr. to:** PO Box 79342, Baltimore, MD 21279-0342.

720 GBR ISSN 1360-2365
NA1
➤ **THE JOURNAL OF ARCHITECTURE.** Text in English. 1996. 5/yr. GBP 429, USD 707 combined subscription to institutions print & online eds. (effective 2006). adv. bibl.; illus. index. back issues avail.; reprint service avail. from PSC. **Document type:** *Journal, Academic/Scholarly.*
Related titles: Online - full text ed.: ISSN 1466-4410. GBP 408, USD 672 to institutions (effective 2006) (from EBSCO Publishing, Gale Group, IngentaConnect, O C L C Online Computer Library Center, Inc., Swets Information Services).
Indexed: AIAP, API, BrCerAb, C&ISA, CerAb, CorrAb, DIP, E&CAJ, EMA, IAA, IBR, IBZ, M&TEA, MBF, METADEX, SUSA, SolStAb, WAA.
—BLDSC (4947.192000), IE, Infotrieve, ingenta, Linda Hall. **CCC.**
Published by: (Royal Institute of British Architects), Routledge (Subsidiary of: Taylor & Francis Group), 4 Park Sq, Milton Park, Abingdon, Oxon OX14 4RN, United Kingdom. TEL 44-1235-828600, FAX 44-1235-829000, info@routledge.co.uk, http://www.tandf.co.uk/journals/titles/13602365.asp, http://www.routledge.co.uk. Ed. Allen Cunningham. **Subscr. in US & Canada to:** Taylor & Francis Inc., Customer Services Dept, 325 Chestnut St, 8th Fl, Philadelphia, PA 19106. TEL 215-625-8900, 800-354-1420, FAX 215-625-8914; **Subscr. to:** Taylor & Francis Ltd, Journals Customer Service, Rankine Rd, Basingstoke, Hants RG24 8PR, United Kingdom. TEL 44-1256-813000, FAX 44-1256-330245, enquiry@tandf.co.uk.

720 JPN ISSN 1346-7581
➤ **JOURNAL OF ASIAN ARCHITECTURE AND BUILDING ENGINEERING.** Text in English. 2002. s-a. **Document type:** *Journal, Academic/Scholarly.* **Description:** Covers building structures and materials, environmental engineering, architectural/urban planning and design, and architectural history and theory.
Related titles: Online - full text ed.: ISSN 1347-2852 (from J-Stage).
—BLDSC (4947.231000), IE.
Published by: Architectural Institute of Japan, 26-20 Shiba 5-chome, Minato-ku, Tokyo, 108-8414, Japan. TEL 81-3-34562017, FAX 81-3-34562058, jaabe@aij.or.jp, http://www.aij.or.jp/eng/jaabe/. Ed. Hyoun Ho Rhee. **Co-sponsors:** Architectural Institute of Korea; Architectural Society of China.

➤ **THE JOURNAL OF CANADIAN ART HISTORY/ANNALES D'HISTOIRE DE L'ART CANADIEN.** see *ART*

➤ **JOURNAL OF DECORATIVE AND PROPAGANDA ARTS.** see *ART*

720 PAK
➤ **JOURNAL OF RESEARCH IN ARCHITECTURE AND PLANNING.** Text in English. 2001. a.
Published by: N E D University of Engineering and Technology, University Rd, Karachi, 75270, Pakistan. coccd@neduet.edu.pk. Ed. Noman Ahmed.

➤ **JOURNAL OF URBAN DESIGN.** see *HOUSING AND URBAN PLANNING*

➤ **JOURNAL OF URBAN TECHNOLOGY.** see *TECHNOLOGY: COMPREHENSIVE WORKS*

➤ **JOURNAL OF WOOD SCIENCE.** see *FORESTS AND FORESTRY—Lumber And Wood*

720 JPN ISSN 0003-8490
KENCHIKU BUNKA/ARCHITECTURAL CULTURE. Text in Japanese; Summaries in English. 1947. q. USD 270. adv. **Description:** Covers the latest trends, design and technology of architecture, as well as its impact on the environment.
Indexed: AIAP.
—BLDSC (5089.375000).
Published by: Shokokusha Publishing Co. Ltd., 25 Saka-Machi, Shinjuku-ku, Tokyo, 160-0002, Japan. TEL 81-3-3359-3231, FAX 81-3-3357-3961. Ed. Hiroyoshi Tajiri. Adv. contact Toshio Takahashi. B&W page JPY 200,000, color page JPY 500,000. Circ: 60,000. **Dist. by:** Intercontinental Marketing Corp., IPO Box 5056, Tokyo 100-30, Japan. TEL 81-3-3661-7458, FAX 81-3-667-9646.

720 JPN
KENCHIKU TECHO/ARCHITECT. Text in Japanese. 1957. m. adv.
Published by: Kinryudo Co. Ltd., 2-3 Higashi-Ueno 5-chome, Taito-ku, Tokyo, 110-0000, Japan. Ed. Shigeru Kikuchi. Circ: 29,000.

712 AUS
KERB. Text in English. a.
Published by: Royal Melbourne Institute of Technology, School of Architecture & Design, GPO Box 2476V, Melbourne, VIC 3001, Australia. i.

720 JPN ISSN 0023-1479
KINDAI KENCHIKU✶ /CONTEMPORARY ARCHITECTURE OF THE WORLD. Text in Japanese. 1946. m. JPY 1,500 newsstand/cover. adv. illus.

Published by: Kindai Kenchikusha, Kanda Bundo Bldg, 4-18 Kanda-Sakuma-cho, Chiyoda-ku, Tokyo, 101-0025, Japan.

KING SAUD UNIVERSITY JOURNAL. ARCHITECTURE AND PLANNING. see *HOUSING AND URBAN PLANNING*

720 KOR
KONCHUK MUNHWA/ARCHITECTURAL TECHNOLOGY INFORMATION. Text in Korean. m. **Description:** Covers architectural culture and news.
Address: 2-ga Songsu, Songdong-gu, Seoul, 273-23, Korea, S. TEL 02-4684701, FAX 02-2697925.

KULTURA. see *LITERATURE*

720 KAZ ISSN 1028-9402
KUMBEZ. Text in Kazakh, Russian. q. **Document type:** *Journal.* **Description:** Focuses on space formation in Kazakhstan and Central Asian arts. Includes news and history of urban planning, architecture, design, construction, restoration, education, and fine arts.
Address: 77 Furmanova, 136, Almaty, 480004, Kazakstan. TEL 7-3272-330767, kumbez@lorton.com, http://www.lorton.com/~kumbez.

700 948 CHE ISSN 1421-086X
KUNST UND ARCHITEKTUR IN DER SCHWEIZ/ART ET ARCHITECTURE EN SUISSE/ARTE E ARCHITETTURA IN SVIZZERA. Text and summaries in French, German, Italian. 1950. 4/yr. CHF 80 (effective 2003). adv. bk.rev. 80 p./no.; back issues avail. **Document type:** *Magazine, Academic/Scholarly.*
Formerly (until 1994): Unsere Kunstdenkmaeler (0566-263X)
Indexed: AIAP, API, BHA, BibInd.
Published by: Gesellschaft fuer Schweizerische Kunstgeschichte/Societe d'Histoire de l'Art en Suisse, Pavillonweg 2, Bern, 3012, Switzerland. TEL 41-31-3083838, FAX 41-31-3016991, gsk@gsk.ch, http://www.gsk.ch. Ed. Isabelle Rucki. adv.: page CHF 2,300; trim 182 x 277. Circ: 8,000.

720 DEU
KUNST UND STADT. Text in German. 1979. 2/yr. adv. bk.rev. **Document type:** *Bulletin.*
Formerly: Kunst am Bau
Published by: Kulturwerks des Berufverbandes Bildender Kuenstler Berlins GmbH, Koethener Str 44, Berlin, 10963, Germany. TEL 030-2611191, FAX 030-2623319. Eds. E Mueller, R Krueger.

KUNTATEKNIIKKA/KOMMUNTEKNIK. see *HOUSING AND URBAN PLANNING*

720 POL ISSN 0023-5865
NA6
KWARTALNIK ARCHITEKTURY I URBANISTYKI. Text in Polish; Summaries in English. 1956. q. price on request. bk.rev. charts; illus. cum.index every 5 yrs. **Document type:** *Journal, Academic/Scholarly.*
Indexed: AIAP, BHA, RASB.
Published by: (Polska Akademia Nauk, Komitet Architektury i Urbanistyki), Oficyna Wydawnicza Politechniki Wroclawskiej, Wybrzeze Wyspianskiego 27, Wroclaw, 50370, Poland. TEL 48-71-3202994, oficwyd@pwr.wroc.pl, http://www.pwr.wroc.pl/~oficwyd/#OFICYNA. Ed. Edmund Malachowicz. Circ: 1,320. **Dist. by:** Ars Polona, Krakowskie Przedmiescie 7, Warsaw, Poland. TEL 48-22-9263914, FAX 48-22-9265324, arspolona@arspolona.com.pl, http://www.arspolona.com.pl.

720 USA
L.A. ARCHITECT; the magazine of design in Southern California. Text in English. 1999. bi-m.
Published by: Balcony Press, 512 E. Wilson, No. 306, Glendale, CA 91206. TEL 818-956-5313, FAX 818-956-5904, http://www.LAArch.com. Circ: 5,000 (paid and controlled).

720 USA
▼ **L A ARCHITECT.** (Los Angeles) Text in English. 2003. bi-m. USD 30 (effective 2003). adv. **Document type:** *Magazine, Trade.* **Description:** Brings together all of the elements and tools that make design work.
Published by: (American Institute of Architects, Los Angeles Chapter), Balcony Media, Inc., 512 E Wilson, Ste 213, Glendale, CA 91206. TEL 818-956-5313, FAX 818-956-5904, balconypress@earthlink.net, http://www.laarch.com/, http://www.balconypress.com/. Ed. Laura Hull. Pub. Ann Gray. Adv. contact Jerri Levi. B&W page USD 2,100; trim 8.875 x 10.75. Circ: 19,500.

712 GBR
L D T MONOGRAPHS. Text in English. irreg. **Document type:** *Monographic series.*
Published by: Landscape Design Trust, 13a West St, Reigate, Surrey RH2 9BL, United Kingdom. TEL 44-1737-225374, FAX 44-1737-224206, info@landscape.co.uk, http://www.landscape.co.uk.

LABYRINTHOS; ermeneutica delle arti figurative dal Medioevo al Novecento. see *ART*

728 747 POL ISSN 1506-3267
LADNY DOM; magazyn budowlany dla ciebie. Text in Polish. 1998. m. PLZ 63.50 domestic; PLZ 132 foreign; PLZ 5.90 newsstand/cover domestic (effective 2003). adv. **Document type:** *Magazine, Consumer.* **Description:** Provides advice on how to build a house and how to design its interior.
Published by: Agora S.A., ul Czerska 8/10, Warsaw, 00732, Poland. TEL 48-22-5554000, FAX 48-22-5554780, ladnydom@agora.pl, prenumerata@gazeta.pl, http://www.ladnydom.pl, http://www.gazeta.pl. Ed. Wieslaw Rudolf. Pub. Adam Wilk. Adv. contact Elzbieta Kaiser. color page PLZ 17,000; trim 275 x 203.

720 DEU
LANDESKONSERVATOR RHEINLAND. ARBEITSHEFT DER RHEINISCHEN DENKMALPFLEGE. Text in German. 1971. irreg., latest vol.52, 1999. price varies. **Document type:** *Monographic series, Academic/Scholarly.*
Formerly: Landeskonservator Rheinland. Arbeitsheft
Indexed: AIAP.
Published by: (Landeskonservator Rheinland), Rheinland Verlag GmbH, Abtei Brauweiler, Postfach 2140, Pulheim, 50250, Germany. TEL 49-2234-9854265, FAX 49-2234-82503. **Dist. by:** Dr. Rudolf Habelt GmbH, Am Buchenhang 1, Bonn 53115, Germany. TEL 49-228-9238322, FAX 49-228-232017. **Co-sponsor:** Landschaftsverband Rheinland.

LANDMARKS OBSERVER. see *HISTORY—History Of North And South America*

720 CAN ISSN 0228-6963
LANDSCAPE ARCHITECTURAL REVIEW/REVUE D'ARCHITECTURE DE PAYSAGE. Text in English, French. 1980. 4/yr. CND 25, USD 25. adv. bk.rev. illus. index. back issues avail.; reprints avail. **Description:** A forum for the exchange, discussion and review of a broad range of ideas and topics related to the theory and practice of landscape architecture, the environmental sciences and related professions.
Indexed: AIAP, CBPI, GardL.
Address: 24 Kensington Ave, Willowdale, ON M2M 1R6, Canada. TEL 416-223-3956, FAX 416-225-8103. Ed. Nick Van Vliet. Circ: 1,400.

712 USA ISSN 0023-8031
SB469
LANDSCAPE ARCHITECTURE. Text in English. 1910. 12/yr. USD 59 domestic; USD 99 foreign (effective 2005). adv. bk.rev. charts; illus.; tr.lit. index. reprints avail. **Document type:** *Magazine, Trade.*
Indexed: ABM, AIAP, API, ASCA, ArchI, ArtHuCI, ArtInd, CurCont, EIA, EIP, EPB, EnerInd, EnerRev, GardL, IBR, IBZ, MEA&I, PCI, RASB, SSCI, Search.
—BLDSC (5153.140000), IDS, IE, Infotrieve, ingenta, Linda Hall.
Published by: American Society of Landscape Architects, 636 Eye St, N W, Washington, DC 20001-3736. TEL 202-898-2444, FAX 202-898-1185, ispeckhardt@asla.org, scahill@asla.org, http://www.asla.org. Ed. Bill Thompson. Adv. contact Mark Frieden. Circ: 25,000 (paid).

720 NLD
LANDSCAPE ARCHITECTURE AND TOWN PLANNING IN THE NETHERLANDS. Text in Dutch, English. 1993. irreg.
Published by: Uitgeverij Thoth, Prins Hendriklaan 13, Bussum, 1404 AS, Netherlands. Ed. Harry Harsema.

712 USA ISSN 0023-754X
SB469
LANDSCAPE ARCHITECTURE NEWS DIGEST. Text in English. 1960. 10/yr. looseleaf. USD 32 to non-members (effective 1998). adv. tr.lit. back issues avail. **Document type:** *Newsletter.* **Description:** Presents current news on congressional, legal, artistic, and business activities in the field of landscape architecture.
Related titles: E-mail ed.: L A N D Online; Microform ed.: (from PQC).
Published by: American Society of Landscape Architects, 636 Eye St, N W, Washington, DC 20001-3736. TEL 202-898-2444, FAX 202-898-1185, scahill@asla.org, http://www.asla.org/Members/land/index.cfm. Ed. Bill Welsh. Circ: 12,000.

LANDSCAPE CONTRACTOR; official publication of the Illinois Landscape Contractors Association. see *GARDENING AND HORTICULTURE*

LANDSCAPE HISTORY. see *HISTORY*

720 GBR ISSN 0265-9786
➤ **LANDSCAPE ISSUES.** Text in English. 1984. s-a. GBP 25 (effective 1998). bk.rev. **Document type:** *Academic/Scholarly.* **Description:** Publishes articles and reports on aspects of landscape architecture, countryside planning, and environmental policy.
Published by: Department of Countryside and Landscape, Cheltenham and Gloucester College of Higher Education, Francis Close Hall, Swindon Rd, Cheltenham, United Kingdom. TEL 44-1242-532930, FAX 44-1242-532997, issues@chelt.ac.uk. Ed. Robert Moore. Circ: 200.

720 712 USA ISSN 0277-2426
SB469
➤ **LANDSCAPE JOURNAL**; design, planning, and management of the land. Text in English. 1981. s-a. USD 50 combined subscription to individuals print & online eds; USD 180 combined subscription to institutions print & online eds (effective 2006). adv. bk.rev. illus. Index. back issues avail.; reprint service avail. from PQC,PSC. **Document type:** *Journal, Academic/Scholarly.*
Related titles: Microform ed.: (from PQC); Online - full text ed.: ISSN 1553-2704. USD 171 to institutions (effective 2006) (from EBSCO Publishing, Gale Group, IngentaConnect).
Indexed: AIAP, API, Agr, ArtInd, BHA, EPB, GardL, IBR, IBZ, SFA, SUSA, WildRev.
—BLDSC (5153.146300), IE, Infotrieve, ingenta. **CCC.**
Published by: (Council of Education in Landscape Architecture), University of Wisconsin Press, Journal Division, 1930 Monroe St, 3rd Fl, Madison, WI 53711-2059. TEL 608-263-0668, FAX 608-263-1173, journals@uwpress.wisc.edu, http://www.wisc.edu/wisconsinpress/journals/journals/lj.html. Eds. James F Palmer, M Elen Deming TEL 315-470-6539. adv.: page USD 370; trim 8.5 x 11. Circ: 700.

➤ **LANDSCAPE MANAGEMENT**; commercial magazine for lawn, landscape and grounds managers. see *GARDENING AND HORTICULTURE*

712 GBR ISSN 0142-6397
BH301.L3 CODEN: LAREDJ
LANDSCAPE RESEARCH. Text in English. 1968. q. GBP 330, USD 545 combined subscription to institutions print & online eds. (effective 2006). adv. bk.rev. illus. Index. reprint service avail. from PSC. **Document type:** *Journal, Academic/Scholarly.* **Description:** Deals with recent research in landscape from all disciplines.
Formerly (until 1976): Landscape Research News (0458-7014)
Related titles: Online - full text ed.: ISSN 1469-9710. GBP 315, USD 520 to institutions (effective 2006) (from EBSCO Publishing, Gale Group, IngentaConnect, Northern Light Technology, Inc., O C L C Online Computer Library Center, Inc., ProQuest Information & Learning, Swets Information Services).
Indexed: API, ASFA, AbHyg, AgrForAb, BHA, BiolAb, BrArAb, DIP, EPB, ESPM, EnerRev, ForAb, GEOBASE, GardL, HerbAb, HortAb, I&DA, IBR, IBZ, M&TEA, NumL, OrnHort, PGegResA, RDA, RRTA, S&F, SWRA, WAE&RSA, WeedAb, WildRev.
—BLDSC (5153.147700), IE, Infotrieve, ingenta. **CCC.**
Published by: (Landscape Research Group Ltd.), Routledge (Subsidiary of: Taylor & Francis Group), 4 Park Sq, Milton Park, Abingdon, Oxon OX14 4RN, United Kingdom. TEL 44-1235-828600, FAX 44-1235-829000, info@routledge.co.uk, http://www.tandf.co.uk/journals/titles/01426397.asp, http://www.routledge.co.uk. Ed. Dr. Ian Thompson. Circ: 650. **Subscr. to:** Taylor & Francis Ltd, Journals Customer Service, Rankine Rd, Basingstoke, Hants RG24 8PR, United Kingdom. TEL 44-1256-813000, FAX 44-1256-330245.

LANDSCAPER. see *HOUSING AND URBAN PLANNING*

721 CAN ISSN 1492-3440
LANDSCAPING & GROUNDSKEEPING JOURNAL. Text in French. 1999. q. **Document type:** *Magazine, Trade.* **Description:** Reports on products, applications and technologies of the landscaping and groundskeeping business.
Published by: Baum Publications Ltd., 201-2323 Boundary Rd, Vancouver, BC V5M 4V8, Canada. TEL 604-291-9900, FAX 604-291-1906, admin@baumpub.com, http://www.baumpub.com.

LANDSCAPING HOMES & GARDENS. see *GARDENING AND HORTICULTURE*

LANDSCHAP; tijdschrift voor landschapsecologie en milieukunde. see *ENVIRONMENTAL STUDIES*

LANDSKAB; tidsskrift for planlaegning af have og landskab, review for garden and landscape planning. see *GARDENING AND HORTICULTURE*

LANDWORKS HOT LINE. see *GARDENING AND HORTICULTURE*

720 ZAF
LEADING ARCHITECTURE AND DESIGN. Text in English; Text occasionally in Afrikaans. 1915; N.S. 1978. bi-m. ZAR 250 domestic; ZAR 331 foreign (effective 2003). adv. bk.rev. bibl.; charts; illus. Supplement avail. **Document type:** *Trade.* **Description:** For architects and those who commission buildings in southern Africa.
Former titles: Architecture S.A. (0250-054X); (until 1978): Plan; (until Dec. 1968): South African Architectural Record (0038-1977)
Related titles: Microfilm ed.: N.S. (from PQC).
Indexed: AIAP, ISAP.
—BLDSC (1601.994000).
Published by: (South African Institute of Architects), Primedia Publishing, 366 Pretoria Ave, Ferndale, Randburg, Transvaal 2194, South Africa. TEL 27-11-787-5725, FAX 27-11-787-5776, http://www.primemags.co.za. Circ: 3,900.

720 USA ISSN 0730-6164
LEARNING BY DESIGN; a school leader's guide to architectural services. Text in English. a. USD 15 per issue (effective 2003). adv.
Related titles: ♦ Supplement to: American School Board Journal. ISSN 0003-0953.
Indexed: CIJE.
Published by: National School Boards Association, 1680 Duke St, Alexandria, VA 22314-3493. learningbydesign@asbj.com, http://www.asbj.com/lbd/, http://www.nsba.org/site/index.asp. Pub. Don E Blom. Adv. contact Deborah Cumbo. B&W page USD 6,500, color page USD 7,259; trim 8.125 x 10.875. Circ: 60,000.

LEGAL HANDBOOK FOR ARCHITECTS, ENGINEERS AND CONTRACTORS. see *LAW*

LEICHHARDT HISTORICAL JOURNAL; Annandale, Balmain, Glebe, Leichhardt, Lilyfield, Rozelle. see *HISTORY—History Of Australasia And Other Areas*

720 DEU
LEONARDO ONLINE; architecture with new media. Text in German. 1988. bi-m. adv. bk.rev. back issues avail.
Document type: *Trade.*
Formerly (until 1996): Leonardo (0935-1108)
Indexed: ArtInd, CMCI.
Published by: W E K A Baufachverlag GmbH, Berliner Allee 28 b-c, Augsburg, 86153, Germany. TEL 49-821-5041-0, FAX 49-821-5041257, info@bau.weka.de, http://www.bau.weka.de/leonardo. Ed. Heike Kappelt. Pub. Dieter Kleber. Adv. contact Reinhard Mueller. Circ: 18,000.

387 USA ISSN 1066-0038
LIGHTHOUSE DIGEST. Text in English. 1992. m. USD 28 domestic; USD 38 in Canada; USD 46 elsewhere (effective 2001). adv. **Description:** Contains news and features on lighthouses throughout the US, information on endangered lighthouses, and a related calendar of events.
Address: PO Box 1690, Wells, ME 04090. TEL 207-646-0515, 800-668-7737, FAX 207-646-0516, lhdigest@lhdigest.com, http://www.lighthousedigest.com. Ed. Timothy Harrison. Adv. contact Kathleen Finnegan. B&W page USD 670, color page USD 825; bleed 8.75 x 11.25. Circ: 25,000.

LIGHTING. see *ENGINEERING—Electrical Engineering*

791.436 USA ISSN 0191-541X
PN2091.E4
LIGHTING DIMENSIONS. Text in English. 1977. 12/yr. USD 34.97 domestic; USD 62 in Canada; USD 80 elsewhere; USD 5.95 newsstand/cover (effective 2005). adv. bk.rev.; film rev.; play rev. charts; illus.; tr.lit. back issues avail.; reprint service avail. from PQC. **Document type:** *Magazine, Trade.* **Description:** For the lighting professional. Lighting design for stage and studio, architecture and interior design.
Related titles: Microfilm ed.: (from PQC); Online - full text ed.: (from bigchalk, Chadwyck-Healey Inc., EBSCO Publishing, Gale Group, H.W. Wilson, LexisNexis, O C L C Online Computer Library Center, Inc.).
Indexed: BPI, IIPA, RASB.
—IE, Infotrieve. **CCC.**
Published by: Primedia Business Magazines & Media, Inc. (Subsidiary of: Primedia, Inc.), 249 W 17th St, New York, NY 10011. TEL 212-462-3600, FAX 212-206-3622, inquiries@primediabusiness.com, http://www.lightingdimensions.com/, http://www.primediabusiness.com. Pubs. Doug MacDonald TEL 212-204-1504, Jacqueline Tien. Adv. contact Doug MacDonald TEL 212-204-1504. color page USD 3,740. Circ: 12,188 (paid).

723 ITA ISSN 1122-0805
LINGUAGGIO DELL'ARCHITETTURA ROMANA. Text in Italian. 1987. irreg., latest vol.2, 1991. price varies. **Document type:** *Monographic series, Academic/Scholarly.*
Published by: Casa Editrice Leo S. Olschki, Viuzzo del Pozzetto 8, Florence, 50126, Italy. TEL 39-055-6530684, FAX 39-055-6530214, celso@olschki.it, http://www.olschki.it.

720 DNK ISSN 0108-4135
NA1208
LIVING ARCHITECTURE; architecture and design from Denmark, Finland, Norway, Sweden. Text in Danish, English. 1980. q. DKK 495 domestic; DKK 165 per issue domestic (effective 2005). adv. illus. back issues avail. **Document type:** *Journal, Trade.* **Description:** Features new and traditional Scandinavian furniture, design and architecture.
Formerly (until 1983): BoligRevy (0107-2986)
Indexed: AIAP, API, BHA.
Published by: Living Architecture Publishing, Bredgade 34, PO Box 2076, Copenhagen K, 1260, Denmark. TEL 45-33-137613, FAX 45-33-326989, la@livingarch.com, www.livingarch.com, http://www.livingarch.com. Ed. Vibe Udsen. Pub., Adv. contact Per Nagel. Circ: 45,000.

720 USA ISSN 1547-4690
NA1
▼ **LOG (NEW YORK).** Text in English. 2003 (Fall). irreg. USD 10 per issue (effective 2003).
Published by: Anyone Corporation, 41 W. 25th St. 11th Fl., New York, NY 10010. TEL 212-645-1400, FAX 212-645-0726, log@anycorp.com, http://www.anycorp.com. Ed. Cynthia Davidson.

720 747 USA ISSN 1072-6063
LOG HOMES ILLUSTRATED; a complete consumer guide. Text in English. 1993. bi-m. USD 25; USD 35 foreign; USD 3.99 newsstand/cover; CND 4.99 newsstand/cover in Canada. adv. **Document type:** *Magazine, Consumer.* **Description:** Guide to log home plans, building techniques, product reviews and decorating ideas.
Published by: Goodman Media Group, Inc., 250 W 57th St, Ste 710, New York, NY 10107-0799. TEL 212-541-7100, FAX 212-245-1241, http://www.loghomesmag.com, http://www.goodmanmediagroup.com. Ed. Roland Sweet. Pub. Jason Goodman. R&P Sandy Kosherick. Adv. contact Laura Lapatin. B&W page USD 4,010, color page USD 5,415; trim 8 x 10.875. Circ: 110,492. **Subscr. to:** PO Box 612, Mt Morris, IL 61054.

720 ESP ISSN 1136-758X
LOGGIA; arquitectura y restauracion. Text in Spanish. 1996. 3/yr. —CINDOC.
Published by: Editorial de los Oficios, Apdo. de Correos 906, Leon, 24080, Spain. edeoficios1@edeoficios.com, http://www.edeoficios.com/.

720 ITA ISSN 1124-9064
NA9
LOTUS INTERNATIONAL; rivista trimestrale di architettura - quarterly architectural review. Text in English, Italian. 1963. 4/yr. EUR 76 (effective 2004). **Document type:** *Magazine, Trade.*
Formerly (until 1970): Lotus (0076-101X)
Indexed: AIAP, ASCA, ArtHuCI, ArtInd, BAS, BHA, CurCont, PCI, SSCI.
—BLDSC (5294.899000), IE, Infotrieve, ingenta.
Published by: Editoriale Lotus, Via Santa Maria 19a, Milan, 20123, Italy. TEL 39-02-45475744, FAX 39-02-45475746, abbonamenti@editorialelotus.it.

720 ITA ISSN 1591-4291
LOTUS NAVIGATOR. Text in Italian. 2000. 3/yr. EUR 34 (effective 2004). **Document type:** *Magazine, Trade.*
Published by: Editoriale Lotus, Via Santa Maria 19a, Milan, 20123, Italy. TEL 39-02-45475744, FAX 39-02-45475746, abbonamenti@editorialelotus.it.

720 747 USA
▼ **LUXE.** Text in English. 2005. q. USD 19.95 (effective 2005). **Document type:** *Magazine, Consumer.* **Description:** Covers luxury architecture and home design in Colorado.
Published by: Sandow Media Corp., 3731 NW 8th Ave., Boca Raton, FL 33431-6452. TEL 561-750-0151, FAX 561-750-0152, info@sandowmedia.com, http://www.luxecolorado.com/, http://www.sandowmedia.com.

M A M A. (Magasin foer Modern Arkitektur) see *GENERAL INTEREST PERIODICALS—Sweden*

720 GBR ISSN 1355-3046
NA1
MAC JOURNAL. Text in English. 1994. irreg., latest vol.3, 1996-97. illus. **Document type:** *Academic/Scholarly.*
Indexed: AIAP, API.
—BLDSC (5320.250400).
Published by: Mackintosh School of Architecture, 177 Renfrew St., Glasgow, Scotland G3 6RQ, United Kingdom. TEL 44-413-534590, FAX 44-413-534703. Eds. Christian Hermansen, James Macaulay.

720 FRA ISSN 1274-5790
MAISONS DE FRANCE. Text in French. 1965. m. (10/yr.). EUR 29 domestic; EUR 46.50 in the European Union; EUR 72 elsewhere (effective 2004).
Formerly (until 1967): Maisons a la Campagne (1274-5782)
Published by: Edinot, B.P. 17, Pompadour, 19230, France. Ed. Jean Michel Reillier.

720 EST
MAJA. Text in Estonian. q. adv.
Published by: Kirjastus Maja Ou, Paldiski Maantee 26a, Tallinn, 10149, Estonia. Ed. Ojari Triin TEL 372-2-5059120. Adv. contact Sild Kulli TEL 372-2-55642682. page EEK 13,000;.

MALAYSIA SOURCE BOOK FOR ARCHITECTS AND DESIGNERS (YEAR). see *BUSINESS AND ECONOMICS—Trade And Industrial Directories*

720 IND ISSN 0025-2913
N1
MARG (BOMBAY). Variant title: Modern Architectural Research Group. Text in English. 1946. q. USD 145 foreign to institutions (effective 2005).
Related titles: Online - full text ed.: (from H.W. Wilson, O C L C Online Computer Library Center, Inc.).
Indexed: AIAP, ArtInd, DIP.
Published by: Marg Publications, Army-Navy Bldg., 3rd Fl., 148 Mahatma Gandhi Rd., Fort, Mumbai, Maharashtra 400 001, India. TEL 91-22-2842520, 91-22-2821151, FAX 91-22-2047102, margpub@tata.com. **Dist. by:** Scientific Publishers, 5-A New Pali Rd., Near Hotel Taj Hari Mahal, PO Box 91, Jodhpur, Rajasthan 342 003, India. info@scientificpub.com, http://www.scientificpub.com.

MARKETING TACTICS. see *BUSINESS AND ECONOMICS—Marketing And Purchasing*

MARMOR. see *MINES AND MINING INDUSTRY*

792 USA ISSN 0025-3928
MARQUEE (ELMHURST). Text in English. 1969. base vol. plus q. updates. USD 45 domestic; USD 67 foreign (effective 2004). adv. bk.rev. illus. index, cum.index: 1969-2000. 32 p./no.; back issues avail. **Document type:** *Journal, Academic/Scholarly.* **Description:** Features theatre buildings.
Related titles: Microform ed.: (from PQC).
Indexed: AIAP, IIPA.
Published by: Theatre Historical Society of America, York Theatre Bldg, Ste 200, 152 N York Rd, Elmhurst, IL 60126-2806. TEL 630-782-1800, FAX 630-782-1802, execdir@historictheatres.org, http://www.historictheatres.org. Ed. Steven Levin. Pub., R&P, Adv. contact Richard Sklenar. Circ: 1,050 (paid).

MASKAN; arkhitektura i stroitel'stvo Uzbekistana, Kazakhstana, Azerbaidzana, Kyrgyzstana, Tadzjikistana, Turkmenistana. see *BUILDING AND CONSTRUCTION*

720 693 624 333.72 GBR ISSN 0950-2289
CODEN: MASIEE
➤ **MASONRY INTERNATIONAL**; journal of the British Masonry Society. Text in English. 1984. 3/yr. GBP 64 to non-members; free to members (effective 2004). bk.rev. charts; illus. back issues avail. **Document type:** *Magazine, Academic/Scholarly.* **Description:** Contains original papers in bulletin-reviews and more practical papers; journal-latest research findings. Focus for all involved in manufacture of masonry materials, design of masonry structures and economical construction, all masonry units such as, clay, concrete, stone plus mortar, etc.
Indexed: BrCerAb, C&ISA, CerAb, CorrAb, E&CAJ, EMA, ICEA, SolStAb, WAA.
—BLDSC (5387.532000), CISTI, IE, ingenta.
Published by: British Masonry Society, Shermanbury, Church Rd, Whyteleafe, Surrey CR3 0AR, United Kingdom. TEL 44-20-8660-3653, FAX 44-20-8668-6983, http://www.masonry.org.uk/publications/mas_int/mas_int.htm. Ed., Pub., R&P, Adv. contact Dr. K Fisher TEL 44-20-8660-3633. Circ: 400 (paid).

720 ITA ISSN 1121-0516
TA401 CODEN: GWORF8
MATERIA. Text in Italian. 1989. 3/yr. EUR 24 (effective 2005). adv. **Document type:** *Magazine, Trade.*
Indexed: CIN, ChemAb, ChemTitl.
Published by: Gruppo Editoriale Motta, Via Branda Castiglioni 7, Milan, MI 20156, Italy. TEL 39-02-300761, FAX 39-02-38010046, http://www.mottaeditore.it. Circ: 80,000.

711.4 DEU ISSN 0176-3539
DER MAUERANKER. Text in German. 1981. q. adv. bk.rev.
Document type: *Bulletin.* **Description:** Provides background information and practical tips for owners and lovers of old buildings.
—**CCC.**
Published by: Interessengemeinschaft Baupflege Nordfriesland e.V., Suederstr 30, Bredstedt, 25821, Germany. TEL 04671-2081, FAX 04671-1333. Ed. Gerd Kuehnast. Circ: 2,500.

DAS MAUERWERK. see *BUILDING AND CONSTRUCTION*

MAUERWERK-KALENDER. see *BUILDING AND CONSTRUCTION*

720 700 BEL
MELANGES D'HISTOIRE DE L'ARCHITECTURE. Text in French. 1973. irreg. price varies. illus. **Document type:** *Monographic series, Academic/Scholarly.*
Indexed: BHA, MLA-IB.
Published by: (Universite Catholique de Louvain, Departement d'Etudes Greques, Latines et Orientales, Publications d'Archeologie et d'Histoire de l'Art), Universite Catholique de Louvain, College Erasme, Pl Blaise Pascal 1, Louvain-la-Neuve, 1348, Belgium. TEL 32-10-474882, FAX 32-10-474870, moucharte@arke.ucl.ac.be, moucharte@fltr.ucl.ac.be, http://juppiter.fltr.ucl.ac.be/FLTR/publications/pub_pahal. R&P Ghislaine Moucharte.

720 ESP ISSN 1135-6146
NA2310.S7
MEMORIA DE PROYECTOS. Text in Spanish. 1995. 3/yr. EUR 7 (effective 2005).
Related titles: Online - full text ed.: (from EBSCO Publishing).

Published by: Ediciones Universidad de Navarra S.A., Pza. Los Sauces, 1-2, Baranain, (Navarra) 31010, Spain. TEL 34-948-256850, FAX 34-948-256854, http://www.unav.es/arquitectura/documentos/publicaciones/publis/3des.htm, http://www.eunsa.es.

690 669 USA ISSN 0885-5781
TH1
METAL ARCHITECTURE. Text in English. 1985. m. free domestic to qualified personnel; USD 45 in Canada & Mexico; USD 125 elsewhere (effective 2005). adv. **Document type:** *Magazine, Trade.*
Indexed: BrCerAb, C&ISA, CerAb, CorrAb, E&CAJ, EMA, IAA, M&TEA, MBF, METADEX, SolStAb, WAA.
—Linda Hall.
Published by: Modern Trade Communications, Inc., 7450 Skokie Blvd, Skokie, IL 60077. TEL 847-674-2200, FAX 847-674-3676, ma@moderntrade.com, http://www.moderntrade.com. Ed. Bob Fittro. Adv. contact John Garvey. B&W page USD 4,300, color page USD 6,370. Circ: 32,000 (controlled).

720 ITA ISSN 0394-6835
METAMORFOSI; quaderni di architettura. Text in Multiple languages. 1985. 3/yr. adv. bk.rev.
Related titles: Online - full text ed.
Indexed: AIAP.
Published by: Mancosu Editore, Via Alfredo Fusco 71, Rome, 00136, Italy. TEL 39-06-351921, FAX 39-06-35409791, http://www.mancosueditore.it.

720 747 USA ISSN 0279-4977
N6535.N5
METROPOLIS; architecture design. Text in English. 1981. 10/yr. USD 32.95 domestic; USD 52.95 in Canada; USD 72.95 elsewhere (effective 2005). adv. bk.rev. illus. reprints avail. **Document type:** *Magazine, Consumer.* **Description:** Covers all aspects of the built world, from architecture to graphic design to products to the city.
Related titles: Online - full text ed.
Indexed: AIAP, ASIP, DAAI, Search.
—BLDSC (5748.937500), IE, ingenta.
Published by: Bellerophon Publications, Inc., 61 W 23rd St, 4th fl, New York, NY 10010. TEL 212-722-5050, 800-344-3046, FAX 212-427-1938, edit@metropolismag.com, http://www.metropolismag.com/. Ed. Susan S Szenasy. Pub. Horace Havemeyer III. R&P Danielle Masar. Adv. contact Judson Green. Circ: 47,000 (paid).

724 USA
METROPOLITAN HISTORIC STRUCTURES ASSOCIATION. NEWS. Text in English. 1976. 4/yr. USD 5. adv. bk.rev.
Published by: Metropolitan Historic Structures Association, Dyckman House Museum, 4881 Broadway, New York, NY 10034. Ed. Jane Sullivan Crowley. Circ: 2,000.

720 690 USA
MILLION DOLLAR PROJECT PLANNED LIST✶. Text in English. 1965. m. USD 150 per issue. back issues avail.
Published by: Live Leads Corp., 35 W 76th St 4, New York, NY 10023-1521. Ed. Thomas Szabo. Circ: 100.

720 TUR ISSN 1300-4212
MIMARLIK DERGISI. Text in Turkish. 1963. bi-m. USD 50. adv. bk.rev. illus. cum.index: 1963-1977, 1979-1982, 1983-1987. back issues avail. **Document type:** *Trade.* **Description:** News of current architectural issues in Turkey and the world, including planning, conservation and environmental issues.
Published by: (T M M O B Mimarlar Odasi), Yapi Endustri Merkezi, Cumhuriyet Cad. 329, Harbiya 80230 Istanbul, Ankara, Turkey. TEL 90-212-2302919, FAX 90-212-2484814. Ed. Asli Ozbay. Pub. Semih Eryildiz. Adv. contact Mrs. Zehra Oztok Ebcim. Circ: 11,000.

MISSISSIPPI HISTORY NEWSLETTER. see *HISTORY—History Of North And South America*

720 USA
MISSISSIPPI. STATE BOARD OF ARCHITECTURE. ANNUAL REPORT. Text in English. 1935. a.
Published by: Board of Architecture, 239 N Lamar St, Ste 502, Jackson, MS 39201-1311. TEL 601-359-6020, FAX 601-359-6159.

720 690 DEU
MITGLIEDERINFORMATION. Text in German. bi-m.
Published by: Bund Deutscher Baumeister Architekten und Ingenieure Landesverband Hessen, Am Waldacker 8, Frankfurt Am Main, 60388, Germany. TEL 06109-3103133, TELEX 4185923.

724 747 USA ISSN 1547-3775
THE MODERNISM MAGAZINE. Text in English. 1998 (Spr.). q. USD 19.95 domestic; USD 24.95 in Canada; USD 29.95 elsewhere; USD 6.95 newsstand/cover domestic; USD 9.95 newsstand/cover in Canada (effective 2003). adv. bk.rev. **Document type:** *Magazine, Consumer.* **Description:** Covers all elements of modern design with spotlights on period designers and schools of thought, architecture, interiors, furniture, ceramics, glass, textiles, photography and art.
Formerly (until 1998): The Modernist (1098-8211)
Related titles: Online - full text ed.: (from Gale Group).
Indexed: AIAP, DAAI.
Published by: Modernism Magazine, 333 N Main St, Lambertville, NJ 08530. TEL 609-397-4104, FAX 609-397-9377, cara@modernismmagazine.com, http://www.modernismmagazine.com. Eds. Cara Greenberg, Dave Cane. R&P Dave Cane. Adv. contact Miriam Assion. Circ: 6,000 (paid and controlled).

THE MODERNIST. see *ART*

720 USA ISSN 0191-4022
NA1
MODULUS. Text in English. 1979. irreg. (approx a.), latest vol.23, 1996. USD 25 (effective 1998). illus. **Document type:** *Academic/Scholarly.*
Indexed: ABM, AIAP, API, BHA.
Published by: University of Virginia, School of Architecture, Campbell Hall, P O Box 400122, Charlottesville, VA 22904. TEL 804-892-4567, FAX 804-982-2678, modulus@palladio.virginia.edu. Ed., R&P Jessie Chapman. **Dist. by:** Princeton Architectural Press, 37 E 7th St, New York, NY 10003. TEL 212-995-9620, FAX 212-995-9454.

720 FRA ISSN 0998-4194
LE MONITEUR ARCHITECTURE - A M C. Text in French. 1967. m. adv. bk.rev. bibl.; illus.
Former titles: A M C (0336-1675); Architecture Mouvement Continuite (0336-1667)
Related titles: CD-ROM ed.
Indexed: AIAP, API, DAAI, RASB.
—BLDSC (5908.609000), IE, Infotrieve, ingenta. **CCC.**
Published by: Groupe Moniteur, 17 rue d'Uzes, Paris, 75002, France. TEL 33-1-40135055, FAX 33-1-40135194. Ed. J F Devron. Adv. contact Marc N Vigier. Circ: 10,532.

720.92 NLD
MONOGRAFIEEN VAN NEDERLANDSE ARCHITECTEN/ MONOGRAPHS OF DUTCH ARCHITECTS. Text in Dutch, English. 1994 (vol.8). irreg., latest vol.10, 1996. **Document type:** *Monographic series.*
Published by: Uitgeverij 010, Watertorenweg 180, Rotterdam, 3063 HA, Netherlands. TEL 31-10-4333509, FAX 31-10-4529825.

MONTEREY MUSEUM OF ART NEWS. see *ART*

720 AUS ISSN 1320-1115
MONUMENT. Text in English. 1993. bi-m. AUD 100 domestic; AUD 120 in New Zealand; AUD 230 elsewhere; AUD 16.45 newsstand/cover (effective 2004). adv. **Document type:** *Magazine, Consumer.* **Description:** Covers architecture, design, and urban and landscape projects.
Published by: Pacific Publications, 35-51 Mitchell St, McMahons Point, NSW 2060, Australia. TEL 61-2-94643300, FAX 61-2-94643375, monument@pacpubs.com.au, subscriptions@pacpubs.com.au, http://www.pacificpubs.com.au/display.cfm?ObjectID=6CA2DC4A-47F5-4CBF-B0A02ED023BB4ACD. Circ: 17,000.

722.6 930 NLD ISSN 0169-8850
➤ **MONUMENTA GRAECA ET ROMANA.** Text in English. 1963. irreg., latest vol.9, 2002. price varies. illus. back issues avail. **Document type:** *Monographic series, Academic/Scholarly.* **Description:** Scholarly monographs on topics in Greek and Roman architecture and art, particularly sculpture.
Published by: Brill Academic Publishers, PO Box 9000, Leiden, 2300 PA, Netherlands. TEL 31-71-53-53-500, FAX 31-71-53-17-532, cs@brill.nl, http://www.brill.nl. Ed. H F Mussche. R&P Elizabeth Venekamp. **Subscr. in N. America to:** PO Box 605, Herndon, VA 20172. TEL 703-661-1585, 800-337-9255, FAX 703-661-1501, cs@brillusa.com. **Distr. outside N. America by:** c/o Turpin Distribution, Stratton Business Park, Pegasus Drive, Biggleswade, BEDFORDSHIRE SG 18 8TQ, United Kingdom. TEL 44-1767-604-954, FAX 44-1767-601-640, brill@turpin-distribution.com.

725.94 DEU ISSN 0941-7125
MONUMENTE; Magazin fuer Denkmalkultur in Deutschland. Text in German. 1991. bi-m. EUR 27.40; EUR 4.60 newsstand/cover (effective 2003). adv. **Document type:** *Journal, Academic/Scholarly.*
Published by: Deutsche Stiftung Denkmalschutz, Koblenzer Str 75, Bonn, 53177, Germany. TEL 49-228-957380, FAX 49-228-9573823, info@denkmalschutz.de, http://www.denkmalschutz.de/publikationen/monumente/index_html. adv.: B&W page EUR 4,250, color page EUR 6,500. Circ: 120,000 (paid and controlled).

720 RUS
MOSKOVSKAYA STROIKA. Text in Russian. 24/yr. USD 145 in United States.
Address: Yaroslavskaya ul 15-8, k 302, Moscow, 129366, Russian Federation. TEL 7-095-9116698, FAX 7-095-2176640. Ed. G B Gilinskii. **US dist. addr.:** East View Information Services, 3020 Harbor Ln. N., Minneapolis, MN 55447. TEL 612-550-0961.

690 NOR ISSN 0332-5733
➤ **MUR**; arkitektur og byggeteknikk. Text in Norwegian. 1976. q. NOK 260 (effective 2003). adv. back issues avail. **Document type:** *Magazine, Academic/Scholarly.* **Description:** Covers buildings and projects in mansonry, science of masonry technology for architects and engineers.
Indexed: AIAP, BHA, RASB.
Published by: Mur Sentret, Forskningsveien 3 B, PO Box 53, Blindern, Oslo, 0313, Norway. TEL 47-22-930760, FAX 47-22-601192, post@mur-sentret.no, http://www.mur-sentret.no. Ed., Pub., R&P Mari Flaata TEL 47-22-930764. Adv. contact Eva Johnsrud. Circ: 1,300 (paid); 1,200 (controlled).

720 625 POL ISSN 0239-6866
MURATOR; domy, wnetrza , ogrody. Text in Polish. 1983. m. EUR 61 foreign (effective 2005). adv. **Document type:** *Magazine, Consumer.*
Related titles: Online - full text ed.: ISSN 1689-0493; Regional ed(s).: Murator Dolnoslaski. ISSN 1643-210X. 2002; Murator Lodzki. ISSN 1643-207X. 2002; Murator Malopolski. ISSN 1643-2061. 2002; Murator Mazowiecki. ISSN 1643-2118. 2002; Murator Pomorski. ISSN 1643-2088. 2002; Murator Slaski. ISSN 1643-2096. 2002; Murator Wielkopolski. ISSN 1643-2053. 2002; Supplement(s): Murator Numer Specjalny. ISSN 1429-8198. 1998.
Indexed: AgrLib.
Published by: Wydawnictwo Murator Sp. z o.o., ul Kamionkowska 45, Warsaw, 03812, Poland. TEL 48-22-5905000, FAX 48-22-5905444, wydawnictwo@murator.com.pl, http://www.muratordom.pl/murator.html, http://www.murator.com.pl. Ed. Wieslaw Rudolf. Pub. Zygmunt Stepinski. Adv. contact Anna Piela. page PLZ 24,300. Circ: 130,000. **Dist. by:** Ars Polona, Krakowskie Przedmiescie 7, Warsaw, Poland. TEL 48-22-9263914, FAX 48-22-9265334, arspolona@arspolona.com.pl, http://www.arspolona.com.pl.

MUSEES. see *MUSEUMS AND ART GALLERIES*

720 693 ESP ISSN 1135-3384
N A: NUEVA ARCHITECTURA CON ARCILLA COCIDA. Text in Spanish. 1995. s-a. **Document type:** *Magazine, Trade.*
Published by: Faenza Editrice Iberica S.L., Pol. Ind Sur Nave 39, Castellon, 12006, Spain. TEL 34-964-216570, FAX 34-964-241010, info@faenza.es. Ed. Benjamin Caervera Canceller. Circ: 14,370.

721 CHN ISSN 1000-0232
NANFANG JIANZHU/SOUTH-CHINA ARCHITECTURE. Text in Chinese. 1981. q. CNY 32 (effective 1998). adv. **Document type:** *Academic/Scholarly.* **Description:** Discusses construction projects and economic theories.
Related titles: Online - full text ed.: (from East View Information Services).
Published by: Guangdong Sheng Tumu Jianzhu Xuehui/Guangdong Association of Architecture, No 85, Liuhua Rd, Guangzhou, Guangdong 510010, China. TEL 86-8667-6522, FAX 86-8667-7463. Ed. Zheng Zhenhong. Adv. contact Tian Yong. Circ: 5,000.

720.624 CHN ISSN 1003-711X
NANJING JIANZHU GONGCHENG XUEYUAN XUEBAO/NANJING ARCHITECTURAL AND CIVIL ENGINEERING INSTITUTE. JOURNAL. Text in Chinese. 1984. q. CNY 4 per issue domestic (effective 2000). back issues avail. **Document type:** *Academic/Scholarly.*
Related titles: Online - full content ed.: (from WanFang Data Corp.); Online - full text ed.: (from East View Information Services).
Published by: Nanjing Jianzhu Gongcheng Xueyuan/Nanjing Architectural and Civil Engineering Institute, 200 Shan Bei Lu, Nanjing, 210009, China. Ed. Miao Kang Zang.

720 USA
E159
NATIONAL TRUST FOR HISTORIC PRESERVATION IN THE UNITED STATES. PRESERVATION BOOKS. Text in English. 1976. irreg. price varies. back issues avail. **Document type:** *Consumer.* **Description:** Provides concise information on basic and frequently used preservation techniques and issues.
Former titles: National Trust for Historic Preservation in the United States. Information Series (1054-6855); National Trust for Historical Preservation. Information (0272-6556)
Indexed: AIAP.
Published by: National Trust for Historic Preservation, 1785 Massachusetts Ave, N W, Washington, DC 20036. TEL 202-588-6296. Pub. Byrd Wood. R&P Robert Wilson TEL 202-588-6217.

712 DEU ISSN 0940-6808
QH77.G3
NATURSCHUTZ UND LANDSCHAFTSPLANUNG. Text in German; Summaries in English, German. 1963. m. EUR 89.60 domestic; EUR 95 foreign; EUR 9 newsstand/cover (effective 2004). adv. **Document type:** *Magazine, Trade.* **Description:** Covers all aspects of landscape planning, architecture and conservation.
Former titles: Landschaft und Stadt (0023-8058); Beitraege zur Landespflege

Indexed: AEA, AgrForAb, AnBrAb, BioCN&I, DIP, ExcerpMed, ForAb, GEOBASE, HerbAb, HortAb, I&DA, IBR, IBZ, KWIWR, OrnHort, PAIS, PBA, PGegResA, RRTA, RefZh, RevApplEntom, S&F, SeedAb, WAE&RSA, WeedAb, ZooRec. —BLDSC (6048.700000), IE, ingenta. **CCC.**
Published by: Verlag Eugen Ulmer GmbH, Wollgrasweg 41, Stuttgart, 70599, Germany. TEL 49-711-45070, FAX 49-711-4507120, info@ulmer.de, http://www.ulmer.de. Ed. Eckhard Jedicke. Adv. contact Dieter Boger. B&W page EUR 870; trim 185 x 260. Circ: 2,336 (paid and controlled).

720   RUS
NEO XXI. Text in Russian. bi-m. **Document type:** *Trade.* **Description:** Covers architecture, art and design, interiors, building materials, and building technology and equipment.
Published by: Pro, Plotinnaya 7, Novosibirsk, 630058, Russian Federation. TEL 7-3832-341844, FAX 7-3832-323621, neo@online.nsk.su, http://www.nsk.su/~neo.

NETHERLANDS INSTITUTE AT ATHENS. PUBLICATIONS. see *ARCHAEOLOGY*

725   NLD
NETHERLANDS. RIJKSDIENST VOOR DE MONUMENTENZORG. JAARVERSLAG. Text in Dutch. 1974. a. illus.; stat. 70 p./no. 2 cols./p.; **Document type:** *Yearbook, Government.*
Published by: Rijksdienst voor de Monumentenzorg, Postbus 1001, Zeist, 3700 BA, Netherlands. TEL 31-30-6983211, FAX 31-30-6916189, http://www.monumentenzorg.nl. Ed. M E Reijn. Circ: 3,000.

725   NLD   ISSN 0929-3035
NETHERLANDS. RIJKSDIENST VOOR DE MONUMENTENZORG. NIEUWSBRIEF. Text in Dutch. 1988. 6/yr. free. bibl.; illus. 12 p./no.; back issues avail. **Document type:** *Newsletter, Government.* **Description:** Discusses cultural heritage, preservation and conservation issues.
Formerly (until 1993): R D M Z Nieuwsbrief (0925-8183)
Published by: Rijksdienst voor de Monumentenzorg, Postbus 1001, Zeist, 3700 BA, Netherlands. TEL 31-30-6983211, FAX 31-30-6916189, http://www.monumentenzorg.nl. Ed. M Bus.

720   DEU
DIE NEUEN ARCHITEKTURFUEHRER. Text in German. 1998. irreg. **Document type:** *Monographic series, Trade.*
Published by: Stadtwandel Verlag, Solmsstr. 22, Berlin, 10961, Germany. TEL 49-30-69504812, FAX 49-30-69504813, info@stadtwandel.de, http://www.stadtwandel.de.

720   GBR   ISSN 0262-558X
N6768
➤ **NEW ARCADIAN JOURNAL.** Text in English. 1981. a. GBP 20 in United Kingdom to individuals; GBP 25 elsewhere to individuals; GBP 25 in United Kingdom to institutions; GBP 30 elsewhere to institutions (effective 2002). illus. back issues avail. **Document type:** *Academic/Scholarly.* **Description:** Explores the cultural politics of designed landscapes in Britain, with particular reference to the 18th century English landscape garden and garden works by contemporary artists.
—BLDSC (6082.082000).
Published by: New Arcadian Press, 13 Graham Grove, Burley, Leeds, LS4 2NF, United Kingdom. TEL 44-113-2304608, FAX 44-1274-753236, patricke@bilk.ac.uk. Ed., Pub., R&P, Adv. contact Patrick Eyres. Circ: 300.

➤ **NEW CRYSTAL PALACE MATTERS.** see *HISTORY—History Of Europe*

▼ ➤ **NEW ENGLAND HOME.** see *INTERIOR DESIGN AND DECORATION*

974.9   USA
NEW JERSEY AND NATIONAL REGISTERS OF HISTORIC PLACES. Text in English. 1977. biennial. USD 15 (effective 2000). **Document type:** *Government.* **Description:** Lists names and addresses of properties registered as historic places and places found eligible by the State Historic Perservation Officer or determined eligible by the National Park Service.
Formerly: State and National Registers of Historic Places
Published by: Department of Environmental Protection, Division of Parks and Forestry, New Jersey Historic Preservation Office, CN 404, P O Box 404, Trenton, NJ 08625-0404. TEL 609-292-2023, 609-292-2028, FAX 609-984-0578. Ed. Robert W Craig. Circ: 2,000.

720   USA   ISSN 0734-4481
NEW ORLEANS PRESERVATION IN PRINT. Text in English. 1975. m. USD 25. adv. bk.rev. charts; illus. **Document type:** *Newsletter.*
Formerly: Preservation Press
Published by: Preservation Resource Center, 923 Tchoupitoulas St., New Orleans, LA 70130-3819. TEL 504-581-7032, FAX 504-522-9275, prc@prcno.org, http://www.prcno.org. Ed. Mary Fitzpatrick. Adv. contact Jackie Derks. B&W page USD 920; trim 13 x 9.63. Circ: 12,000.

NEW STEEL CONSTRUCTION. see *BUILDING AND CONSTRUCTION*

▼ **NEW YORK SPACES.** see *INTERIOR DESIGN AND DECORATION*

▼ **NEW YORK SPACES (NEW JERSEY EDITION).** see *INTERIOR DESIGN AND DECORATION*

720   NZL
NEW ZEALAND BUILDING ECONOMIST; current construction costs. Text in English. 1967. q. NZD 55 (effective 2002). adv. charts; mkt.; stat.; tr.lit. **Document type:** *Consumer.* **Description:** Covers current construction costs including the costs of the various parts of buildings for the different areas of New Zealand. For feasibility studies, cost comparisons, checking tender, final accounts.
Published by: Plans and Specifications Ltd., P.O. Box 35-930, Browns Bay, Auckland, New Zealand. Ed., R&P, Adv. contact Dick Willson TEL 64-9-479-5099. page NZD 850. Circ: 700.

720 510   ITA   ISSN 1522-4600
NA2750
➤ **NEXUS NETWORK JOURNAL**; architecture and mathematics. Text in English. 1999. s-a. EUR 40 to corporations (effective 2003). bk.rev.; Website rev. abstr.; illus.; bibl. back issues avail. **Document type:** *Journal, Academic/Scholarly.* **Description:** Studies in the relationships between architecture and mathematics for professionals, academics and students in both disciplines.
Related titles: Online - full text ed.: free (effective 2005); Print ed.: ISSN 1590-5896. EUR 20 per issue (effective 2002).
Published by: Kim Williams Books, Via Mazzini 7, Fucecchio (Florence), 50054, Italy. TEL 39-0571-20489, FAX 39-0571-22033, kwilliams@kimwilliamsbooks.com, http://www.kimwilliamsbooks.com. Ed. Ms. Kim Williams.

720   BEL
NIEUW - NEUF; architecture and design. Text in Dutch, French. 1965. bi-m. adv. bk.rev. bibl.; charts; illus.; tr.lit. Supplement avail.
Formerly: Neuf
Indexed: AIAP.
Published by: Socorema s.c.r.l., Rue du Merlo 28, Brussels, 1180, Belgium. TEL 02-376-62-28, FAX 02-376-12-80. Ed. J Laffineur. Circ: 10,000.

720   JPN   ISSN 1340-4210
NIHON KENCHIKU GAKKAI KEIKAKU-KEI RONBUNSHU/ JOURNAL OF ARCHITECTURE, PLANNING AND ENVIRONMENTAL ENGINEERING. Text in English, Japanese. 1936. m. JPY 1,500 per issue (effective 2005). bibl. **Document type:** *Journal, Academic/Scholarly.*
Supersedes (in 1994): Nihon Kenchiku Gakkai Keikaku-Kei Ronbun Hokokushu (0910-8017); Supersedes in part (in 1985): Nihon Kenchiku Gakkai Ronbun Hokokushu (0387-1185); Which was formerly (until 1956): Nihon Kenchiku Gakkai Ronbunshu (0387-1177)
Indexed: AIAP, AJEE, BrCerAb, C&ISA, CerAb, CivEngAb, ConcrAb, CorrAb, E&CAJ, EEA, EMA, IAA, INIS AtomInd, M&TEA, MBF, METADEX, SolStAb, WAA.
—BLDSC (4947.200600), CISTI, IE, ingenta, Linda Hall. **CCC.**
Published by: Nihon Kenchiku Gakkai/Architectural Institute of Japan, 26-20 Shiba 5-chome, Minato-ku, Tokyo, 108-0014, Japan. TEL 81-3-34562051, FAX 81-3-34562058, info@aij.or.jp, http://www.aij.or.jp/aijhomej.htm.

720   JPN   ISSN 1340-4202
TA630
NIHON KENCHIKU GAKKAI KOZO-KEI RONBUNSHU/ JOURNAL OF STRUCTURAL AND CONSTRUCTION ENGINEERING. Text in English, Japanese. 1936. m. JPY 33,600 to non-members; JPY 26,400 to members; includes Nihon Kenchiku Gakkai Keikaku-Kei Ronbunshu. **Document type:** *Academic/Scholarly.*
Supersedes (in 1994): Nihon Kenchiku Gakkai Kozo-Kei Ronbun Hokokushu (0910-8025); Supersedes in part (in 1985): Nihon Kenchiku Gakkai Ronbun Hokokushu (0387-1185); Which was formerly (until 1956): Nihon Kenchiku Gakkai Ronbunshu (0387-1177)
Indexed: BrCerAb, C&ISA, CRIA, CRICC, CerAb, CivEngAb, ConcrAb, CorrAb, E&CAJ, EEA, EMA, IAA, ICEA, INIS AtomInd, M&TEA, MBF, METADEX, RASB, SolStAb, WAA.
—CISTI, Linda Hall. **CCC.**
Published by: Nihon Kenchiku Gakkai/Architectural Institute of Japan, 26-20 Shiba 5-chome, Minato-ku, Tokyo, 108-0014, Japan. TEL 81-3-34562051, FAX 81-3-34562058, info@aij.or.jp, http://www.aij.or.jp, http://www.aij.or.jp/aijhomej.htm.

720   JPN   ISSN 0385-0870
NIKKEI ARCHITECTURE. Text in Japanese. 1976. bi-w. JPY 18,000. adv. **Document type:** *Trade.* **Description:** Covers design and planning activities, as well as technological, social, economic, and legal developments relating to architecture.
Published by: Nikkei Business Publications Inc. (Subsidiary of: Nihon Keizai Shimbun, Inc.), 2-7-6 Hirakawa-cho, Chiyoda-ku, Tokyo, 102-8622, Japan. TEL 81-3-8121-8502, FAX 81-3-5210-8123, info@nikkeibpnyc.com, info@nikkeibp-america.com, http://www.nikkeibp.com. Ed. Masatoshi Kawamura. Pub. Shoji Tanabe. Adv. contact Yarada Harada. B&W page JPY 738,000, color page JPY 1,070,000; trim 208 x 280. Circ: 54,462. **Dist. in America by:** Nikkei Business Publications America Inc., 575 Fifth Ave, 20th Fl, New York, NY 10017. TEL 212-867-3278.

720   USA
NO-SPACE. Text in English. 1997. q. **Document type:** *Newsletter.* **Description:** Theory of life in the suburbs with a focus on southern California.
Media: Online - full text.
Address: eknutzen@ucsd.edu, http://www.geocities.com/soho/lofts/7621. Ed. Erik Knutzen.

720   SWE   ISSN 1102-5824
NORDISK ARKITEKTURFORSKNING/NORDIC JOURNAL OF ARCHITECTURAL RESEARCH. Text in Danish, English, Norwegian, Swedish. 1987. q. SEK 325, EUR 35.30 to individuals; SEK 500, EUR 58.90 to institutions; SEK 225, EUR 26.90 to students (effective 2003). adv. bk.rev. back issues avail. **Document type:** *Journal, Academic/Scholarly.* **Description:** Acts as a forum for architectural theory, architecture criticism and debate on architecture and architectural research problems and methods in the Nordic countries.
Formerly (until 1992): Tidskrift foer Arkitekturforskning (0284-2998)
Indexed: BHA, NAA.
Published by: Nordisk Foerening foer Arkitekturforskning, Arkitekturskolan KTH, Stockholm, 10044, Sweden. TEL 46-8-7906000, nordic.journal@a-aarhus.dk, lena@arch.kth.se, http://arkitekturforskning.nu/tidskrift/tidskrift.html, http://www.arch.kth.se. Ed. Pia Bille. Pub. Jerker Lundequist.
Subscr. to: Naetverkstan Ekonomitjaenst, PO Box 31120, Goeteborg 40032, Sweden.

720   NOR   ISSN 0332-6578
NORSKE ARKITEKTKONKURRANSER. Text in Norwegian. 1953. irreg. illus. index. **Document type:** *Monographic series, Trade.*
Published by: Norske Arkitekters Landsforbund/National Association of Norwegian Architects, Josefines Gate 34, Oslo, 0351, Norway. TEL 47-23-33-25-00, FAX 47-23-33-25-50. Ed. Kristin Ytreberg.

720   USA   ISSN 1045-3253
NORTH CAROLINA ARCHITECTURE. Text in English. 1964. q. USD 30. adv. **Document type:** *Trade.*
Former titles (until 1987): North Carolina Architect (0029-2427); (until 1978): N C Architect (0886-0378); (until 1977): North Carolina Architect (0886-0386); Southern Architect
Indexed: AIAP.
Published by: American Institute of Architects, North Carolina Chapter, 115 W Morgan St, Raleigh, NC 27601-1335. TEL 919-833-6656. Ed. John Roth. Circ: 3,500.

720   USA   ISSN 0078-1444
N11
NORTH CAROLINA STATE UNIVERSITY. SCHOOL OF DESIGN. (STUDENT PUBLICATION MAGAZINE). Text in English. 1951. irreg. price varies. adv. bk.rev. **Document type:** *Magazine.*
Indexed: AIAP.
Published by: North Carolina State University, College of Design, Campus Box 7701, Raleigh, NC 27695-7701. TEL 919-737-2202. Circ: 1,000.

720   CAN   ISSN 0834-7816
NOVA SCOTIA ASSOCIATION OF ARCHITECTS. NEWSLETTER. Text in English. m. membership. **Document type:** *Newsletter.*
Published by: Nova Scotia Association of Architects, 1361 Barrington St, Halifax, NS B3J 1Y9, Canada. TEL 902-423-7607, FAX 902-425-7024.

720   ARG   ISSN 0029-5701
NUESTRA ARQUITECTURA ✱. Text in Spanish. 1929. 6/yr. USD 54. adv. bk.rev. illus. index.
Indexed: AIAP, API.
Published by: Editorial Contempra s.r.l., Sarmiento 643, 5o Piso, Buenos Aires, 1382, Argentina. TEL 54-114-451793. Ed. Norberto Mario Muzio. Circ: 10,000.

O P D RESTAURO; rivista dell'Opificio delle Pietre Dure. see *ART*

720   NLD   ISSN 0169-6238
NA673
OASE; tijdschrift voor architectuur. Text in Dutch, English. 1985. 3/yr. EUR 50 in Netherlands; EUR 75 elsewhere (effective 2001). adv. illus. back issues avail. **Document type:** *Academic/Scholarly.*
Supersedes (1981-1985): O - Ontwerp, Onderzoek, Onderwijs (0167-8620)
Published by: (Stichting Oase), Uitgeverij S U N, Postbus 1609, Nijmegen, 6501 BP, Netherlands. TEL 31-24-3221700, FAX 31-24-3235493, info@uitgeverijsun.nl, http://www.uitgeverijsun.nl. Circ: 1,000.

720   ESP   ISSN 0211-6065
OBRADOIRO. Text in Spanish, Catalan. 1978. 3/yr. back issues avail.
Related titles: Online - full text ed.; Supplement(s): Obradoiro. Suplemento. ISSN 0211-6073.
Indexed: AIAP, RILM.
Published by: Colegio Oficial de Arquitectos de Galicia, Plaza de Quintana, s-n, Santiago de Compostela, 15704, Spain. TEL 34-981-580100, FAX 34-981-561655, http://www.coag.es/arteecultura/publicacions/obradoiro/ob29.asp. Ed. Jose Manuel Rey Pichel.

▼ *new title*   ➤ *refereed*   ✱ *unverified*   ◆ *full entry avail.*

A

720 BRA ISSN 1519-7727
NA5
OCULUM ENSAIOS; Revista de Arquitetura e Urbanismo. Text in Portuguese. 1985. s-a. BRL 23 (effective 2001). illus.
Document type: *Academic/Scholarly.*
Formerly (until 2000): Oculum (0104-0308)
Published by: Pontificia Universidade Catolica de Campinas, Faculdade de Arquitectura e Urbanismo, Campus 1, Rodovia D. Pedro I, km 136, Campinas, SP 13089-900, Brazil. TEL 55-19-3756-7082, FAX 55-19-3756-7085, ocensaios@puc-campinas.br. Ed. Jane Victal Ferreira Duduch. Circ: 2,000.

720 USA ISSN 0885-5927
N1
OCULUS. Text in English. 1996 (vol.58). m. USD 40 (effective 1998). illus. **Document type:** *Newsletter.* **Description:** Covers architecture in New York: what's being designed, built, published and discussed in the city, including international events and member information.
Indexed: AIAP.
Published by: American Institute of Architects, New York Chapter, 200 Lexington Ave, New York, NY 10016. TEL 212-683-0023. Ed. Jayne Merkel.

OESTERREICHISCHE INGENIEUR UND ARCHITEKTEN ZEITSCHRIFT. see *ENGINEERING*

645.4 ITA ISSN 1120-9739
OFX OFFICE INTERNATIONAL. Text in Italian. 1991. bi-m. EUR 52 domestic; EUR 78, USD 75 foreign (effective 2001). adv.
Document type: *Magazine, Trade.*
Published by: Design Diffusion Edizioni, Via Lucano 3, Milan, 20135, Italy. TEL 39-02-5516109, FAX 39-02-59902431, info@designdiffusion.com, http://www.designdiffusion.com/riviste/ofx/ofx.html.

OLD HOUSE JOURNAL. see *BUILDING AND CONSTRUCTION*

OLD-HOUSE JOURNAL RESTORATION DIRECTORY. see *BUILDING AND CONSTRUCTION*

OLD MILL NEWS. see *HISTORY—History Of North And South America*

720 CAN ISSN 1481-8280
ON SITE REVIEW; design at work. Text in English; Summaries in English, French. 1999. s-a. CND 15 domestic; USD 15 foreign; CND 7.50 newsstand/cover (effective 2002 - 2003). adv. bk.rev.; software rev. illus. Index. back issues avail.
Document type: *Magazine.* **Description:** Architecture magazine with reviews, articles, letters and photographs of built work. Includes some student projects, competitions and architectural practice in Canada and the United States plus the work of Canadian architects abroad.
Published by: Field Notes Press, 1326 11th Ave SE, Calgary, AB T2G 0Z5, Canada. TEL 403-266-5827, editor@onsitereview.ca. Ed., R&P, Adv. contact Stephanie White TEL 403-266-5827. B&W page CND 500, color page CND 1,000; trim 8.5 x 11. Circ: 500 (paid); 150 (controlled).

720 IRL
ONSITE IRELAND. Text in English. 1997. m. **Description:** Covers Irish architecture: past, present and future.
Media: Online - full text.
Published by: Archeire, 54 SCR, Portabello, Dublin, 8, Ireland. TEL 353-1-676-8996, FAX 353-1-661-3932, pclerkin@connect.ie, http://www.archeire.com/onsite/. Eds. Beth McLendon, Paul Clerkin.

OP CIT; selezione della critica d'arte contemporanea. see *ART*

OPEN HOUSE INTERNATIONAL; the journal of an association of institutes and individuals concerned with housing, design and development in the built environment. see *HOUSING AND URBAN PLANNING*

720 USA
OPENSPACE. Text in English. 1997. irreg.
Media: Online - full content.
Published by: University of Cincinnati, School of Architecture, University of Cincinnati, Box 210016, Cincinnati, OH 45221-0016.

ORDINE DEGLI INGEGNERI DELLA PROVINCIA DI PALERMO. BOLLETTINO. see *BUILDING AND CONSTRUCTION*

OXONIENSIA. see *ARCHAEOLOGY*

720 747 NLD ISSN 1384-4415
P I; vakblad voor projektinrichting in Nederland en Belgie. (Projekt & Interieur) Text in Dutch. 1990. 6/yr. EUR 52; EUR 11.50 newsstand/cover (effective 2005). adv. bk.rev. illus. back issues avail. **Document type:** *Journal, Trade.* **Description:** Covers all aspects of architectural and interior design.
Formerly: Mobilia: Vakblad voor Interieurspecialisten (0165-5302)
Related titles: Fax ed.; Online - full text ed.
Published by: Uitgeverij Triade Benelux BV, Hemonylaan 24, Amsterdam, 1074 BJ, Netherlands. TEL 31-20-6624201, FAX 31-20-4004106, info@interieur.net, pi@interieur.net. Ed. Olga Smalhout Holst. Circ: 10,000.

721 USA
P T I NEWSLETTER. Text in English. 1976. q. membership only. back issues avail. **Document type:** *Newsletter.* **Description:** Disseminates information on post-tensioned design and construction technology and developments in the post-tensioning industry. Audience is post-tensioning materials fabricators and manufacturers of prestressing materials in the US, Canada, Mexico and other countries.
Published by: Post-Tensioning Institute, 8601 N. Black Canyon Hwy., Ste. 103, Phoenix, AZ 85021-4155. TEL 602-870-7540, FAX 602-870-7541. Ed. Gerald J McGuire. Circ: 1,200 (controlled).

720 ITA ISSN 0031-0379
NA4
PALLADIO; rivista di storia dell'architettura e restauro. Text in Multiple languages. 1937; N.S. 1951-1977; resumed 1978. s-a. EUR 62 domestic; EUR 93 foreign (effective 2004). bk.rev. bibl.; charts; illus. index. reprints avail. **Document type:** *Magazine, Trade.*
Indexed: AIAP, API, ArtInd, BHA, DIP, IBR, IBZ.
—IE.
Published by: Istituto Poligrafico e Zecca dello Stato, Piazza Verdi 10, Rome, 00198, Italy. TEL 39-06-85082147, editoriale@ipzs.it, http://www.ipzs.it.

720 USA
PAMPHLET ARCHITECTURE. Text in English. 1977. irreg., latest vol.19, 1996. USD 11.95 per issue. illus. back issues avail.
Document type: *Monographic series.* **Description:** Publishes the work of younger American architects.
Indexed: AIAP, API.
Published by: Princeton Architectural Press, 37 E 7th St, New York, NY 10003. TEL 212-995-9620, FAX 212-995-9454, sales@pap.designsys.com, http://www.designsys.com/pap. **Dist. by:** Chronicle Books, 85 2nd St., San Francisco, CA 94105-3459. TEL 800-722-6657.

PAM'YATKY UKRAINY: ISTORIYA TA KUL'TURA/UKRAINIAN HERITAGE: HISTORY & CULTURE. see *HISTORY—History Of Europe*

PAMYATNIKI OTECHESTVA. see *HISTORY—History Of Europe*

PANSTADIA INTERNATIONAL QUARTERLY REPORT; the definitive journal for the sports facility industry worldwide. see *BUILDING AND CONSTRUCTION*

711.4 ITA ISSN 0031-1731
PARAMETRO. Text in English, Italian; Summaries in English, French, German, Spanish. 1971. 6/yr. EUR 62 domestic; EUR 118 foreign (effective 2004). back issues avail. **Document type:** *Magazine, Trade.* **Description:** International review of architecture and town planning.
Indexed: A&ATA, AIAP, API.
Published by: Gruppo Editoriale Faenza Editrice SpA, Via Pier de Crescenzi 44, Faenza, RA 48018, Italy. TEL 39-0546-670411, FAX 39-0546-660440, info@faenza.com, http://www.faenza.com. Eds. Giorgio Trebbi, Glauco Gresleri. Adv. contact Elvio Neri. Circ: 5,000.

725 CHE ISSN 1420-7095
PATRIMOINE ET ARCHITECTURE. Text in French. 1996. s-a. CHF 30, EUR 19.48 to individuals; CHF 40, EUR 25.97 to institutions (effective 2002). **Document type:** *Journal, Academic/Scholarly.*
Published by: (Republique et Canton de Geneve), Editions Medecine et Hygiene, 78 avenue de la Rosarale, Case Postale 456, Geneva 4, 1211, Switzerland. TEL 41-22-7029311, FAX 41-22-7029355, abonnements@medhyg.ch, http://www.medhyg.ch.

720 USA ISSN 1062-8649
NA730.P4
PENNSYLVANIA ARCHITECT✶. Text in English. q. adv.
Document type: *Trade.*
Published by: T S G Publishing, PO Box 15684, Pittsburgh, PA 15244-0684. TEL 412-344-3360, FAX 412-344-3364. Ed. John A Fatula. Adv. contact Gary Winterhalter. Circ: 5,000.

720 647.9 USA
PENTON'S DESIGNING. Text in English. 2000. 6/yr. free to qualified personnel. adv. **Document type:** *Magazine, Trade.* **Description:** Covers the latest industry trends and products for architects and interior designers serving the hospitality industry.
Published by: Penton Media, Inc. (Subsidiary of: Pittway Company), 1300 E 9th St, Cleveland, OH 44114-1503. TEL 216-696-7000, 800-659-5251, FAX 216-696-7658, information@penton.com, http://www.penton.com/cgi-bin/superdirectory/details.pl?id=364. Ed. Grace Wagner TEL 216-931-9486. Circ: 36,000 (paid and controlled).

720 666 ITA
PERCORSI IN CERAMICA; rivista di segni e immagini magazine di Casalgrande - Padana. Text in Italian, French. irreg.
Description: Dedicated to ceramic in architecture and design. Includes photos and descriptions of recent large scale ceramic design works.
Published by: Ceramica Casalgrande - Padana, 73 via Statale 467, Casalgrande, 42013, Italy. TEL 39-05-229901, FAX 39-05-22996121, info@casalgrande-padana.re.it, http://www.pianeta.it/casalgrande-padana.

PEREGRINATIONS. see *ART*

724 747 GBR ISSN 1476-5349
PERIOD HOUSE; new ideas for homes with character. Text in English. 1990. m. GBP 27 domestic; GBP 55 in Europe; GBP 99 elsewhere (effective 2003). adv. index. back issues avail.
Document type: *Magazine, Consumer.* **Description:** Contains practical, technical, style and gardening features to help the period home owner get the most from their house and garden.
Former titles: Period House and Its Garden (0966-1530); (until 1992): Old House Journal (0961-5962)
Indexed: AIAP.
Published by: Essential Publishing Ltd., The Tower, Phoenix Sq, Colchester, Essex CO4 9HU, United Kingdom. TEL 44-1206-851117, sarah@essentialhomes.com, http://www.essentialhomes.com. Ed. Sarah Wiltshire. R&P Luke Patten. Adv. contact Rob Grainger. B&W page GBP 995, color page GBP 1,295; trim 222 x 298. Circ: 35,000 (paid).
Subscr. to: PO Box 648, Harrow, Mddx HA1 2NW, United Kingdom. **Dist. by:** Comag, Tavistock Works, Tavistock Rd, W Drayton, Middx UB7 7QX, United Kingdom. TEL 44-1895-444055, FAX 44-1895-433602.

720 700 HRV ISSN 0553-6707
N6
PERISTIL. Text in Croatian, English; Summaries in English, German, Italian. 1954. a.
Indexed: ABM, AIAP, BHA, BibInd, RILM.
Published by: Drustvo Povjesnicara Umjetnosti SR Hrvatske, Zrinjski trg 11, Zagreb, 41000, Croatia. TEL 041-433-504.

THE PERMACULTURE ACTIVIST. see *AGRICULTURE*

720 USA ISSN 0079-0958
NA1
PERSPECTA; the Yale architectural journal. Text in English. 1951. a., latest vol.33, 2002. USD 30 (effective 2003). reprint service avail. from PQC,ISI. **Document type:** *Journal, Academic/Scholarly.*
Indexed: AIAP, API, ASCA, ArtHuCI, ArtInd, BHA, CurCont, PCI, RILM.
—BLDSC (6428.107000).
Published by: Yale University, School of Architecture, 180 York St, New Haven, CT 06520. TEL 203-432-2288, FAX 203-432-7175, http://www.architecture.yale.edu.

720 690 747 GBR ISSN 0967-2176
PERSPECTIVE. Text in English. 1992. bi-m. GBP 15 in the European Union; GBP 18 elsewhere; GBP 2.50 newsstand/cover. adv. index. back issues avail. **Document type:** *Consumer.* **Description:** Reviews recent Northern Ireland architecture. Contains news and views of importance and interest to architects and other design professionals, seeking to promote an appreciation of Northern Ireland architecture among the public.
Related titles: Online - full text ed.: (from Northern Light Technology, Inc.).
Indexed: API, BrArAb.
Published by: (Royal Society of Ulster Architects), Adleader Publications, Marlborough House, 348 Lisburn Rd, Belfast, BT9 6GH, United Kingdom. TEL 44-1232-661666, FAX 44-1232-681888, adleader@dial.pipex.com, http://www.dialspace.dial.pipex.com/adleader. Ed., R&P Linda Brooks. Adv. contact Lorraine Gill. Circ: 2,000.

720 690 PHL ISSN 0031-7470
TA1
PHILIPPINE ARCHITECTURE, ENGINEERING & CONSTRUCTION RECORD. Text in English. 1953. m. adv. charts; illus.
Published by: P A E N C O R, Inc., 154 Araneta Ave, P.O. Box 1295, Quezon City, Philippines. TEL 2-7122239. Ed. Placido O Urbanes Jr. Adv. contact Ambrosio Racho.

PICTURE HOUSE. see *MOTION PICTURES*

724 ITA ISSN 1123-993X
PIETRANTICA. Text in Italian. 1996. bi-m. EUR 4.95 newsstand/cover (effective 2003). **Document type:** *Magazine, Consumer.*
Published by: Trentini S.r.l., Via Pier Luigi Nervi 1/B, Argenta, 44011, Italy. TEL 39-0532-318149, FAX 39-0532-310084, info@3ntini.com, http://www.3ntini.com.

720 700 SVN ISSN 1318-007X
NA958
PIRANESI; 1st Middle-European architectural magazine for the culture of environment. Text in English, German, Italian, Slovenian. 1992. s-a. ANG 48. adv. bk.rev. illus. **Document type:** *Monographic series, Academic/Scholarly.* **Description:** Aims to discuss all specific features of architectural production in Middle Europe.
Indexed: AIAP.

Published by: Piranesi Ltd., Bogisiceva 11, Ljubljana, 61000, Slovenia. TEL 386-61-223-039, FAX 386-61-221-226. Eds. Tomaz Brate, Vojteh Ravnikar. Circ: 2,000. Dist. by: Idea Books Amsterdam, Nieuwe Herengracht 11, Amsterdam 1011 RK, Netherlands.

720 ITA ISSN 1591-3163
LA PISCINA. Text in Italian. 1992. s-a. EUR 8 newsstand/cover (effective 2004). **Document type:** *Magazine, Consumer.*
Published by: Di Baio Editore SpA, Via Luigi Settembrini 11, Milan, MI 20124, Italy. TEL 39-02-674951, FAX 39-02-67495228, http://www.dibaio.com.

720 USA ISSN 1062-8657
PLACE. Text in English. 1989. q. USD 10 (effective 1998). **Document type:** *Directory, Consumer.* **Description:** Focuses on all members of the building team: the clients, architects, contractors, and developers who influence Michigan's built environment.
Published by: American Institute of Architects, Michigan Chapter, 553 E Jefferson St, Detroit, MI 48226. TEL 313-965-4100. Ed. Timothy Casai. R&P Lynne Merrill Francis. adv.: B&W page USD 1,200. Circ: 3,500.

711.4 USA ISSN 0731-0455
NA2542.35
➤ **PLACES**; a forum of environmental design . Text in English. 1983. 3/yr., latest vol.14, 2001. USD 55 domestic to libraries; USD 80 in Canada to libraries; USD 90 elsewhere to libraries (effective 2005). adv. bk.rev. illus.; maps. 80 p./no.; back issues avail.; reprint service avail. from PQC. **Document type:** *Journal, Academic/Scholarly.* **Description:** Provides an alternative to both commercial and theoretical architecture and planning-design magazines, covering buildings, landscapes, public art, and more.
Related titles: Online - full text ed.: (from H.W. Wilson, O C L C Online Computer Library Center, Inc.).
Indexed: AIAP, API, ArtHuCI, ArtInd, CurCont, DAAI, GardL, PRA, SUSA, V&AA.
—BLDSC (6506.906000), IE, Infotrieve, ingenta. **CCC.**
Published by: (University of California at Berkeley, Center for Environmental Design, Pratt Institute), Design History Foundation, 201B Higgins Hall, Pratt Institute, 200 Willoughby Ave, Brooklyn, NY 11205. TEL 718-399-4313, FAX 718-399-4332, places@allenpress.com, http://www.places-journal.org. Ed. Donlyn Lyndon. Pub. Richard Shepard. R&P, Adv. contact Todd W Bressi TEL 718-399-4313. B&W page USD 1,200. Circ: 4,200. **Subscr. to:** Allen Press Inc., PO Box 1897, Lawrence, KS 66044. **Dist. by:** Eastern News Distributors Inc., 250 W. 55th St., New York, NY 10019.

➤ **PLAISIRS DE VIVRE/LIVING IN STYLE.** see *INTERIOR DESIGN AND DECORATION*

720 USA
PLAN. Text in English. s-a. free. **Document type:** *Newsletter, Academic/Scholarly.*
Related titles: Online - full content ed.
Published by: Massachusetts Institute of Technology, School of Architecture and Planning, 77 Massachusetts Ave, Cambridge, MA 02139. TEL 617-253-0692, FAX 617-253-9417, plan-news@mit.edu, http://alberti.mit.edu/plan, http://alberti.mit.edu/index.html. Ed. Scott Campbell.

720 IRL ISSN 0376-7302
PLAN. Text in English. 1969. m. looseleaf. EUR 57 (effective 2005). adv. back issues avail. **Document type:** *Magazine, Trade.*
Incorporates: Interior Plan; Build (0791-7759); Which was formerly (until 1988): Build Magazine (0790-8830); (until 1983): Build (0007-3229); (until 1964): Irish Architect and Contractor (0535-6687); (until 1953): The Irish Contractor (0332-2858)
Related titles: Online - full content ed.
Indexed: AIAP.
Published by: Plan Magazines Ltd., 5-7 Main St., Blackrock, Co. Dublin, Ireland. TEL 353-1-2788161, FAX 353-1-2788133, planmag@eircom.net, http://www.planmagazine.ie/main.html. R&P Richard Byrne. Adv. contact Rob Sutton. color page EUR 2,200; bleed 240 x 308. Circ: 3,500 (controlled).

747 728 USA
PLAN HOUSE. Text in English. 2000. q. USD 3.25 newsstand/cover (effective 2001). adv. **Document type:** *Magazine, Consumer.*
Published by: Plan House, Inc., Box 366, Brandon, MS 39043. TEL 800-752-6468, pheckler@planhouse.com, http://www.planhouse.com. Ed., Pub. Peggy S Heckler.

720 GBR
THE PLANAHOME BOOK OF PLANS. Text in English. 1969. a. GBP 14.95. adv. **Document type:** *Consumer.*
Former titles: Custom Homes Book of Plans; Architectural Services Book of Plans
Published by: Custom Publishing Ltd. (Subsidiary of: Glendower Holdings Ltd.), Hatchways House, Burrows Cross, Gomshall, Surrey GUF 9QF, United Kingdom. TEL 44-1483-202001, FAX 44-1483-202847. Eds. John Bailey, Michael Hanson. adv.: page GBP 1,950. Circ: 50,000 (controlled).

720 AUT
PLANEN - BAUEN - WOHNEN. Text in German. bi-m.
Indexed: AIAP.
Address: Linzer Strasse 261, Vienna, W 1140, Austria. TEL 01-945288. Ed. Rudolf Tiffinger. Circ: 8,000.

720 690 ZAF ISSN 0377-2780
TH119.S66
PLANNING. Text in English. 1972. bi-m. ZAR 209 (effective 1998). back issues avail. **Document type:** *Trade.* **Description:** Features architecture projects, property developments, and professional news of interest to architects in South Africa.
Related titles: Online - full text ed.: (from Northern Light Technology, Inc.).
Indexed: API, ISAP.
Published by: Avonwold Publishing Co. (Pty) Ltd., Avonwold House, 24 Baker St, Rosebank, Johannesburg, 2196, South Africa. TEL 27-11-788-1610, FAX 27-11-880-2732. Ed. C Buchanan. Circ: 4,168. **Subscr. to:** PO Box 52068, Saxonwold 2132, South Africa.

720 ITA ISSN 1129-4469
HT51
➤ **PLURIMONDI**; An international forum for research and debate on human settlements. Text in English. 1999. s-a. EUR 32 domestic; EUR 48 foreign (effective 2003). **Document type:** *Journal, Academic/Scholarly.*
Published by: (Politecnico di Bari, Dipartimento di Architettura e Urbanistica), Edizioni Dedalo, Casella Postale BA-19, Bari, BA 70123, Italy. TEL 39-080-5311413, FAX 39-080-5311414, info@edizionidedalo.it, http://www.edizionidedalo.it.

700.5 AUS ISSN 1447-5170
POL OXYGEN; design - art - architecture. Text in English. 2002. q. AUD 70; AUD 17.50 newsstand/cover (effective 2005). **Document type:** *Magazine, Consumer.* **Description:** Contains articles and information about designers, architects and artists.
Published by: POL Publications, 125-127 Little Eveleigh St, Redfern, NSW 2016, Australia. TEL 61-29-3180500, FAX 61-29-95494345.

720 IDN ISSN 0126-0774
POLA. Text in Indonesian. 1975. bi-m. IDR 750 per issue. adv. bk.rev.
Published by: Yayasan Pola, Ruang 20, Departemen Arsitekter Institut Teknologi Bandung, Jalan Ganesha 10, Bandung, Indonesia. Ed. Agus Basuki. Circ: 12,500.

720 POL ISSN 0518-3138
POLITECHNIKA GDANSKA. ZESZYTY NAUKOWE. ARCHITEKTURA. Text in English, French, German, Polish; Summaries in Russian. 1958. irreg. price varies. bibl.; charts; illus. **Document type:** *Academic/Scholarly.* **Description:** Research work on town planning, ship and naval architecture and building technology.
—Linda Hall.
Published by: Politechnika Gdanska, Ul G Narutowicza 11-12, Gdansk, 80952, Poland. **Dist. by:** Osrodek Rozpowszechniania Wydawnictw Naukowych PAN, Palac Kultury i Nauki, Warsaw 00901, Poland.

720 POL
POLITECHNIKA KRAKOWSKA. MONOGRAFIE. SERIA: ARCHITEKTURA. Text in Polish; Summaries in English, French, German, Russian. 1985. irreg price varies. bibl.; charts; illus. **Document type:** *Monographic series, Academic/Scholarly.*
Related titles: ♦ Series of: Politechnika Krakowska. Monografie. ISSN 0860-097X.
Published by: Politechnika Krakowska, Ul Warszawska 24, Krakow, 31155, Poland. TEL 48-12-6374289, FAX 48-12-6374289. Ed. Elzbieta Nachlik. Adv. contact Ewa Malochleb. Circ: 200.

720 POL ISSN 0137-1371
POLITECHNIKA KRAKOWSKA. ZESZYTY NAUKOWE. ARCHITEKTURA. Text in Polish; Summaries in English, French, German, Russian. 1956. irreg. price varies. bibl.; charts; illus. **Document type:** *Academic/Scholarly.*
Published by: Politechnika Krakowska, Ul Warszawska 24, Krakow, 31155, Poland. TEL 48-12-6374289, FAX 48-12-6374289. Ed. Elzbieta Nachlik. Adv. contact Ewa Malochleb. Circ: 200.

720 POL ISSN 1507-6407
POLITECHNIKA POZNANSKA. ZESZYTY NAUKOWE. ARCHITEKTURA I URBANISTYKA. Text in Polish; Summaries in English. 1999. irreg., latest vol.3, 2002. price varies. **Document type:** *Monographic series, Academic/Scholarly.*
Published by: (Politechnika Poznanska), Wydawnictwo Politechniki Poznanskiej, Pl M Sklodowskiej Curie 2, Poznan, 60965, Poland. TEL 48-61-6653516, FAX 48-61-6653583, office_ed@put.poznan.pl, http://www.ed.put.poznan.pl. Ed. Robert Ast. Circ: 130.

720 POL ISSN 0860-0074
NA1455.P6
POLITECHNIKA SLASKA. ZESZYTY NAUKOWE. ARCHITEKTURA. Text in Polish. 1989. irreg.
—Linda Hall.
Published by: Politechnika Slaska, ul Akademicka 5, Gliwice, 44100, Poland. wydawnictwo_mark@polsl.pl. Ed. Andrzej Niezabitowski. Circ: 205. **Dist. by:** Ars Polona, Krakowskie Przedmiescie 7, Warsaw, Poland.

720 ITA
POLITECNICO DI TORINO. ISTITUTO DI SCIENZA DEI SISTEMI ARCHITETTONICI E TERRITORIALI DELLA FACOLTA DI ARCHITETTURA. STUDI E RICHERCHE. Text in Italian. 3/yr. price varies. illus. **Document type:** *Monographic series, Academic/Scholarly.*
Published by: (Politecnico di Torino, Istituto di Scienza dei Sistemi Architettonici e Territoriali della Facolta di Architettura), Giardini Editori e Stampatori (Subsidiary of: Libra Web), Via Giosue Carducci 60, Ghezzano - La Fontina, Pisa 56123, Italy. TEL 39-050-878066, FAX 39-050-878732, giardinieditori@giardinieditori.it, http://www.libraweb.net. Ed. Giacomo Donato.

711.4 POL ISSN 0079-3450
POLSKA AKADEMIA NAUK. ODDZIAL W KRAKOWIE. KOMISJA URBANISTYKI I ARCHITEKTURY. TEKA. Text in Polish; Summaries in English, Russian. 1967. a., latest vol.34, 2002. price varies. **Document type:** *Academic/Scholarly.* **Description:** Presents papers on various problems of architecture: conservation, town planning, fortification and more.
Indexed: AIAP, AgrLib, BHA, IBR, RASB, RILM.
—KNAW.
Published by: (Polska Akademia Nauk, Oddzial w Krakowie, Komisja Urbanistyki i Architektury), Polska Akademia Nauk, Oddzial w Krakowie, ul sw Jana 28, Krakow, 31018, Poland. TEL 48-12-4224853, FAX 48-12-4222791.

720 AUT ISSN 0948-8685
PORTRAITS OESTERREICHISCHER ARCHITEKTEN/ PORTRAITS AUSTRIAN ARCHITECTS. Text in English, German. 1995. irreg., latest vol.4, 2000. price varies. **Document type:** *Monographic series, Academic/Scholarly.* **Description:** Provides international coverage for the work and achievements of Austrian architects.
Published by: (ArchitekturZentrum Wien), Springer-Verlag Wien (Subsidiary of: Springer Science+Business Media) TEL 43-1-3302415-0, FAX 43-1-330242665, books@springer.at, http://www.springer.at. R&P Angela Foessl TEL 43-1-3302415517. **Subscr. to:** Springer-Verlag New York, Inc., 233 Spring St, New York, NY 10013. TEL 800-777-4643, FAX 201-348-4505, orders@springer-ny.com.

727 USA ISSN 1059-7239
NA1996
PRACTICES. Text in English. 1992. s-a. USD 23.50 (effective 1998). **Document type:** *Trade.*
Indexed: AIAP.
Published by: Center for the Study of Practice, College of Design, Architecture, Art, and Planning, University of Cincinnati, Box 210016, Cincinnati, OH 45221-0016.

720 USA ISSN 0883-7279
NA1
PRATT JOURNAL OF ARCHITECTURE. Text in English. 1985. irreg. (approx. biennial). **Document type:** *Academic/Scholarly.*
Indexed: AIAP, API.
Published by: Pratt Institute, School of Architecture, Attn: Anthony Caradonna, 200 Willoughby Ave, Brooklyn, NY 11205. TEL 718-339-4306.

720 USA ISSN 1526-2065
NA1
PRAXIS (CAMBRIDGE); a journal of writing and building. Text in English. 1999. 2/yr. USD 52 domestic to individuals; USD 62 in Canada & Mexico to individuals; USD 72 elsewhere to individuals; USD 96 domestic to institutions; USD 106 in Canada & Mexico to institutions; USD 116 elsewhere to institutions; USD 40 domestic to students; USD 50 in Canada & Mexico to students; USD 60 elsewhere to students (effective 2005).
Indexed: AIAP.
Published by: Praxis, Inc., P O Box 380225, Cambridge, MA 02238-0225. TEL 617-384-9399, FAX 617-384-9409, mail@praxisjournal.net, http://www.praxisjournal.net. Eds. Amanda Reeser, Ashley Schafer.

PRESENZA TECNICA. see *ENGINEERING*

720 USA ISSN 1090-9931
E151
PRESERVATION. Text in English. 1949. bi-m. USD 20 membership; USD 5 newsstand/cover (effective 2005). adv. bk.rev. illus. back issues avail.; reprints avail. **Document type:** *Journal, Academic/Scholarly.* **Description:** Focuses on preservation and restoration of structures, communities, and rural lands important to American history and culture.
Former titles (until vol.48, no.4, 1996): Historic Preservation (0018-2419); (until 1951): National Council for Historic Sites and Buildings Quarterly Report; Which incorporated (1961-1995): Historic Preservation News (1065-3562); Which was formerly (until 1990): Preservation News (0032-7735)
Related titles: Microfilm ed.: (from PQC); Talking Book ed.
Indexed: A&ATA, ABS&EES, AIAP, API, ASCA, AbAn, AmH&L, ArtHuCI, ArtInd, BHA, CurCont, GardL, HistAb, RILM, SSCI, Search.

—BLDSC (6609.778500), IDS, IE, ingenta. **CCC.**
Published by: National Trust for Historic Preservation, 1785 Massachusetts Ave, N W, Washington, DC 20036. TEL 202-588-6388, FAX 202-588-6266, preservation@nthp.org, law@nthp.org, http://www.nationaltrust.org/magazine/. Pub. Bob A Barron. Adv. contact James W Cooke. B&W page USD 17,065, color page USD 35,100; trim 8.125 x 10.875. Circ: 215,000 (paid and controlled).

720.9 340 USA ISSN 0882-715X
KF4310.A15
PRESERVATION LAW REPORTER. Text in English. 1982. q. looseleaf. USD 95 to non-members; USD 55 to members (effective 2004). bibl. cum.index. back issues avail. **Document type:** *Academic/Scholarly.*
Published by: National Trust for Historic Preservation, 1785 Massachusetts Ave, N W, Washington, DC 20036. TEL 202-588-6000, FAX 202-588-6038, law@nthp.org, http://www.nationaltrust.org. Pub. Julia Miller TEL 202-588-6180. Circ: 337.

720.9747 USA
PRESERVATION NEW YORK. Text in English. 1975; N.S. 1993. q. USD 35 to members. illus. **Document type:** *Newsletter.* **Description:** Reports noteworthy developments affecting historic preservation throughout New York, including articles on successful projects.
Formerly (until 1993): Preservation League of New York State. Newsletter (0882-7478)
Indexed: AIAP.
Published by: Preservation League of New York State, 44 Central Ave, Albany, NY 12206. TEL 518-462-5658, FAX 518-462-5684, plnys@worldnet.att.net, http://www.preserve.orglplnysl. Ed. Jonathan Walters. R&P Clark Strickland.

724 974.747 930.1 USA ISSN 0885-7326
PRESERVATION NOTES. Text in English. 1965. a. membership. adv. bk.rev. illus. back issues avail. **Document type:** *Newsletter.* **Description:** Reports on buildings and other sites on Long Island that have historic or cultural importance and are endangered or have been saved. Includes a houses for sale section.
Formerly: Preservation of Long Island Antiquities; Incorporates: Society for the Preservation of Long Island Antiquities. Newsletter (0583-9181)
Indexed: AIAP.
Published by: Society for the Preservation of Long Island Antiquities, PO Box 148, Cold Springs Harbor, NY 11724. TEL 516-692-4664, FAX 516-692-5265, splia@aol.com. Ed. Barbara Ferris Van Liew. Circ: 1,800 (controlled).

720 USA
PRESERVATION PERSPECTIVE. Text in English. 1981. q. looseleaf. USD 35 to individuals (effective 2005). adv. bk.rev. illus.; stat. back issues avail. **Document type:** *Newsletter, Consumer.* **Description:** Covers architecture and historic preservation in New Jersey.
Indexed: AIAP.
Published by: Preservation New Jersey, Inc., 18 W Lafayette St, Trenton, NJ 08608-2002. TEL 609-392-6409, FAX 609-392-6418, info@preservationnj.org, http://www.preservationnj.org. Circ: 3,000 (controlled).

920 USA ISSN 0478-1392
NA1
PRESERVATION PROGRESS (CHARLESTON). Text in English. 1956. q. USD 30 to members. adv. bk.rev. illus. back issues avail. **Document type:** *Newsletter.*
Indexed: HistAb.
Published by: Preservation Society of Charleston, PO Box 521, Charleston, SC 29402. TEL 843-722-4630. Ed. Leigh Allen Murphy. R&P Leigh Murphy. Adv. contact Susan Spearman. B&W page USD 350. Circ: 2,500.

PRESIDENTIAL DESIGN AWARDS. see *ART*

720 GBR
PRINCE OF WALES'S INSTITUTE OF ARCHITECTURE. NEWSLETTER. Text in English. 2/yr. **Document type:** *Newsletter.*
Published by: Prince of Wales's Institute of Architecture, The Prince Of Wales' Institute Of Architecture, 14 Gloucester Gate, Regent's Park, London, NW1 4HG, United Kingdom. TEL 44-20-7916-7380, FAX 44-20-7916-7381, nicks@nwspowia.demon.co.uk, http://www.cf.ac.uk/powia.

720 COL ISSN 0032-9150
NA875
PROA; urbanismo, arquitectura, industrias. Text in Spanish. 1946. irreg. USD 165 (effective 1998). adv. bk.rev. bibl.; charts; illus.; stat. cum.index.
Indexed: AIAP, API, IBR.
Published by: Ediciones Proa, Calle 40 no. 19-52, Bogota, CUND, Colombia. TEL 2456447, FAX 2877402. Ed. Lorenzo Fonseca. Circ: 15,000.

PRODESIGN. see *ART*

PROFESSIONAL LANDSCAPER. see *GARDENING AND HORTICULTURE*

PROFESSIONAL SERVICES MANAGEMENT JOURNAL. see *BUSINESS AND ECONOMICS—Management*

PROFESSIONS AND PROJECTS REGISTER. see *BUILDING AND CONSTRUCTION*

720 USA ISSN 0190-8766
NA53
PROFILE (ATLANTA); the directory of U.S. Architectural Design Firms. Text in English. 1978. a. USD 175 case bound ed.; USD 149 soft bound ed.. adv. **Document type:** *Directory.* **Description:** Provides information on architectural design firms, listing each by city and state, and indicating key staff and their roles, staff size and type, specific project types and services.
Published by: Construction Market Data, Inc., 4126 Pleasantdale Rd, Ste A8, Atlanta, GA 30340. TEL 800-949-0276, FAX 770-613-5978, profile@cmdonl.com. Ed., R&P Dorothy A DeGennaro. Pub. Robert G Rogers. adv.: color page USD 8,500. Circ: 18,000.

720 ITA ISSN 1594-8137
PROGETTARE (MILAN); architettura citta territorio. Text in Italian. 2001. bi-m. EUR 22 domestic (effective 2004). **Document type:** *Magazine, Trade.*
Published by: Tecniche Nuove SpA, Via Eritrea 21, Milan, MI 201, Italy. TEL 39-02-390901, FAX 39-02-7570364, progettare@tecnichenuove.com, info@tecnichenuove.com, http://www.tecnichenuove.com.

720 ITA ISSN 1590-7058
IL PROGETTO (ROME, 1998). Text in Multiple languages. 1998. q. **Document type:** *Journal, Trade.*
Related titles: Online - full text ed.
Published by: Mancosu Editore, Via Alfredo Fusco 71, Rome, 00136, Italy. TEL 39-06-351921, FAX 39-06-35409791, http://www.mancosueditore.it.

720 690 RUS ISSN 1385-2043
PROJECT RUSSIA/PROEKT ROSSIYA; journal on architecture, urbanism, design, technology. Text in Russian, English. 1996. q. RUR 360 domestic to individuals; RUR 720 domestic to institutions; USD 80 in North America (effective 2001). illus. back issues avail. **Document type:** *Journal, Academic/Scholarly.*
Published by: Izdatel'stvo A-Fond, 1-i Kazachii per 8, Moscow, 109017, Russian Federation. TEL 7-095-2323970, prorus@online.ru, project_russia@mtu-net.ru, http://www.prorus.ru. Ed. B Goldkhoorn. Adv. contact Olga Potapova. Circ: 5,000 (paid); 5,000 (controlled). **Dist. by:** East View Information Services, 3020 Harbor Ln. N., Minneapolis, MN 55447. TEL 763-550-0961, FAX 763-559-2931.

720 SVK ISSN 1335-2180
PROJEKT; revue slovenskej architektury. Text in Czech, Slovak; Summaries in English, French, German, Russian. 1959. 10/yr. USD 48 (effective 2000).
Indexed: AIAP, API, EIP.
Published by: (Zvaz Slovenskych Architektov/Socialist Academy of the Slovak Socialist Republic), Obzor, Spitalska 35, Bratislava, 81585, Slovakia. Circ: 5,500. **Dist. by:** Slovart G.T.G. s.r.o., Krupinska 4, PO Box 152, Bratislava 85299, Slovakia. TEL 421-2-63839472, FAX 421-2-63839485, http://www.slovart-gtg.sk.

711.4 HRV ISSN 1330-0652
NA4.5 CODEN: PORREV
PROSTOR. Text in Croatian. 1993. s-a. HRK 75 domestic; EUR 24 in Europe; EUR 27 elsewhere (effective 2004). **Document type:** *Journal, Academic/Scholarly.* **Description:** Publishes results of research in all fields of architecture and urban planning.
Indexed: AIAP, API, BHA, ForAb, RRTA, RefZh, SOPODA.
—BLDSC (6935.652500).
Published by: Sveuciliste u Zagrebu, Arhitektonski Fakultet, Kaciceva 26, Zagreb, 10000, Croatia. TEL 385-1-4561222, FAX 385-1-4828079, prostor@arhitekt.hr, http://www.arhitekt.hr/prostor. Ed. Zlatko Karac.

720 BGR
PROSTRANSTVOTO ARKHITEKTURA/SPACE ARCHITECTURE. Text in Bulgarian. 2000. a.
Published by: (Bulgarian Academy of Sciences, Center for Architectural Studies), Universitetsko Izdatelstvo Sv. Kliment Okhridski/Publishing House of the Sofia University St. Kliment Ohridski, 15 Tsar Osvoboditel Blvd., Sofia, 1504, Bulgaria. TEL 359-2-9792914.

720 ESP ISSN 1133-8849
QUADERNS D'ARQUITECTURA I URBANISME (CATALAN EDITION). Text in Catalan, French. 1944. q. EUR 100 (effective 2002). adv. bk.rev. illus. index. **Description:** Profiles local, national, and international architectural works, accompanied by critical reflections.
Supersedes in part (in 1985): Quaderns d'Arquitectura i Urbanisme (0211-9595); Which was formerly (until 1980): Cuadernos de Arquitectura y Urbanismo (0211-321X); (until 1970): Cuadernos de Arquitectura (0011-2364)
Related titles: Spanish ed.: Quaderns d'Arquitectura i Urbanisme (Spanish Edition). ISSN 1133-8857. EUR 100 (effective 2002).
Indexed: AIAP, API, AmH&L, BHA, HistAb, IECT, RILM.
—BLDSC (7167.500000), CINDOC, IE, ingenta. **CCC.**
Published by: Colegio de Arquitectos de Cataluna/Col.legi d'Arquitectes de Catalunya, Placa Nova 5, Barcelona, 08002, Spain. TEL 34-93-3067814, FAX 34-93-4120068, quaderns@coac.es, http://quaderns.coac.net. Eds. Ivan Bercedo, Jorge Mestre. Adv. contact Robert Guinart. Circ: 10,000. **Subscr. to:** Editorial Gustavo Gili, S.A.. pedidos@ggili.com.

720 975 USA
QUAPAW QUARTER CHRONICLE. Text in English. 1974. bi-m. USD 10 to non-members. adv. bk.rev. charts; illus.
Published by: Quapaw Quarter Association, PO Box 165023, Little Rock, AR 72216. Circ: 15,000.

721 AUS ISSN 1832-8237
▼ ➤ **QUARTERLY ARCHITECTURE ESSAY.** Text in English. 2005. 4/yr. USD 39 per issue to individuals; USD 199 to institutions (effective 2005). **Document type:** *Journal, Academic/Scholarly.* **Description:** Addresses in-depth a particular, specific and contemporarily relevant topical theme on, or contributing to, architecture theory.
Media: Online - full content.
Published by: Scorched Ink Pty Ltd, 163/19 Tusculum St, Potts Point, NSW 2011, Australia. TEL 61-404-261282, FAX 61-2-93802211, info@haecceityinc.com, http://www.haecceityinc.com. Ed., R&P, Adv. contact Daniel Pavlovits.

720 ESP ISSN 1138-5596
R A. REVISTA DE ARQUITECTURA. Text in Spanish. 1997. a. back issues avail.
Related titles: Online - full text ed.; ♦ Supplement(s): Revista de Edificacion. ISSN 0213-8948.
—CINDOC.
Published by: Ediciones Universidad de Navarra S.A., Pza. Los Sauces, 1-2, Baranain, (Navarra) 31010, Spain. TEL 34-948-256850, http://www.unav.es/arquitectura/textos/ra.html.

720 GBR ISSN 0269-0829
R I B A DIRECTORY OF MEMBERS (YEAR). Text in English. a. GBP 52.50. **Document type:** *Directory.*
Published by: (Royal Institute of British Architects), R I B A Publications, Finsbury Mission, 39 Moreland St, London, EC1V 8BB, United Kingdom. TEL 44-20-7251-0791, FAX 44-20-7608-2375.

720 GBR ISSN 0269-0810
R I B A DIRECTORY OF PRACTICES. Text in English. a. GBP 52.50. **Document type:** *Directory.*
Former titles: Architects; R I B A Directory of Practices
—**CCC.**
Published by: (Royal Institute of British Architects), R I B A Publications, Finsbury Mission, 39 Moreland St, London, EC1V 8BB, United Kingdom. TEL 44-20-7251-0791, FAX 44-20-7608-2375.

720 GBR
R I B A DRAWINGS MONOGRAPHS. Text in English. irreg., latest vol.3, 1996.
—BLDSC (7963.682100).
Published by: (Royal Institute of British Architects), Academy Group Ltd., Academy Editions (Subsidiary of: V C H Publishing Group), 42 Leinster Gardens, London, W2 3AN, United Kingdom. Ed. Jill Lever. **U.S. dist. by:** National Book Network Inc., 4720 Boston Way, Lanham, MD 20706.

720 GBR ISSN 1463-9505
NA12
R I B A JOURNAL. Text in English. 1893. m. GBP 70 domestic; EUR 196 in Europe; USD 201 elsewhere (effective 2003). adv. bk.rev. charts; illus.; stat. index. 110 p./no. 3 cols./p.; reprint service avail. from PQC. **Document type:** *Magazine, Trade.*
Incorporates (1986-2003): R I B A Interiors (0950-8910); Former titles (until 1993): Royal Institute of British Architects. Journal (0953-6973); (until 1987): Architect (0950-8902); R I B A Journal (0035-8932)
Related titles: Microform ed.: (from PQC); Online - full text ed.: (from Gale Group, IngentaConnect); ♦ Supplement(s): R I B A Interiors. ISSN 0950-8910.
Indexed: ADPA, AIAP, API, ArtHuCI, ArtInd, BAS, BHA, BldManAb, BrCerAb, BrHumI, BrRB, BrTechI, CurCont, DAAI, EIP, HECAB, RASB, RICS.
—BLDSC (7963.700000), CISTI, IE, ingenta, Linda Hall. **CCC.**
Published by: (Royal Institute of British Architects), Builder Group plc., Exchange Tower, 2 Harbour Exchange Sq, London, E14 9GE, United Kingdom. TEL 44-20-7560-4000, FAX 44-20-7560-4404, http://www.riba.org/riba/advice2.htm. Ed. Amanda Baillieu. Pub. Tony Arnold. Adv. contact Russell Brooks TEL 44-20-7560-4032. Circ: 24,180. **Subscr. to:** Tower Publishing, Lathkill St, Tower House, Sovereign Park, Market Harborough, Leics LE16 9EF, United Kingdom.

721 GBR ISSN 0265-8739
R I B A PRODUCT SELECTOR. Text in English. 1982. a. (in 2 vols.). GBP 40 (effective 2001). adv. 1920 p./no. 4 cols./p.; **Document type:** *Directory.* **Description:** Contains directory of products and suppliers within the UK construction industry.
Related titles: CD-ROM ed.: Product Selector - Plus. ISSN 1363-836X. 1995. GBP 40 (effective 2001).
—**CCC.**

Published by: (Royal Institute of British Architects), R I B A Information Services, 1-3 Dufferin St, London, EC1Y 8NA, United Kingdom. TEL 44-20-7496-8383, FAX 44-20-7374-8200, greenbook@ris.gb.com, http://www.productselector.co.uk, http://www.ris.gb.com. Ed. Sue Quirk. Adv. contact Karen Ball TEL 44-20-7251-7158. Circ: 19,780 (free).

RAKENNUSTAITO/FINNISH CONSTRUCTION MAGAZINE. see *BUILDING AND CONSTRUCTION*

720 ITA ISSN 0392-8608
RASSEGNA DI ARCHITETTURA E URBANISTICA. Text in Italian. 1964. 3/yr. illus. index, cum.index. **Document type:** *Magazine, Trade.* **Description:** Contains studies on urban architecture, giving detailed photos and models for each work.
Formerly (until 1980): Istituto di Architettura e Urbanistica. Rassegna (0021-2458)
Indexed: AIAP, BHA.
Published by: (Universita degli Studi di Roma), Edizioni Kappa, Via Silvio Benco 2, Rome, 00177, Italy. TEL 39-06-273903, FAX 39-06-2147053, edizionikappa@edizionikappa.com, http://www.edizionikappa.com. Ed. Federico Gorio. Circ: 1,500.
Co-sponsor: Istituto di Architettura di Edilizie e di Tecnica Urbanistica.

RASSEGNA TECNICA DEL FRIULI VENEZIA GIULIA. see *ENGINEERING—Civil Engineering*

720 ESP
RATLLES. Text in Spanish. 3/yr.
Published by: Colegio Oficial de Delineantes de Barcelona/Barcelona College of Draftsmen, Mallorca, 257, 2o 2a, Barcelona, 08008, Spain. TEL 3-215-06-66, FAX 3-215-92-49. Ed. Jose M de las Heras. Circ: 10,000.

RAUM UND WOHNEN. see *INTERIOR DESIGN AND DECORATION*

723 946 ESP ISSN 0486-0993
N7101
REALES SITIOS. Text in Spanish. 1964. q. EUR 16.83 domestic; EUR 33.66 foreign (effective 2004). 80 p./no.; **Document type:** *Magazine, Academic/Scholarly.* **Description:** Devoted to the diffusion of news and analysis about the historical and artistic value of Spain's national heritage.
Indexed: ABM, AIAP, BHA, RILM.
—CINDOC.
Published by: Patrimonio Nacional, Palacio Real de Madrid, Bailen s/n, Madrid, 28071, Spain. TEL 34-91-4548700, FAX 34-91-4548841, manuel.gonzalez@patrimonionacional.es, http://www.patrimonionacional.es. Ed. Rosario Diez del Corral. Adv. contact Jose Maria Rodriguez. **Dist. by:** Asociacion de Revistas Culturales de Espana, Hortaleza, 75, Madrid 28004, Spain. TEL 34-91-3086066, FAX 34-91-3199267, info@arce.es, http://www.arce.es.

720 USA ISSN 0277-6219
RECORD INTERIORS. Text in English. 1981. a.
Indexed: AIAP.
Published by: Mcgraw-Hill Construction Dodge (Subsidiary of: McGraw-Hill Construction Information Group), News 2 Penn Plaza 10th Fl, New York, NY 10121. FAX 212-904-2335.

720 USA ISSN 1550-8315
▼ **REFERENCE GUIDES TO NATIONAL ARCHITECTURE.** Text in English. 2004. irreg. price varies. **Document type:** *Monographic series.*
Published by: Greenwood Publishing Group Inc. (Subsidiary of: Harcourt International), 88 Post Rd W, PO Box 5007, Westport, CT 06881. TEL 203-226-3571, 800-225-5800, FAX 603-431-2214, info@greenwoodpublishing.com, http://www.greenwood.com.

REFURBISHMENT PROJECTS. see *BUILDING AND CONSTRUCTION*

720 ITA ISSN 1121-0745
NA1111
REGGIO CALABRIA. DIPARTIMENTO PATRIMONIO ARCHITETTONICO E URBANISTICO. RIVISTA SEMESTRALE. Key Title: Rivista Semestrale del Dipartimento P A U. Cover title: Quaderni P A U. Text in Italian. 1991. s-a. EUR 20.66 domestic (effective 2004). abstr.; bibl.; charts; illus.; maps; stat. index. back issues avail. **Description:** Contains essays on the history of architecture, restoration, anthropology, economy, and human sciences.
Published by: (Calabria. Dipartimento Architettonico e Urbanistico di Reggio Calabria), Gangemi Editore, Piazza San Pantaleo 4, Rome, Italy. TEL 39-06-6872774, FAX 39-06-68806189, gangemieditorerc@tin.it, http://www.gangemieditore.it. Circ: 2,000.

720 GBR ISSN 0306-6967
REGISTER OF ARCHITECTS. Text in English. 1932. a. GBP 50 (effective 2000). **Document type:** *Directory.* **Description:** Serves as a directory of all qualified architects.
Related titles: Diskette ed.: GBP 1,200 (effective 2000).
Published by: Architects Registration Board, 8 Weymouth St, London, W1N 3FB, United Kingdom. TEL 44-20-7580-5861, FAX 44-20-7436-5269, info@arb.org.uk. Circ: 31,000.

728 USA ISSN 1093-359X
NA7205
RESIDENTIAL ARCHITECT. Text in English. 1996. 9/yr. USD 39.95 domestic; USD 49.95 in Canada; USD 132.50 elsewhere; free to qualified personnel (effective 2005). adv. bk.rev. illus. back issues avail. **Document type:** *Magazine, Trade.* **Description:** Delivers editorial on marketing, presentation, products, technology, and business management for architects who design homes.
Related titles: Online - full text ed.: (from Florida Center for Library Automation, Gale Group).
Indexed: Archl.
Published by: Hanley-Wood, LLC (Subsidiary of: J.P. Morgan Chase & Co.), One Thomas Circle, NW, Ste 600, Washington, DC 20005-5701. TEL 202-452-0800, FAX 202-785-1974, cconroy@hanley-wood.com, tjackson@hanleywood.com, http://www.residentialarchitect.com, http://www.hanleywood.com. Ed. S Claire Conroy. Pub. Michael Boyle. Circ: 22,010 (paid).

RESTAURACION HOY. see *ART*

RESTAURACION Y REHABILITACION. see *ART*

720.968 ZAF ISSN 0037-5462
➤ **RESTORICA.** Text in Afrikaans, English. 1960. a. ZAR 25 (effective 1995). adv. bk.rev. illus. **Document type:** *Academic/Scholarly.* **Description:** Preservation and restoration of historical buildings.
Supersedes: Simon van der Stel Foundation. Bulletin
Indexed: ISAP.
Published by: Simon van der Stel Foundation, PO Box 12293, Centrahil, Port Elizabeth 6006, South Africa. TEL 27-41-562849, FAX 27-41-562849. Eds. Albrecht Herholdt, Trudie Wegner. Circ: 3,500.

➤ **RETAIL CONSTRUCTION;** the journal for architecture, design, construction and facilities operation. see *BUILDING AND CONSTRUCTION*

720 ESP
REVISTA BALEAR D'ARQUITECTURA. Text in Spanish. 3/yr. **Description:** Covers architecture, urbanism, interior design and decoration, garden and landscape architecture.
Address: Portella, 14, Palma De Mallorca, Baleares 07001, Spain. TEL 71-72-77-59, FAX 71-72-04-63. Ed. Martin Lucena.

720 ARG ISSN 0327-330X
NA830
REVISTA DE ARQUITECTURA. Text in Spanish. 1904. bi-m. USD 60. adv. illus. **Description:** Covers housing and urban planning, professional meetings, competitions, plans and designs.
Former titles (until 1986): Sociedad Central de Arquitectos. Boletin - Architectural Society Review; (until 1955): Revista de Arquitectura
Indexed: AIAP.
Published by: Sociedad Central de Arquitectos, Montevideo, 938, Capital Federal, Buenos Aires 1019, Argentina. TEL 54-114-8123644, FAX 54-114-9535508. Ed. Ernesto A Grossi. Circ: 8,500 (paid); 8,000 (controlled).

720 ESP ISSN 0213-8948
TH4
REVISTA DE EDIFICACION. Text in Spanish. 1987. 4/yr.
Related titles: Online - full text ed.: (from EBSCO Publishing); ♦ Supplement to: R A. Revista de Arquitectura. ISSN 1138-5596.
Indexed: IECT.
—CINDOC.
Published by: (Escuela Tecnica Superior de Arquitectura, Universidad de Navarra), Universidad de Navarra, Servicio de Publicaciones, Apartado 177, Pamplona, Navarra 31080, Spain. TEL 48-25-2700. Ed. Antonio Garcia Valcarce.

720 COL ISSN 0122-5057
REVISTA E M A; investigacion e innovacion en educacion matematica. Text in Spanish. 1995. 3/yr. **Description:** Focuses on various aspects of architecture for professionals and academics in the field.
Published by: Universidad de los Andes, Carrera 1a, No. 18 A-70, Apartado Aereo 4976, Santafe de Bogota, CUND, Colombia.

REVISTA S A I. see *ENGINEERING*

720 ITA ISSN 1724-6768
▼ **RI - VISTA. RICERCHE PER LA PROGETTAZIONE DEL PAESAGGIO.** Text in Italian. 2003. s-a. free (effective 2005). **Document type:** *Journal, Academic/Scholarly.*
Media: Online - full text.
Published by: Firenze University Press, Borgo Albizi 28, Florence, 50122, Italy. TEL 39-055-2347658, FAX 39-055-242944, e-press@unifi.it, http://www.unifi.it/ri-vista, http://epress.unifi.periodici.it.

721 ITA ISSN 1123-9263
RICERCA E PROGETTO. Text in Italian. 1993. s-a. EUR 18.60 domestic (effective 2004). **Document type:** *Journal, Academic/Scholarly.*

Published by: (Universita degli Sudi di Roma "La Sapienza", Facolta di Architettura), Gangemi Editore, Piazza San Pantaleo 4, Rome, Italy. TEL 39-06-6872774, FAX 39-06-68806189, gangemieditorerc@tin.it, http://www.gangemieditore.it. Ed. Barbara Cacciapuoti.

RIVISTA DI STUDI LIGURI/REVUE D'ETUDES LIGURES. see *HISTORY—History Of Europe*

ROCZNIK HISTORII SZTUKI. see *ART*

ROOFING CONTRACTOR. see *BUILDING AND CONSTRUCTION*

720 GBR
ROYAL SOCIETY OF ULSTER ARCHITECTS. YEARBOOK AND DIRECTORY. Text in English. 1922. a. free to qualified personnel. adv. back issues avail. **Description:** Reviews the year's buildings, information on RSUA registered practices, planning consultants, landscape architects, consultant engineers, chartered quantity surveyors, developers, and government in Northern Ireland.
Formerly: Royal Society of Ulster Architects. Year Book (0080-472X)
Published by: (Royal Society of Ulster Architects), Adleader Publications, Marlborough House, 348 Lisburn Rd, Belfast, BT9 6GH, United Kingdom. TEL 44-1232-661666, FAX 44-1232-681888, adleader@dial.pipex.com. Ed., R&P Alan Mairs. Adv. contact Sinead Balmer. B&W page GBP 525, color page GBP 695. Circ: 4,000.

720 USA ISSN 0898-4948
S A R A SCOPE. Text in English. 1987. bi-m. adv. bk.rev. back issues avail. **Document type:** *Newsletter.* **Description:** Covers society operations, including national, state and chapter news.
Indexed: BioCN&I.
Published by: Society of American Registered Architects, 1411 London Rd, Duluth, MN 55805. TEL 218-728-4293, FAX 218-728-5361, SARA@protonet.com, http://www.protonet.com/SARA. Ed. Raymond J Blesener. Circ: 500 (controlled).

720 SGP ISSN 0217-7668
S I A YEARBOOK✶. (Singapore Institute of Architects) Text in English. 1967. a. SGD 35. adv.
Published by: Singapore Institute of Architects, Publications Board, 20 Orchard Rd, 02-00 SMA House, Singapore, 238830, Singapore. TEL 3388977, FAX 3368708. Circ: 1,700.

720 GBR ISSN 0969-4250
S P A B NEWS. Text in English. 1980. q. GBP 24 in United Kingdom; GBP 32 elsewhere (effective 2000). adv. bk.rev.; video rev. back issues avail. **Document type:** *Newsletter.* **Description:** Reviews and discusses current issues in architectural conservation, both practical and theoretical.
Indexed: API.
Published by: Society for the Protection of Ancient Buildings, 37 Spital Sq, London, E1 6DY, United Kingdom. TEL 44-20-7377-1644, FAX 44-20-7247-5296, info@spab.org.uk, http://www.spab.org.uk. Ed. Philip Venning. R&P Laura Gibbon. Adv. contact Tony Sudweeks. B&W page GBP 530; trim 210 x 300. Circ: 7,000 (paid). **Dist. by:** 21 Farley Hill, Luton, Beds LU1 5EE, United Kingdom.

720 974 USA ISSN 1061-818X
S P N E A'S HISTORIC HOUSES IN NEW ENGLAND. Text in English. a. free. **Description:** Lists historic house museums in New England owned by the society and open to the public.
Formerly: Historic Houses in New England
Published by: Society for the Preservation of New England Antiquities, 141 Cambridge St, Boston, MA 02114. TEL 617-227-3956.

S S C R JOURNAL; promotes the conservation and restoration of historic and artistic objects. see *ART*

690 CHE
S W B - INFORMATION. Text in German. 1984. 4/yr. bk.rev. **Document type:** *Journal, Trade.*
Formerly: Werkbund Material
Published by: Schweizerischer Werkbund, Limmatstr 118, Zuerich, 8031, Switzerland. TEL 41-1-2727176, FAX 41-1-2727506, swb@werkbund.ch, http://www.werkbund.ch.

SAN DIEGO HOME - GARDEN LIFESTYLES. see *INTERIOR DESIGN AND DECORATION*

SANKT-PETERBURGSKAYA PANORAMA. see *BUILDING AND CONSTRUCTION*

SASKATCHEWAN. DEPARTMENT OF CULTURE AND RECREATION. ANNUAL REPORT. see *ART*

720 620 CHE ISSN 0251-0960
TA4 CODEN: IASUD5
SCHWEIZER INGENIEUR UND ARCHITEKT/INGEGNERI E ARCHITETTI SVIZZERI/INGENIEURS ET ARCHITECTES SUISSES; Schweizerische bauzeitung - bulletin technique de la Suisse romande. Text in German. 1883. w. CHF 235 (effective 1999). adv. bk.rev. bibl.; charts; illus. index. **Document type:** *Academic/Scholarly.*

Formerly: Schweizerische Bauzeitung (0036-7524)
Indexed: ApMecR, CISA, ChemAb, DokStr, EnglInd, ExcerpMed, GeotechAb, ICEA, Inspec, RefZh, SoftAbEng.
—CISTI, Linda Hall.
Published by: (Schweizerischer Ingenieur- und Architektenverein/Societe Suisse des Ingenieurs et des Architectes), Verlag der Akademischen Technischen Vereine, Ruedigerstr 11, Postfach, Zuerich, 8021, Switzerland. TEL 41-1-2889060, FAX 41-1-2889070, si_a@swissonline.ch. Eds. Inge Beckel, Martin Grether. Circ: 10,222. **Co-sponsor:** Gesellschaft Ehemaliger Studierender der ETH Zurich, Schweizerische Vereinigung Beratender Ingenieure.

720 CHE ISSN 0036-7370
AP32
SCHWEIZER JOURNAL. Text in German. 1957. m. CHF 215. adv. bk.rev. charts; illus. index.
Indexed: ELLIS, ExcerpMed.
Published by: Meuli & Masueger Media GmbH, Albisriederstr 80A, Zurich, 8003, Switzerland. TEL 41-1-4917188, FAX 41-1-4931176. Ed. Dr. Hans Frey.

SCHWEIZER KUNST/ART SUISSE/ARTE SVIZZERA. see *ART*

720 GBR ISSN 0966-1026
SCROOPE. Text in English. 1989. a. GBP 10 domestic; GBP 12 foreign; GBP 8 to students (effective 2004). back issues avail.
Indexed: AIAP.
Address: University of Cambridge, Faculty of Architecture, 1 Scroope Terrace, Cambridge, CB2 1PX, United Kingdom. TEL 44-1223-332950, FAX 44-1223-332960, arct-info@lists.cam.ac.uk.

SEATTLE HOMES AND LIFESTYLES. see *LIFESTYLE*

720 ESP ISSN 0213-6724
SECUENCIAS DE ARQUITECTURA Y CONSTRUCCION. Key Title: Secuencias. Text in Spanish. 1986. irreg.
—CINDOC.
Published by: Secuencias, Monserrat, 18, Madrid, 28015, Spain. TEL 34-91-5410773. Ed. A Fontes.

SEMINARIO DE ESTUDIOS DE ARTE Y ARQUEOLOGIA. BOLETIN. see *ART*

720 620 CHN ISSN 1003-5990
SHANDONG JIANZHU GONGCHENG XUEYUAN XUEBAO/SHANDONG ARCHITECTURAL AND CIVIL ENGINEERING INSTITUTE. JOURNAL. Text in Chinese. 1986. q. **Document type:** *Journal, Academic/Scholarly.*
Related titles: Online - full text ed.: (from East View Information Services).
—BLDSC (8254.588515).
Published by: Shandong Jianzhu Gongcheng Xueyuan/Shandong Architectural and Civil Engineering Institute, 47 Heping Rd., Jinan, 250014, China. TEL 86-531-6367365, xuebao@sdai.edu.cn. Ed. Zhaohong Fang.

720 690 CHN ISSN 1002-8498
TH4 CODEN: SJSHE4
➤ **SHIGONG JISHU/CONSTRUCTION TECHNOLOGY.** Text in Chinese; Summaries in Chinese, English. 1971. m. CNY 6.50 per issue (effective 2001). adv. bk.rev. abstr.; charts; illus.; pat.; stat. 120 p./no.; back issues avail. **Document type:** *Academic/Scholarly.* **Description:** Covers the latest developments in the field of building and construction as well as relevant policies and regulations.
Related titles: CD-ROM ed.; E-mail ed.; Fax ed.; Online - full text ed.: (from East View Information Services).
Indexed: INIS AtomInd.
Published by: Zhongguo Jianzhu Gongye Chubanshe, c/o Shigong Jishu Bianjibu, Xishimenwai, 19 Chegongzhuang Dajie, Beijing, 100044, China. TEL 86-10-6839-3529, FAX 86-10-6830061, shigong@public.fhnet.cn.net. Ed. Fang Yueying. Adv. contact Ge Li. page CNY 8,000; 210 x 285. Circ: 50,000. **Dist. overseas by:** China International Book Trading Corp, 35 Chegongzhuang Xilu, Haidian District, PO Box 399, Beijing 100044, China. TEL 86-10-68412045, FAX 86-10-68412023, cibtc@mail.cibtc.com.cn, http://www.cibtc.com.cn.

721 CHN ISSN 1000-8373
SHIJIE JIANZHU DAOBAO/WORLD ARCHITECTURE HERALD. Text in Chinese. q.
Related titles: Online - full text ed.: (from East View Information Services).
Published by: Shenzhen Shiwei, Xuanchuan Shiye Fazhan Jijinhui, B-23-6, Nanyang Dasha, Shenzhen, Guangdong 518000, China. TEL 223401. Ed. Zhang Liangjun.

720 JPN ISSN 1342-5447
NA6
SHINKENCHIKU. Text in Japanese. 1925. m. JPY 24,000 domestic; JPY 37,000 foreign (effective 2003). adv. bk.rev.; Website rev. back issues avail. **Document type:** *Magazine, Academic/Scholarly.* **Description:** Provides monthly review of top-level Japanese architecture, mostly featuring the newest pieces of works.
Indexed: AIAP.
—BLDSC (8256.800700).
Published by: Shinkenchiku-sha Co. Ltd./Japan Architect Co., Ltd., 2-31-2 Yushima, Bunkyo-ku, Tokyo, 113-0034, Japan. TEL 81-3-38162635, FAX 81-3-38162937, shinkenchiku@japan-architect.co.jp, http://www.japan-architect.co.jp. Ed. Yasuhiro Teramatsu. Pub. Nobuyuki Yoshida. R&P Ryugo Maru TEL 81-3-3816-2532. Adv. contact Yukinobu Takizawa TEL 81-3-38117109. B&W page JPY 340,000, color page JPY 660,000; trim 297 x 221. Circ: 87,000.

720 JPN
SHOTEN KENCHIKU/COMMERCIAL ARCHITECTURE. Text in Japanese. m. adv. **Description:** Covers architects and shop designers specializing in retail stores and restaurants.
Published by: Shoten Kenchiku Sha Co. Ltd., 7-22-36 Nishi-Shinjuku, Shinjuku-ku, Tokyo, 160-0023, Japan. TEL 81-3-3363-5760, FAX 81-3-3363-5751. Adv. contact Hiroyuki Endo. Circ: 60,000.

720 CHN ISSN 1007-8983
SICHUAN JIANZHU/SICHUAN ARCHITECTURE. Text in Chinese. 1981. q. CNY 3 newsstand/cover. **Document type:** *Academic/Scholarly.*
Related titles: Online - full text ed.: (from East View Information Services).
Published by: (Sichuan Tumu Jianzhu Xuehui/Sichuan Society of Civil Engineering and Architecture), Sichuan Jianzhu Zazhishe, 95, Jiefang Lu 2 Duan, Chengdu, Sichuan 610081, China. TEL 3332322. Ed. Tian Yingju. **Co-sponsor:** Sichuan Jianzhu Gongcheng Gongsi.

720 SGP ISSN 0218-7728
NA1
SINGAPORE ARCHITECT. Text in English. 1966. q. SGD 65. adv. bk.rev. charts; illus. **Document type:** *Trade.*
Formerly (until 1994): S I A J - Singapore Institute of Architects. Journal (0049-0520)
Indexed: API.
Published by: Singapore Institute of Architects, Publications Board, 20 Orchard Rd, 02-00 SMA House, Singapore, 238830, Singapore. TEL 65-226-2668. Ed. Robert Powell. Adv. contact Graeme Burnett. B&W page SGD 600, color page SGD 1,200. Circ: 1,400.

SINGAPORE SOURCE BOOK FOR ARCHITECTS & DESIGNERS. see *BUILDING AND CONSTRUCTION*

SITE RECORDER; for all invloved in site inspections. see *BUILDING AND CONSTRUCTION*

SITES ET MONUMENTS. see *ARCHAEOLOGY*

SOCIETA DEGLI INGEGNERI E DEGLI ARCHITETTI IN TORINO. ATTI E RASSEGNA TECNICA. see *ENGINEERING—Civil Engineering*

720 FRA
SOCIETE FRANCAISE DES ARCHITECTES. BULLETIN. Text in French. q.
Published by: Societe Francaise des Architectes, 247 Rue Saint Jacques, Paris, 75005, France. TEL 33-1-56811025, FAX 33-1-56811026, http://www.sfarchi.org. Circ: 650 (controlled).

973.9 306 USA
SOCIETY FOR COMMERCIAL ARCHEOLOGY. JOURNAL. Text in English. 1977. s-a. free to members. **Document type:** *Academic/Scholarly.* **Description:** Covers roadside and commercial architecture as well as the legacy of the automobile in America.
Supersedes in part (in 1993): Society for Commercial Archeology. News Journal (0735-1399)
Indexed: AIAP.
Published by: Society for Commercial Archeology, c/o Department of Popular Culture, Bowling Green State University, Bowling Green, OH 43403. TEL 419-372-2136, sca_asst@hotmail.com, http://www.sca-roadside.org. Ed. Robert Hadlow. R&P Dan Hershberger TEL 406-994-6904. Circ: 775 (paid).

973.9 306 USA ISSN 1069-0492
SOCIETY FOR COMMERCIAL ARCHEOLOGY. NEWS. Text in English. 1977. q. free to members. bk.rev. back issues avail. **Document type:** *Newsletter.* **Description:** Covers roadside and commercial architecture, as well as the legacy of the automobile in America.
Supersedes in part (in 1993): Society for Commercial Archeology. News Journal (0735-1399)
Indexed: AIAP.
Published by: Society for Commercial Archeology, c/o Department of Popular Culture, Bowling Green State University, Bowling Green, OH 43403. TEL 419-372-2136, sca_asst@hotmail.com, http://www.sca-roadside.org. Ed. Todd Swormstedt. R&P Dan Hershberger TEL 406-994-6904. Circ: 950 (paid).

720 CAN ISSN 1486-0872
➤ **SOCIETY FOR THE STUDY OF ARCHITECTURE IN CANADA. JOURNAL/SOCIETE POUR L'ETUDE DE L'ARCHITECTURE AU CANADA. JOURNAL.** Text in English, French. 1975. q. CND 40, USD 45 to individuals; CND 65, USD 70 to institutions. bk.rev. charts; illus. cum.index: 1980-1989; 1990-1994. back issues avail. **Document type:** *Proceedings, Academic/Scholarly.* **Description:** Covers the examination of the role of the built environment in Canadian society.
Supersedes (in 1998, vol.23): Society for the Study of Architecture in Canada. Bulletin (0228-0744)
Indexed: AIAP.
Published by: Society for the Study of Architecture in Canada/Societe pour l'Etude de l'Architecture au Canada, P O BOX 2302, Sta D, Ottawa, ON K1P 5W5, Canada. Ed. Gordon W Fulton. Circ: 500 (paid).

720 USA ISSN 0037-9808
NA1
➤ **SOCIETY OF ARCHITECTURAL HISTORIANS. JOURNAL.** Text in English. 1940. q. free to members. adv. bk.rev. illus. index. back issues avail.; reprint service avail. from PQC,ISI. **Document type:** *Journal, Academic/Scholarly.*
Formerly: American Society of Architectural Historians. Journal (1544-9890)
Related titles: Microform ed.: (from PQC); Online - full text ed.: (from H.W. Wilson, JSTOR (Web-based Journal Archive), O C L C Online Computer Library Center, Inc.).
Indexed: ABS&EES, AIAP, API, ASCA, AmH&L, ArtHuCI, ArtInd, BAS, BHA, BrArAb, CurCont, GardL, HistAb, IBRH, MEA&I, NumL, PCI, RASB, RILM.
—BLDSC (4880.770000), IDS, IE, Infotrieve, ingenta.
Published by: Society of Architectural Historians, 1365 North Astor St, Chicago, IL 60610-2144. TEL 312-573-1365, FAX 312-573-1141, http://www.sah.org. Ed. Zeynep Celik. Adv. contact Helen Tangires. Circ: 4,000.

720 USA ISSN 0049-1195
SOCIETY OF ARCHITECTURAL HISTORIANS. NEWSLETTER. Text in English. 1957. bi-m. USD 115 to individual members includes subscr. to the Journal of the Society of Architectural Historians; USD 250 to institutional members includes subscr. to the Journal of the Society of Architectural Historians (effective 2005). adv. bibl.; illus. reprint service avail. from PQC,ISI. **Document type:** *Newsletter, Trade.* **Description:** Keeps readers informed about upcoming SAH events, conferences, tours, grants and fellowship opportunities, awards, career postings, publications, and exhibitions.
Indexed: ABS&EES, AIAP, BHA, BibInd, RASB.
—BLDSC (6108.342900), CISTI.
Published by: Society of Architectural Historians, 1365 North Astor St, Chicago, IL 60610-2144. TEL 312-573-1365, FAX 312-573-1141, psaliga@sah.org, info@sah.org, http://www.sah.org/index.php?module=ContentExpress&func=display&btitle=CE&mid=&ceid=52. Eds. Mark Hewitt, Roberta Moudry. Adv. contact Billie Gibson. B&W page USD 500. Circ: 4,000 (paid and controlled).

720 942 GBR
SOCIETY OF ARCHITECTURAL HISTORIANS OF GREAT BRITAIN. NEWSLETTER. Text in English. 1968. s-a. GBP 25; GBP 32 overseas; includes subscr. to Architectural History. bk.rev. bibl. **Document type:** *Newsletter.*
Indexed: AIAP, BHA.
—BLDSC (6107.658000).
Published by: Society of Architectural Historians of Great Britain, Brandon Mead, Old Park Ln, Farnham, Surrey GU9 0AJ, United Kingdom. Circ: 1,150.

720.942 GBR
SOCIETY OF ARCHITECTURAL HISTORIANS OF GREAT BRITAIN. OCCASIONAL PAPER. Text in English. irreg. price varies. **Document type:** *Monographic series.*
Published by: Society of Architectural Historians of Great Britain, Brandon Mead, Old Park Ln, Farnham, Surrey GU9 0AJ, United Kingdom.

720 651 USA
SOCIETY OF DESIGN ADMINISTRATION. NATIONAL PUBLICATION. Text in English. q. USD 75 to non-members (effective 2000). adv. **Document type:** *Newsletter.* **Description:** For owners, managers and administrators in design firm offices.
Formerly (until 1995): Society of Architectural Administrators. News Journal
Published by: Society of Design Administration, c/o Penney De Pas, Executive Director, 4101 Lake Boone Trail, No 201, Raleigh, NC 27607. TEL 919-787-5181, http://www.sdadmin.org. Ed., R&P, Adv. contact Karen Roman TEL 303-738-8877.

SOPRINTENDENZA PER I BENI CULTURALI DELLA VALLE D'AOSTA. QUADERNI. see *ART*

724 333.33 ZAF ISSN 1015-888X
SOUTH AFRICAN HOME OWNER. Text in English. 1990. q. ZAR 242 (effective 1998). **Document type:** *Consumer.* **Description:** Covers practical aspects of renovating, decorating and improving a house, including features on architects' plans, noteworthy projects, gardening and other subjects.

Published by: Avonwold Publishing Co. (Pty) Ltd., Avonwold House, 24 Baker St, Rosebank, Johannesburg, 2196, South Africa. TEL 27-11-788-1610, FAX 27-11-880-2732. Ed. Gail van Zyl-Webber. Circ: 28,164.

720   SGP   ISSN 0218-9593
SOUTHEAST ASIAN ARCHITECTURE. JOURNAL. Text in English. 1996. a.
Indexed: AIAP.
Published by: National University of Singapore, The Department of Architecture, School of Design and Environment, 10 Kent Ridge Crescent, Singapore, 119260, Singapore. TEL 65-7723408, FAX 65-7793078, akijseaa@nus.sg, http://www.nus.edu.sg/#.

SOUTHERN GOLF - LANDSCAPE & RESORT MANAGEMENT. see *GARDENING AND HORTICULTURE*

728   USA   ISSN 1057-3429
NA7211
SOUTHERN LIVING HOUSE PLANS. Text in English. 1987. 3/yr. Included in subscription to Southern Living.. adv. **Document type:** *Magazine, Consumer.*
—CCC.
Published by: Southern Progress Corp. (Subsidiary of: Time Warner, Inc.), 2100 Lakeshore Dr, Birmingham, AL 35209. TEL 205-877-6000, FAX 205-877-6422. Ed. Sarah Jernigan. R&P Jason Burnett TEL 205-877-6731. adv.: page USD 13,430; trim 10.88 x 8.13. Circ: 400,000.

720 747   HKG
SPACE. Text in Chinese, English. 1988. m. HKD 420 domestic; USD 175 foreign; HKD 35 newsstand/cover (effective 2003). adv. bk.rev. 98 p./no.; back issues avail. **Document type:** *Magazine, Trade.* **Description:** Covers commercial interior and architectural design.
Formerly (until 1999): Pace Interior Architecture (1022-5609)
Related titles: E-mail ed.; Fax ed.
Indexed: HongKongiana.
Published by: Pace Publishing Ltd., 27th Fl, 128 Gloucester Rd, Wan Chai, Hong Kong, Hong Kong. TEL 852-2897-1688, FAX 852-2897-2888, pace@pacebase.com, http://www.pacebase.com/02/02.html. Ed. Evelyn Chan. Pub. George Lam. R&P, Adv. contact Olivia Ko TEL 852-2515-7626. color page HKD 11,000; trim 225 x 304. Circ: 25,900.

720   TWN
SPACE. Text in Chinese.
Media: Online - full content.
Published by: Space Magazine Publishing, Yuehli Rd, 45th Ln, no.5, 2nd Fl., Tapei, Taiwan. TEL 886-2-27375655, FAX 886-2-27375654, http://space.com.tw/.

720   KOR
SPACE/KONGGAN. Text in English, Korean. 1966. m. KRW 100,000 domestic; USD 181 in US & Canada (effective 2003). adv. bk.rev. 200 p./no.; **Document type:** *Magazine, Academic/Scholarly.* **Description:** Emphasizes contemporary architecture and art in evaluating Korea's past, present and future.
Published by: Space Group of Korea, 219 Wonseo dong, Chongro-gu, Seoul, 110280, Korea, S. TEL 822-747-2892, FAX 822-747-2894, TELEX SPACE-K-24572, vmspace@vmspace.com, http://www.vmspace.com. Eds. Cheon-Se Kim, Joo-Yeon Lee, Sang-Leem Lee. R&P Joo-Yeon Lee. adv.: page KRW 2,000,000; 280 x 290. Circ: 20,000.

SPACE & CULTURE; the journal. see *GEOGRAPHY*

SPON'S ARCHITECTS' & BUILDERS' PRICE BOOK. see *BUILDING AND CONSTRUCTION*

720   LKA
SRI LANKA ARCHITECT. Text in English. 1960. q. LKR 400; USD 48 in developing nations. adv. bk.rev.
Formerly: Sri Lanka Institute of Architects. Journal
Indexed: API.
Published by: Sri Lanka Institute of Architects, 120-10 Wijerama Mawatha, Colombo, 7, Sri Lanka. TEL 697109. Ed. Vidura Sri Nammuni. adv.: B&W page LKR 2,000, color page LKR 5,000. Circ: 1,000.

SRPSKA AKADEMIJA NAUKA I UMETNOSTI. ODELJENJE DRUSTVENIH NAUKA. SPOMENIK. see *SOCIAL SCIENCES: COMPREHENSIVE WORKS*

ST. LOUIS DESIGN MAGAZINE; art and architecture. see *INTERIOR DESIGN AND DECORATION*

725.804305   GBR
STADIA; the international review of sports venue design, operations & technology. Text in English. 5/yr. adv. **Document type:** *Magazine, Trade.* **Description:** Provides a forum to bring together the views and ideas of leading experts around the world in the area of sports venue design, operations and technology.

Published by: Broadcast Publishing Ltd., Phoenix Hse, 32 West St, Brighton, BN1 2RT, United Kingdom. TEL 44-1273-206222, FAX 44-1273-206205, info@stadia.co.uk, http://www.stadia.co.uk. adv.: color page GBP 2,950; trim 210 x 297.

725.804305   GBR   ISSN 1466-0776
STADIA WORLD; the annual guide to design and build of stadia and arenas. Text in English. 1998. a. GBP 55 domestic; GBP 60 foreign (effective 2000). **Document type:** *Journal, Trade.* **Description:** Reviews developments relating to all aspects of stadium and arena construction and management, from initial project concepts and renovation to day-to-day operations.
Published by: Alliance International Media Ltd., Unicorn House, 3 Plough Yard, London, EC2A 3PW, United Kingdom. TEL 44-20-7422-4200, FAX 44-20-7422-4300. **Subscr. to:** Johnson's International Media Services, 43 Millharbour, London E14 9TR, United Kingdom. TEL 44-20-7538-1164.

720   CZE   ISSN 1210-4825
STAVITEL. Text in Czech. 1992. m. CZK 720; CZK 60 newsstand/cover (effective 2003). adv. **Document type:** *Magazine, Trade.*
Published by: Economia a.s., Dobrovskeho 25, Prague 7 7, 170 55, Czech Republic. TEL 420-2-33071111, FAX 420-2-33072003, economia@economia.cz, http://www.economia.cz. Ed. Jitka Linhova. adv.: page CZK 89,000; trim 185 x 254.

STEDEBOUW EN ARCHITECTUUR. see *BUILDING AND CONSTRUCTION*

STEDEBOUW & RUIMTELIJKE ORDENING. see *HOUSING AND URBAN PLANNING*

720   CAN   ISSN 0712-9092
STEEL DESIGN/CONSTRUCTION METALLIQUE. Text in English. 1971. 2/yr. free to qualified personnel. **Document type:** *Newsletter.* **Description:** Describes the use of steel and steel products in contemporary architectural design.
Related titles: French ed.
Published by: Dofasco, Inc., 1330 Burlington St E, P O Box 2460, Hamilton, ON L8N 3J5, Canada. TEL 905-563-7965. Ed. W D Follis. R&P W.D. Follis. Circ: 24,731 (controlled).

STEN; the Scandinavian stone industries magazine. see *BUILDING AND CONSTRUCTION*

STEUER-BRIEF FUER ARCHITEKTEN UND INGENIEURE. see *ENGINEERING*

STONE & STEIN. see *BUILDING AND CONSTRUCTION*

720   ITA   ISSN 0390-4253
STORIA ARCHITETTURA; rivista di architettura e restauro. Text in Italian. 1982. a. price varies. **Document type:** *Journal, Academic/Scholarly.*
Indexed: AIAP, BHA.
Published by: (Universita Degli Studi Di Roma "La Sapienza", Istituto di Storia dell'Architettura), Bonsignori Editore s.r.l., Viale dei Quattro Venti 47, Rome, RM 00152, Italy. TEL 39-06-5881496, FAX 39-06-5882839.

727   ITA.
STORIA ARCHITETTURA. SAGGI. Text in Italian. irreg. price varies. **Document type:** *Monographic series, Academic/Scholarly.* **Description:** Covers archeological research and studies on restoration.
Published by: Bonsignori Editore s.r.l., Viale dei Quattro Venti 47, Rome, RM 00152, Italy. TEL 39-06-5881496, FAX 39-06-5882839. Eds. G Miarelli Mariani, S Benedetti.

724   USA
STREAMLINE. Text in English. 1987. q. USD 20 (effective 1998). adv. **Document type:** *Newsletter.* **Description:** Contains special events, preservation updates, stories.
Published by: Art Deco Society of the Palm Beaches, 325 S W 29th Ave, Delray Beach, FL 33445. TEL 561-276-9925, FAX 561-276-9925, sharon@flinet.com. Ed., Adv. contact Sharon Koskoff. Circ: 500.

720   RUS
STROITEL'NOE VEDOMOSTI; gazeta dlya stroitelei, proektirovshchikov, rabotnikov stroindustrii i zastroishchikov. Text in Russian. w. RUR 260 in Novosibirsk; RUR 340 elsewhere in Russia (effective 2002). **Document type:** *Newspaper, Consumer.*
Published by: Stroitel'nye Vedomosti, Ul Nemirovicha-Danchenko 165, ofis 313, Novosibirsk, 630087, Russian Federation. http://www.gazeta.sks.ru. Ed. Aleksandr Rusinov.

THE STRUCTURAL DESIGN OF TALL AND SPECIAL BUILDINGS. see *ENGINEERING—Civil Engineering*

727   ITA   ISSN 0390-4296
STRUMENTI. Text in Italian. 1973. irreg. price varies. **Document type:** *Monographic series, Academic/Scholarly.* **Description:** Covers research in the restoration of monuments and historical buildings.

Published by: (Universita degli Studi di Roma "La Sapienza", Scuola di Specializzazione per lo Studio e Restauro dei Monumenti, Universita degli Studi di Roma "La Sapienza"), Bonsignori Editore s.r.l., Viale dei Quattro Venti 47, Rome, RM 00152, Italy. TEL 39-06-5881496, FAX 39-06-5882839. Ed. Giovanni Carbonara.

720   ITA
STUDI E DOCUMENTI DI ARCHITETTURA. Text in Italian. 1973 (no.2). q. USD 8.
Supersedes: Universita degli Studi di Firenze. Istituto di Composizione Architettonica. Quaderni
Indexed: AIAP, API, BHA.
Published by: Universita degli Studi di Firenze, Istituto di Composizione Architettonica, Florence, FI, Italy.

711.4   POL   ISSN 0081-6566
STUDIA I MATERIALY DO TEORII I HISTORII ARCHITEKTURY I URBANISTYKI. Text in Polish; Summaries in English, Russian. 1959. irreg., latest vol.19, 1992. price varies.
Indexed: AIAP, BHA.
Published by: (Polska Akademia Nauk/Polish Academy of Sciences), Wydawnictwo Naukowe P W N SA/Polish Scientific Publishers P W N, ul Miodowa 10, Warsaw, 00251, Poland. TEL 48-22-6954321, FAX 48-22-6954288. **Dist. by:** Ars Polona, Krakowskie Przedmiescie 7, Warsaw, Poland.

STUDIES IN CISTERCIAN ART AND ARCHITECTURE. see *ART*

712   USA
STUDIES IN LANDSCAPE ARCHITECTURE. Text in English. irreg. price varies. **Document type:** *Monographic series.*
Published by: Dumbarton Oaks, 1703 32nd St, N W, Washington, DC 20007. TEL 202-339-6401, FAX 202-339-6419, Landscape@doaks.org, DumbartonOaks@doaks.org, http://www.doaks.org/publications.html.

STUDIES IN THE DECORATIVE ARTS. see *ART*

720   USA   ISSN 1060-8486
STUDIO WORKS. Text in English. 1994. a., latest vol.3, 1996. price varies. illus. back issues avail. **Document type:** *Academic/Scholarly.* **Description:** Showcase for recent work from the design studios of the Harvard University Graduate School of Design.
Indexed: AIAP.
Published by: (Harvard University, Graduate School of Design), Princeton Architectural Press, 37 E 7th St, New York, NY 10003. TEL 212-995-9620, FAX 212-995-9454, sales@pap.designsys.com, http://www.designsys.com/pap, http://www.papress.com/. **Dist by:** Chronicle Books, 85 2nd St., San Francisco, CA 94105-3459. TEL 800-722-6657.

720   ARG   ISSN 0325-4615
NA830
SUMMA✳ ; revista de arquitectura, tecnologia y diseno. Text in Spanish. 1963. m. USD 150. adv. bibl.; charts; illus. index.
Indexed: AIAP, API.
Published by: Ediciones Summa, Piso 7, Casilla Postal 689, Buenos Aires, 1068, Argentina. Ed. Alfredo J Schroeder. Circ: 10,000.

720   ARG   ISSN 0325-6448
SUMMARIOS✳ . Text in Spanish. 1976. 6/yr. USD 55.
Indexed: API.
Published by: Ediciones Summa, Piso 7, Casilla Postal 689, Buenos Aires, 1068, Argentina. Ed. Alfredo J Schroeder.

728   USA
SUNSET BEST SELLING HOME PLANS. Text in English. a. USD 4.99 newsstand/cover; USD 5.99 newsstand/cover in Canada (effective 2001). **Document type:** *Magazine, Consumer.*
Published by: Sunset Publishing Corp., 80 Willow Rd, Menlo Park, CA 94025-3691. TEL 650-321-3600, 800-777-0117, FAX 650-328-6215, openhouse@sunset.com, http://www.sunset.com/books/besthomeplans/bhp.html.

721   GBR   ISSN 0081-9751
SURVEY OF LONDON. Variant title: Survey of London Series. Text in English. 1900. irreg., latest vol.45, 2000. price varies. **Document type:** *Monographic series.* **Description:** Publishes architectural studies of London buildings in various sections of the city.
Indexed: BrArAb.
—CCC.
Published by: (Royal Commission on Historical Monuments), Athlone Press Ltd., 1 Park Dr, London, NW11 7SG, United Kingdom. TEL 44-20-8458-0888, FAX 44-20-8201-8115, athlonepress@btinternet.com. Ed. Tristan Palmer. Pub. Brian Southam. R&P Doris Southam. **Subscr. to:** Transaction Distribution Center, 390 Campus Dr., Somerset, NJ 08873. TEL 732-445-1245, 888-999-6778, FAX 732-748-9801, orders@transactionpub.com, http://www.transactionpub.com.

SWEET'S DIRECTORY. see *BUILDING AND CONSTRUCTION*

T A B. (Technik am Bau) see *HEATING, PLUMBING AND REFRIGERATION*

▼ **T M RAKENNUSMAAILMA.** see *BUILDING AND CONSTRUCTION*

720 FIN ISSN 0359-7105
NA1
TAMPERE UNIVERSITY OF TECHNOLOGY. DEPARTMENT OF ARCHITECTURE. OCCASIONAL PAPERS. Text in English. 1982. irreg. **Document type:** *Monographic series.*
Related titles: ◆ Series of: Tampereen Teknillinen Korkeakoulu. Arkkitehtuurin Osasto. Raportti. ISSN 0356-4843.
—BLDSC (3535.844500).
Published by: Tampereen Teknillinen Korkeakoulu, Arkkitehtuurin Osasto/Tampere University of Technology, Department of Architecture, PO Box 527, Tampere, 33101, Finland. TEL 358-3-311511, FAX 358-3-31153015, http://www.tut.fi.

720 FIN ISSN 0356-4843
TAMPEREEN TEKNILLINEN KORKEAKOULU. ARKKITEHTUURIN OSASTO. RAPORTTI/TAMPERE UNIVERSITY OF TECHNOLOGY. DEPARTMENT OF ARCHITECTURE. REPORT. Text in Multiple languages. 1972. irreg.
Related titles: ◆ Series: Tampere University of Technology. Department of Architecture. Occasional Papers. ISSN 0359-7105.
Published by: Tampereen Teknillinen Korkeakoulu, Arkkitehtuurin Osasto/Tampere University of Technology, Department of Architecture, PO Box 527, Tampere, 33101, Finland. TEL 358-3-311511, FAX 358-3-31153015, http://www.tut.fi.

721 FRA ISSN 0373-0719
TH2
TECHNIQUES ET ARCHITECTURE. Text in English, French. 1942. bi-m. EUR 25 per issue (effective 2004). adv. bk.rev. index. **Document type:** *Magazine, Consumer.*
Indexed: AIAP, BHA, IBR, RASB, RILM.
—BLDSC (8744.400000), IE, Infotrieve, ingenta.
Published by: Editions Jean - Michel Place, 3 rue Lhomond, Paris, 75005, France. TEL 33-1-44320590, FAX 33-1-44320591, place@jmplace.com, http://www.jmplace.com. Eds. Jean-Francois Pousse, Marie Christine Loriers. Circ: 16,800.

724 DEU ISSN 0344-9068
TECHNISCHE KULTURDENKMALE. Text in German. 1966. s-a. adv. bk.rev. back issues avail. **Document type:** *Academic/Scholarly.*
Published by: V.D. Linnepe Verlagsgesellschaft KG, Bahnhofstr 28, Hagen, 58119, Germany. TEL 02331-32078, FAX 02331-32090. Eds. Friederike Kaesting, Holger Heuermann. Circ: 3,000.

TECHNOLOGY AND CONSERVATION; of art, architecture and antiquities. see *ART*

TEGL. see *BUILDING AND CONSTRUCTION*

720 JPN
TELESCOPE (TOKYO). Text in English, Japanese. 1988. q. USD 45. adv. bk.rev. illus. **Description:** Highlights new architectural projects in Japan. Includes exhibitions reviews and reports.
Published by: Workshop for Architecture & Urbanism, YK Aoyama Bldg, 4-7 Shibuya 2-chome, Shibuya-ku, Tokyo, 150-0002, Japan. FAX 03-3407-8753. Circ: 3,000.

720 ITA
TEMPO MATERIA ARCHITETTURA; revista trimestrale di restauro. Variant title: Te M a. Text in Italian. 1993. q.
Related titles: Online - full text ed.
Published by: (Politecnico di Milano, Facolta di Architettura), U T E T SpA, via Montefeltro 6/a, Milano, MI 20156, Italy. FAX 39-02-38086626, abbonamenti@utetperiodici.it, http://www.utet.com.

720 ITA
TERRITORIO (MILANO). Text in Italian. 1996. q. EUR 44 domestic; EUR 58 foreign (effective 2003). **Document type:** *Journal, Academic/Scholarly.*
Published by: (Politecnico di Milano, Dipartimento di Architettura e Pianificazione), Franco Angeli Edizioni, Viale Monza 106, Milan, 20127, Italy. TEL 39-02-2837141, FAX 39-02-26144793, redazioni@francoangeli.it, http://www.francoangeli.it.

720 USA ISSN 0040-4179
NA1
TEXAS ARCHITECT. Text in English. 1950. bi-m. USD 25; USD 15 to students (effective 2005). adv. bk.rev. illus. cum.index. **Document type:** *Magazine, Trade.*
Indexed: AIAP.
Published by: Texas Society of Architects, 816 Congress Ave, Ste 970, Austin, TX 78701-2443. TEL 512-478-7386, FAX 512-478-0528, http://www.texasarchitect.org. Ed. Stephen Sharpe. Pub. Judey Dozeto. Circ: 6,000 (paid and free).

725.82 973 792 USA ISSN 0885-3940
NA6830
THEATRE HISTORICAL SOCIETY. ANNUAL. Text in English. 1973. a. free to members (effective 2004).
Indexed: AIAP.
Published by: Theatre Historical Society of America, York Theatre Bldg, Ste 200, 152 N York Rd, Elmhurst, IL 60126-2806. TEL 630-782-1800, FAX 630-782-1802, http://www.historictheatres.org.

723 DEU
THEISS BURGENFUEHRER. Text in German. 2001. irreg., latest vol.3, 2003. price varies. **Document type:** *Monographic series, Academic/Scholarly.*
Published by: Konrad Theiss Verlag GmbH, Moenchhaldenstr 28, Stuttgart, 70191, Germany. TEL 49-711-255270, FAX 49-711-2552717, service@theiss.de, http://www.theiss.de.

727 DEU ISSN 1434-5919
THEORETISCHE UNTERSUCHUNGEN ZUR ARCHITEKTUR. Text in German. 1997. irreg., latest vol.3, 2000. EUR 29.90 per vol. (effective 2003). **Document type:** *Monographic series, Academic/Scholarly.*
Published by: Waxmann Verlag GmbH, Steinfurter Str 555, Muenster, 48159, Germany. TEL 49-251-26504-0, FAX 49-251-2650426, info@waxmann.com, http://www.waxmann.com. Ed. Eduard Fuehr.

THRESHOLDS (CAMBRIDGE). see *ART*

TIMBER FRAMING. see *BUILDING AND CONSTRUCTION*

720 747 USA ISSN 1090-1361
TIMBER HOMES ILLUSTRATED. Text in English. q. USD 16.97; USD 26.97 foreign; USD 3.99 newsstand/cover; CND 4.99 newsstand/cover in Canada. adv. **Document type:** *Magazine, Consumer.* **Description:** Guide to timber homes in North America. Covers traditional timber frames, log post-and-beam structures that employ elegant, majestic timbers.
Published by: Goodman Media Group, Inc., 250 W 57th St, Ste 710, New York, NY 10107-0799. TEL 212-541-7100, FAX 212-245-1241, http://www.goodmanmediagroup.com/TimberHomes/index.html. Ed. Roland Sweet. Pub. Jason Goodman. Adv. contact Laura Lapatin. page USD 3,220. Circ: 120,000 (paid). **Subscr. to:** PO Box 789, Mt Morris, IL 61054.

TOBISHIMA GIHO, KENCHIKU/TOBISHIMA ENGINEERING REPORT, ARCHITECTURE. see *ENGINEERING—Civil Engineering*

720 747 USA ISSN 1059-5252
NA7205
TODAY'S FAMILY HOME PLANS. Text in English. 1985. a. USD 3.95. **Description:** Features pictures and floor plans of single family detached homes of general interest to home planners and builders.
Published by: Archway Press, Inc., 19 W 44th St, New York, NY 10036. TEL 212-757-5580.

TODAY'S PLAYGROUND. see *CHILDREN AND YOUTH—About*

711.4 USA ISSN 1050-2092
HT51
➤ **TRADITIONAL DWELLINGS AND SETTLEMENTS REVIEW.** Text in English. 1989. s-a. subscr. incld. with membership. bk.rev. **Document type:** *Journal, Academic/Scholarly.* **Description:** Provides a link between tradition and modernity, in any setting throughout the world.
Indexed: AIAP, AICP, API.
—BLDSC (8881.071700), IE, ingenta.
Published by: International Association for the Study of Traditional Environments, 390 Wurster Hall, Department of Architecture, University of California, Berkeley, CA 94720-1839. TEL 510-642-6801, FAX 510-643-5571, iaste@berkeley.edu, http://arch.ced.berkeley.edu/research/iaste/tdsr.htm, http://arch.ced.berkeley.edu/research/iaste/index.htm. Ed. Nezar Alsayyad. R&P David Moffatt. Circ: 350 (paid).

720 ITA ISSN 0082-6006
TRATTATI DI ARCHITETTURA. Text in Italian. 1966. irreg., latest 1995. price varies.
Published by: Edizioni Il Polifilo, Via Borgonuovo, 2, Milan, MI 20121, Italy.

715.2 USA ISSN 1555-1008
▼ **TREE SERVICES**; for tree care/landscape contractors & arborists. Text in English. 2005 (Feb.). m. USD 18 (effective 2005). adv. **Document type:** *Magazine, Trade.*
Published by: Moose River Publishing Co., 374 Emerson Falls Rd., St. Johnsbury, VT 05819. TEL 802-748-8908, 800-422-7147, http://www.treeservicesmagazine.com. Ed. David Cassidy. Pub. Jim Kendrick. Adv. contact Nancy Carpenter.

TRIALOG; Zeitschrift fuer das Planen und Bauen in der Dritten Welt. see *HOUSING AND URBAN PLANNING*

711.4 ISR ISSN 0041-4549
TVAI; periodical for architecture, town planning, industrial design & the plastic arts. Text in Hebrew; Summaries in English. 1966. a. USD 7. adv. bk.rev. illus.
Indexed: AIAP, IHP.
Address: 27, Shlomo Hamelech St., Tel Aviv, Israel. TEL 03-5239152. Ed. Aba Elhanani. Circ: 1,500.

724.6 GBR ISSN 1353-1964
TWENTIETH CENTURY ARCHITECTURE. Text in English. 1981. a. price varies. **Document type:** *Journal.*
Former titles (until 1994): Thirties Society Journal (0964-3486); (until 198?): Thirties Society. Journal (0265-2625)
Indexed: AIAP, DAAI.
—BLDSC (9076.826500).
Published by: Twentieth Century Society, 70 Cowcross St, London, EC1M 6EJ, United Kingdom. TEL 44-20-72503857, FAX 44-20-72518985, http://www.c20society.demon.co.uk/docs/publications/20thjournal.html.

720 GBR ISSN 1365-1951
U.A. INTERNATIONAL; a journal of architecture and building. (Ulster Architect) Text in English. 1984. m. adv. back issues avail. **Document type:** *Journal, Trade.*
Formerly (until 1996): Ulster Architect (0961-8317)
Related titles: CD-ROM ed.
Published by: Architectural Publications Ltd., 182 Ravenhill Rd, Belfast, BT6 8EE, United Kingdom. TEL 44-1232-731636, FAX 44-1232-738927, aaranet@101.dnet.co.uk. Ed. Anne Daley Orr. Adv. contact Andy Allen. B&W page GBP 899, color page GBP 1,112; trim 297 x 210. Circ: 5,000.

720 FRA
U I A NEWSLETTER. Text in English. 1965. bi-m. bk.rev. charts; illus. **Document type:** *Newsletter.* **Description:** Contains information on worldwide architectural events and competitions.
Formerly: U I A Information (0041-6916)
Related titles: French ed.
Published by: Union Internationale des Architectes/International Union of Architects, 51, rue Raynouard, Paris, 75016, France. TEL 33-1-45243688, FAX 33-1-45240278, uia@uia-architectes.org, http://www.uia-architectes.org. Ed. Catherine Hayward.

720 ESP ISSN 0078-8732
UNIVERSIDAD DE NAVARRA. ESCUELA DE ARQUITECTURA. COLECCION DE ARQUITECTURA. Text in Spanish. 1971. irreg., latest vol.18, 1988. price varies.
Formerly: Universidad de Navarra. Escuela de Arquitectura. Manuales: Arquitectura
Published by: (Universidad de Navarra, Escuela de Arquitectura), Ediciones Universidad de Navarra S.A., Pza. Los Sauces, 1-2, Baranain, (Navarra) 31010, Spain. TEL 34-948-256850.

720 ESP
UNIVERSIDAD DE SEVILLA. SERIE: ARQUITECTURA. Text in Spanish. irreg., latest vol.21, 2000. price varies. **Document type:** *Monographic series, Academic/Scholarly.*
Formerly (until 1967): Universidad Hispalense. Anales. Serie: Arquitectura
Published by: Universidad de Sevilla, Secretariado de Publicaciones, Porvenir 27, Sevilla, 41013, Spain. TEL 34-95-4487444, FAX 34-95-4487443, secpub10@us.es, http://www.us.es/publius/inicio.html.

720 MEX
UNIVERSIDAD NACIONAL AUTONOMA DE MEXICO. FACULTAD DE ARQUITECTURA. REVISTA. Short title: Revista F A. Text in Spanish. irreg. (approx. 1/yr.), latest 1986. USD 1.
Indexed: AIAP.
Published by: Universidad Nacional Autonoma de Mexico, Facultad de Arquitectura, c/o Arq. Enrique X. de Anda, Circuito Interior de Cd. Universitaria, Deleg. Coyoacan, Mexico City, DF 04510, Mexico.

720 COL ISSN 0120-2669
UNIVERSIDAD NACIONAL DE COLOMBIA. FACULTAD DE ARQUITECTURA. REVISTA. Text in Spanish. 1976. s-a. per issue exchange basis. adv. bk.rev. illus. **Document type:** *Academic/Scholarly.*
Published by: (Universidad Nacional de Colombia, Facultad de Arquitectura), Editorial Lealon, Biblioteca, Apartado Aereo 1779, Medellin, ANT, Colombia. TEL 57-9-2300040, TELEX 6922 CTX MO-CO. Ed. Nora Elena Mesa Sanchez. Circ: 1,000.

721 ITA
UNIVERSITA DEGLI STUDI DI FIRENZE. DIPARTIMENTO DI PROGETTAZIONE DELL'ARCHITETTURA. QUADERNI. Text in Italian. 1989. a.
Formerly: Universita degli Studi di Firenze. Facolta di Architettura. Quaderni di Storia dell'Architettura
Published by: (Universita degli Studi di Firenze), Alinea Editrice s.r.l., Via Pier Lugi da Palestrina 17-19, Rosso, Florence, FI 50144, Italy. TEL 39-055-333428, FAX 39-055-331013, http://www.alinea.it. Ed. Giuliano Maggiora.

720 ITA ISSN 0392-2898
NA1120
UNIVERSITA DEGLI STUDI DI ROMA. FACOLTA DI ARCHITETTURA. BOLLETINO DELLA BIBLIOTECA. Text in Italian. 1987. s-a. EUR 15.49 newsstand/cover (effective 2001). **Document type:** *Journal, Academic/Scholarly.*
Published by: (Universita degli Studi di Roma, Facolta di Architettura), Gangemi Editore, Piazza San Pantaleo 4, Rome, Italy. TEL 39-06-6872774, FAX 39-06-68806189, gangemieditorerc@tin.it, http://www.gangemieditore.it.

720 ITA ISSN 0485-4152
UNIVERSITA DI ROMA. ISTITUTO DI STORIA DELL'ARCHITETTURA. QUADERNI. Text in Italian. 1953. a. price varies. back issues avail. **Document type:** *Monographic series, Academic/Scholarly.*
Indexed: AIAP, API, BHA, PCI.
Published by: (Universita Degli Studi Di Roma "La Sapienza", Istituto di Storia dell'Architettura), Bonsignori Editore s.r.l., Viale dei Quattro Venti 47, Rome, RM 00152, Italy. TEL 39-06-5881496, FAX 39-06-5882839.

UNIVERSITY OF NEW SOUTH WALES. HANDBOOK: BUILT ENVIRONMENT. see *ENVIRONMENTAL STUDIES*

721.0711 AUS ISSN 1036-0654
UNIVERSITY OF TECHNOLOGY, SYDNEY. FACULTY OF DESIGN ARCHITECTURE AND BUILDING HANDBOOK. Text in English. 1990. a. AUD 14 domestic; AUD 19 foreign (effective 2000). **Document type:** *Catalog, Academic/Scholarly.* **Description:** Contains detailed information about the faculty, staff, courses and subject synopses.
Published by: University of Technology, Sydney, City Campus, PO Box 123, Broadway, NSW 2007, Australia. TEL 61-2-9514-2000, FAX 61-2-9514-1551, publications@uts.edu.au, http://www.uts.edu.au/div/publications. Circ: 6,000.

720 GBR ISSN 0306-0624
UNIVERSITY OF YORK. INSTITUTE OF ADVANCED ARCHITECTURAL STUDIES. RESEARCH PAPERS. Text in English. 1971. irreg. price varies. illus. **Document type:** *Monographic series.*
Published by: University of York, Institute of Advanced Architectural Studies, The King's Manor, York, YO1 2EP, United Kingdom. TEL 44-1904-433988, FAX 44-1904-433949. Circ: 500.

720 690 FRA ISSN 1623-6661
URB.A0. (Assiste par Ordinateur) Text in French. 2000. bi-m. EUR 80 domestic; EUR 95 foreign (effective 2001).
Published by: L' Agence Innovapresse, 29 rue du Faubourg Poissonniere, Paris, 75009, France. TEL 33-1-48240897, FAX 33-1-42470076, abonnement@innovapresse.com, http://www.innovapresse.com. Pub. Jean Audoin.

URBAN DESIGN QUARTERLY. see *HOUSING AND URBAN PLANNING*

711.4 USA ISSN 0895-8076
NA9000
URBAN DESIGN UPDATE. Text in English. 1984. 6/yr. USD 120; USD 170 in Canada; USD 210 elsewhere. **Document type:** *Newsletter.* **Description:** Reports on new projects, cutting edge issues, books and other matters of interest to urban designers.
Published by: Institute for Urban Design, 47 Barrow St, New York, NY 10014-3736. TEL 619-455-1251, FAX 619-450-3680. Ed. Ann Ferebee. **Subscr. to:** 454 W 46th St, Apt 3CN, New York, NY 10036.

729.05 NZL
URBIS. Text in English. 1998. q.
Published by: A G M Publishing Ltd., Newmarket, Private Bag 99 915, Auckland, 1031, New Zealand. TEL 64-9-8464068, FAX 64-9-8468742, agm@agm.co.nz, http://www.agm.co.nz. Ed. Steve Bohling. Pub., R&P Robin Beckett. Circ: 22,100.

720 USA ISSN 1556-5483
▼ **URGENT MATTERS.** Text in English. forthcoming 2006. a. **Document type:** *Journal, Academic/Scholarly.*
Published by: University of Virginia, School of Architecture, Campbell Hall, P O Box 400122, Charlottesville, VA 22904. TEL 434-924-3715, FAX 434-982-2678, arch-web@virginia.edu, http://www.arch.virginia.edu.

UTAH PRESERVATION. see *SOCIAL SERVICES AND WELFARE*

720 DEU
V F A JAHRBUCH. Text in German. 1983. a. bk.rev.; software rev.; Website rev. back issues avail. **Document type:** *Yearbook, Trade.*
Published by: Vereinigung Freischaffender Architekten, Turmstr 33, Berlin, 10551, Germany. TEL 49-30-39494019, FAX 49-30-39494039, info@vfa-architekten.de, http://www.vfa-architekten.de. Circ: 10,000.

720 FRA
V M F. Text in French. 1958. 5/yr. adv. bk.rev. bibl.; charts; illus.; tr.lit. 96 p./no.; back issues avail. **Document type:** *Magazine, Consumer.*
Formerly (until 2001): Vieilles Maisons Francaises (0049-6316)
Indexed: AIAP, BHA.
Published by: Vieilles Maisons Francaises, 93 rue de l'Universite, Paris, 75007, France. TEL 33-1-40626180, FAX 33-1-45511226. Ed., Adv. contact Marie-Claire Colignon. Pub. Jacques De Ladoucette. Circ: 25,000.

720 GBR ISSN 0305-5477
NA208
➤ **VERNACULAR ARCHITECTURE.** Text in English. 1970. a. GBP 20 to individuals (effective 2004). **Document type:** *Journal, Academic/Scholarly.*
Indexed: AIAP.
—BLDSC (9172.900000), IE.
Published by: Vernacular Architecture Group, c/o Mrs Brenda Watkin, Ashley, Willows Green, Great Leighs, Chelmsford, Essex CM3 1QD, United Kingdom. TEL 44-1245-361408, http://www.vag.org.uk.

720 USA ISSN 1071-4898
NA705
VERNACULAR ARCHITECTURE NEWSLETTER. Abbreviated title: V A N. Text in English. 1979. q. free to members (effective 2004). **Document type:** *Newsletter.*
Published by: Vernacular Architecture Forum, P O Box 1511, Harrisonburg, VA 22803-1511. http://www.vernaculararchitectureforum.org. Ed. Philippe Oszuscik.

724 ESP ISSN 1137-7402
NA1311.V32
VIA ARQUITECTURA. Text in Spanish, English. 1997. 3/yr. EUR 56 domestic; EUR 77 in Europe; EUR 120 elsewhere (effective 2004). **Description:** Sheds light on particular aspects of recent international architecture.
Related titles: Online - full content ed.
Indexed: AIAP, API.
—CINDOC.
Published by: (Colegio Oficial de Arquitectos de la Comunidad Valenciana), Papeles de Arquitectura, S.L., Av. de la Estacion, 14, 2o Izda., Alicante, 03005, Spain. TEL 34-65984000, FAX 34-65986232, via@arquired.es, http://www.via-arquitectura.net. Ed. Mercedes Planelles Herrero.

940 GBR ISSN 0083-6079
VICTORIAN SOCIETY. ANNUAL. Text in English. 1958. a. GBP 24 domestic; GBP 32 overseas. adv. bk.rev. **Document type:** *Academic/Scholarly.* **Description:** Includes notes on the main conservation cases of the past year, plus two short articles on subjects of 19th century art and architecture.
Indexed: AIAP, API, BHA.
Published by: Victorian Society, 1 Priory Gardens, London, W4 1TT, United Kingdom. TEL 44-181-742-3438, FAX 44-181-995-4895. Ed. Sarah Whittingham. Adv. contact Richard Seedhouse. Circ: 3,500.

VILLAAEGAREN. see *REAL ESTATE*

720 ITA ISSN 0042-6237
VILLEGIARDINI; casa nel verde. Text in Italian. 1957. 10/yr. EUR 29 (effective 2005). adv. charts; illus. **Document type:** *Magazine, Trade.*
Related titles: Supplement(s): VilleGiardini. Repertorio. ISSN 1122-343X. 1987; Monografie di Ville Giardini. ISSN 1122-3448. 1993.
Indexed: AIAP, API.
—IE, Infotrieve.
Published by: Arnoldo Mondadori Editore SpA, Via Mondadori 1, Segrate, 20090, Italy. TEL 39-02-66814363, FAX 39-030-3198412, http://www.mondadori.com. Circ: 43,000.

VISION MAGAZINE. see *ART*

720 SVN
VISION OF REALITY. Text in English, Italian, Slovenian. 1991. irreg. SIT 10. illus. **Document type:** *Catalog.*
Published by: Piranesi Ltd., Bogisiceva 11, Ljubljana, 61000, Slovenia. TEL 386-61-223-039, FAX 386-61-221-226. Ed. Tomaz Brate. Circ: 2,000 (controlled).

720 FRA ISSN 1265-7034
NA1041
LE VISITEUR; ville, territoire, paysage, architecture. Text in French. 1995. s-a. EUR 59.35 domestic (effective 2004). adv. back issues avail.
Indexed: AIAP, API.
Published by: Societe Francaise des Architectes, 247 Rue Saint Jacques, Paris, 75005, France. TEL 33-1-56811025, FAX 33-1-56811026, http://www.levisiteur.com, http://www.sfarchi.org. Ed. Sebastien Marot. Pub. Sylvestre Nonnier. Adv. contact Sebatian Narot.

VISWASILPI. see *BUILDING AND CONSTRUCTION*

728 ARG ISSN 0505-7981
HD9715.A7
VIVIENDA/DWELLING; la revista de la construccion. Text in Spanish. 1960. m. ARS 88 domestic; ARS 224 foreign; ARS 8 newsstand/cover (effective 2002). adv. abstr.; bibl.; illus. **Description:** For all professionals in the construction field; architects, engineers, builders, construction workers and students.
Related titles: Online - full text ed.
Published by: Revista Vivienda S.r.l., Hipolito Yrigoyen 1176 PB, Buenos Aires, C1086AAT, Argentina. TEL 54-4381-1813, 54-11-43811813, infov@revistavivienda.com.ar, http://www.revistavivienda.com.ar. Adv. contact Maria Murioni. color page USD 1,815; trim 270 x 195. Circ: 12,000.

720 NLD
NA1141
VOLUME. Text in English. 1973. bi-m. EUR 82.50 domestic; EUR 99 foreign; EUR 64 domestic to students; EUR 80.50 foreign to students (effective 2005). adv. bk.rev. illus. **Document type:** *Journal, Trade.* **Description:** For architects, town planners, and artists.
Formerly: Archis (English Edition) (1568-2730); Supersedes in part (in 2001): Archis (0921-8041); Which was formerly (until 1986): Wonen - T A - B K (0165-3504)
Indexed: AIAP, API, BHA, DIP, IBR, IBZ, KES, RILM.
—BLDSC (1597.663000), IE, Infotrieve, ingenta.
Published by: (Stichting Nederlands Instituut voor Architectuur en Stedebouw), Artimo Foundation, Elandsgracht 8, Amsterdam, 1016 TV, Netherlands. TEL 31-20-6253344, FAX 31-20-3204630, info@archis.org, info@artimo.net, http://www.archis.org, http://www.artimo.net. Ed. Ole Bouman. adv.: B&W page EUR 2,250, color page EUR 2,850; 230 x 290. **Dist. by:** Idea Books Amsterdam, Nieuwe Herengracht 11, Amsterdam 1011 RK, Netherlands. TEL 31-20-622-6154, FAX 31-20-620-9299, idea@ideabooks.nl, http://www.ideabooks.nl/frameset.asp.

720 JPN
WASEDA ARCHITECTURAL NEWS. Text in Japanese. 1977. s-a. membership. back issues avail.
Published by: Waseda Architectural Society, Waseda Daigaku Riko-Gakubu, 3-4-1 Okubo, Shinjuku-ku, Tokyo, 160-0000, Japan. TEL 03-208-0640.

720 JPN
WASEDA ARCHITECTURE. Text in Japanese. 1970. a. membership. back issues avail.
Published by: Waseda Architectural Society, Waseda Daigaku Riko-Gakubu, 3-4-1 Okubo, Shinjuku-ku, Tokyo, 160-0000, Japan. TEL 03-208-0640.

627 714 USA ISSN 1522-6581
SB475.8
WATERSHAPES. Text in English. 1999. m. (10/yr). USD 30 domestic; USD 64 foreign (effective 2001). adv. charts; illus.; tr.lit. back issues avail. **Document type:** *Trade.* **Description:** Covers the design, engineering and construction of swimming pools, spas, ponds, waterfalls, streams and waterfeatures of all shapes and sizes.
Published by: McCloskey Communications, Inc., PO Box 306, Woodland, CA 91365. TEL 818-715-9776, FAX 818-715-9059, 818-715-9057, main@watershapes.com, http://www.watershapes.com. Ed., R&P Eric Herman TEL 714-685-1854. Pub. Jim McCloskey. Adv. contact Camma Barsily TEL 310-979-0335. B&W page USD 1,790, color page USD 2,420; trim 10.88 x 8.13. Circ: 13,000 (controlled).

720 ESP
WEB ARCHITECTURE MAGAZINE. Text in English, Spanish. 1996. bi-m.
Media: Online - full content.
Address: Avda Icaria 144-5-2, Barcelona, Spain. wam@arch-mag.com, http://web.arch-mag.com, http://web.arch-mag.com/. Ed. Ulls Mirant.

720 CHE ISSN 0257-9332
NA1.A1
WERK - BAUEN & WOHNEN. Text in French. 10/yr. CHF 200 domestic; CHF 220 foreign; CHF 140 to students; CHF 25 newsstand/cover (effective 2004). adv. **Document type:** *Magazine, Trade.*
Formed by the merger of (1946-1982): Bauen und Wohnen (0005-6529); (1914-1982): Werk (0043-2768)
Related titles: Online - full text ed.: (from H.W. Wilson, O C L C Online Computer Library Center, Inc.).
Indexed: AIAP, API, ArtInd, BAS, BHA, DIP, IBR, IBZ, PCI, RASB.
—BLDSC (9295.742000), IE, Infotrieve, ingenta.
Published by: (Bund Schweizer Architekten), Zollikofer AG, Fuerstenlandstr 122, Postfach 2362, St. Gallen, 9001, Switzerland. TEL 41-71-2727370, FAX 41-71-2727586, leserservice@zollikofer.ch, http://www.werkbauenundwohnen.ch, http://www.zollikofer.ch. Circ: 9,000. **Co-sponsor:** Federation Suisse des Architectes de l'Interieur.

720 DEU ISSN 1617-058X
WERK UND ZEIT. Text in German. 1952. 2/yr. EUR 6.90 (effective 2004). adv. bk.rev. back issues avail. **Document type:** *Magazine, Trade.*
Formerly (until 2000): Werk und Zeit. Brief (1431-9691); Which superseded in part (in 1993): Werk und Zeit (0049-7150)
Indexed: RASB.
Published by: (Deutscher Werkbund e.V.), ardenku Verlag, Eduard-Mueller-Str 2, Hagen, 58097, Germany. TEL 49-2331-303333, FAX 49-2331-303392, mail@ardenkuverlag.de, http://www.werkundzeit.de, http://www.ardenkuverlag.de. Circ: 3,500.

▼ **WESTERN INTERIORS AND DESIGN.** see *INTERIOR DESIGN AND DECORATION*

720 DEU
WETTBEWERBE AKTUELL. Text in German. 1971. m. adv. **Document type:** *Magazine, Trade.* **Description:** Contains information on topical German architectural competitions.
Formerly: Wettbewerbe (0177-9788)

▼ new title ➤ refereed ✶ unverified ♦ full entry avail.

Published by: Wettbewerbe Aktuell Verlagsgesellschaft mbH, Maximilianstr 5, Freiburg Im Breisgau, 79100, Germany. TEL 49-761-77455-0, FAX 49-761-7745599, verlag@wettbewerbe-aktuell.de, http://www.wettbewerbe-aktuell.de. Ed. Thomas Hoffmann-Kuhnt. Pub. Thomas Hoffmann Kuhnt. Adv. contact Antje Vogt. Circ: 13,500.

720 AUT
WETTBEWERBE ARCHITEKTUR JOURNAL. Text in German. bi-m.
Address: Salierigasse 25, Vienna, W 1180, Austria. TEL 01-4706292, FAX 01-475314. Ed. R J Bahula. Circ: 5,000.

WIRTSCHAFTSDIENST FUER INGENIEURE UND ARCHITEKTEN. see *ENGINEERING*

720 USA
WISCONSIN ARCHITECT. Text in English. 1931. bi-m. USD 30. adv. **Document type:** *Directory, Trade.*
Indexed: AIAP.
Published by: (A I A Wisconsin), Wisconsin Architect, Inc., 321 S Hamilton St, Madison, WI 53703-3606. TEL 608-257-8477. Ed., Adv. contact Brenda Taylor. Pub., R&P William Babcock. Circ: 3,700 (controlled).

720 747 DEU
WOHN! DESIGN; internationales Magazin fuer Architektur, Wohnen und Design. Text in German. 6/yr. EUR 35; EUR 6.50 newsstand/cover (effective 2002). adv. **Document type:** *Magazine, Consumer.*
Published by: Trend Medien Verlag GmbH, Herdweg 20, Stuttgart, 70174, Germany. TEL 49-711-18790-0, FAX 49-711-1879045, info@wohndesign.de, http://www.trendmedien.com/1wohndesign/1_f.htm. Ed. Stephan Demmrich. Pub., R&P Klaus Vetterle. Adv. contact Christine Breitkopf. B&W page EUR 5,000, color page EUR 7,000; trim 199 x 278. Circ: 40,542 (paid and controlled).

363.7 DEU ISSN 0176-0513
WOHNUNG & GESUNDHEIT; Fachzeitschrift fuer oekologisches Bauen & Leben. Text in German. 1979. q. USD 45 (effective 2000 & 2001). adv. bk.rev. bibl. Supplement avail.; back issues avail. **Document type:** *Journal, Trade.*
Indexed: DIP, IBR, IBZ, RefZh.
—CISTI.
Published by: Institut fuer Baubiologie und Oekologie, Holzham 25, Neubeuern, 83115, Germany. TEL 49-8035-2039, FAX 49-8035-8164, institut@baubiologie.ibn.de. Ed. Anton Schneider. Circ: 7,500.

728 690 USA ISSN 1550-9729
WOMAN'S DAY HOME REMODELING. Text in English. 1984. 5/yr. USD 3.99 newsstand/cover (effective 2005). adv. illus. **Document type:** *Magazine, Consumer.* **Description:** Covers various aspects of maintaining and upgrading the home.
Supersedes: Woman's Day Home Improvements
Published by: Hachette Filipacchi Media U.S., Inc. (Subsidiary of: Hachette Filipacchi Medias S.A.), 1633 Broadway, New York, NY 10019. http://www.hfmus.com. Ed. Olivia Monjo. Pub. Jim Fraguela. adv.: B&W page USD 31,530, color page USD 45,050; trim 7.88 x 10.5. Circ: 400,000 (paid).

WOOD/BOIS. see *FORESTS AND FORESTRY—Lumber And Wood*

WOOD DESIGN & BUILDING. see *FORESTS AND FORESTRY—Lumber And Wood*

WORLD CULTURAL GUIDES. see *TRAVEL AND TOURISM*

720 USA ISSN 1539-4190
WORLD MONUMENTS ICON. Variant title: Icon. Text in English. 2002 (Fall). q. USD 17.95 (effective 2003).
Published by: World Monuments Fund, 95 Madison Ave. 9th Fl., New York, NY 10016. TEL 646-424-9594, FAX 646-424-9593, http://wmf.org/html/programs/icon.html, http://www.wmf.org. Ed. Angela M. H. Schuster.

720 USA ISSN 1059-4396
NA737.W7
WRIGHT ANGLES. Text in English. 1974. q. USD 45 to individuals; USD 500 to corporations (effective 2000). bk.rev. **Document type:** *Newsletter.* **Description:** Includes a feature article on Wright's early career, architecture, decorative arts, family life and creativity. Contains calendar of events, exhibits, education programs, news items, and other issues of interest to members.
Indexed: AIAP.
Published by: Frank Lloyd Wright Home and Studio Foundation, 951 Chicago Ave, Oak Park, IL 60302. TEL 708-848-1976, FAX 708-848-1248. Ed., R&P Zarine Weil. Circ: 3,600 (controlled).

720 CHN ISSN 1006-7930
XI'AN JIANZHU KEJI DAXUE XUEBAO/XI'AN UNIVERSITY OF ARCHITECTURE AND TECHNOLOGY. JOURNAL. Text in Chinese. 1957. q. CNY 10 newsstand/cover (effective 2004). **Document type:** *Journal, Academic/Scholarly.*
Formerly: Xi'an Yejin Jianzhu Xueyuan Xuebao/Xi'an Institute of Metallurgy & Construction Engineering. Journal (1000-5250)
Related titles: Online - full text ed.: (from East View Information Services, WanFang Data Corp.).
Published by: Xi'an Jianzhu Keji Daxue/Xi'an University of Architecture and Technology, 13, Yanta Lu, Xi'an, 710055, China. TEL 86-29-82202912, xjdxb@webmail.xauat.edu.cn, http://xajzkjdx.periodicals.net.cn/default.html.

YALE PUBLICATIONS IN THE HISTORY OF ART. see *ART*

720 690 TUR ISSN 1300-3437
YAPI; aylik kultur, sanat ve mimarlik dergisi. Text in Turkish; Summaries in English. 1973. m. USD 50 (effective 1994). adv. bk.rev. illus. index. back issues avail. **Document type:** *Trade.* **Description:** Review of culture, art and architecture.
Published by: Yapi Endustri Merkezi, Cumhuriyet Caddesi 329, 80230 Harbiye, Istanbul, Turkey. TEL 90-212-2474185, FAX 90-212-2471101. Ed. Ms. Guner Cilgin. Pub. Dogan Hasol. Adv. contact Mrs. Zehra Oztok Ebcim. B&W page GBP 280, color page GBP 445. Circ: 5,000.

720 USA ISSN 0319-3438
YARDSTICKS FOR COSTING. Variant title: Canadian Architect's Yardsticks for Costing. Text in English. 1971. a., latest 2005. USD 115 domestic (effective 2005). adv. **Document type:** *Trade.* **Description:** Provides cost data for the Canadian construction industry.
—CISTI. **CCC.**
Published by: R.S. Means Company Inc. (Subsidiary of: Reed Construction Data, Associated Construction Publications), 63 Smiths Lane, P O Box 800, Kingston, MA 02364-9988. TEL 800-448-8182. Ed. Jas A Murray. Circ: 2,195.

720.6 GBR ISSN 0959-3640
NA12
YORK GEORGIAN SOCIETY. ANNUAL REPORT. Text in English. 1943. a., latest 2000. GBP 14 domestic; GBP 16 foreign (effective 2001 - 2002). bk.rev. illus. Yes most recent - 1989-1997. 120 p./no. 1 cols./p.; back issues avail. **Document type:** *Proceedings.* **Description:** Reports on the Society's activities. Includes articles on architecture, decorative art, historic restoration work, and related subjects.
Indexed: AIAP, API, BHA.
Published by: York Georgian Society, King's Manor, Yorks YO1 7EW, United Kingdom. Ed., R&P Helen Kirk. Circ: 600.

720 DEU
ZEICHENHILFE. Text in German. 1991. a. adv. **Document type:** *Journal, Trade.*
Published by: Stadtwandel Verlag, Solmsstr. 22, Berlin, 10961, Germany. TEL 49-30-69504812, FAX 49-30-69504813, info@stadtwandel.de, http://www.stadtwandel.de. adv.: B&W page EUR 1,600, color page EUR 1,850. Circ: 8,000 (controlled).

712 CHN ISSN 1000-6664
SB469
ZHONGGUO YUANLIN/CHINESE LANDSCAPE ARCHITECTURE. Text in Chinese. 1985. bi-m. CNY 12 per issue (effective 2004). **Document type:** *Journal, Academic/Scholarly.*
Related titles: Online - full text ed.: (from East View Information Services); Print ed.: (from WanFang Data Corp.).
—BLDSC (9512.831600).
Published by: Zhongguo Fengjing Yuanlin Xuehua/Chinese Society of Landscape Architecture, 9, Sanlihe Lu, Beijing, 100835, China. TEL 86-10-68393918, FAX 86-10-68393333, zgyl@china.com; jcla@china.com, http://zgyl.periodicals.net.cn/default.html, http://www.gardenexpo.cn/. **Dist. by:** China International Book Trading Corp, 35 Chegongzhuang Xilu, Haidian District, PO Box 399, Beijing 100044, China. TEL 86-10-68412045, FAX 86-10-68412023, cibtc@mail.cibtc.com.cn, http://www.cibtc.com.cn.

720 RUS ISSN 0321-5083
ZODCHESTVO. Text in Russian. 1975. irreg.
Formerly: Sovetskaya Arkhitektura
Indexed: RASB.
Published by: (Soyuz Arkhitektorov Rossiiskoi Federatsii), Stroiizdat, Dolgorukovskaya ul 23-a, Moscow, 111442, Russian Federation. TEL 7-095-2516967.

720 RUS
ZODCHESTVO MIRA. Text in Russian. 1995. q. USD 280 in United States (effective 2000).
Indexed: RASB.
Address: Furkasovskii per 12-5, Moscow, 101000, Russian Federation. TEL 7-095-9249741. **Dist. by:** East View Information Services, 3020 Harbor Ln. N., Minneapolis, MN 55447. TEL 763-550-0961, FAX 763-559-2931.

720 ITA ISSN 0394-9230
NA1.A1
ZODIAC (1989); international architecture magazine. Text in English, Italian. 1957-1973; N.S. 1989. s-a. price varies. bk.rev. charts; illus.; maps; pat. back issues avail. **Document type:** *Magazine, Consumer.* **Description:** Examines trends and reports developments in architecture.
Supersedes in part (in 1989): Zodiac (0048-7643)
Indexed: AIAP, ArtInd, DIP, EIP, IBZ.
Published by: Editrice Abitare Segesta SpA, Corso Monforte 15, Milan, MI 20122, Italy. TEL 39-02-76090, FAX 39-02-76090301, abitaremag@abitare.it, http://www.abitare.it. Ed. Guido Canella. Adv. contact Alessandra Fedele.

ZONING PRACTICE. see *HOUSING AND URBAN PLANNING*

720 ESP ISSN 1136-9647
2 G; revista internacional de arquitectura. Variant title: G G. Text in English, Portuguese, Spanish. 1997. q. EUR 95 domestic; EUR 185 foreign (effective 2005). adv.
—**CCC.**
Published by: Editorial Gustavo Gili, S.A., Rosello 87-89, Barcelona, 08029, Spain. TEL 34-93-3228161, FAX 34-93-3229205, info@ggili.com, http://www.ggili.com/2G.cfm?IDIDIOMA=ES. Pub. Pilar Tendero Garcia. adv.: color page EUR 270, B&W page EUR 2,100. Circ: 20,000.

720 USA
▼ **32 BEIJING NEW YORK.** Text in English. 2003. 3/yr. USD 27 (effective 2004). illus.
Address: 450 W 31st St, New York, NY 10001. http://www.32bny.org. Ed. Daniela Fabricius.

747 ITA ISSN 1125-1379
99 IDEE CASA. Text in Italian. 1994. m. EUR 25 (effective 2005). adv. **Document type:** *Magazine, Consumer.*
Published by: Di Baio Editore SpA, Via Luigi Settembrini 11, Milan, MI 20124, Italy. TEL 39-02-674951, FAX 39-02-67495228, http://www.dibaio.com. Ed. Giuseppe Maria Jonghi Lavarini.

747 ITA ISSN 1592-0011
99 IDEE TECH. Text in Italian. 1995. m. **Document type:** *Magazine, Consumer.*
Formerly (until 2000): Why? Perche? (1591-3392)
Published by: Di Baio Editore SpA, Via Luigi Settembrini 11, Milan, MI 20124, Italy. TEL 39-02-674951, FAX 39-02-67495228, http://www.dibaio.com.

720 USA ISSN 1536-1519
NA1.A1
306090; a journal of emergent architecture and design. Variant title: Architecture Journal. Three Hundred Six Thousand Ninety. Text in English. 2001. s-a. **Description:** Promotes the work and the interests of students of architecture and young designers. Addresses themes such as architecture in a social context, or the studio as an educational model, generating productive dialogue amongst geographically and ideologically diverse students and practitioners.
Published by: (306090 Organization), Princeton Architectural Press, 37 E 7th St, New York, NY 10003. TEL 212-995-9620, FAX 212-995-9454, orders@306090.org, sales@pap.designsys.com, http://www.papress.com/. Ed. Jonathan D Solomon.

ARCHITECTURE—Abstracting, Bibliographies, Statistics

720 USA ISSN 0570-6483
Z5941
ARCHITECTURAL INDEX. Text in English. 1951. a., latest 2004. USD 30 (effective 2005). illus. back issues avail.; reprints avail. **Document type:** *Abstract/Index.* **Description:** Index of the major US architectural journals and one British Architectural journal. Articles are listed by building type, design, location and subject.
Related titles: Online - full text ed.
Address: 3498 Iris Court, Boulder, CO 80304. TEL 303-449-7031, FAX 303-449-3748, http://www.archindex.com. Ed., Pub. Jerry Moore. R&P Ervin J Bell. Adv. contact Mary Ellen Bell. Circ: 2,500 (paid).

720 GBR ISSN 1359-740X
Z5941
ARCHITECTURAL PUBLICATIONS INDEX. Text in English. 1973. q. adv. illus. reprints avail. **Document type:** *Abstract/Index.*
Formerly (until 1995): Architectural Periodicals Index (0266-4380); Supersedes: R I B A Library Bulletin (0033-6912)
Related titles: CD-ROM ed.: Architectural Publications Index on Disc. ISSN 1357-0536. GBP 800 (effective 2005); Magnetic Tape ed.; Online - full text ed.
—**CCC.**
Published by: (British Architectural Library), R I B A Publications, 66 Portland Place, London, W1B 1AD, United Kingdom. TEL 44-20-75805533, FAX 44-20-72551541, info@inst.riba.org, http://www.riba.org. Circ: 800.

016.720 AUS
AUSTRALIAN ARCHITECTURE DATABASE. Abbreviated title: A R C H. Text in English. q. **Document type:** *Abstract/Index.* **Description:** Cummulative index to Australian and New Zealand architecture periodicals. Covers architecture, architects, building, interior design, conservation and restoration, and landscape architecture.
Formerly: Australian Architectural Periodicals Index (Print Edition) (0817-2684)
Media: CD-ROM (from R M I T Publishing). **Related titles:** Microfiche ed.: AUD 35 per issue 1910-1983; AUD 50 per issue 1984-1997 (effective 2000); Online - full text ed.

Published by: North Sydney Council, Stanton Library, Reader Services Department, PO Box 12, North Sydney, NSW 2059, Australia. TEL 61-2-99368400, FAX 61-2-99368440, infodesk@northsydney.nsw.gov.au. Ed. Helen Perry.

720 016.5 USA ISSN 1085-2875
Z5945
AVERY INDEX TO ARCHITECTURAL PERIODICALS. Text in English. 1934. a. **Document type:** *Abstract/Index.* **Description:** Provides a comprehensive listing of articles on architecture and design from over 700 scholarly and popular publications.
Related titles: CD-ROM ed.: (from National Information Services Corp. (N I S C)); Online - full text ed.: (from Research Libraries Group).
Published by: (Getty Research Institute of the J. Paul Getty Trust), Columbia University, Avery Architectural and Fine Arts Library, 300 Avery, 1172 Amsterdam Ave, New York, NY 10027. TEL 212-854-3501, avery@libraries.cul.columbia.edu, http://www.getty.edu/research/conducting_research/avery_index/, http://www.columbia.edu/cu/lweb/indiv/avery/.

721 DEU
BAULIT BAUSCHAEDEN. Text in German. 1985. q. adv. bk.rev. back issues avail. **Document type:** *Bulletin, Trade.*
Formerly: Bulldok Bauschaeden (0177-8285)
Related titles: ♦ Supplement to: Arconis. ISSN 0949-7153.
Published by: (Fraunhofer Informationszentrum Raum und Bau), Fraunhofer I R B Verlag, Nobelstr 12, Stuttgart, 70569, Germany. TEL 49-711-9702500, FAX 49-711-9702507, irb@irbdirekt.de, http://www.irbdirekt.de/baulit/. Circ: 1,500.

016.7 USA ISSN 0360-2699
Z5939
BIBLIOGRAPHIC GUIDE TO ART AND ARCHITECTURE. Text in English. a. USD 660 (effective 2005). **Document type:** *Bibliography.* **Description:** Lists non-journal publications on art and architecture from all historic periods and all parts of the world. Includes materials catalogued during the past year by the New York Public Library, Art and Architecture Division, with additional entries from LC MARC tapes.
Formerly: Art and Architecture Book Guide (0098-2822)
Published by: G.K. Hall & Co. (Subsidiary of: Gale Group), 12 Lunar Dr, Woodbridge, CT 06525. TEL 203-397-2600, 800-444-0799, FAX 203-397-8296, remmel.nunn@gale.com, http://www.galegroup.com/gkhall. **Subscr. to:** Simon & Schuster, PO Box 7500, Riverside, NJ 08075-8075. TEL 800-223-2336.

BIO-BIBLIOGRAPHIES IN ART AND ARCHITECTURE. see *ART—Abstracting, Bibliographies, Statistics*

CIMAISE; contemporary art. see *ART—Abstracting, Bibliographies, Statistics*

CONTRIBUTIONS TO THE STUDY OF ART AND ARCHITECTURE. see *ART—Abstracting, Bibliographies, Statistics*

CURRENT BIBLIOGRAPHY ON SCIENCE AND TECHNOLOGY: CIVIL ENGINEERING AND ARCHITECTURE/KAGAKU GIJUTSU BUNKEN SOKUHO. DOBOKU, KENCHIKU KOGAKU HEN. see *ENGINEERING—Abstracting, Bibliographies, Statistics*

DESIGN AND APPLIED ARTS INDEX. see *ART—Abstracting, Bibliographies, Statistics*

721 DEU ISSN 0177-3550
KURZBERICHTE AUS DER BAUFORSCHUNG. Text in German. 1985. bi-m. adv. bk.rev. back issues avail. **Document type:** *Magazine, Trade.*
Formed by the merger of (1960-1985): Kurzberichte aus der Bauforschung. Teil 1 (0343-1282); (1960-1985): Kurzberichte aus der Bauforschung. Teil 2 (0343-1290); Both of which superseded in part (in 1977): Kurzberichte aus der Bauforschung (0343-1118)
Published by: (Fraunhofer Informationszentrum Raum und Bau), Fraunhofer I R B Verlag, Nobelstr 12, Stuttgart, 70569, Germany. TEL 49-711-9702500, FAX 49-711-9702507, irb@irbdirekt.de, http://www.irbdirekt.de. Circ: 400.

720.21 ZWE
ZIMBABWE. CENTRAL STATISTICAL OFFICE. ARCHITECTS BULLETIN. Text in English. q. ZWD 60.50 in Africa; ZWD 75.10 in Europe; ZWD 87.20 elsewhere (effective 2000). **Document type:** *Government.*
Published by: Central Statistical Office, Causeway, PO Box 8063, Harare, Zimbabwe. TEL 263-4-706681, FAX 263-4-728529.

ARCHITECTURE—Computer Applications

720.972 MEX
A M ARQUITECTURA MEXICANA. Short title: A M. Text in Spanish. 1987 (no.2). s-a. MXP 50 per issue (effective 1999). **Description:** Covers contemporary Mexican architecture. Part of the work is based on computer applications.
Formerly: Cuadernos de Arquitectura Docencia
Indexed: AIAP.
Published by: Universidad Nacional Autonoma de Mexico, Facultad de Arquitectura, c/o Arq. Enrique X. de Anda, Circuito Interior de Cd. Universitaria, Deleg. Coyoacan, Mexico City, DF 04510, Mexico. TEL 52-5-6220318, FAX 52-5-6166545, http://ce-atl.posgrado.unam.mx/. Ed. Ramon Vargas Salguero.

720 USA ISSN 1530-0889
QA76.9.F38
INTERNATIONAL CONFERENCE ON DEPENDABLE SYSTEMS AND NETWORKS. PROCEEDINGS. Text in English. 2000. a. USD 285 per vol.; USD 114 per vol. to members (effective 2004). **Document type:** *Proceedings, Trade.* **Description:** Aims to allow researchers, practitioners, and users to learn and exchange information on the latest research results and the state of the practice in dependable systems and networks.
Formed by the merger of (1991-2000): Working Conference on Dependable Computing for Critical Applications. Proceedings; (1971-2000): International Symposium on Fault-Tolerant Computing. Proceedings (0363-8928)
Published by: Institute of Electrical and Electronics Engineers, Inc., 3 Park Ave, 17th Fl, New York, NY 10016-5997. TEL 212-419-7900, FAX 212-752-4929, customer.service@ieee.org, http://www.ieee.org.

720.285 GBR ISSN 1478-0771
NA2728
▼ ➤ **THE INTERNATIONAL JOURNAL OF ARCHITECTUAL COMPUTING.** Text in English. 2003 (Jan). q. GBP 195; GBP 212 combined subscription print & online eds. (effective 2006). **Document type:** *Journal, Academic/Scholarly.*
Related titles: Online - full text ed.: GBP 187 (effective 2006) (from EBSCO Publishing, Gale Group, IngentaConnect, Swets Information Services).
—BLDSC (4542.103300), IE.
Published by: Multi-Science Publishing Co. Ltd., 5 Wates Way, Brentwood, Essex CM15 9TB, United Kingdom. TEL 44-1277-244632, FAX 44-1277-223453, sciencem@hotmail.com, http://www.multi-science.co.uk/ijac.htm. Ed. Andre Brown.

720 JPN
NIKKEI DIGITAL KENSETSU. Text in Japanese. bi-m. JPY 1,200 (effective 2000). adv. back issues avail. **Document type:** *Trade.* **Description:** Offers information on the use of digital equipment and technology in the construction industry.
Published by: Nikkei Business Publications Inc. (Subsidiary of: Nihon Keizai Shimbun, Inc.), 2-7-6 Hirakawa-cho, Chiyoda-ku, Tokyo, 102-8622, Japan. TEL 81-3-5210-8311, FAX 81-3-5210-8530, info@nikkeibpnyc.com, info@nikkeibp-america.com, http://www.nikkeibp.com. Ed. Mutsumi Saito. Pub. Shoji Tanabe. Adv. contact Yunya Seki. B&W page JPY 319,000, color page JPY 440,000; trim 208 x 280. **Dist. in America by:** Nikkei Business Publications America Inc., 575 Fifth Ave, 20th Fl, New York, NY 10017.

ART

see also ADVERTISING AND PUBLIC RELATIONS ; HOBBIES ; MUSEUMS AND ART GALLERIES

615.85156 USA
A A T A NEWSLETTER. Text in English. q. USD 26 domestic; USD 38 foreign (effective 2000). adv. **Document type:** *Newsletter, Academic/Scholarly.*
Former titles: Inklinks (Mundelin); American Art Therapy Association Newsletter (1066-4076)
Published by: American Art Therapy Association, Inc., 1202 Allanson Rd, Mundelein, IL 60060. TEL 847-949-6064, 888-290-0878, FAX 847-566-4580, info@arttherapy.org, http://www.arttherapy.org. Ed. Deborah Mickelsen. Adv. contact Karen Savage. Circ: 5,000.

A A U P BOOK AND JACKET SHOW. see *PUBLISHING AND BOOK TRADE*

765 USA ISSN 1076-6480
A & E MAGAZINE; the magazine for awards & engraving professionals. Variant title: Awards & Engravings Magazine. Text in English. m. USD 38 in US & Canada; USD 85 elsewhere (effective 2005). adv. illus. **Document type:** *Magazine, Trade.* **Description:** Reviews topics and products of interest to engravers.
Published by: National Business Media, Inc., PO Box 1416, Broomfield, CO 80038. TEL 303-469-0424, FAX 303-469-5730, aeeditor@nbm.com, http://www.nbm.com/aemag. Ed. Steve Wieber. Pub. Dave Pomeroy. Circ: 4,400 (paid); 4,700 (controlled).

A & U; America's AIDS magazine. (Art & Understanding) see *LITERATURE*

700 USA
A - C JOURNAL*. Text in English. 1996. s-a. **Document type:** *Bulletin, Government.*
Published by: Michigan Council for the Arts, P O Box 30705, Lansing, MI 48909-8205. TEL 313-256-3731, FAX 313-256-3781. Ed. Jan Fedewa. Circ: 12,000.

A D A MAGAZINE. (Art, Design, Architecture) see *ARCHITECTURE*

A E V NEWS. see *EDUCATION—Teaching Methods And Curriculum*

760 DEU
A G D QUARTAL. Text in German. 1989. q. EUR 7.50 newsstand/cover (effective 2004). adv. **Document type:** *Magazine, Trade.*
Published by: Allianz Deutscher Designer e.V., Steinstr 3, Braunschweig, 38100, Germany. TEL 49-531-16757, FAX 49-531-16989, info@agd.de, http://www.agd.de. adv.: B&W page EUR 1,200, color page EUR 1,650. Circ: 3,600 (paid and controlled).

709 USA
A G S QUARTERLY. Text in English. 1977. q. USD 40 includes membership (effective 2003). adv. bk.rev. bibl.; illus. **Document type:** *Newsletter.* **Description:** Information about projects, literature and research concerning gravestones and about activities of the Association for Gravestone Studies.
Formerly: Association for Gravestone Studies. Newsletter (0146-5783)
Published by: Association for Gravestone Studies, 278 Main St, Ste 207, Greenfield, MA 01301-3230. TEL 413-772-0836, info@gravestonestudies.org, http://www.gravestonestudies.org. Ed., R&P Rosalee Oakley. Adv. contact Andrea Carlin. Circ: 1,100.

700 780 USA ISSN 8755-500X
A H A! HISPANIC ARTS NEWS. Text in English. 1975. q. USD 20 (effective 2001). adv. bk.rev. charts; illus. back issues avail. **Document type:** *Newsletter.* **Description:** Contains opportunities for artists, calendar of events, and editorials on events affecting the arts community.
Formerly: Hispanic Arts (0732-1643)
Published by: Association of Hispanic Arts, 250 W 26th St, 4th Fl, New York, NY 10001. TEL 212-727-7227, FAX 212-727-0549, ahanews@latinoarts.org, http://www.latinoarts.org. Ed., R&P Sandra Perez TEL 212-727-7227 ext 19. Adv. contact Gloria Herrera TEL 212-727-7227 ext 13. Circ: 7,000.

A I A. (Arquitectura, Ingenieria, Artes) see *ARCHITECTURE*

702.88 AUS ISSN 0313-5381
➤ **A I C C M BULLETIN.** Text in English. 1975. s-a. AUD 75 to individuals; AUD 200 to institutions; AUD 30 to students (effective 2000). adv. bk.rev. back issues avail. **Document type:** *Bulletin, Academic/Scholarly.* **Description:** Focuses on conservation of cultural materials.
Indexed: A&ATA, RILM.
—BLDSC (2409.316700), IE, ingenta.
Published by: Australian Institute for the Conservation of Cultural Material Inc., PO Box 1638, Canberra, ACT 2601, Australia. TEL 06-62548695, alexand@dynamite.com.au. Circ: 500.

780 700 USA
A I C F NEWSLETTER. Text in English. 1975. 3/yr. membership. **Document type:** *Newsletter.* **Description:** Covers music, dance, film, theatre, visual arts and other creative and performing arts in Israel.
Formerly: Hadashot
Published by: America-Israel Cultural Foundation, 51 E 42nd St, Ste 400, New York, NY 10017. TEL 212-557-1600, FAX 212-557-1611, usaaicf@aol.com, http://aicf.webnet.org. Ed. Felicity Dell'Aquila. Circ: 3,000.

700 333.7 USA ISSN 1060-3247
A I C NEWS. Text in English. 1975. bi-m. USD 100 to members. adv. **Description:** Reports on conservation issues, conferences, new techniques and materials, as well as AIC activities.
Formerly (until 1991): A I C Newsletter (0887-750X)
Published by: American Institute for Conservation of Historic and Artistic Works, 1717 K St, N W, Ste 301, Washington, DC 20006. TEL 202-452-9545, FAX 202-452-9328, infoAIC@aol.com, http://palimpsest.stanford.edu/aic/. Ed. Lisa Goldberg. Circ: 3,000 (controlled).

700 USA
A I: PERFORMANCE FOR THE PLANET. (Arts International) Cover title: ai. Text in English. 3/yr. USD 50 membership; USD 7.95 newsstand/cover domestic; USD 10.95 newsstand/cover in Canada.
Indexed: RILM.
Published by: Arts International, 251 Park Ave S, 5th Fl, New York, NY 10010. aimagazine@artinternational.org. Ed. Katherine Wessling.

A M S STUDIES IN THE EMBLEM. see *GENEALOGY AND HERALDRY*

700 USA
A P A A NEWSLETTER. Text in English. 1937. s-a. membership. back issues avail. **Document type:** *Newsletter.* **Description:** Contains news and features on the association, announcements of exhibit winners and meetings, minutes of meetings, instructions on entering art exhibits, and a catalog of entries and events.

Published by: American Physicians Art Association, 1130 N Cabrillo, San Pedro, CA 90731. TEL 310-436-9645, FAX 310-436-7119, cbsw70a@mail.prodigy.com. Ed., R&P James S Benedict TEL 310-832-7024. Circ: 300.

A R L I S - N A UPDATE. see *LIBRARY AND INFORMATION SCIENCES*

700   USA   ISSN 0892-3582

A S A ARTISAN. Text in English. 1972. q. **Document type:** *Trade.* **Description:** Information for and about artists and craftspeople, with national calendar of events.
Formerly (until 1982): A S A Bulletin
Published by: American Society of Artists, Inc., PO Box 1326, Palatine, IL 60078. TEL 312-751-2500.

700.1   USA   ISSN 1089-1668

A S A NEWSLETTER. Text in English. 1942. 3/yr. USD 70 domestic membership (effective 2003). adv. bk.rev. **Document type:** *Newsletter, Academic/Scholarly.* **Description:** Articles and announcements about aesthetics, philosophy of the arts, art criticism and theory of the arts.
Related titles: Online - full text ed.
Indexed: RILM.
Published by: American Society for Aesthetics, Marquette University, 707 N 11th, Rm 322, P O Box 1881, Milwaukee, WI 53201-1881. TEL 414-288-7831, FAX 414-288-5415, asastcar@marquette.edu, http://www.aesthetics-online.org. Ed., R&P James Harold. Adv. contact Curtis Carter. Circ: 1,000 (paid).

700   USA   ISSN 0065-0129
QE294   CODEN: HDKUEA

A.W. MELLON LECTURES IN THE FINE ARTS. Text in English. 1956. irreg., latest 2001. price varies. reprint service avail. from PQC. **Document type:** *Monographic series.*
—CCC.
Published by: Princeton University Press, 41 William St, Princeton, NJ 08540-5237. TEL 609-258-4900, 800-777-4726, FAX 609-258-6305, http://pup.princeton.edu/catalogs/series/bsawm.html.

AARET FORTALT I BILLEDER. see *HISTORY—History Of Europe*

700 800 780   DEU   ISSN 0567-4999

ABHANDLUNGEN ZUR KUNST-, MUSIK- UND LITERATURWISSENSCHAFT. Text in German. 1958 (no.3). irreg., latest vol.397, 1997. price varies. **Document type:** *Monographic series.*
Indexed: MLA, MLA-IB, RASB.
Published by: Bouvier Verlag Herbert Grundmann, Am Hof 28, Bonn, 53113, Germany. TEL 49-228-7290184, FAX 49-228-630872, verlag@books.de.

700   ESP   ISSN 0212-6117
NX562.A3

ABRENTE. Text in Spanish. 1969. a.
Indexed: RILM.
—CINDOC.
Published by: Real Academia de Bellas Artes de Nuestra Senora del Rosario, Plaza Pinto Soto Mayor, s-n, Coruna, 15001, Spain.

700   ESP   ISSN 1130-3565

ABSIDE; boletin de la asociacion de amigos de la catedral. Text in Spanish. 1987. 3/yr.
—CINDOC.
Published by: Asociacion de Amigos de la Catedral de Siguenza, Plaza Obispo de Bernando, s-n, Siguenza, Comunidad de Castilla La Mancha 19250, Spain.

700   ESP   ISSN 0567-560X
NX7

ACADEMIA (MADRID, 1881). Text in Spanish. 1881. s-a.
Former titles (until 1951): Real Academia de Bellas Artes de San Fernando. Anales (0210-6418); (until 1939): Real Academia de Bellas Artes de San Fernando. Boletin (0210-640X)
Indexed: PCI, RILM.
—CINDOC.
Published by: Real Academia de Bellas Artes de San Fernando, C. Alcala, 13, Madrid, 28014, Spain. TEL 34-91-5240864, FAX 34-91-5231599, mcutande@terra.es, http://www.rabast.inside.es/.

700   ARG

ACADEMIA NACIONAL DE BELLAS ARTES. ANUARIO. Text in Spanish. 1973. a. USD 120. illus.
Published by: Academia Nacional de Bellas Artes, Sanchez de Bustamante, 2663, Buenos Aires, 1425, Argentina. TEL 54-11-48022469. Circ: 700.

700   BEL

ACADEMIAE ANALECTA. KLASSE VAN DE KUNSTEN. Text in Dutch, English; Summaries in English. 1938. irreg., latest vol.57, no.1, 1998. price varies. back issues avail. **Document type:** *Academic/Scholarly.*

Former titles (until 1980): Koninklijke Academie voor Wetenschappen, Letteren en Schone Kunsten Van Belgie. Mededelingen. Klasse der Schone Kunsten (0770-1349); (until 1972): Koninklijke Vlaamse Academie voor Wetenschappen, Letteren en Schone Kunsten van Belgie. Mededelingen. Klasse der Schone Kunsten (0770-139X)
Indexed: BHA, RILM.
Published by: Koninklijke Vlaamse Academie van Belgie voor Wetenschappen en Kunsten/The Royal Flemish Academy of Belgium for Science and the Arts, Hertogsstraat 1, Brussels, 1000, Belgium. TEL 32-2-5502323, FAX 32-2-5502325, info@kvab.be, http://www.kvab.be. Ed. G Verbeke. Circ: 700.
Dist. by: Brepols Publishers, Begijnhof 67, Turnhout 2300, Belgium. TEL 32-14-40-25-00, FAX 32-14-42-89-19.

700   GBR

ACADEMIC FILE INTERNATIONAL NEWS & PHOTO SYNDICATION. Text in English. q. **Description:** Online information service for the media concerning the developing world.
Media: Online - full text.
Published by: (Centre for Near East Afro-Asian Research (NEAR)), Eastern Art Publishing Group, 27 Wallorton Gardens, London, SW14 8DX, United Kingdom. TEL 44-20-83921122, FAX 44-20-83921422, easternart@compuserve.co.uk. Ed. Shirley Rizvi. Circ: (controlled).

700   BEL   ISSN 0378-7923
AS242

ACADEMIE ROYALE DES SCIENCES, DES LETTRES ET DES BEAUX-ARTS DE BELGIQUE. CLASSE DES BEAUX-ARTS. MEMOIRES. Text in French. 1919. irreg. (1350-1475). price varies. 200 p./no.; **Document type:** *Monographic series.*
Indexed: BHA.
—KNAW.
Published by: Academie Royale des Sciences des Lettres et des Beaux-Arts de Belgique, Palais des Academies, Rue Ducale 1, Brussels, 1000, Belgium. TEL 32-2-5502211, FAX 32-2-25502205, arb@cjwb.be. Ed. Leo Houziaux. Adv. contact Beatrice Denuit TEL 32-2-5502221. Circ: 500 (controlled). **Subscr. to:** Academie Royale de Belgique, Departement Publications, 1 Rue Ducale, Brussels 1000, Belgium. TEL 32-2-5502, FAX 32-2-5502205, luc.moreau@cfwb.be, http://www.arb.cfwb.be.

ACCADEMIA CLEMENTINA. ATTI E MEMORIE. see *HISTORY—History Of Europe*

ACCADEMIA PATAVINA DI SCIENZE LETTERE ED ARTI. ATTI E MEMORIE. see *LITERATURE*

ACCADEMIA PATAVINA DI SCIENZE LETTERE ED ARTI. COLLANA ACCADEMICA. see *LITERATURE*

ACCADEMIA ROVERETANA DEGLI AGIATI. ATTI. FASC. A: CLASSE DI SCIENZE UMANE, LETTERE ED ARTI. see *HUMANITIES: COMPREHENSIVE WORKS*

ACCADEMIA ROVERETANA DEGLI AGIATI. MEMORIE. see *HUMANITIES: COMPREHENSIVE WORKS*

ACCADEMIA ROVERETANA DEGLI AGIATI. PUBBLICAZIONI DIVERSE. see *HUMANITIES: COMPREHENSIVE WORKS*

741.6029   USA   ISSN 1056-4101
NX110

ACCESS (SEATTLE); a guide to the visual arts in Washington State. Text in English. 1972. irreg. (approx. biennial). **Document type:** *Directory.* **Description:** Directory of Washington State exhibition spaces. Includes extensive addenda of arts services, organizations, education and professional training and a bibliography of additional resources.
Published by: Allied Arts of Seattle, 216 1st Ave S., Ste. 253, Seattle, WA 98104-2586. TEL 206-624-0432. Circ: 5,000.

ACE WEEKLY. see *LITERARY AND POLITICAL REVIEWS*

700 780   CAN

ACHE. Text in English. a. USD 3 newsstand/cover (effective 2005). illus. **Description:** Profiling zine and punk culture. It includes interviews with musicians, editors, authors, and local artists, as well as a music review column and the editor's own comics.
Published by: Armen Svadjian, Ed. & Pub., 167 Cortleigh Blvd, Toronto, ON M5N 1P6, Canada. achemag@yahoo.ca, achemag@yahoo.com.

700   CAN

THE ACID-FREE PAPER. Text in English. irreg. back issues avail. **Description:** Covers fine art, literature, poetry and fiction.
Media: Online - full text.
Published by: Acid-Free Paper, Canada. smithk@vianet.on.ca, http://acid-free.simplenet.com/. Ed. Kevin D Smith.

ACTA GRAPHICA; journal of printing science and graphic communications. see *TECHNOLOGY: COMPREHENSIVE WORKS*

700.9   SVN   ISSN 1408-0419
N7255.S56

➤ **ACTA HISTORIAE ARTIS SLOVENICA.** Text in Multiple languages. 1996. a. EUR 20.60 per vol. to individuals; EUR 25.75 per vol. to institutions (effective 2004). bk.rev. illus. 200 p./no. 1 cols./p.; back issues avail. **Document type:** *Journal, Academic/Scholarly.* **Description:** Publishes the results of research studies in the field of the history of art relating to Slovenia and its cultural connections with other European countries.
Related titles: Online - full text ed.
Indexed: DIP, IBR, IBZ.
Published by: (Slovenska Akademija Znanosti in Umetnosti, Znanstvenoraziskovalni Center, Umetnostnozgodovinski Institut Franceta Steleta/Slovenian Academy of Sciences and Arts, Scientific Research Centre, France Stele Institute of Art History), Zalozba Z R C/Scientific Research Centre Publishing, Novi trg 2, P.O. Box 306, Ljubljana, 1001, Slovenia. TEL 386-1-4706474, FAX 386-1-4257719, umzg@zrc-sazu.si, zalozba@zrc-sazu.si, http://www.zrc-sazu.si/www/uifs/acta/, http://www.zrc-sazu.si/zalozba. Ed., R&P Mrs. Alenka Klemenc. Pub. Vojislav Likar TEL 386-1-4706477. Adv. contact Tinka Selic. Circ: 400. **Co-sponsor:** Ministrstvo za Znanost in Tehnologijo in Ministrstvo za Kulturo.

709   HUN   ISSN 0001-5830
N6

ACTA HISTORIAE ARTIUM ACADEMIE SCIENTIARIUM HUNGARICAE; an art-historical journal of the Hungarian Academy of Sciences. Text in English, French, German, Italian. 1953. q. USD 320 (effective 2006). adv. bk.rev. illus.; abstr.; bibl. index. 80 p./no.; back issues avail. **Document type:** *Journal, Academic/Scholarly.* **Description:** Presents papers on the history of art extending from the Middle Ages to contemporary art. Includes critical analyses of research publications.
Related titles: Online - full content ed.: ISSN 1588-2608.
Indexed: AIAP, AmH&L, ArtHuCI, BHA, CurCont, DIP, HistAb, IBR, IBZ, RASB, RILM.
—CCC.
Published by: (Magyar Tudomanyos Akademia/Hungarian Academy of Sciences), Akademiai Kiado Rt. (Subsidiary of: Wolters Kluwer N.V., Prielle Kornelia U. 19, Budapest, 1117, Hungary. TEL 36-1-4648282, FAX 36-1-4648221, journals@akkrt.hu, http://www.akkrt.hu. Ed. Erno Marosi.

709 720   POL   ISSN 0860-4746

ACTA UNIVERSITATIS WRATISLAVIENSIS. HISTORIA SZTUKI. Text in Polish; Summaries in English, German. 1988. irreg. price varies. **Document type:** *Academic/Scholarly.*
Published by: (Uniwersytet Wroclawski), Wydawnictwo Uniwersytetu Wroclawskiego Spolka z o.o., Pl Uniwersytecki 9-13, Wroclaw, 50-137, Poland. TEL 48-71-441006, FAX 48-71-402735. Eds. Jan Wrabec, Zofia Ostrowska Keblowska. Circ: 700.

ACTION (POTTS POINT). see *EDUCATION—Teaching Methods And Curriculum*

709   FRA   ISSN 0293-9789

ACTUALITE DES ARTS PLASTIQUES. Text in French. 3/yr. **Description:** Reference collection dedicated to the development of contemporary art.
Published by: Centre National de Documentation Pedagogique, 29 rue de l'Ulm, Paris, Cedex 5 75230, France. TEL 33-1-46349000, FAX 33-1-46345544. Ed. Bernard Piens. **Subscr. to:** CNDP - Abonnement, B.P. 750, Sainte Genevieve Cedex 60732, France. FAX 33-3-44033013.

700 746.9   BEL   ISSN 1376-3156

AD! DICT. Text in English. 2000. q. EUR 52 domestic; GBP 9 in United States; EUR 60 elsewhere (effective 2003).
Published by: Ad! dict Creative Lab, Delaunoystraat 60, Bruxelles, 1080, Belgium. TEL 32-2-289-5101, FAX 32-2-289-5102, info@addictlab.com, http://www.addictlab.com. Ed. Anja Samson. Pub. Jan van Mol.

ADAM INTERNATIONAL REVIEW. see *LITERATURE*

ADORANTEN. see *ARCHAEOLOGY*

700   ITA   ISSN 1127-1345

AEDON; rivista di arti e diritto on line. Text in Italian. 3/yr. free. **Document type:** *Academic/Scholarly.*
Media: Online - full content.
Published by: Societa Editrice Il Mulino, Strada Maggiore 37, Bologna, 40125, Italy. TEL 39-051-256011, FAX 39-051-256034, riviste@mulino.it, http://www.aedon.mulino.it/, http://www.mulino.it.

AERIAL. see *LITERATURE—Poetry*

AESTHETICA. PRE-PRINT. see *PHILOSOPHY*

700   SWE   ISSN 0349-6708

AESTHETICA UPSALIENSIA. Text in Multiple languages. 1981. irreg., latest vol.7, 1996. price varies. back issues avail. **Document type:** *Monographic series, Academic/Scholarly.*
Related titles: ◆ Series of: Acta Universitatis Upsaliensis. ISSN 0346-5462.

Published by: (Uppsala Universitet), Uppsala Universitet, Acta Universitatis Upsaliensis/University Publications from Uppsala, PO Box 256, Uppsala, 75105, Sweden. TEL 46-18-4713922, http://www.ub.uu.se/upu/auu. Ed. Bengt Landgren. **Dist. by:** Almqvist & Wiksell International.

709.2   NLD

AETA AUREA. Text in English. 1981. irreg., latest vol.12, 1996. price varies. illus. back issues avail. **Document type:** *Monographic series.* **Description:** Publishes monographic studies of notable Dutch painters from the 16th and 17th centuries.
Published by: Davaco Publishers, Beukenlaan 3, Doornspijk, 8085 RK, Netherlands. TEL 31-525-661823, FAX 31-525-662153.

700   GNQ   ISSN 1022-5692

AFRICA 2000. Text in Spanish. q.
Published by: Centro Cultural Hispano-Guineano, Apdo. 180, Malabo, Equatorial Guinea. TEL 240-927220. Ed. Donato Ndongo Bidyogo.

AFRICA E MEDITERRANEO; trimestrale di cultura, politica, economia, societa. see *ANTHROPOLOGY*

709.6   USA   ISSN 0001-9933
NX587

➤ **AFRICAN ARTS.** Text in English. 1967. q. USD 72 in US & Canada to individuals; USD 92 elsewhere to individuals; USD 125 in US & Canada to institutions; USD 145 elsewhere to institutions (effective 2006). adv. bk.rev. charts; illus. index. back issues avail.; reprint service avail. from PQC. **Document type:** *Journal, Academic/Scholarly.*
Related titles: Microform ed.: (from PQC); Online - full text ed.: (from bigchalk, Chadwyck-Healey Inc., EBSCO Publishing, Florida Center for Library Automation, Gale Group, H.W. Wilson, Northern Light Technology, Inc., O C L C Online Computer Library Center, Inc., ProQuest Information & Learning).
Indexed: ABCT, ABM, AIAP, AICP, ASCA, Acal, AnthLit, ArtHuCI, ArtInd, CCA, CurCont, HumInd, IBR, IBRH, IBSS, IIBP, IndIslam, MASUSE, MLA, MLA-IB, PCI, RASB, RILM, SSCI. —BLDSC (0732.315000), IE, Infotrieve, ingenta. **CCC.**
Published by: University of California at Los Angeles, James S. Coleman African Studies Center, 10244 Bunche Hall, 405 Hilgard Ave, Los Angeles, CA 90095-1310. TEL 310-825-3686, FAX 310-206-2250, afriarts@ucla.edu, isacasc@international.ucla.edu, http://www.international.ucla.edu/africa/africanarts/. Adv. contact Greg Cherry. Circ: 5,000. **Dist. by:** M I T Press, c/o Trilateral, 100 Maple Ridge Dr, Cumberland, RI 02864.

➤ **AFRICHE;** quaderni di introduzione alle realta africane. see *HISTORY—History Of Africa*

700   GBR   ISSN 1465-4253

AFTERALL; a journal of art, context and enquiry. Text in English. 1999. s-a. GBP 12 in Europe to individuals; GBP 25 elsewhere to individuals; GBP 25 in Europe to institutions; GBP 35 elsewhere to institutions (effective 2004).
Indexed: ABM.
Published by: Central Saint Martins College of Art & Design, 107-109 Charing Cross Rd, London, WC2H 0DU, United Kingdom. TEL 44-20-75147212, FAX 44-20-75147166, afterall@linst.ac.uk, info@csm.linst.ac.uk, afterall_la@afteralljournal.org, http://www.afteralljournal.org, http://www.csm.linst.ac.uk. Eds. Charles Esche, Mark Lewis.

700 808.8   USA

AFTERNOON MAGAZINE; a magazine of art and literature. Text in English. 1995. irreg. **Description:** International literary magazine.
Media: Online - full text.
Published by: Motley Focus Locus, 788 Columbus Ave 7P, New York, NY 10025. stephenw@escape.com, timber@silcom.com, http://www.motley-focus.com/~timber/afternoon.html. Eds. Stephen Williamson, William Timberman.

700   CAN   ISSN 0829-4801

AGENDA. Text in English. 1985. q. CND 30 domestic; CND 40 in United States; CND 50 elsewhere (effective 2001). adv. **Document type:** *Trade.* **Description:** Includes calls for entries, job opportunities, resources, events and other news.
Published by: Visual Arts Ontario, 1153A Queen's St W, Toronto, ON M6J 1J4, Canada. TEL 416-591-8883, FAX 416-591-2432, zao@wwonline.com. Ed. Melissa Gordon. R&P Hennie Wolff. Adv. contact David McClyment. Circ: 4,000.

AIN SHAMS UNIVERSITY. FACULTY OF ARTS. ANNALS. see *LITERATURE*

AIOLOS; tidskrift foer Litteratur, teori och estetik. see *LITERATURE*

700 666 790.13   USA   ISSN 1040-8509
NC915.A35

AIRBRUSH ACTION. Text in English. 1985. bi-m. USD 26.95 domestic; USD 33 in Canada; USD 50 elsewhere (effective 2005). adv. bk.rev. illus.; tr.lit. back issues avail.; reprints avail. **Document type:** *Magazine, Trade.*
Related titles: Online - full text ed.

Indexed: ABM.
Published by: Airbrush Action, Inc., PO Box 438, Allenwood, NJ 08720. TEL 732-223-7878, FAX 732-223-2855, info@airbrushaction.com, http://www.airbrushaction.com. Ed. Michael Duck. Circ: 55,000 (paid).

751.494   DEU   ISSN 1434-3223
NC915.A35

AIRBRUSH ART & ACTION. Text in German. 1994. bi-m. EUR 48; EUR 4.35 newsstand/cover (effective 2004). adv. **Document type:** *Magazine, Consumer.* **Description:** Contains news and instructions for airbrush artists and fans.
Published by: T V Trend Verlag GmbH, Hertener Markt 7, Herten, 45699, Germany. TEL 49-2366-808100, FAX 49-2366-808190, vmkd@real-net.de. Eds. Aron Cserveny, Eddy Wouters. Pub. Alexander Welke. R&P Arno Welke. Adv. contact Olaf in der Beek TEL 49-2366-808201. B&W page EUR 1,800, color page EUR 2,300; trim 210 x 285. Circ: 23,155 (paid).

751.494   USA   ISSN 1363-5565
NC915.A35

AIRBRUSH ART & ACTION. Text in English. 1994. bi-m. USD 14.95; USD 5.95 newsstand/cover. adv. back issues avail. **Document type:** *Magazine, Trade.* **Description:** Provides step-by-step instructions for airbrush art.
Incorporates (1994-1998): Airbrush Magazine
Published by: Paisano Publications, Inc., PO Box 3075, Agoura Hills, CA 91301. TEL 818-889-8740, FAX 818-889-5214, http://www.easyriders.com/newsstand/aaatoc.html. Ed. Roy Batty. Adv. contact Linda Altus. Circ: 35,000. **Dist. in UK by:** Comag, Tavistock Works, Tavistock Rd, W Drayton, Middx UB7 7QX, United Kingdom. TEL 44-1895-444055, FAX 44-1895-433602.

751.494   DEU

AIRBRUSH TOTAL. Text in German. 1991. bi-m. EUR 5.01 newsstand/cover (effective 2002). adv. **Document type:** *Magazine, Consumer.* **Description:** Contains information, instruction, tips and tricks for airbrush artists.
Published by: H C M Verlags GmbH, Im Buhles 4, Glashuetten-Schlossborn, 61479, Germany. TEL 49-6174-9669-0, FAX 49-6174-966999, airbrushtotal@hcm-verlag.de, mailbox@hcm-verlag.de, http://www.hcm-verlag.de/airbrush-total/. Ed. Torsten Weber. Pub. Helmut Redecker. Adv. contact Karin Redecker. B&W page EUR 1,700, color page EUR 2,000. Circ: 21,200 (paid and controlled).

700 666   DEU

AIRBRUSH-ZEITUNG. Text in German. irreg. adv. **Document type:** *Newsletter.*
Media: Online - full text.
Address: Graeflingsberg 36, Henstedt-Ulzburg, 24558, Germany. TEL 49-4193-892580, FAX 49-4193-892581, http://airbrush-zeitung.de. Ed. C Michael Mette.

700   DEU

AIRBRUSH ZEITUNG (ONLINE EDITION); das erste Deutsche Fachmagazin fuer die Spritzpistole. Text in German. 1986. irreg. adv. bk.rev. back issues avail. **Document type:** *Magazine, Consumer.*
Formerly (until 1994): Airbrush Zeitung (Print Edition)
Media: Online - full content.
Published by: Airbrush Zeitung, Graeflingsberg 36, Henstedt-Ulzburg, 24558, Germany. TEL 49-4193-892580, FAX 49-4193-892581, michael.mette@airbrush-zeitung.de, http://www.airbrush-zeitung.de. Ed., Pub. C Michael Mette. Circ: 10,000.

701.17   CHL   ISSN 0568-3939
BH25

AISTHESIS; revista chilena de investigaciones esteticas. Text in Spanish. 1966. a. USD 31 (effective 1999). adv. bibl. cum.index. **Document type:** *Academic/Scholarly.* **Description:** Examines aesthetics and how it relates to art, literature, architecture and drama, with an emphasis on aesthetic criticism and research in Chile.
Indexed: HAPI, IBR, RILM.
Published by: Pontificia Universidad Catolica de Chile, Instituto de Estetica, Av. Jaime Guzman 3300, Santiago, 22, Chile. TEL 52-2-6865085, FAX 52-2-2741642, aisthesi@puc.cl. Ed. Fidel Sepulveda Llanos. Adv. contact Jorge Montoya Veliz. Circ: 1,000.

AKCENT; literatura i sztuka. see *LITERARY AND POLITICAL REVIEWS*

700   USA

ALABAMA ARTS. Text in English. 1969. s-a. free. illus.
Formerly: Ala-Arts (0146-9398)
Published by: State Council on the Arts, 201 Monroe St, Montgomery, AL 36130. TEL 334-242-4076, FAX 334-240-3269. Ed., R&P Sharon Heflin. Circ: 6,000.

ALADIN; le magazine des chineurs. see *ANTIQUES*

ALASKA GEOGRAPHIC. see *GEOGRAPHY*

700   USA

ALASKA STATE COUNCIL ON THE ARTS. COMMUNIQUE. Text in English. 1973. bi-m. USD 10 out of state; free in state (effective 2005). **Document type:** *Newsletter, Consumer.*

Formerly: Arts In Alaska (0094-3568)
Published by: Alaska State Council on the Arts, 411 W. Fourth Ave., Anchorage, AK 99501-2343. TEL 907-269-6610, FAX 907-269-6601, info@aksca.org. Circ: 6,000 (controlled and free).

792   USA

ALASKA. STATE COUNCIL ON THE ARTS. COMMUNIQUE. Short title: A S C A Communique. Text in English. 1973. m. looseleaf. USD 15 (effective 2000); free in Alaska. back issues avail. **Document type:** *Newsletter.* **Description:** Provides news and opportunities for Alaska artists.
Formerly: Alaska. State Council on the Arts. Bulletin; Which superseded: Arts in Alaska (0094-3568)
Related titles: Online - full text ed.
Indexed: CINAHL.
Published by: State Council on the Arts, 411 W Fourth Ave, Ste 1E, Anchorage, AK 99501-2343. TEL 907-269-6610, FAX 907-269-6601, info@aksca.org, http://www.aksca.org. Ed. Helen Howarth. R&P Pat Oldenburg TEL 907-269-6608. Circ: 1,700.

ALBANY INSTITUTE OF HISTORY & ART. ANNUAL REPORT. see *HISTORY—History Of North And South America*

700   CAN   ISSN 1494-1023

ALBERTA BIENNIAL OF CONTEMPORARY ART. Text in English. 1998. biennial. **Document type:** *Government.*
Published by: Edmonton Art Gallery, 2 Sir Winston Churchill Sq., Edmonton, AB T5J 2C1, Canada. TEL 780-422-6223, FAX 780-426-3105, info@edmontonartgallery.com, http://www.edmontonartgallery.com/index.html.

750 860 770 720   ESP   ISSN 1131-6411
NX456

ALBUM, LETRAS Y ARTES. Text in Spanish. 1986. bi-m. EUR 21.64 domestic; USD 85 in Europe; USD 150 in the Americas (effective 2004). **Document type:** *Magazine, Consumer.* **Description:** Covers painting, photography, architecture and literature to immerse the reader in the fundamental forms of expression and to understand art as the consequence of an age.
Indexed: PCI, RILM.
—CINDOC.
Published by: Album, Letras y Artes S.L., Juan Alvarez Mendizabal 58, 1o A, Madrid, 28008, Spain. TEL 34-91-5479742, FAX 34-91-5599027, albumletras@jazzfree.com. Ed. Jesus Tablate Miquis. Circ: 14,000. **Dist. by:** Asociacion de Revistas Culturales de Espana, Hortaleza, 75, Madrid 28004, Spain. TEL 34-91-3086066, FAX 34-91-3199267, info@arce.es, http://www.arce.es.

THE ALEPH; a journal of global perspectives. see *LITERATURE*

700   AUS

ALL ABOUT ART✳ . Text in English. **Description:** Aims to inform readers of the current trends of the arts world, as well as increase their knowledge in art history and techniques.
Media: Online - full text.
Published by: Coral Coast Emporium, 19 Memory Blvd, Innes Park, Bundaberg, QLD 4070, Australia. TEL 61-7-415-56466, http://www.coralcoast.com/allabourtart.html. Ed. Cecilia Marrington.

ALLA BOTTEGA. see *LITERATURE*

700   USA

ALLIED ARTS NEWSLETTER. Text in English. bi-m. **Document type:** *Newsletter.*
Published by: Allied Arts of Seattle, 216 1st Ave S., Ste. 253, Seattle, WA 98104-2586. TEL 206-624-0432.

ALTERTUMSKUNDE DES VORDEREN ORIENTS. see *ASIAN STUDIES*

700   USA   ISSN 1549-3059

AMERICAN ABSTRACT ARTISTS JOURNAL. Text in English. 1996. irreg.
Published by: American Abstract Artists, P O Box 1076, New York, NY 10013-0862.

700 720   ITA   ISSN 0065-6801
DG12

AMERICAN ACADEMY IN ROME. MEMOIRS. Text in Italian. 1917. irreg. price varies. **Document type:** *Monographic series, Academic/Scholarly.*
Indexed: AIAP, BHA, NumL.
Published by: American Academy in Rome, Via Angelo Masina 5, Rome, 00153, Italy. TEL 39-0658461, FAX 39-06-5810788, hgttp://www.aarome.org.

701 USA ISSN 1073-9300
N6505
➤ **AMERICAN ART;** the journal of the Smithsonian American Art Museum. Text in English. 1987. 3/yr. USD 45 combined subscription to individuals print & online eds.; USD 155 combined subscription to institutions print & online eds.; USD 15 per issue to individuals; USD 45 per issue to institutions (effective 2006). adv. bibl.; illus. back issues avail.; reprints avail. **Document type:** *Academic/Scholarly.* **Description:** Encompasses all aspects of the nation's visual heritage from colonial to contemporary times, including new media, popular culture, and decorative arts and crafts. Primary focus is on fine arts.
Formerly (until 1991): Smithsonian Studies in American Art (0890-4901)
Related titles: Microfiche ed.; Online - full text ed.: ISSN 1549-6503 (from EBSCO Publishing, JSTOR (Web-based Journal Archive)).
Indexed: ABM, AIAP, AcaI, AmH&L, ArtInd, BHA, DIP, HistAb, IBR, IBZ, MASUSE, RILM.
—BLDSC (0810.395000), IE, ingenta.
Published by: (Smithsonian American Art Museum), University of Chicago Press, Journals Division, Journals Division, PO Box 37005, Chicago, IL 60637. TEL 773-753-3347, FAX 773-753-0811, subscriptions@journals.uchicago.edu, http://www.journals.uchicago.edu/AmArt. Ed. Cynthia Mills.
Subscr. to: Membership Services.

702.9 USA ISSN 0065-6968
N50
AMERICAN ART DIRECTORY. Text in English. 1898. biennial. USD 299 per issue (effective 2005). index. **Document type:** *Directory.* **Description:** Identifies characteristics of art museums and libraries, enrollment and programs of art schools, major foreign institutions, and state and local systems. Indexed geographically and by institution, personnel, and subject.
Published by: National Register Publishing (Subsidiary of: Marquis Who's Who), 562 Central Ave, New Providence, NJ 07974. TEL 800-473-7020, FAX 908-673-1189, NRPsales@marquiswhoswho.com, http://www.americanartdir.com, http://www.nationalregisterpub.com.

709 USA ISSN 0002-7359
N6505
➤ **AMERICAN ART JOURNAL.** Text in English. 1969. a., latest vol.32, 2001. USD 35 domestic; USD 40 foreign (effective 2004). bk.rev. illus. Index. 96 p./no.; back issues avail.; reprints avail. **Document type:** *Journal, Academic/Scholarly.*
Related titles: Microform ed.: (from PQC); Online - full text ed.
Indexed: ABCT, ABM, AIAP, ASCA, AmH&L, AmHI, ArtHuCI, ArtInd, BHA, CurCont, HistAb, HumInd, IBR, IBRH, IBZ, PCI, RASB, RILM.
—BLDSC (0810.398000).
Published by: Kennedy Galleries, Inc., 730 Fifth Ave, New York, NY 10019. TEL 212-541-9600, FAX 212-977-3833, aaj@kgny.com, inquiry@kgny.com, http://www.kgny.com/pub_aaj.html. Ed. Jayne A Kuchna. Circ: 2,000.

700 USA ISSN 0092-1327
N6505
AMERICAN ART REVIEW. Text in English. 1973. bi-m. USD 23.50 domestic; USD 41.50 in Canada; USD 47.50 elsewhere (effective 2004). adv. bk.rev. illus. **Description:** Covers museum accessions, exhibitions, contemporary and historical artists and their art.
Indexed: AIAP, ArtInd, BHA, CurCont, MagInd, PCI, RILM.
Address: PO Box 480500, Kansas City, MO 64148. TEL 913-451-8801, amartrev@aol.com, http://www.amartrev.com/. Ed. Thomas Kellaway. Circ: 42,000 (paid).

707 USA ISSN 0002-7375
AMERICAN ARTIST. Text in English. 1937. m. USD 29.95 domestic; USD 39.95 foreign (effective 2005). adv. bk.rev. illus. Index. reprints avail. **Document type:** *Magazine, Consumer.* **Description:** Emphasizes figurative art. Includes interviews with prominent artists and articles on technical aspects of drawing and painting.
Related titles: Microfiche ed.: (from NBI); Microform ed.: ISSN 0364-9865; Online - full text ed.: (from bigchalk, EBSCO Publishing, Florida Center for Library Automation, Gale Group, O C L C Online Computer Library Center, Inc., ProQuest Information & Learning).
Indexed: A&ATA, ABCT, ABM, ABS&EES, AIAP, AcaI, ArtInd, BEL&L, BHA, BRI, CBRI, DIP, IBR, IBZ, MASUSE, MagInd, PCI, PMR, RASB, RGAb, RGPR, RILM, RefSour, TOM.
—BLDSC (0810.410000), IE, Infotrieve, ingenta. **CCC.**
Published by: V N U Business Publications (Subsidiary of: V N U Business Media), 770 Broadway, New York, NY 10003-9595. TEL 646-654-7601, FAX 646-654-5351, bmcomm@vnuinc.com, http://www.myamericanartist.com/americanartist/index.jsp, http://www.vnubusinessmedia.com/. Ed. Stephen Doherty. R&P Simon Adams. Adv. contact Irene Gruen. Circ: 123,300 (paid).

707.1025 USA ISSN 0146-9606
N328
AMERICAN ARTIST DIRECTORY OF ART SCHOOLS & WORKSHOPS. Text in English. 1964. a. adv. **Document type:** *Directory.*
Former titles: American Artist Art School Directory; Art School Directory
Related titles: Microform ed.
Published by: V N U Business Publications (Subsidiary of: V N U Business Media), 770 Broadway, New York, NY 10003-9595. TEL 212-764-7300. Ed. Stephen Doherty. R&P Sylvia Valles. Adv. contact Irene Gruen.

709.73 USA ISSN 1540-9872
N1
AMERICAN ARTS QUARTERLY. Text in English. 1986. q.
Published by: Newington Cropsey Cultural Studies Center, P. O. Box 1654, Cooper Station, New York, NY 10276. TEL 212-260-0176, FAX 212-260-0218, aaq@nccsc.net, http://www.nccsc.net. Ed. James F. Cooper.

760 974 USA
AMERICAN HISTORICAL PRINT COLLECTORS SOCIETY. NEWSLETTER. Text in English. q. USD 35 (effective 2000); includes Imprint. **Document type:** *Newsletter.*
Published by: American Historical Print Collectors Society, Inc., PO Box 201, Fairfield, CT 06430. TEL 810-332-3902. Ed. Donald C O'Brien. R&P Robert Braun TEL 203-255-1627.

709.73 970.1 USA ISSN 0192-9968
E98.A7
➤ **AMERICAN INDIAN ART MAGAZINE.** Text in English. 1975. q. USD 20 domestic; USD 24 foreign (effective 2005). adv. bk.rev. illus. cum.index: vols.1-5, vols.11-15, vols.16-20. back issues avail.; reprints avail. **Document type:** *Magazine, Consumer.* **Description:** Devoted to prehistoric, historic, and contemporary American Indian visual art.
Formerly (until 1977): American Indian Art (0362-2630)
Indexed: ABM, AICP, AbAn, AmH&L, AnthLit, ArtInd, HistAb, PCI, RILM.
—BLDSC (0819.640000), IE, Infotrieve, ingenta.
Published by: American Indian Art, Inc., 7314 E Osborn Dr, Scottsdale, AZ 85251. TEL 480-994-5445, FAX 480-945-9533, http://www.aiamagazine.com. Ed. Roanne P. Goldfein. Pub. Mary G Hamilton. R&P Delinda Ehritz. Adv. contact Ronda L Rawlins. B&W page USD 1,060, color page USD 1,595; trim 8.5 x 11. Circ: 30,000 (paid and controlled).

➤ **AMERICAN INDIAN BASKETRY AND OTHER NATIVE ARTS.** see *ARTS AND HANDICRAFTS*

➤ **AMERICAN INSTITUTE FOR CONSERVATION OF HISTORIC AND ARTISTIC WORKS. ABSTRACTS OF PAPERS PRESENTED AT THE ANNUAL MEETING.** see *ART—Abstracting, Bibliographies, Statistics*

➤ **AMERICAN INSTITUTE FOR CONSERVATION OF HISTORIC AND ARTISTIC WORKS. BOOK & PAPER GROUP ANNUAL.** see *PUBLISHING AND BOOK TRADE*

700 333.7 USA ISSN 1074-7885
N8554
AMERICAN INSTITUTE FOR CONSERVATION OF HISTORIC AND ARTISTIC WORKS. DIRECTORY. Text in English. 1973. a. USD 25 to individuals; USD 50 to institutions. adv. **Document type:** *Directory.* **Description:** Comprehensive listing of AIC members organized by name, specialty, and geographic region; contains additional information on the AIC and the conservation field in general.
Published by: American Institute for Conservation of Historic and Artistic Works, 1717 K St, N W, Ste 301, Washington, DC 20006. TEL 202-452-9545, FAX 202-452-9328, infoAIC@aol.com, http://palimpsest.stanford.edu/aic/. Circ: 3,000.

751.6 USA ISSN 0197-1360
CODEN: JAICDE
➤ **AMERICAN INSTITUTE FOR CONSERVATION OF HISTORIC & ARTISTIC WORKS. JOURNAL.** Text in English. 1961. 3/yr. USD 73; USD 91 foreign. adv. bk.rev. bibl.; charts; illus. index. back issues avail. **Document type:** *Academic/Scholarly.* **Description:** Focuses on the conservation of architectural materials, archaeological objects, books and papers, paintings, photographs and sculpture.
Formerly: American Institute for Conservation of Historic and Artistic Works. Bulletin
Related titles: Online - full text ed.: (from JSTOR (Web-based Journal Archive)).
Indexed: A&ATA, ASCA, ArtHuCI, BHA, BrArAb, BrCerAb, C&ISA, CerAb, CivEngAb, CorrAb, CurCont, E&CAJ, EMA, IAA, M&TEA, MBF, METADEX, NumL, RASB, SolStAb, WAA.
—BLDSC (4686.640000), IE, Infotrieve, ingenta, Linda Hall.
Published by: American Institute for Conservation of Historic and Artistic Works, 1717 K St, N W, Ste 301, Washington, DC 20006. TEL 202-452-9545, FAX 202-452-9328, infoAIC@aol.com, http://palimpsest.stanford.edu/aic/. Ed. Chandra Reedy. Circ: 3,200.

700 620 IRL ISSN 0743-0884
AMERICAN INTERNATIONAL JOURNAL OF ARTS, SCIENCES, ENGINEERING AND MEDICINE. Text in English. 1984. q. looseleaf. USD 100. adv. bk.rev. **Document type:** *Academic/Scholarly.* **Description:** Aimed at providing a link between research and practice for professors, consultants and researchers in various specializations.
Published by: Royal University, Ltd., 6 Lower Hatch St., Dublin, 2, Ireland. FAX 353-1-6686632. Ed. C V Ramasastry.

741 USA ISSN 1071-8745
NC1300
AMERICAN JOURNAL OF ANTHROPOMORPHICS. Text in English. 1993. s-a. USD 40; USD 60 foreign. adv. bk.rev. illus. back issues avail. **Document type:** *Trade.* **Description:** Reference work for freelance artists from around the world who specialize in commercial and commissioned illustration of anthropomorphics, ranging from cartoon animals to realistic illustration and representation of all sorts.
Related titles: Online - full text ed.
Address: PO Box 580009, STA A, Flushing, NY 11358-0009. TEL 973-414-8833, 800-667-7943, FAX 971-414-8844, darrell@vision.nais.com, http://vision.nais.com/siteindex.html. Ed., R&P, Adv. contact Darrell Benvenuto. B&W page USD 400, color page USD 800. Circ: 8,000 (paid).

700 100 USA
AMERICAN LIVING PRESS. Text in English. 1982. q. USD 10. illus. back issues avail. **Description:** Visual magazine depicting past, present and future.
Formerly (until no.25, 1988): American Living
Address: PO Box 901, Allston, MA 02134. TEL 617-522-7782. Eds. Angela Mark, Michael Shores. Circ: 150.

700 USA ISSN 0163-8211
PS501
AMERICAN RAG★. Text in English. 1978. q. USD 11. illus.
Indexed: MusicInd.
Published by: Frederick Douglass Creative Arts Center, 270 W 96th St, New York, NY 10025.

AMERICAN RESEARCH CENTER IN EGYPT. JOURNAL. see *ARCHAEOLOGY*

700 810 USA
AMERICAN REVIEW. Text in English. 1977. m. USD 12. adv. bk.rev.; film rev. illus. back issues avail.; reprints avail.
Formerly: New American Review
Indexed: AES.
Published by: Allen G. Weakland, Ed. & Pub., 15 Burchfield Ave, Cranford, NJ 07016. TEL 201-276-6222. Circ: 2,000.

709 USA ISSN 0890-412X
AMERICAN UNIVERSITY STUDIES. SERIES 20. FINE ARTS. Text in English. 1988. irreg., latest 2004. price varies. **Document type:** *Monographic series, Academic/Scholarly.* **Description:** Explores a wide range of issues in the study of art.
Indexed: MLA-IB.
Published by: Peter Lang Publishing, Inc., 275 Seventh Ave, 28th Fl, New York, NY 10001. TEL 212-647-7700, 212-647-7706, 800-770-5264, FAX 212-647-7707, customerservice@plang.com, http://www.peterlang.com. Ed. David Bergeron. Pub. Christopher Myers. R&P Stephanie Archer. Adv. contact Patricia Mulrane.

700 301.34 USA
AMERICANS FOR THE ARTS. MONOGRAPHS. Text in English. 1993. bi-m. charts; stat. back issues avail. **Document type:** *Monographic series.* **Description:** Covers arts policy, arts education, and community development. Looks to broaden the impact of the arts.
Related titles: Online - full text ed.
Published by: Americans for the Arts, 1 E 53rd St, New York, NY 10022. TEL 800-321-5410, FAX 212-980-4857, pherrick@artsusa.org, http://www.artsusa.org. Ed. Randy I Cohen. R&P Peter Herrick.

700 USA ISSN 1554-9135
N55.A45
THE AMERICAS ART DIRECTORY/DIRECTORIO DE ARTE DE LAS AMERICAS. Text in Spanish, English. a. USD 75 per vol. (effective 2005). **Document type:** *Directory.*
Formerly (until 2002): Directorio de Arte Latinoamericano
Related titles: CD-ROM ed.
Published by: American Art Corporation, 905 Brickwell Bay Dr, Ste 1021, Miami, FL 33131. TEL 305-371-7106, http://www.artealdia.com/. Ed. Diego Costa-Peuser. Adv. contact Hernan Carrara. Circ: 25,000.

704.948 ITA ISSN 0003-1747
AMICO DELL'ARTE CRISTIANA. Text in Italian. 1930. q. adv. 20 p./no.; **Document type:** *Magazine.*
Indexed: DIP.
Published by: Scuola Beato Angelico, Viale San Gimignano, 19, Milan, MI 20146, Italy. TEL 39-02-48302854, FAX 39-02-48301954, bangelic@tin.it. Ed., Adv. contact Valerio Vigorelli.

709 FRA ISSN 0003-1852
AMIS DU CHATEAU DE PAU. BULLETIN. Text in French. 1959. 2/yr. adv. bk.rev. cum.index. **Document type:** *Bulletin.* **Description:** Diffuses information on the cultural activities of the National Museum of the Pau Castle and its Society of Friends, provides texts of lectures, reports on trips, exhibits.
Media: Duplicated (not offset).
Indexed: BHA.
Published by: Societe des Amis du Chateau de Pau, Chateau de Pau, Pau, 64000, France. TEL 33-5-59823810, FAX 33-5-59823818. Ed. Annick Albier. Circ: 1,000.

AMPERLAND; heimatkundliche Vierteljahresschrift fuer die Kreise Dachau, Freising und Fuerstenfeldbruck. see *HISTORY—History Of Europe*

709   TUR   ISSN 0066-1333
ANADOLU SANATI ARASTIRMALARI/RESEARCHES ON ANATOLIAN ART. Text in English, Turkish; Summaries in English. 1968. irreg. TRL 35.
Indexed: AIAP.
Published by: Technical University of Istanbul, Department of the History of Architecture and Preservation/Istanbul Teknik Universitesi, Gumussuyu Caddesi 87, Beyoglu, Istanbul, Turkey. Ed. Dogan Kuban. Circ: 1,000.

ANAGRAM; art and literature of Asian Americans. see *ETHNIC INTERESTS*

ANALES DE HISTORIA DEL ARTE. see *HISTORY*

ANALI. see *HISTORY*

700 800   TJK
ANDESHA. Text in Russian. w.
Address: Chekhova 13, 25-26, Dushanbe, Tajikistan. TEL 992-234936. Ed. Shodi Shokirov.

ANDHRA PRADESH, INDIA. DEPARTMENT OF ARCHAEOLOGY AND MUSEUMS. ARCHAEOLOGICAL SERIES. see *ARCHAEOLOGY*

700   NLD   ISSN 0168-2997
➤ **ANDON**; shedding light on Japanese art. Text in Dutch. 1981. q. EUR 35 in Europe to members; USD 50 elsewhere to members (effective 2003). adv. bk.rev. **Document type:** *Academic/Scholarly.* **Description:** Provides a forum for the dissemination and exchange of ideas and information relating to traditional Japanese arts and crafts.
Indexed: BHA.
Published by: Vereniging voor Japanse Kunst/Society for Japanese Arts, Mr Pankenstraat 12, Bergeijk, 5571 CP, Netherlands. TEL 31-497-572310, FAX 31-497-573657, sja@xs4all.nl. Ed. Henk Herwig. R&P Robert Schaap. Adv. contact Johan Somerwil. Circ: 800 (paid).

➤ **ANGELTREAD**; the lyrian ruse. see *LITERATURE*

▼ ➤ **ANIMATION**; an interdisciplinary journal. see *MOTION PICTURES*

➤ **ANIMATION JOURNAL.** see *MOTION PICTURES*

791.433   USA   ISSN 1041-617X
NC1766.U5
ANIMATION MAGAZINE. Text in English. 1987. m. USD 50 domestic; USD 65 in Canada & Mexico; USD 80 elsewhere (effective 2005). adv. film rev. illus. Supplement avail.; back issues avail. **Document type:** *Magazine, Trade.* **Description:** Covers traditional as well as computer-generated animation. Contains columns by industry professionals and reviews coming events, news, and industry trends.
Related titles: Online - full text ed.: (from H.W. Wilson, O C L C Online Computer Library Center, Inc.).
Indexed: ArtInd.
—BLDSC (0905.207000).
Published by: Terry Thoren Publications, D B A Animation Magazine, 30941 W. Agoura Rd., Ste. 102, Westlake Village, CA 91361. TEL 818-991-2884, FAX 818-991-3773, info@animationmagazine.net, http://www.animationmagazine.net. Ed. Christine Ferriter. Pub. Rita Street. Adv. contact Linda Brown. B&W page USD 1,800, color page USD 2,250; trim 8.38 x 10.88. Circ: 40,000.

741.5   USA   ISSN 1547-3767
ANIME INVASION. Variant title: Wizard Anime Invasion. Text in English. 2001. bi-m. USD 18 domestic; USD 31.50 in Canada; USD 44 elsewhere; USD 6.99 newsstand/cover (effective 2005). **Document type:** *Magazine, Consumer.* **Description:** Contains information on all aspects of anime and manga, including coverage of various creators, sub-categories, manufacturers and more.
Published by: Wizard Entertainment, 151 Wells Ave, Congers, NY 10920. TEL 914-268-2000, FAX 914-268-2392, customerservice@WizardUniverse.com, http://www.wizarduniverse.com.

741.5   JPN
ANIMEDIA. Text in Japanese. 1981. m. JPY 4,560.
Published by: Gakken Co. Ltd., 40-5 Kami-Ikedai 4-chome, Ota-ku, Tokyo, 145-0064, Japan. Ed. Keiichi Oshidari.

741.5   USA   ISSN 1067-0831
ANIMERICA; anime & manga monthly. Text in English. 1992. m. USD 29.95 domestic; USD 41.95 in Canada & Mexico; USD 90 elsewhere; USD 4.95 newsstand/cover; USD 7.95 newsstand/cover in Canada (effective 2004). adv. bk.rev.; music rev.; software rev.; tel.rev.; video rev. abstr.; bibl.; charts; illus.; stat. back issues avail. **Document type:** *Magazine, Consumer.* **Description:** Contains full-length reviews, news, information on the latest Japanese animation releases and "manga" (comic books) for English speaking audiences.

Related titles: Online - full text ed.
Published by: Viz Communications, Inc., PO Box 77010, San Francisco, CA 94107. TEL 415-546-7073, FAX 415-546-7086, anime@sirius.com, media@viz.com, http://www.animerica-mag.com, http://www.viz.com. Ed. Julie Davis. Pub. Seiji Horibuchi. Adv. contact Kristine Givas. B&W page USD 1,300, color page USD 1,800. Circ: 25,000 (paid). **Dist. by:** Viz Shop-By-Mail.

741.5   USA   ISSN 1533-1822
ANIMERICA EXTRA; the anime fan's comic magazine. Text in English. 1998. m. USD 41,95 domestic; USD 60 in Canada; USD 4.95 newsstand/cover (effective 2004). adv. bk.rev.; music rev.; software rev.; tel.rev.; video rev. abstr.; bibl.; charts; illus. back issues avail. **Document type:** *Magazine, Consumer.* **Description:** Serves the reading audience of manga (Japanese comics) and anime (animation.).
Published by: Viz Communications, Inc., PO Box 77010, San Francisco, CA 94107. TEL 415-546-7073, FAX 415-546-7086, extra@viz.com, media@viz.com, http://www.animerica-extra.com, http://www.viz.com. Ed. Bill Flanagan. Adv. contact Kristine Givas. B&W page USD 1,000, color page USD 1,500. Circ: 12,500.

ANKA; revue d'art et de litterature de Turquie. see *LITERATURE*

ANNALES D'ESTHETIQUE/ANNALS FOR AESTHETICS/ CHRONIKA AISTHETIKES. see *PHILOSOPHY*

700   FRA
ANNUAIRE DE L'ART INTERNATIONAL. Text in French. 1961. biennial. adv.bk.rev. illus.
Published by: Patrick Sermadiras Ed. & Pub., 11 rue Arsene Houssaye, Paris, 75008, France. TEL 47-66-51-52, FAX 47-64-10-56. Circ: 20,000.

DER ANSCHNITT; Zeitschrift fuer Kunst und Kultur im Bergbau. see *MINES AND MINING INDUSTRY*

ANTHEM (ST. PETERSBURG); the American experience in words, music and art. see *LITERATURE*

ANTHROPOMORPHIC. see *LITERATURE—Poetry*

709   ESP   ISSN 0213-1498
N7101
ANTIGRAMA. Text in Spanish. 1984. a.
Indexed: RILM.
—CINDOC.
Published by: Universidad de Zaragoza, Departamento de Historia del Arte, C. Pedro Cerbuna, 12, Zaragoza, 50009, Spain. TEL 34-976-762061, FAX 34-976-762114, rartigra@posta.unizar.es, http://www.unizar.es/. Ed. Maria Isabel Alvaro Zamora.

ANTIK & AUKTION. see *ANTIQUES*

ANTIKE KUNST. see *ARCHAEOLOGY*

ANTIKE KUNST. BEIHEFTE. see *ARCHAEOLOGY*

700 800 780 720   BGR
ANTIMOVSKI HAN. Text in Bulgarian. 1997. m. BGL 0.15 newsstand/cover (effective 2002). **Document type:** *Newspaper, Consumer.* **Description:** Covers literature, theater, visual arts, music, cinema, architecture and all areas of culture. The aim of the editors is to preserve, explore and promote the cultural-historical heritage of the Dobrudzha region.
Published by: Writers Association in Dobrich, Chitalishte "Lordan Lovkov", Dobrich, 9300, Bulgaria. TEL 359-5822531, http://www.sca.bg/cultural-periodicals/catalog/antim.htm.

ANTIQUARIAN. see *HISTORY—History Of North And South America*

ANTIQUARIATO. see *ANTIQUES*

ANTIQUESNEWS; the Internet newspaper for the British antiquities trade. see *ANTIQUES*

ANTIQUING DIRECTORY AND TRAVELER'S GUIDE. see *ANTIQUES*

700   ITA   ISSN 0394-0136
N1.A1
ANTOLOGIA DI BELLE ARTI. Text in Italian. 1977. a. adv. **Document type:** *Monographic series, Academic/Scholarly.* **Description:** Includes scholarly and critical articles; each issue focuses on a specific topic of art history.
Indexed: AIAP, BHA, PCI, RASB.
Published by: Umberto Allemandi & C. Srl, Via Mancini 8, Turin, TO 10131, Italy. TEL 39-011-8193133, FAX 39-011-8193090, http://www.allemandi.com. Ed. Alvar Gonzales Palacios. Adv. contact Patrizia Sbodiu.

700   BRA   ISSN 0103-9652
ANUARIO DE INOVACOES EM COMUNICACOES E ARTES. Text in Portuguese. 1989. a.
Indexed: RILM.

Published by: Universidade de Sao Paulo, Escola de Comunicacoes e Artes, Av. Prof. Lucio Martins Rodrigues 443, Butanta, SP 05508-900, Brazil. TEL 818-4112, FAX 814-1324, TELEX 80629 UVSI BR.

709   ESP   ISSN 1130-5517
N7101
ANUARIO DEL DEPARTAMENTO DE HISTORIA Y TEORIA DEL ARTE. Text in Spanish. 1989. a.
Indexed: RILM.
—CINDOC.
Published by: Universidad Autonoma de Madrid, Departamento de Historia y Teoria del Arte, Campus de Cantoblanco, Madrid, 28049, Spain. TEL 34-91-3974611, FAX 34-91-3973835, http://www.uam.es/. Ed. Ismael Gutierrez Pastor.

ANZEIGER DES GERMANISCHEN NATIONALMUSEUMS. see *HISTORY—History Of Europe*

700 745.1   GBR   ISSN 0003-6536
N1
APOLLO; the international magazine of the arts. Text in English. 1925. m. GBP 98 domestic; GBP 114 in Europe; GBP 100 in United States; GBP 125 elsewhere (effective 2004). adv. bk.rev. illus. index. 64 p./no. 3 cols./p.; back issues avail.; reprints avail. **Document type:** *Magazine, Consumer.* **Description:** Deals with art history, antiques, and auctioneering for universities, collectors, dealers, and museums.
Related titles: Microform ed.: (from PQC); Online - full text ed.: (from Gale Group).
Indexed: ABM, AIAP, API, ArtHuCl, ArtInd, BAS, BHA, BRI, BrHumI, CBRI, CurCont, DAAI, DIP, IBR, IBZ, IndIslam, RASB, RILM.
—BLDSC (1568.880000), IDS, IE, Infotrieve, ingenta.
Published by: Apollo Magazine Ltd., 20 Theobald's Rd, London, WC1X 8PF, United Kingdom. TEL 44-20-7235-1998, 44-20-74301262, editorial@apollomag.com, http://www.apollo-magazine.com/. Ed. Dr. David Euserdjian. Pub. Paul Z Josefowitz. R&P Catherine Hockley TEL 44-20-7233-8640. Adv. contact Anthony Law TEL 44-20-7233-8906. B&W page GBP 970, color page GBP 1,450; bleed 244 x 311. **Dist. by:** Spectator Subscriptions, Cary Court, Somerton TA11 6TB, United Kingdom. TEL 44-870-4448661, FAX 44-1458-271146.

700   MEX   ISSN 0188-3992
APOYO A LA DOCENCIA. Text in Spanish. 1990. irreg. price varies.
Published by: Universidad Nacional Autonoma de Mexico, Instituto de Investigaciones Esteticas, Circuito Mario de la Cueva, Zona Cultural, Ciudad Universitaria, Mexico, DF 04510, Mexico. TEL 52-55-56652465, FAX 52-55-56654740.

APPARATUR; tidsskrift for litteratur og kultur. see *LITERATURE*

APPLAUS; Kultur-Magazin. see *THEATER*

700   CAN   ISSN 1196-1775
APPLIED ARTS. Text in English. 1986. 6/yr. CND 49.95 in Canada; USD 49.95 elsewhere; USD 8.95 newsstand/cover (effective 2004). adv. **Document type:** *Magazine, Trade.* **Description:** Presents articles and features of interest to visual communicators working in the design, advertising, multimedia and online communication industries.
Formerly: Applied Arts Quarterly (0829-9242)
Related titles: Online - full text ed.: (from H.W. Wilson, O C L C Online Computer Library Center, Inc.).
Indexed: ABM, ArtInd, CBCARef, CPerl, DAAI.
—BLDSC (1571.680100), IE, ingenta.
Published by: Applied Arts Inc., 18 Wynford Dr, Ste 411, Don Mills, ON M3C 3S2, Canada. TEL 416-510-0909, 800-646-0347, FAX 416-510-0913, editor@appliedartsmag.com, subscribe@appliedartsmag.com, http://www.appliedartsmag.com. Ed. Sara Curtis. Pub. Georges Haroutiun. Adv. contact Sue Rye. Circ: 12,000.

709.2 745.1 769.56   USA   ISSN 1051-0869
N5198
THE APPRAISERS STANDARD; published solely for collectors, auctioneers, dealers, etc. Text in English. 1982. q. USD 20 domestic; USD 25 in Canada; USD 30 elsewhere (effective 2005). adv. bk.rev. **Document type:** *Newsletter, Trade.* **Description:** Assists appraisers of all types in their profession.
Formerly (until 1990): N E A A News (1046-0381)
Published by: New England Appraisers Association, 5 Gill Terrace, Ludlow, VT 05149. TEL 802-228-7444, FAX 802-228-7444, LLT44@ludl.tds.net. Ed., Pub., R&P, Adv. contact Linda L Tucker. Circ: 700 (paid).

ARAB LEAGUE EDUCATIONAL, SCIENTIFIC, AND CULTURAL ORGANIZATION. INFORMATION NEWSLETTER. see *EDUCATION*

ARCHAEOLOGIA. see *ARCHAEOLOGY*

ARCHAEOLOGICAL INSTITUTE OF AMERICA. ABSTRACTS OF THE GENERAL MEETING. see *ARCHAEOLOGY— Abstracting, Bibliographies, Statistics*

ARCHIVES. see *LITERATURE*

709.7 USA ISSN 0003-9853
N11.A735
ARCHIVES OF AMERICAN ART JOURNAL. Text in English. 1960. q. USD 35; USD 15 newsstand/cover (effective 2005). bk.rev. illus. index. **Document type:** *Journal, Academic/Scholarly.* **Description:** Covers all aspects of American art history from the 18th century to the most recent past . Includes fresh and uncommon perspectives on American cultural and social history.
Formerly (until 1964): Archives of American Art. Quarterly Bulletin (0884-6758)
Indexed: ABM, AIAP, ASCA, AmH&L, ArtHuCI, ArtInd, BHA, CurCont, DIP, HistAb, IBR, IBZ.
—BLDSC (1630.950000).
Published by: Smithsonian Institution, Archives of American Art, 750 9th St, NW, Washington, DC 20560-0937. TEL 202-275-1690, FAX 202-275-1955, http://www.aaa.si.edu/pubs.htm. Circ: 1,700. **Subscr. to:** 1285 Ave of the Americas, New York, NY 10019. TEL 212-399-5030, FAX 212-399-6890.

706 BEL ISSN 0066-6637
N7260
➤ **ARCHIVES OF ASIAN ART.** Text in English. 1945. a. EUR 63 in the European Union; EUR 67 elsewhere (effective 2006). illus. cum.index: 1945-93. back issues avail.; reprints avail. **Document type:** *Academic/Scholarly.* **Description:** Recent research by leading scholars on various subjects concerning Asian art.
Formerly (until 1966): Chinese Art Society of America. Archives
Indexed: AIAP, ASCA, ArtHuCI, ArtInd, BAS, CurCont, IBR, IBZ, PCI.
Published by: (Asia Society USA), Brepols Publishers, Begijnhof 67, Turnhout, 2300, Belgium. TEL 32-14-448030, FAX 32-14-428919, periodicals@brepols.net, http://www.brepols.net. Ed. Naomi Noble Richard. Circ: 600.

700 780 ITA ISSN 0392-1999
ARCHIVI DI LECCO. Text in Italian. 1978. q.
Indexed: RILM.
Published by: Associazione Giuseppe Bovara di Lecco, Via Vasena 4, Sala al Barro, Galbiate, 23856, Italy. TEL 39-0341-240724, FAX 39-0341-240734.

ARCHIVIO PER L'ALTO ADIGE; rivista di studi alpini. see *LINGUISTICS*

704.948 ITA
ARCHIVIO SARTORI; documenti di storia e arte. Text in Italian. 1983. irreg. price varies. **Document type:** *Monographic series, Academic/Scholarly.* **Description:** Contains research on local ecclesiastical history and art.
Published by: Centro Studi Antoniani, Piazza del Santo, 11, Padua, PD 35123, Italy. TEL 39-049-8762177, FAX 39-049-8762187. Ed. Giovanni Luisetto.

ARCHIVIST; magazine of the National Archives of Canada. see *HISTORY—History Of North And South America*

709 ESP ISSN 0211-5808
ARCHIVO DE ARTE VALENCIANO. Text in Spanish. 1915. a. back issues avail.
Indexed: PCI, RILM.
—CINDOC.
Published by: Real Academia de Bellas Artes de San Carlos, S. Pio V, 9, Valencia, 46010, Spain. TEL 34-346-3690338, http://www.realacademiasancarlos.com/. Ed. Felipe Maria Garin Ortiz de Taranco.

700 ESP
ARCO (YEAR). Text in Spanish. a. adv. **Document type:** *Catalog.*
Published by: Feria Internacional de Arte Contemporaneo, Parque Ferial Juan Carlos I, Madrid, 28042, Spain. TEL 341-722-50-17, FAX 341-722-57-98. Ed. Rosina Gomez-Baeza. R&P Rosina Gomez Baeza. Circ: 6,000.

700 746.9 CAN
AREA MAGAZINE. Text in English. 1994. q. CND 17.95, USD 21.95. back issues avail. **Document type:** *Consumer.* **Description:** Features entertaining and insightful stories that make Toronto vibrant and unique.
Related titles: Online - full text ed.
Published by: Area Arts, 615 Mt Pleasant Rd, Ste 205, Toronto, ON M4S 3C5, Canada. TEL 416-368-9401, FAX 416-359-0755. Ed., Adv. contact Jason Patton. Pub. Peter Lucas.

ARGENTINA. DEPARTAMENTO DE ESTUDIOS HISTORICOS NAVALES. SERIE H: ICONOGRAFIA. see *MILITARY*

700 DNK ISSN 0900-338X
ARGOS; tidsskrift for kunstvidenskab, visuel kommunikation og kunstpaedagogik. Text in Danish. 1985. irreg., latest vol.8, 1991. DKK 98; DKK 128 per issue (effective 2003). illus. back issues avail. **Document type:** *Monographic series, Academic/Scholarly.*
Published by: Syddansk Universitetsforlag/University Press of Southern Denmark, Campusvej 55, Odense M, 5230, Denmark. TEL 45-66-157999, FAX 45-66-158126, press@forlag.sdu.dk, http://www.universitypress.dk.

ARIANA AFGHAN MAGAZINE. see *ETHNIC INTERESTS*

ARIEL (ENGLISH EDITION); the Israel review of arts and letters. see *HUMANITIES: COMPREHENSIVE WORKS*

ARIZONA ARTISTS GUILD NEWSLETTER. see *MUSEUMS AND ART GALLERIES*

353.9 700 USA ISSN 0098-7387
NX24.A6
ARIZONA COMMISSION ON THE ARTS. REPORT TO THE GOVERNOR (YEAR). Key Title: Report to the Governor - Arizona Commission on the Arts. Text in English. a. free. illus. **Document type:** *Government.* **Description:** A review of the programmatic and financial community service projects supported by the commission in a given fiscal year.
Formerly: Arizona Commission on the Arts and Humanities. Report to the Governor
Related titles: Online - full text ed.
Published by: Commission on the Arts, 417 W Roosevelt St, Phoenix, AZ 85003. TEL 602-255-5882, FAX 602-256-0282, artscomm@primenet.com, http://www.state.az.us/azarts. Ed. Gary Delago. R&P Mollie Lakin TEL 602-229-8226. Circ: 1,500 (controlled).

700 DNK ISSN 1602-9402
ARKEN. BULLETIN. Text in English. 2002. irreg., latest vol.2, 2004. price varies.
Published by: ARKEN, Museum for Moderne Kunst/ARKEN, Museum of Modern Art, Skovvej 100, Ishoej, 2635, Denmark. TEL 45-43-540222, FAX 45-43-540522, reception@arken.dk, http://www.arken.dk/view.asp?ID=11711. Ed. Christian Gether.

700 TUR ISSN 0004-1971
ARKITEKT; yasama sanati. Text in Turkish; Summaries in English. 1931. m. USD 74; USD 70 in North America. adv. bk.rev. **Description:** Covers architecture and the arts, decoration, interior design, antiques, archaeology.
Indexed: AIAP, API.
Published by: Nokta Basin A.S., Buyukdere Cad. Ali Kaya Sok. 8, Levent - Istanbul, 80720, Turkey. TEL 90-212-2819916, FAX 90-212-2798512. Ed. Rifat Dedeoglu. Pub. Engin Vardar. Adv. contact Miss Nuray Berktav. Circ: 10,000; 10,000 (paid).

ARLIS ANNUAL DIRECTORY. see *LIBRARY AND INFORMATION SCIENCES*

ARLIS NEWS-SHEET. see *LIBRARY AND INFORMATION SCIENCES*

ARMAS E TROFEUS; revista de historia, heraldica, genealogia e arte. see *GENEALOGY AND HERALDRY*

709.4 SVK ISSN 0044-9008
N6
ARS. Text and summaries in English, German, Russian, Slovak. 1967. 3/yr. USD 66 foreign (effective 2005). charts; illus. **Document type:** *Journal, Academic/Scholarly.*
Indexed: ABM, AIAP, BHA, RASB.
Published by: (Slovenska Akademia Vied/Slovak Academy of Sciences, Ustav Dejin Umenia/Institute of the history of art), Slovak Academic Press Ltd., Nam Slobody 6, PO Box 57, Bratislava, 81005, Slovakia. sap@sappress.sk, http://www.sappress.sk. Ed. Jan Dekan. Circ: 600.

700 HUN ISSN 0133-1531
N6812
➤ **ARS HUNGARICA.** Text in Hungarian; Summaries in English, French, German. 1973. 2/yr., latest vol.2, 2000. USD 16 (effective 2000); or exchange basis. bk.rev. illus.; bibl. back issues avail. **Document type:** *Journal, Academic/Scholarly.*
Indexed: ABM, AIAP, BHA, BibInd, RILM.
Published by: Magyar Tudomanyos Akademia, Muveszettorteneti Kutato Intezete/Hungarian Academy of Sciences, Institute of Art History, Uri utca 49, Budapest, 1014, Hungary. TEL 36-1-3759011, FAX 36-1-3561849, arthist@arthist.mta.hu, h4517mar@ella.hu, http://www.arthist.mta.hu. Ed., R&P Arpad Timar TEL 36-1-3750493. Circ: 500.

709 ESP ISSN 1130-7099
ARS LONGA; cuadernos de arte. Text in Spanish. 1990. a.
Indexed: RILM.
—CINDOC.
Published by: Universitat de Valencia, Departamento de Historia del Arte, Ave. Blasco Ibanez, 28, Valencia, 26010, Spain. TEL 34-96-3864241, FAX 34-96-3864496, hisarte@uv.es, http://www.uv.es/. Ed. Inmaculada Aguilar Civera.

ARS ORIENTALIS; the arts of Asia, Southeast Asia and Islam. see *ASIAN STUDIES*

700 NLD
ARS PICTURAE. Text in Dutch. 1989. irreg., latest vol.3, 1992. price varies. back issues avail. **Document type:** *Monographic series.* **Description:** Publishes brief scholarly studies of the life and work of Dutch artists of the 17th century.
Published by: Davaco Publishers, Beukenlaan 3, Doornspijk, 8085 RK, Netherlands. TEL 31-525-661823, FAX 31-525-662153.

ARS SACRA. see *ARCHITECTURE*

709 SWE ISSN 0066-7919
ARS SUETICA. Text in Swedish; Summaries in English, German. 1966. irreg., latest vol.20, 2003. price varies. back issues avail. **Document type:** *Monographic series, Academic/Scholarly.*
Related titles: ◆ Series of: Acta Universitatis Upsaliensis. ISSN 0346-5462.
Published by: (Uppsala Universitet, Institute of Art History), Uppsala Universitet, Acta Universitatis Upsaliensis/University Publications from Uppsala, PO Box 256, Uppsala, 75105, Sweden. TEL 46-18-4713922, http://www.ub.uu.se/upu/auu. Ed. Bengt Landgren. **Dist. by:** Almqvist & Wiksell International.

700 ROM ISSN 1220-2789
N7229.T7
ARS TRANSSILVANIAE. Text in Romanian; Summaries in English, French, German. 1990. a.
Indexed: RASB.
Published by: (Academia Romana, Institutul de Arheologie si Istoria Artei, Cluj-Napoca), Editura Academiei Romane/Publishing House of the Romanian Academy, Calea 13 Septembrie 13, Sector 5, Bucharest, 76117, Romania. TEL 40-21-4119008, FAX 40-21-4103983, edacad@ear.ro. Ed. Marius Porumb. **Dist. by:** Rodipet S.A., Piata Presei Libere 1, sector 1, PO Box 33-57, Bucharest 3, Romania. TEL 40-21-2224126, 40-21-2226407, rodipet@rodipet.ro.

700 USA
ARSENAL (EVANSTON); surrealist subversion. Text in English. 1970. irreg., latest 1989. USD 15 per issue (effective 1998). adv. bk.rev. bibl.
Published by: Black Swan Press-Surrealist Editions, PO Box 6424, Evanston, IL 60204. TEL 773-465-7774. Ed. Franklin Rosemont. Adv. contact Laura Valentine. Circ: 3,000.

701.18 DEU ISSN 0173-2781
N3
ART; das Kunstmagazin. Text in German. 1979. m. EUR 7.82 newsstand/cover (effective 2004). adv. reprints avail. **Document type:** *Magazine, Consumer.* **Description:** Contains information on modern and classic art in all mediums, including a calendar of exhibitions.
Indexed: ABM, BHA, DIP, IBR, IBZ, RILM.
—IE.
Published by: Gruner und Jahr AG & Co., Am Baumwall 11, Hamburg, 20459, Germany. TEL 49-40-3703-0, FAX 49-40-37035617, guj-redaktion@guj.de, http://www.guj.de. Ed. Axel Hecht. Adv. contact Angelika Drescher. B&W page EUR 9,000, color page EUR 11,790. Circ: 68,258 (paid).

730 FRA
ART ALBUMS SERIES. Text in English, French; Text occasionally in Spanish. 1953. a. free; price varies.
Formerly: Art (0004-5535)
Published by: (International Association of Art/Association Internationale des Arts Plastiques), UNESCO Publishing, 7 place de Fontenoy, Paris, 75352, France. TEL 33-1-45682654, FAX 33-1-45672287, http://www.unesco.org/publications. Ed. Dunbar Marshall Malagola. Circ: 2,000. **Dist. in the U.S. by:** Bernan Associates, Bernan, 4611-F Assembly Dr., Lanham, MD 20706-4391. TEL 800-865-3450, 800-274-4888, FAX 800-865-3450.

708.7 USA ISSN 0004-296X
N684
ART ALLIANCE BULLETIN. Text in English. 1921. q. membership only. adv. illus. **Description:** Focuses on art exhibits in the area.
Published by: Philadelphia Art Alliance, 251 S 18th St, Philadelphia, PA 19103. FAX 215-545-0767. Ed. Thomas W Yanni. Circ: 2,500.

700 745.5 AUS ISSN 0313-220X
ART ALMANAC. Text in English. 1978. m. (11/yr.). AUD 30 domestic; AUD 48 foreign (effective 2004). adv. back issues avail. **Document type:** *Directory.* **Description:** Covers galleries and information on current exhibitions focusing on contemporary Australian art.
Address: 9/131-145 Glebe Point Rd, PO Box 915, Glebe, NSW 2037, Australia. enquiry@art-almanac.com.au, http://www.art-almanac.com.au. Ed., Pub. Janice E McCulloch. adv.: page AUD 275. Circ: 5,500.

700 USA ISSN 1065-4674
ART? ALTERNATIVES. Text in English. 1992. a. USD 7.95; USD 17.95 foreign. adv. **Document type:** *Consumer.* **Description:** Targets the artworld subculture; features underground, low-brow and outsider art, and tattoo art.
Published by: Outlaw Biker Enterprises, Inc., 5 Marine View Plaza, Ste 207, Hoboken, NJ 07030. TEL 201-653-2700. Ed. Jean Chris Miller. Pub. Casey Exton. R&P Jean-Chris Miller. Adv. contact Ken Knabb. B&W page USD 1,200. Circ: 75,000.

700 780 USA ISSN 1040-7812
ART & ACADEME. Text in English. 1988. s-a.
Indexed: RILM.
Published by: Visual Arts Press, 209 East 23rd St, New York, NY 10010-3994. TEL 212-592-2380.

ART & ANTIQUES. see *ANTIQUES*

701.03 USA
ART AND ARCHAEOLOGY MAGAZINE. Text in English, French, German. irreg. adv. reprints avail. **Description:** Contains news, interviews, in-depth reviews and virtual galleries of major art and archaeology exhibitions in Europe and the United States.
Media: Online - full text.
Published by: Culture Kiosque Publications, Ltd., 164 Madison Ave, 5th Fl, New York, NY 10016-5411. jromero@culturekiosque.com, http://www.culturekisoque.com/art/index.htm. Ed. Joseph Romero. Pub. Philippe Broad.

700 USA ISSN 0197-1093
N8602
ART & AUCTION. Text in English. 1979. m. USD 80 domestic; USD 100 in Canada; USD 120 elsewhere (effective 2005). adv. bk.rev. **Document type:** *Magazine, Consumer.*
Indexed: A&ATA, ArtInd.
—BLDSC (1733.355680).
Address: 11 E 36th St, 9th Fl, New York, NY 10016-3318. TEL 212-447-9555, 800-777-8718, FAX 212-447-5221, 212-532-7321, edit@artandauction.com, info@artandauction.com, http://www.artandauction.com/. Ed. Bruce Wolmer. Circ: 20,000.

709.94 AUS ISSN 0004-301X
ART & AUSTRALIA. Text in English. 1963. q. AUD 63 domestic; USD 108 foreign (effective 2004). adv. bk.rev. illus. index. reprints avail. **Document type:** *Journal, Academic/Scholarly.* **Description:** Includes articles on contemporary Australian art and artists, plus historical articles.
Related titles: Online - full text ed.: (from R M I T Publishing); ♦ Supplement(s): Art AsiaPacific.
Indexed: ABCT, ABM, ABS&EES, ArtInd, AusPAIS, BHA, GdIns, PCI, WBA, WMB.
Published by: Art and Australia Pty Ltd., 42 Chandos St, St Leonards, NSW 2065, Australia. TEL 61-2-99668400, FAX 61-2-99660355, http://www.artaustralia.com. Pub. Eleonora Triguboff. adv.: B&W page USD 1,600, color page USD 1,920; trim 225 x 242. Circ: 150,000 (paid).

ART & CRAFT; a magazine for primary teachers. see *EDUCATION—Teaching Methods And Curriculum*

▼ **THE ART & LAW ELECTRONIC JOURNAL.** see *LAW*

700 821 IND ISSN 0970-1001
ART AND POETRY TODAY. Text in English. q. INR 160 domestic; USD 48 foreign (effective 2003). adv. illus. **Description:** Highlights poetry and art from all over the world.
Formerly (until 1976): Criteria
Published by: Samkaleen Prakashan, 2762 Rajguru Marg, New Delhi, 110 055, India. TEL 91-11-23583520. Ed., R&P, Adv. contact Krishan Khullar. page INR 1,000; trim 180 x 240.

700 340 GBR ISSN 1362-2331
K1 CODEN: AALRC8
➤ **ART, ANTIQUITY, AND LAW.** Text in Dutch. 1996. q. GBP 130 (effective 2003). back issues avail. **Document type:** *Journal, Academic/Scholarly.* **Description:** Publishes research and review articles on the law as it pertains art and antiquities.
Related titles: Online - full text ed.: (from EBSCO Publishing, Gale Group, Kluwer Online, O C L C Online Computer Library Center, Inc.).
Indexed: ABM, ArtInd, CJA, RICS.
—BLDSC (1733.365433), IE, Infotrieve, ingenta. **CCC.**
Published by: Institute of Art and Law, 1-5 Cank St, Leicester, LE1 5GX, United Kingdom. TEL 44-116-2538888, FAX 44-116-2511666, publications@ial.uk.com, info@ial.uk.com, http://www.ial.uk.com/.

➤ **ART, ARTIFACT & ARCHITECTURE LAW.** see *LAW*

709.95 USA
N7260
ART ASIAPACIFIC. Text in English. 1994. q. USD 44 (effective 2004). adv. bk.rev. illus.; mkt. back issues avail. **Document type:** *Academic/Scholarly.* **Description:** Explores and documents the contemporary arts of the Asia and Pacific region. Includes commentary, exhibition reviews, essays, and auction reports.
Formerly: Art and Asia Pacific (1039-3625)
Related titles: ♦ Supplement to: Art & Australia. ISSN 0004-301X.
Indexed: ABM, ArtInd, INZP, WBA, WMB.
Published by: J A K Publishing, 360 West 121st St, New York, NY 10027. TEL 212-870-0617, FAX 212-280-4578, info@aapmag.com, http://www.aapmag.com/. Ed. Franklin Sirmans. Pub. Gang Zhao. Adv. contact Kate Shanley. B&W page USD 980, color page USD 1,320; trim 246 x 265. Circ: 7,000. **Subscr. to:** Subscriptions Department, 2840 Broadway #352, New York, NY 10025. Subscribe@aapmag.com.

700 800 SWE ISSN 1401-2979
THE ART BIN. Text in English. 1995. irreg. free. adv. **Document type:** *Newsletter, Academic/Scholarly.* **Description:** Contains cultural articles, source texts and recent artwork.
Media: Online - full text.
Published by: Nisus Publishing, PO Box 55518, Stockholm, 10204, Sweden. TEL 46-8-344413, tallmo@nisus.se, http://art-bin.com, http://www.nisus.se. Ed., Pub., Adv. contact Karl-Erik Tallmo. Circ: 70,000.

700 720 GBR ISSN 1368-6267
THE ART BOOK. Text in English. 1993. q. EUR 44 combined subscription in Europe to individuals print & online eds.; USD 49 combined subscription in the Americas to individuals & Caribbean, print & online eds.; GBP 29 combined subscription elsewhere to individuals print & online eds.; GBP 83 combined subscription in Europe to institutions print & online eds.; USD 185 combined subscription in the Americas to institutions & Caribbean, print & online eds.; GBP 110 combined subscription elsewhere to institutions print & online eds. (effective 2006). adv. bk.rev. illus. back issues avail.; reprint service avail. from PSC. **Description:** Looks at decorative, fine and applied art, art history, photography, architecture and design. Contains news and reviews by key figures in the art world.
Formerly: International Publishing Review (Fine Arts Edition) (1352-0733)
Related titles: Online - full text ed.: ISSN 1467-8357. GBP 79 in Europe to institutions; USD 176 in the Americas to institutions & Caribbean; GBP 105 elsewhere to institutions (effective 2006) (from Blackwell Synergy, EBSCO Publishing, Gale Group, IngentaConnect, O C L C Online Computer Library Center, Inc., Swets Information Services).
Indexed: ABM, ArtInd.
—BLDSC (1733.367060), IE, Infotrieve. **CCC.**
Published by: Blackwell Publishing Ltd., 9600 Garsington Rd, Oxford, OX4 2ZG, United Kingdom. TEL 44-1865-776868, FAX 44-1865-714591, customerservices@oxon.blackwellpublishing.com, http://www.blackwellpublishing.com/journals/ARTBOOK. R&P Melanie Charge TEL 44-1865-382352.

709 USA ISSN 0004-3079
N11
➤ **ART BULLETIN.** Text in English. 1913. q. membership. adv. bk.rev. charts; illus. index. reprints avail. **Document type:** *Journal, Academic/Scholarly.* **Description:** Scholarly forum for communication; contains research articles on topics from all periods of art history.
Former titles (until 1918): College Art Association of America. Bulletin (0272-8192); (until 1913): College Art Association. Bulletin (0895-0571)
Related titles: Microfiche ed.: (from IDC); Microfilm ed.: (from PQC); Online - full text ed.: (from Chadwyck-Healey Inc., EBSCO Publishing, Florida Center for Library Automation, Gale Group, H.W. Wilson, JSTOR (Web-based Journal Archive), Northern Light Technology, Inc., O C L C Online Computer Library Center, Inc., ProQuest Information & Learning).
Indexed: ABCT, ABM, ABS&EES, AIAP, API, ASCA, AcaI, AmHI, ArtHuCI, ArtInd, BAS, BHA, BRD, BRI, BrArAb, CBRI, CurCont, DIP, HongKongiana, HumInd, IBR, IBRH, IBZ, IndIslam, MASUSE, MEA&I, NumL, PCI, RASB, RI-1, RI-2, RILM, SeedAb.
—BLDSC (1733.368000), IE, ingenta.
Published by: College Art Association, 275 Seventh Ave, New York, NY 10001. TEL 212-691-1051, FAX 212-627-2381, nyoffice@collegeart.org, http://www.collegeart.org/caa/publications/AB/artbulletin.html. Ed. H. Perry Chapman. Adv. contact Paul Skiff. Circ: 9,500.

➤ **ART BULLETIN OF NATIONALMUSEUM STOCKHOLM.** see *MUSEUMS AND ART GALLERIES*

658.91 USA ISSN 0273-5652
N1
➤ **ART BUSINESS NEWS.** Text in English. 1974. m. USD 45 domestic; USD 55 in Canada & Mexico; USD 80 elsewhere (effective 2004). adv. bk.rev. illus. back issues avail. **Document type:** *Magazine, Trade.* **Description:** Provides art galleries, picture framers, art dealers and framers, and art supply stores with timely news and information.
Formerly (until 1980): Art Dealer and Framer (0091-9780)
Related titles: Online - full text ed.: (from bigchalk, EBSCO Publishing, Florida Center for Library Automation, Gale Group, H.W. Wilson, O C L C Online Computer Library Center, Inc., ProQuest Information & Learning).
Indexed: ABIn, ArtInd.
Published by: Pfingsten Publishing, L L C, 6000 Lombardo Center Dr, Ste 420, Seven Hills, OH 44131. TEL 216-328-8926, FAX 216-328-9452, info@pfpublish.com, http://www.artbusinessnews.com, http://www.pfpub.com. Ed. Joe Jancsurak. Pub. Eric Smith. adv.: color page USD 4,002. Circ: 28,000 (controlled).

700 GBR ISSN 0961-6497
ART BUSINESS TODAY. Text in English. 1976. 5/yr. adv. **Document type:** *Trade.*
Formerly (until 1990): Fine Art Trade Guild Journal (0308-0854)
—BLDSC (1733.369550).
Published by: Fine Art Trade Guild, 16-18 Empress Pl, London, SW6 1TT, United Kingdom. TEL 44-20-7381-6616, FAX 44-20-7381-2596. Ed. Annabelle Ruston. Adv. contact Matt Stanley. Circ: 8,580 (controlled).

700 666 770 USA ISSN 0893-3901
N8350
ART CALENDAR; the business magazine for visual artists. Text in English. 1986. m. USD 33 domestic; USD 55 in Canada & Mexico; USD 75 elsewhere (effective 2002). adv. bk.rev.; software rev.; video rev. back issues avail. **Document type:** *Magazine, Consumer.* **Description:** Lists forthcoming professional opportunities in the US and abroad for visual artists. Includes articles on marketing, art law, and career management.
Formerly: Art Calendar - D C
Related titles: Online - full text ed.: USD 33 (effective 2002).
Indexed: ABM.
Address: PO Box 2675, Salisbury, MD 21802. TEL 410-749-9625, FAX 410-749-9625, carolyn@artcalendar.com, http://www.artcalendar.com. Pub. Carolyn Blakeslee Proeber. Adv. contact Dave Proeber TEL 410-749-9625. Circ: 20,000 (paid). **Dist. by:** Ingram Distributors, PO Box 7000, La Vergne, TN 37086-7000. TEL 800-627-6247.

700 RUS ISSN 1607-3983
ART CHRONIKA. Text in Russian. 1999. bi-m. USD 39 in United States; USD 56.90 in Europe; USD 73.90 elsewhere (effective 2001). **Description:** Designed to promote Russian art and antiques and help pave the way for the Russian artists to win international recognition.
Indexed: ABM.
Published by: International Business Development, Stoleshnikov per 11 str 1 ofis 405, Moscow, Russian Federation. TEL 7-095-927-1300, FAX 7-095-927-1213, krouglov@yahoo.com, http://www.artchronika.com. Circ: 30,000.

700 USA ISSN 0732-2852
NX458
ART COM; contemporary art communications. Text in English. 1975. q. USD 8. adv. bk.rev. illus. back issues avail.; reprints avail. **Description:** Reports on the interface between postmodern art and new communication technologies.
Formerly (until vol.4, no.2, 1981): Mamelle Magazine: Art Contemporary
Media: Online - full text. **Related titles:** Microfiche ed.
Published by: (La Mamelle, Inc.), Contemporary Arts Press, Box 3123, Rincon Annex, San Francisco, CA 94119. TEL 415-431-7524, FAX 415-431-7841, TELEX 4946074 ARTCOM. Ed. Carl E Loeffler.

700 745.1 USA
ART CONNOISSEUR. Text in English. 1999. bi-m. USD 30; USD 5 newsstand/cover (effective 1999). illus. **Document type:** *Consumer.* **Description:** Features articles on world art, antiques, and culture. Includes interviews and critiques.
Address: 2547 Hutton Dr., Beverly Hills, CA 90210-1211. TEL 310-256-3200, FAX 310-286-1302.

701 USA ISSN 0195-4148
N7475
➤ **ART CRITICISM.** Text in English. 1979. a. USD 15 to individuals; USD 20 to institutions (effective 2005). **Document type:** *Journal, Academic/Scholarly.*
Related titles: Online - full text ed.: (from H.W. Wilson, O C L C Online Computer Library Center, Inc.).
Indexed: ABM, ABS&EES, AIAP, ASCA, ArtHuCI, ArtInd, BHA, CurCont.
—BLDSC (1733.374000), IDS, IE, ingenta.
Published by: State University of New York at Stony Brook, Department of Art, Staller Center, Stony Brook, NY 11794-5400. TEL 631-632-7250, FAX 631-632-7261, artcriticism@hotmail.com, http://www.art.sunysb.edu/. Ed. Donald B Kuspit. R&P Kirsten Swenson TEL 516-632-7270. Circ: 300.

700 FRA ISSN 0571-1509
ART DE BASSE NORMANDIE. Text in French. 1956. q. back issues avail.
Indexed: BHA.
Published by: Art de Basse-Normandie, c/o Jacques Pougheol, 49 rue Canchy, Caen, 14000, France. FAX 33-2-31502256. Ed. J Pougheol.

707.1141 GBR ISSN 1474-273X
➤ **ART, DESIGN & COMMUNICATION IN HIGHER EDUCATION.** Text in English. 2002. 3/yr. GBP 30 in the European Union to individuals; GBP 38 elsewhere to individuals; GBP 140 combined subscription in the European Union to institutions print & online; GBP 148 combined subscription elsewhere to institutions print & online (effective 2005). back issues avail. **Document type:** *Journal, Academic/Scholarly.* **Description:** Aims to inform, stimulate and promote the development of research with a learning and teaching focus for art, design and communication within higher education.
Related titles: Online - full content ed.; Online - full text ed.: (from EBSCO Publishing, O C L C Online Computer Library Center, Inc., Swets Information Services).
Indexed: ABM, BrEdI, CPE.
—IE.
Published by: (Learning and Teaching Support Network Centre for Art, Design & Communication), Intellect Ltd., PO Box 862, Bristol, BS99 1DE, United Kingdom. TEL 44-117-9589910, FAX 44-117-9589911, journals@intellectbooks.com, info@intellectbooks.com, http://www.intellectbooks.com/journals/adche.htm. Ed. Dr. Linda Drew. R&P, Adv. contact Mr. Robin Beecroft.

▼ new title ➤ refereed ✶ unverified ♦ full entry avail.

700 ITA
ART DIARY INTERNATIONAL; the world's art directory. Text in English. a. EUR 25 (effective 2004). adv. **Document type:** *Directory.* **Description:** Lists more than 30,000 addresses of artists, critics, galleries, museums, art magazines, collections and cultural institutions in 70 countries from the US to Europe and beyond.
Related titles: ♦ English ed.: Art Diary Italia.
Published by: Giancarlo Politi Editore, PO Box 95, Borgo Trevi, PG 06032, Italy. TEL 39-0742-381978, FAX 39-0742-381979, subscription@flashartonline.com, http://www.flashartonline.com. adv.: B&W page USD 2,600, color page USD 3,500; trim 6.88 x 3.13. Circ: 35,000.

700 ITA
ART DIARY ITALIA. Text in English, Italian. 1975. a. EUR 20 (effective 2004). adv. **Document type:** *Directory.* **Description:** Lists more than 30,000 addresses of artists, critics, collectors, galleries, museums, alternative exhibition spaces, libraries, foundations, archives, graphic designers, art conservators, artist's agents, schools, and academies in Italy.
Formerly: Art Diary
Related titles: ♦ English ed.: Art Diary International.
Published by: Giancarlo Politi Editore, PO Box 95, Borgo Trevi, PG 06032, Italy. TEL 39-0742-381978, FAX 39-0742-381979, subscription@flashartonline.com, http://www.flashartonline.com. adv.: B&W page USD 2,600, color page USD 3,500; trim 6.88 x 3.13. Circ: 35,000.

700 659.106 USA ISSN 0735-2026
NC998.5.A1
ART DIRECTORS ANNUAL. Text in English. 1921. a. USD 65 (effective 2005). adv. **Document type:** *Journal, Trade.*
Former titles: Annual of Advertising, Editorial and Television Art and Design with the Annual Copy Awards; (until 1973): Annual of Advertising, Editorial and Television Art and Design (0066-4014)
Published by: Art Directors Club Inc., 106 W 29th St, Ground Fl, New York, NY 10001-5310. TEL 212-643-1440, FAX 212-643-4293, mdavis@adcny.orgnet, http://www.adcglobal.org/main.html. Circ: 15,000 (paid).

ART DOCUMENTATION; bulletin of the Art Libraries Society of North America. see *LIBRARY AND INFORMATION SCIENCES*

700 ITA ISSN 0394-0179
N4
ART E DOSSIER. Text in Italian. 1986. m. (11/yr.). EUR 43.10 domestic; EUR 73.90 foreign (effective 2005). adv. **Document type:** *Magazine, Consumer.*
Indexed: AIAP.
Published by: Giunti Gruppo Editoriale SpA, Via Bolognese 165, Florence, 50139, Italy. TEL 39-055-5062376, FAX 39-055-5062397, informazioni@giunti.it, http://www.giunti.it. Ed. Gioia Mori. Circ: 55,000.

709.426 GBR ISSN 1359-8929
ART EAST. Text in English. 1986. 10/yr. GBP 16 (effective 1998). adv. bk.rev.; film rev.; music rev.; play rev. back issues avail. **Document type:** *Consumer.* **Description:** Covers all arts in the East Anglia area of Great Britain.
Published by: B C Publications, 16C Market Pl, Diss, Norfolk IP22 3AB, United Kingdom. FAX 44-1379-650480. Ed., R&P Simon Tooth. Adv. contact Matthew Denny. page GBP 600; trim 190 x 297. Circ: 6,000.

707 USA ISSN 0004-3125
N81
➤ **ART EDUCATION.** Text in English. 1948. bi-m. USD 50 domestic; USD 75 foreign (effective 2005). adv. bk.rev. illus. Index. reprint service avail. from PQC. **Document type:** *Journal, Academic/Scholarly.*
Incorporates (1970-1980): Art Teacher (0163-3651)
Related titles: Microform ed.: (from PQC); Online - full text ed.: (from H.W. Wilson, JSTOR (Web-based Journal Archive), Northern Light Technology, Inc., O C L C Online Computer Library Center, Inc., ProQuest Information & Learning).
Indexed: ABIn, CIJE, CPE, DIP, EduInd, IBR, IBZ, RASB, YAE&RB.
—BLDSC (1733.400000), IE, ingenta.
Published by: National Art Education Association, 1916 Association Dr, Reston, VA 20191-1590. TEL 703-860-8000, FAX 703-860-2960, kemery@naea-reston.org, http://www.naea-reston.org. adv.: B&W page USD 1,427, color page USD 2,199. Circ: 20,000 (controlled).

700 CAN ISSN 1188-4282
NX120.C2
ART ET CULTURE AU QUEBEC. Text in English. 1991. biennial. CND 52.95 (effective 2000). **Document type:** *Directory.*
Formerly (until 1993): Monde de la Culture au Quebec (0847-4958)
Published by: Quebec dans le Monde, C P 8503, Sainte Foy, PQ G1V 4N5, Canada. TEL 418-659-5540, FAX 418-659-4143. Ed. Denis Turcotte.

708 FRA ISSN 0994-7957
L'ART ET LA MER. Text in French. 1974. q. illus.
Published by: Association des Peintres Officiels de la Marine, Musee de la Marine, Palais de Chaillot, 2 rue Royale, Paris Nava, 75200l, France. TEL 42-60-33-30. Ed. Jean Ducros. Circ: 1,500.

704 FRA ISSN 0066-7951
ART ET LES GRANDES CIVILISATIONS. Text in French. 1965. a.
Published by: Editions Citadelles & Mazenod, 33 rue de Naples, Paris, 75008, France. TEL 33-1-53043060, FAX 33-1-45220427.

700 841 FRA ISSN 0518-7648
ART ET POESIE* . Text in French. 1958. q. adv.
Published by: Societe des Poetes et Artistes de France, 11 rue de la Fontaine-Saint-Laurent, Cosne-sur-Loire, 58200, France.

709 FRA ISSN 1272-1603
ART ET SOCIETE. Text in French. 1976. a. price varies. bk.rev. bibl.; illus. 250 p./no.; **Document type:** *Monographic series, Academic/Scholarly.* **Description:** Collection which covers painting, architecture, applied arts and archaeology.
Formerly (until 1995): Arts de l'Ouest (0220-2220)
Indexed: BHA.
Published by: (Centre de Recherches sur les Arts Anciens et Modernes de l'Ouest de la France, Universite de Rennes II (Universite de Haute Bretagne)), Presses Universitaires de Rennes, Campus de la Harpe, 2 Rue du Doyen Denis-Leroy, Rennes, Cedex 35044, France. TEL 33-2-99141401, FAX 33-2-99141407, http://www.uhb.fr. Ed. Jean Yves Andrieux.

686.5 USA ISSN 1388-249X
ART EXPRESSIONS. Text in English. 1995. q. **Document type:** *Magazine, Trade.*
Published by: Pfingsten Publishing, L L C, 6000 Lombardo Center Dr, Ste 420, Seven Hills, OH 44131. TEL 216-328-8926, 888-772-8926, FAX 216-328-9452.

700 GBR
ART HISTORIANS AND SPECIALISTS IN THE U K. Text in English. 1991. irreg., latest 2000. GBP 20 per issue (effective 2000). **Document type:** *Directory.* **Description:** Detailed bio-bibliographical entries on some 600 individuals involved with the study of the fine and applied arts.
Published by: Peter Marcan Publications, Peter Margan Publications, P.O. Box 3158, London, SE1 4RA, United Kingdom. TEL 44-20-7357-0368. Ed. Peter Marcan. Circ: 400.

709 GBR ISSN 0141-6790
N7480
➤ **ART HISTORY**; journal of the Association of Art Historians. Text in English. 1978. 5/yr. GBP 98, EUR 147 combined subscription in Europe to individuals print & online eds.; USD 208 combined subscription in the Americas to individuals & the Caribbean (print & online eds.); GBP 124 combined subscription elsewhere to individuals print & online eds.; GBP 375 combined subscription in Europe to institutions print & online eds.; USD 724 combined subscription in the Americas to institutions & the Caribbean (print & online eds.); GBP 431 combined subscription elsewhere to institutions print & online eds. (effective 2006). adv. bk.rev. illus. index. back issues avail.; reprint service avail. from PQC,PSC. **Document type:** *Journal, Academic/Scholarly.*
Related titles: Microfilm ed.: (from PQC); Online - full text ed.: ISSN 1467-8365. USD 687 in the Americas to institutions & the Caribbean; GBP 356 in Europe to institutions; GBP 409 elsewhere to institutions (effective 2006) (from Blackwell Synergy, EBSCO Publishing, Gale Group, IngentaConnect, O C L C Online Computer Library Center, Inc., Swets Information Services).
Indexed: ABCT, ABM, AIAP, API, ASCA, AmH&L, ArtHuCI, ArtInd, BAS, BHA, BrHumI, CurCont, DAAI, DIP, HistAb, HumInd, IBR, IBRH, IBZ, NTA, RASB, RILM.
—BLDSC (1733.447000), IDS, IE, Infotrieve, ingenta. **CCC.**
Published by: (Association of Art Historians), Blackwell Publishing Ltd., 9600 Garsington Rd, Oxford, OX4 2ZG, United Kingdom. TEL 44-1865-776868, FAX 44-1865-714591, customerservices@oxon.blackwellpublishing.com, http://www.blackwellpublishing.com/journals/AHIS. Eds. Deborah Cherry, Fintan Cullen. Circ: 2,500.

709 USA ISSN 0004-3214
N1
ART IN AMERICA. Text in English. 1913. m. USD 34.95 domestic; USD 64.95 in Canada; USD 69.95 elsewhere (effective 2005). adv. bk.rev. illus. back issues avail.; reprints avail. **Document type:** *Magazine, Consumer.* **Description:** Covers contemporary art worldwide. The August issue is an annual Museum Guide.
Related titles: Microform ed.: (from PQC); Online - full text ed.: (from EBSCO Publishing, Florida Center for Library Automation, Gale Group, Northern Light Technology, Inc., O C L C Online Computer Library Center, Inc., ProQuest Information & Learning); Supplement(s): Art in America. Annual Guide to Galleries, Museums, Artists. ISSN 0736-7619. 1982.
Indexed: ABM, ABS&EES, AIAP, ASCA, AcaI, AmH&L, AmHI, ArtHuCI, ArtInd, BHA, BRD, BRI, CBRI, ChPerI, CurCont, DAAI, DIP, FLI, HistAb, HumInd, IBR, IBZ, IndIslam, MASUSE, MagInd, PMR, RASB, RGAb, RGPR, RI-1, RI-2, RILM, SSCI.
—BLDSC (1733.345000), IE, Infotrieve, ingenta. **CCC.**
Published by: Brant Publications, Inc., 575 Broadway, 5th Fl, New York, NY 10012. TEL 212-941-2800, FAX 212-941-2819, artinamerica@aol.com, http://www.artinamericamagazine.com/. Ed. Elizabeth C. Baker. Pub. Sandra Brant. Adv. contact Cynthia Zabel. B&W page USD 4,720, color page USD 6,085. Circ: 65,000. **Subscr. to:** PO Box 37003, Boone, IA 50037-0003.

700 CAN ISSN 1700-9995
ART IN PROFILE SERIES. Text in English. 2002. irreg. **Document type:** *Monographic series.*
Published by: University of Calgary Press, University of Calgary, Faculty of Education ETD 722, 2500 University Dr N W, Calgary, AB T2N 1N4, Canada. ucpmail@ucalgary.ca, http://www.ucalgary.ca/ucpress, http://www.uofcpress.com. Eds. Geoffrey Simmins, Michael McMordie.

700 USA
ART IN WISCONSIN* . Text in English. 1984. bi-m. looseleaf. USD 15; (effective June 1993). adv.
Formerly: Wisconsin Painters and Sculptors. Newsletter
Related titles: Diskette ed.: 1984.
Published by: Wisconsin Painters and Sculptors, Inc., 8872 Lime Kiln Rd, Sturgeon Bay, WI 54235-9456. Ed. Kathleen Barlament. Circ: 700.

▼ **ART JEWELRY.** see *JEWELRY, CLOCKS AND WATCHES*

700 DEU ISSN 1437-1340
ART JOURNAL. Text in German. m. free. back issues avail.
Media: Online - full text (from Northern Light Technology, Inc.).
Address: Uhlandstr 8, Hiddenhausen, 32120, Germany. TEL 49-5523-820582, FAX 49-5523-820584, ws@art-joe.com, http://art-quearter.com/beck/joe/aj. Ed. Werner Stuerenburg.

700 USA ISSN 0004-3249
N81
➤ **ART JOURNAL.** Text in English. q. USD 50 domestic to non-member individuals; USD 60 foreign to non-member individuals; USD 75 domestic to non-member institutions; USD 85 foreign to non-member institutions (effective 2005). adv. bk.rev. illus. reprints avail. **Document type:** *Journal, Academic/Scholarly.* **Description:** Journal of ideas and opinions that focuses on critical and aesthetic issues in the visual arts of our times.
Former titles (until 1960): College Art Journal (1543-6322); (until 1941): Parnassus (1543-6314)
Related titles: Microfilm ed.: (from PQC); Online - full text ed.: (from Chadwyck-Healey Inc., EBSCO Publishing, Gale Group, H.W. Wilson, JSTOR (Web-based Journal Archive), O C L C Online Computer Library Center, Inc., ProQuest Information & Learning).
Indexed: A&ATA, ABM, ABS&EES, AIAP, API, ASCA, AcaI, AmHI, ArtHuCI, ArtInd, BAS, BHA, BRI, CBRI, CurCont, DAAI, DIP, HumInd, IBR, IBZ, MASUSE, PCI, RASB, RILM, SSCI.
—BLDSC (1733.460000), IE, ingenta.
Published by: College Art Association, 275 Seventh Ave, New York, NY 10001. TEL 212-691-1051, FAX 212-627-2381, nyoffice@collegeart.org, http://www.collegeart.org/caa/publications/AJ/artjournal.html. Adv. contact Paul Skiff. Circ: 11,000.

776.6 DNK ISSN 1395-5829
ART-LAND INTERNATIONAL. Text in English. 1994. s-a. DKK 25 newsstand/cover (effective 2000). illus. **Document type:** *Magazine, Consumer.* **Description:** Contains theme-based issues mixing art, science, sports and entertainment.
Address: Gothergade 163,3, Copenhagen K, 1123, Denmark. TEL 45-33-32-77-37, FAX 45-33-32-77-47, klykke@apple.agora.dk. Eds. Henrik Heinz Grundsted, Kim Lykke Joergensen.

ART LAW & ACCOUNTING REPORTER. see *LAW*

700 ITA ISSN 1592-1921
ART LEADER; rivista di arte, architettura, informazione, design e cultura. Text in Italian. 1991. m. EUR 5.12 newsstand/cover to individuals (effective 1999). **Description:** Contains articles on current art exhibitions as well as photography, architecture and music festivals. Provides lists of art that is for sale on the open market.
Published by: R M Edizioni S.r.l., Via Volta 19C, Osimo, AN 60027, Italy. TEL 39-071-7202052, FAX 39-071-7108546, ida@imar.net, http://www.artleader.it. Ed. Vania Pasqualini.

ART LIBRARIES JOURNAL. see *LIBRARY AND INFORMATION SCIENCES*

ART LIBRARIES SOCIETY OF NORTH AMERICA. OCCASIONAL PAPERS. see *LIBRARY AND INFORMATION SCIENCES*

700 GBR
ART LINE; international art news. Text in English. 1983. 8/yr. GBP 22, USD 50. bk.rev. back issues avail.
Indexed: DAAI.
Published by: Art Line Magazine, Phoenix House, Phoenix St, Charing Cross Rd, London, WC2H 0DA, United Kingdom. TEL 44-171-497-3545, FAX 44-171-379-4846. Ed. Keith Patrick. Circ: 30,000.

700 UKR
ART LINE. Text in Ukrainian. m.
Address: A-ya 14, Kiev, 254086, Ukraine. TEL 446-81-38, FAX 446-43-11. **US dist. addr.:** East View Information Services, 3020 Harbor Ln. N., Minneapolis, MN 55447. TEL 612-550-0961.

700 USA ISSN 0892-1202
ART LOVER'S ART AND CRAFT FAIR BULLETIN. Text in English. 1977. q. USD 12 (effective 2001). **Document type:** *Trade.* **Description:** Listings of art and craft shows throughout the state of Illinois for visitors to shows.
Published by: American Society of Artists, Inc., PO Box 1326, Palatine, IL 60078. TEL 312-751-2500.

ART MAGIC. see *CHILDREN AND YOUTH—For*

702.8 USA
ART MATERIALS RETAILER. Text in English. 1998. q. free domestic to qualified personnel (effective 2005). adv. **Document type:** *Magazine.* **Description:** Features articles on store design, merchandising, advertising, staffing, finance, written for individuals involved in the artist materials industry.
Published by: Fahy - Williams Publishing, Inc., PO Box 1080, Geneva, NY 14456-8080. tmanzer@fwpi.com, http://www.artmaterialsretailer.com. Ed. Tina Manzer. Pub. Kevin J Fahy. Adv. contact Tim Braden. B&W page USD 1,300, color page USD 1,800. Circ: 12,000 (controlled).

700 GBR ISSN 0142-6702
N1
ART MONTHLY. Text in English. 1976. 10/yr. GBP 38 domestic to individuals; GBP 48 in Europe to individuals; USD 65 in North America to individuals; GBP 62 elsewhere to individuals; GBP 46 domestic to institutions; GBP 58 in Europe to institutions; USD 70 in North America to institutions; GBP 74 elsewhere to institutions; GBP 27 domestic to students; GBP 37 in Europe to students; USD 45 in North Africa to students; USD 48 elsewhere to students (effective 2006). adv. bk.rev.; Website rev. cum.index: 1976-1987, Vol.1 '76-'96, Vol.2 '96-'99, Vol.3 '99-'01. 52 p./no. 3 cols./p.; back issues avail.; reprints avail. **Document type:** *Magazine, Consumer.* **Description:** Contains interviews, features on new artists and trends, gallery and museum reviews from all over the world, and art market information.
Related titles: Audio CD ed.; Online - full text ed.: (from EBSCO Publishing, H.W. Wilson, O C L C Online Computer Library Center, Inc.).
Indexed: ABM, ArtInd, BHA, BrHumI, ChPerI, DIP, IBR, IBZ.
—BLDSC (1733.463200), IE, ingenta.
Published by: Britannia Art Publications Ltd., 4th Fl., 28 Charing Cross Rd, London, WC2H 0DB, United Kingdom. TEL 44-20-7240-0389, FAX 44-20-7497-0726, info@artmonthly.co.uk, http://www.artmonthly.co.uk. Ed. Patricia Bickers. Pubs. Jack Wendler, Nell Wendler. R&P Letty Mooring TEL 44-20-7240-0389. Adv. contact Matthew Hale TEL 44-20-7240-0418. page GBP 1,155. Circ: 5,500.

700 AUS ISSN 1033-4025
ART MONTHLY AUSTRALIA. Text in English. 1987. 10/yr. AUD 70 domestic; AUD 90 in Asia & the Pacific; AUD 120 elsewhere (effective 2004). adv. bk.rev. illus. 52 p./no.; back issues avail. **Document type:** *Magazine, Academic/Scholarly.* **Description:** News, information and discussion of current issues in the visual art world of Australia.
Formerly (until 1989): Australian and International Art Monthly (0819-5838)
Indexed: ABM, AusPAIS, PCI.
Published by: Art Monthly Australia Pty. Ltd., c/o Canberra School of Art, GPO Box 804, Canberra, ACT 2601, Australia. TEL 61-2-62493988, FAX 61-2-61259794, philippa.kelly@anu.edu.au, http://www.artmonthly.org.au. Ed., R&P, Adv. contact Philippa Kelly TEL 61-2-61253986. Circ: 5,000 (paid).

700 USA ISSN 0274-7073
ART NEW ENGLAND; a resource for the visual arts. Text in English. 1979. 6/yr. USD 28 domestic; USD 33 in Canada; USD 40 elsewhere (effective 2005). adv. bk.rev.; film rev. illus. reprints avail. **Document type:** *Bulletin, Consumer.*
Related titles: Online - full text ed.: (from H.W. Wilson, O C L C Online Computer Library Center, Inc.).
Indexed: ArtInd.
Published by: Art New England, Inc., 425 Washington St, Brighton, MA 02135. TEL 617-782-3008, FAX 617-782-4218, advertising@artnewengland.com, http://www.artnewengland.com. Ed. Barbara O'Brien. Pub., Adv. contact Omi Rajpal. R&P Portia Belc. Circ: 30,000.

700 770 NZL ISSN 0110-1102
N7406
ART NEW ZEALAND. Text in English. 1976. q. NZD 35. adv. bk.rev.; film rev.; play rev. illus.
Indexed: ABCT, ABM, BHA, INZP, RILM, WBA, WMB.
—BLDSC (1733.464500), IE, ingenta. **CCC.**
Published by: Art Magazine Press Ltd., Box 10-249, Balmoral, Auckland 4, New Zealand. Ed. William Dart. Circ: 4,000.

700 NZL ISSN 1174-1155
ART NEWS NEW ZEALAND. Text in English. 1981. q. NZD 25 domestic; NZD 45 foreign (effective 2000). adv. illus. back issues avail. **Document type:** *Consumer.*
Published by: Matrix Publishing Ltd., PO Box 99-731, Auckland, New Zealand. TEL 64-9-357-6006, FAX 64-9-358-0606, artnews@industrial.co.nz. Ed. Kart Webster. Pub., R&P Dan Chappell. adv.: B&W page NZD 1,480, color page NZD 1,990; trim 215 x 275.

700 GBR ISSN 0960-6556
N1
THE ART NEWSPAPER (INTERNATIONAL EDITION). Text in English. 1990. 11/yr. adv. bk.rev.; tel.rev. mkt.; stat. **Document type:** *Newspaper, Consumer.* **Description:** Contains comprehensive and international coverage of the world of art: politics, economics, law, exhibitions, opinions, museums, restoration, dealers, galleries, publications and future events.
Incorporated (1988-1989): Journal of Art (1044-9140)
Related titles: ♦ Italian ed.: Il Giornale dell' Arte. ISSN 0394-0543.
Indexed: ABM, ArtInd, RICS, RILM.
—BLDSC (1733.465250), IE. **CCC.**
Published by: The Art Newspaper, 70 South Lambeth Rd, London, SW8 1RL, United Kingdom. TEL 44-207-7353331, FAX 44-207-7353332, contact@theartnewspaper.com, http://www.theartnewspaper.com/, http://artnewspaper.com. Ed. Christina Ruiz. adv.: B&W page GBP 2,300, B&W page USD 4,300; trim 260 x 375. Circ: 14,000 (paid).

700 COL ISSN 0122-1744
ART NEXUS (ENGLISH EDITION). Text in English. 1976. q. USD 32 (effective 2005). back issues avail.
Related titles: Online - full content ed.; Online - full text ed.: (from H.W. Wilson, O C L C Online Computer Library Center, Inc.); ♦ Spanish ed.: Art Nexus (Spanish Edition). ISSN 0121-5639.
Indexed: ABM, ArtInd, BHA, RASB.
Published by: Arte en Colombia Ltda., Apartado Aereo 90193, Bogota, DE, Colombia. TEL 571-3129332, FAX 571-3129252, info@artnexus.com, http://www.artnexus.com/servlet/Reg_Step0. Ed. Celia Sredni de Birbragher. Pub. Ivone Pini. Adv. contact Zulema Roca TEL 305-891-7270.

700 COL ISSN 0121-5639
➤ **ART NEXUS (SPANISH EDITION).** Text in Spanish. 1976. q. USD 32 (effective 2005). adv. bk.rev. illus. back issues avail. **Document type:** *Academic/Scholarly.* **Description:** Covers Latin American art, architecture, films and photography.
Formerly (until 1991): Arte en Colombia Internacional (0120-713X)
Related titles: Online - full text ed.: (from O C L C Online Computer Library Center, Inc.); ♦ English ed.: Art Nexus (English Edition). ISSN 0122-1744.
Indexed: ABCT, ABM, ArtInd, BHA, HAPI, RILM.
—BLDSC (1733.465270), IE, ingenta.
Published by: Arte en Colombia Ltda., Apartado Aereo 90193, Bogota, DE, Colombia. TEL 571-3129332, FAX 571-3129252, info@artnexus.com, http://www.artnexus.com/servlet/Reg_Step0. Ed. Celia Sredni de Birbragher. Pub. Ivone Pini. Adv. contact Zulema Roca TEL 305-891-7270. B&W page USD 1,800, color page USD 2,600; trim 8.5 x 11. Circ: 16,000.

700 USA ISSN 1047-4994
N8214.5.U6
ART OF THE WEST. Text in English. 1987. bi-m. USD 24 domestic; USD 42 foreign (effective 2005). adv. bk.rev. **Document type:** *Magazine, Consumer.* **Description:** Covers landscape and seascapes, Native American art, mountain men art, and "cowboy" art, from old Wild West days to the working cowboy of today.
Published by: Duerr and Tierney Ltd., 15612 Hwy. 7, Ste. 235, Minnetonka, MN 55345. TEL 952-935-5850, FAX 952-935-6546, tom@atow.com, http://www.aotw.com. Ed. Vicki Stavig. Pubs. Allan J Duerr, Thomas F Tierney. R&P Thomas F Tierney. Adv. contact Tom F Tierney. Circ: 33,000 (paid).

769 USA ISSN 1521-7922
NE1
ART ON PAPER. Text in English. 1970. 10/yr. USD 54 domestic; USD 70 in Canada & Mexico; USD 86 elsewhere (effective 2005). adv. bk.rev. illus. reprints avail. **Document type:** *Magazine, Consumer.* **Description:** Presents a balanced range of media and historical periods with features and art market information written by today's specialists. Each issue contains news, announcements, and reviews of current museum and gallery exhibitions as well as independently published artists' books, limited edition prints, and specialized museum and dealer catalogues.
Former titles (until Oct. 1998): On Paper (1089-7909); (until 1996): Print Collector's Newsletter (0032-8537)
Indexed: ABCT, ABM, AIAP, ArtInd, BHA.
—BLDSC (1733.465810).
Published by: Fanning Publishing Co., Inc., 150 W 28th St, Ste 504, New York, NY 10001. TEL 212-675-1968, FAX 212-675-2038, info@artonpaper.com, http://www.artonpaper.com/. Ed., Pub. Peter Nesbett. Adv. contact Jeff Porter. B&W page USD 1,770, color page USD 2,475; 7.375 x 9.875. Circ: 5,000.

700 USA ISSN 1524-9581
NX506
ART PAPERS MAGAZINE. Text in English. 1976. bi-m. USD 35 domestic to non-members; USD 30 domestic to members; USD 40 in Canada & Mexico; USD 75 in Europe; USD 80 in Asia, Africa & Pacific Rim; USD 60 elsewhere (effective 2005). adv. bk.rev.; film rev.; play rev. illus. cum.index: nos. 1-15, 1991. back issues avail.; reprints avail. **Document type:** *Magazine, Consumer.* **Description:** Features diverse perspectives on contemporary art and emerging artists in articles and interviews, original art, reviews, news, and an extensive art resource guide.
Formerly (until 1999): Art Papers (0278-1441); Formed by the 1980 merger of: Contemporary Art - Southeast (0147-6297); Atlanta Art Papers (0271-2083); Formerly (until 1978): Atlanta Art Workers Coalition Newspaper
Related titles: Microfiche ed.: (from PQC); Online - full text ed.: (from H.W. Wilson, O C L C Online Computer Library Center, Inc.).
Indexed: ABM, ABS&EES, ArtInd, BHA, ChPerI, RILM.
—BLDSC (1733.465900), IE, ingenta.
Published by: Atlanta Art Papers, Inc., PO Box 5748, Atlanta, GA 31107. TEL 404-588-1837, FAX 404-588-1836, info@artpapers.org, http://www.artpapers.org. Ed. Sylvie Fortin. adv.: B&W page USD 900, color page USD 1,300. Circ: 155,000.

700 USA
ART POLICE. Variant title: ArtPolice Comics. Text in English, French, Hebrew. 1974. 3/yr. USD 5 to individuals; USD 20 to libraries. back issues avail. **Description:** Provides venues for artists outside mainstream art publications.
Published by: ArtPolice, Inc., 5228 43rd Ave S, Minneapolis, MN 55417-2210. TEL 312-339-3173. Circ: 1,000.

700 PRI ISSN 1548-1468
▼ **ART PREMIUM PUERTO RICO.** Text in Spanish. 2004 (Feb-Mar). bi-m. USD 22 (effective 2004).
Published by: Art Premium, Inc., 1452 Ashford Ave. Ste. 306A, San Juan, PR 00907. TEL 787-721-6021, FAX 787-721-6024, info@artpremium.com, http://www.artpremium.com.

700 FRA ISSN 0245-5676
NX2
ART PRESS; la revue de l'art contemporain. Text in English, French. 1972. m. EUR 6.20 per issue (effective 2005). dance rev.; play rev. abstr.; bibl.; tr.lit. back issues avail. **Description:** Contains artist interviews, reviews of books about artists, reviews of exhibits, articles covering certain themes, and chronicles on different modes of artistic expression including dance, theater and architecture. Also includes a section on the art market and one that explores the artistic activities going on in chosen cities.
Related titles: Microform ed.: (from PQC); Online - full text ed.: (from H.W. Wilson, O C L C Online Computer Library Center, Inc.).
Indexed: ABM, ArtInd, BHA, DIP, IBR, IBZ.
—IE, Infotrieve. **CCC.**
Published by: ArtPublications, 8 rue Francois Villon, Paris, 75015, France. TEL 33-1-53686565, FAX 33-1-53686585, contact@artpress.com, http://www.artpress.com. Ed. Catherine Millet. Pub. Jean-Pierre de Kerraoul. Adv. contact Sylvie Dupuis. Circ: 48,000. **Subscr. to:** 1 rue Robert Bichet, BP 1, Avesnes-sur-Helpe Cedex 59361, France.

700 USA ISSN 1529-6660
ART-PROMO-NEWS. Text in English. 1999. m. adv.
Media: Online - full text.
Published by: Art-Promo News, Box 9, Martin, SD 57551. TEL 605-685-6062, info@armchairpaintclasses.com, http://www.art-promonews.com. Ed., Pub. Madeleine Jacobs. Adv. contact Jack Jacobs.

700 GBR ISSN 0967-4349
ART QUARTERLY. Text in English. 1990. q.
Indexed: ABM.
Published by: National Art Collections Fund, Millais House, 7 Cromwell Place, London, SW7 2JN, United Kingdom. TEL 44-20-7225-4800, FAX 44-20-7225-4848, info@artfund.org, http://www.artfund.org/main_site/1_0home.asp.

700 GBR ISSN 0004-4091
N1
ART REVIEW (LONDON); international art and style. Text in English. 1949. m. GBP 38 domestic; GBP 93 in Europe; USD 99 in US & Canada; GBP 117 elsewhere (effective 2005). adv. bk.rev. illus. index. reprints avail. **Document type:** *Magazine, Consumer.* **Description:** An independent visual art magazine designed to serve the art buyer and gallery visitor.
Formerly: Art News & Review
Related titles: Microfilm ed.: (from BNB, PQC); Online - full text ed.: (from H.W. Wilson, O C L C Online Computer Library Center, Inc.).
Indexed: ABCT, ABM, AIAP, ArtInd, BHA, RASB.
—BLDSC (1733.470920), IE, ingenta. **CCC.**
Published by: Art Review Ltd., Hereford House, 23-24 Smithfield St, London, EC1A 9LF, United Kingdom. TEL 44-20-72364880, FAX 44-20-72364881, info@art-review.co.uk, http://www.art-review.co.uk/. Eds. Daniel Kunitz, David Lee. Circ: 15,000. **Subscr. in the US & Canada to:** Art Review Inc., 33-2212 Hudson St., Jersey City, NJ 07302-6530. TEL 877-363-1310.

▼ new title ➤ refereed ✶ unverified ♦ full entry avail.

700 USA ISSN 1068-7890
ART REVUE. Text in English. 1990. q. USD 15 (effective 2001). adv. bk.rev. back issues avail. **Document type:** *Consumer.*
Formerly: Revue - Art in All Dimensions
Published by: Innovative Artists Agency, 302 W 13th St, Loveland, CO 80537. TEL 970-669-0625, FAX 970-669-0625. Ed. Jan McNutt. Adv. contact Irene Thomson. Circ: 10,000.

700 GBR
ART SALES INDEX: OIL PAINTINGS, DRAWINGS, WATER COLOURS AND SCULPTURE. Text in English, French; Summaries in English. 1968. a. USD 195 (effective 2000). adv. index. **Document type:** *Abstract/Index.* **Description:** Contains over 120,000 sales results for over 35,000 international artists.
Former titles: Annual Art Sales Index: Oil Paintings, Drawings, Water Colours and Sculptures; Annual Art Sales Index: Oil Paintings, Drawings and Watercolours (0308-5910); (until 1979): Annual Art Sales Index (Year) (0143-0688); Formed by the merger of: Annual Art Sales Index: Watercolours and Drawings; Annual Art Sales Index: Oil Paintings
Related titles: Online - full text ed.
—BLDSC (1733.471510).
Published by: Art Sales Index Ltd, 16 Luddington Ave, Virginia Water, Surrey GU25 4DF, United Kingdom. TEL 44-1344-841750, FAX 44-1344-841760, info@art-sales-index.com, http://www.art-sales-index.com/system/index.html. Ed. Duncan Hislop. Pub. Richard Hislop. Circ: 3,000.

700 USA
ART SPIRIT!. Text in English. 1998. 3/yr.
Published by: Art Spirit! Inc., Box 460669, Fort Lauderdale, FL 33346. TEL 954-763-3338, FAX 954-763-4481, sfbiz@mindspring.com. Ed. Sherry Friedlaw. Circ: 20,000 (paid and controlled).

700 USA ISSN 0741-496X
ART-TALK. Text in English. 1981. 9/yr. USD 18. adv. bk.rev. **Document type:** *Newspaper.* **Description:** Covers art news internationally and art events nationally.
Address: PO Box 8508, Scottsdale, AZ 85252-8508. TEL 602-948-1799, FAX 602-994-9284. Ed. Bill Macomber. Pub. Thom Romeo. Adv. contact Kathryn Young. Circ: 40,000.

ART THERAPY; journal of the American Art Therapy Association. see *MEDICAL SCIENCES—Physical Medicine And Rehabilitation*

700 FRA
ART TRADE. Variant title: ADEC - Art Price Annual. Text in English, French. 1987. a. USD 119. back issues avail. **Document type:** *Trade.* **Description:** Guide for prospective buyers and sellers of fine arts, including 250,000 auction results every year.
Related titles: CD-ROM ed.; Online - full text ed.
Published by: Artprice.com, BP 69, St Romain-au-Mont d'Or, 69270, France. TEL 33-478-220000, FAX 33-478-220606, adec@adec.com, http://www.adec.com.

701.18 USA ISSN 1546-7082
N6512.7
▼ **ART U S.** Text in English. 2003. bi-m. USD 30 in US & Canada; USD 55 elsewhere; USD 6 newsstand/cover (effective 2004).
Related titles: Online - full text ed.: (from EBSCO Publishing).
Address: 530 Molino St., Ste 21, Los Angeles, CA 90013. http://www.arttext.org. Ed. Malik Gaines.

700 USA
ART VOICE. Text in English. w. (Wed.). free (effective 2005). **Document type:** *Newspaper.*
Published by: Jamie Moses, 810-812 Main St., Buffalo, NY 14202. TEL 716-881-6604, FAX 716-881-6682, http://www.artvoice.com. Pub. Jamie Moses. Circ: 60,000 (free).

700 GBR
ART WORKERS GUILD. ANNUAL REPORT. Text in English. 1885. a. membership. bibl.; illus. **Description:** Covers the proceedings of the guild.
Published by: Art Workers Guild, 6 Queen St, London, W1X 7PH, United Kingdom. Ed. D G Pullen. Circ: 400 (controlled).

700 ITA
ART WORLD. Text in Italian. 1988. 3/yr.
Indexed: AIAP.
Published by: Michelangelo s.r.l., Via Domenico Cimarosa, 4, Milan, MI 20144, Italy. TEL 02-48021565, FAX 02-48009687. Ed. Marco Lupis di Santa Margherita. Circ: 37,000.

700 USA ISSN 1525-1772
ART WORLD NEWS. Text in English. m. free to qualified subscribers. **Document type:** *Magazine, Trade.* **Description:** Covers the international art and framing community, marketing issues, new products and consumer trends.
Address: 143 Rowayton Ave, Rowayton, CT 06853. TEL 203-854-8566, info.awn@juno.com, http://www.artworldnews.com/.

700 AUS ISSN 1038-3719
ART WRITE. Text in English. 1992. irreg.
Media: Online - full text.
Published by: University of New South Wales, College of Fine Arts, PO Box 259, Paddington, NSW 2021, Australia. TEL 61-2-9385-0706, FAX 61-2-9385-0888, administration@cofa.unsw.edu.au, http://www.cofa.unsw.edu.au/units/artht/artwrite.html.

730 750 ROM ISSN 1220-6865
N8
ARTA. Text and summaries in English, Romanian. 1954. bi-m. ROL 600, USD 39 (effective 1992). adv. bk.rev. **Description:** Covers modern and contemporary visual arts in Rumania and abroad; painting, sculpture, graphics, decorative arts, design, video, installations, performances, film, theater, photography.
Formerly: Arta Plastica Review
Indexed: ABM, BHA, RASB.
Published by: Ministerul Culturii, Piata Presi Libere 1, Sector 1, Bucharest, Romania. TEL 401-6131380, FAX 401-31121939. Ed. Calin Dan. Circ: 2,500. **Co-sponsor:** Soros Foundation for an Open Society.

700 AUS ISSN 1325-6475
ARTBEAT. Text in English. 1996. q. **Document type:** *Newsletter.* **Description:** Cultural newsletter focusing primarily on federal cultural policy, projects and activities.
Media: Online - full text.
Published by: Department of Communications Information Technology and the Arts, 38 Sydney Ave, Forrest, ACT 2603, Australia. TEL 61-2-6277-7480, FAX 61-2-6273-4154, artbeat@dca.gov.au, http://www.dca.gov.au/artbeat.html.

709 ZAF ISSN 0004-3389
N8.A34
➤ **DE ARTE.** Text in Afrikaans, English. 1967. s-a. ZAR 40 domestic; USD 30 foreign (effective 2001). adv. bk.rev.; play rev. bibl.; illus. back issues avail. **Document type:** *Journal, Academic/Scholarly.* **Description:** Articles cover a wide range within art and architectural history as well as applied arts.
Related titles: Online - full text ed.
Indexed: ABM, AIAP, BHA, DIP, IBR, IBZ, ISAP.
Published by: (University of South Africa), Unisa Press, Periodicals, PO Box 392, Pretoria, 0003, South Africa. TEL 27-12-429-3081, FAX 27-12-429-3221, TELEX 350068, unisa-press@unisa.ac.za, http://www.unisa.ac.za/press. Ed. Bernadette van Haute. Pub. P van der Walt. Circ: 750 (paid).

745.2 ITA ISSN 1122-5858
ARTE. Text in Italian. 1970. 11/yr. adv. bk.rev. charts; illus. **Document type:** *Magazine, Consumer.*
Former titles (until 1982): La Rivista dell'Arte (1122-584X); (until 1981): BolaffiArte (0045-236X)
Indexed: ABCT, ABM, AIAP, BHA.
—BLDSC (1733.478700).
Published by: Editoriale Giorgio Mondadori SpA (Subsidiary of: Cairo Communication SpA), Via Tucidide 56, Torre 3, Milan, 20134, Italy. TEL 39-02-748111, FAX 39-02-70100102, info@cairocommunication.it, http://www.cairocommunication.it. Ed. Mario Pancera. Circ: 40,000.

700 780 ITA ISSN 1124-0229
ARTE A BOLOGNA; bollettino dei musei civici d'arte antica. Text in Italian. 1990. a.
Indexed: RILM.
Published by: Nuova Alfa, Via Trentacoste 7, Milano, 20134, Italy. TEL 39-02-215631.

700 USA ISSN 0326-4807
N6502
ARTE AL DIA; international magazine of Latin American art and antique. Text in Spanish, English. 1980. bi-m. USD 48 domestic; USD 68 in Latin America; USD 79 in Europe; USD 85 elsewhere (effective 2001). adv. bk.rev. illus.
Related titles: Online - full text ed.
Published by: American Art Corporation, 905 Brickwell Bay Dr, Ste 1021, Miami, FL 33131. TEL 305-371-7106, http://www.artealdia.com/. Ed. Diego Costa-Peuser. Adv. contact Hernan Carrara. Circ: 24,000.

700 ARG ISSN 0328-2082
ARTE AL DIA INFORMA. Text in Spanish. 1992. 11/yr.
Published by: Editorial Arte al Dia s.r.l., Azcuenaga 1592 PB, Buenos Aires, 1115AAP, Argentina. TEL 54-11-4805-7257, artealdia@artealdia.com, http://www.artealdia.com/. Ed. Jorge Eduardo Costa-Peuse. Circ: 15,000.

700 USA
ARTE AL DIA NEWS. Text in English, Spanish. bi-m. **Document type:** *Newsletter.*
Published by: American Art Corporation, 905 Brickwell Bay Dr, Ste 1021, Miami, FL 33131. TEL 305-371-7106, http://www.artealdia.com/. Ed. Diego Costa-Peuser. Adv. contact Hernan Carrara.

700 MEX
ARTE & ARTES; revista Mexicana de cultura. Text in Spanish. 1998. quadrennial. MXP 400 domestic; USD 80 foreign (effective 2000). **Document type:** *Consumer.*
Published by: Operadora Mexico Viva S.A. de C.V., Rancho de la Laja No 31, Santa Cecilia, Coyoacan, Mexico, D.F., 04930, Mexico. TEL 52-5-594-6406, FAX 52-5-603-1388, gondi_tomas@data.net.mx, http://www.arteyartes.com.mx. Ed. Tomas Gondi-Altamirano.

700 USA
ARTE CONTEMPORARY. Text in English. 1999. q. USD 26.95; USD 6.95 newsstand/cover (effective 2001). adv. **Document type:** *Magazine, Consumer.*
Published by: Perspective Publications, Inc., Box 1951, Santa Fe, NM 87504. TEL 505-988-5007, FAX 505-983-0728, see@artecontemporary.net, http://www.artecontemporary.net. Ed. Benjamin Forde. Pub. Cynthia Stearns.

704.948 ITA ISSN 0004-3400
N7810
ARTE CRISTIANA; rivista internazionale di storia dell'arte e di arti liturgiche. Text in Italian, English. 1913; N.S. 1983. bi-m. EUR 92 (effective 2005). bk.rev. bibl.; charts. index, cum.index. 80 p./no.; **Document type:** *Consumer.*
Indexed: AIAP, BHA, DIP, IBR, IBZ, RILM.
Published by: Scuola Beato Angelico, Viale San Gimignano, 19, Milan, MI 20146, Italy. TEL 39-02-48302854, FAX 39-02-48301954, bangelic@tin.it. Ed. Valerio Vigorelli.

700 ITA ISSN 1121-0524
ARTE DOCUMENTO. Text in Italian. 1988. a.
Indexed: RILM.
Published by: Universita Degli Studi di Udine, Via Palladio 8, Palazzo Florio, Udine, 33100, Italy. TEL 39-0432-556111, FAX 39-0432-507715.

709 913 ITA ISSN 0391-9110
ARTE E ARCHEOLOGIA; studi e documenti. Text in Italian. 1972. irreg., latest vol.25, 1999. price varies. **Document type:** *Monographic series.*
Published by: Casa Editrice Leo S. Olschki, Viuzzo del Pozzetto 8, Florence, 50126, Italy. TEL 39-055-6530684, FAX 39-055-6530214, celso@olschki.it, http://www.olschki.it.

700 ITA
ARTE & CORNICE. Text in Italian; Summaries in English. 1984. q. EUR 15 domestic; EUR 20 foreign (effective 2005). **Document type:** *Magazine, Consumer.* **Description:** Covers all aspects of frames.
Formerly: Aste e Cornici (0393-439X)
Published by: Rima Editrice, Viale Sarca 243, Milan, MI 20126, Italy. TEL 39-02-66103539, FAX 39-02-66103558, rima@rimaedit.it, http://www.rimaedit.it. Circ: 9,800.

700 BRA ISSN 0103-8508
ARTE E CULTURA DA AMERICA LATINA. Text in Portuguese. 1990. s-a. BRL 30, USD 20.
Published by: Sociedade Cientifica de Estudos da Arte, Rua Domingos Cordeiro, 76, VI Morumbi, Sao Paulo, SP 05688-070, Brazil.

700 COL ISSN 0121-506X
NX535.A1
ARTE FACTO. Text in Spanish. 1992. s-a.
Published by: Universidad Nacional de Colombia, Facultad de Artes, Ciudad Universitaria, Santafe de Bogota, 00, Colombia. TEL 57-1-3165000, FAX 57-1-2219891, ori@bacata.usc.unal.edu.co, http://www.unal.edu.co. Circ: 1,000.

700 ESP ISSN 0212-7342
ARTE GALICIA; revista de informacion de las artes plasticas gallegas. Text in Spanish. 1979. q.
Published by: Sociedad Artistica Ferrolana, Apdo. 339, Ferrol, 15480, Spain. TEL 39-81-353474. Adv. contact Gonzalo Palmeiro. Circ: 3,000.

760 ESP
ARTE GRAFICO EN MADRID. Text in Spanish. biennial. free.
Published by: Fundacion C E I M, Diego de Leon, 50 1o, Madrid, 28006, Spain. TEL 4115317, FAX 2627537.

700 ESP ISSN 1131-5598
NX562.A1
ARTE, INDIVIDUO Y SOCIEDAD. Text in Spanish. 1988. a., latest vol.14, 2002. EUR 18 in the European Union; EUR 25 elsewhere (effective 2004). back issues avail. **Document type:** *Journal, Academic/Scholarly.* **Description:** Focuses on artistic education analyzing aesthetic, behaviour and social environment on individuals.
Related titles: CD-ROM ed.: EUR 108 to individuals; EUR 150 to institutions (effective 2003).
Indexed: RILM.
—CINDOC.
Published by: (Universidad Complutense de Madrid, Departamento de Didactica de Expresion Plastica), Universidad Complutense de Madrid, Servicio de Publicaciones, C Isaac Peral s/n, Ciudad Universitaria, Madrid, 28040, Spain. TEL 34-91-3946934, FAX 34-91-3946978, ais@art.ucm.es, servicio@publicaciones.ucm.es, http://www.ucm.es/publicaciones. Ed. Manuel Hernandez Belver.

700 ITA ISSN 0393-7267
N5950
ARTE MEDIEVALE. Text in Italian. 1987. s-a. price varies. **Document type:** *Journal, Academic/Scholarly.* **Description:** International review of medieval art, with contributions in original language.
Indexed: AIAP, BHA, RILM.

Published by: Istituto della Enciclopedia Italiana, Piazza della Enciclopedia Italiana 4, Rome, RM 00186, Italy. TEL 39-6-68984, FAX 39-6-68982175. Ed. Angiola Maria Romanini.

ARTE MUSICA SPETTACOLO. see *LITERATURE*

700 ITA ISSN 0390-1319
ARTE NAIVE. Text in Italian. s-a.
Indexed: ABM.
Published by: Artigianato Grafico Editoriale s.n.c., Via Casorati, 29, Reggio Emilia, RE 42100, Italy. FAX 39-522-921169.

700 ITA ISSN 1591-3694
ARTE STAMPA. Text in Italian. 1950. 3/yr. **Document type:** *Monographic series, Consumer.*
Formerly: Arte Stampa Liguria
Indexed: BHA, MLA-IB.
Published by: Editrice Liguria, Via de Mari 4, Savona, SV 17100, Italy. TEL 39-019-82991, FAX 39-019-8387798, editriceliguria@editriceliguria.it, http://www.editriceliguria.it.

700 BRA ISSN 0102-6550
NX533.A1 CODEN: ARTEES
➤ **ARTE U N E S P.** Text in Portuguese; Abstracts in English. 1985. a., latest vol.14, 1998. USD 30 per vol. (effective 2005); or exchange basis. abstr.; bibl.; illus. back issues avail. **Document type:** *Journal, Academic/Scholarly.* **Description:** Covers Brazilian art, including its history, origin and style.
Indexed: ABM, DIP, IBR, IBZ.
Published by: Fundacao Editora U N E S P, Praca da Se 108, Sao Paulo, SP 01001-900, Brazil. TEL 55-11-32427171, cgb@marilia.unesp.br, http://www.unesp.br. Ed. Jose Leonardo Nascimento.

709 ITA ISSN 0392-5234
N6921.V5
ARTE VENETA; rivista di storia dell'arte. Text in Italian. 1947. a. EUR 36.50 (effective 2004). adv. reprints avail.
Related titles: Online - full text ed.: (from H.W. Wilson, O C L C Online Computer Library Center, Inc.).
Indexed: A&ATA, AIAP, ArtInd, BHA, DIP, IBR, IBZ, RASB, RILM.
Published by: Mondadori Electa, Via Trantacoste 7, Milan, 20134, Italy. TEL 39-02-215631, FAX 39-02-26413121, http://www.electaweb.it. Ed. Rodolfo Pallucchini. Circ: 2,500.

700 ESP ISSN 1136-2006
ARTE Y PARTE. Text in Spanish. 1996. bi-m. EUR 55 domestic; EUR 75 in Europe; USD 80 in North America (effective 2004). bk.rev. 220 p./no.; **Document type:** *Magazine, Consumer.* **Description:** Surveys the Spanish art exhibition scene and keeps the reader updated on debates over the arts.
Related titles: Online - full text ed.
Indexed: ABM.
Published by: Arte y Parte, S.L., C. Tres de Noviembre 13-15, Santander, 39010, Spain. TEL 34-942-373131, FAX 34-942-373130, revista@arteyparte.com, http://www.arteyparte.com. Ed. Fernando Huici. **Dist. by:** Asociacion de Revistas Culturales de Espana, Hortaleza, 75, Madrid 28004, Spain. TEL 34-91-3086066, FAX 34-91-3199267, info@arce.es, http://www.arce.es.

700 DEU
ARTECHOCK KUNST. Text in German. w. **Document type:** *Magazine, Consumer.* **Description:** Provides a forum for discussion on all aspects of art and the art world.
Media: Online - full text.
Published by: Artechock, Medienforum im Literaturhaus, Salvatorplatz 1, Munich, 80333, Germany. TEL 49-89-2422840, FAX 49-89-24228458, kunst@artechock.de, http://www.artechock.de. Eds. Imke Boesch, Milena Greif.

700 ESP
LAS ARTES; catalogo de pintores, escultores y ceramistas en Mallorca. Text in Spanish. a.
Indexed: AIAP.
Published by: Basilio Baltasar Ediciones, Serinya, 9-2o, Palma De Mallorca, 07003, Spain. TEL 72-79-39, FAX 72-72-34.

709.72 MEX ISSN 0300-4953
N7
➤ **ARTES DE MEXICO.** Text in English, Spanish. 1953; N.S. 1988. q. MXP 900 domestic; USD 90 foreign (effective 2005). adv. bk.rev. illus. reprints avail. **Document type:** *Academic/Scholarly.* **Description:** Covers prehistoric art to modern film, colonial paintings to ritual art, Chiapan textiles to viceroyal palaces, architecture to silver works.
Indexed: ABM, AIAP, AICP, ArtInd, BHA, HAPI, RILM, WTA.
Published by: Artes de Mexico y del Mundo S.A., Plaza Rio de Janeiro 52, Col Roma, Mexico City, DF 06700, Mexico. TEL 52-555-5255905, FAX 52-555-5255925, artesdemexico@artesdemexico.com, http://www.artesdemexico.com/. Ed. Ana Maria Perez Rocha. Pub. Alberto Ruy Sanchez. R&P Teresa Vergara. Adv. contact Margarita de Orellana. Circ: 20,000 (paid).

700.9 MEX
ARTES E HISTORIA. Text in English, Spanish. irreg.
Media: Online - full text.
Published by: M Z Milenio Pro, Africa 36, Coyoacan, Mexico City, DF 04020, Mexico. TEL 52-5-6593883, FAX 52-5-6596065, http://www.arts-history.mx/. Ed. Manuel Zavala Y Alonso.

700 DOM ISSN 1681-1577
N6591
ARTES EN SANTO DOMINGO. Text in Spanish. 2001. q. adv. back issues avail.
Related titles: Online - full text ed.: ISSN 1683-6979. 2002.
Address: C. Jose Joaquin Peres No. 1, Gazcue, Santo Domingo, Dominican Republic. TEL 809-6859422, FAX 809-2211877, artes_en_santodomuingo@hotmail.com, http://www.artesensantodomingo.com/. Ed. Maria del Carmen Ossaye.

700 COL ISSN 1657-3242
ARTES. LA REVISTA. Text in Spanish. 2001. s-a. COP 15,000 domestic; USD 15 foreign (effective 2003).
Published by: Universidad de Antioquia, Calle 67, 53-108, Apartado Aereo 1226, Medellin, Colombia. TEL 57-4-2630011, FAX 57-4-2638282, comunicaciones@udea.edu.co, http://www.udea.edu.co.

709 CAN ISSN 1192-7712
N1
ARTFOCUS. Text in English. 1983. 3/yr. CND 15 domestic; USD 20 foreign; CND 4.50 newsstand/cover (effective 2004). adv. bk.rev. back issues avail. **Document type:** *Magazine, Consumer.* **Description:** Contemporary and historical art exhibited in Canada and abroad.
Supersedes (in 1992): Artpost Magazine (0829-0784)
Indexed: ABM, CBCARef.
Published by: Fleisher Fine Arts Inc., P O Box 1063, Sta F, Toronto, ON M4V 2T7, Canada. TEL 416-925-5564, FAX 416-925-2972, info@artfocus.com, http://www.artfocus.com. Ed. Pat Fleisher. adv.: B&W page CND 1,400, color page CND 2,000; trim 11 x 8.5. Circ: 10,000.

700 USA ISSN 1086-7058
N1
ARTFORUM INTERNATIONAL. Text in English. 1962. m. (10/yr.). USD 46 domestic; USD 72 elsewhere; USD 8 newsstand/cover (effective 2005). adv. bk.rev.; film rev.; play rev. abstr.; bibl.; charts; illus. back issues avail.; reprints avail. **Document type:** *Magazine, Consumer.* **Description:** Offers coverage of the contemporary art world, with sections on architecture, music, advertising and reviews of contemporary exhibitions worldwide.
Formerly (until 1982): Artforum (0004-3532)
Related titles: Microfiche ed.; Microform ed.: (from PQC); Online - full text ed.: (from bigchalk, Florida Center for Library Automation, Gale Group, Northern Light Technology, Inc., ProQuest Information & Learning); ♦ Supplement(s): Bookforum. ISSN 1098-3376.
Indexed: ABCT, ABM, ABS&EES, AIAP, ASCA, Acal, ArtHuCI, ArtInd, BAS, BHA, CurCont, DAAI, FLI, HumInd, IBRH, RASB, RILM.
—BLDSC (1733.743000), IE, ingenta. **CCC.**
Published by: Artforum International Magazine, Inc., 350 Seventh Ave, New York, NY 10001. TEL 212-475-4000, FAX 212-529-1257, generalinfo@artforum.com, http://www.artforum.com/inprint. Eds. Jack Bankowsky, Tim Griffin. Pub. Anthony Korner. Adv. contact Knight Landesman. Circ: 32,000.

741.6 USA ISSN 1544-3655
NC978.5.R32
ARTHUR RACKHAM SOCIETY. JOURNAL. Text in English. 1984. 2/yr. USD 20 domestic to individuals; USD 40 domestic to institutions; GBP 12.50 in United Kingdom to individuals; GBP 25 in United Kingdom to institutions; USD 22.50, GBP 15 elsewhere (effective 2003). bk.rev. bibl.; illus. **Document type:** *Journal, Consumer.* **Description:** Covers the life and works of English illustrator Arthur Rackham (1867-1939) and activities of the society.
Formerly (until 1997): Arthur Rackham Society. Newsletter (1076-8912)
Published by: Arthur Rackham Society, 1240 Devil's Gulch Rd, Estes Park, CO 80517-9500. TEL 970-586-4092, owlsnest@charter.net. Eds., Pubs. Dorothy S. Gibbs, Robin Greer. Circ: 150 (paid).

709.5 CHE ISSN 0004-3648
N8
➤ **ARTIBUS ASIAE**; journal of Asian art and archaeology for scholars and connoisseurs. Text in English, French, German. 1925. s-a. CHF 160, USD 105 (effective 2005). bk.rev. bibl.; charts; illus. index. reprint service avail. from SCH. **Document type:** *Journal, Academic/Scholarly.*
Indexed: ABCT, AIAP, ASCA, ArtHuCI, ArtInd, BAS, BRI, CurCont, DIP, IBR, IBRH, IBSS, IBZ, IndIslam, RASB, RILM.
—BLDSC (1734.080000), IE, Infotrieve, ingenta.
Published by: Museum Rietberg Zurich, Gablerstr 15, Zuerich, 8002, Switzerland. TEL 41-1-2063131, FAX 41-1-2063132, artibus.asiae@rietb.stzh.ch, http://inside.bard.edu/~louis/artibus/, http://www.rietberg.ch. Eds. Anne McGannon, Francoise Louis. Pubs. Axel Langer, Eberhard Fischer.

709.5 CHE ISSN 1423-0526
ARTIBUS ASIAE SUPPLEMENTUM. Text in German, French, English. 1937. irreg. price varies. bibl.; illus. back issues avail. **Document type:** *Monographic series, Academic/Scholarly.* **Description:** Series of full-length books dealing with similar topics to "Artibus Asiae".
Published by: Museum Rietberg Zurich, Gablerstr 15, Zuerich, 8002, Switzerland. TEL 41-1-2063131, FAX 41-1-2063132, artibus.asiae@rietb.stzh.ch, http://www.rietberg.ch. Pubs. Axel Langer, Eberhard Fischer.

741.6 POL ISSN 0391-9064
NX1.A1
ARTIBUS ET HISTORIAE; international journal for visual arts. Text in English, French, German, Italian; Summaries in English. 1980. s-a. EUR 129.95 foreign (effective 2005). illus. Index. reprints avail. **Document type:** *Journal, Academic/Scholarly.* **Description:** Covers a broad range of subjects, including photography and film, as well as traditional topics of scholarly art research.
Indexed: AIAP, AmH&L, ArtInd, BHA, HistAb, IBR, IBZ, PCI, RASB, RILM.
—BLDSC (1734.085000), IE, Infotrieve, ingenta.
Published by: IRSA Publishing House, ul Szczepanska 9, Cracow, W 31 011, Poland. TEL 48-12-4219030, FAX 48-12-4214807, irsa@irsa.com.pl, http://www.irsa.com.pl/main.php?ac=11. Ed. Jozef Grabski.

700 CAN ISSN 0847-3277
ARTICHOKE; writings about the visual arts. Text in English. 1989. 3/yr. CND 20 domestic; USD 22.50 in United States; USD 35 elsewhere; CND 6.95 newsstand/cover (effective 2004). adv. bk.rev. back issues avail. **Document type:** *Magazine, Consumer.* **Description:** Features reviews, interviews and commentary about the visual arts, including painting, sculpture, photography, installation art, public art, First Nations art, textiles, ceramics, glass art, metal art, paper making, printmaking and drawing.
Related titles: Online - full text ed.: (from H.W. Wilson, O C L C Online Computer Library Center, Inc.).
Indexed: ABM, ArtInd, CBCARef.
Published by: Artichoke Publishing, 208-901 Jervis St, Vancouver, BC V6E 2B5, Canada. editor@artichoke.ca, http://www.artichoke.ca. Ed. Paula Gustafson. adv.: B&W page CND 375; trim 6.75 x 9.25. Circ: 1,000 (paid).

ARTICLE; art education Victoria. see *EDUCATION—Teaching Methods And Curriculum*

700 USA
ARTIFACTS (COLUMBIA). Text in English. 1976. 4/yr. bk.rev. bibl.; stat. **Document type:** *Newspaper, Government.*
Published by: Arts Commission, 1800 Gervais St, Columbia, SC 29201. TEL 803-734-8696, FAX 803-734-8526. Ed. Jayne Darke. Circ: 17,000.

709 POL ISSN 1644-3888
ARTIFEX. Text in Polish. 2000. q. 40 p./no.; **Document type:** *Journal, Academic/Scholarly.*
Related titles: Online - full content ed.
Published by: (Uniwersytet Kardynala Stefana Wyszynskiego, Kolo Naukowe Studentow Historii Sztuki), Wydawnictwo Uniwersytetu Kardynala Stefana Wyszynskiego, Ul Dewajtis 5, Warsaw, 01815, Poland. artifex@free.art.pl, wydawnictwo@uksw.edu.pl, http://free.art.pl/artifex, http://www.uksw.edu.pl/wydawn/wydawnictwo.htm. Eds. Bartlomiej Gutowski, Piotr Janowczyk. Circ: 200.

ARTINVESTOR. see *BUSINESS AND ECONOMICS—Investments*

700 CHE ISSN 0004-3842
N3
ARTIS. Text in German. 1948. m. CHF 78; CHF 88 foreign (effective 1997). adv. bk.rev. bibl.; illus.; mkt. index. back issues avail. **Document type:** *Bulletin.*
Formerly: Speculum Artis
Indexed: IBR, RASB.
Published by: Hallwag AG, Nordring 4, Bern, 3001, Switzerland. TEL 41-31-3323131, FAX 41-31-3314133, TELEX 912661-HAWA-CH, leserservice.hallwag@hallweb.ch. Ed. Peter Vetsch. Adv. contact Hans Bueschi. Circ: 11,000.

700 GBR ISSN 0004-3877
N1 CODEN: WOSTBE
THE ARTIST; inspiration, instruction & practical udeas for all artists. Text in English. 1931. m. GBP 25.50 domestic; USD 37 foreign (effective 2004). adv. bk.rev.; video rev. illus. Index. 68 p./no.; reprints avail. **Document type:** *Magazine, Consumer.* **Description:** Provides instructional features on painting and drawing, technical advice on materials and techniques, art events, books and workshops.
Incorporates: Art and Artists (0004-3001)
Indexed: AIAP, ArtInd, RASB.
—BLDSC (1735.280000), IE, Infotrieve, ingenta. **CCC.**
Published by: The Artists' Publishing Company Limited, Caxton House, 62-65 High St, Tenterden, Kent TN30 6BD, United Kingdom. TEL 44-1580-763315, 44-1580-763673, FAX 44-1580-765411, http://www.theartistmagazine.co.uk. Ed., Pub., R&P Sally Bulgin. Adv. contact Tim Fleming. Circ: 19,000.

700 DEU ISSN 0936-8930
ARTIST. Text in German. 1989. q. EUR 25 domestic; EUR 35 foreign; EUR 6.20 newsstand/cover (effective 2004). adv. **Document type:** *Magazine, Consumer.*

Published by: Banane Design GmbH, Ausser der Schleifmuehle 51, Bremen, 28203, Germany. TEL 49-421-3398472, FAX 49-421-3398492, info@artist-kunstmagazin.de, info@banane-design.de, http://www.artist-kunstmagazin.de, http://www.banane-design.de. adv.: B&W page EUR 900, color page EUR 1,690; trim 190 x 277. Circ: 4,800 (paid and controlled).

730 DEU ISSN 1430-2918
ARTIST WINDOW. Text in German. 1992. 2/yr. EUR 16 domestic; EUR 26 foreign; EUR 7.65 newsstand/cover (effective 2004). adv. **Document type:** *Magazine, Consumer.*
Published by: Banane Design GmbH, Ausser der Schleifmuehle 51, Bremen, 28203, Germany. TEL 49-421-3398472, FAX 49-421-3398492, info@artist-window.de, info@banane-design.de, http://www.artist-window.de, http://www.banane-design.de. adv.: color page EUR 450. Circ: 12,500 (paid and controlled).

700 ITA ISSN 1120-2459
N6921.T93
ARTISTA. Text in Italian. 1989. a. EUR 51 domestic; EUR 73 foreign (effective 2004). **Document type:** *Journal, Academic/Scholarly.*
Indexed: BHA.
Published by: Casa Editrice le Lettere, Costa San Giorgio 28, Florence, FI 50125, Italy. TEL 39-055-2342710, FAX 39-055-2346010, staff@lelettere.it, www.lelettere.it. Eds. Anna Maria Petrioli Tofani, Carlo Sisi, Carlo del Bravo. Pub. Giovanni Gentile. R&P Gloria Farolfi. **Dist. by:** Licosa SpA, Via Duca di Calabria 1-1, Florence, FI 50125, Italy. TEL 39-055-64831, FAX 39-055-641257, licosa@licosa.com, http://www.licosa.com.

769.566 CAN ISSN 1181-9456
ARTISTAMP NEWS. Text in English. 1971. s-a. looseleaf. CND 12. bk.rev. illus. back issues avail. **Document type:** *Newsletter.* **Description:** Focuses on the emerging field of stamps by artists, with information and news of shows and projects, profiles of artists and reproductions of their works.
Formerly (until 1991): Banana Rag
Address: P O Box 3655, Vancouver, BC V6B 3Y8, Canada. TEL 604-885-7156, FAX 604-885-7183. Ed. Ed Varney. Circ: 100 (paid).

700 USA
THE ARTISTIC FORUM. Text in English. m. **Description:** Covers art events and art trends.
Media: Online - full content.
Published by: Winstanley - Roark Fine Arts, 2759 Main St, Route 6A, Brewster, MA 02631-1948. TEL 800-828-7217, hostmaster@artisticforum.com, wrfa@masterfulart.com, http://artisticforum.com, http://www.masterfulart.com/.

ARTISTIC TRAVELER; architecture & travel with art & photography. see *ARCHITECTURE*

700 USA ISSN 1075-0894
N8600
ARTIST'S AND GRAPHIC DESIGNER'S MARKET; 2,500 places to sell your art and design. Text in English. 1979. a. USD 24.99 (effective 2001). illus. **Document type:** *Directory, Consumer.* **Description:** Lists 2500 places to sell art for ads, albums, cartoons, graphic designs, greeting cards, illustrations, galleries and posters-prints.
Formerly: Artist's Market (0161-0546); Which supersedes in part: Art and Crafts Market (0147-2461); Former titles: Artist's and Photographer's Market (0146-8294); Artist's Market (0361-607X); (until 1973): Cartoonists' Market
Published by: F & W Publications, Inc., 4700 E Galbraith Rd, Cincinnati, OH 45236. TEL 513-531-2690, 800-283-0963, FAX 513-531-2902, wds@fwpubs.com, http://www.fwpublications.com. Ed. Mary Cox.

760 GBR
ARTISTS AND ILLUSTRATORS. Text in English. 1986. m. GBP 25 in United Kingdom; GBP 32 in Europe; GBP 39 rest of world; GBP 2.60 newsstand/cover (effective 2000). adv. bk.rev. cum.index. back issues avail. **Document type:** *Consumer.* **Description:** Focuses on painting and drawing techniques and includes interviews with artists, product reviews and practical demonstrations.
Formerly: Artist's and Illustrator's Magazine (0269-4697)
Indexed: ABM.
—CCC.
Published by: Quarto Magazines plc, The Fitzpatrick Bldg, 188-194 York Way, London, N7 9QR, United Kingdom. TEL 44-20-7700-8500, FAX 44-20-7700-4985. Ed. Jim Manson. Pub., R&P Zarina Hawkins. Adv. contact Paul Harris. B&W page GBP 1,162, color page GBP 1,890; trim 230 x 300. **Subscr. to:** Tower House, Tower House, Sovereign Park, Market Harborough, Leics LE16 9EF, United Kingdom. TEL 44-1858-435307, FAX 44-1858-434958.

748.5 CAN
ARTISTS IN STAINED GLASS. JOURNAL. Text in English. 1978. q. CND 40; USD 50 in United States; CND 65 elsewhere. adv. back issues avail. **Document type:** *Newsletter, Academic/Scholarly.* **Description:** Promotes stained glass as an art form.
Formerly (until 1996): Artists in Stained Glass. Bulletin (0841-8039)
Published by: Artists in Stained Glass, 253 College St, Box 333, Toronto, ON M5T 1R5, Canada. TEL 416-690-0031, FAX 416-977-3552, http://www.aisg.ca. R&P Sue Obata. Adv. contact Gord Hill. Circ: 300.

750 USA ISSN 0741-3351
N7430
THE ARTIST'S MAGAZINE. Text in English. 1984. m. USD 36 domestic; USD 46 in Canada; USD 4.99 newsstand/cover (effective 2005). adv. bk.rev. illus. back issues avail. **Document type:** *Magazine, Consumer.* **Description:** Teaches beginner, intermediate and advanced artists how to improve skills and sell work professionally..
Related titles: Online - full text ed.: (from bigchalk, ProQuest Information & Learning).
Indexed: ABIn, IHTDI.
Published by: F & W Publications, Inc., 4700 E Galbraith Rd, Cincinnati, OH 45236. TEL 513-531-2690, 800-283-0963, FAX 513-891-7153, tamedit@fwpubs.com, www.artistsmagazine.com, http://www.fwpublications.com. Pub. Ulrich Groth. adv.: B&W page USD 10,660, color page USD 11,020; trim 7.75 x 10.75. Circ: 175,000 (paid).

750 AUS
ARTIST'S PALETTE. Text in English. bi-m. AUD 35.96 (effective 2004). **Document type:** *Magazine, Consumer.*
Published by: Express Publications Pty. Ltd., 2 Stanley St, Locked Bag 111, Silverwater, NSW 2128, Australia. TEL 61-2-97480599, 800-801-647, FAX 61-2-97481956, subs@magstore.com.au, http://www.magstore.com.au/.

750 USA
ARTIST'S SKETCHBOOK; your personal guide to discovering the artist within. Text in English. 2000 (Aug.). q. USD 8 newsstand/cover domestic; USD 8.99 newsstand/cover in Canada (effective 2005). adv. **Document type:** *Magazine, Consumer.* **Description:** Contains articles on improving fine art skills as well as developing and expressing creativity.
Published by: F & W Publications, Inc., 4700 E Galbraith Rd, Cincinnati, OH 45236. TEL 513-531-2690, 800-283-0963, FAX 513-531-2902, wds@fwpubs.com, http://www.fwpublications.com. Ed. Sandra Carpenter.

700 DEU ISSN 1015-9797
ARTIUM. Text in English, German. 1994. 3/yr. EUR 15; EUR 7.50 newsstand/cover (effective 2004). adv. **Document type:** *Magazine, Consumer.* **Description:** Covers contemporary art, art of the 19th and 20th centuries, design, and archaeology.
Published by: Art Center GmbH, Holthoke 3A, Essen, 49632, Germany. TEL 49-5434-904136, artcentergmbh@artium.lu, http://www.artium.lu. Ed. Maria Burghagen. Adv. contact Ines Meyers TEL 352-26-440066. B&W page EUR 1,900, color page EUR 3,000; trim 170 x 247. Circ: 6,518 (paid); 3,282 (controlled).

700 USA
ARTLETTER. Text in English. 1980. bi-m. USD 35. back issues avail. **Document type:** *Newsletter.*
Published by: Virginia Beach Center for the Arts, 2200 Park Ave, Virginia Beach, VA 23451. TEL 804-425-0000. Ed. Helen Snow. Circ: 2,500.

707 AUS ISSN 0727-1239
NX590.A1
ARTLINK; Australian contemporary art quarterly. Text in English. 1981. q. AUD 40 domestic to individuals; AUD 76 to individuals to US & Europe; AUD 64 elsewhere to individuals; AUD 72 domestic to institutions; AUD 108 to institutions to US & Europe; AUD 96 elsewhere to institutions (effective 2005). adv. bk.rev. illus. 96 p./no.; back issues avail. **Document type:** *Magazine, Consumer.* **Description:** Covers contemporary art in Australia, all media including electronic, with comment on new work, industry issues, information and publications.
Related titles: CD-ROM ed.
Indexed: ABM, AusPAIS.
—CCC.
Published by: Artlink Australia, 363 Esplanade, Henley Beach, SA 5022, Australia. TEL 61-8-8356-8511, FAX 61-8-8235-1280, artlinkmag@webmedia.com.au, http://www.artlink.com.au. Ed., R&P, Adv. contact Stephanie Britton. Circ: 3,400.

700 USA
ARTNET MAGAZINE. Text in English. 1996. d. free. bk.rev. illus. **Document type:** *Trade.* **Description:** Includes fine art news, reviews, features, images, auction reports, and letters from London, Paris and Tokyo.
Media: Online - full text.
Published by: ArtNet Worldwide Inc., 61 Broadway 23 Fl, New York, NY 10006-2701. TEL 212-497-9700, FAX 212-497-9707, artnet@artnet.com, http://www.artnet.com/Magazine. Ed. Walter Robinson. Pub. Hans Neuendorf. R&P, Adv. contact William Brewster Fine.

707.4 701.18 USA ISSN 0004-3273
N1
ARTNEWS. Text in English. 1902. 11/yr. USD 39.95 domestic; USD 59.95 in Canada; USD 99.95 elsewhere (effective 2005). adv. bk.rev. illus. back issues avail.; reprint service avail. from PQC. **Document type:** *Magazine, Consumer.* **Description:** Covers profiles of artists, surveys of gallery exhibits, and international art news.
Related titles: Microform ed.: (from MIM, PQC); Online - full text ed.: (from O C L C Online Computer Library Center, Inc.).
Indexed: A&ATA, ABM, ABS&EES, AIAP, ARG, ASCA, ArtHuCI, ArtInd, BHA, BRI, BioDAb, CBRI, CurCont, DAAI, IBRH, IIPA, INZP, MASUSE, MEA&I, MagInd, PMR, RASB, RGAb, RGPR, RILM.
—BLDSC (1733.465000), IE, Infotrieve, ingenta.
Published by: Artnews LLC, 48 W 38th St, New York, NY 10018. TEL 212-398-1690, FAX 212-819-0394, info@artnews.com, http://www.artnewsonline.com. Ed., Pub. Milton Esterow. R&P Grace Scalera. Adv. contact Debbie Nelson. Circ: 81,585 (paid). **Subscr. to:** Artnews Subscription Service, PO Box 56590, Boulder, CO 80322. TEL 800-284-4625.

700 USA ISSN 0145-7241
N1
ARTNEWSLETTER; the international bi-weekly business report on the art market. Text in English. 1975. s-m. USD 279 domestic; USD 309 foreign (effective 2005). **Document type:** *Newsletter.*
Published by: Artnews LLC, 48 W 38th St, New York, NY 10018. TEL 212-398-1690, FAX 212-819-0394, http://www.artnewsonline.com/news.cfm. Ed. Kelly Devine Thomas. Pub. Milton Esterow. R&P Grace Scalera.

800 USA ISSN 1085-3391
ARTNOIR SHOWCASE. Text in English. 1995. m. free (effective 2003). adv. **Document type:** *Academic/Scholarly.* **Description:** Specializing in Afro art. For artists, art historians, educators, collectors, museums, and galleries, especially those interested in the art of the diaspora, African American, Afro-Caribbean, Brazilian, Polynesian, and Micronesian.
Media: Online - full text.
Address: 2400 E, Las Olas Blvd, Ste 123, Fort Lauderdale, FL 33301. TEL 954-463-7880, FAX 954-463-7881, coni@dpw-archives.org, http://www.artnoir.com. Ed., R&P, Adv. contact Coni Porter Uzelac.

705 706 AUS ISSN 0066-8095
➤ **ARTS.** Text in English. 1956. a., latest vol.24, 2002. AUD 30 (effective 2003). bk.rev. illus. 130 p./no.; back issues avail. **Document type:** *Journal, Academic/Scholarly.* **Description:** Inaugural lectures, special lectures, occasional papers to graduates and faculty of arts, and research papers in arts.
Indexed: AIAP.
Published by: University of Sydney, Arts Association, English Dept., John Woolley Bldg. A20, Sydney, NSW 2006, Australia. TEL 61-2-93516851, FAX 61-2-93512434. Ed., R&P Geoffrey Little. Circ: 500.

700 USA ISSN 1093-1643
NX663.U6
➤ **ARTS (NEW BRIGHTON)**; the arts in religious and theological studies. Text in English. 1988. s-a. USD 25 (effective 2003). adv. bk.rev. illus. a.index. 48 p./no. 2 cols./p.; back issues avail. **Document type:** *Journal, Academic/Scholarly.* **Description:** Covers the relationship of theology to major art forms and their relevance for theological education and the church.
Related titles: Online - full content ed.; Online - full text ed.: (from EBSCO Publishing, O C L C Online Computer Library Center, Inc., Ovid Technologies, Inc.).
Indexed: RI-1, RILM.
Published by: United Theological Seminary of the Twin Cities, 3000 Fifth St. N.W., New Brighton, MN 55112. TEL 651-633-4311, ext. 109, FAX 651-633-4315, http://artsmag.org/, http://www.unitedseminary-mn.org/. Ed. Wilson Yates. Adv. contact Kimberly Vrudny. page USD 300; 5.25 x 9.75.

➤ **ARTS ACCESS NEWS.** see *HANDICAPPED*

700 BEL
ARTS AFRICAINS. Text in French. irreg. price varies. illus. **Document type:** *Monographic series, Academic/Scholarly.* **Description:** Scholarly monographs on topics in African art.
Published by: (Universite Catholique de Louvain, Departement d'Etudes Greques, Latines et Orientales, Publications d'Archeologie et d'Histoire de l'Art), Universite Catholique de Louvain, College Erasme, Pl Blaise Pascal 1, Louvain-la-Neuve, 1348, Belgium. TEL 32-10-474882, FAX 32-10-474870, moucharte@arke.ucl.ac.be, moucharte@fltr.ucl.ac.be, http://juppiter.fltr.ucl.ac.be/FLTR/publications/pub_pahal. R&P Ghislaine Moucharte.

791.44 306 AUS ISSN 1329-7074
ARTS ALIVE. Text in English. 1997. w. AUD 500 (effective 2004). bk.rev.; dance rev.; music rev.; play rev.; tel.rev.; video rev. abstr.; illus. back issues avail. **Document type:** *Bulletin.* **Description:** Covers Australian arts and culture current affairs.
Media: Online - full text. **Related titles:** Audio cassette/tape ed.: AUD 10 newsstand/cover; AUD 500 (effective 2002); CD-ROM ed.: 1997. AUD 500 (effective 2002).

Published by: (R M I T, School of Applied Communication), Independent Media Foundation, 39 Sydney St, Ascot Vale, VIC 3032, Australia. TEL 61-3-9925-3028, FAX 61-3-9639-1685, vincent.odonnell@rmit.edu.au, http://vicnet.net.au/~artsalive. Ed. Vincent O'Donnell.

ARTS ALIVE!; a magazine promoting the arts. see *THEATER*

ARTS AND ACTIVITIES; the nation's leading arts education magazine. see *EDUCATION—Teaching Methods And Curriculum*

700 USA ISSN 1047-3297

ARTS & CULTURE FUNDING REPORT. Text in English. 1989. m. USD 198 (effective Aug. 2001). back issues avail. **Document type:** *Newsletter.* **Description:** Covers federal budget news, art education news, grants for artists, business-arts partnerships, and funding trends in the arts. Highlights upcoming grant application deadlines for federal and private-sector aid from the federal government, foundations, and corporations.
—CCC.
Published by: Capitol City Publishers, 3485 S. Wakefield St., Arlington, VA 22206-1719. TEL 703-525-3080, FAX 703-525-3044, inquiry@capitolcitypublishers.com, http://capitolcitypublishers.com. Ed. Anita Cosgrove. Pub., R&P Joel Drucker.

ARTS AND HUMANITIES IN HIGHER EDUCATION; an international journal of theory, research and practice. see *HUMANITIES: COMPREHENSIVE WORKS*

370 700 USA ISSN 1534-3499
NX280

➤ **ARTS AND LEARNING RESEARCH**; journal of the Arts and Learning Special Interest Group. Text and summaries in English. 1984. a., latest vol.20, no.1, 2004. USD 24 per issue domestic; USD 25 per issue in Canada; USD 32 per issue in Australia; USD 31 per issue UK, Europe & Israel (effective 2004). bk.rev.; software rev.; video rev. charts; illus.; stat. Index. back issues avail. **Document type:** *Journal, Academic/Scholarly.* **Description:** Covers teacher education and professional development in the arts, curriculum development in the arts and evaluation of educational programs, learning, and adult and child development in the arts. Issues may contain reviews of books, videos and CD-ROMS that are pertinent to arts education. Topics are of interest to art educators, educational administrators, and educational researchers.
Indexed: CIJE.
—CCC.
Published by: American Educational Research Association, Arts & Learning Special Interest Group, c/o Dr. Nancy Ellis, Subscriptions, 328 Shore Rd, Burlington, VT 05401. TEL 802-862-4584, FAX 802-656-0004, nrellis@adelphia.net, http://www.ed.arizona.edu/ALSIG/. Eds. Joan Russell TEL 514-398-2447, Regina Murphy. R&P Regina Murphy.

➤ **ARTS & LEISURE TIMES.** see *LEISURE AND RECREATION*

700 GBR

ARTS AND MEDIA SERIES. Text in English. 1988. irreg., latest vol.6, 1994. **Document type:** *Monographic series.* **Description:** Offers imaginative and provocative accounts of the relationships between art forms, popular cultural practices, technology and audiences.
Published by: University of Luton Press, University of Luton, 75 Castle St, Luton, Beds LU1 3AJ, United Kingdom. TEL 44-1582-743297, FAX 44-1582-743298, ulp@luton.ac.uk.

701.18 745.1 BEL

ARTS, ANTIQUES ET AUCTIONS. Text in Dutch, English, French. 1971. m. (10/yr.). adv. bk.rev. illus.; mkt.; tr.lit. back issues avail. **Document type:** *Magazine, Trade.* **Description:** Publishes information on auctions, antique fairs, art exhibitions in Belgium and abroad including sales results.
Published by: Arts Antiques Auctions S.A., Begijnhoflaan 464, Ghent, 9000, Belgium. TEL 32-9-2691010, FAX 32-9-2691011, aaa@sok.be. Eds. Els Verneulen, J van Langhendenck. Adv. contact J Van Hecke-Comte. Circ: 10,000. **Dist. by:** Rabotsraat 62, Ghent 9000, Belgium.

709.5 FRA ISSN 0004-3958
N2

ARTS ASIATIQUES. Text in French; Text occasionally in English. 1954. a. EUR 40 per issue (effective 2004 - 2005). adv. bk.rev. charts; illus. reprints avail. **Document type:** *Academic/Scholarly.*
Indexed: AIAP, ArtInd, BAS, DIP, IBR, IndIslam, RASB, RILM.
—IE, Infotrieve. **CCC.**
Published by: Ecole Francaise d'Extreme-Orient, 22 Avenue du President Wilson, Paris, 75116, France. TEL 33-1-53701837, FAX 33-1-53701838, efeo-diffusion@efeo.fr, http://www.efeo.fr. Circ: 1,500.

700 CAN ISSN 0704-7916

➤ **ARTS ATLANTIC**; Atlantic Canada's journal of the arts. Text in English. 1977. 3/yr. CND 17.95 domestic to individuals; CND 32.95 foreign to individuals; CND 39.95 domestic to institutions; CND 54.95 foreign to institutions; CND 6.95 newsstand/cover (effective 2004). adv. film rev.; video rev.; Website rev. illus. 64 p./no. 2 cols./p.; back issues avail.; reprints avail. **Document type:** *Magazine, Academic/Scholarly.* **Description:** Features the region's visual arts, crafts, and related cultural activities.
Related titles: Microfilm ed.: (from MML); Microform ed.: (from MML).
Indexed: ABCT, ABS&EES, CBCARef, CBPI, CPerI.
—BLDSC (1736.110000).
Published by: Arts Atlantic Inc., P.O. Box 36007, RPO Spring Garden, Halifax, NS B3J 3S9, Canada. TEL 902-420-5045, FAX 902-491-8624, gillian.collyer@smu.ca, arts.atlantic@stmarys.ca, http://www.artsatlantic.ca. Ed., R&P Mimi Fautley TEL 902-420-5078. Pub. Gillian Collyer. Adv. contact Michael Wile TEL 902-421-2022. page CND 800; trim 10.88 x 8.38. Circ: 2,200.

700 CAN ISSN 0843-2260

ARTS BEAT. Variant title: Artsbeat. Text in English. 1973. bi-m. CND 25 domestic; CND 50 foreign (effective 2002). adv. bk.rev.; dance rev.; music rev.; play rev. illus. back issues avail. **Document type:** *Newsletter.* **Description:** Dedicated to promoting an understanding and appreciation of the arts in all disciplines within the greater Hamilton area, including: craft, dance, literature, music theater and visual arts.
Former titles (until 1987): Art-i-fact (0843-2252); (until 1981): Art-i-fact Bulletin (0382-8638); (until 1975): Art-i-fact (0315-7202)
Published by: Hamilton & Region Arts Council, 2 King St W, Hamilton, ON L8P 1A1, Canada. TEL 905-529-9485, FAX 905-529-9738, artsbeat@harac.on.ca, harac@harac.on.ca, http://www.harac.on.ca. Ed., R&P, Adv. contact Lawson Hunter. B&W page USD 400; trim 14 x 10. Circ: 3,000 (paid).

700 IRL ISSN 0790-1593

ARTS COUNCIL. ANNUAL REPORT/AN CHOMHAIRLE EALAION. TUARASCAIL BHILANTUIL. Text in English, Irish. 1953. a. **Document type:** *Yearbook, Consumer.* **Description:** Provides details on the activities and finances of the Arts Council.
Published by: Arts Council/An Chomhairle Ealaion, 70 Merrion Sq, Dublin, 2, Ireland. TEL 353-1-6180200, FAX 353-1-6610349, info@artscouncil.ie, http://www.artscouncil.ie.

700 GBR ISSN 1464-2123

ARTS COUNCIL OF ENGLAND. ANNUAL LECTURE. Text in English. 1995. a.
—BLDSC (1087.076500).
Published by: Arts Council of England, Information Department, 14 Great Peter St, London, SW1P 3NQ, United Kingdom. TEL 44-845-3006200, FAX 44-20-79736564.

700 GBR
NX28.G72

ARTS COUNCIL OF ENGLAND. ANNUAL REVIEW. Text in English. 1945. a. free (effective 2005). **Document type:** *Trade.* **Description:** Provides an overview of the council's work and records of grants and guarantees offered in the support of the arts.
Former titles (until 1999): Arts Council of England. Annual Report (1361-2999); (until 1995): Arts Council of Great Britain. Annual Report and Accounts (0066-8133)
—BLDSC (0573.797100).
Published by: Arts Council of England, Information Department, 14 Great Peter St, London, SW1P 3NQ, United Kingdom. TEL 44-845-3006200, FAX 44-20-79736564, enquiries@artscouncil.org.uk, http://www.artscouncil.org.uk/information/publication_detail.php?browse=title&id=425.

700 FRA ISSN 0337-1603
NX588.75

ARTS D'AFRIQUE NOIRE. Text in French. 1972. q. adv. bk.rev. illus. index. reprints avail. **Document type:** *Monographic series, Academic/Scholarly.*
Related titles: Online - full text ed.: (from H.W. Wilson, O C L C Online Computer Library Center, Inc.).
Indexed: AICP, AnthLit, ArtInd, PCI, RILM.
Address: B.P. 24, Arnouville-les-Gonesse, 95400, France. Ed., Pub., R&P, Adv. contact Eric Lehuard.

707.1 USA ISSN 1063-2913
NK1160

➤ **ARTS EDUCATION POLICY REVIEW.** Text in English. 1879. bi-m. USD 56 domestic to individuals; USD 72 foreign to individuals; USD 118 domestic to institutions; USD 134 foreign to institutions; USD 19.67 newsstand/cover (effective academic year 2005 - 2006). adv. bk.rev. illus.; charts. Index. 40 p./no.; reprint service avail. from PSC. **Document type:** *Journal, Academic/Scholarly.*
Former titles (until 1992): Design for Arts in Education (0732-0973); (until 1977): Design (0011-9253)
Related titles: CD-ROM ed.: (from ProQuest Information & Learning); Microform ed.: (from PQC); Online - full text ed.: (from bigchalk, Chadwyck-Healey Inc., EBSCO Publishing, Florida Center for Library Automation, Gale Group, H.W. Wilson, Northern Light Technology, Inc., O C L C Online Computer Library Center, Inc., ProQuest Information & Learning).
Indexed: ABIn, ArtInd, BRI, CIJE, CPE, DIP, ERA, EduInd, GAA, IBR, IBZ, MagInd, PCI, PerIslam, RGAb, RGPR, RILM.
—BLDSC (1736.238000), IE, Infotrieve, ingenta. **CCC.**
Published by: (Helen Dwight Reid Educational Foundation), Heldref Publications, 1319 18th St, NW, Washington, DC 20036-1802. TEL 202-296-6267, 800-365-9753, FAX 202-296-5149, 202-293-6130, aepr@heldref.org, subscribe@heldref.org, http://www.heldref.org/aepr.php. Adv. contact Chante Douglas. B&W page USD 455; trim 7 x 10. Circ: 596 (paid). **Co-sponsor:** M E N C: National Association for Music Education.

700 AUS

ARTS FACULTY NEWSLETTER. Text in English. irreg. **Document type:** *Newsletter.* **Description:** Highlights events, awards and administration regarding the Faculty of Arts at Monash University.
Related titles: Online - full text ed.
Published by: Monash University, Faculty of Arts, Wellington Rd, Clayton, VIC 3168, Australia. TEL 61-3-99052107, FAX 61-3-99054209, artsweb@arts.monash.edu.au, http://www.arts.monash.edu.au/news, http://www.arts.monash.edu.au/faculty/newsletter.

700 NZL ISSN 1170-5256

ARTS HORIZON. Text in English. 1975. s-a. **Document type:** *Academic/Scholarly.*
Formerly (1975-1990): New Zealand Arts Horizon (0110-6082)
Published by: New Zealand Guild of Artist Trust, P.O. Box 20170, Glen Eden, Auckland 7, New Zealand. TEL 64-9-8184648, FAX 64-9-8184648. Ed. Pearline Ferguson.

THE ARTS IN PSYCHOTHERAPY. see *PSYCHOLOGY*

ARTS INTERNATIONAL. see *LITERATURE*

700 USA

ARTS JOURNAL; the daily digest of arts and cultural journalism. Text in English. d. Free. **Description:** A digest of current articles and commentary on art and its effects on society.
Media: Online - full content.
Address: http://www.artsjournal.com. Ed. Douglas McLennan.

700 USA

ARTS LINK NEWSLETTER. Text in English. m. membership. adv. **Document type:** *Newsletter.* **Description:** Provides, in summary form, current legislative reports and arts news for arts leaders.
Former titles: Arts Link; A C A Update (1054-3570); (until 1979): Update; A C A Word from Washington (0300-7065)
Published by: Americans for the Arts, 1000 Vermont Ave N W, Ste 12, Washington, DC 20005-4903. TEL 202-371-2830, FAX 202-371-0424, http://www.kwhiteartsusa.org. Ed. Jana Lasorte. Circ: 3,000.

700 960 USA ISSN 1044-8640

ARTS OF AFRICA. Text in English. 1987. a. USD 40 (effective 1998). **Document type:** *Academic/Scholarly.*
Published by: African Studies Association, Rutgers, The State University of New Jersey, 132 George St, New Brunswick, NJ 08901-1400. TEL 732-932-8173, FAX 732-932-3394, ckoch@emory.edu. R&P Christopher Koch.

709.5 HKG ISSN 0004-4083
NX572

ARTS OF ASIA. Text and summaries in English. 1970. bi-m. HKD 520 domestic; USD 85 foreign (effective 2005). adv. bk.rev. illus. index every 3 yrs. back issues avail.; reprints avail. **Document type:** *Journal, Academic/Scholarly.*
Indexed: A&ATA, ABCT, ABM, AIAP, ASCA, ArtHuCI, ArtInd, BAS, CurCont, PCI, RASB, RILM.
—BLDSC (1736.090000), IDS, IE, Infotrieve, ingenta.
Published by: Arts of Asia Publications Ltd., 1309 Kowloon Centre, 29-39 Ashley Rd, Tsimshatsui, Kowloon, Hong Kong. TEL 852-23762228, FAX 852-23763713, artsasia@hk.linkage.net, info@artsofasianet.com, http://www.artsofasianet.com/. Ed. Stephen Markbreiter. Pub., R&P, Adv. contact Tuyet Nguyet. Circ: 18,000.

700 IND

ARTS OF HIMACHAL. Text in English. 1975. irreg. price varies. **Document type:** *Monographic series.*
Published by: State Museum, Simla, Department of Languages and Cultural Affairs, Simla, Himachal Pradesh, India. Ed. Vishwa Chander Ohri. Circ: 1,000.

700 USA ISSN 0740-9214
N1

ARTS QUARTERLY. Text in English. 1978. q. USD 10 domestic; USD 15 foreign (effective 2000). adv. bk.rev. illus. back issues avail. **Document type:** *Newsletter.*
Indexed: BHA.

A

Published by: New Orleans Museum of Art, PO Box 19123, New Orleans, LA 70179. TEL 504-488-2631, FAX 504-484-6662. Ed., R&P Wanda O'Shello TEL 504-483-2665. Adv. contact Karron Lane. Circ: 20,000.

361.73 700 USA
ARTS REACH. Text in English. 10/yr. USD 99 domestic; USD 109 foreign (effective 2002). **Document type:** *Magazine, Trade.* **Description:** Covers planning, marketing and fundraising issues for cultural and education organizations.
Related titles: Online - full content ed.
Published by: Arts Reach Unlimited, 38 Holliday Dr, Novato, CA 94949-6270. TEL 415-883-3414, 800-793-3342, FAX 415-883-7565, ceo@artsreach.com, http://www.artsreach.com. Pub. John Zorn.

700 JAM
ARTS REVIEW. Text in English. 1976. s-a. JMD 0.50.
Published by: University of the West Indies, Creative Arts Centre, Mona, 1 A Aqueduct Flats, Kingston, 7, Jamaica. TEL 809-977-2659, FAX 809-977-2660, salex@uwimona.edu.jm. Ed. Jean Small.

700 USA
ARTS TENNESSEE. Text in English. 1974. q. free (effective 2005). bk.rev.; film rev.; play rev.; music rev. 12 p./no.; back issues avail.; reprint service avail. from PQC. **Document type:** *Newsletter, Government.* **Description:** Contains information on the arts in the state of Tennessee.
Formerly: Tennessee Arts Report
Related titles: Online - full content ed.
Published by: Tennessee Arts Commission, 401 Charlotte Ave, Nashville, TN 37243-0780. TEL 615-741-1701, FAX 615-741-8559, dadkins@mail.state.tn.us, http://www.arts.state.tn.us. Ed. Dennis Adkins. Circ: 3,500 (free).

ARTS THERAPIES RESEARCH LIBRARY. see *MEDICAL SCIENCES*

700 USA
ARTS WIRE CURRENT. Text in English. 1995. w.
Media: Online - full content.
Address: 5306 Ridge View Circle No.5, El Sobrante, CA 94803. jmalloy@artswire.org, htttp://www.artswire.org/current.html. Ed. Judy Malloy.

700 USA
ARTS WIRE: ONLINE COMMUNICATION FOR THE ARTS. Text in English. 1996. m.
Media: Online - full content.
Published by: New York Foundation for the Arts, 155 Ave of the Americas, New York, NY 10013. TEL 212-366-6900, FAX 212-366-1778, nysaweb@nyfa.org, http://www.nyfa.org. Ed. Judy Malloy.

700 AUS
ARTS YARN UP. Text in English. q. free. bk.rev. illus. back issues avail. **Document type:** *Newsletter.*
Related titles: Online - full text ed.
Published by: Australia Council of Arts, PO Box 788, Strawberry Hills, NSW 2012, Australia. TEL 61-2-9950-9175, FAX 91-2-9319-1442, m.burbidge@ozco.gov.au, http://www.ozco.gov.au. Ed., R&P Madelein Burbidge. Circ: 3,500.

700 069 NZL ISSN 1175-0790
ARTSCAPE; a regional arts review. Text in English. 1994. m. NZD 30 domestic; NZD 40 foreign (effective 2001). bk.rev.; music rev.; play rev.; Website rev.; rec.rev. 30 p./no.; back issues avail. **Document type:** *Magazine.*
Published by: Gallery Books & Crafts, P.O. Box 99, Carterton, New Zealand. TEL 06-3796916, FAX 06-3796916, artscape@xtra.co.nz. Ed. Steve Oxenham.

ARTSFOCUS. see *MUSEUMS AND ART GALLERIES*

700 USA ISSN 1541-6089
ARTSHOUSTON; houston's monthly guide to the arts. Text in English. 2001 (May). m. USD 28 (effective 2002). adv.
Published by: H D I Publishers (Subsidiary of: Brain Injury Association, Inc.), 2407 Waugh Dr., 2nd Fl., Houston, TX 77006. TEL 713-526-6900, FAX 713-526-7787, mail@artshouston.com. Ed. Rosemary Ponnekanti. Pub. Chas Haynes. Adv. contact Molly McBirney.

708 ITA
ARTSHOW; guida alle mostre d'arte. Text in Italian. 1986. 8/yr. **Document type:** *Magazine, Consumer.*
Published by: Artshow Edizioni s.r.l., Viale Monza, 48, Milan, MI 20127, Italy. TEL 39-2-26826502, FAX 39-2-26826498. Ed. Giulio Ciavoliello. Adv. contact Pia Quarzo Cerina.

700 AUS ISSN 1033-7318
ARTSLINE. Text in English. 1989. q. free. bibl.; charts; illus. **Document type:** *Newsletter, Government.* **Description:** Highlights role and functions of the department.
Published by: ArtsWA, 573 Hay St., 7th Fl., Perth, W.A. 6000, Australia. TEL 61-08-92247310, FAX 61-08-92247311, info@artswa.mac.wa.gov.au, http://www.imago.com.au/artswa. Ed. Allanan Lucas.

700 GBR ISSN 1474-385X
ARTSPROFESSIONAL. Text in English. 2001 (May). fortn. GBP 3.50 newsstand/cover (effective 2001).
Related titles: Online - full text ed.
Published by: Arts Intelligence Limited, Cottenham, PO Box 957, Cambridge, CB4 8AB, United Kingdom. TEL 44-1954-250600, FAX 44-1954-252600, editors@artsprofessional.co.uk, http://www.artsprofessional.co.uk. Eds. Brian Whitehead, Liz Hill.

700 USA
ARTSUSA UPDATE. Text in English. w. **Document type:** *Newsletter.* **Description:** Includes news and up-to-date information about the Americans for the Arts organizations.
Media: E-mail. **Related titles:** Online - full text ed.
Published by: Americans for the Arts, 1000 Vermont Ave N W, Ste 12, Washington, DC 20005-4903. TEL 202-371-2830, 800-321-5410, FAX 202-371-0424, http://www.artsusa.org/. Ed. Daniel Jones.

700 793.32 AUS ISSN 1323-000X
ARTSWEST; supporting & promoting the arts in Western Sydney. Text in English. 1981. m. AUD 66 (effective 2001). adv. play rev. illus. 10 p./no.; back issues avail. **Document type:** *Newsletter.* **Description:** Covers regional arts news & information, poetry, reviews from members, opinion, political commentary, advocacy with emphasis on cross cultural relationships.
Published by: Artswest Foundation Ltd., PO Box 1424, Parramatta, NSW 2124, Australia. TEL 61-2-98311441, FAX 61-2-98907010, artswest@iprimus.com.au, http://www.artswest.com.au. Ed., Adv. contact Katherine Knight. Circ: 2,500.

750 745 USA
ARTTALK; the free newsletter for visual artists. Text in English. 1990. m. free. **Document type:** *Newsletter.* **Description:** Covers painting, printmaking, sculpture, ceramics, arts and crafts, and more.
Media: Online - full text.
Published by: Paschal Group, Inc., 75 Liberty St, Beacon, NY 12508. TEL 914-831-1043, FAX 914-831-1043, artinc1@aol.com, http://www.arttalk.com. Ed. Jeanne Paschal. Pub. Robert Paschal.

700 ZAF
ARTTHROB; contemporary art in South Africa. Text in English. 1997. m. free (effective 2002). adv. **Document type:** *Magazine, Trade.* **Description:** Reports on the national arts scene and the involvement of South African artists in the international art world.
Media: Online - full content.
Address: P O Box 113, Cape Town, 8000, South Africa. artthrob@mweb.co.za, http://www.artthrob.co.za. Ed. Sophie Perryer.

700 USA
ARTUS. Text in English. 1981. q. USD 30 in US & Canada; USD 55 elsewhere (effective 2004). adv. bk.rev. **Document type:** *Journal, Academic/Scholarly.*
Former titles: Artext (1544-2136); (until 2000): Art & Text (0727-1182)
Related titles: Online - full text ed.: (from H.W. Wilson, O C L C Online Computer Library Center, Inc.).
Indexed: ABM, ArtInd, BHA.
—BLDSC (1733.474105), IE, ingenta.
Published by: (Foundation for International Art Criticism), Artext, PO Box 86187, Los Angeles, CA 90086-9999. TEL 213-625-2010, FAX 213-625-2017, artext@artext.org, artex@unsw.edu.au, http://www.artext.org. Eds. Paul Foss, Paul Taylor. Circ: 3,000.

700 AUS ISSN 0311-0095
ARTVIEWS. Text in English. 197?. irreg. AUD 0.40 per issue.
Indexed: ABM.
Published by: Artists' Guild of Australia, 156 Banksia St, Pagewood, NSW 2035, Australia.

700 USA
ARTVOICE. Text in English. 1990. bi-w. adv. bk.rev. back issues avail. **Document type:** *Newspaper.* **Description:** Covers alternative art and entertainment news.
Related titles: Online - full text ed.
Published by: Jamie Moses, Ed. & Pub., 500 Franklin St, Buffalo, NY 14202. TEL 716-881-6604, FAX 716-881-6682, artvoice@artvoice.com, http://www.artvoice.com. Ed. Jamie Moses. R&P Deborah Ellis. Adv. contact Nancy MacCartney. B&W page USD 1,176, color page USD 1,450; trim 16 x 10. Circ: 57,000 (controlled).

709.7 USA ISSN 0004-4121
N1
ARTWEEK; the national voice of West Coast contemporary art. Text in English. 1970. m. USD 34 domestic; USD 60 foreign (effective 2004). adv. bk.rev. illus. cum.index: vols.1-7, 1977. reprints avail. **Document type:** *Magazine, Consumer.* **Description:** Includes commentary and reviews, interviews, and regular features.
Related titles: Microform ed.: (from MIM, PQC); Online - full text ed.: (from H.W. Wilson, O C L C Online Computer Library Center, Inc.).
Indexed: ABCT, ArtInd, BHA, ChPerI, MagInd.
—BLDSC (1736.865000), IE, ingenta.
Address: PO Box 52100, Palo Alto, CA 94303-0751. TEL 800-733-2916, FAX 262-495-8703, http://www.artweek.com. Ed. Meredith Tromble. Pub., R&P, Adv. contact Kitty Spaulding. Circ: 14,500.

ARTWORK; the North's independent free arts newspaper. see *ARTS AND HANDICRAFTS*

700 AUS ISSN 1323-5885
ARTWORKER. Text in English. 1986. q. AUD 30.80 to individuals; AUD 35 to individual members; AUD 60 to institutional members (effective 2001). adv. **Document type:** *Newsletter.* **Description:** Provides membership information, issue-based articles, and specialist industry columns.
Formerly: Queensland Artworkers Alliance Newsletter
Published by: Artworkers Alliance, Level 1, 381 Brunswick St, Fortitude Valley, QLD 4006, Australia. TEL 61-7-3250-1230, FAX 61-7-3250-1231, info@artworkers.org, info@artworks.org, http://www.artworks.org. Ed. Renai Stonley. Adv. contact Annette Hoberg. B&W page AUD 330; trim 297 x 210. Circ: 1,500 (controlled).

700 374 AUS
ARTWORKS. Text in English. 1978. 2/yr. AUD 5. adv. back issues avail. **Document type:** *Academic/Scholarly.*
Published by: Waverley-Woollahra Arts Centre Co-op Ltd., 138 Bondi Rd, Bondi, NSW 2026, Australia. Eds. Brigid Phecan, Susan Parker. Circ: 6,000.

700 USA ISSN 1062-8312
N6750
ARTWORLD EUROPE. Text in English. 1990. bi-m. USD 59 (effective 1998). bk.rev. back issues avail. **Document type:** *Newsletter.* **Description:** Covers European art world including exhibitions, museum renovations, art fairs, galleries, restorations, and interviews with art professionals.
Published by: Humanities Exchange, Inc., PO Box 1608, Largo, FL 33779. TEL 813-581-7328, FAX 813-585-6398. Ed. S R Howarth. Circ: 1,000.

700 JPN
ASAHI GRAPH BESSATU BIJUTU. Text in Japanese. 1977. 9/yr.
Formerly: Asahi Graph Bessatsu
Published by: Asahi Shimbun Publishing Co., 5-3-2 Tsukiji, Chuo-ku, Tokyo, 104-8011, Japan. Ed. Yoshio Nagata.
Subscr. to: Oversea Courier Service Co. Ltd., 9 Shibaura 2-chome, Minato-ku, Tokyo 108-0023, Japan.

ASIA INSTITUTE. BULLETIN. see *ASIAN STUDIES*

700 HKG ISSN 1023-5884
N7260
ASIAN ART NEWS. Text in English. 1991. bi-m. HKD 240, USD 28; USD 60 in Asia & the Pacific; USD 34 in Canada; GBP 30 in Europe. adv. back issues avail. **Description:** Covers Asia-Pacific art and artists for collectors, museums, galleries and artists.
Address: G/F, 28 Arbuthnot Rd, Central, Hong Kong, Hong Kong. TEL 852-2522-3443, FAX 852-2521-5268, asianart@netvigator.com. Ed. Ian Findlay-Brown. Pub. Ian Findlay Brown. Adv. contact Lynne Gallacher. B&W page USD 2,200, color page USD 2,800; trim 210 x 285.

700 USA
ASIAN ARTS; the online for the study and exhibition of the arts of Asia. Text in English. irreg. **Description:** Dedicated to all aspects of Asian art.
Media: Online - full content. **Related titles:** E-mail ed.
Address: 129 "B" W San Francisco St, Santa Fe, NM 87501. TEL 505-983-7658, FAX 505-983-7613, asianart@webart.com.

700.458 ISR ISSN 0333-6476
N25
ASSAPH: STUDIES IN ART HISTORY. Text in English. 1980. biennial, latest vol.2, 1996. EUR 20 (effective 2003). **Document type:** *Academic/Scholarly.* **Description:** Publishes articles on all aspects, disciplines, and periods of Art History.
Indexed: BHA.
Published by: Tel Aviv University, Department of Art History, Tel Aviv, 69978, Israel. anath@tauex.tau.ac.il, http://www.tau.ac.il/arts/publications. Eds. Asher Ovadiah, Nurit Kenaan-Kedar.
Dist. by: Edizioni Quasar, Via Ajaccio 43, Rome, RM 00198, Italy. TEL 39-6-84241993, FAX 39-6-85833591.

700 USA ISSN 1083-6586
NX1
➤ **ASSOCIATION FOR THE INTERDISCIPLINARY STUDY OF THE ARTS. JOURNAL.** Variant title: J A I S A. Text in English; Text occasionally in French, German, Spanish. 1995. s-a. USD 20 to individuals; USD 30 to institutions; USD 10 to students (effective 2005). bk.rev. **Document type:** *Journal, Academic/Scholarly.*
Indexed: MLA-IB, PhilInd.
Published by: Association for the Interdisciplinary Study of the Arts, c/o John Micheal Crafton, English Department, State University of West Georgia, Carrollton, GA 30118. TEL 770-836-6512, FAX 770-830-2334, http://www.westga.edu/~mhamil/JAISA.html. Ed. Dr. Mustapha Hamil.

➤ **ASSOCIATION INTERNATIONALE D'ETUDES DU SUD-EST EUROPEEN. BULLETIN.** see *HISTORY—History Of Europe*

700   GBR   ISSN 0307-9163
ASSOCIATION OF ART HISTORIANS. BULLETIN. Text in English. 1975. 3/yr. free to members (effective 2005). adv.
Document type: *Bulletin.*
Indexed: BHA.
Published by: Association of Art Historians, 70 Cowcross St, London, EC1M 6EJ, United Kingdom. TEL 44-20-7490-3211, FAX 44-20-7490-3277, ed-bulletin@aah.org.uk, admin@aah.org.uk, http://www.aah.org.uk/pubs/bulletin.html. Ed., R&P Jannet King. Adv. contact Claire Davies. Circ: 1,500.

741.6   GBR   ISSN 0958-3726
ASSOCIATION OF ILLUSTRATORS. JOURNAL. Text in English. 1990. bi-m. membership.
Indexed: DAAI.
Published by: Association of Illustrators, 1 Colville Pl, London, W1P 1HN, United Kingdom. TEL 071-636-4100.

700   PER
ASTERISCO; revista de actualidad y cultura. Text in Spanish. irreg., latest vol.5, 1992. illus.
Published by: Ediciones Fragor, Jiron Jose de Sucre 1083, Huaras, Peru. TEL 72-1177. Ed. Francisco Gonzales.

THE ASTROPHYSICIST'S TANGO PARTNER SPEAKS. see *LITERATURE—Poetry*

700   USA   ISSN 1555-8185
AT L A C M A; museum members magazine. Text in English. bi-m. free to members (effective 2005).
Former titles (until 2004): At the Museum (1065-1101); Los Angeles County Museum of Art. Member's Calendar (0889-3829)
Published by: Los Angeles County Museum of Art, 5905 Wilshire Blvd, Los Angeles, CA 90036. TEL 323-857-6000, publicinfo@lacma.org, http://www.lacma.org/.

700   DEU   ISSN 0176-8530
ATELIER; die Zeitschrift fuer Kuenstler. Text in German. 1982. bi-m. EUR 22.75 domestic; EUR 26 foreign; EUR 4.20 newsstand/cover (effective 2004). adv. bk.rev. **Document type:** *Magazine, Consumer.* **Description:** Information for visual artists. Includes a calendar of art competitions.
Indexed: ABM, DIP, IBR, IBZ.
Published by: Atelier Verlag KG, Hospeltstr 47, Cologne, 50825, Germany. TEL 49-221-9545858, FAX 49-221-9545860, info@atelier-verlag.de, http://members.aol.com/atelier47/index.html, http://www.atelier-verlag.de. Ed. Bence Fritzsche. adv.: B&W page EUR 760, color page EUR 1,444. Circ: 9,500.

ATENEO VENETO; rivista di scienze, lettere ed arti. see *SCIENCES: COMPREHENSIVE WORKS*

ATHENAEUM ANNOTATIONS. see *ARCHITECTURE*

700   ITA
ATLANTI DI RESTAURO. Text in Italian. irreg. **Document type:** *Monographic series.*
Published by: Stefano Patacconi Editore, Corso d Augusto, 115, Rimini, FO 47037, Italy. TEL 39-541-27756, FAX 39-541-54208. Eds. Alfredo Bellandi, Franco Faranda.

700   ESP   ISSN 1132-8428
N6480
ATLANTICA INTERNACIONAL; revista de las artes. Text in Spanish. 1990. 3/yr. EUR 36.06 per issue domestic; EUR 48.08 per issue foreign (effective 2004). 200 p./no.; **Document type:** *Magazine, Consumer.* **Description:** Collects critical works of research in the plastic arts and other art forms.
Formerly (until 1992): Atlantica (1130-7587) —CINDOC.
Published by: Centro Atlantico de Arte Moderno, Los Balcones 9 y 11, Las Palmas de Gran Canaria, Canary Islands 35001, Spain. TEL 34-902-311824, FAX 34-902-321629, comunicacion@caam.net. Ed. Antonio Zaya. **Dist. by:** Asociacion de Revistas Culturales de Espana, Hortaleza, 75, Madrid 28004, Spain. TEL 34-91-3086066, FAX 34-91-3199267, info@arce.es, http://www.arce.es.

700   GBR   ISSN 0267-484X
ATLAS. Text in English. 1985. irreg. adv. back issues avail.
Indexed: BAS, BHA, PAIS.
Published by: Atlas Publishers, 16 Talfourd Rd, London, SE15 5NY, United Kingdom. http://www.thecooker.com. Ed. Jake Tilson. Circ: 2,500.

741.6   USA
ATLAS MAGAZINE. Text in English. 1995. irreg. back issues avail. **Description:** Features editorials and regular columns on graphic design and illustration.
Media: Online - full text.
Address: 11 Carl St, San Francisco, CA 94117. TEL 415-753-2662, FAX 415-902-3898, atlas@atlasmagazine.com, http://www.atlasmagazine.com/. Ed. Oliver Laude.

ATOPIA: PHILOSOPHY, POLITICAL THEORY, AESTHETICS. see *PHILOSOPHY*

700   ESP   ISSN 0214-8293
ATRIO; revista de historia del arte. Text in Spanish. 1988. s-a. —CINDOC.
Published by: Asociacion Cultural de Sevilla, Almudena, 4-3o., Sevilla, Andalucia 41003, Spain. Eds. Fernando Quiles Garcia, Francisco Herrera Garcia.

709.2   ITA
AUCTION BOOK/LIBRO DELLE ASTE; worldwide contemporary art results - risultati delle aste d'arte contemporanea nel mondo. Text in Italian. a. adv. **Document type:** *Directory, Trade.* **Description:** Presents a collection of contemporary art selling prices from the principal international auction houses.
Published by: Giancarlo Politi Editore, PO Box 95, Borgo Trevi, PG 06032, Italy. TEL 39-0742-381978, FAX 39-0742-381979, subscription@flashartonline.com, http://www.flashartonline.com. adv.: B&W page USD 2,600, color page USD 3,500; trim 6.88 x 3.13. Circ: 20,000.

700 860   DOM
AUDITORIUM; revista cultural informativa. Text in Spanish. bi-m. DOP 30 newsstand/cover.
Published by: Direccion General de Bellas Artes, c/o Palacio de Bellas Artes, Av Maximo Gomez 2, Santo Domingo, Dominican Republic. TEL 809-682-1325, FAX 809-682-8622.

709.2   DEU
AUKTIONSPREISE IM KUNSTPREIS JAHRBUCH. BAND 1. Text in German. 1993. a. (in 3 vols.). EUR 126.80 domestic for all 3 vols.; EUR 131.20 foreign for all 3 vols. (effective 2003). adv. illus. **Document type:** *Catalog, Consumer.* **Description:** Verified art auction results from international auction houses.
Formerly: Kunstpreis-Jahrbuch. Band 1 (1435-3946); Which was formed by the merger of part of (1984-1993):
Kunstpreis-Jahrbuch. Teil 1 (1435-392X); (1984-1993):
Kunstpreis-Jahrbuch. Teil 2 (1435-3938); Which were both formed by the merger of part of (1970-1984):
Kunstpreis-Jahrbuch. A (0174-3511); (1980-1984):
Kunstpreis-Jahrbuch. B (0174-352X); Which both superseded in part (1950-1980): Kunstpreisjahrbuch (0172-6765); Which was formerly (until 1970): Kunstpreisverzeichnis (0172-6757); (until 1953): Europaeisches Kunstpreis-Verzeichnis (0172-6730)
Published by: Weltkunst Verlag GmbH, Nymphenburger Str 84, Munich, 80636, Germany. TEL 49-89-1269900, FAX 49-89-12699011, info@weltkunstverlag.de, http://www.weltkunstverlag.de. Ed. Eleonore Pichelkastner. Adv. contact Inge Mueller TEL 49-89-12699021. Circ: 9,000.

709.2   DEU
AUKTIONSPREISE IM KUNSTPREIS JAHRBUCH. BAND 2. Text in German. 1993. a. EUR 126.80 domestic for all 3 vols.; EUR 131.20 foreign for all 3 vols. (effective 2003). **Document type:** *Directory, Trade.*
Formerly: Kunstpreis-Jahrbuch. Band 2 (1435-3954); Which was formed by the merger of part of (1984-1993):
Kunstpreis-Jahrbuch. Teil 1 (1435-392X); (1984-1993):
Kunstpreis-Jahrbuch. Teil 2 (1435-3938); Which were both formed by the merger of part of (1980-1984):
Kunstpreis-Jahrbuch. A (0174-3511); (1980-1984):
Kunstpreis-Jahrbuch. B (0174-352X); Which both superseded in part (1950-1980): Kunstpreisjahrbuch (0172-6765); Which was formerly (until 1970): Kunstpreisverzeichnis (0172-6757); (until 1953): Europaeisches Kunstpreis-Verzeichnis (0172-6730)
Published by: Weltkunst Verlag GmbH, Nymphenburger Str 84, Munich, 80636, Germany. TEL 49-89-1269900, FAX 49-89-12699011, info@weltkunstverlag.de, http://www.weltkunstverlag.de.

709.2   DEU
AUKTIONSPREISE IM KUNSTPREIS JAHRBUCH. BAND 3. Text in German. 1993. a. EUR 126.80 domestic for all 3 vols.; EUR 131.20 foreign for all 3 vols. (effective 2003). **Document type:** *Directory, Trade.*
Formerly: Kunstpreis-Jahrbuch. Band 3 (1435-3962); Which was formed by the merger of part of (1984-1993):
Kunstpreis-Jahrbuch. Teil 1 (1435-392X); (1984-1993):
Kunstpreis-Jahrbuch. Teil 2 (1435-3938); Which were both formed by the merger of part of (1980-1984):
Kunstpreis-Jahrbuch. A (0174-3511); (1980-1984):
Kunstpreis-Jahrbuch. B (0174-352X); Which both superseded in part (1950-1980): Kunstpreisjahrbuch (0172-6765); Which was formerly (until 1970): Kunstpreisverzeichnis (0172-6757); (until 1953): Europaeisches Kunstpreis-Verzeichnis (0172-6730)
Published by: Weltkunst Verlag GmbH, Nymphenburger Str 84, Munich, 80636, Germany. TEL 49-89-1269900, FAX 49-89-12699011, info@weltkunstverlag.de, http://www.weltkunstverlag.de.

700   ITA
AURORA. Text in Italian. bi-m.
Indexed: RILM.
Address: Via Di San Giovanni In Laterano, 276, Rome, RM 00184, Italy. Ed. Vincenzo Lo Faro.

AURORA; Jahrbuch der Eichendorff-Gesellschaft. see *LITERATURE*

709   USA   ISSN 1527-652X
N5300
AURORA (WOODCLIFF LAKE); the journal of the history of art. Text in English. 2000. a. USD 13 per vol. to individuals; USD 21 per vol. to institutions (effective 2004).
Related titles: Online - full text ed.: (from H.W. Wilson).
Indexed: ABM, ArtInd.
Published by: Aurora, 255 Glen Rd, Woodcliff Lake, NJ 07677. Eds., Pubs. Joanna P. Gardner-Huggett, Lilian H. Zirpolo.

AURORA-BUCHREIHE. see *LITERATURE*

700   DEU   ISSN 0067-0642
AUS FORSCHUNG UND KUNST. Text in German. 1968. irreg., latest vol.34, 2001. price varies. **Document type:** *Monographic series, Academic/Scholarly.*
Indexed: DIP, IBR, IBZ.
Published by: (Geschichtsverein fuer Kaernten AUT), Dr. Rudolf Habelt GmbH, Am Buchenhang 1, Bonn, 53115, Germany. TEL 49-228-9238322, FAX 49-228-9238323, info@habelt.de, http://www.habelt.de. Ed. Gotbert Moro.

AUSGABE; ein Literatur- und Kunstmagazin. see *LITERATURE*

700.455   AUS
AUSTRALIA. DEPARTMENT OF ARTS, SPORT, THE ENVIRONMENT AND TERRITORIES. NORFOLK ISLAND ANNUAL REPORT. Text in English. a. price varies. illus.; stat.
Former titles: Australia. Department of Home Affairs. Norfolk Island Annual Report; Australia. Department of Territory of Norfolk Island. Report (0572-0494)
Published by: (Australia. Department of Arts, Sport, the Environment and Territories), AusInfo, GPO Box 1920, Canberra Mc, ACT 2610, Australia. TEL 61-2-62633541, FAX 61-2-62634909.

AUSTRALIAN ABORIGINAL STUDIES. see *ANTHROPOLOGY*

700   AUS   ISSN 1443-4318
N7400.2
AUSTRALIAN AND NEW ZEALAND JOURNAL OF ART. Text in English. 1978. a. AUD 15. adv. bk.rev. back issues avail.
Formerly (until 1999): Australian Journal of Art (0314-6464)
Indexed: AIAP, AusPAIS, BHA.
—BLDSC (1796.884000), IE, ingenta.
Published by: Art Association of Australia and New Zealand, c/o Dept. of Art History, City Art Institute, PO Box 259, Paddington, NSW 2021, Australia. TEL 02-339-9555, FAX 02-3399506. Eds. Dr. Deborah Malor, Dr. Heather Johnson. Circ: 800.

709.2   AUS   ISSN 0819-923X
AUSTRALIAN ART AUCTION RECORDS. Text in English. 1975. biennial. AUD 90 (effective 2001). 540 p./no.; back issues avail. **Document type:** *Directory, Corporate.* **Description:** Publishes records of auction prices for works of art. Includes biographical details of artists.
Related titles: CD-ROM ed.: AUD 295 (effective 2001).
Published by: Australian Art Sales, PO Box 50, Sutherland, NSW 1499, Australia. TEL 61-2-9267-7363, aaauctions@bigpoond.com. Ed., R&P Edward D Craig. Circ: 1,500 (paid).

707.1   AUS   ISSN 1032-1942
➤ **AUSTRALIAN ART EDUCATION.** Text in English. 1976. 2/yr. AUD 60 to individuals; AUD 100 to institutions (effective 2001). bk.rev. abstr.; bibl.; charts; illus. back issues avail. **Document type:** *Journal, Academic/Scholarly.* **Description:** Devoted to the scholarly examination of issues in art education both in Australia and overseas.
Formerly (until 1988): Institute of Art Education. Journal (0729-5995)
Indexed: ABM, AusPAIS, CIJE.
Published by: Australian Institute of Art Education, SRC 150 Palmerston St, Carlton, VIC 3053, Australia. TEL 61-3-9349-5188, FAX 61-3-9349-2050, enquiries@uev.vic.edu.au. Eds. Linda Ashton, Penny Collett. Circ: 300. **Subscr. to:** AIAE membership officer, Ste. 125., 283 Glenhuntly Rd, Elsternwick, VIC 3185, Australia.

750   AUS   ISSN 0813-8095
AUSTRALIAN ARTIST. Text in English. 1984. m. AUD 69.90 (effective 2004). adv. back issues avail. **Document type:** *Consumer.* **Description:** Devoted to developing artistic and creative talents of Australian painters.
Indexed: WBA, WMB.
Published by: Elladrent Pty. Ltd., PO Box 1084, Chatswood, NSW 2057, Australia. TEL 61-2-94916333, FAX 61-2-94115175, sales@artinthemaking.com, http://www.international-artist.com/frameset.asp?lm=a_artist_overview.asp. Ed., Adv. contact Vincent Miller. R&P Terri Dodd. color page AUD 1,600. Circ: 20,000 (paid).

AUSTRALIAN CREATIVE. see *ADVERTISING AND PUBLIC RELATIONS*

700 600   AUS
AUSTRALIAN NETWORK FOR ART AND TECHNOLOGY NEWSLETTER. Text in English. 1988. q. USD 20 to individuals; USD 40 to institutions. **Document type:** *Newsletter.*

Related titles: Online - full text ed.
Published by: Australian Network for Art and Technology, Hindley St, PO Box 8029, Adelaide, SA 5000, Australia. TEL 61-8-82319037, FAX 61-8-82117323, anat@camtech.net.au, http://www.va.com/anat/. Ed. Amanda Mcdonald Crowley.

391.65   AUS
AUSTRALIAN TATTOO. Text in English. 1992. irreg. Document type: Magazine, Consumer.
Published by: Tadevan Holdings P/L, 383 St Pauls Tce, Fortitude Valley, Brisbane, QLD 4006, Australia. TEL 61-7-32528881, http://homepages.ihug.com.au/~pagan/.

AUTHORS & ARTISTS FOR YOUNG ADULTS. see CHILDREN AND YOUTH—For

▼ AUTOFACE INK; the manual for the everyday independent. see MUSIC

750   USA
TL225.2
AUTOGRAPHICS. Text in English. 1995-1999; resumed 2004. bi-m. USD 30 domestic; USD 40 in Canada; USD 45 in Mexico; USD 65 elsewhere (effective 2005). adv. illus. 3 cols./p.; Document type: Magazine, Trade. Description: Focuses exclusively on custom vehicle graphics, pinstriping, airbrushing, custom painting, vinyl graphics, truck lettering, multi-media graphics and more.
Former titles (until 2004): AutoGraphics & Customizing (1092-1834); (until 1996): AutoGraphics (1088-7229)
Published by: National Business Media, Inc., PO Box 1416, Broomfield, CO 80038. TEL 303-469-0424, FAX 303-469-5730, kflees@nbm.com, rpmpublisher@@nbm.com, http://www.nbm.com/autographics. Ed. Kristina Flees. Pub. Terence Wike. Adv. contact Bob Carnahan. B&W page USD 1,120. Circ: 10,000 (controlled).

700 796.77 790.13   USA
AUTOMOTIVE FINE ART. Text in English. 1988. q. USD 24 for 2 yrs. domestic; USD 32 for 2 yrs. in Canada; USD 42 for 2 yrs. elsewhere (effective 2000). adv. bk.rev. Document type: Consumer. Description: Informs the public about the aesthetic value of automotive fine art and keeps collectors abreast of trends in value and availability.
Formerly (until 1998): A F A S Quarterly (0899-9171)
Published by: Automotive Fine Arts Society, PO Box 324, Lake Orion, MI 48361-0324. TEL 248-814-0647, http://www.autoartgallery.com, http://www.autoartgallery.com/afas. Ed. Jack Juratovic. Adv. contact Jan Taylor. Circ: 5,000 (paid and controlled).

AVANT GARDE CRITICAL STUDIES; revue internationale et interdisciplinaire des arts et litteratures du XXe siecle - international and interdisciplinary review of the literatures and arts of the 20th century. see LITERATURE

750 388.324   USA
AVIATION ART GALLERY. Text in English. 1998. q. GBP 2.95 newsstand/cover. Document type: Consumer. Description: Portrays the history of aviation through art and images.
Published by: Y-Visionary Publishing, 265 S Anita Dr, Ste 120, Orange, CA 92868. TEL 714-939-9991. Dist. in UK by: Portman Distribution, Gadoline House, 2 Godstone Rd, Whyteleafe, Surrey CR3 0EA, United Kingdom. TEL 44-20-8645-8200, FAX 44-20-8645-8239.

700   USA
AWARE; an e-zine about expression. Text in English. irreg. Description: Aims to search for awareness through creative expression in art and poetry.
Media: Online - full text.
Address: ktburf@aol.com, http://www.beaware.com/. Ed. Katie Burford.

AXIS; world design journal. see INTERIOR DESIGN AND DECORATION

AZIMUTH. see SCIENCES: COMPREHENSIVE WORKS

AZTLAN; a journal of Chicano studies. see ETHNIC INTERESTS

700 720   CAN
AZURE DESIGN, ARCHITECTURE AND ART. Text in English. 1985. 6/yr.
Address: 20 Maud St Ste 200, Toronto, ON M5V 2M5, Canada. TEL 416-203-9674, FAX 416-522-2357, azure@interlog.com, http://www.azureonline.com. Ed. Nelda Rodger. Circ: 20,000 (paid and controlled).

B A D. (Breakfast All Day) see LITERATURE

B C A NEWS. (Business Committee for the Arts) see BUSINESS AND ECONOMICS

B C S P. (Bollettino del Centro Camuno di Studi Preistorici) see ARCHAEOLOGY

741   ITA   ISSN 1124-8971
B.D. BODY BOOK. Text in Italian. 1996. bi-m. Document type: Magazine, Consumer.

Published by: Trentini S.r.l., Via Pier Luigi Nervi 1/B, Argenta, 44011, Italy. TEL 39-0532-318149, FAX 39-0532-310084, info@3ntini.com, http://www.3ntini.com.

B D K MITTEILUNGEN. see EDUCATION—Teaching Methods And Curriculum

706.0489   DNK   ISSN 0902-7440
B K F - BLADET; billedkunstnernes forbundsblad. Text in Danish. 1960. q. DKK 300 (effective 2004). adv. Document type: Trade.
Former titles (until 1982): Billedkunstnernes Blad (0902-7432); (until 1970): Fagblad for Bildende Kunstnere; (until 1967): Malende Kunstneres Sammenslutning
Published by: Billedkunstnernes Forbund (BKF), Vingaardsstraede 21,3, Copenhagen K, 1070, Denmark. TEL 45-33-128170, FAX 45-33-322839, bkf@bkf.dk, http://www.bkf.dk. Ed. Niels Sylvest. Circ: 2,000.

700 910   ESP   ISSN 0212-5099
BAETICA✱ ; estudios de arte, geografia e historia. Text in Spanish. 1978. a.
—CINDOC.
Published by: Universidad de Malaga, Facultad de Filosofia y Letras, Campus de Teatinos, Malaga, 29071, Spain. TEL 34-95-2131717, http://www.uma.es/. Ed. Isabel Perez de Colosia.

860 700 100   ESP   ISSN 0214-9982
NX7
BALSA DE LA MEDUSA. Text in Spanish. 1987. q. bk.rev. Description: Focuses on cultural and social criticism in the fields of communication, art criticism, philosophy and literature.
Indexed: ABM, PCI, RILM.
—CINDOC.
Published by: Visor Distribuciones S.A., Tomas Breton, 55, Madrid, 28045, Spain. TEL 341-468-11-02, FAX 341-468-10-98. Ed. Carlos Piera. Circ: 3,500.

BAMPTON LECTURES IN AMERICA. see RELIGIONS AND THEOLOGY

BANGLADESH LALIT KALA. see MUSEUMS AND ART GALLERIES

769   CHN   ISSN 1000-4378
BANHUA YISHU/ART OF PRINTS. Text in Chinese. q.
Published by: Shanghai Renmin Meishu Chubanshe/Shanghai People's Art Publishers, No33 Alley 672 Changle Rd, Shanghai, 200040, China. TEL 4374528. Ed. Lu Zongduo.

BARBACANE; revue des pierres et des hommes. see LITERATURE

BARBADOS MUSEUM AND HISTORICAL SOCIETY. JOURNAL. see HISTORY—History Of North And South America

BARCELONA, METROPOLIS MEDITERRANIA (SPANISH EDITION). see HOUSING AND URBAN PLANNING

700   JPN
BARFOUT!/TO EXHALE. Text in Japanese. 1990. m. JPY 10,500 (effective 2002).
Former titles: Bar-f-Out!; (until 1992): Press Cool Resistance
Published by: (T C R C Co., Ltd.), Gentosha Inc., 4-9-7 Sendagaya Shibuya-ku, Tokyo, 151-0051, Japan. TEL 81-3-5411-6211, FAX 81-3-5411-6225, info@gentosha.co.jp, http://www.so-net.ne.jp/barfout/, http://www.gentosha.co.jp/.

700   IDN   ISSN 0005-6138
AP95.I5
BASIS; majalah bulanan kebudayaan umum/monthly for culture in general. Text in Indonesian. 1951. m. USD 20. adv. bk.rev. illus. index.
Indexed: BibLing.
Published by: Yayasan Badan Penerbit Basis, Abu Bakar Ali 14, Yogyakarta, Indonesia. TEL 88283. Ed. Dick Hartoko. Circ: 3,000.

705   ESP   ISSN 0210-0274
BATIK; panorama general de las artes - arte, diseno, arquitectura. Text in Spanish. 1973. bi-m. USD 70. adv. bk.rev.
Indexed: BHA.
Published by: Publiart S.A., Rambla prat. 6 pral. 1a, Barcelona, 08012, Spain. TEL 3-217-45-20. Ed. Manuel Rufi Gibert. Circ: 5,000.

087.5   ITA   ISSN 1721-7121
BATTLE ROYALE. Text in Italian. 2002. m. adv. Document type: Magazine, Consumer.
Published by: Play Press Publishing s.r.l., Via Vitorchiano 123, Rome, RM 00189, Italy. TEL 39-06-33221250, FAX 39-06-33221235, abbonamenti@playpress.com, http://www.playpress.com. Pub. Alessandro Ferri. Adv. contact Lorenza Borroni TEL 39-02-45472867.

BAUART. see ARCHITECTURE

700   DEU   ISSN 0341-9150
N6873
BAYERISCHE DENKMALPFLEGE. JAHRBUCH. Text in German. 1947. a. Document type: Bulletin, Trade.
Indexed: IBR, IBZ, RILM.
Published by: (Bayerisches Landesamt fuer Denkmalpflege), Deutscher Kunstverlag GmbH, Nymphenburger Str 84, Munich, 80636, Germany. TEL 49-89-1269900, FAX 49-89-12151644, info@deutscherkunstverlag.de, http://www.kunstbuecher-online.de.

700   DEU
BAYERISCHE STAATSGEMAELDESAMMLUNGEN. JAHRESBERICHT. Text in German. 1972. a. membership. Document type: Corporate.
Published by: Bayerische Staatsgemaeldesammlungen, Barer Str 29, Munich, 80799, Germany. TEL 49-89-238050. Circ: 1,500.

700   USA
BE TRUE MAGAZINE; the "online" arts magazine for kids. Text in English. m. USD 19.95. Description: Presents educational and entertaining material for kids that adults can read, too.
Media: Online - full text.
Address: FAX 615-832-9404, editor@betruezine.com, http://www.betruezine.com/.

THE BEAT WITHIN; a weekly newsletter of writing and art from the inside. see CHILDREN AND YOUTH—For

BEATTHIEF. see MUSIC

700   USA
BEAUTIFUL / DECAY; interior/exterior subculture. Text in English. 2002. q. USD 20 (effective 2003). adv. illus.
Address: P O Box 2336, Culver City, CA 90231-2336. TEL 410-493-9581, bd@beautifuldecay.com, http://www.beautifuldecay.com.

702   USA
BEAUTIFULLY TATTOOED WOMEN. Text in English. 2001. a. USD 7.98 newsstand/cover (effective 2002). adv. Document type: Consumer.
Published by: Outlaw Biker Enterprises, Inc., 5 Marine View Plaza, Ste 207, Hoboken, NJ 07030. TEL 201-653-2700, FAX 201-653-7892. Ed. Lauren Blake. Pub. Casey Exton.

709   FRA   ISSN 0757-2271
N1
BEAUX ARTS MAGAZINE; actualite des arts. Text in French. 1983. irreg. price varies. adv. illus. Index. reprints avail. Document type: Monographic series, Consumer.
Indexed: ABM, ArtInd, BHA, IBR, RILM.
—IE, Infotrieve. CCC.
Published by: Editions Flammarion, 87 Quai Panhard et Levassor, Paris, 75647 Cedex 13, France. TEL 33-1-40513100, http://www.flammarion.com. Circ: 49,000.

700   SWE   ISSN 1103-4920
BECKERELL. Text in Swedish. 1991. q. SEK 99. Description: Each issue features interviews with a number of real and unreal artists. The subject matter is a mixture from light to serious, cartoons to discussions of art theory.
Address: Fack 17127, Malmo, 20010, Sweden. TEL 46-40-30-72-77, FAX 46-40-30-15-07.

700   DEU   ISSN 0067-5121
BEITRAEGE ZUR KUNST DES CHRISTLICHEN OSTENS. Text in German. 1964. irreg. price varies. illus. Document type: Monographic series.
Published by: Verlag Aurel Bongers, Postfach 100264, Recklinghausen, 45602, Germany.

741.5   NGA
BENBELLA AND LULU. Text in English. 1989. fortn. NGN 12. Document type: Consumer.
Published by: Daily Times of Nigeria Ltd., Publications Division, New Isheri Rd., PMB 21340, Ikeja, Agidingbi, Lagos, Nigeria. TEL 234-64-900850-9, FAX 234-64-21333. Circ: 10,000.

745.5 694   DEU   ISSN 0343-1711
BERGISCHE HANDWERK. Text in German. 1947. m. adv. bk.rev. back issues avail. Document type: Newsletter.
Published by: (Kreishandwerkerschaft Remscheid), J.F. Ziegler KG Druckerei und Verlag, Konrad-Adenauer-Str 2-4, Remscheid, 42853, Germany. TEL 49-2191-909-0, FAX 49-2191-909266. Ed. J F Ziegler. Circ: 3,000.

053.1   DEU
BERLINER. Text in German. q. EUR 32 domestic; EUR 44 in Europe; EUR 60 elsewhere; EUR 9.50 newsstand/cover (effective 2003). adv. Document type: Magazine, Consumer. Description: Contains a variety of features on art, culture and lifestyles.
Published by: Berliner Magazin, Christburger Str 6, Berlin, 10405, Germany. TEL 49-30-44342149, FAX 49-30-44342159, info@berlinermagazin.de, http://www.berlinermagazin.de. Pub. Boris Moshkovits. adv.: page EUR 6,900; trim 215 x 330. Circ: 30,000 (paid and controlled).

700 CHE ISSN 1010-559X
BERNER KUNSTMITTEILUNGEN. Text in German. 1955. 5/yr. adv. bk.rev. illus. cum.index. back issues avail. **Document type:** *Bulletin, Consumer.* **Description:** Covers art exhibitions and events in Bern and Switzerland.
Formerly (until 1970): Kunstmuseum Bern. Mitteilungen (0405-5888)
Indexed: ABM, BHA.
Published by: Kunstmuseum Bern, Hodlerstr 12, Bern, 3011, Switzerland. TEL 41-31-3110944, FAX 41-31-3110955, bhattacharya@kmb.unibe.ch, http://www.kunstmuseumbern.ch. Ed. Therese Bhattacharya. Circ: 4,500. **Co-sponsors:** Bernische Kunstgesellschaft; Verein der Freunde des Berner Kunstmuseums.

BEST EDITORIAL CARTOONS OF THE YEAR. see *LITERARY AND POLITICAL REVIEWS*

741 ITA ISSN 1723-3674
▼ **BEY BLADE.** Text in Italian. 2003. m. adv. **Document type:** *Magazine, Consumer.*
Published by: Play Press Publishing s.r.l., Via Vitorchiano 123, Rome, RM 00189, Italy. TEL 39-06-33221250, FAX 39-06-33221235, abbonamenti@playpress.com, http://www.playpress.com. Pub. Alessandro Ferri. Adv. contact Lorenza Borroni TEL 39-02-45472867.

BIBLIOTECA NAPOLETANA DI STORIA E ARTE. see *HISTORY—History Of Europe*

700 POL ISSN 0067-7698
BIBLIOTEKA KRAKOWSKA. Text in Polish. 1897. irreg., latest vol.137, 1997. price varies.
Published by: Towarzystwo Milosnikow Historii i Zabytkow Krakowa, Ul Sw. Jana 12, Krakow, 31018, Poland. TEL 48-12-4212783, FAX 48-12-4231074. Ed. Wieslaw Bienkowska. **Dist. by:** Ars Polona, Krakowskie Przedmiescie 7, Warsaw, Poland.

709 DEU ISSN 0940-7855
➤ **BIBLIOTHECA HERTZIANA. ROEMISCHES JAHRBUCH.** Text in English, German, Italian. 1937. irreg., latest vol.32, 1997. price varies. illus. 450 p./no.; back issues avail. **Document type:** *Monographic series, Academic/Scholarly.* **Description:** Art history focusing on Rome and Italy.
Formerly (until 1989): Roemisches Jahrbuch fuer Kunstgeschichte (0342-2046)
Indexed: AIAP, ArtInd, BHA, DIP, IBR, IBZ, PCI.
—BLDSC (8020.822000). **CCC.**
Published by: (Bibliotheca Hertziana ITA), Hirmer Verlag, Nymphenburger Str 84, Munich, 80636, Germany. TEL 49-89-1215160, FAX 49-89-12151616, kliemann@biblhertz.it, info@weltkunstverlag.de, http://www.biblhertz.it, http://www.weltkunstverlag.de. Ed., R&P Julian Kliemann. Circ: 300.

➤ **BIBLIOTHEQUE DU C N A M.** (Conservatoire National des Arts et Metiers) see *ENGINEERING—Mechanical Engineering*

➤ **BIBLIS (TIDSKRIFT).** see *PUBLISHING AND BOOK TRADE*

700 USA ISSN 1551-4048
▼ **BIDOUN;** a quarterly forum for middle eastern talent. Text in English. 2004 (Spr.). 4/yr. USD 36 in Middle East & US; USD 38 in Canada; USD 42 in Europe; USD 48 elsewhere (effective 2005). adv. illus. **Document type:** *Magazine, Consumer.* **Description:** Features the latest art, architecture, film, music and fashion from the Middle East and its Diaspora.
Address: PO Box 201, Brooklyn, NY 11222-0201. info@bidoun.com, http://www.bidoun.com. Ed. Lisa Farjam. Circ: 8,000 (paid and controlled).

700 USA ISSN 8756-4777
BIENNIAL EXHIBITION OF CONTEMPORARY AMERICAN PAINTING. Text in English. 1985. biennial.
Published by: Corcoran Gallery of Art, 500 17th St NW, Washington, DC 20006. TEL 202-639-1700, http://www.corcoran.org.

BIG DADDY. see *MUSIC*

BIG SHOULDERS. see *LITERATURE—Poetry*

707 JPN ISSN 0021-9088
BIJUTSU KENKYU/JOURNAL OF ART STUDIES. Text in Japanese; Summaries in English. 1932. bi-m. JPY 2,266 per issue. illus. index. **Document type:** *Journal, Academic/Scholarly.*
Published by: National Research Institute for Cultural Properties, Department of Fine Arts, 13-43 Ueno Park, Taito-Ku, Tokyo, 110-8713, Japan. http://www.tobunken.go.jp/~bijutsu/english/biken/abstract/mokuji.html, http://www.tobunken.go.jp/~bijutsu/index.html. Circ: 600. **Dist. by:** Japan Publications Trading Co., Ltd., Book Export II Dept, PO Box 5030, Tokyo International, Tokyo 101-3191, Japan.

700 JPN ISSN 0287-2218
NX8.J3
BIJUTSU TECHO. Text in Japanese; Summaries in English. 1948. m. JPY 18,000. adv. bk.rev.; film rev.; play rev. back issues avail. **Description:** Covers contemporary art.
Published by: Bijutsu Shuppan-sha, Inaoka Bldg, 2-36 Kanda-Jinbo-cho, Chiyoda-ku, Tokyo, 1010051, Japan. TEL 03-3234-2151, FAX 03-3234-9451.

709 JPN ISSN 0387-2688
BIJUTSUSHIGAKU. Text in Japanese; Summaries in English, Italian, French. 1978. a., latest no.23, 2002. **Document type:** *Journal, Academic/Scholarly.*
—BLDSC (2058.320000).
Published by: Touhoku Daigaku, Daigakuin Bungaku Kenkyuuka Bigaku Bijutsushi Kenkyuushitsu/Tohoku University, Graduate School of Arts and Letters, Department of Art History, Kawauchi, Aoba-ward, Sendai, 980-8576, Japan. TEL 86-22-2176019, FAX 81-22-2176069, art@sal.tohoku.ac.jp, http://www.sal.tohoku.ac.jp/estetica/.

740.7 SWE ISSN 0349-2117
BILD I SKOLAN. Text in Swedish. 1939. q. SEK 160 (effective 2003). adv. 44 p./no. 4 cols./p.; **Document type:** *Magazine, Consumer.*
Formerly (until 1979): Teckning (0346-296X)
Related titles: Online - full text ed.
Published by: Laerarfoerbundet, Tidningsafdelning, Segelbaatsvaegen 15, Box 12229, Stockholm, 10226, Sweden. TEL 46-8-7376500, FAX 46-8-7376569, kansli@lararforbundet.se, http://www.bildiskolan.net/, http://www.lararforbundet.se. Ed., Pub. Arne Kockum. Adv. contact Annelie Bjoernsdotter Lundqvist. B&W page SEK 4,900, color page SEK 6,200; trim 176 x 245. Circ: 3,500.

741.5 SWE ISSN 0347-7096
BILD & BUBBLA/PICTURE AND CAPTION. Text in Swedish. 1968. q. SEK 225 (effective 1998). **Document type:** *Trade.*
Formerly (until 1977): Thud (0346-3133)
Indexed: ChLitAb.
Published by: Seriefraemjandet, Fack 51, Akarp, 23202, Sweden. TEL 46-8-15-95-92, stromberg@mbox301.swipnet.se. Ed. Daniel Atterbom.

750 331.8 SWE ISSN 0348-0615
BILDKONSTNAEREN. Text in Swedish. 1976. q. SEK 400 membership; SEK 100 to students (effective 2004). adv. **Document type:** *Journal.*
Published by: Svenska Konstnaersfoerbundet (SK), Karl Johannsgatan 2, Goeteborg, 41459, Sweden. TEL 46-31-424731, FAX 46-31-143655, info@sv-konstnarsforb.se, http://www.sv-konstnarsforb.se. Ed. Allan Jarden TEL 46-381-611605. Pub. Ulf Johan Tempelman. Circ: 1,000.

750 DNK ISSN 0908-0465
BILLEDKUNST; kritisk videnskabeligt tidsskrift. Text in Danish. 1993. q. DKK 200; DKK 60 newsstand/cover (effective 2004). **Document type:** *Magazine, Academic/Scholarly.*
Published by: Husets Forlag, Havnegade 4, Aarhus C, 8000, Denmark. TEL 45-86-196548, FAX 45-86-196558, husetsforlag@huset-aarhus.dk, http://www.huset-aarhus.dk. Eds., Pubs. Carsten Koed Hansen, Henrik Dalgaard.

700 NOR ISSN 0332-723X
BILLEDKUNSTNEREN. Text in Norwegian. 1975. 10/yr. NOK 250. **Document type:** *Trade.*
Published by: Norske Billedkunstneres Fagorganisasjon, Kongens Gate 3, Oslo, 0153, Norway.

BIOGRAPHY TODAY ARTISTS SERIES. see *BIOGRAPHY*

709 POL ISSN 0006-3967
➤ **BIULETYN HISTORII SZTUKI.** Text in Polish, English, Italian; Summaries in English. 1932. q. EUR 39 per issue foreign (effective 2005). bk.rev. bibl.; illus. index. 120 p./no.; back issues avail. **Document type:** *Journal, Academic/Scholarly.* **Description:** Publishes updates on academic life, reviews of selected exhibitions organized both in Poland and abroad as well as significant articles on art history.
Indexed: ABCT, ABM, AIAP, AmH&L, BHA, BibInd, HistAb, IBR, IBZ, RASB, RILM.
Published by: Polska Akademia Nauk, Instytut Sztuki/Polish Academy of Science, Institute of Art, ul Dluga 28, Warsaw, 00950, Poland. TEL 48-22-5048200, FAX 48-22-8313149, biuletyn.historii.sztuki@ispan.pl, ispan@ispan.pl, http://www.ispan.pl/bhs. Ed. Piotr Paszkiewicz. Circ: 1,000 (paid). **Dist. by:** Ars Polona, Krakowskie Przedmiescie 7, Warsaw, Poland. TEL 48-22-9263914, FAX 48-22-9265334, arspolona@arspolona.com.pl, http://www.arspolona.com.pl. **Co-sponsor:** Stowarzyszenia Historykow Sztuki.

700 POL ISSN 1234-5210
BIULETYN INFORMACYJNY KONSERWATOROW DZIEL SZTUKI. Text in Polish. 1990. q. EUR 52 foreign (effective 2005). 150 p./no.;
Related titles: Online - full content ed.: ISSN 1689-3557.
Indexed: A&ATA.
Published by: Wydawnictwo Konserwatorow Dziel Sztuki, ul Nawrot 36/13, Lodz, 90055, Poland. TEL 48-42-6763465, FAX 48-42-6763465, redakcja@bikds.art.pl, http://www.bikds.art.pl. Ed. Joanna Zajaczkowska-Kloda. Circ: 1,500. **Dist. by:** Ars Polona, Krakowskie Przedmiescie 7, Warsaw, Poland. TEL 48-22-9263914, FAX 48-22-9265334, arspolona@arspolona.com.pl, http://www.arspolona.com.pl.

BIZA NEIRA (BISE NOIRE); sur l'Auvergne et la civilisation Auvergnate. see *HISTORY—History Of Europe*

BLACK BEAR REVIEW. see *LITERATURE—Poetry*

BLACK BOOK; progressive urban culture. see *LIFESTYLE*

BLACK ELVIS; a journal of graphic and literary art. see *LITERATURE—Poetry*

BLACKBIRD; an online journal of literature and the arts. see *LITERATURE*

BLACKFLASH; Canadian journal of photo-based and electronic arts production. see *PHOTOGRAPHY*

BLAETTER DER FREIEN VOLKSBUEHNE BERLIN. see *THEATER*

BLAETTER FUER HEIMATKUNDE. see *HISTORY*

700 CAN ISSN 1203-6692
BLIZZART; Canadian arts and culture news. Text in English, French. 1979. 4/yr. CND 18; CND 23.50 foreign. **Document type:** *Newsletter.*
Former titles (until 1995): Proscenium (Ottawa) (1188-4363); (until 1992): Arts Bulletin (0707-9532); Incorporates (in 1991): Arts News (0843-9583); Which was formerly (1969-1989): Canadian Conference of the Arts. Miscellaneous Reports (0068-8487)
Published by: Canadian Conference of the Arts, 130 Albert St, Ste 804, Ottawa, ON K1P 5G4, Canada. TEL 613-238-3561, FAX 613-238-4849, info@ccarts.ca, http://www.ccarts.ca. Ed. Anita Grace. Circ: (controlled).

700 USA
▼ **THE BLOWUP.** Text in English. 2004. q. USD 10 newsstand/cover (effective 2005).
Published by: Blowup, Llc, 511 Canal St. 4th Fl, New York, NY 10013. TEL 646-283-7259, FAX 212-219-2776, sales@theblowup.com, http://www.theblowupmagazine.com/, http://theblowup.com. Ed. Kate Sennert.

BODENSEE HEFTE; Zeitschrift der Euro-Region Bodensee. see *GEOGRAPHY*

700 GBR ISSN 1470-9120
BODY, SPACE & TECHNOLOGY. Text in English. 2000. s-a. free (effective 2005). **Document type:** *Magazine, Consumer.*
Media: Online - full text.
Published by: Brunel University, Faculty of Arts, Uxbridge, UB8 3PH, United Kingdom. http://people.brunel.ac.uk/bst/home.htm.

700 NLD ISSN 1571-5949
BOEKMAN; tydschrift voor kunst, cultur en beleid. Text mainly in Dutch; Text occasionally in English. 1988. q. EUR 41 domestic to individuals; EUR 48 foreign to individuals; EUR 57 domestic to institutions; EUR 64 foreign to institutions (effective 2003). adv. bk.rev. abstr.; bibl.; illus. index. 120 p./no.; back issues avail. **Document type:** *Journal, Academic/Scholarly.* **Description:** Publishes articles on art and culture, research and management, including national and international policy issues.
Formerly (until 2003): Boekmancahier (0925-0239)
Indexed: ABM, IBSS, SOPODA, SSA.
—IE, KNAW.
Published by: Boekmanstichting, Herengracht 415, Amsterdam, 1017 BP, Netherlands. TEL 31-20-6243736, FAX 31-20-6385239, secretariaat@boekman.nl, http://www.boekman.nl. Ed. Joke J Hermsen. Adv. contact Marielle C E Hendriks. B&W page EUR 600; trim 220 x 134.

700 ESP ISSN 0211-8483
BOLETIN DE ARTE. Text in Spanish. 1980. a.
Indexed: IndIslam, RILM.
—CINDOC.
Published by: Universidad de Malaga, Departamento de Historia del Arte, Campus Universitario de Teatinos s-n, Malaga, 29071, Spain. TEL 34-952-131688, FAX 34-952-131823, http://www.filosofia.uma.es/. Ed. Rosario Camacho Martinez.

700 ESP ISSN 0210-6531
BOLETIN DE BELLAS ARTES. Text in Spanish. 1934. a.
—CINDOC.
Published by: Real Academia de Bellas Artes de Santa Isabel de Hungria, Abades, 12-14, Sevilla, 41004, Spain.

700 ITA ISSN 0394-4573
N4
BOLLETTINO D'ARTE. Variant title: Ministero per i Beni Culturali e Ambientali. Bollettino d'Arte. Text in Italian. 1907. q. EUR 134 domestic; EUR 160 foreign (effective 2004). bk.rev. bibl.; illus. reprints avail. **Document type:** *Bulletin, Academic/Scholarly.*
Formerly (until 1975): Italy. Ministero della Pubblica Istruzione. Bollettino d'Arte (0391-9854)
Related titles: ◆ Supplement(s): Bollettino d'Arte. Supplemento. ISSN 0394-4611.
Indexed: ABM, AIAP, ArtInd, BHA, IndIslam, NumL, RASB, RILM.
—IE.
Published by: (Italy. Ministero per i Beni e le Attivita Culturali), Istituto Poligrafico e Zecca dello Stato, Piazza Verdi 10, Rome, 00198, Italy. TEL 39-06-85082147, editoriale@ipzs.it, http://www.ipzs.it.

A

700 ITA ISSN 0394-4611
BOLLETTINO D'ARTE. SUPPLEMENTO. Text in Italian. 1982. irreg.
Related titles: ◆ Supplement to: Bollettino d'Arte. ISSN 0394-4573.
Indexed: AIAP, BHA.
Published by: (Italy. Ministero per i Beni e le Attivita Culturali), Istituto Poligrafico e Zecca dello Stato, Piazza Verdi 10, Rome, 00198, Italy. TEL 39-06-85082147, editoriale@ipzs.it, http://www.ipzs.it.

791.43 USA ISSN 0743-3204
NX458
BOMB; interviews with artists, writers, musicians, directors and actors. Text in English. 1981. q. USD 18 domestic; USD 40 foreign (effective 2002). adv. bk.rev.; film rev.; music rev.; play rev. illus. back issues avail.; reprints avail. **Document type:** *Magazine, Consumer.* **Description:** Provides original fiction, poetry, essays, interviews and dialogues between artists, fiction writers, musicians, playwrights, directors, actors, photographers and musicians.
Related titles: Online - full text ed.: (from H.W. Wilson, O C L C Online Computer Library Center, Inc.).
Indexed: ABM, AmHI, FLI, HumInd, IAPV, MRD.
Published by: New Art Publications, Inc., 594 Broadway, 905, New York, NY 10012-3233. TEL 212-431-3943, FAX 212-431-5880, bomb@echonyc.com, bombmag@bombsite.com, http://www.bombsite.com. Ed., Pub. Betsy Sussler. R&P Minna Proctor. Adv. contact Maryann Monforton. Circ: 25,000. **Subscr. to:** Bomb Magazine, P O Box 3000, Denville, NJ 07834-9713.

701 IND
BOMBAY ART SOCIETY'S ART JOURNAL. Text in English. 1971. q. INR 4. adv. illus.
Published by: Bombay Art Society, Jehangir Art Gallery, 16-B Mahatma Gandhi Rd., Mumbai, Maharashtra 400 001, India. Ed. Gopal S Adivrekar.

BOOKFORUM; the book review for art, fiction & culture. see *LITERARY AND POLITICAL REVIEWS*

BOOKPLATE JOURNAL. see *PUBLISHING AND BOOK TRADE*

BOOKPLATE SOCIETY NEWSLETTER. see *PUBLISHING AND BOOK TRADE*

B'OR HA-TORAH; science, the arts and modern life in the light of the Torah. see *RELIGIONS AND THEOLOGY—Judaic*

700 792 CAN ISSN 0831-2559
NX313.A3
BORDER CROSSINGS; a magazine of the arts. Text in English. 1982. q. CND 27 domestic; USD 32 foreign (effective 2004). adv. bk.rev. illus. index. reprints avail. **Document type:** *Trade.* **Description:** features articles, artists' profiles and interviews covering the full range of the contemporary arts (visual, performing and literary) in Canada. Also feature articles on American and international art.
Formerly: Arts Manitoba
Related titles: Microfiche ed.: (from MML); Microform ed.: (from MML); Online - full text ed.: (from H.W. Wilson, Micromedia ProQuest, O C L C Online Computer Library Center, Inc.).
Indexed: ABM, ArtInd, BHA, CBCARef, CBPI, CLitI, CPerI.
Published by: Arts Manitoba Publications Inc., 500 70 Arthur St, Winnipeg, MB R3B 1G7, Canada. TEL 204-942-5778, FAX 204-949-0793, bordercr@escape.ca, http://www.bordercrossingsmag.com, http://www.cmpa.ca/va1.html. Ed., R&P Meeka Walsh TEL 204-9434853. Circ: 3,300 (paid).

702.94 745.1 GBR
BOULAY 300: WORLD AUCTION REPORT. Text in English. 1998. 10/yr. USD 500 (effective 1999). illus.
Address: Galleon, Bldg 960, Sittingbourne Research Centre, Sittingbourne, Kent ME9 8DF, United Kingdom.

700 USA ISSN 1552-3160
BOUND & LETTERED. Text in English. 1980. q. USD 25 domestic; USD 33 foreign (effective 2005). bk.rev 64 p./no.; back issues avail. **Document type:** *Newsletter, Consumer.* **Description:** Presents how-to articles for calligraphers, book-binders, book artists, illuminators, and paper crafters.
Former titles (until 2004): Tabellae Ansatae (1534-8814); (until 1999): Letter Arts Book Club Newsletter
Published by: Letter Arts Book Club, Inc., PO Box 9986, Greensboro, NC 27429. TEL 336-272-6139, FAX 336-272-9015, info@johnnealbooks.com, http://www.johnnealbooks.com. Pub. John Neal. Circ: 4,500 (paid).

BRABANT CULTUREEL. see *HUMANITIES: COMPREHENSIVE WORKS*

BRAUNSCHWEIGISCHE HEIMAT; Zeitschrift fuer Natur- u. Heimatpflege, Landes- u. Volkskunde, Geschichte, Kunst u. Kultur Ostfalens. see *HISTORY—History Of Europe*

700 BRA
BRAVO. Text in Portuguese. m. BRL 114 domestic; USD 92.31 foreign (effective 2005). adv. **Document type:** *Magazine, Consumer.*
Related titles: Online - full text ed.
Published by: Editora Abril, S.A., Av. das Nacoes Unidas, 7221, 11 andar Pinheiros, Sao Paulo, SP 05425-902, Brazil. TEL 55-11-50872112, FAX 55-11-50872100, bravo@abril.com.br, http://www.bravoonline.com.br/, http://www.abril.com.br/. adv.: page BRL 19,800. Circ: 32,421.

700 FIN ISSN 1235-662X
BRAVO (PORI). Text in Finnish. 1993. biennial. **Document type:** *Magazine, Consumer.* **Description:** Listings of the cultural events through the year in Pori, Finland.
Published by: Porin Kulttuuritoimisto, Antinkatu 5, Pori, 28100, Finland. TEL 358-2-6211251, FAX 358-2-6211255.

700 BRA ISSN 0103-9636
NX533.A1
BRAZILIAN ART RESEARCH YEARBOOK. Text in Portuguese. 1992. a.
Published by: Universidade de Sao Paulo, Escola de Comunicacoes e Artes, Av. Prof. Lucio Martins Rodrigues 443, Butanta, SP 05508-900, Brazil.

700 305.8 AUS
BRISBANE ETHNIC MUSIC & ARTS CENTRE NEWS. Abbreviated title: B E M A C News. Text in English. 1992. q. free to members. adv. dance rev.; music rev.; play rev. back issues avail. **Document type:** *Newsletter.* **Description:** Covers Brisbane ethnic music and arts, including articles, notice board, funding information.
Formerly: B E M A C Newsletter
Published by: Brisbane Ethnic Music & Arts Centre Inc., PO Box 4169, East Brisbane, QLD 4169, Australia. TEL 61-7-3391-4433, FAX 61-7-3391-2802. Ed. Verity Clisby. Circ: 650 (controlled).

BRITISH ARCHAEOLOGICAL ASSOCIATION. CONFERENCE TRANSACTIONS. see *ARCHAEOLOGY*

BRITISH ARCHAEOLOGICAL ASSOCIATION. JOURNAL. see *ARCHAEOLOGY*

709.4105 GBR ISSN 1467-2006
N6761
➤ **THE BRITISH ART JOURNAL;** the research journal of British art studies. Text in English. 1999 (July). 3/yr. GBP 30 domestic; USD 50 in United States; GBP 35 elsewhere (effective 2005). adv. back issues avail. **Document type:** *Journal, Academic/Scholarly.* **Description:** Publishes original research on British art of all periods and covers most fields of art-historical research, including painting and the graphic arts, books and publishing, sculpture, architecture, the decorative arts, and the history of dress.
Related titles: Online - full content ed.
Indexed: ArtInd.
—BLDSC (2289.182000).
Published by: Art Journals Ltd, 46 Grove Lane, London, SE5, United Kingdom. editor@britishartjournal.co.uk, http://www.britishartjournal.co.uk/. Ed. Robin Simon. adv.: B&W page GBP 1,500, color page GBP 2,500; 210 x 297.

706 USA
BRITISH ARTISTS. Text in English. 1999. irreg., latest 2003. price varies. illus. back issues avail. **Document type:** *Monographic series, Academic/Scholarly.* **Description:** Takes an in-depth look at the lives and careers of the most influential British artists from the eighteenth through the twentieth centuries.
Published by: Princeton University Press, 41 William St, Princeton, NJ 08540-5237. TEL 609-258-4900, 800-777-4726, FAX 609-258-6305, Orders@cpfs.pupress.princeton.edu, http://pup.princeton.edu/catalogs/series/ba.html. **Subscr. addr. in US:** California - Princeton Fulfillment Services, 1445 Lower Ferry Rd, Ewing, NJ 08618. TEL 800-777-4726, FAX 800-999-1958, orders@cpfs.pupress.princeton.edu. **Dist. addr. in Canada:** University Press Group, 164 Hillsdale Ave E, Toronto, ON M4S 1T5, Canada.

BRITISH SCHOOL AT ATHENS. ANNUAL. see *ARCHAEOLOGY*

BRITISH SCHOOL AT ROME. PAPERS. see *ARCHAEOLOGY*

BROOKGREEN JOURNAL. see *GARDENING AND HORTICULTURE*

700 USA
BROOKLYN JOURNAL OF ARTS & URBAN AFFAIRS. Text in English. m.
Published by: Brooklyn Journal Publications, Inc., 129 Montague St, Brooklyn, NY 11201. TEL 718-624-6033, FAX 718-875-5302.

BROT & SPIELE; das Live-Magazin fuer die Region Aschaffenburg. see *MUSIC*

745.61 USA
BROWN LINES. Text in English. 6/yr.
Published by: Ken Brown Studio of Calligraphic Art, PO Box 637, Hugo, OK 74743. TEL 405-326-7544, FAX 405-326-6366. Ed. Ken Brown. Circ: 5,000.

DIE BRUECKE; Kaerntner Kulturzeitschrift. see *LITERARY AND POLITICAL REVIEWS*

708 DEU ISSN 0572-7146
BRUECKE-ARCHIV. Text in German. 1967. irreg., latest vol.9, 1977. price varies. illus.
Indexed: BHA.
Published by: Bruecke-Museum, Bussardsteig 9, Berlin, 14195, Germany. Ed. Magdalena Moeller.

700 USA
BRUTARIAN. Text in English. 1991. q. USD 12 domestic; USD 20 foreign; USD 4 newsstand/cover. bk.rev. back issues avail.
Address: PO Box 25222, Arlington, VA 22202-9998. TEL 703-360-2514. Ed. Dominick J Salemi. adv.: page USD 300. Circ: 3,000.

908 ITA ISSN 0392-3894
BRUTIUM. Text in Italian. 1922. 3/yr. EUR 30 domestic (effective 2004). **Document type:** *Journal, Academic/Scholarly.*
Published by: Gangemi Editore, Piazza San Pantaleo 4, Rome, Italy. TEL 39-06-6872774, FAX 39-06-68806189, gangemieditorerc@tin.it, http://www.gangemieditore.it. Ed. Maria Froncillo.

BUDIVNYTSTVO UKRAINY. see *ARCHITECTURE*

700.482943 JPN ISSN 0004-2889
N8193.A1
BUKKYO GEIJUTSU/ARS BUDDHICA. Text in Japanese; Abstracts and contents page in English. 1948. bi-m. USD 71.75. adv. illus.
Related titles: Microform ed.
Published by: (Buddhist Art Association), Mainichi Shinbunsha/Mainichi Newspapers, 1-1-1 Hitotsubashi, Chiyoda-ku, Tokyo, 100-8051, Japan. Circ: 1,000. **Dist. by:** Japan Publications Trading Co., Ltd., Book Export II Dept, PO Box 5030, Tokyo International, Tokyo 101-3191, Japan.

700 913 HUN ISSN 0133-5545
AM101.B927
BULLETIN DU MUSEE HONGROIS DES BEAUX-ARTS. Text in English, French, German, Hungarian, Italian. 1947. s-a. only on exchange basis. **Document type:** *Bulletin.*
Indexed: A&ATA, ABM, BHA, RASB, RILM.
Published by: Szepmuveszeti Muzeum/Musee des Beaux-Arts, Dozsa Gyorgy ut 41, Budapest 14, 1146, Hungary. TEL 36-1-3439759, FAX 36-1-3438298. Ed. Vilmos Tatrai. R&P Jlona Egyed-Lux. Circ: 700.

BULLETIN MONUMENTAL. see *ARCHAEOLOGY*

709 NZL ISSN 0110-4888
N7406.5
➤ **BULLETIN OF NEW ZEALAND ART HISTORY.** Text in English. 1972. a. price varies. bk.rev. **Document type:** *Bulletin, Academic/Scholarly.* **Description:** Chronicles the history of art in New Zealand, as well as production and activities of artists and museums in other countries which influence New Zealand art.
Indexed: ABM, BHA, INZP.
Published by: University of Otago, Hocken Library, PO Box 56, Dunedin, New Zealand. FAX 64-3-4795-078, TELEX 03-479-1100, hocken@library.otago.ac.nz. R&P S R Strachan. Circ: 200.

➤ **BULLETTINO STORICO EMPOLESE.** see *HISTORY—History Of Europe*

➤ **BUNKAZAI HOZON SYUHUKU GAKKAISI.** see *ANTIQUES*

➤ **BURGEN UND SCHLOESSER;** Zeitschrift fuer Burgenforschung und Denkmalpflege. see *HISTORY—History Of Europe*

➤ **BURGENBOTE;** Oesterreichs Bindenschild. see *CONSERVATION*

745.1 GBR ISSN 0007-6287
N1
➤ **BURLINGTON MAGAZINE.** Text in English. 1903. m. GBP 189 domestic; USD 494 in North America; GBP 215, EUR 322 elsewhere (effective 2004). adv. bk.rev. illus. index, cum.index every 10 yrs.: 1963-1972, 1973-1982. reprints avail. **Document type:** *Journal, Academic/Scholarly.* **Description:** Fine art magazine, international in scope, covering all periods from antiquity to the present day.
Formerly (until 1947): Burlington Magazine for Connoisseurs (0951-0788)
Related titles: Microfiche ed.: (from IDC); Microfilm ed.; Online - full text ed.: (from JSTOR (Web-based Journal Archive)).
Indexed: A&ATA, ABCT, ABM, AIAP, API, ASCA, ArtHuCI, ArtInd, BAS, BEL&L, BHA, BRI, BrArAb, CBRI, CurCont, DAAI, DIP, IBR, IBRH, IBZ, IndIslam, PCI, RASB, RILM, SSCI.
—BLDSC (2931.650000), IE, Infotrieve, ingenta. **CCC.**
Published by: Burlington Magazine Publications Ltd., 14 Dukes Rd, London, WC1H 9AD, United Kingdom. TEL 44-20-7388-1228, FAX 44-20-7388-1230, editorial@burlington.org.uk, burlington@burlington.org.uk, http://www.burlington.org.uk/. Ed. Richard Shone. Adv. contact Mark Scott.

➤ **BUSINESS & TEACHER DIRECTORY (YEAR).** see *ARTS AND HANDICRAFTS*

760 GBR ISSN 1473-1061
BUSINESS RATIO REPORT. DESIGN CONSULTANCIES (YEAR). Variant title: Design Consultancies. Text in English. 1988. a. GBP 275 (effective 2001). charts; stat. **Document type:** *Trade.*
Former titles (until 2001): Business Ratio. Design Consultancies (1469-7335); (until 2000): Business Ratio Plus. Design Consultancies (1358-5231); (until 1994): Business Ratio Report. Design Consultants (0963-6153); (until 1989): Business Ratio Report. Design Consultancy (0953-8143)
Published by: The Prospect Shop Ltd., Field House, 72 Oldfield Rd, Hampton, Middx TW12 2HQ, United Kingdom. TEL 44-20-8461-8730, 44-20-8481-8720, FAX 44-20-8783-1940, info@theprospectshop.co.uk.

700 POL ISSN 0067-947X
BYDGOSKIE TOWARZYSTWO NAUKOWE. WYDZIAL NAUK HUMANISTYCZNYCH. PRACE. SERIA D (SZTUKA). Text in Polish. irreg., latest vol.3, 1965. price varies.
Published by: Bydgoskie Towarzystwo Naukowe, Jezuicka 4, Bydgoszcz, Poland. **Dist. by:** Ars Polona, Krakowskie Przedmiescie 7, Warsaw, Poland.

BYZANTION; revue internationale des etudes byzantines. see *ASIAN STUDIES*

700 CAN ISSN 1480-5472
N6540
C; international contemporary art. Text in English. 1983. q. CND 25.68 domestic to individuals; USD 28 foreign to individuals; CND 36.38 domestic to institutions; USD 38 foreign to institutions; CND 8.25 newsstand/cover (effective 2005). adv. bk.rev.; music rev. illus. back issues avail.; reprints avail. **Document type:** *Magazine, Consumer.* **Description:** Provides a forum for the presentation of contemporary art and the discussion of issues surrounding art in our culture.
Former titles (until 1996): C Magazine (1193-8625); (until 1992): C (0838-0392); (until 1987): C Magazine (0836-6152); (until 1986): C (0829-2906); (until 1984): Impressions
Related titles: Microfiche ed.; Microfilm ed.: (from MML); Microform ed.: (from MML); Online - full text ed.: (from Gale Group, Micromedia ProQuest).
Indexed: ABM, ArtInd, BHA, CBCARef, CBPI, CPerl.
—CCC.
Published by: C The Visual Arts Foundation, P O Box 5, Sta B, Toronto, ON M5T 2T2, Canada. TEL 416-539-9495, FAX 426-539-9903, general@cmagazine.com, http://www.cmagazine.com. Adv. contact Janis Demkiw. B&W page CND 1,150, color page CND 1,990. Circ: 3,000.

700 USA ISSN 1557-511X
N345
C A A NEWS (NEW YORK). Text in English. 1979. bi-m. free to members. adv. bibl. 24 p./no. 3 cols./p.; **Document type:** *Newsletter, Academic/Scholarly.*
Formerly (until 1990): C A A Newsletter (New York)
Related titles: Online - full text ed.
Published by: College Art Association, 275 Seventh Ave, New York, NY 10001. TEL 212-691-1051, FAX 212-627-2381, caanews@collegeart.org, http://www.collegeart.org. Circ: 10,000 (controlled).

709 USA ISSN 1543-950X
C A A REVIEWS. (College Art Association) Text in English. 1998. irreg. Free. **Description:** Devoted to the peer review of new books relevant to the fields of art history, national and international museum and gallery exhibitions, academic conferences, electronic media, as well as books on art-historical criticism, arts education, policy, film curatorial studies, and more.
Media: Online - full content.
Published by: College Art Association, 275 Seventh Ave, New York, NY 10001. TEL 212-691-1051, FAX 212-627-2381, http://www.caareviews.org, http://www.collegeart.org.

700 793.3 780 792 USA
C A NEWS*. Text in English. 1985. q. USD 15 to individuals; USD 50 to institutions. bk.rev. back issues avail. **Document type:** *Newsletter.* **Description:** Highlights conferences and other events around the world. Looks at other organizations and what they are doing.
Published by: Christians in the Arts Networking, Inc., 9 West Minster Ave, Box 242, Arlington, MA 02174-0003. TEL 617-646-1541, FAX 617-646-7725. Ed. Brian Emmet. Circ: 750.

741.5 USA
C B C WEB-MAG. (Comic Books Collectors) Text in English. w. bk.rev. **Document type:** *Consumer.* **Description:** Includes news about the comic book universe and contains interviews and notes from collectors and readers.
Media: Online - full text.
Address: sinofsky@hotmail.com, http://www.sfcentral.com/cbc/. Ed., Pub. David Lewis Sinofsky.

C B D. (Corporate Business Design) see *BUSINESS AND ECONOMICS*

700 GBR ISSN 0263-9475
N6789
C I R C A ART MAGAZINE; Ireland's journal of contemporary visual culture. Text in English. 1981. q. GBP 14 domestic to individuals; EUR 20.30 in Ireland to individuals; EUR 29.45 in Europe to individuals; EUR 45.55, USD 45.50 elsewhere to individuals; GBP 29 domestic to institutions; EUR 44.45 in Ireland to institutions; EUR 56.45 in Europe to institutions; EUR 72.50, USD 71.50 elsewhere to institutions (effective 2003). adv. bk.rev. index. back issues avail. **Document type:** *Magazine, Consumer.*
Formerly: Circa
Indexed: ABM, ArtInd, BHA, FLI, RILM.
—BLDSC (3198.821200), IE, ingenta.
Published by: Circa, 43/44 Temple Bar, Dublin, Ireland 2, United Kingdom. liz@recirca.com, http://www.recirca.com. Circ: 1,000.

741.6 USA
C M Y K MAGAZINE. Text in English. 1996. q. USD 20 domestic; USD 38 in Canada; USD 72 elsewhere; USD 7 newsstand/cover domestic; USD 9.95 newsstand/cover in Canada (effective 2003). adv. **Document type:** *Magazine, Trade.* **Description:** Publishes the best work from students in advertising, design, illustration and photography; also offers student and school profiles and tips from professional designers .
Address: 5B Isadora Duncan Ln, San Francisco, CA 94102. TEL 415-346-1435, 800-467-6532, FAX 415-346-1432, cmykcurt@aol.com, editor@cmykmag.com, http://www.cmykmag.com. Ed. Curtis Clarkson. adv.: B&W page USD 2,950, color page USD 3,700.

700 USA ISSN 1531-1430
NX456
CABINET. Text in English. 2000. q. USD 28 domestic to individuals; USD 34 in Canada to individuals; USD 36 in Europe to individuals; USD 50 elsewhere to individuals; USD 34 domestic to institutions; USD 42 in Canada to institutions; USD 44 in Europe to institutions; USD 60 elsewhere to institutions (effective 2005). 112 p./no. 3 cols./p.; back issues avail. **Document type:** *Magazine, Consumer.* **Description:** Contains articles, interviews, commissioned projects, and special sections on international art and culture.
Published by: Immaterial Incorporated, 181 Wyckoff St, Brooklyn, NY 11217. TEL 718-222-8434, FAX 718-222-3700, cabinet@immaterial.net, subscriptions@immaterial.net, http://www.cabinetmagazine.org, http://www.immaterial.net. Ed. Sina Najafi TEL 718-222-8434.

CADERNOS DE POS-GRADUACAO EM EDUCACAO, ARTE E HISTORIA DA CULTURA. see *HUMANITIES: COMPREHENSIVE WORKS*

THE CAFE REVIEW; a quarterly poetry and arts publication. see *LITERATURE*

CAHIERS ALSACIENS D'ARCHEOLOGIE D'ART ET D'HISTOIRE. see *ARCHAEOLOGY*

CAHIERS BOURBONNAIS; arts, lettres, regionalisme. see *LITERATURE*

CAHIERS DE CIVILISATION MEDIEVALE. see *HISTORY*

CAHIERS DE CIVILISATION MEDIEVALE. BIBLIOGRAPHIE. see *HISTORY*

CAHIERS DE L'IROISE. see *HISTORY—History Of Europe*

THE CAIRN. see *MUSEUMS AND ART GALLERIES*

700 EGY ISSN 1012-6015
CAIRO UNIVERISTY. FACULTY OF ARTS. BULLETIN. Text in English. 1933. s-a. EGP 25, USD 25 newsstand/cover (effective 2003). **Document type:** *Bulletin, Academic/Scholarly.*
Published by: Cairo University, Faculty of Arts, Gamaat El-Qahira Str, Giza, Egypt. TEL 20-2-5676302, FAX 20-2-5729659, http://derp.sti.sci.eg/data/0085.htm. Ed. Dr. Muhammad Khalifa Hasan.

CALCUTTAN. see *POLITICAL SCIENCE*

709 USA ISSN 0068-5909
➤ **CALIFORNIA STUDIES IN THE HISTORY OF ART.** Text in English. 1962. irreg., latest vol.35, 1996. price varies. Supplement avail.; back issues avail. **Document type:** *Monographic series, Academic/Scholarly.* **Description:** Publishes research on the history of all forms of Western art.
—BLDSC (3015.336000).
Published by: University of California Press, Book Series, 2120 Berkeley Way, Berkeley, CA 94720. TEL 510-642-4247, FAX 510-643-7127, askucp@ucpress.edu, http://www.ucpress.edu/books/CSHA.ser.html, http://www.ucpress.edu/books/series.html. **Orders to:** California - Princeton Fulfillment Services, 1445 Lower Ferry Rd, Ewing, NJ 08618. TEL 800-777-4726, FAX 800-999-1958.

➤ **CALYX**; a journal of art & literature by women. see *LITERATURE*

➤ **CAMERAWORK**; a journal of photographic arts. see *PHOTOGRAPHY*

➤ **CAMPUS REVIEW.** see *LITERARY AND POLITICAL REVIEWS*

700 CAN ISSN 0825-3854
N1
CANADIAN ART. Text in English. 1984. q. CND 24 domestic; USD 32 in United States; USD 40 elsewhere; CND 6.95 per issue (effective 2005). adv. bk.rev. illus. back issues avail.; reprints avail. **Document type:** *Magazine, Consumer.* **Description:** Covers visual arts in Canada and internationally.
Formed by the merger of (1940-1984): Arts Canada (0004-4113); Which was formerly (until 1967): Canadian Art (0317-011X); (until 1943): Maritime Art (0317-0101); (19??-1984): Artsmagazine (0318-6644); Which was formerly (until 1974): Art (0004-3257); (until 1969): Society of Canadian Artists. Journal
Related titles: Microfiche ed.: (from MML); Microform ed.: (from MML); Online - full text ed.: (from Micromedia ProQuest).
Indexed: ABM, ArtInd, BHA, CBCARef, CBPI, CPerl.
—CCC.
Published by: Canadian Art Foundation, 51 Front St E, Ste 210, Toronto, ON M5E 1B3, Canada. TEL 416-368-8854, 800-222-4762, FAX 416-368-6135, info@canadianart.ca, http://www.canadianart.ca. Ed. Richard Rhodes. Pub., R&P, Adv. contact Wendy Ingram. B&W page USD 4,275, color page USD 5,040; trim 10.88 x 8.19. Circ: 20,000 (paid).

CANADIAN ART TEACHER. see *EDUCATION*

708.11 CAN ISSN 0383-5405
CANADIAN ARTISTS SERIES. Text in English. 1973. irreg., latest vol.10, 1985. CND 8.95. illus. **Document type:** *Catalog.* **Description:** Examines life and work of significant Canadian artists and their contributions to art in Canada.
Published by: National Gallery of Canada, Publications Division, c/o Irene Lillico, 380 Sussex Dr, Ottawa, ON K1N 9N4, Canada. TEL 613-990-0537, FAX 613-990-7460. Circ: 5,000.

781.542 CAN ISSN 1490-3563
CANADIAN COUNCIL FOR THE ARTS. ANNUAL REPORT/CONSEIL DES ARTS DU CANADA. RAPPORT ANNUEL. Text in English, French. 1958. a. free. charts; stat. **Document type:** *Corporate.*
Formerly (until 1996): Canada Council. Annual Report (0576-4300)
Published by: Canada Council for the Arts, 350 Albert St, P O Box 1047, Ottawa, ON K1P 5V8, Canada. TEL 613-566-4414, 800-263-5588, FAX 613-566-4390, http://www.conseildesarts.ca. Circ: 5,000.

CANADIAN JOURNAL OF NETHERLANDIC STUDIES/REVUE CANADIENNE D'ETUDES NEERLANDAISES. see *LITERATURE*

707 CAN ISSN 0706-8107
➤ **CANADIAN REVIEW OF ART EDUCATION. RESEARCH AND ISSUES/REVUE CANADIENNE D'EDUCATION ARTISTIQUE RECHERCHE ET QUESTIONS D'ACTUALITE ARTISTIQUE.** Text mainly in English; Text occasionally in French. 1977. irreg. price varies. **Document type:** *Academic/Scholarly.*
Formerly (until 1988): Canadian Review of Art Education Research (0384-1839)
Indexed: CEI, CIJE, CPE, SRRA.
—BLDSC (3044.630900). **CCC.**
Published by: Canadian Society for Education Through Art, Faculty of Education, Queen's University, A321 Duncan McArthur Hall, Kingston, ON K7L 3N6, Canada. TEL 613-533-6000 ext 78401, FAX 613-5333-2331, csea@educ.queensu.ca, http://www.csea-scea.ca. Ed. Roger Clark. Circ: 400.

➤ **CANADIAN SOCIETY FOR EDUCATION THROUGH ART. VIEWPOINTS.** see *EDUCATION*

700 USA
CAPE COD ARTS. Text in English. a. USD 2.50 newsstand/cover (effective 2001). **Document type:** *Magazine, Consumer.* **Description:** Covers the active arts culture inspired by and in the Cape Cod region.
Published by: Cape Cod Life, Inc., 270 Communication Way, Unit 6, Hyannis, MA 02601-1883. TEL 508-564-4466, FAX 508-564-4470, capelife@capecodlife.com, http://www.capecodlife.com/CCA/index.html.

700 305.897 CAN ISSN 1704-0639
CAPE DORSET ANNUAL PRINT COLLECTION. Text in English. 1962. a. **Document type:** *Journal, Consumer.*
Former titles (until 199?): Cape Dorset Annual Graphics Collection (0843-2678); (until 1988): Cape Dorset Graphics (0829-1497); (until 1984): Dorset (0382-7747); (until 1975): Cape Dorset Prints (0319-0463); (until 1972): Cape Dorset (0319-0455); (until 1971): Eskimo Graphic Art (0071-1322)
Published by: (West Baffin Eskimo Co-operative), Dorset Fine Arts, 80 Spadina Ave, Ste 309, Toronto, ON M5V 2J4, Canada. TEL 416-961-0511, FAX 416-961-7749, info@dorsetfinearts.com, http://www.dorsetfinearts.com/althome.html.

▼ new title ➤ refereed * unverified ♦ full entry avail.

A

700   USA
CARBON 14. Text in English. q. USD 18; USD 25 in Canada & Mexico; USD 36 elsewhere. back issues avail. **Description:** Covers arts and music.
Related titles: Online - full text ed.
Published by: Leslie Goldam, Ed. & Pub., PO Box 29247, Philadelphia, PA 19127. editor@c14.com, carbon@voicenet.com, http://www.c14.com/.

CARDOZO ARTS & ENTERTAINMENT LAW JOURNAL. see *LAW*

CARIBBEAN STUDIES/ESTUDES DES CARAIBES/ESTUDIOS DEL CARIBE. see *SOCIAL SCIENCES: COMPREHENSIVE WORKS*

700   USA   ISSN 0741-0085
CB235
CARIBE MAGAZINE; visual arts in the Caribbean. Text in English. 1977. irreg. USD 3 per issue. bk.rev. charts; illus. **Description:** Explores the African Diaspora and the cultures of all its descendants residing in the Americas, the Caribbean, and around the world.
Formerly: Pre-Columbian Research Resources Review
Indexed: AICP, SRRA.
Published by: Caribbean Cultural Center, 408 W 58th St, New York, NY 10019. TEL 212-307-7420, FAX 212-315-1086, mail@caribecenter.org, http://www.caribecenter.org/. Ed. Marta Vega. Circ: 2,500.

800 500 700   USA   ISSN 0008-6681
AS36
CARNEGIE MAGAZINE; dedicated to art, and science. Text in English. 1927. bi-m. adv. bk.rev. illus. index. reprint service avail. from PQC. **Description:** Includes articles and photography on the arts, natural history and science.
Incorporates: Carnegie. Annual Report
Related titles: Microform ed.: (from PQC); Online - full text ed.: (from bigchalk).
Indexed: ABM, AIAP, BHA.
Published by: Carnegie Museums of Pittsburgh, 4400 Forbes Ave, Pittsburgh, PA 15213. TEL 412-622-5528, FAX 412-688-8624, carnegiemag@clpgh.org, http://www.carnegiemuseums.org/cmag/. Ed. R Jay Gangewere. R&P R. Jay Gangewere TEL 412-622-3315. Adv. contact Brian B McKee. B&W page USD 1,700, color page USD 2,940; trim 10.88 x 8.25. Circ: 30,000.

▼ CARNET ARTE. see *GENERAL INTEREST PERIODICALS—Italy*

CARRIZOS. see *LITERATURE*

700   ITA   ISSN 0392-3347
DG975.B57
CARROBBIO. Text in Italian. 1975. a. EUR 54.59 (effective 2003).
Indexed: BHA.
Published by: Patron Editore, Via Badini 12, Quarto Inferiore, BO 40050, Italy. TEL 39-051-767003, FAX 39-051-768252, info@patroneditore.com, http://www.patroneditore.com. Eds. Emilio Pasquini, Giancarlo Susini.

741.5 658.8   USA
CARTOON OPPORTUNITIES. Text in English. 1995. m. USD 60 (effective 2004). adv. bk.rev. back issues avail. **Document type:** *Newsletter.* **Description:** Publishes listings of markets that buy cartoons as well as tips on how to draw and market cartoons.
Address: PO Box 248, Chalfont, PA 18914. billkeo@ptd.net. Ed., Pub., R&P, Adv. contact Bill Keough.

CARTOON TIMES. see *MUSEUMS AND ART GALLERIES*

740   USA
CARTOONIST AND COMIC ARTIST MAGAZINE. Text in English. 1992. 4/yr. USD 20 domestic; USD 26 in Canada & Mexico; USD 32 elsewhere. USD 6 newsstand/cover. adv. bk.rev. back issues avail. **Document type:** *Consumer.* **Description:** Guide to better cartooning and comic illustrating for professional and beginning cartoonists.
Formerly: Aspiring Cartoonist (1080-3491)
Address: 2747 N Grand Ave, PMB 250, Santa Ana, CA 92705-8751. cartoonmag@aol.com, http://www.aspiringcartoonist.com. Ed., Pub., R&P, Adv. contact Steve Pastis. Circ: 4,000 (paid and controlled).

741.5   USA   ISSN 0008-7068
NC1300
CARTOONIST PROFILES. Text in English. 1969. q. USD 35 to institutions (effective 2000). adv. charts; illus. **Document type:** *Trade.*
Related titles: Microform ed.: (from PQC).
Address: PO Box 325, Fairfield, CT 06430. Ed., Pub. Jud Hurd.

700   ESP   ISSN 1132-9998
CASTELLUM. Text in Spanish. 1992. irreg.
—CINDOC.
Published by: Universidad Complutense de Madrid, Facultad de Geografia e Historia, Asociacion Cultural Castellum, Ciudad Universitaria, Madrid, 28040, Spain.

CATALOGO DANTE. see *LITERATURE*

708.972   MEX   ISSN 0187-9766
CATALOGO DE LAS EXPOSICIONES DE ARTE. Text in Spanish. 1937. a.
Related titles: ♦ Supplement to: Universidad Nacional Autonoma de Mexico. Instituto de Investigaciones Esteticas. Anales. ISSN 0185-1276.
Published by: Universidad Nacional Autonoma de Mexico, Instituto de Investigaciones Esteticas, Circuito Mario de la Cueva, Zona Cultural, Ciudad Universitaria, Mexico, DF 04510, Mexico. TEL 52-55-56652465, FAX 52-55-56654740, http://www.esteticas-unam.mx. Ed. Durdica Segota.

700   ESP
CATALOGO NACIONAL DE ARTE CONTEMPORANEO. Text in Spanish. a.
Published by: Iberico 2000 S.A., Joaquin Montes Jovellar, 4, 1o Dcha., Madrid, 28002, Spain. TEL 91-261-82-68.

THE CATALOGUE OF ANTIQUES & FINE ARTS. see *ANTIQUES*

700 808.81   USA   ISSN 0739-8506
CATALYST (SEATTLE). Text in English. 1980. s-a. USD 8; USD 11 foreign. back issues avail. **Description:** Literary erotica in irregular collections, with emphasis on modern poetry and illustrated art.
Published by: Laocoon Books, PO Box 20518, Seattle, WA 98102. TEL 206-323-7268. Ed. M Kettner. Circ: 2,000.

CATCH-A-FIRE. see *ETHNIC INTERESTS*

THE CELATOR; journal of ancient and medieval coinage. see *NUMISMATICS*

700   AUS
CELEBRITY, PEOPLE, EVENTS NEWS. Text in English. 1990. w. AUD 120 (effective 2000). **Document type:** *Bulletin.*
Formerly: Media Futures (1037-3381); Supersedes: MediaFax (1035-0802)
Published by: H W W Limited, PO Box 996, Darlinghurst, NSW 2010, Australia. TEL 61-2-8268-8268, FAX 61-2-8268-8267, http://www.hww.com.au.

705   USA
CENTRAL HALL ARTISTS NEWSLETTER∗. Text in English. 1974. q. USD 1. adv. illus.
Published by: Central Hall Artists Inc., c/o L Cohen, 84 Allenwood Rd, Great Neck, NY 11023. Circ: 1,000.

700 780   CMR
CENTRE CULTUREL FRANCAIS DE YAOUNDE. PROGRAMME SAISON. Text in French. a.
Published by: Centre Culturel Francais de Yaounde, BP 513, Yaounde, Cameroon.

CENTRE D'HISTOIRE ET D'ART DE LA THUDINIE. PUBLICATIONS. see *HISTORY—History Of Europe*

CENTRE INTERNATIONAL D'ETUDE DES TEXTILES ANCIENS. BULLETIN. see *TEXTILE INDUSTRIES AND FABRICS*

745.5 677.653   ITA   ISSN 1129-5295
CENTRINI E FILET. Text in Italian. 1998. m. **Document type:** *Consumer.* **Description:** Contains lacework patterns, as well as textual instructions.
Published by: Edizioni G E S, Via A Grandi, 1, Rho, MI 20017, Italy. TEL 39-2-93522201, FAX 39-2-93522203. Ed. Gianni Eusebio. Dist. by: A & G Marco Via Fortezza, Milan, MI, Italy.

CENTRO CAMUNO DI STUDI PREISTORICI. ARCHIVI. see *ARCHAEOLOGY*

CENTRO CAMUNO DI STUDI PREISTORICI. STUDI CAMUNI. see *ARCHAEOLOGY*

709 913   ITA
CENTRO CAMUNO DI STUDI PREISTORICI. SYMPOSIA. Text in Multiple languages. irreg., latest vol.3, 1983. price varies.
Published by: Centro Camuno di Studi Preistorici, Capo di Ponte, BS 25044, Italy. TEL 39-0364-42091, FAX 39-0364-42572, info@ccsp.it, http://www.ccsp.it.

700   CUB   ISSN 1684-2413
CENTRO CULTURAL PABLO DE LA TORRIENTE BRAU. MEMORIA. Key Title: Memoria. Text in Spanish. 1999. m. back issues avail.
Related titles: Online - full text ed.: ISSN 1684-2421. 1999.
Published by: Centro Cultural Pablo de la Torriente Brau, C. de la Muralla No. 63, Entre Oficios e Inquisidor, Havana, Cuba. TEL 53-78-666585, vccasaus@colombus.cu, http://www.portalatino.com/lanzamientos/centropablo/main_new.htm.

700 900 011   ITA
CENTRO DI CULTURA E STORIA AMALFITANA. RASSEGNA. Text in Italian. 1981; N.S. 1991. s-m. USD 20 (effective 2000). bk.rev. bibl. **Document type:** *Monographic series.* **Description:** Contains articles and research on the history and civilization of the Amalfi region.

Indexed: BHA.
Published by: Centro di Cultura e Storia Amalfitana, Via Annunziatella, 44, Amalfi, SA 84011, Italy. TEL 089-871170, FAX 089-873143. Ed. Andrea Cerenza. Circ: 1,000.
Co-sponsor: Ministero Beni Culturali e Ambientali - Rome.

CERAMICS; art and perception. see *CERAMICS, GLASS AND POTTERY*

CHANGJIANG WENYI/YANGTZE LITERATURE AND ART. see *LITERATURE*

700   DNK   ISSN 0109-3479
CHARLOTTENBORG FORAARSUDSTILLINGEN. Text in Danish. 1984. a.
Address: Nyhavn 2, Copenhagen K, 1051, Denmark.

700 363.49   USA   ISSN 1083-8872
CHEROTIC REVOLUTIONARY. Text in English. 1991. irreg., latest vol.8, 1999. USD 5 per issue (effective 2000). adv. bk.rev.; film rev.; play rev.; video rev.; music rev. back issues avail. **Document type:** *Newsletter.* **Description:** Offers a "Zine" about the edge, for and by people on the edge... if not over it.
Published by: Inter - Relations, Inc., PO Box 11445, Berkeley, CA 94712. TEL 510-526-7858, FAX 510-524-2053, fmoore@eroplay.com, http://www.eroplay.com. Ed. Frank Moore. R&P, Adv. contact Linda Mac. Circ: 500.

700   USA   ISSN 1523-6072
CHICAGO ART JOURNAL. Text in English. 1991. a.
Indexed: ABM.
Published by: University of Chicago, Division of Humanities, 1050 E 59th St, Chicago, IL 60637.

708   USA
CHICAGO ARTISTS' NEWS. Text in English. 1975. 11/yr. USD 40 domestic to individual members; USD 62 foreign to individual members; USD 60 domestic to institutional members; USD 82 foreign to institutional members (effective 2000). adv. bk.rev. **Document type:** *Newspaper.* **Description:** Feature articles, list of gallery openings, jobs, space, opportunities including grants information, exhibitions, lectures, workshops, and other information of concern to artists.
Formerly: (until Jan. 1990): C A C News (0890-5908)
Related titles: Online - full text ed.
Published by: Chicago Artists' Coalition, 11 E Hubbard St, 7th Fl, Chicago, IL 60611. TEL 312-670-2060, FAX 312-670-2521, http://www.caconline.org, http://www.caconline.org/home.html. Ed., R&P, Adv. contact Katie Copenhaver. Circ: 2,400 (paid).

709   USA   ISSN 1045-1382
N6487.C52
CHICAGO INTERNATIONAL NEW ART FORMS EXPOSITION∗ Text in English. 1986. a.
Published by: Lakeside Group Inc., General Delivery, Lakeside, MI 49116-9999.

028.5   USA   ISSN 1096-9020
CHILDART. Text in English. 1998 (April). q. USD 30 domestic; USD 40 foreign (effective 2003). **Document type:** *Magazine, Consumer.*
Related titles: Online - full text ed.: (from Gale Group).
Published by: International Child Art Foundation, 1350 Connecticut Ave, N W, Washington, DC 20036-1702. TEL 202-530-1000, FAX 202-530-1080, jadams@icaf.org, http://www.icaf.org/Adults/Magazine.htm.

CHILDREN'S WRITER'S AND ILLUSTRATOR'S MARKET; 800 editors and art directors who buy your writing and illustrations. see *PUBLISHING AND BOOK TRADE*

707.0951 001.3   USA
CHINA INSTITUTE IN AMERICA. BULLETIN. Text in English. q. membership only. bk.rev.
Published by: China Institute in America, Inc., 125 E 65th St, New York, NY 10021. TEL 212-744-8181, info@chinainstitute.org, http://www.chinainstitute.org. Ed. Helen Geraghty. Circ: 1,700.

750   USA   ISSN 0889-8189
CHINA PAINTER. Text in English. 1967. bi-m. USD 30; USD 35 foreign (effective 1999). adv. back issues avail. **Description:** Covers all aspects of the fine art of porcelain china painting.
Published by: World Organization of China Painters, 2641 N W 10, Oklahoma City, OK 73107. TEL 405-521-1234, FAX 405-521-1265, http://www.theshop.wet@wocporg. Ed. Pat Dickerson. Circ: 8,000.

700   HKG
➤ CHINESE TYPE CONTEMPORARY ART. Text in Chinese. 1997. bi-m. free. **Document type:** *Academic/Scholarly.* **Description:** Provides collectors, historians, curators, dealers and critics outside the modern China context with an in-depth look at some of the art making history in China today.
Media: Online - full text.
Published by: New Art Media Limited, 12-F Aon Insurance Tower, 3 Lockhart Rd, Wanchai, Hong Kong, Hong Kong. rbernell@chinese-art.com, rbernell@aol.com, http://www.chinese-art.com, http://www.chinese-art.com. Ed. Yin Jinan. Pub. Robert Bernell.

700 PRK
CHOSON YESUL/KOREAN ARTS. Text in Korean. m.
Indexed: RASB.
Published by: Central Committee of the General Federation of Literature and Arts of Korea, Pyongyang, Korea, N.

DIE CHRISTENGEMEINSCHAFT; Monatsschrift zur religioesen Erneuerung. see *RELIGIONS AND THEOLOGY*

CHRISTIAAN DE WET ANNALE. see *HISTORY—History Of Africa*

700 GBR
N8610
CHRISTIE'S MAGAZINE. Text in English. 1984. 10/yr. GBP 40 domestic; GBP 54 in Europe; USD 85 in United States; GBP 7.50 newsstand/cover. adv. **Document type:** *Consumer.*
Formerly: Christie's International Magazine (0266-1217)
Indexed: ChLitAb.
Published by: Christie's, St James, 8 King St, London, SW1Y 6QT, United Kingdom. TEL 44-20-7839-9060, FAX 44-20-7389-2429, http://www.christies.com. Ed. Sarah Reardon. Adv. contact Dariel Garnettt. B&W page GBP 3,000, color page GBP 4,500; trim 230 x 285. Circ: 50,000.

CHRONICA. see *HISTORY—History Of Europe*

700 BRA ISSN 0103-2380
CHRONOS. Text in Portuguese. 1967. s-a. **Document type:** *Journal, Academic/Scholarly.*
Incorporates (1987-1988): Ato (0103-2399)
Indexed: L&LBA.
Published by: Universidade de Caxias do Sul, Rua Francisco Getulio Vargas, 1130, Caxias do Sul, RS 95070-560, Brazil. informa@ucs.tce.br, http://www.ucs.br/.

CHURCHSCAPE; annual review of the Council for the Care of Churches. see *ARCHITECTURE*

CINMAY SMRTI PATHAGARA. see *LITERATURE*

CITTA DI VITA; bimestrale di religione arte e scienza. see *RELIGIONS AND THEOLOGY*

700 ITA
LA CIVETTA. Text in Italian. 1974 (no.2). irreg., latest vol.6, 1977. price varies. **Document type:** *Monographic series, Academic/Scholarly.*
Published by: Giardini Editori e Stampatori (Subsidiary of: Libra Web), Via Giosue Carducci 60, Ghezzano - La Fontina, Pisa 56123, Italy. TEL 39-050-878066, FAX 39-050-878732, giardinieditori@giardinieditori.it, http://www.libraweb.net. Ed. Nicola Micieli.

700 945 ITA ISSN 0069-4355
CIVILTA VENEZIANA. FONTI E TESTI. SERIE PRIMA: FONTI E TESTI PER LA STORIA DELL'ARTE VENETA. Text in Italian. 1959. irreg., latest vol.8, 1972. price varies. **Document type:** *Monographic series.*
Published by: (Fondazione Giorgio Cini), Casa Editrice Leo S. Olschki, Viuzzo del Pozzetto 8, Florence, 50126, Italy. TEL 39-055-6530684, FAX 39-055-6530214, celso@olschki.it, http://www.olschki.it. Circ: 1,000.

THE CLASSICIST. see *ARCHITECTURE*

745 USA
CLAVE; a journal of Latin American arts and culture. Text in English. q. USD 19.99 to individuals; USD 29.95 to institutions (effective 2002). back issues avail.
Related titles: Online - full text ed.
Indexed: RILM.
Published by: Latin American Folk Institute, 3800 A. 34th St, Mount Rainier, MD 20712-2045. TEL 301-887-9331, FAX 301-887-0308, info@lafi.org, http://www.lafi.org/magazine/magazine.html.

940 NLD
CLAVIS KLEINE KUNSTHISTORISCHE MONOGRAFIEEN. Text in Dutch. 1984. a. price varies. illus. **Document type:** *Monographic series, Academic/Scholarly.* **Description:** Publishes monographic studies on medieval art.
Published by: Clavis Stichting Publicaties Middeleeuwse Kunst, Postbus 1521, Utrecht, 3500 BM, Netherlands. Ed. R E Th M Rijntjes.

940 NLD
CLAVIS KUNSTHISTORISCHE MONOGRAFIEEN. Text in Dutch. 1984. a. price varies. illus. **Document type:** *Monographic series, Academic/Scholarly.* **Description:** Publishes monographic studies on medieval art.
Published by: Clavis Stichting Publicaties Middeleeuwse Kunst, Postbus 1521, Utrecht, 3500 BM, Netherlands. Ed. R E Th M Rijntjes.

CLAY PALM REVIEW: ART AND LITERARY MAGAZINE. see *LITERATURE—Poetry*

CLEMSON UNIVERSITY. COLLEGE OF ARCHITECTURE. JOURNAL; a journal of educational thought. see *ARCHITECTURE*

709 USA ISSN 1554-2254
CLEVELAND ART; Cleveland Museum of Art members magazine. Text in English. 1995. m.
Formerly (until 2005): Cleveland Museum of Art. Members Magazine (1081-7042)
Published by: Cleveland Museum of Art, Publications Department, 11150 E Blvd, Cleveland, OH 44106. TEL 216-421-7340, FAX 216-421-0411.

709 USA ISSN 1092-3934
CLEVELAND STUDIES IN THE HISTORY OF ART. Text in English. 1996. a.
Indexed: ABM, RILM.
Published by: Cleveland Museum of Art, Publications Department, 11150 E Blvd, Cleveland, OH 44106. TEL 216-421-7340, FAX 216-421-0411.

700 MEX
CLON: CYBERZINE DE ARTE Y CULTURA. Text in Spanish. irreg. back issues avail.
Media: Online - full text.
Published by: Universidad Autonoma Metropolitana - Xochimilco, CALZ DEL HUESO 1100, Col Villa Quietud, Mexico City, DF 04960, Mexico. TEL 52-5-7245050, http://alebrije.uam.mx/revista/clon.

700 USA
COAGULA ART JOURNAL; the low down on high art. Text in English. 1992. 6/yr. USD 23.95 (effective 2002). adv.
Description: Reports on insider information about the art world.
Address: 2100 N Main St, #A-8, Lincoln Heights, CA 90031. TEL 213-833-6650, coagula@hotmail.com, http://www.coagula.com. Pub. Mat Gleason.

700 USA
COASTAL ANTIQUES & ART. Text in English. 1996. m. free newsstand/cover. **Document type:** *Magazine, Consumer.*
Description: Contains information on art and museum exhibits, openings, artist profiles, art calendar, antique collecting and show schedules.
Published by: Morris Communications Company LLC, 725 Broad St, Augusta, GA 30901. TEL 800-622-6358, james.parker@savannahnow.com, http://coastalantiques.com, http://morris.com. Ed. Tim Rutherford. Adv. contact Mandi Martin TEL 912-652-0238. Circ: 19,000 (controlled).

COLECCION ETHOS. see *MUSIC*

COLLECTIONS (COLUMBIA). see *MUSEUMS AND ART GALLERIES*

COLLECTOR. see *ADVERTISING AND PUBLIC RELATIONS*

COLLECTOR EDITIONS. see *HOBBIES*

741 ITA ISSN 1129-1745
COLOUR TATTOO. Text in Italian. 1999. bi-m. EUR 4.60 newsstand/cover (effective 2003). **Document type:** *Magazine, Consumer.*
Published by: Trentini S.r.l., Via Pier Luigi Nervi 1/B, Argenta, 44011, Italy. TEL 39-0532-318149, FAX 39-0532-310084, info@3ntini.com, http://www.3ntini.com.

700 340 USA ISSN 1544-4848
K1
COLUMBIA JOURNAL OF LAW & THE ARTS; a quarterly journal of law and the arts, entertainment, communications and intellectual property. Text in English. 1974. q. USD 45 in North America; USD 53 elsewhere; USD 12 newsstand/cover in North America; USD 14 newsstand/cover elsewhere (effective 2005). adv. bk.rev. illus. index. back issues avail.; reprint service avail. from WSH. **Document type:** *Journal, Academic/Scholarly.*
Former titles (until 2001): Columbia - V L A Journal of Law & the Arts (0888-4226); (until 1985): Art and the Law (0743-5266)
Related titles: Microfiche ed.: (from WSH); Microfilm ed.: (from WSH); Online - full text ed.: (from LexisNexis).
Indexed: CLI, ILP, LRI, PCI, RILM.
—BLDSC (3323.047000), IE, ingenta.
Published by: Columbia University, School of Law, Jerome Greene Hall, 435 West 116th St, New York, NY 10027. TEL 212-854-1605, FAX 212-854-2358, http://www.columbia.edu/cu/jla/current.html. Circ: 750.

▼ 700 USA
COLUMBIA SEMINAR ON ART IN SOCIETY. Text in English. 2003. a. **Document type:** *Journal, Academic/Scholarly.*
Published by: Columbia University, Department of Art History and Archaeology, Miriam and Ira D. Wallach Fine Arts Center, 826 Schermerhorn MC5517, 1190 Amsterdam Ave, New York, NY 10027. TEL 212-854-4504, FAX 212-854-7329, http://www.columbia.edu/cu/arthistory.

740 USA ISSN 1542-7447
COMIC ART. Text in English. 2002. q. USD 36; USD 9 newsstand/cover (effective 2004). **Document type:** *Magazine, Consumer.*

Address: 5715 Nottingham Ave, St.Louis, MO 63109. TEL 314-481-7255, todd@comicartmagazine.com, http://www.comicartmagazine.com/. Ed. Todd Hignite. Pub. Daniel Zimmer.

COMICS & GAMES RETAILER. see *BUSINESS AND ECONOMICS—Small Business*

741.5 USA ISSN 0194-7869
PN6700
COMICS JOURNAL; the magazine of comics news & criticism. Text in English. 1976. m. USD 72 domestic; USD 100 foreign (effective 2005). adv. bk.rev.; film rev. illus. back issues avail.
Document type: *Consumer.*
Published by: Fantagraphics Books, Inc., 7563 Lake City Way, Seattle, WA 98115. TEL 206-524-1967, 800-657-1100, FAX 206-524-2104, tcjnews@tcj.com, http://www.tcj.com/. Ed. Gary Groth. R&P Tom Spurgeon. Adv. contact Rhea Patton. page USD 200; trim 10.88 x 8.38. Circ: 12,000.

700 USA ISSN 0887-8943
COMICS VALUES MONTHLY. Text in English. 1986. m. USD 3.95 newsstand/cover.
Published by: Sunrise Publications, 15 Danbury Rd, Ridgefield, CT 06877. TEL 203-438-9652, FAX 203-438-6744.

COMITATUS; a journal of Medieval and Renaissance studies. see *LITERATURE*

741.5 DEU ISSN 0948-4523
COMIXENE. Text in German. 1974-1998; N.S. 2003. 10/yr. EUR 50 domestic; EUR 55 foreign; EUR 5 newsstand/cover (effective 2005). adv. **Document type:** *Magazine, Consumer.*
Description: Covers all aspects of comics and related industries.
Incorporates (in 2002): Hit Comics; Former titles (until 1994): Comixene Newsletter (0722-8392); (until 1982): Comixene (0174-2205)
Published by: Verlag Jurgeit, Krismann und Nobst GbR, Im Sonnengrund 10, Lehrte, 31275, Germany. TEL 49-5175-980230, FAX 49-5175-5337, redaktion@comixene.de, http://www.comixene.de. Ed., Adv. contact Martin Jurgeit. B&W page EUR 400, color page EUR 700; trim 210 x 297. Circ: 6,000 (paid).

COMPETITIONS (LOUISVILLE). see *ARCHITECTURE*

700 AUS ISSN 1322-3267
COMPETITIONS AND FINANCIAL OPPORTUNITIES FOR ARTISTS. Text in English. a. AUD 31.90 to non-members; AUD 20.90 to members (effective 2001). **Document type:** *Directory.* **Description:** Listings of art competitions, prizes, awards, scholarships, grants, fellowships, foundations and professional opportunities for visual artists.
Formerly: Creative Culture
Published by: Artworkers Alliance, Level 1, 381 Brunswick St, Fortitude Valley, QLD 4006, Australia. TEL 48-7-3250-1230, FAX 61-7-3250-1231, info@artworks.org, http://www.artworks.org. Ed. Troy Anthony Baylis. R&P Kyrin Vea Vea. Circ: (controlled).

COMPOSITE ART MANUAL. see *MEDICAL SCIENCES— Forensic Sciences*

700 SWE ISSN 1102-2043
COMPREHENSIVE SUMMARIES OF UPPSALA DISSERTATIONS FROM THE FACULTY OF ARTS. Text in English. 1991. irreg., latest vol.3, 2000. price varies. back issues avail. **Document type:** *Abstract/Index.*
Related titles: ◆ Series of: Acta Universitatis Upsaliensis. ISSN 0346-5462.
Published by: (Uppsala Universitet), Uppsala Universitet, Acta Universitatis Upsaliensis/University Publications from Uppsala, PO Box 256, Uppsala, 75105, Sweden. TEL 46-18-4713922, http://www.ub.uu.se/upu/auu. Ed. Bengt Landgren. **Dist. by:** Almqvist & Wiksell International.

700 810 USA ISSN 1048-8790
NX504
CONCEPTIONS SOUTHWEST; publicacion de literatura y arte de la Universidad de Nuevo Mexico. Text in English, Spanish. 1977. s-a. USD 5 (effective 1999). back issues avail.
Description: Fine arts magazine publishing work of the University of New Mexico staff, faculty and alumni.
Published by: University of New Mexico, Student Publications Board, PO Box 20, Albuquerque, NM 87131. TEL 505-277-7525. Circ: 700.

CONCILIUM MEDII AEVI; Zeitschrift fuer Geschichte, Kunst und Kultur des Mittelalters und der fruehen Neuzeit. see *HISTORY*

CONFERENCE ON EDITORIAL PROBLEMS: UNIVERSITY OF TORONTO. see *LITERATURE*

CONNAISSANCE DE L'EURE. see *HISTORY*

700 FRA ISSN 0293-9274
CONNAISSANCE DES ARTS. Text in French. 1952. m. adv. bk.rev. bibl.; illus.; mkt. reprints avail.
Former titles: Connaissance des Arts-Plaisir (0395-5907); Plaisir de France (0032-048X); Connaissance des Arts (0010-5988)

Indexed: A&ATA, ABM, AIAP, API, ASCA, ArtHuCI, ArtInd, BAS, BHA, CurCont, DAAI, PCI, RASB, RILM.
—BLDSC (3417.568000), IE, ingenta. **CCC.**
Published by: Societe Francaise de Promotion Artistique, 23 rue des jeuneurs, Paris, 75002, France. TEL 33-1-44885500, FAX 33-1-44885188, cda@cdesarts.com. Ed. Philip E Jodidio. R&P Martine Josse. Adv. contact Astrid Calvet. Circ: 39,758.

700 USA ISSN 1532-8872
NX456
CONNECT. Text in English. 2000. s-a. USD 35 domestic; USD 47 foreign; USD 15 newsstand/cover (effective 2002).
Indexed: DIP.
Published by: Arts International, 251 Park Ave S, 5th Fl, New York, NY 10010. aimagazine@artinternational.org, http://www.artsinternational.org.

751.6 USA ISSN 1071-0892
CC135
CONSERVATION; G C I newsletter. Text in English. 1986. 3/yr. free (effective 2004). illus.; tr.lit. 32 p./no.; back issues avail. **Document type:** *Newsletter, Trade.* **Description:** Covers the institute's activities in the conservation of objects and collections, sites and monuments, and sites and monuments. Includes scientific research, conservation education, information documentation and field projects.
Formerly (until 1990): Getty Conservation Institute Newsletter (0898-4808)
Related titles: Online - full text ed.
Indexed: AIAP, BrArAb.
—BLDSC (3417.945000).
Published by: Getty Conservation Institute, 1200 Getty Center Dr, Ste 700, Los Angeles, CA 90049-1684. TEL 310-440-7325, FAX 310-440-7702, gci@getty.edu, http://www.getty.edu/gci. Ed. Jeffrey Levin. Circ: 8,500 (free).

CONSTRUCTIVE CRITICISM; a journal of construct psychology and the arts. see *PSYCHOLOGY*

791.45 GBR ISSN 1475-9853
NX460
CONTEMPORARY. Text in English. 1995 (vol.3). m. GBP 49 to individuals; GBP 59 to institutions; GBP 5.95 newsstand/cover (effective 2005). adv. bk.rev. illus. back issues avail. **Document type:** *Consumer.* **Description:** Provides an overview of art today, covering video, film, photography, performance and installation as well as painting and sculpture. Focuses on British art but also looks at significant international developments.
Former titles (until 2001): Contemporary Visual Arts (1028-5040); (until 1997): Contemporary Art (0968-6711)
Indexed: ABM.
—IE. **CCC.**
Published by: Gordon & Breach Magazines Unlimited, Tower Bridge Business Complex, 100 Clements Rd, Ste. K101, London, SE16 4DG, United Kingdom. TEL 44-20-77401704, FAX 44-20-72523510, cva@gbhap.com, http://www.contemporary-magazine.com. Ed., Pub. Brian Muller. R&P Dawn Fulcher. Adv. contact Emily Palmer. B&W page GBP 700, color page GBP 900; trim 213 x 280. Circ: 45,000.

700 AUS ISSN 0819-677X
CONTEMPORARY ART CENTRE OF SOUTH AUSTRALIA. BROADSHEET. Text in English. 1951. q. AUD 20 domestic (effective 2003); free copies avail. on the streets and to members. adv. bk.rev.; play rev. back issues avail. **Document type:** *Newspaper, Academic/Scholarly.* **Description:** Covers contemporary art, popular culture, film and architecture.
Formerly: Contemporary Art Society of Australia. Broadsheet
Published by: Contemporary Art Centre of South Australia Inc., 14 Porter St, Parkside, SA 5063, Australia. TEL 61-8-8272-2682, FAX 61-8-8373-4286, cacsa@cacsa.org.au, http://www.cacsa.org.au/. Ed. Alan Cruickshank. Adv. contact Karen Boulton. page AUD 525; trim 38.5 x 24.9. Circ: 7,000; 200 (paid).

701.18 USA
CONTEMPORARY ART REVIEW; painting and sculpture. Text in English. 1994. m. USD 97 (effective 2001). bk.rev. abstr.; charts; illus. back issues avail.
Published by: Cromwell - Sloan Publishing Company, 63 Vine Rd, Stamford, CT 06905-2012. TEL 203-323-4810. Ed. Paul Sloan. Circ: 1,100.

002.075 USA ISSN 1066-9434
NE508
CONTEMPORARY IMPRESSIONS. Text in English. 1993. s-a. USD 50; USD 53 in Canada & Mexico; USD 58 elsewhere (effective 2000). adv. bk.rev. illus. back issues avail. **Document type:** *Academic/Scholarly.* **Description:** Contains critical writing on prints, paperworks and artists' books for artists, collectors and the educated public; includes an original print each year.
Indexed: ABM, ArtInd.
Published by: American Print Alliance, 302 Larkspur Turn, Peachtree City, GA 30269-2210. TEL 770-486-6680. Ed., R&P, Adv. contact Carol Pulin. Circ: 2,000.

760 686.2 USA ISSN 1046-9087
NE491
CONTEMPORARY PRINT PORTFOLIO; a guide to prices, new editions & sources. Text in English. 1990. a. USD 85; USD 100 foreign.
Published by: Bon a Tirer Publishing, PO Box 3480, Shawnee Mission, KS 66203. TEL 913-631-4991. Ed. Joseph E Zanatta.

CONTENUTI; trimestrale di lettere e arti. see *LITERATURE*

CONTEXT (NORMAL); a forum for literary arts and culture. see *LITERATURE*

150 GBR ISSN 0069-973X
CONTROL MAGAZINE. Text in English. 1965. a., latest no.16. GBP 9 (effective 2001). back issues avail. **Document type:** *Magazine, Academic/Scholarly.*
Indexed: ABCT.
Address: 5 London Mews, London, W2 1HY, United Kingdom. Ed. S Willats. Circ: 750.

700 800 USA
CORADDI. Text in English. 1897. bi-m. USD 4. adv. bk.rev. illus.
Published by: (University of North Carolina at Greensboro, University Media Board), Coraddi Publications, Elliott Center, Rm 205, Greensboro, NC 27412. TEL 919-379-5572. Ed. Elizabeth House. Circ: 4,000.

700 CAN
CORETEXT. Text in English. 1995. q.
Formerly: CyberStage Online (1201-2564)
Media: Online - full text.
Published by: CyberStage Publications, P.O. Box 652, Don Mills, ON M3C 2T6, Canada. editor@cyberstage.org, http://www.coretext.net. Ed. Mark J Jones.

700 IRL ISSN 0332-2580
CORK REVIEW. Text in English. 1979. a. adv. bk.rev. illus. **Document type:** *Consumer.*
Published by: Triskel Arts Centre, Tobin St., Cork, Ireland. TEL 353-21-4272022, FAX 353-21-4272592, info@triskelartscentre.com, http://www.triskelart.com/. Ed. Thomas McCarthy. Adv. contact Michelle Whelan. Circ: 2,000.

700 DNK ISSN 0107-9794
N7018.5.C6
CORNER. Text in Danish. 1986. a. DKK 30.
Address: Tofte Baeksvej 2, Lyngby, 2800, Denmark. Ed. Uffe Thorlacius.

700 800 USA
CORNER (OAKLAND); an electronic journal dedicated to the avant-grade. Text in English. s-a. **Document type:** *Academic/Scholarly.* **Description:** Dedicated to theoretical and interdisciplinary materials on art and literature.
Media: Online - full text.
Published by: Mills College, 5000 MacArthur Blvd, Oakland, CA 94613. TEL 510-430-3314, FAX 510-430-2356, amach@mills.edu, http://www.cornermag.org/. Ed. Carlota Caulfield.

CORNFIELD REVIEW; an annual of the creative arts. see *LITERATURE*

741.6 USA ISSN 0890-7609
CORPORATE ANNUAL REPORT NEWSLETTER. Abbreviated title: C A R N. Text in English. 1986. m. USD 329. **Document type:** *Newsletter.* **Description:** Designed to aid those responsible for creating, designing and editing their company's annual report.
Published by: Lawrence Ragan Communications, Inc., 316 N Michigan Ave, Ste 300, Chicago, IL 60601. TEL 312-960-4100, 800-878-5331, FAX 312-960-4106, http://www.ragan.com. Ed. Bob Ghelardi. Circ: 500.

750 FRA
CORPUS DE LA PEINTURE DES ANCIENS PAYS-BAS MERIDIONAUX ET DE LA PRINCIPAUTE DE LIEGE AU QUINZIEME SIECLE. Text in French; Text occasionally in English. 1951. irreg., latest 2001. price varies.
Formerly (until 1995): Les Primitifs Flamands. I, Corpus de la Peinture des Anciens Pays-Bas Meridionaux au Quinzieme Siecle (0555-1269)
Published by: Editions de la Reunion des Musees Nationaux, 49, rue Etienne Marcel, Paris, 75039 Cedex 01, France. TEL 33-1-40134966, FAX 33-1-40134973, http://www.rmn.fr.

730 ITA ISSN 0528-5658
CORPUS DELLA SCULTURA ALTOMEDIEVALE. Text in Italian. 1959. irreg., latest vol.16, 1999. price varies. **Document type:** *Monographic series.*
Indexed: PCI.
Published by: Centro Italiano di Studi sull'Alto Medioevo, Palazzo Ancaiani, Piazza della Liberta 12, Spoleto, PG 06049, Italy. FAX 39-07-43232701, cisam@cisam.org, http://www.cisam.org.

091 BEL
➤ **CORPUS OF THE ILLUMINATED MANUSCRIPTS.** Text in English. 1985. irreg., latest vol.9, 1996. price varies. back issues avail. **Document type:** *Monographic series, Academic/Scholarly.* **Description:** Examines the art of illuminated manuscripts from Belgium and the Netherlands.
Published by: (Katholieke Universiteit Leuven), Peeters Publishers, Bondgenotenlaan 153, Leuven, 3000, Belgium. TEL 32-16-235170, FAX 32-16-228500, http://www.peeters-leuven.be.

➤ **CORPUS VASORUM ANTIQUORUM. ITALIA.** see *CLASSICAL STUDIES*

700 FRA ISSN 1639-4348
CORPUS VITREARUM. Variant title: Corpus Vitrearum. France, Etudes. Text in French. 1976. biennial. price varies. adv. bk.rev. index. **Document type:** *Monographic series, Academic/Scholarly.*
Published by: C N R S Editions, 15 Rue Malebranche, Paris, 75005, France. TEL 33-1-53102700, FAX 33-1-53102727, http://www.cnrseditions.fr. Circ: 1,500 (controlled).

700 943 DEU ISSN 0232-1459
CORPUS VITREARUM MEDII AEVI. Text in German. 1976. irreg. **Document type:** *Monographic series, Academic/Scholarly.*
Published by: Akademie Verlag GmbH (Subsidiary of: Oldenbourg Wissenschaftsverlag GmbH), Palisadenstr 40, Berlin, 10243, Germany. TEL 49-30-4220060, FAX 49-30-42200657, info@akademie-verlag.de, http://www.akademie-verlag.de.

CORRIERE DEL MEZZOGIORNO. see *POLITICAL SCIENCE*

700 913 ITA
CORSI INTERNAZIONALI DI CULTURA SULL'ARTE RAVENNATE E BIZANTINA. ATTI. Text in English, French, German, Italian. 1953. irreg., latest vol.43, 1997. price varies. **Document type:** *Yearbook, Academic/Scholarly.* **Description:** Studies on Byzantine culture, art and history.
Indexed: AIAP, BHA.
Published by: (Universita degli Studi di Bologna), Angelo Longo Editore, Via Paolo Costa 33, Ravenna, 48100, Italy. TEL 39-0544-217026, FAX 39-0544-217554, longo-ra@linknet.it, http://www.longo-editore.it. Ed., Pub. Alfio Longo. R&P Marina De Leonardis. Circ: 1,500.

700 CHE
COSMOPOLIS. Text in German, English. 1999.
Media: Online - full text.
Address: Wallruetistr 59, Winterthur, CH-8404, Switzerland. feedback@cosmopolis.ch, http://www.cosmopolis.ch/. Ed. Louis Gerber.

COURTAULD INSTITUTE OF ART. COURTAULD RESEARCH PAPERS. see *MUSEUMS AND ART GALLERIES*

700 HRV ISSN 0011-0728
COVJEK I PROSTOR. Text in Croatian. 1954. m. HRK 292.80 domestic; EUR 50 foreign (effective 2004). adv. bk.rev. abstr. 64 p./no. 2 cols./p.; back issues avail. **Document type:** *Magazine, Academic/Scholarly.* **Description:** Specializes in architectural issues and contemporary arts design.
Indexed: BHA, EIP, RASB.
Published by: Udruzenje Hrvatskih Arhitekata, Trg Bana Jelacica 3-1, Zagreb, 10000, Croatia. TEL 385-1-4816151, FAX 385-1-4816197, covjekiprostor@2amir.net, daz@zg.hinet.hr, http://www.d-a-z.hr. Ed. Zdravko Krasic. Adv. contact Maja Trinajstic. Circ: 2,500.

CRAFT ARTS INTERNATIONAL. see *ARTS AND HANDICRAFTS*

700 AUS
CRAFT CULTURE. Text in English. m. **Document type:** *Academic/Scholarly.*
Media: Online - full content.
Published by: Craft Victoria, 31 Flinders Ln, Melbourne, VIC 3000, Australia. TEL 61-3-96507775, FAX 61-3-96505688, crafvic@craftvic.asn.au, http://www.craftculture.org/, http://www.craftvic.asn.au/.

760 659 USA
CRAP HOUND. Text in English. 1994. irreg., latest vol.4. USD 5 per issue. illus. **Description:** Adult zine that includes graphics from advertising of the 1930s to 1950s positioned so as to give them new meaning.
Address: PO Box 40373, Portland, OR 97240-0373. Ed. Sean Tejaratchi.

700 FRA ISSN 0293-0196
CREATIONS. Text in French. 1959. q. illus. Supplement avail. **Description:** Aims at developing art and creativity in children.
Formerly: Art Enfantin (0004-3133)
Published by: Publications de l'Ecole Moderne Francaise - Pedagogie Freinet, Mouans-Sartoux, Cedex 06376, France. TEL 33-4-92921757. Ed. Robert Poitrenaud.

THE CREATIVE HANDBOOK. see *ARTS AND HANDICRAFTS*

700 DEU ISSN 1437-1359
CREATIVE JOURNAL; do it yourself. Text in German. m. back issues avail.
Media: Online - full text.
Address: Uhlandstr 8, Hiddenhausen, 32120, Germany. TEL 49-5523-820582, FAX 49-5523-820584, ws@art-joe.com, http://art-quarter.com/journals.html#cj. Ed. Werner Stuerenburg.

CREATIVE SOURCE AUSTRALIA; the wizards of Oz. see *ARTS AND HANDICRAFTS*

CREATIVE WOMAN. see *WOMEN'S INTERESTS*

CREATIVITY (GLENBROOK). see *ADVERTISING AND PUBLIC RELATIONS*

CRESCENDO (INTERLOCHEN). see *EDUCATION*

701.18 ITA ISSN 0011-1511
N4
CRITICA D'ARTE. Text in Italian. 1935; N.S. 1954-1989 (Apr.); resumed 1990. q. EUR 93 domestic; EUR 130 foreign (effective 2005). adv. bk.rev. abstr.; bibl.; illus. index.
Document type: *Journal, Academic/Scholarly.*
Indexed: ABM, AIAP, ArtHuCI, BHA, CurCont, RASB, RILM.
Published by: Casa Editrice le Lettere, Costa San Giorgio 28, Florence, FI 50125, Italy. TEL 39-055-2342710, FAX 39-055-2346010, staff@lelettere.it, www.lelettere.it.

CRITICAL CERAMICS. see *CERAMICS, GLASS AND POTTERY*

700 USA ISSN 1057-0993
CRITICAL RESPONSES IN ARTS AND LETTERS. Text in English. 1991. irreg. price varies. **Document type:** *Monographic series, Academic/Scholarly.*
Indexed: MLA-IB.
Published by: Greenwood Publishing Group Inc. (Subsidiary of: Harcourt International), 88 Post Rd W, PO Box 5007, Westport, CT 06881. TEL 203-226-3571, 800-225-5800, FAX 603-431-2214, http://www.greenwood.com.

701.1 USA
CRITICAL REVIEW. Text in English. 1996. irreg. back issues avail. **Description:** Reviews current art exhibitions in the United States and provides a forum for a dialogue about art.
Media: Online - full text.
Address: jgrimm@creview.com, alissa@creview, http://www.creview.com/. Eds. Alissa Schoenfeld, Jay Grimm.

CRONACHE DI ARCHEOLOGIA. see *ARCHAEOLOGY*

CROSSCURRENTS. see *MUSIC*

700 600 IRL ISSN 1649-0460
N72.T4
► **CROSSINGS (DUBLIN)**; electronic journal of art and technology. Text in English. 2001. s-a. free (effective 2005). back issues avail. **Document type:** *Journal, Academic/Scholarly.* **Description:** Aims to explore the areas where technology and art intersect.
Media: Online - full content.
Published by: Trinity College, College Green, Dublin, 2, Ireland. TEL 353-1-608-1000, crossings@tcd.ie, http://crossings.tcd.ie, http://www.tcd.ie. Ed. Mads Haahr.

700 800 USA ISSN 1536-5298
PS325
CROWD MAGAZINE. Text in English. 2001. s-a. USD 20; USD 12 newsstand/cover (effective 2004). **Document type:** *Magazine, Consumer.*
Address: 487 Union St. 3rd Fl, Brooklyn, NY 11231. aimee@crowdmagazine.com, lily@crowdmagazine.com, http://www.crowdmagazine.com/, http://www.crowdmagazine.com/c. Eds. Aimee Kelly, Lily Sant. Pub. Aimee Kelly.

700 384 BGR
CTRL_Z MAGAZINE. Text in Bulgarian. 1999. irreg. **Description:** Aims at providing opportunities for furthering expression beyond the established practices of official and private mass media. Provides the young generation with an alternative pattern of communicating their artistic concerns and expression and stimulates them to encourage similar practices.
Media: Online - full content.
Published by: Ctrl_Z Solutions, 51 Velcho Atanasov St, Ap 16, Sofia, 1505, Bulgaria. TEL 359-2-715084, 359-2-569582, FAX 359-2-9743458, ctrl_z_magazine@yahoo.com, http://www.sca.bg/cultural-periodicals/catalog/zmag.htm, http://www.freespeech.org/ctrl_z/magazine. Eds. Boriana Dragoeva, Vencislav Zankov.

700 ESP ISSN 0214-2821
N7101
CUADERNOS DE ARTE E ICONOGRAFIA. Text in Spanish. 1988. s-a. back issues avail.
Related titles: Online - full text ed.
Indexed: PCI, RILM.
—CINDOC.

Published by: Fundacion Universitaria Espanola, Alcala, 93, Madrid, 28009, Spain. FAX 34-91-5767352, fue2@nova.es, http://www.nova.es/fue/cai.htm, http://www.nova.es/fue/fue.htm. Ed. Jose Manuel Pita Andrade.

700 ARG ISSN 0070-1688
CUADERNOS DE HISTORIA DEL ARTE. Text in Spanish. 1961-1977; resumed 1988. irreg.. latest vol.16, 1997. USD 10 (effective 1999). bk.rev. **Document type:** *Monographic series, Academic/Scholarly.* **Description:** Covers general art and Argentine art, particularly from Mendoza.
Related titles: CD-ROM ed.
Published by: (Instituto de Historia del Arte), Universidad Nacional de Cuyo, Facultad de Filosofia y Letras, Centro Universitario, Parque General San Martin, Mendoza 5500, Argentina. TEL 54-61-230915, FAX 54-61-380457.

709 MEX ISSN 0185-1691
CUADERNOS DE HISTORIA DEL ARTE. Text in Spanish. 1973. irreg., latest 1990. price varies.
Published by: Universidad Nacional Autonoma de Mexico, Instituto de Investigaciones Esteticas, Circuito Mario de la Cueva, Zona Cultural, Ciudad Universitaria, Mexico, DF 04510, Mexico. TEL 52-55-56652465, FAX 52-55-56654740, ereinoso@servidor.unam.mx.

700 ESP ISSN 1138-1299
CUADERNOS DE RESTAURACION. Text in Spanish. 1997. s-a.
—CINDOC.
Published by: Colegio Oficial de Doctores y Licenciados en Bellas Artes de Andalucia, C Teodosio 5 Bajos A y B, Sevilla, 41002, Spain. colbaa@teleline.es.

700 ESP ISSN 0210-3974
CUADERNOS GUADALIMAR. Text in Spanish. 1977. a.
—CINDOC.
Published by: Editorial Guadalimar, Villanueva, 32, Madrid, 28001, Spain.

700 PRI
EL CUARTO DEL QUENEPON. Text in Spanish. 1995. bi-m.
Media: Online - full content.
Published by: El Cuarto del Quenepon, PMB 205, #667 Ponce de Leon, San Juan, 00907, Puerto Rico. quenepas@caribe.net, http://cuarto.quenepon.org, http://cuarto.quenepon.org/. Eds. Marma O'Neill, Rosa Irigoyen.

CUBA INTERNACIONAL. see *POLITICAL SCIENCE— International Relations*

CUENTOS EN ESPANOL/SHORT STORIES IN SPANISH. see *LINGUISTICS*

700 GBR ISSN 0954-8963
NX543
► **CULTURAL TRENDS.** Text in English. q. GBP 224, USD 353 combined subscription to institutions print & online eds. (effective 2006). reprint service avail. from PSC. **Document type:** *Journal, Academic/Scholarly.* **Description:** Presents independent research on essential statistics about the arts and cultural industries in the U.K.
Related titles: Online - full text ed.: ISSN 1469-3690. GBP 213, USD 335 to institutions (effective 2006) (from EBSCO Publishing, Gale Group, IngentaConnect, O C L C Online Computer Library Center, Inc., Swets Information Services).
Indexed: ABM, SociolAb.
—BLDSC (3491.668463), IE, Infotrieve, ingenta. CCC.
Published by: (Policy Studies Institute), Routledge (Subsidiary of: Taylor & Francis Group), 4 Park Sq, Milton Park, Abingdon, Oxon OX14 4RN, United Kingdom. TEL 44-1235-828600, FAX 44-1235-829000, journals@routledge.com, http://www.tandf.co.uk/journals/titles/09548963.asp, http://www.routledge.com. Ed. Sara Selwood.

700 780 GBR ISSN 1368-6348
CULTURAL TRENDS IN SCOTLAND. Text in English. 1992. a.
Document type: *Directory.*
Published by: Policy Studies Institute, 100 Park Village E., London, NW1 3SR, United Kingdom. TEL 44-20-7468-0468, FAX 44-20-7388-0914. **Dist. by:** BEBC Distribution Ltd., B E B C Distribution Ltd, PO Box 1496, Poole, Dorset BH12 3YD, United Kingdom. **Co-sponsor:** Scottish Arts Council.

CULTUREVULTURE.NET; choices for the cognoscenti. see *MOTION PICTURES*

700 USA ISSN 1541-938X
CULTUREWORK. Text in English. 1997. q. (3-4/yr.).
Media: Online - full content.
Indexed: MLA-IB.
Published by: University of Oregon, Institute for Community Arts Studies, Arts & Administration Program, School of Architecture and Allied Arts, Eugene, OR 97403. TEL 541-346-3639, http://aad.uoregon.edu/culturework, http://aad.uoregon.edu/icas. Ed. Richard Bear.

D B 3 BILLEDKUNST. see *EDUCATION—Teaching Methods And Curriculum*

D B C C PHOTOGRAPHIC SOCIETY. NEWSLETTER. see *PHOTOGRAPHY*

745.2 ITA ISSN 1594-8528
D I I D. DISEGNO INDUSTRIALE INDUSTRIAL DESIGN. Text in Multiple languages. 2002. q. EUR 40 domestic (effective 2004). **Document type:** *Magazine, Trade.*
Published by: Gangemi Editore, Piazza San Pantaleo 4, Rome, Italy. TEL 39-06-6872774, FAX 39-06-68806189, gangemieditorerc@tin.it, http://www.gangemieditore.it.

700 TWN
DABIEN. Text in Chinese. 1993 (Feb.). irreg. (approx. 1-2/month).
Document type: *Magazine, Consumer.* **Description:** Contains digital art, comics, prints, photographs and other art medias of various subjects and styles.
Media: Online - full content.
Address: dabien@r703a.chem.nthu.edu.tw, http://r703a.chem.nthu.edu.tw/~dabien/.

DADA - SURREALISM. see *LITERATURE*

DANDELION. see *LITERATURE—Poetry*

DANDELION ARTS MAGAZINE. see *LITERATURE—Poetry*

DANGDAI WENYI TANSUO/CONTEMPORARY LITERATURE AND ART STUDY. see *LITERATURE*

DANSK DESIGNTIDENDE. see *PATENTS, TRADEMARKS AND COPYRIGHTS*

DARK REALMS; exploring the shadows of art, music and culture. see *LITERATURE—Science Fiction, Fantasy, Horror*

DARMSTAEDTER KULTURNACHRICHTEN. see *MUSIC*

700 ITA ISSN 0011-6726
N4
D'ARS; periodico d'arte contemporanea. Text in Italian. 1960. q. EUR 46.50 domestic; EUR 54.50 in Europe; USD 100 in the Americas (effective 2004). adv. bk.rev. **Document type:** *Magazine, Consumer.*
Formerly (until 1967): D'Ars Agency (1125-2340)
Indexed: ABM, BHA.
Published by: Fondazione D'Ars Oscar Signorini Onlus, Via Giardino Aristide Calderini 3, Milan, MI 20123, Italy. TEL 39-02-860290, FAX 39-02-865909, http://www.dars.it. Ed. Pierre Restany. Circ: 5,000.

700 IND ISSN 0045-9658
DARSHAK; a Bengali fortnightly on art news & views. Text in Bengali. 1960. fortn. INR 10, USD 2. adv. bk.rev. illus.
Published by: Nabya Bangla Natya Parishad, 9-3 Tamar Lane, Kolkata, West Bengal 700 009, India. Eds. Deb Kumar Basu, Rabi Mitra. Circ: 2,000.

700 JPN
DARUMA MAGAZINE. Text in English. 1994. 4/yr. (published in Mar., Jun., Sep. and Dec.). JPY 4,000; JPY 75,000 for 2 yrs.; USD 40; USD 75 for 2 yrs.; GBP 20; GBP 38 for 2 yrs.; EUR 28; EUR 53 for 2 yrs.; AUD 50; AUD 95 for 2 yrs.; CND 50; CND 95 for 2 yrs. (effective 2001). back issues avail.
Document type: *Magazine, Consumer.* **Description:** Covers Japanese art and antiques, includes originally articles.
Indexed: BAS.
Published by: Daruma Publishing, c/o Takeguchi Momoko, Mukonoso Higashi 1-12-5, Amagasaki, 661-0032, Japan. TEL 81-6-6436-5874, FAX 81-6-6438-1882, momoko@gao.ne.jp, http://www.darumamagazine.com/.

DAYLIGHT. see *PHOTOGRAPHY*

700 069 USA ISSN 1523-2522
DAYTON ART INSTITUTE. MEMBER QUARTERLY. Text in English. 1997. q. free to members (effective 2005). illus.
Document type: *Magazine, Consumer.* **Description:** Provides art exhibition information, educational programming information, museum special events and full-color art work reproductions.
Published by: Dayton Art Institute, 456 Belmonte Park N, Dayton, OH 45405-4700. TEL 937-223-5277, FAX 937-223-3140, info@daytonartinstitute.org, http://www.daytonartinstitute.org. Pub. Susan Dyer. Circ: 1,000 (paid); 9,000 (controlled).

700 800 CHN
DAZHONG WENYI. Text in Chinese. m. CNY 2.88 newsstand/cover. adv.
Published by: Hebei Sheng Qunzhong Yishu-guan, 10 Hongguang Jie, Xinhua Xilu, Shijiazhuang, Hebei 050081, China. TEL 86-311-3034491. Ed. Tian Zhongxin. Circ: 20,000.

700 GBR
DE-, DIS-, EX-. Text in English. 1996. a. GBP 13.95; USD 19.95 in United States (effective 2001). illus. 208 p./no.; back issues avail. **Document type:** *Journal, Academic/Scholarly.*
Description: Discusses art, architecture, and cultural theory. For a general audience as well as an academic audience.

▼ *new title* ➤ *refereed* ✱ *unverified* ◆ *full entry avail.*

Published by: Black Dog Publishing Ltd., 5 Ravenscroft St., London, E2 7JH, United Kingdom. TEL 44-20-7613-1922, FAX 44 20-7613-1944, info@bdp.demon.co.uk. Ed. Alex Coles. Pub. Duncan McCorquodale.

DEADBEAT MAGAZINE. see *LIFESTYLE*

DECISION; Zeitschrift fuer deutsche und franzoesische Literatur. see *LITERATURE*

DECORATIVE ARTS SOCIETY, 1850 TO THE PRESENT. JOURNAL. see *ARTS AND HANDICRAFTS*

745 USA ISSN 0884-4011
DECORATIVE ARTS SOCIETY NEWSLETTER. Text in English. 1975. 3/yr. USD 25 to individuals; USD 30 to institutions; USD 15 to students (effective 2000). bk.rev. **Document type:** *Newsletter.* **Description:** Provides a forum for those interested in European and American decorative arts of all periods.
Formerly (until 1978): Decorative Arts Newsletter (0740-5634)
Indexed: AIAP, BHA, DAAI.
Published by: Decorative Arts Society, c/o Cooper Hewitt National Design Museum, 2 E 91st St, New York, NY 10128. Eds. Gerald W R Ward, Maria Conelli. R&P Janna Eggebeen TEL 212-849-8346.

DEDISENO; diseno, arquitectura, arte. see *PRINTING*

700 USA
DEEPTAPIOCA; showcasing the creative mind. Text in English. 2002. m. USD 24 (effective 2002). adv. **Document type:** *Magazine, Consumer.* **Description:** Displays the art of local artists, writers and chefs with an entertainment guide to help showcase local events.
Related titles: Online - full text ed.
Published by: Deeptapioca Media Group, 31 N. 2nd St., Ste. 320, San Jose, CA 95113. TEL 408-293-1679, FAX 408-209-4681, info@deeptapioca.com, http://www.deeptapioca.com. Ed. Clarissa Mendiola. Pub., R&P David Brissenden. Adv. contact Joshua Mangan. Circ: 50,000 (paid and free).

700 DEU ISSN 0342-1732
DEIKE-PRESS; international clip art service. Text in German. 1923. 6/yr. **Document type:** *Consumer.*
Published by: Verlag Horst Deike KG, Postfach 100452, Konstanz, 78404, Germany. TEL 07531-8155-0, FAX 07531-815581. Ed. Wolfgang Deike. Circ: 1,500.

700 RUS
DEKORATIVNOE ISKUSSTVO - DIALOG ISTORII I KULTURY. Text in Russian; Summaries in English. 1957. s-a. price varies. adv. illus. index. **Document type:** *Academic/Scholarly.* **Description:** Deals with the history and theory of fine arts, includes articles on painting and sculpture.
Formed by the 1994 merger of: Dialog Istorii i Kultury; Dekorativnoe Iskusstvo (0869-4494); Which was formerly (until 1991): Dekorativnoe Iskusstvo S S S R (0130-3031)
Indexed: ABM, BHA, IBSS, RASB.
Published by: Izdatel'stvo D I - D I K, Tverskaya ul 9, pod 6, etazh 9, Moscow, 103009, Russian Federation. TEL 7-095-2291910. Ed. Aider Kurkchi. Circ: 3,000. **Dist. by:** M K - Periodica, ul Gilyarovskogo 39, Moscow 129110, Russian Federation. TEL 7-095-2845008, FAX 7-095-2813798, info@periodicals.ru, http://www.mkniga.ru; **US dist. addr.:** East View Information Services, 3020 Harbor Ln. N., Minneapolis, MN 55447. TEL 612-550-0961.

DEMOKRATICHESKI PREGLED. see *POLITICAL SCIENCE*

686.3 095 DEU ISSN 0341-2474
CODEN: GTMAER
DENKMAELER DER BUCHKUNST. Text in German. 1976. irreg., latest vol.13, 1997. price varies. **Document type:** *Monographic series, Academic/Scholarly.*
Published by: Anton Hiersemann Verlag, Haldenstr 30, Stuttgart, 70376, Germany. TEL 49-711-549971-0, FAX 49-711-54997121, info@hiersemann.de, http://www.hiersemann.de.

709 DEU ISSN 0947-031X
N3
DIE DENKMALPFLEGE. Text in German. 1934. s-a. adv. bk.rev. bibl. index. **Document type:** *Bulletin, Academic/Scholarly.*
Formerly (until 1994): Deutsche Kunst und Denkmalpflege (0012-0375)
Indexed: A&ATA, AIAP, API, ASCA, ArtHuCI, BHA, CurCont, DIP, IBR, IBZ, RASB, RILM.
—IDS. **CCC.**
Published by: (Vereinigung der Landesdenkmalpfleger in der Bundesrepublik Deutschland), Deutscher Kunstverlag GmbH, Nymphenburger Str 84, Munich, 80636, Germany. TEL 49-89-1269900, FAX 49-89-12151644, info@deutscherkunstverlag.de, http://www.kunstbuecher-online.de. Ed. J Habich. Circ: 1,800.

751.6 DEU ISSN 0342-0027
DENKMALPFLEGE IN BADEN-WUERTTEMBERG. Text in German. 1972. q. free. bk.rev. illus. **Document type:** *Bulletin, Academic/Scholarly.*
Indexed: A&ATA, BHA, DIP, IBR, IBZ.
Published by: Landesdenkmalamt Baden-Wuerttemberg, Berliner Str 12, Esslingen am Neckar, 73712, Germany. TEL 49-711-664630, FAX 49-711-66463444, http://www.landesdenkmalamt-bw.de/nachrichtenblatt.html. Circ: 20,000.

751.6 DEU
DENKMALPFLEGE IN SACHSEN-ANHALT. Text in German. 1993. s-a. **Document type:** *Bulletin.*
Indexed: BHA, IBZ.
Published by: (Sachsen-Anhalt. Landesamt fuer Denkmalpflege Sachsen-Anhalt), Verlag fuer Bauwesen, Am Friedrichshain 22, Berlin, 10407, Germany. TEL 49-30-42151-0, FAX 49-30-42151468. Circ: 1,000 (controlled).

354.489 700 DNK ISSN 0107-2951
NX28.D42
DENMARK. STATENS KUNSTFOND. BERETNING. Text in Danish. 1959. a. free. back issues avail.
Related titles: Online - full text ed.
Published by: Statens Kunstfond/Danish Arts Foundation, Kongens Nytorv 3, Copenhagen K, 1050, Denmark. TEL 45-33-744500, FAX 45-33-744545, skf@statenskunstfond.dk, http://www.kunststyrelsen.dk/69000c, http://www.statenskunstfond.dk. Ed. Vibeke Jakobsen.

DEPAUL JOURNAL OF ART & ENTERTAINMENT LAW. see *LAW*

DESIGN AND ARCHITECTURE. see *INTERIOR DESIGN AND DECORATION*

DESIGN + ART IN GREECE/THEMATA CHOROU + TECHNON. see *ARCHITECTURE*

745 800.9268 BRA ISSN 1413-9456
DESIGN GRAFICO. Text in Portuguese. m. adv.
Published by: Market Press Editora Ltda, Rua Hugo Carotini 445, Parque Previdencia, Sao Paulo, 05532-020, Brazil. TEL 55-11-37211950, designgrafico@marketpress.com.br, http://www.uol.com.br/designgrafico/, http://www.marketpress.com.br. Adv. contact Ana Lucia Borella Guido. page BRL 11,500; 20.5 x 27.5. Circ: 25,000.

745.4 ZAF
DESIGN INDABA MAGAZINE. Text in English. 2000. q. ZAR 160 (effective 2005). adv. **Document type:** *Magazine, Trade.* **Description:** Covers design issues across all disciplines, from graphic design to architectural design and everything in between.
Related titles: Online - full text ed.
Published by: Interactive Africa, PO Box 7735, Roggebaai, 8012, South Africa. TEL 27-21-418-6666, FAX 27-21-418-6333, http://www.designindabamag.com, http://www.interactive.africa.com. Ed. Andi Norton. Pub. Ravi Naidoo. Adv. contact Dale Cupido. color page ZAR 11,000. Circ: 2,500 (paid and controlled).

745.4 900 801.95 USA ISSN 0747-9360
➤ **DESIGN ISSUES**; history/theory/criticism. Text in English. 1984. 3/yr. USD 48 combined subscription in US & Canada to individuals print & online eds.; USD 68 combined subscription elsewhere to institutions print & online eds.; USD 182 combined subscription in US & Canada to institutions print & online eds.; USD 202 combined subscription elsewhere to institutions print & online eds. (effective 2006). adv. bk.rev. illus. Index. back issues avail.; reprint service avail. from PQC. **Document type:** *Journal, Academic/Scholarly.* **Description:** Presents a scholarly forum for the history, theory, and criticism of design. Provokes inquiry into the cultural and intellectual role of non-architectural fields, from graphic design to industrial design.
Related titles: Microfilm ed.: (from PQC); Online - full text ed.: ISSN 1531-4790. USD 43 to individuals; USD 153 to institutions (effective 2005) (from EBSCO Publishing, Gale Group, H.W. Wilson, IngentaConnect, O C L C Online Computer Library Center, Inc., Swets Information Services).
Indexed: ABM, AIAP, ASCA, ArtHuCI, ArtInd, BHA, CurCont, DAAI, DIP, IBR, IBZ.
—BLDSC (3559.976000), IDS, IE, Infotrieve, ingenta. **CCC.**
Published by: M I T Press, 55 Hayward St, Cambridge, MA 02142-1493. TEL 617-253-5646, FAX 617-258-6779, dsc6@andrew.cmu.edu, journals-info@mit.edu, http://mitpress.mit.edu/di. R&P Christina Ellis. adv.: page USD 300; 5.5 x 8.5. Circ: 1,400.

700 JPN ISSN 0914-1103
DESIGN SCENE. Text in English. 1984. s-a. (2-3/yr.).
Indexed: ABM, DAAI.
—BLDSC (3560.185500).
Published by: Kokusai Dezain Koryu Kyokai/Japan Design Foundation, 3-1-800, Umeda1-Chome, Kitaku, Osaka 530-0001, Japan. TEL 81-6-6346-2611, FAX 81-6-6346-2615, info@jdf.or.jp, http://www.jdf.or.jp/jdf_old/book/design/top_dse.html.

700 GBR ISSN 0950-3676
DESIGN WEEK. Text in English. 1986. w. GBP 65 domestic; GBP 108 in Europe; GBP 125 elsewhere; GBP 1.80 newsstand/cover. adv. bk.rev. Supplement avail. **Document type:** *Trade.* **Description:** Dedicated to design, news, and features about the industry worldwide.
Related titles: Microform ed.: (from PQC); Online - full text ed.: (from Northern Light Technology, Inc.); (from EBSCO Publishing, Gale Group, H.W. Wilson, LexisNexis, O C L C Online Computer Library Center, Inc., ProQuest Information & Learning).
Indexed: ABM, BPI, DAAI.
—BLDSC (3560.215000).
Published by: Centaur Publishing, St Giles House, 50 Poland St, London, W1V 4AX, United Kingdom. TEL 44—20-7970-4000, FAX 44-20-7970-4009. Ed. Lynda Relph-Knight. Pub. Morag Arman-Addey. Adv. contact Jessica MacDermott. Circ: 10,406.

700 GBR
DESIGN WEEK ACTION PACK. Text in English. q. free with subscr. to Design Week. adv. back issues avail. **Document type:** *Trade.* **Description:** Aimed at designers, graphic artists, and home-design consultants.
Published by: Centaur Publishing, St Giles House, 50 Poland St, London, W1V 4AX, United Kingdom. TEL 44-20-7439-4222, FAX 44-20-7734-1770. Ed. Lynda Relph Knight. Pub. Roger Beckett. Adv. contact Jessica MacDermott. Circ: 8,500.

702.8 DEU ISSN 0947-899X
DESIGNERS DIGEST; Magazin fuer Gestaltung und Technik. Text in German. 1986. bi-m. EUR 11 newsstand/cover (effective 2004). adv. bk.rev. index. back issues avail.; reprints avail. **Document type:** *Magazine, Trade.*
Incorporates (1948-1992): Photo Design und Technik (0930-2417); Which superseded in part (in 1986): Graphik Visuelles Marketing (0177-6584); Which was formerly (until 1982): Graphik (0341-1745)
Published by: C Q Communication GmbH, Im Haesen 9, Sittensen, 27419, Germany. TEL 49-4282-592023. Ed. Klaus Tiedge. Adv. contact Gabriele Henschel. B&W page EUR 3,200, color page EUR 5,400. Circ: 25,000.

700 USA
DESTROY ALL COMIC BOOKS∗ . Text in English. 6/yr. USD 9. **Document type:** *Newsletter.* **Description:** Information on the alternative comics scene.
Address: 11930 S.W. 70th Ave., Tigard, OR 97223-8565. Ed. Jeff Levine.

701.17 GBR
DETOURS AND DELAYS; an occasional journal of aestetics and politics. Text in English. 199?. irreg. **Document type:** *Academic/Scholarly.* **Description:** Publishes articles on aesthetics and art.
Media: Online - full text.
Published by: (School of Art and Design), University of Derby, Kedleton Rd, Derby, DE22 1GB, United Kingdom. TEL 44-1332-622222, FAX 44-1332-294861, detours@art.derby.ac.uk, http://art.derby.ac.uk/~detours/detours.html. Ed. Stanley Mitchell.

700 USA
DETROIT FOCUS QUARTERLY; a visual arts publication. Text in English. 1978. q. USD 50; USD 20 membership (effective 2005). adv. bk.rev. **Document type:** *Newsletter.*
Published by: Detroit Focus Gallery, PO Box 843, Royal Oak, MI 48068-0843. TEL 248-541-3527, FAX 248-541-3403, http://www.detroitfocus.org. Adv. contact Jerome Magid. Circ: 3,000.

700 USA ISSN 0011-9636
N560
➤ **DETROIT INSTITUTE OF ARTS. BULLETIN.** Text in English. 1919. 2/yr. USD 20 domestic; USD 24 foreign; USD 12 newsstand/cover (effective 2005). illus. 64 p./no.; back issues avail.; reprint service avail. from PQC. **Document type:** *Bulletin, Academic/Scholarly.* **Description:** Devoted to the study of objects in the Museum's permanent collection.
Related titles: Microfiche ed.; Microfilm ed.
Indexed: AIAP, ArtInd, BHA, DIP, IBR, IBZ, NumL.
Published by: Detroit Institute of Arts, 5200 Woodward Ave, Detroit, MI 48202. TEL 313-833-1368, 313-833-7900, FAX 313-833-6409, mhoptman@dia.org, http://www.dia.org. Ed., R&P Maya Hoptman. Circ: 5,000 (paid).

700 DEU ISSN 0012-0693
DIE DEUTSCHE SCHRIFT; Zeitschrift zur Foerderung von Gotisch, Schwabacher und Fraktur. Text in German. 1918. 4/yr. EUR 24; EUR 6 newsstand/cover (effective 2005). adv. bk.rev. illus. **Document type:** *Journal, Academic/Scholarly.*
Published by: Bund fuer Deutsche Schrift und Sprache, Postfach 1145, Seesen, 38711, Germany. TEL 49-5381-46355, FAX 49-5381-46355, verwaltung@bfds.de, http://www.bfds.de. Ed. Wolfgang Hendlmeier. Circ: 2,000.

700 DEU ISSN 0044-2135
N3
DEUTSCHER VEREIN FUER KUNSTWISSENSCHAFT. ZEITSCHRIFT. Text in German. 1934. irreg., latest vol.59, 2005. price varies. illus. back issues avail.; reprints avail. **Document type:** *Journal, Academic/Scholarly.*
Formerly (until 1963): Zeitschrift fuer Kunstwissenschaft (0721-958X)
Related titles: Online - full text ed.: (from H.W. Wilson, O C L C Online Computer Library Center, Inc.).
Indexed: AIAP, ArtHuCI, ArtInd, BHA, CurCont, DIP, IBR, IBZ, PCI, RASB.
—IDS, IE. **CCC.**

Published by: (Deutscher Verein fuer Kunstwissenschaft e.V.), Deutscher Verlag fuer Kunstwissenschaft GmbH, Jebensstr 2, Berlin, 10623, Germany. TEL 49-30-3139932, FAX 49-30-32303824, dvfk@aol.com, http://www.dvfk-berlin.de. Circ: 1,600.

DIABLO MAGAZINE. see *THEATER*

701.18 USA ISSN 0279-568X
DIALOGUE (COLUMBUS); voicing the arts. Text in English. 1978. bi-m. USD 24 domestic; USD 49 in Canada & Mexico; USD 54 elsewhere (effective 2000). adv. bk.rev. back issues avail. **Document type:** *Consumer.* **Description:** Covers visual arts in Ohio and regional states. Offers profiles of artists, communities and art spaces, besides arts criticism, news, exhibition previews, and artist opportunities.
Related titles: Microfiche ed.; Online - full text ed.: (from ProQuest Information & Learning).
Published by: Dialogue Inc., PO Box 2572, Columbus, OH 43216-2572. TEL 614-621-3704, FAX 614-621-2448, dialogarts@aol.com. Ed., R&P Meg Galipault. Adv. contact Laura Chichester. B&W page USD 730, color page USD 1,100; trim 14.5 x 10.5. Circ: 1,300 (paid); 3,700 (controlled).
Dist. by: Ingram Periodicals Inc., 1240 Heil Quaker Blvd, Box 7000, La Vergne, TN 37086-7000. TEL 800-627-6247.

700 FRA ISSN 0070-4776
DICTIONNAIRE DES VALEURS DES MEUBLES ET OBJETS D'ART. Text in French. 1965. irreg.
Published by: Librairie Fischbacher, 33 rue de Seine, Paris, 75006, France. TEL 43-26-84-87, FAX 43-26-48-87. Ed. E Mayer.

DIETSCHE WARANDE EN BELFORT; tijdschrift voor letterkunde en geestesleven. see *LITERARY AND POLITICAL REVIEWS*

700 FIN ISSN 1239-6427
DIMENSIO. Text in Finnish; Summaries in English. 1996. irreg., latest vol.4, 2000. price varies. back issues avail. **Document type:** *Monographic series, Academic/Scholarly.*
Published by: Valtion Taidemuseo/Finnish National Gallery, Kaivokato 2, Helsinki, 00100, Finland. TEL 358-9-173361, FAX 358-9-17336248, info@fng.fi, http://www.fng.fi.

▼ **DIPLO MAGAZINE.** see *LITERARY AND POLITICAL REVIEWS*

700 USA
DIRECT ART. Text in English. s-a. USD 3.95 newsstand/cover domestic; USD 5 newsstand/cover in Canada (effective 2003).
Published by: Slow Art Productions, 51 Wooster St., Flr. 2, New York, NY 10013-2292. da@slowart.com, slowart@aol.com, http://www.directart.org. Ed., Pub. Paul Winslow.

760 770 USA
DIRECT STOCK✶. Text in English. 1992. a. USD 24.95. illus. **Document type:** *Catalog, Trade.* **Description:** Catalogs stock photographs available to graphic designers for purchase.
Published by: Watson - Guptill Publications, 770 Broadway, New York, NY 10003-9522. TEL 212-764-7300.

741.58029 USA
DIRECTORY OF CARTOONISTS - GAGWRITERS - SHORT HUMOR MARKETS. Text in English. 1960. a. USD 12. **Document type:** *Directory.* **Description:** Lists names and addresses of cartoonists and gagwriters seeking and supplying gags for cartoons and markets for short humor.
Published by: Gag Recap Publishers, 12 Hedden Pl, New Providence, NJ 07974-1724. TEL 908-464-1158. Ed., Pub. Al Gottlieb.

700 CAN ISSN 0832-865X
DIRECTORY OF THE ARTS. Text in English, French. biennial. CND 40 to non-members; CND 30 to members. **Document type:** *Directory.* **Description:** Offers a comlete guide to federal and provincial government agencies related to arts and culture, and national and provincial arts service organizations.
Incorporates: Who's Who: A Guide to Federal and Provincial Departments and Agencies, Their Funding Programs and the People Who Head Them (0384-2355); Who Does What: A Guide to National Associations, Service Organizations and Unions Operating in the Arts (0700-2661)
Published by: Canadian Conference of the Arts, 130 Albert St, Ste 804, Ottawa, ON K1P 5G4, Canada. TEL 613-238-3561, FAX 613-238-4849, cca@mail.culturenet.ca, http://www.ccarts.ca. Ed., R&P Sharon Griffiths. Circ: 300 (controlled).

DIRT. see *MOTION PICTURES*

700 NZL
DISRUPT. Text in English. 2002. s-a. **Document type:** *Magazine, Consumer.* **Description:** Covers graffiti and urban art and artistis, also includes music.
Published by: Disrupt Gallery, 145 Karangahape Rd., Auckland, New Zealand. TEL 64-9-3691540, FAX 64-9-3691542, deirdre@disruptiv.com, http://www.disruptiv.com/.

DIX-HUITIEME SIECLE. see *HISTORY—History Of Europe*

700 FRA ISSN 1260-9447
DIZAJN. Text in French. 1994. q. **Document type:** *Journal, Trade.* **Description:** Covers topics in design for student and professional artists.
Published by: Ecole Nationale Superieure de Creation Industrielle, 48, rue Saint-Sabin, Paris, 75011, France. TEL 33-1-49231269, FAX 33-1-49231267, wagner@ensci.com. Ed. Dominique Wagner.

DOCUMENTATION AND REGISTRATION OF ROCK ART IN TANUM; No. 1 Aspeberget (1997), No. 2 Fossum (1999). see *ARCHAEOLOGY*

DOCUMENTI E RICERCHE D'ARTE ALESSANDRINA. see *ARCHAEOLOGY*

700 FIN ISSN 1456-0852
DOKUMENTTI. Text in Finnish. 1995. biennial. back issues avail. **Document type:** *Magazine, Consumer.*
Related titles: Online - full text ed.: ISSN 1456-0860.
Published by: Valtion Taidemuseo/Finnish National Gallery, Kaivokato 2, Helsinki, 00100, Finland. TEL 358-9-173361, FAX 358-9-17336248, info@fng.fi, http://www.fng.fi/fng/rootnew/fi/kka/kka-etusivu.htm.

705 DOM
DOMINICAN REPUBLIC. DIRECCION GENERAL DE BELLAS ARTES. CATALOGO DE LA BIENAL DE ARTES PLASTICAS. Text in Spanish. irreg. illus.
Published by: Direccion General de Bellas Artes, Santo Domingo, Dominican Republic.

700 CHN
DONGHUA DAWANG. Text in Chinese. bi-m.
Published by: Shanghai Renmin Meishu Chubanshe/Shanghai People's Art Publishers, No33 Alley 672 Changle Rd, Shanghai, 200040, China. TEL 4374528. Ed. Huang Qianggen.

DOODGEWOON (ONLINE EDITION); tijdschrift over de dood. see *PHILOSOPHY*

700 FRA ISSN 1161-3122
N2
DOSSIER DE L'ART. Text in French. 10/yr.
Indexed: ABM.
Published by: Editions Faton S.A., 25 rue Berbisey, Dijon, 21000, France. TEL 33-3-80404104.

700 FRA ISSN 0756-5860
LES DOSSIERS DE L'ART PUBLIC. Text in English, French. 1983. irreg., latest vol.6, 1991. bk.rev.
Published by: Association pour la Promotion de l'Art Public (A.P.A.P.), 71 rue d'Hautpoul, Paris, 75019, France. TEL 1-42-41-13-61, FAX 1-42-41-77-18. Ed. Herve Bechy. Circ: 2,000.

DRAGON. see *LITERATURE*

DREAM/GIRL; the arts magazine for girls. see *CHILDREN AND YOUTH—About*

DRUNKEN BOAT. see *LITERARY AND POLITICAL REVIEWS*

700 CHE ISSN 0012-6837
AP32
DU; die Zeitschrift der Kultur. Text in German; Summaries in English. 1941. m. CHF 160; CHF 20 newsstand/cover (effective 2001). adv. bk.rev.; rec.rev. illus. index. **Document type:** *Magazine, Consumer.*
Formerly: Du-Atlantis
Indexed: ABCT, ABM, AIAP, API, ArtHuCI, ArtInd, BHA, CurCont, DIP, IBR, IBZ, RASB, RILM.
—BLDSC (3630.530000), IE, Infotrieve, ingenta.
Published by: T A Media AG, Werdstr 21, Zuerich, 8004, Switzerland. TEL 41-1-2484111, FAX 41-1-2485314, redaktion@dumag.ch, http://www.dumag.ch. Ed. Dieter Bachmann. Adv. contact Yvonne Philipp. Circ: 28,027.

DUMBARTON OAKS CONFERENCE PROCEEDINGS. see *ARCHAEOLOGY*

700 CHN ISSN 1000-6028
ND1042
DUO YUN. Text in Chinese. s-a.
Published by: Shanghai Shu Hua Chubanshe/Shanghai Calligraphy and Painting Publishers, 81 Qinzhou S Rd, Shanghai, 200233, China. TEL 86-21-6451-9008. Ed. Lu Fusheng.

741.6 NLD
DUTCH DESIGN (YEAR). Text in Dutch, English. biennial. EUR 95 per issue (effective 2005). illus. **Document type:** *Trade.* **Description:** Offers a forum in which 220 Dutch designers and design agencies can present their most outstanding and inspirational work.
Published by: Uitgeverij B I S, Postbus 323, Amsterdam, 1000 AH, Netherlands. TEL 31-20-5247560, FAX 31-20-5247557, info@bispublishers.nl, http://www.bispublishers.nl.

EARLY DRAMA, ART, AND MUSIC MONOGRAPH SERIES. see *THEATER*

EARLY DRAMA, ART, AND MUSIC REFERENCE SERIES. see *THEATER*

EARTHSONG. see *MUSEUMS AND ART GALLERIES*

EAST ASIA JOURNAL; studies in material culture. see *ANTHROPOLOGY*

700 956 GBR ISSN 0269-8404
N7260
➤ **EASTERN ART REPORT.** Text in English. 1989. bi-m. GBP 30 in United Kingdom to individuals & Channel Islands; GBP 40, EUR 65 in Europe to individuals Turkey & Cyprus; USD 80 in United States to individuals; GBP 50, USD 80 elsewhere to individuals; GBP 60 in United Kingdom to institutions & Channel Islands; GBP 80, EUR 130 in Europe to institutions Turkey & Cyprus; USD 160 in United States to institutions; GBP 100, USD 160 elsewhere to institutions (effective 2003). adv. illus. Index. back issues avail. **Document type:** *Monographic series, Academic/Scholarly.* **Description:** Combines scholarly articles on the visual arts of Africa, the Far East, and South and Southeast Asia (including China and Japan), with exclusive interviews, previews of exhibitions, art events, books, and exhibition catalogs.
Related titles: Online - full text ed.: Eastern Art Report Online. ISSN 1463-385X.
Indexed: ABM, PerIslam.
Published by: (Centre for Near East Afro-Asian Research (NEAR)), Eastern Art Publishing Group, PO Box 13666, London, SW14 8WF, United Kingdom. TEL 44-20-83921122, FAX 44-20-83921422, ear@eapgroup.ndirect.co.uk, http://www.eapgroup.ndirect.co.uk. Ed. Shirley Rizvi. Pub., R&P Sajid Rizvi. Circ: 9,000.

700 DEU
ECCO; das Buchmagazin fuer Kunst, Kultur & Geschichte. Text in German. 2/yr. free. **Document type:** *Magazine, Consumer.*
Published by: Rossipaul Kommunikation GmbH, Menzinger Str 37, Munich, 80638, Germany. TEL 49-89-179106-0, FAX 49-89-17910622, info@rossipaul.de, http://www.rossipaul.de/ecco.html.

ECOREDESIGN NESLETTER. see *PRINTING*

740 GBR ISSN 1358-6688
THE EDGE (LONDON). Text in English. 1995. bi-m. GBP 21 in Europe; GBP 27 elsewhere; GBP 3 newsstand/cover. adv. bk.rev. illus. index. back issues avail.; reprints avail. **Document type:** *Newsletter, Consumer.* **Description:** Discusses various aspects of calligraphy, present and historic. Updates readers on forthcoming events of interest.
Published by: Calligraphy and Lettering Arts Society, 54 Boileau Rd, London, SW13 9BL, United Kingdom. TEL 44-181-741-7886, FAX 44-181-741-7886, 101344.3245@compuserve.com, http://www.clas.co.uk. Ed. Susan Cavendish. Circ: 1,800 (paid).

700 NLD
EDITIE COLLECTION D'ART. Text in Dutch. 8/yr. bk.rev.
Published by: Collection d'Art Galerie, Keizersgracht 516, Amsterdam, 1017 EJ, Netherlands. Circ: 1,500.

700 900 AUT
EDITION JOANNEUM. Text in English, German. 1998. irreg., latest 1999. price varies. **Document type:** *Monographic series, Academic/Scholarly.* **Description:** Presents and comments upon the various museums, collections and exhibitions under the direction of the State Museum Joanneum.
Published by: (Landesmuseum Joanneum), Springer-Verlag Wien (Subsidiary of: Springer Science+Business Media) TEL 43-1-3302415-0, FAX 43-1-330242665, books@springer.at, http://www.springer.at. R&P Angela Foessl TEL 43-1-3302415517. **Subscr. to:** Springer-Verlag New York, Inc., 233 Spring St, New York, NY 10013. TEL 800-777-4643, FAX 201-348-4505, orders@springer-ny.com.

EDITOR'S CHOICE; fiction, poetry and art from the U.S. small press. see *LITERATURE*

700 CAN
THE EDUCATOR. Text in English. 1962. irreg. **Document type:** *Newsletter.*
Former titles: S S E A Newsletter (0315-9035); (until 1970): S S E A Art Journal (0080-6625); (until 1964): Art Journal (0571-1665)
—CCC.
Published by: Saskatchewan Society for Education Through Art, PO Box 9497, Saskatoon, SK S7K 7E9, Canada. TEL 306-975-0222, 800-667-7732, FAX 306-975-1262, ssea@saskedthroughart.ca, http://www.saskedthroughart.ca/main.html.

EIGHTEENTH CENTURY: A CURRENT BIBLIOGRAPHY. see *BIBLIOGRAPHIES*

EIGHTEENTH-CENTURY LIFE. see *HISTORY—History Of Europe*

▼ new title ➤ refereed ✶ unverified ♦ full entry avail.

EIGHTEENTH-CENTURY STUDIES. see *HISTORY*

EIKON; Beitraege zur antiken Bildersprache. see *CLASSICAL STUDIES*

709.94 USA
ELAN; celebrating the good life in northern Virginia. Text in English. 1999. 10/yr. USD 25 (effective 2003). adv. **Document type:** *Magazine, Consumer.* **Description:** Profiles amateur and professional artists who work or live in Northern Virginia. It also features a historical perspective on a particular building or place of note in Northern Virginia.
Published by: Reynolds & Associates, 1144-F Walker Rd, Great Falls, VA 22066. TEL 703-757-7522, FAX 703-757-7525, info@elanmagazine.com, http://www.elanmagazine.com. adv.: color page USD 3,095; trim 8 x 10.875. Circ: 35,947 (controlled).

EMBLEMATICA; an interdisciplinary journal for emblem studies. see *HISTORY—History Of Europe*

745.61 USA ISSN 1045-3717
NC997.A1
EMIGRE. Text in English. 1984. s-a. USD 25 newsstand/cover (effective 2005). bk.rev. illus. 144 p./no.; back issues avail. **Document type:** *Magazine, Trade.* **Description:** Features both established and emerging graphic design talents from around the world. Focuses on a specific design topic and showcases works, often experimental in nature.
Indexed: ABM, ArtInd, DAAI, MLA-IB.
Published by: Emigre Graphics, 1700 Shattuck Ave., #307, Beakeley, CA 94709. TEL 530-756-2900, FAX 530-756-1300, info@emigre.com, http://www.emigre.com. Ed. Rudy Vanderlans. Circ: 6,000 (paid).

701 USA ISSN 0276-2374
NX1 CODEN: ESAREN
EMPIRICAL STUDY OF THE ARTS. Text in English. 1982. s-a. USD 56 to individuals; USD 176.50 domestic to institutions; USD 182 foreign to institutions (effective 2005). adv. bk.rev. illus. back issues avail. **Document type:** *Journal, Academic/Scholarly.* **Description:** Covers the fields of anthropology, applied aesthetics, psychology, semiotics and discourse analysis, sociology, and computational stylistics.
Related titles: Online - full text ed.: ISSN 1541-4493 (from EBSCO Publishing).
Indexed: DIP, FLI, IBR, IBZ, PsycInfo, PsycholAb, RILM, SOPODA, e-psyche.
—BLDSC (3737.024200), IE, ingenta. **CCC.**
Published by: (International Association of Empirical Aesthetics), Baywood Publishing Co., Inc., 26 Austin Ave, PO Box 337, Amityville, NY 11701-0337. TEL 631-691-1270, FAX 631-691-1770, info@baywood.com, http://www.baywood.com/Journals/PreviewJournal.asp?Id=0276-2374. Ed. Colin Martindale. R&P Julie Krempa. Adv. contacts Marcie Cohen, Valerie Ford.

700 111.85 FRA ISSN 1623-457X
ENCRAGES. Text in French. 1999. irreg. **Document type:** *Journal, Academic/Scholarly.*
Published by: L' Harmattan, 5 rue de l'Ecole Polytechnique, Paris, 75005, France. TEL 33-1-43257651, FAX 33-1-43258203, http://www.editions-harmattan.fr.

700 808.8 USA ISSN 1090-0020
ENTERZONE. Text in English. 1994. q. free. bk.rev.; music rev.; play rev.; video rev. illus. back issues avail. **Document type:** *Academic/Scholarly.* **Description:** Covers arts, literature, and media.
Related titles: Online - full text ed.
Address: 1017 Bay View Ave, Oakland, CA 94612. TEL 510-532-7573, editor@ezone.org, http://ezone.org/ez/. Ed., Pub. Christian Crumlish. R&P Briggs Nisbet. Circ: 30,000.

ENVIRONMENT AND ART LETTER; a forum on architecture and the arts for the Parish. see *RELIGIONS AND THEOLOGY—Roman Catholic*

700 150.19 ARG
EOS; revista Argentina de arte y psicoanalisis. Text in Spanish. 1991. a.?.
Published by: Fundacion Banco Credito Argentino, 11 De Septiembre, 1990, Capital Federal, Buenos Aires 1428, Argentina. TEL 54-114-7833819.

700 USA ISSN 1044-0224
N7668.H6
EQUINE IMAGES; reflections of the equestrian lifestyle . Text in English. 1986. bi-m. USD 29.95 domestic; USD 39.95 in Canada; USD 41.95 foreign (effective 1999). adv. illus. reprints avail. **Description:** Reflects the horse-loving equestrian lifestyle through equine artwork, antiques, and collectibles.
Published by: Heartland Construction Group, Inc., 1003 Central Ave, Fort Dodge, IA 50501. TEL 800-247-2000, FAX 515-574-2213, amy@hlipublishing.com, http://www.equineimages.com. Adv. contact Amelia Presler.

L'ERBAMUSICA. see *MUSIC*

740 CHN ISSN 1003-0468
ERTONG MANHUA/CHILDREN'S CARTOON. Text in Chinese. 1980. m. **Document type:** *Consumer.*
Published by: Renmin Meishu Chubanshe/People's Fine Arts Publishers, 32, Beizongbu Hutong, Beijing, 100735, China. TEL 86-1-552296. Ed. Ding Wu.

700 VEN ISSN 1316-6204
NX7
ESCRITOS; en artes, estetica y cultura. II etapa. Text in Spanish. 1986. s-a. USD 30; USD 15 newsstand/cover (effective 2000). adv. bk.rev. **Description:** Covers art, theatre, music, dance and literature.
Indexed: SOPODA.
Published by: (Escuela de Artes), Universidad Central de Venezuela, Facultad de Humanidades y Educacion, Edificio Trasbordo, Planta Baja, Calle Minerva, Urb los Chaguaramos, Caracas, 1051, Venezuela. Ed. Catalina Gaspar. adv.: page USD 200.

730 CAN ISSN 0821-9222
ESPACE; the magazine of another dimension. Text in English, French. q. CND 33 domestic to individuals; CND 40 domestic to institutions; CND 25 domestic to students; USD 60 foreign; CND 8 newsstand/cover (effective 2003). adv. bk.rev. **Document type:** *Magazine, Consumer.* **Description:** Explores various aspects of contemporary sculpture.
Indexed: ABM, BHA, CPerI.
Published by: Le Centre de Diffusion 3D, 4888 rue Saint-Denis, Montreal, PQ H2J 2L6, Canada. TEL 514-844-9858, FAX 514-844-3661, espace@espace-sculpture.com, http://www.espace-sculpture.com. Ed. Serge Fisette. Circ: 1,400. **Co-sponsors:** Canada Council for the Arts; Canadian Magazine Publishers Association.

709 ESP ISSN 1130-4715
ESPACIO, TIEMPO Y FORMA. SERIE VII. HISTORIA DEL ARTE. Text in Spanish. 1987. a.
Supersedes in part (in 1990): Espacio, Tiempo y Forma (0214-4433)
Indexed: PCI, RILM.
—CINDOC.
Published by: Universidad Nacional de Educacion a Distancia, Bravo Murillo No. 38, Madrid, Spain. TEL 34-91-3986000, FAX 34-91-3986600, http://www.uned.es/.

700 ESP ISSN 1136-5390
ESPEJO DE PACIENCIA; revista de literatura y arte. Text in Spanish. 1998. q.
—CINDOC.
Published by: Universidad de las Palmas de Gran Canaria, C, Juan de Quesada, 30, Las Palmas de Gran Canaria, 35001, Spain. TEL 34-928-451023, FAX 34-928-451022, universidad@ulpgc.es, http://www.ulpgc.es/. Ed. Manuel Diaz Martinez.

800 FRA ISSN 0998-8041
L'ESTAMPILLE - L'OBJET D'ART; art antiquites et artisanat. Text in French. 1969. m. (11/yr.). adv. bk.rev.
Formed by the merger of: Estampille (0184-7724); Objet d'Art (0988-8519)
Indexed: BHA.
Published by: Editions Faton S.A., 25 rue Berbisey, Dijon, 21000, France. TEL 33-3-80404104. Ed. Louis Faton. Circ: 50,000.
Subscr. to: 1 rue des Artisans, BP 90, Quetigny Cedex 21803, France.

700 VEN
▼ **ESTETICA**; revista de arte y estetica contemporanea. Text in English. 2004. a. free (effective 2005). **Document type:** *Journal, Academic/Scholarly.* **Description:** Its goal is to disseminate the knowledge of contemporary esthetics and art.
Media: Online - full text.
Published by: Universidad de los Andes, Merida, Av 4 entre Calles 18 y 19, Edif General Masini, Piso 3, Of A-3, Merida, 5101, Venezuela. TEL 58-274-2524192, info@saber.ula.ve, http://www.saber.ula.ve/estetica/, http://www.ula.ve.

701.17 111.85 801.93 CZE ISSN 0014-1291
ESTETIKA/AESTHETICS. Text in Czech, English, German, Slovak; Summaries in English, German. 1964. q. CZK 25 per issue (effective 2005). adv. bk.rev. charts; illus.; tr.lit. index. **Document type:** *Journal, Academic/Scholarly.* **Description:** Contains studies and articles on general aesthetics and the theory and history of art.
Indexed: ABM, PCI, PhilInd, RILM.
—**CCC.**
Published by: Akademie Ved Ceske Republiky, Ustav Dejin Umeni/Czech Academy of Sciences, Institute of the History of Art, Husova 4, Prague, 11000, Czech Republic. TEL 420-2-22220099, FAX 420-2-22221654, arthist@site.cas.cz, udu@cas.cz, http://www.lib.cas.cz/knav/journals/cz/Estetika.htm, http://www.udu.cas.cz. Ed. Helena Lorenzova. Adv. contact Kybon M Sagner. Circ: 1,400. **Dist. by:** Kubon & Sagner Buchexport - Import GmbH, Hessstr 39-41, Munich 80798, Germany. TEL 49-89-542180, FAX 49-89-54218218, postmaster@kubon-sagner.de, http://www.kubon-sagner.de.

700 ESP ISSN 1139-1634
ESTIGMA; revista de investigacion y de creacion. Text in Spanish. m. back issues avail.
Related titles: Online - full text ed.: 1999.
Published by: Universidad de Malaga, Apdo. de Correos No. 4118, Malaga, 24080, Spain. estigama@lettera.net, http://externos.uma.es/estigama/. Eds. Enrique Carratula Llopis, Juan Jacinto Munoz Rengle.

700 EST
ESTONIAN ART. Text in English. 1997. s-a.
Media: Online - full content.
Published by: Estonian Institute, P.O. Box 3469, Tallinn, 10506, Estonia. TEL 372-6314355, FAX 372-6314356, http://www.einst.ee/Ea/.

709 MEX ISSN 0071-1659
ESTUDIOS DE ARTE Y ESTETICA. Text in Spanish. 1958. irreg., latest 1988. price varies. illus. **Document type:** *Academic/Scholarly.*
Published by: Universidad Nacional Autonoma de Mexico, Instituto de Investigaciones Esteticas, Circuito Mario de la Cueva, Zona Cultural, Ciudad Universitaria, Mexico, DF 04510, Mexico. TEL 52-55-56652465, FAX 52-55-56654740, ereinoso@servidor.unam.mx.

ESTUDIOS HUMANISTICOS: GEOGRAFIA, HISTORIA, ARTE. see *GEOGRAPHY*

709 MEX ISSN 0185-1845
ESTUDIOS Y FUENTES DEL ARTE EN MEXICO. Text in Spanish. 1955. irreg. price varies. illus. **Document type:** *Academic/Scholarly.*
Published by: Universidad Nacional Autonoma de Mexico, Instituto de Investigaciones Esteticas, Circuito Mario de la Cueva, Zona Cultural, Ciudad Universitaria, Mexico, DF 04510, Mexico. TEL 52-55-56652465, FAX 52-55-56654740, ereinoso@servidor.unam.mx.

700 800 PRT ISSN 0870-8584
ESTUDOS ITALIANOS EM PORTUGAL. Text in Italian, Portuguese. 1939. irreg. bk.rev. bibl.; illus.; stat.; tr.lit. cum.index. **Document type:** *Academic/Scholarly.*
Related titles: Cards ed.
Indexed: AmH&L, BHA, HistAb, MLA-IB.
Published by: (Istituto Italiano di Cultura in Portogallo), Papelaria Fernandes, Largo do Rato, 13, Lisbon, 1200, Portugal. Circ: 500.

700 BGR ISSN 0861-9697
NX8.B8
ET CETERA. Text in Bulgarian, Russian. 1993. a. BGL 5 (effective 2002). **Document type:** *Consumer.* **Description:** Presents well-known creators of art and culture, produced with their participation using unpublished works, illustrations, documents, letters found in personal archives and cultural institutions, and texts written especially for the almanac.
Published by: Et Cetera Foundation, KV Hipodruma, block 134a, entr A, Sofia, 1612, Bulgaria. TEL 359-2-872080, maiapramatarova@hotmail.com, http://www.sca.bg/cultural-periodicals/catalog/etcetera.htm. Ed. Maia Pramatarova.

700 CAN ISSN 0835-7641
ETC. MONTREAL. Text in English. 1987. q. CND 35 domestic to individuals; CND 55 foreign to individuals; CND 58 to institutions (effective 2002). adv. bk.rev. **Document type:** *Consumer.* **Description:** Deals with contemporary art and art criticism.
Related titles: Online - full text ed.: (from Gale Group).
Indexed: ABM, CPerI.
Published by: Revue d'Art Contemporain Etc Inc., 307 St Catherine Ouest, Bureau 620, Montreal, PQ H2X 2A3, Canada. TEL 514-848-1125, FAX 514-848-0071, etcmtl@dsuper.net. Ed., R&P, Adv. contact Isabelle Lelarge. Circ: 2,500.

709 BEL ISSN 0071-1969
ETUDES D'HISTOIRE DE L'ART. Text in French. 1964. irreg., latest vol.7, 1993. price varies. back issues avail. **Document type:** *Monographic series.* **Description:** Studies on art history, with emphasis on the relations between Belgian artists and Italy.
Published by: (Institut Historique Belge de Rome), Brepols Publishers, Begijnhof 67, Turnhout, 2300, Belgium. FAX 32-14-42-89-19, publishers@brepols.com, periodicals@brepols.net. Circ: (controlled).

EUROPA DOKUMENTARO. see *HISTORY—History Of Europe*

EUROPEAN AND AMERICAN PAINTING, SCULPTURE AND DECORATIVE ARTS, VOLUME 1: 1300-1800. see *MUSEUMS AND ART GALLERIES*

741.5 GBR ISSN 0378-9012
EUROPEAN ILLUSTRATION. Text in English, French, German. 1975. a. GBP 38. illus.
Address: 80 Charlotte St, London, W1A 1AQ, United Kingdom. Ed. Edward Booth Clibborn. Circ: 10,000.

EUROPEAN MEDIA ART FESTIVAL. see *MOTION PICTURES*

EUROPEAN PHOTOGRAPHY. see *PHOTOGRAPHY*

EUROPEAN STUDIES JOURNAL. see *HISTORY—History Of Europe*

EVALUATOR. see *ANTIQUES*

700 800 ITA
EVENTI E INTERVENTI. Text in Italian. irreg., latest vol.8. price varies. **Document type:** *Monographic series, Academic/Scholarly.*
Published by: Angelo Longo Editore, Via Paolo Costa 33, Ravenna, 48100, Italy. TEL 39-0544-217026, FAX 39-0544-217554, longo-ra@linknet.it, http://www.longo-editore.it. Ed., Pub. Alfio Longo. R&P Marina De Leonardis. Circ: 1,500.

700 GBR ISSN 1361-7699
EVERYTHING. Text in English. 1992. irreg. USD 3.50 newsstand/cover (effective 2005). **Document type:** *Magazine, Consumer.* **Description:** Covers contemporary visual arts in London.
Indexed: ABM.
Published by: Everything Publications, Camberwell Business Centre, Unit 126, 99-103 Lomond Grove, Camberwell, London, SE5 7HN, United Kingdom. giraffe@easynet.co.uk, http://www.backspace.org/everything/e/ecentre.html, http://www.bak.spc.org. Pubs. Luci Eyers, Steve Rushton.

EXETER STUDIES IN AMERICAN & COMMONWEALTH ARTS. see *LITERATURE*

701.17 USA
THE EXHIBITIONIST. Text in English. bi-m. USD 21.50; USD 4.95 newsstand/cover. **Document type:** *Magazine, Consumer.*
Published by: The Exhibitionist, 20 W 22nd St, 11th Fl, New York, NY 10010. TEL 212-473-7050, FAX 212-604-0823. Ed. Christian Viveros-Faune. Pub. James Heaton.

700 ESP ISSN 1577-2721
EXIT, IMAGEN Y CULTURA. Key Title: Exit. Text in English, Spanish. 2000. q. EUR 80 domestic; EUR 100 in Europe; EUR 140 in the Americas (effective 2004). 168 p./no.; back issues avail. **Document type:** *Magazine, Consumer.* **Description:** Deals with the most representative visual arts of the 21st century, featuring photography, video, and cinema.
Published by: Rosa Olivares y Asociados, S.L., C. Juan de Mena 25 2o. Izq, Madrid, 28014, Spain. TEL 34-91-4049878, FAX 34-91-3260012, exit@exitmedia.net, http://www.exitmedia.net. Ed. Rosa Olivares. **Dist. by:** Asociacion de Revistas Culturales de Espana, Hortaleza, 75, Madrid 28004, Spain. TEL 34-91-3086066, FAX 34-91-3199267, info@arce.es, http://www.arce.es.

760 DEU ISSN 0172-2859
➤ **EXLIBRISKUNST UND GRAPHIK. JAHRBUCH.** Text in German. 1891. a. EUR 70 membership (effective 2003). adv. **Document type:** *Bulletin, Academic/Scholarly.* **Description:** Contains articles on the art of bookplates.
Formerly (until 1979): Exlibriskunst und Graphik (0075-2630)
Published by: Deutsche Exlibris-Gesellschaft e.V., Joachim-Karnatz-Allee 19, Berlin, 10557, Germany. TEL 49-30-20671990, FAX 49-30-20671991, birgit.goebel@t-online.de, http://www.exlibris-gesellschaft.de. Ed. Heinz Decker. R&P Birgit Goebel.

➤ **EXPERIMENT/EKSPERIMENT**; a journal of Russian culture. see *ETHNIC INTERESTS*

740 720 ESP ISSN 1133-9675
EXPERIMENTA; revista para la cultura del proyecto. Text in Spanish. 1994. bi-m. EUR 59.90 domestic; EUR 97 in Europe; EUR 136 newsstand/cover elsewhere (effective 2004). adv. bk.rev.; software rev. abstr.; bibl.; illus. 120 p./no.; back issues avail. **Document type:** *Monographic series, Consumer.* **Description:** Design magazine covering the culture of projects.
Related titles: E-mail ed.; Fax ed.; Online - full text ed.; ♦ Supplement(s): Industria & Diseno. ISSN 1577-8029; ♦ Grafica y Diseno. ISSN 1577-8037.
Published by: Experimenta S.L., Churruca 27, 4o, Madrid, 28004, Spain. TEL 34-91-5214049, FAX 34-91-5213212, suscribe@revistaexperimenta.com, http://www.revistaexperimenta.com. Ed., R&P Pierluigi Cattermole. Adv. contact Sonia Santamaria. Circ: 10,000. **Dist. by:** Asociacion de Revistas Culturales de Espana, Hortaleza, 75, Madrid 28004, Spain. TEL 34-91-3086066, FAX 34-91-3199267, info@arce.es, http://www.arce.es.

EXPLORING (SAN FRANCISCO). see *SCIENCES: COMPREHENSIVE WORKS*

EXPOSURE (OXFORD). see *PHOTOGRAPHY*

EXPRESSION; revue culturelle feminine internationale. see *WOMEN'S INTERESTS*

700 USA ISSN 1537-3010
EXPRESSION (SAN DIEGO); sharing the spirit of creative arts. Text in English. bi-m. USD 19.95 domestic; USD 34.95 foreign (effective 2002). adv. **Description:** Inspires artists on all levels in various creative arts. Includes information on supplies, materials, and techniques. Covers the paper and letter arts, jewelry-making/wire-working, and home decoration.
Related titles: Online - full text ed.: (from Gale Group).
Published by: Expression Magazine, 591 Camino de la Reina, 200, San Diego, CA 92108. TEL 619-819-4530, FAX 619-297-5353, ed@expressionartmagazine.com, http://www.expressionartmagazine.com. Circ: 65,000.

700 GBR ISSN 0960-779X
NC1
EYE; the international review of graphic design. Text in English. 1990. q. GBP 63 (effective 2005). adv. **Document type:** *Magazine, Trade.*
Indexed: ArtInd, DAAI.
—BLDSC (3854.566500), IE, Infotrieve. **CCC.**
Published by: Quantum Business Media Ltd., Quantum House, 19 Scarbrook Rd, Croydon, Surrey CR9 1LX, United Kingdom. TEL 44-20-85654200, FAX 44-20-85654444, enquiries@quantumbusinessmedia.com, http://www.quantumbusinessmedia.com. Ed. Rick Poyner. Circ: 9,000.

776.6 AUS ISSN 0818-8734
EYELINE. Text in English. 1987. 3/yr. (Autumn/Winter, Spring, Summer). AUD 26 domestic to individuals; AUD 46 in New Zealand to individuals; AUD 49 in Asia & the Pacific to individuals; AUD 53 in US & Canada to individuals; AUD 56 in Europe to individuals; AUD 42 domestic to institutions; AUD 61 in New Zealand to institutions; AUD 64 in Asia & the Pacific to institutions; AUD 68 in US & Canada to institutions; AUD 71 in Europe to institutions (effective 2001). adv. bk.rev.; film rev. 60 p./no.; back issues avail. **Description:** Covers contemporary visual art, craft, design, visual culture. Includes artist monographs, specialist columns, and researched articles.
Published by: Eyeline Publishing Ltd., Victoria Park Rd, Kelvin Grove, QLD 4059, Australia. TEL 61-7-3864-5521, FAX 61-7-3864-3974, s.follent@qut.edu.au, http://www.qut.edu.au/eyeline/. Ed., R&P Sarah Follent TEL 61-7-38643862. Adv. contact Debra Beattie. B&W page AUD 520, color page AUD 1,000; trim 288 x 245. Circ: 2,000 (controlled).

707.11 USA ISSN 1090-3372
➤ **F A T E IN REVIEW.** Text in English. 1975. a. USD 10 per issue (effective 2000). bk.rev. **Document type:** *Academic/Scholarly.* **Description:** Contains articles on college level core courses in studio, art history and critical studies in visual art and design.
Published by: Foundations in Art Theory and Education, Art Department, University of Hawaii, Honolulu, HI 96822. TEL 808-956-5250, FAX 808-956-9043, http://www.louisville.edu/groups/finearts~www/fate.html. Ed., R&P Laura Ruby. Circ: 900.

700 055.1 ITA ISSN 0394-0462
N4
F M R. (Franco Maria Ricci) Text in English, French, Spanish. 1982. bi-m. EUR 159.50 (effective 2005). adv. illus. reprints avail. **Document type:** *Magazine, Consumer.*
Related titles: French ed.: ISSN 0394-0454; Italian ed.: ISSN 0393-0033; Spanish ed.
Indexed: AIAP, ArtInd, BHA, DAAI, RASB.
—Infotrieve.
Published by: Franco Maria Ricci SpA, Via Benedetto Croce 38, Naples, 80134, Italy. http://www.fmrnapoli.it. Ed. Carole Aghion. Pub. Franco Maria Ricci. R&P Raffaella Russo. Circ: 43,000.

700 600 ESP ISSN 1578-5998
FABRIKART. Text in Spanish. 2001. a. EUR 18 (effective 2004). **Document type:** *Journal, Academic/Scholarly.*
Published by: Universidad del Pais Vasco, Servicio Editorial, Apartado 1397, Bilbao, 48080, Spain. TEL 34-94-6015126, FAX 34-94-4801314, luxedito@lg.ehu.es, http://www.ehu.es/servicios/se_az/.

700 USA
FACE✶; the face of the congress. Text in English. 1992. q. USD 10. bk.rev.
Published by: Fa Ga Ga Ga, 155 N Washington St, Delaware, OH 43015-1609. TEL 216-744-4116. Eds. Mark Corroto, Melinda Otto Corroto. Circ: 175.

THE FADER. see *MUSIC*

FAENZA; rivista di studi di storia e di tecnica dell'arte ceramica. see *CERAMICS, GLASS AND POTTERY*

FAITH AND FORM; journal of religion, art and architecture. see *ARCHITECTURE*

FANTASIA. see *LITERATURE—Science Fiction, Fantasy, Horror*

700 646.72 746.9 GBR ISSN 1362-704X
TT500
FASHION THEORY; journal of dress, body and culture. Text in English. 1997. q. GBP 44 to individuals; GBP 116 to institutions (effective 2004). adv. bk.rev. bibl.; illus. annual. 120 p./no.; back issues avail. **Document type:** *Journal, Consumer.* **Description:** Offers an interdisciplinary forum for the rigorous analysis of the role of fashion in the cultural construction of embodied identity. Each issue contains at least four essays on topics ranging from the history of costume to the place of fashion in contemporary art, literature and commerce.
Related titles: Online - full text ed.: (from EBSCO Publishing, Gale Group, H.W. Wilson, IngentaConnect, O C L C Online Computer Library Center, Inc.).
Indexed: ABM, ArtInd, DAAI, IBSS, SociolAb.
—BLDSC (3897.118850), IE, Infotrieve, ingenta. **CCC.**
Published by: (The Fashion Institute of Technology, Museum USA), Berg Publishers, Angel Court, 1st Fl, 81 St Clements St, Oxford, Berks OX4 1AW, United Kingdom. TEL 44-1865-245104, FAX 44-1865-791165, steelemajor@earthlink.net, enquiry@bergpublishers.com, http://www.bergpublishers.com/uk/fashion/fashion_contents.htm. Ed. Valerie Steele. R&P Kathryn Earle. Adv. contact Jennifer Howell. Circ: 1,000 (paid). **Dist. by:** Extenza - Turpin, Pegasus Dr, Stratton Business Park, Biggleswade, Beds SG18 8TQ, United Kingdom. TEL 44-1462-672555, FAX 44-1462-480-947, custservturpin@turpinltd.com.

700 913 ITA ISSN 0391-7517
FELIX RAVENNA; rivista di antichita ravennati, cristiane e bizantine. Text in Italian. 1911. a., latest 1990, no.139-140. bk.rev. **Document type:** *Monographic series, Academic/Scholarly.* **Description:** Covers ancient art and archaeology, and old Christian and Byzantine art from all over the world.
Indexed: AIAP, BHA.
Published by: (Universita degli Studi di Bologna, Istituto di Antichita Ravennati e Bizantine), Edizioni del Girasole s.r.l., Via P Costa, 10, Ravenna, RA 48100, Italy. TEL 39-544-212830, FAX 39-544-38432, info@europart.it, http://www.europart.it/girasole. Ed. Raffaella Farioli Campanati. R&P Ivan Simonini. Circ: 500. **Co-sponsor:** Fondazione Cassa di Risparmio, Ravenna.

DAS FENSTER; Tiroler Kulturzeitschrift. see *LITERATURE*

745 USA ISSN 0164-324X
TT697
FIBERARTS; the magazine of textiles. Text in English. 1974. bi-m. (5/yr.). USD 24 (effective 2004). adv. bk.rev. illus. index. back issues avail.; reprints avail. **Document type:** *Magazine, Consumer.* **Description:** Covers profiles and interviews with individual artists, including photoportfolios of their work, techniques and life-styles, for enthusiasts of contemporary weaving, knitting, crochet, needlework, quilting, dyeing tapestry and basketry..
Formerly (until 1977): Fibercraft Newsletter
Related titles: Online - full text ed.: (from H.W. Wilson, O C L C Online Computer Library Center, Inc.).
Indexed: A&ATA, ArtInd, DAAI, IHTDI, Inspec, TTI, WTA.
—BLDSC (3914.690000), IE, ingenta.
Published by: Interweave Press, Inc., 201 E Fourth St, Loveland, CO 80537. TEL 970-669-7672, FAX 970-667-8317, customerservice@interweave.com, http://www.interweave.com. adv.: B&W page USD 1,050. Circ: 24,500.

709 SWE ISSN 0071-481X
N25
FIGURA. NOVA SERIES; Uppsala studies in the history of art. Text in English, German. 1951; N.S. 1959. irreg., latest vol.28, 2002. price varies. back issues avail. **Document type:** *Monographic series, Academic/Scholarly.*
Related titles: ♦ Series of: Acta Universitatis Upsaliensis. ISSN 0346-5462.
—KNAW.
Published by: (Uppsala Universitet, Institute of Art History), Uppsala Universitet, Acta Universitatis Upsaliensis/University Publications from Uppsala, PO Box 256, Uppsala, 75105, Sweden. TEL 46-18-4713922, http://www.ub.uu.se/upu/auu. Ed. Bengt Landgren. **Dist. by:** Almqvist & Wiksell International.

FIKRUN WA FANN. see *LITERARY AND POLITICAL REVIEWS*

FILOZOFSKI FAKULTET - ZADAR. RAZDIO POVIJESNIH ZNANOSTI. RADOVI. see *ARCHAEOLOGY*

700 USA
FINE ART MARKET REPORT. Text in English. 1995. m. USD 197 (effective 2001). bk.rev. abstr.; charts; illus. back issues avail.
Published by: Cromwell - Sloan Publishing Company, 63 Vine Rd, Stamford, CT 06905-2012. TEL 203-323-4810. Ed. Paul Sloan. Circ: 1,900.

700 GBR
FINE ART TRADE GUILD. DIRECTORY. Text in English. 1910. a. GBP 40. adv. **Document type:** *Trade.*
Incorporates (1994-1997): Sources; Formerly (until 1996): Picture and Prints Directory
Published by: Fine Art Trade Guild, 16-18 Empress Pl, London, SW6 1TT, United Kingdom. TEL 44-20-7381-6616, FAX 44-20-7381-2596, info@fineart.co.uk. Ed. Anne Beaton. Adv. contact Matt Stanley. Circ: 1,800 (controlled).

FINE F A C T A. see *EDUCATION*

700 AUS ISSN 1442-4894
FINEART FORUM; art and technology network news service. Text in English. 1987. m. free. adv. bk.rev.; music rev.; software rev.; video rev. illus. back issues avail. **Document type:** *Newsletter, Consumer.*
Media: Online - full text. **Related titles:** E-mail ed.

A

Published by: FineArt Forum, Art Science and Technology Network, PO Box 3603, South Brisbane, QLD 4101, Australia. TEL 61-7-3856-1207, 61-7-413-893-258, FAX 61-7-3864-5569, editor@fineartforum.org, http://www.msstate.edu/Fineart_Online/home.html, http://www.fineartforum.org. Ed., R&P, Adv. contact Nisar Keshvani. Circ: 7,000.

700 ITA ISSN 0394-1493
N1.A1
FLASH ART INTERNATIONAL. Text in English. 1980. bi-m. EUR 50 in Europe; EUR 90 Oceania; EUR 70 elsewhere (effective 2004). adv. bk.rev. charts; illus. reprints avail. **Document type:** *Newspaper.* **Description:** Contains news of the contemporary art world.
Related titles: Online - full text ed.: (from H.W. Wilson, O C L C Online Computer Library Center, Inc.); ♦ Italian ed.: Flash Art Italia.
Indexed: ABM, AIAP, ArtInd, BHA, DAAI, IBR, IBZ.
—BLDSC (3950.021000), IE, Infotrieve, ingenta.
Published by: Giancarlo Politi Editore, PO Box 95, Borgo Trevi, PG 06032, Italy. TEL 39-0742-381978, FAX 39-0742-381979, subscription@flashartonline.com, http://www.flashartonline.com. Eds. Giancarlo Politi, Helena Kontova. adv.: B&W page USD 3,200, color page USD 4,300; trim 9.63 x 7.06. Circ: 55,000. **US subscr. to:** Flash Art, 799 Broadway Rm 226, New York, NY 10003.

700 ITA
N1.A1
FLASH ART ITALIA. Text in Italian. 1967. bi-m. EUR 50 in Europe; EUR 90 Oceania; EUR 70 elsewhere (effective 2004). bk.rev. charts; illus. **Description:** Presents the spectrum of international contemporary art, with a special focus on Italy. Includes design, fashion, literature and philosophy.
Formed by the merger of (1973-1979): Heute Kunst (0391-6472); Flash Art (Edizione Italiana) (0015-3524); Which was formerly (until 1967): Flash (0394-1485)
Related titles: ♦ English ed.: Flash Art International. ISSN 0394-1493.
Indexed: ABCT, BHA, DAAI.
Published by: Giancarlo Politi Editore, PO Box 95, Borgo Trevi, PG 06032, Italy. TEL 39-0742-381978, FAX 39-0742-381979, subscription@flashartonline.com, http://www.flashartonline.com. Eds. Giancarlo Politi, Helena Kontova. Circ: 40,000. **US subscr. to:** Flash Art, 799 Broadway Rm 226, New York, NY 10003.

700 GBR ISSN 1461-0558
FLUX. Text in English. 1997. bi-m. GBP 17; GBP 2.80 newsstand/cover domestic; USD 9.99 newsstand/cover in United States (effective 2002).
Published by: Flux Magazine, 42 Edge St, Second Fl, Manchester, M4 1HN, United Kingdom. TEL 44-161-8320300, editorial@fluxmagazine.com, http://www.fluxmagazine.com. Ed. Lee Taylor.

700 790.1 CAN
FOCUS ON FESTIVALS. Text in English. 1980. 3/yr. CND 20 to members (effective 1998). adv. back issues avail. **Document type:** *Newsletter.* **Description:** News about Manitoba's 38 local community arts festivals, the Manitoba Community Arts Development, and provincial festival events.
Published by: Associated Manitoba Arts Festivals, Inc., 424 100 Arthur St, Winnipeg, MB R3B 1H3, Canada. TEL 204-945-4578, FAX 204-948-2073. Ed., Pub. Karen Oliver. Adv. contact Beverley Atkinson. Circ: 500.

709 POL ISSN 0071-6723
N6
FOLIA HISTORIAE ARTIUM. Text in Polish; Summaries in French. 1964. a. price varies. **Document type:** *Academic/Scholarly.* **Description:** Papers concerning European and occasionally Eastern art from early Christianity to modern times.
Indexed: ABCT, AIAP, AmH&L, BHA, HistAb, IBR, RASB.
—KNAW.
Published by: (Komisja Teorii i Historii Sztuki), Polska Akademia Nauk, Oddzial w Krakowie, ul sw Jana 28, Krakow, 31018, Poland. TEL 48-12-224853, FAX 48-12-222791. Ed. L Kalinowski.

745 USA ISSN 1067-3067
NK805
FOLK ART; magazine of the American Folk Art Museum. Text in English. 1971. q. USD 65 to individual members; USD 50 to students member; USD 8 newsstand/cover (effective 2005). adv. bk.rev. illus. Index. reprints avail. **Document type:** *Magazine, Consumer.*
Formerly (until 1992): Clarion (0197-6850)
Indexed: ABCT, ArtInd, BHA.
—BLDSC (3974.571210), IE.
Published by: American Folk Art Museum, 45 W 53rd St, New York, NY 10019. TEL 212-265-1040, FAX 212-265-2350, info@folkartmuseum.org, http://www.folkartmuseum.org. Ed., Pub. Tanya Heinrich. Circ: 10,000.

700 USA
FOLK ART AND ARTISTS. Text in English. irreg.
Indexed: MLA-IB.

Published by: University Press of Mississippi, 3825 Ridgewood Rd, Jackson, MS 39211-6492. TEL 601-432-6205, 800-737-7788, FAX 601-432-6217, press@ihl.state.ms.us, http://www.upress.state.ms.us.

FOLK ART AND DECORATIVE PAINTING. see *HOBBIES*

745 USA ISSN 1043-5026
N5312
➤ **FOLK ART MESSENGER.** Text in English. 1987. 3/yr. USD 25 domestic; USD 50 foreign (effective 2003). bk.rev.; video rev. illus. cum.index: 1987-2002. 40 p./no.; back issues avail. **Document type:** *Journal, Academic/Scholarly.* **Description:** Promotes the discovery, study and documentation of folk and self-taught art, folk artists and folk art environments, with an emphasis on the contemporary.
Indexed: ArtInd.
Published by: Folk Art Society of America, PO Box 17041, Richmond, VA 23226. TEL 804-285-4532, FAX 804-285-4532, fasa@folkart.org, http://www.folkart.org. Ed., Pub., R&P Ann Oppenhimer. Circ: 1,000 (paid).

709 900 ITA
FONTI E STUDI PER LA STORIA DI BOLOGNA E DELLE PROVINCE EMILIANE E ROMAGNOLE. Text in Italian. 1969. irreg., latest vol.7, 1981. price varies.
Published by: ALFA Edizioni, Via Santo Stefano, 13, Bologna, BO 40125, Italy. Circ: 4,000.

700 CAN ISSN 1488-8912
FOR THE ARTS/POUR LES ARTS. Text in English, French. 1983. q.
Former titles (until 1999): Canada Council. Bulletin (0846-4723); (until 1989): Canada Council. Quarterly Bulletin (0822-0506); (until 1983): Canada Council. Bulletin (0826-063X)
Related titles: Online - full text ed.: ISSN 1488-8920.
Published by: Canada Council for the Arts, 350 Albert St, P O Box 1047, Ottawa, ON K1P 5V8, Canada. TEL 613-566-4414, 800-263-5588, FAX 613-566-4390, http://www.canadacouncil.ca/news/newsletters/. Eds. Lolita Boudreault, Terry O'Grady.

700 USA ISSN 0890-2992
FOR YOUR INFORMATION (NEW YORK); practical information for those who create and work in the arts. Short title: F Y I. Text in English. 1985. q. USD 50 donation (effective 2004). adv. bk.rev. back issues avail. **Document type:** *Newsletter.* **Description:** Condensed information on issues, events, and opportunities for artists and arts workers. Includes funding deadlines and information on residencies.
Formerly: F.Y.I.
Published by: New York Foundation for the Arts, 155 Ave of the Americas, New York, NY 10013. TEL 212-366-6900, FAX 212-366-1778, nysaweb@nyfa.org, http://www.nyfa.org. Ed. Alan Gilbert. R&P Joseph Hannan. Adv. contact Shu Mei Chan. Circ: 30,000 (paid and controlled).

FORM FUNCTION FINLAND. see *ARCHITECTURE*

700 POL ISSN 0867-2555
FORMAT; pismo artystyczne. Text in Polish. 1990. q. illus. 112 p./no.; **Document type:** *Magazine, Consumer.*
Published by: Redakcja Format, Plac Polski 3/4, Wroclaw, 50156, Poland. TEL 48-71-3438031, ext 209, FAX 48-71-3460327, format@cybis.asp.wroc.pl, asa@cybis.asp.wroc.pl, http://www.asp.wroc.pl/asp/format/Formatwebpage. Ed. Andrzej Saj. Circ: 2,500.

FORSCHUNGEN UND BERICHTE ZUR BAU- UND KUNSTDENKMALPFLEGE IN BADEN-WUERTTEMBERG. see *ARCHAEOLOGY*

709 913 DEU ISSN 0532-2189
N3
FORSCHUNGEN ZUR KUNSTGESCHICHTE UND CHRISTLICHEN ARCHAEOLOGIE. Text in German. irreg., latest vol.19, 1998. price varies. **Document type:** *Monographic series, Academic/Scholarly.*
Indexed: AIAP.
Published by: Franz Steiner Verlag Stuttgart GmbH, Birkenwaldstr 44, Stuttgart, 70191, Germany. TEL 49-711-25820, FAX 49-711-2582390, franz.steiner.verlag@t-online.de, http://www.steiner-verlag.de. Eds. Otto Feld, Richard Hamann-MacLean. R&P Sabine Koerner.

FOTOGRAF. see *PHOTOGRAPHY*

700 USA
FOUND MAGAZINE. Text in English. 2002. 3/yr. USD 22.21 domestic; USD 36 in Canada; USD 30 elsewhere (effective 2002). **Document type:** *Magazine, Consumer.* **Description:** Covers found objects such as notes, photos, and poems that offers a glimpse into someone's life or an event.
Address: 3455 Charing Cross Rd, Ann Arbor, MI 48108-1911. info@foundmagazine.com, http://www.foundmagazine.com/. Circ: 20,000.

700 ZAF
FOUNDATION FOR THE CREATIVE ARTS. ANNUAL REPORT/STIGTING VIR DIE SKEPPENDE KUNSTE. JAARVERSLAG. Text in English. 1994. a. illus. **Document type:** *Corporate.*
Published by: Foundation for the Creative Arts, PO Box 91122, Auckland Park, Johannesburg 2006, South Africa.

700 FIN ISSN 1459-6288
FRAMEWORK. Text in English. 2000. biennial. EUR 23.20 domestic; EUR 31.50 in the European Union; EUR 37.40 in Europe; EUR 53.30 elsewhere (effective 2005). adv. **Document type:** *Journal.* **Description:** Information about Contemporary Finnish art.
Formerly (until 2004): Frame News
Published by: F R A M E Finnish Fund for Art Exchange, Merimiehenkatu 36 D, Helsinki, 00150, Finland. TEL 358-9-6126420, FAX 358-9-61264230, info@framework.fi, http://www.framework.fi, http://www/frame-fund.fi. adv.: page EUR 1,100; 240 x 340.

681.43 694.2 USA
▼ **FRAMING MONTHLY;** the educations resource for the custom framer. Text in English. 2003. m. USD 26; USD 3.50 newsstand/cover (effective 2004). adv. **Document type:** *Magazine, Trade.* **Description:** Dedicated to bringing art and framing retailers all the news, trends, products, services and up-to-date framing techniques that will help their businesses thrive.
Formerly: Framing Business News
Published by: Pfingsten Publishing, L L C, 6000 Lombardo Center Dr, Ste 420, Seven Hills, OH 44131. TEL 216-328-8926, FAX 216-328-9452, info@pfpublish.com, http://www.framingbusinessnews.com/, http://www.pfpub.com. Ed. Amy Leibrock. Pub. Julie Macdonald. Adv. contact Andrea Mullen. color page USD 3,295; trim 10.75 x 14.5. Circ: 13,397.

FRANK; an international journal of contemporary writing and art. see *LITERARY AND POLITICAL REVIEWS*

760 USA
FREELANCER'S NEWS. Text in English. 1989. 8/yr. USD 25. **Description:** Discusses marketing and selling, trade practices, case histories in the freelance graphic arts field.
Published by: Creative Independent Communications, Inc., PO BOX 437, MURRAY HILL STA, New York, NY 10156-0437. TEL 212-686-3514. Ed. Barbara Gordon.

700 USA ISSN 0071-9382
FREER GALLERY OF ART, WASHINGTON, D.C. OCCASIONAL PAPERS. Text in English. 1947. irreg., latest vol.4, 1971.
Published by: Freer Gallery of Art, Smithsonian Institution, Jefferson Dr, S W at 12th St, Washington, DC 20560. TEL 202-357-1432.

700 USA
FRIENDS OF FRENCH ART; art de vivre into art conservation. Text in English. 1979. a. USD 40 donation. **Description:** Covers annual trip to France to raise money for art conservation and restoration, and exchange of art conservation students to museums.
Address: Villa Narcissa, 100 Vanderlip Dr, Rancho Palos Verdes, CA 90275. TEL 310-377-4444, FAX 310-377-4584. Ed. Elin Vanderlip. Circ: 10,000.

700 GBR ISSN 0962-0672
N6480
FRIEZE; contemporary art and culture. Text in English. 1991. 8/yr. GBP 29 domestic to individuals; GBP 41 foreign to individuals; GBP 40 domestic to institutions; GBP 47 foreign to institutions (effective 2003). adv. back issues avail. **Document type:** *Magazine, Consumer.* **Description:** Covers international contemporary art and the culture it reflects.
Related titles: Online - full text ed.: (from EBSCO Publishing).
Indexed: ABM, DAAI.
—BLDSC (4039.170000), IE.
Published by: Durian Publications, 5-9 Hatton Wall, London, EC1N 8HX, United Kingdom. TEL 44-20-78135555, FAX 44-20-78137779, editors@frieze.demon.co.uk, admin@frieze.com, http://www.frieze.com. Ed. James Roberts. Pub. Matthew Slotover TEL 20- 7371 -1533. Adv. contact Michael Benevento. page USD 2,400; trim 230 x 300.

FRITID & KULTUR I SVERIGE. see *LEISURE AND RECREATION*

730 USA
FROM THE MAYOR'S DOORSTEP. Text in English. 1996. bi-m. USD 20 domestic; USD 25 in Canada; USD 30 elsewhere (effective 2000).
Related titles: Online - full text ed.: free.
Published by: Piri Halasz, Ed. & Pub., 520 E 76th St Apt 3A, New York, NY 10121-3162. piri@mindspring.com, http://piri.home.mindspring.com.

FUCK. see *LITERARY AND POLITICAL REVIEWS*

FUEHRER ZU ARCHAEOLOGISCHEN DENKMAELERN IN BADEN-WUERTTEMBERG. see *ARCHAEOLOGY*

FUEHRER ZU ARCHAEOLOGISCHEN DENKMAELERN IN DEUTSCHLAND. see *ARCHAEOLOGY*

700.985 PER
FUNDACION MARINA NUNEZ DEL PRADO DE FALCON. INFORMATIVO. Text in Spanish. 1996. m.
Published by: Fundacion Marina Nunez del Prado de Falcon, Antero Aspillaga, 300, San Isidro, Lima 27, Peru. TEL 51-14-4220208.

FUNDE UND AUSGRABUNGEN IM BEZIRK TRIER. see *ARCHAEOLOGY*

FUOCO; rassegna di cultura e d'arte. see *LITERARY AND POLITICAL REVIEWS*

700 306 CAN ISSN 0838-603X
NX513.A1
➤ **FUSE MAGAZINE**; a magazine about issues of art and culture. Text in English. 1976. q. CND 20 domestic to individuals; USD 24 foreign to individuals; CND 32 domestic to institutions; USD 38 foreign to institutions; CND 5.50 newsstand/cover (effective 2004). adv. bk.rev.; film rev.; music rev.; tel.rev.; video rev. illus. back issues avail.; reprints avail. **Document type:** *Magazine, Consumer.* **Description:** Addresses issues in visual and media arts, film, contemporary thought and cultural politics. Writers and artists from a range of communities offer diverse perspectives on the intersection of culture and the arts.
Former titles: Fuse (0226-8086); Centerfold
Related titles: Microfiche ed.: (from MML); Microfilm ed.: (from MML); Microform ed.: (from MML).
Indexed: AltPI, CBCARef, CBPI, CPerI, CWPI.
—CCC.
Published by: Arton's Publishing, 401 Richmond St W, Ste 454, Toronto, ON M5V 3A8, Canada. TEL 416-340-8026, FAX 416-340-0494, subscriptions@fusemagazine.org, http://www.fusemagazine.org/. Ed. Izida Zorde. Pub., R&P Michael Maranda. adv.: B&W page CND 500, color page CND 600; 10.75 x 8.25. Circ: 2,500 (paid).

➤ **FYNSKE MINDER.** see *HISTORY—History Of Europe*

➤ **G A HOUSES.** (Global Architecture) see *ARCHITECTURE*

700 780 DEU
G I AKTUELL. Text in German. q. **Document type:** *Bulletin.* **Description:** Contains information about various cultural events sponsored by the Goethe-Institut throughout the world.
Published by: Goethe-Institut zur Pflege der Deutschen Sprache im Ausland und zur Foederung der Internationalen Kulturellen Zusammenarbeit, Helene-Weber-Allee 1, Munich, 80637, Germany. TEL 49-89-15921-0, FAX 49-89-15921414, zv@goethe.de.

G L B. see *EDUCATION*

741.5 808.87 USA
GAG RECAP. Text in English. 1954. m. USD 55; USD 65 foreign (effective 1999). back issues avail. **Document type:** *Newsletter, Trade.* **Description:** Market information for cartoonists and gagwriters.
Published by: Gag Recap Publishers, 12 Hedden Pl, New Providence, NJ 07974-1724. TEL 908-464-1158. Ed., Pub. Al Gottlieb.

759.2 GBR ISSN 1351-2021
GAINSBOROUGH'S HOUSE REVIEW. Text in English. 1989. a. GBP 5.95, USD 10 to individuals; GBP 8.95, USD 15 to institutions (effective 2001). adv. illus. back issues avail. **Document type:** *Academic/Scholarly.* **Description:** Includes articles on aspects of the life and work of Thomas Gainsborough and related subjects.
Formerly (until 1992): Gainsborough's House Society Annual Report (0960-8176)
Indexed: BHA.
Published by: Gainsborough's House Society, Gainsborough's House, 46 Gainsborough St, Sudbury, Suffolk CO10 2EU, United Kingdom. TEL 44-1787-372958, FAX 44-1787-376991, mail@gainsboroughorg.demon.co.uk, mail@gainsborough.org. Ed., R&P Hugh Belsey. Adv. contact Jennifer Prowse TEL 44-1787-228027. Circ: 700.

700 001.3 NLD
GALATEA. Text in Dutch. 1996. q. illus. **Document type:** *Academic/Scholarly.* **Description:** Interdisciplinary contributions on culture, literature and the arts.
Media: Online - full text.
Published by: Vrije Universiteit Amsterdam, Word & Image Studies, De Boelelaan 1105, Amsterdam, 1081 HV, Netherlands. TEL 31-20-5987777, FAX 31-20-5985611, galatea@let.vu.nl, http://www.let.vu.nl/e-zine/galatea.

700 BGR ISSN 1311-1450
NX567.A1
GALERIA IZKUSTVO I KULTURA/CULTURE AND ART GALLERY. Text in Bulgarian. 1996. m. BGL 2 newsstand/cover (effective 2002). **Document type:** *Magazine, Consumer.* **Description:** Presents and introduces to the reader the best examples from Bulgaria and the world in past and contemporary art and culture.
Published by: MAKTA Co., 26 Lajos Kossuth St., Sofia, 1606, Bulgaria. TEL 359-2-9515175, http://www.sca.bg/cultural-periodicals/catalog/galerkul.htm. Ed. Hristo Kovachevski.

700 708.2 GBR ISSN 0265-7511
GALLERIES. Text in English. 1983. m. GBP 21.75 domestic; GBP 25 in Europe; GBP 40 in United States; GBP 35 elsewhere (effective 2005). adv. bk.rev. illus.; maps. 88 p./no.; back issues avail. **Document type:** *Magazine, Consumer.* **Description:** Contains listings, exhibition previews, market analysis, map locations, and topical news of fine art in the UK.
Related titles: Online - full text ed.
Published by: Barrington Publications, 54 Uxbridge Rd, London, W12 8LP, United Kingdom. artefact@artefact.co.uk, http://www.artefact.co.uk/a-gind.htm#!. Ed. Andrew Aitken. Pub., R&P Paul Hooper. Adv. contact Rosemary Clunie. B&W page GBP 445, color page GBP 775; trim 214 x 151. Circ: 20,000 (controlled).

700 ZWE ISSN 1561-1574
GALLERY. Text in English. 1995. q. ZWD 210 domestic; USD 28 in Africa; GBP 18 in Europe; USD 28 in the Americas (effective 2004). illus. **Document type:** *Magazine.* **Description:** Covers contemporary visual art and events in Zimbabwe and around the African continent.
Indexed: ABM.
Published by: Gallery Publications, 373 Union Ave, PO Box UA, Harare, Zimbabwe. gallery@icon.co.zw. Ed. Barbara Murray.

700 USA ISSN 1058-9112
A GATHERING OF THE TRIBES; the multicultural arts magazine. Text in English. 1991. 2/yr. USD 17.50; USD 10 newsstand/cover (effective 1999). adv. bk.rev.; dance rev.; film rev.; music rev.; play rev.; software rev.; tel.rev.; video rev. bibl.; illus.; maps; mkt.; stat.; tr.lit. back issues avail. **Document type:** *Trade.* **Description:** Aimed at exposing intercultural and intergenerational expressions disregarding borders.
Related titles: Audio cassette/tape ed.; Diskette ed.; Online - full text ed.; Video ed.
Published by: Steve Cannon, Ed. & Pub., PO BOX 20693, TOMPKINS SQ STA, New York, NY 10009. TEL 212-674-3778, FAX 212-674-5576, tribes@pop.interport.net, http://www.interport.net/~tribes. Eds. Patrick Koseiwisz, Steve Cannon. R&P, Adv. contact Steve Cannon. page USD 495. Circ: 2,000. **Dist. by:** Ubiquity Distributors Inc., 607 DeGraw St, Brooklyn, NY 11217. TEL 718-875-5491.

EL GATO TUERTO/ONE-EYED CAT; gaceta de arte, literatura, etcetera, etcetera. see *LITERATURE*

750 891.851008 POL ISSN 1231-7020
N6
GAZETA MALARZY I POETOW. Text in Polish. 1994. bi-m. 52 p./no.; **Document type:** *Magazine, Consumer.*
Published by: Galeria Miejska Arsenal, Stary Rynek 3, Poznan, 61772, Poland. office@arsenal.info.poznan.pl. Ed. Wojciech Makowiecki. Circ: 800.

701.18 FRA ISSN 1169-2294
LA GAZETTE DE L'HOTEL DROUOT; l'hebdomadaire des ventes publiques. Text in French. 1891. w. FRF 550; FRF 780 foreign. adv. **Description:** Includes news of art, antiques, auctions.
Formerly (until 1891): Hotel Drouot (1169-2286)
Published by: Gazette de l'Hotel Drouot, 10 rue du Faubourg Montmartre, Paris, Cedex 9 75441, France. TEL 33-1-47709300, FAX 33-1-47709394, gazette@gazette-drouot.com, http://www.gazette-drouot.com. Ed. Yves Gairaud. Adv. contact Jacques Boussac. Circ: 50,000.

GAZZETTA ANTIQUARIA. see *ANTIQUES*

701.18 JPN ISSN 0435-1657
NX440
GEIJUTSU SHINCHO. Text in Japanese. 1950. m. adv. **Description:** Covers fine arts, music, architecture, drama and design.
Address: Shincho-Sha, 71 Yarai-cho, Shinjuku-ku, Tokyo, 162-0805, Japan. TEL 03-3266-5381, FAX 03-3266-5387, TELEX 27433. Ed. Midori Yamakawa. Circ: 150,000.

GENAVA; revue d'archeologie et d'histoire de l'art. see *ARCHAEOLOGY*

GENERATOR. see *LITERATURE—Poetry*

700 CAN ISSN 1488-1063
GENOUS, FIRST PEOPLES ART OF CANADA. Text in English. 1999. q. CND 24 to individuals; CND 18 to institutions (effective 2000). **Document type:** *Magazine, Consumer.*
Indexed: CBCARef.
Published by: Genous, Inc, 6-2400 Dundas St, Ste 712, Mississauga, ON L5K 2R8, Canada. TEL 905-271-1977, genousmag@aol.com.

700 720 BEL ISSN 0772-7151
N9
➤ **GENTSE BIJDRAGEN TOT DE KUNSTGESCHIEDENIS.** Text and summaries in Dutch, English, French, German. 1934. a., latest vol.32, 1997. EUR 45 (effective 2005). illus. back issues avail. **Document type:** *Monographic series, Academic/Scholarly.*
Formerly (until 1973): Gentse Bijdragen tot de Kunstgeschiedenis en Oudheidkunde (0772-7143)
Related titles: Online - full text ed.
Indexed: ABM, AIAP, BHA, RILM.
Published by: (Rijksuniversiteit te Gent, Sectie Kunstgeschiedenis en Oudheidkunde, Sectie Kunstgeschiedenis en Oudheidkunde), Peeters Publishers, Bondgenotenlaan 153, Leuven, 3000, Belgium. TEL 32-16-235170, FAX 32-16-228500, peeters@peeters-leuven.be, http://poj.peeters-leuven.be/content.php?url=journal&journal_code=GBI, http://www.peeters-leuven.be. Ed. Anna Bergmans. Circ: 120.

700 USA ISSN 0147-1902
N514.A8
GEORGIA MUSEUM OF ART. BULLETIN. Text mainly in English. 1974. a. USD 10. back issues avail. **Document type:** *Bulletin.* **Description:** Contains an annual report and scholarly articles dealing with works from the museum's collections.
Indexed: ABM, BHA.
Published by: Georgia Museum of Art, University of Georgia, Athens, GA 30602. TEL 706-542-4662, FAX 706-542-1051, buramsey@arches.uga.edu, http://www.uga.edu/gamuseum/. Ed. Bonnie Ramsey. R&P Annelies Mondi TEL 706-542-0439. Circ: 1,000.

709 940 USA ISSN 0016-920X
N6280
➤ **GESTA.** Text in English. 1963. s-a. subscr. incld. with membership. adv. bk.rev. bibl.; charts; illus. cum.index. reprints avail. **Document type:** *Journal, Academic/Scholarly.*
Related titles: Online - full text ed.: (from JSTOR (Web-based Journal Archive)).
Indexed: AIAP, ASCA, ArtHuCI, ArtInd, BHA, BrArAb, CurCont, DIP, IBR, IBZ, NumL, RASB, RI-1, RI-2, RILM.
—BLDSC (4163.300000), IDS, IE, Infotrieve, ingenta.
Published by: International Center of Medieval Art, The Cloisters, Fort Tryon Park, New York, NY 10040. TEL 212-928-1146, FAX 212-928-9946, ICMA@medievalart.org, http://www.medievalart.org. Ed. Anne D Hedeman. Circ: 975.

707 DEU ISSN 0340-6172
DIE GESTALT; Vierteljahreszeitschrift fuer bildnerische Erziehung. Text in German. 1972. q. EUR 18. index. **Document type:** *Journal, Academic/Scholarly.*
Supersedes in part (in 1972): Bildnerische Erziehung (0006-243X); Which was formerly (until 1965): Kunst- und Werk-Erziehung (0172-0082); (until 1960): Kunst und Jugend (0451-081X)
Indexed: DIP, IBR, IBZ, RASB.
Published by: E O S Verlag, Erzabtei St. Ottilien, St.Ottilien, 86941, Germany. TEL 49-8193-71261, FAX 49-8193-6844, mail@eos-verlag.de, http://www.eos-verlag.de. Circ: 6,000.

700 DEU ISSN 0342-104X
GIESSENER BEITRAEGE ZUR KUNSTGESCHICHTE. Text in German. 1970. irreg., latest vol.10, 1997. price varies. **Document type:** *Monographic series, Academic/Scholarly.*
Indexed: AIAP, BHA.
Published by: Wilhelm Schmitz Verlag, Am Weidacker 12, Wettenberg-Launsbach, 35435, Germany. TEL 49-641-8773939, kontakt@wilhelm-schmitz-verlag.de, http://www.wilhelm-schmitz-verlag.de.

700 IRQ
GILAGAMESH✶; journal of modern Iraqi arts. Text in English. 1986. q. IQD 5, USD 20. adv. bk.rev.
Published by: Dar Al-Ma'mum for Translation and Publishing, Karantina, P O Box 624, Baghdad, Iraq. TEL 9641-5383171. Ed. Naji Al Hadithi. Circ: 15,000.

THE GILCREASE JOURNAL. see *HISTORY—History Of North And South America*

700 ITA ISSN 0394-0543
IL GIORNALE DELL' ARTE; mensile di informazione, cultura, economia. Text in Italian. 1983. m. EUR 80 domestic; EUR 120 in Europe; EUR 145 elsewhere (effective 2005). adv. bk.rev. illus. **Document type:** *Consumer.* **Description:** Provides comprehensive coverage of the art world, including news of exhibitions, books, restoration, archaeology, galleries, the marketplace, and auction results.
Related titles: Online - full text ed.; ♦ English ed.: The Art Newspaper (International Edition). ISSN 0960-6556; Supplement(s): Vernissage. ISSN 1591-4348. 1985.
Indexed: ABM.
Published by: Umberto Allemandi & C. Srl, Via Mancini 8, Turin, TO 10131, Italy. TEL 39-011-8193133, FAX 39-011-8193090, http://www.ilgiornaledellarte.com, http://www.allemandi.com. Eds. Gianna Marini, Umberto Allemandi. R&P Germana Moro. Adv. contact Patrizia Sbodio. Circ: 20,000.

A

700 666.1 USA ISSN 0278-9426
NK5112
GLASS ART SOCIETY JOURNAL. Text in English. 1981. a. USD 27 in North America to non-members; USD 32 elsewhere to non-members (effective 2003). adv. charts; illus.; tr.lit. back issues avail.; reprints avail. **Document type:** *Journal, Academic/Scholarly.*
Indexed: ABM, ArtInd, DAAI.
Published by: Glass Art Society, 3131 Western Ave., Ste. 414, Seattle, WA 98121-1028. TEL 206-382-1305, FAX 206-382-2630, info@glassart.org, http://www.glassart.org. Ed. Susan Frantz. R&P Penny Berk. Adv. contact Tamara Childress. Circ: 2,500.

GLASS ON METAL; the enamelist's magazine. see *CERAMICS, GLASS AND POTTERY*

GLENDORA REVIEW; an African quarterly on the arts. see *LITERATURE*

700 USA ISSN 1082-8338
NX456.5.M35
GLOBAL MAIL✶ ; the hole to the underground. Text in English. 1992. 3/yr. USD 9; USD 3 newsstand/cover; USD 12 foreign (effective 1996). back issues avail. **Document type:** *Directory, Consumer.* **Description:** Provides more than 700 listings of cultural projects from over 40 nations for artists, activists, writers, and publishers.
Related titles: Diskette ed.: 1992; Online - full text ed.: 1992.
Published by: Soapbox June, PO Box 22320, Lexington, KY 40522-2320. Ed. Ashley Parker Owens. Circ: 5,000.

700 AUS ISSN 1324-8030
GLOBE E JOURNAL OF CONTEMPORARY ART. Text in English. 1995. 3/yr. bk.rev. back issues avail. **Document type:** *Academic/Scholarly.* **Description:** Covers contemporary visual culture from an Australian perspective.
Media: Online - full text.
Published by: Monash University, Visual Arts Department, Wellington Rd, Clayton, VIC 3168, Australia. TEL 61-3-9905-4222, FAX 61-3-9905-4209, globe@arts.monash.edu.au, http://www.arts.monash.edu.au/visarts/globe/ghome.html. Ed. Robert Schubert. **Co-sponsor:** Vicarts, Gordon Darling Foundation, Australian Council.

GLOSSOLALIA; electronic journal for experimental literature & arts. see *LITERATURE*

651.6 SWE ISSN 0284-6578
GOETEBORG STUDIES IN CONSERVATION. Text mainly in English. 1988. irreg., latest vol.9, 2002. price varies; also exchange basis. **Document type:** *Monographic series, Academic/Scholarly.*
Related titles: ◆ Series of: Acta Universitatis Gothoburgensis. ISSN 0346-7740.
Published by: Acta Universitatis Gothoburgensis, Renstroemsgatan 4, P O Box 222, Goeteborg, 40530, Sweden. TEL 46-31-773-17-33, FAX 46-31-163-797. Ed. Jan Rosvall.

700 USA ISSN 0160-6298
NE85
GORDON'S PRINT PRICE ANNUAL (YEAR). Text in English. 1978. a. (plus 1 update). USD 245; USD 299 includes updates. **Description:** Lists over 35,000 prints sold during the past year in the world's major auctions and galleries.
Related titles: CD-ROM ed.: USD 595.
Published by: Gordon's Art Reference, Inc., 306 W Coronado Rd, Phoenix, AZ 85003-1147. TEL 941-434-6842, FAX 602-253-2104, infor@gordonart.com, http://www.gordonart.com. Ed. Jodie Benson.

709 720 SWE ISSN 0348-4114
GOTHENBURG STUDIES IN ART AND ARCHITECTURE. Text mainly in Swedish. 1978. irreg., latest vol.12, 2002. price varies; also exchange basis. **Document type:** *Monographic series, Academic/Scholarly.*
Related titles: ◆ Series of: Acta Universitatis Gothoburgensis. ISSN 0346-7740.
Published by: Acta Universitatis Gothoburgensis, Renstroemsgatan 4, P O Box 222, Goeteborg, 40530, Sweden. TEL 46-31-773-17-33, FAX 46-31-163-797. Ed. Lena Johannesson.

700 ESP ISSN 0017-2715
N7
➤ **GOYA**; revista de arte. Text in Spanish. 1954. bi-m. EUR 42.50 domestic; EUR 98 foreign (effective 2005). adv. bk.rev. illus.; abstr. 64 p./no.; back issues avail. **Document type:** *Magazine, Academic/Scholarly.*
Related titles: Online - full text ed.: (from H.W. Wilson, O C L C Online Computer Library Center, Inc.).
Indexed: ABCT, ABM, AIAP, ASCA, ArtHuCI, ArtInd, BHA, CurCont, DIP, HistAb, IBR, IBZ, PCI, RASB, RILM, SSCI.
—BLDSC (4206.100000), CINDOC, IDS, IE, Infotrieve, ingenta.
Published by: Fundacion Lazaro Galdiano, C Serrano, 122, Madrid, 28006, Spain. TEL 34-91-5616084, FAX 34-91-5617793, goya@flg.es, http://www.flg.es. Ed. Carlos Saguar Quer. Circ: 2,000.

720 ESP ISSN 1577-8037
GRAFICA Y DISENO. Text in Spanish. 1989. bi-m.
Supersedes in part (in 1997): Experimenta Informa (1133-9667); Which was formerly (until 1992): Experimenta (1133-9659)
Related titles: ◆ Supplement to: Experimenta. ISSN 1133-9675.
Published by: Experimenta S.L., Churruca 27, 4o, Madrid, 28004, Spain. TEL 34-91-5214049, FAX 34-91-5213212, suscribe@revistaexperimenta.com, http://www.revistaexperimenta.com. Ed. Pierluigi Cattermole.

GRAMMATEION; the St. Michael's Journal of the Arts. see *LITERARY AND POLITICAL REVIEWS*

700 330 659.1 USA ISSN 1547-9617
▼ **GRAPHIC & DESIGN BUSINESS.** Text in English. 2004. q. free to qualified personnel. **Document type:** *Magazine, Trade.*
Published by: North American Publishing Co., 1500 Spring Garden St., Ste 1200, Philadelphia, PA 19130-4094. http://www.gdbmag.com/, http://www.napco.com.

741.6092 USA
GRAPHIC ARTISTS GUILD. DIRECTORY OF ILLUSTRATIONS. Text in English. a. illus. **Document type:** *Directory, Trade.*
Published by: (Graphic Artists Guild), Serbin Communications, Inc., 813 Reddick St., Santa Barbara, CA 93103-3124. TEL 805-963-0439.

700 CAN
GRAPHIC EXCHANGE. Text in English. 1991. 6/yr. CND 29. adv.
Published by: Brill Communications, 25 Elm Ave, P O Box 65090, Toronto, ON M4W 1M9, Canada. TEL 416-961-1325, FAX 416-961-0941, gxo@tube.com, mail@gxo.com. Ed., Pub. Dan Brill. adv.: color page CND 3,600; trim 10.75 x 8.25. Circ: 18,000.

700 USA
GRAPHIC WORK OF BIRGER SANDZEN. Text in English. 1952. irreg., latest vol.4, 2001. USD 7.50 per issue (effective 2003). bk.rev. **Document type:** *Academic/Scholarly.* **Description:** A catalog of the prints produced by Birger Sandzen by year, title, size, and number of editions.
Published by: Birger Sandzen Memorial Foundation, PO Box 348, Lindsborg, KS 67456-0348. TEL 913-227-2220, FAX 913-227-4170, fineart@sandzen.org, http://www.sandzen.org. Ed. Charles P Greenough III. Adv. contact Larry Griffis. Circ: 2,000 (paid).

760 GBR ISSN 1350-0937
NC997.A1
GRAPHICS INTERNATIONAL; the magazine for the creative graphic design business. Variant title: Graphics. Text in English. 1988. m. adv. bk.rev.; software rev. illus. back issues avail. **Document type:** *Magazine, Trade.* **Description:** Presents innovative corporate identity, packaging, graphic design, illustration, and computer graphics work from the international circuit.
Formerly (until 1992): Hot Graphics (0962-7308)
Indexed: BrCerAb, DAAI.
—CCC.
Published by: Archant Specialist Ltd. (Subsidiary of: Archant), The Mill, Bearwalden Business Park, Royston Rd, Wendens Ambo, Essex CB11 4GB, United Kingdom. TEL 44-1799-544200, farine.clarke@archant.co.uk, http://www.archant.co.uk/. adv.: page GBP 950; trim 275 x 380. Circ: 8,000. **Dist. by:** Comag, Tavistock Works, Tavistock Rd, W Drayton, Middx UB7 7QX, United Kingdom. TEL 44-1895-444055, FAX 44-1895-433602.

760 GBR ISSN 0142-8853
GRAPHICS WORLD. Text in English. 1977. bi-m. GBP 28.50 domestic; GBP 47.25 in Europe; GBP 52.50 elsewhere. **Document type:** *Trade.*
Indexed: ABIPC, ABM, BMT, DAAI, EngInd, FLUIDEX, GALA.
—IE, Infotrieve. **CCC.**
Published by: Datateam Publishing Ltd, 15a London Rd, Maidstone, Kent ME16 8LY, United Kingdom. TEL 44-1622-687031, FAX 44-1622-757646, info@datateam.co.uk, http://www.datateam.co.uk/home/home.htm. Ed. Charles Walker. Pub. Nick Carpenter. Adv. contact Barry Morgan. Circ: 7,000.

760 659.1 USA ISSN 0017-3452
N8 CODEN: GRPHAB
GRAPHIS; international journal of visual communication. Text in English, French, German. 1944. bi-m. USD 90 domestic; USD 125 foreign (effective 2004). adv. bk.rev. illus.; stat. index. cum.index: 1944-1953. back issues avail.; reprints avail. **Document type:** *Trade.* **Description:** Provides information about product design, graphics, illustration, photography and architecture.
Related titles: Online - full text ed.: (from ProQuest Information & Learning).
Indexed: ABM, ASCA, ArtHuCI, ArtInd, BHA, ChLitAb, CurCont, DAAI, FLI, PCI, RASB.
—BLDSC (4212.527000), CASDDS, IE, Infotrieve, ingenta.
Published by: Graphis Inc, 307 Fifth Ave, 10th Fl, New York, NY 10016. TEL 212-532-9387, FAX 212-213-3229, info@graphis.com, http://www.graphis.com/journals. Ed. Jamie Reynolds. Pub. Martin B Pedersen. Adv. contact Marian Mayers. Circ: 23,000.

700 CHE
GRAPHIS ANNUAL REPORTS. Text in English. 1991. a. USD 75. illus. **Document type:** *Trade.* **Description:** Reviews how successful corporate publications were designed.
—BLDSC (4212.528100).
Published by: B Martin Pedersen Graphis Press Corp, Dufourstr 107, Zuerich, 8008, Switzerland. Ed. B Martin Pedersen. **Dist. in the U.S. by:** Watson-Guptill Publications, 1695 Oak St, Lakewood, NJ 08701. TEL 800-451-1741, FAX 908-363-0338.

700 CHE
GRAPHIS CORPORATE IDENTITY. Text in English. 1993. a. USD 75. illus. **Document type:** *Trade.* **Description:** Takes an in-depth look at the corporate-identity programs of 50 design firms from around the world.
Published by: B Martin Pedersen Graphis Press Corp, Dufourstr 107, Zuerich, 8008, Switzerland. Ed. B Martin Pedersen. **Dist. in the U.S. by:** Watson-Guptill Publications, 1695 Oak St, Lakewood, NJ 08701. TEL 800-451-1741, FAX 908-363-0338.

659.1 760 CHE ISSN 1012-9340
GRAPHIS DESIGN; international annual of design and illustration. Text in English, French, German. 1952. a. USD 69. index. **Document type:** *Trade.* **Description:** Presents more than 800 examples of excellence in illustrative and photographic visual communication from around the world.
Formerly: Graphis Annual (0072-5528)
Indexed: RASB.
—BLDSC (4212.528300).
Published by: B Martin Pedersen Graphis Press Corp, Dufourstr 107, Zuerich, 8008, Switzerland. Ed. B Martin Pedersen. Circ: 16,000. **Dist. in the U.S. by:** Watson-Guptill Publications, 1695 Oak St, Lakewood, NJ 08701. TEL 908-363-0338, 800-451-1741, FAX 908-363-0338.

700 686.2 CHE
GRAPHIS LETTERHEAD. Text in English. 1993. a. USD 69. illus. index. **Document type:** *Trade.* **Description:** Reproduces the best stationery designs created during the previous two years from around the world. Presents ideas to guide graphic design professionals in this area of corporate identity.
Published by: B Martin Pedersen Graphis Press Corp, Dufourstr 107, Zuerich, 8008, Switzerland. Ed. B Martin Pedersen. **Dist. in the U.S. by:** Watson-Guptill Publications, 1695 Oak St, Lakewood, NJ 08701. TEL 800-451-1741, FAX 908-363-0338.

700 686.2 CHE
GRAPHIS LOGO. Text in English. 1993. a. USD 60. illus. index. **Document type:** *Trade.* **Description:** Features more than 300 innovative, top-quality corporate logos and brand trademarks from around the world. Presents ideas for running a successful corporate identity program.
Published by: B Martin Pedersen Graphis Press Corp, Dufourstr 107, Zuerich, 8008, Switzerland. Ed. B Martin Pedersen. **Dist. in the U.S. by:** Watson-Guptill Publications, 1695 Oak St, Lakewood, NJ 08701. TEL 800-451-1741, FAX 908-363-0338.

769.5 CHE ISSN 1021-2892
GRAPHIS POSTERS; international annual of poster art. Text in English, French, German. 1973. a. CHF 123, USD 69. illus. **Document type:** *Trade.*
Published by: B Martin Pedersen Graphis Press Corp, Dufourstr 107, Zuerich, 8008, Switzerland. Ed. B Martin Pedersen. Circ: 8,500. **Dist in the U.S. by:** Watson-Guptill Publications, 1695 Oak St, Lakewood, NJ 08701. TEL 800-451-1741, FAX 908-363-0338.

760 746.92 CHE
GRAPHIS T - SHIRT DESIGN. Text in English. 1994. a. USD 75. illus. **Document type:** *Trade.* **Description:** Presents innovative T-shirt designs in creative fashion photographs.
Published by: B Martin Pedersen Graphis Press Corp, Dufourstr 107, Zuerich, 8008, Switzerland. Ed. B Martin Pedersen. **Dist. in the U.S. by:** Watson-Guptill Publications, 1695 Oak St, Lakewood, NJ 08701. TEL 800-451-1741, FAX 908-363-0338.

700 DEU ISSN 0342-3158
GRAPHISCHE KUNST; Zeitschrift fuer Graphikfreunde. Text in German. 1973. s-a. EUR 28 (effective 2001). bk.rev. illus. back issues avail. **Document type:** *Magazine, Consumer.* **Description:** Covers the art of graphic prints within this century.
Related titles: Microfilm ed.: (from BHP).
Indexed: ABM, DIP, IBR, IBZ, RASB.
—IE, Infotrieve.
Published by: Edition Curt Visel, Weberstr 36, Memmingen, 87700, Germany. TEL 49-8331-2853, FAX 49-8331-490364, visel@edition-curt-visel.de, info@edition-curt-visel.de, http://www.edition-curt-visel.de. Ed. Curt Visel. Circ: 1,000.

GREY ROOM. see *ARCHITECTURE*

GRUNDSCHULE KUNST. see *EDUCATION—Teaching Methods And Curriculum*

700 ESP ISSN 0210-1254
GUADALIMAR; revista de las artes. Text in Spanish. 1975. bi-m. EUR 27.05 domestic; EUR 39.07 in Europe; EUR 66.11 elsewhere (effective 2003). **Description:** Covers artistic creation in the plastic arts.
Indexed: BHA.
—CINDOC.

Published by: Miguel Fernandez-Braso Ed. & Pub., Villanueva, 22, Madrid, 28001, Spain. **Dist. by:** Asociacion de Revistas Culturales de Espana. info@arce.es, http://www.arce.es.

700　　　CHN　　　ISSN 1003-3343
GUANG YU YING/LIGHT AND SHADOW. Text in Chinese. 1981. q.
Published by: Jiangsu Renmin Chubanshe/Jiangsu People's Publishing House, 165 Zhongyang Road, Nanjing, Jiangsu 210009, China. TEL 86-25-6634309, FAX 86-25-3379766, http://www.book-wind.com/. Ed. Xiao Zhuang.

GUGONG WENWU YUEKAN/NATIONAL PALACE MUSEUM. MONTHLY OF CHINESE ART. see *MUSEUMS AND ART GALLERIES*

700　　　FRA　　　ISSN 0533-5167
GUIDE EMER. Text in French. 1947. biennial. adv. **Document type:** *Directory.* **Description:** Contains information on the art trade and antique dealers in France and neighboring countries.
Formerly: Guide Europeen de l'Amateur d'Art, de l'Antiquaire et du Bibliophile (0066-3069)
Published by: Editions Froville, 73 rue Notre Dame des Champs, Paris, 75006, France. TEL 33-1-44073166, FAX 33-1-44072161. Pub. Jacques Guespereau. Circ: 10,000 (paid).

700　　　FRA
GUIDE INTERNATIONAL DES EXPERTS & SPECIALISTES; guide juridique de l'art - liste des catalogues raisonnes. Text in French. a.
Published by: Editions des Catalogues Raisonnes, 18 rue Godefroy Cavaignac, Paris, 75011, France. TEL 1-43-56-29-50, FAX 1-43-56-29-27. Ed. Armand Israel.

353.77　　　USA
GUIDE TO ARTS ADMINISTRATION TRAINING RESEARCH (YEARS). Text in English. 1975. biennial. USD 12.95 (effective 1999). **Document type:** *Consumer.*
Formerly: Survey of Arts Administration Training
Published by: Americans for the Arts, 1000 Vermont Ave N W, Ste 12, Washington, DC 20005-4903. TEL 202-371-2830, FAX 202-371-0424. Ed. Dan J Martin. Circ: 1,500.

GUIDE TO LITERARY AGENTS; 500 agents who sell what you write. see *PUBLISHING AND BOOK TRADE*

700　　　USA　　　ISSN 0360-3407
NX398
GUIDE TO NATIONAL ENDOWMENT FOR THE ARTS. Cover title: National Endowment for the Arts. A New Look. Text in English. 1972. a. free. **Document type:** *Government.*
Formerly: National Endowment for the Arts. Guide to Programs (0547-6658)
Published by: U.S. National Endowment for the Arts, Public Information Office, 1100 Pennsylvania Ave, N W, Washington, DC 20506. TEL 202-682-5400, http://www.arts.endow.gov, http://www.nea.gov. Circ: 20,000.

760　　　USA　　　ISSN 1099-2316
GUILD NEWS. Text in English. bi-m. bk.rev. **Document type:** *Newspaper, Trade.* **Description:** Covers legal and industry issues in visual communications.
Formerly (until 199?): Graphic Artists Guild. News (1096-6366)
Published by: Graphic Artists Guild, 90 John St, Ste 403, New York, NY 10038-3202. TEL 212-791-3400, FAX 212-791-0333, execdir@gag.org, http://www.gag.org/news/index.php. Ed., R&P Steven R Schubert. Circ: 5,000 (controlled).

GUILD SOURCEBOOKS: THE ARCHITECT'S SOURCEBOOK - ARCHITECTURAL ARTS & SCULPTURE. see *ARCHITECTURE*

GUILD SOURCEBOOKS: THE DESIGNER'S SOURCEBOOK - ART FOR THE WALL, FURNITURE & ACCESSORIES. see *INTERIOR DESIGN AND DECORATION*

790　　　USA
GUILDNOTES. Text in English. bi-m. free membership. **Document type:** *Newsletter.* **Description:** Information about issues, programs and funding related to the field of community arts schools.
Published by: National Guild of Community Schools of Art, 520 Eighth Ave, 3rd Fl, Ste 302, New York, NY 10018. TEL 212-268-3337, FAX 212-268-3995, info@natguild.org, http://www.nationalguild.org. Ed. Lolita Mayadas. Circ: 2,000.

GUNMA UNIVERSITY, FACULTY OF EDUCATION. ANNUAL REPORT: ART, TECHNOLOGY, HEALTH & PHYSICAL EDUCATION, AND SCIENCE OF HUMAN LIVING SERIES. see *EDUCATION—Higher Education*

700　　　CHN　　　ISSN 1005-6912
GUOHUA JIA. Text in Chinese. q. USD 28.30. **Description:** Covers traditional Chinese painting.
Formerly: Yingchun Hua

Published by: Tianjin Renmin Meishu Chubanshe/Tianjin People's Fine Art Publishing House, 150 Machang Dao, Heping-qu, Tianjin 300050, China. TEL 86-2-328-0984, FAX 86-2-3313358. Ed. Du Ziling. **Dist. overseas by:** China International Book Trading Corp, 35 Chegongzhuang Xilu, Haidian District, PO Box 399, Beijing 100044, China.

700 792 780 720　　　DEU　　　ISSN 0947-3882
H D K MAGAZIN. (Hochschule der Kuenste Berlin) Text in German. 1975. s-a. free. bk.rev. back issues avail. **Document type:** *Academic/Scholarly.*
Formerly: H D K Info
Published by: Hochschule der Kuenste Berlin, Presse- und Informationsstelle, Ernst-Reuter-Platz 10, Berlin, 10587, Germany. TEL 49-30-31852450, FAX 49-30-3185-2635, http://www.hdk-berlin.de. Ed. Verena Tafel. Circ: 4,800.

745.5　　　DEU
H K H PERSPEKTIVEN. (Holz und Kunststoffverarbeitende Handwerk) Text in German. 1973. m. adv.
Formerly: Info Holz und Kunststoff
Published by: Fachverband Holz und Kunststoff Nordrhein-Westfalen, Kreuzstr 108-110, Dortmund, 44137, Germany. TEL 0231-9120100, FAX 0231-91201010. Ed. Ralf Bickert.

741.6　　　DEU
H S AKTUELL. Text in German. 1985. bi-m. bk.rev. illus. back issues avail. **Document type:** *Consumer.*
Published by: Heinrich Schmid GmbH und Co., Lederstr 33, Reutlingen, 72764, Germany. TEL 07121-326111, FAX 07121-326165. Circ: 4,000.

741.5　　　USA
H U P. Text in English. 1985. biennial. USD 6. back issues avail. **Description:** Contains cartoon art for adults.
Published by: Last Gasp of San Francisco, 777 Florida St, San Francisco, CA 94110. TEL 415-824-6636, FAX 415-824-1836. Ed. R Crumb. Circ: 25,000.

745.5　　　DNK　　　ISSN 0903-0425
HAAND & VAERK. Text in Danish. 1900. 10/yr. free membership. adv.
Former titles (until 1967): Haandvaerkerbladet; (until 1960): Medlemsblad for Haandvaerkerforeningen i Kjoebenhavn
Published by: Haandvaerkerforeningen i Kjoebenhavn, Dronningens Tvaergade 2 A, Copenhagen K, 1302, Denmark. TEL 45-33-12-27-17, FAX 45-33-14-16-25. Ed. Adam Pade. adv.: B&W page DKK 4,800; 200 x 135. Circ: 2,836.

745　　　DNK　　　ISSN 0109-4564
HAANDVAERKSHISTORISK TIDSSKRIFT. Text in Danish. 1983. q. membership. illus.
Published by: Haadverkshistorisk Selskab, c/o Birgit C Villumsen, Foerlev, Illerupvej 2, Skanderborg, 8660, Denmark.

709.4　　　DEU　　　ISSN 0072-9205
HABELTS DISSERTATIONSDRUCKE. REIHE KUNSTGESCHICHTE. Text in German. 1953. irreg., latest vol.8, 1985. price varies. **Document type:** *Monographic series, Academic/Scholarly.*
Published by: Dr. Rudolf Habelt GmbH, Am Buchenhang 1, Bonn, 53115, Germany. TEL 49-228-9238322, FAX 49-228-9238323, info@habelt.de, http://www.habelt.de.

700　　　DNK　　　ISSN 0085-1361
HAFNIA: COPENHAGEN PAPERS IN THE HISTORY OF ART. Text in English, French, German. 1970. irreg. price varies. back issues avail. **Document type:** *Monographic series, Academic/Scholarly.*
Indexed: AIAP, BHA, NAA.
Published by: Koebenhavns Universitet, Afdeling for Kunsthistorie/University of Copenhagen. Department of Art History, Bygning 21, Karen Blixens Vej 1, Copenhagen S, 2300, Denmark. TEL 45-35-328195, FAX 45-35-328222. Eds. Hannemarie Ragn Jensen, Oystein Hjort. Circ: 600.

HANDBUCH DER ORIENTALISTIK. 7. ABTEILUNG. KUNST UND ARCHAEOLOGIE/HANDBOOK OF ORIENTAL STUDIES. SECTION 7. ART AND ARCHEOLOGY. see *ASIAN STUDIES*

HARDCORE INK. see *MUSIC*

708.144　　　USA　　　ISSN 1065-6448
HARVARD UNIVERSITY ART MUSEUMS. BULLETIN. Text in English. 1992. 3/yr. **Document type:** *Bulletin, Academic/Scholarly.*
Indexed: AIAP, ArtInd.
—BLDSC (4270.773000).
Published by: Harvard University Art Museums, 32 Quincy St, Cambridge, MA 02138. TEL 617-495-9400, FAX 617-496-9762, mbarone@fas.harvard.edu, http://www.artmuseums.harvard.edu.

HARVESTER. see *LITERATURE*

HAWAII ANTIQUES, ART, & COLLECTIBLES QUARTERLY. see *ANTIQUES*

700　　　GBR　　　ISSN 1353-9760
P96.S45
HEADPRESS. Text in English. 1991. 3/yr. GBP 16 domestic; GBP 20 in Europe; GBP 8.50 newsstand/cover (effective 2000). adv. bk.rev.; film rev. illus. **Document type:** *Consumer.* **Description:** Covers bizarre culture, deviant conceptions and cinematic extremes, including artist interviews.
Address: 40 Rossall Ave, Radcliffe, Manchester M26 IJD, United Kingdom. TEL 44-161-796-1935, FAX 44-161-796-1935, david.headpress@zen.co.uk, http://www.headpress.com/. Ed., Pub., R&P, Adv. contact David Kerekes. Circ: 3,000.

THE HEALING MUSE. see *LITERATURE*

HEARD MUSEUM JOURNAL. see *MUSEUMS AND ART GALLERIES*

HEARTLANDS; a magazine of midwest life and art. see *LITERATURE*

HEDGEHOG (FT. LAUDERDALE). see *LITERATURE—Poetry*

700　　　USA　　　ISSN 1091-9708
THE HEDGEHOG (SAN FRANCISCO); international arts review. Text in English. 1996. q. USD 20 domestic; USD 30 foreign (effective 2001).
Published by: The Lively Foundation, 2565 Washington St., San Francisco, CA 94115. http://www.livelyfoundation.org. Eds. Jonathan Clark, Leslie Friedman.

HENRY'S AUKTIONEN. see *ANTIQUES*

700 669　　　DEU　　　ISSN 0942-7511
HEPHAISTOS; internationale Zeitschrift fuer Metallgestalter. Text in German. 1992. 6/yr. bk.rev. **Document type:** *Journal, Trade.*
Indexed: AIAP, BHA, MLA-IB.
—BLDSC (4295.847000).
Published by: Verlag Hephaistos, Gnadenberger Weg 4, Immenstadt, 87509, Germany. TEL 49-8379-728016, FAX 49-8379-728018. Ed., R&P, Adv. contact Peter Elgass. Circ: 2,000.

704.918　　　DEU　　　ISSN 0942-7562
NX655
HERMENEIA; Beitraege zu Kultur und Kunst, Ikonen und Theologie des christlichen Ostens. Text in German. 1985. q. adv. bk.rev. back issues avail. **Document type:** *Academic/Scholarly.* **Description:** Presents information on all aspects of Orthodox and Eastern Orthodox sacred art, hagiography, liturgy and liturgical music.
Former titles (until 1992): Zeitschrift fuer Ostkirchliche Kunst Hermeneia (0930-6897); (until 1986): Ermenia (0178-4323)
Indexed: BHA, DIP, IBR, IBZ.
Published by: Typos Verlag, Gruener Weg 40A, Bochum, 44791, Germany. TEL 49-234-501932, FAX 49-234-503576, 101763.2306@compuserve.com. Ed., R&P Nikolaus Thon. Adv. contact Kerstin Keller. Circ: 1,000.

709　　　USA　　　ISSN 0899-9856
HERMENEUTICS OF ART. Text in English. irreg., latest 2001. price varies. **Document type:** *Monographic series, Academic/Scholarly.* **Description:** Presents original research in the history and theoretical foundations of the visual arts.
Published by: Peter Lang Publishing, Inc., 275 Seventh Ave, 28th Fl, New York, NY 10001. TEL 212-647-7700, 212-647-7706, 800-770-5264, FAX 212-647-7707, customerservice@plang.com, http://www.peterlang.com. Ed. Moshe Barasch.

700 800　　　DEU　　　ISSN 0946-9923
HERZOG AUGUST BIBLIOTHEK. AUSSTELLUNGSKATALOGE. Text in German. irreg., latest vol.82, 2003. price varies. adv. **Document type:** *Monographic series, Academic/Scholarly.*
Published by: (Herzog August Bibliothek), Harrassowitz Verlag, Taunusstr 14, Wiesbaden, 65183, Germany. TEL 49-611-5300, FAX 49-611-530570, verlag@harrassowitz.de, http://www.harrassowitz.de. R&Ps Albrecht Weddigen, Michael Langfeld. Adv. contact Robert Gietz.

700　　　SWE　　　ISSN 1103-1832
HETEROGENESIS/REVISTA DE ARTES VISUALES/TIDSKRIFT FOER VISUELL KONST; revista de artes visuales; tidskrift foer visuell konst. Text in Spanish, Swedish. 1992. q. SEK 150 domestic; SEK 40 per issue domestic; EUR 25 in Europe; EUR 7 per issue in Europe; USD 32 elsewhere; USD 9 per issue elsewhere (effective 2004). **Document type:** *Journal, Academic/Scholarly.*
Related titles: Online - full content ed.: ISSN 1402-4632. 1996.
Published by: Konstfoereningen Mulato Gil, PO Box 760, Lund, 22007, Sweden. heterogenesis@telia.com, http://www.heterogenesis.com. Ed. Ximena Narea TEL 46-46-2220946.

700　　　USA
HIBELETTER; current events of the Edna Hibel Society. Text in English. 1978. q. membership. illus. **Document type:** *Newsletter, Consumer.* **Description:** Features a variety of subjects relating to Edna Hibel.
Formerly: Edna Hibel Society Newsletter

A

Published by: Edna Hibel Society, PO Box 9721, Coral Springs, FL 33705. TEL 561-533-6872, FAX 561-533-0174, http://www.hibel.org. Ed., R&P Ralph Burg TEL 954-731-6699. Circ: 4,500.

HIGHLANDER. see *GEOGRAPHY*

HIRMAGAZIN - MAGYAR IPARSZOVETSEG. see *LABOR UNIONS*

700 GBR
HISLOP'S ART SALES INDEX. Text in English. a. GBP 250 domestic; EUR 375 in Europe (effective 2004); USD 375 elsewhere (effective 2000). adv. mkt. back issues avail. **Document type:** *Consumer.* **Description:** Contains 140,000 entries of fine art sold at auction worldwide. Essential for collectors, dealers, galleries, museums and libraries.
Formerly (until 2004): Art Sales Index
Related titles: CD-ROM ed.; E-mail ed.; Fax ed.; Online - full text ed.
—BLDSC (4315.699000).
Published by: Art Sales Index Ltd, 16 Luddington Ave, Virginia Water, Surrey GU25 4DF, United Kingdom. TEL 44-1344-841750, FAX 44-1344-841760, asi@art-sales-index.com, http://www.art-sales-index.com/system/index.html. Ed. Duncan Hislop. adv.: B&W page USD 2,000, color page USD 3,000; trim 297 x 210.

700 USA ISSN 0738-5625
NX7
HISPANIC AMERICAN ARTS✶ ; all you want or must know, about everything, in all the fields of Hispanic American arts. Text in Spanish, English. 1974. 3/yr. USD 42. bk.rev.; film rev.; play rev. bibl.; illus. index.
Published by: E. Darino, Ed. & Pub., 222 Park Ave S, Apt 2A, New York, NY 10003.

700 FRA ISSN 0992-2059
N7480
➤ **HISTOIRE DE L'ART**; revue de recherche et d'information. Text in French; Abstracts in English. 1988. 2/yr. EUR 45 (effective 2005). adv. **Document type:** *Academic/Scholarly.*
Indexed: ABM, AIAP, BHA.
Published by: (Association des Professeurs d'Archeologie et d'Histoire de l'Art des Universites), A.P.A.H.A.U., Centre d'Histoire, 3 rue Michelet, Paris, 75006, France. TEL 33-1-40469390, FAX 33-1-40469390. Ed. Marie-Felicie Perez. R&P, Adv. contact Laetitia Temporelli.

700 800 SWE ISSN 0348-6958
HJAERNSTORM. Variant title: Tidskriften Hjaernstorm. Text in Swedish. 1977. q. SEK 200; SEK 70 per issue (effective 2004). **Document type:** *Bulletin, Academic/Scholarly.*
Related titles: Online - full text ed.: ISSN 1402-5167.
Published by: Kulturfoereningen Hjaernstorm, PO Box 34237, Stockholm, 10026, Sweden. bo-p@telia.com, http://hjarnstorm.com/index.html, http://www.tvs.se/hjaernstorm. Ed. Staffan Kling. Pub., Adv. contact Bo Pettersson.

741.5 USA ISSN 1074-7354
HOGAN'S ALLEY; the magazine of the cartoon arts. Text in English. 1994. s-a. USD 21.95 domestic for 4 nos.; USD 30.95 foreign for 4 nos.; USD 6.95 newsstand/cover (effective 2000). adv. bk.rev. illus. back issues avail. **Document type:** *Consumer.* **Description:** Focuses on cartooning with special emphasis on newspaper strips.
Related titles: Online - full text ed.: (from CompuServe Inc.).
Published by: Bull Moose Publishing Corp., PO Box 47684, Atlanta, GA 30362. TEL 770-458-2624, FAX 770-458-3657, 71061.43@compuserve.com, http://www.eagle.com/hogan, http://www.cagle.com/hogan. Ed., Pub., R&P, Adv. contact Tom Heintjes. B&W page USD 250; trim 10.75 x 8.25. Circ: 5,000 (paid).

700 IRN ISSN 1025-9570
HONAR-HA-YE-ZIBA/JOURNAL OF FACULTY OF FINE ARTS. Text in Persian, Modern; Abstracts in English. 1995. s-a. IRR 7,000 (effective 2005). **Description:** Research-based journal in the field of Urban and Regional Planning, Architecture, Industrial Design, Visual Arts, Performing Arts and Music.
Published by: University of Tehran/Danishgah-i Tihran, Faculty of Fine Arts, Tehran, Iran. TEL 98-21-6415282, FAX 98-21-6461504, fineartj@ut.ac.ir. Ed. Mohammad M Azizi.

700 USA ISSN 0360-4756
N576.H6
HONOLULU ACADEMY OF ARTS. JOURNAL. Text in English. 1974. irreg., latest vol.4, 1986. **Document type:** *Monographic series.*
Indexed: BHA.
Published by: Honolulu Academy of Arts, 900 S Beretania St, Honolulu, HI 96814.

750 NLD ISSN 1567-8717
THE HOOGSTEDER JOURNAL. Text in English. 1996. irreg., latest vol.6, 1999. F, free; free. illus. back issues avail. **Document type:** *Journal, Consumer.* **Description:** Takes a close look at various exhibitions and art reviews.
Related titles: Online - full content ed.
Published by: (Kunsthandel Hoogsteder & Hoogsteder BV), Hoogsteder & Hoogsteder, Lange Vijverberg 15, The Hague, 2513 AC, Netherlands. info@hoogsteder.com, http://www.hoogsteder.com/journal. Ed. Marike Dickmann-Wijnand.

700 780 USA
HOOK (IRVINGTON); art, ideas & evolution. Text in English. d. music rev. **Description:** Offers on-line arts and entertainment e-zine featuring art, music, interactive shockwave games, QTVR demos, audio and video clips, and more.
Media: Online - full text.
Published by: (Market Vision Studios), Edward Greenberg, Ed. & Pub., Trent Bldg, 50 S Buckhout St, Irvington, NY 10533. TEL 914-591-3320, FAX 914-591-3321, webmaster@thehook.com, http://www.thehook.com. R&P Ed Greenberg.

HORTUS ARTIUM MEDIEVALIUM. see *HISTORY—History Of Europe*

HRVATSKA REVIJA. see *LITERARY AND POLITICAL REVIEWS*

700 DNK ISSN 0901-5795
HRYMFAXE; kunsttidsskrift. Text in Danish, Norwegian. 1971. q. DKK 250 (effective 2005). adv. back issues avail. **Document type:** *Magazine.*
Indexed: ABM.
Published by: Forlaget Hrymfaxe, Janus Bygningen, Laerkevej 25, Tistrup, 6862, Denmark. TEL 45-75-299825, FAX 45-75-291272, mail@janusbygningen.dk, http://www.janusbygningen.dk/velkomst.php?menu=hrymfaxe. Ed. Arne Mumgaard. Adv. contact Flemming Beck-Petersen. page DKK 2,190. Circ: 2,300.

HUDEBNI VYCHOVA. see *EDUCATION*

HUESO HUMERO. see *LITERATURE*

HUG'N'AKISS. see *LIFESTYLE*

HUMBOLDT (PORTUGUESE EDITION); revista para o mondo Luso-Brasileiro. see *LITERARY AND POLITICAL REVIEWS*

HUNT INSTITUTE FOR BOTANICAL DOCUMENTATION. BULLETIN. see *BIOLOGY—Botany*

HUNTINGTON LIBRARY QUARTERLY; studies in English and American history and literature. see *LITERATURE*

700 JOR
HUWAT AL-FUNOUN✶ **/ARTS AMATEURS.** Text in Arabic; Section in English, German. 1968. m. adv. bk.rev.
Published by: Club of Arts Amateurs, P O Box 6370, Amman, Jordan. Ed. Nayef Kamal Naanah. Circ: 10,000.

HVEDEKORN. see *LITERATURE*

700 500 MEX ISSN 0536-2571
I C A C H✶ ; organo de divulgacion cultural. Text in Spanish. 1973 (no.7). s-a.
Published by: Instituto de Ciencias y Artes de Chiapas, 2a y 3a Oriente, Tuxtla, Gutierrez, Chiapas, Mexico.

700 GBR ISSN 0957-2465
I C A DOCUMENTS. (Institute of Contemporary Arts) Text in English. 198?. irreg. **Document type:** *Monographic series.*
—BLDSC (4360.176500).
Published by: Institute of Contemprary Art, The Mall, London, SW1Y 5AH, United Kingdom. TEL 44-20-79303647, http://www.ica.org.uk.

700 792 GBR
I C A MONTHLY BULLETIN. Text in English. 1977. m. GBP 25 to members. illus. **Document type:** *Bulletin.* **Description:** Gallery, theater, cinema and talks, events and news of the Institute of Contemporary Arts.
Formerly (until Oct. 1977): I C A Quarterly
Published by: Institute of Contemporary Arts, The Mall, London, SW1, United Kingdom. TEL 44-20-7930-0493, FAX 44-20-7873-0051, info@ica.org.uk, http://www.illumin.co.uk/ica/. Circ: 31,000.

700 913 USA
I C S NEWSLETTER. Text in English. 1982. biennial. membership. back issues avail. **Document type:** *Newsletter.*
Published by: International Catacomb Society, 61 Beacon St, Boston, MA 02108. TEL 617-742-1285. Circ: 1,000.

343 700 USA ISSN 1098-1195
N8554
I F A R JOURNAL. Text in English. 1984. q. USD 65 domestic; USD 85 foreign; USD 100 domestic associate (active subscriber); USD 120 foreign associate (active subscriber) (effective 2003). adv. bk.rev. illus. cum.index. reprints avail. **Document type:** *Journal, Academic/Scholarly.* **Description:** Publishes articles on authentication, art theft, fraud, recovery, legal issues, and cultural property laws.
Formerly (until 1998): I F A R Reports (8756-7172); Which was formed by the merger of (1981-1984): Art Research News (0884-2892); (1979-1984): Stolen Art Alert (0197-0208); Which was formerly (until 1980): Art Theft Archive Newsletter (0736-8712)
Indexed: ABM, ArtInd.
Published by: International Foundation for Art Research, Inc., 500 Fifth Ave, New York, NY 10110. TEL 212-391-6234, FAX 212-391-8794, http://www.ifar.org. Ed. Sharon Flescher. R&P, Adv. contact Kathleen Ferguson. Circ: 1,500.

I F O STUDIEN ZU KULTUR UND WIRTSCHAFT. see *BUSINESS AND ECONOMICS*

700 020 USA ISSN 0741-2940
NE3000
➤ **I S C A QUARTERLY.** Text in English. 1982. q. USD 90 domestic; USD 110 foreign (effective 2003). back issues avail. **Document type:** *Journal, Academic/Scholarly.* **Description:** Promotes xerography as a creative tool and art form for prints and artists' books. Original artist contributed print editions are collated.
Published by: International Society of Copier Artists Ltd., 759 President St, # 2H, Brooklyn, NY 11215. TEL 718-638-3264, isca4art2b@aol.com, http://members.aol.com/isca4art2b/I.S.C.A.homepage.html/. Ed., Pub., R&P Louise Neaderland. Circ: 125 (paid).

769.562 NLD
I U O M A MAGAZINE. Text in English. 1991. a. membership. illus. index. **Description:** Discusses international projects and activities of the union and its members, with addresses, calls for submissions and notices of projects.
Published by: International Union of Mail Artists, PO Box 10388, Tilburg, 5000 JJ, Netherlands. Ed. Ruud Janssen. Circ: 10,000.

IBDA'/INNOVATION. see *LITERATURE*

ICARUS. see *LITERATURE*

760 659.1 GBR
ICOGRADA MESSAGE BOARD. Text in English. 1963. q. free to members. bk.rev. back issues avail. **Document type:** *Newsletter.* **Description:** Contains articles on professional design, new designs, an international design calendar, information relating to intellectual property, reproduction rights, and copyright issues, educational matters, and news of members.
Indexed: DAAI.
Published by: International Council of Graphic Design Associations, International Council Of Graphic Design Associatio, PO Box 398, London, W11 4UG, United Kingdom. TEL 44-171-603-8494, FAX 44-171-371-6040, 106065.2235@compuserve.com. R&P, Adv. contact Mary V Mullin. Circ: 2,200.

704.9 USA ISSN 1547-8793
N8185.5
▼ **ICONOFILE.** Text in English. 2003 (Spr.). q. USD 56 domestic; USD 68 foreign (effective 2004). **Document type:** *Journal.*
Address: 1250 Maize Way, Willits, CA 95490-9587. info@iconofile.com, http://www.iconofile.com. Ed. George O'Hanlon. Pub. Tanya Zaytseva.

755 ITA
ICONOGRAPHIA FRANCISCANA. Text in Italian. 1973. irreg., latest vol.11, 1999. price varies.
Published by: Frati Minori Cappuccini, Istituto Storico, Circonv. Occidentale 6850, Casella Postale 18382, Rome, RM 00163, Italy. TEL 39-6-660521, FAX 39-6-66162401.

704.948 DNK ISSN 0106-1348
N7957
ICONOGRAPHISK POST; nordisk tidsskrift for ikonografi - Nordic iconographic review. Variant title: I C O Den Iconographiske Post. Nordic Review of Iconography. Text in Danish, Norwegian, Swedish; Summaries in English. 1970. q. DKK 175; DKK 50 per issue (effective 2005). bk.rev. bibl.; illus. cum.index: 1970-1974, 1975-1984, 1985-1994. **Document type:** *Journal, Academic/Scholarly.*
Formerly (until 2001): Iconographiske Post
Indexed: BHA, NAA, RILM.
—IE, Infotrieve.
Published by: Koebenhavns Universitet, Afdeling for Kirkehistorie. Center for Kunst og Kristendom/University of Copenhagen. Section for Church History, Koebmagergade 44-46, PO Box 2164, Copenhagen K, 1150, Denmark. TEL 45-35-323621, 45-35-323610, FAX 45-35-323639. Ed. Louise Lillie TEL 45-35-323628. Circ: 1,500.

704.948 NLD
➤ **ICONOGRAPHY OF RELIGIONS.** Text in Dutch. 1973. irreg., latest 1996. price varies. illus. Supplement avail. **Document type:** *Monographic series, Academic/Scholarly.* **Description:** Scholarly studies discussing religious iconography in traditions from all parts of the world.
—BLDSC (4362.063000).

Published by: (Rijksuniversiteit Groningen/University of Groningen, Institute of Religious Iconography), Brill Academic Publishers, PO Box 9000, Leiden, 2300 PA, Netherlands. TEL 31-71-53-53-500, FAX 31-71-53-17-532, http://www.brill.nl. R&P Elizabeth Venekamp. **Subscr. in N. America to:** PO Box 605, Herndon, VA 20172. TEL 703-661-1585, 800-337-9255, FAX 703-661-1501, cs@brillusa.com. **Distr. outside N. America by:** c/o Turpin Distribution, Stratton Business Park, Pegasus Drive, Biggleswade, BEDFORDSHIRE SG 18 8TQ, United Kingdom. TEL 44-1767-604-954, FAX 44-1767-601-640, brill@turpin-distribution.com.

755 NLD ISSN 0169-8184
➤ **ICONOGRAPHY OF RELIGIONS. SECTION 10, NORTH AMERICA.** Text in Dutch. 1973. irreg., latest vol.7, 1986. price varies. illus. **Document type:** *Monographic series, Academic/Scholarly.* **Description:** Scholarly monographs on the iconography of indigenous North American religions.
Published by: (Rijksuniversiteit Groningen/University of Groningen, Institute of Religious Iconography), Brill Academic Publishers, PO Box 9000, Leiden, 2300 PA, Netherlands. TEL 31-71-53-53-500, FAX 31-71-53-17-532, cs@brill.nl, http://www.brill.nl. R&P Elizabeth Venekamp. **Subscr. in N. America to:** PO Box 605, Herndon, VA 20172. TEL 703-661-1585, 800-337-9255, FAX 703-661-1501, cs@brillusa.com. **Distr. outside N. America by:** c/o Turpin Distribution, Stratton Business Park, Pegasus Drive, Biggleswade, BEDFORDSHIRE SG 18 8TQ, United Kingdom. TEL 44-1767-604-954, FAX 44-1767-601-640, brill@turpin-distribution.com.

755 NLD ISSN 0169-9970
➤ **ICONOGRAPHY OF RELIGIONS. SECTION 11, ANCIENT AMERICA.** Text in Dutch. irreg., latest vol.4, 1981. price varies. illus. **Document type:** *Monographic series, Academic/Scholarly.* **Description:** Scholarly monographs on the iconography of pre-Columbian American religions.
Published by: (Rijksuniversiteit Groningen/University of Groningen, Institute of Religious Iconography), Brill Academic Publishers, PO Box 9000, Leiden, 2300 PA, Netherlands. TEL 31-71-53-53-500, FAX 31-71-53-17-532, cs@brill.nl, http://www.brill.nl. R&P Elizabeth Venekamp. **Subscr. in N. America to:** PO Box 605, Herndon, VA 20172. TEL 703-661-1585, 800-337-9255, FAX 703-661-1501, cs@brillusa.com. **Distr. outside N. America by:** c/o Turpin Distribution, Stratton Business Park, Pegasus Drive, Biggleswade, BEDFORDSHIRE SG 18 8TQ, United Kingdom. TEL 44-1767-604-954, FAX 44-1767-601-640, brill@turpin-distribution.com.

755 NLD ISSN 0169-9725
➤ **ICONOGRAPHY OF RELIGIONS. SECTION 12, EAST AND CENTRAL ASIA.** Text in Dutch. irreg., latest vol.13, 1985. price varies. illus. **Document type:** *Monographic series, Academic/Scholarly.* **Description:** Scholarly monographs on the iconography of East and Central Asian religions, including Chinese and Korean Buddhism, Confucianism, and other religious traditions.
Published by: (Rijksuniversiteit Groningen/University of Groningen, Institute of Religious Iconography), Brill Academic Publishers, PO Box 9000, Leiden, 2300 PA, Netherlands. TEL 31-71-53-53-500, FAX 31-71-53-17-532, cs@brill.nl, http://www.brill.nl. R&P Elizabeth Venekamp. **Subscr. in N. America to:** PO Box 605, Herndon, VA 20172. TEL 703-661-1585, 800-337-9255, FAX 703-661-1501, cs@brillusa.com. **Distr. outside N. America by:** c/o Turpin Distribution, Stratton Business Park, Pegasus Drive, Biggleswade, BEDFORDSHIRE SG 18 8TQ, United Kingdom. TEL 44-1767-604-954, FAX 44-1767-601-640, brill@turpin-distribution.com.

755 NLD ISSN 0169-8133
➤ **ICONOGRAPHY OF RELIGIONS. SECTION 13, INDIAN RELIGIONS.** Text in Dutch. 1973. irreg., latest vol.17, 1995. price varies. illus. **Document type:** *Monographic series, Academic/Scholarly.* **Description:** Scholarly monographs on the iconography of Indian religions, including Buddhism, Jainism, Sikhism, in India and neighboring geographical regions.
Published by: (Rijksuniversiteit Groningen/University of Groningen, Institute of Religious Iconography), Brill Academic Publishers, PO Box 9000, Leiden, 2300 PA, Netherlands. TEL 31-71-53-53-500, FAX 31-71-53-17-532, cs@brill.nl, http://www.brill.nl. R&P Elizabeth Venekamp. **Subscr. in N. America to:** PO Box 605, Herndon, VA 20172. TEL 703-661-1585, 800-337-9255, FAX 703-661-1501, cs@brillusa.com. **Distr. outside N. America by:** c/o Turpin Distribution, Stratton Business Park, Pegasus Drive, Biggleswade, BEDFORDSHIRE SG 18 8TQ, United Kingdom. TEL 44-1767-604-954, FAX 44-1767-601-640, brill@turpin-distribution.com.

755 NLD ISSN 0169-9873
➤ **ICONOGRAPHY OF RELIGIONS. SECTION 14, IRAN.** Text in Dutch. 1980. irreg., latest vol.4, 1980. EUR 41, USD 49 per vol. (effective 2003). illus. **Document type:** *Monographic series, Academic/Scholarly.* **Description:** Scholarly monographs on the iconography of Iranian religions, including Zoroastrianism and Parsism.

Published by: (Rijksuniversiteit Groningen/University of Groningen, Institute of Religious Iconography), Brill Academic Publishers, PO Box 9000, Leiden, 2300 PA, Netherlands. TEL 31-71-53-53-500, FAX 31-71-53-17-532, cs@brill.nl, http://www.brill.nl. R&P Elizabeth Venekamp. **Subscr. in N. America to:** PO Box 605, Herndon, VA 20172. TEL 703-661-1585, 800-337-9255, FAX 703-661-1501, cs@brillusa.com.

755 NLD ISSN 0169-8036
➤ **ICONOGRAPHY OF RELIGIONS. SECTION 15, MESOPOTAMIA AND THE NEAR EAST.** Text in Dutch. 1976. irreg., latest vol.15, 1976. price varies. illus. **Document type:** *Monographic series, Academic/Scholarly.* **Description:** Scholarly monographs on the religious iconography of the ancient Near East.
Published by: (Rijksuniversiteit Groningen/University of Groningen, Institute of Religious Iconography), Brill Academic Publishers, PO Box 9000, Leiden, 2300 PA, Netherlands. TEL 31-71-53-53-500, FAX 31-71-53-17-532, cs@brill.nl, http://www.brill.nl. R&P Elizabeth Venekamp. **Subscr. in N. America to:** PO Box 605, Herndon, VA 20172. TEL 703-661-1585, 800-337-9255, FAX 703-661-1501, cs@brillusa.com. **Distr. outside N. America by:** c/o Turpin Distribution, Stratton Business Park, Pegasus Drive, Biggleswade, BEDFORDSHIRE SG 18 8TQ, United Kingdom. TEL 44-1767-604-954, FAX 44-1767-601-640, brill@turpin-distribution.com.

755 NLD ISSN 0169-8338
➤ **ICONOGRAPHY OF RELIGIONS. SECTION 16, EGYPT.** Text in Dutch. 1982. irreg., latest vol.10, 1988. illus. **Document type:** *Monographic series, Academic/Scholarly.* **Description:** Scholarly monographs on the religious iconography of ancient Egypt.
Published by: (Rijksuniversiteit Groningen/University of Groningen, Institute of Religious Iconography), Brill Academic Publishers, PO Box 9000, Leiden, 2300 PA, Netherlands. TEL 31-71-53-53-500, FAX 31-71-53-17-532, cs@brill.nl, http://www.brill.nl. R&P Elizabeth Venekamp. **Subscr. in N. America to:** PO Box 605, Herndon, VA 20172. TEL 703-661-1585, 800-337-9255, FAX 703-661-1501, cs@brillusa.com. **Distr. outside N. America by:** c/o Turpin Distribution, Stratton Business Park, Pegasus Drive, Biggleswade, BEDFORDSHIRE SG 18 8TQ, United Kingdom. TEL 44-1767-604-954, FAX 44-1767-601-640, brill@turpin-distribution.com.

755 NLD ISSN 0169-9822
➤ **ICONOGRAPHY OF RELIGIONS. SECTION 17, GREECE AND ROME.** Text in Dutch. 1976. irreg., latest vol.3, 1976. illus. **Document type:** *Monographic series, Academic/Scholarly.* **Description:** Scholarly monographs on the religious iconography of ancient Greece and Rome.
Published by: (Rijksuniversiteit Groningen/University of Groningen, Institute of Religious Iconography), Brill Academic Publishers, PO Box 9000, Leiden, 2300 PA, Netherlands. TEL 31-71-53-53-500, FAX 31-71-53-17-532, cs@brill.nl, http://www.brill.nl. R&P Elizabeth Venekamp. **Subscr. in N. America to:** PO Box 605, Herndon, VA 20172. TEL 703-661-1585, 800-337-9255, FAX 703-661-1501, cs@brillusa.com. **Distr. outside N. America by:** c/o Turpin Distribution, Stratton Business Park, Pegasus Drive, Biggleswade, BEDFORDSHIRE SG 18 8TQ, United Kingdom. TEL 44-1767-604-954, FAX 44-1767-601-640, brill@turpin-distribution.com.

755 NLD ISSN 0169-9679
➤ **ICONOGRAPHY OF RELIGIONS. SECTION 19, ANCIENT EUROPE.** Text in Dutch. 1985. irreg. price varies. illus. **Document type:** *Monographic series, Academic/Scholarly.* **Description:** Scholarly monographs on the iconography of ancient European religions.
Published by: (Rijksuniversiteit Groningen/University of Groningen, Institute of Religious Iconography), Brill Academic Publishers, PO Box 9000, Leiden, 2300 PA, Netherlands. TEL 31-71-53-53-500, FAX 31-71-53-17-532, cs@brill.nl, http://www.brill.nl. R&P Elizabeth Venekamp. **Subscr. in N. America to:** PO Box 605, Herndon, VA 20172. TEL 703-661-1585, 800-337-9255, FAX 703-661-1501, cs@brillusa.com. **Distr. outside N. America by:** c/o Turpin Distribution, Stratton Business Park, Pegasus Drive, Biggleswade, BEDFORDSHIRE SG 18 8TQ, United Kingdom. TEL 44-1767-604-954, FAX 44-1767-601-640, brill@turpin-distribution.com.

755 NLD
➤ **ICONOGRAPHY OF RELIGIONS. SECTION 2, NEW ZEALAND.** Text in Dutch. 1986. irreg., latest vol.1, 1986. price varies. illus. **Document type:** *Monographic series, Academic/Scholarly.* **Description:** Scholarly monographs on topics in religious iconography.
Published by: (Rijksuniversiteit Groningen/University of Groningen, Institute of Religious Iconography), Brill Academic Publishers, PO Box 9000, Leiden, 2300 PA, Netherlands. TEL 31-71-53-53-500, FAX 31-71-53-17-532, cs@brill.nl, http://www.brill.nl. R&P Elizabeth Venekamp. **Subscr. in N. America to:** PO Box 605, Herndon, VA 20172. TEL

703-661-1585, 800-337-9255, FAX 703-661-1501, cs@brillusa.com. **Distr. outside N. America by:** c/o Turpin Distribution, Stratton Business Park, Pegasus Drive, Biggleswade, BEDFORDSHIRE SG 18 8TQ, United Kingdom. TEL 44-1767-604-954, FAX 44-1767-601-640, brill@turpin-distribution.com.

755 NLD ISSN 0169-8435
➤ **ICONOGRAPHY OF RELIGIONS. SECTION 20, MANICHAEISM.** Text in Dutch. 1982. irreg., latest vol.1, 1982. illus. **Document type:** *Monographic series, Academic/Scholarly.* **Description:** Scholarly monographs on the religious iconography of Manichaeism.
Published by: (Rijksuniversiteit Groningen/University of Groningen, Institute of Religious Iconography), Brill Academic Publishers, PO Box 9000, Leiden, 2300 PA, Netherlands. TEL 31-71-53-53-500, FAX 31-71-53-17-532, cs@brill.nl, http://www.brill.nl. R&P Elizabeth Venekamp. **Subscr. in N. America to:** PO Box 605, Herndon, VA 20172. TEL 703-661-1585, 800-337-9255, FAX 703-661-1501, cs@brillusa.com. **Distr. outside N. America by:** c/o Turpin Distribution, Stratton Business Park, Pegasus Drive, Biggleswade, BEDFORDSHIRE SG 18 8TQ, United Kingdom. TEL 44-1767-604-954, FAX 44-1767-601-640, brill@turpin-distribution.com.

755 NLD ISSN 0169-9776
➤ **ICONOGRAPHY OF RELIGIONS. SECTION 21, MANDAEISM.** Text in Dutch. 1978. irreg., latest vol.1, 1978. price varies. illus. **Document type:** *Monographic series, Academic/Scholarly.* **Description:** Scholarly monographs on the religious iconography of Mandaeism.
Published by: (Rijksuniversiteit Groningen/University of Groningen, Institute of Religious Iconography), Brill Academic Publishers, PO Box 9000, Leiden, 2300 PA, Netherlands. TEL 31-71-53-53-500, FAX 31-71-53-17-532, cs@brill.nl, http://www.brill.nl. R&P Elizabeth Venekamp. **Subscr. in N. America to:** PO Box 605, Herndon, VA 20172. TEL 703-661-1585, 800-337-9255, FAX 703-661-1501, cs@brillusa.com. **Distr. outside N. America by:** c/o Turpin Distribution, Stratton Business Park, Pegasus Drive, Biggleswade, BEDFORDSHIRE SG 18 8TQ, United Kingdom. TEL 44-1767-604-954, FAX 44-1767-601-640, brill@turpin-distribution.com.

700.48297 NLD ISSN 0169-8389
➤ **ICONOGRAPHY OF RELIGIONS. SECTION 22, ISLAM.** Text in Dutch. 1970. irreg., latest vol.3, 1985. price varies. illus. **Document type:** *Monographic series, Academic/Scholarly.* **Description:** Scholarly monographs on the religious iconography of Islam.
Published by: (Rijksuniversiteit Groningen/University of Groningen, Institute of Religious Iconography), Brill Academic Publishers, PO Box 9000, Leiden, 2300 PA, Netherlands. TEL 31-71-53-53-500, FAX 31-71-53-17-532, cs@brill.nl, http://www.brill.nl. R&P Elizabeth Venekamp. **Subscr. in N. America to:** PO Box 605, Herndon, VA 20172. TEL 703-661-1585, 800-337-9255, FAX 703-661-1501, cs@brillusa.com. **Distr. outside N. America by:** c/o Turpin Distribution, Stratton Business Park, Pegasus Drive, Biggleswade, BEDFORDSHIRE SG 18 8TQ, United Kingdom. TEL 44-1767-604-954, FAX 44-1767-601-640, brill@turpin-distribution.com.

700.48296 NLD ISSN 0169-8281
➤ **ICONOGRAPHY OF RELIGIONS. SECTION 23, JUDAISM.** Text in Dutch. 1975. irreg., latest vol.5, 1987. price varies. illus. **Document type:** *Monographic series, Academic/Scholarly.* **Description:** Scholarly monographs on topics in the iconography of Judaism.
Published by: (Rijksuniversiteit Groningen/University of Groningen, Institute of Religious Iconography), Brill Academic Publishers, PO Box 9000, Leiden, 2300 PA, Netherlands. TEL 31-71-53-53-500, FAX 31-71-53-17-532, cs@brill.nl, http://www.brill.nl. R&P Elizabeth Venekamp. **Subscr. in N. America to:** PO Box 605, Herndon, VA 20172. TEL 703-661-1585, 800-337-9255, FAX 703-661-1501, cs@brillusa.com. **Distr. outside N. America by:** c/o Turpin Distribution, Stratton Business Park, Pegasus Drive, Biggleswade, BEDFORDSHIRE SG 18 8TQ, United Kingdom. TEL 44-1767-604-954, FAX 44-1767-601-640, brill@turpin-distribution.com.

704.948 246 NLD ISSN 0169-992X
➤ **ICONOGRAPHY OF RELIGIONS. SECTION 24, CHRISTIANITY.** Text in Dutch. irreg., latest vol.13, 1979. price varies. illus. **Document type:** *Monographic series, Academic/Scholarly.* **Description:** Scholarly monographs on topics in Christian iconography.
Published by: (Rijksuniversiteit Groningen/University of Groningen, Institute of Religious Iconography), Brill Academic Publishers, PO Box 9000, Leiden, 2300 PA, Netherlands. TEL 31-71-53-53-500, FAX 31-71-53-17-532, cs@brill.nl, http://www.brill.nl. R&P Elizabeth Venekamp. **Subscr. in N. America to:** PO Box 605, Herndon, VA 20172. TEL 703-661-1585, 800-337-9255, FAX 703-661-1501, cs@brillusa.com. **Distr. outside N. America by:** c/o Turpin Distribution, Stratton Business Park, Pegasus Drive, Biggleswade, BEDFORDSHIRE SG 18 8TQ, United Kingdom. TEL 44-1767-604-954, FAX 44-1767-601-640, brill@turpin-distribution.com.

755   NLD   ISSN 0169-8087
➤ ICONOGRAPHY OF RELIGIONS. SECTION 5, AUSTRALIAN ABORIGINAL RELIGION. Text in Dutch. 1974. irreg., latest vol.4, 1974. price varies. illus. **Document type:** *Monographic series, Academic/Scholarly.* **Description:** Scholarly monographs on the iconography of Australian aboriginal religions.
Published by: (Rijksuniversiteit Groningen/University of Groningen, Institute of Religious Iconography), Brill Academic Publishers, PO Box 9000, Leiden, 2300 PA, Netherlands. TEL 31-71-53-53-500, FAX 31-71-53-17-532, cs@brill.nl, http://www.brill.nl. R&P Elizabeth Venekamp. **Subscr. in N. America to:** PO Box 605, Herndon, VA 20172. TEL 703-661-1585, 800-337-9255, FAX 703-661-1501, cs@brillusa.com. **Distr. outside N. America by:** c/o Turpin Distribution, Stratton Business Park, Pegasus Drive, Biggleswade, BEDFORDSHIRE SG 18 8TQ, United Kingdom. TEL 44-1767-604-954, FAX 44-1767-601-640, brill@turpin-distribution.com.

755   NLD   ISSN 0169-8230
➤ ICONOGRAPHY OF RELIGIONS. SECTION 7, AFRICA. Text in Dutch. 1974. irreg., latest vol.1, 1985. price varies. illus. **Document type:** *Monographic series, Academic/Scholarly.* **Description:** Scholarly monographs on the iconography of African religions.
Published by: (Rijksuniversiteit Groningen/University of Groningen, Institute of Religious Iconography), Brill Academic Publishers, PO Box 9000, Leiden, 2300 PA, Netherlands. TEL 31-71-53-53-500, FAX 31-71-53-17-532, cs@brill.nl, http://www.brill.nl. R&P Elizabeth Venekamp. **Subscr. in N. America to:** PO Box 605, Herndon, VA 20172. TEL 703-661-1585, 800-337-9255, FAX 703-661-1501, cs@brillusa.com. **Distr. outside N. America by:** c/o Turpin Distribution, Stratton Business Park, Pegasus Drive, Biggleswade, BEDFORDSHIRE SG 18 8TQ, United Kingdom. TEL 44-1767-604-954, FAX 44-1767-601-640, brill@turpin-distribution.com.

755   NLD   ISSN 0169-9628
➤ ICONOGRAPHY OF RELIGIONS. SECTION 8, ARCTIC PEOPLES. Text in Dutch. 1985. irreg., latest vol.2, 1985. price varies. illus. **Document type:** *Monographic series, Academic/Scholarly.* **Description:** Scholarly monographs on the iconography of Eskimo and Arctic religions.
Published by: (Rijksuniversiteit Groningen/University of Groningen, Institute of Religious Iconography), Brill Academic Publishers, PO Box 9000, Leiden, 2300 PA, Netherlands. TEL 31-71-53-53-500, FAX 31-71-53-17-532, cs@brill.nl, http://www.brill.nl. R&P Elizabeth Venekamp. **Subscr. in N. America to:** PO Box 605, Herndon, VA 20172. TEL 703-661-1585, 800-337-9255, FAX 703-661-1501, cs@brillusa.com. **Distr. outside N. America by:** c/o Turpin Distribution, Stratton Business Park, Pegasus Drive, Biggleswade, BEDFORDSHIRE SG 18 8TQ, United Kingdom. TEL 44-1767-604-954, FAX 44-1767-601-640, brill@turpin-distribution.com.

755   NLD   ISSN 0921-0334
➤ ICONOGRAPHY OF RELIGIONS. SECTION 9, SOUTH AMERICA. Text in Dutch. 1987. irreg., latest vol.1, 1987. illus. **Document type:** *Monographic series, Academic/Scholarly.* **Description:** Scholarly monographs on the iconography of South American Indian religions.
—CCC.
Published by: (Rijksuniversiteit Groningen/University of Groningen, Institute of Religious Iconography), Brill Academic Publishers, PO Box 9000, Leiden, 2300 PA, Netherlands. TEL 31-71-53-53-500, FAX 31-71-53-17-532, cs@brill.nl, http://www.brill.nl. R&P Elizabeth Venekamp. **Subscr. in N. America to:** PO Box 605, Herndon, VA 20172. TEL 703-661-1585, 800-337-9255, FAX 703-661-1501, cs@brillusa.com. **Distr. outside N. America by:** c/o Turpin Distribution, Stratton Business Park, Pegasus Drive, Biggleswade, BEDFORDSHIRE SG 18 8TQ, United Kingdom. TEL 44-1767-604-954, FAX 44-1767-601-640, brill@turpin-distribution.com.

704.948   NLD
➤ ICONOGRAPHY OF RELIGIONS. SUPPLEMENTS. Text in Dutch. 1980. irreg., latest vol.1, 1980. price varies. illus. **Document type:** *Monographic series, Academic/Scholarly.*
Published by: (Rijksuniversiteit Groningen/University of Groningen, Institute of Religious Iconography), Brill Academic Publishers, PO Box 9000, Leiden, 2300 PA, Netherlands. TEL 31-71-53-53-500, FAX 31-71-53-17-532, cs@brill.nl, http://www.brill.nl. R&P Elizabeth Venekamp. **Subscr. in N. America to:** PO Box 605, Herndon, VA 20172. TEL 703-661-1585, 800-337-9255, FAX 703-661-1501, cs@brillusa.com. **Distr. outside N. America by:** c/o Turpin Distribution, Stratton Business Park, Pegasus Drive, Biggleswade, BEDFORDSHIRE SG 18 8TQ, United Kingdom. TEL 44-1767-604-954, FAX 44-1767-601-640, brill@turpin-distribution.com.

709.37   NLD
ICONOLOGICAL STUDIES IN ROMAN ART. Text in English. 1994. irreg., latest vol.3, 1994. EUR 45 per vol. (effective 2003). illus. back issues avail. **Document type:** *Academic/Scholarly.*

Published by: J.C. Gieben, Entrepotdok 72b, Amsterdam, 1018 AD, Netherlands. TEL 31-20-6234709, FAX 31-20-6275170, http://www.teachtext.net/gieben/. Ed. F J G M Miller. **Dist. in N. America by:** John Benjamins Publishing Co., PO Box 27519, Philadelphia, PA 19118-0519. TEL 215-836-1200.

741   ITA   ISSN 1123-6450
IDEA TATTOO. Text in Italian. 1995. m. EUR 4.60 newsstand/cover (effective 2003). adv. **Document type:** *Magazine, Consumer.*
Related titles: Spanish ed.: ISSN 1593-5647. 1998; English ed.: ISSN 1129-1303. 1999; French ed.: ISSN 1593-5655. 1998; Dutch ed.: ISSN 1593-5671. 1998; German ed.: ISSN 1593-5663. 2000.
Published by: Trentini S.r.l., Via Pier Luigi Nervi 1/B, Argenta, 44011, Italy. TEL 39-0532-318149, FAX 39-0532-310084, info@3ntini.com, http://www.3ntini.com/periodici.htm.

700   DEU
IKONENKALENDER. Text in German. a. illus. **Document type:** *Bulletin.*
Published by: Verlag Aurel Bongers, Postfach 100264, Recklinghausen, 45602, Germany.

700   POL   ISSN 0860-5769
N380
➤ IKONOTHEKA. Text in French, Polish; Summaries in French, German. 1990. irreg., latest vol.13, 1998. price varies. bk.rev. **Document type:** *Journal, Academic/Scholarly.* **Description:** Covers history of European art.
Indexed: BHA.
Published by: Uniwersytet Warszawski, Instytut Historii Sztuki, Ul. Krakowskie Przedmiescie 26-28, Warsaw, 00-927 , Poland. TEL 48-22-8261574, FAX 48-22-8281154. Ed. Andrzej Grzybkowski. Circ: 600.

700   USA   ISSN 0445-3387
AM101
ILLINOIS. STATE MUSEUM. HANDBOOK OF COLLECTIONS. Text in English. 1963. irreg., latest vol.6, 1988. **Document type:** *Monographic series.*
Published by: Illinois State Museum, Spring & Edwards Sts, Springfield, IL 62706. TEL 217-782-7386, FAX 217-782-1254, editor@museum.state.il.us, http://www.museum.state.il.us.

741   USA   ISSN 1543-4737
NC975
ILLUSTRATION. Text in English. 2001. q. USD 36 domestic; USD 72 foreign (effective 2003).
Published by: Illustration Magazine, 540 Wooddell Ct., Kirkwood, MO 63122. TEL 314-822-1580, FAX 314-822-2721, http://www.illustration-magazine.com. Ed., Pub. Dan Zimmer.

700   DEU   ISSN 0019-2457
NC960
ILLUSTRATION 63; Zeitschrift fuer die Buchillustration. Text in German. 1963. 3/yr. EUR 110 (effective 2001). bk.rev. illus. 40 p./no.; back issues avail. **Document type:** *Magazine, Consumer.* **Description:** Covers graphics and book illustration of this century.
Indexed: ABM, DIP, IBR, IBZ, RASB.
Published by: Edition Curt Visel, Weberstr 36, Memmingen, 87700, Germany. TEL 49-8331-2853, FAX 49-8331-490364, visel@edition-curt-visel.de, info@edition-curt-visel.de, http://www.edition-curt-visel.de. Ed. Curt Visel. Circ: 700.

760   JPN
ILLUSTRATION IN JAPAN. Text in Japanese, English. 1972. a.
Published by: (Daiichi Shuppan Center), Kodansha Ltd., 2-12-21 Otowa, Bunkyo-ku, Tokyo, 112-8001, Japan. TEL 81-3-3946-6201, FAX 81-3-3944-9915, http://www.kodansha.co.jp, http://www.toppan.co.jp/kodansha.

707   USA   ISSN 0019-2465
NC997.A1
ILLUSTRATOR. Text in English. 1916. a. USD 10 for 5 yrs. (effective 2004). illus.; tr.lit. 24 p./no.; **Document type:** *Academic/Scholarly.*
Indexed: DAAI.
Published by: Art Instruction Schools, 3400 Technology Dr., Minneapolis, MN 55418-6000. TEL 612-362-5060, FAX 612-362-5260, http://www.artists-ais.com. Pub. Steve Unverzagt. Circ: 30,000.

700 946   ESP   ISSN 0213-392X
N7101
IMAFRONTE. Text in Spanish; Summaries in English. 1955. irreg., latest vol.14, 1999. back issues avail. **Document type:** *Academic/Scholarly.* **Description:** Covers the history of Murcian and Baroque art.
Supersedes in part (in 1985): Universidad de Murcia. Anales. Filosofia y Letras (0463-9863)
Indexed: BHA, PCI, RILM.
—CINDOC.
Published by: (Universidad de Granada, Departamento de Historia del Arte), Universidad de Murcia, Servicio de Publicaciones, Edificio Saavedra Fajardo, C/ Actor Isidoro Maiquez 9, Murcia, 30007, Spain. TEL 34-968-363887, FAX 34-968-363414, vgm@um.es, http://www.um.es/spumweb. Ed. Jesus Francisco Rivas Carmona TEL 34-968-363183, Circ: 174.

IMAGE (SEATTLE); a journal of the arts & religion. see RELIGIONS AND THEOLOGY

700   ZAF   ISSN 1021-1497
➤ IMAGE & TEXT. Text in English. 1992. a. ZAR 25 (effective 2001). bk.rev. **Document type:** *Journal, Academic/Scholarly.* **Description:** A Journal for design, focuses on the South African context and provides a forum in which anyone interested in design and the study of design, can exchange and communicate ideas, opinions, experiences and research findings. The emphasis of the journal is a in-depth consideration of concerns related to all designers, educators and students can draw.
Published by: University of Pretoria, Faculty of Arts: Visual Art & Art History/Universiteit van Pretoria, Pretoria, 0002, South Africa. TEL 27-12-4202353, FAX 27-12-4203686, TELEX 3-22723 SA, leeflang@libarts.up.ac.za, leeflan@postino.up.ac.za. Ed. Marian D Sauthoff. Circ: 2,000 (paid and controlled).

➤ IMAGEN LATINOAMERICANA. see ETHNIC INTERESTS

051   USA
THE IMP. Text in English. irreg.
Published by: The Imp, 5046 S. Blackstone Ave., # 3, Chicago, IL 60615-3006. Ed. Dan Braeburn.

700 808.81   USA   ISSN 1044-7490
IMPETUS. Text in English. 1984. irreg. USD 20 domestic; USD 30 foreign (effective 2000). adv. bk.rev. back issues avail. **Document type:** *Journal, Consumer.* **Description:** Presents Social protest expressed through the means of poetry, artwork, editorials and articles.
Published by: Impetus Implosion Press, 4975 Comanche Trail, Stow, OH 44224. TEL 216-688-5210, FAX 216-688-5120, IMPETUS@aol.com. Ed. Cheryl A Townsend. R&P Cheryl Townsend. Circ: 1,000 (paid and controlled).

IMPREMPRES; revista tecnica de la industria grafica. see PAPER AND PULP

700   POL   ISSN 1234-8686
IMPRESJE; magazyn artystyczny. Text in Polish. 1995. q.
Document type: *Magazine, Consumer.*
Published by: Fundacja Pro Arte, Plac Szczepanski 5, Krakow, 31011, Poland. TEL 48-12-4231580, pro-arte@free.ngo.pl. Ed. Urszula Orman.

700 950   USA
➤ IMPRESSIONS (NEW YORK). Text in English. 1976. a. USD 60 to members (effective 2003). adv. bk.rev. 120 p./no. 1 cols./p.; back issues avail. **Document type:** *Journal, Academic/Scholarly.* **Description:** Devoted to the study and art of Japanese woodblock prints.
Published by: Ukiyo-e Society of America, Inc., PO BOX 665, F D R STA, New York, NY 10150. ukiyoe@earthlink.net, http://www.ukiyo-e.org. Ed. Julia D Meech. Adv. contact Allison Tolman TEL 212-489-7696. B&W page USD 475, color page USD 825; 7 x 9.5. Circ: 1,000.

700 800   ZAF   ISSN 1021-8629
IMPRINT; a magazine of the arts. Text in English. 1993. 3/yr. ZAR 22.80. illus. **Document type:** *Magazine, Consumer.*
Published by: Justified Press, PO Box 5091, Rivonia, Gauteng 2128, South Africa. TEL 27-11-8032500, FAX 27-11-8035094.

760 974   USA   ISSN 0277-7061
NE505
IMPRINT (FAIRFIELD). Text in English. 1976. s-a. free to members (effective 2005). adv. bk.rev. illus. back issues avail. **Document type:** *Academic/Scholarly.* **Description:** Scholarly articles concerning history, meanings, and techniques of prints made in America or about American subjects before 1900.
Indexed: AmH&L, BHA, HistAb.
Published by: American Historical Print Collectors Society, Inc., PO Box 201, Fairfield, CT 06430. TEL 810-332-3902. Ed. Sue Raincy. R&P Robert Braun TEL 203-255-1627. Adv. contact Donald O'Brien. Circ: 600.

700   USA
IN BRIEF (SAN FRANCISCO, 1974). Text in English. 1974. q. USD 12 to members. adv. bk.rev. illus.; stat.; tr.lit. **Document type:** *Newsletter.*
Formerly: Graphiti
Indexed: ChLitAb, NPI.
Published by: Artists in Print, Inc., 665 Third St, Ste 530, San Francisco, CA 94107. TEL 415-243-8244, FAX 415-495-3155. Ed. R Biggs. Circ: 3,000.

IN FOCUS (LOS ANGELES). see MOTION PICTURES

391   USA   ISSN 1088-2448
IN THE FLESH. Text in English. 1995. q. USD 6.95 newsstand/cover. **Document type:** *Consumer.* **Description:** Covers piercings, tattoos, and other art that modifies the human body.
Published by: Art & Ink Enterprises, 5 Marine View Plaza No 207, Hoboken, NJ 07030. TEL 201-653-2700, FAX 201-653-7892, tattoo1@ix.netcom.com, http://www.darkskinart.com. Ed., R&P Jean-Chris Miller. Pub. Casey Exton. Adv. contact Ken Knabb.

707 USA ISSN 1097-3710
HM623
IN VISIBLE CULTURE. Text in English. 1998. bi-m. **Description:** Features essays and art projects that address contemporary issues within visual studies.
Media: Online - full text.
Address: 424 Morey Hall, Rochester, NY 14627. TEL 716-275-9249, FAX 716-442-1692, nvisible@uhura.cc.rochester.edu, http://www.rochester.edu/in_visible_culture. Eds. Mario A Caro, Tina T Takemoto.

INCONTRI; rivista di studi italo-nederlandesi. see *HISTORY—History Of Europe*

THE INDEPENDENT MIND. see *LITERATURE*

700 USA
INDEX. Text in English. 1996. bi-m. USD 15; USD 50 foreign (effective 1998). film rev.; music rev. **Document type:** *Consumer.* **Description:** Covers the art, music and film scene. Publishes extensive interviews with performers, artists and film-makers, reviews of cultural events, fabulations and critical essays.
Address: 526 W 26th St, Ste 920, New York, NY 10001. TEL 212-243-1428, FAX 212-243-1603, editor@indexmagazine.com, http://www.indexmagazine.com. Ed. Bob Nickas. Pub. Peter Halley. R&P Cory Speyer. Adv. contact Ariana Speyer. Circ: 6,000.

INDIA STAR; a literary and arts magazine. see *LITERATURE*

720 ESP ISSN 1577-8029
INDUSTRIA & DISENO. Text in Spanish. 1989. bi-m.
Supersedes in part (in 1997): Experimenta Informa (1133-9667); Which was formerly (until 1992): Experimenta (1133-9659)
Related titles: ♦ Supplement to: Experimenta. ISSN 1133-9675.
Published by: Experimenta S.L., Churruca 27, 4o, Madrid, 28004, Spain. TEL 34-91-5214049, FAX 34-91-5213212, suscribe@revistaexperimenta.com, http://www.revistaexperimenta.com. Ed. Pierluigi Cattermole.

INFOBRIEF: FOTOGRAFIE; ein Kulleraugen Informationsdienst. see *PHOTOGRAPHY*

INSITES (CHICAGO). see *ARCHITECTURE*

700 AUS ISSN 1443-3680
INSPIRASI. Text in English. 1999. q. **Description:** Aims to promote Indonesian culture and cultural exchange.
Formerly (until 1999): A I A A Newsletter (Australia Indonesia Arts Alliance) (1443-3850)
Media: Online - full text.
Published by: Australia Indonesia Arts Alliance, PO Box 484, Byron Bay, NSW 2481, Australia. TEL 61-2-6685-7789, indoartsalliance@hotmail.com, indoarts@dingoblue.net.au, http://www.aiaa.org.au/news, http://ww.aiaa.org.au. Eds. Cande Chapman, Judith Shelley. R&P, Adv. contact Judith Shelley.

INSTITUT ARCHEOLOGIQUE DU LUXEMBOURG. ANNALES. see *ARCHAEOLOGY*

INSTITUT ARCHEOLOGIQUE DU LUXEMBOURG. BULLETINS; archeologie-art-histoire-folklore. see *ARCHAEOLOGY*

INSTITUT ARCHEOLOGIQUE LIEGEOIS. BULLETIN. see *ARCHAEOLOGY*

700 BEL ISSN 0085-1892
N13
➤ **INSTITUT ROYAL DU PATRIMOINE ARTISTIQUE. BULLETIN/KONINKLIJK INSTITUUT VOOR HET KUNSTPATRIMONIUM. BULLETIN.** Text and summaries in Dutch, French. 1958. a., latest vol.27, 2000, for the years 1996-1998. price varies. back issues avail. **Document type:** *Bulletin, Academic/Scholarly.* **Description:** Covers topics relating to Belgian art and conservation.
Indexed: A&ATA, BHA, RASB, RILM.
—IE, Linda Hall.
Published by: Institut Royal du Patrimoine Artistique, Parc du Cinquantenaire 1, Brussels, 1000, Belgium. TEL 32-2-739-6711, FAX 32-2-732-0105. Ed. Dominique Vanwijnsberghe. R&P M Serck-Dewaide. Circ: 1,100.

700 USA
INSTITUTE ITEMS. Text in English. m. USD 50 (effective 2000). tr.lit. back issues avail. **Document type:** *Newsletter.* **Description:** Keeps members updated on issues of interest, including legislation and regulations, association services, etc.
Published by: Art and Creative Materials Institute, 1280 Main St, PO Box 479, Hanson, MA 02341. TEL 781-293-4100, FAX 781-294-0808. Ed., R&P Debbie Gustafson. Circ: 350.

INSTITUTO BRASIL - ESTADOS UNIDOS. BOLETIM. see *EDUCATION*

INSTITUTO CARO Y CUERVO. NOTICIAS CULTURALES. see *LITERATURE*

INTANGIBLE. see *LITERATURE*

INTERFERENCES, ARTS, LETTRES. see *LITERATURE*

796.56 CAN
INTERNATIONAL ART POST. Text in English. 1988. a., latest vol.13, 2001. CND 25; USD 30 in United States; USD 35 in Europe (effective 2000). back issues avail. **Description:** Consists of full-color gummed and pin-hole perforated stamps by artists, cooperatively published.
Published by: Banana Productions, RR22, 3747 Sunshine Coast Hwy, Roberts Creek, BC V0N 2W2, Canada. TEL 604-885-7156, FAX 604-885-7183, a_banana@sunshine.net, http://www.bigpacific.com/anna_banana, http://www.vis-soft.com/banana/. Ed., R&P Anna Banana. Circ: 100 (paid).

700 AUS ISSN 1440-1320
INTERNATIONAL ARTIST; the magazine for artists by artists from around the world. Text in English. 1998. bi-m. AUD 49.50 domestic; AUD 52 in New Zealand; GBP 19 in United Kingdom; EUR 27 in Europe; USD 27 in United States; USD 42.80 in Canada; AUD 69 elsewhere (effective 2004). adv. illus. **Document type:** *Consumer.* **Description:** Presents arts from around the world in geographic sections. Includes articles on art methods and materials.
Published by: Elladrent Pty. Ltd., P0 Box 1084, Chatswood, NSW 2057, Australia. TEL 61-2-94916333, FAX 61-2-94115175, intartmag@aol.com, sales@artinthemaking.com, http://www.international-artist.com. Pub. Vincent Miller.

700 GBR ISSN 1355-6169
NX760
INTERNATIONAL ARTS MANAGER. Text in English. 1987. 10/yr. GBP 55 domestic; GBP 65 foreign (effective 2005). adv. **Document type:** *Magazine, Trade.* **Description:** Contains news and feature articles on performing arts managers, venues, and companies from all parts of the world.
Published by: Alain Charles Arts Publishing Ltd., 27 Wilfred St, London, SW1E 6PR, United Kingdom. TEL 44-20-78347676, FAX 44-20-79730076, subs@alaincharles.com, http://www.api.co.uk/acapnewiam.htm. Ed. Eva Johannson. Pub., Adv. contact Martin Huber. B&W page GBP 1,448, color page GBP 2,490. Circ: 4,500 (paid and controlled).

700 USA
INTERNATIONAL ASSOCIATION FOR THE FANTASTIC IN THE ARTS NEWSLETTER. Text in English. 1987. q. membership. film rev. bibl. back issues avail. **Document type:** *Newsletter.*
Published by: International Association for the Fantastic in the Arts, c/o Robert A. Collins, Dorothy F.Schmidt College of Arts & Letters, Florida Atlantic University, 777 Glades Rd, Boca Raton, FL 33431-0991. TEL 407-367-3838. Ed. Robert Collins. Circ: 400.

700 FRA
INTERNATIONAL ASSOCIATION OF PERFORMING ARTS LIBRARIES AND MUSEUMS. CONGRESS PROCEEDINGS. (Publisher of Proceedings varies) Text in French. 1957. biennial. **Document type:** *Proceedings.*
Formerly: International Society for Performing Arts Libraries and Museums. Congress Proceedings (0074-7882)
Published by: International Association of Performing Arts Libraries and Museums, 1 rue De Sully, Paris, 75004, France.

701.18 USA ISSN 1541-0447
N6502
INTERNATIONAL CENTER FOR THE ARTS OF THE AMERICAS. Text in English. 2002. irreg. USD 29.95 newsstand/cover (effective 2002).
Published by: Museum of Fine Arts, Houston, 6826, Houston, TX 77265-6826.

709 USA
INTERNATIONAL CENTER OF MEDIEVAL ART. NEWSLETTER. Text in English. 3/yr. membership. **Document type:** *Newsletter.*
Published by: International Center of Medieval Art, The Cloisters, Fort Tryon Park, New York, NY 10040. TEL 212-928-1146, FAX 212-928-9946, ICMA@medievalart.org, http://www.medievalart.org. Ed. Geneva Kornbluth.

INTERNATIONAL CHINESE SNUFF BOTTLE SOCIETY. JOURNAL. see *ANTIQUES*

709 FRA ISSN 0074-4190
INTERNATIONAL CONGRESS ON THE HISTORY OF ART. PROCEEDINGS. Text in French. 1873. quinquennial. reprints avail. **Document type:** *Proceedings, Trade.*
Published by: Orient - Express, c/o Institut d'Art et d'Archeologie, 3 rue Michelet, Paris, 75006, France. FAX 33-1-44070179. Eds. Aude Mantoux, Anne-Elizabeth Dunn-Vaturi. Adv. contact Aline Tenu.

700 JPN
INTERNATIONAL DESIGN YEARBOOK. Text in Japanese. a. JPY 13,800.
Published by: Bijutsu Shuppan-sha, Inaoka Bldg, 2-36 Kanda-Jinbo-cho, Chiyoda-ku, Tokyo, 1010051, Japan. TEL 03-3234-2151, FAX 03-3234-9451.

INTERNATIONAL DESIGN YEARBOOK. see *INTERIOR DESIGN AND DECORATION*

700 DEU ISSN 0074-4565
INTERNATIONAL DIRECTORY OF ARTS. Text in English, French, German, Italian, Spanish. 1949. biennial (in 3 vols.). USD 295 (effective 2001). adv. index. **Document type:** *Directory, Academic/Scholarly.* **Description:** Provides a comprehensive guide to art sources and markets in 137 countries. Contains more than 150,000 names and addresses of art restorers, publishers, libraries, art dealers and galleries, museums, associations.
Related titles: ♦ Series: International Directory of Arts & Museums of the World CD-ROM; ♦ Museums of the World.
Published by: K.G. Saur Verlag GmbH (Subsidiary of: Gale Group), Ortlerstr 8, Munchen, 81373, Germany. TEL 49-89-769021321, FAX 49-89-76902150, customerservice_saur@csi.com, http://www.saur.de. Adv. contact Constanze Gueldner. Circ: 10,000.

708 DEU
INTERNATIONAL DIRECTORY OF ARTS & MUSEUMS OF THE WORLD CD-ROM. Text in English. 1999. a. USD 525 (effective 2001). **Document type:** *Directory, Trade.* **Description:** Lists virtually all the people, publications, and institutions that make up today's art culture, both in the West and the East.
Media: CD-ROM (from K. G. Saur Verlag GmbH & Co.). **Related titles:** ♦ Series: International Directory of Arts. ISSN 0074-4565; ♦ Museums of the World.
Published by: K.G. Saur Verlag GmbH (Subsidiary of: Gale Group), Ortlerstr 8, Munchen, 81373, Germany. TEL 49-89-76902-0, FAX 49-89-76902150, customerservice_saur@csi.com, http://www.saur.de.

700 USA
INTERNATIONAL DIRECTORY OF CHRISTIAN ARTS ORGANIZATIONS✶. Text in English. 1991. irreg. USD 35. **Document type:** *Directory.* **Description:** Lists Christian arts organizations, including contact information, activities and publications.
Published by: Christians in the Arts Networking, Inc., 9 West Minster Ave, Box 242, Arlington, MA 02174-0003. TEL 617-646-1541, FAX 617-696-7725. adv.: B&W page USD 375.

741.4 USA ISSN 1068-7688
NK1170
INTERNATIONAL DIRECTORY OF DESIGN. Text in English. 1992. m. (in 12 vols.). USD 624.50 (effective 2000). adv. **Document type:** *Directory, Trade.* **Description:** Comprises design educational programs, professional organizations, and periodical publications; covers every major design discipline and every region of the world.
Related titles: Online - full text ed.
Published by: Penrose Press, PO Box 470925, San Francisco, CA 94147. TEL 415-567-4157, FAX 415-567-4165, orders@penrose-press.com, http://www.penrose-press.com/IDD/. Pub. Ray Lauzzana. R&P Denise Penrose. adv.: B&W page USD 200; trim 8.05 x 4. Circ: 500 (paid).

760 DNK ISSN 0020-6830
INTERNATIONAL GRAFIK; original graphics review. Text in Danish, English, French, German. 1969-1975; resumed 1976. s-a. DKK 60. adv. illus. index.
Indexed: RASB.
Address: PO Box 109, Frederikshavn, 9900, Denmark. Eds. Helmer Fogedgaard, Klaus Roedel.

INTERNATIONAL JOURNAL OF ART & DESIGN EDUCATION. see *EDUCATION—Teaching Methods And Curriculum*

INTERNATIONAL JOURNAL OF ART THERAPY; inscape. see *MEDICAL SCIENCES—Physical Medicine And Rehabilitation*

700 CAN ISSN 1480-8986
NX760
INTERNATIONAL JOURNAL OF ARTS MANAGEMENT. Text in English; Abstracts in English, French, Spanish. 1998. 3/yr. CND 64 domestic to individuals; USD 50 foreign to individuals; CND 128 domestic to institutions; USD 100 foreign to institutions; CND 38 domestic to students; USD 29 foreign to students (effective 2004). bk.rev. 80 p./no.; **Document type:** *Academic/Scholarly.*
Related titles: Online - full text ed.: (from Micromedia ProQuest, O C L C Online Computer Library Center, Inc., ProQuest Information & Learning).
Indexed: ABIn.
—BLDSC (4542.105200), IE, ingenta. **CCC.**
Published by: Ecole des Hautes Etudes Commerciales, 3000 Chemin de la Cote Sainte Catherine, Montreal, PQ H3T 2A7, Canada. TEL 514-340-5629, FAX 514-340-6432, http://www.hec.ca/ijam. Ed. Francois Colbert.

700 GBR ISSN 0940-7391
CC135
➤ **INTERNATIONAL JOURNAL OF CULTURAL PROPERTY.** Text in English. 1992-2002; resumed 2005. q. GBP 148 to institutions; USD 250 in North America to institutions; GBP 164 combined subscription to institutions; USD 275 combined subscription in North America to institutions (effective 2006). adv. back issues avail.; reprints avail. **Document type:** *Journal, Academic/Scholarly.* **Description:** Covers cultural property policy, ethics, preservation, economics and law.

Related titles: Online - full text ed.: ISSN 1465-7317. 2005. GBP 134 to institutions; USD 225 in North America to institutions (effective 2006) (from EBSCO Publishing, Gale Group, O C L C Online Computer Library Center, Inc., Swets Information Services).
Indexed: A&ATA, ABM, AIAP, AnthLit, BHA, BrArAb, FLP, IBR, IBZ, ILP, NumL.
—BLDSC (4542.181000), IE, Infotrieve, ingenta. **CCC.**
Published by: Cambridge University Press, The Edinburgh Bldg, Shaftesbury Rd, Cambridge, CB2 2RU, United Kingdom. TEL 44-1223-312393, FAX 44-1223-315052, journals@cambridge.org, http://journals.cambridge.org/jid_JCP, http://uk.cambridge.org/journals. Ed. Alexander A Bauer. adv.: page GBP 420, page USD 756. Circ: 750. **Subscr. to:** Cambridge University Press, 100 Brook Hill Dr, West Nyack, NY 10994. TEL 845-353-7500, FAX 845-353-4141, journals_subscriptions@cup.org

➤ **INTERNATIONAL JOURNAL OF EDUCATION AND THE ARTS.** see *EDUCATION*

▼➤ **INTERNATIONAL JOURNAL OF EDUCATION THROUGH ART.** see *EDUCATION*

➤ **INTERNATIONAL JOURNAL OF IMAGE AND GRAPHICS.** see *COMPUTERS—Computer Graphics*

700 USA ISSN 1045-0920
NX164.N4
➤ **INTERNATIONAL REVIEW OF AFRICAN AMERICAN ART**; an international publication. Text in English. 1976. q. USD 36 domestic; USD 44 foreign (effective 2004). adv. bk.rev. illus. reprints avail. **Document type:** *Journal, Academic/Scholarly.* **Description:** Covers art and culture of black people in the Americas.
Formerly: Black Art (0145-8116)
Related titles: Online - full text ed.: (from Chadwyck-Healey Inc., H.W. Wilson, O C L C Online Computer Library Center, Inc.).
Indexed: ABM, AIAP, ASCA, AmHI, ArtHuCI, ArtInd, BHA, CurCont, IIBP, PCI.
Address: Hampton University Museum, Hampton, VA 23668-0101. TEL 804-727-5142, FAX 804-727-5170, jbowles@hamptona.edu, http://www.hamptonu.edu/museum/publication.htm. Circ: 5,000.

391.65 USA ISSN 1065-643X
INTERNATIONAL TATTOO ART. Text in English. 1992. 6/yr. USD 29.95; USD 44.95 foreign; USD 4.99 newsstand/cover; GBP 2.90 newsstand/cover in United Kingdom; CND 5.99 newsstand/cover in Canada (effective 1999). adv. **Document type:** *Consumer.*
Indexed: ABM.
Published by: Butterfly Publications, Ltd., 462 Broadway, 4th Fl, New York, NY 10013. TEL 212-966-8400, FAX 212-960-9366. Ed. Chris Pfouts. Pub. Jason Childs. Adv. contact Nancy McCrary. **Subscr. to:** Jiffy Fulfillment Inc., PO Box 1102, Cranford, NJ 07016-1102. **Dist. in UK by:** Seymour Distribution Ltd, 86 Newman St, London W1T 3EX, United Kingdom. FAX 44-207-396-8002, enquiries@seymour.co.uk.

INTERPLAY (MALIBU); proceedings of symposia in comparative literature and the arts. see *LITERATURE*

INTERSPECIES NEWSLETTER. see *COMMUNICATIONS*

700 900 100 ITA
INTERVENTI CLASSENSI. Text in Italian, English. irreg., latest vol.19. price varies. **Document type:** *Monographic series, Academic/Scholarly.* **Description:** Studies on art, history, collection of classic libraries.
Indexed: MLA-IB.
Published by: (Biblioteca Classense di Ravenna), Angelo Longo Editore, Via Paolo Costa 33, Ravenna, 48100, Italy. TEL 39-0544-217026, FAX 39-0544-217554, longo-ra@linknet.it, http://www.longo-editore.it. Ed., Pub. Alfio Longo. R&P Marina De Leonardis. Circ: 3,500.

700 ITA ISSN 1124-6456
INTERVISTA; the "other" art magazine. Text in Italian. 1996. bi-m. USD 25 domestic; USD 35 in Europe; USD 55 elsewhere (effective 2001). **Document type:** *Magazine, Consumer.* **Description:** Contains interviews and large photos of artists, musicians, trendsetters and their creations.
Published by: Giancarlo Politi Editore, PO Box 95, Borgo Trevi, PG 06032, Italy. TEL 39-0742-381978, FAX 39-0742-381979, subscription@flashartonline.com, http://www.flashartonline.com.

700 305.897 CAN ISSN 0831-6708
E99.E7
INUIT ART QUARTERLY. Text in English. 1986. q. CND 26.75 domestic; USD 25 in United States; CND 39 elsewhere; CND 6.25 newsstand/cover (effective 2005). adv. bk.rev. illus. Index. reprints avail. **Document type:** *Journal, Academic/Scholarly.* **Description:** Features, profiles and news about Inuit art and artists as well as reviews of exhibitions.
Indexed: ABM, AICP, AbAn, ArtInd, CBCARef, DIP, IBR, IBZ, SRRA.
—**CCC.**
Published by: Inuit Art Foundation, 2081 Merivale Rd, Nepean, ON K2G 1G9, Canada. TEL 613-224-8189, FAX 613-224-2907, iaq@inuitart.org, http://www.inuitart.org/iaq.htm. Ed. Marybelle Mitchell. R&P Sheila Sturk-Green. Adv. contact Sheila Sturk Green. Circ: 1,923 (paid); 1,862 (controlled).

700 745.1 GBR ISSN 1471-3497
INVALUABLE & TRACE MAGAZINE. Text in English. 1989. m. adv. **Document type:** *Magazine.* **Description:** Publishes details of stolen objects which are made available to law enforcement agencies and auction houses.
Formerly (until 2000): Trace (0968-1388)
Published by: Invaluable, Catherine House, 76 Gloucester Pl, London, W1U 6HJ, United Kingdom. TEL 44-20-74873401, FAX 44-20-74874211, customer.services@invaluable.com, http://www.invaluable.com.

INVENTAIRE GENERAL DES MONUMENTS ET DES RICHESSES ARTISTIQUES DE LA FRANCE. see *ARCHITECTURE*

INVESTING IN ART. see *BUSINESS AND ECONOMICS—Investments*

700 500 970.1 USA ISSN 0021-0331
PS536.2
IO. Text in English. 1964. a. USD 40; USD 50 foreign. illus. back issues avail.
Published by: (Society for the Study of Native Arts and Sciences), North Atlantic Books, PO Box 12327, Berkeley, CA 94712. TEL 510-559-8277, FAX 510-559-8279. Ed. Richard Grossinger. Pub. Richard Glassinger. R&P Lindy Hough. Circ: 3,000.

IOWA STUDIES IN AFRICAN ART. see *ANTHROPOLOGY*

IPROPAGANDA. see *MUSIC*

708 IRL ISSN 1649-217X
N6782
➤ **IRISH ARTS REVIEW.** Text in English. 1984. q. (plus annual). EUR 56 in Ireland (includes N. Ireland); EUR 65 in United Kingdom; EUR 67 in Europe; USD 70 in United States; EUR 77 elsewhere (effective 2003). adv. bk.rev. illus. 272 p./no.; back issues avail. **Document type:** *Journal, Academic/Scholarly.* **Description:** Discusses Irish visual and decorative arts from pre-history to the present.
Former titles (until 2002): Irish Arts Review Yearbook (0791-3540); (until 1990): The G P A Irish Arts Review Yearbook (0791-038X); (until 1988): Irish Arts Review (0790-178X)
Related titles: Online - full text ed.: (from H.W. Wilson, O C L C Online Computer Library Center, Inc.).
Indexed: ABM, AIAP, ArtInd, BHA, DAAI, RILM.
—BLDSC (4568.870000).
Address: State Apartments, Dublin Castle, Dublin, 2, Ireland. TEL 353-1-6793525, FAX 353-1-6793503, editorial@irishartsreview.com, subscriptions@irishartsreview.com, http://www.irishartsreview.com. Ed. John Mulcahy. Adv. contact Yvonne Smalley. Circ: 3,000 (paid).

704.94897 956 USA ISSN 0739-3261
N6260
ISLAMIC ART. Text in English. 1981. irreg. price varies. **Document type:** *Monographic series, Academic/Scholarly.*
Indexed: AIAP.
—BLDSC (4583.019550).
Published by: Oxford University Press (Subsidiary of: Oxford University Press), 198 Madison Ave, New York, NY 10016. TEL 212-726-6000, 800-334-4249, http://www.us.oup.com.

709 956 USA ISSN 0742-1125
ISLAMIC ART AND ARCHITECTURE. Text in English. 1981. irreg. price varies.
Indexed: AIAP.
Published by: Mazda Publishers, PO Box 2603, Costa Mesa, CA 92626. TEL 714-751-5252. Ed. A Daneshvari.

700 746.9 USA
ISSUE (NEW YORK). Text in English. q. USD 30 domestic; USD 60 foreign (effective 2001). **Document type:** *Magazine, Consumer.*
Published by: Issue, Inc., 600 Braodway, Studio 4F, New York, NY 10012. http://www.issueinc.com. Pub. Jan-Willem Dikkers.

ISTITUTO NAZIONALE DI ARCHEOLOGIA E STORIA DELL'ARTE. RIVISTA. see *ARCHAEOLOGY*

709 940 ITA ISSN 0393-0904
ISTITUTO SICILIANO DI STUDI BIZANTINI E NEOELLENICI. MONUMENTI. Text in Italian. 1962. irreg., latest vol.6, 2000. **Document type:** *Monographic series.*
Published by: Istituto Siciliano di Studi Bizantini e Neoellenici, Via Noto, 34, Palermo, PA 90141, Italy. TEL 39-91-6259541, FAX 39-91-6259541.

700 800 ITA ISSN 0394-0411
ISTITUTO UNIVERSITARIO ORIENTALE DI NAPOLI. SEMINARIO DI STUDI DELL'EUROPA ORIENTALE. ARTE E LETTERATURA. Text in Italian. 1979. a.
Supersedes in part: Istituto Universitario Orientale di Napoli. Sezione Slava. Annali (0077-2771)
Indexed: MLA-IB.
Published by: Universita degli Studi di Napoli, L'Orientale/Dipartimento di Studi dell'Europa Orientale, Palazzo Giusso, Largo San Giovanni Maggiore, 30, Naples, NA 80134, Italy. TEL 39-81-7605430, FAX 39-81-5517914.

709 ITA
ISTITUTO VENETO DI SCIENZE, LETTERE ED ARTI. MONUMENTA VENETA. Text in Italian. irreg.
Published by: Istituto Veneto di Scienze, Lettere ed Arti, Campo S Stefano 2945, Venezia, 30124, Italy.

509 ITA
ISTITUTO VENETO DI SCIENZE, LETTERE ED ARTI. STUDI DI ARTE VENETA. Text in Italian. irreg.
Published by: Istituto Veneto di Scienze, Lettere ed Arti, Campo S Stefano 2945, Venezia, 30124, Italy.

745 620 NLD ISSN 1381-4249
ITEMS (VAKEDITIE); tijdschrift voor vormgeving. Text in Dutch. 1985. 6/yr. EUR 75 (effective 2005). adv. illus. **Document type:** *Trade.* **Description:** News and information in the fields of design, visual communication and architecture for design professionals.
Formerly (until 1993): Industrieel Ontwerpen (0920-0118)
—BLDSC (4588.584000).
Published by: Uitgeverij B I S, Postbus 323, Amsterdam, 1000 AH, Netherlands. TEL 31-20-5247560, FAX 31-20-5247557, items@bispublishers.nl, info@bispublishers.nl, http://www.bispublishers.nl/Items/htm_item/items.htm. Ed. Diana Krabbendam. Pub. Rudolf van Wezel. adv.: B&W page EUR 1,950; 216 x 274. Circ: 8,000.

700 ITA ISSN 0390-2498
ITERARTE. Text in Italian. 1974. bi-m. adv. illus.
Published by: Circolo Artistico di Bologna, Via di Roncrio 7A, Bologna, BO 40124, Italy. TEL 39-051-229490. Ed. Giovanni M Accame.

IWALEWA FORUM; working papers in African art and culture. see *GENERAL INTEREST PERIODICALS—Africa*

IZ STAROG I NOVOG ZAGREBA. see *ARCHITECTURE*

700 BGR ISSN 0861-9905
N7188
IZKUSTVO/ART IN BULGARIA. Text in Bulgarian. 1993. 10/yr. BGL 25; BGL 3 newsstand/cover (effective 2002). **Description:** Presents the latest tendencies in Bulgarian contemporary art, criticism, new ideas and events forming the Bulgarian culture.
Published by: AYA Promotion House, 17 Nishava St., ZHK Hipodruma, Sofia, 1612, Bulgaria. TEL 359-2-5815289, azholding@aster.net, azholding@usa.net, http://www.sca.bg/cultural-periodicals/catalog/izkustvo.htm. Ed. Dimitar Grozdanov.

IZLOZBENE SVESKE GALERIJE SRPSKE AKADEMIJE NAUKA I UMETNOSTI. see *HISTORY—History Of Europe*

700 BEL ISSN 0066-3174
JAARBOEK DER SCHONE KUNSTEN/ALGEMEEN JAARBOEK DER SCHONE KUNSTEN. Text in Dutch, French. 1928. a. USD 15. adv. bk.rev.
Formerly: Dessinateurs, Peintres et Sculpteurs de Belgique (0070-3869)
Indexed: BHA.
Published by: Editions ARTO, Av Winston Churchill 85, Brussels, 1180, Belgium. Circ: 4,000.

JAPAN. see *BUSINESS AND ECONOMICS*

700 616.89 JPN ISSN 0916-6688
RC489.A7
➤ **JAPANESE BULLETIN OF ARTS THERAPY.** Text in Japanese, Multiple languages. 1969. s-a. JPY 10,000 (effective 2001). adv. bk.rev. bibl.; charts; illus.; stat. back issues avail. **Document type:** *Bulletin, Academic/Scholarly.*
Indexed: e-psyche.
—**CCC.**
Published by: Societe Japonaise de Psychopathologie de l'Expression, c/o Neuropsychiatric Research Institute, 91 Bentencho, Shin Juku-ku, Tokyo, 162-0851, Japan. TEL 81-3-3260-5598, FAX 81-3-3260-5598. Ed. Dr. Makio Iimori.

➤ **JAPANESE SWORD SOCIETY OF THE U S BULLETIN.** see *ANTIQUES*

➤ **JASZKUNSAG**; social and artistic journal. see *LITERATURE*

700 890 491.93 780 CAN ISSN 0448-9179
AP95.L4
JAUNA GAITA. Text in Latvian; Summaries in English. 1955. bi-m. CND 35 domestic; USD 30 in United States (effective 2004). bk.rev. cum.index. back issues avail. **Document type:** *Magazine, Consumer.*
Indexed: MLA, MLA-IB.

Address: 23 Markland Dr, Etobicoke, ON M9C 1M8, Canada. TEL 416-621-0898, FAX 416-621-9717, ibulmanis@sympatico.ca, http://faculty.stcc.edu/zagarins/JG/htm. Ed. R Ekmanis. R&P Ingrida Bulmanis. Circ: 1,200.

JEOPARDY. see *LITERATURE*

700.48296 ISR ISSN 0792-0660
N7415

JEWISH ART. Text in English. 1974. a., latest vol.24, 1998. USD 640 full set (effective 2005); price varies per volume. bk.rev. bibl.; illus. back issues avail.; reprint service avail. from PQC. **Document type:** *Academic/Scholarly.* **Description:** Studies of Jewish art through the ages.
Formerly: Journal of Jewish Art (0160-208X)
Related titles: Microform ed.: (from PQC).
Indexed: ABM, AIAP, ASCA, ArtHuCI, ArtInd, BHA, CurCont, IJP, PCI, RILM.
—BLDSC (4668.351250).
Published by: Hebrew University of Jerusalem, Center for Jewish Art, Mount Scopus Humanities Bldg., Jerusalem, 91905, Israel. TEL 972-2-5882281, 972-2-5882285, FAX 972-2-5400105, cja@vms.huji.ac.il, http://www.hum.huji.ac.il/cja. Ed. Dr. Aliza Cohen-Mushlin. Circ: 2,000.

JEWISH CULTURE NEWS. see *ETHNIC INTERESTS*

750 CHN ISSN 1005-6890

JIANGSU HUAKAN/JIANGSU ART MONTHLY. Text in Chinese. 1974. m. USD 240 (effective 2001). 64 p./no.; **Document type:** *Magazine, Consumer.*
Published by: Jiangsu Meishu Chubanshe/Jiangsu Fine Arts Publishing House, 165 Zhongyang Lu, Nanjing, Jiangsu 210009, China. TEL 86-25-3242472, huakan@public1.ptt.js.cn. Ed. Liu Dianzhang. Pub. Wei Zheng. R&P Da Fan TEL 86-25-3354465. Circ: 25,000. **Dist. in US by:** China Books & Periodicals Inc, 360 Swift Ave., Ste. 48, S San Fran, CA 94080-6220. info@chinabooks.com, http://www.chinabooks.com/.

700 NLD ISSN 0168-9193
N6947

➤ **JONG HOLLAND**; tijdschrift voor kunst en vormgeving na 1850. Text in Dutch; Summaries in English. 1985. q. adv. bk.rev. illus. **Document type:** *Magazine, Academic/Scholarly.* **Description:** Publishes studies of art and design after 1850, including critical appraisals of individual artists and thematic studies.
Indexed: ABM, API, ArtInd, BHA.
—IE, Infotrieve.
Published by: Stichting Jong Holland, Postbus 90418, The Hague, 2509 LK, Netherlands. TEL 31-70-385-2415, FAX 31-70-333-9757. Ed. Marty Bax. R&P Patricia van Ulzen. Circ: 1,850.

700 USA

THE JOURNAL BRAVO. Text in English. 1975. bi-w. (Thu.). free domestic locally; USD 20 domestic area (effective 2005). adv. **Document type:** *Newspaper.*
Formerly: The Springfield Journal
Published by: Reminder Publications, Inc., 280 N Main St, East Longmeadow, MA 01028. TEL 413-525-6661, FAX 413-525-5882, news@reminderpublications.com, http://www.thereminder.com. Ed. Sarah M Corigliano. adv.: B&W page USD 900. Circ: 18,000 (free).

700 FRA ISSN 1245-1495

LE JOURNAL DES ARTS. Text in French. 1994. bi-m. **Description:** Offers international coverage of contemporary art, architecture, photography, books, multimedia.
Indexed: RILM.
Published by: Publications Artistiques Francaises, 23 av. Villemain, Paris, 75014, France. TEL 33-1-45438260, FAX 33-1-45438140. Ed. Emmanuel Fessy. Pub. Jacques Dodeman. Circ: 30,000.

704.9 DEU ISSN 1432-9506
N380

➤ **JOURNAL FUER KUNSTGESCHICHTE.** Text in German. 1997. q. EUR 32; EUR 9 newsstand/cover (effective 2005). adv. bk.rev. back issues avail. **Document type:** *Journal, Academic/Scholarly.*
Indexed: DIP, IBR, IBZ.
Published by: Verlag Schnell und Steiner GmbH, Leibnizstr 13, Regensburg, 93055, Germany. TEL 49-941-787850, FAX 49-941-7878516, post@schnell-und-steiner.de, http://www.schnell-und-steiner.de. Eds. Juergen Krueger, Volker Herzner. R&P Albrecht Weiland. Adv. contact Bernhard Fetsch. B&W page EUR 265; trim 125 x 186. Circ: 1,050 (controlled).

701.1 USA ISSN 0021-8529
N1

➤ **JOURNAL OF AESTHETICS AND ART CRITICISM.** Text in English. 1941. q. USD 161 combined subscription in the Americas to institutions & Caribbean (print & online eds.); GBP 124 combined subscription elsewhere to institutions print & online eds. (effective 2006). adv. bk.rev. bibl.; illus. index. reprint service avail. from PQC. **Document type:** *Journal, Academic/Scholarly.* **Description:** Takes an interdisciplinary approach to exploring aesthetics, as related to visual arts, literature, music, and theater.
Related titles: Microform ed.: (from MIM, PQC); Online - full text ed.: ISSN 1540-594X. USD 153 in the Americas to institutions & Caribbean; GBP 118 elsewhere to institutions (effective 2006) (from Blackwell Synergy, EBSCO Publishing, Gale Group, IngentaConnect, JSTOR (Web-based Journal Archive), O C L C Online Computer Library Center, Inc., Swets Information Services).
Indexed: ABM, ABS&EES, AES, AIAP, ASCA, AcaI, AmHI, ArtHuCI, ArtInd, BAS, BHA, BRD, BRI, CBRI, CRCL, CurCont, DIP, FLI, HumInd, IBR, IBRH, IBZ, IIMP, IIPA, IPB, IndIslam, MLA, MLA-IB, MusicInd, PhilInd, PsycholAb, RASB, RILM, SSCI.
—BLDSC (4919.985000), IE, Infotrieve, ingenta.
Published by: (American Society for Aesthetics), Blackwell Publishing, Inc. (Subsidiary of: Blackwell Publishing Ltd.), Commerce Place, 350 Main St, Malden, MA 02148. TEL 781-388-8206, FAX 781-388-8232, feagin@temple.edu, subscrip@blackwellpub.com, http://www.blackwellpublishing.com/journals/JAAC. Ed. Susan Feagin. adv.: page USD 310; 5.5 x 8. Circ: 2,700 (paid).

709 JPN ISSN 0021-907X

JOURNAL OF ART HISTORY/BIJUTSU SHI. Text in Japanese. 1950. q. USD 22.25. illus. index.
Indexed: RASB.
Published by: Japan Art History Society/Bijutsu-shi Gakkai, c/o Tokyo National Research Institute of Cultural Properties, Ueno Park, Tokyo, Japan. Ed. Kaho Yonezawa. Circ: 800.

709 USA ISSN 1085-1461
N7433.3

JOURNAL OF ARTISTS' BOOKS. Short title: J A B. Text in English. 1994. s-a. USD 20 in North America to individuals; USD 22 elsewhere to individuals; USD 35 in North America to institutions; USD 45 elsewhere to institutions (effective 2002). bk.rev. illus. **Document type:** *Journal.*
Related titles: Online - full text ed.: (from H.W. Wilson, O C L C Online Computer Library Center, Inc.).
Indexed: ABM, ArtInd.
Published by: Nexus Press, 535 Means St, Atlanta, GA 30318. TEL 404-577-3579, jabeditor@earthlink.net, http://www.nexuspress.org.

700 720 CAN ISSN 0315-4297
N6540

➤ **THE JOURNAL OF CANADIAN ART HISTORY/ANNALES D'HISTOIRE DE L'ART CANADIEN.** Text in English, French. 1974. s-a. CND 25; CND 30 foreign (effective 1999). adv. bk.rev. bibl.; charts; illus. index. back issues avail.; reprints avail. **Document type:** *Academic/Scholarly.* **Description:** Devoted to the publications of scholarly articles on the history of Canadian art, architecture and the decorative arts.
Related titles: Microfiche ed.: (from MML); Microfilm ed.: (from MML); Microform ed.: (from MML); Online - full text ed.: (from H.W. Wilson, O C L C Online Computer Library Center, Inc.).
Indexed: AIAP, AmH&L, ArtHuCI, ArtInd, BHA, CBCARef, CBPI, CPerI, CurCont, DIP, HistAb, IBR, IBZ, PCI, PdeR.
Published by: Journal of Canadian Art History, 9 Campus Dr, Saskatoon, SK S7N 5A5, Canada. TEL 306-966-5794, FAX 306-966-5852, spaik@gemini.concordia.ca. Ed., Pub. Sandra Paikowsky. R&P, Adv. contact Brenda Dionne Hutchinson. Circ: 700.

➤ **JOURNAL OF CULTURAL ECONOMICS.** see *BUSINESS AND ECONOMICS—Economic Systems And Theories, Economic History*

707 USA
N7428.5

➤ **JOURNAL OF CULTURAL RESEARCH IN ART EDUCATION.** Text in English. 1983. a. USD 25 membership to individuals; USD 30 membership to institutions (effective 2003); journal comes with membership. adv. bk.rev. reprints avail. **Document type:** *Journal, Academic/Scholarly.*
Formerly (until 2001): Journal of Multicultural and Cross-Cultural Research in Art Education (0740-1833)
Related titles: Online - full text ed.: (from O C L C Online Computer Library Center, Inc.).
Indexed: CPE, ERA, ETA, MEA, RHEA, SEA, SENA, SOMA, TEA.
—BLDSC (4965.847700), IE, ingenta.
Published by: United States Society for Education Through Art, Department of Art Education, 126 MCH, Florida State University, Tallahassee, FL 32306-4480. http://www.public.asu.edu/~ifmls/usseafolder/usseа.html. Ed. Tom Anderson TEL 850-644-2331.

741.6 USA ISSN 0888-7314
NK1

JOURNAL OF DECORATIVE AND PROPAGANDA ARTS. Text in English. 1986-1990 (no.17); resumed 1992. a. USD 25 per issue (effective 2005). adv. illus. Supplement avail.; back issues avail.; reprints avail. **Document type:** *Academic/Scholarly.* **Description:** Contains scholarly articles of international scope on decorative and propaganda arts, including art, architecture, design and material culture from 1875 to 1945.
Indexed: ABM, ABS&EES, AIAP, ArtInd, BHA, DAAI, PerIslam, RASB, RILM.
—BLDSC (4967.900000), IE, ingenta.
Published by: Wolfson Foundation of Decorative and Propaganda Arts, Wolfsonian - F I U, 1001 Washington Ave, Miami, FL 33139. TEL 305-535-2613, FAX 305-531-2133, dapa@thewolf.fiu.edu. Ed., Pub., R&P, Adv. contact Cathy Leff TEL 305-535-2615. Circ: 5,000.

JOURNAL OF DESIGN & TECHNOLOGY EDUCATION. see *EDUCATION—Teaching Methods And Curriculum*

700 747 GBR ISSN 0952-4649
NK1175

➤ **JOURNAL OF DESIGN HISTORY.** Text in English. 1988. q. GBP 132, USD 224, USD 198 to institutions; GBP 139, USD 236, EUR 209 combined subscription to institutions print & online eds. (effective 2006). adv. bk.rev. illus. back issues avail.; reprint service avail. from PSC. **Document type:** *Journal, Academic/Scholarly.* **Description:** Provides a forum for dialog and debate, for publishing new research, and for addressing current issues of interest on a wide and interdisciplinary basis.
Related titles: Online - full text ed.: ISSN 1741-7279 (from EBSCO Publishing, Gale Group, HighWire Press, IngentaConnect, JSTOR (Web-based Journal Archive), O C L C Online Computer Library Center, Inc., Oxford University Press Online Journals, Swets Information Services).
Indexed: ABM, AIAP, AmH&L, ArtInd, BHA, DAAI, DIP, HistAb, IBR, IBSS, IBZ, PCI.
—BLDSC (4968.815000), IE, Infotrieve, ingenta. **CCC.**
Published by: (Design History Society), Oxford University Press, Great Clarendon St, Oxford, OX2 6DP, United Kingdom. TEL 44-1865-556767, FAX 44-1865-556646, jnl.orders@oup.co.uk, http://jdh.oxfordjournals.org/, http://www.oxfordjournals.org/. Pub. Nina Curtis. R&P Fiona Bennett. Adv. contact Helen Pearson. B&W page GBP 275, B&W page USD 460; 150 x 210. Circ: 900. **Subscr. in the Americas to:** Oxford University Press, 2001 Evans Rd, Cary, NC 27513. jnlorders@oup-usa.org.

➤ **JOURNAL OF EARLY SOUTHERN DECORATIVE ARTS.** see *ANTIQUES*

➤ **JOURNAL OF EUROPEAN STUDIES.** see *HISTORY—History Of Europe*

➤ **JOURNAL OF MEDIEVAL AND EARLY MODERN STUDIES.** see *HUMANITIES: COMPREHENSIVE WORKS*

➤ **JOURNAL OF PRE-RAPHAELITE STUDIES.** see *LITERATURE*

510 USA

JOURNAL OF REGIONAL CRITICISM. Text in English. 1979. irreg. looseleaf. price varies. dance rev.; film rev. **Document type:** *Monographic series, Academic/Scholarly.* **Description:** Manuscript copy on proceedings in experimental surrealism, differential logic, visual poetics for objective and dynamic forms, decorative and symbolic arts, criticism and aesthetics, and quantum notation in the context of dance and martial arts.
Published by: (Institute of Martial Arts, Inc.), Arjuna Library Press, 1025 Garner St D Space 18, Colorado Springs, CO 80905-1774. TEL 719-475-2787. Ed. Joseph A. Uphoff Jr.

JOURNAL OF ROMANCE STUDIES. see *LINGUISTICS*

707.1 USA ISSN 1057-0292

JOURNAL OF SOCIAL THEORY IN ART EDUCATION. Text in English. 1981. a. USD 20 (effective 2005). adv. **Document type:** *Journal, Academic/Scholarly.* **Description:** Promotes the use of theoretical concepts from the social sciences to study visual culture and the teaching of art.
Related titles: Online - full text ed.: (from ProQuest Information & Learning).
Indexed: CIJE.
Published by: (Caucus of Social Theory and Art Education), National Art Education Association, 1916 Association Dr, Reston, VA 20191-1590. TEL 703-860-8000, http://www.art.ttu.edu/cstae/journal/journal.html. Ed., Adv. contact Janice Davenport. R&P Cam Luccarelli. Circ: 150. **Subscr. to:** Caucus of Social Theory and Art Education, c/o Sara Wilson McKay, University of Houston, Dept of Curriculum & Instruction, Art Education Program, Houston, TX 77204-5872 . TEL 713-861-9326, FAX 713-743-4990, skwmckay@pop.uh.edu, http://www.art.ttu.edu/cstae/cstae.html.

711 NLD ISSN 1367-6679
TS171.4 CODEN: JSPDB6

THE JOURNAL OF SUSTAINABLE PRODUCT DESIGN; balancing economic, environmental, ethical and social issues in product design and development. Text in English. 1997. q. EUR 204, USD 205, GBP 134 combined subscription to institutions print & online eds. (effective 2005). adv. reprint service avail. from PSC. **Document type:** *Academic/Scholarly.*
Related titles: Online - full text ed.: ISSN 1573-1588 (from EBSCO Publishing, Gale Group, IngentaConnect, Kluwer Online, O C L C Online Computer Library Center, Inc., Swets Information Services).
Indexed: BibLing, DAAI, ESPM, EnvEAb, PollutAb.
—BLDSC (5067.733000), IE, Infotrieve, ingenta. **CCC.**

Published by: (Surrey Institute of Art and Design, Faculty of Design GBR, Centre for Sustainable Design GBR), Springer-Verlag Dordrecht (Subsidiary of: Springer Science+Business Media), Van Godewijckstraat 30, Dordrecht, 3311 GX, Netherlands. TEL 31-78-6576050, FAX 31-78-6576474, http://springerlink.metapress.com/openurl.asp?genre=journal&issn=1367-6679, http://www.springeronline.com. Ed. Martin Charter.

700 GBR ISSN 1470-2029
➤ **JOURNAL OF VISUAL ART PRACTICE.** Text in English. 3/yr. GBP 30 in the European Union to individuals; GBP 38 elsewhere to individuals; GBP 140 combined subscription in the European Union to institutions print & online; GBP 148 combined subscription elsewhere to institutions print & online (effective 2005). back issues avail. **Document type:** *Journal, Academic/Scholarly.* **Description:** Publishes scholarly research and informed commentary on visual art practice seen from a broadly educational perspective. Seeks to represent the full spectrum of intellectual positions and modes of educational practice that have developed out of, or in reaction to, the traditional notions of "fine art" practice.
Related titles: Online - full content ed.; Online - full text ed.: (from EBSCO Publishing, O C L C Online Computer Library Center, Inc., Swets Information Services).
Indexed: ABM.
Published by: (University of West of England, Faculty of Art, Media and Design), Intellect Ltd., PO Box 862, Bristol, BS99 1DE, United Kingdom. TEL 44-117-9589910, FAX 44-117-9589911, journals@intellectbooks.com, http://www.intellectbooks.com/journals/jvap.htm. Ed. Richard Woodfield. R&P, Adv. contact Mr. Robin Beecroft.

➤ **JOURNAL OF VISUAL CULTURE.** see *HUMANITIES: COMPREHENSIVE WORKS*

➤ **JOURNAL OF VISUAL LITERACY.** see *EDUCATION—Teaching Methods And Curriculum*

700 800 USA ISSN 0738-2669
AP2
THE JUGGLER. Text in English. 1920. s-a. **Description:** The University of Notre Dame arts and literature magazine.
Published by: University of Notre Dame Press, 310 Flanner Hall, Notre Dame, IN 46556. juggler@nd.edu.

052 NZL
▼ ➤ **JUNCTURES;** journal for thematic dialogue. Text in English. 2003. s-a. NZD 40 domestic to individuals; NZD 65 foreign to individuals; NZD 100 domestic to institutions; NZD 140 foreign to institutions (effective 2005). bk.rev.; dance rev.; film rev.; music rev.; software rev.; tel.rev.; video rev.; Website rev. illus. back issues avail. **Document type:** *Journal, Academic/Scholarly.* **Description:** Academic journal with interdisciplinary focus, designed around themes.
Related titles: Online - full content ed.
Published by: Otago Polytechnic, Private Bag 1910, Dunedin, New Zealand. TEL 64-377-3014, FAX 643-471-6870, http://www.junctures.org, http://www.tekotago.ac.nz/. Ed., R&P Annemarie Jutel.

700 DEU ISSN 0933-307X
JUNGE KUNST. Text in German. 1987. 4/yr. EUR 23 domestic; EUR 27 in Europe; EUR 33 elsewhere; EUR 6 newsstand/cover (effective 2003). adv. **Document type:** *Magazine, Consumer.*
Indexed: ABM, DIP, IBR, IBZ.
Published by: Ritterbach Verlag GmbH, Postfach 1820, Frechen, 50208, Germany. TEL 49-2234-18660, FAX 49-2234-186690, anzeigen@ritterbach.de, verlag@ritterbach.de, http://www.ritterbach.de. Ed. Barbara Rotzoll Golly. R&P Marie Luise Coeln TEL 49-2234-186632. Adv. contact Sonja Erdmann TEL 49-2234-186695. B&W page EUR 742, color page EUR 1,187. Circ: 9,900 (paid).

700 USA ISSN 1077-8411
N6512.5.P79
JUXTAPOZ. Text in English. 1994. 8/yr. USD 19.95 domestic; USD 33 in Canada; USD 4.99 newsstand/cover (effective 2005). adv. bk.rev.; film rev.; music rev.; rec.rev.; Website rev. back issues avail. **Document type:** *Magazine, Consumer.* **Description:** Offers a gallery of underground artists. Includes full color layouts featuring painters, sculptors, cartoonists, and photographers along with portfolios, sketches, interviews and reviews.
Published by: High Speed Productions, Inc., 1303 Underwood Ave, San Francisco, CA 94124. TEL 415-822-3083, FAX 415-822-8359, editor@juxtapoz.com, http://www.juxtapoz.com, http://www.wrtiscirc.com. Ed. Jamie O'Shea. Pub. Edward Riggins. Adv. contact William Haugh. B&W page USD 2,000; trim 10.88 x 8.5. Circ: 105,000 (paid and free). **Dist. by:** Curtis CIRC Company, 730 River Rd., New Milford, NJ 07646. TEL 201-634-7420, FAX 201-634-7475.

700 FIN ISSN 0075-4633
JYVASKYLA STUDIES IN THE ARTS. Text in Finnish. 1967. irreg. price varies; available on exchange.
Published by: Jyvaskylan Yliopisto/University of Jyvaskyla, PO Box 35, Jyvaeskylae, 40014, Finland. TEL 941-601-211, FAX 603-371, TELEX 28219 JYK SF. Eds. Erkki Pekkila, Kalevi Poykko. Circ: 450.

700 RUS
K A K - ZHURNAL DLYA DIZAINEROV - GRAFIKOV I PROSTO KHUDOZHNIKOV. Text in Russian. 1997. q. USD 124 in North America (effective 2000).
Published by: Redaktsiya K A K, Tsvetnoi bul 30, Moscow, 103051, Russian Federation. TEL 7-095-2002432, FAX 7-095-2002442. **Dist. by:** East View Information Services, 3020 Harbor Ln. N., Minneapolis, MN 55447. TEL 763-550-0961, FAX 763-559-2931.

K W M NEWSLETTER; the quarterly journal of the kendall whaling museum. see *MUSEUMS AND ART GALLERIES*

K48. see *LITERARY AND POLITICAL REVIEWS*

KALAVA HA SAHITYAYA. see *LITERATURE*

KALDRON. see *LITERATURE—Poetry*

KALEIDOSCOPE (AKRON); exploring the experience of disability through literature and the fine arts. see *HANDICAPPED*

700 ESP ISSN 0214-6762
KALIAS; revista de arte. Text in Catalan, Spanish. 1989. s-a.
Indexed: ABM.
—CINDOC.
Published by: Generalitat Valenciana, Conselleria de Cultura i Educacio, Plaza de Manise, 3, Valencia, 46003, Spain. TEL 34-96-3866170, FAX 34-96-3803478, infomacio@cult.gva.es, http://www.gva.es.

700 AUS ISSN 0047-312X
KALORI. Text in English. 1959. q. AUD 10. adv. bk.rev.
Document type: *Academic/Scholarly.*
Published by: Royal South Australian Society of Arts, North Terr, 122 Kintore Ave, Adelaide, SA 5000, Australia. TEL 61-8-223-4704. Ed. P W Grisci. Circ: 800.

KANINA; revista de artes y letras. see *LITERATURE*

700 POL ISSN 0075-5257
KATALOG ZABYTKOW SZTUKI W POLSCE. Text in Polish. 1953. irreg. price varies. **Document type:** *Catalog.* **Description:** Each volume covers a part of Poland's territory and contains inventory descriptions of architecture, sculpture, painting and objects of applied art.
Published by: (Polska Akademia Nauk/Polish Academy of Sciences, Instytut Sztuki), Wydawnictwa Artystyczne i Filmowe, Pulawska 61, Warsaw, 02595, Poland. TEL 48-22-45-53-01, FAX 48-22-455584. Ed. Jerzy Zygmunt Lozinski. Circ: 3,250. **Dist. by:** Ars Polona, Krakowskie Przedmiescie 7, Warsaw, Poland.

741.5 DEU
KAWAII; anime - manga - nippon - otaku. Text in German. m. EUR 3.90 newsstand/cover (effective 2003). adv. **Document type:** *Magazine, Consumer.*
Formerly (until 2003): MonsterFun
Published by: Pro Verlag Gesellschaft fuer Publikationen mbH, Berner Str 38, Frankfurt Am Main, 60437, Germany. TEL 49-69-5008050, FAX 49-69-5008051, office@proverlag.com, http://www.proverlag.com. adv.: page EUR 3,900; trim 210 x 280.

KAYHAN KARIKATUR. see *LITERARY AND POLITICAL REVIEWS*

741.092 USA ISSN 0163-1861
N6537.K44
KENT COLLECTOR. Text in English. 1974. 3/yr. USD 20 (effective 2004). adv. bk.rev. **Document type:** *Newsletter, Academic/Scholarly.* **Description:** Devoted to the life and work of Rockwell Kent and the American art of the first half of the twentieth century. Includes auction and dealer news.
Indexed: ABM.
Published by: State University of New York at Plattsburgh, Rockwell Kent Gallery, SUNY Plattsburgh, Plattsburgh, NY 12901. TEL 518-564-2813. Ed., R&P, Adv. contact Marguerite Eisinger. Circ: 225.

KERAMISCHE ZEITSCHRIFT. see *CERAMICS, GLASS AND POTTERY*

700 RUS ISSN 0131-7555
N6
KHUDOZHNIK. Text in Russian. 1958. q. USD 96. illus. index.
Indexed: NumL, RASB.
—East View.
Published by: (Soyuz Khudozhnikov Rossiiskoi Federatsii), Izdatel'stvo Khudozhnik, Ul Pokrovka 37, Moscow, 103062, Russian Federation. TEL 7-095-9174951. **US dist. addr.:** East View Information Services, 3020 Harbor Ln. N., Minneapolis, MN 55447. TEL 612-550-0961.

700 800 SAU ISSN 1018-3612
➤ **KING SAUD UNIVERSITY JOURNAL. ARTS.** Key Title: Majallat Jami'at al-Malik Sa'ud, al-Adab. (Other sections avail.: Administrative Sciences, Agricultural Sciences, Architecture and Planning, Computer and Information Sciences, Educational Sciences and Islamic Studies, Engineering Sciences, Science) Text in Arabic, English. 1989. s-a. USD 5 (effective 2001). charts; illus. **Document type:** *Academic/Scholarly.*
Indexed: BibLing, MLA-IB.
Published by: King Saud University, University Libraries, P O Box 22480, Riyadh, 11495, Saudi Arabia. TEL 966-1-4676148, FAX 966-1-4676162. Ed. Khalid A. Al-Hamoudi. R&P Dr. Sulaiman Saleh Al-Ogle. Circ: 3,000.

➤ **KINO-TEATR.** see *MOTION PICTURES*

700 USA
KITCHEN SINK. Text in English. 2002. q. USD 20; USD 5.95 newsstand/cover (effective 2002). **Document type:** *Magazine, Consumer.* **Description:** Covers various issues in independent art, identity, culture, and politics.
Address: 5245 College Ave #301, Oakland, CA 94618. TEL 510-653-9529, http://www.kitchensinkmag.com/index.php. Ed. Jen Loy. Pub., Adv. contact Antonia Blue.

KNOTGRASS; a creative online journal. see *LITERATURE*

700 ESP ISSN 0214-7955
N7109.P25
KOBIE, REVISTA DE BELLAS ARTES Y CIENCIAS: SERIE BELLAS ARTES. Key Title: Kobie. Arte Ederrak. Text in English, German, Spanish; Summaries in Basque, English, French, German. 1969. a. back issues avail.
Supersedes in part (in 1984): Kobie (0211-1942)
Indexed: ABM, BHA, RILM.
—CINDOC.
Published by: Diputacion Foral de Bizkaia, Departamento de Cultura, PO Box 97, Bilbao, 48070, Spain. TEL 34-4-4157217, FAX 34-4-4162981.

KODIKAS - CODE - ARS SEMEIOTICA; an international journal of semiotics. see *SOCIOLOGY*

KODIKAS - CODE SUPPLEMENT. see *SOCIOLOGY*

700 JPN ISSN 0023-2785
N8
KOKKA/ESSENCES OF JAPAN. Text in Japanese. 1889. m. USD 405.
Related titles: Microform ed.: (from PQC).
Published by: Asahi Shimbun Publishing Co., 5-3-2 Tsukiji, Chuo-ku, Tokyo, 104-8011, Japan. Ed. Yuzo Yamane. Circ: 2,000. **Dist. by:** Japan Publications Trading Co., Ltd., Book Export II Dept, PO Box 5030, Tokyo International, Tokyo 101-3191, Japan.

709 GBR ISSN 0023-3609
N8
➤ **KONSTHISTORISK TIDSKRIFT/JOURNAL OF ART HISTORY.** Text in English, Swedish; Summaries in English; Text occasionally in Danish, Norwegian. 1932. q. GBP 90, USD 149 combined subscription to institutions print & online eds. (effective 2006). adv. bk.rev. bibl.; illus. Index. reprint service avail. from PSC. **Document type:** *Journal, Academic/Scholarly.* **Description:** Coverage includes historical investigations on a particular theme, artist, period or work of art.
Related titles: Online - full text ed.: ISSN 1651-2294. GBP 86, USD 142 to institutions (effective 2006) (from EBSCO Publishing, Gale Group, H.W. Wilson, IngentaConnect, O C L C Online Computer Library Center, Inc., Swets Information Services).
Indexed: ABCT, ABM, AIAP, ASCA, ArtHuCI, ArtInd, BHA, CurCont, DIP, IBR, IBRH, IBZ, RASB, RILM.
—IDS, IE, Infotrieve. **CCC.**
Published by: (National Museum of Art in Stockholm SWE, Stockholm University, Department of Art History SWE), Routledge (Subsidiary of: Taylor & Francis Group), 4 Park Sq, Milton Park, Abingdon, Oxon OX14 4RN, United Kingdom. TEL 44-1235-828600, FAX 44-1235-829000, info@routledge.co.uk, http://www.tandf.co.uk/journals/titles/00233609.asp, http://www.routledge.co.uk. Ed. Margaretha Rossholm Lagerlof. Circ: 500. **Subscr. to:** Taylor & Francis Ltd, Journals Customer Service, Rankine Rd, Basingstoke, Hants RG24 8PR, United Kingdom. TEL 44-1256-813000, FAX 44-1256-330245, enquiry@tandf.co.uk, http://www.tandf.co.uk/journals.

750 SWE ISSN 0283-2887
KONSTNAEREN. Text in Swedish. 1940. q. SEK 250; SEK 45 newsstand/cover (effective 2001). adv. 32 p./no. 4 cols./p.; **Document type:** *Magazine, Consumer.*
Former titles (until 1985): K R O - Konstnaeren (0281-4927); (until 1979): Konstnaeren (0347-5239); (until no.4, 1976): Medlemsblad - K R O (0345-6587)
Indexed: BHA.

Published by: Konstnaernas Riksorganisation (KRO), Enkehuset, Norrtullsgatan 45, Stockholm, 11345, Sweden. TEL 46-8-54542080, FAX 46-8-54542089, konstnaren@kro.se, kro@kro.se, http://www.kro.se/konstnaren. Ed., Adv. contact Jan Nordwall. Pub. Maria Sundstroem. color page SEK 9,000; trim 190 x 250. Circ: 4,300. **Co-sponsor:** Foereningen Sveriges Konsthantverkare och Industriformgivare (KIF).

720 SWE ISSN 0347-4453
KONSTPERSPEKTIV; Nordens stoersta konsttidskrift. Text in Swedish. 1975. q. SEK 250. adv.
Related titles: Audio cassette/tape ed.
Indexed: BHA.
Published by: Sveriges Konstfoereningars Riksfoerbund, Fack 600 65, Malmo, 20125, Sweden. TEL 46-40-16-41-10, FAX 46-46-16-26-07, info@skr.se. Ed. Uno Kampmark. Adv. contact Monica Larsson.

720 SWE ISSN 1101-8623
KONSTTIDNINGEN. Text in Swedish. 1990. SEK 175 (effective 1999).
Published by: Vindeld AB, c/o Lars Kolberg, Ehrensvardsgatan 3 nb, Stockholm, 11235, Sweden. TEL 46-8-651-70-17, FAX 46-8-651-70-17. **Subscr. to:** Foerlagsdata RK AB, Fack 982, Vaesteraas 72123, Sweden. TEL 46-21-554-21.

700 745.1 SWE
KONSTVAERLDEN & DISAJN; art, architecture, interior. Text in Swedish. 1992. bi-m. SEK 199 (effective 2001). adv. **Document type:** *Magazine, Consumer.*
Formerly: Konstvaerlden (1103-663X)
Published by: Mediafabriken Conny & Teddy Hallin AB, Box 3101, Stockholm, 10362, Sweden. TEL 46-8-587-07-500, FAX 46-8-587-07-501, http://www.disajn.com. Ed., Pub. Goeran Hellstroem. Adv. contact Per Asp. page SEK 23,900; trim 192 x 269. Circ: 20,000. **Subscr. to:** Pressdata, Fack 3263, Stockholm 10365, Sweden. TEL 46-8-98-88-80.

700 POL ISSN 1230-6142
NK7
KONTEKSTY. POLSKA SZTUKA LUDOWA; antropologia kultury, etnografia, sztuka. Text in Polish; Summaries in English. 1947. q. EUR 33 foreign (effective 2005). bk.rev. illus. index. back issues avail.; reprints avail. **Document type:** *Journal, Academic/Scholarly.* **Description:** Covers Polish folk art. Combines research of culture and art using different methods of cultural anthropology.
Formerly (until 1990): Polska Sztuka Ludowa (0032-3721)
Indexed: ABM, AICP, BHA, IBR, IBSS, MLA, MLA-IB, RASB.
Published by: Polska Akademia Nauk, Instytut Sztuki/Polish Academy of Science, Institute of Art, ul Dluga 28, Warsaw, 00950, Poland. TEL 48-22-5048200, FAX 48-22-8313149, konteksty@ispan.pl, ispan@ispan.pl, http://www.konteksty.pl, http://www.ispan.pl. Eds. Aleksander Jackowski, Zbigniew Benedyktowicz. Circ: 1,200 (paid). **Dist. by:** Ars Polona, Krakowskie Przedmiescie 7, Warsaw, Poland. TEL 48-22-9263914, FAX 48-22-9265334, arspolona@arspolona.com.pl, http://www.arspolona.com.pl.

700 HRV ISSN 1330-4976
KONTURA. Text in Croatian. 1991. m. **Document type:** *Magazine, Consumer.*
Published by: Kontura d.o.o., Nova cesta 89a, Zagreb, 10000, Croatia. TEL 385-1-3822074, FAX 385-1-3820924, kontura@zg.tel.hr. Ed. Zdravko Mihocinec.

KOREANA; Korean art and culture. see *ASIAN STUDIES*

709 DEU ISSN 0340-7403
KRITISCHE BERICHTE; Zeitschrift fuer Kunst- und Kulturgeschichte. Text in German. 1973. q. EUR 35 domestic; EUR 46.13 foreign (effective 2003). adv. bk.rev. **Document type:** *Journal, Academic/Scholarly.*
Indexed: AIAP, BHA, DIP, IBR, IBZ.
—CCC.
Published by: (Ulmer Verein, Verband fuer Kunst- und Kulturwissenschaften), Jonas Verlag, Weidenhaeuser Str 88, Marburg, 35037, Germany. TEL 49-6421-25132, FAX 49-6421-210572, jonas@jonas-verlag.de, http://www.kunst.kulturnetz.de/kritische-berichte/index.html, http://www.jonas-verlag.de. Circ: 1,500.

709 NLD ISSN 0166-0381
N5
KRONIEK VAN HET REMBRANDTHUIS. Text in Dutch; Summaries in English. 1946. 2/yr. EUR 20 (effective 2003). adv. illus. **Document type:** *Academic/Scholarly.* **Description:** Covers Rembrandt and his surroundings, including his redecessors, pupils and followers, 17th century art, etching techniques, and history.
Formerly (until 1969): Vriendenkring van Het Rembrandthuis. Kroniek (0042-9171)
Indexed: BHA.
Published by: Vereniging van Vrienden van Het Museum Het Rembrandthuis, Jodenbreestraat 4, Amsterdam, 1011 NK, Netherlands. TEL 31-20-5200400, FAX 31-20-5200401, museum@rembrandthuis.nl, http://www.rembrandthuis.nl. Ed. M E A Enklaar.

700 DEU ISSN 0934-1730
KUENSTLER - KRITISCHES LEXIKON DER GEGENWARTSKUNST. Text in German. 1988. q. EUR 148 domestic; EUR 158 foreign (effective 2003). **Document type:** *Magazine, Academic/Scholarly.*
Indexed: ABM.
Published by: Weltkunst Verlag GmbH, Nymphenburger Str 84, Munich, 80636, Germany. TEL 49-89-1269900, FAX 49-89-12699011, info@weltkunstverlag.de, http://www.weltkunstverlag.de. Ed. Detlef Bluemler.

700 331.8 DEU ISSN 0946-3100
DIE KUENSTLERGILDE; bildende Kunst, Literatur, Musik, Photographie, Publizistik, Theater. Text in German. 1954. q. adv. bk.rev. **Document type:** *Magazine, Consumer.*
Published by: Kuenstlergilde e.V., Hafenmarkt 2, Esslingen Am Neckar, 73728, Germany. TEL 49-711-3969010, FAX 49-711-39690123, kuenstlergilde@t-online.de. Ed. Dr. Hanna Nogossek. adv.: B&W page EUR 521; trim 180 x 240. Circ: 1,800.

700 800 BGR ISSN 1310-6511
KULA/TOWER. Text in Bulgarian. 1923. q. BGL 4; BGL 1 newsstand/cover (effective 2002). **Description:** Stresses spiritual values and aims at uniting authors without ideological prejudices, presenting contemporary poetry and prose, texts on the culture of the region as well as on general problems of arts and ideas of philosophy, religion, and history of culture.
Published by: Municipality of Kazanlak, 37A Nikola Petkov Blvd., Kazalnak, 6100, Bulgaria. TEL 359-431-25401, http://www.sca.bg/cultural-periodicals/catalog/kula.htm. Ed. Stefan Bakardiev.

700 830 DEU ISSN 1437-5958
KULTUR NEWS; Mitteilungen des Kulturrings in Berlin. Text in German. 1991. m. EUR 0.25 newsstand/cover (effective 2005). adv. bk.rev.; film rev.; music rev.; play rev. bibl.; illus. back issues avail. **Document type:** *Newsletter, Consumer.*
Formerly (until 1995): Kulturbund Informationen
Published by: Kulturring in Berlin e.V., Giselastr 12, Berlin, 10317, Germany. TEL 49-30-5139749, FAX 49-30-51656005, vorstand@kulturring.org, http://www.kulturring.org/kulturnews.htm. Ed., R&P, Adv. contact Ingo Knechtel. Circ: 1,500 (controlled).

KULTUR UND TECHNIK. see *MUSEUMS AND ART GALLERIES*

KULTURA. see *LITERATURE*

700 DEU
KULTURA-EXTRA; das online-magazin. Text in German. 2000. m. adv. **Document type:** *Magazine, Consumer.* **Description:** Contains reports, portraits, and reviews on and beyond all cultural activities.
Media: Online - full content.
Published by: Kultura e.V. TEL 49-7071-440488, FAX 49-7071-440488, redaktion@kultura-extra.de, http://www.kultura-extra.de. Ed., R&P, Adv. contact Susanne Parth.

700 AUT ISSN 0023-5121
KULTURBERICHTE AUS NIEDEROESTERREICH✶. Variant title: N O Kulturberichte. Text in German. 1950. m. charts; illus. **Document type:** *Magazine, Consumer.*
Related titles: Supplement(s): Amtliche Nachrichten.
Published by: Niederoesterreichische Landesregierung, Niederoesterreich-Fonds, Landhausplatz 1, St. Polten, W 3109, Austria. TEL 43-2742-900513130, FAX 43-2742-900516390, post.k1@noel.gv.at, http://www.noel.gv.at.

700 DEU
KULTURJOURNAL. Text in English, French, German, Russian, Spanish. 1983. bi-m. free. bk.rev. bibl.; illus. **Document type:** *Journal, Academic/Scholarly.* **Description:** Devoted to news and views concerning art, literature, theatre, education and science, architecture, photography, film, television and music in Germany. Includes list of events and exhibitions.
Formerly (until 2004): Kulturchronik (0724-343X)
Related titles: English ed.: Kulturjournal (English Edition). 1958.
Indexed: RASB.
Published by: Goethe Institut Inter Nationes, Neue Schoenhauser Str 20, Berlin, 10178, Germany. TEL 49-30-259063, FAX 49-30-259064, berlin@goethe.de, http://www.goethe.de. Ed. Jan Thorn-Prikker. Circ: 45,000.

KULTURO; tidsskrift for moderne kultur. see *LITERATURE*

700 IND ISSN 0023-5342
KUMAR. Text in Gujarati; Summaries in Gujarati. 1924. m. INR 150, USD 25; INR 15 newsstand/cover (effective 2000). adv. bk.rev.; music rev.; play rev. abstr.; charts; illus.; maps. back issues avail. **Document type:** *Academic/Scholarly.* **Description:** Promotes arts, culture and literature of various states and countries in Gujarati.
Published by: Kumar Karyalaya Ltd., 1454 Raipur Chakla, Ahmedabad, Gujarat 380 001, India. TEL 91-2143745. Ed., R&P Dhiru Parikh. adv.: B&W page INR 1,000, color page INR 2,000. Circ: 3,900 (paid); 100 (controlled).

KUNGLIGA VITTERHETS HISTORIE OCH ANTIKVITETS AKADEMIEN. AARSBOK. see *HISTORY—History Of Europe*

709 913 SWE ISSN 0083-6737
KUNGLIGA VITTERHETS HISTORIE OCH ANTIKVITETS AKADEMIEN. ANTIKVARISKT ARKIV. Text in English, German, Swedish. 1954. irreg., latest vol.80, 1999. price varies. index. back issues avail. **Document type:** *Monographic series, Academic/Scholarly.*
Indexed: AIAP, BHA, NAA.
—KNAW.
Published by: Kungliga Vitterhets Historie och Antikvitets Akademien/Royal Academy of Letters, History and Antiquities, PO Box 5622, Stockholm, 11486, Sweden. TEL 46-8-4404280, FAX 46-8-4404290, http://www.vitterhetsakad.se/publikationer/kap01-e.htm. **Dist. by:** Almqvist & Wiksell International, P O Box 7634, Stockholm 10394, Sweden. TEL 46-8-6136100, FAX 46-8-217050.

948.5 745.1 SWE ISSN 0083-6761
KUNGLIGA VITTERHETS HISTORIE OCH ANTIKVITETS AKADEMIEN. HANDLINGAR. ANTIKVARISKA SERIEN/ROYAL ACADEMY OF LETTERS, HISTORY AND ANTIQUITIES. PROCEEDINGS. ANTIQUARIAN SERIES. Text in English, French, German, Swedish. 1954. irreg., latest vol.43, 1999. price varies. back issues avail. **Document type:** *Monographic series, Academic/Scholarly.*
Indexed: RASB.
Published by: Kungliga Vitterhets Historie och Antikvitets Akademien/Royal Academy of Letters, History and Antiquities, PO Box 5622, Stockholm, 11486, Sweden. TEL 46-8-4404280, FAX 46-8-4404290, kansli@vitterhetsakad.se, http://www.vitterhetsakad.se/publikationer/kap01-e.htm. **Dist. by:** Almqvist & Wiksell International, P O Box 7634, Stockholm 10394, Sweden. TEL 46-8-6136100, FAX 46-8-217050.

700 NOR ISSN 1503-2442
KUNST. Text in Norwegian. 1984. q. NOK 180 to individuals; NOK 150 to students; NOK 65 per issue (effective 2002). adv. illus. **Description:** Covers art from different times and countries with emphasis on the contemporary Norwegian art scene.
Formerly (until 2002): Vi Ser paa Kunst (0800-675X)
Indexed: ABM.
Published by: Norske Kunstforeningers Landsforbund Kunstforlag A-S, Sentrum, P O Box 477, Oslo, 0105, Norway. TEL 47-22-42-20-35, FAX 47-22-41-61-77, nklf@nklf.no, http://www.kunstmag.no. Ed. Aashild Grana.

700 CHE ISSN 1013-6940
DAS KUNST-BULLETIN. Text in German, French. 1968. 10/yr. CHF 50 domestic; CHF 61 in Europe (effective 2001). bk.rev. **Document type:** *Bulletin, Consumer.*
Indexed: ABM, BHA, DIP, IBR, IBZ.
Published by: Schweizerischer Kunstverein, Postfach, Zuerich, 8026, Switzerland. TEL 41-1-2416300, FAX 41-1-2416373, info@kunstbulletin.ch, http://www.kunstbulletin.ch/. Ed., R&P Claudia Jolles. Adv. contact Nino Osswald. Circ: 17,000. **Subscr. to:** Kunst-Bulletin Leserservice, Postfach, Luzern 6002, Switzerland. TEL 41-41-2484444, FAX 41-41-2484488.

KUNST EN WETENSCHAP. see *SCIENCES: COMPREHENSIVE WORKS*

KUNST IN KOELN. see *MUSEUMS AND ART GALLERIES*

705 AUT ISSN 0075-7241
KUNST-KATALOG: AUKTIONEN. Text in German. 1947. irreg. price varies. adv. bk.rev. **Document type:** *Catalog.*
Published by: Dorotheum, Dorotheergasse 17, Vienna, W 1011, Austria. TEL 43-1-51560-0, marketing.dorotheum@telecom.at, http://www.dorotheum.com. Ed. Dieter Rauch. Adv. contact Brigitte Zierhut Bosch. Circ: 2,000.

700 NOR ISSN 0023-5415
N8
KUNST OG KULTUR; Norwegian journal for pictorial art, architecture and handicrafts. Text in Norwegian; Summaries in English. 1911. q. NOK 495 to individuals; NOK 695 to institutions; NOK 200 to students; NOK 110 per issue (effective 2004). adv. bk.rev. illus. index. **Document type:** *Journal, Academic/Scholarly.* **Description:** Devoted to pictorial art, architecture and handicraft.
Indexed: ABCT, ABM, BHA, BibInd, DIP, IBR, IBZ.
Published by: (National Gallery of Art), Universitetsforlaget AS/Scandinavian University Press (Subsidiary of: Aschehoug & Co.), Sehesteds Gate 3, Postboks 508, Oslo, 0105, Norway. TEL 47-24-147500, FAX 47-24-147501, post@universitetsforlaget.no, http://www.universitetsforlaget.no/tidsskrifter/article.jhtml?articleID=319, http://www.universitetesforlaget.no. Ed. Ellen Lerbjerg.

704.948 DEU ISSN 0023-5431
KUNST UND KIRCHE; Oekumenische Zeitschrift fuer Architektur und Kunst. Text in German. 1923. q. EUR 37; EUR 32 to students; EUR 11 newsstand/cover (effective 2004). adv. bk.rev. illus. index. **Document type:** *Magazine, Consumer.*
Indexed: ABCT, ABM, AIAP, CERDIC, RILM.
—BLDSC (5129.800000), IE, ingenta. **CCC.**
Published by: Verlag das Beispiel GmbH, Spreestr 9, Darmstadt, 64295, Germany. TEL 49-6151-33557, FAX 49-6151-313089, verlag@das-beispiel.de, http://www.verlag-das-beispiel.de/kunstkirche/html/impressum_frameset.htm. adv.: B&W page EUR 2,250, color page EUR 4,050.

700 800 DEU ISSN 0946-5243
KUNST UND KULTUR. Text in German. 8/yr. **Document type:** *Trade.*
Published by: Vereinte Dienstleistungsgewerkschaft, Paula-Thiede-Ufer 10, Berlin, 10179, Germany. info@verdi.de, http://www.verdi.de. Circ: 24,000.

KUNST UND POLITIK. see *POLITICAL SCIENCE—International Relations*

KUNST UND STADT. see *ARCHITECTURE*

720 730 CHE ISSN 0023-5458
KUNST UND STEIN. Text in German. 1956. bi-m. CHF 78 to members; CHF 84 to non-members (effective 2001). adv. bk.rev. **Document type:** *Magazine, Consumer.*
Indexed: RASB.
Published by: (Verband Schweizer Bildhauer- und Steinmetzmeister), Verlag Kunst und Stein, Schwarztorstr 26, Postfach 6922, Bern, 3001, Switzerland. TEL 41-31-3822322, FAX 41-31-3822670. Ed. Markus Christen. Adv. contact Werner Hulliger. Circ: 1,800.

707 370 DEU ISSN 0931-7112
KUNST UND UNTERRICHT; Zeitschrift fuer Kunstpaedagogik. Text in German. 1985. 10/yr. EUR 91; EUR 10 newsstand/cover (effective 2005). adv. bibl.; charts; illus. index. **Document type:** *Journal, Academic/Scholarly.*
Formed by the 1985 merger of: K und U (0170-6225); Which was formerly (1968-1978): Kunst und Unterricht (0023-5466); (1972-1985): Zeitschrift fuer Kunstpaedagogik (0340-6180); Which superseded in part: Bildnerische Erziehung (0006-243X); Which was formerly (until 1965): Kunst- und Werk-Erziehung (0172-0082); (until 1960): Kunst und Jugend (0451-081X)
Indexed: DIP, IBR, IBZ, RASB.
—CCC.
Published by: Erhard Friedrich Verlag GmbH, Im Brande 17, Seelze, 30926, Germany. TEL 49-511-400040, FAX 49-511-40004170, info@friedrich-verlag.de, http://www.friedrich-verlag.de. adv.: B&W page EUR 1,290, color page EUR 1,940. Circ: 6,705.

705 DNK ISSN 0107-6957
KUNSTAVISEN. Text in Danish. 1981. 11/yr. DKK 429; DKK 39 newsstand/cover (effective 2005). adv. bk.rev. illus. **Document type:** *Newspaper, Consumer.* **Description:** Covers the present art scene in Denmark.
Published by: Forlaget Kunst-Avisen, Egoejevej 114 B, Koege, 4600, Denmark. TEL 45-56-639900, FAX 45-56-639919, kunstavisen@kunstavisen.dk, http://www.kunstavisen.dk. Eds. Tom Joergensen, Soeren Juhl. Pub. Soeren Juhl. Circ: 8,000.

700 NLD ISSN 0165-1129
N5
KUNSTBEELD. Text in Dutch. 1976. 10/yr. EUR 79; EUR 68 to students (effective 2005). adv. **Document type:** *Consumer.*
—IE, Infotrieve.
Published by: P/F-Kunstbeeld vof, Marshallplein 37-39, Postbus 318, Rijswijk, 2280 AH, Netherlands. TEL 31-70-3941007, FAX 31-70-3938382, info@profoto.nl, http://www.kunstbeeld.nl/, http://pf-kunstbeeld.nl. Ed. Robbert Roos. Pubs. Jan van der Schans, Wiggele Warnar. Adv. contact Wanda Bergman. color page EUR 1,997; 220 x 290. Circ: 15,000.

700 DEU ISSN 0177-3674
N6480
KUNSTFORUM INTERNATIONAL. Text in German. 1973. 5/yr. EUR 99 (effective 2004). illus. **Document type:** *Journal, Trade.*
Indexed: ABM, AIAP, ArtInd, DIP, IBR, IBZ, RILM.
—IE, Infotrieve. **CCC.**
Published by: Kunstforum, Zum Brunnentor 7, Ruppichteroth, 53809, Germany. TEL 49-2295-5023, FAX 49-2295-5021, verwaltung@kunstforum.de, http://www.kunstforum.de.

700 CHE ISSN 1421-1726
KUNSTHALLE BASEL. Text in German, English. 1996. irreg., latest vol.61, 2003. price varies. adv. **Document type:** *Monographic series, Academic/Scholarly.*
Published by: Schwabe und Co. AG, Steinentorstr 13, Basel, 4010, Switzerland. TEL 41-61-2789565, FAX 41-61-2789566, verlag@schwabe.ch, http://www.schwabe.ch. Ed. Peter Pakesch. Circ: 1,200.

700 DEU ISSN 0023-5504
DER KUNSTHANDEL; Zeitschrift fuer Bild und Rahmen. Text in German. 1908. m. bk.rev. charts; illus. **Document type:** *Magazine, Trade.*
Published by: Transmedia Projekt und Verlags GmbH, Ludolf-Krehl-Str 13-17, Mannheim, 68167, Germany. TEL 49-621-37070, FAX 49-621-3707111, transmedia@transmedia-mannheim.de, http://www.transmedia-mannheim.de. Circ: 3,426.

709 AUT ISSN 0075-2312
➤ **KUNSTHISTORISCHE SAMMLUNGEN IN WIEN. JAHRBUCH.** Text in German. 1926. a. price varies. **Document type:** *Academic/Scholarly.*
Related titles: Online - full text ed.: (from H.W. Wilson).
Indexed: AIAP, ArtInd, BHA, IBR, IBZ, NumL.
Published by: (Kunsthistorisches Museum in Wien), Verlag Anton Schroll und Co., Spengergasse 39, Vienna, W 1051, Austria. FAX 43-1-544564166. Ed., R&P Georg Kugler.

700 900 ITA
KUNSTHISTORISCHES INSTITUT IN FLORENZ. MITTEILUNGEN. Text in English, German, Italian, French. 1908. 2/yr. EUR 90 (effective 2003). bibl.; illus. index. reprints avail. **Document type:** *Journal, Academic/Scholarly.*
Indexed: AIAP, ArtHuCI, ArtInd, BHA, CurCont, IBZ, RASB.
Published by: Kunsthistorisches Institut in Florenz, Max-Panck-Institut, Via Giuseppe Giusti 44, Florence, 50121, Italy. TEL 39-055-2491147, FAX 39-055-2491155, http://www.khi.fi.it. Eds. Max Seidel, Wolfger A Bulst. Circ: 900 (controlled). **Dist. by:** Art&libri s.a.s., Via dei Fossi 32 r, Florence 50123, Italy. TEL 39-055-264186, http://www.artlibri.it, FAX 39-055-264187, artlibri@tin.it.

705 AUT ISSN 0454-6601
N6836.L5
KUNSTJAHRBUCH DER STADT LINZ. Text in German. 1961. a. bk.rev. **Document type:** *Journal, Academic/Scholarly.*
Formerly: Linzer Jahrbuch fuer Kunstgeschichte (0075-9732)
Indexed: ABM, BHA.
Published by: Nordico - Museum der Stadt Linz, Dametzstr 23, Linz, O 4020, Austria. TEL 43-732-70701912, FAX 43-732-793518, nordico@mag.linz.at, http://www.nordico.at/nordico.html. Eds. Herfried Thaler, Willibald Katzinger. Circ: 450.

700 DNK
KUNSTMAGASINET 1%. Text in Danish. 1997. q. DKK 152.50; DKK 40 newsstand/cover (effective 2001). illus. **Document type:** *Magazine, Consumer.* **Description:** Covers the contemporary art scene and includes catalogs for exhibitions in Denmark and major European cities.
Published by: Sanne Fandrup & Tine Nygaard, Eds. & Pubs., Dampfaergevej 29, 425, Copenhagen OE, 3200, Denmark. TEL 45-35-26-44-40, info@kunstmagasinet.dk, http://www.kunstmagasinet.dk. Eds., Pubs. Sanne Fandrup, Tine Nygaard.

701.17 DEU
KUNSTPHILOSOPHIE. Text in German. 2002. irreg., latest vol.5, 2003. price varies. **Document type:** *Monographic series, Academic/Scholarly.*
Published by: Mentis Verlag GmbH, Schulze-Delitzsch-Str 19, Paderborn, 33100, Germany. TEL 49-5251-687902, FAX 49-5251-687905, webmaster@mentis.de, http://www.mentis.de.

700 NLD ISSN 0166-7297
KUNSTSCHRIFT. Text in Dutch. 1957. 6/yr. EUR 62.50 (effective 2003); includes Tentoonstellingsboekje. adv. **Document type:** *Magazine, Consumer.*
Formerly (until 1980): Openbaar Kunstbezit (0166-7394)
Indexed: BHA.
—IE, Infotrieve.
Published by: (Netherlands. Openbaar Kunstbezit), Waanders Uitgevers, Postbus 1129, Zwolle, 8001 BC, Netherlands. TEL 31-38-4658628, FAX 31-38-4655989, info@waanders.nl, http://www.waanders.nl. Ed. Mariet Haveman. Circ: 10,000 (paid).

707.1 DEU
KUNSTSTUNDE; Unterrichtsbeispiele zur aesthetischen Erziehung. Text in German. 1980. 2/yr. looseleaf. EUR 14 (effective 2005). illus. cum.index: 1980-1999. back issues avail. **Document type:** *Journal, Academic/Scholarly.*
Published by: A L S Verlag GmbH, Voltastr 3, Dietzenbach, 63128, Germany. TEL 49-6074-82160, FAX 49-6074-27322, info@als-verlag.de, http://www.als-verlag.de. Ed. Ingrid Kreide. R&P Maria Landji.

700 DEU ISSN 1618-8101
KUNSTTEXTE.DE. Text in German, English. 2001. q. free (effective 2005). **Document type:** *Journal, Academic/Scholarly.*
Media: Online - full text.
Published by: Humboldt-Universitaet zu Berlin, Unter den Linden 6, Berlin, 10099, Germany. TEL 49-30-2093-0, FAX 49-30-20932770, redaktion@kunsttexte.de, hu-presse@uv.hu-berlin.de, http://www.kunsttexte.de, http://www.hu-berlin.de.

700 FIN ISSN 1238-4100
KUVATAITEN KESKUSARKISTO/CENTRAL ART ARCHIVES. Text in English, Finnish. a., latest vol.8, 2002. price varies. back issues avail. **Document type:** *Monographic series, Academic/Scholarly.*
Published by: Valtion Taidemuseo/Finnish National Gallery, Kaivokato 2, Helsinki, 00100, Finland. TEL 358-9-173361, FAX 358-9-17336248, info@fng.fi, http://www.fng.fi.

KYOWA HAKKO KOGYO. ANNUAL REPORT. see *ADVERTISING AND PUBLIC RELATIONS*

700 USA
L I A: LIFE IMITATING ART. Abbreviated title: L I A. Text in English. 2002. bi-m. USD 24.95 domestic; CND 29.95 in Canada; USD 34.95 elsewhere; USD 6.50 newsstand/cover domestic; CND 8.50 newsstand/cover in Canada (effective 2003). adv. illus. **Document type:** *Magazine, Consumer.*
Published by: Life Imitating Art Magazine, 97 Ashland Avenue, 4A, Bala Cynwnd, PA 19004. TEL 610-771-0727, FAX 610-771-0348, editorial@liamagazine.com, http://www.liamagazine.com. Ed. Sammy DePasquale.

700 746.92 GBR ISSN 1473-3374
▼ **LAB MAGAZINE.** Text in English. 2003. 3/yr. GBP 4.95, USD 9.90 newsstand/cover (effective 2004). **Document type:** *Magazine, Consumer.*
Address: P O Box 31590, London, W11 1ZA, United Kingdom. subscribe@labmagazine.co.uk, http://www.labmagazine.co.uk.

LABIRINTI DEL FANTASTICO. see *LITERATURE*

700 ESP ISSN 1130-5762
LABORATORIO DE ARTE. Text in Spanish. 1988. a., latest vol.13, 2000. EUR 30 per issue (effective 2005). **Document type:** *Journal, Academic/Scholarly.*
Indexed: BHA.
—CINDOC.
Published by: Universidad de Sevilla, Secretariado de Publicaciones, Porvenir 27, Sevilla, 41013, Spain. TEL 34-95-4487444, FAX 34-95-4487443, secpub10@us.es, http://www.us.es/publius/inicio.html.

700 720 900 800 ITA ISSN 0393-0807
N6916
LABYRINTHOS; ermeneutica delle arti figurative dal Medioevo al Novecento. Text in English, French, German, Italian. 1982. 3/yr. EUR 68 domestic; EUR 88 foreign (effective 2004). adv. bk.rev. back issues avail. **Document type:** *Journal, Academic/Scholarly.*
Indexed: AIAP, BHA.
Published by: Casa Editrice le Lettere, Costa San Giorgio 28, Florence, FI 50125, Italy. TEL 39-055-2342710, FAX 39-055-2346010, staff@lelettere.it, www.lelettere.it. Circ: 2,000.

709 IND ISSN 0458-6506
LALIT KALA. Text in English. 1955. irreg., latest vol.27, 1993. INR 250. **Description:** Covers ancient Indian art and archaeology.
Indexed: ABM, BAS, IBSS, IndIslam.
Published by: National Academy of Art/Lalit Kala Akademi, Rabindra Bhavan, New Delhi, 110 001, India.

709 IND ISSN 0023-7396
N1
LALIT KALA CONTEMPORARY. Text in English. 1962. s-a. INR 60. adv. bk.rev. **Description:** Devoted to contemporary Indian art.
Indexed: ABM, BAS.
Published by: National Academy of Art/Lalit Kala Akademi, Rabindra Bhavan, New Delhi, 110 001, India. Ed. S A Krishnan.

700 ESP ISSN 0214-4573
N6280
LAMBARD; estudis d'art medieval. Text in Catalan. 1977. irreg.
—CINDOC.
Published by: Institut d'Estudis Catalans, C. del Carme, 47, Barcelona, 08001, Spain. TEL 34-932-701621, FAX 34-932-701180, piec@iec.es, http://www.iec.es/.

LANDFALL; New Zealand arts & letters. see *LITERARY AND POLITICAL REVIEWS*

LANTERN; cultural journal. see *EDUCATION*

700 ESP ISSN 0212-1700
LAPIZ; revista international de arte. Text in Spanish. 1982. m. (10/yr.). EUR 72 domestic; EUR 99 in Europe; EUR 142 in the Americas; EUR 189 elsewhere (effective 2005). 100 p./no.; **Document type:** *Magazine, Consumer.* **Description:** Informs on developments in the plastic arts, both in Spain and abroad.
Indexed: ABM.
—CINDOC, IE, Infotrieve.
Published by: Publicaciones de Estetica y Pensamiento S.L., Gravina 10, 1o, Madrid, 28004, Spain. TEL 34-91-5222972, FAX 34-91-5224707, lapiz@retemail.es. Ed. Jose Alberto Lopez. Adv. contact Isabel Debusto. Circ: 18,000. **Dist. by:** Asociacion de Revistas Culturales de Espana, Hortaleza, 75, Madrid 28004, Spain. TEL 34-91-3086066, FAX 34-91-3199267, info@arce.es, http://www.arce.es.

741.5 GBR ISSN 1473-3625
LARA CROFT TOMB RAIDER. Variant title: Tomb Raider. Text in English. 2001. m. USD 51; USD 4.99 newsstand/cover in United States; USD 5.99 newsstand/cover in Canada (effective 2001). **Document type:** *Magazine, Consumer.*
Published by: Titan Magazines (Subsidiary of: Titan Books Ltd.), Titan House, 144 Southwark St, London, SE1 0UP, United Kingdom. TEL 44-20-7620-0200, FAX 44-20-7803-1803. Ed. Nick Jones. Pub. Nick Landau. Adv. contact Scott Ferguson-Caisley. **Dist. by:** Comag Marketing Group, LLC, 250 W 55th St, New York, NY 10019. TEL 212-649-4468, FAX 212-262-1239.

THE LATIN AMERICANIST. see *HISTORY*

700 USA ISSN 0362-7047
N6995.L3
LATVJU MAKSLA. Text in Latvian. 1975. irreg. USD 15. adv. bk.rev. illus. **Document type:** *Monographic series.*
Published by: American Latvian Association in the United States, Inc., 400 Hurley Ave, Box 4578, Rockville, MD 20849-4578. TEL 301-340-1914, FAX 301-762-5438. Ed., R&P, Adv. contact Raits Eglitis. Circ: 1,500 (paid).

700 398 075 ITA ISSN 0047-4231
LAZIO IERI E OGGI; rivista mensile di cultura, arte, turismo. Text in Italian. 1965. m. EUR 25.83 domestic (effective 2004). bk.rev. illus. index. **Document type:** *Magazine, Consumer.*
Address: Via Taranto, 178, Rome, RM 00182, Italy. TEL 39-6-7020663, FAX 39-6-7020663, wpocino@ats.it. Ed. Willy Pocino.

LEIDSE UNIVERSITEITSBIBLIOTHEEK. KUNSTPUBLIKATIES. see *LIBRARY AND INFORMATION SCIENCES*

750 GBR ISSN 0024-0710
LEISURE PAINTER. Text in English. 1967. m. GBP 25.50 domestic; GBP 37 foreign (effective 2004). adv. bk.rev. illus. **Document type:** *Magazine, Consumer.* **Description:** Provides painting instruction and guidance.
Indexed: RASB.
—CCC.
Published by: The Artists' Publishing Company Limited, Caxton House, 62-65 High St, Tenterden, Kent TN30 6BD, United Kingdom. TEL 44-1580-763315, 44-1580-763673, FAX 44-1580-765411, http://www.leisurepainter.co.uk. Ed. Jane Stroud. Circ: 24,000.

LEODIUM. see *HISTORY—History Of Europe*

LEONARDO: ART SCIENCE AND TECHNOLOGY; oriented towards readers interested in the application of contemporary science and technology to music and the arts. see *MUSIC*

709.94 GBR
LEONARDO DA VINCI SOCIETY NEWSLETTER. Text in English. 1982. 2/yr. GBP 5 to members. bibl. back issues avail. **Document type:** *Newsletter.* **Description:** Includes a current select bibliography, news of events, exhibitions, conferences and lectures on Leonardo da Vinci.
Supersedes in part (in 1989): Newsletter for Leonardisti (0741-9597)
Published by: Leonardo da Vinci Society, c/o Francis Ames-Lewis Ed, Dept. of History of Art Birkbeck College, 43 Gordon St, London, WC1H 0AH, United Kingdom. TEL 44-171-631-6108, FAX 44-171-631-6107, f.ames-lewis@hart.bbk.ac.uk. R&P Francis Ames Lewis. Circ: 150.

LEONARDO MUSIC JOURNAL. see *MUSIC*

700.294 USA ISSN 0747-6566
N8602
LEONARD'S ANNUAL PRICE INDEX OF ART AUCTIONS. Text in English. 1981. a. USD 245 (effective 1999). **Document type:** *Abstract/Index.* **Description:** Listings of sales from nineteen major American auction galleries.
Formerly (until 1982): Leonard's Annual Index of Art Auctions (0733-5342)
Published by: Auction Index, Inc., 30 Valentine Park, Box 650190, Newton, MA 02465-0190. TEL 617-964-2867, FAX 617-969-9912.

700.294 USA
LEONARD'S PRICE INDEX OF LATIN AMERICAN ART AT AUCTION. Text in English. 1998. a. USD 125 (effective 1999).
Published by: Auction Index, Inc., 30 Valentine Park, Box 650190, Newton, MA 02465-0190. TEL 617-964-2876, FAX 617-969-9912, theran@auctionindex.com.

700 370 USA
LESLEY UNIVERSITY SERIES IN ART AND EDUCATION. Text in English. 2002. irreg., latest 2004. price varies. **Document type:** *Monographic series.*
Published by: Peter Lang Publishing, Inc., 275 Seventh Ave, 28th Fl, New York, NY 10001. TEL 212-647-7700, 800-770-5264, FAX 212-647-7707, customerservice@plang.com, http://www.peterlangusa.com. Ed. Elijah Mirochnik.

700 800 DOM
LETRA GRANDE, ARTE Y LITERATURA. Text in Spanish. 1980. m. USD 65. adv.
Published by: Letra Grande Arte y Literatura, Mirador del Sur, Leonardo da Vinci 13, Santo Domingo, Dominican Republic. TEL 809-531-2225, FAX 809-541-2855. Ed. Juan Ramon Quinones M. Adv. contact Berenice Canaham.

LETRAS DEL ECUADOR. see *LITERATURE*

LETRAS E ARTES. see *LITERATURE*

745.61 USA ISSN 1076-7339
Z43.A1
LETTER ARTS REVIEW. Text in English. 1982. q. USD 45 domestic; USD 49 in Canada & Mexico; USD 67 elsewhere (effective 2005). adv. bk.rev. illus. index, cum.index. back issues avail.; reprints avail. **Document type:** *Magazine, Consumer.* **Description:** Dedicated to the art and craft of hand lettering and calligraphy. Provides in-depth articles and quality reproductions about artists, calligraphic works past, present and future, typography, artists' books, practical commercial applications and unbiased book fonts and exhibition reviews.
Former titles (until vol.11, no.2, 1994): Calligraphy Review (0895-7819); (until 1987): Calligraphy Idea Exchange (0737-318X)
Related titles: Online - full text ed.: (from H.W. Wilson, O C L C Online Computer Library Center, Inc.).
Indexed: ABM, ArtInd, DAAI, DIP, IBR, IBZ.
—BLDSC (5185.126770).
Published by: Letter Arts Review, Inc., 212 Hillsboro Dr, Silver Spring, MD 20902. mail@letterarts.com, http://www.letterarts.com. Ed., Pub., R&P, Adv. contact Karyn L Gilman. Circ: 5,500.

LETTER BOMB. see *PHILATELY*

▼ **LETTERATURA & ARTE.** see *LITERATURE*

745 USA
LETTERHEADS; the international annual of letterhead design. Text in English. 1977. a. USD 19.95 (effective 2000). adv. **Document type:** *Trade.*
Published by: Art Direction Book Co., Inc., 456 Glenbrook Rd., Glenbrook, CT 06906. TEL 203-353-1441, FAX 203-353-1371. Ed. Don Barron. Circ: 6,200 (paid).

LETTRES EOLIENNES/EOLIKA GRAMMATA; revue bimensuelle d'art de Lesbos. see *LITERATURE*

792 780 700 CAN ISSN 0227-227X
LIAISON; la revue des arts en Ontario francais. Text in French. 1978. 5/yr. CND 26 (effective 2000). adv. bk.rev. illus. **Document type:** *Magazine, Consumer.* **Description:** Artistic and cultural activities by Franco-Ontariens; includes creative writing, profiles of artists, current events.
Related titles: Online - full text ed.: (from Northern Light Technology, Inc.).
Indexed: CPerl, RehabLit.
Published by: Editions L' Interligne, 255 Montreal Rd, Vanier, PQ K1L 6C4, Canada. TEL 613-748-0850, FAX 613-748-0852. Ed., R&P Stefan Psenak. Adv. contact Rachel Carriere. Circ: 1,500.

700 CHN
LIANHUAN HUABAO/PICTURE STORIES. Text in Chinese. m. USD 54; USD 4.50 newsstand/cover (effective 2001). illus.
Published by: Renmin Meishu Chubanshe/People's Fine Arts Publishers, 32, Beizongbu Hutong, Beijing, 100735, China. TEL 86-1-5122587. Ed. Meng Qingjiang. **Dist. by:** China International Book Trading Corp, 35 Chegongzhuang Xilu, Haidian District, PO Box 399, Beijing 100044, China. TEL 86-10-68412045, FAX 86-10-68412023, cibtc@mail.cibtc.com.cn, http://www.cibtc.com.cn.

700 USA
LIBRARY OF GREAT PAINTERS. Text in English. irreg. USD 49.50. **Document type:** *Monographic series.*
Published by: Harry N. Abrams, Inc., 100 Fifth Ave, New York, NY 10011. TEL 212-206-7715, FAX 212-654-8437.

LICHTUNGEN; Zeitschrift fuer Literatur, Kunst und Zeitkritik. see *LITERATURE*

700 NLD ISSN 0925-8191
➤ **LIER EN BOOG**; series of philosophy of art & art theory. Text in English. 1975. a. price varies. adv. bk.rev. **Document type:** *Monographic series, Academic/Scholarly.*
Related titles: Online - full text ed.: (from Gale Group, IngentaConnect, Swets Information Services).
Published by: Editions Rodopi B.V., Tijnmuiden 7, Amsterdam, 1046 AK, Netherlands. TEL 31-20-6114821, FAX 31-20-4472979, F.van.der.Zee@rodopi.nl, info@rodopi.nl, http://www.rodopi.nl. Ed. Mr. Fred van der Zee. Circ: 1,200.

700 FRA ISSN 0989-6023
LIGEIA; dossiers sur l'art. Text in French. 1988. q.
Indexed: BHA.
Published by: Association Ligeia, 53 Galerie des Damiers, Paris-la-Defense, Courbevoie, 92400, France. TEL 33-1-46930367, FAX 33-1-46390362. Ed., Pub. Giovanni Lista. **Subscr. to:** B.P. 327, Paris Cedex 6 75266, France.

700 USA ISSN 0161-4223
➤ **LIGHTWORKS**; illuminating thresholds of new art. Text in English. 1975. irreg., latest no.22, 2000. bk.rev.; film rev.; music rev. illus.; bibl. 96 p./no.; back issues avail. **Document type:** *Monographic series, Academic/Scholarly.* **Description:** Presents approaches to new and experimental art including intermedial art forms, photography, Ray Johnson, xerography, artist's books, mail art and fringe research. The accent is on far-reaching exploration within the creative arts. Upcoming issue will focus on private and institutional archives of ephemera and mail art.
Published by: Lightworks Magazine, Inc., PO Box 1202, Birmingham, MI 48012-1202. TEL 248-626-8026, FAX 248-737-0046, lightworks_mag@hotmail.com. Ed. Andrea D Martin. Pub., R&P Charlton Burch. Circ: 2,000.

700 BGR
LIK. Text in Bulgarian. 1994. m. BGL 36; BGL 3 newsstand/cover (effective 2001). 64 p./no.; **Description:** Presents information concerning world cultural events, processes, trends, creators; portrays famous Bulgarian artists; draws the route of art on the map of contemporary Europe and Bulgaria.
Published by: Bulgarian News Agency, 49 Tzarigradsko Chausee Blvd., Sofia, 1040, Bulgaria. TEL 359-2-926242, FAX 359-2-9461123, bta@bta.bg, http://www.sca.bg/cultural-periodicals/catalog/lik.htm, http://www.bta.bg/site/en/indexe.shtml. Eds. Maria Velkovska, Panayot Denev, Yana Kozuharova Kozuharova.

700 AUS ISSN 1327-5445
LIKE, ART MAGAZINE. Text in English. 1988. 3/yr. AUD 20 domestic to individuals; AUD 45 foreign to individuals; AUD 30 domestic to institutions; AUD 55 foreign to institutions (effective 2000); AUD 6 newsstand/cover. adv. bk.rev.; film rev. illus. index. **Document type:** *Academic/Scholarly.* **Description:** Discusses contemporary visual art and culture.
Formerly: Agenda: Australian Contemporary Art (1033-1115)
Indexed: ABM.
Published by: Royal Melbourne Institute of Technology, Faculty of Art, Design & Communication, GPO Box 2476 V, Melbourne, VIC 3001, Australia. TEL 61-3-9225-5636, FAX 61-3-9925-5363, like@rmit.edu.au, http://art.rmit.edu.au/like. Ed. Robyn McKenzie. Adv. contact Sarah Ritson. page AUD 500; trim 240 x 340. Circ: 1,300.

745.4 USA ISSN 1528-6193
N6480
LIMN; magazine of international design. Text in English. 1997. q. USD 30. illus.
Address: 290 Townsend St, San Francisco, CA 94107. info@limn.com, http://www.limn.com. Eds. Andrew Wagner, Stephanie Ray.

LINDEY ON ENTERTAINMENT, PUBLISHING AND THE ARTS. see *LAW*

700 USA ISSN 1544-4716
N330.N52
LINEA (NEW YORK); the journal of the Art Students League of New York. Text in English. 1948. s-a. free to qualified personnel (effective 2003). illus. 24 p./no. 3 cols./p.; back issues avail. **Document type:** *Newsletter, Academic/Scholarly.* **Description:** Written by artists to forge a distinctive voice for those who practice and write about art.
Formerly (until 1997): Art Students League News
Published by: Art Students League of New York, 215 W 57th St, New York, NY 10019. TEL 212-247-4510, FAX 212-541-7024, stephanie@artstudentsleague.org, http://www.theartstudentsleague.org. Ed. Stephanie Cassidy. Circ: 7,400.

700 ITA
LINEAVERDE; periodico di arte attualita e cultura. Text in Italian. 1973. bi-m. free. adv. bk.rev. illus. 4 p./no. 3 cols./p.; **Document type:** *Newspaper, Newspaper-distributed.* **Description:** Provides poets, writers, painters, and academics with information to spread Italian culture.
Related titles: Fax ed.; Microform ed.
Published by: Rossieditore, Via L. Giordano 56, Casella Postale 1008, Vomero, NA 80100, Italy. pi.erre@inwind.it, http://www.puntostampa.freeweb.supereva.it. Ed., Pub., Adv. contact Paolo Rossi. Circ: 3,000.

700 USA ISSN 1097-9700
NX511.B35
LINK (BALTIMORE); a critical journal on the arts in Baltimore and the world. Text in English. 1996. s-a. USD 25 to individuals; USD 50 to institutions; USD 10 per issue (effective 2002). adv. **Document type:** *Journal, Academic/Scholarly.*
Related titles: Online - full text ed.: (from ProQuest Information & Learning, SoftLine Information).
Indexed: AltPI.
Published by: Link Arts, Inc., PO Box 22228, Baltimore, MD 21203. TEL 410-327-4001, editors@baltolink.org, ads@baltolink.org, http://www.baltolink.org. adv.: page USD 250.

700 ESP ISSN 0211-2574
LINO: REVISTA DE ARTE. Text in Spanish. 1980. a. price varies.
—CINDOC.

Published by: Universidad de Oviedo, Servicio de Publicaciones, Campus de Humanidades, Oviedo, Asturias 33001, Spain. TEL 34-85-210160, FAX 34-85-218352. Ed. Carlos Cid Priego.

THE LISTENING EYE. see LITERATURE

LITERARY SALT; a journal of art and literature. see LITERATURE

LITERATURA I MASTATSTVA. see LITERATURE

LITERATURE AND THE VISUAL ARTS: NEW FOUNDATIONS. see LITERATURE

LITERATUREN FORUM. see LITERATURE

LITERATUREN GLAS. see LITERATURE

LITERATURNAYA ROSSIYA. see LITERARY AND POLITICAL REVIEWS

LITHOPHANE COLLECTOR'S CLUB BULLETIN. see MUSEUMS AND ART GALLERIES

LITORAL; revista de poesia, arte y pensamiento. see LITERATURE—Poetry

700 800   USA   ISSN 0271-7735
PS571.K2
LITTLE BALKANS REVIEW; Southeast Kansas literary and graphics quarterly. Text in English. 1980. q. USD 10. adv. bk.rev. illus. index. back issues avail.
Indexed: IAPV.
Published by: Little Balkans Press, Inc., 601 Grandview Heights Terrace, Pittsburg, KS 66762. Ed. Gene Degruson. Circ: 1,500.

700 500.9   USA   ISSN 0024-5283
QH1   CODEN: LIMUAR
THE LIVING MUSEUM. Text in English. 1939. q. free. illus. index, cum.index: 1939-1955. Document type: Academic/Scholarly. Description: Describes Illinois' natural history, art, and anthropology.
Related titles: Braille ed.
Indexed: ABS&EES, BiolAb, BiolDig, SFA, WildRev. —Linda Hall.
Published by: Illinois State Museum, Spring & Edwards Sts, Springfield, IL 62706. TEL 217-782-7386, FAX 217-782-1254, editor@museum.state.il.us, http://www.museum.state.il.us. Circ: 19,000.

700   FRA
LIVRE DU CONGRES L'A F T P V. Text in French. biennial. Description: Gathers the full text of the lectures pronounced during the AFTPV Congress.
Published by: (Etudes et Realisations de la Couleur), E R E C, 68 rue Jean Jaures, Puteaux, 92800, France. TEL 47-73-01-23. Ed. Annik Chauvel. Circ: 800.

709.9305   NZL   ISSN 1174-2216
LOG ILLUSTRATED. Text in English. 1997. 3/yr. NZD 15 domestic; NZD 20 in Australia; NZD 22 in United Kingdom; NZD 22 newsstand/cover in United States; NZD 5 newsstand/cover domestic; NZD 7 newsstand/cover in Australia; NZD 8 newsstand/cover in United Kingdom; NZD 8 newsstand/cover in United States (effective 2002). adv.
Formerly: Physics Room Journal (1174-0264)
Published by: Physics Room, P.O. Box 22-351, Christchurch, New Zealand. TEL 64-3-379-5583, FAX 64-3-379-6063, log@physicsroom.org.nz, http://www.physicsroom.org.nz/log. adv.: page NZD 550; 260 x 370. Circ: 1,000.

▼ LOOK-LOOK; the magazine by young photographers, writers and artists. see CHILDREN AND YOUTH—For

LOST GENERATION JOURNAL. see LITERATURE

700   DNK   ISSN 0024-6891
NX28.S8
LOUISIANA REVY. Text in Danish; Abstracts in English. 1960. 2/yr. DKK 296 (effective 2005). adv. illus. index, cum.index: vols.1-35. Document type: Catalog. Description: Serves as a catalog for major art exhibitions at the Louisiana Museum of Modern Art (Denmark).
Indexed: ABCT, ABM, BHA, RASB, RILM.
Published by: Louisiana Museum of Modern Art, Gl Strandvej 13, Humlebaek, 3050, Denmark. TEL 45-49-190719, FAX 45-49-193505, curator@louisiana.dk, http://www.louisiana.dk. Circ: 40,000.

THE LOW COUNTRIES; arts and society in Flanders and The Netherlands: a yearbook. see HUMANITIES: COMPREHENSIVE WORKS

LOWDOWN; youth performing arts in Australia. see CHILDREN AND YOUTH—For

750 796.77   USA   ISSN 1527-4209
HN1
LOWRIDER ARTE. Text in English. 1990. bi-m. adv. Document type: Magazine, Consumer. Description: Presents art and artists expressing individual and cultural pride as well as enthusiasm for custom cars.
—CCC.
Published by: Primedia Automotive Group (Subsidiary of: Primedia Enthusiast Media), 2400 E Katella Ave, 11th Fl, Anaheim, CA 92806. TEL 714-939-2400, 800-777-5489, lowrider@mcmullenargus.com, http://www.lowridermagazine.com, http://www.mcmullenargus.com. Pub. Rudy Rivas.

700   USA
LOYAL. Text in English. q. USD 8, EUR 7 newsstand/cover (effective 2005).
Published by: Loyal New York, 159 Rivington St #2, New York, NY 10002. http://www.loyalmagazine.com. Eds. Kristian Bengtsson, Martin Lilja.

LUDICA; arte y cultura del diseno. see COMPUTERS—Computer Graphics

LUNGFULL MAGAZINE. see LITERATURE

731.76   USA   ISSN 0192-2491
M B NEWS. Text in English. 1944. m. USD 70 domestic; USD 80 in Canada; USD 95 elsewhere (effective 2005). adv. bk.rev. Document type: Magazine, Trade. Description: Includes news of the trade, meetings, features, and memorial designs for monument retailers, wholesalers and quarriers.
Formerly: Monument Builder News
Published by: Monument Builders of North America, 401 N Michigan Ave, Ste 2200, Chicago, IL 60611. TEL 312-321-5143, FAX 312-673-6732, info@minumentbuildres.org, http://www.monumentbuilders.org. Ed. Alice Konopasek. adv.: B&W page USD 765, color page USD 1,265. Circ: 1,300 (paid and free).

700   USA
M C A C A BULLETIN*. Text in English. bi-m. Document type: Bulletin, Government.
Formerly: M C A News
Published by: Michigan Council for the Arts, P O Box 30705, Lansing, MI 48909-8205. TEL 313-256-3731, FAX 313-256-3781. Circ: 12,000.

700   NLD   ISSN 1566-6247
M M NIEUWS. (Marketing Management Nieuws) Text in Dutch. 1999. 10/yr. EUR 95 (effective 2005). adv. bk.rev. charts; stat. index. back issues avail. Document type: Newsletter. Description: Deals with marketing the arts and culture. For professionals in museums and stage arts institutions.
Formed by the merger of (1992-1999): Culturele Marketing Nieuwsbrief (0927-6742); (1995-1999): Vakblad Management Knust en Cultuur (1382-4333)
Published by: Bureau Menno Heling, Johan van Hasseltweg 118, Amsterdam, 1022 WZ, Netherlands. TEL 31-20-6235001, FAX 31-20-6382196, redactie@mmnieuws.nl, http://www.mmnieuws.nl/inhoud/. Ed. Menno Heling. Circ: 1,000 (paid).

MACEDONIAN REVIEW; history, culture, literature, arts. see LITERATURE

700   CAN   ISSN 0228-7749
MADE IN CANADA; artists in books. Text in French, English. 1980. a.
Published by: National Library of Canada, 395 Wellington St, Ottawa, ON K1A 0N4, Canada. TEL 613-996-5115, 866-578-7777, FAX 613-943-1112, publications@nlc-bnc.ca, http://www.nlc-bnc.ca.

700   ESP   ISSN 1139-5362
DP302.M1
MADRID. Variant title: Madrid, Revista de Arte, Geografia e Historia. Text in Spanish. 1998. a.
Indexed: RILM.
Published by: Comunidad de Madrid, Servicio de Publicaciones, Gran Via, 3, Madrid, 28013, Spain. TEL 34-91-7200952, FAX 34-91-7200831, http://www3.madrid.org/edupubli/.

MAGALLAT AL-FAISAL. see LITERATURE

700   DNK   ISSN 0907-3612
MAGASINET KUNST. Text in Danish. 1992. 6/yr. DKK 360 (effective 2005). adv. bk.rev. 52 p./no.; Document type: Journal, Consumer. Description: Features articles on the Danish and international modern art scene along with exhibition and artist reviews.
Published by: Horisont Gruppen A/S, Center Boulevard 5, Copenhagen S, 2300, Denmark. TEL 45-32-473230, FAX 45-32-473239, red@magasinetkunst.dk, info@horisontgruppen.dk, http://www.magasinetkunst.dk, http://www.horisontgruppen.dk. Eds. Michel Henri TEL 45-20-227309, Ole Lindboe TEL 45-20-161477. Adv. contact Jan Dupont TEL 45-32-473230. color page DKK 12,875; 185 x 274. Circ: 3,142.

700   CAN
MAGAZIN ART. Text in English; Section in French. q. CND 34.95 domestic; USD 40 in United States; USD 50 elsewhere; USD 10.95 newsstand/cover (effective 2001). Document type: Magazine, Consumer. Description: Features articles on Canadian art, artists, Canadian galleries and museums.
Address: PO Box 4066, Westmount Stn, Westmount, PQ H3Z 2X3, Canada. TEL 514-685-5425, 800-641-9552, FAX 514-685-9011, magazinart@videotron.ca. Circ: 10,000 (paid); 10,000 (controlled).

700   POL   ISSN 1231-6709
MAGAZYN SZTUKI. Text in Polish. 1993. q. PLZ 40 domestic; USD 40 foreign. adv. 96 p./no.; back issues avail. Document type: Magazine, Consumer. Description: Presents contemporary art - Polish and international as well.
Related titles: Online - full text ed.: ISSN 1689-1295. 1999; English ed.
Published by: Ryszard Ziarkiewicz Ed. & Pub., Ul Zakopianska 32 b-4, Gdansk, 80142, Poland. TEL 48-58-321001, FAX 48-58-321001, magazynsztuki@home.pl, cultbalt@softel.gda.pl, http://magazynsztuki.home.pl. Ed. Ryszard Ziarkiewicz. Adv. contact Beata Maciejewska. Circ: 1,000.

700   USA   ISSN 0196-8432
MAGIC CHANGES*; the biannual for independent artists. Text in English. 1979. s-a. USD 5. adv. bk.rev. back issues avail.
Published by: (Order of the Celestial Otter), Celestial Otter Press, c/o John Sennett, Ed., 237 Parktrail Ct., Schaumberg, IL 60173-2150. TEL 708-416-3111. Adv. contact Kaela Sennett. Circ: 500.

MAGICAL BLEND; a transformative journey. see NEW AGE PUBLICATIONS

745   HUN   ISSN 1217-9833
MAGYAR NEPMUVESZET. Text in Hungarian; Summaries in English, German. 1951-1955; resumed 1994. a. HUF 1,000. Document type: Monographic series.
Published by: Neprajzi Muzeum/Ethnographical Museum, Kossuth Lajos ter 12, Budapest, 1055, Hungary. TEL 36-1-326340, FAX 36-2-692419. Ed. Attila Selmeczi Kovacs.

790 910.03   USA   ISSN 0149-0729
MAHOGANY*. Text in English. 1977. w. free. adv.
Published by: Ike DuBose, 1520 Royster Rd, Fort Worth, TX 76134-3604. Circ: 150,000.

700 793.3   GBR   ISSN 0959-0013
MAILOUT; arts work with people. Text in English. 1988. bi-m. GBP 15 to individuals; GBP 21 to non-profit organizations; GBP 25 all others; GBP 4 per issue (effective 2003). adv. bk.rev.; film rev.; music rev.; play rev.; rec.rev.; video rev. Website rev. illus. cum.index. 32 p./no. 3 cols./p.; back issues avail. Document type: Magazine, Consumer. Description: Covers all forms of participatory arts work.
Published by: Mailout Trust, 87 New Sq, Chesterfield, Derbys S40 1AH, United Kingdom. TEL 44-1246-207070, FAX 44-1246-238319, info@e-mailout.org, ads@e-mailout.org, http://www.e-mailout.org. Eds. Huw Champion, Jules Cadie. R&P Huw Champion. adv.: page GBP 300; 190 x 277. Circ: 1,300.

MAIN DE SINGE. see LITERARY AND POLITICAL REVIEWS

MAINFRAENKISCHES JAHRBUCH FUER GESCHICHTE UND KUNST. see HISTORY—History Of Europe

943 913 709   DEU   ISSN 0076-2792
DD901.M2
MAINZER ZEITSCHRIFT; Mittelrheinisches Jahrbuch fuer Archaeologie, Geschichte und Kunst. Text in German. 1906. a. price varies. Document type: Yearbook, Academic/Scholarly.
Indexed: AIAP, BHA, BrArAb, DIP, IBR, IBZ, RASB. —BLDSC (5352.670000).
Published by: Mainzer Altertumsverein e.V., Rheinallee 3B, Mainz, 55116, Germany. TEL 49-6131-229442, FAX 49-6131-123569, brigitte.barwinski@t-online.de, http://www.mainzer-altertumsverein.de. Ed. Wolfgang Dobras. Circ: 770.

MAISONNEUVE; eclectic curiosity. see SOCIOLOGY

700 605.4   GBR   ISSN 1365-8190
➤ MAKE; the magazine of women's art. Text in English. 1983. q., latest no.92. GBP 18 for 18 mos. in United Kingdom to individuals; GBP 23 for 18 mos. in Europe to individuals; GBP 22 in United Kingdom to institutions 4 issues per year; GBP 29 in Europe to institutions 4 issues per year; GBP 3 newsstand/cover (effective 2000). adv. bk.rev.; video rev. back issues avail. Document type: Academic/Scholarly.
Description: Vital coverage of British art currently led by a new generation of women artists - provocative and informative news, features and reviews. Reflects the contemporary discourse provoked by the issues, themes and concepts in the work of women artists today.
Formerly (until 1996): Women's Art Magazine (0961-1460)
Related titles: Online - full text ed.: (from H.W. Wilson, O C L C Online Computer Library Center, Inc.).
Indexed: ABM, ArtInd, BHA, BrHumI, DIP, FemPer, IBZ.

—BLDSC (5353.694910). **CCC.**
Published by: (Arts Council of England), Make Magazine, 107-109 Charing Cross Rd, London, WC2H ODU, United Kingdom. TEL 44-20-7384-1110, 44-20-7584-8860, FAX 44-20-7384-1110, 44-20-7584-8864, make@csm.linst.ac.uk, womensart.lib@ukonline.co.uk, http://www.makemagazine.net/, http://www.womensart.org.uk. R&P Ceri Hand. Adv. contact Taru Elfving TEL 44-171-384-1110. B&W page GBP 440, color page GBP 600; trim 230 x 310. Circ: 20,000. **Dist. by:** Central Books Ltd., 99 Wallis Rd, London E9 5LN, United Kingdom. TEL 44-20-8986-4854.

700 808.81 USA ISSN 0888-0972
MALLIFE✶. Text in English. 1981. s-a. USD 10. adv. bk.rev.; film rev. back issues avail. **Description:** Writing and art dealing with greed inherent in capitalist economies.
Published by: Bomb Shelter Props, 3030 N 15th St, Phoenix, AZ 85014-5636. TEL 602-253-4430. Ed. Mike Miskowski. Circ: 300.

700 GBR ISSN 1470-8817
MANGA MAX. Text in English. 1993. m. GBP 3.25 newsstand/cover (effective 2000). adv. back issues avail. **Document type:** *Magazine, Consumer.*
Formerly (until 1998): Manga Mania (0968-9575)
Published by: Titan Magazines (Subsidiary of: Titan Books Ltd.), Titan House, 144 Southwark St, London, SE1 0UP, United Kingdom. TEL 44-20-7620-0200, FAX 44-20-7803-1803, mangamaxmail@titanemail.com. Pub. Nick Landau. Adv. contact Scott Ferguson-Caisley. **Dist. by:** Comag, Tavistock Works, Tavistock Rd, W Drayton, Middx UB7 7QX, United Kingdom. TEL 44-1895-433600, FAX 44-1715-433606.

700 895.1 CHN ISSN 1003-2746
MANGYUAN. Text in Chinese. bi-m. CNY 3 per issue. illus. **Description:** Literary magazine.
Published by: Henan Sheng Wenlian, No 34 Jing 7 Lu, Zhengzhou, Henan 450003, China. TEL 334646. Ed. Qian Jiyang. **Dist. overseas by:** China International Book Trading Corp, 35 Chegongzhuang Xilu, Haidian District, PO Box 399, Beijing 100044, China. TEL 86-10-68412045, FAX 86-10-68412023, cibtc@mail.cibtc.com.cn, http://www.cibtc.com.cn.

700 USA ISSN 1524-4180
MANHATTAN ARTS INTERNATIONAL. Text in English. 1983. bi-m. USD 20 domestic; USD 35 foreign (effective 2000). adv. bk.rev. **Document type:** *Consumer.* **Description:** Promotes new artists on the horizon. Covers art events and includes interviews with world art leaders and reviews of exhibitions.
Formerly: Manhattan Arts
Address: 200 E 72nd St, New York, NY 10021. TEL 212-472-1660, FAX 212-794-0324, manarts@aol.com, http://wwwManhattanArts.com. Ed., R&P Renee Phillips. Adv. contact Richard Davis. Circ: 10,000 (paid); 40,000 (controlled).

MANILA REVIEW; Philippines journal of literature and the arts. see *LITERATURE*

700 DEU ISSN 0178-3556
MANIPULATOR. Text in English, German, Italian; Summaries in English. 1982. q. adv. back issues avail.
Published by: Moser und Colby GmbH, Duisburger Str 44, Duesseldorf, 40477, Germany. TEL 0211-4982068, FAX 0211-4983424. Ed. Wilhelm Moser. Circ: 24,000.

MANUSKRIPTE; Zeitschrift fuer Literatur. see *LITERATURE*

070.5 GBR
MARCAN HANDBOOK OF ARTS ORGANISATIONS. Text in English. 1983. triennial. GBP 20 per issue (effective 2000). **Document type:** *Directory.* **Description:** Covers national and international organizations in all areas of the arts, pure and applied, with details of activities and publications.
Formerly: Arts Address Book
Published by: Peter Marcan Publications, Peter Margan Publications, P.O. Box 3158, London, SE1 4RA, United Kingdom. TEL 44-20-7357-0368. Circ: 750.

700 IND ISSN 0972-1444
N1
MARG (MUMBAI). Variant title: Marg Art Magazine. Text in English. 1946. q. USD 145 to institutions (effective 2006). adv. bk.rev. illus. back issues avail. **Document type:** *Journal, Academic/Scholarly.* **Description:** Covers the arts of India and related cultures. Presents four or five articles on a theme, plus non-thematic articles and exhibition notes.
Related titles: Online - full text ed.
Indexed: A&ATA, AIAP, ArtInd, IBR, RASB.
Published by: (National Centre for the Performing Arts), Scientific Publishers, 5-A New Pali Rd., Near Hotel Taj Hari Mahal, PO Box 91, Jodhpur, Rajasthan 342 003, India. TEL 91-291-2433323, FAX 91-291-2512580, info@scientificpub.com, http://www.scientificpub.com/bookdetails.php?booktransid=459&bookid=455. Circ: 1,500. **Dist. by:** H P C Publishers Distributors Pvt. Ltd., 4805 Bharat Ram Rd, 24 Darya Ganj, New Delhi 110 002, India; **Dist. by:** Art Media Resources, Ltd., Paragon Book Gallery.

709 USA ISSN 0277-8726
E159.5
MARKERS. Text in English. 1979. a. price varies. **Document type:** *Academic/Scholarly.* **Description:** Scholarly articles relating to many aspects of funerary art, preservation, and history in different parts of the United States.
Indexed: AmH&L, HistAb, MLA-IB.
Published by: Association for Gravestone Studies, 278 Main St, Ste 207, Greenfield, MA 01301-3230. TEL 413-772-0836, info@gravestonestudies.org, http://www.gravestonestudies.org. R&P Gary E Collison.

709.2 DEU ISSN 1437-1375
MARKETING MUSING ON ART; sell fine art for a change. Text in German. m. back issues avail. **Document type:** *Trade.*
Media: Online - full text.
Address: Uhlandstr 8, Hiddenhausen, 32120, Germany. TEL 49-5523-820582, FAX 49-5523-820584, ws@art-joe.com, http://art-quarter.com/beck/joe/aj. Ed. Werner Stuerenburg.

701 709 CZE ISSN 1211-7390
N17
MASARYKOVA UNIVERZITA. FILOZOFICKA FAKULTA. SBORNIK PRACI. F: RADA UMENOVEDNA. OPUSCULA HISTORIAE ARTIUM. Text in Czech; Summaries in Multiple languages. 1957. a. price varies. bk.rev. **Document type:** *Academic/Scholarly.* **Description:** Articles about the theory and history of the arts.
Formerly: Univerzita J.E. Purkyne. Filozoficka Fakulta. Sbornik Praci. F: Rada Umenovedna (0231-5025)
Published by: Masarykova Univerzita, Filozoficka Fakulta, A Novaka 1, Brno, 66088, Czech Republic. TEL 420-5-41121102, FAX 420-5-41121406, exchange@phil.muni.cz. Ed. Milos Stedron TEL 420-5-41121337.

741 USA ISSN 0025-5025
NC1
➤ **MASTER DRAWINGS**; devoted exclusively to the study and illustration of drawings. Text in English. 1963. q. USD 95 domestic; USD 105 foreign (effective 2005). adv. bk.rev. illus. index, cum.index: 1963-1997. back issues avail.; reprints avail. **Document type:** *Journal, Academic/Scholarly.*
Indexed: AIAP, ASCA, ArtHuCI, ArtInd, BHA, CurCont, DIP, IBR, IBRH, IBZ, RASB.
—IE, Infotrieve.
Published by: Master Drawings Association, Inc., 29 E 36th St, New York, NY 10016. TEL 212-590-0369, FAX 212-685-4740, administrator@masterdrawings.org, http://www.masterdrawings.org. Ed. Anne Marie Logan. R&P, Adv. contact Asher Miller TEL 212-685-0008 ext. 369. Circ: 1,250 (paid and free).

708.11 CAN ISSN 0383-5391
MASTERPIECES IN THE NATIONAL GALLERY OF CANADA/CHEFS-D'OEUVRE DE LA GALERIE NATIONALE DU CANADA. Text in English, French. 1971. irreg., latest vol.12, 1978. CND 1.95. illus. **Document type:** *Monographic series.* **Description:** Details study, history and criticism of individual paintings in the National Gallery's collection.
Published by: National Gallery of Canada, Publications Division, c/o Irene Lillico, 380 Sussex Dr, Ottawa, ON K1N 9N4, Canada. TEL 613-990-0537, FAX 613-990-7460. Eds. Charles Hill, Michael Pantazzi. Circ: 5,000. **Dist. by:** University of Chicago, 5801 S Ellis Ave, Chicago, IL 60637.

700 ESP ISSN 1579-2641
MATERIA. Text in Catalan, Spanish. 1972. irreg. bk.rev. back issues avail. **Document type:** *Monographic series, Academic/Scholarly.* **Description:** Includes a list and short abstract of the theses (first degree and doctoral dissertations) that have been read at the History of Art Department of the University of Barcelona.
Formerly (until 1998): D'Art (0211-0768)
Indexed: ABM, BHA, RILM.
—CINDOC.
Published by: (Universitat de Barcelona, Departament d'Historia de l'Art), Universitat de Barcelona, Servei de Publicacions, Gran Via Corts Catalanes 585, Barcelona, 08007, Spain. TEL 34-93-4021100, http://www.publicacions.ub.es. Ed. Dr. Pere Salabert. Circ: 1,000.

▼ **MATERIAL RELIGION**; the journal of objects, art & belief. see *RELIGIONS AND THEOLOGY*

MATERIALI E STRUTTURE; problemi di conservazione. see *CONSERVATION*

700 930.1 USA ISSN 1095-1318
CC135 CODEN: MRSPDH
MATERIALS ISSUES IN ART AND ARCHAEOLOGY. Text in English. 1988. a.
Indexed: AnthLit.
Published by: Materials Research Society, 506 Keystone Dr, Warrendale, PA 15086-7573. TEL 724-779-3003, FAX 724-779-8313, info@mrs.org.

MATRIART; a Canadian feminist art journal. see *WOMEN'S STUDIES*

800 700 CAN ISSN 0318-3610
MATRIX. Text in English. 1975. 3/yr. CND 21 domestic to individuals; CND 25 domestic to institutions; USD 25 in United States; USD 35 elsewhere (effective 2005). adv. bk.rev. **Document type:** *Magazine, Consumer.* **Description:** Publishes fiction, essays, poems, short articles, and book reviews.
Related titles: Microfiche ed.: (from MML); Microform ed.: (from MML).
Indexed: CBCARef, CLitI, CPerI.
—**CCC.**
Published by: Matrix Magazine, 1400 de Maisonneuve W, Ste LB-502, Montreal, PQ H3G 1M8, Canada. matrix@alcor.concordia.ca, http://alcor.concordia.ca/~matrix. Circ: 2,000.

A MATTER OF WIT. see *LITERATURE*

700 FRA ISSN 1422-8122
MAYER. Text in French. 1995. a. FRF 1,200.
Formed by the merger of (1967-1995): International Auction Records (English Edition) (1422-822X); (19??-1995): International Auction Records (English-German Edition) (1422-8262); (1991-1995): Il Libro Internazionale delle Vendite all'Asta (1422-819X); (1963-1995): Le Livre International des Ventes (1154-5445); Which was formerly (until 1988): Annuaire International des Ventes (1154-5437)
Related titles: English ed.
Published by: Guide Mayer, 18 rue Godefroy-Cavaignac, Paris, 75011, France. TEL 33-1-43796361, http://www.guidemayer.com.

500 808 USA ISSN 0272-5657
ME. Variant title: Dirigo Me. Text in English, French, Italian. 1980. irreg. (approx. q.). USD 20. adv. bk.rev. illus. back issues avail. **Document type:** *Newsletter.*
Formerly: Me, Too
Published by: (International Mail Art Network), Pittore Euforico, PO Box 182, Bowdoinham, ME 04008-0182. TEL 207-666-8453. Ed. Carlo Pittore. Circ: 1,000.

700 USA ISSN 1551-2045
▼ **ME MAGAZINE.** Text in English. 2004. q. USD 25 domestic; USD 35 in Canada & Mexico; USD 55 elsewhere; USD 7.50 newsstand/cover (effective 2004). **Document type:** *Magazine, Consumer.*
Address: 126 Winding Ridge Rd, White Plains, NY 10603. office@memagazinenyc.com, http://www.memagazinenyc.com. Ed. Angel Chang.

THE MEDAL. see *NUMISMATICS*

MEDIA AND ARTS LAW REVIEW. see *LAW*

709 ITA
MEDIAEVALIA. Text in Italian. 1983. irreg., latest vol.3, 1990. price varies. **Document type:** *Monographic series, Academic/Scholarly.* **Description:** Covers the history of medieval art.
Indexed: IPB.
Published by: (Universita degli Studi di Roma "La Sapienza"), L'Erma di Bretschneider, Via Cassiodoro, 19, PO Box 6192, Rome, RM 00193, Italy. TEL 39-06-6874127, FAX 39-06-6874129, edizioni@lerma.it, http://www.lerma.it. Ed. Angiola Maria Romanini.

MEDIAEVALIA. see *HISTORY—History Of Europe*

MEDIAEVALIA GRONINGANA. see *HISTORY—History Of Europe*

700 DEU
MEDIAEVALIS. Text in German. 2000. irreg., latest vol.3, 2001. **Document type:** *Monographic series, Academic/Scholarly.*
Published by: S H Verlag GmbH, Osterather Str 42, Cologne, 50739, Germany. TEL 49-221-9561740, FAX 49-221-9561741, info@sh-verlag.de, http://www.sh-verlag.de. Eds. Klaus Beuckers, Stefanie Lieb.

384.558 NLD ISSN 1571-2559
MEDIAMATIC OFF-LINE. Text in Dutch, English. 1986. irreg. adv. bk.rev. illus. reprints avail. **Document type:** *Academic/Scholarly.* **Description:** Covers books, films, software reviews, illustrations.
Formerly (until 2001): Mediamatic (0920-7864)
Related titles: CD-ROM ed.
Indexed: ABM.
—IE.
Published by: Mediamatic Foundation, Postbus 17490, Amsterdam, 1001 JL, Netherlands. TEL 31-20-6389901, FAX 31-20-6387969, mail@mediamatic.nl, http://www.mediamatic.nl. Circ: 4,000.

MEDIEVAL ACADEMY BOOKS. see *HISTORY—History Of Europe*

MEDIEVALIA ET HUMANISTICA; studies in medieval and renaissance culture. see *HISTORY—History Of Europe*

MEDITERRANEAN STUDIES. see *HISTORY—History Of The Near East*

A

700 750 CHN ISSN 1003-1774
N7340
MEISHU/ART. Text in Chinese; Contents page in English. 1954. m. USD 98.40; USD 8.20 newsstand/cover (effective 2001). bk.rev. illus. **Description:** Covers art history, painting. Includes interviews with artists and articles on the art world.
Related titles: Online - full text ed.: (from East View Information Services).
Indexed: RASB.
Address: Wenlian Dalou 13th Fl, 10 Nongzhanguan Nanli, Beijing, 100026, China. TEL 86-1-5003278. Ed. Shao Dazhen. **Dist. in US by:** China Books & Periodicals Inc, 360 Swift Ave., Ste. 48, S San Fran, CA 94080-6220. TEL 415-282-2994; **Dist. outside China by:** China International Book Trading Corp, 35 Chegongzhuang Xilu, Haidian District, PO Box 399, Beijing 100044, China. TEL 86-10-68412045, FAX 86-10-68412023, cibtc@mail.cibtc.com.cn, http://www.cibtc.com.cn.

700 CHN
MEISHU BAO/CHINA ART WEEKLY. Text in Chinese. w. CNY 78 (effective 2004). **Document type:** *Consumer.*
Published by: Zhejiang Ribao Baoye Jituan/Zhejiang Daily Newspaper Group, 178, Tiyuchang Lu, Hangzhou, Zhejiang 310039, China. TEL 86-571-85311124, FAX 86-571-85195207, http://www.zjdaily.com.cn/msb/. **Dist. by:** China International Book Trading Corp, 35 Chegongzhuang Xilu, Haidian District, PO Box 399, Beijing 100044, China. TEL 86-10-68412045, FAX 86-10-68412023, cibtc@mail.cibtc.com.cn, http://www.cibtc.com.cn.

700 CHN
MEISHU DAGUAN/ART PANORAMA. Text in Chinese. m. USD 49.20; USD 4.10 newsstand/cover (effective 2001). **Document type:** *Academic/Scholarly.*
Published by: Liaoning Meishu Chubanshe, 29 Minzu Beijie, Heping-qu, Shenyang, Liaoning 110001, China. Ed. Zhang Xiushi. **Dist. by:** China International Book Trading Corp, 35 Chegongzhuang Xilu, Haidian District, PO Box 399, Beijing 100044, China. TEL 86-10-68412045, FAX 86-10-68412023, cibtc@mail.cibtc.com.cn, http://www.cibtc.com.cn.

709 CHN ISSN 1006-8899
MEISHU GUANCHA/ART OBSERVATION. Text in Chinese. 1981. q. USD 23.70.
Formerly (until 1995): Meishu Shilun (1002-9680)
Related titles: Online - full text ed.: (from East View Information Services).
Published by: (Zhongguo Yishu Yanjiuyuan/Chinese Academy of Arts, Meishu Yanjiusuo/Institute of Fine Art), Meishu Shilun Bianjibu, 17 Qianhai Xijie, Beijing, 100009, China. TEL 651128. Ed. Shui Tianzhong. **Dist. in US by:** China Books & Periodicals Inc, 360 Swift Ave., Ste. 48, S San Fran, CA 94080-6220. TEL 415-282-2994.

700 CHN
MEISHU JIE/AIR CIRCLE. Text in Chinese. bi-m.
Published by: Guangxi Wenlian, 28 Jianzheng Lu, Nanning, Guangxi 530023, China. TEL 27225. Ed. Guo Ling.

700 CHN ISSN 1003-0441
MEISHU XIANGDAO/GUIDE TO ART. Text in Chinese. 1985. bi-m. CNY 58.80 (effective 2004). **Document type:** *Magazine, Academic/Scholarly.*
Related titles: Online - full text ed.: (from East View Information Services).
Published by: Renmin Meishu Chubanshe/People's Fine Arts Publishers, 32, Beizongbu Hutong, Beijing, 100735, China. TEL 86-10-85114277, http://msxd.periodicals.net.cn/default.html. **Dist. by:** China International Book Trading Corp, 35 Chegongzhuang Xilu, Haidian District, PO Box 399, Beijing 100044, China. TEL 86-10-68412045, FAX 86-10-68412023, cibtc@mail.cibtc.com.cn, http://www.cibtc.com.cn.

701 CHN ISSN 0461-6855
N8.C5
MEISHU YANJIU/ART RESEARCH. Text in Chinese; Contents page in English. 1957. q. USD 25.20; USD 6.30 newsstand/cover (effective 2001). illus. **Description:** Covers art, art education, and art criticism worldwide.
Related titles: Online - full text ed.: (from East View Information Services).
Indexed: RASB.
Published by: Zhongyang Meishu Xueyuan/Central Academy of Arts, 5 Xiaowei Hutong, Dongcheng-qu, Beijing, 100730, China. Eds. Du Zhesen, Tong Jinghan. **Dist. in US by:** China Books & Periodicals Inc, 360 Swift Ave., Ste. 48, S San Fran, CA 94080-6220. TEL 415-282-2994; **Dist. outside China by:** China International Book Trading Corp, 35 Chegongzhuang Xilu, Haidian District, PO Box 399, Beijing 100044, China. TEL 86-10-68412045, FAX 86-10-68412023, cibtc@mail.cibtc.com.cn, http://www.cibtc.com.cn.

070.5 700 CHN ISSN 1003-045X
MEISHU ZHI YOU/FRIEND OF FINE ARTS. Text in Chinese. 1982. bi-m. CNY 5.88.
Related titles: Online - full text ed.: (from East View Information Services).
Published by: Renmin Meishu Chubanshe/People's Fine Arts Publishers, 32, Beizongbu Hutong, Beijing, 100735, China. TEL 81-1-5122583. Eds. Shen Peng, Wu Baolun. Circ: 50,000.

700 CHN
MEISHU ZHIYOU/FRIEND OF CHINESE FINE ARTS. Text in Chinese. bi-m. USD 22.20; USD 3.70 newsstand/cover (effective 2001). **Document type:** *Academic/Scholarly.*
Published by: Renmin Meishu Chubanshe/People's Fine Arts Publishers, 32, Beizongbu Hutong, Beijing, 100735, China. **Dist. by:** China International Book Trading Corp, 35 Chegongzhuang Xilu, Haidian District, PO Box 399, Beijing 100044, China. TEL 86-10-68412045, FAX 86-10-68412023, cibtc@mail.cibtc.com.cn, http://www.cibtc.com.cn.

707 DEU ISSN 0171-3973
MEISTERWERKE DER KUNST. Text in German. 19??. a. EUR 3.50 per issue (effective 2003). **Document type:** *Monographic series, Academic/Scholarly.*
Published by: Neckar Verlag GmbH, Postfach 1820, Villingen-Schwenningen, 78008, Germany. TEL 49-7721-89870, FAX 49-7721-898750, service@neckar-verlag.de, http://www.neckar-verlag.de.

750 CHN ISSN 1003-5605
➤ **MEIYUAN/LU XUN ACADEMY OF FINE ART. JOURNAL.** Variant title: Lu Xun Meishu Xueyuan Xuebao. Text in Chinese; Contents page in English. 1980. bi-m. USD 43.80; USD 7.30 newsstand/cover (effective 2001). adv. bk.rev. illus. **Document type:** *Academic/Scholarly.* **Description:** Covers traditional Chinese painting.
Related titles: Online - full text ed.: (from East View Information Services).
Published by: Lu Xun Meishu Xueyuan, 19 Sanhao Jie, Heping-qu, Shenyang, Liaoning 110003, China. TEL 3920125, FAX 390334. Ed. Song Huimin. Adv. contact Li Fengying. Circ: 11,000 (paid). **Dist. by:** China International Book Trading Corp, 35 Chegongzhuang Xilu, Haidian District, PO Box 399, Beijing 100044, China. TEL 86-10-68412045, FAX 86-10-68412023, cibtc@mail.cibtc.com.cn, http://www.cibtc.com.cn.

709 913 FRA ISSN 0076-230X
DP1
LES MELANGES DE LA CASA DE VELAZQUEZ/CASA DE VELASQUEZ, MADRID. MISCELLANIES. Text in French, Spanish. 1965. a. price varies.
Indexed: AmH&L, BHA, HistAb, PCI, RILM.
—BLDSC (5536.811000), CINDOC.
Published by: (Casa de Velazquez), De Boccard Edition - Diffusion, 11 rue de Medicis, Paris, 75006, France. TEL 33-1-43260037, FAX 33-1-43548583, http://www.casadevelazquez.org, http://www.deboccard.com.

MELANGES D'HISTOIRE DE L'ARCHITECTURE. see *ARCHITECTURE*

701.17 AUS
➤ **MELBOURNE ART JOURNAL.** Text in English. 1997. a. AUD 40 domestic member individuals; AUD 50 foreign membership individuals; AUD 75 domestic membership institutions; AUD 85 foreign membership institutions. illus. back issues avail. **Document type:** *Journal, Academic/Scholarly.* **Description:** Covers topics in the fine arts and art history from around the world.
Published by: (Fine Arts Society), University of Melbourne, Department of Classical and Near Eastern Studies, Old Pathology Bldg, Parkville, VIC 3010, Australia. TEL 61-3-9344-5565, FAX 61-3-9344-5563, http://www.sfca.unimelb.edu.au/maj, http://www.sfca.unimelb.edu.au/school/about.html.

➤ **MEMOIRES DE LA DELEGATION ARCHEOLOGIQUE FRANCAISE EN IRAN.** see *ARCHAEOLOGY*

➤ **MERIDIAN: CROSSING AESTHETICS.** see *PHILOSOPHY*

➤ **MERVYN PEAKE REVIEW.** see *LITERATURE—Science Fiction, Fantasy, Horror*

778.53 AUS ISSN 1326-8694
MESH; film video - digital media - installation - performance - art. Text in English. 1993. a. adv. bk.rev. back issues avail. **Document type:** *Academic/Scholarly.* **Description:** Covers experimental media arts, including digital media, film, video, sound, performance, installation and visual arts.
Media: Online - full content.
Published by: Experimenta Media Arts, PO Box 1102, St Kilda South, VIC 3182, Australia. TEL 61-3-95255025, FAX 61-3-95255105, experimenta@experimentg.org, http://www.experimenta.org. Ed., R&P Keely Macarow.

760 USA ISSN 0895-5719
MESSAGES. Text in English. 1987. 6/yr. USD 20 domestic; USD 30 in Canada; USD 40 elsewhere (effective 2000). adv. bk.rev. back issues avail. **Document type:** *Newsletter.* **Description:** Reports on the society's news and events. Regular columns include A.D.A. update, S.E.G.D. regional news, member news, Allied Organization News, and resources.
Indexed: DAAI.
Published by: Society for Environmental Graphic Design, 401 F St, N W, Ste 333, Washington, DC 20001. TEL 202-638-5555, FAX 202-638-0891. Ed., R&P, Adv. contact Elisabeth Banks. page USD 750; trim 11 x 8.5. Circ: 1,200 (controlled).

700 NLD ISSN 0168-9053
METROPOLIS M; tijdschrift over hedendaagse kunst. Text in Dutch. 1979. bi-m. EUR 51; EUR 44 to senior citizens (effective 2005). adv. illus. index. 72 p./no. 4 cols./p.; back issues avail. **Document type:** *Magazine, Consumer.* **Description:** Covers contemporary art.
—IE, Infotrieve.
Published by: Stichting Metropolis M, Postbus 19263, Utrecht, 3501 DG, Netherlands. TEL 31-30-2342125, redactie@metropol.nl, info@metropol.nl, http://www.metropolism.org/. Ed. Domeniek Ruyters. Adv. contact Richard Derks TEL 31-26-4422194. B&W page EUR 750, color page EUR 1,385; 184 x 244.

700 USA ISSN 0740-7661
N610
METROPOLITAN MUSEUM OF ART. ANNUAL REPORT OF THE TRUSTEES. Text in English. 1870. a., latest 2004.
Published by: Metropolitan Museum of Art, 1000 Fifth Ave, New York, NY 10028. TEL 212-535-7710, http://www.metmuseum.org.

METRO'S PLUS BUSINESS. see *ADVERTISING AND PUBLIC RELATIONS*

MICHIGAN ACADEMICIAN. see *HUMANITIES: COMPREHENSIVE WORKS*

700 USA
MICHIGAN ART FAIRS✶. Text in English. a. **Document type:** *Catalog, Government.*
Published by: Michigan Council for the Arts, P O Box 30705, Lansing, MI 48909-8205. TEL 313-256-3731, FAX 313-256-3781. Circ: 20,000.

340 700 USA
MICHIGAN COUNCIL FOR THE ARTS. LEGISLATIVE REPORT✶. Text in English. 1969. a. free.
Published by: Michigan Council for the Arts, P O Box 30705, Lansing, MI 48909-8205. TEL 313-256-3731, FAX 313-256-3781. Ed. Martha Gibiser Shea. Circ: 500.

709 USA
MICHIGAN STATE UNIVERSITY. MUSEUM PUBLICATIONS. FOLK ART SERIES. Text in English. irreg. price varies. **Document type:** *Monographic series.*
Published by: Michigan State University, Museum, MSU Library, East Lansing, MI 48824. TEL 517-355-2370.

MIDATLANTIC ANTIQUES MAGAZINE; monthly guide to antiques, auctions, art & collectibles. see *ANTIQUES*

MIDCOASTER. see *LITERATURE*

700 USA
MIDWEST ART FAIRS. Text in English. 1977. s-a. USD 13.95 (effective 2000). adv. **Document type:** *Directory.* **Description:** Lists arts and crafts fairs and festivals in Minnesota, Wisconsin, Iowa and the Dakotas, as well as more than 400 artists, artisans, suppliers, arts organizations and services in the region.
Former titles: Minnesota Arts Directory (1060-3107); (until 1989): Minnesota Arts Fairs
Published by: New North Publishing, PO Box 72, Pepin, WI 54759. TEL 715-442-2022, 800-871-0813, FAX 715-442-3027, newnorth@cannon.net, http://www.midwestartfairs.com. Ed., Pub., Adv. contact James W Schiller. Circ: 7,500.

700 069.1 USA
MIDWEST MUSEUM BULLETIN. Text in English. 1979. bi-m. free to members. **Document type:** *Bulletin.* **Description:** Reviews of exhibitions, schedule of events, film showing, lectures and classes for members and interested public.
Published by: Midwest Museum of American Art, 429 S Main St, Box 1812, Elkhart, IN 46515. TEL 219-293-6660. Ed. Brian D Byrn. Circ: 700.

MINDPRINTS. see *LITERATURE*

700 ITA
MINIATURA E ARTI MINORI IN CAMPANIA. Text in Italian. 1975 (no.10). irreg., latest vol.13, 1978. price varies.
Published by: (Banca Sannitica), Societa Editrice Napoletana s.r.l., Corso Umberto I, 1-34, Naples, NA 80138, Italy. Ed. Mario Rotili.

MINIATURE COLLECTOR. see *HOBBIES*

MINT NEWS OF THE MINT MUSEUMS. see *MUSEUMS AND ART GALLERIES*

700 CHN ISSN 1003-2584
MINZU YILIN/WORLD OF NATIONAL ART. Text in English. bi-m. CNY 36 (effective 2004). **Document type:** *Journal, Academic/Scholarly.*
Related titles: Online - full text ed.: (from WanFang Data Corp.).

Address: 23, Wenhua Dongjie, Yinchuan, 750004, China. TEL 86-951-6024301, http://mzyl.periodicals.net.cn/default.html. **Dist. by:** China International Book Trading Corp, 35 Chegongzhuang Xilu, Haidian District, PO Box 399, Beijing 100044, China. TEL 86-10-68412045, FAX 86-10-68412023, cibtc@mail.cibtc.com.cn, http://www.cibtc.com.cn.

700 808.81 USA
MIRAGE; the magazine of the arts. Text in English. a. illus. **Description:** Showcases talent from all parts of Cochise county in Southern Arizona.
Published by: Cochise College, 4190 W Hwy 80, Douglas, AZ 85607. TEL 520-364-7943. Eds. Mark Litwicki, Norman Bates. Circ: 2,000.

781.542 USA
MIRROR MAGAZINE. Text in English. 1996. q. film rev. **Description:** Covers new art, original writing, music, fiction, poetry, restaurant, bar and movies.
Media: Online - full text.
Address: PO Box 182, Bolinas, CA 94118. http://www.mirrormagazine.com. Ed. Joel Braverman.

700 ISR ISSN 0334-9810
N8.H4
MISHKAFAYIM. Text in Hebrew. 1987. q. ILS 51. adv. **Description:** Art for the general public.
Indexed: IHP.
Published by: Israel Museum, Youth Department, P O Box 71117, Jerusalem, 91710, Israel. TEL 972-2-708823, FAX 972-2-631833. Ed. Tamir Rauner. Circ: 16,000. **Subscr. to:** 5 Mikunis St, Tel Aviv 67772, Israel.

MISSISSIPPI HISTORY NEWSLETTER. see *HISTORY—History Of North And South America*

708.95195 KOR ISSN 0540-4568
NK1073.6.A1
MISUL CHARYO/NATIONAL MUSEUM JOURNAL OF ARTS. Key Title: Misur Jaryo. Text in Korean; Summaries in Korean, English. 1960. s-a. illus.
Published by: National Museum of Korea, Department of Fine Arts/Gujrib Juhhah Bagmurgwan, 1 Sejong, Chongno-gu, Seoul, 110050, Korea, S. TEL 02-720-4723.

220.93 930.1 AUT ISSN 1025-6555
BR133.A9
MITTEILUNGEN ZUR CHRISTLICHEN ARCHAEOLOGIE. Text in German. 1995. a. EUR 26 (effective 2003). **Document type:** *Journal, Academic/Scholarly.*
Indexed: DIP, IBR, IBZ.
Published by: Verlag der Oesterreichischen Akademie der Wissenschaften, Postfach 471, Vienna, W 1011, Austria. TEL 43-1-515813402, FAX 43-1-515813400, verlag@oeaw.ac.at, http://verlag.oeaw.ac.at. Ed. Renate Pillinger.

MITTEILUNGEN ZUR SPAETANTIKEN ARCHAEOLOGIE UND BYZANTINISCHEN KUNSTGESCHICHTE. see *ARCHAEOLOGY*

700 CAN ISSN 1204-5349
MIX; independent art & culture magazine. Text in English, French. 1976. q. CND 25 domestic to individuals; USD 25 foreign to individuals; CND 40 domestic to institutions; USD 40 foreign to institutions (effective 2002). adv. bk.rev. **Document type:** *Magazine, Consumer.* **Description:** Covers the work of independent multi-media artists across the country and abroad. Offers a pan-national showcase of artwork, directory to Canadian artist-run centres, opinion features, critical writing, reviews, radio & television, and the prison arts.
Formerly (until 1995): Parallelogramme (0703-8712)
Related titles: Microfilm ed.: (from MMP); Online - full content ed.; French ed.
Indexed: ABM, CBCARef, CBPI, IIPA.
Published by: Parallelogramme Artist-Run Culture and Publishing Inc., 446-401 Richmond St W, Ste 446, Toronto, ON M5V 3A8, Canada. TEL 416-506-1012, FAX 416-340-8458, mix@web.ca, http://www.mixmagazine.com. Ed. Rosemary Heather. Adv. contact Chandra Bulucon. page CND 900; 9 x 12. Circ: 3,000 (paid and controlled).

707 USA
MIXED MEDIA. Text in English. q. free. adv.
Published by: Maine Art Education Association, PO Box 10463, Portland, ME 04104. Ed. Diane Noble. Circ: 700.

MIZIA. see *LITERATURE*

700 JPN
MIZUE. Text in Japanese. 1905. q. JPY 2,800.
Indexed: SIA.
Published by: Bijutsu Shuppan-sha, Inaoka Bldg, 2-36 Kanda-Jinbo-cho, Chiyoda-ku, Tokyo, 1010051, Japan. TEL 03-3234-2151, FAX 03-3234-9451. Ed. Tatsumi Shinoda. Circ: 30,000.

700 RUS
MODERN KLASSIKI. Text in Russian. 1994. s-a. USD 70 in North America (effective 2000).
Published by: Izdatel'stvo Tanais, Ul Tverskaya 6 pod 9 9 etazh, Moscow, 119332, Russian Federation. TEL 7-095-2291910. **Dist. by:** East View Information Services, 3020 Harbor Ln. N., Minneapolis, MN 55447. TEL 763-550-0961, FAX 763-559-2931.

759 USA ISSN 0738-0429
MODERN MASTER SERIES. Cover title: Abbeville Modern Masters. Text in English. 1983. irreg. price varies. illus. **Description:** Covers the creative and influential artists of the post-war era.
Published by: Abbeville Press, 137 Varick St, 5th Flr, New York, NY 10013. TEL 212-366-5585, FAX 212-366-6966, abbeville@abbeville.com, http://www.abbeville.com.

700 GBR ISSN 0953-6698
N6480
MODERN PAINTERS. Text in English. 1988. q. GBP 35.90 domestic; GBP 45, EUR 64.50 in Europe; USD 59.99 in United States; CND 75 in Canada; GBP 55, USD 69 per issue elsewhere (effective 2005). adv. back issues avail. **Document type:** *Magazine, Consumer.*
Related titles: Online - full text ed.: (from H.W. Wilson, O C L C Online Computer Library Center, Inc.).
Indexed: ABM, ArtInd, BHA, BrHumI, DAAI, RILM. —BLDSC (5890.766000), IE, ingenta. **CCC.**
Published by: Fine Art Journals Ltd., 52 Bermondsey Street, 3rd Fl, London, SE1 3UD, United Kingdom. TEL 44-20-74079247, info@modernpainters.co.uk, http://www.modernpainters.co.uk. Ed. Karen Wright. Adv. contact Haydon Rainsford TEL 44-20-75599826. Circ: 20,726. **Subscr. in the UK to:** Modern Painters Subscriptions, Customer Interface, Freepost LON 15765, Patchway, Bristol TA11 6ZA, United Kingdom. TEL 0800-0852757, FAX 44-1454-620080, modernpainters@cisubs.co.uk; **Subscr. in the US & Canada to:** Modern Painters Subscriptions, c/o Express Mag, PO Box 2769, Plattsburg, NY 12901-0239. TEL 877-363-1310; **Subscr. to:** Modern Painters Subscriptions, Bradley Pavilions, Bradley Stoke North, Bristol TA11 6ZA, United Kingdom. TEL 44-1454-642510.

THE MODERNISM MAGAZINE. see *ARCHITECTURE*

709 720 USA
THE MODERNIST✶. Text in English. 1981. q. USD 20. adv. bk.rev. back issues avail. **Description:** Surveys modern movements in the arts, architecture, design, and performance past, present, and future, through features, photo-essays, critiques, news and notes.
Formerly: Art Deco News (0743-3522)
Published by: Art Deco Society of New York, c/o William Weber, 242 Heath Vlg, Hackettstown, NJ 07840-4026. Ed. Glenn Loney. Circ: 1,000.

709 POL ISSN 1641-9715
N17
MODUS. Text in Polish; Summaries in French, Russian. 1962. irreg. price varies. **Document type:** *Monographic series, Academic/Scholarly.*
Formerly (until 1999): Uniwersytet Jagiellonski. Zeszyty Naukowe. Prace z Historii Sztuki (0083-4424)
Indexed: AIAP, BHA.
Published by: (Uniwersytet Jagiellonski, Instytut Historii Sztuki), Wydawnictwo Uniwersytetu Jagiellonskiego/Jagiellonian University Press, ul Grodzka 26, Krakow, 31044, Poland. TEL 48-12-4312364, FAX 48-12-4301995, wydaw@if.uj.edu.pl, http://www.wuj.pl. **Dist. by:** Ars Polona, Krakowskie Przedmiescie 7, Warsaw, Poland.

700 028.5 USA
MONKEYSHINES ON ART AND GREAT ARTISTS. Text in English. irreg. USD 26.95 per issue (effective 2003). **Document type:** *Consumer.* **Description:** Covers prehistoric, Classical, Medieval, Gothic, Renaissance, Baroque, Rococo, Romantic, Realism, Impressionism, Post Impressionism, Expressionism, Abstract Expressionism, Surrealism, and Pop Art are all included for the reader to explore. Contains illustrations, art terms, materials, glossary, full index, projects, and artists' biographies from the renaissance up to the present.
Published by: Monkeyshines Publications, PO Box 10245, Greensboro, NC 27404. mkshines@infionline.net, http://www.monkeyshinespublishers.com.

730 DEU ISSN 0944-0828
MONOGRAPHIEN ZUR BILDENDEN KUNST/MONOGRAFIE DELL'ARTE/MONOGRAPHS ON ART. Text in German. 1993. irreg., latest vol.5, 1995. EUR 52.30 per vol. (effective 2003). **Document type:** *Monographic series, Academic/Scholarly.*
Published by: Peter Lang GmbH Europaeischer Verlag der Wissenschaften, Eschborner Landstr 42-50, Frankfurt Am Main, 60489, Germany. TEL 49-69-7807050, FAX 49-69-78070543, zentrale.frankfurt@peterlang.com, http://www.peterlang.de. Ed. Juerg Meyer zur Capellen.

700 USA ISSN 0544-845X
MONOGRAPHS ON AMERICAN ART. Text in English. 1968. irreg., latest vol.4, 1975. price varies. illus. **Document type:** *Monographic series.*
Published by: Sheldon Memorial Art Gallery, 12th & R Sts, University of Nebraska, Lincoln, NE 68588. TEL 402-472-2461.

700 USA ISSN 1053-976X
MONOGRAPHS ON THE FINE ARTS. Text in English. irreg. price varies. **Document type:** *Monographic series.*
Formerly: Monographs on Archaeology and Fine Arts (0077-0981) —BLDSC (5915.436300), IE, ingenta.
Published by: (College Art Association of America), University of Washington Press, PO Box 50096, Seattle, WA 98145-5096. TEL 206-543-8870, FAX 206-543-3932.

700 DEU ISSN 1614-5445
▼ **MONOPOL**; Magazin fuer Kunst und Leben. Text in German. 2004. bi-m. EUR 38 domestic; EUR 41 foreign; EUR 7 newsstand/cover (effective 2005). adv. **Document type:** *Magazine, Consumer.* **Description:** Merges contemporary art, culture, design, fashion and topics involving upscale lifestyles.
Published by: Juno Verlag GmbH & Co. KG, Choriner Str 20, Berlin, 10435, Germany. TEL 49-30-44013440, FAX 49-30-44013443, info@monopol-magazin.de, http://www.monopol-magazin.de. Eds. Amelie von Heydebreck, Florian Illies. Adv. contact Alexander von Oheimb. page EUR 4,190; trim 203 x 262. Circ: 65,000 (paid and controlled).

708.1 745.5 USA
MONTEREY MUSEUM OF ART NEWS. Text in English. 1986. bi-m. USD 35. adv. **Document type:** *Newsletter.* **Description:** Exhibitions at and acquisitions by the museum; activity and program information.
Formerly: Monterey Peninsula Museum of Art News
Published by: Monterey Museum of Art, 559 Pacific St, Monterey, CA 93940. TEL 408-372-5477, FAX 408-372-5680. Ed. Richard W Gadd. Adv. contact Pat Seiling. Circ: 3,000.

700 JPN ISSN 0910-4364
MONTHLY ART/GEKKAN BIJUTSU. Text in Japanese. 1975. m. JPY 21,600.
Published by: Jitsugyo no Nihon Sha Ltd., 3-9 Ginza 1-chome, Chuo-ku, Tokyo, 104-0061, Japan. TEL 81-3-3563-5636, FAX 81-3-3562-3200, lebo2234@niftyserve.or.jp. Ed. Minoru Nakano.

MONUMENTA ARTIS ROMANAE. see *ARCHAEOLOGY*

730 ITA ISSN 0545-008X
MONUMENTI ETRUSCHI. Text in Italian. 1968. irreg., latest vol.8, 1998. price varies. **Document type:** *Monographic series, Academic/Scholarly.*
Published by: Casa Editrice Leo S. Olschki, Viuzzo del Pozzetto 8, Florence, 50126, Italy. TEL 39-055-6530684, FAX 39-055-6530214, celso@olschki.it, http://www.olschki.it.

MOONLIGHT CHRONICLES; a wandering artists journal. see *GENERAL INTEREST PERIODICALS—United States*

MOSAIC (ST. PETERSBURG). see *MUSEUMS AND ART GALLERIES*

700 ITA ISSN 0394-4271
N4
MOSTRE E MUSEI. Text in Italian. 1975. irreg., latest vol.8, 1983. price varies.
Published by: Societa Editrice Napoletana s.r.l., Corso Umberto I, 1-34, Naples, NA 80138, Italy. Ed. Raffaello Causa.

700 800 780 USA ISSN 8756-890X
MOVEMENTS IN THE ARTS. Text in English. 1985. irreg. price varies. **Document type:** *Monographic series, Academic/Scholarly.*
Published by: Greenwood Publishing Group Inc. (Subsidiary of: Harcourt International), 88 Post Rd W, PO Box 5007, Westport, CT 06881. TEL 203-226-3571, FAX 203-226-1502, webmaster@greenwood.com, http://www.greenwood.com.

MUDFISH; art and poetry. see *LITERATURE—Poetry*

709 DEU ISSN 0077-1899
N9
➤ **MUENCHENER JAHRBUCH DER BILDENDEN KUNST.** Text in German. 1906. a. back issues avail. **Document type:** *Academic/Scholarly.* **Description:** Art historical journal with emphasis on archeology, architecture, painting and sculpture.
Indexed: AIAP, ArtInd, BHA, IBR, IBZ, RASB. —BLDSC (5983.735000), IE.
Published by: Staatliche Kunstsammlungen Bayerns, Prinzregentenstr 3, Munich, 80538, Germany. TEL 49-89-211241, FAX 49-89-21124201. Ed. Konrad Renger. R&P Lorenz Seelig TEL 49-89-21124-215. Circ: 700.

704.9 DEU ISSN 0027-299X
N3
➤ **DAS MUENSTER**; Zeitschrift fuer Christliche Kunst und Kunstwissenschaft. Text in German; Summaries in English, French. 1947. q. EUR 49; EUR 12.90 newsstand/cover (effective 2005). adv. bk.rev. bibl.; illus. index. **Document type:** *Journal, Academic/Scholarly.* **Description:** Covers aspects of traditional and modern arts from a Christian viewpoint.
Indexed: ABM, AIAP, ArtInd, BHA, CERDIC, DIP, IBR, IBZ, RASB, RILM. —BLDSC (5985.550000), IE, ingenta.

Published by: Verlag Schnell und Steiner GmbH, Leibnizstr 13, Regensburg, 93055, Germany. TEL 49-941-787850, FAX 49-941-7878516, das.muenster@schnell-und-steiner.de, post@schnell-und-steiner.de, http://www.schnell-und-steiner.de. Ed. Barbara Polaczek. R&P Albrecht Weiland. Adv. contact Bernhard Fetsch. page EUR 690; trim 159 x 237. Circ: 2,100 (paid and free).

➤ **MULTI-STOREY.** see *LITERATURE*

704.948 297.38 NLD ISSN 0732-2992
N6260
➤ **MUQARNAS**; an annual on the visual culture of the Islamic world. Text in Dutch. 1983. a., latest vol.19, 2002. price varies. illus. cum.index: vols.1-10 in vol.10. back issues avail. **Document type:** *Academic/Scholarly.* **Description:** Scholarly contributions on historical, cultural and technical aspects of Islamic art, ceramics and architecture, from all regions of the Islamic world, in the medieval and modern periods. Serves as a forum for discussion among scholars and students in the Western and Islamic world.
Related titles: ♦ Supplement(s): Muqarnas, Supplements. ISSN 0921-0326.
Indexed: AIAP, API, IndIslam, RI-1, RI-2.
—BLDSC (5985.860000), IE, ingenta. **CCC.**
Published by: Brill Academic Publishers, PO Box 9000, Leiden, 2300 PA, Netherlands. TEL 31-71-53-53-500, FAX 31-71-53-17-532, cs@brill.nl, http://www.brill.nl. Ed. Gulru Necipoglu. R&P Elizabeth Venekamp. **Subscr. in N. America to:** PO Box 605, Herndon, VA 20172. TEL 703-661-1585, 800-337-9255, FAX 703-661-1501, cs@brillusa.com. **Distr. outside N. America by:** c/o Turpin Distribution, Stratton Business Park, Pegasus Drive, Biggleswade, BEDFORDSHIRE SG 18 8TQ, United Kingdom. TEL 44-1767-604-954, FAX 44-1767-601-640, brill@turpin-distribution.com.

704.948 297.38 NLD ISSN 0921-0326
➤ **MUQARNAS, SUPPLEMENTS.** Key Title: Studies in Islamic Art and Architecture. Supplements to Muqarnas. Text in Dutch. 1987. irreg., latest vol.10, 2001. price varies. illus. back issues avail. **Document type:** *Monographic series, Academic/Scholarly.* **Description:** Scholarly historical examinations of topics and issues in Islamic art, architecture and culture.
Related titles: ♦ Supplement to: Muqarnas. ISSN 0732-2992.
—BLDSC (8490.785400). **CCC.**
Published by: Brill Academic Publishers, PO Box 9000, Leiden, 2300 PA, Netherlands. TEL 31-71-53-53-500, FAX 31-71-53-17-532, cs@brill.nl, http://www.brill.nl. R&P Elizabeth Venekamp. **Subscr. in N. America to:** PO Box 605, Herndon, VA 20172. TEL 703-661-1585, 800-337-9255, FAX 703-661-1501, cs@brillusa.com. **Distr. outside N. America by:** c/o Turpin Distribution, Stratton Business Park, Pegasus Drive, Biggleswade, BEDFORDSHIRE SG 18 8TQ, United Kingdom. TEL 44-1767-604-954, FAX 44-1767-601-640, brill@turpin-distribution.com.

700 JPN ISSN 0288-6030
MUSASHINO ART UNIVERSITY. BULLETIN. Text in Japanese; Summaries in English. 1963. irreg., latest vol.25, 1994. free. illus. **Document type:** *Bulletin.*
Indexed: ABM, RILM.
—BLDSC (2623.550000).
Published by: Musashino Art University, 1-736 Ogawa-cho, Kodaira-shi, Tokyo-to 187-0032, Japan.

913 708 USA ISSN 0077-2194
N584.M5
MUSE (COLUMBIA). Text in English. 1967. a. USD 15 (effective 2002). **Document type:** *Yearbook.*
Indexed: BHA, NumL.
Published by: University of Missouri at Columbia, Museum of Art and Archaeology, One Pickard Hall, Columbia, MO 65211-1420. TEL 573-882-3591, FAX 573-884-4039. Ed. Marlene Perchinske. R&P B Cox. Circ: 2,500.

▼ **MUSE SQUARED**; a quarterly journal of poetry and visual art. see *LITERATURE—Poetry*

700 USA ISSN 1086-301X
MUSEA. Text in English. 1992. m. USD 10 (effective 2003). bk.rev.; dance rev.; film rev.; music rev.; play rev.; rec.rev.; tel.rev.; video rev.; Website rev. 8 p./no. 2 cols./p.; back issues avail. **Document type:** *Newsletter.* **Description:** Includes the latest news on arts.
Related titles: Online - full text ed.
Published by: Tom Hendricks, Ed. & Pub., 4000 Hawthorne, 5, Dallas, TX 75219-2275. TEL 214-526-3524, tomhendricks474@cs.com, http://musea.digitalchainsaw.com. Circ: 400 (paid and controlled).

MUSEA NOSTRA. see *MUSEUMS AND ART GALLERIES*

709.4 FRA ISSN 1141-4782
MUSEE INGRES. BULLETIN. (Spacial nos. avail.) Text in French. 1956. a. bk.rev. illus. **Document type:** *Bulletin.* **Description:** Discusses new acquisitions by the Musee d'Ingres and covers special exhibits. Reviews the year's news of the museum.
Indexed: BHA.
Published by: Societe des Amis du Musee d'Ingres, 7 rue Emile Pouvillon, Montauban, 82000, France. Ed. Evelyne Dayrens. Circ: 800.

MUSEES. see *MUSEUMS AND ART GALLERIES*

700 CHL ISSN 0716-1530
F2230.1.A7
➤ **MUSEO CHILENO DE ARTE PRECOLOMBINO. BOLETIN.** Text in Spanish. 1986. irreg. USD 10 domestic; USD 17 foreign. back issues avail. **Document type:** *Bulletin, Academic/Scholarly.* **Description:** Contains essays, research reports, and commentary on aboriginal art of the Americas, namely pre-European art.
Indexed: AICP, AnthLit.
Published by: Museo Chileno de Arte Precolombino, Casilla 3687, Bandera, 361, Santiago, Chile. TEL 695-3851, FAX 697-2779. Ed. Jose Berenguer R. R&P Jose Berenguer R TEL 695-3627. Circ: 500.

700 ITA ISSN 0393-0750
MUSEO CIVICO DI STUDI. BOLLETTINO. Text in Italian. 1899. a.
Indexed: RILM.
Published by: Museo Civico di Studi, Piazza del Santo, Padova, Italy.

MUSEU DE ARQUEOLOGIA E ETNOLOGIA. REVISTA. see *ARCHAEOLOGY*

708.6 ESP ISSN 1133-6455
N7109.c7
MUSEU NACIONAL D'ART DE CATALUYNA. BUTLLETI. Text in Catalan, English, French, German, Spanish; Summaries in Catalan, English, Spanish. 1993. a. bk.rev. **Document type:** *Bulletin, Bibliography.* **Description:** Includes papers on art history and museology, museum news and research works on the collection, exhibition reviews and studies of art from other collections.
—CINDOC.
Published by: Museu Nacional d'Art de Catalunya, Palau Nacional, Parc de Montjuic, Barcelona, 08038, Spain. TEL 34-3-4237199, FAX 34-3-3255773. Ed. Eduard Carbonell Esteller. Pub. Maria Montserrat Guma. Circ: 1,500.

MUSEUM FUER VOELKERKUNDE, BERLIN. VEROEFFENTLICHUNGEN. NEUE FOLGE. ABTEILUNG: AMERIKANISCHE NATURVOELKER. see *ANTHROPOLOGY*

709 USA ISSN 0027-4097
N714.P7
MUSEUM NOTES (PROVIDENCE). Text in English. 1913. irreg. **Document type:** *Bulletin.* **Description:** Includes articles relating to the museum's collections.
Formerly: Rhode Island School of Design. Bulletin
Indexed: AIAP, ArtInd, BHA.
Published by: (Museum of Art), Rhode Island School of Design, 224 Benefit St, Providence, RI 02903-2723. TEL 401-454-6500, FAX 401-454-6556, museum@risd.edu, http://www.risd.edu. Ed. Judith A Singsen. R&P Melody Ennis TEL 401-454-6535. Circ: 7,400.

MUSEUM NOTES (SPOKANE). see *MUSEUMS AND ART GALLERIES*

MUSEUM OF FAR EASTERN ANTIQUITIES. BULLETIN. see *MUSEUMS AND ART GALLERIES*

MUSEUM YEAR. see *MUSEUMS AND ART GALLERIES*

MUSIC & ART. see *MUSIC*

MUSIC IN ART; international journal for music iconography. see *MUSIC*

MUSIC OF THE SPHERES; a quarterly magazine of art and music for the New Age. see *NEW AGE PUBLICATIONS*

MUSICA, CINEMA, IMMAGINE, TEATRO. see *MUSIC*

MUSICWORKS; journal of sound exploration. see *MUSIC*

709 HUN ISSN 0027-5247
MUVESZETTORTENETI ERTESITO/BULLETIN FOR HISTORY OF ARTS. Text in Hungarian; Abstracts occasionally in English, French, German. 1952. q. USD 100 (effective 2006). adv. bk.rev. charts; illus.; abstr.; bibl. index. 80 p./no.; back issues avail. **Document type:** *Journal, Academic/Scholarly.* **Description:** Results of research on the world and Hungarian history of the arts from the Middle Ages up to now. Special attention to the antecedents of the modern art and to studies on modern art.
Related titles: Online - full text ed.: ISSN 1588-2802.
Indexed: ABCT, AIAP, BHA, HistAb, NumL, RASB, RILM.
Published by: (Hungarian National Gallery), Akademiai Kiado Rt. (Subsidiary of: Wolters Kluwer N.V.), Prielle Kornelia U. 19, Budapest, 1117, Hungary. TEL 36-1-4648282, FAX 36-1-4648221, info@akkrt.hu, http://www.akkrt.hu. Ed. Anna Javor.

700 IRN ISSN 1010-6618
MUZAH'HA. Text in Persian, Modern. 1962. m.
Supersedes (1962-1977): Hunar va Mardum - Art and People (1010-6464)
Published by: Sazman-i Miras-i Farhangi Kishvar, Idarah-i Kull-i Muzah'ha-yi, 60 Khayaban-e- Laristan, Ustad Mutahhari Ave., Tehran, Iran.

700 POL ISSN 0068-4678
MUZEUM GORNOSLASKIE W BYTOMIU. ROCZNIK. SERIA SZTUKA. Text in Polish; Summaries in German, English. 1964. irreg. USD 15; price varies. **Document type:** *Monographic series.*
Published by: Muzeum Gornoslaskie w Bytomiu/The Museum of Upper Silesia, Pl Jana III Sobieskiego 2, Bytom, 41902, Poland. TEL 48-32-28182941, dobosz@us.edu.pl, mgbytom@us.edu.pl.

MUZEUM NARODOWE W KRAKOWIE. KATALOGI ZBIOROW/NATIONAL MUSEUM IN CRACOW. CATALOGUES OF THE COLLECTIONS. see *MUSEUMS AND ART GALLERIES*

707 USA ISSN 0160-6395
N105
N A E A NEWS. Text in English. 1958. bi-m. USD 50 domestic to non-members; USD 75 in Canada to non-members; free to members (effective 2005). adv. bk.rev. **Document type:** *Newsletter, Trade.* **Description:** List of current association events and news affecting visual art education.
—BLDSC (6011.377000).
Published by: National Art Education Association, 1916 Association Dr, Reston, VA 20191-1590. TEL 703-860-8000, FAX 703-860-2960, http://www.naea-reston.org. Ed. Thomas A Hatfield. R&P Cam Luccarelli. Adv. contact Janice Davenport. Circ: 20,000 (paid and controlled).

702.8 USA
N A M T A NEWS & VIEWS. Text in English. 1960. m. (10/yr.). USD 25 to members. bk.rev. **Document type:** *Newsletter, Trade.*
Published by: National Art Materials Trade Association, 10115 Kincey Ave, Ste 260, Huntersville, NC 28078. TEL 704-948-5554, FAX 704-948-5658. Pub. Stephen Lefebvre. Circ: 1,500.

700 792.8 GBR
N C A NEWS. Text in English. 1986. q. GBP 50 to individual members waged; GBP 25 to individual members consessions (effective 2005). adv. **Document type:** *Bulletin, Consumer.*
Former titles (until 2004): Arts News (1368-2431); (until 1996): N C A News (0957-9044)
—BLDSC (6067.761800).
Published by: National Campaign for the Arts, Pegasus House, 37-43 Sackville St, London, W1S 3EH, United Kingdom. TEL 44-20-73330375, FAX 44-20-73330660, nca@artscampaign.org.uk, http://www.artscampaign.org.uk. Ed., Adv. contact Helen Gould. Circ: 3,500.

700 780 USA ISSN 0894-8585
N D. Text in English. 1982. 2/yr. USD 9 domestic; USD 16 foreign (effective 2000). adv. bk.rev.; music rev. illus. reprints avail. **Document type:** *Consumer.* **Description:** Devoted to documenting experimental works and artists. Serves as a forum for exchange and contact within the international community of artists, networkers and musicians.
Address: PO Box 4144, Austin, TX 78765. TEL 512-440-7609, FAX 512-416-8007, plunkett@ND.org, plunkett@nd.org, http://nd.org., http://www.nd.org. Ed., R&P Daniel Plunkett. Circ: 2,500 (paid).

▼ **THE N E P ERA**; Russian culture and politics 1921-1928. (New Economic Policy) see *HISTORY—History Of Europe*

N G C S A NARRATIVE REPORT. (National Guild of Community Schools of the Arts) see *EDUCATION*

700 USA
N H ARTS NEWS. (New Hampshire) Short title: N H Arts. Text in English. 1987 (vol.4). q. free (effective 2005). bk.rev. back issues avail. **Document type:** *Newsletter, Government.* **Description:** Provides information of interest to artists and art organizations in New Hampshire.
Former titles: New Hampshire Arts Newsletter; Artsheaf
Published by: New Hampshire State Council on the Arts, 2-1/2 Beacon St, 2nd Fl, Concord, NH 03301-4974. TEL 603-271-2789, FAX 603-271-3584, ystahr@nharts.state.nh.us, http://www.state.nh.us/nharts. Ed. Yvonne Stahr. Circ: 6,000 (free).

700 DEU ISSN 0935-2341
NB198
N I K E. Text in English, German. 1983. 10/yr. adv. bk.rev. **Document type:** *Magazine, Consumer.*
Formerly (until 1985): Neue Kunst in Europa (0175-0038)
Indexed: BHA.
—**CCC.**
Published by: Verlag Gerhard Goetze, Schellingstr 139, Munich, 80798, Germany. TEL 49-89-340013, FAX 49-89-340069. Ed. Gerhard Goetze. Circ: 10,000.

709 305.896 USA ISSN 1075-7163
NX587
➤ N K A; journal of contemporary African art. Text in English.
1994. s-a. USD 27 domestic to individuals; USD 47 foreign to
individuals; USD 43 domestic to institutions; USD 63 foreign
to institutions (effective 2000). illus. back issues avail.
Document type: Journal, Academic/Scholarly. Description:
Explores all areas of contemporary African and African
diaspora art.
Indexed: ABM.
Published by: Mario Einaudi Center for International Studies
(Subsidiary of: Cornell University), 170 Uris Hall, Africana
Studies and Research Center, Cornell University, Ithaca, NY
14853-7601. TEL 607-255-6370, FAX 607-254-5000,
nka_journal@cornell.edu, http://www.einaudi.cornell.edu/NKA.
Eds. Okwui Enwezor, Olu Oguibe, Salah Hassan.

750 GBR
N P G REVIEW. Text in English. a. Document type: Corporate.
Formerly (until 1999): N P G Triennial Report
Published by: National Portrait Gallery, St Martin's Pl, London,
WC2H 0HE, United Kingdom. TEL 44-171-306-0055.

700 305.4 GBR ISSN 1461-0434
N72.F45
➤ N.PARADOXA; international feminist art journal. Text in
English. 1998 (Jan.). s-a. GBP 18 in Europe to individuals
including the UK; USD 38 rest of world to individuals; GBP 32
in Europe to institutions including the UK; USD 72 rest of
world to institutions; GBP 7.95 newsstand/cover in Europe
including the UK; USD 12 newsstand/cover rest of world
(effective 2005); Online access free. adv. bk.rev. 96 p./no.;
back issues avail. Document type: Journal,
Academic/Scholarly. Description: International art journal of
feminist theory and the work of contemporary women artists.
Related titles: Online - full text ed.: ISSN 1461-0426. 1996. free.
Indexed: ABM, ArtInd, DIP, IBR, IBZ.
Published by: K T Press, 38 Bellot St, East Greenwich, London,
SE10 0AQ, United Kingdom. TEL 44-20-8858-3331,
k.deepwell@ukonline.co.uk, http://web.ukonline.co.uk/
n.paradoxa/index.htm. Ed., R&P, Adv. contact Katy Deepwell.
B&W page USD 1,100, color page USD 1,350. Circ: 1,000.
Dist. by: Art Data, 12 Bell Industrial Estate, 50 Cunningham
St, London W4 5HB, United Kingdom. artdata@btinternet.com.

730 USA ISSN 1081-1478
N S S NEWS BULLETIN. Text in English. 1935. bi-m.
membership. Document type: Newsletter. Description:
Contains member news, listings of opportunities for artists to
show work, technical information about sculpting, and
information about learning sculpture.
Published by: National Sculpture Society, 237 Park Ave, New
York, NY 10017-3140. TEL 212-764-5645, FAX 212-764-5651,
nss1893@aol.com, gp@sculpturereview.com. Pubs. Amy Kelly,
Kathleen Hahn. Circ: 900 (paid).

700 USA
N Y ARTS. Text in English. 11/yr. USD 60 domestic; USD 120
foreign; USD 10 newsstand/cover (effective 2005). Document
type: Magazine, Consumer.
Published by: NY Arts Magazine, 473 Broadway 7th Fl, New
York, NY 10013. TEL 212-274-8993, FAX 212-226-3400,
info@nyartsmagazine.com, http://www.nyartsmagazine.com.
Ed., Pub. Abraham Lubelski.

709.4 ITA ISSN 0027-7835
NK155.Z9
NAPOLI NOBILISSIMA; rivista di arti figurative, archeologia ed
urbanistica. Text in Italian. 1961. 6/yr., latest vol.2, 2001, Serie
V. EUR 62 domestic; EUR 78 foreign (effective 2003). illus.
240 p./no.; Document type: Magazine, Consumer.
Indexed: AIAP, BHA.
Published by: Editrice Arte Tipografica, c/o Editore Bardi, Via
Piave 7, Rome, 00187, Italy. TEL 39-06-4817656, FAX
39-06-4891274, bardied@tin.it, http://www.bardieditore.com.
Ed. Roberto Pane.

THE NATION. see LITERARY AND POLITICAL REVIEWS

700 USA ISSN 0191-0825
NATIONAL ACADEMY OF DESIGN. ANNUAL EXHIBITION
CATALOGUE. Text in English. 1826. a. USD 10; USD 18
foreign. adv. illus. back issues avail. Document type: Catalog.
Description: Provides listing of exhibition, history of the
National Academy of Design, and members of the national
academy.
Published by: National Academy of Design, 1083 Fifth Ave, New
York, NY 10128. TEL 212-369-4880, FAX 212-360-6795. Ed.
Deena Abu-Lughod. Adv. contact Deena Abu Lughod. B&W
page USD 800; trim 6 x 9. Circ: 1,500.

700 CAN ISSN 0382-1455
NATIONAL ARTS CENTRE. ANNUAL REPORT. Text in English.
1968. a.
Published by: National Arts Centre, Ste B, Box 1534, Ottawa,
ON K1P 5W1, Canada.

700 USA ISSN 0190-8049
N6505
NATIONAL ARTS GUIDE*. Text in English. 1979. bi-m. USD 50.
Indexed: BHA.

Published by: National Arts Guide, Inc., 209 Lake Shore Dr,
Chicago, IL 60611. TEL 312-642-9001.

707.4 USA
NATIONAL ASSOCIATION OF WOMEN ARTISTS. ANNUAL
EXHIBITION CATALOG. Text in English. 1889. a. USD 12
(effective 2001). adv. Document type: Catalog.
Published by: National Association of Women Artists, 41 Union
Sq W, Rm 906, New York, NY 10003. TEL 212-675-1616,
FAX 212-675-1616, nawomena@msn.com. Ed. Harriet Regina
Marion. Circ: 1,000 (controlled).

NATIONAL DIRECTORY OF ART & ANTIQUES BUYERS &
SPECIALISTS. see ANTIQUES

700.715 USA ISSN 1043-092X
NX396.6
NATIONAL DIRECTORY OF ART INTERNSHIPS. Text in English.
1983. biennial. USD 75 (effective 2001). Document type:
Directory.
Published by: National Network for Artist Placement, 935 W
Avenue 37, Los Angeles, CA 90065. TEL 323-222-4035. Ed.
Warren Christensen.

700 792.8 USA ISSN 0882-245X
NX398
NATIONAL FOUNDATION FOR ADVANCEMENT IN THE ARTS.
ANNUAL REPORT. Text in English. 1981. a. free. Document
type: Corporate.
Published by: National Foundation for Advancement in the Arts,
800 Brickell Ave 5, Miami, FL 33131-2944. TEL 305-377-1140,
FAX 305-377-1149. Ed., R&P Suzette L Prude. Circ: 1,000
(controlled).

708.2 GBR ISSN 0140-7430
ND1630
NATIONAL GALLERY, LONDON. TECHNICAL BULLETIN. Text
in English. 1977-1989; N.S. 1993. a., latest vol.23. GBP 25
per issue (effective 2003). illus. 96 p./no. 2 cols./p.; back
issues avail. Document type: Bulletin, Academic/Scholarly.
Description: Contains technical studies of easel paintings, art
conservation, and articles in museology.
Indexed: A&ATA, AIAP, BHA.
—BLDSC (6023.980000), IE, ingenta.
Published by: National Gallery Company Ltd., St Vincent House,
30 Orange St, London, WC2H 7HH, United Kingdom. TEL
44-20-77472870, FAX 44-20-78390367. Ed. Ashok Roy. Pub.
Kate Bell. R&P Jan Green TEL 44-20-7475983. Circ: 2,000.

700 USA ISSN 0091-7222
N856
NATIONAL GALLERY OF ART. ANNUAL REPORT. Text in
English. 1970. a. price varies. illus. Document type:
Corporate.
Indexed: ArtInd.
Published by: National Gallery of Art, 2000B South Club Dr, Door
#7, Landover, MD 20785. TEL 202-842-6353,
cl-messineo@nga.gov. Circ: 5,500.

705 708.11 CAN ISSN 1183-7608
NATIONAL GALLERY OF CANADA. ANNUAL REPORT. Text in
English. 1969. a.
Supersedes in part (in 1991): National Museums of Canada.
Annual Report (0704-1616)
Related titles: French ed.: Musee des Beaux-Arts du Canada.
Rapport Annuel. ISSN 1489-7067.
—CISTI.
Published by: National Gallery of Canada, Publications Division,
c/o Irene Lillico, 380 Sussex Dr, Ottawa, ON K1N 9N4,
Canada. subscriptions@gallery.ca, http://
www.national.gallery.ca.

NATIONAL GALLERY OF CANADA CATALOGUE. CANADIAN
ART. see MUSEUMS AND ART GALLERIES

705 CAN ISSN 1492-8035
NATIONAL GALLERY OF CANADA REVIEW. Text in English,
French. 2000. a. CND 25 (effective 2004). Document type:
Journal.
Indexed: ArtInd.
Published by: National Gallery of Canada, Publications Division,
PO Box 427, Stn A, Ottawa, ON K1N 9N4, Canada. TEL
613-990-1985, FAX 613-993-4385, info@gallery.ca,
http://www.national.gallery.ca.

700 JPN ISSN 0914-7489
N8.J28
NATIONAL MUSEUM OF MODERN ART, TOKYO. BULLETIN.
Text in Japanese; Summaries in English. 1987. biennial.
Document type: Bulletin, Academic/Scholarly. Description:
Publishes research articles on modern and contemporary arts
including crafts and films.
Published by: National Museum of Modern Art Tokyo, 3
Kitano-Marukoen, Chiyoda-ku, Tokyo, 102-8322, Japan. TEL
81-3-3561-1400, FAX 81-3-3561-8100. Circ: 1,000.

750 GBR
NATIONAL PORTRAIT GALLERY. REPORT. Text in English. a.
Document type: Corporate.
Published by: National Portrait Gallery, St Martin's Pl, London,
WC2H 0HE, United Kingdom. TEL 44-171-306-0055.

750 USA
➤ NATIONAL SOCIETY OF MURAL PAINTERS. NEWSLETTER.
Text in English. 1895. q. USD 25 membership. adv. bk.rev.
back issues avail. Document type: Newsletter,
Academic/Scholarly. Description: Contains news and
illustrations covering current and historic activities of muralists.
Published by: National Society of Mural Painters, c/o American
Fine Arts Society, 215 W 57th St, New York, NY 10019. TEL
212-777-8570, FAX 212-473-8268, reginas@anny.org,
http://www.anny.org. Ed. Jack Stewart. R&P Stewart. Adv.
contact Regina Stewart. Circ: 200.

709 NLD ISSN 0169-6726
N5
NEDERLANDS KUNSTHISTORISCH JAARBOEK. Text in Dutch,
English. 1950. a., latest vol.52, 2002. EUR 105 (effective
2005). back issues avail. Document type: Yearbook,
Academic/Scholarly.
Indexed: ABM, AIAP, ArtInd, BHA, IBR, IBZ, RASB.
—IE. CCC.
Published by: Waanders Uitgevers, Postbus 1129, Zwolle, 8001
BC, Netherlands. TEL 31-38-4658628, FAX 31-38-4655989,
info@waanders.nl, http://www.waanders.nl. Circ: 550.

700 800 LUX
NEEUROPA. Text in French. 1971. biennial. USD 50. adv. bk.rev.
Published by: Europeditor, P.O. Box 212, Luxembourg,
Luxembourg. Eds. Georges Astalos, Pino Mariano. Circ:
10,000.

700 GRL ISSN 0906-2254
NERIUSAAQ/REGNBUEN; tidsskrift for kunst og kultur i
Groenland. Text in Danish, Inuktitut; Some issues in English,
Inuktitut. 1990. q. DKK 110 (effective 2001). adv. 32 p./no.;
Description: Provides information on art and culture related
to Greenland.
Published by: Foreningen Neriusaaq (Regnbuen), P O Box 1555,
Nuuk, 3900, Greenland. TEL 299-32-6838, FAX 299-32-7911,
burkal@greennet.gl. Ed. Michael Thomsen.

NERTER; una revista dedicada a la literatura, el arte y el
conocimiento. see LITERATURE

700 DEU ISSN 0941-6501
N3
NEUE BILDENDE KUNST; Zeitschrift fuer Kunst und Kritik. Text
in German. 1953. bi-m. bk.rev. charts; illus. Document type:
Magazine, Consumer. Description: Provides reports, criticism,
essays, interviews, news and reviews of contemporary art as
well as an international exhibition calendar.
Formerly (until 1990): Bildende Kunst (0006-2391)
Indexed: A&ATA, ABCT, ABM, BAS, BHA, IBR, IBZ, RASB, RILM.
Published by: Neue Bildende Kunst Redaktion GmbH, Littenstr
106, Berlin, 10179, Germany. TEL 49-30-2465760, FAX
49-30-24657649, nbk.bln@t-online.de, http://www.gbhap.com/
neue_bildende_kunst. Ed. Matthias Fluegge. Adv. contact
Katrin Wittneven TEL 49-30-24657616. Circ: 10,000.

700 DEU
NEUE REIHE ZUR AKTUELLEN KUNST. Text in German. irreg.,
latest vol.21, 2001. Document type: Monographic series,
Academic/Scholarly.
Published by: Isensee Verlag, Haarenstr 20, Oldenburg, 26122,
Germany. TEL 49-441-25388, FAX 49-441-17872,
verlag@isensee.de, http://www.isensee.de.

750 USA ISSN 1066-2235
ND212
NEW AMERICAN PAINTINGS. Text in English. 1993. bi-m. USD
89 in North America; USD 119 elsewhere; USD 20
newsstand/cover domestic; USD 25 newsstand/cover in
Canada (effective 2003). illus. Document type: Magazine,
Consumer. Description: Publishes work of 46 winners of
regional juried competitions.
Published by: The Open Studios Press, 450 Harrison Ave., #304,
Boston, MA 02118. TEL 781-235-2235, 888-235-2783,
szevitas@newamericanpaintings.com, http://
www.newamericanpaintings.com. Ed. Steven T Zevitas. Pub.
H I Gliick.

NEW ARCADIAN JOURNAL. see ARCHITECTURE

NEW COLLAGE MAGAZINE. see LITERATURE

700 792 NGA ISSN 0331-7080
NEW CULTURE; a review of contemporary African arts. Text in
English. 1978. 10/yr. NGN 15, USD 40. bk.rev. back issues
avail.
Published by: African Designs Development Centre Ltd., New
Culture Studios, Oremji, N6A Adeola Crescent, PMB 5162,
Ibadan, Oyo, Nigeria. Ed. D Nwoko.

NEW DEPARTURES; international review of literature & the lively
arts. see LITERATURE

701.18 GBR
NEW ENGLISH ART CLUB. Text in English. a. Document type:
Catalog.
Published by: Federation of British Artists, 17 Carlton House Terr,
London, SW1Y 5BD, United Kingdom. TEL 44-20-7930-6844,
FAX 44-20-7839-7830, http://www.mallgalleries.org.uk.

▼ new title ➤ refereed * unverified ◆ full entry avail.

NEW MUSE OF CONTEMPT. see *LITERATURE*

700 USA ISSN 0737-5387
NX504
NEW OBSERVATIONS. Text in English. 1982. q. USD 22 domestic; USD 38 foreign (effective 2000). back issues avail.
Description: Centers on contemporary visual art from the artist's perspective.
Indexed: ABM.
Published by: New Observations Ltd., 320 W 37th St, Fl 6, New York, NY 10018-4232. TEL 212-971-0440, mail@newobservations.org, http://newobservations.org. Ed. Diane R Karp. R&P Erika Knerr. Circ: 1,500 (paid).

THE NEW RENAISSANCE; an international magazine of ideas and opinions, emphasizing literature & the arts. see *LITERATURE*

700 USA
NEW WORLD ARTS MAGAZINE. Text in English. 1996. bi-m. free. **Document type:** *Bulletin.* **Description:** Experiment of freedom of speech and visual expression.
Former titles: Art Notes; Antholo-Gee! -Zine
Media: Online - full text.
Published by: (Fine Art Inc.), New World Internet Publishing, 12 Bowman Sq, Bowman, GA 30624. TEL 706-245-4900, FAX 706-245-4990, art@fineartinc.com, http://www.hilson.org/NW/. Ed. Harry Hilson. Pub. Harry Wilson.

700 USA ISSN 1081-8847
N6485.3
NEW YORK CONTEMPORARY ART GALLERIES; the complete annual guide. Text in English. 1995. a., latest 2002. USD 19.95 (effective 2002). mkt.; stat. **Document type:** *Directory.*
Description: Comprehensive resource containing over 1,000 profiles of galleries, museums, private dealers, corporate art consultants and other art professional resources.
Related titles: CD-ROM ed.
Published by: Manhattan Arts International, 200 E 72nd St, New York, NY 10021. TEL 212-472-1660, FAX 212-794-0324, info@manhattanarts.com, http://www.manhattanarts.com. Ed., R&P Renee Phillips. Pub. Michael Jason.

700 USA ISSN 1422-6243
NEW YORK CONTEMPORARY ART REPORT. Text in English. 10/yr. USD 75 domestic; USD 100 in Canada; USD 110 elsewhere (effective 2001). **Document type:** *Consumer.*
Description: Provides information on 60 of New York's leading galleries for collectors, curators, dealers and art enthusiasts.
Address: 885 Third Ave, Ste 2900, New York, NY 10022. TEL 212-829-5748, FAX 212-829-5505, nycartreport@hotmail.com, http://www.nycartreport.com/.

NEW YORK NIGHTS. see *LITERARY AND POLITICAL REVIEWS*

700 USA ISSN 0737-4003
NEWSBANK REVIEW OF THE ARTS: FINE ARTS AND ARCHITECTURE. Text in English. 1972. m. (q. and a. index). price varies. cum.index (paper or CD-ROM).
Supersedes in part: NewsBank Review of the Arts
Related titles: Microfiche ed.
Published by: Newsbank, Inc., 58 Pine St, New Canaan, CT 06840-5426. TEL 203-966-1100, FAX 203-966-6254. Ed. Jim Branch.

700 930.1 950 USA ISSN 8755-4593
N7336
NEWSLETTER EAST ASIAN ART & ARCHAEOLOGY. Short title: Newsletter E A A A. Text in English. 1977. 3/yr. USD 15 domestic; USD 18 foreign (effective 2005). adv. bk.rev. back issues avail.; reprints avail. **Document type:** *Newsletter, Academic/Scholarly.* **Description:** Informs readers about Asian art activities regarding worldwide exhibitions, symposia, lectures, and book dealers.
Published by: University of Michigan, Center for Japanese Studies, Tappan Hall, Rm 40, Ann Arbor, MI 48109-1357. TEL 734-936-2539, FAX 734-647-4121, nhilgen@umich.edu, http://www.umich.edu/~hartspc/NEAAA/issue76/76NEAAA.html. Ed., Adv. contact Nathan Hilgendorf TEL 734-763-2874. page USD 125. Circ: 450.

700 745.1 USA ISSN 1056-7143
N8604.S66
NEWSLETTER - SOTHEBY'S. Text in English. 1973. 7/yr. USD 25 in US & Canada; USD 35 elsewhere (effective 2005).
Document type: *Newsletter.*
Former titles (until 1984): Sotheby's Newsletter (0741-7306); (until 1981): Sotheby Parke Bernet Inc. Newsletter (0741-7292)
Published by: Sotheby's Inc., 1334 York Ave, New York, NY 10021. TEL 212-606-7000, 212-606-7000, FAX 541-312-5684. Ed. Lynn Stowell Pearson. Circ: 55,000.

741.5 USA ISSN 1541-4817
NC1766.J3
NEWTYPE U S A; the moving pictures magazine. Text in English. 2002 (Nov.). m. USD 89.95 domestic; USD 145 in Canada & Mexico; USD 165 elsewhere; USD 9.95 newsstand/cover (effective 2002). adv. film rev.; video rev. **Document type:** *Magazine, Consumer.* **Description:** Provides a source for information about anime, manga and Japanese culture.
Published by: A.D. Vision, Inc., 5750 Bintliff No.216, Houston, TX 77036. TEL 713-341-7100, info@newtype-usa.com, info@advfilms.com, http://www.newtype-usa.com, http://www.advfilms.com. Ed. Kimberly Guerre.

700 ITA ISSN 0394-6428
CODEN: IKNEE3
NEXT. Text in English, French, Italian. 1985. q. USD 40 (effective 1999). adv. **Document type:** *Consumer.*
Published by: Joyce & Co. - Associazione Culturale, Via Natale Del Grande, 51, Rome, RM 00153, Italy. TEL 39-6-5899285, FAX 39-06-58390672. Eds. Anna Di Biagio, Emma Ercoli.

709 DEU ISSN 0078-0537
N3
NIEDERDEUTSCHE BEITRAEGE ZUR KUNSTGESCHICHTE. Text in German. 1961. a. **Document type:** *Journal, Academic/Scholarly.*
Indexed: AIAP, BHA, DIP, IBR, IBZ, NAA.
Published by: (Niedersaechsisches Landesmuseum, Hannover), Deutscher Kunstverlag GmbH, Nymphenburger Str 84, Munich, 80636, Germany. TEL 49-89-1269900, FAX 49-89-12151644, info@deutscherkunstverlag.de, http://www.kunstbuecher-online.de. Ed. Heide Grape Albers. Circ: 800.

740 CHN
NIENHUA YISHU/ART OF NEW YEAR PICTURE. Text in Chinese. s-a.
Published by: Tianjin Renmin Meishu Chubanshe/Tianjin People's Fine Art Publishing House, 150 Machang Dao, Heping-qu, Tianjin 300050, China. TEL 313820. Ed. Qing Baiyin.

709.52 JPN ISSN 0546-0255
NIHON BIJUTSU NENKAN/YEAR BOOK OF JAPANESE ART. Text in Japanese. 1936. a. **Document type:** *Yearbook, Academic/Scholarly.*
Published by: National Research Institute for Cultural Properties, Department of Fine Arts, 13-43 Ueno Park, Taito-Ku, Tokyo, 110-8713, Japan. http://www.tobunken.go.jp/~bijutsu/japanese/nenkan/nenkan.html, http://www.tobunken.go.jp/~bijutsu/index.html.

700 JPN ISSN 0549-401X
NIHON NO BIJUTSU/VISUAL ART IN JAPAN. Text in Japanese. 1966. m. JPY 1,650 newsstand/cover (effective 2004).
Document type: *Journal, Academic/Scholarly.*
Published by: Shibundo Co., 4-2, Nishi-Gokencho, Shinjuku-ku, Tokyo, 162-0812, Japan. TEL 81-3-32682441, FAX 81-3-32683550, eigyo@imail.plala.or.jp, http://www.shibundo.co.jp/.

709.034 USA ISSN 1543-1002
N6450
➤ **NINETEENTH-CENTURY ART WORLDWIDE.** Text in English. 2002. s-a. free (effective 2005). **Description:** Devoted to the study of nineteenth-century painting, sculpture, graphic arts, photography, architecture, and decorative arts across the globe.
Media: Online - full content. **Related titles:** Online - full text ed.: (from H.W. Wilson, O C L C Online Computer Library Center, Inc.).
Indexed: ArtInd.
Published by: Association of Historians of Nineteenth-Century Art, Dept. of Art and Archaeology, University of MD, College Park, MD 20742-1335. http://19thc-artworldwide.org, http://www.inform.umd.edu/arth/ahnca/index.html.

➤ **NINETEENTH-CENTURY STUDIES.** see *LITERATURE*

700 FRA ISSN 1155-1240
NINETY. Text in French. 1983. bi-m. FRF 500 (effective 1999). adv.
Formerly: Eighty (0294-1880)
Indexed: BHA.
Published by: Flohic Editions, 28 av. Jean Jaures, BP 33, Charenton-le-Pont, Cedex 94222, France. TEL 33-1-45180900, FAX 33-1-45189039, flohi@club-internet.fr. Ed. Catherine Flohic. Pub. Jean Luc Flohic. Adv. contact Frederic Baujard.

709 ESP ISSN 0213-2214
N7101
NORBA: ARTE. Text in Spanish. 1980. irreg., latest vol.10, 1990. illus. **Description:** Covers art history, with preference to aspects of Spanish art: theory, analysis, documentation, commentaries.
Supersedes in part (in 1983): Norba (0211-0636)
Indexed: ABM, BHA, PCI.
—CINDOC.
Published by: Universidad de Extremadura, Departamento de Historia del Arte, Calle Pizarro 8, Caceres, 10071, Spain. TEL 34-927-247650.

NORDISK TIDSKRIFT FOR VETENSKAP, KONST OCH INDUSTRI. see *LITERARY AND POLITICAL REVIEWS*

700 808 USA ISSN 0739-2974
NX456
NORTHERN LIGHTS STUDIES IN CREATIVITY. Text in English. 1984. irreg., latest vol.3, 1991. adv. bk.rev. back issues avail.
Published by: University of Maine, Presque Isle, 181 Main St, Presque Isle, ME 04769. TEL 207-762-0311. Ed. Stanley Scott. Circ: 500.

NORTHWEST REVIEW. see *LITERATURE*

700 ITA ISSN 0029-3814
NOSTRO TEMPO; settimanale cattolico. Text in Italian. 1946. bi-m. adv. bk.rev.; film rev. illus. index.
Published by: Centro Giornali Cattolici, Corso Giacomo Matteotti, 11, Turin, TO 10121, Italy. Ed. Domenico Agasso.

700 ITA ISSN 0029-4322
NOTIZIARIO D'ARTE. Text in Italian; Summaries in English, French, German. 1949. bi-m. adv. bk.rev. bibl.; illus.
Published by: Ennio Francia Ed. & Pub., Via del Babuino 197, Rome, RM, Italy. Circ: 2,000.

709 ITA ISSN 0391-4364
N380
NOTIZIE DA PALAZZO ALBANI. Text in Italian. 1972. a. EUR 40 domestic; EUR 60 foreign (effective 2004). bk.rev. illus.
Document type: *Journal, Academic/Scholarly.*
Indexed: AIAP, BHA, BibInd, RILM.
Published by: (Universita degli Studi di Urbino, Istituto di Storia dell'Arte Medievale e Moderna), Edizioni Quattroventi, Piazza Rinascimento 4, Urbino, PS 61029, Italy. TEL 39-072-22588, FAX 39-072-2320998, info@edizioniquattroventi.it, http://www.edizioniquattroventi.it.

NOUVELLE REVUE NEUCHATELOISE. see *HISTORY—History Of Europe*

760 FRA ISSN 0029-4888
NE1
NOUVELLES DE L'ESTAMPE. Text in French. 1963. 5/yr. EUR 60 domestic; EUR 75 in the European Union; EUR 80 elsewhere (effective 2005). bk.rev. **Document type:** *Trade.*
Indexed: ABCT, ABM, BHA, DIP, IBR, IBZ.
—IE, Infotrieve.
Published by: Comite National de la Gravure Francaise, 58 rue de Richelieu, Paris, 75002, France. TEL 33-1-53798388, FAX 33-1-53798307, http://www.bnf.fr/pages/collections/esta-nouv.htm. Ed., R&P Gerard Sourd. Adv. contact Philippe Zani. Circ: 1,200.

700 COL ISSN 0029-4969
NOVA*; revista de arte y literatura. Text in Spanish. 1964. bi-m. COP 3.50. adv. charts; illus.
Address: Apartado Aereo 15858, Bogota, CUND, Colombia. Ed. David Consuegra U.

700 RUS ISSN 0869-7361
AP50
NOVAYA YUNOST'. Text in Russian. 1993. bi-m. USD 115 in North America (effective 2000).
Related titles: Online - full text ed.: (from East View Information Services).
Indexed: RASB.
Published by: Tvorcheskii Tsentr Novaya Yunost', Bersenevskaya nab 20-2, Moscow, 109072, Russian Federation. TEL 7-095-2300605. Ed. E B Laputin. **Dist. by:** East View Information Services, 3020 Harbor Ln. N., Minneapolis, MN 55447. TEL 763-550-0961, FAX 763-559-2931.

NOVUM; Forum fuer Kommunikations-Design. see *ADVERTISING AND PUBLIC RELATIONS*

700 RUS ISSN 1560-8697
N6981
NOVYI MIR ISKUSSTVA; zhurnal kul'turnoi stolitsy. Text in Russian. 1998. bi-m. RUR 70 domestic; EUR 10 in Europe; USD 12 elsewhere (effective 2004). **Document type:** *Magazine, Consumer.* **Description:** Provides information on cultural life in Russia and abroad: painting, graphic arts, sculpture, fashion, architecture, decorative and applied arts.
Address: Izhorskaia ul,13/39, Sankt-Petersburg, 197198, Russian Federation. art@worldart.ru, http://www.worldart.ru. Ed. Vera Bibinova.

NUEVA LUZ; photographic journal. see *PHOTOGRAPHY*

NUOVA RASSEGNA; attualita, lettere, storia, scienze, cinema, teatro. see *LITERARY AND POLITICAL REVIEWS*

NY CARLSBERG GLYPTOTEK. MEDDELELSER. see *ARCHAEOLOGY*

708.9493 BEL ISSN 1379-7271
O K V TENTO. (Openbaar Kunstbezit in Vlaanderen) Text in Dutch. 1963. q. EUR 25 domestic; EUR 28 in Europe; EUR 34 elsewhere (effective 2005). bk.rev. index. back issues avail.
Document type: *Academic/Scholarly.* **Description:** Presents art in Belgian museums and public collections.
Formerly (until 2003): Openbaar Kunstbezit in Vlaanderen (1373-4873)

Published by: Openbaar Kunstbezit in Vlaanderen v.z.w., Grote Markt 46, St-Niklaas, 9100, Belgium. TEL 32-3-7601640, FAX 32-3-7601641, openbaar.kunstbezit@planetinternet.be, http://www.tento.be/home/index.cfm?id=185&l=1, http://www.okvweb.org. Ed., Pub., R&P Rudy Vercruysse. Adv. contact Jan Bergmans. Circ: 10,000.

751.6 ITA ISSN 1120-2513
O P D RESTAURO; rivista dell'Opificio delle Pietre Dure. Text in Italian; Section in English. 1986; N.S. 1989. a., latest vol.14. EUR 50 domestic; EUR 65 foreign (effective 2004). adv. bk.rev. **Document type:** *Academic/Scholarly.* **Description:** Covers art restoration technique and history and the activities of the Opificio.
Indexed: A&ATA, AIAP, BHA.
Published by: (Italy. Ministero per i Beni e le Attivita Culturali), Centro Di, Lungarno Serristori 35, Florence, FI 50125, Italy. TEL 39-055-2342668, FAX 39-055-2342667, centrodi@centrodi.it, http://www.centrodi.it.

700 HKG
THE OBSERVATION POST/CH'UN CH'IU. Text in Chinese. m.
Published by: Observation Post, 60 Leighton Rd 6th Fl, Hong Kong, Hong Kong. TEL 5-765123.

740 SVN
OBVESTILA. Text in Slovenian; Summaries in English. 1975. irreg. (4-5/yr.). looseleaf. free.
Published by: Drustvo Exlibris Sloveniae, Trubarjeva 14, Ljubljana, 61000, Slovenia. TEL 386-61-312332.

700 JPN ISSN 0472-4682
OCHANOMIZU JOSHI DAIGAKU JINBUN KAGAKU KIYO/OCHANOMIZU UNIVERSITY STUDIES IN ARTS AND CULTURE. Text in Japanese. 1952. a. **Document type:** *Academic/Scholarly.*
Indexed: MLA-IB.
Published by: Ochanomizu Joshi Daigaku/Ochanomizu University, Faculty of Letters and Education, 2-1-1 Otsuka, Bunkyo-Ku, Tokyo, 112-8610, Japan.

700 POL ISSN 0029-8247
DK409
OCHRONA ZABYTKOW. Text in Polish; Summaries in English. 1948. q. EUR 37 foreign (effective 2005). bk.rev. abstr.; bibl.; charts; illus. index. 120 p./no.; **Document type:** *Magazine, Trade.* **Description:** Covers restoration techniques, procedures, and projects.
Related titles: CD-ROM ed.; Microfilm ed.
Indexed: A&ATA, AIAP, BHA, RASB.
—BLDSC (6235.122000).
Published by: (Osrodek Dokumentacji Zabytkow), Wydawnictwo DiG, ul Nowy Swiat 39, Warsaw, 00029, Poland. biuro@dig.com.pl, http://www.dig.com.pl. Ed. Wojciech Fijalkowski. Circ: 800. **Dist. by:** Ars Polona, Krakowskie Przedmiescie 7, Warsaw, Poland. TEL 48-22-9263914, FAX 48-22-9265334, arspolona@arspolona.com.pl, http://www.arspolona.com.pl.

700 USA ISSN 0162-2870
NX1
➤ **OCTOBER.** Text in English. 1976. q. USD 46 combined subscription in US & Canada to individuals print & online eds.; USD 66 combined subscription elsewhere to individuals print & online eds.; USD 166 combined subscription in US & Canada to institutions print & online eds.; USD 186 combined subscription elsewhere to institutions print & online eds. (effective 2006). illus. reprint service avail. from PQC. **Document type:** *Academic/Scholarly.* **Description:** Presents current texts by and about leading contemporary artists, scholars and critics. Topics include film, painting, music, photography and more.
Related titles: Microform ed.: (from PQC); Online - full text ed.: ISSN 1536-013X. USD 43 to individuals; USD 149 to institutions (effective 2006) (from EBSCO Publishing, Gale Group, H.W. Wilson, IngentaConnect, JSTOR (Web-based Journal Archive), O C L C Online Computer Library Center, Inc., Swets Information Services).
Indexed: ABM, ABS&EES, AIAP, AltPI, AmHI, ArtHuCI, ArtInd, BHA, CurCont, FLI, MLA-IB, RILM.
—BLDSC (6235.151490), IDS, IE, Infotrieve, ingenta. **CCC.**
Published by: M I T Press, 55 Hayward St, Cambridge, MA 02142-1493. TEL 617-253-5646, FAX 617-258-6779, octobermagazine@nyc.rr.com, journals-info@mit.edu, http://mitpress.mit.edu/october. Ed. Rosalind Krauss TEL 212-809-1404. Circ: 4,000.

700 949.2 NLD ISSN 0923-0033
OCULI. Text in Dutch. 1987. irreg., latest vol.6, 1996. price varies. **Document type:** *Monographic series.* **Description:** Historical research in the arts of the Low Countries, from the 14th and 15th centuries to the present. Includes monographs, catalogues, and critical studies.
—IE.
Published by: John Benjamins Publishing Co., PO Box 36224, Amsterdam, 1020 ME, Netherlands. TEL 31-20-6304747, FAX 31-20-6792956, http://www.benjamins.nl. Eds. Bert W Meijer, Rob Ruurs. **Co-publisher:** Forsten.

700 900 AUT ISSN 0029-9626
N3
OESTERREICHISCHE ZEITSCHRIFT FUER KUNST UND DENKMALPFLEGE. Text in German. 1856. 5/yr. EUR 27.50; EUR 7 newsstand/cover (effective 2005). adv. bk.rev. charts; illus. **Document type:** *Journal, Academic/Scholarly.*
Indexed: A&ATA, ABM, AIAP, API, AmH&L, BHA, BibInd, DIP, HistAb, IBR, IBZ, RASB, RILM.
—IE, Infotrieve.
Published by: (Austria. Bundesdenkmalamt Oesterreich), Verlag Ferdinand Berger und Soehne GmbH, Wienerstr 80, Horn, N 3580, Austria. TEL 43-2982-41610, FAX 43-2982-4161268, office@berger.at, http://www.berger.at. Circ: 150.

OESTERREICHISCHES MUSEUM FUER VOLKSKUNDE. VEROEFFENTLICHUNGEN. see *FOLKLORE*

709 USA ISSN 0731-3284
NX24.O3
OHIO ARTS COUNCIL. BIENNIAL REPORT. Text in English. 1965. biennial. membership only. stat. **Document type:** *Corporate.*
Formerly: Ohio Arts Council. Annual Report
Published by: Ohio Arts Council, 727 E Main St, Columbus, OH 43205. TEL 614-466-2613. Circ: 500.

780.89 NLD
OIDEION; the performing arts world-wide. Text in English. 1993. irreg. bk.rev. **Description:** Contains articles, book and CD-reviews and reports on the study of the performing arts in the non-Western world.
Indexed: AnthLit.
Published by: Research School of Asian, African and Amerindian Studies, P.O. Box 9515, Leiden, 2300 RA, Netherlands. TEL 31-71-5272171, FAX 31-71-5272939, cnws@let.leidenuniv.nl.

700 DNK ISSN 0108-3511
OMKRING ET KUNSTVAERK. Text in Danish. 1980. irreg. DKK 2 per issue. illus.
Published by: Randers Kunstmuseum, Stemannsgade 2, Randers, 8900, Denmark. Ed. Nina Hobolth.

700 ESP ISSN 1137-4403
N7109.P25
ONDARE. Text in Spanish. 1982. irreg. price varies. **Document type:** *Monographic series, Academic/Scholarly.*
Formerly (until 1997): Sociedad de Estudios Vascos. Cuadernos de Seccion. Artes Plasticas y Monumentales (0212-3215)
Related titles: Online - full text ed.
Published by: Eusko Ikaskuntza/Sociedad de Estudios Vascos, Palacio Miramar, Miraconcha 48, Donostia, San Sebastian 20007, Spain. TEL 34-943-310855, FAX 34-943-213956, ei-sev@sc.ehu.es, http://www.eusko-ikaskuntza.org/.

700 CAN ISSN 0701-5429
ONTARIO ARTS COUNCIL. ANNUAL REPORT/CONSEIL DES ARTS DE L'ONTARIO. RAPPORT ANNUEL. Text in English, French. 1963. a. free.
Published by: Ontario Arts Council/Conseil des Arts de l'Ontario, Ste 500, 151 Bloor St W, Toronto, ON M5S 1T6, Canada. TEL 416-961-1660, 800-387-0058, FAX 416-961-7796. Circ: 3,500.

700 ITA ISSN 0030-3305
OP CIT; selezione della critica d'arte contemporanea. Text in Italian. 1964. 3/yr. adv. bk.rev. bibl. **Document type:** *Academic/Scholarly.*
Indexed: ABCT, ABM, BHA, HAPI, MLA-IB.
—BLDSC (6265.550000).
Published by: Electa Napoli, Via Francesco Caracciolo 13, Naples, NA 80122, Italy. info@ena.it, http://www.ena.it. Ed. Renato De Fusco. Circ: 1,000.

OPEN SPACE MONOGRAPHS. see *PHOTOGRAPHY*

700 800 BGR ISSN 0861-4334
AP58.B8
ORFEY/ORPHEUS. Text in Bulgarian. 1991. q. BGL 4 newsstand/cover (effective 2002). **Document type:** *Magazine, Trade.* **Description:** Aims to inform about the latest tendencies in art and literature worldwide by publishing mostly new and unpublished works, often still as-yet unfinished.
Published by: Spisanie Orfey ST Publishing House, 1 Veliko Tarnovo St., Sofia, 1504, Bulgaria. TEL 359-2-446016, FAX 359-2-466858, malinova@omega.bg, http://www.sca.bg/cultural-periodicals/catalog/orfey.htm. Ed. Lyubomir Levchev.

ORIENS; journal of the International Society for Oriental Research. see *ASIAN STUDIES*

ORIENTAL ART; devoted to the study of all forms of Oriental art. see *ASIAN STUDIES*

700 USA ISSN 0078-6551
ORIENTAL STUDIES. Text in English. 1970 (no.8). irreg. price varies.
Published by: Freer Gallery of Art, Smithsonian Institution, Jefferson Dr, S W at 12th St, Washington, DC 20560. TEL 202-357-1432.

950 HKG ISSN 0030-5448
DS501
ORIENTATIONS; the monthly magazine for collectors and connoisseurs of Oriental art. Text in English. 1970. m. (10/yr., Jan-Jun, Sep-Dec). HKD 442 domestic; JPY 7,260 in Japan; SGD 104 in Singapore; AUD 94.25 in Australia; USD 68.25 in United States; CND 96.85 in Canada; EUR 61.75 in Europe; GBP 42.25 in United Kingdom; USD 58.50 elsewhere (effective 2004). adv. bk.rev. illus. Index. 72 p./no.; back issues avail.; reprints avail. **Document type:** *Magazine, Consumer.* **Description:** For collectors and connoisseurs of Asian art. Presents the ancient arts of painting, calligraphy, bronzes, and ceramics, as well as the decorative arts and crafts. Includes coverage of contemporary artists.
Indexed: A&ATA, AIAP, ArtInd, BAS, BHA, RASB, SPPI.
—BLDSC (6291.220100), IE, Infotrieve, ingenta. **CCC.**
Published by: Orientations Magazine Ltd., 17th Fl, 200 Lockhart Rd, Hong Kong, Hong Kong. TEL 852-2511-1368, FAX 852-2507-4620, omag@netvigator.com, http://www.orientations.com.hk/. Adv. contact Elizabeth Knight. page USD 1,750; trim 210 x 286. Circ: 5,000.

ORIGINA. see *PRINTING*

700 USA ISSN 0030-5529
THE ORIGINAL ART REPORT; committed to the preservation, comprehension, and progress of artists, art, and the broader society. Abbreviated title: T O A R. Text in English. 1967. irreg. (12 nos./vol.). USD 31 per vol.. bk.rev. back issues avail. **Document type:** *Newsletter.* **Description:** Probes the way art works in the real world. Contains objective and subjective opinions and inquiries based on generally available knowledge, usually with a twist.
Published by: Original Art Report, 3024 Sunnyside Dr, Rockford, IL 61114-6025. Ed. Frank Salantrie. Pub. June Salantrie.

ORNAMENT; a quarterly of jewelry and personal adornment. see *JEWELRY, CLOCKS AND WATCHES*

730 POL ISSN 1230-6703
ORONSKO; kwartalnik rzezby. Text in Polish; Summaries in English. 1990. q. PLZ 10 domestic; USD 12 foreign (effective 2003). adv. bk.rev. **Description:** Covers contemporary sculpture, installations, art objects, and more.
Published by: Centrum Rzezby Polskiej, Ul Topolowa 1, Oronsko, 26681, Poland. crporo@polbox.com, http://www.rzezba-oronsko.pl. Ed., R&P Tomasz Palacz. Adv. contact Lech Karwowski. Circ: 500.

700 800 BIH
OSNOVAC. Text in Serbo-Croatian. 1977. q.
Published by: Udruzena Osnovna Skola, M Tita 8, Derventa, Bosnia Herzegovina. TEL 074-833-934.

709 NLD ISSN 0030-672X
DJ1
OUD-HOLLAND; driemaandelijks tijdschrift voor Nederlandse kunstgeschiedenis. Text in Dutch; Summaries in English. 1885. q. bk.rev. illus. index. back issues avail.; reprints avail. **Document type:** *Journal, Academic/Scholarly.*
Indexed: ABCT, AIAP, ASCA, ArtHuCI, ArtInd, BHA, CurCont, DIP, IBR, IBZ, RASB, RILM.
—IE.
Published by: (Stichting tot Exploitatie van het Rijksbureau voor Kunsthistorische Documentatie), Uitgeverij Nauta, Postbus 1, Zutphen aan den Rijn, 7200 AA, Netherlands. TEL 31-5750-13614. Circ: 750.

700 CHE
▼ **OUR MAGAZINE.** Text in English. 2003. 3/yr. USD 13.50 newsstand/cover (effective 2004).
Address: Gasometerstrasse 32, Zurich, 8031, Switzerland. http://www.our-magazine.ch. Eds. Martin Jaeggi, Melanie Hofmann.

700 709 GBR ISSN 0142-6540
N1
➤ **OXFORD ART JOURNAL.** Text in English. 1978. 3/yr. GBP 120, USD 216, EUR 180 to institutions; GBP 126, USD 227, EUR 189 combined subscription to institutions print & online eds. (effective 2006). adv. bk.rev. illus. cum.index. 208 p./no.; back issues avail.; reprint service avail. from PSC. **Document type:** *Journal, Academic/Scholarly.* **Description:** Addresses historical and philosophical issues concerning visual culture while seeking to provide an alternative to mainstream art history journals.
Related titles: Microform ed.; Online - full text ed.: ISSN 1741-7287 (from Chadwyck-Healey Inc., EBSCO Publishing, Gale Group, HighWire Press, IngentaConnect, JSTOR (Web-based Journal Archive), O C L C Online Computer Library Center, Inc., Oxford University Press Online Journals, ProQuest Information & Learning, Swets Information Services).
Indexed: ABM, AIAP, ASCA, AltPI, AmH&L, ArtHuCI, ArtInd, BHA, ChPerI, CurCont, DAAI, HistAb, PCI, RILM.
—BLDSC (6320.597000), IDS, IE, Infotrieve, ingenta. **CCC.**

A

Published by: Oxford University Press, Great Clarendon St, Oxford, OX2 6DP, United Kingdom. TEL 44-1865-556767, FAX 44-1865-556646, jnl.orders@oup.co.uk, http://oaj.oxfordjournals.org/, http://www.oxfordjournals.org/. Ed. Jon Bird. Pub. Clare Morton. R&P Fiona Bennett. Adv. contact Helen Pearson. B&W page GBP 275, B&W page USD 460; 169 x 220. Circ: 900.

790 800 USA ISSN 1067-2222
P - FORM* ; a journal of interdisciplinary and performance art. Text in English. 1986. q. USD 17.50 to individuals; USD 25 to institutions. adv. bk.rev.; play rev. illus. back issues avail. **Document type:** *Academic/Scholarly.* **Description:** Covers the experimental time-based arts, including performance, video, audio or sound art, theater, dance and film.
Indexed: ABM, AltPI, IIPA.
Published by: Randolph Street Gallery, 1136 13th Ave, Apt 101, Seattle, WA 98122-4405. TEL 206-320-9447, pform@mailexcite.com, http://fileroom.aaup.uic.edu/RSG/pformhomepage.html. Ed., R&P, Adv. contact Ken Thompson. B&W page USD 220; trim 7.5 x 10. Circ: 1,500.

700 FRA ISSN 1286-5923
P L G. (Plein la Gueule) Text in French. 1978. a. adv. bk.rev. **Document type:** *Monographic series.* **Description:** Contains interviews with comic book authors and young artists.
Formerly: P L G P P U R (0223-0844)
Published by: Association pour la Promotion des Jeunes Auteurs de la Bande Dessinee, 3 rue de la Vanne, Montrouge, 92120, France. TEL 33-1-46556604, FAX 33-1-46556604, morin100@aol.com, http://www.ifrance.com/plg. Ed. Philippe Morin. Pub. Dominique Poncet. R&P Frederic Debomy. Adv. contact Thomas Berthelot. Circ: 1,500.

750 DEU ISSN 1437-1367
PABLO JOURNAL; the Louvre test. Text in German. 1998. m. illus. back issues avail. **Document type:** *Academic/Scholarly.*
Media: Online - full text.
Address: Flagenstr 28, Loehne, 32584, Germany. TEL 49-5224-997407, FAX 49-5224-997409, ws@art-joe.com, http://art-quarter.com/beck/joe/aj. Ed. Werner Stuerenburg.

740 USA ISSN 1018-4252
N7410
PACIFIC ARTS. Text in English. 1975. a., latest 1994, nos. 9-10. USD 40 membership (effective 2005). bk.rev.; film rev. bibl. **Document type:** *Academic/Scholarly.* **Description:** Articles, commentary and reviews about research museums, exhibitions, and publications on Pacific arts and material culture.
Formerly (until no.29, 1989): Pacific Arts Newsletter (0111-5774)
Indexed: ABM, AICP, AnthLit, INZP, RILM, SPPI.
Published by: Pacific Arts Association, c/o Metropolitan Museum of Art, Dept AAOA, 1000 Fifth Ave, New York, NY 10028. Ed. Philip J C Dark. Circ: 300.

700 945 ITA ISSN 1120-9755
PADOVA E IL SUO TERRITORIO. Text in Italian. 1986. bi-m.
Published by: Editrice la Garangola, Via E. della Costa 6, Padua, 35129, Italy. TEL 39-049-8075557, FAX 39-049-7806580, info@garangola.it, http://www.garangola.it.

700 USA
PAINT RAG. Text in English. 1926. m. USD 30 to members (effective 1999). adv. **Document type:** *Newsletter.* **Description:** To promote and stimulate growth and ability among members of the art community, and to contribute to the cultural life of the state of Hawaii.
Published by: Association of Hawaii Artists, PO Box 10202, Honolulu, HI 96816. TEL 808-395-3238. Ed. Murray Breen. R&P J Rothschild. Circ: 500.

PALAESTRA. see *LITERATURE*

700 BEL
LE PALAIS DES BEAUX-ARTS. Text in French. m. adv. back issues avail.
Formerly (until 1992): Vie et Culture
Published by: Palais des Beaux-Arts - Charleroi, Pl du Manege, Charleroi, 6000, Belgium. TEL 32-71-314420, FAX 32-71-334207.

700 SWE ISSN 0031-0352
N8
➤ **PALETTEN.** Text in Swedish. 1940. q. SEK 300 to individuals; SEK 400 to institutions; SEK 270 to students (effective 2005). adv. bk.rev. illus. back issues avail. **Document type:** *Bulletin, Academic/Scholarly.*
Indexed: ABCT, ABM, BHA, DIP, IBR, IBZ.
Published by: Stiftelsen Paletten, Heurlins Plats 1, Goeteborg, 41301, Sweden. TEL 46-31-7439915, FAX 46-31-7439916, redaktor@paletten.tk, info@paletten.tk, http://www.paletten.tk/. Ed. Anna van de Vliet. Adv. contact Therese Lundberg. Circ: 5,500.

700 913 RUS
PAMYATNIKI KUL'TURY. NOVYE OTKRYTIYA/MONUMENTS OF CULTURE. NEW DISCOVERIES. Text in Russian; Summaries in English. 1974. irreg. price varies. illus.
Indexed: RASB.
Published by: (Rossiiskaya Akademiya Nauk/Russian Academy of Sciences), Izdatel'stvo Nauka, Sankt-Peterburgskoe Otdelenie, Mendeleevskaya liniya 1, St Petersburg, 199034, Russian Federation. **Dist. by:** M K - Periodica, ul Gilyarovskogo 39, Moscow 129110, Russian Federation. TEL 7-095-2845008, FAX 7-095-2813798, info@periodicals.ru, http://www.mkniga.ru.

PAN; c'est myotique!. see *LINGUISTICS*

PANDULIPI. see *LITERARY AND POLITICAL REVIEWS*

702.88 GBR ISSN 0140-1033
PAPER CONSERVATION NEWS. Text in English. 1976. 3/yr.
Indexed: A&ATA, LISA.
—BLDSC (6360.750000).
Published by: International Institute for Conservation of Historic and Artistic Works, 6 Buckingham St, London, WC2N 6BA, United Kingdom. TEL 44-20-78395975, FAX 44-20-79761564, iic@iiconservation.org, http://www.iiconservation.org.

700 ESP ISSN 1131-9267
PAPERS D'ART. Text in Catalan. 1987. s-a. EUR 24.04 domestic; EUR 34.26 in Europe; EUR 45.08 in the Americas (effective 2004). **Document type:** *Magazine, Consumer.* **Description:** Presents a discussion forum in which diverse topics are tacked that concern the world of art and culture.
Indexed: ABM.
Published by: Fundacio Espais d'Art Contemporani, Bisbe Lorenzana 31-33, Gerona, 17002, Spain. TEL 34-972-202530, FAX 34-972-208498. Ed. Carmen Ortiz. **Dist. by:** Asociacion de Revistas Culturales de Espana, Hortaleza, 75, Madrid 28004, Spain. TEL 34-91-3086066, FAX 34-91-3199267, info@arce.es, http://www.arce.es.

PAPOTAGE. see *LITERARY AND POLITICAL REVIEWS*

PAPYRUS; the post contemporary journal of poetry and art. see *LITERATURE—Poetry*

700 CAN ISSN 0318-7020
PARACHUTE; contemporary art magazine. Text in English, French. 1975. q. CND 57 domestic to individuals; CND 84 foreign to individuals; CND 125 domestic to institutions; CND 149 foreign to institutions (effective 2005). adv. bk.rev. back issues avail. **Document type:** *Magazine, Consumer.* **Description:** Presents contemporary Canadian and international art and criticism. Includes articles, interviews, exhibition reviews, and a debate section.
Related titles: Microfiche ed.: (from MML); Online - full text ed.: (from Gale Group, H.W. Wilson, O C L C Online Computer Library Center, Inc.).
Indexed: ABM, ArtInd, BHA, CBCARef, CPerI, PdeR, RASB.
—BLDSC (6404.710000), IE, ingenta. **CCC.**
Published by: Editions Parachute, 4060 bd St Laurent, Ste 501, Montreal, PQ H2W 1Y9, Canada. TEL 514-842-9805, FAX 514-842-9319, parachut@citenet.net, http://www.parachute.ca/. Ed. Chantal Pontbriand. R&P, Adv. contact Monica Gyorkos. B&W page CND 795; trim 10.5 x 8. Circ: 5,000.

PARADOXISM. see *LITERATURE*

PARALLAX. see *LITERATURE*

PARES CUM PARIBUS; revista de literatura y arte. see *LITERATURE*

700 CHE ISSN 0256-0917
NX456
PARKETT. Text in English, German. 1984. 3/yr. EUR 82 in Europe; USD 80 in US & Canada; EUR 98 elsewhere (effective 2005). adv. bk.rev. illus. cum.index: nos.1-25. reprints avail. **Document type:** *Magazine, Consumer.* **Description:** Documents European and American contemporary art. Each issue covers several important artists and is produced in close collaboration with those artists.
Indexed: ABCT, ABM, ArtInd, BHA, DIP, IBR, IBZ, RILM.
—BLDSC (6406.771000), IE, Infotrieve, ingenta.
Published by: Parkett Verlag AG, Quellenstr 27, Zuerich, 8031, Switzerland. TEL 41-1-2718140, FAX 41-1-2724301, info@parkettart.com, http://www.parkettart.com. Ed. Bice Curiger. Pub. Dieter von Graffenried. Adv. contact Therese Faessler. Circ: 10,000. **Subscr. in US to:** Parkett Publishers, 155 Ave of the Americas, 2nd Fl, New York, NY 10013. TEL 212-673-2660, 212-271-0704.

700 BEL ISSN 0773-9532
LA PART DE L'OEIL. Text in French. 1985. a.
Published by: Le Part de l'Oeil, 144, rue du Midi, Bruxelles, 1000, Belgium. FAX 32-2-514-1841, lapartdeloeil@brunette.brucity.be, http://www.aca-bxl.be/oeil/part/index.htm.

700 860 ESP ISSN 1130-0388
EL PASEANTE. Text in Spanish. 1985. q. adv. **Document type:** *Monographic series.* **Description:** Reviews the main cultural features of our times, from literary creation to the plastic arts.
Published by: Ediciones Siruela S.A., El Pabellon, Plaza Manuel Becerra, 15, Madrid, 28028, Spain. TEL 34-1-355-57-20, FAX 34-1-355-22-01, siruela@siruela.com. Ed. Jacobo Fitz James Stewart. Adv. contact Mamen Fernandez Damborenea. Circ: 15,000.

PASSAGEN; Zeitschrift fuer Literatur und Kunst. see *LITERATURE*

709 DNK ISSN 0908-5351
PASSEPARTOUT; skrifter for kunsthistorie. Text in Danish. 1993. 2/yr. DKK 180 (effective 2004). back issues avail. **Document type:** *Monographic series, Academic/Scholarly.*
Published by: Aarhus Universitet, Institut for Kunsthistorie, Langelandsgade 139, Aarhus C, 8000, Denmark. TEL 45-89-421864, FAX 45-89-421855, passepartout@hum.aau.dk, http://www.hum.au.dk/kunsthis/passepartout/. Eds. Peter Brix Soendergaard, Steen Hammerhoey Andersen.

741 USA ISSN 1524-9034
THE PASTEL JOURNAL; the magazine for artists who work in soft pastel. Text in English. 1999. bi-m. USD 27 domestic; USD 37 foreign; USD 5.99 newsstand/cover domestic; USD 7.75 newsstand/cover foreign (effective 2004). adv. illus. back issues avail. **Document type:** *Magazine, Consumer.* **Description:** Contains high quality images of pastel art works, interviews with artists, and other related information.
Published by: F & W Publications, Inc., 4700 E Galbraith Rd, Cincinnati, OH 45236. TEL 513-531-2690, FAX 513-531-0798, pjedit@fwpubs.com, wds@fwpubs.com, http://pasteljournal.com, http://www.familytreemagazine.com. Adv. contact Stephanie Curtis TEL 877-234-6829. B&W page USD 2,250. Circ: 38,000.

741 ITA ISSN 1721-2170
PEACH GIRL. Text in Italian. 2002. m. adv. **Document type:** *Magazine, Consumer.*
Published by: Play Press Publishing s.r.l., Via Vitorchiano 123, Rome, RM 00189, Italy. TEL 39-06-33221250, FAX 39-06-33221235, abbonamenti@playpress.com, http://www.playpress.com. Pub. Alessandro Ferri. Adv. contact Lorenza Borroni TEL 39-02-45472867.

PEAKE STUDIES; dedicated to the life and work of Mervyn Peake (1911-1968). see *LITERARY AND POLITICAL REVIEWS*

PEN WORLD. see *HOBBIES*

PENFINDER. see *HOBBIES*

PEQUOD. see *LITERATURE*

709.02 723 USA ISSN 1554-8678
N5950
PEREGRINATIONS. Text in Multiple languages. 2002. irreg. free (effective 2005). **Document type:** *Journal, Academic/Scholarly.*
Media: Online - full content.
Published by: International Society for the Study of Pilgrimage Arts, Art History Dept Kenyon College, Gambier, OH 43022. TEL 740-427-5347, http://peregrinations.kenyon.edu, http://peregrinations.kenyon.edu/about.html. Eds. Rita Tekippe, Sarah Blick.

700 CAN
PERFORMANCE (ROYAL THOMSON - MASSEY HALL EDITION). Text in English. 1982. bi-m. adv. **Document type:** *Consumer.*
Formerly: Bravo (0714-6981)
Published by: St. Clair Group, 30 St Clair Ave W 805, Toronto, ON M4V 3A1, Canada. TEL 416-926-7595, FAX 416-926-0407. Ed. Laurie Payne.

PERISTIL. see *ARCHITECTURE*

700 FRA
PERMANENT FOOD. Text in English. 1995. irreg. USD 11.50 newsstand/cover. **Document type:** *Magazine, Consumer.*
Published by: Les Presses du Reel, 16 rue Quentin, Dijon, 21000, France. FAX 33-1-42-38-26-04. Ed. Maurizio Cattelan. **Dist. by:** Idea Books Amsterdam, Nieuwe Herengracht 11, Amsterdam 1011 RK, Netherlands.

PESARO CITTA E CONTA; rivista della Societa pesarese di studi storici. see *HISTORY—History Of Europe*

700 HRV ISSN 0031-6296
PETNAEST DANA/FIFTEEN DAYS; casopis za kulturu i umjetnost. Text in Croatian. 1957. bi-m. USD 20. bk.rev. illus. cum.index.
Formerly: Petnaest - Fifteen Dana
Indexed: RILM.
Published by: Radnicko Sveuciliste "Mosa Pijade", Proletarskih br 68, Zagreb, 41000, Croatia. Ed. Slavko Kovac. Circ: 2,000.

PHAROS. see *ARCHAEOLOGY*

▼ **PHILAMENT.** see *HUMANITIES: COMPREHENSIVE WORKS*

709 USA ISSN 0193-8061
N5300
PHOEBUS (TEMPE); a journal of art history. Text in English. 1978. a. USD 12. bk.rev. illus.
Indexed: BHA.
Published by: Arizona State University, School of Art, Tempe, AZ 85287. TEL 602-965-6439. Ed. Anthony Lacy Gully. Circ: 1,200.

PHOTOGRAPH COLLECTOR; for collectors, curators and dealers. see *PHOTOGRAPHY*

PHOTOGRAPHIC ART MARKET: AUCTION PRICES (YEAR). see *PHOTOGRAPHY*

700 770 MEX
▼ **PICNIC.** Text in Spanish. 2004. bi-m. MXP 55 domestic; USD 15 in United States; EUR 12 in Europe (effective 2005).
Published by: Ediciones Flavours, Tabasco 77, col. Roma Norte, Mexico D.F., CP 06700, Mexico. contacto@picnic-mag.com, http://www.picnic-mag.com. Eds. Veronique Ricardoni, Victor Manuel Rodriguez.

709 BEL
➤ **PICTURA NOVA**; studies in 16th and 17th century Flemish painting and drawing. Text in English, German. 1996. irreg., latest vol.8, 2001. price varies. bibl.; illus. back issues avail. **Document type:** *Monographic series, Academic/Scholarly.* **Description:** Publishes monographic studies of specific artists and studies on various themes and topics in Flemish painting and drawing of the 16th and 17th centuries.
Published by: Brepols Publishers, Begijnhof 67, Turnhout, 2300, Belgium. FAX 32-14-42-89-19, publishers@brepols.com, periodicals@brepols.net. Eds. Hans Vlieghe, Katlijne van der Stighelen.

➤ **PICTURA & POESIS.** see *LITERATURE*

338.76176 GBR ISSN 1362-1238
PICTURE BUSINESS. Text in English. 1994. 10/yr. GBP 28 (effective 2004). adv. **Document type:** *Magazine, Trade.*
Incorporates (1985-199?): Framing & Art Buyer's World
Published by: Write Angle Publishing Ltd., Paynetts Business Centre, Unit 2C, Cranbrook Rd, Goudhurst, Kent, TN17 1DY, United Kingdom. TEL 44-1580-212717, FAX 44-1580-212414, info@picturebusiness.uk.com, http://www.picturebusiness.uk.com. adv.: color page GBP 2,050; trim 230 x 326. Circ: 4,665 (paid and controlled).

700 GBR
(YEAR) PICTURE PRICE GUIDE. Text in English. 1988. a. GBP 120 per issue domestic; GBP 125, USD 225, EUR 190 per issue foreign (effective 2005). charts; illus.; mkt. **Document type:** *Catalog, Consumer.* **Description:** Provides information about fine art sold at public auctions in the UK.
Supersedes (in 199?): Miller's Picture Price Guide (1352-3996)
Published by: Art Sales Index Ltd, 16 Luddington Ave, Virginia Water, Surrey GU25 4DF, United Kingdom. TEL 44-1344-841750, FAX 44-1344-841760, info@art-sales-index.com, asi@art-sales-index.com, http://www.art-sales-index.com. Ed. Duncan Hislop.

PIEDRA IMAN. see *LITERATURE*

THE PIG IRON SERIES. see *LITERATURE*

740 770 RUS ISSN 1561-3488
N6981
PINAKOTEKA. Text in Russian, English; Summaries in English. q. USD 65; USD 165 foreign. adv. illus. **Document type:** *Academic/Scholarly.* **Description:** Focuses on a new subject in art history every issue. Examines art via historical, systematic, and critical approaches.
Address: M Bronnaya 32, kv 2, Moscow, 103001, Russian Federation. TEL 7-095-2904112, FAX 7-095-2023795, pinak@mail.cnt.ru, http://www.pinakoteke.artinfo.ru. Ed. Natalia Osipovskaya. Pub. Natalia Sipovskaya. R&P Andrei Tolstoy. Adv. contact Ekaterina Vyazova. B&W page USD 1,100, color page USD 1,800. Circ: 3,000. **US dist. addr.:** East View Information Services, 3020 Harbor Ln. N., Minneapolis, MN 55447. TEL 612-550-0961.

700 BRA ISSN 0104-3358
NX533.A1
PIRACEMA; arte e cultura. Text in Portuguese. 1993. 3/yr.
Indexed: RILM.
Published by: Instituto Brasileiro de Arte e Cultura, Palacio Gustavo Capanema, Rua da Imprensa, 16 Andar 7, Centro, Rio De Janeiro, RJ 20030-120, Brazil. TEL 55-21-2976116, FAX 55-21-2624895. Ed. Ivan Junqueira.

PIRANESI; 1st Middle-European architectural magazine for the culture of environment. see *ARCHITECTURE*

700 705 DNK ISSN 0107-6442
PIST PROTTA. Text in Danish. 1981. 2/yr. DKK 100; DKK 50 newsstand/cover (effective 2000). illus. **Description:** A medium for experimental art worldwide with emphasis on contemporary art. Theme issues in different physical formats and looks.
Published by: Space Poetry, Ahlefeldtsgade 24,3, Copenhagen K, 1359, Denmark. TEL 45-33-15-30-81, FAX 45-33-15-30-81. Eds. Aase Eg Joergensen, Jesper Fabricius.

▼ **PISTIL MAGAZINE.** see *WOMEN'S INTERESTS*

700 DEU ISSN 0945-9936
PLAKAT JOURNAL. Text in English, German. 1994. q. USD 65 elsewhere. **Document type:** *Consumer.*
Indexed: DAAI.
Published by: PlakatKonzepte Grohnert und Weigelt, Oskar-Winter-Str 3, Hannover, 30161, Germany. TEL 49-511-628376, FAX 49-511-628377.

700 POL ISSN 1428-8931
PLAMA; pismo artystyczne. Text in Polish. 1997. q. 94 p./no.
Published by: Towarzystwo Kulturalno-Sportowe Kuznia, ul Podmiejska 1, Rybnik, 44207, Poland. TEL 48-32-7391898, sekretariat@kuznia.rybnik.pl. Ed. Marian Bednarek. Circ: 400.

PLANET; the Welsh internationalist. see *LITERATURE*

700 DEU ISSN 0938-6602
DAS PLATEAU. Text in German. 1990. bi-m. **Document type:** *Bulletin.* **Description:** Contains essays on general cultural interests.
Indexed: DIP, IBR, IBZ.
Published by: Radius-Verlag GmbH, Olgastr 114, Stuttgart, 70180, Germany. TEL 49-711-6076666, FAX 49-711-6075555. Ed. Wolfgang Erk. Circ: 1,500.

741 ITA ISSN 1127-3364
PLAY X. Text in Italian. 1998. bi-m. adv. **Document type:** *Magazine, Consumer.*
Published by: Play Press Publishing s.r.l., Via Vitorchiano 123, Rome, RM 00189, Italy. TEL 39-06-33221250, FAX 39-06-33221235, abbonamenti@playpress.com, http://www.playpress.com. Ed. Maurizio Di Stefano. Pub. Alessandro Ferri. Adv. contact Lorenza Borroni TEL 39-02-45472867.

700 781.64 USA ISSN 1085-4525
AP2
PLAZM. Text in English. 1993. q. USD 20 domestic; USD 25 in Canada & Mexico; USD 50 elsewhere; USD 6 newsstand/cover domestic; USD 7.50 newsstand/cover in Canada & Mexico (effective 2001). adv. illus. **Document type:** *Magazine, Consumer.* **Description:** Features young artists and describes their talents.
Address: PO Box 2863, Portland, OR 97208-2863. TEL 503-222-6389, 800-524-4944, FAX 503-222-6356, editor@plazm.com, http://www.plazm.com. Ed., R&P Jon Raymond. Pub., Adv. contact Josh Berger.

PLEINE MARGE; cahiers de litterature, d'arts plastiques et de critique. see *LITERATURE*

PLUG; cultureel informatieblad voor houders van een Cultureel Jongeren Pasport in Noord-Holland. see *THEATER*

POBOCZA; kwartalnik literacko-artystyczny. see *LITERATURE*

700 ITA ISSN 0079-242X
POCKET LIBRARY OF STUDIES IN ART. Text in Italian. 1948. irreg., latest vol.34, 2000. price varies. **Document type:** *Monographic series, Academic/Scholarly.*
Published by: Casa Editrice Leo S. Olschki, Viuzzo del Pozzetto 8, Florence, 50126, Italy. TEL 39-055-6530684, FAX 39-055-6530214, celso@olschki.it, http://www.olschki.it. Circ: 1,200.

POETS, PAINTERS, COMPOSERS. see *LITERATURE*

701.18 POL ISSN 1231-9562
N69.P7
POKAZ; pismo krytyki artystycznej. Text in Polish. 1997. q. 64 p./no.;
Related titles: Online - full text ed.: ISSN 1689-1325.
Published by: (Galeria Krytykow Pokaz), Mazowieckie Centrum Kultury i Sztuki, ul Elektoralna 12, Warsaw, 00139, Poland. TEL 48-22-6204836, pokazpismo@free.art.pl, http://free.art.pl/pokazpismo. Ed. Magdalena Hniedziewicz. Circ: 600.

POL OXYGEN; design - art - architecture. see *ARCHITECTURE*

700 MEX ISSN 1405-0560
N6555
POLIESTER; pintura y no pintura. Text in English, Spanish. 1992. q. MXP 170 domestic; USD 50 in Latin America and Europe (effective 2000). adv. **Document type:** *Consumer.* **Description:** Covers contemporary art of the Americas. Includes interviews with curators and reviews of exhibitions.
Indexed: ABM.
Address: PUERTO REAL 20, Col Condesa, Mexico City, DF 06140, Mexico. TEL 52-5-5534813, FAX 525-2114039, poliester@intranet.com.mx, http://www.poliester.com. Eds. Geraldine Ripol, Kurt Hollander. Circ: 5,000.

700 AUT ISSN 0259-0824
POLYAISTHESIS; Beitraege zur Integration der Kuenste und der Wissenschaften und zu ihrer Umsetzung in die Paedagogische Praxis. Text in German. 1986. a. price varies. **Document type:** *Academic/Scholarly.*
Indexed: IBR, RILM.
Published by: (Internationale Gesellschaft fuer Polyaesthetische Erziehung), Oesterreichischer Kunst- und Kulturverlag, Postfach 17, Vienna, W 1016, Austria.

POLYMERS PAINT COLOR YEAR BOOK (YEAR). see *PAINTS AND PROTECTIVE COATINGS*

700 943 DEU ISSN 0032-4167
POMMERN; Zeitschrift fuer Kultur und Geschichte. Text in German. 1963. q. EUR 20; EUR 6 newsstand/cover (effective 2003). adv. bk.rev. abstr.; bibl.; charts; illus. **Document type:** *Journal, Academic/Scholarly.*
Formerly: Unser Pommern
Published by: Pommerscher Landsmannschaft Zentralverband e.V., Europaweg 3, Luebeck, 23570, Germany. TEL 49-4502-8030, FAX 49-4502-803131, post@pommern-z.de, http://pommern-z.de. Eds. Jens Ruediger, Michael Hammermeister. Circ: 1,500.

POP. see *CLOTHING TRADE—Fashions*

POSMOTRI. see *GENERAL INTEREST PERIODICALS—Russia*

776.6 USA
POST-DOGMATIST QUARTERLY; the arts & letters journal of the International Post-Dogmatist Group. Text in English. 4/yr. **Description:** Aims to advance creative endeavor in all of its multifarious expressions.
Media: Online - full text.
Published by: International Post-Dogmatist Group webmaster@post-dogmatist-arts.net, http://post-dogmatist-arts.net/quarterly/. Ed. Cecil Orion Touchon.

800 700 USA
POSTCARD ART - POSTCARD FICTION. Text in English. 1974. irreg. (1-2/yr.). USD 5.
Published by: Martha Rosler, Ed. & Pub., 143 McGuinness Blvd, Brooklyn, NY 11222. TEL 718-383-2277. Circ: 600.

709 POL ISSN 0079-466X
➤ **POZNANSKIE TOWARZYSTWO PRZYJACIOL NAUK. KOMISJA HISTORII SZTUKI. PRACE.** Text in Polish; Summaries in English. 1923. irreg., latest vol.32, 2002. price varies. charts; illus. **Document type:** *Monographic series, Academic/Scholarly.*
Published by: (Poznanskie Towarzystwo Przyjaciol Nauk, Komisja Historii Sztuki), Poznanskie Towarzystwo Przyjaciol Nauk/Poznan Society for the Advancement of the Arts and Sciences, ul Sew Mielzynskiego 27-29, Poznan, 61725, Poland. TEL 48-61-8527441, FAX 48-61-8522205, sekretariat@ptpn.poznan.pl, wydawnictwo@ptpn.poznan.pl, http://www.ptpn.poznan.pl. **Dist. by:** Ars Polona, Krakowskie Przedmiescie 7, Warsaw, Poland. TEL 48-22-9263914, FAX 48-22-9265334, arspolona@arspolona.com.pl, http://www.arspolona.com.pl.

060 709 POL ISSN 0138-0516
PRACE POPULARNONAUKOWE. ZABYTKI POLSKI POLNOCNEJ. Text in Polish. 1975. irreg., latest vol.9, 1991. price varies. **Document type:** *Monographic series.*
Related titles: ♦ Series of: Towarzystwo Naukowe w Toruniu. Prace Popularnonaukowe. ISSN 0079-4805.
Published by: Towarzystwo Naukowe w Toruniu, Ul Wysoka 16, Torun, 81100, Poland. TEL 48-56-23941. Ed. Cecylia Iwaniszewska. Circ: 7,000.

PRATIBHA INDIA; journal of Indian art, culture and literature. see *LITERATURE*

PRATO - STORIA ED ARTE. see *HISTORY—History Of Europe*

PRATT INSTITUTE CREATIVE ARTS THERAPY REVIEW. see *MEDICAL SCIENCES—Physical Medicine And Rehabilitation*

700 800 NLD ISSN 1124-5093
NX552.A1
PRAZ!. Text in Italian. 1994. 3/yr. EUR 25 in Europe; EUR 35 elsewhere; EUR 11 per issue (effective 2005). adv. bk.rev. abstr.; bibl.; illus. index, cum.index. back issues avail. **Document type:** *Monographic series.* **Description:** Covers literature, criticism, art, poetry and music fields.
Related titles: Diskette ed.
Published by: Semar Publishers S.r.l., Nachtegaallan 1, The Hague, 2566JJ, Netherlands. TEL 31-703-459038, FAX 31-703-602471. Ed. Dr. Luciano Sahlan Momo. adv.: page USD 1,200. Circ: 5,000 (paid).

700 USA ISSN 1049-541X
NK1404
PRESIDENTIAL DESIGN AWARDS. Text in English. 1984. quadrennial. free. **Document type:** *Government.*
Published by: (Publication Office), National Endowment for the Arts, 1100 Penn Ave, N W, Washington, DC 20506. TEL 202-682-5437, FAX 202-682-5669.

700 069 GBR ISSN 0962-2470
PREVIEW; friends of glasgow museums. Text in English. 1991. q.
Document type: *Bulletin.*
Indexed: AESIS.
Published by: Glasgow City Council, Cultural and Leisure Services, 16 Albion St, Glasgow, G1 1LH, United Kingdom. TEL 0141-2875387, FAX 0141-2875557, paul.kane@cls.glasgow.gov.uk. Ed. Paul Kane. Circ: 30,000 (free).

PREVUE. see *MOTION PICTURES*

391 USA
PRICK; the world's first free tattoo & piercing lifestyle magazine. Text in English. 2000. m. free newsstand/cover. adv.
Document type: *Magazine, Consumer.* **Description:** Contains articles and features on all aspects of the tattoo and piercing lifestyle.
Published by: C D B Enterprises, PO Box 381, Tucker, GA 30085. TEL 770-723-9824, chuckbrank@prickmag.net, http://www.prickmag.net. Ed., Pub. Charles Brank. Adv. contact Geoffrey Stephenson. B&W page USD 350, color page USD 500; trim 10 x 12. Circ: 30,000 (controlled).

PRIMI PIANI; mensile d'arte, costume, cultura, scienza, spettacolo e turismo. see *MUSIC*

PRINCETON ESSAYS ON THE ARTS. see *HUMANITIES: COMPREHENSIVE WORKS*

700 913 USA ISSN 0079-5208
PRINCETON MONOGRAPHS IN ART AND ARCHAEOLOGY. Text in English. 1932. irreg., latest 1990. price varies. bibl.; charts; illus.; maps. back issues avail.; reprint service avail. from PQC. **Document type:** *Monographic series, Academic/Scholarly.* **Description:** Discusses specific topics in art and archaeology.
—CCC.
Published by: Princeton University Press, 41 William St, Princeton, NJ 08540-5237. TEL 609-258-4900, 800-777-4726, FAX 609-258-6305. **Subscr. to:** California - Princeton Fulfillment Services, 1445 Lower Ferry Rd, Ewing, NJ 08618. TEL 800-777-4726, FAX 800-999-1958. **Dist. by:** University Press Group, 164 Hillsdale Ave E, Toronto, ON M4S 1T5, Canada.; John Wiley & Sons Ltd., The Atrium, Southern Gate, Chichester, West Sussex PO19 8SQ, United Kingdom.

338.4768620971 CAN ISSN 1481-9287
PRINT ACTION. Text in English. 1962. 12/yr. CND 28.95 domestic; USD 34.35 in United States; USD 55 elsewhere (effective 2005). adv. bk.rev. stat.; tr.lit. **Document type:** *Magazine, Trade.* **Description:** Covers the graphic arts and printing industries in Canada.
Incorporates (1997-2001): Print on Demand (1481-9708); Former titles (until 1971): Applied Graphics (0003-6889); (until 1965): Applied Graphics and Materials (0837-0699)
Related titles: ◆ Supplement(s): PrintAction National Directory of Services & Equipment for the Trade. ISSN 1481-9309.
Published by: Youngblood Publishing Ltd., 4580 Dufferin St, Ste 404, Toronto, ON M3H 5Y2, Canada. TEL 416-665-7333, 800-363-3261, FAX 416-665-7226, info@printaction.com, http://www.printaction.com/. Ed. Jon Robinson. Adv. contact Gerald Fruehwirth. B&W page CND 4,970, color page CND 6,070; trim 10.375 x 13.5. Circ: 10,500.

741.6 GBR ISSN 0265-8305
NE1
➤ **PRINT QUARTERLY.** Text in English. 1984. q. GBP 43 domestic; EUR 79 in Europe eurozone; USD 96 in US & Canada; GBP 52 elsewhere (effective 2005). adv. bk.rev. illus. back issues avail.; reprints avail. **Document type:** *Journal, Academic/Scholarly.* **Description:** Devoted to the history of prints and printmaking from the fifteenth century to the present.
Indexed: ABM, AIAP, ASCA, AmH&L, ArtHuCI, ArtInd, BHA, CurCont, HistAb, PCI, RASB, RILM.
—BLDSC (6613.218000), IDS, IE, Infotrieve.
Published by: Print Quarterly Publications, 52 Kelso Pl, London, W8 5QQ, United Kingdom. TEL 44-20-77954987, FAX 44-20-77954988, admin@printquarterly.co.uk, http://www.printquarterly.com/. Ed., R&P David Landau. Adv. contact Jocelyne Bancel. page GBP 396, page USD 572, page EUR 639; 159 x 206. Circ: 1,300.

760 GBR ISSN 0960-9253
NE1
PRINTMAKING TODAY. Text in English. 1990. q. GBP 18 domestic to individuals; USD 37.50 in North America to individuals; GBP 25 elsewhere to individuals; GBP 25 domestic to institutions; USD 48 in North America to institutions. adv. bk.rev. **Document type:** *Academic/Scholarly.* **Description:** Reports on contemporary international printmaking.
Indexed: ABM, ArtInd.
—BLDSC (6615.285000), IE, ingenta. **CCC.**
Published by: Farrand Press, 50 Ferry St, London, E14 3DT, United Kingdom. TEL 44-20-7515-7322, FAX 44-20-7537-3559, fitrrandprs@aol.com. Ed. Anne Desmet. Adv. contact Geoff Munday. Circ: 2,000 (paid).

PRISMA (KASSEL). see *SCIENCES: COMPREHENSIVE WORKS*

700 USA
PRIVATE VIEW. Text in English. m. free. **Document type:** *Newsletter.* **Description:** Displays art on binary attachments.
Media: E-mail.
Address: solvista@binternet.com.

700 800 POL ISSN 1426-2398
AP54
PRO ARTE; czasopismo kulturalno-literackie. Text in Polish. 1996. q. 120 p./no.;
Related titles: Online - full content ed.: ISSN 1689-1856.
Published by: Stowarzyszenia Inicjatywa Kulturalna Pro Arte, ul Kraszewskiego 24/6, Poznan, 60519, Poland. TEL 48-61-6627314, redakcja@proarte.net.pl, stowarzyszenie@proarte.net.pl, http://proarte.net.pl. Ed. Karol Francuzik. Circ: 1,500.

700 BGR ISSN 0032-9371
PROBLEMI NA IZKUSTVOTO/PROBLEMS OF ART. Summaries in English, French, German, Russian. 1968. q. BGL 1.80 per issue; USD 40 foreign (effective 2002). bk.rev.; film rev.; play rev. illus. reprint service avail. from IRC. **Document type:** *Journal.* **Description:** Contains studies about theory and history of art; materials in all fields of art - fine and applied art, theatre, music, cinema, TV.
Indexed: ABCT, ABM, BHA, RILM.
Published by: (Bulgarska Akademiya na Naukite/Bulgarian Academy of Sciences, Institut za Izkustvoznanie), Universitetsko Izdatelstvo Sv. Kliment Okhridski/Publishing House of the Sofia University St. Kliment Ohridski, Akad G Bonchev 6, Sofia, 1113, Bulgaria. http://musicart.imbm.bas.bg/journals.htm#art_studies. Ed. A Stoikov. Circ: 1,360. **Dist. by:** Hemus, 6 Rouski Blvd., Sofia 1000, Bulgaria; **Dist. by:** Sofia Books, ul Silivria 16, Sofia 1404, Bulgaria. TEL 359-2-9586257, info@sofiabooks-bg.com, http://www.sofiabooks-bg.com.

PROCESOS HISTORICOS; revista semestral de historia, arte y ciencias ociales. see *HISTORY*

747 720 NZL ISSN 1171-8897
PRODESIGN. Text in English. 1992. 6/yr. NZD 36.95. adv. charts; illus.; tr.lit. **Document type:** *Trade.* **Description:** For the professional design community as well as their clients. Provides information, comment and debate on design and design matters including new products and projects, key issues, events and awards, overseas trends, people and practice profiles, professional development and education.
Indexed: DAAI, INZP.
Published by: A G M Publishing Ltd., Newmarket, Private Bag 99 915, Auckland, 1031, New Zealand. TEL 64-9-8464068, FAX 64-9-8468742. Eds. Kristy Robertson, Robin Beckett. Pub., R&P Robin Beckett. Adv. contact Stephaniie Watson. Circ: 8,500.

PROFESSIONAL APPRAISERS INFORMATION EXCHANGE. see *ANTIQUES*

700 URY
PROGRAMA; por un programa de trabajo de la cultura. Text in Spanish. bi-m. UYP 360, USD 10.
Published by: Editorial Imago s.r.l., Treinta Y Tres, 1324, Montevideo, 11007, Uruguay. Ed. Luis Carrizo.

709 ITA ISSN 0394-0802
N4
PROSPETTIVA; rivista di storia dell'arte antica e moderna. Text in Italian. 1975. q. EUR 92.96 domestic; EUR 123.95 foreign (effective 2004). adv. bk.rev. illus. **Document type:** *Academic/Scholarly.* **Description:** Covers methodological problems, essays, contributions, and exhibitions. Includes art history from antiquity up to modern times.
Indexed: AIAP, ASCA, ArtHuCI, BHA, CurCont, RASB.
—IE.
Published by: (Universita degli Studi di Siena, Facolta di Lettere e Filosofia), Centro Di, Lungarno Serristori 35, Florence, FI 50125, Italy. TEL 39-055-2342668, FAX 39-055-2342667, centrodi@centrodi.it, http://www.centrodi.it. Circ: 600.

741.5 USA ISSN 1087-9013
PROTOONER. Text in English. 1995. m. USD 60 domestic; USD 65 in Canada (effective 2003). adv. bk.rev. bibl.; illus. back issues avail. **Document type:** *Magazine, Trade.* **Description:** For cartoonists producing a variety of nationally known cartoons accompanied by short comments on their history and origin. Also includes a list of publications advertising for cartoons to be submitted.
Address: PO Box 2270, Daly City, CA 94017-2270. protooner@earthlink.net, http://protooner.lookscool.com. Ed., Adv. contact Joyce Miller. Pub. Ladd A Miller. Circ: 1,050 (paid).

700 800 USA ISSN 1053-5012
PROVINCETOWN ARTS. Text in English. 1985. a. USD 10 (effective 1999). adv. bk.rev. illus. back issues avail.
Document type: *Trade.* **Description:** Covers artists and writers in and around Provincetown, with interviews, essays, discussions of current gallery offerings, fiction, poetry and a calendar of exhibitions.
Related titles: Online - full text ed.: (from EBSCO Publishing).
Indexed: AmHI.
Published by: Provincetown Arts Press, Inc., 650 Commercial St., Provincetown, MA 02657-1725. TEL 508-487-3167, FAX 508-487-8634, press@CapeCodAccess.com. Ed. Jennifer Liese. Pub., R&P Christopher Busa. Adv. contact Margaret Bergman. B&W page USD 990, color page USD 1,300; trim 12 x 9. Circ: 8,000.

PROZA; literary and art magazine. see *LITERATURE*

700 FRA
PUBLIC ART. Text in English, French. 2000. m. free to members (effective 2002). **Document type:** *Newsletter, Trade.*
Description: Covers art, architecture and urban design.
Media: Online - full content.
Published by: Art - Public, 21 Bd de la Madeleine, Paris, 75001, France. TEL 33-1-40200220, FAX 33-1-40200380, info@art-public.com, http://www.art-public.com/.

701.18 USA ISSN 1062-5089
N8908.A1
PUBLIC ART ISSUES. Text in English. 1983. 4/yr. free.
Document type: *Newsletter.* **Description:** Covers issues related to the field of public art.
Former titles: In Process (1060-6734); (until 1991): Public Art Fund Newsletter
Indexed: AIAP.
Published by: Public Art Fund Inc., 1 E 53rd St, 11th Fl, New York, NY 10022. TEL 212-980-4575, FAX 212-980-3610. Circ: 2,000.

700 USA ISSN 1040-211X
N8700
➤ **PUBLIC ART REVIEW.** Text in English. 1989. s-a. USD 17 domestic; USD 23 in Canada & Mexico; USD 28 elsewhere (effective 2004). bk.rev. 52 p./no.; back issues avail.
Document type: *Magazine, Academic/Scholarly.* **Description:** Critical dialogue, reviews, profiles and listings on public art.
Related titles: Online - full text ed.: (from H.W. Wilson, O C L C Online Computer Library Center, Inc.).
Indexed: ABM, ArtInd.
—BLDSC (6962.791300), IE, ingenta.
Published by: Forecast Public Artworks, 2324 University Ave. W., Ste. 102, St. Paul, MN 55114-1802. TEL 651-641-1128, FAX 651-641-0028, publicartreview@visi.org, forecast@visi.com, http://www.publicartreview.org, http://www.forecastart.org. Pub. Jack Becker. Adv. contact Rebecca Ryan. Circ: 2,500 (paid).

700 USA
PUBLIC ILLUMINATION MAGAZINE. Text in English. 1979. irreg. USD 3 (effective 2000). **Description:** Contains dada art submitted and published pseudonymously.
Related titles: Online - full text ed.
Address: 30 73 47th St, Long Island City, NY 11103. TEL 718-721-0946, casasorci@krenet.it, http://www.mondorondo.com/pim/. Ed., Pub. Zagreus Bowery. R&P Ron Kolm. Circ: 1,000.

730 GBR
PUBLIC SCULPTURE OF BRITAIN. Text in English. 1997. irreg. back issues avail. **Document type:** *Monographic series, Academic/Scholarly.*
Published by: Liverpool University Press, 4 Cambridge St, Liverpool, L69 7ZU, United Kingdom. TEL 44-151-794-2233, FAX 44-151-794-2235, http://www.liverpool-unipress.co.uk/. Pub. Robin Bloxsidge. Adv. contact Sandra Robinson.

700 860 MEX ISSN 1405-1680
F1261
PUENTELIBRE. Text in Spanish. 1993. q. USD 50. adv. bk.rev. illus. reprints avail. **Description:** Promotes recent artistic, literary and cultural manifestations of Latin America.
Published by: Puentelibre Editores, Apdo. Postal 1860-B, Cd. Juarez, Chihuahua, Mexico. Ed. Rosario Sanmiguel.

PUNCTURE; a magazine of music and the arts. see *MUSIC*

PUNGOLO VERDE; arti-science e lettere. see *LITERARY AND POLITICAL REVIEWS*

700 ITA
QUADERNI DI STORIA DELL'ARTE. Text in Italian. 1966. irreg., latest vol.15, 1988. price varies.
Published by: (Istituto di Storia dell'Arte), Universita degli Studi di Parma, Piazzale della Pace, 7 A, Parma, PR 43100, Italy. TEL 0521-283089, FAX 0521-207125.

QUICK & EASY PAINTING. see *HOBBIES*

709 CAN ISSN 0315-9906
N1
R A C A R. (Revue d'Art Canadienne - Canadian Art Review) Text in English, French. 1974. s-a. CND 35 domestic; USD 35 foreign (effective 2005). bk.rev. bibl.; illus. back issues avail.; reprints avail. **Document type:** *Academic/Scholarly.*
Related titles: Microfilm ed.: 1974 (from MML).
Indexed: ABM, AIAP, ASCA, AmH&L, ArtHuCI, ArtInd, BHA, CBCARef, CBPI, CPerI, CurCont, HistAb.
—BLDSC (7225.872000). **CCC.**

Published by: Association d'Art des Universites du Canada, Department of History in Art, University of Victoria, Box 1700, Victoria, BC V8W 2Y2, Canada. bwinters@finearts.uvic.ca, http://www.uaac-aauc.com/racar/racar.html. Ed. Barbara Winters. Circ: 900.

700 GBR ISSN 0956-9332
R A MAGAZINE. (Royal Academy) Text in English. 1983. q. GBP 20 in Europe; GBP 28 elsewhere (effective 2004).
Indexed: ABM.
—BLDSC (7225.605000).
Published by: Royal Academy of Arts, Burlington House, Piccadilly, London, W1J 0BD, United Kingdom. TEL 44-20-7300-8000, http://195.172.125.151. Ed. Sarah Greenberg TEL 44-20-7300-5826.

THE R B S GAZETTE. (Rubber Band Society) see *LITERATURE*

707 338 381 GBR ISSN 0958-0433
T1
➤ **R S A JOURNAL.** Text in English. 1852. q. GBP 60 in the European Union; GBP 70 elsewhere (effective 1999). adv. charts; illus. index. reprint service avail. from PQC. **Document type:** *Proceedings, Academic/Scholarly.* **Description:** Proceedings of the Royal Society for the Encouragement of Arts, Manufactures and Commerce. Editorial includes RSA lectures, reports on the RSA Programe of work, news and reviews of exhibitions, books etc. The main fields of interest are: business and industry, design and technology, eduation,the arts and the environment.
Formerly: Royal Society of Arts. Journal (0035-9114)
Related titles: Microfiche ed.: (from BHP); Microfilm ed.: (from PMC, PQC).
Indexed: ADPA, AIAP, API, BHA, BldManAb, BrArAb, BrCerAb, BrHumI, BrTechI, ChemAb, DAAI, DIP, FCA, HerbAb, IBR, IBRH, IBZ, IMMAb, M&MA, MLA-IB, PCI, RASB, RHEA, RICS, RILM, RRTA, SPPI, WAE&RSA.
—BLDSC (8036.704200), CISTI, IE, Infotrieve, ingenta, Linda Hall. **CCC.**
Published by: Royal Society for the Encouragement of Arts Manufactures and Commerce, Royal Society For The Encouragement Of Arts, 8 John Adam St, London, WC2N 6EZ, United Kingdom. TEL 44-20-7930-5115, FAX 44-20-7839-7831, editor@rsajournal.co.uk, http://www.cs.mdx.ac.uk/rsa/. Ed., R&P Celia Joicey. Adv. contact Jackie Lea. Circ: 22,000 (paid).

➤ **R S V P: THE DIRECTORY OF ILLUSTRATION AND DESIGN.** see *BUSINESS AND ECONOMICS—Trade And Industrial Directories*

790.2 700.74 NLD
R U I T MAGAZINE. Text in Dutch. 1972. 10/yr. USD 30; free combined subscription per issue (effective 1999). adv. illus. 32 p./no. 6 cols./p.; **Document type:** *Consumer.* **Description:** Covers what is going on in theaters, concert halls, galleries, and museums.
Formerly (until 1997): Magazijn: Uitgaan in Rotterdam (0167-9813)
Published by: V V V Rotterdam, Dienst Recreatie Rotterdam, Postbus 21550, Rotterdam, 3001 AN, Netherlands. TEL 31-10-402-3253, FAX 31-10-413-0124. Ed. Helmut de Hoogh. Adv. contact Ad Kleingeld. Circ: 50,000.

RABENFLUG; Literatur - Kunst - Geschichte. see *LITERATURE*

700 800 851 ITA
RADAR - SEI; rivista mensile di attualita-arte-cultura. Text in Italian. 1973. m. EUR 15.49 (effective 2004). adv. bk.rev. back issues avail. **Document type:** *Magazine, Consumer.*
Published by: Organizzazione "X" di Armando Rositani, Corso Cavour, 113, Bari, BA 70121, Italy. TEL 39-80-5214363, FAX 39-80-5214363. Ed. Armando Rositani. Adv. contact Mariuccia Verrone. Circ: 6,000.

706 USA ISSN 0886-7771
NX510.C2
RADIUS (SAN FRANCISCO)✶ ; resources for local arts. Text in English. 1985. bi-m. USD 30. adv. bk.rev. back issues avail. **Document type:** *Trade.* **Description:** Presents information for funding and services as well as programs for local arts groups.
Published by: California Assembly of Local Arts Agencies, 693 Sutter St, 3rd Fl, San Francisco, CA 94102-1023. TEL 415-979-2345, FAX 415-394-5000. Ed. Ken Larsen. Circ: 2,000.

700 USA
RAMBLES; a cultural arts magazine. Text in English. 1999. irreg.
Media: Online - full text.
Address: feedback@rambles.net, http://www.rambles.net/. Ed., Pub. Tom Knapp.

700 FRA ISSN 1276-6267
RAMDAM. Text in French. 1996. bi-m. illus. **Description:** Covers the visual, literary, musical, and dramatic arts in southern France.
Address: 6 Place Roguet, Toulouse, 31300, France. TEL 33-5-62485252, ramdam@internetclub.fr, http://www.ramdam.presse.fr. Ed. Pierre Combes.

750 800 780 CAN ISSN 0834-3551
NX1
RAMPIKE MAGAZINE. Text in English, French. 1979. s-a. CND 16 domestic to individuals; USD 18 foreign to individuals; CND 18 domestic to institutions; CND 8 newsstand/cover (effective 2003). adv. cum.index: 1979-1984. back issues avail. **Document type:** *Magazine, Academic/Scholarly.* **Description:** Thematic art and writing journal featuring select international talent.
Published by: (Ontario Arts Council/Conseil des Arts de l'Ontario), Rampike, 81 Thorneloe Cres., Sault-st. Marie, ON P6A 4J4, Canada. TEL 705-949-6498, jirgens@thunderbird.auc.on.ca, http://www.auc.on.ca. Ed. Karl E Jirgens. Circ: 2,000.

RASKRASKI, KOTORYE UCHAT. see *CHILDREN AND YOUTH—For*

700 GBR ISSN 0955-1182
CODEN: TIMUEH
➤ **RAW VISION**; international journal of intuitive and visionary art, outsider art and contemporary folk art. Text in English. 1989. 4/yr. GBP 23 domestic to individuals; GBP 30, EUR 44 in Europe to individuals; USD 74 in United States to individuals; GBP 33 elsewhere to individuals; GBP 33 domestic to institutions; GBP 40, EUR 64 in Europe to institutions; USD 59 in United States to institutions; GBP 43 elsewhere to institutions (effective 2003). adv. bk.rev. 80 p./no.; back issues avail. **Document type:** *Magazine, Academic/Scholarly.* **Description:** Coverage of outsider art subjects from all around the world.
Indexed: ABM, AIAP, ArtInd, BHA, IBR, IBZ.
Published by: Raw Vision Ltd., 42 Llanvanor Rd, London, NW2 2AP, United Kingdom. TEL 44-1923-856644, FAX 44-1923-859897, info@rawvision.com, http://www.rawvision.com. Ed., Pub. John Maizels. R&P Julia Duckett. Adv. contact Maggie Jackman. Circ: 9,000 (paid and controlled). **Subscr. addr. in France:** Raw Vision, 37 rue de Gergovie, Paris, France. TEL 40-44-9646; **Subscr. addr. in US:** Raw Vision, 163 Amsterdam Ave, #203, New York, NY 10023-5001. TEL 212-714-8381, FAX 212-724-4441.

700 780 USA
RE-SOUNDINGS. Text in English. irreg. **Document type:** *Bulletin.* **Description:** Creates an environment in which scholars and artists can create and discuss texts, sharing and building commentary in a variety of media, integrating sound and graphics as well as written materials.
Media: Online - full text.
Address: resound@marauder.millersv.edu, http://www.millersv.edu/~resound/.

700 ESP ISSN 1133-0341
REAL ACADEMIA CATALANA DE BELLES ARTS SAN JORDI. BUTLLETI. Text in Catalan, Spanish. 1986. a.
Indexed: RILM.
—CINDOC.
Published by: Reial Academia Catalana de Belles Arts de Sant Jordi, Consolat de Mar, 2-4, Casa Llotja de Mar, Barcelona, 08003, Spain. TEL 34-93-3192432, FAX 34-93-3190216, http://www.ba-stjordi.org/. Ed. Eduard Ripoll i Perello.

730 929.82 USA ISSN 1069-1855
RECOGNITION REVIEW. Text in English. 1979. m. free to members; USD 5.50 per issue (effective 2001). adv. software rev.; video rev. charts; tr.lit. back issues avail. **Document type:** *Trade.* **Description:** Presents general business articles and industry-specific process articles to retailers and suppliers in the awards industry.
Former titles (until 1993): T D M A Today; Trophy Dealer; T D M A Newsletter (1063-8261)
Published by: Awards and Recognition Association (A R A), 4700 W Lake Ave, Glenview, IL 60025. TEL 847-375-4800, FAX 847-375-6309, dbergeson@amtec.com, http://www.ara.org. Ed. Joe Agnew. R&P Stacy MacTaggert. Adv. contact Lynn Walsh. B&W page USD 1,240, color page USD 1,790; trim 10.88 x 8.25. Circ: 8,000 (paid).

720 ITA
RECUPERO E CONSERVAZIONE. Text in Italian. 1994. bi-m. EUR 38 (effective 2005). adv. **Document type:** *Magazine, Trade.*
Published by: De Lettera Editore, Via Tabino 25, Milan, MI 20131, Italy. http://www.delettera.it. Ed. Fiorino Ivan de Lettera.

RED BASS. see *LITERARY AND POLITICAL REVIEWS*

RED MAGAZINE. see *MUSIC*

700 DEU
REIHE KUNSTGESCHICHTE. Text in German. 1979. irreg., latest vol.82, 2004. price varies. **Document type:** *Monographic series, Academic/Scholarly.*
Published by: Herbert Utz Verlag GmbH, Zieblandstr 7, Munich, 80799, Germany. TEL 49-89-27779100, FAX 49-89-27779101, utz@utzverlag.com, http://www.utzverlag.de.

RELIGION AND THE ARTS. see *RELIGIONS AND THEOLOGY*

RENAISSANCE QUARTERLY. see *LITERATURE*

700 DEU
RENOVATIO IMPERII; Zeitschrift fuer Tradition, Kunst und geistige Ueberlieferung. Text in German. 4/yr. EUR 30; EUR 8 newsstand/cover (effective 2003). **Document type:** *Journal, Academic/Scholarly.*
Published by: Renovatio Verlag, Postfach 120518, Heidelberg, 69067, Germany. renovatio@t-online.de, http://www.renovatio-verlag.de.

700 FRA ISSN 0761-4241
REPERES (PARIS, 1947); cahiers d'art contemporain. Text in French. 1947. irreg., latest vol.114, 2001. price varies. illus.
Formerly (until 1982): Derriere le Miroir (0011-9113)
Indexed: ABM, BHA.
Published by: Galerie Lelong, 13 rue de Teheran, Paris, 75008, France. TEL 33-1-45-63-13-19, FAX 33-1-42-89-34-33, lelong.editions@wanadoo.fr. Ed. Daniel Lelong.

RES; anthropology and aesthetics. see *ARCHAEOLOGY*

700 800 ESP ISSN 1578-9926
RESENA. Text in Spanish. 1964. 11/yr. EUR 43 domestic; EUR 73 in Europe; EUR 85 in Latin America and Africa; EUR 86 in US & Canada; EUR 109 elsewhere (effective 2003). adv. cum.index: 1964-1973. 48 p./no.; back issues avail. **Document type:** *Journal, Academic/Scholarly.* **Description:** Critiques plastic arts, cinema, television, theater, music, fiction and poetry.
Formerly (until 2001): Resena de Literatura, Arte y Espectaculos (0080-1763)
Indexed: RASB.
Published by: Compania de Jesus, Centro Loyola de Estudios y Comunicacion Social, Pablo Aranda 3, Madrid, 28006, Spain. TEL 34-91-5624930, FAX 34-91-5634073, http://www.jesuitas.es. Ed., R&P Luis Urbez. Adv. contact Carmen Gonzalez. B&W page EUR 601.01, color page EUR 751.27; 208 x 269. Circ: 3,000. **Dist. by:** Asociacion de Revistas Culturales de Espana. info@arce.es, http://www.arce.es.

700 USA
RESOUNDINGS. Text in English. 1996. s-a.
Media: Online - full content.
Published by: Millersville University, Dept. of English, Millersville, PA 17551. http://marauder.millersville.edu/~resound/. Ed. Bonnie Duncan.

700 USA ISSN 1550-8420
N6512.7
RESOURCE LIBRARY. Text in English. 1997. irreg. free (effective 2005). **Document type:** *Journal, Academic/Scholarly.* **Description:** Devoted to American representational art, including aspects of both a scholarly journal and a popular magazine.
Formerly (until 2004): Resource Library Magazine
Media: Online - full text.
Published by: Traditional Fine Arts Organization, Inc., PMB 392, 8502 East Chapman Ave, Orange, CA 92869-2461, http://tfaoi.org/resourc.htm, http://www.tfaoi.com.

700 720 COL ISSN 0121-5264
RESTAURACION HOY. Text in Spanish. 1986. s-a. USD 40 for 2 yrs.. bk.rev. **Document type:** *Academic/Scholarly.*
Published by: (Instituto Colombiano de Cultura), Centro Nacional de Restauracion, Calle 9 no. 8-31, Bogota, CUND, Colombia. TEL 57-1-284-8595, FAX 57-1-282-8759. Ed. Beatriz Restrepo. Circ: 1,000.

700 ESP ISSN 1134-4571
RESTAURACION Y REHABILITACION. Variant title: R & R. Text in Spanish. 1994. bi-m. back issues avail.
—CINDOC.
Published by: Editorial America Iberica, Miguel Yuste 33bis, Madrid, 28037, Spain. TEL 34-91-3277950, FAX 34-91-3044746, http://www.eai.es/. Ed. Isabel Martin.

751.6 DEU ISSN 0933-4017
ND1259
RESTAURO; Zeitschrift fuer Kunsttechniken, Restaurierung und Museumsfragen. Text in German. 8/yr. EUR 116.40 domestic; EUR 122.40 foreign; EUR 92.40 domestic to students; EUR 98.40 foreign to students; EUR 16 newsstand/cover (effective 2004). adv. bk.rev. illus. back issues avail. **Document type:** *Magazine, Trade.*
Formerly (until 1988): Maltechnik-Restauro (0025-1445)
Indexed: A&ATA, AIAP, BHA, DIP, IBR, IBZ, RASB, RILM, RefZh.
—IE, Infotrieve. **CCC.**
Published by: Callwey Verlag, Streitfeldstr 35, Munich, 81673, Germany. TEL 49-89-4360050, FAX 49-89-436005113, info@restauro.de, a.hagenkord@callwey.de, http://www.restauro.de, http://www.callwey.de. Ed. Ulrike Besch. Adv. contact Beate Muck. B&W page EUR 1,130, color page EUR 2,330. Circ: 5,281 (paid).

700 CAN ISSN 1496-4554
THE REVIEW; a monthly arts and entertainment e-zine. Text in English, Spanish. 1997. m. free. music rev.; play rev. back issues avail. **Document type:** *Consumer.* **Description:** Covers entertainment, theater, opera, symphonic and chamber music, and art exhibitions in Vancouver.
Media: Online - full text.

Published by: Farolan Communications Ltd., 11816 88th Ave, Unite 218, Delta, BC V4C 3C5, Canada. TEL 604-599-4527, FAX 604-599-4527, efaro26164@aol.com, http://members.aol.com/efaro26164/review.html. Ed., Pub. Ed Farolan.

REVIEW OF SOUTHERN AFRICAN STUDIES; a multidisplinary journal of arts, social and behavioural sciences. see *SOCIAL SCIENCES: COMPREHENSIVE WORKS*

REVISTA CAMPINENSE DE CULTURA. see *LITERATURE*

REVISTA COMUNICACOES E ARTES. see *SOCIOLOGY*

700 ARG ISSN 0327-3687
REVISTA DE ESTETICA/AESTHETICS MAGAZINE. Text in English, Spanish. 1983. biennial. USD 15.
Related titles: Microform ed.
Published by: Centro de Arte y Comunicacion, Escuela de Altos Estudios/Center of Art and Communication, Elpidio Gonzalez, 4070, Capital Federal, Buenos Aires 1407, Argentina. TEL 54-1-5674594, FAX 54-1-5663867, TELEX 18660 DELPHI AR. Ed. Jorge Glusberg. Circ: 3,000.

REVISTA DO PATRIMONIO. see *HISTORY—History Of North And South America*

781.68 BRA
REVISTA GOIANA DE ARTES. Text in Portuguese. a. BRL 4 (effective 1998). **Document type:** *Academic/Scholarly.*
Published by: Universidade Federal de Goias, Caixa Postal 254, Goiania, GO 74001-970, Brazil. http://www.ufg.br.

700 BEL ISSN 0035-077X
N2
REVUE BELGE D'ARCHEOLOGIE ET D'HISTOIRE DE L'ART/BELGISCH TIJDSCHRIFT VOOR OUDHEIDKUNDE EN KUNSTGESHIEDENIS. Text in French. 1931. a. EUR 50 (effective 2003). bk.rev. bibl.; illus. cum.index: vols.1-59, 1931-1990. reprints avail. **Document type:** *Bulletin, Academic/Scholarly.* **Description:** Publishes topics relating to archaeology and art history, with particular emphasis on Belgium and Belgian art.
Formed by the merger of (1897-1929): Academie Royale d'Archeologie de Belgique. Annales (0776-0035); (1927-1930): Academie Royale d'Archeologie de Belgique. Bulletin (0776-0051); Which was formerly (until 1926): Academie d'Archeologie de Belgique. Annales (0776-0027); (until 1847): Academie d'Archeologie de Belgique. Bulletin et Annales (0776-0019)
Indexed: A&ATA, ABM, AIAP, ArtInd, BHA, DIP, IBR, IBZ, NumL, PCI, RASB, RILM.
Published by: Academie Royale d'Archeologie de Belgique/Koninklijke Academie voor Oudheidkunde van Belgie, 10 Parc du Cinquantenaire, Brussels, 1000, Belgium. Ed. C Dumortier. Circ: 400.

LA REVUE DE BELLES-LETTRES. see *LITERARY AND POLITICAL REVIEWS*

700 FRA ISSN 0035-1326
N2
REVUE DE L'ART. Text in French; Summaries in English, German. 1968. q. bk.rev. abstr.; charts; illus. reprints avail. **Document type:** *Magazine, Consumer.* **Description:** Presents for reflection and criticism those activities, proceedings and interpretations roused or being roused by art and its history as well as works and their creators throughout time and civilization.
Indexed: A&ATA, ABM, AIAP, ASCA, ArtHuCI, ArtInd, BHA, CurCont, DIP, IBR, IBZ, RASB, RILM.
—BLDSC (7891.180000), IE, Infotrieve, ingenta. **CCC.**
Published by: Ophrys, 5 allee du Torrent, Gap, 05000, France. TEL 33-4-92538572, FAX 33-4-92517865, editions.ophrys@ophrys.fr, http://www.ophrys.fr.

REVUE D'ESTHETIQUE. see *PHILOSOPHY*

REVUE D'HISTOIRE ET D'ART DE LA BRIE ET DU PAYS DE MEAUX. see *HISTORY—History Of Europe*

REVUE HISTORIQUE DU CENTRE OUEST. see *HISTORY—History Of Europe*

700 960 FRA ISSN 1157-4127
NX588.75
REVUE NOIRE; art contemporain africain - African contemporary art. Text in English, French. 1991. q. adv. bk.rev. illus. Index. back issues avail.; reprints avail.
Indexed: ABM, ArtInd, CCA.
Address: 8 rue Cels, Paris, 75014, France. TEL 33-1-43209200, FAX 33-1-43229260, http://www.revuenoire.com. Eds. N'Gone Fall, Simon Njami. Pub. Jean Loup Pivin. R&P Pascal Martin Saint Leon. Adv. contact Gwenaele Guigon.

709 ROM ISSN 0556-8080
REVUE ROUMAINE D'HISTOIRE DE L'ART. SERIE BEAUX-ARTS. Text in Romanian. 1963. a. ROL 50, USD 45.
Formerly: Revue Roumaine de l'Histoire de l'Art. Serie Arts Plastiques (0080-262X)
Related titles: Online - full text ed.
Indexed: AIAP, BHA, NumL, RASB.
—KNAW.
Published by: (Academia Romana, Institutul de Istoria Artei George Oprescu), Editura Academiei Romane/Publishing House of the Romanian Academy, Calea 13 Septembrie 13, Sector 5, Bucharest, 76117, Romania. TEL 40-21-4119008, FAX 40-21-4103983, edacad@ear.ro. Ed. Remus Niculescu. **Dist. by:** Rodipet S.A., Piata Presei Libere 1, sector 1, PO Box 33-57, Bucharest 3, Romania. TEL 40-21-2224126, 40-21-2226407, rodipet@rodipet.ro.

RICEPAPER. see *LITERATURE*

750 ITA
RICERCHE SUL '600 NAPOLETANO. Text in Italian. 1982. a.
Indexed: BHA.
Published by: Electa Napoli, Via Francesco Caracciolo 13, Naples, NA 80122, Italy. info@ena.it, http://www.ena.it. Ed. Giuseppe Devito. Circ: 1,000.

779.28 USA
RICHARDSON. Text in English. 2000. irreg. USD 37 newsstand/cover (effective 2002). **Document type:** *Magazine, Consumer.*
Address: 22 Prince St, Ste 108, New York, NY 10012. TEL 212-219-9198, http://www.richardsonmag.com/. Ed. Andrew Richardson. **Dist. by:** Oedious, LLC.

709.4 NLD ISSN 0165-9510
N2460
RIJKSMUSEUM. BULLETIN. Key Title: Bulletin van het Rijksmuseum. Text in Dutch; Summaries in English. 1953. q. EUR 21 domestic; EUR 25 foreign; EUR 7 newsstand/cover (effective 2005). bk.rev. illus. index. reprints avail. **Document type:** *Bulletin.*
Former titles: Netherlands. Rijksmuseum Amsterdam. Bulletin (0569-9665); Netherlands. Rijksmuseum. Bulletin (0028-3002)
Indexed: ABM, AIAP, ArtInd, BHA, DIP, IBR, IBZ.
—IE, Infotrieve.
Published by: Waanders Uitgevers, Postbus 1129, Zwolle, 8001 BC, Netherlands. TEL 31-38-4673400, FAX 31-38-4673401, info@waanders.nl, http://www.waanders.nl. **Co-sponsor:** Prepared by: Rijksmuseum, Amsterdam.

RIJKSMUSEUMKUNSTKRANT. see *MUSEUMS AND ART GALLERIES*

700 ISR
RIMONIM. Text in Hebrew. 1983. irreg., latest vol.7, 1999. USD 40 (effective 2001). **Document type:** *Bulletin.* **Description:** Studies forms and styles of Jewish art through the ages.
Published by: Society for Jewish Art, P O Box 4262, Jerusalem, 91042, Israel. TEL 972-2-6586605, FAX 972-2-6586672, cja@vms.huji.ac.il, http://www.hum.huji.ac.il/cja/. Ed. Shalom Zabar. Circ: 1,000.

700 BRA
RIO ARTES. Text in Portuguese. 1991. m. BRL 20,000.
Formerly (until 1992): Rio Artes e Literatura
Address: Rua Rumania 14, Laranjeiras, RJ 22240, Brazil. TEL 285-5344. Ed. Wilson Coutinho.

RIVER STYX. see *LITERARY AND POLITICAL REVIEWS*

700 811 USA
RIVET; discover. inquire. repeat. Text in English. 2001. q. USD 16; USD 5 newsstand/cover (effective 2005).
Published by: The Shunpike Arts Collective, 3518 Fremont Ave., N, P O Box 18, Seattle, WA 98103. TEL 206-795-4388, info@theshunpike.org, http://www.rivetmagazine.org, http://www.theshunpike.org. Ed. Leah Baltus.

RIVISTA DALMATICA. see *HISTORY—History Of Europe*

701 ITA ISSN 0393-9898
RIVISTA DI PSICOLOGIA DELL'ARTE. Text in Italian. 1979. a. USD 30 to individuals; USD 50 to institutions (effective 2004). adv. bk.rev. back issues avail. **Document type:** *Journal, Academic/Scholarly.* **Description:** Publishes experimental and theoretical studies in the field of psychology of art and empirical aesthetics.
Indexed: ABM, PsycholAb, e-psyche.
Address: Via dei Pianellari 20, Rome, 00186, Italy. TEL 39-06-68307590, FAX 39-06-6867824, sergio.lombardo@iol.it. Ed., R&P Sergio Lombardo. Circ: 3,000.

720.22 ITA ISSN 1126-4772
RIVISTA DI STORIA DELLA MINIATURA. Text in Italian. 1988. a. EUR 124 domestic; EUR 150 foreign (effective 2004).
Supersedes (in 1996): Miniatura
Published by: (Societa Internazionale di Studi si Storia della Miniatura), Centro Di, Lungarno Serristori 35, Florence, FI 50125, Italy. TEL 39-055-2342668, FAX 39-055-2342667, centrodi@centrodi.it, http://www.centrodi.it.

700 930.1 ITA
RIVISTA INGAUNA E INTEMELIA. Text in Italian. 1946. a. EUR 30 (effective 2004). index. back issues avail. **Document type:** *Journal, Academic/Scholarly.* **Description:** Covers art, handicrafts, archaeology, history and architecture of west of Liguria.
Indexed: BHA.
Published by: Istituto Internazionale di Studi Liguri/International Institute of Ligurian Studies, Via Romana 39, Bordighera, IM 18012, Italy. TEL 39-0184-263601, FAX 39-0184-266421, iisl@istitutostudi.191.it, http://www.iisl.it. Circ: 2,000.

700 NZL
ROBERT MCDOUGALL ART GALLERY. BULLETIN. Text in English. q. NZD 12 domestic; NZD 4 newsstand/cover domestic (effective 2002). back issues avail. **Document type:** *Journal, Consumer.*
Published by: Public Art Museum of Christchurch, Robert McDougall Art Gallery, Botanic Gardens, Rolleston Ave, PO Box 2626, Christchurch, New Zealand. TEL 64-3-941-7970, FAX 64-3-941-7987, art.gallery@ccc.govt.nz, http://www.mcdougall.org.nz/Bulletin/.

ROCK ART RESEARCH. see *ANTHROPOLOGY*

700 USA
ROCKHURST REVIEW; a fine arts journal. Text in English. 1988. a. **Description:** Presents poetry, prose, photography and drawings.
Published by: Rockhurst College, 1100 Rockhurst Rd, Kansas City, MO 64110-2561. Ed. Patricia Cleary Miller.

709 POL ISSN 0080-3472
N9.6
➤ **ROCZNIK HISTORII SZTUKI.** Text in Polish; Summaries in English, French, German, Italian. 1956. a., latest 2002, vol.27. PLZ 45 domestic; USD 29 foreign (effective 2003). illus. 270 p./no. 1 cols./p.; back issues avail. **Document type:** *Yearbook, Academic/Scholarly.* **Description:** Devoted to the past and contemporary history of art and architecture in Poland and Europe.
Indexed: AIAP, BHA, DIP, IBR, IBZ, RASB.
Published by: (Polska Akademia Nauk, Komitet Nauk o Sztuce), Wydawnictwo Neriton, Rynek Starego Miasta 29/31, Warsaw, 00-272, Poland. TEL 48-22-8310261, FAX 48-22-8310261, neriton@ihpan.edu.pl, http://www.neriton.apnet.pl. Ed. Andrzej Grzybkowski. Pub., R&P Andrzej Wronski TEL 48-22-8310061. Circ: 450. **Co-sponsor:** Komitet Badan Naukowych/Committee of Scientific Research.

700 780 792 CAN
RODMAN HALL BULLETIN. Text in English. 1970. m. free. back issues avail. **Document type:** *Bulletin.*
Published by: Rodman Hall Arts Centre, 109 St Paul Crescent, St Catharines, ON L2S 1M3, Canada. TEL 416-684-2925, FAX 416-682-2950. Circ: 1,500.

709 DEU ISSN 0175-9434
ROEMISCHE FORSCHUNGEN DER BIBLIOTHECA HERTZIANA. Text in German. 1912. irreg. **Document type:** *Monographic series, Academic/Scholarly.*
Published by: Hirmer Verlag, Nymphenburger Str 84, Munich, 80636, Germany. TEL 49-89-1215160, info@weltkunstverlag.de, http://www.weltkunstverlag.de.

741.5 800 NGA
ROMANCE OF LIFE. Text in English. 1989. irreg. NGN 3. **Document type:** *Consumer.*
Published by: Daily Times of Nigeria Ltd., Publications Division, New Isheri Rd., PMB 21340, Ikeja, Agidingbi, Lagos, Nigeria. TEL 234-64-900850-9, FAX 234-64-21333. Ed. David Ajoboye.

ROMANIA LITERARA. see *LITERATURE*

729.5 733 DNK ISSN 0107-2366
NK1285
ROMANSKE STENARBEJDER. Text in Danish. 1981. irreg., latest vol.5, 2003. price varies. illus. back issues avail. **Document type:** *Monographic series, Academic/Scholarly.* **Description:** Publishes articles on stone art in Danish Romanesque churches.
Published by: Forlaget Hikuin, Moesgaard, Hoejbjerg, 8270, Denmark. TEL 45-89-424603, 45-86-272443, henvendelser@hikuin.dk, http://www.hikuin.dk/romanske_stenarbejder.asp. Ed., Pub. Jens Vellev.

ROMANTIC RUSSIA. see *LITERATURE*

850 ITA
ROMANTICISMO E DINTORNI. Text in Italian. 1984. irreg., latest vol.7, 1998. price varies. adv. **Document type:** *Monographic series.*
Published by: Liguori Editore srl, Via Posillipo 394, Naples, 80123, Italy. TEL 39-81-7206111, FAX 39-81-7206244, http://www.liguori.it. Pub. Guido Liguori. Adv. contact Maria Liguori.

570 700 CAN ISSN 0035-8495
AM101
ROTUNDA. Text in English. 1968. 3/yr. USD 12.84 domestic; CND 18 foreign; CND 4.25 newsstand/cover (effective 2000). adv. bk.rev. charts; illus.; stat. index. **Document type:** *Consumer.* **Description:** Reports the latest information on the endeavours of humankind and the ways of nature, both past and present.
Related titles: Microfiche ed.: (from MML); Microform ed.: (from MML); Online - full text ed.: (from Gale Group, Micromedia ProQuest).

Indexed: AmH&L, BHA, CBCARef, CBPI, CPerI, DAAI, HistAb, RILM.
Published by: Royal Ontario Museum, Publications Dept, 100 Queen s Park, Toronto, ON M5S 2C6, Canada. TEL 416-586-5590, FAX 416-586-5887, sandras@rom.on.ca, http://www.rom.on.ca/ebuff/aboutarc.htm. Ed., R&P Sandra Shaul. Circ: 25,000.

750 GBR
ROYAL INSTITUTE OF OIL PAINTERS. EXHIBITION CATALOGUE. Text in English. a. GBP 2 (effective 2001). **Document type:** *Catalog.*
Published by: (Royal Institute of Oil Painters), Federation of British Artists, 17 Carlton House Terr, London, SW1Y 5BD, United Kingdom. TEL 44-20-7930-6844, FAX 44-20-7839-7830, http://www.mallgalleries.org.uk.

706 GBR
ROYAL SOCIETY OF BRITISH ARTISTS. PUBLICATION. Text in English. 1890. a. GBP 2 (effective 2001). **Document type:** *Catalog, Trade.*
Published by: (Royal Society of British Artists), Federation of British Artists, 17 Carlton House Terr, London, SW1Y 5BD, United Kingdom. TEL 44-20-7930-6844, FAX 44-20-7839-7830, http://www.mallgalleries.org.uk. Circ: 5,000.

706 GBR
ROYAL SOCIETY OF MARINE ARTISTS. EXHIBITION CATALOGUE. Text in English. 1946. a. GBP 2 (effective 2001). **Document type:** *Catalog.*
Published by: (Royal Society of Marine Artists), Federation of British Artists, 17 Carlton House Terr, London, SW1Y 5BD, United Kingdom. TEL 44-20-7930-6844, FAX 44-20-7839-7830, http://www.mallgalleries.org.uk.

700 GBR
ROYAL SOCIETY OF MINIATURE PAINTERS, SCULPTORS AND GRAVERS. PUBLICATION. Text in English. 1895. a. GBP 39.50. **Document type:** *Catalog.*
Published by: Royal Society of Miniature Painters, Sculptors and Gravers, 1 Knapp Cottages, Wyke, Gillingham, Dorset SP8 4NQ, United Kingdom. TEL 44-1747-825718. Ed., R&P Suzanne Lucas.

757 GBR
ROYAL SOCIETY OF PORTRAIT PAINTERS. PUBLICATION. Text in English. 1981. a. GBP 6 (effective 2001). **Document type:** *Catalog, Trade.*
Published by: (Royal Society of Portrait Painters), Federation of British Artists, 17 Carlton House Terr, London, SW1Y 5BD, United Kingdom. TEL 44-20-7930-6844, FAX 44-20-7839-7830, http://www.mallgalleries.org.uk.

741.5 USA
RUSS COCHRAN NEWSLETTER. Text in English. 1973. s-a. USD 1. **Document type:** *Newsletter.* **Description:** Updates on the progress of reprinting the complete EC comic book line. Introduces new products in the comic line.
Published by: Russ Cochran Publisher, Ltd., PO Box 469, W. Plains, MO 65775-0469. TEL 417-256-2224, FAX 417-256-5555. Ed. Russ Cochran. Circ: 8,000.

709 USA ISSN 0194-049X
N1
RUTGERS ART REVIEW; the journal of graduate research in art history. Text in English. 1980. a. USD 9. **Document type:** *Journal, Academic/Scholarly.* **Description:** Presents original research by current graduate students in the history of art, architecture, and related fields.
Indexed: ABM, AIAP, AmH&L, BHA, HistAb.
—CCC.
Published by: Rutgers, the State University of New Jersey, Department of Art History, Voorhees Hall, 71 Hamilton St, New Brunswick, NJ 08901-1248. TEL 732-932-7041 ext 27, http://arthistory.rutgers.edu/rar/rar.htm. Eds. David Boffa, Kandice Rawlings, Yelena Kalinsky.

S A C NEWSMONTHLY; national news and listings of art & craft shows. (Southern Art and Crafts) see *ARTS AND HANDICRAFTS*

S P N E A NEWS. see *HISTORY*

751.6 GBR ISSN 0959-2369
➤ **S S C R JOURNAL**; promotes the conservation and restoration of historic and artistic objects. Text in English. 1980. q. GBP 38 domestic to individuals; GBP 41 elsewhere to individuals; GBP 75 domestic to institutions; GBP 80 elsewhere to institutions; GBP 20 domestic to students; GBP 25 elsewhere to students (effective 2000); includes membership. adv. bk.rev. **Document type:** *Academic/Scholarly.* **Description:** Discusses the projects and techniques of professional conservators.
Former titles (until 1990): Scottish Society for Conservation and Restoration. Bulletin (0264-9039); (until 1983): Scottish Society for Conservation and Restoration. Newsletter (0261-703X); (until 1980): Scottish Society for the Conservation and Restoration of Historic and Artistic Works. Newsletter (0260-5597); (until 1979): S S C R Newsletter
Indexed: A&ATA.
Published by: Scottish Society for Conservation and Restoration, The Glasite Meeting House, 33 Barony St, Edinburgh, EH3 6NX, United Kingdom. TEL 44-131-556-8417, FAX 44-131-557-5977, admin@sscr.demon.co.uk, http://www.sscr.demon.co.uk, http://www.sscr.demon.co.uk/. Ed. Jane Hutchison. R&P, Adv. contact Elaine Martay. Circ: 400.

➤ **SABAZIA.** see *HISTORY*

709 ITA ISSN 0392-713X
N4
SAGGI E MEMORIE DI STORIA DELL'ARTE. Text in Italian. 1957. irreg., latest vol.23, 1999. price varies. **Document type:** *Monographic series, Academic/Scholarly.*
Indexed: AIAP, BHA.
Published by: (Fondazione Giorgio Cini, Centro di Cultura e Civilta), Casa Editrice Leo S. Olschki, Viuzzo del Pozzetto 8, Florence, 50126, Italy. TEL 39-055-6530684, FAX 39-055-6530214, celso@olschki.it, http://www.olschki.it. Circ: 500.

SAINT ANN'S REVIEW. see *LITERATURE*

700 USA ISSN 0749-6435
SALOME; a journal of the performing arts. Text in English. 1975. q. USD 12. adv. bk.rev.; film rev. **Description:** Interviews, reviews, photo documentation and artwork concerning the performing arts.
Indexed: AIPP.
Published by: Ommation Press, 5548 N Sawyer Ave, Chicago, IL 60625. Ed. Effie Mihopoulos. Circ: 1,000.

SALT E-ZINE. see *MUSIC*

SALT FOR SLUGS; contemporary literature for the random reader. see *MUSIC*

SAMNIUM. see *HISTORY—History Of Europe*

SAMPEL; jong kultuurtijdschrift. see *LITERARY AND POLITICAL REVIEWS*

700 USA ISSN 0581-4766
HV97.S25
SAMUEL H. KRESS FOUNDATION. ANNUAL REPORT. Text in English. 1963. a. **Document type:** *Corporate.* **Description:** Describes the foundation's grant programs in art history, conservation and preservation.
Published by: Samuel H. Kress Foundation, 174 E 80th St, New York, NY 10021. TEL 212-861-4993, FAX 212-628-3146, http://www.shkf.org. R&P Lisa Ackerman. Circ: 2,500.

700 PER ISSN 0254-8151
SAN MARCOS. Text in Spanish. 1947. q. bk.rev. bibl.
Published by: Universidad Nacional Mayor de San Marcos, Direccion de Biblioteca y Publicaciones, Rep. de Chile 295, Of. 508, Lima, Peru. Ed. Juan de Dios Guevara.

700 810 USA
SANDBOX MAGAZINE. Text in English. 2/yr. USD 8 domestic; USD 11 in Canada; USD 17 elsewhere; USD 5 newsstand/cover. **Document type:** *Consumer.* **Description:** Provides a forum for experimentation in the visual arts, performing arts, music and digital arts with particular emphasis on interactive and multi-media work.
Published by: Sandbox Open Arts Inc., PO Box 150098, Brooklyn, NY 11215-0098. sandbox@echonyc.com, http://www.echonyc.com/~sandbox. Ed. Sylvie Myerson. Pubs. Sylvie Myerson, Vidyut Jain.

700 810 USA
SANDBOX WEB-ZINE. Text in English. 2/yr. **Document type:** *Consumer.* **Description:** Presents articles, reviews and interactive art exploiting the creative potential of the World Wide Web.
Media: Online - full text.
Published by: Sandbox Open Arts Inc., PO Box 150098, Brooklyn, NY 11215-0098. sandbox@echonyc.com, http://www.echonyc.com/~sandbox. Ed. Sylvie Myerson.

IL SANTO; rivista francescana di storia dottrina arte. see *RELIGIONS AND THEOLOGY—Roman Catholic*

354 CAN ISSN 0701-6433
NX28.C32
SASKATCHEWAN CENTRE OF THE ARTS. ANNUAL REPORT. Text in English. a. adv. **Document type:** *Corporate.*
Published by: Saskatchewan Centre of the Arts, 200 Lakeshore Dr, Regina, SK S4P 3V7, Canada. TEL 306-584-5050. Adv. contact Louise Yates.

700 CAN
SASKATCHEWAN. DEPARTMENT OF CULTURE AND RECREATION. ANNUAL REPORT✶. Text in English. 1972. a. free. illus. **Document type:** *Government.*
Formerly: Saskatchewan. Department of Culture and Youth. Annual Report (0317-4344)
Published by: Department of Municipal Affairs, Culture and Housing, 1855 Victoria Ave 7th Fl, Regina, SK S4P 3V7, Canada. TEL 306-787-5759. Ed. Clay Serby. Circ: 800.

709.9 JAM ISSN 0036-5068
F1601
SAVACOU; a journal of the Caribbean artists movement. Text in English. 1970. irreg. (1-2/yr.). USD 15. adv. bk.rev. bibl.
Indexed: MLA, MLA-IB.
Published by: (Caribbean Artists Movement), Savacou Publications, Mona, PO Box 170, Kingston, 7, Jamaica. Ed. Edward Kamau Brathwaite. Circ: 2,000.

▼ **SCAN**; journal of media arts culture. see *SOCIOLOGY*

709 DNK ISSN 0906-3447
NK1160
➤ **SCANDINAVIAN JOURNAL OF DESIGN HISTORY.** Text in English. 1991. a. DKK 250, GBP 21, EUR 36, USD 31 (effective 2005). bk.rev. cum.index: vols. 1-10. back issues avail. **Document type:** *Academic/Scholarly.*
Related titles: Online - full text ed.: (from H.W. Wilson, O C L C Online Computer Library Center, Inc.).
Indexed: ABM, AmH&L, ArtInd, BHA, DAAI, HistAb.
—BLDSC (8087.505530), IE, ingenta.
Published by: (Danish Museum of Decorative Art), Rhodos A/S, Holtegaard, Hoersholmsvej 17, Humlebaek, 3050, Denmark. TEL 45-32-543020, FAX 45-32-543022, design@rhodos.dk, rhodos@rhodos.dk, www.rhodos.dk, http://www.rhodos.dk. Ed. Mirjam Gelfer-Joergensen.

700 780 CHE ISSN 1016-9415
SCENES MAGAZINE; mensuel suisse d'information culturelle. Text in French. 1986. m. CHF 75; CHF 100 foreign (effective 2000). adv. bk.rev. **Document type:** *Magazine, Consumer.*
Address: Case Postale 129, Geneva 4, 1211, Switzerland. TEL 41-22-3469643. Ed. F Fredenrich. Adv. contact N Bastar. Circ: 5,000.

943 ITA ISSN 0036-6145
DB1
SCHLERN; Zeitschrift fuer Suedtiroler Landeskunde. Text in German. 1920. m. adv. bk.rev. illus. index, cum.index. back issues avail. **Document type:** *Consumer.*
Indexed: BHA, BibInd, DIP, IBR, IBZ, RILM.
Published by: Verlagsanstalt Athesia, Lauben, 41, Postfach 417, Bozen, BZ 39100, Italy. TEL 39-471-925111, FAX 39-471-925599. Ed. Dr. Hans Griessmair. Adv. contact Sonja Scharrer. Circ: 1,600.

SCHOLASTIC ART. see *EDUCATION—Teaching Methods And Curriculum*

700 DEU ISSN 1617-8610
SCHRIFTEN ZUR KUNSTGESCHICHTE. Text in German. 2001. irreg., latest vol.9, 2005. price varies. **Document type:** *Monographic series, Academic/Scholarly.*
Published by: Verlag Dr. Kovac, Arnoldstr 49, Hamburg, 22763, Germany. TEL 49-40-3988800, FAX 49-40-39888055, info@verlagdrkovac.de, http://www.verlagdrkovac.de/8-11.htm.

700 375.001 DEU ISSN 1613-138X
▼ **SCHRIFTEN ZUR KUNSTPAEDAGOGIK UND AESTHETISCHEN ERZIEHUNG.** Text in German. 2004. irreg., latest vol.3, 2005. price varies. **Document type:** *Monographic series, Academic/Scholarly.*
Published by: Verlag Dr. Kovac, Arnoldstr 49, Hamburg, 22763, Germany. TEL 49-40-3988800, FAX 49-40-39888055, info@verlagdrkovac.de, http://www.verlagdrkovac.de/7-20.htm.

700 DEU ISSN 0080-7176
Z5961.G4
SCHRIFTTUM ZUR DEUTSCHEN KUNST. Text in German. 1934; N.S. 1962. irreg., latest vol.63, 1999. price varies. **Document type:** *Monographic series, Bibliography.*
Published by: (Deutscher Verein fuer Kunstwissenschaft e.V.), Deutscher Verlag fuer Kunstwissenschaft GmbH, Jebensstr 2, Berlin, 10623, Germany. TEL 49-30-3139932, FAX 49-30-32303824, dvfk@aol.com, http://www.dvfk-berlin.de.

700 720 CHE ISSN 1016-2879
SCHWEIZER KUNST✶ /ART SUISSE/ARTE SVIZZERA. Text in French, German, Italian. 1972. m. CHF 16. adv. bk.rev. bibl.; illus.
Published by: Gesellschaft Schweizerischer Maler Bildhauer und Architekten, Postfach, Basel, 4007, Switzerland.

751.6 FRA ISSN 0988-3789
SCIENCE ET TECHNOLOGIE DE LA CONSERVATION ET DE LA RESTORATION DES OEUVRES D'ART ET DU PATRIMOINE. Text in French. 1988. s-a.
Indexed: RILM.
Published by: (Etudes et Realisations de la Couleur), E R E C, 68 rue Jean Jaures, Puteaux, 92800, France. TEL 47-73-01-23, FAX 49-00-05-91. Ed. Annik Chauvel. Circ: 5,000.

SCREEN & DISPLAY GRAPHICS. see *PRINTING*

741.6 AUS ISSN 1328-9756
➤ **SCREENING THE PAST.** Text in English. 1997. irreg. bk.rev. **Document type:** *Journal, Academic/Scholarly.* **Description:** Publishes material of interest to historians of visual media, film, and the arts.
Media: Online - full text.

▼ *new title* ➤ *refereed* ✶ *unverified* ◆ *full entry avail.*

Indexed: AmH&L, HistAb.
Published by: La Trobe University, Kingsbury Dr, Bundoora, Melbourne, VIC 3086, Australia. screen@latrobe.edu.au, http://www.latrobe.edu.au/www/screeningthepast. Ed. Peter Hughes.

700 NLD ISSN 0080-8350
SCRIPTA ARTIS MONOGRAPHIA. Text in English, French, German. 1968. irreg. price varies. **Document type:** *Monographic series.*
Published by: Academic Publishers Associated, Postbus 806, Amsterdam, 1000 AV, Netherlands. TEL 31-30-436166, FAX 31-30-420250.

730 USA ISSN 1541-7514
SCULPTURAL PURSUIT. Text in English. 2002. q. USD 28 domestic; USD 38 in Canada; USD 45 elsewhere; USD 8 newsstand/cover (effective 2002). adv.
Published by: Hammer & Pen Productions, LLC, P. O. Box 262283, Highlands Ranch, CO 80163-2283. contactus@sculpturalpursuit.com, http://www.sculpturalpursuit.com. Ed. Nancy DeCamillis. Pub. Diana Dietvorst.

730 USA ISSN 0889-728X
NB1
SCULPTURE. Text in English. 1982. 10/yr. subscr. incld. with membership. adv. bk.rev. illus. reprints avail. **Document type:** *Magazine, Consumer.* **Description:** Features studio visits and interviews with established and emerging artists, profiles, news, exhibition and book reviews, as well as a variety of art-related advertising.
Incorporates (1993-1995): Maquette (1079-8811); Former titles (until Jan. 1987): International Sculpture (0887-5472); (until Apr. 1985): Sculptors International (0730-675X); (until 1981): International Sculpture Center Bulletin (0277-240X); National Sculpture Center Bulletin (0891-1983)
Related titles: Online - full text ed.: (from H.W. Wilson, O C L C Online Computer Library Center, Inc.).
Indexed: ABM, AIAP, ArtInd, BHA.
—BLDSC (8213.295000), IE, ingenta.
Published by: International Sculpture Center, 1529 18th St NW, Washington, DC 20036. TEL 609-689-1051, FAX 609-689-1061, isc@sculpture.org, http://www.sculpture.org/. Ed. Glenn Harper. Adv. contact Amy Blankstein. Circ: 22,000.

730 USA ISSN 0747-5284
NB1
SCULPTURE REVIEW. Text in English. 1951. q. USD 24 domestic; USD 50 foreign (effective 2005). adv. bk.rev. illus. cum.index. back issues avail.; reprint service avail. from PQC. **Document type:** *Consumer.* **Description:** Primary mission is to educate and inform the public of contemporary figurative sculpture. Publishes educational articles, candid interviews, and historical essays in every issue, highlighted by photography. Annual collectors' issue and special features on conservation, reliefs, and the history of sculpture tools.
Former titles: Sculpture (0272-6807); (until 1971): National Sculpture Review (0028-0127)
Related titles: CD-ROM ed.; Microform ed.: (from PQC); Online - full text ed.: (from H.W. Wilson, O C L C Online Computer Library Center, Inc.).
Indexed: AIAP, ASCA, ArtHuCI, ArtInd, BHA, BRI, CBRI, CurCont, DIP, IBR, IBZ, NumL.
—BLDSC (8213.297000), IDS, IE, Infotrieve, ingenta.
Published by: National Sculpture Society, 237 Park Ave, New York, NY 10017-3140. TEL 212-529-1763, FAX 212-260-1732, gp@sculpturereview.com, http://www.sculpturereview.com/. Ed. Giancarlo Biagi. Pub. Stanley Bleifeld. R&P Gwen Pier. Adv. contact Amy Kelly. B&W page USD 1,210; trim 11 x 8.25. Circ: 3,200 (paid).

700 USA
SEATTLE ARTS. Text in English. 1972. q. adv. illus.; stat. **Document type:** *Newsletter, Government.* **Description:** Provides news about the commission's activities and achievements, along with job and volunteer positions available in the arts.
Formerly: Seattle and King County Arts Commission. Newsletter
Published by: City of Seattle Arts Commission, 312 First Ave N, Seattle, WA 98109-4501. TEL 206-684-7306, 206-684-7171, FAX 206-684-7172, 206-684-7306, http://www.pan.ci.seattle.wa.us. Ed. Amy Painter. Circ: 12,000 (paid and free).

SECOND SHIFT. see *WOMEN'S INTERESTS*

700 ESP ISSN 0487-3491
➤ **SEMINARIO DE ARTE ARAGONES.** Text in Spanish. 1945. irreg. EUR 18.03 per issue (effective 2002). adv. **Document type:** *Academic/Scholarly.*
Indexed: AIAP, BHA, PCI.
—CINDOC.
Published by: Institucion Fernando el Catolico, Plaza de Espana 2, Zaragoza, 50071, Spain. TEL 34-976-288878, FAX 34-976-288869, ifc@dpz.es, http://ifc.dpz.es. Ed. Gonzalo Borras Gualis. R&P Felix Sanchez TEL 34-976-288858. Adv. contact Maria Luz Cortes TEL 34-976-288879. Circ: 750.

700 720 ESP ISSN 0210-9573
SEMINARIO DE ESTUDIOS DE ARTE Y ARQUEOLOGIA. BOLETIN. Text in Spanish. 1939. a. cum.index: 1939-1984. **Document type:** *Bulletin, Academic/Scholarly.*
Indexed: BHA, NumL, PCI.
—CINDOC.
Published by: Universidad de Valladolid, Secretariado de Publicaciones, Juan Mambrilla, 14, Valladolid, 47003, Spain. TEL 34-83-294499, FAX 34-83-290300.

741.5 DNK ISSN 0109-3797
SERIE KUREREN; Fokus pa Tegneseriemediet. Text in Danish. 1984. bi-m. illus.
Published by: Viking, Gabelsparken 81, Bramming, 6740, Denmark.

700 ITA
➤ **SETTORE CULTURA E MUSEI. RASSEGNA DI STUDI E DI NOTIZIE.** Text in Italian. 1973. a., latest vol.26, 2002. EUR 20 (effective 2003). illus. **Document type:** *Academic/Scholarly.* **Description:** Articles deal with objects and collections of the organization, essays on related subjects and on new acquisitions.
Formerly: Settore Cultura e Spettacolo. Rassegna di Studi e di Notizie
Indexed: BHA.
Published by: Settore Cultura e Musei, Civiche Raccolte d'Arte Applicata ed Incisioni, Castello Sforzesco, Milan, 20121, Italy. TEL 39-02-88463635, FAX 39-02-88463812. Ed. Claudio Salsi. R&P Giovanna Mori. Circ: 750.

➤ **SEVERNIAK.** see *LITERATURE*

➤ **SEVRES.** see *ARTS AND HANDICRAFTS*

➤ **SHANGHAI YISHUJIA/SHANGHAI ARTISTS.** see *THEATER*

➤ **SHAONIAN WENYI (SHANGHAI)/JUVENILE LITERATURE.** see *CHILDREN AND YOUTH—For*

700 CHN ISSN 1000-8683
SHIJIE MEISHU/WORLD ART. Text in Chinese. 1979. q. USD 25.20 (effective 2001); USD 6.30 newsstand/cover. **Description:** Introduces to Chinese readers foreign art streams and schools, foreign artists and their works, art history and theories, as well as art techniques and materials.
Related titles: Online - full text ed.: (from East View Information Services).
Published by: (Zhongyang Meishu Xueyuan/Central Academy of Arts), Renmin Meishu Chubanshe/People's Fine Arts Publishers, 32, Beizongbu Hutong, Beijing, 100735, China. **Dist. in US by:** China Books & Periodicals Inc, 360 Swift Ave., Ste. 48, S San Fran, CA 94080-6220. TEL 415-282-2994; **Dist. outside China by:** China International Book Trading Corp, 35 Chegongzhuang Xilu, Haidian District, PO Box 399, Beijing 100044, China. TEL 86-10-68412045, FAX 86-10-68412023, cibtc@mail.cibtc.com.cn, http://www.cibtc.com.cn.

700 CHN ISSN 1000-4483
SHIYONG MEISHU/APPLIED FINE ART. Text in Chinese. q.
Published by: Shanghai Renmin Meishu Chubanshe/Shanghai People's Art Publishers, No33 Alley 672 Changle Rd, Shanghai, 200040, China. TEL 4374528. Ed. Zhou Feng.

741 808.83 USA ISSN 1545-7818
▼ **SHONEN JUMP.** Text in English. 2003. m. USD 29.95 domestic; USD 41.95 in Canada; USD 4.95 newsstand/cover (effective 2005). adv. **Document type:** *Magazine, Consumer.* **Description:** Contains over 300 pages of Japanese manga, plus artist interviews, card games, videogames, toys and anime information.
Published by: Viz Communications, Inc., PO Box 77010, San Francisco, CA 94107. TEL 415-546-7073, FAX 415-546-7086, fanart@shonenjump.com, media@viz.com, http://www.shonenjump.com, http://www.viz.com. Adv. contact Kristine Givas.

741.6029 USA ISSN 1554-6268
NC998.5.A1
SHOWCASE ILLUSTRATION. Text in English. 1977. a. (in 2 vols.). USD 95 per vol. (effective 2005). adv. back issues avail. **Document type:** *Directory.* **Description:** Presents trend-setting examples (5,000 images) of illustration and design for books, magazines, advertisements, posters and packaging. Lists names and addresses of over 9,500 illustrators, reps, and designers, arranged topically for easy access.
Formerly (until 200?): American Showcase Illustration (0278-8128); Which superseded in part (in 1982): American Showcase (0742-6100)
Published by: American Showcase Inc., 915 Broadway, 14th Fl, New York, NY 10010-7108. TEL 212-673-6600, 800-894-7469, FAX 212-673-9795. Pub. Ira Shapiro. R&P Ann Middlebrook. Adv. contact Karen Hadam. Circ: 20,000. **Dist. outside US by:** Rotovision SA, 112-116 Western Rd, Hove, E Sussex BN3 1DD, United Kingdom. TEL 44-1273-727268.

700 USA ISSN 1097-5985
NC998.5.A1
SHOWCASE STOCK PREMIER ILLUSTRATION. Text in English. 1998. a. USD 21.95 newsstand/cover (effective 2000). adv. illus. back issues avail. **Document type:** *Directory.* **Description:** Contains a collection of the finest stock art available. Includes highly specific image ideas, allowing for search by subject, style, or medium.
Published by: American Showcase Inc., 915 Broadway, 14th Fl, New York, NY 10010-7108. TEL 212-673-6600, FAX 212-673-9795, info@amshow.com, http://www.showcase.com. Pub. Ira Shapiro. R&P Ann Middlebrook. Adv. contact Karen Hadam. Circ: 500 (paid); 25,500 (controlled).

745.61 CHN ISSN 1000-6214
SHU YU HUA/CALLIGRAPHY AND PAINTING. Text in Chinese. bi-m. USD 28.80; USD 2.40 newsstand/cover (effective 2001).
Published by: Shanghai Shu Hua Chubanshe/Shanghai Calligraphy and Painting Publishers, 81 Qinzhou S Rd, Shanghai, 200233, China. TEL 86-21-6451-9008. **Dist. by:** China International Book Trading Corp, 35 Chegongzhuang Xilu, Haidian District, PO Box 399, Beijing 100044, China. TEL 86-10-68412045, FAX 86-10-68412023, cibtc@mail.cibtc.com.cn, http://www.cibtc.com.cn.

745.61 CHN ISSN 1000-6036
NK3634.A2
SHUFA/CHINESE CALLIGRAPHY. Text in Chinese. 1978. bi-m. USD 52.80; USD 4.40 newsstand/cover (effective 2001). illus. **Description:** Covers Chinese calligraphy, both ancient and modern, traditional and avant-garde. Includes numerous samples of calligraphy.
Published by: Shanghai Shu Hua Chubanshe/Shanghai Calligraphy and Painting Publishers, 81 Qinzhou S Rd, Shanghai, 200233, China. TEL 86-21-6451-9008. Ed. Lu Fusheng. **Dist. in US by:** China Books & Periodicals Inc, 360 Swift Ave., Ste. 48, S San Fran, CA 94080-6220. TEL 415-282-2994; **Dist. outside China by:** China International Book Trading Corp, 35 Chegongzhuang Xilu, Haidian District, PO Box 399, Beijing 100044, China. TEL 86-10-68412045, FAX 86-10-68412023, cibtc@mail.cibtc.com.cn, http://www.cibtc.com.cn.

745.61 CHN
SHUFA BAO/CALLIGRAPHIC ART WEELY. Text in Chinese. 1984. w. CNY 20.28. adv. **Document type:** *Newspaper.* **Description:** Covers calligraphy and seal cutting art as well as trends and activities home and abroad.
Published by: (Hubei Shufajia Xiehui), Shufa Baoshe, No 4, Shuiguo Hu Heng Lu, Wuhan, Hubei 430071, China. TEL 86-27-781-7557, FAX 86-27-783-4954. Circ: 150,000 (paid). **Dist. overseas by:** China International Book Trading Corp, 35 Chegongzhuang Xilu, Haidian District, PO Box 399, Beijing 100044, China. TEL 86-10-68412045, FAX 86-10-68412023, cibtc@mail.cibtc.com.cn, http://www.cibtc.com.cn.

745.61 CHN ISSN 1004-213X
SHUFA SHANGPING/CALLIGRAPHY APPRECIATION. Text in Chinese. 1988. q. USD 20.40; USD 3.40 newsstand/cover (effective 2001). **Document type:** *Academic/Scholarly.*
Published by: Zhongguo Shufajia Xiehui, Heilongjiang Fenhui/China Calligraphers' Association, Heilongjiang Chapter, Fu 16, Yaojing Jie, Nangang-qu, Harbin, Heilongjiang 150006, China. TEL 330933. Ed. Li Kemin. Circ: 20,000. **Dist. by:** China International Book Trading Corp, 35 Chegongzhuang Xilu, Haidian District, PO Box 399, Beijing 100044, China. TEL 86-10-68412045, FAX 86-10-68412023, cibtc@mail.cibtc.com.cn, http://www.cibtc.com.cn.

745.61 CHN
SHUFA SHIJIE/FRIEND OF CALLIGRAPHY. Text in Chinese. 1992. m. CNY 96 (effective 2003). **Document type:** *Academic/Scholarly.*
Formerly: Shufa zhi You (1006-0669)
Published by: Anhui Meishu Chubanshe, 283, Jinzhai Lu, Hefei, 230063, China. **Dist. by:** China International Book Trading Corp, 35 Chegongzhuang Xilu, Haidian District, PO Box 399, Beijing 100044, China. TEL 86-10-68412045, FAX 86-10-68412023, cibtc@mail.cibtc.com.cn, http://www.cibtc.com.cn.

745.61 CHN ISSN 1000-6044
NK3634.A2
SHUFA YANJIU/STUDIES IN CALLIGRAPHY. Text in Chinese. 1979. bi-m. USD 17.40, USD 2.90 (effective 2001).
Published by: Shanghai Shu Hua Chubanshe/Shanghai Calligraphy and Painting Publishers, 81 Qinzhou S Rd, Shanghai, 200233, China. TEL 86-21-6451-9008. **Dist. in US by:** China Books & Periodicals Inc, 360 Swift Ave., Ste. 48, S San Fran, CA 94080-6220. TEL 415-282-2994; **Dist. outside of China by:** China International Book Trading Corp, 35 Chegongzhuang Xilu, Haidian District, PO Box 399, Beijing 100044, China. TEL 86-10-68412045, FAX 86-10-68412023, cibtc@mail.cibtc.com.cn, http://www.cibtc.com.cn.

700 CHN ISSN 1004-4809
SHUHUA YISHU/PAINTING & CALLIGRAPHY ARTS. Text in English. 1990. bi-m. CNY 34.80 (effective 2004). **Document type:** *Academic/Scholarly.*
Related titles: Online - full text ed.: (from East View Information Services).

Published by: Wuxi Wenhua Yishu Xuexiao, Meishu Zhuanye, 12, Qianrong Lu, Wuxi, 214063-1, China. TEL 86-510-5517029, wxwhyx@pub.wx.jsinfo.net, http://wxyx.wxjy.com.cn/. Dist. by: China International Book Trading Corp, 35 Chegongzhuang Xilu, Haidian District, PO Box 399, Beijing 100044, China. TEL 86-10-68412045, FAX 86-10-68412023, cibtc@mail.cibtc.com.cn, http://www.cibtc.com.cn.

792   CHN   ISSN 1003-7500
PN2875.S78
SICHUAN XIJU✶ /SICHUAN DRAMA. Text in Chinese. 1980. bi-m. CNY 5 newsstand/cover (effective 2004). Document type: Academic/Scholarly.
Related titles: Online - full text ed.: (from East View Information Services).
Published by: Chuanju Yishu Yanjiushi/Sichuan Drama Research Office, 21, Xiawangjiaguai Jie, Chengdu, Sichuan 610015, China. TEL 86-28-86113570, FAX 86-28-86124110, http://scxj.periodicals.net.cn/default.html. Ed. Wang Ding'ou. Dist. by: China International Book Trading Corp, 35 Chegongzhuang Xilu, Haidian District, PO Box 399, Beijing 100044, China. TEL 86-10-68412045, FAX 86-10-68412023, cibtc@mail.cibtc.com.cn, http://www.cibtc.com.cn.

709   THA   ISSN 0037-5314
SILPAKON✶ . Text in Thai; Contents page in English. 1957. bi-m. THB 40, USD 3. charts; illus. index.
Published by: Government House Press, Fine Arts Department, Thanon Na Phra That, Bangkok, Thailand. Ed. Nai Prapat Treenarong. Circ: 1,000.

THE SILVER AGE; Russian literature and culture 1881-1921. see LITERATURE

709   NLD   ISSN 0037-5411
N5
SIMIOLUS; Netherlands quarterly for the history of art. Text in English. 1966. q. adv. bk.rev. bibl.; illus. back issues avail.; reprints avail. Document type: Journal, Academic/Scholarly.
Indexed: ABCT, AIAP, ASCA, ArtHuCl, ArtInd, BHA, CurCont, DIP, IBR, IBRH, IBZ, PCI, RASB.
—BLDSC (8284.200000), IE, Infotrieve, ingenta.
Published by: Stichting voor Nederlandse Kunsthistorische Publicaties/Foundation for Dutch Art - Historical Publications, Kromme Nieuwegracht 29, Utrecht, 3512 HD, Netherlands. TEL 31-30-392278, FAX 32-30-392167. Ed. P Hecht. Circ: 950.

SINALEFA. see LITERATURE—Poetry

SKETCH. see LITERATURE

700   USA
SKETCH BOOK. Text in English. 1937. a. USD 10 (effective 2005). Document type: Directory, Academic/Scholarly.
Published by: Kappa Pi International Honorary Art Fraternity, 400 South Bolivar Ave, Cleveland, MS 38732-3745. TEL 662-846-4729, koehler@tecinfo.com, http://ntweb.deltastate.edu/kappa_pi/index.htm. Ed. Ron Koehler. Circ: 2,000 (controlled).

700   USA
SKETCHES. Text in English. 1995. m.
Media: Online - full content.
Published by: The Mining Company, PO Box 6572, New York, NY 10128-0006. http://finearts.miningco.com/blnews1.htm. Ed. Chris Jeffries.

700   USA
THE SKETCHPAD. Text in English. a. USD 10 (effective 2005). Document type: Directory, Academic/Scholarly.
Formerly: Sketch Board Bulletin
Published by: Kappa Pi International Honorary Art Fraternity, 400 South Bolivar Ave, Cleveland, MS 38732-3745. TEL 662-846-4729, koehler@tecinfo.com, http://ntweb.deltastate.edu/kappa_pi/index.htm.

391   USA   ISSN 1061-3013
SKIN ART. Text in English. 1992. 9/yr. USD 32.95; USD 42.95 foreign. adv. illus. Document type: Consumer.
Published by: Outlaw Biker Enterprises, Inc., 5 Marine View Plaza, Ste 207, Hoboken, NJ 07030. TEL 201-653-2700. Ed. Jean-Chris Miller. Pub. Casey Exton. R&P Jean Chris Miller. Adv. contact Ken Knabb.

391   USA   ISSN 1067-2060
SKIN ART PRESENTS. Text in English. 1993. 9/yr. adv. illus. Document type: Consumer.
Published by: Outlaw Biker Enterprises, Inc., 5 Marine View Plaza, Ste 207, Hoboken, NJ 07030. TEL 201-653-2700. Ed. Jean-Chris Miller. Pub. Casey Exton. R&P Jean Chris Miller. Adv. contact Ken Knabb.

745   GBR   ISSN 0966-4351
SKIN DEEP; the European tattoo magazine. Text in English. 1994. m. GBP 39.50 domestic; GBP 55.34 in Europe; GBP 68.78 in Australasia; GBP 66.86 elsewhere (effective 2003). illus. Document type: Magazine, Consumer. Description: Explores the art and culture of the tattoo.

Published by: Jazz Publishing, PO Box 23619, London, E7 9TY, United Kingdom. sally@skindeep.co.uk, http://www.skindeep.co.uk. Dist. by: M M C Ltd., Octagon House, White Hart Meadows, Ripley, Woking, Surrey GU23 6HR, United Kingdom.

741 960   ZAF
SKOTAVILLE GRAPHIC SERIES. Text in English. irreg., latest vol.2. Document type: Monographic series.
Published by: Skotaville Publishers, PO Box 32483, Braamfontein, Johannesburg 2017, South Africa. Dist. outside Africa by: African Books Collective Ltd., The Jam Factory, 27 Park End St, Oxford, Oxon OX1 1HU, United Kingdom. TEL 0865-726686, FAX 0865-796298.

730   DNK   ISSN 0107-4911
NB198
SKULPTUR VEKSOELUND. Text in Danish. 1978. a. DKK 25. illus.
Published by: Veksoelund, c/o Poul Hansen, Kirkestraede 6, Veksoe, 3670, Denmark.

700   USA
SLASH MAGAZINE. Text in English. q. USD 9.99 newsstand/cover (effective 2005).
Address: 113 W Gaston St., 4th Fl, Savannah, GA 31401. TEL 478-320-7173, FAX 912-236-4996, info@slashmagazine.com, http://www.slashmagazine.com. Ed., Pub. K Hinton.

708   CAN   ISSN 0821-2287
SLATE. Text in English. 1979. 8/yr. CND 22; CND 30 foreign (effective 1997). adv. maps. Description: Lists gallery exhibitions, studio shows, opening receptions and events.
Formerly (until 1982): Slate Gallery Guide (0821-2279); (until 1981): Slate (0821-2260)
—CCC.
Address: 155 King St E, Kingston, ON K7L 2Z9, Canada. TEL 613-542-3717, FAX 613-542-1447, admin@slateartguide.com, http://www.slate.com. Ed. Allan Lochhead. Circ: 150 (paid); 12,100 (controlled).

SLIPSTREAM (NIAGARA FALLS). see LITERATURE—Poetry

700 500   SVN   ISSN 0374-0315
AS346
SLOVENSKA AKADEMIJA ZNANOSTI IN UMETNOSTI. LETOPIS/SLOVENIAN ACADEMY OF SCIENCES AND ARTS. YEARBOOK. Text in Slovenian, English. 1938. a. Document type: Yearbook, Academic/Scholarly.
Indexed: BHA, RefZh.
—CISTI, Linda Hall.
Published by: Slovenska Akademija Znanosti in Umetnosti/Slovenian Academy of Sciences and Arts, Novi trg 3-5, Ljubljana, 1000, Slovenia. TEL 386-1-4706100, FAX 386-1-4253462, sazu@sazu.si, http://www.sazu.si. Ed. Lidija Andolsek Jeras. Pub. Dusan Merhar.

SLOVENSKE POHLADY NA LITERATURU A UMENIE. see LITERATURE

700 362.4   POL   ISSN 1426-6628
SLOWEM I KSZTALTEM. Text in Polish. 1996. q.
Published by: Fundacja Sztuki Osob Niepelnosprawnych, ul Zielna 41, Krakow, 30320, Poland. fson@idn.org.pl, http://www.idn.org.pl/fson/kwart7/podzial.htm. Ed. Janusz Kopczynski. Circ: 2,000.

700   USA   ISSN 1540-3297
N6512
SMOCK; a modern art attitude. Text in English. 2000. q. USD 25 domestic; USD 35 in Canada; USD 45 elsewhere; USD 5.50 newsstand/cover (effective 2005). Document type: Magazine, Consumer. Description: Covers today's art scene, fashion, and design; featuring emerging and established artists.
Published by: Smock Magazine, Inc., 49 Walker St, 2nd Fl, New York, NY 10013. TEL 212-226-4442, FAX 212-226-8250, contact@smockonline.com, http://www.smockonline.com/. Pub. Scott Bennett. Circ: 400,000 (paid).

SOCIETA PER GLI STUDI STORICI, ARCHEOLOGICI ED ARTISTICI DELLA PROVINCIA DI CUNEO. BOLLETTINO. see ARCHAEOLOGY

SOCIETA PIEMONTESE DI ARCHEOLOGIA E BELLE ARTI. BOLLETTINO. see ARCHAEOLOGY

SOCIETA ROMANA DI STORIA PATRIA. ARCHIVIO. see MUSIC

SOCIETA STORICA VALTELLINESE. BOLLETTINO (1953). see HISTORY

709 943   BEL   ISSN 0776-1295
SOCIETE D'ART ET D'HISTOIRE DU DIOCESE DE LIEGE. BULLETIN. Text in French. 1881. irreg. cum.index: vols.16-55. Document type: Bulletin.
Indexed: BHA.
Published by: Societe d'Art et d'Histoire du Diocese de Liege, Rue Bonne Fortune 6, Liege, 4000, Belgium. Circ: 3,500.

SOCIETE DES SCIENCES, LETTRES ET ARTS DE BAYONNE. BULLETIN. see LITERATURE

SOCIETY FOR ARMENIAN STUDIES. JOURNAL. see ETHNIC INTERESTS

SOCIETY FOR RENAISSANCE STUDIES. BULLETIN. see LITERATURE

750   USA
SOCIETY OF ANIMAL ARTISTS NEWSLETTER✶ . Text in English. 1960. 4/yr. membership. adv. bk.rev. illus.; stat. Document type: Newsletter.
Published by: Society of Animal Artists, 47 5th Ave, New York, NY 10003-4303. Ed. Patricia Bott. Circ: 200.

SOCIETY OF PHOTOGRAPHER AND ARTIST REPRESENTATIVES. NEWSLETTER. see PHOTOGRAPHY

706   GBR
SOCIETY OF WILDLIFE ARTISTS. PUBLICATION. Text in English. a. GBP 1 (effective 2001). Document type: Catalog. Description: Catalog for annual exhibition in July or August.
Published by: (Society of Wildlife Artists), Federation of British Artists, 17 Carlton House Terr, London, SW1Y 5BD, United Kingdom. TEL 44-20-7930-6844, FAX 44-20-7839-7830, http://www.mallgalleries.org.uk.

700 301   FRA   ISSN 0779-1674
SOCIOLOGIE DE L'ART. Text in French. 1988. irreg. Price varies.
Published by: L' Harmattan, 5 rue de l'Ecole Polytechnique, Paris, 75005, France. TEL 33-1-43257651, FAX 33-1-43258203, http://www.editions-harmattan.fr.

700   IRL
SOLAS OCCASIONAL RESEARCH PAPERS IN ART AND DESIGN EDUCATION; an anthology of student research. Text in English. 2/yr.?.
—BLDSC (8327.234000).
Published by: National College of Art and Design, 100 Thomas St., Dublin, 8, Ireland.

700 780   FRA
SON!✶ . Text in French. 1984 (no.3). bi-m.
Address: 63 av. des Champs-Elysees, Paris, 75008, France. Ed. Frank Tenot.

SONIC THE COMIC. see LITERATURE—Science Fiction, Fantasy, Horror

709 726   ITA
SOPRINTENDENZA PER I BENI CULTURALI DELLA VALLE D'AOSTA. QUADERNI. Text in Italian. 1981. irreg., latest vol.7, 1992. price varies. Document type: Monographic series, Academic/Scholarly.
Published by: (Soprintendenza per i Beni Culturali della Valle d'Aosta), L'Erma di Bretschneider, Via Cassiodoro, 19, PO Box 6192, Rome, RM 00193, Italy. TEL 39-06-6874127, FAX 39-06-6874129, edizioni@lerma.it, http://www.lerma.it.

SOTHEBY'S INTERNATIONAL PREVIEW. see BUSINESS AND ECONOMICS—Domestic Commerce

THE SOUND MAGAZINE. see LITERATURE

709   USA   ISSN 0737-4453
➤ SOURCE: NOTES IN THE HISTORY OF ART. Text in English. 1981. q. USD 25 domestic; USD 28 in Canada & Mexico; USD 30 elsewhere (effective 2003 - 2004). bk.rev. illus. back issues avail.; reprints avail. Document type: Journal, Academic/Scholarly. Description: Scholarly journal devoted to short notes, articles and reviews in art history and archaeology.
Indexed: ABM, AIAP, ASCA, ArtHuCl, ArtInd, BHA, CurCont, RILM.
—BLDSC (8330.575100), IDS.
Published by: Ars Brevis Foundation, Inc., c/o Laurie Adams, Ed, 224 E 68th St, New York, NY 10021. TEL 212-501-3051, FAX 212-501-3099. Ed. Laurie Schneider Adams. Pub.- R&P Susan Weber. Circ: 1,000 (paid).

700   USA   ISSN 1043-5158
N1
SOUTHEASTERN COLLEGE ART CONFERENCE REVIEW. Short title: S E C A C Review. Text in English. 1967. a. USD 30 to individuals; USD 100 to institutions; USD 10 to students (effective 2005). bk.rev. illus. Document type: Academic/Scholarly.
Formerly (until 1973): S E C A C Review and Newsletter (0584-4118)
Indexed: AIAP, BHA.
—BLDSC (8352.357000).
Address: PO Box 656, Carrboro, NC 27510-0656. secac@ncrrbiz.com, http://www.furman.edu/secac. Ed. Michael Duffy. Circ: 500.

700 800   USA   ISSN 0886-067X
SOUTHEASTERN FRONT. Text in English. 1993. irreg.?. free. adv. bk.rev. Description: Publishes new art, fiction and poetry.
Address: 565 17th St, N W, Cleveland, TN 37311. TEL 615-479-3244. Ed. Robin Merritt. Circ: 1,500.

SOUTHERN INDIANA REVIEW. see LITERATURE

▼ new title   ➤ refereed   ✶ unverified   ◆ full entry avail.

SOUTHERN QUARTERLY; a journal of the arts in the South. see *HUMANITIES: COMPREHENSIVE WORKS*

705 USA ISSN 0192-4214
N6525
SOUTHWEST ART. Text in English. 1971. m. USD 32 domestic; USD 44 foreign; USD 5.99 per issue (effective 2005). adv. bk.rev. illus. Index. back issues avail.; reprints avail.
Document type: *Magazine, Consumer.* **Description:** Focuses on representational arts west of the Mississippi River. Includes interviews with painters, sculptors, museum professionals, collectors and dealers.
Former titles: Southwest Art Magazine (0091-8830); Southwest Art Gallery; Incorporates (1985-1987): Western Art Digest (0883-8992); Which was formed by the merger of (1977-1985): Art West; Artist of the Rockies and the Golden West (0364-3379); Which was formerly: Artists of the Rockies
Related titles: Online - full text ed.: (from bigchalk, ProQuest Information & Learning).
Indexed: ABCT, ABM, ASIP, ArtInd, BHA, ChPerI.
—BLDSC (8356.280000), IE, ingenta.
Published by: Southwest Art Publishing, 5444 Westheimer Ste 1400, Houston, TX 77056. TEL 713-296-7900, FAX 713-850-1314, southwestart@southwestart.com, http://www.southwestart.com. Ed. Kristin Bucher. Circ: 60,173 (paid).

SPACE/KONGGAN. see *ARCHITECTURE*

SPANNER (LONDON, 1974). see *LITERARY AND POLITICAL REVIEWS*

740 USA
SPANNER N Y C. Text in English. 1978. s-a. USD 4 per issue. illus.
Published by: Aloes Books U S A, PO Box 5, Canal St Sta, New York, NY 10013. Eds. Dick Miller, Terry Slotkin. Circ: 1,000.

700 USA
SPARKS. Text in English. 8/yr. USD 55 domestic to individuals; USD 89 domestic family (effective 2005). **Document type:** *Newsletter, Consumer.*
Published by: Boston Museum of Science, Science Park, Boston, MA 02114. TEL 617-723-2500, FAX 617-589-0363, http://www.mos.org. Circ: 330,000 (paid).

SPECULUM; a journal of Medieval studies. see *HISTORY—History Of Europe*

708.1 USA ISSN 0733-866X
N582.L25
SPENCER MUSEUM OF ART. REGISTER. Text in English. 1951. a. USD 15 domestic; USD 20 foreign (effective 2000). illus.
Document type: *Academic/Scholarly.* **Description:** Scholarly articles on works of art in the collection along with the museum annual report.
Formerly: University of Kansas. Museum of Art. Register (0041-9672)
Indexed: BHA.
Published by: University of Kansas, Spencer Museum of Art, 1301 Mississippi St, Lawrence, KS 66045-7500. TEL 785-864-4710, FAX 785-864-3112, http://www.falconcc.ukans.edu/~sma. Ed. Sally Hayden. Circ: 900.

▼ **SPIRIT.** see *ETHNIC INTERESTS*

354 CAN
SPOTLIGHT. Cover title: Saskatchewan Centre Spotlight. Text in English. 5/yr. adv. **Description:** Contains a regular calendar of upcoming performances, local arts information, program performance details, a restaurant guide as well as other related articles.
Published by: Saskatchewan Centre of the Arts, 200 Lakeshore Dr, Regina, SK S4P 3V7, Canada. TEL 306-565-4500, FAX 306-565-3274. Adv. contact Louise Yates. page CND 720; trim 5.5 x 8.5.

700 JPN
SPROUT (TOKYO). Text in English. irreg. JPY 1,200 (effective 2005). **Document type:** *Magazine, Consumer.*
Published by: Sprout Japan, Inc., Roppongi Hiss Residence, D-Tower, 6-12-4, Poppongi, Minatoku, Tokyo, 10006, Japan. http://www.sproutmag.com. Ed., Pub. Yoshikazu Shinga.

700 SCG ISSN 0586-4887
SRPSKA AKADEMIJA NAUKA I UMETNOSTI. GALERIJA S A N U. Text in Serbo-Croatian. a.
Indexed: DIP, IBR, IBZ.
Published by: Srpska Akademija Nauka i Umetnosti/Serbian Academy of Arts and Sciences, Knez Mihailova 35, Belgrade, 11000. TEL 381-11-3342400, FAX 381-11-182825, SASApres@bib.sanu.ac.yu, http://www.sanu.ac.yu.

700 780 SCG ISSN 0081-4008
SRPSKA AKADEMIJA NAUKA I UMETNOSTI. ODELJENJE LIKOVNE I MUZICKE UMETNOSTI. POSEBNA IZDANJA. Text in Serbo-Croatian; Summaries in English, French, German, Russian. 1954. irreg. price varies.
Indexed: IBR, IBZ.
Published by: Srpska Akademija Nauka i Umetnosti/Serbian Academy of Arts and Sciences, Knez Mihailova 35, Belgrade, 11000. TEL 381-11-3342400, FAX 381-11-182825, SASApres@bib.sanu.ac.yu, http://www.sanu.ac.yu. Circ: 1,000.
Dist. by: Prosveta, Terazije 16, Belgrade, Serbia, Yugoslavia.

700 DEU
STADTMUSEUM OLDENBURG. VEROEFFENTLICHUNGEN. Text in German. 1987. irreg., latest vol.47, 2003. price varies.
Document type: *Monographic series, Academic/Scholarly.*
Published by: (Stadtmuseum Oldenburg), Isensee Verlag, Haarenstr 20, Oldenburg, 26122, Germany. TEL 49-441-25388, FAX 49-441-17872, verlag@isensee.de, http://www.isensee.de.

700 DEU ISSN 0585-0118
N9
STAEDEL JAHRBUCH. Text in German. 1967. biennial.
Document type: *Monographic series.* **Description:** Art historical journal with emphasis on archeology, architecture, painting and sculpture.
Indexed: BHA, IBR, IBZ.
Published by: (Staedelsches Museum-Verein und Stadt Frankfurt am Main), Prestel Verlag, Koeniginstr 9, Munich, 80539, Germany. info@prestel.de, http://www.prestel.de. Ed. Michael Maegraith. Pub. Juergen Tesch. R&P Karin Kirmaier.

STARGREEN; the magazine for the modern sentimentalist. see *MUSIC*

700 051 DEU ISSN 1619-2052
STARSHIP. Text in English. 1998. irreg. USD 6 newsstand/cover (effective 2005). **Document type:** *Magazine, Consumer.*
Published by: Starship e.V., Skalitzer Str 135a, Berlin, 10999, Germany. TEL 49-30-4491683, redaktion@starship-magazine.org, http://www.starship-magazine.org. Pub. Hans-Christian Dany.

700.25 USA
STATE ARTS AGENCY DIRECTORY. Text in English. m. USD 12.50 per issue (effective 1999). **Document type:** *Directory.*
Description: Lists state arts agency executive directors and chairs alphabetically including addresses. Also includes names, addresses, and phone numbers for the seven regional arts organizations.
Published by: National Assembly of State Arts Agencies, 1029 Vermont Ave, N W, 2nd Fl, Washington, DC 20005-3517. TEL 202-347-6352, FAX 202-737-0562, nasaa@nasaa-arts.org. Ed. Pat Prater.

709 DNK ISSN 1398-1609
N1915
STATENS MUSEUM FOR KUNST. JOURNAL. Variant title: Kunstmuseets Aarsskrift. New series. Text in English. 1914. a. illus. **Document type:** *Academic/Scholarly.*
Formerly (until 1993): Kunstmuseets Aarsskrift (0107-8933)
Indexed: BHA.
Published by: Statens Museum for Kunst, Soelvgade 48-50, Copenhagen K, 1307, Denmark. TEL 45-33-748494, FAX 45-33-748404, smk@smk.dk, http://www.smk.dk. Ed. Jan Garff.

700 948 NOR ISSN 0333-0656
AS283
STAVANGER MUSEUM. AARBOK. Text in Norwegian; Summaries in English. 1890. a. NOK 150 (effective 2003). illus. back issues avail. **Document type:** *Yearbook, Academic/Scholarly.*
Former titles (until 1947): Stavanger Museum. (0333-3884); (until 1901): Stavanger Museums Aarsberetning (0333-3892)
Indexed: BHA, DIP, IBR, IBZ, RASB, ZooRec.
—Linda Hall.
Published by: Stavanger Museum, Musegate 16, Stavanger, 4010, Norway. TEL 47-51-842700, FAX 47-51-842701, firmapost@stavanger.museum.no, http://www.stavanger.museum.no. Circ: 1,000.

702.88 AUT ISSN 0039-1026
STEINE SPRECHEN. Text in German. 1962. q. EUR 22 membership (effective 2005). adv. bk.rev. bibl.; illus.; maps. 24 p./no. 3 cols./p.; back issues avail. **Document type:** *Bulletin, Consumer.* **Description:** Covers the history, the care and upkeep of historical monuments, buildings, and gardens.
Related titles: Supplement(s): Steinschlag.
Indexed: BHA.
Published by: Oesterreichische Gesellschaft fuer Denkmal und Ortsbildpflege, Karlsplatz 5, Vienna, 1010, Austria. TEL 43-664-5436382, FAX 43-1-5232374, redaktion@steine-sprechen.at, gesellschaft@denkmal-ortsbildpflege.at, http://www.denkmalschutz.at/steine-sprechen/, http://www.denkmalschutz.at/denkmal-ortsbildpflege/. Ed. Mario Schwarz. Adv. contact Elisabeth Bobrowsky. Circ: 1,000.

740 750 GBR ISSN 1462-0421
THE STEP-BY-STEP ART COURSE. Text in English. 1998. fortn.
Document type: *Consumer.* **Description:** Offers adults and children over 14 years of age the opportunity to enhance their drawing and paintings skills in a step-by-step manner.
Published by: DeAgostini (UK) Ltd., PO Box 6000, Hastings, E Sussex TN35 4TJ, United Kingdom. TEL 44-870-8702575, FAX 44-870-8702577, enquiries@deagostini.co.uk, http://www.deagostini.co.uk.

STERZ; Zeitschrift fuer Literatur, Kunst und Kulturpolitik. see *LITERATURE*

709 SWE ISSN 0491-0850
STOCKHOLM STUDIES IN HISTORY OF ART. Text in Multiple languages. 1956. irreg., latest vol.36, 1992. price varies.
Document type: *Monographic series, Academic/Scholarly.*
Related titles: ♦ Series of: Acta Universitatis Stockholmiensis. ISSN 0346-6418.
Published by: Stockholms Universitet, Acta Universitatis Stockholmiensis, c/o Stockholms Universitetsbibliotek, Universitetsvaegen 10, Stockholm, 10691, Sweden. FAX 46-8-157776. **Dist. by:** Almqvist & Wiksell International, P O Box 7634, Stockholm 10394, Sweden. TEL 46-8-6136100, FAX 46-8-242543, info@akademibokhandeln.se, http://www.akademibokhandeln.se.

745.5 SWE
STOCKHOLMS-FOERETAGAREN. Text in Swedish. 1970. q. SEK 25. adv. bk.rev. **Document type:** *Newsletter.*
Published by: Stockholms Stads Hantverksfoerening/Stockholm Craft and Small Industry Association, Gotgatan 61, Stockholm, 11621, Sweden. TEL 4-608-644-0090, FAX 4-608-643-7134. Ed. Haakan Wallensten. Circ: 4,110.

720.22 ITA ISSN 0081-5845
STORIA DELLA MINIATURA. STUDI E DOCUMENTI. Text in Italian. 1962. irreg., latest vol.7, 1992. price varies. **Document type:** *Monographic series, Academic/Scholarly.*
Published by: Casa Editrice Leo S. Olschki, Viuzzo del Pozzetto 8, Florence, 50126, Italy. TEL 39-055-6530684, FAX 39-055-6530214, celso@olschki.it, http://www.olschki.it. Circ: 1,000.

709 ITA ISSN 0392-4513
STORIA DELL'ARTE. Text in Italian. 1969. 3/yr. EUR 73.66 domestic; EUR 93.53 in Europe; EUR 113.53 elsewhere (effective 2005). **Document type:** *Journal, Academic/Scholarly.*
Related titles: Online - full text ed.: (from H.W. Wilson, O C L C Online Computer Library Center, Inc.).
Indexed: ABCT, ABM, AIAP, ASCA, ArtHuCI, ArtInd, BHA, CurCont, PCI, RASB.
Published by: CAM Editrice Roma, Via Capo di Ferro 4, Rome, 00186, Italy. TEL 39-06-68300889, info@cameditrice.com, http://www.cameditrice.com/storiarivista.htm.

709 ITA
STORIA DELL'ARTE E DELLA CRITICA D'ARTE. Text in Italian. 1990. irreg., latest vol.9, 1998. price varies. adv. **Document type:** *Monographic series.*
Published by: Liguori Editore srl, Via Posillipo 394, Naples, 80123, Italy. TEL 39-81-7206111, FAX 39-81-7206244, http://www.liguori.it. Ed. Alfredo De Paz. Pub. Guido Liguori. Adv. contact Maria Liguori.

LO STRANIERO/ETRANGER/EXTRANJERO/FREMDE/STRANGER; Stranger - Etranger - Fremde - Extranjero. see *LITERARY AND POLITICAL REVIEWS*

STRANITSA/PAGE. see *LITERATURE*

741.5 CHE ISSN 1424-2575
STRAPAZIN. Text in German. 1984. q. CHF 30 domestic; CHF 40 foreign (effective 2000). **Document type:** *Magazine, Consumer.* **Description:** Contains a wide variety of cartoons, comics and graphic stories and articles.
Published by: Strapazin Ateliers, Eglistr 8, Zurich, 8004, Switzerland. TEL 41-1-4919682, FAX 41-1-4011944, post@strapazin.ch, http://www.strapazin.ch.

STREAMLINE. see *ARCHITECTURE*

700 371.42 USA
STREET ARTISTS' NEWSLETTER. Text in English. 1978. a. looseleaf. USD 25 to individuals (effective 2005). adv. bk.rev. back issues avail. **Document type:** *Newsletter.* **Description:** Covers locations, legal issues, profiles and reviews. Includes festival and event listings.
Published by: Community Arts Advocates, PO Box 300112, Jamaica Plain, MA 02130. TEL 617-522-3407, info@communityartsadvocates.org, http://www.communityartsadvocates.org, http://www.communityartsadvocates.org/. Ed., Pub. Stephen Baird. Circ: 1,000.

741.509 DNK ISSN 1398-0742
STRIP!. Text in Danish. 1998. q. DKK 150 domestic; DKK 170 in Scandinavia; DKK 200 elsewhere (effective 2001). **Document type:** *Magazine, Consumer.* **Description:** Covers cartoons from around the world with reviews and news.
Published by: Serieforeningen STRIP, Mysundevej 9, st., Copenhagen V, 1668, Denmark. TEL 45-33-79-78-76, FAX 45-38-88-16-16, fahrenheit@email.dk, http://www.natdag.dk/strip. Ed. Paw Mathiesen.

709 707 CAN ISSN 0081-6027
N9
THE STRUCTURIST. Text in English. 1960. biennial, latest vol.44, 2004. CND 32 per vol. to individuals; CND 60 per vol. to institutions (effective 2005). bk.rev. cum.index: nos.1-40. back issues avail.; reprint service avail. from PQC. **Document type:** *Journal, Academic/Scholarly.* **Description:** Focuses on ideas relating to architecture and the arts - including painting, sculpture, design, photography, music and literature - their histories and relationships to each other, as well as to science, technology, and Nature.
Related titles: CD-ROM ed.: (from H.W. Wilson); Microfilm ed.: (from PQC); Online - full text ed.: (from H.W. Wilson, O C L C Online Computer Library Center, Inc.).
Indexed: ABM, AIAP, API, AmHI, ArtInd, BHA, EIP, PCI.
—BLDSC (8479.320000).
Published by: The Structurist, PO Box 378, RPO University, University of Saskatchewan, Saskatoon, SK S7N 4J8, Canada. TEL 306-966-4198, FAX 306-966-4197, eli.bornstein@usask.ca, http://www.usask.ca/structurist. Ed., Pub. Eli Bornstein. Circ: 1,200.

STRUMA. see *LITERATURE*

STUDI BITONTINI. see *HISTORY—History Of Europe*

709 ITA ISSN 1123-5683
STUDI DI STORIA DELL'ARTE. Text in English, French, German, Italian. 1990. a. price varies. bk.rev. index. back issues avail. **Document type:** *Monographic series, Academic/Scholarly.*
Indexed: AIAP, BHA.
Published by: Ediart Editrice, Localita Montelupino, Todi, PG 06059, Italy. TEL 39-0758-943594, FAX 39-0758-942411, ediart@ediart.it, http://www.ediart.it. Ed. Filippo Todini. Circ: 1,000.

709 ITA
STUDI DI STORIA DELLE ARTI. Text in Italian. 1977. a. USD 15 (effective 1993). back issues avail. **Document type:** *Academic/Scholarly.*
Indexed: BHA.
Published by: Istituto di Storia dell'Arte, Universita di Genova, Via Balbi, 4, Genoa, GE 16126, Italy. TEL 010-2099749. Ed. Gildo Fossati. Circ: 1,000.

709 701.18 ITA
STUDI E TESTI DI STORIA E CRITICA DELL'ARTE. Text in Italian. 1975. irreg., latest vol.12, 1984. price varies.
Published by: Societa Editrice Napoletana s.r.l., Corso Umberto I, 1-34, Naples, NA 80138, Italy.

STUDI GERMANICI. see *LITERATURE*

709 ITA ISSN 1124-3910
STUDI SUL SETTECENTO ROMANO. Text in Italian. 1984. a. price varies. **Document type:** *Journal, Academic/Scholarly.* **Description:** Covers research on Roman art of the 18th century.
Published by: (Universita degli Studi di Roma "La Sapienza", Istituto Storia dell'Arte Medievale e Moderna), Bonsignori Editore s.r.l., Viale dei Quattro Venti 47, Rome, RM 00152, Italy. TEL 39-06-5881496, FAX 39-06-5882839. Ed. Elisa Debenedetti.

709 POL
STUDIA NAD SZTUKA RENESANSU I BAROKU/STUDIES IN ART OF RENAISSANCE AND BAROQUE. Text in Polish.
Published by: Katolicki Uniwersytet Lubelski, Towarzystwo Naukowe, Ul Gliniana 21, Lublin, 20616, Poland. TEL 55-01-93. Ed. Antoni Maslinski.

701 POL ISSN 0081-7104
STUDIA Z HISTORII SZTUKI. Text in Polish; Summaries in English, French, German. 1953. irreg., latest vol.49, 1995. price varies. **Document type:** *Monographic series.*
Published by: Polska Akademia Nauk, Instytut Sztuki/Polish Academy of Science, Institute of Art, ul Dluga 28, Warsaw, 00950, Poland. TEL 48-22-5048200, FAX 48-22-8313149, ispan@ispan.pl, http://www.ispan.pl.

709 DEU ISSN 0081-7228
➤ **STUDIEN ZUR DEUTSCHEN KUNSTGESCHICHTE.** Text in German. 1894. irreg., latest vol.369, 2002. price varies. back issues avail.; reprints avail. **Document type:** *Monographic series, Academic/Scholarly.* **Description:** Concerning the history of German art.
Published by: Verlag Valentin Koerner GmbH, Postfach 100164, Baden-Baden, 76482, Germany. TEL 49-7221-22423, FAX 49-7221-38697, valentin.koerner@t-online.de, http://www.koernerverlag.de. Circ: 1,000.

707 DEU ISSN 1617-3961
STUDIEN ZUR KUNST AM OBERRHEIN. Text in German. 2001. irreg. EUR 34.80 per vol. (effective 2003). **Document type:** *Monographic series, Academic/Scholarly.*
Published by: Waxmann Verlag GmbH, Steinfurter Str 555, Muenster, 48159, Germany. TEL 49-251-26504-0, FAX 49-251-2650426, info@waxmann.com, http://www.waxmann.com. Ed. Wilhelm Schlink.

700 DEU ISSN 0175-9558
STUDIEN ZUR KUNSTGESCHICHTE. Text in German. irreg., latest vol.138, 2001. price varies. **Document type:** *Monographic series, Academic/Scholarly.*
Published by: Georg Olms Verlag, Hagentorwall 7, Hildesheim, 31134, Germany. TEL 49-5121-1501-0, FAX 49-5121-150150, info@olms.de, http://www.olms.de. R&P Christiane Busch.

709 950 DEU ISSN 0170-3684
STUDIEN ZUR OSTASIATISCHEN SCHRIFTKUNST. Text in German. 1970. irreg., latest vol.5, 2002. price varies. **Document type:** *Monographic series, Academic/Scholarly.*
Published by: Franz Steiner Verlag Stuttgart GmbH, Birkenwaldstr 44, Stuttgart, 70191, Germany. TEL 49-711-25820, FAX 49-711-2582390, franz.steiner.verlag@t-online.de, http://www.steiner-verlag.de. Ed. Dietrich Seckel. R&P Sabine Koerner.

091 745.6 NLD
STUDIES AND FACSIMILES OF NETHERLANDISH ILLUMINATED MANUSCRIPTS. Text in English. 1986. irreg., latest vol.3, 1991. price varies. **Document type:** *Monographic series.*
Published by: Davaco Publishers, Beukenlaan 3, Doornspijk, 8085 RK, Netherlands. TEL 31-525-661823, FAX 31-525-662153.

STUDIES IN AESTHETICS. see *PHILOSOPHY*

700 200 USA
➤ **STUDIES IN ART AND RELIGIOUS INTERPRETATION.** Text in English. 1982. irreg., latest vol.31, 2003. price varies. **Document type:** *Monographic series, Academic/Scholarly.*
—BLDSC (8489.525000), ingenta.
Published by: Edwin Mellen Press, 415 Ridge St, P.O. Box 450, Lewiston, NY 14092. TEL 716-754-2266, FAX 716-754-4056, cservice@mellenpress.com, http://www.mellenpress.com/.

707 USA ISSN 0039-3541
N81
➤ **STUDIES IN ART EDUCATION;** a journal of issues and research in art education. Text in English. 1959. q. USD 25 domestic; USD 45 foreign (effective 2005). bk.rev. bibl.; charts; illus. Index. reprint service avail. from PQC. **Document type:** *Journal, Academic/Scholarly.* **Description:** Research and issues pertaining to visual art education.
Related titles: Microform ed.: (from PQC); Online - full text ed.: (from bigchalk, H.W. Wilson, JSTOR (Web-based Journal Archive), Northern Light Technology, Inc., O C L C Online Computer Library Center, Inc., ProQuest Information & Learning).
Indexed: ABCT, ABIn, ABM, CIJE, CPE, ERA, ETA, EduInd, MEA, RHEA, SEA, SENA, SOMA, SWA, TEA.
—BLDSC (8489.530000), IE, Infotrieve, ingenta.
Published by: National Art Education Association, 1916 Association Dr, Reston, VA 20191-1590. TEL 703-860-8000, FAX 703-860-2960, kemery@naea-reston.org, http://www.naea-reston.org/publications-artedu.html. Ed. Janice Davenport. R&P Cam Luccarelli. Circ: 3,500.

➤ **STUDIES IN ASIAN ART AND ARCHAEOLOGY.** see *ASIAN STUDIES*

700 USA
STUDIES IN BRITISH ART. Text in English. irreg., latest 1992. price varies. **Document type:** *Monographic series.*
Published by: (Paul Mellon Centre for Studies in British Art), Yale University Press, PO Box 209040, New Haven, CT 06520. TEL 203-432-0940, FAX 616-592-2618, chla@mlc.lib.mi.us, ysm@yale.edu, http://www.yale.edu, http://www.yalepress.yale.edu.

700 720 USA ISSN 1555-4058
N7853.5
STUDIES IN CISTERCIAN ART AND ARCHITECTURE. Text in English. 1982. irreg., latest vol.4, 1993. price varies. **Document type:** *Monographic series, Academic/Scholarly.*
Published by: Cistercian Publications, Western Michigan University, 1903 W Michigan Ave, Kalamazoo, MI 48008-5415. TEL 269-387-8920, FAX 269-387-8390, cistpub@wmich.edu, http://www.spencerabbey.org/cistpub. Ed. Meredith Parsons Lillich. R&P E Royanne Elder. Circ: 1,000.

751.6 913 GBR ISSN 0039-3630
N8560 CODEN: SCONAH
➤ **STUDIES IN CONSERVATION.** Text in English; Summaries in French, German, Spanish. 1952. q. GBP 50; free to members (effective 2005). adv. bk.rev. illus. index. 72 p./no. 2 cols./p.; back issues avail.; reprints avail. **Document type:** *Journal, Academic/Scholarly.* **Description:** Contains original work and reviews on advances in conservation and restoration, covering both practical and scientific aspects, together with technical research on materials and methods of fabrication.
Indexed: A&ATA, ABM, AESIS, AIAP, ASCA, AnthLit, ArtHuCI, ArtInd, BAS, BHA, BrArAb, CCI, CIN, ChemAb, ChemTitl, CurCont, DIP, EngInd, FPA, IBR, IBZ, MSB, NumL, PCI, RASB, RILM, WSCA.
—BLDSC (8490.290000), CASDDS, IDS, IE, Infotrieve, ingenta, Linda Hall. **CCC.**
Published by: International Institute for Conservation of Historic and Artistic Works, 6 Buckingham St, London, WC2N 6BA, United Kingdom. TEL 44-20-78395975, FAX 44-20-79761564, studies@iiconservation.org, iic@iiconservation.org, http://www.iiconservation.org/publications/scguide.php. Circ: 4,000.

769.9492 NLD
STUDIES IN DUTCH GRAPHIC ART. Text in English. 1996. irreg. illus. **Document type:** *Academic/Scholarly.*
Published by: Museum Het Rembrandthuis, Jobenbreestraat 4-6, Amsterdam, 1011 NK, Netherlands. TEL 31-20-6384668, FAX 31-20-6232246. **Co-sponsor:** Rembrandt Information Center.

704 USA ISSN 0148-1029
NX1
➤ **STUDIES IN ICONOGRAPHY.** Text in English. 1975. a., latest vol.21. USD 20 per issue to individuals; USD 40 per issue to institutions (effective 2005). **Document type:** *Academic/Scholarly.* **Description:** Contains original essays about the visual culture of the period before 1600.
Related titles: Online - full text ed.: (from H.W. Wilson, O C L C Online Computer Library Center, Inc.).
Indexed: ABM, AIAP, ArtInd, BHA, MLA, MLA-IB, RILM.
—BLDSC (8490.714000).
Published by: Medieval Institute Publications, Western Michigan University, Walwood Hall, 1903 W Michigan, Kalamazoo, MI 49008-5432. TEL 269-387-8755, FAX 269-387-8750, http://www.wmich.edu/medieval/mip/journals/iconog.htm. Ed. Richard K Emmerson.

740 USA ISSN 0081-8178
P1
➤ **STUDIES IN MANUSCRIPT ILLUMINATION.** Text in English. 1954. irreg., latest 1995. price varies. charts; illus. reprint service avail. from PQC. **Document type:** *Monographic series, Academic/Scholarly.* **Description:** Explores issues in the illumination artwork in early manuscripts.
Published by: Princeton University Press, 41 William St, Princeton, NJ 08540-5237. TEL 609-258-4900, FAX 609-258-6305, http://pup.princeton.edu/catalogs/series/smi.html. Ed. Herbert H Kessler. **Subscr. to:** California - Princeton Fulfillment Services, 1445 Lower Ferry Rd, Ewing, NJ 08618. TEL 800-777-4726, FAX 800-999-1958, orders@cpfs.pupress.princeton.edu. **Dist. by:** University Press Group, 164 Hillsdale Ave E, Toronto, ON M4S 1T5, Canada.; John Wiley & Sons Ltd., The Atrium, Southern Gate, Chichester, West Sussex PO19 8SQ, United Kingdom.

700 USA ISSN 1058-997X
N6512
STUDIES IN MODERN ART. Text in English. 1991. a. USD 25. illus. reprints avail. **Description:** Devoted to modern and contemporary art. Concentrates on the museum's collection and programs as well as topics broadly related to the museums holdings. Each issue focuses on a single topic, such as an historical period, a movement, technique or individual work.
Indexed: ArtInd, BHA.
Published by: Museum of Modern Art, 11 W 53rd St, New York, NY 10019. TEL 212-708-9730, FAX 212-708-9779, TELEX 62370 MODART. Ed. John Elderfield.

STUDIES IN PRE-COLUMBIAN ART AND ARCHAEOLOGY. see *ARCHAEOLOGY*

740 745.1 720 USA ISSN 1069-8825
NK1
➤ **STUDIES IN THE DECORATIVE ARTS.** Text in English. 1993. s-a. USD 30 domestic; USD 35 in Canada & Mexico; USD 37 elsewhere (effective 2005). bk.rev. illus. back issues avail. **Document type:** *Journal, Academic/Scholarly.* **Description:** Publishes new research and interpretation in the history of the decorative arts. Studies all periods and cultures.
Indexed: ABM, AIAP, AmH&L, ArtInd, BHA, BRI, CBRI, DAAI, HistAb.
—BLDSC (8490.330500), IE, ingenta.
Published by: Bard Graduate Center for Studies in the Decorative Arts, 18 W 86th St, New York, NY 10024. TEL 212-501-3058, FAX 212-501-3089, http://www.bgc.bard.edu/aboutbgc/publications.shtml. Ed., R&P Sarah B Sherrill. Circ: 1,000 (paid).

708 USA ISSN 0091-7338
N386.U5
STUDIES IN THE HISTORY OF ART. Text in English. 1971. irreg., latest vol.65, 2004. price varies. charts; illus. **Document type:** *Monographic series, Academic/Scholarly.*
Formerly: Report and Studies in the History of Art (0080-1240)
Indexed: ABM, AIAP, ASCA, ArtHuCI, ArtInd, BHA, CurCont, PCI.
—BLDSC (8490.653000), IE, Infotrieve, ingenta.
Published by: National Gallery of Art, 2000B South Club Dr, Door #7, Landover, MD 20785. TEL 202-842-6353, cl-messineo@nga.gov. Circ: 6,000.

700 333.77 USA ISSN 1537-7199
N6921.V5
STUDIES IN VENETIAN ART AND CONSERVATION. Text in English. 1999. biennial.
Published by: Save Venice Inc., 15 East 74th St, New York, NY 10021. TEL 212-737-3141, FAX 212-249-0510, newyork@savevenice.org, http://www.savevenice.org.

▼ new title ➤ refereed ✶ unverified ♦ full entry avail.

700   ISR   ISSN 0792-4038
➤ **STUDIO/SETWDEYW**; art magazine. Text in English, Hebrew. 1989. m. ILS 320, USD 67 (effective Apr. 2003). adv. bk.rev.; film rev. illus. Index. 80 p./no.; back issues avail.; reprints avail. **Document type:** *Magazine, Consumer.*
Indexed: IHP.
Published by: Havatzeleth Cultural and Educational Institutes of Hashomer Hatzair, P O Box 23570, Tel Aviv, 61231, Israel. TEL 972-3-525-5701, FAX 972-3-525-5702, studio@netvision.net.il. Ed. Sarah Breitberg Semel. Adv. contact Rachel Michaeli. Circ: 4,000.

➤ **SUEDOSTDEUTSCHES KULTURWERK. VEROEFFENTLICHUNGEN. REIHE A: KULTUR UND DICHTUNG.** see *HISTORY—History Of Europe*

700 658.8   USA   ISSN 1081-6542
SUNSHINE ARTIST; America's premier show & festival guide for artists and craftspeople. Text in English. 1972. m. USD 34.95 domestic; USD 46.95 in Canada & Mexico; USD 50.95 elsewhere (effective 2005). adv. back issues avail. **Document type:** *Magazine, Trade.*
Formerly: Sunshine Artists U S A (0199-9370)
Related titles: Online - full text ed.
Published by: Palm House Publishing, Inc., 3210 Dade Ave., Orlando, FL 32804-4018. business@sunshineartist.com, webmaster@sunshineartist.com, http://www.sunshineartist.com/magazine/archives.htm. Ed. Cameron Meier. Pub. Ron Jones. Adv. contact Angel Ross. color page USD 1,581, B&W page USD 1,107. Circ: 15,000 (paid).

SUOMEN MUINAISMUISTOYHDISTYKSEN AIKAKAUSKIRJA/ FINSKA FORNMINNESFOERENINGENS TIDSKRIFT. see *ARCHAEOLOGY*

700 810   USA
SUPER A M; the journal for the science of leisure and the technology of art. Text in English. q. adv. **Document type:** *Consumer.* **Description:** Creative journal of art and ideas with art and technical sponsorships.
Address: 3373 Rowena Ave., Los Angeles, CA 90027. TEL 323-664-5431, sfosterj@pacbell.net, tompaul@earthlink.net, http://www.superam.com. Ed. Foster Johnson. Adv. contact Tom Wilson.

745   USA
NK8800
SURFACE DESIGN. Text in English. 1978. q. USD 45 domestic; USD 60 foreign; USD 7 newsstand/cover (effective 2000). adv. bk.rev. illus. back issues avail. **Document type:** *Trade.* **Description:** Covers contemporary textile art with emphasis on surface treatment.
Former titles (until 1999): Surface Newsletter; Surface Design Journal (0197-4483)
Related titles: Online - full text ed.: (from H.W. Wilson, O C L C Online Computer Library Center, Inc.).
Indexed: ArtInd, BRI, CBRI, DAAI, WTA.
—BLDSC (8547.820000), IE, ingenta.
Published by: Surface Design Association, PO Box 360, Sebastopol, CA 95473. TEL 707-829-3110, FAX 707-829-3285, surfacedesign@mail.com, http://www.art.uidaho.edu/sda, http://www.surfacedesign.org. Ed., R&P Patricia Malarcher TEL 201-568-1084. Pub. Nancy Jones Wetmore. Adv. contact Joy Stocksdale. B&W page USD 370, color page USD 605; trim 10.25 x 8.25. Circ: 5,600. **Dist. by:** Eastern News Distributors Inc., 250 W. 55th St., New York, NY 10019. TEL 212-649-4149.

SVETA GORA. see *LITERATURE*

700   SWE   ISSN 1651-4564
SWEDEN. STATENS KONSTRAAD. KATALOG. Text in Swedish; Summaries in English. 1980. a., latest vol.32, 2003. illus. back issues avail. **Document type:** *Yearbook.* **Description:** Includes descriptions of installed, commissioned public art in Sweden.
Formerly (untill 2002): Statens Konstraad (0349-8220)
Published by: Statens Konstraad/The National Public Art Council, Wallingatan 20-22, PO Box 3084, Stockholm, 10361, Sweden. TEL 46-8-4401280, FAX 46-8-4401281, info@statenskonstrad.se, http://www.statenskonstrad.se.

SWINDLE. see *MUSIC*

700   NLD   ISSN 0923-9073
➤ **SYMBOLA ET EMBLEMATA.** Text in Dutch. 1989. irreg., latest vol.10, 2000. price varies. illus. back issues avail. **Document type:** *Monographic series, Academic/Scholarly.* **Description:** Scholarly monographs and papers on the history of emblems in Europe.
—BLDSC (8581.690000).
Published by: Brill Academic Publishers, PO Box 9000, Leiden, 2300 PA, Netherlands. TEL 31-71-53-53-500, FAX 31-71-53-17-532, cs@brillusa.com, http://www.brill.nl. R&P Elizabeth Venekamp. **Subscr. in N. America to:** PO Box 605, Herndon, VA 20172. TEL 703-661-1585, 800-337-9255, FAX 703-661-1501, cs@brillusa.com. **Distr. outside N. America by:** c/o Turpin Distribution, Stratton Business Park, Pegasus Drive, Biggleswade, BEDFORDSHIRE SG 18 8TQ, United Kingdom. TEL 44-1767-604-954, FAX 44-1767-601-640, brill@turpin-distribution.com.

➤ **SYMMETRY:** culture and science. see *SCIENCES: COMPREHENSIVE WORKS*

➤ **SYRIA**; revue d'art oriental et d'archeologie. see *ARCHAEOLOGY*

700   POL   ISSN 0324-8232
N6
SZTUKA. Text in Polish; Summaries in English, French. 1974. m. PLZ 24, USD 48. bk.rev. bibl.; illus. **Description:** Color and black and white pictures, critical and theoretical texts on contemporary art in Poland and in the world; reviews, interviews, and chronicles.
Formerly: Przeglad Artystyczny (0033-2011)
Indexed: ABCT, ABM, BHA, RASB.
Published by: Studio Wydawnicze "Sztuka", Ul Miodowa 12 m 57, Warsaw, 00261, Poland. Ed. Andrzej Skoczylas.

700 100   POL
SZTUKA I FILOZOFIA. Text in Polish. s-a. PLZ 19 per issue (effective 2003). **Document type:** *Journal, Academic/Scholarly.*
Published by: (Uniwersytet Warszawski, Instytut Filozofii/Warsaw University, Institute of Philosophy), Wydawnictwo Naukowe Scholar, ul Krakowskie Przedmiescie 62, Warsaw, 00322, Poland. TEL 48-22-6357404 ext 218, FAX 48-22-8289391, info@scholar.com.pl, http://www.scholar.com.pl.

700.957   AUS   ISSN 1037-6674
NX572.A1
T A A S A REVIEW; journal of the Asian Arts Society of Australia. Text in English. 1992. q. AUD 55 domestic; AUD 85 foreign (effective 2003). adv. bk.rev.; music rev.; film rev. 28 p./no.; back issues avail. **Document type:** *Journal, Consumer.* **Description:** Contains articles and reviews on Asian fine and decorative arts and their impact on the arts of the other cultures including Australia. Concerned with the historical continuum to the present including West, Central, South, Southeast and East Asia.
Indexed: ABM.
Published by: Asian Arts Society of Australia, PO Box 996, Potts Point, NSW 2011, Australia. TEL 61-2-92251861, FAX 61-2-92251894, farfor@ozemail.com.au. Eds. Ann MacArthur, Sandra Forbes TEL 61-2-9363-2003. Adv. contact Sabrina Snow TEL 61-2-9363-1661.

700   NLD
T A M BULLETIN. Text in English. 1984. bi-m. free. bk.rev. illus.; stat. **Document type:** *Bulletin.* **Description:** Features mail-art news, projects and publications through a computer bulletin board service.
Related titles: Online - full text ed.
Published by: Travelling Art Mail, Ruud Janssen - TAM, PO Box 10388, Tilburg, 5000 JJ, Netherlands. TEL 31-13-5366103, webmaster@iuoma.org, http://www.iuoma.org/. Ed. Ruud Janssen. Circ: (controlled).

740   ESP   ISSN 0210-3761
T G; revista de las artes decorativas. Text in Spanish. 1968. bi-m. adv. bk.rev. illus.
Indexed: BHA.
Published by: Tapicerias Gancedo, Velazquez 21, Madrid, 28001, Spain. TEL 34-91-5768701, FAX 34-91-5765024, madrid@tapicerias-gancedo.com, http://www.tapicerias-gancedo.com. Circ: 10,000 (controlled).

700   NLD   ISSN 0166-4492
TABLEAU; fine arts magazine. Text in Dutch, English. 1978. bi-m. EUR 49.50 (effective 2005). adv. illus. back issues avail. **Document type:** *Magazine, Consumer.* **Description:** Covers the international art world, including museum and gallery exhibitions, auctions, art and antiques fairs, and profiles of artists.
Indexed: AIAP, BHA.
—IE, Infotrieve.
Published by: Sanoma Uitgevers B.V., Postbus 1900, Hoofddorp, 2130 JH, Netherlands. TEL 31-23-5565377, FAX 31-23-5565376, tableau@tijdschriften.sanoma.com, http://www.sanoma-uitgevers.nl. Ed. Ronald Kraayeveld. Circ: 9,961.

TABLEAU (WINNIPEG); involving people in the visual arts. see *MUSEUMS AND ART GALLERIES*

391   USA
TABU TATTOO. Text in English. bi-m. USD 20.98 (effective 2002). **Address:** 5 Marine View Plaza, 207, Hoboken, NJ 07030. TEL 201-653-2700, FAX 201-653-7892. Pub. Casey Exton.

790.13   DEU   ISSN 1614-9394
TAETOWIERMAGAZIN. Text in German. 1994. m. EUR 52 domestic; EUR 75 foreign; EUR 5 newsstand/cover (effective 2005). adv. **Document type:** *Magazine, Consumer.*
Published by: Huber Verlag GmbH & Co. KG, Ottenhoefer Str 8, Mannheim, 68239, Germany. TEL 49-621-483610, FAX 49-621-4836111, postmaster@taetowiermagazin.de, h.heim@huber-verlag.de, http://www.taetowiermagazin.de, http://www.huber-verlag.de. Ed. Dirk-Boris Roedel. Pub. Guenther Brecht. Adv. contact Petra Thiele. color page EUR 2,100; trim 184 x 256. Circ: 17,666 (paid and controlled).

700   FIN   ISSN 0039-8977
N8
TAIDE. Text in Finnish; Summaries in English. 1960. bi-m. EUR 55. adv. bk.rev. illus. **Document type:** *Magazine, Academic/Scholarly.*
Indexed: ABM, BHA, RASB, RILM.
—BLDSC (8598.502700).
Published by: Suomen Taiteilijaseura/Artists' Association of Finland, Nilsiaenkatu 11-13, Helsinki, 00510, Finland. TEL 358-9-6129210, FAX 358-9-61292160, taide@artists.fi, aaf@artists.fi, http://www.artists.fi/taide-kustannus/lehti/lehti-index.html. Ed. Otso Kantokorpi. Circ: 6,500.

709   FIN   ISSN 0355-1938
TAIDEHISTORIALLISIA TUTKIMUKSIA/STUDIES IN ART HISTORY. Text in English, Finnish. 1974. a., latest vol.30, 2004. prce varies. back issues avail. **Document type:** *Monographic series, Academic/Scholarly.*
Indexed: AIAP.
Address: c/o Taidehistorian Oppiano, Helsinki Universitet, PO Box 3, Helsinki, 00014, Finland. johanna.vuolasto@luakku.com, http://www.taidehistorianseura.fi/.

TALOHA. see *MUSEUMS AND ART GALLERIES*

TAMIL KALAI; research journal on Tamilology. see *HISTORY—History Of Asia*

700   GBR   ISSN 1464-3472
TANK (LONDON). Text in English. 2001 (May). s-a. GBP 72. **Document type:** *Magazine, Consumer.* **Description:** Presents contemporary art.
Indexed: LID&ISL.
Published by: Tank Publications Ltd., 58 Frith St, London, W1V 5TA, United Kingdom. http://www.tankmagazine.com. Eds. Andreas Laeufer, Masoud Golsorkhi.

700   UAE
AT-TASHKIL. Text in Arabic. 1987. irreg. free. **Description:** Covers fine arts activities in the U.A.E., including exhibition listings and cinema.
Published by: Emirates Society for Fine Arts, Cultural Group, PO Box 2355, Sharjah, United Arab Emirates. TEL 375262. Ed. Muhammas Yussif Ali. Circ: 500.

705   GBR   ISSN 1743-8853
TATE ETC. Text in English. 1993. 3/yr. **Document type:** *Magazine, Consumer.* **Description:** An independent art magazine for the general reader interested in the art scene.
Formerly (until 2004): Tate (London) (1351-3737)
Related titles: Online - full content ed.
Indexed: ABM, BHA.
—BLDSC (8608.555000), IE, ingenta.
Published by: Tate Etc., 20 John Islip St, London, SW1P 4G, United Kingdom. TEL 44-20-78878000, FAX 44-20-78878729, tateetc@tate.org.uk, http://www.tate.org.uk/tateetc. Ed. Simon Grant. Pub. Matt Watkins.

391   FRA   ISSN 1289-5369
TATOUAGE. Text in French. 199?. q. EUR 32.13 (effective 2002). adv. **Document type:** *Magazine, Consumer.*
Published by: Editions Lariviere, Espace Clichy, 12 rue Mozart, Clichy, Cedex 92587, France. TEL 33-1-41403105, FAX 33-1-41403250, abo@editions-lariviere.fr, http://www.editions-lariviere.fr.

391   USA   ISSN 1041-3146
GT2345
TATTOO; magazine of skin art. Text in English. m. USD 34.95 domestic; USD 51.95 foreign; USD 5.99 newsstand/cover (effective 2005). adv. **Document type:** *Magazine, Consumer.*
Published by: Paisano Publications, Inc., 28210 Dorothy Dr, Box 3075, Agoura Hills, CA 91301. TEL 818-889-8740, FAX 818-889-4726. Ed. Dave Nichols. Pub., R&P Joseph Teresi. adv.: B&W page USD 1,795, color page USD 2,830. Circ: 106,955 (paid).

391   USA   ISSN 1079-9443
TATTOO FLASH. Text in English. bi-m. USD 19.95; USD 4.99 newsstand/cover (effective 2001). adv. **Document type:** *Magazine, Consumer.*
Formerly: Flash (Agoura Hills) (1070-1184)
Published by: Paisano Publications, Inc., 28210 Dorothy Dr, Box 3075, Agoura Hills, CA 91301. TEL 818-889-8740, FAX 818-889-4726, http://www.easyriders.com. Ed. Keith Ball. Pub. Joseph Teresi. R&P Brian Wood. Adv. contact Sandie Nilsen. **Dist. in UK by:** Comag, Tavistock Works, Tavistock Rd, W Drayton, Middx UB7 7QX, United Kingdom. TEL 44-1895-444055, FAX 44-1895-433602.

741   ITA   ISSN 1591-1772
TATTOO ONE. Text in Italian. 2001. bi-m. EUR 4.60 newsstand/cover (effective 2003). adv. **Document type:** *Magazine, Consumer.*
Published by: Trentini S.r.l., Via Pier Luigi Nervi 1/B, Argenta, 44011, Italy. TEL 39-0532-318149, FAX 39-0532-310084, info@3ntini.com, http://www.3ntini.com.

700   **USA**
TATTOO PLANET. Text in English. 2000. bi-m. USD 29.70 domestic; USD 37.97 in Canada; USD 42.97 elsewhere; USD 5.99 newsstand/cover domestic; USD 7.50 newsstand/cover in Canada (effective 2002). illus.; tr.lit. 80 p./no.; **Document type:** *Magazine, Trade.* **Description:** Covers tattoo arts and culture with features on tattoo artists, news of tattoo events and conventions, and articles on tattoo history throughout the world. Provides a "cultural background" for tattoo artists and serves as a forum for tattoo artists to share ideas.
Published by: Multi Media International L L C, 1359 Broadway, 1203, New York, NY 10018. http://www.tattoolife.com. Ed. Robert Butcher. **Subscr. to:** Veer Publishing Co, 7154 N University Dr, 132, Tamarac, FL 33321.

700   **USA**   ISSN 1047-1499
TATTOO REVIEW. Text in English. 9/yr. USD 32.95. adv. back issues avail. **Document type:** *Consumer.*
Published by: Outlaw Biker Enterprises, Inc., 5 Marine View Plaza, Ste 207, Hoboken, NJ 07030. TEL 201-653-2700. Ed. Jean-Chris Miller. Pub. Casey Exton. R&P Jean Chris Miller. Adv. contact Ken Knabb. Circ: 170,000.

702   **USA**
TATTOO REVIEW SPECIALS. Text in English. q. USD 5.95 newsstand/cover. adv. **Document type:** *Consumer.*
Published by: Outlaw Biker Enterprises, Inc., 5 Marine View Plaza, Ste 207, Hoboken, NJ 07030. TEL 201-653-2700. Ed. Jean-Chris Miller. Pub. Casey Exton. R&P Jean Chris Miller. Adv. contact Ken Knabb.

391   **USA**   ISSN 1072-8384
TATTOO SAVAGE. Variant title: Savage. Text in English. 1994. bi-m. USD 19.95; USD 4.99 newsstand/cover (effective 2001). adv. illus. **Document type:** *Magazine, Consumer.*
Published by: Paisano Publications, Inc., 28210 Dorothy Dr, Box 3075, Agoura Hills, CA 91301. TEL 818-889-8740, FAX 818-889-4726, http://www.easyriders.com/newsstand/savagetoc.html. Ed. Keith Ball. Pub. Joseph Teresi. R&P Brian Wood. Adv. contact Sandie Nilsen. **Subscr. to:** Tattoo Savage Subscriptions, PO Box 469062, Escondido, CA 92046-9062. **Dist. in UK by:** Comag, Tavistock Works, Tavistock Rd, W Drayton, Middx UB7 7QX, United Kingdom. TEL 44-1895-444055, FAX 44-1895-433602.

391   **DEU**   ISSN 1438-2083
TATTOO SCENE LIVE. Text in German. 1998. bi-m. EUR 4.50 newsstand/cover (effective 2002). adv. **Document type:** *Magazine, Consumer.* **Description:** Contains articles and feautres on tattoo artists, conventions, and enthusiasts.
Published by: T V Trend Verlag GmbH, Hertener Markt 7, Herten, 45699, Germany. TEL 49-2366-808100, FAX 49-2366-808190, vmkd@real-net.de. Ed. Michael Stein. Pub. Alexander Welke. R&P Arno Welke. Adv. contact Olaf in der Beek TEL 49-2366-808201. B&W page EUR 3,300, color page EUR 4,500; trim 210 x 285. Circ: 23,000 (paid).

391.65   **CAN**
TATTOOS.COM EZINE. Text in English. 1995. d. **Description:** Covers tattoos and body modification.
Media: Online - full text.
Address: 2234 Kingston Rd, Toronto, ON M1N 1T9, Canada. tats@inforamp.net, http://tattoos.com. Ed. Damian McGrath.

702   **USA**   ISSN 1070-7247
TATTOOS FOR MEN. Text in English. 1993. bi-m. USD 5.95 newsstand/cover; GBP 2.99 newsstand/cover in United Kingdom. adv. **Document type:** *Consumer.*
Published by: Outlaw Biker Enterprises, Inc., 5 Marine View Plaza, Ste 207, Hoboken, NJ 07030. TEL 201-653-2700, FAX 201-653-7892. Ed. Jean-Chris Miller. Pub. Casey Exton. R&P Jean Chris Miller. Adv. contact Ken Knabb. **Dist. in UK by:** Comag, Tavistock Works, Tavistock Rd, W Drayton, Middx UB7 7QX, United Kingdom. TEL 44-1895-444055, FAX 44-1895-433602.

702   **USA**   ISSN 1088-2456
TATTOOS FOR WOMEN. Text in English. 1995. bi-m. USD 5.95 newsstand/cover; GBP 2.99 newsstand/cover in United Kingdom. adv. **Document type:** *Consumer.*
Published by: Outlaw Biker Enterprises, Inc., 5 Marine View Plaza, Ste 207, Hoboken, NJ 07030. TEL 201-653-2700, FAX 201-653-7892. Ed. Jean-Chris Miller. Pub. Casey Exton. R&P Jean Chris Miller. Adv. contact Ken Knabb. **Dist. in UK by:** Comag, Tavistock Works, Tavistock Rd, W Drayton, Middx UB7 7QX, United Kingdom. TEL 44-1895-444055, FAX 44-1895-433602.

702   **DEU**   ISSN 1614-9408
TATTOOSTYLE. Text in German. 2002. q. EUR 18 domestic; EUR 26 foreign; EUR 5 newsstand/cover (effective 2005). adv. **Document type:** *Magazine, Consumer.*
Published by: Huber Verlag GmbH & Co. KG, Ottenhoefer Str 8, Mannheim, 68239, Germany. TEL 49-621-483610, FAX 49-621-4836111, h.heim@huber-verlag.de, http://www.huber-verlag.de. Ed. Dirk-Boris Roedel. Adv. contact Petra Thiele. color page EUR 2,100; trim 184 x 256. Circ: 17,666 (paid and controlled).

700   **USA**
TATTOOTIME. Text in English. 1982. irreg.

Published by: Hardy Marks Publications, 700 Lombard St, San Francisco, CA 94133-1615. TEL 415-433-9437, FAX 415-433-0229. Ed. D E Hardy. Circ: 10,000.

700 370   **USA**   ISSN 1541-1796
NX303
▼ **THE TEACHING ARTIST JOURNAL.** Text in English. 2003. q. USD 230 in US & Canada to institutions; USD 260 elsewhere to institutions; USD 240 combined subscription in US & Canada to institutions print & online eds.; USD 270 combined subscription elsewhere to institutions print & online eds. (effective 2006). adv. back issues avail. **Document type:** *Journal, Academic/Scholarly.* **Description:** Provides an authoritative, timely, ongoing professional development resource to clarify, enrich, and advance Teaching Artist research and practice.
Related titles: Online - full content ed.: ISSN 1541-180X. 2003. USD 215 worldwide to institutions (effective 2006); Online - full text ed.: (from EBSCO Publishing, Gale Group, O C L C Online Computer Library Center, Inc., Swets Information Services).
—BLDSC (8614.040500), IE. **CCC.**
Published by: Lawrence Erlbaum Associates, Inc., 10 Industrial Ave, Mahwah, NJ 07430-2262. TEL 201-258-2200, 800-926-6579, FAX 201-236-0072, journals@erlbaum.com, http://www.leaonline.com/loi/taj, http://www.erlbaum.com. Ed. Eric Booth. adv.: page USD 250; trim 5 x 8.

700   **USA**
TEAR. Text in English. q. USD 29 (effective 2002). adv. illus.
Published by: Tattoo Planet, 1089 Broadway, 3rd Fl, Brooklyn, NY 11221. TEL 718-455-5130, tat2planet@aol.com, http://www.tattooplanet.com/Tear. Ed. Yahsa Yough. **Subscr. to:** Veer Publishing Co, 7154 N University Dr, 132, Tamarac, FL 33321.

▼ **TECHNOETIC ARTS**; a journal of speculative research. see *TECHNOLOGY: COMPREHENSIVE WORKS*

751.6 720   **USA**   ISSN 0146-1214
N8554   **CODEN: TECODM**
TECHNOLOGY AND CONSERVATION; of art, architecture and antiquities. Text in English. 1976. q. USD 28 domestic; USD 60 foreign (effective 2005). adv. bk.rev. illus.; tr.lit. **Document type:** *Magazine, Trade.* **Description:** Covers the analysis, preservation, restoration, security, environmental protection, and documentation of art (paintings, sculptures, textiles, ceramics, antiquities etc.), photography, manuscripts, books, and architecture (buildings, monuments, historic sites).
Indexed: A&ATA, AIAP, API, AbAn, ArtInd, BHA, BrArAb, ChemAb, GALA, PCI.
—CISTI.
Published by: Technology Organization Inc., 76 Highland Ave, Somerville, MA 02143. TEL 617-623-4488. Ed., Pub., Adv. contact Susan E Schur. Circ: 15,500.

740   **SWE**   ISSN 0347-7673
TECKNAREN. Text in Swedish. 1977. 6/yr. SEK 250 to non-members (effective 2004). adv. bk.rev. 32 p./no.; **Document type:** *Trade.* **Description:** Forum for debate, feature stories, and news relevant to professional illustrators and graphic designers.
Published by: Foereningen Svenska Tecknare, Goetgatan 48, Stockholm, 11826, Sweden. TEL 46-8-55602910, FAX 46-8-55602919, tecknaren@svensktecknare.se, info@svensktecknare.se, http://www.svensktecknare.se/index2.asp?avdelning=1, http://www.svensktecknare.se. Ed., R&P Dick Schyberg TEL 46-8-55602918. Circ: 1,350.

700   **ITA**   ISSN 1128-6601
TEMA CELESTE; arte contemporanea. Text in Italian. 1983. bi-m. EUR 43 domestic; EUR 70 in Europe; EUR 98 elsewhere; USD 11 newsstand/cover in United States; USD 17.50 newsstand/cover in Canada (effective 2005). adv. **Document type:** *Magazine, Consumer.*
Indexed: BHA.
Published by: Gabrius SpA, Piazza Borromeo 10, Milan, 20123, Italy. TEL 39-02-8065171, FAX 39-02-80651743, http://www.temaceleste.com, http://www.gabrius.com. Ed., Pub. Alberica Cetti Serbelloni.

700   **ESP**   ISSN 0214-6258
TEMAS DE ESTETICA Y ARTE. Text in Spanish. 1985. irreg.
Indexed: RILM.
—CINDOC.
Published by: Real Academia de Bellas Artes de Santa Isabel de Hungria, Abades, 12-14, Sevilla, 41004, Spain.

TEMENOS ACADEMY REVIEW. see *LITERATURE*

700   **CHE**   ISSN 1016-0809
TEMPORALE; rivista d'arte e di cultura. Text in Italian. 1983. q. CHF 36.
Published by: Edizioni Dabbeni - Lugano, Casella Postale 2461, Lugano, 6900, Switzerland. TEL 091-23-29-80, FAX 091-23-12-11. Ed. Stefano Dabbeni.

TERRA PLANA. see *TRAVEL AND TOURISM*

753   **ITA**   ISSN 0390-0355
TERZO OCCHIO; rivista trimestrale d'arte contemporanea. Text in Italian. 1975. q. adv. bk.rev. illus.
Indexed: ABM, BHA, RILM.
Published by: Edizioni Bora S.N.C., Via Jacopo di Paolo, 42, Bologna, BO 40128, Italy. TEL 39-51-356133, FAX 39-51-374394, daniele.brandani@mailbox.dsnet.it. Ed. Patrizia Bonfiglioli. Pub. Edoardo Brandani. R&P Arnalda Franciosi. Adv. contact Valentina Brandani. Circ: 10,000.

700   **DEU**   ISSN 0940-9459
TEXTE ZUR KUNST. Text in German. 1990. q. adv. bk.rev.; film rev.; play rev.; video rev.; Website rev. back issues avail. **Document type:** *Journal, Academic/Scholarly.*
Indexed: BHA.
Published by: Texte zur Kunst Verlag GmbH und Co. KG, Torstr 141, Berlin, 10119, Germany. TEL 49-30-28484939, FAX 49-30-28484938, verlag@textezurkunst.de, http://www.textezurkunst.de. Ed. Isabelle Graw. Pub., R&P Wilhelm von Werthern. Adv. contact Anke Ulrich TEL 49-30-28047911.

THE TEXTILE MUSEUM JOURNAL. see *TEXTILE INDUSTRIES AND FABRICS*

700   **UAE**
THAQAFA WA FANN/CULTURE AND ART. Text in Arabic. 1989. d. **Description:** Covers the activities of the foundation: exhibitions, film series, lectures, meeting, publications.
Published by: Cultural Foundation, Culture and Arts Department, P O Box 2380, Abu Dhabi, United Arab Emirates. TEL 215300, FAX 336059, TELEX 2214 CULCEN EM. Circ: 500 (controlled).

THEORIE UND GESCHICHTE DER LITERATUR UND DER SCHOENEN KUENSTE. see *LITERATURE*

700   **GBR**   ISSN 0952-8822
NX596.3.A1
➤ **THIRD TEXT**; third world perspectives on contemporary art & culture. Text in English. 1987. bi-m. GBP 262, USD 395 combined subscription to institutions print & online eds. (effective 2006). adv. bk.rev. reprint service avail. from PSC. **Document type:** *Journal, Academic/Scholarly.* **Description:** Scholarly journal focusing on the fields of art criticism, art history and cultural studies.
Related titles: Online - full text ed.: ISSN 1475-5297. GBP 249, USD 375 to institutions (effective 2006) (from EBSCO Publishing, Gale Group, IngentaConnect, O C L C Online Computer Library Center, Inc., Swets Information Services).
Indexed: ABM, ArtInd, BHA, DIP, FLI, IBR, IBSS, IBZ, LeftInd, PerIslam.
—BLDSC (8820.143200), IE, Infotrieve, ingenta. **CCC.**
Published by: Routledge (Subsidiary of: Taylor & Francis Group), 4 Park Sq, Milton Park, Abingdon, Oxon OX14 4RN, United Kingdom. TEL 44-1235-828600, FAX 44-1235-829000, editorial@thirdtext.com, journals@routledge.com, http://www.tandf.co.uk/journals/titles/09528822.asp, http://www.routledge.co.uk. Eds. Rasheed Araeen, Ziauddin Sardar. Circ: 2,500. **Subscr. to:** Taylor & Francis Ltd, Journals Customer Service, Rankine Rd, Basingstoke, Hants RG24 8PR, United Kingdom. TEL 44-1256-813000, FAX 44-1256-330245, enquiry@tandf.co.uk.

➤ **THORVALDSENS MUSEUM. MEDDELELSER.** see *MUSEUMS AND ART GALLERIES*

720 700 770 791.43   **USA**   ISSN 1091-711X
NA2000
THRESHOLDS (CAMBRIDGE). Text in English. 1992. s-a. USD 18 domestic; USD 23 foreign; USD 10 per issue domestic; USD 13 per issue foreign (effective 2004). **Document type:** *Journal, Academic/Scholarly.*
Indexed: AIAP.
Published by: Massachusetts Institute of Technology, Department of Architecture, 77 Massachusetts Ave, Cambridge, MA 02139. TEL 617-258-8439, FAX 617-258-9455, thresh@mit.edu, http://architecture.mit.edu/threshholds.

700   **AUS**   ISSN 1444-1594
THYLAZINE; Australian arts and literature on landscape and animals. Text in English. 2000. s-a.
Media: Online - full text.
Published by: Thylazine Publishing Australia, PO Box 527, Ingleborn, NSW 1890, Australia. TEL 61-4-1851-5411, coralhull@thylazine.org, http://www.thylazine.org. Eds. Coral Hull, John Kinsella.

TIROLER HEIMATBLAETTER. see *HISTORY—History Of Europe*

700   **USA**   ISSN 1539-1183
TODAY'S CREATIVE HOME ARTS. Text in English. 2001. bi-m. adv. **Document type:** *Magazine, Consumer.*
Published by: North American Media Group, Inc. (Subsidiary of: North American Membership Group, Inc.), 12301 Whitewater Dr, Ste 260, Minnetonka, MN 55343. TEL 952-936-9333, 800-922-4888, FAX 952-936-9755, namghq@namginc.com, http://www.namginc.com/ACmediaKit.asp. Ed. Kelly March O'Hara. Pub. Marynell Christenson. adv.: B&W page USD 5,650, color page USD 8,250. Circ: 275,000 (controlled).

A

700 JPN ISSN 0563-8151
TOKYO GEIJUTSU DAIGAKU BIJUTSU GAKUBU KIYO/TOKYO NATIONAL UNIVERSITY OF FINE ARTS AND MUSIC. FACULTY OF FINE ARTS. BULLETIN. Text in Japanese. 1965. a. **Document type:** *Journal, Academic/Scholarly.*
Published by: Tokyo Geijutsu Daigaku, Bijutsu Gakubu/Tokyo National University of Fine Arts and Music, Faculty of Fine Arts, 12-8 Ueno Kouen, Taito-ku, Tokyo, 110-8714, Japan. jkikaku@off.geidai.ac.jp, http://www.geidai.ac.jp/guid/arts.html.

741.5 GBR ISSN 1466-0997
TOMB RAIDER - WITCHBLADE. Text in English. 1999. bi-m. **Document type:** *Magazine, Consumer.*
Published by: Marvel Comics Ltd. (Subsidiary of: Panini UK Ltd.), Panini House, Coach & Horses Passage, The Pantiles, Tunbridge Wells, Kent TM2 5UJ, United Kingdom. TEL 44-1892-500100, FAX 44-1892-545666.

700 ITA ISSN 0392-498X
IL TORCHIO ARTISTICO E LETTERARIO; organo ufficiale di stampa dell'Accademia Culturale d'Europa. Text in Italian. 1978. m. bk.rev. back issues avail.
Published by: Accademia Culturale d'Europa, Viale IV Novembre, 1, Bassano Romano, VT 01030, Italy. TEL 0761 634115. Ed. Rino Pompei.

700 POL ISSN 0082-5514
TOWARZYSTWO NAUKOWE W TORUNIU. KOMISJA HISTORII SZTUKI. TEKA. Text in Polish; Summaries in French. 1959. irreg., latest vol.6, 1992. price varies. **Document type:** *Monographic series.*
Related titles: ◆ Series of: Wydzial Filologiczno-Filozoficzny. Prace. ISSN 0208-497X.
Indexed: BHA.
Published by: Towarzystwo Naukowe w Toruniu, Ul Wysoka 16, Torun, 81100, Poland. TEL 48-56-23941. Ed. Marian Szarmach. Circ: 600.

TRACE (NEW YORK, 1998); transcultural styles & ideas. see *LIFESTYLE*

700 808.87 USA
TRADE JOURNAL RECAP. Text in English. 1973. m. USD 20 (effective 1999). back issues avail. **Document type:** *Newsletter, Trade.* **Description:** Describes cartoons printed in trade journals and house organs during the previous months. Includes frequency of publication, issue date, cartoon editor, address, price paid, and cartoonist's name.
Published by: Gag Recap Publishers, 12 Hedden Pl, New Providence, NJ 07974-1724. TEL 908-464-1158. Ed. Al Gottlieb.

700 USA ISSN 1093-0973
➤ **TRADICION REVISTA**; the journal of contemporary & traditional Spanish colonial art and culture. Text in English. 1996 (Jan.). q. USD 30 domestic to individuals; USD 66 foreign to individuals (effective 2004). adv. bk.rev.; music rev.; video rev. charts; illus.; maps. 96 p./no.; back issues avail. **Document type:** *Magazine, Academic/Scholarly.* **Description:** Provides regular information on the Hispanic art and culture of the Southwest as well as other areas of the Spanish Borderlands. Covers history, archaeology, architecture, culture and art.
Published by: L P D Press, 925 Salamanca NW, Albuquerque, NM 87107-5647. TEL 505-344-9382, FAX 505-345-5129, info@nmsantos.com, http://www.nmsantos.com/. Ed., Pub., R&P, Adv. contact Paul Rhetts TEL 505-344-9382. B&W page USD 320, color page USD 800; trim 8 x 10.5. Circ: 5,000.

700 800 USA ISSN 1084-9432
NX458
TRANS: ARTS CULTURES MEDIA. Text in English, Spanish, French, Portuguese. 1995. 3/yr. USD 40 (effective 2000). adv. bk.rev. illus. **Document type:** *Academic/Scholarly.* **Description:** Devoted to developing and extending a dialogue on the diversity of cultural and artistic production in the Americas.
Related titles: Online - full text ed.
Published by: Passim, Inc., 511 W. 25th St., # 502, New York, NY 10001-5501. TEL 212-929-0226, FAX 212-366-4813, trans@echonyc.com, http://www.echonyc.com/~TRANS. Ed. Sandra Antelo-Suarez. R&P Sandra Antelo Suarez. Adv. contact Elizabeth Fiore.

701.17 DNK ISSN 1399-1353
➤ **TRANSFIGURATION**; Nordisk tidsskrift for kunst og kristendom. Text in Danish; Text occasionally in Swedish, Norwegian. 1999. s-a., latest vol.2, 2001. DKK 150 domestic; USD 25 elsewhere (effective 2005). **Document type:** *Journal, Academic/Scholarly.* **Description:** Discusses the relationship between the arts and Christianity from the early Church to the present day.
Related titles: Online - full content ed.: ISSN 1604-3049.
Indexed: RILM.
Published by: Museum Tusculanum Press, c/o University of Copenhagen, Njalsgade 94, Copenhagen S, 2300, Denmark. TEL 45-35-329109, FAX 45-35-329113, mtp@mtp.dk, http://www.mtp.dk. Ed. Nils Holger Petersen. **Dist. by:** International Specialized Book Services Inc.

700 ARG
TRASTIENDA; revista del mercado de arte y antiguedades. Text in Spanish. m.?. USD 40.
Address: Tte. Gral. Peron 1454, 1o '6', Capital Federal, Buenos Aires 1037, Argentina. Ed. Julia Raggi. Pub. Mario Gilardoni.

TRAVAUX D'HUMANISME ET RENAISSANCE. see *HISTORY—History Of Europe*

700 FRA ISSN 0336-9730
TRAVERSES. Text in French. 1997. 3/yr. back issues avail.
Media: Online - full text.
Published by: (Centre National d'Art et de Culture Georges Pompidou), Edition du Centre Pompidou, Paris, Cedex 4 75191, France. TEL 33-1-4478-1233, FAX 33-1-4478-1205, TELEX CNACGP 212 726, seac@cnac-gp.fr, http://www.cnac-gp-fr/traverses.

TRIBUS; Jahrbuch des Linden-Museums Stuttgart. see *ANTHROPOLOGY*

TRICYCLE; the Buddhist review. see *RELIGIONS AND THEOLOGY—Buddhist*

TRIERER ZEITSCHRIFT FUER GESCHICHTE UND KUNST DES TRIERER LANDES UND SEINER NACHBARGEBIETE. see *ARCHAEOLOGY*

TRIVIUM. see *LITERATURE*

750 730 FRA
TROUVAILLES. Text in French. m. adv. illus. **Description:** Antiques in painting, sculpture, decorations.
Published by: Joel Garcia, 1-3 rue du Depart, Paris, 75014, France. Eds. Anne Vaujour, Rene Margeridon.

745.1 070.5 USA
THE TRUMPET (NEW YORK). Text in English. 1986. q. free. illus. **Document type:** *Newsletter.* **Description:** Provides news of forthcoming sales of rare books, photographs, autographs and art at auctions, as well as brief notes on recently held sales, and the prices brought in by notable pieces.
Published by: Swann Galleries, Inc., 104 E 25th St, New York, NY 10010-2977. TEL 212-254-4710, FAX 212-979-1017, swann@swanngalleries.com. Eds. Annie Livingston, Caroline Birenbaum. Circ: 45,000.

700 BGR ISSN 1310-7283
N7188
TSENITEL/CONNOISSEUR. Text in Bulgarian. 1996. s-a. BGL 7 newsstand/cover (effective 2002). **Description:** Presents contemporary and classical Bulgarian art, young artists, international events and personalities.
Published by: Business Week Ltd., 33 Lulin Planina St., Sofia, 1618, Bulgaria. TEL 359-2-541055, FAX 359-2-543007, http://www.sca.bg/cultural-periodicals/catalog/zenitel.htm. Ed. Jura Shishkova.

700 780 792 GBR ISSN 0260-8383
TUITION, ENTERTAINMENT, NEWS, VIEWS. Text in English. 197?. 2/yr. GBP 0.20. illus.
Formerly: Oxford Area Arts Council. Newsletter
Published by: Oxford Area Arts Council, Old Fire Station Arts Centre, Oxford, United Kingdom.

709 RUS ISSN 0131-6877
TVORCHESTVO. Text in Russian. 1957. q. USD 58 (effective 1998). bk.rev. illus. index.
Indexed: ABCT, ABM, AIAP, NumL, RASB.
Published by: (Soyuz Khudozhnikov Rossiiskoi Federatsii), Izdatel'stvo Khudozhnik, Ul Chernyakhovskogo 4-a, Moscow, 125319, Russian Federation. TEL 095-151-2502. Ed. Alexander Rozhin. Circ: 14,000. **Dist. in U.S. by:** Victor Kamkin Inc., 220 Girard St, Ste 1, Gaithersburg, MD 20877. TEL 901-881-5973, http://www.kamkin.com.

790 USA
U N I M A - U S A MEMBERSHIP GUIDE AND DIRECTORY. Text in English. 1966. a. membership. **Document type:** *Directory.* **Description:** Lists North American puppeteers for persons who use their art to promote international and intercultural peace and understanding.
Published by: Union Internationale de la Marionette, 1404 Spring St, N W, Atlanta, GA 30309-2820. TEL 404-873-3089, FAX 404-873-9907. Eds. Angela Benefield, Mark Smythe.

700 USA ISSN 0899-1782
N6505
U S ART. Text in English. 1982. 12/yr. USD 32.95 (effective 2000). adv. bk.rev. **Document type:** *Consumer.* **Description:** Aimed at collectors and enthusiasts of limited-edition realist print art in America, including wildlife, landscape, Americana, Western, still-life and florals.
Formerly: Midwest Art (0744-6217)
Published by: M S P Communications, Pillsbury Ctr, S Tower, 220 S Sixth St, Ste 500, Minneapolis, MN 55402. TEL 612-339-7571, FAX 612-339-5806. Ed., R&P Sara Gilbert. Pub. Frank Sisser. Adv. contact Laurie Scheel. Circ: 55,000.

700 USA ISSN 0083-2103
NX22
U.S. NATIONAL ENDOWMENT FOR THE ARTS. ANNUAL REPORT. Text in English. 1967. a., latest 2003. free (effective 2005). **Document type:** *Corporate.* **Description:** Lists grants awarded to artists and arts organizations; contains names, funded amount, and a brief description of the grant.
Related titles: Online - full content ed.
Published by: U.S. National Endowment for the Arts, Public Information Office, 1100 Pennsylvania Ave, N W, Washington, DC 20506. TEL 202-682-5400, http://www.nea.gov. Circ: 4,000 (controlled).

U.S. NATIONAL ENDOWMENT FOR THE ARTS. GRANTS TO ORGANIZATIONS. see *EDUCATION—Higher Education*

U.S. ROCKER MAGAZINE. see *MUSIC*

700 USA
➤ **U - TURN E - ZINE**✶; an art journal. Text in English. 1998. 3/yr. USD 20 per issue (effective 2000). back issues avail. **Document type:** *Academic/Scholarly.* **Description:** Each issue features a special topic on the art theory, art criticism and online artwork.
Media: Online - full text. **Related titles:** CD-ROM ed.
Published by: U-Turn E-Zine, 454 Iowa St, Oak Park, IL, IL 60302-2268. TEL 773-561-8039, jim@uturn.org, http://www.uturn.org. Ed., Pub. James Hugunin.

➤ **ULM UND OBERSCHWABEN**; Zeitschrift fuer Geschichte und Kunst. see *HISTORY—History Of Europe*

➤ **ULUM WA FUNOUN AL-MUSIQA/MUSIC SCIENCE AND ART.** see *MUSIC*

700 USA ISSN 0160-0699
N1
UMBRELLA. Text in English. 1978. irreg. USD 20 worldwide to individuals; USD 25 domestic to institutions; USD 30 foreign to institutions (effective 2005). adv. bk.rev. illus. 40 p./no.; back issues avail.; reprints avail. **Document type:** *Newsletter.* **Description:** Covers news and publications made by artists, including books, photography and mail art.
Indexed: ABM.
Published by: Umbrella Associates, PO Box 3640, Santa Monica, CA 90408. TEL 310-399-1146, FAX 310-399-5070, umbrella@ix.netcom.com, http://colophon.com/journal. Ed., Pub. Judith A Hoffberg. Circ: 500 (paid).

709 CZE ISSN 0049-5123
N6
UMENI/ART. Text and summaries in Czech, English, German. 1953. 6/yr. EUR 175 (effective 2004). illus. **Description:** Specialized studies and essays dealing with the history of the arts in general; studies on Bohemian and Central European painting, sculpture, architecture and applied arts.
Indexed: ABCT, AIAP, BHA, DIP, IBR, IBZ, RASB.
Published by: Akademie Ved Ceske Republiky, Ustav Dejin Umeni/Czech Academy of Sciences, Institute of the History of Art, Husova 4, Prague, 11000, Czech Republic. TEL 420-2-22220099, FAX 420-2-22221654, art@udu.cas.cz, udu@cas.cz, http://www.intimate.cz/umeni, http://www.udu.cas.cz. Circ: 800. **Dist. in Western countries by:** Kubon & Sagner Buchexport - Import GmbH, Hessstr 39-41, Munich 80798, Germany. TEL 49-89-542180, FAX 49-89-54218218, postmaster@kubon-sagner.de, http://www.kubon-sagner.de.

UNICA; revista de artes y humanidades de la Universidad Catolica Cecilio Acosta. see *LITERATURE*

UNIR: ECHO DE SAINT LOUIS. see *LITERATURE*

THE UNIT CIRCLE; a magazine. see *LITERARY AND POLITICAL REVIEWS*

700 500 370.1 800 PHL ISSN 0041-7149
LH7.M28
➤ **UNITAS**; a quarterly review for the arts and sciences. Text and summaries in English, Tagalog. 1923. q. PHP 400, USD 30; USD 9 newsstand/cover (effective 2003). bk.rev. charts; illus.; bibl. index. back issues avail. **Document type:** *Journal, Academic/Scholarly.* **Description:** Contains articles and studies, university forum, the world of books and review articles. Schlolarly works and researches.
Related titles: Online - full text ed.: (from Northern Light Technology, Inc.).
Indexed: AmH&L, BAS, HistAb, IPP, MLA-IB.
Published by: University of Santo Tomas Publishing House, Beato Angelico Bldg, UST Compound, Espana, Sampaloc, Manila, Philippines. TEL 63-2-7313522 ext 8252/8278, FAX 63-2-7313522, publish@ust.edu.ph, http://www.ust.edu.ph. Eds. Dr. Mecheline I Manalastas, Winston F Cabading. Circ: 500.

700 ESP ISSN 0210-962X
NX7 CODEN: CAUGFB
➤ **UNIVERSIDAD DE GRANADA. CUADERNOS DE ARTE.** Text in Spanish. 1974. a. price varies. illus. **Document type:** *Monographic series, Academic/Scholarly.*

Related titles: Online - full text ed.: (from H.W. Wilson, O C L C Online Computer Library Center, Inc.).
Indexed: ABM, ArtInd, BHA, PCI, RILM, SOPODA.
—CINDOC.
Published by: (Universidad de Granada, Departamento de Historia del Arte), Editorial Universidad de Granada, Antiguo Colegio Maximo, Campus de Cartuja, Granada, 18071, Spain. TEL 34-958-246220, FAX 34-958-243931, comunicacion@editorialugr.com, http://www.editorialugr.com. Ed. Emilio Angel Villanueva Munoz.

700 800   GTM
UNIVERSIDAD DE SAN CARLOS. REVISTA; artes - literatura - ciencias humanas. Text in Spanish. m. bibl.; illus.
Published by: Universidad de San Carlos de Guatemala, Ciudad Universitaria, zona 12, Edificio de Rectoria, Of. 307, Guatemala, Guatemala. Ed. Julio Penados del Barrio. Circ: 2,000.

700   ESP
UNIVERSIDAD DE SEVILLA. SERIE: ARTE. Text in Spanish. irreg., latest vol.17, 2001. price varies. illus. **Document type:** Monographic series, Academic/Scholarly.
Published by: Universidad de Sevilla, Secretariado de Publicaciones, Porvenir 27, Sevilla, 41013, Spain. TEL 34-95-4487444, FAX 34-95-4487443, secpub10@us.es, http://www.us.es/publius/inicio.html.

700 300   BOL   ISSN 0041-8609
UNIVERSIDAD MAYOR DE SAN ANDRES. GACETA UNIVERSITARIA✳. Text in Spanish. m. charts; illus.
Published by: Universidad Mayor de San Andres, Departamento de Relaciones Publicas, Casilla, La Paz, 4787, Bolivia. Ed. Abel Elias Sainz.

700   MEX   ISSN 0188-9583
UNIVERSIDAD NACIONAL AUTONOMA DE MEXICO. ESCUELA NACIONAL DE ARTES PLASTICAS. REVISTA. Text in Spanish. s-a. MXP 30, USD 8 (effective 2000). **Description:** Publishes original articles and case reports on sculpture, painting and art related issues.
Indexed: BHA.
Published by: Universidad Nacional Autonoma de Mexico, Escuela Nacional de Artes Plasticas, Ave Constitucion 600, Barrio de la Concha, Xochimilco, Mexico City, DF 16210, Mexico. TEL 52-5-676-2621, FAX 52-5-653-0281, http://www.unam.mx/enap/. Ed. Fernando Alba Aldave.

700   MEX   ISSN 0185-1276
N16
➤ **UNIVERSIDAD NACIONAL AUTONOMA DE MEXICO. INSTITUTO DE INVESTIGACIONES ESTETICAS. ANALES.** Text in Spanish. 1937. s-a. USD 20 newsstand/cover (effective 2005); no subscription available at this moment. bk.rev. bibl.; illus. 200 p./no.; back issues avail. **Document type:** Journal, Academic/Scholarly. **Description:** Publishes articles, notes and news on Mexican and Latin American art.
Related titles: Online - full text ed.; ◆ Supplement(s): Catalogo de las Exposiciones de Arte. ISSN 0187-9766.
Indexed: AIAP, AICP, AmH&L, BHA, BibInd, HAPI, IBR, RILM.
Published by: Universidad Nacional Autonoma de Mexico, Instituto de Investigaciones Esteticas, Circuito Mario de la Cueva, Zona Cultural, Ciudad Universitaria, Mexico, DF 04510, Mexico. TEL 52-55-56652465, FAX 52-55-56654740, redaccion@analesiie.unam.mx, http://www.analesiie.unam.mx/, http://www.esteticas-unam.mx. Ed. Durdica Segota. Circ: 1,500.

700   MEX   ISSN 0185-1799
UNIVERSIDAD NACIONAL AUTONOMA DE MEXICO. INSTITUTO DE INVESTIGACIONES ESTETICAS. MONOGRAFIAS DE ARTE. Text in Spanish. 1977. irreg., latest 1990. price varies. **Document type:** Monographic series.
Published by: Universidad Nacional Autonoma de Mexico, Instituto de Investigaciones Esteticas, Circuito Mario de la Cueva, Zona Cultural, Ciudad Universitaria, Mexico, DF 04510, Mexico. TEL 52-55-56652465, FAX 52-55-56654740, ereinoso@servidor.unam.mx.

701.18   ITA
UNIVERSITA DEGLI STUDI DI PARMA. ISTITUTO DI STORIA DELL'ARTE. CATALOGHI. (Each issue devoted to an individual artist) Text in Italian. 1968. irreg., latest vol.26, 1975. price varies. bk.rev. bibl.; illus.
Published by: (Instituto di Storia dell'Arte), Universita degli Studi di Parma, Piazzale della Pace, 7 A, Parma, PR 43100, Italy. TEL 0521-283089, FAX 0521-207125. Circ: 1,000.

709   DEU
UNIVERSITAET BONN. SEMINAR FUER ORIENTALISCHE KUNSTGESCHICHTE. VEROEFFENTLICHUNGEN. REIHE B. ANTIQUITATES ORIENTALES. Text in German. 1977. irreg. price varies. **Document type:** Monographic series, Academic/Scholarly.
Published by: (Universitaet Bonn, Forschungsstelle fuer Orientalische Kunstgeschichte), Dr. Rudolf Habelt GmbH, Am Buchenhang 1, Bonn, 53115, Germany. TEL 49-228-9238322, FAX 49-228-9238323, info@habelt.de, http://www.habelt.de.

700   AUT
UNIVERSITAET INNSBRUCK. KUNSTGESCHICHTLICHE STUDIEN✳. Text in German. 1972. irreg. price varies.
Related titles: Series of: Universitaet Innsbruck. Veroeffentlichungen.
Published by: (Universitaet Innsbruck), Oesterreichische Kommissionsbuchhandlung, Glasmalereistr 6, Innsbruck, T 6020, Austria. TEL 43-512-587039, FAX 43-512-5870394, oekobuch@aon.at, http://www.oekobuch.com. Ed. Otto Lutterotti.

707   AUT
UNIVERSITAET MOZARTEUM SALZBURG. JAHRESBERICHT. Text in German. 1920. a. adv. **Document type:** Bulletin, Academic/Scholarly. **Description:** Contains information about the activities of the university and its teachers and students.
Formerly: Hochschule fuer Musik und Darstellende Kunst Mozarteum in Salzburg. Jahresbericht
Published by: Universitaet Mozarteum Salzburg, Alpenstrasse 48, Salzburg, Sa 5020, Austria. TEL 43-662-6198-2210, FAX 43-662-6198-2219, http://www.moz.ac.at. Ed. Susanne Delincee. Circ: 500.

709 950   DEU   ISSN 0170-3692
UNIVERSITAET ZU KOELN. KUNSTHISTORISCHES INSTITUT. ABTEILUNG ASIEN. PUBLIKATIONEN. Text in German. 1977. irreg., latest vol.6, 1990. price varies. **Document type:** Monographic series, Academic/Scholarly. **Description:** Asian art history.
Published by: (Universitaet zu Koeln, Kunsthistorisches Institut), Franz Steiner Verlag Stuttgart GmbH, Birkenwaldstr 44, Stuttgart, 70191, Germany. TEL 49-711-25820, FAX 49-711-2582390, franz.steiner.verlag@t-online.de, http://www.steiner-verlag.de. R&P Sabine Koerner.

UNIVERSITAS (GERMAN EDITION); Orientierung in der Wissenschaft. see SCIENCES: COMPREHENSIVE WORKS

709   BEL
UNIVERSITE CATHOLIQUE DE LOUVAIN. DEPARTEMENT D'ARCHEOLOGIE ET D'HISTOIRE DE L'ART. DOCUMENTS DE TRAVAIL. Text in French. 1970. irreg., latest vol.30, 1998. price varies. illus. **Document type:** Monographic series.
Published by: (Universite Catholique de Louvain, Departement d'Etudes Greques, Latines et Orientales, Publications d'Archeologie et d'Histoire de l'Art), Universite Catholique de Louvain, College Erasme, Pl Blaise Pascal 1, Louvain-la-Neuve, 1348, Belgium. moucharte@arke.ucl.ac.be, http://juppiter.fltr.ucl.ac.be/FLTR/publications/pub_pahal. R&P Ghislaine Moucharte.

709 913   MDG
UNIVERSITE DE MADAGASCAR. MUSEE D'ART ET D'ARCHEOLOGIE. TRAVAUX ET DOCUMENTS. Text in French. 1970. irreg., latest vol.26, 1987. MGF 3,000. **Description:** Ancient and contemporary geography, art, history and ethnology of Madagascar.
Published by: Universite de Madagascar, Musee d'Art et d'Archeologie, Isoraka, BP 564, Antananarivo, Madagascar.

UNIVERSITE DE POITIERS. CENTRE D'ETUDES SUPERIEURES DE CIVILISATION MEDIEVALE. PUBLICATIONS. see HISTORY

700 913   BEL   ISSN 0771-2723
UNIVERSITE LIBRE DE BRUXELLES. FACULTE DE PHILOSOPHIE ET LETTRES. ANNALES D'HISTOIRE DE L'ART ET D'ARCHEOLOGIE. Text in French. 1979. a.
Indexed: RILM.
Published by: Universite Libre de Bruxelles, Faculte de Philosophie et Lettres, Campus du Solbosch, Avenue F.D. Roosevelt 50, C P 175, Bruxelles, 1050, Belgium. TEL 32-2-6502402.

700   CAN   ISSN 0315-940X
UNIVERSITIES ART ASSOCIATION OF CANADA. JOURNAL/ASSOCIATION D'ART DES UNIVERSITES DU CANADA. JOURNAL. Text in English, French. 1972. 3/yr. CND 10 (effective 1999). adv. bk.rev. **Document type:** Bulletin.
Published by: Universities Art Association of Canada, c/o Department of Fine Arts, University of Waterloo, Waterloo, ON N2L 3G1, Canada. TEL 519-888-4567, FAX 519-746-4982, jmcoutu@artsech.watstar.uwaterloo.ca. Ed. Joan Coutu. Circ: 350.

UNIVERSITY OF CALIFORNIA AT LOS ANGELES. FOWLER MUSEUM OF CULTURAL HISTORY. MONOGRAPH SERIES. see MUSEUMS AND ART GALLERIES

UNIVERSITY OF CALIFORNIA AT LOS ANGELES. FOWLER MUSEUM OF CULTURAL HISTORY. OCCASIONAL PAPERS. see MUSEUMS AND ART GALLERIES

700 378   USA
UNIVERSITY OF ILLINOIS AT URBANA-CHAMPAIGN. SCHOOL OF ART AND DESIGN. NEWSLETTER. Text in English. 1951. a. USD 15. **Document type:** Newsletter. **Description:** Contains information on the school for faculty and students.
Formerly (until 1976): University of Illinois at Urbana-Champaign. Department of Art. Newsletter (0073-5256)

Published by: University of Illinois at Urbana-Champaign, Continuing Education and Public Service-Visual Arts, 136 Art and Design Bldg, 590, Champaign, IL 61820. TEL 217-333-2439, FAX 217-244-7388, http://www.gnofn.org/~nopl/lama/lama.htm. Ed., R&P Oliver Ramsey TEL 217-265-8464. Circ: 6,000 (controlled).

UNIVERSITY OF KENTUCKY ART MUSEUM NEWSLETTER. see MUSEUMS AND ART GALLERIES

UNIVERSITY OF LONDON. INSTITUTE OF GERMANIC STUDIES. BITHELL MEMORIAL LECTURES. see LITERATURE

700   AUS   ISSN 1322-9575
UNIVERSITY OF NEW SOUTH WALES. HANDBOOK: ART AND SOCIAL SCIENCES. Text in English. 1976. a. AUD 6.
Former titles (until 1993): University of New South Wales. Faculty Handbooks: Art and Social Sciences (1037-9843); (until 1992): University of New South Wales. Faculty Handbooks: Arts (0811-7608)
Published by: University of New South Wales, Sydney, NSW 2052, Australia. TEL 61-2-385-2840, FAX 61-2-662-2163.

700 913 780   SVK   ISSN 0083-4130
UNIVERZITA KOMENSKEHO. FILOZOFICKA FAKULTA. ZBORNIK: MUSAICA. Text in Czech, Slovak; Summaries in English, German. 1961. irreg. free domestic (effective 2005). **Document type:** Academic/Scholarly. **Description:** Discusses philosophic aspects of the study and teaching of art.
Indexed: RASB.
Published by: Univerzita Komenskeho, Filozoficka Fakulta, Ustredna Kniznica, Gondova 2, Bratislava, 81801, Slovakia. Circ: 700.

700   POL   ISSN 0556-1019
UNIWERSYTET IM. ADAMA MICKIEWICZA. HISTORIA SZTUKI. Text in Polish; Summaries in German, English. 1959. irreg., latest vol.25, 1996. price varies. **Document type:** Monographic series, Academic/Scholarly. **Description:** Contains current research results of the university's scholars of history of art, their Ph.D. works and monographs. Each volume contains the work of one author.
Former titles (until 1969): Uniwersytet im. Adama Mickiewicza w Poznaniu. Wydzial Filozoficzno-Historyczny. Prace. Seria Historia Sztuki (0860-1399); Uniwersytet im. Adama Mickiewicza w Poznaniu. Zeszyty Naukowe. Historia Sztuki (0083-4270)
Indexed: AIAP.
Published by: Wydawnictwo Naukowe Uniwersytetu im. Adama Mickiewicza/Adam Mickiewicz University Press, Nowowiejskiego 55, Poznan, 61-734, Poland. TEL 48-61-527380, FAX 48-61-527701. Pub. Maria Jankowska. R&P Malgorzata Bis.

700   GBR   ISSN 0969-9716
UNTITLED; a review of contemporary art. Text in English. 1993. s-a. GBP 3.50 newsstand/cover (effective 2004). **Document type:** Magazine.
Indexed: ABM.
Address: c/o Central Books Ltd., 99 Wallis Rd., London, E9 5LN, United Kingdom. TEL 44-845-4589925, FAX 44-845-4589912, magazines@centralbooks.com.

700   USA
URBAN AUTOGRAFF. Text in English. q. **Document type:** Magazine, Consumer.
Address: PO Box 398, Winfield, IL 60196.

700 780   USA
URBAN DESIRES. Text in English. 1994. bi-m. **Description:** Contains works by artists and musicians.
Media: Online - full text.
Address: 665 Broadway, 9th Fl, New York, NY 10012. TEL 212-358-8220, gaby@desires.com, info@agency.com, http://www.desires.com. Ed. Gabrielle Shannon.

746.92 391   USA   ISSN 1539-185X
TT502
V MAGAZINE. Text in English. 1999. 6/yr. USD 35 domestic; USD 75 Canada, Europe & South America; USD 100 Asia, Australia and New Zealand; USD 6.95 newsstand/cover domestic; GBP 7.50 newsstand/cover in United Kingdom; EUR 12.50 newsstand/cover Italy & Germany; EUR 12 newsstand/cover in France; EUR 13.90 newsstand/cover in Netherlands (effective 2004).
Related titles: Online - full text ed.
Published by: Visionaire Publishing, 11 Mercer St, New York, NY 10013. TEL 212-274-8959, FAX 212-343-2595, vmagazine@visionaireworld.com, http://www.vmagazine.com, http://www.visionaireworld.com. Ed. Stephen Gan. Adv. contact Jorge Garcia.

▼ **new title**   ➤ **refereed**   ✳ **unverified**   ◆ **full entry avail.**

700 USA ISSN 1543-9313
NC968
VADEBONCOEUR COLLECTION OF IMAGES. Variant title: ImageS. Text in English. 2001. 3/yr., latest no.2. USD 50 domestic; USD 60 foreign; USD 20 newsstand/cover (effective 2004). **Document type:** *Magazine, Consumer.* **Description:** A collectible volume of reproductions of classic illustrations from the years 1890-1923. Often called, "The Golden Age of Illustration," the era produced such artists as Howard Pyle, Harvey Dunn, Gustaf Tenggren and J.C. Leyendecker. Publisher Jim Vadeboncoeur has keep text to a minimum, with captions acting as the sole information, preferring to let the images-many of which were originally created for magazine publication—speak for themselves. The reproductions of well-known and rare work from the period are excellent and are printed on a lightweight cardboard stock. The images are sure to delight any collector or enthusiast, and contemporary visual artist may find "The Vadeboncoer Collection of Images" a useful reference. Due to its lack of text and the slightly esoteric nature of the content, this publication is recommended only for large art collections.
Published by: J V J Publishing, 3809 Laguna Ave, Palo Alto, CA 94306-2629. TEL 650-493-3841, FAX 650-493-1145, images@bpib.com, http://www.bpib.com/images.htm. Ed., Pub., R&P Jim Vadeboncoeur Jr. Circ: 1,500 (paid). **Dist. by:** Bud Plant Comic Art, PO Box 1689, Grass Valley, CA 95945. TEL 530-273-2166, bud@budplant.com, http://www.budplant.com.

VALLUM; contemporary poetry. see *LITERATURE—Poetry*

700 SWE ISSN 0283-751X
➤ **VALOER**; konstvetenskapliga studier. Text in Swedish. 1986-1998; resumed 2000. q. SEK 225 to individuals; SEK 250 to institutions; SEK 60 per issue (effective 2004). bk.rev. **Document type:** *Journal, Academic/Scholarly.* **Description:** Features articles on architecture and fine and decorative arts. Publishes results of art historical research in progress and gives accounts of conferences.
Published by: Foereningen Valoer, c/o Konstvetenskapliga Institutionen, Slottet, Soedra Tornet, inngaang HO, Uppsala, 75237, Sweden. TEL 46-18-4712896, FAX 46-18-4712892, valoer@hotmail.com. Ed. Britt-Inger Johansson. R&P Britt Inger Johansson. Circ: 500 (paid); 50 (controlled).

700 GBR ISSN 0954-8815
VARIANT. Text in English. 1996. irreg. (1-3/yr. approx.). GBP 7.50 newsstand/cover domestic to individuals; GBP 9.50 newsstand/cover in the European Union to individuals; GBP 15 newsstand/cover elsewhere to individuals; GBP 20 newsstand/cover to institutions (effective 2005). back issues avail. **Document type:** *Magazine, Academic/Scholarly.*
Address: 1/2, 189b Maryhill Rd, Glasgow, G20 7XJ, United Kingdom. TEL 44-141-3339522, variant@ndirect.co.uk, http://www.variant.randomstate.org/. Eds. Daniel Jewesbury, Leigh French.

700 BEL ISSN 0042-3440
VENT - ART✶. Text in French. 1967. q. adv. illus.
Address: c/o Jean Schwartz, Rue de la Laiterie 36, Brussels, Belgium. Ed. Joan Marti.

VENUE MAGAZINE. see *THEATER*

VERBICIDE. see *MUSIC*

VERBUM; analecta neolatina. see *LITERATURE*

VEREIN FUER VOLKSKUNDE IN WIEN. SONDERSCHRIFTEN. see *FOLKLORE*

700 BEL ISSN 0770-0849
VERHANDELINGEN. KLASSE VAN DE KUNSTEN. Text in Dutch, English, French, German. 1943. irreg., latest vol.66, 1998. price varies. back issues avail. **Document type:** *Monographic series.*
Formerly (until 1972): Koninklijke Vlaamse Academie voor Wetenschappen, Letteren en Schone Kunsten van Belgie. Verhandelingen. Klasse der Schone Kunsten (0770-089X)
Indexed: Inspec, RASB.
Published by: Koninklijke Vlaamse Academie van Belgie voor Wetenschappen en Kunsten/The Royal Flemish Academy of Belgium for Science and the Arts, Hertogsstraat 1, Brussels, 1000, Belgium. TEL 32-2-5502323, FAX 32-2-5502325, info@kvab.be, http://www.kvab.be. **Dist. by:** Brepols Publishers, Begijnhof 67, Turnhout 2300, Belgium. TEL 32-14-40-25-00, FAX 32-14-42-89-19.

707.11 USA
VERMONT ACADEMY OF ARTS AND SCIENCES. STUDENT SYMPOSIUM AND ANNUAL CONFERENCE. OCCASIONAL PAPERS. Text in English. 1965. s-a. USD 2.50. **Document type:** *Proceedings.*
Published by: Vermont Academy of Arts and Sciences, 2 Buxton Ave, Middletown Springs, VT 05757. TEL 802-235-2302. Ed. Frances B Krouse. Circ: 750.

700 DEU ISSN 1434-5986
N3
VERNISSAGE. Text in German. 1993. irreg. (12-15/yr.). EUR 24.80 domestic; EUR 38 foreign; EUR 5 newsstand/cover (effective 2002). adv. **Document type:** *Magazine, Consumer.*
Indexed: DIP, IBR, IBZ, RILM.
Published by: Vernissage Verlag, Bergheimer Str 104-106, Heidelberg, 69115, Germany. TEL 49-6221-161061, FAX 49-6221-161575, vernissage@vernissageverlag.de, http://www.vernissageverlag.de. adv.: B&W page EUR 2,667, color page EUR 3,551. Circ: 27,000 (controlled).

700 FRA ISSN 1270-0614
NX2
VERSO ARTS ET LETTRES. Text in French. 1967. q. bk.rev.; dance rev.; music rev. illus. back issues avail.; reprint service avail. from PQC. **Description:** Includes reviews and interviews with artists.
Formerly: Opus International (0048-2056)
Related titles: Microfilm ed.: (from PQC).
Indexed: ABM, BHA, RASB.
—Infotrieve.
Published by: Editions Verso, 2 rue de Nevers, Paris, 75006, France. TEL 33-1-46336245, FAX 33-1-44070828. Ed. Jean-Luc Chalumeau. Pub. Jean Luc Chalumeau. R&P J L Chalumeau TEL 33-6-03447952. Circ: 5,000.

745 USA
VESTERHEIM ROSEMALING LETTER. Text in English. 1969. q. looseleaf. USD 35 domestic; USD 39 in Canada & Mexico; USD 40 elsewhere (effective 2002). bk.rev. illus.; maps. back issues avail. **Document type:** *Newsletter, Consumer.* **Description:** Covers rosemaling, decorative Norwegian folk paintings, and related folk arts. Includes history, how-to advice, events, awards, workshops, patterns, and personal experiences.
Published by: Vesterheim Norwegian-American Museum, PO Box 379, Decorah, IA 52101. TEL 319-382-9681, FAX 319-382-8828, vesterheim@vesterheim.org. Ed. Sara Tollefson. R&P, Adv. contact Charles Langton. Circ: 1,650 (paid).

700 800 ITA ISSN 0393-6147
IL VESUVIO; fiaccola ercolanese. Variant title: Vesuv. Text in Italian. 1964. d. USD 50. adv. bk.rev. illus.
Published by: Vesuvio, Via Liberta, San Sebastiano Al Vesuvio, NA 80040, Italy. FAX 39-81-7715870. Ed. Vincenzo Ascione.

VETERA CHRISTIANORUM. see *ARCHAEOLOGY*

700 800 780 792.8 USA ISSN 1077-6788
VICE; art and entertainment newsmagazine. Text in English. 1994. 10/yr. USD 30 domestic; CND 30 in Canada; USD 70 elsewhere (effective 2003). adv. bk.rev.; dance rev.; film rev.; music rev.; play rev.; tel.rev.; video rev. bibl.; illus.; tr.lit. back issues avail. **Document type:** *Magazine, Consumer.* **Description:** Covers artists, books, cabaret, dance, film, illustrations, music, opera, photography, poetry, psychology, restaurants, short stories, theatre, travel, health and fitness.
Related titles: Online - full text ed.
Published by: Vice Publishing, Inc., 75 N Fourth St, 3rd Fl, Brooklyn, NY 11211. TEL 212-727-2787, FAX 212-727-3190, vice@viceland.com, http://www.viceland.com. Ed., Pub., R&P, Adv. contact William A Zeoli. page USD 6,517; trim 7.75 x 10. Circ: 50,000; 4,700 (paid).

VIDEO GUIDE. see *COMMUNICATIONS—Video*

700 CAN ISSN 0042-5435
VIE DES ARTS. Text in French. 1956. q. CND 24 domestic; CND 39 foreign; CND 7.50 newsstand/cover (effective 2000). adv. bk.rev. illus. cum.index: 1956-66, 1966-76, 1976-86, 1986-91. reprints avail. **Document type:** *Consumer.* **Description:** Features articles on artists, the art market, and trends in contemporary art and architecture in Canada and around the world.
Related titles: Microfilm ed.: (from BNQ).
Indexed: ABCT, ABM, ArtInd, BHA, CBCARef, CBPI, CPerI, PdeR, RILM.
—CCC.
Published by: Societe la Vie des Arts, 200 St Jacques St, Ste 600, Montreal, PQ H2Y 1M1, Canada. TEL 514-282-0205, FAX 514-282-0235, http://www.viedesarts.com/000/profil.html. Ed. Bernard Levy. Circ: 7,500.

VIEWFINDER JOURNAL OF FOCAL POINT GALLERY. see *PHOTOGRAPHY*

700 720 PHL ISSN 0042-692X
VISION MAGAZINE. Text in English, Tagalog. 1964. s-a. USD 22. bk.rev. charts; illus. **Description:** Serves as a gallery of the students' best works. Features articles related to architecture and fine arts.
Published by: (University of Santo Tomas), University of Santo Tomas, College of Architecture and Fine Arts (Subsidiary of: University of Santo Tomas), Espana St, Sampaloc, Manila, Philippines. Ed. Pebbles B Tan Gatue. Circ: 3,000.

VISIONAIRE. see *CLOTHING TRADE—Fashions*

VISIONS WEST - NATIONAL CENTER FOR AMERICAN WESTERN ART. see *MUSEUMS AND ART GALLERIES*

700 GBR ISSN 1368-5236
VISITING ARTS. Text in English. 1986. 3/yr. free (effective 2001). **Description:** Provides information on developing or promoting international arts activities and collaborations or touring opportunities.
Published by: British Council, British Council Publications, Bridgewater House, 58 Whitworth St, Manchester, M1 6BB, United Kingdom. TEL 44-161-9577184, FAX 44-161-9577168, publications@visitingarts.demon.co.uk, publications.information@britishcouncil.org, http://www.britishcouncil.org/publications.

741.67 ESP ISSN 1133-0422
VISUAL. Text in Spanish. 1989. bi-m. EUR 51.09 domestic; EUR 108.18 in Europe; EUR 168.28 elsewhere (effective 2004). **Document type:** *Magazine, Consumer.* **Description:** Aims at being the presentation and analysis of the communicative elements of visual communication.
Related titles: Online - full text ed.: ISSN 1576-7868. 1999.
—IE, Infotrieve.
Published by: Blur Ediciones, S.L., Ave. Mediterraneo 9,1o, Madrid, 28007, Spain. TEL 34-91-5214049, FAX 34-91-5213212, informa@visual.gi, http://www.visual.gi. Ed. Alvaro Sobrino. Circ: 7,500. **Dist. by:** Asociacion de Revistas Culturales de Espana, Hortaleza, 75, Madrid 28004, Spain. TEL 34-91-3086066, FAX 34-91-3199267, info@arce.es, http://www.arce.es.

760.071025 USA ISSN 1552-7751
NX303
VISUAL AND PERFORMING ARTS. Text in English. 1995. a. USD 26.95 per issue (effective 2005). **Document type:** *Directory.* **Description:** Covers more than 600 accredited U.S. and Canadian colleges and universities granting undergraduate and graduate degree programs in the areas of art, dance, music, and theater.
Former titles (until 2003): Professional Degree Programs in the Visual and Performing Arts; (until 2002): Peterson's Professional Degree Programs in the Visual and Performing Arts (1073-2020)
Published by: Thomson Peterson's (Subsidiary of: Thomson Corporation), Princeton Pike Corporate Center, 2000 Lenox Dr, 3rd Fl, Lawrenceville, NJ 08648. TEL 609-243-9111, FAX 609-243-9150, http://www.petersons.com. Ed. Barbara Lawrence.

709.716 CAN ISSN 0704-0512
VISUAL ARTS NEWS. Text in English. 1978. q. CND 12.50, USD 16 domestic; CND 18 foreign (effective 1998). adv. back issues avail. **Document type:** *Newsletter.* **Description:** Offers features, interviews and reviews with a focus on living Nova Scotian artists. Promotes a knowledge of the artists and their work.
Published by: Visual Arts Nova Scotia, 1113 Marginal Rd, Halifax, NS B3H 4P7, Canada. TEL 902-423-4694, FAX 902-422-0881, vans@visualarts.ns.ca, http://www.vans.ednet.ns.ca. Ed. Rick Janson. Adv. contact Kim Goodson. Circ: 650.

707.1 USA ISSN 0736-0770
N81
➤ **VISUAL ARTS RESEARCH**; educational, historical, philosophical and psychological perspectives. Text in English. 1973. s-a. USD 25 domestic to individuals; USD 32 foreign to individuals; USD 36 domestic to institutions; USD 43 foreign to institutions (effective 2000 - 2001). adv. illus. back issues avail.; reprints avail. **Document type:** *Journal, Academic/Scholarly.*
Former titles (until 1982): Review of Research in Visual Arts Education (0160-3221); (until 1975): Review of Research in Visual and Environmental Education (0160-3256)
Indexed: ABIn, BHA, CIJE, EduInd, PsycInfo, PsycholAb, e-psyche.
—BLDSC (9241.230000), IE, Infotrieve, ingenta.
Published by: University of Illinois at Urbana-Champaign, School of Art and Design, 143 Art and Design Bldg, 408 E Peabody Dr, Champaign, IL 61820. TEL 217-333-8952, FAX 217-244-7688. Ed. Christine Thompson. R&P Carole Smith. Circ: 400.

700 USA
VISUAL ARTS TRENDS. Text in English. q.
Media: Online - full text. **Related titles:** ◆ Supplement(s): Visual Arts Trends Es.
Published by: Colonial Communications Corp, 794 W Fingergoard Rd, Staten Island, NY 10305. http://www.visualartstrends.com. Ed. Keith Williams.

700 USA
VISUAL ARTS TRENDS ES. Text in English. bi-m. **Document type:** *Newsletter.*
Media: Online - full text. **Related titles:** ◆ Supplement to: Visual Arts Trends.
Published by: Colonial Communications Corp, 794 W Fingergoard Rd, Staten Island, NY 10305. http://www.visualartstrends.com/eS/eS.html. Ed. Keith Williams.

700 GBR ISSN 1471-4787
N6761
VISUAL CULTURE IN BRITAIN. Text in English. 2000. 2/yr. GBP 30, EUR 60, USD 60 to individuals; GBP 65, EUR 130, USD 130 to institutions includes online access (effective 2005). adv. bk.rev. abstr. 144 p./no.; back issues avail. **Document type:** *Journal, Academic/Scholarly.* **Description:** Addresses a range of contemporary debates involving constructions of racial, ethnic and gender identities, nationality and internationalism, colonialism, high and low culture, the role of institutions and cultural groupings, models of production and consumption.
Related titles: Online - full text ed.: (from EBSCO Publishing).
Indexed: ABM, ArtInd.
—BLDSC (9241.235500). **CCC.**
Published by: Manchester University Press, Oxford Rd, Manchester, Lancs M13 9NR, United Kingdom. TEL 44-161-2752310, FAX 44-161-2743346, mup@manchester.ac.uk, http://www.manchesteruniversitypress.co.uk/information_areas/journals/visualculture/visualcult.htm. Ed. Ysanne Holt.

700 GBR ISSN 0197-3762
N3998 CODEN: VRVRDZ
➤ **VISUAL RESOURCES**; an international journal of documentation. Text in English. 1980. q. GBP 413, USD 551 to institutions (effective 2006). adv. bk.rev. illus. index. back issues avail.; reprint service avail. from PSC. **Document type:** *Journal, Academic/Scholarly.* **Description:** Explores how visual language is structured and visual meaning communicated and also illustrates how picture collections are acquired, organized, indexed, and preserved.
Related titles: Microfiche ed.; Microfilm ed.; Online - full text ed.: (from EBSCO Publishing, IngentaConnect, O C L C Online Computer Library Center, Inc.).
Indexed: ABM, ArtInd, BAS, BHA, DAAI, DIP, IBR, IBZ, InfoSAb, Inspec.
—BLDSC (9241.320000), Infotrieve. **CCC.**
Published by: Routledge (Subsidiary of: Taylor & Francis Group), 4 Park Sq, Milton Park, Abingdon, Oxon OX14 4RN, United Kingdom. TEL 44-1235-828600, FAX 44-1235-829000, info@routledge.co.uk, http://www.tandf.co.uk/journals/titles/01973762.asp, http://www.routledge.co.uk. Eds. Christine Sundt, Helene E Roberts. **Subscr. to:** Taylor & Francis Ltd, Journals Customer Service, Rankine Rd, Basingstoke, Hants RG24 8PR, United Kingdom. TEL 44-1256-813000, FAX 44-1256-330245, enquiry@tandf.co.uk.

700 020 USA ISSN 1046-9001
N72.P5
VISUAL RESOURCES ASSOCIATION BULLETIN. Variant title: V R A Bulletin. Text in English. 1974. q. USD 100 (effective 2005). index. back issues avail. **Document type:** *Bulletin.* **Description:** Contains association news, updates readers on conferences and workshops, and provides information on various aspects of managing visual resources collections.
Formerly (until 1989): International Bulletin for Photographic Documentation of the Visual Arts (0197-8020)
Indexed: ABM.
—BLDSC (9258.707025), IE, ingenta.
Published by: Visual Resources Association, Tappan Hall, Rm 20, History of Art Department, University of Michigan, Ann Arbor, MI 48109. TEL 313-763-6114, FAX 313-747-4123, taormina@duke.edu, http://www.vraweb.org/vrabulletin.html. Ed. Pompelia Mark. Circ: 769.

VISWA RACHANA/WORLD WRITING; illustrated fortnightly. see *LITERATURE*

700 USA
LA VITRINA. Text in English, Spanish. irreg. back issues avail. **Description:** Includes articles and events related to Mexican art and culture.
Media: Online - full text.
Published by: Mexican Consulate at New York, Mexican Cultural Institute, 27 E 39th St, New York, NY 10016. TEL 212-217-6422, FAX 212-217-6425, mexcult@quicklink.com, http://www.lavitrina.com/. Ed., R&P Monica de la Torre.

700 747 RUS
VITRINA I TORGOVYI DIZAIN. Text in Russian. bi-m. USD 145 in United States.
Address: Krasnopresnenskaya nab 12, Moscow, 123610, Russian Federation. TEL 7-095-2531618. Ed. S A Markov. **US dist. addr.:** East View Information Services, 3020 Harbor Ln. N., Minneapolis, MN 55447. TEL 612-550-0961.

700 BEL ISSN 0042-7683
VLAANDEREN; tijdschrift voor kunst en cultuur. Text mainly in Dutch; Text occasionally in English, French, German. 1951. bi-m. USD 35. adv. bk.rev. charts; illus.; tr.lit. index. **Document type:** *Magazine, Academic/Scholarly.* **Description:** Publishes thematic articles about art, culture, and cultural events.
Formerly: West-Vlaanderen
Published by: Christelijk Vlaams Kunstenaarsverbond vzw, c/o Dirk Rommens, Sec, Sint Pietersstraat 39, Kuurne, 8520, Belgium. TEL 32-56-360364, dirk.rommens@pandora.be, http://www.http://www.cuku-vlaanderen.be. Ed. Patrick Lateur. Adv. contact Adiel Vandaele. Circ: 3,000.

681.43 USA
▼ **VOLUME**; serving the contract framing industry. Text in English. 2004. q. adv. **Document type:** *Magazine, Trade.*
Published by: Pfingsten Publishing, L L C, 6000 Lombardo Center Dr, Ste 420, Seven Hills, OH 44131. TEL 216-328-8926, 888-772-8926, FAX 216-328-9452, info@pfpublish.com, http://www.pfpub.com. adv.: color page USD 2,950. Circ: 3,733.

740 747 688 GBR
THE VOLUME FRAMER. Text in English. 1986. m. free to qualified personnel. adv. bk.rev. back issues avail. **Document type:** *Trade.* **Description:** Informs industry leaders in the volume picture framing industry on key issues and current affairs.
Former titles: Framing and Art (0957-929X); (until 1989): Framing, Fine Art and Wall Decor (0952-3197); (until 1987): Framing and Wall Decor
Related titles: Fax ed.
Published by: Vic Faulkner Associates, 48 Longfield Dr, Amersham, Bucks HP6 5HE, United Kingdom. TEL 44-1494-791451, FAX 44-1494-778224, Vic_Faulkner@compuserve.com. Ed., Pub., Adv. contact Vic Faulkner. page USD 1,200. Circ: 5,000 (controlled).

VOODOO SOULS QUARTERLY. see *LITERATURE*

700 RUS
VOPROSY ISKUSSTVOZNANIYA. Text in Russian. q.
Indexed: RASB.
Published by: Izdatel'stvo Galart, Ul Chernyakhovskogo 4a, kom 9, Moscow, 125319, Russian Federation. TEL 7-095-1513891, FAX 7-095-1513761. Ed. V T Sheveleva. **US dist. addr.:** East View Information Services, 3020 Harbor Ln. N., Minneapolis, MN 55447. TEL 612-550-0961.

700 NLD ISSN 0169-6858
VORM EN INDUSTRIE IN NEDERLAND. Text in Dutch. 1984. irreg.
Published by: Uitgeverij 010, Watertorenweg 180, Rotterdam, 3063 HA, Netherlands. TEL 31-10-4333509, FAX 31-10-4529825.

778.53 SVK ISSN 0042-9392
VYTVARNICTVO, FOTOGRAFIA, FILM; mesacnik pre zaujmovu umelecku cinnost. Text in Czech, Slovak; Summaries in English, German, Russian. 1963. m. USD 58. illus. index.
Published by: (Osvetovy Ustav/Union of the Czechoslovak-Soviet Friendship), Obzor, Spitalska ul 35, Bratislava, 81585, Slovakia. Ed. Jaroslav Ciljak. **Dist. by:** Slovart G.T.G. s.r.o., Krupinska 4, PO Box 152, Bratislava 85299, Slovakia. TEL 421-2-63839472, FAX 421-2-63839485, http://www.slovart-gtg.sk.

700 SVK ISSN 0139-7214
VYTVARNY ZIVOT. Text in Czech, Slovak; Summaries in English, German, Russian. 10/yr. USD 102.
Indexed: RASB.
Published by: Slovenska Vytvarna Unia, Dostojeskieho rad 2, Bratislava, 81109, Slovakia.

700 USA ISSN 1052-0066
N8554
W A A C NEWSLETTER. Text in English. 1979. 3/yr. free to members (effective 2004). bk.rev.; film rev. bibl.; illus.; tr.lit. cum.index: 1978-1988. **Document type:** *Newsletter, Consumer.* **Description:** Serves professionals in conservation and restoration of artistic and cultural works with news, ideas, and information.
Related titles: Online - full text ed.
Indexed: A&ATA.
Published by: Western Association for Art Conservation, 5905 Wilshire Blvd, Los Angeles, CA 90036. TEL 602-433-0461, http://palimpsest.stanford.edu/waac/. Ed. Carolyn Tallent. Circ: 400.

800 792 780 MWI
W A S I. Text in English. 1992. 3/yr. bk.rev. **Description:** Covers art, literature, music and drama. Aims to include Chiyao language and literature, putting it on the national scene.
Published by: Writers and Artists Services International, PO Box 317, Zomba, Malawi. Ed. Steve Chimombo.

709 DEU
WALLRAF-RICHARTZ-JAHRBUCH; WESTDEUTSCHES JAHRBUCH FUER KUNSTGESCHICHTE. NEUE FOLGE. Text in German. 1924. a. EUR 109 (effective 2005). **Document type:** *Journal, Academic/Scholarly.*
Formerly (until 1979): Wallraf-Richartz-Jahrbuch; Westdeutsches Jahrbuch fuer Kunstgeschichte (0083-7105)
Related titles: Online - full text ed.: (from H.W. Wilson, O C L C Online Computer Library Center, Inc.).
Indexed: AIAP, ArtInd, BHA, DIP, IBR, IBZ, PCI.
—BLDSC (9261.630000), IE, ingenta. **CCC.**
Published by: (Freunde des Wallraf-Richartz-Museums), DuMont Buchverlag, Amsterdamer Str 192, Cologne, 50735, Germany. TEL 49-221-2241877, FAX 49-221-2241973, info@DuMontLiteraturundKunst.de, http://www.dumontliteraturundkunst.de. Circ: 800.

700 GBR ISSN 0141-0016
WALPOLE SOCIETY. VOLUME. Key Title: Volume of the Walpole Society. Text in English. 1912. biennial.
Published by: Walpole Society, c/o Hugh Brigstocke, Editor, 118 Mickelgate, York, Y01 6JX, United Kingdom. TEL 44-190-462-6013, http://www.walpolesociety.org.uk/.

709 USA ISSN 0083-7148
WALTER W.S. COOK ALUMNI LECTURE. Text in English. 1960. irreg. USD 5. index.
Published by: (New York University, Institute of Fine Arts), J.J. Augustin, Inc., PO Box 311, Locust Valley, NY 11560. TEL 516-676-1510.

705 709 USA
N5220
➤ **WALTERS ART MUSEUM. JOURNAL.** Text in English. 1938. a. USD 52 domestic; USD 55 foreign (effective 2002). illus. back issues avail.; reprints avail. **Document type:** *Journal, Academic/Scholarly.* **Description:** Covers art history, particularly focusing on pieces in the Walters collection.
Formerly (until 2000): Walters Art Gallery. Journal (0083-7156)
Related titles: Online - full text ed.: (from H.W. Wilson, O C L C Online Computer Library Center, Inc.).
Indexed: A&ATA, AIAP, ArtInd, BAS, BHA, PCI, RILM.
Published by: Walters Art Museum, 600 N Charles St, Baltimore, MD 21201-5185. TEL 410-547-9000, FAX 410-752-4797, info@thewalters.org, http://www.thewalters.org/. Ed., R&P Deborah Horowitz. Circ: 1,000.

708.1 USA ISSN 1541-8863
N5220
THE WALTERS MAGAZINE. Text in English. 1948. q. USD 35 domestic; USD 47 foreign (effective 2000). illus. **Document type:** *Newsletter.* **Description:** Reviews exhibitions and events at the Walters Art Gallery. Includes calendar, membership information, and programs.
Former titles (until 2001): The Walters (1044-8683); (until 1983): Walters Art Gallery. Bulletin (0043-0188)
Indexed: BHA, RASB.
Published by: Walters Art Museum, 600 N Charles St, Baltimore, MD 21201-5185. TEL 410-547-9000, FAX 410-752-4797, info@thewalters.org, magazine@thewalters.org, http://www.thewalters.org/. Ed. Ann Ingraham. Circ: 10,000.

700 USA ISSN 0163-903X
WASHINGTON REVIEW. Text in English. 1975. bi-m. USD 15 (effective 1999). adv. bk.rev.; film rev.; play rev. illus. back issues avail. **Description:** Contains fiction, short stories, poetry, essays and art.
Former titles: Washington Review: a Quarterly Review of the Arts; Washington Review of the Arts
Related titles: Microform ed.
Indexed: AIPP, AmHI, IAPV.
Published by: Friends of the Washington Review of the Arts, Inc., PO Box 50132, Washington, DC 20091-0132. TEL 202-638-0515. Ed. Clarissa Wittenberg. R&P, Adv. contact Mary Swift. Circ: 1,500.

750 USA ISSN 1053-3915
ND1700
WATERCOLOR. Text in English. q. USD 23.95 domestic; USD 27.95 foreign; USD 8.50 newsstand/cover (effective 2005). **Document type:** *Magazine, Trade.* **Description:** Showcase of specially commissioned artists and step-by-step demonstrations totally devoted to watercolor.
Related titles: Online - full text ed.: (from bigchalk, Gale Group, ProQuest Information & Learning).
Published by: V N U Business Publications (Subsidiary of: V N U Business Media), 770 Broadway, New York, NY 10003-9595. TEL 646-654-7604, FAX 312-240-0686, mail@myamericanartist.com, bmcomm@vnuinc.com, http://myamericanartist.com, http://www.vnubusinessmedia.com/. Ed. M. Stephen Doherty. Pub. Jackie Leigh. Circ: 38,868 (paid).

750 USA ISSN 1079-5936
WATERCOLOR MAGIC. Text in English. 1993. q. USD 16.96 (effective 2005). adv. back issues avail. **Document type:** *Consumer.* **Description:** Provides instruction, technical information, and creative ideas to artists working in water media. Also includes information on new painting materials.
Published by: F & W Publications, Inc., 4700 E Galbraith Rd, Cincinnati, OH 45236. TEL 513-531-2690, 800-283-0963, FAX 513-531-2902, wcmedit@fwpubs.com, wds@fwpubs.com, http://www.watercolormagic.com, http://www.fwpublications.com. Ed. Ann Abbott. Pub. Jeffry Lapin. Adv. contact Joe Wood TEL 513-336-9760. B&W page USD 3,375, color page USD 3,775; trim 7.75 x 10.75. Circ: 90,000.
Subscr. to: PO Box 5439, Harlan, IA 51593.

750 GBR
WATERCOLOUR CHALLENGE. Text in English. w. GBP 1.80 newsstand/cover (effective 2001). **Document type:** *Magazine, Consumer.* **Description:** Contains tips and advice on how to master watercolor techniques and applications.
Published by: Eaglemoss Publications Ltd., 5 Cromwell Rd, London, SW7 2HR, United Kingdom. TEL 44-20-7590-8300, FAX 44-20-7590-8301, hjames@woodgt.co.uk, http://www.watercolourmag.co.uk, http://www.eaglemoss.co.uk.

A

750 CAN
WATERCOLOUR NEWS. Text in English, French. 4/yr. CND 30 to members. adv. back issues avail. **Document type:** *Newsletter.* **Description:** For professional watercolour artists and those interested in the form.
Published by: Canadian Society of Painters in Water Colour/Societe Canadienne de Peintres en Aquarelle, 258 Wallace Ave, Toronto, ON M6P 3M9, Canada. TEL 416-533-5100. Ed., Adv. contact Shirley Barrie. Circ: 400.

WEBCREATE. see *COMPUTERS—Internet*

DIE WEBEREIZEITUNG. see *GENERAL INTEREST PERIODICALS—Germany*

700 DEU ISSN 1437-1383
WEEKLY WORK; art and anecdotes. Text in German. w. back issues avail. **Document type:** *Consumer.*
Media: Online - full text.
Address: Uhlandstr 8, Hiddenhausen, 32120, Germany. TEL 49-5523-820582, FAX 49-5523-820584, ws@art-joe.com, http://art-quarter.com/beck/joe/aj. Ed. Werner Stuerenburg.

WEIMAR AND NOW: GERMAN CULTURAL CRITICISM. see *LITERATURE*

WELTKUNST; aktuelle Zeitschrift fuer Kunst und Antiquitaeten. see *ANTIQUES*

WENYI BAO/LITERATURE & ART GAZETTE. see *LITERATURE*

700 CHN ISSN 0510-0380
WENYI XUEXI/ART STUDIES. Text in Chinese. 1954. m.
Indexed: AIAP.
Published by: Zhongguo Wenlian Chuban Gongsi, 10 Nongzhanguan Nanli, Beijing, 100026, China. TEL 5005588.

WENYI YANJIU/LITERATURE AND ART STUDIES. see *LITERATURE*

WEST BY NORTHWEST. see *LITERATURE*

WEST COAST PEDDLER; oldest journal of antiques, art & collectibles in the Pacific states. see *ANTIQUES*

700 USA ISSN 0043-3357
N6530.C2
WESTART; west coast's art news scene. Text in English. 1962. m. USD 16 (effective 2000). adv. bk.rev. illus. reprint service avail. from PQC. **Document type:** *Newspaper, Trade.*
Related titles: Microfilm ed.: (from PQC).
Indexed: CalPI.
Published by: WestArt Publications, PO Box 6868, Auburn, CA 95604. TEL 530-885-0969, westart@vfr.net. Ed., R&P, Adv. contact Martha Garcia. Pub. Bud Pisarek. page USD 420. Circ: 4,000 (paid).

THE WESTMINSTER COLLEGE LIBRARY OF BIBLICAL SYMBOLISM. see *RELIGIONS AND THEOLOGY*

700 800 280 770 USA ISSN 0508-6191
➤ **WESTWIND (LOS ANGELES)**; U C L A's journal of the arts. Text in English. 1957. a. USD 15; USD 20 foreign. adv. **Document type:** *Academic/Scholarly.*
Published by: University of California at Los Angeles, A-265 Murphy Hall, 405 Hilgard Ave., Los Angeles, CA 90095. TEL 310-206-1225, westwind@hup.ucla.edu. Ed. Arnold Barba. adv.: page USD 140; 6 x 9. Circ: 1,100.

700 GBR ISSN 0269-9214
WESTWORDS. Text in English. 1987. 2/yr. GBP 5. adv. bk.rev. back issues avail.
Address: Devonshire, 15 Trelawney Rd, Peverell, Plymouth, Devon PL3 4JS, United Kingdom. TEL 0752-262877. Ed. David Woolley. Circ: 450.

500 USA ISSN 0190-9835
N1
WHITE WALLS; a journal of language and art. Text in English. 1978. 2/yr. USD 15; USD 8 newsstand/cover (effective 1999). adv. bk.rev. tr.lit.; illus. back issues avail.; reprints avail. **Document type:** *Magazine.* **Description:** Run by artists, supports and publishes artwork that explores relationships between language, visual arts, and contemporary culture.
Indexed: ABM.
Published by: White Walls, Inc., PO Box 8204, Chicago, IL 60680. aeelm@aol.com. Ed., R&P, Adv. contact Anthony Elms. B&W page USD 130. Circ: 1,000.

700 USA ISSN 1043-3260
N6512
WHITNEY MUSEUM OF AMERICAN ART. BIENNIAL EXHIBITION. Text in English. biennial.
Former titles (until 1973): Whitney Museum of American Art. Annual Exhibition; (until 1968): Whitney Museum of American Art. Annual Exhibition of Contemporary Painting; (until 1967): Whitney Museum of American Art. Annual Exhibition; (until 1960): Whitney Museum of American Art. Annual Exhibition of Contemporary American Painting; (until 1959): Whitney Museum of American Art. Annual Exhibition, Sculpture, Paintings, Watercolors, Drawings; (until 1959): Whitney Museum of American Art. Annual Exhibition, Sculpture, Paintings, Watercolors; (until 1957): Whitney Museum of American Art. Annual Exhibition, Sculpture, Paintings, Watercolors, Drawings; Which was formed by the 1956 merger of: Whitney Museum of American Art. Annual Exhibition of Contemporary American Painting; Whitney Museum of American Art. Annual Exhibition of Contemporary American Sculpture, Watercolors, and Drawings
Published by: Whitney Museum of American Art, 945 Madison Ave at 75 St, New York, NY 10021. TEL 212-570-3600, 800-944-8639, http://www.whitney.org/.

WHOLE ARTS DIRECTORY. see *BUSINESS AND ECONOMICS—Trade And Industrial Directories*

WHO'S WHO IN ART. see *BIOGRAPHY*

709.2 USA
WHO'S WHO IN ART MATERIALS. Text in English. a. USD 200 to non-members (effective 1999). **Document type:** *Directory, Trade.* **Description:** Geared to manufacturers and representatives, retailers, wholesalers, importers and publishers of art materials.
Published by: National Art Materials Trade Association, 10115 Kincey Ave, Ste 260, Huntersville, NC 28078. TEL 704-948-5554, FAX 704-948-5658. Ed. Stephen Lefebvre. Circ: 2,000.

700 AUT ISSN 0083-9981
N9
WIENER JAHRBUCH FUER KUNSTGESCHICHTE. Text in English, German. 1921. a. EUR 69 (effective 2004). bk.rev. illus. **Document type:** *Journal, Academic/Scholarly.*
Indexed: ABM, AIAP, BHA, DIP, IBR, IBZ, RASB, RILM.
Published by: (Bundesdenkmalamt Wien), Boehlau Verlag GmbH & Co.KG., Sachsenplatz 4-6, Vienna, W 1201, Austria. TEL 43-1-33024270, FAX 43-1-3302432, boehlau@boehlau.at, http://www.boehlau.at. Eds. E Frodl Kraft, G Schmidt. Circ: 500. **Co-sponsor:** Universitaet Wien. Kunsthistorisches Institut.

700 AUT
WIENZEILE; internationales kunstmagazin. Text in German. q. **Document type:** *Consumer.*
Published by: V I Z A Literaturfoerderungsverein, Hahngasse 15, Vienna, W 1090, Austria. TEL 01-315222. Circ: 3,000.

WILBOUR MONOGRAPHS. see *HISTORY*

WILD HEART JOURNAL. see *LIFESTYLE*

700 USA ISSN 1084-7855
N7660
WILDLIFE ART. Text in English. 1982. bi-m. USD 19.95 domestic; USD 29.95 in Canada; USD 40.95 elsewhere; USD 6.95 newsstand/cover (effective 2005). adv. bk.rev. illus. back issues avail. **Document type:** *Magazine, Consumer.* **Description:** For wildlife art collectors. Contains interviews with artists, a calendar of events and business news.
Formerly: Wildlife Art News (0746-9640)
Related titles: Supplement(s): Art Collector's Edition.
Indexed: ABM, WildRev.
Published by: Pothole Publications, Inc., 1428 E Cliff Rd, Burnsville, MN 55337. TEL 952-736-1020, 800-221-6547, FAX 952-736-1030, publisher@winternet.com, http://www.wildlifeartmag.com. Ed. Mary Nelson. Pub. Robert J Koenke. Adv. contact Paul Montag. B&W page USD 2,095, color page USD 2,820; trim 8.25 x 10.75. Circ: 41,950 (paid and controlled).

700 975 USA
WILLIAMSBURG DECORATIVE ARTS SERIES. Text in English. 1974. irreg., latest 1997. price varies. **Document type:** *Trade.*
Published by: Colonial Williamsburg Foundation, PO Box 1776, Williamsburg, VA 23187-1776. TEL 757-220-7342. Ed. Donna C Sheppard. R&P Joseph N Rountree.

WINDHAM PHOENIX. see *LITERATURE*

WINDSCRIPT. see *LITERATURE*

700 USA ISSN 0084-0416
N9
➤ **WINTERTHUR PORTFOLIO**; a journal of American material culture. Text in English. 1964. 3/yr., latest vol.37, 2002, Spring. USD 39 combined subscription to individuals print & online eds.; USD 160 combined subscription to institutions print & online eds.; USD 18 per issue to individuals; USD 62 per issue to institutions (effective 2006). adv. bk.rev. illus. Index. back issues avail.; reprint service avail. from PQC,ISI. **Document type:** *Journal, Academic/Scholarly.* **Description:** Contains articles on the arts in America and the historical context in which they developed. Emphasizes analytical studies that integrate artifacts into their cultural context.
Incorporates: Winterthur Conference Report (0084-0408)
Related titles: Online - full text ed.: ISSN 1545-6927. USD 144 to institutions (effective 2006) (from EBSCO Publishing, Florida Center for Library Automation, Gale Group, JSTOR (Web-based Journal Archive)).
Indexed: ABCT, ABM, AIAP, API, ASCA, AmH&L, ArtHuCI, ArtInd, BHA, CurCont, DIP, HistAb, IBR, IBRH, IBZ, MLA, MLA-IB, PCI, RI-1, RI-2, SOPODA, SSA, SSCI.
—BLDSC (9319.800000), IDS, IE, Infotrieve, ingenta. **CCC.**
Published by: (Henry Francis du Pont Winterthur Museum), University of Chicago Press, Journals Division, Journals Division, PO Box 37005, Chicago, IL 60637. TEL 773-753-3347, 877-705-1878, FAX 773-753-0811, 877-705-1879, llock@winterthur.org, subscriptions@press.uchicago.edu, http://www.journals.uchicago.edu/WP. Ed. Lisa L Lock. adv.: page USD 385; trim 8.5 x 11. Circ: 1,000 (paid).

➤ **WIRED ART FROM WIRED HEARTS.** see *LITERATURE*

➤ **WISCONSIN ACADEMY OF SCIENCES, ARTS AND LETTERS. TRANSACTIONS.** see *SCIENCES: COMPREHENSIVE WORKS*

➤ **WISCONSIN ACADEMY REVIEW.** see *LITERARY AND POLITICAL REVIEWS*

700 BEL ISSN 0774-8523
DE WITTE RAAF. Text in Dutch. 1986. bi-m. EUR 18.59 domestic; EUR 18.59 in Netherlands; EUR 5 per issue domestic (effective 2005). illus. 44 p./no.; back issues avail. **Document type:** *Newspaper.* **Description:** Aimed at persons seeking to reflect and be informed on the visual arts.
Published by: (Vlaamse Gemeenschap), D W R - T W R vzw, Postbus 1428, Brussel, 1000, Belgium. TEL 32-2-223-1450, FAX 32-2-223-2318, info@dewitteraaf.be, dewitteraaf@skynet.be, http://www.dewitteraaf.be. Ed. Sven Luettichen. R&P, Adv. contact Etienne Wynants. Circ: 17,000 (paid).

WITTENBERG REVIEW OF LITERATURE AND ART. see *LITERATURE*

THE WITTLIFF GALLERY SERIES. see *PHOTOGRAPHY*

741.5 USA ISSN 0892-9807
NC1300
WITTYWORLD; international cartoon bulletin. (Includes a magazine and 11 bulletins.) Text in English. 1987. 11/yr. USD 56; USD 64 foreign (effective 1997). adv. bk.rev.; video rev. illus. reprints avail. **Document type:** *Bulletin, Trade.* **Description:** Covers all aspects of cartooning art: political, comic strip, animation, and caricature. Includes interviews with leading cartoonists, dates and reports on competitions, and examples of cartoons.
Published by: WittyWorld Publications, 214 School St, North Wales, PA 19454. TEL 215-699-2626, FAX 215-699-0627, www.wittyworld.com. Ed., Pub. Joseph George Szabo. Adv. contact Flora Toth. Circ: 5,000.

700 305.4 USA ISSN 0270-7993
N72.F45
➤ **WOMAN'S ART JOURNAL.** Text in English. 1980. s-a. USD 20 domestic to individuals; USD 28 foreign to individuals; USD 40 domestic to institutions; USD 48 foreign to institutions (effective 2004). adv. bk.rev. illus. Index. 60 p./no.; back issues avail. **Document type:** *Journal, Academic/Scholarly.* **Description:** Covers women and issues related to women in all areas of the visual arts. Each issue features articles covering time periods from antiquity to the present. Also includes about 20 book and catalogue reviews.
Related titles: Microform ed.: (from PQC); Online - full text ed.: (from H.W. Wilson, JSTOR (Web-based Journal Archive), O C L C Online Computer Library Center, Inc.).
Indexed: ABM, ABS&EES, AIAP, ASCA, ArtHuCI, ArtInd, BHA, CurCont, DAAI, FemPer, PCI.
—BLDSC (9343.171900), IDS, IE, ingenta.
Published by: Woman's Art, Inc., 1711 Harris Rd., Laverock, PA 19038-7208. Ed., Pub. Elsa Honig Fine. Circ: 4,000.

704.042 USA
N6512
WOMEN ARTISTS NEWS BOOK REVIEW. Text in English. 1975. a. USD 6 to individuals; USD 7 to institutions (effective 2000). adv. bk.rev. illus. index. back issues avail.; reprints avail. **Document type:** *Trade.* **Description:** Includes reviews of books on art and literature, women artists, and women's issues.
Former titles (until 1993): Women Artists News (0149-7081); N A W A News; Women Artist Newsletter (0361-9117)
Related titles: Online - full text ed.: (from O C L C Online Computer Library Center, Inc., ProQuest Information & Learning).
Indexed: ABCT, AltPI, ArtInd, BHA, FemPer, GendWatch, IBZ.
Published by: (Midmarch Associates), Midmarch Arts Press, 300 Riverside Dr, New York, NY 10025. TEL 212-666-6990. Ed. Sylvia Moore. Circ: 5,000.

700 USA ISSN 1058-7217
N858.N36
WOMEN IN THE ARTS. Text in English. 1983. q. free to members. adv. bk.rev. **Document type:** *Journal.* **Description:** Provides information on museum activities related to promoting knowledge about women in the arts, notices of exhibitions across the country of works by women artsts, and articles on women's contributions to the arts.

Formerly (until 1991): National Museum of Women in the Arts News (0891-1827)
Published by: National Museum of Women in the Arts, 1250 New York Ave N W, Washington, DC 20005-3920. TEL 202-783-5000, 800-222-7270, FAX 202393-3235, http://www.nmwa.org/pubs/wia_main.asp. Ed. Laureen Schipsi. R&P Randi Greenberg. Adv. contact Mary Frances Wain. Circ: 60,000 (controlled).

700 305.42 USA
WOMEN IN THE ARTS NEWSLETTER. Text in English. 1971. bi-m. USD 9 to individuals; USD 15 domestic to institutions; USD 19 foreign to institutions (effective 2000). adv. bk.rev. **Document type:** *Newsletter.*
Formerly: Women in the Arts Bulletin - Newsletter
Published by: Women in the Arts Foundation, Inc., 1175 York Ave, No 2G, c o R Crown, New York, NY 10021. TEL 212-751-1915. Ed., R&P, Adv. contact Erin Butler. Circ: 300.

700 USA
WOMEN'S CAUCUS FOR ART. HONOR AWARDS CATALOGUE. Text in English. 1980. a. USD 8 to non-members. bibl. back issues avail. **Document type:** *Catalog.* **Description:** Honors five women for their life work in the visual arts. Includes essays and a chronology.
Published by: Women's Caucus for Art, Moore College of Art, 20th & Parkway, Philadelphia, PA 19103. TEL 215-854-0922. Circ: 4,000.

700 USA ISSN 1052-4959
NX180.F4
WOMEN'S CAUCUS FOR ART. NATIONAL UPDATE. Text in English. 1978. q. membership. **Description:** Contains information of interest to women in all visual arts professions. Includes short articles and new material, as well as job listings and exhibition opportunities.
Published by: Women's Caucus for Art, Moore College of Art, 20th & Parkway, Philadelphia, PA 19103. TEL 215-854-0922. Circ: 4,000.

WONKA VISION; your source for independent art, music & thoughts. see *MUSIC*

700 790 NLD ISSN 0084-1498
WORLD COLLECTORS ANNUARY✶. Text in English. 1950. a., latest 44th, for 1993-1995. USD 195. adv. cum.index (1946-1982). **Description:** Alphabetical listing of each object (painting, drawing, pastel, gouache, and watercolor) sold at auction, with price realized (and conversion into US dollars), factual and scholarly description, and provenance index.
Published by: World Collectors Publishers, Prof Velicstraat 47, Nijmegen, 6524 NN, Netherlands. FAX 31-243-237747. Ed. M J van Laake. Circ: 1,000.

WORLD CULTURAL GUIDES. see *TRAVEL AND TOURISM*

700 745.1 USA
WORLD FINE ART. Text in English. 1982. bi-m. USD 75 (effective 1999). bk.rev. **Document type:** *Newsletter.*
Published by: Art Baron Management Corp., PO Box 5365, Scottsdale, AZ 85261. TEL 602-957-3215. Ed., R&P Steve Shipp. Pub. Jeff Coffin.

WORLD OF ANTIQUES AND ART. see *ANTIQUES*

700 ISR
WORLD OF ART. Text in Hebrew. 1977. s-a. ILS 60, USD 30. adv. bk.rev. back issues avail.
Indexed: IHP.
Published by: World of Art Inc., 190 Ben Yehuda St, Tel Aviv, 63471, Israel. TEL 3-5237115, FAX 3-5272570. Ed. Joseph A Melamed. Circ: 4,000.

THE WORLD OF TRIBAL ARTS/MONDE DE L'ART TRIBAL. see *MUSEUMS AND ART GALLERIES*

730 HKG ISSN 1024-087X
WORLD SCULPTURE NEWS. Text in English. 1995. q. HKD 140, USD 17.50; USD 22 in Canada; USD 30 in Asia & the Pacific. adv. back issues avail. **Description:** Covers all aspects of modern and contemporary sculpture and installation, worldwide.
—IE.
Published by: Asian Art News, G/F, 28 Arbuthnot Rd, Central, Hong Kong, Hong Kong. TEL 852-2522-3443, FAX 852-2521-5268, asianart@netvigator.com. Ed., R&P Ian Findlay-Brown. Pub. Ian Findlay Brown. Adv. contact Lynne Gallacher. B&W page USD 1,500, color page USD 1,900; trim 210 x 285. **Dist. by:** PO Box 469111, Escondido, CA 92046-9111.

741 GBR
Z43.A1
WRITING MATTERS; the journal and newsletter of the society for italic handwriting. Text in English. 1962. q. GBP 15 domestic; USD 25 foreign. adv. bk.rev. charts; illus. **Document type:** *Newsletter.* **Description:** Promotion of the use of italic handwriting for everyday use in educational and other areas.
Former titles (until 2000): Society for Italic Handwriting. Newsletter (1358-3921); Society for Italic Handwriting. Journal (0037-9743)
Indexed: BHA.
Published by: Society for Italic Handwriting, 205 Dyas Ave, Great Barr, Birmingham, W Mids B42 1HN, United Kingdom. TEL 44-121-358-0032, http://www.argonet.co.uk/users/quilljar/sih.html. Ed. Nicholas Caulkin. Circ: 500.

700 POL ISSN 0084-2982
WROCLAWSKIE TOWARZYSTWO NAUKOWE. KOMISJA HISTORII SZTUKI. ROZPRAWY. Text in Polish; Summaries in English, French. 1960. irreg., latest vol.12, 1991. price varies. **Document type:** *Monographic series.* **Description:** Monographs and studies in Polish painting, sculpture, artistics industry and handicraft on comparative background.
Indexed: AIAP.
Published by: (Poznanskie Towarzystwo Przyjaciol Nauk, Komisja Historii Sztuki), Wroclawskie Towarzystwo Naukowe, Ul Parkowa 13, Wroclaw, 50616, Poland. TEL 48-71-484-061. Circ: 1,000.

WYDZIAL FILOLOGICZNO-FILOZOFICZNY. PRACE. see *PHILOSOPHY*

730 POL ISSN 0860-9071
WYZSZA SZKOLA PEDAGOGICZNA IM. KOMISJI EDUKACJI NARODOWEJ W KRAKOWIE. ROCZNIK NAUKOWO-DYDAKTYCZNY. PRACE Z WYCHOWANIA PLASTYCZNEGO. Text in Polish. 1988. irreg. price varies.
Published by: (Wyzsza Szkola Pedagogiczna im. Komisji Edukacji Narodowej w Krakowie), Wydawnictwo Naukowe W S P, Ul Karmelicka 41, Krakow, 31128, Poland. TEL 33-78-20.
Co-sponsor: Ministerstwo Edukacji Nrodowej.

XERO; quaderni di Heliopolis. see *LITERATURE—Poetry*

700 CHN ISSN 1005-7889
XIAOYISHUJIA/LITTLE ARTIST. Text in Chinese. 1993. m. CNY 66 (effective 2004). **Document type:** *Journal, Academic/Scholarly.*
Address: 15, Yingyuan Lu, Guangzhou, 510040, China. TEL 86-20-83556422. **Dist. by:** China International Book Trading Corp, 35 Chegongzhuang Xilu, Haidian District, PO Box 399, Beijing 100044, China. TEL 86-10-68412045, FAX 86-10-68412023, cibtc@mail.cibtc.com.cn, http://www.cibtc.com.cn.

700 CHN
XINMEISHU/NEW ARTS. Text in Chinese. 1980. q. USD 48 (effective 2004). **Document type:** *Journal, Academic/Scholarly.*
Published by: Zhejiang Meishu Xueyuan Chubanshe/Zhejiang Academy of Fine Art Publishing House, 218, Nanshan Lu, Hangzhou, 310002, China. **Dist. by:** China International Book Trading Corp, 35 Chegongzhuang Xilu, Haidian District, PO Box 399, Beijing 100044, China. TEL 86-10-68412045, FAX 86-10-68412023, cibtc@mail.cibtc.com.cn, http://www.cibtc.com.cn.

700 CHN
XIZANG YISHU YANJIU/TIBETAN ART STUDIES. Text in Chinese. q. (Tibetan ed. s-a.). CNY 20 domestic for Chinese ed.; USD 24 foreign for Chinese ed.; CNY 10 domestic for Tibetan ed.; USD 12 foreign for Tibetan ed.. **Document type:** *Academic/Scholarly.* **Description:** Covers Tibetan culture, including music and dance, literature, painting and artists.
Related titles: Tibetan ed.: CNY 10 domestic; USD 12 foreign (effective 1999).
Published by: Xizang Zizhiqu Minzu Yishu Yanjiusuo, Wenhuating Yuan Nei, 2 Duodi Lu, Lhasa, Xizang (Tibet) 850000, China. TEL 86-891-6326538. Eds. Da Wa Sang Bu, Liu Zhiqun. **Dist. overseas by:** Jiangsu Publications Import & Export Corp., 56 Gao Yun Ling, Nanjing, Jiangsu, China.

700 792 AUS ISSN 0817-4628
XPRESS✶. Text in English. 1986. bi-m. AUD 48. adv. bk.rev. back issues avail. **Description:** Discusses popular culture topics including art, fashion design and theatre.
Indexed: AEI.
Published by: A & E Xpress, PO Box 1195, Potts Point, NSW 2011, Australia. TEL 02 358 4077. Ed. Alexandra Morphett.

700 USA
XTREME BODY MOD; piercing, branding, tattooing & more. Text in English. 2001 (Oct.). bi-m. USD 17.97 domestic; USD 23.97 foreign; USD 5.99 newsstand/cover; USD 6.99 newsstand/cover in Canada (effective 2001). adv. **Document type:** *Magazine, Consumer.* **Description:** Contains in-depth articles and features on body modification, including tattooing, branding, piercing and scarification.
Published by: Body Mod Productions, 170 Hamilton Ave, Ste 212, White Plains, NY 10601. TEL 914-949-0250, 800-964-6247, FAX 914-949-0249, extremeditor@aol.com, http://www.xtremebodymod.com. Pub. Warren Tabatch. Adv. contact Kevin Kelly TEL 760-485-0650. color page USD 1,710. Circ: 50,000 (paid). **Dist. by:** Curtis Circulation Co., 730 River Road, New Milford, NJ 07646. TEL 201-634-7400, FAX 201-634-7499, http://www.curtiscirc.com.

700 USA ISSN 0084-3415
YALE PUBLICATIONS IN THE HISTORY OF ART. Text in English. 1939. irreg. price varies.
Published by: Yale University Press, PO Box 209040, New Haven, CT 06520. TEL 203-432-0940, FAX 616-592-2618, chla@mlc.lib.mi.us, ysm@yale.edu, http://www.yale.edu, http://www.yalepress.yale.edu.

YAPI; aylik kultur, sanat ve mimarlik dergisi. see *ARCHITECTURE*

700 801 USA ISSN 1074-5629
PN1
YEFIEF; a narrative of culture at the end of the century. Text in English. 1994. irreg. USD 24.95 per vol. (effective 2000). bk.rev. back issues avail. **Description:** Contains fine art, literature and newforms. Constructed to create a narrative of culture at the end of the century which draws on the diversity of contemporary life.
Published by: Images for Media, PO Box 8505, Santa Fe, NM 87504. TEL 505-753-3648, FAX 505-753-7049, arr@imagesformedia.com, http://www.imagesformedia.com. Ed., Pub., R&P Ann Racuya-Robbins. Adv. contact Ann Racuya Robbins. Circ: 2,000.

700 CHN ISSN 1003-9104
➤ **YISHU BAIJIA/HUNDRED SCHOOLS IN ART.** Text in Chinese. 1985. q. USD 50. adv. bk.rev. **Document type:** *Academic/Scholarly.*
Related titles: Online - full text ed.: (from East View Information Services).
Published by: Jiangsu Sheng Wenhua Yishu Yanjiusuo/Jiangsu Provincial Institute of Culture and Art, Xuanwu-qu, Longpanzhong Road, Huashan Fandian South, 2nd Floor, Room 110, Nanjing, Jiangsu 210016, China. TEL 86-25-3353056. Ed. Weidong Su. R&P, Adv. contact Yongjing Wang. page USD 300. Circ: 3,000.

700 CHN ISSN 1003-9481
YISHU SHENGHUO/ART & LIFE. Text in Chinese. 1988. bi-m. CNY 33.60 (effective 2004). **Document type:** *Academic/Scholarly.*
Address: 31, Wushiyi Beilu, 13 Luo, Fuzhou, Fujian 7534506, China. **Dist. by:** China International Book Trading Corp, 35 Chegongzhuang Xilu, Haidian District, PO Box 399, Beijing 100044, China. TEL 86-10-68412045, FAX 86-10-68412023, cibtc@mail.cibtc.com.cn, http://www.cibtc.com.cn.

700 CHN ISSN 1005-7722
YISHU SHIJIE/WORLD OF ART. Text in Chinese. bi-m. USD 75 (effective 2001); USD 6.30 newsstand/cover. adv. illus.
Published by: Shanghai Wenyi Chubanshe, 74 Shaoxing Lu, Shanghai, 200020, China. TEL 86-21-6437-2608. Ed. Baoping Chen. R&P Zengi Yu TEL 86-21-6437-6396. Adv. contact Jie Fang. **Dist. in US by:** China Books & Periodicals Inc, 360 Swift Ave., Ste. 48, S San Fran, CA 94080-6220. TEL 415-282-2994; **Dist. outside China by:** China International Book Trading Corp. cibtc@mail.cibtc.com.cn, http://www.cibtc.com.cn.

700 CHN
YISHU YU SHIDAI. Text in Chinese. bi-m.
Published by: Hubei Sheng Wenlian, 1 Dongting 2 Lu, Donghu, Wuchang, Wuhan, Hubei 430071, China. TEL 356377. Ed. Chen Dongcheng.

700 CHN
YISHUJIA/ARTIST. Text in Chinese. bi-m. CNY 1.50 per issue. illus. **Description:** Presents profiles, interviews, and biographical articles about Chinese and foreign artists in all media. Also contains articles and discussion on issues pertaining to art and society.
Published by: (Tianjin Wenxue Yishujie Lianhehui/Tianjin Federation of the Literary and Art Circle), Yishujia Zazhishe, 237 Xinhua Lu, Heping-qu, Tianjin 300040, China. Ed. Feng Jicai.

700 TWN ISSN 1016-4170
N8.C5
YISHUJIA/ARTIST. Text in Chinese. 1975. m. TWD 2,300, USD 87. adv. bk.rev. illus.
Published by: Artist Magazine, 6F, 147 Chungking S. Rd Sec 1, Taipei, Taiwan. TEL 02-371-9692, FAX 02-331-7096. Ed. Flora Yang. Pub. Ho Cheng Kuang. Adv. contact Grace Huang. color page USD 550. Circ: 22,000.

700 GBR ISSN 0951-9084
YORKSHIRE ARTSCENE. Text in English. 1976. 10/yr. GBP 12. adv. bk.rev.; film rev.; music rev.; play rev. abstr.; bibl.; illus. back issues avail. **Document type:** *Consumer.*
Formerly (until 1986): Arts Yorkshire (0264-7699)
Published by: (Yorkshire and Humberside Arts), White Knight Music Ltd., Dean Clough Industrial Park, Halifax, W Yorks HX3 5AX, United Kingdom. TEL 44-1422-322527, FAX 44-1422-322518. Ed. Vic Allen. Adv. contact David Nesbitt. B&W page GBP 385, color page GBP 655. Circ: 25,000.

YOUR FLESH QUARTERLY. see *MUSIC*

YUNYI KHUDOZHNIK. see *CHILDREN AND YOUTH—For*

730 CHN ISSN 1009-7635
ZAOXING YISHU/PLASTIC ART. Text in Chinese. 1978. bi-m. USD 66 (effective 2004). 120 p./no.; **Document type:** *Journal, Academic/Scholarly.* **Description:** Covers paintings, calligraphy, sculpture, handcrafts, photography and other art forms.
Formerly: Zaoxing Yishu Yanjiu (1001-3296)
Published by: Zhongguo Renmin Daxue, Shubao Zilio Zhongxin/Renmin University of China, Information Center for Social Server, Dongcheng-qu, 3, Zhangzizhong Lu, Beijing, 100007, China. TEL 86-10-64039458, FAX 86-10-64015080, kyes@163.net, http://www.confucius.cn.net/bkdetail.asp?fzt=J7. **Dist. in US by:** China Publications Service, PO Box 49614, Chicago, IL 60649. TEL 312-288-3291, FAX 312-288-8570.

700 SCG
ZBORNIK NARODNOG MUZEJA O BEOGRADU. ISTORIYA UMETNOSTI. Text in Multiple languages. 1982. irreg., latest 2002. price varies. **Document type:** *Monographic series, Academic/Scholarly.*
Supersedes in part (in 1981): Zbornik Narodnog Muzeja o Beogradu (0522-8352)
Published by: Narodni Muzej Beograd, Trg. Republike 1a, Beograd. TEL 381-11-624322, FAX 381-11-627721, narodnimuzej@narodnimuzej.org.yu, http://www.narodnimuzej.org.yu.

700 CHE
ZEICHNEN UND GESTALT. Text in German. 1912. 3/yr. CHF 6. **Document type:** *Bulletin.*
Related titles: ♦ Supplement to: Schweizer Lehrerinnen- und Lehrerzeitung. ISSN 1422-0660.
Indexed: PsycInfo.
Published by: Gesellschaft Schweizerischer Zeichenlehrer, Im Geeren 7, Otelfingen, 8112, Switzerland. TEL 01-8441209. Ed. M Poertner Hayoz. Circ: 1,000.

ZEITSCHRIFT FUER AESTHETIK UND ALLGEMEINE KUNSTWISSENSCHAFT. see *PHILOSOPHY*

709 DEU ISSN 0044-2992
N3
ZEITSCHRIFT FUER KUNSTGESCHICHTE. Text in English, French, German, Italian. 1932. 4/yr. EUR 92; EUR 28 newsstand/cover (effective 2005). adv. bk.rev. charts; illus. index. reprints avail. **Document type:** *Journal, Academic/Scholarly.*
Formed by the merger of (1876-1932): Repertorium fuer Kunstwissenschaft (0932-1179); (1866-1932): Zeitschrift fuer Bildende Kunst (0863-5838); (1905-1932): Jahrbuch fuer Kunstwissenschaft (0863-582X); Which was formerly (until 1923): Monatshefte fuer Kunstwissenschaft (0863-5811); (until 1908): Monatshefte der Kunstwissenschaftlichen Literatur (0932-1136)
Indexed: ABM, AIAP, ASCA, AmH&L, ArtHuCI, ArtInd, BHA, CurCont, DIP, HistAb, IBR, IBRH, IBZ, IndIslam, NTA, PCI, RASB, RILM.
—IDS, IE, Infotrieve. **CCC.**
Published by: Deutscher Kunstverlag GmbH, Nymphenburger Str 84, Munich, 80636, Germany. TEL 49-89-1269900, FAX 49-89-12151644, zsfkg-kunsthist@unibas.ch, info@deutscherkunstverlag.de, http://pages.unibas.ch/zsfkg/, http://www.kunstbuecher-online.de. Eds. Andreas Beyer, Andreas Toennesmann. Circ: 900.

700 DEU ISSN 0931-7198
N8554
ZEITSCHRIFT FUER KUNSTTECHNOLOGIE UND KONSERVIERUNG. Text in German. 1987. s-a. adv. **Document type:** *Bulletin.*
Indexed: AIAP, BHA, RILM.
Published by: (Deutscher Restauratorenverbandes e.V.), Wernersche Verlagsgesellschaft mbH, Liebfrauenring 17-19, Worms, 67547, Germany. TEL 06241-43574, FAX 06241-45564. Ed., Adv. contact Juergen Hirschauer.

ZEITSCHRIFT FUER SCHWEIZERISCHE ARCHAEOLOGIE UND KUNSTGESCHICHTE/REVUE SUISSE D'ART ET D'ARCHEOLOGIE. see *ARCHAEOLOGY*

ZEITZOO; Zeitschrift fuer Literatur und bildende Kunst. see *LITERATURE*

ZEN RUBIES; an eclectic display of words and pictures. see *LITERATURE*

ZHAZHDA/THIRST. see *LITERATURE*

700 CHN ISSN 1007-094X
ZHONG GUO KA TONG/CARTOON OF CHINA. Text in Chinese. 1996. m. CNY 58.80; USD 36 foreign. adv. bk.rev. illus. back issues avail. **Document type:** *Consumer.*
Related titles: Fax ed.
Published by: Zhongguo Shaonian Ertong Chubanshe, 21 Dongsi 12 Tiao, Beijing, 100708, China. TEL 86-10-6403-2266, FAX 86-10-6401-2262. Ed. Shi Mingli.

760 CHN ISSN 1005-0787
NE768
ZHONGGUO BANHUA. Text in Chinese. q.
Formerly: Banhua Shijie
Published by: Renmin Meishu Chubanshe/People's Fine Arts Publishers, 32, Beizongbu Hutong, Beijing, 100735, China. TEL 86-1-5122583. Ed. Liu Yushan.

745.61 CHN ISSN 1007-2942
ZHONGGUO GANGBI SHUFA/PEN CALLIGRAPHY OF CHINA. Text in Chinese. 1987. m. CNY 57.60 (effective 2004). **Document type:** *Journal, Academic/Scholarly.*
Address: Hangzhou Sheng Fudayuan, no.2 Building, Zhejiang, 310025, China. http://www.zgshj.com/Html/2004182262-1.html. **Dist. by:** China International Book Trading Corp, 35 Chegongzhuang Xilu, Haidian District, PO Box 399, Beijing 100044, China. TEL 86-10-68412045, FAX 86-10-68412023, cibtc@mail.cibtc.com.cn, http://www.cibtc.com.cn.

750 CHN
ZHONGGUO HUA/CHINESE PAINTING. Text in Chinese. 1957. q. **Document type:** *Academic/Scholarly.* **Description:** Focuses on traditional Chinese painting and artists.
Published by: (Zhongguo Beijing Huayuan), Zhongguo Hua Bianjibu, 13 Yu er Hutong, Di'anmen, Beijing, 100009, China. TEL 86-10-4040179, FAX 86-10-4035322. Ed. Wen Guanwang. **Dist. in US by:** China Books & Periodicals Inc, 360 Swift Ave., Ste. 48, S San Fran, CA 94080-6220. TEL 415-282-2994.

741.5 CHN ISSN 1005-6955
ZHONGGUO MANHUA/CHINA CARTOONS. Text in Chinese. bi-m. USD 16.20.
Published by: Tianjin Renmin Meishu Chubanshe/Tianjin People's Fine Art Publishing House, 150 Machang Dao, Heping-qu, Tianjin 300050, China. TEL 86-2-3313358. Ed. Liu Jingping. **Dist. overseas by:** China International Book Trading Corp, 35 Chegongzhuang Xilu, Haidian District, PO Box 399, Beijing 100044, China.

745.61 CHN
ZHONGGUO SHUFA/CHINESE CALLIGRAPHY. Text in Chinese. bi-m. USD 30.50. illus.
Published by: Zhongguo Zhufajia Xiehui, 2 Shatan Beijie, Beijing, 100009, China. **Dist. in US by:** China Books & Periodicals Inc, 360 Swift Ave., Ste. 48, S San Fran, CA 94080-6220. TEL 415-282-2994; **Dist. overseas by:** China International Book Trading Corp, 35 Chegongzhuang Xilu, Haidian District, PO Box 399, Beijing 100044, China. TEL 86-10-68412045, FAX 86-10-68412023, cibtc@mail.cibtc.com.cn, http://www.cibtc.com.cn.

750 CHN
ZHONGGUO SHUHUA/CHINESE CALLIGRAPHY AND PAINTING. Text in Chinese; Contents page in English. m. CNY 96. illus. **Description:** Covers Chinese painting.
Published by: Renmin Meishu Chubanshe/People's Fine Arts Publishers, 32, Beizongbu Hutong, Beijing, 100735, China. TEL 81-1-5122583. Ed. Shen Peng.

700 CHN ISSN 1003-0433
ZHONGGUO YISHU/CHINESE ART. Text in Chinese. q. USD 48.40; USD 12.10 newsstand/cover (effective 2001).
Published by: Renmin Meishu Chubanshe/People's Fine Arts Publishers, 32, Beizongbu Hutong, Beijing, 100735, China. TEL 86-1-5122375. Ed. Chen Yunhe. **Dist. by:** China International Book Trading Corp, 35 Chegongzhuang Xilu, Haidian District, PO Box 399, Beijing 100044, China. TEL 86-10-68412045, FAX 86-10-68412023, cibtc@mail.cibtc.com.cn, http://www.cibtc.com.cn.

750 CHN ISSN 1005-6920
ZHONGGUO YOUHUA/CHINA OIL PAINTING. Text in Chinese. q. USD 26.60.
Published by: Tianjin Renmin Meishu Chubanshe/Tianjin People's Fine Art Publishing House, 150 Machang Dao, Heping-qu, Tianjin 300050, China. TEL 86-2-3313358, FAX 86-2-3313358. Ed. Du Ziling. **Dist. overseas by:** China International Book Trading Corp, 35 Chegongzhuang Xilu, Haidian District, PO Box 399, Beijing 100044, China.

740 CHN ISSN 0412-3662
ZHUANGSHI/DECORATION. Text in Chinese. q. illus. 56 p./no.; **Description:** Covers decorative art and design as well as advertising designs.
Related titles: Online - full text ed.: (from East View Information Services).
Published by: (Zhongyang Gongyi Meishu Xueyuan), China International Book Trading Corp/Zhongguo Guoji Tushu Maoyi Zonggongsi, 35 Chegongzhuang Xilu, Haidian District, PO Box 399, Beijing, 100044, China. **Dist. in US by:** China Books & Periodicals Inc, 360 Swift Ave., Ste. 48, S San Fran, CA 94080-6220. TEL 415-282-2994.

ZINE-ON-THE-WEB. see *MUSIC*

700 FRA ISSN 0044-4952
N2
ZODIAQUE. Text in French. 1951. s-a. adv. bk.rev. index. back issues avail. **Document type:** *Consumer.*
Indexed: BHA, RILM.
Published by: Editions Zodiaque, Abbaye de la Pierre-Qui-Vire, St Leger Vauban, 89630, France. TEL 33-3-86331924, FAX 33-3-86331925, http://www.edition-zodiaque.fr. Ed. Matthieu Collin. R&P Alban Toucas. Adv. contact Vincent Lescanne. Circ: 2,000.

700 GBR ISSN 1466-2124
TR640
ZOO (LONDON,1999). Text in English. 1999. q. GBP 420 domestic; GBP 460, USD 736 in Europe; GBP 480, USD 768 in North America; GBP 500, USD 800 elsewhere; GBP 110 newsstand/cover domestic; GBP 120, USD 192 newsstand/cover in Europe; GBP 125, USD 200 newsstand/cover in North America; GBP 130, USD 208 newsstand/cover elsewhere (effective 2001). **Document type:** *Academic/Scholarly.* **Description:** Contains diverse array of both emerging and established talent encompassing advertising, architecture, art, photography, design and moving image.
Related titles: Online - full content ed.
Published by: Purple House, 245 Old Marylebone Rd, London, NW1 5QT, United Kingdom. TEL 44-20-7258-6900, FAX 44-20-7258-6901, office@zooworld.net, http://www.zooworld.net/home.html. Pub. Sibylle Koehler.

760 JPN ISSN 0387-5512
QA90
ZUGAKU KENKYU/JOURNAL OF GRAPHIC SCIENCE OF JAPAN. Text in Japanese; Summaries in English. 1967. s-a. abstr.
Indexed: JPI.
—**CCC.**
Published by: Nihon Zugakkai/Japan Society for Graphic Science, c/o Tokyo Daigaku Kyoyogakubu, 8-1 Komaba 3-chome, Meguro-ku, Tokyo, 153-0041, Japan.

740 NLD
ZWART EN WIT. Text in Dutch. 3/yr.
Published by: Ravenberg Pers, Paasberg 26, Oosterbeek, 6862 CC, Netherlands. Circ: 500.

ZYZZYVA; the last word: west coast writers and artists. see *LITERATURE*

00TAL; tidskrift om litteratur och konst. see *LITERATURE*

700 746.9 DEU
032C; fashion, art & conflict. Text in English. q. USD 15, EUR 10, JPY 1,890 newsstand/cover (effective 2005). **Document type:** *Magazine, Consumer.*
Published by: 032c Workshop, Anklamer Str.35, Berlin, 10115, Germany. TEL 49-30-44050980, FAX 49-30-44050981, office@032c.com, http://www.032c.com. Ed. Joerg Koch.

700 DEU
2X PROVINZ. Text in German. 1986. q. back issues avail. **Document type:** *Bulletin.*
Former titles: No News; Tiegel und Tumult
Published by: No-Institute, Niederfeldstr 35, Kassel, 34128, Germany. TEL 49-561-884694, FAX 49-561-884694. Ed. Juergen Olbrich.

741 USA ISSN 1546-640X
▼ **3 X 3 MAGAZINE**; the magazine of contemporary illustration. Text in English. 2003. 3/yr. USD 36 domestic; USD 46 foreign; USD 12.50 newsstand/cover (effective 2005). adv. **Document type:** *Magazine, Consumer.* **Description:** Devoted to contemporary illustration and illustrators.
Published by: 3x3 Magazine, 244 Fifth Ave, Ste F269, New York, NY 10001. TEL 212-591-2566, FAX 212-591-6534, chively@3x3mag.com, http://www.3x3mag.com. Ed., Pub., R&P, Adv. contact Charles Hively. B&W page USD 1,150, color page USD 1,500. Circ: 4,300 (paid and controlled).

700 USA ISSN 1092-549X
15 CREDIBILITY STREET. Cover title: Fifteen Credibility Street. Text in English. 1995. q. **Description:** Publishes innovative, modern art and theory, including graphic art, music, poetry, short fiction, essays and manifestoes.
Media: Online - full text.
Address: Wright Hall, Smith College, Northampton, MA 01063. tshortel@sophia.smith.edu, http://www.smith.edu/15cst. Ed. Timothy Shortell.

700 FRA ISSN 0762-3291
303; arts, recherches et creations. Variant title: Trois-cent-trois. Text in French. 1984. q. **Description:** Explores the architectural, artistic and historical heritage of the Pays-de-Loire region.
Indexed: BHA, RILM.
Published by: Association 303, Hotel de la Region, Ile Beaulieu, Nantes, Cedex 2 44266, France. TEL 33-2-40358600, FAX 33-2-40358608, revue.303@mail.cr-pays-de-la-loire.fr, http://www.cr-pays-de-la-loire.fr.

ART—Abstracting, Bibliographies, Statistics

016.7516 USA
AM141
AMERICAN INSTITUTE FOR CONSERVATION OF HISTORIC AND ARTISTIC WORKS. ABSTRACTS OF PAPERS PRESENTED AT THE ANNUAL MEETING. Key Title: Abstracts of Papers Presented at the Annual Meeting- American Institute for Conservation of Historic and Artistic Works. Text in English. a. USD 10. **Document type:** *Abstract/Index.*

Formerly: American Institute for Conservation of Historic and Artistic Works. Preprints of Papers Presented at the Annual Meeting (0272-3727)
Indexed: A&ATA, TTI.
Published by: American Institute for Conservation of Historic and Artistic Works, 1717 K St, N W, Ste 301, Washington, DC 20006. TEL 202-452-9545, FAX 202-452-9328, infoAIC@aol.com, http://palimpsest.stanford.edu/aic/. Circ: 1,200.

016.70904 USA ISSN 0898-7300
Z5935.3
ANNUAL BIBLIOGRAPHY OF MODERN ART. Text in English. a. USD 360 (effective 2005). **Document type:** *Bibliography.* **Description:** Computer-derived bibliography of acquisitions catalogued in the past year by MOMA Library. Covers literature published in various languages worldwide, with emphasis on the U.S., Europe and Japan.
Related titles: Microfilm ed.
Published by: (Museum of Modern Art), G.K. Hall & Co. (Subsidiary of: Gale Group), 12 Lunar Dr, Woodbridge, CT 06525. TEL 203-397-2600, 800-444-0799, FAX 203-397-8296, remmel.nunn@gale.com, http://www.galegroup.com/gkhall. **Subscr. to:** Simon & Schuster, PO Box 7500, Riverside, NJ 08075-8075. TEL 800-223-2336.

016.7 USA ISSN 1092-146X
Z5937
ART ABSTRACTS. Text in English. 1995. m. price varies. **Document type:** *Abstract/Index.* **Description:** Offers full text plus abstracts and indexing of an international array of peer-selected publications with expanded coverage of Latin American, Canadian, Asian and other non-Western art, new artists, contemporary art, exhibition reviews, and feminist criticism.
Formerly (until 1997): Wilson Art Abstracts (1084-0206)
Media: CD-ROM (from H.W. Wilson). **Related titles:** ♦ Online - full text ed.: Art Full Text; USD 3,525 in US & Canada (effective 2006).
Published by: H.W. Wilson Co., 950 University Ave, Bronx, NY 10452-4224. TEL 718-588-8400, 800-367-6770, FAX 718-590-1617, 800-590-1617, custserv@hwwilson.com, http://www.hwwilson.com.

700 571 016 USA
AM1 CODEN: AATABU
ART AND ARCHAEOLOGY TECHNICAL ABSTRACTS (ONLINE EDITION); abstracts of the technical literature on archaeology, architecture, and the fine and applied arts. Text in English. 1955. q. free (effective 2005). abstr. index. back issues avail. **Document type:** *Database, Abstract/Index.*
Former titles (until 2002): Art and Archaeology Technical Abstracts (Print Edition) (0004-2994); (until 1966): I I C Abstracts
Media: Online - full content.
Indexed: AESIS, BHA, RASB, RILM, TTI.
—BLDSC (1733.350000).
Published by: Getty Conservation Institute, 1200 Getty Center Dr, Ste 700, Los Angeles, CA 90049-1684. TEL 310-440-6809, FAX 310-440-7712, aata@getty.edu, http://aata.getty.edu, http://www.getty.edu/. Circ: 1,200. **Co-sponsor:** International Institute for Conservation of Historic and Artistic Works (London).

016.7 USA
ART FULL TEXT. Text in English. 1997. d. USD 5,040 in US & Canada (effective 2006). **Document type:** *Abstract/Index.* **Description:** Contains full text articles, article abstracts and indexing for art journals.
Media: Online - full text. **Related titles:** ♦ CD-ROM ed.: Art Abstracts. ISSN 1092-146X; ISSN 1529-9848; ♦ Print ed.: Art Index. ISSN 0004-3222.
Published by: H.W. Wilson Co., 950 University Ave, Bronx, NY 10452-4224. TEL 718-588-8400, 800-367-6770, FAX 718-590-1617, 800-590-1617, custserv@hwwilson.com, http://www.hwwilson.com/Databases/artindex.htm.

700 016 USA ISSN 0004-3222
Z5937
ART INDEX. Text in English. 1929. q. USD 540 in US & Canada (effective 2006). **Document type:** *Abstract/Index.* **Description:** Author and subject index to domestic and foreign art periodicals and museum bulletins covering archaeology, architecture, art history, city planning, crafts, graphic arts, industrial design, and interior design.
Related titles: CD-ROM ed.: ISSN 1076-7290 (from H.W. Wilson, SilverPlatter Information, Inc.); Magnetic Tape ed.; ♦ Online - full text ed.: Art Full Text; USD 2,310 in US & Canada (effective 2006); Cumulative ed(s).
Indexed: RASB.
—BLDSC (1733.450000).
Published by: H.W. Wilson Co., 950 University Ave, Bronx, NY 10452-4224. TEL 718-588-8400, 800-367-6770, FAX 718-590-1617, 800-590-1617, custserv@hwwilson.com, http://www.hwwilson.com/Databases/artindex.htm. Ed. Margaret Richter.

700 USA ISSN 1529-9767
ART INDEX RETROSPECTIVE. Text in English. 1984. irreg. USD 6,680 in US & Canada single user (effective 2006). illus. **Document type:** *Abstract/Index.*
Media: CD-ROM (from H.W. Wilson). **Related titles:** Online - full content ed.
Published by: H.W. Wilson Co., 950 University Ave, Bronx, NY, New York 10452. http://www.hwwilson.com/Databases/artretro.htm, http://www.hwwilson.com/default.cfm.

016.7 USA ISSN 0193-6867
ART REFERENCE COLLECTION. Text in English. 1980. irreg., latest 2002. price varies.
Published by: Greenwood Publishing Group Inc. (Subsidiary of: Harcourt International), 88 Post Rd W, PO Box 5007, Westport, CT 06881. TEL 203-226-3571, FAX 203-226-1502, http://www.greenwood.com.

016.7 USA
Z5937
ARTBIBLIOGRAPHIES CURRENT TITLES (EMAIL EDITION). Abbreviated title: A C T. Text in English. 1972. bi-m. USD 190 (effective 2006); Free to subscribers of ART Bibliographies Modern. illus.; abstr.; bibl. 36 p./no. 2 cols./p.; back issues avail.; reprints avail. **Document type:** *Journal, Bibliography.* **Description:** Provides the table of contents listings from art, craft, photography and design journals.
Formerly (until 2003): ARTbibliographies Current Titles (Print Edition) (0307-9961)
Media: E-mail. **Related titles:** Online - full text ed.: USD 190 (effective 2003).
Published by: C S A Journal Division (Subsidiary of: Cambridge Information Group), 7200 Wisconsin Ave, Ste 715, Bethesda, MD 20814. TEL 301-961-6798, 800-843-7751, FAX 301-961-6799, journals@csa.com, service@csa.com, http://www.csa.com. Pub. Mr. Matt Dunie.

016.7 USA ISSN 0300-466X
Z5935
ARTBIBLIOGRAPHIES MODERN; abstracts of the current literature of modern art, photography and design. Abbreviated title: A B M. Text in English. 1969. s-a. USD 1,875 combined subscription in North America to institutions print & online eds. (effective 2006); For institutions with an annual book fund of $50,000 or more; complimentary access to ACT Current Titles. abstr.; bibl. 2 cols./p.; back issues avail.; reprints avail. **Document type:** *Abstract/Index.* **Description:** Indexes and abstracts current literature on 20th century art, crafts, history of photography and design.
Supersedes (in 1971): L O M A Literature on Modern Art (0090-7235)
Related titles: E-mail ed.: USD 190 (effective 2005); Online - full content ed.: A B M on I D S. ISSN 1528-3461. 1999.
—CINDOC. **CCC.**
Published by: C S A Journal Division (Subsidiary of: Cambridge Information Group), 7200 Wisconsin Ave, Ste 715, Bethesda, MD 20814. TEL 301-961-6798, 800-843-7751, FAX 301-961-6799, journals@csa.com, service@csa.com, http://www.csa.com. Pub. Mr. Matt Dunie.

016.7 USA ISSN 1541-955X
▼ **ARTISTS OF AN ERA.** Text in English. 2003 (Jun.). irreg. **Document type:** *Bibliography.*
Published by: Greenwood Publishing Group Inc. (Subsidiary of: Harcourt International), 88 Post Rd W, PO Box 5007, Westport, CT 06881. TEL 203-226-3571, FAX 203-226-1502, http://www.greenwood.com.

001.3 016 USA ISSN 0162-8445
AI3
ARTS & HUMANITIES CITATION INDEX. Short title: A & H C I. Text in English. 1976. 3/yr. (includes a. cumulation). USD 6,490. illus. cum.index: 1975-79, 1980-89. reprints avail. **Document type:** *Abstract/Index.* **Description:** Multidisciplinary indexing of all fields of arts and humanities, including dance, film, radio and television, language, music and literature.
Related titles: CD-ROM ed.: ISSN 1060-9202 (from Thomson I S I); Magnetic Tape ed.; Online - full text ed.
Indexed: RASB.
—CINDOC.
Published by: Thomson I S I (Subsidiary of: Thomson Corporation), 3501 Market St., Philadelphia, PA 19104. TEL 215-386-0100, FAX 215-386-2911, http://www.isnet.com, http://www.isinet.com.

700.021 AUS ISSN 1328-4460
AUSTRALIA. BUREAU OF STATISTICS. CULTURAL FUNDING, AUSTRALIA. Text in English. 1995. a., latest 1998. AUD 19 (effective 2003). **Document type:** *Government.*
Published by: Australian Bureau of Statistics, PO Box 10, Belconnen, ACT 2616, Australia. TEL 61-2-6252-5249, FAX 61-2-6252-6778, http://www.abs.gov.au.

097 016 DNK
BIBLIOGRAFI OVER EUROPAEISKE KUNSTNERES EX LIBRIS/EUROPAEISCHE EX LIBRIS/EUROPEAN BOOK PLATES/EX LIBRIS D'EUROPE. Text in Danish, English, French, German. 1967. a. (combines 1976-77), latest 1978. DKK 120. **Document type:** *Bibliography.*
Published by: Klaus Roedel Ed. & Pub., PO Box 109, Frederikshavn, 9900, Denmark. Circ: 300.

700 016 DEU
BIBLIOGRAPHIE DER ANTIQUARIATS-, AUKTIONS- UND KUNSTKATALOGE. Text in German. 1975. irreg., latest vol.14, 2001. **Document type:** *Bibliography.*
Published by: Bibliographie der Antiquariats- Auktions- und Kunstkataloge, Lausner Weg 36B, Leipzig, 04207, Germany. FAX 49-341-4213818. Ed., Pub. Gerhard Loh.

016.7 USA ISSN 1085-5092
Z5937
BIBLIOGRAPHY OF THE HISTORY OF ART. Text in English, French. 1996. a. **Document type:** *Bibliography.* **Description:** Provides access to literature and scholarship on issues of Western from the late antique period to the present.
Formed by the merger of (1975-1996): International Repertory of the Literature of Art / Repertoire International de la Litterature de l'Art (RILA) (1085-5106); (19??-1996): Repertoire d'Art et d'Archeologie (CD-ROM) (1085-5114)
Media: CD-ROM (from National Information Services Corp. (N I S C)). **Related titles:** Online - full text ed.: (from National Information Services Corp. (N I S C), Research Libraries Group, The Dialog Corporation).
Indexed: RASB.
Published by: Getty Trust Publications, 1200 Getty Center Dr, Los Angeles, CA 90049-1679. TEL 310-440-7300, http://www.getty.edu/publications. **Subscr. to:** INIST - CNRS, 2 allee du Parc de Brabois, Vandoeuvre-les-Nancy Cedex 54514, France. TEL 33-3-83504664, FAX 33-3-83504666, http://www.inist.fr.

016.72 USA ISSN 1055-6826
BIO-BIBLIOGRAPHIES IN ART AND ARCHITECTURE. Text in English. 1991. irreg. price varies. **Document type:** *Monographic series, Bibliography.*
Published by: Greenwood Publishing Group Inc. (Subsidiary of: Harcourt International), 88 Post Rd W, PO Box 5007, Westport, CT 06881. TEL 203-226-3571, FAX 203-226-1502, bookinfo@greenwood.com, http://www.greenwood.com.

700 720 FRA ISSN 0009-6830
N1.A1
CIMAISE; contemporary art. Text in English, French. 1953-2000; resumed 2002 (Resumed with Jan/Feb). bi-m. adv. bk.rev. bibl.; illus. 80 p./no. 2 cols./p.; back issues avail. **Document type:** *Abstract/Index.* **Description:** Focuses on contemporary art and exhibits.
Indexed: ABCT, ABM, ASCA, ArtHuCI, ArtInd, BHA, CurCont, RASB.
—IDS, IE, Infotrieve.
Published by: Cimaise S.A.R.L., 95 rue Vieille du Temple, Paris, 75003, France. TEL 33-1-42744092, FAX 33-1-42744092. Ed. Martine Arnault Tran. Circ: 15,000.

COMPREHENSIVE SUMMARIES OF UPPSALA DISSERTATIONS FROM THE FACULTY OF ARTS. see *ART*

700 720 USA ISSN 1058-9120
CONTRIBUTIONS TO THE STUDY OF ART AND ARCHITECTURE. Text in English. 1992. irreg. price varies. **Document type:** *Monographic series.*
Published by: Praeger Publishers (Subsidiary of: Greenwood Publishing Group Inc.), 88 Post Rd W, Box 5007, Westport, CT 06881-5007. TEL 203-226-3571, FAX 203-222-1502.

700.11 FRA ISSN 1246-8258
Z5935
CRITIQUES D'ART; revue critique et bibliographique. Text in French; Summaries in English. 1993. s-a. **Document type:** *Bibliography.* **Description:** Offers views and reviews on French-language publications about today's international art.
Published by: Archives de la Critique d'Art, 3 rue de Noyal, Chateaugiron, 35410, France. TEL 33-2-99375529, FAX 33-2-99375084. Ed. Sylvie Mokhtari. Pub. Jean Marc Poinsot.

016.7 016.6862 016.79013 USA ISSN 1353-1298
NK1160 CODEN: JOFTED
DESIGN AND APPLIED ARTS INDEX. Short title: D A A I. Text in English. m. price varies. adv. bk.rev. illus. reprints avail. **Document type:** *Abstract/Index.* **Description:** Annotated index to 300 current international architecture, design and crafts journals.
Media: CD-ROM. **Related titles:** Online - full content ed.: 2001 (June). USD 2,750 (effective 2004).
—BLDSC (3559.886400).
Published by: C S A Journal Division (Subsidiary of: Cambridge Information Group), 7200 Wisconsin Ave, Ste 715, Bethesda, MD 20814. TEL 301-961-6700, FAX 301-961-6720, journals@csa.com, http://www.csa.com.

700 011 USA
FINE ARTS PERIODICALS✶; an international directory of the visual arts. Text in English. irreg. USD 89. index. **Document type:** *Directory.* **Description:** Covers more than 2700 current fine arts publications, classified by subject, indicating the scope, purpose and focus of each title. Indexed by title, publisher, subject, country and ISSN.
Published by: Peri Press (Subsidiary of: Schwann Publications), 20 Shad Way, Voorheesville, NY 12186-4940. TEL 518-765-3163, 800-677-4992, FAX 518-765-3158. Ed. Doris Robinson.

700 686.2 GBR
GRAPHIC DESIGNERS' INDEX. Text in English. 198?. a. illus. **Document type:** *Directory, Trade.* **Description:** Presents the latest trends in art direction; computer graphics; and corporate, display, environmental, packaging, industrial, interior, and textile design. Lists major photographers and illustrators.
Published by: Rotovision S.A., 112-116A Western Rd, Hove, East Sussex BN3 1DD, United Kingdom. TEL 44-1273-716010, FAX 44-1273-727269, sales@rotovision.com, http://www.rotovision.com. **Dist. in the U.S. by:** Watson-Guptill Publications, 1695 Oak St, Lakewood, NJ 08701. TEL 800-451-1741, FAX 908-363-0338.

700 800 GRC ISSN 0256-3606
GREECE. NATIONAL STATISTICAL SERVICE. CULTURAL STATISTICS. Text in Greek. 1973. a., latest 1993-94. back issues avail. **Document type:** *Government.*
Published by: National Statistical Service of Greece, Statistical Information and Publications Division/Ethniki Statistiki Yperesia tes Ellados, 14-16 Lykourgou St, Athens, 101 66, Greece. TEL 30-1-3289-397, FAX 30-1-3241-102, http://www.statistics.gr, http://www.statistics.gr/Main_eng.asp.

INDEX OF JEWISH ART. see *ABSTRACTING AND INDEXING SERVICES*

011 700 USA ISSN 0893-0139
N8580
INDEX TO REPRODUCTIONS IN ART PERIODICALS. Text in English. 1987. q. USD 60; USD 70 foreign (effective 1999). **Document type:** *Abstract/Index.* **Description:** Provides cover-to-cover indexing of art reproduced in five art periodicals (Art in America, American Craft, Arts of Asia, African Arts, American Indian Art). Indexes by artist, title, media, and subject.
Published by: Data Arts, PO Box 30789, Seattle, WA 98103. TEL 206-783-9580. Ed., Pub. Eugene C Burt.

016.700 RUS ISSN 0208-2071
N6
IZOBRAZITEL'NOE ISKUSSTVO; referativno-bibliograficheskaya informatsiya. Text in Russian. bi-m. USD 95 foreign. **Document type:** *Bibliography.* **Description:** Includes abstracts of Russian and foreign publications on different problems in the visual arts.
Related titles: CD-ROM ed.
Published by: Idatel'stvo Rossiiskoi Gosudarstvennoi Biblioteki Pashkov Dom/Russian State Library, Vozdizhenka 3/5, Moscow, 101000, Russian Federation. TEL 7-095-2033731, FAX 7-095-2039390, aisnik@rsl.ru, pashkov_dom@rsl.ru, http://www.rsl.ru, http://www.rsl.ru/pub.asp. Ed. T Lapteva. Circ: 350. **US dist. addr.:** East View Information Services, 3020 Harbor Ln. N., Minneapolis, MN 55447. TEL 800-477-1005, FAX 800-800-3839, eastview@eastview.com, http://www.eastview.com.

016.7009 USA
KEY GUIDE TO ELECTRONIC RESOURCES: ART AND ART HISTORY. Text in English. 1996. irreg. USD 39.50 (effective 2001). **Document type:** *Directory.* **Description:** Coverage includes commercial online databases, CD-ROM databases, OPAC-accessible collections, bulletin board systems, and all network-based electronic journals, newsletters and discussion groups related to art and art history.
Related titles: ♦ Series of: The Key Guide Series.
Published by: Information Today, Inc., 143 Old Marlton Pike, Medford, NJ 08055-8750. TEL 609-654-6266, FAX 609-654-4309, custserv@infotoday.com, http://www.infotoday.com. Ed. Martin Raish.

KUNGLIGA VITTERHETS HISTORIE OCH ANTIKVITETS AKADEMIEN. KONFERENSER. see *MEETINGS AND CONGRESSES*

700 DEU
MARBURGER INDEX; Wegweiser zur Kunst in Deutschland. Text in English, German. a. **Document type:** *Catalog, Abstract/Index.* **Description:** Provides a pictorial source for all those who work with texts or pictorial matters from all areas of historical studies.
Media: CD-ROM (from K. G. Saur Verlag GmbH & Co.).
Published by: K.G. Saur Verlag GmbH (Subsidiary of: Gale Group), Ortlerstr 8, Munchen, 81373, Germany. TEL 49-89-76902232, FAX 49-89-76902150, customerservice_saur@csi.com, http://www.saur.de.

016.730 GBR ISSN 1366-2724
NB1
THE SCULPTURE JOURNAL. Text in English. 1997. a. USD 50 (effective 2000). **Document type:** *Abstract/Index.* **Description:** Features articles by leading international scholars relating to European sculpture from the sixteenth century to the present.
Indexed: ABM.
Published by: Public Monuments & Sculpture Association, 72 Lissenden Mansions, Lissenden Gardens, London, NW5 1PR, United Kingdom. **Subscr. to:** Getty Trust Publications. TEL 310-440-7333, 800-223-3431, FAX 818-779-0051, http://www.getty.edu/publications.

TURKEY. DEVLET ISTATISTIK ENSTITUSU. KULTUR ISTATISTIKLERI/TURKEY. STATE INSTITUTE OF STATISTICS. CULTURAL STATISTICS. see *STATISTICS*

016.7 016.8 CHN
WENYI LILUN WENZHAI KA/LITERATURE AND ART THEORIES ABSTRACTS ON CARDS. Text in Chinese. q. CNY 24 (effective 2004). **Document type:** *Abstract/Index.*
Media: Cards.
Published by: Zhongguo Renmin Daxue, Shubao Zilio Zhongxin/Renmin University of China, Information Center for Social Server, Dongcheng-qu, 3, Zhangzizhong Lu, Beijing, 100007, China. TEL 86-10-64039458, FAX 86-10-64015080, kyes@163.net, http://www.confucius.cn.net/bkdetail.asp?fzt=WJ1. **Dist. by:** China International Book Trading Corp, 35 Chegongzhuang Xilu, Haidian District, PO Box 399, Beijing 100044, China. TEL 86-10-68412045, FAX 86-10-68412023, cibtc@mail.cibtc.com.cn, http://www.cibtc.com.cn; China Publications Service, PO Box 49614, Chicago, IL 60649. TEL 312-288-3291, FAX 312-288-8570.

ART—Computer Applications

A S I F A NEWS. see *MOTION PICTURES*

700 004 GBR ISSN 0966-3363
ARTBYTE: COMPUTERS IN ART & ART HISTORY. Text in English. 5/yr. GBP 25 to individuals; GBP 50 to institutions. **Document type:** *Academic/Scholarly.*
Published by: Eastern Art Publishing Group, PO Box 13666, London, SW14 8WF, United Kingdom. TEL 44-20-83921122, FAX 44-20-83921422, ear@eapgroup.ndirect.co.uk, http://www.eapgroup.ndirect.co.uk. R&P Sajid Rizvi.

BEFORE & AFTER; how to design cool stuff. see *COMPUTERS—Computer Graphics*

700 GRC
COMPUTER ARTS. Text in Greek. 1998. bi-m. USD 33 domestic; USD 56 foreign (effective 2000). adv. software rev. illus. back issues avail. **Document type:** *Magazine, Consumer.* **Description:** Contains tutorials and how-to advice in the graphic arts field; information on the latest software and systems in the area of design technology.
Published by: Technical Press SA, 2-4 Helioupopeos St, Athens, 172 37, Greece. TEL 30-1-979-2500, FAX 30-1-979-2528, arts@techlink.gr, tpress@techlink.gr, http://www.computerarts.gr/home.htm, http://www.techlink.gr. Ed. Costas Cavathas. Pub. Sophia Cavatha. R&P Costas Sakellariadis. Adv. contact Dimitra Koutsiouba. B&W page GRD 450,000, color page GRD 500,000; trim 280 x 230. Circ: 10,000 (paid). **Dist. by:** Europe Distribution Agency SA, Amifiaraou 15-17, Athens 104 42, Greece. TEL 30-1-519-9900, FAX 30-1-519-9901.

CREATIVE TECHNOLOGY. see *COMPUTERS—Computer Graphics*

750 USA ISSN 1097-5926
NC997.A1
DIGITAL GRAPHICS MAGAZINE. Text in English. 1997. m. USD 24 domestic; USD 40 in Canada; USD 51 in Mexico; USD 67 elsewhere (effective 2005). adv. illus. back issues avail. **Document type:** *Magazine, Trade.* **Description:** Reviews large-format digital output in multiple applications.
Published by: National Business Media, Inc., PO Box 1416, Broomfield, CO 80038. TEL 303-469-0424, FAX 303-469-5730, http://www.nbm.com/digitalgraphics. Ed. Ken Mergentime. Adv. contact Scott Kiker. Circ: 20,000 (controlled).

702.85 005.72 USA
DIGITAL WEB MAGAZINE. Text in English. m. **Document type:** *Magazine, Trade.* **Description:** Targets design professionals who are active in web site development and production.
Media: Online - full content.
Address: 16055 SW Walker Rd #253, Beaverton, OR 97006-4942. http://www.digital-web.com. Ed. Nick Finck.

705 USA ISSN 1071-4391
N6480
LEONARDO ELECTRONIC ALMANAC. Text in English. 1993. m. USD 35 in US & Canada to individuals; USD 75 in US & Canada to institutions; USD 20 in US & Canada to students (effective 2005). **Description:** Provides a forum for those interested in the realm where art, science and technology converge.
Media: Online - full text (from EBSCO Publishing).
Published by: (International Society for the Arts, Sciences, and Technology (ISAST)), M I T Press, 55 Hayward St, Cambridge, MA 02142-1493. TEL 617-253-5646, FAX 617-258-6779, lea@mitpress.mit.edu, journals-info@mit.edu, http://mitpress.mit.edu/LEA. Ed. Nisar Keshvani.

MEDIAMATIC OFF-LINE. see *ART*

776.6029 CAN
PIXEL - THE COMPUTER ANIMATION DICTIONARY; a compilation of new media terms. Text in English. 1997. a. CND 24.95 (effective 2000). back issues avail. **Document type:** *Academic/Scholarly.* **Description:** Includes over 4,000 entries.
Published by: Pixel - The Computer Animation News People, Inc., 109 Vanderhoof Ave, Ste 2, Toronto, ON M4G 2H7, Canada. TEL 416-424-4657, FAX 416-424-1812, pixel@inforamp.net, http://www.pixelnews.com. Ed., Pub. Robi Roncarelli.

776.6029 CAN
PIXEL - THE COMPUTER ANIMATION DIRECTORY. (Print version avail. on request) Text in English. a. USD 89 (effective 2000). **Document type:** *Directory.*
Former titles: Directory of Computer Animation Producers (1202-5941); International Directory of Computer Animation Producers (0840-5905)
Media: Online - full text. **Related titles:** Diskette ed.
Published by: Pixel - The Computer Animation News People, Inc., 109 Vanderhoof Ave, Ste 2, Toronto, ON M4G 2H7, Canada. TEL 416-424-4657, FAX 416-424-1812, pixel@inforamp.net, http://www.pixelnews.com. Ed., Pub. Robi Roncarelli.

700 CAN ISSN 1202-1156
RONCARELLI REPORT ON THE COMPUTER ANIMATION INDUSTRY. Text in English. 1984. a. USD 1,695 (effective 2000). back issues avail. **Description:** Report and analysis of the current state of the global computer animation industry with comments and forecasts.
Formerly (until 1992): Roncarelli Report (0838-2271)
Published by: Pixel - The Computer Animation News People, Inc., 109 Vanderhoof Ave, Ste 2, Toronto, ON M4G 2H7, Canada. TEL 415-424-4657, FAX 415-424-1812, pixel@inforamp.net, http://www.pixelnews.com. Ed., Pub. Robi Roncarelli.

741.6 702.85 USA ISSN 1551-4595
NK1510
▼ **S E G D DESIGN.** (Society for Environmental Graphic Design) Text in English. 2003. q. USD 25 domestic; USD 35 foreign (effective 2004). **Document type:** *Magazine.*
Published by: Society for Environmental Graphic Design, 1000 Vermont Ave NW Ste 400, Washington, DC 20005. TEL 202-638-5555, FAX 202-638-0891, segd@segd.org, http://www.segd.org.

700 USA
T385
S I G G R A P H ELECTRONIC ART AND ANIMATION CATALOG. (Special Interest Group on Computer Graphics and Interactive Techniques) Text in English. irreg.
Media: Online - full content. **Related titles:** CD-ROM ed.: ISSN 1098-6162; Print ed.: ISSN 1098-6154.
Published by: Association for Computing Machinery, Inc., 1515 Broadway, 17th Fl, New York, NY 10036-5701. TEL 212-626-0500, FAX 212-869-0481.

700 694 CAN ISSN 1200-8923
SIGNS CANADA. Text in English. 1994. 6/yr. CND 36 domestic; USD 42 in United States; USD 55 elsewhere (effective 2005). adv. software rev. charts; illus.; tr.lit. **Document type:** *Newsletter, Trade.* **Description:** Reports on the latest trends and management issues affecting sign makers. Covers topics like neon, vinyl and sign design, etc.
Related titles: Online - full content ed.
Published by: (Sign Association of Canada), Kenilworth Media Inc., 710 -15 Wertheim Court, Richmond Hill, ON L4B 3H7, Canada. TEL 905-771-7333, 877-738-7624, FAX 905-771-7336, publisher@kenilworth.com, http://www.signscanada.com, http://www.kenilworth.com. adv.: B&W page USD 985; trim 10.75 x 8.13. Circ: 5,090.

SILICON GRAPHICS WORLD. see *COMPUTERS—Computer Graphics*

621.3 001.6 USA ISSN 1042-2994
NX260
SYMPOSIUM ON SMALL COMPUTERS IN THE ARTS. PROCEEDINGS✶. Text in English. 1981. a. **Document type:** *Proceedings.*
Published by: Small Computers in the Arts Network, Inc., 209 Upland Rd., Merton Sta., PA 19066-1821.

ARTIFICIAL INTELLIGENCE

see COMPUTERS—Artificial Intelligence

ARTS AND HANDICRAFTS

see also HOBBIES

A F D A FORUM. see *HOBBIES*

745.5 USA ISSN 0194-8008
NK1
AMERICAN CRAFT. Text in English. 1941. bi-m. USD 40 domestic; USD 55 foreign; USD 5 newsstand/cover (effective 2005). adv. bk.rev. illus. back issues avail.; reprints avail. **Document type:** *Magazine, Consumer.* **Description:** Covers a variety of crafts, including fiber, clay, metal, wood, and glass. Includes artist profiles, exhibition reviews, lists of museum and gallery exhibits, and discussions of historical as well as contemporary crafts.
Former titles (until 1979): Craft Horizons with Craft World (0164-9191); (until 1979, vol.39, no.3): Craft Horizons (0011-0744); Incorporates: Craft World
Related titles: CD-ROM ed.: (from ProQuest Information & Learning); Microform ed.: (from PQC); Online - full text ed.: (from bigchalk, Northern Light Technology, Inc., O C L C Online Computer Library Center, Inc., ProQuest Information & Learning).
Indexed: ABM, AIAP, ArtInd, BAS, BRI, CBRI, DAAI, IBRH, IBZ, MRD, MagInd, PMR, RASB, RGAb, RGPR.
—BLDSC (0812.660000), IE, Infotrieve, ingenta.
Published by: American Craft Council, 72 Spring St, New York, NY 10012. TEL 212-274-0630, FAX 212-274-0650, amcraft@craftcouncil.org, council@craftcouncil.org, http://www.craftcouncil.org. Ed., R&P Lois Moran. Pub. John Gourlay. adv.: B&W page USD 2,625, color page USD 3,725; trim 8.25 x 10.875. Circ: 40,000 (paid and free).

746.41208997 970.1 USA
AMERICAN INDIAN BASKETRY AND OTHER NATIVE ARTS. Text in English. 1979. 4/yr. USD 30. adv. bk.rev. bibl.; illus. back issues avail.
Formerly: American Indian Basketry
Indexed: AICP, AnthLit.
Published by: (Institute for the Study of Traditional American Indian Arts), John M. Gogol, Ed. & Pub., PO Box 66124, Portland, OR 97266. TEL 503-233-8131. Circ: 5,000.

745.5 USA ISSN 1078-8425
NK805
AMERICAN STYLE; the art of living creatively . Text in English. 1995. q. USD 24.99 domestic; USD 33 in Canada; USD 36 elsewhere (effective 2004). adv. illus. reprints avail.
Published by: Rosen Group, 3000 Chestnut Ave, Baltimore, MD 21211-2743. TEL 410-889-3093, 800-272-3893, http://www.americanstyle.com. Ed. Hope Daniels. Pub. Wendy Rosen. Adv. contact John Stefancik. Circ: 60,000.

AMPERSAND. see *PUBLISHING AND BOOK TRADE*

745.5 DEU
ANNA WINDOW COLOR. Text in German. 4/yr. adv. **Document type:** *Magazine, Consumer.*
Former titles: Anna Weihnachten mit Window Color Farben; Burda Umstandsmode (0944-6400)
Published by: Verlag Aenne Burda GmbH & Co. KG, Am Kestendamm 1, Offenburg, 77652, Germany. TEL 49-781-846270, FAX 49-781-843242, info@burdamode.com, http://www.burdamode.com. Ed. Veronika Hark. Adv. contact Sabine Burda. B&W page EUR 3,000, color page EUR 5,000.

745.5 USA ISSN 1556-8113
▼ **ANNIE'S PLASTIC CANVAS**; creative designs for home & holiday. Text in English. 2004. bi-m. USD 19.97 domestic; USD 24.97 in Canada; USD 29.97 elsewhere (effective 2006). **Document type:** *Magazine, Consumer.*
Formed by the merger of (2000-2004): Plastic Canvas Home & Holiday; (2002-2004): Plastic Canvas Today (1541-7603); Which was formerly (until 2002): Plastic Canvas World (1072-6373)
Published by: Annie's Attic, Inc., 103 N Pearl St, P O Box 9001, Big Sandy, TX 75755. TEL 903-636-4303, 800-829-5865, FAX 888-848-4414, http://www.anniesplasticcanvas.com. Ed. Vivki Blizzard.

745.5 CAN ISSN 1189-4555
ANNUAL CRAFT SHOWS IN ONTARIO✶ . Text in English. 1975. a. CND 14 to non-members; CND 10 to members. **Document type:** *Directory.* **Description:** Designed for craftspeople looking for shows as a market for their work.
Published by: Ontario Crafts Council, Designers Walk, 170 Bedford Rd, Ste 300, Toronto, ON M5R 2K9, Canada. TEL 416-925-4222, FAX 416-925-4223. Ed. Jane Moore. Circ: 2,000.

745.5 USA ISSN 0889-177X
TT218
THE ANVIL'S RING. Text in English. 1973. q. USD 45 domestic to individuals; USD 65 foreign to individuals; USD 35 domestic to libraries; USD 40 to senior citizens (effective 2003). adv. bk.rev. charts; illus.; tr.lit. 60 p./no.; back issues avail.; reprints avail. **Document type:** *Trade.* **Description:** Blacksmithing, metal arts, tools technique, design and events.
—Linda Hall.
Published by: Artists-Blacksmith Association of North America, Inc., PO Box 816, Farmington, GA 30638-0816. TEL 706-310-1030, FAX 706-769-7147, abana@abana.org, http://www.abana.org/membership/publications/publications.html. Ed., Adv. contact Rob Edwards TEL 530-333-2687. Circ: 5,000 (paid).

ARIADNE AT HOME. see *INTERIOR DESIGN AND DECORATION*

ART ALMANAC. see *ART*

ART & CRAFT; a magazine for primary teachers. see *EDUCATION—Teaching Methods And Curriculum*

ART ATTACK. see *CHILDREN AND YOUTH—For*

745.5 028.5 USA
ART DOLL QUARTERLY. Text in English. q. USD 34.95 domestic; USD 44.95 in Canada; USD 9.95 newsstand/cover domestic; USD 14.95 newsstand/cover in Canada (effective 2004).
Published by: Stampington & Company, LLC, 22992 Mill Creek, Ste B, Laguna Hills, CA 92653. TEL 877-782-6737, http://www.artdollquarterly.com. Ed. Sharilyn Miller.

ART REVUE. see *ART*

687.3 ITA ISSN 1129-0218
ARTE FEMMINILE. Text in Italian. 1996. m. **Document type:** *Magazine, Consumer.*
Published by: Edizioni Mimosa Srl, Piazza E de Angeli 9, Milan, 20146, Italy. TEL 39-02-48713813, FAX 39-02-48713805, artefemminile@fastwebnet.it, segreteria@edizionimimosa.it, http://www.edizionimimosa.it.

687.3 ITA ISSN 1720-3996
ARTE FEMMINILE SPECIAL. Text in Italian. 2002. bi-m. **Document type:** *Magazine, Consumer.*
Published by: Edizioni Mimosa Srl, Piazza E de Angeli 9, Milan, 20146, Italy. TEL 39-02-48713813, FAX 39-02-48713805, segreteria@edizionimimosa.it, http://www.edizionimimosa.it.

745.5 ITA ISSN 0391-707X
ARTIGIANATO OGGI. Text in Italian. 1977. m. adv. bk.rev.
Published by: Confederazione Nazionale Artigianato, Via G A Guattani 13, Rome, 00161, Italy. TEL 39-06-441881, FAX 39-06-44249513, cna@cna.it, http://www.cna.it. Ed. Sergio Cecchini. Circ: 200,000.

ARTISTS IN STAINED GLASS. JOURNAL. see *ART*

745 USA ISSN 1073-7618
ARTS & CRAFTS. Key Title: Michaels Arts & Crafts. Text in English. 1992. 6/yr. USD 19.99 domestic; USD 30.97 foreign (effective 2005). adv. **Document type:** *Magazine, Consumer.* **Description:** Covers home decorations, clothing, and accessories; additional feature stories include items of interest to crafters.
Published by: Krause Publications, Inc. (Subsidiary of: F & W Publications, Inc.), 700 E State St, Iola, WI 54990-0001. TEL 715-445-2214, 800-258-0929, FAX 715-445-4087, info@krause.com, http://www.krause.com/crafts/ac/. Ed. Althea Reetz. Pub. Debbie Knauer TEL 715-445-2214 ext 487. Adv. contacts Thomas P Paar, Marilyn Duquaine TEL 715-445-2214 ext 549. B&W page USD 3,730, color page USD 4,550; trim 8.125 x 10.875. Circ: 166,557 (paid and free).

745.5 CAN
ARTS & CRAFTS CANADA. Text in English. 2000 (Fall). bi-m. CND 28.65 in ON; CND 30.80 in PQ, NB, NS, NF; USD 27.95 elsewhere (effective 2001). adv. back issues avail. **Document type:** *Magazine, Consumer.* **Description:** Provides information about decorative arts & crafts with a "Canadian slant.".
Address: 83 Queen St E, PO Box 1870, St Marys, ON N4X 1C2, Canada. TEL 519-284-2787, 877-565-2787, FAX 519-284-0858, http://www.artsandcraftscanada.com/. Ed. Maridon Duncanson. Pub. Brad Neufeld. adv.: color page USD 2,446.50, B&W 1/2 page USD 1,127.50, color page CND 3,495, B&W 1/2 page CND 1,895; 7.25 x 9.75. Circ: 30,000.

ARTS BEAT. see *ART*

745.5 USA ISSN 1071-6289
ARTS 'N CRAFTS SHOWGUIDE; a market guide to arts, crafts fairs and other events. Text in English. 1985. 6/yr. USD 21.95 (effective 1998 & 1999). adv. bk.rev. **Document type:** *Consumer.* **Description:** Lists national art and craft events, fairs, and festivals. Contains information, opportunities, resources and a nationwide show list.
Former titles (until vol.6, no.5, 1991): A C N Showtime; A C N Art and Craft News
Published by: A C N Publications, PO Box 25, Jefferson City, MO 65102. TEL 314-636-0491, 800-832-7674, FAX 314-636-2112, acnpubs@plnet.net. Ed., R&P, Adv. contact Dan Engle. Circ: 10,000.

745.5 GBR
ARTWORK; the North's independent free arts newspaper. Text in English. 1983. bi-m. GBP 7.50 (effective 2001). adv. bk.rev.; dance rev.; film rev.; music rev.; play rev.; rec.rev. 18 p./no. 8 cols./p.; back issues avail. **Document type:** *Newspaper, Newspaper-distributed.* **Description:** Informs readers about the arts, theatre shows and events.
Related titles: Diskette ed.; Online - full text ed.
Published by: Famedram Publishers Ltd., PO Box 3, Ellon, Aberdeenshire AB41 9EA, United Kingdom. TEL 44-1651-842429, FAX 44-1651-842180, editorial@artwork.co.uk, http://www.artwork.co.uk. Ed., Pub. Bill Williams. R&P Eleanor Stewart. Adv. contact Sandra Moore TEL 44-1436-673327. Circ: 20,000.

745.5 USA ISSN 1554-5016
ASH BREEZE. Text in English. q. USD 4 newsstand/cover (effective 2003); free to members. **Document type:** *Journal, Consumer.*
Published by: Traditional Small Craft Association, PO Box 350, Mystic, CT 06355. http://www.tsca.net/tscaash.html. Ed., Pub. Dan Drath.

745.5 USA
BALLOONS & PARTIES; innovations for the party professional. Text in English. 1986. bi-m. USD 34.95 domestic; USD 49.95 foreign (effective 2005). adv. tr.lit.; illus. back issues avail. **Document type:** *Magazine, Trade.* **Description:** Presents full color designs and decorations using balloons. Geared towards retailers selling balloons and party supplies and trade managers for industry.
Former titles: Balloons and Parties Today; Balloons Today (1049-9970)
Published by: Partilife Publications, LLC, 65 Sussex St, Hackensack, NJ 07601-4205. TEL 201-441-4224, FAX 201-342-8118, info@balloonsandparties.com, http://www.balloonsandparties.com. Ed. Andrea P Zettler. Pub. Mark Zettler. Adv. contact Francine Chabora. B&W page USD 1,488, color page USD 2,063; trim 8.125 x 10.875. Circ: 8,000 (paid).

745.592 USA
BASKET BITS. Text in English. 1989. q. USD 16 (effective 1998). adv. **Description:** Provides step-by-step instructions for basket weaving. Includes interviews with basket makers and basketry suppliers, and a calendar of events.
Published by: Jim Rutherford, Ed. & Pub., PO Box 8, Loudonville, OH 44842. TEL 419-994-3256. Circ: 1,800.

745.58 USA ISSN 1543-7086
▼ **BEAD DREAMS**; inspiration and technique for beading artistry. Text in English. 2003 (Jun.). a. USD 6.95 newsstand/cover domestic; USD 10.95 newsstand/cover elsewhere (effective 2003).
Published by: Kalmbach Publishing Co., 21027 Crossroads Circle, PO Box 1612, Waukesha, WI 53187-1612. TEL 262-796-8776, 800-533-6644, FAX 262-796-1615, customerservice@kalmbach.com, http://www.kalmbach.com. Ed. Alice Korach.

745.58 USA ISSN 1544-354X
▼ **BEAD STYLE**; fast, fashionable, fun. Text in English. 2003 (Sept.). bi-m. USD 19.95 domestic; USD 26 foreign; USD 4.95 newsstand/cover domestic; USD 7.50 newsstand/cover foreign (effective 2004). adv. **Document type:** *Magazine, Consumer.* **Description:** Offers more than 18 necklace, bracelet, and earring projects simple enough for beginners, yet stylish enough to interest seasoned beaders. The easy-to-follow directions are well-illustrated with photos, and every project is tested by the editors.
Published by: Kalmbach Publishing Co., 21027 Crossroads Circle, PO Box 1612, Waukesha, WI 53187-1612. TEL 262-796-8776, 888-350-2413, FAX 262-796-1615, customerservice@kalmbach.com, http://www.kalmbach.com/kpc/html/magazines/bds/bds.asp. adv.: B&W page USD 2,150, color page USD 2,473; trim 8.25 x 10.75.

745.58 USA ISSN 1549-8646
▼ **BEAD UNIQUE.** Text in English. 2004 (Sum.). q. USD 19.97 (effective 2004). adv. **Document type:** *Magazine, Consumer.*
Published by: All American Crafts, Inc., 7 Waterloo Rd., Stanhope, NJ 07874-2621. http://www.allamericancrafts.com. Pub. Jerry Cohen. Adv. contact Sandy Moncelsi.

745.582 USA ISSN 1528-5634
BEADWORK. Text in English. 1997. bi-m. USD 24 domestic; USD 31 foreign; USD 4.99 newsstand/cover (effective 2005). adv. bk.rev. illus. reprints avail. **Document type:** *Magazine, Consumer.*
Published by: Interweave Press, Inc., 201 E Fourth St, Loveland, CO 80537. TEL 970-669-7672, 800-272-2193, FAX 970-667-8317, beadwork@interweave.com, customerservice@interweave.com, http://www.interweave.com. Eds. Marlene Blessing, Jean Campbell. Pub. Linda C. Ligon. Adv. contact Marilyn Koponen.

745.5 AUS ISSN 1325-8427
BEAR CREATIONS. Variant title: Australian Bear Creations. Text in English. 1996. bi-m. AUD 53.94; AUD 8.99 newsstand/cover (effective 2004). adv. **Document type:** *Magazine, Consumer.* **Description:** Contains bear patterns and wardrobe suggestions with creative touches.
Published by: Express Publications Pty. Ltd., 2 Stanley St, Locked Bag 111, Silverwater, NSW 2128, Australia. TEL 61-2-97480599, 800-801-647, FAX 61-2-97481956, subs@magstore.com.au, http://www.magstore.com.au/. **Dist. by:** Quilters' Resource Inc., PO Box 148850, Chicago, IL 60614-8850. TEL 773-278-1348, FAX 773-278-5695.

▼ new title ➤ refereed ✶ unverified ♦ full entry avail.

A

745.5 JPN
BENIBANA. Text in Japanese. 1974. irreg. free. index. **Document type:** *Monographic series.* **Description:** Focuses on the techniques and history of paper-making, dyeing and textiles in China and Japan.
Published by: Tsutomu Yamaguchi, Ed. & Pub., 32 Koyama-Minami, Kamifusa-cho, Kita-ku, Kyoto-shi, 603-8149, Japan. TEL 81-75-451-3568, FAX 81-3-75-791-9482. R&P Tsutomu Yamaguchi. Circ: 300.

745.5 USA ISSN 1085-1526
BETTER HOMES AND GARDENS CROSS-STITCH CHRISTMAS. Text in English. 1990. a. USD 6.95 per academic year (effective 2005). adv. illus.; tr.lit. **Document type:** *Magazine, Consumer.* **Description:** Devoted to cross-stitch projects for Christmas. Includes instructions, charts and photographs for each project.
Published by: Meredith Corp., 1716 Locust St, Des Moines, IA 50309-3023. TEL 515-284-3000, 800-556-9184, FAX 515-284-3657, http://www.bhg.com, http://www.meredith.com. Ed. Marjoan Schaefer. Pub. Steve Levinson. Adv. contact Diane Claude. B&W page USD 17,658, color page USD 23,409; trim 10.5 x 8. Circ: 600,000 (paid).

745.5 USA ISSN 0278-7490
TT1
BETTER HOMES AND GARDENS HOLIDAY CRAFTS. Text in English. 1974. s-a. (spring & fall). USD 6.95 per issue (effective 2005). adv. illus. **Document type:** *Magazine, Consumer.* **Description:** Features crafts projects themed to each holiday, as well as special occasions such as birthdays, weddings, and graduations.
Published by: Meredith Corp., 1716 Locust St, Des Moines, IA 50309-3023. TEL 515-284-3000, 800-556-9184, FAX 515-284-3657, http://www.bhg.com, http://www.meredith.com. Ed. Patricia McClure. Pub. Steve Levinson. Adv. contact Diane Claude. B&W page USD 17,658, color page USD 23,409. Circ: 650,000 (paid).

745.5 USA ISSN 1088-2944
BETTER HOMES AND GARDENS SANTA CLAUS. Variant title: Santa Claus. Text in English. 1991. a. USD 4.99 newsstand/cover domestic; USD 5.99 newsstand/cover in Canada (effective 2004). adv. illus. **Document type:** *Magazine, Consumer.* **Description:** Contains 40 to 50 crafts projects featuring Santa Claus.
Published by: Meredith Corp., 1716 Locust St, Des Moines, IA 50309-3023. TEL 515-284-3000, 800-556-9184, FAX 515-284-3657, http://www.bhg.com, http://www.meredith.com. Ed. Beverly Rivers. Pub. Steve Lacy. Circ: 400,000 (paid).

BRIDAL CRAFTS. see *MATRIMONY*

745.54 736.982 GBR ISSN 1745-3410
BRITISH ORIGAMI. Text in English. 1967. bi-m. GBP 23 domestic membership; GBP 17.50 domestic membership junior (under 17); GBP 28.50 in Europe membership; GBP 36 elsewhere membership (effective 2005). bk.rev. illus. back issues avail. **Document type:** *Magazine, Consumer.* **Description:** Contains diagrams, news. reviews and articles on origami from around the world.
Published by: British Origami Society, Secretary, 16 Stamford St, Newmarket, Cambs CB8 8JB, United Kingdom. http://www.britishorigami.org.uk. Ed. Nick Robinson. Pub. David Petty. **Subscr. to:** Membership Secretary, 2a The Chestnuts, Countesthorpe, Leics LE8 5TL, United Kingdom.

BRITISH SOCIETY OF SCIENTIFIC GLASSBLOWERS. JOURNAL. see *CERAMICS, GLASS AND POTTERY*

745.5 747 700 USA
BUSINESS & TEACHER DIRECTORY (YEAR). Text in English. 1991. a. USD 12 per issue (effective 2005). adv. **Document type:** *Directory, Trade.* **Description:** Lists artists, teachers, retailers, wholesalers, manufacturers, importers, exporters, and publishers in the decorative painting industry.
Related titles: Online - full text ed.
Published by: Society of Decorative Painters, 393 N McLean Blvd, Wichita, KS 67203-5916. TEL 316-269-9300, FAX 316-269-9191, sdp@decorativepainters.org, http://www.decorativepainters.org. Ed. Cheryl Capps. Adv. contact Sara Perkins. Circ: 4,000 (controlled).

745.5 USA
BUTTERFLY NET. Text in English. 1977. 6/yr. USD 20 to members. adv. **Document type:** *Newsletter, Academic/Scholarly.* **Description:** Includes informative articles on Fenton glass and advertising listings from members showing items wanted or for sale.
Published by: Fenton Art Glass Collectors of America, Inc., PO Box 384, Williamstown, WV 26187-0384. TEL 304-375-6196. Ed. Ferill J Rice. R&P Art Gilbert. Adv. contact Debbie Nielsen. Circ: 3,600.

745.5 746 USA ISSN 1525-7940
C N A; turning creative ideas into retail profit. Text in English. 1943. m. (& annual directory). USD 30; USD 5 newsstand/cover; free to qualified personnel (effective 2004). adv. bk.rev. illus.; mkt.; stat.; tr.mk. **Document type:** *Magazine, Trade.* **Description:** Contains trend articles, timely product showcases, and special sections that focus on fine arts, sewing and textiles, and scrapbooking.
Former titles: Craft and Needlework Age (0887-9818); Craft and Needlework Age - World of Miniatures (0744-2319); Supersedes in part (in 1982): Craft, Model and Hobby Industry (0011-0752)
Published by: Krause Publications, Inc. (Subsidiary of: F & W Publications, Inc.), 700 E State St, Iola, WI 54990-0001. TEL 715-445-2214, 800-258-0929, FAX 715-445-4087, info@krause.com, http://www.krause.com/crafts/cn/. Ed. Karen Ancona TEL 570-646-8524. Pub. Debbie Knauer TEL 715-445-2214 ext 487. Adv. contact Marilyn Duquaine TEL 715-445-2214 ext 549. B&W page USD 4,185, color page USD 3,437; trim 7.75 x 10.5. Circ: 22,462 (controlled and free).

CANADIAN BOOKBINDERS & BOOK ARTISTS GUILD NEWSLETTER. see *PUBLISHING AND BOOK TRADE*

745.531 CAN ISSN 0045-5121
CANADIAN LEATHERCRAFT. Text in English. 1951. q. CND 25 to members. adv. bk.rev. **Document type:** *Newsletter.*
Published by: Canadian Society of Creative Leathercraft, c/o Lois MacPherson, 1506 205 Queen Mary Dr, Oakville, ON L6K 3K8, Canada. Eds. Betsy Rennie, Lois MacPherson. Circ: 90 (controlled).

745.5 USA
CANDLE INFO MAPPING NEWSLETTER. Text in English. 1985. biennial. USD 7 newsstand/cover (effective 2005). **Document type:** *Newsletter.*
Formerly: Candle Makers Instruction Etc. Update
Published by: Prosperity and Profits Unlimited, PO Box 416, Denver, CO 80201-0416. TEL 303-575-5676, FAX 303-575-1187, starsuccess@excite.com, http://www.prosperityandprofitsunlimited.com. Ed., R&P A Doyle TEL 303-575-5676. Circ: 600.

745.5 GBR
▼ **CARD MAKING & PAPERCRAFT.** Text in English. 2004. m. GBP 39; GBP 3.25 newsstand/cover (effective 2004). adv. **Document type:** *Magazine, Consumer.* **Description:** Contains quick and easy paper craft card designs, great ideas, tips and tricks and useful guides to making last minute cards.
Published by: Origin Publishing Ltd., 14th Fl, Tower House, Fairfax St, Bristol, BS1 3BN, United Kingdom. TEL 44-117-927-9009, FAX 44-117-934-9008, origin@subscription.co.uk, http://www.cardmakingandpapercraft.com, http://www.originpublishing.co.uk. Ed. Anna Davenport. Pub. Catherine Potter. Adv. contact Nicky Marsh.

736 USA ISSN 1546-6809
▼ **CARVING MAGAZINE.** Text in English. 2003. q. USD 19.95 domestic; USD 23.95 in Canada; USD 25.95 elsewhere (effective 2004). adv. **Document type:** *Magazine, Consumer.* **Description:** Provides a forum for information, advice and ideas involving a variety of carving techniques and styles.
Published by: All American Crafts, Inc., 7 Waterloo Rd., Stanhope, NJ 07874-2621. editors@carvingmagazine.com, readersvc@allamericancrafts.com, http://www.carvingmagazine.com, http://www.allamericancrafts.com. Ed. Marnie Whillock. Adv. contact Lee Jaworski TEL 973-383-8080 ext 114.

745.5 941 GBR ISSN 1351-6272
CELTIC CONNECTIONS MAGAZINE. Text in English. 1992. q. GBP 9 in United Kingdom; GBP 13.50 elsewhere; GBP 2 newsstand/cover (effective 2001). adv. **Document type:** *Magazine, Academic/Scholarly.* **Description:** Covers the history and art of the Celts, folklore, legends, ancient sites, books, music, private schools, etc.
Published by: Celtic Connections Publications, Orchard Cottage, Waddon, Portesham, Weymouth, Dorset DT3 4ER, United Kingdom. TEL 44-1305-871065, editor@celtic-connections.freeserve.co.uk, http://www.celtic-connections-magazine.co.uk/. Ed., Pub., Adv. contact David James. B&W page GBP 40, color page GBP 120. Circ: 2,000 (paid).

CHARLES RENNIE MACKINTOSH SOCIETY NEWSLETTER. see *ARCHITECTURE*

698.3 USA ISSN 0577-9294
TT199.7
CHIP CHATS. Text in English. 1953. bi-m. USD 14 domestic; USD 16 foreign (effective 2001). adv. bk.rev. illus. back issues avail.; reprints avail. **Document type:** *Trade.*
Indexed: IHTDI.
Published by: (National Wood Carvers Association), Edward F. Gallenstein, Ed. & Pub., 7424 Miami Ave, Cincinnati, OH 45243. TEL 513-561-0627, http://www.terranet.ab.ca:80/~bjndt/ChipChats_Mag/ChipChats.html. R&P Edward F Gallenstein. Circ: 40,000 (paid).

CHRISTMAS: YEAR ROUND NEEDLEWORK & CRAFT IDEAS. see *NEEDLEWORK*

745.5 USA ISSN 1087-7614
NK3700
CLAY TIMES; the journal of ceramic trends & techniques. Text in English. 1995. bi-m. USD 26 domestic; USD 36 in Canada; USD 66 elsewhere; USD 5.95 newsstand/cover domestic; USD 8.25 newsstand/cover foreign (effective 2005). adv. back issues avail. **Document type:** *Journal, Trade.* **Description:** Provides current ceramic news and useful techniques to clay artists at all levels.
Indexed: DAAI.
Published by: Clay Times Journal, 15481 Second St, PO Box 365, Waterford, VA 20197. TEL 540-882-3576, 1-800-356-2529, FAX 540-882-4196, claytimes@aol.com, ctmagsubs@aol.com, http://www.claytimes.com/. Ed. Polly Beach. Adv. contact Carolyn Melton. B&W page USD 1,186, color page USD 1,611.

COLLECTIONS (COLUMBIA). see *MUSEUMS AND ART GALLERIES*

745.5 USA ISSN 0897-7216
TT25.W55
COLONIAL WILLIAMSBURG HISTORIC TRADES. Text in English. 1988. irreg. price varies. **Description:** Presents articles on crafts practiced in Colonial America.
Published by: Colonial Williamsburg Foundation, PO Box 1776, Williamsburg, VA 23187-1776. TEL 757-220-7342. Ed. Donna C Sheppard. R&P Joseph N Rountree.

745.5 USA
COLOR. Text in English. 2001. q. USD 7.50 newsstand/cover (effective 2002). **Document type:** *Consumer.*
Published by: V N U Business Publications (Subsidiary of: V N U Business Media), 770 Broadway, New York, NY 10003-9595. TEL 646-654-5600. Ed. Stephen Doherty.

745.5 AUS ISSN 1444-9552
COMPUTER CRAFT. Text in English. 2001. bi-m. AUD 5.95 newsstand/cover (effective 2004).
Related titles: Online - full text ed.
Published by: Pride Publishing, PO Box 645, Rozelle, NSW 2039, Australia. TEL 61-2-9555-9322, FAX 61-2-9555-6188, info@pridepublishing.com.au, http://www.pridepublishing.com.au/.

745 USA ISSN 1526-2146
COUNTRY CRAFTS. Text in English. 1998. m. free (effective 2005). adv. bk.rev. back issues avail. **Document type:** *Newsletter, Consumer.* **Description:** Includes crafts, tips, show listings and more.
Media: Online - full text. **Related titles:** E-mail ed.
Published by: Country Cuts, 3065 Tuscaloosa Ln, Lexington, KY 40515. TEL 606-263-3527, CountryCuts@worldnet.att.net, http://home.att.net/~DLeddy/newsletter.html. Pub. Fresca Leddy. Circ: 3,550.

394.2663 USA ISSN 1538-2885
COUNTRY LIVING HOLIDAYS. Text in English. 1992. a. USD 3.95; USD 4.95 in Canada (effective 2001). adv. illus. **Document type:** *Magazine, Consumer.* **Description:** Offers cooking, home-decorating, and party ideas for the holiday season.
Published by: Hearst Corporation, Hearst Special Publications, 1790 Broadway, New York, NY 10019. TEL 212-830-2900, FAX 212-586-3455, http://www.hearstcorp.com. Eds. Rachel Newman, Robin Long Mayer. Pub. Brian J Doyle. Circ: 1,000,000 (paid).

658 USA ISSN 1097-7848
COUNTRY MARKETPLACE. Text in English. 1991. bi-m. USD 19.95 domestic; USD 29.95 in Canada; USD 45.95 elsewhere (effective 2003). adv. Supplement avail. **Document type:** *Magazine, Consumer.* **Description:** Contains the latest in handcrafted items, decorative ideas, market trends, informative articles, plus free patterns and projects.
Related titles: Online - full text ed.
Published by: Emmis Publishing LP, 707 Kautz Rd., St. Charles, IL 60174. TEL 630-377-8000, FAX 630-377-8194, pattern@cscrafts.com, http://www.sampler.com/countrymarketplace/index.html. Ed. Donna Marcel. adv.: color page USD 5,000. **Subscr. to:** PO Box 420235, Palm Coast, FL 32142-0235. TEL 386-447-6304.

745.5 USA ISSN 1047-3955
COUNTRY SAMPLER. Text in English. 1984. bi-m. USD 19.96 domestic; USD 29.96 in Canada; USD 35.96 elsewhere; USD 5.99 newsstand/cover domestic; USD 8.50 newsstand/cover in Canada (effective 2005). adv. illus. **Document type:** *Magazine, Consumer.* **Description:** Contains information about country home accessories, decorating, and crafts. Also includes crafter advertising for direct purchase of their products.
Published by: Emmis Publishing LP, 707 Kautz Rd., St. Charles, IL 60174. TEL 630-377-8000, FAX 630-377-8194, http://www.countrysampler.com, http://www.sampler.com. Ed. Donna Marcel. Adv. contact Betty Lou Turner. color page USD 11,590. Circ: 300,027 (paid). **Subscr. to:** PO Box 420235, Palm Coast, FL 32142-0235. TEL 386-447-6304.

COUNTRY SAMPLER'S DECORATING IDEAS. see *INTERIOR DESIGN AND DECORATION*

745.5 700 AUS ISSN 1038-846X
CRAFT ARTS INTERNATIONAL. Text in English. 1984. q. AUD 52 domestic; AUD 56 in Asia & the Pacific (effective 2003); AUD 75 elsewhere (effective 2000). adv. back issues avail. **Document type:** *Magazine, Academic/Scholarly.* **Description:** Specialises in the presentation and documentation of creative works, with emphasis on the visual and applied arts. Examines concepts that challenge conventional aesthetic experience.
Formerly: Craft Arts Magazine (0814-6586)
Related titles: Online - full text ed.: (from EBSCO Publishing).
Indexed: ABM, ArtInd, DAAI.
—BLDSC (3486.577500).
Published by: Craft Arts International Pty Ltd., PO Box 363, Neutral Bay Junction, NSW 2089, Australia. TEL 61-2-99084797, FAX 61-2-99531576, http://www.craftarts.com.au/. Ed. Ken Lockwood. Adv. contact Jenie Thomas.

745.5 USA ISSN 1193-3208
CRAFT CONNECTION. Text in English. 1974. q. USD 35 (effective 2000). bk.rev. **Document type:** *Newspaper.* **Description:** Contains interviews with artists, reviews of exhibits, grant information for artists, calendar listings of festivals, exhibitions and workshops, and general news of interest to professionals in the arts and crafts industry.
Published by: Minnesota Crafts Council, Hennepin Center for the Arts, 528 Hennepin Ave, Rm 216, Minneapolis, MN 55403. TEL 612-204-0409, FAX 612-332-8131, mncraft@mtn.org, http://www.mncraft.org. Ed., Adv. contact Tom Polzine. R&P David Glenn. Circ: 4,000.

CRAFT - CRAFTS. see *RELIGIONS AND THEOLOGY—Other Denominations And Sects*

745.5 CAN ISSN 0228-7498
THE CRAFT FACTOR. Text in English. 1975. 2/yr. CND 15 domestic; USD 15 foreign; CND 6 newsstand/cover (effective 2000). adv. illus. back issues avail. **Document type:** *Newsletter.* **Description:** Covers all types of fine craft from glass to knives, from pottery to knitting.
Former titles (until 1977): Saskatchewan Craft Council News (0228-748X); (until 1976): Saskatchewan Craft Council Newsletter (0228-7471); (until 1976): Saskatchewan Craft Council IS (0228-7463)
Published by: Saskatchewan Craft Council, 813 Broadway Ave, Saskatoon, SK S7N 1B5, Canada. TEL 306-653-3616, FAX 306-244-2711, saskcraftcouncil@home.com. Ed. Leslie Millikin. Circ: 600 (paid).

745.5 USA ISSN 1053-2013
CRAFT RELATED NEWSLETTERS, PERIODICALS & PUBLICATIONS; an updating reference. Text in English. 1990. biennial. USD 19.95 (effective 2001). 12 p./no.; **Description:** Lists references for crafts, crafts patterns, products, and fairs.
—CCC.
Published by: Continnuus, c/o Prosperity & Profits Unlimited Distribution Services, P O Box 416, Denver, CO 80201-0416. TEL 303-575-5676. Ed., R&P A C Doyle. Circ: 2,000.

745.5 GBR ISSN 1469-3992
CRAFT STAMPER. Text in English. 2000. m. GBP 42 domestic; GBP 47.20 in Europe; USD 67.95 in United States; GBP 55.20 rest of world; GBP 3.50, USD 7.95 newsstand/cover (effective 2005). **Document type:** *Magazine, Consumer.* **Description:** Contains projects, instructional articles, competitions, new product reviews, and other information for art stamping enthusiasts.
Published by: Traplet Publications Ltd, Traplet House, Severn Dr, Upton-upon-Severn, Worcs WR8 0JL, United Kingdom. TEL 44-1684-588500, FAX 44-1684-578558, cs@traplet.com, orders@traplet.com, customerservice@traplet.com, http://www.craftstamper.com, http://www.traplet.com. Ed. Jane Pinder. Adv. contact Liz Lane TEL 44-1684-595388. **Dist. in Australia:** Traplet Publications Australia, Ste 11B Southern Corporate Centre, 35-37 Railway Parade, Engadine, NSW 2233, Australia. TEL 61-2-9520-0933, FAX 61-2-9520-0032, aus@traplet.com; **Dist. in the US:** Traplet Distribution USA Ltd., 1405, Champaign, IL 61824-1405. TEL 800-695-0208, usa@traplet.com.

745.5 USA
CRAFT TIMES. Text in English. 11/yr. USD 22.95 domestic (effective 2005). adv. **Document type:** *Newsletter, Consumer.* **Description:** Provides information about arts and crafts shows in southern California.
Address: P O Box 1938, Lakeside, CA 92040. TEL 619-390-7646, crafttimes@cox.net, http://www.CraftTimes.com. Ed. Carol S Hayes. adv.: B&W page USD 60.

745.5 ZAF ISSN 1023-5248
CRAFTART; a quarterly publication promoting South African crafts. Text in English. 1994. q. ZAR 19.50, USD 10 per issue. illus.
Published by: CraftArt Publishers, PO Box 650737, Benmore, Johannesburg 2010, South Africa.

790 USA ISSN 1082-1376
CRAFTING TRADITIONS. Text in English. 1983. bi-m. USD 14.98 domestic; CND 19.98 in Canada; USD 25.98 elsewhere; USD 3.99 newsstand/cover (effective 2005). illus. **Document type:** *Magazine, Consumer.* **Description:** Suggests craft ideas and projects for memorable holidays and family occasions.
Formerly (until 1995): Country Handcrafts (0745-3116)
Published by: Reiman Publications, LLC (Subsidiary of: Reader's Digest Association), 5400 S 60th St, Greendale, WI 53129. TEL 414-423-0100, 800-344-6913, FAX 414-423-8463, editors@craftingtraditions.com, subscriberservices@reimanpub.com, http://www.craftingtraditions.com, http://www.reimanpub.com. Ed. Kathleen Anderson. Circ: 5,000,000 (paid). **Subscr. to:** PO Box 996, Greendale, WI 53129.

745 AUS ISSN 1442-9233
CRAFTMARK. Text in English. 1999. q.
Media: Online - full text.
Published by: Craftmark Australia, Level 5, 414-418 Elizabeth St, Surry Hills, NSW 2010, Australia. TEL 61-2-9211-1445, FAX 61-2-9211-1443, http://www.craftaus.com.au. Ed. Jennifer Mors.

745.5 USA ISSN 1061-3064
CRAFTMASTER NEWS. Text in English. 1982. m. USD 30 (effective 1998). back issues avail. **Document type:** *Trade.* **Description:** For arts and crafts vendors. Lists show events with promoters name, address, fees for show, etc. Covers California, Arizona, Nevada, Oregon.
Address: PO Box 39429, Downey, CA 90242. TEL 562-869-5882, FAX 562-904-0546. Ed. Marsha Reed. adv.: page USD 190; trim 9.75 x 7.25. Circ: 4,000.

745 USA ISSN 0897-6341
CRAFTRENDS. Text in English. 1982. m. USD 26 in North America; USD 44 elsewhere (effective 2005). adv. bk.rev. **Document type:** *Magazine, Trade.* **Description:** Targets craft, needlework and fabric retailers, manufacturers, and wholesalers with editorial content on industry events, news, and products.
Related titles: Online - full text ed.
—CCC.
Published by: Primedia Enthusiast Media (Subsidiary of: Primedia Consumer Media & Magazine Group), 741 Corporate Circle, Ste A, Golden, CO 80401. TEL 303-278-1010, FAX 303-277-0370, craftrends@primedia.com, information@primedia.com, http://www.craftrends.com, http://www.primedia.com. Ed. Bill Gardner. Adv. contact Mike Irish TEL 309-679-5302. B&W page USD 3,070, color page USD 4,493. Circ: 22,000 (controlled).

745 USA
CRAFTRENDSTODAY. Text in English. 1993. 24/yr. **Document type:** *Newsletter.*
Published by: Primedia Enthusiast Media (Subsidiary of: Primedia Consumer Media & Magazine Group), 741 Corporate Circle, Ste A, Golden, CO 80401. TEL 303-278-1010, FAX 303-277-0370, mike@craftrends.com, information@primedia.com, http://www.craftrends.com, http://www.primedia.com.

745 GBR ISSN 0306-610X
TT1
CRAFTS; the decorative & applied arts magazine. Text in English. 1973. bi-m. GBP 27 in United Kingdom to individuals; GBP 35 in Europe to individuals; USD 56 in United States to individuals; GBP 42 elsewhere to individuals; GBP 33 in United Kingdom to institutions; GBP 45 in Europe to institutions; USD 75 in United States to institutions; GBP 55 elsewhere to institutions (effective 2001). adv. bk.rev. illus. index. back issues avail.; reprint service avail. from PQC. **Document type:** *Consumer.* **Description:** Britain's decorative arts publication featuring work by craftsmen and women worldwide; includes buyers' guide and calendar of craft events.
Related titles: Microform ed.: (from PQC); Online - full text ed.: (from H.W. Wilson, O C L C Online Computer Library Center, Inc.).
Indexed: ABM, ArtInd, DAAI, WTA.
—BLDSC (3486.750000), IE, Infotrieve, ingenta. **CCC.**
Published by: Crafts Council, 44a Pentonville Rd, London, N1 9BY, United Kingdom. TEL 44-20-7278-7700, FAX 44-20-7837-0858, crafts@craftscouncil.org.uk, http://www.craftscouncil.org.uk. Ed. Geraldine Rudge. Pub., R&P Andrew Ryan TEL 44-20-7806-2540. Adv. contact Nichola Bath. Circ: 15,500 (paid).

745.5 GBR ISSN 1350-1984
CRAFTS BEAUTIFUL. Text in English. 1993. m. GBP 25 domestic; GBP 33.75 in Europe; GBP 35.50 in United States; GBP 47.45 elsewhere; GBP 2.60 newsstand/cover. adv. bk.rev. back issues avail. **Document type:** *Consumer.* **Description:** Contains regular features on stencils, rubber stamping, decoupage, stitching, home decorations, knitting, quilling, ceramics, quilting, painting, doughcraft and plastercrafts. Includes giveaways, competitions, drawings, and free patterns each month.
Published by: Aceville Publications Ltd., Castle House, 97 High St, Colchester, Essex CO1 2QN, United Kingdom. TEL 44-1206-563363, FAX 44-1206-769512, mail@maze.u-net.com. Ed. Helen Tudor. Pub. Matthew Tudor. Adv. contact Martin Lack. B&W page GBP 425, color page GBP 670; trim 210 x 297. Circ: 30,000 (paid). **Dist. by:** Seymour Distribution Ltd, 86 Newman St, London W1T 3EX, United Kingdom. FAX 44-207-396-8002, enquiries@seymour.co.uk.

745.5 USA ISSN 0273-7957
CRAFTS FAIR GUIDE. Text in English. 1974. q. USD 45 (effective 2000). adv. bk.rev. **Description:** Reviews, rates, and evaluates arts and crafts fairs in the Western states.
Address: PO Box 688, Corte Madera, CA 94976. TEL 415-924-3259, 800-871-2341, FAX 415-924-3259, leecfg@pacbell.net. Ed. Dianne Spiegel. Circ: 3,500.

745.5 USA ISSN 0146-6607
TT855
CRAFTS 'N THINGS. Text in English. 1975. 8/yr. USD 21.97 domestic; USD 25.97 in Canada; USD 29.97 elsewhere (effective 2005). adv. bk.rev. illus. index. back issues avail. **Document type:** *Magazine, Consumer.*
Incorporates (1967-1986): Creative Crafts and Miniatures (0734-0176); Which was formed by the merger of: Creative Craft (0011-0884); Miniature Magazine (0162-5632)
Related titles: Online - full text ed.: (from Gale Group, Northern Light Technology, Inc.).
Indexed: BRI, IHTDI, MELSA, MagInd, RGAb, RGPR.
Published by: Clapper Communications Companies, 2400 E Devon Ave, Ste 375, Des Plaines, IL 60018-4618. TEL 847-635-5800, FAX 847-635-6311, cntcs@clapper.com, http://www.craftideas.com, http://www.clapper.com. Pub. Jeff Clapper. Adv. contact Bobbie Zych. B&W page USD 4,400, color page USD 7,300. Circ: 310,000 (paid). **Dist. in UK by:** Seymour Distribution Ltd, 86 Newman St, London W1T 3EX, United Kingdom. FAX 44-207-396-8002, enquiries@seymour.co.uk.

745.5 USA ISSN 0899-9724
CRAFTS NEWS. Text in English. 1986. q. USD 35 (effective 2005). adv. 16 p./no.; back issues avail. **Document type:** *Newsletter, Consumer.* **Description:** International crafts effort, artisan profiles, sources of technical assistance, equipment, materials, trends, trade issues, and microcredit information.
Related titles: E-mail ed.; Online - full text ed.
Indexed: ABM.
Published by: Crafts Center at C H F International, 8601 Georgia Ave, Ste 800, Silver Spring, MD 20910. TEL 301-587-4700, FAX 301-587-7315, craftscenter@chfng.org, info@craftscenter.org, http://www.craftscenter.org. Ed. Caroline Ramsay. adv.: col. inch USD 180. Circ: 6,000 (paid and controlled).

745.5 USA ISSN 0160-7650
THE CRAFTS REPORT. Text in English. 1974. m. USD 29 domestic; USD 41 foreign; USD 6.95 newsstand/cover domestic; USD 10 newsstand/cover foreign (effective 2005). adv. bk.rev.; Website rev. illus. reprint service avail. from PQC. **Document type:** *Magazine, Trade.* **Description:** Business newsmonthly for professional craftspersons, gallery and shop owners. Covers sales and marketing, management, finance and crafts industry trends. Lists fairs and shows throughout the US, and reports on issues such as taxes, health, law, copyright, and computers.
Incorporates: Working Craftsman (0149-0206)
Related titles: Microform ed.: (from PQC).
Indexed: ArtInd, DAAI.
Published by: Crafts Report Publishing Co., Inc., 100 Rogers Rd, PO Box 1992, Wilmington, DE 19801. TEL 302-656-2209, theeditor@craftsreport.com, http://www.craftsreport.com. Ed. Heather Skelly. Pubs. Deborah Copeland, Lammont Copeland Jr. Circ: 25,000 (paid and free).

745.5 GBR ISSN 0953-9190
THE CRAFTSMAN MAGAZINE. Text in English. 1983. m. GBP 25 domestic; GBP 40 in Europe; GBP 50 elsewhere; GBP 2.50 newsstand/cover. adv. bk.rev. back issues avail. **Document type:** *Consumer.* **Description:** Contains the most up-to-date crafts information available.
Published by: P S B Design and Print Consultants Ltd., Lowthorpe, PO Box 5, Driffield, E Yorks YO25 8JD, United Kingdom. TEL 44-1377-255213, FAX 44-1377-255730, angie@craftsman-magazine.co.uk, http://www.craftsman-magazine.co.uk. Ed. Angie Boyer. R&P Paul Boyer. Adv. contact Andrea Garnett. Circ: 15,000. **Subscr. to:** FREEPOST YO558, Driffield, E Yorks YO25 8BR, United Kingdom. **Dist. by:** Lakeside Publishing Services, Unit 1D, Tideway Industrial Estate, 87 Kirtling St, London SW8 5BP, United Kingdom. TEL 44-20-77206680, FAX 44-20-74989616.

745.5 GBR ISSN 0968-4506
CRAFTWORKER'S YEAR BOOK. Text in English. 1981. a. GBP 12, USD 25 (effective 2001). adv. 232 p./no. 2 cols./p.; back issues avail. **Document type:** *Directory, Yearbook, Consumer.* **Description:** Details on 1900 craft retailing events, the companies that organise them, plus guilds, associations, societies, magazines, & craft course providers.
Formerly (until 1992): Craftman's Directory (Year) Part 1 (0261-2135)

A

Published by: Write Angle Press, 44 Kingsway, Stoke-on-Trent, Staffs ST4 1JH, United Kingdom. TEL 44-1782-749919, 44-1778-342948, FAX 44-1782-747061, 44-1778-342976, charleswallin@btclick.com, charles.wallin@btclick.com, charles.wallin@btclick.com. Ed., R&P Charles Wallin. adv.: B&W page GBP 350, B&W page USD 525, color page GBP 700, color page USD 1,000; trim 126 x 196. Circ: 2,000 (paid). **Subscr. to:** Mail Order Department, PO Box 560, Sutton, Surrey SM2 5ZY, United Kingdom.

745.5 USA
CREATE AND DECORATE. Text in English. 1985. 8/yr. USD 19.97 domestic; USD 26.97 in Canada; USD 33.97 elsewhere (effective 2005). adv. bk.rev. illus. **Document type:** *Magazine, Consumer.* **Description:** For craft enthusiasts, featuring original craft projects, designs, instructions, and diagrams for all skill levels.
Former titles: Craftworks; Craftworks for the Home (0891-0588)
Related titles: Online - full text ed.
Published by: All American Crafts, Inc., 7 Waterloo Rd, Stanhope, NJ 07874-2621. TEL 973-347-6900, 800-877-5527, FAX 973-347-6909, http://www.createanddecorate.com/. Ed. Trish Swenson. Pub. Jerry Cohen. Adv. contact Lee Jaworski TEL 973-383-8080 ext 114. Circ: 180,000 (paid).

745.5 USA ISSN 1091-3580
CREATING KEEPSAKES; scrapbook magazine. Text in English. 1996. m. USD 24.97 domestic; USD 36.97 in Canada; USD 68.97 elsewhere (effective 2005). adv. illus. **Document type:** *Magazine, Consumer.* **Description:** Offers highly creative ideas for creating unusual and captivating scrapbooks, keepsake boxes, and album covers.
Published by: Primedia Enthusiast Media (Subsidiary of: Primedia Consumer Media & Magazine Group), 14850 Pony Express Rd., Riverton, UT 84065-4801. editorial@creatingkeepsakes.com, http://www.creatingkeepsakes.com, http://www.primedia.com. Ed. Tracey White. Pub. Mark Seastrand. Adv. contact Becky Lowder TEL 909-613-1961. Circ: 250,000 (paid).

745.5 GBR ISSN 1365-9189
CREATIVE CRAFTS FOR THE HOME. Text in English. m. GBP 32.95 domestic; USD 65 in United States; GBP 37.95 elsewhere; GBP 2.95 newsstand/cover. **Document type:** *Consumer.* **Description:** Provides detailed information and ideas on a wide range of crafts from experts and professionals for the home crafter.
Published by: G M C Publications Ltd., 166 High St, Lewes, E Sussex BN7 1XU, United Kingdom. TEL 44-1273-477374, FAX 44-1273-478606. Ed. Lisa Leonard. **Dist. by:** Comag, Tavistock Works, Tavistock Rd, W Drayton, Middx UB7 7QX, United Kingdom. TEL 44-1895-444055, FAX 44-1895-433602.

745 AUS
CREATIVE EXPRESSIONS: WITH JENNY HASKINS. Text in English. m. AUD 32.50 domestic; NZD 57.50 in New Zealand (effective 2004).
Published by: Pride Publishing, PO Box 645, Rozelle, NSW 2039, Australia. TEL 61-2-9555-9322, FAX 61-2-9555-6188, info@pridepublishing.com.au, http://www.jennyhaskins.com/, http://www.pridepublishing.com.au/.

700 GBR ISSN 1364-1719
HF5808.E85
THE CREATIVE HANDBOOK. Text in English. 1973. a. GBP 140 in United Kingdom; USD 240 overseas (effective 2000). adv. **Document type:** *Directory.* **Description:** Showcase for British talent, covering design, illustration, photography, picture libraries, photographic services, print, commercials, sound, live events, etc.
—CCC.
Published by: Variety Media Publications (Subsidiary of: Reed Business Information Ltd.), 6 Bell Yard, London, WC2A 2JR, United Kingdom. TEL 44-20-7520-5233, FAX 44-20-7520-5237, richard.wooley@rbi.co.uk, http://www.chb.com. Ed. Sara Tyler TEL 44-13-4985-2839. Pub. Richard Woolley. Adv. contact Jerry Odlin. B&W page GBP 2,850, color page GBP 4,750; trim 130 x 270. Circ: 8,000.

CREATIVE HOME. see *INTERIOR DESIGN AND DECORATION*

745.5 USA ISSN 1062-8207
CREATIVE OUTLETS. Text in English. 1984. q. USD 5 per issue. adv. bk.rev. **Document type:** *Newsletter.* **Description:** Dedicated to home based business with an emphasis on the arts and crafts industry. Features listings of shops and shows buying or consigning handicrafts.
Published by: Country Press, PO Box 5024, Durango, CO 81301. Ed. J L Walker.

745.593 AUS ISSN 1446-1595
CREATIVE SCRAPBOOKING FOR KEEPS. Text in English. 2001. q.
Published by: Pride Publishing, PO Box 645, Rozelle, NSW 2039, Australia. TEL 61-2-9555-9322, FAX 61-2-9555-6188, info@pridepublishing.com.au, http://www.pridepublishing.com.au/.

700 770 AUS ISSN 0726-3589
CREATIVE SOURCE AUSTRALIA✶; the wizards of Oz. Text in English. 1980. every 18 mos. USD 70 (effective 1999). adv. illus. back issues avail. **Document type:** *Directory.* **Description:** Comprehensive source of what's happening in Australia's creative circles today.
Published by: Armadillo Publishers Pty. Ltd., 410 Elizabeth Street, PO Box 12358, Melbourne, VIC 8006, Australia. TEL 61-3-52896137, FAX 61-3-52896137. Ed., Pub., R&P, Adv. contact Elaine Howell. Circ: 4,000.

745.5 790.132 GBR ISSN 0262-7140
CRESTED CIRCLE; a bi-monthly magazine for collectors of the products of the crested china manufacturers. Text in English. 1980. bi-m. GBP 4. adv. bk.rev.
Address: c/o F. Owen, 26 Urswick Rd, Dagenham, Essex RM9 6EA, United Kingdom. Circ: 400.

CROCHET HOME. see *NEEDLEWORK*

745.5 USA ISSN 1095-4996
KFT1215
CROCHET WITH HEART. Text in English. bi-m.
Published by: Leisure Arts, PO Box 420126, Palm Coast, FL 32142. TEL 501-868-8800.

CROSS STITCH. see *NEEDLEWORK*

CROSS STITCH COLLECTION; the most beautiful cross stitch designs. see *NEEDLEWORK*

CROSS STITCH! MAGAZINE. see *NEEDLEWORK*

CROSS-STITCHER. see *NEEDLEWORK*

CROSS STITCHER. see *NEEDLEWORK*

745.5 USA ISSN 0893-1097
DECORATIVE ARTIST'S WORKBOOK. Text in English. 1987. bi-m. USD 19.96 domestic; USD 26.96 foreign (effective 2005). adv. **Document type:** *Magazine, Consumer.* **Description:** Instructs decorative painters of all levels step-by-step from other artists and illustrations.
Related titles: Microform ed.: (from PQC); Online - full text ed.: (from Northern Light Technology, Inc., ProQuest Information & Learning).
Indexed: IHTDI.
Published by: F & W Publications, Inc., 4700 E Galbraith Rd, Cincinnati, OH 45236. TEL 513-531-2690, 800-283-0963, FAX 513-531-2902, wds@fwpubs.com, http://www.decorativeartist.com, http://www.fwpublications.com. Ed. Anne Hevener. Pub. Jeffry Lapin. Adv. contact Stephanie Curtis TEL 877-234-6829. B&W page USD 2,015, color page USD 2,565; trim 7.75 x 10.75. Circ: 93,920.

745.0941 GBR ISSN 0260-9568
DECORATIVE ARTS SOCIETY, 1850 TO THE PRESENT. JOURNAL. Text in English. 1976. a. GBP 10 to individuals; GBP 20 to institutions. adv. bk.rev. bibl.; illus. cum.index. **Document type:** *Academic/Scholarly.*
Formerly (until 1978): Decorative Arts Society 1890 - 1940. Bulletin
Indexed: ABM, API, BHA, DAAI.
—BLDSC (4732.675000). **CCC.**
Published by: Decorative Arts Society 1850 to the Present, c/o Helen Grogan Hon Secy, Decorative Arts Society, PO Box 844, Lewes, E Sussex BN7 3NG, United Kingdom. TEL 44-1798-831734. adv.: page USD 120. Circ: 500. **Subscr. to:** 47 Coombe Crescent, Bury, Pulborough, W Sussex RH20 1PE, United Kingdom.

745.5 FRA ISSN 0994-2114
DECORATIVE CROCHET. Text in French. 1988. bi-m. USD 19.95 (effective 1999). illus. **Document type:** *Consumer.* **Description:** Contains patterns for doilies, lacework, filet, tablecloths, and curtains; also includes illustrations, photographs, and instructions.
Published by: Les Editions de Saxe S.A., 20 rue Croix Barret, Lyon, Cedex 7 69358, France. TEL 33-4-78729254, FAX 33-4-78726418.

745.5 747 USA ISSN 1096-3278
THE DECORATIVE PAINTER. Text in English. 199?. bi-m. USD 35 domestic individual membership; USD 65 foreign individual membership; USD 65 domestic business membership; USD 95 foreign business membership (effective 2005). **Document type:** *Magazine, Trade.*
Published by: Society of Decorative Painters, 393 N McLean Blvd, Wichita, KS 67203-5916. TEL 316-269-9300, FAX 316-269-9191, sdp@decorativepainters.org, http://www.decorativepainters.org/thedp.asp.

746 DEU ISSN 1434-0437
DIANA SPECIAL. Text in German. 19??. irreg. adv. **Document type:** *Magazine, Consumer.*
Published by: OZ Verlag GmbH, Roemerstr 90, Rheinfelden, 79618, Germany. TEL 49-7623-964-0, FAX 49-7623-96464200, vollmar@oz-bpv.de, http://www.oz-verlag.com. adv.: B&W page EUR 1,800, color page EUR 2,400.

745.592 USA ISSN 0746-9624
DOLL CRAFTER; published for creators and collectors. Text in English. 1983. m. USD 39.95 domestic; USD 54.95 foreign; USD 4.95 newsstand/cover (effective 2005). adv. illus. reprints avail. **Document type:** *Magazine, Consumer.* **Description:** Publishes for the doll creator and collector.
Incorporates (19??-2003): Doll Artisan (1040-6336); (1994-2003): Dollmaking (1093-9911); Which was formerly (until 1996): Dollmaking Crafts & Designs (1081-0773); Which was formed by the merger of (1985-1994): Dollmaking Projects & Plans (0885-2707); (198?-1994): Doll Designs (1050-4796); Which was formerly (1979-198?): National Doll World Omnibook (0199-1043)
Indexed: IHTDI.
Published by: Jones Publishing, Inc., N 7450 Aanstad Rd, PO Box 5000, Iola, WI 54945. TEL 715-445-5000, 800-331-0038, FAX 715-445-4053, http://www.jonespublishing.com. Ed. Pat Duchene. Pub. Joe Jones. adv.: B&W page USD 1,510, color page USD 1,890. Circ: 42,000 (paid).

DOLLS, BEARS, AND COLLECTABLES. see *HOBBIES*

688.7 738.8 USA ISSN 1544-6158
▼ **DOLLS BEAUTIFUL.** Text in English. 2003 (Spr.). q.
Published by: (Doll Artisan Guild), Seeley's Ceramic Service, Inc., P. O. Box 669, Oneonta, NY 13820. TEL 607-433-1240, FAX 607-432-2042, seeley@seeleys.com, http://www.seeleys.com. Adv. contact Karlyn Grzymkowski.

746 AUS ISSN 1033-4513
DOWN UNDER QUILTS. Text in English. 1988. q. adv. back issues avail. **Document type:** *Consumer.*
Published by: Pride Publishing, PO Box 645, Rozelle, NSW 2039, Australia. TEL 61-2-9555-9322, FAX 61-2-9555-6188, info@pridepublishing.com.au, http://www.pridepublishing.com.au/.

745.5 DEU ISSN 0720-0528
DRECHSELN. Text in German. 1878. q. adv. bk.rev. **Document type:** *Consumer.* **Description:** Covers all aspects of the art and craft of lathe-turning.
Former titles (until 1991): Holz und Elfenbein; Deutsche Drechsler Zeitung
Published by: Kettler Verlag, Robert Bosch Str 14, Boenen, 59199, Germany. TEL 49-2383-5118, FAX 49-2383-3052. Ed. Georg Panz. Circ: 975.

745.5 800 GBR
DUE SOUTH; the biggest guide to what's on in the South. Text in English. 1984. m. GBP 8.50. back issues avail.
Published by: Lastcode Ltd., 106 St Mary's Rd, Southampton, Hants SO2 0AN, United Kingdom. TEL 0703-332233. Ed. Sally O'Shaughnessy. Circ: 16,000.

E D V UND KOMMUNIKATION FUER DAS HANDWERK. (Elektronische Datenverarbeitung) see *COMPUTERS*

EARLY AMERICAN LIFE; traditions, period style, antiques, architecture, history. see *INTERIOR DESIGN AND DECORATION—Furniture And House Furnishings*

745.5 USA
EAST COAST ARTISAN. Text in English. bi-m. USD 30 (effective 2005). **Document type:** *Magazine, Trade.* **Description:** Provides news and reviews of arts and crafts shows in Connecticut and the surrounding states.
Formerly (until 2005): The Craft Digest
Address: PO Box 4056, Monroe, CT 06468. TEL 860-626-7360, 860-225-8875, FAX 860-496-1830, 860-225-7325, harry@craftdigest.com, joe@craftdigest.com, http://www.eastcoastartisan.com/.

EESTI NAINE; a magazine for women. see *WOMEN'S INTERESTS*

745.5 738 GBR ISSN 0264-5041
EUROPEAN TABLEWARE BUYERS GUIDE. Text in English. 1971. a. GBP 51.94 per issue domestic; USD 109.45, GBP 62.54 per issue foreign (effective 2005). adv. **Document type:** *Directory, Trade.* **Description:** List of European manufacturers of tableware, housewares and quality giftware. All entries are fully comprehensive and include full name and address, telephone, fax, E-mail, Web Address and the names of up to three senior executives.
Former titles: Tableware Reference Book; Tableware and Pottery Gazette Reference Book (0082-1438)
Published by: D M G World Media Ltd. (Subsidiary of: Daily Mail and General Trust PLC), Queensway House, 2 Queensway, Redhill, Surrey RH1 1QS, United Kingdom. TEL 44-1737-768611, FAX 44-1737-855469, info@uk.dmgworldmedia.com, http://www.tablewareinternational.com, http://www.dmgworldmedia.com. Ed. Stephen Wadey. Pub. Robin Beaman TEL 44-1737-855211.

292 398 GBR
EVERLASTING CIRCLE. Text in English. irreg. free. **Document type:** *Newsletter.* **Description:** Reviews and reports Ebat (Pagan bard) music and folklore and folk events.
Published by: Acca and Adda, B C M Akademia, London, WC1N 3XX, United Kingdom. Ed. S Bate.

745.5 BRA
FACA FACIL. Text in Portuguese. m. adv. illus. **Document type:** *Consumer.* **Description:** Promotes and teaches all types of crafts techniques. Covers ceramics, paper handiwork, embroidery, crochet, sewing, knitting and tapestry.
Related titles: ♦ Supplement(s): Faca Facil Especial. Papel Vegetal. ISSN 1413-3490.
Published by: Editora Globo S.A., Rua Domingos Sergio dos Anjos, 277, Pirituba, Jd S Elias, Sao Paulo, SP 05136-170, Brazil. TEL 55-11-836-5000, atendimento@edglobo.com.br, http://editoraglobo.globo.com/. Pub. Jose Francisco Queiroz. adv.: color page USD 11,700; trim 274 x 208. Circ: 166,000 (paid).

781.7 IRN
➤ **FASLNAMEH-I HONAR**; the art quarterly. Text in Persian, Modern. 1988. q. IRR 960 per issue. abstr. **Document type:** *Magazine, Academic/Scholarly.* **Description:** Covers Iranian music.
Formerly: Ahang
Published by: Center of Music and Revolutionary Songs, Vahdat Hall, Arfa St., Hafiz Ave., Teheran, Iran. TEL 98-21-672-5827, 98-21-070-5101, honar@neda.net. Ed. Mohammed Reza Zahouti.

➤ **FINE TOOL JOURNAL.** see *ANTIQUES*

745.5 USA ISSN 1539-7157
FIRED ARTS & CRAFTS. Text in English. 1955. m. USD 32.95; USD 3.95 newsstand/cover (effective 2005). adv. illus.; tr.lit. **Document type:** *Magazine, Consumer.*
Formerly (until 2002): Ceramic Arts & Crafts (0009-0190)
Related titles: Microfilm ed.: (from PQC).
Indexed: IHTDI.
Published by: Jones Publishing, Inc., N 7450 Aanstad Rd, PO Box 5000, Iola, WI 54945. TEL 715-445-5000, FAX 715-445-4053, jonespub@jonespublishing.com, http://www.jonespublishing.com. R&P Mike Harbridge. adv.: B&W page USD 710, color page USD 1,400. Circ: 15,000 (paid).

745.92 GBR ISSN 0046-421X
THE FLOWER ARRANGER. Text in English. 1961. q. GBP 8.50; GBP 10 foreign. adv. bk.rev. illus. index. **Document type:** *Consumer.*
Published by: National Association of Flower Arrangement Societies, 21 Denbigh St, London, SW1V 2HF, United Kingdom. TEL 44-171-828-5145. Ed., R&P Jill Grayston. Circ: 55,000. **Subscr. to:** Taylor Bloxham Ltd., Nugent St, Leicester LE3 5HH, United Kingdom.

372.5 700 NOR ISSN 0805-9144
CODEN: IEKRDI
FORM; et fagpedagogisk tidsskrift. Text in Norwegian. 1967. bi-m. NOK 250; NOK 55 newsstand/cover (effective 2000). adv. bk.rev. back issues avail. **Document type:** *Journal, Academic/Scholarly.*
Former titles (until 1995): Forming i Skolen (0333-2217); (until 1981): Ide og Form (0046-8525)
—CASDDS. **CCC.**
Published by: Landslaget Formgiving, Kunst og Handverk, Tollbugt 28, Oslo, 0157, Norway. TEL 47-22-42-29-71, FAX 47-22-41-93-83, fiskolen@online.no, http://skolenettet.nls.no/dok/sn/fag/kunst/felleskunst/magasiner/form. Ed. Hilde Degerud. Adv. contact Berit Landet Holoyen. Circ: 2,100.

FORM; designtidskriften. see *INTERIOR DESIGN AND DECORATION*

FUSIONS. see *CERAMICS, GLASS AND POTTERY*

745.5 AUT
GESTALTEN MIT FLIESEN. Text in German. 4/yr. **Document type:** *Journal, Trade.*
Published by: Verlag Lorenz, Ebendorferstr 10, Vienna, W 1010, Austria. TEL 43-1-40566950, FAX 43-1-4068693, k+r@verlag-lorenz.at, office@verlag-lorenz.at, http://www.verlag-lorenz.at. Ed. Gertraud Kosicek. Adv. contact Regina Hersey. Circ: 6,500 (paid and controlled).

688 664 USA ISSN 1050-0316
GIFT BASKET REVIEW; the magazine of the gift basket industry. Text in English. 1990. m. USD 39.95 domestic; USD 59 foreign (effective 2004). adv. charts; illus.; stat.; tr.lit. 48 p./no. 3 cols./p.; back issues avail. **Document type:** *Magazine, Trade.* **Description:** Features full color design ideas for gift baskets. For retailers and distributors in the gift industries.
Published by: Festivities Publications, Inc., 815 Haines St, Jacksonville, FL 32206-6050. TEL 904-634-1902, FAX 904-633-8764, reader@festivities-pub.com, info@festivities-pub.com, http://www.festivities-pub.com. Pub., R&P, Adv. contact David L Paulk. page USD 2,229; trim 10.88 x 8.13. Circ: 20,000 (paid and controlled).

745.5 666 USA ISSN 1041-6684
TT298
GLASS PATTERNS QUARTERLY. Text in English. 1985. q. USD 24 domestic; USD 29 foreign (effective 2003). adv. bk.rev. index. **Document type:** *Consumer.* **Description:** Every issue contains step-by-step instructions, how-to photos, and patterns for creating more than a dozen projects.
Published by: Glass Patterns Quarterly, Inc., 8300 Hidden Valley Rd, Box 69, Westport, KY 40077. TEL 502-222-5631, 800-719-0769, FAX 502-222-4527, gpqmag@aol.com, info@glasspatterns.com, http://www.glasspatterns.com. Ed., R&P Maureen James. Pub. Steven James. Adv. contact Sarah Smith TEL 502-222-5631. Circ: 45,000 (paid).

748 USA ISSN 0017-1077
GLASS WORKSHOP✶ . Text in English. 1969. q. USD 8. adv. bk.rev. illus. **Document type:** *Consumer.*
Indexed: BHA.
Published by: Stained Glass Club, 4481 Edinbridge Circle, Sarasota, FL 34235-2284. Ed. Seymour Isenberg. Circ: 2,000.

A GUIDE TO ART & DESIGN COURSES. see *EDUCATION—Teaching Methods And Curriculum*

745.5 ESP
GURE ARTEA; margoketa, eskultura, grabaketa, argazkxia. Text in Spanish, Basque; Summaries in Spanish, Basque. 1985. a. **Document type:** *Catalog.*
Published by: Eusko Jaurlaritzaren Argitalpen-Zerbitzu Nagusia/Servicio Central de Publicaciones del Gobierno Vasco, Donostia-San Sebastian, 1, Vitoria-gasteiz, Alava 01010, Spain. TEL 34-945-018561, FAX 34-945-018709, hac-sabd@ej-gv.es, http://www.ej-gv.net/publicaciones.

745.5 DNK ISSN 0105-9416
HAANDVAERKET MED MASKINEN. Text in Danish. 1976. 6/yr.
Address: PO Box 92, Hellerup, 2900, Denmark.

745.5 GBR ISSN 0142-0798
NK2808
HALI; the international magazine of antique carpet and textile art. Text in English. 1978. bi-m. GBP 90 domestic; GBP 101 in Europe; GBP 137 in United States; GBP 164 elsewhere (effective 2005). adv. bk.rev. bibl.; illus.; stat.; tr.lit. index. back issues avail. **Document type:** *Magazine, Consumer.* **Description:** Covers all aspects of fine antique carpets and textiles, providing scholarly research, reviews of public and private exhibitions, and marketplace news.
Indexed: A&ATA, ABM, AICP, ArtInd, PerIslam, RASB, WTA.
—BLDSC (4240.375000), IE, ingenta. **CCC.**
Published by: Hali Publications Ltd. (Subsidiary of: Centaur Communications Ltd.), St. Giles House, 50 Poland St, London, W1F 7AX, United Kingdom. TEL 44-20-79704600, FAX 44-20-75787222, hali@centaur.co.uk, http://www.hali.com/. Ed., R&P Daniel Shaffer TEL 44-20-79704600. Pub. Sebastian Ghandchi. Adv. contact Maro Artimatas. Circ: 7,500 (paid).

746 GBR ISSN 1356-7985
THE HALI ANNUAL (YEAR). Text in English. 1994. a.
Published by: Hali Publications Ltd. (Subsidiary of: Centaur Communications Ltd.), St. Giles House, 50 Poland St, London, W1F 7AX, United Kingdom. TEL 44-20-7970-4600, FAX 44-20-7578-7222, hali@centaur.co.uk, http://www.hali.com/. Ed. Jill Tilden.

HAND PAPERMAKING. see *PAPER AND PULP*

HAND PAPERMAKING NEWSLETTER. see *PAPER AND PULP*

745.5 USA ISSN 1072-0529
HANDCRAFT ILLUSTRATED. Text in English. 1993. q. USD 24.95; USD 30.95 in Canada; USD 36.95 elsewhere. illus. reprints avail. **Document type:** *Consumer.* **Description:** Presents detailed instructions and advice on craft and home decorating ideas, including flower arrangement, framing, gilding, antiquing, wreath making and similar projects.
Published by: Boston Common Press, 17 Station St, Brookline, MA 02445. TEL 617-232-1000, FAX 617-232-1572, hndcftill@aol.com. Ed. Mary Ann Hall. Pub. Christopher Kimball. **Subscr. to:** PO Box 7446, Red Oak, IA 51591-0446.

745.5 USA ISSN 0198-8212
TT848
HANDWOVEN. Text in English. 1979. 5/yr. USD 27 domestic; USD 33 foreign; USD 5.99 newsstand/cover (effective 2005). adv. bk.rev. illus. reprints avail. **Document type:** *Magazine, Consumer.* **Description:** Provides woven projects, step-by-step instructions, in-depth articles, reviews, columns, tips and product information. Features cover special techniques, history, people and weaving lore. Projects include fashions, fabrics and accessories for the home.
Incorporates (197?-1981): Interweave (0198-8220)
Indexed: ABM, IHTDI, WTA.
Published by: Interweave Press, Inc., 201 E Fourth St, Loveland, CO 80537. TEL 970-669-7672, 800-272-2193, FAX 970-667-8317, customerservice@interweave.com, http://www.interweave.com. Ed. Madelyn van der Hoogt. Pub. Marilyn Murphy. Adv. contact Sharon Altergott. Circ: 36,000.

738 USA
HAVILAND COLLECTORS INTERNATIONALE FOUNDATION NEWSLETTER. Text in English. 1989. q. USD 40 membership (effective 2005). adv. illus. back issues avail. **Document type:** *Newsletter, Consumer.* **Description:** Features articles on Haviland china, its art, artists, and the foundation.
Related titles: Fax ed.
Published by: Haviland Collectors International Foundation, PO Box 271383, Fort Collins, CO 80527. tclyde37@aol.com, haviland@aeroinc.net, http://www.havilandcollectors.com. Ed., Pub., R&P Keith J. Waterbrook. Circ: 415.

745.5 SWE ISSN 0345-4649
HEMSLOEJDEN. Text in Swedish. 1933. 6/yr. SEK 297 domestic; SEK 387 in Scandinavia; SEK 474 elsewhere; SEK 267 domestic to students (effective 2004). adv. bk.rev. illus.; bibl. cum index: 1984-2002. 52 p./no.; back issues avail. **Document type:** *Magazine, Consumer.*
Published by: Svenska Hemsloejdsfoereningarnas Riksfoerbund - S H R, Torsplan 7, Stockholm, 11364, Sweden. TEL 46-8-54549453, FAX 46-8-54549459, tidsskriften@hemslojden.org, kansli@hemslojden.org, http://www.hemslojden.org/index.1061.html. Eds. Anette Olofsson TEL 46-90718303, Celia Dackenberg TEL 46-90-718302. Pub. Celia Dackenberg TEL 46-90-718302. Adv. contact Liz Larsson TEL 46-46-399940. B&W page SEK 13,050, color page SEK 14,300. Circ: 16,200.

745.5 DEU
HOBEL UND SPAN; Holz- und Kunststoffverarbeitendes Handwerk Rheinland-Pfalz. Text in German. 1951. m.
Published by: Landesfachverband Holz und Kunststoff Rheinland-Pfalz, Postfach 946, Koblenz Am Rhein, 56009, Germany. TEL 0261-34445.

745.5 USA ISSN 1521-5806
HOLIDAY DECORATING. Text in English. 1995. a. USD 5.99 newsstand/cover (effective 2003).
Published by: Meredith Corp., 1716 Locust St, Des Moines, IA 50309-3023. TEL 515-284-3000, 800-556-9184, FAX 515-284-3657, http://www.meredith.com.

745.5 USA ISSN 1544-0923
▼ **HOLIDAY PAINTING.** Text in English. 2003 (Nov.). q. USD 19.97 (effective 2003).
Published by: E G W Publishing Co., 1041 Shary Circle, Concord, CA 94518. TEL 925-671-9852, FAX 925-671-0692, http://www.egw.com.

HOOKED ON CROCHET!. see *NEEDLEWORK*

745.5 USA
HORIZONS (ELMWOOD PARK). Text in English. 1982. 4/yr. membership only. back issues avail. **Document type:** *Newsletter.* **Description:** Provides information regarding the Association and industry events.
Published by: Hobby Industry Assn., 319 E 54th St, PO Box 348, Elmwood Park, NJ 07407. TEL 201-794-1133, FAX 201-797-0657, hia@ix.netcom.com. Eds. Beth Mauro, Susan Brandt. Circ: 4,200 (controlled and free).

746 DNK ISSN 0108-481X
HUSFLID. Variant title: Dansk Husflid. Text in Danish. 1881. 6/yr. DKK 375 membership; DKK 280 to students (effective 2005). adv. **Document type:** *Journal, Academic/Scholarly.*
Formerly (until 1972): Dansk Husflidstidende
Published by: Dansk Husflidsselskab, Tyrebakken 11, Kerteminde, 5300, Denmark. TEL 45-63-322096, FAX 45-63-322097, dansk@husflid.dk, http://www.husflid.dk. Ed. Ib Solvang. Adv. contact Inge Bay. B&W page DKK 4,135; trim 261 x 191. Circ: 8,000.

745.5 ARG
IDEAS (BUENOS AIRES). Text in Spanish. m. adv. **Document type:** *Magazine, Consumer.*
Published by: Editorial Televisa Argentina, Av Paseo Colon 275, Piso 10, Buenos Aires, Buenos Aires 1063, Argentina. TEL 54-11-4343-2225, FAX 54-11-4345-0955, http://www.televisa.com.ar.

746 ESP ISSN 1139-7055
IDEAS Y PUNTOS. Text in Spanish. 1994. m. EUR 19.80 domestic; EUR 42.65 in Europe; EUR 105.35 elsewhere (effective 2005). adv. back issues avail. **Document type:** *Magazine, Consumer.*
Published by: H Y M S A, Grupo Editorial Edipresse, Muntaner, 40-42, Barcelona, 08011, Spain. TEL 34-93-5087000, FAX 34-93-4542321, hymsa@hymsa.com, http://www.hymsa.com. Ed. Antoine Pasche. Pub. Eulalia Ubach.

INDIAN ARTS & CRAFTS ASSOCIATION NEWSLETTER. see *ETHNIC INTERESTS*

745.5 700 USA
INFORM (SYRACUSE)✶ . Text in English. 1981. q. USD 30 to members. adv. bk.rev. **Document type:** *Newsletter.*
Formerly: Information (Poughkeepsie)
Indexed: P&BA.
Published by: Empire State Crafts Alliance, Inc., 501 West Fayette St, Syracuse, NY 13204-2925. TEL 315-472-4245. Ed., R&P Megan White. Circ: 1,100.

INK & GALL; the marbling journal. see *PUBLISHING AND BOOK TRADE*

INSTRUMENTENBAU REPORT; aktuelle Informationen fuer Musikfreunde und Instrumentenbauer. see *MUSIC*

A

INUIT ART QUARTERLY. see *ART*

ITALIC HANDWRITING NEWSLETTER; a newsletter for people who care about legibility. see *EDUCATION—Teaching Methods And Curriculum*

745.5 USA
IVY COTTAGE SCRAPBOOK MAGAZINE. Text in English. 199?. bi-m. USD 19.95 (effective 2002). adv. **Document type:** *Magazine, Consumer.* **Description:** Covers scrapbooking ideas and projects.
Formerly (until Jun. 2001): Ivy Cottage Creations (1532-4338)
Published by: Ivy Cottage Creations, 325 N. 550 E., Orem, UT 84097-4809. TEL 888-303-1375, info@ivycottagecreations.com, http://www.ivycottagecreations.com.

745 USA
JO-ANN ETC. Text in English. 1999. q. USD 11.85 domestic; USD 20 in Canada; USD 4.95 newsstand/cover (effective 2003). adv. illus. **Document type:** *Magazine, Consumer.* **Description:** Features the various crafts and clothing that can be made using implements and materials purchased at the Jo-Ann stores. Each issue includes a section highlighting what is currently trendy in crafts as well as a 'creative kids' section and a store listing of Jo-Ann locations.
Related titles: Online - full text ed.
Published by: (Jo-Ann Stores, Inc.), Soho Publishing Company, 161 Ave of the Americas, New York, NY 10013. TEL 212-620-2500, 800-766-3619, FAX 212-620-2731, http://www.joann.com, http://www.butterick.com. Ed. Trisha Malcolm. Pub. Barbara Semen. Adv. contact Doreen Connors-Spellman TEL 212-620-2539.

745.5 USA ISSN 0075-4250
NK5100 CODEN: JGLSAE
➤ **JOURNAL OF GLASS STUDIES.** Text in English. 1959. a. USD 43 per issue domestic; USD 43.75 per issue foreign (effective 2004). adv. illus. cum.index: vols.1-15. back issues avail.; reprint service avail. from PQC. **Document type:** *Journal, Academic/Scholarly.* **Description:** Articles on the artistic, historical, and archeological aspects of glass from classical antiquity through the 19th century.
Related titles: Microform ed.: (from PQC).
Indexed: A&ATA, ABM, AIAP, AICP, ASCA, ArtHuCI, ArtInd, BHA, BrArAb, ChemAb, CurCont, DIP, IBR, IBZ, IndIslam, NumL, PCI.
—CASDDS, IE, Infotrieve. **CCC.**
Published by: Corning Museum of Glass, One Museum Way, Corning, NY 14830-2253. TEL 607-937-5371, info@cmog.org, http://www.cmog.org/. Ed. Richard Price. R&P David Whitehouse TEL 607-974-8424. Circ: 1,500.

745.5 USA
KAREN'S KUNTRY KHRONICLE. Text in English. bi-w. free. **Document type:** *Newsletter, Consumer.* **Description:** Includes articles on country decoration, country crafts, country music, country living and lots of other country tips, tricks and news.
Media: E-mail.
Published by: Karen's Kuntry Klutter TEL 352-694-7690, FAX 365-694-7690. Ed., Pub. Karen Mead.

KEEPSAKE CALENDAR; (year) cross-stitch collection. see *NEEDLEWORK*

745.5 CHE ISSN 0023-0553
NK3700
KERAMIK-FREUNDE DER SCHWEIZ. MITTEILUNGSBLATT/ AMIS SUISSES DE LA CERAMIQUE. BULLETIN. Text in English, French, German, Italian. 1946. irreg. membership. bk.rev. abstr.; charts; illus.; mkt. **Document type:** *Bulletin, Consumer.*
Indexed: ABM, BHA.
Published by: Keramik-Freunde der Schweiz, Plattenstr 86, Zuerich, 8032, Switzerland. TEL 41-1-2612155. Ed., R&P Rudolf Schnyder.

745.5 DEU ISSN 0172-6102
KERAMIKMAGAZIN. Text in German. 1979. 6/yr. EUR 35 domestic; EUR 38 in Europe; EUR 44 elsewhere; EUR 6 newsstand/cover (effective 2003). adv. **Document type:** *Magazine, Consumer.*
Incorporates (in 1991): Keramik Creativ (0720-9126)
Indexed: ABM, DAAI, DIP, IBR, IBZ.
Published by: Ritterbach Verlag GmbH, Postfach 1820, Frechen, 50208, Germany. TEL 49-2234-18660, FAX 49-2234-186690, anzeigen@ritterbach.de, verlag@ritterbach.de, http://www.kunstwelt-online.de/verlag/kunstwelt/keramikmagazin/index.asp, http://www.ritterbach.de. Ed. Gabi Dewald. R&P Marie Luise Coeln TEL 49-2234-186632. Adv. contact Sonja Erdmann TEL 49-2234-186695. B&W page EUR 916, color page EUR 1,280. Circ: 8,200 (paid).

745.5 AUT
KERAMISCHE RUNDSCHAU KLIMA UND RAUM. Short title: K & R. Text in German. 12/yr. EUR 72 domestic; EUR 99 foreign (effective 2005). adv. **Document type:** *Journal, Trade.*
Indexed: BrCerAb, RefZh.
Published by: Verlag Lorenz, Ebendorferstr 10, Vienna, W 1010, Austria. TEL 43-1-40566950, FAX 43-1-4068693, k+r@verlag-lorenz.at, office@verlag-lorenz.at, http://www.verlag-lorenz.at/keramik/index.html. Ed., Adv. contact Regina Hersey. B&W page EUR 1,645, color page EUR 2,970; trim 185 x 264. Circ: 2,200 (paid and controlled).

KINDER BASTELSPASS. see *CHILDREN AND YOUTH—For*

KOTAPRESS JOURNALS ONLINE. see *LITERATURE—Poetry*

745.5 NLD ISSN 1382-368X
KREAPLUS; hobby magazine. Text in Dutch. 1995. q. EUR 17 domestic (effective 2005). adv. illus. back issues avail. **Document type:** *Magazine, Consumer.* **Description:** Offers craftspersons and other hobbyists detailed directions to make a wide variety of creative projects.
Published by: De Kleine Leeuw, Antwoordnummer 10747, 's-Hertogenbosch, 5200 WB, Netherlands. TEL 31-73-642-6224, FAX 31-73-641-2012, info@kreaplus.nl, http://www.kreaplus.nl. Ed. Tonni Dowes-Snel.

745.5 DEU
KREATIV. Text in German. 1999. 9/yr. adv. **Document type:** *Magazine, Consumer.*
Published by: Marken Verlag GmbH, Bonner Str 323, Cologne, 50968, Germany. TEL 49-221-9574270, FAX 49-221-95742777, marken-info@markenverlag.de, http://www.markenverlag.de. adv.: page EUR 2,600. Circ: 82,967 (controlled).

745.5 DEU
KREATIV: BASTELN & NAEHEN. Text in German. q. EUR 14.60 domestic; EUR 19.60 foreign; EUR 3.10 newsstand/cover (effective 2003). adv. **Document type:** *Magazine, Consumer.*
Published by: Dollami Verlag GmbH, Schillerstr 22, Eschwege, 37269, Germany. TEL 49-5651-7467-0, FAX 49-5651-746719, verlag@dollami.de, http://www.dollami.de. Ed. Christiane Freitag. Adv. contact Andrea Eckert. B&W page EUR 750, color page EUR 1,000; trim 178 x 255. Circ: 60,000 (paid and controlled).

745.5 DEU ISSN 1434-3630
KREATIV JOURNAL. Text in German. 1993. m. EUR 3.53 newsstand/cover (effective 2003). adv. **Document type:** *Magazine, Consumer.*
Formerly (until 1996): C M - Magazin fuer Creative Leute (0947-6946)
Published by: H C M Verlags GmbH, Im Buhles 4, Glashuetten-Schlossborn, 61479, Germany. TEL 49-6174-9669-0, FAX 49-6174-966999, kreativjournal@hcm-verlag.de, mailbox@hcm-verlag.de, http://www.hcm-verlag.de/kreativ-journal/. Ed. Edda Mueller. Pub. Helmut Redecker. Adv. contact Karin Redecker. B&W page EUR 2,200, color page EUR 2,500. Circ: 40,920 (paid and controlled).

745.5 DEU ISSN 0941-9179
NK925
KUNSTHANDWERK UND DESIGN. Text in German. 1965. bi-m. EUR 46 domestic; EUR 57 in Europe; EUR 62 overseas; EUR 8 newsstand/cover (effective 2003). adv. bk.rev. **Document type:** *Magazine, Consumer.*
Formerly: Kunst und Handwerk (0454-6539)
Indexed: ABM, DAAI, DIP, IBR, IBZ, RASB, WTA.
—BLDSC (5130.688800).
Published by: Ritterbach Verlag GmbH, Postfach 1820, Frechen, 50208, Germany. TEL 49-2234-18660, FAX 49-2234-186690, anzeigen@ritterbach.de, verlag@ritterbach.de, http://www.kunstwelt-online.de/verlag/kunstwelt/kunsthandwerk/index.asp, http://www.ritterbach.de. Ed. Uta Klotz. R&P Marie Luise Coeln TEL 49-2234-186632. Adv. contact Sonja Erdmann TEL 49-2234-186695. B&W page EUR 880, color page EUR 1,250. Circ: 4,500 (paid).

745.5 DNK ISSN 1603-9092
KUNSTUFF/DANISH CRAFTS; artcraftdesign. Text in Danish, English. 1986. q. DKK 250; DKK 65 per issue (effective 2005). adv. bk.rev. illus. back issues avail. **Document type:** *Journal, Consumer.* **Description:** Features articles on art policy and professional issues; includes workshop portraits, reviews and debates.
Former titles (until 2004): Dansk Kunsthandvaerk (0902-2163); (until 1986): Danske Kunsthaandvaerkeres Landssammenslutning (0107-2153); (until 1980): Orientering fra Danske Kunsthaandvaerkeres Landssammenslutning (0105-3868)
Indexed: DAAI.
Published by: Danske Kunsthaandvaerkere/Danish Arts and Crafts Association, Herredsvejen 7, Nimtofte, 8581, Denmark. TEL 45-86-398464, FAX 45-86-398442, mail@kunstuff.dk, http://www.kunstuff.dk, http://www.crafts.dk/magazine. Ed. Merete Erbou Laurent. Circ: 2,500.

745.5 BEL ISSN 0779-1534
KWINTESSENS. Text in Dutch, English. 1992. q. bk.rev. illus. back issues avail. **Document type:** *Government.*
Published by: Vlaams Instituut voor het Zelfstandig Ondernemen, Kanselarijstraat 19, Brussels, 1000, Belgium. TEL 32-2-2276393, FAX 32-2-2276398, info@vizo.be, http://www.designvlaanderen.be/kwintessens, http://www.vizo.be. Ed., Pub. Johan Valcke. Circ: 882.

745.5 USA ISSN 1553-0256
▼ **LASTING MOMENTS**; inspiration and ideas for meaningful scrapbook albums. Text in English. 2004. bi-m. USD 23.97 domestic; CND 35.97 in Canada (effective 2005).
Published by: Meredith Corp., 1716 Locust St, Des Moines, IA 50309-3023. TEL 515-284-3000, FAX 515-284-3697, http://www.meredith.com.

745.5 USA
LEADING THE ARTFUL LIFE. Text in English. 2000. bi-m. USD 18.95 domestic; USD 34.95 foreign (effective 2000). adv. **Document type:** *Newsletter, Consumer.* **Description:** Includes easy craft projects, simple recipes, useful gardening tips, essays from readers, and hands-on decorating ideas.
Published by: Mary Engelbreit Enterprises, Inc. (Subsidiary of: Belvoir Media Group, LLC), 6358 Delmar Blvd, Ste 450, St Louis, MO 63130. TEL 816-932-6700, 877-817-3829, http://www.maryengelbreit.com.

THE LEATHER CRAFTERS & SADDLERS JOURNAL. see *LEATHER AND FUR INDUSTRIES*

745.5 ITA ISSN 0393-8190
NX4
M C M : LA STORIA DELLE COSE; rivista delle arti minori. (Manualita Creativita Maestria) Text in Italian; Summaries in English, Italian. 1985. q. USD 65.31 (effective 2005). adv. bk.rev. back issues avail. **Document type:** *Magazine, Consumer.* **Description:** Includes news on a wide variety of topics: the history of painting, the art of hand blown glass, tapestries, making and working with metals and fabrics, clay, pottery, fiber, gold, silver, wood and mosaic.
Published by: Maria Cristina de Montemayor Editore, Viale Alessandro Volta, 173, Florence, FI 50131, Italy. TEL 39-55-224227. Ed. Maria Cristina de Montemayor. Adv. contact Marino Giani. Circ: 10,000.

745.5 ITA ISSN 1594-9060
MACRAME. Text in Italian. 2002. 5/yr. EUR 24 domestic; EUR 33 foreign (effective 2005). **Document type:** *Magazine, Consumer.*
Published by: Edizioni Gruppo Abele, Corso Trapani 95, Turin, TO 10141, Italy. TEL 39-011-3841011, FAX 39-011-3841031, segreteria@gruppoabele.org, http://www.gruppoabele.org.

738.15 NOR ISSN 1504-1808
MALEGLEDER; med farger og pensler. Text in Danish, Norwegian, Swedish; Text occasionally in English, German. 1980. 5/yr. NOK 285 domestic; NOK 295 elsewhere (effective 2004). adv. 60 p./no. 3 cols./p.; back issues avail. **Document type:** *Consumer.* **Description:** Meant for amateurs as well as professionals, the magazine contains ideas and information mainly about porcelain painting, but also includes other painting genres.
Formerly (until 2003): Porselensmaling (0333-4872); Incorporates (1998-2003): Porselensmaling (English and German) (1501-0554); Which was formed by the merger of (1995-1998): Porcelain Painting (0807-741X); (1995-1998): Porzellanmalerei (0807-7428)
Related titles: English ed.: Porcelain Painting. ISSN 0807-741X. 1995; German ed.: Porzellanmalerei. ISSN 0807-7428. 1995.
Published by: Tema Forlag A-S, Evjebakken, Kirkenaer, 2260, Norway. TEL 47-62-946650, FAX 47-62-946651, post@maleglede, http://www.maleglede.no. Ed. Bjarne H Reenskaug. Adv. contact Else Enger. B&W page NOK 5,700, color page NOK 6,800; trim 264 x 185.

MALSPASS KINDERLEICHT. see *CHILDREN AND YOUTH—For*

745.5 ITA ISSN 1593-4101
MANUALI D'ARTE. Text in Italian. 2001. irreg. price varies. **Document type:** *Monographic series, Consumer.*
Published by: Alexandra Editrice, Largo Lanciani 1, Roma, 00162, Italy. TEL 39-06-86320393, FAX 39-06-86320481, alexandra@alexandra.it, http://www.alexandra.it.

745.5 USA ISSN 1096-5289
TX311
MARY ENGELBREIT'S HOME COMPANION; leading the artful life. Text in English. 1996. bi-m. USD 19.95 domestic; USD 36.95 in Canada; USD 28.95 elsewhere (effective 2006). adv. illus. back issues avail. **Document type:** *Magazine, Consumer.* **Description:** Provides real options for real people. It offers timely and seasonal insights that are meant to inspire readers to create the lives they want. Articles highlight fascinating homes created by the people who live in them and reflect a variety of styles.
Published by: Mary Engelbreit Enterprises, Inc. (Subsidiary of: Belvoir Media Group, LLC), 6358 Delmar Blvd, Ste 450, St Louis, MO 63130. TEL 314-726-6070, contactus@maryengelbreit.com, http://www.maryengelbreit.com/MEHC/index.htm. Ed. Mary Engelbreit. Pub. Philip L Penny. R&P Greg Hoffman TEL 314-762-5646. Adv. contact Laura Straub. B&W page USD 21,600, color page USD 27,000; trim 8 x 10.8. Circ: 525,000 (paid). **Subscr. to:** PO Box 5459, Harlan, IA 51593-0959.

745.5 AUS
MELBOURNE SHEEP AND WOOL. Text in English. 1878. a. AUD 45 (effective 1999). adv. back issues avail. **Document type:** *Catalog, Trade.* **Description:** Promotes improvement in the breed and quality of emulation amongst all engaged in pastoral pursuits by holding Shows at such times and place as the Committee may appoint, and by offering and awarding prizes and trophies at such Shows.
Former titles: Victorian Producers' Sheep and Wool Show; Weekly Times Melbourne Sheep and Woolcraft Show
Published by: Australian Sheep Breeders Association Inc., Royal Melbourne Showgrounds, Epsom Rd, Ascot Vale, VIC 3032, Australia. FAX 61-3-9376-2973, peter.fraser@rasv.melbourne.net. Ed., Pub., R&P, Adv. contact Peter Fraser TEL 61-3-9281-7443. Circ: 700.

745.5 770 USA ISSN 1520-2860
MEMORY MAKERS; the first source for scrapbooking ideas. Text in English. 1996. bi-m. USD 21.96 domestic; USD 36.96 in Canada; USD 51.96 elsewhere (effective 2005). adv. bk.rev.; software rev.; video rev. back issues avail. **Document type:** *Magazine, Consumer.* **Description:** Features ideas and stories of scrapbookers across the US and other countries. Dedicated to the craft of scrapbook making.
Published by: F & W Publications, Inc., 12365 Huron St, Ste 500, Denver, CO 80234-3438. TEL 303-452-0048, FAX 303-452-3582, editorial@memorymakersmagazine.com, wds@fwpubs.com, http://www.memorymakersmagazine.com, http://www.fwpublications.com. adv.: color page USD 5,917; trim 8.375 x 10.875. Circ: 200,000.

745.5 USA
MEMORY MAKERS SCRAPBOOK IDEA GALLERY. Text in English. 2000. bi-m. USD 24.95; USD 9.95 newsstand/cover (effective 2001). adv. **Document type:** *Magazine, Consumer.*
Published by: Satellite Press (Subsidiary of: F & W Publications, Inc.), 12365 Huron St, Ste 500, Denver, CO 80234. TEL 303-920-5341, http://www.memorymakersmagazine.com. Ed. Deborah Mock. Pub. Tim Gilmour.

745.5 669 USA ISSN 0270-1146
NK6400
METALSMITH. Text in English. 5/yr. USD 29 in North America to non-members; USD 41 elsewhere to non-members; free to members (effective 2005). adv. bk.rev. charts; illus. index. back issues avail. **Document type:** *Magazine, Trade.* **Description:** Devoted solely to the metal arts.
Former titles (1977-1980): Goldsmith's Journal (0197-0127); Golddust
Related titles: Online - full text ed.: (from EBSCO Publishing, H.W. Wilson, O C L C Online Computer Library Center, Inc.).
Indexed: ArtInd, DAAI.
—BLDSC (5699.610000), IE, ingenta.
Published by: Society of North American Goldsmiths, 1300 Iroquois Ave, Ste 160, Naperville, Du Page, IL 60563-6614. TEL 630-778-6385, FAX 630-416-3333, info@SNAGmetalsmith.org, info@snagmetalsmith.org, http://www.snagmetalsmith.org/metalsmith/default.asp. Eds. Nancy Monkman, Suzanne Ramljak TEL 203-792-5599. Adv. contact Jean Savarese TEL 908-901-9767. B&W page USD 710, color page USD 1,288; trim 10.88 x 8.38. Circ: 13,300.

745.5 USA ISSN 1533-9084
MICHAELS CREATE!. Text in English. 2001. bi-m. USD 21.97; USD 4.99 newsstand/cover (effective 2005). adv. **Document type:** *Magazine, Consumer.* **Description:** Features the best in contemporary do-it-yourself designs from high fashion to trendy home decor.
Published by: Krause Publications, Inc. (Subsidiary of: F & W Publications, Inc.), 700 E State St, Iola, WI 54990-0001. TEL 715-445-2214, 800-258-0929, FAX 715-445-4087, sparkss@krause.com, info@krause.com, https://www.krause.com/subscribe/mc/index.asp, http://www.krause.com. Ed. Jane Beard TEL 715-445-2214 ext 487. Pub. Debbie Knauer TEL 715-445-2214 ext 487. Adv. contact Marilyn Duquaine TEL 715-445-2214 ext 549. B&W page USD 4,340, color page USD 5,785; trim 8.125 x 7.875. Circ: 211,919 (paid and free).

MIDWEST ART FAIRS. see *ART*

MONTEREY MUSEUM OF ART NEWS. see *ART*

745.5 USA ISSN 0739-1544
NK4005
N C E C A JOURNAL. Text in English. 1980. a. price varies. charts; illus. **Document type:** *Magazine, Trade.* **Description:** Record of the annual conference proceedings.
Published by: National Council on Education for the Ceramic Arts, 77 Erie Village Sq, Ste 280, Erie, CO 80516-6996. TEL 303-828-2811, FAX 303-828-0911, http://www.nceca.net. Circ: 3,000.

745.5 USA
N C E C A NEWS. Text in English. 1977. q. membership. **Document type:** *Newsletter, Trade.* **Description:** Includes pertinent information about the annual conference, other NCECA activities, and member news.
Formerly (until 1986): N C E C A Newsletter (0739-1552)
Published by: National Council on Education for the Ceramic Arts, 77 Erie Village Sq, Ste 280, Erie, CO 80516-6996. TEL 303-828-2811, FAX 303-828-0911. Circ: 3,000.

745 RUS ISSN 0235-5051
HD8522
NARODNOE TVORCHESTVO. Text in Russian. 1937. bi-m. USD 49 foreign (effective 2003). adv.
Indexed: RASB.
—East View.
Published by: Ministerstvo Kul'tury Rossiiskoi Federatsii, Tsentr Russkogo Fol'klora/Ministy of Culture of the Russian Federation, Centre of Russian Folklore, Kropotkinskii per 10, Moscow, 119034, Russian Federation. TEL 7-095-2468417, FAX 7-095-2463389. Ed., Adv. contact Anatoli Kargin. page USD 300. Circ: 10,000. **Dist. by:** M K - Periodica, ul Gilyarovskogo 39, Moscow 129110, Russian Federation. TEL 7-095-2845008, FAX 7-095-2813798, info@periodicals.ru, http://www.mkniga.ru; **US dist. addr.:** East View Information Services, 3020 Harbor Ln. N., Minneapolis, MN 55447. TEL 612-550-0961. **Co-sponsor:** Ministerstvo Kul'tury Rossiiskoi Federatsii.

745.5 ZAF ISSN 1015-2369
NATIONAL CERAMICS QUARTERLY. Text in English. 1974. q. USD 20. adv. bk.rev. **Document type:** *Consumer.* **Description:** Brings the reader up-to-date on news from around the world, new technical developments, an in-depth look at ceramics in the home, the people who make them, as well as the firms that supply the necessary materials.
Supersedes (in 1984): Sgraffiti
Indexed: DAAI.
Published by: (Association of Potters of Southern Africa), Guassardo - National Ceramics, PO Box 568, Anerley, KwaZulu-Natal 4230, South Africa. TEL 27-39-6813216, FAX 27-39-6813216. Ed. Michael Guassardo. Circ: 2,000 (paid).

NEEDLEWORK. see *NEEDLEWORK*

745.5 USA
NETCRAFTS ONLINE MAGAZINE. Text in English. m. **Description:** Covers topics for the arts & crafts consumer and retailer.
Media: Online - full content.
Published by: Mill Hollow, P O Box 14351, Scottsdale, AZ 85267-4351. editor@netcrafts.com, info@netcrafts.com, http://www.netcrafts.com. Pub. Ms. Chris Wallace.

700 DEU ISSN 0723-2454
NK5100
NEUES GLAS/NEW GLASS; magazine on contemporary glass art. Text in English, German. 1980. q. EUR 36 domestic; EUR 38 in Europe; EUR 41 elsewhere; EUR 9 newsstand/cover (effective 2003). adv. back issues avail. **Document type:** *Magazine, Consumer.*
Indexed: ABM, ArtInd, DAAI, DIP, IBR, IBZ.
—BLDSC (6077.985500), IE, ingenta.
Published by: Ritterbach Verlag GmbH, Postfach 1820, Frechen, 50208, Germany. TEL 49-2234-18660, FAX 49-2234-186690, anzeigen@ritterbach.de, verlag@ritterbach.de, http://www.ritterbach.de. Ed. Uta Klotz. R&P Marie Luise Coeln TEL 49-2234-186632. Adv. contact Sonja Erdmann TEL 49-2234-186695. B&W page EUR 990, color page EUR 1,450. Circ: 5,500 (paid).

THE NEW BOOKBINDER; journal of designer bookbinders. see *PUBLISHING AND BOOK TRADE*

745.5 USA ISSN 0275-469X
NK5110
NEW GLASS REVIEW. Text in English. 1976. a. USD 11.50 per vol. domestic; USD 12 per vol. foreign (effective 2003). adv. illus. back issues avail.; reprint service avail. from PQC. **Document type:** *Journal, Trade.* **Description:** Compendium of contemporary glass made in previous calendar year.
Formerly (until 1979): Contemporary Glass; Supersedes (in 1978): Contemporary Glass Microfiche Program
Indexed: ABM, DAAI.
Published by: Corning Museum of Glass, One Museum Way, Corning, NY 14830-2253. TEL 607-937-5371, FAX 607-937-3352. Ed. Richard Price. R&P David Whitehouse TEL 607-974-8424. Adv. contact Stephanie Specchio TEL 607-974-8124.

NEW IDEA. see *HOME ECONOMICS*

680 NOR ISSN 0048-0592
NORSK HUSFLID. Text in Norwegian. 1965. 5/yr. NOK 273 domestic; NOK 373 elsewhere; NOK 52 per issue (effective 2002). adv.
Formerly (until 1966): Husflidsbladet (0333-0540)
Published by: Norges Husflidslag, Postboks 860, Sentrum, Oslo, 0104, Norway. TEL 47-22-00-87-00, FAX 47-22-00-87-50. Ed. Berit Solhaug TEL 47-22-00-87-25. Adv. contact Kari Loevland TEL 47-22-17-35-36. B&W page NOK 9,850, color page NOK 14,800; 185 x 260. Circ: 27,273.

745.5 CAN ISSN 1193-011X
NOVA SCOTIA CRAFT NEWS. Text in English. 1973. q. CND 57.50 (effective 1999). adv. bibl.; mkt.; stat.; tr.lit. back issues avail. **Document type:** *Newsletter, Trade.* **Description:** Newsletter of the non-profit, charitable organization which aims at communicating information to the crafts industry.
Former titles (until 1992): Nova Scotia Designer Crafts Council. Newsletter (0834-3829); (until 1986): N S D C C Newsletter (0834-3136); (until 1985): N S D C Newsletter (0709-0374)
Related titles: Diskette ed.; E-mail ed.; Online - full text ed.
Published by: Nova Scotia Designer Crafts Council, 1113 Marginal Rd, Halifax, NS B3H 4P7, Canada. TEL 902-423-3837, FAX 902-422-0881, office@nsdcc.ns.ca, http://www.nsdcc.ns.ca. Ed. Grace Butland. Pub. Susan Hanrahan. R&P, Adv. contact Bernard Burton. B&W page CND 230; trim 9 x 7. Circ: 500 (paid); 1,000 (controlled).

745.5 AUS ISSN 1038-1856
NB1100.2
➤ **OBJECT.** Text in English. 1964. q. AUD 34 domestic to individuals; USD 39, GBP 27 to individuals in US & Europe; USD 35 in Asia to individuals; NZD 49, AUD 40 to individuals in New Zealand & the Pacific; AUD 44 to institutions (effective 2002). adv. bk.rev. illus. back issues avail.; reprints avail. **Document type:** *Academic/Scholarly.* **Description:** Presents critical and theoretical writing on crafts-based art and design issues.
Formerly (until 1995): Crafts New South Wales (0726-6758)
Indexed: DAAI.
Published by: Centre for Contemporary Craft, 3rd Fl, Customs House, 31 Alfred St, Circular Quay, NSW 2000, Australia. TEL 61-2-92479126, FAX 61-2-92472641, object@object.com.au, http://www.object.com.au. Ed., R&P Ian Were. Adv. contact Nicole Berman. B&W page USD 440, color page USD 950; trim 210 x 275. Circ: 10,000.

745.5 ESP ISSN 1135-1152
OFICIO Y ARTE; noticias de artesania. Text in Spanish. 1992. bi-m. bk.rev. **Document type:** *Bulletin.* **Description:** Provides information on exhibitions, galleries, shops, fairs, museums, technical articles and more.
Published by: Organizacion de los Artesanos de Espana, Camino de la Iglesia 38, A Coruna, 15009, Spain. TEL 34-981-288104, FAX 34-981-133569, 34-981-133569, correo@oficioyarte.org. Ed. Manual Gonzalez Arias. Adv. contact Manuel Gonzalez Arias. Circ: 5,000.

745.5 CAN ISSN 0229-1320
ONTARIO CRAFT. Text in English. 1981. 4/yr. CND 53.50 membership (effective 2000); CND 7 newsstand/cover (effective 1998). adv. illus. reprints avail. **Document type:** *Consumer.*
Incorporates (1975-1996): Craftnews (0319-7832); Supersedes: Craftsman (0319-7840)
Related titles: Microfiche ed.: (from MML); Microfilm ed.: (from MML).
Indexed: ABM, CBCARef, CBPI, CPerl, DAAI.
Published by: Ontario Crafts Council, Designers Walk, 170 Bedford Rd, Ste 300, Toronto, ON M5R 2K9, Canada. TEL 416-925-4222, FAX 416-925-4223, katherin@brasch.com, hgttp://www.craft.on.ca. Ed. Anne McPherson. Adv. contact Susan Browne. B&W page CND 930; trim 11 x 8.13. Circ: 4,000.

ORIENTAL CERAMIC SOCIETY OF HONG KONG. BULLETIN. see *CERAMICS, GLASS AND POTTERY*

745.5 USA ISSN 0030-901X
PACK - O - FUN. Text in English. 1951. 6/yr. USD 21.97 domestic; USD 25.97 in Canada; USD 29.97 elsewhere (effective 2005). adv. illus. back issues avail.; reprints avail. **Document type:** *Magazine, Consumer.*
Related titles: Online - full text ed.
Published by: Clapper Communications Companies, 2400 E Devon Ave, Ste 375, Des Plaines, IL 60018-4618. TEL 847-635-5800, 800-444-0441, FAX 847-635-6311, packofun@palmcoastd.com, imueller@clapper.com, http://www.pack-o-fun.com, http://www.pack-o-fun.com. Ed. Billie Ciancio. Pub. Marie Clapper. Adv. contact John Dziewiatkowski. Circ: 102,000.

745.5 USA ISSN 1079-6819
PAINTING. Text in English. 1985. 6/yr. USD 23.95 domestic; USD 26.62 in Canada; USD 27.95 elsewhere (effective 2005); includes Source Guide. adv. bk.rev. back issues avail. **Document type:** *Magazine, Consumer.* **Description:** Directed toward those interested in learning, or increasing skills, in tole and decorative painting.
Former titles (until 1995): Decorative Arts Painting (1067-0068); (until 1993): Decorative Arts Digest (0888-076X)
Related titles: Online - full text ed.
—Ei.
Published by: Clapper Communications Companies, 2400 E Devon Ave, Ste 375, Des Plaines, IL 60018-4618. TEL 847-635-5800, 800-272-3871, FAX 847-635-6311, http://www.painting.com, http://www.craftnet.org/painting. Pub. Jeff Clapper. Adv. contact Bobbie Zych. Circ: 100,000 (paid).

745.5 USA ISSN 1077-5404
PAINTWORKS. Text in English. 1991. 9/yr. USD 28.97 domestic; USD 37.97 in Canada; USD 46.47 elsewhere (effective 2005). adv. **Document type:** *Magazine, Consumer.* **Description:** Features craft and decorative painting for painters and hobbyists.
Published by: All American Crafts, Inc., 7 Waterloo Rd, Stanhope, NJ 07874-2621. TEL 973-347-6900, FAX 973-347-6909, http://www.allamericancrafts.com. Ed. Linda Heller. Pub. Jerry Cohen. Adv. contacts Lee Jaworski TEL 973-383-8080 ext 114, Robert Becker. B&W page USD 900, color page USD 1,500; trim 10.5 x 7.88. Circ: 170,000.

▼ new title ➤ refereed ✶ unverified ♦ full entry avail.

745.5 USA
TT1
PAPER CRAFTS. Text in English. 1978. 8/yr. USD 15.97 domestic; USD 21.97 in Canada; USD 26.97 elsewhere (effective 2005). adv. bk.rev. illus. **Document type:** *Magazine, Consumer.* **Description:** Covers general handicrafts, including needlecrafts, tile painting, doll making, kids' crafts, and gift-giving crafts.
Formerly (until 2004): Crafts Magazine (0148-9127)
Related titles: Online - full content ed.; ♦ Special ed(s).: Last Minute Gifts.
Indexed: IHTDI, RASB.
—CCC.
Published by: Primedia Enthusiast Media (Subsidiary of: Primedia Consumer Media & Magazine Group), 260 Madison Ave, 8th Fl, New York, NY 10016. TEL 917-256-2267, FAX 917-256-2282, editor@papercraftsmag.com, information@primedia.com, http://www.papercraftsmag.com/, http://www.primedia.com. Ed. Stacey Groninger. Pub. Tony Golden. adv.: B&W page USD 7,580, color page USD 9,610; trim 10.5 x 7.88. Circ: 175,000 (paid). **Subscr. to:** PO Box 420494, Palm Coast, FL 32142-9524. TEL 800-727-2387, FAX 386-447-2321.

745.5 GBR
▼ **PAPERCRAFT INSPIRATIONS.** Text in English. 2004 (Sep.). m. GBP 3.35 newsstand/cover (effective 2004). adv. **Document type:** *Magazine, Consumer.* **Description:** Includes in-depth features, tips and step-by-step instructions on how to create paper crafts, cards and gifts.
Published by: Future Publishing Ltd., Beauford Court, 30 Monmouth St, Bath, Avon BA1 2BW, United Kingdom. TEL 44-1225-442244, FAX 44-1225-446019, customerservice@futurenet.co.uk, http://www.thefuturenetwork.plc.uk. Ed. Debora Bradley. Pub. Katherine Raderecht.

745.5 USA
PAPERKUTS POWER BOOK. Abbreviated title: P K Power Book. Text in English. 2001. a. USD 13.99 newsstand/cover (effective 2004).
Published by: Possibilities Publishing LLC, 232 W 540 N Holland Square, Orem, UT 84057. http://www.paperkuts.com.

745.5 028.5 USA ISSN 1531-3646
PAPERKUTS SCRAPBOOK MAGAZINE. Text in English. 2000. bi-m. USD 22.95 (effective 2003). adv. **Document type:** *Magazine, Consumer.*
Published by: Possibilities Publishing LLC, 232 W 540 N Holland Square, Orem, UT 84057. http://www.paperkuts.com. Ed. Angie Randall.

746 USA ISSN 1548-7385
TT740
PAPERWORKS; paper crafts with creative style. Text in English. 1986. bi-m. USD 19.97 domestic; USD 24.97 in Canada (effective 2005). adv. bk.rev.; software rev. charts; illus.; mkt. back issues avail. **Document type:** *Magazine, Consumer.* **Description:** Contains 20 to 30 patterns, offers designs in various crafts.
Former titles (until 2004): Creative Crafter (1541-762X); (until 2002): Quick & Easy Crafts (1048-3659); (until 1990): Women's Circle Country Needlecraft (0892-8223)
Published by: House of White Birches, 306 E Parr Rd, Berne, IN 46711. TEL 260-589-4000, FAX 260-589-8093, Customer_Service@whitebirches.com, http://www.paperworksmagazine.com, http://www.whitebirches.com. Ed. Vicki Blizzard. Pub. Beth Wheeler. Adv. contact John Boggs TEL 219-589-4000 ext 354. color page USD 2,400; trim 8.625 x 10.875. Circ: 175,700; 250,000 (paid).

745.5 DEU ISSN 1434-5080
PATCHWORK MAGAZIN. Text in German. 1996. bi-m. EUR 5.01 newsstand/cover (effective 2003). adv. **Document type:** *Magazine, Consumer.*
Published by: H C M Verlags GmbH, Im Buhles 4, Glashuetten-Schlossborn, 61479, Germany. TEL 49-6174-9669-0, FAX 49-6174-966999, patchwork-magazin@hcm-verlag.de, mailbox@hcm-verlag.de, http://www.hcm-verlag.de/patchwork-magazin. Ed. Gudula Reiser. Pub. Helmut Redecker. Adv. contact Karin Redecker. B&W page EUR 1,100, color page EUR 1,400. Circ: 26,200 (paid and controlled).

745.5 MEX
PEQUENA DIANA. Text in Spanish. 1984. m.
Address: LUCIO BLANCO 435, Col. Juan Tlihuaca, Mexico City, DF 02400, Mexico. TEL 5-352-6056. Ed. Javier Ortiz Camorlinga. Circ: 200,000.

PERISTIL. see *ARCHITECTURE*

745.5 USA ISSN 1052-9977
PICTURE FRAMING MAGAZINE. Text in English. 1990. m. USD 20 domestic; USD 40 in Canada & Mexico; USD 120 elsewhere (effective 2003). adv. back issues avail. **Document type:** *Magazine, Trade.* **Description:** For independent retailers, gallery owners, chain store buyers, wholesalers, manufacturers and designers of frames and related framing supplies. Editorial emphasis is on education and technique in custom framing.
Related titles: Online - full text ed.
Published by: Hobby Publications, Inc., 207 Commercial Ct., PO Box 102, Morganville, NJ 07751-0102. TEL 732-536-5160, FAX 732-536-5761, pfm@hobbypub.com, http://www.pictureframingmagazinee.com. Eds. Anne Vazquez, Laura Caiaccia. Pub., Adv. contact Bruce Gherman. Circ: 27,632.

PIECEWORK; all this by hand. see *NEEDLEWORK*

745.5 ITA ISSN 1121-8509
PITTURA SU TESSUTO E SETA. Text in Italian. 1986. q. EUR 14.28 (effective 2004). **Document type:** *Magazine, Consumer.*
Published by: Alexandra Editrice, Largo Lanciani 1, Roma, 00162, Italy. TEL 39-06-86320393, FAX 39-06-86320481, alexandra@alexandra.it, http://www.alexandra.it.

PLASTIC CANVAS! MAGAZINE. see *NEEDLEWORK*

745.5 GBR ISSN 0144-2937
POPULAR CRAFTS. Text in English. 1974. m. GBP 28.50 domestic; GBP 37.50 in Europe; GBP 39.50 in United States; GBP 43 elsewhere (effective 2004). adv. bk.rev. illus. index. back issues avail. **Document type:** *Magazine, Consumer.* **Description:** Offers advice and projects for arts and crafts enthusiasts, embracing every area of traditional and contemporary handicrafts.
Incorporates: Gem Craft (0140-5977)
—BLDSC (6550.325000), IE, ingenta.
Published by: Highbury Leisure Publishing Ltd (Subsidiary of: Highbury House Communications PLC), Berwick House, 8-10 Knoll Rise, Orpington, Kent BR6 0EL, United Kingdom. TEL 44-1689-887200, FAX 44-1689-886666, info@nexusmedia.com, http://www.popularcrafts.com, http://www.hhc.co.uk/. Ed. Debbie Moss TEL 44-1322-660070 ext 2421. Adv. contact Nikki Drew TEL 44-1322-660070 ext 2425. B&W page GBP 570, color page GBP 820; trim 230 x 300. **Subscr. in US to:** Wise Owl Worldwide Publications, 5674 El Camino Real., Ste. D, Carlsbad, CA 92008-7130. TEL 310-375-6258.

745.5 GBR ISSN 0969-6946
POPULAR PATCHWORK; patchwork - quilting - applique - patterns - designs - ideas. Text in English. 1993. 8/yr. GBP 22.80 domestic; GBP 28.64 in Europe; USD 57 in United States; GBP 35.84 elsewhere; GBP 2.85 newsstand/cover. illus. back issues avail. **Document type:** *Consumer.* **Description:** Offers clear instruction for patchwork quilt projects for beginners and experts alike.
Published by: Nexus Media Ltd. (Subsidiary of: Highbury House Communications PLC), Nexus House, Azalea Dr, Swanley, Kent BR8 8HU, United Kingdom. TEL 44-1322-660070, FAX 44-1322-667633. Ed. Brenda Ross. Pub. Tony Debell. **Subscr. in US to:** Wise Owl Worldwide Publications, 5674 El Camino Real., Ste. D, Carlsbad, CA 92008-7130. TEL 310-375-6258; **Subscr. to:** Nexus Subscription Services, Tower House, Sovereign Park, Lathkill St, Market Harborough, Leics LE16 9EF, United Kingdom. TEL 44-1858-435344. **Dist. by:** Comag, Tavistock Works, Tavistock Rd, W Drayton, Middx UB7 7QX, United Kingdom. TEL 44-1895-444055, FAX 44-1895-433602.

745.5 USA
POTPOURRI SIMPLE & EASY UPDATE. Text in English. 1992. a. looseleaf. USD 5 (effective 2001). **Document type:** *Newsletter.* **Description:** Offers potpourri recipes.
Published by: Prosperity & Profits Unlimited Distribution Services, PO Box 416, Denver, CO 80201-0416. TEL 303-575-5676, FAX 970-292-2136, mail@curriculumresourceonline.com, http://www.telemarketingscripts.20m.com/. Ed. A Doyle. Circ: 3,200 (paid).

745.5 AUS ISSN 0048-4954
POTTERY IN AUSTRALIA. Text in English. 1962. q. AUD 58 domestic; AUD 71 in New Zealand (effective 2005). adv. bk.rev. illus. cum.index: 1962-1997. reprints avail. **Document type:** *Magazine, Academic/Scholarly.* **Description:** Showcases the best of Australian ceramics and includes exhibition reviews, artists profiles, technical information and news of competition and events.
Indexed: ABM, DAAI, GdIns, Pinpoint.
—BLDSC (6566.100000), IE, ingenta.
Published by: Potters' Society of Australia, PO Box 105, Erskineville, NSW 2043 , Australia. TEL 1300-720124, FAX 61-2-95173690, mail@australianceramics.com, society@potteryinaustralia.com, http://www.australianceramics.com/MAG/index_mag.html, http://www.potteryinaustralia.com/PS/index_ab.html. Ed. Suzanne Buckle. Adv. contact Christina Fitzgerald. Circ: 5,000.

745.5 GBR
PRACTICAL CRAFTS; making things better. Text in English. 1993. m. GBP 35.40 domestic; GBP 42.40 in Europe; USD 64 in United States; GBP 55.40 elsewhere; GBP 2.95 newsstand/cover; USD 6.25 newsstand/cover in United States (effective 2005). adv. **Document type:** *Magazine, Consumer.* **Description:** Filled with creative and stimulating ideas and tips for a wide variety of crafting projects.
Formerly: Practical Craft (1350-1151)
Published by: Traplet Publications Ltd, Traplet House, Severn Dr, Upton-upon-Severn, Worcs WR8 0JL, United Kingdom. TEL 44-1684-588500, FAX 44-1684-578558, practicalcraft@traplet.com, customerservice@traplet.com, http://www.traplet.com. Ed. Michelle Powell. Adv. contact Alice Padley TEL 44-1684-595348.

748 666.1 USA ISSN 1543-5717
PROFITABLE GLASS QUARTERLY. Text in English. 1998. q. USD 29 (effective 2003). adv.
Related titles: CD-ROM ed.: ISSN 1543-5709.
Published by: Glass Patterns Quarterly, Inc., 8300 Hidden Valley Rd, Box 69, Westport, KY 40077. TEL 502-222-5631, 800-719-0769, FAX 502-222-4527, info@glasspatterns.com, http://www.glasspatterns.com. Pub. Steven James. R&P Maureen James. Adv. contact Sarah Smith TEL 502-222-5631.

QUEENSLAND BOOKBINDERS' GUILD. NEWSLETTER. see *PUBLISHING AND BOOK TRADE*

QUICK & EASY PLASTIC CANVAS. see *NEEDLEWORK*

QUILTS JAPAN. see *NEEDLEWORK*

745.5 738.1 GBR ISSN 0953-0436
REAL POTTERY; a review of craft pottery. Text in English. 1954. irreg. (approx. a.). GBP 10. adv. bk.rev. illus. index. reprint service avail. from PQC.
Former titles: Pottery Quarterly (0032-5678); Real Pottery
Related titles: Microfilm ed.: (from PQC).
Indexed: BrCerAb.
Address: Northfields Studio, Northfields, Tring, Herts HP23 5QW, United Kingdom. TEL 01442-85229. Ed. M Fieldhouse. Circ: 2,500.

RECIPE GREETINGS UPDATE. see *HOME ECONOMICS*

683 DEU ISSN 0934-411X
ROLLADEN & SONNENSCHUTZ; Fachzeitschrift fuer das Rolladen- und Jalousiebauer-Handwerk. Variant title: R S Rolladen Sonnenschutz. Text in German. 1961. 10/yr. EUR 54 domestic; EUR 72 in Europe; EUR 82 elsewhere (effective 2005). adv. bk.rev. pat. **Document type:** *Magazine, Trade.* **Description:** Covers the shutter and sunscreen industry, with marquees, shades, blinds, awnings, security shutters. Includes list of advertisers.
Published by: Bundesverband Rolladen & Sonnenschutz e.V., Hopmannstr 2, Bonn, 53177, Germany. TEL 49-228-952100, FAX 49-228-328099, info@bv-rolladen.de, http://www.bv-rolladen.de. Ed., R&P Hans Stoffels. Adv. contact Hannelore Prevot. B&W page EUR 536; trim 185 x 260. Circ: 1,750 (paid).

745.5 IND ISSN 0035-8215
N8
ROOPA - LEKHA; an illustrated journal of Indian arts and crafts. Text in English. 1929. s-a. USD 20. adv. bk.rev. illus.
Indexed: AIAP, BAS.
Published by: All-India Fine Arts and Crafts Society, Rafi Marg, New Delhi, 110 001, India. Ed. S S Bhagat. Circ: 1,000.

730 USA ISSN 0746-7672
RUBBERSTAMPMADNESS. Text in English. 1980. bi-m. USD 24.95 domestic; USD 30 foreign (effective 2002). adv. bk.rev.; video rev.; Website rev. illus. 132 p./no.; back issues avail. **Document type:** *Magazine, Consumer.* **Description:** Devoted to the creative use of artistic rubber stamps. Includes stories on artists using stamps and provides techniques on ways to use rubber stamps to make cards, jewelry, and different art works.
Published by: Rubberstampmadness, Inc., 610, Corvallis, OR 97339-0610. TEL 541-752-0075, FAX 541-752-5475, rsm@rsmadness.com, http://www.rsmadness.com. Ed., R&P Roberta Sperling TEL 541-752-0075. Pub. Michael Malan. Adv. contact Don Nelson TEL 877-782-6762. B&W page USD 1,270, color page USD 1,555; trim 11 x 8.5. Circ: 8,000 (paid); 16,000 (controlled).

790.13 700 745.5 USA
S A C NEWSMONTHLY; national news and listings of art & craft shows. (Southern Art and Crafts) Text in English. 1986. m. USD 24 print edition only; USD 36 print and online editions (effective 2002). adv. bk.rev. 64 p./no. 4 cols./p.; back issues avail. **Document type:** *Newsletter.* **Description:** Lists art and crafts shows and festivals nationwide. Includes details on place, time, deadlines, and fees involved.
Incorporates: Art and Crafts Catalyst; Former titles: National Arts and Crafts Network; National Calendar of Open Competitive Exhibitions; Lisa's Report; Craft Show Bulletin
Related titles: Online - full text ed.
Published by: S A C, Inc, PO Box 159, Bogalusa, LA 70429-0159. TEL 504-732-5616, 800-825-3722, FAX 504-732-3744, info@SACNewsmonthly.com, http://www.SACNewsmonthly.com. Ed., Pub., R&P Wayne Smith. Adv. contact Sue Martin. page USD 390; 13 x 10. Circ: 4,000.

700   AUS   ISSN 0819-2936
S.A. CRAFTS. (South Australia) Text in English. 1985. q. USD 65. adv. bk.rev. back issues avail. **Description:** Focuses on Cratsouth projects, national and state crafts news. Provides current information on funding opportunities, workshops, exhibitions, and festivals.
Formerly (until June 1986): S.A. Crafts News (0814-9933)
Published by: Craftsouth, Centre for Contemporary Craft & Design Inc., PO Box 8067, Station Arcade, SA 5000, Australia. TEL 61-8-84101822, FAX 61-8-82320004. Ed., Pub., R&P, Adv. contact Jane Andrew. Circ: 500.

700 746   USA
S A G A NEWS. Variant title: SagaNews. Text in English. 1979. q. USD 28 domestic membership; USD 32 foreign membership. bk.rev. **Document type:** *Newsletter.*
Formerly (until Jan. 1988): Smocking Arts
Published by: Smocking Arts Guild of America, 1926 Waukegan Rd, Glenview, IL 60025-1770. TEL 847-657-6804, FAX 847-657-6819. R&P Patricia Sistler. Circ: 4,000 (paid).

745.5 669   USA
S N A G NEWSLETTER. Text in English. 5/yr. USD 69 in North America membership; USD 85 elsewhere membership (effective 2005). **Document type:** *Newsletter, Trade.*
Description: Features information on exhibitions, workshops, conferences, and job opportunities throughout North America.
Published by: Society of North American Goldsmiths, 1300 Iroquois Ave, Ste 160, Naperville, Du Page, IL 60563-6614. TEL 630-778-6385, FAX 630-416-3333, nanman@earthlink.net, info@snagmetalsmith.org, http://www.snagmetalsmith.org/infocentral/newsletter.asp.

745.5   USA   ISSN 0748-8378
S P A C E S; notes on America's folk art environments. Text in English. 1982. irreg. USD 15 to individuals; USD 25 to institutions (effective 2001). bk.rev.; film rev. bibl.; illus. back issues avail. **Document type:** *Newsletter.*
Published by: Saving and Preserving Art and Cultural Environments, 1804 N Van Ness, Los Angeles, CA 90028. TEL 323-463-1629. Ed. Seymour Rosen. Circ: 1,000.

745.5   USA
SCENTERPIECE UPDATE. Text in English. 1990. a. looseleaf. USD 5 (effective 2000). 4 p./no.; **Document type:** *Newsletter.*
Description: Contains potpourri recipes and explains the origins of various fragrances.
Published by: Continnuus, c/o Prosperity & Profits Unlimited Distribution Services, P O Box 416, Denver, CO 80201-0416. TEL 303-575-5676. Ed. A C Doyle TEL 303-575-5676. R&P A C Doyle.

SCHOOL ARTS; the art education magazine for teachers. see *EDUCATION—Teaching Methods And Curriculum*

SCOTTISH HOME AND COUNTRY. see *WOMEN'S INTERESTS*

745.5   GBR   ISSN 0144-1302
SCOTTISH POTTERY HISTORICAL REVIEW. Text in English. 1980. a. adv. bk.rev.
Published by: Scottish Pottery Society, c/o Mr. Graeme Cruickshank, 21 Warrender Park Terr, Edinburgh, United Kingdom. Circ: 300.

745.5   USA   ISSN 1545-6315
SCRAP & STAMP ARTS. Text in English. 1999. 8/yr. USD 29.90 domestic; USD 37.90 foreign (effective 2005). adv. illus.
Document type: *Magazine, Consumer.* **Description:** Explores and explains various arts and crafts projects using stamp pads.
Formerly (until 2003): Stamping Arts & Crafts (1525-3775)
Published by: Scott Publications, 30595 Eight Mile, Livonia, MI 48152-1798. TEL 248-477-6650, 800-458-8237, FAX 248-477-6795, contactus@scottpublications.com, http://www.scottpublications.com. Ed. Joy Moss. Adv. contact Jane Adams.

745.5   USA
SCRAP BITS. Text in English. q. USD 19.95 (effective 2002). **Description:** Publishes ideas and instructions for paper piecing crafts.
Published by: Mill Hollow, P O Box 14351, Scottsdale, AZ 85267-4351. bits@scrapeasy.com, info@scrapeasy.com, http://www.scrapeasy.com. Pub. Ms. Chris Wallace.

745.5   USA   ISSN 1532-5091
SCROLL SAW WORKSHOP; the how-to magazine for scrollers. Text in English. 1999. 4/yr. USD 19.95 (effective 2005). adv. back issues avail. **Document type:** *Magazine, Consumer.*
Description: Promotes scrolling as an art form and enjoyable pasttime while inspiring creativity and building skills.
Published by: Fox Chapel Publishing Company, 1970 Broad St, East Petersburg, PA 17520. TEL 717-560-4703, FAX 717-560-4702, editors@scrollsawer.com, comments@carvingworld.com, http://www.scrollsawer.com, http://www.carvingworld.com. Ed. Cathy Hart. Pub., R&P Alan Giagnocavo. Adv. contact Barbara Zercher. B&W page USD 900, color page USD 1,100. Circ: 23,000 (paid).

745.5 749   RUS
SEL'SKAYA ZHIZN'. Text in Russian. 1918. s-w. USD 245 in United States.

Related titles: Microfilm ed.: (from EVP).
Indexed: RASB.
Address: Ul Pravdy 24, A-ya 137, GSP, Moscow, 125869, Russian Federation. TEL 7-095-2575151, 7-095-2575353, FAX 7-095-2575839. Eds. M V Sharov, Sh Kagermanov. Circ: 102,000. **US dist. addr.:** East View Information Services, 3020 Harbor Ln. N., Minneapolis, MN 55447. TEL 612-550-0961.

738 748   FRA   ISSN 1169-2537
SEVRES. Summaries in English. 1955. q. adv. bk.rev. back issues avail.
Formerly: Cahiers de la Ceramique, du Verre et des Arts du Feu (0007-9790)
Indexed: BHA.
Published by: (Societe des Amis du Musee National de Ceramique), Editions des Cahiers de la Ceramique, B.P. 5, Paris, Cedex 12 75562, France. Ed. Bernard Pernes.

745.5   CHN   ISSN 1005-071X
SHANGHAI GONGYI MEISHU/SHANGHAI ARTS & CRAFTS. Text in Chinese. 1984. q. CNY 32 (effective 2004). **Document type:** *Journal, Academic/Scholarly.*
Published by: Shanghai Gongyi Meishu Zhonggongsi, 190, Nanjin Xilu, Shanghai, 200003, China. TEL 86-21-63272623, FAX 86-21-63272908, sharts@public.sta.net.cn, http://www.setways.com. **Dist. by:** China International Book Trading Corp, 35 Chegongzhuang Xilu, Haidian District, PO Box 399, Beijing 100044, China. TEL 86-10-68412045, FAX 86-10-68412023, cibtc@mail.cibtc.com.cn, http://www.cibtc.com.cn.

745.5   USA
SHOW WEST MAGAZINE. Text in English. USD 29.95 domestic; USD 5 newsstand/cover domestic (effective 2001). **Document type:** *Magazine, Trade.* **Description:** Provides information and reviews of arts and crafts shows in Arizona, California, Colorado, Nevada, New Mexico and Utah.
Published by: Show West, P O Box 6278, Phoenix, AZ 85005-6278. TEL 623-873-3350, showwest@showwestmag.com, http://www.showwestmag.com.

SIMPLY CROSS STITCH. see *NEEDLEWORK*

372.55   DNK   ISSN 0106-9608
SLOEJD. Text in Danish. 1978. 6/yr. DKK 380 (effective 2004). adv. bk.rev. back issues avail.
Formed by the merger of (1919-1978): Sloejdbladet (0108-4070); (1919-1978): Dansk Skolesloejd (0108-4062)
Published by: Danmarks Sloejdlaererforening, c/o Henning Birk Andersen, Appenaes Bygade 33, Naestved, 4700, Denmark. TEL 45-55-776760, FAX 45-55-776783, henning.andersen@skolekom.dk, http://www.slojd.dk. Ed. Soeren Moeller TEL 45-98-921345. Adv. contact Poul Steen Rasmussen TEL 45-75-653396.

745 746   SWE   ISSN 0346-0509
SLOEJDFORUM. Text in Swedish. 1973. 6/yr. SEK 240 (effective 2003). adv. 50 p./no. 2 cols./p.; **Document type:** *Magazine, Consumer.*
Formed by the merger of (1921-1973): Svensk Sloejdtidning (0039-6710); Sloejdlaeraren
Related titles: Online - full text ed.
Published by: Laerarfoerbundet, Tidningsafdelning, Segelbaatsvaegen 15, Box 12229, Stockholm, 10226, Sweden. TEL 46-8-7376500, FAX 46-8-7376569, kansli@lararforbundet.se, http://www.slojdforum.net/default.asp, http://www.lararforbundet.se. Ed. Hasse Hedstroem. Adv. contact Lisen Skeppstedt. B&W page SEK 6,500, color page SEK 9,750; trim 182 x 266. Circ: 7,100.

745.5922   USA   ISSN 1096-5254
SOFT DOLLS & ANIMALS. Text in English. bi-m. USD 26.95 domestic; USD 32.95 foreign (effective 2004). adv. illus.
Document type: *Magazine, Consumer.* **Description:** Contains full details on how professionals create cloth dolls and animals. Provides ideas and possible projects.
Published by: Scott Publications, 30595 Eight Mile, Livonia, MI 48152-1798. TEL 248-477-6650, 800-458-8237, FAX 248-477-6795, contactus@scottpublications.com, http://softdollsandanimals.com, http://www.scottpublications.com. Ed. Barbara Campbell. Pub. Robert Keessen. Adv. contacts Cathy Schnoes, Mary Grayson.

745.5   AUS
SOFT TOYS. Text in English. q. USD 25. **Document type:** *Consumer.* **Description:** Contains craft projects, patterns and tips.
Published by: Express Publications Pty. Ltd., 2 Stanley St, Locked Bag 111, Silverwater, NSW 2128, Australia. TEL 61-2-97480599, 800-801-647, FAX 61-2-97481956, subs@magstore.com.au, http://www.magstore.com.au/. **Dist. by:** Quilters' Resource Inc., PO Box 148850, Chicago, IL 60614-8850. TEL 773-278-5695.

745.5   USA   ISSN 1096-5823
SOMERSET STUDIO; paper arts, art stamping, letter arts. Text in English. 1997. bi-m. USD 25.95; USD 39.95 in Canada; USD 64.95 foreign; USD 5.95 newsstand/cover (effective 2001). adv. bk.rev.; video rev. index. back issues avail. **Description:** For paper artists, book artists, stampers, stencilers and calligraphers. Intends to elevate these crafts to the level of an artform. Audience is 99 percent female, including professional and amateur artists.
Published by: Stampington & Company, LLC, 22992 Mill Creek, Ste B, Laguna Hills, CA 92653. TEL 949-380-7318, 877-782-6737, FAX 949-380-9355, sompublisher@aol.com, somerseted@aol.com, http://www.somersetstudio.com. Ed. Sharilyn Miller. Pub., R&P Kellene Giloff. Adv. contact Lesley Ann Hamilton. Circ: 50,000.

745.5   USA   ISSN 0198-8239
TT847
SPIN-OFF; the magazine for handspinners. Text in English. 1977. 4/yr. USD 24 domestic; USD 31 foreign; USD 6.99 newsstand/cover (effective 2005). adv. bk.rev. illus. reprints avail. **Document type:** *Magazine, Consumer.* **Description:** Offers new ideas, approaches and special projects to the hand spinner.
Indexed: IHTDI.
Published by: Interweave Press, Inc., 201 E Fourth St, Loveland, CO 80537. TEL 970-669-7672, 800-272-2193, FAX 970-667-8317, spinoff@interweave.com, customerservice@interweave.com, http://www.interweave.com. Ed. Amy C. Clarke. Pub. Marilyn Murphy. Adv. contact Vicki Yost. Circ: 18,000.

SPINCRAFT PATTERN NEWSLETTER; the handspinner's craft pattern newsletter. see *NEEDLEWORK*

745.5   USA   ISSN 1067-8867
NK5300
STAINED GLASS; devoted to the craft of architectural stained and decorative art glass. Text in English. 1906. q. USD 36 domestic; USD 44 in Canada & Mexico; USD 50 elsewhere (effective 2006). adv. bk.rev. bibl.; illus. cum.index: 1906-1987. back issues avail.; reprints avail. **Document type:** *Magazine, Trade.* **Description:** Preserves the techniques of the past and illustrates the trends of the future in stained glass crafts. For hobbyists, professional artists, interior decorators, architects, and restoration specialists.
Former titles (until 1990): Stained Glass Quarterly (0895-7002); (until 1986): Stained Glass (0038-9161)
Related titles: Microfiche ed.; Microfilm ed.; Online - full text ed.: (from H.W. Wilson, O C L C Online Computer Library Center, Inc.)
Indexed: AIAP, ASCA, ArtInd, BHA, DAAI, DIP, IBR, IBZ. —BLDSC (8430.013000), IE, ingenta.
Published by: Stained Glass Association of America, 10009 E 62nd St, Raytown, MO 64133. TEL 816-737-2090, 800-438-9581, FAX 816-737-2801, sgmagaz@kcnet.com, http://www.stainedglass.org. Ed. Richard Gross. R&P, Adv. contact Katei Gross. Circ: 3,000.

745.5   USA
STAMP IT!. Text in English. 2002. 2/yr. USD 4.99 newsstand/cover domestic; USD 5.99 newsstand/cover in Canada (effective 2003); Not avail. by subscr.; newsstand only. **Document type:** *Magazine, Consumer.* **Description:** Contains information on rubber stamping for the creative craft maker.
Published by: Primedia Enthusiast Media (Subsidiary of: Primedia Consumer Media & Magazine Group), 741 Corporaate Cir., Golden, CO 80401. TEL 303-277-0370, FAX 303-278-1010, stampit@primediasi.com, http://primedia.com. Ed. Tracy White.

745.5   AUS
STAMPING AND PAPERCRAFT. Text in English. bi-m. AUD 53.70 for 2 yrs.; AUD 7.95 newsstand/cover (effective 2001). **Document type:** *Magazine, Consumer.* **Description:** Contains articles and information on creative rubber stamp making, arts, and related topics.
Published by: Express Publications Pty. Ltd., 2 Stanley St, Locked Bag 111, Silverwater, NSW 2128, Australia. TEL 61-2-97480599, 800-801-647, FAX 61-2-97481956, subs@magstore.com.au, http://www.magstore.com.au/.

THE STEP-BY-STEP ART COURSE. see *ART*

STITCHER'S WORLD. see *NEEDLEWORK*

745.5   IRL
STOPRESS. Text in English. 1992. 10/yr. looseleaf. EUR 35 (effective 2005). back issues avail. **Document type:** *Newsletter, Consumer.*
Formerly: Crafts Council. Newsletter
Published by: Crafts Council of Ireland, Castle Yard, Kilkenny, Ireland. TEL 353-56-7761804, FAX 353-56-7763754, info@ccoi.ie, http://www.ccoi.ie/publications/index.html. Circ: 1,500.

391.7   USA
STRINGING. Text in English. q. USD 7.99 newsstand/cover domestic; USD 9.99 newsstand/cover in Canada (effective 2005).

Published by: Interweave Press, Inc., 201 E Fourth St, Loveland, CO 80537. TEL 970-669-7672, 800-272-2193, FAX 970-667-8317, customerservice@interweave.com, http://www.interweave.com. Ed. Jamie Hogsett.

745.5 USA ISSN 0091-6641
NK3700
STUDIO POTTER. Text in English. 1972. s-a. USD 30 domestic; USD 33 in Canada; USD 35 elsewhere (effective 2004). bk.rev. illus. cum.index in vol.5. back issues avail.; reprints avail. **Document type:** *Magazine, Trade.* **Description:** Devoted to the interests of working potters and ceramic artists, covering technology, aesthetics, history, and biography. Each issue explores a single theme.
Related titles: Online - full text ed.: (from H.W. Wilson, O C L C Online Computer Library Center, Inc.).
Indexed: ABM, ArtInd, BAS, DAAI.
—BLDSC (8500.628600), IE, ingenta.
Address: PO Box 70, Goffstown, NH 03045. TEL 603-774-3582, FAX 603-774-6313, http://www.studiopotter.org/. Ed. Gerry Williams. Circ: 6,000.

STYLE 1900; the quarterly journal of the arts and crafts movement. see *ANTIQUES*

SYMPOSIUM ON THE ART OF SCIENTIFIC GLASSBLOWING. PROCEEDINGS. see *CERAMICS, GLASS AND POTTERY*

745.5 FIN ISSN 1235-6875
TAITO. Text in Finnish. 1907. 6/yr. EUR 45 domestic; EUR 61 in Europe; EUR 65 elsewhere (effective 2005). adv. **Document type:** *Magazine, Consumer.* **Description:** Contains articles on Finnish handicrafts, events, interviews, and gives instruction on patterns and models for weaving, knitting, woodwork and other related handicrafts.
Former titles (until 1991): Kotiteollisuus (0355-7421); (until 1935): Lastu ja Lanka
Published by: Kasi- ja Taideteollisuusliitto/Finnish Crafts Organization, Kalevankatu 61, PO Box 186, Helsinki, 00181, Finland. TEL 358-9-75191900, FAX 358-9-75191950, ktl@taitogroup.fi, http://www.taitogroup.fi. Ed. Marketta Luutonen TEL 358-9-75191975. Pub. Stellatum Oy. Adv. contact Paula Niemela TEL 358-9-682-3600. Circ: 8,000 (controlled). **Subscr.to:** Laserma, Kuoppmaaent 3A, Tampere 33800, Finland. TEL 358-3-225-1948.

TEDDY TODAY. see *HOBBIES*

TEXTILE FIBRE FORUM; the fibre magazine of the Australian region. see *TEXTILE INDUSTRIES AND FABRICS*

TEXTILE FORUM (DEUTSCHE AUSGABE). see *TEXTILE INDUSTRIES AND FABRICS*

THE TEXTILE MUSEUM JOURNAL. see *TEXTILE INDUSTRIES AND FABRICS*

745.5 SWE ISSN 1652-3687
▼ **TIDSKRIFTEN SVENSKT KONSTHANTVERK.** Variant title: Svenskt Konsthantverk. Text in Swedish. 2004. q. SEK 290; SEK 65 per issue (effective 2005). adv. **Document type:** *Magazine.*
Related titles: Online - full text ed.
Address: Svinningevaegen 100, Aakersberga, 18494, Sweden. TEL 46-8-54027920, info@svensktkonsthantverk.se, http://www.svensktkonsthantverk.se. Ed. Peter Oehlen. Adv. contact Leslie Spenner TEL 46-42-147040. Circ: 8,000.

745.5 USA ISSN 0199-4514
TOLE WORLD; creative ideas for decorative painting. Text in English. 1977. bi-m. USD 19.97 (effective 2005). adv. back issues avail. **Document type:** *Magazine, Consumer.* **Description:** Features painting projects for decorative artists, emphasizing projects for intermediate painters on a variety of mediums. Includes columns on technique and new products.
Related titles: Online - full text ed.
Indexed: IHTDI.
Published by: E G W Publishing Co., 1041 Shary Circle, Concord, CA 94518. TEL 925-671-9852, 800-777-1164, FAX 925-671-0692, editor@toleworld.com, http://www.toleworld.com. Eds. Sandy Yarmolich, Judy Swager. Adv. contact Rickie Wilson. B&W page USD 2,097, color page USD 2,726; trim 8 x 10.5. Circ: 90,000 (paid).

745.5 GBR ISSN 0951-6751
TORQUAY POTTERY COLLECTORS SOCIETY. MAGAZINE. Text in English. 1976. q. GBP 12. adv. bk.rev. illus. **Document type:** *Newsletter.* **Description:** History of the potteries that operated in South Devon, England from 1870 to 1970.
Formerly: Torquay Pottery Collectors Society. Newsletter (0143-5590)
Published by: Torquay Pottery Collectors Society, c/o Virginia Brisco, Ed, 218 Sandridge Rd, St Albans, Herts AL1 4AL, United Kingdom. tpcs@macatala.demon.co.uk, lornadance@hotmail.com. Circ: 1,100.

THE TRUMPETER. see *THEATER*

745 398 POL ISSN 0860-4126
TWORCZOSC LUDOWA. Text in Polish. 1986. q. USD 10. bk.rev. bibl.; illus. **Description:** Covers folk art and folk culture.
Published by: Stowarzyszenie Tworcow Ludowych, Zarzad Glowny, Ul Grodzka 14, Lublin, 20112, Poland. TEL 48-81-24974.

VAEVMAGASINET; Scandinavian weaving magazine. see *NEEDLEWORK*

745.5 SWE ISSN 1652-3415
▼ **VENUE**; arena foer graensloes design. Text in Swedish. 2004. 3/yr. SEK 100 (effective 2005). adv. **Document type:** *Magazine, Consumer.* **Description:** Focus on all areas of design.
Address: c/o Community, Gustav Adolfs Torg 10B, Malmoe, 21139, Sweden. info@venuemagazine.se, http://www.venuemagazine.se/, http://www/venuemagazine.se. Ed. Christel Brost. Adv. contact Mija Carlsson TEL 46-702-582498.

VESTERHEIM ROSEMALING LETTER. see *ART*

745.5 ROM
VIATA C M. Text in Romanian. 1953. m.
Formerly (until 1991): Viata Cooperatiei Mestesugaresti
Address: Calea Plevnei 46, Bucharest, Romania. Ed. Marin Petre. Circ: 65,000.

VICTORIAN CHRISTMAS. see *NEEDLEWORK*

VISUAL ARTS NEWS. see *ART*

745.5 NLD ISSN 0927-748X
VORMEN UIT VUUR. Text in Dutch. 1953. q. EUR 39 to individuals; EUR 57 to institutions; EUR 23 to students (effective 2005). adv. bk.rev. cum.index. back issues avail. **Document type:** *Bulletin, Academic/Scholarly.* **Description:** Covers all types of glass and ceramics, from all periods.
Former titles (until 1992): Nederlandse Vereniging van Vrienden van de Ceramiek. Mededelingen (0920-1009); (until 1979): Vrienden van de Nederlandse Ceramiek. Mededelingenblad (0165-814X); Vereniging van Vrienden van de Nederlandse Ceramiek. Mededelingenblad (0042-3858)
Indexed: BHA.
Published by: Nederlandse Vereniging van Vrienden van Ceramiek en Glas/Dutch Society of Friends of Ceramics and Glass, Postbus 15757, Amsterdam, 1001 NG, Netherlands. http://www.vormenuitvuur.nl/. Ed. Christien Smits. Circ: 700.

WHO'S WHO IN ART MATERIALS. see *ART*

745.5 DEU
WINDOW COLOR; Gestalten und Dekorieren mit abziehbaren Fensterfarben. Text in German. q. EUR 1.90 newsstand/cover (effective 2003). adv. **Document type:** *Magazine, Consumer.*
Published by: OZ Verlag GmbH, Roemerstr 90, Rheinfelden, 79618, Germany. TEL 49-7623-964-0, FAX 49-7623-96464200, vollmar@oz-bpv.de, http://www.oz-verlag.com. adv.: B&W page EUR 4,200, color page EUR 5,400; trim 210 x 280. Circ: 118,000 (paid and controlled).

745.56 USA
THE WIRE WORKER; making wire jewelry the easy way. Text in English. bi-m. free to qualified personnel (effective 2003). **Document type:** *Academic/Scholarly.* **Description:** Dedicated to anyone who would like to learn the ancient method of making handcrafted wire jewelry.
Media: Online - full text.
Published by: Wire Worker preuther@wire-sculpture.com, http://www.wire-sculpture.com/, http://www.wire-sculpure.com. Pub. Preston J Reuther.

745.5 USA ISSN 1096-2816
TT199.7
WOOD CARVING ILLUSTRATED; every carver's how-to magazine. Text in English. 1997. 4/yr. USD 19.95 (effective 2004). adv. illus. back issues avail. **Document type:** *Magazine, Consumer.* **Description:** Covers everything from realistic carving to abstract wood sculpture. Step-by-step articles offer a series of photos and text that illustrate projects.
Published by: Fox Chapel Publishing Company, 1970 Broad St, East Petersburg, PA 17520. TEL 717-560-4703, FAX 717-560-4702, editors@carvingworld.com, comments@carvingworld.com, http://www.carvingworld.com. Ed. Cathy Hart. Pub., R&P Alan Giagnocavo. Adv. contact Barbara Zercher. B&W page USD 900, color page USD 1,100. Circ: 39,000 (paid).

WOOD STROKES & WOODCRAFTS. see *BUILDING AND CONSTRUCTION—Carpentry And Woodwork*

WOODCARVING. see *BUILDING AND CONSTRUCTION—Carpentry And Woodwork*

745.5 USA ISSN 1551-7772
▼ **WOODWORKING FOR WOMEN.** Text in English. 2004 (Mar.). bi-m. USD 19.97 domestic; USD 24.97 in Canada (effective 2004). adv. **Document type:** *Magazine, Consumer.* **Description:** Contains woodworking plans and advice aimed at women.
Published by: D R G Texas, LP, 103 N Pearl St, Big Sandy, TX 75755. TEL 903-636-4012, 800-538-5354, FAX 903-636-4088, editor@woodworkingforwomenmagazine.com, http://www.woodworkingforwomenmagazine.com. Ed. Jeanne Stauffer. adv.: color page USD 1,575; trim 8.625 x 10.875.

WORLD OF WOOD. see *FORESTS AND FORESTRY—Lumber And Wood*

747 CHN
YISHU - SHENGHUO/ART - LIFE. Text in Chinese. q. CNY 350,001. **Description:** Covers researches in arts and crafts, interior design and design of daily utensils.
Published by: Fujian Sheng Gongyi Meishu Xuexiao, 22 Hexi Lu, Fuzhou, Fujian 350001, China. TEL 534506. Ed. Zheng Likuo. **Dist. overseas by:** Jiangsu Publications Import & Export Corp., 56 Gao Yun Ling, Nanjing, Jiangsu, China.

745 398 RUS ISSN 0204-3432
GR203.17
ZHIVAYA STARINA; zhurnal o russkom fol'klore i traditsionnoi kul'ture. Text in Russian. 1890. q. USD 110 in United States (effective 2005). adv. bk.rev. index. **Document type:** *Journal.* **Description:** Covers traditional Slavic culture and folk arts.
Related titles: Microfiche ed.: (from IDC).
Indexed: RASB.
—East View.
Published by: Ministerstvo Kul'tury Rossiiskoi Federatsii, Tsentr Russkogo Fol'klora/Ministy of Culture of the Russian Federation, Centre of Russian Folklore, Kropotkinskii per 10, Moscow, 119034, Russian Federation. TEL 7-095-2468417, FAX 7-095-2463389, http://www.arts.ualberta.ca/SEEFA/RUSSIAN.HTM#ZhS. Ed. N I Tolstoi. Adv. contact Anatoli Kargin. page USD 600. Circ: 3,000. **US dist. addr.:** East View Information Services, 3020 Harbor Ln. N., Minneapolis, MN 55447. TEL 763-550-0961, FAX 763-559-2931, eastview@eastview.com, http://www.eastview.com.
Co-sponsor: Ministerstvo Kul'tury Rossiiskoi Federatsii.

ARTS AND HANDICRAFTS—Abstracting, Bibliographies, Statistics

745.5 ECU
CENTRO INTERAMERICANO DE ARTESANIAS Y ARTES POPULARES. CENTRO DE DOCUMENTACION. BOLETIN. Text in Spanish. 1991. 3/yr. per issue exchange basis. adv. **Document type:** *Bulletin.*
Published by: Centro Interamericano de Artesanias y Artes Populares, HERMANO MIGUEL, 3-23 (Escalinata, Apdo 01 01 1943, Cuenca, Azuay, Ecuador. TEL 593-7-829451, FAX 593-7-831450. Ed. Joaquin Moreno. Adv. contact Manual Jadan. Circ: 1,000.

745.5 011 AUS ISSN 1034-8174
INDEX TO CRAFT JOURNALS. Text in English. 1979. irreg., latest 1989-90. AUD 118 domestic; AUD 125 foreign (effective 2000). back issues avail. **Document type:** *Abstract/Index.* **Description:** Access to information in 74 craft periodicals classified by authors, craftsperson's name, subject heading, studio-workshop name.
Published by: Craft of Australia, Level 5, 414-418 Elizabeth St, Surry Hills, NSW 2010, Australia. TEL 61-2-211-1445, FAX 61-2-211-1443. Ed. Beth Hatton. Circ: 140.

745.5097 970.1 CAN ISSN 1192-4373
TERRES EN VUES/ASSI NUKUAN. Text in French. q. CND 20; CND 6 newsstand/cover. adv. bk.rev.; film rev.; music rev.; play rev.; video rev. back issues avail. **Description:** American Native people's cultural magazine with a focus on arts, handicraft, lifestyle and festivals.
Published by: Terres en Vues - Societe pour la Diffusion de la Culture Autochtone, 770 rue Rachel E, Montreal, PQ H2S 2H5, Canada. TEL 514-521-2714, FAX 514-521-9480. Ed., Adv. contact Andre Dudemaine. Pub. Danie Corvec. page CND 1,000. Circ: 3,000.

ASIAN STUDIES

see also HISTORY—History Of Asia ; LINGUISTICS ; LITERATURE ; PHILOSOPHY

950 IND ISSN 0304-6214
DS401
A I I S QUARTERLY NEWSLETTER. Text in English. 1974. q. adv. bk.rev. bibl.; illus.
Published by: American Institute of Indian Studies, D-176 Defence Colony, New Delhi, 110 024, India. Ed. P R Mehendiratta. Circ: 1,500.

950 BEL
➤ **A R A M.** Text in English. 1988. a., latest vol.16, 2004. EUR 44 (effective 2004). adv. bk.rev. illus.; maps. back issues avail. **Document type:** *Monographic series, Academic/Scholarly.* **Description:** Deals primarily with Aramaic culture, which was a focal point of the ancient Syrio-Mesopotamian civilizations.
Published by: (A R A M Society, Oxford GBR), Peeters Publishers, Bondgenotenlaan 153, Leuven, 3000, Belgium. TEL 32-16-235170, FAX 32-16-228500, http://www.peeters-leuven.be. Ed. S Abou Zaud.

A

950 IND
A S H PUBLICATION SERIES. Text in English. irreg., latest vol.2, 1992. **Document type:** *Monographic series.* **Description:** Explores the civilization of the Himalaya Mountains region.
Published by: (Association of Studies on Himalayas), Shree Almora Book Depot, Mall Rd., Almora, Uttar Pradesh 263 601, India.

950 DEU ISSN 0567-4980
PJ5
ABHANDLUNGEN FUER DIE KUNDE DES MORGENLANDES. Text in English, French, German. 1857. irreg. price varies. reprints avail. **Document type:** *Monographic series, Academic/Scholarly.*
Related titles: Microfiche ed.: (from BHP).
Indexed: BAS, RASB.
Published by: (Deutsche Morgenlaendische Gesellschaft), Ergon Verlag, Grombuehlstr 7, Wuerzburg, 97080, Germany. TEL 49-931-280084, FAX 49-931-282872, service@ergon-verlag.de, http://www.ergon-verlag.de.

950 LBN ISSN 0002-3973
AS595.A6
➤ **AL-ABHATH.** Text in Arabic, English. 1948. a. USD 22 in the Middle East; USD 22 in Africa; USD 22 in Europe; USD 25 elsewhere (effective 1999). bk.rev. bibl. **Document type:** *Academic/Scholarly.* **Description:** Includes information on Middle Eastern history, Arab linguistics, and political affairs.
Indexed: AmH&L, BibLing, HistAb, IBSS, NumL, PerIslam.
Published by: American University of Beirut, Faculty of Arts and Sciences, AUB Post Hall 106, Beirut, Lebanon. TEL 96-1-353465, FAX 212-478-1995, TELEX 20801 LE, publications@aub.edu.lb, http://www.aub.edu.lb/. Ed. Farid El Khazen. R&P Helga Seeden. Circ: 1,000. **Subscr. to:** P O Box 11 0236 31, Beirut, Lebanon.

➤ **ABSTRACTA IRANICA.** see *HISTORY—Abstracting, Bibliographies, Statistics*

➤ **ACADEMIA SINICA. INSTITUTE OF ETHNOLOGY. BULLETIN.** see *ANTHROPOLOGY*

950 JPN ISSN 0567-7254
DS12
ACTA ASIATICA. Text in English. 1961. s-a. JPY 8,400 (effective 2002). bibl. 128 p./no.; back issues avail. **Document type:** *Bulletin, Academic/Scholarly.* **Description:** Introduces recent academic contributions by leading Japanese scholars in the field of Asian and Japanese studies.
Indexed: AnthLit, BAS, IBSS, IndIslam, MLA, MLA-IB, PerIslam, RASB, RILM.
Published by: Toho Gakkai/Institute of Eastern Culture, 4-1 Nishi-Kanda 2-chome, Chiyoda-ku, Tokyo, 101-0065, Japan. TEL 81-3-3262-7221, FAX 81-3-3262-7227, tohogakkai@mc.nextlink.ne.jp. R&P Hiroshi Yanase. Circ: 1,000.

950 BEL ISSN 0378-4215
ACTA IRANICA. Text in Dutch. 1974. irreg. price varies. back issues avail. **Document type:** *Monographic series, Academic/Scholarly.*
Published by: Peeters Publishers, Bondgenotenlaan 153, Leuven, 3000, Belgium. TEL 32-16-235170, FAX 32-16-228500, peeters@peeters-leuven.be, http://www.peeters-leuven.be.

951.9 KOR ISSN 1520-7412
DS904
➤ **ACTA KOREANA.** Text in English. 1998. s-a. USD 20 to individuals; USD 36 to institutions (effective 2005). illus. Index. **Document type:** *Journal, Academic/Scholarly.*
Related titles: Online - full text ed.
Indexed: L&LBA, SSA, SociolAb.
—BLDSC (0628.600000), IE.
Published by: Keimyung University, Academia Koreana, 1000 Sindang-Dong, Dalseo-Gu, Daegu, 704701, Korea, S. TEL 82-53-5805578, acta@kmu.ac.kr, http://www.actakoreana.org/publs/.

950 NOR ISSN 0001-6438
PJ1
➤ **ACTA ORIENTALIA.** Text in English, French, German. 1922. a., latest vol.65, no.1, 2003. NOK 400 per issue (effective 2005). bk.rev. illus. reprint service avail. from ISI. **Document type:** *Academic/Scholarly.* **Description:** Devoted to the studies of the languages, history, archaeology and religions of the Orient from the earliest times down to our day.
Formerly: Le Monde Orientale
Indexed: BAS, BibLing, CurCont, DIP, IBR, IBSS, IBZ, IndIslam, MEA&I, MLA, MLA-IB, OTA, PerIslam, RASB, RI-1, RI-2, RILM, ZooRec.
—IE, Infotrieve. **CCC.**
Published by: (Oriental Societies of Denmark, Finland, Norway and Sweden DNK), Novus Forlag, Herman Foss Gate 19, Oslo, 0171, Norway. TEL 47-22-717450, FAX 47-22-718107, novus@novus.no, http://www.novus.no. Ed. Per Kvaerne. Circ: 500.

950 HUN ISSN 0001-6446
DS1
➤ **ACTA ORIENTALIA ACADEMIAE SCIENTIARUM HUNGARICAE.** Text mainly in English; Text occasionally in French, German, Russian. 1950. q. USD 292 (effective 2006). adv. bk.rev. illus.; abstr.; bibl. index. 120 p./no. 1 cols./p.; **Document type:** *Journal, Academic/Scholarly.* **Description:** Provides an international forum for original papers in the field of oriental studies, including Turkish, Mongolian, Manchurian, Chinese, Tibetan, Indian, Iranian, and Semitic philology, literature and history.
Related titles: Online - full text ed.: ISSN 1588-2667. 1998 (from EBSCO Publishing, Gale Group, IngentaConnect, Swets Information Services).
Indexed: AmH&L, BAS, BibLing, DIP, HistAb, IBR, IBZ, IndIslam, MLA, MLA-IB, OTA, PCI, RASB, SOPODA.
—IE, Infotrieve. **CCC.**
Published by: (Magyar Tudomanyos Akademia/Hungarian Academy of Sciences), Akademiai Kiado Rt. (Subsidiary of: Wolters Kluwer N.V.), Prielle Kornelia U. 19, Budapest, 1117, Hungary. TEL 36-1-4648282, FAX 36-1-4648221, http://www.akkrt.hu. Ed. Andras Rona-Tas.

949.502 HUN ISSN 0139-2751
ACTA UNIVERSITATIS SZAGEDIENSIS. OPUSCULA BYZANTINA. Text in English, French, German, Greek, Hungarian, Italian. 1972. irreg., latest vol.9, 1994. exchange basis. **Document type:** *Monographic series, Academic/Scholarly.* **Description:** Journal of Byzantine and medieval Latin studies.
Published by: (Szegedi Tudomanyegyetem, Bolcseszettudomanyi Kar, Bizantinologia- es Kozeplatin Filologia Tanszeki Csoport/University of Szeged, Faculty of Arts, Research Group of Medieval Latin and Byzantine Studies), Szegedi Tudomanyegyetem/University of Szeged, c/o E Szabo, Exchange Librarian, Dugonics ter 13, PO Box 393, Szeged, 6701, Hungary. TEL 36-62-544009, FAX 36-62-420895, Eneh.Szabo@bibl.u-szeged.hu, http://www.u-szeged.hu. Ed. Terez Olajos. Circ: 500.

950 DEU ISSN 0720-9061
AEGYPTEN UND ALTES TESTAMENT; Studien zu Geschichte, Kultur und Religion Aegyptens und des Alten Testaments. Text in German. 1979. irreg., latest vol.57, 2003. price varies. **Document type:** *Monographic series, Academic/Scholarly.*
Indexed: RASB.
Published by: Harrassowitz Verlag, Taunusstr 14, Wiesbaden, 65183, Germany. TEL 49-611-5300, FAX 49-611-530570, verlag@harrassowitz.de, http://www.harrassowitz.de. Ed. Manfred Goerg. R&P Michael Langfeld. Adv. contact Robert Gietz.

956 DEU ISSN 0568-0476
AEGYPTOLOGISCHE ABHANDLUNGEN. Text in German. 1960. irreg., latest vol.65, 2003. price varies. adv. **Document type:** *Monographic series, Academic/Scholarly.*
Indexed: MathR, RASB.
Published by: Harrassowitz Verlag, Taunusstr 14, Wiesbaden, 65183, Germany. TEL 49-611-5300, FAX 49-611-530570, verlag@harrassowitz.de, http://www.harrassowitz.de. Ed. Ursula Roessler Koehler. R&P Michael Langfeld. Adv. contact Robert Gietz.

950 DEU ISSN 0931-282X
AETAS MANJURICA. Text in German. 1987. irreg., latest vol.9, 2001. price varies. adv. **Document type:** *Monographic series, Academic/Scholarly.*
Indexed: RASB.
Published by: Harrassowitz Verlag, Taunusstr 14, Wiesbaden, 65183, Germany. TEL 49-611-5300, FAX 49-611-530570, verlag@harrassowitz.de, http://www.harrassowitz.de. R&P Michael Langfeld. Adv. contact Robert Gietz.

950 DEU ISSN 0170-3196
AETHIOPISTISCHE FORSCHUNGEN. Text in English, German. irreg., latest vol.62, 2003. price varies. **Document type:** *Monographic series, Academic/Scholarly.*
Published by: Harrassowitz Verlag, Taunusstr 14, Wiesbaden, 65183, Germany. TEL 49-611-5300, FAX 49-611-530570, verlag@harrassowitz.de, http://www.harrassowitz.de. Ed. Siegbert Uhlig. R&P Michael Langfeld. Adv. contact Robert Gietz.

AFRICAN AND ASIAN STUDIES. see *SOCIOLOGY*

AFRO-ASIA. see *HUMANITIES: COMPREHENSIVE WORKS*

950 DEU ISSN 0568-4447
AKADEMIE DER WISSENSCHAFTEN UND DER LITERATUR, MAINZ. ORIENTALISCHE KOMMISSION. VEROEFFENTLICHUNGEN. Text in French, German. irreg., latest vol.47, 2001. price varies. **Document type:** *Monographic series, Academic/Scholarly.*
Published by: (Akademie der Wissenschaften und der Literatur, Mainz, Orientalische Kommission), Harrassowitz Verlag, Taunusstr 14, Wiesbaden, 65183, Germany. TEL 49-611-5300, FAX 49-611-530570, verlag@harrasowitz.de, http://www.harrassowitz.de. Ed. Walter Mueller. R&P Michael Langfeld. Adv. contact Robert Gietz.

950 IND ISSN 0970-0994
ALIGARH JOURNAL OF ORIENTAL STUDIES. Text in English; Summaries in Arabic, Persian, Modern, Sanskrit. 1984. s-a. INR 100, USD 20. bk.rev. bibl. back issues avail. **Document type:** *Academic/Scholarly.* **Description:** Publishes original contributions on all areas represented in the All-India Oriental Conference.
Indexed: BibLing, IBR.
Published by: Viveka Publications, 3-39 Samad Rd., Aligarh, Uttar Pradesh 202 001, India. TEL 0571-24681. Ed. Umesh Chandra Sharma. adv.: page INR 700. Circ: 500.

950 NLD ISSN 0065-6593
➤ **ALTBABYLONISCHE BRIEFE IM UMSCHRIFT UND UEBERSETZUNG.** Text in Dutch. 1964. irreg., latest vol.13, 1993. price varies. back issues avail. **Document type:** *Monographic series, Academic/Scholarly.* **Description:** Publishes ancient Babylonian letters from museums and collections throughout the world, with translations and scholarly commentary.
Published by: Brill Academic Publishers, PO Box 9000, Leiden, 2300 PA, Netherlands. TEL 31-71-53-53-500, FAX 31-71-53-17-532, http://www.brill.nl. Ed. W H van Soldt. R&P Elizabeth Venekamp.

902 DEU ISSN 0948-1737
➤ **ALTERTUMSKUNDE DES VORDEREN ORIENTS.** Text in English, French, German. 1992. irreg., latest vol.11, 2002. price varies. **Document type:** *Monographic series, Academic/Scholarly.* **Description:** Publishes monographs on ancient Near Eastern art and archaeology.
Published by: Ugarit-Verlag, Ricarda-Huch-Str 6, Muenster, 48161, Germany. TEL 49-2534-1590, FAX 49-2534-539983, verlag@ugarit-verlag.de, http://www.ugarit-verlag.de. Eds. Manfred L.G. Dietrich, Oswald Loretz.

➤ **ALTORIENTALISCHE FORSCHUNGEN.** see *HISTORY—History Of The Near East*

495.1 951 USA ISSN 0742-5929
➤ **AMERICAN JOURNAL OF CHINESE STUDIES.** Text in English. 1984. s-a. USD 30 (effective 2005). adv. bk.rev. charts; stat.; illus. index. back issues avail.; reprints avail. **Document type:** *Academic/Scholarly.* **Description:** Publishes original articles on China in all disciplines of social sciences and humanities.
Former titles: Journal of Chinese Studies; American Association for Chinese Studies. Bulletin; American Association for Chinese Studies Newsletter; American Association of Teachers of Chinese Language and Culture. Newsletter
Indexed: AmH&L, BAS, HistAb, MLA-IB, PAIS.
Published by: American Association for Chinese Studies, Dept of Political Science, University of Texas at San Antonio, San Antonio, TX 78249-0603. TEL 210-458-4628, FAX 210-458-4621. Ed., R&P, Adv. contact Dr. Thomas J Bellows. Pub. Dr. Peter C Y Chow. Circ: 550 (paid).

950 USA ISSN 0065-9541
AMERICAN ORIENTAL SERIES. Text in English. 1925. irreg. price varies. bk.rev. reprints avail. **Document type:** *Monographic series, Academic/Scholarly.*
Published by: American Oriental Society, Harlan Hatcher Graduate Library, University of Michigan, Ann Arbor, MI 48109-1205. TEL 734-647-4760. Ed. Paul Kroll. **Dist. by:** Eisenbrauns, PO Box 275, Winona Lake, IN 46590-0275.

950 USA ISSN 0003-0279
PJ2
➤ **AMERICAN ORIENTAL SOCIETY. JOURNAL.** Text in English, French, German. 1842. q. USD 70 membership (effective 2005). adv. bk.rev. charts; illus. index. back issues avail.; reprint service avail. from PQC. **Document type:** *Academic/Scholarly.*
Related titles: Microfiche ed.: (from IDC); Microform ed.: (from PMC, PQC); Online - full text ed.: (from bigchalk, EBSCO Publishing, Florida Center for Library Automation, Gale Group, H.W. Wilson, JSTOR (Web-based Journal Archive), O C L C Online Computer Library Center, Inc., ProQuest Information & Learning).
Indexed: ABS&EES, AIAP, ASCA, AbAn, AmHI, ArtHuCI, BAS, BibLing, CurCont, DIP, HumInd, IBR, IBRH, IBSS, IBZ, IPB, IndIslam, L&LBA, LRI, MLA-IB, NTA, NumL, OTA, PhilInd, R&TA, RASB, RI-1, RI-2, RILM, SOPODA, SSCI.
—BLDSC (4689.390000), IDS, IE, Infotrieve, ingenta, Linda Hall.
Published by: American Oriental Society, Harlan Hatcher Graduate Library, University of Michigan, Ann Arbor, MI 48109-1205. TEL 734-647-4760, jrodgers@umich.edu, http://www.umich.edu/~aos/, http://www.umich.edu/vaos/. Ed. Paul Kroll. Circ: 2,300.

950 USA ISSN 0003-097X
DS101
➤ **AMERICAN SCHOOLS OF ORIENTAL RESEARCH. BULLETIN.** Abbreviated title: B A S O R. Text in English. 1919. q. USD 60 to individuals; USD 150 to institutions (effective 2005). adv. bk.rev. charts; illus. index. back issues avail.; reprint service avail. from PQC. **Document type:** *Bulletin, Academic/Scholarly.* **Description:** Presents technical reports of original research and ASOR-sponsored excavations, and reviews of current scholarship in the field.

Formerly (until 1921): American School of Oriental Research in Jerusalem. Bulletin (0276-7732)
Related titles: Microform ed.: (from PQC); Online - full text ed.: ISSN 1557-5586 (from EBSCO Publishing, H.W. Wilson, JSTOR (Web-based Journal Archive), O C L C Online Computer Library Center, Inc., ProQuest Information & Learning).
Indexed: AICP, AnthLit, ArtInd, BHA, BibLing, DIP, IBR, IBSS, IBZ, IndIslam, L&LBA, NTA, NumL, OTA, PCI, R&TA, RASB, RI-1, RI-2, RILM, SOPODA.
—BLDSC (2392.700000), IE, ingenta. **CCC.**
Published by: American Schools of Oriental Research, 825 Houston Mill Rd, Atlanta, GA 30329. TEL 404-727-8989, FAX 404-727-2348, asorpubs@asor.org, http://www.asor.org/pubs/basor/basor.html. Ed. James Weinstein. adv.: B&W page USD 300; trim 11 x 8.5. Circ: 2,100 (paid).

951 930.1 USA ISSN 0361-6029
DS101
AMERICAN SCHOOLS OF ORIENTAL RESEARCH. NEWSLETTER. Variant title: A S O R Newsletter. Text in English. 1938. q. USD 20 domestic to individuals; USD 30 foreign to individuals; USD 35 domestic to institutions; USD 45 foreign to institutions (effective 2005). bk.rev. tr.lit. 28 p./no.; back issues avail.; reprint service avail. from PQC. **Document type:** *Newsletter, Academic/Scholarly.* **Description:** Presents brief summaries of research work done under ASOR auspices and reports on the various activities of ASOR's overseas centers in Amman, Jerusalem, and Nicosia.
Formerly (until 1966): Archeological Newsletter
Related titles: Microform ed.: (from PQC); Online - full text ed.: (from EBSCO Publishing).
Indexed: AICP, AnthLit, PerIslam, RI-1, RI-2.
—CCC.
Published by: American Schools of Oriental Research, 825 Houston Mill Rd, Atlanta, GA 30329. TEL 404-727-0807, FAX 404-727-4719, bcollin@emory.edu, asorpubs@asor.org, http://www.asor.org/pubs/news/news.html. Ed. Billie Jean Collins. Circ: 1,700 (paid and controlled).

950 ITA ISSN 1590-7430
➤ **ANALECTA ORIENTALIA.** Text in Italian, German, French, English. 1931. irreg., latest vol.55, 1999. price varies. **Document type:** *Academic/Scholarly.* **Description:** Devoted to the languages, literatures and history of ancient Near Eastern non-biblical cultures.
Published by: (Pontificio Istituto Biblico, Facolta degli Studi per l'Oriente Antico) Pontificio Istituto Biblico/Pontifical Biblical Institute, Via della Pilotta 25, Rome, 00187, Italy. TEL 39-06-695261, FAX 39-06-695266151, pibsegr@pib.ur, http://www.pib.urbe.it.

956 939 TUR ISSN 1018-1946
➤ **ANATOLIA ANTIQUA/ESKI ANADOLU.** Text in French, Turkish. irreg., latest vol.6, 1998. price varies. illus.; maps. back issues avail. **Document type:** *Monographic series, Academic/Scholarly.* **Description:** Explores ancient Anatolia, now modern-day Turkey.
Published by: Institut Francais d'Etudes Anatoliennes a Istanbul/Fransiz Anadolu Arastirmalari Enstitusu, Palais de France, Nuru Ziya Sokak, 22, PK 54, Beyoglu, Istanbul 80072, Turkey. TEL 90-212-244-1717, 90-212-244-3327, FAX 90-212-252-8091, ifeai@superonline.com, http://www.geocities.com/Athens/Styx/7236/publint.html.

956 TUR ISSN 1297-8094
DR401
➤ **ANATOLIA MODERNA/YENI ANADOLU.** Text in French, Turkish. 1991. irreg., latest vol.7, 1997. price varies. illus.; maps. back issues avail. **Document type:** *Monographic series, Academic/Scholarly.* **Description:** Explores the recent history and culture of Anatolia, part of modern-day Turkey.
Published by: Institut Francais d'Etudes Anatoliennes a Istanbul/Fransiz Anadolu Arastirmalari Enstitusu, Palais de France, Nuru Ziya Sokak, 22, PK 54, Beyoglu, Istanbul 80072, Turkey. TEL 90-212-244-1717, 90-212-244-3327, FAX 90-212-252-8091, ifeai@superonline.com, http://www.geocities.com/Athens/Styx/7236/publint.html.

➤ **ANATOLIAN ARCHAEOLOGICAL STUDIES.** see *ARCHAEOLOGY*

➤ **ANATOLIAN ARCHAEOLOGY.** see *ARCHAEOLOGY*

➤ **ANATOLIAN STUDIES.** see *ARCHAEOLOGY*

➤ **ANCIENT NEAR EAST STUDIES SUPPLEMENTS.** see *ARCHAEOLOGY*

950 USA ISSN 0897-6074
DS41
➤ **ANCIENT NEAR EASTERN SOCIETY. JOURNAL.** Abbreviated title: J A N E S. Text in English. 1968. a. USD 15 to individuals; USD 25 to institutions (effective 1999). adv. illus. back issues avail. **Document type:** *Academic/Scholarly.* **Description:** Presents articles on all aspects of the ancient Near East.
Formerly (until 1982): Columbia University. Ancient Near Eastern Society. Journal (0010-2016)
Related titles: Microfilm ed.
Indexed: AnthLit, BibLing, MEA&I, NTA, OTA, R&TA, RI-1, RI-2.
—BLDSC (4697.740000).
Published by: Ancient Near Eastern Society, Jewish Theological Seminary, 3080 Broadway, New York, NY 10027-4649. TEL 212-678-8856, FAX 212-678-8961, damarcus@jtsa.eou. Ed. Edward L Greenstein. R&P David Marcus TEL 212-280-2556. Circ: 400.

➤ **ANCIENT NEAR EASTERN STUDIES.** see *ARCHAEOLOGY*

954 913 NPL
ANCIENT NEPAL. Text in English, Nepali. 1967. bi-m. NPR 50 (effective 2000). **Document type:** *Academic/Scholarly.*
Indexed: AIAP, IBSS.
Published by: Department of Archaeology, Ramshahpath, Kathmandu, Nepal. TEL 977-1-250683, FAX 977-1-231856, dcu@doa.wlink.com.np. Ed. Riddhi Pradhan. Circ: 500.

953 ESP ISSN 1133-8571
DP102
AL-ANDALUS-MAGREB. Text in Spanish. 1993. a. back issues avail.
—CINDOC.
Published by: Universidad de Cadiz, Servicio de Publicaciones, Rectorado Ancha 16, Cadiz, 11001, Spain. TEL 34-956-0150000, http://minerva.uca.es/publicaciones/seccion.asp?secc=R-AA, http://www.uca.es/.

950 FRA ISSN 0980-5842
DS41
ANNALES DU LEVANT. Text in French. 1985. a. **Description:** Studies the economic and political relationships between industrialized and developing countries in the Middle East.
Indexed: IPSA.
Published by: (Universite de Rennes II (Universite de Haute Bretagne), Centre Interdisciplinaire de Recherche sur les Relations Internationales au Moyen-Orient), Presses Universitaires de Rennes, Campus de la Harpe, 2 Rue du Doyen Denis-Leroy, Rennes, Cedex 35044, France. TEL 33-2-99141401, FAX 33-2-99141407, pur@uhb.fr, http://www.uhb.fr. **Co-sponsor:** Equipe de Recherche sur le Systeme Industriel.

297 EGY ISSN 0254-282X
ANNALES ISLAMOLOGIQUES. SUPPLEMENT. Key Title: Supplement aux Annales Islamologiques. Variant title: Cahiers des Annales Islamologiques. Text occasionally in English; Text mainly in French. 1981. irreg. (approx a.), latest vol.20, 2001. EGP 98, EUR 30.50 (effective 2001). back issues avail. **Document type:** *Monographic series.* **Description:** Scholarly studies of historical topics, texts and inscriptions relating to Islamic Egypt and neighboring regions.
Published by: Institut Francais d'Archeologie Orientale du Caire, Kasr el-Aini, 37 Sharia Sheikh Aly Youssef, Mounira, P O Box 11562, Cairo, Egypt. TEL 20-2-3571622, FAX 20-2-3544635, ventes@ifao.egnet.net. Adv. contact Marie-Christine Michel TEL 20-2-7971622. **Dist. by:** Boustany's Publishing House, 29 Faggalah St, Cairo 11271, Egypt. TEL 20-2-5195315, FAX 20-2-4177915, http://www.boustany.com.

950 IND
ANNALS OF ORIENTAL RESEARCH. Text in English. a.
Indexed: BAS, BibLing, IBR, IBZ.
Published by: University of Madras, c/o Director, Publications Division, Chennai, Tamil Nadu 600 005, India. TEL 91-44-568778, FAX 91-44-566693.

ANNUAL OF URDU STUDIES. see *LINGUISTICS*

953 USA ISSN 1083-4753
DS36
➤ **ARAB STUDIES JOURNAL.** Text in English. 1993. 2/yr. USD 25 domestic to individuals; USD 40 foreign to individuals; USD 40 domestic to institutions; USD 55 foreign to institutions (effective 2005). bk.rev. **Document type:** *Journal, Academic/Scholarly.*
Indexed: CCME, IBSS, IndIslam.
—BLDSC (1583.295700).
Published by: Georgetown University, Center for Contemporary Arab Studies, ICC 241, Washington, DC 20057. TEL 202-687-0904, FAX 202-687-7100, http://www.arabstudiesjournal.org. Ed. Bassam S A Haddad.

953 NLD ISSN 0570-5398
PJ6001
➤ **ARABICA;** journal of Arabic and Islamic studies. Text in Arabic, English, French, German. 1954. q. USD 132 in the Americas to individuals; EUR 102 subscr - carrier delivery elsewhere to individuals; USD 394 combined subscription in the Americas to institutions print & online eds.; EUR 325 combined subscription elsewhere to institutions print & online eds. (effective 2006). bk.rev. bibl. index. back issues avail.; reprint service avail. from PSC. **Document type:** *Journal, Academic/Scholarly.* **Description:** Studies, documents and notes on the language, literature, history and civilization of the Arab world, with emphasis on multidisciplinary studies of ancient and contemporary problems concerning Arab societies.
Related titles: Microform ed.: (from SWZ); Online - full content ed.: ISSN 1570-0585. USD 355 in the Americas to institutions; EUR 284 elsewhere to institutions (effective 2006); Online - full text ed.: (from EBSCO Publishing, Gale Group, IngentaConnect, Kluwer Online, O C L C Online Computer Library Center, Inc., Springer LINK, Swets Information Services).
Indexed: AmH&L, BHA, BibInd, BibLing, DIP, HistAb, IBR, IBSS, IBZ, IndIslam, MLA, MLA-IB, NumL, PCI, PerIslam, RASB, RI-1, RI-2.
—BLDSC (1583.350000), IE, Infotrieve, ingenta. **CCC.**
Published by: (France. Centre National de la Recherche Scientifique FRA), Brill Academic Publishers, PO Box 9000, Leiden, 2300 PA, Netherlands. TEL 31-71-53-53-500, FAX 31-71-53-17-532, cs@brill.nl, http://www.brill.nl/m_catalogue_sub6_id7990.htm. Ed. M Arkoun. R&P Elizabeth Venekamp. Adv. contact F S Geuze. **Subscr. in N. America to:** PO Box 605, Herndon, VA 20172. TEL 703-661-1585, 800-337-9255, FAX 703-661-1501, cs@brillusa.com. **Distr. outside N. America by:** c/o Turpin Distribution, Stratton Business Park, Pegasus Drive, Biggleswade, BEDFORDSHIRE SG 18 8TQ, United Kingdom. TEL 44-1767-604-954, FAX 44-1767-601-640, brill@turpin-distribution.com.

➤ **ARABISTISCHE TEXTE UND STUDIEN.** see *LITERATURE*

950 FRA ISSN 0044-8613
DS501
ARCHIPEL; etudes interdisciplinaires sur le monde insulindien. Text in English, French, Indonesian. 1971. s-a. EUR 130 per issue (effective 2005). adv. bk.rev. bibl.; charts; illus. **Document type:** *Journal, Academic/Scholarly.*
Indexed: AICP, AmH&L, BAS, BibInd, BibLing, EI, HistAb, IBSS, IPSA, IndIslam, RASB.
—CCC.
Published by: Association Archipel, Ehess Bureau 732, 54 bd. Raspail, Paris, 75006, France. TEL 33-1-49542564, FAX 33-1-45449311, archipel@ehess.fr. Ed. Claude Guillot. Circ: 700.

950 960 CZE ISSN 0044-8699
DS1
➤ **ARCHIV ORIENTALNI/ORIENTAL ARCHIVES;** quarterly journal of African and Asian studies. Text in English, French, German. 1929. q. EUR 263 (effective 2006). bk.rev. bibl.; charts; illus.; abstr. 150 p./no.; back issues avail. **Document type:** *Journal, Academic/Scholarly.* **Description:** Publishes original papers, review articles and book reviews pertaining to the history, economy, culture and society of African and Asian countries.
Related titles: Microfiche ed.: (from IDC); ♦ Supplement(s): Archiv Orientalni. Supplementa. ISSN 0570-6815.
Indexed: AICP, AmH&L, BAS, BibInd, BibLing, EI, HistAb, IBSS, IndIslam, L&LBA, MEA&I, MLA, MLA-IB, OTA, PCI, PerIslam, RASB, RI-1, RI-2, SOPODA, SSA.
—BLDSC (1621.570000), IE, Infotrieve, ingenta.
Published by: Akademie Ved Ceske Republiky, Orientalni Ustav/Czech Academy of Sciences, Oriental Institute, Pod Vodarenskou vezi 4, Prague, 18208, Czech Republic. TEL 420-2-66052483, FAX 420-2-6897260, aror@orient.cas.cz. Ed., R&P Stanislava Vavrouskova. Circ: 500. **Dist. by:** John Benjamins Publishing Co.. customer.services@benjamins.nl.

950 CZE ISSN 0570-6815
DS1
➤ **ARCHIV ORIENTALNI. SUPPLEMENTA.** Text in English, French, German. 1953. irreg., latest vol.9, 2000. USD 60 (effective 2001). abstr.; charts; illus.; maps. back issues avail. **Document type:** *Monographic series, Academic/Scholarly.*
Related titles: ♦ Supplement to: Archiv Orientalni. ISSN 0044-8699.
Published by: Akademie Ved Ceske Republiky, Orientalni Ustav/Czech Academy of Sciences, Oriental Institute, Pod Vodarenskou vezi 4, Prague, 18208, Czech Republic. TEL 420-2-66052483, FAX 420-2-6897260, aror@orient.cas.cz, http://www.lib.cas.cz/knav/journals/eng/archiv_orientalni.htm. Ed., R&P L'ubica Obuchova. Circ: 950 (paid).

956 DEU ISSN 0724-8822
DS327
ARCHIVUM EURASIAE MEDII AEVI. Text in English, French. 1975. a. EUR 89 (effective 2006). adv. bk.rev. **Document type:** *Journal, Academic/Scholarly.* **Description:** Focuses on the Eurasian steppes and adjoining regions from the fifth through the twelfth centuries.
Indexed: BHA, IBR, IBZ, NumL.
Published by: Harrassowitz Verlag, Taunusstr 14, Wiesbaden, 65183, Germany. TEL 49-611-5300, FAX 49-611-530560, verlag@harrassowitz.de, http://www.harrassowitz.de. Ed. T Allsen. R&P Michael Langfeld. Adv. contact Robert Gietz.

950 709 USA ISSN 0571-1371
N7260
➤ **ARS ORIENTALIS;** the arts of Asia, Southeast Asia and Islam. Text in English. 1954. a. USD 40 (effective 2005). bk.rev. illus. back issues avail. **Document type:** *Academic/Scholarly.*
Supersedes: Ars Islamica
Related titles: Online - full text ed.: (from H.W. Wilson, O C L C Online Computer Library Center, Inc.).
Indexed: AIAP, ArtInd, BAS, RASB.

Published by: Department of History of Art, Tappan Hall, University of Michigan, Ann Arbor, MI 48109-1357. TEL 734-647-3307, FAX 734-763-8976, http://www.asia.si.edu/visitor/arsorientalis.htm, http://www-personal.umich.edu/~plourie. Ed., R&P Margaret A Lourie. Circ: 500.

950 ITA
ARTE ORIENTALE IN ITALIA. Text in Italian. 1971. irreg. price varies. illus.
Related titles: Series of: Museo Nazionale d'Arte Orientale. Pubblicazione.
Published by: Museo Nazionale d'Arte Orientale, Via Merulana, 248, Rome, RM 00185, Italy. Ed. Giovanni Poncini. Circ: 1,000.

ARTIBUS ASIAE; journal of Asian art and archaeology for scholars and connoisseurs. see *ART*

ARTIBUS ASIAE SUPPLEMENTUM. see *ART*

ARTS ASIATIQUES. see *ART*

950 USA ISSN 0890-4464
N7280.A1
➤ **ASIA INSTITUTE. BULLETIN.** Text in English, French, German. 1987. a. USD 65 (effective 2003). adv. bk.rev. charts; illus.; maps. Index. 250 p./no.; back issues avail. **Document type:** *Journal, Academic/Scholarly.* **Description:** For universities, museums, historians, and collectors. Promotes current studies in the art, archaeology, history, language, and religion of early to mid-Islamic Iran and Central Asia and interconnections with the Far East.
Indexed: AIAP, BAS, BibLing, RASB.
Published by: Carol Altman Bromberg, Ed. & Pub., 3287 Bradway Blvd, Bloomfield Hills, MI 48301. TEL 248-647-7917, FAX 248-647-9223, BAI34@aol.com, http://www.bulletinasiainstitute.org. R&P, Adv. contact Carol Altman Bromberg. Circ: 300 (paid).

950 USA ISSN 0004-4482
DS501
➤ **ASIA MAJOR**; a journal of Far Eastern Studies. Text in English. 1923; N.S. 1949-1975; N.S. 1988. s-a. USD 45 domestic to individuals; USD 49 foreign to individuals; USD 65 domestic to institutions; USD 69 foreign to institutions; USD 30 domestic to students; USD 34 foreign to students (effective 2005). adv. bk.rev. bibl.; illus.; maps. reprint service avail. from SCH. **Document type:** *Academic/Scholarly.* **Description:** Covers all periods of Chinese history, literature, ideas, and culture in general. Included are the histories and cultures of other East and Central Asian peoples in their relations with China.
Indexed: AmH&L, HistAb, IBSS, IndIslam, MLA-IB, RILM.
Published by: Academia Sinica, Institute of History and Philology, c/o Howard L Goodman, Ed, 4427 49th Ave, S W, Seattle, WA 98116-4021. hlgoodman@compuserve.com, pubsvc@tsp.sheridan.com, http://www.ihp.sinica.edu.tw/~asiamajor/. Ed., R&P, Adv. contact Howard L Goodman. Circ: 500. **Subscr. to:** PO Box 465, Hanover, PA 17331.

950 JPN
ASIA - PACIFIC CULTURAL CENTRE FOR UNESCO. ORGANIZATION AND ACTIVITIES. Text in English. biennial. illus.
Formerly: Asian Cultural Centre for UNESCO. Organization and Activities
Published by: Asia-Pacific Cultural Centre for UNSECO, 6 Fukuro-Machi, Shinjuku-ku, Tokyo, 162-0828, Japan. TEL 81-3-3269-4435, FAX 81-3-3269-4510, general@accu.or.jp, http://www.accu.or.jp.

950 GBR ISSN 0306-8374
DS1
ASIAN AFFAIRS. Text in English. 1903; N.S. 2000. 3/yr. GBP 125, USD 208 combined subscription to institutions print & online eds. (effective 2006). adv. bk.rev. charts; illus. index. back issues avail.; reprint service avail. from PSC. **Document type:** *Journal, Academic/Scholarly.*
Formerly: Royal Central Asian Society. Journal (0035-8789)
Related titles: Online - full text ed.: ISSN 1477-1500. GBP 119, USD 198 to institutions (effective 2006) (from EBSCO Publishing, Gale Group, H.W. Wilson, IngentaConnect, O C L C Online Computer Library Center, Inc., Swets Information Services).
Indexed: APEL, AmH&L, BAS, BRI, CJA, DIP, HistAb, IBR, IBZ, IPSA, IndIslam, MASUSE, MEA&I, PAIS, PCI, PSA, PerIslam, RASB, RI-1, RI-2, SSI, WBA, WMB.
—BLDSC (1742.270000), IE, Infotrieve, ingenta.
Published by: (Royal Society for Asian Affairs), Routledge (Subsidiary of: Taylor & Francis Group), 4 Park Square, Milton Park, Abingdon, Oxon OX14 4RN, United Kingdom. TEL 44-1235-828600, FAX 44-1235-829000, info@routledge.co.uk, http://www.tandf.co.uk/journals/titles/03068374.html, http://www.routledge.com. Ed. Michael Sheringham. Circ: 1,600 (paid).

ASIAN AMERICA. see *ETHNIC INTERESTS*

950 960 490 890 SVK ISSN 1335-1257
DS1 CODEN: AAFSEH
ASIAN AND AFRICAN STUDIES. Text in English. 1965. s-a. USD 60 foreign (effective 2005). bk.rev. index. **Document type:** *Journal, Academic/Scholarly.*
Indexed: APEL, BAS, BibLing, CCA, EI, HistAb, IndIslam, L&LBA, PSA, RASB, SSA, SociolAb.
Published by: (Slovenska Akademia Vied, Kabinet Orientalistiky/Slovak Academy of Sciences, Institute of Oriental and African Studies), Slovak Academic Press Ltd., Nam Slobody 6, PO Box 57, Bratislava, 81005, Slovakia. sap@sappress.sk, http://www.sappress.sk. Ed. Jozef Genzor.

ASIAN CHURCH TODAY. see *RELIGIONS AND THEOLOGY*

ASIAN CULTURAL STUDIES. see *HISTORY—History Of Asia*

THE ASIAN FOODBOOKERY; a quarterly exploration of Asian foods and cooking elsewhere. see *HOME ECONOMICS*

950 500 610 USA ISSN 1541-8219
QH305.2.A78 CODEN: AISNDK
ASIAN INFORMATION - SCIENCE - LIFE. Text in English. 2002. q. USD 275 (effective 2005). **Document type:** *Journal, Academic/Scholarly.* **Description:** Focuses on applied mathematics, information science, parallel processing, computational biology, electronic communications, bioscience, medical engineering, and pharmaceutical science.
Published by: Nova Science Publishers, Inc., 400 Oser Ave, Ste 1600, Hauppauge, NY 11788-3619. TEL 631-231-7269, FAX 631-231-8175, novascience@earthlink.net, http://www.novapublishers.com. Ed. Hisamatsu Nakano.

950 TWN
ASIAN PACIFIC CULTURE QUARTERLY. Text in English. 1973. q. TWD 960; USD 36 foreign. adv. bk.rev. index. **Description:** General articles on Asian-Pacific culture and creative writings.
Formerly: Asian Culture Quarterly (0378-8911)
Indexed: BAS, IBSS, RILM.
Published by: Asian-Pacific Cultural Center, Asian-Pacific Parliamentarians' Union, 6F, 66 Aikuo East Rd, Taipei, 107, Taiwan. TEL 886-2-2322-2139, FAX 886-2-2322-2138, apccapcc@ms23.hinet.net, 101400.2076@compuserve.com. Ed. Eric T S Wu. Circ: 3,000.

950 USA ISSN 1526-8675
ASIAN PAGES. Text in English. 1990. bi-w.
Related titles: Online - full text ed.: (from SoftLine Information).
Indexed: DYW.
Published by: Kita Associates, Inc., Box 11932, St. Paul, MN 55111-1932. TEL 952-884-3265, FAX 952-888-9373, asianpages@att.net, http://www.asianpages.com. Ed. Cheryl Weiberg. Circ: 75,000.

ASIAN PHILOSOPHY; an international journal of Indian, Chinese, Japanese, Buddhist, Persian and Islamic philosophical traditions. see *PHILOSOPHY*

950 CAN ISSN 0304-8675
DS1
➤ **ASIAN PROFILE.** Text in English. 1973. bi-m. USD 70 to individuals; USD 90 to institutions (effective 2004). adv. bk.rev. charts; illus.; maps; stat. back issues avail. **Document type:** *Journal, Academic/Scholarly.* **Description:** Covers issues on Asia from scholars in and outside of Asia.
Indexed: APEL, ARDT, AgrForAb, AmH&L, BAS, CJA, ForAb, HistAb, HortAb, IBSS, IPSA, IndVet, MEA&I, PAIS, PCI, PRA, PhilInd, ProtozoAb, RASB, RDA, REE&TA, RRTA, RevApplEntom, S&F, TriticAb, WAE&RSA.
—BLDSC (1742.731000), IE, Infotrieve, ingenta. **CCC.**
Published by: Asian Research Service, 108-4800 Kingsway, PO Box 1211, Burnaby, BC V5H 4J2, Canada. TEL 604-276-8115, FAX 604-276-0813, info@AsianResearchService.com, http://www.asianresearchservice.com/Pub.htm.

950 JPN ISSN 0917-1479
DS32.9.E18
ASIAN RESEARCH TRENDS; a humanities and social science review. Text in English. 1962. a. JPY 2,200 (effective 2000). **Document type:** *Academic/Scholarly.* **Description:** Presents recent trends in the research on Asia and North Africa done by regional specialists in the various disciplines concerning these areas.
Supersedes (in 1991): East Asian Cultural Studies (0012-8414)
Indexed: AICP, BAS, IBSS, RASB, RDA, WAE&RSA.
—BLDSC (1742.744700), IE, ingenta.
Published by: Centre for East Asian Cultural Studies for UNESCO, Bunko (Oriental Library), 2-28-21 Honkomagome, Bunkyo-ku, Tokyo, 113-0021, Japan. TEL 81-3-3942-0124, FAX 81-3-3942-0120, ceacs@toyo-bunko.or.jp, http:/www.toyo-bunko.or.jp/ceacs/. Ed. Yoneo Ishii. Circ: 1,500.

950 PHL ISSN 0004-4679
DS1
ASIAN STUDIES. Text in English. 1963. a. USD 12.50 (effective 1989). charts; illus.; stat. reprints avail.
Indexed: APEL, BAS, BibLing, EI, IPP, IndIslam, MLA, MLA-IB, RILM.
Published by: University of the Philippines, Asian Center, Diliman, Quezon City Mm, 1128, Philippines. FAX 992863, TELEX 2231 UPDIL PU. Circ: 500.

950 AUS ISSN 0156-0182
ASIAN STUDIES ASSOCIATION OF AUSTRALIA. CONFERENCE PAPERS. Text in English. 1978. biennial. price varies. **Document type:** *Proceedings.*
Media: Microfiche.
Published by: (Asian Studies Association of Australia), University of New South Wales, Library, PO Box 1, Kensington, NSW 2033, Australia. FAX 02-663-4017.

950 USA ISSN 0362-4811
DS1
ASIAN STUDIES NEWSLETTER. Text in English. 1955. 5/yr. USD 25; USD 35 foreign (effective 1998). adv. illus. back issues avail.; reprint service avail. from PQC. **Document type:** *Newsletter.* **Description:** Contains association news, and information on grants, publications, study programs, meetings, exhibits, and employment opportunities.
Formerly (until 1971): Association for Asian Studies. Newsletter (0004-5403)
Indexed: AICP, EI.
Published by: Association for Asian Studies, Inc., 1021 E Huron St, Ann Arbor, MI 48104. TEL 734-665-2490, FAX 734-665-3801, aarizala@aasianst.org, http://www.assianst.org. Circ: 8,500.

ASIAN STUDIES REVIEW. see *HISTORY—History Of Asia*

ASIAN SURVEY; a monthly review of contemporary Asian affairs. see *POLITICAL SCIENCE*

ASIAN THEATRE JOURNAL. see *THEATER*

950 USA ISSN 0893-6870
ASIAN THOUGHT AND CULTURE. Text in English. 1989. irreg., latest vol.58, 2004. price varies. **Document type:** *Monographic series, Academic/Scholarly.* **Description:** Covers Asian thought and culture in a broad perspective, including comparative philosophy and religion, history, political and social thought, literature, music, fine arts and related areas.
Indexed: MLA-IB.
Published by: Peter Lang Publishing, Inc., 275 Seventh Ave, 28th Fl, New York, NY 10001. TEL 212-647-7700, 212-647-7706, 800-770-5264, FAX 212-647-7707, customerservice@plang.com, http://www.peterlang.com. Ed. Sandra A. Wawrytko. Pub. Christopher Myers. R&P Stephanie Archer. Adv. contact Patricia Mulrane.

025.0695 USA ISSN 1098-9145
DS1
ASIANDOC ELECTRONIC NEWSLETTER. Text in English. 1998. q. **Document type:** *Newsletter.* **Description:** Supports scholars, librarians, and researchers world-wide who are developing text and image databases in the various fields of Asian studies.
Media: Online - full text.
Published by: Ohio State University Libraries, 1858 Neil Ave Mall, 328 Main Library, Columbus, OH 43210. TEL 614-292-3502, donovan.1@osu.edu, http://asiandoc.lib.ohio-state.edu. Ed., Pub. Maureen Donovan.

950 FRA ISSN 1298-0358
THE ASIANISTS' ASIA. Text in English. 2000. a. **Description:** Devoted to humanitites and social sciences.
Media: Online - full text.
Published by: Centre de Recherche Sur les Etudes Asiatiques/Research Centre in Asian Studies, 5, Blvd Pablo Picasso, Paris, 94000, France. http://members.aol.com/_ht_a/wignesh/AA2BContents.htm. Ed. T Wignesan.

950 IND ISSN 0571-3161
ASIATIC SOCIETY, CALCUTTA. JOURNAL. Text in English. 1976 (vol.18). a. USD 9. bk.rev. bibl.; charts; illus. reprint service avail. from PQC.
Related titles: Microfiche ed.: (from BHP); Microfilm ed.: (from PQC).
Indexed: AICP, AmH&L, BAS, IBSS, NumL, RASB.
Published by: Asiatic Society Calcutta, One Park St., Kolkata, West Bengal 700 016, India. TEL 91-033-290779, FAX 91-033-290355, TELEX 021 5238 ASIA IN.

950 IND
ASIATIC SOCIETY, CALCUTTA. MONOGRAPH SERIES. Text in English. irreg. USD 10 per vol.. **Document type:** *Monographic series.*
Published by: Asiatic Society Calcutta, One Park St., Kolkata, West Bengal 700 016, India. TEL 91-033-290779, FAX 91-033-290355.

950 IND
ASIATIC SOCIETY, CALCUTTA. SEMINAR SERIES. Text in English. irreg.
Published by: Asiatic Society Calcutta, One Park St., Kolkata, West Bengal 700 016, India. TEL 91-033-290779, FAX 91-033-290355, TELEX 021 5238 ASIA IN.

950 IND ISSN 0368-3303
ASIATIC SOCIETY. JOURNAL. Text in English. 1959. irreg. **Document type:** *Journal, Academic/Scholarly.*

▼ new title ➤ refereed ✶ unverified ♦ full entry avail.

A

Formed by the merger of (19??-1959): Journal of the Asiatic Society. Letters; (1904-1959): Journal of the Asiatic Society. Science (0368-4326); Which was formerly (until 1951): Journal of the Royal Asiatic Society of Bengal. Science (0368-3990); (until 1936): Journal of the Asiatic Society of Bengal. Science (0368-1076); Which superseded in part (in 1935): Asiatic Society of Bengal. Journal and Proceedings (0368-3451); Which was formed by the merger of (1832-1904): Asiatic Society of Bengal. Journal (0368-1068); (1854-1904): Asiatic Society of Bengal. Proceedings (0369-8416)
Indexed: RefZh.
Published by: Asiatic Society Calcutta, One Park St., Kolkata, West Bengal 700 016, India. TEL 91-33-290779, FAX 91-33-290355.

068.549 954 BGD
ASIATIC SOCIETY OF BANGLADESH. ANNUAL GENERAL MEETING: REPORT OF THE GENERAL SECRETARY. Text in English. a. **Document type:** *Academic/Scholarly.*
Published by: Asiatic Society of Bangladesh, Ramna, 5 Old Secretariat Rd Nimtali, Dhaka, 1000, Bangladesh. TEL 2-866582.

ASIATIC SOCIETY OF BANGLADESH. JOURNAL: HUMANITIES. see *HUMANITIES: COMPREHENSIVE WORKS*

ASIATIC SOCIETY OF BANGLADESH. JOURNAL: SCIENCE; man and nature of Asia. see *SCIENCES: COMPREHENSIVE WORKS*

950 IND ISSN 0004-4709
➤ **ASIATIC SOCIETY OF BOMBAY. JOURNAL.** Text in English. 1841; N.S. 1925. a. INR 350. bk.rev. illus. **Document type:** *Journal, Academic/Scholarly.* **Description:** Presents articles on Indology, Sanskrit and Prakrit literature, history, archaeology and other oriental subjects.
Formerly (until 1954): Royal Asiatic Society. Bombay Branch. Journal (0970-2237)
Indexed: AICP, BAS, BibLing, DIP, HistAb, IBR, IBZ, MLA-IB, NumL, RASB.
Published by: Asiatic Society of Bombay, Town Hall, Mumbai, Maharashtra 400 023, India. FAX 91-22-2665139, asbl@bom2.vsnl.net.in. Ed. Devengana Desai. R&P Vimal Shah TEL 91-22-2660956. Circ: 1,000. **Subscr. to:** Arthur Probsthain, 41 Great Russell St, London WC1B 3PL, United Kingdom.

950 952 JPN ISSN 0913-4271
AS552
ASIATIC SOCIETY OF JAPAN. TRANSACTIONS. 4TH SERIES. Text in English. 1872. a. JPY 8,000 (effective 2003). adv. bk.rev. back issues avail.; reprints avail. **Document type:** *Academic/Scholarly.* **Description:** Publishes articles on historical and cultural subjects, chiefly concerning Japan.
Former titles (until 1985): Asiatic Society of Japan. Transactions. 3rd Series (0287-6051); (until 1940): Asiatic Society of Japan. Transactions. 2nd Series (0287-6043); (until 1922): Asiatic Society of Japan. Transactions. 1st Series (0287-6035)
Related titles: Microfilm ed.: (from BHP).
Indexed: BAS, IBSS, MLA-IB, RILM.
Published by: Asiatic Society of Japan, 3-42-3 Otsuka, Bunkyo-ku, Tokyo, 112-0012, Japan. info@asjapan.org, http://ww.asjapan.org. Ed. George Sioris. R&P Hugh E Wilkinson. Circ: 500.

956 DEU ISSN 0571-320X
ASIATISCHE FORSCHUNGEN. Text in German. 1959. irreg., latest vol.146, 2002. price varies. **Document type:** *Monographic series, Academic/Scholarly.*
Published by: (Universitaet Bonn, Seminar fuer Sprach- und Kulturwissenschaft Zentralasiens), Harrassowitz Verlag, Taunusstr 14, Wiesbaden, 65183, Germany. TEL 49-611-5300, FAX 49-611-530570, verlag@harrassowitz.de, http://www.harrassowitz.de. R&P Michael Langfeld. Adv. contact Robert Gietz.

950 CHE ISSN 0004-4717
DS1
➤ **ASIATISCHE STUDIEN/ETUDES ASIATIQUES.** Text in English, French, German. 1939. 4/yr. CHF 95; EUR 66 in Austria & Germany; EUR 62 in Europe; GBP 43, USD 74 (effective 2006). bk.rev. bibl.; illus. index. reprint service avail. from SCH. **Document type:** *Journal, Academic/Scholarly.*
Formerly (until 1947): Schweizerische Gesellschaft der Freunde Ostasiatischer Kultur. Mitteilungen (1420-6854)
Indexed: BAS, BibLing, DIP, IBR, IBZ, IndIslam, MLA, MLA-IB, PCI, RASB.
—IE, Infotrieve.
Published by: (Schweizerische Asiengesellschaft), Verlag Peter Lang AG, Hochfeldstr. 32, Postfach 746, Bern 9, 3000, Switzerland. TEL 41-31-3061717, FAX 41-31-3061727, info@peterlang.com, http://www.peterlang.com. Circ: 600.

950 DNK ISSN 1397-1158
ASIATISKE SKRIFTER. Text in Danish. 1996. irreg., latest vol.8, 2000. DKK 60 (effective 2003). back issues avail. **Document type:** *Monographic series, Academic/Scholarly.*
Published by: Koebenhavns Universitet, Asian Instituttet/Copenhagen University. Department of Asian Studies, Leifsgade 33, Copenhagen S, 2300, Denmark. TEL 45-35-328822, FAX 45-35-328835, asia@hum.ku.dk, http://www.hum.ku.dk/asien/d_publikationer.html.

950 DEU ISSN 0721-5231
DS1
➤ **ASIEN;** deutsche Zeitschrift fuer Politik, Wirtschaft und Kultur. Text in English, German; Summaries in English. 1981. q. EUR 50 (effective 2005). bk.rev. bibl. back issues avail. **Document type:** *Journal, Academic/Scholarly.* **Description:** Contains articles, conference reports, research, book reviews, and lectures on Asia and the South Pacific.
Indexed: APEL, BAS, DIP, ForAb, IBR, IBZ, RDA.
—CCC.
Published by: Deutsche Gesellschaft fuer Asienkunde e.V., Rothenbaumchaussee 32, Hamburg, 20148, Germany. TEL 49-40-445891, FAX 49-40-4107945, post@asienkunde.de, http://www.asienkunde.de/asienzeitschrift/index.html. Ed. Christine Berg. Circ: 1,000.

950 079.6 DEU
ASIEN- UND AFRIKA- STUDIEN DER HUMBOLDT UNIVERSITAET ZU BERLIN. Text in German. 1998. irreg., latest vol.4, 1998. price varies. **Document type:** *Monographic series.*
Former titles (until 1998): Berliner Studien zur Politik in Afrika (0930-7303); (until 1982): Berliner Studien zur Politik in Afrika und Asien (0171-6689)
Published by: Harrassowitz Verlag, Taunusstr 14, Wiesbaden, 65183, Germany. TEL 49-611-530555, FAX 49-611-530559, verlag@harrassowitz.de, http://www.harrassowitz.de. R&P Michael Langfeld. Adv. contact Robert Gietz.

950 DEU ISSN 1437-3688
ASIEN UND PAZIFIK. Text in German. 1999. irreg., latest vol.3, 2002. EUR 39.90 per vol. (effective 2003). **Document type:** *Monographic series, Academic/Scholarly.* **Description:** Presents interdisciplinary studies on Asia, Southeast Asia and the South Pacific.
Published by: Waxmann Verlag GmbH, Steinfurter Str 555, Muenster, 48159, Germany. TEL 49-251-26504-0, FAX 49-251-2650426, info@waxmann.com, http://www.waxmann.com. Ed. Juergen Henze.

950 ESP ISSN 0571-3692
DS1
ASOCIACION ESPANOLA DE ORIENTALISTAS. BOLETIN. Text in Multiple languages. 1965. a., latest vol.37, 2001. bk.rev. charts; illus. back issues avail. **Document type:** *Bulletin, Academic/Scholarly.*
Indexed: AmH&L, BAS, BHA, BibLing, DIP, HistAb, IBR, IBSS, IndIslam, RILM.
—CINDOC.
Published by: Asociacion Espanola de Orientalistas, Universidad Autonoma, Edificio Rectorado, Madrid, 28049, Spain. TEL 34-91-3974112. Ed. Fernando Valderrama. Circ: 500.

950 USA
ASSOCIATION FOR ASIAN STUDIES. ABSTRACTS OF THE ANNUAL MEETING. Text in English. 1992. a.
Formerly (until 2004): Association for Asian Studies. Abstracts of the Annual Meeting (Print) (1066-1603)
Media: Online - full content.
Published by: Association for Asian Studies, Inc., 1 Lane Hall, Univ of Michigan, Ann Arbor, MI 48109. http://www.assianst.org.

ASSOCIATION FOR ASIAN STUDIES. MONOGRAPHS. see *HISTORY—History Of Asia*

ASSYRIOLOGICAL STUDIES. see *LINGUISTICS*

ATELIER A S E M I. see *ANTHROPOLOGY*

950 ESP ISSN 0212-5730
DS56
AULA ORIENTALIS. Text in Spanish. 1983. s-a.
Indexed: NTA, OTA, RI-1.
—CINDOC.
Published by: Editorial Ausa, Apdo. 101, Sabadell, Barcelona 08200, Spain. http://www.ub.es/ipoa/arbor1.htm. Eds. Ignacio Marquez Rowe, Manuel Molina.

955 IRN ISSN 1017-4109
AYANDEH; Persian journal of Iranian studies. Text in Persian, Modern. 1926. m. USD 50 (effective 2001). adv. bk.rev. bibl.; illus. index. **Document type:** *Journal, Academic/Scholarly.*
Former titles (until 1979): Rahnama-yi Kitab (0033-8699); (until 1958): Ayandah (0259-9252)
Indexed: BibLing, MLA, MLA-IB.
Published by: Iraj Afshar, Ed. & Pub., Niyavaran, P O Box 19575-583, Teheran, Iran. TEL 98-21-2283254. Circ: 4,000.

950 NLD ISSN 0922-1751
AZIE. Text in Dutch. 1987. bi-m. EUR 26.70 domestic; EUR 29.10 in Belgium; EUR 5.25 newsstand/cover (effective 2005). adv. **Document type:** *Magazine, Consumer.* **Description:** For those with an interest in Asia.
Published by: Azie Magazine Productions, Striensestraat 100, Rosmalen, 5241 AZ, Netherlands. TEL 31-73-5218801, FAX 31-73-5218842, info@aziemagazine.nl, http://www.aziemagazine/nl. Ed. Eildert de Boer. Circ: 18,000 (paid).

950.05 CAN
➤ **B C ASIAN REVIEW (ONLINE EDITION).** (British Columbia) Text in English. 1987. a. free (effective 2005). back issues avail. **Document type:** *Academic/Scholarly.* **Description:** Features graduate research on Asia related topics, including textual studies and other forms of critical analysis, as well as translations and reviews.
Formerly (until 1998): B C Asian Review (Print Edition) (0835-6432)
Media: Online - full text.
Published by: University of British Columbia, Department of Asian Studies, Asian Centre, 403 - 1871 West Mall, Vancouver, BC V6T 1Z2, Canada. TEL 604-822-0019, FAX 604-822-8937, astudies@interchange.ubc.ca, http://www2.arts.ubc.ca/bcar/, http://www.asia.ubc.ca. Ed. Allen Haaheim.

➤ **BANGALORE THEOLOGICAL FORUM.** see *RELIGIONS AND THEOLOGY*

950 490 AUT ISSN 0259-0654
BEIHEFTE ZUR WIENER ZEITSCHRIFT FUER DIE KUNDE DES MORGENLANDES. Text in German. irreg., latest vol.15, 1989. price varies. **Document type:** *Monographic series.*
Published by: Universitaet Wien, Institut fuer Orientalistik, Spitalgasse 2, Hof 4, Vienna, W 1090, Austria. Michaela.Weszeli@univie.ac.at, http://www.univie.ac.at/orientalistik/. Ed. Arne A Ambros.

956 DEU ISSN 1432-6949
BEITRAEGE ZUR INDOLOGIE. Text in German. 1968. irreg., latest vol.39, 2002. price varies. **Document type:** *Monographic series, Academic/Scholarly.*
Formerly: Freiburger Beitraege zur Indologie (0340-6261)
Published by: Harrassowitz Verlag, Taunusstr 14, Wiesbaden, 65183, Germany. TEL 49-611-5300, FAX 49-611-530570, verlag@harrassowitz.de, http://www.harrassowitz.de. Ed. Konrad Meisig. R&P Michael Langfeld. Adv. contact Robert Gietz.

952 AUT ISSN 0522-6759
BEITRAEGE ZUR JAPANOLOGIE. Text in English, German; Summaries in English, Japanese. 1955. irreg., latest vol.35, 1998. price varies. bk.rev. **Document type:** *Monographic series, Academic/Scholarly.*
Indexed: AICP, IBSS.
Published by: Universitaet Wien, Institut fuer Ostasienwissenschaften - Japanologie, Spitalgasse 2, Vienna, W 1090, Austria. TEL 43-1-427743801, FAX 43-1-42779438, a7611dae@vm.univie.ac.at, japanologie.ostasien@univie.ac.at. Ed. Sepp Linhart. Circ: 300.

950 DEU ISSN 0948-2806
BEITRAEGE ZUR KENNTNIS SUEDASIATISCHER SPRACHEN UND LITERATUREN. Text in German. 1996. irreg., latest vol.11, 2003. price varies. **Document type:** *Monographic series, Academic/Scholarly.*
Published by: Harrassowitz Verlag, Taunusstr 14, Wiesbaden, 65183, Germany. TEL 49-611-5300, FAX 49-611-530570, verlag@harrassowitz.de, http://www.harrassowitz.de. Ed. Dieter Kapp. R&P Michael Langfeld. Adv. contact Robert Gietz.

959 DEU ISSN 1619-7593
BERLINER SUEDOSTASIEN-STUDIEN/BERLIN STUDIES ON SOUTHEAST ASIA. Text in German. 2002. irreg., latest vol.3, 2003. price varies. **Document type:** *Monographic series, Academic/Scholarly.*
Published by: Logos Verlag Berlin, Comeniushof, Gubener Str 47, Berlin, 10243, Germany. TEL 49-30-42851090, FAX 49-30-42851092, redaktion@logos-verlag.de, http://www.logos-verlag.de.

950 DEU ISSN 0138-4228
BERLINER TURFANTEXTE. Text in English, German. 1971. irreg. **Document type:** *Monographic series, Academic/Scholarly.*
Published by: Akademie Verlag GmbH (Subsidiary of: Oldenbourg Wissenschaftsverlag GmbH), Palisadenstr 40, Berlin, 10243, Germany. TEL 49-30-4220060, FAX 49-30-42200657, info@akademie-verlag.de, http://www.akademie-verlag.de.

954 IND ISSN 0378-1143
PK101
➤ **BHANDARKAR ORIENTAL RESEARCH INSTITUTE. ANNALS.** Text in English. 1919. a., latest vol.79, 1998. price varies. bk.rev. back issues avail. **Document type:** *Journal, Academic/Scholarly.* **Description:** Comparative, historical, literary, linguistic and text-critical studies of ancient and medieval Indian literature from the Indo-Aryan languages, for purposes of Indologists and Orientologists.
Indexed: AICP, BAS, BibLing, IBR, MLA, MLA-IB, NumL.
Published by: Bhandarkar Oriental Research Institute, Deccan Gymkhana, Pune, Maharashtra 411 004, India. TEL 91-20-5656932, FAX 91-20-5661362, bori1@vsnl.net. Eds. M G Dhadphale, S D Laddu. Pub., Adv. contact Saroja Bhate. Circ: 1,500.

> **BIBLICA ET ORIENTALIA.** see *RELIGIONS AND THEOLOGY—Roman Catholic*

> **BIBLIOTECA DEGLI STUDI CLASSICI E ORIENTALI.** see *CLASSICAL STUDIES*

> **BIBLIOTHECA ORIENTALIS.** see *HISTORY—Abstracting, Bibliographies, Statistics*

950 490   HUN   ISSN 0067-8104
BIBLIOTHECA ORIENTALIS HUNGARICA. Text in English, French, German. 1955. irreg., latest vol.48, 2003. price varies. bk.rev. bibl.; illus. back issues avail. **Document type:** *Monographic series, Academic/Scholarly.*
Indexed: NTA, OTA.
Published by: Akademiai Kiado Rt. (Subsidiary of: Wolters Kluwer N.V.), Prielle Kornelia U. 19, Budapest, 1117, Hungary. TEL 36-1-4648282, FAX 36-1-4648221, pp@akkrt.hu, http://www.akkrt.hu. Ed. Gyorgy Hazai.

955   BEL
BIBLIOTHEQUE IRANIENNE. Text in English, French. 1975. irreg., latest vol.46, 1996. price varies. back issues avail. **Document type:** *Monographic series.*
Address: Bondgenotenlaan 153, Leuven, 3000, Belgium. TEL 32-16-235170, FAX 32-16-228500, http://www.peeters-leuven.be.

952   FRA   ISSN 0293-0684
BIBLIOTHEQUE JAPONAISE. Variant title: Collection Bibliotheque Japonaise. Text in French. 1978. irreg. price varies. bibl. **Document type:** *Monographic series, Academic/Scholarly.* **Description:** Publishes scholarship on Japan and her culture.
Formerly (until 1981): P O F Etudes. Bibliotheque Japonaise (0184-0231)
Published by: Publications Orientalistes de France, 1 bd de l'Oise, Cergy, 95030, France. TEL 33-1-34223002, FAX 33-1-30734400, http://www.afaa.asso.fr/desa/5-ficheo.htm.

951   DEU   ISSN 1436-0845
BOCHUMER CHINAREIHE. Text in German. 1998. irreg., latest vol.6, 2001. price varies. **Document type:** *Monographic series, Academic/Scholarly.*
Published by: Bochumer Universitaetsverlag GmbH, Querenburger Hoehe 281, Bochum, 44801, Germany. TEL 49-234-9719780, FAX 49-234-9719786, bou@bou.de, http://bou.de.

500   DEU   ISSN 0170-0006
> **BOCHUMER JAHRBUCH ZUR OSTASIENFORSCHUNG.** Text in German. 1978. a. EUR 51 domestic; EUR 52 foreign (effective 2003). bk.rev. **Document type:** *Journal, Academic/Scholarly.*
Indexed: BAS, BibLing, IBR.
Published by: (Ruhr Universitaet Bochum, Fakultaet fuer Ostasienwissenschaften), Iudicium Verlag, Hans-Graessel-Weg 13, Munich, 81375, Germany. TEL 49-89-718747, FAX 49-89-7142039, andreas.v.pigulla@rz.ruhr-uni-bochum.de, info@iudicium.de, http://www.iudicium.de. Eds. Andreas Pigulla, Christine Moll Murata. Circ: 80.

952   DEU   ISSN 0173-7902
BONNER JAPANFORSCHUNGEN. Text in German. 1979. irreg. back issues avail. **Document type:** *Monographic series, Academic/Scholarly.*
Published by: Bonner Verein zur Foerderung der Japanforschung e.V., Regina-Pacis-Weg 7, Bonn, 53113, Germany. TEL 49-228-739693, FAX 49-228-737020. Ed. Josef Kreiner. Circ: 500 (controlled).

950   DEU   ISSN 0947-1200
BONNER SAMMLUNG VON AEGYPTIACA. Text in German. 1995. irreg., latest vol.4, 2001. price varies. **Document type:** *Monographic series, Academic/Scholarly.*
Published by: Harrassowitz Verlag, Taunusstr 14, Wiesbaden, 65183, Germany. TEL 49-611-5300, FAX 49-611-530570, verlag@harrassowitz.de, http://www.harrassowitz.de. Ed. Ursula Roessler Koehler. R&P Michael Langfeld. Adv. contact Robert Gietz.

BOSTON COLLEGE THIRD WORLD LAW JOURNAL. see *LAW—International Law*

954   USA   ISSN 1542-0094
DS331
> **BRIDGES (OAKLAND);** Berkeley research journal on South and Southeast Asia. Text in English. 2002 (Fall). a. **Document type:** *Academic/Scholarly.* **Description:** Features articles and reviews by graduate students, faculty, and independent scholars focusing on various topics within the broad fields of South and Southeast Asian studies.
Related titles: Online - full text ed.: ISSN 1542-0108.
Published by: Bridges Magazine, 6701 San pablo Ave, Ste 210, Oakland, CA 94608. TEL 510-642-4912, adheesh@socrates.berkeley.edu, http://brjss.berkeley.edu. Ed. Anita Anantharan.

954   NLD   ISSN 0925-2916
> **BRILL'S INDOLOGICAL LIBRARY.** Text in English. 1991. irreg., latest vol.17, 2001. price varies. back issues avail. **Document type:** *Monographic series, Academic/Scholarly.* **Description:** Scholarly monographs on topics in Indian religion, language, history and philosophy.
Published by: Brill Academic Publishers, PO Box 9000, Leiden, 2300 PA, Netherlands. TEL 31-71-53-53-500, FAX 31-71-53-17-532, cs@brill.nl, http://www.brill.nl. Ed. Johannes Bronkhorst. R&P Elizabeth Venekamp. **Subscr. in N. America to:** PO Box 605, Herndon, VA 20172. TEL 703-661-1585, 800-337-9255, FAX 703-661-1501, cs@brillusa.com. **Distr. outside N. America by:** c/o Turpin Distribution, Stratton Business Park, Pegasus Drive, Biggleswade, BEDFORDSHIRE SG 18 8TQ, United Kingdom. TEL 44-1767-604-954, FAX 44-1767-601-640, brill@turpin-distribution.com.

952   NLD   ISSN 0925-6512
> **BRILL'S JAPANESE STUDIES LIBRARY.** Text in Dutch. 1990. irreg., latest vol.17, 2002. price varies. back issues avail. **Document type:** *Monographic series, Academic/Scholarly.* **Description:** Scholarly studies of Japanese literary history and traditions, and related topics in linguistics.
Published by: Brill Academic Publishers, PO Box 9000, Leiden, 2300 PA, Netherlands. TEL 31-71-53-53-500, FAX 31-71-53-17-532, cs@brill.nl, http://www.brill.nl. R&P Elizabeth Venekamp. **Subscr. in N. America to:** PO Box 605, Herndon, VA 20172. TEL 703-661-1585, 800-337-9255, FAX 703-661-1501, cs@brillusa.com. **Distr. outside N. America by:** c/o Turpin Distribution, Stratton Business Park, Pegasus Drive, Biggleswade, BEDFORDSHIRE SG 18 8TQ, United Kingdom. TEL 44-1767-604-954, FAX 44-1767-601-640, brill@turpin-distribution.com.

950 305.8951 028.5   GBR   ISSN 1360-0923
BRUSHSTROKES; a collection of British Chinese writings and drawings. Text in English, Chinese. 1995. 3/yr. GBP 8 in United Kingdom; GBP 11 in Europe; GBP 16 rest of world (effective 2001). adv. bk.rev. illus. back issues avail. **Document type:** *Magazine.* **Description:** Contains factual or creative writing and artwork by British Chinese. Its purpose is to encourage British Chinese to discuss and reflect on their lives and experiences; document the history of the Chinese in Britain.
Address: Avril Robarts Learning Resource Centre, Liverpool John Moores University, 79 Tithebarn St, Liverpool, L2 2ER, United Kingdom. TEL 44-151-231-4015, FAX 44-151-231-4479, g.k.chan@livjm.ac.uk. Ed. Graham Chan. adv.: B&W page GBP 200. Circ: 500; 60 (paid).

950   HUN   ISSN 0139-4614
BUDAPEST ORIENTAL REPRINTS, SERIES A. Text in Hungarian. 1977. irreg. per issue exchange basis. **Document type:** *Monographic series.*
Published by: (Korosi Csoma Tarsasag), Magyar Tudomanyos Akademia, Konyvtara, Arany Janos utca 1, PO Box 1002, Budapest, 1245, Hungary. TEL 36-1-338-2344, FAX 36-1-331-6954. Eds. E Schutz, Eva Apor.

BUDDHIST TRADITION SERIES. see *RELIGIONS AND THEOLOGY—Buddhist*

BULLETIN CRITIQUE DES ANNALES ISLAMOLOGIQUES (CD-ROM EDITION). see *RELIGIONS AND THEOLOGY—Islamic*

950   FRA   ISSN 1162-5058
BULLETIN DE L'OEUVRE D'ORIENT. Key Title: Oeuvres d'Orient. Text in French. 1856. bi-m.
Formerly (1857-1931): Oeuvre des Ecoles d'Orient (1162-5066); Which incorporates (1858-1874): Bulletin de l'Oeuvre des Pelerinages en Terre-Sainte (1160-3941)
Published by: Association de l'Oeuvre d'Orient, 20 rue du Regard, Paris, 75006, France. Ed. Jean Maksud. Circ: 150,000.

950   FRA   ISSN 0253-1623
BULLETIN D'ETUDES ORIENTALES. Text in Arabic, English, French, German. 1931. irreg., latest vol.50, 1999. **Document type:** *Monographic series, Academic/Scholarly.*
Indexed: BHA, BibLing, CCMJ, MathR, MathSciNet, PCI.
Published by: Librairie d'Amerique et d'Orient, 11 rue Saint-Sulpice, Paris, 75006, France. FAX 33-1-43545954.

952   DEU   ISSN 0932-268X
BUNKEN; Studien und Materialen zur japanischen Literatur. Text in German. 1987. irreg., latest vol.9, 2003. price varies. **Document type:** *Monographic series, Academic/Scholarly.*
Published by: Harrassowitz Verlag, Taunusstr 14, Wiesbaden, 65183, Germany. TEL 49-611-5300, FAX 49-611-530570, verlag@harrassowitz.de, http://www.harrassowitz.de. Ed. Ekkehard May. R&P Michael Langfeld. Adv. contact Robert Gietz.

949.5   DEU   ISSN 0007-7704
PA5000
BYZANTINISCHE ZEITSCHRIFT. Text in Multiple languages. 1892. s-a. EUR 228; EUR 114 newsstand/cover (effective 2006). adv. bk.rev. bibl.; illus. index, cum.index: vols.1-12. back issues avail.; reprint service avail. from SCH. **Document type:** *Journal, Academic/Scholarly.* **Description:** Covers research in Byzantine history.
Indexed: ASCA, ArtHuCI, BHA, BibLing, CurCont, DIP, IBR, IBZ, IPB, IndIslam, MLA, MLA-IB, MathSciNet, NumL, PCI, RASB, RI-1, RI-2, RILM.
—IDS, IE, Infotrieve. **CCC.**
Published by: K.G. Saur Verlag GmbH (Subsidiary of: Gale Group), Ortlerstr 8, Munchen, 81373, Germany. TEL 49-89-769020, FAX 49-89-76902150, info@saur.de, http://www.saur.de/Journals/jbyze.htm. Ed. Albrecht Berger. Circ: 1,000.

949.5 487   CZE   ISSN 0007-7712
CB231
> **BYZANTINOSLAVICA;** revue internationale des etudes byzantines. Text in English, French, German, Italian, Russian. 1929. irreg., latest vol.62, 2005. EUR 110 per vol. foreign (effective 2006). bk.rev. bibl.; illus.; maps. index, cum index. 360 p./no.; back issues avail. **Document type:** *Monographic series, Academic/Scholarly.* **Description:** Focuses on all aspects of Byzantine studies and provides an extensive bibliography of contemporary international publications in Byzantinology.
Indexed: ASCA, ArtHuCI, BHA, BibInd, BibLing, CERDIC, CurCont, DIP, IBR, IBZ, IndIslam, MLA, MLA-IB, NumL, RASB, RI-1, RI-2.
Published by: Akademie Ved Ceske Republiky, Slovansky Ustav, Valentinska 1, Prague 1, 110 00, Czech Republic. TEL 420-224-300251, FAX 420-224-800252, byzslav@slu.cas.cz, http://www.lib.cas.cz/knav/journals/eng/Byzantinoslavica.htm. Ed. Vladimir Vavrinek. Circ: 1,100.

900   BEL   ISSN 0378-2506
PA5000
BYZANTION; revue internationale des etudes byzantines. Text in English, French, German, Greek, Italian, Spanish. 1924. s-a. EUR 50 in Europe; EUR 60 elsewhere (effective 2005). bk.rev. bibl. reprints avail. **Document type:** *Academic/Scholarly.*
Indexed: BHA, BibLing, DIP, IBR, IBZ, IPB, MLA, MLA-IB, NumL, PCI, RASB.
—IE, Infotrieve.
Published by: (Byzantion asbl), Universa Press (Wetteren), Rue Hoender 24, Wetteren, 9230, Belgium. FAX 32-9-366-0199, universa.press@pop.KPN.be, http://www.kbr.be/~tnazyb. Ed. Panayotis Yannopoulos.

950   LBN
> **C E M A M REPORTS.** (Centre pour l'Etude du Monde Arabe Moderne) Text in French. 1974. a. price varies. **Document type:** *Academic/Scholarly.*
Published by: (Centre pour l'Etude du Monde Arabe Modern), Dar el-Machreq S.A.R.L., Ashrafieh, P O Box 166778, Beirut, Lebanon. TEL 961-1-202423, machreq@cyberia.net.lb. Pub. Hechaime Camille.

950   USA
D1
C H U S NEWSLETTER. Text in English. q. USD 20 to members. **Document type:** *Newsletter.* **Description:** Promotes exchange among historians in China and the United States.
Published by: Chinese Historians in the United States, Inc., 225 Keith Hall, Indiana University of Pennsylvania, Indiana, PA 15705-1087. TEL 724-357-2237, FAX 724-357-6478, ch-review@iup.edu, http://216.32.70.150/affiliates/chus.htm, http://www.chss.iup.edu/history/CHR/. Ed. Xi Wang. Circ: 202.

C W A S NEWSLETTER. see *WOMEN'S STUDIES*

CAHIERS DE LINGUISTIQUE ASIE ORIENTALE. see *LINGUISTICS*

CAHIERS DU MONDE RUSSE; Empire Russe, Union Sovietique, etats independants. see *HISTORY—History Of Europe*

950   AUT   ISSN 1215-7279
CAHIERS FRANCOPHONES D'EUROPE CENTRE ORIENTALE. Text in French. 1991. a. price varies. **Document type:** *Journal, Academic/Scholarly.*
Indexed: IBZ.
Published by: (Association des Etudes Francophones d'Europe Centre Orientale), Wilhelm Braumueller Universitaets-Verlagsbuchhandlung GmbH, Servitengasse 5, Vienna, 1092, Austria. TEL 43-1-3191159, FAX 43-1-3102805, office@braumueller.at, http://www.braumueller.at. Eds. Arpad Vigh, Fritz Peter Kirsch.

956.1   FRA   ISSN 0337-3371
CAHIERS TURCICA. Text in French. 1975. irreg. price varies. illus.; maps. back issues avail. **Document type:** *Monographic series, Academic/Scholarly.* **Description:** Publishes research in various disciplines in the study of ancient Turkey.
Related titles: ◆ Supplement to: Turcica. ISSN 0082-6847.
Published by: Publications Orientalistes de France, 1 bd de l'Oise, Cergy, 95030, France. TEL 33-1-34223002, FAX 33-1-30734400, http://www.afaa.asso.fr/desa/5-ficheo.htm.

950 GBR
CAMBRIDGE ASIA - PACIFIC STUDIES. Text in English. 1994. irreg., latest 2002. price varies. **Document type:** *Monographic series, Academic/Scholarly.* **Description:** Provides a focus and forum for scholarly work on the Asia-Pacific region as a whole, and its component sub-regions, namely Northeast Asia, Southeast Asia and the Pacific Islands.
Published by: Cambridge University Press, The Edinburgh Bldg, Shaftesbury Rd, Cambridge, CB2 2RU, United Kingdom. TEL 44-1223-312393, FAX 44-1223-315052, information@cambridge.org, http://publishing.cambridge.org/series/capc.

956 GBR
CAMBRIDGE MIDDLE EAST STUDIES. Text in English. irreg., latest vol.3, 1995. **Document type:** *Monographic series.* **Description:** Aims to provide new and original interpretations of aspects of Middle Eastern societies and their histories.
—BLDSC (3015.962780).
Published by: University of Cambridge, Press Syndicate, The Pitt Bldg, Trumpington St, Cambridge, Cambs CB2 1RP, United Kingdom. TEL 44-1223-315052. Ed. Charles Tripp.

CELESTINESCA. see *LITERATURE*

CENTER PAPYROLOGICAL STUDIES. BULLETIN/MAGALLAT MARKAZ AL-DIRASAT AL-BARDIYAT. see *HISTORY—History Of Africa*

958 PAK ISSN 1729-9802
DS785.A1
➤ **CENTRAL ASIA.** Text in English. 1978. s-a. PKR 90, USD 25 (effective 2004). **Document type:** *Journal, Academic/Scholarly.*
Indexed: BAS, IBR, MLA-IB, PerIslam, RASB.
Published by: University of Peshawar, Area Study Center (Russia, China and Central Asia), Peshawar, Pakistan. TEL 92-91-921670120, FAX 92-91-9216470, zauop@yahoo.com, http://upesh.edu/centres/asc/asc.html. Ed. Mohammad Anwar Khan. R&P Dr. Azmat Hayat Khan. Adv. contact Dr. Zahid Anwar Khan. Circ: 200.

➤ **CENTRAL ASIA-CAUCASUS ANALYST.** see *POLITICAL SCIENCE*

950 490 890 DEU ISSN 0008-9192
DS327 CODEN: CAJOFE
➤ **CENTRAL ASIATIC JOURNAL**; international periodical for the languages, literatures, history and archaeology of Central Asia. Text in English, French, German. 1955. s-a. EUR 84; CHF 142 in Switzerland (effective 2006). adv. bk.rev. bibl.; charts; illus. index. back issues avail.; reprints avail. **Document type:** *Journal, Academic/Scholarly.*
Indexed: ASCA, ArtHuCI, ArtInd, BAS, BibInd, BibLing, CurCont, DIP, IBR, IBSS, IBZ, MEA&I, MLA-IB, NumL, PCI, RASB.
—IDS, IE, Infotrieve. **CCC.**
Published by: Harrassowitz Verlag, Taunusstr 14, Wiesbaden, 65183, Germany. TEL 49-611-5300, FAX 49-611-530560, verlag@harrassowitz.de, http://www.harrassowitz.de. Ed. Giovanni Stary. R&P Michael Langfeld. Adv. contact Robert Gietz. Circ: 550.

959 490 CAN ISSN 0839-4555
➤ **CENTRE D'ETUDES DE L'ASIE DE L'EST. CAHIERS**; recherche sur l'Asie de l'Est. Text in Chinese, English, French, Japanese. 1980. irreg., latest vol.19. CND 8 per issue (effective 1998). bk.rev. back issues avail. **Document type:** *Academic/Scholarly.* **Description:** Presents a multidisciplinary forum that covers all aspects of the Far East. Publishes original manuscripts, notes, essays, documents, bibliographical studies in the field of humanities by specialists of East and Southeast Asia.
Published by: (Centre d'Etudes de l'Asie de l'Est), Universite de Montreal, Faculte des Arts et des Sciences, Succ Centre Ville, C P 6128, Montreal, PQ H3C 3J7, Canada. TEL 514-343-5970, FAX 514-343-7716. Ed. Claude Comtois. Circ: 500.

950 GBR
CENTRE FOR ASIA-PACIFIC STUDIES NEWS. Text in English. q. **Document type:** *Newsletter.* **Description:** Promotes new academic research, contributes to postgraduate and undergraduate study, and provides a service to the local, regional and national communities in relation to the countries of the Asia-Pacific.
Media: Online - full text.
Published by: Centre for Asia-Pacific Studies, United Kingdom. ins3mcneij@ntu.ac.uk, http://human.ntu.ac.uk/foh/caps.html. Ed. Jane McNeil.

959 GBR ISSN 0269-1760
CENTRE FOR SOUTH-EAST ASIAN STUDIES. BIBLIOGRAPHY AND LITERATURE SERIES. Text in English. 1986. irreg., latest vol.13, special issues available. price varies. back issues avail. **Document type:** *Monographic series, Bibliography.*
—BLDSC (2002.080000).
Published by: Centre for South-East Asian Studies, University of Hull, Cottingham Rd, Hull, HU6 7RX, United Kingdom. TEL 44-1482-465967, s.ryan@pol-as.hull.ac.uk. Ed. V T King.

CENTRE FOR SOUTH-EAST ASIAN STUDIES. OCCASIONAL PAPERS. see *HISTORY—History Of Asia*

950 IND
CHAUKHAMBHA ORIENTAL RESEARCH STUDIES. Text in English. 1976. irreg., latest vol.35, 1989. price varies. **Document type:** *Monographic series.*
Published by: Chaukhambha Orientalia, Gokul Bhawan, K 37-109 Gopal Mandir Ln., Varanasi, Uttar Pradesh 221 001, India.

951 GBR ISSN 0920-203X
DS701
➤ **CHINA INFORMATION**; a journal on contemporary China studies. Text in English. 1967. 3/yr. GBP 286, USD 499 to institutions; GBP 297, USD 520 combined subscription to institutions print & online eds. (effective 2006). adv. bk.rev. 180 p./no.; back issues avail. **Document type:** *Journal, Academic/Scholarly.* **Description:** Presents timely and in-depth analyses of major developments in contemporary China and overseas Chinese communities in the areas of politics, economics, law, ecology, culture, and society, including literature and the arts.
Formerly (until 1986): China Informatie (0577-8832)
Related titles: Online - full content ed.; Online - full text ed.: ISSN 1741-590X. GBP 283, USD 494 to institutions (effective 2006) (from EBSCO Publishing, O C L C Online Computer Library Center, Inc., Sage Publications, Inc., Swets Information Services).
Indexed: BAS, IBSS, IPSA, KES, MLA-IB, RDA, RILM.
—BLDSC (3180.170700), IE, ingenta. **CCC.**
Published by: (Universiteit Leiden, Institute of Sinology NLD, Documentation and Research Centre for Modern China NLD), Sage Publications Ltd. (Subsidiary of: Sage Publications, Inc.), 1 Oliver's Yard, 55 City Rd, London, EC1 1SP, United Kingdom. TEL 44-20-73248500, FAX 44-20-73248600, info@sagepub.co.uk, http://www.sagepub.co.uk/journal.aspx?pid=105836. Ed. Tak-Wing Ngo TEL 31-71-527-2528. Circ: 375. **Subscr. in the Americas to:** Sage Publications, Inc., 2455 Teller Rd, Thousand Oaks, CA 91320. TEL 805-499-0721, FAX 805-499-0871, journals@sagepub.com.

320 AUS ISSN 1324-9347
DS701
➤ **THE CHINA JOURNAL.** Text in English. 1979. s-a. (Jan. & Jul.). AUD 25 domestic to individuals; USD 25 foreign to individuals; AUD 40, USD 40 domestic to institutions (effective 2004). adv. bk.rev. illus. Index. 230 p./no.; back issues avail.; reprints avail. **Document type:** *Academic/Scholarly.* **Description:** Focuses on topics relating to China, Hong Kong and Taiwan since 1949, plus studies of the major issues that contribute to understanding of Communist Party history and contemporary events.
Formerly (until Jul. 1995): Australian Journal of Chinese Affairs (0156-7365)
Related titles: Microform ed.: (from PQC); Online - full text ed.: (from EBSCO Publishing, JSTOR (Web-based Journal Archive), ProQuest Information & Learning).
Indexed: APEL, ASCA, AmH&L, ArtHuCI, AusPAIS, BAS, CurCont, DIP, FamI, GEOBASE, HistAb, IBR, IBSS, IBZ, IPSA, PAIS, PCI, PSA, RDA, RILM, RRTA, SSCI, SUSA, SociolAb, WAE&RSA, WTA.
—BLDSC (3180.179900), IDS, IE, Infotrieve, ingenta. **CCC.**
Published by: Contemporary China Centre, Australian National University, Research School of Pacific and Asian Studies, Canberra, ACT 0200, Australia. TEL 61-2-62494150, FAX 61-2-62573642, ccc@coombs.anu.edu.au, http://rspas.anu.edu.au/ccc/journal.htm, http://rspas.anu.edu.au/ccc/home.htm. Eds. Anita Chan, Jonathan Unger. R&P Sarah Leeming TEL 61-2-92490152. Adv. contact Heli Brecht. Circ: 1,300.

951 DEU
CHINA-JOURNAL. Text in German. 2002. irreg. price varies. **Document type:** *Monographic series, Academic/Scholarly.*
Published by: Deutsche China Gesellschaft e.V./German China Association, c/o Prof. Dr. Gregor Paul, Klauprechtstr. 41, Karlsruhe, 76137, Germany. TEL 49-721-816802, FAX 49-721-9812500, dcg@dcg.de, http://www.dcg.de/journal/index.html, http://dcg.de.

951 GBR ISSN 0305-7410
DS701
➤ **THE CHINA QUARTERLY**; an international journal for the study of China. Text in English. 1959. q. USD 166 in North America to institutions; GBP 100 elsewhere to institutions; USD 172 combined subscription in North America to institutions print & online eds.; GBP 96 combined subscription elsewhere to institutions print & online eds. (effective 2006). adv. bk.rev. bibl.; charts; maps; illus. index. reprints avail. **Document type:** *Journal, Academic/Scholarly.* **Description:** Covers all aspects of modern China studies.
Related titles: Microfilm ed.: (from PQC); Online - full text ed.: ISSN 1468-2648. USD 160 in North America to institutions; GBP 96 elsewhere to institutions (effective 2006) (from JSTOR (Web-based Journal Archive), O C L C Online Computer Library Center, Inc., Swets Information Services).
Indexed: ABCPolSci, APEL, ASCA, Acal, AmH&L, ArtHuCI, BAS, CJA, CurCont, DIP, EI, FamI, GEOBASE, HistAb, IBR, IBSS, IBZ, ILD, IPSA, JEL, KES, MEA&I, MLA, MLA-IB, PAIS, PRA, PSA, RASB, RDA, RRTA, RefSour, SSA, SSCI, SSI, SociolAb, TriticAb, WAE&RSA.
—BLDSC (3180.230000), IE, Infotrieve, ingenta.
Published by: (University of London), Cambridge University Press, The Edinburgh Bldg, Shaftesbury Rd, Cambridge, CB2 2RU, United Kingdom. TEL 44-1223-312393, FAX 44-1223-315052, journals@cambridge.org, http://titles.cambridge.org/journals/journal_catalogue.asp?historylinks=ALPHA&mnemonic=CQY, http://www.cup.cam.ac.uk/. Ed. Julia Strauss. adv.: B&W page USD 590; 200 x 135. Circ: 2,700. **Subscr. to:** Cambridge University Press, 100 Brook Hill Dr, West Nyack, NY 10994. TEL 845-353-7500, FAX 845-353-4141, journals_subscriptions@cup.org

➤ **CHINA REVIEW.** see *GENERAL INTEREST PERIODICALS—China*

951 DEU ISSN 1616-1556
CHINA - SCIENCE & SCHOLARSHIP. Text in English, German. 2000. irreg., latest vol.5, 2002. price varies. **Document type:** *Monographic series, Academic/Scholarly.*
Published by: Bochumer Universitaetsverlag GmbH, Querenburger Hoehe 281, Bochum, 44801, Germany. TEL 49-234-9719780, FAX 49-234-9719786, bou@bou.de, http://bou.de.

CHINESE AMERICA, HISTORY AND PERSPECTIVES. see *ETHNIC INTERESTS*

950 USA ISSN 1547-402X
D1
THE CHINESE HISTORICAL REVIEW; the journal of Chinese historians in the United States. Text in English. 1987. s-a. USD 30 to individuals; USD 50 to institutions; USD 20 to students (effective 2004). bk.rev. **Document type:** *Academic/Scholarly.* **Description:** Provides original research on the history of China, China's historical relations with the world, historical experiences of the overseas Chinese, as well as comparative studies of history.
Former titles (until 2004): Chinese Historians (1043-643X); (until 1987): Historian (Athens)
Indexed: AmH&L, HistAb.
Published by: Chinese Historians in the United States, Inc., 225 Keith Hall, Indiana University of Pennsylvania, Indiana, PA 15705-1087. TEL 724-357-2237, FAX 724-357-6478, ch-review@iup.edu, http://www.chss.iup.edu/history/CHR/. Ed. Xi Wang. Circ: 202.

951 USA
CHINESE STUDIES. Text in English. 1995. irreg. (3-4/y.), latest vol.29, 2003. **Document type:** *Monographic series, Academic/Scholarly.*
Published by: Edwin Mellen Press, 415 Ridge St, P.O. Box 450, Lewiston, NY 14092. TEL 716-754-2266, FAX 716-754-4056, cservice@mellenpress.com, http://www.mellenpress.com/.

CHINESE STUDIES IN HISTORY; a journal of translations. see *HISTORY*

CHING FENG; a journal on Christianity and Chinese religion and culture. see *RELIGIONS AND THEOLOGY*

951 895.1 USA ISSN 0193-7774
PL2253
➤ **CHINOPERL PAPERS.** Cover title: Chung-kuo Yen Ch'ang Wen i Yen Chiu Hui Lun Chi. Text in Chinese, English. 1969. irreg., latest vol.18, 1995. price varies. adv. bk.rev. bibl. back issues avail. **Document type:** *Academic/Scholarly.* **Description:** Deals primarily with oral Chinese literature (popular storytelling, opera, ceremonial chanting and folksongs) and various genres of Chinese verse and prose.
Formerly: Chinoperl News
Indexed: BAS, RILM.
Published by: Conference on Chinese Oral and Performing Literature, c/o Bell Yung, Music Department, University of Pittsburgh, Pittsburgh, PA 15260. TEL 412-624-4061, FAX 412-624-4186. Eds. Lindy Li Mark, Samuel H N Cheung. R&P, Adv. contact Dianne Dakis. Circ: 200.

962 BEL ISSN 0009-6067
DT57
CHRONIQUE D'EGYPTE. Text in English, French, German, Italian. 1925. s-a. bk.rev. bibl.; illus. cum.index: vols.1-10, 11-35, 36-50. back issues avail. **Document type:** *Academic/Scholarly.*
Indexed: BHA, BibInd, BibLing, IBR, IndIslam, MLA, MLA-IB, NTA, RASB.
Published by: Fondation Egyptologique Reine Elisabeth, Parc du Cinquantenaire 10, Brussels, 1000, Belgium. TEL 32-2-7417364. Eds. H de Meulenaere, J Bingen. Circ: 1,000.

CINERAIDER. see *LITERARY AND POLITICAL REVIEWS*

952 FRA ISSN 1164-5857
DS801
CIPANGO. Text in French. a. price varies. **Description:** Interdisciplinary study of Japan, past and present.
Published by: Institut National des Langues et Civilisations Orientales (INALCO), 2 rue de Lille, Paris, Cedex 7 75343, France. TEL 33-01-49264274, FAX 33-01-49264299, http://www.inalco.fr.

950 DEU ISSN 0340-6393
CODICES ARABICI ANTIQUI. Text in German. 1972. irreg., latest vol.8, 2003. price varies. **Document type:** *Monographic series, Academic/Scholarly.*
Published by: Harrassowitz Verlag, Taunusstr 14, Wiesbaden, 65183, Germany. TEL 49-611-5300, FAX 49-611-530570, verlag@harrassowitz.de, http://www.harrassowitz.de. Ed. R G Khoury. R&P Michael Langfeld. Adv. contact Robert Gietz.

950 ARG
COLECCION ORIENTE-OCCIDENTE. Text in Spanish. 1976. irreg. price varies.
Published by: Universidad del Salvador, Instituto Latinoamericano de Investigaciones Comparadas Oriente-Occidente, Avda. Callao, 853, Capital Federal, Buenos Aires 1023, Argentina. Ed. I Quiles. Circ: 2,000.

952 FRA ISSN 1160-3305
COLLECTION TAMA. Variant title: Tama. Text in French. 1992. irreg. illus. **Document type:** *Monographic series, Academic/Scholarly.* **Description:** Publishes research in Japanese studies.
Published by: Publications Orientalistes de France, 1 bd de l'Oise, Cergy, 95030, France. TEL 33-1-34223002, FAX 33-1-30734400, http://www.afaa.asso.fr/desa/5-ficheo.htm. Pub. Simone Maviel-Sieffert.

956.1 BEL
➤ **COLLECTION TURCICA.** Text in English, French. 1981. irreg., latest vol.8, 1995. price varies. back issues avail. **Document type:** *Monographic series, Academic/Scholarly.* **Description:** Publishes contributions on topics relating to the history and culture of the Ottoman Empire, Turkey and other Turkic-speaking areas.
Related titles: ♦ Supplement to: Turcica. ISSN 0082-6847.
Published by: Peeters Publishers, Bondgenotenlaan 153, Leuven, 3000, Belgium. TEL 32-16-235170, FAX 32-16-228500, http://www.peeters-leuven.be.

➤ **COLLECTIONS BAUR. BULLETIN.** see *MUSEUMS AND ART GALLERIES*

951 FRA ISSN 0337-792X
COLLEGE DE FRANCE. INSTITUT DES HAUTES ETUDES CHINOISES. MEMOIRS. Text in French. 1975. irreg. price varies. illus. reprints avail. **Document type:** *Monographic series, Academic/Scholarly.*
Published by: (Institut des Hautes Etudes Chinoises), College de France, 11 Place Marcelin Berthelot, Paris, 75231 Cedex 05, France. TEL 33-1-44271101, FAX 33-1-44271109, contact@college-de-france.fr, http://www.college-de-france.fr. **Dist. by:** De Boccard Edition - Diffusion, 11 rue de Medicis, Paris 75006, France.

950 FRA ISSN 0248-5095
COLLOQUES LANGUES'O. Text in French. irreg. price varies. **Document type:** *Academic/Scholarly.*
Published by: Institut National des Langues et Civilisations Orientales (INALCO), 2 rue de Lille, Paris, Cedex 7 75343, France. TEL 49-26-42-74. Ed. Andre Bourgey. R&P Sylvie Plan.

COLUMBIA EAST ASIAN REVIEW. see *POLITICAL SCIENCE*

COLUMBIA JOURNAL OF ASIAN LAW. see *LAW*

950 USA
COLUMBIA UNIVERSITY. EAST ASIAN INSTITUTE. STUDIES. Variant title: East Asian Institute Series. Text in English. 1962. irreg., latest 1995. price varies. **Document type:** *Monographic series.*
Published by: Columbia University Press, 61 W 62nd St, New York, NY 10023. TEL 212-666-1000. Ed. Kate Witterberg. R&P Lisa Simmars.

COMMONWEALTH NOVEL IN ENGLISH. see *LITERATURE*

COMPUTER AIDED RESEARCH IN NEAR EASTERN STUDIES. see *HISTORY—Computer Applications*

CONTEMPORARY CHINA INSTITUTE PUBLICATIONS. see *HISTORY—History Of Asia*

950 306.4 USA
CONTEMPORARY ISSUES IN ASIA AND THE PACIFIC. Text in English. 1995. irreg., latest vol.4, 1999. price varies. back issues avail. **Document type:** *Monographic series, Academic/Scholarly.* **Description:** Examines cultural and socio-political issues in Asia and the Pacific Rim.
Published by: Stanford University Press (Subsidiary of: Stanford University), 1450 Page Mill Rd., Palo Alto, CA 94304-1124. TEL 650-723-9434, FAX 650-725-3457, http://www.sup.org/search/index.html. **In Europe:** Cambridge University Press, The Edinburgh Bldg, Shaftesbury Rd, Cambridge CB2 2RU, United Kingdom. TEL 44-1223-312393, FAX 44-1223-315052; **In the Americas:** Cambridge University Press Distribution Center, 110 Brookhill Dr., West Nyack, NY 10994-2140. TEL 800-872-7423.

950 USA ISSN 1053-1866
CODEN: PPTRDD
CONTRIBUTIONS IN ASIAN STUDIES. Text in English. 1991. irreg. price varies. **Document type:** *Monographic series, Academic/Scholarly.*
Published by: Greenwood Publishing Group Inc. (Subsidiary of: Harcourt International), 88 Post Rd W, PO Box 5007, Westport, CT 06881. TEL 203-226-3571, FAX 203-226-1502, webmaster@greenwood.com, http://www.greenwood.com.

CONTRIBUTIONS TO NEPALESE STUDIES. see *HISTORY—History Of Asia*

CONTRIBUTIONS TO SOUTHEAST ASIAN ETHNOGRAPHY. see *ANTHROPOLOGY*

950 DNK ISSN 1395-4199
DS501
➤ **COPENHAGEN JOURNAL OF ASIAN STUDIES.** Text in English. 1987. biennial. DKK 300, EUR 40; DKK 250, EUR 30 to students; DKK 175, EUR 25 per issue (effective 2005). adv. bk.rev. back issues avail. **Document type:** *Journal, Academic/Scholarly.* **Description:** Covers East and Southeast Asia from a wide range of angles within the social sciences and humanities. While international in scope, the journal is also meant to act as a window on the ongoing Nordic research on East and Southeast Asia.
Formerly (until 1995): Copenhagen Papers in East and Southeast Asian Studies (0903-2703)
Indexed: APEL, BAS, GEOBASE, IBR, IPSA.
—BLDSC (3466.104500). **CCC.**
Published by: Copenhagen Business School, Asia Research Centre, Porcelaenshaven 24 B, 3, Frederiksberg, 2000, Denmark. TEL 45-38-152515, FAX 45-38-152500, cjas.int@cbs.dk, arc.int@cbs.dk, http://www.cbs.dk/arc. Ed. Kjeld Erik Broedsgaard.

950 USA ISSN 0734-449X
Z688.A75
CORMOSEA BULLETIN. Text in English. 1974 (vol.7). s-a. USD 10. bk.rev. bibl. **Document type:** *Bulletin.* **Description:** Bibliographies and reviews of research materials in Southeast Asian Studies.
Formerly: Cormosea Newsletter
Indexed: BAS, EI.
Published by: Association for Asian Studies, Inc., Committee for Research Materials on Southeast Asia, University of Michigan, One Lane Hall, Ann Arbor, MI 48109. TEL 313-665-2490, FAX 608-265-2754. Ed. Carol Mitchell. Circ: 200.

950 USA ISSN 1050-2955
➤ **CORNELL EAST ASIA SERIES.** Text in English. 1973. irreg., latest vol.108, 2001. price varies. **Document type:** *Academic/Scholarly.* **Description:** Publishes manuscripts on a wide variety of scholarly topics pertaining to East Asia (China, Japan, Korea).
Formerly (until 1991): Cornell East Asia Papers (8756-5293)
—BLDSC (3470.940900), IE, ingenta.
Published by: Cornell University, East Asia Program, 140 Uris Hall, Ithaca, NY 14853-7601. TEL 607-255-6222, FAX 607-255-1388, ceas@cornell.edu, kks3@cornell.edu, http://www.einaudi.cornell.edu/eastasia/CEASbooks/. Ed. J Victor Koschmann. Circ: 2,000.

959 011 USA
➤ **CORNELL MODERN INDONESIA PROJECT PUBLICATIONS.** Text in English. 1958. irreg., latest vol.74, 1995. price varies. **Document type:** *Monographic series, Academic/Scholarly.*
Former titles (until no.72, 1993): Cornell University. Modern Indonesia Project Publications. Monographs, Translations, Bibliographies, Interim Reports (0589-7300); Cornell University. Modern Indonesia Project Publications. Monographs, Translations, Bibliographies; Cornell University. Modern Indonesia Project. Monographs
Published by: Cornell University, Cornell Modern Indonesia Project, 640 Stewart Ave, Ithaca, NY 14850. TEL 607-255-4359, FAX 607-277-1904, TELEX WUI 6713054. Ed. Deborah Homsher.

950 USA
CORNELL UNIVERSITY. SOUTHEAST ASIA PROGRAM. TRANSLATION SERIES. Text in English. 1990. irreg., latest vol.4, 1995. price varies. back issues avail. **Document type:** *Monographic series.* **Description:** Offers translations of key studies of the history and culture of the Far East.
Published by: Cornell University, Southeast Asia Program, 640 Stewart Ave, Ithaca, NY 14850. TEL 877-865-2432, FAX 607-255-7534. R&P David J Stotz. **Subscr. to:** S E A P Publications, Cornell University, E Hill Plaza, Ithaca, NY 14850.

CORPUS SCRIPTORUM CHRISTIANORUM ORIENTALIUM: ARABICA. see *RELIGIONS AND THEOLOGY—Eastern Orthodox*

CORPUS SCRIPTORUM CHRISTIANORUM ORIENTALIUM: COPTICA. see *RELIGIONS AND THEOLOGY—Eastern Orthodox*

CORPUS SCRIPTORUM CHRISTIANORUM ORIENTALIUM: SUBSIDIA. see *RELIGIONS AND THEOLOGY—Eastern Orthodox*

CORPUS SCRIPTORUM CHRISTIANORUM ORIENTALIUM: SYRIACA. see *RELIGIONS AND THEOLOGY—Eastern Orthodox*

CRITICAL ASIAN STUDIES. see *POLITICAL SCIENCE—International Relations*

956 GBR ISSN 1066-9922
DS41 CODEN: CRITF7
➤ **CRITIQUE (ST PAUL);** critical Middle Eastern studies. Text in English. 1992. 3/yr. GBP 212, USD 348 combined subscription to institutions print & online eds. (effective 2006). adv. bk.rev. back issues avail.; reprint service avail. from PSC. **Document type:** *Journal, Academic/Scholarly.* **Description:** Takes a critical look at the social, economic, and cultural aspects of the Middle Eastern societies.
Related titles: Online - full text ed.: ISSN 1473-9666. GBP 202, USD 332 to institutions (effective 2006) (from EBSCO Publishing, Gale Group, IngentaConnect, O C L C Online Computer Library Center, Inc., Swets Information Services).
Indexed: AltPI, CCME, IndIslam, MLA-IB, PSA, SOPODA, SSA, SociolAb.
—IE, Infotrieve. **CCC.**
Published by: Routledge (Subsidiary of: Taylor & Francis Group), 4 Park Sq, Milton Park, Abingdon, Oxon OX14 4RN, United Kingdom. TEL 44-1235-828600, FAX 44-1235-829000, critique@gw.hamline.edu, info@routledge.co.uk, http://www.tandf.co.uk/journals/carfax/10669922.asp, http://www.routledge.com. Ed. Eric Hooglund. adv.: B&W page USD 150; 5 x 8. Circ: 400.

➤ **CROSSROADS: AN INTERDISCIPLINARY JOURNAL OF SOUTHEAST ASIAN STUDIES.** see *HISTORY—History Of Asia*

950 ESP
CUADERNOS DEL I E O. (Cuadernos del Instituto de Europa Oriental) Text in Spanish. 1994. q.
—CINDOC.
Published by: Instituto de Europa Oriental (Subsidiary of: Universidad Complutense de Madrid, Servicio de Publicaciones), Campus de Somosaguas, Madrid, 28223, Spain. TEL 34-91-3942481, FAX 34-91-3942487. Ed. Justo Villafane Gallego.

956 TUR ISSN 0011-281X
CULTURA TURCICA. Text in English, French, German. 1964. irreg. USD 10 (effective 1999). bk.rev.; dance rev.; film rev. abstr.; charts; illus. index. **Document type:** *Academic/Scholarly.*
Related titles: Microfiche ed.: (from IDC).
Indexed: PerIslam, RefZh.
Published by: Turk Kulturunu Arastirma Enstitusu/Turkish Cultural Research Institute, 17 Sok. 38, Bahcelievler, Ankara, Turkey. Ed. Sukru Elcin. Circ: 1,000.

951.9 USA
D P R K - DEMOCRATIC PEOPLE'S REPUBLIC OF KOREA. Text in English. 1997. w. **Description:** A virtual library on North Korea, covering press, scholars, military, and business.
Media: Online - full text.
Indexed: BAS.
Published by: Korean Nationalists Association, PO Box 340827, Columbus, OH 43234. TEL 740-393-3938, FAX 740-393-3993, ysk@kimsoft.com, http://www.kimsoft.com/dprk.htm. Ed. Young S Kim.

950 CHN ISSN 1007-161X
DANGDAI YA-TAI/CONTEMPORARY ASIA-PACIFIC STUDIES. Text in Chinese. 1992. m. CNY 120 domestic; USD 50.40 foreign (effective 2005). **Document type:** *Journal, Academic/Scholarly.*
Formerly (until 1994): Ya-Tai Yanjiu/Asia-Pacific Studies (1003-9724)
Related titles: Online - full text ed.: (from East View Information Services, WanFang Data Corp.).
Published by: Zhongguo Shehui Kexueyuan, Yadasuo, Dongcheng-qu, 3, Zizhong Lu, Beijing, 100007, China. TEL 86-10-64063921, FAX 86-10-64063041, bjb-yts@cass.org.cn, http://ddyt.periodicals.net.cn/. **Dist. by:** China International Book Trading Corp, 35 Chegongzhuang Xilu, Haidian District, PO Box 399, Beijing 100044, China. TEL 86-10-68412045, FAX 86-10-68412023, cibtc@mail.cibtc.com.cn, http://www.cibtc.com.cn.

DAYAN CENTER NEWS. see *HISTORY—History Of The Near East*

DAYAN CENTER PAPERS. see *HISTORY—History Of The Near East*

DELEGATION ARCHEOLOGIQUE FRANCAISE EN IRAN. CAHIERS. see *ARCHAEOLOGY*

951 DEU ISSN 1436-8048
DS701
DEUTSCHE CHINA GESELLSCHAFT. MITTEILUNGSBLATT. Variant title: Mitteilungsblatt der Deutschen China Gesellschaft. Text in German. 1998. irreg., latest vol.9, 2002. price varies. **Document type:** *Monographic series, Academic/Scholarly.*

A

▼ new title ➤ refereed ∗ unverified ♦ full entry avail.

Published by: (Deutsche China Gesellschaft e.V./German China Association), MultiLingua Verlag GmbH, Querenburger Hoehe 281, Bochum, 44801, Germany. TEL 49-234-707088, contact@multi-lingua.com, http://www.multi-lingua.com.

951 DEU
DEUTSCHE CHINA GESELLSCHAFT. SCHRIFTEN. Variant title: Schriften der Deutschen China Gesellschaft. Text in German. irreg., latest vol.7, 2000. price varies. **Document type:** *Monographic series, Academic/Scholarly.*
Published by: (Deutsche China Gesellschaft e.V./German China Association), MultiLingua Verlag GmbH, Querenburger Hoehe 281, Bochum, 44801, Germany. TEL 49-234-707088, contact@multi-lingua.com, http://www.multi-lingua.com.

951 DEU ISSN 1436-0837
DEUTSCHE CHINAREIHE. Text in German. 1998. irreg., latest vol.7, 2002. price varies. **Document type:** *Monographic series, Academic/Scholarly.*
Published by: Bochumer Universitaetsverlag GmbH, Querenburger Hoehe 281, Bochum, 44801, Germany. TEL 49-234-9719780, FAX 49-234-9719786, bou@bou.de, http://bou.de.

950 DEU ISSN 0341-0137
PJ5
DEUTSCHE MORGENLAENDISCHE GESELLSCHAFT. ZEITSCHRIFT. Text in English, German, French. 1847. s-a. EUR 84 (effective 2006). adv. bk.rev. bibl. index. Supplement avail.; back issues avail.; reprints avail. **Document type:** *Journal, Academic/Scholarly.*
Related titles: Microfiche ed.: (from BHP, IDC); Supplement(s): Deutsche Morgenlandischen Gesellschaft. Zeitschrift. Supplement. ISSN 0341-0803. 1969.
Indexed: ArtHuCI, BibInd, BibLing, CurCont, DIP, IBR, IBZ, IndIslam, MLA-IB, NTA, NumL, OTA, RASB, RI-1, RI-2.
—IDS, IE. **CCC.**
Published by: (Deutsche Morgenlaendische Gesellschaft), Harrassowitz Verlag, Taunusstr 14, Wiesbaden, 65183, Germany. TEL 49-611-5300, 49-611-5300, FAX 49-611-530560, verlag@harrassowitz.de, http://www.harrassowitz.de. Ed. Florian Reiter. Adv. contact Robert Gietz. Circ: 1,200.

950 DEU
DS57
DEUTSCHE MORGENLAENDISCHE GESELLSCHAFT. ZEITSCHRIFT. SUPPLEMENTA. Text in German. irreg., latest vol.11, 1998. price varies. **Document type:** *Monographic series, Academic/Scholarly.*
Related titles: Microfiche ed.: (from BHP).
Published by: (Deutsche Morgenlaendische Gesellschaft), Franz Steiner Verlag Stuttgart GmbH, Birkenwaldstr 44, Stuttgart, 70191, Germany. TEL 49-711-25820, FAX 49-711-2582390, franz.steiner.verlag@t-online.de, http://www.steiner-verlag.de. R&P Sabine Koerner.

956 DEU ISSN 0012-1169
DS111.A1
DEUTSCHER PALAESTINA-VEREIN. ZEITSCHRIFT. Text in English, French, German. 1978. 2/yr. EUR 50 (effective 2006). adv. bk.rev. illus. back issues avail.; reprints avail. **Document type:** *Journal, Academic/Scholarly.*
Related titles: Microfiche ed.: (from IDC).
Indexed: AIAP, ArtHuCI, BHA, BibInd, BibLing, CurCont, DIP, IBR, IBZ, IHP, MEA&I, NTA, OTA, RASB, RI-1, RI-2.
—IDS, Infotrieve. **CCC.**
Published by: (Deutscher Verein zur Erforschung Palaestinas), Harrassowitz Verlag, Taunusstr 14, Wiesbaden, 65183, Germany. TEL 49-611-5300, FAX 49-611-530560, verlag@harrassowitz.de, http://www.harrassowitz.de. Ed. Dieter Vieweger. R&P Michael Langfeld. Adv. contact Robert Gietz. Circ: 600.

956 DEU ISSN 0173-1904
DEUTSCHER PALAESTINAVEREIN. ABHANDLUNGEN. Text in German. 1969. irreg., latest vol.31, 2003. price varies. adv. **Document type:** *Monographic series, Academic/Scholarly.*
Published by: Harrassowitz Verlag, Taunusstr 14, Wiesbaden, 65183, Germany. TEL 49-611-5300, FAX 49-611-530570, verlag@harrassowitz.de, http://www.harrassowitz.de. Eds. Dieter Viewegar, Jens Kamlah. R&P Michael Langfeld. Adv. contact Robert Gietz.

954 IND
DHANIRAM BHALLA GRANTHAMALA. Text in Hindi, Sanskrit. irreg., latest vol.19, 1972. price varies.
Published by: Vishveshvaranand Vedic Research Institute, P.O. Sadhu Ashram, Hoshiarpur, Punjab 146 021, India. Ed. Vishva Bandhu.

950 282 BEL
➤ **DICTIONAIRE DES RACINES SEMITIQUES.** Text in French. 1972. irreg., latest vol.8, 1999. price varies. bk.rev. back issues avail. **Document type:** *Monographic series, Academic/Scholarly.*
Published by: Peeters Publishers, Bondgenotenlaan 153, Leuven, 3000, Belgium. TEL 32-16-235170, FAX 32-16-228500, http://www.peeters-leuven.be. Ed. D Cohen.

956 USA ISSN 1060-4367
DS41
➤ **DIGEST OF MIDDLE EAST STUDIES.** Abbreviated title: D O M E S. Text in English. 1992. s-a. USD 50 (effective 2000). bk.rev. **Document type:** *Journal, Academic/Scholarly.*
Description: Contains articles and reviews on all topics concerning Islam, Arab countries, Israel, Turkey and Iran. Includes the texts of important Middle East agreements and transcriptions of notable speeches by experts.
Related titles: Online - full text ed.: (from EBSCO Publishing, ProQuest Information & Learning, SoftLine Information).
Indexed: BRD, BRI, BibInd, CCME, ENW, IndIslam, PerIslam.
Published by: University of Wisconsin at Milwaukee, Milwaukee School of Library and Information Science, PO Box 413, Milwaukee, WI 53201. TEL 414-229-4707, FAX 414-229-4848, TELEX 4909991372, barajas@slis.wwu.edu, http://www.slis.uwm.edu. Ed. Mohammed Aman. Circ: 500.

956 DEU ISSN 0949-6807
DISKURSE DER ARABISTIK. Text in German. 1997. irreg., latest vol.7, 2003. price varies. **Document type:** *Monographic series, Academic/Scholarly.*
Indexed: MLA-IB.
Published by: Harrassowitz Verlag, Taunusstr 14, Wiesbaden, 65183, Germany. TEL 49-611-530555, FAX 49-611-530559, verlag@harrassowitz.de. Eds. Angelika Neuwirth, Hartmut Bobzin. R&P Michael Langfeld. Adv. contact Robert Gietz.

950 895 495 CZE ISSN 0419-4268
DISSERTATIONES ORIENTALES. Text in English, German, French. 1964. irreg., latest vol.48. price varies. **Document type:** *Monographic series, Academic/Scholarly.*
Indexed: RASB.
Published by: Akademie Ved Ceske Republiky, Orientalni Ustav/Czech Academy of Sciences, Oriental Institute, Pod Vodarenskou vezi 4, Prague, 18208, Czech Republic. TEL 420-2-66052483, FAX 420-2-6897260, aror@orient.cas.cz, http://www.lib.cas.cz/knav/journals/eng/archiv_orientalni.htm.

950 DEU ISSN 0945-5639
DOCUMENTA ARABICA ANTIQUA. Text in German. 1995. irreg., latest vol.4, 1997. price varies. **Document type:** *Monographic series, Academic/Scholarly.*
Published by: Harrassowitz Verlag, Taunusstr 14, Wiesbaden, 65183, Germany. TEL 49-611-5300, FAX 49-611-530570, verlag@harrassowitz.de, http://www.harrassowitz.de. Ed. Werner Diem. R&P Michael Langfeld. Adv. contact Robert Gietz.

950 FRA ISSN 0768-4053
DOCUMENTS D'HISTOIRE MAGHREBINE. Text in French. 1972. irreg.
Published by: Librairie Orientaliste Paul Geuthner, 12 rue Vavin, Paris, 75006, France. TEL 33-1-46-34-71-30, FAX 33-1-43-29-75-64. Ed. Chantal de la Veronne.

890 KOR
DONG-A MUNHUA/EAST ASIA CULTURE. Text in Korean. 1963. irreg., latest vol.29. KRW 1,500. bk.rev.
Published by: (Institute of Asian Studies), Seoul National University, San 56-1 Sinlim-dong, Kwanak-ku, Seoul, 151742, Korea, S. FAX 02-871-7244. Circ: 500.

950 CHN ISSN 1005-7110
DONGFANG LUNTAN/ORIENTAL FORUM. Text in Chinese. 1988. bi-m. CNY 48 domestic; USD 20.40 foreign (effective 2005). **Document type:** *Journal, Academic/Scholarly.*
Related titles: Online - full text ed.: (from WanFang Data Corp.).
Address: 308, Ningxia Lu, Qingdao, 266071, China. dflt@qdu.edu.cn, http://dflt.periodicals.net.cn/. **Dist. by:** China International Book Trading Corp, 35 Chegongzhuang Xilu, Haidian District, PO Box 399, Beijing 100044, China. TEL 86-10-68412045, FAX 86-10-68412023, cibtc@mail.cibtc.com.cn, http://www.cibtc.com.cn.

954 CHN ISSN 1000-7970
DONGNANYA/SOUTH ASIAN. Text in Chinese. 1983. q. CNY 32 domestic; USD 13.60 foreign (effective 2005). **Document type:** *Journal, Academic/Scholarly.*
Related titles: Online - full text ed.: (from East View Information Services).
Published by: Yunnan Sheng Shehui Kexue Dongnanya Yanjiusuo, 577, Huancheng Xilu, Kunming, 650034, China. TEL 86-871-4175672. **Dist. by:** China International Book Trading Corp, 35 Chegongzhuang Xilu, Haidian District, PO Box 399, Beijing 100044, China. TEL 86-10-68412045, FAX 86-10-68412023, cibtc@mail.cibtc.com.cn, http://www.cibtc.com.cn.

950 CHN ISSN 1008-6099
DONGNANYA YANJIU/SOUTHEAST ASIAN STUDIES. Text in Chinese. 1960. bi-m. CNY 60 domestic; USD 25.20 foreign (effective 2005). **Document type:** *Journal, Academic/Scholarly.*
Related titles: Online - full text ed.: (from East View Information Services).
Published by: Jinan Daxue, Dongnanya Yanjiusuo, 4F, Wenxueyuanlou, Guangzhou, 510632, China. odnypj@jnu.edu.cn, http://dnyyj.periodicals.net.cn/. **Dist. by:** China International Book Trading Corp, 35 Chegongzhuang Xilu, Haidian District, PO Box 399, Beijing 100044, China. TEL 86-10-68412045, FAX 86-10-68412023, cibtc@mail.cibtc.com.cn, http://www.cibtc.com.cn.

DONGNANYA ZONGHENG/ALL-ROUND SOUTHEAST ASIA. see *SOCIAL SCIENCES: COMPREHENSIVE WORKS*

950 KOR ISSN 1229-1234
DONG'YANG SAHOE SA'SANG/JOURNAL OF EAST ASIAN SOCIAL THOUGHTS. Text in Korean. 1998. a.
Indexed: SociolAb.
—BLDSC (3619.229050).
Published by: Dong'yang Sahoe Sa'sang Haghoe/Association of East Asian Social Thoughts, Seoul, Korea, S. http://www.asian-thoughts.org.

950 MNG
DORNO, ORNO/EAST & WEST. Text in Mongol; Summaries in English. 1978. 2/yr. **Document type:** *Academic/Scholarly.*
Description: Covers social, political events, history, culture and foreign relations.
Formerly (until 1991, no.3): Dornodahiny Sudlal - Oriental Studies
Indexed: RASB.
Published by: (Institute of International Studies), Academy of Sciences, PO Box 48 17, Ulan Bator, Mongolia. Ed. Ts Batbayar.

959 DEU ISSN 1431-4975
DRAMA UND THEATER IN SUEDASIEN. Text in German. 1997. irreg., latest vol.2, 2003. price varies. **Document type:** *Monographic series, Academic/Scholarly.* **Description:** Study of theater and the performing arts in Southeast Asia.
Published by: Harrassowitz Verlag, Taunusstr 14, Wiesbaden, 65183, Germany. TEL 49-611-530555, FAX 49-611-5305590, verlag@harrassowitz.de. Ed. Heidrun Brueckner. R&P Michael Langfeld. Adv. contact Robert Gietz.

950 011 GBR
DURHAM MIDDLE EAST PAPERS. Text in English. 1972. 6/yr. price varies. adv. bibl. **Document type:** *Monographic series.*
Former titles: Durhan Middle Eastern Papers; (until 1998): C M E I S Occasional Papers (1357-7522); (until 1995): University of Durham. Centre for Middle Eastern and Islamic Studies. Occasional Papers Series (0307-0654)
—BLDSC (3632.347100).
Published by: University of Durham, Centre for Middle Eastern and Islamic Studies, Southend House, South Rd, Durham, DH1 3TG, United Kingdom. TEL 44-191-374-2822, FAX 44-191-374-2830, n.m.quilliam@durham.ac.uk, neilquilliam@hotmail.com, http://www.dur.ac.uk/~dme0www/, http://www.dur.ac.uk/~dme0www/pub.htm. Ed., Adv. contact Dr. Neil Quilliam. page GBP 50.

950 HKG
➤ **E-JOURNAL ON HONG KONG CULTURAL AND SOCIAL STUDIES.** Text in English. 2002. s-a. **Document type:** *Academic/Scholarly.*
Media: Online - full content.
Published by: University of Hong Kong, Centre of Asian Studies, Pokfulam Rd, Hong Kong, Hong Kong. TEL 852-2859-2463, FAX 852-2559-3185, http://www.hku.hk/hkcsp/ccex/ehkcss01/. Ed. Elizabeth Sinn.

➤ **EAST.** see *GENERAL INTEREST PERIODICALS—Japan*

950 ITA ISSN 0012-8376
AP37
➤ **EAST AND WEST.** Text in English. 1950. q. EUR 72.30 (effective 2003). bk.rev. bibl.; charts; illus. index. back issues avail. **Document type:** *Journal, Academic/Scholarly.*
Indexed: AmH&L, AnthLit, BAS, BHA, BibLing, DIP, HistAb, IBR, IBZ, IndIslam, MLA-IB, NumL, RI-1, RI-2.
—BLDSC (3645.400000), IE, Infotrieve, ingenta.
Published by: Istituto Italiano per l'Africa e l'Oriente, Via Ulisse Aldrovandi 16, Rome, 00197, Italy. TEL 39-06-328551, FAX 39-06-3225348, biblio.dir@isiao.it, http://www.isiao.it. Ed. Gherardo Gnoli. Circ: 1,500. **Dist. by:** Herder Editrice e Libreria s.r.l., Piazza di Montecitorio 117-120, Rome 00186, Italy.

➤ **EAST ASIAN HISTORY.** see *HISTORY—History Of Asia*

950 SGP
EAST ASIAN INSTITUTE CONTEMPORARY CHINA SERIES. Text in English. 1997. irreg., latest no.34. price varies. **Document type:** *Monographic series, Academic/Scholarly.*
Published by: World Scientific Publishing Co. Pte. Ltd., 5 Toh Tuck Link, Singapore, 596224, Singapore. TEL 65-466-5775, FAX 65-467-7667, wspc@wspc.com.sg, series@wspc.com.sg, http://www.wspc.com.sg/books/series/eaiccs_series.shtml, http://www.worldscientific.com. **Dist. by:** World Scientific Publishing Co., Inc., 1060 Main St, River Edge, NJ 07661. TEL 201-487-9655, 800-227-7562, FAX 201-487-9656, 888-977-2665; World Scientific Publishing Ltd., 57 Shelton St, London WC2H 9HE, United Kingdom. TEL 44-20-78360888, FAX 44-20-78362020, sales@wspc.co.uk.

950 020 USA ISSN 1079-8021
Z733.G47
EAST ASIAN LIBRARY JOURNAL. Text in English. 1986. s-a. USD 40; USD 50 foreign (effective 2001). adv. bk.rev. 225 p./no. 1 cols./p.; back issues avail. **Document type:** *Academic/Scholarly.* **Description:** Presents significant historical and literary scholarship on East Asia with special reference to bibliographical research, book history, publishing, and print culture; occasional reports on the Gest Library and its collections; notes on relevant activities and new publications on the book in East Asia.
Formerly (until 1994): Gest Library Journal (0891-0553)
Indexed: BAS.
—BLDSC (3645.937000), IE, ingenta.
Address: 211 Jones Hall, Princeton University, Princeton, NJ 08544-1008. TEL 609-258-4846, FAX 609-258-2461, EALJ@princeton.edu, sedgren@princeton.edu. Ed., R&P, Adv. contact Nancy Norton Tomasko TEL 609-258-4746. Circ: 200.

950 USA
EAST ASIAN RESEARCH AIDS AND TRANSLATIONS. Text in English. 1984. irreg., latest vol.6, 1998. price varies. **Document type:** *Monographic series.*
Published by: Western Washington University, Center for East Asian Studies, Bellingham, WA 98225-9056. TEL 206-650-3448. Ed. Edward H Kaplan.

950 JPN ISSN 1342-8047
DS501
EAST ASIAN REVIEW. Variant title: Osaka University of Economics and Law. Asian Research Institute. Annual Journal. Text in English. 1997. a.
Published by: Osaka University of Economics and Law, Asian Research Institute, 6-10 Gakuonji, Yao, Osaka 581-8511, Japan.

▼ **EASTERN CHRISTIAN ART**; in the Late Antique and Islamic contexts. see *ARCHAEOLOGY*

950 FRA ISSN 0336-1519
DS531
ECOLE FRANCAISE D'EXTREME-ORIENT. BULLETIN. Text in French; Text occasionally in English. 1901. a. EUR 55 per issue (effective 2004 - 2005). **Document type:** *Bulletin, Academic/Scholarly.*
Related titles: Microfiche ed.: (from IDC).
Indexed: AICP, AmH&L, AnthLit, BHA, BibLing, DIP, EI, HistAb, IBR, IBSS, IBZ, MLA-IB, PCI, RASB.
Published by: Ecole Francaise d'Extreme-Orient, 22 Avenue du President Wilson, Paris, 75116, France. TEL 33-1-53701837, FAX 33-1-53701838, efeo-diffusion@efeo.fr, http://www.efeo.fr.

954 GBR
EDINBURGH PAPERS IN SOUTH ASIAN STUDIES. Text in English. irreg., latest vol.5, 1995. GBP 2 (effective 1999). **Document type:** *Monographic series, Academic/Scholarly.*
—BLDSC (3661.015500).
Published by: University of Edinburgh, Centre for South Asian Studies, c/o Dr Roger Jeffery, Ed, Dept of Sociology, 18 Buccleuch Pl, Edinburgh, EH8 9LN, United Kingdom. TEL 44-131-650-3976, FAX 44-131-650-3989, r.jeffery@ed.ac.uk.

950 USA ISSN 1090-6851
DS32.8
EDUCATION ABOUT ASIA. Text in English. 1996. 3/yr. USD 25 foreign to individual members; USD 15 domestic to individual members; USD 25 domestic to individuals non-members; USD 32 foreign to individuals non-members; USD 31 domestic to institutions; USD 38 foreign to institutions (effective 2005). adv. bk.rev. back issues avail. **Document type:** *Academic/Scholarly.* **Description:** Focuses on the enhancement of classroom teaching on Asia. For educators at all academic levels, from elementary through university.
Indexed: BAS.
Published by: Association for Asian Studies, Inc., 1021 E Huron St, Ann Arbor, MI 48104. TEL 734-665-2490, FAX 734-665-3801, http://www.aasianst.org/eaa-toc.htm. Ed. Lucien Ellington. Circ: 9,000.

950 GBR ISSN 1476-9158
DS801
➤ **ELECTRONIC JOURNAL OF CONTEMPORARY JAPANESE STUDIES.** Text in English. 2001. irreg. free (effective 2005). Index. **Document type:** *Journal, Academic/Scholarly.*
Media: Online - full content.
Published by: University of Sheffield, School of East Asian Studies, Fl 5, The Arts Tower, Western Bank, Sheffield, S Yorks S10 2TN, United Kingdom. http://www.japanesestudies.org.uk/contents/intro.html. Ed. Peter Matanle.

950 NLD ISSN 0928-6802
DS36
➤ **ELECTRONIC JOURNAL OF ORIENTAL STUDIES.** Key Title: E J O S. Text in Multiple languages. 1998. irreg., latest vol.5, 2002. free (effective 2005). illus. Index. back issues avail. **Document type:** *Journal, Academic/Scholarly.* **Description:** Devoted to the study of multi- and inter-disciplinary focus covering the full range of the humanities in Oriental studies.
Media: Online - full text.
Published by: Universiteit Utrecht, Faculty of Arts, Department of Arabic, Persian and Turkic Languages and Cultures, Drift 15, Utrecht BR, 3512, Netherlands. TEL 31-30-2536128, FAX 31-30-2536138, hans.theunissen@let.uu.nl, http://www2.let.uu.nl/Solis/anpt/ejos/EJOS-1.html. Ed. Hans Theunissen.

954 USA ISSN 1084-7561
BL1112.26
➤ **ELECTRONIC JOURNAL OF VEDIC STUDIES.** Text in English. 1995. irreg. free (effective 2005). illus. Index. **Document type:** *Journal, Academic/Scholarly.*
Media: Online - full content.
Address: ejvs-list@shore.net, witzel@fas.harvard.edu, http://www1.shore.net/~india/ejvs. Ed. Michael E Witzel.

950 CHN ISSN 1009-721X
ELUOSI YANJIU/RUSSIA STUDIES. Text in Chinese. 1981. q. CNY 32 domestic; USD 13.60 foreign (effective 2005). **Document type:** *Journal, Academic/Scholarly.*
Published by: Huadong Shifan Daxue/East China Normal University, 3663 Zhongshan Beilu, 15F, Wenke Dalou, Shanghai, 200062, China. russiastudies@163.net, http://elsyj.periodicals.net.cn/. **Dist. by:** China International Book Trading Corp, 35 Chegongzhuang Xilu, Haidian District, PO Box 399, Beijing 100044, China. TEL 86-10-68412045, FAX 86-10-68412023, cibtc@mail.cibtc.com.cn, http://www.cibtc.com.cn.

950 MEX ISSN 0185-0164
DS1
ESTUDIOS DE ASIA Y AFRICA. Text in Spanish. 1966. 3/yr. USD 64 (effective 1999). adv. bk.rev. cum.index. back issues avail.; reprint service avail. from PQC.
Supersedes (in 1974): Estudios Orientales (0185-0156)
Indexed: AmH&L, BAS, HistAb, IBSS, IndIslam, MLA, MLA-IB, PSA, SociolAb.
—IE, Infotrieve.
Published by: Colegio de Mexico, A.C., Departamento de Publicaciones, Camino al Ajusco 20, Col. Pedregal Santa Teresa, Mexico City, DF 10740, Mexico. TEL 52-5-4493077, FAX 52-5-4493083, emunos@colmex.mx. Ed., R&P Francisco Gomez Ruiz TEL 525-449-3080. Adv. contact Maria Cruz Mora. Circ: 1,500.

950 DEU ISSN 1432-0266
ETHNO-ISLAMICA. Text in German. 1991. irreg., latest vol.8, 1997. **Document type:** *Monographic series.*
Published by: Ergon Verlag, Grombuehlstr 7, Wuerzburg, 97080, Germany. TEL 49-931-280084, FAX 49-931-282872, ergon-verlag@t-online.de, service@ergon-verlag.de. Ed. P Heine.

951 FRA ISSN 0755-5857
DS734.97.F8
ETUDES CHINOISES. Text in French. 1981. s-a.
Formerly (until 1982): Association Francaise d'Etudes Chinoises. Bulletin (1169-0186)
Published by: Association Francaise d'Etudes Chinoises/French Association for Chinese Studies, 54 Bvld Raspail, Paris, 75006, France. afec_fr@yahoo.fr, http://www.assoc.wanadoo.fr/afec/.

959 BEL ISSN 0531-1926
ETUDES ORIENTALES. Text in French. 1963. irreg., latest vol.11, 1983. price varies. back issues avail. **Document type:** *Monographic series.*
Indexed: BibLing, IBR.
Published by: Librairie-Editions Thanh-Long, Rue Dekens 34, Brussels, 1040, Belgium.

ETUDES URBAINES. see *HOUSING AND URBAN PLANNING*

950 NLD ISSN 1568-0584
DS501
EUROPEAN JOURNAL OF EAST ASIAN STUDIES. Text in English. 2001. 2/yr. USD 55 in the Americas to individuals; EUR 44 elsewhere to individuals; USD 160 combined subscription in the Americas to institutions print & online eds.; EUR 128 combined subscription elsewhere to institutions print & online eds. (effective 2006). back issues avail.; reprint service avail. from PSC. **Document type:** *Journal, Academic/Scholarly.* **Description:** Covers social science and modern history of the broader East Asian region, including Southeast as well as Northeast Asia.
Related titles: Online - full text ed.: ISSN 1570-0615. USD 144 in the Americas to institutions; EUR 115 elsewhere to institutions (effective 2006) (from EBSCO Publishing, Gale Group, IngentaConnect, Kluwer Online, O C L C Online Computer Library Center, Inc., Springer LINK, Swets Information Services).
Indexed: AmH&L, CJA, IndIslam.
—IE. CCC.
Published by: Brill Academic Publishers, PO Box 9000, Leiden, 2300 PA, Netherlands. TEL 31-71-53-53-500, FAX 31-71-53-17-532, cs@brill.nl, http://www.brill.nl/m_catalogue_sub6_id9449.htm. Eds. Christian Henriot, Paul Waley. **Subscr. in N. America to:** PO Box 605, Herndon, VA 20172. TEL 703-661-1585, 800-337-9255, FAX 703-661-1501, cs@brillusa.com. **Distr. outside N. America by:** c/o Turpin Distribution, Stratton Business Park, Pegasus Drive, Biggleswade, BEDFORDSHIRE SG 18 8TQ, United Kingdom. TEL 44-1767-604-954, FAX 44-1767-601-640, brill@turpin-distribution.com.

915.66 NLD ISSN 0922-7768
EVLIYA CELEBI'S BOOK OF TRAVELS. Text in English, German, Turkish. 1988. irreg., latest vol.5, 2000. price varies. illus.; maps. back issues avail. **Document type:** *Monographic series.* **Description:** Publishes scholarly editions of portions of the Seyahatname, with English translation and commentary.
Published by: Brill Academic Publishers, PO Box 9000, Leiden, 2300 PA, Netherlands. TEL 31-71-53-53500, FAX 31-71-53-17-532, cs@brill.nl, http://www.brill.nl. R&P Elizabeth Venekamp. **Subscr. in N. America to:** PO Box 605, Herndon, VA 20172. TEL 703-661-1585, 800-337-9255, FAX 703-661-1501, cs@brillusa.com. **Distr. outside N. America by:** c/o Turpin Distribution, Stratton Business Park, Pegasus Drive, Biggleswade, BEDFORDSHIRE SG 18 8TQ, United Kingdom. TEL 44-1767-604-954, FAX 44-1767-601-640, brill@turpin-distribution.com.

951.9 KOR
EXTERNAL ENVIRONMENT FOR UNIFICATION AND NORTH-SOUTH KOREAN RELATIONS. Text in Korean. a.
Published by: Korea Institute for National Unification, 535-353 Suyu 6-dong, Kangbuk-ku, Seoul, 142-076, Korea, S.

955 800 IRN ISSN 0014-7788
DS251
FARHANG-E IRAN ZAMIN. Text mainly in Persian, Modern; Text occasionally in English, French. 1952. q. USD 40 (effective 2001). bk.rev. **Document type:** *Academic/Scholarly.*
Related titles: Microfiche ed.
Indexed: BibLing, IndIslam, MLA, MLA-IB, RASB.
Published by: Iraj Afshar, Ed. & Pub., Niyavaran, P O Box 19575-583, Teheran, Iran. TEL 021-283254. Circ: 2,000.

FLAVOR AND FORTUNE; dedicated to the art and science of Chinese cuisine. see *ETHNIC INTERESTS*

950 AUS ISSN 0085-0586
DS1
FLINDERS ASIAN STUDIES LECTURE. Text in English. 1970. a. AUD 8 per issue. back issues avail. **Document type:** *Monographic series.*
Published by: Flinders University of South Australia, Department of Asian Studies and Languages, Director of Asian Studies, GPO Box 2100, Adelaide, SA 5001, Australia. TEL 61-8-8201-2404, FAX 61-8-8201-2566. R&P Colin Brown.

950 AUS
FLINDERS ASIAN STUDIES MONOGRAPH. Text in English. 1981. irreg., latest vol.6, 1996. price varies. back issues avail. **Document type:** *Monographic series, Academic/Scholarly.*
Published by: Flinders University of South Australia, School of Social Sciences, Director of Asian Studies, GPO Box 2100, Adelaide, SA 5001, Australia. TEL 61-8-8201-2404, FAX 61-8-8201-2566. R&P Colin Brown.

950 SWE ISSN 0346-7449
FOERENINGEN FOER ORIENTALISKA STUDIER. SKRIFTER. Text in Multiple languages. 1969. irreg., latest vol.28, 1997. pice varies. back issues avail. **Document type:** *Monographic series, Academic/Scholarly.*
Published by: Foereningen for Orientaliska Studier/Society for Oriental Studies, Stockholm University, Kraeftriket 4 B, Stockholm, 10691, Sweden. TEL 46-8-164273, FAX 46-8-155464, http://www.orientaliskastudier.se/boklista.htm.

950 POL ISSN 0015-5675
FOLIA ORIENTALIA. Text in English, French, German. 1959. a. price varies. bk.rev. abstr.; bibl. **Document type:** *Academic/Scholarly.* **Description:** Monographs and research reports from Oriental studies in Poland.
Indexed: BAS, BibLing, IBR, IndIslam, MLA, MLA-IB, NTA, NumL, OTA, PCI, PerIslam, RASB, RILM.
—KNAW.
Published by: (Komisja Orientalistyczna), Polska Akademia Nauk, Oddzial w Krakowie, ul sw Jana 28, Krakow, 31018, Poland. TEL 48-12-224853, FAX 48-12-222791. Ed. Stanislaw Stachowski. Circ: 590.

950 DEU ISSN 0170-3307
FREIBURGER ALTORIENTALISCHE STUDIEN. Text in German. irreg., latest vol.21, 1998. price varies. **Document type:** *Monographic series, Academic/Scholarly.*
Published by: Franz Steiner Verlag Stuttgart GmbH, Birkenwaldstr 44, Stuttgart, 70191, Germany. TEL 49-711-25820, FAX 49-711-2582390, franz.steiner.verlag@t-online.de, http://www.steiner-verlag.de. Ed. Burkhart Kienast. R&P Sabine Koerner.

950 DEU ISSN 0724-4703
FREIBURGER FERNOESTLICHE FORSCHUNGEN. Text in German. 1983. irreg., latest vol.5, 2001. price varies. **Document type:** *Monographic series, Academic/Scholarly.*
Published by: Harrassowitz Verlag, Taunusstr 14, Wiesbaden, 65183, Germany. TEL 49-611-5300, FAX 49-611-530570, verlag@harrassowitz.de, http://www.harrassowitz.de. Ed. Peter Greiner. R&P Michael Langfeld. Adv. contact Robert Gietz.

951 DEU ISSN 0429-6656
FREIES ASIEN. Text in German. 1959. s-m. looseleaf. bk.rev. back issues avail. **Document type:** *Newsletter, Consumer.*
Published by: Deutsch-Chinesische Gesellschaft e.V., Markgrafenstr 35, Berlin, 10117, Germany. TEL 49-30-20361440, FAX 49-30-20361410, dcg-bonn@t-online.de, http://freies-asien.de. Ed. Sophie-Caroline Zillessen. Circ: 3,500.

FU JEN STUDIES; literature & linguistics. see *LITERATURE*

950 IND
➤ **GANGANATHA JHA KENDRIYA SANSKRIT VIDYAPEETHA. JOURNAL**; a research journal devoted to the oriental studies in general and indian studies in particular. Text in English, Hindi, Sanskrit. 1943. q. INR 80, USD 16 (effective 2001). bk.rev. illus. index. 150 p./no. 1 cols./p.; back issues avail.; reprints avail. **Document type:** *Journal, Academic/Scholarly.* **Description:** Devoted to oriental studies in general, and India studies in particular.
Formerly: Ganganatha Jha Research Institute. Journal (0016-4461)
Indexed: BAS, DIP, IBR, MLA-IB.
Published by: Ganganatha Jha Kendriya Sanskrit Vidyapeetha, Chandrashakhar Azad Park, Allahabad, Uttar Pradesh 211 002, India. TEL 91-532-460957, FAX 91-532-466625. Ed., R&P Gaya Charan Tripathi. Circ: 500 (paid).

890 297 BIH ISSN 0350-1418
DB240.5
GAZI HUSREVBEGOVA BIBLIOTEKA. ANALI. Text in Serbo-Croatian; Summaries in English. 1972. a.
Indexed: AmH&L, HistAb.
Published by: Gazi Husrevbegova Biblioteka, Obala Pariske Komune 4, Sarajevo, 71000, Bosnia Herzegovina. Ed. Abdurahman Hukic. Circ: 1,500. **Co-sponsor:** Starjesinstvo Islamske Zajednice.

GESCHICHTE DES ARABISCHEN SCHRIFTTUMS. see *LITERATURE*

950 DEU ISSN 0016-9080
GESELLSCHAFT FUER NATUR- UND VOELKERKUNDE OSTASIENS. NACHRICHTEN; Zeitschrift fuer Kultur und Geschichte Ostasiens. Text in English, German. 1926. s-a. EUR 50 to non-members; EUR 40 to members (effective 2003). bk.rev. bibl.; charts; illus. back issues avail. **Document type:** *Journal, Academic/Scholarly.*
Indexed: AmH&L, BAS, DIP, HistAb, IBR, IBZ, RASB.
—CCC.
Published by: Universitaet Hamburg, Asien-Afrika Institut, Abteilung fuer Sprache und Kultur Japans, ESA 1 - Ost, Hamburg, 20146, Germany. TEL 49-40-428384884, FAX 49-40-428386200, hworm@uni-hamburg.de, or7a018@rrz.uni-hamburg.de, http://www.uni-hamburg.de. Ed. Herbert Worm. Circ: 350.

950 DEU ISSN 0170-3455
GLASENAPP-STIFTUNG. Text in German. irreg., latest vol.40, 2001. price varies. **Document type:** *Monographic series, Academic/Scholarly.*
Indexed: MLA-IB.
Published by: (Glasenapp-Stiftung), Franz Steiner Verlag Stuttgart GmbH, Birkenwaldstr 44, Stuttgart, 70191, Germany. TEL 49-711-25820, FAX 49-711-2582390, franz.steiner.verlag@t-online.de, http://www.steiner-verlag.de. R&P Sabine Koerner.

959 USA ISSN 1080-4153
DS401
GLOBAL STUDIES: INDIA AND SOUTH ASIA. Text in English. 1993. irreg., latest 2003, 6th ed. USD 23.12 per vol. (effective 2004). illus. **Document type:** *Academic/Scholarly.* **Description:** Provides comprehensive background information and selected world press articles on the regions and countries of the world. Features an overview of South Asia and country reports for Afghanistan, Bangladesh, Bhutan, Maldives, Nepal, Pakistan, and Sri Lanka. An annotated list of World Wide Web sites guides students to additional resources.
Published by: McGraw-Hill - Dushkin (Subsidiary of: McGraw-Hill Higher Education), 2460 Kerper Blvd, Dubuque, IA 52001. TEL 800-243-6532, customer.service@mcgraw-hill.com, http://www.dushkin.com/text-data/catalog/0072850248.mhtml. Ed. James Norton. Pub. Ian Nielsen. R&P Cheryl Greenleaf.

954 300 IND ISSN 0970-1427
GLORY OF INDIA; quarterly on Indology. Text in English, Hindi. 1977. q. INR 40, USD 22. adv. bk.rev. abstr.; bibl.
Published by: Motilal Banarsidass (Delhi), Jawahar Nagar, 40, U.A. Bungalow Rd., New Delhi, 110 007, India. TEL 11-2911985, FAX 011-2930689. Ed. N P Jain.

956 297 NLD ISSN 0169-8257
DE GOEJE STICHTING. UITGAVEN✱ /GOEJE FUND. PUBLICATIONS. Text in Dutch. 1956. irreg., latest vol.27, 1997. price varies. adv. **Document type:** *Monographic series, Academic/Scholarly.*
Published by: De Goeje Stichting/De Goeje Fund, c/o Nederlands Instituut voor het Nabije Oosten, PO Box 9515, Leiden, 2300 RA, Netherlands. R&P J Deroos TEL 31-71-5272036. Adv. contact J. de Roos.

935 950 DEU ISSN 0340-6326
GOETTINGER ORIENTFORSCHUNGEN. REIHE I: SYRIACA. Text in German. irreg., latest vol.36, 1997. price varies. **Document type:** *Monographic series, Academic/Scholarly.*
Published by: Harrassowitz Verlag, Taunusstr 14, Wiesbaden, 65183, Germany. TEL 49-611-5300, FAX 49-611-530570, verlag@harrassowitz.de, http://www.harrassowitz.de. R&P Michael Langfeld. Adv. contact Robert Gietz.

950 DEU ISSN 0173-2358
GOETTINGER ORIENTFORSCHUNGEN. REIHE II: STUDIEN ZUR SPAETANTIKEN UND FRUEHCHRISTLICHEN KUNST. Text in German. 1980. irreg., latest vol.4, no.4, 1993. price varies. **Document type:** *Monographic series, Academic/Scholarly.*
Published by: Harrassowitz Verlag, Taunusstr 14, Wiesbaden, 65183, Germany. TEL 49-611-5300, FAX 49-611-530570, verlag@harrassowitz.de, http://www.harrassowitz.de. R&P Michael Langfeld. Adv. contact Robert Gietz.

932 DEU ISSN 0340-6342
GOETTINGER ORIENTFORSCHUNGEN. REIHE IV: AEGYPTEN. Text in German. 1973. irreg., latest vol.44, 2003. price varies. **Document type:** *Monographic series, Academic/Scholarly.*
Published by: Harrassowitz Verlag, Taunusstr 14, Wiesbaden, 65183, Germany. TEL 49-611-5300, FAX 49-611-530570, verlag@harrassowitz.de, http://www.harrassowitz.de. Eds. Friedrich Junge, Wolfhart Westendorf. R&P Michael Langfeld. Adv. contact Robert Gietz.

954 NLD ISSN 1382-3442
GONDA INDOLOGICAL STUDIES. Text in English. 1994. irreg., latest vol.4, 1995. back issues avail. **Document type:** *Monographic series, Academic/Scholarly.*
Published by: Forsten, Postbus 6148, Groningen, 9702 HC, Netherlands. FAX 31-50-5275618, info@forsten.nl, http://www.forsten.nl. **Dist. in N. America by:** John Benjamins Publishing Co., PO Box 27519, Philadelphia, PA 19118-0519. TEL 215-836-1200.

950 NLD ISSN 0924-8846
GRONINGEN ORIENTAL STUDIES. Text in English. 1986. irreg., latest vol.11, 1995. price varies. illus. back issues avail. **Document type:** *Monographic series, Academic/Scholarly.* **Description:** Publishes studies of Indian religion, art, medicine, science and literature.
—BLDSC (4217.975000).
Published by: Forsten, Postbus 6148, Groningen, 9702 HC, Netherlands. FAX 31-50-5275618, info@forsten.nl, http://www.forsten.nl. **Dist. in N. America by:** John Benjamins Publishing Co., PO Box 27519, Philadelphia, PA 19118-0519. TEL 215-836-1200.

951 CHN
GUIZHOU MINZU YANJIU/STUDY OF GUIZHOU NATIONALITIES. Text in Chinese. q. USD 20.40.
Published by: Guizhou Sheng Minzu Yanjiusuo/Guizhou Nationality Research Institute, No 16 Bianjing Xiang, Bajiaoyan, Guiyang, Guizhou 550001, China. TEL 625623. Ed. Wu Yongqing. **Dist. in US by:** China Books & Periodicals Inc, 360 Swift Ave., Ste. 48, S San Fran, CA 94080-6220. TEL 415-282-2994.

950 ISR ISSN 0017-7083
DS41
➤ **HAM-MIZRAH HE-HADASH/NEW EAST.** Text in Hebrew; Summaries in English. 1949. a. USD 30 (effective 2000). bk.rev. bibl.; charts; stat. index. **Document type:** *Academic/Scholarly.*
Indexed: IHP, OTA.
Published by: (Israel Oriental Society), Magnes Press (Subsidiary of: Hebrew University of Jerusalem), Hebrew University, Jerusalem, PO Box 39099, Jerusalem, 91390, Israel. TEL 972-2-5660341, FAX 972-2-5883688. Ed. Jacob M Landau. Circ: 2,500 (controlled).

951.9 KOR ISSN 1225-8091
HAN-GUG GUGJE GYORYU JAEDAN SOSIG. Text in Korean. 1993. q. Free. **Document type:** *Newsletter.*
Related titles: ◆ English ed.: Korea Foundation Newsletter. ISSN 1225-8105.
Published by: Korea Foundation, Publication & Reference Materials Team, 1376-1, Seocho-2-dong, Seocho-gu, Seoul, 137072, Korea, S. TEL 82-2-34635684, FAX 82-2-34636086, publication@kf.or.kr, http://www.kf.or.kr/newsletter/view.asp?lang=k, http://www.kofo.or.kr. Pub. In-ho Lee TEL 82-2-8463-5684. R&P Jung-sok Song. Circ: 1,500.

950 TWN
HANDBOOK OF ASIAN PACIFIC COUNTRIES AND REGIONS. Text in English. irreg., latest vol.3, 1995.
Published by: Asian-Pacific Cultural Center, Asian-Pacific Parliamentarians' Union, 6F, 66 Aikuo East Rd, Taipei, 107, Taiwan. TEL 886-2-2322-2139, FAX 886-2-2322-2138, apccapcc@ms23.hinet.net, 101400.2076@compuserve.com. Eds. Chen Tai Chu, Francis Fine.

HANDBOOK OF GERMAN - INTERNATIONAL RELATIONS. see *POLITICAL SCIENCE—International Relations*

950 NLD ISSN 0169-9423
➤ **HANDBUCH DER ORIENTALISTIK. 1. ABTEILUNG. DER NAHE UND DER MITTLERE OSTEN/HANDBOOK OF ORIENTAL STUDIES. SECTION 1. THE NEAR AND MIDDLE EAST.** Text in Dutch. 1952. irreg., latest vol.68. price varies. bibl. back issues avail. **Document type:** *Monographic series, Academic/Scholarly.* **Description:** Scholarly monographs, bibliographic works and research tools pertaining to the political, economic, and social history of the Near and Middle East, encompassing studies of religions, the sciences, archaeology (including Egyptology) and linguistics.
Published by: Brill Academic Publishers, PO Box 9000, Leiden, 2300 PA, Netherlands. TEL 31-71-53-53-500, FAX 31-71-53-17-532, cs@brill.nl, http://www.brill.nl. R&P Elizabeth Venekamp. **Subscr. in N. America to:** PO Box 605, Herndon, VA 20172. TEL 703-661-1585, 800-337-9255, FAX 703-661-1501, cs@brillusa.com. **Distr. outside N. America by:** c/o Turpin Distribution, Stratton Business Park, Pegasus Drive, Biggleswade, BEDFORDSHIRE SG 18 8TQ, United Kingdom. TEL 44-1767-604-954, brill@turpin-distribution.com, brill@turpin-distribution.com.

954 NLD ISSN 0169-9377
Z3208.A6
➤ **HANDBUCH DER ORIENTALISTIK. 2. ABTEILUNG. INDIEN/HANDBOOK OF ORIENTAL STUDIES. SECTION 2. SOUTH ASIA.** Text in Dutch. 1966. irreg., latest vol.16, 2002. price varies. **Document type:** *Monographic series, Academic/Scholarly.* **Description:** Scholarly monographs, bibliographies and research tools pertaining to the political, economic, social, linguistic and religious history of the Indian sub-continent.
Published by: Brill Academic Publishers, PO Box 9000, Leiden, 2300 PA, Netherlands. TEL 31-71-53-53-500, FAX 31-71-53-17-532, cs@brill.nl, http://www.brill.nl. R&P Elizabeth Venekamp. **Subscr. in N. America to:** PO Box 605, Herndon, VA 20172. TEL 703-661-1585, 800-337-9255, FAX 703-661-1501, cs@brillusa.com. **Distr. outside N. America by:** c/o Turpin Distribution, Stratton Business Park, Pegasus Drive, Biggleswade, BEDFORDSHIRE SG 18 8TQ, United Kingdom. TEL 44-1767-604-954, FAX 44-1767-601-640, brill@turpin-distribution.com.

959 NLD ISSN 0169-9571
➤ **HANDBUCH DER ORIENTALISTIK. 3. ABTEILUNG. INDONESIEN, MALAYSIA UND DIE PHILIPPINEN, UNTER EINSCHLUSS DER KAP-MALAIEN IN SUDAFRIKA/ HANDBOOK OF ORIENTAL STUDIES. SECTION 2. SOUTHEAST ASIA.** Text in Dutch. 1972. irreg., latest vol.14, 2003. price varies. **Document type:** *Monographic series, Academic/Scholarly.* **Description:** Scholarly monographs on topics in the history, religions, culture and linguistics of Indonesia, the Philippines and Malaysia, including the Cape-Malays in South Africa.
Published by: Brill Academic Publishers, PO Box 9000, Leiden, 2300 PA, Netherlands. TEL 31-71-53-53-500, FAX 31-71-53-17-532, cs@brill.nl, http://www.brill.nl. Ed. B Spuler. R&P Elizabeth Venekamp. **Subscr. in N. America to:** PO Box 605, Herndon, VA 20172. TEL 703-661-1585, 800-337-9255, FAX 703-661-1501, cs@brillusa.com. **Distr. outside N. America by:** c/o Turpin Distribution, Stratton Business Park, Pegasus Drive, Biggleswade, BEDFORDSHIRE SG 18 8TQ, United Kingdom. TEL 44-1767-604-954, FAX 44-1767-601-640, brill@turpin-distribution.com.

951 NLD ISSN 0169-9520
➤ **HANDBUCH DER ORIENTALISTIK. 4. ABTEILUNG. CHINA/HANDBOOK OF ORIENTAL STUDIES. SECTION 4. CHINA.** Text in Dutch. 1976. irreg., latest vol.16, 2000. price varies. **Document type:** *Monographic series, Academic/Scholarly.* **Description:** Scholarly studies and research tools on topics in the history, religions, culture and linguistics of China.
Published by: Brill Academic Publishers, PO Box 9000, Leiden, 2300 PA, Netherlands. TEL 31-71-53-53-500, FAX 31-71-53-17-532, cs@brill.nl, http://www.brill.nl. R&P Elizabeth Venekamp. **Subscr. in N. America to:** PO Box 605, Herndon, VA 20172. TEL 703-661-1585, 800-337-9255, FAX 703-661-1501, cs@brillusa.com. **Distr. outside N. America by:** c/o Turpin Distribution, Stratton Business Park, Pegasus Drive, Biggleswade, BEDFORDSHIRE SG 18 8TQ, United Kingdom. TEL 44-1767-604-954, FAX 44-1767-601-640, brill@turpin-distribution.com.

952 NLD ISSN 0921-5239
➤ **HANDBUCH DER ORIENTALISTIK. 5. ABTEILUNG. JAPAN/HANDBOOK OF ORIENTAL STUDIES. SECTION 5. JAPAN.** Text in Dutch. 1988. irreg., latest vol.8, 1998. price varies. **Document type:** *Monographic series, Academic/Scholarly.* **Description:** Scholarly studies on topics in the religious, literary, social, economic, legal and political history of Japan.

Published by: Brill Academic Publishers, PO Box 9000, Leiden, 2300 PA, Netherlands. TEL 31-71-53-53-500, FAX 31-71-53-17-532, cs@brill.nl, http://www.brill.nl. R&P Elizabeth Venekamp. **Subscr. in N. America to:** PO Box 605, Herndon, VA 20172. TEL 703-661-1585, 800-337-9255, FAX 703-661-1501, cs@brillusa.com. **Distr. outside N. America by:** c/o Turpin Distribution, Stratton Business Park, Pegasus Drive, Biggleswade, BEDFORDSHIRE SG 18 8TQ, United Kingdom. TEL 44-1767-604-954, FAX 44-1767-601-640, brill@turpin-distribution.com.

950 700 NLD ISSN 0169-9474
➤ **HANDBUCH DER ORIENTALISTIK. 7. ABTEILUNG. KUNST UND ARCHAEOLOGIE/HANDBOOK OF ORIENTAL STUDIES. SECTION 7. ART AND ARCHEOLOGY.** Text in English. 1975. irreg., latest no.8, 1992. price varies.
Document type: *Monographic series, Academic/Scholarly.*
Description: Scholarly monographs, bibliographies, and research tools pertaining to the art and archaeology of the ancient Near East and Asia.
—BLDSC (4254.055500).
Published by: Brill Academic Publishers, PO Box 9000, Leiden, 2300 PA, Netherlands. TEL 31-71-53-53-500, FAX 31-71-53-17-532, cs@brill.nl, http://www.brill.nl. Ed. B Spuler. **Subscr. in N. America to:** PO Box 605, Herndon, VA 20172. TEL 703-661-1585, 800-337-9255, FAX 703-661-1501, cs@brillusa.com. **Distr. outside N. America by:** c/o Turpin Distribution, Stratton Business Park, Pegasus Drive, Biggleswade, BEDFORDSHIRE SG 18 8TQ, United Kingdom. TEL 44-1767-604-954, FAX 44-1767-601-640, brill@turpin-distribution.com.

494 NLD ISSN 0169-8524
➤ **HANDBUCH DER ORIENTALISTIK. 8. ABTEILUNG. HANDBOOK OF URALIC STUDIES/HANDBOOK OF ORIENTAL STUDIES. SECTION 8. URALIC AND CENTRAL ASIAN STUDIES.** Text in Dutch. 1988. irreg., latest vol.7, 2002. price varies. back issues avail. **Document type:** *Monographic series, Academic/Scholarly.* **Description:** Discusses the history and culture of the Central Asian regions, including linguistics of the Uralic languages.
Published by: Brill Academic Publishers, PO Box 9000, Leiden, 2300 PA, Netherlands. TEL 31-71-53-53-500, FAX 31-71-53-17-532, cs@brill.nl, http://www.brill.nl. Ed. B Spuler. R&P Elizabeth Venekamp. **Subscr. in N. America to:** PO Box 605, Herndon, VA 20172. TEL 703-661-1585, 800-337-9255, FAX 703-661-1501, cs@brillusa.com. **Distr. outside N. America by:** c/o Turpin Distribution, Stratton Business Park, Pegasus Drive, Biggleswade, BEDFORDSHIRE SG 18 8TQ, United Kingdom. TEL 44-1767-604-954, FAX 44-1767-601-640, brill@turpin-distribution.com.

950 DEU ISSN 0948-8650
HANDSCHRIFTEN DES ALTAEGYPTISCHEN TOTENBUCHES. Text in German. 1995. irreg., latest vol.7, 2001. price varies. **Document type:** *Monographic series, Academic/Scholarly.*
Published by: Harrassowitz Verlag, Taunusstr 14, Wiesbaden, 65183, Germany. TEL 49-611-5300, FAX 49-611-530570, verlag@harrassowitz.de, http://www.harrassowitz.de. Eds. Heinz Josef Thissen, Ursula Roessler Koehler. R&P Michael Langfeld. Adv. contact Robert Gietz.

HARVARD ARMENIAN TEXTS AND STUDIES. see *HISTORY—History Of The Near East*

HARVARD ASIA PACIFIC REVIEW. see *POLITICAL SCIENCE*

950 USA ISSN 0073-0548
DS501
➤ **HARVARD JOURNAL OF ASIATIC STUDIES.** Text in English. 1936. s-a. USD 30 to individuals; USD 45 to institutions (effective 2004). bk.rev. illus. cum.index: 1936-80; index every 5 yrs. back issues avail.; reprint service avail. from PQC,SCH. **Document type:** *Journal, Academic/Scholarly.* **Description:** Covers the literatures, cultures, and histories of the countries in Eastern and Central Asia, but not contemporary political and social sciences.
Related titles: Microform ed.: (from MIM, PQC); Online - full text ed.: (from JSTOR (Web-based Journal Archive)).
Indexed: ASCA, AmH&L, AnthLit, ArtHuCI, BAS, BRI, BibLing, CBRI, CurCont, HistAb, HumInd, IBR, IBRH, IBSS, IBZ, IndIslam, MEA&I, MLA, MLA-IB, PCI, RASB, RILM, SSI.
—IDS, IE, Infotrieve.
Published by: Harvard-Yenching Institute, 2 Divinity Ave, Cambridge, MA 02138. TEL 617-495-2758, FAX 617-495-7798, yenching@fas.harvard.edu, http://hcl.harvard.edu/harvard-yenching, http://www-hcl.harvard.edu/hyl/hylhome.html. Eds. Joanna Handlin Smith, Wilt Idema. Circ: 1,200.

410 CHE ISSN 0073-0971
HAUTES ETUDES ORIENTALES. Text in French. 1968. irreg., latest vol.34, 2001. **Document type:** *Monographic series, Academic/Scholarly.* **Description:** Discusses studies of military, literature and poetry from the Far East.
—CCC.
Published by: (Ecole Pratique des Hautes Etudes FRA, Centre de Recherches d'Histoire et de Philologie FRA), Librairie Droz S.A., 11 rue Massot, Geneva 12, 1211, Switzerland. TEL 41-22-3466666, FAX 41-22-3472391, droz@droz.org, http://www.droz.org. Circ: 600.

935 BEL ISSN 0776-2666
➤ **HETHITICA.** Text in Dutch, French. 1972. irreg., latest vol.14, 1999. price varies. back issues avail. **Document type:** *Monographic series, Academic/Scholarly.*
Related titles: ♦ Series of: Institut de Linguistique de Louvain. Bibliotheque des Cahiers. ISSN 0779-1666.
Indexed: BibLing, RI-2.
Published by: (Universite Catholique de Louvain, Faculte de Philosophie et Lettres, Universite Catholique de Louvain, Institut de Linguistique), Peeters Publishers, Bondgenotenlaan 153, Leuven, 3000, Belgium. TEL 32-16-235170, FAX 32-16-228500, http://www.peeters-leuven.be. Eds. R Lebrun, Y Duhoux. Pub. G Juquois.

958 NPL
HIMALAYAN CULTURE. Text in English, Nepali. 1978. q. NPR 38, USD 6.
Published by: Hari Bangsha Kirant, 20-136 Kamal Pokhari, Kathmandu, 711000, Nepal.

956 USA ISSN 1097-3702
DS59.J24
➤ **HUGOYE: JOURNAL OF SYRIAC STUDIES.** Text in English. 1998. s-a. free. bk.rev. **Document type:** *Academic/Scholarly.* **Description:** Dedicated to the study of the Syriac tradition.
Media: Online - full text.
Indexed: RI-1.
Published by: Syriac Computing Institute, c/o Dr. G. Kiraz, Bell-Labs, Rm. 2D-446, 700 Mountain Ave., Murray Hill, NJ 07974. TEL 908-582-4074, FAX 908-582-3306, webmaster@bethmardutho.org, http://syrcom.cua.edu/Hugoye/, http://www.bethmardutho.org. Ed. George Anton Kiraz.

890 TUN ISSN 0018-862X
AS653
I B L A. Text mainly in French; Text occasionally in Arabic, English. 1937. s-a. TND 12 domestic; USD 30 foreign (effective 2003). adv. bk.rev. bibl. index. 200 p./no.; **Document type:** *Academic/Scholarly.* **Description:** Covers questions in the field of arts and human sciences concerning the Arab-Muslim world, with special reference to Tunisia.
Related titles: Microfiche ed.
Indexed: AICP, AmH&L, BibInd, BibLing, DIP, HistAb, IBR, IBSS, IBZ, L&LBA, MLA, MLA-IB, RASB, SOPODA.
Published by: Institut des Belles Lettres Arabes, 12 rue Jamaa el Haoua, Tunis, 1008, Tunisia. TEL 216-71560133, FAX 216-71572683, ibla@gnet.tn. Ed. Jean Fontaine. Circ: 800.

I I A S NEWSLETTER. see *HISTORY—History Of Asia*

950 DEU
IAPONIA INSULA. Text in German. 1994. irreg., latest vol.9, 2000. price varies. **Document type:** *Monographic series, Academic/Scholarly.*
Published by: Iudicium Verlag, Hans-Graessel-Weg 13, Munich, 81375, Germany. TEL 49-89-718747, FAX 49-89-7142039, info@iudicium.de, http://www.iudicium.de.

954 800 IND
IMAGE. Text in English. 1977 (vol.2). s-a. INR 10, USD 3. adv. bk.rev.
Published by: Image Publication, Sahadevkhunta, Balasore, Orissa 756001, India. Ed. Indu Bhusan Kar.

INDIAN HORIZONS. see *HISTORY—History Of Asia*

954 IND
INDIAN JOURNAL OF NEPALESE STUDIES. Text in English. 1987. s-a. INR 40, USD 8 (effective 2001). **Document type:** *Journal, Academic/Scholarly.*
Published by: Centre for the Study of Nepal, Banaras Hindu University, Faculty of Social Sciences, Varanasi, Uttar Pradesh 221 005, India. TEL 91-542-307427, FAX 91-542-368174, cs_nepal@usa.net. Ed. M D Dharamdasani.

954 IND ISSN 0019-686X
DS401
INDICA. Text in English. 1964. s-a. USD 15 (effective 2000). adv. bk.rev. illus. index, cum.index. back issues avail. **Document type:** *Academic/Scholarly.* **Description:** Publishes articles on history, literature, archeology, art and religion.
Indexed: AmH&L, BAS, HistAb, IBR, IBZ, IndIslam, RASB.
Published by: Heras Institute of Indian History and Culture, St. Xavier's College, Mumbai, Maharashtra 400 001, India. TEL 91-22-262-0662. Ed. Aubrey Mascarenhas S J. Circ: 400.

INDO-IRAN JOURNAL. see *POLITICAL SCIENCE—International Relations*

891 955 NLD ISSN 0019-7246
PK1 CODEN: IIRJAU
➤ **INDO-IRANIAN JOURNAL.** Text in Dutch, English. 1957. q. EUR 448, USD 458, GBP 285 combined subscription to institutions print & online eds. (effective 2005). adv. bk.rev. index. reprint service avail. from PSC. **Document type:** *Journal, Academic/Scholarly.* **Description:** Publishes original scholarship on ancient and medieval Indian and Iranian languages, literatures and linguistics, as well as related philosophical and textual issues.
Related titles: Microform ed.: (from PQC); Online - full text ed.: ISSN 1572-8536 (from EBSCO Publishing, Gale Group, IngentaConnect, Kluwer Online, O C L C Online Computer Library Center, Inc., Springer LINK, Swets Information Services).
Indexed: ASCA, ArtHuCI, BAS, BibLing, CurCont, DIP, IBR, IBRH, IBSS, IBZ, IndIslam, L&LBA, MEA&I, MLA, MLA-IB, PhilInd, RASB, RI-1, RI-2, RILM, SOPODA.
—BLDSC (4437.590000), IDS, IE, Infotrieve, ingenta. **CCC.**
Published by: Springer-Verlag Dordrecht (Subsidiary of: Springer Science+Business Media), Van Godewijckstraat 30, Dordrecht, 3311 GX, Netherlands. TEL 31-78-6576050, FAX 31-78-6576474, http://springerlink.metapress.com/openurl.asp?genre=journal&issn=0019-7246, http://www.springeronline.com. Eds. H T Bakker, Oskar von Hinueber.

954 491 ITA ISSN 1023-3881
PK1
➤ **INDOLOGICA TAURINENSIA.** Text in Multiple languages. 1973. a. EUR 46.48 domestic; EUR 80 foreign (effective 2003). bk.rev. back issues avail. **Document type:** *Academic/Scholarly.* **Description:** Contains research about Indological studies with particular reference to Sanskrit literature.
Indexed: BibLing, IBR.
Address: c/o C E S M E O, Via Cavour 17, Turin, 10123, Italy. TEL 39-011-546564, FAX 39-011-545031. Ed. Oscar Botto.
Dist. by: Edizioni dell' Orso.

959.8 USA ISSN 0019-7289
DS611
➤ **INDONESIA.** Text in English. 1966. s-a. USD 32 domestic; USD 34 foreign (effective 2005). adv. bk.rev. bibl.; charts; illus.; stat. index every 3 yrs. back issues avail.; reprint service avail. from PQC. **Document type:** *Academic/Scholarly.* **Description:** Interdisciplinary journal devoted to Indonesia's culture, history and socio-political problems.
Related titles: Microform ed.: (from PQC); Online - full text ed.: (from bigchalk, Northern Light Technology, Inc., ProQuest Information & Learning).
Indexed: APEL, AmH&L, BAS, DIP, EI, HistAb, IBR, IBSS, IPSA, IndIslam, MLA-IB, PCI, RASB.
—BLDSC (4437.630000), IE, Infotrieve, ingenta.
Published by: Cornell University, Southeast Asia Program, 180 Uris Hall, Ithaca, NY 14857-7601. TEL 607-255-2370, FAX 607-254-5000, SEAP-Pubs@cornell.edu, http://www.einaudi.cornell.edu:591/SEAPpubs, http://www.einaudi.cornell.edu/SoutheastAsia/. Ed. Deborah Homsher. R&P, Adv. contact David J Stotz. Circ: 900. **Subscr. to:** Cornell University, 95 Brown Rd., Ste. 1004, Ithaca, NY 14850-1257.

➤ **INDONESIA AND THE MALAY WORLD.** see *HISTORY—History Of Asia*

954 AUS ISSN 0816-8091
INDONESIAN STUDIES NEWSLETTER. Text in English. 1985. s-a. AUD 10 to individuals; AUD 15 to institutions. **Document type:** *Newsletter.* **Description:** Explores all aspects of Indonesian culture, with emphasis on Indonesian as a language taught in high schools and universities.
Media: Online - full text.
Published by: (Asian Studies Association of Australia), Australian National University, G.P.O. Box 4, Canberra, ACT 2601, Australia. TEL 61-2-6249-3163, FAX 61-2-6249-0745, VirginiaHooker@anu.edu.au, http://www.anu.edu.au/asianstudies/indonnews/. Ed. Virginia Hooker.

950 DEU
INSCHRIFTEN DES TEMPELS VON EDFU. ABTEILUNG I: UEBERSETZUNGEN. Text in German. 1998. irreg. price varies. **Document type:** *Monographic series, Academic/Scholarly.*
Published by: Harrassowitz Verlag, Taunusstr 14, Wiesbaden, 65183, Germany. TEL 49-611-5300, FAX 49-611-530570, verlag@harrassowitz.de, http://www.harrassowitz.de. Ed. Dieter Kurth. R&P Michael Langfeld. Adv. contact Robert Gietz.

950 DEU ISSN 0937-8413
INSCHRIFTEN DES TEMPELS VON EDFU. BEGLEITHEFTE. Text in German. 1990. irreg., latest vol.3, 2002. price varies. **Document type:** *Monographic series, Academic/Scholarly.*
Published by: Harrassowitz Verlag, Taunusstr 14, Wiesbaden, 65183, Germany. TEL 49-611-5300, FAX 49-611-530570, verlag@harrassowitz.de, http://www.harrassowitz.de. Ed. Dieter Kurth. R&P Michael Langfeld. Adv. contact Robert Gietz.

INSTITUT DE RELATIONS INTERNATIONALES. ETUDES ET DOCUMENTS. see *POLITICAL SCIENCE—International Relations*

935 955 BEL ISSN 1288-8931
➤ **INSTITUT DES ETUDES IRANIENNES. TRAVAUX ET MEMOIRES.** Key Title: Travaux et Memoires de l'Institut d'Etudes Iraniennes. Text in French. 1966. irreg., latest vol.18, 1997. price varies. back issues avail. **Document type:** *Monographic series, Academic/Scholarly.* **Description:** Publishes studies on the history, language and culture of Iran from ancient times to the present.

▼ new title ➤ refereed ∗ unverified ♦ full entry avail.

A

Formerly (until 1995): Institut des Etudes Iraniennes. Travaux (0553-2841)
Published by: (Universite de Paris III (Sorbonne-Nouvelle) FRA, Institut des Etudes Iraniennes FRA), Peeters Publishers, Bondgenotenlaan 153, Leuven, 3000, Belgium. TEL 32-16-235170, FAX 32-16-228500, http://www.peeters-leuven.be.

➤ **INSTITUT DOMINICAIN D'ETUDES ORIENTALES DU CAIRE. MELANGES.** see *HISTORY—History Of The Near East*

➤ **INSTITUT FRANCAIS D'ARCHEOLOGIE ORIENTALE DU CAIRE. BIBLIOTHEQUE D'ETUDE.** see *ARCHAEOLOGY*

➤ **INSTITUT FRANCAIS D'ARCHEOLOGIE ORIENTALE DU CAIRE. BIBLIOTHEQUE GENERALE.** see *ARCHAEOLOGY*

➤ **INSTITUT FRANCAIS D'ARCHEOLOGIE ORIENTALE DU CAIRE. BULLETIN.** see *ARCHAEOLOGY*

950 IND ISSN 0073-8352
INSTITUT FRANCAIS DE PONDICHERY. DEPARTEMENT D'INDOLOGIE. PUBLICATIONS. Text in English, French. 1956. irreg. (approx. 4/yr.). price varies. bk.rev. index.
Formerly: Institut Francais d'Indologie. Publications
Published by: Institut Francais de Pondichery/French Institute of Pondicherry, P O Box 33, Pondicherry, Tamil Nadu 605 001, India. TEL 91-413-34-170, FAX 91-413-39-534, instfran@giasmd01.vsnl.net.in. Ed. F Grimalh. Circ: 500. **Dist. outside India:** Librairie d'Amerique et d'Orient, 11 rue Saint-Sulpice, Paris 75006, France. TEL 33-1-43268635, 33-1-43545954.

INSTITUTE OF ASIAN STUDIES. JOURNAL. see *SOCIOLOGY*

INTERCONTINENTA. see *HISTORY—History Of Europe*

026.95 USA ISSN 0161-7397
Z688.A75
INTERNATIONAL ASSOCIATION OF ORIENTALIST LIBRARIANS. BULLETIN. Text in English. 1971. s-a. USD 20; USD 12 to individuals; institutions (effective 1999). adv. bk.rev. **Document type:** *Bulletin, Trade.*
Formerly (until 1976): International Association of Orientalist Librarians. Newsletter (0146-6992)
Indexed: BAS.
Published by: University of Wisconsin Madison, 412A Memorial Library, 728 State St, Madison, Belgium, WI 53706. TEL 608-262-0344, FAX 608-265-2754, thahn@macc.wisc.edu. Pub., R&P, Adv. contact Thomas Hahn. Circ: 300.

950 001.3 300 JPN
PJ21
INTERNATIONAL CONFERENCE OF EASTERN STUDIES. TRANSACTIONS. Text in English. 1957. a. JPY 2,000 (effective 2002). 130 p./no.; back issues avail. **Document type:** *Proceedings.* **Description:** Publishes full texts and abstracts of the papers presented at the Conference.
Formerly (until Feb. 1995): International Conference of Orientalists in Japan. Transactions (0538-6012)
Indexed: BAS, MLA, MLA-IB, RASB.
Published by: Toho Gakkai/Institute of Eastern Culture, 4-1 Nishi-Kanda 2-chome, Chiyoda-ku, Tokyo, 101-0065, Japan. TEL 81-3-3262-7221, FAX 81-3-3262-7227, tohogakkai@mc.nextlink.ne.jp. Ed. Hattori Masaaki. Circ: 1,300.

INTERNATIONAL INSTITUTE FOR ASIAN STUDIES. ANNUAL REPORT. see *HISTORY—History Of Asia*

950 GBR ISSN 1479-5914
DS1
▼➤ **INTERNATIONAL JOURNAL OF ASIAN STUDIES.** Text in English. 2003. s-a. GBP 92 to institutions; USD 138 in North America to institutions; GBP 94 combined subscription to institutions print & online eds.; USD 142 combined subscription in North America to institutions print & online eds. (effective 2006). illus. **Document type:** *Journal, Academic/Scholarly.*
Related titles: Online - full text ed.: ISSN 1479-5922. GBP 86 to institutions; USD 130 in North America to institutions (effective 2006) (from EBSCO Publishing, O C L C Online Computer Library Center, Inc., Swets Information Services).
Indexed: AmH&L, HistAb.
Published by: Cambridge University Press, The Edinburgh Bldg, Shaftesbury Rd, Cambridge, CB2 2RU, United Kingdom. TEL 44-1223-312393, FAX 44-1223-315052, journals@cambridge.org, http://titles.cambridge.org/journals/journal_catalogue.asp?historylinks=ALPHA&mnemonic=ASI, http://www.cup.cam.ac.uk/. Eds. Gaynor Sekimori, Haruka Yanagisawa, Takeshi Hamashita. **Subscr. to:** Cambridge University Press, 100 Brook Hill Dr, West Nyack, NY 10994. TEL 845-353-7500, FAX 845-353-4141, journals_subscriptions@cup.org

956 CAN ISSN 1206-789X
➤ **INTERNATIONAL JOURNAL OF ISLAMIC STUDIES**★ **.** Text in Arabic, English. 1997. q. CND 400 (effective 2000). adv. bk.rev. **Document type:** *Journal, Academic/Scholarly.* **Description:** Designed for concise, cooperative publication of simple and creative practical ideas for society development using available resources.
Published by: M.I. Ismail, Ed. & Pub., P O Box 98029, Mississauga, ON L5L 3A0, Canada. FAX 516-277-2875.

951.9 KOR ISSN 1229-6902
DS917.44
INTERNATIONAL JOURNAL OF KOREAN UNIFICATION STUDIES. Text in English. 2000. s-a.
Indexed: PAIS.
Published by: Korea Institute for National Unification, 535-353 Suyu 6-dong, Kangbuk-ku, Seoul, 142-076, Korea, S.

956 GBR ISSN 0020-7438
DS41 CODEN: IJMECN
➤ **INTERNATIONAL JOURNAL OF MIDDLE EAST STUDIES.** Text in English. 1970. q. (plus two bulletins). GBP 176 to institutions; USD 280 in North America to institutions; GBP 190 combined subscription to institutions print & online eds.; USD 306 combined subscription in North America to institutions print & online eds. (effective 2006); Subscr. includes Middle East Studies Association Bulletin (0026-3184) in July & Dec.. adv. bk.rev. illus. back issues avail.; reprint service avail. from PQC,PSC. **Document type:** *Journal, Academic/Scholarly.* **Description:** Features research on the Middle East from the seventh century to the present day: history, politics, economics, anthropology, sociology, literature and folklore, comparative religion and law.
Related titles: Microform ed.: (from PQC); Online - full text ed.: ISSN 1471-6380. GBP 160 to institutions; USD 255 in North America to institutions (effective 2006) (from EBSCO Publishing, JSTOR (Web-based Journal Archive), O C L C Online Computer Library Center, Inc., Swets Information Services).
Indexed: ABCPolSci, AICP, ASCA, AbAn, AmH&L, ArtHuCI, BRI, BibLing, CCME, CJA, CommAb, CurCont, DIP, FamI, GEOBASE, HistAb, IBR, IBSS, IBZ, IPSA, IndIslam, L&LBA, MEA&I, MLA, MLA-IB, PAIS, PCI, PRA, PSA, PerIslam, PhilInd, RASB, RDA, RRTA, SOPODA, SSA, SSCI, SSI, SociolAb, WAE&RSA.
—BLDSC (4542.358000), IDS, IE, Infotrieve, ingenta. **CCC.**
Published by: (Middle East Studies Association of North America - M E S A USA), Cambridge University Press, The Edinburgh Bldg, Shaftesbury Rd, Cambridge, CB2 2RU, United Kingdom. TEL 44-1223-312393, FAX 44-1223-315052, journals@cambridge.org, http://uk.cambridge.org/journals/mes/. Ed. Judith Tucker. R&P Linda Nicol TEL 44-1223-325757. Adv. contact Rebecca Curtis TEL 44-1223-325757. **Subscr. to:** Cambridge University Press, 100 Brook Hill Dr, West Nyack, NY 10994. TEL 845-353-7500, FAX 845-353-4141, journals_subscriptions@cup.org

956 CAN ISSN 1206-7849
INTERNATIONAL JOURNAL OF SCIENTIFIC AMERICA & MIDDLE EAST STUDIES★ **.** Text in Arabic, English. 1997. q. CND 400 (effective 2000). adv. bk.rev. **Document type:** *Journal, Academic/Scholarly.* **Description:** Designed for concise, cooperative publication of simple economic and practical creative ideas for solution of societal problems.
Published by: M.I. Ismail, Ed. & Pub., P O Box 98029, Mississauga, ON L5L 3A0, Canada. FAX 516-277-2875.

950 HKG
INTERNATIONAL SYMPOSIA ON ASIAN STUDIES. PROCEEDINGS. Text in Chinese. 1979. a. USD 125. **Document type:** *Proceedings.*
Published by: Asian Research Service, GPO Box 2232, Hong Kong, Hong Kong. TEL 852-2570-7227, FAX 852-2512-8050, arsmart@in2nett.com. R&P Nelson Leung.

950 DEU ISSN 0020-9449
➤ **INTERNATIONALES ASIENFORUM**; international quarterly for Asian studies. Text in English, German; Summaries in English. 1970. q. EUR 65 (effective 2002). adv. bk.rev. **Document type:** *Journal, Academic/Scholarly.* **Description:** Focuses on current developments in Asian countries.
Related titles: Online - full text ed.: (from ProQuest Information & Learning).
Indexed: APEL, AmH&L, BAS, DIP, EI, HistAb, IBR, IBSS, IBZ, ILD, IPSA, KES, MEA&I, PAIS, RASB, RI-1, RI-2, SSCI.
—BLDSC (4557.003000), IE, ingenta. **CCC.**
Published by: Arnold-Bergstraesser-Institut fuer Kulturwissenschaftliche Forschung, Windausstr 16, Freiburg Im Breisgau, 79110, Germany. TEL 49-761-888780, FAX 49-761-8887878, abifr@abi.uni-freiburg.de, http://www.arnold-bergstraesser.de. Eds. Alois Graf von Waldburg-Zeil, Detlef Kantowsky. Circ: 350 (paid).

➤ **INTERSECTIONS**; gender, history & culture in the Asian context. see *MEN'S STUDIES*

955 NLD ISSN 1609-8498
DS266
IRAN & CAUCASUS. Text in English. 1997. s-a., latest vol.10, 2006. USD 41 in the Americas to individuals; EUR 33 elsewhere to individuals; USD 124 combined subscription in the Americas to institutions print & online eds.; EUR 99 combined subscription elsewhere to institutions print & online eds. (effective 2006). back issues avail. **Document type:** *Journal, Academic/Scholarly.* **Description:** Focuses on the history of the Caucasian and Iranian people.
Related titles: Online - full text ed.: ISSN 1573-384X. USD 112 in the Americas to institutions; USD 89 elsewhere to institutions (effective 2006) (from EBSCO Publishing, Gale Group, IngentaConnect, O C L C Online Computer Library Center, Inc., Swets Information Services).
Published by: Brill Academic Publishers, PO Box 9000, Leiden, 2300 PA, Netherlands. TEL 31-71-53-53-500, FAX 31-71-53-17-532, cs@brill.nl, http://www.brill.nl/m_catalogue_sub6_id9559.htm. Ed. Garnik Asatrian. **Subscr. in N. America to:** PO Box 605, Herndon, VA 20172. TEL 703-661-1585, 800-337-9255, FAX 703-661-1501, cs@brillusa.com. **Distr. outside N. America by:** c/o Turpin Distribution, Stratton Business Park, Pegasus Drive, Biggleswade, BEDFORDSHIRE SG 18 8TQ, United Kingdom. TEL 44-1767-604-954, FAX 44-1767-601-640, brill@turpin-distribution.com.

955 USA
THE IRANIAN★ **.** Text in English. 1995. bi-m. **Description:** Features Iranian art, culture, history, politics, life in Iran and abroad, including issues of identity facing expatriates of the Iranian community as well as others who are interested.
Media: Online - full text.
Published by: Iranian, PO Box 34842, Bethesda, MD 20827-0842. bulletin@iranian.com, http://www.iranian.com. Ed. Jahanshah Javid.

955 GBR ISSN 0021-0862
CODEN: IRSTEK
➤ **IRANIAN STUDIES.** Text in English. 1968. q. GBP 173, USD 285 combined subscription to institutions print & online eds. (effective 2006); includes SIS News. adv. bk.rev. bibl.; charts; illus. Index. reprint service avail. from PSC. **Document type:** *Journal, Academic/Scholarly.* **Description:** Devoted to Iranian and Persian history, literature, and society.
Related titles: Online - full text ed.: ISSN 1475-4819. GBP 165, USD 272 to institutions (effective 2006) (from EBSCO Publishing, Gale Group, IngentaConnect, O C L C Online Computer Library Center, Inc., Swets Information Services).
Indexed: AmH&L, AnthLit, BibLing, DIP, HistAb, IBR, IBZ, IPSA, IndIslam, MEA&I, MLA, MLA-IB, PCI, PSA, PerIslam, RILM, SOPODA, SSA, SociolAb.
—IE.
Published by: (International Society for Iranian Studies USA), Routledge (Subsidiary of: Taylor & Francis Group), 4 Park Sq, Milton Park, Abingdon, Oxon OX14 4RN, United Kingdom. TEL 44-1235-828600, FAX 44-1235-829000, info@routledge.co.uk, http://www.tandf.co.uk/journals/titles/00210862.asp, http://www.routledge.co.uk. Ed. Homa Katouzian. Adv. contact Kambiz Eslami. Circ: 600. **Subscr. in N. America to:** Taylor & Francis Inc., Customer Services Dept, 325 Chestnut St, 8th Fl, Philadelphia, PA 19106. TEL 215-625-8900, 800-354-1420, FAX 215-625-8914, customerservice@taylorandfrancis.com; **Subscr. to:** Taylor & Francis Ltd, Journals Customer Service, Rankine Rd, Basingstoke, Hants RG24 8PR, United Kingdom. TEL 44-1256-813000, FAX 44-1256-330245.

950 DEU ISSN 0944-1271
IRANICA. Text in German. 1993. irreg., latest vol.6, 2003. price varies. **Document type:** *Monographic series, Academic/Scholarly.*
Published by: Harrassowitz Verlag, Taunusstr 14, Wiesbaden, 65183, Germany. TEL 49-611-5300, FAX 49-611-53070, verlag@harrassowitz.de, http://www.harrassowitz.de. Ed. Maria Macuch. R&P Michael Langfeld. Adv. contact Robert Gietz.

IRANICA ANTIQUA. see *ARCHAEOLOGY*

IRANICA ANTIQUA SUPPLEMENTA. see *ARCHAEOLOGY*

955 DEU ISSN 0578-7076
DS251
IRANISTISCHE MITTEILUNGEN. Text in English, German. 1967. irreg. (2-4/yr.). bk.rev. back issues avail. **Document type:** *Academic/Scholarly.* **Description:** Iranian studies.
Indexed: BibLing.
Published by: Antigone-Verlag, Postfach 1147, Allendorf, 35105, Germany. TEL 49-6452-1800. Ed. Helmhart Kanus Crede. Circ: 50.

IRAQ. see *ARCHAEOLOGY*

ISLAMIC ART. see *ART*

ISLAMIC HISTORY AND CIVILIZATION. see *RELIGIONS AND THEOLOGY—Islamic*

ISLAMIC QUARTERLY; a review of Islamic Culture. see *RELIGIONS AND THEOLOGY—Islamic*

ISRAEL EXPLORATION JOURNAL. see *ARCHAEOLOGY*

ISSUES & STUDIES; an international quarterly on China, Taiwan, and East Asian affairs. see *POLITICAL SCIENCE—International Relations*

ISTANBULER MITTEILUNGEN. see *ARCHAEOLOGY*

ISTITUTO UNIVERSITARIO ORIENTALE DI NAPOLI. DIPARTIMENTO DI STUDI DEL MONDO CLASSICO E DEL MEDITERRANEO ANTICO. SEZIONE LINGUISTICA. ANNALI. see *CLASSICAL STUDIES*

950 401   ITA
ISTITUTO UNIVERSITARIO ORIENTALE. DIPARTIMENTO DI STUDI ASIATICI. SERIES MINOR. Text in Italian. 1974. irreg.
Indexed: MLA-IB.
Published by: Universita degli Studi di Napoli, L'Orientale/Dipartimento di Studi Asiatici, Piazza San Domenico Maggiore 12, Palazzo Corigliano, Naples, 80134 , Italy. Dist. by: Herder Editrice e Libreria s.r.l., Piazza di Montecitorio 117-120, Rome 00186, Italy. TEL 39-6-6794628.

950   ITA
ISTITUTO UNIVERSITARIO ORIENTALE. DIPARTIMENTO DI STUDI ASIATICI. SEZIONE ORIENTALE. ANNALI. Text in English, French, Italian. 1940. q.
Indexed: MLA-IB.
Published by: Universita degli Studi di Napoli, L'Orientale/Dipartimento di Studi Asiatici, Piazza San Domenico Maggiore 12, Palazzo Corigliano, Naples, 80134 , Italy. Ed. Giovanni Verardi. Dist. by: Herder Editrice e Libreria s.r.l., Piazza di Montecitorio 117-120, Rome 00186, Italy. TEL 39-6-6794628, FAX 39-6-6784751, http://www.herder.it. Co-publisher: Universita degli Studi di Napoli, L'Orientale/Dipartimento di Studi e Ricerche su Africa e Paesi Arabi.

952   DEU   ISSN 0937-2008
IZUMI; Quellen, Studien und Materialen zur Kultur Japans. Text in German. 1989. irreg., latest vol.8, 2002. price varies.
Document type: *Monographic series, Academic/Scholarly.*
Published by: Harrassowitz Verlag, Taunusstr 14, Wiesbaden, 65183, Germany. TEL 49-611-5300, FAX 49-611-530570, verlag@harrassowitz.de, http://www.harrassowitz.de. Ed. Klaus Kracht. R&P Michael Langfeld. Adv. contact Robert Gietz.

950   SGP
J S E A S SPECIAL PUBLICATION SERIES. (Journal of Southeast Asian Studies) Text in English. 1990. irreg., latest vol.3, 1996. Document type: *Monographic series, Academic/Scholarly.*
Published by: Singapore University Press, Ground Floor Yusof Ishak House, 10 Kent Ridge Crescent, Singapore, 119260, Singapore. TEL 65-7761148, FAX 65-7740652, supbooks@nus.edu.sg, http://www.nus.sg/sup. Ed. George Ofori.

952 059.956   JPN   ISSN 0385-2318
DS821
JAPAN FOUNDATION NEWSLETTER. Text in English. 1973. q. free. bk.rev. illus. Index. back issues avail.; reprints avail.
Document type: *Newsletter.* Description: Features cultural highlights, research reports, and foundation activities. Intended for those interested in Japanese culture and international cultural exchange.
Indexed: BAS, RASB.
Published by: Japan Foundation, Ark-Mori Bldg 20th Fl, 1-12-32 Akasaka, Minato-ku, Tokyo, 107-0052, Japan. TEL 81-3-5562-3532, FAX 81-3-5562-3501, jfnl@jpf.go.jp. Circ: 4,000.

JAPAN LETTER. see *BUSINESS AND ECONOMICS—Economic Situation And Conditions*

952   DEU   ISSN 1436-879X
JAPAN-MAGAZIN. Text in German. 1990. m. adv. Document type: *Magazine, Consumer.* Description: Provides information and features on all aspects of Japan and Japanese culture.
Incorporates (in 1999): Japan-Journal
Published by: Verlag Dieter Born, Karl-Legien-Str 156, Bonn, 53117, Germany. TEL 49-228-55925-0, FAX 49-228-5592555, verlag@dieter-born.de, http://www.japan-magazin.de, http://www.dieter-born.de.

950   DEU
JAPANESE INSTITUE OF ANATOLIAN ARCHAEOLOGY. BULLETIN. Text in German. 1984. irreg. price varies.
Document type: *Monographic series, Academic/Scholarly.*
Formerly (until 2000): Middle Eastern Culture Center, Japan. Bulletin (0177-1647)
Indexed: DIP, IBR.
Published by: (Japanese Institute of Anatolian Archaeology JPN), Harrassowitz Verlag, Taunusstr 14, Wiesbaden, 65183, Germany. TEL 49-611-5300, FAX 49-611-530570, verlag@harrassowitz.de, http://www.harrassowitz.de. Ed. H I H Prince Takahito Mikasa. R&P Michael Langfeld. Adv. contact Robert Gietz.

JAPANESE SWORD SOCIETY OF THE U S BULLETIN. see *ANTIQUES*

952   DEU   ISSN 0934-9995
JAPANISCHE FACHTEXTE. Text in German. 1980. irreg., latest vol.3, 1988. price varies. Document type: *Monographic series, Academic/Scholarly.*
Published by: Harrassowitz Verlag, Taunusstr 14, Wiesbaden, 65183, Germany. TEL 49-611-5300, FAX 49-611-530570, verlag@harrassowitz.de, http://www.harrassowitz.de. Ed. Bruno Lewin. R&P Michael Langfeld. Adv. contact Robert Gietz.

952   DEU   ISSN 1433-3473
DS820.8
JAPONICA HUMBOLDTIANA. Text in German, English. 1997. a. EUR 49 (effective 2006). Document type: *Monographic series, Academic/Scholarly.*
Indexed: DIP, IBR, IBZ.
Published by: (Humboldt-Universitaet zu Berlin, Mori-Ogai-Gedenkstaette), Harrassowitz Verlag, Taunusstr 14, Wiesbaden, 65183, Germany. TEL 49-611-5300, FAX 49-611-530560, verlag@harrassowitz.de, http://www.harrassowitz.de. Ed. Klaus Kracht. R&P Michael Langfeld. Adv. contact Robert Gietz.

952   NLD
JAPONICA NEERLANDICA. Text in English. 1985. irreg., latest vol.5, 1992. price varies. Document type: *Monographic series.* Description: Publishes scholarly studies on topics relating to Japanese history and culture.
Published by: Hotei Publishing, Royal Tropical Institute, PO Box 95001, Amsterdam, 1090 HA, Netherlands. TEL 31-20-5688330, FAX 31-20-568-8286, info@hotei-publishing.com, http://www.kit.nl/hotei/html.

950   USA
JAVANESE LITERATURE IN SURAKARTU MANUSCRIPTS. Text in English. 1993. irreg. price varies. Document type: *Bibliography.*
Published by: Cornell University, Southeast Asia Program, 640 Stewart Ave, Ithaca, NY 14850. TEL 607-255-4359, FAX 607-255-7534. Ed. Deborah Homsher. R&P David J Stotz. Subscr. to: S E A P Publications, Cornell University, E Hill Plaza, Ithaca, NY 14850.

THE JEWISH QUARTERLY REVIEW. see *RELIGIONS AND THEOLOGY—Judaic*

950   JPN   ISSN 0289-1417
JOCHI AJIAGAKU/JOURNAL OF SOPHIA ASIAN STUDIES. Text in Japanese. 1983. a. Document type: *Journal, Academic/Scholarly.*
Published by: Jochi Daigaku, Ajia Bunka Kenkyujo/Sophia University, Institute of Asian Cultures, 7-1 Kioi-cho, Chiyoda-Ku, Tokyo, 102-8554, Japan. TEL 81-3-32383697, FAX 81-3-32383690, http://www.sophia.ac.jp/J/research.nsf/Content/ajia.

950   BEL   ISSN 0021-762X
➤ JOURNAL ASIATIQUE. Text mainly in French; Text occasionally in English, German, Italian, Spanish. 1822. s-a. EUR 85 (effective 2006). adv. bk.rev. illus. index. reprint service avail. from SCH. Document type: *Journal, Academic/Scholarly.* Description: Disseminates highly scholarly research in orientalist philology and history, as well as other humanities and social sciences disciplines covering the area stretching from the Near East to Japan.
Related titles: Microfiche ed.: (from IDC); Online - full text ed.: (from EBSCO Publishing).
Indexed: BAS, Biblnd, BibLing, DIP, EI, IBR, IBZ, IndIslam, MLA, MLA-IB, PCI, PerIslam, RASB, RI-1, RI-2.
—IE, Infotrieve. CCC.
Published by: (Societe Asiatique FRA), Peeters Publishers, Bondgenotenlaan 153, Leuven, 3000, Belgium. TEL 32-16-235170, FAX 32-16-228500, peeters@peeters-leuven.be, http://poj.peeters-leuven.be/content.php?url=journal&journal_code=JA, http://www.peeters-leuven.be. Ed. C Scherrer-Schaub.

956   AUS   ISSN 1320-7199
DS36
➤ JOURNAL OF ARABIC, ISLAMIC AND MIDDLE EASTERN STUDIES. Text in English. s-a. AUD 50 to individuals; AUD 120 to institutions. Document type: *Academic/Scholarly.* Description: Aims to be a forum for discourse on the broad range of issues related to Arabic, Islamic and Middle Eastern studies.
—BLDSC (4947.164500).
Published by: Deakin University, Faculty of Arts (Burwood), 221 Burwood Hwy, Burwood, VIC 3125, Australia. TEL 61-3-9244-3915, FAX 61-3-9244-6755, hisha@deakin.edu.au. Ed. Abdel Hakeem Kasem.

➤ JOURNAL OF ARABIC LITERATURE. see *LITERATURE*

950   USA   ISSN 0162-6795
DS1
JOURNAL OF ASIAN CULTURE. Text in English. 1977. a. USD 7 per issue domestic to individuals; USD 9 per issue foreign to individuals; USD 10 per issue domestic to institutions; USD 12 per issue foreign to institutions; USD 5 per issue domestic to students (effective 2005). adv. bk.rev. charts; illus. Document type: *Academic/Scholarly.* Description: Publishes the work of graduate students whose research involves various aspects of Asian studies.
Indexed: AmH&L, BAS, HistAb, SOPODA.
Published by: University of California at Los Angeles, Department of East Asian Languages and Cultures, PO Box 951540, Los Angeles, CA 90024-1540. TEL 213-206-8235, http://www.humnet.ucla.edu/jac/index2.html. Ed. Nick Morrissey. Circ: 500.

950 796.8   USA   ISSN 1057-8358
GV1100.69.A2
➤ JOURNAL OF ASIAN MARTIAL ARTS. Text in English. 1992. q. USD 32 domestic to individuals; USD 34 in Canada & Mexico to individuals; USD 35 elsewhere to individuals; USD 75 domestic to institutions; USD 77 in Canada & Mexico to institutions; USD 78 elsewhere to institutions; USD 10 per issue to individuals; USD 20 per issue to institutions (effective 2004). adv. bk.rev.; video rev.; software rev. bibl.; illus. index. 124 p./no.; back issues avail.; reprints avail. Document type: *Journal, Academic/Scholarly.* Description: Covers all historical and cultural aspects of the Asian martial traditions with high academic and aesthetic standards.
Indexed: PEI.
Published by: Via Media Publishing Company, 821 W 24th St, Erie, PA 16502. TEL 814-455-9517, FAX 814-455-2726, info@goviamedia.com, http://www.goviamedia.com/journal/description.html. Ed., Pub., R&P, Adv. contact Michael A DeMarco. B&W page USD 950; 10.875 x 8.375. Circ: 12,000 (paid and controlled). Subscr. to: 30 Amberwood Parkway, PO Box 338, Ashland, OH 44805. TEL 419-281-1802, 800-247-6553, FAX 419-281-6883, order@bookmaster.com.

950   USA   ISSN 0021-9118
DS501
➤ JOURNAL OF ASIAN STUDIES. Text in English. 1941. q. USD 70 domestic; USD 80 foreign; free to members (effective 2005). adv. bk.rev. bibl.; charts; illus.; stat. index. back issues avail.; reprint service avail. from PQC. Document type: *Academic/Scholarly.* Description: Contains articles about the humanities and social sciences in reference to Asia.
Formerly (until 1956): The Far Eastern Quarterly (0363-6917)
Related titles: Microform ed.: (from PQC); Online - full text ed.: (from Chadwyck-Healey Inc., JSTOR (Web-based Journal Archive), Northern Light Technology, Inc., O C L C Online Computer Library Center, Inc., ProQuest Information & Learning).
Indexed: ABCPolSci, ABIn, ABM, ABS&EES, APEL, ASCA, Acal, AmH&L, AnthLit, ArtHuCl, BAS, BRI, BibLing, CBRI, CJA, ChPerl, CurCont, DIP, EI, FamI, ForAb, HistAb, HumInd, IBR, IBRH, IBSS, IBZ, IPSA, IndIslam, JEL, JOF, MLA, MLA-IB, PCI, RASB, RDA, RI-1, RI-2, RILM, RefSour, SSCI, SWA, SociolAb, WAE&RSA, WBA, WMB.
—BLDSC (4947.250000), IE, Infotrieve, ingenta.
Published by: Association for Asian Studies, Inc., 1021 E Huron St, Ann Arbor, MI 48104. TEL 734-665-2490, FAX 734-665-3801, http://www.aasianst.org/catalog/jas.htm. Ed. Ann Waltner. Circ: 10,000.

950   KOR   ISSN 1226-4385
DS1
JOURNAL OF ASIATIC STUDIES/ASE'A YEON'GU. Text in Korean; Text occasionally in English. 1958. s-a. USD 50.
Indexed: AmH&L, BAS, HistAb, MEA&I, PerIslam.
Published by: (Korea University, Asiatic Research Center), Korea University Press, 1 Anam-dong, Sungbuk-ku, Seoul, 136-70, Korea, S. TEL 82-2-9261926, FAX 82-2-923-4661, TELEX KOREA-KU-K34138. Ed. Choi Song Yong.

JOURNAL OF BURMA STUDIES. see *HISTORY—History Of Asia*

JOURNAL OF CHINESE LANGUAGE AND COMPUTING. see *LINGUISTICS—Computer Applications*

JOURNAL OF CHINESE PHILOSOPHY. see *PHILOSOPHY*

JOURNAL OF CHINESE RELIGIONS. see *RELIGIONS AND THEOLOGY—Other Denominations And Sects*

JOURNAL OF CUNEIFORM STUDIES. see *ARCHAEOLOGY*

950   USA   ISSN 1598-2408
DS501
➤ JOURNAL OF EAST ASIAN STUDIES. Text in English. 2001. 3/yr. USD 48 domestic to individuals print & online eds.; USD 60 foreign to individuals print & online eds.; USD 105 domestic to institutions print & online eds.; USD 115 foreign to institutions print & online eds. (effective 2005). adv. bk.rev. bibl.; maps; abstr.; illus. Index. 200 p./no.; back issues avail. Document type: *Journal, Academic/Scholarly.* Description: Contains research on the entire region of East Asia, addressing the challenges facing each nation ranging from democratic governance to military security, from political culture to economic reforms, from human rights to environmental concerns.

Related titles: Online - full text ed.: (from EBSCO Publishing, Gale Group).
Indexed: IPSA, PAIS.
—BLDSC (4971.475000), IE.
Published by: (East Asia Institute KOR), Lynne Rienner Publishers, 1800 30th St, Ste 314, Boulder, CO 80301-1026. TEL 303-444-6684, FAX 303-444-0824, peacock@rienner.com, http://www.rienner.com/viewbook.cfm?BOOKID=1354. Ed. Stephan Haggard. R&P, Adv. contact Martha Peacock. Circ: 500 (paid). **Co-sponsor:** Korea University, Department of Political Science, East Asian Studies Program.

950 PHL ISSN 0022-0450
JOURNAL OF EAST ASIATIC STUDIES. Text in English. 1951. s-a. USD 12. adv. charts; illus. index.
Indexed: AICP, BAS, HistAb.
Published by: University of Manila, 546 Dr. M.V. de los Santos St, Sampaloc, Manila, D-403, Philippines. Ed. Charles O Houston Jr. Circ: 500.

JOURNAL OF FUKIEN HISTORY. see *HISTORY—History Of Asia*

JOURNAL OF INDIAN PHILOSOPHY. see *PHILOSOPHY*

952 USA ISSN 0095-6848
DS801
➤ **JOURNAL OF JAPANESE STUDIES.** Text in English. 1974. s-a. USD 42 domestic; USD 47 foreign (effective 2002). adv. bk.rev. illus. back issues avail.; reprint service avail. from PSC. **Document type:** *Journal, Academic/Scholarly.*
Description: Takes a multidisciplinary approach to the study of Japan.
Related titles: Online - full text ed.: ISSN 1549-4721 (from JSTOR (Web-based Journal Archive), O C L C Online Computer Library Center, Inc., Project MUSE).
Indexed: ASCA, AmH&L, ArtHuCI, BAS, CurCont, FamI, HistAb, HumInd, IBSS, IPSA, MLA, MLA-IB, PCI, RASB, RILM, SSCI, SSI.
—BLDSC (5009.300000), IE, Infotrieve, ingenta.
Published by: Society for Japanese Studies, University of Washington, Box 353650, Seattle, WA 98195-3650. TEL 206-543-9302, FAX 206-685-0668, jjs@u.washington.edu, http://depts.washington.edu/jjs. Eds. John Whitter Treat, Susan B Hanley. Circ: 1,900.

950 IND ISSN 0022-3301
PK101
JOURNAL OF ORIENTAL RESEARCH. Text in English, Sanskrit. 1927. irreg. (approx. a.). bk.rev. illus. index. **Description:** Contributions to Sanskrit and Indological research.
Related titles: Microfiche ed.: (from IDC).
Indexed: BAS.
Published by: Kuppuswami Sastri Research Institute, 84 Royapettah High Rd., Mylapore, Chennai, Tamil Nadu 600 004, India. TEL 847320. Ed. S S Janaki. Circ: 500.

950 HKG ISSN 0022-331X
DS501
JOURNAL OF ORIENTAL STUDIES. Text in Chinese, English. 1954. s-a. HKD 225, USD 30 to individuals; HKD 300, USD 40 to institutions (effective 2005). adv. bk.rev. Index. back issues avail.; reprint service avail. from PQC. **Document type:** *Journal, Academic/Scholarly.* **Description:** Covers research from China, Japan and Southeast Asia concerning traditional and contemporary issues in various social sciences.
Related titles: Microform ed.: (from PQC).
Indexed: ABM, AmH&L, BAS, DIP, HistAb, IBR, IBRH, IBZ, MLA-IB, PerIslam, RASB.
—BLDSC (5027.400000).
Published by: University of Hong Kong, Department of Chinese, Pokfulam Rd., Hong Kong, Hong Kong. TEL 852-2859-2426, 852-2859-7923, FAX 852-2858-1334, http://www.hku.hk/chinese/. Ed. C Y Sin. adv.: page HKD 320, page USD 40. Circ: 300.

951 JPN
JOURNAL OF SINOLOGICAL STUDIES/SHINAGAKU KENKYU. Text in Japanese; Summaries in English. 1948. s-a.
Published by: Sinological Society of Hiroshima/Hiroshima Shinagakkai, c/o Hiroshima University, Faculty of Literature, 1-1-89 Higashi-Senda-machi, Hiroshima, Japan.

JOURNAL OF SOUTHEAST ASIAN STUDIES. see *HISTORY—History Of Asia*

JOURNAL OF STUDIES IN THE BHAGAVADGITA. see *RELIGIONS AND THEOLOGY—Hindu*

951 USA ISSN 1059-3152
DS751
JOURNAL OF SUNG-YUAN STUDIES. Text in Chinese, English. 1970. a. USD 15 to individuals; USD 25 to institutions; USD 10 to students. adv. bk.rev. bibl.; illus. **Document type:** *Academic/Scholarly.*
Former titles (until no.22, 1989): Bulletin of Sung-Yuan Studies (0275-4118); (until vol.14, 1978): Sung Studies Newsletter (0049-254X)
Indexed: BAS, RASB, RILM.
Address: c/o James M Hargett, Ed, Department of East Asian Studies, HU 210, State University of New York at Albany, Albany, NY 12222. TEL 518-422-4233, FAX 518-442-4188, hargett@cnsvax.albany.edu. Circ: 400.

950 TWN ISSN 1022-6230
JOURNAL OF SUNOLOGY. Text in Chinese. 1985. q. USD 50. bk.rev. **Document type:** *Academic/Scholarly.*
Published by: National Sun Yat-sen University, Sun Yat-sen Institute, 70 Lien-hai Rd, Kaohsiung, 800, Taiwan. TEL 07-5329387003. Ed. Wen Chun Chen. Circ: 1,000.

JOURNAL OF THE ECONOMIC AND SOCIAL HISTORY OF THE ORIENT/JOURNAL D'HISTOIRE ECONOMIQUE ET SOCIALE DE L'ORIENT. see *HISTORY—History Of The Near East*

950 GBR
K.R. NORMAN COLLECTED PAPERS. Text in English. 1990. irreg., latest vol.6, 1996. GBP 19.50 (effective 1999). **Document type:** *Academic/Scholarly.*
Published by: Pali Text Society, 73 Lime Walk, Headington, Oxford, Oxon OX3 7AD, United Kingdom. TEL 44-1865-742125, http://www.pts@palitext.demon.co.uk, http://www.palitext.demon.co.uk/. R&P S B Hamilton.

954 IND ISSN 0022-9210
KASHMIR AFFAIRS. Text in English. 1959. bi-m. INR 7.50. adv. bk.rev. charts. cum.index.
Address: Karan Nagar, Jammu, Jammu & Kashmir, India. Ed. Balraj Puri.

958 DEU
KATALOG DER TIBETISCHEN UND MONGOLISCHEN SACHKULTUR IN EUROPAEISCHEN MUSEEN UND PRIVATSAMMLUNGEN. Text in German. 1989. irreg. price varies. adv. back issues avail. **Document type:** *Catalog, Academic/Scholarly.*
Published by: Harrassowitz Verlag, Taunusstr 14, Wiesbaden, 65183, Germany. TEL 49-611-5300, FAX 49-611-530570, verlag@harrassowitz.de, http://www.harrassowitz.de. Eds. Hans Roth, Veronika Ronge. R&P Michael Langfeld. Adv. contact Robert Gietz. Circ: 250 (paid).

KEILSCHRIFTTEXTE AUS BOGHAZKOI. see *ARCHAEOLOGY*

950 HUN ISSN 0133-6193
KELETI TANULMANYOK/ORIENTAL STUDIES. Text in English, French, German, Hungarian. 1976. irreg. per issue exchange basis. **Document type:** *Monographic series.* **Description:** Oriental studies and papers on the documents and the history of the Oriental collection of the Academy Library of Hungary.
Published by: Magyar Tudomanyos Akademia, Konyvtara, Arany Janos utca 1, PO Box 1002, Budapest, 1245, Hungary. TEL 36-1-338-2344, FAX 36-1-331-6954. Ed. Eva Apor.

KENKYUJOHO. see *RELIGIONS AND THEOLOGY*

950 NLD ISSN 0169-8907
➤ **KERN INSTITUTE, LEIDEN. MEMOIRS.** Text in Dutch. 1955. irreg., latest vol.5, 1992. price varies. **Document type:** *Monographic series, Academic/Scholarly.*
Published by: (Kern Institute, Leiden), Brill Academic Publishers, PO Box 9000, Leiden, 2300 PA, Netherlands. TEL 31-71-53-53-500, FAX 31-71-53-17-532, cs@brill.nl, http://www.brill.nl. R&P Elizabeth Venekamp. **Subscr. in N. America to:** PO Box 605, Herndon, VA 20172. TEL 703-661-1585, 800-337-9255, FAX 703-661-1501, cs@brillusa.com. **Distr. outside N. America by:** c/o Turpin Distribution, Stratton Business Park, Pegasus Drive, Biggleswade, BEDFORDSHIRE SG 18 8TQ, United Kingdom. TEL 44-1767-604-954, FAX 44-1767-601-640, brill@turpin-distribution.com.

950 DEU ISSN 0937-2105
KHOJ; a series of modern South Asian studies. Text in German. 1988. irreg., latest vol.7, 2003. price varies. **Document type:** *Monographic series, Academic/Scholarly.*
Published by: Harrassowitz Verlag, Taunusstr 14, Wiesbaden, 65183, Germany. TEL 49-611-5300, FAX 49-611-530570, verlag@harrassowitz.de, http://www.harrassowitz.de. Eds. Ali Asani, Monika Thiel Horstmann. R&P Michael Langfeld. Adv. contact Robert Gietz.

950 PHL ISSN 0115-6012
KINAADMAN/WISDOM; a journal of the southern Philippines. Text in English. 1979. a. PHP 300 (effective 2000). bk.rev. bibl. **Document type:** *Academic/Scholarly.* **Description:** Covers the Southern Philippines and Mindanao topics.
Indexed: BAS, IPP.
Published by: Xavier University, Cagayan De Oro, 9000, Philippines. TEL 63-8822-72-6069, FAX 63-8822-72-6355. R&P Miguel A Bernad. Circ: 800. **Dist. in the U.S. by:** Book Bin, 215 SW 4th St., Corvallis, OR 97333-4624.

959.8 DEU ISSN 0948-3314
KITA✶ ; das Magazin der Deutsch-Indonesischen Gesellschaft. Text in German, Indonesian. 1991. 3/yr. bk.rev.; dance rev.; music rev. tr.lit. back issues avail. **Document type:** *Magazine, Consumer.*
Formerly (until 1995): D I G Magazin (0944-9876)
Published by: Deutsch-Indonesische Gesellschaft e.V., Adrian-Kiels-Str 7, Cologne, 51149, Germany. TEL 49-221-9522709, FAX 49-221-9522707, kulturkontakt@t-online.de, dig.koeln@gmx.de. Circ: 500.

956 DEU ISSN 0343-1088
KLEINE AEGYPTISCHE TEXTE. Text in German. 1969. irreg., latest vol.14, 2004. price varies. adv. **Document type:** *Monographic series, Academic/Scholarly.*
Published by: Harrassowitz Verlag, Taunusstr 14, Wiesbaden, 65183, Germany. TEL 49-611-5300, FAX 49-611-530570, verlag@harrassowitz.de, http://www.harrassowitz.de. Ed. Hartwig Altenmueller. R&P Michael Langfeld. Adv. contact Robert Gietz.

KOKUSAI KORYU. see *ETHNIC INTERESTS*

KONGZI YANJIU/STUDIES ON CONFUCIUS. see *RELIGIONS AND THEOLOGY—Other Denominations And Sects*

951.9 DEU ISSN 0944-8373
KOREA FORUM. Text in German. 1991. 2/yr. adv. bk.rev. **Document type:** *Bulletin.*
Published by: Korea-Verband im Asienhaus, Bullmannaue 11, Essen, 45327, Germany. TEL 49-201-8303812, FAX 49-201-8303830, koreaverband@asienhaus.org, http://www.asienhaus.org. Circ: 600 (controlled).

951.9 KOR
KOREA FOUNDATION ANNUAL REPORT. Text in English, Korean. a.
Published by: Korea Foundation, 526 Namdaemunno 5 ga, Chung-gu, Seoul, 100095, Korea, S. TEL 81-2-757-2041, FAX 82-2-753-3462.

951.9 KOR
KOREA INSTITUTE FOR NATIONAL UNIFICATION. CURRENT ISSUE PAPERS. Text in Korean. irreg.
Published by: Korea Institute for National Unification, 535-353 Suyu 6-dong, Kangbuk-ku, Seoul, 142-076, Korea, S.

951.9 KOR
KOREA INSTITUTE FOR NATIONAL UNIFICATION. K I N U TRANSLATION SERIES. Text in English. irreg.
Published by: Korea Institute for National Unification, 535-353 Suyu 6-dong, Kangbuk-ku, Seoul, 142-076, Korea, S.

951.9 KOR
KOREA INSTITUTE FOR NATIONAL UNIFICATION. RESEARCH MONOGRAPHS. Text in Korean. irreg.
Published by: Korea Institute for National Unification, 535-353 Suyu 6-dong, Kangbuk-ku, Seoul, 142-076, Korea, S.

951.9 KOR
KOREA INSTITUTE FOR NATIONAL UNIFICATION. SEMINAR PROCEEDINGS. Text in Korean. irreg.
Published by: Korea Institute for National Unification, 535-353 Suyu 6-dong, Kangbuk-ku, Seoul, 142-076, Korea, S.

KOREA INSTITUTE FOR NATIONAL UNIFICATION. WHITE PAPER ON HUMAN RIGHTS IN NORTH KOREA. see *POLITICAL SCIENCE—Civil Rights*

951.9 KOR ISSN 0023-3919
DS901
➤ **KOREA OBSERVER.** Text in English. 1968. q. USD 60 (effective 2005). adv. bk.rev. abstr.; charts; stat.; illus. back issues avail.; reprints avail. **Document type:** *Journal, Academic/Scholarly.* **Description:** Covers the fields of the humanities and social sciences, and promotes cultural exchanges with other nations.
Related titles: Online - full text ed.: (from Northern Light Technology, Inc., ProQuest Information & Learning).
Indexed: APEL, BAS, IBSS, IPSA, PAIS, RASB.
—BLDSC (5113.467000), IE, ingenta.
Published by: Institute of Korean Studies, 135-080, Rm 802 PLAZA654 B/D, 654-3 Yeoksam-dong, Kangnam-gu, Seoul, 100634, Korea, S. TEL 82-2-5695574, FAX 82-2-5641190, journal@iks.or.kr, webmaster@iks.or.kr, http://www.iks.or.kr/koreaobserver/near.asp, http://www.iks.or.kr/default.asp. Ed. Myong Whai Kim. Circ: 3,500.

951.9 305.89519073 USA ISSN 0749-7970
KOREAN AND KOREAN-AMERICAN STUDIES BULLETIN. Text in English. 1984. s-a. USD 26. **Document type:** *Bulletin, Academic/Scholarly.*
Published by: East Rock Institute, 251 Dwight St, New Haven, CT 06511. TEL 203-624-8619, FAX 203-624-7933, Eri3@pantheon.yale.edu, http://www.eastrockinstitute.org/eastrock/.

951.9 KOR ISSN 1225-6072
JC599.K7
KOREAN JOURNAL OF NATIONAL UNIFICATION. Text in English. 1992. a.
Indexed: PAIS.
Published by: Korea Institute for National Unification, 535-353 Suyu 6-dong, Kangbuk-ku, Seoul, 142-076, Korea, S.

950 USA ISSN 0145-840X
DS901 CODEN: KOSTEL
➤ **KOREAN STUDIES.** Text in English. 1977. s-a. (a. pre-vol.25). USD 20 to individuals; USD 30 to institutions; USD 15 to students (effective 2003). adv. bk.rev. cum.index: 1977-1996. back issues avail.; reprint service avail. from PQC,ISI,PSC. **Document type:** *Journal, Academic/Scholarly.* **Description:** Features interdisciplinary scholarly essays and articles on Korea. For Korea specialists, those whose interests touch on Korea, and the Korean community abroad.
Related titles: Microfiche ed.; Online - full text ed.: ISSN 1529-1529. 2000 (from bigchalk, EBSCO Publishing, Florida Center for Library Automation, Gale Group, O C L C Online Computer Library Center, Inc., Project MUSE, ProQuest Information & Learning, Swets Information Services).
Indexed: AmH&L, BAS, HistAb, IBSS, IBibSS, L&LBA, MLA-IB, PAIS, PSA, RILM, SOPODA, SSA, SociolAb.
—IE. **CCC.**
Published by: (University of Hawaii at Manoa, Center for Korean Studies), University of Hawaii Press, Journals Department, 2840 Kolowalu St, Honolulu, HI 96822-1888. TEL 808-956-8833, FAX 808-988-6052, uhpjourn@hawaii.edu, http://www.uhpress.hawaii.edu/journals/ks/index.html. Ed. Karl E Kim. R&P Joel Bradshaw TEL 808-956-6790. Adv. contact Norman Kaneshiro. B&W page USD 200; 4.375 x 7.75. Circ: 180.

951.9 CAN ISSN 1195-8448
KOREAN STUDIES IN CANADA. Text in English. q.?.
Published by: University of Toronto, Centre for Korean Studies, 130 St George St, Rm 8001, Toronto, ON ON M5S 1A5, Canada. TEL 416-978-7568, FAX 416-978-5711. Ed. Eung-Jin Baek.

951.9 700 KOR ISSN 1016-0744
NX584.6.A1
KOREANA; Korean art and culture. Text in English. 1987. q. KRW 18,000 domestic; USD 33 in Japan, Hong Kong, Taiwan & China; USD 37 elsewhere (effective 2005). adv. bk.rev.; dance rev.; music rev.; play rev. maps. 100 p./no.; back issues avail. **Document type:** *Magazine, Consumer.* **Description:** Covers Korean traditional and contemporary culture and arts.
Related titles: Online - full text ed.: 1998 (from H.W. Wilson, O C L C Online Computer Library Center, Inc.); Chinese ed.: Goryeoa'na. ISSN 1225-8083; Spanish ed.: Cultura Y las Artes de Corea. ISSN 1225-4606. 1990.
Indexed: ABM, ArtInd, BAS, MLA, MLA-IB, RILM.
Published by: Korea Foundation, Publication & Reference Materials Team, 1376-1, Seocho-2-dong, Seocho-gu, Seoul, 137072, Korea, S. TEL 82-2-34635684, FAX 82-2-34636086, koreana@kf.or.kr, http://www.koreana.or.kr/. Ed. Jeong-yeop Park. Pub. In Hyuk Kwon. Circ: 9,000. **Dist. in N. America by:** Yeong & Yeong Book Co.

952 JPN ISSN 0913-5200
DS801
➤ **KYOTO JOURNAL**; perspectives on Asia. Text in English. 1986. q. JPY 3,200 domestic; USD 39 in North America; USD 50 elsewhere (effective 2005). adv. bk.rev. 122 p./no.; **Document type:** *Journal, Academic/Scholarly.* **Description:** Contains interviews, translations, humor, fiction, essays, poetry and reviews, accompanied by photo-essays, original illustrations and design.
Published by: Heian Bunka Center, 35 Minamigoshomachi, Okazaki, Sakyo-ku, Kyoto-shi, 606-8334, Japan. TEL 81-75-7611433, FAX 81-75-7511196, feedback@kyotojournal.org, http://kyotojournal.org/, http://www.kampo.co.jp/. Ed., R&P, Adv. contact John Einarsen. Pub. Shokei Harada. Circ: 6,000. **Subscr. in N America to:** Kampo Cultural Center, 31 Bond St, New York, NY 10012.

950 895 IND
LALBHAI DALPATBHAI INSTITUTE OF INDOLOGY. PUBLICATIONS. Text in Multiple languages. irreg. INR 80 per issue. **Document type:** *Monographic series.*
Published by: Lalbhai Dalpatbhai Institute of Indology, Near Gujarat University, P.O. Navarangpura, Ahmedabad, Gujarat 380 009, India. TEL 91-79-442463. Circ: 500.

950 DEU ISSN 1436-5413
LANDESSPRACHEN INSTITUT NORDHEIN-WESTFALEN. PUBLIKATIONEN. Text in German. 1998. irreg. price varies. **Document type:** *Monographic series, Academic/Scholarly.*
Published by: Harrassowitz Verlag, Taunusstr 14, Wiesbaden, 65183, Germany. TEL 49-611-530555, FAX 49-611-530-55590, verlag@harrassowitz.de, http://www.harrassowitz.de/verlag. R&P Michael Langfeld. Adv. contact Robert Gietz.

LATE IMPERIAL CHINA. see *HISTORY—History Of Asia*

LAW, SOCIETY, AND CULTURE IN CHINA. see *HISTORY—History Of Asia*

LEBANON REPORT. see *POLITICAL SCIENCE—International Relations*

932 NLD
LECTIONES ORIENTALES. Text in French, English, German. 1948. irreg., latest vol.3, 1995. price varies. illus. **Document type:** *Monographic series, Academic/Scholarly.* **Description:** Publishes research in ancient Near Eastern archaeology.
Published by: Nederlands Instituut voor het Nabije Oosten/Netherlands Institute for the Near East, Witte Singel 25, Leiden, 2311 BG, Netherlands. TEL 31-71-5272036, FAX 31-71-5272018, http://www.leidenuniv.nl/nino/nino.html. R&P J de Roos TEL 31-71-527-2036. **Subscr. to:** Postbus 9515, Leiden 2300 RA, Netherlands. FAX 31-71-5272038, beurs@rullet.leidenuniv.nl.

LEVANT MORGENLAND. see *RELIGIONS AND THEOLOGY*

495 DEU
LEXICOGRAPHIA ORIENTALIS. Text in German. irreg., latest vol.4. price varies. **Document type:** *Monographic series, Academic/Scholarly.*
Published by: Helmut Buske Verlag GmbH, Richardstr. 47, Hamburg, 22081, Germany. TEL 49-40-2999580, FAX 49-40-2993614, info@buske.de, http://www.buske.de. Ed. Jost Gippert.

LINGUISTIC AND ORIENTAL STUDIES FROM POZNAN. see *LINGUISTICS*

LIVERPOOL MONOGRAPHS IN ARCHAEOLOGY AND ORIENTAL STUDIES. see *ARCHAEOLOGY*

LONDON ORIENTAL AND AFRICAN LANGUAGE LIBRARY. see *LINGUISTICS*

954 GBR ISSN 0142-601X
LONDON STUDIES ON SOUTH ASIA. Text in English. 1980. irreg. price varies. bibl. index. **Document type:** *Academic/Scholarly.*
—BLDSC (5294.153000). **CCC.**
Published by: (University of London, University of London, School of Oriental and African Studies), Curzon Press Ltd., 15 The Quadrant, 6-8 Church Rd, Richmond, Surrey TW9 1BP, United Kingdom. Ed. Peter Robb. Pub. M Campbell.

951 BEL
LOUVAIN CHINESE STUDIES. Text in Multiple languages. 2000. irreg. price varies. **Document type:** *Academic/Scholarly.*
Published by: Leuven University Press, Blijde Inkomststraat 5, Leuven, 3000, Belgium. TEL 32-16-325345, FAX 32-16-325352, university.press@upers.kuleuven.ac.be, http://www.kuleuven.ac.be/upers.

M A A S JOURNAL OF ISLAMIC SCIENCE. see *RELIGIONS AND THEOLOGY—Islamic*

M E E D PRACTICAL GUIDE. SAUDI ARABIA. (Middle East Economic Digest) see *TRAVEL AND TOURISM*

M E E D PRACTICAL GUIDE. UNITED ARAB EMIRATES. (Middle East Economic Digest) see *TRAVEL AND TOURISM*

327 ISR
➤ **M E R I A JOURNAL.** (Middle East Review of International Affairs) Text in English. 1997. q. free (effective 2005); includes Current Contents of Periodicals of the Middle East. back issues avail. **Document type:** *Journal, Academic/Scholarly.* **Description:** Publishes scholarly articles on issues and topics concerning the Middle East.
Media: Online - full content.
Published by: Global Research in International Affairs, Interdisciplinary Center, Herzliya, Israel. TEL 972-9-960-2736, FAX 972-9-960-2736, gloria@idc.ac.il, http://meria.idc.ac.il, http://gloria.idc.ac.il. Ed. Barry Rubin. Circ: 10,065 (controlled).

327 ISR
M E R I A NEWS. (Middle East Review of International Affairs) Text in English. m. **Document type:** *Newsletter.* **Description:** Newsletter covering Middle East studies.
Media: Online - full text.
Published by: Bar-Ilan University, Begin-Sadat Center for Strategic Studies, Israel. TEL 972-3-531-8959, FAX 972-3-535-9195, rubinb@mail.biu.ac.il, besa@mail.biu.ac.il, http://www.biu.ac.il/soc/besa/meria.html. Ed. Barry Rubin.

950 LBN
➤ **AL-MACHRIQ**; cultural magazine. Text in Arabic; Abstracts in French. 1898. 2/yr. EUR 40 in Europe & Africa; USD 40 US, Canada & Australia (effective 2005). bk.rev. **Document type:** *Academic/Scholarly.*
Published by: Dar el-Machreq S.A.R.L., Ashrafieh, P O Box 166778, Beirut, Lebanon. TEL 961-1-202423, machreq@cyberia.net.lb. Pub. Hechaime Camille.

952 001.3 300 BEL ISSN 0495-7725
MAISON FRANCO-JAPONAISE. BULLETIN. Text in French; Summaries in English, French. 1927; N.S. 1951. irreg. (every 2-3 yrs.). price varies. bibl. reprints avail. **Document type:** *Bulletin, Academic/Scholarly.*
Indexed: MLA, MLA-IB, RASB.
—CCC.
Published by: (Maison Franco-Japonaise JPN), Peeters Publishers, Bondgenotenlaan 153, Leuven, 3000, Belgium. TEL 32-16-235170, FAX 32-16-228500, http://www.peeters-leuven.be. Circ: 7,000.

956 USA ISSN 1086-170X
DT96
➤ **MAMLUK STUDIES REVIEW.** Text in English. 1997. s-a. USD 90 per vol. (effective 2004). **Document type:** *Academic/Scholarly.*
Published by: University of Chicago, Middle East Documentation Center, 5828 S University Ave, Pick Hl 201, Chicago, IL 60637. http://www.lib.uchicago.edu/e/su/mideast/medoc.html.

495 895 RUS ISSN 1238-5018
MANUSCRIPTA ORIENTALIA. Text in English. 1995. q. USD 200 to individuals; USD 250 to institutions (effective 2004). illus. back issues avail. **Document type:** *Journal, Academic/Scholarly.* **Description:** Devoted to Oriental textology, comparative codicology, and palaeography.
—**CCC.**
Published by: (Russian Academy of Sciences, Institute of Oriental Studies. Saint Petersburg Branch), Thesa Company, ul Dobrolubova 14, Office 358, Saint Petersburg, 197198, Russian Federation. TEL 7-812-2389594, FAX 7-812-2335916, order@thesa.ru, http://orient.thesa.ru, http://www.thesa.ru. Ed. Efim A. Rezvan.

MANUSCRIPTS OF THE MIDDLE EAST; journal devoted to the study of handwritten materials of the Middle East. see *HISTORY—History Of The Near East*

951.03 CHN ISSN 1000-7873
PL471
➤ **MANYU YANJIU/JOURNAL OF MANCHU STUDIES.** Text in Chinese. 1983. s-a. CNY 24, CNY 40.80; CNY 12 per issue (effective 1999). adv. **Document type:** *Journal, Academic/Scholarly.* **Description:** Studies on Manchu culture and language.
Related titles: Online - full text ed.: (from East View Information Services).
Indexed: BibLing.
Published by: (Heilongjiang Manyu Yanjiusuo/Heilongjiang Provincial Man Language Research Institute), Manchu Studies Editorial Office, 74 Qingbin Rd, Nangang, Harbin, Heilongjiang 150080, China. TEL 86-451-6358213. Ed., Pub., R&P, Adv. contact Zhao Aping. Circ: 1,000. **Dist. in US by:** China Books & Periodicals Inc, 360 Swift Ave., Ste. 48, S San Fran, CA 94080-6220. TEL 415-282-2994.

➤ **MANZU WENXUE/MANCHU LITERATURE.** see *LITERATURE*

950 ITA
MATERIALI PER IL VOCABOLARIO NEOSUMERICO. COLLANA. Text in Italian. 1974. a. price varies. back issues avail. **Document type:** *Monographic series, Academic/Scholarly.*
Published by: (Unione Accademica Nazionale), Bonsignori Editore s.r.l., Viale dei Quattro Venti 47, Rome, RM 00152, Italy. TEL 39-06-5881496, FAX 39-06-5882839.

MATERIALS AND STUDIES FOR KASSITE HISTORY. see *HISTORY—History Of The Near East*

MATRIX (URBANA). see *LITERATURE—Poetry*

956 950 DEU ISSN 0543-1719
MAX FREIHERR VON OPPENHEIM-STIFTUNG. SCHRIFTEN. Text in German. 1955. irreg., latest vol.14, 1988. price varies. reprints avail. **Document type:** *Monographic series, Academic/Scholarly.*
Published by: (Max Freiherr von Oppenheim-Stiftung), Gebr. Mann Verlag, Neue Gruenstr 17, Berlin, 10179, Germany. TEL 49-30-2790760, FAX 49-30-27907655, vertrieb-kunstverlage@reimer-verlag.de, http://www.gebrmannverlag.de. R&P Elisabeth Roosens.

950 410 DEU ISSN 0179-1621
MEDITERRANEAN LANGUAGE AND CULTURE MONOGRAPH SERIES. Text in German. 1985. irreg., latest vol.14, 1998. price varies. **Document type:** *Monographic series, Academic/Scholarly.*
Published by: Harrassowitz Verlag, Taunusstr 14, Wiesbaden, 65183, Germany. TEL 49-611-5300, FAX 49-611-530570, verlag@harrassowitz.de, http://www.harrassowitz.de. R&P Michael Langfeld. Adv. contact Robert Gietz.

950 410 DEU ISSN 0724-7567
P381.M4
MEDITERRANEAN LANGUAGE REVIEW. Text in English, French, German, Italian. 1983. a. EUR 74 (effective 2006). **Document type:** *Monographic series, Academic/Scholarly.* **Description:** Aims to stimulate and promote inquiry into the linguistic and cultural history of the Mediterranean.
Indexed: BibLing, DIP, IBR, IBZ, L&LBA, LingAb, MLA-IB, PCI, SOPODA.
—BLDSC (5534.737000), IE.
Published by: Harrassowitz Verlag, Taunusstr 14, Wiesbaden, 65183, Germany. TEL 49-611-5300, FAX 49-611-530560, verlag@harrassowitz.de, http://www.harrassowitz.de. Ed. Marcel Erdal. R&P Michael Langfeld. Adv. contact Robert Gietz. Circ: 350.

299.5 BEL
➤ **MELANGES CHINOIS ET BOUDDHIQUES. NOUVELLE SERIE.** Text mainly in French; Text occasionally in English. 1931. irreg., latest vol.28, 1997. price varies. back issues avail. **Document type:** *Monographic series, Academic/Scholarly.* **Description:** Publishes studies on the history, cultures and religions of China and surrounding areas, including Nepal, Tibet and Mongolia.
Supersedes (in 1951): Melanges Chinois et Bouddhiques (0775-4612)
Indexed: BAS.
Published by: (Institut Belge des Hautes Etudes Chinoises), Peeters Publishers, Bondgenotenlaan 153, Leuven, 3000, Belgium. TEL 32-16-235170, FAX 32-16-228500, http://www.peeters-leuven.be.

950 DEU ISSN 0138-3663
MEORITICA; Schriften zur Altsudanesischen Geschichte und Archaeologie. Text in English, French, German. 1973-1994 (vol.14); resumed 1999. irreg., latest vol.17, 2000. price varies. **Document type:** *Monographic series, Academic/Scholarly.* **Description:** Supplies monographs and source material on ancient Sudanese history and archaeology.
Indexed: AnthLit.
Published by: (Humboldt-Universitaet zu Berlin, Bereich Aegyptologie und Sudan Archaeologie), Harrassowitz Verlag, Taunusstr 14, Wiesbaden, 65183, Germany. TEL 49-611-530555, FAX 49-611-530559, verlag@harrassowitz.de. Ed. Steffen Wenig. R&P Michael Langfeld. Adv. contact Robert Gietz.

MERIDIANS (COLUMBIA); redefining health. see *ALTERNATIVE MEDICINE*

951.9 USA ISSN 1050-3935
DS901
MID ATLANTIC BULLETIN OF KOREAN STUDIES. Text in English. 1984. 2/yr. USD 5. adv. **Document type:** *Bulletin.*
Published by: Georgetown University, School of Foreign Service, Asian Studies Program, Washington, DC 20057. TEL 202-687-8987, FAX 202-687-1431, ohb@gunet.georgetown.edu. Ed. Bonnie B C Oh.

MIDDLE EAST STUDIES ASSOCIATION BULLETIN. see *SOCIAL SCIENCES: COMPREHENSIVE WORKS*

MIDDLE EASTERN LECTURES. see *HISTORY—History Of The Near East*

950 USA ISSN 0147-037X
DS753
➤ **MING STUDIES.** Text in English. 1975. s-a. USD 25 to individuals; USD 40 to institutions; USD 15 to students (effective 2005). adv. bk.rev. bibl. back issues avail. **Document type:** *Academic/Scholarly.* **Description:** Contains articles, reviews, and news notes on Chinese history from the Ming period (1368-1644).
Formerly: Ming Studies Newsletter
Indexed: AmH&L, BAS, HistAb, IBR, IBZ, MLA-IB, RASB.
Published by: University of Minnesota, Department of History, 267 19th Ave S, Minneapolis, MN 55455. TEL 612-624-7301, FAX 612-624-7096, http://cla.umn.edu/farmer/studies.htm. Ed. Anita M Andrew. Circ: 250.

➤ **MINZU HUABAO/NATIONALITY PICTORIAL.** see *ETHNIC INTERESTS*

951 CHN ISSN 1009-7457
MINZU WENTI YANJIU/STUDIES OF ETHNIC PROBLEMS. Text in Chinese. m. CNY 93.60 (effective 2004). 112 p./no.; **Document type:** *Journal, Academic/Scholarly.* **Description:** Contains articles and studies on the history, economics, politics and traditions of Chinese minority nationalities.
Former titles (until 2001): Minzu Yanjiu (1005-4278); (until 2000): Zhongguo Shaoshu Minzu (1001-0882)
Indexed: RASB.
Published by: Zhongguo Renmin Daxue, Shubao Zilio Zhongxin/Renmin University of China, Information Center for Social Server, Dongcheng-qu, 3, Zhangzizhong Lu, Beijing, 100007, China. TEL 86-10-84043003, FAX 86-10-64015080, http://www.confucius.cn.net/bkdetail.asp?fzt=D5. **Dist. in US by:** China Publications Service, PO Box 49614, Chicago, IL 60649. TEL 312-288-3291.

951 CHN ISSN 0256-1891
DS701
MINZU YANJIU (BEIJING, 1979)/STUDY IN NATIONALITIES. Text and summaries in Chinese; Contents page in English. 1979. bi-m. CNY 6.60, USD 26.10. bk.rev. **Description:** Contains historical, social, and economic studies of minority nationalities.
Related titles: Online - full text ed.: (from East View Information Services).
Indexed: BibLing, RILM.
Published by: Zhongguo Shehui Kexueyuan, Minzu Yanjiusuo/Chinese Academy of Social Sciences, National Minorities Institute, 27 Baishiqiao Lu, Beijing, 100081, China. TEL 8022288. Ed. Du Rongkun. Circ: 5,000 (controlled). **Dist. in US by:** China Books & Periodicals Inc, 360 Swift Ave., Ste. 48, S San Fran, CA 94080-6220. TEL 415-282-2994; **Dist. outside China by:** China International Book Trading Corp, 35 Chegongzhuang Xilu, Haidian District, PO Box 399, Beijing 100044, China. TEL 86-10-68412045, FAX 86-10-68412023, cibtc@mail.cibtc.com.cn, http://www.cibtc.com.cn.

MIRAS-E FARHANGI. see *ARCHAEOLOGY*

950 ESP ISSN 0544-408X
PJ3001
MISCELANEA DE ESTUDIOS ARABES Y HEBRAICOS. Text in Spanish. 1952. 2/yr. price varies. **Document type:** *Monographic series, Academic/Scholarly.*
Indexed: AmH&L, BHA, BibLing, DIP, HistAb, IBR, IBZ, MLA-IB, OTA, PCI.
—CINDOC. **CCC.**
Published by: Editorial Universidad de Granada, Antiguo Colegio Maximo, Campus de Cartuja, Granada, 18071, Spain. TEL 34-958-246220, FAX 34-958-243931, comunicacion@editorialugr.com, http://www.editorialugr.com. Eds. Lola Ferre Cano, Mercedes del Amo Fernandez.

950 DEU ISSN 0938-9024
MIZAN; Studien und Texte zur Literatur des Orients. Text in German. 1990. irreg., latest vol.10, 2002. price varies. **Document type:** *Monographic series, Academic/Scholarly.*
Indexed: BAS.
Published by: Harrassowitz Verlag, Taunusstr 14, Wiesbaden, 65183, Germany. TEL 49-611-5300, FAX 49-611-530570, verlag@harrassowitz.de, http://www.harrassowitz.de. Ed. Petra Kappert. R&P Michael Langfeld. Adv. contact Robert Gietz.

320.9 GBR ISSN 0026-749X
DS1
➤ **MODERN ASIAN STUDIES.** Text in English. 1967. q. GBP 205 to institutions; USD 340 in North America to institutions; GBP 218 combined subscription to institutions print & online eds.; USD 362 combined subscription in North America to institutions print & online eds. (effective 2006). adv. bk.rev. illus. Index. back issues avail.; reprint service avail. from PSC. **Document type:** *Journal, Academic/Scholarly.* **Description:** Covers Asia from Pakistan to Japan; studies the impact of modernization during the 19th and 20th centuries on the ancient cultures of these nations.
Related titles: Microform ed.: (from PQC); Online - full text ed.: ISSN 1469-8099. GBP 192 to institutions; USD 319 in North America to institutions (effective 2006) (from EBSCO Publishing, JSTOR (Web-based Journal Archive), O C L C Online Computer Library Center, Inc., Swets Information Services).
Indexed: ABCPolSci, APEL, ASCA, AmH&L, ArtHuCI, BAS, CurCont, DIP, EI, FamI, ForAb, GEOBASE, HistAb, HumInd, I&DA, IBR, IBSS, IBZ, IPSA, IndIslam, JEL, L&LBA, MEA&I, PCI, PHN&I, PSA, PerIslam, RASB, RDA, RI-1, RI-2, RILM, RRTA, RiceAb, S&F, SOPODA, SRRA, SSA, SSCI, SSI, SociolAb, TriticAb, WAE&RSA.
—BLDSC (5883.650000), IDS, IE, Infotrieve, ingenta. **CCC.**
Published by: Cambridge University Press, The Edinburgh Bldg, Shaftesbury Rd, Cambridge, CB2 2RU, United Kingdom. TEL 44-1223-312393, FAX 44-1223-315052, modernasianstudies@cambridge.org, journals@cambridge.org, http://uk.cambridge.org/journals/ass. Ed. Gordon Johnson. R&P Linda Nicol TEL 44-1223-325757. **Subscr. to:** Cambridge University Press, 100 Brook Hill Dr, West Nyack, NY 10994. TEL 845-353-7500, FAX 845-353-4141, journals_subscriptions@cup.org

➤ **MODERN CHINA**; an international quarterly of history and social science. see *HISTORY—History Of Asia*

➤ **MODERN CHINESE LITERATURE.** see *LITERATURE*

➤ **MODERN MIDDLE EAST SERIES.** see *HISTORY—History Of Asia*

951 ITA ISSN 0390-2811
DS701
MONDO CINESE. Text in Italian. 1973. q. adv. bk.rev. bibl.; charts; stat. back issues avail. **Document type:** *Academic/Scholarly.* **Description:** Covers the development of relations between the Chinese and Italian cultures.
Indexed: AmH&L, BAS, HistAb, PCI, RASB.
Published by: Istituto Italo Cinese per gli Scambi Economici e Culturali, Via Giosue' Carducci, 18, Milan, MI 20123, Italy. TEL 39-02-862765, FAX 39-02-72000236, china-italy@planet.it, http://www.china-italy.com. Ed. Franco Demarchi. Adv. contact Alcide Luini. Circ: 1,200.

951.7005 USA ISSN 0190-3667
DS793.M7
➤ **MONGOLIAN STUDIES.** Text in English. 1962. a. USD 20 (effective 1997). adv. bk.rev. abstr.; bibl.; charts; stat.; illus. reprints avail. **Document type:** *Academic/Scholarly.* **Description:** Scholarly research articles and multidisciplinary approaches to Mongolia, past and present.
Supersedes (in 1974): Mongolian Society Bulletin (0026-9654); Which superseded: Mongolia Society Newsletter
Indexed: ABS&EES, AmH&L, BAS, BibLing, HistAb, IBSS, MLA, MLA-IB, RILM.
Published by: Mongolia Society, Inc., 322 Goodbody Hall, Indiana University, Bloomington, IN 47405-2401. TEL 812-855-4078, FAX 812-855-7500, monsoc@indiana.edu, http://www.bluemarket.net/~mitch/monsoc/monsocj.html. Ed. Christopher Atwood. Circ: 475.

954 DEU ISSN 0170-8864
MONOGRAPHIEN ZUR INDISCHEN ARCHAEOLOGIE, KUNST UND PHILOLOGIE. Text in German. irreg., latest vol.16, 2002. price varies. back issues avail. **Document type:** *Monographic series, Academic/Scholarly.*
Published by: (Stiftung Ernst Waldschmidt), Dietrich Reimer Verlag GmbH, Neue Gruenstr 17, Berlin, 10179, Germany. TEL 49-30-2790760, FAX 49-30-27907655, vertrieb-kunstverlage@reimer-verlag.de, http://www.dietrichreimerverlag.de. Ed. Marianne Yaldiz. R&P Beate Behrens.

952 390 JPN ISSN 0027-0741
DS821.A1
➤ **MONUMENTA NIPPONICA**; studies in Japanese culture. Text in English. 1938. q. JPY 4,480 domestic; USD 40, EUR 42 foreign (effective 2004). adv. bk.rev. illus. cum.index: vols.1-50. reprints avail. **Document type:** *Journal, Academic/Scholarly.*
Related titles: Microform ed.: (from PQC); Online - full text ed.: ISSN 1880-1390 (from JSTOR (Web-based Journal Archive), Project MUSE).
Indexed: ASCA, AmH&L, ArtHuCI, BAS, CurCont, HistAb, IBR, IBRH, IBSS, IBZ, MLA, MLA-IB, RASB, RI-1, RI-2, RILM, SSCI.
—BLDSC (5966.230000), IE, Infotrieve, ingenta.
Published by: Sophia University, 7-1 Kioi-cho, Chiyoda-ku, Tokyo, 102-8554 , Japan. TEL 81-3-32383544, FAX 81-3-32383835, kw-nakai@hoffman.cc.sophia.ac.jp, http://monumenta.cc.sophia.ac.jp/, http://www.sophia.ac.jp/. Ed., R&P Kate Wildman Nakai. Adv. contact Lynne E. Riggs. Circ: 1,150.

950 DEU ISSN 0254-9948
DS701
MONUMENTA SERICA; journal of Oriental studies. Text in English, French, German. 1934. a. EUR 85 (effective 2004). bk.rev. 500 p./no.; back issues avail. **Document type:** *Journal, Academic/Scholarly.* **Description:** Scholarly journal dealing with traditional China in the fields of history, language, literature, philosophy and religion.
Indexed: AIAP, AmH&L, BAS, BibInd, DIP, HistAb, IBR, IBSS, IBZ, IndIslam, MLA-IB, RASB.
—IE, Infotrieve. **CCC.**
Published by: Institut Monumenta Serica, Arnold-Janssen-Str 20, Sankt Augustin, 53757, Germany. TEL 49-2241-237431, FAX 49-2241-206770, monumenta.serica@t-online.de, http://www.steyler.de/monumenta.serica/, http://www.monumenta-serica.de. Ed. Roman Malek. Circ: 400. **Dist. by:** Steyler Verlag, Postfach 2460, Nettetal 41311, Germany. TEL 49-2157-120220, FAX 49-2157-120222, steyl.buch@t-online.de.

950 DEU ISSN 0179-261X
MONUMENTA SERICA MONOGRAPH SERIES. Text in English, French, German. 1937. irreg., latest vol.50. price varies. back issues avail. **Document type:** *Monographic series, Academic/Scholarly.* **Description:** Covers various topics in Chinese history, language, literature, philosophy and religion.
Published by: Institut Monumenta Serica, Arnold-Janssen-Str 20, Sankt Augustin, 53757, Germany. TEL 49-2241-237431, FAX 49-2241-206770, monumenta.serica@t-online.de, http://www.monumenta-serica.de. Ed. Roman Malek. Circ: 500. **Dist. by:** Steyler Verlag, Postfach 2460, Nettetal 41311, Germany. TEL 49-2157-120220, FAX 49-2157-120222, steyl.buch@t-online.de.

MOSHE DAYAN CENTER. DATA AND ANALYSIS SERIES. see *HISTORY—History Of The Near East*

950 RUS ISSN 0320-8095
DS1
MOSKOVSKII GOSUDARSTVENNYI UNIVERSITET. VESTNIK. SERIYA 13: VOSTOKOVEDENIE. Text in Russian. 1970. q. USD 36 foreign (effective 2004). bk.rev. bibl. index. **Document type:** *Journal, Academic/Scholarly.*
Indexed: IAA, IBSS, RASB, RefZh.
—East View.
Published by: (Moskovskii Gosudarstvennyi Universitet im. M.V. Lomonosova/M.V. Lomonosov Moscow State University), Izdatel'stvo Moskovskogo Gosudarstvennogo Universiteta im. M. V. Lomonosova/Publishing House of Moscow State University, B Nikitskaya 5/7, Moscow, 103009, Russian Federation. TEL 7-095-2295091, FAX 7-095-2036671, kd_mgu@rambler.ru, http://www.msu.ru/depts/MSUPubl. **Dist. by:** M K - Periodica, ul Gilyarovskogo 39, Moscow 129110, Russian Federation. TEL 7-095-2845008, FAX 7-095-2813798, info@periodicals.ru, http://www.mkniga.ru.

950 DEU ISSN 0170-3668
MUENCHENER OSTASIATISCHE STUDIEN. Text in English, German. irreg., latest vol.76, 1999. price varies. **Document type:** *Monographic series, Academic/Scholarly.* **Description:** Publishes studies in East Asian culture, religion, art, and literature.
Published by: Franz Steiner Verlag Stuttgart GmbH, Birkenwaldstr 44, Stuttgart, 70191, Germany. TEL 49-711-25820, FAX 49-711-2582390, franz.steiner.verlag@t-online.de, http://www.steiner-verlag.de. R&P Sabine Koerner.

950 DEU ISSN 0170-3676
MUENCHENER OSTASIATISCHE STUDIEN. SONDERREIHE. Text in English, German. 1976. irreg., latest vol.4, 1992. price varies. **Document type:** *Monographic series, Academic/Scholarly.*
Published by: Franz Steiner Verlag Stuttgart GmbH, Birkenwaldstr 44, Stuttgart, 70191, Germany. TEL 49-711-25820, FAX 49-711-2582390, franz.steiner.verlag@t-online.de, http://www.steiner-verlag.de. R&P Sabine Koerner.

MUSEO NAZIONALE D'ARTE ORIENTALE. SCHEDE. see *MUSEUMS AND ART GALLERIES*

950 BEL ISSN 0771-6494
AS242
➤ **LE MUSEON;** revue d'etudes orientales. Text in English, French, German, Italian. 1881. s-a. EUR 80 (effective 2006). bk.rev. bibl. cum.index 1882-1931, 1932-1973. Supplement avail. **Document type:** *Journal, Academic/Scholarly.* **Description:** Studies all aspects of the Christian Near East.
Related titles: Online - full text ed.: (from EBSCO Publishing); ♦ Supplement(s): Universite Catholique de Louvain. Institut Orientaliste. Publications. ISSN 0076-1265.
Indexed: BHA, BibInd, BibLing, DIP, IBR, IBZ, IPB, IndIslam, MLA-IB, NTA, NumL, RASB, RILM.
—IE, Infotrieve.
Published by: (Universite Catholique de Louvain, Faculte de Philosophie et Lettres, Universite Catholique de Louvain, Institut Orientaliste), Peeters Publishers, Bondgenotenlaan 153, Leuven, 3000, Belgium. TEL 32-16-235170, FAX 32-16-228500, peeters@peeters-leuven.be, http://poj.peeters-leuven.be/content.php?url=journal&journal_code=MUS, http://www.peeters-leuven.be. Ed. A Schmidt.

➤ **MUSEUM OF FAR EASTERN ANTIQUITIES. BULLETIN.** see *MUSEUMS AND ART GALLERIES*

954 IND ISSN 0580-4396
PK401
MYSORE ORIENTALIST. Text in English, Sanskrit. 1967. a. USD 5 (effective 2000). bk.rev. **Document type:** *Academic/Scholarly.* **Description:** Contains studies on Indic peoples.
Indexed: BAS, DIP, IBR.
Published by: University of Mysore, Oriental Research Institute, Mysore, Karnataka 5, India. TEL 91-821-443136. Ed. Dr. K V Ramesh. Circ: 300.

950.072048 DNK ISSN 0904-4337
HB1413 CODEN: MSIPE9
N I A S NYTT/NORDIC NEWSLETTER OF ASIAN STUDIES; Asia insight. Text in Multiple languages. 1976. 4/yr. free (effective 2004). back issues avail. **Document type:** *Monographic series, Academic/Scholarly.* **Description:** Issues of topical interest. For anyone interested in modern Asia and its developments.
Former titles (until 1988): C I N A - Nytt (0109-4203); (until 1980): Asien-Studier i Skandinavien (0105-7340)
Related titles: Online - full text ed.
Published by: Nordisk Institut for Asienstudier/Nordic Institute of Asian Studies, Leifsgade 33, Copenhagen S, 2300, Denmark. TEL 45-35-329500, FAX 45-35-329549, http://www.nias.ku.dk. Ed. Joergen Delman. Circ: 3,000.

950 DEU ISSN 0935-1051
DS41
NAHOST JAHRBUCH. Text in German. 1988. a. EUR 24.90 (effective 2004). bk.rev. **Document type:** *Journal, Academic/Scholarly.*
Indexed: DIP, IBR, IBZ.
Published by: (Deutsches Orient-Institut), V S - Verlag fuer Sozialwissenschaften (Subsidiary of: Springer Science+Business Media), Abraham-Lincoln-Str 46, Wiesbaden, 65189, Germany. TEL 49-611-78780, FAX 49-611-7878400, info@vs-verlag.de, http://www.vs-verlag.de. Eds. Hanspeter Mattes, Thomas Koszinowski.

950 JPN ISSN 1341-5670
NAIRIKU AJIA GENGO NO KENKYU/STUDIES ON THE INNER ASIAN LANGUAGES. Text in Japanese. 1992. a. **Document type:** *Journal, Academic/Scholarly.*
Supersedes in part: Kobe-shi Gaikokugo Daigaku Gaikokugaku Kenkyu (0289-9256)
—BLDSC (6015.320300).
Published by: Chuo Yurashiagaku Kenkyukai/Society of Central Eurasian Studies, Osaka University, Faculty of Letters, Department of Asian History, 1-5 Machikaneyama, Toyonaka, 560-8532, Japan. FAX 81-6-68505091, moriyasu@let.osaka-u.ac.jp, http://www.let.osaka-u-ac.jp/toyosi/sial/front-e.html.

951 305 NLD ISSN 1387-6805
HQ1075.5.C6
➤ **NAN NU;** men, women, and gender in early Imperial China. Text in Dutch. 1999. s-a. USD 59 in the Americas to individuals; EUR 47 elsewhere to individuals; USD 178 combined subscription in the Americas to institutions print & online eds.; EUR 142 combined subscription elsewhere to institutions print & online eds. (effective 2006). reprint service avail. from PSC. **Document type:** *Journal, Academic/Scholarly.* **Description:** An interdisciplinary journal on men, women, and gender in China, from the beginnings of civilization to the early 20th century.
Related titles: Online - full text ed.: ISSN 1568-5268. USD 160 in the Americas to institutions; EUR 128 elsewhere to institutions (effective 2006) (from EBSCO Publishing, Gale Group, IngentaConnect, Kluwer Online, O C L C Online Computer Library Center, Inc., Springer LINK, Swets Information Services).
Indexed: AmH&L, BAS, FemPer, HistAb, MLA-IB, SociolAb.
—CCC.
Published by: Brill Academic Publishers, PO Box 9000, Leiden, 2300 PA, Netherlands. TEL 31-71-53-53500, FAX 31-71-53-17532, cs@brill.nl, http://www.brill.nl/m_catalogue_sub6_id8603.htm. Ed. Harriet Zurndorfer. **Subscr. in N. America to:** PO Box 605, Herndon, VA 20172. TEL 703-661-1585, 800-337-9255, FAX 703-661-1501, cs@brillusa.com. **Distr. outside N. America by:** c/o Turpin Distribution, Stratton Business Park, Pegasus Drive, Biggleswade, BEDFORDSHIRE SG 18 8TQ, United Kingdom. TEL 44-1767-604-954, FAX 44-1767-601-640, brill@turpin-distribution.com.

954 CHN ISSN 1004-1508
NANYA YANJIU JIKAN/SOUTH ASIAN STUDIES QUARTERLY. Text in Chinese. 1979. q. CNY 12, USD 40.
Related titles: Online - full text ed.: (from East View Information Services).
Published by: Sichuan University, South Asian Studies Institute, Sichuan Daxue Nei, Jiuyanqiao, Chengdu, Sichuan 610064, China. TEL 86-28-85412638, FAX 86-28-85417102. Ed. Wen Fude. Circ: 1,000.

950 CHN ISSN 1003-9856
DS520
NANYANG WENTI YANJIU/SOUTHEAST ASIAN STUDIES. Text in Chinese. q. USD 20. **Document type:** *Academic/Scholarly.*
Related titles: Online - full text ed.: (from East View Information Services).
Indexed: HistAb, PerIslam.
Published by: (Nanyang Yanjiusuo), Xiamen Daxue/Xiamen University, c/o Xiamen Daxue Tushuguan, Xiamen, Fujian 361005, China. TEL 86-592-218-6144. Ed. Liao Shaolian.

950 CHN
NANYANG ZILIAO YICONG/SOUTH ASIAN AFFAIRS: A QUARTERLY JOURNAL OF TRANSLATION. Text in Chinese. q. **Document type:** *Academic/Scholarly.*
Published by: (Nanyang Yanjiusuo), Xiamen Daxue/Xiamen University, c/o Xiamen Daxue Tushuguan, Xiamen, Fujian 361005, China. TEL 86-592-218-6144. Ed. Liao Shaolian.

NANZAN INSTITUTE FOR RELIGION AND CULTURE. BULLETIN. see *RELIGIONS AND THEOLOGY*

NATIONAL PALACE MUSEUM. NEWSLETTER. see *MUSEUMS AND ART GALLERIES*

951.9 KOR
NATIONAL UNIFICATION AND NORTH KOREAN SOCIAL CULTURE. Text in Korean. 1994. s-a.
Formerly: Studies on Culture for a Unified Korea
Published by: Korea Institute for National Unification, 535-353 Suyu 6-dong, Kangbuk-ku, Seoul, 142-076, Korea, S.

950 DEU ISSN 0932-2728
NEAR AND MIDDLE EAST MONOGRAPHS. Text in German. 1987. irreg., latest vol.3, 1990. price varies. **Document type:** *Monographic series, Academic/Scholarly.*
Published by: Harrassowitz Verlag, Taunusstr 14, Wiesbaden, 65183, Germany. TEL 49-611-5300, FAX 49-611-530570, verlag@harrassowitz.de, http://www.harrassowitz.de. R&P Michael Langfeld. Adv. contact Robert Gietz.

NEAR EASTERN ARCHAEOLOGY. see *ARCHAEOLOGY*

320.9 NPL ISSN 0251-2653
NEPAL - ANTIQUARY; journal of social-historical research and digest. Text in Nepali. 1974-1991; resumed 2001. bi-m. USD 30 per issue (effective 2004). back issues avail.
Published by: Nepal Antiquary, P O Box 5140, Kathmandu, Nepal. TEL 977-1-4475037. Ed. Jagadish Chandra Regmi. Circ: 75.

958 DEU ISSN 0178-8612
➤ **NEPAL INFORMATION.** Text in German. 1967. 2/yr. EUR 41 membership (effective 2005). adv. bk.rev. bibl. 100 p./no.; back issues avail. **Document type:** *Journal, Academic/Scholarly.* **Description:** Information on all fields relevant to the socio-economic development of Nepal.
Indexed: DIP, IBR, IBZ.
Published by: Deutsch-Nepalische Gesellschaft e.V., Postfach 190327, Cologne, 50500, Germany. TEL 49-221-2338380, FAX 49-221-2338382, info@deutsch-nepal.de, http://www.deutsch-nepal.de. Ed. Wolf Donner. Circ: 500 (paid).

950 DEU ISSN 0720-6615
NEPAL RESEARCH CENTRE. JOURNAL. Text in English. 1977. a. price varies. **Document type:** *Journal, Academic/Scholarly.*
Indexed: BAS, BibLing, DIP, IBR, IBZ.
Published by: (Nepal Research Centre), Franz Steiner Verlag Stuttgart GmbH, Birkenwaldstr 44, Stuttgart, 70191, Germany. TEL 49-711-25820, FAX 49-711-2582390, franz.steiner.verlag@t-online.de, http://www.steiner-verlag.de. Ed. Albrecht Wezler. R&P Sabine Koerner.

956 USA ISSN 0081-8291
NEW YORK UNIVERSITY. STUDIES IN NEAR EASTERN CIVILIZATION. Text in English. 1968. irreg., latest vol.12. **Document type:** *Monographic series.*
Published by: New York University Press, 70 Washington Square So, New York, NY 10012. TEL 212-998-2575, 800-996-6987, FAX 212-995-3833. Ed. Peter Chelkowski. R&P Susan Conn.

959 NZL ISSN 1174-8915
➤ **NEW ZEALAND JOURNAL OF ASIAN STUDIES.** Text in English. 1993. s-a. NZD 40 to individuals; NZD 60 to institutions (effective 2000 - 2001). bk.rev. **Document type:** *Academic/Scholarly.* **Description:** Considers a wide range of Asia-related items for publication, such as academic papers, research reports, reviews, extended review articles, essays, poems and letters to the editor.
Formerly (until 1999): New Zealand Journal of East Asian Studies (1172-3823)
Indexed: BAS.
—BLDSC (6093.150000), IE, ingenta.
Published by: New Zealand Asian Studies Society, Inc., c/o Department of East Asian Studies, University of Waikato, Private Bag 3105, Hamilton, New Zealand. TEL 64-7-838-4116, FAX 64-7-838-4638, robertsm@waikato.ac.nz, http://www.nzasia.waikato.ac.nz. Ed. Kenneth G Henshall. Circ: 125.

950 TWN ISSN 0253-2875
DS734.97.T28
NEWSLETTER FOR RESEARCH IN CHINESE STUDIES. Text in Chinese. 1982. q. USD 40. adv. bk.rev. **Document type:** *Newsletter, Government.*
Indexed: BAS, RASB.
Published by: Center for Chinese Studies, c/o National Central Library, 20 Chung Shan S. Rd, Taipei, 100-01, Taiwan. TEL 886-2-2314-7321, FAX 886-2-2371-2126, ccsnews@msg.ncl.edu.tw, http://ccs.ncl.edu.tw. Ed. Yen-hui Tsui. Pub. Fang Rung Juang. R&P Yen Hui Tsui. Circ: 2,400.

952 JPN ISSN 0915-0889
DS820.8
NICHIBUNKEN. Text in Japanese. 1988. s-a.
Indexed: RASB.
Published by: International Research Center for Japanese Studies (Nichibunken)/Kokusai Nihon Bunka Kenkyu Senta, 3-2 Oeyama-cho, Goryo, Nishikyo-ku, Kyoto-shi, 610-1192, Japan. TEL 81-75-3352222, FAX 81-75-3352091.

952 JPN ISSN 0915-0986
DS820.8
➤ **NICHIBUNKEN JAPAN REVIEW.** Text in English; Summaries in English, Japanese. 1990. a. free to qualified personnel; JPY 2,500 newsstand/cover (effective 2005). Index. back issues avail. **Document type:** *Journal, Academic/Scholarly.* **Description:** Covers the advancement of comparative and interdisciplinary studies of Japan in fields including history, literature, religious studies, anthropology, sociology, archaeology, art history, language and linguistics, philosophy, political science, and psychology.
Indexed: BAS, RASB.
—BLDSC (6109.899000).
Published by: International Research Center for Japanese Studies (Nichibunken)/Kokusai Nihon Bunka Kenkyu Senta, 3-2 Oeyama-cho, Goryo, Nishikyo-ku, Kyoto-shi, 610-1192, Japan. TEL 81-75-3352222, FAX 81-75-3352093, shuppan@nichibun.ac.jp, http://www.nichibun.ac.jp. Ed. James C. Baxter. Pub. Yamaori Tetsuo. R&P Sakamoto Yasuyuki.

952 JPN ISSN 0914-6482
NICHIBUNKEN NEWSLETTER/NIHON BUNKA. Text in English, Japanese. 1988. s-a. **Document type:** *Newsletter.*
Indexed: RASB.
Published by: International Research Center for Japanese Studies (Nichibunken)/Kokusai Nihon Bunka Kenkyu Senta, 3-2 Oeyama-cho, Goryo, Nishikyo-ku, Kyoto-shi, 610-1192, Japan. TEL 81-75-3352222, FAX 81-75-3352091. Ed. Ito Shuntaro.

NIPPON CHUGOKU GAKKAIHO/BULLETIN OF THE SINOLOGICAL SOCIETY OF JAPAN. see *HISTORY—History Of Asia*

950 GBR ISSN 1359-0421
NORDIC INSTITUTE OF ASIAN STUDIES. MONOGRAPH SERIES. Text in English. 1969. irreg. price varies. **Document type:** *Monographic series.*

Formerly (until 1994): Scandinavian Institute of Asian Studies. Monograph Series (0069-1712)
Published by: (Nordisk Institut for Asienstudier/Nordic Institute of Asian Studies DNK), Curzon Press Ltd., 15 The Quadrant, 6-8 Church Rd, Richmond, Surrey TW9 1BP, United Kingdom. Circ: 1,100.

958   GBR
NORDIC INSTITUTE OF ASIAN STUDIES. OCCASIONAL PAPERS. Text in English. 1987. irreg.
Formerly: Scandinavian Institute of Asian Studies. Occasional Papers (0266-206X)
Published by: Curzon Press Ltd., 15 The Quadrant, 6-8 Church Rd, Richmond, Surrey TW9 1BP, United Kingdom.

950   DNK   ISSN 1398-313X
DS32.9.S34
NORDIC INSTITUTE OF ASIAN STUDIES. REPORT SERIES. Text in Danish. 1968. irreg. bk.rev. **Document type:** *Monographic series, Academic/Scholarly.* **Description:** Working paper series on Asian studies.
Former titles (until 1996): N I A S Report (0904-597X); (until 1989): Scandinavian Institute of Asian Studies. Annual Newsletter (0106-3871); (until 1974): Scandinavian Institute of Asian Studies. Newsletter (0906-978X)
Indexed: BAS, IBSS, SPPI.
Published by: Nordisk Institut for Asienstudier/Nordic Institute of Asian Studies, Leifsgade 33, Copenhagen S, 2300, Denmark. TEL 45-35-329500, FAX 45-35-329549, sec@nias.ku.dk, http://www.nias.ku.dk. Circ: 300.

NORTHERN ILLINOIS UNIVERSITY. MONOGRAPH SERIES ON SOUTHEAST ASIA. see HISTORY—History Of Asia

950   CZE   ISSN 0029-5302
DS1
NOVY ORIENT/NEW ORIENT. Text in Czech. 1945. 10/yr, USD 60 in Europe; USD 75 elsewhere (effective 1999). bk.rev. charts; illus.; maps. index. **Document type:** *Journal, Academic/Scholarly.* **Description:** Deals with the cultures and civilizations of Asia and Africa, regularly including studies on developing countries and information about current problems of the Third World.
Indexed: AmH&L, BAS, HistAb, MLA-IB, RASB.
Published by: Akademie Ved Ceske Republiky, Orientalni Ustav/Czech Academy of Sciences, Oriental Institute, Pod Vodarenskou vezi 4, Prague, 18208, Czech Republic. TEL 42-2-66053523, FAX 42-2-6897260, novor@orient.cas.cz, http://www.lib.cas.cz/knav/journals/eng/archiv_orientalni.htm. Ed. Svetozar Pantucek. Circ: 2,050.

320   GBR   ISSN 0960-7935
Z792.B85932
O I O C NEWSLETTER. Text in English. 1974. s-a. free. adv. bk.rev. bibl. **Document type:** *Newsletter.* **Description:** News of activities of the library and articles pertaining to its acquisitions, collections, recent publications.
Former titles: India Office Library and Records Oriental Collections Newsletter (0265-1386); India Office Library and Records Newsletter (0307-6008)
Indexed: BAS.
—BLDSC (6252.638000).
Published by: (British Library, Oriental and India Office Collections), British Library Board, 96 Euston Rd, London, NW1 2DB, United Kingdom. oioc-enquiries@bl.uk. Ed. David Plumb. Circ: 880. **Subscr. to:** British Library, Oriental and India Office Collections, 197 Blackfriars Rd, London SE1 8NG, United Kingdom. TEL 44-171-412-7000, 44-171-412-7641.

950   DEU   ISSN 0949-0795
OKAMATSU BUNKO; japanwissenschaftliche Beitraege zur interkulturellen Kommunikation. Text in German. 1995. irreg., latest vol.3, 2000. price varies. **Document type:** *Monographic series, Academic/Scholarly.*
Published by: Harrassowitz Verlag, Taunusstr 14, Wiesbaden, 65183, Germany. TEL 49-611-5300, FAX 49-611-530570, verlag@harrassowitz.de, http://www.harrassowitz.de. Ed. Johannes Laube. R&P Michael Langfeld. Adv. contact Robert Gietz.

950   DEU   ISSN 0949-7927
OPERA SINOLOGICA. Text in German. 1996. irreg., latest vol.13, 2001. price varies. **Document type:** *Monographic series, Academic/Scholarly.*
Published by: Harrassowitz Verlag, Taunusstr 14, Wiesbaden, 65183, Germany. TEL 49-611-5300, FAX 49-611-530570, verlag@harrassowitz.de, http://www.harrassowitz.de. Eds. Erling von Mende, Lutz Bieg. R&P Michael Langfeld. Adv. contact Robert Gietz.

ORBIS MUSICAE; Assaph studies in the arts. see MUSIC

950   NLD   ISSN 0078-6527
DS1
➤ ORIENS; journal of the International Society for Oriental Research. Text in English, French, German. 1948. irreg. (approx. biennial), latest vol.36, 2001. price varies. bk.rev. illus.; maps. cum.index: vols.1-10 (1948-1957). back issues avail. **Document type:** *Monographic series, Academic/Scholarly.* **Description:** Studies in the culture of Asia and North Africa from antiquity to the present focusing on language, literature, religion and art.

Indexed: AmH&L, BAS, BibLing, DIP, HistAb, IBR, IBZ, IndIslam, PerIslam, RASB.
—CCC.
Published by: (Internationale Gesellschaft fuer Orientforschung), Brill Academic Publishers, PO Box 9000, Leiden, 2300 PA, Netherlands. TEL 31-71-53-53-500, FAX 31-71-53-17-532, cs@brill.nl, http://www.brill.nl/product_id7413.htm. Ed. R Sellheim. R&P Elizabeth Venekamp. **Subscr. in N. America to:** PO Box 605, Herndon, VA 20172. TEL 703-661-1585, 800-337-9255, FAX 703-661-1501, cs@brillusa.com. **Distr. outside N. America by:** c/o Turpin Distribution, Stratton Business Park, Pegasus Drive, Biggleswade, BEDFORDSHIRE SG 18 8TQ, United Kingdom. TEL 44-1767-604-954, FAX 44-1767-601-640, brill@turpin-distribution.com.

950 490 890   DEU   ISSN 0030-5197
DS501
ORIENS EXTREMUS; Zeitschrift fuer Sprache, Kunst und Kultur der Laender des fernen Ostens. Text in English, French, German. 1954. a. EUR 64; CHF 109 in Switzerland (effective 2006). charts; illus. index. back issues avail. **Document type:** *Journal, Academic/Scholarly.* **Description:** Contains articles on the language, art and culture of the Far East.
Indexed: AmH&L, BAS, BHA, BibLing, DIP, EI, HistAb, IBR, IBSS, IBZ, IndIslam, MLA, MLA-IB, RASB, RILM.
—IE. CCC.
Published by: Harrassowitz Verlag, Taunusstr 14, Wiesbaden, 65183, Germany. TEL 49-611-5300, FAX 49-611-530560, verlag@harrassowitz.de, http://www.uni-hamburg.de/Wiss/FB/10/JapanS/Zeitschr/oe.html, http://www.harrassowitz.de. Ed. Roland Schneider. R&P Michael Langfeld. Adv. contact Robert Gietz. Circ: 350.

950   DEU   ISSN 0030-5227
DS41
ORIENT; Deutsche Zeitschrift fuer Wirtschaft und Politik des Orients - German journal for politics and economics of the Middle East. Text in German. 1960. q. EUR 84 domestic; EUR 89 foreign; EUR 59.70 domestic to students; EUR 64.70 foreign to students; EUR 23.20 newsstand/cover (effective 2004). adv. bk.rev. bibl.; charts; illus.; maps. reprint service avail. from SCH. **Document type:** *Journal, Academic/Scholarly.* **Description:** Deals with the politics, economy and society of the modern Near and Middle East.
Indexed: BAS, BibLing, CCME, DIP, ELLIS, GEOBASE, IBR, IBSS, IBZ, IPSA, IndIslam, KES, MLA-IB, PAIS, PerIslam, RASB.
—BLDSC (6291.138000), IE, Infotrieve, ingenta. CCC.
Published by: (Deutsches Orient-Institut), V S - Verlag fuer Sozialwissenschaften (Subsidiary of: Springer Science+Business Media), Abraham-Lincoln-Str 46, Wiesbaden, 65189, Germany. TEL 49-611-78780, FAX 49-611-7878400, info@vs-verlag.de, http://www.vs-verlag.de.

950   FRA   ISSN 1161-0344
DS56
ORIENT EXPRESS; notes et nouvelles d'archeologie orientale. Text in French. 1991. q. EUR 18.29 to individuals; EUR 13.72 to students (effective 2002). adv. **Document type:** *Newsletter, Academic/Scholarly.* **Description:** International bulletin specializing in oriental archaeology.
Published by: Orient - Express, c/o Institut d'Art et d'Archeologie, 3 rue Michelet, Paris, 75006, France. FAX 33-1-44070179, annezaza@easynet.fr. Eds. Aude Mantoux, Anne-Elizabeth Dunn-Vaturi. Adv. contact Anna Vivante.

950   DEU   ISSN 1617-4488
ORIENT JOURNAL. Text in German. 2000. s-a. **Document type:** *Journal, Academic/Scholarly.*
Published by: (Deutsches Orient-Institut), Lit Verlag, Grevener Str. 179, Muenster, 48159, Germany. TEL 49-251-235091, FAX 49-251-231972, lit@lit-verlag.de, http://www.lit-verlag.de/journale/orient/. Ed. Udo Steinbach. Circ: 15,000 (controlled).

709.5   SGP   ISSN 0030-5278
N8
ORIENTAL ART; devoted to the study of all forms of Oriental art. Text in English. 1948; N.S. 1955. 5/yr. USD 80, GBP 60 (effective 2005). adv. bk.rev. bibl.; illus. index. back issues avail.; reprints avail. **Document type:** *Magazine, Consumer.* **Description:** Devoted entirely to Eastern art. Includes reports from the dealer's markets of Europe and the US.
Indexed: A&ATA, ABCT, ABM, AIAP, ASCA, ArtHuCI, ArtInd, BHA, CurCont, DIP, IBR, IBRH, IBZ, IndIslam, PCI, RASB, RI-1, RI-2.
—BLDSC (6291.163000), IE, Infotrieve, ingenta. CCC.
Published by: Oriental Art Magazine, 47 Hill St, #06-06, Singapore, 179365, Singapore. TEL 65-6737-9931, FAX 65-6737-3190, orientalart@orientalartmag.com, http://www.orientalartmagazine.com/. adv.: B&W page GBP 670, color page GBP 790; trim 210 x 297. **Dist. addr. in the US:** Oriental Art Magazine, 300 Park Ave, PMB #1725, 17th Fl., New York, NY 10022.

ORIENTAL INSTITUTE COMMUNICATIONS. see ARCHAEOLOGY

ORIENTAL INSTITUTE MUSEUM PUBLICATIONS. see MUSEUMS AND ART GALLERIES

950   AUS   ISSN 0030-5340
DS41
➤ ORIENTAL SOCIETY OF AUSTRALIA. JOURNAL. Text in English. 1961. a. AUD 30 membership (effective 2005); subscr. incld. with membership. adv. bk.rev. charts; illus. index. **Document type:** *Journal, Academic/Scholarly.*
Indexed: AmH&L, AusPAIS, BAS, DIP, EI, HistAb, IBR, RASB.
Published by: Oriental Society of Australia, The University of Sydney, School of Languages & Cultures, Sydney, NSW 2006, Australia. TEL 61-2-93514500, FAX 61-2-93512319, yasuko.claremont@arts.usyd.edu.au, http://www.arts.usyd.edu.au/publications/JOSA/journals.htm, http://www.arts.usyd.edu.au/publications/JOSA/index.htm. Ed. Leith D Morton. Circ: 500.

939.4   ITA   ISSN 0030-5367
PJ6
➤ ORIENTALIA. Text in English, French, German, Italian. 1920. q. EUR 61.97, USD 110 (effective 2001). bk.rev. bibl.; charts; illus. index. back issues avail. **Document type:** *Academic/Scholarly.* **Description:** Consists of ancient Near Eastern studies.
Related titles: Microfiche ed.: (from IDC).
Indexed: BAS, BHA, BibInd, BibLing, DIP, IBR, IBSS, IBZ, IndIslam, MLA-IB, NTA, OTA, PCI, RASB, RI-1, RI-2.
—IE.
Published by: Pontificio Istituto Biblico/Pontifical Biblical Institute, Via della Pilotta 25, Rome, 00187, Italy. TEL 39-06-695261, FAX 39-06-695266151, pibsegr@pib.ur, http://www.pib.urbe.it. Circ: 700.

➤ ORIENTALIA BIBLICA ET CHRISTIANA. see RELIGIONS AND THEOLOGY—Roman Catholic

282   ITA
ORIENTALIA CHRISTIANA ANALECTA. Text in English, French, German, Italian. 1923. irreg. (approx. 3/yr.) price varies. **Document type:** *Monographic series, Academic/Scholarly.*
Formerly (until 1935): Orientalia Christiana
Indexed: RASB.
Published by: (Pontificio Istituto Orientale/Pontificum Institutum Studiorum Orientalium), Edizioni Orientalia Cristiana (Subsidiary of: Pontificio Istituto Orientale/Pontificum Institutum Studiorum Orientalium), Piazza Santa Maria Maggiore, 7, Rome, RM 00185, Italy. TEL 39-06-4465589, FAX 39-06-4465576. Ed. Robert Taft. Circ: 1,000.

950   SWE   ISSN 0078-656X
ORIENTALIA GOTHOBURGENSIA. Text in English. 1969. irreg., latest vol.17, 2003. price varies. **Document type:** *Monographic series, Academic/Scholarly.*
Related titles: ◆ Series of: Acta Universitatis Gothoburgensis. ISSN 0346-7740.
Indexed: MLA-IB.
Published by: Acta Universitatis Gothoburgensis, Renstroemsgatan 4, P O Box 222, Goeteborg, 40530, Sweden. TEL 46-31-773-17-33, FAX 46-31-163-797. Ed. Jan Retsoe.

950   BEL   ISSN 0777-978X
➤ ORIENTALIA LOVANIENSIA ANALECTA. Text in English, French, German. 1974. irreg., latest vol.102, 2001. price varies. back issues avail. **Document type:** *Monographic series, Academic/Scholarly.* **Description:** Publishes studies on the history, cultures, languages, religions and cultures of the ancient and modern Near East, North Africa and South Asian regions.
Related titles: ◆ Series: Studia Phoenicia; ◆ Supplement to: Orientalia Lovaniensia Periodica. ISSN 0085-4522.
Indexed: CCMJ, MLA-IB, RI-2.
Published by: (Katholieke Universiteit Leuven, Departement Oosterse en Slavische Studies), Peeters Publishers, Bondgenotenlaan 153, Leuven, 3000, Belgium. TEL 32-16-235170, FAX 32-16-228500, http://www.peeters-leuven.be.

950   BEL   ISSN 0085-4522
ORIENTALIA LOVANIENSIA PERIODICA. Text in English, French, German; Summaries in English. 1970. a., latest vol.31, 2000. EUR 50 (effective 2006). bk.rev. abstr.; charts; illus. cum.index. **Document type:** *Monographic series, Academic/Scholarly.*
Related titles: Online - full text ed.: (from EBSCO Publishing); ◆ Supplement(s): Orientalia Lovaniensia Analecta. ISSN 0777-978X.
Indexed: BAS, BibLing, IBR, MLA, MLA-IB, NTA, NumL, OTA, PCI, RI-1, RI-2, SOPODA.
—BLDSC (6291.187400), KNAW.
Published by: (Katholieke Universiteit Leuven, Departement Oosterse en Slavische Studies), Peeters Publishers, Bondgenotenlaan 153, Leuven, 3000, Belgium. TEL 32-16-235170, FAX 32-16-228500, jozefa.delcon@arts.kuleuven.ac.be, peeters@peeters-leuven.be, http://poj.peeters-leuven.be/content.php?url=journal&journal_code=OLP, http://www.peeters-leuven.be. Ed., R&P G Pollet. Circ: 300.

950   NLD   ISSN 0169-9504
➤ ORIENTALIA RHENO-TRAIECTINA. Text in Dutch. 1949. irreg., latest vol.35, 1990. price varies. back issues avail. **Document type:** *Monographic series, Academic/Scholarly.*

Published by: Brill Academic Publishers, PO Box 9000, Leiden, 2300 PA, Netherlands. TEL 31-71-53-53-500, FAX 31-71-53-17-532, cs@brill.nl, http://www.brill.nl. Ed. J Gonda. R&P Elizabeth Venekamp. **Subscr. in N. America by:** PO Box 605, Herndon, VA 20172. TEL 703-661-1585, 800-337-9255, FAX 703-661-1501, cs@brillusa.com. **Distr. outside N. America by:** c/o Turpin Distribution, Stratton Business Park, Pegasus Drive, Biggleswade, BEDFORDSHIRE SG 18 8TQ, United Kingdom. TEL 44-1767-604-954, FAX 44-1767-601-640, brill@turpin-distribution.com.

950 809.5 SWE ISSN 0078-6578
➤ **ORIENTALIA SUECANA**; an international journal of Indological, Iranian, Semitic and Turkic studies. Text in Swedish. 1952. a., latest vol.50, 2001. price varies. bk.rev. back issues avail. **Document type:** *Academic/Scholarly.*
Indexed: BAS, BibLing, IBR, MLA, MLA-IB, NTA, NumL, PCI, PerIslam, RASB.
Published by: Uppsala Universitet, Institutionen foer Afro-Asiatiske Spraak/Department of Asian and African Languages, PO Box 527, Uppsala, 75120, Sweden. TEL 48-18-4711090, FAX 48-18-4711094, info@afro.uu.se, http://www.afro.uu.se/orientalia/oriental.html. Ed. Gunilla Green-Eklund. Circ: 600.

950 SWE ISSN 0345-8997
CODEN: SRUNEK
ORIENTALISKA STUDIER. Text mainly in Swedish; Text occasionally in English. 1969. q. SEK 120 in Scandinavia to individuals; SEK 150 in Scandinavia to institutions; SEK 300 elsewhere (effective 2005). bk.rev. Index. **Document type:** *Journal, Academic/Scholarly.*
Indexed: BAS, IndIslam.
Published by: Foereningen for Orientaliska Studier/Society for Oriental Studies, Stockholm University, Kraeftriket 4 B, Stockholm, 10691, Sweden. TEL 46-8-164273, FAX 46-8-155464, redaktionen@orientaliskastudier.se, http://www.orientaliskastudier.se/. Ed. Fredrik Fallman.

950 DEU
ORIENTALISTIK BIBLIOGRAPHIEN UND DOKUMENTATIONEN. Text in German. 1996. irreg., latest vol.19, 2003. price varies. adv. **Document type:** *Monographic series, Academic/Scholarly.*
Formerly: Orientalistik Bibliographien (1432-3338)
Published by: Harrassowitz Verlag, Taunusstr 14, Wiesbaden, 65183, Germany. TEL 49-611-5300, FAX 49-611-530570, verlag@harrassowitz.de, http://www.harrassowitz.de. R&P Michael Langfeld. Adv. contact Robert Gietz.

890 DEU ISSN 0030-5383
➤ **ORIENTALISTISCHE LITERATURZEITUNG**; Zeitschrift fuer die Wissenschaft vom ganzen Orient und seinen Beziehungen zu den angrenzenden Kulturkreisen. Text in English, French, German. 1898. bi-m. EUR 282 domestic; EUR 292 foreign; EUR 54 domestic to students; EUR 58 foreign to students (effective 2005). adv. bk.rev. bibl. reprint service avail. from SCH. **Document type:** *Journal, Academic/Scholarly.* **Description:** Review journal for the entire field of Oriental studies.
Related titles: Microfiche ed.: (from IDC).
Indexed: BAS, BibLing, DIP, IBR, IBZ, NTA, OTA, PCI, RASB, RI-1, RI-2.
—IE, Infotrieve. **CCC.**
Published by: Akademie Verlag GmbH (Subsidiary of: Oldenbourg Wissenschaftsverlag GmbH), Palisadenstr 40, Berlin, 10243, Germany. TEL 49-30-4220060, FAX 49-30-42200657, info@akademie-verlag.de, http://www.akademie-verlag.de. Ed. Peter Heine.

➤ **ORIENTATIONS**; the monthly magazine for collectors and connoisseurs of Oriental art. see *ART*

950 ITA ISSN 0030-5472
D461
ORIENTE MODERNO; rivista d'informazione e di studi per la diffusione della conoscenza della cultura dell'oriente sopratutto musulmano. Text in Italian. 1921. irreg., latest vol.80, 2000. bk.rev. index, cum.index: 1921-1973. back issues avail.; reprints avail. **Document type:** *Academic/Scholarly.*
Indexed: ASD, AmH&L, BAS, BibInd, BibLing, DIP, HistAb, IBR, IBZ, IPSA, IndIslam, PCI, RASB.
—IE.
Published by: Istituto per l'Oriente C.A. Nallino, Via A. Caroncini 19, Rome, 00197, Italy. TEL 39-06-8084106, FAX 39-06-8079395. Ed. F Castro. Circ: 800. **Dist. by:** Herder Editrice e Libreria s.r.l., Piazza di Montecitorio 117-120, Rome 00186, Italy. TEL 39-06-6794628, FAX 390-6-3225348, 39-6-6784751.

950 410 IND ISSN 0474-9030
OUR HERITAGE. Text in English, Bengali, Sanskrit. 1972 (vol.19). s-a. bibl. **Description:** Covers literary subjects.
Indexed: RASB.
—BLDSC (6314.330000).
Published by: Sanskrit College, Department of Postgraduate Training and Research, 1 Bankim Chatterjee St., Kolkata, West Bengal 700 012, India. Ed. B Bhattacharya.

954 GBR
OXFORD INDIA PAPERBACKS. Text in English. irreg., latest 2002. price varies. back issues avail. **Document type:** *Monographic series.* **Description:** Explores the history, culture (including arts and religions), and politics of colonial and modern India.
Published by: Oxford University Press, Great Clarendon St, Oxford, OX2 6DP, United Kingdom. TEL 44-1865-556767, FAX 44-1865-556646, enquiry@oup.co.uk, http://www.oup-usa.org/catalogs/general/series/Oxford_India_Paperbacks.html, http://www.oup.co.uk/.

950 GBR
OXFORD ORIENTAL INSTITUTE MONOGRAPHS. Text in English. 1978. irreg., latest vol.15, 1996. price varies. **Document type:** *Monographic series, Academic/Scholarly.* **Description:** Publishes academic studies of aspects of Chinese, Japanese, and Arabic cultures, past and present. Subjects have included poetry, criticism, legends, literature, scholars, and more.
Published by: Ithaca Press (Subsidiary of: Garnet Publishing), 8 Southern Ct, South St, Reading, Berks RG1 4QS, United Kingdom. TEL 44-1189-597847, FAX 44-1189-597356, enquiries@garnet-ithaca.demon.co.uk, http://www.garnet-ithaca.demon.co.uk. Pub., R&P Emma Hawker.

951 TWN
PACIFIC CULTURAL FOUNDATION. ANNUAL REPORT. Text in English, Chinese. a.
Published by: Pacific Cultural Foundation, Palace Office Bldg, Ste. 807, 346 Nanking East Rd, Sec 3, Taipei, Taiwan. TEL 02-752-7424, FAX 02-752-7429. Ed. Brian P Lew. Pub. Yu Sheng Chang.

950 AUS ISSN 1443-8976
THE PACIFIC STUDIES W W W MONITOR. Text in English. 2000. m. free. **Document type:** *Journal, Academic/Scholarly.*
Media: Online - full text.
Published by: Australian National University, Internet Publications Bureau, Research School of Pacific & Asian Studies, Canberra, ACT 0200, Australia. tmciolek@coombs.anu.edu.au, http://coombs.anu.edu.au/pacific-www-monitor.html, http://coombs.anu.edu.au/RSPAS-ipb.html. Ed. T Matthew Ciolek TEL 61-2-61250110.

959 CUB
PAGINAS. Text in Spanish. a. USD 8 in South America; USD 10 in North America; USD 12 elsewhere.
Published by: (Centro de Estudio Asia y Oceania), Ediciones Cubanas, Obispo No. 527, Apdo. 605, Havana, Cuba.

894 494 947.87 USA ISSN 0031-5508
PERMANENT INTERNATIONAL ALTAISTIC CONFERENCE (PIAC). NEWSLETTER. Text in German. 1966. irreg. (2-3/yr.). free. adv. bibl. **Document type:** *Newsletter.*
Media: Duplicated (not offset).
Indexed: BibLing.
Published by: Indiana University, Permanent International Altaistic Conference, Goodbody Hall 216, Indiana University, Bloomington, IN 47405. Circ: 750.

950 USA
PERSPECTIVES ON CENTRAL ASIA. Text in English. m. **Document type:** *Newsletter.*
Indexed: PAIS.
Published by: The Center for Political and Strategic Studies, 1050 17th St, N W, Ste 600, Washington, DC 20036.

THE PHILIPPINES: NEWS AND VIEWS. see *POLITICAL SCIENCE—International Relations*

950 PNG ISSN 0253-2913
POINT SERIES. Text in English. 1982. s-a. USD 12. bk.rev. back issues avail.
Indexed: RI-1, RI-2.
Published by: Melanesian Institute for Pastoral & Socio-Economic Service, PO Box 382, Goroka, EHP, Papua New Guinea. TEL 657-7321777, FAX 675-7321214. Ed. N de Groot. Circ: 1,000.

950 POL ISSN 0079-4783
POLSKA AKADEMIA NAUK. KOMITET NAUK ORIENTALISTYCZNYCH. PRACE ORIENTALISTYCZNE. Text and summaries in English, French, German, Polish, Russian. 1954. irreg., latest vol.39, 1997. price varies. **Document type:** *Academic/Scholarly.*
Published by: (Polska Akademia Nauk/Polish Academy of Sciences, Polska Akademia Nauk, Komitet Nauk Orientalistycznych), Wydawnictwo Naukowe P W N SA/Polish Scientific Publishers P W N, ul Miodowa 10, Warsaw, 00251, Poland. TEL 48-22-6954321, FAX 48-22-6954288. Circ: 1,200.

950 POL ISSN 0079-3426
POLSKA AKADEMIA NAUK. ODDZIAL W KRAKOWIE. KOMISJA ORIENTALISTYCZNA. PRACE. Text in English, French, German, Polish. 1962. irreg., latest vol.21, 1990. price varies. **Document type:** *Monographic series.* **Description:** Presents Arabic sources concerning the history of Central and Eastern Europe. Also important literary and linguistic works on Oriental subjects.
—BLDSC (6588.147300), KNAW.
Published by: (Komisja Orientalistyczna), Polska Akademia Nauk, Oddzial w Krakowie, ul sw Jana 28, Krakow, 31018, Poland. TEL 48-12-224853, FAX 48-12-222791. Ed. Stanislaw Stachowski. Circ: 700.

PORTA LINGUARUM ORIENTALIUM. see *LINGUISTICS*

950 USA ISSN 1067-9847
DS501 CODEN: POSIFA
➤ **POSITIONS**; East Asia cultures critique. Text in English. 1993. 3/yr. USD 33 to individuals; USD 135 to institutions; USD 150 combined subscription to institutions print & online eds. (effective 2006). adv. back issues avail.; reprint service avail. from PSC. **Document type:** *Journal, Academic/Scholarly.* **Description:** Offers a forum of debate for all concerned with the social, intellectual, and political events unfolding in East Asia and within the Asian diaspora.
Related titles: Online - full text ed.: ISSN 1527-8271. 1999. USD 135 to institutions (effective 2006) (from EBSCO Publishing, Gale Group, IngentaConnect, O C L C Online Computer Library Center, Inc., Project MUSE, Swets Information Services).
Indexed: AmH&L, ArtHuCI, BAS, CurCont, HistAb, MLA-IB, PSA, SOPODA, SSA, SociolAb.
—BLDSC (6558.846900), IDS, IE, Infotrieve. **CCC.**
Published by: (Washington University), Duke University Press, 905 W Main St, Ste 18 B, Durham, NC 27701. TEL 919-687-3600, FAX 919-688-3524, subscriptions@dukeupress.edu, http://dukeupress.edu/journals/j_titles.php3?user_id=, http://www.dukeupress.edu. Ed. Tani Barlow. R&P Kay Robin Alexander. Adv. contact Mandy Dailey-Berman TEL 919-687-3636. page USD 200; trim 5.875 x 6.5. Circ: 660 (paid and controlled).

954 IND
➤ **PRACHYA PRATIBHA.** Text in English, Hindi, Sanskrit. 1973. s-a. INR 150, USD 30 (effective 1996). bk.rev. **Document type:** *Academic/Scholarly.* **Description:** A research journal which carries contributions from scholars and savants on Indology. Regular features include Indian history and culture, archaeology, epigraphy, museology and numismatics.
Related titles: Microfilm ed.
Published by: Birla Institute of Art and Music, Prachya Niketan, Museum, P.O. Vallabh Bhavan, Bhopal, Madhya Pradesh 462 004, India. TEL 0755-551388. Ed. Susmita Pande. Pub. Aparna Bajpai. Circ: 500.

950 490 USA
PRINCETON LIBRARY OF ASIAN TRANSLATIONS. Text in English. 1953. irreg., latest 2001. price varies. back issues avail. **Document type:** *Monographic series, Academic/Scholarly.* **Description:** Publishes translations of noteworthy classic Asian literature.
Published by: Princeton University Press, 41 William St, Princeton, NJ 08540-5237. TEL 609-258-4900, FAX 609-258-6305, http://pup.princeton.edu/catalogs/series/plat.html. **Subscr. addr.:** California - Princeton Fulfillment Services, 1445 Lower Ferry Rd, Ewing, NJ 08618. TEL 800-777-4726, FAX 800-999-1958, orders@cpfs.pupress.princeton.edu. **Dist. addr. in Canada:** University Press Group, 164 Hillsdale Ave E, Toronto, ON M4S 1T5, Canada.; **Dist. addr. in UK:** John Wiley & Sons Ltd., The Atrium, Southern Gate, Chichester, West Sussex PO19 8SQ, United Kingdom.

THE PRINCETON PAPERS; interdisciplinary journal of Middle Eastern studies. see *HISTORY—History Of The Near East*

PRINCETON STUDIES IN MUSLIM POLITICS. see *RELIGIONS AND THEOLOGY—Islamic*

PRINCETON STUDIES ON THE NEAR EAST. see *HISTORY—History Of The Near East*

956 NLD ISSN 0169-9601
➤ **PROBLEME DER AEGYPTOLOGIE.** Text in Dutch. 1953. irreg., latest vol.19, 2001. price varies. back issues avail. **Document type:** *Monographic series, Academic/Scholarly.* **Description:** Interpretations of religious, historical and cultural topics in Egyptology.
Published by: Brill Academic Publishers, PO Box 9000, Leiden, 2300 PA, Netherlands. TEL 31-71-53-53-500, FAX 31-71-53-17-532, cs@brill.nl, http://www.brill.nl. Ed. W Helck. R&P Elizabeth Vennekamp. **Subscr. in N. America to:** PO Box 605, Herndon, VA 20172. TEL 703-661-1585, 800-337-9255, FAX 703-661-1501, cs@brillusa.com. **Distr. outside N. America by:** c/o Turpin Distribution, Stratton Business Park, Pegasus Drive, Biggleswade, BEDFORDSHIRE SG 18 8TQ, United Kingdom. TEL 44-1767-604-954, FAX 44-1767-601-640, brill@turpin-distribution.com.

954 IND
PUNJAB UNIVERSITY INDOLOGICAL SERIES. Text in English. 1979 (no.24). irreg. price varies.
Published by: (Panjab University), Vishveshvaranand Vedic Research Institute, P.O. Sadhu Ashram, Hoshiarpur, Punjab 146 021, India. Ed. S Bhaskaran Nair.

▼ *new title* ➤ *refereed* ✶ *unverified* ♦ *full entry avail.*

A

950 DEU ISSN 0931-9158
PURANA RESEARCH PUBLICATIONS, TUEBINGEN. Text in German. 1987. irreg., latest vol.6, 1997. price varies. **Document type:** *Monographic series, Academic/Scholarly.*
Published by: Harrassowitz Verlag, Taunusstr 14, Wiesbaden, 65183, Germany. TEL 49-611-5300, FAX 49-611-530570, verlag@harrassowitz.de, http://www.harrassowitz.de. Ed. Heinrich von Stietencron. R&P Michael Langfeld. Adv. contact Robert Gietz.

QADMONIYOT; journal for the antiquities of Eretz-Israel and Biblical lands. see *ARCHAEOLOGY*

951.47 CHN ISSN 1000-5447
QINGHAI MINZU XUEYUAN XUEBAO/QINGHAI INSTITUTE OF NATIONALITIES. JOURNAL. Text in Chinese. 1975. q. CNY 14. bk.rev. **Document type:** *Academic/Scholarly.* **Description:** Focuses on local and ethnic history, minority languages and literatures (including folk literature), economics, education, government policy, religion, law, and arts pertaining to nationalities in Qinghai Province.
Related titles: Online - full text ed.: (from East View Information Services).
Published by: Qinghai Minzu Xueyuan/Qinghai Institute of Nationalities, 3 Bayi Lu, Xining, Qinghai 810007, China. TEL 86-971-8124652. Ed. Wenyuan Nan. Circ: 1,500.

950 ITA
QUADERNI ASIATICI. Text in Italian. 1983. 4/yr. adv. bk.rev.; film rev.; music rev. bibl.; illus. index. back issues avail.
Published by: Centro di Cultura Italia Asia, Corso di Porta Ticinese 39, Milan, MI 20123, Italy. Ed., R&P Jolanda Guardi. Adv. contact Daniele Pirola.

953 ITA ISSN 1121-2306
DS36.8
QUADERNI DI STUDI ARABI. Text in English, French, Italian. 1983. a., latest vol.17, 1999. price varies. back issues avail. **Document type:** *Journal, Academic/Scholarly.*
Indexed: BibLing, DIP, IBR, IBSS, IBZ, PerIslam.
Published by: Universita degli Studi di Venezia, Dipartimento di Scienze dell'Antichita e del Vicino Oriente, Palazzo Capello, Calle Larga San Polo, 2035, Venice, VE 30125, Italy. TEL 39-041-5287687, FAX 39-041-5241891. Ed. Francesca Picchetti Lucchetta. **Dist. by:** Herder Editrice e Libreria s.r.l., Piazza di Montecitorio 117-120, Rome 00186, Italy. TEL 39-6-6794628, FAX 390-6-6784751.

951.9 KOR
QUARTERLY TRENDS IN NORTH KOREA. Text in Korean. 1997. q.
Published by: Korea Institute for National Unification, 535-353 Suyu 6-dong, Kangbuk-ku, Seoul, 142-076, Korea, S.

R A A S. (Reports on Asian and African Studies) see *LINGUISTICS*

RECHERCHES D'ARCHEOLOGIE, DE PHILOLOGIE ET D'HISTOIRE. see *ARCHAEOLOGY*

RECORDS OF CIVILIZATION, SOURCES AND STUDIES. see *HISTORY*

RELIGIONS IN THE GRAECO-ROMAN WORLD. see *RELIGIONS AND THEOLOGY*

950 HKG ISSN 0377-3515
PL2658.E1
➤ **RENDITIONS**; a Chinese-English translation magazine. Text in Chinese. 1973. s-a. HKD 150 domestic; USD 28 foreign to individuals; HKD 45 foreign to institutions (effective 2005). adv. bk.rev. bibl.; illus. Index. reprints avail. **Document type:** *Journal, Academic/Scholarly.* **Description:** Offers top China scholars, students, other specialists and general readers worldwide a rich variety of Chinese literary works from classical to modern poetry, prose, fiction and drama.
Related titles: E-mail ed.; Fax ed.
Indexed: ArtHuCI, BAS, CurCont, MLA, MLA-IB.
Published by: Chinese University of Hong Kong, Research Centre for Translation, Sha Tin, New Territories, Hong Kong. TEL 852-26097407, FAX 852-26035110, TELEX 50301-CUHK-HX, renditions@cuhk.edu.hk, rct@cuhk.edu.hk, http://www.renditions.org/renditions/index.html, http://www.cuhk.edu.hk/rct/index.html. Eds. Ms. Audrey Heijns, Dr. Eva Hung. Adv. contact Mrs. Cecilia Ip. B&W page USD 280; trim 5.88 x 8.75. Circ: 1,000 (paid); 500 (controlled). **Dist by:** Tai Yip Art Book Centre, 1 F., Hong Kong Museum of Art, 10 Salisbury Rd, Ocowloon, Tsim Sha Tsui, Kowloon, Hong Kong. TEL 852-2732-2088, FAX 852-2312-1208; **Dist. in Australia by:** China Books, 2nd Fl, 234 Swanston St, Melbourne, VIC 3000, Australia. TEL 61-03-9663-882, FAX 61-03-9663-8822, info@chinabooks.com.au, http://www.chinabooks.com.au; **Dist. in the US by:** Cheng & Tsui Co., 25 West St, Boston, MA 02111-1268. TEL 617-426-6074, FAX 617-426-3669, service@cheng-tsui.com, http://www.cheng-tsui.com.

492.7 EGY
REPERTOIRE CHRONOLOGIQUE D'EPIGRAPHIE ARABE. Text in French. 1931. irreg., latest vol.18, 1991. price varies. back issues avail. **Document type:** *Monographic series.*
Published by: Institut Francais d'Archeologie Orientale du Caire, Kasr el-Aini, 37 Sharia Sheikh Aly Youssef, Mounira, P O Box 11562, Cairo, Egypt. TEL 20-2-3571622, FAX 20-2-3544635, mcmichel@fao.egnet.net, bph@ritsec3.com.eg. **Dist. by:** Boustany's Publishing House, 29 Faggalah St, Cairo 11271, Egypt. TEL 20-2-5195315, FAX 20-2-4177915.

956 BEL ISSN 1142-2831
DS41
RES ORIENTALES. Text in French. 1989. a., latest vol.9, 1996. price varies. back issues avail. **Document type:** *Monographic series, Academic/Scholarly.* **Description:** Discusses topics and research in oriental and middle-eastern studies.
Published by: (Groupe d'Etudes pour la Civilisation du Moyen-Orient), Peeters Publishers, Bondgenotenlaan 153, Leuven, 3000, Belgium. TEL 32-16-235170, FAX 32-16-228500, http://www.peeters-leuven.be. Ed. R Gyeselen.

951.9 KOR ISSN 1229-0076
DS901
REVIEW OF KOREAN STUDIES. Text in Multiple languages. 1998. s-a. USD 75 (effective 2004). back issues avail.
Published by: Academy of Korean Studies, 50 Unjung-dong, Pundang-gu, Songnam, Kyonggi 463-791, Korea, S. TEL 82-31-7098111, FAX 82-31-7094168, review@aks.ac.kr, http://review.aks.ac.kr, http://www.aks.ac.kr. Ed. Kim Keong-il.

REVISTA AFRICA Y MEDIO ORIENTE. see *GENERAL INTEREST PERIODICALS—Africa*

956 FRA
PJ3103
REVUE D'ASSYRIOLOGIE. Text in French. 1884. s-a. EUR 75 domestic; EUR 80 foreign (effective 2005). reprints avail. **Document type:** *Journal, Academic/Scholarly.*
Formerly (until 2004): Revue d'Assyriologie et d'Archeologie Orientale (0373-6032)
Related titles: Microfiche ed.: (from IDC).
Indexed: BibLing, DIP, IBSS, IBZ, MEA&I, OTA, PCI, RASB, RI-1, RI-2.
—IE. **CCC.**
Published by: Presses Universitaires de France, 6 Avenue Reille, Paris, 75685 Cedex 14, France. TEL 33-1-58103100, FAX 33-1-58103182, revues@puf.com, http://www.puf.com.

REVUE DE QUMRAN. see *RELIGIONS AND THEOLOGY*

REVUE D'EGYPTOLOGIE. see *ARCHAEOLOGY*

REVUE DES ETUDES ARMENIENNES. NOUVELLE SERIE. see *HISTORY—History Of The Near East*

297 FRA ISSN 0336-156X
BP1
REVUE DES ETUDES ISLAMIQUES. Text in French. 1927. 2/yr. abstr.; charts. back issues avail.; reprints avail. **Document type:** *Academic/Scholarly.* **Description:** Cultural, sociological and historical studies of Islamic world.
Supersedes (1906-1926): Revue du Monde Musulman
Related titles: Microfiche ed.: (from IDC).
Indexed: BibInd, BibLing, EI, IBR, IPB, MLA, MLA-IB, PCI, RASB.
Published by: Librairie Orientaliste Paul Geuthner, 12 rue Vavin, Paris, 75006, France. TEL 33-1-46-34-71-30, FAX 33-1-43-29-75-64. Ed. D Sourdel.

950 CHN ISSN 1004-2458
RIBEN WENTI YANJIU/JOURNAL OF JAPANESE STUDIES. Text in Chinese. q. **Document type:** *Academic/Scholarly.*
Related titles: Online - full text ed.: (from East View Information Services).
Published by: Hebei Daxue/Hebei University, 1 Hezuolu Rd, Baoding, Hebei 071002, China. TEL 86-312-5079413, FAX 86-312-5022648. Ed. Hanwen Sun. Circ: 1,000.

950 ITA ISSN 0392-4866
PJ6 CODEN: BUMVA4
RIVISTA DEGLI STUDI ORIENTALI. Text in English, French, German, Italian, Spanish. 1907. q. EUR 150 domestic; EUR 350 foreign (effective 2004). adv. bk.rev. bibl. reprints avail. **Document type:** *Journal, Academic/Scholarly.* **Description:** Covers all fields of Oriental studies, from the ancient Near East to modern Japan.
Related titles: Microfiche ed.: (from IDC).
Indexed: BAS, BibLing, DIP, IBR, IBZ, IZBG, MLA, MLA-IB, NTA, OTA, PerIslam, RASB, RI-1, RI-2.
—IE.
Published by: (Universita degli Studi di Roma, Dipartimento di Studi Orientali), Istituti Editoriali e Poligrafici Internazionali (Subsidiary of: Libra Web), Via Giosue' Carducci, 60, Ghezzano - La Fontina, PI 56010, Italy. TEL 39-050-878066, FAX 39-050-878732, iepi@iepi.it, http://www.libraweb.net/riviste.php?chiave=38, http://www.iepi.it. Circ: 300.

950 POL ISSN 0080-3545
ROCZNIK ORIENTALISTYCZNY/YEARBOOK OF ORIENTAL STUDIES. Text in English, French, German, Polish, Russian. 1914. irreg., latest vol.52, 1999. price varies. **Document type:** *Academic/Scholarly.*
Indexed: AmH&L, BAS, BibInd, BibLing, DIP, HistAb, IBR, IBZ, IndIslam, MLA, MLA-IB, PCI, RASB.
Published by: (Polska Akademia Nauk, Komitet Nauk Orientalistycznych), Wydawnictwo Naukowe P W N SA/Polish Scientific Publishers P W N, ul Miodowa 10, Warsaw, 00251, Poland. TEL 48-22-6954181, FAX 48-22-6954288, ksiegarnia@pwn.pl, http://en.pwn.pl. Circ: 470.

951 GBR
ROUTLEDGE STUDIES IN CHINA IN TRANSITION. Text in English. 1996. irreg., latest vol.11, 2001, Aug. price varies. **Document type:** *Monographic series, Academic/Scholarly.* **Description:** Participates in the intellectual developments by focusing on social, political and cultural change in the China of the 1990s and beyond.
—BLDSC (8026.519250).
Published by: Routledge (Subsidiary of: Taylor & Francis Group), 4 Park Square, Milton Park, Abingdon, Oxon OX14 4RN, United Kingdom. TEL 44-1235-828600, FAX 44-1235-829000, info@routledge.co.uk, http://www.tandf.co.uk, http://www.routledge.co.uk. Ed. David Goodman.

950 HKG ISSN 0085-5774
DS1
ROYAL ASIATIC SOCIETY. HONG KONG BRANCH. JOURNAL. Text in English. 1961. a., latest vol.41, 2001. HKD 5,650 combined subscription to members for vols.1-41 & indexes (effective 2003); price varies per issue. bk.rev. cum.index: vols. 1-10, 11-20. back issues avail.; reprints avail. **Document type:** *Journal, Academic/Scholarly.* **Description:** Specializes in Hong Kong and South China studies, especially local history, social anthropology, and natural history.
Indexed: AICP, AmH&L, BAS, HistAb, MLA-IB.
Published by: Royal Asiatic Society, Hong Kong Branch, GPO Box 3864, Hong Kong, Hong Kong. membership@royalasiaticsociety.org.hk, http://www.royalasiaticsociety.org.hk. Ed. Peter Halliday. Circ: 1,000.

950 GBR ISSN 1356-1863
AS122
➤ **ROYAL ASIATIC SOCIETY. JOURNAL.** Variant title: Journal of the Royal Asiatic Society. Text in English. 1827; N.S. 1865; N.S. 1991 (3rd). 3/yr. GBP 98 to institutions; USD 163 in North America to institutions; GBP 104 combined subscription to institutions print & online eds.; USD 174 combined subscription in North America to institutions print & online eds. (effective 2006). adv. bk.rev. illus. index. back issues avail.; reprint service avail. from SCH. **Document type:** *Journal, Academic/Scholarly.* **Description:** Covers Asian languages, literatures, history, archaeology, arts, philosophies and religions.
Former titles (until 1991): Royal Asiatic Society of Great Britain and Ireland. Journal (0035-869X); Formerly (until 1835): Royal Asiatic Society of Great Britain and Ireland. Transactions (0950-4737); Incorporates: Society of Biblical Archaeology. Proceedings
Related titles: Microfiche ed.: (from BHP, IDC); Online - full text ed.: ISSN 1474-0591. GBP 89 to institutions; USD 148 in North America to institutions (effective 2006) (from EBSCO Publishing, O C L C Online Computer Library Center, Inc., Swets Information Services).
Indexed: AICP, ASCA, AmH&L, ArtHuCI, BAS, BibLing, BrHumI, CurCont, DIP, HistAb, IBR, IBSS, IBZ, IndIslam, MEA&I, MLA-IB, NumL, PCI, RASB, RI-1, RI-2, SFA.
—BLDSC (4853.810000), IDS, IE, Infotrieve. **CCC.**
Published by: (Royal Asiatic Society of Great Britain and Ireland), Cambridge University Press, The Edinburgh Bldg, Shaftesbury Rd, Cambridge, CB2 2RU, United Kingdom. TEL 44-1223-312393, FAX 44-1223-315052, journals@cambridge.org, http://www.cup.cam.ac.uk/. Ed. Sarah Ansari. R&P Linda Nicol TEL 44-1223-325757. Adv. contact Rebecca Curtis TEL 44-1223-325757. **Subscr. to:** Cambridge University Press, 100 Brook Hill Dr, West Nyack, NY 10994. TEL 845-353-7500, FAX 845-353-4141, journals_subscriptions@cup.org

➤ **RTAM.** see *LINGUISTICS*

950 FRA ISSN 1144-5726
SAHAND; a Persian journal of political & cultural studies. Text in French. 1984. q. **Document type:** *Academic/Scholarly.*
Address: B.P. 931 Bienvenue, Paris, Cedex 15 75519, France. Ed. R Sharifi.

950 IND
SAMBODHI. Text in English, Gujarati, Hindi, Sanskrit. 1972. q. INR 320. bk.rev. **Document type:** *Academic/Scholarly.*
Published by: Lalbhai Dalpatbhai Institute of Indology, Near Gujarat University, P.O. Navarangpura, Ahmedabad, Gujarat 380 009, India. TEL 91-79-442463. Circ: 500.

SANAL TURKOLOJI ARASTIRMALARI DERGISI/VIRTUAL JOURNAL OF TURKOLOGY RESEARCHES. see *LINGUISTICS*

950 DEU ISSN 0940-0265
SANTAG; Arbeiten und Untersuchungen zur Keilschriftkunde. Text in German. 1990. irreg., latest vol.7, 2002. price varies. **Document type:** *Monographic series, Academic/Scholarly.*
Published by: Harrassowitz Verlag, Taunusstr 14, Wiesbaden, 65183, Germany. TEL 49-611-5300, FAX 49-611-530570, verlag@harrassowitz.de, http://www.harrassowitz.de. Eds. Karl Hecker, Walter Sommerfeld. R&P Michael Langfeld. Adv. contact Robert Gietz.

954 GBR ISSN 0141-0156
SCHOOL OF ORIENTAL AND AFRICAN STUDIES. COLLECTED PAPERS ON SOUTH ASIA. Text in English. 1978. irreg. price varies. adv. **Document type:** *Monographic series.*
—BLDSC (3306.490000).
Published by: (University of London, University of London, School of Oriental and African Studies), Curzon Press Ltd., 15 The Quadrant, 6-8 Church Rd, Richmond, Surrey TW9 1BP, United Kingdom. Ed. Peter Robb. Pub. M Campbell.

950 CHE ISSN 0172-3375
SCHWEIZER ASIATISCHE STUDIEN. Text in German. 1980. irreg., latest vol.31, 1998. CHF 81, USD 57.95. **Document type:** *Monographic series, Academic/Scholarly.* **Description:** Disseminates research and studies of Asian culture, art, history and religion.
Indexed: MLA-IB.
Published by: Verlag Peter Lang AG, Hochfeldstr. 32, Postfach 746, Bern 9, 3000, Switzerland. TEL 41-31-3061717, FAX 41-31-3061727, langwerbung@datacomm.ch, info@peterlang.com, http://www.peterlang.ch, http://www.peterlang.com.

950 CHE ISSN 0171-7391
SCHWEIZER ASIATISCHE STUDIEN. STUDIENHEFTE. Text in German. 1978. irreg., latest vol.15, 1997. CHF 39, USD 31.95. **Document type:** *Academic/Scholarly.* **Description:** Disseminates research and studies of Asian culture, art, history, and religion.
Published by: Verlag Peter Lang AG, Hochfeldstr. 32, Postfach 746, Bern 9, 3000, Switzerland. TEL 41-31-3061717, FAX 41-31-3061727, langwerbung@datacomm.ch, info@peterlang.com, http://www.peterlang.ch, http://www.peterlang.com.

SCRIPTA MEDITERRANEA. see *HISTORY—History Of The Near East*

SEMAIAN. see *HISTORY—History Of Asia*

950 DNK ISSN 0905-9717
DS1
SEMIRAMIS. Text in Danish. 1990. a. DKK 125 per issue (effective 2003). back issues avail. **Document type:** *Monographic series, Academic/Scholarly.*
Published by: (Orientalsk Forum/Oriental Forum), Syddansk Universitetsforlag/University Press of Southern Denmark, Campusvej 55, Odense M, 5230, Denmark. TEL 45-66-157999, FAX 45-66-158126, press@forlag.sdu.dk, http://www.universitypress.dk.

SEMITIC STUDY SERIES; new series. see *LINGUISTICS*

951.9 KOR ISSN 1225-0201
DS901
SEOUL JOURNAL OF KOREAN STUDIES. Text in English. 1988. a. KRW 8,000 domestic; USD 20 foreign (effective 2000). **Document type:** *Academic/Scholarly.*
Indexed: BAS.
Published by: Seoul National University, Institute of Korean Studies, Seoul, 151742, Korea, S. TEL 02-888-5833, FAX 02-871-7244, hanyon@chollian.net, hanyon@hitel.net. Ed. Ryong-geun Lee.

SHAMAN; journal of the International Society for Shamanistic Research. see *ALTERNATIVE MEDICINE*

950 DEU ISSN 0941-8415
SHAMANICA MANCHURICA COLLECTA. Text in German. 1992. irreg., latest vol.6, 1998. price varies. **Document type:** *Monographic series, Academic/Scholarly.*
Published by: Harrassowitz Verlag, Taunusstr 14, Wiesbaden, 65183, Germany. TEL 49-611-5300, FAX 49-611-530570, verlag@harrassowitz.de, http://www.harrassowitz.de. Ed. Giovanni Stary. R&P Michael Langfeld. Adv. contact Robert Gietz.

953 ESP ISSN 0213-3482
SHARQ AL-ANDALUS. Text in Spanish, Catalan. 1984. a.
—CINDOC.
Published by: Centro de Estudios Mujedares (Subsidiary of: Instituto de Estudios Turolenses), Apdo. de Correos 77, Teruel, 44080, Spain. estudios.turolenses@trl.servicom.es, http://www.ua.es/dfint/arabe/revista.htm. Ed. Maria Jesus Rubiera Mata.

950 IND
SHREYE; international research quarterly. Text in English, Hindi. 1971. q. free to members. adv. bk.rev. **Document type:** *Academic/Scholarly.*
Published by: Bharatiya Sahityakar Sangh, Guru Gavind Singh Marg, 51-1 New Market, New Delhi, 110 005, India. TEL 11-5725707. Ed. Dr. Mohan Lal Srivastava. Circ: 1,000.

951 JPN ISSN 0495-9930
SHUKAN TOYOGAKU. Abbreviated title: Chinese and Oriental Studies. Text in Japanese. 1959. s-a. **Document type:** *Journal, Academic/Scholarly.*
Published by: Chugoku Bunshitetsu Kenkyukai/Society for the Study of Chinese Literature, History and Philosophy, Tohoku University, Faculty of Arts and Letters, Aoba-ku, Kawauchi 27-1, Sendai, 980-8576, Japan. TEL 81-22-2176002, FAX 81-22-2176086, http://www.sal.tohoku.ac.jp/index-j.html.

SINICA LEIDENSIA. see *HISTORY—History Of Asia*

951 DEU ISSN 0170-3706
SINOLOGICA COLONIENSIA; Ostasiatische Beitraege der Universitaet zu Koeln. Text in German. 1972. irreg., latest vol.20, 1998. price varies. **Document type:** *Monographic series, Academic/Scholarly.*
Published by: (Universitaet zu Koeln), Franz Steiner Verlag Stuttgart GmbH, Birkenwaldstr 44, Stuttgart, 70191, Germany. TEL 49-711-25820, FAX 49-711-2582390, franz.steiner.verlag@t-online.de, http://www.steiner-verlag.de. Ed. Martin Gimm.

950 FRA ISSN 0183-6080
DJK1
SLOVO. Text in French. 1979. a. price varies. **Document type:** *Academic/Scholarly.* **Description:** Studies the culture and civilization of the people occupying the Soviet territory.
Indexed: BHA, BibLing, IBSS.
Published by: Institut National des Langues et Civilisations Orientales (INALCO), 2 rue de Lille, Paris, Cedex 7 75343, France. TEL 33-01-49264274, FAX 33-01-49264299, http://www.inalco.fr.

SOCIETE FRANCAISE D'EGYPTOLOGIE. BULLETIN. see *ARCHAEOLOGY*

951 895.1 TWN ISSN 1027-1163
SOOCHOW JOURNAL OF CHINESE STUDIES. Key Title: Dongwu Chungwen Xuebao. Text in Chinese. 1995. a. USD 15. **Document type:** *Academic/Scholarly.* **Description:** Covers Chinese studies and Chinese literature.
Published by: Soochow University, Wai Shuang Hsi, Shih Lin, Taipei, Taiwan. FAX 886-2-8838555, tch@www.scu.edu.tw.

950 GBR ISSN 0262-7280
DS331
➤ **SOUTH ASIA RESEARCH.** Text in English. 1980. 3/yr. GBP 173, USD 303 to institutions; GBP 180, USD 315 combined subscription to institutions print & online eds. (effective 2006). bk.rev. back issues avail. **Document type:** *Journal, Academic/Scholarly.* **Description:** Constitutes an interdisciplinary journal concerned with history, ecology, anthropology, languages and literatures, legal systems and religions of South Asia.
Related titles: Microfiche ed.; Online - full text ed.: ISSN 1741-3141. GBP 171, USD 300 to institutions (effective 2006) (from EBSCO Publishing, O C L C Online Computer Library Center, Inc., Sage Publications, Inc., Swets Information Services).
Indexed: ABM, AmH&L, BAS, ESPM, HistAb, IBSS, MLA-IB, PCI, PSA, PerIslam, RDA, RiskAb, SociolAb.
—BLDSC (8348.584000), IE, Infotrieve, ingenta. **CCC.**
Published by: (University of London, University of London, School of Oriental and African Studies), Sage Publications Ltd. (Subsidiary of: Sage Publications, Inc.), 1 Oliver's Yard, 55 City Rd, London, EC1 1SP, United Kingdom. TEL 44-20-73248500, FAX 44-20-73248600, info@sagepub.co.uk, http://www.sagepub.co.uk/journal.aspx?pid=105785. Ed. Werner F Menski. Circ: 500. **Subscr. in the Americas to:** Sage Publications, Inc., 2455 Teller Rd, Thousand Oaks, CA 91320. TEL 805-499-0721, FAX 805-499-0871, journals@sagepub.com; **Subscr. to:** Scientific Publishers, 5-A New Pali Rd., Near Hotel Taj Hari Mahal, PO Box 91, Jodhpur, Rajasthan 342 003, India.

950 IND ISSN 0970-3764
➤ **SOUTH ASIAN SOCIAL SCIENTIST.** Text in English. 1985. s-a. USD 15 to individuals; USD 23 to institutions. adv. bk.rev. **Document type:** *Academic/Scholarly.* **Description:** Offers a forum for discussions between researchers and scholars on the theoretical and empirical on various aspects of the social sciences.
Indexed: BAS.
Published by: South Asian Social Scientists Association, Department of Anthropology, University of Madras, Chennai, Tamil Nadu 600 005, India. TEL 568778, TELEX 41-6376-UNOM-IN. Ed. N Subba Reddy. Circ: 325.

950 954 IND ISSN 0038-285X
DS335
SOUTH ASIAN STUDIES. Text in English. 1965. s-a. INR 60, USD 72. bk.rev. bibl.
Indexed: AmH&L, BAS, DIP, IBR, IPSA, RASB.
Published by: University of Rajasthan, South Asian Studies Centre, Research Centre Building, Jaipur, Rajasthan 302 004, India. Ed. Dr. Ramakaut.

954 DEU ISSN 0584-3170
SOUTH ASIAN STUDIES. Text in English. irreg., latest vol.38, 2001. price varies. **Document type:** *Monographic series, Academic/Scholarly.*
Indexed: PerIslam.
Published by: (Universitaet Heidelberg, Suedasien Institut, New Delhi IND), Franz Steiner Verlag Stuttgart GmbH, Birkenwaldstr 44, Stuttgart, 70191, Germany. TEL 49-711-25820, FAX 49-711-2582390, franz.steiner.verlag@t-online.de, http://www.steiner-verlag.de. R&P Sabine Koerner.

950 DEU ISSN 0945-9286
SOUTH CHINA AND MARITIME ASIA. Text in English. 1994. irreg., latest vol.10, 2001. price varies. **Document type:** *Monographic series, Academic/Scholarly.*
Published by: Harrassowitz Verlag, Taunusstr 14, Wiesbaden, 65183, Germany. TEL 49-611-5300, FAX 49-611-530570, verlag@harrassowitz.de, http://www.harrassowitz.de. Ed. Roderich Ptak. R&P Michael Langfeld. Adv. contact Robert Gietz.

959 USA
➤ **SOUTHEAST ASIA PAPERS.** Text in English. 1973. irreg. (1-2/yr.). bibl. back issues avail. **Document type:** *Monographic series, Academic/Scholarly.* **Description:** Publishes research on Southeast Asia and the Pacific islands, as well as translations of contemporary Southeast Asian literature.
Formerly: Southeast Asian Studies Working Paper Series
Indexed: BAS, HRIR, SeedAb.
Published by: University of Hawaii at Manoa, Center for Southeast Asian Studies, c/o Program Coordinator, 1890 East West Rd, Moore Hall 416, Honolulu, HI 96822. TEL 808-956-2688, FAX 808-956-2682, cseas@hawaii.edu, http://www2.hawaii.edu/shops/southeastasia. Circ: 150.

959 USA
SOUTHEAST ASIA PROGRAM SERIES; monographs, translations, bibliographies. Text in English. 1986. irreg., latest vol.24, 1998. price varies. adv. back issues avail. **Document type:** *Monographic series.* **Description:** Explores the culture and history of Southeast Asia.
Published by: Cornell University, Southeast Asia Program, 640 Stewart Ave, Ithaca, NY 14850. TEL 877-865-2432, FAX 607-255-7534, http://www.einaudi.cornell.edu:591/SEAPpubs. Ed. Deborah Homsher. R&P, Adv. contact David J Stotz. **Subscr. to:** S E A P Publications, Cornell University, E Hill Plaza, Ithaca, NY 14850.

950 USA
SOUTHEAST ASIA SERIES. Text in English.
—BLDSC (7741.556600).
Published by: Ohio University, Center for International Studies, Scott Quadrangle, Athens, OH 45701.

SOUTHEAST ASIAN LANGUAGE TEXT SERIES. see *LINGUISTICS*

950 USA ISSN 1083-074X
DS1
➤ **SOUTHEAST REVIEW OF ASIAN STUDIES.** Text in English. 1979. a. USD 15 membership (effective 2005). adv. **Document type:** *Academic/Scholarly.*
Supersedes (in 1994, vol.16): Association for Asian Studies. Southeast Conference. Annals (0883-8909)
Published by: Association for Asian Studies, Inc., Southeast Conference, c/o Avinash C Maheshwary, South Asia Collection, Duke University Library, Durham, NC 27708-0195. TEL 919-660-5841, FAX 919-684-2855, dmetraux@mbc.edu, acm@mail.lib.duke.edu. Ed. Daniel Metraux. Circ: 200.

950 SCG ISSN 0354-2742
SRPSKA AKADEMIJA NAUKA I UMETNOSTI. ZBORNIK ZA ORIJENTALNE STUDIJE/ACADEMIE SERBE DES SCIENCES ET DES ARTS. RECUEIL D'ETUDES ORIENTALES. Text in Serbo-Croatian. 1992. irreg.
Published by: Srpska Akademija Nauka i Umetnosti/Serbian Academy of Arts and Sciences, Knez Mihailova 35, Belgrade, 11000. TEL 381-11-3342400, FAX 381-11-182825, SASApres@bib.sanu.ac.yu, http://www.sanu.ac.yu.

950 USA ISSN 1550-767X
DS501
STANFORD JOURNAL OF EAST ASIAN AFFAIRS. Abbreviated title: S J E A A. Text in English. 2001 (Spr.). s-a.
Published by: Stanford University, Center for East Asian Studies, Bldg 50, Stanford, CA 94305. http://www.stanford.edu/dept/CEAS/.

STATE ARCHIVES OF ASSYRIA CUNEIFORM TEXTS; the standard Babylonian epic of Anzu. see *HISTORY—History Of The Near East*

950 SWE ISSN 0284-883X
THE STOCKHOLM JOURNAL OF EAST ASIAN STUDIES. Text in English. 1988. a., latest vol.13, 2003. USD 20 (effective 2005). back issues avail. **Document type:** *Monographic series, Academic/Scholarly.*
Published by: Stockholm University, Center for Pacific Asia Studies, Kraeftriket, Hus 4, University of Stockholm, Stockholm, 10691, Sweden. TEL 46-8-162897, FAX 46-8-168810, cpas@orient.su.se, http://www.orient.su.se/cpas/publications.html.

950 SWE ISSN 0585-3559
STOCKHOLM ORIENTAL STUDIES. Text in Multiple languages. 1961. irreg., latest vol.17, 2002. price varies. back issues avail. **Document type:** *Monographic series, Academic/Scholarly.*
Related titles: ◆ Series of: Acta Universitatis Stockholmiensis. ISSN 0346-6418.
Published by: Stockholms Universitet, Acta Universitatis Stockholmiensis, c/o Stockholms Universitetsbibliotek, Universitetsvaegen 10, Stockholm, 10691, Sweden. FAX 46-8-157776. **Dist. by:** Almqvist & Wiksell International, P O Box 7634, Stockholm 10394, Sweden. TEL 46-8-6136100, FAX 46-8-242543, info@akademibokhandeln.se, http://www.akademibokhandeln.se.

950 ITA
STUDI ORIENTALI. Text in Italian. 1943. irreg., latest vol.15, 1997. price varies. **Document type:** *Monographic series, Academic/Scholarly.*
Indexed: BibLing.
Published by: (Universita degli Studi di Roma, Dipartimento di Studi Orientali), Bardi Editore, Via Piave 7, Rome, 00187, Italy. TEL 39-06-4817656, FAX 39-06-48912574, bardied@tin.it, http://www.bardieditore.com.

340.09 NLD ISSN 0169-8168
➤ **STUDIA ET DOCUMENTA AD IURA ORIENTIS ANTIQUI PERTINENTIA.** Text in Multiple languages. 1936. irreg., latest vol.11, 1984. price varies. **Document type:** *Monographic series, Academic/Scholarly.* **Description:** Scholarly studies of law and related issues in the ancient Near East.
Published by: (Stichting voor het Niet-Westers Recht), Brill Academic Publishers, PO Box 9000, Leiden, 2300 PA, Netherlands. TEL 31-71-53-53-500, FAX 31-71-53-17-532, cs@brill.nl, http://www.brill.nl. R&P Elizabeth Venekamp. **Subscr. in N. America to:** PO Box 605, Herndon, VA 20172. TEL 703-661-1585, 800-337-9255, FAX 703-661-1501, cs@brillusa.com. **Distr. outside N. America by:** c/o Turpin Distribution, Stratton Business Park, Pegasus Drive, Biggleswade, BEDFORDSHIRE SG 18 8TQ, United Kingdom. TEL 44-1767-604-954, FAX 44-1767-601-640, brill@turpin-distribution.com.

955 BEL ISSN 0221-5004
➤ **STUDIA IRANICA.** Text in French, English, German. 1971. s-a. EUR 55 (effective 2006). adv. bk.rev. bibl.; illus.; stat. Index. **Document type:** *Journal, Academic/Scholarly.*
Related titles: Online - full text ed.: (from EBSCO Publishing); ◆ Supplement(s): Abstracta Iranica. ISSN 0240-8910; ◆ Studia Iranica. Cahiers. ISSN 0993-8699.
Indexed: BibLing, DIP, IBR, IBSS, IBZ, MLA, MLA-IB, NumL, PCI. —Infotrieve.
Published by: (Association pour l'Avancement des Etudes Iraniennes), Peeters Publishers, Bondgenotenlaan 153, Leuven, 3000, Belgium. TEL 32-16-235170, FAX 32-16-228500, http://poj.peeters-leuven.be/content.php?url=journal&journal_code=SI, http://www.peeters-leuven.be. Ed. M Bazin.

955 BEL ISSN 0993-8699
➤ **STUDIA IRANICA. CAHIERS.** Variant title: Cahiers de "Studia Iranica". Text in English, French. 1982. irreg., latest vol.29, 1998. price varies. bibl.; illus. back issues avail. **Document type:** *Monographic series, Academic/Scholarly.*
Related titles: ◆ Supplement to: Studia Iranica. ISSN 0221-5004.
Published by: (Association pour l'Avancement des Etudes Iraniennes), Peeters Publishers, Bondgenotenlaan 153, Leuven, 3000, Belgium. TEL 32-16-235170, FAX 32-16-228500, peeters@peeters-leuven.be, http://www.peeters-leuven.be. Eds. M Bazin, Ph Gignoux.

950 DEU ISSN 0943-7908
STUDIA MELITENSIA. Text in German. 1994. irreg. price varies. **Document type:** *Monographic series, Academic/Scholarly.*
Published by: Harrassowitz Verlag, Taunusstr 14, Wiesbaden, 65183, Germany. TEL 49-611-5300, FAX 49-611-530570, verlag@harrassowitz.de, http://www.harrassowitz.de. Ed. Alexander Borg. R&P Michael Langfeld. Adv. contact Robert Gietz.

950 FIN ISSN 0039-3282
➤ **STUDIA ORIENTALIA.** Text in English, French, German. 1925. irreg., latest vol.94, 2001. price varies. bk.rev. charts; illus. cum.index. **Document type:** *Monographic series, Academic/Scholarly.*
Indexed: BAS, BibLing, IBR, IBSS, IndIslam, RASB.
Published by: Finnish Oriental Society, c/o University of Helsinki, Institute for Asian and African Studies, PL 59, Helsinki, 00014, Finland. TEL 358-191-22224, FAX 358-191-22094, juha.laulainen@helsinki.fi. Ed. Juha Lauleinen. Circ: 700.

950 SWE ISSN 0281-4528
➤ **STUDIA ORIENTALIA LUNDENSIA.** Text in English. 1983. irreg., latest vol.4, 1990. price varies. **Document type:** *Monographic series, Academic/Scholarly.*
Indexed: L&LBA, SOPODA.
Published by: Lunds Universitet, Department of Middle Eastern Languages/Lund University, Bredgatan 4, Lund, 22221, Sweden. TEL 46-46-222 00 00, FAX 46-46-222 44 28.

➤ **STUDIA PHOENICIA.** see *HISTORY—History Of The Near East*

950 ITA
➤ **STUDIA POHL.** Text in Multiple languages. 1967. irreg., latest vol.15, 1990. price varies. **Document type:** *Academic/Scholarly.* **Description:** Studies concerning the ancient Near East.
Published by: Pontificio Istituto Biblico/Pontifical Biblical Institute, Via della Pilotta 25, Rome, 00187, Italy. TEL 39-06-695261, FAX 39-06-695266151, pibsegr@pib.ur, http://www.pib.urbe.it.

950 POL ISSN 1425-1973
STUDIA TURCOLOGICA CRACOVIENSIA/CRACOW TURKOLOGICAL STUDIES. Text in Polish. 1995. irreg., latest vol.3, 1997. USD 29 per vol. foreign (effective 2003). **Document type:** *Monographic series, Academic/Scholarly.*
Published by: (Uniwersytet Jagiellonski, Instytut Filologii Orientalnej), Wydawnictwo Uniwersytetu Jagiellonskiego/Jagiellonian University Press, ul Grodzka 26, Krakow, 31044, Poland. TEL 48-12-4312364, FAX 48-12-4301995, wydaw@if.uj.edu.pl, http://www.wuj.pl. Ed. Marek Stachowski.

950 930.1 DEU
STUDIEN ZUM ALTAEGYPTISCHEN TOTENBUCH. Text in German. 1998. irreg., latest vol.8, 2004. price varies. **Document type:** *Monographic series, Academic/Scholarly.*
Formerly: Studien zum Altaegyptischen Studienbuch (1430-9726)
Published by: Harrassowitz Verlag, Taunusstr 14, Wiesbaden, 65183, Germany. TEL 49-611-530555, FAX 49-611-530559, verlag@harrassowitz.de. Eds. Heinz Josef Thissen, Ursula Roessler Koehler. R&P Michael Langfeld. Adv. contact Robert Gietz.

STUDIEN ZUR OSTASIATISCHEN SCHRIFTKUNST. see *ART*

STUDIES IN ANCIENT ORIENTAL CIVILIZATION. see *HISTORY—History Of The Near East*

306 950 NLD ISSN 1380-782X
➤ **STUDIES IN ASIAN ART AND ARCHAEOLOGY.** Text in Dutch. 1969. irreg., latest vol.24, 2002. price varies. back issues avail. **Document type:** *Monographic series, Academic/Scholarly.* **Description:** Scholarly studies of subjects relating to the arts, religions and cultures of Asian societies in prehistoric, ancient and modern periods, with emphasis on art, sculpture and architecture.
Formerly (until vol.16, 1994): Studies in South Asian Culture (0169-9865)
—BLDSC (8489.546000).
Published by: Brill Academic Publishers, PO Box 9000, Leiden, 2300 PA, Netherlands. TEL 31-71-53-53-500, FAX 31-71-53-17-532, cs@brill.nl, http://www.brill.nl. Ed. Jan Fonten. R&P Elizabeth Venekamp.

➤ **STUDIES IN ASIAN THOUGHT AND RELIGION.** see *RELIGIONS AND THEOLOGY—Other Denominations And Sects*

950 390 USA ISSN 0081-8321
STUDIES IN ORIENTAL CULTURE. Text in English. 1966. irreg., latest vol.21, 1988. **Document type:** *Monographic series.*
Published by: Columbia University Press, 61 W 62nd St, New York, NY 10023. TEL 212-666-1000. Ed. Kate Witterberg. R&P Lisa Simmars.

950 USA ISSN 1554-3749
DS1
➤ **STUDIES ON ASIA (ONLINE).** Text in English. 1960. s-a. free (effective 2005). illus. **Document type:** *Journal, Academic/Scholarly.* **Description:** Covers any and all aspects of Asia, past and present, including translations, poetry, prose, and pedagogy.
Formerly (until 2004): Studies on Asia (Print) (0081-881X)
Media: Online - full content.
Published by: Michigan State University, Asian Studies Center, 301 International Center, East Lansing, MI 48824. TEL 517-353-1680, FAX 517-432-2659, asiansc@msu.edu, http://www.isp.msu.edu/studiesonasia/.

954 GBR ISSN 0142-6028
STUDIES ON ASIAN TOPICS. Text in English. 1980. irreg. price varies.
Indexed: RASB.
Published by: (Nordisk Institut for Asienstudier/Nordic Institute of Asian Studies DNK), Curzon Press Ltd., 15 The Quadrant, 6-8 Church Rd, Richmond, Surrey TW9 1BP, United Kingdom.

950 USA
STUDIES ON EAST ASIA. Text in English. 1971. irreg., latest vol.20, 1997. price varies. **Document type:** *Monographic series.*
Formerly (until vol.13): Western Washington State College. Program in East Asian Studies. Occasional Papers
Published by: Western Washington University, Center for East Asian Studies, Bellingham, WA 98225-9056. TEL 206-650-3448. Ed. Edward H Kaplan.

959 USA
STUDIES ON SOUTHEAST ASIA. Text in English. 1985. irreg. price varies. adv. back issues avail. **Document type:** *Monographic series.* **Description:** Explores the politics, culture, and history of Southeast Asia.
Published by: Cornell University, Southeast Asia Program, 640 Stewart Ave, Ithaca, NY 14850. TEL 877-865-2432, FAX 607-255-7534, http://www.einaudi.cornell.edu:591/SEAPpubs. Ed. Deborah Homsher. R&P, Adv. contact David J Stotz. **Subscr. to:** S E A P Publications, Cornell University, E Hill Plaza, Ithaca, NY 14850.

SUI YUAN WEN HSIEN. see *ETHNIC INTERESTS*

T A A S A REVIEW; journal of the Asian Arts Society of Australia. see *ART*

950 613.7 USA ISSN 0730-1049
GV504
T'AI CHI; the leading international magazine of T'ai Chi Ch'uan. Text in English. 1977. bi-m. USD 20 domestic; USD 30 foreign; USD 3.95 newsstand/cover domestic; USD 6.25 newsstand/cover foreign (effective 2004). adv. bk.rev. back issues avail. **Document type:** *Magazine, Consumer.* **Description:** Takes a comparative look at the various styles of T'ai Chi Ch'uan practice, Qigong, and Chinese philosophy and health principles.
Published by: Wayfarer Publications, PO Box 39938, Los Angeles, CA 90039. TEL 328-665-7773, FAX 328-665-1627, taichi@tai-chi.com, http://www.tai-chi.com. Ed., Pub., R&P, Adv. contact Marvin Smalheiser. Circ: 30,000 (paid).

950 GBR ISSN 1355-8307
TAI CHI & ALTERNATIVE HEALTH. Text in English. q. GBP 12 domestic; GBP 16 in Europe; GBP 20 elsewhere; GBP 2.70 newsstand/cover; USD 6 newsstand/cover in United States (effective 2001). **Document type:** *Magazine, Consumer.* **Description:** Features in-depth articles on all aspects of Tai Chi Chuan - history, theory, martial applications as well as interviews with leading Tai Chi masters.
Address: PO Box 6404, London, E18 1EX, United Kingdom. TEL 44-20-85029307, FAX 44-20-85517553, tcah@taichiwl.demon.co.uk, http://www.taichiwl.demon.co.uk. **Dist. by:** International Publishers Direct, 27500 Riverview Center Blvd, Bonita Springs, FL 34134. TEL 858-320-4563, FAX 858-677-3220.

950 TWN
▼ **TAIWAN JOURNAL OF EAST ASIAN STUDIES.** Text in English. 2004 (Jun.). s-a.
Indexed: AmH&L, HistAb.
Published by: National Taiwan University, No.1, Section 4, Roosevelt Rd, Taipei, 106, Taiwan.

950 USA ISSN 1048-2342
TAIWAN STUDIES NEWSLETTER. Text in English. 1982. s-a. USD 10.
Published by: Taiwan Studies Group, Asian Studies Center, Michigan State University, E, Lansing, MI 48824. TEL 517-353-1680, FAX 517-336-2659. Ed. Jack Williams. **Co-sponsors:** China and Inner Asia Council; Association for Asian Studies, Inc.

951.01 USA ISSN 0737-5034
DS749.3
➤ **T'ANG STUDIES.** Text in English. 1982. a. USD 30 to individuals; USD 40 to institutions; USD 15 to students (effective 2005). adv. reprint service avail. from SCH. **Document type:** *Journal, Academic/Scholarly.* **Description:** Surveys scholarly articles relating to China's T'ang Dynasty (618-907).
Indexed: BAS.
Published by: T'ang Studies Society, c/o David B Honey, Dept of Asian & Near Eastern Languages, Brigham Young Univ, 1031 E JKHB, Provo, UT 84602-6117. TEL 801-378-3443, FAX 801-378-5866, david_honey@byu.edu, http://www.colorado.edu/ealc/tss/Tang.htm. Ed. Paul W Kroll. R&P, Adv. contact David Honey. Circ: 250.

➤ **TAXILA INSTITUTE OF ASIAN CIVILIZATIONS. QUAID-I-AZAM UNIVERSITY. PUBLICATIONS.** see *HISTORY—History Of Asia*

➤ **TEL AVIV UNIVERSITY. INSTITUTE OF ARCHAEOLOGY. MONOGRAPH SERIES.** see *ARCHAEOLOGY*

➤ **TEL AVIV UNIVERSITY. INSTITUTE OF ARCHAEOLOGY. OCCASIONAL PUBLICATIONS.** see *ARCHAEOLOGY*

951.5 IND ISSN 0970-5368
DS785.A1
➤ **THE TIBET JOURNAL;** a publication of Tibetian studies. Text in English. 1975. q. INR 260 domestic; USD 25 foreign; INR 70 newsstand/cover domestic; USD 7.50 newsstand/cover foreign (effective 2005). adv. bk.rev.; film rev.; rec.rev. bibl.; charts; illus. cum.index: 1975-1994. 100 p./no. 1 cols./p.; back issues avail.; reprints avail. **Document type:** *Journal, Academic/Scholarly.* **Description:** Devoted to the presentation of scholarly and general interest articles on Tibetan culture and civilization by Tibetans and non-Tibetans.
Related titles: Diskette ed.; Online - full text ed.: (from EBSCO Publishing).
Indexed: BAS, DIP, IBR, IBSS, RASB, RILM.
—BLDSC (8820.637000), IE, ingenta.

A

Published by: Library of Tibetan Works and Archives, Gangchen Kyishong, Dharamsala, Himachal Pradesh 176 215, India. TEL 91-1892-22467, FAX 91-1892-23723, ltwa@ndf.vsnl.net.in, http://www.lib.virginia.edu/area-studies/Tibet/Tserials/TibetJour/tibJour.html, http://www.lib.virginia.edu/area-studies/Tibet/Tserials/Tibet.Jour/tibJour.html. Ed. Thupten K Rikey. Pub. Achok Rindoche. adv.: B&W page USD 35. Circ: 1,000. **Subscr. to:** Biblia Impex Pvt. Ltd., 2-18 Ansari Rd, New Delhi 110 002, India.

950 GBR ISSN 0735-1364
DS785.A1
TIBET SOCIETY JOURNAL. Text in English, French, German, Tibetan. 1981. q. GBP 15 domestic membership; GBP 25 foreign membership (effective 1999). bk.rev. **Document type:** *Academic/Scholarly.* **Description:** Devoted to all areas of research on Tibet and regions influenced by Tibetan culture, with the aim of raising public awareness of the threat to the culture and civil liberties by the occupying Chinese government.
Indexed: BAS.
—**CCC.**
Published by: Tibet Society,, 114 Tottenham Court Rd, London, Mddx W1P 9HL, United Kingdom. members@tibet-society.org.uk, http://www.tibet-society.org. Circ: 450.

958 DEU ISSN 0935-7505
TIBETAN AND INDO-TIBETAN STUDIES. Text in German. 1989. irreg., latest vol.8, 1999. price varies. **Document type:** *Monographic series, Academic/Scholarly.*
Indexed: MLA-IB.
Published by: (University of Hamburg, Institute for the Culture and History of India and Tibet), Franz Steiner Verlag Stuttgart GmbH, Birkenwaldstr 44, Stuttgart, 70191, Germany. TEL 49-711-25820, FAX 49-711-2582390, franz.steiner.verlag@t-online.de, http://www.steiner-verlag.de. R&P Sabine Koerner.

950 297 JPN ISSN 0304-2448
DS701
TOHO GAKUHO/DONGFANG XUEBAO. Text in Japanese; Text occasionally in Chinese. 1931. a. illus. **Document type:** *Academic/Scholarly.* **Description:** Covers humanities in East Asia.
Indexed: AmH&L, HistAb, RASB.
—BLDSC (5027.410000), IE, ingenta.
Published by: Kyoto University, Institute for Research in Humanities/Kyoto Daigaku Jinbun Kagaku Kenkyusho, Ushinomiya-cho, Yoshida, Sakyo-ku, Kyoto-shi, 606-8501, Japan. Ed. Shosin Kuwayama.

900 JPN ISSN 0495-7199
DS734.97.E18
TOHOGAKU/EASTERN STUDIES. Text in Japanese; Abstracts in English. 1951. s-a. JPY 4,000 (effective 2002). bk.rev. 224 p./no.; back issues avail. **Description:** Publishes articles on oriental studies, covering such fields as history, religion, literature, linguistics, art and archaeology.
Indexed: MLA, MLA-IB, RASB, RILM.
Published by: Toho Gakkai/Institute of Eastern Culture, 4-1 Nishi-Kanda 2-chome, Chiyoda-ku, Tokyo, 101-0065, Japan. TEL 81-3-3262-7221, FAX 81-3-3262-7227, tohogakkai@mc.nextlink.ne.jp. R&P Hiroshi Yanase.

951.9 KOR ISSN 1225-6064
JQ1721.A1
TONG'IL YEON'GU NONCONG/KOREAN JOURNAL OF UNIFICATION STUDIES. Text in Korean. 1992. s-a.
Published by: Korea Institute for National Unification, 535-353 Suyu 6-dong, Kangbuk-ku, Seoul, 142-076, Korea, S.

950 NLD ISSN 0082-5433
DS501
➤ **T'OUNG PAO**; international journal of Chinese studies. Text mainly in English; Text occasionally in French, German. 1890. s-a. USD 99 in the Americas to individuals; EUR 80 elsewhere to individuals; USD 299 combined subscription in the Americas to institutions print & online eds.; EUR 240 combined subscription elsewhere to institutions print & online eds. (effective 2006). bk.rev. abstr.; illus. index, cum.index: vols.38-55, 1948-1969. back issues avail.; reprint service avail. from PSC. **Document type:** *Journal, Academic/Scholarly.* **Description:** Publishes articles on topics in art, history, linguistics, literature, history of science, and other fields furthering knowledge of traditional Chinese civilization.
Related titles: Microfilm ed.: (from BHP); Online - full text ed.: ISSN 1568-5322. USD 269 in the Americas to institutions; EUR 216 elsewhere to institutions (effective 2006) (from Chadwyck-Healey Inc., EBSCO Publishing, Gale Group, IngentaConnect, Kluwer Online, O C L C Online Computer Library Center, Inc., Springer LINK, Swets Information Services); ♦ Supplement(s): T'oung Pao. Monographies. ISSN 0169-832X.
Indexed: AIAP, ASCA, AmH&L, ArtHuCI, BAS, BibLing, CurCont, DIP, HistAb, IBR, IBZ, IndIslam, MLA, MLA-IB, PCI, RASB, RILM.
—IDS, IE, Infotrieve. **CCC.**

Published by: Brill Academic Publishers, PO Box 9000, Leiden, 2300 PA, Netherlands. TEL 31-71-53-53500, FAX 31-71-53-17532, cs@brill.nl, http://www.brill.nl/m_catalogue_sub6_id7547.htm. Eds. B ter Haar, P E Will. R&P Elizabeth Venekamp. **Subscr. in N. America to:** PO Box 605, Herndon, VA 20172. TEL 703-661-1585, 800-337-9255, FAX 703-661-1501, cs@brillusa.com. **Distr. outside N. Amerca by:** c/o Turpin Distribution, Stratton Business Park, Pegasus Drive, Biggleswade, BEDFORDSHIRE SG 18 8TQ, United Kingdom. TEL 44-1767-604-954, FAX 44-1767-601-640, brill@turpin-distribution.com.

951 NLD ISSN 0169-832X
➤ **T'OUNG PAO. MONOGRAPHIES.** Text in English, French, German. 1954. irreg., latest vol.16, 1989. price varies. back issues avail. **Document type:** *Monographic series, Academic/Scholarly.* **Description:** Scholarly translations of Chinese historical texts, and critical studies on specific issues in the arts, literature, social, cultural, religious and political history of ancient and modern China.
Related titles: ♦ Supplement to: T'oung Pao. ISSN 0082-5433.
—**CCC.**
Published by: Brill Academic Publishers, PO Box 9000, Leiden, 2300 PA, Netherlands. TEL 31-71-53-53-500, FAX 31-71-53-17-532, cs@brillusa.com, cs@brill.nl, http://www.brill.nl/product_id7549.htm. R&P Elizabeth Venekamp. **Subscr. in N. America to:** PO Box 605, Herndon, VA 20172. TEL 703-661-1585, 800-337-9255, FAX 703-661-1501, cs@brillusa.com. **Distr. outside N. America by:** c/o Turpin Distribution, Stratton Business Park, Pegasus Drive, Biggleswade, BEDFORDSHIRE SG 18 8TQ, United Kingdom. TEL 44-1767-604-954, FAX 44-1767-601-640, brill@turpin-distribution.com.

➤ **TRANSLATIONS FROM THE ASIAN CLASSICS.** see *LITERATURE*

800 950 ARG ISSN 1666-7050
TRANSOXIANA; journal libre de estudios orientales. Text in Spanish. 2000. irreg. free (effective 2005). **Document type:** *Journal, Academic/Scholarly.*
Media: Online - full text.
Published by: Universidad del Salvador, Escuela de Estudios Orientales http://www.transoxiana.com.ar/.

950 DEU ISSN 0938-0051
TRAVAUX DU GROUPE DE RECHERCHES ET D'ETUDES SEMITIQUES ANCIENNES. Text in German. 1982. irreg., latest vol.5, 1998. price varies. **Document type:** *Monographic series, Academic/Scholarly.*
Published by: Harrassowitz Verlag, Taunusstr 14, Wiesbaden, 65183, Germany. TEL 49-611-5300, FAX 49-611-530570, verlag@harrassowitz.de, http://www.harrassowitz.de. R&P Michael Langfeld. Adv. contact Robert Gietz.

950 DEU ISSN 0946-0349
TUNGUSO SIBIRICA. Text in German. 1995. irreg., latest vol.12, 2003. price varies. **Document type:** *Monographic series, Academic/Scholarly.*
Published by: Harrassowitz Verlag, Taunusstr 14, Wiesbaden, 65183, Germany. TEL 49-611-5300, FAX 49-611-530570, verlag@harrassowitz.de, http://www.harrassowitz.de. Eds. Hans Rainer Kaempfe, Michael Weiers. R&P Michael Langfeld. Adv. contact Robert Gietz.

956.1 494 BEL ISSN 0082-6847
DR401
➤ **TURCICA**; revue d'etudes turques: peuples, langues, cultures, etats. Text in English, French, German. 1968. a., latest vol.35, 2003. EUR 55 (effective 2006). adv. bk.rev. illus. index. **Document type:** *Journal, Academic/Scholarly.* **Description:** Studies the peoples, languages, cultures, and political entities of ancient Turkic peoples.
Related titles: Online - full text ed.: (from EBSCO Publishing); ♦ Supplement(s): Collection Turcica; ♦ Cahiers Turcica. ISSN 0337-3371.
Indexed: AmH&L, BibLing, DIP, HistAb, IBR, IBSS, IBZ, IndIslam.
—BLDSC (9071.840000).
Published by: (Association pour le Developpement des Etudes Turques FRA, Universite de Strasbourg II (Marc Bloch/Sciences Humaines) FRA), Peeters Publishers, Bondgenotenlaan 153, Leuven, 3000, Belgium. TEL 32-16-235170, FAX 32-16-228500, peeters@peeters-leuven.be, http://poj.peeters-leuven.be/content.php?url=journal&journal_code=TURC, http://www.peeters-leuven.be. Ed. Irene Melikoff. **Co-sponsor:** Institut Francais d'Etudes Anatoliennes a Istanbul/Fransiz Anadolu Arastirmalari Enstitusu.

950 DEU ISSN 0177-4743
TURCOLOGICA. Text in German. 1977. irreg., latest vol.55, 2003. price varies. **Document type:** *Monographic series, Academic/Scholarly.*
Formerly (until 1985): Frankfurter Tuerkologische Arbeitsmittel (0342-1082)
Indexed: MLA-IB.
Published by: Harrassowitz Verlag, Taunusstr 14, Wiesbaden, 65183, Germany. TEL 49-611-5300, FAX 49-611-530570, verlag@harrassowitz.de, http://www.harrassowitz.de. Ed. Lars Johanson. R&P Michael Langfeld. Adv. contact Robert Gietz.

956 TUR ISSN 0041-4239
TURK KULTURU. Text in Turkish. 1962. m. USD 25 (effective 1999). bk.rev.; film rev.; play rev. abstr.; bibl.; charts; illus.; stat. index. **Document type:** *Academic/Scholarly.*
Related titles: Microfiche ed.: (from IDC).
Indexed: Perlslam, RASB.
Published by: Turk Kulturunu Arastirma Enstitusu/Turkish Cultural Research Institute, 17 Sok. 38, Bahcelievler, Ankara, Turkey. Ed. Sukru Elcin. Circ: 5,000.

956.1 TUR ISSN 0564-5093
AP95.T8
TURK KULTURU ARASTIRMALARI. Text in Turkish. 1964. a. USD 10 (effective 1999). bk.rev.; film rev.; play rev. abstr.; bibl.; charts; illus.; stat. index. **Document type:** *Academic/Scholarly.*
Indexed: Perlslam.
Published by: Turk Kulturunu Arastirma Enstitusu/Turkish Cultural Research Institute, 17 Sok. 38, Bahcelievler, Ankara, Turkey. Ed. Sukru Elcin. Circ: 1,000.

TURK TARIH KURUMU. BELGELER. see *HISTORY—History Of The Near East*

TURK TARIH KURUMU. BELLETEN. see *HISTORY—History Of The Near East*

TURKIC LANGUAGES. see *LINGUISTICS*

956 DEU ISSN 0934-4403
TURKOLOGIE UND TUERKEIKUNDE. Text in German. 1988. irreg., latest vol.6, 2003. price varies. **Document type:** *Monographic series, Academic/Scholarly.*
Published by: Harrassowitz Verlag, Taunusstr 14, Wiesbaden, 65183, Germany. TEL 49-611-5300, FAX 49-611-530570, verlag@harrassowitz.de, http://www.harrassowitz.de. Ed. Klaus Kreisa. R&P Michael Langfeld. Adv. contact Robert Gietz.

TURKOLOGISCHER ANZEIGER/TURKOLOGY ANNUAL. see *ASIAN STUDIES—Abstracting, Bibliographies, Statistics*

UNIVERSITE CATHOLIQUE DE LOUVAIN. INSTITUT ORIENTALISTE. PUBLICATIONS. see *HISTORY—History Of Asia*

955 200 LBN
UNIVERSITE SAINT-JOSEPH. FACULTE DES LETTRES ET DES SCIENCES HUMAINES. RECHERCHES. SERIE B: ORIENT CHRETIEN. Text in French. 1956; N.S. 1971. irreg. price varies. **Document type:** *Monographic series, Academic/Scholarly.*
Indexed: BibLing.
Published by: (Universite Saint-Joseph, Faculte des Lettres et des Sciences Humaines, Universite Saint Joseph), Dar el-Machreq S.A.R.L., Ashrafieh, P O Box 166778, Beirut, Lebanon. TEL 961-1-202423, machreq@cyberia.net.lb. Pub. Hechaime Camille.

UNIVERSITY OF CHICAGO ORIENTAL INSTITUTE. PUBLICATIONS. see *HISTORY—History Of The Near East*

950 DNK
➤ **UNIVERSITY OF COPENHAGEN. DEPARTMENT OF ASIAN STUDIES. OCCASIONAL PAPERS.** Text in English. 1988. irreg., latest vol.9, 1992. free (effective 2003). back issues avail. **Document type:** *Monographic series, Academic/Scholarly.*
Formerly: University of Copenhagen. East Asian Institute. Occasional Papers (0903-6822)
Published by: Koebenhavns Universitet, Asian Institutet/Copenhagen University. Department of Asian Studies, Leifsgade 33, Copenhagen S, 2300, Denmark. TEL 45-35-328822, FAX 45-35-328835, asia@hum.ku.dk, http://www.hum.ku.dk/asien/d_publikationer.html. R&P Yoichi Nagashima.

950 HKG ISSN 0378-2689
UNIVERSITY OF HONG KONG. CENTRE OF ASIAN STUDIES. OCCASIONAL PAPERS AND MONOGRAPHS. Key Title: Occasional Papers and Monographs - Centre of Asian Studies. Text in Chinese, English. 1970. irreg., latest vol.140, 1999. price varies. back issues avail. **Document type:** *Monographic series.*
Indexed: ZooRec.
—BLDSC (3106.467000).
Published by: University of Hong Kong, Centre of Asian Studies, Pokfulam Rd, Hong Kong, Hong Kong. TEL 852-2859-2463, FAX 852-2559-3185, casgen@hkucc.hku.hk, http://www.hku.hk/cas/mono.htm. Ed. Wong Siu-Lun.

951 GBR ISSN 0308-6119
UNIVERSITY OF LONDON. CONTEMPORARY CHINA INSTITUTE. RESEARCH NOTES AND STUDIES. Text in English. 1976. irreg., latest vol.12, 1998. GBP 9.50. **Document type:** *Academic/Scholarly.*
—BLDSC (7749.760000).
Published by: University of London, School of Oriental and African Studies, Thornhaugh St, Russell Sq, London, WC1H 0XG, United Kingdom. TEL 44-171-637-2388, FAX 44-171-436-3844. R&P Martin Daly. **Co-sponsor:** Contemporary China Institute.

▼ *new title* ➤ *refereed* ✶ *unverified* ♦ *full entry avail.*

UNIVERSITY OF LONDON. SCHOOL OF ORIENTAL AND AFRICAN STUDIES. BULLETIN. see *HUMANITIES: COMPREHENSIVE WORKS*

915.4 IND ISSN 0304-8233
DS339.9.I4
UNIVERSITY OF RAJASTHAN. SOUTH ASIAN STUDIES CENTRE. ANNUAL REPORT. Text in English. 1966. irreg., latest 1973.
Published by: University of Rajasthan, South Asian Studies Centre, Research Centre Building, Jaipur, Rajasthan 302 004, India.

UNIVERZITA KOMENSKEHO. FILOZOFICKA FAKULTA. ZBORNIK: GRAECOLATINA ET ORIENTALIA. see *CLASSICAL STUDIES*

VARENDRA RESEARCH MUSEUM. JOURNAL. see *MUSEUMS AND ART GALLERIES*

956 936 TUR ISSN 1013-9559
➤ **VARIA ANTIQUA.** Text in French. 1987. irreg., latest vol.9, 1997. price varies. illus. back issues avail. **Document type:** *Monographic series, Academic/Scholarly.* **Description:** Explores cutural artifacts of ancient Anatolia, now modern-day Turkey.
Published by: Institut Francais d'Etudes Anatoliennes a Istanbul/Fransiz Anadolu Arastirmalari Enstitusu, Palais de France, Nuru Ziya Sokak, 22, PK 54, Beyoglu, Istanbul 80072, Turkey. TEL 90-212-244-1717, 90-212-244-3327, FAX 90-212-252-8091, ifeai@superonline.com, http://www.geocities.com/Athens/Styx/7236/publint.html.

956 TUR
➤ **VARIA TURCICA.** Text in French. 1985. irreg., latest vol.32, 1998. price varies. illus. back issues avail. **Document type:** *Monographic series, Academic/Scholarly.* **Description:** Analyzes social, sociopolitical, and political issues in modern Turkish history.
Published by: Institut Francais d'Etudes Anatoliennes a Istanbul/Fransiz Anadolu Arastirmalari Enstitusu, Palais de France, Nuru Ziya Sokak, 22, PK 54, Beyoglu, Istanbul 80072, Turkey. TEL 90-212-244-1717, 90-212-244-3327, FAX 90-212-252-8091, ifeai@superonline.com, http://www.geocities.com/Athens/Styx/7236/publint.html.

890 967 MUS
➤ **VASANT.** Text in Hindi. 1978. q. MUR 80, USD 6 (effective 2003). bk.rev. back issues avail. **Document type:** *Magazine, Academic/Scholarly.* **Description:** Provides a representation of Hindi literature being written in Mauritius consolidating a geographical identity while keeping in touch with trends of world Hindi literature.
Published by: Mahatma Gandhi Institute, Moka, Mauritius. TEL 230-4331277, FAX 230-4332235. Ed. Dr. B Jugasing. Circ: 500.

950 DEU ISSN 0506-7936
VERZEICHNIS DER ORIENTALISCHEN HANDSCHRIFTEN IN DEUTSCHLAND. Short title: V O H D. Text in English, German. 1961. irreg., latest vol.37, 1999. price varies. **Document type:** *Monographic series, Academic/Scholarly.*
Published by: (Deutsche Morgenlaendische Gesellschaft), Franz Steiner Verlag Stuttgart GmbH, Birkenwaldstr 44, Stuttgart, 70191, Germany. TEL 49-711-25820, FAX 49-711-2582390, franz.steiner.verlag@t-online.de, http://www.steiner-verlag.de. Ed. Hartmut Ortwin Feistel. R&P Sabine Koerner.

950 DEU ISSN 0506-7944
VERZEICHNIS DER ORIENTALISCHEN HANDSCHRIFTEN IN DEUTSCHLAND. SUPPLEMENTBAENDE. Abbreviated title: V O H D Supplementbaende. Text in English, German. 1963. irreg., latest vol.35, 1995. price varies. **Document type:** *Monographic series, Academic/Scholarly.*
Published by: (Deutsche Morgenlaendische Gesellschaft), Franz Steiner Verlag Stuttgart GmbH, Birkenwaldstr 44, Stuttgart, 70191, Germany. TEL 49-711-25820, FAX 49-711-2582390, franz.steiner.verlag@t-online.de, http://www.steiner-verlag.de. Ed. Hartmut Ortwin Feistel. R&P Sabine Koerner.

VESTNIK DREVNEI ISTORII/JOURNAL OF ANCIENT HISTORY. see *HISTORY*

VIETNAMESE STUDIES. see *HISTORY—History Of Asia*

954 IND
VISHVA VICHARAMALA. Text in Hindi, Sanskrit. irreg. price varies.
Published by: Vishveshvaranand Vedic Research Institute, P.O. Sadhu Ashram, Hoshiarpur, Punjab 146 021, India. Ed. S Bhaskaran Nair.

954 IND
VISHVESHVARANAND VEDIC RESEARCH INSTITUTE. RESEARCH AND GENERAL PUBLICATIONS. Text in English, Hindi, Sanskrit. 1921. irreg. price varies.
Published by: Vishveshvaranand Vedic Research Institute, P.O. Sadhu Ashram, Hoshiarpur, Punjab 146 021, India.

VOICES FROM ASIA. see *LITERATURE—Poetry*

VOORAZIATISCH-EGYPTISCH GENOOTSCHAP "EX ORIENTE LUX". JAARBERICHT; annuaire de la Societe Orientale Neerlandaise "Ex Oriente Lux". see *HISTORY—History Of The Near East*

VOORAZIATISCH-EGYPTISCH GENOOTSCHAP "EX ORIENTE LUX". MEDEDELINGEN EN VERHANDELINGEN. see *HISTORY—History Of The Near East*

950 RUS ISSN 1681-7559
DS1
➤ **VOSTOCHNAYA KOLLEKTSIYA.** Text in Russian. 2000. bi-m. RUR 308 (effective 2004). adv. bk.rev. illus.; abstr.; bibl.; maps. 160 p./no.; **Document type:** *Journal, Academic/Scholarly.* **Description:** Covers the history and peoples of the East, both within Russia and abroad, cultural masterpieces, traditions, customs, and life today. Also includes perspectives on development.
Published by: (Rossiiskaya Gosudarstvennaya Biblioteka/Russian State Library), Idatel'stvo Rossiiskoi Gosudarstvennoi Biblioteki Pashkov Dom/Russian State Library, Vozdizhenka 3/5, Moscow, 101000, Russian Federation. TEL 7-095-2033731, FAX 7-095-2039390, pashkov_dom@rsl.ru, http://www.rsl.ru/pub.asp. Ed. Aleksandr Poleshchuk. Circ: 800 (paid); 1,000 (controlled). **Dist. by:** East View Information Services, 3020 Harbor Ln. N., Minneapolis, MN 55447. TEL 800-477-1005, FAX 800-800-3839, eastview@eastview.com, http://www.eastview.com.

950 960 RUS ISSN 0869-1908
DS1
VOSTOK; Afro-aziatskie obshchestva - istoria i sovremennost'. Text in Russian; Summaries in English; Contents page in English, French. 1955. bi-m. RUR 250 for 6 mos. domestic; USD 153 foreign (effective 2004). bk.rev. bibl.; charts; illus. index. **Document type:** *Journal, Academic/Scholarly.*
Former titles (until 1991): Narodny Azii i Afriki (0130-6995); (1959-1961): Problemy Vostokovedeniya
Related titles: Microfiche ed.: (from EVP); Online - full text ed.: (from East View Information Services).
Indexed: AmH&L, BAS, BibLing, HistAb, IBR, ILD, IPSA, IndIslam, NumL, RASB, RefZh, WAE&RSA.
—East View, KNAW.
Published by: (Rossiiskaya Akademiya Nauk, Institut Vostokovedeniya), Izdatel'stvo Nauka, Profsoyuznaya ul 90, Moscow, 117864, Russian Federation. TEL 7-095-3347151, FAX 7-095-4202220, secret@naukaran.ru, http://www.naukaran.ru. Circ: 3,700. **Dist. by:** M K - Periodica, ul Gilyarovskogo 39, Moscow 129110, Russian Federation. TEL 7-095-2845008, FAX 7-095-2813798, info@periodicals.ru, http://www.mkniga.ru. **Co-sponsor:** Rossiiskaya Akademiya Nauk, Institut Afriki.

962 EGY ISSN 0257-4098
VOYAGEURS OCCIDENTAUX EN EGYPTE. Key Title: Collection des Voyageurs Occidentaux en Egypte. Text in French. 1970. irreg., latest vol.26, 1990. price varies. back issues avail. **Document type:** *Monographic series.* **Description:** Publishes early travel accounts and studies of early European travellers in Egypt, up to and including the Napoleonic invasion.
Published by: Institut Francais d'Archeologie Orientale du Caire, Kasr el-Aini, 37 Sharia Sheikh Aly Youssef, Mounira, P O Box 11562, Cairo, Egypt. TEL 20-2-3571622, FAX 20-2-3544635, http://www.ifao.egnet.net. **Dist. by:** Boustany's Publishing House, 29 Faggalah St, Cairo 11271, Egypt. TEL 20-2-5915315, FAX 20-2-4177915.

WACANA. see *EDUCATION—Higher Education*

WAQA'I DAWLAT AL-IMARAT/EMIRATES EVENTS. see *HISTORY—History Of The Near East*

WASHINGTON - JAPAN JOURNAL. see *POLITICAL SCIENCE—International Relations*

AL-WATHA'IQ AL-FILASTINIYYAH/PALESTINIAN DOCUMENTS. see *HISTORY—History Of The Near East*

WATHA'IQ DAWLAT AL-IMARAT/EMIRATES DOCUMENTS. see *HISTORY—History Of The Near East*

AL-WATHIQA. see *HISTORY—History Of The Near East*

WENSHI ZHISHI/KNOWLEDGE OF LITERATURE AND HISTORY. see *SOCIAL SCIENCES: COMPREHENSIVE WORKS*

956 AUT ISSN 0084-0076
PJ5
WIENER ZEITSCHRIFT FUER DIE KUNDE DES MORGENLANDES. Text in English, French, German, Italian. 1887. a. EUR 52.30 (effective 2005). adv. bk.rev. reprint service avail. from SCH. **Document type:** *Journal, Academic/Scholarly.*
Indexed: BAS, BibLing, DIP, IBR, IBZ, MLA, MLA-IB, PerIslam, RASB, RI-1.
Published by: Universitaet Wien, Institut fuer Orientalistik, Spitalgasse 2, Hof 4, Vienna, W 1090, Austria. Michaela.Weszeli@univie.ac.at, http://www.univie.ac.at/orientalistik/Wzkm.html. Circ: 400.

WOMEN IN ASIA PUBLICATION SERIES. see *WOMEN'S STUDIES*

XIANGQI KURIER; Chinesisches Schach. see *SPORTS AND GAMES*

951 CHN ISSN 1001-5558
DS730
➤ **XIBEI MINZU YANJIU/NORTHWEST MINORITIES RESEARCH.** Text in Chinese; Summaries in English. 1986. q. CNY 54 domestic (effective 2003 & 2004). bk.rev. bibl. 208 p./no.; back issues avail. **Document type:** *Journal, Academic/Scholarly.* **Description:** Covers Tibetan, Mongolia, Turkilogy, DunHuang and Tanggut studies.
Related titles: CD-ROM ed.; Online - full text ed.: (from East View Information Services, WanFang Data Corp.).
Published by: Xibei Minzu Xueyuan Shehui Renleixue Minsuxue Xi Yanjiusuo/Department & Institute of Social Anthropology and Folklore, No 1, Xibei Xincun, Lanzhou, Gansu 730030, China. TEL 86-931-8185645, FAX 86-931-8157162, xbmzyj@236.net, http://saga.chinajournal.net.cn, http://www.xbmu.edu.cn/shxx. Eds. Sumin Hao, Ma Jianchun. Pub. Man Ke. R&P Hao Sumin. Adv. contact Aodun Bilig TEL 86-931-8152822. Circ: 1,000 (controlled). **Dist. in US by:** China Books & Periodicals Inc, 360 Swift Ave., Ste. 48, S San Fran, CA 94080-6220. TEL 415-282-2994.

➤ **XIZANG WENXUE/TIBETAN LITERATURE.** see *LITERATURE*

951 CHN ISSN 1000-0003
DS785.A1
XIZANG YANJIU/TIBETAN STUDIES. Text in Chinese, Tibetan. 1981. q. (English ed. s-a). USD 24 for Chinese ed.; USD 21 for Tibetan ed.. **Description:** Covers Tibetan politics, economics, history, religion, literature, art, language, medicine, law and archaeology.
Related titles: Online - full text ed.: (from East View Information Services); Chinese ed.; English ed.; Tibetan ed.
Indexed: RILM.
Published by: Xizang Zizhiqu Shehui Kexueyuan/Tibetan Autonomous Region Academy of Social Sciences, Lhasa, Xizang (Tibet) 850000, China. TEL 22638. Ed. Shilai Daoji. **Dist. in US by:** China Books & Periodicals Inc, 360 Swift Ave., Ste. 48, S San Fran, CA 94080-6220. TEL 415-282-2994.

951 CHN ISSN 1003-7942
XUEYU WENHUA/TIBETAN CULTURE. Text in Chinese. 1989. q. CNY 10. adv. **Description:** Features Tibetan customs, arts, religion, ancient relics and tourism.
Related titles: Tibetan ed.
Published by: Xueyu Wenhua Zazhishe, 2 Dolsingar Rd, Lhasa, Xizang (Tibet) 850000, China. TEL 22024, FAX 26689. Ed. Gyamco. Adv. contact Zhong Zhang. Circ: 7,000. **Dist. overseas by:** China International Book Trading Corp, 35 Chegongzhuang Xilu, Haidian District, PO Box 399, Beijing 100044, China.

950 USA ISSN 0513-4501
YALE SOUTHEAST ASIA STUDIES. MONOGRAPH SERIES. Text in English. 1961. irreg., latest vol.43, 1996. adv. reprint service avail. from PQC. **Document type:** *Monographic series.*
—IE.
Published by: Yale University, Council on Southeast Asia Studies, 34 Hillhouse Ave, PO Box 208206, New Haven, CT 06520. TEL 203-432-3431, FAX 203-432-9381. Ed. M K Mansfield.

951 CHN ISSN 1003-7527
YANG GUAN. Text in Chinese. 1979. bi-m. CNY 6. adv. bk.rev. **Description:** Includes literary works, profiles of historical figures, legends, and ancient relics and art works along the Silk Road in Western China.
Published by: (Jiuquan Diqu Wenlian), Yang Guan Zazhishe, Xi Dajie, Jiuquan, Guansu 735000, China. TEL 86-937-2614195. Ed. Zhao Shuming. Circ: 4,000. **Dist. overseas by:** Jiangsu Publications Import & Export Corp., 56 Gao Yun Ling, Nanjing, Jiangsu, China.

YAQEEN INTERNATIONAL. see *RELIGIONS AND THEOLOGY—Islamic*

953 ITA
YEMEN; studi archeologici, storici e filologici sull'Arabia meridionale. Text in Italian. 1992. irreg. **Document type:** *Monographic series.*
Indexed: BibLing.
Published by: Istituto Italiano per l'Africa e l'Oriente, Via Ulisse Aldrovandi 16, Rome, 00197, Italy. TEL 39-06-328551, FAX 39-06-3225348, biblio.dir@isiao.it, http://www.isiao.it. Ed. Alessandro de Maigret.

951.35 CHN ISSN 1001-8913
➤ **YUNNAN MINZU XUEYUAN XUEBAO/YUNNAN INSTITUTE OF NATIONALITIES. JOURNAL.** Text in Chinese. 1983. q. CNY 12 (effective 1996). adv. bk.rev. **Document type:** *Academic/Scholarly.* **Description:** Contains research papers and reports on political science, philosophy, economics, literature, history, and linguistics relating to ethnic groups in Yunnan Province.
Related titles: Online - full text ed.: (from East View Information Services).

Published by: Yunnan Minzu Xueyuan/Yunnan Institute of Nationalities, Lianhua Chi, Kunming, Yunnan 650031, China. TEL 86-871-5154458. Ed. Huikun Huang. Circ: 2,500. **Dist. overseas by:** China International Book Trading Corp, 35 Chegongzhuang Xilu, Haidian District, PO Box 399, Beijing 100044, China.

932 490 DEU ISSN 0044-216X
PJ1004
➤ **ZEITSCHRIFT FUER AEGYPTISCHE SPRACHE UND ALTERTUMSKUNDE.** Text in English, French, German. 1863. 2/yr. EUR 144 domestic; EUR 154 foreign; EUR 64 domestic to students; EUR 70 foreign to students (effective 2005). bk.rev. bibl.; illus. index. **Document type:** *Journal, Academic/Scholarly.* **Description:** Dedicated to the entire field of Egyptology, including Demotic, Coptic and Meroitic studies.
Related titles: Microfiche ed.: (from IDC).
Indexed: ASCA, ArtHuCI, BHA, BibLing, CurCont, IBR, IBZ, PCI, RASB.
—IDS, IE, Infotrieve. **CCC.**
Published by: Akademie Verlag GmbH (Subsidiary of: Oldenbourg Wissenschaftsverlag GmbH), Palisadenstr 40, Berlin, 10243, Germany. TEL 49-30-4220060, FAX 49-30-42200657, info@akademie-verlag.de, http://zaes.akademie-verlag.de, http://www.akademie-verlag.de. Ed. Sebastian Richter.

950 340 DEU ISSN 0948-0587
ZEITSCHRIFT FUER ALTORIENTALISCHE UND BIBLISCHE RECHTSGESCHICHTE. Text in English, French, German. 1995. a. EUR 84 (effective 2006). **Document type:** *Journal, Academic/Scholarly.*
Indexed: DIP, IBR, IBZ, OTA.
—IE, Infotrieve.
Published by: Harrassowitz Verlag, Taunusstr 14, Wiesbaden, 65183, Germany. TEL 49-611-5300, FAX 49-611-530560, verlag@harrassowitz.de, http://www.harrassowitz.de. Ed. Eckart Otto. R&P Michael Langfeld. Adv. contact Robert Gietz.

956 DEU ISSN 0179-4639
ZEITSCHRIFT FUER GESCHICHTE DER ARABISCH-ISLAMISCHEN WISSENSCHAFTEN. Text in Arabic, English, French, German. 1984. a. price varies. bk.rev.
Indexed: BibLing, CCMJ, DIP, IBR, MathR, MathSciNet.
—BLDSC (9463.075500), IE, Infotrieve, ingenta.
Published by: Institut fuer Geschichte der Arabisch-Islamischen Wissenschaften, Beethovenstr 32, Frankfurt Am Main, 60325, Germany. TEL 069-756009-0. Ed. Fuat Sezgin.

956.1 DEU ISSN 0934-0696
HC491
ZEITSCHRIFT FUER TUERKEISTUDIEN✶. Text in German. 2/yr. **Document type:** *Journal, Academic/Scholarly.*
Indexed: DIP, IBR, IBZ, IndIslam, PerIslam.
Published by: Zentrum fuer Tuerkeistudien, Altendorfer Str 3, Essen, 45127, Germany. TEL 49-201-3198-0, FAX 49-201-3198333, zft@uni-essen.de, http://www.zft-online.de.

951 TWN
➤ **ZHONGGUO DALU YANJIU/MAINLAND CHINA STUDIES.** Text in Chinese. 1958. bi-m. USD 39 (effective 2003). adv. charts; illus.; maps; abstr.; bibl.; stat. Index. 100 p./no.; back issues avail.; reprint service avail. from PQC,ISI. **Document type:** *Monographic series, Academic/Scholarly.* **Description:** Specializes in academic analysis of the political, military, foreign policy, economic, cultural, educational and social issues of China.
Former titles: Zhongguo Dalu (0257-9456); Which incorporated (1958-1985): Feiqing Yebao/Chinese Communist Affairs Monthly (0014-9675); (until 1974): Zhongguo Dalu Yanjiu (1017-0251); (until 1971): Zhonggong Dongtai Fenxi (0578-1469); (until 1965): Zhongguo Dalu Yanjiu (1013-2716)
Related titles: Microform ed.: (from PQC); Online - full text ed.
Indexed: RASB.
—BLDSC (5352.323400), IE, ingenta.
Published by: National Chengchi University, Institute of International Relations, 64 Wanshou Road, Wenshan District, Taipei, 116, Taiwan. TEL 886-2-82377277, FAX 886-2-22344919, iir@nccu.edu.tw, http://iir.nccu.edu.tw/english/dirkinde2.htm. Ed. Szu-Yin Ho. R&P, Adv. contact Chia-mei Chuang. Circ: 458 (paid); 1,750 (controlled).

➤ **ZHONGGUO SHEHUI JINGJISHI YANJIU/JOURNAL OF CHINESE SOCIAL AND ECONOMIC HISTORY.** see *HISTORY—History Of Asia*

951 HKG ISSN 1016-4464
ZHONGGUO WENHUA YANJIUSUO XUEBAO/JOURNAL OF CHINESE STUDIES. Text in Chinese, English. 1968; N.S. 2000 (No.9). a., latest no.9, 2000. HKD 300 (effective 2001). bk.rev. abstr.; bibl.; charts; illus. 400 p./no.; back issues avail. **Document type:** *Journal, Academic/Scholarly.* **Description:** Covers Chinese history, literature, philosophy, language, archaeology, human and economic geography and China's relations with the world.
Formerly (until Dec., 1992): Institute of Chinese Studies of the Chinese University of Hong Kong. Journal
Indexed: AmH&L, HistAb.
Published by: (Chinese University of Hong Kong, Institute of Chinese Studies), Zhongwen Daxue Chubanshe/Chinese University Press, The Chinese University of Hong Kong, Shatin, New Territories, Hong Kong. TEL 852-2609-6508, FAX 852-2603-7355, cup@cuhk.edu.hk, http://www.cuhk.edu.hk/cupress/, http://www.chineseupress.com/. Ed., R&P Hok-Lam Chan. Adv. contact Kwok-Fan Chu.

951 CHN ISSN 1002-9060
ZHONGGUO ZANGXUE/CHINA TIBETOLOGY. Text in Chinese. 1988. q. CNY 24 (effective 2004). **Document type:** *Journal, Academic/Scholarly.*
Related titles: Tibetan ed.
Published by: Zhongguo Zangxue Yanjiu Zhongxin, 131, Beisihuan Donglu, Beijing, 100101, China. TEL 86-10-64937928, FAX 86-10-64917619, zhanghong@tibetology.ac.cn, http://www.tibetology.ac.cn. **Dist. in US by:** China Books & Periodicals Inc, 360 Swift Ave., Ste. 48, S San Fran, CA 94080-6220. TEL 415-282-2994; **Dist. by:** China International Book Trading Corp, 35 Chegongzhuang Xilu, Haidian District, PO Box 399, Beijing 100044, China. TEL 86-10-68412045, FAX 86-10-68412023, cibtc@mail.cibtc.com.cn, http://www.cibtc.com.cn.

950 DEU ISSN 0934-6155
ZWISCHEN ORIENT UND OKZIDENT. Text in German. 1988. irreg., latest vol.5, 1998. **Document type:** *Monographic series.*
Published by: (Rueckert Gesellschaft e.V.), Ergon Verlag, Grombuehlstr 7, Wuerzburg, 97080, Germany. TEL 49-931-280084, FAX 49-931-282872, ergon-verlag@t-online.de, service@ergon-verlag.de.

ASIAN STUDIES—Abstracting, Bibliographies, Statistics

ANNUAL EGYPTOLOGICAL BIBLIOGRAPHY/BIBLIOGRAPHIE EGYPTOLOGIQUE ANNUELLE/JAEHRLICHE AEGYPTOLOGISCHE BIBLIOGRAPHIE. see *HISTORY—Abstracting, Bibliographies, Statistics*

016.65 AUS ISSN 1329-9778
DS1
ASIAN STUDIES W W W MONITOR. (World Wide Web) Text in English. 1994. every 10 days. free. illus. back issues avail.; reprints avail. **Document type:** *Journal, Academic/Scholarly.* **Description:** Monitors new Web sites and electronic journals in Asian Studies and provides objective summaries of these resources.
Formerly: What's New in W W W Asian Studies
Media: Online - full text.
Published by: Australian National University, Internet Publications Bureau, Research School of Pacific & Asian Studies, Canberra, ACT 0200, Australia. tmciolek@coombs.anu.edu.au, http://coombs.anu.edu.au/asia-www-monitor.html, http://coombs.anu.edu.au/RSPAS-ipb.html. Ed. T Matthew Ciolek TEL 61-2-61250110.

950 015 IND ISSN 0006-1212
BIBLIOGRAPHIA ASIATICA. Text in English. 1968. m. INR 1,800, USD 250 (effective 2000). abstr.; bibl. index. **Document type:** *Bibliography.*
Related titles: Microform ed.
Indexed: PAIS.
Published by: K.K. Roy (Private) Ltd., 55 Gariahat Rd., P O Box 10210, Kolkata, West Bengal 700 019, India. Ed. K K Roy. R&P M Misra TEL 91-33-475-4872. Circ: 1,600.

950 USA ISSN 1046-8765
Z3001
BIBLIOGRAPHIC GUIDE TO EAST ASIAN STUDIES. Text in English. 1990. a. USD 360 (effective 2005). **Document type:** *Bibliography.* **Description:** Covers China, Hong Kong, Taiwan, North and South Korea, and Japan, with approximately 3500 listings from LCMARC tapes and the Oriental Division of the New York Public Library. Includes publications about East Asia, materials published in any of the relevant countries, and publications in Chinese, Korean, and Japanese (transliterated into Roman letters).
Published by: G.K. Hall & Co. (Subsidiary of: Gale Group), 12 Lunar Dr, Woodbridge, CT 06525. TEL 203-397-2600, 800-444-0799, FAX 203-397-8296, remmel.nunn@gale.com, http://www.galegroup.com/gkhall.

016.951 DEU ISSN 0724-8415
Z3106
BIBLIOGRAPHY OF CHINESE STUDIES; selected articles on China in Chinese, English and German. Text in Chinese, English, German. 1983. a. EUR 14 (effective 2003). bibl. 150 p./no. 2 cols./p.; back issues avail. **Document type:** *Monographic series, Bibliography.*
Published by: Deutsches Uebersee-Institut, Uebersee-Dokumentation, Neuer Jungfernstieg 21, Hamburg, 20354, Germany. TEL 49-40-42825598, FAX 49-40-42825512, dok@duei.de, http://www.duei.de/dok. Ed. Uwe Kotzel. Adv. contact Joerg Joswiak. Circ: 90.

BULLETIN D'ARABE CHRETIEN. BIBLIOGRAPHIE DES AUTEURS ARABES CHRETIENS. see *HISTORY—Abstracting, Bibliographies, Statistics*

950 016 USA ISSN 0008-9044
Z7043
CENTER FOR CHINESE RESEARCH MATERIALS. NEWSLETTER. Text in English. 1968. s-a. free. bibl.; charts. **Document type:** *Newsletter.*
—Linda Hall.
Published by: Center for Chinese Research Materials, PO Box 3090, Oakton, VA 22124. TEL 703-715-2688, FAX 703-715-7913. Ed. Pingfeng Chi. Circ: 1,400.

950 016 USA
CORNELL UNIVERSITY. LIBRARY. JOHN M. ECHOLS COLLECTION ON SOUTHEAST ASIA. ACCESSIONS LIST. Text in English. 1959. q. USD 30 (effective 1999). bibl. back issues avail. **Document type:** *Bibliography.*
Formerly (until 1978): Cornell University. Library. Wason Collection. Southeast Asia Accessions List (0589-7351)
Published by: Cornell University, Kroch Library, Echols Collection, Ithaca, NY 14853. TEL 607-255-4189, FAX 607-255-8438, TELEX WUI-6713054. Ed., R&P Allen Riedy TEL 607-255-8889. Circ: 50 (controlled).

950 016 IND
INDEX ASIA SERIES IN HUMANITIES. Text in English. 1965. irreg. price varies. bk.rev. **Document type:** *Monographic series, Abstract/Index.* **Description:** Cumulative index to writings in journals on all aspects of South Asian and Buddhistic studies as well as bibliographies on specific topics.
Published by: Centre for Asian Dokumentation, K-15, CIT Bldg., Christopher Rd., Kolkata, West Bengal 700 014, India. TEL 2461186. Ed. S Chaudhuri.

950 015 IND ISSN 0019-3852
Z3001
INDEX INDO-ASIATICUS. Text in Bengali, English, Hindi, Sanskrit, Multiple languages. 1968. q. INR 400 in Asia & the Pacific; INR 1,250 elsewhere. adv. bk.rev. bibl. cum.index. **Document type:** *Abstract/Index.* **Description:** Indexes international periodicals of all languages, whose topics relate to the culture of India and ancient Asia.
Published by: Centre for Asian Dokumentation, K-15, CIT Bldg., Christopher Rd., Kolkata, West Bengal 700 014, India. TEL 2461186. Ed. Sibadas Chaudhuri. Circ: 400. **Subscr. to:** Central News Agency, P O Box 374, New Delhi 110 001, India. **Dist. overseas by:** Verlag Otto Harrassowitz, Taunusstr 6, Postfach 2929, Wiesbaden 65019, West Germany.

650 IND
INDEX INTERNATIONALIS INDICUS. Text in English. 1970. triennial. INR 1,000; INR 3,000 foreign (effective 2001). adv. **Document type:** *Abstract/Index.* **Description:** Lists cumulative articles on Indological and Buddhistic studies published in Indian and foreign periodicals.
Published by: Centre for Asian Dokumentation, K-15, CIT Bldg., Christopher Rd., Kolkata, West Bengal 700 014, India. TEL 2461186. Ed. S Chaudhuri. Circ: 500. **Dist. by:** Central News Agency, P O Box 374, New Delhi 110 001, India; Verlag Otto Harrassowitz, Taunusstr 6, Postfach 2929, Wiesbaden 65019, Germany. TEL 0611-530-0, FAX 0611-530570.

959 016 SGP ISSN 0046-984X
INSTITUTE OF SOUTHEAST ASIAN STUDIES. LIBRARY. ACCESSIONS LIST. Text in English. 1968. irreg., latest vol.8, no.14. free. bibl. **Document type:** *Bibliography.*
Media: Duplicated (not offset).
Published by: Institute of Southeast Asian Studies, 30 Heng Mui Keng Terrace, Pasir Panjang, Singapore, 119614, Singapore. libadm1@iseas.edu.sg, http://www.iseas.edu.sg/.

016.9519 KOR
KOREA INSTITUTE FOR NATIONAL UNIFICATION. K I N U RESEARCH ABSTRACTS. Text in English. 1997. irreg.
Published by: Korea Institute for National Unification, 535-353 Suyu 6-dong, Kangbuk-ku, Seoul, 142-076, Korea, S.

011 SAU
MARKAZ AL-MALIK FAISAL LIL-BUHUTH WAL-DIRASAT AL-ISLAMIYYAH. FIHRIS AL-MAKHTUTAT/KING FAISAL CENTER FOR RESEARCH AND ISLAMIC STUDIES. MANUSCRIPT CATALOGUE. Text in Arabic. 1985. irreg. **Document type:** *Bibliography.*
Published by: King Faisal Center for Research and Islamic Studies, P O Box 51049, Riyadh, 11543, Saudi Arabia. TEL 4652255, FAX 4659993, TELEX 205470.

011.75 590 DNK ISSN 1398-1315
NORDIC DIRECTORY OF DISSERTATION PROJECTS IN ASIAN STUDIES. Text in Multiple languages. 1993. biennial. free. **Document type:** *Directory.* **Description:** Lists ongoing and completed Nordic dissertation projects in Asian studies.
Published by: Nordisk Institut for Asienstudier/Nordic Institute of Asian Studies, Leifsgade 33, Copenhagen S, 2300, Denmark. TEL 45-32-54-88-44, FAX 45-32-96-25-30, erik@nias.ku.dk, http://nias.ku.dk. Eds. Erik R Skaaning, Gerald Jackson. Circ: 500.

016.65 AUS ISSN 1440-9127
R S O A S PRINT NEWS. Text in English. 1998. irreg. free. back issues avail. **Document type:** *Bulletin, Bibliography.* **Description:** Announces and summarizes important print and electronic research publications in all areas of Asian studies.
Media: Online - full text.

Published by: (Australian National University, Research School of Pacific & Asian Studies), Coombs Academic Publishing, Canberra, ACT 0200, Australia. TEL 61-2-6249-3269, FAX 61-2-6249-4986, aandrews@coombs.anu.edu.au, http://coombs.anu.edu.au/rspas-print-news.htm. Ed. Ann Andrews. Circ: 630.

016.95   RUS
SOTSIAL'NYE I GUMANITARNYE NAUKI. ZARUBEZHNAYA LITERATURA. VOSTOKOVEDENIE I AFRIKANISTIKA; referativnyi zhurnal. Text in Russian. 1972. q. USD 130 in United States (effective 2004). **Document type:** Abstract/Index. **Description:** Contains abstracts of foreign books devoted to Oriental and African studies acquired lately by INION.
Formerly: Obshchestvennye Nauki za Rubezhom. Vostokovedenie i Afrikanistika (0132-7348)
Indexed: RASB.
—East View.
Published by: Rossiiskaya Akademiya Nauk, Institut Nauchnoi Informatsii po Obshchestvennym Naukam, Nakhimovskii pr-t 51/21, Moscow, 117997, Russian Federation. TEL 7-095-1288930, FAX 7-095-4202261, info@inion.ru, http://www.inion.ru. Ed. S N Kuznetsova. **US dist. addr.:** East View Information Services, 3020 Harbor Ln. N., Minneapolis, MN 55447. TEL 800-477-1005, FAX 800-800-3839, eastview@eastview.com, http://www.eastview.com.

950   AUT   ISSN 0255-5425
Z2831
TURKOLOGISCHER ANZEIGER/TURKOLOGY ANNUAL. Text in English, German, Turkish. 1975. a. back issues avail.
Document type: Bibliography. **Description:** Provides bibliographic information on new publications on Turkish language, literature, and history.
Published by: Universitaet Wien, Institut fuer Orientalistik, Spitalgasse 2, Hof 4, Vienna, W 1090, Austria. TEL 43-1-427743401, FAX 43-1-42779434, Michaela.Weszeli@univie.ac.at, http://www.univie.ac.at/orientalistik/. Circ: 400.

950 016   HKG   ISSN 0441-1900
Z3107.H7
UNIVERSITY OF HONG KONG. CENTRE OF ASIAN STUDIES. BIBLIOGRAPHIES AND RESEARCH GUIDES. Text in Chinese, English. 1970. irreg., latest vol.24, 1987. price varies. back issues avail. **Document type:** Bibliography.
Published by: University of Hong Kong, Centre of Asian Studies, Pokfulam Rd, Hong Kong, Hong Kong. TEL 852-2859-2463, FAX 852-2559-3185, TELEX 71919-CEREB-HX, casgen@hkucc.hku.hk, http://www.hku.hk/cas/. Ed. Frank H H King.

ASTROLOGY

see also NEW AGE PUBLICATIONS

133.5   USA   ISSN 1049-6181
A F A N NEWSLETTER. Text in English. 1988. q. membership.
Document type: Newsletter.
Published by: (Association for Astrological Networking), Matrix Software, 1921 Cambridge Rd., Ann Arbor, MI 48104-3650. TEL 616-796-2483, FAX 616-796-3060. Ed. Gloria Star.

133.5   ITA
ALTRA; rivista trimestrale di astrologia, psicologia, spiritualita. Text in Italian. 1992. q.
Published by: Jupiter Edizioni, Casella Postale 25, San Benedetto, PI 56026, Italy. Ed. Gabriella Verdone.

133.5   USA   ISSN 0002-7529
AMERICAN ASTROLOGY. Text in English. 1933. m. USD 23 (effective 2004). adv. bk.rev. illus. Index. reprints avail.
Document type: Consumer.
Related titles: Microform ed.: (from PQC).
Published by: (American Astrology, Inc.), Starlog Group, Inc., 475 Park Ave S, 7th Fl, New York, NY 10016. TEL 212-689-2830, http://www.starlog.com. Eds. Ken Irving, Lee Chapman. Circ: 185,000.

133.5   USA   ISSN 0516-9550
AMERICAN ASTROLOGY DIGEST. Text in English. 1956. a. USD 2.99 newsstand/cover; CND 4.50 newsstand/cover in Canada. adv. charts; illus.; tr.lit. **Document type:** Consumer.
Description: Publishes in the interest of astrology and its practical application to everyday life.
Published by: (American Astrology, Inc.), Kappa Publishing Group, Inc., J B H Publishing, 6198 Butler Pike., Ste. 200, Blue Bell, PA 19422-2606. TEL 215-643-6385. Eds. Ken Irving, Lee Chapman. R&P Kenneth Irving.

ARIES; journal for the study of western esotericism. see *NEW AGE PUBLICATIONS*

133.5   HRV   ISSN 1332-3474
ASTRA. Text in Croatian. 1995. m. **Document type:** Magazine, Consumer.
Formerly (until 2000): Vas Astrolog (1331-2480)
Published by: A N K H - Centar za Poboljsanje Kvalitete Zivota, Petrova 101, Zagreb, 10000, Croatia. TEL 385-1-226536, FAX 385-1-226536.

133.5   ITA   ISSN 0392-226X
ASTRA. Text in Italian. 1977. m. EUR 34.80 (effective 2005). adv. illus. **Document type:** Magazine, Consumer. **Description:** Covers topics in astrology and offers readers horoscopes for the near future. Includes articles on parapsychology, esoterica, magic, alternative medicine, and various New Age themes.
Published by: R C S Periodici (Subsidiary of: R C S Mediagroup), Via Angelo Rizzoli, 2, Milan, MI 20132, Italy. TEL 39-2-25845413, FAX 39-2-25845444, info@periodici.rcs.it, http://www.rcsmediagroup.it/siti/periodici.php. Ed. Rudy Stauder. Adv. contact Flavio Biondi. Circ: 133,000 (paid). **Dist. in UK by:** Seymour Distribution Ltd, 86 Newman St, London W1T 3EX, United Kingdom. TEL 44-20-73968000, FAX 44-20-73968002.

133.5   DEU   ISSN 1434-0658
ASTRAL. Text in German. 1989. a. **Document type:** Magazine, Consumer.
Published by: OZ Verlag GmbH, Roemerstr 90, Rheinfelden, 79618, Germany. TEL 49-7623-964-0, FAX 49-7623-96464200, vollmar@oz-bpv.de, http://www.oz-verlag.com.

133.5   FRA
ASTRES. Text in French. 1948. m. adv. illus.
Related titles: ♦ Supplement(s): Guide Astrologique.
Published by: Editions Francois de Villac, 6 rue de Savoie, Paris, 75006, France. TEL 33-1-53102600, FAX 33-1-53102601. Circ: 110,000.

133.5   DEU
ASTRO. Variant title: Die Neue Frau - Astro. Text in German. a. EUR 1.95 newsstand/cover (effective 2002). adv. **Document type:** Magazine, Consumer.
Published by: Klambt Verlag GmbH, Im Neudeck 1, Speyer, 67346, Germany. TEL 49-6232-3100, FAX 49-6232-310226, anzeigen@klambt.de, http://www.klambt.de. Adv. contact Anita Weiss. B&W page EUR 3,320, color page EUR 4,114. Circ: 73,807 (paid).

133.5   USA
ASTRO ANALYTICS NEWSLETTER. Text in English. 1978. 4/yr. bk.rev. **Document type:** Newsletter. **Description:** Features articles, comments, astrological product reviews, and other related items.
Formerly: Astro Analytics
Address: PO Box 16927, Encino, CA 91416-6927. TEL 818-997-8684. Ed. Craig Greeno. Circ: 4,000.

133.5   USA
ASTRO! GO. Text in English. irreg. **Description:** Designed to entertain and explore meaningless perspectives in astrology.
Media: Online - full text.
Address: ccheung@aw.sgi.com, http://reality.sgi.com/ccheung_tor.Ed. Christopher Cheung.

THE ASTRO-INVESTOR; a newsletter for investors. see *BUSINESS AND ECONOMICS—Investments*

133.52   HRV   ISSN 1331-2308
ASTRO MAGAZIN. Text in Croatian. 1990. m. **Document type:** Magazine, Consumer.
Former titles (until 1997): Astro Express (1330-8289); (until 1995): Astro Magazin (0353-8613)
Published by: Arena d.d., Slavonska Avenija 4, Zagreb, 10000, Croatia. TEL 385-1-6166666, FAX 385-1-6162032, astro@eph.hr. Ed. Mladen Gerovac.

133.52   HRV   ISSN 1331-3185
ASTRO MAGAZIN POSEBNO IZD. Text in Croatian. 1996. a.
Formerly (until 1997): Godisnjak Astro Express (1330-8009)
Published by: Arena d.d., Slavonska Avenija 4, Zagreb, 10000, Croatia. TEL 385-1-6166666, FAX 385-1-6162032, astro@eph.hr.

133.5   HRV   ISSN 1331-4408
ASTRO VODIC. Text in Croatian. 1997. 2/yr. **Document type:** Magazine, Consumer.
Published by: A N K H - Centar za Poboljsanje Kvalitete Zivota, Petrova 101, Zagreb, 10000, Croatia. TEL 385-1-226536, FAX 385-1-226536.

133.5   RUS
ASTROLOG. Text in Russian. m. USD 99.95 in United States.
Published by: Firma Konek, A-ya 151, Moscow, 119048, Russian Federation. TEL 7-095-2641201, FAX 7-095-2641201, astrolog@deol.ru. Ed. V M Kopylov. **US dist. addr.:** East View Information Services, 3020 Harbor Ln. N., Minneapolis, MN 55447. TEL 612-550-0961.

133.5   CHE   ISSN 0257-9235
ASTROLOG; Fachzeitschrift fuer astrologische Psychologie. Text in German. 1981. bi-m. CHF 63, EUR 40 (effective 2005). **Document type:** Magazine, Consumer.
Published by: Astrologisch-Psychologisches Institut, Obertilistr 4, Postfach 614, Adliswil, 8134, Switzerland. TEL 41-1-7103776, FAX 41-1-7103786, huber_api@compuserve.com, http://www.astro-api.ch.

133.5   IND   ISSN 0004-6140
BF1651
➤ **THE ASTROLOGICAL MAGAZINE.** (A Journal dedicated to Science of Astrology in articular and other aspects or Indian culture like Yoga and Vastu etc.) Text in English. 1936. m. INR 265 domestic; USD 45 foreign (effective 2003). adv. bk.rev. charts. index. 80 p./no. 2 cols./p.; back issues avail.
Document type: Magazine, Academic/Scholarly. **Description:** Covers Jyotisha, Vastu or ancient Indian architecture, Yoga, Indian culture and allied subjects.
Published by: Raman Publications, Sri Rajeswari, 28 Nagappa St (Nehru Circle), Seshadripuram, Bangalore, Kanartaka 560 020, India. TEL 91-80-3348646, FAX 91-80-3313260, info@astrologicalmagazine.com, http://www.astrologicalmagazine.com/. Ed., R&P Gayatri Devi Vasudev. Pub., Adv. contact B Niranjan Babu. page USD 600; 5.5 x 8. Circ: 25,000.

133.5   USA   ISSN 0044-9784
BF1651
ASTROLOGICAL REVIEW∗ . Text in English. 4/yr. USD 20.
Published by: Astrologers' Guild of America, 5 Fair Meadow Dr, Brewster, NY 10509. Ed. Susanne Neuschulz.

133.5   CHE
ASTROLOGIE HEUTE. Text in German. 1986. bi-m. CHF 65 (effective 1999). adv. bk.rev. back issues avail. **Document type:** Consumer.
Published by: Astrodata AG, Chilenholzstr 8, Wettswil, 8907, Switzerland. TEL 41-1-4935130, FAX 41-1-4935135, astrologieheute@compuserve.com. Ed. Claude Weiss. Pub. Armando Bertozzi. Circ: 11,000 (paid).

133.5   RUS
ASTROLOGIYA. Text in Russian. q. USD 89 in United States.
Published by: Firma Konek, A-ya 151, Moscow, 119048, Russian Federation. TEL 7-095-2641201, FAX 7-095-2641202, astrolog@deol.ru. Ed. V M Kopylov. **US dist. addr.:** East View Information Services, 3020 Harbor Ln. N., Minneapolis, MN 55447. TEL 612-550-0961.

133.5   USA
ASTROLOGY AND PSYCHIC NEWS. Text in English. 1989 (vol.66, no.18). q. membership. back issues avail.
Published by: California Astrology Association, Department V, PO Box 810, N. Hollywood, CA 91603.

133.5   USA
ASTROLOGY ANNUAL. Text in English. a. **Document type:** Consumer.
Published by: Hachette Filipacchi Media U.S., Inc. (Subsidiary of: Hachette Filipacchi Medias S.A.), 1633 Broadway, 41st Fl, New York, NY 10019. TEL 212-767-6000.

133.5   USA   ISSN 0004-6191
ASTROLOGY GUIDE∗ . Text in English. 1937. bi-m. USD 7.50. adv. bk.rev. charts; illus. **Document type:** Consumer.
Published by: Dorchester Media, 35 Wilbur St, Lynbrook, NY 11563. TEL 516-593-1220.

133.5   GBR   ISSN 1464-0589
ASTROLOGY QUARTERLY. Text in English. 1926. q. GBP 22 in Europe; GBP 25 US, Canada,India, S.Africa, S.America; GBP 27 Far East, Australia, N. Zealand, S.E. Asia, Japan (effective 2000). adv. bk.rev. charts. index. **Document type:** Academic/Scholarly. **Description:** Serves as the journal of the A.L.L. Dedicated to the study of all branches of astrology. Aims to serve as a forum for high quality debate.
Formerly: Astrology (0004-6183)
Published by: Astrological Lodge of London, 50 Gloucester Pl, London, SW1V 4EH, United Kingdom. Ed. Gerasime Patilas. Circ: 700.

133.5   USA   ISSN 0195-0851
BF1651
ASTROLOGY: YOUR DAILY HOROSCOPE. Text in English. m. USD 42; USD 3.50 newsstand/cover (effective 2004). illus.
Document type: Magazine, Consumer.
Published by: Kappa Publishing Group, Inc., 6198 Butler Pike., Ste. 200, Blue Bell, PA 19422-2606.

133.5   USA
ASTROMIND. Text in English. m. free. **Description:** Explores astrology beyond sun signs.
Media: Online - full text.
Address: AstroMind1@aol.com, http://members.aol.com/Astromind1/. Ed. Randall Collins. Pub. Randall Collins.

133.5   USA   ISSN 1529-1278
ASTROSOLUTIONS. Text in English. 1999. w. **Document type:** Newsletter. **Description:** Includes original articles, horoscope readings, weekly affirmations for each astrology sign.
Media: E-mail.
Published by: Circles of Light, Box 140, Sedona, AZ 86339. FAX 707-215-2820, newsletter@astroevolution.com, http://astroevolution.com. Ed. Jeri Noble. Circ: 450.

133.5 USA
ASTROTALK BULLETIN. Text in English. 1983. q. USD 9.95 domestic; USD 17.95 foreign. bk.rev. illus.; stat. **Document type:** *Bulletin.* **Description:** Bulletin for the Matrix user's group with information on the developments in the Matrix software field. Includes astrological and time cycles, and stock market correspondence to cyclical data.
Formerly: Astro Talk (0740-6738)
Published by: Matrix Software, 1921 Cambridge Rd., Ann Arbor, MI 48104-3650. TEL 616-796-2483, FAX 616-796-3060. Ed. Michael Erlewine. Circ: 1,000.

133.5 DEU
ASTROWOCHE. Text in German. w. (Thu.). EUR 83.20 domestic; EUR 119.60 foreign; EUR 1.75 newsstand/cover (effective 2004). adv. **Document type:** *Magazine, Consumer.*
Published by: Astro Zeitschriftenverlags GmbH, Medienstr 5, Passau, 94036, Germany. TEL 49-851-802201, FAX 49-851-802837, service@astrowoche.de, http://www.astrowoche.de. Ed. Rudolf Kollboeck. Adv. contact Heidi Scheitza. B&W page EUR 2,250, color page EUR 2,914. Circ: 58,202. **Subscr. to:** P M S GmbH & Co. KG, Grafenberger Allee 100, Duesseldorf 40237, Germany. TEL 49-211-69078936, FAX 49-211-69078950, pms.duesseldorf@cityweb.de.

133.5 GBR
BLUE AQUARIUS. Text in English. 1997. m. bk.rev. **Description:** Aims to be a collage or reflection of astrology on the Web, and features articles, horoscopes and web reviews.
Media: Online - full text.
Address: United Kingdom. venice@vastro.force9.co.uk, http://www.vastro.force9.co.uk/blueaqua.htm. Ed., Pub. Venice Sedwick.

133.5 FRA ISSN 0007-9596
CAHIERS ASTROLOGIQUES; revue d'astrologie traditionnelle. Text in French. 1938. 6/yr. adv. bk.rev. abstr.; bibl.; charts; illus.; stat. index.
Published by: Editions des Cahiers Astrologiques, 7 rue Condorcet, Paris, 75009, France. Ed. Paul Rogel. Circ: 1,200.

CASTER. see *MOTION PICTURES*

CHURCH OF LIGHT QUARTERLY. see *NEW AGE PUBLICATIONS*

133.5 USA ISSN 1066-4920
BF1621
CONSIDERATIONS. Text in English. 1983. q. USD 40 domestic; USD 45 foreign (effective 2004). bk.rev.; software rev. illus.; charts. 96 p./no.; back issues avail. **Document type:** *Journal, Academic/Scholarly.*
Address: PO Box 655, Mount Kisco, NY 10549. TEL 914-232-4452, kwgmkg@aol.com, http://www.considerations-mag.com. Ed., Pub. Kennet Gillman. Circ: 1,500 (paid).

133.5 USA ISSN 1529-126X
COSMIC MAILBOX FROM CIRCLES OF LIGHT. Text in English. 1998. w. **Document type:** *Newsletter.* **Description:** Focuses on astrology and metaphysics.
Formerly: Circles of Light Newsletter
Media: Online - full text. **Related titles:** E-mail ed.
Published by: Circles of Light, Box 140, Sedona, AZ 86339. TEL 707-204-1875, FAX 707-215-2820, newsletters@circlesoflight.com, http://www.circlesoflight.com/news.shtml. Ed. Jeri Noble. Circ: 2,600.

133.5 USA ISSN 1548-7512
▼ **COSMIC PLANETARY INFLUENCES.** Abbreviated title: Cosmic P I. Text in English. 2003 (Oct. 28). w. free (effective 2005). **Document type:** *Consumer.* **Description:** Contains entertaining forecasts of celestial influences along with inspirational advice using feng shui astrology.
Media: Online - full content.
Published by: China Rose, 2428 Earl St, Los Angeles, CA 90039. TEL 323-953-8388, FAX 323-913-0299, thegoldpig@msn.com, http://www.cosmicpi.com. Ed. Matthew Rose. Pub., R&P Rose China.

133.5 USA
COSMOBIOLOGY INTERNATIONAL JOURNAL. Text in English, German. 1969. 3/yr. USD 15 (effective 2004). bk.rev. charts; illus. **Document type:** *Journal, Trade.*
Former titles (until 1993): Cosmobiology International; (until 1983): Cosmobiology Journal; (until 1973): Cosmobiology International (0045-8694)
Published by: Cosmobiology Research Foundation, PO Box 1844, Englewood, CO 80150-1844. rlgraphics@earthlink.net, http://www.inkdrop.net/cosmobiology/cosmo.html. Eds. Nelda Louise Tanner, Patricia Petty Munns. Circ: 1,500.

133.5 520 GBR ISSN 1368-6534
BF1651
➤ **CULTURE AND COSMOS.** Text in English. 1997. s-a. GBP 13 domestic to individuals; GBP 15 foreign to individuals; GBP 22 domestic to institutions; GBP 24 foreign to institutions (effective 2002). back issues avail. **Document type:** *Journal, Academic/Scholarly.* **Description:** Devoted to the study of the history of astrology and cultural astronomy.
Indexed: RefZh.
Address: P.O. Box 1071, Bristol, BS99 1HE, United Kingdom. culture@caol.demon.co.uk, http://www.cultureandcosmos.com/. Ed. Nicholas Campion.

133.5 USA ISSN 1080-1421
DELL HOROSCOPE. Text in English. 1935. 13/yr., latest vol.67. USD 39.87 domestic (effective 2005). adv. bk.rev. charts; illus. 128 p./no. 2 cols./p.; reprint service avail. from PQC.
Document type: *Magazine, Consumer.* **Description:** Daily in-depth horoscope guide and authoritative feature articles.
Formerly (until 199?): Horoscope (0018-5116)
Related titles: Microform ed.: 1935 (from PQC).
Indexed: BRI, CBRI.
Published by: Dell Magazines (Subsidiary of: Penny Publications LLC), 475 Park Ave S, 11 Fl, New York, NY 10016-6901. TEL 212-686-7188, 800-333-3311, FAX 212-686-7414, horoscope@dellmagazines.com, juliamcevoy@dellmagazines.com, http://www.dellhoroscope.com. Ed. Ronnie Grishman. adv.: B&W page USD 1,100; 5 x 8. Circ: 240,000 (paid).

133.5 USA
DELL HOROSCOPE PURSE BOOKS✶. Text in English. 6/yr. adv. **Document type:** *Consumer.*
Published by: Dell Magazines (Subsidiary of: Penny Publications LLC), 475 Park Ave S, 11 Fl, New York, NY 10016-6901. TEL 212-698-1313, FAX 212-698-1198. Ed. Ronnie Grishman. Pub. Peter Kanter. R&P Kathleen Halligan.

133.5 BRA ISSN 0104-8716
DESTINO. Text in Portuguese. m. illus. **Document type:** *Consumer.* **Description:** Includes horoscopes, star predictions, mysteries, personality traits and health. Covers numerology, cartomancy, past lives and dream analysis.
Related titles: ♦ Supplement(s): Destino Edicao Especial. ISSN 1413-4225.
Published by: Editora Globo S.A., Rua Domingos Sergio dos Anjos, 277, Pirituba, Jd S Elias, Sao Paulo, SP 05136-170, Brazil. TEL 55-11-836-5000, atendimento@edglobo.com.br. Pub. Jose Francisco Queiroz. adv.: color page USD 3,600; trim 274 x 208. Circ: 49,000 (paid).

133.5 BRA ISSN 1413-4225
DESTINO EDICAO ESPECIAL. Text in Portuguese. 1996. a. adv. illus.
Related titles: ♦ Supplement to: Destino. ISSN 0104-8716.
Published by: Editora Globo S.A., Rua Domingos Sergio dos Anjos, 277, Pirituba, Jd S Elias, Sao Paulo, SP 05136-170, Brazil. TEL 55-11-836-5000, atendimento@edglobo.com.br, http://www.editoraglobo.com.br, http://editoraglobo.globo.com/. Pub. Jose Francisco Queiroz.

133.52 POL ISSN 1506-0403
DOBRE RADY. HOROSKOP. Variant title: Horoskop. Text in Polish. 2001. a. adv. **Document type:** *Magazine, Consumer.*
Published by: Wydawnictwo Burda Polska Sp. z.o.o., ul Strzegomska 236a, Wroclaw, 54432, Poland. TEL 48-71-3737280, prenumerata@burda.pl, http://www.burda.pl. adv.: page PLZ 4,000. Circ: 100,000 (controlled).

133.5 332.6 USA ISSN 1055-8527
CODEN: CASTE5
FINANCIAL CYCLES; wealth creation & investment success through person-centered financial astrology. Text in English. 1988. m. USD 55; USD 79 foreign (effective 1998). adv. bk.rev. charts; illus. back issues avail.; reprints avail.
Document type: *Newsletter.* **Description:** Explores the use of technical analysis and financial astrology in promoting the esoteric understanding of economic trends, geocosmic cycles, geopolitical events, and market movements.
Published by: Bost Communications - Support of Nature, PO Box 1657, Sarasota, FL 34230-1657. TEL 941-953-3545, FAX 941-953-3732, timbost@pipeline.com. Ed., Pub., R&P, Adv. contact Timothy Lee Bost. Circ: 125.

133.5 GBR ISSN 0071-8084
FOULSHAM'S ORIGINAL OLD MOORE'S ALMANACK✶. Text in English. 1697. a. **Document type:** *Consumer.* **Description:** Contains astrological predictions for a twelve month period.
Published by: W. Foulsham & Co. Ltd., Chippenham, Bennetts Close, Slough, Bucks SL1 5AP, United Kingdom. TEL 44-1753-26769, TELEX 849041 SHARET G.

133.5 USA ISSN 1080-6415
GEOCOSMIC✶. Text in English. 1978. 2/yr. USD 35 to members. adv. bk.rev. bibl.; charts; illus.; stat. back issues avail.
Document type: *Academic/Scholarly.*
Formerly: Geocosmic News
Published by: National Council for Geocosmic Research, Inc., 9307 Thronewood Dr, Baltimore, MD 21234-3219. TEL 301-812-2593, ncgr@allware.com, http://www.geocosmic.org/www/publi.html. Ed. Frances McEvoy. Pub. Mary Downing. Adv. contact Arlene Nimark. Circ: 3,000.

133.5 DEU
DAS GROSSE HOROSKOP - MEINE STERNSTUNDEN. Text in German. a. EUR 1.95 newsstand/cover (effective 2002). adv. **Document type:** *Magazine, Consumer.*
Published by: Klambt Verlag GmbH, Im Neudeck 1, Speyer, 67346, Germany. TEL 49-6232-3100, FAX 49-6232-310226, anzeigen@klambt.de, http://www.klambt.de. Adv. contact Anita Weiss. B&W page EUR 3,320, color page EUR 4,114. Circ: 79,248 (paid).

133.5 FRA
GUIDE ASTROLOGIQUE. Text in French. 1970. a. adv. illus.
Related titles: ♦ Supplement to: Astres.
Published by: Editions Francois de Villac, 6 rue de Savoie, Paris, 75006, France. TEL 33-1-53102600, FAX 33-1-53102601. Circ: 120,000.

133.5 GBR ISSN 0954-9587
HOROSCOPE; the world's premier astrological magazine. Text in English. 1954. m. GBP 20 in United Kingdom; GBP 28 in Europe; GBP 41 elsewhere; GBP 2.10 newsstand/cover (effective 2000). bk.rev. illus. **Document type:** *Consumer.* **Description:** Covers the zodiac and astrology, feature articles on each zodiac sign, daily horoscopes.
Published by: Wimborne Publishing Ltd. (Subsidiary of: Crosstown Publications), 408 Wimborne Rd E, Ferndown, Doreset BH22 9ND, United Kingdom. TEL 44-1202-881749, FAX 44-1202-841692, enquiries@wimborne.co.uk. Ed. Mike Kenward.

133.5 CAN
HOROSCOPE QUOTIDIEN. Text in French. 1956. m. CND 32.99 (effective 1998). adv. **Document type:** *Consumer.*
Formerly: Horoscope Quotidien Eclair (0018-5124)
Published by: Super Magazine (Subsidiary of: Editions du Boise, Inc.), 3065 Blvd Levesque Ouest, Laval, PQ H7V 1C5, Canada. TEL 450-681-6361, FAX 450-681-1638. Ed. Paul Henri Goulet. Pub. Jean Pare. R&P Celine Forest. Adv. contact Claude David. Circ: 25,000.

133.5 BRA ISSN 0104-1576
HOROSCOPO; a revista dos astros. Text in Portuguese. 1972. m. adv. illus. Supplement avail. **Document type:** *Magazine, Consumer.* **Description:** Covers the zodiac and astrology. Includes feature articles on each zodiac sign and daily horoscopes.
Former titles (until 1990): Horoscopo Caricia; (until 1986): Horoscopo Capricho
Published by: Editora Abril, S.A., Av. das Nacoes Unidas, 7221, 11 andar Pinheiros, Sao Paulo, SP 05425-902, Brazil. TEL 55-11-30374858, FAX 55-11-30371961, horoscopo.atleitor@abril.com.br, relacoes.corporativas@abril.com.br, http://www.abril.com.br/. Ed. Regina Gianetti. R&P Ana Vidotti TEL 55-11-30372125. Adv. contact Enio Vergeiro. color page USD 4,240; 134 x 190. Circ: 130,000 (paid).

133.5 DEU
HOROSKOP IM MONAT. Text in German. m. EUR 2.50 newsstand/cover (effective 2003). adv. **Document type:** *Magazine, Consumer.*
Published by: Der Heisse Draht Verlag GmbH und Co., Drostestr 14-16, Hannover, 30161, Germany. TEL 49-511-390910, FAX 49-511-39091252, zentrale@dhd.de, http://www.dhd.de. adv.: B&W page EUR 1,500, color page EUR 1,650.

133.5 USA
➤ **INTERNATIONAL ASTROLOGER.** Text in English. 1968. q. USD 35 (effective 1999). adv. bk.rev. charts; illus. **Document type:** *Academic/Scholarly.* **Description:** Contains timed birthdates of known personalities and persons listed by category.
Formerly: Kosmos (0047-3650)
Published by: International Society for Astrological Research, Inc., PO Box 38613, Los Angeles, CA 90038-0613. TEL 805-525-0461, FAX 805-525-0461, mmacycles@mail.msn.com, http://www.isarastrology.com. Ed., Adv. contact Bette Denlinger. R&P Marguerite Dar Boggia. Circ: 1,000 (controlled).

➤ **J. GRUBER'S HAGERSTOWN TOWN AND COUNTRY ALMANACK.** see *ENCYCLOPEDIAS AND GENERAL ALMANACS*

133.5 IND
JANMABHOOMI KHAGOL SIDDHA SUKSHMA NIRAYANA BHARATIYA PANCHANG (GUJARATI EDITION). Text in Hindi. 1945. a. INR 200; INR 30 newsstand/cover (effective 1999). adv. bk.rev. back issues avail. **Description:** Annual almanac of astrology-palmistry.
Related titles: Microfilm ed.; Gujarati ed.
Published by: Saurashtra Trust, Janmabhoomi Bhavan, Janmabhoomi Marg, Fort, P O Box 62, Mumbai, Maharashtra 400 001, India. TEL 91-22-2873438, FAX 91-22-2874097, bhoomi@bom3.vsnl.net.in. Ed. Jyoti Bhatt. Pub. Dhirubhai J Desai. Adv. contact N G Patel. Circ: 50,000.

133.5 IND
JANMABHOOMI KHAGOL SIDDHA SUKSHMA NIRAYANA BHARATIYA PANCHANG (HINDI EDITION). Text in Hindi. 1991. a. INR 150; INR 15 newsstand/cover (effective 1999). adv. bk.rev. **Description:** Annual almanac of astrology-palmistry.
Related titles: Microfilm ed.; Gujarati ed.

▼ *new title* ➤ *refereed* ✶ *unverified* ♦ *full entry avail.*

Published by: Saurashtra Trust, Janmabhoomi Bhavan, Janmabhoomi Marg, Fort, P O Box 62, Mumbai, Maharashtra 400 001, India. TEL 91-22-2873438, FAX 91-22-2874097, bhoomi@bom3.vsnl.net.in. Ed. Jyoti Bhatt. Pub. Dhirubhai J Desai. Adv. contact N G Patel. Circ: 8,000.

133.5 IND
JANMABHOOMI PANCHANG. Text in Gujarati. 1945. a. INR 80. adv. **Description:** Annual almanac with special interest articles on astrology.
Published by: Saurashtra Trust, Janmabhoomi Bhavan, Janmabhoomi Marg, Fort, P O Box 62, Mumbai, Maharashtra 400 001, India. TEL 2870831. Ed. Jyoti Bhatt. Circ: 47,000.

133.5 NLD ISSN 0022-7463
DE KAARSVLAM. Text in Dutch. 1947. bi-m. EUR 27 (effective 2005). adv. bk.rev.; film rev.; play rev. **Document type:** *Monographic series, Consumer.*
Published by: Mellie Uyldert, Ed.& Pub., Lomanlaan 7, Bussum, 1405 BK, Netherlands. TEL 31-35-6940423, http://www.uyldert.nl/html/kaarsvlam.html. R&P Satyamo Uyldert. Circ: 1,000.

133.5 640 IND
KALNIRNAY. Text in English, Hindi, Marathi, Gujarati, Kannada, Tamil, Telugu, Bengali. 1973. a., latest 2001. looseleaf. INR 14, USD 4 (effective Oct. 2002). adv. 12 p./no.; back issues avail.; reprints avail. **Document type:** *Consumer.* **Description:** Caimanac Date Pad information, Railway Time information. Articles by Welknown authors.
Related titles: Online - full text ed.
Published by: Sumangal Publishing Co., 172 M M G S Marg, Dadar, P O Box 5547, Mumbai, Maharashtra 400 014, India. TEL 91-022-4130885, FAX 91-022-4146939, kalnirnay@kalnirnay.com, http://www.kalnirnay.com. Ed. Jayant Salgaonkar. Pub. JayRaj Salgaokar. Adv. contact Shirish Vaidya. page USD 40,000; 25 x 8. Circ: 5,076,666 (paid).

133.5 IND
KUMUDAM JOTHIDAM. Text in Tamil. w. INR 350 domestic; USD 50 foreign (effective 2003).
Related titles: Online - full text ed.
Published by: Kumudam Publications Pvt. Ltd., 151 Purasawalkam High Rd, Chennai, Tamil Nadu 600 010, India. TEL 91-44-26422146, FAX 91-44-26425041, kumudam@vsnl.com, kumudamweb@indiatimes.com, http://www.kumudam.com/jothidam/mainpage.php. Pub. P V Parthasarathy. Adv. contact A Jawahar Palaniappan TEL 91-44-26422147.

133.5 ITA
➤ **LINGUAGGIO ASTRALE.** Text in Italian. 1971. q. EUR 40 (effective 2003). adv. bk.rev. charts; illus. 200 p./no.; back issues avail. **Document type:** *Magazine, Academic/Scholarly.* **Description:** Sound researches and surveys on astrological field.
Published by: Centro Italiano di Astrologia (CIDA), Via Monzanbano 13, Milan, 20159, Italy. TEL 39-02-69005576, http://wwww.cida.net. Ed., Pub., R&P Dante Valente. Circ: 2,000.

133.52 RUS ISSN 1606-8726
LIZA. GOROSKOP. Text in Russian. 2000. m. RUR 32 newsstand/cover (effective 2003). adv. **Document type:** *Magazine, Consumer.* **Description:** Contains full descriptions of each sign of the Zodiac for all areas of life: romance and relationships, career and finance, travel, as well as happiness and health.
Published by: Izdatel'skii Dom Burda, ul Pravdy 8, Moscow, 125040, Russian Federation. TEL 7-095-7979849, FAX 7-095-2571196, vertrieb@burda.ru, http://www.burda.ru. adv.: page USD 2,600. Circ: 150,000 (paid and controlled).

133.52 UKR
LIZA. GOROSKOP. Text in Russian. m. UAK 17.46 for 6 mos. domestic (effective 2004). **Document type:** *Magazine, Consumer.*
Published by: Burda Ukraina, Zhyljanskaja ul. 29, Kiev, 01033, Ukraine. TEL 38-044-4908363, FAX 38-044-4908364, advert@burdaua.com, http://www.burda.com.ua.

133.5 USA ISSN 1554-6373
BF1728.A2
▼ **LLEWELLYN'S STARVIEW ALMANAC;** an astrological look at people, events & trends. Text in English. 2005. a. USD 8.95 per vol. (effective 2005).
Published by: Llewellyn Publications, 84 South Wabasha St, P O Box 64383, St. Paul, MN 55164. TEL 651-291-1970, FAX 651-291-1908, http://www.llewellyn.com.

133.532 529.3 USA
➤ **LUNAR CALENDAR (YEAR);** dedicated to the goddess in her many guises. Text in English. 1976. a., latest 27th edition. USD 23 (effective 2002). bibl.; charts; illus. 32 p./no.; back issues avail. **Document type:** *Academic/Scholarly.* **Description:** Features works from twenty-three poets and artists and gives complete astrological and astronomical moon-data; the lunar year at a glance and all the phases of the moon. Inspired by Robert Graves' The White Goddess, this 13-month lunar calendar teaches moon lore.

Published by: Luna Press, PO Box 15511, Kenmore Sta, Boston, MA 02215-0009. TEL 617-427-9846, thelunapress@aol.com, http://www.thelunapress.com. Ed. Nancy F.W. Passmore. R&P Nancy F W Passmore. Circ: 7,000 (paid).

133.5 IND
MATHAJOTHIDAM; astrological Tamil monthly. Text in Tamil. 1949. m.
Address: 3 Arasamaram, N.A.A. Dist., Vellore, Tamil Nadu, India. Ed. A K Thulasiraman. Pub. A.K. Thulasiraman. Circ: 8,000.

133.5 DEU
MEIN HOROSKOP. Variant title: Heim und Welt - Mein Horoskop. Text in German. a. EUR 1.95 newsstand/cover (effective 2002). adv. **Document type:** *Magazine, Consumer.*
Published by: Klambt Verlag GmbH, Im Neudeck 1, Speyer, 67346, Germany. TEL 49-6232-3100, FAX 49-6232-310226, anzeigen@klambt.de, http://www.klambt.de. Adv. contact Anita Weiss. B&W page EUR 3,320, color page EUR 4,114. Circ: 77,128 (paid).

133.5 USA
MIDNIGHT HOROSCOPE✶. Text in English. 1980. 4/yr. USD 9.97. adv. bk.rev. illus.
Published by: Rosenbloom Family Publishing, 3 E 54th St, 15th Fl, New York, NY 10022-3108. TEL 800-472-7744. Ed. Carlson Wade. Circ: 50,000.

133.5 USA ISSN 1079-1345
THE MOUNTAIN ASTROLOGER. Text in English. 1987. 6/yr. USD 36 in US & Canada; USD 54 elsewhere in the Americas; USD 64 in Europe; USD 76 in Asia & the Pacific; USD 5.95 newsstand/cover domestic; CND 7.95 newsstand/cover in Canada (effective 2004). adv. bk.rev.; software rev.; Website rev. bibl.; charts; illus.; stat. back issues avail. **Document type:** *Magazine, Consumer.* **Description:** Targets anyone serious learning or practicing astrology. Contains articles, global forecasts, and astro-humor.
Related titles: E-mail ed.; Fax ed.; Online - full text ed.
Published by: Mountain Astrologer, PO Box 970, Cedar Ridge, CA 95924-0970. TEL 530-477-8839, 800-287-4828, FAX 530-477-9423, subs@mountainastrologer.com, http://www.mountainastrologer.com. Ed., R&P Nan Geary TEL 530-477-7756. Pub. Tem Tarriktar. Adv. contact Judy Schwein. B&W page USD 745; trim 10.75 x 8.25. Circ: 20,000 (paid).

133.5 ESP ISSN 1577-9084
EL MUNDO DE LOS ASTROS. Text in Spanish. 1999. q. **Document type:** *Magazine, Consumer.*
Published by: H. Bauer Ediciones S.L. (Subsidiary of: Heinrich Bauer Verlag), Jacometrezo 15, Madrid, 28013, Spain. TEL 34-91-5476800, FAX 34-91-5413523.

133.5 USA ISSN 0892-5429
MUTABLE DILEMMA. Text in English. 1977. q. USD 20; USD 30 foreign (effective 1999). bk.rev. back issues avail. **Document type:** *Academic/Scholarly.*
Published by: Los Angeles Community Church of Religious Science, 838 Fifth Ave, Los Angeles, CA 90005. TEL 213-487-1000, FAX 213-487-7853, markpottenger@msn.com. Ed., R&P Mark Pottenger. Circ: 250.

133.5 USA ISSN 0296-5569
N C G R JOURNAL✶. Text in English. 1984. 2/yr. USD 35 to members. adv. bk.rev. back issues avail. **Document type:** *Academic/Scholarly.* **Description:** Education and research regarding the correspondence between events in the cosmos and events on earth.
Published by: National Council for Geocosmic Research, Inc., 9307 Thronewood Dr, Baltimore, MD 21234-3219. TEL 301-812-2593, ncgr@allware.com, http://www.geocosmic.org. Ed. Loraine Welsh. Pub., R&P Mary Downing. Adv. contact Arlene Nimark. Circ: 3,000.

133.5 USA
NATIONAL COUNCIL FOR GEOCOSMIC RESEARCH. MEMBERLETTER✶. Text in English. 1984. m. membership. adv. bk.rev. **Document type:** *Newsletter.*
Published by: National Council for Geocosmic Research, Inc., 9307 Thronewood Dr, Baltimore, MD 21234-3219. TEL 301-812-2593, ncgr@allware.com, http://www.geocosmic.org. Ed. Martha Ramsey. Pub. Mary Downing. Adv. contact Arlene Nimark. Circ: 3,000.

ORACLE (SIERRA MADRE). see *PARAPSYCHOLOGY AND OCCULTISM*

133.5029 USA
POWER AGENT. Text in English. 1993. 3/yr., latest vol.5, 2001. USD 19.95 (effective 2001). adv. dance rev.; film rev.; music rev.; play rev.; tel.rev.; video rev. illus.; stat.; tr.lit. 108 p./no.; back issues avail. **Document type:** *Directory, Trade.* **Description:** Comprehensive listing of motion picture and television nationwide astrological signs, addresses and phone numbers, sign descriptions and agency breakdowns. Plus vital industry survival information and lead articles with industry celebrities.
Formerly: Taaffe O'Connell's Astro Agents (1065-7584)
Related titles: Series of: The Industry's Edge Series.

Published by: Canoco Publishing, 11611 Chenault St, Ste 118, Los Angeles, CA 90049. TEL 310-471-2287, FAX 310-471-1944, industryedge@earthlink.net, http://www.hollywoodnetwork.com/astrohollywood. Ed. Taaffe C O'Connell. Pub., R&P Taaffe O'Connell. Adv. contact Susan Moore. B&W page USD 900; 4.5 x 7.5. Circ: 100,000.

133.5 IND
POYYAMOZHI; astrological Tamil monthly. Text in Tamil. 1972. m. INR 36. adv. bk.rev. charts; illus.
Published by: P. Adimoolam Ed.& Pub., 64 Gaudiamath Rd., Chennai, Tamil Nadu 600 014, India. FAX 868780. Circ: 2,500.

133.5 GBR ISSN 0079-4953
PREDICTION ANNUAL. Text in English. a. GBP 3.95 (effective 1999). adv. bk.rev. **Document type:** *Consumer.* **Description:** Presents astrological forecasts for each sign of the Zodiac; includes Tarot card projections.
Published by: I P C Country & Leisure Media Ltd. (Subsidiary of: I P C Media Ltd.), Focus House, Dingwall Ave, Croydon, Surrey CR9 2TA, United Kingdom. TEL 44-208-686-2599, FAX 44-20-8781-1159. Ed. Jo Logan.

133.5 GBR
RAPHAEL'S ASTROLOGICAL ALMANAC✶. Text in English. 1819. a. **Document type:** *Consumer.* **Description:** Provides reference material for the astrologer as well as predictions for the year ahead.
Published by: W. Foulsham & Co. Ltd., Chippenham, Bennetts Close, Slough, Bucks SL1 5AP, United Kingdom. TEL 44-1753-26769.

133.5 ITA
SESTILE. Text in Italian. 1992. m. (11/yr.). EUR 20 (effective 2003). **Document type:** *Newsletter.* **Description:** Covers professional astrology.
Published by: Centro Italiano di Astrologia (CIDA), Via Monzanbano 13, Milan, 20159, Italy. TEL 39-02-69005576, http://wwww.cida.net. Ed. Grazia Mirti.

133.5 USA
SIDEREALIST. Text in English. 4/yr. USD 14.50.
Published by: Sidereal Registry & Exchange, 11 Valley St, Endwell, NY 13760. Ed. Norman Bones.

STAR BEACON. see *NEW AGE PUBLICATIONS*

133.5 USA
STARSCROLL. Text in English. m. USD 0.89 newsstand/cover. **Document type:** *Consumer.*
Published by: Twelve Signs, Inc., 3369 S Robertson Blvd, Los Angeles, CA 90034. TEL 310-553-8000, FAX 310-836-0110. Pub. Richard W Houseman.

133.5 USA
STARSIGNS. Text in English. m. USD 0.99 newsstand/cover. **Document type:** *Consumer.*
Published by: Twelve Signs, Inc., 3369 S Robertson Blvd, Los Angeles, CA 90034. TEL 310-553-8000, FAX 310-836-0110. Pub. Richard W Housman.

133.5 HRV ISSN 1331-2472
STELLA. Text in Croatian. 1994. m. **Document type:** *Magazine, Consumer.*
Published by: A N K H - Centar za Poboljsanje Kvalitete Zivota, Petrova 101, Zagreb, 10000, Croatia. TEL 385-1-226536, FAX 385-1-226536. Ed. Osama Shreim.

133.5 USA
STELLIUM QUARTERLY✶; an astrological journal. Text in English. 1975. q. USD 6.50. adv. bk.rev. charts; illus. back issues avail.
Published by: Stellium Inc., 101 Interpromontory Rd, Great Falls, VA 22066-3218. Ed. Katherine Boehrer.

133.5 LKA
SUBASETHA. Text in Singhalese. 1967. w.
Address: Lake House, D.R. Wijewardene Mawatha, P O Box 248, Colombo, 10, Sri Lanka. TEL 1-21181. Ed. K Chandra Sri Kularatne. Circ: 80,000.

133.5 USA ISSN 0737-6154
BF1728.A2
SUN SIGN BOOK. Text in English. 1983. a. USD 7.95 per vol. (effective 2005). adv.
Published by: Llewellyn Publications, 84 S, Wabasha, MN 55164. TEL 612-291-1970, FAX 612-291-1970. Circ: 40,000.

133.5 NLD ISSN 0925-2878
SYMBOLON; tijdschrift voor astrologie en haar raakvlakken. Text in Dutch. 1990. 4/yr. EUR 22.50 (effective 2005). adv. bk.rev. index. back issues avail. **Document type:** *Academic/Scholarly.* **Description:** Covers serious astrological subjects for professional astrologers.
Address: Amsterdamseweg 156, Amstelveen, 1182 HK, Netherlands. TEL 31-20-6436979, symbolon@wxs.nl. Ed., Pub., R&P, Adv. contact A J Hamaker.

133.5 GBR
TAKE A BREAK'S FATE & FORTUNE. Variant title: Fate & Fortune. Text in English. 2001 (Nov.). bi-m. GBP 1.50 newsstand/cover (effective 2003). adv. **Document type:** *Magazine, Consumer.* **Description:** Contains articles and features on health, fashion and real life stories linked to astrology and psychic phenomena.
Published by: H. Bauer Publishing Ltd. (Subsidiary of: Heinrich Bauer Verlag), Academic House, 24-28 Oval Rd, London, NW1 7DT, United Kingdom. TEL 44-20-72418000, FAX 44-20-72418056, simon.priston@bauer.co.uk. Ed. Elayne DeLaurian. Pub. Liz Watkinson. Adv. contact Elaine Traynor. page GBP 2,800; trim 210 x 280.

133.5 USA ISSN 1067-1439
BF1651
TODAY'S ASTROLOGER. Text in English. 1938. m. USD 45 (effective 2004). bk.rev. charts; illus. index. back issues avail.; reprints avail. **Document type:** *Academic/Scholarly.* **Description:** Contains astrological articles, data information, news releases and a calendar of activities of members and affiliates.
Formerly: American Federation of Astrologers Bulletin (0735-4797)
Published by: American Federation of Astrologers, Inc., 6535 S Rural Rd, Box 22040, Tempe, AZ 85283-9760. TEL 602-838-1751, FAX 602-838-8293, afa@msn.com, http://www.astrologers.com. Ed., R&P Kris Brandt Riske. Circ: 2,700 (controlled).

133.5 DNK ISSN 0108-2450
TRIGON; magazine for professional astrology. Text in Danish. 1981. 3/yr. DKK 65. adv. bk.rev. illus.
Published by: Forlaget Stjernerne, Irene Christensen Institutet, Farimagsgade 63-1, Copenhagen K, 1364, Denmark. FAX 33141303. Ed. Christian Borup. Circ: 1,000.

613.262 USA
VEGETARIAN ASTROLOGER. Text in English. irreg.
Address: 4216 Tod Ave, East Chicago, IN 46312. TEL 219-397-9297. Ed. Ted Pandeva.

133.5 FRA
VOTRE SIGNE ASTRAL ET VOUS. Text in French. 1949. a. adv. illus.
Formerly: Astral (1250-5005)
Published by: Editions Francois de Villac, 6 rue de Savoie, Paris, 75006, France. TEL 33-1-53102600, FAX 33-1-53102601. Circ: 55,000.

133.5 USA ISSN 0747-8968
WELCOME TO PLANET EARTH; journal of new astrology in the contemporary world. Text in English. 1979. m. USD 45 (effective 2004). adv. bk.rev. illus. reprints avail. **Description:** Includes information on workshops, services, other periodicals. New age topics are covered as well.
Former titles: Pass the Word; Great Bear
Published by: Great Bear Press, PO Box 5164, Eugene, OR 97405. http://www.mcn.org/greatbear/. Ed. Mark Lerner. Circ: 2,100.

133.5 USA ISSN 0044-1082
BF1651
YOUR PERSONAL ASTROLOGY MAGAZINE★ . Text in English. 1939. q. USD 5. adv. bk.rev. charts. **Document type:** *Consumer.*
Published by: Dorchester Media, 35 Wilbur St, Lynbrook, NY 11563. TEL 516-593-1220. Ed. Marsha Kaplan.

ASTRONOMY

522.1 AUS ISSN 1326-2270
A A O NEWSLETTER. Text in English. 1994. 3/yr. (q. until 2002). free. back issues avail. **Document type:** *Newsletter, Academic/Scholarly.* **Description:** Contains updates on current research, new telescope instrumentation, sofware developments, personnel and general information of interest to telescope users.
Media: Online - full text.
Published by: Anglo-Australian Observatory, PO Box 296, Epping, NSW 1710 , Australia. lib@aaoepp.aao.gov.au, http://www.aao.gov.au/library/news.html.

520 USA ISSN 1046-5200
A A S JOB REGISTER. Text in English. 1980. m. looseleaf. membership only. adv. back issues avail. **Description:** Covers current job openings in astronomy for Ph.D. astronomers.
Published by: American Astronomical Society, 2000 Florida Ave, N W, Ste 400, Washington, DC 20009. TEL 202-328-2010, FAX 202-234-2560. Ed. Judy Johnson. Circ: 2,000.

520 USA ISSN 8750-9350
A A S NEWSLETTER. Text in English. 197?. 5/yr. membership. **Document type:** *Newsletter.*
Published by: American Astronomical Society, 2000 Florida Ave, N W, Ste 400, Washington, DC 20009. TEL 202-328-2010, FAX 202-234-2560, http://www.aas.org. R&P Robert W Milkey. Circ: 6,000.

520 USA
A A V S O ALERT NOTICE. Text in English. 1974. irreg. USD 7.50 per issue; USD 10 per issue foreign; USD 15 per issue by fax; USD 20 per issue foreign by fax (effective 2001). **Description:** Alerts persons interested to the discovery of novae, unusual activities of variable stars, and special requests from astronomers for simultaneous AAVSO observations.
Related titles: Fax ed.
Published by: American Association of Variable Star Observers, 25 Birch St, Cambridge, MA 02138. TEL 617-354-0484, FAX 617-354-0665, aavso@aavso.org, http://www.aavso.org. Ed. Janet A Mattei. Circ: 600.

523.8 USA ISSN 0516-9518
A A V S O BULLETIN; predicted dates of maxima and minima of long period variables for (year). Text in English. 1937. a. looseleaf. USD 25 domestic to individuals; USD 30 foreign to individuals; USD 40 domestic to institutions; USD 45 foreign to institutions (effective 2001). back issues avail. **Document type:** *Bulletin, Academic/Scholarly.* **Description:** Provides annual predicted dates of maxima and minima of 600 long-period variable stars.
Indexed: A&AAb, Inspec, RefZh.
—Linda Hall.
Published by: American Association of Variable Star Observers, 25 Birch St, Cambridge, MA 02138. TEL 617-354-0484, FAX 617-354-0665, aavso@aavso.org, http://www.aavso.org. Ed. Janet A Mattei. Circ: 1,500.

520 USA
A A V S O EPHEMERIDES. Text in English. 1981. a. USD 10 domestic to individuals; USD 15 foreign to individuals; USD 35 domestic to institutions; USD 40 foreign to institutions (effective 2001). back issues avail.
Published by: American Association of Variable Star Observers, 25 Birch St, Cambridge, MA 02138. TEL 617-354-0484, FAX 617-354-0665, aavso@aavso.org, http://www.aavso.org.

520 USA ISSN 0271-9053
QB835 CODEN: JAAODA
➤ **A A V S O JOURNAL.** Text in English. 1972. s-a. USD 25 to individuals; USD 30 foreign to individuals; USD 40 to institutions; USD 45 foreign to institutions (effective 2001). bk.rev. illus. index. back issues avail.; reprints avail. **Document type:** *Academic/Scholarly.* **Description:** Publishes scientific papers on variable-star research, AAVSO activities, and letters to editor.
Indexed: A&AAb, Inspec, RefZh.
—AskIEEE, Linda Hall.
Published by: American Association of Variable Star Observers, 25 Birch St, Cambridge, MA 02138. TEL 617-354-0484, FAX 617-354-0665, aavso@aavso.org, http://www.aavso.org/journal.html. Ed. Charles A Whitney. Circ: 1,500.

520 USA
A A V S O MONOGRAPHS AND MONOGRAPH SUPPLEMENTS. Text in English. irreg. USD 10 per issue; USD 15 per issue foreign (effective 2001); supplements free with monographs. **Document type:** *Monographic series.* **Description:** Contains AAVSO observations of one star as computer-generated lighted light curves and covers many years. Each supplement to Monograph continues the light curves of the Monograph's star for an additional five years.
Indexed: Inspec.
Published by: American Association of Variable Star Observers, 25 Birch St, Cambridge, MA 02138. TEL 617-354-0484, FAX 617-354-0665, aavso@aavso.org, http://www.aavso.org.

520 USA
A A V S O NEWSLETTER. Text in English. s-a. back issues avail.
Related titles: Online - full text ed.
Indexed: RefZh.
Published by: American Association of Variable Star Observers, 25 Birch St, Cambridge, MA 02138. TEL 617-354-0484, FAX 617-354-0665, aavso@aavso.org, http://www.aavso.org.

522 USA
A A V S O PHOTOELECTRIC PHOTOMETRY NEWSLETTER. Text in English. 1979. irreg. (3-4/yr.). looseleaf. USD 10 to individuals; USD 15 foreign to individuals (effective 2001). back issues avail. **Document type:** *Newsletter.* **Description:** Contains brief reports on small-amplitude variables, requests for PEP observations, and photoelectric hardware and software.
Published by: American Association of Variable Star Observers, 25 Birch St, Cambridge, MA 02138. TEL 617-354-0484, FAX 617-354-0665, aavso@aavso.org, http://www.aavso.org. Circ: 200.

520 USA ISSN 0271-8480
A A V S O SOLAR BULLETIN. Text in English. 1945. m. looseleaf. USD 25 to individuals; USD 30 foreign to individuals; USD 40 to institutions; USD 45 foreign to institutions (effective 2001). **Document type:** *Bulletin.* **Description:** Provides daily American and international sunspot numbers; sudden ionospheric disturbance data.
Indexed: Inspec.
Published by: American Association of Variable Star Observers, 25 Birch St, Cambridge, MA 02138. TEL 617-354-0484, FAX 617-354-0665, aavso@aavso.org, http://www.aavso.org. Ed. Joseph Lawrence. Circ: 300.

520 FRA
A G B NEWSLETTER. (Asymptotic Giant Branch) Text in French. 1994. m. **Document type:** *Newsletter.* **Description:** Covers stellar evolution on the asymptotic giant branch and beyond.
Media: Online - full text.
Published by: Universite de Grenoble II (Pierre Mendes-France), BP 47X, Grenoble, 38040, France. TEL 33-4-76825400, FAX 33-4-76825654, agbnews@gag.observ-gr.fr, http://gag.observ-gr.fr/liens/agbnews.html, http://www.upmf-grnoble.fr.

520 USA
A S P CATALOG. Text in English. 1976. s-a. free (effective 2005). **Document type:** *Catalog.* **Description:** Includes astronomy posters, videotapes, books, slides, globes, slide sets, and educational materials.
Formerly: A S P Selectory
Published by: Astronomical Society of the Pacific, 390 Ashton Ave, San Francisco, CA 94112. TEL 415-337-1100, 800-335-2624, FAX 415-337-5205, editor@astrosociety.org, service@astrosociety.org, http://www.astrosociety.org. Ed., R&P Joycelin Craig. Circ: 300,000.

523.01 DEU ISSN 0374-1583
ABHANDLUNGEN AUS DER HAMBURGER STERNWARTE. Text in German. 1966.
Formerly: Astronomische Abhandlungen der Hamburger Sternwarte (0374-0196)
—Linda Hall.
Published by: (Institut fuer Theoretische Astrophysik), Hamburger Sternwarte, Gojenbergsweg 12, Hamburg, 21029, Germany. TEL 49-40-428914112, FAX 49-40-428914198, sternwarte@hs.uni-hamburg.de, http://www.hs.uni-hamburg.de.

520 USA ISSN 0733-6314
ABRAMS PLANETARIUM SKY CALENDAR; an aid to enjoying the changing sky. Text in English. 1969. q. looseleaf. USD 10 domestic; USD 14 in Canada & Mexico (effective 2004). illus. back issues avail.; reprints avail. **Description:** Provides a night-by-night description of noteworthy sky events and includes a simplified star chart of the month's evening sky. On the calendar, text and drawings guide to bright planets at dusk and dawn, to the bright zodiac stars as the moon passes them, and to sights that can be enjoyed with binoculars.
Published by: Michigan State University, Talbert & Leota Abrams Planetarium, 113 Angell Bldg, East Lansing, MI 48824-1234. TEL 517-355-4676, ladiski@pilot.msu.edu, http://www.pa.msu.edu/abrams/SkyCalendar. Ed. Robert C Victor. Circ: 15,000.

ACADEMIE DES SCIENCES. COMPTES RENDUS. PHYSIQUE. see *CHEMISTRY—Physical Chemistry*

520 POL ISSN 0001-5237
QB1 CODEN: AASWAM
➤ **ACTA ASTRONOMICA**; an international quarterly journal. Text in English. 1925. q. EUR 169 (effective 2005). adv. bk.rev. back issues avail. **Document type:** *Journal, Academic/Scholarly.* **Description:** Publishes original, scientific papers from the domain of astrophysics and astronomy.
Indexed: ASCA, CIN, ChemAb, ChemTitl, CurCont, IAA, ISR, Inspec, SCI.
—BLDSC (0596.800000), AskIEEE, CASDDS, CISTI, IDS, IE, Infotrieve, ingenta, Linda Hall.
Published by: Copernicus Foundation for Polish Astronomy, Al Ujazdowskie 4, Warsaw, 00478, Poland. FAX 48-22-6294967, acta@astrouw.edu.pl, mk@astrouw.edu.pl, http://www.astrouw.edu.pl/~acta/acta.html. Eds. Andrzej Udalski, Marcin Kubiak TEL 48-22-6295346. R&P Marcin Kubiak TEL 48-22-6295346. Circ: 250 (paid). **Dist. by:** Ars Polona, Krakowskie Przedmiescie 7, Warsaw, Poland. TEL 48-22-9263914, FAX 48-22-9265334, arspolona@arspolona.com.pl, http://www.arspolona.com.pl.

520 DEU ISSN 1422-8521
ACTA HISTORICA ASTRONOMIAE. Text in English, German. 1998. irreg., latest vol.28, 2005. price varies. bk.rev. back issues avail. **Document type:** *Monographic series, Academic/Scholarly.* **Description:** Contains monographs, proceedings of conferences, and collections of scientific articles from all fields of the history of astronomy.
Related titles: Online - full text ed.
Published by: (Astronomische Gesellschaft, Arbeitskreis Astronomie), Verlag Harri Deutsch, Graefstr 47, Frankfurt Am Main, 60486, Germany. TEL 49-69-77015860, FAX 49-69-77015869, verlag@harri-deutsch.de, http://www.astro.uni-bonn.de/~pbrosche/aa/acta/, http://www.harri-deutsch.de/verlag. Ed. Juergen Hamel. Adv. contact Wolfgang Dick. Circ: 300 (controlled).

523.01 SGP ISSN 0218-0251
ADVANCED SERIES IN ASTROPHYSICS AND COSMOLOGY. Text in English. 1991. irreg., latest vol.13, 2000. price varies. **Document type:** *Monographic series, Academic/Scholarly.*
—BLDSC (0696.927200).

Published by: World Scientific Publishing Co. Pte. Ltd., 5 Toh Tuck Link, Singapore, 596224, Singapore. TEL 65-466-5775, FAX 65-467-7667, wspc@wspc.com.sg, http://www.wspc.com.sg/books/series/asac_series.shtml, http://www.worldscientific.com. Eds. L Z Fang, R Ruffini. **Dist. by:** World Scientific Publishing Co., Inc., 1060 Main St, River Edge, NJ 07661. TEL 201-487-9655, FAX 201-487-9656, 888-977-2665; World Scientific Publishing Ltd., 57 Shelton St, London WC2H 9HE, United Kingdom. TEL 44-20-78360888, FAX 44-20-78362020, sales@wspc.co.uk.

525   DEU   ISSN 1610-8957
▼ **ADVANCES IN ASTROBIOLOGY AND BIOGEOPHYSICS.**
Text in English. 2004. irreg., latest 2006. price varies.
Document type: *Monographic series, Academic/Scholarly.*
Description: Contains articles encompassing all aspects of research into the origins of life - from the creation of matter to the emergence of complex life forms - and the study of both structure and evolution of planetary ecosystems under a given set of astro- and geophysical parameters.
Published by: Springer-Verlag (Subsidiary of: Springer Science+Business Media), Tiergartenstr 17, Heidelberg, 69121, Germany. TEL 49-6221-3450, FAX 49-6221-345229, subscriptions@springer.de, http://www.springer.de. Eds. A Brack, J Baross. Adv. contact Stephan Kroeck TEL 49-30-827875739.

500.5   DEU   ISSN 1430-9602
ADVANCES IN SPATIAL SCIENCE. Text in German. 1995. irreg., latest 2002. price varies. **Document type:** *Monographic series, Academic/Scholarly.* **Description:** Publishes relevant research in this area of economics.
Indexed: CCMJ.
Published by: Springer-Verlag (Subsidiary of: Springer Science+Business Media), Haber Str 7, Heidelberg, 69126, Germany. TEL 49-30-82787-448, subscriptions@springer.de, http://www.springer-sbm.de. **Subscr. in N. America to:** Springer-Verlag New York, Inc., Journal Fulfillment, PO Box 2485, Secaucus, NJ 07096-2485. TEL 212-460-1500, FAX 212-473-6272.

520   ESP
AGRUPACION ASTRONOMICA DE SABADELL. CIRCULAR INFORMATIVA. Text in Spanish. 1981 (no.267). a. membership.
Formerly: Agrupacion Astronomica de Sabadell. Circular Mensual
Published by: Agrupacio Astronomica de Sabadell, Apdo de Correos 50, Sabadell, 08200, Spain. TEL 34-93-7255373, FAX 34-93-7272941, secretaria@astrosabadell.org, http://www.astrosabadell.org.

THE AIR ALMANAC. see *AERONAUTICS AND SPACE FLIGHT*

520   DNK   ISSN 0905-8958
AKTUEL ASTRONOMI. Text in Danish. 1977. q. DKK 21,500 (effective 1999). adv. bk.rev. illus. **Document type:** *Academic/Scholarly.*
Former titles (until 1991): Astronomi og Rumfart (0107-2862); (until 1980): Dansk Amatoer Astronomi (0105-9815)
Published by: (Tycho Brahe Planetarium), I S Astronomisk Forlag, Gl Kongevej 10, Copenhagen V, 1610, Denmark. TEL 45-33-14-28-88, FAX 45-33-14-28-88, tycho@tycho.dk, http://www.tycho.dk. Ed. Henry Norgaard. Pub. Astrono Misk Forlag. R&P Bjorn Jorgensen TEL 45-33-14-48-88. Adv. contact Gitte Jorgensen. Circ: 12,000.

520 001.942 NZL   ISSN 1173-5988
ALIENS (AUCKLAND). Text in English. 1995. s-a.
Indexed: ZooRec.
Published by: University of Auckland, Department of Geography and Environmental Science, Private Bag 92019, Auckland, New Zealand. TEL 64-9-3737599, FAX 64-9-3737434, http://www.geog.auckland.ac.nz.

520   PHL   ISSN 0569-0838
ALMANAC FOR GEODETIC ENGINEERS. Text in English. a. PHP 40. **Document type:** *Government.* **Description:** Data of the sun and selected stars for surveying purposes.
Published by: Philippine Atmospheric, Geophysical and Astronomical Services Administration, 1424 Quezon Ave, Quezon City, 1101, Philippines. TELEX 42021-PAGASA-PM. Ed. Leoncio A Amadore. Circ: 1,500.

528.6   ESP   ISSN 0210-735X
QB8.S73
ALMANAQUE NAUTICO. Text in Spanish. 1792. a. EUR 12.02 (effective 2001). illus. **Document type:** *Yearbook, Trade.* **Description:** Provides data required for astronomical navigation at sea.
Formerly: Almanaque Nautico para Uso de los Navegantes (0210-7341)
Related titles: CD-ROM ed.: Almanaue Nautico ... para PC. ISSN 1138-3550. 1998. EUR 1.80 (effective 2001).
Indexed: IECT.
—CINDOC.
Published by: Real Instituto y Observatorio de la Armada, Cecilio Pugazon s-n, San Fernando, Cadiz 11100, Spain. TEL 34-956-599367, FAX 34-956-599366, jcoma@roa.es, http://www.roa.es. Circ: 3,000 (paid).

520   USA
AMATEUR ASTRONOMY. Text in English. 1994. q. USD 20 domestic; USD 26 in Canada; USD 30 overseas (effective 2001). back issues avail. **Document type:** *Magazine, Consumer.* **Description:** Provides news and information to amateur astronomers about observing and telescopes.
Published by: Amateur Astronomy Magazine, 5450 N W 52 Ct, Chiefland, FL 32626. TEL 352-490-9101, tom@amateurastronomy.com, http://www.amateurastronomy.com.

520   USA
AMATEUR TELESCOPE MAKERS OF BOSTON NEWSLETTER. Text in English. 1996. m. **Document type:** *Newsletter.* **Description:** Contains astro-photos and articles and links to astronomy related sites.
Media: Online - full text.
Published by: Amateur Telescope Makers of Boston nugentrp@nenlifesci.com, nugentrp@aol.com, http://www.jovian.com/atmob/news.html.

520   USA
THE AMERICAN ASTRONOMER. Text in English. q. USD 25 membership (effective 2005). **Document type:** *Newsletter, Academic/Scholarly.*
Published by: American Association of Amateur Astronomers, 3131 Custer Rd., Ste. 175/175, Plano, TX 75075. http://www.astromax.com, http://www.corvus.com/.

520   USA   ISSN 0002-7537
QB1   CODEN: AASBAR
AMERICAN ASTRONOMICAL SOCIETY. BULLETIN. Text in English. 1969. q. USD 30 in North America; USD 55 elsewhere (effective 2005). abstr.; illus. reprints avail. **Document type:** *Bulletin.*
Related titles: Microfilm ed.: (from AIP).
Indexed: Inspec.
—BLDSC (2386.200000), CISTI, IE, Infotrieve, ingenta, Linda Hall.
Published by: American Astronomical Society, 2000 Florida Ave, N W, Ste 400, Washington, DC 20009. TEL 202-328-2010, FAX 202-234-2560, ssavoy@aas.org, http://www.aas.org/publications/baas/baas.html. Ed. P B Boyce. **Subscr. to:** American Institute of Physics, PO Box 503284, St Louis, MO 63150-3284. TEL 516-576-2270, 800-344-6902, FAX 516-349-9704, subs@aip.org, http://librarians.aip.org.

520   BGR   ISSN 1310-3571
ANDROMEDA. Text in Bulgarian. 1994. m. USD 60 foreign (effective 2004). **Document type:** *Magazine, Academic/Scholarly.*
Published by: Astronomical Association - Sofia, 49 Tsar Asen St, Sofia, 1463, Bulgaria. TEL 359-2-9793202, aas@cl.bas.bg, http://www.geocities.com/aas_sofia_bg. Ed. Boriana Bontcheva TEL 359-87-894056.

ANG TAGAMASID. see *METEOROLOGY*

522.1   JPN   ISSN 0915-5392
                          CODEN: ARKOED
ANNUAL REPORT OF THE KISO OBSERVATORY. Text in English. 1979. a.
Formerly (until 1988): Kiso Information Bulletin (0286-1380)
Indexed: Inspec.
Published by: University of Tokyo, Kiso Observatory, University of Tokyo Institute of Astronomy, Kiso Observatory, Tarusawa, Mitake-mura, Kiso-gun, Nagano, 397-0101, Japan. TEL 81-264-52-3360, FAX 81-264-52-3361, http://www.ioa.s.u-tokyo.ac.jp/kisohp.

520   USA   ISSN 0066-4146
QB1   CODEN: ARAAAJ
➤ **ANNUAL REVIEW OF ASTRONOMY AND ASTROPHYSICS.**
Text in English. 1963. a. USD 196 to institutions print or online ed.; USD 235 combined subscription to institutions print & online eds. (effective 2006). bibl.; charts; abstr. index, cum.index. back issues avail.; reprint service avail. from PSC. **Document type:** *Academic/Scholarly.* **Description:** Synthesizes and filters primary research to identify the principal contributions in the fields of astrophysics and astronomy.
Related titles: Microfilm ed.: (from PQC); Online - full text ed.: ISSN 1545-4282. USD 180 (effective 2003) (from bigchalk, EBSCO Publishing, H.W. Wilson, HighWire Press, O C L C Online Computer Library Center, Inc., ProQuest Information & Learning, Swets Information Services).
Indexed: ASCA, BrCerAb, C&ISA, CIN, CerAb, ChemAb, ChemTitl, CorrAb, CurCont, E&CAJ, EMA, GSI, IAA, ISR, Inspec, M&GPA, M&TEA, MBF, METADEX, MRD, PhysBer, SCI, WAA.
—CASDDS, CISTI, IDS, IE, Infotrieve, Linda Hall. **CCC.**
Published by: Annual Reviews, 4139 El Camino Way, Palo Alto, CA 94303-0139. TEL 650-493-4400, 800-523-8635, FAX 650-424-0910, service@annualreviews.org, http://arjournals.annualreviews.org/loi/astro, http://www.annualreviews.org. Eds. Geoffrey Burbidge, Samuel Gubins. R&P Laura Folkner.

➤ **ANNUAL REVIEW OF EARTH AND PLANETARY SCIENCES.**
see *EARTH SCIENCES*

520   ITA   ISSN 0392-2987
ANNUARIO DELLA SPECOLA CIDNEA. Text in Italian. 1953. a.
Formerly (until 1965): Guardare il Firmamento dalla Specola Cidnea (0392-2979)
Indexed: Inspec.
Published by: Specola Astronomica Cidnea, c/o Civici Musei di Scienze, via Ozanam 4, Brescia, 25128, Italy.

523.2   USA   ISSN 0270-7179
ANTARCTIC METEORITE NEWSLETTER. Text in English. 1978. 2/yr. free (effective 2005). **Document type:** *Newsletter, Government.* **Description:** Lists classifications and descriptions of meteorites returned as part of the US Antarctic Meteorite Program.
Published by: Antarctic Meteorite Program, Mail Code ST, Johnson Space Center, 2101 NASA Pkwy, Houston, TX 77058-3696. TEL 713-483-5135, FAX 713-483-5347, carlton.c.allen1@jsc.nasa.gov, http://www-curator.jsc.nasa.gov/curator/antmet/amn/amn.htm, http://www-curator.jsc.nasa.gov/curator/antmet/antmet.htm. Eds. Cecilia Satterwhite, Kevin Righter. Circ: 600.

520   CAN   ISSN 0843-6061
➤ **APEIRON (MONTREAL);** studies in infinite nature. Text in English. 1987. q. free (effective 2005). back issues avail.
Document type: *Journal, Academic/Scholarly.* **Description:** Consists of original articles focusing on new approaches to fundamental physics and astrophysics, new models of cosmology, elementary particles and forces, aimed at a specialist or informed lay audience.
Media: Online - full text (from Gale Group).
Indexed: Inspec.
—CISTI.
Published by: C. Roy Keys Inc., 4405 St Dominique, H2W ZBZ, Montreal, PQ H2W 2B2, Canada. FAX 514-842-3667, apeiron@vif.com, http://redshift.vif.com/Apeiron%20Home.htm. Ed., R&P C Roy Keys. Circ: 70.

520   DEU   ISSN 0174-254X
QB9
APPARENT PLACES OF FUNDAMENTAL STARS. Text in English. a.
—Linda Hall.
Published by: Astronomisches Rechen-Institut Heidelberg, Monchhofstrasse 12-14, Heidelberg, D-69120, Germany. TEL 49-6221-405-0, FAX 49-6221-405-297, http://www.ari.uni-heidelberg.de.

ARCHAEOASTRONOMY; the journal of astronomy culture. see *ARCHAEOLOGY*

ARCHAEOASTRONOMY & ETHNOASTRONOMY NEWS. see *ARCHAEOLOGY*

520   DEU   ISSN 0570-6262
ARCHENHOLD-STERNWARTE. VORTRAEGE UND SCHRIFTEN. Text in German. 1959. irreg., latest vol.7, no.70, 1989. price varies. adv. bk.rev. **Document type:** *Monographic series.* **Description:** Documents the history of astronomy.
—Linda Hall.
Published by: Archenhold-Sternwarte, Alt-Treptow 1, Berlin, 12435, Germany. TEL 49-30-2727493, FAX 49-30-2318083. Ed. D B Herrmann. Circ: 1,500.

520   USA   ISSN 1529-1294
THE ARMCHAIR ASTRONOMER. Text in English. 1994. irreg. free. **Description:** Compiles articles and commentaries on the study of astronomy and its applications and impact on the average layperson.
Media: Online - full text.
Published by: Armchair Astronomer, 49 Woodbine St., No. 4, Wollaston, MA 02170. TEL 617-923-6616, FAX 617-923-5116, vanhoose@lalaland.cl.msu.edu, http://lalaland.cl.msu.edu/~vanhoose/astro.html. Ed., Pub. Todd Ellis Van Hoosear.

520   USA   ISSN 1525-3996
PS648.S3
ARTEMIS; science and fiction for a space-faring age. Text in English. 2000. q. USD 15; USD 4.95 newsstand/cover (effective 2002). adv. illus.
Published by: L C R Publications, 1380 E 17th St, Ste 201, Brooklyn, NY 11230-6011. letters@lrcpubs.com, http://www.LRCPublications.com, http://www.tlrc.com. Ed., Pub. Ian Randal Strock.

520   ARG
ASOCIACION ARGENTINA DE ASTRONOMIA. BOLETIN (ONLINE). Text in Spanish. 1958. irreg. **Description:** This official organ of the Argentine Astronomy Association serves to make known its scientific activity.
Formerly (until 1995): Asociacion Argentina de Astronomia. Boletin (Print Edition) (0571-3285)
Media: Online - full text.
Published by: Asociacion Argentina de Astronomia, Facultad de Ciencias Astronomicas y Geofisicas, Paseo del Bosque s/n, La Plata, 1900, Argentina. TEL 54-221-4217308, FAX 54-221-4211761, aaacd@fcaglp.unlp.edu.ar, http://www.casleo.gov.ar/webaaa/indexaaa.htm, http://www.iafe.uba.ar.

520 CHL ISSN 0716-2049
QB1
ASOCIACION CHILENA DE ASTRONOMIA Y ASTRONAUTICA. BOLETIN. Text in Spanish. 1957. m.
Related titles: Online - full text ed.
Published by: Asociacion Chilena de Astronomia y Astronautica, Marcoleta 485, Of.H, Santiago, Chile. contacto@achaya.cl, http://www.achaya.cl.

520 PER ISSN 0044-9318
ASOCIACION PERUANA DE ASTRONOMIA. BOLETIN✶ . Text in Spanish. 1947. q. bk.rev.
Media: Duplicated (not offset).
Indexed: AICP.
Published by: Juan Fanning Ed.& Pub., 354 Miraflores, Lima, 18, Peru. Ed. Gustavo A Estremadoyro.

523 USA ISSN 0039-2502
QB1 CODEN: STASAD
➤ **ASSOCIATION OF LUNAR AND PLANETARY OBSERVERS. JOURNAL.** Variant title: Strolling Astronomer. Text in English. 1947. q. USD 26 in North America; USD 33 elsewhere (effective 2004). adv. bk.rev. charts; illus.; stat.; maps. 46 p./no.; back issues avail.; reprints avail. **Document type:** *Journal, Academic/Scholarly.*
Indexed: A&AAb, Inspec.
—AskIEEE, Linda Hall.
Published by: Association of Lunar and Planetary Observers, P O Box 13456, Springfield, IL 62791-3456. poshedly@bellsouth.net, poshedly@bellsouth.nt, http://www.LPL.Arizona.edu/~rhill/alpo/member.html. Ed. John E Westfall. Pub., Adv. contact Ken Poshedly. Circ: 410 (paid).

522.1 FRA ISSN 0249-7522
ASSOCIATION POUR LE DEVELOPPEMENT INTERNATIONAL DE L'OBSERVATOIRE DE NICE. BULLETIN. Text in English, French. 1964. a. charts; illus. **Document type:** *Bulletin.*
Formerly (until 1974): Association pour le Developpement International de l'Observatoire de Nice. Bulletin d'Information (0004-5861)
Published by: Association pour le Developpement International de l'Observatoire de Nice, BP 4229, Nice, 06304, France. Circ: 400.

ASTROBIOLOGY. see *BIOLOGY*

523.01 ARM ISSN 0571-7132
QB461 CODEN: ASTKBG
ASTROFIZIKA. Text in Russian. 1965. q. **Document type:** *Journal, Academic/Scholarly.*
Related titles: ◆ English Translation: Astrophysics. ISSN 0571-7256.
Indexed: INIS AtomInd, Inspec.
—Linda Hall.
Published by: Yerevan State University, 1 A Manoukian St, Yerevan, 375049, Armenia. TEL 7-8852-554702, FAX 7-8852-151087.

522.63 USA ISSN 0094-1417
QB121
ASTROGRAPH✶ . Text in English. 1973. bi-m. USD 10; USD 15 foreign. bk.rev. **Description:** Covers astrophotography: astronomical photography of the Moon, planets, galaxies, nebulae and stars.
Address: PO Box 369, Dumfries, VA 22026-0369. TEL 703-892-6846. Ed. Robert C Price. adv.: color page USD 625. Circ: 1,200.

520 FRA ISSN 0398-074X
ASTROLAB. Text mainly in French; Summaries in English, Italian, Spanish. 1976. q. EUR 37 (effective 2002). adv. bk.rev. **Document type:** *Journal.* **Description:** Practical and theoretical ideas on astronomy and space. Includes new books and materials available.
Published by: Philippe Bury Ed. & Pub., 185 rue de Solignac, Limoges, 87000, France. buryph@voila.fr.

520 FRA ISSN 0764-2997
ASTROLETTRE. Text in French. 1984. irreg. (approx. 5/yr.). EUR 13 (effective 2002). adv. bk.rev. **Document type:** *Newsletter.*
Published by: Philippe Bury Ed. & Pub., 185 rue de Solignac, Limoges, 87000, France. buryph@voila.fr.

520 GBR ISSN 0950-138X
➤ **THE ASTRONOMER.** Text in English. 1964. m. GBP 21 domestic; GBP 25 in Europe; GBP 28 elsewhere (effective 2001). adv. bk.rev.; software rev. charts; illus.; stat. 32 p./no. 1 cols./p.; back issues avail. **Document type:** *Magazine, Academic/Scholarly.*
Related titles: Online - full text ed.
Indexed: Inspec.
—AskIEEE.
Published by: Astronomer, 6 Chelmerton Avenue, Chelmsford, Essex CM2 9RE, United Kingdom. TEL 44-1245-475885, secretary@theastronomer.org, http://www.theastronomer.org/. Ed., R&P, Adv. contact Guy M Hurst. Pub. Guy Hurst. Circ: 300; 300 (paid).

520 NOR ISSN 0802-7587
ASTRONOMI. Text in Norwegian. 1971. bi-m. NOK 190 to individual members (effective 2003). adv. bk.rev. 48 p./no.; back issues avail.
Former titles (until 1989): Amatoerastronomen (0802-7609); (until 1972): Amatoerkontakt (0802-7595)
Related titles: Online - full text ed.
Published by: Norsk Astronomisk Selskap/Norwegian Astronomical Society, 1029 Blindern, Postboks 250, Oslo, 0315, Norway. nas-astronomi@astro.uio.no, http://www.astro.uio.no/nas/index.html. Ed. Trond Erik Hillstad. Circ: 1,100.

520 ITA ISSN 1129-7662
L'ASTRONOMIA (MILAN). Text in Italian. 1979. m. adv. bk.rev. **Document type:** *Magazine, Consumer.*
Published by: Media Presse Edizioni, Via Nino Bixio, 30, Milan, MI 20129, Italy. TEL 39-2-2043941, FAX 39-2-2046507, lastronomia@galactica.it. Ed., R&P Corrado Lamberti. Pub. Cesare Vacchelli. Adv. contact Luigi Vacchelli. Circ: 70,000.

523 USA ISSN 0737-6421
QB8.U6 CODEN: ASALET
THE ASTRONOMICAL ALMANAC. Text in English. 1766. a. USD 55 (effective 2004). back issues avail. **Document type:** *Government.* **Description:** Contains precise ephemerides of the sun, moon, and planets and satellites, as well as data for eclipses and other astronomical phenomena.
Supersedes (1960-1981): Astronomical Ephemeris (0066-9962); (1852-1980): American Ephemeris and Nautical Almanac (0065-8189); (1766-1852): Nautical Almanac and Astronomical Ephemeris
Indexed: Inspec.
—BLDSC (1749.780000), Linda Hall.
Published by: U.S. Naval Observatory, c/o Dr D D McCarthy, Department of the Navy, Washington, DC 20392-5100. http://aa.usno.navy.mil/publications/docs/NewASA.htm. **Subscr. also to:** U.S. Government Printing Office, Superintendent of Documents; **Subscr. in the U.K. to:** H.M.S.O., Publications Centre, PO Box 276, London SW8 5DT, United Kingdom. TEL 44- 207-873-9090, 44-207-873-8200, FAX 44-20-7873-8200. **Co-sponsor:** H.M. Nautical Almanac Office (UK).

520 GBR ISSN 1055-6796
QB1 CODEN: AATREG
➤ **ASTRONOMICAL AND ASTROPHYSICAL TRANSACTIONS.** Text in English. 1991. bi-m. (in 2 vols., 6 nos./vol.). GBP 2,193, USD 2,892 combined subscription to institutions print & online eds. (effective 2006). reprint service avail. from PSC. **Document type:** *Journal, Academic/Scholarly.* **Description:** Covers all modern and classical fields of astronomy and astrophysics. Includes astronomical instrumentation and related fundamental sciences.
Related titles: Microform ed.; Online - full text ed.: ISSN 1476-3540. GBP 2,083, USD 2,747 to institutions (effective 2006) (from EBSCO Publishing, Gale Group, IngentaConnect, O C L C Online Computer Library Center, Inc., Swets Information Services).
Indexed: Inspec.
—BLDSC (1749.790000), AskIEEE, CISTI, IE. **CCC.**
Published by: (Eurasian Astronomical Society RUS), Taylor & Francis Ltd (Subsidiary of: Taylor & Francis Group), 4 Park Sq, Milton Park, Abingdon, OX14 4RN, United Kingdom. TEL 44-1235-828600, FAX 44-1235-829000, info@tandf.co.uk, http://www.tandf.co.uk/journals/titles/10556796.asp. Ed. Nikolai G Bochkarev.

520 IND ISSN 0066-9970
ASTRONOMICAL EPHEMERIS OF GEOCENTRIC PLACES OF PLANETS. Text in English; Summaries in Hindi. 1942. a. INR 13. **Document type:** *Government.*
Published by: Shree Jiwaji Observatory, Ujain, Madhya Pradesh, India. Ed. Jyotishastracharya K K Joshi. Circ: 500.

520 CZE ISSN 1211-9105
ASTRONOMICAL INSTITUTE OF THE ACADEMY OF SCIENCES OF THE CZECH REPUBLIC. PUBLICATIONS. Text in English. 1977. a. **Description:** Publishes papers presented at conferences organized by the institute.
Supersedes (in 1993): Czechoslovak Academy of Sciences. Astronomical Institute. Publication (0862-3082)
Indexed: Inspec, RefZh.
—BLDSC (7025.897000), Linda Hall.
Published by: Akademie Ved Ceske Republiky, Astronomicky Ustav/Academy of Sciences of the Czech Republic, Astronomical Institite, Fricova 1, Ondrejov, 25165, Czech Republic. TEL 42-2-04857141, FAX 42-2-881611, had@dsunstel.asu.cas.cz, http://www.lib.cas.cz/knav/journals/eng/Publications_of_the_Astronomical_Institute.htm, http://www.asu.cas.cz. Ed. Petr Hadrova.

520 USA ISSN 0004-6256
QB1 CODEN: ANJOAA
➤ **THE ASTRONOMICAL JOURNAL.** Text in English. 1849. m. USD 550 combined subscription print & online eds.; USD 53 per issue (effective 2006). abstr.; bibl.; charts; illus. cum.index: vols.1-50, 1849-1944; vols.51-80, 1944-1975. back issues avail.; reprints avail. **Document type:** *Journal, Academic/Scholarly.* **Description:** Covers quasars, supernova remnants, and studies of the interstellar medium as well as more traditional areas of astronomy.
Related titles: Microform ed.: (from AIP); Online - full text ed.: ISSN 1538-3881. USD 425 (effective 2006) (from EBSCO Publishing).
Indexed: ASCA, ApMecR, CIN, CPI, ChemAb, ChemTitl, CivEngAb, CompR, CurCont, GPAA, ISR, Inspec, MathR, PhysBer, RefZh, SCI, SPINweb.
—BLDSC (1752.000000), AskIEEE, CASDDS, CISTI, IDS, IE, Infotrieve, ingenta, Linda Hall. **CCC.**
Published by: American Astronomical Society, 2000 Florida Ave, N W, Ste 400, Washington, DC 20009. TEL 202-328-2010, FAX 202-234-2560, astroj@astro.washington.edu, http://www.journals.uchicago.edu/AJ/home.html, http://www.aas.org. Ed. John S. Gallagher III. **Subscr. to:** University of Chicago Press, Journals Division, Journals Division, PO Box 37005, Chicago, IL 60637. TEL 773-753-3347, FAX 773-753-0811, subscriptions@journals.uchicago.edu, http://www.press.uchicago.edu/.

520 SVK ISSN 0862-920X
ASTRONOMICAL OBSERVATORY ON SKALNATE PLESO. CONTRIBUTIONS. Text in English; Summaries in Russian, Slovak. 1977 (vol.8). irreg. price varies.
Formerly (until 1990): Astronomicke Observatorie na Skalnatom Plese. Prace (0583-466X)
Indexed: Inspec, RefZh.
—CISTI.
Published by: (Slovenska Akademia Vied/Slovak Academy of Sciences, Astronomicky Ustav), Vydavatel'stvo Slovenskej Akademie Vied Veda/Veda, Publishing House of the Slovak Academy of Sciences, Dubravska cesta 9, Bratislava, 84234, Slovakia. **Dist. by:** Slovart G.T.G. s.r.o., Krupinska 4, PO Box 152, Bratislava 85299, Slovakia. TEL 421-2-63839472, FAX 421-2-63839485, http://www.slovart-gtg.sk.

523 USA ISSN 0083-2421
QB9
ASTRONOMICAL PHENOMENA. Text in English. 1951. a. USD 6.50 (effective 2002). back issues avail. **Document type:** *Government.* **Description:** Preprints data from the Astronomical Almanac, including the calendar, anniversaries and festivals, chronological eras and cycles, equinoxes and solstices, phase of the moon, visibility and configurations of the planets, elipses, equation of time and declination of the sun, rising and setting of the sun and moon, and the position of the Polaris.
—Linda Hall.
Published by: U.S. Naval Observatory, c/o Dr D D McCarthy, Department of the Navy, Washington, DC 20392-5100. TEL 202-783-3238. **Subscr. in the U.K. to:** H.M.S.O., Publications Centre, PO Box 276, London SW8 5DT, United Kingdom. TEL 44- 207-873-9090, FAX 44-20-7873-8200. **Dist. by:** Bernan Associates, Bernan, 4611-F Assembly Dr., Lanham, MD 20706-4391. TEL 301-459-0056, 800-274-4447. **Co-sponsor:** H.M. Nautical Almanac Office (UK).

520 AUS
➤ **ASTRONOMICAL SOCIETY OF AUSTRALIA. PUBLICATIONS (ONLINE EDITION).** Text in English. q. AUD 70 in Australasia to individuals; USD 60 elsewhere to individuals; AUD 260 in Australia & New Zealand to institutions; USD 275 elsewhere to institutions (effective 2002). bk.rev. charts; stat. back issues avail.; reprints avail. **Document type:** *Journal, Academic/Scholarly.* **Description:** Publishes new and significant research in all areas of astronomy and astrophysics, including instrumentation.
Media: Online - full text (from EBSCO Publishing, Gale Group, O C L C Online Computer Library Center, Inc., Swets Information Services).
Published by: C S I R O Publishing, 150 Oxford St, PO Box 1139, Collingwood, VIC 3066, Australia. TEL 61-3-96627500, FAX 61-3-96627611, pasa@publish.csiro.au, publishing@csiro.au, http://www.publish.csiro.au/journals.pasa/. Ed. M C Storey.

520 IND ISSN 0304-9523
QB1 CODEN: BANID3
➤ **ASTRONOMICAL SOCIETY OF INDIA. BULLETIN.** Text in English. 1973. q. USD 100 to institutions (effective 2006). adv. bk.rev. back issues avail.; reprints avail. **Document type:** *Bulletin, Academic/Scholarly.* **Description:** Publishes original research papers, review articles, reports on scientific meetings, reports from astronomical centres, and proceedings.
Related titles: Online - full text ed.
Indexed: A&AAb, ChemAb, Inspec.
—AskIEEE, CASDDS, Linda Hall.
Published by: Astronomical Society of India, Indian Institute of Astrophysics, Koramangala, Bangalore, Karnataka 560 034, India. TEL 91-80-5530672, FAX 91-80-5534043, basi@iiap.ernet.in, http://www.scientificpub.com/bookdetails.php?booktransid=470&bookid=466, http://www.rri.res.in/asi/. Ed., Pub., R&P, Adv. contact H C Bhatt. Circ: 900 (paid). **Subscr. to:** Scientific Publishers, 5-A New Pali Rd., Near Hotel Taj Hari Mahal, PO Box 91, Jodhpur, Rajasthan 342 003, India. TEL 91-291-2433323, FAX 91-291-2512580, info@scientificpub.com, http://www.scientificpub.com.

520 USA
ASTRONOMICAL SOCIETY OF NEW YORK. NEWSLETTER. Text in English. 1976. s-a. USD 12 (effective 2001). **Document type:** *Newsletter.*
Indexed: A&AAb.

Published by: L. Davis Press, Inc., 1125 Oxford Pl, Schenectady, NY 12308. TEL 518-374-5636. Ed. A G Davis Philip. Circ: 100.

520 AUS ISSN 0044-9806
ASTRONOMICAL SOCIETY OF SOUTH AUSTRALIA. BULLETIN. Text in English. 1892. m. AUD 36 (effective 2000). bk.rev. **Document type:** *Newsletter.*
Published by: Astronomical Society of South Australia, GPO Box 199, Adelaide, SA 5001, Australia. TEL 61-8-8338-1231, FAX 61-8-8379-4145, info@assa.org.au, http://www.assa.org.au. Ed. Janita Hill TEL 61-8-83708248. R&P Tomy Beresfood TEL 61-8-8338-1231. Circ: 450.

520 ZAF ISSN 0024-8266
CODEN: MASAAK
➤ **ASTRONOMICAL SOCIETY OF SOUTHERN AFRICA. MONTHLY NOTES.** Short title: M N A S S A. Text in English. 1941. bi-m. ZAR 100 per issue domestic; USD 45 per issue foreign (effective 2006). adv. bk.rev.; software rev. bibl.; charts; illus. back issues avail. **Document type:** *Journal, Academic/Scholarly.*
Indexed: A&AAb, Inspec.
—AskIEEE.
Published by: Astronomical Society of Southern Africa, PO Box 9, Observatory, Cape Town 7935, South Africa. TEL 27-21-5315250, FAX 27-21-4473639, cliffturk@yebo.co.za, http://da.saao.ac.za/assa. Ed., R&P Auke Slotegraaf. Adv. contact Cliff Turk. page ZAR 200; 13 x 20. Circ: 500.

➤ **ASTRONOMICAL SOCIETY OF THE PACIFIC. CONFERENCE PROCEEDINGS.** see *MEETINGS AND CONGRESSES*

520 AUS ISSN 0067-0006
QB4.9.A8
ASTRONOMICAL SOCIETY OF VICTORIA. ASTRONOMICAL YEARBOOK. Text in English. 1964. a. AUD 15 (effective 2003). index. **Document type:** *Yearbook, Academic/Scholarly.* **Description:** Contains data for local observations and other general astronomical information, as well as informative summaries of various celestial objects.
Published by: Astronomical Society of Victoria, GPO Box 1059 J, Melbourne, VIC 3001, Australia. http://www.asv.org.au/. R&P Chris Johnston. Circ: 900.

520 BGR ISSN 0861-1270
QB4
ASTRONOMICHESKI KALENDAR. Text in Bulgarian. 1954. a. BGL 1.26. reprint service avail. from IRC.
Formerly (until 1984): Astronomicheski Kalendar na Observatoriiata v Sofia (0324-1408)
—Linda Hall.
Published by: (Bulgarska Akademiya na Naukite/Bulgarian Academy of Sciences, Sektsiia po Astronomiia), Universitetsko Izdatelstvo Sv. Kliment Okhridski/Publishing House of the Sofia University St. Kliment Ohridski, Akad G Bonchev 6, Sofia, 1113, Bulgaria. Ed. L Levicharska. Circ: 2,640. **Dist. by:** Hemus, 6 Rouski Blvd., Sofia 1000, Bulgaria.

520 RUS ISSN 0373-3343
ASTRONOMICHESKII EZHEGODNIK/ASTRONOMICAL YEARBOOK. Text in Russian. 1921. a., latest 2003. **Document type:** *Yearbook, Academic/Scholarly.* **Description:** Contains the ephemerides of the Sun, Moon, major planets, and stars. Also gives information on various astronomical phenomena: lunar and solar eclipses, planetary configurations, rises and sets of the Sun and Moon, etc.
Formerly (until 1993): Astronomicheskii Ezhegodnik SSSR (0205-4590)
—Linda Hall.
Published by: Rossiiskaya Akademiya Nauk, Institut Prikladnoi Astronomii/Russian Academy of Sciences, Institute of Applied Astronomy, Naberezhnaya Kutuzova 10, St Petersburg, 191187, Russian Federation. TEL 8-812-2751118, FAX 7-812-2751119, ipa@ipa.nw.ru, http://www.ipa.rssi.ru.

520 RUS ISSN 0320-930X
QB1 CODEN: ASVEA7
ASTRONOMICHESKII VESTNIK. Text in Russian; Summaries in English. 1967. 6/yr. RUR 770 for 6 mos. domestic (effective 2004). back issues avail. **Document type:** *Journal, Academic/Scholarly.* **Description:** Publishes articles concerning the bodies of the Solar System: planets and their satellites, asteroids, comets, meteroic substances, and cosmic dust; the physics and dynamics of these bodies, their origin and evolution, and investigative methods are covered.
Related titles: Online - full text ed.; ♦ English Translation: Solar System Research. ISSN 0038-0946.
Indexed: CIN, ChemAb, ChemTitl, Inspec, RefZh.
—AskIEEE, CASDDS, East View, KNAW, Linda Hall. **CCC.**
Published by: (Rossiiskaya Akademiya Nauk/Russian Academy of Sciences), Izdatel'stvo Nauka, Profsoyuznaya ul 90, Moscow, 117864, Russian Federation. TEL 7-095-3347151, FAX 7-095-4202220, astvest@maik.ru, secret@naukaran.ru, http://www.maik.rssi.ru/journals/solsys.htm, http://www.naukaran.ru. Circ: 2,300.

520 RUS ISSN 0004-6299
CODEN: ASZHA2
ASTRONOMICHESKII ZHURNAL. Text in Russian. 1924. bi-m. RUR 1,230 for 6 mos. domestic; USD 396 foreign (effective 2004). bk.rev. index. **Description:** Publishes original papers on astronomy, including theoretical and observational astrophysics, physics of the Sun, planetary astrophysics, radioastronomy, stellar astronomy, celestial mechanics, and astronomy methods and instrumentation.
Related titles: Online - full text ed.; ♦ English Translation: Astronomy Reports. ISSN 1063-7729.
Indexed: ASCA, BrCerAb, C&ISA, CIN, CerAb, ChemAb, ChemTitl, CivEngAb, CorrAb, CurCont, E&CAJ, EMA, IAA, ISR, Inspec, M&TEA, MBF, METADEX, MathR, PhysBer, RefZh, SCI, WAA, ZentMath.
—AskIEEE, CASDDS, East View, IDS, Linda Hall. **CCC.**
Published by: (Rossiiskaya Akademiya Nauk/Russian Academy of Sciences), Izdatel'stvo Nauka, Profsoyuznaya ul 90, Moscow, 117864, Russian Federation. TEL 7-095-3347151, FAX 7-095-4202220, astrep@maik.ru, secret@naukaran.ru, http://www.maik.rssi.ru/cgi-bin/list.pl?page=astrus, http://www.naukaran.ru. **Dist. by:** M K - Periodica, ul Gilyarovskogo 39, Moscow 129110, Russian Federation. TEL 7-095-2845008, FAX 7-095-2813798, info@periodicals.ru, http://www.mkniga.ru.

520 FRA ISSN 0004-6302
QB1
L'ASTRONOMIE. Text in French. 1882. m. adv. bk.rev. bibl.; charts; illus. index. **Document type:** *Bulletin.* **Description:** Contains scientific articles for amateur astronomers.
Indexed: A&AAb, Inspec, RefZh.
—AskIEEE, Linda Hall. **CCC.**
Published by: Societe Astronomique de France, 3 rue Beethoven, Paris, 75016, France. TEL 33-01-42241374, FAX 33-01-42307547, saf@calvanet.fr, http://www.iap.fr/saf. Ed. Monique Gros. R&P, Adv. contact Elisabeth Sable. Circ: 3,000.

520 DEU ISSN 1616-0894
ASTRONOMIE. Text in German. 2000. irreg. price varies. **Document type:** *Monographic series, Academic/Scholarly.*
Published by: Bochumer Universitaetsverlag GmbH, Querenburger Hoehe 281, Bochum, 44801, Germany. TEL 49-234-9719780, FAX 49-234-9719786, bou@bou.de, http://bou.de.

520 FRA ISSN 0989-6236
ASTRONOMIE ET SCIENCES HUMAINES. Text in French. 1988. s-a. **Document type:** *Proceedings.*
Indexed: AICP.
Published by: Observatoire Astronomique de Strasbourg, 11 rue de l'Universite, Strasbourg, 67000, France. FAX 88-25-01-60, TELEX 890506 STAROB S, gerard@simbad.u-strasbg.fr. Ed. Gerard Jasniewicz. Circ: 450.

520 CAN ISSN 1183-5362
ASTRONOMIE QUEBEC. Text in English. 1972. bi-m. CND 32. illus. **Description:** Disseminates astronomical and astronautical information including observation reports, member news, general information, and more.
Formerly: Quebec Astronomique (0318-0492)
Indexed: PdeR.
Published by: Editions Astronomique Inc., 4545 Ave Pierre de Coubertin, Montreal, PQ H1V 3R2, Canada. TEL 514-252-3038, FAX 514-251-8038. Ed. Jean Pierre Urbain. adv.: B&W page CND 625. Circ: 2,500.

520 DEU ISSN 0948-4388
ASTRONOMIE UND RAUMFAHRT. Text in German. 1964. bi-m. EUR 35.40; EUR 17.70 to students; EUR 8 newsstand/cover (effective 2004). adv. bk.rev. bibl.; charts; illus.; stat. index. **Document type:** *Journal, Academic/Scholarly.*
Formerly: Astronomie in der Schule (0004-6310)
Published by: Erhard Friedrich Verlag GmbH, Im Brande 17, Seelze, 30926, Germany. TEL 49-511-40004-0, FAX 49-511-40004119, info@friedrich-verlag.de, http://www.friedrich-verlag.de. adv.: B&W page EUR 808, color page EUR 1,212. Circ: 3,500.

520 DEU ISSN 0934-4438
CODEN: AGESEK
ASTRONOMISCHE GESELLSCHAFT. ABSTRACT SERIES. Text in English. 1988. irreg. EUR 500 per vol. (effective 2001). back issues avail. **Document type:** *Monographic series.* **Description:** Covers abstracts and contributed talks presented at the annual meeting.
Indexed: Inspec.
Published by: Astronomische Gesellschaft, c/o Reinhard E. Schielicke, Astrophysikalisches Inst und Univ-Sternwaerte Jena, Schillergaesschen 2, Jena, 07745, Germany. TEL 49-3641-94-75-01, FAX 49-3641-94-75-02, schie@astro.uni-jena.de, http://www.astro.uni-jena.de/Astron_Ges/.

520 DEU ISSN 0374-1958
ASTRONOMISCHE GESELLSCHAFT. MITTEILUNGEN. Text in German. 1866. a. **Description:** Includes annual reports of astronomical institutions, reports on meetings of the executive committee, and minutes of the regular meetings.
Formerly (until 1944): Astronomische Gesellschaft. Vierteljahrsschrift (1011-0690); Incorporates (1966-1991): Astronomischer Institute. Jahresberichte (0172-5483)
Indexed: Inspec.
—Linda Hall.
Published by: Astronomische Gesellschaft, c/o Reinhard E. Schielicke, Astrophysikalisches Inst und Univ-Sternwaerte Jena, Schillergaesschen 2, Jena, 07745, Germany. TEL 49-3641-94-75-01, FAX 49-3641-94-75-02, schie@astro.uni-jena.de, http://www.astro.uni-jena.de/Astron_Ges/.

520 DEU ISSN 0067-0014
ASTRONOMISCHE GRUNDLAGEN FUER DEN KALENDER. Text in German. 1949. a. EUR 75 (effective 2005). **Document type:** *Journal, Academic/Scholarly.*
Published by: (Astronomisches Rechen-Institut Heidelberg), G. Braun Buchverlag (Subsidiary of: D R W Verlag Weinbrenner GmbH & Co.), Kaiserallee 87, Karlsruhe, 76185, Germany. TEL 49-721-509860, FAX 49-721-509889, info@gbraun-buchverlag.de, http://www.ari.uni-heidelberg.de/publikationen/kal/, http://www.gbraun-buchverlag.de. Ed. T Lederle. Circ: 1,000.

520 DEU ISSN 0004-6337
QB1 CODEN: ASNAAN
➤ **ASTRONOMISCHE NACHRICHTEN/ASTRONOMICAL NOTES.** Text in English. 1821. 10/yr. EUR 1,018 in Europe; CHF 1,794 Switzerland & Liechtenstein; USD 1,248 elsewhere; EUR 1,120 combined subscription in Europe print & online eds.; CHF 1,974 combined subscription in Switzerland & Liechtenstein for print & online eds; USD 1,373 combined subscription elsewhere print & online eds. (effective 2006). charts; illus. index. **Document type:** *Journal, Academic/Scholarly.* **Description:** Publishes original manuscripts on all fields of astronomy and astrophysics and review papers on special and current topics.
Related titles: Online - full text ed.: ISSN 1521-3994. 2000. EUR 1,018 in Europe to institutions; CHF 1,794 to institutions in Switzerland & Liechtenstein; USD 1,248 elsewhere to institutions (effective 2006) (from EBSCO Publishing, Swets Information Services, Wiley InterScience).
Indexed: ASCA, CCMJ, CIN, ChemAb, ChemTitl, CurCont, ISR, Inspec, MathR, MathSciNet, PhysBer, RefZh, SCI, SSCI, ZentMath.
—AskIEEE, CASDDS, IDS, IE, Linda Hall. **CCC.**
Published by: (Astrophysikalisches Institut Potsdam), Wiley - V C H Verlag GmbH & Co. KGaA (Subsidiary of: John Wiley & Sons, Inc.), Boschstr 12, Weinheim, 69469, Germany. TEL 49-6201-6060, FAX 49-6201-606328, subservice@wiley-vch.de, http://www.wiley-vch.de/home/an. Ed. K G Strassmeier. R&P Claudia Rutz. Circ: 300. **Subscr. in the Americas to:** John Wiley & Sons, Inc., 111 River St, Hoboken, NJ 07030-5774. TEL 201-748-6645, FAX 201-748-6088, uscs-wis@wiley.com, http://www.wiley.com; **Subscr. outside Germany, Austria & Switzerland to:** John Wiley & Sons Ltd., The Atrium, Southern Gate, Chichester, West Sussex PO19 8SQ, United Kingdom. TEL 44-1243-779777, FAX 44-1243-775878.

520 USA ISSN 0091-6358
QB1 CODEN: ASTRD5
ASTRONOMY. Text in English. 1973. m. USD 42.95 domestic; USD 58 in Canada (effective 2005). adv. bk.rev. charts; illus. index. back issues avail.; reprint service avail. from PQC. **Document type:** *Magazine, Consumer.* **Description:** Explores the planets, stars, and galaxies, and probes other facets of space. Includes monthly star charts with tips about star-gazing.
Related titles: Online - full text ed.: (from bigchalk, EBSCO Publishing, Florida Center for Library Automation, Gale Group, H.W. Wilson, Northern Light Technology, Inc., O C L C Online Computer Library Center, Inc., ProQuest Information & Learning).
Indexed: Acal, BRI, CBRI, CPerI, GSI, IHTDI, Inspec, MASUSE, MagInd, PMR, RGAb, RGPR, RefZh, TOM, WBA, WMB.
—BLDSC (1762.900000), AskIEEE, CISTI, EI, IE, Infotrieve, ingenta, Linda Hall.
Published by: Kalmbach Publishing Co., 21027 Crossroads Circle, PO Box 1612, Waukesha, WI 53187-1612. TEL 262-796-8776, 888-350-2413, FAX 262-796-1615, editor@kalmbach.com, http://www.astronomy.com, http://www.kalmbach.com. Ed. David Eicher. Pub. James J Slocum. Adv. contact Howard Hoerl. B&W page USD 4,854, color page USD 7,136. Circ: 152,821 (paid).

520 523.01 FRA ISSN 0004-6361
QB1 CODEN: AAEJAF
➤ **ASTRONOMY & ASTROPHYSICS;** a European journal. Text in English, French, German; Summaries in English. 1930. 48/yr. (in 16 vols., 3 nos./vol.). EUR 541 combined subscription worldwide to individuals print & online eds.; EUR 3,489 combined subscription worldwide to institutions print & online eds. (effective 2006). adv. bibl.; charts; illus. index, cum.index. reprint service avail. from ISI. **Document type:** *Journal, Academic/Scholarly.* **Description:** Presents papers on all aspects of astronomy and astrophysics - theoretical, observational, and instrumental - regardless of the techniques used - optical, radio, particles, space vehicles, and numerical analysis.

Superseded in part (in 1968): Zeitschrift fuer Astrophysik (0372-8331); Incorporated (1947-1992): Astronomical Institutes of Czechoslovakia. Bulletin (0004-6248); (1966-2000): Astronomy & Astrophysics. Supplement Series (0365-0138); Which was formerly (until 1970): Astronomical Institutes of the Netherlands. Bulletin. Supplement Series (0365-8910); Which incorporated (1900-1960): Kapteyn Astronomical Laboratory at Groningen. Publications (0927-3107); Which was formerly (until 1924): Astronomical Laboratory at Groningen. Publications (0929-6255)
Related titles: Microform ed.: (from PQC); Online - full text ed.: ISSN 1432-0746. EUR 212 in the European Union to individuals; EUR 211 elsewhere to individuals; EUR 2,563 in the European Union to institutions; EUR 2,617 elsewhere to institutions (effective 2006) (from EBSCO Publishing, Swets Information Services).
Indexed: ASCA, ApMecR, BrCerAb, C&ISA, CIN, CIS, CMCI, CerAb, ChemAb, ChemTitl, CivEngAb, CorrAb, CurCont, E&CAJ, EMA, Englnd, IAA, ISR, Inspec, M&GPA, M&TEA, MBF, METADEX, MSB, MathR, RefZh, SCI, WAA.
—BLDSC (1762.970000), AskIEEE, CASDDS, CISTI, Ei, IDS, IE, Infotrieve, ingenta, Linda Hall. **CCC.**
Published by: (European Southern Observatory DEU), E D P Sciences, 17 Ave du Hoggar, Parc d'Activites de Courtaboeuf, BP 112, Cedex A, Les Ulis, F-91944, France. TEL 33-1-69187575, FAX 33-1-69860678, subscribers@edpsciences.org, http://www.edpsciences.org.

520 DEU ISSN 0935-4956
QB1 CODEN: AASREB
➤ **THE ASTRONOMY AND ASTROPHYSICS REVIEW.** Text in English. 1989. q. EUR 358 combined subscription to institutions print & online eds. (effective 2005). adv. illus. Index. back issues avail.; reprint service avail. from PSC. **Document type:** *Journal, Academic/Scholarly.* **Description:** Encompasses all areas of astronomy and astrophysics, including bordering subjects.
Related titles: Online - full text ed.: ISSN 1432-0754 (from EBSCO Publishing, ProQuest Information & Learning, Springer LINK, Swets Information Services).
Indexed: ASCA, BrCerAb, C&ISA, CerAb, CorrAb, CurCont, E&CAJ, EMA, Englnd, IAA, ISR, Inspec, M&GPA, M&TEA, MBF, METADEX, RefZh, SCI, WAA.
—BLDSC (1762.971700), AskIEEE, CISTI, Ei, IDS, IE, Infotrieve, ingenta, Linda Hall. **CCC.**
Published by: Springer-Verlag (Subsidiary of: Springer Science+Business Media), Tiergartenstr 17, Heidelberg, 69121, Germany. TEL 49-6221-3450, FAX 49-6221-345229, http://link.springer.de/link/service/journals/00159/index.htm. Eds. L Woltjer, M C E Huber. Adv. contact Stephan Kroeck TEL 49-30-827875739. **Subscr. in the Americas to:** Springer-Verlag New York, Inc., Journal Fulfillment, PO Box 2485, Secaucus, NJ 07096-2485. TEL 800-777-4643, 201-348-4033, FAX 201-348-4505, journals@springer-ny.com, http://www.springer-ny.com; **Subscr. to:** Springer GmbH Auslieferungsgesellschaft, Haberstr 7, Heidelberg 69126, Germany. TEL 49-6221-345-0, FAX 49-6221-345-4229, subscriptions@springer.de.

520 GBR ISSN 1366-8781
QB1 CODEN: ASGEF5
➤ **ASTRONOMY & GEOPHYSICS.** Text in English. 1960. bi-m. GBP 86, EUR 129 combined subscription in Europe to individuals print & online eds.; USD 160 combined subscription in the Americas to individuals & the Caribbean (print & online eds.); GBP 86 combined subscription elsewhere to individuals print & online eds.; GBP 193 combined subscription in Europe to institutions print & online eds.; USD 358 combined subscription in the Americas to institutions & the Caribbean (print & online eds.); GBP 213 combined subscription elsewhere to institutions print & online eds. (effective 2006). adv. bibl.; illus. index. back issues avail.; reprint service avail. from ISI. **Document type:** *Journal, Academic/Scholarly.* **Description:** Publishes scientific articles on major developing themes in astronomy and geophysics in a succinct, readable, and accessible format. Its primary objective is to promote communications among and between astronomers and geophysicists.
Formerly (until 1997): Royal Astronomical Society. Quarterly Journal (0035-8738)
Related titles: Microform ed.: (from PQC); Online - full text ed.: ISSN 1468-4004. GBP 183 in Europe to institutions; USD 339 in the Americas to institutions & Caribbean; GBP 202 elsewhere to institutions (effective 2006) (from Blackwell Synergy, EBSCO Publishing, Gale Group, IngentaConnect, O C L C Online Computer Library Center, Inc., Swets Information Services).
Indexed: ASCA, CIN, ChemAb, ChemTitl, CurCont, ISR, Inspec, MathR, PhysBer, RefZh, SCI.
—BLDSC (1762.975000), AskIEEE, CASDDS, CISTI, IDS, IE, Infotrieve, ingenta, Linda Hall. **CCC.**
Published by: (Royal Astronomical Society), Blackwell Publishing Ltd., 9600 Garsington Rd, Oxford, OX4 2ZG, United Kingdom. TEL 44-1865-776868, FAX 44-1865-714591, customerservices@oxon.blackwellpublishing.com, http://www.blackwellpublishing.com/journals/AAG. Ed. Sue Bowler. Circ: 3,700. **Dist. by:** Marston Book Services Ltd., Marston Book Services Ltd, Box 269, Abingdon, Oxon OX14 4YN, United Kingdom. TEL 44-1235-465500, FAX 44-1235-465555.

520 IRL ISSN 0791-8062
ASTRONOMY & SPACE. Variant title: Astronomy and Space (London). Text in English. 1990. m. EUR 40 (effective 2005). adv. bk.rev. **Document type:** *Consumer.* **Description:** Covers British, Irish and international astronomy and space news.
Formerly (until 1993): Journal of Astronomy Ireland (0791-3974)
Indexed: Inspec.
Published by: Astronomy Ireland, PO Box 2888, Dublin, 5, Ireland. TEL 353-1-8470777, FAX 353-1-8470771, info@astronomy.ie, http://www.astronomy.ie/magazine.html. Ed., Pub., R&P, Adv. contact David Moore. **Dist. by:** Diamond Magazine Distribution, Rye Wharf, Harbour Rd, Rye, E Sussex TN31 7TE, United Kingdom. TEL 44-1797-225229.

520 USA ISSN 1539-1515
ASTRONOMY EDUCATION REVIEW; a lively electronic compedium of research, news, resources and opinion. Text in English. 2002. q. free (effective 2005). bk.rev. back issues avail. **Document type:** *Journal, Academic/Scholarly.*
Media: Online - full content.
Published by: National Optical Astronomy Observatory, 950 N Cherry Ave, Tucson, AZ 85719. aer@noao.edu, http://aer.noao.edu/. Eds. Andrew Fraknoi, Sydney C Wolff.

520 MEX
ASTRONOMY IN LATIN AMERICA. Text in English, Portuguese, Spanish. irreg. **Document type:** *Academic/Scholarly.* **Description:** Contains summaries of recent research and theses, information on astronomical projects and resources, and announcements of jobs and meetings.
Media: Online - full text.
Address: Mexico. ala@carina.astro.ugto.mx, http://www.astro.ugto.mx/~ala/. Ed. Philippe Eenens.

520 RUS ISSN 1063-7737
QB1 CODEN: ALETEO
➤ **ASTRONOMY LETTERS**; a journal of astronomy and space astrophysics. Text in English. 1975. m. USD 1,687 combined subscription in United States to institutions; USD 1,712 combined subscription to institutions in Canada, Mexico, Central and South America & Caribbean; USD 1,717 combined subscription to institutions in Europe, Asia, Middle East, Africa & Oceania (effective 2004); print & online eds.. bibl.; charts; illus. index. back issues avail. **Document type:** *Journal, Academic/Scholarly.* **Description:** Contains papers in the fields of astronomy and astrophysics; including cosmology, theoretical and relativistic astrophysics, high energy astrophysics, optical and radio astronomy, and planetary physics.
Formerly: Soviet Astronomy Letters (0360-0327)
Related titles: Online - full text ed.: ISSN 1562-6873. USD 1,350 worldwide (effective 2004) (from EBSCO Publishing, Swets Information Services); ♦ Translation of: Pis'ma v Astronomicheskii Zhurnal. ISSN 0320-0108.
Indexed: ASCA, CPI, CurCont, GPAA, IAA, ISR, Inspec, PhysBer, SCI, SPINweb, SSCI.
—BLDSC (0404.773000), AskIEEE, CISTI, IDS, IE, Infotrieve, ingenta. **CCC.**
Published by: (Rossiiskaya Akademiya Nauk/Russian Academy of Sciences), M A I K Nauka - Interperiodica, Profsoyuznaya ul 90, Moscow, 117997, Russian Federation. TEL 7-095-3347420, FAX 7-095-3360666, pazh@maik.ru, compmg@maik.ru, http://www.maik.ru/journals/letters.htm. Ed. Rashid A Sunyaev. **Subscr. to:** American Institute of Physics, PO Box 503284, St Louis, MO 63150-3284. TEL 516-576-2270, 800-344-6902, FAX 516-349-9704, subs@aip.org.

520 GBR ISSN 0951-9726
CODEN: ASNOEZ
ASTRONOMY NOW. Text in English. 1987. m. GBP 31 domestic; EUR 35 in the European Union; USD 56 elsewhere; GBP 3.20 per issue domestic; EUR 3.70 per issue in the European Union (effective 2005). adv. bk.rev. illus.; maps. index. back issues avail. **Document type:** *Academic/Scholarly.* **Description:** Explores the world of astronomy and space exploration.
Related titles: Online - full text ed.
Indexed: BiolDig, Inspec, RefZh.
—BLDSC (1762.979200), AskIEEE, Ei, IE, Infotrieve, ingenta, Linda Hall.
Published by: Pole Star Publications Ltd., PO Box 175, Tonbridge, Kent, United Kingdom. http://www.astronomynow.com. Ed. Pam Spence. Pub., R&P Chris Courtiour TEL 44-1903-266165. Adv. contact Lucien Taylor. Circ: 25,000. **Subscr. to:** AIM Ltd., PO Box 10, Gateshead, Tyne and Wear NE11 0GA, United Kingdom. TEL 44-191-487-8333, FAX 44-191-487-6333. **Dist. by:** M M C Ltd., Octagon House, White Hart Meadows, Ripley, Woking, Surrey GU23 6HR, United Kingdom. TEL 44-1483-211222, FAX 44-1483-224541.

520 USA ISSN 1089-4926
ASTRONOMY PRESENTS EXPLORE THE UNIVERSE. Variant title: Explore The Universe. Text in English. 1995. a. USD 5.95 newsstand/cover domestic; USD 7.95 newsstand/cover foreign (effective 2001). **Document type:** *Magazine, Consumer.* **Description:** Provides a guide to all the best astronomy events in the coming year, including maps, diagrams, and photos, along with expert viewing tips.
Formerly (until 1997): Astronomy Presents Observer's Guide (1077-5153)
Published by: Kalmbach Publishing Co., 21027 Crossroads Circle, PO Box 1612, Waukesha, WI 53187-1612. TEL 262-796-8776, 888-558-1544, FAX 262-796-383, editor@kalmbach.com, http://www.astronomy.com, http://www.kalmbach.com.

520 RUS ISSN 1063-7729
QB1 CODEN: ATROES
➤ **ASTRONOMY REPORTS.** Text in English. 1924. m. USD 2,849 combined subscription in United States; USD 2,874 combined subscription in Canada, Mexico, Central and South America & Caribbean; USD 2,884 combined subscription in Europe, Asia, Middle East, Africa & Oceania (effective 2005); print & online eds.. bk.rev. bibl.; charts; illus. index. back issues avail.; reprints avail. **Document type:** *Journal, Academic/Scholarly.* **Description:** Publishes original papers on astronomy, including theoretical and observational astrophysics, physics of the sun, planetary astrophysics, radioastronomy, stellar astronomy, celestial mechanics, and astronomy methods and instrumentation.
Former titles (until 1993): Soviet Astronomy (0038-5301); (until 1974): Soviet Astronomy A.J. (0278-3495)
Related titles: Online - full text ed.: ISSN 1562-6881. USD 2,279 worldwide (effective 2005) (from EBSCO Publishing, Swets Information Services); ♦ Translation of: Astronomicheskii Zhurnal. ISSN 0004-6299.
Indexed: CPI, CurCont, GPAA, IAA, ISR, Inspec, MathR, PhysBer, SCI, SPINweb.
—BLDSC (0404.775000), AskIEEE, CISTI, IDS, IE, Infotrieve, ingenta, Linda Hall. **CCC.**
Published by: (Rossiiskaya Akademiya Nauk/Russian Academy of Sciences), M A I K Nauka - Interperiodica, Profsoyuznaya ul 90, Moscow, 117997, Russian Federation. TEL 7-095-3347420, FAX 7-095-3360666, astrep@maik.ru, compmg@maik.ru, http://www.maik.ru/cgi-bin/journal.pl?name=asteng&page=main. Ed. Alexander A Boyarchuk. **Subscr. to:** American Institute of Physics, PO Box 503284, St Louis, MO 63150-3284. TEL 516-576-2270, 800-344-6902, FAX 516-349-9704.

520 USA
ASTRONOMY THROUGH PRACTICAL INVESTIGATION. Text in English. 1973. base vol. plus a. updates. USD 1 per issue.
Published by: L.S.W. Publications, Inc., PO Box 909, Mattituck, NY 11952-0915. Circ: 1,000.

523.013 NLD ISSN 0927-6505
QB463 CODEN: APHYEE
➤ **ASTROPARTICLE PHYSICS.** Text in English. 1993. 12/yr. EUR 743 in Europe to institutions; JPY 98,700 in Japan to institutions; USD 830 to institutions except Europe and Japan (effective 2006). illus. back issues avail. **Document type:** *Journal, Academic/Scholarly.* **Description:** Publishes experimental and theoretical research papers focusing on new developments in high energy cosmic ray physics and astrophysics, particle cosmology and astrophysics, neutrino and gamma-ray astronomy, and relevant advances in instrumentation and detectors.
Related titles: Microform ed.: (from PQC); Online - full text ed.: (from EBSCO Publishing, Gale Group, IngentaConnect, ScienceDirect, Swets Information Services).
Indexed: ASCA, BrCerAb, C&ISA, CerAb, CorrAb, CurCont, E&CAJ, EMA, IAA, ISR, Inspec, M&TEA, MBF, METADEX, RefZh, SCI, WAA.
—BLDSC (1762.993000), AskIEEE, CISTI, IDS, IE, Infotrieve, ingenta, Linda Hall. **CCC.**
Published by: Elsevier BV, North-Holland (Subsidiary of: Elsevier Science & Technology), Sara Burgerhartstraat 25, Amsterdam, 1055 KV, Netherlands. TEL 31-20-485-3911, FAX 31-20-485-2457, nlinfo-f@elsevier.nl, http://www.elsevier.com/locate/astropartphys, http://www.elsevier.nl.

523.01 USA ISSN 0004-637X
QB1 CODEN: ASJOAB
➤ **THE ASTROPHYSICAL JOURNAL**; an international review of astronomy and astronomical physics. Text in English. 1895. 36/yr. (in 18 vols., 2 nos./vol.). USD 1,950 combined subscription print & online eds.; USD 59 per issue (effective 2006). bk.rev. bibl.; charts; illus. biennial index, cum.index. 500 p./no.; back issues avail.; reprint service avail. from PQC,ISI. **Document type:** *Journal, Academic/Scholarly.* **Description:** Covers galactic structure and dynamics, solar physics, cosmology, the interstellar medium, and other areas of astronomy and astrophysics.
Related titles: Microform ed.: (from PMC, PQC); Online - full text ed.: ISSN 1538-4357. USD 1,300 worldwide (effective 2003) (from EBSCO Publishing); ♦ Supplement(s): The Astrophysical Journal Supplement Series. ISSN 0067-0049.
Indexed: ASCA, CCI, CIN, ChemAb, ChemTitl, CurCont, Englnd, INIS AtomInd, ISR, Inspec, M&GPA, MEDLINE, MSB, MathR, PhysBer, RefZh, SCI.
—BLDSC (1764.000000), AskIEEE, CASDDS, CISTI, Ei, IDS, IE, Infotrieve, ingenta, Linda Hall.
Published by: (American Astronomical Society), University of Chicago Press, Journals Division, Journals Division, PO Box 37005, Chicago, IL 60637. TEL 773-753-3347, FAX 773-753-0811, apj@journals.uchicago.edu, subscriptions@press.uchicago.edu, http://www.journals.uchicago.edu/ApJ, http://www.press.uchicago.edu/. Ed. Dr. Robert C. Kennicutt Jr. Circ: 2,900 (paid).

▼ *new title* ➤ *refereed* ✶ *unverified* ♦ *full entry avail.*

523.01 USA
THE ASTROPHYSICAL JOURNAL LETTERS. Text in English. 1971. 3/m.
Formerly: Astrophysical Journal Letters to the Editor
Related titles: Online - full text ed.
Indexed: Inspec.
Published by: (American Astronomical Society), University of Chicago Press, Journals Division, Journals Division, PO Box 37005, Chicago, IL 60637. TEL 773-753-3347, FAX 775-753-0811, subscriptions@press.uchicago.edu, http://www.journals.uchicago.edu. Ed. Alexander Dalgarno.

523.01 USA ISSN 0067-0049
CODEN: APJSA2
➤ **THE ASTROPHYSICAL JOURNAL SUPPLEMENT SERIES.** Text in English. 1953. m. USD 200; USD 2,100 combined subscription for Journal & Supplement Series; print & online eds.; USD 27 per issue (effective 2006). cum.index. reprint service avail. from PQC,ISI. **Document type:** *Journal, Academic/Scholarly.*
Related titles: Microform ed.: (from AIP); Online - full text ed.: ISSN 1538-4365. USD 1,460 combined subscription for Journal & Supplement Series (effective 2005) (from EBSCO Publishing); ♦ Supplement to: The Astrophysical Journal. ISSN 0004-637X.
Indexed: ASCA, CCI, CIN, ChemAb, ChemTitl, CurCont, ISR, Inspec, M&GPA, MSB, PhysBer, RefZh, SCI.
—BLDSC (1765.000000), AskIEEE, CASDDS, CISTI, IDS, IE, Infotrieve, ingenta, Linda Hall. **CCC.**
Published by: (American Astronomical Society), University of Chicago Press, Journals Division, Journals Division, PO Box 37005, Chicago, IL 60637. TEL 773-753-3347, FAX 773-753-0811, subscriptions@journals.uchicago.edu, http://www.journals.uchicago.edu. Ed. Dr. Robert C. Kennicutt Jr. Circ: 1,500.

523.01 USA ISSN 0571-7256
QB461 CODEN: ATPYAA
➤ **ASTROPHYSICS.** Text in English. 1965. q. EUR 2,218, USD 2,258, GBP 1,385 combined subscription to institutions print & online eds. (effective 2005). adv. bk.rev. charts; illus. index. back issues avail.; reprints avail. **Document type:** *Journal, Academic/Scholarly.* **Description:** Presents recent theoretical and experimental advances in the field, translated from the Russian.
Related titles: Microfilm ed.: (from PQC); Online - full text ed.: ISSN 1573-8191 (from EBSCO Publishing, Gale Group, IngentaConnect, Kluwer Online, O C L C Online Computer Library Center, Inc., Springer LINK, Swets Information Services); ♦ Translation of: Astrofizika. ISSN 0571-7132.
Indexed: ApMecR, BibLing, BrCerAb, C&ISA, CIN, CerAb, ChemAb, ChemTitl, CorrAb, CurCont, E&CAJ, EMA, EnerRA, IAA, Inspec, M&GPA, M&TEA, MBF, METADEX, MathR, WAA.
—BLDSC (0404.780000), AskIEEE, CISTI, IE, Infotrieve, ingenta. **CCC.**
Published by: (Armenian Academy of Sciences ARM), Consultants Bureau (Subsidiary of: Springer-Verlag New York, Inc.), 233 Spring St, New York, NY 10013. TEL 212-460-1500, FAX 212-460-1575, service@springer-ny.com, http://springerlink.metapress.com/openurl.asp?genre=journal&issn=0571-7256, http://www.springeronline.com. Ed. D M Sedrakyan. **Subscr. to:** Springer-Verlag New York, Inc., Journal Fulfillment, PO Box 2485, Secaucus, NJ 07096-2485. TEL 201-348-4033, FAX 201-348-4505, journals@springer-ny.com.

523.01 NLD ISSN 0004-640X
QB460 CODEN: APSSBE
➤ **ASTROPHYSICS AND SPACE SCIENCE;** an international journal of astronomy, astrophysics and space science. Text in English. 1968. s-m. EUR 3,298, USD 3,358, GBP 2,065 combined subscription to institutions print & online eds. (effective 2005). adv. bk.rev. illus. index. reprint service avail. from PSC. **Document type:** *Journal, Academic/Scholarly.* **Description:** Publishes original contributions in the entire domain of astrophysics and related fields, including observational and theoretical papers, as well as discussions of techniques and instrumentation.
Incorporates (1970-1972): Cosmic Electrodynamics; (1975-1981): Space Science Instrumentation (0377-7936)
Related titles: Microform ed.: (from PQC); Online - full text ed.: ISSN 1572-946X (from EBSCO Publishing, Gale Group, IngentaConnect, Kluwer Online, O C L C Online Computer Library Center, Inc., Springer LINK, Swets Information Services); ♦ Supplement(s): Experimental Astronomy. ISSN 0922-6435.
Indexed: A&AAb, ASCA, BibLing, BrCerAb, C&ISA, CCMJ, CIN, CIS, CerAb, ChemAb, ChemTitl, CivEngAb, CorrAb, CurCont, E&CAJ, EMA, EngInd, GeophysAb, IAA, ISR, Inspec, M&GPA, M&TEA, MBF, METADEX, MathR, PhysBer, RefZh, SCI, WAA, ZentMath.
—BLDSC (1765.048000), AskIEEE, CASDDS, CISTI, Ei, IDS, IE, Infotrieve, ingenta, Linda Hall. **CCC.**
Published by: Springer-Verlag Dordrecht (Subsidiary of: Springer Science+Business Media), Van Godewijckstraat 30, Dordrecht, 3311 GX, Netherlands. TEL 31-78-6576050, FAX 31-78-6576474, http://springerlink.metapress.com/openurl.asp?genre=journal&issn=0004-640X, http://www.springeronline.com.

520 NLD ISSN 0067-0057
CODEN: ASSLAD
➤ **ASTROPHYSICS AND SPACE SCIENCE LIBRARY;** a series of books on the developments of space science and of general astronomy and astrophysics published in connection with the journal Space Science Reviews. Text in Dutch. 1965. irreg., latest vol.330, 2005. price varies. back issues avail. **Document type:** *Monographic series, Academic/Scholarly.*
Indexed: ApMecR, CCMJ, CIN, ChemAb, ChemTitl, EngInd, Inspec, MathR, PhysBer.
—BLDSC (1765.050000), AskIEEE, CASDDS, CISTI, Ei, IE, ingenta. **CCC.**
Published by: Springer-Verlag Dordrecht (Subsidiary of: Springer Science+Business Media), Van Godewijckstraat 30, Dordrecht, 3311 GX, Netherlands. TEL 31-78-6576050, FAX 31-78-6576474, http://www.springeronline.com.

523.01 DEU ISSN 1810-6528
▼ ➤ **ASTROPHYSICS AND SPACE SCIENCES TRANSACTIONS (A S T R A).** Text in English. 2004. irreg. **Document type:** *Journal, Academic/Scholarly.* **Description:** Dedicated to the publication and public discussion of high quality original research on all fields of astrophysics and space sciences and related technology.
Related titles: Online - full text ed.: ISSN 1810-6536. free (effective 2005).
Published by: Copernicus GmbH, Max-Planck Str 13, Katlenburg-Lindau, 37191, Germany. TEL 49-5556-91099, info@copernicus.org, http://www.astra-science.net/site/index.html, http://www.copernicus.org.

327.0 520 GBR ISSN 1477-7622
▼ **ASTROPOLITICS;** the international journal of space power and policy. Text in English. 2003 (Sum.). 3/yr. GBP 174, USD 280 combined subscription to institutions print & online eds. (effective 2006). **Document type:** *Journal, Academic/Scholarly.*
Related titles: Online - full text ed.: ISSN 1557-2943. GBP 165, USD 266 to institutions (effective 2006) (from EBSCO Publishing, Gale Group, IngentaConnect, O C L C Online Computer Library Center, Inc., Swets Information Services).
Indexed: ESPM, PAIS, RiskAb.
—BLDSC (1765.077000), IE.
Published by: Routledge (Subsidiary of: Taylor & Francis Group), 4 Park Sq, Milton Park, Abingdon, Oxon OX14 4RN, United Kingdom. TEL 44-1235-828600, FAX 44-1235-829000, info@routledge.co.uk, http://www.tandf.co.uk/journals/titles/14777622.asp, http://www.routledge.com.

520 NLD ISSN 1384-7546
ASTRUIM; spacemagazine. Text in Dutch. 1975. bi-m. EUR 3 newsstand/cover (effective 2005). adv.
Published by: Nederlandse Jeugdvereniging voor Ruimtevaart en Sterrenkunde, Postbus 38, Oss, 5340 AA, Netherlands. TEL 31-24-6419929, info@njrs.nl, http://www.njrs.nl/.

520 ESP ISSN 0210-4105
ASTRUM. Text in Spanish. 1960. bi-m. EUR 78 domestic membership; EUR 116 foreign membership (effective 2005). adv. abstr.; bibl.; illus.; stat.
—BLDSC (1765.200000).
Published by: Agrupacio Astronomica de Sabadell, Apdo de Correos 50, Sabadell, 08200, Spain. TEL 34-93-7272941, secretaria@astrosabadell.org, http://www.astrosabadell.org/es/4_publicacions/astrum.asp. Circ: 2,000.

551.56 NOR ISSN 0373-4854
QC830.T75
AURORAL OBSERVATORY. MAGNETIC OBSERVATIONS. Text in English. 1932. a. free.
Formerly (until 1971): Norske Institutt for Kosmisk Fysikk. Magnetic Observations
—CCC.
Published by: University of Tromsoe, Auroral Observatory, Tromsoe, 9001, Norway. FAX 47-83-89-85-2.

520 LTU ISSN 1392-0049
QB1
BALTIC ASTRONOMY. Text in English. 1992. q. USD 85 (effective 2001).
Indexed: CivEngAb, CurCont, IAA, Inspec, RefZh.
—Linda Hall.
Published by: Institute of Theoretical Physics and Astronomy, A Gostauto 12, Vilnius, 2600, Lithuania. TEL 370-2-613440, FAX 370-2-224694, straizys@itpa.lt, http://www.itpa.lt. Ed. V Straizys.

523.8 USA ISSN 0296-3140
➤ **BE STAR NEWSLETTER.** Text in English. 1980. s-a. free. back issues avail. **Document type:** *Academic/Scholarly.* **Description:** Contains reports, abstracts and contributions on new research on active B stars, which are hot stars, 2-5 times hotter than our sun.
Related titles: Online - full text ed.
Published by: University of Southern California, Space Sciences Center, University Park, Los Angeles, CA 90089-1341. TEL 404-651-1366, FAX 404-651-1389, gjpeters@mucen.usc.edu, http://www.limber.org/benews/. Ed. Geraldine J Peters. Circ: 350.

➤ **BOLETIM I G - U S P. PUBLICACAO ESPECIAL.** see *EARTH SCIENCES*

➤ **BOLETIM I G - U S P. SERIE CIENTIFICA.** see *EARTH SCIENCES*

➤ **BOLETIM I G - U S P. SERIE DIDATICA.** see *EARTH SCIENCES*

520 ESP ISSN 1132-2306
BOLETIN DE ASTRONOMIA. Text in Spanish. 1977. q.
Document type: *Bulletin.*
Former titles (until 1987): Sociedad de Ciencias Aranzadi. Seccion de Astronomia. Circular; (until 1979): Asociacion Guipuzcoana de Astronomia. Circular (1132-2314)
Published by: Sociedad de Ciencias Aranzadi/Zientzi Elkartea, Calle del Alto de Zorroaga 11, Donostia, San Sebastian 20014, Spain. TEL 34-943-466142, FAX 34-943-455811, idazkatitza@aranzadi-zientziak.org, http://www.aranzadi-zientziak.org.

520 GBR ISSN 0264-4185
CODEN: BAACDM
BRITISH ASTRONOMICAL ASSOCIATION. CIRCULAR. Text in English. 1923. irreg.
Indexed: Inspec.
—Linda Hall.
Published by: British Astronomical Association, Burlington House, Picadilly, London, W1J 0DU, United Kingdom.

520 GBR ISSN 0068-130X
CODEN: BAAHAY
➤ **BRITISH ASTRONOMICAL ASSOCIATION. HANDBOOK.** Text in English. 1922. a. GBP 9 per issue (effective 2003). adv. **Document type:** *Academic/Scholarly.* **Description:** Provides astronomical data.
Formerly: British Astronomical Association. Observer's Handbook
Indexed: Inspec.
—Linda Hall.
Published by: British Astronomical Association, Burlington House, Picadilly, London, W1J 0DU, United Kingdom. http://www.britastro.org. Ed. J Mitton. Circ: 4,000.

520 GBR ISSN 0007-0297
QB1 CODEN: JBAAA6
➤ **BRITISH ASTRONOMICAL ASSOCIATION. JOURNAL.** Text in English. 1890. bi-m. GBP 35.10 (effective 2002). adv. bk.rev. illus. index. reprints avail. **Document type:** *Academic/Scholarly.*
Related titles: Online - full text ed.: (from EBSCO Publishing).
Indexed: Inspec, RefZh.
—BLDSC (4713.000000), AskIEEE, IE, ingenta, Linda Hall.
Published by: British Astronomical Association, Burlington House, Picadilly, London, W1J 0DU, United Kingdom. 100257.735@compuserve.com, http://www.star.ncl.ac.uk/~hwm/, http://www.britastro.org. Ed. H McGee. Adv. contact T Boles. Circ: 3,500.

523.8 GBR ISSN 0267-9272
CODEN: CBASEL
BRITISH ASTRONOMICAL ASSOCIATION. VARIABLE STAR SECTION CIRCULAR. Text in English. 1922. 4/yr. GBP 3 in British Isles to members; GBP 4 in Europe to members; GBP 6.50 rest of world to members; GBP 5 in British Isles to non-members; GBP 6 in Europe to non-members; GBP 8.50 rest of world to non-members (effective 2002). **Description:** Provides notification of special events.
Indexed: Inspec.
Published by: (British Astronomical Association, Variable Star Section), British Astronomical Association, Burlington House, Picadilly, London, W1J 0DU, United Kingdom. http://www.britastro.org. Ed. Karen Holland.

520 SCG ISSN 0354-2955
BULLETIN ASTRONOMIQUE DE BELGRADE. Text in English. 1936. irreg. YUN 150, USD 50 to individuals; YUN 300 to institutions (effective 2002). **Document type:** *Bulletin.* **Description:** Covers all researches and original observations in all branches of astronomy.
Formerly (until 1992): Bulletin de l'Observatoire Astronomique de Belgrade (0373-3734)
Indexed: Inspec.
Published by: Observatoire Astronomique de Belgrade/Belgrade Astronomical Observatory, Volgina 7, Belgrade, 11160. TEL 381-11-401320, bull@aob.aob.bg.ac.yu, contact@aob.bg.ac.yu, http://www.aob.bg.ac.yu. Ed. Milan S. Dimitrijevic. **Co-publisher:** Mathematical Faculty, Department of Astronomy.

523.8 FRA ISSN 0764-9614
QB61
C D S. PUBLICATION SPECIALE. Text in French. 197?. irreg. **Document type:** *Monographic series.*
Indexed: Inspec.
Published by: (Centre de Donnees Astronomiques de Strasbourg), Observatoire de Strasbourg, 11 rue de l'Universite, Strasbourg, 67000, France. TEL 33-3-90242410, FAX 33-3-90242432, http://cdsweb.u-strasbg.fr/CDS-f.html, http://astro.u-strasbg.fr.

523.01 384.5 FRA
C R A F NEWS. (Committee on Radio Astronomy Frequencies) Text in English. s-a.
Related titles: Online - full text ed.

Published by: European Science Foundation, 1 quai Lezay Marnesia, Strasbourg, 67080 Cedex, France. TEL 33-3-88767100, FAX 33-3-88370532, esf@esf.org, http://www.esf.org.

520 GBR ISSN 0950-141X
CODEN: CASEES
CAMBRIDGE ASTROPHYSICS SERIES. Text in English. 1979. irreg., latest 2003. price varies. **Document type:** *Monographic series.*
Indexed: Inspec.
—BLDSC (3015.941400), IE, ingenta.
Published by: Cambridge University Press, The Edinburgh Bldg, Shaftesbury Rd, Cambridge, CB2 2RU, United Kingdom. TEL 44-1223-312393, FAX 44-1223-315052, information@cambridge.org, https://booktrade.cambridge.org/series.asp?series=CAPS, http://www.cup.cam.ac.uk/.

CAMBRIDGE MONOGRAPHS ON PLASMA PHYSICS. see *PHYSICS*

520 551 GBR ISSN 0265-3044
CAMBRIDGE PLANETARY SCIENCE SERIES. Text in English. 1981. irreg. price varies. **Document type:** *Monographic series.*
Indexed: Inspec.
Published by: Cambridge University Press, The Edinburgh Bldg, Shaftesbury Rd, Cambridge, CB2 2RU, United Kingdom. TEL 44-1223-312393, FAX 44-1223-315052, information@cambridge.org, http://www.cup.cam.ac.uk/. R&P Linda Nicol TEL 44-1223-325757.

520 USA ISSN 0099-4936
AS32 CODEN: CIWPAV
CARNEGIE INSTITUTION OF WASHINGTON. PUBLICATION. Text in English. 1902. irreg.
Indexed: Inspec.
—CISTI.
Published by: Carnegie Institution of Washington, 1530 P St, N W, Washington, DC 20005-1910. TEL 202-939-1121, FAX 202-387-8092, http://www.carnegieinstitution.org.

523.75 FRA ISSN 1290-0230
QB528 CODEN: PBJOAN
CARTES SYNOPTIQUES DE L'ACTIVITE SOLAIRE. Text in French. 1928. biennial. free. adv. maps. **Document type:** *Academic/Scholarly.* **Description:** Contains solar activity maps and tables containing parameters of features given in maps, as well as scientific discussions of solar activity.
Former titles (until 1999): Cartes Synoptique de la Chromosphere Solaire et Catalogues des Filaments et des Centres d'Activite (0373-7713); Cartes Synoptiques de la Chromosphere Solaire (0085-4778)
Related titles: Online - full text ed.
Indexed: A&AAb.
Published by: Observatoire de Paris, DASOP, 5 place Jules Janssen, Meudon, Cedex 92195, France. TEL 33-1-45077800, FAX 33-1-45077959, TELEX 634 103 OBSASTR, mouradian@obspm.fr, http://www.mesola.obspm.fr. Ed. Z. Mouradian. R&P Z Mouradian. Circ: 300.

520 CAN ISSN 0715-4747
CASSIOPEIA. Text in English, French. 1973. q. free. bk.rev. index. **Document type:** *Newsletter.*
Published by: Canadian Astronomical Society/Societe Canadienne d'Astronomie, c/o Dept of Mathematics, Physics & Engineering, Mount Royal College, 4825 Richard Rd, S W, Calgary, AB T3E 6K6, Canada. TEL 403-240-6029, FAX 430-240-6664. Ed., R&P Jack Penfold. Circ: 400 (controlled).

520 NLD ISSN 0923-2958
QB351 CODEN: CLMCAV
➤ **CELESTIAL MECHANICS AND DYNAMICAL ASTRONOMY;** an international journal of space dynamics. Text in English. 1969. m. EUR 1,738, USD 1,768, GBP 1,088 combined subscription to institutions print & online eds. (effective 2005). adv. bk.rev. illus. Index. reprint service avail. from PSC. **Document type:** *Journal, Academic/Scholarly.* **Description:** Concerns with the broadest range of dynamical astronomy and its applicati ons, as well as with peripheral fields.
Formerly: Celestial Mechanics (0008-8714)
Related titles: Microform ed.: (from PQC); Online - full text ed.: ISSN 1572-9478 (from EBSCO Publishing, Gale Group, IngentaConnect, Kluwer Online, O C L C Online Computer Library Center, Inc., Springer LINK, Swets Information Services).
Indexed: A&AAb, ApMecR, BibLing, C&ISA, CCMJ, CurCont, E&CAJ, IAA, ISR, Inspec, M&GPA, MathR, MathSciNet, PhysBer, RefZh, SCI, ZentMath.
—BLDSC (3097.551000), AskIEEE, CISTI, IDS, IE, Infotrieve, ingenta, Linda Hall. **CCC.**
Published by: Springer-Verlag Dordrecht (Subsidiary of: Springer Science+Business Media), Van Godewijckstraat 30, Dordrecht, 3311 GX, Netherlands. TEL 31-78-6576050, FAX 31-78-6576474, http://springerlink.metapress.com/openurl.asp?genre=journal&issn=0923-2958, http://www.springeronline.com. Ed. Sylvio Ferraz-Mello.

520 ROM
CENTRE DE L'ASTRONOMIE ET DES SCIENCES SPATIALES. OBSERVATIONS SOLAIRES. Text in French. 1956. a. bk.rev.
Formerly: Institutul Astronomic din Bucuresti. Observations Solaires (0068-3094)
Indexed: A&AAb.
Published by: (Institutul Astronomic din Bucuresti), Editura Academiei Romane/Publishing House of the Romanian Academy, Calea 13 Septembrie 13, Sector 5, Bucharest, 76117, Romania. Ed. Georgeta Maris. Circ: 500. **Dist. by:** Rodipet S.A.. TEL 40-21-2224126, 40-21-2226407, rodipet@rodipet.ro.

522 ROM ISSN 0256-5277
CENTRUL DE ASTRONOMIE SI STIINTE SPATIALE. ANUARUL ASTRONOMIC. Text in Romanian. 1940. a.
Formerly: Institutul Astronomic din Bucuresti. Anuarul (0068-3086)
Indexed: A&AAb.
Published by: (Institutul Astronomic din Bucuresti), Editura Academiei Romane/Publishing House of the Romanian Academy, Calea 13 Septembrie 13, Sector 5, Bucharest, 76117, Romania. Circ: 1,600. **Dist. by:** Rodipet S.A., Piata Presei Libere 1, sector 1, PO Box 33-57, Bucharest 3, Romania. TEL 40-21-2224126, 40-21-2226407, rodipet@rodipet.ro.

520 KOR ISSN 1225-1534
CEONMUNHAG NONCONG/KOREAN ASTRONOMICAL SOCIETY. PUBLICATIONS. Text in Korean. 1984. a.
Indexed: Inspec.
Published by: Korean Astronomical Society/Han'gug Ceonmun Haghoe, 61 Whaam-Dong, Deajeon, 305-348, Korea, S. TEL 82-42-865-3255, FAX 82-42-865-3207, kas@kao.re.kr, http://www-kas.or.kr.

522.682 USA
THE CHANDRA CHRONICLES; gateway to the hot universe of x-ray astronomy. Text in English. irreg. (approx fortn). free. illus. back issues avail. **Document type:** *Newsletter, Academic/Scholarly.* **Description:** Informs the public of discoveries made under NASA's Chandra x-ray observatory program.
Media: Online - full content.
Published by: Harvard - Smithsonian Center for Astrophysics, Chandra X-Ray Observatory Center, 60 Garden St, Cambridge, MA 02138. TEL 617-496-7941, FAX 617-495-7356, cxcpub@cfa.harvard.edu, http://chandra.harvard.edu/chronicle. **Co-sponsor:** U.S. National Aeronautics and Space Administration, Public Affairs Office.

520 GBR ISSN 0275-1062
QB1 CODEN: CASGEY
➤ **CHINESE ASTRONOMY AND ASTROPHYSICS.** Text in English. 1977. 4/yr. EUR 1,437 in Europe to institutions; JPY 190,700 in Japan to institutions; USD 1,608 to institutions except Europe and Japan (effective 2006). adv. back issues avail. **Document type:** *Journal, Academic/Scholarly.* **Description:** Presents the results of current Chinese research in all disciplines of astronomy and astrophysics.
Formerly: Chinese Astronomy (0146-6364)
Related titles: Microfilm ed.: (from PQC); Online - full text ed.: (from EBSCO Publishing, Gale Group, IngentaConnect, ScienceDirect, Swets Information Services); ♦ Chinese ed.: Tianwen Xuebao. ISSN 0001-5245; ♦ English ed.: Chinese Journal of Astronomy and Astrophysics. ISSN 1009-9271; ♦ Partial Chinese translation(s): Kongjian Kexue Xuebao. ISSN 0254-6124.
Indexed: BrCerAb, C&ISA, CCMJ, CerAb, CorrAb, CurCont, E&CAJ, EMA, IAA, Inspec, M&TEA, MBF, METADEX, MathR, PhysBer, WAA.
—BLDSC (3180.272500), AskIEEE, CISTI, IE, Infotrieve, ingenta. **CCC.**
Published by: Pergamon (Subsidiary of: Elsevier Science & Technology), The Boulevard, Langford Ln, East Park, Kidlington, Oxford OX5 1GB, United Kingdom. TEL 44-1865-843000, FAX 44-1865-843010, http://www.elsevier.com/locate/chinastron. Ed. Wang Shouguan. **Subscr. to:** Elsevier BV, PO Box 211, Amsterdam 1000 AE, Netherlands. TEL 31-20-485-3757, FAX 31-20-485-3432, nlinfo-f@elsevier.nl, http://www.elsevier.nl.

523.01 CHN ISSN 1009-9271
QB461 CODEN: CJAAAJ
➤ **CHINESE JOURNAL OF ASTRONOMY AND ASTROPHYSICS.** Text in English. 1980. bi-m. (q. until 2001). adv. **Document type:** *Journal, Academic/Scholarly.* **Description:** Contains articles on theoretical and observational astrophysics, astronomical methods and techniques, and research notes.
Formerly (until 2001): Tianti Wuli Xuebao (0253-2379)
Related titles: Online - full content ed.: (from WanFang Data Corp.); Online - full text ed.: (from East View Information Services); ♦ English ed.: Chinese Astronomy and Astrophysics. ISSN 0275-1062; ♦ Chinese ed.: Tianwen Xuebao. ISSN 0001-5245.
Indexed: CCMJ, CIN, ChemAb, ChemTitl, CurCont, Inspec, MathR.
—BLDSC (3180.295230), AskIEEE, CASDDS, CISTI, Linda Hall.
Published by: (Chinese Academy of Sciences, National Astronomical Observatories), Kexue Chubanshe/Science Press, 16 Donghuang Cheng Genbei Jie, Beijing, 100717, China. TEL 86-10-64000246, FAX 86-10-64030255, zjz@bao.ac.cn, http://ttwlxb.periodicals.com.cn/default.html. Eds. Cheng Fang, Jingxiu Wang. Circ: 6,000.

520 FRA ISSN 0373-9139
CIEL ET ESPACE. Text in French. 1947. m. adv. bk.rev. **Document type:** *Newspaper.*
Indexed: Inspec, RefZh.
Published by: Association Francaise d'Astronomie, Observatoire du Parc Montsouris, 17 rue Emile-Deutsch de la Meurthe, Paris, 75014, France. TEL 33-1-45898144, FAX 33-1-45650895, ceespace@francenet.fr, revue@cieletespace.fr. Ed. Francoise Harrois-Monin. Pub. Alain Cirou. Adv. contact Valerie D'Auria. Circ: 90,000. **Subscr. to:** 5-7 rue Marcelin - Berthelot, Antony Cedex 92762, France.

520 551 BEL ISSN 0009-6709
QB1 CODEN: CIELAV
➤ **CIEL ET TERRE.** Text in French. 1880. bi-m. EUR 40 domestic; EUR 55 in the European Union; EUR 58 elsewhere (effective 2002). adv. bk.rev. illus. index. **Document type:** *Academic/Scholarly.*
Indexed: A&AAb, ChemAb, IndIslam, Inspec, RefZh.
—BLDSC (3193.000000), AskIEEE, IE, Infotrieve, ingenta, Linda Hall.
Published by: Societe Royale Belge d'Astronomie de Meteorologie et de Physique du Globe, Av Circulaire 3, Brussels, 1180, Belgium. TEL 32-2-373-0253, FAX 32-2-374-9822, TELEX 21565 OBSBEL. Ed. R Dejaiffe. Circ: 1,200.

520 ITA
IL CIELO; l'astronomia: gli uomini, gli strumenti, le tecniche. Text in Italian. 1996. 11/yr.
Published by: Biroma Editore, Via San Pio X, 108, Galliera Veneta, PD 35015, Italy. TEL 39-49-9422177, mc2212@mclink.it, http://www.mclink.it/com/biroma/ilcielo. Ed. Dr. Gastone Favero.

520 COL ISSN 0120-2758
COLOMBIA. OBSERVATORIO ASTRONOMICO NACIONAL. ANUARIO. Text in Spanish. a. USD 1.50; or exchange basis.
Published by: Universidad Nacional de Colombia, Observatorio Astronomico Nacional, Apartado Aereo 2584, Bogota, CUND, Colombia.

522.1 COL ISSN 0067-9518
COLOMBIA. OBSERVATORIO ASTRONOMICO NACIONAL. PUBLICACIONES. Text in Spanish, English; Summaries in Spanish, English. 1967. irreg., latest vol.6, 1980.
Published by: Universidad Nacional de Colombia, Observatorio Astronomico Nacional, Apartado Aereo 2584, Bogota, CUND, Colombia. Circ: 500.

523.3 523.4 USA ISSN 0099-6416
QB4 CODEN: AULCBY
COMMUNICATIONS OF THE LUNAR AND PLANETARY LABORATORY. Text in English. 1962. irreg. **Document type:** *Monographic series.*
Indexed: Inspec.
Published by: (University of Arizona, Lunar and Planetary Laboratory), University of Arizona Press, 355 S Euclid Ave, Ste 103, Tucson, AZ 85719. TEL 520-621-1441, FAX 520-621-8899.

520 USA ISSN 0889-9630
COMPARATIVE EPHEMERIS (YEAR). Text in English. 1979. a. USD 12 (effective 2003). **Description:** Provides the daily celestial positions of the sun, moon, Mercury, Venus, Mars, Jupiter and Saturn arranged side-by-side, on two facing pages per month, for easy comparison of positions and sight recognition of phenomena.
Published by: Astronomical Data Service, 3922 Leisure Lane, Colorado Springs, CO 80917-3502. TEL 719-597-4068, sky_watcher@att.net.

551.6 FRA ISSN 0181-3048
QB8
CONNAISSANCE DES TEMPS. Text in French, English. 1795. a. EUR 41.16 (effective 2002). **Description:** High precision ephemeris for professional and amateur astronomers which gives the coordinates of the Sun, Moon, planets and Galilean satellites of Jupiter, as well as formulae useful to achieve some classical astronomical calculations.
Incorporates (in 1996): Ephemerides of the Satellites of Mars, Jupiter, Saturn and Uranus
Related titles: ♦ Supplement(s): Satellites Galileens de Jupiter. ISSN 0769-1033; ♦ Ephemerides of the Faint Satellites of Jupiter and Saturn. ISSN 0769-1041; ♦ Satellites de Saturne I to VIII. ISSN 0769-1025.
Published by: (France. Bureau des Longitudes), E D P Sciences, 17 Ave du Hoggar, Parc d'Activites de Courtaboeuf, BP 112, Cedex A, Les Ulis, F-91944, France. TEL 33-1-69187575, FAX 33-1-69860678, subscribers@edpsciences.org, http://www.edpsciences.org. Ed. J E Arlot. Circ: 1,000.

520 USA ISSN 1547-8890
QB54
▼ ➤ **CONTACT IN CONTEXT;** a journal of research on life in the universe. Text in English. 2003. s-a. free (effective 2005). **Description:** Intended as a scientific forum for research in astroanalytical chemistry, astrobiology and in the search for intelligent life in the universe.
Media: Online - full text.

A

Published by: S E T I League, Inc., 433 Liberty St, Box 555, Little Ferry, NJ 07643. TEL 201-641-1771, FAX 800-828-7384, info@setileague.org, http://cic.setileague.org/cic/CIC_home.htm, http://www.setileague.org. Ed. Robert Lodder.

520.09 NLD
CORPUS DES ASTRONOMES BYZANTINS. Text in English, French. 1983. irreg., latest vol.6, 1993. price varies. back issues avail. **Document type:** *Monographic series.* **Description:** Publishes scholarly studies of Byzantine astronomers and their work, and critical editions of important texts.
Published by: J.C. Gieben, Entrepotdok 72b, Amsterdam, 1018 AD, Netherlands. TEL 31-20-6234709, FAX 31-20-6275170, http://www.teachtext.net/gieben/. Ed. Anne Tihon. **Dist. in N. America by:** John Benjamins Publishing Co., PO Box 27519, Philadelphia, PA 19118-0519. TEL 215-836-1200. **Co-publisher:** A.M. Hakkert, Calle Alfambra, 26, 35010 Las Palmas de Gran Canaria, Spain.

523.1 JPN
COSMIC RAY INTENSITY. Text in English. 1959. irreg., latest vol.10, 2002. stat. **Document type:** *Academic/Scholarly.*
Published by: Nagoya University, Solar-Terrestrial Environment Laboratory, Chikusa-ku, Nagoya-shi, Aichi-ken 464-8601, Japan. FAX 81-52-789-4313, muraki@stelab.nagoya-u.ac.jp. Ed. Yasushi Muraki.

520 USA ISSN 0190-2717
QB1 CODEN: BCAOD4
CRIMEAN ASTROPHYSICAL OBSERVATORY. BULLETIN. Key Title: Bulletin of the Crimean Astrophysical Observatory. Text in English. 1977. irreg., latest vol.98. USD 600 per vol. (effective 2006). abstr.; charts; illus. back issues avail. **Document type:** *Bulletin, Academic/Scholarly.* **Description:** Emphasis on solar astrophysics, stellar spectroscopy, extra galactic radio sources, and astrophysical equipment.
Formerly (until 1979): Academy of Sciences of the U S S R. Crimean Astrophysical Observatory. Bulletin
Related titles: ◆ Translation of: Krymskaya Astrofizicheskaya Observatoriya. Izvestiya. ISSN 0367-8466.
Indexed: Inspec, PhysBer.
—BLDSC (0409.150000), AskIEEE, IE, ingenta. **CCC.**
Published by: (Crimean Astrophysical Observatory RUS), Allerton Press, Inc., 18 W 27th St, New York, NY 10001. TEL 646-424-9686, FAX 646-424-9695, journals@allertonpress.com, http://www.allertonpress.com/journals/cao.htm. Ed. Nikolai V Steshenko.

CULTURE AND COSMOS. see *ASTROLOGY*

CURRENT PAPERS IN PHYSICS; containing about 78,000 titles of research articles from the world's physics journals. see *PHYSICS—Abstracting, Bibliographies, Statistics*

520 JPN
DAIKIKYU SHINPOJUMU. Text in Japanese. a. **Description:** Contains papers on observation balloons.
Published by: Institute of Space and Aeronautical Science/Uchu Kagaku Kenkyujo, 1-1 Yoshinodai 3-chome, Sagamihara-shi, Kanagawa-ken 229-0022, Japan.

520 GBR ISSN 0260-7794
DARLINGTON ASTRONOMICAL SOCIETY. NEWSLETTER. Text in English. 1980. irreg. membership. adv. bk.rev. illus. **Document type:** *Newsletter.*
Published by: Darlington Astronomical Society, c/o Paul Tate, Ed, 59 Eden Cres., Darlington Co., Durham DL1 5TN, United Kingdom.

520 GBR
DAVE'S ASTRONOMY MAGAZINE. Text in English. m. **Document type:** *Magazine, Consumer.*
Media: Online - full content.
Address: webmaster@astromag.co.uk, http://www.astromag.co.uk.Ed. Dave Johnson.

520 IRL ISSN 0967-6139
THE DEEP-SKY OBSERVER. Text in English. 1992. q. GBP 16 domestic membership; GBP 18, USD 30 in Europe membership; GBP 20.50, USD 37, AUD 52 elsewhere membership (effective 2005). adv. bk.rev. charts. cum.index. 2 cols./p.; back issues avail. **Document type:** *Journal, Academic/Scholarly.* **Description:** Intended as educational, for advanced amateur astronomers, membership world-wide.
Incorporates (1969-1999): Webb Society Quarterly Journal (0043-1680)
Media: Duplicated (not offset).
Published by: Webb Society, c/o Robert W. Argyle, Pres., Lyndhurst, Ely Rd, Water Beach, Cambs CB5 9NW, United Kingdom. TEL 44-1223-862551, 353-23-92591146, FAX 44-23-92862466, don@webbsoc.demon.co.uk, rwa@ast.cam.ac.uk, http://www.webbsociety.freeserve.co.uk/wperiodical.html#deep. Ed., Adv. contact Owen Brazell TEL 44-1403-750633. Pub. Don Miles. Circ: 450.

DIRECTORY OF PHYSICS & ASTRONOMY STAFF (YEAR). see *PHYSICS*

520 CAN ISSN 1209-0182
DOINGS ONLINE. Key Title: Doings of the Department of Astronomy and the David Dunlap Observatory (Online). Text in English. 1997. irreg. **Document type:** *Newsletter.*
Media: Online - full content.
Published by: David Dunlap Observatory, Station A, PO Box 360, Richmond Hill, ON C4C 4T6, Canada. http://ddo.astro.utoronto.ca/ddohome/doings/. Ed. Brian Beattie.

520 IRL ISSN 0070-7643
DUNSINK OBSERVATORY. PUBLICATIONS; communications of the Dublin Institute for Advanced Studies, Series C. Text in English. 1960. irreg., latest vol.1, no.7. price varies. **Document type:** *Monographic series.*
—CISTI.
Published by: Dublin Institute for Advanced Studies, 10 Burlington Rd., Dublin, 4, Ireland. TEL 353-1-680748, FAX 353-1-680561.

520 FRA ISSN 1633-4760
E A S PUBLICATIONS SERIES. Variant title: European Astronomical Society Publication Series. Text in English. 2001. irreg. (4-6/yr). EUR 230 combined subscription in the European Union print & online eds.; EUR 236 combined subscription elsewhere print & online eds. (effective 2006). **Description:** Contains a diffusion of papers of general interest in astronomy: proceedings of conferences, monographs, etc.
Related titles: Online - full text ed.: ISSN 1638-1963. EUR 164 (effective 2006) (from Swets Information Services).
Published by: (European Astronomical Society), E D P Sciences, 17 Ave du Hoggar, Parc d'Activites de Courtaboeuf, BP 112, Cedex A, Les Ulis, F-91944, France. TEL 33-1-69187575, FAX 33-1-69860678, subscribers@edpsciences.org, http://www.edpsciences.org/journal/index.cfm?edpsname=eas. Ed. Jean-Paul Zahn.

520 NLD ISSN 0379-6566
TL787
E S A - S P. (European Space Agency Special Publication) Variant title: European Space Agency. Special Publication. Text in English. irreg. price varies. **Document type:** *Monographic series, Trade.* **Description:** Contains information on missions, scientific/technical activities, and proceedings of papers presented at conferences and symposia.
Related titles: CD-ROM ed.: ISSN 1609-042X. 1998; Online - full text ed.: ISSN 1609-0438. 1995.
Indexed: BrCerAb, C&ISA, CerAb, CorrAb, E&CAJ, EMA, IAA, Inspec, M&GPA, M&TEA, MBF, METADEX, WAA.
—BLDSC (3830.150000), CISTI, IE, ingenta. **CCC.**
Published by: European Space Agency, Publications Division/Agence Spatiale Europeenne, Keplerlaan 1, Noordwijk, 2200 AG, Netherlands. TEL 31-071-5653405, FAX 31-071-5655433, frits.de.zwaan@esa.int, http://www.esa.int/SPECIALS/ESA_Publications/index.html.

523.01 DEU ISSN 1431-2433
E S O ASTROPHYSICS SYMPOSIA. (European Southern Observatory) Text in English. 1995. irreg., latest vol.19, 2005. price varies. **Document type:** *Monographic series, Academic/Scholarly.* **Description:** Contains both theory and the most recent observational data from telescope observations.
Indexed: Inspec.
Published by: Springer-Verlag (Subsidiary of: Springer Science+Business Media), Haber Str 7, Heidelberg, 69126, Germany. TEL 49-6221-3450, FAX 49-6221-229, service@springer.de, http://www.springer.de. Ed. P Crane. **Subscr. in N. America to:** Springer-Verlag New York, Inc., Journal Fulfillment, PO Box 2485, Secaucus, NJ 07096-2485. TEL 212-460-1500, FAX 212-473-6272.

520 DEU
E S O MESSENGER. (European Southern Observatory) Text in English. 1995. q.
Related titles: Online - full text ed.
Published by: European Southern Observatory, Karl Schwarzschild Str 2, Garching, 85748, Germany. TEL 49-89-320060, FAX 49-89-3202362, ips@eso.org, http://www.eso.org/gen-fac/pubs/messenger/.

523.3 NLD ISSN 0167-9295
QB581 CODEN: EMPLD3
➤ **EARTH, MOON, AND PLANETS**; an international journal of comparative planetology. Text in English. 1969. 8/yr. EUR 998, USD 1,015, GBP 628 combined subscription to institutions print & online eds. (effective 2005). adv. bk.rev. bibl.; illus. index. reprint service avail. from PSC. **Document type:** *Journal, Academic/Scholarly.* **Description:** Provides an interdisciplinary medium for the publication of original investigations of all aspects of planetary systems studies; including such theoretical aspects as the origin and evolution of planetary systems and related topics.
Former titles: Moon and the Planets (0165-0807); Moon (0027-0903)
Related titles: Microform ed.: (from PQC); Online - full text ed.: ISSN 1573-0794 (from EBSCO Publishing, Gale Group, IngentaConnect, Kluwer Online, O C L C Online Computer Library Center, Inc., Ovid Technologies, Inc., Springer LINK, Swets Information Services).
Indexed: A&AAb, ASCA, BibLing, BrCerAb, C&ISA, CIN, CerAb, ChemAb, ChemTitl, CorrAb, CurCont, E&CAJ, EMA, GEOBASE, GeophysAb, IAA, ISR, Inspec, M&GPA, M&TEA, MBF, METADEX, PhysBer, RefZh, SCI, WAA, ZentMath.
—BLDSC (3643.195000), AskIEEE, CASDDS, IDS, IE, Infotrieve, ingenta, Linda Hall. **CCC.**
Published by: Springer-Verlag Dordrecht (Subsidiary of: Springer Science+Business Media), Van Godewijckstraat 30, Dordrecht, 3311 GX, Netherlands. TEL 31-78-6576050, FAX 31-78-6576474, http://springerlink.metapress.com/openurl.asp?genre=journal&issn=0167-9295, http://www.springeronline.com. Eds. Giovanni B Valsecchi, Mark E Bailey.

➤ **EARTH, PLANETS AND SPACE.** see *EARTH SCIENCES*

520 CAN ISSN 0840-6502
EDGES; new planetary patterns. Text in English. 1988. 3/yr. CND 3 (effective 2004). **Document type:** *Newsletter.* **Description:** Discusses issues of the day intending that its readers shift their image of what is going on planet-wise in society.
Related titles: Online - full text ed.: (from Micromedia ProQuest).
Published by: The Canadian Institute of Cultural Affairs, 579 Kingston Rd, Toronto, ON M4E 1R3, Canada. TEL 416-691-2316, 877-691-1422, FAX 416-691-2491, http://www.icacan.ca.

520 PRT ISSN 0870-1199
EFEMERIDES ASTRONOMICAS. Text in Portuguese. 1803. a.
—BLDSC (3664.000000).
Published by: Universidade de Coimbra, Observatorio Astronomico, Santa Clara, Coimbra, 3040, Portugal. TEL 351-239-802370, FAX 351-239-802379, http://www.astro.mat.uc.pt.

520 RUS ISSN 0201-7806
QB8
EFEMERIDY MALYKH PLANET/EPHEMERIDES OF MINOR PLANETS. Text in English, Russian. 1948. a., latest 2003. price varies. **Document type:** *Yearbook, Academic/Scholarly.* **Description:** Contains information on orbital elements and photometric parameters of all the numbered minor planets and tables of their positions in the sky during the time intervals suitable for observations (near opposition ephemerides).
Indexed: Inspec.
—Linda Hall.
Published by: Rossiiskaya Akademiya Nauk, Institut Prikladnoi Astronomii/Russian Academy of Sciences, Institute of Applied Astronomy, Naberezhnaya Kutuzova 10, St Petersburg, 191187, Russian Federation. TEL 8-812-2751118, FAX 7-812-2751119, ipa@ipa.nw.ru, http://www.ipa.rssi.ru.

528.6 ESP ISSN 0080-5971
QB8
EFERMERIDES ASTRONOMICAS. Text in Spanish. 1971. a. EUR 12.02 (effective 2001). **Document type:** *Yearbook, Government.* **Description:** Provides the high accuracy data require for astronomical observations.
Indexed: IECT.
—CINDOC, Linda Hall.
Published by: Real Instituto y Observatorio de la Armada, Cecilio Pugazon s-n, San Fernando, Cadiz 11100, Spain. TEL 34-956-599367, FAX 34-956-599366, jcoma@roa.es. Circ: 700 (paid).

520 HUN ISSN 0238-2423
CODEN: PADUE8
EOTVOS UNIVERSITY. ASTRONOMY DEPARTMENT. PUBLICATIONS. Text in English, Hungarian. 1975. irreg.
Formerly (until 1977): Eotvos Lorand Tudomanyegyetem. Csillagaszati Tanszekenek Kozlemenyei (0324-3621)
Indexed: Inspec.
Published by: (Magyar Tudomanyos Akademia, Konkoly Observatory/Hungarian Academy of Sciences), Eotvos Lorand Tudomanyegyetem, Department of Astronomy/Eotvos Lorand University, XI Pazmany Peter, Setany 1/A, Pf 32, Budapest, 1518, Hungary. TEL 36-1-3722946, FAX 36-1-3722940, astro@astro.elte.hu, http://ninlil.elte.hu.

520 FRA ISSN 1169-0437
EPHEMERIDES ASTRONOMIQUES (YEAR); annuaire du Bureau des Longitudes. Text in French. 1977. a. EUR 35 (effective 2003).
Formerly (until 1983): Ephemerides (1162-9819)
Published by: (France. Bureau des Longitudes), Dunod, 5 rue Laromiguiere, Paris, 75005, France. TEL 33-1-40463500, FAX 33-1-40464995, infos@dunod.com, http://www.dunod.com.

520 FRA ISSN 0769-1041
QB404
EPHEMERIDES OF THE FAINT SATELLITES OF JUPITER AND SATURN. Text in English, French. 1985. a. **Document type:** *Academic/Scholarly.*
Related titles: ◆ Supplement to: Connaissance des Temps. ISSN 0181-3048.
Published by: (Institut de Mecanique Celeste et de Calcul des Ephemerides), Bureau des Longitudes, Palais de l"Institut, 3 Rue Mazarine, Paris, 75006, France. FAX 33-1-46332834, contact@bureau-des-longitudes.fr, http://www.bdl.fr, http://www.bureau-des-longitudes.fr. Ed. J E Arlot.

520 AUS ISSN 0312-1305
EPHEMERIS★. Text in English. a. AUD 8. **Description:** Data book on predicted astronomical phenomena occurring during the year. Contains physical details of the solar system.
Former titles (until 1973): Yearbook of Astronomy. Ephemeris (0312-1291); (until 1972): Astronomy Yearbook. Ephemeris
Published by: Astronomical Society of New South Wales Incorporated, c/o Astronomical Society of South Australia, GPO Box 1123, Sydney, NSW 10043, Australia. FAX 61-2-9337-3378, asnsw@ozmail.com.au, http://www.ozmail.com.au/~lmacdonald/universe/universe.htm. Circ: 1,000.

EPIMENIDES/EPIMENIS. see *TRANSPORTATION—Ships And Shipping*

520 DEU ISSN 0531-4496
QB82.G42
EUROPEAN SOUTHERN OBSERVATORY. ANNUAL REPORT. Text in English, French, German. 1964. a. free.
Incorporates (19??-1979): European Southern Observatory. Rapport Annuel (0343-4826)
—BLDSC (1245.600000).
Published by: European Southern Observatory, Karl Schwarzschild Str 2, Garching, 85748, Germany. TEL 49-89-320060, FAX 49-89-3202362. Circ: 1,600.

520 NLD ISSN 0922-6435
QB84.5 CODEN: EXASER
➤ **EXPERIMENTAL ASTRONOMY**; an international journal on astronomical instrumentation and data analysis. Text in English. 1989. bi-m. EUR 598, USD 608, GBP 378 combined subscription to institutions print & online eds. (effective 2005). illus. back issues avail.; reprint service avail. from PSC. **Document type:** *Journal, Academic/Scholarly.* **Description:** Publishes short and long research articles, research letters and reviews on advances in astronomical detection techniques, in instruments and in techniques of data analysis and image-processing.
Related titles: Microform ed.: (from PQC); Online - full text ed.: ISSN 1572-9508 (from EBSCO Publishing, Gale Group, IngentaConnect, Kluwer Online, O C L C Online Computer Library Center, Inc., Springer LINK, Swets Information Services); ♦ Supplement to: Astrophysics and Space Science. ISSN 0004-640X.
Indexed: BibLing, C&ISA, CurCont, E&CAJ, IAA, Inspec, M&GPA, RefZh.
—BLDSC (3838.744000), AskIEEE, CISTI, IDS, IE, Infotrieve, ingenta, Linda Hall. **CCC.**
Published by: Springer-Verlag Dordrecht (Subsidiary of: Springer Science+Business Media), Van Godewijckstraat 30, Dordrecht, 3311 GX, Netherlands. TEL 31-78-6576050, FAX 31-78-6576474, http://springerlink.metapress.com/openurl.asp?genre=journal&issn=0922-6435, http://www.springeronline.com.

520 USA ISSN 0146-7662
EYEPIECE. Text in English. 1954. m. USD 40; (includes subscr. to Sky and Telescope). back issues avail. **Document type:** *Newsletter.* **Description:** News on astronomy and related topics for astronomers in New York metropolitan area.
Incorporates: Urban Observers
Published by: Amateur Astronomers Association, 1010 Park Ave, New York, NY 10028. TEL 212-535-2922, RN.5305@ROSE.COM. Ed. Jack Dittrick. Circ: 700.

520 GBR
F A S HANDBOOK. Text in English. 1977. a. GBP 2.80. adv. **Description:** Provides data on suppliers, places to visit, speakers, information sources, astronomical organizations, mainly within the UK.
Published by: Federation of Astronomical Societies, 17 Havelock St, Thornton, Bradford, W Yorks BD13 3HA, United Kingdom. Ed. Brian Jones. Circ: 300.

520 ESP ISSN 0210-8127
FENOMENOS ASTRONOMICOS. Text in Spanish. 1980. biennial. EUR 2.25 (effective 2001). **Document type:** *Government.* **Description:** Provides information on the principal phenomena of the Sun and the Moon.
Indexed: IECT.
Published by: Real Instituto y Observatorio de la Armada, Cecilio Pugazon s-n, San Fernando, Cadiz 11100, Spain. TEL 34-956-599367, FAX 34-956-599366, jcoma@roa.es. Circ: 250 (paid).

FIZIKA SOZNANIYA I ZHYZNI, KOSMOLOGIYA I ASTROFIZIKA. see *PHYSICS*

FOUNDATIONS OF PHYSICS; an international journal devoted to the conceptual and fundamental theories of modern physics, biophysics, and cosmology. see *PHYSICS*

523.01 GBR ISSN 1460-5600
FRONTIERS. Text in English. 1995. 3/yr. **Document type:** *Journal, Academic/Scholarly.* **Description:** Contains updates and in-depth features on the many research projects currently funded by the Research Council, plus news of events and activities involving PPARC-funded scientists.
Formerly (until 1997): Particle Physics and Astronomy Research Council. Bulletin (1361-2646)
Indexed: ABM.
Published by: Particle Physics and Astronomy Research Council, Polaris House, North Star Ave., Swindon, SN2 1SZ, United Kingdom. TEL 44-1793-442000, FAX 44-1793-442002, webmaster@pparc.ac.uk, http://www.pparc.ac.uk/frontiers/.

523.8 FRA ISSN 1148-6252
G E O S. CIRCULAR ON ECLIPSING BINARIES. Text in English; Abstracts in French, Italian, Spanish. irreg.
Indexed: Inspec.
Published by: Groupe Europeen d'Observation Stellaire, 3 Promenade Venezia, Versailles, 78000, France. TEL 33-1-30219023, http://www.upv.es/geos/.

523.8 FRA
G E O S. CIRCULAR ON RR LYR TYPE VARIABLES. Text in English; Abstracts in French, Italian, Spanish. irreg.
Indexed: Inspec.
Published by: Groupe Europeen d'Observation Stellaire, 3 Promenade Venezia, Versailles, 78000, France. TEL 33-1-30219023, http://www.upv.es/geos/.

523.8 FRA
G E O S. NOTE CIRCULAIRE. Text in English, French. irreg. **Description:** Contains preliminary results, state of current studies, monthly reports, and general comments.
Indexed: Inspec.
Published by: Groupe Europeen d'Observation Stellaire, 3 Promenade Venezia, Versailles, 78000, France. TEL 33-1-30219023, http://www.upv.es/geos/.

520 028.5 NZL
GALAXY. Text in English. q. USD 25 for families with 3 children or less; USD 5 newsstand/cover (effective 2001). **Document type:** *Magazine, Consumer.* **Description:** Contains puzzles, stories, star maps, cartoons related to astronomy.
Published by: Royal Astronomical Society of New Zealand, Education Section, Box 24 187, Auckland, New Zealand. TEL 64-9-624-1246, johnd@stardome.org.nz, http://www.rasnz.org.nz/. Ed. Marilyn Head.

520 DEU ISSN 0435-1452
GAUSS-GESELLSCHAFT. MITTEILUNGEN. Text in German. 1964. a. EUR 25 membership (effective 2004). adv. bk.rev. back issues avail. **Document type:** *Journal, Academic/Scholarly.*
Indexed: CCMJ, MathSciNet, ZentMath.
Published by: Gauss-Gesellschaft e.V., Geismarlandstr 11, Goettingen, 37083, Germany. TEL 49-551-395045, wolfschmidt@math.uni-hamburg.de, wittmann@uni-sw.gwdg.de, http://www.math.uni-hamburg.de/math/ign/gauss/mitteil.html, http://www.math.uni-hamburg.de/math/ign/gauss/gaussges.html. Ed. Gudrun Wolfschmidt.

520 JPN ISSN 0288-4216
GEKKAN TENMON. Text in Japanese. 1934. m. JPY 6,600, USD 99. adv. bk.rev.
—CISTI.
Published by: Chijin Shokan Co. Ltd., 15 Naka-cho, Shinjuku-ku, Tokyo, 162-0835, Japan. TEL 03-3235-4422, FAX 03-3235-8984. Ed. Akira Tsuda.

GEOINFO. see *EARTH SCIENCES—Geophysics*

551 523.01 NLD ISSN 0165-1307
CODEN: GAMOD3
➤ **GEOPHYSICS AND ASTROPHYSICS MONOGRAPHS**; a series of graduate-level textbooks and monographs on plasma astrophysics and geophysics, including magnetospheric, solar, and stellar physics. Text in English. 1972. irreg., latest vol.31, 1990. price varies. **Document type:** *Monographic series, Academic/Scholarly.*
Indexed: Inspec.
—CISTI.
Published by: Springer-Verlag Dordrecht (Subsidiary of: Springer Science+Business Media), Van Godewijckstraat 30, Dordrecht, 3311 GX, Netherlands. TEL 31-78-6576050, FAX 31-78-6576474, http://www.springeronline.com. Ed. Billy M McCormac.

➤ **GEORESURSY.** see *EARTH SCIENCES—Geology*

520 ITA ISSN 0390-1106
QB33.I8
GIORNALE DI ASTRONOMIA. Text in Italian. 1975. q. EUR 16 domestic; EUR 32 foreign (effective 2004). bk.rev. **Document type:** *Journal, Academic/Scholarly.*
Related titles: Arabic ed.: Al - Magella Al - Falakyya. EUR 30 domestic; EUR 60 foreign (effective 2004).
Indexed: RefZh.
Published by: Societa Astronomica Italiana, Largo Enrico Fermi 5, Florence, 50125, Italy. TEL 39-055-2752270, FAX 39-055-220039, sait@arcetri.astro.it, http://www.sait.it. Ed. Achille Leani.

520 GBR ISSN 0952-326X
GNOMON★; Newsletter of the Association for Astronomy Education. Text in English. 1981. 3/yr., latest vol.20, 2001. membership. adv. bk.rev.; software rev.; Website rev. 8 p./no.; **Document type:** *Newsletter.*
Former titles (until 1987): A A E Newsletter (0950-5083); (until 1983): A A E News (0262-3099)
Indexed: IndIslam, SSCI.
Published by: Association for Astronomy Education, 35 Gundreda Rd, Lewes, E Sussex BN7 1PT, United Kingdom. gnomon.editor@virgin.net, http://www.aae.org.uk. Ed., Pub., Adv. contact Richard Knox TEL 44-1736-362947. Circ: 300.

GRADUATE PROGRAMS: PHYSICS, ASTRONOMY, AND RELATED FIELDS (YEAR). see *PHYSICS*

520 GBR
THE GRADUATE SERIES IN ASTRONOMY. Text in English. 199?. irreg. price varies. **Document type:** *Monographic series.* **Description:** Covers all aspects of theoretical and experimental astronomy and astrophysics for graduate students.
Published by: (Institute of Physics), Institute of Physics Publishing, Dirac House, Temple Back, Bristol, BS1 6BE, United Kingdom. TEL 44-117-9297481, FAX 44-117-9294318, custserv@iop.org, http://www.iop.org/. Eds. R E White, R J Taylor. **Dist. addr. in the US & Canada:** Institute of Physics Publishing, Inc, c/o A I D C, 50 Wintersport Ln, PO Box 20, Williston, VT 05495-0020. TEL 802-862-0095, 800-632-0880, FAX 802-864-7626, orders@aidcvt.com; **Dist. addr. outside N America:** Marston Book Services Ltd., PO Box 269, Abingdon, Oxon OX14 4YN, United Kingdom. TEL 44-1235-465500, FAX 44-1235-465555, direct.order@marston.co.uk.

520 GRC ISSN 0072-7385
GREEK NATIONAL COMMITTEE FOR ASTRONOMY. ANNUAL REPORTS OF THE ASTRONOMICAL INSTITUTES OF GREECE. Text in English. 1960. a. per issue exchange basis.
Published by: Greek National Committee for Astronomy, 14 Anagnostopolou St, Athens, 106 73, Greece.

520 GBR ISSN 0264-4177
GREENWICH TIME REPORT. Text in English. 1968. q.
Supersedes in part: Royal Observatory Bulletins. Series B
Indexed: Inspec.
Published by: Royal Greenwich Observatory, London, E Essex SE10 9NF, United Kingdom. TEL 020-8858-4422, http://www.rog.nmm.ac.uk.

520 USA ISSN 0195-3982
QB1
GRIFFITH OBSERVER. Text in English. 1937. m. USD 18 domestic; USD 25 in Canada; USD 26 in Mexico; USD 30 elsewhere (effective 2000). bk.rev. illus. index. reprints avail. **Document type:** *Journal, Consumer.* **Description:** Charts, photographs, and illustrative articles on astronomy and related sciences, with monthly sky calendar and illustration of celestial events.
—CISTI.
Published by: Griffith Observatory, 2800 E Observatory Rd, Los Angeles, CA 90027. TEL 323-664-1181, FAX 323-663-4323, info@GriffithObs.org, http://www.griffithobs.org/Observer.html. Ed. E C Krupp. R&P E.C. Krupp. Circ: 2,000 (paid).

523.3 DEU
GRUPPE BERLINER MONDBEOBACHTER. PROTOKOLL DER SITZUNG. Text in German. 1954. m. adv. bk.rev. **Document type:** *Newspaper, Academic/Scholarly.*
Published by: (Gruppe Berliner Mondbeobachter), Wilhelm-Forster-Sternwarte e.V., Munsterdamm 90, Berlin, 12169, Germany. TEL 49-30-790093-0, FAX 49-30-790093-12. Ed. Adolf Voigt. Circ: 650.

520 BEL ISSN 0772-6422
HEELAL. Text in Dutch. 1956. m. EUR 23 domestic; EUR 33 foreign (effective 2003). adv. bk.rev. illus. index. 28 p./no.; back issues avail. **Document type:** *Magazine, Consumer.* **Description:** Covers topics of interest to amateur astronomers.
Published by: Vereniging voor Sterrenkunde v.z.w., Brieversweg 147, Bruges, 8310, Belgium. TEL 32-50-358872, FAX 32-50-355007, heelal@vvs.be, http://www.vvs.be. Ed., R&P, Adv. contact Frank Tamsin. B&W page EUR 250, color page EUR 500; trim 27 x 27. Circ: 2,100 (paid).

520 JPN ISSN 0389-7605
HOKKYOKUSEI HOIKAKUHYO/POLARIS ALMANAC FOR AZIMUTH DETERMINATION. Text in Japanese. a. JPY 650. charts; stat. **Document type:** *Government.*
Published by: (Suirobu), Kaijo Hoan Kyokai/Maritime Safety Association, 3-1 Tsuki-Ji 5-chome, Chuo-ku, Tokyo, 104-0045, Japan.

520 JPN
HOSHI. Text in Japanese. irreg. **Description:** Contains news of the organization and relevant subjects.
Published by: Kawasaki Tenmon Dokokai/Kawasaki Astronomical Circle, c/o Mr Mikio Kawamura, 5-224 Hosoyama, Asao-ku, Kawasaki-shi, Kanagawa-ken 215-0001, Japan.

520 JPN ISSN 0389-2131
HOSHI NO TECHO. Text in Japanese. 1978. q. JPY 3,200.
Published by: Kawade Shobo Shinsha, 32-2 Sendagaya 2-chome, Shibuya-ku, Tokyo, 151-0051, Japan.

▼ new title ➤ refereed ★ unverified ♦ full entry avail.

523.51 JPN ISSN 0389-0341
HOSHI NO TOMO/FRIEND OF STARS. Text in Japanese. 195?. a. JPY 3,600 to members.
Published by: Nippon Ryusei Kenkyukai/Nippon Meteor Society, Yabu Tenmondai, 878 Maruyama-cho, Omihachiman-shi, Shiga-ken 523-0805, Japan. TEL 0748-32-4539, FAX 0748-33-4892. Ed. Yasuo Yabu.

522.1 HRV ISSN 0351-2657
HVAR OBSERVATORY BULLETIN. Text in English; Summaries in Croatian, English. 1977. a. free. back issues avail.
Description: Highlights solar and stellar physics.
Indexed: A&AAb, IAA, Inspec.
—AskIEEE.
Published by: Hvar Observatory, Faculty of Geodesy, Kaciceva 26, Zagreb, 41000, Croatia. FAX 38-41-445-410, TELEX 22203 IFS YU. Ed. Vladis Vujnovic. Circ: 400.

523.8 CZE ISSN 0862-173X
HVEZDARNA A PLANETARIUM MIKULASE KOPERNIKA V BRNE. PRACE/NICHOLAS COPERNICUS OBSERVATORY AND PLANETARIUM IN BRNO. CONTRIBUTIONS. Text in Czech, English. 1964. irreg.
Indexed: Inspec.
Published by: Hvezdarna a Planetarium Mikulase Kopernika v Brne, Kravi Hora 2, Brno, 61600, Czech Republic. TEL 420-5-41321287, FAX 420-5-41233389, e-mail@hvezdarna.cz, http://www.hvezdarna.cz.

521 JPN ISSN 0919-8296
QC484.8
I C R R ANNUAL REPORT. Text in English. a. **Document type:** *Academic/Scholarly.* **Description:** Contains research activities of the institute.
Published by: University of Tokyo, Institute for Cosmic Ray Research/Tokyo Daigaku Uchusen Kenkyujo, 5-1-5, Kashiwanoha, Kashiwa-shi, Ciba, 277-8582, Japan.

532.019 JPN
I C R R HOKOKU. Text in Japanese. 1976. 10/yr.
Related titles: ♦ English ed.: I C R R Report. ISSN 1340-3745.
Published by: University of Tokyo, Institute for Cosmic Ray Research/Tokyo Daigaku Uchusen Kenkyujo, 5-1-5, Kashiwanoha, Kashiwa-shi, Ciba, 277-8582, Japan.

520 JPN
I C R R NEWS. Text in Japanese. 4/yr. **Description:** Covers ICRR news and activities.
Published by: University of Tokyo, Institute for Cosmic Ray Research/Tokyo Daigaku Uchusen Kenkyujo, 5-1-5, Kashiwanoha, Kashiwa-shi, Ciba, 277-8582, Japan.

532.019 JPN ISSN 1340-3745
CODEN: ICRPEY
I C R R REPORT. Text in English. 1976. 30/yr.
Related titles: ♦ Japanese ed.: I C R R Hokoku.
Indexed: ChemAb.
—CASDDS.
Published by: University of Tokyo, Institute for Cosmic Ray Research/Tokyo Daigaku Uchusen Kenkyujo, 5-1-5, Kashiwanoha, Kashiwa-shi, Ciba, 277-8582, Japan.

520 JPN
I S A S LUNAR AND PLANETARY SYMPOSIUM. PROCEEDINGS. Text and summaries in English. a. **Document type:** *Proceedings.*
Published by: Institute of Space and Aeronautical Science/Uchu Kagaku Kenkyujo, 1-1 Yoshinodai 3-chome, Sagamihara-shi, Kanagawa-ken 229-0022, Japan.

520 JPN ISSN 0285-2861
I S A S NYUSU. Text in Japanese. 1981. m. **Description:** News of the institute.
Published by: Institute of Space and Aeronautical Science/Uchu Kagaku Kenkyujo, 1-1 Yoshinodai 3-chome, Sagamihara-shi, Kanagawa-ken 229-0022, Japan.

520 JPN
I S A S RESEARCH NOTE. Text and summaries in English, Japanese. 1981. irreg.
Published by: Institute of Space and Aeronautical Science/Uchu Kagaku Kenkyujo, 1-1 Yoshinodai 3-chome, Sagamihara-shi, Kanagawa-ken 229-0022, Japan.

523.8 GBR ISSN 1354-9820
I S O/I R A S NEWSLETTER. Text in English. 1991. irreg.
Indexed: Inspec.
Published by: Walker, Ed. & Pub., Helen, Rutherford Appleton Laboratory R68, Chilton, Didcot, Oxon OX11 0QX, United Kingdom. h.walker@rl.ac.uk.

523.2 USA ISSN 0019-1035
QB1 CODEN: ICRSA5
➤ **ICARUS.** Text in English. 1962. 12/yr. EUR 4,306 in Europe to institutions; JPY 449,700 in Japan to institutions; USD 3,377 to institutions except Europe and Japan; EUR 227 in Europe to students; JPY 23,700 in Japan to students; USD 198 to students except Europe and Japan (effective 2006). adv. bk.rev. bibl.; charts; illus. index. back issues avail.; reprints avail. **Document type:** *Journal, Academic/Scholarly.*
Description: Publishes original contributions in the field of planetary science. Reports the results of new research - observational, experimental, or theoretical - concerning the astronomy, geology, meteorology, physics, chemistry, biology, and other scientific aspects of the solar or extrasolar systems.
Related titles: Online - full text ed.: ISSN 1090-2643. USD 3,512 (effective 2002) (from EBSCO Publishing, Gale Group, IngentaConnect, O C L C Online Computer Library Center, Inc., ScienceDirect, Swets Information Services).
Indexed: BrCerAb, C&ISA, CCI, CIN, CerAb, ChemAb, ChemTitl, CivEngAb, CorrAb, CurCont, E&CAJ, EMA, GSI, IAA, ISR, Inspec, M&GPA, M&TEA, MBF, METADEX, PhysBer, RefZh, SCI, WAA.
—BLDSC (4360.250000), AskIEEE, CASDDS, CISTI, Ei, IDS, IE, Infotrieve, ingenta, Linda Hall. **CCC.**
Published by: (American Astronomical Society), Academic Press (Subsidiary of: Elsevier Science & Technology), 525 B St, Ste 1900, San Diego, CA 92101-4495. TEL 619-231-6616, 800-894-3434, apsubs@acad.com, http://www.elsevier.com/locate/icarus, http://www.academicpress.com. Ed. P. D. Nicholson.

➤ **IKOMAYAMA UCHU KAGAKUKAN NYUSU.** see *MUSEUMS AND ART GALLERIES*

528 IND
INDIAN ASTRONOMICAL EPHEMERIS. Text in English. 1958. a. INR 400 (effective 2000). index.
Formerly: Indian Ephemeris and Nautical Almanac (0537-1546)
Published by: Meteorological Department, Lodi Rd., New Delhi, 110 003, India. TEL 91-11-4618241, 91-11-4651287. Circ: 375. **Dist. by:** Controller of Publications, Civil Lines, New Delhi 110 006, India.

523.01 IND ISSN 0367-8393
QC801 CODEN: IJRSAK
INDIAN JOURNAL OF RADIO & SPACE PHYSICS. Text in English. 1972. bi-m. USD 120 (effective 2003). illus. back issues avail. **Document type:** *Academic/Scholarly.*
Description: Devoted to research communication in areas of radio and space science.
Indexed: BrCerAb, C&ISA, CIN, CerAb, ChemAb, ChemTitl, CivEngAb, CorrAb, CurCont, E&CAJ, EMA, EngInd, IAA, ISR, Inspec, M&GPA, M&TEA, MBF, METADEX, RefZh, SCI, SolStAb, WAA.
—BLDSC (4420.900000), AskIEEE, CASDDS, CISTI, Ei, IDS, IE, ingenta, Linda Hall.
Published by: (India. Council of Scientific and Industrial Research, Publications & Information Directorate), Scientific Publishers, 5-A New Pali Rd., Near Hotel Taj Hari Mahal, PO Box 91, Jodhpur, Rajasthan 342 003, India. TEL 91-291-2433323, FAX 91-291-2512580, info@scientificpub.com, http://www.scientificpub.com. Ed. R P Goal. **Dist. by:** H P C Publishers Distributors Pvt. Ltd. **Co-sponsor:** Indian National Science Academy.

520 HUN ISSN 0374-0676
CODEN: IBVSDL
➤ **INFORMATION BULLETIN ON VARIABLE STARS.** Text in English, French. 1961. irreg. (approx. 200/yr.). HUF 1,600, USD 65. back issues avail. **Document type:** *Bulletin, Academic/Scholarly.*
Related titles: CD-ROM ed.: ISSN 1587-6578. 1961; Online - full content ed.: ISSN 1587-2440. 1961. free (effective 2005).
Indexed: Inspec, RefZh.
—BLDSC (4485.560000), AskIEEE, IE, ingenta.
Published by: (International Astronomical Union), Magyar Tudomanyos Akademia, Konkoly Observatory/Hungarian Academy of Sciences, Konkoly Thege ut 13, PF 67, Budapest, 1525, Hungary. TELEX 61-227460 KONOB H, http://www.konkoly.hu/ibvs/. Eds. K Olah, L Szabados. Circ: 500.

520 RUS
INSTITUT PRIKLADNOI ASTRONOMII. TRUDY/I A A TRANSACTIONS. Text in Russian. 1952. irreg. price varies. **Document type:** *Academic/Scholarly.*
Formerly (until 1998): Institut Teoreticheskoi Astronomii. Trudy (0568-6016)
Indexed: Inspec.
Published by: Rossiiskaya Akademiya Nauk, Institut Prikladnoi Astronomii/Russian Academy of Sciences, Institute of Applied Astronomy, Naberezhnaya Kutuzova 10, St Petersburg, 191187, Russian Federation. TEL 8-812-2751118, FAX 7-812-2751119, ipa@ipa.nw.ru, http://www.ipa.rssi.ru.

INSTITUT ROYAL METEOROLOGIQUE DE BELGIQUE. BULLETIN MENSUEL: OBSERVATIONS IONOSPHERIQUES ET DU RAYONNEMENT COSMIQUE/KONINKLIJK METEOROLOGISCHE INSTITUUT VAN BELGIE. MAANDBULLETIN: WAARNEMINGEN VAN DE IONOSFEER EN DE KOSMISCHE STRALING. see *METEOROLOGY*

INSTITUT ROYAL METEOROLOGIQUE DE BELGIQUE. BULLETIN QUOTIDIEN DU TEMPS/KONINKLIJK METEOROLOGISCH INSTITUUT VAN BELGIE. DAGELIJKS WEERBULLETIN. see *METEOROLOGY*

520 JPN ISSN 0285-6808
UNC CODEN: IASRDU
INSTITUTE OF SPACE AND AERONAUTICAL SCIENCE. REPORT. Text in English. 1921. irreg. index. **Document type:** *Academic/Scholarly.*
Former titles (until 1981): University of Tokyo. Institute of Space and Aeronautical Science. Report (0372-1418); (until 1965): University of Tokyo. Aeronautical Research Institute. Report (0376-1061)
Indexed: Inspec, RefZh.
—BLDSC (7522.724000), CASDDS, CISTI, Linda Hall.
Published by: Institute of Space and Aeronautical Science/Uchu Kagaku Kenkyujo, 1-1 Yoshinodai 3-chome, Sagamihara-shi, Kanagawa-ken 229-0022, Japan.

520 JPN ISSN 0288-433X
INSTITUTE OF SPACE AND ASTRONAUTICAL SCIENCE. REPORT. SPECIAL PUBLICATION. Text and summaries in English. 1983. a.
Indexed: RefZh.
—BLDSC (7522.724500), CISTI.
Published by: Institute of Space and Aeronautical Science/Uchu Kagaku Kenkyujo, 1-1 Yoshinodai 3-chome, Sagamihara-shi, Kanagawa-ken 229-0022, Japan.

520 910.02 ESP ISSN 0213-6198
➤ **INSTITUTO DE ASTRONOMIA Y GEODESIA. PUBLICACION.** Text in English, Spanish. 1949. irreg., latest vol.194, 1999. price varies. back issues avail. **Document type:** *Academic/Scholarly.*
Formerly (until 1985): Seminario de Astronomia y Geodesia. Publicacion (0211-8289)
Indexed: IECT.
—CINDOC.
Published by: Instituto de Astronomia y Geodesia, c/o Fac. de Matematicas, Univ. Complutense de Madrid, Madrid, 28040, Spain. TEL 34-91-3944615, FAX 34-91-3944615, flora@iagmat1.mat.ucm.es, http://www.mat.ucm.es/deptos/iag/index.htm.

520 USA ISSN 0886-6961
INTERNATIONAL AMATEUR - PROFESSIONAL PHOTOELECTRIC PHOTOMETRY. COMMUNICATION. Text in English. 1980. irreg. **Document type:** *Academic/Scholarly.*
Published by: International Amateur - Professional Photoelectric Photometry, c/o Dr. Douglas S. Hall, Dyer Observatory, 1000 Oman Dr., Brentwood, TN 37027-4143. TEL 615-373-4897, hall@astro.dyer.vanderbilt.edu, http://www.hposoft.com/IAPPP/IAPPP.html.

520 USA ISSN 0081-0304
CODEN: IANUAB
INTERNATIONAL ASTRONOMICAL UNION. CENTRAL BUREAU FOR ASTRONOMICAL TELEGRAMS. CIRCULAR. Text in English. 1922. irreg., latest 1997. price varies.
Formerly (until 1964): Union Astronomique International. Bureau Central de Telegrammes Astronomiques. Circulaire
Related titles: Online - full text ed.
Indexed: Inspec.
—AskIEEE, Linda Hall.
Published by: (International Astronomical Union/Union Astronomique Internationale FRA), Smithsonian Institution Astrophysical Observatory, 60 Garden St, Cambridge, MA 02138. TEL 617-495-7280, FAX 617-495-7231, iausubs@cfa.harvard.edu. Ed. B G Marsden. R&P B.G. Marsden TEL 617-495-7244. Circ: 600.

520 GBR
INTERNATIONAL ASTRONOMICAL UNION. GENERAL ASSEMBLY. HIGHLIGHTS OF ASTRONOMY. Text in Dutch. triennial. price varies. **Document type:** *Proceedings, Academic/Scholarly.*
Formerly: International Astronomical Union. General Assembly. Proceedings
Published by: (International Astronomical Union/Union Astronomique Internationale FRA), Cambridge University Press, The Edinburgh Bldg, Shaftesbury Rd, Cambridge, CB2 2RU, United Kingdom. TEL 44-1223-312393, FAX 44-1223-315052, information@cambridge.org, http://www.cup.cam.ac.uk/.

520 FRA ISSN 0538-4753
QB1
INTERNATIONAL ASTRONOMICAL UNION. INFORMATION BULLETIN. Text in Multiple languages. 1959. s-a.
—BLDSC (4482.850000), Linda Hall.
Published by: International Astronomical Union/Union Astronomique Internationale, IAU-UAI Secretariat, 98bis Blvd Arago, Paris, 75014, France. TEL 33-1-43258358, FAX 33-1-43252616, iau@iap.fr, http://www.iau.org.

520 USA ISSN 0736-6884
CODEN: MPCIB2
INTERNATIONAL ASTRONOMICAL UNION. MINOR PLANET CENTER. MINOR PLANET CIRCULARS - MINOR PLANETS AND COMETS. Text in English. 1947. irreg. (approx. m.), latest no.2890, 1997. illus. reprints avail.

Former titles (until 1978): Cincinnati Observatory. Minor Planet Circulars; Smithsonian Institution. Astrophysical Observatory. Minor Planet Circulars - Minor Planets and Comets
Related titles: Online - full text ed.
Indexed: Inspec.
—AskIEEE, Linda Hall.
Published by: (International Astronomical Union/Union Astronomique Internationale FRA), Smithsonian Institution Astrophysical Observatory, 60 Garden St, Cambridge, MA 02138. TEL 617-495-7280, FAX 617-495-7231, TELEX 710-320-6842 ASTROGRAM CAM, iausubs@cfa.harvard.edu, http://cfa-www.harvard.edu/cfa/ps/services/MPC.html. Ed., R&P Brian G Marsden TEL 617-495-7244. Circ: 250.

520 GBR ISSN 1743-9213
INTERNATIONAL ASTRONOMICAL UNION. PROCEEDINGS. Text in English. 10/yr. GBP 550 to institutions; USD 935 in North America to institutions; GBP 610 combined subscription to institutions print & online eds.; USD 1,045 combined subscription in North America to institutions print & online eds. (effective 2006). **Description:** Covers astrophysical developments around the world.
Related titles: Online - full text ed.: ISSN 1743-9221. GBP 505 to institutions; USD 860 in North America to institutions (effective 2006) (from EBSCO Publishing, Swets Information Services).
Published by: (International Astronomical Union/Union Astronomique Internationale FRA), Cambridge University Press, The Edinburgh Bldg, Shaftesbury Rd, Cambridge, CB2 2RU, United Kingdom. TEL 44-1223-312393, FAX 44-1223-315052, journals@cambridge.org, http://uk.cambridge.org/journals. Ed. Karel A van der Hucht. **Subscr. to:** Cambridge University Press, 100 Brook Hill Dr, West Nyack, NY 10994. TEL 845-353-7500, FAX 845-353-4141, journals_subscriptions@cup.org

520 NLD ISSN 0074-1809
CODEN: IASYAE
INTERNATIONAL ASTRONOMICAL UNION. PROCEEDINGS OF SYMPOSIA. Text in Dutch. 1955. irreg., latest vol.187, 2002. price varies. **Document type:** *Proceedings, Academic/Scholarly.*
Indexed: ChemAb, Englnd, ISR, Inspec, SCI.
—BLDSC (8584.000000), AskIEEE, CASDDS, CISTI, IE, ingenta. **CCC.**
Published by: (International Astronomical Union/Union Astronomique Internationale FRA), Springer-Verlag Dordrecht (Subsidiary of: Springer Science+Business Media), Van Godewijckstraat 30, Dordrecht, 3311 GX, Netherlands. TEL 31-78-6576050, FAX 31-78-6576474, http://www.springeronline.com.

520 USA ISSN 0251-107X
QB1
INTERNATIONAL ASTRONOMICAL UNION. TRANSACTIONS. Text in Dutch. 1922. triennial (in 2 vols.). USD 125 per vol. to non-members; USD 80 per vol. to members (effective 2005). **Document type:** *Proceedings, Academic/Scholarly.*
Formerly: International Astronomical Union. Transactions and Highlights; Incorporating: Reports on Astronomy
Indexed: Inspec.
—CISTI.
Published by: (International Astronomical Union/Union Astronomique Internationale FRA), Astronomical Society of the Pacific, 390 Ashton Ave, San Francisco, CA 94112. TEL 415-337-1100, 800-335-2624, FAX 415-337-5205, service@astrosociety.org, http://www.astrosociety.org.

520 USA ISSN 0736-6922
CODEN: ICOQDL
➤ **INTERNATIONAL COMET QUARTERLY.** Text in English. 1979. q. (plus a. handbook). USD 31 domestic; USD 46 foreign (effective 2005). adv. bk.rev. charts; illus. index. back issues avail.; reprints avail. **Document type:** *Journal, Academic/Scholarly.* **Description:** Includes photometric observations of comets, general reviews of recent studies and observations, and reviews and research articles by cometary astronomers on various aspects of cometary research.
Indexed: A&AAb, Inspec.
—AskIEEE, Linda Hall.
Address: Smithsonian Astrophysical Observatory, M S 18, 60 Garden St, Cambridge, MA 02138. TEL 617-495-7440, icq@cfa.harvard.edu, http://cfa-www.harvard.edu/cfa/ps/icq.html. Ed. Daniel W.E. Green. R&P Daniel W E Green. Circ: 500.

525.3 551 FRA
INTERNATIONAL EARTH ROTATION SERVICE. ANNUAL REPORT. Text in English. 1964. a. avail. on exchange or request. **Document type:** *Academic/Scholarly.*
Former titles: International Polar Motion Service. Annual Report.; Bureau International de l'Heure . Rapport Annuel (0074-7432)
Published by: International Earth Rotation Service (IERS), c/o Dr. D. Gambis, 61 avenue de l'Observatoire, Paris, 75014, France. TEL 33-1-40512226, FAX 33-1-40512291, iers@obspm.fr, http://hpiers.obspm.fr.

525.3 FRA
INTERNATIONAL EARTH ROTATION SERVICE. MONTHLY BULLETIN. Text in English. 1962. m. avail. on exchange or request. **Document type:** *Bulletin.*
Former titles: Bureau International de l'Heure. Circulaire D; International Polar Motion Service. Monthly Notes (0020-8337)
Published by: International Earth Rotation Service (IERS), c/o Dr. D. Gambis, 61 avenue de l'Observatoire, Paris, 75014, France. TEL 33-1-40512226, FAX 33-1-40512291, iers@obspm.fr.

520 FRA
INTERNATIONAL EARTH ROTATION SERVICE. SPECIAL BULLETIN C. Text in French. irreg. **Document type:** *Bulletin.*
Published by: International Earth Rotation Service (IERS), c/o Dr. D. Gambis, 61 avenue de l'Observatoire, Paris, 75014, France. TEL 33-1-40512226, FAX 33-1-40512291, iers@obspm.fr, http://hpiers.obspm.fr.

520 FRA
INTERNATIONAL EARTH ROTATION SERVICE. SPECIAL BULLETIN D. Text in French. irreg. **Document type:** *Bulletin.*
Published by: International Earth Rotation Service (IERS), c/o Dr. D. Gambis, 61 avenue de l'Observatoire, Paris, 75014, France. TEL 33-1-40512226, FAX 33-1-40512291, iers@obspm.fr, http://hpiers.obspm.fr.

520 FRA ISSN 1019-4568
INTERNATIONAL EARTH ROTATION SERVICE. TECHNICAL NOTES. Text in French. 1989. irreg. **Document type:** *Monographic series.*
Published by: International Earth Rotation Service (IERS), c/o Dr. D. Gambis, 61 avenue de l'Observatoire, Paris, 75014, France. TEL 33-1-40512226, FAX 33-1-40512291, iers@obspm.fr, http://hpiers.obspm.fr.

520 USA
INTERNATIONAL EARTH ROTATION SERVICE. WEEKLY BULLETIN A. Text in English. w. **Document type:** *Bulletin, Government.*
Published by: (International Earth Rotation Service (IERS) FRA), U.S. Naval Observatory, c/o Dr D D McCarthy, Department of the Navy, Washington, DC 20392-5100. TEL 202-762-1837.

INTERNATIONAL JOURNAL OF ASTROBIOLOGY. see *BIOLOGY*

520 NLD ISSN 1385-7525
INTERNATIONAL SPACE SCIENCE INSTITUTE. SPACE SCIENCE SERIES. Text in English. 1996. irreg., latest vol.19, 2005. price varies. **Document type:** *Monographic series, Academic/Scholarly.* **Description:** Contributes to the achievement of a deeper understanding of the results from space-research missions.
Formerly: Space Telescope Science Institute Symposium Series (0951-659X)
—BLDSC (8585.784500).
Published by: (International Space Science Institute), Springer-Verlag Dordrecht (Subsidiary of: Springer Science+Business Media), Van Godewijckstraat 30, Dordrecht, 3311 GX, Netherlands. TEL 31-78-6576050, FAX 31-78-6576474, http://www.springeronline.com.

INTERNATIONAL WORKSHOP ON THE IDENTIFICATION OF DARK MATTER. PROCEEDINGS. see *PHYSICS*

520 GBR
J C M T NEWSLETTER. Text in English. q. **Document type:** *Newsletter.*
Published by: Royal Observatory Edinburgh, Royal Observatory Edinburgh, Blackford Hill, Edinburgh, EH9 3HJ, United Kingdom. TEL 44-131-668-8100, FAX 44-131-662-1668.

520 GBR ISSN 0021-8286
QB15 CODEN: JHSAA2
➤ **JOURNAL FOR THE HISTORY OF ASTRONOMY.** Text in English. 1970. 4/yr., latest vol.33. USD 192 in the Americas to institutions & Japan; GBP 96 elsewhere to institutions; USD 56 per issue in the Americas to institutions & Japan; GBP 28 per issue elsewhere to institutions (effective 2006). bk.rev. bibl.; charts; illus. index. back issues avail.; reprints avail. **Document type:** *Journal, Academic/Scholarly.* **Description:** History of astronomy, astrophysics, cosmology and related sciences.
Incorporates (1979-2002): Archaeoastronomy (0142-7253)
Related titles: ♦ Supplement(s): Archaeoastronomy. ISSN 0142-7253.
Indexed: AbAn, AmH&L, ArtHuCI, BrArAb, CCMJ, CurCont, DIP, GSI, HistAb, IBR, IBZ, IndIslam, Inspec, MEA&I, MathR, NumL, PhilInd, RASB.
—BLDSC (5000.580000), AskIEEE, CISTI, IE, Infotrieve, ingenta, Linda Hall. **CCC.**
Published by: Science History Publications Ltd., 16 Rutherford Rd, Cambridge, CB2 2HH, United Kingdom. TEL 44-1638-605464, FAX 44-1638-605465, journals@shpltd.co.uk, http://www.shpltd.co.uk/jha.html. Ed. M A Hoskin. Pub., R&P, Adv. contact Bernard Hoskin. Circ: 650.

520 AUS ISSN 1440-2807
QB15
JOURNAL OF ASTRONOMICAL HISTORY AND HERITAGE. Abbreviated title: J A H2. Text in English. 1998. s-a. AUD 75 domestic; GBP 27 foreign (effective 2003). bk.rev. 96 p./no.; back issues avail. **Document type:** *Journal, Academic/Scholarly.* **Description:** Features review papers, research papers, short communications, and book reviews that covers all aspects of astronomical history, including studies which place the evolution of astronomy in political, economic and cultural context.
Indexed: Inspec.
—Linda Hall.
Published by: Astral Press, PO Box 107, Wembley, W.A. 6014, Australia. TEL 61-8-9387-4250, FAX 61-8-9387-3981, astral@iinet.net.au, http://www.astralpress.com.au.

520 551 EGY ISSN 1687-0980
JOURNAL OF ASTRONOMY AND ASTROPHYSICS. Text in English. 1930. s-a. **Document type:** *Journal, Academic/Scholarly.*
Supersedes in part (in 2002): National Research Institute of Astronomy and Geophysics. Section A. Astronomy. Bulletin (1110-1695); Which superseded in part (in 1981): Helwan Institute of Astronomy and Geophysics. Bulletin; Which was formerly (until 1970): Helwan Observatory Bulletin
Published by: National Research Institute of Astronomy and Geophysics, Egyptian Economic Center, Haroun Tower, 18 El Mansoura St, Heliopolis, Cairo, Egypt. TEL 20-2-2437710.

523.01 IND ISSN 0250-6335
QB460 CODEN: JASRD7
➤ **JOURNAL OF ASTROPHYSICS AND ASTRONOMY.** Text in English. 1980. q. USD 100 to institutions (effective 2006). illus.; abstr. 100 p./no. 1 cols./p.; back issues avail. **Document type:** *Journal, Academic/Scholarly.* **Description:** Original research papers on all aspects of Astrophysical and Astronomy including instrumentation.
Related titles: Online - full text ed.: free (effective 2005).
Indexed: ASCA, BrCerAb, C&ISA, CIN, CerAb, ChemAb, ChemTitl, CorrAb, CurCont, E&CAJ, EMA, IAA, ISR, Inspec, M&GPA, M&TEA, MBF, METADEX, PhysBer, RefZh, SCI, WAA.
—BLDSC (4947.550000), AskIEEE, CASDDS, CISTI, IDS, IE, ingenta, Linda Hall.
Published by: Indian Academy of Sciences, C.V. Raman Ave., Sadashivanagar, P O Box 8005, Bangalore, Karnataka 560 080, India. TEL 91-80-23612546, FAX 91-80-23616094, jaa@ias.ernet.in, http://www.ias.ac.in/jaa. Ed. R Nityananda. R&P G Madhavan. Circ: 1,000. **Subscr. to:** Scientific Publishers, 5-A New Pali Rd., Near Hotel Taj Hari Mahal, PO Box 91, Jodhpur, Rajasthan 342 003, India. http://www.scientificpub.com.

➤ **JOURNAL OF ATMOSPHERIC AND SOLAR - TERRESTRIAL PHYSICS.** see *EARTH SCIENCES—Geophysics*

▼ ➤ **JOURNAL OF COSMOLOGY AND ASTROPARTICLE PHYSICS.** see *PHYSICS*

➤ **JOURNAL OF MATHEMATICAL SCIENCES.** see *MATHEMATICS*

➤ **KAIJO HOANCHO. SUIROBU KANSOKU HOKOKU. TENMON SOKUCHI HEN/DATA REPORT OF HYDROGRAPHIC OBSERVATIONS. SERIES OF ASTRONOMY AND GEODESY.** see *EARTH SCIENCES—Geophysics*

523.01 USA ISSN 0884-5913
QB460 CODEN: KPCBEU
➤ **KINEMATICS AND PHYSICS OF CELESTIAL BODIES.** Text in English. 1985. bi-m. USD 1,860 per vol. in US & Canada; USD 2,160 per vol. elsewhere (effective 2006). abstr.; charts; illus.; maps. back issues avail. **Document type:** *Journal, Academic/Scholarly.* **Description:** Covers solar physics, astronomic catalogs and databases, positional and theoretical astronomy, stars and interstellar space, planetary physics, earth rotation and geodynamics, galactic structure and dynamics.
Related titles: Russian Translation: Kinematika i Fizika Nebesnykh Tel. ISSN 0233-7665.
Indexed: CIN, ChemAb, ChemTitl, IAA, Inspec.
—BLDSC (0415.405000), AskIEEE, CISTI, IE, ingenta. **CCC.**
Published by: (Natsional'na Akademiya Nauk Ukrainy UKR, Division of Physics and Astronomy UKR), Allerton Press, Inc., 18 W 27th St, New York, NY 10001. TEL 646-424-9686, FAX 646-424-9695, journals@allertonpress.com, http://www.allertonpress.com/journals/kin.htm. Ed. Yaroslav S Yatskiv.

➤ **KNJIZNICA SIGMA.** see *PHYSICS*

520 IND ISSN 0374-3632
KODAIKANAL OBSERVATORY BULLETIN. SERIES A. Text in English. irreg.
Indexed: Inspec.
Published by: (Kodaikanal Solar Observatory), Government of India, Department of Publications, Patiala House, Tilak Marg, New Delhi, 110 001, India. TEL 91-11-3387983, FAX 91-11-3387341, indiapub@nda.vsnl.net.in, http://www.nic.in/indiapublications/.

A

520 IND ISSN 0374-3667
KODAIKANAL OBSERVATORY BULLETIN. SERIES B. Text in English. 1969. irreg.
Indexed: Inspec.
Published by: (Kodaikanal Solar Observatory), Government of India, Department of Publications, Patiala House, Tilak Marg, New Delhi, 110 001, India. TEL 91-11-3387983, FAX 91-11-3387341, indiapub@nda.vsnl.net.in, http://www.nic.in/indiapublications/.

522.1 JPN ISSN 0915-8863
KOKURITSU TENMONDAI NYUSU. Text in Japanese. 1988. 10/yr. **Description:** News of the observatory.
Published by: National Astronomical Observatory, Kokuritsu Tenmondai, 21-1 Osawa 2-chome, Mitaka-shi, Tokyo-to 181-0015, Japan. FAX 81-422-34-3690.

520 JPN ISSN 0915-6321
QB1 CODEN: KTENE2
KOKURITSU TENMONDAIHO/NATIONAL ASTRONOMICAL OBSERVATORY. REPORT. Text in Japanese. 1932. 2/yr. available on exchange basis only.
Formerly (until 1989): Tokyo Astronomical Observatory. Report (0374-4639)
Indexed: Inspec, RefZh.
—BLDSC (7560.025000), AskIEEE.
Published by: National Astronomical Observatory, Kokuritsu Tenmondai, 21-1 Osawa 2-chome, Mitaka-shi, Tokyo-to 181-0015, Japan. FAX 81-422-34-3690. Circ: 600.

520 KOR ISSN 0253-3065
QB1 CODEN: CHACDE
KOREAN ASTRONOMICAL SOCIETY. JOURNAL. Text in English. 1968. s-a. KRW 10,000, USD 20. **Document type:** *Academic/Scholarly.* **Description:** Covers the entire domain of astronomy, astrophysics and related fields.
Indexed: Inspec.
—BLDSC (4811.900000), AskIEEE.
Published by: (Korean Astronomical Society/Han'gug Ceonmun Haghoe), Seoul National University, San 56-1 Sinlim-dong, Kwanak-ku, Seoul, 151742, Korea, S. TEL 02-884-9055, FAX 02-887-1435. Ed. Minn Y K. Circ: 500.

520 SVK ISSN 0323-049X
KOZMOS. Text in Slovak. 1970. bi-m. USD 25 (effective 2000).
Published by: Slovenska Ustredna Hvezdaren, Hurbanovo, 94701, Slovakia.

529 NLD ISSN 1567-715X
KRONOSCOPE; journal for the study of time. Text in English. 2001. 2/yr. USD 42 in the Americas to individuals; EUR 33 elsewhere to individuals; USD 124 combined subscription in the Americas to institutions print & online eds.; EUR 99 combined subscription elsewhere to institutions print & online eds. (effective 2006). back issues avail.; reprint service avail. from PSC. **Document type:** *Journal, Academic/Scholarly.* **Description:** Offers an open-ended platform for the cross-fertilization of scholarly and scientific ideas acquainted with the nature of time.
Related titles: Online - full text ed.: ISSN 1568-5241. USD 112 in the Americas to institutions; EUR 89 elsewhere to institutions (effective 2006) (from EBSCO Publishing, Gale Group, IngentaConnect, Kluwer Online, O C L C Online Computer Library Center, Inc., Springer LINK, Swets Information Services).
Indexed: e-psyche.
—BLDSC (5118.550250), IE. **CCC.**
Published by: Brill Academic Publishers, PO Box 9000, Leiden, 2300 PA, Netherlands. TEL 31-71-53-53-500, FAX 31-71-5317531, 31-71-53-17-532, cs@brill.nl, cs@brill.nl, http://www.brill.nl/m_catalogue_sub6_id9587.htm. Ed. Marlene Soulsby. **Subscr. in N. America to:** PO Box 605, Herndon, VA 20172. TEL 703-661-1585, 800-337-9255, FAX 703-661-1501, cs@brillusa.com. **Distr. outside N. America by:** c/o Turpin Distribution, Stratton Business Park, Pegasus Drive, Biggleswade, BEDFORDSHIRE SG 18 8TQ, United Kingdom. TEL 44-1767-604-954, FAX 44-1767-601-640, brill@turpin-distribution.com.

523 UKR ISSN 0367-8466
QB1 CODEN: IKAOAW
KRYMSKAYA ASTROFIZICHESKAYA OBSERVATORIYA. IZVESTIYA. Text in Russian; Summaries in English, Russian. 1946. s-a. free. **Document type:** *Journal, Academic/Scholarly.*
Related titles: ♦ English Translation: Crimean Astrophysical Observatory. Bulletin. ISSN 0190-2717.
Indexed: ChemAb, IAA, Inspec.
—AskIEEE, CASDDS, KNAW, Linda Hall. **CCC.**
Published by: Krymskaya Astrofizicheskaya Observatoriya/ Crimean Astrophysical Observatory, Nauchny, Bahchisarai, Crimea 334413, Ukraine. TEL 380-655-471166, FAX 380-655-471754, postmaster@crao.crimea.ua, http://www.crao.crimea.ua.

KVANT; tidsskrift for fysik og astronomi. see *PHYSICS*

520 JPN ISSN 0388-0230
KYOTO UNIVERSITY. DEPARTMENT OF ASTRONOMY. CONTRIBUTIONS. Text and summaries in English. 1960. irreg. **Document type:** *Academic/Scholarly.*
Published by: (Department of Astrophysics), Kyoto University, Faculty of Science/Kyoto Daigaku Rigakubu, Kita-Shirakawaoiwake-cho, Sakyo-ku, Kyoto-shi, 606-8224, Japan. TEL 81-75-753-3900, FAX 81-75-753-3897, ikemura@kusastro.kyoto-u.ac.jp.

522.1 JPN ISSN 0388-2349
CODEN: IJCRDD
KYOTO UNIVERSITY. KWASAN AND HIDA OBSERVATORIES. CONTRIBUTIONS. Text and summaries in English. 1948. irreg. **Document type:** *Academic/Scholarly.*
—Linda Hall.
Published by: Kyoto University, Faculty of Science, Kwasan Observatory/Kyoto Daigaku Rigakubu Fuzoku Kazan Tenmondai, Omine-cho, Kita-Kazan, Yamashina-ku, Kyoto-shi, 607, Japan. Ed. Hiroki Kurokawa.

523 USA ISSN 0161-5297
CODEN: LPCODB
L P I CONTRIBUTION. Text in English. irreg. price varies. **Document type:** *Monographic series.*
Formerly (until 197?): L S I Contribution (0145-143X)
Indexed: Inspec.
—Linda Hall.
Published by: Lunar and Planetary Institute, 3600 Bay Area Blvd, Houston, TX 77058-1113. TEL 281-486-2172, 281-486-2172, FAX 281-486-2186, lpibed@lpi.usra.edu, http://www.lpi.usra.edu.

520 530 DEU ISSN 1614-4961
▼ **LIVING REVIEWS IN SOLAR PHYSICS.** Text in English. 2004. irreg. free (effective 2005). **Document type:** *Journal, Academic/Scholarly.* **Description:** Publishes up-to-date reviews on all aspects of solar physics.
Media: Online - full text.
Published by: Max-Planck-Institut for Solar System Research, Max-Planck-Str 2, Katlenburg-Lindau, 37191, Germany. TEL 49-5556-979154, FAX 49-5556-979240, presseinfo@linmpi.mpg.de, http://solarphysics.livingreviews.org/.

520 USA ISSN 0889-9622
QB601
LOCAL PLANET VISIBILITY REPORT (YEAR). Text in English. 1978. a. USD 15 (effective 2003). **Description:** Contains local visibility information for each of five planets, Mercury, Venus, Mars, Jupiter, and Saturn, computed for your latitude, longitude, and time zone.
Published by: Astronomical Data Service, 3922 Leisure Lane, Colorado Springs, CO 80917-3502. TEL 719-597-4068, sky_watcher@att.net. Pub. Roger L Mansfield.

523.4 USA ISSN 1534-6587
QB500 CODEN: LPIBE3
LUNAR AND PLANETARY INFORMATION BULLETIN. Text in English. 1970. q. free (effective 2004); . bk.rev. illus. reprints avail. **Document type:** *Bulletin.* **Description:** Covers solar system exploration.
Media: Online - full content.
Indexed: IAA, Inspec, RefZh.
Published by: Lunar and Planetary Institute, 3600 Bay Area Blvd, Houston, TX 77058-1113. TEL 281-486-2172, FAX 281-486-2186, lpibed@lpi.usra.edu, http://www.lpi.usra.edu/publications/lpib. Ed., R&P D Brian Anderson. Circ: 5,500.

LUNAR CALENDAR (YEAR); dedicated to the goddess in her many guises. see *ASTROLOGY*

523 USA
THE MAGELLANIC CLOUDS NEWSLETTER. Text in English. bi-m.
Media: Online - full content.
Published by: University of Illinois, Department of Astronomy, 1002 W Green St, Urbana, IL 61801. mcnews@astro.uiuc.edu, http://www.astro.uiuc.edu/projects/mcnews/MCNews.html.

MAJALLAH-I FIZIK/IRANIAN JOURNAL OF PHYSICS. see *PHYSICS*

MANITOBA MUSEUM OF MAN AND NATURE. HAPPENINGS. see *MUSEUMS AND ART GALLERIES*

MARDAILY. see *AERONAUTICS AND SPACE FLIGHT*

MATHEMATICAL PROCEEDINGS OF THE ROYAL IRISH ACADEMY. see *MATHEMATICS*

523.01 DEU ISSN 0943-2930
MAX-PLANCK-INSTITUT FUER PHYSIK. WERNER-HEISENBERG-INSTITUT. JAHRESBERICHT. Text in German. 1971. a. **Document type:** *Journal, Academic/Scholarly.*
Former titles (until 1992): Max-Planck-Institut fuer Physik und Astrophysik. Werner-Heisenberg-Institut (0932-9021); (until 1982): Max-Planck-Institut fuer Physik und Astrophysik. Institut fuer Physik. Jahresbericht (0173-6256)
—BLDSC (4635.925000).
Published by: Max-Planck-Institut fuer Physik, Werner-Heisenberg-Institut, Foehringer Ring 6, Munich, 80805, Germany. TEL 49-89-323540, FAX 49-89-3226704, altmann@mppmu.mpg.de, http://www.mppmu.mpg.de.

520 USA ISSN 0047-6773
QB1 CODEN: MRCYAT
MERCURY (SAN FRANCISCO). Text in English. 1972. bi-m. USD 48 in North America to institutions; USD 57 elsewhere to institutions (effective 2005); includes membership in the Astronomical Society of the Pacific. adv. bk.rev. charts; illus. index, cum.index. back issues avail.; reprint service avail. from PQC. **Document type:** *Magazine, Consumer.* **Description:** Nontechnical magazine about astronomy for the general reader or amateur astronomer.
Related titles: Online - full text ed.: (from EBSCO Publishing, Florida Center for Library Automation, Gale Group, H.W. Wilson, O C L C Online Computer Library Center, Inc.).
Indexed: A&AAb, CIJE, DIP, GSI, Inspec, MASUSE, RefZh.
—BLDSC (5679.850000), AskIEEE, CISTI, IE, Infotrieve, ingenta, Linda Hall.
Published by: Astronomical Society of the Pacific, 390 Ashton Ave, San Francisco, CA 94112. TEL 415-337-1100, FAX 415-337-5205, editor@astrosociety.org, service@astrosociety.org, http://www.astrosociety.org/pubs/mercury/mercury.html. Ed., R&P, Adv. contact Robert Naeye. page USD 650; trim 11 x 9. Circ: 7,000.

523.41 USA
MERCURY MESSENGER. Text in English. 1987 (Dec.). irreg. free (effective 2004). **Document type:** *Newsletter.* **Description:** Concerned with exploration of the planet Mercury.
Media: Online - full content.
Published by: Lunar and Planetary Institute, 3600 Bay Area Blvd, Houston, TX 77058-1113. TEL 281-486-2172, FAX 281-486-2186, lpibed@lpi.usra.edu, http://www.lpi.usra.edu/publications/newsletters/mercmessenger/.

520 DEU ISSN 0722-6691
QB1 CODEN: MESSE4
THE MESSENGER/MENSAJERO. Text in English; Abstracts occasionally in Spanish. 1974. q. free. illus. Index. reprints avail. **Document type:** *Newsletter.* **Description:** Covers research and findings of astronomical and astrophysical observatories in Europe and of the European Southern Observatory in La Silla, Chile. Includes reports and list of events.
Indexed: Inspec, RefZh.
—BLDSC (5682.690000), AskIEEE, Linda Hall. **CCC.**
Published by: European Southern Observatory, Karl Schwarzschild Str 2, Garching, 85748, Germany. TEL 49-89-320060, FAX 49-89-3202362, ips@eso.org, http://www.hq.eso.org/messenger.html, http://www.eso.org. Ed. M H Ulrich.

523.5 USA ISSN 0146-9959
METEOR NEWS. Text in English. 1970. irreg. (3-4/yr.). USD 6; USD 9 foreign (effective 1998). adv. bk.rev. charts. cum.index every 5 yrs. **Document type:** *Newsletter.* **Description:** Reports on meteor observations and meteorite falls worldwide.
Media: Duplicated (not offset).
Published by: Callahan Astronomical Society, 3859 Woodland Heights, Callahan, FL 32011. TEL 904-879-2646. Ed. Karl Simmons. Pub. Wanda Simmons. Circ: 350 (paid).

523.5 NZL ISSN 1173-2245
METEORITE!. Text in English. 1995. q. USD 35 (effective 2004). **Document type:** *Magazine, Academic/Scholarly.* **Description:** Contains articles and features on meteors and asteroids.
Published by: Pallasite Press, Takapuna, PO Box 33-1218, Auckland, New Zealand. TEL 64-9-486-2428, FAX 64-9-489-6750, j.schiff@auckland.ac.nz, http://www.meteor.co.nz. Ed. Joel Schiff.

523.4 550 USA ISSN 1086-9379
QB741 CODEN: MPSCFY
➤ **METEORITICS AND PLANETARY SCIENCE.** Text in English. 1953. m. USD 900 in North America to institutions; USD 950 elsewhere to institutions; free to members (effective 2005). adv. bk.rev.; video rev. charts; illus.; stat. index. 150 p./no.; Supplement avail.; back issues avail.; reprints avail. **Document type:** *Journal, Academic/Scholarly.* **Description:** Publishes primary research articles and invited reviews in such areas as asteroids, comets, craters, interplanetary dust, interstellar medium, lunar samples, meteors, meteorites, natural satellites, planets, tektites and the origin and history of the Solar System.
Formerly (until 1996): Meteoritics (0026-1114)
Related titles: Microform ed.: (from PQC); Online - full content ed.; Online - full text ed.: (from Gale Group, IngentaConnect).
Indexed: AESIS, ASCA, ChemAb, ChemTitl, CurCont, GEOBASE, IAA, ISR, Inspec, MSB, MinerAb, RefZh, SCI.
—BLDSC (5703.350000), AskIEEE, CASDDS, CISTI, IDS, IE, Infotrieve, ingenta, Linda Hall. **CCC.**
Published by: Meteoritical Society, Dept. of Geosciences, University of Arizona, 4717 E. Fort Lowell Road, Room 104, Tucson, AZ 85712-1201. TEL 520-881-0857, FAX 520-881-0554, meteor@uark.edu, http://meteoritics.org, http://www.uark.edu/meteor, http://www.meteorite.ch/metsoc2.htm. Ed. Dr. A J Timothy Jull TEL 520-621 6816. R&P, Adv. contact Hazel Sears TEL 501-575-5204. Circ: 1,200 (paid). **Subscr. to:** Allen Press Inc.

520 DEU ISSN 0944-1999
MITTEILUNGEN ZUR ASTRONOMIEGESCHICHTE. Text in German, English. 1992. s-a. EUR 3; EUR 1.50 newsstand/cover (effective 2005). 6 p./no.; back issues avail. **Document type:** *Newsletter, Academic/Scholarly.* **Description:** Contains news from all fields of the history of astronomy.
Related titles: Online - full text ed.: Electronic Newsletter for the History of Astronomy. 1994.
Published by: Astronomische Gesellschaft, Arbeitskreis Astronomiegeschichte, c/o Wolfgang R. Dick, Otterkiez 14, Potsdam, 14478, Germany. TEL 49-331-863199, wdi@potsdam.ifag.de, http://www.astro.uni-bonn.de/~pbrosche/aa/aa-ejourn.html. Ed. Wolfgang R Dick.

520 JPN ISSN 0916-6343
QB330
MIZUSAWA ASTROGEODYNAMICS OBSERVATORY. ANNUAL REPORT. Text in English. 1988. a. **Document type:** *Bulletin.* **Description:** Annual summary of the time service and geophysical observations performed in the Mizusawa Astronomical Observatory.
Published by: (Mizusawa Astrogeodynamics Observatory), National Astronomical Observatory, Division of Earth Rotation/Kokuritsu Tenmondai Chikyu Kaiten Kenkyukei Mizusawa Kansoku Senta, 2-12 Hoshigaoka-cho, Mizusawa-shi, Iwate-ken 023-0861, Japan. TEL 81-197-22-7111, FAX 81-197-22-7120, syomu@miz.nao.ac.jp. Ed. Seiji Manabe. Circ: 200.

520 GBR ISSN 1368-0919
MODERN ASTRONOMER; the monthly bulletin for astronomers. Text in English. 1996. m. GBP 2.49 newsstand/cover. **Document type:** *Consumer.* **Description:** Contains articles of interest and headline news on astronomy.
—Linda Hall.
Published by: Top Events & Publishing Ltd., Bowmere House, Birch Heath Rd, Tarporley, Ches CW6 9UR, United Kingdom. TEL 44-1829-733268, FAX 44-1829-730247, topeventsltd@binternet.com, http://www.topevents.co.uk. Ed. Geoffrey H Lindop. **Dist. by:** Comag, Tavistock Works, Tavistock Rd, W Drayton, Middx UB7 7QX, United Kingdom. TEL 44-1895-433600, FAX 44-189-543-3606.

523 623.89 RUS
MORSKOI ASTRONOMICHESKII EZHEGODNIK/NAVAL ASTRONOMICAL YEARBOOK. Text in Russian. a., latest 2003. **Document type:** *Yearbook, Academic/Scholarly.* **Description:** Intends to provide the users at any time moment with Greenwich hourly angles as well as with the declanations of the celestial bodies and with other values, which can be used for the naval astronavigation problems. The main content of the Yearbook is the daily tables.
Published by: Rossiiskaya Akademiya Nauk, Institut Prikladnoi Astronomii/Russian Academy of Sciences, Institute of Applied Astronomy, Naberezhnaya Kutuzova 10, St Petersburg, 191187, Russian Federation. TEL 8-812-2751118, FAX 7-812-2751119, ipa@ipa.nw.ru, http://www.ipa.rssi.ru.

MOSKOVSKII GOSUDARSTVENNYI UNIVERSITET. VESTNIK. SERIYA 3: FIZIKA I ASTRONOMIYA. see *PHYSICS*

MOZAMBIQUE. INSTITUTO NACIONAL DE METEOROLOGIA. INFORMACOES DE CARACTER ASTRONOMICO (ASTRONOMICAL INFORMATION). see *EARTH SCIENCES—Geophysics*

520 USA ISSN 0894-5985
N R A O NEWSLETTER. Text in English. 1981. q. free to qualified personnel. **Document type:** *Newsletter.* **Description:** Covers news, policies and instrumentation of interest to NRAO employees, telescope users, and others in the astronomical community.
Related titles: Online - full content ed.
—Linda Hall.
Published by: National Radio Astronomy Observatory, 520 Edgemont Rd, Charlottesville, VA 22903. TEL 434-296-0211, FAX 434-296-0278, http://www.nrao.edu/news/newsletters/index.html. Circ: 700.

522.1 JPN
N R O GIJUTSU HOKOKU/N R O TECHNICAL REPORT. Text in English, Japanese; Summaries in English. 1981. irreg. **Document type:** *Academic/Scholarly.*
Published by: National Astronomical Observatory, Nobeyama Radio Observatory/Kokuritsu Tenmondai Nobeyama Uchu Denpa Kansokujo, Nobeyama, Minamisaku-gun, Minamimaki-mura, Nagano-ken 384-1305, Japan.

522.1 JPN ISSN 0911-5501
N R O REPORT. Text and summaries in English. 1982. irreg. **Description:** Contains original research papers.
Published by: National Astronomical Observatory, Nobeyama Radio Observatory/Kokuritsu Tenmondai Nobeyama Uchu Denpa Kansokujo, Nobeyama, Minamisaku-gun, Minamimaki-mura, Nagano-ken 384-1305, Japan.

522.1 JPN
N R O YUZAZU MITINGU. Text in Japanese. 1983. a. **Document type:** *Proceedings.* **Description:** Contains proceedings from the observatory's users' meeting.
Published by: National Astronomical Observatory, Nobeyama Radio Observatory/Kokuritsu Tenmondai Nobeyama Uchu Denpa Kansokujo, Nobeyama, Minamisaku-gun, Minamimaki-mura, Nagano-ken 384-1305, Japan.

523.1 JPN ISSN 0919-875X
NAGOYA UNIVERSITY. JOURNAL OF EARTH AND PLANETARY SCIENCES. Text in English. 1992. a.
Indexed: BIOSIS Prev, BiolAb, INIS AtomInd, RefZh, ZooRec.
—Linda Hall.
Published by: Nagoya University, Solar-Terrestrial Environment Laboratory, Chikusa-ku, Nagoya-shi, Aichi-ken 464-8601, Japan.

520 SVN ISSN 1318-0614
NASE NEBO; astronomske efemeride. Text in Slovenian. 1973. a. SIT 1,200 in Slovenia to individuals; SIT 1,500 in Slovenia to institutions (effective 2004). adv. stat.; charts. **Document type:** *Journal, Academic/Scholarly.*
Former titles (until 1987-1992): Nase Nebo in Zemlja; (until 1986): Nase Nebo
Published by: Drustvo Matematikov, Fizikov in Astronomov - Zaloznistvo/Society of Mathematicians, Physicists and Astronomers - Publishing, Jadranska 19, pp 2964, Ljubljana, 1001, Slovenia. TEL 386-1-4232460, FAX 386-1-2517281, dmfa.zaloznistvo@fmf.uni-lj.si, http://vega.fmf.uni-lj.si/~zaloznistvo/. Ed. Mr. Herman Mikuz. Adv. contact Mr. Vladimir Bensa. Circ: 350 (paid and free).

520 JPN ISSN 0915-3780
QC851
NATIONAL ASTRONOMICAL OBSERVATORY. MIZUSAWA ASTROGEODYNAMICS OBSERVATORY. MIZUSAWA KANSOKU CENTER. TECHNICAL REPORT. Text and summaries in Japanese. 1988. a. **Document type:** *Academic/Scholarly.*
Published by: (Mizusawa Kansoku Center), National Astronomical Observatory, Mizusawa Astrogeodynamics Observatory/Kokuritsu Tenmondai, 2-12 Hoshigaoka-cho, Mizusawa-shi, Iwate-ken 023-0861, Japan. TEL 0197-22-7111, FAX 0197-22-7120, TELEX 837628-ILSMIZ-J. Ed. T Tsubokawa.

522.1 JPN ISSN 0915-3640
QB4.K68 CODEN: PNAJEH
NATIONAL ASTRONOMICAL OBSERVATORY. PUBLICATIONS/KOKURITSU TENMONDAI OBUN HOKOKU. Text in English. 1922. 2/yr. per issue exchange basis.
Former titles (until 1989): National Astronomical Observatory. Annals; Tokyo Astronomical Observatory. Annals (0082-4704); Supersedes (in 1937): Observatoire Astronomique de Tokyo. Annales
Indexed: BrCerAb, C&ISA, CerAb, ChemAb, CorrAb, E&CAJ, EMA, IAA, Inspec, M&GPA, M&TEA, MBF, METADEX, RefZh, WAA.
—BLDSC (7096.853000), AskIEEE, CASDDS, Linda Hall.
Published by: National Astronomical Observatory, Kokuritsu Tenmondai, 21-1 Osawa 2-chome, Mitaka-shi, Tokyo-to 181-0015, Japan. FAX 81-422-34-3690. Circ: 1,100.

520 JPN ISSN 0915-0021
NATIONAL ASTRONOMICAL OBSERVATORY. REPRINT. Text in English. 1938. irreg., latest 1997. per issue exchange basis.
Formerly (until 1988): Tokyo Astronomical Observatory. Reprints (0082-4712)
Indexed: IAA.
Published by: National Astronomical Observatory, Kokuritsu Tenmondai, 21-1 Osawa 2-chome, Mitaka-shi, Tokyo-to 181-0015, Japan. FAX 81-422-34-3690. Circ: 100.

THE NAUTICAL ALMANAC. see *TRANSPORTATION—Ships And Shipping*

528.3 DEU ISSN 0077-6211
NAUTISCHES JAHRBUCH, ODER EPHEMERIDEN UND TAFELN. Text in German. 1878. a. EUR 25.60 (effective 2005). **Document type:** *Journal, Academic/Scholarly.*
Published by: Bundesamt fuer Seeschiffahrt und Hydrographie, Bernhard-Nocht-Str 78, Hamburg, 20359, Germany. TEL 49-40-31900, FAX 49-40-31905000, posteingang@bsh.de, http://www.bsh.de/de/Produkte/Buecher/Nautisches%20Jahrbuch/index.jsp. Circ: 5,200.

520 572 UKR
NEIZVEDANNYE MIRY/UNEXPLORED WORLDS. Text in Russian. 1999. m. USD 48 domestic; USD 132 foreign; USD 22 newsstand/cover (effective 2002). **Document type:** *Newspaper.*
Published by: Mezhdunarodnyi Institut Sotsioniki/International Socionics Institute, a/s 23, Kiev, 02206, Ukraine. TEL 380-44-5580935, socionic@ukrpack.net, nm@socionics.ibc.com.ua, http://www.socionics.ibc.com.ua/esocint.html. Eds. A. V. Dr. Bukalov, G. A. Shulman, G. V. Chykyrysova, O. B. Karpenko. Circ: 12,000 (paid).

520 NLD ISSN 1384-1076
QB1
➤ **NEW ASTRONOMY.** Text in English. 1996. 8/yr. EUR 161 in Europe to individuals; JPY 21,300 in Japan to individuals; USD 181 to individuals except Europe and Japan; EUR 632 in Europe to institutions; JPY 83,900 in Japan to institutions; USD 706 to institutions except Europe and Japan (effective 2006). illus. back issues avail.; reprints avail. **Document type:** *Journal, Academic/Scholarly.* **Description:** Publishes articles in all fields of astronomy and astrophysics: theoretical, observational and instrumental. Includes full length research articles and letter articles. Covers solar, planetary, stellar, galactic and extragalactic astronomy and astrophysics. Reports on original research in all wavelength bands, ranging from radio to gamma-ray.
Related titles: Online - full text ed.: ISSN 1384-1092 (from EBSCO Publishing, Gale Group, IngentaConnect, ScienceDirect, Swets Information Services).
Indexed: BrCerAb, C&ISA, CerAb, CorrAb, CurCont, E&CAJ, EMA, EngInd, IAA, Inspec, M&TEA, MBF, METADEX, WAA.
—BLDSC (6082.114000), CASDDS, CISTI, IE, Infotrieve, ingenta. **CCC.**
Published by: Elsevier BV, North-Holland (Subsidiary of: Elsevier Science & Technology), Sara Burgerhartstraat 25, Amsterdam, 1055 KV, Netherlands. TEL 31-20-485-3911, FAX 31-20-485-2457, nlinfo-f@elsevier.nl, http://www.elsevier.com/locate/newast, http://www.elsevier.nl. Ed. W. D. Cochran. **Subscr. to:** Elsevier BV, PO Box 211, Amsterdam 1000 AE, Netherlands. TEL 31-20-485-3757, FAX 31-20-485-3432, http://www.elsevier.nl.

520 NLD ISSN 1387-6473
QB1 CODEN: NAREF9
➤ **NEW ASTRONOMY REVIEWS.** Text in English. 1958. 12/yr. EUR 929 in Europe to institutions; JPY 123,400 in Japan to institutions; USD 1,039 to institutions except Europe and Japan (effective 2006). adv. illus.; abstr. index. back issues avail.; reprints avail. **Document type:** *Journal, Academic/Scholarly.* **Description:** Publishes review articles in all fields of astronomy and astrophysics: theoretical, observational and instrumental.
Formerly: Vistas in Astronomy (0083-6656); Incorporates (1977-1991): Astronomy Quarterly (0364-9229)
Related titles: Microfilm ed.: (from PQC); Online - full text ed.: (from EBSCO Publishing, Gale Group, IngentaConnect, ScienceDirect, Swets Information Services).
Indexed: BAS, CIN, ChemAb, CurCont, IAA, Inspec, MathR, PhysBer, RefZh.
—BLDSC (6082.115000), AskIEEE, CASDDS, CISTI, IE, Infotrieve, ingenta, Linda Hall. **CCC.**
Published by: Elsevier BV, North-Holland (Subsidiary of: Elsevier Science & Technology), Sara Burgerhartstraat 25, Amsterdam, 1055 KV, Netherlands. TEL 31-20-485-3911, FAX 31-20-485-2457, nlinfo-f@elsevier.nl, http://www.elsevier.com/locate/newastrev, http://www.elsevier.nl. Ed. J. Audouze. **Subscr. to:** Elsevier BV, PO Box 211, Amsterdam 1000 AE, Netherlands. TEL 31-20-485-3757, FAX 31-20-485-3432, http://www.elsevier.nl.

520 USA ISSN 1546-9743
QB1
▼ **NIGHT SKY.** Text in English. 2004 (May/Jun.). bi-m. USD 17.99 domestic; USD 24.99 in Canada; USD 29.99 elsewhere; USD 3.99 newsstand/cover (effective 2004). adv. **Document type:** *Magazine, Consumer.* **Description:** Provides information for novice astronomy practitioners, containing non-technical writing, tips, new product announcements, and many images.
Related titles: Online - full text ed.: (from EBSCO Publishing, Gale Group, ProQuest Information & Learning).
—**CCC.**
Published by: Sky Publishing Corp., 49 Bay State Rd, Cambridge, MA 02138. TEL 617-864-7360, 800-253-0245, FAX 617-864-6117, custserv@nightskymag.com, info@skyandtelescope.com, http://www.nightskymag.com/, http://www.skypub.com. Ed. J Kelly Beatty. adv.: B&W page USD 1,150, color page USD 1,670; bleed 8.6875 x 11.1875. Circ: 50,000.

520 JPN
NIHON TENMON KENKYUKAI KANSOKU GEPPO/JAPAN ASTRONOMICAL STUDY ASSOCIATION. MONTHLY BULLETIN. Text in Japanese. 1964. m. stat. **Document type:** *Bulletin.*
Published by: Nihon Tenmon Kenkyukai/Japan Astronomical Study Association, c/o Kokuritsu Kagaku Hakubutsukan, Rikagaku Kenkyubu, 7 Ueno-Koen, Taito-ku, Tokyo, 110-0007, Japan.

522.1 JPN ISSN 0911-5870
NOBEYAMA NEWSLETTER. Text in English. 1985. s-a. **Document type:** *Newsletter.*
Published by: National Astronomical Observatory, Nobeyama Radio Observatory/Kokuritsu Tenmondai Nobeyama Uchu Denpa Kansokujo, Nobeyama, Minamisaku-gun, Minamimaki-mura, Nagano-ken 384-1305, Japan.

522.1 JPN ISSN 0911-5242
NOBEYAMA UCHU DENPA KANSOKUJO NYUSU. Text in Japanese. 1982. irreg. **Description:** News of the observatory.

A

Published by: National Astronomical Observatory, Nobeyama Radio Observatory/Kokuritsu Tenmondai Nobeyama Uchu Denpa Kansokujo, Nobeyama, Minamisaku-gun, Minamimaki-mura, Nagano-ken 384-1305, Japan.

523 USA
NORTH AMERICAN SKIES. Text in English. 1996. m.
Media: Online - full content.
Published by: Final Copy, 6874 E Harvard Ave., Denver, CO 80224. starman@usa.net, http://webcom.com/safezone/NAS/. Ed. Larry Sessions.

NOTIZIARIO U F O. (Unidentified Flying Objects) see *AERONAUTICS AND SPACE FLIGHT*

NOVA ACTA REGIAE SOCIETATIS SCIENTIARUM UPSALIENSIS. A, ASTRONOMY AND MATHEMATICAL SCIENCES. see *SCIENCES: COMPREHENSIVE WORKS*

520 DEU ISSN 0078-2246
NOVA KEPLERIANA. NEUE FOLGE. Text in German; Abstracts occasionally in English. 1969. irreg., latest vol.8, 1992. price varies. **Document type:** *Monographic series, Academic/Scholarly.*
Related titles: ♦ Series of: Bayerische Akademie der Wissenschaften. Mathematisch-Naturwissenschaftliche Klasse. Abhandlungen. ISSN 0005-6995.
Published by: (Kepler-Kommission), Verlag C.H. Beck oHG, Wilhelmstr 9, Munich, 80801, Germany. TEL 49-89-38189338, FAX 49-89-38189398, bestellung@beck.de, http://www.beck.de.

520 ITA ISSN 1122-7869
NUOVO ORIONE. Text in Italian. 1977. m. adv. **Document type:** *Consumer.*
Published by: Sirio Srl, Via Bronzino, 3, Milan, MI 20133, Italy. TEL 39-02-2046510, FAX 39-02-2049593, http://www.orione.it. Ed. Paola Dameno. Circ: 30,000.

522.1 USA
OBSERVATION OF THE WEEK. Text in English. 1995. w. **Document type:** *Government.* **Description:** Covers earth sciences, the Sun and solar system, stars, galaxies, the universe, and space history.
Media: Online - full text.
Published by: U.S. National Aeronautics and Space Administration, Observatorium, 110 University Dr, Fairmont, WV 26554. TEL 304-367-8331, FAX 304-367-8211, curator@rspac.ivv.nasa.gov, http://observe.ivv.nasa.gov/nasa/core.shtml.

520 FRA ISSN 0769-0878
OBSERVATIONS ET TRAVAUX. Text in French. q. adv. **Document type:** *Bulletin.*
Indexed: RefZh.
Published by: Societe Astronomique de France, 3 rue Beethoven, Paris, 75016, France. TEL 33-01-42241374, FAX 33-01-42307547, saf@calvanet.fr, http://www.iap.fr/saf. Ed. Gros. Adv. contact Elisabeth Sable.

520 DZA ISSN 0065-6232
OBSERVATOIRE ASTRONOMIQUE D'ALGER. ANNALES. Variant title: Universite d'Alger. Observatoire Astronomique. Annales. Text in French. irreg., latest vol.5, 1979.
Indexed: RASB.
Published by: Universite d'Alger, Observatoire Astronomique, Bouzareah, Algeria.

520 CHE
OBSERVATOIRE DE GENEVE. PRE-PUBLICATIONS. SERIE C. Text in English, French. 1986. irreg. (approx. 4/yr.). free.
Published by: Observatoire de Geneve, Sauverny, 1290, Switzerland.

520 CHE ISSN 0085-0942
OBSERVATOIRE DE GENEVE. PUBLICATIONS. SERIE A. Text in English, French. 1928. irreg. (approx. a). CHF 15. **Description:** Astronomical and astrophysical research.
Indexed: A&AAb.
Published by: Observatoire de Geneve, Sauverny, 1290, Switzerland.

520 CHE ISSN 0435-2939
OBSERVATOIRE DE GENEVE. PUBLICATIONS. SERIE B. Text in English, French. 1967. irreg. price varies. **Description:** Astronomical and astrophysical research.
Indexed: A&AAb.
Published by: Observatoire de Geneve, Sauverny, 1290, Switzerland.

520 FRA ISSN 0750-6651
OBSERVATOIRE DE HAUTE PROVENCE. RAPPORT D'ACTIVITE. Text in French. a.
Published by: (France. Centre National de la Recherche Scientifique), C N R S Editions, 15 Rue Malebranche, Paris, 75005, France. TEL 33-1-53102700, FAX 33-1-53102727, cnrseditions@cnrseditions.fr, http://www.cnrs.fr.

520 BEL ISSN 1370-298X
OBSERVATOIRE ROYAL DE BELGIQUE. ANNUAIRE (BILINGUAL EDITION). Text in English, French. a. —Linda Hall.
Published by: Observatoire Royal de Belgique, Av. Circulaire, 3, Bruxelles, 1180, Belgium. TEL 32-2-373-02-11, FAX 32-2-374-98-22.

520 BEL ISSN 0373-0697
OBSERVATOIRE ROYAL DE BELGIQUE. BULLETIN ASTRONOMIQUE. Text in French. 1931. a. **Document type:** *Monographic series, Academic/Scholarly.*
—Linda Hall.
Published by: Observatoire Royal de Belgique, Av. Circulaire, 3, Bruxelles, 1180, Belgium. TEL 32-2-373-02-11, FAX 32-2-374-98-22.

520 BEL ISSN 0524-7888
OBSERVATOIRE ROYAL DE BELGIQUE. COMMUNICATIONS. SERIE A. Text in French. 1966. irreg. **Document type:** *Monographic series, Academic/Scholarly.*
Supersedes in part (1948-1966): Observatoire Royal de Belgique. Communications (0779-2123)
—Linda Hall.
Published by: Observatoire Royal de Belgique, Av. Circulaire, 3, Bruxelles, 1180, Belgium. TEL 32-2-373-02-11, FAX 32-2-374-98-22.

520 BEL ISSN 0524-7896
OBSERVATOIRE ROYAL DE BELGIQUE. COMMUNICATIONS. SERIE B. Text in French. 1948. irreg.
Incorporates in part: Observatoire Royal de Belgique. Communications (0779-2123)
—Linda Hall.
Published by: Observatoire Royal de Belgique, Av. Circulaire, 3, Bruxelles, 1180, Belgium. TEL 32-2-373-02-11, FAX 32-2-374-98-22.

522.1 ESP ISSN 0373-5125
OBSERVATORIO ASTRONOMICO DE MADRID. ANUARIO. Text in Spanish. 1860; N.S. 1907. a. price varies. **Document type:** *Monographic series, Academic/Scholarly.* **Description:** contains the ephemerides of the astronomical bodies within the solar system, the explanation about how to use such data, and brief catalogs of interesting celestial objects for students and amateur observers.
Formerly (until 1926): Observatorio de Madrid. Anuario (0210-7619); Incorporates (1862-1905): Observatorio de Madrid. Observaciones Meteorologicas (0214-1671)
Indexed: IECT.
—CINDOC.
Published by: Observatorio Astronomico Nacional, Apartado 1143, Alcala De Henar, Madrid 28800, Spain. Ed. Pere Planesas. Circ: 2,000. **Co-sponsor:** Instituto Geografico Nacional.

520 ARG ISSN 0302-2277
QB1
OBSERVATORIO ASTRONOMICO MUNICIPAL DE ROSARIO. BOLETIN. Text in Spanish; Summaries in English. irreg. adv. illus. **Document type:** *Bulletin.*
Published by: Observatorio Astronomico Municipal de Rosario, Parque Urquiza, Rosario, Argentina. TEL 54-347-4802533. Ed., Pub. Roberto Oscar Aquilano. Adv. contact Daniel Davoli.

OBSERVATORIO DEL EBRO. PUBLICACIONES. MEMORIA. see *EARTH SCIENCES—Geophysics*

522.1 BRA
OBSERVATORIO NACIONAL RIO DE JANEIRO. EFEMERIDES ASTRONOMICAS. Text in Portuguese. 1885. a. BRL 20.
Formerly (until 1977): Observatorio Nacional Rio de Janeiro. Anuario
Published by: Observatorio Nacional, Coordenacao de Informacao e Documentacao, Rua General Jose Cristino, 77, Sao Cristovao, RJ 20921, Brazil.

520 551 BRA
OBSERVATORIO NACIONAL RIO DE JANEIRO. PUBLICACOES. Text in English, French, Portuguese. 1977; N.S. 1980. irreg. free.
Published by: Observatorio Nacional, Coordenacao de Informacao e Documentacao, Rua General Jose Cristino, 77, Sao Cristovao, RJ 20921, Brazil.

520 GBR ISSN 0029-7704
QB1 CODEN: OBSEAR
➤ **THE OBSERVATORY**; a review of astronomy. Text in English. 1877. bi-m. GBP 48, USD 85 to institutions; GBP 10, USD 18 newsstand/cover (effective 2004). adv. bk.rev.; software rev. illus. index, cum.index. 72 p./no. 1 cols./p.; back issues avail.; reprints avail. **Document type:** *Journal, Academic/Scholarly.*
Indexed: A&AAb, ASCA, ChemAb, ChemTitl, CurCont, ISR, Inspec, MathR, RefZh, SCI.
—BLDSC (6206.000000), AskIEEE, CASDDS, CISTI, IDS, IE, Infotrieve, ingenta, Linda Hall.
Published by: Observatory, c/o Dr. D.J. Stickland, Ed, Space and Astrophysics Div., Rutherford Appleton Laboratory, Chilton, Didcot, Oxon OX11 0QX, United Kingdom. TEL 44-1235-446523, FAX 44-1235-445848, TELEX 83159, obs@astro1.bnsc.rl.ac.uk, http://www.ulo.ucl.ac.uk/obsmag. R&P D J Stickland. adv.: page GBP 120. Circ: 1,000 (paid).

520 USA
OBSERVED MINIMA TIMINGS OF ECLIPSING BINARIES. Text in English. irreg., latest vol.3. USD 3; USD 5 foreign (effective 2001); included with AAVSO Publication Package. **Document type:** *Monographic series.* **Description:** Each volume contains times of minima, derived from AAVSO observations, of 50 eclipsing binary stars covering several to many years in graphical and tabular form.
Indexed: RefZh.
Published by: American Association of Variable Star Observers, 25 Birch St, Cambridge, MA 02138. TEL 617-354-0484, FAX 617-354-0665, aavso@aavso.org, http://www.aavso.org.

OBZORNIK ZA MATEMATIKO IN FIZIKO. see *MATHEMATICS*

520 USA ISSN 0737-6766
OCCULTATION NEWSLETTER. Text in English. 1974. q. USD 20 domestic; USD 25 foreign (effective 2001). charts; stat. back issues avail. **Document type:** *Newsletter, Academic/Scholarly.* **Description:** Contains predictions, methods of observing lunar occultations, asteroidal occultations, lunar and solar eclipses.
Related titles: Online - full content ed.
Published by: International Occultation Timing Association, Arthur Lucas 5403 Bluedbird Trail, Stillwaten, OK 74074. TEL 785-232-3693, editor@occultations.org, business@occultation.org, http://www.occultations.org. Ed. Rex L Easton. Pub. Tony Murray. Circ: 270 (paid).

ODYSSEY (PERU); adventures in science. see *CHILDREN AND YOUTH—For*

520 CHE ISSN 0030-557X
QB1
ORION. Text in French, German, English. 1943. 6/yr. CHF 52 domestic; CHF 60 foreign; CHF 25 to students (effective 2005). adv. bk.rev. charts; illus. index. back issues avail. **Document type:** *Journal, Academic/Scholarly.*
Related titles: CD-ROM ed.
Indexed: RGAb.
Published by: Societe Astronomique de Suisse/Schweizerische Astronomische Gesellschaft, c/o Sue Kernen, Gristenbuehl 13, Neukirch, 9315, Switzerland. TEL 41-71-4771743, sag.orion@bluewin.ch, http://www.astronomie.ch/literat/orion/, http://www.astronomie.ch/sag/. Ed. Noel Cramer. Adv. contact Fabio Barblan. Circ: 2,800.

523.01 GBR
PARTICLE PHYSICS AND ASTRONOMY RESEARCH COUNCIL. OPERATING PLAN. Text in English. 19??. a. **Document type:** *Monographic series, Academic/Scholarly.*
Formerly: Particle Physics and Astronomy Research Council. Business Plan (1464-0864)
—BLDSC (6579.138950).
Published by: Particle Physics and Astronomy Research Council, Polaris House, North Star Ave., Swindon, SN2 1SZ, United Kingdom. TEL 44-1793-442000, FAX 44-1793-442002, webmaster@pparc.ac.uk, http://www.pparc.ac.uk.

520 AUS ISSN 0155-3704
PERTH OBSERVATORY. COMMUNICATIONS. Text in English. 1964. irreg., latest vol.5, 1986. per issue exchange basis. **Description:** Documents position of comets and minor planets.
Indexed: A&AAb.
Published by: Perth Observatory (Subsidiary of: Department of Conservation and Land Management), Walnut Rd, Bickley, W.A. 6076, Australia. TEL 61-8-9293-8255, FAX 61-8-9293-8138, perthobs@iinet.net.au, http://www.wa.gov.au/perthobs/. Circ: 200.

520 PHL ISSN 0115-1207
PHILIPPINE ASTRONOMICAL HANDBOOK. Text in English. 1950. a. PHP 40, USD 1.50. **Document type:** *Government.* **Description:** Annual publication containing data on the sun, moon, planets and eclipses.
Published by: Philippine Atmospheric, Geophysical and Astronomical Services Administration, 1424 Quezon Ave, Quezon City, 1101, Philippines. Ed. Leoncio A Amadore. Circ: 300.

520 USA ISSN 1093-118X
PHOTOGRAPHER'S ALMANAC OF THE SUN & MOON (YEAR). Text in English. 1988. a. USD 20 (effective 2003). **Description:** Computed for the purchaser's latitude, longitude, and time zone, and contains everything about the daily astronomical circumstances of sunlight and moonlight that a landscape photographer might need to know.
Published by: Astronomical Data Service, 3922 Leisure Lane, Colorado Springs, CO 80917-3502. TEL 719-597-4068, sky_watcher@att.net.

PHYSICS ABSTRACTS. see *PHYSICS—Abstracting, Bibliographies, Statistics*

520 RUS ISSN 0320-0108
QB1 CODEN: PAZHDA
PIS'MA V ASTRONOMICHESKII ZHURNAL. Text in Russian; Summaries in English. 1975. m. USD 364 foreign (effective 2005). **Document type:** *Journal, Academic/Scholarly.*
Related titles: Online - full text ed.; ♦ English Translation: Astronomy Letters. ISSN 1063-7737.
Indexed: ChemAb, ChemTitl, Inspec, PhysBer, RefZh, SCI.

—AskIEEE, CASDDS, CISTI, East View, KNAW, Linda Hall. **CCC.**
Published by: (Rossiiskaya Akademiya Nauk/Russian Academy of Sciences, Astrosovet), Izdatel'stvo Nauka, Profsoyuznaya ul 90, Moscow, 117864, Russian Federation. TEL 7-095-3347151, FAX 7-095-4202220, secret@naukaran.ru, http://www.maik.rssi.ru/cgi-bin/list.pl?page=pisma, http://www.naukaran.ru. **Dist. by:** M K - Periodica, ul Gilyarovskogo 39, Moscow 129110, Russian Federation. TEL 7-095-2845008, FAX 7-095-2813798, info@periodicals.ru, http://www.mkniga.ru.

522.1 USA ISSN 0090-3213
QB1
PLANETARIAN. Text in English. 1972. q. USD 36 to libraries (effective 2004). adv. bk.rev. illus. index. reprint service avail. from PQC. **Document type:** *Academic/Scholarly.*
Related titles: Microform ed.: (from PQC).
—Linda Hall.
Published by: International Planetarium Society, Griffith Observatory, 2800 E Observatory Rd, Los Angeles, CA 90027. FAX 323-663-4323, jmosley@griffithObs.org, http://www.griffithobs.org/IPSPlanetarian.html. Ed. John E Mosley. R&P John Mosley. Circ: 750.

520 GBR ISSN 0032-0633
QC801 CODEN: PLSSAE
➤ **PLANETARY AND SPACE SCIENCE.** Text in English. 1959. 15/yr. EUR 3,011 in Europe to institutions; JPY 399,600 in Japan to institutions; USD 3,368 to institutions except Europe and Japan; EUR 331 in Europe to qualified personnel; JPY 44,000 in Japan to qualified personnel; USD 370 to qualified personnel except Europe and Japan (effective 2006). adv. bk.rev. illus. Index. reprints avail. **Document type:** *Academic/Scholarly.* **Description:** Publishes papers in cosmology and origins; small bodies, dust and rings; terrestrial planets and satellites; outer planets; planetary atmospheres, magnetospheres and ionospheres; exobiology; celestial mechanics; and the history of planetary and space research.
Related titles: Microfilm ed.: (from PQC); Online - full text ed.: (from EBSCO Publishing, Gale Group, IngentaConnect, ScienceDirect, Swets Information Services).
Indexed: ASCA, ASFA, ApMecR, BrCerAb, C&ISA, CCI, CIN, CerAb, ChemAb, ChemTitl, CivEngAb, CorrAb, CurCont, E&CAJ, EMA, EPB, Englnd, ExcerpMed, IAA, ISR, Inspec, M&GPA, M&TEA, MBF, METADEX, MSB, PhysBer, RefZh, SCI, SSCI, WAA.
—BLDSC (6508.320000), AskIEEE, CASDDS, CISTI, Ei, IDS, IE, Infotrieve, ingenta, Linda Hall. **CCC.**
Published by: (European Geophysical Society USA), Pergamon (Subsidiary of: Elsevier Science & Technology), The Boulevard, Langford Ln, East Park, Kidlington, Oxford OX5 1GB, United Kingdom. TEL 44-1865-843000, FAX 44-1865-843010, http://www.elsevier.com/locate/pss. Ed. T. Encrenaz. Circ: 1,250. **Subscr. to:** Elsevier BV, PO Box 211, Amsterdam 1000 AE, Netherlands. TEL 31-20-485-3757, FAX 31-20-485-3432, nlinfo-f@elsevier.nl, http://www.elsevier.nl.

523.2 USA
PLANETARY PHOTOJOURNAL. Text in English. 1996. m.
Media: Online - full content.
Address: 4800 Oak Grove Dr, Pasadena, CA 91009. http://photojournal.jpl.nasa.gov.

522 USA ISSN 0736-3680
QB600
PLANETARY REPORT. Text in English. 1980. bi-m. USD 30 domestic; USD 45 foreign (effective 2005). bk.rev. charts; illus. back issues avail. **Document type:** *Newsletter.* **Description:** Focuses on planetary exploration and the search for extraterrestrial intelligence.
Related titles: Online - full text ed.
Indexed: RefZh.
—Linda Hall.
Published by: Planetary Society, 65 N Catalina Ave, Pasadena, CA 91106-2301. TEL 626-793-5100, FAX 626-793-5528, TELEX 757511, tps@planetary.org, http://planetary.org. Ed. Charlene M Anderson. R&P Jennifer Vaughn. Circ: 100,000 (paid).

POLISH ACADEMY OF SCIENCES. BULLETIN. MATHEMATICS. see *MATHEMATICS*

520 SWE ISSN 1650-7177
CODEN: ANTKBF
➤ **POPULAER ASTRONOMI.** Text in Swedish. 1920. 4/yr. SEK 220 domestic; SEK 270 elsewhere (effective 2004). adv. bk.rev. charts; illus. index. Supplement avail. **Document type:** *Magazine, Academic/Scholarly.* **Description:** Contains news on astronomy, articles on the history of astronomy, society activities and other things of interest to amateur astronomers.
Former titles (until 2001): Astronomisk Tidskrift (1404-9295); (until 1999): Astronomisk Tidsskrift (0004-6345); (until 1968): Nordisk Astronomisk Tidsskrift (0909-4865)
Indexed: Inspec, RefZh.
—Linda Hall.
Published by: Svenska Astronomiska Saellskapet/Swedish Astronomical Society, PO Box 43, Lund, 22100, Sweden. gunnar.welin@astro.uu.se, http://www.popast.nu. Ed. Gunnar Welin. Circ: 1,300.

520 GBR ISSN 0261-0892
POPULAR ASTRONOMY. Text in English. 1953. q. GBP 12; GBP 16 in Europe; GBP 20 elsewhere. adv. bk.rev. illus. reprints avail. **Document type:** *Bulletin.*
Formerly: Hermes
Published by: Society for Popular Astronomy, c/o Tom Hosking, Ed, 6 Queensberry Pl, Friars Ln., Richmond, Surrey TW9 1NW, United Kingdom. spa@stones.com, http://www.u-net.com/ph/spa/spapop. Adv. contact Stewart McLaughlin. Circ: (controlled). **Subscr. to:** 36 Fairway, Keyworth, Nottingham NG12 5DU, United Kingdom.

520 POL ISSN 0032-5414
QB1 CODEN: PYAIAJ
➤ **POSTEPY ASTRONOMII.** Text in Polish. 1953. q. PLZ 20, USD 46 (effective 1998). adv. bk.rev. charts; illus. index. **Document type:** *Academic/Scholarly.* **Description:** Contains review articles, news, people in astronomy, astronomical centers in Poland, occasionally interviews.
Indexed: ChemAb, Inspec.
—CASDDS, Linda Hall.
Published by: Polskie Towarzystwo Astronomiczne/Polish Astronomical Society, Ul Bartycka 18, Warsaw, 00716, Poland. TEL 48-22-410041, FAX 48-22-410046, aw@astri.uni.torun.pl. Ed. A Woszczyk. R&P A. Woszczyk. Circ: 1,000. **Dist. also by:** M K - Periodica, ul Gilyarovskogo 39, Moscow 129110, Russian Federation. TEL 7-095-2845008, FAX 7-095-2813798, info@periodicals.ru, http://www.mkniga.ru; **Dist. by:** Ars Polona, Krakowskie Przedmiescie 7, Warsaw, Poland.

➤ **PRESEK**; list za mlade matematike, fizike, astronome in racunalnikarje. see *SCIENCES: COMPREHENSIVE WORKS*

523.1 USA
PRINCETON SERIES IN ASTROPHYSICS. Text in English. 1987. irreg., latest vol.6, 1999. price varies. illus. **Document type:** *Monographic series, Academic/Scholarly.* **Description:** Publishes research and new findings in astrophysics.
Indexed: CCMJ.
Published by: Princeton University Press, 41 William St, Princeton, NJ 08540-5237. TEL 609-258-4900, FAX 609-258-6305, http://pup.princeton.edu/catalogs/series/psa.html. Ed. Jeremiah P Ostriker. **Subscr.addr. in US:** California - Princeton Fulfillment Services, 1445 Lower Ferry Rd, Ewing, NJ 08618. TEL 800-777-4726, FAX 800-999-1958, orders@cpfs.pupress.princeton.edu. **Dist. add. in Canada:** University Press Group, 164 Hillsdale Ave E, Toronto, ON M4S 1T5, Canada.; **Dist. addr. in UK:** John Wiley & Sons Ltd., The Atrium, Southern Gate, Chichester, West Sussex PO19 8SQ, United Kingdom.

520 JPN ISSN 0004-6264
QB1 CODEN: PASJAC
➤ **PUBLICATIONS OF ASTRONOMICAL SOCIETY OF JAPAN/NIHON TENMON GAKKAI OBUN KENKYU HOKOKU.** Text and summaries in English. 1949. bi-m. JPY 20,000 combined subscription domestic print & online eds.; JPY 23,000 combined subscription foreign print & online eds. (effective 2003). adv. reprint service avail. from ISI. **Document type:** *Academic/Scholarly.* **Description:** Publishes papers on all aspects of Astronomy, Astrophysics, and fields closely related to them.
Related titles: Online - full text ed.: (from EBSCO Publishing).
Indexed: ASCA, CIN, ChemAb, ChemTitl, CurCont, ISR, Inspec, JPI, JTA, PhysBer, RefZh, SCI.
—BLDSC (7029.000000), AskIEEE, CASDDS, CISTI, IDS, IE, Infotrieve, ingenta, Linda Hall.
Published by: Nihon Tenmon Gakkai/Astronomical Society of Japan, c/o National Astronomical Observatory, 2-21-1 Osawa, Mitaka-shi, Tokyo-to 181-0015, Japan. TEL 81-422-31-5488, FAX 81-422-31-5487, office@pasj.asj.or.jp, http://www.asj.or.jp/pasj/. Ed. I Hachisu. **Dist. by:** Maruzen Co., Ltd., 3-10 Nihonbashi 2-chome, Chuo-ku, Tokyo 103-0027, Japan. TEL 81-3-3273-3230, http://www.maruzen.co.jp.

520 USA ISSN 0004-6280
QB1 CODEN: PASPAU
➤ **PUBLICATIONS OF THE ASTRONOMICAL SOCIETY OF THE PACIFIC.** Text in English. 1889. m. USD 365 combined subscription to institutions print & online eds.; USD 37 per issue (effective 2006). illus. cum.index: vols.1-94. reprint service avail. from PQC. **Document type:** *Journal, Academic/Scholarly.* **Description:** Research reports, PhD abstracts and review articles in astronomy and astrophysics.
Related titles: Microfiche ed.; Online - full text ed.: ISSN 1538-3873. USD 345 to institutions (effective 2006) (from EBSCO Publishing).
Indexed: A&AAb, ASCA, ChemAb, CivEngAb, CurCont, Englnd, ISR, Inspec, MathR, PhysBer, RefZh, SCI, SPINweb.
—BLDSC (7030.000000), AskIEEE, CASDDS, CISTI, Ei, IE, Infotrieve, ingenta, Linda Hall. **CCC.**
Published by: (Astronomical Society of the Pacific), University of Chicago Press, Journals Division, Journals Division, PO Box 37005, Chicago, IL 60637. TEL 773-753-3347, 877-705-1878, FAX 773-753-0811, 877-705-1879, subscriptions@press.uchicago.edu, http://www.journals.uchicago.edu/PASP/home.html. Eds. Anne P Cowley, David Hartwick. Circ: 3,000.

523.2 JPN ISSN 0048-6167
QUARTERLY BULLETIN ON SOLAR ACTIVITY. Text in English, French. 1928. q. USD 30. **Document type:** *Bulletin.*
—Linda Hall.
Published by: (International Astronomical Union/Union Astronomique Internationale FRA), National Astronomical Observatory, Kokuritsu Tenmondai, 21-1 Osawa 2-chome, Mitaka-shi, Tokyo-to 181-0015, Japan. FAX 81-422-34-3700. Circ: 500.

QUEST (GRAND FORKS); the history of spaceflight quarterly. see *AERONAUTICS AND SPACE FLIGHT*

520 USA ISSN 0034-2963
THE REFLECTOR NEWSLETTER. Text in English. 1956. q. USD 8 domestic; USD 11 in Canada & Mexico; USD 16 elsewhere (effective 2005). adv. bk.rev. charts; illus.; stat. **Document type:** *Newsletter, Academic/Scholarly.* **Description:** Covers amateur astronomy news.
Related titles: Online - full text ed.: (from CompuServe Inc.).
Indexed: RefZh.
Published by: Astronomical League, 9201 Ward Pkwy, Ste 100, Kansas City, MO 64114. TEL 816-333-7759, reflectorphotos@swbell.net, http://www.astroleague.org/al/reflectr/reflmain.html. Ed. Kent Marts. adv.: B&W page USD 500. Circ: 13,000.

523.1 531.14 530.11 USA
▼ **RELATIVITY, GRAVITATION, COSMOLOGY.** Text in English. 2004. irreg. **Document type:** *Monographic series.*
Published by: Nova Science Publishers, Inc., 400 Oser Ave, Ste 1600, Hauppauge, NY 11788-3619. TEL 631-231-7269, FAX 631-231-8175, novascience@earthlink.net, http://www.novapublishers.com.

REVIEWS OF GEOPHYSICS. see *EARTH SCIENCES—Geophysics*

520 ARG ISSN 0374-4272
REVISTA ASTRONOMICA. Text in Spanish. 1929. q. USD 20 (effective 1999). adv. bk.rev. back issues avail. **Document type:** *Academic/Scholarly.* **Description:** Covers amateur astronomy, observation guides, telescopes and the ephemerides.
Indexed: Inspec.
Published by: Asociacion Argentina Amigos de la Astronomia, Av Patricias Argentinas 550, Buenos Aires, 1405, Argentina. TEL 54-11-4863-3366, FAX 54-11-486-33366, postmaster@asaramas.com, http://www.asaramas.com. Ed., R&P Cristian Rusquellas. Adv. contact Mauricio Berthet. Circ: 1,500.

REVISTA BRASILEIRA DE CARTOGRAFIA. see *GEOGRAPHY*

520 MEX ISSN 0185-1101
QB1 CODEN: RMAAD4
➤ **REVISTA MEXICANA DE ASTRONOMIA Y ASTROFISICA.** Text in English; Summaries in English, Spanish. 1974. s-a. cum.index: 1974-1994. back issues avail. **Document type:** *Academic/Scholarly.* **Description:** Includes original research papers in all branches of astronomy, astrophysics and closely related fields.
Indexed: A&AAb, ASCA, ChemAb, ChemTitl, CurCont, ISR, Inspec, MathR, PhysBer, RefZh, SCI.
—AskIEEE, CASDDS, IDS, Linda Hall.
Published by: Universidad Nacional Autonoma de Mexico, Instituto de Astronomia, Apdo Postal 70-264, Mexico DF, 04510 , Mexico. TEL 52-5-622-3909, FAX 52-5-616-0653, rmaa@astroscu.unam.mx, http://www.astroscu.unam.mx/rmaa.html. Eds. Jorge Canto, Luis Rodriguez. Circ: 200 (paid); 800 (controlled).

520 523.01 MEX ISSN 1405-2059
CODEN: RMAAF6
REVISTA MEXICANA DE ASTRONOMIA Y ASTROFISICA SERIE DE CONFERENCIAS. Text in English; Summaries in English, Spanish. 1995. irreg., latest vol.7, 1998. **Document type:** *Proceedings.* **Description:** Publishes the proceedings of astronomical symposia that take place in Latin America.
Indexed: CIN, ChemAb, ChemTitl, Inspec, RefZh.
—AskIEEE, CASDDS, CISTI, Linda Hall.
Published by: Universidad Nacional Autonoma de Mexico, Instituto de Astronomia, Apdo Postal 70-264, Mexico DF, 04510 , Mexico. TEL 52-5-622-3909, FAX 52-5-616-0653, rmaa@astroscu.unam.mx, http://www.astroscu.unam.mx/rmaa.html. Ed. Silvia Torres-Peimbert. Circ: 200 (paid); 800 (controlled).

520 CZE ISSN 0035-5550
RISE HVEZD✶. Text in Czech, Slovak. 1920. m. USD 21.70. bk.rev.; film rev. bibl.; charts. index. **Document type:** *Consumer.* **Description:** Astronomical journal for amateurs.
Published by: Informacni a Poradenske Stredisko pro Misti Kulturu, Ul Blanicka 4, Prague, 12021, Czech Republic. Ed. Eduard Skoda. Circ: 5,000.

520 ROM ISSN 1220-5168
ROMANIAN ASTRONOMICAL JOURNAL. Text in English, French; Summaries in English. 1991. s-a.
Supersedes (1956-1974): Studii si Cercetari de Astronomie (0039-3894); Which was formerly (until 1963): Studii si Cercetari de Astronomie si Seismologie (1220-062X)

Related titles: Online - full text ed.
—CISTI, Linda Hall.
Published by: (Academia Romana, Observatul Astronomic), Editura Academiei Romane/Publishing House of the Romanian Academy, Calea 13 Septembrie 13, Sector 5, Bucharest, 76117, Romania. TEL 40-21-4119008, FAX 40-21-4103983, edacad@ear.ro, http://www.ear.ro. Ed. Arpad Pal. **Dist. by:** Rodipet S.A., Piata Presei Libere 1, sector 1, PO Box 33-57, Bucharest 3, Romania. TEL 40-21-2224126, 40-21-2226407, rodipet@rodipet.ro.

520 RUS
ROSSIISKII KOSMICHESKII BYULLETEN'. Text in Russian. q. USD 135 in United States.
Address: Profsoyuznaya ul 84-32, Moscow, 117485, Russian Federation. TEL 7-095-3334134, FAX 7-095-3301200. **US dist. addr.:** East View Information Services, 3020 Harbor Ln. N., Minneapolis, MN 55447. TEL 612-550-0961.

520 GBR ISSN 0035-8711
QB1 CODEN: MNRAA4
➤ **ROYAL ASTRONOMICAL SOCIETY. MONTHLY NOTICES.** Variant title: Monthly Notices of the Royal Astronomical Society. Text in English. 1827. 36/yr. GBP 453, EUR 680 combined subscription in Europe to individuals print & online eds.; USD 837 combined subscription in the Americas to individuals & Caribbean, print & online eds.; GBP 498 combined subscription elsewhere to individuals print & online eds.; GBP 3,146 combined subscription in Europe to institutions print & online eds.; USD 5,813 combined subscription in the Americas to institutions & Caribbean, print & online eds.; GBP 3,460 combined subscription elsewhere to institutions print & online eds. (effective 2006). adv. illus. index, cum.index: vols.1-91, 1827-1931 (in 4 vols.). back issues avail.; reprint service avail. from ISI. **Document type:** *Journal, Academic/Scholarly.* **Description:** Publishes the results of original research in positional and dynamical astronomy, astrophysics, radio astronomy, cosmology, space research and the design of astronomical instruments.
Related titles: Microform ed.: (from PQC); Online - full text ed.: ISSN 1365-2966. GBP 2,989 in Europe to institutions; USD 5,522 in the Americas to institutions & Caribbean; GBP 3,287 elsewhere to institutions (effective 2006) (from Blackwell Synergy, EBSCO Publishing, Gale Group, IngentaConnect, O C L C Online Computer Library Center, Inc., Swets Information Services).
Indexed: ASCA, BrCerAb, C&ISA, CCI, CIS, CerAb, ChemAb, ChemTitl, CivEngAb, CorrAb, CurCont, E&CAJ, EMA, IAA, ISR, Inspec, M&TEA, MBF, METADEX, MathR, PhysBer, RefZh, SCI, WAA.
—BLDSC (5943.000000), AskIEEE, CASDDS, CISTI, Ei, IDS, IE, Infotrieve, ingenta, Linda Hall. **CCC.**
Published by: (Royal Astronomical Society), Blackwell Publishing Ltd., 9600 Garsington Rd, Oxford, OX4 2ZG, United Kingdom. TEL 44-1865-776868, FAX 44-1865-714591, customerservices@oxon.blackwellpublishing.com, http://www.blackwellpublishing.com/journals/MNR. Ed. A C Fabian. Pub. Sue Hewitt. R&P Sophie Savage. Adv. contact Jenny Applin. Circ: 1,130.

520 CAN ISSN 0035-872X
QB1 CODEN: JRASA2
ROYAL ASTRONOMICAL SOCIETY OF CANADA. JOURNAL. Text in English. 1907. bi-m. CND 80, USD 90 to institutions (effective 2000). adv. bk.rev. bibl.; illus. index, cum.index: vols.1-25, 26-60. **Document type:** *Academic/Scholarly.*
Description: Contains articles on Canadian astronomers and current activities of the RASC, research and review papers by professional and amateur astronomers, and articles of a historical, biographical, or educational nature of general interest to the astronomical community.
Incorporates (1978-1997): Royal Astronomical Society of Canada. Bulletin (1187-1571); Which was formerly (until 1991): Royal Astronomical Society of Canada. Newsletter (0846-8877); (until 1989): Royal Astronomical Society of Canada. National Newsletter (0846-8494)
Related titles: Microform ed.: (from PQC).
Indexed: A&AAb, ASCA, CBCARef, ChemAb, CurCont, IAA, Inspec, RefZh.
—BLDSC (4854.000000), AskIEEE, CASDDS, CISTI, IE, Infotrieve, ingenta, Linda Hall. **CCC.**
Published by: Royal Astronomical Society of Canada/Societe Royale d'Astronomie du Canada, 136 Dupont St, Toronto, ON M5R 1V2, Canada. TEL 416-924-7973, FAX 416-924-2911, rasc@rasc.ca, nationaloffice@rasc.ca, http://www.rasc.ca. Ed., R&P Wayne Barkhouse. Adv. contact David Lane. Circ: 3,500.

522 CAN ISSN 0080-4193
QB9
ROYAL ASTRONOMICAL SOCIETY OF CANADA. OBSERVER'S HANDBOOK. Text in English. 1908. a. USD 25.95 (effective 2004). illus. index. reprints avail.
Related titles: Microform ed.: (from PQC).
—Linda Hall.
Published by: Royal Astronomical Society of Canada/Societe Royale d'Astronomie du Canada, 136 Dupont St, Toronto, ON M5R 1V2, Canada. TEL 416-924-7973, FAX 416-924-2911, rasc@rasc.ca, nationaloffice@rasc.ca, http://www.rasc.ca. Ed. Dr. Rajiv Gupta. Circ: 12,000.

523.8 JPN ISSN 0385-0994
RYUSEIJIN KAIHO/CIRCULAR OF METEORIC DUST. Text in Japanese. 1964. bi-m. stat.
Published by: Morikubo Shigeru Ed. & Pub., 1058 Oikawa, Atsugi-shi, Kanagawa-ken 243-0212, Japan.

520 ZAF ISSN 1017-7787
S A A O NEWSLETTER. Text in English. 1983. s-a. free. back issues avail. **Document type:** *Newsletter.*
Related titles: Online - full text ed.
Published by: South African Astronomical Observatory, PO Box 9, Observatory, Cape Town 7935, South Africa. TEL 27-21-447-0025, FAX 27-21-447-3639, ethleen@saao.ac.za, http://www.saao.ac.za. Ed. Ethleen Lastovica. Circ: 700.

629.4 JPN
S P A R C JIMUKYOKUHO/S P A R C NEWS. Text in Japanese. 1967. irreg. **Description:** Contains news of the association.
Published by: Space Research Co-Operative Association/Uchu Kukan Kenkyusha Kyogikai, Nagoya Daigaku Rigakubu Butsurigaku Kyoshitsu, Furo-cho, Chikusa-ku, Nagoya-shi, Aichi-ken 464-0814, Japan.

SANKT-PETERBURGSKII UNIVERSITET. VESTNIK. SERIYA: MATEMATIKA, MEKHANIKA I ASTRONOMIYA. see *MATHEMATICS*

520 FRA ISSN 0769-1025
SATELLITES DE SATURNE I TO VIII. Text in English, French. 1985. a. **Document type:** *Academic/Scholarly.*
Related titles: ◆ Supplement to: Connaissance des Temps. ISSN 0181-3048.
Published by: (Institut de Mecanique Celeste et de Calcul des Ephemerides), Bureau des Longitudes, Palais de l'Institut, 3 Rue Mazarine, Paris, 75006, France. FAX 33-1-46332834, contact@bureau-des-longitudes.fr, http://www.bdl.fr, http://www.bureau-des-longitudes.fr. Ed. J E Arlot. **Subscr. to:** A F A, 17 rue Deutch de la Meurthe, Paris 75014, France.

520 FRA ISSN 0769-1033
SATELLITES GALILEENS DE JUPITER; phenomenes et configurations. Text in English, French. 1979. a. **Document type:** *Academic/Scholarly.*
Related titles: ◆ Supplement to: Connaissance des Temps. ISSN 0181-3048.
Published by: (Institut de Mecanique Celeste et de Calcul des Ephemerides), Bureau des Longitudes, Palais de l'Institut, 3 Rue Mazarine, Paris, 75006, France. FAX 33-1-46332834, contact@bureau-des-longitudes.fr, http://www.bdl.fr, http://www.bureau-des-longitudes.fr. Ed. J E Arlot.

523.01 SGP
THE SCIENCE AND CULTURE SERIES - ASTROPHYSICS. Text in English. 1992. irreg., latest 1999. price varies. **Document type:** *Monographic series, Academic/Scholarly.*
Related titles: ◆ Series: The Science and Culture Series - Advanced Scientific Culture; ◆ The Science and Culture Series - Environmental Sciences; ◆ The Science and Culture Series - Ethology; ◆ The Science and Culture Series - Materials Science; ◆ The Science and Culture Series - Mathematics; ◆ The Science and Culture Series - Medicine; ◆ The Science and Culture Series - Nuclear Strategy and Peace Technology; ◆ The Science and Culture Series - Physics; ◆ The Science and Culture Series - Spectroscopy.
Published by: World Scientific Publishing Co. Pte. Ltd., 5 Toh Tuck Link, Singapore, 596224, Singapore. TEL 65-466-5775, FAX 65-467-7667, wspc@wspc.com.sg, series@wspc.com.sg, http://www.wspc.com.sg/books/series/scsa_series.shtml, http://www.worldscientific.com. Ed. A Zichichi. **Dist. by:** World Scientific Publishing Co., Inc., 1060 Main St, River Edge, NJ 07661. TEL 201-487-9655, 800-227-7562, FAX 201-487-9656, 888-977-2665; World Scientific Publishing Ltd., 57 Shelton St, London WC2H 9HE, United Kingdom. TEL 44-20-78360888, FAX 44-20-78362020.

SCIENCE IN CHINA. SERIES A: MATHEMATICS. see *MATHEMATICS*

SCIENCE IN CHINA. SERIES G: PHYSICS, MECHANICS & ASTRONOMY. see *PHYSICS*

520 CZE
SCRIPTA ASTRONOMICA. Text in Czech. irreg. **Document type:** *Academic/Scholarly.* **Description:** Covers the history of astronomy in Bohemian lands.
Published by: Akademie Ved Ceske Republiky, Astronomicky Ustav/Academy of Sciences of the Czech Republic, Astronomical Institite, Fricova 1, Ondrejov, 25165, Czech Republic. TEL 42-2-04857111, FAX 42-2-881611, had@dsunstel.asu.cas.cz, http://sunkl.asu.cas.cz. Ed. Petr Hadrova.

523.1 USA ISSN 1096-5599
SEARCHLITES. Text in English. 1995. q. USD 50 to members (effective 2000). **Document type:** *Newsletter.* **Description:** Provides a forum for members to discuss their thoughts and findings in their search for intelligent extraterrestrial intelligence.
Published by: S E T I League, Inc., 433 Liberty St, Box 555, Little Ferry, NJ 07643. TEL 201-641-1770, 800-TAU-SETI, FAX 201-641-1771, info@setileague.org, http:// www.setileague.org. Ed. H Paul Shuch.

520 USA
SELENOLOGY✶. Text in English. 1982. q. USD 12 (effective 1998). bk.rev. **Document type:** *Academic/Scholarly.*
Description: Devoted to the science of the Earth's moon.
Related titles: Microform ed.: 1982.
Published by: American Lunar Society, 417 Franklin St, E, Pittsburgh, PA 15112-1067. TEL 412-829-8901. Ed. Francis G Graham. Circ: 200.

520 JPN ISSN 0386-0817
SENDAI ASTRONOMIAJ REPORTOJ. Text and summaries in English. 1930. irreg. free. **Document type:** *Academic/Scholarly.*
Published by: Tohoku Daigaku, Rigakubu/Tohoku University, Faculty of Science, Laboratory of Nuclear Science, Aramaki, Aoba-ku, Sendai-shi, Miyagi-ken 981-0945, Japan. Ed. Mine Takeuti.

520 AUS ISSN 1035-932X
SKY AND SPACE. Text in English. 1988. bi-m. AUD 41 (effective 2004).
Formerly (until 1992): Southern Astronomy (1030-0015)
Address: PO Box 1690, Bondi Junction, NSW 1355, Australia. TEL 61-2-9369-3344, FAX 61-2-9369-3366, info@skyadspace.com.au, http://www.skyandspace.com.au.

520 USA ISSN 0037-6604
QB1 CODEN: SKTEA3
SKY & TELESCOPE; the essential magazine of astronomy. Text in English. 1941. m. USD 42.95 domestic; USD 49.95 in Canada; USD 61.95 elsewhere (effective 2005). adv. bk.rev.; film rev. charts; illus.; maps. s-a. index. back issues avail.; reprints avail. **Document type:** *Magazine, Consumer.*
Description: Discusses astronomy and space science. Contains items by leading professionals, activities of amateur astronomers and current celestial events.
Former titles: Telescope: Drama of the Skies; Sky (0361-8242)
Related titles: Microform ed.: (from PQC); Online - full text ed.: (from bigchalk, EBSCO Publishing, Gale Group, H.W. Wilson, Northern Light Technology, Inc., O C L C Online Computer Library Center, Inc., ProQuest Information & Learning); Alternate Frequency ed(s).: Sky & Telescope's Weekly News Bulletin.
Indexed: A&AAb, ASCA, Acal, BRI, BiolDig, CBRI, CIS, CurCont, DIP, GSI, IAA, IHTDI, Inspec, LRI, MagInd, PMR, RGAb, RGPR, RefZh.
—BLDSC (8309.000000), AskIEEE, CISTI, IE, Infotrieve, ingenta, Linda Hall. **CCC.**
Published by: Sky Publishing Corp., 49 Bay State Rd, Cambridge, MA 02138. TEL 617-864-7360, 800-253-0245, FAX 617-864-6117, info@skyandtelescope.com, http://www.SkyandTelescope.com, http://www.skypub.com. Ed. Richard T Fienberg. Pub. Susan B. Lit. R&P Imelda Joson. Adv. contact Peter D. Hardy Jr. Circ: 111,528 (paid).

520 ZAF
SKY GUIDE AFRICA SOUTH. Text in English. 1946. a. ZAR 50 domestic; USD 25 foreign (effective 2006). adv. charts; illus. 100 p./no.; back issues avail. **Document type:** *Yearbook, Academic/Scholarly.* **Description:** Provides astronomical notes and predictions for the year.
Formerly: Astronomical Handbook for Southern Africa (0571-7191)
Published by: Astronomical Society of Southern Africa, PO Box 9, Observatory, Cape Town 7935, South Africa. TEL 27-21-5315250, FAX 27-21-4473639, http://da.saao.ac.za/ assa. Ed., R&P Auke Slotegraaf. Adv. contact Cliff Turk. page ZAR 400; 14 x 21. Circ: 1,500 (paid).

520 JPN ISSN 0911-7652
SKY WATCHER. Text in Japanese. 1983. m. JPY 620. adv. bk.rev. **Document type:** *Consumer.*
Published by: Rippu Shobo Inc., 5-8 Kami-Meguro 5-chome, Meguro-ku, Tokyo, 153-0051, Japan. TEL 03-5721-0561. Ed. Masaya Kawaguchi.

520 CAN ISSN 0840-8939
QB1
SKYNEWS; the Canadian magazine of astronomy and stargazing. Text in English. bi-m. CND 28.72 domestic; USD 26 in United States (effective 2004). illus. reprints avail. **Description:** Includes star charts, research articles by astronomy experts and equipment reviews.
Indexed: CBCARef, CPerI, RefZh.
Published by: Canada Science and Technology Museum Corp/Musee National des Sciences et de la Technologie, P O Box 9724, Sta T, Ottawa, ON K1G 5A3, Canada. TEL 800-267-3999, FAX 613-990-3635, skynewseditor@compuserve.com, cmgroup@interlog.com, http://www.science-tech.nmstc.ca. Ed. Terence Dickinson.

520 USA ISSN 1089-4888
SKYWATCH; tour guide for stargazing and space exploration. Text in English. 1996. a. USD 4.99 newsstand/cover domestic; USD 5.99 newsstand/cover foreign (effective 2004). adv. **Document type:** *Magazine, Consumer.* **Description:** Contains articles and features on astronomy, space science, and other tools for beginning and seasoned astronomers.
Related titles: Microform ed.: (from PQC); Online - full text ed.: (from EBSCO Publishing, Gale Group, ProQuest Information & Learning).
—CCC.

A

Published by: Sky Publishing Corp., 49 Bay State Rd, Cambridge, MA 02138. TEL 617-864-7360, 800-253-0245, FAX 617-864-6117, info@skyandtelescope.com, http://www.skypub.com. Circ: 85,000 (paid and controlled).

520 USA ISSN 0889-9614
SKYWATCHERS ALMANAC (YEAR). Text in English. 1976. a. USD 20 (effective 2003). illus. back issues avail.; reprints avail. **Description:** Provides information about the sun, moon, planets, stars, and constellations in an easy-to-use, quick-reference format. Computed for purchaser's latitude and longitude.
Published by: Astronomical Data Service, 3922 Leisure Lane, Colorado Springs, CO 80917-3502. TEL 719-597-4068, sky_watcher@att.net. Pub. Roger L Mansfield. **Subscr. to:** PO Box 26180, Colorado Springs, CO 80936.

520 ITA ISSN 0037-8720
QB1 CODEN: MSATAB
SOCIETA ASTRONOMICA ITALIANA. MEMORIE/ITALIAN ASTRONOMICAL SOCIETY. JOURNAL. Text in Multiple languages. 1872. q. EUR 80 domestic; EUR 160 foreign (effective 2004). bk.rev. charts; illus. index. **Document type:** *Journal, Academic/Scholarly.*
Formerly (until 1920): Societa degli Spettroscopisti Italiani. Memorie
Related titles: Online - full text ed.: ISSN 1824-016X.
Indexed: ChemAb, IAA, Inspec, MathR, RefZh.
—BLDSC (5675.055000), AskIEEE, CASDDS, IE, ingenta.
Published by: Societa Astronomica Italiana, Largo Enrico Fermi 5, Florence, 50125, Italy. TEL 39-055-2752270, FAX 39-055-220039, sait@arcetri.astro.it, http://www.sait.it. Ed. Roberto Pallavicini. Circ: 400.

SOCIETA ITALIANA DI FISICA. NUOVO CIMENTO B. GENERAL PHYSICS, RELATIVITY, ASTRONOMY, AND MATHEMATICAL PHYSICS AND METHODS. see *PHYSICS*

520 FRA ISSN 0081-0738
SOCIETE ASTRONOMIQUE DE BORDEAUX. BULLETIN✶. Text in French. 1961. a. price varies.
Published by: Societe Astronomique de Bordeaux, Hotel des Societes Savantes, 71 rue du Loup, Bordeaux, 33000, France.

523.01 551 USA
QB524
SOLAR-GEOPHYSICAL DATA. PART 1 - PROMPT REPORTS. Text in English. 1957. m. (plus a. descriptive text issue). USD 105; USD 120 foreign; includes both parts. **Document type:** *Government.* **Description:** Presents historical data on the sun's activity and effects on the Earth.
Supersedes in part: Solar-Geophysical Data (0038-0911)
Related titles: CD-ROM ed.; Microfiche ed.: (from NTI).
Published by: (National Oceanic and Atmospheric Administration), U.S. National Geophysical Data Center, 325 Broadway, E CG4, Boulder, CO 80303-3328. TEL 303-497-6836, FAX 303-497-6513, info@ngdc.noaa.gov, http://www.ngdc.noaa.gov.

523.01 551 USA
QB524
SOLAR-GEOPHYSICAL DATA: PART 2 - COMPREHENSIVE REPORTS. Text in English. 1955. m. USD 105; USD 120 foreign; includes both parts. **Document type:** *Government.* **Description:** Presents historical data on the sun's activity and effects on the Earth.
Supersedes in part: Solar-Geophysical Data (0038-0911)
Related titles: CD-ROM ed.; Microfiche ed.: (from NTI).
Published by: (National Oceanic and Atmospheric Administration), U.S. National Geophysical Data Center, 325 Broadway, E CG4, Boulder, CO 80303-3328. TEL 303-497-6836, FAX 303-497-6513, info@ngdc.noaa.gov, http://www.ngdc.noaa.gov, http://www.ngdc.noaa.gov. Eds. Helen E Coffey, John A McKinnon. Circ: 800.

523.01 NLD ISSN 0038-0938
QB521 CODEN: SLPHAX
➤ **SOLAR PHYSICS**; a journal for solar and solar-stellar research and the study of solar terrestrial physics. Text in Dutch. 1967. 14/yr. EUR 3,538, USD 3,588, GBP 2,208 combined subscription to institutions print & online eds. (effective 2005). adv. bk.rev. illus. index, cum.index vols. 1-100. back issues avail.; reprint service avail. from PSC. **Document type:** *Journal, Academic/Scholarly.* **Description:** Treats all aspects of solar physics, ranging from the internal structure of the Sun and its evolution to the outer corona and solar wind in interplanetary space.
Related titles: Microform ed.: (from PQC); Online - full text ed.: ISSN 1573-093X (from EBSCO Publishing, Gale Group, IngentaConnect, Kluwer Online, O C L C Online Computer Library Center, Inc., Springer LINK, Swets Information Services).
Indexed: A&AAb, ASCA, BibLing, CIN, ChemAb, ChemTitl, CurCont, EngInd, IAA, IBR, IBZ, ISR, Inspec, M&GPA, PhysBer, RefZh, SCI.
—BLDSC (8327.205000), AskIEEE, CASDDS, CISTI, IDS, IE, Infotrieve, ingenta, Linda Hall. **CCC.**
Published by: Springer-Verlag Dordrecht (Subsidiary of: Springer Science+Business Media), Van Godewijckstraat 30, Dordrecht, 3311 GX, Netherlands. TEL 31-78-6576050, FAX 31-78-6576474, http://springerlink.metapress.com/openurl.asp?genre=journal&issn=0038-0938, http://www.springeronline.com. Eds. Jack W Harvey, Oddbjorn Engvold, Zdenek Svestka.

621.47 523.01 RUS ISSN 0038-0946
QB501 CODEN: SSYRAL
➤ **SOLAR SYSTEM RESEARCH.** Text in English. 1967. bi-m. EUR 2,678, USD 2,398, GBP 1,672 combined subscription to institutions print & online eds. (effective 2005). illus. back issues avail.; reprints avail. **Document type:** *Journal, Academic/Scholarly.* **Description:** Publishes articles concerning the bodies of the Solar System: planets and their satellites, asteroids, comets, meteroic substances, and cosmic dust; the physics and dynamics of these bodies, their origin and evolution, and investigative methods are covered.
Related titles: Online - full text ed.: ISSN 1608-3423 (from EBSCO Publishing, Gale Group, IngentaConnect, Kluwer Online, O C L C Online Computer Library Center, Inc., Springer LINK, Swets Information Services); ♦ Translation of: Astronomicheskii Vestnik. ISSN 0320-930X.
Indexed: BibLing, CurCont, EngInd, Inspec.
—BLDSC (0420.825000), AskIEEE, IE, Infotrieve, ingenta, Linda Hall. **CCC.**
Published by: (Rossiiskaya Akademiya Nauk/Russian Academy of Sciences), M A I K Nauka - Interperiodica, Profsoyuznaya ul 90, Moscow, 117997, Russian Federation. TEL 7-095-3347420, FAX 7-095-3360666, compmg@maik.ru, http://www.maik.rssi.ru/journals/solsys.htm, http://www.maik.ru. Ed. M Ya Marov. **Subscr. to:** Springer-Verlag Dordrecht, Journals Department, PO Box 322, Dordrecht, Netherlands. TEL 31-78-6576392, FAX 31-78-6576474.

520 DEU ISSN 0721-0094
SONNE; Mitteilungsblatt der Amateursonnenbeobachter. Text in German; Abstracts in English. 1977. q. USD 22 (effective 2001). adv. bk.rev. abstr.; bibl.; charts; illus.; stat. index. back issues avail. **Document type:** *Bulletin, Consumer.* **Description:** Observations of the sun.
Related titles: Online - full text ed.
Indexed: A&AAb.
Published by: Vereinigung der Sternfreunde e.V., Fachgruppe Sonne, c/o Wilhelm-Foerster-Sternwarte e.V., Munsterdamm 90, Berlin, 12169, Germany. konto@vds-sonne.de, http://sonneonline.org. Ed. Michael Schwab. Adv. contact Robert Hilz. Circ: 350.

522.19687 ZAF ISSN 0250-0671
QB82.S62
SOUTH AFRICAN ASTRONOMICAL OBSERVATORY. ANNUAL REPORT. Key Title: Report for the Year Ending - South African Astronomical Observatory. Text in English. 1977. a. **Document type:** *Corporate.*
—BLDSC (7608.820000).
Published by: (Foundation for Research and Development), South African Astronomical Observatory, PO Box 9, Observatory, Cape Town 7935, South Africa. TEL 27-21-470025, FAX 27-21-473639, TELEX 5-20309 SA, ethleen@saao.ac.za. R&P R S Stobie.

520 NZL ISSN 0049-1640
QB1
➤ **SOUTHERN STARS.** Text in English. 1934. q. NZD 50 to non-members (effective 2002). adv. bk.rev.; software rev. Index. **Document type:** *Journal, Academic/Scholarly.* **Description:** Covers astronomical research and reports especially as caried out in New Zealand.
Indexed: A&AAb, Inspec, RefZh.
—Linda Hall. **CCC.**
Published by: Royal Astronomical Society of New Zealand (Inc.), PO Box 3181, Wellington, New Zealand. TEL 64-3-213-0329, FAX 64-3-318-7659, rasnz@rasnz.org.nz, http://www.rasnz.org.nz/. Ed., R&P R W Evans. adv.: page NZD 50. Circ: 300 (paid).

629.4072 JPN
SPACE RESEARCH IN JAPAN. Text in English. 2/yr. abstr.
Published by: (Nihon Gakujutsu Kaigi/Science Council of Japan, Uchu Kukan Kenkyu Renraku Iinkai), Institute of Space and Aeronautical Science/Uchu Kagaku Kenkyujo, 1-1 Yoshinodai 3-chome, Sagamihara-shi, Kanagawa-ken 229-0022, Japan.

629.4 NLD ISSN 0038-6308
QB1 CODEN: SPSRA4
➤ **SPACE SCIENCE REVIEWS.** Text in English. 1962. 24/yr. EUR 2,268, USD 2,308, GBP 1,418 combined subscription to institutions print & online eds. (effective 2005). adv. bk.rev. illus. back issues avail.; reprint service avail. from PSC. **Document type:** *Academic/Scholarly.* **Description:** Publishes review papers on scientific research carried out by means of rockets, rocket-propelled vehicles, stratospheric balloons, and at observatories on the Earth.
Related titles: Microform ed.: (from PMC, PQC); Online - full text ed.: ISSN 1572-9672 (from EBSCO Publishing, Gale Group, IngentaConnect, Kluwer Online, O C L C Online Computer Library Center, Inc., Springer LINK, Swets Information Services).
Indexed: A&AAb, ASCA, BibLing, BrCerAb, C&ISA, CerAb, ChemAb, CivEngAb, CorrAb, CurCont, E&CAJ, EMA, IAA, IBR, IBZ, ISR, Inspec, M&GPA, M&TEA, MBF, METADEX, MSB, PhysBer, RefZh, SCI, WAA.
—BLDSC (8361.650000), AskIEEE, CISTI, IDS, IE, Infotrieve, ingenta, Linda Hall. **CCC.**
Published by: Springer-Verlag Dordrecht (Subsidiary of: Springer Science+Business Media), Van Godewijckstraat 30, Dordrecht, 3311 GX, Netherlands. TEL 31-78-6576050, FAX 31-78-6576474, http://springerlink.metapress.com/openurl.asp?genre=journal&issn=0038-6308, http://www.springeronline.com. Ed. Hans Bloemen.

520 USA ISSN 1053-8534
SPACE SCIENCE SERIES. Text in English. 1974. irreg. price varies. **Document type:** *Monographic series.*
Indexed: Inspec.
Published by: University of Arizona Press, 355 S Euclid Ave, Ste 103, Tucson, AZ 85719. TEL 520-621-1441, FAX 520-621-8899, http://www.uapress.arizona.edu.

520 USA ISSN 1542-7390
▼ ➤ **SPACE WEATHER**; the international journal of research and applications. Text in English. 2003. q. USD 210 to institutions (effective 2006). **Document type:** *Journal, Academic/Scholarly.* **Description:** Provides the latest news and findings in the emerging field of space .
Media: Online - full content (from EBSCO Publishing). **Related titles:** Print ed.: ISSN 1539-4956.
Indexed: CurCont.
Published by: American Geophysical Union, 2000 Florida Ave, NW, Washington, DC 20009-1277. TEL 202-462-6900, 800-966-2481, FAX 202-328-0566, institutions@agu.org, http://www.agu.org/journals/spaceweather. Ed. Louis Lanzerotti.

➤ **SPACEDAILY.** see *AERONAUTICS AND SPACE FLIGHT*

520 DEU
STAR FORMATION NEWSLETTER. Text in English. 1992. m.
Media: Online - full content.
Published by: European Southern Observatory, Karl Schwarzschild Str 2, Garching, 85748, Germany. TEL 49-89-320060, FAX 49-89-3202362, ips@eso.org, http://www.eso.org/gen-fac/pubs/starform/. Ed. Bo Reipurth.

520 USA ISSN 0893-4614
STAR TECH; the real cosmic connection. Text in English. 1987. m. USD 16.50; USD 25 foreign. back issues avail. **Description:** For people who are interested in contemporary ideas, techniques, and tools for understanding the connections between human experience and the cosmic environment.
Published by: Richard Nolle, Ed. & Pub., PO Box 26599, Tempe, AZ 85285-6599. TEL 602-838-3245.

520 USA ISSN 0889-3098
STARDATE. Text in English. 1972. bi-m. USD 21 domestic; USD 25 in Canada & Mexico; USD 36 elsewhere (effective 2001). bk.rev. illus. reprints avail. **Document type:** *Magazine, Consumer.*
Formerly: McDonald Observatory News
Related titles: Online - full content ed.
Indexed: BiolDig.
Published by: University of Texas, Austin, McDonald Observatory, PO Box 1337, Fort Davis, TX 79734-1337. TEL 432-426-4188, FAX 432-426-3641, TELEX 9108741351, http://stardate.org/. Eds. Gary Harrison, Damond Beeningfield. Pub. Sandra Preston. R&P Damond Beeningfield. Circ: 11,000 (paid).

520 USA
STARGAZINE. Text in English. 1998. m.
Media: Online - full text.
Published by: University of Texas, Austin, McDonald Observatory, PO Box 1337, Fort Davis, TX 79734-1337. TEL 432-426-4188, FAX 432-426-3641, http://www.stardate.org/. Ed. Doug Addison.

520 DEU ISSN 0039-1263
QB1 CODEN: STUWAN
STERNE UND WELTRAUM; Zeitschrift fuer Astronomie. Text in German. 1962. m. adv. bk.rev.; software rev.; video rev.; Website rev. abstr.; charts; illus.; bibl. index. 100 p./no.; back issues avail. **Document type:** *Magazine, Academic/Scholarly.*
Incorporates (1921-1997): Sterne (0039-1255)
Indexed: CIN, ChemAb, ChemTitl, DIP, Inspec, RefZh.
—AskIEEE, CASDDS, IE, Infotrieve, Linda Hall. **CCC.**
Published by: (Max-Planck-Institut fuer Astronomie), Verlag Sterne und Weltraum, Huethig GmbH & Co. KG, Im Weiher 10, Heidelberg, 69121, Germany. TEL 49-6221-489283, FAX 49-6221-489258, quetz@mpia-hd.mpg.de, hvs_zeitschrift@huethig.de, http://www.mpia.de/suw, http://www.huethig.de. Ed. Dr. Jakob Staude. Adv. contact Friedrich Limperg TEL 49-6181-72904. Circ: 22,000.

520 AUT ISSN 0039-1271
DER STERNENBOTE; Oesterreichische Astronomische Monatsschrift. Text in German. 1958. m. EUR 15 (effective 2003). adv. bk.rev. bibl. **Document type:** *Bulletin, Academic/Scholarly.*

Published by: Astronomisches Buero, Hasenwartgasse 32, Vienna, W 1238, Austria. TEL 43-1-88935410, FAX 43-1-889354111, astbuero@astronomisches-buero-wien.or.at, http://members.ping.at/astbuero. Ed., R&P Hermann Mucke. Circ: 2,000.

520 NLD ISSN 0925-6806
➤ **STUDIA COPERNICANA - BRILL SERIES.** Text in Dutch. 1991. irreg., latest vol.2, 2002. price varies. **Document type:** *Monographic series, Academic/Scholarly.*
Published by: Brill Academic Publishers, PO Box 9000, Leiden, 2300 PA, Netherlands. TEL 31-71-53-53-500, FAX 31-71-53-17-532, cs@brill.nl, http://www.brill.nl. Ed. Pawel Czartoryski. R&P Elizabeth Venekamp. **Subscr. in N. America to:** PO Box 605, Herndon, VA 20172. TEL 703-661-1585, 800-337-9255, FAX 703-661-1501, cs@brillusa.com. **Distr. outside N. America by:** c/o Turpin Distribution, Stratton Business Park, Pegasus Drive, Biggleswade, BEDFORDSHIRE SG 18 8TQ, United Kingdom. TEL 44-1767-604-954, FAX 44-1767-601-640, brill@turpin-distribution.com.

520 POL ISSN 0082-5573
STUDIA SOCIETATIS SCIENTIARUM TORUNENSIS. SECTIO F. ASTRONOMIA. Text in English; Summaries in Polish. 1956. irreg., latest vol.6, no.4, 1987. price varies. charts; illus. index. **Document type:** *Monographic series.*
Published by: Towarzystwo Naukowe w Toruniu, Ul Wysoka 16, Torun, 81100, Poland. TEL 48-56-23941. Ed. Cecylia Iwaniszewska. Circ: 650.

529 USA ISSN 0170-9704
QB209
THE STUDY OF TIME. Variant title: International Society for the Study of Time. Proceedings. Text in English. 1972. irreg., latest vol.7. price varies. bibl.; illus. reprint service avail. from ISI. **Document type:** *Proceedings, Academic/Scholarly.*
—BLDSC (8501.215000).
Published by: International Society for the Study of Time, c/o Dr Marlene Soulsby, Box 6195, Bloomington, IN 47407. http://www.studyoftime.org.

522 PHL ISSN 0115-3307
QB216
TABLE OF SUNRISE, SUNSET, TWILIGHT, MOONRISE AND MOONSET. Text in English. a. PHP 40, USD 1.50. **Document type:** *Government.* **Description:** Sunrise and moonrise data for the Philippines.
Published by: Philippine Atmospheric, Geophysical and Astronomical Services Administration, 1424 Quezon Ave, Quezon City, 1101, Philippines. Ed. Leoncio A Amadore. Circ: 450.

TAIYOKEI KAGAKU SHINPOJUMU. see *ASTRONOMY—Abstracting, Bibliographies, Statistics*

520 629 SWE ISSN 1651-6346
TELESCOPIUM. Text in Swedish. 1972. q. SEK 190 to individual members; SEK 1,000 to institutional members (effective 2003). adv. bk.rev. 24 p./no. 3 cols./p.; **Document type:** *Magazine.*
Former titles (until 2002): Astro (0280-7173); Which incorporates (1990-2001): Amatoerastronomen (1102-6901); (until 1982): Scanam: the Scandinavian Amateur Astronomer (0348-7156); (until 1978): The Scandinavian Amateur Astronomer (0347-9951)
Published by: Svensk Amatoerastronomisk Foerening (SAAF), c/o Daniel Soederstroem, Sturegatan 9:34, Uppsala, 75314, Sweden. TEL 46-18-261993, FAX 46-70-3645088, telescopium@swipnet.se, http://www.saaf.se. Ed. Daniel Soederstroem.

520 BGR ISSN 1311-3879
TELESKOP. Text in Bulgarian. bi-w. USD 100 foreign (effective 2004). **Document type:** *Newspaper, Academic/Scholarly.* **Description:** Covers space and science news, and activities of Association.
Published by: Astronomical Association - Sofia, 49 Tsar Asen St, Sofia, 1463, Bulgaria. TEL 359-2-9793202, newspaper@aas.stilrad.bas.bg, aas@cl.bas.bg, http://www.geocities.com/aas_andromeda//tel.htm, http://www.geocities.com/aas_sofia_bg. Ed. Boriana Bontcheva TEL 359-87-894056. **Dist. by:** Sofia Books, ul Silivria 16, Sofia 1404, Bulgaria. TEL 359-2-9586257, info@sofiabooks-bg.com, http://www.sofiabooks-bg.com.

520 JPN ISSN 0288-1977
TENMON GAIDO✶ /GUIDE TO ASTRONOMY. Text in Japanese. 1965. m. JPY 14,460.
Published by: Seibundo Shinkosha Inc., 3-3-11 Hongo, Bunkyoku, Tokyo, 164-0013, Japan. Ed. Yukihiro Takatsuki. Circ: 200,000.

520 JPN ISSN 0374-2466
QB1 CODEN: TGEPAC
TENMON GEPPO/ASTRONOMICAL HERALD. Text in Japanese. 1908. m. JPY 8,400. adv. bk.rev. index.
Indexed: CIN, ChemAb, ChemTitl, Inspec, JPI, RefZh.
—AskIEEE, CASDDS, CISTI.
Published by: Nihon Tenmon Gakkai/Astronomical Society of Japan, c/o National Astronomical Observatory, 2-21-1 Osawa, Mitaka-shi, Tokyo-to 181-0015, Japan. geppou@asj.or.jp, http://www.asj.or.jp/geppou/. Ed. M Veno. Circ: 3,000. **Dist. by:** Universal Academy Press, Inc., BR-Hongo-5 Bldg, 6-16-2, Hongo, Bunkyo-ku, Tokyo 113-0033, Japan.

523.51 JPN ISSN 0388-5852
TENMON KAIHO/ASTRONOMICAL CIRCULAR. Text in Japanese. 1950. q. **Document type:** *Academic/Scholarly.*
Formerly: Tenmon Sokuho
Published by: Nippon Ryusei Kenkyukai/Nippon Meteor Society, Yabu Tenmondai, 878 Maruyama-cho, Omihachiman-shi, Shiga-ken 523-0805, Japan. TEL 0748-32-4539, FAX 0748-33-4892. Ed. Yasuo Yabu.

520 CHN ISSN 0493-2285
TIANWEN AIHAOZHE/AMATEUR ASTRONOMER. Text in Chinese. 1956. m. (bi-m. until 2004). CNY 75.60 per issue (effective 2004). **Document type:** *Journal, Academic/Scholarly.*
Related titles: Online - full text ed.: (from East View Information Services).
Address: 138, Xizhimen Wei Dajie, Beijing, 100044, China. **Dist. by:** China International Book Trading Corp, 35 Chegongzhuang Xilu, Haidian District, PO Box 399, Beijing 100044, China. TEL 86-10-68412045, FAX 86-10-68412023, cibtc@mail.cibtc.com.cn, http://www.cibtc.com.cn.

520 CHN ISSN 0001-5245
QB1 CODEN: TIWHAO
➤ **TIANWEN XUEBAO/ACTA ASTRONOMICA SINICA.** Text in Chinese; Summaries in English. 1953. q. CNY 120 (effective 2004). adv. **Document type:** *Journal, Academic/Scholarly.* **Description:** Includes papers on theoretical astronomy, analysis of astronomical observations, application of the results of astronomical study, development of astronomical instruments, and the history of astronomy.
Related titles: Online - full text ed.: (from East View Information Services); ◆ English ed.: Chinese Astronomy and Astrophysics. ISSN 0275-1062; ◆ English ed.: Chinese Journal of Astronomy and Astrophysics. ISSN 1009-9271.
Indexed: CCMJ, IAA, Inspec, M&TEA, ZentMath.
—BLDSC (0598.500000), AskIEEE, IE, ingenta, Linda Hall.
Published by: (Zhongguo Kexueyuan, Xijinshan Tianwentai/Chinese Academy of Sciences, Purple Mountain Observatory), Kexue Chubanshe/Science Press, 16 Donghuang Cheng Genbei Jie, Beijing, 100717, China. TEL 86-10-64000246, FAX 86-10-64030255, twxb@pmo.ac.cn, http://www.pmo.ac.cn/pmolj/indexlj.htm, http://www.sciencep.com/. Circ: 7,000. **Dist. by:** China International Book Trading Corp, 35 Chegongzhuang Xilu, Haidian District, PO Box 399, Beijing 100044, China. TEL 86-10-68412045, FAX 86-10-68412023, cibtc@mail.cibtc.com.cn, http://www.cibtc.com.cn.

520 CHN ISSN 1000-8349
QB1 CODEN: TIJIEY
➤ **TIANWENXUE JINZHAN/PROGRESS IN ASTRONOMY.** Text in Chinese; Summaries in English. 1983. q. CNY 40 (effective 2004). adv. **Document type:** *Journal, Academic/Scholarly.*
Related titles: Online - full text ed.: (from East View Information Services, WanFang Data Corp.).
Indexed: Inspec.
Published by: (Zhongguo Kexueyuan, Shanghai Tianwentai/Chinese Academy of Sciences, Shanghai Astronomical Observatory), Kexue Chubanshe/Science Press, 16 Donghuang Cheng Genbei Jie, Beijing, 100717, China. TEL 86-10-64000246, FAX 86-10-64030255, twxjz@cencer.shao.ac.cn, http://twxjz.periodicals.net.cn/default.html, http://www.sciencep.com/. Circ: 5,000. **Dist. by:** China International Book Trading Corp, 35 Chegongzhuang Xilu, Haidian District, PO Box 399, Beijing 100044, China. TEL 86-10-68412045, FAX 86-10-68412023, cibtc@mail.cibtc.com.cn, http://www.cibtc.com.cn.

520 CZE
TIME AND LATITUDE. Text in English. q. **Description:** Provides data on observations of variations in width and world time using optical astrometry.
Published by: Akademie Ved Ceske Republiky, Astronomicky Ustav/Academy of Sciences of the Czech Republic, Astronomical Institute, Fricova 1, Ondrejov, 25165, Czech Republic. TEL 42-2-04857111, FAX 42-2-04881611, assu@asu.cas.cz, vondrak@ig.cas.cz, http://www.lib.cas.cz/knav/journals/cz/Time_and_Latitude.htm. Ed. Jan Vondrak.

TODAY AT N A S A. see *AERONAUTICS AND SPACE FLIGHT*

TOHOKU UNIVERSITY. SCIENCE REPORTS. SERIES 8: PHYSICS AND ASTRONOMY. see *PHYSICS*

520 ESP ISSN 0213-5892
TRIBUNA DE ASTRONOMIA Y UNIVERSO. Text in Spanish. 1985. m.
—CINDOC.
Published by: Equipo Sirius, Ave. Rafael Finat, 34, Madrid, 28044, Spain. TEL 34-91-7107349, FAX 34-91-7054304, http://www.equiposirius.com/tribuna/.

520 JPN ISSN 0285-2853
QB495
UCHU KAGAKU KENKYUJO HOKOKU/BULLETIN OF THE INSTITUTE OF SPACE AND AERONAUTICAL SCIENCE. UNIVERSITY OF TOKYO A. Text in Japanese. 1965. irreg. **Document type:** *Monographic series.*
Supersedes in part (in 1981): Tokyo Daigaku Uchu Koku Kenkyusho Hokoku (0563-8100)
Indexed: INIS AtomInd, Inspec, RefZh.
—BLDSC (9079.621050), CISTI, Linda Hall.
Published by: Institute of Space and Aeronautical Science/Uchu Kagaku Kenkyujo, 3-1-1 Yoshinodai, Sagamihara, Kanagawa, 229-8510, Japan. TEL 81-42-751-3911, FAX 81-42-759-4251.

520 JPN ISSN 0285-9920
UCHU KAGAKU KENKYUJO HOKOKU. TOKUSHU/BULLETIN OF THE INSTITUTE OF SPACE AND AERONAUTICAL SCIENCE. UNIVERSITY OF TOKYO B. Text in Japanese. 1965. a.
Supersedes in part (in 1981): Tokyo Daigaku Uchu Koku Kenkyusho Hokoku (0563-8100)
Indexed: INIS AtomInd, Inspec, RefZh.
—BLDSC (9079.621070), CISTI, Linda Hall.
Published by: Institute of Space and Aeronautical Science/Uchu Kagaku Kenkyujo, 3-1-1 Yoshinodai, Sagamihara, Kanagawa, 229-8510, Japan. TEL 81-42-751-3911, FAX 81-42-759-4251.

UCHU SEIBUTSU KAGAKU/BIOLOGICAL SCIENCES IN SPACE. see *BIOLOGY*

520 AUS ISSN 0049-5506
UNIVERSE. Text in English. 1955. m. AUD 40 domestic membership; AUD 55 foreign (effective 1999). adv. bk.rev. back issues avail. **Document type:** *Newsletter, Academic/Scholarly.* **Description:** Provides information for members on astronomy and related topics.
Published by: Astronomical Society of New South Wales Incorporated, c/o Astronomical Society of South Australia, GPO Box 1123, Sydney, NSW 10043, Australia. FAX 61-2-9337-3378, asnsw@ozmail.com.au, http://www.ozemail.com.au/~lmacdonald/universe/universe.htm, http://www.ozmail.com.au/~lmacdonald/universe/universe.htm. Ed. Peter Northfield. Circ: 300.

THE UNIVERSE IN THE CLASSROOM; a newsletter on astronomy for teachers. see *EDUCATION—Teaching Methods And Curriculum*

520 MEX ISSN 0185-2752
UNIVERSIDAD DE GUADALAJARA. INSTITUTO DE ASTRONOMIA Y METEOROLOGIA. BOLETIN INFORMATIVO MENSUAL. Text in Spanish. 1965. m. MXP 180; USD 36 foreign. charts. **Document type:** *Bulletin.* **Description:** Covers astronomy news, astronomical phenomena, climatology, regional meteorological information, popularization articles on astronomy and meteorology.
Formerly: Universidad de Guadalajara. Instituto de Astronomia y Meteorologia. Informacion (0041-8404)
Media: Duplicated (not offset).
Published by: Universidad de Guadalajara, Instituto de Astronomia y Meteorologia, Av. Vallarta Num. 2602, Guadalajara, Jal. 44110, Mexico. TEL 52-3-6164937, FAX 52-3-6159829, dalba@udgserv.cencar.udg.mx. Circ: 150.

520 BEL
UNIVERSITEIT TE GENT. STERRENKUNDIG OBSERVATORIUM. MEDEDELINGEN. Text and summaries in Dutch, English. 1939. irreg. free. **Document type:** *Academic/Scholarly.*
Formerly: Rijksuniversiteit te Gent. Sterrenkundig Observatorium. Mededelingen: Astronomie (0072-4432)
Published by: Universiteit te Gent, Sterrenkundig Observatorium, Krijgslaan 281, Ghent, 9000, Belgium. TEL 32-9-2644798, FAX 32-9-2644989.

UNIVERSITY OF BRITISH COLUMBIA. PHYSICS SOCIETY. JOURNAL. see *PHYSICS*

523.01 GBR
UNIVERSITY OF LEICESTER. X-RAY ASTRONOMY GROUP. SPECIAL REPORT. Text in English. irreg. GBP 20 (effective 1999). **Document type:** *Monographic series, Academic/Scholarly.*
Related titles: Online - full text ed.
Published by: University of Leicester, X-Ray Astronomy Group, Leicester, Leics LE1 7RH, United Kingdom. TEL 44-1162-523494, FAX 44-1162-523311, par@star.le.ac.uk, http://www.star.le.ac.uk/.

523.51 USA ISSN 0085-3968
➤ **UNIVERSITY OF NEW MEXICO. INSTITUTE OF METEORITICS. SPECIAL PUBLICATION.** Text in English. 1970. irreg. (2-4/yr.). USD 10. back issues avail. **Document type:** *Academic/Scholarly.*
Published by: University of New Mexico, Institute of Meteoritics, Department of Earth and Planetary Sciences, Northrop Hall, Albuquerque, NM 87131. TEL 505-277-2747, FAX 505-277-3577. Ed. James J Papike. Circ: 1,000.

520 JPN ISSN 0563-8038
UNIVERSITY OF TOKYO. DEPARTMENT OF ASTRONOMY. CONTRIBUTIONS. Text and summaries in English. 1959. irreg. **Document type:** *Academic/Scholarly.*
Published by: (Department of Astronomy), University of Tokyo, Graduate School of Science, Chirigaku Kyoshitsu, 3-1, Hongo 7-chome, Bunkyo-ku, Tokyo, 113-0033, Japan.

520 ESP ISSN 1135-2876
UNIVERSO. Text in Spanish. 1995. m.
—CINDOC.
Published by: Antares, Ciencias y Ediciones, Gran Via Corts Catalanes, Barcelona, 08007, Spain. TEL 34-93-3011717, FAX 34-93-3011765, universo@antares.es. Ed. Jose Maria Rodriguez.

520 MEX ISSN 0374-0501
UNIVERSO. Text in Spanish. 1973 (vol.27). q. MXP 32, USD 12. charts; illus.
Published by: Sociedad Astronomica de Mexico, Jardin Felipe Xicotencatl, Mexico 13, DF, Mexico. Ed. Antonio R Viaud.

520 USA
UNIVERSO ONLINE. Text in Spanish. 1997. m.
Media: Online - full content.
Published by: University of Texas, Austin, McDonald Observatory, PO Box 1337, Fort Davis, TX 79734-1337. TEL 432-426-4188, FAX 432-426-3641, http://universo.utexas.edu/. Ed. Gary Harrison.

520 POL ISSN 0554-8233
UNIWERSYTET IM. ADAMA MICKIEWICZA. ASTRONOMIA. Text in English, Polish; Summaries in English. 1964. irreg., latest vol.4, 1992. price varies. **Document type:** *Monographic series, Academic/Scholarly.* **Description:** Contains current research results of the university's astronomers, their Ph.D. works, monographs and scientific works.
Formerly (until 1976): Uniwersytet im. Adama Mickiewicza w Poznaniu. Wydzial Matematyki, Fizyki i Chemii. Prace. Seria Astronomia (0208-6492)
Published by: (Uniwersytet im. Adama Mickiewicza w Poznaniu/Adam Mickiewicz University), Wydawnictwo Naukowe Uniwersytetu im. Adama Mickiewicza/Adam Mickiewicz University Press, Nowowiejskiego 55, Poznan, 61-734, Poland. TEL 48-61-527380, FAX 48-61-527701. Pub. Maria Jankowska. R&P Malgorzata Bis.

520 POL
QB9
UNIWERSYTET JAGIELLONSKI. OBERWATORIUM KRAKOWSKIE. ROCZNIK ASTRONOMICZNY/ SUPPLEMENTO AD ANNUARIO CRACOVIENSE. Cover title: S A C - Rocznik Astronomiczny Obserwatorium Krakowskiego. Text in English. 1922. a., latest 2002. PLZ 11 per issue domestic; USD 13 per issue foreign (effective 2003). Website rev. **Document type:** *Yearbook, Academic/Scholarly.*
Description: Stimulates the observations of eclipsing binaries and RR Lyrae type variables with period changes or other pecularities in their light curves. Contains a list of selected eclipsing binary stars and list of elements for RR Lyrae stars.
Related titles: Online - full content ed.; Supplement(s): Uniwersytet Jagiellonski. Oberwatorium Krakowskie. Rocznik Astronomiczny. Dodatek Miedzynarodowy. ISSN 0075-7047.
Published by: (Uniwersytet Jagiellonski, Oberwatorium Krakowskie/Jagiellonian University, Cracow Observatory), Wydawnictwo Uniwersytetu Jagiellonskiego/Jagiellonian University Press, ul Grodzka 26, Krakow, 31044, Poland. TEL 48-12-4312364, FAX 48-12-4301995, sac@oa.uj.edu.pl, wydaw@if.uj.edu.pl, http://www.oa.uj.edu.pl/ktt/rocznik/rcznk.html, http://www.wuj.pl. Ed. Maria Kurpinska-Winiarska. R&P Maria Kurpinska Winiarska. Circ: 400.

520 ESP ISSN 0211-4844
URANIA. Text in Spanish. 1911. q.
Formerly (until 1934): Sociedad Astronomica de Espana y America. Revista (0211-4836)
Related titles: Supplement(s): Suplemento de Urania.
Published by: Sociedad Astronomica de Espana y America, Avenida Diagonal 377, Barcelona, 08008, Spain.

520 POL ISSN 0042-0794
QB1
URANIA. Text in Polish; Contents page in English, Russian. 1922. m. PLZ 588, USD 13.20. adv. bk.rev. charts; illus. index.
Description: Popular scientific magazine dealing with different aspects of astronomic research and space conquest.
Indexed: A&AAb, RefZh.
Published by: Polskie Towarzystwo Milosnikow Astronomii/Polish Association of Friends of Astronomy, Ul Solskiego 30 m 8, Krakow, 31027, Poland. TEL 386-25. Ed. K Ziolkowski. Circ: 3,500. **Dist. by:** Ars Polona, Krakowskie Przedmiescie 7, Warsaw, Poland.

523.8 JPN ISSN 0917-2211
VARIABLE STAR BULLETIN. Text in English. 1987. irreg.
Indexed: Inspec.
Published by: Variable Star Observers League in Japan, c/o Keiichi Saijo National Science Museum, Ueno-Park, Tokyo, Japan. Ed. Seeichiro Kiyota.

522.1 VAT
VATICAN OBSERVATORY ANNUAL REPORT. Text in English. 1970. a. free. back issues avail. **Document type:** *Academic/Scholarly.*
Supersedes in part (in 1994): Vatican Observatory Publications (0083-5293)
Indexed: A&AAb.
—BLDSC (1486.526000).
Published by: Specola Vaticana/Vatican Observatory, Vatican City, 00120, Vatican City. TEL 39-06-69885266, FAX 39-06-69884671. Ed. George V Coyne. Circ: 500. **Affiliate:** Vatican Observatory Research Group.

520 DEU ISSN 0340-9821
VEROEFFENTLICHUNGEN DER ASTRONOMISCHEN INSTITUT DER UNIVERSITAET BONN. Text in German; Summaries in English. 1930. irreg. price varies. **Document type:** *Monographic series, Academic/Scholarly.*
Published by: Astronomische Institute der Universitaet Bonn - Sternwarte, Auf dem Huegel 71, Bonn, 53121, Germany. TEL 49-228-733655, FAX 49-228-733672, sek-stw@astro.uni-bonn.de, http://www.astro.uni-bonn.de/~webstw/.

520 USA
VIA STELLARIS. Text in English. 1958. m. looseleaf. USD 10 (effective 2000). bk.rev. **Document type:** *Newsletter.*
Description: Contains information on astronomy and astrophotography. Includes calendar of local events and meetings.
Published by: Von Braun Astronomical Society, Inc., PO Box 1142, Huntsville, AL 35807. TEL 205-539-0316. Ed., R&P Michael Cissell. Circ: 200.

520 RUS
VSELENNAYA I MY; nauchno-khudozhestvennyi almanakh. Text in Russian; Summaries in English. 1993. irreg. back issues avail. **Description:** Covers astronomy for general audience, teachers, and students.
Published by: Astronomicheskoe Obshchestvo/Astronomical Society, Universitetskii pr-t 13, Moscow, 119899, Russian Federation. TEL 7-095-9391626, FAX 7-095-9328841, konon@sai.msu.su. Ed. E V Kononovich. **Co-sponsor:** Astronomo-Geodizecheskoe Obshchestvo.

523.01 USA ISSN 0363-3675
CODEN: WIASDH
WISCONSIN ASTROPHYSICS. Text in English. 1974. m. free (effective 2003). **Document type:** *Academic/Scholarly.*
Related titles: Online - full text ed.
—CISTI, Linda Hall.
Published by: University of Wisconsin at Madison, Department of Astronomy, 5534 Sterling Hall, 475 N Charter St, Madison, WI 53706. TEL 608-262-3071, FAX 608-262-6386, astrolib@astro.wisc.edu, http://www.astro.wisc.edu.

523.01 SGP ISSN 1793-1320
WORLD SCIENTIFIC SERIES IN ASTRONOMY AND ASTROPHYSICS. Text in English. 1995. irreg., latest vol.5. price varies. **Document type:** *Monographic series, Academic/Scholarly.*
Published by: World Scientific Publishing Co. Pte. Ltd., 5 Toh Tuck Link, Singapore, 596224, Singapore. TEL 65-466-5775, FAX 65-467-7667, wspc@wspc.com.sg, series@wspc.com.sg, http://www.wspc.com.sg/books/series/wsaa_series.shtml, http://www.worldscientific.com. Ed. J V Narlikar. **Dist. by:** World Scientific Publishing Co., Inc., 1060 Main St, River Edge, NJ 07661. TEL 201-487-9655, 800-227-7562, FAX 201-487-9656, 888-977-2665; World Scientific Publishing Ltd., 57 Shelton St, London WC2H 9HE, United Kingdom. TEL 44-20-78360888, FAX 44-20-78362020.

522.1 CHN ISSN 1001-7526
QB4
YUNNAN TIANWENTAI TAIKAN/YUNNAN OBSERVATORY. PUBLICATIONS. Text in Chinese. 1977. q. CNY 5 newsstand/cover (effective 2002). **Document type:** *Journal, Academic/Scholarly.*
Related titles: Online - full content ed.: (from WanFang Data Corp.); Online - full text ed.: (from East View Information Services).
Indexed: Inspec.
—CISTI.
Published by: Yunnan Tianwentai/Yunnan Observatory (Subsidiary of: Zhongguo Kexueyuan/Chinese Academy of Sciences), Dongjiao Yangfangao Fenghuangshan, PO Box 110, Kunming, 650011, China. TEL 86-871-3840472, FAX 86-871-3911845, ynaotk@public.km.yn.cn, http://periodicals.wanfangdata.com.cn/gyjs.asp?ID=79812.

ZEITSCHRIFT FUER NATURFORSCHUNG. SECTION A: A JOURNAL OF PHYSICAL SCIENCES. see *PHYSICS*

520 RUS ISSN 0044-3948
QB1 CODEN: ZEVSAM
ZEMLYA I VSELENNAYA. Text in Russian. 1965. bi-m. RUR 200 for 6 mos. domestic; USD 99 foreign (effective 2004). index. **Document type:** *Journal, Academic/Scholarly.*
Indexed: BiolAb, ChemAb, IAA, RASB, RefZh.
—BLDSC (0072.080000), CISTI, East View, KNAW, Linda Hall.
Published by: (Rossiiskaya Akademiya Nauk/Russian Academy of Sciences), Izdatel'stvo Nauka, Profsoyuznaya ul 90, Moscow, 117864, Russian Federation. TEL 7-095-3347151, FAX 7-095-4202220, secret@naukaran.ru, http://www.naukaran.ru. Circ: 20,000. **Dist. by:** M K - Periodica, ul Gilyarovskogo 39, Moscow 129110, Russian Federation. TEL 7-095-2845008, FAX 7-095-2813798, info@periodicals.ru, http://www.mkniga.ru.

520 NLD ISSN 0165-0211
ZENIT. Text in Dutch. 1974. m. EUR 51; EUR 4.95 newsstand/cover (effective 2005). adv. bk.rev.; software rev. charts; illus. index. **Document type:** *Magazine, Consumer.*
Description: Discusses topics in amateur astronomy.
Formed by the 1974 merger of: Hemel en Dampkring (0018-0289); Macro (Utrecht)
Indexed: A&AAb, ExcerpMed.
—IE, Infotrieve, Linda Hall.
Published by: Stichting De Koepel, Zonnenburg 2, Utrecht, 3512 NL, Netherlands. TEL 31-30-2311360, FAX 31-30-2342852, zenit@dekoepel.nl, info@dekoepel.nl, http://www.dekoepel.nl/zenit/. Circ: 7,500 (paid).

ZHONGGUO KEXUE. G JI: WULIXUE, TIANWENXUE. see *PHYSICS*

522.1 CHN ISSN 1000-3681
ZIJINSHAN TIANWENTAI TAIKAN/PURPLE MOUNTAIN OBSERVATORY. PUBLICATIONS. Text in Chinese. 1982. q. **Document type:** *Journal, Academic/Scholarly.*
Related titles: Online - full text ed.: (from East View Information Services).
Indexed: Inspec.
Published by: Zhonghua Kexueyuan, Zijinshan Tianwentai/Chinese Academy of Sciences, Purple Mountain Observatory, 2, Beijing Xilu, Nanjing, 210008, China. TEL 86-25-83332000, zjtt@chinajournal.net.cn, http://zjstwttk.periodicals.net.cn/, http://www.pmo.ac.cn/.

ASTRONOMY—Abstracting, Bibliographies, Statistics

016.52 RUS ISSN 0486-2236
QB1 CODEN: RZASAA
REFERATIVNYI ZHURNAL. ASTRONOMIYA. Text in Russian. 1953. m. USD 670 foreign (effective 2006). **Document type:** *Abstract/Index.*
Related titles: CD-ROM ed.; Online - full text ed.
—East View, Linda Hall.
Published by: Vserossiiskii Institut Nauchnoi i Tekhnicheskoi Informatsii (VINITI), Ul Usievicha 20, Moscow, 125190, Russian Federation. TEL 7-095-1526441, FAX 7-095-9430060, dir@viniti.ru, http://www.viniti.ru. Ed. Yurii Arskii. **Dist. by:** Informnauka Ltd., Ul Usievicha 20, Moscow 125190, Russian Federation. alfimov@viniti.ru.

016.62 525 RUS ISSN 0233-6480
Z6004.R38
REFERATIVNYI ZHURNAL. ISSLEDOVANIE ZEMLI IZ KOSMOSA. Text in Russian. 1985. m. USD 163 foreign (effective 2006). **Document type:** *Abstract/Index.*
Related titles: CD-ROM ed.; Online - full text ed.
—East View.
Published by: Vserossiiskii Institut Nauchnoi i Tekhnicheskoi Informatsii (VINITI), Ul Usievicha 20, Moscow, 125190, Russian Federation. TEL 7-095-1526441, FAX 7-095-9430060, dir@viniti.ru, http://www.viniti.ru. Ed. Yurii Arskii. **Dist. by:** Informnauka Ltd., Ul Usievicha 20, Moscow 125190, Russian Federation. alfimov@viniti.ru.

523.2 JPN
SOLAR TERRESTRIAL ACTIVITY CHART. Text in English. a. charts; stat.
Published by: (Joho Kokusaika), Nihon Gakujutsu Kaigi/Science Council of Japan, 22-34 Roppongi 7-Chome, Minato-Ku, Tokyo, 1060032, Japan.

016.5232 JPN
TAIYOKEI KAGAKU SHINPOJUMU. Text in Japanese. a. abstr.
Description: Contains abstracts from the Institute's symposium on solar system sciences.
Published by: Institute of Space and Aeronautical Science/Uchu Kagaku Kenkyujo, 1-1 Yoshinodai 3-chome, Sagamihara-shi, Kanagawa-ken 229-0022, Japan.

AUTOMATION

see COMPUTERS—Automation

AUTOMOBILES

see TRANSPORTATION—Automobiles

BAKERS AND CONFECTIONERS

see FOOD AND FOOD INDUSTRIES—Bakers And Confectioners

BALL GAMES

see SPORTS AND GAMES—Ball Games

BANKING AND FINANCE

see BUSINESS AND ECONOMICS—Banking And Finance

BEAUTY CULTURE

see also BEAUTY CULTURE—Perfumes And Cosmetics

646.72 USA
A A C S NEWS REPORT✶. Text in English. m. adv. **Document type:** *Newsletter, Trade.*
Former titles: A A C S News; N A A C S News
Published by: American Association of Cosmetology Schools, 15825 N 71st St, Ste 100, Scottsdale, AZ 85254-2187. TEL 480-281-0431, 800-831-1086, FAX 480-905-0993, http://www.beautyschools.org. Circ: 1,000.

▼ **THE AESTHETIC BOOK.** see *MEDICAL SCIENCES*

AGRO FOOD INDUSTRY HI-TECH. see *AGRICULTURE*

646.72 ITA ISSN 1121-9580
ALLURE CLUB. Text in Italian. 1993. bi-m. adv. **Document type:** *Magazine, Consumer.* **Description:** For operators in the accessory business: firm managers, beauty consultants, retailers and business agents.
Published by: Target Editore s.r.l., Via Antonio Bondi 23/2, Bologna, BO 40138, Italy. TEL 39-051-342426, FAX 39-051-345554, allure@allure.it. Ed. Rosetta Sannelli. Pub. Luciano Parisini. R&P Diana Baravelli.

646.72 MEX
ALTO PEINADO. Text in Spanish. 1969. m. MXP 120, USD 70. adv. film rev. illus. **Document type:** *Consumer.*
Published by: Editorial Famari, NORTE 72-A no. 6120,, Col Gertrudis Sanchez, Mexico City, DF 07830, Mexico. TEL 760-9391, FAX 751-5918. Ed. Francisco Martinez Rios.

646.72 USA
AMAZE MAGAZINE. Text in English. q. **Description:** Covers fashion, beauty advise, health and home.
Formerly: V:Magazine
Media: Online - full content.
Published by: Venus Imaging, LLC, 16818 SE 34th Way, Vancouver, WA 98683. TEL 360-882-4416, divas@venusimaging.com, http://www.venusimaging.com/.

646.72 USA
AMERICAN LOOKS✶. Text in English. 1972. s-a. USD 7 to non-members (effective 1997). adv. back issues avail. **Document type:** *Trade.* **Description:** Shows trends in hair, makeup, nails, and fashion.
Published by: National Cosmetology Association, 401 N Michigan Ave, Chicago, IL 60611-4255. TEL 314-534-7980, FAX 314-534-8618. Ed., Adv. contact Julie Becker. page USD 7,000. Circ: 32,000.

646.724 USA ISSN 0741-5737
TT950
AMERICAN SALON. Text in English. 1877. m. USD 26.50 domestic; USD 35.50 in Canada & Mexico; USD 40.50 elsewhere; USD 3.50 newsstand/cover domestic; USD 5 newsstand/cover in Canada & Mexico; USD 8 newsstand/cover elsewhere (effective 2005). adv. bk.rev. illus.; tr.lit. Supplement avail.; back issues avail. **Document type:** *Magazine, Trade.* **Description:** Provides salon owners, managers and stylists coverage of the professional beauty industry. Combines information on business and style, intending to both advise and inspire beauty professionals.
Incorporates (1993-1997): American Stylist; Formerly: American Hairdresser - Salon Owner (0095-1404); Which incorporated: Salon Owner (0036-3553); Which was formerly: American Hairdresser
Related titles: Microfilm ed.: (from PQC); Online - full text ed.: (from Northern Light Technology, Inc., ProQuest Information & Learning).
Indexed: ABIn.
—CCC.
Published by: (National Hairdressers and Cosmetologists Association), Advanstar Communications, Inc., One Park Ave, 2nd Fl, New York, NY 10016. TEL 212-951-6600, FAX 212-951-6793, rmcclain@advanstar.com, info@advanstar.com, http://www.americansalonmag.com, http://www.advanstar.com. Ed., R&P Robbin McClain TEL 212-951-6640. Pub. Brett Vinovich. Adv. contact Bonnie Tokofsky TEL 212-951-6685. B&W page USD 12,900, color page USD 16,087; trim 8.875 x 10.75. Circ: 132,042 (paid and controlled).

646.72 USA ISSN 1044-8705
AMERICAN SALON'S GREEN BOOK; the annual manufacturer's & distributor's marketing & reference guide for the professional salon industry. Text in English. a. USD 225 (effective 2004). adv. **Document type:** *Directory, Trade.* **Description:** Covers marketing and buying guide providing listings of distributors, manufacturers, products and services, key executives and demographics.
Formerly: Green Book (Cleveland)
—CCC.
Published by: Advanstar Communications, Inc., One Park Ave, 2nd Fl, New York, NY 10016. TEL 212-951-6600, FAX 212-951-6793, info@advanstar.com, http://www.salon-greenbook.com, http://www.advanstar.com. Pub. Karen Eagle. Circ: 30,000. **Subscr. to:** Advanstar Marketing Services, Customer Service Department, 131 West, First St, Duluth, MN 55802. TEL 218-723-9200, 800-598-6008, FAX 218-723-9437.

646.72 USA ISSN 1523-486X
RA794
AMERICAN SPA. Text in English. 1997. m. USD 27 domestic; USD 45 in Canada & Mexico; USD 63 elsewhere; USD 6 newsstand/cover domestic; USD 8 newsstand/cover foreign (effective 2005). adv. **Document type:** *Magazine, Trade.* **Description:** Covers industry trend, wellness, fitness, business, new products, and industry issues for spa owners and managers, and professionals in upscale salons offering skin services. Includes coverage of all segments of the spa market: day, destination, resort, club, and medical.
Related titles: Online - full text ed.
—CCC.
Published by: Advanstar Communications, Inc., One Park Ave, 2nd Fl, New York, NY 10016. TEL 212-951-6600, FAX 212-951-6793, americanspa@advanstar.com, info@advanstar.com, http://www.americanspamag.com, http://www.advanstar.com. adv.: B&W page USD 3,435, color page USD 4,435; trim 8.875 x 10.75. Circ: 28,147 (paid). **Subscr. to:** Advanstar Marketing Services, Customer Service Department, 131 West, First St, Duluth, MN 55802. TEL 218-723-9200, 800-598-6008, FAX 218-723-9437.

646 AUS ISSN 1442-8083
ANTI-AGING & COSMETIC SURGERY MAGAZINE: MEN'S GUIDE. Text in English. 2001. a. USD 9.99 newsstand/cover (effective 2002). adv. **Document type:** *Consumer.*
Published by: Gadfly Media, 645 Harris St, Ultimo Sydney, NSW 2007, Australia. TEL 61-2-9281-7523, FAX 61-2-9281-7528. Ed. Michelle Kearney. Pub. Ben Crawford.

646.72 USA
THE ART OF COSMETIC BEAUTY. Text in English. 2000. bi-m. USD 15.90; USD 7.95 newsstand/cover (effective 2001). adv. **Document type:** *Magazine, Consumer.*
Published by: Deyan Pty Ltd., 8642 Diceman Dr, Dallas, TX 75218. TEL 214-319-6700, FAX 214-319-6707, tracy@cosmeticbeauty.net, http://www.cosmeticbeauty.net. Ed., Pub. Tracy Grujovic.

646.7 688.8 GBR
ASIA PACIFIC PERSONAL CARE. Text in English. bi-m. adv. **Description:** Addresses scientific and technical issues relating to the formulation, development, manufacture and packaging of personal care products for the Asia Pacific region.
Published by: Step Communications Ltd., Step House, North Farm Rd, Tumbridge Wells, Kent TN2 3DR, United Kingdom. TEL 44-1892-518877, FAX 44-1892-616177, mail@stepex.co.uk, http://www.stepex.co.uk. **Subscr. to:** Subscriptions Dept, Shadwell House, 65 Lower Green, Rusthall, Tunbridge Wells TN4 8TW, United Kingdom. TEL 44-1892-518877, FAX 44-1892-616177.

646.724 USA
ATLANTA HAIR MAGAZINE. Text in English. q.
Published by: Voila Communications, PO Box 191244, Atlanta, GA 31119-1244. TEL 770-495-4856, FAX 770-476-2666, info@atlantahairmag.com, http://www.atlantahairmag.com.

646.72 DEU
AYK AKTIV. Text in German. q. **Document type:** *Newsletter.*
Published by: (Ayk Beauty Sun-Sonnenstudios), Vereinigte Verlagsanstalten GmbH, Hoeherweg 278, Duesseldorf, 40231, Germany. TEL 49-211-7357589, FAX 49-211-7357507, am@vva.de, info@vva.de, http://www.vva.de. Circ: 100,000 (controlled).

646.72 USA
B B S I. (Beauty & Barber Supply Institute) Text in English. 1994. bi-m. free domestic to members (effective 2005). adv. **Document type:** *Magazine, Trade.* **Description:** Covers beauty and barber supplies distribution trends, regulations, technology, and trade show news.
Formerly (until July 2001): Beauty Inc. (1078-1781)
Published by: Beauty & Barber Supply Institute, Inc., 15825 N 71st St No.100, Scottsdale, AZ 85254-2187. TEL 480-281-0424, 800-468-2274, FAX 480-905-0708, denise@bbsi.org, http://www.bbsi.org. Ed., R&P Denise M Rucci TEL 480-281-0424 ext 112. Pubs. Jon Hiler, Michael A Spano. Adv. contact Sandy Domin. B&W page USD 1,425, color page USD 2,025. Circ: 6,891 (paid and controlled).

646.72 FRA ISSN 1620-2716
BEAUTE SERVICE INTERNATIONAL✶; magazine des professionnels de l'esthetique - cosmetique. Text in French. 1979. m. bk.rev. back issues avail. **Document type:** *Magazine, Trade.* **Description:** Beauty care; aesthetics, cosmetics, perfumes, fitness, dieting.
Formerly (until 2000): Beaute Service (1156-7635)
Related titles: Online - full text ed.
Published by: Creation Service, 2 bis rue du Moulin de Mars, Argeles Plage, Argeles-sur-Mer, 66700, France. TEL 33-4-68958506, FAX 33-4-68958507, Beaute.Service@mipnet.fr, http://www.beaute-service.mipnet.fr. Ed. J.F. Vidal. Pub. J F Vidal. R&P V. Thevenod. Adv. contact V Thevenod. Circ: 17,000 (paid).

646.72 DEU
BEAUTY & MORE. Text in German. d. adv. **Document type:** *Consumer.* **Description:** Covers all aspects of beauty, cosmetic and health issues and products.
Media: Online - full text.
Published by: Network Orange Medien Service, Monumentenstr 33-34, Berlin, 10829, Germany. TEL 49-30-780994-0, FAX 49-30-78099418, info@beauty-and-more.de, network@orange.de, http://www.beauty-and-more.de. Ed. Petra Stueben. Adv. contact Doris Eckardt.

646.72 USA ISSN 1545-567X
HD9970.5.T65
BEAUTY BIZ. Text in English. 2001. m. **Document type:** *Magazine, Trade.* **Description:** Covers and analyzes events, trends and personalities in beauty retailing and related industries.
Related titles: Online - full text ed.: (from Gale Group, O C L C Online Computer Library Center, Inc.).
—CCC.
Published by: Fairchild Publications, Inc., 7 W 34th St, New York, NY 10001-8191. TEL 212-630-4000, 800-289-0273, FAX 212-630-4201, http://www.fairchildpub.com. Ed. Jenny B Fine. Circ: 44,000 (controlled).

646.72 FRA ISSN 1620-302X
BEAUTY BUSINESS NEWS. Text in English. 2000. 42/yr. EUR 985, USD 985 (effective 2002). adv. **Document type:** *Newsletter, Trade.* **Description:** Reports on the news concerning beauty markets worldwide.
Published by: Cosmedias International, 4 rue de Seze, Paris, 75009, France. TEL 33-1-44945060, FAX 33-1-44945069, circ@cosmedias.fr, http://www.cosmetiquenews.com/. Ed. Fabienne Colin. Adv. contact Sylvie Borin.

646.72 DEU
BEAUTY CARE SUPPLY GUIDE. Text in English. 1989. a. adv. back issues avail. **Document type:** *Directory, Trade.* **Description:** International purchasing handbook for importers, distributors, agents and traders in over 180 countries.
Related titles: CD-ROM ed.
Published by: Made in Europe Marketing Organisation GmbH, Unterhainstr 50, Aschaffenburg, 63743, Germany. TEL 49-6021-391850, FAX 49-6021-3918525, mie@miesys.com, http://www.miesys.com. Ed., Pub., R&P Martin Romer. Adv. contact Franziska Bastanier. Circ: 15,000.

646.72025 GBR
BEAUTY DIRECTORY. Text in English. a. GBP 31; GBP 53 foreign. **Document type:** *Directory.* **Description:** Comprehensive industry guide for products, equipment, training and services.
Published by: Reed Business Information Ltd. (Subsidiary of: Reed Business), Quadrant House, The Quadrant, Brighton Rd, Sutton, Surrey SM2 5AS, United Kingdom. TEL 44-208-652-3500, rbp.subscriptions@rbi.co.uk, rbi.subscriptions@qss-uk.com, http://www.reedbusiness.com, http://www.reedinfo.co.uk/. **Subscr. to:** Quadrant Subscription Services, PO Box 302, Haywards Heath, W Sussex RH16 3YY, United Kingdom. TEL 44-1444-445566, FAX 44-1444-445447.

646.7 POL ISSN 1427-1508
BEAUTY FORUM. Text in Polish. 1996. 10/yr. PLZ 95 (effective 2004). adv. **Document type:** *Magazine, Trade.*
Published by: Health and Beauty Media Sp.z.o.o, ul Koniczynowa 11, Warsaw, 03-612, Poland. TEL 48-22-6793198, FAX 48-22-6796934, biuro@beauty-forum.com.pl, http://www.beauty-forum.com.pl. adv.: page PLZ 4,950; trim 184 x 263. Circ: 3,000 (controlled).

646.72 HUN ISSN 1219-6290
BEAUTY FORUM. Text in Hungarian. 1994. q. **Document type:** *Magazine, Trade.*
Formerly (until 1995): Beauty Forum Hungary (1219-6746)
Published by: Health and Beauty Business Media Hungary Kft, Varosmajor u 33, Budapest, 1122, Hungary. TEL 36-1-4570067, FAX 36-1-2013248, azsilak@health-and-beauty.hu.

646.72 DEU ISSN 0944-0364
BEAUTY FORUM. Text in German. 1992. m. EUR 69 domestic; EUR 81 foreign (effective 2005). adv. **Document type:** *Magazine, Trade.*
Formed by the merger of (1986-1992): Beauty (0932-7398); (1985-1992): Cosmetic Forum (0938-8176); Which was formerly (until 1990): Forum fuer Schoenheit, Besonnung und Fitness (0937-6720); (until 1989): Forum fuer Schoenheit, Besonnung und Gesundheit (0933-9396); (until 1987): Forum fuer Besonnung, Schoenheit und Gesundheit (0178-8035)
Published by: Health and Beauty Business Media GmbH & Co. KG, Karl-Friedrich-Str 14-18, Karlsruhe, 76133, Germany. TEL 49-721-165833, FAX 49-721-165618, juergen.volpp@health-and-beauty.com, http://www.beauty-forum.com, http://www.health-and-beauty.com. adv.: B&W page EUR 2,932, color page EUR 3,952. Circ: 22,833 (paid).

646.7 DEU ISSN 1610-1235
BEAUTY FORUM BOERSE. Text in German. 1997. m. **Document type:** *Magazine, Trade.*
Published by: Health and Beauty Business Media GmbH & Co. KG, Karl-Friedrich-Str 14-18, Karlsruhe, 76133, Germany. TEL 49-721-165833, FAX 49-721-165618, juergen.volpp@health-and-beauty.com, http://www.health-and-beauty.com. Circ: 18,000 (controlled).

646.72 AUT ISSN 1605-4555
BEAUTY LIFE. Text in German. 1982. 10/yr. EUR 19 domestic; EUR 51 in Europe (effective 2005). bk.rev. back issues avail. **Document type:** *Magazine, Consumer.*
Formerly (until 1992): Neue Beauty
Related titles: Online - full text ed.: ISSN 1605-4563.
Published by: H.J. Pichler Verlagsgesellschaft, Geweygasse 4A/2/5, Postfach 16, Vienna, W 1195, Austria. TEL 43-1-36931310, FAX 43-1-369313120, office@beauty.at, http://www.beauty.at. Ed., Adv. contact Hans Joachim Pichler. Circ: 80,000 (controlled).

646.72 USA ISSN 1098-0660
BEAUTY STORE BUSINESS. Text in English. 1995. bi-m. USD 24 domestic; USD 35 in Canada & Mexico; USD 60 elsewhere (effective 2000). adv. back issues avail. **Document type:** *Trade.* **Description:** Provides information on business management for full-service distributors, satellite stores, independent beauty stores, ethnic beauty supply dealers and salons offering retail products.
Published by: Creative Age Communications, Inc., 7628 Densmore Ave, Van Nuys, CA 91406-2042. TEL 818-782-7328, FAX 818-782-7450. Ed., R&P Marc Birenbaum. Pub. Deborah Carver. adv.: B&W page USD 2,095, color page USD 3,160; trim 13.5 x 10.88. Circ: 15,000 (controlled). **Subscr. to:** PO Box 10751, Riverton, NJ 08076-0751.

646.7 ITA
BEAUTY TRENDS. Text in Italian. 2/yr. **Document type:** *Magazine, Consumer.*
Formerly (until 1999): Beauty MKT
Published by: Sfera Editore SpA (Subsidiary of: R C S Mediagroup), Via Angelo Rizzoli 2, Milan, MI 20132, Italy. TEL 39-02-25841. Ed. Antonella Grua.

646.72 ZAF ISSN 1027-4189
BEAUTYWORX; professional beauty, nails. Text in English. 1994. m. ZAR 88.50 (effective 2000). adv. illus. **Document type:** *Trade.*
Formerly (until 1996): Aesthetics
Published by: Toxic Ratman, PO Box 1707, Four Ways, 2055, South Africa. TEL 27-11-804-6835. Ed., Pub. Lance G Whatmore. R&P, Adv. contact Philene Robertson.

053.1 DEU
BELLISSIMA; Qualitaet is weiblich. Text in German. d. adv. **Document type:** *Consumer.* **Description:** Contains articles and information on beauty, fashion, entertainment and other items of interest to women.
Media: Online - full text.
Published by: Endemann!! Internet AG Neuss, Gerhard-Hoehme-Allee 1, Neuss, 41466, Germany. http://www.bellissima.de. Ed. Cornela Lingott.

BIBA. see *CLOTHING TRADE—Fashions*

646.724 GBR ISSN 0263-3213
BLACK BEAUTY & HAIR. Text in English. 1982. bi-m. GBP 12; GBP 2 newsstand/cover (effective 1999). adv. back issues avail. **Document type:** *Consumer.*
—CCC.
Published by: Hawker Consumer Publishing Ltd., 140 Battersea Park Rd, London, SW11 4NB, United Kingdom. TEL 44-171-720-2108, FAX 44-171-498-3023. Ed. Irene Shelley. Pub., Adv. contact Pat Petker. Circ: 21,101 (paid). **Subscr. to:** ESCO Business Services Ltd., PO Box 935, Braintree, Essex CM7 4LN, United Kingdom. TEL 44-1371-810433, FAX 44-1371-811065. **Dist. by:** Comag, Tavistock Works, Tavistock Rd, W Drayton, Middx UB7 7QX, United Kingdom. TEL 44-1895-433600, FAX 44-189-543-3606.

646.724 USA
BLACK CELEBRITY GUIDE: BLACK RADIANCE HAIRSTYLING GUIDE. Text in English. 2001. m. USD 4 newsstand/cover (effective 2001). adv. **Document type:** *Consumer.*
Published by: Celebrity Style Inc., 1359 Broadway., Rm. 1203, New York, NY 10018-7874. TEL 212-244-0559, FAX 212-244-1752.

646.724 USA
BLACK CELEBRITY STYLE HAIR & BRAIDS. Text in English. 2000. irreg. USD 5.95 newsstand/cover (effective 2001). adv. **Document type:** *Consumer.*
Published by: Celebrity Style Inc., 1359 Broadway., Rm. 1203, New York, NY 10018-7874.

646.724 GBR
BLACK HAIR; the no.1 for hair and beauty. Text in English. bi-m. GBP 12 domestic; GBP 18 in Europe; GBP 35 elsewhere; GBP 2.20 newsstand/cover. illus. **Document type:** *Consumer.*
Published by: James Kimber Publishing Ltd., Kimber House, 134 King St, London, W6 0QU, United Kingdom. TEL 44-181-563-2288, FAX 44-181-563-2299. Ed. Deidre Forbes. **Subscr. to:** Freepost LON986, London SW6 4YZ, United Kingdom. **Dist. by:** Comag, Tavistock Works, Tavistock Rd, W Drayton, Middx UB7 7QX, United Kingdom. TEL 44-1895-433600, FAX 44-189-543-3606.

646.724 USA ISSN 1533-8800
BLACK HAIR & BRAIDS. Text in English. 2001. m. USD 5.99 newsstand/cover (effective 2002). adv. **Document type:** *Consumer.*
Published by: Celebrity Worldwide, 20 E Sunrise Hwy, Ste 202, Valley Stream, NY 11581. TEL 516-823-1212, FAX 516-823-1561. Ed. Susan Jones Dorsainville. Pub. Eddison Bramble.

646.72 USA ISSN 1058-0956
BLACTRESS. Text in English. bi-m. USD 5.95 newsstand/cover (effective 2003). **Document type:** *Magazine, Consumer.*
Published by: Harris Publications, Inc., 800 Kennesaw Ave, Ste 220, Marietta, GA 30060. TEL 212-807-7100, FAX 212-627-4678.

646.72 746.9 USA
BLI. Text in English. 2001. m. adv. **Document type:** *Consumer.*
Published by: Bliss, Inc., 121 W. Alabama St., Florence, AL 35630. TEL 256-764-6699, FAX 256-764-6690, blissmagshoals@aol.com.

BOA FORMA. see *PHYSICAL FITNESS AND HYGIENE*

646.72 IND
BODY & BEAUTY CARE. Text in English. 1982. fortn.
Published by: Publicity Society of India Ltd., Free Press House, 215 Nariman Point, Mumbai, Maharashtra 400 021, India. TEL 2853335. Ed. M S Kamath. Pub. R Mani. adv.: B&W page INR 9,000, color page INR 18,000; trim 240 x 163.

646.72 HUN ISSN 1586-2720
BODY LIFE. Text in Hungarian. 2000. q. HUF 2,200 (effective 2004). **Document type:** *Magazine, Trade.*
Published by: Health and Beauty Business Media Hungary Kft, Varosmajor u 33, Budapest, 1122, Hungary. TEL 36-1-4570067, FAX 36-1-2013248, azsilak@health-and-beauty.hu.

646.72 POL ISSN 1641-0106
BODY LIFE. Text in Polish. 2000. m. **Document type:** *Magazine, Trade.*
Published by: Health and Beauty Media Sp.z.o.o, ul Koniczynowa 11, Warsaw, 03-612, Poland. TEL 48-22-6793198, FAX 48-22-6796934.

BOOTS HEALTH & BEAUTY. see *WOMEN'S INTERESTS*

646.724 USA ISSN 1078-1811
BRAIDS & BEAUTY. Text in English. 1994. q. GBP 2.50 newsstand/cover. adv. **Document type:** *Consumer.*
Published by: T B W Publishing Group, 210 Rte 4 E, Ste 401, Paramus, NJ 07652. TEL 201-843-4004, FAX 201-843-8636. **Dist. in UK by:** Comag, Tavistock Works, Tavistock Rd, W Drayton, Middx UB7 7QX, United Kingdom. TEL 44-1895-444055, FAX 44-1895-433602.

646.724 301.42 GBR ISSN 1460-8154
BRIDES' HAIR. Text in English. 1998. s-a. GBP 2.50 newsstand/cover. adv. **Document type:** *Consumer.* **Description:** Offers practical tips and advice on hair and beauty styles for brides.
Published by: James Kimber Publishing Ltd., Kimber House, 134 King St, London, W6 0QU, United Kingdom. TEL 44-181-563-2266, FAX 44-181-563-2299. **Dist. by:** Comag, Tavistock Works, Tavistock Rd, W Drayton, Middx UB7 7QX, United Kingdom. TEL 44-1895-444055, FAX 44-1895-433602.

646.72 DEU ISSN 0170-8473
BRILLE UND MODE. Text in German. 1978. s-a. adv. **Document type:** *Magazine, Trade.*
Published by: D O Z Verlag - Optische Fachveroeffentlichung GmbH, Luisenstr 14, Heidelberg, 69115, Germany. TEL 49-6221-905170, FAX 49-6221-905171, doz@doz-verlag.de, http://www.doz-verlag.de/brilleundmode.php. adv.: B&W page EUR 2,600, color page EUR 4,400; trim 179 x 260. Circ: 15,000 (controlled).

646.724 HUN ISSN 1586-0981
BURDA FRIZURA. Text in Hungarian. 2000. s-a. **Document type:** *Magazine, Consumer.*
Published by: M-Medien Group, 14-16 Ecseri Str., Budapest, 1033, Hungary. TEL 36-1-2808949, FAX 36-1-2826817, medien@ax.hu.

687 CHE
BURDA MODEN (ARABIC EDITION). Text in Arabic. 1985. m. **Document type:** *Consumer.*
Published by: I P M International Press & Marketing S.A., 2 Cours de Rive, Geneva, 1204, Switzerland. TEL 022-3105357, FAX 022-3105327, TELEX 423052-CH. Ed. A Hazan. Circ: 94,092. **Subscr. to:** Verlag Aenne Burda GmbH & Co. KG, Am Kestendamm 1, Offenburg 77652, Germany.

343.0786467 USA
CALIFORNIA. STATE BARBERING AND COSMETOLOGY PROGRAM. RULES AND REGULATIONS. Text in English. 1929. irreg. free. **Document type:** *Government.* **Description:** Alerts readers to updates and revisions in the California state rules and regulations affecting the barber and cosmetology sectors.
Former titles: California. State Board of Barbering and Cosmetology. Rules and Regulations; California. State Board of Cosmetology. Rules and Regulations (0094-4327)
Published by: State Barbering and Cosmetology Bureau, 400 R St 4080, Sacramento, CA 95814-6213. TEL 916-445-7061.

B

646.724 USA
CALIFORNIA STYLIST & SALON; The Business of Hair, Skin & Nails. Text in English. 1995. m. USD 20; USD 30 foreign (effective 2001). adv. back issues avail. **Document type:** *Newspaper, Trade.* **Description:** Official publication for the cosmetology unit of the California Dept. of Consumer Affairs.
Published by: Holland Graphics Inc., 1750 S W Skyline Blvd, Ste 24, Portland, OR 97221-2533. TEL 503-297-7010, FAX 503-297-7022, editor@stylistnewspapers.com, hollandgfx@aol.com, http://www.californiastylist.com. Ed., Pub. Linda Holland. Adv. contact Joel Holland. Circ: 41,000.

646.72 USA ISSN 1041-0430
CAMEO; exaltation of woman. Text in English. 1988. bi-m. USD 6 per issue. adv. **Description:** Covers hair styles, manicures, skin care, makeup and fashion.
Published by: Pygmalion Publications, 7 Morningwood Dr, Laguna Niguel, CA 92677. TEL 714-661-1674. Ed. Daniel Nicolas. Circ: 100,000.

CAWAII. see *WOMEN'S INTERESTS*

646.724 USA ISSN 1533-8797
CELEBRITY CUTS HAIRSTYLES & TRENDS. Text in English. 2001. m. USD 4.50 newsstand/cover (effective 2002). adv. **Document type:** *Consumer.*
Published by: Celebrity Worldwide, 20 E Sunrise Hwy, Ste 202, Valley Stream, NY 11581. TEL 516-823-1212, FAX 516-823-1561. Ed. Yvonne Mathison.

646.724 USA ISSN 1058-305X
CELEBRITY HAIRSTYLES. Text in English. 1984. q. GBP 2 newsstand/cover. adv. **Document type:** *Consumer.* **Description:** Presents the latest and hottest hairstyles worn by stars and celebrities.
Published by: Harris Publications, Inc., 800 Kennesaw Ave, Ste 220, Marietta, GA 30060. TEL 212-807-7100, 888-456-6247, FAX 212-627-4678, harrismags@aol.com, http://www.harrispublications.com, http://www.harris-pub.com/. **Dist. by:** Comag, Tavistock Works, Tavistock Rd, W Drayton, Middx UB7 7QX, United Kingdom. TEL 44-1895-444055, FAX 44-1895-433602.

646.724 USA
CELEBRITY HAIRSTYLES PRESENTS: BRIDAL STAR HAIRSTYLES. Text in English. 2000. s-a. USD 3.95 newsstand/cover (effective 2001). **Document type:** *Consumer.*
Published by: Harris Publications, Inc., 800 Kennesaw Ave, Ste 220, Marietta, GA 30060. TEL 212-807-7100. Ed. Mary Greenberg. Pub. Stanley R Harris.

646.724 USA
CELEBRITY HAIRSTYLES PRESENTS: TEEN STAR HAIRSTYLES. Text in English. 2000. 3/yr. USD 3.50 newsstand/cover (effective 2001). **Document type:** *Consumer.*
Published by: Harris Publications, Inc., 800 Kennesaw Ave, Ste 220, Marietta, GA 30060. TEL 212-807-7100. Ed. A J Hanley. Pub. Stanley R Harris.

CELEBRITY LOOKS. see *CLOTHING TRADE—Fashions*

646.72 384.554 USA
CELEBRITY STYLE: SOAP STARS AT HOME. Text in English. 2000. m. USD 3.99 newsstand/cover (effective 2001). adv. **Document type:** *Consumer.*
Published by: Celebrity Style Inc., 1359 Broadway., Rm. 1203, New York, NY 10018-7874. Ed. Lucille Barilla.

CHIMICA OGGI/CHEMISTRY TODAY. see *CHEMISTRY*

646.72 ITA ISSN 1591-6596
CIPRIA. Text in Italian. 1994. m. **Document type:** *Magazine, Consumer.*
Published by: Sfera Editore SpA (Subsidiary of: R C S Mediagroup), Via Angelo Rizzoli 2, Milan, MI 20132, Italy. TEL 39-02-25841.

CLIN D'OEIL. see *CLOTHING TRADE—Fashions*

646.742 DEU
CLIPS; das Fachmagazin fuer Topfriseure. Text in German. 1984. m. EUR 72 (effective 2004). adv. bk.rev. charts; illus.; tr.lit. index. **Document type:** *Magazine, Trade.* **Description:** Trade publication for hairdressers and beauty salons. Covers new fashion hairstyles, hair care, beauty care, reports of events, tips, and new cosmetic products.
Incorporates (1947-1993): Frisur und Kosmetik (0323-410X); Which was formerly: Frisur (0016-1489)
Published by: Clips Verlags GmbH, Wilhelm-Backhaus-Str 2, Cologne, 50931, Germany. TEL 49-221-944067-0, FAX 49-221-94406710, clips_verlags_gmbh@t-online.de. Ed. Heidrun Barbie. adv.: B&W page EUR 2,035, color page EUR 3,565; trim 230 x 297. Circ: 17,344 (paid and controlled).

B

646.724 DEU
CLIVIA; Friseurkunden-Zeitschrift fuer Haarkosmetik. Text in German. m. adv. **Document type:** *Magazine, Consumer.*
Published by: Deutscher Supplement Verlag GmbH, Breslauer Str 300, Nuernberg, 90471, Germany. TEL 49-911-8003161, FAX 49-911-8003639, info@supplement-verlag.de, http://www.deutscher-supplement-verlag.de. adv.: B&W page EUR 5,830, color page EUR 8,690; trim 193 x 240. Circ: 552,217 (controlled).

646.724 NLD ISSN 0165-3679
COIFFURE; vaktijdschrift voor de kapper/ondernemer. Text in Dutch. 1972. m. (11/yr.). EUR 114.75 (effective 2005). adv. bk.rev. index. **Document type:** *Trade.*
Published by: It's Amazing Business Communication bv, Postbus 7104, Zoetermeer, 2701 AC, Netherlands. TEL 31-79-3438383, FAX 31-79-3438399, itsabc@itsamazing.nl, http://www.itsamazing.nl. Circ: 4,430 (controlled).

382 FRA ISSN 1161-899X
COIFFURE ET STYLES. Text in French. 1946. m. adv. **Document type:** *Trade.* **Description:** Information about laws concerning hairdressers, hair fashion and beauty profession news.
Formerly (until 1991): Coiffeur de France (0750-3563)
Published by: (Federation Nationale de la Coiffure), Edizioni Esav S.r.l., Estyle S.A., 1-3 place de la Bourse, Paris, 75002, France. TEL 33-1-42602561, FAX 33-1-42602440, info@estetica.it, http://www.estetica.it. Ed. Claude Vauthrin. Adv. contact Valerie Lacoste. Circ: 37,300.

646.72 ESP ISSN 0214-5790
COIFFURE PROFESSIONNELLE. Text in Spanish. 1983. 11/yr. EUR 43 domestic; EUR 77 foreign (effective 2005). adv. **Document type:** *Trade.*
Published by: Editorial Tecnico Cientifica de Prensa Hispano Americana S.L., C/ Gascuena, 41, Madrid, 28022, Spain. TEL 34-91-747-8000, FAX 34-91-747-9056, redaccion@coiffeureprofessionnelle.net, http://www.coiffureprofessionnelle.net. Ed., Pub. Angeles Mora. Adv. contact Patricia Cordero. Circ: 20,000.

646.72 USA
COLOR NEWS. Text in English. 1986. q. USD 20. stat. back issues avail. **Document type:** *Newsletter.* **Description:** Examines all aspects of color in everyday life, both professional and personal.
Published by: Pantone, Inc., 590 Commerce Blvd, Carlstadt, NJ 07072. TEL 201-935-5500, FAX 201-896-0242. Ed. Leatrice Eiseman. Circ: 100,000.

646.72 USA
COSMETIC REPORT; your complete source for no nonsense cosmetic information and advice. Text in English. 1996. w. **Description:** Brings you up-to-date information about cosmetic products and trends so you can make educated buying decisions.
Media: Online - full text.
Published by: Cosmetic Connection heather@kleinman.com, http://www.kleinman.com/cosmetic/. Ed. Heather Kleinman.

668.5 USA ISSN 0589-8447
COSMETIC WORLD. Text in English. 1967. 50/yr. USD 125 domestic; USD 200 foreign; USD 5 newsstand/cover (effective 2005). adv. bk.rev. 12 p./no.; back issues avail. **Document type:** *Newsletter, Trade.* **Description:** Covers marketing, sales, retailing and technical management of the cosmetic, fragrance and toiletry industry.
Related titles: Online - full text ed.
Address: 8 W, 38th St., Ste 200, New York, NY 10018. TEL 212-840-8800, FAX 212-840-7246, http://www.cosmeticworld.com/. Ed. John G. Ledes. Pub. George Ledes. Adv. contact Michelle Krell Kydd. color page USD 5,800, B&W page USD 3,500; trim 7 x 10. Circ: 5,560 (paid).

646.72 CAN ISSN 1494-8109
COSMETICS; Canada's business magazine for the cosmetics, fragrance, toiletry and personal care industry. Text in English. 1972. bi-m. CND 42 (effective 2001). **Document type:** *Magazine, Trade.* **Description:** Meets the specialized needs of the cosmetics, fragrance, toiletry, health and beauty aids, personal care and allied industries in Canada.
Published by: Rogers Media Publishing Ltd, One Mount Pleasant Rd, 11th Fl, Toronto, ON M4Y 2Y5, Canada. TEL 416-764-2000, FAX 416-764-3941, http://www.cosmeticsmag.com, http://www.rogers.com. Ed. Ronald Wood TEL 416-596-5817. Pub. James Hicks. Adv. contact Pam Chodda TEL 416-596-5918. Circ: 13,000 (paid).

646.72 FRA ISSN 1297-4773
COSMETIQUE HEBDO. Text in French. 1989. 42/yr. EUR 475 domestic; EUR 525 foreign (effective 2002). adv. 12 p./no.; **Document type:** *Newsletter, Trade.* **Description:** Covers current news about the beauty market in France.
Former titles (until 1999): La Lettre de Cosmetique News (1266-5088); (until 1995): Cosmetique Newsletter (1150-7594)
Published by: Cosmedias International, 4 rue de Seze, Paris, 75009, France. TEL 33-1-44945060, FAX 33-1-44945069, circ@cosmedias.fr, http://www.cosmetiquenews.com/. Ed. Marie-Laure Prost. Adv. contact Sylvie Borin.

646.72 FRA ISSN 1297-4781
COSMETIQUE MAGAZINE. Text in French. 1999. 10/yr. EUR 68 domestic; EUR 88 in Europe; EUR 128 elsewhere (effective 2004). **Document type:** *Magazine, Trade.* **Description:** Covers the French beauty market in all distribution channels and market segments: fragrances, cosmetics, skin care, hair care, and toiletries.
Formed by the merger of (1986-1999): Cosmetique News (0980-0875); (1990-1999): Cosmetica (1286-1243); Which was formerly (until 1993): Cosmetica Distribution (1150-1677)
Published by: Cosmedias International, 4 rue de Seze, Paris, 75009, France. TEL 33-1-44945060, FAX 33-1-44945069, circ@cosmedias.fr, http://www.cosmetiquenews.com/. Ed. Marie-Laure Prost. Adv. contact Sylvie Borin.

646.72 RUS
▼ **COSMO BEAUTY.** Text in Russian. 2003. m. USD 8.30 domestic; USD 45 foreign (effective 2005). adv. **Document type:** *Magazine, Consumer.*
Published by: Independent Media (Moscow), ul Vyborgskaya dom 16, str 1, Moscow, 125212, Russian Federation. TEL 7-095-2323200, FAX 7-095-2329265, cosmobeauty@imedia.ru, podpiska@imedia.ru, http://www.independent-media.ru. Ed. Elena Vasil'eva. Circ: 180,000.

COUTURE MALAYSIA; ultimate fashion and beauty guide for women. see *CLOTHING TRADE—Fashions*

646.72 GBR
CUTTING EDGE. Text in English. 11/yr.
Indexed: SRRA.
Address: 32 Vauxhall Bridge Rd, London, SW1V 2SS, United Kingdom. TEL 071-973-6636, FAX 071-233-5081. Ed. Damian Hockney. Circ: 25,000.

646.72 USA ISSN 1089-3199
DAYSPA. Text in English. 1996. m. USD 36 domestic; USD 60 in Canada & Mexico; USD 72 foreign; USD 7.25 newsstand/cover (effective 2000). adv. back issues avail. **Document type:** *Trade.* **Description:** Provides owners and managers of premium salons and day spas with operational and business information. Also covers product, legal regulatory and financial information. Management topics include facility planning, marketing and promotion, fashion and beauty, and wellness services.
Published by: Creative Age Communications, Inc., 7628 Densmore Ave, Van Nuys, CA 91406-2042. TEL 818-782-7328, FAX 818-782-7450, dayspamag@aol.com, http://www.dayspamag.com. Ed. Linda W Lewis. Pub. Deborah Carver. R&P Amy Hamaker. Adv. contact Diane Walker Richey. B&W page USD 2,641, color page USD 3,633; trim 10.75 x 8. Circ: 3,522 (paid); 27,008 (controlled). **Subscr. to:** PO Box 10566, Riverton, NJ 08076-0566.

DE MODA. see *CLOTHING TRADE—Fashions*

DEMI. see *CHILDREN AND YOUTH—For*

646.72 USA
DERMASCOPE; the encyclopedia of aesthetics and spa therapy. Text in English. 1973. 13/yr., latest 2001, Jul. USD 35 domestic; USD 55 in Canada; USD 75 elsewhere (effective 2001). adv. bk.rev. back issues avail. **Document type:** *Trade.* **Description:** Covers a wide variety of subjects related to skin care, make up and body spa therapy with related subjects which affect the beauty and aging of the skin. Also includes business articles on the industry.
Published by: Aestheticians International Association, Dermascope Magazine, 2611 N. Belt Line Rd., Ste. 140, Sunnyvale, TX 75182-9357. TEL 972-682-9510, 800-961-3777, FAX 972-226-2339, dermascope@aol.com, http://www.dermascope.com. Ed. Saundra Wallens. Adv. contact Mulene Hays. Circ: 15,000.

DETOUR. see *WOMEN'S INTERESTS*

687.5 POL ISSN 1509-6858
DOBRE RADY. FRYZURY. Text in Polish. 2000. 2/yr. adv. **Document type:** *Magazine, Consumer.* **Description:** Features a wide variety of information ranging from top styling tips to basic hair care.
Published by: Wydawnictwo Burda Polska Sp. z.o.o., ul Strzegomska 236a, Wroclaw, 54432, Poland. TEL 48-71-3737280, prenumerata@burda.pl, http://www.burda.pl. adv.: page PLZ 12,000. Circ: 100,000 (paid and controlled).

EBONY. see *ETHNIC INTERESTS*

646.724 FRA ISSN 1153-950X
ECLAIREUR DES COIFFEURS. Text in French. 1904. 44/yr. EUR 51.50 domestic; EUR 77.50 foreign (effective 2004). adv.
Published by: Promotion Presse Internationale, 7 Cour des Petites-Ecuries, Paris, 75010, France. TEL 33-1-42471205, FAX 33-1-47703394. Circ: 36,000.

ELECTROLYSIS WORLD. see *MEDICAL SCIENCES—Dermatology And Venereology*

ELEGANTISSIMA. see *CLOTHING TRADE—Fashions*

ELLE; Hong Kong. see *WOMEN'S INTERESTS*

646.7 ITA
ESTETICA DEUTSCHE AUSGABE. Text mainly in German; Text occasionally in Multiple languages. 6/yr. adv.
Published by: Edizioni E S A V Srl, Via Cavour 50, Turin, TO 10123, Italy. TEL 39-011-8174061, FAX 39-011-8125661, editorial@estetica.it, http://www.estetica.it. adv.: color page USD 3,100. Circ: 11,000.

646.7 ITA
ESTETICA ESPANA. Text mainly in Spanish; Text occasionally in Multiple languages. 5/yr. adv.
Published by: Edizioni E S A V Srl, Via Cavour 50, Turin, TO 10123, Italy. TEL 39-011-8174061, FAX 39-011-8125661, editorial@estetica.it, http://www.estetica.it. adv.: color page USD 1,600.

646.7 ITA
ESTETICA ESPANA Y SUD AMERICA. Text in Spanish. 5/yr. adv.
Published by: Edizioni E S A V Srl, Via Cavour 50, Turin, TO 10123, Italy. TEL 39-011-8174061, FAX 39-011-8125661, editorial@estetica.it, http://www.estetica.it. adv.: color page USD 2,600. Circ: 13,000.

646.7 ITA
ESTETICA FRANCE. Text mainly in French; Text occasionally in Multiple languages. 5/yr.
Published by: Edizioni E S A V Srl, Via Cavour 50, Turin, TO 10123, Italy. TEL 39-011-8174061, FAX 39-011-8125661, editorial@estetica.it, http://www.estetica.it. Circ: 11,000.

646.72 ITA
ESTETICA ITALIA/ESTETICA HAIRFASHION. Text in Italian. 1946. 8/yr. EUR 54.80 domestic (effective 2005). adv. **Document type:** *Magazine, Consumer.* **Description:** Presents hairstyles from all over the world. Contains news, tips, reports, and techniques.
Formerly: Estetica Modacapelli - Estetica Hairfashion
Related titles: Online - full text ed.
Published by: Edizioni E S A V Srl, Via Cavour 50, Turin, TO 10123, Italy. TEL 39-011-83921111, FAX 39-011-8171188, editorial@estetica.it, http://www.estetica.it. Ed. Roberto Pissimiglia. adv.: color page USD 4,300; trim 257 x 187. Circ: 31,000.

646.7 ITA
ESTETICA U.K. Text mainly in English; Text occasionally in Multiple languages. 5/yr.
Related titles: ♦ Regional ed(s).: Estetica USA.
Published by: Edizioni E S A V Srl, Via Cavour 50, Turin, TO 10123, Italy. TEL 39-011-8174061, FAX 39-011-8125661, editorial@estetica.it, http://www.estetica.it.

646.7 ITA
ESTETICA USA. Text in English. 5/yr. USD 92, CND 124 in United States (effective 2000). adv. **Document type:** *Magazine, Consumer.*
Related titles: ♦ Regional ed(s).: Estetica U.K.; ♦ Estetica World (Asia and Oceania).
Published by: Edizioni E S A V Srl, Via Cavour 50, Turin, TO 10123, Italy. TEL 39-011-8174061, FAX 39-011-8125661, editorial@estetica.it, http://www.estetica.it. adv.: color page USD 3,000. Circ: 10,000.

646.7 ITA
ESTETICA WORLD (ASIA AND OCEANIA). Text mainly in English; Text occasionally in Multiple languages. 5/yr.
Related titles: ♦ Regional ed(s).: Estetica USA.
Published by: Edizioni E S A V Srl, Via Cavour 50, Turin, TO 10123, Italy. TEL 39-011-8174061, FAX 39-011-8125661, editorial@estetica.it, http://www.estetica.it.

646.72 NLD ISSN 0014-1321
ESTHETICIENNE. Text in Dutch. 1965. m. EUR 74 domestic; EUR 78 in Belgium (effective 2005). adv. illus. **Document type:** *Trade.*

Published by: Koggeschip Vakbladen B.V., Postbus 1198, Amsterdam, 1000 BD, Netherlands. TEL 31-20-3113990, FAX 31-20-6960396, http://www.estheticienne.nl. Circ: 7,500.

646.72   FRA   ISSN 0220-1941
ESTHETIQUE. Text in French. 1969. 11/yr.
Formerly (until 1976): Revue Francaise de l'Esthetique (0220-195X)
Address: 8 rue Fort Notre Dame, Marseille, 13007, France. TEL 91-33-45-20, FAX 91-54-48-06. Ed. J M Mondoloni. Circ: 6,500.

646.72   HUN   ISSN 1216-8114
ESZTETIKA. Text in Hungarian. 1992. q. **Document type:** Magazine, Trade.
Published by: Health and Beauty Business Media Hungary Kft, Varosmajor u 33, Budapest, 1122, Hungary. TEL 36-1-4570067, FAX 36-1-2013248, azsilak@health-and-beauty.hu.

EVA. see CLOTHING TRADE—Fashions

EVE ESSENTIALS. see CLOTHING TRADE—Fashions

646.724   USA   ISSN 1523-424X
FAMOUS SALONS PRESENTS; Hollywood hairstyles - short and easy hair styles. Text in English. 1999. bi-m. USD 3.99 newsstand/cover; CND 4.99 newsstand/cover in Canada. adv. illus. back issues avail. **Document type:** Consumer.
Published by: Roxbury Media, LLC, 27 Glen Rd, PO Box 140, Sandy Hook, CT 06482. TEL 203-426-9533, FAX 203-426-9533. **Subscr. to:** Sunbelt Fulfillment Services, 307 Southgate Ct, Brentwood, TN 37027. **Dist. by:** Curtis Circulation Co., 730 River Road, New Milford, NJ 07646. TEL 201-634-7400, FAX 201-634-7499.

646.724   ITA   ISSN 1125-6214
FASHION PARADE. Text in Italian, English. 1979. q. 36 p./no.; back issues avail.
Published by: SEPEM s.r.l., Via Grado 9, Milan, MI 20125, Italy. R&P Franco Mattei.

FASHION THEORY; journal of dress, body and culture. see ART

FASHIONSTANCE. see CLOTHING TRADE—Fashions

FEINE ADRESSEN BERLIN. see GENERAL INTEREST PERIODICALS—Germany

FEINE ADRESSEN BODENSEE. see GENERAL INTEREST PERIODICALS—Germany

FEINE ADRESSEN BRAUNSCHWEIG. see GENERAL INTEREST PERIODICALS—Germany

FEINE ADRESSEN BREMEN - WESER-EMS. see GENERAL INTEREST PERIODICALS—Germany

FEINE ADRESSEN DORTMUND. see GENERAL INTEREST PERIODICALS—Germany

FEINE ADRESSEN DUISBURG - ESSEN - MUELHEIM. see GENERAL INTEREST PERIODICALS—Germany

FEINE ADRESSEN FRANKFURT - RHEIN-MAIN. see GENERAL INTEREST PERIODICALS—Germany

FEINE ADRESSEN HAMBURG. see GENERAL INTEREST PERIODICALS—Germany

FEINE ADRESSEN HANNOVER. see GENERAL INTEREST PERIODICALS—Germany

FEINE ADRESSEN HOF - OBERFRANKEN - PLAUEN. see GENERAL INTEREST PERIODICALS—Germany

FEINE ADRESSEN INTERNATIONAL. see GENERAL INTEREST PERIODICALS—Germany

FEINE ADRESSEN KARLSRUHE - BADEN-BADEN. see GENERAL INTEREST PERIODICALS—Germany

FEINE ADRESSEN KASSEL - KURHESSEN. see GENERAL INTEREST PERIODICALS—Germany

FEINE ADRESSEN KOELN. see GENERAL INTEREST PERIODICALS—Germany

FEINE ADRESSEN MUENCHEN. see GENERAL INTEREST PERIODICALS—Germany

FEINE ADRESSEN NUERNBERG - FRANKEN. see GENERAL INTEREST PERIODICALS—Germany

FEINE ADRESSEN STUTTGART - SCHWABEN. see GENERAL INTEREST PERIODICALS—Germany

FEINE ADRESSEN SYLT. see GENERAL INTEREST PERIODICALS—Germany

646.72   USA   ISSN 1522-8703
FIRST HOLD. Cover title: 1stHold. Text in English. q. USD 27.50 domestic (effective 2000). adv. back issues avail. **Document type:** Magazine, Trade. **Description:** Covers news and issues about the freelance styling industry for hair, makeup and fashion designers.
Published by: Set The Pace Publishing Group, 4237 Los Nietos Dr, Los Angeles, CA 90027-2911. TEL 323-913-0773, FAX 323-913-0900, info@setthepacepubgroup.com, http://www.setthepacepubgroup.com. Ed., Pub. Crystal A. Wright. adv.: color page USD 2,590.

646.724   DEU   ISSN 1430-4104
FRISEURWELT; Magazin fuer das Friseurhandwerk. Text in German. 1949. m. EUR 77; EUR 7 newsstand/cover (effective 2003). adv. charts; illus.; stat.; tr.illt. 64 p./no.; **Document type:** Magazine, Trade.
Former titles: Friseurwelt Aktuell (0724-1291); (until 1983): Friseurwelt (0016-1470)—CCC.
Published by: Terra Verlag GmbH, Neuhauser Str 21, Konstanz, 78464, Germany. TEL 49-7531-812238, FAX 49-7531-812299, info@terra-verlag.de, http://www.terra-verlag.de/friseurwelt.html. adv.: B&W page EUR 1,992, color page EUR 3,187. Circ: 19,700.

646.72   NOR   ISSN 0805-8024
FRISOER. Text in Norwegian. 1937. 6/yr. membership. adv.
Formerly (until 1995): Norske Dame- og Herrefrisoer (0333-4562); Which was formed by the merger of (1931-1937): Damefrisoeren (0332-5016); (1932-1937): Norske Frisoer (0805-8016); Which was formerly (1901-1931): Norske Barber og Frisoer (0805-8008)
Published by: Norges Frisoermesterforbund, Essendrupsgt 3, PO Box 7017, Oslo, 0368, Norway. TEL 47-23-08-79-60, FAX 47-23-08-79-70. Adv. contact Robin Hasle TEL 47-22-98-00-65. B&W page NOK 11,900, color page NOK 28,400.

646.724   DNK
FRISOERFAGET. Text in Danish. 1959. m. (11/yr.). DKK 450, USD 13 (effective 2000). adv. **Document type:** Trade.
Formerly: Frisoerfagene (0901-2737)
Published by: ReproHuset, Dueoddevej 14, Herning, 7400, Denmark. TEL 45-38-33-22-90, FAX 45-31-87-75-36, frisormester@vip.cybercity.dk. Ed. Jens Erik Behrndtz. R&P Karen Linger. Adv. contact Helle Jensen. B&W page DKK 7,000, color page DKK 14,000; trim 277 x 190. Circ: 6,200.

646.724   DEU
FRISUREN UND TRENDS. Text in German. m. adv. **Document type:** Magazine, Trade.
Published by: Marken Verlag GmbH, Bonner Str 323, Cologne, 50968, Germany. TEL 49-221-9574270, FAX 49-221-95742777, marken-info@markenverlag.de, http://www.markenverlag.de. adv.: page EUR 4,980. Circ: 176,500 (controlled).

646.72   JPN
FUJINGAHO/WOMEN'S GRAPHIC BEAUTY. Text in Japanese. 1951. m. JPY 1,100 newsstand/cover (effective 2002). adv. **Document type:** Magazine, Consumer. **Description:** Aimed at affluent women over forty with a deep appreciation for the beauty of Japanese lifestyles and culture, yet an open-minded curiosity for overseas fashion.
Published by: Hachette Fujingaho Co. Ltd. (Subsidiary of: Hachette Filipacchi Medias S.A.), 2-9-1 Nishi Shinbashi, Minato-ku, Tokyo, 105-0003, Japan. TEL 81-3-3506-6601, FAX 81-3-3506-6606, http://www.hfm.co.jp. Circ: 187,000 (paid).

GLAMOUR. see CLOTHING TRADE—Fashions

GLAMOUR. see CLOTHING TRADE—Fashions

GLAMOUR. see CLOTHING TRADE—Fashions

GLAMOUR. see CLOTHING TRADE—Fashions

GLAMOUR. see CLOTHING TRADE—Fashions

646.72   USA   ISSN 1556-2131
GLAMOUR LATINOAMERICA. Text in Spanish. 1998 (Mar.). m. USD 12 domestic; USD 24 in Canada; MXP 180 in Mexico; USD 30 elsewhere (effective 2001). adv. **Document type:** Magazine, Consumer.
Formerly (until 2005): Glamour en Espanol (1097-699X)
Related titles: ♦ English ed.: Glamour. ISSN 0017-0747.
Published by: Conde Nast Americas, 1101 Brickell Ave 15th Fl, Miami, FL 33131. TEL 305-371-9393, 800-792-5999, FAX 305-371-9392, glamour@ideaspublishinggroup.com, http://www.ideaspublishinggroup.com/magazines/glamour.html. adv.: page USD 3,350; trim 8 x 10.875. Circ: 394,000 (paid and controlled).

646.72   MNG
GOO MARAL/BEAUTIFUL DOE. Text in Mongol. 1990. bi-m.
Related titles: ♦ Supplement(s): Mongoljin Goo.
Published by: Association of Women, Ulan Bator, Mongolia. TEL 21035. Circ: 50,000.

646.72   ITA
LA GRIFFE. Text in Italian. 1960. bi-m. USD 100 foreign (effective 2001). adv.
Former titles (until 1988): Zeffiro Italia; Zeffiro
Published by: Fregoli Editore s.r.l., Via Bernardino Lanino, 5, Milan, MI 20144, Italy. TEL 39-02-48952284, FAX 39-02-48952716. Ed. Fregoli Altilio. Adv. contact Marisa Leali. Circ: 18,000.

646.72   USA
GUIDE TO TALENT & MODELING AGENCIES. Text in English. a. USD 23.99 (effective 2001). **Document type:** Directory, Consumer. **Description:** Comprehensive directory of agency schools, conferences, and scouts for those interested in modeling.
Published by: F & W Publications, Inc., 4700 E Galbraith Rd, Cincinnati, OH 45236. TEL 513-531-2690, FAX 513-531-2902, wds@fwpubs.com, http://www.fwpublications.com. Ed. Rachel Vater.

646.724   AUS
HAIR +; every day is a good hair day. Text in English. m. AUD 49.95 domestic; AUD 73.95 in New Zealand; AUD 133.95 elsewhere (effective 2004). adv. **Document type:** Magazine, Trade. **Description:** Covers over 600 new hair trends, cutting edge hairstyles, the latest colors, hairdressers' tips & advice, makeovers, cosmetic trends, celebrity secrets and the latest in hair and beauty news.
Published by: Derwent Howard, PO Box 1037, Bondi Junction, NSW 1355, Australia. TEL 61-2-93846666, 800-007-820, FAX 61-2-93864288, enquiries@derwenthoward.com.au, http://www.derwenthoward.com.au/. Ed. Nicola Conville. Adv. contact Jane Slingo.

646.724   GBR   ISSN 0143-7968
HAIR. Text in English. 1977. bi-m. GBP 15.77 domestic; USD 35.72 in United States (effective 2004). adv. **Document type:** Consumer. **Description:** Features an exciting visual mix of the latest hairstyles, tips, techniques, make-up and fashion, combined with advice and step-by-step guides.
Published by: I P C SouthBank (Subsidiary of: I P C Media Ltd.), Kings Reach Tower, Stamford St, London, SE1 9LS, United Kingdom. TEL 44-161-8722144, http://www.ipcmedia.com/. Ed. Kate Barlow TEL 44-20-72616974. Pub. Kirstin Lee TEL 44-20-72617443. adv.: color page GBP 3,950. Circ: 152,602. **Subscr. to:** I P C Media Ltd., Perrymount Rd, Haywards Heath RH16 3DA, United Kingdom. TEL 44-1444-475675, FAX 44-1444-445599, ipcsubs@qss-uk.com. **Dist. by:** MarketForce UK Ltd, 247 Tottenham Court Rd, London, Middx W1T 7AU, United Kingdom. TEL 44-207-2615199, FAX 44-207-2617341.

646.72   JPN
HAIR & BEAUTY. Text in Japanese. 4/yr. **Document type:** Consumer. **Description:** Beauty magazine for 15-28 year olds.
Published by: Kodansha Ltd., 2-12-21 Otowa, Bunkyo-ku, Tokyo, 112-8001, Japan. TEL 81-3-3946-6201, FAX 81-3-3944-9915, http://www.kodansha.co.jp, http://www.toppan.co.jp/kodansha. Ed. Takashi Sasagawa. Circ: 150,000.

646.724   GBR   ISSN 1360-3701
HAIR & BEAUTY. Text in English. 1995. bi-m. GBP 12 domestic; GBP 25 in Europe; USD 35 in United States; GBP 35 elsewhere; GBP 2 newsstand/cover domestic; USD 5.75 newsstand/cover in United States; CND 9.50 newsstand/cover in Canada. adv. **Document type:** Consumer. **Description:** Presents new hair and make-up looks and ideas.
Published by: Style Publishing, 126 Great Portland St, London, W1N 5PH, United Kingdom. TEL 44-20-7436-9766, FAX 44-20-7436-9957, hair.beautymag@btinternet.com. Ed. Kate Barlow. Pub. Damian Hockney. Adv. contact Kirsten Sangster. Circ: 79,787 (paid). **Dist. by:** M M C Ltd., Octagon House, White Hart Meadows, Ripley, Woking, Surrey GU23 6HR, United Kingdom. TEL 44-1483-211222, FAX 44-1483-224541.

646.724   ZAF
HAIR & BEAUTY FASHION. Text in English. 1994. bi-m. ZAR 98.50. adv. illus. **Document type:** Trade.
Former titles (until 2000): Black Salon Africa; Black Salon
Published by: Toxic Ratman, PO Box 1707, Four Ways, 2055, South Africa. TEL 27-11-804-6835. Ed., Pub. Lance G Whatmore. R&P, Adv. contact Philene Robertson.

646.724   GBR
HAIR IDEAS. Text in English. 9/yr. GBP 1.95 newsstand/cover (effective 2004). adv. **Document type:** Magazine, Consumer. **Description:** Contains information and advice on hair styles, product tests and makeovers.
Published by: Origin Publishing Ltd., 14th Fl, Tower House, Fairfax St, Bristol, BS1 3BN, United Kingdom. TEL 44-117-927-9009, FAX 44-117-934-9008, origin@subscription.co.uk, http://www.originpublishing.co.uk.

646.72   USA   ISSN 0887-803X
HAIR INTERNATIONAL NEWS. Text in English. bi-m. USD 25. adv. back issues avail.
Published by: (Associated Master Barbers and Beauticians of America), Hair International, 2017 Church St., Lebanon, PA 17046-2733. Ed. Franz Singer. Adv. contact Linda Yiengst. Circ: 700.

B

646.724 GBR ISSN 1362-8496
HAIR NOW. Text in English. 1996. 10/yr. GBP 2 newsstand/cover.
Document type: *Consumer.* **Description:** Shows fun ways of experimenting with hair cuts and coloring.
Published by: Style Publishing, 126 Great Portland St, London, W1N 5PH, United Kingdom. TEL 44-20-7436-9766, FAX 44-20-7436-9957. Ed. Laleh Gullanpour. Pub. Damian Hockney. Circ: 116,655 (paid). **Dist. by:** M M C Ltd., Octagon House, White Hart Meadows, Ripley, Woking, Surrey GU23 6HR, United Kingdom. TEL 44-1483-211222, FAX 44-1483-224541.

646.724 GBR
▼ **HAIR STYLE & BEAUTY.** Text in English. 2004 (Sep.). m. GBP 2.70 newsstand/cover (effective 2004). adv. **Document type:** *Magazine, Consumer.* **Description:** Helps keep readers up-to-date with the latest hair styles and fashions, as well as premium brand hair and skin care products and cosmetics.
Published by: Future Publishing Ltd., Beauford Court, 30 Monmouth St, Bath, Avon BA1 2BW, United Kingdom. TEL 44-1225-442244, FAX 44-1225-446019, customerservice@futurenet.co.uk, http://www.thefuturenetwork.plc.uk. Ed. Becky Skuse. Pub. Katherine Raderecht.

646.724 HUN
HAIR STYLE FORUM. Text in Hungarian. bi-m. adv. **Document type:** *Magazine, Trade.*
Published by: Health and Beauty Business Media Hungary Kft, Varosmajor u 33, Budapest, 1122, Hungary. TEL 36-1-4570067, FAX 36-1-2013248, azsilak@health-and-beauty.hu. adv.: page HUF 460,000; trim 225 x 310.

646.724 USA ISSN 1058-0980
HAIRDO IDEAS. Text in English. bi-m. USD 3.50 newsstand/cover; GBP 1.95 newsstand/cover in United Kingdom. **Document type:** *Consumer.* **Description:** Contains photos of hairstyles and styling tips.
Published by: Harris Publications, Inc., 800 Kennesaw Ave, Ste 220, Marietta, GA 30060. **Dist. in UK by:** Comag, Tavistock Works, Tavistock Rd, W Drayton, Middx UB7 7QX, United Kingdom. TEL 44-1895-444055, FAX 44-1895-433602.

646.724 GBR ISSN 0143-6910
HAIRDRESSERS' JOURNAL INTERNATIONAL. Text in English. 1882. w. GBP 67 domestic; GBP 75, USD 112 in United States; GBP 85, USD 128 elsewhere (effective 2000). adv. bk.rev. illus.; tr.mk. **Document type:** *Trade.* **Description:** Covers industry and product news, business advice, step-by-step tips, creative trends, consumer surveys, interiors, and classified advertising.
Formerly: Hairdressers' Journal (0017-6761)
Related titles: Online - full text ed.: (from Gale Group).
—CCC.
Published by: Reed Business Information Ltd. (Subsidiary of: Reed Business), Quadrant House, The Quadrant, Brighton Rd, Sutton, Surrey SM2 5AS, United Kingdom. TEL 44-208-652-3500, FAX 44-208-652-8975, rbi.subscriptions@qss-uk.com, http://www.reedinfo.co.uk/. Ed. Jayne Lewis-Orr TEL 44-20-8652-8255. Pub. Leon Clifford. Circ: 15,500. **Subscr. to:** Quadrant Subscription Services, Rockwood House, 9-17 Perrymount Rd, Haywards Heath, W. Sussex RH16 3DH, United Kingdom. TEL 44-1444-441212, FAX 44-1444-440620. **Dist. by:** MarketForce UK Ltd, 247 Tottenham Court Rd, London, Middx W1T 7AU, United Kingdom. TEL 44-20-72616996, FAX 44-207-2616951.

646.724 GBR ISSN 0954-2787
HAIRFLAIR. Key Title: Hair Flair. Text in English. 1982. bi-m. GBP 13 domestic; GBP 20 in Europe; GBP 26 elsewhere; GBP 2.20 newsstand/cover. adv. **Document type:** *Consumer.* **Description:** Profiles what is new in beauty including products and makeovers. A section is devoted to horoscopes.
Published by: James Kimber Publishing Ltd., Kimber House, 134 King St, London, W6 0QU, United Kingdom. TEL 44-181-563-2266, FAX 44-181-563-2299. Ed. Rebecca Barnes. Pub., R&P James Kimber. Adv. contact Stella Ramiah. B&W page GBP 1,400, color page GBP 2,495; trim 220 x 300. Circ: 76,200 (paid). **Subscr. to:** Hairflair Magazine, FREEPOST LON986, London SW6 4YZ, United Kingdom.

HAIRSTYLE!. see *LIFESTYLE*

646 USA ISSN 1058-3025
HAIRSTYLE. Text in English. 1984. q. USD 4.75 newsstand/cover; GBP 1.95 newsstand/cover in United Kingdom. **Document type:** *Consumer.* **Description:** Contains hairstyle ideas and photos.
Published by: Harris Publications, Inc., 800 Kennesaw Ave, Ste 220, Marietta, GA 30060.

646.724 AUS ISSN 1320-9469
HAIRTELL. Text in English. 1959. bi-m. AUD 40 domestic to non-members; AUD 55 foreign to non-members (effective 2000). adv. cum.index. **Document type:** *Newsletter, Trade.* **Description:** Provides industrial news of the hairdressing and industry.
Formerly (until 1989): Hair Fashions Magazine
Published by: Professional Hairdressers' Association, Level 10, 60 Pitt St, Sydney, NSW 2000, Australia. TEL 61-2-9247-5500, FAX 61-2-9247-5553. Ed., R&P, Adv. contact Linden Swan TEL 61-2-9977-1669. Circ: 1,600.

646.724 ISL
HAR OG FEGURD/HAIR AND BEAUTY MAGAZINE; timarit harsnyrtiidnadarins og Felags Islenskra Snyrtifraedinga. Text in Icelandic. 1980. 3/yr. ISK 1,400, USD 27 (effective 1996). **Description:** Publishes articles and other information on fashion in hair styling, clothes design, cosmetics and make-up, as well as on environmental protection.
Published by: Timaritid Har og Fegurd, Skulagata 54, Reykjavik, 105, Iceland. TEL 354-562-8141, FAX 354-562-8141, pmelsted@vortex.is, http://www.vortex.is/fashion. Ed. Petur Melsted.

646.72 GBR
HEADLINE NEWS. Text in English. 1974. m. GBP 88 to members. adv. bk.rev. **Document type:** *Newsletter.*
Formerly: National Hairdresser
Published by: National Hairdressers Federation, 11 Goldington Rd, Bedford, United Kingdom. TEL 44-1234-360332, FAX 44-1234-269337. Ed. R J Seymour. R&P John Patterson. Circ: 5,000.

646.72 GBR
HEALTH & BEAUTY SALON; for health and beauty therapists. Text in English. 1980. bi-m. GBP 35 domestic; GBP 58, USD 87 elsewhere (effective 2000). adv. illus. **Document type:** *Trade.* **Description:** Offers comprehensive information on all aspects of the health and beauty industry.
Formerly: Beauty Salon (0261-4146)
Related titles: Online - full text ed.: (from EBSCO Publishing, H.W. Wilson, O C L C Online Computer Library Center, Inc.).
Indexed: BPI.
—CCC.
Published by: Reed Business Information Ltd. (Subsidiary of: Reed Business), Quadrant House, The Quadrant, Brighton Rd, Sutton, Surrey SM2 5AS, United Kingdom. TEL 44-208-652-3500, FAX 44-208-652-8977, rbi.subscriptions@qss-uk.com, http://www.reedbusiness.co.uk/. Ed. Jayne Lewis-Orr TEL 44-20-8652-8255. Pub. Leon Clifford. Circ: 9,100. **Subscr. to:** Quadrant Subscription Services, PO Box 302, Haywards Heath, W Sussex RH16 3YY, United Kingdom. TEL 44-1444-445566, FAX 44-1444-445447.

646.72 AUS ISSN 1442-3200
HIGHLIGHTS. Text in English. 1992. s-a. AUD 60. adv. back issues avail. **Document type:** *Trade.*
Published by: Highlights Publications, 77 Beattie St, Balmain, NSW 2041, Australia. TEL 61-2-95552520, FAX 61-2-95552477, think@geko.net.au. Ed., Pub., Adv. contact Mark Stapleton. Circ: 20,000.

646.724 USA ISSN 1533-8789
HOLLYWOOD WORLDWIDE BLACK HAIRSTYLES & TRENDS. Variant title: Black Hairstyles & Trends. Text in English. 2001. m. USD 4.99 newsstand/cover (effective 2002). **Document type:** *Consumer.*
Published by: Celebrity Worldwide, 20 E Sunrise Hwy, Ste 202, Valley Stream, NY 11581. TEL 516-823-1212, FAX 516-823-1561, http://www.hairweb.com. Ed. Susan Jones Dorsainville. Pub. Eddison Bramble.

646.724 USA ISSN 1099-9426
HYPE HAIR. Text in English. 1992. bi-m. USD 27 (effective 2004). adv. **Document type:** *Magazine, Consumer.* **Description:** Covers beauty haircare for black women.
Published by: T B W Publishing Group, 210 Rte 4 E, Ste 401, Paramus, NJ 07652. TEL 201-843-4004, FAX 201-843-8636. Ed. Adrienne Moore. Pub. John Blassingame. Adv. contact Steve Gross TEL 212-490-1895. Circ: 75,000. **Dist. in UK by:** Comag, Tavistock Works, Tavistock Rd, W Drayton, Middx UB7 7QX, United Kingdom. TEL 44-1895-444055, FAX 44-1895-433602.

I F M T MAGAZINE. (International Fashion Model & Talent) see *CLOTHING TRADE—Fashions*

646.7 GBR
INSTITUTE OF ELECTROLYSIS. LIST OF QUALIFIED OPERATORS. SYLLABUS PROSPECTUS. Text in English. 1962. a. membership. **Document type:** *Newsletter.*
Published by: Institute of Electrolysis, 138 Downs Barn Blvd, Milton Keynes, Bucks MK14 7RP, United Kingdom. TEL 44-1908-695297, institute@electrolysis.co.uk, http://electrolysis.co.uk. Circ: (controlled).

646.72 FRA ISSN 1264-6539
INTERNATIONAL COSMETIQUE NEWS. Abbreviated title: I C N. Text in English. 1994. 9/yr. EUR 95, USD 95 (effective 2002). adv. **Document type:** *Magazine, Trade.* **Description:** Covers the international beauty market in all the major countries, market segments and distribution channels.
Published by: Cosmedias International, 4 rue de Seze, Paris, 75009, France. TEL 33-1-44945060, FAX 33-1-44945069, circ@cosmedias.fr, http://www.cosmetiquenews.com/. Ed. Jane Williams. Adv. contact Sylvie Borin.

INTERNATIONAL DIRECTORY OF BEAUTY SUPPLIES, COSMETICS AND TOILETRIES IMPORTERS. see *BUSINESS AND ECONOMICS—Trade And Industrial Directories*

INTERNATIONAL DIRECTORY OF PAGEANTS. see *WOMEN'S INTERESTS*

646.724 ROM
IOANA FRIZURI. Text in Romanian. 2/yr. adv. **Document type:** *Magazine, Consumer.*
Published by: Burda Romania, Str. Izvor nr. 78, sector 5, Bucharest, Romania. TEL 40-21-4105212, FAX 40-21-4110168, sandi@burda.ro, http://www.burda.ro. adv.: page USD 2,000. Circ: 45,000 (controlled).

646.72 BEL ISSN 0775-8952
KAPPER EN KAPSELS; maandblad van het kappersvak. Text in Dutch. 1949. 9/yr. adv. **Document type:** *Trade.* **Description:** For the hairdressing trade.
Supersedes (in 1988): Kapper (0775-8936); Coiffeur (0775-8928)
Related titles: French ed.: Coiffeur et Coiffures. ISSN 0775-8944.
Published by: A.P.I.C., Dieweg 294, Brussels, 1180, Belgium. TEL 32-2-375-4444, FAX 32-2-375-5257. Circ: 6,000.

646.724 CZE
KATKA UCESY. Text in Czech. s-a. CZK 49 newsstand/cover (effective 2003). adv. **Document type:** *Magazine, Consumer.*
Published by: Burda Praha spol. s.r.o., Uruguayska 17, Prague 2, 120 00, Czech Republic. TEL 420-2-22520618, FAX 420-2-22522648, klincokova@burda.cz, http://www.burda.cz. adv.: page CZK 90,000. Circ: 150,000 (paid and controlled).

646.72 FIN ISSN 0047-3308
KAUNEUS JA TERVEYS. Text in Finnish. 1956. m. EUR 98.10 domestic; EUR 100.50 in Europe; EUR 111.30 elsewhere (effective 2005). adv. **Document type:** *Magazine, Consumer.* **Description:** Health and beauty magazine for female readers from 25 - 45 years.
Published by: A-Lehdet Oy, Risto Rytin tie 33, Helsinki, 00081, Finland. TEL 358-9-75961, FAX 358-9-7598600, a-tilaus@a-lehdet.fi, http://www.a-lehdet.fi/lehti/kauneus_ja_terveys/. Ed. Irmeli Castren. Adv. contact Matti Sahravuo TEL 358-9-7596385. color page EUR 5,650; 187 x 241. Circ: 74,791 (controlled).

646.72 GBR ISSN 1363-7096
KEY NOTE MARKET REPORT: BATHS & SANITARYWARE. Variant title: Baths & Sanitaryware. Text in English. irreg., latest 2001, Mar. GBP 340 per issue (effective 2002). **Document type:** *Trade.* **Description:** Provides an overview of a specific UK market segment and includes executive summary, market definition, market size, industry background, competitor analysis, current issues, forecasts, company profiles, and more.
Formerly (until 1996): Key Note Report: Baths and Sanitaryware (0957-7300)
Related titles: CD-ROM ed.; Online - full text ed.
Published by: Key Note Ltd., Field House, 72 Oldfield Rd, Hampton, Middx TW12 2HQ, United Kingdom. TEL 44-20-8481-8750, FAX 44-20-8783-0049, info@keynote.co.uk, http://www.keynote.co.uk. Ed. Jenny Baxter.

646.72 658 GBR ISSN 1367-2304
KEY NOTE PLUS MARKET REPORT. TOILETRIES. Variant title: Toiletries Plus Market Report. Text in English. irreg., latest 2002, May. GBP 455 per issue (effective 2002). **Document type:** *Trade.* **Description:** Provides an overview of a specific UK market segment and includes executive summary, market definition, market size, industry background, competitor analysis, current issues, forecasts, company profiles, and more.
Formerly (until 1996): Key Note Report: Toiletries (0950-1541)
Related titles: CD-ROM ed.; Online - full text ed.
Published by: Key Note Ltd., Field House, 72 Oldfield Rd, Hampton, Middx TW12 2HQ, United Kingdom. TEL 44-20-8481-8750, FAX 44-20-8783-0049, info@keynote.co.uk, http://www.keynote.co.uk.

646.72 DEU ISSN 1439-5541
KONKRETER ERFOLG. Text in German. 1991. m. EUR 65 domestic; EUR 71 foreign (effective 2004). **Document type:** *Magazine, Trade.*
Former titles (until 1998): Beauty Forum Konkret (0946-0950); (until 1994): Cosmetic Konkret (0940-1245)
Published by: Health and Beauty Business Media GmbH & Co. KG, Karl-Friedrich-Str 14-18, Karlsruhe, 76133, Germany. TEL 49-721-165833, FAX 49-721-165618, juergen.volpp@health-and-beauty.com, http://www.health-and-beauty.com.

KOSMETIK INTERNATIONAL. see *BEAUTY CULTURE—Perfumes And Cosmetics*

646.72 THA
THE LADY. Text in Thai. m.
Published by: Lady, 77 Rama V Rd, Bangkok, Thailand. Ed. Princess Ngarmchitr Prem Purachatra.

646.724 DEU
LEA - FRISUREN. Text in German. 2001. 4/yr. EUR 1.95 newsstand/cover (effective 2003). adv. **Document type:** *Magazine, Consumer.* **Description:** Contains ideas and advice on a variety of new hairstyles.

Published by: Klambt Verlag GmbH, Im Neudeck 1, Speyer, 67346, Germany. TEL 49-6232-3100, FAX 49-6232-310226, anzeigen@klambt.de, http://www.klambt.de. Adv. contact Anita Weiss. B&W page EUR 3,420, color page EUR 4,114. Circ: 68,553 (paid).

646.72 FRA ISSN 1284-9715
L'ESSENTIEL DE LA COIFFURE. Text in French. 1997. 10/yr. EUR 61 domestic; EUR 72 foreign; EUR 32 to students (effective 2003).
Published by: Editions de Courcelles (Subsidiary of: Groupe Meditions), 1 et 3 Rue du Depart, Paris, 75014, France. TEL 33-1-40640075, FAX 33-1-43222699, groupemeditions@wanadoo.fr.

646.724 SCG
LISA FRIZURE. Text in Serbian. 2/yr. **Document type:** *Magazine, Consumer.* **Description:** Provides information on styling tips and basic hair care.
Published by: Isdavacka Kuca Burda Beograd, Takovska 45, Beograd, 11000. sandi@burda.co.yu. Circ: 45,000 (controlled).

THE LITTLE BLACK BOOK. see *BUSINESS AND ECONOMICS—Trade And Industrial Directories*

646.724 RUS ISSN 1681-3464
LIZA. MODNYE PRICHESKI. Text in Russian. 2001. 2/yr. adv. **Document type:** *Magazine, Consumer.* **Description:** Features a wide variety of information on hair ranging from top styling tips to basic hair care.
Published by: Izdatel'skii Dom Burda, ul Pravdy 8, Moscow, 125040, Russian Federation. TEL 7-095-7979849, FAX 7-095-2571196, vertrieb@burda.ru, http://www.burda.ru. adv.: page USD 5,100. Circ: 150,000 (paid and controlled).

THE LOOK. see *CLOTHING TRADE—Fashions*

LOOKING FIT. see *PHYSICAL FITNESS AND HYGIENE*

646.72 613 DNK ISSN 1603-726X
▼ **LOOKS**; fordi skoenhed kommer udefra. Text in Danish. 2004. q. DKK 149; DKK 48.50 per issue (effective 2004). **Document type:** *Magazine, Consumer.*
Published by: Aller Press A-S, Vigerslev Alle 18, Valby, 2500, Denmark. TEL 45-36-152000, FAX 45-36-152696, looks@aller.dk, direktionen@aller.dk, http://www.aller.dk.

646.72 NLD ISSN 1573-6334
LOOKS. Text in Dutch. 1979. q. EUR 114.75 (effective 2005). adv. illus. **Document type:** *Trade.*
Former titles (until 2003): Coiffure Looks (1566-1644); (until 1999): Coiffure Gallery (0927-7927); (until 1992): Photo Gallery (0927-7919)
Published by: It's Amazing Business Communication bv, Postbus 7104, Zoetermeer, 2701 AC, Netherlands. TEL 31-79-3438383, FAX 31-79-3438399, itsabc@itsamazing.nl, http://www.itsamazing.nl. Circ: 2,200.

LUMIERE. see *CLOTHING TRADE—Fashions*

LUXURY BRIEFING. see *CLOTHING TRADE*

646.72 USA ISSN 1523-1232
MAKE-UP ARTIST MAGAZINE. Text in English. 1996. bi-m. USD 24.95 domestic; USD 34.95 in Canada; USD 49.95 elsewhere; USD 6.50 newsstand/cover (effective 2001). **Document type:** *Magazine, Trade.* **Description:** Features cover stories and articles on the entertainment industry's top make-up artists, innovative make-up techniques, and current product news.
Related titles: Online - full text ed.
Address: 4018 NE 112th Ave., Ste. 8, Vancouver, WA 98682-5703. TEL 818-504-6770, FAX 818-504-6257, editor@makeupmag.com, http://www.makeupmag.com. **Dist. by:** International Publishers Direct, 27500 Riverview Center Blvd, Bonita Springs, FL 34134. TEL 858-320-4563, FAX 858-677-3220.

MARIE CLARIE EN ESPANOL. see *WOMEN'S INTERESTS*

MCSISTER. see *CHILDREN AND YOUTH—For*

MINI. see *CLOTHING TRADE—Fashions*

MINI. see *WOMEN'S INTERESTS*

MISS BEAUTY. see *CHILDREN AND YOUTH—For*

646.72 659.152 ITA
MIXART NEWS. Text in Italian. 1998. s-a.?. **Document type:** *Trade.*
Published by: SEPEM s.r.l., Via Grado 9, Milan, MI 20125, Italy. TEL 39-02-26825553, FAX 39-02-26823952. Ed. Franco Mattei.

MODA TOP. see *CLOTHING TRADE—Fashions*

646.72 USA ISSN 0148-4001
RL76.A1
MODERN SALON MAGAZINE. Text in English. 1924. m. USD 20 domestic; USD 29.50 in Canada; USD 36 elsewhere; USD 4 newsstand/cover (effective 2005). adv. bk.rev. illus.; tr.lit. index. **Document type:** *Magazine, Trade.* **Description:** Features hair styles and business trends.
Incorporates: Visions (Lincolnshire); Formerly (until 1977): Modern Beauty Shop (0026-7511)
Related titles: Microform ed.: (from PQC).
—CCC.
Published by: Vance Publishing Corp., 400 Knightsbridge Pkwy, Lincolnshire, IL 60069. TEL 847-634-2600, 800-255-5113, FAX 847-634-7885, matherton@vancepublishing.com, http://www.modernsalon.com, http://www.vancepublishing.com. Ed. Mary Atherton. Adv. contact Sherry Fisher. B&W page USD 10,695, color page USD 12,490. Circ: 120,000 (paid and controlled).

646.724 DEU
MOD'S HAIR. Text in German. 2/yr. adv. **Document type:** *Magazine, Consumer.*
Published by: Vereinigte Verlagsanstalten GmbH, Hoeherweg 278, Duesseldorf, 40231, Germany. TEL 49-211-73570, FAX 49-211-7357123, info@vva.de, http://www.vva.de. adv.: B&W page EUR 3,100, color page EUR 4,900. Circ: 120,000 (controlled).

646.72 MNG
MONGOLJIN GOO/MONGOLIAN BEAUTY. Text in Mongol. bi-m.
Related titles: ◆ Supplement to: Goo Maral.
Address: PO Box 2106 44, Ulan Bator, Mongolia. TEL 21035. Ed. B Enhtuyaa.

646.72 USA ISSN 1064-5926
N A C C A S REVIEW. Text in English. 1981. bi-m. USD 65 (effective 2001). adv. Website rev. 20 p./no.; back issues avail. **Document type:** *Newsletter, Trade.* **Description:** Covers issues relating to the development and implementation of standards in post-secondary education in cosmetology.
Published by: National Accrediting Commission of Cosmetology Arts & Sciences, 4401 Ford Ave., Ste. 1300, Alexandria, VA 22302-1432. TEL 703-527-7600, FAX 703-527-8811, naccas@erols.com, naccas@naccas.org, http://www.naccas.org. Ed., Adv. contact Clifford A Culbreath TEL 703-527-7600 ext 35. R&P Mary E Bird. Circ: 4,100.

624.7 USA ISSN 0896-193X
NAILS. Text in English. 1983. m. (plus Factbook in July). USD 20 domestic; USD 57 in Canada; USD 87 elsewhere (effective 2005). adv. illus. **Document type:** *Magazine, Trade.* **Description:** Provides business advice for professional manicurists, nail salon owners, and beauty supply distributors. Includes information on new products and application techniques.
Related titles: Online - full text ed.: (from Northern Light Technology, Inc., ProQuest Information & Learning).
Published by: Bobit Business Media, 3520 Challenger St, Torrance, CA 90503. TEL 310-533-2400, FAX 310-533-2500, nailsmag@bobit.com, http://www.nailsmag.com, http://www.bobit.com. Pubs. Cyndy Drummey. Circ: 50,000.

646.72 305.896 USA
▼ **NAPTURAL ROOTS.** Text in English. 2005 (Nov.). bi-m. free in Seattle Metro area; USD 10 out of area (effective 2006). **Document type:** *Magazine, Consumer.* **Description:** Promotes a positive self-imagine of African American women through asserting their natural beauty, healthy mind, body and soul.
Published by: Akili Technologies Publishing, LLC, PO Box 68926, Seattle, WA 98168. TEL 206-331-4984, FAX 206-331-4985, http://napturalrootsmagazine.com.

NATIONAL ALOPECIA AREATA FOUNDATION NEWSLETTER. see *MEDICAL SCIENCES—Dermatology And Venereology*

646.724 DEU
DIE NEUE FRAU - FRISUREN. Text in German. 2/yr. EUR 1.95 newsstand/cover (effective 2002). adv. **Document type:** *Magazine, Consumer.*
Published by: Klambt Verlag GmbH, Im Neudeck 1, Speyer, 67346, Germany. TEL 49-6232-3100, FAX 49-6232-310226, anzeigen@klambt.de, http://www.klambt.de. Adv. contact Anita Weiss. B&W page EUR 3,320, color page EUR 4,114. Circ: 71,798 (paid).

▼ **NEW BEAUTY**; the magazine about cosmetics enhancement. see *MEDICAL SCIENCES—Surgery*

646.72 USA
NEW ENGLAND BEAUTY JOURNAL. Text in English. m. USD 18. **Description:** For the hair salon trade.
Published by: Bay Colony Publications, 105 Orchard St, Lynn, MA 01905. TEL 617-592-9157.

646.724 USA ISSN 1058-0964
NEW IDEAS FOR HAIR STYLING. Text in English. bi-m. USD 17.97; USD 3.75 newsstand/cover; GBP 1.95 newsstand/cover in United Kingdom. adv. charts; illus.
Published by: Harris Publications, Inc., 800 Kennesaw Ave, Ste 220, Marietta, GA 30060. TEL 212-807-7100, FAX 212-627-4678. Ed. Lyla Aubry.

NON FOOD ALIMARKET. see *GIFTWARE AND TOYS*

646.724 USA
NORTHWEST STYLIST & SALON; The Business of Hair, Skin & Nails. Text in English. 1983. m. USD 20; USD 30 foreign (effective 2001). adv. bk.rev. back issues avail. **Document type:** *Newspaper, Trade.* **Description:** For salon and beauty school owners, practitioners, and students in Oregon, Idaho, and Washington.
Published by: Holland Graphics Inc., 1750 S W Skyline Blvd, Ste 24, Portland, OR 97221-2533. TEL 503-297-7010, FAX 503-297-7022, editor@stylistnewspapers.com, hollandgfx@aol.com, http://www.nwstylist.com, http://www.ohiostylist.com. Ed., Pub. Linda Holland. R&Ps Alby Hesedia, Linda Holland. Adv. contact Joel Holland. Circ: 22,000.

B

646.72 USA ISSN 1043-9641
LES NOUVELLES ESTHETIQUES (AMERICAN EDITION). Text in English. 1985. m. USD 45 domestic; USD 55 in Canada; USD 140 for 2 yrs. elsewhere (effective 2004). adv. illus.; tr.lit. back issues avail.; reprints avail. **Document type:** *Magazine, Consumer.* **Description:** Includes articles and news on skin, spas, business, medicine, and other features. Contains industry trends, products, equipment, techniques, ingredients and services.
Published by: Les Nouvelles Esthetiques, Inc., 3929 Ponce de Leon Blvd, Miami, FL 33134-7323. TEL 305-433-2322, 800-471-0229, FAX 305-443-1664, subscriptins@lneonline.com, http://www.lneonline.com. Ed. Monica J Schuloff-Smith. Pub. Jean Jacques Legrand. R&P Rodolphe Legrand. Adv. contact Larry L Solomon. B&W page USD 2,870, color page USD 4,160; trim 8.375 x 10.875. Circ: 20,000 (paid and controlled).

646.72 FRA ISSN 0029-490X
LES NOUVELLES ESTHETIQUES (FRENCH EDITION). Text in French. 1952. 11/yr. EUR 46 domestic; EUR 64 DOM-TOM; EUR 73 elsewhere (effective 2004). bk.rev. illus. **Document type:** *Magazine, Trade.*
Published by: Les/Nouvelles Esthetiques, 7 av. Stephane Mallarme, Paris, 75017, France. TEL 33-1-43800647, FAX 33-1-43808363, http://www.nouvelles-esthetiques.com/. Ed. Michelle de Lattre TEL 33-4-43807129. Pub. M Pierantoni. Circ: 14,000.

646.72 ITA
LES NOUVELLES ESTHETIQUES (ITALIAN EDITION). Text in Italian. 9/yr. EUR 62 domestic; EUR 99 in Europe; EUR 130 elsewhere (effective 2003). adv. **Document type:** *Magazine, Trade.* **Description:** Intended for those in the beauty industry. Contains articles and advertisements on beauty technology.
Published by: A L A Editrice s.r.l., Via Macedonio Melloni, 36, Milan, MI 20129, Italy. TEL 39-02-747656, FAX 39-02-70100018, nsantelli@alalne.com. Ed. Nennella Santelli. Adv. contact Alberto Fossati.

646.724 AUT ISSN 0029-9065
DER OESTERREICHISCHE FRISEUR; offizielles Fachorgan der Friseure Oesterreichs. Text in German. 1948. m. adv. **Document type:** *Magazine, Trade.* **Description:** Trade publication for hairdressers and owners of beauty salons. Covers new hair fashions, product information, sales promotion, and association news. Includes reports and announcements of events and exhibitions, classified ads, list of courses.
Published by: Landesinnung Wien der Friseure, Mollardgasse 1, Vienna, W 1060, Austria. TEL 43-1-5870420, FAX 43-1-587042020, friseure@wkw.at. Ed. Lui Vemzely. Circ: 4,200 (paid and controlled).

646.72 DEU
PASSION LADY. Text in English. q. **Document type:** *Trade.*
Published by: Trend Design GmbH, Bruederstr 16, Herford, 32052, Germany. TEL 05221-54900, FAX 05221-56890.

646.724 DEU
PASSION MEN; international hair magazine. Text in English. q. **Document type:** *Trade.*
Published by: Trend Design GmbH, Bruederstr 16, Herford, 32052, Germany. TEL 05221-54900, FAX 05221-56890.

687.5 ESP ISSN 1575-1724
PELO NEW LOOK. Text in Spanish. 1994. m. EUR 24.36 (effective 2004). adv. **Document type:** *Magazine, Consumer.*
Published by: Globus Comunicacion (Subsidiary of: Bonnier AB), Covarrubias 1, Madrid, 28010, Spain. TEL 34-91-4471202, FAX 34-91-4471043, pelonewlook@globuscom.es, txhdez@globuscom.es, http://www.globuscom.es/sum/pelo1.htm. Ed. Ines Revuelta. Adv. contact Ana Madero. color page EUR 3,820; trim 21 x 28.5.

646.724 ESP ISSN 1134-5608
PELUQUERIAS DE GRAN SELECCION; revista tecnica del peinado. Text in English, French, Italian, Spanish. 1969. 11/yr. USD 79 (effective 2001). adv. film rev.; play rev. illus. **Document type:** *Trade.* **Description:** Contains hairstyles and how to do them.
Related titles: Russian ed.: Priceski. ISSN 1134-5624. 1994; Includes: Revista Tecnica de Peluqueria y Belleza; Supplement(s): Peluquerlas. Suplemento Informativo. ISSN 1134-5616. 1993.

Published by: Ediciones Prensa y Video, S.L., Plaza de las Navas, 11, Barcelona, 08004, Spain. TEL 34-93-2925840, FAX 34-93-292-5841, info@hair_styles.com, info@hair-styles.com, http://www.hair-factory.com/, http://www.hair-styles.com/. Ed. Juan Prat. Pub. Luis Llongueras Batlle. Adv. contact Pauli Sole. Circ: 25,000.

POINT OF VIEW. see *CLOTHING TRADE—Fashions*

PRETTY STYLE. see *CLOTHING TRADE—Fashions*

646.724 USA
PROCESS. Text in English. bi-m. USD 29 domestic; USD 41 in Canada; USD 47 elsewhere (effective 2005). adv. **Document type:** *Magazine, Trade.*
Published by: Vance Publishing Corp., 400 Knightsbridge Pkwy, Lincolnshire, IL 60069. TEL 847-634-2600, FAX 847-634-4379, http://www.vancepublishing.com.

646.72 GBR
PURE BEAUTY. Text in English. 1997. m. GBP 50; GBP 75 foreign. adv. bk.rev. bibl.; tr.lit. back issues avail. **Document type:** *Trade.* **Description:** News and features on all aspects of beauty retailing.
Published by: Podium Publications, 2M Cooper House, 2 Michael Rd, London, SW6 2AD, United Kingdom. TEL 44-171-371-7900, FAX 44-171-371-7949. Ed. Janice Hallett. Pub., R&P, Adv. contact Sian Rees. color page GBP 2,300. Circ: 14,500 (controlled).

646.726 USA
▼ **RENEW**; the modern spirit of professional skin care. Text in English. 2004. bi-m. free to qualified personnel. adv. **Document type:** *Magazine, Trade.* **Description:** Contains information for and about the hands-on skin care therapist.
Published by: Vance Publishing Corp., 400 Knightsbridge Pkwy, Lincolnshire, IL 60069. TEL 847-634-2600, FAX 847-634-4379, http://www.vancepublishing.com.

SABRINA'S SECRETS. see *CHILDREN AND YOUTH—For*

646.724 ITA
SALON. Text in Italian. 10/yr.
Address: Via Romolo Gessi, 28, Milan, MI 20146, Italy. TEL 2-42-39-443, FAX 2-41-23-405. Ed. Giuseppe Tirabasso. Circ: 13,000.

646.724 POL ISSN 1230-9656
SALON I ELEGANCJA. Text in Polish. 1993. m. PLZ 78 (effective 1999). adv. illus. **Document type:** *Trade.* **Description:** Contains professional articles and beauty information, reports, interviews, descriptions of new products and worldwide correspondence interesting to cosmeticians and heirdressers.
Published by: Warsaw Voice S.A., Ksiecia Janusza 65, Warsaw, 01452, Poland. TEL 48-22-366377, FAX 48-22-371995, voice@warsawvoice.com.pl, http://www.warsawvoice.com.pl. Ed. Joanna Kwiatkowska. Adv. contact Joanna Stniszewska. page PLZ 7,800; 261 x 180.

646.724 CAN ISSN 1197-1495
TT950
SALON MAGAZINE. Text in English. 1992. 8/yr. CND 40; CND 50 in United States; CND 60 elsewhere. adv. **Document type:** *Trade.*
—CCC.
Published by: Salon Communications Inc., 365 Bloor St East, Ste 1902, Toronto, ON M4W 3L4, Canada. TEL 416-869-3131, FAX 416-869-3008, salon@beautynet.com, http://www.beautynet.com/. Eds. Alison Wood, Deirdre Hanna. Pub. Greg Robins. adv.: B&W page CND 2,800, color page CND 3,410; trim 10.88 x 8.63. Circ: 23,000.

646.72 USA ISSN 1071-5606
SALON NEWS. Text in English. 1993. m. USD 39 domestic; USD 65 in Canada & Mexico; USD 95 elsewhere (effective 2002). adv. **Document type:** *Magazine, Trade.* **Description:** Discusses business news and issues salon owners need to know, along with fashion and hair style trends.
Related titles: Online - full text ed.: (from Florida Center for Library Automation, Gale Group); Supplement(s): Salon News Look Book.
Published by: Fairchild Publications, Inc., 7 W 34th St, New York, NY 10001-8191. TEL 212-630-4000, salonedit@fairchildpub.com, http://www.salonnews.com, http://www.fairchildpub.com. Pub. Robert Mugnai. Circ: 77,568 (controlled).

646.724 USA
SALON REPORT✶. Text in English. q. **Document type:** *Newsletter.*
Published by: Salon Development Corporation, 1381 Summit Ave., St. Paul, MN 55105-2219. TEL 612-690-1613. Ed. Bill Perron.

646.724 USA ISSN 0743-6394
SALON TODAY. Text in English. 1983. bi-m. USD 42 domestic; USD 60 foreign (effective 2005). 80 p./no.; back issues avail. **Document type:** *Magazine, Trade.*
Related titles: Online - full content ed.
—CCC.
Published by: Vance Publishing Corp., 400 Knightsbridge Pkwy, Lincolnshire, IL 60069. TEL 847-634-2600, 800-255-5113, FAX 847-634-4379, http://www.modernsalon.com, http://www.vancepublishing.com. Circ: 40,000.

646.727 DNK ISSN 0109-596X
SAMMENSLUTNINGEN AF DANSKE FODPLEJERE - FAGTIDSSKRIFT. Text in Danish. 1976. q.
Former titles (until 1983): Fodplejeren (0107-3362); (until 1978): Fodspecialisten (0107-4148)
Published by: Sammenslutningen af Danske Fodplejere, c/o Hartvig Pedersen, Tegelvaerksvej 20, Brundby, Tranebjerg, 8791, Denmark.

646.72 NLD ISSN 0168-9630
DE SCHOONHEIDSSPECIALIST. Text in Dutch. 1966. m. EUR 85 domestic; EUR 111 foreign; EUR 51 to students; EUR 7 newsstand/cover (effective 2005). adv. illus. back issues avail. **Document type:** *Journal, Trade.* **Description:** Business magazine for beauty therapists.
Published by: (Algemene Nederlandse Branche Organisatie Schoonheidsverzorging - A N B O S/Dutch Association of Beauty Therapists), Uitgeverij Lakerveld BV, Turfschipper 53, Postbus 160, Wateringen, 2290 AD, Netherlands. TEL 31-174-315000, FAX 31-174-315001, redactie@lakerveld.nl, uitgeverij@lakerveld.nl, http://www.schoonheidsspecialist.nl/, http://www.lakerveld.nl. Ed. Saskia Petit. Pub., R&P Ad van Gaalen. adv.: B&W page EUR 1,572, color page EUR 2,502; trim 185 x 268. Circ: 7,343.

SHINE; for a happier, healthier, sexier you. see *WOMEN'S HEALTH*

646.724 USA
SHORT & EASY HAIRCUTS. Text in English. q. USD 3.99 per issue (effective 2001). adv. **Description:** Features new hairstyles and haircuts of the stars.
Published by: Roxbury Media, LLC, 27 Glen Rd, PO Box 140, Sandy Hook, CT 06482. TEL 203-426-6533, FAX 203-426-9021. Pub. Kevin Montanaro.

391.65 USA ISSN 1071-7684
SKIN & INK; the tattoo magazine. Text in English. 1993. bi-m. USD 17.95 (effective 2005). **Document type:** *Magazine, Consumer.*
Published by: L F P, Inc., 8484 Wilshire Blvd., Ste. 900, Beverly Hills, CA 90211. http://www.skinandink.com. Ed. Bob Baxter. Pub. Larry Flynt.

646.72 617.952 USA
SKIN DEEP. Text in English. q. (bi-m. in 2006). USD 6.96 newsstand/cover (effective 2005). **Document type:** *Magazine, Consumer.* **Description:** Covers plastic surgery, skin care, cosmetic dentistry, vision, finance information, statistics and more.
Published by: Meducation, Inc., 5052 S. Jones Blvd.#110, Las Vegas, NV 89118. http://www.skindeepworld.com/Magazine.

646.724 USA ISSN 1042-5276
SOPHISTICATE'S BLACK HAIR; styles and care guide. Text in English. 8/yr. USD 26.70; USD 37.40 foreign; USD 4.95 newsstand/cover; CND 5.99 newsstand/cover in Canada; GBP 2.50 newsstand/cover in United Kingdom (effective 1999). adv. **Document type:** *Consumer.* **Description:** Shows African American women step by step how they can create beautiful hair styles. Covers the hairstyles of celebrities.
Published by: Associated Publications, Inc., 875 N Michigan Ave, Ste 3434, Chicago, IL 60611-1901. TEL 312-266-8680. Adv. contact Beverly Coley Morris. **Dist. in the UK:** by Comag, Tavistock Rd, West Drayton, Mddx UB7 7QE, United Kingdom. TEL 44-1895-444055, FAX 44-1895-433602.

646.724 USA ISSN 1041-7125
TT950
SOPHISTICATE'S HAIRSTYLE GUIDE. Text in English. bi-m. USD 20.75; USD 36.30 foreign; GBP 2.20 newsstand/cover (effective 1999). illus. **Document type:** *Consumer.* **Description:** Displays a wide variety of hairstyles as worn by celebrities.
Published by: Associated Publications, Inc., 875 N Michigan Ave, Ste 3434, Chicago, IL 60611-1901. TEL 312-266-8680. Ed. Bonnie Krueger. Pub. James Spurlock. **Dist. in UK by:** Comag, Tavistock Works, Tavistock Rd, W Drayton, Middx UB7 7QX, United Kingdom. TEL 44-1895-444055, FAX 44-1895-433602.

SOUTH AFRICA. STATISTICS SOUTH AFRICA. CENSUS OF SOCIAL, RECREATIONAL AND PERSONAL SERVICES - HAIRDRESSING AND BEAUTY SERVICES. see *BEAUTY CULTURE—Abstracting, Bibliographies, Statistics*

646.72 ZAF
SOUTH AFRICAN HAIRDRESSERS JOURNAL. Text in English. 1946. m. ZAR 62.70 domestic; ZAR 122 foreign (effective 2000). adv. bk.rev. charts; illus. **Document type:** *Trade.* **Description:** Journal for the hairdressing and cosmetology industry.
Formerly: S.A. Hairdressing and Beauty Culture (0036-0759)
Published by: (S A Hairdressers & Cosmetologists Association), Trade Focus Publications, PO Box 18733, Sunward Park, 1470, South Africa. TEL 27-011-9133044, FAX 27-011-9133045. Circ: 45,000 (paid and controlled).

646.726 616.5 USA
▼ **SPA 20/20;** covering the emerging sunless tanning & skincare markets. Text in English. 2003. q. USD 26 domestic; USD 32 in Canada; USD 82 elsewhere; USD 15 per issue (effective 2005). adv. **Document type:** *Magazine, Trade.* **Description:** Addresses the growth of the anti-aging skincare market. Also profiles successful salons offering skincare, bodycare, sunless tanning and anti-aging products to their customers.
Published by: Virgo Publishing, Inc., 3300 N. Central Ave., Ste 300, Phoenix, AZ 85012. TEL 480-990-1101, FAX 480-990-0819, cs@vpico.com, http://www.spa20-20.com, http://www.vpico.com. Pub. Jennifer Bolton TEL 480-990-1101 ext 1133. adv.: B&W page USD 2,950; trim 8.125 x 10.875. Circ: 15,600 (paid and free).

646.726 DEU
SPA MANAGER. Text in German. bi-m. EUR 62 domestic; EUR 74 foreign (effective 2004). **Document type:** *Magazine, Trade.*
Published by: Health and Beauty Business Media GmbH & Co. KG, Karl-Friedrich-Str 14-18, Karlsruhe, 76133, Germany. TEL 49-721-165833, FAX 49-721-165618, juergen.volpp@health-and-beauty.com, http://www.health-and-beauty.com. Circ: 6,500 (controlled).

646.724 DNK ISSN 0038-7266
SPEJLET. Text in Danish. 1912. m. DKK 175 (effective 1997). adv. bk.rev.
Published by: Dansk Frisoerforbund/Union of Danish Hairdressers and Beauticians, Lersoe Parkalle 21, Copenhagen Oe, 2100, Denmark. FAX 35-82-14-62. Ed. Poul Monggaard. Circ: 5,000.

646.724 USA
STAR HAIRDO. Text in English. bi-m. USD 2.95 newsstand/cover.
Published by: G C R Publishing Group, Inc., 1700 Broadway, 34th Fl, New York, NY 10019. TEL 212-541-7100, FAX 212-245-1241. Pub. Jason Goodman.

646.724 DEU
STAR LOOK. Text in German. 2002. m. EUR 3.20 newsstand/cover (effective 2002). adv. **Document type:** *Magazine, Consumer.*
Formerly (until 2002): Star Styling
Published by: Panini Verlags GmbH, Ravensstr 48, Nettetal, 41334, Germany. TEL 49-711-947680, FAX 49-711-94768830, info@panini-dino.de, http://www.panini-media.de. adv.: page EUR 3,500. Circ: 100,000 (paid and controlled).

646.724 ITA
STUDIO. Text in Italian. 1981. m. adv.
Published by: Studio s.r.l., Corso Casale, 410 20, Turin, TO 10132, Italy. TEL 39-11-8981502, FAX 39-11-8987073, TELEX 216258 STUDIO I. Ed. Fernando Trono. Circ: 24,000.

646.724 ITA
STUDIO U S A; hair fashion. Text in English. bi-m. (7/yr.). adv. **Description:** Covers new hairstyles and makeup from America and Europe. Includes personality profiles and interviews.
Published by: Studio s.r.l., Corso Casale, 410 20, Turin, TO 10132, Italy. TEL 11-898-1502, FAX 11-898-7073. adv.: B&W page USD 4,000, color page USD 6,000; trim 11.38 x 9.13.

646.724 DEU
STYLE. Text in German. q. adv. **Document type:** *Consumer.*
Address: Feldstr 75, Duesseldorf, 40479, Germany. TEL 0211-4912448, FAX 0211-4982844. Ed. Brigitte Schiller Domke. Adv. contact Karin Schulz. Circ: 93,922.

646.72 SWE ISSN 0346-0657
SVENSKA FRISOERTIDNINGEN. Text in Swedish. 1902. 9/yr. adv. 64 p./no. 3 cols./p.; **Document type:** *Magazine, Trade.* **Description:** Contains articles on exhibitions, hair fashion competitions, education and legislation for hairdressers in Sweden.
Published by: Sveriges Frisoerfoeretagare/Swedish Hairdressers Association, Frisoerernas Hus, Per Ekstroems Vaeg 3, Bromma, 16851, Sweden. TEL 46-8-870430, FAX 46-8-4458800, tidning@frisor.com, info@frisor.com, http://www.frisorforetagarna.se/omoss/frisortidningen/. Ed. Jens Kuhn. Adv. contact Rasmus Thomas. B&W page SEK 8,000, color page SEK 15,000; 164 x 254. Circ: 7,400.

646.724 CHE
SWISS HAIR PROFESSIONAL. Text in French, German, Italian. m. CHF 168 (effective 2000). adv. **Document type:** *Trade.* **Description:** Magazine for hairdressers, covering information about new hairstyles and association activities.
Formerly: Swiss Hair Intern
Published by: Coiffure Suisse/Swiss Association of Master Hairdressers, Moserstr 52, Bern, 3014, Switzerland. TEL 41-31-3327942, FAX 41-31-3314500. Ed. Rolf Fauser. Adv. contact Monika Moser. Circ: 8,000.

646.72 CHE
SWISS HAIR SHOP. Text in English. 1991. 24/yr. CHF 168 (effective 2000). adv. **Document type:** *Bulletin, Trade.* **Description:** Presents information on the activities of SAMH for fellow hairdressers.
Related titles: French ed.; German ed.; Italian ed.

Published by: Coiffure Suisse/Swiss Association of Master Hairdressers, Moserstr 52, Bern, 3014, Switzerland. TEL 41-31-3327942, FAX 41-31-3314500. Ed. Rolf Fauser. Circ: 8,000.

TABU TATTOO. see *ART*

646.726 DEU
TAN BIZ. Text in German. bi-m. EUR 53.50 domestic; EUR 65.50 foreign (effective 2004). adv. **Document type:** *Magazine, Trade.*
Published by: Health and Beauty Business Media GmbH & Co. KG, Karl-Friedrich-Str 14-18, Karlsruhe, 76133, Germany. TEL 49-721-165833, FAX 49-721-165618, juergen.volpp@health-and-beauty.com, http://www.health-and-beauty.com. Adv. contact Ruth Reif. Circ: 9,000 (paid).

646 USA
TEEN EXTREME. Text in English. 2001. USD 0.99 newsstand/cover (effective 2002). **Document type:** *Consumer.*
Published by: Compendium Systems Corporation, 346 N. Main St, Port Chester, NY 10573. TEL 914-935-1000, FAX 914-935-1063, editor@beauty-handbook.com. Ed. Joy Pecoraro. Pub. John McAuliffe.

646.724 USA ISSN 1533-8762
TEEN HAIRSTYLES & TRENDS. Variant title: Celebrity Worldwide Teen Hairstyles & Trends. Text in English. 12/yr. adv. **Description:** Keeps teenage girs up-to-date on the latest celebrity hairstyles. Also contains entertainment news.
Published by: Celebrity Worldwide, 20 E Sunrise Hwy, Ste 202, Valley Stream, NY 11581. TEL 516-823-1212, FAX 516-823-1561. Adv. contact Allison Cooper.

THOI TRANG TRE/NEW FASHION. see *WOMEN'S INTERESTS*

646.724 ESP ISSN 1139-4641
TOCADO; magazine de peluqueria y moda. Text in Spanish. 1956. 11/yr. EUR 45 domestic; EUR 125 in Europe; EUR 150 elsewhere (effective 2005). **Document type:** *Trade.*
Former titles (until 1984): Nuevo Tocado (1139-4803); (until 1979): Tocado (1139-479X)
Published by: Ediciones Cosmobelleza - Tocado y Vida Estetica, C Muntaner, 401, Barcelona, 08021, Spain. TEL 34-93-2414690, FAX 34-93-2001544, info@editocado.com, http://www.editocado.com/. Ed. Jaime Juez Codina. Pub. Antonio Castro Morera. Adv. contact Agustin Angosta. Circ: 15,000.

646.72 AUS
TOILETRIES MONITOR. Text in English. d. **Document type:** *Trade.*
Media: Online - full content.
Published by: Roy Morgan Research, PO Box 2282 U, Melbourne, VIC 3001, Australia. TEL 61-3-96296888, FAX 61-3-96291250, http://www.roymorgan.com.

646.724 DEU ISSN 1430-9122
TOP HAIR INTERNATIONAL. Text in English. 1985. s-m. EUR 88; EUR 5 newsstand/cover (effective 2005). adv. **Document type:** *Magazine, Consumer.*
Formerly (until 1995): Top Hair (0178-9805); Which was formed by the merger of (1969-1985): Friseurhandwerk Friseurspiegel (0016-1454); (1956-1985): Deutsche Friseur-Zeitung (0724-9799); Which was formerly (until 1980): Deutsche Friseur-Zeitung. Hauptausgabe (0011-491X)
Related titles: Dutch ed.; German ed.
Indexed: RASB.
Published by: Top Hair International GmbH, Eisenwerkstr 11, Gaggenau, 76571, Germany. TEL 49-7225-9160, FAX 49-7225-916305, info@tophair.de, http://www.tophair.de. Ed. Rolf Wilms. Adv. contact Uwe Wolff. B&W page EUR 4,130, color page EUR 5,980; trim 220 x 297. Circ: 26,251 (paid and controlled). **Subscr. in US to:** GLP International. TEL 201-871-1010, FAX 201-871-0870.

646.72 DEU ISSN 0939-6802
TOP TAN; Journal for Wellness and Tanning. Text in German. 1989. 6/yr. EUR 36.60; EUR 7 newsstand/cover (effective 2003). adv. 64 p./no.; **Document type:** *Magazine, Trade.*
Formerly (until 1990): Top in Form (0936-2541)
Published by: Terra Verlag GmbH, Neuhauser Str 21, Konstanz, 78464, Germany. TEL 49-7531-8122-0, FAX 49-7531-812299, info@terra-verlag.de, http://www.terra-verlag.de/toptan.html. Ed. Monika Baumann. Adv. contact Ulrike Buchta. B&W page EUR 2,040, color page EUR 3,408. Circ: 13,800 (paid).

646.724 DEU
TREND FRISUREN. Text in German. 1989. 2/yr. EUR 2.95 newsstand/cover (effective 2002). adv. **Document type:** *Magazine, Consumer.* **Description:** Presents advice and ideas on all the various hair styles and products available.
Published by: Marken Verlag GmbH, Bonner Str 323, Cologne, 50968, Germany. TEL 49-221-9574270, FAX 49-221-95742777, marken-info@markenverlag.de, http://www.markenverlag.de. Adv. contact Frank Krauthaeuser. page EUR 4,500; trim 210 x 285. Circ: 80,000 (paid and controlled).

TRENDI. see *WOMEN'S INTERESTS*

646.724 USA ISSN 1076-8092
TRY IT YOURSELF HAIR. Text in English. 1992. bi-m. USD 18; USD 23 foreign; GBP 2.50 newsstand/cover (effective 1999). adv. **Document type:** *Consumer.* **Description:** Provides black women with an abundance of hairstyles to choose from, beauty ideas, skin care advice, and sensational celebrity fashion styles.
Published by: T B W Publishing Group, 210 Rte 4 E, Ste 401, Paramus, NJ 07652. TEL 201-843-4004, FAX 201-843-8636. Ed. Adrienne Moore. Pub. John Blassingame. Adv. contact Steve Gross TEL 212-490-1895. Circ: 75,000. **Subscr. to:** PO Box 785, Mount Morris, IL 61054-7920. **Dist. in UK by:** Comag, Tavistock Works, Tavistock Rd, W Drayton, Middx UB7 7QX, United Kingdom. TEL 44-1895-444055, FAX 44-1895-433602.

TWOJ STYL. see *CLOTHING TRADE—Fashions*

646.724 USA ISSN 1523-4231
ULTIMATE BLACK HAIR GUIDE. Variant title: Premier Hair. Text in English. 1999. bi-m. USD 3.99 newsstand/cover; CND 4.99 newsstand/cover in Canada (effective 2001). adv. illus. back issues avail. **Document type:** *Consumer.*
Published by: Roxbury Media, LLC, 27 Glen Rd, PO Box 140, Sandy Hook, CT 06482. TEL 203-426-6533, FAX 203-426-9021. Pub. Kevin Montanaro. **Subscr. to:** Sunbelt Fulfillment Services, 307 Southgate Ct, Brentwood, TN 37027. **Dist. by:** Curtis Circulation Co., 730 River Road, New Milford, NJ 07646. TEL 201-634-7400, FAX 201-634-7499.

646.72 POL ISSN 0500-7194
URODA. Text in Polish. 1957. m. PLZ 64.80 domestic; PLZ 150 foreign (effective 2005). illus. **Document type:** *Magazine, Consumer.*
Published by: Edipresse Polska S A, Ul Wiejska 19, Warsaw, 00-480, Poland. TEL 48-22-5842516, FAX 48-22-5842500, uroda.redakcja@edipresse.pl, http://www.uroda.com.pl. Ed. Dorota Maj. Circ: 50,000.

646.72 CAN
VISAGE. Text in English, French. 1989. bi-m. USD 19 domestic; USD 28 foreign. adv.
Published by: Literati Publishing Corp., 50 Charles St E, Ste 966, Toronto, ON M4Y 2N9, Canada. TEL 416-963-9709, FAX 416-963-5119. Ed. Linda Wright. Circ: 31,491.

VIVER SANI E BELLI; settimanale di salute e bellezza. see *PHYSICAL FITNESS AND HYGIENE*

VOGUE (FRANCE). see *CLOTHING TRADE—Fashions*

VOGUE AUSTRALIA. see *CLOTHING TRADE—Fashions*

VOGUE ITALIA. see *CLOTHING TRADE—Fashions*

646.72 FRA ISSN 0042-8965
RA778.A1
VOTRE BEAUTE. Text in French. 1933. 10/yr. adv. bk.rev. **Document type:** *Magazine, Consumer.*
Incorporates (1946-1970): Votre Sante (1259-1815)
Published by: (Societe d'Editions Modernes Parisiennes), Groupe Marie Claire, 10 Boulevard des Freres Voisins, Issy-les-Moulineaux, 92792 Cedex 9, France. TEL 33-1-41468888, FAX 33-1-41468686, http://www.groupemarieclaire.com. Ed. Natalie Charon. Adv. contact Henri J Nijdam. Circ: 100,000.

WEDDING HAIR & BEAUTY. see *MATRIMONY*

646.724 DEU
WELT DER FRAU FRISUREN. Text in German. 4/yr. EUR 1.95 newsstand/cover (effective 2002). adv. **Document type:** *Magazine, Consumer.*
Published by: Klambt Verlag GmbH, Im Neudeck 1, Speyer, 67346, Germany. TEL 49-6232-310-0, FAX 49-6232-310226, anzeigen@klambt.de, http://www.klambt.de. adv.: B&W page EUR 3,320, color page EUR 4,114. Circ: 88,056 (paid and controlled).

WINK. see *CLOTHING TRADE—Fashions*

646.726 CHE
WOMAN'S BEAUTY; das Magazin fuer die Schoenheit. Text in German. q. CHF 15 (effective 2002). adv. **Document type:** *Magazine, Consumer.*
Published by: Mediax AG, Schneebergstr 7, Sankt Gallen, 9000, Switzerland. TEL 41-71-2264040, FAX 41-71-2264045, info@mediaxag.ch, http://www.mediaxag.ch. adv.: color page CHF 5,600; trim 225 x 300. Circ: 30,000 (paid and controlled).

WOMEN'S HEALTH & BEAUTY; exclusively at Rite Aid. see *WOMEN'S HEALTH*

646.72 HKG
YOUNG GIRL MAGAZINE. Text in Chinese. 1987. bi-w.
Address: B2, 14-F, Fuk Keung Ind. bldg.,, 66-68 Tong Mei Rd, Taikoktsui, Kowloon, Hong Kong. TEL 3910668, FAX 7893868. Ed. Vincent Leung. Circ: 65,000.

646.724 GBR ISSN 1472-0809
YOUR HAIR (BRISTOL). Text in English. 2001. 11/yr. GBP 25.74 domestic; GBP 40.39 in Europe; GBP 58.01 elsewhere (effective 2004). **Document type:** *Magazine, Consumer.*
Published by: Origin Publishing Ltd., 14th Fl, Tower House, Fairfax St, Bristol, BS1 3BN, United Kingdom. TEL 44-117-927-9009, FAX 44-117-934-9008, origin@subscription.co.uk, http://www.yourhair.co.uk, http://www.originpublishing.co.uk. Ed. Alison Worthington. Pub. Andy Marshall. Adv. contact Nicky Marsh.

646.724 GBR ISSN 0955-0372
YOUR HAIR (LONDON). Text in English. 1978. m. GBP 16. **Document type:** *Magazine, Consumer.*
Incorporates: Hair Fashion and Style
Published by: Health Digest Publications, 10 Woodberry Way, London, E4 7DX, United Kingdom. Ed. Pat Herbert.

646.72 USA
ZDROWIE, URODA I ZYCIE. Text in Polish. 1988. m. USD 25. adv. back issues avail. **Document type:** *Consumer.* **Description:** Provides health, fitness and beauty tips.
Published by: Back to Nature, Inc., 5627 N Milwaukee, Chicago, IL 60646. TEL 312-585-0402. Ed., Adv. contact Barbara Radlinski. Pub., R&P Marcin Hencz. page USD 325. Circ: 15,000.

646.72 ITA
ZEFFIRO CAPELLI. Text in Italian. 6/yr. **Document type:** *Magazine, Trade.*
Published by: Zeffiro Capelli & Company, Via Cavour 46, Turin, TO 10123, Italy. TEL 11-83-66-63, FAX 11-83-79-67. Ed. Paola Gallotti. Circ: 24,500.

ZEST; the health and beauty magazine. see *WOMEN'S INTERESTS*

BEAUTY CULTURE—Abstracting, Bibliographies, Statistics

016.66854 USA ISSN 0275-7044
CODEN: CACCD9
C A SELECTS. COSMETIC CHEMICALS. Text in English. s-w. USD 315 to non-members; USD 95 to members (effective 2005). **Document type:** *Abstract/Index.* **Description:** Covers the synthesis or manufacture of chemical substances of use in cosmetics; formulation of cosmetic preparations.
Published by: Chemical Abstracts Service (C A S) (Subsidiary of: American Chemical Society), 2540 Olentangy River Rd., Columbus, OH 43210-0012. TEL 614-447-3600, FAX 614-447-3713, help@cas.org, http://www.cas.org, http://caselects.cas.org. **Subscr. to:** PO Box 3012, Columbus, OH 43210. TEL 800-753-4227, FAX 614-447-3751.

016.6685 USA ISSN 1083-2688
CODEN: CSPFF7
C A SELECTS PLUS. FLAVORS & FRAGRANCES. Text in English. s-w. USD 315 to non-members; USD 95 to members (effective 2005). **Document type:** *Abstract/Index.* **Description:** Covers substances affecting senses of smell and taste; aromas, odorants, deodorants, perfumes, essential oils, flavoring materials, artificial sweeteners, acidulants, taste-modifying compounds; and synthetic methods for these compounds.
Formerly: C A Selects. Flavors and Fragrances (0148-2327)
Published by: Chemical Abstracts Service (C A S) (Subsidiary of: American Chemical Society), 2540 Olentangy River Rd., Columbus, OH 43210-0012. TEL 614-447-3600, FAX 614-447-3713, help@cas.org, http://www.cas.org, http://caselects.cas.org. **Subscr. to:** PO Box 3012, Columbus, OH 43210. TEL 800-753-4227, FAX 614-447-3751.

646.72021 ZAF
SOUTH AFRICA. STATISTICS SOUTH AFRICA. CENSUS OF SOCIAL, RECREATIONAL AND PERSONAL SERVICES - HAIRDRESSING AND BEAUTY SERVICES. Text in English. irreg., latest 1990. ZAR 4.40 domestic; ZAR 4.80 foreign (effective 2000). **Document type:** *Government.*
Formerly (until Aug.1998): South Africa. Central Statistical Service. Census of Social, Recreational and Personal Services - Hairdressing and Beauty Services
Published by: Statistics South Africa/Statistieke Suid-Afrika, Private Bag X44, Pretoria, 0001, South Africa. TEL 27-12-310-8911, FAX 27-12-310-8500, info@statssa.pwv.gov.za, http://www.statssa.gov.za.

BEAUTY CULTURE—Perfumes And Cosmetics

AERZTLICHE PRAXIS. DERMATOLOGIE. see *MEDICAL SCIENCES—Dermatology And Venereology*

668.5 AUT
AESTHETIK. Text in German. bi-m.
Address: Ziegelofengasse 31, Vienna, W 1050, Austria. TEL 01-551345. Ed. Gerhard Schuppich. Circ: 1,200.

B

668.5 ITA ISSN 1120-5415
ALLURE. (In 2 editions: trade and consumer) Text in Italian. 1985. 10/yr. EUR 31 (effective 2004). adv. **Document type:** *Magazine, Consumer.* **Description:** For operators in the perfume business: firm managers, beauty consultants, retailers and business agents.
Related titles: CD-ROM ed.: EUR 68 (effective 2004).
Published by: Target Editore s.r.l., Via Antonio Bondi 23/2, Bologna, BO 40138, Italy. TEL 39-051-342426, FAX 39-051-345554, allure@target-editore.it, http://www.allure.it/. Ed. Rosetta Sannelli. Pub. Luciano Parisini. R&P Diana Baravelli. Adv. contact Alessandro Parisini. Circ: 35,000 (controlled).

668.55 GBR
AVON CONTACT. Text in English. 1966. m. free. bk.rev. **Document type:** *Newspaper.*
Published by: Avon Cosmetics Ltd., Nunn Mills Rd, Northampton, United Kingdom. TEL 44-1604-232425, FAX 44-1604-618628. Ed., R&P Judith Wojtowicz. Circ: 3,000.

B

668.5 USA ISSN 0887-414X
BEAUTY AGE✶. Text in English. 1985. bi-m. USD 25. adv. back issues avail. **Description:** Describes cosmetic, fragrance and cosmetic accessory products.
Address: 75-144 Liberty Ave, No E-18, Jersey City, NJ 07306-5029. TEL 212-580-2756. Ed. Paul M Cohen. Circ: 27,719.

668.5 USA ISSN 0005-7487
BEAUTY FASHION. Text in English. 1916. m. USD 25 domestic; USD 50 in Canada & Mexico; USD 175 elsewhere; USD 10 newsstand/cover (effective 2005). adv. bk.rev. **Document type:** *Magazine, Trade.* **Description:** Covers perfumes, cosmetics, skincare and toiletries.
Published by: Beauty Fashion, Inc., 8 W 38th St, Ste 200, New York, NY 10018. TEL 212-840-8800, FAX 212-840-7246, http://www.beautyfashion.com. Ed., Pub., R&P John G Ledes. Adv. contacts Megan Shaner, Michelle Krell Kydd. B&W page USD 6,950, color page USD 7,900; trim 8.375 x 10.875. Circ: 18,396 (paid).

668.5 GBR
BEAUTY MAGAZINE. Text in English. m. GBP 53, GBP 93 (effective 2000). adv. **Document type:** *Trade.* **Description:** Provides trade information for beauty sales personnel.
Published by: Communications International Group, 307 Linen Hall, 162-168 Regent St, London, W1R 5TB, United Kingdom. TEL 44-20-7434-1530, FAX 44-20-7437-0915. Ed. Clare Grundy. Pub. Richard Koegh. Adv. contact Simon Whiten. Circ: 13,659 (controlled).

668.5 DEU
BEAUTY TALK. Text in German. bi-m. adv. **Document type:** *Magazine, Consumer.*
Published by: (parma Aurel GmbH & Co. KG), G & J Corporate Media GmbH (Subsidiary of: Gruner und Jahr AG & Co.), Griegstr 75, Hamburg, 22763, Germany. TEL 49-40-88303401, FAX 49-40-88303402, http://www.guj-corporate-media.de. Ed. Birgit Klitzing. Circ: 230,000 (controlled).

BLACK BEAUTY & HAIR. see *BEAUTY CULTURE*

668.55 GBR ISSN 1470-7160
BUSINESS RATIO. THE TOILETRIES & COSMETICS INDUSTRY. Text in English. 1978. a. GBP 275 (effective 2001). **Document type:** *Trade.*
Former titles (until 2000): Business Ratio Plus: The Toiletries and Cosmetics Industry (1357-6801); (until 1994): Business Ratio Report: Toiletries and Cosmetics Industry (0261-9636)
Published by: The Prospect Shop Ltd., Field House, 72 Oldfield Rd, Hampton, Middx TW12 2HQ, United Kingdom. TEL 44-20-8461-8730, 44-20-8481-8720, FAX 44-20-8783-1940, info@theprospectshop.co.uk.

C A SELECTS. COSMETIC CHEMICALS. see *BEAUTY CULTURE—Abstracting, Bibliographies, Statistics*

C A SELECTS PLUS. FLAVORS & FRAGRANCES. see *BEAUTY CULTURE—Abstracting, Bibliographies, Statistics*

C H P PACKER INTERNATIONAL. (Cosmetics, Healthcare, Pharmaceuticals) see *PACKAGING*

C H P PACKER INTERNATIONAL DIRECTORY (YEAR). (Cosmetics, Healthcare, Pharmaceuticals) see *PACKAGING*

665.55029 GBR
C I DIRECTORY. (Cosmetics International) Text in English. a. GBP 125 (effective 2000). adv. **Document type:** *Directory, Trade.*
Published by: Communications International Group, 307 Linen Hall, 162-168 Regent St, London, W1R 5TB, United Kingdom. TEL 44-20-7434-1530, FAX 44-20-7437-0915. Ed. Wendy Copping. Pub., R&P Felim O'Brien. Adv. contact Simon Whiten.

668.5 USA ISSN 1086-119X
CATEGORY REPORT - HEALTH & BEAUTY AIDS. Text in English. m. USD 1,100 (effective 2000). **Document type:** *Newsletter.* **Description:** Contains detailed product and packaging description and analysis of new foreign and domestic consumer packaged goods.
Published by: Marketing Intelligence Service Ltd., 6473D Route 64, Naples, NY 14512-9726. TEL 716-374-6326, FAX 716-374-5217, mi@productscan.com, http://www.productscan.com. Eds. Daniel Smith, Thomas Vierhile. Pub., R&P Daniel Smith.

668.5 USA ISSN 1086-1203
CATEGORY REPORT - HOUSEHOLD, PET & MISCELLANEOUS PRODUCTS. Text in English. m. USD 1,100 (effective 2000). back issues avail. **Document type:** *Newsletter.* **Description:** Contains detailed product and packaging description and analysis of new foreign and domestic consumer packaged goods.
Published by: Marketing Intelligence Service Ltd., 6473D Route 64, Naples, NY 14512-9726. TEL 716-374-6326, FAX 716-374-5217, mi@productscan.com, http://www.productscan.com. Eds. Daniel Smith, Thomas Vierhile. Pub., R&P Daniel Smith.

CHEMEXCIL EXPORT BULLETIN. see *BUSINESS AND ECONOMICS—International Commerce*

668.5 GRC
CHRYSES SELIDES ESTHITIKIS/AESTHETIC GOLDEN PAGES. Text in Greek. 1985. 3/yr. free to qualified personnel. bk.rev. back issues avail. **Document type:** *Trade.* **Description:** Lists beauticians and cosmetologists in Greece and Cyprus.
Published by: I C O International, 3A Barbanou St, PO Box 190 25, Athens, 117 10, Greece. TEL 30-1-9017-806, FAX 30-1-9016-663. Ed. Stella Tsirimocou. Pub. Dimitrios E Tsirimocos. Circ: 12,000.

668.55 ITA
COSMESI. Text in Italian. 1969. 2/yr. adv.
Published by: Schwegler Editore s.n.c., Via Senato, 18, Milan, MI 20121, Italy. TEL 2-79-50-75, FAX 2-76-00-68-92. Ed. Carla Catani. Circ: 12,000.

668.5 USA ISSN 1069-1448
COSMETIC BENCH REFERENCE. Text in English. a. USD 190 domestic; USD 210 foreign (effective 2001). **Document type:** *Journal, Trade.*
Published by: Allured Publishing Corp., 362 S Schmale Rd, Carol Stream, IL 60188-2787. TEL 630-653-2155, FAX 630-653-2192, allured@allured.com, http://www.cbr.thecosmeticsite.com, http://www.allured.com.

668.5 ITA ISSN 1125-6222
COSMETIC NEWS; bimestrale tecnico-scientifico di cosmetologia e dermocosmesi. Text in Italian; Summaries in English. 1978. 6/yr. adv. bk.rev. 84 p./no.; back issues avail. **Document type:** *Magazine, Consumer.* **Description:** Deals with scientific advances in the cosmotology industry.
Indexed: CIN, ChemAb, ChemTitl.
Published by: SEPEM s.r.l., Via Grado 9, Milan, MI 20125, Italy. TEL 39-02-26825553, FAX 39-02-26823952, sepem@libero.it. Ed., R&P, Adv. contact Franco Mattei. Circ: 3,000 (controlled).

668.5 USA ISSN 1087-5441
COSMETIC - PERSONAL CARE PACKAGING. Text in English. 1996. bi-m. free to qualified personnel. adv. back issues avail. **Document type:** *Magazine, Trade.* **Description:** Provides decision makers in cosmetic and personal care markets information on trends, new materials, containers, and latest developments in machinery and equipment.
Related titles: Online - full text ed.
Indexed: IPackAb.
Published by: Canon Communications LLC, 11444 W Olympic Blvd, Ste 900, Los Angeles, CA 90064-1549. TEL 310-445-4269, FAX 310-445-4299, cpcpkg@aol.com, http://www.cpcpkg.com, http://www.cancom.com. Ed. John Bethune. Adv. contact Patricia Spinner. B&W page USD 3,185, color page USD 4,070. Circ: 8,000 (controlled).

COSMETIC SCIENCE AND TECHNOLOGY SERIES. see *MEDICAL SCIENCES*

668.55 GBR
COSMETIC SCIENCE MONOGRAPHS. Text in English. 1997. irreg., latest vol.2, 1998. **Document type:** *Monographic series.*
—BLDSC (3477.175770).
Published by: Micelle Press, 10-12 Ullswater Cres., Weymouth, Dorset DT3 5HE, United Kingdom. TEL 44-1305-781574, http://www.wdi.co.uk. **Dist. in US and Canada by:** Scholuim International Inc., 14 Vanderventer Ave, PO Box 1519, Port Washington, NY 11050-0306. TEL 516-767-7171.

668.5 ITA ISSN 1127-6312
COSMETIC TECHNOLOGY; rivista di scienze cosmetologiche. Text in Italian. 1998. bi-m.
—BLDSC (3477.175770).
Published by: C E C Editore, Viale Legioni Romane 55, Milan, 20147, Italy. TEL 39-02-4152943, FAX 39-02-416737, ceclebovich@tin.it.

668.5 GBR ISSN 0305-0319
TP983 CODEN: CSWNAR
COSMETIC WORLD NEWS; the international news magazine of the perfumery, cosmetics and toiletries industry. Text in English. 1950. 6/yr. USD 192. adv. bk.rev. abstr. reprint service avail. from PQC. **Document type:** *Trade.*
Formerly (until 1974): International Perfumer (0020-8248)
Related titles: Microfilm ed.: (from PQC); Online - full text ed.: (from Gale Group).
Indexed: ChemAb, KES, PROMT.
Published by: World News Publications, 130 Wigmore St, London, W1H 0AT, United Kingdom. FAX 44-171-487-5436. Ed. M A Murray Pearce. Circ: 6,000.

668.5 ESP ISSN 0212-3991
COSMETICA Y AROMATICA. Text in Spanish. 1983. 6/yr.
Address: Travesera de Gracia 15, Barcelona, 08021, Spain. TEL 3-204-79-33, FAX 3-209-69-18.

668.5 USA ISSN 0361-4387
TP983 CODEN: CTOIDG
COSMETICS AND TOILETRIES; the international journal of cosmetic technology. Text in English. 1906. m. USD 98 domestic; USD 137 in Canada; USD 189 elsewhere (effective 2004). adv. bk.rev. abstr.; bibl.; charts; illus.; mkt.; tr.lit. index. reprint service avail. from PQC. **Document type:** *Magazine, Trade.* **Description:** Covers ingredient application, formulation ideas and research.
Former titles (until 1975): Cosmetics and Perfumery (0090-6581); (until 1973): American Cosmetics and Perfumery (0090-5852); (until 1972): American Perfumer and Cosmetics (0003-0392); (until 1962): American Perfumer (0096-0896); (until 1960): American Perfumer and Aromatics (0517-4252); American Perfumer and Essential Oil Review (0161-9977); (until 1939): American Perfumer, Cosmetics, Toilet Preparations; (until 1936): American Perfumer (0096-087X); American Perfumer and Essential Oil Review (0096-0888); American Perfumer (0162-8593)
Related titles: Microform ed.: (from PQC); Online - full text ed.: (from Gale Group, H.W. Wilson, O C L C Online Computer Library Center, Inc.).
Indexed: AS&TI, BPI, CIN, ChemAb, ChemTitl, ESPM, EngInd, H&SSA, IPA, MSB, PROMT.
—BLDSC (3477.184500), CASDDS, CINDOC, CISTI, Ei, GNLM, IE, Infotrieve, ingenta, Linda Hall. **CCC.**
Published by: Allured Publishing Corp., 362 S Schmale Rd, Carol Stream, IL 60188-2787. TEL 630-653-2155, FAX 630-653-2192, cosmtoil@allured.com, allured@allured.com, http://www.cosmeticsandtoiletries.com/, http://www.allured.com. Ed. Laruie DiBerardino. Pub., Adv. contact Nancy Allured. B&W page USD 2,130, color page USD 3,205. Circ: 5,200 (paid and free).

COSMETICS & TOILETRIES & HOUSEHOLD PRODUCTS MARKETING NEWS IN JAPAN. see *BUSINESS AND ECONOMICS—Marketing And Purchasing*

668.55 USA ISSN 1063-2107
COSMETICS COUNTER UPDATE✶. Text in English. 1992. bi-m. USD 25; USD 35 foreign. back issues avail. **Document type:** *Newsletter, Consumer.* **Description:** Reviews and evaluations by Paula Begoun, a consumer advocate of new beauty products.
Related titles: E-mail ed.; Online - full text ed.: 1992.
Published by: Beginning Press, 13075 Gateway Dr, Seattle, WA 98168-3342. TEL 206-723-6300, 800-831-4088, FAX 206-722-5765, dearpaula@cosmeticscop.com, http://www.cosmeticscop.com. Ed. Paula Begoun. Circ: 5,000 (paid).

668.55 BRA ISSN 0103-4030
COSMETICS E TOILETRIES. Variant title: Revista de Cosmeticos & Tecnologia. Text in Portuguese. 1989. bi-m. BRL 55, USD 55 (effective 2001). adv. **Document type:** *Trade.* **Description:** Presents scientific articles and information for cosmetics researchers.
Published by: Tecnopress Editora, Rua Alvaro de Menezes, 74, Vl Mariana, Sao Paulo, SP 04007-020, Brazil. TEL 55-11-3884-8756, FAX 55-11-3887-8271, tpress@uol.com.br. Ed. Hamilton Dos Santos. Adv. contact Edesia Gaiao TEL 55-11-3884-8756. page BRL 2,800. Circ: 5,000.

668.55 GBR ISSN 0963-6137
CODEN: COSIDZ
COSMETICS INTERNATIONAL; the news bulletin of the cosmetics industry. Text in English. 1975. bi-w. GBP 348 domestic; GBP 362 rest of Europe; USD 606 in North America (effective 2003); includes C I Directory. adv. stat.; tr.lit. back issues avail. **Document type:** *Newsletter, Trade.* **Description:** Covers market trends, mergers, acquisitions, financial reports and company profiles.
Related titles: Online - full text ed.: (from Florida Center for Library Automation, Gale Group, Northern Light Technology, Inc., O C L C Online Computer Library Center, Inc.).
Indexed: B&I, IPackAb, LRI.
—BLDSC (3477.187000).

Published by: Communications International Group, 307 Linen Hall, 162-168 Regent St, London, W1R 5TB, United Kingdom. TEL 44-20-7434-1530, FAX 44-20-7437-0915, cosmeticsint@1530.com, http://www.cosmeticsint.co.uk. Ed. Wendy Copping. Pub. Felim O'Brien. R&P, Adv. contact Simon Whiten. B&W page GBP 950, color page GBP 1,290; trim 210 x 297. Circ: 3,000 (paid). **Subscr. addr.:** TCO, Unit 1, Hainault Rd, Little Heath, Romford RM6 5RX, United Kingdom. TEL 44-1815-970181, FAX 44-1815-974040. **Dist. by:** Mercury VMD, Mills Rd, Quarry Wood, Aylesford, Kent ME20 7WZ, United Kingdom. TEL 44-1622-792111, FAX 44-1622-792444.

668.55 GBR ISSN 1358-3387
COSMETICS INTERNATIONAL. COSMETIC PRODUCTS REPORT. Text in English. 1994. m. GBP 235 in United Kingdom; GBP 285 rest of Europe; GBP 298 rest of world rest of Europe (effective 2000). adv. **Document type:** *Trade.* **Description:** Covers all product launches of cosmetics worldwide.
Formerly: Cosmetics international. New Products Report
Related titles: Online - full text ed.: (from Gale Group).
Published by: Communications International Group, 307 Linen Hall, 162-168 Regent St, London, W1R 5TB, United Kingdom. TEL 44-20-7434-1530, FAX 44-20-7437-0915. Ed. Wendy Copping. Pub., R&P Felim O'Brien. Adv. contact Simon Whiten.

668.55 USA
COSMETICS: LATIN AMERICAN INDUSTRIAL REPORT✶. (Avail. for each of 22 Latin American countries) Text in English. 1985. a. USD 435; per country report.
Published by: Aquino Productions, P O Box 15760, Stamford, CT 06901-0760.

D C A T DIGEST. see *PHARMACY AND PHARMACOLOGY*

D W: DROGISTEN WEEKBLAD; onafhankelijk vakblad voor drogisterij, parfumerie, reformzaak. see *PHARMACY AND PHARMACOLOGY*

DERMATOLOGIE PRATIQUE. see *MEDICAL SCIENCES—Dermatology And Venereology*

DIARY. see *CLOTHING TRADE—Fashions*

668.55 USA ISSN 1073-290X
DR. HAIR COSMETOLOGY NEWS JOURNAL. Text in English. 1994. bi-m. USD 12. charts; illus. **Document type:** *Consumer.* **Description:** Acts as a forum for professional and student cosmetologists.
Published by: (Dr. Hair Product Company), Michael's Hair Design Studio, 12777 Jones Rd, Ste 425, Houston, TX 77070. TEL 713-897-9171, FAX 713-370-8887. Ed. R Michael Tucker. adv.: page USD 380. Circ: 1,500.

668.5 DEU ISSN 0366-9645
CODEN: DRFSDW
DRAGOCO REPORT. Text in German. 1956. 4/yr. free. bibl.; charts; illus.; stat. 60 p./no.; back issues avail. **Document type:** *Magazine, Trade.* **Description:** Presents articles concerning new fragrance and flavor products of company.
Incorporates (1956-1998): Dragoco Report: Flavoring Information Service (0720-1249)
Related titles: Online - full text ed.; French ed.: ISSN 0174-321X; English ed.: ISSN 0931-5454; Spanish ed.: ISSN 0174-3236; Portuguese ed.: ISSN 0932-9374.
Indexed: ChemAb, DIP, FS&TA, IBZ, IPA.
—CASDDS. **CCC.**
Published by: Dragoco Gerberding & Co. AG, Dragocostr 1, Holzminden, 37603, Germany. TEL 49-5531-97-0, FAX 49-5531-971391, info@eu.dragoco.com, http://www.dragoco.com. Eds. Katja Derow, Marlies Knirsch. Circ: 20,000.

668.5 ESP ISSN 1135-4224
DROGUERIA & PERFUMERIA; revista professional del sector de la drogueria y perfumeria. Variant title: D & P. Text in Spanish. 1985. m. EUR 53.24 domestic; EUR 58.55 foreign (effective 2004). adv. **Document type:** *Trade.*
Formerly (until 1993): Tiendas de Drogueria y Perfumeria (0213-0858)
Published by: Tecnipublicaciones Espana, S.L., Avda de Manoteras 44, 3a Planta, Madrid, 28050, Spain. TEL 34-91-2972000, FAX 34-91-2972154, tp@tecnipublicaciones.com, http://www.tecnipublicaciones.com. adv.: B&W page EUR 1,160, color page EUR 1,665; bleed 210 x 285. Circ: 15,000.

668.5 GBR ISSN 1364-9922
ESPRIT. Text in English. 1988. m. GBP 75 in United Kingdom; GBP 100 in Europe; GBP 125 elsewhere (effective 2001). adv. **Document type:** *Trade.* **Description:** Information source for the perfumery, cosmetics, skincare and premium toiletries industry.
Indexed: ABM, ArtHuCI, IndIslam.
Published by: Sandron Publishing, Bouverie House, 43A Effra Rd, Wimbledon, London, SW19 8PS, United Kingdom. TEL 44-20-8543-9799, FAX 44-20-8540-6519, esprit@esprit-magazine.co.uk. Ed. Lorraine Wilson Morris. Pub., R&P Andrea Jones. Adv. contact Jonathan Charles. color page GBP 2,100. Circ: 5,400.

668.5 ESP ISSN 1576-351X
ESTETICISTAS, FEDERACION NACIONAL. Text in Spanish. 1986. bi-m. adv. bk.rev.
Formerly (until 1998): Estetica Espanola (1130-0590)
Published by: Federacion Nacional de Asociacioes de Esteticistas, San Bernardo, 8 3o, Madrid, 28015, Spain. TEL 34-91-5213765, FAX 34-5212434, info@fanae.org, http://www.fanae.org/revista.php. Ed. G Garcia Vaquero. Circ: 7,000.

668.5 FRA ISSN 1146-5794
ESTHETICA PROFESSIONNEL. Text in French. 1985. 10/yr.
Formerly (until 1990): Esthetica (0769-6507)
Address: 58 rue Saint Georges, Paris, 75009, France. TEL 42-85-51-00, FAX 42-85-41-45, TELEX 281 078 F. Ed. Joelle Ilous. Circ: 10,000.

668.5 DEU ISSN 0944-8942
EURO COSMETICS; the international magazine for cosmetics and fragrances - das internationale Fachmagazin fuer die Kosmetika- und Riechstoff-Industrie. Text in German, English. 1993. 11/yr. EUR 155 domestic; EUR 175 foreign (effective 2003). adv. **Document type:** *Magazine, Trade.* **Description:** Discusses trends in the cosmetics and perfume industries.
—BLDSC (3829.230608), IE, ingenta. **CCC.**
Published by: Inter-Euro Medien GmbH, Kaiser-Wilhem-Str 76, Starnberg, 82319, Germany. TEL 49-8151-559260, FAX 49-8151-5592611, info@eurocosmetics-magazine.com, http://www.eurocosmetics-magazine.com. Ed. Anja Kunzmann. Pub. Detlev Melcher. Adv. contact Helga Reichert. Circ: 950 (paid); 5,980 (controlled).

668.5 GBR ISSN 0957-1515
EUROPEAN COSMETIC MARKETS. Text in English. 1983. m. GBP 675; GBP 720 in Europe; USD 1,195 in US & Canada. adv. **Document type:** *Trade.* **Description:** Publishes market reports, along with news and product launches in the cosmetics industry.
Related titles: Online - full text ed.: (from Factiva, Gale Group, Northern Light Technology, Inc., O C L C Online Computer Library Center, Inc.).
Indexed: B&I.
—IE, Infotrieve.
Published by: Wilmington Publishing Ltd. (Subsidiary of: Wilmington Group Plc), Maidstone Rd, Footscray, Sidcup, Kent DA14 5HZ, United Kingdom. TEL 44-1322-277788, FAX 44-1322-276476, wbp@wilmington.co.uk. Ed. Charlotte Sharpe. Circ: 5,000 (paid).

668.5 ESP
EXPERTOS EN ESTETICA. Text in Spanish. 1977. 11/yr. EUR 50 domestic; EUR 84 foreign (effective 2005). adv. **Description:** Provides data about the latest aesthetic treatment and make-up trends.
Formerly (until 2002): La Estetica Profesional (0214-5774)
Published by: Editorial Tecnico Cientifica de Prensa Hispano Americana S.L., C/ Gascuena, 41, Madrid, 28022, Spain. TEL 34-91-747-8000, FAX 34-91-747-9056, http://www.expertosenestetica.net/revista-estetica/la-revista.asp. Ed., Pub. Angeles Mora. Adv. contact Patricia Cordero. Circ: 20,000.

668.5 ITA
EXPORT MAGAZINE - BEAUTY DISTRIBUTOR. Text in English, Italian. 10/yr.
Address: Via Romolo Gessi, 28, Milan, MI 20146, Italy. TEL 2-42-39-443, FAX 2-412-34-05. Ed. Giuseppe Tirabasso. Circ: 15,000.

668.5 USA ISSN 1070-1281
KF3896.A15
F M A REGULATORY AND LEGISLATIVE UPDATE. Text in English. 1990. q. looseleaf. back issues avail. **Document type:** *Newsletter.*
Former titles (until 1991): F M A Update, Regulatory and Legislative News (1070-1273); (until 1990): F M A Regulatory Update (1070-1265)
Published by: Fragrance Materials Association of the United States, 1620 I St, N W, Ste 950, Washington, DC 20006. TEL 202-293-5800, FAX 202-463-8998. Ed. Glenn Roberts. Circ: 300.

FARMACIA DISTRIBUICAO. see *PHARMACY AND PHARMACOLOGY*

FINANCIAL SURVEY. TOILETRIES AND COSMETICS INDUSTRY; company data for success. see *BUSINESS AND ECONOMICS—Trade And Industrial Directories*

FLAVOUR & FRAGRANCE JOURNAL. see *CHEMISTRY—Organic Chemistry*

FOOD, DRUG, COSMETIC, AND MEDICAL DEVICE LAW DIGEST. see *LAW*

FOR FORMULATION CHEMISTS ONLY. see *CHEMISTRY—Analytical Chemistry*

668.5 USA
FRAGRANCE FORUM. Text in English. q. USD 100 domestic to non-members; USD 130 foreign to non-members; USD 75 domestic to members; USD 105 foreign to members. bk.rev. charts; illus. back issues avail. **Document type:** *Newsletter.* **Description:** Provides information on the marketing of fragrance in the 90s. Addresses changing trends, technologies, sociological developments and future markets.
Related titles: Online - full text ed.
Published by: Fragrance Foundation, 145 E 32nd St, New York, NY 10016. TEL 212-725-2755, FAX 212-779-9058, address-info@fragrance.org, http://www.fragrance.org. Ed. Annette Green.

668.5 JPN ISSN 0288-9803
FRAGRANCE JOURNAL/FUREGURANSU JANARU. Text in Japanese. m. JPY 2,800 per issue domestic; JPY 34,000 per issue foreign (effective 2003). **Document type:** *Journal, Trade.*
—BLDSC (4032.112300), IE, ingenta.
Published by: Fureguransu Janarusha/Fragrance Journal Ltd., 1-5-9 Iidabashi, Chiyoda-ku, Tokyo, 102-0072 , Japan. TEL 81-3-32640125, FAX 81-3-32640148, http://www.fragrance-j.co.jp/books/index.html.

668.54 AUS
FRAGRANCES OF THE WORLD (YEAR)/PARFUMS DU MONDE. Text in English, French. a., latest 2001. **Document type:** *Directory, Trade.* **Description:** Contains an encyclopedic references for perfumers and evaluators, industry professionals and collectors.
Related titles: CD-ROM ed.: Fragrance Adviser CD-ROM.
Published by: Michael Edwards & Co., Blakehurst, PO Box 14, Sydney, NSW 2221, Australia. mk@fragrance-editions.com, http://www.fragrance-editions.com/home.htm.

668.5 CHE
FUER SIE MADAME. Text in French, German. 10/yr. adv. **Document type:** *Consumer.*
Address: Merkurstr 34, Zuerich, 8032, Switzerland. TEL 41-1-2524522, FAX 41-1-2611986. Ed. Anuschka Moser. Pub. Ruedi Schueder. Adv. contact Ursula McCormack. Circ: 140,000.

668.55 RUS
GAZETA DLYA ZHENSHCHIN: DOMA RUSSKOI KOSMETIKI. Text in English, Russian. 1990. m. USD 20 foreign. adv. **Document type:** *Newspaper.*
Published by: Uchebno-Nauchnoizdatel'skii Tsentr Doma Russkoi Kosmetiki, Ul Kosygina 15, etazh 3-l, Moscow, 117334, Russian Federation. TEL 7-095-9298224, FAX 7-095-9398224, drk@imbs.com, http://drk.imbs.com. Ed. S V Sikorskaya. Pub. Anna Sikorskaya. R&P Svetlana Sikorskaya TEL 7-095-9398225. Adv. contact Dmitri Kuznetsov. page USD 2,000. Circ: 50,000 (controlled). **US dist. addr.:** East View Information Services, 3020 Harbor Ln. N., Minneapolis, MN 55447. TEL 612-550-0961.

668.55 USA ISSN 1523-9470
RS1 CODEN: DCINAQ
GLOBAL COSMETIC INDUSTRY. Text in English. 1914. 13/yr., latest vol.166. USD 43 domestic; USD 59 in Canada & Mexico; USD 99 elsewhere; USD 5 newsstand/cover; free to qualified personnel (effective 2005). adv. bk.rev. abstr.; illus.; mkt.; pat.; tr.mk. index. reprints avail. **Document type:** *Magazine, Trade.* **Description:** Formulation, raw material procurement, production and packaging for marketers and manufacturers of cosmetics, personal products and OTC pharmaceuticals.
Former titles (until 1999): D C I (1096-4819); (until May 1997): Drug and Cosmetic Industry (0012-6527); Which incorporated (1931-1997): Drug and Cosmetic Catalog (0732-0760)
Related titles: Microform ed.: (from PMC, PQC); Online - full text ed.: (from EBSCO Publishing, Factiva, Florida Center for Library Automation, Gale Group, H.W. Wilson, Northern Light Technology, Inc., O C L C Online Computer Library Center, Inc., ProQuest Information & Learning, The Dialog Corporation).
Indexed: ABIn, B&I, BPI, BiolAb, BusI, CBNB, CIN, Cadscan, ChemAb, ChemTitl, CurCont, CurPA, ESPM, H&SSA, HlthInd, IPA, IPackAb, LeadAb, PROMT, RefZh, T&II, ToxAb, Zincscan.
—BLDSC (4195.384850), CASDDS, GNLM, IE, Infotrieve, ingenta, Linda Hall. **CCC.**
Published by: Allured Publishing Corp., 362 S Schmale Rd, Carol Stream, IL 60188-2787. TEL 630-653-2155, FAX 630-653-2192, gci@allured.com, allured@allured.com, http://www.globalcosmetic.com/ME2/Audiences/default.asp, http://www.allured.com. Ed. Karen Newman. Circ: 16,129 (paid).

668.55 USA
GRAYSON REPORT✶. Text in English. 1972. bi-m. USD 45 (effective 1988). **Document type:** *Trade.* **Description:** Covers marketing analysis for the cosmetics and toiletries industry.
Published by: Grayson Associates, Inc., 30482 Via Andalusia, San Juan Capistrano, CA 92675-1730. TEL 805-564-1313, FAX 805-564-8800. Ed. Suzanne Grayson.

GUIDE INTERNATIONAL DES FOURNISSEURS DE LA BEAUTE/GENERAL DIRECTORY OF THE PERFUME AND COSMETIC INDUSTRY. see *BUSINESS AND ECONOMICS—Trade And Industrial Directories*

668.55 DEU ISSN 1615-0694
HAND & NAILS. Text in German. 2000. q. EUR 27 domestic; EUR 30.10 in Europe; EUR 90 elsewhere; EUR 6.75 newsstand/cover (effective 2005). adv. **Document type:** *Magazine, Trade.* **Description:** Contains information for the hand and nail cosmetics industry.
Published by: KOSMETIK International Verlag GmbH, Eisenwerkstr 11, Gaggenau, 76571, Germany. TEL 49-7225-9160, FAX 49-7225-916109, ki@ki-verlag.de, http://www.ki-online.de/html/hand-nails.html. Ed. Franka Haenig. Adv. contact Birgit Hartmann. B&W page EUR 1,715, color page EUR 2,795; trim 210 x 297. Circ: 6,348 (paid and controlled).

HOUSEHOLD & PERSONAL PRODUCTS INDUSTRY; the magazine for the detergent, soap, cosmetic and toiletries, wax, polish and aerosol industries. see *BUSINESS AND ECONOMICS—Marketing And Purchasing*

668.5 540 DEU ISSN 1520-4561
TP983
I F S C C MAGAZINE. (International Federation of Societies of Cosmetic Chemists) Text in English. 1998. q. EUR 220 (effective 2005). **Document type:** *Journal, Academic/Scholarly.*
—BLDSC (4363.343552).
Published by: International Federation of Societies of Cosmetic Chemists, IFSCC Magazine Publishing Offices, Verlag fuer Chemische Industrie, Beethovenstr. 16, Augsburg, 86150, Germany. ifscc.mag@sofw.com, http://www.ifscc.org/pubs.htm. Adv. contact Natalie Bader.

668.54 ITA
IMAGINE. Text in Italian. 1975. bi-w. adv. illus. **Document type:** *Magazine, Consumer.*
Related titles: Online - full text ed.
Published by: (Federazione Nazionale Profumieri Italiani), Sfera Editore SpA (Subsidiary of: R C S Mediagroup), Via Angelo Rizzoli 2, Milan, MI 20132, Italy. Ed. Antonella Grua. Circ: 12,000 (paid and controlled).

668.54 IND ISSN 0019-607X
CODEN: IPERAS
INDIAN PERFUMER. Text in English. 1957. q. USD 150 (effective 2003). adv. bk.rev. abstr.; charts; illus.; pat.; stat.
Indexed: BiolAb, CIN, ChemAb, ChemTitl, CurCont, RiceAb.
—BLDSC (4425.500000), CASDDS, IE, ingenta.
Published by: Essential Oil Association of India, Dua Complex, 24 Veer Savarkar Block, Sakarpur, Vikas Marg, New Delhi, 110 092, India. FAX 11-2204284, TELEX 31-62434 SIVA IN. Ed. S N Sobti. Circ: 500. **Subscr. to:** Scientific Publishers, 5-A New Pali Rd., Near Hotel Taj Hari Mahal, PO Box 91, Jodhpur, Rajasthan 342 003, India. info@scientificpub.com, http://www.scientificpub.com.

668.5 GBR ISSN 0142-5463
TP983 CODEN: IJCMDW
➤ **INTERNATIONAL JOURNAL OF COSMETIC SCIENCE.** Text in English, French. bi-m. GBP 693 combined subscription in Europe to institutions print & online eds.; USD 1,282 combined subscription in the Americas to institutions & Caribbean (print & online eds.); GBP 763 combined subscription elsewhere to institutions print & online eds. (effective 2006). adv. back issues avail.; reprint service avail. from ISI,PSC. **Document type:** *Journal, Academic/Scholarly.* **Description:** Provides a current presentation of pure and applied scientific research in cosmetics, toiletries, perfumery, and allied fields.
Related titles: Online - full text ed.: ISSN 1468-2494. GBP 658 in Europe to institutions; USD 1,218 in the Americas to institutions & Caribbean; GBP 725 elsewhere to institutions (effective 2006) (from Blackwell Synergy, EBSCO Publishing, Gale Group, IngentaConnect, O C L C Online Computer Library Center, Inc., Ovid Technologies, Inc., Swets Information Services).
Indexed: ASCA, BIOSIS Prev, BiolAb, CIN, CISA, ChemAb, ChemTitl, CurCont, DBA, ESPM, EngInd, ExcerpMed, H&SSA, IPA, ISR, IndMed, RefZh, RiskAb, SCI.
—BLDSC (4542.178400), CASDDS, CISTI, Ei, GNLM, IE, Infotrieve, ingenta. **CCC.**
Published by: (Societe Francaise de Cosmetologie FRA, Society of Cosmetic Scientists), Blackwell Publishing Ltd., 9600 Garsington Rd, Oxford, OX4 2ZG, United Kingdom. TEL 44-1865-776868, FAX 44-1865-714591, customerservices@oxon.blackwellpublishing.com, http://www.blackwellpublishing.com/journals/ICS. Ed. Anthony Rawlings. Pub. Elaine Stott. R&P Lindsay Doyle. Adv. contact Martine Cariou Keen. Circ: 2,750.

➤ **INTERNATIONAL PHARMACEUTICAL REGULATORY MONITOR**; a legal, medical & scientific information series for the pharmaceutical and biotech industry. see *PHARMACY AND PHARMACOLOGY*

➤ **INTERNATIONAL PRODUCT ALERT.** see *BUSINESS AND ECONOMICS—Marketing And Purchasing*

668.55 JPN ISSN 0287-1238
CODEN: NKKAEV
JAPANESE COSMETIC SCIENCE SOCIETY. JOURNAL. Text in Japanese. 1976. q. JPY 12,000. adv. bk.rev. **Document type:** *Academic/Scholarly.*
—BLDSC (4809.253000), CASDDS. **CCC.**
Published by: Japanese Cosmetic Science Society, 3-3165 Higashi-Tamagawagakuen, Machida-shi, Tokyo-to 194-0042, Japan. FAX 81-427-23-3585. **Dist. by:** Business Center for Academic Societies Japan, 5-16-19 Honkomagome, Bunkyo-ku, Tokyo 113-0021, Japan. TEL 81-3-58145811.

668.5 USA ISSN 1525-7886
TP983.A1 CODEN: JSCCA5
➤ **JOURNAL OF COSMETIC SCIENCE.** Text in English. 1947. bi-m. USD 200 to non-members; free membership (effective 2004). adv. bk.rev. **Document type:** *Journal, Academic/Scholarly.* **Description:** Studies the sciences underlying cosmetics.
Formerly (until 1998): Society of Cosmetic Chemists. Journal (0037-9832)
Related titles: Microform ed.: (from PMC).
Indexed: ASCA, AgeL, CCI, CIN, ChemAb, ChemTitl, CurCont, EngInd, IPA, RCI.
—BLDSC (4965.430400), CASDDS, CISTI, Ei, GNLM, IDS, IE, ingenta, Linda Hall. **CCC.**
Published by: Society of Cosmetic Chemists, 120 Wall St, Ste 2400, New York, NY 10005-4088. TEL 212-668-1500, FAX 212-668-1504, dscelso@scconline.org, http://www.scconline.org. Ed. Mindy Goldstein. adv.: B&W page USD 450, color page USD 900; trim 6.75 x 9.75. Circ: 4,200.

668.54 USA ISSN 1041-2905
TP958 CODEN: JEOREG
JOURNAL OF ESSENTIAL OIL RESEARCH. Text in English. 1989. bi-m. USD 660 in US & Canada; USD 690 elsewhere (effective 2005). adv. **Document type:** *Journal, Academic/Scholarly.* **Description:** Contains original research papers on all aspects of production, processing and analysis of essential oils and related natural products relative to their use in flavor and fragrances.
Related titles: Online - full text ed.: (from EBSCO Publishing, H.W. Wilson, O C L C Online Computer Library Center, Inc., ProQuest Information & Learning).
Indexed: AbHyg, AgBio, Agr, AgrForAb, B&BAb, BBCI, BPI, BibAg, BioCN&I, BioEngAb, C&ISA, CIN, CPA, ChemAb, ChemTitl, ChemoAb, CurCont, E&CAJ, ESPM, EngInd, FCA, FPA, FS&TA, ForAb, HerbAb, HortAb, IPA, MBA, MSB, NemAb, NutrAb, OrnHort, PBA, PGegResA, PHN&I, ProtozoAb, RA&MP, RM&VM, RPP, RefZh, RevApplEntom, S&F, SeedAb, SolStAb, TDB, WeedAb.
—BLDSC (4979.550000), CASDDS, CISTI, Ei, IE, Infotrieve, ingenta, Linda Hall. **CCC.**
Published by: Allured Publishing Corp., 362 S Schmale Rd, Carol Stream, IL 60188-2787. TEL 630-653-2155, FAX 630-653-2192, allured@allured.com, http://www.perfumerflavorist.com/ME2/Audiences/default.asp, http://www.allured.com. Eds. Jeb Gleason, Brian M. Lawrence. Pub. Matt Gronlund. adv.: B&W page USD 1,700, color page USD 3,540.

668.5 GBR
KEY NOTE MARKET REVIEW: U K TOILETRIES & COSMETICS MARKET. Variant title: U K Toiletries & Cosmetics Market. Text in English. 1992. irreg. GBP 375 (effective 1999). **Document type:** *Trade.*
Related titles: CD-ROM ed.; Online - full text ed.
Published by: Key Note Ltd., Field House, 72 Oldfield Rd, Hampton, Mddx TW12 2HQ, United Kingdom. TEL 44-20-8481-8750, FAX 44-20-8783-0049, info@keynote.co.uk, http://www.keynote.co.uk.

668.5 GBR
KEY NOTE PLUS MARKET REPORT. COSMETICS & FRAGRANCES. Text in English. irreg., latest 2001, Aug. GBP 455 per issue (effective 2002). **Document type:** *Trade.* **Description:** Provides an overview of the UK cosmetics and fragrances sectors, including industry structure, market size and trends, developments, prospects, and major company profiles.
Former titles (until 2001): Key Note Market Report: Cosmetics & Fragrances; (until 1995): Key Note Report: Cosmetics and Fragrances
Related titles: CD-ROM ed.; Online - full text ed.
Published by: Key Note Ltd., Field House, 72 Oldfield Rd, Hampton, Mddx TW12 2HQ, United Kingdom. TEL 44-20-8481-8750, FAX 44-20-8783-0049, info@keynote.co.uk, http://www.keynote.co.uk. Ed. Lyndsey Barker.

668.5 JPN ISSN 0368-6558
CODEN: KORYAR
KORYO✶. Text in English. 1947. q.
—BLDSC (5113.900000), Linda Hall. **CCC.**
Published by: Japan Perfumery Flavouring Association, c/o Nitta Bldg. 4F, 8-2-1, Ginza, Chuo-ku, Tokyo, 102, Japan.

668.5 ITA ISSN 1590-1505
KOSMETICA. Text in Italian. 1999. bi-m. EUR 43 domestic (effective 2004). **Document type:** *Magazine, Consumer.*
Published by: Tecniche Nuove SpA, Via Eritrea 21, Milan, MI 201, Italy. TEL 39-02-390901, FAX 39-02-7570364, Kosmetica@tecnichenuove.com, info@tecnichenuove.com, http://www.tecnichenuove.com.

668.5 NLD ISSN 0165-2192
KOSMETIEK; vakblad voor de cosmeticabranche. Text in Dutch. 1972. m. (11/yr.). EUR 59.75 (effective 2005). adv. **Document type:** *Trade.*
Related titles: ◆ Supplement(s): Kosmetiek Apropos. ISSN 1381-8864.
Indexed: KES.
Published by: It's Amazing Business Communication bv, Postbus 7104, Zoetermeer, 2701 AC, Netherlands. TEL 31-79-3438383, FAX 31-79-3438399, kosmetiek@itsamazing.nl, itsabc@itsamazing.nl, http://www.kosmetiek.nl, http://www.itsamazing.nl. Circ: 4,000.

668.5 NLD ISSN 1381-8864
KOSMETIEK APROPOS. Text in Dutch. 1987. 6/yr. adv. illus. **Document type:** *Trade.*
Related titles: ◆ Supplement to: Kosmetiek. ISSN 0165-2192.
Published by: Samsom Bedrijfsinformatie BV (Subsidiary of: Wolters Kluwer N.V.), Postbus 4, Alphen aan den Rijn, 2400 MA, Netherlands. TEL 31-172-446954, FAX 31-172-422804. Ed. P Weijers. R&P E Stolwerk. Adv. contact N van der Does. Circ: 10,000.

665.58 SWE ISSN 1403-0497
KOSMETIK. Text in Swedish. 1996. bi-m. SEK 300 (effective 2001). adv. **Document type:** *Magazine, Trade.*
Published by: Melizma AB, Box 21016, Stockholm, 10031, Sweden. TEL 46-8-34-35-90, FAX 46-8-34-35-95, melizma@swipnet.se. Ed., Pub., Adv. contact Liz Husberg. color page SEK 16,000; trim 187 x 265.

668.5 DEU ISSN 0342-2976
KOSMETIK INTERNATIONAL. Text in German. 1951. m. EUR 73 domestic; EUR 87.90 in Europe; EUR 6.10 newsstand/cover (effective 2005). adv. bk.rev. illus. **Document type:** *Magazine, Trade.*
Formerly: Kosmetikerinnen-Fachzeitung - Parfuemerie Journal (0023-4176)
Indexed: RASB.
Published by: KOSMETIK International Verlag GmbH, Eisenwerkstr 11, Gaggenau, 76571, Germany. TEL 49-7225-9160, FAX 49-7225-916109, ki@ki-verlag.de, http://www.ki-online.de/html/ki-magazin.html. Ed. Heinrich Grossmann. Adv. contact Birgit Hartmann. B&W page EUR 2,930, color page EUR 4,040; trim 230 x 310. Circ: 25,599 (paid and controlled).

668.55 DEU
KOSMETIK REPORT; aktuelle Informationen. Text in German. 1971. 3/m. adv. **Document type:** *Trade.*
Published by: Orbis Werbung, Neuhauser Str 21, Konstanz, 78464, Germany. TEL 49-7531-882247, FAX 49-7531-812299. Ed. Sabine Bursy. Circ: 750.

668.55 DEU
KOSMETIKJAHRBUCH. Text in German. a. **Document type:** *Trade.*
Published by: Verlag fuer Chemische Industrie H. Ziolkowsky GmbH, Beethovenstr 16, Augsburg, 86150, Germany. TEL 49-821-32583-0, FAX 49-821-3258323, vci@sofw.com. Ed. Bernd Ziolkowsky.

646.726 DEU ISSN 1432-9018
KOSMETISCHE PRAXIS. Text in German. 1996. bi-m. EUR 43 domestic; EUR 48 foreign (effective 2004). adv. **Document type:** *Magazine, Trade.*
Published by: Health and Beauty Business Media GmbH & Co. KG, Karl-Friedrich-Str 14-18, Karlsruhe, 76133, Germany. TEL 49-721-165833, FAX 49-721-165618, juergen.volpp@health-and-beauty.com, http://www.health-and-beauty.com. adv.: B&W page EUR 2,148. Circ: 4,910 (paid).

668.5 ITA
LISTINO DI IMAGINE. Text in Italian. 1959. 5/yr. adv. illus. **Document type:** *Catalog, Consumer.*
Formerly: Nuove Armonie
Published by: (Associazione Profumieri Milano), Sfera Editore SpA (Subsidiary of: R C S Mediagroup), Via Angelo Rizzoli 2, Milan, MI 20132, Italy. TEL 39-02-25841, http://www.sferaeditore.it. Ed. Maruska Colantoni. Circ: 8,000 (paid and controlled).

668.5 USA ISSN 0740-3852
LOOKOUT - NONFOODS. Text in English. 1978. s-m. USD 700 (effective 2000). **Document type:** *Newsletter.* **Description:** Reviews the most innovative and influential new product entries, complete with analyses and illustrations.
Supersedes in part: Lookout (Naples)
Related titles: Online - full text ed.
Indexed: B&I.
—**CCC.**
Published by: Marketing Intelligence Service Ltd., 6473D Route 64, Naples, NY 14512-9726. TEL 716-374-6326, FAX 716-374-5217, mi@productscan.com, http://www.productscan.com. Eds. Daniel Smith, Thomas Vierhile. Pub., R&P Daniel Smith.

MEGA; the Philippines' best fashion magazine. see *CLOTHING TRADE*

668.5 ESP
N C P DOCUMENTA. (Noticias de Cosmetica y de Perfumeria) Text in Spanish. 1977. m. USD 8. charts.
Published by: (Sociedad Espanola de Quimicos Cosmeticos), Romargraf S.A., Juventud 55-57, Hospitalet del Llobregat, Barcelona, 08001, Spain.

668.55 USA
N I C BULLETIN. Text in English. 1954. bi-m. membership. **Document type:** *Bulletin.* **Description:** Covers topics relating to cosmetology licensing, testing, regulation and enforcement.
Formerly: National Interstate Council of State Boards of Cosmetology. Bulletin
Published by: National - Interstate Council of State Boards of Cosmetology, 8 Hills Rd., Ballston, NY 12019. brookstg@global2000.net. Ed. Gerald Brooks. Circ: 600. **Subscr. to:** T. Gerald Brooks, 45 Birch St., Apt. 14A, Kingston, NY 12401-1068. TEL 518-899-5798, FAX 518-899-5702.

668.55 GBR ISSN 1352-2639
NAIL NEWS. Text in English. 1993. bi-m. GBP 15 domestic; GBP 21, USD 32 elsewhere (effective 2000). **Document type:** *Trade.* **Description:** All the news, developments and step-by-step techniques from the world of nail care.
—CCC.
Published by: Reed Business Information Ltd. (Subsidiary of: Reed Business), Quadrant House, The Quadrant, Brighton Rd, Sutton, Surrey SM2 5AS, United Kingdom. TEL 44-208-652-3500, FAX 44-208-652-8977, rbi.subscriptions@qss-uk.com, http://www.reedbusiness.co.uk/. **Subscr. to:** Quadrant Subscription Services, PO Box 302, Haywards Heath, W Sussex RH16 3YY, United Kingdom. TEL 44-1444-445566, FAX 44-1444-445447.

668.55 USA ISSN 1049-4553
NAILPRO. Text in English. 1990. m. USD 24 domestic to individuals; USD 89 foreign to individuals (effective 2005). adv. **Document type:** *Magazine, Trade.* **Description:** Covers the technical, business and management aspects of the nailcare industry, with emphasis on how to effectively build a nail salon business and new manicuring techniques and products.
Formerly: N - The Magazine for Nail Professionals
Published by: Creative Age Publications, Inc., 7628 Densmore Ave, Van Nuys, CA 91406-2042. TEL 818-782-7328, nailpro@aol.com, http://www.nailpro.com. Ed., R&P Karie L Frost. Pub., Adv. contact Deborah Carver. B&W page USD 4,036, color page USD 5,316; trim 10.75 x 8. Circ: 50,713.

NIEUWE DROGIST. see *PHARMACY AND PHARMACOLOGY*

668.5 ESP ISSN 0213-1579
NOTICIAS DE COSMETICA Y DE PERFUMERIA. Short title: N C P. Text in Spanish. 1971. m. free. adv. bk.rev. abstr.; pat.; stat.; illus. index. Supplement avail.; back issues avail.
Published by: (Sociedad Espanola de Quimicos Cosmeticos), Romargraf S.A., Juventud 55-57, Hospitalet del Llobregat, Barcelona, 08001, Spain. Ed. Miguel Margalef. Circ: 3,000.

668.5 ESP ISSN 0210-4245
NUEVA ESTETICA. Text in Spanish. 1964. m. (10/yr.). USD 135. adv. bk.rev. abstr.; illus. index. back issues avail.
Published by: Ediciones Tecnicas Especializadas, Traversera de Gracia 15, 4, Barcelona, 08021, Spain. TEL 3-2097933, FAX 3-2096918. Ed. Alejandra Puig. Circ: 15,000.

NUTRACOS. see *FOOD AND FOOD INDUSTRIES*

668.5 AUT
DER OESTERREICHISCHE KOSMETIKER - FUSSPFLEGER - MASSEUR. Text in German. 1964. m. membership. **Document type:** *Trade.*
Published by: Verbaende der Oesterreichischen Fachkosmetikerinnen, Kaigasse 31, Salzburg, Sa 5020, Austria. TEL 43-662-843457, FAX 43-662-843457. Ed. Marga Schicho.

668.54 DEU ISSN 0723-1989
PARFUEMERIE AKTUELL. Text in German. 1982. 9/yr. EUR 55.60; EUR 6 newsstand/cover (effective 2003). adv. **Document type:** *Magazine, Trade.*
—CCC.
Published by: Terra Verlag GmbH, Neuhauser Str 21, Konstanz, 78464, Germany. TEL 49-7531-8122-0, FAX 49-7531-812299, info@terra-verlag.de, http://www.terra-verlag.de/parfuemerie.html. Ed. Heidi Stolz. adv.: B&W page EUR 2,472, color page EUR 4,272. Circ: 13,400.

668.55 DEU ISSN 1434-5749
PARFUEMERIE JOURNAL. Text in German. 1991. bi-m. EUR 48 domestic; EUR 55.50 in Europe; EUR 96.80 elsewhere; EUR 8 newsstand/cover (effective 2005). adv. **Document type:** *Magazine, Trade.*
Formerly (until 1998): Cosmetic Management International (0947-0603)
Published by: KOSMETIK International Verlag GmbH, Eisenwerkstr 11, Gaggenau, 76571, Germany. TEL 49-7225-9160, FAX 49-7225-916109, ki@ki-verlag.de, http://www.ki-online.de/html/pj.html. Ed. Susanne Stoll. Adv. contact Birgit Hartmann. B&W page EUR 1,650, color page DEM 3,090; trim 210 x 297. Circ: 5,208 (paid and controlled).

668.5 FRA
PARFUMS-BEAUTE INTERNATIONAL. Text in French. 1931. a. EUR 103.68 domestic; EUR 124 foreign.
Formerly: Parfums-Beaute (0751-5537)
Published by: Editions Louis Johanet, 38 bd Henri Sellier, Suresnes, 92156, France.

668.5 FRA ISSN 1267-0812
TP983 CODEN: PCARDV
PARFUMS, COSMETIQUES, ACTUALITES; partenaire des industries cosmetiques et aromatiques. Text in French. bi-m. adv. charts; illus.; tr.lit. **Document type:** *Trade.*
Former titles (until Sep. 1995): Parfums, Cosmetiques, Aromes (0337-3029); (until 1975): Parfums, Cosmetiques, Savons de France (0031-1960); Which was formed by the merger of (1958-1970): Parfumerie, Cosmetique, Savons (0369-9099); (1957-1970): France et Ses Parfums (0532-9094)
Indexed: CBNB, CIN, ChemAb, ChemTitl, KES, PROMT, RefZh.
—BLDSC (6406.579500), CASDDS, CINDOC, CISTI, Ei, IE, Infotrieve, Linda Hall. **CCC.**
Published by: (Societe d'Expansion Technique et Economique S.A.), P C A Media, 4, rue de Seze, Paris, 75439, France. TEL 33-01-44945060, FAX 33-01-44945075, http://www.infochimie.presse.fr. Ed. Francoise Basset.

668.54 GBR ISSN 1462-043X
PERFUME COLLECTION; discover the world's most enduring fragrances. Text in English. 1998. bi-w. illus. **Document type:** *Consumer.* **Description:** Discusses the world's most enduring fragrances, with histories and profiles of world-class perfumers and famous brand names.
Published by: Orbis Publishing Ltd., Griffin House, 161 Hammersmith Rd, London, W6 8SD, United Kingdom. http://www.perfume-collection.com.

668.55 USA ISSN 0272-2666
TP983 CODEN: PEFLDI
PERFUMER & FLAVORIST. Text in English. 1940. bi-m. USD 135 in US & Canada; USD 175 elsewhere; USD 30 newsstand/cover in US & Canada; USD 36 newsstand/cover elsewhere (effective 2005). adv. bk.rev. reprint service avail. from PQC. **Document type:** *Magazine, Trade.* **Description:** International business magazine for the flavor and fragrance industry. Covers the creative, scientific and commercial aspects of this business.
Formerly (until 1980): Perfumer and Flavorist International (0361-8587); Which superseded in part (in 1976): Cosmetics and Perfumery (0090-6581); Which was formerly (until 1973): American Cosmetics and Perfumery (0090-5852); (until 1972): American Perfumer and Cosmetics (0003-0392); (until 1962): American Perfumer (0096-0896); (until 1960): American Perfumer and Aromatics (0161-9993); (until 1956): The American Perfumer and Essential Oil Review (0161-9977)
Related titles: Microform ed.: (from PQC); Online - full text ed.: (from H.W. Wilson, O C L C Online Computer Library Center, Inc.).
Indexed: ASFA, AgBio, AgrForAb, B&BAb, BPI, CPA, ChemAb, ChemTitl, ChemoAb, FPA, FS&TA, ForAb, HortAb, IPA, OrnHort, PBA, PGegResA, PHN&I, PotatoAb, RA&MP, RDA, SeedAb, TriticAb, WAE&RSA.
—BLDSC (6423.950000), CASDDS, CISTI, IE, Infotrieve, ingenta, Linda Hall. **CCC.**
Published by: Allured Publishing Corp., 362 S Schmale Rd, Carol Stream, IL 60188-2787. TEL 630-653-2155, FAX 630-653-2192, allured@allured.com, http://www.perfumerflavorist.com, http://www.allured.com. Eds. Stanley E Allured, Brian Lawrence. Adv. contact Stanley E Allured. B&W page USD 1,700, color page USD 3,540. Circ: 1,900 (paid).

668.54 ESP
PERFUMERIA AL DIA. Text in Spanish. 6/yr.
Address: Via Agusta 59, 8o Of. 812, Barcelona, 08006, Spain. TEL 3-2378865, FAX 3-415-86-88. Ed. Salvador Beltran Nunez. Circ: 20,000.

668.5 MEX ISSN 0185-6588
PERFUMERIA MODERNA/MODERN PERFUMING. Text in Spanish. 1969. m. USD 50. adv. **Description:** Suppliers' guide to perfumes, cosmetics, aerosols, detergents, insecticides, pharmaceuticals, and chemical products.
Published by: Bravo Grupo Editorial S.A., Jose Maria Bustillos 49, Col Algarin, Mexico City, DF 06880, Mexico. TEL 5-530-6062, FAX 5-538-86-79. Ed. Lazaro Bravo Bernabe. Circ: 5,000.

668.55 ZAF ISSN 1015-4760
CODEN: PCRVDQ
PHARMACEUTICAL & COSMETIC REVIEW; devoted to the manufacture & marketing of medicines, toiletries, soaps, detergents in South Africa. Text in English. 1974. bi-m. ZAR 191.84 (effective 1999). adv. illus. **Document type:** *Trade.* **Description:** Reports on new equipment, ingredients, processes, packaging materials, legislative and marketing trends and overseas developments for manufacturers, packers and distributors of pharmaceutical, cosmetic and related products.
Formerly: South African Pharmaceutical and Cosmetic Review (0257-2028)
Indexed: IPA, ISAP.
—BLDSC (6442.750000), IE, ingenta.
Published by: National Publishing (Pty) Ltd., PO Box 2271, Clareinch, 7740, South Africa. TEL 27-21-611140, FAX 27-21-611389, accirc@natpub.co.za. Ed. Lindy Hughson. Circ: 2,000. **Co-sponsors:** Aerosol Manufacturers' Association; Society of Cosmetic Chemists; South African Association of Industrial Flavor and Fragrance Manufacturers.

PHARMACEUTICAL FORMULATION & QUALITY BUYERS' GUIDE. see *PHARMACY AND PHARMACOLOGY*

PRODUCT ALERT. see *FOOD AND FOOD INDUSTRIES*

668.55 DEU ISSN 0944-4025
CODEN: ANKODI
PROFI KOSMETIK; Fachmedium fuer die praktizierende Kosmetikerin. Text in German. 1956. m. EUR 46.80 (effective 2003). adv. illus.; stat. **Document type:** *Magazine, Trade.*
Former titles (until 1993): Profi Kosmetik Journal (0942-3788); (until 1992): Kosmetik Journal (0342-2968); (until 1977): Angewandte Kosmetik (0003-3138)
—CASDDS. **CCC.**
Published by: Terra Verlag GmbH, Neuhauser Str 21, Konstanz, 78464, Germany. TEL 49-7531-812228, FAX 49-7531-812299, info@terra-verlag.de, http://www.terra-verlag.de/profikosmetik.html. Ed. Heidi Stolz. adv.: B&W page EUR 2,100, color page EUR 3,000. Circ: 14,800.

668.54 ITA
PROFUMERIA DA COLLEZIONE. Text in Italian. m. **Description:** Dedicated to perfume collectors. Contains articles on determining authenticity of perfume antiques. Provides photos, descriptions and value estimates of various antique perfume objects.
Published by: Sound Project Sas, Via Fauche, 36, Milano, Italy. TEL 39-02-3495161, FAX 39-02-33611676, mignon@tin.it.

REFERATIVNYI ZHURNAL. TEKHNOLOGIYA PROIZVODSTVA PRODUKTOV BYTOVOI KHIMII. PARFUMERIYA I KOSMETIKA. see *CHEMISTRY—Abstracting, Bibliographies, Statistics*

668.5 664.5 ITA ISSN 0392-0445
TP983 CODEN: RIEPD7
➤ **RIVISTA ITALIANA E P P O S.** (Essenze Profumi Piante Officianali Saponi) Short title: Rivista Italiana Eppos. Text in Italian. 1939. s-a. EUR 77.47 (effective 2005). adv. bk.rev. abstr.; charts; illus.; mkt. index. back issues avail. **Document type:** *Academic/Scholarly.* **Description:** Publishes original papers and reviews on; aroma, medicinal plants, sensory analysis, essences, ingredients and additives, perfumes, instrumental analysis, hygiene, microbiology and chemometrics.
Former titles (until 1979): Rivista Italiana Essenze, Profumi, Piante Officianali, Aromatizzanti, Syndets, Saponi, Cosmetici, Aereosols (0391-4658); (until 1978): Rivista Italiana Essenze, Profumi, Piante Officianali, Aromi, Saponi, Cosmetici, Aereosol (0035-6948); (until 1965): Rivista Italiana Essenze, Profumi, Piante Officianali, Aromi, Saponi, Cosmetici (0370-677X); (until 1962): Rivista Italiana Essenze, Profumi, Piante Officianali, Olii Vegetali, Saponi (0370-5730)
Related titles: Supplement(s): Symposium on Essential Oils. Proceedings.
Indexed: AbHyg, AgBio, BiolAb, CPA, ChemAb, DSA, FCA, FPA, FS&TA, HortAb, IPA, MSB, OrnHort, PBA, PGegResA, PGrRegA, PHN&I, ProtozoAb, RA&MP, RM&VM, RPP, RRTA, S&F, SeedAb, TDB, WAE&RSA, WeedAb.
—BLDSC (7987.330000), CISTI, IE, ingenta, Linda Hall.
Published by: Istituto Tetrahedron, Via Capitani di Mozzo, 12, Mozzo, BG 24030, Italy. TEL 39-035-468511, FAX 39-035-463803. Ed. Enrico Colombo. Adv. contact Silvia Sarlo. Circ: 5,000.

➤ **RIYONG HUAXUE GONGYE/CHINA SURFACTANT, DETERGENT & COSMETICS.** see *CLEANING AND DYEING*

668.5 USA ISSN 1530-1222
THE ROSE SHEET. Text in English. 1980. 51/yr. looseleaf. USD 1,015 to institutions (effective 2006). back issues avail.; reprints avail. **Document type:** *Newsletter, Trade.* **Description:** Provides executives in the toiletries, fragrances, skin care and related industries with specialized regulatory, legislative, scientific, financial and legal news.
Formerly (until 2000): F D C Reports. Toiletries, Fragrances and Skin Care (0279-1110)
Related titles: Online - full text ed.: The Rose Sheet on the Web (from Data-Star, EBSCO Publishing).
Indexed: PNI.
—CCC.
Published by: F-D-C Reports, Inc. (Subsidiary of: Elsevier Health Sciences), 5550 Friendship Blvd, Ste One, Chevy Chase, MD 20815-7278. TEL 301-657-9830, 800-332-2181, FAX 301-656-3094, http://www.elsevier.com/locate/rose, http://www.fdcreports.com. Eds. J Merrill, Karl Uhlendorf. R&P Michael Keville.

B

668.5 DEU ISSN 0942-7694
TP1 CODEN: SOFJEE
S OE F W JOURNAL. Text in German. 1874. 12/yr. (plus 2 special issues). EUR 210; EUR 235 combined subscription print & online eds.; EUR 21 newsstand/cover (effective 2004). adv. bk.rev. bibl.; charts; illus.; mkt.; pat.; tr.mk. index.
Document type: *Journal, Trade.* **Description:** Provides information in the field of scientific developments in the personal care industry.
Incorporates (1927-1991): Kosmetika, Aerosole, Riechstoffe (0931-055X); Which was formerly (until 1980): Kosmetik und Aerosole (0931-0150); (until 1971): Kosmetik (0931-0142); (until 1948): Der Parfuemeur (0369-8378); Former titles (until 1992): S Oe F W - Seifen, Oele, Fette, Wachse (0173-5500); (until 1980): Seifen, Oele, Fette, Wachse (0037-0983); (until 1948): Seifensieder-Zeitung (0371-3296); Which incorporated (1922-1943): Allgemeine Oel- und Fett-Zeitung (0365-5202)
Related titles: English ed.: 1999 (Jan. 1st).
Indexed: BiolAb, ChemAb, DBA, ExcerpMed, FPA, FS&TA, IPA, IPackAb, KES, NutrAb, PROMT, RefZh.
—BLDSC (8321.483000), CASDDS, CISTI, IE, Infotrieve, ingenta, Linda Hall. **CCC.**
Published by: (Specialists in Soaps, Perfumes, Detergents (SEPAWA)), Verlag fuer Chemische Industrie H. Ziolkowsky GmbH, Beethovenstr 16, Augsburg, 86150, Germany. TEL 49-821-32583-0, FAX 49-821-3258323, vci@sofw.com, http://www.sofw.com. Ed. Bernd Ziolkowsky. adv.: B&W page EUR 1,740; trim 178 x 264. Circ: 1,358 (paid and controlled).
Co-sponsor: Vereinigung der Seifen-, Parfuem-, und Waschmittelfachleute e.V.

B

668.5 GBR ISSN 1365-4926
S P C ASIA. (Soap, Perfumery and Cosmetics) Text in English. 1996. bi-m. GBP 65 in Europe; USD 172 in US & Canada; GBP 120 elsewhere. **Document type:** *Trade.*
Related titles: Online - full text ed.: (from EBSCO Publishing, Gale Group, O C L C Online Computer Library Center, Inc., ProQuest Information & Learning).
Indexed: ABIn, B&I.
Published by: Wilmington Publishing Ltd. (Subsidiary of: Wilmington Group Plc), Maidstone Rd, Footscray, Sidcup, Kent DA14 5HZ, United Kingdom. TEL 44-1322-277788, FAX 44-1322-276474, spc@wilmington.co.uk.

668.5 ESP ISSN 1695-7237
SELECTIVO. Text in Spanish. 2000. q. EUR 59.16 domestic; EUR 63.65 foreign (effective 2004). adv. **Description:** Directed at all those involved in the high quality perfumes and beauty products market.
Published by: Tecnipublicaciones Espana, S.L., Avda de Manoteras 44, 3a Planta, Madrid, 28050, Spain. TEL 34-91-2972000, FAX 34-91-2972154, tp@tecnipublicaciones.com, http://www.tecnipublicaciones.com. adv.: B&W page EUR 2,250; bleed 210 x 280.

668.55 JPN
SHISEIDO ANNUAL REPORT. Text in Japanese. a. **Document type:** *Corporate.* **Description:** Offers a review of the year's highlights, economic status of the company, market trends, and future plans.
Published by: Shiseido Co. Ltd., 7-5-5 Ginza, Chuo-ku, Tokyo, 104-0061, Japan. TEL (03) 572-5111, FAX 03-572-6973.

668.55 JPN
SHISEIDO SEMI-ANNUAL REPORT. Text in Japanese. s-a. **Document type:** *Corporate.*
Published by: Shiseido Co. Ltd., 7-5-5 Ginza, Chuo-ku, Tokyo, 104-0061, Japan. TEL 03(572)5111, FAX 03-572-6973, TELEX J24548.

SKIN INC.; business and science for skin care professionals. see *MEDICAL SCIENCES—Dermatology And Venereology*

SO YOUNG!; dedicated to a youthful body, mind and spirit. see *PHYSICAL FITNESS AND HYGIENE*

668.5 USA ISSN 1523-9225
TP1 CODEN: SCCSC8
SOAP AND COSMETICS. Text in English. 1925. m. USD 60 domestic; USD 85 in Canada & Mexico; USD 119 elsewhere (effective 2005). adv. bk.rev. bibl.; illus.; mkt.; pat.; tr.lit.; tr.mk. reprint service avail. from PQC. **Document type:** *Magazine, Trade.* **Description:** Edited for manufacturers of detergents, soaps, cosmetics, aerosols, waxes, polishers, insecticides, disinfectants, and other chemical specialty products.
Former titles (until 1999): Soap, Cosmetics, Chemical Specialties (0091-1372); (until 1971): Soap and Chemical Specialties (0037-7481)
Related titles: Microform ed.: (from PMC, PQC); Online - full text ed.: ISSN 1523-0481 (from Florida Center for Library Automation, Gale Group, O C L C Online Computer Library Center, Inc.).
Indexed: A&ATA, ASCA, B&I, BiolAb, BusI, CBNB, CIN, ChemAb, ChemTitl, CurCont, CurPA, EngInd, ExcerpMed, HlthInd, IPA, PROMT, RefZh, T&II, TTI.
—BLDSC (8315.006000), CASDDS, CISTI, Ei, IE, ingenta, Linda Hall. **CCC.**
Published by: Cygnus Business Media, Inc., 3 Huntington Quadrangle, Ste 301N, Melville, NY 11747-3601. Circ: 17,050.

668.5 GBR ISSN 0037-749X
CODEN: SSPCD2
SOAP, PERFUMERY & COSMETICS. Text in English. 1928. m. adv. bk.rev. abstr.; bibl.; charts; illus.; mkt.; pat.; tr.mk. index. **Document type:** *Directory, Trade.*
Incorporating: Soap Trade Review
Related titles: Online - full text ed.: (from EBSCO Publishing, Florida Center for Library Automation, Gale Group, O C L C Online Computer Library Center, Inc., ProQuest Information & Learning).
Indexed: ABIn, B&I, BrTechI, CBNB, ChemAb, CurPA, IPA, IPackAb, KES, LRI, PROMT.
—BLDSC (8316.000000), CINDOC, CISTI, IE, Infotrieve, ingenta, Linda Hall. **CCC.**
Published by: Wilmington Publishing Ltd. (Subsidiary of: Wilmington Group Plc), Maidstone Rd, Footscray, Sidcup, Kent DA14 5HZ, United Kingdom. spc@wilmington.co.uk, http://www.spc-magazine.com/, http://www.wilmington.co.uk/, http://www.cosmeticsbusiness.com/. Ed. Clare Henderson. Circ: 3,400.

668.5 IND ISSN 0379-5608
CODEN: SDTRDU
SOAPS, DETERGENTS & TOILETRIES REVIEW. Text in English. 1965. m. USD 50.
Indexed: ChemAb.
—CASDDS.
Published by: Wadhera Publications, General Assurance Bldg., 232 Dr D.N. Rd., Mumbai, Maharashtra 400 001, India. Ed. Roshanlal Wadhera. Circ: 4,000.

SOCIEDAD ARGENTINA PARA LA INVESTIGACION DE PRODUCTOS AROMATICOS. ANALES. see *BIOLOGY—Botany*

668.5 JPN ISSN 0387-5253
SOCIETY OF COSMETIC CHEMISTS OF JAPAN. JOURNAL. Variant title: Journal of S C C J. Text in English. 1963. q. free to members (effective 2005). **Document type:** *Journal, Trade.*
Formerly (until 1975): Japan Cosmetic Chemists Association. Journal (0289-1379)
—BLDSC (4869.700000), IE. **CCC.**
Published by: Nihon Keshohin Gijutsushakai/Society of Cosmetic Chemists of Japan, 2-2-1 Hayabuchi, Tsuzuki-ku, Yokohama, 224-8558, Japan. TEL 81-45-5906025, FAX 81-45-5906093, http://www.sccj-ifscc.com/journal/journal.html.

668.5 USA
STATE OF THE ART. Text in English. 1976. m. USD 12; USD 1 newsstand/cover (effective 2005); free to qualified personnel. **Document type:** *Magazine.*
Formerly: National Beauty News
Published by: State Service Systems, 10405-B E 55th Pl, Tulsa, OK 74146-6502. TEL 918-627-8000, http://www.statebeauty.com. Circ: 35,500 (paid and controlled).

668.5 ITA
UP - BEAUTY & BIJOUX. Text in Italian. 6/yr.
Published by: Raddicchi Editore S.R.L., Via San Giovanni B. De La Salle, 4, Milan, MI 20132, Italy. TEL 2-26-30-03-30. Ed. Rossella Radicchi.

668.5 ESP ISSN 1136-1433
VENTAS DE PERFUMERIA Y COSMETICA. Text in Spanish. 1980. 12/yr. EUR 75 domestic; EUR 145 foreign (effective 2005). **Document type:** *Trade.* **Description:** Covers retail trade in perfumes and cosmetics.
Related titles: Supplement(s): Quien es Quien.
Published by: Ediciones 4 Mas 4, C. Portala 27-6, Barcelona, 08023, Spain. TEL 34-3-4188718, FAX 34-3-4189041, http://www.perfumedia.com/. Ed. Carles Solsona. Pub. Antonio Bergillos. Adv. contact Francisco Borroso. Circ: 8,000.

668.5 DEU ISSN 1618-4807
WER UND WAS - KOERPERPFLEGE-, WASCH- UND REINIGUNGSMITTEL-INDUSTRIE. Text in German. 1977. biennial. EUR 137.50 (effective 2003). adv. **Document type:** *Directory, Trade.*
Formerly (until 2001): Wer und Was in der Deutschen Koerperpflege-, Wasch- und Reinigungsmittel-Industrie (0171-4341)
Published by: B. Behr's Verlag GmbH & Co. KG, Averhoffstr. 10, Hamburg, 22085, Germany. TEL 49-40-2270080, FAX 49-40-2201091, info@behrs.de, http://www.behrs.de. Adv. contact Frau Nuesslein.

668.5 USA ISSN 1073-3086
WOMAN'S DAY BEAUTY. Text in English. 1995 (vol.5, no.1). q. illus. **Document type:** *Consumer.*
Published by: (Mary Kay Cosmetics), Hachette Filipacchi Media U.S., Inc. (Subsidiary of: Hachette Filipacchi Medias S.A.), 1633 Broadway, New York, NY 10019. TEL 212-767-6000, http://www.hfmus.com. Ed. Nancy Kalish. Pub. Beth Ann Burgon.

668.55 658.8 GBR
WORLD COSMETICS AND TOILETRIES MARKETING DIRECTORY; the definitive information source for the world cosmetics and toiletries industry. Text in English. 1999. a., latest 2002/2003. GBP 745 domestic (effective Nov. 2002); EUR 1,190 in Europe; USD 1,190 elsewhere (effective Nov. 2003). **Document type:** *Directory, Trade.* **Description:** Directory of the world's top cosmetics and toiletries manufacturers and retailers together with market business information.
Incorporates: European Cosmetics and Toiletries Marketing Report
Published by: Euromonitor, 60-61 Britton St, London, EC1 5UX, United Kingdom. TEL 44-20-7251-8024, FAX 44-20-7608-3149, info@euromonitor.com, http://www.euromonitor.com.

THE WORLD MARKET FOR COSMETICS AND TOILETRIES. see *BUSINESS AND ECONOMICS—Marketing And Purchasing*

THE WORLD MARKET FOR ETHNIC COSMETICS & TOILETRIES. see *BUSINESS AND ECONOMICS—Marketing And Purchasing*

668.5 CHN ISSN 1004-5163
ZHONGGUO HUAZHUANGPIN/CHINA COSMETICS REVIEW. Text in Chinese. 1993. bi-m. CNY 12 domestic; USD 10 foreign (effective 2001). 112 p./no.; back issues avail. **Document type:** *Magazine, Consumer.*
Published by: (Guojia Guonei Maoyi Ju, Zhongguo Baihuo Fangzhipin Gongsi/China general Merchandise & Textile Co.), Zhongguo Huazhuangpin Bianjibu, 45 Fuxingmennei Dajie, Beijing, 100801, China. TEL 86-1-6609-4405, 86-1-6609-4445, FAX 81-1-6601-8261, cghzp@ihw.com.cn. Ed. Li Zhanrong. R&P Li Kong TEL 86-1-6609-4445. Adv. contact Shen Lizhen TEL 86-1-6609-4406. Circ: 50,000. **Dist. overseas by:** China International Book Trading Corp, 35 Chegongzhuang Xilu, Haidian District, PO Box 399, Beijing 100044, China. TEL 86-10-68412045, FAX 86-10-68412023, cibtc@mail.cibtc.com.cn, http://www.cibtc.com.cn.

646.72 CHN ISSN 1006-9216
ZHONGHUA YIXUE MEIRONG ZAZHI/CHINESE JOURNAL OF MEDICAL AETHETICS AND COSMETOLOGY. Text in Chinese. bi-m. CNY 10, USD 2.90 newsstand/cover (effective 2003). **Document type:** *Academic/Scholarly.*
Published by: Zhonghua Yixuehui Zazhishe/Chinese Medical Association Publishing House, 42 Dongsi Xidajie, Beijing, 100710, China. **Dist. by:** China International Book Trading Corp, 35 Chegongzhuang Xilu, Haidian District, PO Box 399, Beijing 100044, China. TEL 86-10-68412045, FAX 86-10-68412023, cibtc@mail.cibtc.com.cn, http://www.cibtc.com.cn.

BEVERAGES

see also FOOD AND FOOD INDUSTRIES ; PACKAGING

663 USA
A B A NEWSLETTER. Text in English. 1983. m. USD 38 to members. bk.rev. **Document type:** *Newsletter.*
Indexed: e-psyche.
Published by: American Bartenders' Association, PO Box D, Plant City, FL 33564. TEL 800-935-3232, FAX 813-752-2768. Ed. Linda Harrell.

641.3 DEU
A F G WIRTSCHAFT - DAS ERFRISCHUNGSGETRAENK. Text in German. 1948. m. EUR 138 (effective 2004). adv. **Document type:** *Newspaper, Trade.*
Former titles: Das Erfrischungsgetraenk; Erfrischungsgetraenk - Mineralwasser-Zeitung (0342-2232); (until 1968): Mineralwasser-Zeitung (0343-110X)
Indexed: FS&TA.
Published by: (Bundesverband der Deutschen Erfrischungsgetraenke-Industrie e.V.), Matthaes Verlag GmbH, Olgastr 87, Stuttgart, 70180, Germany. TEL 49-711-2133245, FAX 49-711-2133350, kontaktm@matthaes.de, http://www.matthaes.de. Ed. Roswitha Volkhardt. Pub. Amalie Marga Matthaes. Adv. contact Rudolf Goeth. B&W page EUR 2,060, color page EUR 3,140; trim 187 x 262. Circ: 2,793.

A PROPOS CULINA; Beitraege zur Kulturgeschichte des Essens und Trinkens. see *SOCIAL SCIENCES: COMPREHENSIVE WORKS*

663.3 USA ISSN 0149-7308
A S B C NEWSLETTER. Text in English. q. USD 27 domestic to non-members; USD 33 foreign to non-members; USD 95 to individual members; USD 195 to corporations; USD 26 to students (effective 2003). adv. **Document type:** *Newsletter.*
Published by: American Society of Brewing Chemists, 3340 Pilot Knob Rd., St. Paul, MN 55121-2097. TEL 651-454-7250, FAX 651-454-0766, http://www.aaccnet.org.

663 NLD ISSN 0929-6247
ADFUNDUM; vakblad voor de drankenbranche. Text in Dutch. 1993. m. EUR 52 domestic; EUR 78 foreign; EUR 5 newsstand/cover (effective 2005). adv. charts; illus.; stat. back issues avail. **Document type:** *Journal, Trade.* **Description:** Business magazine for the beverage trade.
Published by: Uitgeverij Lakerveld BV, Turfschipper 53, Postbus 160, Wateringen, 2290 AD, Netherlands. TEL 31-174-315000, FAX 31-174-315001, redactie@lakerveld.nl, uitgeverij@lakerveld.nl, http://www.adfundum.nl/, http://www.lakerveld.nl. Pub., R&P Ad van Gaalen. adv.: B&W page EUR 1,265, color page EUR 2,160; trim 185 x 268. Circ: 1,542.

AGRICULTURE, FOOD AND BEVERAGES. see *AGRICULTURE*

663 616.861 USA ISSN 1067-3105
ALCOHOL ISSUES INSIGHTS. Text in English. 1983. m. USD 360 (effective 2005). 4 p./no.; back issues avail. **Document type:** *Newsletter, Consumer.* **Description:** Covers alcohol policy issues, including excise tax, drunk driving laws, advertising and availability restrictions, and alcohol and health.
Published by: Beer Marketer's Insights, Inc., PO Box 264, West Nyack, NY 10994. TEL 845-624-2337, FAX 845-624-2340, http://www.beerinsights.com. Ed. Eric Shepard. Pub. Benj Steinman. R&P Jim Sullivan.

663 USA ISSN 0889-3519
ALCOHOLIC BEVERAGE EXECUTIVES' NEWSLETTER. Text in English. 1940. w. looseleaf. USD 320 (effective 2005). adv. back issues avail. **Document type:** *Newsletter, Trade.* **Description:** Covers beer, wine and spirits.
Published by: Alcoholic Beverage Executives' Newsletter, Inc., 1120 S 96th St, Omaha, NE 68124-1122. TEL 402-397-5514, FAX 402-397-3843. Ed., Pub., R&P, Adv. contact Patricia Kennedy. page USD 550.

663.4 USA
ALE STREET NEWS. Text in English. 1993 (vol.2). bi-m. USD 18.95 domestic; USD 33.95 in Europe & S. America; USD 36.95 elsewhere (effective 2005). adv. illus. **Document type:** *Newspaper, Consumer.*
Published by: Tuscarora Inc., PO Box 1125, Maywood, NJ 07607. TEL 201-368-9100, 800-351-2537, FAX 201-368-9101, tony@alestreetnews.com, http://www.alestreetnews.com. Ed., Adv. contact Tony Forder. Pubs. Jack Babin, Tony Forder. Circ: 110,000 (controlled).

663 ESP ISSN 1134-8127
ALIMARKET. BEBIDAS. Text in Spanish. 1993. a. price varies. adv.
Related titles: Online - full text ed.
Published by: Publicaciones Alimarket S.A., Albasanz 14 3o, Madrid, 28037, Spain. TEL 34-91-3274340, FAX 34-91-3274522, informa@alimarket.es, http://www.alimarket.es. R&P Carlos Guerrero.

663.1 DEU ISSN 0002-5496
ALKOHOL-INDUSTRIE; deutsche Spirituosen-Zeitung und Brennerei-Zeitung. Text in German. 1887. s-m. adv. bk.rev. charts; illus.; mkt.; pat. index. **Document type:** *Trade.*
Indexed: BiolAb, ChemAb, FS&TA.
—BLDSC (0788.540000), CISTI.
Published by: Team Verlag GmbH und Fachzeitschriften KG, Auwanne 19, Karlstein, 63791, Germany. Ed. Horst P Czerner. Circ: 3,000.

663.4 USA ISSN 0898-9001
ALL ABOUT BEER. Text in English. 1980. bi-m. USD 19.99 domestic; USD 29.99 in Canada & Mexico; USD 39.99 elsewhere (effective 2005). adv. bk.rev. 86 p./no.; back issues avail.; reprints avail. **Document type:** *Magazine, Consumer.* **Description:** Contains information about travel, collectibles, homebrewing, beer history, beer cultures in other countries, food and beer.
Related titles: Online - full text ed.
Published by: Chautauqua Press, 501-H Washington Street, Durham, NC 27701. TEL 919-530-8150, 800-977-2337, FAX 919-530-8160, editor@allaboutbeer.com, publisher@allaboutbeer.com, http://www.allaboutbeer.com/aabmhome.html. Ed. Julie Johnson Bradford. Pub. Daniel Fuller Bradford. Adv. contact Catherine Lemin. Circ: 26,000 (paid).

663.2 634.8 FRA ISSN 0769-8372
AMATEUR DE BORDEAUX. Text in French. 1981. 8/yr. **Document type:** *Monographic series, Consumer.* **Description:** Cultivates the art of the good life in the heart of the Bordeaux wine country.
Published by: Societe d'Editions Specialisees, 22 rue des Reculettes, Paris, 75013, France. TEL 33-1-43314499, FAX 33-1-43314115. Ed. Nicholas Faith. Pub. Michel Guillard. Adv. contact Georges Savi de Tove.

663.3 USA ISSN 1536-0792
HD9397.U5
AMERICAN BREWER AND DISTILLER; the business of beer. Text in English. 1987. q. USD 50 in US & Canada (effective 2005). adv. bk.rev. tr.lit.; illus. back issues avail. **Document type:** *Trade.* **Description:** Covers craft beer-brewing and distillery business start-up and is geared toward those who work in microbreweries and brewpubs as well as those who enjoy craft-brewed beer.
Formerly (until 2001): American Brewer Magazine (1055-470X); Formed by the merger of (1986-1987): Amateur Brewer (0887-7416); (1983-1987): Home Fermenter's Digest (0742-4590)
Related titles: Online - full text ed.
Indexed: RefZh.
—GNLM. **CCC.**
Published by: American Brewer Magazine, P O Box 510, Hayward, CA 94543-0510. TEL 510-538-9500, FAX 510-538-7644, ambrew@aol.com, http://www.ambrew.com. Eds. Pamela Evans, Bill Owens. Pub. Bill Owens. Adv. contact Karen Dolan. B&W page USD 1,050, color page USD 1,550; trim 10.88 x 8.38. Circ: 3,000 (controlled); 3,000 (paid). **Dist. by:** Eastern News Distributors Inc., 250 W. 55th St., New York, NY 10019. TEL 212-649-4484, FAX 212-265-6239.

663.3 USA
AMERICAN BREWER MAGAZINE. Text in English. 1868-198?; resumed 1986. q. USD 50 (effective 2005). **Document type:** *Magazine.*
Formerly: American Brewer Magazine & Distiller
Published by: American Brewer, Inc., PO Box 650, East Amherst, NY 14051. TEL 508-653-7929, ambrew@aol.com, http://www.americanbrewer.com/. Pubs. Bill Metzer, Jim Dorsch. Circ: 6,000 (controlled and free).

AMERICAN BREWERIANA JOURNAL. see *HOBBIES*

AMERICAN INSTITUTE OF WINE & FOOD. NEW YORK AREA CHAPTER. NEWS. see *FOOD AND FOOD INDUSTRIES*

663.2 634.8 USA ISSN 0002-9254
CODEN: AJEVAC
➤ **AMERICAN JOURNAL OF ENOLOGY AND VITICULTURE.** Text in English. 1954. q. USD 200 domestic; USD 220 foreign; USD 400 combined subscription domestic print & online eds.; USD 440 combined subscription foreign print & online eds. (effective 2005). adv. abstr.; bibl.; charts. index. reprint service avail. from PQC. **Document type:** *Journal, Academic/Scholarly.* **Description:** Examines grape growing and wine making research.
Related titles: Microfilm ed.: (from PQC); Online - full text ed.: (from HighWire Press).
Indexed: AEA, ASCA, AgBio, Agr, BCI, BIOBASE, BIOSIS Prev, BioDAb, BiolAb, CPA, ChemAb, CurCont, CurPA, DBA, DSA, ExcerpMed, FCA, FPA, FS&TA, ForAb, HerbAb, HortAb, I&DA, IABS, ISR, MSB, NemAb, NutrAb, OrnHort, PBA, PGegResA, PGrRegA, PHN&I, PlantSci, RA&MP, RM&VM, RPP, RefZh, RevApplEntom, S&F, SCI, SIA, SeedAb, TriticAb, VITIS, WAE&RSA, WeedAb.
—BLDSC (0824.525000), CASDDS, CINDOC, CISTI, IDS, IE, Infotrieve, ingenta, Linda Hall. **CCC.**
Published by: American Society for Enology and Viticulture, PO Box 1855, Davis, CA 95617. TEL 916-753-3142, FAX 916-753-3318, http://www.ajevonline.org. Ed. Joanne Rantz. Circ: 3,300.

663.3 663.4 USA ISSN 0361-0470
CODEN: JSBCD3
➤ **AMERICAN SOCIETY OF BREWING CHEMISTS. JOURNAL.** Variant title: Journal of the American Society of Brewing Chemists. Text in English. 1942. q. USD 204 domestic; USD 218 foreign (effective 2005). adv. charts. index, cum.index: 1940-1945, 1955-1964. back issues avail. **Document type:** *Journal, Academic/Scholarly.*
Formerly (until vol.34, 1976): American Society of Brewing Chemists. Proceedings (0096-0845)
Indexed: ASCA, AgBio, Agr, BCI, BIOBASE, BIOSIS Prev, BiolAb, CIN, CPA, ChemAb, ChemTitl, CurCont, CurPA, DSA, FCA, FS&TA, HortAb, ISR, MSB, NutrAb, PBA, PGrRegA, PHN&I, RM&VM, RPP, RefZh, RevApplEntom, SCI, SIA, SeedAb, TriticAb, WeedAb.
—BLDSC (4692.545000), CASDDS, CISTI, IDS, IE, Infotrieve, ingenta, Linda Hall. **CCC.**
Published by: American Society of Brewing Chemists, 3340 Pilot Knob Rd., St. Paul, MN 55121-2097. TEL 651-454-7250, 800-328-7560, FAX 651-454-0766, aacc@scisoc.org, http://www.asbcnet.org/Journal/, http://www.aaccnet.org. Ed. Charlie Bamforth. R&P Karen Cummings. Circ: 850.

663.2 641.5 USA
AMERICAN WINE ON THE WEB. Text in English. 1988. 12/yr. adv. **Document type:** *Consumer.* **Description:** Covers the wine industry in the Americas. Focuses on new wine releases, winery profiles, wine art, and wine events.
Former titles (until 1995): Southwest Internacional Wine and Food Review; Southwest International Wine
Media: Online - full text.
Published by: Gerry Troy, Pub., 969 Kevin Ave, Redlands, CA 92373-5855. TEL 909-338-9776, FAX 909-338-4956, winefreak@aol.com, http://www.2way.com/food/wine. Ed. Richard Jones. R&P, Adv. contact Gerry Troy.

663.2 USA ISSN 0149-6778
AMERICAN WINE SOCIETY BULLETIN. Text in English. 1973. irreg. USD 3. back issues avail. **Document type:** *Bulletin.*
Published by: American Wine Society, 3006 Latta Rd, Rochester, NY 14612. TEL 716-225-7613. Pub. Angel Nardone. Circ: 3,000.

663 USA ISSN 0364-698X
TP544.A46
AMERICAN WINE SOCIETY JOURNAL. Text in English. 1974 (vol.6). q. USD 36; includes manual & bulletin. **Description:** Contains articles on all aspects of wine appreciation, grape growing, winemaking, travel, health, and food.
Indexed: Agr, BibAg.
Published by: American Wine Society, 3006 Latta Rd, Rochester, NY 14612. TEL 716-225-7613. Ed. Jane Moulton. Pub., R&P Angel Nardone.

663.2 USA ISSN 0149-676X
AMERICAN WINE SOCIETY MANUAL. Text in English. irreg. price varies. back issues avail.
Published by: American Wine Society, 3006 Latta Rd, Rochester, NY 14612. TEL 716-225-7613. R&P Angel Nardone.

663.2 USA ISSN 1543-205X
AMERICAN WINE SOCIETY NEWS. Text in English. 1990 (vol.4). q. membership. **Description:** Contains news of the society; profiles the society's members; and lists calendar of events.
Published by: American Wine Society, 3006 Latta Rd, Rochester, NY 14612. TEL 716-225-7613. Ed. Robert Miller. R&P Angel Nardone.

663 CAN ISSN 1203-6528
ANNUAL PRODUCTION OF SOFT DRINKS. Text in English. 1954. a. **Document type:** *Yearbook, Trade.*
Former titles (until 1996): Monthly Production of Soft Drinks (0527-575X); (until 1964): Monthly Production of Carbonated Beverages (0380-593X)
—CISTI.
Published by: Statistics Canada, Manufacturing, Construction and Energy Division, Ste 1500 Main Bldg Holland Ave, Ottawa, ON K1A OT6, Canada. TEL 613-951-8116, infostats@statcan.ca.

663.2 ITA
ANNUARIO DEI MIGLIORI VINI ITALIANI; i migliori vini italiani descritti e valutati punto per punto. Text in Italian. 1993. a. EUR 49 (effective 2005). adv. charts; illus. **Document type:** *Directory, Consumer.* **Description:** Presents Luca Maroni's organoleptic fact sheets and tables on the best wines of Italy, along with labels and profiles of wine producers.
Formerly (until 1997): Annuario dei Vini Italiani
Published by: L m Srl, Via Flaminia, 1007, Rome, RM 00189, Italy. TEL 39-06-33219811, FAX 39-06-33219843, lmonline@lmonline.com, http://www.lmonline.com. Ed., Pub., R&P Luca Maroni. Adv. contact Tania Wolodimeroff.

APERITIF; tidningen foer en baettre restaurang- och dryckeskultur. see *HOTELS AND RESTAURANTS*

663.1 USA ISSN 0164-6281
ARIZONA BEVERAGE ANALYST. Text in English. 1936. m. USD 15 (effective 2005). adv. bk.rev. illus. **Document type:** *Magazine, Trade.* **Description:** Examines the liquor industry.
Formerly (until 1977): Arizona Beverage Journal (0004-1432)
Published by: Golden Bell Press Inc., 2403 Champa St, Denver, CO 80205. TEL 303-296-1600, FAX 303-295-2159, print@goldenbellpress.com, http://www.goldenbellpress.com. R&P Larry Bell. Adv. contact Susan Sherwood. Circ: 2,600 (paid).

ART CULINAIRE; the international magazine in good taste. see *FOOD AND FOOD INDUSTRIES*

THE ART OF EATING. see *FOOD AND FOOD INDUSTRIES*

663 GBR ISSN 1354-7240
ASIA - PACIFIC DRINKS BUYER. Text in English; Summaries in Chinese, Japanese, Korean, Thai. 1994. bi-m. GBP 55, USD 94 in Asia & the Pacific; GBP 70, USD 110 elsewhere (effective 2000). adv. back issues avail. **Document type:** *Trade.* **Description:** Discusses matters of interest to major purchasing companies of drinks in all Asian and Pacific nations.
Published by: Crier Publications Ltd., Arctic House, Rye Ln, Dunton Green, Sevenoaks, Kent TN14 5HB, United Kingdom. TEL 44-1732-451515, FAX 44-1732-451383, hbuckle@crier.co.uk. Ed. Sandy Guthrie. Pub., R&P Heather Buckle. Adv. contact Philip McLean. Circ: 10,200.

663.3 ESP
ASOCIACION ESPANOLA DE TECNICOS DE CERVEZA Y MALTA. ANUARIO. Text in Spanish. a. adv.
—CINDOC.
Published by: Asociacion Espanola de Tecnicos de Cerveza y Malta, C Ramirez de Prado, 8-1o F, Madrid, 28045, Spain. TEL 34-91-5277255, FAX 34-91-5285507, secretaria@aetcm.es, http://www.aetcm.es. adv.: B&W page EUR 470.

B

▼ new title ➤ refereed ✶ unverified ◆ full entry avail.

663 GTM ISSN 0066-8567
ASOCIACION NACIONAL DEL CAFE. DEPARTAMENTO DE ASUNTOS AGRICOLAS. INFORME ANUAL. Text in Spanish. 1962. a. free.
Formerly: Asociacion Nacional del Cafe. Departamento de Asuntos Agricolas. Annual Memory
Published by: (Departamento de Asuntos Agricolas), Asociacion Nacional del Cafe, Edificio Etisa, Plazuela Espana, Zona 9, Guatemala City, Guatemala.

ASSAM DIRECTORY & TEA AREAS HANDBOOK. see *BUSINESS AND ECONOMICS—Trade And Industrial Directories*

663 USA
ASSOCIATION OF WINE SUPPLIERS. BANKRUPTCY UPDATE. Text in English. irreg.
Published by: Association of Wine Suppliers, 21 Tamal Vistal Blvd, 196, Corte Madera, CA 94925. TEL 415-924-2640.

663 USA ISSN 0044-9881
ATLANTIC CONTROL STATES BEVERAGE JOURNAL. (North Carolina, Virginia and West Virginia Editions) Text in English. 1967. m. USD 18 (effective 2005). adv. bk.rev. **Document type:** *Magazine, Trade.* **Description:** News publication for West Virginia, Virginia and North Carolina liquor licenses and restaurants.
Published by: Club & Tavern, Inc., 3 12th St, Wheeling, WV 26003. TEL 304-232-7620, FAX 304-233-1236, bevjournalch@swave.net, http://www.bevnetwork.com. Pub., R&P, Adv. contact Arnold Lazarus. Circ: 6,379.

AUSTRALIA. BUREAU OF STATISTICS. SALES OF AUSTRALIAN WINE AND BRANDY BY WINEMAKERS. see *BEVERAGES—Abstracting, Bibliographies, Statistics*

663.2029 AUS ISSN 1033-7954
HD9388.A8
AUSTRALIAN AND NEW ZEALAND WINE INDUSTRY DIRECTORY. Text in English. 1983. a., latest 2003, 21st Ed. AUD 95 domestic; AUD 98 in New Zealand; AUD 120 elsewhere (effective 2004). adv. stat. 548 p./no.; **Document type:** *Directory, Trade.* **Description:** Directory of all wineries in Australia and New Zealand, plus listings of personnel, suppliers, consultants, distributors, writers, and organizations.
Formerly (until 1987): Australian Wine Industry Directory (0811-1324)
Published by: Wine Publishers Pty Ltd, PO Box 6015, Halifax St, SA 5000, Australia. TEL 61-8-82234799, FAX 61-8-82234790, wid@winetitles.com.au, info@winetitles.com.au, http://www.winetitles.com.au/wid. Ed. Michael Major. Adv. contact Ron Redford. B&W page AUD 1,782, color page AUD 2,255; trim 210 x 297. Circ: 3,000.

663.2 630 AUS ISSN 0819-2421
AUSTRALIAN AND NEW ZEALAND WINE INDUSTRY JOURNAL. Text in English. 1986. bi-m. AUD 88 domestic; AUD 80 in New Zealand; AUD 120 elsewhere (effective 2004). adv. index. 108 p./no. 2 cols./p.; back issues avail. **Document type:** *Journal, Trade.* **Description:** Contains wine-making, grape growing, finance & marketing information, including papers, industry news, market reports, new products.
Formerly: Australian Wine Industry Journal (0817-427X)
Indexed: AEA, AESIS, AgBio, CPA, FPA, FS&TA, HortAb, I&DA, NutrAb, PBA, PHN&I, RDA, RPP, RRTA, RevApplEntom, S&F, SIA, VITIS, WAE&RSA, WeedAb.
—BLDSC (1797.360000), IE, ingenta.
Published by: Wine Publishers Pty Ltd, PO Box 6015, Halifax St, SA 5000, Australia. TEL 61-8-82234799, FAX 61-8-82234790, wij@winetitles.com.au, info@winetitles.com.au, http://www.winetitles.com.au/wij. Ed. Anthony Madigan. R&P Paul Clancy. Adv. contact Ron Redford. color page AUD 1,705; trim 210 x 297. Circ: 3,000.

AUSTRALIAN HOTELIER. see *HOTELS AND RESTAURANTS*

663.2 634.8 AUS ISSN 1322-7130
AUSTRALIAN JOURNAL OF GRAPE AND WINE RESEARCH. Text in English. 1995. 3/yr. **Document type:** *Journal, Trade.*
Indexed: AEA, AgBio, CPA, CurCont, DSA, FPA, FS&TA, HortAb, I&DA, NemAb, NutrAb, OrnHort, PBA, PGegResA, PGrRegA, PHN&I, RM&VM, RPP, S&F, SIA, SeedAb, SoyAb, VITIS.
—BLDSC (1808.350000), IE, ingenta.
Published by: Australian Society of Viticulture and Oenology, P.O. Box 197, Glen Osmond, SA 5064, Australia. TEL 61-8-83036607, FAX 61-8-83036803, editor.ajgwr@asvo.com.au, http://www.asvo.com.au/front_ajgwr.html. Ed. Paul Kriedemann.

663.1 AUS
AUSTRALIAN LIQUOR REASEARCH. Text in English. 5/yr. **Document type:** *Magazine, Trade.*
Published by: N P G Media, 97 Victoria St, Potts Point, NSW 2011, Australia. TEL 61-2-93577277, FAX 61-2-93577244, npg@npg.com.au, http://www.npg.com.au/. Ed. Katrina Holden. Adv. contact Ashley Pini.

634.8 AUS ISSN 1329-0436
AUSTRALIAN VITICULTURE. Text in English. 1997. bi-m. AUD 55 domestic; AUD 60 in New Zealand; AUD 70 elsewhere (effective 2004). adv. Index. 112 p./no.; back issues avail. **Document type:** *Magazine, Trade.* **Description:** Provides practical vineyard management information and transfer of technical extension information from state agricultural departments and organizations.
Indexed: VITIS.
Published by: Wine Publishers Pty Ltd, PO Box 6015, Halifax St, SA 5000, Australia. TEL 61-8-82234799, FAX 61-8-82234790, viti@winetitles.com.au, info@winetitles.com.au, http://www.winetitles.com.au/ausvit. Ed. Cindie Smart. R&P Paul Clancy. Adv. contact Ron Redford. B&W page AUD 1,254, color page AUD 1,650; trim 210 x 297. Circ: 4,000 (paid).

663.2 AUS ISSN 0816-0805
➤ **AUSTRALIAN WINE RESEARCH INSTITUTE TECHNICAL REVIEW.** Text in English. 1981. bi-m. AUD 40.30 domestic; AUD 50 foreign; AUD 22 domestic to students; AUD 33.30 foreign to students (effective Jan. 2002). bk.rev. abstr. 50 p./no.; back issues avail. **Document type:** *Academic/Scholarly.* **Description:** Technical abstracts for winemakers, research articles, and industry news.
Published by: Australian Wine Research Institute, PO Box 197, Glen Osmond, SA 5064, Australia. TEL 61-8-83036600, FAX 61-8-83036601, ioats@awri.adelaide.edu.au. Ed., Adv. contact Creina Stockley. R&P Rae Blair. Circ: 1,120 (controlled).

➤ **AUSTRIA. HOEHERE BUNDESLEHRANSTALT UND BUNDESAMT FUER WEIN- UND OBSTBAU. MITTEILUNGEN KLOSTERNEUBURG**; Rebe und Wein, Obstbau und Fruechteverwertung. see *AGRICULTURE—Crop Production And Soil*

663.2 CAN ISSN 1188-1348
B C WINE TRAILS. Key Title: British Columbia Wine Trails. Text in English. 1991. q. CND 15 domestic; USD 18 in United States; CND 20 foreign (effective 2005). adv. bk.rev. back issues avail. **Document type:** *Magazine, Consumer.* **Description:** Guides readers into the vineyards, cellars and tasting roads of British Columbia wineries.
Published by: Wine Trails Publishing, PO Box 1319, Summerland, BC V0H 1Z0, Canada. TEL 250-494-7733, FAX 250-494-7737, winetrails@shaw.ca, http://www.winetrails.ca. Ed., Pub., Adv. contact Dave Gamble. B&W page CND 1,375; trim 15.5 x 11.5. Circ: 15,000.

B L R A STATISTICAL HANDBOOK; a compilation of drinks industry statistics. see *BEVERAGES—Abstracting, Bibliographies, Statistics*

663.2 ITA
BACCHUS. Text in German. 1978. s-a. adv. **Document type:** *Magazine, Trade.* **Description:** Explores Italian wines and food.
Related titles: ♦ Italian ed.: Civilta del Bere. ISSN 0390-1572.
Published by: Editoriale Lariana s.r.l., Via Ciro Menotti 11-D, Milan, MI 20129, Italy. TEL 39-02-76110303, FAX 39-02-713847. Ed. Pino Khail. Adv. contact Antonella Khail. Circ: 46,000.

663 DEU ISSN 0172-0937
DER BADISCHE WINZER. Text in German. 1978. m. EUR 2.50 newsstand/cover (effective 2004). adv. **Document type:** *Magazine, Trade.*
Indexed: VITIS.
Published by: Badischer Weinbauverband e.V., Merzhauser Str 115, Freiburg im Breisgau, 79100, Germany. TEL 49-761-459100, FAX 49-761-408026, info@badischer-weinbauverband.de, http://www.badischer-weinbauverband.de. adv.: B&W page EUR 2,635.20, color page EUR 4,366.20. Circ: 9,569 (controlled).

663.2 BGR
BAKHUS. Text in Bulgarian. 1999. m. BGL 48 domestic; EUR 50 in Europe; EUR 110 elsewhere (effective 2005). **Document type:** *Magazine, Trade.*
Published by: Economedia, ul Ivan Vazov 20, et. 2, Sofia, Bulgaria. TEL 359-2-9376444, FAX 359-2-9376236.

BARBEQUE & BEVERAGE. see *HOME ECONOMICS*

663.2 CAN ISSN 0228-5452
LA BARRIQUE. Text in English. 1971. 7/yr. CND 23. adv. back issues avail. **Document type:** *Trade.* **Description:** Wine and spirits information for consumers and restaurateurs in the Quebec province.
Published by: Kylix Media Inc., 5165 Sherbrooke St W, Ste 414, Montreal, PQ H4A 1T6, Canada. TEL 514-481-5892, FAX 514-481-9699, ryann@odyssee.net. Ed. Tony Aspler. Pub. Barbara Leslie. R&P Anne Walby. Adv. contact Judy Rochester. Circ: 11,045.

663 USA ISSN 0199-8404
BARTENDER; the authority on bartending and on-premise. Text in English. 1979. q. USD 30 domestic; USD 45 in Canada; USD 60 elsewhere (effective 2005). adv. bk.rev. back issues avail. **Document type:** *Magazine, Trade.* **Description:** For the full-service on-premise industry.
Published by: Foley Publishing Corp., PO Box 158, Liberty Corner, NJ 07938. TEL 800-463-7465, info@bartender.com, http://www.bartender.com. Ed. Jaclyn Wilson Foley. Pub., Adv. contact Raymond Foley. B&W page USD 14,000, color page USD 15,000. Circ: 148,170 (paid and controlled).

BARTENDER INTERNATIONAL. see *OCCUPATIONS AND CAREERS*

BARTENDEREN. see *OCCUPATIONS AND CAREERS*

663.2 USA
SB387
THE BAXEVANIS AMERICAN WINE REVIEW. Text in English. 1974. bi-m. USD 25 (effective 2001). adv. bk.rev. index, cum.index: 1974-1984. **Document type:** *Newsletter.* **Description:** Informs, educates, and fosters discourse on the wines and geography of the world's major and minor wine-producing regions.
Formerly (until 1994): Vinifera Wine Growers Journal (0095-3563)
Indexed: Agr.
—CISTI.
Published by: John J. Baxevanis, Ed. & Pub., 1947 Hillside Dr, Stroudsburg, PA 18360. TEL 717-424-6076. Circ: 2,500 (paid).

663 USA ISSN 0005-7533
CODEN: BBDSDO
BEBIDAS. Text in Spanish, English. 1942. bi-m. USD 30 domestic; USD 95 foreign (effective 2005). adv. bk.rev. 60 p./no.; reprints avail. **Document type:** *Magazine, Trade.* **Description:** Written for producers and distributors of soft drinks, beer, bottled water, juice and wine in 22 countries of Latin America plus Spain and Portugal.
Related titles: Supplement(s): Bebidas Para Mexico.
Published by: Global Beverage Publishers Inc., PO Box 16116, Cleveland, OH 44116. TEL 440-331-9100, FAX 440-331-9020, bebidaspub@aol.com. Ed., Adv. contact William R Dolan. B&W page USD 3,620; trim 11.25 x 8.25. Circ: 11,300 (controlled and free).

663 MEX ISSN 0188-8080
BEBIDAS MEXICANAS. Text in Spanish. bi-m. USD 25; USD 55 foreign. adv. **Document type:** *Trade.* **Description:** Presents technological, legal, business and marketing aspects of the beverage sector.
Published by: Alfa Editores Tecnicos S.A., Cumbres de Acultzingo 83, Col. Narvarte, Mexico City, DF 03020, Mexico. TEL 525-579-3333, FAX 525-582-3342, alfotec@telmex.net.mx, http://www.industria-alimentaria.com. Ed., R&P, Adv. contact Alejandro Garduno Torres. B&W page USD 504, color page USD 756. Circ: 5,000 (controlled).

663.4 642.5 USA
BEER & TAVERN CHRONICLE. Text in English. 1994. m. USD 30; USD 36 in Canada; USD 50 elsewhere. adv. **Document type:** *Newspaper.*
Published by: Beer & Tavern Chronicle, Inc., 244 Madison Ave, Ste 164, New York, NY 10016. TEL 212-685-8334, 800-343-4677, gsmithbeer@aol.com. Ed., R&P Gregg Smith. Pub., Adv. contact Liz Branch. Circ: 120,000.

663.42 USA
BEER BUSINESS DAILY. Text in English. d. USD 380 (effective 2005). **Document type:** *Newsletter, Trade.* **Description:** Contains brief, concise, insider beer news with analysis by industry participants and observers.
Media: Online - full content.
Published by: BeerNet Communications, Inc., 601 E Ashby, Ste 200, San Antonio, TX 78212. TEL 210-805-8006, hs@beernet.com, http://www.beernet.com/aboutpubs/bbd.html. Ed., Pub. Harry Schuhmacher.

BEER CANS & BREWERY COLLECTIBLES. see *HOBBIES*

663.42 USA
BEER DISTRIBUTOR MONTHLY. Text in English. m. USD 490 (effective 2005). **Document type:** *Newsletter, Trade.* **Description:** Filled with ideas to save costs and increase revenue and margins for beer and beverage distributors.
Published by: BeerNet Communications, Inc., 601 E Ashby, Ste 200, San Antonio, TX 78212. TEL 210-805-8006, hs@beernet.com, http://www.beernet.com/aboutpubs/dpl.html. Ed., Pub. Harry Schuhmacher.

662.3 658.8 USA
BEER HANDBOOK. Variant title: Adams Beer Handbook. Text in English. a. USD 350. charts; stat. **Document type:** *Trade.* **Description:** Reports trends, statistics, and analyses for the beer industry.
Published by: Adams Business Media, 2101 S Arlington Heights Rd, 150, Arlington, IL 60005. TEL 847-427-9512, 800-396-3939, FAX 847-427-2097, http://www.abm.net.

663.4 USA
BEER INDUSTRY UPDATE. Text in English. 1982. a. USD 845 (effective 1999). charts. back issues avail. **Document type:** *Trade.* **Description:** Statistical overview of US beer industry, with written analysis. Provides data for total beer shipments by state, brewer and region.
Published by: Beer Marketer's Insights, Inc., PO Box 264, West Nyack, NY 10994. TEL 914-624-2337. Ed. Jerry Steinman.

663.3 USA ISSN 0300-7480
BEER MARKETER'S INSIGHTS. Text in English. 1970. s-m. USD 595 (effective 2005). bk.rev. stat. 4 p./no.; back issues avail. **Document type:** *Newsletter, Trade.* **Description:** Analyzes shipments, sales in beer industry (domestic and import), plus social, political, legal trends which affect sales.
Published by: Beer Marketer's Insights, Inc., PO Box 264, West Nyack, NY 10994. TEL 845-624-2337, FAX 845-624-2340, http://www.beerinsights.com. Ed., Pub. Benj Steinman.

663.4 310 USA ISSN 0164-4831
BEER STATISTICS NEWS. Text in English. 1974. 24/yr. USD 360 (effective 1999). charts. **Document type:** *Bulletin.* **Description:** Reports shipments by major brewers in 39 states. Includes state, region, summary reports with graphs, maps, written analysis.
Published by: Beer Marketer's Insights, Inc., PO Box 264, West Nyack, NY 10994. TEL 914-624-2337. Ed. Eric Shepard.

BEST 'N' MOST IN D F S. (Duty Free Shopping) see *BUSINESS AND ECONOMICS—International Commerce*

658.8 USA
BEVERAGE ALCOHOL BUSINESS SCENE✶. Text in English. 1963. m. (8/yr.). USD 30. adv. **Document type:** *Trade.* **Description:** For beverage alcohol licensees buying at least $1,000,000 of liquor, wine and or beer at wholesale prices.
Former titles: Spirits, Wine and Beer Marketing in Iowa (0747-3214); Iowa Beverage Journal (0191-4650)
Published by: Diamond Publications, PO Box 398, Hopkins, MN 55343-0398. TEL 612-449-9446, FAX 612-449-9447. Ed. Gary L Diamond. Circ: 26,000.

663 USA ISSN 0736-220X
BEVERAGE ALCOHOL MARKET REPORT. Text in English. 1982. 20/yr. USD 210 domestic; USD 235 foreign (effective 2005). adv. bk.rev. charts; stat. 8 p./no. 1 cols./p.; **Document type:** *Newsletter, Trade.* **Description:** For executives in the international beer, wine and spirits industries, including producers, wholesalers and retailers.
Published by: Peregrine Communications, 160 E 48th St, New York, NY 10017. TEL 212-371-5237, perl160 @aol.com, perl160@aol.com. Ed., Pub., R&P Perry Luntz. adv.: B&W page USD 970. Circ: 3,000 (paid).

663.3 DEU
BEVERAGE AND BREWING INTERNATIONAL SUPPLIERS' GUIDE. Text in English. a. EUR 30 (effective 2003). adv. **Document type:** *Directory, Trade.*
Published by: Dr. Harnisch Verlagsgesellschaft GmbH, Blumenstr 15, Nuernberg, 90402, Germany. TEL 49-911-20180, FAX 49-911-2018100, service@harnisch.com, http://www.harnisch.com/beverage_brewing/index.htm. Circ: 14,500 (paid and controlled).

663 664 IND ISSN 0970-6194
BEVERAGE AND FOOD WORLD. Text in English. 1974 (vol.3). m. INR 450, USD 50 (effective 2001). adv. **Document type:** *Journal, Trade.* **Description:** Provides information on processed foods and beverage products, equipment, and ingredients.
Incorporates: Brewer - Distiller and Bottler
Published by: Amalgamated Press, Narang House, 2nd Fl, 41 Ambalal Doshi Marg Fort, Mumbai, Maharashtra 400 001, India. TEL 91-22-2650268, 91-22-2654184, FAX 91-22-264-1275, dasilva@vsnl.com. Ed., Pub. Norman J Da Silva. adv.: B&W page INR 5,500, B&W page USD 450, color page INR 8,500, color page USD 750; trim 240 x 186. Circ: 8,000.

663 USA
BEVERAGE COMMUNICATOR. Text in English. 1972. q. USD 18; USD 20 foreign.
Published by: Beverage Communicator, Inc., 5 Barker Ave, Ste 501, White Plains, NY 10601. TEL 914-761-7700, FAX 914-997-2617. Circ: 6,250.

663 330 USA
BEVERAGE DIGEST. Text in English. 1982. s-m. (22/yr). USD 665 domestic includes supplement; USD 765 foreign includes supplement (effective 2005). bk.rev. charts; mkt.; stat. Supplement avail.; back issues avail.; reprints avail. **Document type:** *Newsletter, Trade.* **Description:** Covers the soft drink industry and related markets.
Formerly: Jesse Meyers' Beverage Digest (0738-8853)
Related titles: Supplement(s): Fact Book.
Published by: Beverage Digest Company, LLC, 2 Depot Plaza, Ste 101-A, PO Box 621, Bedford, NY 10507-0621. TEL 914-244-0700, FAX 914-244-0774, bevnews@beverage-digest.com, http://www.beverage-digest.com. Ed., Pub., R&P John Sicher.

663 658 USA ISSN 1523-0392
BEVERAGE DYNAMICS. Text in English. 1934. 9/yr. USD 35 domestic; USD 50 in Canada & Mexico; USD 75 elsewhere; free to qualified personnel (effective 2005). adv. charts; illus.; stat. **Document type:** *Magazine, Trade.* **Description:** Covers the retail trade in specialty food items, sundries, gourmet and deli products, and the beverage trade, including alcohol.
Former titles (until 1999): Jobson's Beverage & Food Dynamics (1077-0666); (until 1994): Beverage Dynamics (1077-0763); Jobson's Beverage Dynamics (1046-1973); (until 1989): Liquor Store (1058-5273); (until 1983): Liquor Store Magazine (0024-4236)
Related titles: Online - full text ed.: (from Florida Center for Library Automation, Gale Group).
Published by: Adams Business Media, Beverage Group, 257 Park Ave. S, 3d Fl, New York, NY 10010. TEL 646-654-2000, FAX 646-654-2099, http://www.beveragenet.net. Ed. Richard Brandes. Pub. Seymour Leikind. adv.: B&W page USD 11,575, color page USD 15,040. Circ: 65,000 (controlled).

663.6 USA ISSN 0148-6187
CODEN: BEVIAY
BEVERAGE INDUSTRY. Text in English. 1946. m. USD 85.05 domestic; USD 150.05 foreign; USD 15.05 per issue; free to qualified personnel (effective 2004). adv. illus. Index. reprints avail. **Document type:** *Magazine, Trade.* **Description:** Edited for executives in beverage markets, with emphasis on marketing, technology, and distribution activities.
Former titles (until 1973): Soft Drink Industry (0038-0547); (until 1966): Bottling Industry
Related titles: Microform ed.: (from PQC); Online - full text ed.: (from EBSCO Publishing, Florida Center for Library Automation, Gale Group, Northern Light Technology, Inc., O C L C Online Computer Library Center, Inc., ProQuest Information & Learning); ♦ Supplement(s): Beverage Industry Annual Manual. ISSN 8755-0717.
Indexed: ABIn, B&I, BPI, BusI, ChPerI, CurPA, H&TI, HospI, IPackAb, PROMT, SRI, T&II.
—BLDSC (1947.255000), IE, ingenta.
Published by: Stagnito Communications, Inc. (Subsidiary of: Ascend Media), 155 Pfingsten Rd., Ste. 205, Deerfield, IL 60015. TEL 847-205-5660, FAX 847-205-5680, info@stagnito.com, http://www.bevindustry.com, http://www.stagnito.com. Eds. Joan Holleran, Sarah Theodore. Pubs. Jim Karwowski, Tom Bachmann. Adv. contact Catherine Wynn. B&W page USD 5,590, color page USD 7,690; trim 10.825 x 14.5. Circ: 34,000 (controlled).

663 USA ISSN 8755-0717
HD9348.U5
BEVERAGE INDUSTRY ANNUAL MANUAL. Text in English. 1967. a. USD 55.05 (effective 2003). adv. stat. **Document type:** *Trade.* **Description:** Contains statistical material for beverage industry executives and department managers.
Related titles: ♦ Supplement to: Beverage Industry. ISSN 0148-6187.
Indexed: SRI.
Published by: Stagnito Communications, Inc. (Subsidiary of: Ascend Media), 155 Pfingsten Rd., Ste. 205, Deerfield, IL 60015. TEL 847-205-5660, FAX 847-205-5680, info@stagnito.com, http://www.stagnito.com. Ed. Joan Holleran. Pub. Tom Bachmann. Adv. contact Anngail Norris. Circ: 34,000.

663.1 USA ISSN 1054-0423
BEVERAGE INDUSTRY NEWS. Text in English. 1935. m. USD 49 (effective 2005). adv. bk.rev. abstr.; bibl.; charts; illus.; stat. index. **Document type:** *Magazine, Trade.* **Description:** Covers all news relevant to the alcoholic beverage industry.
Incorporates (1970-1994): Beverage Industry News Merchandiser (0271-9894); Formerly (until 1988): Beverage Industry News of California (0274-9041)
Published by: B I N Publications, 171 Mayhew Way Ste 202, Pleasant Hill, CA 94523-4348. TEL 925-932-4999, FAX 925-932-4966, dlpage@earthlink.net. Ed. John Coleman. Pub., R&P, Adv. contact David L Page. Circ: 15,000.

663 USA ISSN 1050-4427
THE BEVERAGE JOURNAL. Text in English. 1982. m. USD 26 (effective 2005). adv. bk.rev.; software rev.; Website rev. 100 p./no. 3 cols./p.; reprints avail. **Document type:** *Journal, Trade.*
Published by: Michigan Licensed Beverage Association, 920 N Fairview Ave, Lansing, MI 48912. TEL 518-374-9611, FAX 518-374-1165, ashock@mlba.org, editor@mlba.org, http://www.mlba.org. Ed. Peter Broderick. Pub. Lou Adado. adv.: page USD 300. Circ: 3,700 (paid); 400 (free).

663 USA ISSN 1057-5030
HD9348.U5
THE BEVERAGE MARKETING DIRECTORY (YEAR). Text in English. 1978. a. USD 845 softcover ed; USD 865 hardcover ed (effective 2000). adv. **Document type:** *Directory, Trade.* **Description:** Guide to the beverage industry in the United States and Canada. Comprehensive company-by-company listing of more than 12,000 producers, bottlers, importers, wholesalers and distributors in every beverage category.
Former titles (until 1991): National Beverage Marketing Directory (0197-3061); (until 1980): National Beverage Marketing Directory of Telephone Numbers and Addresses (0160-9580)
Related titles: Diskette ed.
Published by: Beverage Marketing Corporation, 2670 Commercial Ave, Mingo, OH 43938. TEL 740-598-4133, FAX 740-598-3977. Ed. Terry Welling. Circ: 2,300.

663 USA ISSN 0006-0372
BEVERAGE MEDIA. Text in English. 1936. m. USD 99 NYC (effective 2005); subscr. price varies by state. adv. bk.rev. illus.; mkt.; stat.; tr.lit. **Document type:** *Magazine, Trade.*
Published by: Beverage Media, Ltd., 161 Ave of the Americas, New York, NY 10013. TEL 212-734-0322, FAX 212-620-0473, info@bevaccess.com, http://www.beveragemedia.com. Ed. William G Slone. Circ: 19,000 (paid).

641.2 USA ISSN 1524-6566
BEVERAGE RETAILER MAGAZINE. Text in English. bi-m. USD 30 domestic; USD 45 in Canada; USD 95 elsewhere (effective 2001). **Document type:** *Magazine, Trade.* **Description:** Covers the marketing and merchandising of alcoholic beverages by off-premise retailers.
Published by: Oxford Publishing, Inc., 307 W Jackson Ave, Oxford, MS 38655-2154. TEL 662-236-5510, 800-247-3881, FAX 662-236-5541, br@beverage-retailer.com, http://www.beverage-retailer.com. Ed. Benita Whitehorn. Pub. Ed Meek.

663.6 USA ISSN 0098-2318
TP659.A1 CODEN: BEWODQ
BEVERAGE WORLD. Text in English. 1882. m. USD 79 domestic; USD 84 in Canada; USD 148 elsewhere; USD 10 newsstand/cover (effective 2005). adv. charts; illus.; mkt.; pat.; tr.lit.; tr.mk. index. back issues avail.; reprint service avail. from PQC. **Document type:** *Magazine, Trade.* **Description:** Provides in-depth editorial feature, essential news and research on the issues, trends, people and companies shaping the best-changing beverage market.
Former titles (until 1975): Soft Drinks (0038-0571); (until 1966): National Bottler's Gazette (0097-2061)
Related titles: Microfilm ed.: (from PQC); Online - full text ed.: (from EBSCO Publishing, Factiva, Florida Center for Library Automation, Gale Group, H.W. Wilson, O C L C Online Computer Library Center, Inc., ProQuest Information & Learning, The Dialog Corporation); ♦ Spanish ed.: Beverage World en Espanol. ISSN 1076-8149.
Indexed: ABIn, BPI, BPIA, BusI, CurPA, ExcerpMed, H&TI, HospI, IPackAb, PAIS, PROMT, T&II.
—BLDSC (1947.265000), CISTI, IE, Infotrieve, ingenta, Linda Hall. **CCC.**
Published by: V N U Business Publications (Subsidiary of: V N U Business Media), 770 Broadway, New York, NY 10003-9595. TEL 646-654-7601, FAX 646-654-5351, akaplan@beverageworld.com, bmcomm@vnuinc.com, http://www.beverageworld.com/, http://www.vnubusinessmedia.com/. adv.: page USD 5,970; trim 8 x 10.875. Circ: 30,000 (controlled). **Subscr. to:** PO Box 2054, Skokie, IL 60076-9724.

663 USA ISSN 1076-8149
BEVERAGE WORLD EN ESPANOL. Text in Spanish, English. 1946-1989; resumed 1994. bi-m. USD 79 domestic; USD 125 foreign; USD 10 per issue (effective 2005). adv. **Document type:** *Magazine, Trade.* **Description:** Provides close-up looks at people, industry, products and trends of the Latin American beverage market.
Related titles: Online - full content ed.; ♦ English ed.: Beverage World. ISSN 0098-2318.
—CCC.
Published by: V N U Business Media, 770 Broadway, New York, NY 10003 . TEL 646-654-5000, FAX 646-654-7212, bmcomm@vnuinc.com, http://www.beverageworld.com/, http://www.vnubusinessmedia.com/. Ed. Jeff Cioletti. adv.: page USD 3,170; trim 8 x 10.875. Circ: 11,708 (controlled).

663 USA
BEVERAGE WORLD'S DATABANK. Text in English. 1984. a. free with subscr. to Beverage World. adv. **Document type:** *Trade.*
Former titles: Beverage World's Daily Desk Reference Living Directory; Beverage World's Living Directory
Published by: V N U Business Media, 770 Broadway, New York, NY 10003 . TEL 646-654-5000, FAX 646-654-7727, bmcomm@vnuinc.com, http://www.vnubusinessmedia.com/. Ed. Andrea Foote. Pub. Kevin Francella. Circ: 34,000.

663 USA
BEVERAGES: LATIN AMERICAN INDUSTRIAL REPORT✶. (Avail. for each of 22 Latin American countries) Text in English. 1985. a. USD 435; per country report.
Published by: Aquino Productions, P O Box 15760, Stamford, CT 06901-0760. Ed. Andres C Aquino.

663.4 NLD ISSN 1383-309X
HET BIERBLAD. Text in Dutch. 1987. 10/yr. **Document type:** *Magazine, Consumer.*
Published by: (Heineken Brouwerijen), B J Media bv, Postbus 53, Bloemendaal AB, 2060, Netherlands. TEL 31-23-5411726, FAX 31-23-5411826. Circ: 25,000 (controlled).

641 DEU
DER BIERGROSSHANDEL - DER GETRAENKEGROSSHANDEL. Text in German. 1949. m. EUR 144 (effective 2004). adv. **Document type:** *Magazine, Trade.*
Formerly: Biergrosshandel (0341-4914)
Indexed: FS&TA, KES.
Published by: Matthaes Verlag GmbH, Olgastr 87, Stuttgart, 70180, Germany. TEL 49-711-2133245, FAX 49-711-2133350, kontaktm@matthaes.de, http://www.matthaes.de/biergrosshandel/. adv.: B&W page EUR 2,380, color page EUR 3,460. Circ: 8,445 (paid and controlled).

B

▼ new title ➤ refereed ✶ unverified ♦ full entry avail.

663 CAN
BILLY'S BEST BOTTLES. Text in English. 1973. bi-m. CND 40; CND 50 foreign (effective 1999). bk.rev. back issues avail. **Document type:** *Newsletter.* **Description:** Review of all wines sold in Canada as well as restaurant and travel tips.
Former titles: Best Bottles Wineletter (1196-9539); (until 1987): Best Bottles (0827-7478); (until 1984): William Munnelly's Private Guide to the Best Bottles (0827-746X)
Published by: Best Bottles Inc., P O Box 21011, Stratford, ON N5A 7V4, Canada. TEL 519-273-5517, FAX 519-273-5517. Ed., Pub. William Munnelly. Circ: 5,000.

BINSTED'S BOTTLING DIRECTORY (YEAR). see *BUSINESS AND ECONOMICS—Trade And Industrial Directories*

663.4 ITA ISSN 0006-3770
BIRRA E MALTO. Text in Italian. 1954. 3/yr. free to qualified personnel. adv. bk.rev. **Document type:** *Academic/Scholarly.* **Description:** Publishes articles on the art and science of brewing and technological progress.
Indexed: FS&TA, RefZh.
—BLDSC (2094.080000).
Published by: Associazione Italiana Tecnici Birra e Malto/Italian Brewmasters Association, Via Trento, 79, Pedavena, BL 32034, Italy. TEL 0439-303737. Ed. Tullio Zangrando. Circ: 950.

B

663 DEU ISSN 1619-4969
DIE BLUME. Text in German. 1951. 4/yr. EUR 40.35 domestic; EUR 45.60 in Europe; EUR 46.60 elsewhere; EUR 6.65 newsstand/cover (effective 2005). adv. **Document type:** *Journal, Trade.*
Published by: (Fachverband Getraenkeschankanlagen e.V.), Fachverlag Hans Carl, Andernacher Str 33A, Nuernberg, 90411, Germany. TEL 49-911-952850, FAX 49-911-9528560, info@hanscarl.com, http://www.hanscarl.com. adv.: B&W page EUR 421, color page EUR 1,000. Circ: 1,200 (paid and controlled).

663 FRA ISSN 0760-1999
BOISSONS DE FRANCE - JEAN PRIMUS. Text in French. 1936. m. adv. bk.rev. bibl.; charts; illus.; stat. index.
Formerly: Boissons de France "Saines et Legeres" (0006-5803)
Published by: Federation Nationale des Boissons, 49 rue de la Glaciere, Paris, 75013, France. TEL 45-87-21-41, FAX 45-87-11-69, TELEX 260 076 F. Ed. Claude Boissin. Circ: 7,000.

BON VIVANT. see *TRAVEL AND TOURISM*

663.19 USA
BOTTLED WATER REPORTER. Text in English. bi-m. USD 50 to non-members; USD 25 to members. adv. bk.rev. **Document type:** *Trade.*
Published by: International Bottled Water Association, 1700 Diagnol Rd, Ste 650, Alexandria, VA 22314-2973. TEL 703-683-5213, FAX 703-683-4074, mbeusetti@erols.com, http://www.bottledwater.org. Ed. Max Beusetti. Adv. contact Ann F Carberry. Circ: 3,000.

663.2 ESP ISSN 0211-1071
BOUQUET. Text in Spanish. 1980. m. **Document type:** *Consumer.*
Published by: Ediciones Sociales S.L., Rossello, 186-4o, Barcelona, 08036, Spain. TEL 34-3-323-14-91, FAX 34-3-4548665. Ed. Julio Cayuela Torno.

663.1 DEU ISSN 0006-9159
CODEN: BWWSAP
DIE BRANNTWEINWIRTSCHAFT; Zeitschrift fuer Spiritusindustrie. Text in German. 1857. s-m. EUR 131.50 domestic; EUR 158.25 foreign (effective 2002). adv. bk.rev. charts; illus.; pat.; tr.lit. index. **Document type:** *Magazine, Trade.*
Indexed: BiolAb, CISA, ChemAb, FS&TA, VITIS.
—BLDSC (2271.000000), CASDDS.
Published by: Versuchs- und Lehranstalt fuer Spiritusfabrikation und Fermentationstechnologie, Seestr 13, Berlin, 13467, Germany. TEL 49-30-45080-0, FAX 49-30-4536067, info@vlsf.de, http://www.vlsf.de. Ed. R Beckmann. Circ: 2,880.

663.3 DEU ISSN 0179-2466
CODEN: MONBAS
BRAUEREI-FORUM; Fachzeitung fuer Brauereien, Maelzereien und Getraenkeindustrie. Text in German. 1985. fortn. EUR 95 (effective 2005). adv. bk.rev. **Document type:** *Newspaper, Trade.*
Formed by the merger of (1943-1985): Tageszeitung fuer Brauerei (0039-8942); Which was formerly (until 1961): Die Brauerei (0366-2683); Which superseded in part (in 1946): Die Deutsche Brauerei (0366-869X); (1948-1985): Forum der Brauerei (0723-6891); Which superseded in part (in 1982): Monatsschrift fuer Brauerei (0369-1233); Which was formerly (until 1960): Die Brauerei. Wissenschaftliche Beilage (0366-2691); (1963-1985): Der Brauer- und Maelzer-Lehrling (0520-7568)
Indexed: AnalAb, BiolAb, ChemAb, DSA, FCA, FS&TA, HerbAb, PST.
—BLDSC (2275.901000), CASDDS, CISTI, Linda Hall. **CCC.**
Published by: (Versuchs- und Lehranstalt fuer Brauerei in Berlin), Westkreuz Verlag GmbH Berlin-Bonn, Buehlenstr 10-14, Bad Muenstereifel, 53902, Germany. TEL 49-2257-811, FAX 49-2257-7853, redaktion@brauerei-forum.de, verlag@westkreuz.de, http://www.vlb-berlin.org/forum/, http://www.westkreuz.de. Ed. Olaf Hendel. Adv. contact Hannelore Gautsch. B&W page EUR 1,805, color page EUR 2,825; trim 185 x 263. Circ: 4,725 (paid).

663.3 DEU ISSN 0172-0589
BRAUEREI JOURNAL. Text in German. 1882. m. adv. charts; illus. **Document type:** *Magazine, Trade.*
Former titles (until 1972): D B B - Der Brauereibesitzer und Braumeister (0172-0600); (until 1955): Brauereibesitzer und Braumeister (0006-9280)
Indexed: CISA.
—CCC.
Published by: Dreistern Verlag GmbH, Andreas-Hofer-Str 1, Munich, 81547, Germany. TEL 49-89-6936730, FAX 49-89-69367370, brauerei.journal@dreistern.de, cp@dreistern.de, http://www.brauereijournal.de, http://www.dreistern.de. Ed. Dr. Guenter Thoss. Adv. contact Sylvia Bolkart.

663.3 DEU ISSN 0068-0710
BRAUEREIEN UND MAELZEREIEN IN EUROPA. Text in German. 1910. a. EUR 227.52 (effective 1999). adv. **Document type:** *Directory.*
Published by: Hoppenstedt Bonnier Zeitschriften GmbH, Havelstr. 9, Darmstadt, 64295, Germany. TEL 49-6151-380-0, FAX 49-6151-380-360. Circ: 2,000.

663.4 DEU ISSN 0341-7115
CODEN: BRINDA
BRAUINDUSTRIE. Text in German. 1915. m. EUR 55; EUR 5.20 newsstand/cover (effective 2004). adv. bk.rev. index. **Document type:** *Magazine, Trade.*
Formerly: Brauer und Maelzer (0045-2718)
Indexed: CEABA, CIN, ChemAb, ChemTitl, PST, RefZh.
—BLDSC (2275.930000), CASDDS, CISTI, IE, ingenta. **CCC.**
Published by: Verlag W. Sachon GmbH & Co., Schloss Mindelburg, Mindelheim, 87714, Germany. TEL 49-8261-9990, FAX 49-8261-999132, info@sachon.de, http://www.sachon.de. Ed. Marcus Steiner. Adv. contact Martina Zimmermann. B&W page EUR 3,610, color page EUR 4,990; trim 210 x 297. Circ: 7,995 (paid and controlled).

663.3 DEU ISSN 0724-696X
CODEN: BRUWAQ
BRAUWELT; Zeitschrift fuer das gesamte Brauwesen und die Getraenkewirtschaft. Text in German; Summaries in English, French. 1943. 3/m. EUR 182.50 domestic; EUR 222.50 in Europe; EUR 237 elsewhere; EUR 8.55 newsstand/cover (effective 2005). adv. bk.rev. abstr.; charts; illus.; pat.; tr.lit. index. Supplement avail. **Document type:** *Magazine, Trade.* **Description:** Provides up-to-date information on technical and marketing developments in the brewing, distilling and soft drink industries.
Incorporates (1984-1993): Getraenketechnik (0177-784X); (1969-1987): Brautechnik Aktuell (0006-9310); Former titles (until 1978): Brauwelt. Ausgabe B (0340-9945); (until 1948): Die Brauwelt (0006-9329); Which superseded in part (in 1946): Die Deutsche Brauerei (0366-869X); Which was formed by the merger of (1861-1943): Allgemeine Brauer- und Hopfenzeitung (0365-0707); (1885-1943): Allgemeine Braumeister-Zeitung (0723-3213); (188?-1943): Allgemeiner Anzeiger fuer Brauereien, Maelzereien und Hopfenbau (0723-3205); (1903-1943): Tageszeitung fuer Brauerei (0723-3396); (1866-1943): Zeitschrift fuer das Gesamte Brauwesen (0372-8706); Which was formerly (until 1878): Der Bayerische Bierbrauer (0723-3965)
Indexed: CIN, CISA, ChemAb, ChemTitl, ExcerpMed, FS&TA, IPackAb, NutrAb, RefZh.
—BLDSC (2277.049000), CISTI, IE, ingenta, Linda Hall. **CCC.**
Published by: Fachverlag Hans Carl, Andernacher Str 33A, Nuernberg, 90411, Germany. TEL 49-911-952850, FAX 49-911-9528560, info@hanscarl.com, http://www.brauwelt.de, http://www.hanscarl.com. Ed. Karl-Ullrich Heyse. Adv. contact Bettina Lehmacher. B&W page EUR 3,247, color page EUR 4,663; trim 185 x 275. Circ: 5,931 (paid and controlled).

663.3 DEU ISSN 1431-522X
BRAUWELT - BREVIER (YEAR). Text in German. 1975. a. EUR 29.90 (effective 2003). **Document type:** *Yearbook, Trade.*
—BLDSC (2277.090000).
Published by: Fachverlag Hans Carl, Andernacher Str 33A, Nuernberg, 90411, Germany. TEL 49-911-952850, FAX 49-911-9528560, info@hanscarl.com, http://www.hanscarl.com. Ed. K U Heyse.

663.3 DEU ISSN 0934-9340
HD9397.A1 CODEN: BRINEB
BRAUWELT INTERNATIONAL. Text in English. 1983. 6/yr. EUR 93.50; EUR 17.20 newsstand/cover (effective 2005). adv. index. back issues avail. **Document type:** *Magazine, Trade.* **Description:** Reports on technical and marketing developments in the brewing, distilling and soft drinks industries.
Related titles: Russian ed.: Mir Piva. ISSN 1029-3914. 1995. EUR 93.50; EUR 17.20 newsstand/cover (effective 2005); Chinese ed.: ISSN 1435-8042. EUR 93.50; EUR 17.20 newsstand/cover (effective 2005); Spanish ed.: EUR 123.30; EUR 29.50 newsstand/cover (effective 2005).
Indexed: AbHyg, AgBio, DSA, FCA, FS&TA, HortAb, NutrAb, PBA, PHN&I, RDA, RPP, RevApplEntom, S&F, SIA, TDB, TriticAb, WAE&RSA, WeedAb.
—BLDSC (2277.110000), IE, ingenta. **CCC.**
Published by: Fachverlag Hans Carl, Andernacher Str 33A, Nuernberg, 90411, Germany. TEL 49-911-952850, FAX 49-911-9528548, info@hanscarl.com, http://www.hanscarl.com. Ed. Karl-Ullrich Heyse. Adv. contact Christine Bach. B&W page EUR 2,455, color page EUR 3,850; trim 185 x 275. Circ: 11,379.

663.3 GBR
BREW-INFO; monthly industry review. Text in English. 1952. m. bk.rev. Supplement avail.
Former titles: Brewing Research Foundation. Current Awareness Monthly; Brewing Research Foundation. Bulletin of Current Literature; Brewing Industry Research Foundation. Bulletin of Current Literature (0300-4619)
Indexed: AEA.
Published by: Brewing Research International, Lyttel Hall, Nutfield, Redhill, Surrey RH1 4HY, United Kingdom. TEL 44-1737-822205, FAX 44-1737-822380, suehendn@brewingresearch.co.uk. Circ: 400 (controlled).

663.4 USA ISSN 1081-826X
TP570
BREW YOUR OWN; the how-to homebrew beer magazine. Text in English. 1995. 8/yr. USD 24.95 domestic; USD 29.95 in Canada & Mexico; USD 39.95 elsewhere (effective 2005). adv. bk.rev. back issues avail. **Document type:** *Magazine, Consumer.* **Description:** Provides practical hands-on tips and techniques to brew great tasting beer for hobbyists who make their own beer.
Address: 5053 Main St, Ste A, Manchester Center, VT 05255. TEL 802-362-3981, FAX 802-362-2377, byo@byo.com, http://www.byo.com/. Ed. Chris Colby. Pub., R&P Brad Ring. Adv. contact Kiev Rattee. Circ: 105,000 (paid).

663.3 GBR
TP500 CODEN: BREWDH
THE BREWER & DISTILLER. Text in English. 2000. m. GBP 60 domestic to non-members; GBP 75 foreign to non-members (effective 2005). adv. bk.rev. charts; illus.; stat. index. back issues avail. **Document type:** *Magazine, Trade.* **Description:** Contains review articles, and serves as a training, revision, and more general communications vehicle, with news and views from industry.
Formerly (until 2005): The Brewer International; Formed by the merger of (1988-2000): Ferment (0957-7041); (1911-2000): The Brewer (0006-9736); Which was formerly (until 1971): Brewers' Guild Journal (0366-2764); (until 1950): Incorporated Brewers' Guild. Journal (0368-2439)
Related titles: E-mail ed.; Online - full text ed.
Indexed: BiolAb, BrTechI, CurPA, FS&TA, PST.
—BLDSC (2279.847000), CASDDS, CISTI, IE, ingenta.
Published by: Institute & Guild of Brewing, 33 Clarges St, London, W1J 7EE, United Kingdom. TEL 44-20-74998144, FAX 44-20-74991156, enquiries@igb.org.uk, http://www.igb.org.uk/igbsite/publications/brewer.asp. Ed. Michael Parsons. Adv. contact Julie Barker TEL 44-20-74046999. Circ: 4,500.

663 USA
BREWERS ALMANAC. Text in English. 1946. a. USD 170 (effective 1999). charts; stat. **Document type:** *Trade.* **Description:** Documents historical and current information on the American brewing industry, including production, consumption and trade statistics.
Published by: Beer Institute, 122 C St, N W, Ste 750, Washington, DC 20001-2109. TEL 202-737-2337, FAX 202-737-7004, http://www.beerinst.org. Ed. Matthew A Hein. R&P Matthew Hein. Circ: 1,400.

663.3 USA ISSN 0006-971X
TP500 CODEN: BRDGAT
BREWERS DIGEST. Text in English. 1926. bi-m. USD 30 domestic; USD 40 foreign (effective 2005). adv. bk.rev. abstr.; bibl.; illus.; stat.; tr.lit. index. 72 p./no.; **Document type:** *Magazine, Trade.*
Related titles: Special ed(s).: Brewers Digest. Annual Buyers' Guide.
Indexed: BiolAb, ChemAb, CurCont, CurPA, FS&TA, IPackAb, NutrAb.
—BLDSC (2280.000000), CASDDS, CISTI, IE, ingenta, Linda Hall.
Published by: Siebel Publishing Co., Inc., PO Box 677, Thiensville, WI 53092. TEL 262-242-6105. Ed. Dori Whitney. Pub. Thomas Volke. adv.: B&W page USD 728, color page USD 898. Circ: 2,000 (paid).

663.3029 USA
BREWERS DIGEST ANNUAL BUYERS GUIDE AND BREWERY DIRECTORY✶. Variant title: Brewers Digest Brewery Directory. Text in English. 1926. a. USD 50. adv. **Document type:** *Directory, Trade.*

Published by: Siebel Publishing Co., Inc., PO Box 677, Thiensville, WI 53092. TEL 312-463-3401. Ed. Dori Whitney. Pub. Leonard Kay TEL 773-463-7484. Circ: 3,104.

663.3 GBR ISSN 0006-9728
TP500
BREWERS' GUARDIAN. Text in English. 1871. m. GBP 60 in Europe; USD 180 in US & Canada; JPY 28,000 in Japan; GBP 110 rest of world (effective 2001). adv. bk.rev. charts; illus.; mkt.; stat.; tr.lit. index. 44 p./no. 3 cols./p.; back issues avail.; reprint service avail. from PQC. **Document type:** *Magazine, Trade.*
Indexed: BiolAb, ChemAb, CurPA, FS&TA, IPackAb, PST.
—BLDSC (2281.000000), CISTI, IE, ingenta.
Published by: P J B Publications Ltd. (Subsidiary of: T & F Informa plc), 5th Fl, Telephone House, 69-77 Paul Street, London, EC2A 4LQ, United Kingdom. TEL 44-20-70176979, FAX 44-20-70176969, info@pjbpubs.com, http://www.pjbpubs.com. Ed. Larry Nelson. Pub. Dr. Philip Brown. R&P Annette Watts TEL 44-20-83328961. Adv. contact Hazel Swinton. page GBP 660; trim 186 x 267. Circ: 2,800; 400 (paid); 2,600 (controlled). **Subscr. addr. in N America:** Pharmabooks Ltd., 270 Madison Ave., # 4, New York, NY 10016-0601.

663.3029 GBR ISSN 0309-7625
BREWERS GUILD DIRECTORY. Text in English. 1923. a. GBP 60 in British Isles; GBP 70 rest of world (effective 1999). adv. **Document type:** *Directory.*
Published by: Brewers Guild Publications Ltd., 8 Ely Pl, London, EC1N 6SD, United Kingdom. TEL 44-171-405-4565, FAX 44-171-831-4995. Ed. J A Barker. Adv. contact Julie Barker. Circ: 2,000.

663.3029 GBR
BREWERY MANUAL & WHO'S WHO IN BRITISH BREWING & SCOTCH WHISKY DISTILLING INDUSTRIES. Text in English. 1915. a. GBP 80, USD 120 (effective 2001). adv. **Document type:** *Directory.* **Description:** Gives names, addresses, financial details and personnel of all British breweries and Scotch whisky distillers maltsters and hop merchants. Lists all brands, wholesalers, organizations, conferences and conventions. Contains material of interest to beer importers, pub operators, cider makers, and manufacturers of soft drinks.
Published by: P J B Publications Ltd. (Subsidiary of: T & F Informa plc), 5th Fl, Telephone House, 69-77 Paul Street, London, EC2A 4LQ, United Kingdom. TEL 44-20-70176979, FAX 44-20-70176969, info@pjbpubs.com, http://www.pjbpubs.com. Ed. Larry Nelson. R&P Annette Watts TEL 44-20-83328961. Adv. contact Peter Coltart TEL 44-20-83328802.

663.42 DEU
BREWING AND BEVERAGE INDUSTRY CHINA. Text in Chinese. 1996. 2/yr. EUR 7.80 newsstand/cover (effective 2004). adv. **Document type:** *Magazine, Trade.*
Published by: Verlag W. Sachon GmbH & Co., Schloss Mindelburg, Mindelheim, 87714, Germany. TEL 49-8261-9990, FAX 49-8261-999132, info@sachon.de, http://www.sachon.de. Ed. Margit Pietzke. Adv. contact Sabine Berchtenbreiter. B&W page EUR 3,200, color page EUR 4,520; trim 210 x 297. Circ: 9,050 (paid and controlled).

663.42 DEU ISSN 1439-5452
BREWING AND BEVERAGE INDUSTRY ESPANOL. Text in Spanish. 1999. 2/yr. EUR 7.80 newsstand/cover (effective 2004). adv. **Document type:** *Magazine, Trade.*
Published by: Verlag W. Sachon GmbH & Co., Schloss Mindelburg, Mindelheim, 87714, Germany. TEL 49-8261-9990, FAX 49-8261-999132, info@sachon.de, http://www.sachon.de. Ed. Margit Pietzke. Adv. contact Sabine Berchtenbreiter. B&W page EUR 2,740, color page EUR 3,940; trim 210 x 297. Circ: 6,595 (paid and controlled).

663 DEU ISSN 0949-8877
BREWING AND BEVERAGE INDUSTRY INTERNATIONAL. Text in English. 1989. q. EUR 6 newsstand/cover (effective 2004). adv. back issues avail. **Document type:** *Magazine, Trade.*
Indexed: RefZh.
—CISTI.
Published by: Verlag W. Sachon GmbH & Co., Schloss Mindelburg, Mindelheim, 87714, Germany. TEL 49-8261-9990, FAX 49-8261-999132, info@sachon.de, http://www.sachon.de. Ed. Margit Pietzke. Adv. contact Sabine Berchtenbreiter. B&W page EUR 3,550, color page EUR 4,915. Circ: 12,300 (paid and controlled).

663.1 GBR ISSN 0308-1265
CODEN: BDINDE
BREWING & DISTILLING INTERNATIONAL. Text in English. 1865. m. GBP 48 domestic; GBP 82 foreign (effective 2000). adv. bk.rev. charts; illus.; mkt.; tr.lit. **Document type:** *Trade.* **Description:** Covers news, views new products and plant applications. Includes regular technical features on all aspects of the brewing and distilling processes.
Formerly (until 1974): International Brewing and Distilling (0020-6210)
Indexed: B&I, ChemAb, FS&TA, IPackAb, NutrAb, PST, RefZh.
—BLDSC (2282.700000), CISTI, IE, ingenta.
Published by: Brewery Traders Publications Ltd., 52 Glenhouse Rd, Eltham, London, SE19 1JQ, United Kingdom. TEL 44-20-8859-4300, FAX 44-20-8859-5813, bdilondon@dial.pipex.com, http://www.bdinews.com, http://www.bdinews.co.uk. Ed., Pub., R&P Bruce J Stevens TEL 44-20-8859-4300. Adv. contact Sarah-Jane Cropper TEL 44-1543-672641. Circ: 3,100 (paid and controlled).

663.3 CAN ISSN 0068-094X
BREWING AND MALTING BARLEY RESEARCH INSTITUTE. ANNUAL REPORT. Text in English. 1952. a. free to qualified persons. **Document type:** *Corporate.*
Indexed: FS&TA.
Published by: Brewing and Malting Barley Research Institute, 303-161 Portage Ave, East, Winnipeg, MB R3B 2L6, Canada. TEL 204-927-1407, FAX 204-947-5960. Circ: 700 (controlled).

663 BEL ISSN 1371-2438
HET BROUWERSBLAD. Text in Flemish. 1893. q. EUR 30 domestic; EUR 50 foreign (effective 2005). adv. bk.rev. **Document type:** *Trade.*
Former titles: Kleine Brouwersblad; Renseignements Techniques
Related titles: ♦ French ed.: Le Journal du Brasseur. ISSN 1371-0052; English ed.: ISSN 1376-6392. 2000. EUR 30 domestic; EUR 50 foreign (effective 2005).
Published by: Confederation des Brasseries de Belgique/Confederation of Belgian Breweries, Maison des Brasseurs, Grand' Place 10, Brussels, 1000, Belgium. TEL 32-2-511-4987, FAX 32-2-511-3259, http://www.beerparadise.be. Ed. Rik Cooreman. R&P Jan Debrabanter. Adv. contact Alain Mathieu Medial. Circ: 10,000.

663.3 658.8 GBR ISSN 1467-4521
BUSINESS RATIO. BREWERS. Text in English. 1974. a. GBP 275 (effective 2001). charts; stat. **Document type:** *Trade.*
Former titles (until 1999): Business Ratio Plus: Brewers (1354-8743); (until 1993): Business Ratio Report: Brewers (0261-748X)
Published by: The Prospect Shop Ltd., Field House, 72 Oldfield Rd, Hampton, Middx TW12 2HQ, United Kingdom. TEL 44-20-8461-8730, 44-20-8481-8720, FAX 44-20-8783-1940, info@theprospectshop.co.uk.

663 GBR ISSN 1473-3919
BUSINESS RATIO REPORT. DISTILLERS (YEAR). Text in English. 1973. a. GBP 275 (effective 2001). charts; stat. **Document type:** *Trade.*
Former titles (until 2000): Business Ratio. Distillers (1469-2635); (until 1999): Business Ratio Plus. Distillers (1358-2321); (until 1994): Business Ratio Report. Distillers (0261-7803)
Published by: The Prospect Shop Ltd., Field House, 72 Oldfield Rd, Hampton, Middx TW12 2HQ, United Kingdom. TEL 44-20-8461-8730, 44-20-8481-8720, FAX 44-20-8783-1940, info@theprospectshop.co.uk.

663.2 GBR ISSN 1470-7055
BUSINESS RATIO. WINE & SPIRIT MERCHANTS. Text in English. 1973. a. GBP 275 (effective 2001). **Document type:** *Trade.*
Former titles (until 2000): Business Ratio Plus: Wine & Spirit Merchants (1354-8727); (until 1995): Business Ratio Report: Wine and Spirit Merchants (0261-9695)
Published by: The Prospect Shop Ltd., Field House, 72 Oldfield Rd, Hampton, Middx TW12 2HQ, United Kingdom. TEL 44-20-8461-8730, 44-20-8481-8720, FAX 44-20-8783-1940, info@theprospectshop.co.uk.

CAFE REVUE (EDITION FRANCAISE). see *HOTELS AND RESTAURANTS*

CAFE REVUE (NEDERLANDSE EDITIE). see *HOTELS AND RESTAURANTS*

641.2 USA
CALIFORNIA BEVERAGE NEWS. Text in English. 1936. m. USD 24 (effective 2004). adv. **Document type:** *Magazine, Trade.*
Former titles: California Beverage Bulletin (1096-5491); (until 199?): Beverage Bulletin (1074-2085); Southern California Beverage Bulletin (0192-1835)
Published by: Interactive Color, Inc., 4910 San Fernando Rd, Glendale, CA 91204. http://www.beveragelink.com. Ed. Meridith May. Circ: 20,000 (controlled).

663.2 USA ISSN 0883-4423
TP557
CALIFORNIA WINE WINNERS; the best from the competitions. Text in English. 1983. a. USD 10.95 (effective 2005). adv. back issues avail. **Document type:** *Consumer.* **Description:** Covers the major Western wine judgings and reports on specific awards given during each contest.
Published by: Varietal Fair, PO Box 432, Graton, CA 95444-0432. TEL 707-874-3105, FAX 707-874-1323. Eds. J T Devine, T Ahlstrom. R&P T. Ahlstrom. Adv. contact J.T. Devine. Circ: 11,000 (paid).

663.3 USA ISSN 1086-2587
CELEBRATOR BEER NEWS. Text in English. 1988. bi-m. USD 19.95 domestic (effective 2005). adv. bk.rev. 52 p./no. 4 cols./p.; back issues avail. **Document type:** *Newspaper, Consumer.*
Published by: Celebrator Publications, 22455 Maple Ct, Hayward, CA 94541. TEL 510-538-3739, FAX 510-889-7780, tdalldorf@celebrator.com, http://www.celebrator.com/, http://www.celebrator.com/celebrator/. Ed., Pub. Tom Dalldorf. Circ: 50,000 (paid and controlled).

663 674.94 USA
CELLAR NOTES. Text in English. 1981. bi-m. USD 15. bk.rev. back issues avail.
Published by: Cellar Notes Inc., 5 Muirfield Ln., St. Louis, MO 63141-7355. TEL 314-576-4143, FAX 314-919-8801. Ed. Eileen M Carr. Circ: 400.

663.3 BEL ISSN 1373-7163
CODEN: CERBE8
CEREVISIA (EDITION BILINGUE); Belgian journal of brewing and biotechnology. Text in Dutch, English, French, German. 1939. q. bk.rev. abstr.; charts; illus.; tr.lit. index. reprint service avail. from PQC. **Document type:** *Bulletin, Trade.* **Description:** Covers developments in the brewing sciences and other sectors of fermentation and non-alcoholic beverage technology.
Formerly (until 1995): Cerevisia and Biotechnology (0778-2640); Formed by the 1991 merger of: Belgian Journal of Food Chemistry and Biotechnology (0773-6177); Which was formerly (1946-1985): Revue des Fermentations et des Industries Alimentaires (0035-2071); Cerevisia (0770-1713); Which was formed by the 1976 merger of: Fermentatio (0015-0053); B I F (0773-4964); Which was formerly: Association des Anciens Etudiants en Brasserie de Bruxelles. Bulletin
Related titles: Microform ed.
Indexed: AgBio, AgrForAb, B&BAb, BiolAb, CBTA, CIN, ChemAb, ChemTitl, CurCont, DSA, FS&TA, GenetAb, HGA, HortAb, IndVet, NutrAb, PBA, PHN&I, PST, RM&VM, RPP, RefZh, SIA, TriticAb, WeedAb.
—BLDSC (3120.050000), CASDDS, CISTI, IE, ingenta, Linda Hall.
Published by: Cerevisia, Groene Dreef 11, St-Martens-Latem, 9830, Belgium. TEL 32-9-282-5695, FAX 32-9-221-6370, cerevisia@skynet.be. Eds. Eric van Schoonenbeerghe, Joseph Lenges. Pub., R&P, Adv. contact Jacques Vander Stricht. Circ: 2,000.

B

663.3 ESP ISSN 0300-4481
CODEN: CEMADD
CERVEZA Y MALTA. Text in Spanish. 1964. q. EUR 75 domestic; EUR 150 foreign (effective 2005). adv. bk.rev. abstr.; bibl.; charts; illus.; pat.; stat. cum.index. back issues avail. **Document type:** *Magazine, Trade.* **Description:** Contains scientific, technical and professional articles about the beer and malt industry.
Related titles: Online - full text ed.
Indexed: CIN, ChemAb, ChemTitl, IECT.
—CASDDS, CINDOC. **CCC.**
Published by: Asociacion Espanola de Tecnicos de Cerveza y Malta, C Ramirez de Prado, 8-1o F, Madrid, 28045, Spain. TEL 34-91-5277255, FAX 34-91-5285507, secretaria@aetcm.es, http://www.aetcm.es/revista.htm. Ed. F Xavier Castante Sitjas. adv.: B&W page EUR 470. Circ: 1,500 (controlled).

▼ **CHOW;** Food. Drink. Fun. see *FOOD AND FOOD INDUSTRIES*

641 ITA ISSN 0390-1572
CIVILTA DEL BERE; mensile di informazione, documentazione e difesa della qualita. Text in Italian. 1974. m. (11/yr.). illus. **Document type:** *Magazine, Trade.* **Description:** Covers winemaking, wines, alcoholic beverages and food.
Related titles: ♦ German ed.: Bacchus.
Published by: Editoriale Lariana s.r.l., Via Ciro Menotti 11-D, Milan, MI 20129, Italy. TEL 39-02-76110303, FAX 39-02-713847, editorialelariana@civiltadelbere.com. Ed. Bruno Donati. Adv. contact Antonella Khail. Circ: 49,000.

647.95 663.1 GBR
CLASS; the magazine of bar culture. Text in English. 1997. m. GBP 33 domestic; GBP 60 in Europe; GBP 90 elsewhere (effective 2005). adv. **Document type:** *Magazine, Trade.* **Description:** Covers the bar culture within the drinks industry.
Formerly: C L A S S - Cocktail Liqueur and Specialty Spirt (1464-0430)
Published by: William Reed Publishing Ltd., Broadfield Park, Brighton Rd, Pease Pottage, Crawley, W Sussex RH11 9RT, United Kingdom. TEL 44-7714-451955, subs@william-reed.co.uk, http://www.william-reed.co.uk/magazines/s_class.html. Ed. Paul Wootton. Pub. Russell Dodd. Adv. contact Beth Pedersen. Circ: 9,591.

663 USA
CLOCKDIAL. Text in English. 1938. q. free. **Document type:** *Magazine, Trade.* **Description:** For the employees and management of Dr Pepper bottling plants worldwide.
Published by: Dr Pepper - Seven Up, Inc., PO Box 869077, Plano, TX 75086-9077. TEL 972-673-7000, FAX 972-673-7867, jill_haerle@dpsu.com. Ed., R&P Jill Haerle TEL 972-673-7819. Circ: 10,000.

663 DEU
COCA-COLA JOURNAL. Text in German. 1934. q. free. back issues avail. **Document type:** *Corporate.*

Published by: Coca-Cola GmbH, Max-Keith-Str 66, Essen, 45136, Germany. TEL 49-201-18211377, FAX 49-201-8211110, ulindenberg@lus.v.o.com. Ed. Ursula Kindenberg. Circ: 16,300.

663   CHE
COCKTAIL BAR. Text in French, German, Italian. q. **Document type:** Trade.
Published by: Gastronomie & Tourisme SA, Case Postale 231, Lugano-Pregassona, 6963, Switzerland. TEL 41-91-9413828, FAX 41-91-9413825. Ed. Alberto Dell'Acqua.

663   USA   ISSN 0010-1516
COLORADO BEVERAGE ANALYST. Text in English. 1936. m. USD 16 (effective 2005). adv. illus.; stat.; tr.lit. **Document type:** Magazine, Trade.
Published by: Golden Bell Press Inc., 2403 Champa St, Denver, CO 80205. TEL 303-296-1600, FAX 303-295-2159, print@goldenbellpress.com, http://www.goldenbellpress.com. Pub. Lawrence Bell. Adv. contact Susan Sherwood. Circ: 2,300 (paid).

COMPENSATION IN FOOD & BEVERAGE PROCESSING. see BUSINESS AND ECONOMICS—Labor And Industrial Relations

663   USA   ISSN 0191-8818
CONNECTICUT BEVERAGE JOURNAL. Text in English. 1943. m. USD 37.10 in state; USD 35 elsewhere (effective 2005). adv. illus.; mkt. **Document type:** Magazine, Trade.
Description: Reports on news and developments in the Connecticut beverage industry.
Published by: Beverage Publications, Inc, 2508 Whitney Ave, Ste C, Box 185159, Hamden, CT 06518. TEL 203-288-3375, FAX 203-288-2693, thebeveragejournal@snet.net, http://www.ctbeveragejournal.com. Ed., Pub. Gerald P Slone. Circ: 5,636 (paid).

663.2 686.2   USA   ISSN 0161-6668
CONNOISSEURS GUIDE TO CALIFORNIA WINE. Text in English. 1974. m. looseleaf. USD 50; USD 75 foreign (effective 1999). index. back issues avail. **Document type:** Newsletter.
Address: PO Box V, Alameda, CA 94501. TEL 510-865-3150, cgcw@aol.com. Eds. Charles Olken, Earl Singer. Circ: 11,000.

663.2   ITA
CORRIERE VINICOLO; commercio vinicolo. Text in Italian. 1928. w. EUR 154 (effective 2005); includes subscription to Focuswine. bk.rev. mkt.; stat. 24 p./no.; Supplement avail.; back issues avail. **Document type:** Newspaper. **Description:** Discusses viticulture and enology.
Related titles: CD-ROM ed.; Online - full text ed.; ◆ Supplement(s): Enotria.
Published by: Unione Italiana Vini, Via San Vittore al Teatro 3, Milan, 20123, Italy. TEL 39-02-7222281, FAX 39-02-866226, info@uiv.it, http://www.corrierevinicolo.com, http://www.uiv.it. Ed. Marco Mancini. Adv. contact Giordano Chiesa TEL 39-02-72222843. Circ: 9,000 (paid).

663   FRA   ISSN 1257-2187
LA COTE DES VINS. Text in French. s-m. **Document type:** Newsletter.
Published by: Jour-Azur S.A., 17 rue d'Uzes, Paris, Cedex 2 75108, France. TEL 33-1-40133500, FAX 33-1-40419363.

CUISINE ET VINS DE FRANCE. see FOOD AND FOOD INDUSTRIES

663   DEU   ISSN 0944-4645
                                    CODEN: WEWIAW
D D W - DIE WEINWISSENSCHAFT; viticultural and enological sciences. Text in English, French, German. 1946. 4/yr. EUR 11.50 newsstand/cover (effective 2004). adv. bk.rev. back issues avail. **Document type:** Magazine, Trade.
Former titles (until 1989): Die Weinwissenschaft (0375-8818); (until 1954): Der Deutsche Weinbau. Wissenschaftliche Beihefte (0173-7392); (until 1952): Der Deutsche Weinbau (0012-0979); (until 1952): Der Weinbau (0342-5924)
Indexed: FS&TA, HortAb, PGrRegA, RefZh, VITIS.
—CASDDS. **CCC.**
Published by: Fachverlag Dr. Fraund GmbH, An der Brunnenstube 33-35, Mainz, 55120, Germany. TEL 49-6131-62050, FAX 49-6131-620544, verlag@fraund.de, http://www.fraund.de. Ed. K Schaller. adv.: B&W page EUR 500. Circ: 1,600 (paid and controlled).

663.2   GBR   ISSN 0954-4240
DECANTER; the world's best wine magazine. Text in English. 1975. m. GBP 34.40 domestic; USD 49.99 in United States (effective 2004). adv. bk.rev. illus.; tr.lit. reprints avail. **Document type:** Magazine, Consumer. **Description:** Discusses wine and wine making.
Former titles (until 1985): Decanter Magazine (0141-6014); (until 1975): Wine-Butler (0043-5783)

Published by: I P C Country & Leisure Media Ltd. (Subsidiary of: I P C Media Ltd.), 1st Fl, Broadway House, 2-6 Fulham Broadway, London, SW6 5UA, United Kingdom. TEL 44-20-76103929, marketing@decanter.com, http://www.decanter.com, http://www.ipcmedia.com. Ed. Amy Wislocki TEL 44-20-7261-3929. Pub. Sarah Kemp. Adv. contact Stephen Hobley. Circ: 36,000 (paid). **Subscr. to:** I P C Media Ltd., Perrymount Rd, Haywards Heath RH16 3DA, United Kingdom. TEL 44-1444-475675, FAX 44-1444-445599.

663   FRA   ISSN 1254-2733
DECISION BOISSONS; le premier journal hebdomadaire des decideurs du monde des liquides. Text in French. 1995. w. (42/yr).
Published by: Editions Litteraires Techniques et Artistiques (ELTA), 16 rue Saint Fiacre, Paris, 75002, France. TEL 33-1-42-36-9559, FAX 33-1-42338324. Ed. Norbert Brousse. Pub. Michel Burton. R&P Brigitte Borel.

663   USA
DELAWARE BEVERAGE MONTHLY. Text in English. 1984. m. USD 38 (effective 1998). adv. **Document type:** Magazine, Trade. **Description:** State distributors' monthly pricing of alcoholic beverages for licensees in the state of Delaware.
Published by: Melton Communications Inc., 1518 N Van Buren St, Wilmington, DE 19806. TEL 302-655-2800, FAX 302-655-2805. Ed., Pub. Dale W Melton. Adv. contact Fran Baldt. page USD 240. Circ: 1,800 (controlled).

DELICATESSE (FRENCH EDITION). see FOOD AND FOOD INDUSTRIES

DELTA MAG; the magazine of the Delta guide. see HOTELS AND RESTAURANTS

641.2 362.29   USA   ISSN 0094-3940
HV5297.V8
DEPARTMENT OF ALCOHOLIC BEVERAGE CONTROL. ANNUAL REPORT. Text in English. 1972. a. **Document type:** Government.
Published by: Virginia. Department of Alcoholic Beverage Control, 2901 Hermitage Rd, Richmond, VA 23220. TEL 804-213-4687, 800-552-3200, http://www.abc.state.va.us/admin/reports/annual.htm.

DESKTOP PRODUCTS GUIDE. see BUSINESS AND ECONOMICS—Trade And Industrial Directories

663   DEU   ISSN 0724-4266
DEUTSCHE GETRAENKE WIRTSCHAFT; Wirtschaftsmagazin fuer Fachhandel und Gastronomie. Text in German. 1983. 10/yr. EUR 56 domestic; EUR 74.50 foreign; EUR 7 newsstand/cover (effective 2004). adv. **Document type:** Magazine, Trade. **Description:** Covers beer, wine, champagne, spirits, trade fairs, management and news.
Formerly (until 1983): Deutsche Getraenke-Industrie (0012-0227)
Indexed: FS&TA.
Published by: D G W Verlag Monika Busch und Timur Dosdogru GbR, Nansenstr 11, Wetter, 58300, Germany. TEL 49-2335-739801, FAX 49-2335-739802, Red@deutschegetraenkewirtschaft.de, http://www.deutsche-getraenke-wirtschaft.de. Eds. Monika Busch, Timur Dosdogru. adv.: B&W page EUR 2,686, color page EUR 4,464; trim 210 x 280. Circ: 12,000 (paid and controlled).

663   DEU   ISSN 0944-3177
DER DEUTSCHE WEINBAU. Text in German. 1993. 24/yr. EUR 73.20; EUR 3.10 newsstand/cover (effective 2004). adv. **Document type:** Magazine, Trade.
Formed by the merger of (1968-1993): Weinwirtschaft Anbau (0932-3309); Which was formerly (until 1987): Winzer-Kurier (0343-5156); (1971-1993): Die Weinwirtschaft Technik (0723-1369); Which superseded in part (in 1983): Die Weinwirtschaft (0341-6364); Which was formerly (until 1975): Allgemeine Deutsche Weinfachzeitung (0012-0960); Which was formed by the merger of (1903-1971): Das Weinblatt (0170-0650); (1864-1971): Deutsche Wein-Zeitung (0366-8967); Which incorporated (192?-1967): Illustrierte Wein-Zeitung (0724-598X)
Indexed: FS&TA, VITIS.
—Infotrieve. **CCC.**
Published by: Meininger Verlag GmbH, Maximilianstr 7-17, Neustadt, 67433, Germany. TEL 49-6321-8908-0, FAX 49-6321-890873, contact@meininger.de, http://www.der-deutsche-weinbau.de, http://www.meininger.de. Ed. Rudolf Nickenig. adv.: color page EUR 3,850, B&W page EUR 2,500. Circ: 7,897 (paid and controlled).

663.4   DEU   ISSN 0172-3774
DEUTSCHER BRAUMEISTER- UND MALZMEISTER-BUND. MITTEILUNGSBLATT. Text in German. 4/yr. (plus a issue). EUR 79.50 domestic; EUR 84.75 in Europe; EUR 85.75 elsewhere; EUR 9.65 newsstand/cover (effective 2005). adv. **Document type:** Newsletter, Trade.
Published by: (Deutscher Braumeister- und Malzmeister-Bund e.V.), Fachverlag Hans Carl, Andernacher Str 33A, Nuernberg, 90411, Germany. TEL 49-911-952850, FAX 49-911-9528560, info@hanscarl.com, http://www.hanscarl.com. Eds. Karl-Ullrich Heyse, Karlheinz Limpert. Adv. contact Bettina Lehmacher. B&W page EUR 1,490, color page EUR 2,537; trim 185 x 275. Circ: 3,570.

DIRECTORIO DE LA INDUSTRIA MEXICANA DE BEBIDAS. see BUSINESS AND ECONOMICS—Trade And Industrial Directories

663   DEU   ISSN 0344-6816
DER DOEMENSIANER. Text in German. 1960. q. adv. **Document type:** Journal, Trade.
Published by: Verlag W. Sachon GmbH & Co., Schloss Mindelburg, Mindelheim, 87714, Germany. TEL 49-8261-9990, FAX 49-8261-999132, info@sachon.de, http://www.sachon.de. Ed. G Zentgraf. Adv. contact Martina Zimmermann. B&W page EUR 1,661, color page EUR 3,164. Circ: 4,978 (controlled).

DRAM SHOP AND ALCOHOL REPORTER. see LAW

663 658.8   NLD   ISSN 0165-2745
DRANKENDETAIL. Text in Dutch. 1902. 10/yr. adv. bk.rev.; software rev. illus.; mkt.; stat.; tr.lit.; tr.mk. back issues avail. **Document type:** Magazine, Trade. **Description:** For specialized retailers of wine, spirits, beer and non-alcoholic beverages, their suppliers, and allied trades.
Formerly (until 1978): Gastrovin (1385-6979)
Published by: Theo Jaegers B.V., Hoefbladhof 61, Houten, 3991 GG, Netherlands. TEL 31-30-6371780, FAX 31-30-6351034. Ed., R&P Theo Jaegers.

663   GBR
DRINK BUYER AMERICAS. Text in English, Spanish. 1996. q. GBP 50, USD 80 in Latin America and Caribbean; GBP 75, USD 110 elsewhere. adv. **Document type:** Trade. **Description:** Discusses matters of interest to major purchasing companies of drinks in all Latin American nations.
Former titles (until 1999): Bebidas Latino Americanas; Latin American Drinks Buyer
Published by: Crier Publications Ltd., Arctic House, Rye Ln, Dunton Green, Sevenoaks, Kent TN14 5HB, United Kingdom. TEL 44-1732-451515, FAX 44-1732-451383, editorial@crier.co.uk. Ed. Sandy Guthrie. Pub., R&P Heather Buckle. Adv. contact Philip McLean. Circ: 15,000.

663   GBR   ISSN 1468-6880
DRINK BUYER EUROPE. Text in English. 1991. bi-m. GBP 55 in Europe; GBP 80 elsewhere (effective 2000). adv. back issues avail. **Document type:** Trade. **Description:** Discusses matters of interest to major companies purchasing drinks in all European nations.
Formerly (until 1999): European Drinks Buyer (1351-4911)
Indexed: B&I.
Published by: Crier Publications Ltd., Arctic House, Rye Ln, Dunton Green, Sevenoaks, Kent TN14 5HB, United Kingdom. TEL 01732-451515, FAX 01732-451383, edhart@crier.co.uk. Ed. Sandy Guthrie. Pub., R&P Heather Buckle. Adv. contact Philip McLean. Circ: 10,942.

663   GBR   ISSN 0951-7723
THE DRINK FORECAST. Text in English. q. GBP 695 (effective 2000). **Document type:** Trade. **Description:** Provides a monitor of trends in all the main alcoholic and soft drink sectors.
Published by: N T C Publications Ltd. (Subsidiary of: World Advertising Research Center Ltd.), PO Box 69, Henley-on-Thames, Oxon RG9 1GB, United Kingdom. TEL 44-1491-411000, FAX 44-1491-571188, info@ntc.co.uk.

663   GBR   ISSN 0965-5360
DRINK POCKET BOOK (YEAR). Text in English. 1989. a. GBP 35 per issue (effective 2000). **Document type:** Trade. **Description:** Provides detailed statistical drink industry data for those working in drink manufacturing, retailing, advertising and marketing.
—CCC.
Published by: N T C Publications Ltd. (Subsidiary of: World Advertising Research Center Ltd.), Farm Rd, Henley-on-Thames, Oxon RG9 1EJ, United Kingdom. TEL 44-1491-411000, FAX 44-1491-571188, info@ntc.co.uk.
Co-sponsor: A C Nielson.

663   DEU   ISSN 1433-1594
DRINK TECHNOLOGY AND MARKETING. Text in English. 1997. q. adv. back issues avail. **Document type:** Magazine, Trade. **Description:** Publishes a magazine of the worldwide beverage industry for readers interested in the brewing, dairing and mineral water industries, manufacturers of non-alcoholic drinks, wine and bottled waters.
Indexed: FS&TA.
—BLDSC (3627.031700).
Published by: Dr. Harnisch Verlagsgesellschaft GmbH, Blumenstr 15, Nuernberg, 90402, Germany. TEL 49-911-20180, FAX 49-911-2018100, drink@harnisch.com, service@harnisch.com, http://www.harnisch.com/drink_technology/index.htm. Ed. Ian Healey. Pub. Benno Keller. Adv. contact Claudine Hebestreit. B&W page EUR 3,300, color page EUR 4,500; trim 210 x 297. Circ: 13,750.

663   CHE
DRINKS. Text in German. 1985. bi-m. EUR 6 newsstand/cover (effective 2005). adv. **Document type:** Magazine, Trade.
Published by: (Deutsche Barkeeper Union e.V. DEU), Die Medienbotschaft GmbH, Villa Rheinblick, Oberstr 2, Taegerwilen, 8274, Switzerland. TEL 41-71-6693670, FAX 41-71-6693674, info@medienbotschaft.com. adv.: B&W page EUR 2,690, color page EUR 4,050. Circ: 5,900.

663 GBR
DRINKS BUYER CHINA. Text in Chinese. 1996. q. GBP 20, USD 34 in Asia & the Pacific; GBP 30, USD 51 elsewhere (effective 2000). adv. **Document type:** *Trade.* **Description:** Discusses matters of interest to major purchasing companies of drinks in China.
Formerly (until 1999): Chinese Drinks Buyer
Published by: Crier Publications Ltd., Arctic House, Rye Ln, Dunton Green, Sevenoaks, Kent TN14 5HB, United Kingdom. TEL 44-1732-451515, FAX 44-1732-451383, editorial@crier.co.uk. Ed. Sandy Guthrie. Pub. Heather Buckle. Adv. contact Philip McLean. Circ: 11,000.

641.2 IRL
DRINKS INDUSTRY IRELAND. Text in English. m. adv. **Document type:** *Magazine, Trade.*
Published by: Louisville Publishing Ltd., Louisville, Enniskerry, Co. Wicklow, Ireland. TEL 353-2046230, FAX 353-2046231. adv.: color page EUR 1,898. Circ: 4,500 (paid and controlled).

641.2 GBR
DRINKSNET✶ . Text in English. d. mkt.; stat.; tr.lit. **Document type:** *Newspaper, Trade.* **Description:** World's daily business news agency for drinks industry.
Media: Large Type (12 pt.). **Related titles:** E-mail ed.; Fax ed.
Published by: Drinksnet Ltd., 43 Whitehouse Rd, Edinburgh, EH4, United Kingdom. FAX 44-131-5503863, mac.news@btinternet.com. Ed. Jamie Sempill.

663.2 DEU ISSN 0172-391X
E W R; Schriftenreihe zum europaeischen Weinrecht. Text in German. 1979. irreg. **Document type:** *Monographic series, Trade.*
Indexed: ELLIS.
Published by: (Institut fuer Weinrecht der Gesellschaft fuer Rechtspolitik, Trier), Deutscher Fachverlag GmbH, Mainzer Landstr 251, Frankfurt Am Main, 60326, Germany. TEL 49-69-759501, FAX 49-69-75952999, info@dfv.de, http://www.dfv.de.

641.2 DEU
ECKES. ANNUAL REPORT. Text in English. a. **Document type:** *Yearbook, Corporate.* **Description:** Details the economic and market conditions of the Eckes beverage distribution company.
Published by: Eckes AG, Ludwig-Eckes-Allee 6, Nieder-Olm, 55268, Germany. TEL 49-6136-35-0, FAX 49-6136-351400.

663.2 ITA ISSN 0390-2048
ENOHOBBY. Text in Italian. 1974. m.
Address: Via di San Tarcisio, 5, Rome, RM 00178, Italy. Ed. Franco Tomassoli.

663.2 ITA ISSN 1593-6112
L'ENOLOGO. Text in Italian. 1890. 10/yr. EUR 33.57 domestic; EUR 46.49 foreign (effective 2000). adv. bk.rev. charts; illus.; stat.
Formerly (until 2000): Enotecnico (0392-176X)
Indexed: FS&TA, HortAb.
—BLDSC (3775.693200), IE, ingenta.
Published by: Associazone Enologi Enotecnici Italiani, Viale Murillo 17, Milan, MI 20149, Italy. TEL 39-02-40072460, FAX 39-02-48704951, info@assoenologi.it. Ed. Giuseppe Martelli. Adv. contact Giacomo Moretti. Circ: 7,500.

ENOTECA WINE AND FOOD MAGAZINE; for the connoisseur in you. see *HOTELS AND RESTAURANTS*

641 ITA
ENOTRIA; annuario della vite e del vino. Text in Italian. 1920. a. EUR 15.50 per issue (effective 2003). adv. **Document type:** *Magazine, Trade.*
Related titles: ♦ Supplement to: Corriere Vinicolo.
Published by: Unione Italiana Vini, Via San Vittore al Teatro 3, Milan, 20123, Italy. TEL 39-02-7222281, FAX 39-02-866226, info@uiv.it, http://www.uiv.it. Ed. Marco Mancini. Adv. contact Giordano Chiesa TEL 39-02-72222843. Circ: 30,000.

663.2 664 USA
EPICUREAN TRAVELER. Text in English. 1999. q. USD 28 domestic; USD 36 foreign; USD 4.50 per issue (effective 2003). adv. bk.rev. 84 p./no. 2 cols./p.; **Document type:** *Magazine, Consumer.* **Description:** Covers food, wine, spirits and travel.
Formerly (until 2002): Epicurean (1532-8317)
Related titles: CD-ROM ed.; Online - full content ed.
Published by: Fezziwig Publishing Co., L L C, 740 Stetson St, Moss Beach, CA 94038. TEL 650-728-5389, FAX 650-728-5390, editor@epicurean-traveler.com, http://www.epicurean-traveler.com. Ed., Pub., R&P Scott Clemens. Adv. contacts Dana Jung TEL 925-831-8775, Roger Dexter. page USD 2,800; trim 8.5 x 10.875. Circ: 125,000 (paid and controlled).

ESSEN UND TRINKEN. see *FOOD AND FOOD INDUSTRIES*

663 ESP
ETIQUETA DE EDICIONES MARCO REAL. Text in Spanish. 1993. bi-m. **Document type:** *Consumer.* **Description:** Covers gastronomy, wines, beer and spirits.
Published by: Ediciones Marco Real S.A., Ronda de Poniente, 8 Bajo Izq, Madrid, 28760, Spain. TEL 34-91-8041759, FAX 34-91-8041946, etiqueta@marcoreal.com, http://www.marcoreal.com/. Ed. J J Delgado.

663.3 DEU ISSN 0367-018X
EUROPEAN BREWERY CONVENTION. PROCEEDINGS OF THE CONGRESS. Text in English, French, German. 1947. biennial, latest vol.29, 2003. price varies. back issues avail. **Document type:** *Proceedings, Trade.*
Indexed: CIN, ChemAb, ChemTitl, FS&TA.
—BLDSC (6843.301000), CISTI. **CCC.**
Published by: (European Brewery Convention GBR), Fachverlag Hans Carl, Andernacher Str 33A, Nuernberg, 90411, Germany. TEL 49-911-952850, FAX 49-911-9528560, info@hanscarl.com, http://www.hanscarl.com. Circ: 1,500.

663 GBR
EUROPEAN CAN MAKERS REPORT. Text in English. 1981. biennial, latest 2002. free (effective 2005). **Document type:** *Newsletter, Trade.* **Description:** Contents relate to soft drinks and beer.
Formerly (until 2001): The Can Makers Report (0956-8018)
—BLDSC (3016.406400).
Published by: Can Makers Information Service, 1 Chelsea Towers, 1 Chelsea Manor Gardens, London, SW3 5PN, United Kingdom. TEL 44-20-7349-5024, FAX 44-20-7352-6246, canmakers@gciuk.com, http://www.canmakers.co.uk. Circ: 3,000 (controlled).

663 GBR
F.O. LICHT'S WORLD DISTILLERIES GUIDE (YEARS). Text in English. a. GBP 195 per vol. domestic; GBP 205 per vol. in Europe; GBP 215 per vol. elsewhere (effective 2005). **Description:** Provides a complete listing of over 4000 distilleries in 144 countries and is a valuable source to buyers and traders in the alcohol distilling industry.
Published by: Agra Europe (London) Ltd. (Subsidiary of: T & F Informa plc), 80 Calverley Rd, Tunbridge Wells, Kent TN1 2UN, United Kingdom. TEL 44-1892-533813, FAX 44-1892-544895, marketing@agra-net.com, http://www.agra-net.com.

663 COL ISSN 0084-7941
FEDERACION NACIONAL DE CAFETEROS DE COLOMBIA. BOLETIN DE INFORMACION ESTADISTICA SOBRE CAFE. Text in Spanish. a.
Published by: (Departamento de Informacion Cafetera), Federacion Nacional de Cafeteros de Colombia, Calle 73, 8-13 Piso 10 B, Bogota, DE, Colombia.

663.63 FRA ISSN 0074-5952
FEDERATION INTERNATIONALE DES PRODUCTEURS DE JUS DE FRUITS. COMPTE-RENDU DU CONGRES/ INTERNATIONAL FEDERATION OF FRUIT JUICE PRODUCERS. PROCEEDINGS OF CONGRESS. Text in French. 1948. irreg., latest 12th, Interlaken. **Document type:** *Proceedings.*
Published by: Federation Internationale des Producteurs de Jus de Fruits/International Federation of Fruit Juice Producers, 23 bd. des Capucines, Paris, 75002, France. TEL 33-1-47428280, FAX 33-1-47422928

663.2 USA ISSN 1045-0971
FINE WINE FOLIO; an appreciation of vineyards and vintages. Text in English. 1988. m. USD 46.50; USD 57 foreign (effective 1999). back issues avail. **Document type:** *Consumer.* **Description:** Each issue is a profile of one of the world's wine-production areas; including leading producers and their labels, information on recent vintages.
Published by: Holland & Edwards Publishing Inc., 250 Mercer St A203, New York, NY 10012. TEL 212-673-5773, FAX 212-995-8956. Ed. Karen Holland. Pub., R&P Edward Holland. Circ: 75,000 (paid).

658.8 DEU ISSN 0947-4560
FIZZZ; fuer die Szenengastronomie. Text in German. m. **Document type:** *Trade.*
Former titles: Getraenke Gastronomie (0937-3926); Getraenke
Published by: Meininger Verlag GmbH, Maximilianstr 7-17, Neustadt, 67433, Germany. TEL 49-6321-8908-0, FAX 49-6321-890873. Ed. Annette Koenig. Circ: 8,389.

663.63 DEU ISSN 0015-4539
CODEN: FLOBA3
FLUESSIGES OBST. Text in German. 1930. m. EUR 144 domestic; EUR 153 in Europe; EUR 166 elsewhere; EUR 14 newsstand/cover (effective 2004). adv. bk.rev. index. **Document type:** *Magazine, Trade.*
Former titles (until 1948): Der Landbote. Beihefte fuer Garungslose Fruechteverwertung (0179-9924); (until 1947): Fluessiges Obst (0179-9916); (until 1939): Garungslose Fruechteverwertung (0179-9908)
Indexed: CIN, ChemAb, ChemTitl, DSA, FPA, FS&TA, HortAb, NutrAb, PBA, PHN&I, RA&MP, SIA, VITIS, WAE&RSA.
—BLDSC (3962.280000), CASDDS, CISTI, IE, Infotrieve, ingenta, Linda Hall. **CCC.**
Published by: (Verband der Deutschen Fruchtsaft-Industrie e.V.), Confructa Medien GmbH, Raiffeisenstr 27, Strassenhaus, 56587, Germany. TEL 49-2634-92350, FAX 49-2634-923535, info@fluessiges-obst.de, info@confructa-medien.com, http://www.fluessiges-obst.de, http://www.confructa-medien.com. Ed., R&P Evi Brennlich. Pub. Philipp Possmann. Adv. contact Cornelia Hebbe. B&W page EUR 1,810, color page EUR 2,620; trim 175 x 250. Circ: 1,649 (paid and controlled).

FOOD & BEVERAGE NEWS. see *LAW*

663 664 CAN ISSN 1188-5335
FOOD & DRINK/BON VERRE, BONNE TABLE. Text in English. 1988. bi-m. CND 20 domestic; CND 30 in United States (effective 2004). adv. **Document type:** *Government.*
Published by: Liquor Control Board of Ontario, 55 Lake Shore Blvd E, Toronto, ON M5E 1A4, Canada. TEL 800-668-5226, foodanddrink@lcbo.com, http://www.lcbo.com. Ed. Michelle Oosterman. Pub. Stephanie Blanshay. adv.: B&W page CND 11,407, color page CND 12,675. Circ: 520,000.

▼ **FOOD & DRINK LAW MONTHLY.** see *LAW*

FOOD AND DRINK TRADE HANDBOOK. see *FOOD AND FOOD INDUSTRIES*

FOOD & DRINK WEEKLY. see *FOOD AND FOOD INDUSTRIES*

FOOD & WINE. see *FOOD AND FOOD INDUSTRIES*

FOOD & WINE ANNUAL COOKBOOK; an entire year of recipes. see *HOME ECONOMICS*

FOOD & WINE MAGAZINE. see *HOME ECONOMICS*

663.2 USA ISSN 1549-6465
TP544
FOOD & WINE MAGAZINE'S WINE GUIDE. Text in English. 1998. a. USD 11.95 newsstand/cover (effective 2004). adv. **Document type:** *Magazine, Consumer.*
Formerly (until 2002): Food & Wine Magazine's Official Wine Guide (1522-001X)
Published by: American Express Publishing Corp., 1120 Ave of the Americas, New York, NY 10036. TEL 212-382-5600, FAX 212-382-5887, http://www.foodandwine.com/, http://www.amexpub.com.

FOOD MANAGEMENT; vakblad voor de voedings- en genotmiddelenindustrie. see *FOOD AND FOOD INDUSTRIES*

FOOD QUALITY BUYERS' GUIDE. see *FOOD AND FOOD INDUSTRIES*

FOOD QUALITY MAGAZINE; quality control and quality assurance for the food and beverage industries. see *FOOD AND FOOD INDUSTRIES*

FOODS ADLIBRA BEVERAGE EDITION. see *BEVERAGES—Abstracting, Bibliographies, Statistics*

663.73 USA ISSN 1094-8228
FRESH CUP MAGAZINE; the voice of the specialty beverage industry. Text in English. 1992. m. USD 38 domestic; USD 45 in Canada & Mexico; USD 75 elsewhere (effective 2005). adv. bk.rev. illus.; tr.mk. 90 p./no.; **Document type:** *Magazine, Trade.* **Description:** Provices specialty coffee and tea professionals with cutting-edge business information. Monthly columns assist readers with specific business advice and marketing tips, while feature articles provide in-depth examinations of industry issues.
Related titles: Online - full text ed.
Indexed: H&TI.
Published by: Fresh Cup Publishing Co., PO Box 14827, Portland, OR 97293-0827. TEL 503-236-2587, FAX 503-236-3165, freshcup@freshcup.com, http://www.freshcup.com. Ed. Julie Beals. Pub. Ward Barbee. Adv. contact Greg Ingram. Circ: 15,000.

663.2 USA ISSN 0364-9474
TP544
FRIENDS OF WINE✶ . Text in English. 1964. bi-m. USD 18. adv. bk.rev. reprint service avail. from PQC.
Related titles: Microfiche ed.: 1964 (from PQC).
Indexed: Consl.
Published by: Les Amis du Vin, O A Picone, 5015 Glenoak Dr, Louisville, OH 44641-8831. TEL 301-588-0980. Ed. Ronald J Fonte. Circ: 80,000.

663.63 DEU ISSN 0939-4435
CODEN: FRPREY
FRUIT PROCESSING. Text in English. 1991. bi-m. EUR 101 domestic; EUR 110 in Europe; EUR 119 elsewhere; EUR 14 newsstand/cover (effective 2004). adv. bk.rev. abstr.; bibl.; charts; illus.; tr.lit. back issues avail. **Document type:** *Magazine, Trade.* **Description:** Focuses on special technologies for the manufacture of fruit juice, juice concentrates, fruit-based beverages, purees and fruit preparations.

Indexed: AgrForAb, CIN, ChemAb, ChemTitl, DSA, FS&TA, HortAb, OrnHort, PBA, PGegResA, PHN&I, RA&MP, RM&VM, SIA, SeedAb, VITIS, WAE&RSA.
—BLDSC (4042.870000), CASDDS, CISTI, IE, ingenta. **CCC.**
Published by: Confructa Medien GmbH, Raiffeisenstr 27, Strassenhaus, 56587, Germany. TEL 49-2634-92350, FAX 49-2634-923535, info@confructa-medien.com, http://www.fruit-processing.com, http://www.confructa-medien.com. Ed., Pub., R&P Evi Brennlich. Adv. contact Cornelia Hebbe. B&W page EUR 2,030, color page EUR 2,840; trim 175 x 250. Circ: 2,450 (controlled).

663   DEU
GAULT MILLAU WEINGUIDE DEUTSCHLAND. Text in German. 1994. a. EUR 28 newsstand/cover (effective 2003). adv. back issues avail. **Document type:** *Directory, Consumer.*
Published by: Christian Verlag GmbH, Amalienstr 62, Munich, 80799, Germany. TEL 49-89-38180317, FAX 49-89-38180381, info@christian-verlag.de, http://www.weinguide.de, http://www.christian-verlag.de. adv.: B&W page EUR 2,850, color page EUR 4,100. Circ: 23,720 (paid).

GEFSI/TASTE. ya na zoumi kalitera. see *FOOD AND FOOD INDUSTRIES*

663   USA   ISSN 1074-0759
GEORGE WELLS' WASHINGTON BEVERAGE INSIGHT. Text in English. 1974. w. looseleaf. USD 375; USD 425 foreign (effective 1995). tr.lit. index. **Document type:** *Newsletter.*
Description: Covers national legislation, regulation and litigation affecting the soft drink and alcoholic beverage industries.
Formerly: Washington Beverage Insight (0890-8060)
Related titles: Online - full text ed.: (from Factiva).
Published by: George Wells & Associates, 2942 S Columbus St, Ste A 2, Arlington, VA 22206. TEL 703-671-8140. Ed., Pub., R&P George Wells.

663   DEU   ISSN 1860-8922
HD9397.G2
GESELLSCHAFT FUER GESCHICHTE DES BRAUWESENS. JAHRBUCH. Text in German. 1928. a. EUR 15 (effective 2005). bk.rev. **Document type:** *Yearbook, Academic/Scholarly.*
Formerly (until 2004): Gesellschaft fuer die Geschichte und Bibliographie des Brauwesens. Jahrbuch (0072-422X)
Indexed: IBZ.
Published by: Gesellschaft fuer Geschichte des Brauwesens e.V., Seestr 13, Berlin, 13353, Germany. TEL 49-30-45080264, FAX 49-30-4536069, ggb@vlb-berlin.org, http://www.ggb-berlin.de. Ed. Heinrich Letzing. Circ: 800.

641.2   DEU   ISSN 1435-3571
GETRAENKE-RING AKTIV. Text in German. 1997. s-a. EUR 7.80 newsstand/cover (effective 2003). adv. **Document type:** *Magazine, Trade.*
Published by: Verlag W. Sachon GmbH & Co., Schloss Mindelburg, Mindelheim, 87714, Germany. TEL 49-8261-9990, FAX 49-8261-999132, info@sachon.de, http://www.sachon.de. Ed. Dirk Omlor. Adv. contact Helga Ress. B&W page EUR 2,030, color page EUR 2,780. Circ: 4,128 (paid and controlled).

663   DEU   ISSN 1431-4428
GETRAENKE! TECHNOLOGIE UND MARKETING. Text in German. 1997. 5/yr. adv. bk.rev. back issues avail. **Document type:** *Magazine, Trade.*
Published by: Dr. Harnisch Verlagsgesellschaft GmbH, Blumenstr 15, Nuernberg, 90402, Germany. TEL 49-911-2018235, FAX 49-911-2018100, gtm@harnisch.com, service@harnisch.com, http://www.harnisch.com/GTM/Index.htm. Ed., Adv. contact Gertrude Schoeneberg. Pub. Benno Keller. B&W page EUR 3,094, color page EUR 4,294; trim 210 x 297. Circ: 9,902 (controlled).

663   DEU   ISSN 0947-5141
GETRAENKE ZEITUNG. Text in German. 1968. 24/yr. adv. **Document type:** *Trade.*
Former titles (until 1994): Getraenke Handel (0937-390X); Getraenke Revue (0343-3919)
—**CCC.**
Published by: Meininger Verlag GmbH, Maximilianstr 7-17, Neustadt, 67433, Germany. TEL 49-6321-8908-0, FAX 49-6321-890873. Ed. Reiner Mihr. Circ: 12,260.

663   DEU   ISSN 0724-6153
GETRAENKEFACHGROSSHANDEL. Text in German. 1982. 11/yr. EUR 42; EUR 4 newsstand/cover (effective 2003). adv. **Document type:** *Magazine, Trade.*
Published by: Verlag W. Sachon GmbH & Co., Schloss Mindelburg, Mindelheim, 87714, Germany. TEL 49-8261-9990, FAX 49-8261-999132, info@sachon.de, http://www.sachon.de. Adv. contact Helga Ress. B&W page EUR 5,160, color page EUR 6,840. Circ: 16,479 (paid and controlled).

663   DEU   ISSN 0016-9331
DER GETRAENKEHANDEL. Text in German. 1966. q. EUR 40 (effective 2001). adv. bk.rev. illus.; mkt.; tr.lit. **Document type:** *Magazine, Trade.* **Description:** Provides information and content on the wholesale beverage trade.
Published by: Zeitungs- und Zeitschriftenverlag Heinrichs, Brueggekamp 1, Barsinghausen, 30890, Germany. TEL 49-5105-2289. Ed., Pub. Gerhard Heinrichs.

663   DEU   ISSN 0016-9323
GETRAENKEINDUSTRIE. Text in German. 1946. m. EUR 44; EUR 4 newsstand/cover (effective 2003). adv. abstr.; illus. **Document type:** *Magazine, Trade.*
Indexed: RefZh, VITIS.
—BLDSC (4165.150000), IE, ingenta.
Published by: Verlag W. Sachon GmbH & Co., Schloss Mindelburg, Mindelheim, 87714, Germany. TEL 49-8261-9990, FAX 49-8261-999132, info@sachon.de, http://www.sachon.de. Eds. Marcus Steiner, Margit Pietzke. Adv. contact Sabine Berchtenbreiter. B&W page EUR 4,280, color page EUR 5,660. Circ: 9,749 (paid and controlled).

663   DEU   ISSN 0721-8389
GETRAENKEMARKT; Zeitschrift fuer Marketing und Technik im Getraenkehandel. Text in German. 1981. m. EUR 84.75 domestic; EUR 101.50 in Europe; EUR 107.95 elsewhere; EUR 9.65 newsstand/cover (effective 2005). adv. bk.rev. back issues avail. **Document type:** *Magazine, Trade.* **Description:** Covers marketing and engineering topics for beverage wholesalers.
Incorporates (1990-1998): Bier und Getraenke (0937-1958)
—**CCC.**
Published by: Fachverlag Hans Carl, Andernacher Str 33A, Nuernberg, 90411, Germany. TEL 49-911-952850, FAX 49-911-9528560, info@hanscarl.com, http://www.hanscarl.com. Ed. Karl-Ullrich Heyse. Adv. contact Bettina Lehmacher. B&W page EUR 3,830, color page EUR 5,297; trim 191 x 268. Circ: 16,712.

663   DEU   ISSN 0943-4704
GETRAENKEREPORT; fuer Handel und Gastronomie. Text in German. 1991. 6/yr. EUR 15.50; EUR 2.50 newsstand/cover (effective 2004). adv. **Document type:** *Magazine, Trade.*
Published by: L F G Verlag, Augustenstr 33, Munich, 80333, Germany. TEL 49-89-5426290, FAX 49-89-54262928, info@verlagsgruppe-gindler.de, http://www.getraenke-report.de. Ed. Frank J. Gindler. adv.: B&W page EUR 4,400, color page EUR 7,100; trim 178 x 270. Circ: 27,000.

663   USA
GOLDEN STATE BEVERAGE TIMES✱ . Text in English. 1991. m. **Description:** Covers problems, trends and purchasing information for the alcoholic beverage industry.
Published by: Diamond Publications, PO Box 398, Hopkins, MN 55343-0398. TEL 612-449-9446, FAX 612-449-9447. adv.: B&W page USD 1,725, color page USD 2,475; trim 11 x 8.5. Circ: 13,500.

663.4   GBR   ISSN 0265-0681
GOOD BEER GUIDE; 5000 best pubs in Britain. Text in English. 1974. a. GBP 11.99 (effective 2001). adv. bk.rev. maps. 780 p./no. 2 cols./p.; back issues avail. **Document type:** *Consumer.*
Published by: (Campaign for Real Ale Ltd.), C A M R A Books, 230 Hatfield Rd, St Albans, Herts AL1 4LW, United Kingdom. TEL 44-1727-867201, FAX 44-1727-867670, camra@camra.org.uk, http://www.camra.org.uk. Ed. Roger Protz. Adv. contact Louise Ashworth. Circ: 60,000.

GOURMET FARE MAGAZINE. see *FOOD AND FOOD INDUSTRIES*

641.22   ESP
GOURMETS WINE GUIDE/GUIA DE VINOS GOURMETS. Text in Spanish, English, French, German, Japanese. 1983. a. EUR 20 domestic; EUR 44.34 foreign (effective 2001). adv. **Document type:** *Trade.*
Published by: Club G. S.A., Aniceto Marinas 92, Madrid, 28008, Spain. TEL 34-91-577-0418, FAX 34-91-5487133, reyes@gourmets.net, http://www.gourmets.net. Ed. Francisco Lopez Canis. Adv. contact Ana Maria Palmieri.

663.42   USA
GREAT LAKES BREWING NEWS; celebrating a region's beer and culture. Text in English. bi-m. USD 17 (effective 2005). **Document type:** *Newspaper, Trade.*
Address: 214 Muegel Rd, East Amherst, NY 14051. TEL 716-689-5841, FAX 716-689-5789, http://www.brewingnews.com/greatlakes. Pub., R&P, Adv. contact Bill Metzger. Circ: 55,000.

663.3   GRD
GRENADA BREWERIES ANNUAL REPORT. Text in English. a. **Document type:** *Corporate.*
Published by: Grenada Breweries, Grand Anse, St. George's, Grenada.

663   GBR
GRIST INTERNATIONAL. Text in English. 6/yr. **Document type:** *Trade.*
Address: 2 Balfour Rd, London, N5 2HB, United Kingdom. TEL 071-359-8323, FAX 071-354-3962. Ed. Elisabeth Baker. Circ: 2,500.

663.2   ITA
GUIDA AI VINI DEL MONDO. Text in Italian, Spanish. 1992. biennial. price varies. adv. **Document type:** *Directory, Trade.* **Description:** Lists wineries and wines by country, from all over the world.

Published by: Arcigola Slow Food Editore, Via Mendicita Istruita 14, Bra, CN 12042, Italy. TEL 39-0172-419611, FAX 39-0172-421293, slowinfo@slowfood.com, http://www.slowfood.com. Ed. Carlo Petrini. Circ: 20,000.

663.2   ITA
GUIDA DEI VINI ITALIANI; le piu importanti aziende vinicole italiane analizzate vino per vino. Text in Italian. 1997. a. EUR 34 (effective 2004). adv. charts; illus. **Document type:** *Directory, Consumer.* **Description:** Presents thousands of wines tasted by Luca Maroni. Lists hundreds of wine producers and offers detailed classification, along with fruit-wine ratings of Italy's best wines.
Related titles: English ed.: Guide to Italian Wines; German ed.: Fuehrer zu den Italienischen Weinen.
Published by: L m Srl, Via Flaminia, 1007, Rome, RM 00189, Italy. TEL 39-06-33219811, FAX 39-06-33219843, lmonline@lmonline.com, http://www.lmonline.com. Ed., Pub., R&P Luca Maroni. Adv. contact Tania Wolodimeroff.

GUIDE TO THE WINELANDS OF THE CAPE. see *TRAVEL AND TOURISM*

663.3   GBR
GUINNESS GLOBE. Text in English. 1984. bi-m. free. **Description:** Presents news and information of interest to employees and pensioners of Guiness Brewing and associated companies worldwide.
Published by: Guinness, Park Royal Brewery, Park Royal, London, NW10 7RR, United Kingdom. FAX 44-181-965-1882, TELEX 23882. Ed., R&P Claire Grundy. Circ: 10,500.

663.1   GBR   ISSN 1367-9082
HARPERS; the wine and spirit weekly. Text in English. 1878. w. GBP 115 domestic; GBP 140 in Europe; GBP 190 elsewhere; GBP 2.95 newsstand/cover (effective 2003); subscr. includes supplements & Harpers Wine & Spirit Directory. adv. bk.rev. mkt.; stat.; tr.mk. Supplement avail. **Document type:** *Magazine, Trade.* **Description:** Covers the wine and spirits trade business.
Formerly (until Sep. 1996): Harpers Wine and Spirit Gazette (0017-7903)
Published by: Highbury Harpers (Subsidiary of: Highbury House Communications PLC), 47 Brunswick Pl, London, N1 6EB, United Kingdom. TEL 44-20-75755600, FAX 44-20-76086520, info@harpers-wine.com, http://www.hhc.co.uk/harpersweekly. Ed. Tim Atkin TEL 44-20-75755627. Adv. contact Kevin Moore TEL 44-20-75755631. B&W page GBP 1,550, color page GBP 1,950; 230 x 300. Circ: 4,000.

663.1   GBR   ISSN 1467-7946
HARPERS ON RETAIL. Text in English. 1999. 10/yr. GBP 30 domestic; GBP 35 in Europe; GBP 55 elsewhere (effective 2000). adv. **Document type:** *Magazine, Trade.* **Description:** Contains specialist information on the retail drinks sector in the U.K. and across Europe.
Published by: Harper Trade Journals Ltd., 47-51 Great Suffolk St, London, SE1 0BS, United Kingdom. TEL 44-20-7575-5600, FAX 44-20-7633-0281, subs@harpers-wine.com, http://www.harpers-wine.com.

663.1   GBR   ISSN 1470-2517
HARPERS ON TRADE. Abbreviated title: H O T. Text in English. 2000. 10/yr. free to qualified personnel. adv. **Document type:** *Magazine, Trade.* **Description:** Contains business-focussed and drinks-led information for the restaurant, hotel, bars and clubs trade in the U.K. and across Europe.
Formed by the merger of (1997-2000): Harpers on Restaurants (1461-6564); Harpers on Bars & Clubs
Published by: Highbury Harpers (Subsidiary of: Highbury House Communications PLC), 47 Brunswick Pl, London, N1 6EB, United Kingdom. TEL 44-20-75755600, FAX 44-20-76086520, info@harpers-wine.com, http://www.hhc.co.uk/. Ed. James Aufenast. Adv. contact Christopher Bennett. B&W page USD 1,550, color page USD 2,100; 230 x 300.

663.2   GBR   ISSN 1367-9090
HARPERS WINE AND SPIRIT DIRECTORY. Text in English. 1914. a., latest vol.70, 1999. incl. with subscr. to Harpers. adv. back issues avail. **Document type:** *Directory, Trade.* **Description:** Lists distilleries, wineries, shippers, wholesalers, trade agencies and associations connected to the wine and spirit industry worldwide,.
Former titles: Harpers Wine and Spirit Annual (0952-0856); Harpers Directory of the Wine and Spirit Trade; Harpers Directory and Manual of the Wine and Spirit Trade (0073-0408)
Related titles: Online - full content ed.: GBP 100 (effective 2003).
Published by: Highbury Harpers (Subsidiary of: Highbury House Communications PLC), 47 Brunswick Pl, London, N1 6EB, United Kingdom. TEL 44-20-75755600, FAX 44-20-76086520, info@harpers-wine.com, http://www.harpers-wine.com/directory/login.cfm, http://www.hhc.co.uk/. Circ: 3,500.

HARVEST (LAKEVILLE-MIDDLEBORO). see *AGRICULTURE*

663   USA   ISSN 0017-8543
HAWAII BEVERAGE GUIDE. Text in English. 1949. m. USD 35; USD 5 newsstand/cover (effective 2005). adv. stat. **Document type:** *Magazine, Trade.* **Description:** Presents news of interest about the beverage industry in Hawaii, both national and local, plus wholesale price listings.

Published by: (Associated Beverage Publications), Service Publications, Inc. (Honolulu), 1311 Kapiolani Blvd, Ste 301, Honolulu, HI 96814-0000. TEL 808-591-0049, FAX 808-591-0038, hibevgde@aloha.net. Ed. Christopher Teves. Circ: 2,000 (paid and controlled).

HOPFEN - RUNDSCHAU. see *AGRICULTURE—Crop Production And Soil*

HORTICULTURE NEWS. see *GARDENING AND HORTICULTURE*

HOTEL F & B EXECUTIVE; the magazine for hospitality food & beverage professionals. see *HOTELS AND RESTAURANTS*

663.1 CHN
HUAXIA JIUBAO/CHINA ALCOHOLIC BEVERAGES WEEKLY. Text in Chinese. 3/w. CNY 78 (effective 2004). **Document type:** *Newspaper, Trade.* **Description:** Covers the important issues in the Chinese alcoholic beverages industries and agencies.
Address: 115-6, Yantaiyuanshan Lu, Shandong, 264001, China. TEL 86-535-6231990, FAX 86-535-6218838. **Dist. by:** China International Book Trading Corp, 35 Chegongzhuang Xilu, Haidian District, PO Box 399, Beijing 100044, China. TEL 86-10-68412045, FAX 86-10-68412023, cibtc@mail.cibtc.com.cn, http://www.cibtc.com.cn.

663.19 USA ISSN 1058-3289
I B W A NEWS. Text in English. 1980. bi-m. membership. **Document type:** *Newsletter.* **Description:** Covers the events and activities of the IBWA and the bottled water industry throughout the world.
Published by: International Bottled Water Association, 1700 Diagnol Rd, Ste 650, Alexandria, VA 22314-2973. TEL 703-683-5213, FAX 703-683-4074, http://www.bottledwater.org. Ed. Ann F Carberry. Circ: 2,500 (controlled).

663.19 USA
I B W A TECHNICAL BULLETIN. Text in English. 1980. q. membership. **Document type:** *Newsletter.* **Description:** Covers technical subjects pertaining to the bottled water industry worldwide.
Published by: International Bottled Water Association, 1700 Diagnol Rd, Ste 650, Alexandria, VA 22314-2973. TEL 703-683-5213, FAX 703-683-4074, http://www.bottledwater.org. Ed. Tyrone P Wilson. Circ: 2,500 (controlled).

663.1 USA
ILLINOIS BEVERAGE GUIDE. Text in English. 2001. m. USD 25; USD 5 per issue (effective 2005). adv. **Document type:** *Magazine, Trade.*
Published by: The Beverage Network (Subsidiary of: The Beverage Media Group), 116 John St, 23rd Fl, New York, NY 10038. TEL 800-7-BEVERAGE (800-723-8372), FAX 212-571-4443, info@bevmedia.com, http://www.bevnetwork.com/. Ed., Pub. Stewart Baxter. adv.: color page USD 20,400; trim 8.25 x 10.875.

663 USA ISSN 0019-1892
ILLINOIS BEVERAGE JOURNAL. Text in English. 1944. m. USD 30 (effective 2004). adv. **Document type:** *Magazine, Trade.* **Description:** Covers all branches of beer, wine, liquor and related products in the alcoholic beverage field in Illinois, merchandising developments, people, new lines, association news, etc.
Published by: Illinois Beverage Media, Inc. (Subsidiary of: The Beverage Network), 2260 Bracken Ln, Northfield, IL 60093. TEL 847-441-7776, FAX 847-441-7796. Ed., R&P Linda J O'Brien. Adv. contact Tracy S Bruning. Circ: 6,000 (paid).

IMBOTTIGLIAMENTO. see *PACKAGING*

663 338.47 USA
IMPACT (NEW YORK); U S news and research for the wine, spirits and beer industries. Variant title: Impact Newsletter. Text in English. 1970. s-m. USD 595 in US & Canada (effective 2004). adv. bk.rev. Index. back issues avail. **Document type:** *Newsletter, Trade.* **Description:** Focuses on news related to the United States alcoholic beverage industry.
Former titles: Impact: Wine and Spirits Newsletter (0363-9444); Impact Alcoholic Beverage Newsletter
Indexed: CPerl.
Published by: Marvin R. Shanken Communications, Inc., 387 Park Ave S, New York, NY 10016. TEL 212-684-4224, FAX 212-684-5424. Pub. Marvin R Shanken.

663 338.47 USA ISSN 0268-8212
IMPACT INTERNATIONAL; global news and research for the international drinks executive. Text in English. 1986. s-m. USD 425. adv. charts; illus. **Document type:** *Trade.* **Description:** Focuses on regular rankings of world's top selling brands, drinking trends around the globe, and new product performance.
Indexed: Perlslam, RASB.
Published by: Marvin R. Shanken Communications, Inc., 387 Park Ave S, New York, NY 10016. TEL 212-684-4224, FAX 212-684-5424.

IMPACT WORLD DIRECTORY; leading spirits, wine & beer companies; who's who of industry executives. see *BUSINESS AND ECONOMICS—Trade And Industrial Directories*

663 USA
IMPACT WORLDWIDE DISTILLED SPIRITS REPORT. Text in English. 1991. a. USD 2,360. charts. **Document type:** *Trade.* **Description:** Utilizing the IMPACT Databank, the report analyzes all segments of the U.S. and international distilled spirits market.
Formerly: International Spirits Market Report (1061-4923)
Published by: Marvin R. Shanken Communications, Inc., 387 Park Ave S, New York, NY 10016. TEL 212-684-4224, FAX 212-684-5424. Ed. Marvin R Shanken.

663.2 USA
IMPACT WORLDWIDE WINE REPORT. Text in English. 1991. a. USD 1,560. charts. **Document type:** *Trade.* **Description:** Analyzes all segments of the U.S. and international wine market.
Formerly: International Wine Market Report (1061-9305)
Published by: Marvin R. Shanken Communications, Inc., 387 Park Ave S, New York, NY 10016. TEL 212-684-4224, FAX 212-684-5424. Ed. Marvin R Shanken.

663.4 USA
IMPORT - SPECIALTY INSIGHTS. Text in English. 1984. a. USD 675 (effective 1999). charts. back issues avail. **Document type:** *Trade.* **Description:** Statistical overview of import and specialty market in US, with written analysis. Provides statistics for total import shipments in 19 states by major importers.
Formerly: Import Insights
Published by: Beer Marketer's Insights, Inc., PO Box 264, West Nyack, NY 10994. TEL 914-624-2337. Ed. Jerry Steinman.

663.1 340 USA
INDIANA ALCOHOLIC BEVERAGE LAWS AND RULES. Text in English. a. USD 26 (effective 2005). 389 p./no.; **Description:** Provides all the statutes and rules governing Indiana's alcoholic beverage industry.
Published by: Michie Company (Subsidiary of: LexisNexis North America), 701 E Water St, Charlottesville, VA 22902-5389. TEL 434-972-7600, 800-446-3410, FAX 434-972-7677, http://www.michie.com.

663.3 USA ISSN 0274-547X
HD9348.I6
INDIANA BEVERAGE JOURNAL. Text in English. 1945. m. USD 26.50 (effective 2005). adv. **Document type:** *Magazine, Trade.*
Published by: Indiana Beverage Life, PO Box 5067, Zionsville, IN 46077. TEL 317-733-0527, FAX 317-733-0528, sntsb19@indy.net. Ed., Pub. Stewart N Baxter. Circ: 3,500 (paid). **Affiliate:** Associated Beverage Publications.

663 663.2 663.19 ITA ISSN 0390-0541
CODEN: INBEEW
INDUSTRIE DELLE BEVANDE. Text in Italian; Summaries in English. 1971. bi-m. EUR 50 in Europe; EUR 85 elsewhere (effective 2005). bk.rev. **Document type:** *Magazine, Trade.* **Description:** Covers all branches of the beverage industry; mineral waters, wines, soft drinks, aperitifs, beers, spirits, and fruit juices.
Indexed: AgBio, CIN, CPA, ChemAb, ChemTitl, DSA, FPA, FS&TA, ForAb, HortAb, IPackAb, MSB, MaizeAb, NutrAb, OrnHort, PBA, PGegResA, PHN&I, PST, RA&MP, RM&VM, RefZh, RevApplEntom, S&F, SIA, TriticAb, VITIS, WAE&RSA.
—BLDSC (4464.900000), CASDDS, IE, ingenta, Linda Hall. **CCC.**
Published by: Chiriotti Editori S p A, Viale Rimembranza 60, Pinerolo, TO 10064, Italy. TEL 39-0121-393127, FAX 39-0121-794480, info@chiriottieditori.it, http://www.industriedellebevande.com, http://www.chiriottieditori.com. Ed. Mrs. Christina Sarti. Pub., R&P Mr. Alberto Chiriotti. Adv. contact Mr. Giuseppe Chiriotti. Circ: 4,800.

663 USA
INDUSTRY WORLD. Text in English. bi-m. **Description:** Features developments in the industry. Includes association news.
Formerly: Industry Woman
Published by: World Association of Alcohol Beverage Industries, Inc., 1250 Eye St N W, Ste 900, Washington, DC 20005. TEL 202-628-3544.

663.2 FRA
INSTITUT NATIONAL DES APPELLATIONS D'ORIGINE. BULLETIN. (Special nos. avail.) Text in French. 1938. q. bk.rev. **Description:** Covers texts, data and statistics of the wine industry.
Formerly: Institut National des Appellations d'Origine des Vins et Eaux-de-Vie. Bulletin (0020-2401)
Published by: Institut National des Appellations d'Origine, 138 av. des Champs Elysees, Paris, 75008, France. TEL 1-45-62-54-75. Circ: 450.

663.4 GBR ISSN 0046-9750
CODEN: JINBAL
➤ **INSTITUTE OF BREWING. JOURNAL.** Text in English. 1904. q. GBP 200 (effective 2004). bk.rev. illus. **Document type:** *Journal, Academic/Scholarly.* **Description:** Features original research articles on all aspects of brewing science. Also contains Institute news and abstracts of research from other publications.
Formerly: Federated Institutes of Brewing. Journal
Indexed: AEA, ASCA, AgBio, Agr, AnalAb, BCI, BIOSIS Prev, BiolAb, BrTechI, CBTA, CIN, CISA, CPA, ChemAb, ChemTitl, CurCont, DBA, DSA, ESPM, FCA, FS&TA, HerbAb, HortAb, ISR, NutrAb, PBA, PGegResA, PGrRegA, PHN&I, PollutAb, RA&MP, RM&VM, RPP, RefZh, S&F, SCI, SIA, SeedAb, TriticAb, VITIS.
—BLDSC (4771.000000), CASDDS, CINDOC, CISTI, IDS, IE, Infotrieve, ingenta, Linda Hall. **CCC.**
Published by: Institute & Guild of Brewing, 33 Clarges St, London, W1J 7EE, United Kingdom. TEL 44-20-74998144, FAX 44-20-74991156, ingerussell@sympatico.ca, enquiries@igb.org.uk, http://www.igb.org.uk/igbsite/publications/journal.asp. Ed. Dr. Inge Russell. Circ: 4,200.

➤ **INTERMEZZO (MELROSE).** see *LIFESTYLE*

663 GBR
INTERNATIONAL BOTTLER AND PACKER. Text in English. 1927. m. GBP 57, USD 137, CND 148; GBP 8 per issue (effective 2003). adv. illus. **Document type:** *Journal, Trade.*
Incorporating: International Beverage News (0020-6199); Which incorporated: Wine and Spirit Chronicle
Indexed: DSA, FS&TA, IPackAb, KES, RAPRA, RefZh.
—BLDSC (4537.500000), IE. **CCC.**
Published by: Binsted Group Plc, Attwood House, Mansfield Park, Four Marks, Alton, Hants GU34 5PZ, United Kingdom. TEL 44-1420-568900, FAX 44-1420-565994, info@binstedgroup.com, http://www.binstedpublications.com/html/bottlerandpacker/, http://www.binsteadgroup.com/. Ed., Pub. Edward C Binsted. Adv. contact Andrew Flew. Circ: 6,000.

663 CHE
INTERNATIONAL BREWER'S DIRECTORY. DISTILLERS AND SOFT DRINK GUIDE. Text in English, French, German. 1928. every 7 yrs., latest vol.11, 2000. CHF 600. **Document type:** *Directory.*
Former titles: International Brewer's Directory (0074-9796); Internationales Firmenregister der Brauindustrie, Malzerien, Brennereien, Mineralwasser und Erfrischungsgetraenke
Published by: Verlag fuer Internationale Wirtschaftsliteratur GmbH, Postfach 28, Zuerich, 8047, Switzerland. TEL 41-1-4926130, FAX 41-1-4010545. Ed. Walter Hirt.

INTERNATIONAL DIRECTORY OF FOOD AND BEVERAGES IMPORTERS. see *BUSINESS AND ECONOMICS—Trade And Industrial Directories*

INTERNATIONAL FOOD ABSTRACTS. BEVERAGES AND SOFT DRINKS DISK. see *BEVERAGES—Abstracting, Bibliographies, Statistics*

663.2 GBR ISSN 0954-7541
HD9370.1
➤ **THE INTERNATIONAL JOURNAL OF WINE MARKETING.** Text in English. 1989. 3/yr. EUR 1,899 in Europe; USD 1,949 in North America; AUD 969 in Australasia; GBP 1,269 in the UK & elsewhere (effective 2005). back issues avail.; reprint service avail. from PSC. **Document type:** *Journal, Academic/Scholarly.* **Description:** Provides in-depth information on all aspects of marketing wine from international sources.
Related titles: Online - full text ed.: (from O C L C Online Computer Library Center, Inc., ProQuest Information & Learning).
Indexed: ABIn, H&TI.
—BLDSC (4542.701300), IE, ingenta. **CCC.**
Published by: (University of Surrey, Department of Management Studies), Barmarick Publications, Enholmes Hall, Patrington, Hull, East Yorkshire HU12 0PR, United Kingdom. TEL 44-1964-630033, FAX 44-1964-631716, hr24@dial.pipex.com. Ed. Michael Howley. Circ: 100 (paid). **Dist. by:** Emerald Group Publishing Limited, 60-62 Toller Ln, Bradford, W Yorks BD8 9BY, United Kingdom. TEL 44-1274-777700, FAX 44-1274-785200; **Dist. in the US:** Emerald Group Publishing Ltd., 44 Brattle St, 4th Fl, Cambridge, MA 02138. TEL 617-497-2175, 888-622-0075, FAX 617-354-6875, america@emeraldinsight.com.

➤ **INTERNATIONAL PRODUCT ALERT.** see *BUSINESS AND ECONOMICS—Marketing And Purchasing*

663.2 ITA ISSN 0374-5791
ISTITUTO SPERIMENTALE PER L'ENOLOGIA ASTI. ANNALI. Text in Italian; Summaries in English, German, French. 1970. a., latest vol.27, 1997. charts. back issues avail. **Document type:** *Yearbook, Academic/Scholarly.*
Indexed: BiolAb, VITIS.
Published by: Istituto Sperimentale per l'Enologia, Via P Micca, 35, Asti, AT 14100, Italy. TEL 39-0141-433811, FAX 39-0141-436829, enologia@tin.it. Circ: 500.

B

ITALIAN FOOD AND BEVERAGE TECHNOLOGY. see *FOOD AND FOOD INDUSTRIES*

663.2 ITA
ITALIAN WINES & SPIRITS (U S AND CANADA EDITION). Text in English. 1977. q. USD 23. adv. **Document type:** *Magazine, Trade.*
Published by: Editoriale Lariana s.r.l., Via Ciro Menotti 11-D, Milan, MI 20129, Italy. TEL 39-02-76110303, FAX 39-02-713847. Ed. Pino Khail. Adv. contact Antonella Khail. Circ: 50,000.

663.2 ITA
ITALIAN WINES & SPIRITS (UK EDITION). Text in English. 1979. q. USD 23. adv. **Document type:** *Magazine, Trade.*
Description: Covers Italian wines and food.
Published by: Editoriale Lariana s.r.l., Via Ciro Menotti 11-D, Milan, MI 20129, Italy. TEL 39-02-76110303, FAX 39-02-713847. Ed. Pino Khail. Adv. contact Antonella Khail. Circ: 25,000.

663.2 DEU
JACQUES JOURNAL. Text in German. q. **Document type:** *Magazine, Consumer.*
Published by: (Jacques Weindepot), Journal International Verlags- und Werbegesellschaft mbH, Hanns-Seidel-Platz 5, Munich, 81737, Germany. TEL 49-89-642797-0, FAX 49-89-64279777, info@journal-international.de, http://www.journal-international.de. Circ: 310,000 (controlled).

663.3 BEL ISSN 1371-0052
LE JOURNAL DU BRASSEUR. Text in French. 1893. q. EUR 30 domestic; EUR 50 foreign; EUR 8.70 per issue (effective 2005). bk.rev. bibl.; charts; illus.; mkt.; pat.; tr.lit. index. **Document type:** *Trade.* **Description:** Covers production and marketing of Belgian beers.
Formerly (until 1993): Petit Journal du Brasseur (0031-6253)
Related titles: ◆ Flemish ed.: Het Brouwersblad. ISSN 1371-2438; English ed.: ISSN 1376-6392. 2000. EUR 30 domestic; EUR 50 foreign (effective 2005).
Indexed: BiolAb, ChemAb, FS&TA, NutrAb.
Published by: Confederation des Brasseries de Belgique/Confederation of Belgian Breweries, Maison des Brasseurs, Grand' Place 10, Brussels, 1000, Belgium. TEL 32-2-511-4987, FAX 32-2-511-3259, http:// www.beerparadise.be. Ed. Rik Cooreman. R&P Jan Debrabanter. Adv. contact Alain Mathieu Medial. Circ: 10,000.

JOURNAL OF WINE RESEARCH. see *AGRICULTURE—Crop Production And Soil*

663.2 FRA ISSN 0151-4393
JOURNEE VINICOLE. Text in English, French. 1927. d. adv. bk.rev. illus.; stat. **Document type:** *Newspaper, Trade.* **Description:** Daily international newspaper on wine and spirits.
Published by: Promovin, B. P. 1064, Montpellier, 34007, France. TEL 33-4-67079101, FAX 33-4-67479363. Ed. J C Causse. R&P Jean Christophe Causse. Adv. contact Stephane Gardere. Circ: 15,900 (controlled).

663 JPN ISSN 1342-2510
JOZO KENKYUJO HOKOKU/RESEARCH INSTITUTE OF BREWING. REPORT. Text in Japanese. 1905. a. free or exchange basis. **Document type:** *Monographic series, Academic/Scholarly.* **Description:** Includes coverage of sake and various types of wine.
Formerly (until no.168, 1996): Jozo Shikenjo Hokoku (0389-9136)
Published by: National Research Institute of Brewing, 3-7-1 Kagamiyama, Higashihiroshima-shi, Hiroshima-ken 739-0046, Japan. TEL 81-824-20-0800, FAX 81-824-20-0802.

663.2 DEU ISSN 1437-708X
KAESE UND WEIN. Text in German. 1997. 4/yr. **Document type:** *Magazine, Consumer.*
Published by: Meininger Verlag GmbH, Maximilianstr 7-17, Neustadt, 67433, Germany. TEL 49-6321-8908-0, FAX 49-6321-890873, contact@meininger.de, http:// www.meininger.de.

663 USA ISSN 0023-0138
KENTUCKY BEVERAGE JOURNAL. Text in English. 1949. m. USD 24 (effective 2005). adv. illus.; mkt. **Document type:** *Magazine, Trade.*
Published by: Midway Publications, PO Box 346, Midway, KY 40347-0346. mtucker@pop.uky.edu. Ed. John D Meyers. Adv. contact Sharon Turner. B&W page USD 535, color page USD 1,600. Circ: 1,800 (paid).

663 GBR
KEY NOTE MARKET ASSESSMENT. BOTTLED WATER. Variant title: Bottled Water Market Assessment. Text in English. irreg., latest 2001, Sept. GBP 730 per issue (effective 2002). **Document type:** *Trade.* **Description:** Provides an in-depth strategic analysis across a broad range of industries and contains an examination on the scope, dynamics and shape of key UK markets in the consumer, financial, lifestyle and business to business sectors.
Former titles: Key Note Market Report: Bottled Waters; Key Note Report: Bottled Waters; Key Note Report: Mineral Water (0957-7386)
Related titles: CD-ROM ed.; Online - full text ed.
Published by: Key Note Ltd., Field House, 72 Oldfield Rd, Hampton, Mddx TW12 2HQ, United Kingdom. TEL 44-20-8481-8750, FAX 44-20-8783-0049, info@keynote.co.uk, http://www.keynote.co.uk. Ed. Simon Taylor.

641.2 658 GBR
KEY NOTE MARKET ASSESSMENT. HOT BEVERAGES. Text in English. irreg., latest 2001, Feb. GBP 730 per issue (effective 2002). **Document type:** *Trade.* **Description:** Provides an in-depth strategic analysis across a broad range of industries and contains an examination on the scope, dynamics and shape of key UK markets in the consumer, financial, lifestyle and business to business sectors.
Formerly: Key Note Market Report: Hot Drinks
Related titles: CD-ROM ed.; Online - full text ed.
Published by: Key Note Ltd., Field House, 72 Oldfield Rd, Hampton, Mddx TW12 2HQ, United Kingdom. TEL 44-20-8481-8750, FAX 44-20-8783-0049, info@keynote.co.uk, http://www.keynote.co.uk.

663 GBR
KEY NOTE MARKET REPORT: AFTER DINNER DRINKS. Variant title: After Dinner Drinks. Text in English. irreg., latest 1994, Nov. GBP 340 per issue (effective 2002). **Document type:** *Trade.* **Description:** Provides an overview of a specific UK market segment and includes executive summary, market definition, market size, industry background, competitor analysis, current issues, forecasts, company profiles, and more.
Formerly: Key Note Report: After Dinner Drinks (0954-4542)
Related titles: CD-ROM ed.; Online - full text ed.
Published by: Key Note Ltd., Field House, 72 Oldfield Rd, Hampton, Mddx TW12 2HQ, United Kingdom. TEL 44-20-8481-8750, FAX 44-20-8783-0049, info@keynote.co.uk, http://www.keynote.co.uk.

663.4 GBR
KEY NOTE MARKET REPORT: BREWERIES & THE BEER MARKET. Variant title: Breweries & the Beer Market. Text in English. 1991. a., latest 2001, June. GBP 340 per issue (effective 2002). **Document type:** *Trade.* **Description:** Provides an overview of a specific UK market segment and includes executive summary, market definition, market size, industry background, competitor analysis, current issues, forecasts, company profiles, and more.
Formerly: Key Note Report: Breweries and the Beer Market (1352-5492)
Related titles: CD-ROM ed.; Online - full text ed.
Published by: Key Note Ltd., Field House, 72 Oldfield Rd, Hampton, Mddx TW12 2HQ, United Kingdom. TEL 44-20-8481-8750, FAX 44-20-8783-0049, info@keynote.co.uk, http://www.keynote.co.uk. Ed. Simon Howitt.

663 338 GBR
KEY NOTE MARKET REPORT: CIDER. Variant title: Cider. Text in English. 1993. irreg., latest 1993, May. GBP 340 (effective 2002). **Document type:** *Trade.* **Description:** Provides an overview of the UK cider sector, including industry structure, market size and trends, developments, prospects, and major company profiles.
Formerly: Key Note Report: Cider (0951-9122)
Related titles: CD-ROM ed.; Online - full text ed.
Published by: Key Note Ltd., Field House, 72 Oldfield Rd, Hampton, Mddx TW12 2HQ, United Kingdom. TEL 44-20-8481-8750, FAX 44-20-8783-0049, info@keynote.co.uk, http://www.keynote.co.uk.

663.52 658 GBR
KEY NOTE MARKET REPORT: DISTILLERS (WHISKY). Variant title: Distillers (Whisky). Text in English. irreg., latest 1993, Dec. GBP 340 per issue (effective 2002). **Document type:** *Trade.* **Description:** Provides an overview of the UK whiskey distillers market, including industry structure, market size and trends, developments, prospects, and major company profiles.
Formerly: Key Note Report: Distillers (Whisky) (0954-4569)
Related titles: CD-ROM ed.; Online - full text ed.
Published by: Key Note Ltd., Field House, 72 Oldfield Rd, Hampton, Mddx TW12 2HQ, United Kingdom. TEL 44-20-8481-8750, FAX 44-20-8783-0049, info@keynote.co.uk, http://www.keynote.co.uk.

663 658 GBR ISSN 1368-4051
KEY NOTE MARKET REPORT: FRUIT JUICES & HEALTH DRINKS. Variant title: Fruit Juices & Health Drinks. Text in English. 198?. irreg., latest vol.6, 1997. GBP 340 per issue (effective 2002). **Document type:** *Trade.* **Description:** Provides and overview of a specific UK market segment and includes executive summary, market definition, market size, industry background, competitor analysis, current issues, forecasts, company profiles, and more.
Formerly (until 1997): Key Note Report: Fruit Juices and Health Drinks (0954-4666)
Related titles: CD-ROM ed.; Online - full text ed.
Published by: Key Note Ltd., Field House, 72 Oldfield Rd, Hampton, Mddx TW12 2HQ, United Kingdom. TEL 44-20-8481-8750, FAX 44-20-8783-0049, info@keynote.co.uk, http://www.keynote.co.uk. Ed. Lyndsey Barker.

663 GBR
KEY NOTE MARKET REPORT: LOW ALCOHOL DRINKS. Variant title: Low Alcohol Drinks. Text in English. 1989. irreg., latest 1994, Dec. GBP 340 per issue (effective 1999). **Document type:** *Trade.* **Description:** Provides and overview of a specific UK market segment and includes executive summary, market definition, market size, industry background, competitor analysis, current issues, forecasts, company profiles, and more.
Formerly: Key Note Report: Low Alcohol Drinks (0957-736X)
Related titles: CD-ROM ed.; Online - full text ed.
—CCC.
Published by: Key Note Ltd., Field House, 72 Oldfield Rd, Hampton, Mddx TW12 2HQ, United Kingdom. TEL 44-20-8481-8750, FAX 44-20-8783-0049, info@keynote.co.uk, http://www.keynote.co.uk.

663.1 658 GBR ISSN 1366-6193
KEY NOTE MARKET REPORT: THE TAKE HOME TRADE. Text in English. 19??. irreg. (13th Edition), latest 2000, July. GBP 340 per issue (effective 2002). **Document type:** *Trade.* **Description:** Provides an overview of the fastest growing sector in the UK alcoholic drinks market and includes executive summary, market definition, market size, industry background, competitor analysis, current issues, forecasts, company profiles, and more.
Former titles (until 1996): Key Note Market Report: Off-License Trade (0956-2036); Key Note Report: Off-License Trade
Related titles: CD-ROM ed.; Online - full text ed.
Published by: Key Note Ltd., Field House, 72 Oldfield Rd, Hampton, Mddx TW12 2HQ, United Kingdom. TEL 44-20-8481-8750, FAX 44-20-8783-0049, info@keynote.co.uk, http://www.keynote.co.uk.

663 658 GBR ISSN 1360-1873
KEY NOTE MARKET REVIEW: U K DRINKS MARKET. Text in English. irreg., latest 2001, Nov. GBP 565 per issue (effective 2002). **Document type:** *Trade.* **Description:** Provides an overview of the UK drinks market, including industry structure, market size and trends, developments, prospects, and major company profiles.
Formerly: Key Note Market Review: U K Drinking Habits
Related titles: CD-ROM ed.; Online - full text ed.
Published by: Key Note Ltd., Field House, 72 Oldfield Rd, Hampton, Mddx TW12 2HQ, United Kingdom. TEL 44-20-8481-8750, FAX 44-20-8783-0049, info@keynote.co.uk, http://www.keynote.co.uk. Ed. Jenny Baxter.

663 GBR ISSN 1461-5312
KEY NOTE PLUS MARKET REPORT. DARK SPIRITS & LIQUEURS. Text in English. 1997. irreg., latest 2001, July. GBP 455 per issue (effective 2002). **Description:** Provides an overview of a specific UK market segment and includes executive summary, market definition, market size, industry background, competitor analysis, current issues, forecasts, company profiles, and more.
Published by: Key Note Ltd., Field House, 72 Oldfield Rd, Hampton, Mddx TW12 2HQ, United Kingdom. TEL 44-20-8481-8750, FAX 44-20-8783-0049, info@keynote.co.uk, http://www.keynote.co.uk. Ed. Emily Pattullo.

663.4 658.8 GBR
KEY NOTE PLUS MARKET REPORT. PREMIUM LAGERS, BEERS & CIDERS. Text in English. 1992. irreg., latest 2000, July. GBP 455 per issue (effective 2002). **Document type:** *Trade.* **Description:** Provides an overview of a specific UK market segment and includes executive summary, market definition, market size, industry background, competitor analysis, current issues, forecasts, company profiles, and more.
Former titles (until 2000): Key Note Market Report: Premium Lagers, Beers and Ciders (1368-3721); (until 1997): Key Note Report: Premium Lagers, Beers and Ciders (1352-6944)
Related titles: CD-ROM ed.; Online - full text ed.
Published by: Key Note Ltd., Field House, 72 Oldfield Rd, Hampton, Mddx TW12 2HQ, United Kingdom. TEL 44-20-8481-8750, FAX 44-20-8783-0049, info@keynote.co.uk, http://www.keynote.co.uk. Ed. Dominic Fenn.

663.6 658 GBR
KEY NOTE PLUS MARKET REPORT. SOFT DRINKS. Text in English. 2002 (May). irreg., latest 2002, May. GBP 455 per issue (effective 2002). **Document type:** *Trade.* **Description:** Provides an overview of a specific UK market segment and includes executive summary, market definition, market size, industry background, competitor analysis, current issues, forecasts, company profiles, and more.
Formed by the merger of (1992-2002): Key Note Market Review: U K Soft Drinks Market (1356-6199); (19??-2002): Key Note Market Report: Soft Drinks (Carbonated & Concentrated); Which was formerly: Key Note Report. Soft Drinks. Carbonated & Concentrated (0954-450X)
Published by: Key Note Ltd., Field House, 72 Oldfield Rd, Hampton, Mddx TW12 2HQ, United Kingdom. TEL 44-20-8481-8750, FAX 44-20-8783-0049, info@keynote.co.uk, http://www.keynote.co.uk.

663.1 658 GBR ISSN 1462-2319
KEY NOTE PLUS MARKET REPORT. WHITE SPIRITS AND SPECIALITY DRINKS. Cover title: Market Report Plus. White Spirits & Specialty Drinks. Text in English. 1997. irreg., latest 1997, Dec. **Description:** Provides an overview of a specific UK market segment and includes executive summary, market definition, market size, industry background, competitor analysis, current issues, forecasts, company profiles, and more.
Incorporates: Key Note Market Report: White Spirits
Published by: Key Note Ltd., Field House, 72 Oldfield Rd, Hampton, Mddx TW12 2HQ, United Kingdom. TEL 44-20-8481-8750, FAX 44-20-8783-0049, info@keynote.co.uk, http://www.keynote.co.uk. Ed. Richard Caines.

663.2 658 GBR
KEY NOTE PLUS MARKET REPORT. WINE. Text in English. irreg., latest 2002, Jan. GBP 455 per issue (effective 2002). **Document type:** *Trade.* **Description:** Provides an overview of a specific UK market segment and includes executive summary, market definition, market size, industry background, competitor analysis, current issues, forecasts, company profiles, and more.
Former titles (until 2000): Key Note Market Report: Wine; Key Note Report: Wine (0954-5034)
Related titles: CD-ROM ed.; Online - full text ed.
Published by: Key Note Ltd., Field House, 72 Oldfield Rd, Hampton, Mddx TW12 2HQ, United Kingdom. TEL 44-20-8481-8750, FAX 44-20-8783-0049, info@keynote.co.uk, http://www.keynote.co.uk. Ed. Emily Pattullo.

663.3 JPN
KIRIN BREWERY COMPANY. ANNUAL REPORT. Text in Japanese. 1956. a.
Published by: (Technology Development Department), Kirin Brewery Co. Ltd./Kirin Biru K.K. Gijutsubu, 26-1 Jingu-Mae 6-chome, Shibuya-ku, Tokyo, 150-0001, Japan. TEL 03-3499-6111, FAX 03-3499-6151.

KOMPASS PROFESSIONNEL. AGRICULTURE, ALIMENTATION. see *BUSINESS AND ECONOMICS—Trade And Industrial Directories*

663.1 340 USA
LAWS AND REGULATIONS OF THE STATE OF MARYLAND RELATING TO ALCOHOLIC BEVERAGES AND TOBACCO TAX. (YEAR) CUMULATIVE SUPPLEMENT. Text in English. a., latest 2002. USD 60 (effective 2003). 495 p./no.; **Description:** A compilation of Laws and Regulations that contains Article 2B Alcoholic Beverages from the Annotated Code of Maryland as well as numerous related statutes covering taxes and business regulation. In addition, it contains related regulations from the Code of Maryland Administrative Regulations (COMAR) such as Alcoholic Beverage Regulations, Subtitle 02 Alcohol and Tobacco Tax.
Published by: Michie Company (Subsidiary of: LexisNexis North America), 701 E Water St, Charlottesville, VA 22902-5389. TEL 434-972-7600, 800-446-3410, FAX 434-972-7677, http://www.michie.com.

DIE LEBENSMITTEL- UND GETRAENKE-INDUSTRIE DER SCHWEIZ/L'INDUSTRIE DES PRODUITS ALIMENTAIRES ET DES BOISSONS EN SUISSE. see *BUSINESS AND ECONOMICS—Trade And Industrial Directories*

663.2 FRA ISSN 1010-3074
OFFICE INTERNATIONAL DE LA VIGNE ET DU VIN. LA LETTRE. Key Title: La Lettre de l'O I V. Text in French. 11/yr. EUR 51 in the European Union; EUR 56 elsewhere (effective 2004). **Document type:** *Newsletter.* **Description:** Covers the activities of the organization, the introduction of vineyards and the publication of new journals.
Related titles: English ed.: ISSN 1010-3066; ♦ Supplement(s): Office International de la Vigne et du Vin. La Lettre Vin, Nutrition et Sante (French Edition). ISSN 1027-4863.
Published by: Office International de la Vigne et du Vin, 18 rue d'Aguesseau, Paris, 75008, France. TEL 33-1-44948080, FAX 33-1-42669063, oiv@oiv.int, http://www.oiv.int. Ed. Yann Juban.

663.2 FRA ISSN 1027-4863
OFFICE INTERNATIONAL DE LA VIGNE ET DU VIN. LA LETTRE VIN, NUTRITION ET SANTE (FRENCH EDITION). Variant title: Lettre Vin, Nutrition et Sante de l'O I V. Text in French. 11/yr. EUR 50 in the European Union plus La lettre; EUR 55 elsewhere plus La lettre (effective 2002). **Description:** Covers the activities of the vineyards and the publication of new journals.
Formerly (until 1996): Nutrition et Sante (1024-3119)
Related titles: English ed.: Office International de la Vigne et du Vin. La Lettre Vin, Nutrition et Sante (English Edition). ISSN 1560-3938; ♦ Supplement to: Office International de la Vigne et du Vin. La Lettre. ISSN 1010-3074.
Published by: Office International de la Vigne et du Vin, 18 rue d'Aguesseau, Paris, 75008, France. TEL 33-1-44948080, FAX 33-1-42669063, oiv@oiv.int, http://www.oiv.int.

338.47 GBR
LICENSED AND CATERING NEWS. Text in English. 1944. m. GBP 25. **Document type:** *Trade.*
Formerly: Ulster Licensed Trade News
Published by: Ulster Magazines Ltd., 58 Rugby Rd, Belfast, Co Antrim BT7 1NT, United Kingdom. TEL 44-1232-230425, FAX 44-1232-243595. Ed. Larry Nixon. Circ: 4,500.

LICENSING LAWS N S W: LIQUOR ACT & REGULATIONS. see *LAW*

663 IRL ISSN 1393-0826
LICENSING WORLD. Text in English. 1978. m. adv. bk.rev. index. **Document type:** *Magazine, Trade.*
Formerly (until 1993): Vintners World (0790-2158); Which was formed by the merger of (1947-1978): Licensing World (0790-2166); Which was formerly (until 1974): Irish Licensing World (0790-2182); (1935-1978): The Vintner (0790-2174); Which was formerly (until 1974): The Licensed Vintner (0024-2799); (until 1959): The Licensed Vintner and Grocer (0790-2190); Which was formed by the merger of (1935-1935): The Licensed Trader (0790-2204); (1934-1935): The Irish Vintner and Licensed Grocer (0790-2212)
Published by: Jemma Publications Ltd., Marino House, 52 Glasthule Rd., Sandycove, Co. Dublin, Ireland. TEL 353-1-2800000, FAX 353-1-2801818, edit@jemma.ie. Ed. Pat Nolan. adv.: B&W page EUR 1,630, color page EUR 2,230; trim 210 x 297. Circ: 3,912 (controlled).

663.3 FRA ISSN 1299-6793
LIQUIDES & CONDITIONNEMENT. Variant title: Bios Liquides et Conditionnement. Text in French; Summaries in English, French, German. 1970. 6/yr. bk.rev. abstr.; bibl.; stat.; tr.lit. index. **Document type:** *Trade.* **Description:** Deals with the evolutions and the technological innovations in the following sectors: raw materials and ingredients; manufacturing processes; packaging and bottling; packing; handling and logistics; control, measurement, analysis and hygiene.
Former titles (until 2000): Bios Boissons Conditionnement (1266-2925); (until 1995): Bios Boissons (1252-1248); (until 1993): Bios (0366-2284); (until 1972): Cahiers de Bio (0150-648X); Bios Brasserie Malterie Biotechnique (1274-0225)
Indexed: BiolAb, BiolDig, CBTA, CIN, ChemAb, ChemTitl, DBA, DSA, FS&TA, PST, RefZh.
—CASDDS, CISTI, Linda Hall.
Published by: P C I Presse et Communication de l'Institut, 176 rue du Temple, Paris, 75003, France. TEL 33-1-44593838, FAX 33-1-44593839. Ed. Frederic Reux. Pub. Jean Lavie. R&P Catherine Leclerq Bourbon. Adv. contact Catherine Leclercq Bourdon. Circ: 3,000.

LIQUOR CONTROL LAW REPORTS; federal and all states. see *BUSINESS AND ECONOMICS—Public Finance, Taxation*

LIQUOR LAWS VICTORIA. see *LAW*

663.1 340 USA
LIQUOR LIABILITY LAW. Text in English. 1987. 2 base vols. plus irreg. updates. looseleaf. USD 300 base vol(s). (effective 2002). Supplement avail. **Description:** Comprehensive coverage of civil liability of tavern owners, social hosts, employers, and others, for negligent service of alcohol to intoxicated persons and minors. Who can sue, who can be sued, and what actions give rise to liability are some of the issues that are fully explored. Both common law and statutory claims are discussed. Includes all dram shop statutes.
Published by: Matthew Bender & Co., Inc. (Subsidiary of: LexisNexis North America), 1275 Broadway, Albany, NY 12204. international@bender.com, http://bender.lexisnexis.com. Ed. James Mosher.

LOCALI TOP; mensile di informazione e di aggiornamento per i professionisti del bar. see *HOTELS AND RESTAURANTS*

663.4 GBR ISSN 0144-7866
LONDON DRINKER. Text in English. 1979. bi-m. GBP 3 domestic; GBP 6 foreign (effective 2001). adv. bk.rev. 48 p./no. 2 cols./p.; back issues avail. **Document type:** *Magazine, Consumer.* **Description:** Covers real ale, in and around London.
Published by: Campaign for Real Ale Ltd., London Branches, 122 Manor Way, Uxbridge, Mddx UB8 2BH, United Kingdom. Ed., R&P I H Amy TEL 44-20-7305-3988. Adv. contact P Tonge TEL 44-20-8300-7693. Circ: 8,000.

634.8 663.2 BGR ISSN 0458-4244
CODEN: LOVIAA
LOZARSTVO I VINARSTVO. Short title: L & V. Text in Bulgarian; Summaries in English. 1952. 6/yr., latest vol.3, 2001. BGL 5.80; BGL 72 foreign (effective 2002). abstr.; bibl.; illus.; mkt.; stat.; tr.lit.; tr.mk. 64 p./no.; back issues avail. **Document type:** *Journal.* **Description:** Covers vine-growing and winemaking.
Formerly (until 1952): Lozarski Pregled
Indexed: CIN, ChemAb, ChemTitl, FS&TA, HortAb, RASB, RefZh, VITIS, WAE&RSA.
—CASDDS.
Address: 19 Lavele ul, Sofia, 1000, Bulgaria. TEL 359-2-9810879. Eds. Margarita Hristova, Snezhana Zhivkova. R&P Gergana Hristova. Circ: 1,500. **Dist. by:** Hemus, 6 Rouski Blvd., Sofia 1000, Bulgaria; **Dist. by:** Sofia Books, ul Silivria 16, Sofia 1404, Bulgaria. TEL 359-2-9586257, info@sofiabooks-bg.com, http://www.sofiabooks-bg.com.

MAJOR FOOD & DRINK COMPANIES OF EUROPE (YEAR). see *BUSINESS AND ECONOMICS—Trade And Industrial Directories*

MAJOR FOOD & DRINK COMPANIES OF THE FAR EAST & AUSTRALASIA (YEAR). see *BUSINESS AND ECONOMICS—Trade And Industrial Directories*

MAJOR FOOD & DRINK COMPANIES OF THE WORLD (YEAR). see *BUSINESS AND ECONOMICS—Trade And Industrial Directories*

663 FIN ISSN 0356-3014
TP577 CODEN: MAOLD2
MALLAS JA OLUT. Text in Finnish; Summaries in English. 1935. 6/yr. adv. bk.rev. illus.; stat. **Document type:** *Journal, Trade.* **Description:** Covers brewing and soft drinks industry.
Formerly (until 1977): Mallasjuomat (0025-1380)
Indexed: RefZh.
—BLDSC (5356.240400), CASDDS, IE, ingenta.
Published by: Panimolaboratorio - Bryggerilaboratorium AB, Tietotie 2, PO Box 16, Espoo, 02151, Finland. TEL 358-9-464472, FAX 358-9-4552103. Ed. Matti Linko. Circ: 200.

641.21 USA ISSN 1086-4199
MALT ADVOCATE; beer and whisky magazine. Text in English. 1994. q. USD 18 domestic; USD 24 in Canada; USD 40 elsewhere (effective 2005). adv. bk.rev. back issues avail. **Document type:** *Consumer.*
Related titles: Online - full text ed.
Published by: Malt Advocate, Inc., PO Box 158, Emmaus, PA 18049-0158. TEL 610-967-1083, FAX 610-965-2995, info@maltadvocate.com, http://www.whiskeypages.com. Ed. John Hansell. adv.: color page USD 2,700; trim 10.88 x 8.38. Circ: 40,000.

663 ESP
MARCO REAL; periodico economico de vinos, cervezas y espirituosos. Text in Spanish. 1987. s-m. (except Aug.). bk.rev. **Document type:** *Trade.* **Description:** Provides the latest news on the companies and products in the world of wine, beer, and spirits. Includes restaurant and drink critiques, results of wine tasting events, opinions on fairs and congresses, and editorials on legislation.
Published by: Ediciones Marco Real S.A., Ronda de Poniente, 8 Bajo Izq, Madrid, 28760, Spain. TEL 34-91-8041759, FAX 34-91-8041946, etiqueta@marcoreal.com, http://www.marcoreal.com/. Ed. J J Delgado. Circ: 15,000.

663.2 USA ISSN 0277-9277
HD9350.1
MARKET WATCH (NEW YORK). Text in English. 1981. m. USD 60 (effective 2005). adv. **Document type:** *Magazine, Trade.* **Description:** Provides market intelligence on the wine, spirit, and beer businesses.
Indexed: H&TI, PROMT.
Published by: Marvin R. Shanken Communications, Inc., 387 Park Ave S, New York, NY 10016. TEL 212-684-4224, FAX 212-684-5424. Ed. Marvin R Shanken. Adv. contact Diane Leech. Circ: 57,000 (paid and controlled).

MARMITE. see *FOOD AND FOOD INDUSTRIES*

641.2 USA
MARYLAND BEVERAGE JOURNAL. Text in English. 1938. m. USD 37.80 (effective 2005). adv. **Document type:** *Magazine, Trade.*
Published by: Beverage Journal, Inc., PO Box 8900, Elkridge, MD 21075-8900. spatten@beerwineliquor.com, http://www.beerwineliquor.com/. Ed. Lee W Murray. adv.: page USD 595. Circ: 5,000 (paid and controlled).

663 USA ISSN 1090-9214
MASSACHUSETTS BEVERAGE BUSINESS. Text in English. 1944. m. USD 62 (effective 2004). adv. maps; mkt. 430 p./no.; back issues avail. **Document type:** *Magazine, Trade.* **Description:** Contains wholesale prices for spirits, wine and malt beverages, news and reports of trade events.
Former titles (until 1996): Massachusetts Beverage Price Journal (1084-1113); Massachusetts Beverage Journal
Published by: New Beverage Publications, Inc., PO Box 932, Boston, MA 02117-0932. TEL 617-598-1900, FAX 617-598-1940, sistone@beveragebusiness.com, http://www.beveragebusiness.com. Pub. J C Stone. Adv. contact Jack Chisholm TEL 617-598-1913. B&W page USD 1,600, color page USD 3,200; trim 7 x 10. Circ: 9,880 (paid and controlled).

663.3 USA
MASTER BREWERS ASSOCIATION OF THE AMERICAS. COMMUNICATOR. Variant title: M B A A Communicator. Text in English. 1940. q. charts; illus. **Document type:** *Newsletter.* **Description:** Acts as an internal newsletter.
Formerly: Master Brewers Association of America. Communications
Related titles: ♦ Issued with: Master Brewers Association of the Americas. Technical Quarterly. ISSN 0743-9407.
Published by: Master Brewers Association of the Americas, 3340 Pilot Knob Rd., Saint Paul, MN 55121-2097. TEL 651-454-7250, FAX 651-454-0766, mbaa@mbaa.com, http://www.mbaa.com. Circ: 2,700.

663.3 USA ISSN 0743-9407
MASTER BREWERS ASSOCIATION OF THE AMERICAS. TECHNICAL QUARTERLY. Text in English. 1964. q. USD 158 domestic; USD 168 foreign; USD 45 newsstand/cover domestic; USD 51 newsstand/cover foreign (effective 2004). adv. abstr.; charts; illus. index. **Description:** Features papers on brewing ingredients, the brewing process, brewing by-products, brewery ecological matters, beer packaging, and beer flavor and physical stability.
Formerly (until 1977): Master Brewers Association of America. Technical Quarterly (0542-9811)
Related titles: CD-ROM ed.; ♦ Includes: Master Brewers Association of the Americas. Communicator.
Indexed: Agr, CIN, ChemAb, ChemTitl, FS&TA, NutrAb. —BLDSC (8710.740100), Infotrieve, ingenta.
Published by: Master Brewers Association of the Americas, 3340 Pilot Knob Rd., Saint Paul, MN 55121-2097. TEL 651-454-7250, FAX 651-454-0766, mbaa@mbaa.com, http://www.mbaa.com/TechQuarterly/. Ed. Ray Klimovitz. adv.: B&W page USD 1,170; trim 8.5 x 11. Circ: 2,700.

641.2 DEU ISSN 1618-0194
MEININGER MAGAZIN. Text in German. 1988. irreg. (4-6/yr.). **Document type:** *Magazine, Consumer.*
Published by: Meininger Verlag GmbH, Maximilianstr 7-17, Neustadt, 67433, Germany. TEL 49-6321-8908-0, FAX 49-6321-890873, contact@meininger.de, http://www.meininger.de.

663.42 USA
MID-ATLANTIC BREWING NEWS. Text in English. 1999. bi-m. USD 17, CND 25; USD 50 foreign (effective 2000); free newsstand. adv. bk.rev. illus. **Document type:** *Newspaper, Trade.* **Description:** Covers brewing news for the Mid-Atlantic states of the US.
Address: PO Box 20268, Alexandria, VA 22320-1268. Ed. Greg Kitsock. Pubs. Bill Metzger, Jim Dorsch TEL 703-567-1962. Adv. contacts Jim Dorsch TEL 703-567-1962, Melissa Hochberg TEL 703-591-1944. Circ: 35,000.

663.61 DEU ISSN 0171-5720
DER MINERALBRUNNEN. Text in German. 1951. m. EUR 1.60 newsstand/cover (effective 2005). adv. bk.rev. illus. **Document type:** *Magazine, Trade.* **Description:** Communicates views on all issues affecting the mineral water industry.
Formerly (until 1971): Naturbrunnen (0028-0828)
Indexed: FS&TA, NutrAb.
Published by: Genossenschaft Deutscher Brunnen e.G., Kennedyallee 36, Bonn, 53175, Germany. TEL 49-228-959590, FAX 49-228-9595977, info@gdb.de, http://www.gdb.de. Eds. Andreas Rottke, Wolfgang Stubbe. Adv. contact Ulrich Wermke. B&W page EUR 950, color page EUR 1,940. Circ: 2,800 (paid and controlled).

663 ITA
MIXER. Text in Italian. 1976. 10/yr. adv. bk.rev. illus. **Document type:** *Trade.*
Former titles (until 1983): Mixer il Barman; Barman
Published by: (Associazione Italiana Barmen e Sostenitori/Italian Bartenders Association), Gruppo E.S. s.r.l., Via Andrea Solari, 19, Milan, MI 20144, Italy. TEL 39-02-58102128, FAX 39-02-89406970. Circ: 128,000.

664 USA
MIXIN'. Text in English. 1983. m. USD 38. **Document type:** *Newsletter.* **Description:** Bartending, wine and spirit information. Includes bar product news and editorials.
Published by: American Bartenders' Association, PO Box D, Plant City, FL 33564. TEL 800-935-3232, FAX 813-752-2768. Circ: 5,000.

663.3 USA ISSN 0026-7538
MODERN BREWERY AGE. Text in English. 1933. bi-m. USD 95 (effective 2005). adv. bk.rev. charts; illus.; stat.; tr.lit. Supplement avail. **Document type:** *Magazine, Trade.*
Related titles: Online - full text ed.: (from Gale Group, Northern Light Technology, Inc., O C L C Online Computer Library Center, Inc.); ♦ Supplement(s): Modern Brewery Age Blue Book. ISSN 0076-9932.
Indexed: B&I, BiolAb, LRI, PROMT. —BLDSC (5883.750000).
Published by: Business Journals, 50 Day St, Norwalk, CT 06856. TEL 203-853-6015, FAX 203-852-8175, pete@breweryage.com, http://www.breweryage.com, http://www.busjour.com/. Ed., Pub. Peter Reid. Adv. contact Diane Apicelli. B&W page USD 2,560, color page USD 4,180. Circ: 5,400.

663.3 USA ISSN 0076-9932
MODERN BREWERY AGE BLUE BOOK. Text in English. 1941. a. USD 265 (effective 1999). **Document type:** *Academic/Scholarly.*
Related titles: ♦ Supplement to: Modern Brewery Age. ISSN 0026-7538.
Published by: Business Journals, 50 Day St, Norwalk, CT 06856. TEL 203-853-6015. Ed. Peter Reid.

663.3 USA
MODERN BREWERY AGE: TABLOID EDITION. Text in English. 1958. w. USD 85 (effective 1999). adv. **Document type:** *Trade.*
Published by: Business Journals, 50 Day St, Norwalk, CT 06856. TEL 203-853-6015. Circ: 1,944.

MODERN DRUNKARD. see *LIFESTYLE*

MONATSSCHRIFT FUER BRAUWISSENSCHAFT (ONLINE EDITION). see *BEVERAGES—Abstracting, Bibliographies, Statistics*

663.4 ITA ISSN 1121-1598
IL MONDO DELLA BIRRA; mensile d'informazione, attualita e costume della birra. Text in Italian. 1982. m. EUR 30 domestic; EUR 40 foreign (effective 2005). adv. bk.rev. **Document type:** *Magazine, Trade.* **Description:** Covers beer for pubs, bars, pizzerias, discos, restaurants, hotels, breweries, importers, distributors, wholesalers, and supermarkets.
Published by: Tuttopress Editrice s.r.l., Viale Lunigiana 40, Milan, MI 20125, Italy. TEL 39-02-6691692, FAX 39-02-6695596, monbirr@tin.it, http://www.ilmondodellabirra.it/. Ed. Silvano Rusmini. Circ: 44,000.

642.5 647.95 GBR ISSN 1471-1958
MORNING ADVERTISER. Text in English. 1794. w. GBP 78 domestic; GBP 130 in Europe; GBP 200 elsewhere (effective 2005). adv. bk.rev. charts; illus. **Document type:** *Newspaper, Trade.* **Description:** Britain's premier news magazine for the pub, club and leisure industry.
Formerly (until 1994): The Licensee and Morning Advertiser (1356-0034)
Related titles: ♦ Regional ed(s).: Morning Advertiser Scotland; ♦ Supplement(s): PubChef.
Published by: (Society of Licensed Victuallers), William Reed Publishing Ltd., Broadfield Park, Brighton Rd, Pease Pottage, Crawley, W Sussex RH11 9RT, United Kingdom. TEL 44-7714-451955, subs@william-reed.co.uk, http://www.william-reed.co.uk/magazines/s_morn_ad.html. Ed. Andrew Pring TEL 44-1293-610480. Adv. contact David Griffiths TEL 44-1293-610432. Circ: 12,652 (paid).

642.5 941.1 GBR
MORNING ADVERTISER SCOTLAND. Variant title: M A Scotland. Text in English. fortn. GBP 38 domestic; GBP 90 in Europe; GBP 170 elsewhere (effective 2005). adv. **Document type:** *Newspaper, Trade.* **Description:** Addresses issues and news specifically affecting the Scottish industry.
Related titles: ♦ Regional ed(s).: Morning Advertiser. ISSN 1471-1958.
Published by: (Society of Licensed Victuallers), William Reed Publishing Ltd., Broadfield Park, Brighton Rd, Pease Pottage, Crawley, W Sussex RH11 9RT, United Kingdom. TEL 44-7714-451955, subs@william-reed.co.uk, http://www.william-reed.co.uk/magazines/s_morn_ad_scotland.htm. Ed. Tom Stainer. Adv. contact Aileen Byrne. Circ: 10,011.

663 AUT
MOSTVIERTLER. Text in German. m.
Address: Eggersdorferstrasse 51, Postfach 12, Amstetten, N 3302, Austria. TEL 7472-337536. Circ: 12,000.

663.2 SWE ISSN 0345-8202
MUNSKAENKEN MED VINJOURNALEN. Variant title: Tidskriften Munskaenken. Text in Swedish. 1958. 10/yr. adv. bk.rev. back issues avail. **Document type:** *Bulletin.*
Published by: Foereningen Munskaenkarna, Nybohovsbacken 61, PO Box 47147, Stockholm, 10074, Sweden. TEL 46-8-301043, FAX 46-8-301152, kansli@munskankarna.a.se, http://www.munskankarna.a.se. Ed. Ulf Jansson. Adv. contact Anne-Marie Sandstroem TEL 46-8-54512024. Circ: 6,000.

663 USA
N B W A HANDBOOK. Text in English. a. membership only. **Document type:** *Directory, Trade.*
Published by: National Beer Wholesalers Association, 1101 King St., Ste. 600, Alexandria, VA 22314-2965. TEL 703-578-4300. Ed. Tamara Tyrell.

663 USA
N B W A LEGISLATIVE AND REGULATORY ISSUES ALERT. Text in English. q. membership only. **Document type:** *Trade.*
Published by: National Beer Wholesalers Association, 1101 King St., Ste. 600, Alexandria, VA 22314-2965. TEL 703-578-4300. Ed. Tamara Tyrell.

344.0541 USA
N C S L A MINUTES OF ANNUAL MEETING. Text in English. 1937. a. USD 25.
Published by: National Conference of State Liquor Administrators, 300 Centennial Mall S, Lincoln, NE 68509. TEL 402-471-2571. Ed. Randy Yarbrough. Circ: 100.

344.0541 USA
N C S L A OFFICIAL DIRECTORY. Text in English. a. USD 5. **Document type:** *Directory.* **Description:** Directory of all state agencies administrating alcoholic beverage laws.
Published by: National Conference of State Liquor Administrators, 300 Centennial Mall S, Lincoln, NE 68509. TEL 402-471-2571. Ed. Randy Yarbrough. Circ: 100.

N W PALATE MAGAZINE; wine, food, & travel of the Pacific Northwest. see *TRAVEL AND TOURISM*

663 USA
NATIONAL ASSOCIATION OF BEVERAGE IMPORTERS. BULLETIN✶. Text in English. irreg.
Published by: National Association of Beverage Importers, 607 Aster Blvd, Rockville, MD 20850-2035. TEL 202-638-1617, FAX 202-638-3122.

663 USA
NATIONAL ASSOCIATION OF BEVERAGE IMPORTERS. IMPORT REPORT✶. Text in English. irreg. membership only.
Published by: National Association of Beverage Importers, 607 Aster Blvd, Rockville, MD 20850-2035. TEL 202-638-1617, FAX 202-638-3122.

NATIONAL ASSOCIATION OF BEVERAGE IMPORTERS. STATISTICAL REPORT. see *BEVERAGES—Abstracting, Bibliographies, Statistics*

663 USA
NATIONAL ASSOCIATION OF BEVERAGE RETAILERS. NEWS AND VIEWS. Text in English. q. membership only. **Document type:** *Newsletter.*
Formerly: National Liquor Stores Association. News and Views
Published by: National Association of Beverage Retailers, 5101 River Rd, Ste 108, Bethesda, MD 20816. TEL 301-656-1494, FAX 301-656-7539. Ed. Stephen Kay. Circ: 15,000 (controlled).

663 USA ISSN 1062-0990
NATIONAL BEER WHOLESALERS ASSOCIATION. BEER PERSPECTIVES NEWSLETTER. Key Title: Beer Perspectives. Text in English. w. membership only. **Document type:** *Newsletter, Trade.*
Published by: National Beer Wholesalers Association, 1101 King St., Ste. 600, Alexandria, VA 22314-2965. TEL 703-578-4300. Ed. Tamara Tyrell.

663 USA
NATIONAL BEER WHOLESALERS ASSOCIATION. DISTRIBUTOR PRODUCTIVITY REPORT. Text in English. biennial. **Document type:** *Trade.*
Published by: National Beer Wholesalers Association, 1101 King St., Ste. 600, Alexandria, VA 22314-2965. TEL 703-683-4300. Ed. Tamara Tyrell.

663.1 AUS ISSN 0816-0430
NATIONAL LIQUOR NEWS. Text in English. 1984. m. adv. cum.index. **Document type:** *Magazine, Trade.* **Description:** Covers only trade aspects around all liquor brands sold in Australia.
Formerly: National Thomson's Liquor Guide (0812-3705)
Published by: N P G Media, 97 Victoria St, Potts Point, NSW 2011, Australia. TEL 61-2-93577277, FAX 61-2-93577244, npg@npg.com.au, http://www.npg.com.au/nln/. Ed. Katrina Holden. Adv. contact Ashley Pini. B&W page AUD 3,495, color page AUD 3,990; trim 210 x 297. Circ: 9,735.

663 USA ISSN 0028-1808
NEBRASKA BEVERAGE ANALYST. Text in English. 1936. m. USD 12 (effective 2006). adv. illus.; mkt.; stat. **Document type:** *Magazine, Trade.*
Published by: Golden Bell Press Inc., 2403 Champa St, Denver, CO 80205. TEL 303-296-1600, FAX 303-295-2159, print@goldenbellpress.com, http://www.goldenbellpress.com. Pub. Lawrence Bell. Adv. contact Susan Sherwood. Circ: 3,150 (paid).

663 USA ISSN 1053-6345
CODEN: CTTEEU
NEVADA BEVERAGE ANALYST. Text in English. 19??. m. USD 12 (effective 2005). adv. **Document type:** *Magazine, Trade.*
Formerly (until 19??): Nevada Beverage Index (0191-4723)
Published by: Golden Bell Press Inc., 2403 Champa St, Denver, CO 80205. TEL 303-296-1600, FAX 303-295-2159, print@goldenbellpress.com, http://www.goldenbellpress.com. Pub. Larry Bell. Adv. contact Susan Sherwood. Circ: 5,000 (free).

663.3 USA ISSN 0741-0506
THE NEW BREWER; the magazine for micro and pub brewers. Text in English. 1983. bi-m. USD 85 domestic; USD 95 foreign (effective 2005). adv. bk.rev. cum.index: 1983-1996. back issues avail. **Document type:** *Magazine, Trade.* **Description:** For those interested in the business of operating small breweries, including restaurateurs, and entrepreneurs. Includes all aspects of brewing.
Indexed: H&TI, RefZh. —BLDSC (6082.382300), IE, ingenta.
Published by: (Association of Brewers), Institute for Brewing Studies, 736 Pearl St, Box 1679, Boulder, CO 80306. TEL 303-447-0816, FAX 303-447-2825, mike@aob.org, http://www.beertown.org/craftbrewing/newbrewer.html. Ed. Ray Daniels. Adv. contact Julia Herz. Circ: 6,000.

641.2 664 GBR ISSN 1461-4642
NEW FOOD; the quarterly business review of new technology for European food & drink manufacturers. Text in English. 1998. q. GBP 60 (effective 2003). adv. tr.lit. 96 p./no.; back issues avail.; reprints avail. **Document type:** *Magazine, Trade.* **Description:** Reviews food and beverage industry business and technology.
Indexed: FS&TA.
—BLDSC (6084.176000), IE, ingenta.
Published by: Russell Publishing Ltd., Court Lodge, Hogtrough Hill, Brasted, Kent TN16 1NU, United Kingdom. TEL 44-1959-563311, FAX 44-1959-563123, airport@russellpublishing.com, admin@russellpublishing.com, http://www.russellpublishing.com/pages/food/food1.html. Ed. Tim Lloyd. Pub. Ian Russell. R&P Tim Dean. Adv. contacts Simon Raey, Tim Dean. color page GBP 3,977. Circ: 145 (paid); 14,779 (controlled).

663.1 USA ISSN 0028-5552
NEW JERSEY BEVERAGE JOURNAL. Text in English. 1949. m. USD 49 (effective 2005). adv. bk.rev. illus.; mkt. **Document type:** *Magazine, Trade.* **Description:** News and information on the alcoholic beverage industry in the state, including package stores, restaurants, bars, grills, taverns, hotels, clubs, seasonal bars, and distributor salespersons.
Published by: Gem Publishers, Inc., 2414 Morris Ave, Union, NJ 07083-5708. TEL 908-964-5060, FAX 908-964-1472, http://www.bevaccess.com/. Ed., Pub. Harry Slone. adv.: B&W page USD 895. Circ: 9,342.

663.1 USA ISSN 0194-813X
NEW MEXICO BEVERAGE ANALYST. Text in English. 1947. m. USD 10 (effective 2005). adv. bk.rev. illus. **Document type:** *Magazine, Trade.*
Formerly: New Mexico Beverage Journal (0028-6141)
Published by: Golden Bell Press Inc., 2403 Champa St, Denver, CO 80205. TEL 303-296-1600, FAX 303-295-2159, http://www.goldenbellpress.com. Circ: 1,000.

663.1 340 USA
NEW YORK ALCOHOLIC BEVERAGE CONTROL LAW. Cover title: Gould's Alcoholic Beverage Control Law of New York. Variant title: Alcoholic Beverage Control Law of New York. Text in English. 1990. a. USD 6 (effective 2000). **Document type:** *Government.* **Description:** Contains complete presentation of Chapter 3-B of the Consolidated Laws of New York, including a comprehensive index.
Published by: Gould Publications, Inc. (Subsidiary of: LexisNexis), 1333 North US Hwy 17-92, Longwood, FL 32750-3724. TEL 407-695-9500, 800-717-7917, FAX 407-695-2906, info@gouldlaw.com, http://www.gouldlaw.com.

663.1 659.9 310 NZL
NEW ZEALAND. STATISTICS NEW ZEALAND. ALCOHOL AND TOBACCO AVAILABLE FOR CONSUMPTION. Text in English. stat. **Document type:** *Government.* **Description:** Provides estimates of the quantity of alcoholic beverages and tobacco available for consumption in New Zealand.
Published by: Statistics New Zealand/Te Tari Tatau, PO Box 2922, Wellington, New Zealand. TEL 64-4-495-4600, FAX 64-4-473-2626, info@stats.govt.nz, http://www.stats.govt.nz.

663.1 310 NZL
NEW ZEALAND. STATISTICS NEW ZEALAND. ALCOHOL AVAILABLE FOR CONSUMPTION. Text in English. q. **Document type:** *Government.* **Description:** Provides statistical data on alcohol comsumption in New Zealand.
Published by: Statistics New Zealand/Te Tari Tatau, PO Box 2922, Wellington, New Zealand. TEL 64-4-495-4600, FAX 64-4-473-2626, info@stats.govt.nz, http://www.stats.govt.nz.

663.1 CHN ISSN 1002-8110
NIANGJIU. Text in Chinese. 1974. bi-m. CNY 8 per issue domestic (effective 2000). back issues avail. **Document type:** *Academic/Scholarly.*
Related titles: Online - full content ed.: (from WanFang Data Corp.); Online - full text ed.: (from East View Information Services).
Published by: (Heilongjiang Sheng Niangjiu Zhuanye Xiehui), Niangjiu, 43 Duan Jie, Daoli-qu, Ha'erbin, 150010, China. TEL 86-451-4654008, FAX 86-451-4615315. Ed. Tong Zhao. **Co-sponsors:** Heilongjiang Sheng Qinggongye Yanjiusuo; Zhongguo Baijiu Zhuanye Xuehui.

663.3 CHN ISSN 1001-9286
TP544
NIANGJIU KEJI. Text in Chinese; Summaries in English. 1980. bi-m. CNY 60 domestic; USD 60 foreign (effective 2003). adv. bk.rev.; Website rev. Index. 128 p./no.; **Document type:** *Journal, Trade.* **Description:** Covers spirits, beers, wines, liqueurs, foreign research trends, cultures of alcoholic beverages, and new products.
Related titles: CD-ROM ed.; E-mail ed.; Fax ed.; Online - full text ed.: (from East View Information Services).
Indexed: FS&TA.
—BLDSC (5221.943400), IE, ingenta.
Published by: Niangjiu Keji Zazhishe/China Alcoholic Beverage Information Centre, 58 Shachong Zhonglu, Guiyang, Guizhou 550002, China. TEL 86-851-5796163, FAX 86-851-5776394, 1mst@publicl.gy.gz.cn, lmst@public.gz.cn, http://www.gy.gz.cn/gzoline/gzrx.htm, http://www.lmst.com.cn/. Ed., Pub., R&P, Adv. contact Ping Huang. B&W page USD 400, color page USD 2,000; trim 185 x 260. Circ: 16,000 (paid). **Dist. overseas by:** China International Book Trading Corp, 35 Chegongzhuang Xilu, Haidian District, PO Box 399, Beijing 100044, China.

641.2 JPN ISSN 0914-7314
NIPPON JOZO KYOKAISHI/BREWING SOCIETY OF JAPAN. JOURNAL. Text in Japanese. m. **Document type:** *Journal, Trade.*
Former titles (until 1987): Nippon Jozo Kyokai Zasshi (0369-416X); (until 1914): Jozo Kyokai Zasshi
Indexed: FS&TA.
—BLDSC (4712.200000), CISTI.
Published by: Nippon Jozo Kyokai/Brewing Society of Japan, 2-6-30 Takinogawa, Kita-ku, Tokyo, 114-0023, Japan. TEL 81-3-39103853, FAX 81-3-39103748, http://www.jozo.or.jp/i.kennsaku.htm.

NORTH AMERICAN BREWERS RESOURCE DIRECTORY. see *BUSINESS AND ECONOMICS—Trade And Industrial Directories*

663.1 ITA ISSN 0017-0119
NUOVO GIORNALE DEI DISTILLATORI; alcoli - acquaviti - liquori. Variant title: Giornale dei Distillatori. Text in Italian. 1962. m. bk.rev. stat. **Document type:** *Newspaper, Trade.* **Description:** Covers economic, technical and legislative information in the distillation and liqueur industry.
Published by: Guido Scialpi Editore, Via Ugo De Carolis, 7, Rome, RM 00136, Italy. TEL 39-6-33679865, FAX 39-6-33679865. Ed. Guido Scialpi. Circ: 3,000.

663 CHE ISSN 1023-2958
CODEN: SZOWAZ
OBST- UND WEINBAU. Text in German. 1864. 26/yr. CHF 65; CHF 91 in Europe; CHF 116 elsewhere (effective 2000). adv. bk.rev. **Document type:** *Magazine, Trade.*
Formerly: Schweizerische Zeitschrift fuer Obst und Weinbau (0371-4942)
Indexed: AEA, AgBio, BioCN&I, BiolAb, CPA, ChemAb, DBA, DSA, ExcerpMed, FPA, FS&TA, ForAb, HortAb, NemAb, NutrAb, OrnHort, PBA, PGegResA, PGrRegA, PHN&I, PotatoAb, RA&MP, RPP, RevApplEntom, S&F, SIA, SeedAb, VITIS, WAE&RSA, WeedAb.
—BLDSC (6208.116000), CASDDS, IE, Infotrieve, ingenta.
Published by: Eidgenoessische Forschungsanstalt, Postfach 185, Waedenswil, 8820, Switzerland. TEL 41-1-7836111, FAX 41-1-7836211, margrit.bueeler@faw.admin.ch. Ed. Walter Mueller. Circ: 4,000.

663.3 DNK ISSN 1604-2115
OELKASSEN. Text in Danish. 1983. q. **Document type:** *Magazine, Consumer.*
Incorporates (19??-2004): Samlernyt (0109-3460); Which superseded in part (in 1984): Samlerringen (0105-3442)
Published by: Skandinavisk Bryggerisouvenir Samlerforening/Scandinavian Breweriana Collectors Association, c/o Michael Buus, Valbylangggade 120, Valby, 2500, Denmark. TEL 45-36450773, michaelbuus@privat.dk, http://www.scanbrew.dk. Ed. Finn Christiansen TEL 45-39-698214.

663.1 AUT
OESTERREICHISCHES GETRAENKE INSTITUT. MITTEILUNGEN. Text in German. 1947. 6/yr. EUR 47.70 domestic; EUR 86.50 foreign (effective 2005). adv. bk.rev. charts; illus.; stat. Index. **Document type:** *Newspaper, Trade.*
Formerly: Versuchsstation fuer das Gaerungsgewerbe in Wien. Mitteilungen (0042-4390)
Indexed: BiolAb, FS&TA, RefZh.
Published by: Oesterreichisches Getraenke Institut, Michaelerstr 25, Vienna, W 1180, Austria. TEL 43-1-47969240, FAX 43-1-479692411, office@oegi.at, http://www.oegi.at. Ed. Helmuth Schwarz. adv.: page EUR 1,509.70; trim 185 x 257. Circ: 550 (paid and controlled).

663.1 GBR ISSN 0043-5775
OFF LICENCE NEWS; the voice of drinks retailing. Text in English. 1970. w. GBP 65 domestic; GBP 110 in Europe; GBP 170 elsewhere (effective 2005). adv. illus.; stat. **Document type:** *Magazine, Trade.* **Description:** Aimed at buyers and retailers of alcoholic drinks.
Related titles: Online - full text ed.: (from LexisNexis).
Indexed: H&TI.
—BLDSC (6236.510000).
Published by: William Reed Publishing Ltd., Broadfield Park, Brighton Rd, Pease Pottage, Crawley, W Sussex RH11 9RT, United Kingdom. TEL 44-7714-451955, graham.holter@william-reed.co.uk, subs@william-reed.co.uk, http://www.william-reed.co.uk/magazines/s_oln.html. Ed. Graham Holter. Pub. Russell Dodd. Adv. contact Nina Suckling. Circ: 18,329 (paid and controlled).

663.2 634.8 FRA ISSN 0029-7127
CODEN: BLOVAJ
OFFICE INTERNATIONAL DE LA VIGNE ET DU VIN. BULLETIN; revue internationale. Key Title: Bulletin de l'O I V. Text in English, French. 1928. bi-m. EUR 133 in the European Union; EUR 159 elsewhere (effective 2004). bk.rev. abstr.; bibl.; charts. index. **Document type:** *Bulletin.* **Description:** Explores wine growing, producing and appreciation, as well as economics and legal issues in wine making.
Related titles: ♦ Supplement(s): Situation et Statistiques Mondiales du Secteur Viticole.
Indexed: AbHyg, AgBio, BioCN&I, BiolAb, CIN, CPA, ChemAb, ChemTitl, FS&TA, HortAb, I&DA, NutrAb, PBA, PGegResA, PGrRegA, PHN&I, RA&MP, RDA, RM&VM, RPP, RefZh, RevApplEntom, S&F, SIA, SeedAb, TDB, VITIS, VetBull, WAE&RSA, WeedAb.
—BLDSC (2668.300000), CASDDS, CISTI, IE, Infotrieve, ingenta.
Published by: Office International de la Vigne et du Vin, 18 rue d'Aguesseau, Paris, 75008, France. TEL 33-1-44948080, FAX 33-1-42669063, oiv@oiv.int, http://www.oiv.int. Ed. M O Boissenot. Circ: 1,000.

663 FRA
OFFICE INTERNATIONAL DE LA VIGNE ET DU VIN. REGLEMENTS DE LA C E E. Text in French. irreg. EUR 82 in the European Union; EUR 97 elsewhere (effective 2004).
Formerly: Office International de la Vigne et du Vin. Reglements
Related titles: English ed.; Spanish ed.
Published by: Office International de la Vigne et du Vin, 18 rue d'Aguesseau, Paris, 75008, France. TEL 33-1-44948080, FAX 33-1-42669063, oiv@oiv.int, http://www.oiv.int.

641 USA ISSN 0740-1361
OHIO BEVERAGE JOURNAL; first trade journal of Ohio's beverage, restaurant and hotel industry. Text in English. 1934. m. USD 18 (effective 2005). adv. bk.rev. illus.; mkt.; tr.lit. 48 p./no.; **Document type:** *Journal, Trade.* **Description:** Covers the alcohol and restaurant industries, with state, national and international news.
Former titles: Buckeye Beverage Journal (0007-2826); Buckeye Tavern
Published by: Midwest Beverage Publications, Inc., 3 12th St, Wheeling, WV 26003. TEL 304-232-7620, FAX 304-233-1236, bevjournalch@swave.net, http://www.bevnetwork.com. Ed., Pub., R&P, Adv. contact Arnold Lazarus. page USD 870. Circ: 7,200 (controlled and free).

641 USA ISSN 0030-1183
OHIO TAVERN NEWS. Text in English. 1939. bi-w. USD 18 (effective 2005). adv. bk.rev. illus. **Document type:** *Magazine, Trade.* **Description:** Serves Ohio's on- and off-premise liquor permit holders, beverage alcohol manufacturers, distributors and wholesalers, related industry associations, and other representatives of the state's hospitality industry. Covers industry trends and local, state and federal legislation as it pertains to the alcoholic beverage and hospitality industries.
Published by: Daily Reporter Inc., 580 S High St, Ste 316, Columbus, OH 43215. TEL 614-228-6397, FAX 614-224-8649, otn@sourcenews.com, http://www.ohiotavernnews.com. Ed. Chris Bailey. Pub., R&P Dan Shillingburg. Adv. contact Bret Greiner. Circ: 8,215 (paid and free).

647.95 663 USA ISSN 1051-4562
ON PREMISE. Text in English. 1985. bi-m. USD 15 to non-members (effective 2001). adv. tr.lit. back issues avail. **Document type:** *Magazine, Trade.* **Description:** For owners, managers, and employees of taverns, restaurants, resorts, hotel/motel lounges, and nightclubs.
Formerly (until 1990): TopShelf (0749-2022)
Published by: (Tavern League of Wisconsin), Slack Attack Advertising, 5113 Monona Dr., Monona, WI 53716-2719. TEL 608-222-7630, FAX 608-222-0262, bslack@slackattack.com, http://www.tlw.org. Ed. Chuck Taylor. Pub. Barbara Slack. R&P Melody Bruckner. Adv. contact Janet Vinje. B&W page USD 725, color page USD 1,325; trim 10.88 x 8.38. Circ: 5,000. **Subscr. to:** T L W, 2817 Fish Hatchery Rd, Madison, WI 53713. TEL 800-445-9221.

ONTARIO GRAPE GROWER. see *AGRICULTURE—Crop Production And Soil*

663.2 GBR ISSN 1352-1195
OZ CLARK'S WINE GUIDE (YEAR). Text in English. 1984. a. GBP 9.99. adv. back issues avail. **Document type:** *Consumer.*
Formerly (until 1992): Websters Wine Guide (0957-7777)
Published by: Websters Wine Guide Ltd., Axe & Bottle Ct, 70 Newcomen St, London, SE1 1YT, United Kingdom. TEL 44-171-407-5956, FAX 44-171-407-6437. Ed. Claire Harcup. R&P Adrian Webster. Adv. contact Tim Bradshaw. B&W page GBP 1,100; trim 130 x 198. Circ: 40,000 (paid).

PASTA; the journal of fine wines and italian cuisine. see *HOME ECONOMICS*

663 USA
PATTERSON'S CALIFORNIA BEVERAGE JOURNAL. Text in English. 1962. m. USD 48 (effective 2005). mkt.; stat. **Document type:** *Magazine, Trade.* **Description:** The voice of California's wine & spirits industry.

Former titles: Patterson's Beverage Journal (0895-3872); (until 1987): Patterson's California Beverage Journal (0192-1797)
Published by: Interactive Color, Inc., 4910 San Fernando Rd, Glendale, CA 91204. TEL 818-547-4507, FAX 818-547-4607, nswords@interactivecolor.com, http://www.beveragelink.com. Ed. Meridith May. Circ: 20,000 (paid).

663 USA ISSN 1542-3107
PENNSYLVANIA'S OFFICIAL WINE - SPIRITS QUARTERLY. Text in English. 1985. q. adv.
Formerly (until 2001): Pennsylvania's Official Wine and Liquor Quarterly
Published by: Metrocorp, 1818 Market St, Philadelphia, PA 19103. TEL 215-564-7700, FAX 215-656-3536, http://winespirits-pa.com. Ed. Emily McManus. Pub. David H. Lipson Jr. Adv. contact Meredith Bass Edelman. B&W page USD 6,800, color page USD 8,500; trim 10.88 x 8. Circ: 325,000.

663.4 NLD ISSN 1380-6084
PINT - NIEUWS. Text in Dutch. 1980. bi-m. EUR 18 (effective 2005). adv. bk.rev.; software rev. illus.; stat.; tr.lit. index. back issues avail. **Document type:** *Newsletter, Consumer.*
Published by: Pint, PO Box 3757, Amsterdam, 1001 AN, Netherlands. info@pint.nl, http://www.pint.nl/. Circ: 4,000.

663 GBR
PINTPOT. Text in English. 1960. q. free. **Document type:** *Trade.*
Published by: Manners PR, 20 Grove Pl, Bedford, MK40 3JJ, United Kingdom. TEL 44-1234-357274, FAX 44-1234-210282. Ed. Jacquie Manners. Circ: 10,000.

641.23 SCG ISSN 0554-2308
PIVARSTVO✶. Text in Serbo-Croatian; Summaries in English, German. 1967. q. YUN 9,000, USD 12. adv. index, cum.index: 1967-1977, 1978-1987. back issues avail.
Published by: Poslovna Zajednica Industrije Piva i Slada Jugoslavije/Beer and Malt Industry of Yugoslavia Business Association, Deligradska 18, Belgrade, Serbia 11000. TEL 011-644-953. Circ: 1,000.

PLAISIRS DE LA TABLE. see *FOOD AND FOOD INDUSTRIES*

PODRAVKA; znanstveno-strucni casopis. see *AGRICULTURE*

663 CZE ISSN 0862-2159
POTRAVINARSKE AKTUALITY. NAPOJOVY PRUMYSL. Text in Czech. 1958. 10/yr. CZK 400 (effective 2000). adv. **Document type:** *Consumer.*
Formerly (until 1983): Potravinarske Aktuality. Rada G (0139-5785)
Published by: Ustav Zemedelskych a Potravinarskych Informaci, Potravinarske Aktuality/Institute of Agricultural and Food Information, Slezska 7, Prague 2, 120 56, Czech Republic. TEL 420-2-24257939, FAX 420-2-22514003, insav@login.cz, insav@uzpi.cz, http://www.uzpi.cz. Adv. contact L Masakova.

663.2 USA ISSN 0739-8077
TP544
PRACTICAL WINERY & VINEYARD; in-depth coverage from vine to market. Text in English. 1980. bi-m. USD 31 domestic; USD 36 in Canada; USD 49 elsewhere (effective 2004). adv. bk.rev. index. back issues avail.; reprints avail. **Document type:** *Magazine, Consumer.*
Formerly: Practical Winery
Published by: P W V Incorporated, 58-D Paul Drive, San Rafael, CA 94903. TEL 415-479-5819, FAX 415-492-9325, http://www.practicalwinery.com/. Ed., Pub. Don Neel. Adv. contact Ron Sweeney. B&W page USD 1,215; 8.5 x 11. Circ: 3,000 (paid).

663.2 ESP
LA PRENSA DEL RIOJA. Text mainly in Spanish; Some issues in English. 1985. 10/yr. EUR 45 (effective 2002). adv. bk.rev. **Document type:** *Magazine, Consumer.* **Description:** Covers wine, gastronomy, tourism and the wine-growing region of Rioja.
Related titles: English ed.: ESP 4,800 for 3 yrs. (effective 2000).
Published by: Prensa del Rioja, C/ Padre Claret, 3 bajo, Logrono, La Rioja 26004, Spain. TEL 34-941-237520, FAX 34-941-237518, info@laprensadelrioja.com, http://www.laprensadelrioja.com. Ed., Pub. Javier Pascual Corral. Adv. contact Mirian Terroba. page EUR 1,111; 210 x 285. Circ: 7,500 (paid).

663.2 FRA ISSN 0221-301X
PRESSE DU VIN-VINETEC. Text in French; Summaries in English. 1978. m. adv. bk.rev. charts; illus.; stat.
Published by: S.F.P. Vinitec, 79 rue Raymond Poincare, Le Bouscat, 33110, France. Ed. Philippe Dourthe. Circ: 10,000.

663.42 DEU ISSN 1435-3601
DIE PRIVATBRAUEREI. Text in German. 1998. m. EUR 36.81 domestic; EUR 49.08 foreign (effective 2000). **Document type:** *Journal, Trade.*
Published by: Verlag W. Sachon GmbH & Co., Schloss Mindelburg, Mindelheim, 87714, Germany. TEL 49-8261-9990, FAX 49-8261-999132, info@sachon.de, http://www.sachon.de. Ed. Lucas Goebel. Adv. contact Martina Zimmermann.

PROCESSED FOODS & BEVERAGES DIRECTORY (YEAR). see *BUSINESS AND ECONOMICS—Trade And Industrial Directories*

PRODUCT ALERT. see *FOOD AND FOOD INDUSTRIES*

663.1 GBR ISSN 1365-5817
THE PUBLICAN NEWSPAPER. Text in English. 1975. w. adv. illus. reprint service avail. from PQC. **Document type:** *Newspaper, Trade.*
Formerly (until 1996): Publican (0142-0755)
Related titles: Microfilm ed.: (from PQC).
—BLDSC (7012.201750). **CCC.**
Published by: United Business Media, Riverbank House, Angel Ln, Tonbridge, Kent TN9 1SE, United Kingdom. TEL 44-20-79215000, communications@unitedbusinessmedia.com, http://www.unitedbusinessmedia.com. Circ: 33,000.

663.2 641.5 USA ISSN 0740-1248
TP544
QUARTERLY REVIEW OF WINES. Text in English. 1977. q. USD 17.95 domestic; USD 22.95 in Canada; USD 39.95 in Europe; USD 4.95 newsstand/cover (effective 2005). adv. bk.rev. illus.; maps. 124 p./no. 3 cols./p.; back issues avail.; reprints avail. **Document type:** *Magazine, Consumer.* **Description:** Articles on wines, food and travel.
Published by: Q R W, Inc., 24 Garfield Ave, Winchester, MA 01890. TEL 781-729-7132, 800-752-2587, FAX 781-721-0572, qrwinc@qrw.com, qrwine@qrw.com, http://qrw.com, http://www.qrw.com. Ed. Randolph G Sheahan. Pub., R&P Richard L Elia. Adv. contact Jack Lynch. Circ: 25,000 (free); 165,000 (paid and controlled).

663.2 ESP
R I V E. (Revista Internacional de Vinos Espanoles) Text in Spanish. 10/yr.
Address: Baeza, 6, Madrid, 28002, Spain. TEL 1-415-90-72. Ed. Jose L Dorado.

641.2 FRA ISSN 1247-2077
RAYON BOISSONS. Text in French. 1993. m. (11/yr.). EUR 55 domestic; EUR 70 foreign (effective 2004). **Document type:** *Magazine, Trade.*
Published by: Editions du Boisbaudry, 13 Square du Chene Germain, Cesson Sevigne, 355773, France. TEL 33-2-99322121, http://www.editionsduboisbaudry.com.

634.8 663.2 DEU ISSN 0034-1118
REBE UND WEIN. Text in German. 1947. m. adv. bk.rev. charts; illus. index. **Document type:** *Bulletin.*
Indexed: VITIS.
Published by: Jahrbuch Verlag, Schwabstr 20, Weinsberg, 74189, Germany. Ed. Hans Roeck. Circ: 6,600.

RESTAURANT WINE; buying - selling - serving: the full-service guide to on sale beverage profits. see *HOTELS AND RESTAURANTS*

REVISTA DE GASTRONOMIA Y ENOLOGIA. see *HOTELS AND RESTAURANTS*

634.8 PRT ISSN 0874-372X
REVISTA DE VINHOS; para apreciadores exigentes. Text in Portuguese. 1989. m. EUR 34.91 (effective 2002). adv. **Document type:** *Magazine, Trade.*
Published by: Edicoes Expansao Economica Lda., Rue Mario Castelhano, 40-1, Queluz de Baixo, Barcarena, 2749-502, Portugal. TEL 351-21-496-95-40, FAX 351-21-436-95-39, webmaster@expansao.iol.pt, http://www.revistadevinhos.iol.pt, http://www.expansao.iol.pt. Ed. Luis Lopes.

634.8 FRA ISSN 0760-9868
TP544
REVUE D'OENOLOGUES ET DES TECHNIQUES VITI-VINICOLES ET OENOLOGIQUES. Text in French. 1974. 5/yr. bk.rev. **Document type:** *Trade.*
Indexed: FS&TA, RefZh, VITIS.
—BLDSC (7938.750000), IE, ingenta.
Published by: Oeno Plurimedia, Chateau de Chaintre, Cidex 453 Bis, Chaintre, 71570, France. TEL 33-3-85374321, FAX 33-3-85371983, oenee@club-internet.fr, infos@mail.oeno.tm.fr. Ed. M Gautier. Pub. H.L. Arnould. Adv. contact H L Arnould. Circ: 15,000.

663.2 634.8 FRA ISSN 1634-7625
REVUE DU VIN DE FRANCE. Text in French. 1981. m. FRF 100; EUR 5.80 newsstand/cover (effective 2005). adv. bk.rev. bibl.; charts; illus.; mkt.; stat. index. **Document type:** *Magazine, Trade.*
Formerly (until 1986): Revue du Vin de France, Sommeliers du Monde (0750-358X); Which was formed by the merger of (1927-1982): Revue du Vin de France (0035-273X); (1980-1981): Sommeliers du Monde (0246-246X)
Indexed: KES.
Published by: Groupe Marie Claire, 10 Boulevard des Freres Voisins, Issy-les-Moulineaux, 92792 Cedex 9, France. TEL 33-1-41468888, FAX 33-1-41468686, http://www.groupemarieclaire.com. Circ: 40,000.

663 USA ISSN 0035-4562
RHODE ISLAND BEVERAGE JOURNAL. Text in English. 1945. m. USD 35 (effective 2005). adv. bk.rev. mkt.; tr.lit. back issues avail. **Document type:** *Magazine, Trade.* **Description:** Provides price listings for package stores, restaurants and other liquor permittees.
Published by: Rhode Island Beverage Journal, Inc., 2508 Whitney Ave, P O Box 185159, Hamden, CT 06518. TEL 203-288-3375, FAX 203-288-2693, thebeveragejournal@snetnet, thebeveragejournal@snet.net, http://www.bevaccess.com/, http://www.ribeveragejournal.com. Ed., Pub., R&P Gerald P Slone. adv.: B&W page USD 385, color page USD 1,135; trim 8.25 x 10.88. Circ: 1,400 (paid).

RIVISTA DI VITICOLTURA E DI ENOLOGIA. see *AGRICULTURE—Crop Production And Soil*

▼ **ROAST MAGAZINE**; dedicated to the success of coffee roasters. see *FOOD AND FOOD INDUSTRIES*

663.2 AUT
ROTWEINGUIDE (YEAR). Text in German. a. EUR 12.10 newsstand/cover (effective 2005). **Document type:** *Directory, Consumer.* **Description:** Guide to various brands and types of red wine.
Published by: Falstaff Verlag, Bueropark Donau, Inkustr 1-7, Stg 4, Klosterneuburg, N 3400, Austria. TEL 43-2243-34798, FAX 43-2243-25840, redaktion@falstaff.at, http://www.falstaff.at.

663.1 AUS
ROY MORGAN ALCOHOLIC BEVERAGE MONITOR. Text in English. q. **Document type:** *Trade.*
Published by: Roy Morgan Research, PO Box 2282 U, Melbourne, VIC 3001, Australia. TEL 61-3-96296888, FAX 61-3-96291250, http://www.roymorgan.com.

641.2 AUS
ROY MORGAN NON-ALCOHOLIC BEVERAGE MONITOR. Text in English. m. **Document type:** *Trade.*
Published by: Roy Morgan Research, PO Box 2282 U, Melbourne, VIC 3001, Australia. TEL 61-3-96296888, FAX 61-3-96291250, http://www.roymorgan.com.

663.3 DNK ISSN 0105-3442
SAMLERRINGEN; tidsskrift for bryggerisouvenirs og bryggerihistorie. Text in Danish. 19??. biennial. **Document type:** *Newsletter, Consumer.* **Description:** Abour beer history and bottle collecting.
Published by: Skandinavisk Bryggerisouvenir Samlerforening/Scandinavian Breweriana Collectors Association, c/o Michael Buus, Valbylangggade 120, Valby, 2500, Denmark. TEL 45-36450773, michaelbuus@privat.dk, http://www.scanbrew.dk.

663.2 USA
▼ **SAVEUR'S WINE COUNTRY.** Text in English. 2005 (Aug.). a. (s-a. in 2006). adv. **Document type:** *Magazine, Consumer.* **Description:** Covers West Coast wineries, hotels, spas, restaurants and other attractions.
Published by: World Publications LLC, 460 N Orlando Ave, Ste 200, Winter Park, FL 32789. TEL 407-628-4802, FAX 407-628-7061, info@worldpub.net, http://www.saveurswinecountry.com/, http://www.worldpub.net. Ed. Bill Marken. Pub. Michael Earls. adv.: color page USD 7,200. Circ: 150,000.

SAVOIR-VIVRE; Journal fuer Geniesser. see *FOOD AND FOOD INDUSTRIES*

663.2 910.91 USA
SAVOR WINE COUNTRY. Text in English. 2002. q. adv. **Document type:** *Magazine, Consumer.*
Related titles: Online - full content ed.
Published by: The Press Democrat, 427 Mendocino Ave., Santa Rosa, CA 95401. TEL 707-546-2020, http://www.savorwinecountry.com. Pub. Michael J Parman. Adv. contact Joanne Davey. color page USD 4,807; trim 8.375 x 10.875. Circ: 165,000.

663.3 DNK CODEN: BRYGAW
SCANDINAVIAN BREWERS' REVIEW. Text in English. 1944. bi-m. DKK 200; DKK 40 per issue (effective 2002). adv. bk.rev. abstr.; charts; illus.; pat.; stat.; tr.lit. index. **Document type:** *Trade.* **Description:** For and about the Nordic brewery and soft drink industry.
Formerly (until 2002): Brygmesteren (0007-2737)
Indexed: BiolAb, ChemAb, FS&TA, PST.
—BLDSC (8087.471700), CASDDS, IE, ingenta.
Published by: Dansk Brygmester Forening/Danish Master Brewers' Association, c/o Benny Poulsen, Dansk Brygmester Forening, Ny Carlsberg Vej 100, Copenhagen V, 1799, Denmark. TEL 45-33-27-12-87, http://www.brygmesteren.dk. Ed. Steen Kledal. Circ: 1,000. **Co-sponsors:** Norsk Bryggerlaug; Sveriges Bryggeritekniker Foerening.

SCANDINAVIAN FOOD AND DRINK REPORT. see *FOOD AND FOOD INDUSTRIES*

663.2 CHE ISSN 0036-7796
SCHWEIZERISCHE WEINZEITUNG/JOURNAL VINICOLE SUISSE. Text in French, German. 1893. 14/yr. CHF 150 domestic; CHF 160 foreign (effective 2001). **Document type:** *Newspaper, Trade.*
Published by: Schweizerische Weinzeitung Verlag AG, Hofstr 3, Postfach 69, Glattfelden, 8192, Switzerland. TEL 41-1-8672300, FAX 41-1-8672308, swz@active.ch. Ed. Othmar Staeheli. Circ: 1,700 (paid).

641 GBR ISSN 0036-9322
SCOTTISH LICENSED TRADE NEWS. Text in English. 1964. 24/yr. GBP 56 domestic; GBP 70 foreign (effective Oct. 2002). adv. **Document type:** *Trade.* **Description:** For retailers of liquor in stores, hotels and bars.
—CCC.
Published by: Peebles Media Group, Bergius House, Clifton St, Glasgow, G3 7LA, United Kingdom. TEL 44-141-567-6000, FAX 44-141-353-2336, info@peeblesmedia.com, http://www.peeblesmedia.com/sltn/index.htm. Ed. Pat Duffy. Adv. contact Sharon Wilson. Circ: 15,800 (controlled).

641.2 AUS
SHARE OF THORAT MONITOR. Text in English. d. **Document type:** *Trade.*
Media: Online - full content.
Published by: Roy Morgan Research, PO Box 2282 U, Melbourne, VIC 3001, Australia. TEL 61-3-96296888, FAX 61-3-96291250, http://www.roymorgan.com.

663.1 USA ISSN 0887-2783
SOCIAL HISTORY OF ALCOHOL REVIEW✶ . Text in English. 1980. s-a. USD 15 to individuals; USD 20 to institutions. bk.rev. **Document type:** *Academic/Scholarly.* **Description:** Provides a forum for the exchange of ideas among scholars in all disciplines who are interested in any aspect of alcohol use, abuse, production, and control within given societies or countries.
Former titles (until 1985): Alcohol in History: A Multidisciplinary Newsletter (0749-7989); Alcohol and Temperance History Group Newsletter
Published by: Alcohol & Temperance History Group, Southwest Regional Laboratory, 4665 Lampson Ave, Los Alamitos, CA 90720-5139. TEL 904-392-0271. Ed. W Scott Haine. Circ: 150. **Subscr. to:** c/o Prof. Richard F. Hamm, SHAR Sec -Treas, Dept of History, State University of New York at Albany, Social Sciences Bldg 341, Albany, NY 12222.

663.6 USA
THE SODA FOUNTAIN NEWSLETTER. Text in English. irreg. free. adv. **Document type:** *Newsletter.*
Media: Online - full text.
Published by: Soda Fountain Newsletter, 140 Bourne Ave, Ste 21, Rumford, RI 02916. TEL 401-455-8415, FAX 401-431-1836. Pub., Adv. contact David Ivey.

663.6 GBR ISSN 1367-8302
CODEN: SDMIE3
SOFT DRINKS INTERNATIONAL. Text in English. 1888. m. GBP 80 EU member states; GBP 100 elsewhere (effective 2005); GBP 80 elsewhere. adv. bk.rev. charts; illus.; pat.; tr.lit. index. **Document type:** *Journal, Trade.* **Description:** Provides in depth coverage on the manufacture, distribution, and marketing of soft drinks, fruit juices, and bottled water throughout Europe and the rest of the world.
Former titles (until Jan. 1996): Soft Drinks Management International (0953-4776); (until 1988): Soft Drinks; (until 1985): Soft Drinks Trade Journal (0038-058X)
Indexed: FS&TA, IPackAb, KES.
—BLDSC (8321.352700), IE, Infotrieve, ingenta. **CCC.**
Published by: A S A P Publishing Ltd., PO Box 4173, Winborne, Dorset BH21 1YX, United Kingdom. TEL 44-1202-842222, FAX 44-1202-848494, subs@softdrinksjournal.com, aands@oxfordshire.co.uk, http://www.softdrinksjournal.com/. Ed. Stewart Farr. Adv. contact Tom Faux TEL 44-1622-850555. B&W page GBP 680, color page GBP 1,190. Circ: 3,500 (paid).

663.2 ESP
SOMMELIER. Text in Spanish. 12/yr. **Document type:** *Consumer.*
Published by: Ediciones Sociales S.L., Rossello, 186-4o, Barcelona, 08036, Spain. TEL 34-3-323-14-91, FAX 34-3-4348565. Ed. Susana Cayuela.

663.2 DEU
SOMMELIER MAGAZIN. Text in German. 2000. 4/yr. EUR 23.40; EUR 6.10 newsstand/cover (effective 2002). adv. **Document type:** *Magazine, Trade.*
Published by: Meininger Verlag GmbH, Maximilianstr 7-17, Neustadt, 67433, Germany. TEL 49-6321-8908-0, FAX 49-6321-890873, baeder@meininger.de, contact@meininger.de, http://www.sommelier-magazin.de, http://www.meininger.de. Ed. Julia Kloeckner. adv.: B&W page EUR 2,400, color page EUR 2,650. Circ: 4,806 (paid and controlled).

663.2 634.8 ZAF ISSN 0253-939X
CODEN: SAJVD5
SOUTH AFRICAN JOURNAL FOR ENOLOGY AND VITICULTURE. Text in English. 1980. s-a.
Indexed: AgBio, AgrForAb, BioCN&I, CPA, FS&TA, HortAb, I&DA, NemAb, NutrAb, OrnHort, PBA, PGegResA, PGrRegA, PHN&I, PoultAb, RDA, RM&VM, RPP, S&F, SIA, WAE&RSA.
—BLDSC (8338.867000), CISTI, IE, ingenta.
Published by: South African Society for Enology and Viticulture, PO Box 2092, Dennesig, 7601, South Africa. TEL 27-21-8093123, FAX 27-21-8896335, sasev@infruit.agric.za, http://www.sasev.co.za/.

663.2 USA
SOUTHCOAST WINE; Southern & Baja California's guide to great living. Text in English. 1997. q. USD 14 for 6 nos.; USD 2.95 newsstand/cover. adv. bk.rev. **Document type:** *Consumer.* **Description:** Covers the wine industry of Southern and Baja California. Winery profiles, local food and wine events, local recreational activities.
Published by: Gerry Troy, Pub., 969 Kevin Ave, Redlands, CA 92373-5855. TEL 909-338-9776, FAX 909-338-4956, winefreak@aol.com. Ed. Richard Jones. R&P, Adv. contact Gerry Troy. Circ: 10,000.

663 USA ISSN 0193-0613
SOUTHERN BEVERAGE JOURNAL. Text in English. 1948. m. USD 35 (effective 2005). **Document type:** *Magazine, Trade.*
Published by: S B J Publishing, Inc., PO Box 561107, Miami, FL 33256-1107. TEL 305-233-7230, FAX 305-252-2580, sobevjrnl@aol.com, http://www.bevnetwork.com. Ed., R&P Wanda Rowe. Pub. William Slone. Circ: 25,000.

663.93 USA ISSN 1077-3460
TX945
SPECIALTY COFFEE RETAILER; the coffee business monthly. Text in English. 1994. m. USD 39 domestic; USD 48 in Canada; USD 110 elsewhere (effective 2005). adv. illus. back issues avail. **Document type:** *Magazine, Trade.* **Description:** Provides owners and managers of coffee houses and coffee retail operations with information on products and equipment, merchandising, retailing trends and management strategies.
Related titles: Online - full text ed.: (from Florida Center for Library Automation, Gale Group, O C L C Online Computer Library Center, Inc.).
Indexed: B&I.
—CCC.
Published by: Adams Business Media, 420 S. Palm Canyon Dr., 2nd Fl, Palm Springs, CA 92262. TEL 847-427-9512, 760-318-7000, FAX 847-427-2079, 760-323-4877, http://www.retailmerchandising.net/coffee/, http://www.abm.net. Ed. Sue Gillerlain. Adv. contact Brian Grau. B&W page USD 1,695. Circ: 7,500.

658.8 USA ISSN 0747-3206
SPIRITS, WINE & BEER MARKETING IN MINNESOTA, NORTH & SOUTH DAKOTA✶ . Text in English. 1934. m. USD 24. adv. **Document type:** *Trade.*
Formerly: Northwest Beverage Journal
Published by: Diamond Publications, PO Box 398, Hopkins, MN 55343-0398. TEL 612-449-9446, FAX 612-449-9447. Ed. Gary L Diamond. Circ: 11,500.

663.53 DEU ISSN 0081-3729
SPIRITUOSEN-JAHRBUCH. Text in German. 1950. a. adv. **Document type:** *Trade.*
Published by: Versuchs- und Lehranstalt fuer Spiritusfabrikation und Fermentationstechnologie, Seestr 13, Berlin, 13467, Germany. TEL 49-30-45080-0, FAX 49-30-4536067. Ed. R Beckmann. Circ: 4,500.

663 DEU ISSN 0038-7657
DER SPIRITUOSEN- UND WEINHANDEL. Text in German. 1966. q. EUR 40 (effective 2001). adv. bk.rev. charts; stat.; tr.lit. **Document type:** *Magazine, Trade.* **Description:** Covers the wholesale wine and spirits trade.
Published by: Zeitungs- und Zeitschriftenverlag Heinrichs, Brueggekamp 1, Barsinghausen, 30890, Germany. TEL 49-5105-2289. Ed., Pub. Gerhard Heinrichs.

663.2 USA
SPOTLIGHT'S WINE COUNTRY GUIDE. Text in English. 1989. m. USD 3.50 per issue (effective 2005); free in hotels, wineries, and AAA offices. adv. illus. 96 p./no.; **Document type:** *Magazine, Consumer.* **Description:** For northern California's visitors and wineries. Covers wine tasting, dining, entertainment, sights, shopping and sports.
Published by: Spotlight Publishing Inc., 5 Kenilworth Ct, Novato, CA 94945. TEL 415-898-7908, FAX 415-898-7751, bill@winecountryguide.com, http://www.winecountryguide.com. Ed. Reggie Winner. Pub., R&P William Schoen. Adv. contact Bill Schoer TEL 415-898-7908. B&W page USD 1,620, color page USD 1,929; 3.5 x 10. Circ: 720,000.

663.2 GBR
SPYGLASS; the wine magazine with refreshing acidity. Text in English. m. GBP 2 newsstand/cover. **Document type:** *Consumer.*
Published by: N H Publishing, Downside House, Shepton Mallet, Somers BA4 4JL, United Kingdom.

STAGNITO'S NEW PRODUCTS MAGAZINE. see *FOOD AND FOOD INDUSTRIES*

663.3 USA ISSN 0279-2133
HD9351
STATEWAYS. Text in English. 1972. bi-m. USD 20 domestic; USD 25 in Canada & Mexico; USD 50 elsewhere (effective 2004). adv. bk.rev. **Document type:** *Magazine, Trade.* **Description:** Directed to the 19 Alcohol Beverage Control markets.
Related titles: Online - full text ed.: (from Florida Center for Library Automation, Gale Group).
Published by: Adams Business Media, 420 S Palm Canyon Dr, 2nd Fl, Palm Springs, CA 92262. TEL 847-427-9512, 760-318-7000, FAX 847-882-6842, 760-323-4877, rbrandes@mail.aip.com, http://www.beveragenet.net, http://www.abm.net. Eds. Michael Applehaum, Richard Brandes. Pub. Seymour Leikind. R&P Michael Applehaum. Adv. contacts John Pennacchio, Anthony Bongiovanni. B&W page USD 4,980, color page USD 7,555. Circ: 10,000 (controlled).

663 USA ISSN 0081-931X
KF3920
SUMMARY OF STATE LAWS AND REGULATIONS RELATING TO DISTILLED SPIRITS. Text in English. 1935. biennial. USD 23 (effective 2000). **Document type:** *Consumer.*
Published by: Distilled Spirits Council of the United States, Inc., Office of General Counsel, 1250 Eye St, N W, Ste 400, Washington, DC 20005. TEL 202-682-8820, FAX 202-682-8877, tbudoff@discus.org, http://www.discus.health.org. Circ: (controlled).

663.2 ITA
THE TASTER OF WINE AND FOOD; il periodico per conoscere ed apprezzare il vino e la degustazione. Text in Italian. 1998. q. EUR 52 domestic; EUR 57 in Europe; EUR 67 elsewhere (effective 2005). adv. charts; illus. **Document type:** *Magazine, Consumer.* **Description:** Evaluates hundreds of Italian and foreign wines. Interviews key persons, presents updates on wine-tasting techniques, and provides a dialogue with readers.
Published by: L m Srl, Via Flaminia, 1007, Rome, RM 00189, Italy. TEL 39-06-33219811, FAX 39-06-33219843, lmonline@lmonline.com, http://www.lmonline.com. Ed., Pub., R&P Luca Maroni. Adv. contact Tania Wolodimeroff.

380.141 IND
TEA DIRECTORY. Text in English. 1960. irreg., latest 1982. INR 35.
Published by: Tea Board, 14 B.T.M .Sarani (Brabourne Rd.), P O Box 2172, Kolkata, West Bengal 700 001, India. TEL 26-0210, TELEX 021-4527. Ed. Shri R N Mondal.

663.94 IND ISSN 0375-3077
TEA RESEARCH ASSOCIATION. ADVISORY BULLETIN. Text in English. 1971. irreg., latest vol.11, 1986. price varies. cum.index every 5 yrs. **Document type:** *Bulletin.*
Indexed: ATA, HortAb.
Published by: Tea Research Association, Tocklai Experimental Station, Jorhat, Assam 785 008, India.

663 633 IND
TEA RESEARCH ASSOCIATION. MEMORANDUM. Text in English. 1938. irreg., latest vol.30, 1977. price varies. charts.
Indexed: ATA, HortAb.
Published by: Tea Research Association, Tocklai Experimental Station, Jorhat, Assam 785 008, India.

663 633 IND
TEA RESEARCH ASSOCIATION. OCCASIONAL SCIENTIFIC PAPERS. Text in English. 1968. irreg., latest vol.12. price varies. bibl.; charts.
Indexed: HortAb.
Published by: Tea Research Association, Tocklai Experimental Station, Jorhat, Assam 785 008, India.

663 630 IND ISSN 0564-6723
TEA RESEARCH ASSOCIATION. TOCKLAI EXPERIMENTAL STATION. SCIENTIFIC ANNUAL REPORT. Text in English. a. price varies.
Indexed: ATA, BiolAb, HortAb, RPP, RevApplEntom.
Published by: Tea Research Association, Tocklai Experimental Station, Jorhat, Assam 785 008, India.

TEA TALK; a newsletter on the pleasures of tea. see *FOOD AND FOOD INDUSTRIES*

663.3 JPN ISSN 0916-6491
CODEN: RLKBAD
TECHNICAL REPORT OF KIRIN. Text in English, German. 1958. a. free or exchange basis. **Document type:** *Corporate.*
Formerly: Kirin Brewery Company, Tokyo. Research Laboratory. Report (0075-6229)
Indexed: BiolAb, FS&TA.
—CASDDS.
Published by: Kirin Brewery Co. Ltd./Kirin Biru K.K. Gijutsubu, 26-1 Jingu-Mae 6-chome, Shibuya-ku, Tokyo, 150-0001, Japan. Ed. Hiroshi Yokoyama.

663.2 ESP ISSN 1578-6153
TECNOLOGIA DEL VINO. Text in Spanish. 2001. bi-m. EUR 51 domestic; EUR 79 in Europe; EUR 128 elsewhere (effective 2003).
Related titles: Online - full text ed.
—CINDOC.

▼ new title ➤ refereed ✶ unverified ♦ full entry avail.

Published by: Editorial Alcion Ingenieria Quimica, S.A., Medea, 4, Madrid, 28037, Spain. TEL 34-91-3456400, FAX 34-91-3453945, alcion@tsai.es, http://www.alcion.es.

THOMAS FOOD AND BEVERAGE MARKET PLACE. see *BUSINESS AND ECONOMICS—Trade And Industrial Directories*

663.2 910.2 USA ISSN 1098-8866
TOURING AND TASTING; wine, food, travel. Text in English. 1995. s-a. USD 9 (effective 2003). **Description:** Contains gourmet recipes, intriguing winery histories and exotic wine travel articles.
Related titles: Online - full text ed.
Published by: Touring and Tasting Club, 207 E Victoria St., Santa Barbara, CA 93101. TEL 800-850-4370, FAX 805-965-2873, wine@touringandtasting.com, http://www.touringandtasting.com/subscribe.htm.

663 DEU
THE TRADE WITH BEVERAGES/HANDEL MIT GETRAENKEN. Text in English, German. q. EUR 40 (effective 2001). adv. **Document type:** *Magazine, Trade.*
Published by: Zeitungs- und Zeitschriftenverlag Heinrichs, Brueggekamp 1, Barsinghausen, 30890, Germany. TEL 49-5105-2289. Ed., Pub. Gerhard Heinrichs.

663 664 GRC ISSN 1106-3718
TROFIMA KAI POTA/FOOD & BEVERAGES. Text in Greek; Summaries in English. 1976. m. USD 100. adv. bk.rev. illus. back issues avail. **Document type:** *Trade.* **Description:** Provides a tool for managers in the food and beverage industries, packaging and plastics, and hotels and restaurants.
Related titles: English ed.: Galaktomia. ISSN 1106-3734. 1991.
Published by: Triaina Publishing Co., 110 Syngrou Ave, Athens, 117 41, Greece. TEL 30-210-924-0748, FAX 30-210-924-2650, info@triaina.com. Ed. Kyriakos Korovilas. Adv. contact Catherine Stergion. Circ: 8,500.

664 IND ISSN 0496-6201
CODEN: TAABAA
TWO AND A BUD. Text in English. 1954. s-a. INR 420; USD 18 foreign. adv. bk.rev. bibl.; charts; tr.lit.
Indexed: AEA, ATA, AgBio, AgrForAb, BioCN&I, BiolAb, CPA, ChemAb, FS&TA, ForAb, HortAb, I&DA, PBA, PGegResA, PGrRegA, PHN&I, RA&MP, RM&VM, RPP, RRTA, RevApplEntom, S&F, SeedAb, WAE&RSA, WeedAb, ZooRec. —CASDDS.
Published by: Tea Research Association, Tocklai Experimental Station, Jorhat, Assam 785 008, India.

663.4 USA ISSN 1059-6887
HD9397.U5
THE U S BEER MARKET: IMPACT DATABANK REVIEW AND FORECAST. Text in English. 1980. a. USD 845; USD 865 foreign (effective 1997). charts. **Document type:** *Trade.* **Description:** Provides research on the U.S. beer market.
Formerly: Impact American Beer Market Review and Forecast (0198-9952)
Published by: Marvin R. Shanken Communications, Inc., 387 Park Ave S, New York, NY 10016. TEL 212-684-4224, FAX 212-684-5424. Ed. Marvin R Shanken.

U.S. BUREAU OF ALCOHOL, TOBACCO AND FIREARMS. QUARTERLY BULLETIN. see *CRIMINOLOGY AND LAW ENFORCEMENT*

663.1 USA
HD9390.U6
THE U S DISTILLED SPIRITS MARKET: IMPACT DATABANK REVIEW AND FORECAST. Text in English. 1976. a. USD 845; USD 865 foreign (effective 1997). charts. **Document type:** *Trade.* **Description:** Provides research on the U.S. market for distilled spirits.
Formerly: Impact American Distilled Spirits Market Review and Forecast (0163-9536)
Published by: Marvin R. Shanken Communications, Inc., 387 Park Ave S, New York, NY 10016. TEL 212-684-4224, FAX 212-684-5424. Ed. Marvin R Shanken.

663.2 USA
HD9374
THE U S WINE MARKET: IMPACT DATABANK REVIEW AND FORECAST. Text in English. 1975. a. USD 845; USD 865 foreign (effective 1997). charts. back issues avail. **Document type:** *Trade.* **Description:** Provides research on the U.S. market for wine.
Formerly: Impact American Wine Market Review and Forecast (0163-9544)
Published by: Marvin R. Shanken Communications, Inc., 387 Park Ave S, New York, NY 10016. TEL 212-684-4224, FAX 212-684-5424. Ed. Marvin R Shanken.

ULSTER FOOD TRADER. see *FOOD AND FOOD INDUSTRIES*

663 FRA ISSN 1161-3580
UNION FRANCAISE DES OENOLOGUES. ANNUAIRE. Text in French. 1969 (2nd ed.). a. adv.
Formerly: Union National des Oenologues. Annuaire (1161-3572)
Related titles: ◆ Supplement to: Revue Francaise d'Oenologie. ISSN 0395-899X.

Published by: Revue Francaise d'Oenologie, Maison des Agriculteurs, Mas de Saporta, Lattes, 34970, France. TEL 33-4-67586906, FAX 33-4-67586891. Ed. Dominique Traxel. Adv. contact Magali Dumas.

641.2 IRL
V F I UPDATE. Text in English. 9/yr. adv. **Document type:** *Magazine, Trade.*
Published by: Vintners Federation of Ireland, 25 Dawson St., Dublin, 2, Ireland. TEL 353-1-6705866, FAX 353-1-6627424, vfiupdate@eircom.net. adv.: color page EUR 1,841. Circ: 6,500 (controlled).

V W D - GETRAENKE. see *BUSINESS AND ECONOMICS—Investments*

VIGIE. AGRONOMIE & INDUSTRIE ALIMENTAIRE. see *FOOD AND FOOD INDUSTRIES*

VIGNERON CHAMPENOIS; organe de la vigne et du vin de champagne. see *AGRICULTURE—Crop Production And Soil*

VIGNEVINI. see *AGRICULTURE—Crop Production And Soil*

663.2 SWE ISSN 1400-6715
VIN OCH SPRIT. Text in Swedish. 1994. m. adv. **Document type:** *Magazine, Trade.*
Published by: Vin och Sprit AB, Stockholm, 11797, Sweden. TEL 46-8-744-70-00, FAX 46-8-744-74-44, info@vinsprit.se, http://www.vinsprit.se. Circ: 90,000 (controlled).

VINEYARD AND WINERY MANAGEMENT; the bottom line resource for grower and vintner. see *AGRICULTURE—Crop Production And Soil*

663.2 BRA ISSN 1516-2648
VINHO MAGAZINE. Text in Portuguese. 1999. m. BRL 7 newsstand/cover (effective 2002). adv. bk.rev. back issues avail. **Document type:** *Magazine, Consumer.*
Published by: Market Press Editora Ltda, Rua Hugo Carotini 445, Parque Previdencia, Sao Paulo, 05532-020, Brazil. TEL 55-11-3721-1950, FAX 55-11-3721-5558, editora@vinhomagazine.com.br, http://www.vinhomagazine.com.br/, http://www.marketpress.com.br. adv.: page BRL 10,000; 22.5 x 30. Circ: 25,000.

663.2 RUS
VINNAYA KARTA. Text in Russian. 1999. m. (11/yr.). RUR 50 per issue (effective 2004). adv. **Document type:** *Newspaper, Trade.*
Published by: Vitrina, ul Verkhnyaya 34, ofis 707, Moscow, 125040, Russian Federation. serdyuk@vitrina.com.ru, vitrina@vitrina.com.ru, http://www.vitrinapress.ru/magazines/vk/index.htm. Ed., Pub. Igor' Serdyuk. Circ: 40,000.

663.2 ESP ISSN 1131-5997
VINO Y GASTRONOMIA. Text in Spanish. 1981. m. adv. **Document type:** *Monographic series, Consumer.*
Former titles (until 1991): Vina, Vino y Gastronomia (1130-2917); (until 1989): Vina y Vino (0211-8947)
Address: Santa Hortensia, 27 bajo, Madrid, 28002, Spain. TEL 34-91-415-1662, FAX 34-91-519-4887, vyg@vino-y-gastronomia.com. Ed., Pub. Luis Magana Ruiz. R&P, Adv. contact Sofia Magana. Circ: 20,000 (paid); 20,000 (controlled).

663.2 ESP
VINOS DE ESPANA. Text in Spanish. bi-m.
Published by: G y J Espana Ediciones S.L., Albasanz, 15 Edificio A, Madrid, 28037, Spain. TEL 34-91-4369800, FAX 34-91-5751280, http://www.gyj.es.

634.8 663.2 FRA ISSN 0042-6334
VINS D'ALSACE; revue viticole et vinicole mensuelle. Text in French, German. 1911. m. adv. bk.rev. bibl.; stat.; tr.lit. index. **Document type:** *Corporate.*
Published by: Association des Viticulteurs d'Alsace, Maison des Vins d'Alsace, 12 av. de la Foire-aux-Vins, BP 1225, Colmar, Cedex 68012, France. TEL 33-3-89242400, FAX 33-3-89240781, s.kieffer@viticulteurs-alsace.asso.fr. Ed. Keiffer Simone.

663 FRA
VINS MAGAZINE. Text in French. m.
Published by: Gilbert & Gaillard Multimedia, Bailly, 78870, France. http://www.gilbertgaillard.com.

641.2021 663.2 AUS ISSN 1442-780X
VINTAGE; the Australian wine industry statistical yearbook. Text in English. 1998. a., latest 2002. AUD 38.50 per issue (effective 2005). adv. stat. back issues avail. **Document type:** *Yearbook, Trade.* **Description:** Covers the Australian wine industry, including an update on major issues and activities of the Winemakers' Federation throughout the year, vintage report, wine show results, export trends, domestic market analysis, and much more.
Published by: (Winemakers' Federation of Australia), Wine Publishers Pty Ltd, PO Box 6015, Halifax St, SA 5000, Australia. TEL 61-8-82234799, FAX 61-8-82234790, info@winetitles.com.au, http://www.winetitles.com.au. R&P Paul Clancy. Adv. contact Ron Redford.

663 CHE ISSN 0177-2570
TP544
VINUM. Text in German. 1981. 10/yr. CHF 124 domestic; CHF 148 foreign (effective 2002). adv. bk.rev. **Document type:** *Magazine, Consumer.*
Related titles: French ed.; Spanish ed.
Published by: Intervinum AG, Klosbachstr 85, Zuerich, 8030, Switzerland. TEL 41-1-2685240, FAX 41-1-2685205, redaktion@vinum.ch, info@vinum.ch, http://www.vinum.ch. Ed. Rolf Bichsel. R&P, Adv. contact Natascha Kriesi. Circ: 50,000.

663 USA
W S S A GRAPEVINE. Text in English. 6/yr. membership. **Description:** Summary of transportation rates, regulations, and other developments of interest to beverage importers.
Published by: Wine and Spirits Shippers Association, 11800 Sunrise Valley Dr, Ste 332, Reston, VA 22091. TEL 703-860-2300, FAX 703-860-2422, info@wssa.ccom. Circ: 2,000.

663.1 USA
WASHINGTON D C BEVERAGE JOURNAL. Text in English. 1938. m. USD 36 (effective 2005). adv. bk.rev. charts; illus.; mkt. **Document type:** *Magazine, Trade.* **Description:** Covers the beer, wine, and liquor industry in Maryland and Washington, DC.
Former titles: Maryland - Washington Beverage Journal (1058-9341); Maryland - Washington - Delaware Beverage Journal (0037-0045); Seaboard Beverage Journal
Published by: Beverage Journal, Inc., PO Box 8900, Elkridge, MD 21075-8900. spatten@beerwineliquor.com, http://www.beerwineliquor.com. Ed. Lee W Murray. Adv. contact Stephen Patten. B&W page USD 595; trim 8.375 x 10.875. Circ: 6,700.

663 USA ISSN 1075-5586
HD9377.W2
WASHINGTON WINESTYLE*. Text in English. 1993. bi-m. USD 18. adv. **Document type:** *Consumer.*
Published by: Forward Publishing, Inc., 538 Shelton Place N E, Renton, WA 98056-3984. TEL 206-232-8681, FAX 206-232-0846, winestyle@aol.com. Ed. Kathy Ward. Adv. contact Bill Ward. B&W page USD 895. Circ: 7,500.

663 DEU ISSN 0171-5089
DER WEIHENSTEPHANER. Text in German. 1924. q. EUR 70.10 domestic; EUR 75.35 in Europe; EUR 76.35 elsewhere; EUR 9.65 newsstand/cover (effective 2005). adv. **Document type:** *Newsletter, Trade.*
Indexed: FS&TA.
—BLDSC (9288.280000), IE, ingenta.
Published by: (Verband Ehemaliger Weihenstephaner e.V.), Fachverlag Hans Carl, Andernacher Str 33A, Nuernberg, 90411, Germany. TEL 49-911-952850, FAX 49-911-9528560, info@hanscarl.com, http://www.hanscarl.com. Adv. contact Bettina Lehmacher. B&W page EUR 1,184, color page EUR 21,170. Circ: 2,719.

663.2 DEU
WEIN & SPEISEN. Text in German. 2002 (Oct.). bi-m. EUR 1.90 newsstand/cover (effective 2002). adv. **Document type:** *Magazine, Consumer.*
Published by: Goeller Verlag GmbH, Aschmattstr 8, Baden-Baden, 76532, Germany. TEL 49-7221-502200, FAX 49-7221-502222, verlag@goeller-verlag.de, http://www.goeller-verlag.de. Ed. Jochen Bielefeld. Pub. Ulrich Goeller. Adv. contact Branka Di Stefano. color page EUR 12,400. Circ: 200,000 (controlled).

663.2 DEU
WEIN GOURMET; das internationale Wein Magazin. Variant title: Der Feinschmecker Wein Gourmet. Text in German. 2000. 4/yr. EUR 23.60; EUR 6 newsstand/cover (effective 2005). adv. **Document type:** *Magazine, Consumer.* **Description:** Contains informative articles and features for wine enthusiasts of all levels.
Published by: Jahreszeiten Verlag GmbH (Subsidiary of: Ganske Verlagsgruppe), Possmoorweg 5, Hamburg, 22301, Germany. TEL 49-40-27170, FAX 49-40-27172056, redaktion@weingourmet.de, jahreszeitenverlag@jalag.de, http://www.der-feinschmecker-club.de/go/home, http://www.jalag.de. Ed. Madeleine Jakits. adv.: B&W page EUR 6,590, color page EUR 8,900. Circ: 46,201 (paid and controlled).

663.2 DEU ISSN 1439-6440
WEIN UND MARKT; Das Wirtschaftsmagazin fuer Handel und Erzeuger. Text in German. 2000. m. EUR 58.80 domestic; EUR 65.40 foreign; EUR 4.90 newsstand/cover (effective 2004). adv. **Document type:** *Magazine, Trade.*
Indexed: RefZh, VITIS.
Published by: Fachverlag Dr. Fraund GmbH, An der Brunnenstube 33-35, Mainz, 55120, Germany. TEL 49-6131-62050, FAX 49-6131-620544, info@wein-und-markt.de, verlag@fraund.de, http://www.wein-und-markt.de, http://www.fraund.de. adv.: B&W page EUR 2,800, color page EUR 3,700. Circ: 9,053 (paid and controlled).

663.2 DEU ISSN 1618-5366
WEINE UND WINZER. Variant title: Weine und Winzer an Rhein und Nahe. Text in German. 2001. a. EUR 5.01 newsstand/cover (effective 2002). adv. **Document type:** *Magazine, Trade.*
Published by: Ute Behrens P R & Rheingauer Publikationen, Am Schwarzenstein 16a, Johannisberg, 65366, Germany. TEL 49-6722-980611, FAX 49-6722-980610, derrheingauer@t-online.de, http://www.weineundwinzer.de. Ed. Ute Behrens. Pub. Karl-Heinz Behrens. adv.: page EUR 2,100; trim 210 x 297. Circ: 30,000 (controlled).

663.2 DEU ISSN 1437-7276
WEINWELT; das Magazin fuer Geniesser. Text in German. 1999. bi-m. EUR 24.50; EUR 4.35 newsstand/cover (effective 2002). adv. **Document type:** *Magazine, Consumer.*
Related titles: Online - full text ed.
Published by: Meininger Verlag GmbH, Maximilianstr 7-17, Neustadt, 67433, Germany. TEL 49-6321-8908-0, FAX 49-6321-890873, weinwelt@meininger.de, contact@meininger.de, http://www.wein-marktplatz.de, http://www.meininger.de. adv.: B&W page EUR 4,850, color page EUR 5,350. Circ: 39,830 (paid and controlled).

663.2 DEU
HD9383.1
WEINWIRTSCHAFT. Text in German. 1864. 26/yr. adv. bk.rev. charts; illus.; mkt.; pat.; tr.lit. index. **Document type:** *Trade.*
Former titles: Weinwirtschaft - Markt (0723-1350); Weinwirtschaft - German Wine Review; Allgemeine Deutsche Weinfachzeitung (0012-0960)
Indexed: BiolAb, ChemAb, ExcerpMed, RRTA, VITIS, WAE&RSA. —CCC.
Published by: Meininger Verlag GmbH, Maximilianstr 7-17, Neustadt, 67433, Germany. TEL 49-6321-8908-0, FAX 49-6321-890873. Ed. Hermann Pilz.

663 DEU ISSN 1610-2150
HD9348.G3
WER UND WAS - GETRAENKE-INDUSTRIE. Text in German. 1978. biennial. EUR 147 (effective 2003). **Document type:** *Directory, Trade.*
Former titles (until 2002): Wer und Was in der Deutschen Getraenke - Industrie (0171-4457); (until 1979): Wer und Was in der Deutschen Getraenke - Technik (0170-1150)
Published by: B. Behr's Verlag GmbH & Co. KG, Averhoffstr. 10, Hamburg, 22085, Germany. TEL 49-40-2270080, FAX 49-40-2201091, info@behrs.de, http://www.behrs.de. Adv. contact Frau Nuesslein.

663 338 USA
WHAT'S BREWING✶. Text in English. 10/yr. membership.
Published by: National Coffee Service Association, 8201 Greensboro Dr., Ste. 300, Mclean, VA 22102-3814. TEL 703-273-9008, FAX 703-273-9011. Circ: 650.

663.3 GBR
WHAT'S BREWING. Text in English. 1972. m. GBP 14 (effective 2001). adv. bk.rev.; software rev.; Website rev. **Document type:** *Consumer.* **Description:** Covers beer, brewing and pubs in Britain and worldwide.
Published by: (Campaign for Real Ale Ltd.), C A M R A Books, 230 Hatfield Rd, St Albans, Herts AL1 4LW, United Kingdom. TEL 44-1727-867201, FAX 44-1727-867670, camra@camra.org.uk, http://www.camra.org.uk. Ed. Ted Bruning. Adv. contact Peter Tonge. Circ: 60,000.

641 CHE
DER WHISKY-BOTSCHAFTER; Journal fuer Kenner und Geniesser. Text in German. 4/yr. CHF 39 domestic; EUR 22 in Germany; EUR 24 in Austria (effective 2005). adv. **Document type:** *Magazine, Consumer.*
Published by: Die Medienbotschaft GmbH, Villa Rheinblick, Oberstr 2, Taegerwilen, 8274, Switzerland. TEL 41-71-6693670, FAX 41-71-6693674, chefredaktion@whiskybotschafter.com, info@medienbotschaft.com, http://www.whiskybotschafter.com. Ed. Karl Rudolf. Pub., Adv. contact Christian Rosenberg. color page CHF 6,075, B&W page CHF 4,035; trim 190 x 260.

641 GBR ISSN 1464-7648
WHISKY MAGAZINE. Text in English. 1998. 7/yr. GBP 34 domestic; GBP 41.25 in Europe; GBP 35.68 in United States; GBP 40.51 in Canada; GBP 49 elsewhere (effective 2004). adv. **Document type:** *Magazine, Consumer.* **Description:** Examines the history and culture of whisky, and the lifestyle of the whisky drinker.
Published by: Paragraph Publishing, St Faiths House, Mountergate, Norwich, NRI, United Kingdom. TEL 44-1603-633808, FAX 44-1603-632808, office@whiskymag.com, publishing@paragraph.co.uk, http://www.whiskymag.com/, http://www.paragraph.co.uk/. Pub. Marcin Miller. adv.: color page USD 7,495; trim 8.5 x 11.25.

663.2 BEL
WIJNKRONIEK; gastronomisch magazine. Text in Dutch. 1977. q.
Published by: Vlaamse Wijngilde, Forthoekstraat 12, Blankenberge, 8370, Belgium. TEL 32-50-412003. Ed. A Aspeslagh.

663 GBR ISSN 0269-9443
WINE. Text in English. 1984. m. GBP 39.80 domestic; GBP 42.95 in Europe; GBP 59.95 elsewhere; GBP 3.10 newsstand/cover; USD 6.95 newsstand/cover in United States (effective 2000). adv. bk.rev. **Document type:** *Magazine, Consumer.* **Description:** Features wine tastings and notes, regional insights and travelogues, the latest wine world news, and advice on food and wine pairings.
Formerly: What Wine? (0267-4157)
Published by: Wilmington Publishing, 6-8 Underwood St, London, N1 7JQ, United Kingdom. TEL 44-20-7549-2548, FAX 44-20-7549-2550. Ed. Susan Vumback Low. Pub., Adv. contact Jim Cooper. Circ: 35,000. **Dist. by:** Seymour Distribution Ltd, 86 Newman St, London W1T 3EX, United Kingdom. TEL 44-20-73968000, FAX 44-20-73968002.

663.2 ZAF ISSN 1021-1454
WINE; a taste of good living. Text in English. 1993. m. ZAR 125; ZAR 195 foreign (effective 1999). adv. bk.rev. **Document type:** *Consumer.* **Description:** Presents news and feature articles on South African and other wines, food, wine accessories, retail information and other topics of interest to local wine consumers.
Indexed: ISAP.
Published by: Ramsay, Son & Parker (Pty) Ltd., PO Box 180, Howard Place, Cape Town 7450, South Africa. TEL 27-21-530-3100, FAX 27-21-5312212, wine@rsp.co.za. Ed. Mike Froud. Adv. contact Andrew Stodel. B&W page ZAR 5,050, color page ZAR 7,510; trim 210 x 280. Circ: 11,557 (paid).

663.2 CAN ISSN 1483-4340
WINE ACCESS. Text in English. 1991. m. (9/yr). CND 47.67 domestic; USD 40 in United States; USD 60 elsewhere (effective 2004). adv. **Document type:** *Magazine, Consumer.* **Description:** Covers international and Canadian wines from a Canadian point of view.
Formerly (until 1996): David Lawrason's Wine Access (1205-0423)
Related titles: Online - full content ed.
Published by: RedPoint Media Group Inc., 161 Frederick St, Toronto, ON M5A 4P3, Canada. TEL 416-596-1480, FAX 416-596-9793, info@wineaccess.ca, http://www.wineaccess.ca/. Adv. contact Lisa Brooksbank TEL 416-596-1480 ext 228. Circ: 1,750 (paid).

663.2 USA
▼ **WINE ADVENTURE.** Text in English. 2005 (Jul.). bi-m. USD 30 (effective 2005). **Document type:** *Magazine, Consumer.* **Description:** Covers wine related food, travel, and culture geared toward the female audience.
Address: 12513 El Camino Real Ste C, San Diego, CA 92130. TEL 858-432-0581, info@WAmagazine.com, http://www.wamagazine.com/. Ed. Michele Ostrove. Pub. Lucien Bonnafoux.

663.2 USA ISSN 0887-8463
WINE ADVOCATE. Text in English. bi-m. USD 60 domestic; USD 75 in Canada & Mexico; USD 100 elsewhere (effective 2005). back issues avail. **Document type:** *Journal, Consumer.*
Address: PO Box 311, Monkton, MD 21111-0311. TEL 301-329-6477, FAX 301-357-4504. Ed. Robert M Parker.

WINE & DINE (LAS VEGAS). see *FOOD AND FOOD INDUSTRIES*

WINE & DINE E-ZINE. see *HOTELS AND RESTAURANTS*

663 GBR
WINE & SPIRIT INTERNATIONAL. Text in English. 1874. m. GBP 90; GBP 100 in Europe; USD 135 in Canada & Mexico; GBP 155 elsewhere (effective 1999). adv. bk.rev. illus.; stat. **Document type:** *Trade.* **Description:** Industry news for commercial wine and spirit makers, importers-exporters and retailers. Features include reviews and profiles, auction results, U.K. and international news and services guide.
Former titles: Wine & Spirit (0264-4797); (until 1973): Wine & Spirit Trade International
Indexed: KES.
Published by: Wilmington Publishing, 6-8 Underwood St, London, N1 7JQ, United Kingdom. TEL 44-20-7549-2548, FAX 44-20-7549-2550. Ed. Chris Losch. Pub. Colin Bailey Wood. Adv. contact Lee Sharkey. Circ: 7,110.

663.2029 GBR
WINE AND SPIRIT INTERNATIONAL YEAR BOOK. Text in English. 1898. a. GBP 90 domestic; GBP 95 foreign (effective 1999). adv. **Document type:** *Directory.* **Description:** Lists wine producers, their key personnel, brands, and agents worldwide.
Formerly: Wine and Spirit Trade International Year Book (0306-8846)
Published by: Wilmington Publishing, 6-8 Underwood St, London, N1 7JQ, United Kingdom. TEL 44-20-7549-2548, FAX 44-20-7549-2550. Ed. Chris Losh. Pub. Chris Mitchell. Adv. contact Carole White.

663 JPN
WINE & SPIRITS. Text in Japanese. bi-m.
Published by: Ohta Publications Co. Ltd., Dame Ginza Bldg, 7-18 Ginza 6-chome, Chuo-ku, Tokyo, 104-0061, Japan. TEL 81-3-3571-1181, FAX 81-3-3574-1650. Ed. Kazuhiko Haruguchi. Pub. Tonosuke Ohta. Circ: 22,000. **Subscr. in US to:** Ken Kamimoto, One Executive Dr, 2F, Fort Lee, NJ 07024.

663.1 USA ISSN 0890-0299
WINE & SPIRITS; the practical guide to wine . Text in English. 1981. 8/yr. USD 26 domestic; USD 36 in Canada; USD 56 elsewhere (effective 2005). adv. bk.rev. illus. back issues avail.; reprints avail. **Document type:** *Magazine, Consumer.*
Formerly: Wine and Spirits Buying Guide
Indexed: H&TI.
Published by: Wine & Spirits Magazine, Inc., 2 W. 32nd St., Ste. 601, New York, NY 10001. TEL 212-695-4660, FAX 212-695-2920, info@wineandspiritsmagazine.com, http://www.wineandspiritsmagazine.com. Eds. Joshua Greene, Marcy Crimmins. Pub. Joshua Greene. adv.: B&W page USD 4,760, color page USD 6,639. Circ: 70,000 (paid).

663.2029 USA
WINE & SPIRITS INDUSTRY MARKETING. Text in English. 1971. a. USD 215 (effective 1999). **Document type:** *Directory, Trade.* **Description:** Lists individual companies in the wine and spirits industry, along with professional organizations, suppliers, importers, and marketers.
Former titles (until 1996): Jobson's Wine and Spirits Industry Marketing; Jobson's Wine Marketing Handbook; Wine Marketing Handbook
Indexed: SRI.
Published by: Adams Business Media, 2101 S Arlington Heights Rd, 150, Arlington, IL 60005. TEL 847-427-9512, 800-396-3939, FAX 847-427-2097, http://www.abm.net.

663.2 330 USA ISSN 1057-8544
WINE BUSINESS INSIDER. Text in English. 1991. w. USD 192. back issues avail. **Document type:** *Newsletter, Trade.* **Description:** Covers the wine business including sales, marketing, who's who in the industry, and more.
Related titles: Online - full text ed.: (from Factiva, Northern Light Technology, Inc.).
Published by: SmartWired Inc., 867 W Napa St, Sonoma, CA 95476. TEL 707-939-0822, FAX 707-939-0833, winebiz@aol.com, http://smartwine.com. Ed. Rich Cartiere. Pub. W Lewis Perdue.

663 USA ISSN 1075-7058
WINE BUSINESS MONTHLY; & grower and cellar news. Text in English. 1994. m. USD 69; USD 5.95 newsstand/cover. adv. back issues avail. **Document type:** *Newspaper, Trade.* **Description:** Contains articles on wine production and vineyards as well as information on wine sales, stocks and other aspects of the wine business.
Published by: SmartWired Inc., 867 W Napa St, Sonoma, CA 95476. TEL 707-939-0822, FAX 707-939-0833, winebiz@aol.com, http://smartwine.com. Ed. Rich Cartiere. Pub. W Lewis Perdue. Adv. contact Jennifer Popish. page USD 1,725; trim 10 x 13.5. Circ: 9,000.

663.2 USA ISSN 0897-8492
TP557
WINE COUNTRY GUIDE TO CALIFORNIA; the complete guide to wineries, restaurants and lodging in California wine country. Text in English. 1984. a. USD 6.95. adv. index. **Document type:** *Directory, Trade.* **Description:** Covers nine wine growing areas of California.
Formerly (unitl 1989): Wine Spectator Wine Maps (0882-7206)
Published by: Marvin R. Shanken Communications, Inc., 387 Park Ave S, New York, NY 10016. TEL 212-684-4224, FAX 212-684-5424. Ed. Marvin R Shanken.

663 USA ISSN 1544-9726
WINE COUNTRY LIVING. Text in English. 1993. bi-m. USD 21 in United States; USD 35 in Canada & Mexico; USD 45 in United Kingdom; USD 55 elsewhere (effective 2001). adv. illus. back issues avail. **Document type:** *Magazine, Consumer.* **Description:** Covers homes, cooking, culture, lifestyle, wine and cooking.
Former titles (until 2002): Appellation (1099-548X); (until 199?): Napa Valley Appellation (1072-5717)
Published by: Appellation L L C, 489 First St, W, Sonoma, CA 95476. TEL 707-935-0111, FAX 707-935-4848, info@appellation.com, http://www.appellation.com/. Eds. Thom Elkjer, Jim Gordon. Pub. Michael Earls. Adv. contact Jodana Beck. B&W page USD 4,500, color page USD 6,000. Circ: 100,000.

663 USA ISSN 0892-662X
TP544
WINE EAST. Text in English. 1974. bi-m. USD 22 domestic; USD 30 foreign (effective 2005). adv. bk.rev. illus. **Document type:** *Magazine, Trade.* **Description:** Includes features on winemaking, grape growing and marketing.
Published by: L & H Photojournalism, 620 N Pine St, Lancaster, PA 17603. TEL 717-393-0943, FAX 717-393-7398, editor@wineeast.com, http://www.wineeast.com. Eds. Hudson Cattell, Linda Jones McKee. Circ: 1,300.

▼ new title ➤ refereed ✶ unverified ♦ full entry avail.

663.2 USA ISSN 1078-3318
WINE ENTHUSIAST. Text in English. 1988. 13/yr. USD 26.95 domestic; USD 74.95 foreign (effective 2004). adv. bk.rev.
Document type: *Magazine, Consumer.* **Description:** Covers domestic and world wine regions, cellaring, and wine news.
Formerly (until 1990): Wine Times
Address: 103 Fairview Pk Dr., Elmsford, NY 10523-1553. TEL 914-345-8463, 800-829-5901, FAX 914-345-3028, winenthmag@aol.com, http://www.wineenthusiast.com. Pub. David Talbot. Circ: 95,000 (paid and free).

663 USA ISSN 1059-0234
TP546.5
WINE INDUSTRY PHONE BOOK. Text in English. 1989. a. USD 15. adv. **Document type:** *Directory.* **Description:** Lists phone numbers of all grape- and wine-affiliated wineries and personnel, suppliers, and services available throughout the U.S., Canada, and the world.
Published by: Vineyard & Winery Services, Inc., PO Box 231, Watkins Glen, NY 14891. TEL 607-535-7133, FAX 607-535-2998. Ed. J. William Moffett. R&P J William Moffett. Adv. contact Rob Merletti. Circ: 4,000.

641.22 IRL ISSN 1393-9890
WINE IRELAND. Text in English. 2000. 10/yr. EUR 38 domestic; GBP 39.95 in United Kingdom; EUR 79 in Europe; EUR 102 elsewhere (effective 2002). adv. **Document type:** *Magazine, Trade.* **Description:** Contains articles and features on making wine drinking more pleasurable.
Related titles: Online - full text ed.
Published by: Computer Publications Group, CPG House, Glenageary Office Park, Dun Laoghaire, Co. Dublin, Ireland. TEL 353-1-2847777, FAX 353-1-2847584, wine@cpg.ie, http://www.winewatch.ie, http://www.cpg.ie. Ed. John Doyle. Pub. Colette O'Connor. Adv. contact Ian Mulvaney. color page EUR 2,533; trim 232 x 330. Circ: 10,000 (paid and controlled).

663 GBR
WINE LINE. Text in English. 6/yr.
Published by: Academy of Wine Service, 40 Foscote Rd, London, NW4 3SD, United Kingdom. TEL 081-202-6770. Ed. Ann Satchell. Circ: 10,000.

663.2 AUS ISSN 1441-0141
WINE MAGAZINE. Text in English. 1997. bi-m. AUD 74; AUD 6.95 newsstand/cover (effective 2004). adv. **Document type:** *Magazine, Consumer.* **Description:** Provides wine recommendations for all budgets and occasions, for beginners and experts.
Formerly (until 1998): Australian Gourmet Traveller Wine Magazine (1329-5721)
Related titles: Online - full text ed.
Published by: A C P Publishing Pty. Ltd., 54-58 Park St, Sydney, NSW 1028, Australia. TEL 61-2-9282-8000, FAX 61-2-9267-4361, info@acp.com.au, http://lifestyle.ninemsn.com.au/winemagazine/, http://www.acp.com.au. Ed. Judy Sarris. Adv. contact Patricia Connolly. Circ: 26,161 (paid and controlled).

663 USA ISSN 1065-4895
TP544
THE WINE NEWS. Text in English. 1985. bi-m. USD 25 domestic; USD 60 foreign; USD 5 newsstand/cover (effective 2005). adv. bk.rev. illus. reprints avail. **Document type:** *Magazine, Consumer.* **Description:** Educates, guides, and entertains readership about wine through interviews, commentary, historical perspectives, as well as food and wine pairing tips for both the novice and collector.
Published by: T.E. Smith, Ed. & Pub., PO Box 142096, Coral Gables, FL 33114. TEL 305-740-7170, FAX 305-740-7153, wineline@aol.com, http://www.thewinenews.com. Pub. Tom E Smith. adv.: B&W page USD 4,200. Circ: 60,000 (paid and controlled).

663.2 USA ISSN 1053-4776
WINE ON LINE; food and wine magazine. Text in English. 1980. w. adv. bk.rev.; software rev.; Website rev. tr.lit. **Document type:** *Magazine, Consumer.* **Description:** Discusses wine and food with reviews and educational articles.
Related titles: CD-ROM ed.; Magnetic Tape ed.; Online - full text ed.
Published by: Enterprises Publishing, 400 E 59th St, Ste 9F, New York, NY 10022. TEL 212-755-4363, FAX 212-755-4365, wireonline@usa.net, http://www.wineonline.net/. Ed. Nancy Preiser. Circ: 600,000 (controlled).

663.2 USA
WINE PRESS NORTHWEST. Text in English. 2000. q. USD 8; USD 3 newsstand/cover (effective 2001). adv. **Document type:** *Consumer.*
Address: 107 N Cascade St, Kennewick, WA 99336. TEL 509-582-1564, FAX 509-582-1453, editor@winepressnw.com, http://www.winepressnw.com. Ed. Andy Perdue.

663.2 USA ISSN 0193-497X
CODEN: WISPEV
WINE SPECTATOR. Text in English. 1976. s-m. (18/yr.). USD 45 domestic; USD 58.85 in Canada; USD 135 elsewhere (effective 2005). adv. illus. back issues avail.; reprints avail. **Document type:** *Magazine, Consumer.* **Description:** Reports on European and California wines; discusses fine foods and which wines best accompany them.
Related titles: Online - full text ed.: (from EBSCO Publishing).
Indexed: MagInd.
Published by: Marvin R. Shanken Communications, Inc., 387 Park Ave S, New York, NY 10016. TEL 212-481-8610, FAX 212-481-1540, ws.online@mshanken.com, http://www.winespectator.com. Ed. Marvin R Shanken. **Dist. in UK by:** Seymour Distribution Ltd, 86 Newman St, London W1T 3EX, United Kingdom. TEL 44-20-73968000, FAX 44-20-73968002.

663.2 USA ISSN 1544-8576
TP544
WINE SPECTATOR MAGAZINE'S ULTIMATE GUIDE TO BUYING WINE. Variant title: Ultimate Guide to Buying Wine. Text in English. 1992-1993; resumed. biennial. **Document type:** *Directory.* **Description:** Lists fine wines by type, producer and country.
Formerly (until 1995): The Wine Spectator's Ultimate Guide to Buying Wine (1058-5729)
Published by: Marvin R. Shanken Communications, Inc., 387 Park Ave S, New York, NY 10016. FAX 212-684-5424. Pub. Marvin R Shanken.

663.2 CAN ISSN 0228-6157
WINE TIDINGS. Text in English. 1973. 8/yr. CND 26.54 domestic; CND 38 in United States; CND 42 elsewhere; CND 3.95 newsstand/cover (effective 2000). adv. bk.rev. illus. **Document type:** *Consumer.* **Description:** Wine appreciation, food, recipes and travel to wine-producing countries.
Formerly: Tidings (0381-730X)
Indexed: CBCARef.
Published by: Kylix Media Inc., 5165 Sherbrooke St W, Ste 414, Montreal, PQ H4A 1T6, Canada. TEL 514-481-5892, FAX 514-481-9699, winetidings@opim.ca, http://www.cmpa.ca. Ed. Tony Aspler. Pub., Adv. contact Judy Rochester. Circ: 13,391.

663.2 USA ISSN 1527-3784
WINE X MAGAZINE; wine, food and an intelligent slice of vice. Text in English. 1997. bi-m. USD 21 (effective 2005). adv. bk.rev.; film rev.; music rev.; tel.rev.; video rev. 100 p./no.; back issues avail. **Document type:** *Magazine, Consumer.* **Description:** Lifestyle magazine for young adults about wine and other beverages.
Former titles (until 1995): Wines International; (until 1994): Wines International Quarterly
Related titles: Online - full content ed.
Address: 4184 Sonoma Mountain Rd., Santa Rosa, CA 95404-8557. TEL 888-229-4639, winex@winexwired.com, http://www.winexwired.com. Ed. Angelina Malhotsa-Singh. Pub. Darryl M Roberts TEL 707-545-0992. Circ: 50,000 (paid).

663.2 AUS ISSN 1442-8415
WINEDARK SEA. Text in English. 2000. q.
Related titles: Online - full text ed.
Published by: Winedark Sea Pty Ltd, Southgate, PO Box 367, Sylvania, NSW 2224, Australia. TEL 61-2-9699-9636, editors@winedark.com, http://www.winedark.com/home.hmtl.

663.2 USA
▼ **WINEMAKER;** creating your own great wines. Text in English. 2003. bi-m. USD 22 domestic; USD 23 in Canada; USD 45 elsewhere (effective 2005). **Document type:** *Magazine, Consumer.* **Description:** Publishes articles about making wine at home.
Published by: Battenkill Communications LLP, 5053 Main St., Ste. A, Manchester Center, VT 05255. TEL 802-362-3981, FAX 802-362-2377, wm@winemakermag.com, http://www.winemakermag.com/. Ed. Chris Colby. Pub. Brad Ring. Adv. contact Kiev Rattee. Circ: 108,500 (paid and controlled). **Subscr. to:** P O Box 469118, Escondido, CA 92046.

663.2 RUS CODEN: VIVSA6
TP559.R8
WINEMAKING AND VITICULTURE. Text in Russian. 1887. 8/yr. USD 145. illus. index. **Description:** Covers winemaking technology and viticulture, recent developments in machinery and equipment, and reports on conferences, exhibitions, trade fairs and seminars.
Former titles: Vinograd i Vino Rossii (0869-3625); Vinodelie i Vinogradarstvo S.S.S.R. (0042-6318)
Indexed: BiolAb, ChemAb, FS&TA, HortAb, NutrAb, PBA, PGrRegA, RASB, RefZh, VITIS, WeedAb.
—CASDDS, East View, Linda Hall.
Published by: Izdatel'stvo Pishchevaya Promyshlennost', Sadovaya-Spasskaya 18, kom 601-606, Moscow, 107807, Russian Federation. TEL 7-095-2071770, FAX 7-095-2077958. Ed. Diana Mkrchian. **US dist. addr.:** East View Information Services, 3020 Harbor Ln. N., Minneapolis, MN 55447. TEL 612-550-0961.

663.2 ZAF
WINENEWS. Text in English. w. **Document type:** *Trade.* **Description:** Reports on news and trends about the South African wine industry.
Media: Online - full content. **Related titles:** E-mail ed.
Published by: WineNet (Pty) Ltd., Office 5 Village Gate, P O Box 27067, Hout Bay, 7872, South Africa. TEL 27-21-7902482, FAX 27-21-7902504, editor@winenews.co.za, info@wine.co.za, http://www.winenews.co.za/, http://www.wine.co.za. Ed. Lesley Beake.

634.8 663.2 USA ISSN 0043-583X
HD9372
WINES AND VINES; the authoritative voice of the grape and wine industry. Text in English. 1919. m. USD 32.50 domestic; USD 50 foreign (effective 2005). adv. bk.rev. bibl.; charts; illus.; mkt.; stat. back issues avail. **Document type:** *Magazine, Trade.*
Related titles: Online - full text ed.: (from Florida Center for Library Automation, Gale Group).
Indexed: ChemAb, PROMT.
—CISTI, Linda Hall.
Published by: Hiaring Co., 1800 Lincoln Ave, San Rafael, CA 94901-1298. TEL 415-453-9700, FAX 415-453-2517, geninfo@winesandvines.com, http://www.winesandvines.com. Circ: 4,000 (paid and free).

WINES AND VINES: DIRECTORY OF THE WINE INDUSTRY IN NORTH AMERICA. see *BUSINESS AND ECONOMICS—Trade And Industrial Directories*

663.1 IND
WINES, WHISKY, RUM, GIN, BEER REPORT. Text in English. 1970. w. looseleaf. INR 735, USD 85 (effective 1999). bk.rev. index. **Document type:** *Newsletter.* **Description:** Contains a report about industry relating to alchohol in India.
Formerly: Fermented Wines, Liqueurs, Brandy, Gin, Rum, Whisky, Beer and Alcoholic Drinks (0047-0945)
Media: Duplicated (not offset).
Published by: International Press Cutting Service, PO Box 121, Allahabad, Uttar Pradesh 211 001, India. TEL 91-532-622392. Ed. Nandi Khanna. Circ: 1,200.

663.2 910.09 AUS ISSN 0156-6490
WINESTATE. Text in English. 1978. bi-m. AUD 60 domestic; AUD 69 in New Zealand; AUD 99 in Asia & the Pacific; AUD 113 elsewhere (effective 2004). adv. bk.rev. index. back issues avail. **Description:** Contains feature articles, news and reviews of Australian and imported wine, beer and spirits.
Published by: Winestyle Nominees Pty. Ltd., 81 King William Rd, Unley, SA 5061, Australia. TEL 61-8-8357-9277, FAX 61-8-8357-9212, http://www.winestate.com.au/. Ed. Timothy D H Bannister. adv.: B&W page AUD 1,380, color page AUD 2,280; trim 210 x 297. Circ: 30,000.

663.2 634.8 DEU ISSN 0935-5723
DIE WINZER ZEITSCHRIFT. Abbreviated title: D W Z. Text in German. 1986. m. EUR 28.20 (effective 2004). adv. **Document type:** *Magazine, Trade.*
Indexed: VITIS.
Published by: Landvolk Verlag landvolk.redaktion@t-online.de. Ed. Gerd Knebel. adv.: B&W page EUR 2,204, color page EUR 3,248; trim 205 x 290. Circ: 5,400 (paid and controlled).

663.1 USA ISSN 0043-6399
WISCONSIN BEVERAGE JOURNAL. Text in English. 1942. m. USD 20 (effective 2004). adv. bk.rev. illus.; mkt.; stat. **Document type:** *Magazine, Trade.* **Description:** Offers trade news for the beverage alcohol industry in Wisconsin.
Address: 7379 Fox Hollow Ridge, Zionsville, IN 46077. TEL 317-733-0527, FAX 317-733-0528, http://www.bevaccess.com. Pub. Stewart Baxter. Circ: 6,000 (paid).

663.2 USA
WOMEN ON WINE CHAPTER FLYER. Text in English. m.
Published by: Women on Wine, 6110 Sunset Ranch Dr, Riverside, CA 92506. TEL 714-784-3096.

663.2 USA
WOMEN ON WINE NATIONAL NEWS. Text in English. m. USD 10 to non-members. adv. **Description:** Includes regional reports and a calendar of events.
Published by: Women on Wine, 6110 Sunset Ranch Dr, Riverside, CA 92506. TEL 714-784-3096.

663 GBR ISSN 0969-8159
WORLD DRINK TRENDS. Text in English. a. GBP 33 per issue (effective 2000). **Document type:** *Trade.* **Description:** Compilation of worldwide statistics describing world trends in alcohol production, country-by-country statistics and charts on drink consumption.
—CCC.
Published by: (Productschap voor Gedistilleerde Dranken NLD), N T C Publications Ltd. (Subsidiary of: World Advertising Research Center Ltd.), Farm Rd, Henley-on-Thames, Oxon RG9 1EJ, United Kingdom. TEL 44-1491-411000, FAX 44-1491-571188, info@ntc.co.uk.

641.2029 GBR
WORLD DRINKS DATABOOK. Text in English. 1995. irreg. charts; stat. **Document type:** *Directory.* **Description:** Analyzes the European alcoholic and nonalcoholic beverage industries.
Published by: Euromonitor, 60-61 Britton St, London, EC1 5UX, United Kingdom. TEL 44-20-7251-8024, FAX 44-20-7608-3149, info@euromonitor.com, http://www.euromonitor.com.

641.202 658.8 GBR
WORLD DRINKS MARKETING DIRECTORY; the ultimate guide to the global drinks industry. Text in English. 1999. a., latest 2002/2003. GBP 745 domestic; EUR 1,190 in Europe; USD 1,190 elsewhere (effective Nov. 2002). **Document type:** *Directory, Trade.* **Description:** Provides access to the world's top drinks manufacturers and retailers together with global market briefings.
Incorporates: European Drinks Marketing Directory
Published by: Euromonitor, 60-61 Britton St, London, EC1 5UX, United Kingdom. TEL 44-20-7251-8024, FAX 44-20-7608-3149, info@euromonitor.com, http://www.euromonitor.com. **Dist. by:** Current Pacific Ltd., PO Box 36-536, Northcote, Auckland, New Zealand. TEL 64-9-480-1388, FAX 64-9-480-1387, info@cplnz.com, http://www.cplnz.com.

663 GBR ISSN 1360-7995
WORLD DRINKS REPORT. Text in English. 25/yr. GBP 413 domestic; GBP 452 in Europe; GBP 490 elsewhere (effective 2005). **Document type:** *Newsletter, Trade.* **Description:** Business report for the global drinks industry. Contains company news, mergers and acquisitions, new legislation and Brussels report.
Related titles: Online - full text ed.
Published by: Agra Europe (London) Ltd. (Subsidiary of: T & F Informa plc), 80 Calverley Rd, Tunbridge Wells, Kent TN1 2UN, United Kingdom. TEL 44-1892-533813, FAX 44-1892-544895, marketing@agra-net.com, http://www.agra-net.com.

THE WORLD MARKET FOR ALCOHOLIC DRINKS. see *BUSINESS AND ECONOMICS—Marketing And Purchasing*

663.42 658.8 GBR
THE WORLD MARKET FOR BEER. Text in English. 1998. a. GBP 5,050 per vol. domestic; EUR 7,900 per vol. in Europe; USD 7,900 per vol. elsewhere (effective Apr. 2002). **Document type:** *Trade.* **Description:** Provides a comprehensive and strategic review of the beer market from a global perspective.
Related titles: Series of: Strategy 2000 Series.
Published by: Euromonitor, 60-61 Britton St, London, EC1 5UX, United Kingdom. TEL 44-20-7251-8024, FAX 44-20-7608-3149, info@euromonitor.com, http://www.euromonitor.com.

663 330.9 GBR
THE WORLD MARKET FOR HOT DRINKS. Text in English. irreg., latest 2002. GBP 5,050 domestic; EUR 7,900 in Europe; USD 7,900 elsewhere (effective Jun. 2002). **Document type:** *Directory, Trade.* **Description:** Contains global and regional market analyses, product trends and developments, corporate profiles, and market forecasts.
Published by: Euromonitor, 60-61 Britton St, London, EC1 5UX, United Kingdom. TEL 44-20-7251-8024, FAX 44-20-7608-3149, info@euromonitor.com, http://www.euromonitor.com.

663.6 658.8 GBR
THE WORLD MARKET FOR SOFT DRINKS. Text in English. 1998. irreg., latest 2002, Aug. GBP 5,050 domestic; EUR 7,900 in Europe; USD 7,900 elsewhere (effective Aug. 2002). **Document type:** *Directory, Trade.* **Description:** Provides a comprehensive and strategic review of soft drink markets and services from a global perspective.
Related titles: Series of: Strategy 2000 Series.
Published by: Euromonitor, 60-61 Britton St, London, EC1 5UX, United Kingdom. TEL 44-20-7251-8024, FAX 44-20-7608-3149, info@euromonitor.com, http://www.euromonitor.com.

663.5 658.8 GBR
THE WORLD MARKET FOR SPIRITS. Text in English. irreg. GBP 3,950, USD 7,900. **Document type:** *Trade.* **Description:** Provides strategic analysis at a global level for the spirit alcohol markets and industries.
Related titles: Series of: Strategy 2000 Series.
Published by: Euromonitor, 60-61 Britton St, London, EC1 5UX, United Kingdom. TEL 44-20-7251-8024, FAX 44-20-7608-3149, info@euromonitor.com, http://www.euromonitor.com.

663.2 658.8 GBR
THE WORLD MARKET FOR WINE. Text in English. irreg. GBP 5,050 per vol. domestic; EUR 7,900 per vol. in Europe; USD 7,900 per vol. elsewhere (effective Apr. 2002). **Document type:** *Trade.* **Description:** Provides strategic analysis at a global level for the wine market and industry.
Formerly: Wines: A World Survey
Related titles: Series of: Strategy 2000 Series.
Published by: Euromonitor, 60-61 Britton St, London, EC1 5UX, United Kingdom. TEL 44-20-7251-8024, FAX 44-20-7608-3149, info@euromonitor.com, http://www.euromonitor.com.

663.4 ITA ISSN 1121-158X
THE WORLD OF BEER; news and views on the best of international brewing. Text in English, French, German, Spanish. 1987. s-a. free to qualified personnel (effective 2005). adv. **Document type:** *Magazine, Trade.* **Description:** Contains reports about marketing, statistics, market strategies, legislation and all that you can be interested in, about the beer market.
Published by: Tuttopress Editrice s.r.l., Viale Lunigiana 40, Milan, MI 20125, Italy. TEL 39-02-6691692, FAX 39-02-6695596, monbirit@tin.it, http://www.ilmondodellabirra.it/. Ed. Silvano Rusmini. R&P Vanda Loda. Adv. contact Alessandra Costanzo. color page EUR 4,400; 225 x 285. Circ: 20,000.

WORLD OF FOOD & BEVERAGE. see *FOOD AND FOOD INDUSTRIES*

663.3 USA ISSN 0196-5921
ZYMURGY. Text in English. 1978. q. USD 33 domestic; USD 39 in Canada; USD 50 elsewhere. adv. bk.rev. index. back issues avail. **Document type:** *Magazine, Consumer.* **Description:** For the home brewer and beer enthusiast.
Related titles: Online - full text ed.
Indexed: RefZh.
Published by: American Homebrewers Association Inc., PO Box 1679, Boulder, CO 80306-1679. TEL 303-447-0816, FAX 303-447-2825, dena@aob.org, http://www.beertown.org. Ed., R&P Dena Niskek. Adv. contact Linda Starck. Circ: 24,000 (paid).

BEVERAGES—Abstracting, Bibliographies, Statistics

663.021 AUS ISSN 0312-925X
AUSTRALIA. BUREAU OF STATISTICS. SALES OF AUSTRALIAN WINE AND BRANDY BY WINEMAKERS. Text in English. 1975. m. AUD 18.50 (effective 2003). **Document type:** *Government.* **Description:** Provides the quantity of wine sales classified by type and brandy, including seasonally adjusted figures and trend estimates.
Published by: Australian Bureau of Statistics, PO Box 10, Belconnen, ACT 2616, Australia. TEL 61-2-6252-5249, FAX 61-2-6252-6778, http://www.abs.gov.au.

663.021 GBR
B L R A STATISTICAL HANDBOOK; a compilation of drinks industry statistics. Text in English. 1973. a. **Document type:** *Trade.*
Formerly: Brewers' Society (0306-6002)
Published by: Brewers and Licensed Retailers Association, 42 Portman Sq, London, W1H 0BB, United Kingdom.

016.6412 DEU
BRAUDATENBANKEN. Text in German. m. EUR 135 (effective 2005). **Document type:** *Abstract/Index.* **Description:** Contains comprehensive country and company specific information on all aspects of the beverage industry.
Media: Online - full content.
Published by: Fachverlag Hans Carl, Andernacher Str 33A, Nuernberg, 90411, Germany. TEL 49-911-952850, FAX 49-911-9528560, info@hanscarl.com, http://www.braudatenbanken.de, http://www.hanscarl.com.

016.663 USA
FOODS ADLIBRA BEVERAGE EDITION. Text in English. m. USD 125; USD 150 foreign (effective 1998). **Document type:** *Abstract/Index.*
Related titles: Online - full text ed.
Published by: (General Mills, Inc.), Foods Adlibra Publications, 9000 Plymouth Ave N, Minneapolis, MN 55427. TEL 612-540-4759, FAX 612-540-3166. Ed. J E O'Connell.

016.6636 GBR
INTERNATIONAL FOOD ABSTRACTS. BEVERAGES AND SOFT DRINKS DISK. Text in English. bi-m. GBP 355 (effective 2000). **Document type:** *Abstract/Index.*
Media: CD-ROM.
Published by: Leatherhead Food International Ltd., Randalls Rd, Leatherhead, Surrey KT22 7RY, United Kingdom. TEL 44-1372-376761, FAX 44-1372-386228, hbennett@lfra.co.uk.

016.663 DEU ISSN 1613-2041
CODEN: MOBRDJ
➤ **MONATSSCHRIFT FUER BRAUWISSENSCHAFT (ONLINE EDITION).** Text in German; Summaries in English, German. 1948. m. EUR 119 (effective 2005). adv. bk.rev. abstr.; bibl.; charts; illus.; tr.lit. index, cum.index. reprints avail. **Document type:** *Journal, Academic/Scholarly.*
Former titles (until 2004): Monatsschrift fuer Brauwissenschaft (Print Edition) (0723-1520); (until 1983): Brauwissenschaft (0006-9337)
Media: Online - full content.
Indexed: AnalAb, BiolAb, CIN, CPA, ChemAb, ChemTitl, CurCont, EngInd, ExcerpMed, FCA, FS&TA, HortAb, IBR, ISR, NutrAb, PBA, PGegResA, PHN&I, RA&MP, RPP, RefZh, S&F, SeedAb, TriticAb, VITIS.
—BLDSC (5906.260000), CASDDS, CISTI, Ei, IDS, IE, ingenta, Linda Hall. **CCC.**
Published by: (Technische Universitaet Muenchen und Berlin), Fachverlag Hans Carl, Andernacher Str 33A, Nuernberg, 90411, Germany. TEL 49-911-952850, FAX 49-911-9528560, info@hanscarl.com, http://www.brauwissenschaft.de, http://www.hanscarl.com. Eds. Karl-Ullrich Heyse, Wolfgang Popp. Adv. contact Bettina Lehmacher. B&W page EUR 574, color page EUR 913. Circ: 2,800. **Co-publisher:** Westkreuz-Verlag.

663.021 USA
NATIONAL ASSOCIATION OF BEVERAGE IMPORTERS. STATISTICAL REPORT✶. Text in English. m. (plus q. & a. compilations). USD 425 to non-members. **Description:** Provides statistics on beverage importers arranged by product. Includes a comparison of tax payments.
Published by: National Association of Beverage Importers, 607 Aster Blvd, Rockville, MD 20850-2035. TEL 202-638-1617, FAX 202-638-3122.

663.1021 RUS
PROIZVODSTVO I OBOROT ETILIVOGO SPIRTA I ALKOGOL'NOI PRODUKTSII V ROSSIISKOI FEDERATSII/PRODUCTION AND TURNOVER OF ALCOHOLIC PRODUCTS IN RUSSIAN FEDERATION. Text in Russian. m. RUR 5,940 (effective 2005). **Document type:** *Bulletin, Government.* **Description:** Provides data on production and shipment of ethyl spirit and alcohol output in Russian Federation.
Related titles: Online - full content ed.: RUR 6,372 (effective 2005).
Published by: Gosudarstvennyi Komitet Rossiiskoi Federatsii po Statistike/Federal State Statistics Office, ul Myasnitskaya 39, Moscow, 107450, Russian Federation. TEL 7-095-2074902, FAX 7-095-2074087, stat@gks.ru, http://www.gks.ru.

641.2021 SWE ISSN 1650-0245
HV5537
SWEDEN. STATENS FOLKHAELSOINSTITUT. ALKOHOLSTATISTIK/SWEDEN. NATIONAL INSTITUTE OF PUBLIC HEALTH. ALCOHOL STATISTICS. (Subseries of: Sveriges Officiella Statistik) Text in English, Swedish. 1873-1999; resumed 2002. a. stat. **Document type:** *Government.*
Former titles (until 1996): Sweden. Socialstyrelsen. Alkoholstatistik (0586-156X); (until 1968): Rusdrycksfoersaeljningen; Accispliktiga Naeringar, Rusdrycksfoersaeljningen; Accispliktiga Naeringar, Braennvinsfoersaeljningen; Accispliktiga Naeringar; Braennvins Tillverkning och Foersaeljning Samt Socker-och Maltdryckstillverkningen; Braennvins Tillverkning och Foersaeljning Samt Hvitbetssocker-och Maltdryckstillverkningen; Braenvins Tillverkning och Foersaeljning Samt Hvitbetssockertillverkni
Published by: Statens Folkhaelsoinstitut/National Institute of Public Health in Sweden, Olof Palmes Gata 17, Stockholm, 10352, Sweden. TEL 46-8-56613500, FAX 46-8-56613505, info@fhi.se, http://www.fhi.se. **Subscr. to:** Fritzes Kundtjaenst.

VINTAGE; the Australian wine industry statistical yearbook. see *BEVERAGES*

BIBLIOGRAPHIES

see also ABSTRACTING AND INDEXING SERVICES ; LIBRARY AND INFORMATION SCIENCES ; PUBLISHING AND BOOK TRADE ; and also Abstracting, Bibliographies, Statistics subheadings under specific subjects

A A B'S BIBLIOGRAPHY OF RARE & OUT-OF-PRINT TITLES FOR SALE. see *PUBLISHING AND BOOK TRADE—Abstracting, Bibliographies, Statistics*

A A B'S BRITISH BIBLIOGRAPHY OF RARE & OUT OF PRINT PUBLICATIONS REPORTED AVAILABLE FOR SALE THIS WEEK BY THE LEGITIMATE OWNERS. BY SUBJECTS. SPECIAL ISSUE. see *PUBLISHING AND BOOK TRADE—Abstracting, Bibliographies, Statistics*

A A B'S BRITISH BIBLIOGRAPHY OF RARE AND OUT-OF-PRINT TITLES AVAILABLE. see *LIBRARY AND INFORMATION SCIENCES—Abstracting, Bibliographies, Statistics*

A A B'S REGISTER OF WANTED PUBLICATIONS; updated daily. see *PUBLISHING AND BOOK TRADE—Abstracting, Bibliographies, Statistics*

A B A BOOK BUYER'S HANDBOOK (YEAR). see *PUBLISHING AND BOOK TRADE*

011 AUS ISSN 1449-776X
THE A B & P BOOK BUYER'S GUIDE; the authoritative guide to forthcoming books. (Australian Bookseller & Publisher) Text in English. 1990. q. AUD 120 domestic; AUD 180 foreign (effective 2004). adv. **Document type:** *Directory, Bibliography.* **Description:** Provides a complete listing of new books, along with bibliographic details and descriptive annotations.
Formerly (until 2004): Guide to New Australian Books (1035-5391)

B

▼ *new title* ➤ *refereed* ✶ *unverified* ♦ *full entry avail.*

Related titles: CD-ROM ed.
Published by: (Monash University), Thorpe - Bowker (Subsidiary of: R.R. Bowker LLC), Bldg C3, 85 Turner St, Port Melbourne, VIC 3207, Australia. TEL 61-3-86450301, subscriptions@thorpe.com.au, http://www.thorpe.com.au. Ed. Bianca Simpson. Pub. Andrew Wilkins. Adv. contact Mr. Robert Hamilton-Jones TEL 61-3-86450308. Circ: 540.

A B AS BIBLIOGRAFISKE SERIE. (Arbejderbevaegelsens Bibliotek og Arkiv) see *POLITICAL SCIENCE—Abstracting, Bibliographies, Statistics*

A B C BLUE BOOK: CANADIAN WEEKLY NEWSPAPERS. see *ADVERTISING AND PUBLIC RELATIONS—Abstracting, Bibliographies, Statistics*

A B C BLUE BOOK: U S AND CANADIAN FARM PUBLICATIONS. see *AGRICULTURE—Abstracting, Bibliographies, Statistics*

A B C BLUE BOOK: U S DAILY NEWSPAPERS. see *ADVERTISING AND PUBLIC RELATIONS—Abstracting, Bibliographies, Statistics*

A B C BLUE BOOK: U S WEEKLY NEWSPAPERS. see *ADVERTISING AND PUBLIC RELATIONS—Abstracting, Bibliographies, Statistics*

A C U BULLETIN. see *EDUCATION—Abstracting, Bibliographies, Statistics*

A I B NOTIZIE. see *LIBRARY AND INFORMATION SCIENCES*

016.05   DEU
A I D A. (Articoli Italiani di Periodici Accademici) Text in Italian, English, German. 1997. 2/yr. EUR 638 (effective 2003). **Document type:** *Bibliography.* **Description:** Bibliography of Italian academic periodical literature.
Media: CD-ROM. **Related titles:** Online - full text ed.
Published by: K.G. Saur Verlag GmbH (Subsidiary of: Gale Group), Hirschberger Str. 17b, Osnabrueck, 49086, Germany. TEL 49-541-404590, FAX 49-541-41255, g.hochgeladen@saur.de, http://www.saur.de.

A L A'S GUIDE TO BEST READING. see *LIBRARY AND INFORMATION SCIENCES—Abstracting, Bibliographies, Statistics*

A S T I S OCCASIONAL PUBLICATIONS. see *EARTH SCIENCES—Abstracting, Bibliographies, Statistics*

011   USA
A TO ZOO; subject access to children's picture books. Text in English. triennial, latest 6th ed. USD 75, GBP 48.50 (effective 2003). 1800 p./no.; **Document type:** *Consumer.* **Description:** Indexes more than 18,000 fiction and nonfiction picture books for children in preschool through the second grade.
Published by: Greenwood Publishing Group Inc. (Subsidiary of: Harcourt International), 88 Post Rd W, PO Box 5007, Westport, CT 06881. TEL 203-226-3571, FAX 203-226-1502, http://www.greenwood.com/books/BookDetail.asp?dept_id=1&sku=BO2069.

011   DNK   ISSN 1396-7789
AARETS LYDBOEGER. Text in Danish. a. DKK 35 (effective 2004). illus.
Former titles (until 1995): Nye Lydboeger (0907-1709); (until 1992): Gode Lydboeger (0107-5209); (until 1981): Lydbogskatalog
Related titles: Online - full text ed.
Published by: Dansk BiblioteksCenter AS, Tempovej 7-11, Ballerup, 2750, Denmark. TEL 45-44-867777, FAX 45-44-867892, dbc@dbc.dk, http://www.dbc.dk.

AARHUS UNIVERSITET. TEOLOGISKE FAKULTET. BIBLIOGRAFI. see *RELIGIONS AND THEOLOGY— Abstracting, Bibliographies, Statistics*

ABSTRACTA IRANICA. see *HISTORY—Abstracting, Bibliographies, Statistics*

011   ESP
ACADEMIA ALFONSO X EL SABIO. CUADERNOS BIBLIOGRAFICOS. Text in Spanish. 1977. irreg., latest vol.10, 1986. **Document type:** *Bibliography.*
Published by: Academia Alfonso X el Sabio, Murcia, Spain.

011   EST   ISSN 1406-3530
ACTA BIBLIOTHECAE NATIONALIS ESTONIAE. Text in Estonian, English. 1990. a. **Document type:** *Monographic series, Bibliography.*
Indexed: AmH&L, HistAb.
Published by: (Eesti Rahvaluule Arhiiv), National Library of Estonia/Eesti Rahvusraamatukogu, Tonismagi 2, Tallinn, 15189, Estonia. TEL 372-6307611, nlib@nlib.ee, http://www.nlib.ee/.

ACTUALIDAD BIBLIOGRAFICA DE FILOSOFIA Y TEOLOGIA; selecciones de libros. see *RELIGIONS AND THEOLOGY—Abstracting, Bibliographies, Statistics*

ADVERTISING, MARKETING, AND PUBLIC RELATIONS RESOURCES; an internet miniguide. see *BUSINESS AND ECONOMICS—Abstracting, Bibliographies, Statistics*

AEROSPACE MEDICINE AND BIOLOGY; a continuing bibliography. see *MEDICAL SCIENCES—Abstracting, Bibliographies, Statistics*

AFRICA BIBLIOGRAPHY. see *HISTORY—Abstracting, Bibliographies, Statistics*

AFRICA GEOSCIENCE REVIEW. see *EARTH SCIENCES—Geology*

THE AFRICAN BOOK PUBLISHING RECORD. see *PUBLISHING AND BOOK TRADE—Abstracting, Bibliographies, Statistics*

015.6   DEU   ISSN 0306-9516
Z3501
AFRICAN BOOKS IN PRINT/LIVRES AFRICAINS DISPONIBLES. Text in English. 1975. irreg. (in 2 vols.), latest vol.5, 2000. USD 790 (effective 2005). **Document type:** *Bibliography.* **Description:** Provides full bibliographic and acquisition information on some 40,000 books published - in English and in French - in 43 African countries by over 1,100 publishers. Includes a substantial number of books in over 120 African languages.
—BLDSC (0732.365000).
Published by: K.G. Saur Verlag GmbH (Subsidiary of: Gale Group), Ortlerstr 8, Munchen, 81373, Germany. TEL 49-89-769020, FAX 49-89-76902150, info@saur.de, http://www.saur.de. Ed. Hans Zell.

960 016   IND   ISSN 0001-9941
AFRICAN BOOKS NEWSLETTER. Text in English. 1965. m. looseleaf. USD 52 (effective 2000). adv. mkt. index.
Document type: *Newsletter.*
Related titles: Microfilm ed.
Published by: K.K. Roy (Private) Ltd., 55 Gariahat Rd., P O Box 10210, Kolkata, West Bengal 700 019, India. Ed. K K Roy. R&P M Misra TEL 91-33-475-4872. Circ: 2,300.

AFRICAN SPECIAL BIBLIOGRAPHIC SERIES. see *HISTORY—Abstracting, Bibliographies, Statistics*

AFRICAN URBAN AND REGIONAL SCIENCE INDEX. see *SCIENCES: COMPREHENSIVE WORKS—Abstracting, Bibliographies, Statistics*

AGRICOLA C R I S. see *AGRICULTURE—Abstracting, Bibliographies, Statistics*

AGRICULTURAL ENGINEERING INDEX (YEARS). see *AGRICULTURE*

011   JPN
AICHI-KEN KYODO SHIRYO SOGO MOKUROKU. Text in Japanese. 1964. irreg., latest 1987. JPY 4,000. bibl.
Published by: Aichi Library Association/Aichi Toshokan Kyokai, 1-12-1 Higashi-Sakura, Higashi-ku, Nagoya-shi, Aichi-ken 461-0005, Japan.

AIDS LEGAL BIBLIOGRAPHY. (Acquired Immune Deficiency Syndrome) see *LAW—Abstracting, Bibliographies, Statistics*

AKADEMIA ROLNICZA WE WROCLAWIU. ZESZYTY NAUKOWE. BIBLIOGRAFIE. see *AGRICULTURE— Abstracting, Bibliographies, Statistics*

ALBERTA. PUBLIC AFFAIRS BUREAU. CATALOGUE - ALBERTA. QUEEN'S PRINTER. see *PUBLIC ADMINISTRATION—Abstracting, Bibliographies, Statistics*

017 070.5   USA
THE ALDINE PRESS; catalogue of the Ahmanson-Murphy collection of books by or relating to the press in the library of the University of California, Los Angeles: incorporating works recorded elsewhere. Text in English. 2001. **Document type:** *Bibliography.*
Published by: University of California Press, Book Series, 2120 Berkeley Way, Berkeley, CA 94720. TEL 510-642-4247, FAX 510-643-7127, askucp@ucpress.edu, http://www.ucpress.edu/books/series.html.

ALE SEFER; a journal of Hebrew bibliography and booklore. see *LIBRARY AND INFORMATION SCIENCES—Abstracting, Bibliographies, Statistics*

011   GBR   ISSN 0964-3400
Z921.B854
ALPHANUMERIC REPORTS PUBLICATIONS INDEX. Text in English. 1992. irreg. GBP 27; GBP 33 foreign (effective 2001). **Document type:** *Abstract/Index.*
Published by: British Library, Document Supply Centre, c/o Mike Marcus, British Library, Boston Spa, Wetherby, W Yorkshire LS23 7BQ, United Kingdom. TEL 44-1937-546080, FAX 44-1937-546586, http://portico.bl.uk/.

ALTERNATIVE ALTERNATIVE. see *SOCIOLOGY—Abstracting, Bibliographies, Statistics*

011   USA   ISSN 1094-4559
ALTERNATIVE PUBLISHERS OF BOOKS IN NORTH AMERICA. Text in English. 1994. biennial. USD 39.95 (effective 2003). 185 p./no. 1 cols./p.; **Document type:** *Directory, Academic/Scholarly.* **Description:** Lists name, address, ISBN, phone, fax, e-mail, Internet address, previous names, editor, year founded, average number of books published per year, average press run, other materials produced, and a narrative description of 162 alternative presses. Includes bibliography and subject index.
Published by: C R I S E S Press, Inc., 1716 S W Williston Rd, Gainesville, FL 32608. TEL 352-335-2200, willett@liblib.com, http://www.liblib.com. Ed. Byron Anderson. **Co-sponsors:** Alternatives in Print Task Force; American Library Association, Social Responsibilities Round Table; American Library Association.

378.3 011   IND
ALUMNI PUBLICATIONS: A CATALOGUE. Text in English. 1976. quinquennial. free.
Published by: United States Educational Foundation in India, Fulbright House, 12 Hailey Rd., New Delhi, 110 001, India. Ed. P D Sayal.

AMERICAN BIBLIOGRAPHY OF SLAVIC AND EAST EUROPEAN STUDIES. see *HISTORY—Abstracting, Bibliographies, Statistics*

AMERICAN INDIAN BIBLIOGRAPHIC SERIES. see *NATIVE AMERICAN STUDIES*

AMERICAN SOCIETY OF AGRICULTURAL ENGINEERS. COMPREHENSIVE INDEX OF PUBLICATIONS. see *AGRICULTURE*

AMSTERDAM STUDIES IN THE THEORY AND HISTORY OF LINGUISTIC SCIENCE. SERIES 5: LIBRARY AND INFORMATION SOURCES IN LINGUISTICS. see *LINGUISTICS—Abstracting, Bibliographies, Statistics*

ANATOMY OF WONDER; a critical guide to science fiction. see *LITERATURE—Abstracting, Bibliographies, Statistics*

ANNALES DE NORMANDIE; revue d'etudes regionales. see *HISTORY—Abstracting, Bibliographies, Statistics*

L'ANNEE PHILOLOGIQUE; bibliographie critique et analytique de l'antiquite greco-latine. see *CLASSICAL STUDIES— Abstracting, Bibliographies, Statistics*

016.011   USA   ISSN 0748-5190
ANNOTATED BIBLIOGRAPHIES OF SERIALS: A SUBJECT APPROACH. Text in English. 1986 (no.5). irreg., latest 1989. price varies. **Document type:** *Bibliography.*
Published by: Greenwood Publishing Group Inc. (Subsidiary of: Harcourt International), 88 Post Rd W, PO Box 5007, Westport, CT 06881. TEL 203-226-3571, 800-225-5800, FAX 603-431-2214, bookinfo@greenwood.com, http://www.greenwood.com.

ANNOTATED BIBLIOGRAPHY FOR ENGLISH STUDIES. see *LITERATURE—Abstracting, Bibliographies, Statistics*

016.334   IND
ANNOTATED BIBLIOGRAPHY OF LITERATURE ON COOPERATIVE MOVEMENTS IN SOUTH-EAST ASIA. Text in English. 1963. s-a. INR 15, USD 2. abstr. **Document type:** *Bibliography.*
Formerly: Annotated Bibliography of Literature Produced by the Cooperative Movements in South-East Asia (0003-5084)
Media: Duplicated (not offset).
Published by: International Cooperative Alliance, Regional Office and Education Centre for South-East Asia, 43 Friends Colony, P O Box 3312, New Delhi, 110 014, India. Ed. B D Pandey. Circ: 500. **Publications of regional offices can also be ordered from:** International Cooperative Alliance, World Headquarters, 11 Upper Grosvenor St, London W1X 9PA, United Kingdom.

ANNOTATED GUIDE TO CURRENT NATIONAL BIBLIOGRAPHIES. see *LIBRARY AND INFORMATION SCIENCES—Abstracting, Bibliographies, Statistics*

ANNUAL BIBLIOGRAPHY OF ENGLISH LANGUAGE AND LITERATURE. see *LITERATURE—Abstracting, Bibliographies, Statistics*

ANNUAL BIBLIOGRAPHY OF MODERN ART. see *ART—Abstracting, Bibliographies, Statistics*

ANNUAL BIBLIOGRAPHY OF ORTHOPAEDIC SURGERY. see *MEDICAL SCIENCES—Abstracting, Bibliographies, Statistics*

ANNUAL BIBLIOGRAPHY OF THE HISTORY OF THE PRINTED BOOK AND LIBRARY. see *PUBLISHING AND BOOK TRADE—Abstracting, Bibliographies, Statistics*

ANNUAL BIBLIOGRAPHY OF VICTORIAN STUDIES. see *LITERATURE—Abstracting, Bibliographies, Statistics*

ANNUAL EGYPTOLOGICAL BIBLIOGRAPHY/BIBLIOGRAPHIE EGYPTOLOGIQUE ANNUELLE/JAEHRLICHE AEGYPTOLOGISCHE BIBLIOGRAPHIE. see *HISTORY—Abstracting, Bibliographies, Statistics*

011   COL   ISSN 0570-393X
Z1731
ANUARIO BIBLIOGRAFICO COLOMBIANO. Text in Spanish. 1951. irreg., latest vol.24, 1995. price varies.
Published by: Instituto Caro y Cuervo, Seccion de Publicaciones, Apartado Aereo 51502, Bogota, Cund, Colombia. carocuer@apenway.cam.co.

015   CRI   ISSN 0066-5010
Z1453
ANUARIO BIBLIOGRAFICO COSTARRICENSE. Text in Spanish. 1956. irreg. free.
Published by: Asociacion Costarricense de Bibliotecarios, Apdo. 3308, San Jose, Costa Rica. Circ: 500.

015   DOM
ANUARIO BIBLIOGRAFICO DOMINICANO* . Text in Spanish. a.
Published by: Biblioteca Nacional, Cesar Nicolas Penson, Santo Domingo, Dominican Republic.

011   ECU   ISSN 0252-8649
ANUARIO BIBLIOGRAFICO ECUATORIANO. (Published as the 6th issue each year of Bibliografia Ecuatoriana) Text in Spanish. 1975. a.
Published by: (Biblioteca General), Universidad Central del Ecuador, Apdo 3291, Quito, Pichincha, Ecuador.

011   URY   ISSN 0304-8861
Z1881
ANUARIO BIBLIOGRAFICO URUGUAYO. Text in Spanish. 1946-1949; resumed 1968. a. per issue exchange basis.
Indexed: RASB.
Published by: Biblioteca Nacional de Uruguay, c/o Director General, Av. Dieciocho De Julio, 1790, Montevideo, 11210, Uruguay. TEL 598-2-485030, FAX 598-2-496902. Ed. Luis Alberto Musso. Circ: 600.

APENDICE AL INDICE PROGRESIVO DE LEGISLACION. see *LAW—Abstracting, Bibliographies, Statistics*

011   USA
APPALACHIAN BIBLIOGRAPHY. Text in English. 1980. irreg., latest 1980. USD 15 (effective 2000). **Document type:** *Bibliography.* **Description:** Covers all aspects of Appalachian regional culture.
Related titles: ♦ Supplement(s): Appalachian Outlook. ISSN 0003-6625.
Published by: West Virginia University, Charles C. Wise, Jr. Library, Main Office, Box 6069, Morgantown, WV 26506-6069. TEL 304-293-3640. Ed. J B Brown.

ARBITRIUM; Zeitschrift fuer Rezensionen zur germanistischen Literaturwissenschaft. see *LITERARY AND POLITICAL REVIEWS*

011   USA   ISSN 0195-7163
ARCADIA BIBLIOGRAPHICA VIRORUM ERUDITORUM. Text in English. 1979. irreg., latest vol.18, 2001. price varies. **Document type:** *Bibliography.* **Description:** Presents bibliographical monographs of scholars whose work is of international significance in the area of the humanities.
Indexed: RASB.
Published by: Eurolingua, PO Box 101, Bloomington, IN 47402-0101.

011   ITA   ISSN 0390-1009
DG655.6
ARCHIVIO STORICO CIVICO E BIBLIOTECA TRIVULZIANA. LIBRI & DOCUMENTI. Text in Italian. 1975. 3/yr. per issue exchange basis only. bk.rev. bibl.; illus. cum.index: 1975-1994. 502 p./no.; back issues avail. **Document type:** *Academic/Scholarly.* **Description:** Featuring articles in history, literature and philology.
Indexed: BHA, RILM.
—BLDSC (5207.320000).
Published by: Archivio Storico Civico e Biblioteca Trivulziana, Castello Sforzesco, Milan, MI 20121, Italy. TEL 39-2-86454638, FAX 39-2-875926. Ed. Giovanni Piazza. Circ: 500.

015   MEX   ISSN 0187-5817
Z1425
ARCHIVO GENERAL DE LA NACION. BOLETIN BIBLIOGRAFICO. Text in Spanish. 1987. bi-m. **Document type:** *Bibliography.*
Media: Diskette.
Published by: (Direccion de Informacion y Documentacion), Archivo General de la Nacion, c/o Eduardo Molina y Albaniles, Col. Penitenciaria Ampliacion s-n, Mexico, DF 15350, Mexico. TEL 7-95-73-11, FAX 7-89-52-96.

ARCHIVUM BIBLIOGRAPHICUM CARMELI TERESIANI. see *RELIGIONS AND THEOLOGY—Abstracting, Bibliographies, Statistics*

ARCHIVUM HISTORIAE PONTIFICAE. see *RELIGIONS AND THEOLOGY—Abstracting, Bibliographies, Statistics*

982 015   ARG
ARGENTINA. CONGRESO DE LA NACION. BIBLIOTECA. BOLETIN. Text in Spanish. 1918-1990 (no.117); resumed 1995. a. per issue exchange basis. bibl. **Document type:** *Bulletin.*
Formerly: Argentina. Congreso. Biblioteca. Boletin (0004-1009)
Indexed: FLP.
Published by: Congreso de la Nacion, Biblioteca, Avda. Rivadavia, 1850, Capital Federal, Buenos Aires 1033, Argentina. TEL 54-114-3715595. Circ: 1,500.

ARGENTINA. DEPARTAMENTO DE ESTUDIOS HISTORICOS NAVALES. SERIE J: LIBROS Y IMPRESOS RAROS. see *MILITARY—Abstracting, Bibliographies, Statistics*

ARGENTINA. MINISTERIO DE CULTURA Y EDUCACION. BOLETIN BIBLIOGRAFICO. see *EDUCATION—Abstracting, Bibliographies, Statistics*

ARGENTINA. SECRETARIA DE GUERRA. DIRECCION DE ESTUDIOS HISTORICOS. BOLETIN BIBLIOGRAFICO. see *MILITARY—Abstracting, Bibliographies, Statistics*

ARGENTINA. SERVICIO DE INTELIGENCIA NAVAL. BIBLIOTECAS DE LA ARMADA. BOLETIN BIBLIOGRAFICO. see *MILITARY—Abstracting, Bibliographies, Statistics*

ART REFERENCE COLLECTION. see *ART—Abstracting, Bibliographies, Statistics*

▼ **ARTISTS OF AN ERA.** see *ART—Abstracting, Bibliographies, Statistics*

ASIA AND PACIFIC BIBLIOGRAPHY. see *HISTORY—Abstracting, Bibliographies, Statistics*

ASIAN AND PACIFIC COCONUT COMMUNITY. BIBLIOGRAPHY SERIES. see *AGRICULTURE—Abstracting, Bibliographies, Statistics*

890 015   IND   ISSN 0004-4547
ASIAN BOOKS NEWSLETTER. Text in English. 1966. m. USD 48 (effective 2000). adv. index. **Document type:** *Newsletter.*
Related titles: Microfilm ed.
Published by: K.K. Roy (Private) Ltd., 55 Gariahat Rd., P O Box 10210, Kolkata, West Bengal 700 019, India. Ed. K K Roy. R&P M Misra TEL 91-33-475-4872. Circ: 2,300.

ASIAN SOCIAL SCIENCE BIBLIOGRAPHY WITH ANNOTATIONS AND ABSTRACTS. see *SOCIAL SCIENCES: COMPREHENSIVE WORKS—Abstracting, Bibliographies, Statistics*

ASIAN STUDIES W W W MONITOR. (World Wide Web) see *ASIAN STUDIES—Abstracting, Bibliographies, Statistics*

ASSOCIATION FOR GERONTOLOGY IN HIGHER EDUCATION. BRIEF BIBLIOGRAPHY. see *GERONTOLOGY AND GERIATRICS—Abstracting, Bibliographies, Statistics*

ASSOCIATION OF AFRICAN UNIVERSITIES. BIBLIOGRAPHY ON HIGHER EDUCATION IN AFRICA. see *EDUCATION—Abstracting, Bibliographies, Statistics*

011   ITA   ISSN 0392-4270
ASSOCIAZIONE CENTRO DI DOCUMENTAZIONE. NOTIZIARIO. Key Title: Notiziario del Centro di Documentazione. Text in Italian. 1970. m. USD 15 (effective 2000).
Formerly: Cooperativa Centro di Documentazione. Notiziario
Published by: Associazione Centro di Documentazione, Casella Postale 347, Via Orafi, 29, Pistoia, PT 51100, Italy. TEL 39-0573-977353, FAX 39-0573-977353, cdocumen@tin.it, giorlima@tin.it.

011   USA
ATHENAEUM BOOKSHELF. Text in English. 1976. bi-m. membership. bk.rev. **Document type:** *Bibliography.*
Published by: Athenaeum of Philadelphia, 219 S Sixth St, Philadelphia, PA 19106-3794. TEL 215-925-2688, FAX 215-925-3755, athena@libertynet.org, http://www.libertynet.org/~athena. Circ: 1,400.

ATTITUDES AND ARABESQUES. see *DANCE—Abstracting, Bibliographies, Statistics*

AUS DEM ANTIQUARIAT. see *PUBLISHING AND BOOK TRADE*

AUSSTELLUNGSKATALOGE ZUR ARBEITERKULTUR. see *SOCIOLOGY—Abstracting, Bibliographies, Statistics*

011   AUS   ISSN 0067-172X
Z4011
AUSTRALIAN BOOKS IN PRINT; including information on book trade associations. Text in English. 1956. a. USD 159 (effective 2003). bk.rev. bibl. index. **Document type:** *Bibliography.* **Description:** Provides bibliographic information on over 80,000 in-print books published in Australia. Details more than 11,000 publishers and distributors whose titles are represented, plus information on Australian representation, associacions, and book series.
—BLDSC (1798.020000), CISTI. **CCC.**
Published by: Thorpe - Bowker (Subsidiary of: R.R. Bowker LLC), Bldg C3, 85 Turner St, Port Melbourne, VIC 3207, Australia. TEL 61-3-9245-7370, FAX 61-3-9245-7395, customer.service@thorpe.com.au, subscriptions@thorpe.com.au, http://www.thorpe.com.au. Ed. Karen Hewitt. Circ: 4,000. **Subscr. to:** R.R. Bowker LLC, Order Dept., PO Box 32, New Providence, NJ 07974-9903. TEL 800-521-8110.

AUSTRALIAN INSTITUTE OF ABORIGINAL AND TORRES STRAIT ISLANDER STUDIES. ANNUAL BIBLIOGRAPHY. see *ANTHROPOLOGY—Abstracting, Bibliographies, Statistics*

015   ESP
AUTORIDADES DE LA BIBLIOTECA NACIONAL DE ESPANA EN CD-ROM. Text in Spanish. 1996. s-a. USD 1,189.
Description: Provides the bibliographic authority database of the National Library.
Media: CD-ROM (from Chadwyck-Healey Inc.).
Published by: Biblioteca Nacional de Espana, Paseo Recoletos, 20, Madrid, 28001, Spain. editor@chadwyck.es, http://www.chadwyck.com. **Dist. in Spain and Latin America by:** Proquest Information & Learning (Spain), Juan Bravo, 18, 2o C, Madrid 28006, Spain. TEL 34-91-575-5597, FAX 34-91-575-9885.

028.5   USA   ISSN 1055-792X
Z1037
AWARD-WINNING BOOKS FOR CHILDREN AND YOUNG ADULTS. Text in English. 1989. irreg., latest 1990-1991. price varies. **Document type:** *Monographic series, Bibliography.*
Published by: Scarecrow Press, Inc. (Subsidiary of: Rowman & Littlefield Publishers, Inc.), 4501 Forbes Blvd., Suite 200, Lanham, MD 20706. TEL 301-459-3366, FAX 301-429-5748, custserv@rowman.com, http://www.scarecrowpress.com.

015   MEX   ISSN 0188-901X
AZTECA BOLETIN BIBLIOGRAFICO INTERNACIONAL. Text in Spanish. 1990. q. free. **Document type:** *Bibliography.*
Published by: Fondo de Cultura Economica, Carretera PICACHO AJUSCO 227, Col Bosques del Pedregal, Mexico City, DF 14200, Mexico. TEL 52-55-52274662, FAX 52-55-52274659. Ed. Ali Chumacero. Circ: 10,000.

015.942   GBR   ISSN 0968-3097
B N B ON CD-ROM. (British National Bibliography) (Colleges edition avail. (bi-m.); Schools edition avail. (3/yr.)) Text in English. 1950. m. GBP 1,080 domestic to institutions; GBP 1,225 foreign to institutions (effective 2002). cum. files (1950-1985; 1986-). back issues avail. **Document type:** *Bibliography.* **Description:** Lists more than 1.7 million books and serials published in the UK and Ireland since 1950.
Media: CD-ROM (from Chadwyck-Healey Inc.).
Published by: British Library, National Bibliographic Service, c/o Mike Marcus, Boston Spa, Wetherby, W Yorks LS23 7BQ, United Kingdom. TEL 44-1937-546585, FAX 44-1937-546586, nbs-info@bl.uk, http://www.bl.uk. **Dist. in US by:** ProQuest Information & Learning, 300 N Zeeb Rd., PO Box 1346, Ann Arbor, MI 48106-1346. FAX 703-683-7589; **Dist. by:** Extenza - Turpin, Pegasus Dr, Stratton Business Park, Biggleswade, Beds SG18 8TQ, United Kingdom. TEL 44-1462-672555, FAX 44-1462-480-947.

011   BHR
BAHRAIN BIBLIOGRAPHY. Text in English. a. **Document type:** *Bibliography.*
Published by: Ministry of Education, Manama Central Library, PO Box 43, Manama, Bahrain. TEL 258550, FAX 274036.

001.3 015   COL   ISSN 0006-6184
BANCO DE LA REPUBLICA. BIBLIOTECA LUIS ANGEL ARANGO. BOLETIN CULTURAL Y BIBLIOGRAFICO. Text in Spanish. 1958-1973; resumed 1978. 3/yr. COP 15,000, USD 30 (effective 1998). bk.rev. bibl.; charts; illus. **Document type:** *Bulletin.*
Indexed: ABM, AICP, AmH&L, HAPI, HistAb, MLA, MLA-IB, PCI, RASB, RILM.
Published by: Banco de la Republica, Biblioteca Luis Angel Arango, Barrio de la Candelaria, Calle 11, 4-14, Bogota, CUND, Colombia. TEL 57-1-2813146, FAX 57-1-2811191. Ed. Dario Jaramillo Agudelo. Circ: 4,000.

015   IND
BANGIYA SAHITYAKOSHA/SAHITYIK BARSAPANJEE. Text in Bengali. 1970. a. price varies. bk.rev. bibl. 200 p./no.; **Document type:** *Yearbook, Bibliography.*
Published by: Bangla Bhasa Sahitya-o-Samskriti Gabesane Samastha, c/o Little Magazine Stall & Bektigata Prakashani, 6 B Ramanath Mazumder St., Kolkata, West Bengal 700 009, India. TEL 03212-59622. Ed. Asok Kumar Kundu. Circ: 1,100.

▼ *new title*   ➤ *refereed*   ✱ *unverified*   ♦ *full entry avail.*

015 BGD
BANGLADESH NATIONAL BIBLIOGRAPHY. Text in Bengali, English. 1972. a. **Document type:** *Abstract/Index.* **Description:** Index of articles published in the daily newspaper.
Published by: National Library of Bangladesh, Directorate of Archives and Libraries, Sher.-&-Bangla Nagar(agargaon), Dhaka, 1207, Bangladesh. Circ: 2,000.

016 940 DEU
BAYERISCHE STAATSBIBLIOTHEK. OSTEUROPA-KATALOG AUF CD-ROM. Text in German. 1972. s-a. **Document type:** *Government.*
Formerly (until 1997): Bayerische Staatsbibliotek. Osteuropa-Neuerwerbungen
Media: CD-ROM.
Published by: Bayerische Staatsbibliothek, Ludwigstr 16, Munich, 80539, Germany. TEL 49-89-28638-0, FAX 49-89-28638-2200, direktion@bsb-muenchen.de, http://www.bsb-muenchen.de. Ed. Hermann Leskien.

BELGIUM. INSTITUT NATIONAL DE STATISTIQUE. CATALOGUE DES PRODUITS ET SERVICES. see *STATISTICS*

BELGIUM. NATIONAAL INSTITUUT VOOR DE STATISTIEK. CATALOGUS VAN DE PRODUKTEN EN DIENSTEN. see *STATISTICS*

LA BERIO; rivista semestrale di storia locale e di informazioni bibliografiche. see *HISTORY—History Of Europe*

015 BMU ISSN 0255-0067
Z1591
BERMUDA NATIONAL BIBLIOGRAPHY. Text in English. 1984. q. (plus a. cumulation). BMD 14 domestic to individuals; BMD 17.50 foreign to individuals; BMD 19 domestic to institutions; BMD 23.50 foreign to institutions (effective 2001). back issues avail. **Document type:** *Bibliography.* **Description:** Lists all new materials added to the Bermudiana collection.
Published by: Bermuda National Library, Technical Services, Par-la-Ville, 13 Queen St, Hamilton, HM11, Bermuda. TEL 441-295-2905, FAX 441-292-8443, bdanatlibts@bdagov.bm. Ed. Patrice A Carvell. R&P Grace Rawlins. Circ: 100.

011 USA
BEST BOOK CATALOG IN THE WORLD. Text in English. 1975. a. USD 5 (effective 2000). adv. Supplement avail. **Document type:** *Catalog.* **Description:** Source for anarchists, survivalists, iconoclasts, self-liberators, mercenaries, investigators, drop outs, and researchers.
Formerly: Loompanics Book Catalog
Published by: Loompanics Unlimited, PO Box 1197, Port Townsend, WA 98368. TEL 360-385-5087, FAX 360-385-7785, loompanx@olympus.net, http://loompanics.com. Ed., R&P Gia Cosindas. Adv. contact Audrey Lee. Circ: 30,000.

BEST BOOKS FOR CHILDREN; preschool through grade 6. see *CHILDREN AND YOUTH—Abstracting, Bibliographies, Statistics*

011 BEL
BIBLIO-FLASH (ONLINE). Text in English. 1987. irreg. **Document type:** *Bibliography.*
Former titles (until Jun. 2003): Biblio-flash (Print); (until 1998): Communautes Europeennes. Office des Publications Officielles. Biblio-flash (1015-0390)
Related titles: French ed.
Published by: European Commission, Central Library/Commission Europeenne, Bibliotheque Centrale, Building (VM18), Rue Van Maerlant, 18, Bruxelles, B-1049, Belgium. TEL 32-2-2999064, FAX 32-2-2960657, http://europa.eu.int/comm/libraries/sb_europa/biblioflash/polonia_en.htm, http://europa.eu.int/comm/libraries/centrallibrary/index_en.htm.

011 BEL
BIBLIO INTERNATIONAL (ONLINE). Text in English. 1993. q. free. **Document type:** *Bibliography.*
Former titles (until Jun. 2002): Biblio International (Print) (1680-2233); (until 1999): Biblio Country Reports (1024-1868)
Media: Online - full content. **Related titles:** Online - full content ed.
Published by: European Commission, Central Library/Commission Europeenne, Bibliotheque Centrale, Building (VM18), Rue Van Maerlant, 18, Bruxelles, B-1049, Belgium. TEL 32-2-2999064, FAX 32-2-2960657, http://europa.eu.int/comm/libraries/sb_europa/bibliocr/index_en.htm, http://europa.eu.int/comm/libraries/centrallibrary/index_en.htm.

015 IDN ISSN 0523-1639
Z3273
BIBLIOGRAFI NASIONAL INDONESIA/INDONESIAN NATIONAL BIBLIOGRAPHY. Text in Indonesian. 1953. q. (plus a. cumulation). free. adv. bk.rev.
Published by: Perpustakaan Nasional R.I./National Library of Indonesia, P.O. Box 3624, Jakarta, 1000s, Indonesia. TEL 021-310-3553, FAX 021-310-3554. Ed. Dady P Rachmananta. Circ: 1,000.

BIBLIOGRAFIA ANALITYCZNA BIBLIOTEKOZNAWSTWA I INFORMACJI NAUKOWEJ; pismiennictwo zagraniczne. see *LIBRARY AND INFORMATION SCIENCES—Abstracting, Bibliographies, Statistics*

011 POL ISSN 0860-6579
Z2521.A1
BIBLIOGRAFIA BIBLIOGRAFII POLSKICH/BIBLIOGRAPHY OF POLISH BIBLIOGRAPHIES. Text in Polish. 1937. a., latest 1998. PLZ 18 domestic; USD 12 foreign (effective 2001).
Document type: *Bibliography.*
Formerly (until 1981): Bibliografia Bibliografii i Nauki o Ksiazce. Cz. 1: Bibliografia Bibliografii Polskich (0860-8385); Which superseded in part (in 1969): Bibliografia Bibliografii i Nauki o Ksiazce (0509-6413)
Related titles: Online - full text ed.
—Linda Hall.
Published by: Biblioteka Narodowa, Instytut Bibliograficzny, Al Niepodleglosci 213, Warsaw, 02086, Poland. TEL 48-22-6082412, FAX 48-22-8255251, przybysz@bn.org.pl, http://www.bn.org.pl. Eds. Danuta Urbanska, Marzena Przybysz.

BIBLIOGRAFIA BRASILEIRA DE ODONTOLOGIA (ONLINE EDITION). see *MEDICAL SCIENCES—Abstracting, Bibliographies, Statistics*

015 CHL ISSN 0716-176X
BIBLIOGRAFIA CHILENA. Text in Spanish. 1877. irreg. CLP 1,000, USD 10. bibl. **Document type:** *Bibliography.*
Description: Provides a listing of publications issued in Chile.
Formerly (until 1981): Anuario de la Prensa Chilena
Published by: Direccion de Bibliotecas Archivos y Museos, Biblioteca Nacional, Alameda, 651, Santiago, Chile. TEL 6380461, FAX 6381975. Circ: 1,000.

011 BRA ISSN 0006-0992
BIBLIOGRAFIA CLASSIFICADA∗ . Text in Portuguese. 1968. bi-m.
Published by: Centro de Investigacao e Documentacao, Petropolis, Centro, Caixa Postal 23, Rio De Janeiro, RJ 20001-970, Brazil. Ed. Arcangelo Raimundo Buzzi.

015.7291 CUB ISSN 0067-6705
Z1511
BIBLIOGRAFIA CUBANA. Text in Spanish. 1959. a. USD 35. **Description:** Compiles all books, magazines, postals, catalogues of expositions, and programs of musical reference.
Indexed: RASB.
Published by: Biblioteca Nacional Jose Marti, Ave. Independencia y 20 de Mayo, Plaza de la Revolucion, Havana, Cuba. TEL 70-5092, FAX 53-7-335072, TELEX 511963 CU. Circ: 500.

BIBLIOGRAFIA DE LA LITERATURA HISPANICA. see *LITERATURE—Abstracting, Bibliographies, Statistics*

BIBLIOGRAFIA DO IDOSO. see *GERONTOLOGY AND GERIATRICS—Abstracting, Bibliographies, Statistics*

BIBLIOGRAFIA E STORIA DELLA CRITICA. see *LITERATURE—Abstracting, Bibliographies, Statistics*

BIBLIOGRAFIA ERITYSIRYHMIEN LIIKUNNAN TUTKIMUKSESTA/BIBLIOGRAPHY ON RESEARCH IN PHYSICAL EDUCATION AND SPORT FOR THE HANDICAPPED. see *EDUCATION—Abstracting, Bibliographies, Statistics*

011 ESP ISSN 1133-9519
Z6027.S72
BIBLIOGRAFIA ESPANOLA. CARTOGRAFIA. Text in Spanish. 1980. a.
Formerly (until 1991): Bibliografia Espanola. Suplemento de Cartografia (0214-4441)
Published by: Biblioteca Nacional de Espana, Paseo Recoletos, 20, Madrid, 28001, Spain. TEL 1-5447443. Circ: 1,000.
Co-sponsor: Ministerio de Cultura, Direccion General del Libro y Bibliotecas.

BIBLIOGRAFIA ESPANOLA DE REVISTAS CIENTIFICAS DE CIENCIA Y TECNOLOGIA. see *SCIENCES: COMPREHENSIVE WORKS—Abstracting, Bibliographies, Statistics*

BIBLIOGRAFIA ESPANOLA DE REVISTAS CIENTIFICAS DE CIENCIAS SOCIALES Y HUMANIDADES/SPANISH BIBLIOGRAPHY OF SCIENTIFIC JOURNALS IN SOCIAL SCIENCES AND HUMANITIES. see *SOCIAL SCIENCES: COMPREHENSIVE WORKS—Abstracting, Bibliographies, Statistics*

015 ESP
BIBLIOGRAFIA ESPANOLA DESDE 1976 EN CD-ROM. Text in Spanish. 1993. q. USD 1,449 (effective 1996). **Document type:** *Bibliography.*
Media: CD-ROM (from Chadwyck-Healey Inc.).
—CINDOC.

Published by: Biblioteca Nacional de Espana, Paseo Recoletos, 20, Madrid, 28001, Spain. **Dist. in Spain and Latin America by:** Proquest Information & Learning (Spain), Juan Bravo, 18, 2o C, Madrid 28006, Spain. TEL 34-91-575-5597, FAX 34-91-575-9885.

015 ESP ISSN 1133-858X
Z2685
BIBLIOGRAFIA ESPANOLA. MONOGRAFIAS. Text in Spanish. 1969. m. adv. reprints avail. **Document type:** *Monographic series, Bibliography.*
Former titles (until 1994): Bibliografia Espanola (0525-3675); Boletin del Deposito Legal de Obras Impresas (0006-6362)
Indexed: RASB.
—BLDSC (1949.340000).
Published by: (Biblioteca Nacional de Espana), Ministerio de Educacion, Cultura y Deporte, Centro de Publicaciones, c/o Ciudad Universitaria, S/N, Madrid, 28040, Spain. TEL 34-91-453-9800, FAX 34-91-4539884. Circ: 1,000.
Co-sponsor: Ministerio de Cultura, Direccion General del Libro y Bibliotecas.

011 ESP ISSN 1133-8563
Z2685
BIBLIOGRAFIA ESPANOLA. MONOGRAFIAS. INDICES ACUMULATIVOS. Text in Spanish. 1958. a. price varies. reprints avail. **Document type:** *Monographic series, Bibliography.*
Formerly (until 1993): Bibliografia Espanola. Anual (0523-1760)
Related titles: Microfiche ed.: (from BHP).
Published by: Biblioteca Nacional de Espana, Paseo Recoletos, 20, Madrid, 28001, Spain. TEL 1-5447443. Circ: 1,000.
Co-sponsor: Ministerio de Cultura, Direccion General del Libro y Bibliotecas.

011 ESP
BIBLIOGRAFIA ESPANOLA. MUSICA IMPRESA. Text in Spanish. 1985. a. **Document type:** *Bibliography.*
Formerly: Bibliografia Espanola. Suplemento de Musica Impresa (1130-1392)
Published by: Biblioteca Nacional de Espana, Paseo Recoletos, 20, Madrid, 28001, Spain. TEL 1-5447443. Circ: 1,000.
Co-sponsor: Ministerio de Cultura, Direccion General del Libro y Bibliotecas.

011 ESP ISSN 0210-8372
Z6956.S7
BIBLIOGRAFIA ESPANOLA. SUPLEMENTO DE PUBLICACIONES PERIODICAS. Text in Spanish. 1979. a.
Published by: Biblioteca Nacional de Espana, Plaza del Rey, 1, Madrid, 28004, Spain. TEL 1-5447443. Circ: 1,000. **Dist. by:** Distribuidora de Publicaciones, Fernando el Catolico, 77, Madrid 28015, Spain. **Co-sponsor:** Ministerio de Cultura, Direccion General del Libro y Bibliotecas.

BIBLIOGRAFIA FILOSOFICA ITALIANA. see *PHILOSOPHY—Abstracting, Bibliographies, Statistics*

BIBLIOGRAFIA FORESTAL DE VENEZUELA. see *FORESTS AND FORESTRY—Abstracting, Bibliographies, Statistics*

015 850 ITA ISSN 1122-2220
Z2355.A2
BIBLIOGRAFIA GENERALE DELLA LINGUA E DELLA LETTERATURA ITALIANA. Text in Italian. 1991. a. EUR 150 domestic to individuals; EUR 170 domestic to institutions; EUR 210 in the European Union; EUR 230 elsewhere (effective 2005). adv. bk.rev. **Document type:** *Bibliography.*
Related titles: CD-ROM ed.
Indexed: MLA-IB.
Published by: (Centro Pio Rajna), Salerno Editrice, Via Valadier 52, Rome, 00193, Italy. TEL 39-06-3608201, FAX 39-06-3223132, info@salernoeditrice.it, http://www.salernoeditrice.it. Ed. Enrico Malato. Circ: 1,000. **Dist. by:** Casalini Libri, Via Benedetto da Maiano 3, Fiesole, FI 50014, Italy. TEL 39-55-50181, FAX 39-55-5018201.

BIBLIOGRAFIA GEOGRAFII POLSKIEJ/BIBLIOGRAPHY OF POLISH GEOGRAPHY. see *GEOGRAPHY—Abstracting, Bibliographies, Statistics*

BIBLIOGRAFIA GEOLOGICA SI GEOFIZICA A ROMANIEI/GEOLOGICAL AND GEOPHYSICAL BIBLIOGRAPHY OF ROMANIA. see *EARTH SCIENCES—Abstracting, Bibliographies, Statistics*

BIBLIOGRAFIA GEOLOGICZNA POLSKI. see *EARTH SCIENCES—Abstracting, Bibliographies, Statistics*

BIBLIOGRAFIA HISTORII POLSKIEJ. see *HISTORY—Abstracting, Bibliographies, Statistics*

BIBLIOGRAFIA ITALIANA DI STORIA DELLA SCIENZA. see *SCIENCES: COMPREHENSIVE WORKS—Abstracting, Bibliographies, Statistics*

BIBLIOGRAFIA ITALIANA DI STUDI SULL'UMANESIMO ED IL RINASCIMENTO. see *HUMANITIES: COMPREHENSIVE WORKS*

B

015 ALB
BIBLIOGRAFIA KOMBETARE E LIBRIT QE BOTOHET NE REPUBLIKEN E SHQIPERISE. Text in Albanian. 1960. q. USD 16 (effective 1999). adv. **Document type:** *Bibliography.* **Description:** Lists books and other non-periodical publications of Albania.
Former titles (until 1991): Bibliografia Kombetare e Libritqe Botohet ne Republiken Popullore Socialiste te Shqiperise; (until 1985): Bibliografia Kombetare e Republikes Popullore Socialiste te Shqiperise. Libri Shqip (0250-5053); (until 1976): Bibliografia Kombetare e Repulikes Popullore te Shqiperise. Libri Shqip (0523-1841); (until 1964): Bibliografia e Republikes Popullore te Shqiperise. Vepra Origjinale dhe Perkthime
Indexed: RASB.
Published by: Biblioteka Kombetare, Tirana, Albania. Ed. Maksim Gjinaj. R&P Aurel Plasar. Adv. contact Ardian Basha.

015 ALB
BIBLIOGRAFIA KOMBETARE E REPUBLIKES SE SHQIPERISE. ARTIKUJT E PERIODIKUT SHQIPTAR. Text in Albanian. 1961. m. USD 72 (effective 1999). adv. **Document type:** *Bibliography.* **Description:** Lists articles published in Albanian periodicals.
Former titles (until 1991): Bibliografia Kombetare e Republikes Popullore Socialiste te Shqiperise. Artikujt e Periodikut Shqiptar; (until 1985): Bibliografia Kombetare e Republikes Popullore Socialiste te Shqiperise. Artikujt e Periodikut Shqip (0250-5061); (until 1976): Bibliografia Kombetare e Republikes Popullore te Shqiperise. Artikujt e Periodikut Shqip (0523-1833); (until 1964): Bibliografia e Periodikut te Republikes Popullore te Shqiperise
Indexed: RASB.
Published by: Biblioteka Kombetare, Tirana, Albania. TEL 355-42-238-43. Ed. Maksim Gjinaj. R&P Aurel Plasari. Adv. contact Adrian Basha.

015.8 MEX ISSN 0185-2884
Z1605
BIBLIOGRAFIA LATINOAMERICANA; trabajos publicados por latinoamericanos en revistas extranjeras. Text in English. 1980. s-a. MXP 150, USD 190 (effective 2000). **Document type:** *Bibliography.* **Description:** Bibliographic index that covers 3,000 serials on social sciences and the humanities written by Latin American authors.
Published by: (Centro de Informacion Cientifica y Humanistica), Universidad Nacional Autonoma de Mexico, Direccion General de Bibliotecas, Apdo. Postal 70-392, Mexico City, DF 04510, Mexico. TEL 52-5-6223958, FAX 52-5-6162557, biblat@selene.cichcu.unam.mx, http://www.dgbiblio.unam.mx. Ed., R&P Octavio Alonso Gamboa.

015 MEX ISSN 0006-1069
Z1411
BIBLIOGRAFIA MEXICANA. Text in Spanish. 1967. a. USD 200 (effective 1998). reprints avail. **Document type:** *Bibliography.*
Published by: Universidad Nacional Autonoma de Mexico, Instituto de Investigaciones Bibliograficas, Ciudad Universitaria, Coyoacan, Mexico City, DF 04510, Mexico. TEL 52-5-6226807, FAX 52-5-6650951, libros@biblional.bibliog.unam.mx. Ed. Jose G Moreno de Alba. Circ: 1,000. **Co-sponsor:** Biblioteca Nacional.

BIBLIOGRAFIA MISSIONARIA. see *RELIGIONS AND THEOLOGY—Abstracting, Bibliographies, Statistics*

015 BGR ISSN 0204-7373
BIBLIOGRAFIA NA BULGARSKATA BIBLIOGRAFIIA/ BIBLIOGRAPHY OF BULGARIAN BIBLIOGRAPHIES. Text in Bulgarian. 1965. a. BGL 4 per issue (effective 2003). **Document type:** *Bibliography.*
Published by: Narodna Biblioteka Sv. sv. Kiril i Metodii/Cyril and Methodius National Library, 88 Levski Blvd, Sofia, 1504, Bulgaria. TEL 359-2-9881600, FAX 359-2-435495, nbkm@nl.otel.net. Ed., R&P T Pancheva TEL 359-2-9882811 ext 360. Circ: 280.

015 USA
BIBLIOGRAFIA NACIONAL PORTUGUESA EM CD-ROM. Text in English. s-a. USD 450 (effective 1999). **Document type:** *Bibliography.*
Media: CD-ROM (from Chadwyck-Healey Inc.).
Published by: (Biblioteca Nacional Portuguesa), ProQuest Information & Learning, 300 N Zeeb Rd., PO Box 1346, Ann Arbor, MI 48106-1346. FAX 703-683-7589, info@il.proquest.com, http://www.chadwyck.com.

016.05 ROM ISSN 1454-7430
Z5961.R65
BIBLIOGRAFIA NATIONALA ROMANA. ARTICOLE DIN PUBLICATII PERIODICE. CULTURA. Text in Romanian. 2000. m. ROL 720,000 (effective 2002). Index. 250 p./no.; back issues avail. **Document type:** *Bibliography.* **Description:** Contains the titles of articles that appear every month in cultural reviews. Includes author and subject indexes.
Published by: Biblioteca Nationala a Romaniei, Str. Ion Ghica 4, Sector 3, Bucharest, 79708, Romania. TEL 40-21-3157063, FAX 40-21-3123381, go@bibnat.ro, http://www.bibnat.ro. Ed. Sanda Ciucur.

015 ROM ISSN 1221-9126
Z2923
BIBLIOGRAFIA NATIONALA ROMANA. CARTI. ALBUME. HARTI. Text in Romanian. 1957. s-m. ROL 840,000 (effective 2003). Index. 150 p./no.; **Document type:** *Bibliography.*
Former titles (until 1990): Bibliografia Romaniei. Carti, Albume, Harti (1220-5842); (until 1989): Bibliografia Republicii Socialiste. Carti, Albume, Harti (1220-5834); Supersedes in part (in 1967): Bibliografia Republicii Socialiste Romania. Carti, Albume, Harti, Note Muzicale (0254-6035); Which was formerly (until 1965): Bibliografia Republicii Populare Romane. Carti, Albume, Harti, Note Muzicale (0254-6027)
Indexed: RASB.
Published by: Biblioteca Nationala a Romaniei, Str. Ion Ghica 4, Sector 3, Bucharest, 79708, Romania. TEL 40-21-3157063, FAX 40-21-3123381, go@bibnat.ro, http://www.bibnat.ro. Ed. Sanda Ciucur.

015 ROM ISSN 1583-3194
Z2923
BIBLIOGRAFIA NATIONALA ROMANA. DOCUMENTA ROMANIAE. Text in Romanian. 1993. a., latest vol.7, 2002. ROL 80,000 (effective 2003). Index. 300 p./no.; back issues avail. **Document type:** *Bibliography.*
Former titles (until 2001): Bibliografia Nationala Romana. Romanica (1453-0465); (until 1993): Bibliografia Nationala Romana. Lucrari Aparute in Strainatate (1221-4515)
Published by: Biblioteca Nationala a Romaniei, Str. Ion Ghica 4, Sector 3, Bucharest, 79708, Romania. TEL 40-21-3157063, FAX 40-21-3123381, go@bibnat.ro, http://www.bibnat.ro. Ed. Actarian Emanuel Hrant.

015 ROM ISSN 1221-9134
ML120.R64
BIBLIOGRAFIA NATIONALA ROMANA. NOTE MUZICALE. DISCURI. CASETE. Text in Romanian. 1957. q. ROL 72,000 (effective 2003). Index. 65 p./no.; back issues avail. **Document type:** *Bibliography.*
Former titles (until 1990): Bibliografia Romaniei. Note Muzicale, Discuri, Casete (1220-5877); (until 1989): Bibliografia Republicii Socialiste Romania. Note Muzicale, Discuri, Casete (1220-5869); (until 1979): Bibliografia Republicii Socialiste Romania. Note Muzicale, Discuri (1220-5850); Supersedes in part (in 1967): Bibliografia Republicii Socialiste Romania. Carti, Albume, Harti, Note Muzicale (0254-6035); Which was formerly (until 1965): Bibliografia Republicii Populare Romane. Carti, Albume, Harti, Note Muzicale (0254-6027)
Published by: Biblioteca Nationala a Romaniei, Str. Ion Ghica 4, Sector 3, Bucharest, 79708, Romania. TEL 40-21-3157063, FAX 40-21-3123381, go@bibnat.ro, http://www.bibnat.ro. Ed. Doina Nemes.

016.05 ROM ISSN 1221-180X
AI19.R8
BIBLIOGRAFIA NATIONALA ROMANA. PUBLICATII SERIALE. Text in Romanian. 1992. a., latest vol.11, 2002. ROL 65,000 (effective 2001). Index. 400 p./no.; back issues avail. **Document type:** *Bibliography.*
Published by: Biblioteca Nationala a Romaniei, Str. Ion Ghica 4, Sector 3, Bucharest, 79708, Romania. TEL 40-21-3157063, FAX 40-21-3123381, go@bibnat.ro, http://www.bibnat.ro. Ed. Sanda Ciucur.

015 ROM ISSN 1223-7485
Z2923
BIBLIOGRAFIA NATIONALA ROMANA. TEZE DE DOCTORAT. Text in Romanian. 1995. a., latest vol.8, 2002. ROL 430,000 (effective 2003). Index. 500 p./no.; back issues avail. **Document type:** *Bibliography.*
Published by: Biblioteca Nationala a Romaniei, Str. Ion Ghica 4, Sector 3, Bucharest, 79708, Romania. TEL 40-21-3157063, FAX 40-21-3123381, go@bibnat.ro, http://www.bibnat.ro. Ed. Sanda Ciucur.

BIBLIOGRAFIA NAZIONALE ITALIANA. MONOGRAFIE. see *PUBLISHING AND BOOK TRADE—Abstracting, Bibliographies, Statistics*

BIBLIOGRAFIA POMORZA ZACHODNIEGO. PISMIENNICTWO POLSKIE/BIBLIOGRAPHY OF WEST POMERANIA. POLISH LITERATURE. see *LITERATURE—Abstracting, Bibliographies, Statistics*

015 POL ISSN 0138-0702
BIBLIOGRAFIA POMORZA ZACHODNIEGO. PISMIENNICTWO ZAGRANICZNE/BIBLIOGRAPHY OF WEST POMERANIA. FOREIGN LITERATURE. Text in Polish. 1978. irreg. price varies. bk.rev. **Document type:** *Bibliography.* **Description:** Includes foreign literature of western Pomerania in original languages.
Related titles: Microfilm ed.
Published by: Ksiaznica Pomorska im. Stanislawa Staszica, Podgorna 15/16, Szczecin, 70205, Poland. TEL 48-91-4341662, FAX 48-91-4339678. Ed. Stanislaw Krzywicki.

BIBLIOGRAFIA PUBLIKACJI PRACOWNIKOW NAUKOWYCH AKADEMII EKONOMICZNEJ W KRAKOWIE (ONLINE EDITION). see *BUSINESS AND ECONOMICS—Abstracting, Bibliographies, Statistics*

BIBLIOGRAFIA SELECCIONADA DE ESPECIES Y TOPICOS FORESTALES. see *FORESTS AND FORESTRY—Abstracting, Bibliographies, Statistics*

015 POL ISSN 0523-1930
BIBLIOGRAFIA SLASKA. Text in Polish. 1963. a. PLZ 15 domestic (effective 2002). bk.rev. back issues avail. **Document type:** *Bibliography.*
Published by: Biblioteka Slaska, Plac Rady Europy 1, Katowice, 40021, Poland. TEL 48-32-2083875, FAX 48-32-2553572, bsl@libra.bs.katowice.pl, bsl@bs.katowice.pl, http://www.bs.katowice.pl. Ed. Jan Malicki. Circ: 500.

BIBLIOGRAFIA TEMATICA SOBRE JUDAISMO ARGENTINO. see *RELIGIONS AND THEOLOGY—Abstracting, Bibliographies, Statistics*

BIBLIOGRAFIA TEOLOGICA COMENTADA DEL AREA IBEROAMERICANA. see *RELIGIONS AND THEOLOGY—Abstracting, Bibliographies, Statistics*

015 POL ISSN 0239-4421
Z6956.P7
BIBLIOGRAFIA WYDAWNICTW CIAGLYCH/BIBLIOGRAPHY OF POLISH SERIALS. Text in Polish. 1957. a., latest 1998. PLZ 50 domestic; USD 33.33 foreign (effective 2001). **Document type:** *Bibliography.*
Formerly: Bibliografia Czasopism i Wydawnictw Zbiorowych (0523-1736)
Related titles: Online - full text ed.
Published by: Biblioteka Narodowa, Instytut Bibliograficzny, Al Niepodleglosci 213, Warsaw, 02086, Poland. TEL 48-22-6082409, FAX 48-22-8255251, polonica@bn.org.pl, http://www.bn.org.pl. Ed. Grazyna Federowicz. **Dist. by:** P.P. CHZ Ars Polona, Krakowskie Przedmiescie 7, Warsaw 00068, Poland.

011 POL ISSN 0239-5606
Z2523
BIBLIOGRAFIA WYDAWNICTW CIAGLYCH NOWYCH, ZAWIESZONYCH I ZMIENIAJACYCH TYTUL. Text in Polish. 1976. bi-m. EUR 15 foreign (effective 2005). index. **Document type:** *Bibliography.*
Related titles: ♦ Supplement to: Przewodnik Bibliograficzny. ISSN 0033-2518.
Published by: Biblioteka Narodowa, Instytut Bibliograficzny, Al Niepodleglosci 213, Warsaw, 02086, Poland. TEL 48-22-6082409, FAX 48-22-8255251, polonica@bn.org.pl, http://www.bn.org.pl. Ed. Grazyna Federowicz. **Dist. by:** Ars Polona, Krakowskie Przedmiescie 7, Warsaw, Poland. TEL 48-22-9263914, FAX 48-22-9265334, arspolona@arspolona.com.pl, http://www.arspolona.com.pl.

011 POL ISSN 0006-1093
AI15
BIBLIOGRAFIA ZAWARTOSCI CZASOPISM. Text in Polish. 1947. m. PLZ 14 per issue domestic; USD 9.33 per issue foreign (effective 2001). **Document type:** *Bibliography.*
Related titles: CD-ROM ed.: ISSN 1428-6793. PLZ 5.49 domestic; USD 3.66 foreign; Online - full text ed.
Indexed: RASB.
Published by: Biblioteka Narodowa, Instytut Bibliograficzny, Al Niepodleglosci 213, Warsaw, 02086, Poland. TEL 48-22-6082409, FAX 48-22-8255251, polonica@bn.org.pl, http://www.bn.org.pl. Ed. Alina Ciedrogi-Kwietkowska. **Dist. by:** P.P. CHZ Ars Polona, Krakowskie Przedmiescie 7, Warsaw 00068, Poland.

BIBLIOGRAFIAS DE HISTORIA DE ESPANA. see *HISTORY—Abstracting, Bibliographies, Statistics*

BIBLIOGRAFICA FOLCLORICA. see *FOLKLORE—Abstracting, Bibliographies, Statistics*

BIBLIOGRAFIE BOTANICZNE/BOTANICAL BIBLIOGRAPHIES. see *BIOLOGY—Abstracting, Bibliographies, Statistics*

BIBLIOGRAFIE NEDERLANDSE SOCIALE WETENSCHAPPEN (ONLINE EDITION); vakbibliografie voor nederland en Nederlandstalig Belgie. see *SOCIOLOGY—Abstracting, Bibliographies, Statistics*

BIBLIOGRAFIJA JUGOSLAVIJE. CLANCI I PRILOZI U SERIJSKIM PUBLIKACIJAMA. SERIJA A: DRUSTVENE NAUKE. see *SOCIAL SCIENCES: COMPREHENSIVE WORKS—Abstracting, Bibliographies, Statistics*

BIBLIOGRAFIJA JUGOSLAVIJE. CLANCI I PRILOZI U SERIJSKIM PUBLIKACIJAMA. SERIJA B: PRIRODNE, PRIMENJENE, MEDICINSKE I TEHNICKE NAUKE. see *SCIENCES: COMPREHENSIVE WORKS—Abstracting, Bibliographies, Statistics*

B

016 SCG ISSN 0352-5996
AI15
BIBLIOGRAFIJA JUGOSLAVIJE. CLANCI I PRILOZI U SERIJSKIM PUBLIKACIJAMA. SERIJA C: UMETNOST, SPORT, FILOLOGIJA, KNJIZEVNOST. Text in Serbo-Croatian. 1950. bi-m. 80 p./no. 2 cols./p.; **Document type:** *Bibliography.* **Description:** Bibliography of articles in books and serials, covering literature, linguistics, architecture, arts (painting, music, theatre), sports.
Formerly (until 1985): Bibliografija Jugoslavije. Serija C: Umetnost, Sport, Filologija, Knjizevnost i Muzikalije (0373-6377)
Related titles: Online - full text ed.
Indexed: MLA-IB, RASB.
Published by: Jugoslovenski Bibliografsko-Informacijski Institut (YUBIN)/Yugoslav Institute for Bibliography and Information, Terazije 26, Belgrade. FAX 381-11-687760, yubin@jbi.bg.ac.yu 1, http://www.yugoslavia.com/culture/yubin. Ed. Radomir Glavicki. Adv. contact Tanja Ostojic.

015 SCG ISSN 0523-2201
Z2951
BIBLIOGRAFIJA JUGOSLAVIJE. KNJIGE, BROSURE I MUZIKALIJE. Text in Serbo-Croatian. 1950. bi-m. USD 552 (effective 2002). 80 p./no. 2 cols./p.; **Document type:** *Bibliography.* **Description:** Bibliography of books, pamphlets and music scores, covering all fields of knowledge.
Related titles: Online - full text ed.
Indexed: RASB.
Published by: Jugoslovenski Bibliografsko-Informacijski Institut (YUBIN)/Yugoslav Institute for Bibliography and Information, Terazije 26, Belgrade. FAX 381-11-687760, yubin@jbi.bg.ac.yu, http://www.yugoslavia.com/culture/yubin. Ed. Radomir Glavicki. Adv. contact Tanja Ostojic.

079 015 SCG ISSN 0350-0349
Z6956.Y9
BIBLIOGRAFIJA JUGOSLAVIJE. SERIJSKE PUBLIKACIJE. Text in Serbo-Croatian. 1959. a. index. 100 p./no. 2 cols./p.; **Document type:** *Bibliography.* **Description:** Bibliography of serial publications.
Formerly (until 1975): Bibliografia Jugoslovenske Periodike (0006-1158)
Indexed: RASB.
Published by: Jugoslovenski Bibliografsko-Informacijski Institut (YUBIN)/Yugoslav Institute for Bibliography and Information, Terazije 26, Belgrade. FAX 381-11-687760, yubin@jbi.bg.ac.yu, http://www.yugoslavia.com/culture/yubin. Ed. Radomir Glavicki. Adv. contact Tanja Ostojic.

015 SCG ISSN 0354-6551
Z2957.V64
BIBLIOGRAFIJA KNJIGA U VOJVODINI. Text in Multiple languages. 1983. a. bibl. **Document type:** *Bibliography.*
Formerly (until 1992): Bibliografija Vojvodine. Serija 1. Monografske Publikacije (0352-3241)
Indexed: RASB.
Published by: Biblioteka Matica Srpska, Matice Srpske 1, Novi Sad, 21000. TEL 381-21-25859, FAX 381-21-28574, bms@bms.ns.ac.yu. Ed. Miro Vuksanovic. Circ: 400 (controlled).

015 SCG ISSN 0354-4710
Z6514.T7
BIBLIOGRAFIJA PREVODA U S R J. Text in Serbo-Croatian. 1969. a., latest vol.52, 2001. 100 p./no. 2 cols./p.; **Document type:** *Bulletin, Bibliography.* **Description:** Bibliography of translated books published in Yugoslavia.
Formerly: Bibliografija Prevoda u S F R J (0350-9974)
Related titles: Online - full text ed.
Indexed: RASB.
Published by: Jugoslovenski Bibliografsko-Informacijski Institut (YUBIN)/Yugoslav Institute for Bibliography and Information, Terazije 26, Belgrade. FAX 381-11-687760, yubin@jbi.bg.ac.yu, http://www.yugoslavia.com/culture/yubin. Ed. Radomir Glavicki. Adv. contact Tanja Ostojic.

920 SCG ISSN 0351-6016
BIBLIOGRAFIJA RECENZIJA IZ DOMACIH LISTOVA I CASOPISA. Text in Macedonian, Serbo-Croatian, Slovenian. 1979. q. free. **Document type:** *Bibliography.*
Formerly: Bilten Recenzija iz Damacih Listova i Casopisa
Published by: Biblioteka Grada Geograda, Knez Mihailova 56, Belgrade, 11000. TEL 381-11-2024000, info@bgb.org.yu, http://www.bgb.org.yu. Circ: 100.

BIBLIOGRAFIJA ROTO STAMPE I STRIPOVA. see *LITERATURE—Abstracting, Bibliographies, Statistics*

015 SCG ISSN 0354-4761
Z2953
BIBLIOGRAFIJA ZVANICNIH PUBLIKACIJA S R J. KNJIGE, SERIJSKE PUBLIKACIJE. Text in Serbo-Croatian. 1972. a., latest vol.29, 2000. 80 p./no. 2 cols./p.; **Document type:** *Bulletin, Bibliography.* **Description:** Bibliography of official publications in Yugoslavia.
Formerly: Bibliografija Zvanicnih Publikacija S F R J (0351-2843)
Published by: Jugoslovenski Bibliografsko-Informacijski Institut (YUBIN)/Yugoslav Institute for Bibliography and Information, Terazije 26, Belgrade. FAX 381-11-687760, yubin@jbi.jbi.bg.ac.yu, http://www.yugoslavia.com/culture/yubin. Ed. Radomir Glavicki. Adv. contact Tanja Ostojic.

025.3 LTU ISSN 1392-1738
Z2537
BIBLIOGRAFIJOS ZINIOS. KNYGOS/BIBLIOGRAPHICAL NEWS. BOOKS; Lietuvos valstybines bibliografijos rodykle. Text in Lithuanian, English. 1947. m. **Document type:** *Bibliography.*
Supersedes in part (in 1995): Bibliografijos Zinios (1392-0308); Which was formerly (until 1992): Letopis' Pecati (0135-1354)
Published by: Martynas Mazvydas National Library of Lithuania, Centre of Bibliography and Book Science, Sv Ignoto 6, Vilnius, 2600, Lithuania. TEL 370-2-629023, FAX 370-2-627129, info@tb.lt, http://www.tb.lt. **Co-publisher:** Ministry of Culture. **Co-sponsor:** Ministry of Culture.

025.3 LTU ISSN 1392-1762
Z2537
BIBLIOGRAFIJOS ZINIOS. LITUANIKA/BIBLIOGRAPHICAL NEWS. LITUANICA. Text in Lithuanian, English. 1951. m. **Document type:** *Bibliography.*
Supersedes in part (in 1995): Bibliografijos Zinios (1392-0308); Which was formerly (until 1992): Letopis' Pecati (0135-1354)
Published by: Martynas Mazvydas National Library of Lithuania, Centre of Bibliography and Book Science, Sv Ignoto 6, Vilnius, 2600, Lithuania. TEL 370-2-629023, FAX 370-2-627129, info@tb.lt, http://www.tb.lt. **Co-publisher:** Ministry of Culture. **Co-sponsor:** Ministry of Culture.

025.3 LTU ISSN 1392-1754
Z6956.L5
BIBLIOGRAFIJOS ZINIOS. SERIALINIAI LEIDINIAI/ BIBLIOGRAPHICAL NEWS. SERIALS; Lietuvos valstybines bibliografijos rodykle. Text in Lithuanian, English. 1949. a. **Document type:** *Bibliography.*
Supersedes in part (in 1995): Bibliografijos Zinios (1392-0308); Which was formerly (until 1992): Letopis' Pecati (0135-1354)
Published by: Martynas Mazvydas National Library of Lithuania, Centre of Bibliography and Book Science, Sv Ignoto 6, Vilnius, 2600, Lithuania. TEL 370-2-629023, FAX 370-2-627129, info@tb.lt, http://www.tb.lt. **Co-publisher:** Ministry of Culture. **Co-sponsor:** Ministry of Culture.

025.3 LTU ISSN 1392-1746
Z2537
BIBLIOGRAFIJOS ZINIOS. STRAIPSNIAI/BIBLIOGRAPHICAL NEWS. ARTICLES; Lietuvos valstybines bibliografijos rodykle. Text in Lithuanian, English. 1949. m. **Document type:** *Bibliography.*
Supersedes in part (in 1995): Bibliografijos Zinios (1392-0308); Which was formerly (until 1992): Letopis' Pecati (0135-1354)
Published by: Martynas Mazvydas National Library of Lithuania, Centre of Bibliography and Book Science, Sv Ignoto 6, Vilnius, 2600, Lithuania. TEL 370-2-629023, FAX 370-2-627129, info@tb.lt, http://www.tb.lt. **Co-publisher:** Ministry of Culture. **Co-sponsor:** Ministry of Culture.

015 RUS ISSN 0869-6020
BIBLIOGRAFIYA. Text in Russian. 1929. bi-m. RUR 330 for 6 mos. domestic; USD 65 for 6 mos. foreign (effective 2004). adv. bk.rev. illus. index. 160 p./no.; back issues avail. **Document type:** *Academic/Scholarly.* **Description:** Contains articles on the history, theory, methods and organization of bibliographies.
Formerly (until 1992): Sovetskaya Bibliografiya (0131-6265)
Media: Large Type. **Related titles:** Online - full text ed.
Indexed: LibLit, RASB, RILM, RefZh.
—East View.
Published by: Rossiiskaya Knizhnaya Palata/Book Chamber International, Ostozhenka 4, Moscow, 119034, Russian Federation. TEL 7-095-2911278, FAX 7-095-2919630, bookch@postman.ru, http://www.bookchamber.ru/international/bibliography_mag.html. adv.: page USD 150. Circ: 3,000.

011 RUS ISSN 0204-3386
Z2491.A1
BIBLIOGRAFIYA ROSSIISKOI BIBLIOGRAFII. Text in Russian. 1941. a. (in 1 vol., 2 nos./vol.), latest 2003. USD 50 per issue foreign (effective 2004). 360 p./no.; back issues avail. **Document type:** *Bibliography.* **Description:** Informs readers about all bibliography materials published in Russia. Includes a number of subsidiary indexes.
Published by: Rossiiskaya Knizhnaya Palata/Book Chamber International, Ostozhenka 4, Moscow, 119034, Russian Federation. TEL 7-095-2911278, FAX 7-095-2919630, bookch@postman.ru, http://www.bookchamber.ru/international/letopis_biblio.html. Ed. E Belaeva. Circ: 1,000.

BIBLIOGRAFSKI VJESNIK. see *HISTORY—Abstracting, Bibliographies, Statistics*

960 015 IND ISSN 0006-1190
BIBLIOGRAPHIA AFRICANA. Text in English. 1970. m. INR 2,200, USD 300 (effective 2000). abstr. index.
Related titles: Microform ed.
Published by: K.K. Roy (Private) Ltd., 55 Gariahat Rd., P O Box 10210, Kolkata, West Bengal 700 019, India. Ed. K K Roy. R&P M Misra TEL 91-33-475-4872. Circ: 2,000.

011 BEL ISSN 0409-3747
BIBLIOGRAPHIA BELGICA. Text in Dutch, English, French. 1952. irreg. **Document type:** *Bibliography.*
—Linda Hall.
Published by: Commission Belge de Bibliographie et de Bibliologie, 4 Bd de l'Empereur, Brussels, 1000, Belgium. FAX 32-80-510465. Ed. Christian F Verbecke. R&P Mireille M Vanlaecken. Circ: 350.

BIBLIOGRAPHIA CARTOGRAPHICA; international documentation of cartographical literature. see *GEOGRAPHY—Abstracting, Bibliographies, Statistics*

BIBLIOGRAPHIA DE INTERLINGUA. see *LINGUISTICS—Abstracting, Bibliographies, Statistics*

BIBLIOGRAPHIA FRANCISCANA. see *RELIGIONS AND THEOLOGY—Abstracting, Bibliographies, Statistics*

BIBLIOGRAPHIA PHYTOSOCIOLOGICA SYNTAXONOMICA. see *BIOLOGY—Abstracting, Bibliographies, Statistics*

BIBLIOGRAPHIC GUIDE TO ANTHROPOLOGY AND ARCHAEOLOGY. see *ANTHROPOLOGY—Abstracting, Bibliographies, Statistics*

BIBLIOGRAPHIC GUIDE TO ART AND ARCHITECTURE. see *ARCHITECTURE—Abstracting, Bibliographies, Statistics*

BIBLIOGRAPHIC GUIDE TO BLACK STUDIES. see *ETHNIC INTERESTS—Abstracting, Bibliographies, Statistics*

011 USA ISSN 0360-2729
Z5051
BIBLIOGRAPHIC GUIDE TO CONFERENCE PUBLICATIONS. Text in Multiple languages. 1974. a. USD 660 (effective 2005). **Document type:** *Bibliography.* **Description:** Indexes approximately 26,000 private and government conference publications, including proceedings, reports, and summaries of conferences, meetings, and symposia in all fields.
Formerly (until 1975): Conference Publications Guide (0091-7907)
Indexed: RASB.
—BLDSC (1964.890000).
Published by: G.K. Hall & Co. (Subsidiary of: Gale Group), 12 Lunar Dr, Woodbridge, CT 06525. TEL 203-397-2600, 800-444-0799, FAX 203-397-8296, http://www.galegroup.com/gkhall. **Subscr. to:** Simon & Schuster, PO Box 7500, Riverside, NJ 08075-8075. TEL 800-223-2336.

BIBLIOGRAPHIC GUIDE TO DANCE. see *DANCE—Abstracting, Bibliographies, Statistics*

BIBLIOGRAPHIC GUIDE TO EAST ASIAN STUDIES. see *ASIAN STUDIES—Abstracting, Bibliographies, Statistics*

BIBLIOGRAPHIC GUIDE TO EDUCATION. see *EDUCATION—Abstracting, Bibliographies, Statistics*

015 USA ISSN 0360-280X
Z7164.G7
BIBLIOGRAPHIC GUIDE TO GOVERNMENT PUBLICATIONS - FOREIGN. Text in English. 1980. a. USD 880 (effective 2005). **Document type:** *Bibliography.* **Description:** Lists materials catalogued during the past year by the New York Public Library, including additional entries from LC MARC tapes.
—BLDSC (1964.893300).
Published by: G.K. Hall & Co. (Subsidiary of: Gale Group), 12 Lunar Dr, Woodbridge, CT 06525. TEL 203-397-2600, 800-444-0799, FAX 203-397-8296, remmel.nunn@gale.com, http://www.galegroup.com/gkhall. **Subscr. to:** Simon & Schuster, PO Box 7500, Riverside, NJ 08075-8075. TEL 800-223-2336.

011 USA ISSN 0360-2796
Z7164.G7
BIBLIOGRAPHIC GUIDE TO GOVERNMENT PUBLICATIONS - U S. Text in Multiple languages. 1982. a. USD 750 (effective 2005). **Document type:** *Bibliography.* **Description:** Covers all state, regional and federal government literature.
Formerly: Government Publications Guide (0091-7915)
Published by: G.K. Hall & Co. (Subsidiary of: Gale Group), 12 Lunar Dr, Woodbridge, CT 06525. TEL 203-397-2600, 800-444-0799, FAX 203-397-8296, remmel.nunn@gale.com, http://www.galegroup.com/gkhall. **Subscr. to:** Simon & Schuster, PO Box 7500, Riverside, NJ 08075-8075. TEL 800-223-2336.

015 USA ISSN 0162-5314
Z1610
BIBLIOGRAPHIC GUIDE TO LATIN AMERICAN STUDIES. Text in English. 1971. a. USD 935 (effective 2005). **Document type:** *Bibliography.* **Description:** Includes 31,000 new acquisitions by the Nettie Lee Benson Latin American Collection in the Texas Library, Austin, and the Library of Congress. Covers all library materials written by Latin American authors, materials published anywhere in the world pertaining to Latin America, and materials in any language, including Indian dialects of Latin America.
Former titles (until 1977): Catalog of the Nettie Lee Benson Latin American Collection. Supplement (0732-2178); (until 1975): Catalog of the Latin American Collection. Supplement (0098-8804)

Published by: G.K. Hall & Co. (Subsidiary of: Gale Group), 12 Lunar Dr, Woodbridge, CT 06525. TEL 203-397-2600, 800-444-0799, FAX 203-397-8296, remmel.nunn@gale.com, http://www.galegroup.com/gkhall. Subscr. to: Simon & Schuster, PO Box 7500, Riverside, NJ 08075-8075. TEL 800-223-2336.

BIBLIOGRAPHIC GUIDE TO LAW. see *LAW—Abstracting, Bibliographies, Statistics*

BIBLIOGRAPHIC GUIDE TO MAPS AND ATLASES. see *GEOGRAPHY—Abstracting, Bibliographies, Statistics*

011   USA   ISSN 0891-3749
Z1033.M5
BIBLIOGRAPHIC GUIDE TO MICROFORM PUBLICATIONS. Text in English. 1986. a. **Document type:** *Bibliography.* **Description:** Covers U.S. and foreign books and non-serial publications; includes fiche and film, monographs, government publications, pamphlets and ephemeral material.
Published by: G.K. Hall & Co. (Subsidiary of: Gale Group), 12 Lunar Dr, Woodbridge, CT 06525. TEL 203-397-2600, 800-444-0799, FAX 203-397-8296, remmel.nunn@gale.com, http://www.galegroup.com/gkhall.

BIBLIOGRAPHIC GUIDE TO MUSIC. see *MUSIC—Abstracting, Bibliographies, Statistics*

BIBLIOGRAPHIC GUIDE TO NORTH AMERICAN HISTORY. see *HISTORY—Abstracting, Bibliographies, Statistics*

BIBLIOGRAPHIC GUIDE TO PSYCHOLOGY. see *PSYCHOLOGY—Abstracting, Bibliographies, Statistics*

BIBLIOGRAPHIC GUIDE TO SLAVIC, BALTIC, AND EURASIAN STUDIES. see *HISTORY—Abstracting, Bibliographies, Statistics*

600 016   USA   ISSN 0360-2761
Z5854
BIBLIOGRAPHIC GUIDE TO TECHNOLOGY. Text in English. 1974. a. USD 660 (effective 2005). **Document type:** *Bibliography.* **Description:** Covers all aspects of technology.
Formerly: Technology Book Guide (0091-7885)
Published by: G.K. Hall & Co. (Subsidiary of: Gale Group), 12 Lunar Dr, Woodbridge, CT 06525. TEL 203-397-2600, 800-444-0799, FAX 203-397-8296, remmel.nunn@gale.com, http://www.galegroup.com/gkhall. Subscr. to: Simon & Schuster, PO Box 7500, Riverside, NJ 08075-8075. TEL 800-223-2336.

BIBLIOGRAPHIC GUIDE TO THE ENVIRONMENT. see *ENVIRONMENTAL STUDIES—Abstracting, Bibliographies, Statistics*

011   USA   ISSN 0006-1255
Z1002
BIBLIOGRAPHIC INDEX; a subject list of bibliographies in English and foreign languages. Text in English. 1937. 4/yr. USD 455 in US & Canada (effective 2006). reprints avail. **Document type:** *Abstract/Index.* **Description:** Lists bibliographies with 50 or more citations published in books, pamphlets, or periodicals.
Related titles: Online - full text ed.: 2003 (Spring). USD 1,100 in US & Canada (effective 2006).
Indexed: RASB.
Published by: H.W. Wilson Co., 950 University Ave, Bronx, NY 10452-4224. TEL 718-588-8400, 800-367-6770, FAX 718-590-1617, 800-590-1617, custserv@hwwilson.com, http://www.hwwilson.com. Ed. Laurel Cooley.

010.92   USA   ISSN 0737-0458
Z1008
BIBLIOGRAPHIC SOCIETY OF AMERICA. LIST OF MEMBERS. Text in English. a. **Document type:** *Directory.*
Published by: Bibliographical Society of America, PO Box 1537, Lenox Hill Sta, New York, NY 10021. bsa@bibsocamer.org, http://www.bibsocamer.org.

BIBLIOGRAPHICA JUDAICA. see *RELIGIONS AND THEOLOGY—Abstracting, Bibliographies, Statistics*

010   CAN   ISSN 0709-3756
BIBLIOGRAPHICAL SOCIETY OF CANADA. BULLETIN. Text in English. 1973. s-a. membership. back issues avail. **Document type:** *Newsletter.* **Description:** Provides news of the Society and its members as well as information about lectures, exhibitions, research and publication.
Related titles: CD-ROM ed.
Published by: Bibliographical Society of Canada/La Societe Bibliographique du Canada, P O Box 575, Sta P, Toronto, ON M5S 2T1, Canada. mcgaughe@yorku.ca, http://www.library.utoronto.ca/bsc. Ed. Patricia Belier. Circ: 400 (controlled).

010   CAN   ISSN 0067-6896
➤ **BIBLIOGRAPHICAL SOCIETY OF CANADA. PAPERS/SOCIETE BIBLIOGRAPHIQUE DU CANADA. CAHIERS.** Text in English, French. 1962. s-a. CND 35 to individuals; CND 50 to institutions (effective 2003). bk.rev. **Document type:** *Academic/Scholarly.* **Description:** Offers scholarly articles and book reviews on all aspects of bibliography and print culture including printing and publishing history and textual studies.
Supersedes: Bibliographical Society of Canada. Newsletter
Related titles: CD-ROM ed.; Online - full text ed.: (from Gale Group).
Indexed: AmH&L, BibInd, CBCARef, CPerI, HistAb, MLA-IB, RI-1, RILM.
Published by: Bibliographical Society of Canada/La Societe Bibliographique du Canada, P O Box 575, Sta P, Toronto, ON M5S 2T1, Canada. mcgaughe@yorku.ca, http://www.library.utoronto.ca/bsc. Ed. Sheila Latham. Circ: 400.

016   ARG
BIBLIOGRAPHICAS; revista de bibliografia y cultura. Text in Spanish. 2001. irreg.
Formerly (until 2002): El Rubi (1515-8462)
Media: Online - full text.
Published by: El Rubi http://www.elrubi.com.ar. Ed. Eduardo Luis Rubi.

015   MDG   ISSN 0067-6926
Z3701
BIBLIOGRAPHIE ANNUELLE DE MADAGASCAR. Text in French. 1964. a. MGF 500, USD 2. index.
Published by: Universite de Madagascar, Bibliotheque Universitaire, BP 908, Antananarivo, Madagascar. Circ: 1,500.

011   CHE   ISSN 1012-1331
BIBLIOGRAPHIE ANNUELLE DES LETTRES ROMANDES. Text in French. 1979. a. CHF 30 (effective 2003). **Document type:** *Bibliography.*
Published by: Schweizerische Landesbibliothek/Bibliotheque Nationale Suisse, Hallwylstr 15, Bern, 3003, Switzerland. TEL 41-31-3228911, FAX 41-31-3228463, marie-therese.lathion@slb.admin.ch, slb-bns@slb.admin.ch, http://www.snl.ch/. Ed. Marie Therese Lathion. Dist. by: Editions de l' Aire, 15 rue de l'Union, Vevey 1800, Switzerland. TEL 41-21-9236836, FAX 41-21-9236823.

BIBLIOGRAPHIE ANNUELLE DU MOYEN AGE TARDIF; auteurs et textes latins, vers 1300-1500. see *HISTORY—Abstracting, Bibliographies, Statistics*

015   BEL   ISSN 0006-1336
Z2405   CODEN: BIBEBJ
BIBLIOGRAPHIE DE BELGIQUE/BELGISCHE BIBLIOGRAFIE. Text in Dutch, French. 1875. m. index. reprints avail. **Document type:** *Bibliography.*
Media: Online - full text. Related titles: CD-ROM ed.
Indexed: RASB.
Published by: Bibliotheque Royale Albert 1er/Koninklijke Bibliotheek Albert I, Bd de l'Empereur 4, Brussels, 1000, Belgium. TEL 32-2-519-5311, FAX 32-2-519-5533, http://www.kbr.be/bb/fr/Bbstr1.htm. Ed. W Vanderpijpen.

015 966   CIV   ISSN 0084-7860
Z3689
BIBLIOGRAPHIE DE LA COTE D'IVOIRE. Text in French. 1969. a. XOF 3,000.
Media: Duplicated (not offset).
Published by: Bibliotheque Nationale, BP V180, Abidjan, Ivory Coast.

BIBLIOGRAPHIE DE LA PHILOSOPHIE/BIBLIOGRAPHY OF PHILOSOPHY. see *PHILOSOPHY—Abstracting, Bibliographies, Statistics*

BIBLIOGRAPHIE DE L'AFRIQUE SUD-SAHARIENNE; sciences humaines et sociales. see *SOCIAL SCIENCES: COMPREHENSIVE WORKS—Abstracting, Bibliographies, Statistics*

011 016   DZA   ISSN 0523-2392
BIBLIOGRAPHIE DE L'ALGERIE/AL-BIBLIYUGRAFYA AL-DJAZAIRIYAH. Text in Arabic, French. 1964. s-a. DZD 40, USD 20. adv. back issues avail. **Document type:** *Bibliography.* **Description:** Lists Algerian publications deposited at the National Library.
Published by: (Service du Depot Legal), Bibliotheque Nationale, 1 Ave Frantz Fanon, Algiers, 16000, Algeria. TEL 63-06-32. Circ: 1,500.

BIBLIOGRAPHIE DER BERNER GESCHICHTE/BIBLIOGRAPHIE DE L'HISTOIRE BERNOISE. see *HISTORY—Abstracting, Bibliographies, Statistics*

BIBLIOGRAPHIE DER BUCH- UND BIBLIOTHEKSGESCHICHTE. see *LIBRARY AND INFORMATION SCIENCES—Abstracting, Bibliographies, Statistics*

BIBLIOGRAPHIE DER DEUTSCHEN SPRACH- UND LITERATURWISSENSCHAFT. see *LITERATURE—Abstracting, Bibliographies, Statistics*

BIBLIOGRAPHIE DER FRANZOESISCHEN LITERATURWISSENSCHAFT. see *LITERATURE—Abstracting, Bibliographies, Statistics*

011 900   CHE   ISSN 0378-4584
Z2786
BIBLIOGRAPHIE DER SCHWEIZERGESCHICHTE/ BIBLIOGRAPHIE DE L'HISTOIRE SUISSE. Text in French, German. 1913. a. CHF 32.65 (effective 2003). reprints avail. **Document type:** *Bibliography.*
Indexed: RASB.
Published by: Schweizerische Landesbibliothek/Bibliotheque Nationale Suisse, Hallwylstr 15, Bern, 3003, Switzerland. TEL 41-31-3228911, FAX 41-31-3228463, pierre.surchat@slb.admin.ch, slb-bns@slb.admin.ch, http://www.snl.ch. Ed. Pierre Louis Surchat.

011   DEU   ISSN 0340-6121
BIBLIOGRAPHIE DER WIRTSCHAFTSWISSENSCHAFTEN. Text in German. 1905. s-a. price varies. reprints avail. **Document type:** *Bibliography.*
Former titles (until 1971): Bibliographie der Sozialwissenschaften (0177-0594); (until 1950): Bibliographie der Staats- und Wirtschaftswissenschaften (0177-0470); (until 1937): Bibliographie der Sozialwissenschaften (0177-0748) —CCC.
Published by: Vandenhoeck und Ruprecht, Robert-Bosch-Breite 6, Goettingen, 37079, Germany. TEL 49-551-508440, FAX 49-551-5084422, info@v-r.de, http://www.vandenhoeck-ruprecht.de.

BIBLIOGRAPHIE DES SCHWEIZERISCHEN RECHTS. see *LAW—Abstracting, Bibliographies, Statistics*

015.7   CAN   ISSN 0006-1441
BIBLIOGRAPHIE DU QUEBEC. Text in French. 1968. m. CND 140 (effective 2002). index. **Document type:** *Bibliography.*
Indexed: RASB.
Published by: Bibliotheque Nationale du Quebec, Section de l'Edition, 2275 rue Holt, Montreal, PQ H2G 3H1, Canada. TEL 514-873-1100, FAX 514-873-9932, publications@biblinat.gouv.qc.ca, http://www.biblinat.gouv.qc.ca. Ed., R&P Suzanne Dubois-Rousseau.

016.966   SEN   ISSN 0378-9942
Z3711
BIBLIOGRAPHIE DU SENEGAL. Text in French. 1962. s-a. per issue exchange basis. Supplement avail. **Document type:** *Bibliography.*
Published by: Secretariat General du Gouvernement, Direction des Archives du Senegal, Immeuble Administratif, Dakar, Senegal. TEL 221-821-70-21, FAX 221-822-55-78, bdas@telecomplus.sn. R&P Nkunku Henriette Tavares.

BIBLIOGRAPHIE GEOGRAPHIQUE INTERNATIONALE (PARIS, 1996). see *GEOGRAPHY—Abstracting, Bibliographies, Statistics*

BIBLIOGRAPHIE LINGUISTISCHER LITERATUR/ BIBLIOGRAPHY OF LINGUISTIC LITERATURE; bibliography of general linguistics and of English, German and Romance linguistics. see *LITERATURE—Abstracting, Bibliographies, Statistics*

949.3 011   LUX   ISSN 0253-1631
BIBLIOGRAPHIE LUXEMBOURGEOISE. Text in French. 1944. a. back issues avail.; reprints avail. **Document type:** *Bibliography.* **Description:** Official current Luxembourg bibliography. Lists publications printed in Luxembourg or concerning Luxembourg and those published by Luxembourgers.
Indexed: RASB.
Published by: Bibliotheque Nationale, 37 Boulevard F.D. Roosevelt, Luxembourg, L-2450, Luxembourg. TEL 352-229755-1, FAX 352-475672, http://www.bibnatlux.etat.lu.

BIBLIOGRAPHIE NATIONALE FRANCAISE. LIVRES. see *PUBLISHING AND BOOK TRADE—Abstracting, Bibliographies, Statistics*

011   FRA   ISSN 1626-0082
BIBLIOGRAPHIE NATIONALE FRANCAISE. LIVRES, PUBLICATIONS EN SERIE ET DOCUMENTS ELECTRONIQUES. Text in French. 1989. bi-m. **Document type:** *Bibliography.*
Formerly (until 1997): Bibliographie Nationale Francaise sur CD-ROM (1284-1757)
Media: CD-ROM (from Chadwyck-Healey Inc.)
Published by: Bibliotheque Nationale de France, Site Francois Mitterand, Quai Francois Mauriac, Paris, 75706, France. TEL 33-1-53795950, FAX 33-1-53795045, produits.bibliographiques@bnf.fr.

BIBLIOGRAPHIE NATIONALE FRANCAISE. MUSIQUE. see *MUSIC—Abstracting, Bibliographies, Statistics*

015   FRA   ISSN 1626-0112
Z2161
BIBLIOGRAPHIE NATIONALE FRANCAISE. PUBLICATIONS EN SERIE. Text in French. 1946. m. index. **Document type:** *Bibliography.*

Former titles (until 2001): Bibliographie Nationale Francaise. Publications en Serie (Print) (1142-3269); until 1990): Bibliographie de la France. Supplement 1. Publications en Serie (0150-1399); (until 1977): Bibliographie de la France. 1ere Partie, Bibliographie Officielle. Supplement 1, Publications en Serie (1147-6869); (until 1975): Bibliographie de la France. Supplement A, Periodiques (1147-6850); Which superseded in part (in 1946): Bibliographie de la France (0006-1344)
Media: Online - full content.
—Linda Hall.
Published by: Bibliotheque Nationale de France, Site Francois Mitterand, Quai Francois Mauriac, Paris, 75706, France. TEL 33-1-53795950, FAX 33-1-53795045, http:// bibliographienationale.bnf.fr/Series/BibNatFraSeries.html. Ed. P A Berend. **Subscr. to:** Mereau, 175 bd. Anatole France, BP 189, Saint-Denis Cedex 93208, France. TEL 33-1-48133858, FAX 33-1-48130908.

BIBLIOGRAPHIE PAPYROLOGIQUE. see *ARCHAEOLOGY— Abstracting, Bibliographies, Statistics*

011   FRA   ISSN 0291-123X
BIBLIOGRAPHIE PROSPECTIVE. Text in French. 1982. m. EUR 200 (effective 2004). **Document type:** *Newsletter, Consumer.*
Related titles: Online - full text ed.
Published by: Futuribles International, 55 rue de Varenne, Paris, 75007, France. TEL 33-1-53633770, FAX 33-1-42226554, forum@futuribles.com, http://www.futuribles.com.

BIBLIOGRAPHIE PSYCHOLOGISCHER LITERATUR AUS DEN DEUTSCHSPRACHIGEN LAENDERN. see *PSYCHOLOGY—Abstracting, Bibliographies, Statistics*

BIBLIOGRAPHIE ZUR GESCHICHTE DER DEUTSCHEN ARBEITERBEWEGUNG. see *BUSINESS AND ECONOMICS—Abstracting, Bibliographies, Statistics*

016.940   DEU   ISSN 0177-3631
BIBLIOGRAPHIEN ZUR GESCHICHTE UND LANDESKUNDE OSTMITTELEUROPAS. Text in German. 1985. irreg., latest vol.31, 2003. price varies. back issues avail. **Document type:** *Monographic series, Bibliography.*
Published by: Herder Institut e.V., Gisonenweg 5-7, Marburg, 35037, Germany. TEL 49-6421-184-0, FAX 49-6421-184139, herder@mailer.uni-marburg.de, http://www.uni-marburg.de/ herder-institut.

BIBLIOGRAPHIEN ZUR PHILOSOPHIE. see *PHILOSOPHY*

BIBLIOGRAPHIES AND INDEXES IN AFRO-AMERICAN AND AFRICAN STUDIES. see *HISTORY—Abstracting, Bibliographies, Statistics*

BIBLIOGRAPHIES AND INDEXES IN AMERICAN HISTORY. see *HISTORY—Abstracting, Bibliographies, Statistics*

BIBLIOGRAPHIES AND INDEXES IN AMERICAN LITERATURE. see *LITERATURE—Abstracting, Bibliographies, Statistics*

BIBLIOGRAPHIES AND INDEXES IN ANTHROPOLOGY. see *ANTHROPOLOGY—Abstracting, Bibliographies, Statistics*

BIBLIOGRAPHIES AND INDEXES IN ECONOMICS AND ECONOMIC HISTORY. see *BUSINESS AND ECONOMICS—Abstracting, Bibliographies, Statistics*

BIBLIOGRAPHIES AND INDEXES IN EDUCATION. see *EDUCATION—Abstracting, Bibliographies, Statistics*

BIBLIOGRAPHIES AND INDEXES IN ETHNIC STUDIES. see *ETHNIC INTERESTS—Abstracting, Bibliographies, Statistics*

BIBLIOGRAPHIES AND INDEXES IN GEOGRAPHY. see *GEOGRAPHY—Abstracting, Bibliographies, Statistics*

BIBLIOGRAPHIES AND INDEXES IN GERONTOLOGY. see *GERONTOLOGY AND GERIATRICS—Abstracting, Bibliographies, Statistics*

BIBLIOGRAPHIES AND INDEXES IN LATIN AMERICAN AND CARIBBEAN STUDIES. see *HISTORY—Abstracting, Bibliographies, Statistics*

BIBLIOGRAPHIES AND INDEXES IN LAW AND POLITICAL SCIENCE. see *POLITICAL SCIENCE—Abstracting, Bibliographies, Statistics*

BIBLIOGRAPHIES AND INDEXES IN LIBRARY AND INFORMATION SCIENCE. see *LIBRARY AND INFORMATION SCIENCES—Abstracting, Bibliographies, Statistics*

BIBLIOGRAPHIES AND INDEXES IN MILITARY STUDIES. see *MILITARY—Abstracting, Bibliographies, Statistics*

BIBLIOGRAPHIES AND INDEXES IN PHILOSOPHY. see *PHILOSOPHY—Abstracting, Bibliographies, Statistics*

BIBLIOGRAPHIES AND INDEXES IN PSYCHOLOGY. see *PSYCHOLOGY—Abstracting, Bibliographies, Statistics*

BIBLIOGRAPHIES AND INDEXES IN RELIGIOUS STUDIES. see *RELIGIONS AND THEOLOGY—Abstracting, Bibliographies, Statistics*

BIBLIOGRAPHIES AND INDEXES IN SCIENCE AND TECHNOLOGY. see *SCIENCES: COMPREHENSIVE WORKS—Abstracting, Bibliographies, Statistics*

BIBLIOGRAPHIES AND INDEXES IN SCIENCE FICTION, FANTASY, AND HORROR. see *LITERATURE—Abstracting, Bibliographies, Statistics*

BIBLIOGRAPHIES AND INDEXES IN SOCIOLOGY. see *SOCIOLOGY—Abstracting, Bibliographies, Statistics*

BIBLIOGRAPHIES AND INDEXES IN THE PERFORMING ARTS. see *THEATER—Abstracting, Bibliographies, Statistics*

BIBLIOGRAPHIES AND INDEXES IN WOMEN'S STUDIES. see *WOMEN'S STUDIES—Abstracting, Bibliographies, Statistics*

BIBLIOGRAPHIES AND INDEXES IN WORLD HISTORY. see *HISTORY—Abstracting, Bibliographies, Statistics*

BIBLIOGRAPHIES AND INDEXES IN WORLD LITERATURE. see *LITERATURE—Abstracting, Bibliographies, Statistics*

016   FRA   ISSN 1160-3283
LES BIBLIOGRAPHIES DU C I R A D. (Centre de Cooperation Internationale en Recherche Agronomique pour le Developpement) Text in French. 1992. irreg. price varies. **Document type:** *Monographic series, Bibliography.*
Indexed: BIOSIS Prev, BioCN&I, FPA, ForAb, HortAb, PHN&I, WAE&RSA.
Published by: C I R A D, Avenue Agropolis, Montpellier, 34398 Cedex 5, France. TEL 33-4-67614417, FAX 33-4-67615547, librairie@cirad.fr, http://www.cirad.fr.

BIBLIOGRAPHIES IN TECHNOLOGY AND SOCIAL CHANGE. see *SOCIOLOGY—Abstracting, Bibliographies, Statistics*

011   USA
BIBLIOGRAPHIES OF AMERICAN NOTABLES. Text in English. 1990. irreg. price varies. **Document type:** *Monographic series, Bibliography.*
Published by: Praeger Publishers (Subsidiary of: Greenwood Publishing Group Inc.), 88 Post Rd W, Box 5007, Westport, CT 06881-5007. TEL 203-226-3571, FAX 203-222-1502.

BIBLIOGRAPHIES OF BATTLES AND LEADERS. see *MILITARY—Abstracting, Bibliographies, Statistics*

BIBLIOGRAPHIES OF BRITISH STATESMEN. see *POLITICAL SCIENCE—Abstracting, Bibliographies, Statistics*

BIBLIOGRAPHIES OF THE PRESIDENTS OF THE UNITED STATES. see *POLITICAL SCIENCE—Abstracting, Bibliographies, Statistics*

BIBLIOGRAPHIES OF WORLD LEADERS. see *POLITICAL SCIENCE—Abstracting, Bibliographies, Statistics*

BIBLIOGRAPHIES ON THE HISTORY OF SCIENCE AND TECHNOLOGY. see *SCIENCES: COMPREHENSIVE WORKS—Abstracting, Bibliographies, Statistics*

BIBLIOGRAPHISCHE INFORMATIONEN ZUR ITALIENISCHEN GESCHICHTE IM 19. UND 20. JAHRHUNDERT. see *HISTORY—Abstracting, Bibliographies, Statistics*

BIBLIOGRAPHY AND INDEX OF GEOLOGY. see *EARTH SCIENCES—Abstracting, Bibliographies, Statistics*

BIBLIOGRAPHY AND INDEX OF MICROPALEONTOLOGY (ONLINE EDITION). see *PALEONTOLOGY—Abstracting, Bibliographies, Statistics*

BIBLIOGRAPHY AND SUBJECT INDEX OF SOUTH AFRICAN GEOLOGY. see *EARTH SCIENCES—Abstracting, Bibliographies, Statistics*

BIBLIOGRAPHY OF ASIAN STUDIES (ONLINE EDITION). see *HISTORY—Abstracting, Bibliographies, Statistics*

BIBLIOGRAPHY OF BIOETHICS. see *MEDICAL SCIENCES—Abstracting, Bibliographies, Statistics*

BIBLIOGRAPHY OF CHINESE STUDIES; selected articles on China in Chinese, English and German. see *ASIAN STUDIES—Abstracting, Bibliographies, Statistics*

BIBLIOGRAPHY OF DOCTORAL DISSERTATIONS: NATURAL AND APPLIED SCIENCES. see *SCIENCES: COMPREHENSIVE WORKS—Abstracting, Bibliographies, Statistics*

BIBLIOGRAPHY OF DOCTORAL DISSERTATIONS: SOCIAL SCIENCES AND HUMANITIES. see *SOCIAL SCIENCES: COMPREHENSIVE WORKS—Abstracting, Bibliographies, Statistics*

BIBLIOGRAPHY OF ECONOMIC AND SOCIAL DEVELOPMENT SRI LANKA. see *BUSINESS AND ECONOMICS— Abstracting, Bibliographies, Statistics*

BIBLIOGRAPHY OF ECONOMIC AND STATISTICAL PUBLICATIONS ON TANZANIA. see *BUSINESS AND ECONOMICS—Abstracting, Bibliographies, Statistics*

BIBLIOGRAPHY OF ECONOMIC GEOLOGY. see *EARTH SCIENCES—Abstracting, Bibliographies, Statistics*

BIBLIOGRAPHY OF EDUCATION THESES IN AUSTRALIA. see *EDUCATION—Abstracting, Bibliographies, Statistics*

BIBLIOGRAPHY OF EUROPEAN PALAEOBOTANY & PALYNOLOGY. see *PALEONTOLOGY—Abstracting, Bibliographies, Statistics*

BIBLIOGRAPHY OF INDIAN WRITING IN ENGLISH SERIES. see *LITERATURE—Abstracting, Bibliographies, Statistics*

BIBLIOGRAPHY OF LATIN AMERICAN AND CARIBBEAN BIBLIOGRAPHIES. see *HISTORY—Abstracting, Bibliographies, Statistics*

BIBLIOGRAPHY OF MATERIALS FATIGUE/ZAIRYO NO HIRO NI KANSURU KENKYU NO SUSEI. see *ENGINEERING— Abstracting, Bibliographies, Statistics*

BIBLIOGRAPHY OF MEDIAEVAL LATIN LEXICOLOGY/ BIBLIOTHECA LEXICOLOGIAE MEDII AEVI. see *LINGUISTICS—Abstracting, Bibliographies, Statistics*

BIBLIOGRAPHY OF MODERN HEBREW LITERATURE IN TRANSLATION. see *LITERATURE—Abstracting, Bibliographies, Statistics*

BIBLIOGRAPHY OF PUBLICATIONS FROM ECONOMIC RESEARCH CENTRES IN INDIA. see *BUSINESS AND ECONOMICS—Abstracting, Bibliographies, Statistics*

BIBLIOGRAPHY OF SYSTEMATIC MYCOLOGY. see *BIOLOGY—Abstracting, Bibliographies, Statistics*

BIBLIOGRAPHY OF THE GEOLOGY OF FIJI. see *EARTH SCIENCES—Abstracting, Bibliographies, Statistics*

BIBLIOGRAPHY OF THE GEOLOGY OF MISSOURI. see *EARTH SCIENCES—Abstracting, Bibliographies, Statistics*

BIBLIOGRAPHY OF THE HISTORY OF ART. see *ART—Abstracting, Bibliographies, Statistics*

BIBLIOGRAPHY OF THE HISTORY OF MEDICINE. see *MEDICAL SCIENCES—Abstracting, Bibliographies, Statistics*

BIBLIOGRAPHY OF THE MIDDLE EAST. see *HISTORY—Abstracting, Bibliographies, Statistics*

015   GBR   ISSN 0968-0748
Z2071
BIBLIOGRAPHY OF WALES. Key Title: Llyfryddriaeth Cymru. Text in English. 1909. irreg. (approx. biennial), latest 1997, for 1993. GBP 40. index. reprints avail. **Document type:** *Bibliography.*
Formed by the 1992 merger of: Bibliotheca Celtica (0067-7914); (1978-199?): Subject Index to Welsh Periodicals (0140-265X)
Indexed: BrArAb.
Published by: National Library of Wales/Llyfrgell Genedlaethol Cymru, National Library Of Wales, Penglais, Aberystwyth, Ceredigion, Wales SY23 3BU, United Kingdom. FAX 44-1970-615709, holi@llgc.org.uk, http://www.llgc.org.uk. R&P Mari Wyn. Circ: 450.

BIBLIOGRAPHY ON CABLE TELEVISION. see *COMMUNICATIONS—Abstracting, Bibliographies, Statistics*

BIBLIOGRAPHY ON COLD REGIONS SCIENCE & TECHNOLOGY. see *ENGINEERING—Abstracting, Bibliographies, Statistics*

BIBLIOGRAPHY ON IRRIGATION, DRAINAGE, RIVER TRAINING AND FLOOD CONTROL/BIBLIOGRAPHIE DE LA C I I D. IRRIGATION, DRAINAGE ET MAITRISE DES CRUES. see *WATER RESOURCES—Abstracting, Bibliographies, Statistics*

BIBLIOGRAPHY ON SMOKING AND HEALTH. see *PHYSICAL FITNESS AND HYGIENE—Abstracting, Bibliographies, Statistics*

BIBLIOGRAPHY ON SOILLESS CULTURE. see *AGRICULTURE—Abstracting, Bibliographies, Statistics*

BIBLIOMEDICA (CD-ROM EDITION). see *MEDICAL SCIENCES—Abstracting, Bibliographies, Statistics*

BIBLIONEWS AND AUSTRALIAN NOTES AND QUERIES; journal for book collectors. see *PUBLISHING AND BOOK TRADE*

011   USA   ISSN 0148-9011
BIBLIOSCAN H-L∗. Text in English. 1975. m. USD 70.
Published by: Elsim Co., c/o Chivers, 89 Turner St, Ste 1, Brighton, MA 02135-2525.

011   USA   ISSN 0148-8996
BIBLIOSCAN Q-Z∗. Text in English. 1974. m. USD 70.
Published by: Elsim Co., c/o Chivers, 89 Turner St, Ste 1, Brighton, MA 02135-2525.

BIBLIOTECA AMADEU AMARAL. SERIE REFERENCIA. see *FOLKLORE—Abstracting, Bibliographies, Statistics*

015   ITA   ISSN 0067-7418
BIBLIOTECA DI BIBLIOGRAFIA ITALIANA. Text in Italian. 1923. irreg., latest vol.168, 2001. price varies. **Document type:** *Monographic series.*
Indexed: CCMJ.
Published by: Casa Editrice Leo S. Olschki, Viuzzo del Pozzetto 8, Florence, 50126, Italy. TEL 39-055-6530684, FAX 39-055-6530214, celso@olschki.it, http://www.olschki.it. Circ: 1,000.

020 011   URY   ISSN 0006-1697
F2781.A2
BIBLIOTECA "JOSE ARTIGAS". BOLETIN - JUNTA DE VECINOS. Text in Spanish. 1969. q. free. abstr.; bibl. **Document type:** *Bulletin.*
Formerly (until 1974): Junta Departamental de Montevideo. Boletin (0797-1745)
Media: Duplicated (not offset).
Published by: Biblioteca "Jose Artigas", Veinticinco De Mayo, 609, Montevideo, 11004, Uruguay. Circ: 300 (controlled).

011   BRA   ISSN 0104-0863
BIBLIOTECA MARIO DE ANDRADE. REVISTA. Variant title: Sao Paulo. Biblioteca Mario de Andrade. Revista. Text in Portuguese. 1943. a. free. bk.rev. illus. **Document type:** *Government.* **Description:** Provides information focusing on the Brazilian culture in the field of literature and arts. Points out the cultural changes of Sao Paulo city thoughout the years.
Formerly (until vol.49, 1988): Biblioteca Mario de Andrade. Boletim Bibliografico (0100-4948)
Published by: Sao Paulo. Departamento de Bibliotecas Publicas, Divisao de Documentacao e Comunicacao, c/o Heloisa Guiotti Amendola, Rua Frei Caneca, 1402 Andar 7, Consolacao, Sao Paulo, SP 01307-002, Brazil. TEL 55-11-2532331 ext. 271, FAX 55-11-2894645, bp@prodam.pmsp.sp.gov.br, http://www.prodam.sp.gov.br/bib/bp. Circ: 3,000.

015   BRA   ISSN 0102-3144
BIBLIOTECA NACIONAL. BIBLIOGRAFIA BRASILEIRA. Text in Portuguese. 1918. m. BRL 10, USD 4.50. bibl.; illus.; stat.
Formerly (until 1983): Biblioteca Nacional. Boletim Bibliografico (0100-1876); Which incorporated (1967-1982): Bibliografia Brasileira Mensal (0006-0976)
Related titles: Microfiche ed.; Online - full text ed.
Published by: Biblioteca Nacional, Av Rio Branco, 219, Centro, Rio De Janeiro, RJ 20040008, Brazil. Ed. Aureo Ottoni.

015   PER
BIBLIOTECA NACIONAL DE PERU. BIBLIOGRAFIA PERUANA. Text in Spanish. 1943. a., latest 2000. PEN 50 domestic; USD 45 foreign (effective 2003). bk.rev. bibl. 300 p./no.; **Document type:** *Catalog, Bibliography.* **Description:** Peruvian bibliographic compilation.
Formerly (until 1976): Biblioteca Nacional de Peru. Anuario Bibliografico Peruano
Published by: Biblioteca Nacional del Peru, Ave. Abancay 4ta. Cuadra, Lima, 01, Peru. TEL 51-14-287690, FAX 51-14-277331, dn@binape.gob.pe, http://www.binape.gob.pe. Ed. Carmen Ochoa de Di Franco. R&P Sinesio Lopez Jimenez. Circ: 300.

015   ROM   ISSN 1453-8008
Z2923
BIBLIOTECA NATIONALA A ROMANIEI. BIBLIOGRAFIA CARTILOR IN CURS DE APARITIE. Variant title: C I P. Text in Romanian. 1997. m. ROL 480,000 (effective 2003). 200 p./no.; back issues avail. **Document type:** *Bibliography.* **Description:** Contains the titles of books that appear every month. Includes title, author, subject, and publisher indexes.
Related titles: CD-ROM ed.
Published by: Biblioteca Nationala a Romaniei, Str. Ion Ghica 4, Sector 3, Bucharest, 79708, Romania. TEL 40-21-3157063, FAX 40-21-3123381, go@bibnat.ro, http://www.bibnat.ro. Ed. Laura Margarit.

011   ITA
BIBLIOTECA STATALE E LIBRERIA CIVICA DI CREMONA. MOSTRE. Text in Italian. 1978. irreg., latest vol.19, 1996. per issue exchange basis. **Description:** Covers historical biographies of various artists.

Published by: Biblioteca Statale di Cremona, Via Ugolani Dati, 4, Cremona, CR 26100, Italy. Ed. Emilia Brichi Piccioni. Circ: 1,780.

011   ITA
BIBLIOTECA STATALE. FONTI E SUSSIDI. Text in Italian. 1979. irreg., latest vol.4, 1992. price varies. **Document type:** *Monographic series.* **Description:** Lists bibliographic resources available at the Library.
Published by: Biblioteca Statale di Cremona, Via Ugolani Dati, 4, Cremona, CR 26100, Italy. Ed. Emilia Bricchi Piccioni.

010   ITA   ISSN 0067-7531
BIBLIOTECONOMIA E BIBLIOGRAFIA. SAGGI E STUDI. Text in Italian. 1964. irreg., latest vol.28, 1999. price varies. **Document type:** *Bibliography.*
Published by: Casa Editrice Leo S. Olschki, Viuzzo del Pozzetto 8, Florence, 50126, Italy. TEL 39-055-6530684, FAX 39-055-6530214, celso@olschki.it, http://www.olschki.it. Ed. Piero Innocenti. Circ: 1,000.

BIBLIOTEKA CHEMII. see *CHEMISTRY—Abstracting, Bibliographies, Statistics*

011   SCG   ISSN 0354-7655
BIBLIOTEKA MATICE SRPSKE. BILTEN PRINOVLJENIH KNJIGA NA STRANIM JEZICIMA. Text in Serbo-Croatian. 1986. s-a. **Document type:** *Bulletin.*
Formerly (until 1995): Biblioteka Matice Srpske. Bilten Prinovljenih Stranih Knjiga (0354-5717)
Published by: Biblioteka Matica Srpska, Matice Srpske 1, Novi Sad, 21000. TEL 381-21-25859, FAX 381-21-28574, bms@bms.ns.ac.yu. Ed. Miro Vuksanovic. R&P Dorde Vilovski TEL 381-21-420199.

BIBLIOTHECA ASCETICO-MYSTICA. see *RELIGIONS AND THEOLOGY—Abstracting, Bibliographies, Statistics*

016   DEU   ISSN 0067-7884
BIBLIOTHECA BIBLIOGRAPHICA AURELIANA. Text in English, French, German, Latin. 1959. irreg., latest vol.200, 2003. price varies. index. back issues avail. **Document type:** *Monographic series, Academic/Scholarly.* **Description:** Bibliographies and monographs dealing with Renaissance, humanism and Reformation studies.
Related titles: ◆ Series: Bibliotheca Dissidentium. ISSN 0931-3346.
Published by: Verlag Valentin Koerner GmbH, Postfach 100164, Baden-Baden, 76482, Germany. TEL 49-7221-22423, FAX 49-7221-38697, valentin.koerner@t-online.de, http://www.koernerverlag.de.

011   NLD   ISSN 1570-2162
BIBLIOTHECA BIBLIOGRAPHICA NEERLANDICA. Text in Dutch. 1968. irreg., latest vol.37, 2000. price varies. **Document type:** *Monographic series, Bibliography.*
Indexed: MLA-IB.
Published by: Hes & De Graaf Publishers BV, Tuurzdijk 16, 't Goy-Houten, 3997 MS, Netherlands. TEL 31-30-6011955, FAX 31-30-6011813, info@hesdegraaf.com, http://www.forum-hes.nl. Ed. B Hesselink.

011 273   DEU   ISSN 0931-3346
➤ **BIBLIOTHECA DISSIDENTIUM.** Text in English, French, German, Italian. 1980. irreg., latest vol.22, 2003. price varies. bibl. back issues avail. **Document type:** *Monographic series, Academic/Scholarly.* **Description:** Bibliographies and monographs of 16th and 17th century religious dissidents.
Related titles: ◆ Series of: Bibliotheca Bibliographica Aureliana. ISSN 0067-7884.
Published by: Verlag Valentin Koerner GmbH, Postfach 100164, Baden-Baden, 76482, Germany. TEL 49-7221-22423, FAX 49-7221-38697, valentin.koerner@t-online.de, http://www.koernerverlag.de. Circ: 1,000.

011   GBR   ISSN 0006-193X
THE BIBLIOTHECK; a Scottish journal of bibliography and allied topics. Text in English. 1956. 3/yr. adv. bk.rev. bibl. cum.index: 1956-1970.
Indexed: AES, BibInd, IBR, LIFT, MLA, MLA-IB, PCI, RILM.—BLDSC (2019.680000).
Published by: Library Association, Scottish Group, George IV Bridge, Edinburgh, Midlothian, Scotland EH1 1EW, United Kingdom. Ed. W Kelly. Circ: 300.

011   DEU
BIBLIOTHEK SELTENER TEXTE. Text in German. irreg., latest vol.10, 2003. price varies. **Document type:** *Monographic series, Bibliography.* **Description:** Publishes bibliographies of rare books and texts.
Published by: Weidler Buchverlag Berlin, Luebecker Str 8, Berlin, 10559, Germany. TEL 49-30-3948668, FAX 49-30-3948698, weidler_verlag@yahoo.de, http://www.weidler-verlag.de. Ed. Hans-Gert Roloff.

960 016   BEL   ISSN 0774-8353
BIBLIOTHEQUE AFRICAINE. LISTE DES ACQUISITIONS. Text in French. 1983. q. free. **Document type:** *Bibliography.* **Description:** Lists recent acquisitions in the field of African studies.
Related titles: Online - full text ed.

Published by: Bibliotheque Africaine, Rue des Petits Carmes 19, Brussels, 1000, Belgium. TEL 32-2-5013544, FAX 32-2-5013669, TELEX 25731. Circ: 1,000.

011   COD
BIBLIOTHEQUE NATIONALE. BIBLIOGRAPHIE NATIONALE. Text in French. 1971. irreg., latest 1975.
Published by: Bibliotheque Nationale, BP 3090, Kinshasa-Gombe, Congo, Dem. Republic.

011   FRA   ISSN 0989-635X
BIBLIOTHEQUE NATIONALE DE FRANCE. AUTORITES COLLECTIVITES. Text in French. 1989. s-a.
Media: Microfiche.
Published by: Bibliotheque Nationale de France, Site Francois Mitterand, Quai Francois Mauriac, Paris, 75706, France. TEL 33-1-53798625, FAX 33-1-53798150, produits.bibliographiques@bnf.fr. **Subscr. to:** c/o Service Commercial, 2 rue Vivienne, Paris Cedex 2 75084, France. TEL 33-1-47038173, FAX 33-1-47038172.

011   FRA   ISSN 1140-5570
BIBLIOTHEQUE NATIONALE DE FRANCE. AUTORITES PERSONNES PHYSIQUES. Text in French. 1991. s-a. **Document type:** *Bibliography.*
Media: Microfiche.
Published by: Bibliotheque Nationale de France, Site Francois Mitterand, Quai Francois Mauriac, Paris, 75706, France. TEL 33-1-53798625, FAX 33-1-53798150, produits.bibliographiques@bnf.fr. **Subscr. to:** c/o Service Commercial, 2 rue Vivienne, Paris Cedex 2 75084, France. TEL 33-1-47038173, FAX 33-1-47038172.

011   FRA   ISSN 1140-5589
BIBLIOTHEQUE NATIONALE DE FRANCE. AUTORITES TITRES UNIFORMES. Text in French. 1991. s-a. **Document type:** *Bibliography.*
Media: Microfiche.
Published by: Bibliotheque Nationale de France, Site Francois Mitterand, Quai Francois Mauriac, Paris, 75706, France. TEL 33-1-53798625, FAX 33-1-53798150, produits.bibliographiques@bnf.fr. **Subscr. to:** c/o Service Commercial, 2 rue Vivienne, Paris Cedex 2 75084, France. TEL 33-1-47038173, FAX 33-1-47038172.

015   BOL
BIO BIBLIOGRAFIA BOLIVIANA. Text in Spanish. 1962. a. USD 170 (effective 2000). adv. bk.rev. index. back issues avail. **Document type:** *Monographic series, Bibliography.*
Formerly: Bibliografia Boliviana (0067-6578)
Published by: Los Amigos del Libro, Casilla 450, Cochabamba, Bolivia. TEL 591-42-504150, FAX 591-411-5128, gutten@amigol.bo.net. Ed., R&P Werner Guttentag. Circ: 500.

BIO-BIBLIOGRAPHIES IN AFRO-AMERICAN AND AFRICAN STUDIES. see *ETHNIC INTERESTS—Abstracting, Bibliographies, Statistics*

BIO-BIBLIOGRAPHIES IN AMERICAN LITERATURE. see *LITERATURE—Abstracting, Bibliographies, Statistics*

BIO-BIBLIOGRAPHIES IN ART AND ARCHITECTURE. see *ART—Abstracting, Bibliographies, Statistics*

BIO-BIBLIOGRAPHIES IN ECONOMICS. see *BUSINESS AND ECONOMICS—Abstracting, Bibliographies, Statistics*

BIO-BIBLIOGRAPHIES IN EDUCATION. see *EDUCATION—Abstracting, Bibliographies, Statistics*

BIO-BIBLIOGRAPHIES IN LAW AND POLITICAL SCIENCE. see *LAW—Abstracting, Bibliographies, Statistics*

BIO-BIBLIOGRAPHIES IN MUSIC. see *MUSIC—Abstracting, Bibliographies, Statistics*

BIO-BIBLIOGRAPHIES IN SOCIOLOGY. see *SOCIOLOGY—Abstracting, Bibliographies, Statistics*

BIO-BIBLIOGRAPHIES IN THE PERFORMING ARTS. see *THEATER—Abstracting, Bibliographies, Statistics*

BIO-BIBLIOGRAPHIES IN WORLD LITERATURE. see *LITERATURE—Abstracting, Bibliographies, Statistics*

BIOBIBLIOGRAPHIES ET EXPOSES. see *LINGUISTICS—Abstracting, Bibliographies, Statistics*

BIULETIN ZA NOVONABAVENI KNIGI NA CHUZHDI EZITZI. SERIYA B: ESTESTVENI I PRILOZHNI NAUKI. MEDIZINA. TEKHNIKA. SELSKO STOPANSTVO. see *BIOLOGY—Abstracting, Bibliographies, Statistics*

BIULETIN ZA NOVONABAVENI KNIGI NA CHUZHDI EZTIZI. SERIIA A: OBSHTESTVENI I HUMANITARNI NAUKI. see *SOCIAL SCIENCES: COMPREHENSIVE WORKS—Abstracting, Bibliographies, Statistics*

B

▼ *new title*   ➤ *refereed*   ∗ *unverified*   ◆ *full entry avail.*

B

011 ARG
BOLETIN BIBLIOGRAFICO. Text in Spanish. 1985. q. back issues avail.
Related titles: Online - full text ed.
Published by: Fundacion Bariloche, Casilla de Correos 138, San Carlos de Bariloche, Rio Negro 8400, Argentina. TEL 54-2944-422050, FAX 54-2944-462550, fb@bariloche.com.ar, http://www.bariloche.com.ar/fb.

011 BOL ISSN 0006-6141
BOLETIN BIBLIOGRAFICO BOLIVIANO✶. Text in Spanish; Summaries in English, Spanish. 1955. m. BOB 80, USD 10. adv. bk.rev. bibl.; mkt. index.
Address: Dept. 3F, Ave. Manco Kapac, 269, La Paz, 30, Bolivia. Ed. Antonio Paredes Candia. Circ: 500.

010 ARG ISSN 0328-1701
Z1634.N67
BOLETIN BIBLIOGRAFICO I I G H I. Text in Spanish. 1993. irreg. price varies. **Document type:** *Catalog.* **Description:** Highlights information found in the database of IIGHI Library Catalog;especially that which refers to Northeast Argentina, Paraguay and South Brazil.
Related titles: Diskette ed.; Online - full text ed.
Published by: Consejo Nacional de Investigaciones Cientificas y Tecnicas, Instituto de Investigaciones Geohistoricas, Av Castelli 930, Casilla de Correos 438, Resistencia, Chaco 3500, Argentina. TEL 54-3722-476727, FAX 54-3722-473314, iighi@bib.unne.edu.ar, http://www.conicet.gov.ar/webue/iighi/. Ed. Norma C Meichtry. Circ: 200 (free).

015 COL ISSN 0121-2400
BOLETIN BIBLIOGRAFICO I S B N. (International Standard Book Number) Text in Spanish. 1989. s-a. free. **Document type:** *Bibliography.* **Description:** Lists Colombian books registered under their ISBN system.
Published by: Camara Colombiana del Libro, Carrera 17A No. 37-27, Bogota, CUND, Colombia. TEL 57-1-288-6188, FAX 57-1-287-3320. Ed. Miguel Laverde Espejo.

BOLETIN BIBLIOGRAFICO MEXICANO. see *PUBLISHING AND BOOK TRADE—Abstracting, Bibliographies, Statistics*

011 ITA ISSN 0006-6680
BOLLETTINO DELLE ACCESSIONI DI PERIODICI E LIBRI✶. Text in Italian. 1959. s-a. USD 4 to non-members. bk.rev. bibl.; charts; stat.
Published by: Vilmy Ricerche, Via C Cavour, 24, Casalgrande, RE 42013, Italy. Ed. Mirko A Montanari. Circ: 2,450.

BOOKPLATE JOURNAL. see *PUBLISHING AND BOOK TRADE*

BOOKS ABOUT SINGAPORE; a select bibliography. see *TRAVEL AND TOURISM—Abstracting, Bibliographies, Statistics*

011 USA ISSN 0951-838X
Z7164.C81 CODEN: BPONER
BOOKS & PERIODICALS ONLINE. Text in English. 1987. a. USD 399 (effective 2004). **Document type:** *Directory, Bibliography.* **Description:** Lists 106,000 newspapers, periodicals, wire services, newsletters and reference works available online.
Incorporates (1985-1991): Directory of Periodicals Online - Law and Business (0884-089X); (1989-1994): Directory of Periodicals Online - Science and Technology (0884-0911); (in 1991): Directory of Periodicals Online - Medical and Humanities
Published by: Library Technology Alliance, Ltd., 264 Lexington Ave 4C, New York, NY 10016-4182. TEL 212-686-8816, FAX 212-686-8778, info@booksandperiodicals.com, http://www.booksandperiodicals.com. Ed., Pub., R&P Nuchine Nobari. Circ: 1,050.

011 USA ISSN 0147-0787
Z733.P958
BOOKS AT BROWN. Text in English. 1938. a. USD 10.
Indexed: MLA, MLA-IB, PCI.
Published by: Brown University Library, Friends of the Library, PO Box A, Providence, RI 02912. TEL 401-863-2146. Ed. John Stanley. Circ: 400.

BOOKS FROM FINLAND. see *PUBLISHING AND BOOK TRADE—Abstracting, Bibliographies, Statistics*

BOOKS FROM KOREA. see *PUBLISHING AND BOOK TRADE—Abstracting, Bibliographies, Statistics*

010 PAK ISSN 0068-0206
BOOKS FROM PAKISTAN. Text in English. 1967. a. PKR 15.
Formerly: English Language Publications from Pakistan
Published by: National Book Council of Pakistan, Theosophical Hall, M.A. Jinnah Rd., Karachi, Pakistan.

015.942 GBR ISSN 0045-2572
BOOKS IN ENGLISH; a bibliography compiled from UK and US MARC sources. Text in English. 1970. bi-m. GBP 615 domestic to institutions; GBP 770 foreign to institutions (effective 2002). cum.index: 1971-1980, 1981-1992. **Document type:** *Bibliography.* **Description:** Author/title listing of English-language books published worldwide.
Media: Microfiche.
—BLDSC (2250.180000).
Published by: British Library, National Bibliographic Service, c/o Mike Marcus, Boston Spa, Wetherby, W Yorks LS23 7BQ, United Kingdom. TEL 44-1937-546585, FAX 44-1937-546586, http://www.bl.uk/services. Circ: 200. **Subscr. to:** Extenza - Turpin, Pegasus Dr, Stratton Business Park, Biggleswade, Beds SG18 8TQ, United Kingdom. TEL 44-1462-672555, FAX 44-1462-480-947.

015 USA ISSN 0068-0214
Z1215
BOOKS IN PRINT. Text in English. 1947. a. (in 8 vols.). USD 799 (effective 2005). **Document type:** *Directory, Bibliography.* **Description:** Lists all currently published books, some 1.7 million, with price, ISBN and publisher information under 65,000 U.S. Library of Congress subject headings.
Related titles: ◆ CD-ROM ed.: Books in Print on Disc; Magnetic Tape ed.; ◆ Online - full text ed.: Booksinprint.com; ◆ Supplement(s): Forthcoming Books. ISSN 0015-8119; ◆ Books in Print Supplement. ISSN 0000-0310.
Indexed: RASB.
—BLDSC (2250.210000), CISTI, Linda Hall.
Published by: R.R. Bowker LLC (Subsidiary of: Cambridge Information Group), 630 Central Ave., New Providence, NJ 07974. TEL 908-286-1090, 800-526-9537, FAX 908-219-0098, info@bowker.com, http://www.booksinprint.com, http://www.bowker.com. Ed. Andrew Grabois. **Subscr. to:** Order Dept., PO Box 32, New Providence, NJ 07974-9903. TEL 800-521-8110.

011 USA
Z1215
BOOKS IN PRINT ON DISC. Text in English. 1986. m. USD 1,925 single user (effective 2005). **Document type:** *Directory, Bibliography.* **Description:** Includes 1.6 million active records from Books in Print, Bowker's Video Directory and Words on Cassette.
Formerly (until Dec. 1997): Books in Print Plus (1062-5100)
Media: CD-ROM (from R.R. Bowker LLC). **Related titles:** Magnetic Tape ed.; ◆ Online - full text ed.: Booksinprint.com; ◆ Print ed.: Books in Print. ISSN 0068-0214; International ed.: Books in Print on Disc, Canadian Edition. USD 1,995 single user (effective 2005).
—BLDSC (2250.210100).
Published by: R.R. Bowker LLC (Subsidiary of: Cambridge Information Group), 630 Central Ave., New Providence, NJ 07974. TEL 908-286-1090, 800-526-9537, FAX 908-219-0098, info@bowker.com, http://www.bowker.com. Pub. Marin Mixon.

015 USA ISSN 0000-0310
Z1215
BOOKS IN PRINT SUPPLEMENT; a mid-year updating service listing new and forthcoming books, price changes, and out-of-print titles. Text in English. 1973. a. (in 3 vols.). USD 425 3 vol. set. **Document type:** *Directory, Bibliography.* **Description:** Covers the six months since publication of current Books in Print volumes. Includes publisher address and phone number changes.
Related titles: Magnetic Tape ed.; Microfiche ed.; ◆ Supplement to: Books in Print. ISSN 0068-0214.
—CISTI.
Published by: R.R. Bowker LLC (Subsidiary of: Cambridge Information Group), 630 Central Ave., New Providence, NJ 07974. TEL 908-286-1090, 800-526-9537, FAX 908-219-0098, info@bowker.com, http://www.booksinprint.com, http://www.bowker.com. **Subscr. to:** Order Dept., PO Box 32, New Providence, NJ 07974-9903. TEL 800-521-8110.

011 USA ISSN 1542-7218
Z1215
BOOKS IN PRINT WITH BOOK REVIEWS ON DISC. Text in English. 1987. m. USD 2,495 single user (effective 2005). **Document type:** *Directory, Bibliography.* **Description:** Contains active and out-of-print records from Books In Print, Bowker's Video Directory and Words on cassette, with more than 300,000, full-text book reviews from Library Journal, Publishers Weekly, School Library Journal, Choice, Booklist, Reference and Research Book News, Sci-Tech Book News, University Press Book Mews, Kirkus Reviews, Voya, and BIOSIS.
Formerly (until Dec. 1997): Books in Print with Book Reviews Plus
Media: CD-ROM (from R.R. Bowker LLC, SilverPlatter Information, Inc.). **Related titles:** Online - full text ed.: Booksinprint.com with Book Reviews. USD 2,550 to individuals single user; USD 5,195 to institutions 5 users (effective 2005); International ed.: Books in Print with Book Reviews on Disc, Canadian Edition. USD 2,600 single user (effective 2005).
Published by: R.R. Bowker LLC (Subsidiary of: Cambridge Information Group), 630 Central Ave., New Providence, NJ 07974. TEL 908-286-1090, 800-526-9537, FAX 908-219-0098, info@bowker.com, http://www.bowker.com.

BOOKS IN SPANISH/LIBROS EN ESPANOL; braille and talking books. see *HANDICAPPED—Abstracting, Bibliographies, Statistics*

011 JPN ISSN 1347-7684
▼ **BOOKS ON JAPAN.** Text in English. 2003. q. **Document type:** *Directory, Academic/Scholarly.*
Media: Online - full content.
Published by: National Diet Library/Kokuritsu Kokkai Toshokan, Reference & Special Collections Department, 1-10-1 Nagata-cho, Chiyoda-ku, Tokyo, 100-0014, Japan. TEL 81-3-35812331, webmaster@ndl.go.jp, http://www.ndl.go.jp/en/publication/books_on_japan/boj_top_E.html.

016 USA ISSN 0000-1805
ZA4750
BOOKS OUT LOUD; Bowker's guide to audiobooks. Variant title: Books on Tape. Text in English. 1985. a. (in 2 vols.). USD 255 (effective 2004). **Document type:** *Directory, Bibliography.* **Description:** Covers more than 85,500 audiocassettes, and features more than 12,000 new releases, with title, authors-readers-performers, and producer-distributor indexes.
Formerly (until 2003): Words on Cassette (Year) (0000-1791); Which incorporated (1989-1992): On Cassette (0000-1260); (1984-1992): Words on Tape (8755-3759)
Related titles: CD-ROM ed.; Magnetic Tape ed.
Published by: R.R. Bowker LLC (Subsidiary of: Cambridge Information Group), 630 Central Ave., New Providence, NJ 07974. TEL 908-286-1090, 800-526-9537, FAX 908-219-0098, info@bowker.com, http://www.bowker.com. **Subscr. to:** Order Dept., PO Box 32, New Providence, NJ 07974-9903. TEL 800-521-8110.

011 USA
Z1000.5
BOOKS OUT-OF-PRINT ONLINE. Text in English. 1999. irreg. USD 875 (effective 2005). **Document type:** *Directory, Bibliography.* **Description:** Lists more than 680,000 titles declared out-of-print or out-of-stock.
Media: Online - full content.
Published by: R.R. Bowker LLC (Subsidiary of: Cambridge Information Group), 630 Central Ave., New Providence, NJ 07974. TEL 908-286-1090, 800-526-9537, FAX 908-219-0098, info@bowker.com, http://www.bowker.com. **Subscr. to:** Order Dept., PO Box 32, New Providence, NJ 07974-9903. TEL 800-521-8110.

015 USA
BOOKSINPRINT.COM. Text in English. 1999. m. USD 2,075 to individuals single user; USD 3,875 to institutions 5 users (effective 2005). **Document type:** *Directory, Bibliography.* **Description:** Lists all currently published books, some 1.7 million, with price, ISBN, and bibliographic information under 65,000 U.S. Library of Congress headings.
Media: Online - full text. **Related titles:** ◆ CD-ROM ed.: Books in Print on Disc; Magnetic Tape ed.; ◆ Print ed.: Books in Print. ISSN 0068-0214; International ed.: Bowker's Spanishbooksinprint.com. 2003. USD 595 academic libraries; USD 950 public libraries; USD 850 corporate libraries (effective 2005).
Published by: R.R. Bowker LLC (Subsidiary of: Cambridge Information Group), 630 Central Ave., New Providence, NJ 07974. TEL 908-286-1090, 800-526-9537, FAX 908-219-0098, info@bowker.com, http://www.booksinprint.com, http://www.bowker.com.

011 USA ISSN 0896-4521
THE BOOKWATCH. Text in English. 1981. m. USD 12 (effective 2005). adv. bk.rev. back issues avail. **Document type:** *Newsletter, Trade.* **Description:** Contains reviews of quality books from large and small presses throughout the United States, targeted toward acquisitions librarians and subscribers.
Formerly: Midwest Bookwatch
Related titles: Online - full text ed.: (from Gale Group).
Indexed: BRI, CBRI.
Published by: Midwest Book Review, 278 Orchard Dr, Oregon, WI 53575. TEL 608-835-7937, mbr@execpc.com, mwbookrevw@aol.com, http://www.midwestbookreview.com. Eds. Diane C Donovan, James A. Cox. Circ: 50,000.

BORCLAR - TICARET VE BANKA HUKUKU BIBLIYOGRAFYASI. see *LAW—Abstracting, Bibliographies, Statistics*

BOTSWANA. GEOLOGICAL SURVEY DEPARTMENT. ANNOTATED BIBLIOGRAPHY AND INDEX OF THE GEOLOGY OF BOTSWANA. see *EARTH SCIENCES—Abstracting, Bibliographies, Statistics*

011 USA ISSN 0000-1775
Z1219
▼ **THE BOWKER BUYER'S GUIDE.** Text in English. 2003. s-a. free (effective 2003). adv. **Description:** A 4-color collection of upcoming titles including cover images, annotations, and advertising; arranged by subject, and alphabetical by publisher within each subject.
Published by: R.R. Bowker LLC (Subsidiary of: Cambridge Information Group), 630 Central Ave., New Providence, NJ 07974. TEL 908-286-1090, 800-526-9537, FAX 908-219-0098, info@bowker.com, http://www.bowker.com. adv.: page USD 2,100; trim 7.5 x 10. Circ: 10,000. **Subscr. to:** Order Dept., PO Box 32, New Providence, NJ 07974-9903. TEL 800-521-8110.

015 USA
BOWKER'S GLOBAL BOOKS IN PRINT. Text in English. d. USD 2,895 to individuals single user; USD 6,025 to institutions 5 users (effective 2005). **Description:** Contain comprehensive databases of U.S., Canadian, & U.K. books, audios, and videos. Covers over 5 million titles including more than 165,000 worldwide publishers & distributors listings, along with direct links to their website & e-mail.
Media: Online - full text. **Related titles:** ♦ CD-ROM ed.: Bowker's Global Books in Print on Disc.
Published by: R.R. Bowker LLC (Subsidiary of: Cambridge Information Group), 630 Central Ave., New Providence, NJ 07974. TEL 908-286-1090, 800-526-9537, FAX 908-219-0098, info@bowker.com, http://www.bowker.com. **Subscr. to:** Order Dept., PO Box 32, New Providence, NJ 07974-9903. TEL 800-521-8110.

011 USA
BOWKER'S GLOBAL BOOKS IN PRINT ON DISC. Text in English. 1993. m. USD 2,695 single user (effective 2005). **Document type:** *Abstract/Index.* **Description:** Contains more than two million English-language book entries from Bowker's Books in Print Plus, Whitaker's Bookbank, D.W. Thorpe's Australian and New Zealand Books In Print and K.G. Saur's International Books In Print.
Former titles: Bowker - Whitaker Global Books in Print on Disc (1542-6696); (until June 1998): Bowker - Whitaker Global Books in Print Plus
Media: CD-ROM (from R.R. Bowker LLC). **Related titles:** ♦ Online - full text ed.: Bowker's Global Books in Print.
Published by: R.R. Bowker LLC (Subsidiary of: Cambridge Information Group), 630 Central Ave., New Providence, NJ 07974. TEL 908-286-1090, 800-526-9537, FAX 908-219-0098, info@bowker.com, http://www.bowker.com. **Subscr. to:** Order Dept., PO Box 32, New Providence, NJ 07974-9903. TEL 800-521-8110. **Co-publisher:** J. Whitaker & Sons.

▼ **BOWKER'S GUIDE TO CHARACTERS IN FICTION.** see *LITERATURE—Abstracting, Bibliographies, Statistics*

BRAILLE BOOKS. see *HANDICAPPED—Abstracting, Bibliographies, Statistics*

910 016 GBR ISSN 0268-2400
Z1601
BRITISH BULLETIN OF PUBLICATIONS ON LATIN AMERICA, THE CARIBBEAN, PORTUGAL AND SPAIN. Text in English. 1949. s-a. GBP 15 (effective 1998). adv. bk.rev. bibl. **Document type:** *Bibliography.* **Description:** Contains information about recently published books and periodical articles in English about Latin America, the Caribbean, Portugal and Spain.
Formerly: British Bulletin of Publications on Latin America, the West Indies, Portugal and Spain (0007-036X)
Related titles: Microfilm ed.
Published by: Hispanic and Luso-Brazilian Council, Canning House, 2 Belgrave Sq, London, SW1X 8PJ, United Kingdom. TEL 44-171-235-2303, FAX 44-171-235-3587. Eds. Carmen Suarez, Philip Davies. Adv. contact Carmen Suarez. Circ: 1,000. **Subscr. to:** World Wide Subscription Service Ltd., Unit 4, Gibbs Reed Farm, Ticehurst, E Sussex TN5 7HE, United Kingdom. TEL 44-1580-200657, FAX 44-1580-200616.

BRITISH GENEALOGICAL BIBLIOGRAPHIES. see *GENEALOGY AND HERALDRY—Abstracting, Bibliographies, Statistics*

BRITISH INSTITUTE OF LEARNING DISABILITIES. CURRENT AWARENESS SERVICE. see *EDUCATION—Abstracting, Bibliographies, Statistics*

016.05 GBR ISSN 0959-4914
BRITISH LIBRARY. DOCUMENT SUPPLY CENTRE. CURRENT SERIALS RECEIVED (YEAR). Text in English. 1965. a. GBP 100 domestic to institutions; GBP 130 foreign to institutions (effective 2002). **Document type:** *Bibliography.*
Formerly (until 1986): British Library. Lending Division. Current Serials Received (0309-0655)
—BLDSC (3504.025000), CISTI, GNLM, KNAW. **CCC.**
Published by: British Library, Document Supply Centre, c/o Mike Marcus, British Library, Boston Spa, Wetherby, W Yorkshir LS23 7BQ, United Kingdom. TEL 44-1937-546080, FAX 44-1937-546286, http://www.bl.uk/services/document/sed.html. Circ: 2,500. **Subscr. to:** Extenza - Turpin, Pegasus Dr, Stratton Business Park, Biggleswade, Beds SG18 8TQ, United Kingdom. TEL 44-1462-672555.

015.942 GBR ISSN 0007-1544
Z2001 CODEN: BRNBBV
BRITISH NATIONAL BIBLIOGRAPHY. Text in English. 1950. w. (plus a. & interim cumulations). GBP 645 domestic to institutions; GBP 750 foreign to institutions (effective 2002). cum.index on microfiche (1950-1984, 1981-1992). back issues avail. **Document type:** *Bibliography.* **Description:** Lists new books and first issues of serial titles received by the Legal Deposit Office of the British Library. All subjects are covered, including fiction and children's literature.
Related titles: CD-ROM ed.; Microfiche ed.: (from BNB); Online - full text ed.
Indexed: BEL&L, RASB.
—BLDSC (2330.995000), CASDDS, Linda Hall.
Published by: British Library, National Bibliographic Service, c/o Mike Marcus, Boston Spa, Wetherby, W Yorks LS23 7BQ, United Kingdom. TEL 44-1937-546613, FAX 44-1937-546586, nbs-info@bl.uk, http://www.bl.uk/services/bsds/nbs/. Circ: 2,500. **Subscr. to:** Extenza - Turpin, Pegasus Dr, Stratton Business Park, Biggleswade, Beds SG18 8TQ, United Kingdom. TEL 44-1462-672555, FAX 44-1462-480-947.

659.1 016 GBR ISSN 0263-3515
BRITISH RATE AND DATA. Abbreviated title: B.R.A.D. Text in English. 1954. m. GBP 497; GBP 275 newsstand/cover (effective 2000). adv. **Document type:** *Directory, Trade.* **Description:** Provides up-to-date, easy-to-use and comprehensive data and rates on different sectors of advertising media.
Incorporates (1961-1988): B R A D Directories and Annuals (0263-1040)
Related titles: Online - full text ed.: (from EBSCO Publishing).
—BLDSC (2265.900000).
Published by: Emap Business Communications Ltd., 33-39 Bowling Green Ln, London, EC1R 0DA, United Kingdom. TEL 44-20-7505-8265, FAX 44-20-7505-8264, custserv@readerlink.emap.co.uk, http://www.brad.co.uk. Ed. Adeline Bonnet. Pub. Catherine Pusey. Adv. contact Nicole Rinaldi. Circ: 2,140 (paid).

015 940 BGR ISSN 0323-9969
BULGARIA V CHUZHDATA LITERATURA/BULGARIA IN FOREIGN LITERATURE. Text in Bulgarian. 1966. a. BGL 4.40 per issue (effective 2003). bibl. **Document type:** *Bibliography.*
Published by: Narodna Biblioteka Sv. sv. Kiril i Metodii/Cyril and Methodius National Library, 88 Levski Blvd, Sofia, 1504, Bulgaria. TEL 359-2-9881600, FAX 359-2-435495, nbkm@nl.otel.net. Ed., R&P M Maksimova TEL 359-2-9882811 ext 201. Circ: 350.

015 BGR
BULGARIAN ACADEMIC BOOKS. Text in English. 1969. a. free. bibl. reprint service avail. from IRC.
Related titles: Bulgarian ed.; Russian ed.
Published by: (Bulgarska Akademiya na Naukite/Bulgarian Academy of Sciences), Universitetsko Izdatelstvo Sv. Kliment Okhridski/Publishing House of the Sofia University St. Kliment Ohridski, Akad G Bonchev 6, Sofia, 1113, Bulgaria. Circ: 1,000.

016 BGR ISSN 0323-9411
Z5055.B87
BULGARSKI DISERTATSII. Text in Bulgarian. 1897. a. BGL 3.60 per issue (effective 2003). bibl. index. **Document type:** *Bibliography.*
Formerly: Bulgarski Knigopis. Seriya 2: Sluzhebni Izdaniia i Disertatsii (0323-9667); Supersedes in part: Bulgarski Knigopis (0007-3997)
Indexed: RASB.
—BLDSC (0018.631200).
Published by: Narodna Biblioteka Sv. sv. Kiril i Metodii/Cyril and Methodius National Library, 88 Levski Blvd, Sofia, 1504, Bulgaria. TEL 359-2-9881600, FAX 359-2-435495, nbkm@nl.otel.net. Ed., R&P S Pencheva TEL 359-2-9882811 ext 355. Circ: 430.

015 BGR ISSN 0323-9713
Z2893
BULGARSKI KNIGOPIS. KUMULATZIA. Text in Bulgarian. 1969. a. BGL 5.20 per issue (effective 2003). **Document type:** *Bulletin, Bibliography.*
Indexed: RASB.
Published by: Narodna Biblioteka Sv. sv. Kiril i Metodii/Cyril and Methodius National Library, 88 Levski Blvd, Sofia, 1504, Bulgaria. TEL 359-2-9881600, FAX 359-2-435495, nbkm@nl.otel.net. Ed., R&P E Angelova. Circ: 570.

015 BGR ISSN 0323-9616
Z2893
BULGARSKI KNIGOPIS. SERIA 1; knigi, ofizialni, notni, graficni i kartografskii isdania. Text in Bulgarian. 1897. m. BGL 13.20 (effective 2003). index. **Document type:** *Bibliography.*
Supersedes in part: Bulgarski Knigopis (0007-3997)
Related titles: Diskette ed.
Indexed: RASB.
Published by: Narodna Biblioteka Sv. sv. Kiril i Metodii/Cyril and Methodius National Library, 88 Levski Blvd, Sofia, 1504, Bulgaria. TEL 359-2-9881600, FAX 359-2-435495, angelova@nationallibrary.bg, nbkm@nl.otel.net. Ed., R&P E Angelova. Circ: 500. **Dist. by:** Hemus, 6 Rouski Blvd., Sofia 1000, Bulgaria.

070 015 BGR ISSN 0323-9764
BULGARSKI PERIODICHEN PECHAT/BULGARIAN PERIODICALS; vestnitsi, spisaniia, biuletini i periodichni sbornitsi. Text in Bulgarian. 1967. a. BGL 4 per issue (effective 2003). bibl. **Document type:** *Bulletin, Bibliography.*
Published by: Narodna Biblioteka Sv. sv. Kiril i Metodii/Cyril and Methodius National Library, 88 Levski Blvd, Sofia, 1504, Bulgaria. TEL 359-2-9881600, FAX 359-2-435495, nbkm@nl.otel.net. Ed., R&P I Kaloyanova TEL 359-2-9882811 ext 273. Circ: 320.

BULLETIN CRITIQUE DU LIVRE EN FRANCAIS. see *PUBLISHING AND BOOK TRADE—Abstracting, Bibliographies, Statistics*

BULLETIN D'ARABE CHRETIEN. BIBLIOGRAPHIE DES AUTEURS ARABES CHRETIENS. see *HISTORY—Abstracting, Bibliographies, Statistics*

BUSINESS RESOURCES; an internet miniguide. see *BUSINESS AND ECONOMICS—Abstracting, Bibliographies, Statistics*

016.05 GBR
BYPASS. Text in English. 199?. irreg. USD 10. adv. bk.rev. illus. **Description:** Focuses on British zine producers, self-publishers, small presses, pamphleteers, DIY media creators and others.
Published by: Slab-O-Concrete, PO Box 148, Hove, E Sussex BN3 3DQ, United Kingdom.

C A SELECTS. NEW BOOKS IN CHEMISTRY. see *CHEMISTRY—Abstracting, Bibliographies, Statistics*

011 500 FRA ISSN 0991-6342
C N R S PLUS. Text in French. 1988. irreg. price varies. **Document type:** *Monographic series, Academic/Scholarly.*
Published by: (France. Centre National de la Recherche Scientifique), C N R S Editions, 15 Rue Malebranche, Paris, 75005, France. TEL 33-1-53102700, FAX 33-1-53102727, http://www.cnrseditions.fr.

B

016.05 CAN ISSN 0707-3747
C O N S E R MICROFICHE; a computer-output-microfiche listing of serial records in the CONSER database and authenticated by the National Library of Canada and the Library of Congress. (Cooperative Online Serials) Text in English, French. 1979. a. **Document type:** *Bibliography.*
Media: Microfiche. **Related titles:** Magnetic Tape ed.; Online - full text ed.
—BLDSC (3417.890000), CISTI.
Published by: (Acquisitions and Bibliographic Services Branch), National Library of Canada, Canadiana Editorial Division, 395 Wellington St, Ottawa, ON K1A 0N4, Canada. TEL 819-994-6912, FAX 819-953-0291. Circ: 150.

C O S S A WASHINGTON UPDATE. see *PUBLIC ADMINISTRATION—Abstracting, Bibliographies, Statistics*

C S A POLITICAL SCIENCE & GOVERNMENT; a guide to periodical literature. (Cambridge Scientific Abstracts) see *PUBLIC ADMINISTRATION—Abstracting, Bibliographies, Statistics*

C S I R BUILDING TECHNOLOGY. COMPLETE LIST OF PUBLICATIONS. see *BUILDING AND CONSTRUCTION—Abstracting, Bibliographies, Statistics*

CAB INTERNATIONAL. ABSTRACT JOURNAL. see *FORESTS AND FORESTRY—Abstracting, Bibliographies, Statistics*

CAHIERS HENRI BOSCO. see *LITERATURE—Abstracting, Bibliographies, Statistics*

016.028 USA
CALDECOTT (YEAR) MEDAL BOOKS. Text in English. a. USD 18 for package of 50. **Document type:** *Bibliography.* **Description:** Lists the current Caldecott medal and honor books, along with those children's picture books that were awarded the prestigious medal since 1938.
Published by: (American Library Association, Association for Library Service to Children), American Library Association, 50 E Huron St, Chicago, IL 60611-2795. TEL 800-545-2433, http://www.ala.org. **Subscr. to:** PO Box 932501, Atlanta, GA 31193-2501. TEL 866-746-7252, FAX 770-442-9742, ala-orders@pbd.com.

CALGARY UNION LIST OF PERIODICALS. see *LIBRARY AND INFORMATION SCIENCES—Abstracting, Bibliographies, Statistics*

CALIFORNIA HANDBOOK; a comprehensive guide to sources of current information and action. see *PUBLIC ADMINISTRATION*

011 USA
CALIFORNIA PERIODICALS ON MICROFILM✶. Text in English. 1978. a. USD 345; price includes California Periodicals Index. bk.rev.
Media: Microfilm.
Published by: Gabriel Micrographics, 15813 NE 18th Ct, Vancouver, WA 98686-1474. TEL 815-895-6842. Ed. Marcia Gabriel.

015 USA ISSN 0008-1574
Z1223.5.C2
CALIFORNIA STATE PUBLICATIONS. Text in English. 1947. m. (plus a. cumulation). free to libraries. bibl. **Document type:** *Bibliography.* **Description:** Lists official California state documents received by the Government Publication Section, California State Library.
Related titles: Microfiche ed.
—Linda Hall.

Published by: California State Library, PO Box 942837, Sacramento, CA 94237-0001. TEL 916-654-0261, FAX 916-654-8777, cslgps@library.ca.gov, http://www.lib.state.ca.us/Web2/tramp2.exe/log_in?guest&SETTING_KEY=English&screen=csp_index.html, http://www.library.ca.gov. Ed. Marianne Leach. Circ: 800.

015 ARG ISSN 0327-9189
Z1611
CAMARA ARGENTINA DEL LIBRO. BOLETIN BIBLIOGRAFICO BIMESTRAL. Text in Spanish. 1993. bi-m. USD 72. **Document type:** *Bibliography.* **Description:** Presents information on Argentine books registered with the ISBN commission.
Published by: Camara Argentina del Libro, Avda. Belgrano, 1580 Piso 6, Buenos Aires, 1093, Argentina. TEL 54-114-3819277, FAX 54-114-3819253.

CAMBRIDGE BIBLIOGRAPHICAL SOCIETY. TRANSACTIONS. see *LIBRARY AND INFORMATION SCIENCES*

016 956 GBR
CAMBRIDGE UNIVERSITY LIBRARY. GENIZAH SERIES. Text in English. irreg. price varies. **Document type:** *Bibliography.*
Published by: Cambridge University Press, The Edinburgh Bldg, Shaftesbury Rd, Cambridge, CB2 2RU, United Kingdom. TEL 44-1223-312393, FAX 44-1223-315052, information@cambridge.org, http://www.cup.cam.ac.uk/. R&P Linda Nicol TEL 44-1223-325757.

CAMERA DI COMMERCIO, INDUSTRIA, E AGRICOLTURA DI GENOVA. SEGNALAZIONI BIBLIOGRAFICHE. see *BUSINESS AND ECONOMICS—Abstracting, Bibliographies, Statistics*

CANADIAN ADVERTISING RATES AND DATA. see *ADVERTISING AND PUBLIC RELATIONS—Abstracting, Bibliographies, Statistics*

015 CAN ISSN 0068-8398
Z1365
CANADIAN BOOKS IN PRINT - AUTHOR AND TITLE INDEX. Text in English; Text occasionally in French. 1967. a. CND 195 per issue (effective 2005). **Document type:** *Directory, Bibliography.* **Description:** Contains a list of approximately 52,000 titles, published by primarily English-language Canadian publishers.
Related titles: Microfiche ed.
—BLDSC (3017.630000).
Published by: University of Toronto Press, Reference Division, 10 St Mary St, Ste 700, Toronto, ON M4Y 2W8, Canada. TEL 416-978-2239, FAX 416-978-4738, utpbooks@utpress.utoronto.ca, http://www.utpress.utoronto.ca. Ed. M Butler. Circ: 3,500.

011 CAN ISSN 0315-1999
Z1365
CANADIAN BOOKS IN PRINT - SUBJECT INDEX. Text in English; Text occasionally in French. 1973. a. CND 175 per issue (effective 2005). **Document type:** *Directory, Bibliography.* **Description:** Contains a list of approximately 52,000 titles, published by primarily English-language Canadian publishers, with titles organized under subject headings.
Formerly: Subject Guide to Canadian Books in Print (0318-8493)
—CCC.
Published by: University of Toronto Press, Reference Division, 10 St Mary St, Ste 700, Toronto, ON M4Y 2W8, Canada. TEL 416-978-2239, FAX 416-978-4738, utpbooks@utpress.utoronto.ca, http://www.utpress.utoronto.ca. Ed. M Butler.

015 CAN ISSN 0225-3216
CANADIANA ON MICROFICHE. Text in English, French. 1978. m. (plus quinquennial cumulation). price varies. **Document type:** *Bibliography.*
Published by: National Library of Canada, Marketing and Publishing Services/Bibliotheque Nationale du Canada, 395 Wellington St, Ottawa, ON K1A 0N4, Canada. TEL 613-995-7969, FAX 613-991-9871, publications@nlc-bnc.ca. Ed. Margo Wiper.

015 CAN ISSN 1183-6849
CANADIANA PRE-1901. Text in English, French. 1980. biennial. price varies. **Document type:** *Bibliography.*
Formerly (until 1991): Canadiana 1867-1900: Monographs (Microfiche Edition)
Related titles: Online - full text ed.
Published by: National Library of Canada, 395 Wellington St, Ottawa, ON K1A 0N4, Canada. TEL 819-994-6912, FAX 819-996-0291. Ed. Margo Wiper. **Subscr. to:** Canada Communication Group, 45 Sacre-Coeur Blvd, Hull, PQ K1A 0S7, Canada.

015.71 015 CAN ISSN 0008-5391
CANADIANA: THE NATIONAL BIBLIOGRAPHY. Text in English, French. 1953. irreg. price varies. **Document type:** *Bibliography.* **Description:** Comprehensive bibliography which documents, collects, conserves and describes a wide variety of Canadian publications and sound recordings.
Related titles: CD-ROM ed.: ISSN 1480-7378; Microfiche ed.; Microform ed.; Online - full text ed.
Indexed: RASB.
—Linda Hall.
Published by: National Library of Canada, Marketing and Publishing Services/Bibliotheque Nationale du Canada, 395 Wellington St, Ottawa, ON K1A 0N4, Canada. TEL 613-995-7969, FAX 613-991-9871, publications@nlc-bnc.ca, http://www.nlc-bnc.ca/canadiana/ecancd.htm. Ed. David Balatti.

CANDLELIGHTERS CHILDHOOD CANCER FOUNDATION BIBLIOGRAPHY AND RESOURCE GUIDE. see *MEDICAL SCIENCES—Abstracting, Bibliographies, Statistics*

011 TTO ISSN 0251-9089
Z7165.C3
CARIBBEAN DOCUMENTATION CENTRE. CURRENT AWARENESS BULLETIN. Text in English. 1978. bi-m. free. back issues avail. **Document type:** *Bulletin.* **Description:** Alerts readers to highlights of recent acquisitions received at the center.
Published by: (United Nations Economic Commission for Latin America and the Caribbean CHL, Subregional Headquarters for the Caribbean), Caribbean Documentation Center, 63 Park St, 3rd Fl, Port-of-Spain, Trinidad, Trinidad & Tobago. FAX 868-623-8485, TELEX 623 8485, registry@eclacpos.org, http://www.eclacpos.org/. Circ: 79.

011 ROM
CARTI IN CURS DE APARITIE. Text in Romanian. q.
Published by: Centrala Editoriala, Piata Scinteii 1, Bucharest, 79715, Romania.

CATALOG OF CAPTIONED FILMS FOR THE DEAF. see *MOTION PICTURES—Abstracting, Bibliographies, Statistics*

CATALOGO COLECTIVO DE PUBLICACIONES PERIODICAS EXISTENTES EN BIBLIOTECAS CIENTIFICAS Y TECNICAS ARGENTINA. see *PUBLISHING AND BOOK TRADE—Abstracting, Bibliographies, Statistics*

011 BRA
CATALOGO COLETIVO NACIONAL DE PUBLICACOES PERIODICAS (IN MICROFICHES). Text in Portuguese. irreg. USD 100.
Formerly: Catalogo Coletivo de Publicacoes Periodicas (in Microfiches)
Media: Microfiche. **Related titles:** CD-ROM ed.
Published by: Instituto Brasileiro de Informacao em Ciencia e Tecnologia, SAS Quadra 5, Lote 6, Bloco H, Brasilia, DF 70070914, Brazil. TEL 55-61-217-6161, FAX 55-61-226-2677.

015.85 PER
CATALOGO DE PUBLICACIONES DE LA BIBLIOTECA NACIONAL DEL PERU. Text in Spanish. 1997. a., latest 2001. PEN 10 domestic; USD 25 foreign (effective 2003). 170 p./no.; back issues avail. **Document type:** *Catalog, Bibliography.*
Published by: Biblioteca Nacional del Peru, Ave. Abancay 4ta. Cuadra, Lima, 01, Peru. TEL 51-14-287690, FAX 51-14-277331, dn@binape.gob.pe, http://www.binape.gob.pe. Ed. Carmen Ochoa de Di Franco. R&P Sinesio Lopez Jimenez. Circ: 1,000.

016.05 ESP ISSN 1136-7563
CATALOGO DE REVISTAS CULTURALES DE ESPANA. Text in Spanish, English. 1987. a. free. **Document type:** *Catalog, Bibliography.* **Description:** Provides information on Spanish cultural magazines.
Formerly (until 1992): Catalogo de Revistas Culturales Espanolas (1136-8381)
Published by: Asociacion de Revistas Culturales de Espana, Hortaleza, 75, Madrid, 28004, Spain. info@arce.es, http://www.arce.es.

015.72 MEX ISSN 0188-2341
CATALOGO DE VENTAS. Cover title: Publicaciones UNAM. Text in Spanish. 1989. s-a. **Description:** Includes bibliographic descriptions of all books published by the University.
Published by: Universidad Nacional Autonoma de Mexico, Coordinacion de Humanidades, c/o Departamento de Publicidad y Relaciones Publicas, Mexico, INSURGENTES SUR 3744, Centro Tlalpan, Mexico City, DF 14000, Mexico. TEL 52-5-6663496, FAX 52-5-6663749, libros@bibliounam.unam.mx, http://bibliounam.unam.mx/libros. Ed. Alberto Dallal Castillo. Circ: 5,000.

011 ITA
CATALOGO DEI LIBRI IN COMMERCIO/ITALIAN BOOKS IN PRINT. Text in Italian. 1970. a. (in 6 vols.). price varies. back issues avail. **Document type:** *Directory, Bibliography.* **Description:** Includes information on publications from approximately 3,000 publishers: some 335,800 titles in print and over 48,000 new titles from Italy and Italian-speaking regions.
Formerly (until 1975): Catalogo dei Libri Italiani in Commercio (0069-1054)
Related titles: CD-ROM ed.
Published by: (Associazione Italiana Editori), Editrice Bibliografica SpA, Via Bergonzoli 1-5, Milan, MI 20127, Italy. TEL 39-02-28315996, FAX 39-02-28315906, bibliografica@bibliografica.it, http://www.bibliografica.it. Circ: 2,500. **Dist. outside of Italy by:** K.G. Saur Verlag GmbH, Postfach 701620, Munich 81316, Germany. TEL 49-89-76902232, 49-89-76902150, FAX 49-89-76902150.

011 ITA
CATALOGO DEI LIBRI IN COMMERCIO - CD-ROM/ITALIAN BOOKS IN PRINT ON CD-ROM. Short title: A L I C E - C D. Text in Italian. m. USD 1,220 for standalone version; USD 1,620 for network version (effective 2000). adv. **Document type:** *Bibliography.* **Description:** Provides access to more than 360,000 Italian-language titles in print, and profiles 3,000 publishers.
Media: CD-ROM (from K. G. Saur Verlag GmbH & Co.).
Published by: Informazioni Editoriali, Via Begonzoli 1-5, Milan, MI 20127, Italy. TEL 39-02-283151, FAX 39-02-28315900. Ed. Simonetta Pillon. Pub. Mauro Zerbini. Adv. contact Mauro Morellini. **Europe subscr. to:** K.G. Saur Verlag GmbH, Postfach 701620, Munich 81316, Germany. TEL 49-89-76902-2, FAX 49-89-76902150.

015 ITA
CATALOGO DEI PERIODICI ITALIANI. Text in Italian. 1983. a. price varies. **Document type:** *Directory, Bibliography.* **Description:** Reference guide to 14,000 Italian serials in print.
Published by: Editrice Bibliografica SpA, Via Bergonzoli 1-5, Milan, MI 20127, Italy. TEL 39-02-28315996, FAX 39-02-28315906, bibliografica@bibliografica.it, http://www.bibliografica.it. Ed. Roberto Maini. Circ: 1,000.

011 JPN
CATALOGUE OF BOOKS RECOMMENDED FOR LIBRARIES/SENTEI TOSHO SOMOKUROKU. Text in Japanese. a. JPY 6,500. **Document type:** *Catalog.*
Published by: Nihon Toshokan Kyokai/Japan Library Association, 1-11-14, Shinkawa, chuo-ku, Tokyo, 104-0033, Japan. FAX 81-3-3421-7588.

015.41053 USA ISSN 0260-5619
Z2009
CATALOGUE OF BRITISH OFFICIAL PUBLICATIONS NOT PUBLISHED BY H.M.S.O. Text in English. 1980. bi-m. (plus a. cumulation). GBP 295 (effective 1999). **Document type:** *Catalog.* **Description:** Catalogs 11,000 publications from more than 500 official organizations.
Related titles: CD-ROM ed.: (from Chadwyck-Healey Inc.); Microform ed.: (from PQC).
—BLDSC (3086.341000).
Published by: ProQuest Information & Learning, 300 N Zeeb Rd., PO Box 1346, Ann Arbor, MI 48106-1346. FAX 703-683-7589, TELEX 93121 02281 CH G, info@il.proquest.com, http://www.chadwyck.com. Ed. Alison Moss.

CATALOGUE OF I T U PUBLICATIONS. see *COMMUNICATIONS—Abstracting, Bibliographies, Statistics*

011 ROM ISSN 1221-0935
CATALOGUL CARTILOR STRAINE INTRATE IN BIBLIOTECILE DIN ROMANIA. Text in Romanian. 1957. q. ROL 260,000 (effective 2003). bk.rev. 200 p./no.; back issues avail. **Document type:** *Catalog, Bibliography.* **Description:** Contains the titles of foreign books held by Romanian libraries.
Published by: Biblioteca Nationala a Romaniei, Str. Ion Ghica 4, Sector 3, Bucharest, 79708, Romania. TEL 40-21-3157063, FAX 40-21-3123381, go@bibnat.ro, http://www.bibnat.ro. Ed. Marina Iliescu.

282 011 USA ISSN 0008-8307
Z6951
CATHOLIC PRESS DIRECTORY; official media reference guide to Catholic newspapers, magazines, newsletters, general publishers, and diocesan directories of the United States and Canada. Text in English. 1923. a. USD 48.85 to non-members; USD 23.85 to members (effective 2005). adv. index. **Document type:** *Directory, Consumer.* **Description:** Provides a reference to Catholic publications in North America.
Published by: Catholic Press Association, 3555 Veterans Memorial Hwy, Unit O, Ronkonkoma, NY 11779-7637. TEL 631-471-4730, FAX 631-471-4804, cathjourn@aol.com, http://www.catholicpress.org/. Eds. Felicia M Morales, Mary Iapalucci. Circ: 2,500 (paid and controlled).

011.3 GBR
CD-ROM FACTS AND FIGURES. Text in English. 1991. a. GBP 35 (effective 1998). **Document type:** *Trade.*
Published by: Macmillan Reference Ltd., 25 Eccleston Pl, London, W13 0RA, United Kingdom. TEL 44-171-881-8000, FAX 44-171-881-8001.

CD-ROM FINDER. see *PUBLISHING AND BOOK TRADE—Abstracting, Bibliographies, Statistics*

011 USA ISSN 0891-8198
TK7882.C56
CD-ROMS IN PRINT. Text in English. 1987. a. USD 195 (effective 2004). **Document type:** *Directory, Trade.*
Related titles: CD-ROM ed.
—BLDSC (3096.306000), CISTI. **CCC.**

Published by: Gale Group (Subsidiary of: Thomson Corporation), 27500 Drake Rd, Farmington Hills, MI 48331-3535. TEL 248-699-4253, 800-347-4253, FAX 248-699-8035, gale.galeord@thomson.com, http://www.galegroup.com.

CEHUI WENZHAI (CEHUIXUE)/ABSTRACTS OF SURVEYING AND MAPPING. see *GEOGRAPHY—Abstracting, Bibliographies, Statistics*

011 POL ISSN 0239-8931
Z6945
CENTRALNY KATALOG ZAGRANICZNYCH WYDAWNICTW CIAGLYCH W BIBLIOTEKACH POLSKICH. Text in Polish. 1971. a. (in 5 vols.). PLZ 110 (effective 2002). bibl. index. 2280 p./no. 2 cols./p.; back issues avail.; reprints avail. **Document type:** *Catalog.* **Description:** Contains a union catalog of foreign serials preserved in Polish libraries.
Formerly (until 1983): Centralny Katalog Biezacych Czasopism Zagranicznych w Bibliotekach Polskich
Related titles: Online - full text ed.
Published by: Biblioteka Narodowa, Dzial Katalogow Centralnych i Dokumentow Elektronicznych, Al. Niepodleglosci 213, Warsaw, 00-973, Poland. TEL 48-22-6082349, FAX 48-22-6082695, bnckczag@bn.org.pl, promocja@bn.org, http://www.bn.org.pl. Ed. Hanna Biedrzycka. R&P Ewa Krysiak. Circ: 300.

CENTRE FOR SPORTS SCIENCE AND HISTORY. SERIAL HOLDINGS. see *EDUCATION—Abstracting, Bibliographies, Statistics*

944 015 FRA ISSN 0756-3442
CENTRE INTERNATIONAL DE DOCUMENTATION OCCITANE. SERIE BIBLIOGRAPHIQUE. Text in French. 1977. irreg., latest vol.9. price varies.
Published by: Centre International de Documentation Occitane, B. P. 4202, Beziers, Cedex 34325, France.

CENTRO DI CULTURA E STORIA AMALFITANA. RASSEGNA. see *ART*

CENTRO INTERAMERICANO DE INVESTIGACION Y DOCUMENTACION SOBRE FORMACION PROFESIONAL. SERIE BIBLIOGRAFICA. see *EDUCATION—Abstracting, Bibliographies, Statistics*

057.86 015 CZE
CESKA NARODNI BIBLIOGRAFIE. CLANKY V NOVINACH A CASOPISECH (CD-ROM EDITION). Text in Czech. 1953. q. adv. index. **Document type:** *Bibliography.* **Description:** Cumulative bibliography of Czech journal and book production in librarianship, bibliography of information science and related fields.
Former titles (until 1999): Ceska Narodni Bibliografie. Clanky, State v Ceskem Tisku (Diskette Edition) (1212-3927); (until 1997): Ceska Narodni Bibliografie. Clanky v Novinach a Casopisech (Diskette Edition) (1210-8952); (until 1994): Bibliograficky Katalog C S F R: Clanky v Ceskych Casopisech (Print Edition) (0862-9269); (until 1990): Bibliograficky Katalog C S S R: Clanky v Ceskych Casopisech (0006-1115); (until 1954): Bibliograficky Katalog C S S R. Ceske Casopisy; Which superseded: Ceske Casopisy
Media: CD-ROM. **Related titles:** Online - full text ed.
Indexed: RASB.
Published by: Narodni Knihovna Ceske Republiky/National Library of the Czech Republic, Klementinum 190, Prague, 11001, Czech Republic. TEL 420-2-221663262, FAX 420-2-281013333, public.ur@nkp.cz, http://www.nkp.cz. Ed. Bohdana Stoklasova TEL 420-2-221663293. Circ: 850. **Subscr. to:** Albertina Icome Praha, Stepanska 16, Prague 11000, Czech Republic. TEL 420-2-22231212, FAX 420-2-22231313, eva.silhava@aip.cz, http://www.aipberoun.cz.

057.86 015 CZE
Z5949.C9
CESKA NARODNI BIBLIOGRAFIE. GRAFIKA (CD-ROM EDITION). Text in Czech, English. 1958. a. **Document type:** *Bibliography.* **Description:** Bibliography of Czech graphic documents.
Former titles (until 1996): Ceska Narodni Bibliografie. Grafika (Print Edition); (until 1995): Narodni Bibliografie Ceske Republiky. Grafika (1211-1341); Supersedes in part (in 1994): Narodni Bibliografie Ceske Republiky. Grafika a Mapy (1210-8936); Which was formerly (until 1993): Bibliograficky Katalog C S F R: Ceske Knihy. Ceska Grafika a Mapy za Rok (Year) (0862-9226); (until 1990): Bibliograficky Katalog C S S R: Ceske Knihy. Ceska Grafika a Mapy za Rok (Year) (0323-1712)
Media: CD-ROM. **Related titles:** Online - full content ed.
Published by: Narodni Knihovna Ceske Republiky/National Library of the Czech Republic, Klementinum 190, Prague, 11001, Czech Republic. TEL 420-2-221663262, FAX 420-2-281013333, public.ur@nkp.cz, sekret.ur@nkp.cz, http://www.nkp.cz. Ed. Bohdana Stoklasova TEL 420-2-221663293. R&P Adolf Knoll. Circ: 300. **Dist. by:** Albertina Icome Praha, Stepanska 16, Prague 11000, Czech Republic. TEL 420-2-22231212, FAX 420-2-22231313, eva.silhava@aip.cz, http://www.aipberoun.cz/.

CESKA NARODNI BIBLIOGRAFIE. HUDEBNINY (CD-ROM EDITION). see *MUSIC—Abstracting, Bibliographies, Statistics*

057.86 015 CZE
Z2131
CESKA NARODNI BIBLIOGRAFIE. KNIHY (CD-ROM EDITION). Text in Czech, English. 1922. q. CZK 4,300 domestic; USD 145 foreign (effective 2003). index. **Document type:** *Bibliography.* **Description:** Bibliography of Czech books.
Former titles (until 2000): Ceska Narodni Bibliografie. Knihy (Print Edition) (1210-8898); (until 1994): Narodni Bibliografie Ceske Republiky. Knihy (1210-888X); (until 1993): Bibliograficky Katalog C S F R: Ceske Knihy (0862-9218); (until 1990): Bibliograficky Katalog C S S R: Ceske Knihy (0323-1615); (until 1955): Ceska Kniha; Which superseded: Bibliograficky Katalog Ceskoslovenske Republiky. Pt. A: Knihy Ceske 1922-1950
Media: CD-ROM. **Related titles:** Online - full text ed.: ISSN 1210-8928.
Indexed: RASB.
Published by: Narodni Knihovna Ceske Republiky/National Library of the Czech Republic, Klementinum 190, Prague, 11001, Czech Republic. TEL 420-2-221663262, FAX 420-2-281013333, public.ur@nkp.cz, sekret.ur@nkp.cz, http://www.nkp.cz. Ed. Bohdana Stoklasova TEL 420-2-221663293. Circ: 600. **Dist. by:** Albertina Icome Praha, Stepanska 16, Prague 11000, Czech Republic. TEL 420-2-22231212, FAX 420-2-22231313, eva.silhava@aip.cz, http://www.aipberoun.cz/.

015 CZE
Z2133
CESKA NARODNI BIBLIOGRAFIE. ZAHRANICNI BOHEMIKA (CD-ROM EDITION). Text in Czech. 1956. a. CZK 240 domestic (effective 2003). **Document type:** *Catalog, Bibliography.* **Description:** Bibliography of foreign Bohemica deposited or sent to the Czech National Library.
Former titles (until 1997): Ceska Narodni Bibliografie. Zahranicni Bohemika (Print Edition) (1211-4375); (until 1994): Narodna Bibliografie Ceske Republiky. Zakranicni Bohemika (1210-8987); (until 1993): Bibliograficky Katalog C S F R. Zaharanicni Bohemika (1210-4523); (until 1990): Bibliograficky Katalog C S S R. Ceske Knihy, Zakhranicni Bohemika a Slovacika v Roce (0323-1917)
Media: CD-ROM. **Related titles:** Online - full content ed.
Published by: Narodni Knihovna Ceske Republiky/National Library of the Czech Republic, Klementinum 190, Prague, 11001, Czech Republic. TEL 420-2-221663262, FAX 420-2-281013333, public.ur@nkp.cz, http://www.nkp.cz. Ed. Bohdana Stoklasova TEL 420-2-221663293. Circ: 300. **Dist. by:** Albertina Icome Praha, Stepanska 16, Prague 11000, Czech Republic. TEL 420-2-22231212, FAX 420-2-22231313, eva.silhava@aip.cz, http://www.aipberoun.cz/.

CESKA NARODNI BIBLIOGRAFIE. ZVUKOVE DOKUMENTY (CD-ROM EDITION). see *MUSIC—Abstracting, Bibliographies, Statistics*

CESKA ZEMEDELSKA A POTRAVINARSKA BIBLIOGRAFIE. see *AGRICULTURE—Abstracting, Bibliographies, Statistics*

CHECKLIST OF OFFICIAL PUBLICATIONS OF THE STATE OF NEW YORK. see *PUBLIC ADMINISTRATION—Abstracting, Bibliographies, Statistics*

CHICANO DATABASE. see *ETHNIC INTERESTS—Abstracting, Bibliographies, Statistics*

011 USA
CHICOREL INDEX SERIES. Text in English. 1970. irreg., latest vol.26, 1986. USD 125 per vol. (effective 2000). bk.rev. **Document type:** *Directory, Abstract/Index.* **Description:** Comprises series of subject guides to various fields in the humanities and social sciences, such as indexes to plays, poetry and short stories in anthologies, on audio and video. Abstracting services for reading and learning disabilities, and the mental health fields.
Related titles: Microform ed.: (from PQC).
Published by: American Library Publishing Co., PO Box 4272, Sedona, AZ 86340-4272. TEL 520-282-4922. Ed., R&P Marietta S Chicorel.

CHILDREN'S BOOKS IN PRINT; an author, title, and illustrator index to books for children and young adults. see *LITERATURE—Abstracting, Bibliographies, Statistics*

CHILDREN'S BOOKWATCH. see *CHILDREN AND YOUTH—Abstracting, Bibliographies, Statistics*

CHILDREN'S CATALOG. see *CHILDREN AND YOUTH—Abstracting, Bibliographies, Statistics*

CHILDREN'S CHOICES. see *CHILDREN AND YOUTH—Abstracting, Bibliographies, Statistics*

CHUZHDESTRANNI PERIODICHNI IZDANIIA V BULGARIA. see *SCIENCES: COMPREHENSIVE WORKS—Abstracting, Bibliographies, Statistics*

CINEGRAPH; Lexikon zum deutschsprachigen Film. see *MOTION PICTURES—Abstracting, Bibliographies, Statistics*

011 USA
EL CLARIN DE LA BUSCA. Text in English. 1994. q. USD 25; USD 30 foreign; includes La Busca. adv. bk.rev. **Document type:** *Bibliography.* **Description:** Provides a forum for ideas on the literature of La Fiesta Brava through book reviews, criticism, and commentary.
Published by: Taurine Bibliophiles America, c/o Ronn A Philips, 106 S Walnut, La Crescent, MN 55947. TEL 507-895-6640. Ed. Jane Hurwitz. **Subscr. to:** Donald K. Conover, Treasurer, 2171 Twining Rd., Newton, PA 18940. TEL 610-968-0608.

CLOVER INFORMATION INDEX. see *PUBLISHING AND BOOK TRADE—Abstracting, Bibliographies, Statistics*

010 NLD ISSN 0169-8672
CODICES MANUSCRIPTI BIBLIOTHECAE UNIVERSITATIS LEIDENSIS. Text in Dutch. 1910. irreg., latest vol.26, 1988. price varies. back issues avail. **Document type:** *Monographic series, Bibliography.* **Description:** Descriptive catalogues of manuscript holdings at Leiden University and other collections in the Netherlands, including Arabic, Hebrew, Balinese and Latin manuscripts.
Published by: Brill Academic Publishers, PO Box 9000, Leiden, 2300 PA, Netherlands. TEL 31-71-53-53500, FAX 31-71-53-17-532, cs@brill.nl, http://www.brill.nl. R&P Elizabeth Venekamp. **Subscr. in N. America to:** PO Box 605, Herndon, VA 20172. TEL 703-661-1585, 800-337-9255, FAX 703-661-1501, cs@brillusa.com. **Distr. outside N. America by:** c/o Turpin Distribution, Stratton Business Park, Pegasus Drive, Biggleswade, BEDFORDSHIRE SG 18 8TQ, United Kingdom. TEL 44-1767-604-954, FAX 44-1767-601-640, brill@turpin-distribution.com. **Co-publisher:** Leiden University Press.

015 BRA
COLECCAO RODOLFO GARCIA. Text in Portuguese. 1966. irreg.
Formerly (until vol.20, 1983): Biblioteca Nacional. Colecao Rodolfo Garcia. Serie B. Catalogos e Bibliografias
Published by: Biblioteca Nacional, Av Rio Branco, 219, Centro, Rio De Janeiro, RJ 20040008, Brazil. TEL 021-262-8255, FAX 021-220-4173. Circ: 1,000.

COLECCION BIBLIOGRAFICA CIENTIFICA ECUATORIANA. see *SCIENCES: COMPREHENSIVE WORKS—Abstracting, Bibliographies, Statistics*

COLEGIO DE MEXICO. BIBLIOTECA. LISTA DE OBRAS EN CANJE. PUBLICACIONES PERIODICAS. see *JOURNALISM—Abstracting, Bibliographies, Statistics*

COLLECTANEA BIBLIOGRAPHICA CARMELITANA. see *RELIGIONS AND THEOLOGY—Abstracting, Bibliographies, Statistics*

COLLEGE CATALOG COLLECTION ON MICROFICHE. see *EDUCATION—Abstracting, Bibliographies, Statistics*

016 BEL
COMMISSION BELGE DE BIBLIOGRAPHIE ET DE BIBLIOLOGIE. BULLETIN. Text in French. 1957. a. bk.rev. index. **Document type:** *Bulletin.*
Formerly: Commission Belge de Bibliographie. Bulletin (0408-9006)
Published by: Commission Belge de Bibliographie et de Bibliologie, 4 Bd de l'Empereur, Brussels, 1000, Belgium. FAX 32-80-510465. Ed. Christian F Verbecke. R&P Mireille M Vanlaecken. Circ: 300.

COMPENDIUM OF TOURISM STATISTICS. see *TRAVEL AND TOURISM—Abstracting, Bibliographies, Statistics*

COMPETITIVE INTELLIGENCE RESOURCES; an internet miniguide. see *COMPUTERS—Abstracting, Bibliographies, Statistics*

THE COMPLETE DIRECTORY OF LARGE PRINT BOOKS AND SERIALS. see *HANDICAPPED—Abstracting, Bibliographies, Statistics*

011 USA
CONGRESSIONAL RESEARCH REPORT. Text in English. 1986. m. USD 198 (effective 2000). back issues avail. **Document type:** *Newsletter.* **Description:** Includes descriptions and ordering information for all publications of U.S. Congressional Research Service of U.S. Congress.
Formerly: New Products from C R S
Related titles: Online - full text ed.
Published by: Penny Hill Press, 25411 Paine St., Damascus, MD 20872-2349. TEL 301-229-8229, FAX 301-229-6988. Ed., Pub. Walt Seager.

011 ESP
CONSEJO SUPERIOR DE INVESTIGACIONES CIENTIFICAS. BASES DE DATOS. Text in Spanish. 199?. 3/yr.
Media: CD-ROM.
Published by: Consejo Superior de Investigaciones Cientificas, Calle Vitruvio 8, Madrid, 28006, Spain. TEL 34-91-5629633, FAX 34-91-5629634, publ@orgc.csic.es, http://www.csic.es.

B

▼ new title ➤ refereed ✶ unverified ♦ full entry avail.

B

640   **USA**
CONSUMER INFORMATION CATALOG. Text in English. 1971. q.
free (effective 2005). bibl. **Document type:** *Catalog,
Government.* **Description:** Contains descriptive listings of
about 200 free or low-cost Federal publications.
Formerly: Consumer Information
Related titles: Online - full text ed.
Indexed: MEDOC.
Published by: U.S. General Services Administration, Consumer
Information Center, FCIC-05C, PO Box 100, Pueblo, CO
81009. TEL 888-878-3256, FAX 719-948-9724,
cic.info@pueblo.gsa.gov, http://www.pueblo.gsa.gov. Circ:
12,000,000.

CONTEMPORARY PROBLEMS OF CHILDHOOD; a bibliographic
series. see *CHILDREN AND YOUTH—Abstracting,
Bibliographies, Statistics*

**CONTEMPORARY SOCIAL ISSUES: A BIBLIOGRAPHIC
SERIES.** see *SOCIOLOGY—Abstracting, Bibliographies,
Statistics*

CONTENTSDIRECT. see *SCIENCES: COMPREHENSIVE
WORKS—Abstracting, Bibliographies, Statistics*

015   **ITA**
COPTIC BIBLIOGRAPHY. Text in Italian. 1982. a. USD 40.
Supplement avail. **Document type:** *Bibliography.*
Published by: Centro Italiano Microfiches, Piazzale Di Ponte
Milvio, 28, Rome, RM 00191, Italy. FAX 6-3333457. Ed. Tito
Orlandi. Circ: 150.

015.942 025.3   **USA**
**COPYRIGHT CATALOGING: MONOGRAPHS AND
DOCUMENTS.** Text in English. 1978. w. USD 31,500.
Document type: *Bibliography.* **Description:** Compiles MARC
data on such copyright information as author, title, copyright
claimant name, and registration number.
Media: Online - full text.
Published by: U.S. Library of Congress, Copyright Office, First
St, N E, Washington, DC 20559. cdsinfo@loc.gov. **Dist. by:**
U.S. Library of Congress. TEL 202-707-6100, FAX
202-707-1334.

015.942 025.3   **USA**
COPYRIGHT CATALOGING: SERIALS. Text in English. 1994.
s-a. USD 2,000. **Document type:** *Bibliography.* **Description:**
Provides U.S. Copyright Office cataloging data for registrations
of copyright since 1978.
Media: Online - full text.
Published by: (Customer Service Section), U.S. Library of
Congress, Cataloging Distribution Service, 101 Independence
Ave, S E, Washington, DC 20541-4912. TEL 202-707-6100,
FAX 202-707-1334, cdsinfo@loc.gov, http://www.loc.gov/cds.

CORNELL MODERN INDONESIA PROJECT PUBLICATIONS.
see *ASIAN STUDIES*

COSTUME SOCIETY OF AMERICA BIBLIOGRAPHY. see
CLOTHING TRADE—Abstracting, Bibliographies, Statistics

COSTUME SOCIETY OF AMERICA. SYMPOSIA ABSTRACTS.
see *CLOTHING TRADE—Abstracting, Bibliographies,
Statistics*

**COUNCIL OF EUROPE. DOCUMENTATION SECTION. BIBLIO
BULLETIN. SERIES: POLITICAL, ECONOMIC AND SOCIAL
AFFAIRS.** see *POLITICAL SCIENCE—Abstracting,
Bibliographies, Statistics*

COUNTY GENEALOGICAL BIBLIOGRAPHIES. see
*GENEALOGY AND HERALDRY—Abstracting, Bibliographies,
Statistics*

**COUR INTERNATIONALE DE JUSTICE. BIBLIOGRAPHIE/
INTERNATIONAL COURT OF JUSTICE. BIBLIOGRAPHY.**
see *LAW—Abstracting, Bibliographies, Statistics*

CRITICAL BIBLIOGRAPHY OF FRENCH LITERATURE. see
LITERATURE—Abstracting, Bibliographies, Statistics

CRITICAS; an English speaker's guide to the latest Spanish
language titles. see *LIBRARY AND INFORMATION
SCIENCES*

CRITIQUES D'ART; revue critique et bibliographique. see
ART—Abstracting, Bibliographies, Statistics

CROYDON BIBLIOGRAPHIES FOR REGIONAL SURVEY. see
*SCIENCES: COMPREHENSIVE WORKS—Abstracting,
Bibliographies, Statistics*

016   **FRA**   ISSN 0398-8074
Z282
CURIOSPRESS INTERNATIONAL; annuaire international des
editeurs de publications etranges et curieuses. Text in English,
French, German, Italian, Spanish. 1974. biennial. illus.
Address: c/o Ed. Pierre Birukoff, INFOS al International, B.P. 127,
Paris, 75563, France.

CURRENT BASEBALL PUBLICATIONS. see *SPORTS AND
GAMES—Abstracting, Bibliographies, Statistics*

CURRENT BIBLIOGRAPHY ON AFRICAN AFFAIRS. see
POLITICAL SCIENCE—Abstracting, Bibliographies, Statistics

**CURRENT BIBLIOGRAPHY ON SCIENCE AND TECHNOLOGY:
ENERGY/KAGAKU GIJUTSU BUNKEN SOKUHO.
ENERUGI-HEN.** see *ENERGY—Abstracting, Bibliographies,
Statistics*

**CURRENT BIBLIOGRAPHY ON SCIENCE AND TECHNOLOGY:
ENVIRONMENTAL POLLUTION/KAGAKU GIJUTSU
BUNKEN SOKUHO. KANKYO KOGAI-HEN.** see
*ENVIRONMENTAL STUDIES—Abstracting, Bibliographies,
Statistics*

**CURRENT BIBLIOGRAPHY ON SCIENCE AND TECHNOLOGY:
LIFE SCIENCES/KAGAKU GIJUTSU BUNKEN SOKUHO.
RAIFUSAIENSU HEN.** see *BIOLOGY—Abstracting,
Bibliographies, Statistics*

CURRENT CONTENTS: ARTS & HUMANITIES. see
*HUMANITIES: COMPREHENSIVE WORKS—Abstracting,
Bibliographies, Statistics*

011   **JPN**   ISSN 0386-7293
AI19.J3
CURRENT CONTENTS OF ACADEMIC JOURNALS IN JAPAN;
the humanities and social sciences. Text in English. 1971. a.
USD 85 (effective 2001). **Document type:** *Yearbook,
Abstract/Index.*
Related titles: Online - full text ed.
Published by: Center for Publications Japan, 2-14-6 Yayoi,
Bunkyo-ku, Tokyo, 113-0032, Japan. TEL 81-3-3817-5825,
FAX 81-3-3817-5830, capj@crisscross.com. Ed. Ichiro Suzuki.
Circ: 1,000. **Dist. by:** Business Center for Academic Societies
Japan, 5-16-19 Honkomagome, Bunkyo-ku, Tokyo 113-0021,
Japan; **Dist. in U.S. by:** International Specialized Book
Services Inc., 5804 N E Hassalo St, Portland, OR
97213-3644.

CURRENT DIGEST OF THE POST-SOVIET PRESS. see
POLITICAL SCIENCE—Abstracting, Bibliographies, Statistics

CURRENT GENEALOGICAL PUBLICATIONS. see *GENEALOGY
AND HERALDRY—Abstracting, Bibliographies, Statistics*

CURRENT GEOGRAPHICAL PUBLICATIONS. see
GEOGRAPHY—Abstracting, Bibliographies, Statistics

CURRENT JAPANESE PERIODICALS FOR (YEAR). see
*PUBLISHING AND BOOK TRADE—Abstracting,
Bibliographies, Statistics*

CURRENT MATHEMATICAL PUBLICATIONS. see
MATHEMATICS—Abstracting, Bibliographies, Statistics

CURRENT PAPERS ON COMPUTERS & CONTROL. see
COMPUTERS—Abstracting, Bibliographies, Statistics

CURRENT PUBLICATIONS IN LEGAL AND RELATED FIELDS.
see *LAW—Abstracting, Bibliographies, Statistics*

**CURRENT RESEARCH IN FRENCH STUDIES AT
UNIVERSITIES IN THE UNITED KINGDOM AND IRELAND.**
see *LINGUISTICS—Abstracting, Bibliographies, Statistics*

015   **CZE**
CZECH BOOKS FOR YOU. Text in Czech. 1974. 4/yr. free. adv.
bk.rev.
Formerly (until 1991): Czech Books in Print (0862-447X)
Published by: Artia Pegas Press Co. Ltd., Palac Metro, Narodni
trida 25, PO Box 825, Prague, 110 00, Czech Republic. FAX
42-2-266568, TELEX 121065 ARTA C.

025.309   **DNK**
D A N B I B. Text in Danish. 1901. a. DKK 260 per quarter
(effective 2001). **Description:** Union catalogue of acquisitions
of foreign literature in Danish research libraries, special
libraries and public libraries, from 1980; also including Danish
national bibliography.
Former titles: Dansk BiblioteksCenter. A L B A -
Accessionskatalogen; Statens Bibliotekstjeneste. ALBA -
Accessionskatalogen; (until 1990): Rigsbibliotekarembedet.
ALBA - Accessionskatalogen (0109-9256); (until 1984):
Rigsbibliotekarembedet. Accessionskatalog (0084-9715); (until
1953): Rigsbibliotekarembedet. Katalog over Erhvervelser af
Nyere Udenlandsk Litteratur ved Statens Offentlige Biblioteker
(0105-7995)
Media: Online - full text.
Published by: Dansk BiblioteksCenter AS, Tempovej 7-11,
Ballerup, 2750, Denmark. TEL 45-44-867777, FAX
45-44-867892, dbc@dbc.dk, http://www.dbc.dk. Ed. Mogens
Brabrand Jensen.

015.54   **IND**   ISSN 0971-4448
D K NEWSLETTER; a journal of news and reviews of Indian
publications in English. Text in English. 1975. q. USD 10
(effective 2002). adv. bk.rev. **Document type:** *Journal,
Bibliography.*
Published by: D.K. Agencies Pvt. Ltd., A-15-17, D K Ave, Mohan
Garden, Najaf Garh Rd., New Delhi, 110 059, India. TEL
91-11-535-7104, FAX 91-11-535-7103,
custserv@dkagencies.com, http://www.dkagencies.com. Pub.
R.K. Mittal. Circ: 3,100 (paid and controlled).

D L A P S. (Defense Logistics Agency Publishing System) see
*PUBLIC ADMINISTRATION—Abstracting, Bibliographies,
Statistics*

DAGSPRESSENS DETALJSPRIDNING. see *PUBLISHING AND
BOOK TRADE—Abstracting, Bibliographies, Statistics*

016.05   **UAE**
**DALIL AD-DAWRIAT LI-DAWLAT AL-IMARAT AL-ARABIYYAH
AL-MUTTAHIDAH/DIRECTORY OF THE PERIODICALS IN
THE UNITED ARAB EMIRATES.** Text in Arabic, English.
1990. biennial. **Document type:** *Bibliography.* **Description:**
Contains comprehensive bibliographic information on all
periodicals published in the U.A.E. since 1961.
Published by: Cultural Foundation, National Library, P O Box
2380, Abu Dhabi, United Arab Emirates. TELEX 22414
CULCEN EM. Ed. Jumaa Al Qubaisi.

011   **LBY**
► **DALIL AD-DAWRIYAT AL-LIBIYA WA MUHTAWAYATUHA/
INDEX OF LIBYAN PERIODICALS AND THEIR CONTENTS.**
Text in Arabic. a. USD 6 (effective 1998). **Document type:**
Academic/Scholarly.
Published by: Libyan Studies Center, Sidi Munaider St., P O Box
5070, Tripoli, Libya. TEL 218-21-3333996, FAX
218-21-3331616. Ed. Hamed Uheida.

► **DANCE RESEARCH.** see *DANCE—Abstracting,
Bibliographies, Statistics*

015.489   **DNK**   ISSN 0106-2743
**DANSK BOGFORTEGNELSE. AARSKATALOG/DANISH
NATIONAL BIBLIOGRAPHY, BOOKS. ANNUAL LIST.** Text in
Danish. 1851. a. DKK 3,265; DKK 2,220 to libraries (effective
2005).
Published by: Dansk BiblioteksCenter AS, Tempovej 7-11,
Ballerup, 2750, Denmark. TEL 45-44-867777, FAX
45-44-867892, dbc@dbc.dk, http://www.dbc.dk.

DAVISON'S GOLD BOOK. see *TEXTILE INDUSTRIES AND
FABRICS—Abstracting, Bibliographies, Statistics*

DEPUTADOS BRASILEIROS: REPERTORIO BIOGRAFICO. see
POLITICAL SCIENCE—Abstracting, Bibliographies, Statistics

DEUTSCHE BUECHER; Forum fuer Literatur. see *POLITICAL
SCIENCE—Abstracting, Bibliographies, Statistics*

015   **DEU**
DEUTSCHE NATIONALBIBLIOGRAPHIE (CD-ROM AKTUELL).
Text in German. 1989. bi-m. **Document type:** *Bibliography.*
Formerly: Deutsche Bibliographie (CD-ROM Edition)
Media: CD-ROM.
Published by: (Deutsche Bibliothek), M V B - Marketing- und
Verlagsservice des Buchhandels GmbH, Postfach 100442,
Frankfurt Am Main, 60004, Germany. TEL 49-69-1306-243,
FAX 49-69-1306255, info@mvb-online.de, http://
www.buchhaendler-vereinigung.de.

015.43   **DEU**   ISSN 0939-0421
Z2221   **CODEN: DNBAEX**
**DEUTSCHE NATIONALBIBLIOGRAPHIE. REIHE A,
MONOGRAPHIEN UND PERIODIKA DES
VERLAGSBUCHHANDELS.** Text in German. 1947. w. bibl.
index. **Document type:** *Bibliography.*
Former titles: Deutsche Nationalbibliographie. Wochentliches
Verzeichnis. Ausgabe 1 Amtsblatt der Deutschen Bibliothek;
Deutsche Bibliographie. Woechentliches Verzeichnis. Ausgabe
1 Amtsblatt der Deutschen Bibliothek (0170-1037)
Indexed: RASB.
—Linda Hall.
Published by: (Deutsche Bibliothek), M V B - Marketing- und
Verlagsservice des Buchhandels GmbH, Postfach 100442,
Frankfurt Am Main, 60004, Germany. TEL 49-69-1306-243,
FAX 49-69-1306255, info@mvb-online.de, http://
www.buchhaendler-vereinigung.de.

015.431   **DEU**   ISSN 0940-2721
Z2221
**DEUTSCHE NATIONALBIBLIOGRAPHIE. REIHE D,
MONOGRAPHIEN UND PERIODIKA. HALBJAHRES-
VERZEICHNIS.** Text in German. 1951. s-a. bibl. index.
Document type: *Bibliography.*
Formerly: Deutsche Bibliographie. Halbjahres-Verzeichnis
(0532-5854)
Indexed: RASB.
—GNLM, Linda Hall.

B

Published by: (Deutsche Bibliothek), M V B - Marketing- und Verlagsservice des Buchhandels GmbH, Postfach 100442, Frankfurt Am Main, 60004, Germany. TEL 49-69-1306-243, FAX 49-69-1306255, info@mvb-online.de, http://www.buchhaendler-vereinigung.de.

015.43   DEU   ISSN 0942-4318
Z2221
DEUTSCHE NATIONALBIBLIOGRAPHIE. REIHE E, MONOGRAPHIEN UND PERIODIKA. FUENFJAHRES-VERZEICHNIS. Text in German. 1945. irreg. price varies. bibl. index. **Document type:** *Bibliography.*
Formerly: Deutsche Bibliographie. Fuenfjahres-Verzeichnis (0418-8233)
—GNLM, Linda Hall.
Published by: (Deutsche Bibliothek), M V B - Marketing- und Verlagsservice des Buchhandels GmbH, Postfach 100442, Frankfurt Am Main, 60004, Germany. TEL 49-69-1306-243, FAX 49-69-1306255, info@mvb-online.de, http://www.buchhaendler-vereinigung.de.

015.43   DEU   ISSN 0939-057X
Z2221
DEUTSCHE NATIONALBIBLIOGRAPHIE. REIHE G, FREMDSPRACHIGE GERMANICA UND UEBERSETZUNGEN DEUTSCHSPRACHIGER WERKE. Text in German. 1954. q. bibl. cum.index: 1954-1963. **Document type:** *Bibliography.* **Description:** Covers works in all fields and subjects. Includes a systematic author and publisher index.
Formed by 1992 merger of: Bibliographie der Uebersetzungen Deutschsprachiger Werke (0006-1409); Bibliographie Fremdsprachiger Germanica (0323-3154)
Indexed: RASB.
Published by: (Deutsche Bibliothek), M V B - Marketing- und Verlagsservice des Buchhandels GmbH, Postfach 100442, Frankfurt Am Main, 60004, Germany. TEL 49-69-1306-243, FAX 49-69-1306255, info@mvb-online.de, http://www.buchhaendler-vereinigung.de.

DEUTSCHE NATIONALBIBLIOGRAPHIE. REIHE H, HOCHSCHULSCHRIFTEN. see *EDUCATION—Abstracting, Bibliographies, Statistics*

DEUTSCHE NATIONALBIBLIOGRAPHIE. REIHE M, MUSIKALIEN UND MUSIKSCHRIFTEN. see *MUSIC—Abstracting, Bibliographies, Statistics*

015   DEU
DEUTSCHE NATIONALBIBLIOGRAPHIE. REIHE N, VORANKUENDIGUNGEN, MONOGRAPHIEN UND PERIODIKA (CIP). Text in German. 1975. w. **Document type:** *Bibliography.* **Description:** Bibliography of new publications.
Formerly: Deutsche Nationalbibliographie: Vorankuendigungen, Monographien und Periodika; **Incorporates:** Deutsche Nationalbibliographie. Reihe A: Neuerscheinungen des Buchhandels (0323-3596); Deutsche Bibliographie: Neuerscheinungen-Sofortdienst (0340-3416)
Indexed: RASB.
—GNLM, Linda Hall.
Published by: (Deutsche Bibliothek), M V B - Marketing- und Verlagsservice des Buchhandels GmbH, Postfach 100442, Frankfurt Am Main, 60004, Germany. TEL 49-69-1306-243, FAX 49-69-1306255, info@mvb-online.de, http://www.buchhaendler-vereinigung.de.

DICTIONARY OF DICTIONARIES AND EMINENT ENCYCLOPEDIAS; comprising dictionaries, encyclopedias, and other selected works in English. see *ENCYCLOPEDIAS AND GENERAL ALMANACS—Abstracting, Bibliographies, Statistics*

DIRASAT. EDUCATIONAL SCIENCES. see *EDUCATION—Abstracting, Bibliographies, Statistics*

011   USA   ISSN 0899-353X
Z5771   CODEN: DIPREH
DIRECTORIES IN PRINT. Text in English. 1980. irreg. (in 3 vols.), latest vol.24, 2004. USD 625 (effective 2004). **Document type:** *Directory, Trade.* **Description:** Details of current projects and associated literature worldwide, with information on funding agencies and the communications infrastructure.
Formerly (until 1988): Directory of Directories (0275-5580)
Related titles: Online - full text ed.: (from The Dialog Corporation).
—BLDSC (3590.533500), CISTI, Linda Hall.
Published by: Gale Group (Subsidiary of: Thomson Corporation), 27500 Drake Rd, Farmington Hills, MI 48331-3535. TEL 248-699-8061, 800-877-4253, FAX 248-699-4253, galeord@gale.com, http://www.gale.com. Eds. Charles B Montney, Julie E Towell.

DIRECTORIO DE REVISTAS ESPANOLAS DE CIENCIA Y TECNOLOGIA (ONLINE EDITION). see *SCIENCES: COMPREHENSIVE WORKS—Abstracting, Bibliographies, Statistics*

DIRECTORIO DE REVISTAS ESPANOLAS DE CIENCIAS SOCIALES Y HUMANAS (ONLINE EDITION). see *SOCIAL SCIENCES: COMPREHENSIVE WORKS—Abstracting, Bibliographies, Statistics*

DIRECTORIO M P M - MEDIOS AUDIO-VISUALES/M P M - MEXICAN AUDIOVISUAL MEDIA RATES & DATA; tarifas y datos-cine, radio y television. (Medios Publicitarios Mexicanos) see *ADVERTISING AND PUBLIC RELATIONS—Abstracting, Bibliographies, Statistics*

DIRECTORIO M P M - MEDIOS IMPRESOS/M P M - MEXICAN PRINT MEDIA RATES & DATA; tarifas y datos-anuncio exterior, periodicos y revistas. (Medios Publicitarios Mexicanos) see *ADVERTISING AND PUBLIC RELATIONS—Abstracting, Bibliographies, Statistics*

011   GBR
DIRECTORY OF ACRONYMS. Text in English. 1993. biennial. GBP 27; GBP 33 foreign (effective 2001). **Document type:** *Bibliography.* **Description:** Provides details of more than 8,000 acronyms present in the Document Supply Centre's Conference Index database of over 300,000 records.
Published by: British Library, Document Supply Centre, c/o Mike Marcus, British Library, Boston Spa, Wetherby, W Yorkshir LS23 7BQ, United Kingdom. TEL 44-1937-546080, FAX 44-1937-546586, http://www.bl.uk/services/document/sed.html.
Subscr. to: Extenza - Turpin, Pegasus Dr, Stratton Business Park, Biggleswade, Beds SG18 8TQ, United Kingdom. TEL 44-1462-672555.

DIRECTORY OF EDITORS. see *PUBLISHING AND BOOK TRADE*

011 808.87   USA
DIRECTORY OF HUMOR MAGAZINES & HUMOR ORGANIZATIONS IN AMERICA (AND CANADA). Text in English. 1985. triennial. USD 34.95 (effective 2000). adv. **Document type:** *Directory.* **Description:** Covers humor and anything related to it.
Published by: Wry-Bred Press, Inc., 630 1st Ave., Apt. 32P, Madison Sq Sta, New York, NY 10016-3783. TEL 212-689-5473, FAX 212-689-6859, info@psychhumor.com, http://www.psychhumor.com. Ed., Pub., R&P, Adv. contact Glenn Ellenbogen.

015   IRN   ISSN 1028-7035
Z6958.I7
DIRECTORY OF IRANIAN PERIODICALS AND NEWSPAPERS/RAHNAMAY-I MAJALLAH-HA VA RUZNAMEHA-YI IRAN. Text in Persian, Modern. 1974. a. USD 30 (effective 2000). **Document type:** *Bibliography.* **Description:** Contains bibliographic information on all periodicals and newspapers published in Iran, plus the addresses, telephone and fax numbers of the publishers.
Incorporates: Directory of Iranian Newspapers; Former titles (until 1995): Rahnamay-i Majallah-ha-yi Iran (0378-7443); Directory of Iranian Periodicals (0084-9960)
Published by: National Library of Iran, Shahid Bahonar St., Tehran, 19548, Iran. TEL 98-21-2280937, FAX 98-21-2288680. Eds. Poori Soltani, Reza Eqtedar. Circ: 1,500.

DIRECTORY OF PERIODICALS PUBLISHED IN INDIA. see *PUBLISHING AND BOOK TRADE*

DIRECTORY OF POLITICAL NEWSLETTERS. see *PUBLIC ADMINISTRATION—Abstracting, Bibliographies, Statistics*

011   TWN   ISSN 1607-923X
DIRECTORY OF TAIWAN/TAIWAN ZHINAN. Text in Chinese, English. 1951. a. USD 15.40; USD 41.30 foreign. adv. **Document type:** *Directory.* **Description:** Lists phone numbers and names of chief executives for government, embassies, banks, business organizations, associations, airlines, insurance companies and more.
Published by: China News, 40 Tung Hsing Rd, 10th Fl, Taipei, Taiwan. TEL 886-2-27686002, FAX 886-2-27686773. Ed. Daisy C H Liao. Adv. contact Chiu Chi Sen.

DISKOGRAFIA. see *MUSIC—Abstracting, Bibliographies, Statistics*

DIVIDENDS FROM WOOD RESEARCH; recent publications of the Forest Products Laboratory. see *FORESTS AND FORESTRY—Abstracting, Bibliographies, Statistics*

334 011   IND
DOCUMENTATION BULLETIN FOR SOUTH-EAST ASIA✳ . Text in English. 1969. q. INR 30, USD 4.
Formerly: International Cooperative Alliance. Regional Office and Education Centre for South-East Asia. Documentation Bulletin (0012-4591)
Media: Duplicated (not offset).
Published by: International Cooperative Alliance, Regional Office and Education Centre for South-East Asia, 43 Friends Colony, P O Box 3312, New Delhi, 110 014, India. Ed. B D Pandey. Circ: 500.

016   ITA   ISSN 0070-6906
Z4
DOCUMENTI SULLE ARTI DEL LIBRO. Text in Italian. 1962. irreg., latest 1995. price varies.
Published by: Edizioni II Polifilo, Via Borgonuovo, 2, Milan, MI 20121, Italy. Ed. Alberto Vigevani.

DOKUMENTATIONSDIENST AFRIKA. AUSGEWAEHLTE NEUERE LITERATUR. see *POLITICAL SCIENCE—Abstracting, Bibliographies, Statistics*

DOKUMENTATIONSDIENST AFRIKA. KURZBIBLIOGRAPHIE. see *POLITICAL SCIENCE—Abstracting, Bibliographies, Statistics*

DOKUMENTATIONSDIENST ASIEN UND SUEDPAZIFIK. AUSGEWAEHLTE NEUERE LITERATUR. see *POLITICAL SCIENCE—Abstracting, Bibliographies, Statistics*

DOKUMENTATIONSDIENST ASIEN UND SUEDPAZIFIK. KURZBIBLIOGRAPHIE. see *POLITICAL SCIENCE—Abstracting, Bibliographies, Statistics*

DOKUMENTATIONSDIENST ASIEN UND SUEDPAZIFIK. REIHE A. see *POLITICAL SCIENCE—Abstracting, Bibliographies, Statistics*

DOKUMENTATIONSDIENST LATEINAMERIKA. AUSGEWAEHLTE NEUERE LITERATUR/DOCUMENTACION LATINOAMERICANA. BOLETIN BIBLIOGRAFICO. see *POLITICAL SCIENCE—Abstracting, Bibliographies, Statistics*

DOKUMENTATIONSDIENST VORDERER ORIENT. KURZBIBLIOGRAPHIE. see *POLITICAL SCIENCE—Abstracting, Bibliographies, Statistics*

DOKUMENTATIONSDIENST VORDERER ORIENT. REIHE A. see *POLITICAL SCIENCE—Abstracting, Bibliographies, Statistics*

DRUK BELARUSI. see *PUBLISHING AND BOOK TRADE—Abstracting, Bibliographies, Statistics*

DURHAM MIDDLE EAST PAPERS. see *ASIAN STUDIES*

E P A PUBLICATIONS BIBLIOGRAPHY QUARTERLY ABSTRACTS BULLETIN. (Environmental Protection Agency) see *ENVIRONMENTAL STUDIES—Abstracting, Bibliographies, Statistics*

E R I C CLEARINGHOUSE PUBLICATIONS. see *EDUCATION—Abstracting, Bibliographies, Statistics*

015   GBR   ISSN 0046-0958
EAST ANGLIAN BIBLIOGRAPHY. Text in English. 1960. q. GBP 30 in British Isles; GBP 44 foreign (effective 2001). adv. **Document type:** *Bibliography.* **Description:** Lists all local material added to public library collections in East Anglia.
Published by: East Anglian Librarian's Consultative Committee, Central Library, St Andrews St N, Bury St Edmunds, Suffolk IP33 1TZ, United Kingdom. TEL 44-1284-352551, FAX 44-1284-352566, http://www.suffolkcc.gov.uk/libraries_and_heritage. R&P Ed Button. Adv. contact Alan Leventhal. Circ: 65.

EAST ASIA BIBLIOGRAPHY; a review of new publications on China & the Far East. see *BUSINESS AND ECONOMICS—Abstracting, Bibliographies, Statistics*

EBSCO BULLETIN OF SERIALS CHANGES. see *LIBRARY AND INFORMATION SCIENCES*

015   GBR   ISSN 0140-7082
EDINBURGH BIBLIOGRAPHICAL SOCIETY TRANSACTIONS. Text in English. 1938. irreg., latest 2001, vol.VI, part 5. GBP 10 to individual members; GBP 15 to corporations; GBP 5 to students (effective 2001). back issues avail. **Document type:** *Academic/Scholarly.*
Formerly: Edinburgh Bibliographical Society. Publications
Published by: Edinburgh Bibliographical Society, c/o National Library of, George IV Bridge, Edinburgh, Scotland EH1 1EW, United Kingdom. TEL 44-131-226-4531, FAX 44-131-220-6662, TELEX 72638 NLSEDI G, library@admin.nls.uk. Ed., R&P Kenneth Dunn. Circ: 200.

EDITOR & PUBLISHER INTERNATIONAL YEAR BOOK; encyclopedia of the newspaper industry. see *JOURNALISM—Abstracting, Bibliographies, Statistics*

EDUCATION GUIDELINES. see *EDUCATION—Abstracting, Bibliographies, Statistics*

EDUCATIONAL LEGISLATION INDEX. see *LAW—Abstracting, Bibliographies, Statistics*

THE EFFICIENT HOUSE SOURCEBOOK; an annotated bibliography and directory of helpful organizations. see *BUILDING AND CONSTRUCTION*

EGYPTIAN MUSEUM. LIBRARY. CATALOGUE. see *ARCHAEOLOGY—Abstracting, Bibliographies, Statistics*

▼ *new title*   ➤ *refereed*   ✳ *unverified*   ◆ *full entry avail.*

B

011 800   USA   ISSN 0161-0996
Z5579.6
➤ **EIGHTEENTH CENTURY: A CURRENT BIBLIOGRAPHY.** Text in English. 1975. a. price varies. bk.rev.; dance rev.; music rev.; play rev. bibl. index. 600 p./no.; back issues avail. **Document type:** Academic/Scholarly. **Description:** Bibliography of books and articles in literature, art, history, philosophy and science from or about the eighteenth century.
Related titles: ◆ Supplement(s): Philological Quarterly. ISSN 0031-7977.
Published by: A M S Press, Inc., 63 Flushing Ave., # 417, Brooklyn, NY 11205-1005. TEL 212-777-4700, FAX 212-995-5413, amserve@earthlink.net. Eds. Kevin L Cope TEL 225-578-2864, Robert C Leitz.

➤ **EKONOMIKA. EKONOMICHNI NAUKY.** see BUSINESS AND ECONOMICS—Abstracting, Bibliographies, Statistics

➤ **EL-HI TEXTBOOKS AND SERIALS IN PRINT;** including related teaching materials K-12. see EDUCATION—Abstracting, Bibliographies, Statistics

➤ **ELECTRONIC JOURNAL OF AFRICANA BIBLIOGRAPHY.** see HISTORY—Abstracting, Bibliographies, Statistics

011   FRA   ISSN 1021-6928
ELEMENTS DE BIBLIOGRAPHIE SUR LES PAYS DU SAHEL/ELEMENTS FOR A BIBLIOGRAPHY ON THE SAHELIAN COUNTRIES. Text in French. 1976. a. free. **Document type:** Government.
Related titles: Microfiche ed.
Published by: Organization for Economic Cooperation and Development, 2 Rue Andre Pascal, Paris, 75775 Cedex 16, France. TEL 33-1-45248200, FAX 33-1-45248500, http://www.oecd.org. **U.S. orders to:** O E C D Turpin North America, PO Box 194, Downingtown, PA 19335-0194. TEL 610-524-5361, 800-456-6323, FAX 610-524-5417, bookscustomer@turpinna.com.

ELENCHUS OF BIBLICA. see RELIGIONS AND THEOLOGY—Abstracting, Bibliographies, Statistics

ENERGY INFORMATION DIRECTORY (YEAR). see ENERGY

EOTVOS LORAND TUDOMANYEGYETEM. TUDOMANYOS TAJEKOZTATO. see SCIENCES: COMPREHENSIVE WORKS—Abstracting, Bibliographies, Statistics

ERLANGER BAUSTEINE ZUR FRAENKISCHEN HEIMATFORSCHUNG. see HISTORY

ESTUARIES AND COASTAL WATERS OF THE BRITISH ISLES; an annual bibliography of recent scientific papers. see ENVIRONMENTAL STUDIES—Abstracting, Bibliographies, Statistics

015   ETH   ISSN 0071-1772
Z3521
ETHIOPIAN PUBLICATIONS: BOOKS, PAMPHLETS, ANNUALS AND PERIODICAL ARTICLES. Text in English. 1963. irreg. USD 5. back issues avail. **Document type:** Bibliography.
Indexed: AICP.
Published by: Addis Ababa University, Institute of Ethiopian Studies, PO Box 1176, Addis Ababa, Ethiopia. TEL 251-1-119469, FAX 251-1-552688, IES@padis.gn.apc.org. Ed. Abdussamad H Ahmad. Circ: 1,000.

ETUDES STRATEGIQUES ET MILITAIRES (COLLECTION). see LINGUISTICS—Abstracting, Bibliographies, Statistics

EUDORA WELTY NEWSLETTER. see LITERATURE

EUROPEAN BIBLIOGRAPHY OF SLAVIC AND EAST EUROPEAN STUDIES/BIBLIOGRAPHIE EUROPEENNE DES TRAVAUX SUR L'EX-URSS ET L'EUROPE DE L'EST/EUROPAEISCHE BIBLIOGRAPHIE OESTEUROPASTUDIEN. see HISTORY—Abstracting, Bibliographies, Statistics

EUROPEAN ORGANIZATION FOR NUCLEAR RESEARCH. LIST OF SCIENTIFIC PUBLICATIONS/CONSEIL EUROPEEN POUR LA RECHERCHE NUCLEAIRE. LISTE DES PUBLICATIONS SCIENTIFIQUES. see PHYSICS—Abstracting, Bibliographies, Statistics

EXTENSION BIBLIOGRAFICA. see SOCIAL SCIENCES: COMPREHENSIVE WORKS—Abstracting, Bibliographies, Statistics

F A S - F A X REPORTS: BUSINESS PUBLICATIONS. see ADVERTISING AND PUBLIC RELATIONS—Abstracting, Bibliographies, Statistics

F A S - F A X REPORTS: MAGAZINE, FARM AND RELIGIOUS PUBLICATIONS. see ADVERTISING AND PUBLIC RELATIONS—Abstracting, Bibliographies, Statistics

F & S INDEX. UNITED STATES (ANNUAL). see BUSINESS AND ECONOMICS—Abstracting, Bibliographies, Statistics

F I A F INTERNATIONAL FILMARCHIVE CD-ROM. (International Federation of Film Archives) see MOTION PICTURES—Abstracting, Bibliographies, Statistics

FACHBUCHVERZEICHNIS GEISTESWISSENSCHAFTEN. see EDUCATION—Abstracting, Bibliographies, Statistics

FACHBUCHVERZEICHNIS MEDIZIN. see MEDICAL SCIENCES—Abstracting, Bibliographies, Statistics

FACHBUCHVERZEICHNIS NATURWISSENSCHAFTEN. see BIOLOGY—Abstracting, Bibliographies, Statistics

015.71036   CAN   ISSN 0832-6045
Z1365
FACSIMILE. Text in English, French. 1986. s-a. free (effective 2004). **Document type:** Newsletter.
Published by: Canadian Institute for Historical Microreproductions/Institut Canadien de Microreproductions Historiques, 395 Wellington St, Rm 468, Ottawa, ON K1A 0N4, Canada. TEL 613-235-2628, FAX 613-235-9752, cihmicmh@nlc-bnc.ca, http://www.collectionscanada.ca/cihm/cihmftoc.htm, http://www.nlc-bnc.ca/cihm/.

FACTS ON FILE. see HISTORY—Abstracting, Bibliographies, Statistics

016.05   USA   ISSN 1059-6852
Z6941
FAXON GUIDE TO SERIALS. Text in English. 1931. a. USD 25; free to qualified personnel. adv. illus. **Document type:** Catalog.
Former titles: Faxon Librarians' Guide to Serials (0275-8466); Faxon Librarians' Guide (0146-2660); Faxon Librarians' Guide to Periodicals (0092-0487); Faxon Indexed Periodicals —Linda Hall.
Published by: Faxon Library Services from RoweCom (Subsidiary of: RoweCom, Inc.), 249 Vanderbilt Ave., Norwood, MA 02062-5033. TEL 617-329-3350, FAX 617-320-0141, TELEX 681-7238. Circ: 10,000.

011   PRI   ISSN 0015-0592
Z1201   CODEN: FBHIDO
FICHERO BIBLIOGRAFICO HISPANOAMERICANO✳ . Text in Spanish. 1961. 11/yr. USD 75. adv. bk.rev. index. reprint service avail. from PQC. **Document type:** Bibliography. **Description:** Lists new books in Spanish published in the Americas and Spain.
Related titles: Microfilm ed.: 1961 (from PQC).
Indexed: RASB.
—CASDDS, Linda Hall.
Published by: Melcher Ediciones, c/o Margaret Melcher, P O Box 41291, San Juan, 00940-1291, Puerto Rico. TEL 787-724-1352, FAX 787-724-2886.

011 956 011   LBN   ISSN 0257-439X
FIHRIST; index to Arabic periodical literature. Text in Arabic; Text occasionally in English, French, German, Spanish. 1981. q. LBP 500, USD 200. adv. bk.rev. index.
Published by: Al-Fihrist Academic Research Institute, Abu Hishmah Bldg., Farabi St., Watwat (al-zarif), P O Box 14 5968, Beirut, Lebanon. Ed. Samir Shaykh. Circ: 1,500.
Subscr. to: Syrian Lebanese Commercial Bank (Account no. for Al-Fihrist 20195), Hamra Branch, P O Box 118701, Beirut, Lebanon.

FILM & VIDEO FINDER. see COMMUNICATIONS—Abstracting, Bibliographies, Statistics

FILMATISEREDE BOEGER. see MOTION PICTURES

FILMSTATISTISCHES TASCHENBUCH. see MOTION PICTURES—Abstracting, Bibliographies, Statistics

FINE ARTS PERIODICALS; an international directory of the visual arts. see ART—Abstracting, Bibliographies, Statistics

FIRST NATIONS PERIODICAL INDEX. see ETHNIC INTERESTS—Abstracting, Bibliographies, Statistics

FOLKESKOLEN. KATALOG. see EDUCATION—Abstracting, Bibliographies, Statistics

FONTI E STUDI FRANCESCANI. see RELIGIONS AND THEOLOGY—Abstracting, Bibliographies, Statistics

FOR YOUNGER READERS, BRAILLE AND TALKING BOOKS. see HANDICAPPED—Abstracting, Bibliographies, Statistics

011   USA   ISSN 0015-8119
Z1219
FORTHCOMING BOOKS. Text in English. 1966. 3/yr. USD 299.95 free "Bowker's Buyer's Guide" (effective 2004). **Document type:** Directory, Bibliography. **Description:** Lists just-published and to-be-published books, with ISBNs and U.S. Library of Congress numbers.
Incorporates (1967-1986): Subject Guide to Forthcoming Books (0000-0264)
Related titles: Magnetic Tape ed.; Microfiche ed.; Online - full text ed.; ◆ Supplement to: Books in Print. ISSN 0068-0214.

Indexed: CBCARef, RASB.
—Linda Hall.
Published by: R.R. Bowker LLC (Subsidiary of: Cambridge Information Group), 630 Central Ave., New Providence, NJ 07974. TEL 908-286-1090, 800-526-9537, FAX 908-219-0098, info@bowker.com, http://www.bowker.com. **Subscr. to:** Order Dept., PO Box 32, New Providence, NJ 07974-9903. TEL 800-521-8110.

FRANCE. MINISTERE DE L'AMENAGEMENT DU TERRITOIRE ET DE L'ENVIRONNEMENT. BULLETIN DE DOCUMENTATION DE L'ENVIRONNEMENT. see ENVIRONMENTAL STUDIES—Abstracting, Bibliographies, Statistics

FREE MARKET ENVIRONMENTAL BIBLIOGRAPHY. see ENVIRONMENTAL STUDIES—Abstracting, Bibliographies, Statistics

FRENCH 20 BIBLIOGRAPHY; critical and biographical references for the study of French literature since 1885. see LINGUISTICS—Abstracting, Bibliographies, Statistics

FRENTE DE AFIRMACION HISPANISTA. see LITERATURE—Abstracting, Bibliographies, Statistics

011   USA   ISSN 1040-8258
Z6941   CODEN: FSONEO
FULLTEXT SOURCES ONLINE. Text in English. 1989. s-a. USD 149 (effective 2006). **Document type:** Directory, Trade. **Description:** Lists periodicals, journals, newspapers, newsletters and newswires available online in full text. Also lists URLs and dates of coverage for each title.
Related titles: Online - full text ed.: F S O Online. USD 249 (effective 2005).
—BLDSC (4055.564500), CISTI. **CCC.**
Published by: Information Today, Inc., 143 Old Marlton Pike, Medford, NJ 08055-8750. TEL 609-654-6266, FAX 609-654-4309, custserv@infotoday.com, http://www.fso-online.com/, http://www.infotoday.com. Ed. Mary Glose.

FUTURES RESEARCH QUARTERLY. see SCIENCES: COMPREHENSIVE WORKS

011 020   USA
G P O SALES PUBLICATIONS REFERENCE FILE: MAGNETIC TAPE. Text in English. irreg., latest vol.11, 1999, Feb. USD 11 newsstand/cover per vol. domestic for vol.11; USD 26.25 newsstand/cover per vol. foreign for vol.11 (effective 2004). **Document type:** Bibliography.
Media: Magnetic Tape.
Published by: U.S. Government Printing Office, 732 N Capitol St NW, Washington, DC 20401. TEL 202-512-1530, 888-293-6498, FAX 202-512-1262, http://www.gpo.gov. **Subscr. to:** U.S. Government Printing Office, Superintendent of Documents.

011 800   GBR
GALACTIC CENTRAL BIBLIOGRAPHIES. Text in English. 1990. irreg., latest vol.52, 1999. GBP 20 per issue to libraries (effective 2003 & 2004). **Document type:** Bibliography. **Description:** Provides current bibliographies of science fiction and fantasy writers. Includes all of the authors stories, books, poems, edited works, nonfiction works.
Published by: Galactic Central Publications, c/o Phil Stephensen-Payne Ed, 25a Copgrove Rd, Leeds, W Yorks LS8 2SP, United Kingdom. philsp@compuserve.com, http://www.philsp.com. Pub. Phil Stephensen-Payne. R&P Phil Stephensen Payne. **Outside UK orders to:** Chris Drumm, PO Box 445, Polk City, IA 50226.

011   USA
GALE DIRECTORY OF DATABASES. ONLINE DATABASES. Text in English. irreg., latest 2004. USD 360 per vol. (effective 2004). **Document type:** Directory, Trade.
Published by: Gale Group (Subsidiary of: Thomson Corporation), 27500 Drake Rd, Farmington Hills, MI 48331-3535. TEL 248-696-4253, 800-877-4253, FAX 248-399-8061, galeord@gale.com, international@gale.com.

016.05   USA   ISSN 1048-7972
Z6951
GALE DIRECTORY OF PUBLICATIONS AND BROADCAST MEDIA. Text in English. 1869. a. (in 5 vols.), latest 2004, 139th Ed. USD 905 (effective 2005); includes Gale Directory of Publications and Broadcast Media Update. **Document type:** Directory, Trade. **Description:** Bibliography of newspapers, magazines and trade publications.
Former titles (until 1990): Gale Directory of Publications (0892-1636); (until 1987): I M S Directory of Publications (0892-7715); (until 1986): The IMS Ayer Directory of Publications (0738-372X); (until 1983): Ayer Directory of Publications (0145-1642); (until 1972): Ayer Directory of Newspapers, Magazines, and Trade Publications (0067-2696)
Related titles: Online - full text ed.: (from The Dialog Corporation).
—BLDSC (4066.776000), CISTI.
Published by: Gale Group (Subsidiary of: Thomson Corporation), 27500 Drake Rd, Farmington Hills, MI 48331-3535. TEL 248-699-4253, 800-877-4253, FAX 248-699-8035, 800-414-5043, galeord@gale.com, http://www.galegroup.com. Ed. Erin Braun.

GARDEN LITERATURE INDEX. see *GARDENING AND HORTICULTURE—Abstracting, Bibliographies, Statistics*

GEOREF. see *EARTH SCIENCES—Abstracting, Bibliographies, Statistics*

GEOREF SERIALS LIST. see *EARTH SCIENCES—Abstracting, Bibliographies, Statistics*

GEORGE ELIOT - GEORGE HENRY LEWES STUDIES. see *LITERARY AND POLITICAL REVIEWS*

GEORGE MEANY MEMORIAL ARCHIVES LIBRARY CURRENT ACQUISITIONS. see *LABOR UNIONS—Abstracting, Bibliographies, Statistics*

GEOSOURCES. see *EARTH SCIENCES—Abstracting, Bibliographies, Statistics*

GEOTITLES; geoscience bibliography. see *EARTH SCIENCES—Abstracting, Bibliographies, Statistics*

015 DEU
GERMAN BOOKS OUT OF PRINT ON CD-ROM/VERZEICHNIS VERGRIFFENE BUECHER. Text in English, German. a. **Document type:** *Bibliography.* **Description:** Includes 380,000 titles dating back to 1987 from over 9,000 publishers.
Media: CD-ROM (from K. G. Saur Verlag GmbH & Co.). **Related titles:** ◆ Supplement to: Verzeichnis Lieferbarer Buecher - CD-ROM.
Published by: K.G. Saur Verlag GmbH (Subsidiary of: Gale Group), Ortlerstr 8, Munchen, 81373, Germany. TEL 49-89-76902-0, FAX 49-89-76901250, customerservice_saur@csi.com, http://www.saur.de.

015 DEU ISSN 1435-4039
GERMANY. DEUTSCHER BUNDESTAG. WISSENSCHAFTLICHE DIENSTE. AKTUELLE BIBLIOGRAPHIEN DER BIBLIOTHEK. Text in German. 1962. irreg. free. **Document type:** *Government.*
Formerly (until 1996): Germany. Deutscher Bundestag. Wissenschaftliche Dienste. Bibliographien
Published by: Deutscher Bundestag, Abteilung Wissenschaftliche Dienste, Platz der Republik, Berlin, 11011, Germany. TEL 49-30-227-0, FAX 49-30-22736878, mail@bundestag.de, http://www.bundestag.de.

015 DEU ISSN 1435-4918
GERMANY. DEUTSCHER BUNDESTAG. WISSENSCHAFTLICHE DIENSTE. LAENDERBIBLIOGRAPHIEN DER BIBLIOTHEK. Text in German. 1996. irreg. free. **Document type:** *Government.*
Published by: Deutscher Bundestag, Abteilung Wissenschaftliche Dienste, Platz der Republik, Berlin, 11011, Germany. TEL 49-30-227-0, FAX 49-30-22736878, mail@bundestag.de, http://www.bundestag.de.

GERMANY. DEUTSCHER BUNDESTAG. WISSENSCHAFTLICHE DIENSTE. NEUE AUFSAETZE IN DER BIBLIOTHEK. see *SCIENCES: COMPREHENSIVE WORKS—Abstracting, Bibliographies, Statistics*

011 DEU ISSN 0931-3397
GERMANY. DEUTSCHER BUNDESTAG. WISSENSCHAFTLICHE DIENSTE. NEUERWERBUNGEN DER BIBLIOTHEK. Text in German. 1961. 6/yr. free. **Document type:** *Government.*
Formerly: Germany (Federal Republic, 1949-). Deutscher Bundestag Wissenschaftliche Dienste. Neuerwerbungen
Published by: Deutscher Bundestag, Abteilung Wissenschaftliche Dienste, Platz der Republik, Berlin, 11011, Germany. TEL 49-30-227-0, FAX 49-30-22736878, mail@bundestag.de, http://www.bundestag.de. Circ: 1,350.

016 DEU
GESAMTVERZEICHNIS (YEAR). Text in German. a.
Published by: Bohlau Verlag Gmbh & Cie, Theodor-Heuss-Str 76, Cologne, 51149, Germany. TEL 49-2203-307021, FAX 49-2203-307349.

GEST-GUEST QUARTERLY; a historical & genealogical newsletter for Gest, Gist, Guess & Guest Families. see *GENEALOGY AND HERALDRY—Abstracting, Bibliographies, Statistics*

GET READY SHEET. see *COMMUNICATIONS—Abstracting, Bibliographies, Statistics*

015 GHA ISSN 0855-0093
GHANA NATIONAL BIBLIOGRAPHY. Text in English. 1967. bi-m. USD 60. bibl. **Document type:** *Bibliography.* **Description:** Covers material published in Ghana, including new serials, books by Ghanaians about Ghana published abroad, theses and dissertations, periodical articles about Ghana, and a list of publishers whose publications are listed in particular issues and their addresses.
Formerly: Ghana: A Current Bibliography (0072-4378)
Published by: Ghana Library Board, George Padmore Research Library of African Affairs, PO Box 2970, Accra, Ghana. TEL 233-21-223526. Circ: 200.

016 ITA ISSN 0085-2317
GIUNTA CENTRALE PER GLI STUDI STORICI, ROME. BIBLIOGRAFIA STORICA NAZIONALE. Text in Italian. 1939. a. price varies. reprints avail. **Document type:** *Directory, Bibliography.*
Published by: (Giunta Centrale per gli Studi Storici), Laterza Editori, Via di Villa Sacchetti 17, Rome, 00197, Italy. TEL 39-06-3218393, FAX 39-06-3223853, http://www.laterza.it.

015 ITA
GIUNTA REGIONALE DEL VENETO. NOTIZIARIO BIBLIOGRAFICO. Text in Italian. 3/yr. free.
Published by: Giunta Regionale del Veneto, 168 Palazzo Sceriman, Venice, VE 30121, Italy. Circ: 15,000.

GLOBAL ACCUMULATIVE BIBLIOGRAPHY OF ACTION LEARNING. see *EDUCATION—Abstracting, Bibliographies, Statistics*

011 USA
GLOBAL BOOKS IN PRINT WITH BOOK REVIEWS. Text in English. d. USD 3,475 to individuals single user; USD 7,500 to institutions 5 users (effective 2005). bk.rev. **Document type:** *Directory, Trade.* **Description:** Contains information on over 11 million book, audio book, and video titles.
Media: Online - full text.
Published by: R.R. Bowker LLC (Subsidiary of: Cambridge Information Group), 630 Central Ave., New Providence, NJ 07974. TEL 908-286-1090, 800-526-9537, FAX 908-219-0098, info@bowker.com, http://www.globalbooksinprint.com/, http://www.bowker.com.

354 015 CAN ISSN 0709-0412
GOVERNMENT OF CANADA PUBLICATIONS QUARTERLY CATALOGUE; a comprehensive listing of all Government publications with index. Text in English, French. 1953. q. CND 76 domestic; USD 91.20 foreign. index.
Formerly: Canadian Government Publications Monthly Catalogue (0008-3690)
Indexed: PopulInd, RASB.
—Linda Hall.
Published by: Government of Canada Publications, Publishing and Depository Services, Public Works and Government Services Canada, Ottawa, ON K1A 0S9, Canada. TEL 819-956-5365, FAX 819-956-5134. Circ: 2,800.

GREAT AMERICAN ORATORS. see *HISTORY—Abstracting, Bibliographies, Statistics*

GREAT BRITAIN. DEPARTMENT OF THE ENVIRONMENT, TRANSPORT AND THE REGIONS. LIBRARY SERVICES. PUBLICATIONS ISSUED IN (YEAR). see *ENVIRONMENTAL STUDIES—Abstracting, Bibliographies, Statistics*

GREAT BRITAIN. DEPARTMENT OF THE ENVIRONMENT, TRANSPORT AND THE REGIONS. LIBRARY SERVICES. PUBLICATIONS MONTHLY LIST. see *ENVIRONMENTAL STUDIES—Abstracting, Bibliographies, Statistics*

011 GBR ISSN 0267-1727
GREAT BRITAIN. H.M.S.O. BOOKS IN PRINT. Variant title: H.M.S.O. in Print. Text in English. 1985. bi-m. **Document type:** *Catalog, Government.* **Description:** Lists all H.M.S.O. publications in print and available from the Publications Centre.
Media: Microfiche. **Related titles:** Online - full text ed.: (from The Dialog Corporation).
Published by: H.M.S.O. Books, 51 Nine Elms Ln, London, SW8 5DA, United Kingdom. TEL 44-20-7873-0011, FAX 44-20-7873-8247. **Subscr. to:** PO Box 276, London SW8 5DJ, United Kingdom. TEL 44-20-7873-8499, FAX 44-20-7873-8222.

011 GBR ISSN 0951-8843
GREAT BRITAIN. H.M.S.O. DAILY LIST. Text in English. d. (5/w.). **Document type:** *Catalog, Government.* **Description:** Lists all U.K. government publications published or sold by H.M.S.O., including Parliamentary and non-Parliamentary publications, Statutory Instruments, and agency and Northern Ireland publications.
Formerly (until 1986): Daily List of Government Publications (0263-743X)
Related titles: Online - full text ed.: (from The Dialog Corporation).
Published by: H.M.S.O. Books, 51 Nine Elms Ln, London, SW8 5DA, United Kingdom. TEL 44-20-7873-0011. **Subscr. to:** PO Box 276, London SW8 5DJ, United Kingdom. TEL 44-20-7873-8499, FAX 44-20-7873-8222.

011 GBR ISSN 0955-7601
GREAT BRITAIN. H.M.S.O. PUBLICATIONS CATALOGUE. Text in English. a. **Document type:** *Catalog, Government.* **Description:** Lists all the publications received at H.M.S.O. during the calendar year from the British, European and international organizations for which H.M.S.O. is an agent.
Related titles: Online - full text ed.: (from The Dialog Corporation).
Published by: H.M.S.O. Books, 51 Nine Elms Ln, London, SW8 5DA, United Kingdom. TEL 44-20-7873-0011, FAX 44-20-7873-8247. **Subscr. to:** PO Box 276, London SW8 5DJ, United Kingdom. TEL 44-20-7873-8499, FAX 44-20-7873-8222.

011 GBR
GREAT BRITAIN. H.M.S.O. STATUTORY INSTRUMENTS LIST. Text in English. m. **Document type:** *Catalog, Government.* **Description:** Lists H.M.S.O. Statutory Instruments, which are not included in the monthly and annual catalogs. Includes Northern Ireland Statutory Rules.
Related titles: CD-ROM ed.: Justis U K Statutory Instruments. ISSN 1464-3871. GBP 900 (from Context Ltd.); Online - full text ed.: (from Context Ltd., The Dialog Corporation).
Indexed: RevApplEntom.
Published by: H.M.S.O. Books, 51 Nine Elms Ln, London, SW8 5DA, United Kingdom. TEL 44-20-7873-0011, FAX 44-20-7873-8247. **Subscr. to:** PO Box 276, London SW8 5DJ, United Kingdom. TEL 44-20-7873-8499, FAX 44-20-7873-8222.

011 GBR ISSN 1462-0022
Z2009
GREAT BRITAIN. STATIONERY OFFICE. ANNUAL CATALOGUE. Text in English. a. price varies. **Document type:** *Catalog, Government.* **Description:** Lists the publications that the Stationery Office received during the calendar year, except for Statutory Instruments.
Former titles (until 1996): Great Britain. H.M.S.O. Annual Catalogue (0951-8584); (until 1986): Great Britain. H.M.S.O. Government Publications (0143-9499); (until 1973): Great Britain. H.M.S.O. Catalogue of Government Publications
Related titles: Online - full text ed.: (from The Dialog Corporation).
—BLDSC (8447.294500), CISTI, Linda Hall.
Published by: Stationery Office, 51 Nine Elms Ln, London, SW8 5DA, United Kingdom. TEL 44-20-7873-0011. Circ: 6,600.

B

011 GBR
GREAT BRITAIN. STATIONERY OFFICE. CHAIRMEN REPORTS OF OFFICIAL COMMITTEES. INDEX. Text in English. 1985. q. **Document type:** *Catalog, Government.* **Description:** Lists the chairmen of committee reports published by the Stationery Office.
Formerly: Great Britain. H.M.S.O. Committee Reports Index (0267-2146)
Related titles: Online - full text ed.: (from The Dialog Corporation).
Published by: Stationery Office, 51 Nine Elms Ln, London, SW8 5DA, United Kingdom. TEL 44-20-7873-0011, FAX 44-20-7873-8463, book.orders@theso.co.uk, http://www.national-publishing.co.uk. **Subscr. to:** PO Box 276, London SW8 5DT, United Kingdom.

015.68 ZAF
GREY BIBLIOGRAPHIES. Text in English. 1946. irreg., latest vol.21, 1997. price varies. **Document type:** *Bibliography.* **Description:** Bibliographies of subjects of South African interest.
Published by: National Library of South Africa, PO Box 496, Cape Town, 8000, South Africa. TEL 27-21-4246320, FAX 27-21-4233359, http://www.nlsa.ac.za.

053.1 DEU ISSN 0017-4599
GROSS WARTENBERGER HEIMATBLATT. Text in German. 1955. bi-m. EUR 22.60 (effective 2003). adv. bk.rev. **Document type:** *Newsletter, Consumer.*
Published by: Helmut Preussler Verlag, Dagmarstr 8, Nuernberg, 90482, Germany. TEL 49-911-954780, FAX 49-911-542486, preussler-verlag@t-online.de, http://www.preussler-verlag.de. Ed. Karl Heinz Eisert.

050 ITA
GUIDA DELLA STAMPA PERIODICA ITALIANA. Text in Italian. 1969. biennial. price varies. adv. **Document type:** *Directory, Trade.* **Description:** Lists periodical publishers in Italy. Includes the statutes and organs of the union and legislation.
Published by: Unione della Stampa Periodica Italiana, Viale Battista Bardanzellu, 95, Rome, 00155, Italy. TEL 39-06-4065941, FAX 39-06-4066859, uspi@uspi.it, http://www.uspi.it. Circ: 10,000.

GUIDE DES BANQUES DE DONNEES FACTUELLES FRANCAISES SUR LES MATERIAUX. see *ENGINEERING—Computer Applications*

016 658.8 USA ISSN 0533-5248
Z5771
GUIDE TO AMERICAN DIRECTORIES. Text in English. 1947. biennial. USD 95 (effective 2000). **Document type:** *Directory.* **Description:** Covers over 200 classifications of business, industry and the professions.
Published by: B. Klein Publications, PO Box 635, Nyack, NY 10960-0635. TEL 914-358-6213, 800-747-1056, FAX 914-358-1059, toddpub@aol.com, http://www.toddpublications.com. Ed. Bernard Klein. Pub. Barry Klien. Circ: 5,000.

614.7 016 IND ISSN 0252-7979
GUIDE TO CURRENT LITERATURE IN ENVIRONMENTAL HEALTH ENGINEERING AND SCIENCE. Text in English. 1970. m. INR 20 to individuals; INR 60 to institutions.
Media: Duplicated (not offset).
Published by: National Environmental Engineering Research Institute, c/o The Director, Research Institute, Nehru Marg, Nagpur, Maharashtra 440 020, India. **Affiliate:** Council of Scientific and Industrial Research.

011 JPN
GUIDE TO EXHIBITIONS IN THE WORLD. Text in English. 1977. a. JPY 6,500. **Document type:** *Bibliography.* **Description:** Lists the schedules of major world exhibitions, trade fairs, international conferences and scientific conferences.
Published by: Convention Forum, Omori Bldg, 2-2-2 Kandatsu-Kasa-Machi, Chiyoda-ku, Tokyo, 101-0048, Japan. TEL 81-3-5294-6777. Ed. Yoko Omori.

GUIDE TO GOVERNMENT-LOAN FILMS VOLUME 1: THE CIVILIAN AGENCIES. see *MOTION PICTURES—Abstracting, Bibliographies, Statistics*

011 GBR
GUIDE TO INTERNATIONAL JOURNALS & PERIODICALS. Text in English. 1887. a. free. adv. **Document type:** *Directory.* **Description:** Lists 8,500 journals and other periodicals in all major subject areas.
Former titles: Little Red Book (0265-5810); Guide to the Press of the World (0072-8748)
Published by: RoweCom UK, Ltd. (Subsidiary of: RoweCom, Inc.), Dawson (Uk) Ltd, Cannon House, Park Farm Rd, Folkestone, Kent CT19 5EE, United Kingdom. TEL 44-1303-850101, FAX 44-1303-850440, http://www.dawson.co.uk. Ed. Reinhild Coles. Adv. contact Marion Watts. Circ: 6,000.

B

017 DEU ISSN 0163-8386
Z1033.M5
GUIDE TO MICROFORMS IN PRINT. SUBJECT. Variant title: Subject Guide to Microforms in Print (Year). Text in German. 1975. a. USD 430 (effective 2001). index. **Document type:** *Directory, Trade.* **Description:** Provides subject access to all the microform publications listed in Guide to Microform in Print. Titles are categorized under subject headings based on the Dewey Decimal System.
Incorporates: International Microforms in Print; Formerly (until 1978): Subject Guide to Microforms in Print (0090-290X)
—CISTI.
Published by: K.G. Saur Verlag GmbH (Subsidiary of: Gale Group), Ortlerstr 8, Munchen, 81373, Germany. TEL 49-89-76902-0, FAX 49-89-76902150, customerservice_saur@csi.com, http://www.saur.de. Circ: 1,500.

011 DEU ISSN 0164-0739
Z1033.M5
GUIDE TO MICROFORMS IN PRINT. SUPPLEMENT. Text in German. 1977. a. USD 185 (effective 2001). adv. bibl. back issues avail. **Document type:** *Directory, Bibliography.* **Description:** Provides both author-title and subject listings of new titles published since the previous edition of the two main volumes.
Formerly (until 1979): Microlist (0362-1014)
Published by: K.G. Saur Verlag GmbH (Subsidiary of: Gale Group), Ortlerstr 8, Munchen, 81373, Germany. TEL 49-89-76902-0, FAX 49-89-76902150, customerservice_saur@csi.com, http://www.saur.de. Circ: 1,000.

GUIDE TO REFERENCE BOOKS FOR SCHOOL MEDIA CENTERS. see *LIBRARY AND INFORMATION SCIENCES—Abstracting, Bibliographies, Statistics*

011.02 USA
GUIDE TO REFERENCE SOURCES. Text in English. 1902. a., latest vol.12, 2000. USD 275 to non-members; USD 247.50 to members (effective 2003). **Description:** Comprehensive coverage of reference books in all fields.
Formerly (until 2000): Guide to Reference Books (Year) (0072-8624)
—CCC.
Published by: American Library Association, 50 E Huron St, Chicago, IL 60611-2795. TEL 800-545-2433, FAX 312-944-8741, http://www.ala.org. Ed. Robert Kieft. **Subscr. to:** PO Box 932501, Atlanta, GA 31193-2501. TEL 866-746-7252, FAX 770-442-9742, ala-orders@pbd.com.

011 DEU ISSN 1439-2747
GUIDE TO REPRINTS. AUTHOR - TITLE. Text in Multiple languages. 1967. a. EUR 298 domestic; USD 328 foreign (effective 2004).
Supersedes in part (in 2000): Guide to Reprints (0072-8667)
—Linda Hall.
Published by: K.G. Saur Verlag GmbH (Subsidiary of: Gale Group), Ortlerstr 8, Munchen, 81373, Germany. TEL 49-89-769020, FAX 49-89-76902150, saur.info@thomson.com, http://www.saur.de.

011 DEU ISSN 1439-2755
Z1000.5
GUIDE TO REPRINTS. SUBJECTS. Text in English, French, German, Italian, Latin, Spanish. 1967. a. (in 1 vol., 2 nos./vol.). EUR 298 (effective 2004). adv. **Document type:** *Bibliography.*
Supersedes in part (in 2000): Guide to Reprints (0072-8667)
—Linda Hall.
Published by: K.G. Saur Verlag GmbH (Subsidiary of: Gale Group), Ortlerstr 8, Munchen, 81373, Germany. TEL 49-89-76902223, FAX 49-89-76902150, customerservice_saur@csi.com, http://www.saur.de. Ed. Chrisiane Raabe. R&P, Adv. contact Christiane Raabe. Circ: 2,000.

GUIDE TO THE AMERICAN RIGHT; directory and bibliography. see *POLITICAL SCIENCE—Abstracting, Bibliographies, Statistics*

011.53 USA
A GUIDE TO U S GOVERNMENT INFORMATION; subject bibliography index. Text in English. a. free. **Document type:** *Bibliography.* **Description:** Lists individual subject bibliographies available from the U.S. Government Printing Office.
Published by: U.S. Government Printing Office, 732 N Capitol St NW, Washington, DC 20401. TEL 202-512-1530, 888-293-6498, FAX 202-512-1262. **Subscr. to:** U.S. Government Printing Office, Superintendent of Documents. orders@gpo.gov.

GUIDES TO INFORMATION SOURCES SERIES. see *LIBRARY AND INFORMATION SCIENCES*

015 GUY ISSN 0376-5202
Z1791
GUYANESE NATIONAL BIBLIOGRAPHY. Text in English. 1973. q. GYD 100, USD 30 (effective 1995). index. **Document type:** *Bibliography.*
Published by: National Library, 76-77 Main and Church Sts., PO Box 10240, Georgetown, Guyana. TEL 592-2-74053, natlib@sdnp.org.gy. Ed. Karen Sills. R&P Gwyneth Browman. Circ: 250.

GYMNASIET OG HF. see *EDUCATION—Abstracting, Bibliographies, Statistics*

H C I M A QUARTERLY CURRENT AWARENESS BULLETIN FOR HOSPITALITY MANAGEMENT. see *HOTELS AND RESTAURANTS—Abstracting, Bibliographies, Statistics*

012 GBR ISSN 1462-477X
H M S O AGENCY CATALOGUE. (Her Majesty's Stationery Office) Text in English. a. **Document type:** *Catalog, Government.*
—BLDSC (8447.294200).
Published by: H.M.S.O., Publications Centre, PO Box 276, London, SW8 5DT, United Kingdom. TEL 44-20-7873-0011, http://www.hmso.gov.uk.

011 DEU
HAMBURG-BIBLIOGRAPHIE. Text in German. 1995. a. **Document type:** *Bibliography.*
Published by: (Staats- und Universitaetsbibliothek Hamburg), K.G. Saur Verlag GmbH (Subsidiary of: Gale Group), Ortlerstr 8, Munchen, 81373, Germany. TEL 49-89-76902-0, FAX 49-89-76902150, customerservice_saur@csi.com, http://www.saur.de.

016.05 NLD ISSN 0440-1875
Z6956.N45
HANDBOEK VAN DE NEDERLANDSE PERS EN PUBLICITEIT. Text in Dutch. 1953. s-a. EUR 275 (effective 2005). adv. bk.rev. **Document type:** *Directory, Academic/Scholarly.* **Description:** Provides comprehensive information on Dutch periodical publications, including advertising rates and contact names, and an index to publishing, advertising and publicity companies.
Related titles: CD-ROM ed.: Nijgh Media Disc.
Published by: Nijgh Periodieken B.V., Postbus 122, Schiedam, 3100 AC, Netherlands. TEL 31-10-4274100, FAX 31-10-4739911, hnp@nijgh.nl, info@nijgh.nl, http://www.handboeknederlandsepers.nl, http://www.nijgh.nl. Ed. Christel Lieskamp TEL 31-10-4274126. Pub. Rinus Vissers. Adv. contact Irshaad Raghoebar TEL 31-10-4274150. B&W page EUR 2,090, color page EUR 3,505; 129 x 183. Circ: 5,000.

016 300 ISR
➤ **HARRY S. TRUMAN RESEARCH INSTITUTE FOR THE ADVANCEMENT OF PEACE. REPRINT SERIES.** Text in English. 1971. irreg. per issue exchange basis. bibl. **Document type:** *Academic/Scholarly.*
Formerly: Harry S Truman Research Institute, Jerusalem. Occasional Papers
Published by: Hebrew University of Jerusalem, Harry S. Truman Research Institute for the Advancement of Peace, Mount Scopus, Jerusalem, Israel. TEL 972-2-5882300, FAX 972-2-5828076, mstruman@pluto.mscc.huji.ac.il. Ed., R&P Lisa Perlman TEL 972-2-5882315. Circ: 500.

026 059.992 USA
HARVARD - YENCHING LIBRARY BIBLIOGRAPHICAL SERIES. Text in English. 1970. irreg. (approx. every 4 or 5 yrs.), latest vol.4. price varies. **Document type:** *Academic/Scholarly.*
Published by: Harvard - Yenching Library, 2 Divinity Ave, Cambridge, MA 02138. TEL 617-495-3327, FAX 617-496-6008. Circ: 200.

015 USA
HAWAIIAN ACQUISITION LIST; a quarterly bibliography. Text in English. 1944. q. free. **Document type:** *Bibliography.*
Formerly (until 1985): Current Hawaiiana (0011-3522)
Media: Duplicated (not offset).
Published by: University of Hawaii Library, Hawaiian Collection, 2550 the Mall, Honolulu, HI 96822. TEL 808-956-7923, FAX 808-956-5968, http://www2.hawaii.edu/~speccoll/h.html/. Ed. Chieko Tachihata. Circ: 180 (controlled).

HEALTH INDUSTRY QUICKSOURCE; a complete descriptive reference to healthcare information resources. see *MEDICAL SCIENCES—Abstracting, Bibliographies, Statistics*

HEALTHCARE RESOURCES; an internet miniguide. see *MEDICAL SCIENCES—Abstracting, Bibliographies, Statistics*

015 DEU ISSN 0171-1423
Z2244.H5
HESSISCHE BIBLIOGRAPHIE. Text in German. 1977. a. price varies. **Document type:** *Bibliography.*
Related titles: CD-ROM ed.: (from K. G. Saur Verlag GmbH & Co.); Online - full text ed.
Published by: (Stadt- und Universitatsbibliothek Frankfurt am Main), K.G. Saur Verlag GmbH (Subsidiary of: Gale Group), Ortlerstr 8, Munchen, 81373, Germany. TEL 49-89-76902-0, FAX 49-89-76902150, customerservice_saur@csi.com, http://www.saur.de.

015 DEU ISSN 0170-2408
HIERSEMANNS BIBLIOGRAPHISCHE HANDBUECHER. Text in German. 1979. irreg., latest vol.15, 2002. price varies. **Document type:** *Monographic series, Bibliography.*
Published by: Anton Hiersemann Verlag, Haldenstr 30, Stuttgart, 70376, Germany. TEL 49-711-549971-0, FAX 49-711-54997121, info@hiersemann.de, http://www.hiersemann.de.

HIGH BROWSE. see *HANDICAPPED—Abstracting, Bibliographies, Statistics*

HISPANIC MEDIA & MARKET SOURCE. see *ADVERTISING AND PUBLIC RELATIONS—Abstracting, Bibliographies, Statistics*

015 AUS
HISTORICAL SOCIETY OF SOUTH AUSTRALIA. GUIDESHEET. Text in English. 1978. irreg. free. back issues avail. **Document type:** *Monographic series.*
Published by: Historical Society of South Australia Inc., Institute Bldg., 122 Kintore Ave, Adelaide, SA 5000, Australia. TEL 61-8-82264000. Ed. Brian Samuels. Circ: 2,000.

011 ARG ISSN 0073-327X
HONTANAR✶. Text in Spanish. irreg.
Published by: Editorial Universitaria de Buenos Aires, Avda. Rivadavia, 1571-1573, Capital Federal, Buenos Aires 1033, Argentina.

HUMAN RIGHTS ORGANIZATIONS & PERIODICALS DIRECTORY. see *POLITICAL SCIENCE—Abstracting, Bibliographies, Statistics*

850 011 DEU ISSN 0177-9478
HUMANISTISCHE BIBLIOTHEK. REIHE I: ABHANDLUNGEN. Text in German. 1967. irreg., latest vol.47. **Document type:** *Monographic series.*
Published by: Wilhelm Fink Verlag, Ohmstr 5, Munich, 80802, Germany. TEL 49-89-348017, FAX 49-89-341378, http://www.fink.de. R&P Marlene Braun.

850 011 DEU ISSN 0177-9486
HUMANISTISCHE BIBLIOTHEK. REIHE II: TEXTE. Text in German. 1968. irreg., latest vol.32, 1997. adv. **Document type:** *Monographic series.*
Indexed: BHA.
Published by: Wilhelm Fink Verlag, Ohmstr 5, Munich, 80802, Germany. TEL 49-89-348017, FAX 49-89-341378, http://www.fink.de. R&P Marlene Braun. Adv. contact Axel Korlendick.

850 011 DEU ISSN 0177-9494
HUMANISTISCHE BIBLIOTHEK. REIHE III: SKRIPTEN. Text in German. 1972. irreg., latest vol.4. **Document type:** *Monographic series.*
Published by: Wilhelm Fink Verlag, Ohmstr 5, Munich, 80802, Germany. TEL 49-89-348017, FAX 49-89-341378, http://www.fink.de. R&P Marlene Braun.

HYDROTITLES; hydroscience bibliography. see *EARTH SCIENCES—Abstracting, Bibliographies, Statistics*

001 016 DEU ISSN 1618-923X
I B Z - INTERNATIONALE BIBLIOGRAPHIE DER GEISTES- UND SOZIALWISSENSCHAFTLICHEN ZEITSCHRIFTENLITERATUR/INTERNATIONAL BIBLIOGRAPHY OF PERIODICAL LITERATURE FROM ALL FIELDS OF KNOWLEDGE. Short title: I B Z. Text in Multiple languages. N.S. 1965. 2/yr. EUR 3,066, CHF 5,277 (effective 2005). illus. index. reprints avail. **Document type:** *Bibliography.*

Former titles (until 2000): I B Z - Internationale Bibliographie der Zeitschriftenliteratur aus Allen Gebieten des Wissens (0177-8773); (until 1984): Internationale Bibliographie der Zeitschriftenliteratur aus Allen Gebieten des Wissens (0020-9201)
Related titles: CD-ROM ed.: N.S. EUR 3,014 (effective 2005); Online - full content ed.: N.S. EUR 3,014 (effective 2005).
Indexed: RASB.
—BLDSC (4554.020000), Linda Hall.
Published by: K.G. Saur Verlag GmbH (Subsidiary of: Gale Group), Ortlerstr 8, Munchen, 81373, Germany. TEL 49-89-769020, FAX 49-89-76902150, saur.info@thomson.com, http://www.saur.de.

I C S S R UNION CATALOGUE OF SOCIAL SCIENCE PERIODICALS. see *SOCIAL SCIENCES: COMPREHENSIVE WORKS—Abstracting, Bibliographies, Statistics*

011 NLD
I D C PUBLISHERS. CATALOGUE OF CATALOGUES. Text in English. 1993. biennial. free. illus. **Document type:** *Catalog.* **Description:** Provides a comprehensive guide to 271 available microform collections of historical and current materials, grouped by general subject areas in the arts, history, religion, law and sciences, with brief synopses describing the scope of each individual collection. Also includes information on CD-ROM publications.
Formerly: Inter Documentation Company. Catalogue of Catalogues
Published by: I D C Publishers, PO Box 11205, Leiden, 2301 EE, Netherlands. TEL 31-71-5142700, FAX 31-71-5131721, info@idc.nl, http://www.idc.nl.

I E C CATALOGUE OF PUBLICATIONS. see *ELECTRONICS*

016.05 FRA ISSN 1018-4783
CODEN: ILSAEN
I S S N COMPACT; CD-ROM edition of the ISSN Register. (International Standard Serial Number) Text in English, French. 1992. q. back issues avail. **Document type:** *Bibliography.* **Description:** Bibliographic information for all serial publications that have been assigned an ISSN, with a listing of abbreviations used as key words.
Media: CD-ROM. **Related titles:** ♦ Magnetic Tape ed.: I S S N Register (Tape Edition). ISSN 1021-500X; ♦ Online - full text ed.: I S S N Portal. ISSN 1819-1819.
Published by: International Centre for the Registration of Serials, I S S N International Centre/Centre International d'Enregistrement des Publications en Serie, 20 rue Bachaumont, Paris, 75002, France. TEL 33-1-44882220, FAX 33-1-40263243, issnic@issn.org, portal@issn.org, http://www.issn.org.

016.05 FRA ISSN 1819-1819
I S S N PORTAL. (International Standard Serial Number) Text in English, French. 1998. base vol. plus m. updates. **Document type:** *Database, Bibliography.* **Description:** Bibliographic information for all serial publications that have been assigned an ISSN, with a listing of abbreviations used as key words.
Formerly (until 2005): I S S N Online (1560-1560)
Media: Online - full text (from International Network for the Availability of Scientific Publications, African Journals Online). **Related titles:** ♦ CD-ROM ed.: I S S N Compact. ISSN 1018-4783; ♦ Magnetic Tape ed.: I S S N Register (Tape Edition). ISSN 1021-500X.
—BLDSC (4583.976260).
Published by: International Centre for the Registration of Serials, I S S N International Centre/Centre International d'Enregistrement des Publications en Serie, 20 rue Bachaumont, Paris, 75002, France. TEL 33-1-44882220, FAX 33-1-40263243, portal@issn.org, http://portal.issn.org.

011 FRA ISSN 1021-500X
I S S N REGISTER (TAPE EDITION)/REGISTRE DE L'I S S N (EDITION SUR BANDE MAGNETIQUE). (International Standard Serial Number) Text in French. 1974. q.
Formerly (until 1993): I S D S Register (Tape Edition) (0256-8888)
Media: Magnetic Tape. **Related titles:** ♦ CD-ROM ed.: I S S N Compact. ISSN 1018-4783; ♦ Online - full text ed.: I S S N Portal. ISSN 1819-1819.
Published by: International Centre for the Registration of Serials, I S S N International Centre/Centre International d'Enregistrement des Publications en Serie, 20 rue Bachaumont, Paris, 75002, France. TEL 33-1-44882220, FAX 33-1-40263243, issnic@issn.org, portal@issn.org, http://www.issn.org. Circ: 50.

IMPRESSUM BULLETIN. see *JOURNALISM—Abstracting, Bibliographies, Statistics*

IMPRESSUM - SCHWEIZERISCHES MEDIENHANDBUCH. see *JOURNALISM—Abstracting, Bibliographies, Statistics*

INDEX OF AIRWORTHINESS DIRECTIVES APPLICABLE IN CANADA/INDEX DES CONSIGNES DE NAVIGABILITE EN VIGUEUR AU CANADA. see *AERONAUTICS AND SPACE FLIGHT—Abstracting, Bibliographies, Statistics*

050 016.5 IDN ISSN 0216-6216
AI19.I55
INDEX OF INDONESIAN LEARNED PERIODICALS/INDEKS MADJALAH ILMIAH INDONESIA. Text in English, Indonesian. 1960. s-a. IDR 35,000, USD 40 (effective 2001).
Indexed: EI.
Published by: Pusat Dokumentasi dan Informasi Ilmiah, Lembaga Ilmu Pengetahuan Indonesia/Center for Scientific Documentation and Information, Indonesian Institute of Science, Jl. Jend. Gatot Subroto 10, Jakarta, 12710, Indonesia. TEL 62-21-5250719, FAX 62-21-5733467, admin@pdii.lipi.go.id, info@pdii.lipi.go.id. Ed. Endang Sir Rusmiyati Rahayu Mahmudah. Circ: 500. **Subscr. to:** Yayasan Memajukan Jasa Informasi (YASMIN), Gedung PDII-LIPI Lt. V, Jl Jend Gatot Subroto 10, Jakarta 12710, Indonesia.

INDEX TO BRITISH LITERARY BIBLIOGRAPHY. see *LITERATURE—Abstracting, Bibliographies, Statistics*

016 059.924 ISR
INDEX TO HEBREW PERIODICALS (CD-ROM EDITION). Text in Hebrew. 2/yr. USD 320 (effective 1999). **Document type:** *Abstract/Index.*
Supersedes: Index to Hebrew Periodicals (Microfiche Edition)
Media: CD-ROM.
Published by: University of Haifa Library, Haifa, 31905, Israel. maos@geo.haifa.ac.il. Ed. Amira Kehat. **Subscr. to:** C D I Systems, P O Box 45064, Jerusalem, Israel. FAX 972-2-5870115.

950 IND ISSN 0073-6090
DS405
INDIA: A REFERENCE ANNUAL. Text in English. 1953. a. USD 23. **Document type:** *Government.*
—BLDSC (4391.228000).
Published by: Ministry of Information & Broadcasting, Publications Division, Patiala House, Tilak Marg, New Delhi, 110 001, India. Circ: 20,000.

INDIA AND WORLD AFFAIRS: AN ANNUAL BIBLIOGRAPHY. see *POLITICAL SCIENCE—Abstracting, Bibliographies, Statistics*

015 IND
INDIA. DEPARTMENT OF PUBLICATION. PUBLICATIONS. Text in English. 1932. m. free. **Description:** Government publications catalog.
Published by: Government of India, Department of Publications, Civil Lines, New Delhi, 110 054, India. Circ: 300.

INDIAN BOOKS. see *PUBLISHING AND BOOK TRADE—Abstracting, Bibliographies, Statistics*

011 IND ISSN 0971-1589
Z3201
INDIAN BOOKS IN PRINT; a bibliography of Indian books published in the English language. Text in English. 1969. a. INR 7,500, USD 188 (effective 2000). back issues avail. **Document type:** *Bibliography.* **Description:** Contains complete bibliographical details of about 125,000 Indian books in print.
Related titles: CD-ROM ed.
—BLDSC (4393.150000).
Published by: Indian Bibliographies Bureau, 219, 'Kadambari', 19 IX Rohini, New Delhi, 110 085, India. TEL 91-11-7264112, FAX 91-11-7256502. Eds. Bhawna Singh, Sher Singh. Circ: 2,000.

INDIAN LITERATURE IN ENVIRONMENTAL ENGINEERING; a bibliographic review. see *ENVIRONMENTAL STUDIES—Abstracting, Bibliographies, Statistics*

015 IND ISSN 0019-6002
Z3201.A2
INDIAN NATIONAL BIBLIOGRAPHY. Text in English, Sanskrit. 1957. m. (plus a. cumulation). INR 540, USD 144; price varies for annual cums.. **Document type:** *Bibliography.* **Description:** Bibliographical record of current India publications in 14 major languages of India, received by the National Library under the Delivery of Books Act.
Related titles: Assamese ed.; Bengali ed.; Oriya ed.; Sanskrit ed.; Tamil ed.; Hindi ed.; Malayalam ed.
Indexed: RASB.
—Linda Hall.
Published by: Central Reference Library, Belvedere, Kolkata, West Bengal 700 027, India. TEL 91-479-1721-22. Circ: 500.

015 IND ISSN 0073-6708
INDIAN STATISTICAL INSTITUTE. LIBRARY. BIBLIOGRAPHIC SERIES✶ . Text in English. 1959. irreg. price varies.
Published by: Indian Statistical Institute, 203 Barrackpore Trunk Rd., Kolkata, West Bengal 700 108, India.

L'INDICE DEI LIBRI DEL MESE. see *PUBLISHING AND BOOK TRADE*

INDICE PROGRESIVO DE JURISPRUDENCIA. see *LAW—Abstracting, Bibliographies, Statistics*

011 AUS ISSN 0310-6659
Z3279
INDONESIAN ACQUISITIONS LIST/DAFTAR PENGADAAN BAHAN INDONESIA. Text in English. 1971. irreg. free. reprint service avail. from PQC,ISI. **Document type:** *Bibliography.* **Description:** Lists indonesian published books and serials acquired by the National Library of Australia.
Published by: National Library of Australia, Public Programs, Canberra, ACT 2600, Australia. TEL 61-6-262-1365, FAX 61-6-2734493, omann@nla.gov.au, http://www.nla.gov.au/asian/pub/ial/. Circ: 300.

011 FRA
INDUSTRIATHEQUE. Text in French. m.
Published by: Ministere de l'Industrie et de l'Amenagement de Territoire, 101, rue de Grenelle, Paris, Cedex 75700, France.

INFORMATION ALERTS. see *EDUCATION—Abstracting, Bibliographies, Statistics*

658 USA ISSN 0733-8961
CODEN: IRPTD4
THE INFORMATION REPORT. Text in English. 1974. m. bk.rev. bibl. s-a. index. back issues avail. **Document type:** *Newsletter, Bibliography.* **Description:** Informs managers about studies, surveys, reports, directories, and periodicals. Provides full ordering information.
Related titles: Online - full text ed.
Indexed: LibLit.
Published by: Washington Researchers, Ltd., 1655 N Fort Myer Dr, Ste 800, Arlington, VA 22209. TEL 703-312-2863, FAX 703-527-4586, research@researchers.com, http://www.washingtonresearchers.com. Ed. Laurie Schlagel. R&P Ellen O'Kane.

INSTITUT NATIONAL DES TECHNIQUES DE LA DOCUMENTATION. BULLETIN BIBLIOGRAPHIQUE. see *LIBRARY AND INFORMATION SCIENCES—Abstracting, Bibliographies, Statistics*

011 020 BEL
INSTITUT PROVINCIAL D'ETUDES ET RECHERCHES BIBLIOTHECONOMIQUES. MEMOIRES. Text in French. 1978. irreg. bk.rev. abstr.; bibl. back issues avail.
Published by: Institut Provincial d'Etudes et Recherches Bibliotheconomiques, Rue des Croisiers 15, Liege, 4000, Belgium. Circ: 1,000.

INSTITUT ZA NUKLEARNE NAUKE, VINCA. BIBLIOGRAFIJA RADOVA. see *ENERGY—Abstracting, Bibliographies, Statistics*

INSTITUTE OF DEVELOPMENT STUDIES. DEVELOPMENT BIBLIOGRAPHY SERIES. see *BUSINESS AND ECONOMICS—Abstracting, Bibliographies, Statistics*

011 IND
INSTITUTE OF ECONOMIC GROWTH. BOOK REVIEW LIST. Text in English. m. **Document type:** *Bibliography.*
Published by: Institute of Economic Growth, University of Enclave, New Delhi, 110 007, India. TEL 7257101.

011 IND
INSTITUTE OF ECONOMIC GROWTH. LIST OF PERIODICAL HOLDING IN THE I E G LIBRARY. Text in English. irreg. **Document type:** *Bibliography.*
Published by: Institute of Economic Growth, University of Enclave, New Delhi, 110 007, India. TEL 7257101.

011 IND
INSTITUTE OF ECONOMIC GROWTH. LIST OF PERIODICALS CURRENTLY RECEIVED IN THE I E G LIBRARY. Text in English. irreg. **Document type:** *Bibliography.*
Published by: Institute of Economic Growth, University of Enclave, New Delhi, 110 007, India. TEL 7257101.

011 IND
INSTITUTE OF ECONOMIC GROWTH. MICRO DOCUMENT LIST. Text in English. m. **Document type:** *Bibliography.*
Published by: Institute of Economic Growth, University of Enclave, New Delhi, 110 007, India. TEL 7257101.

011 IND
INSTITUTE OF ECONOMIC GROWTH. SELECTIVE LIST OF BOOKS AND DOCUMENTS ADDED TO THE LIBRARY. Text in English. m. **Document type:** *Bibliography.*
Published by: Institute of Economic Growth, University of Enclave, New Delhi, 110 007, India. TEL 7257101.

015 COL ISSN 0073-991X
INSTITUTO CARO Y CUERVO. SERIE BIBLIOGRAFICA. Text in Spanish. 1960. irreg., latest vol.15, 1995. price varies.
Indexed: IBR, IBZ.
Published by: Instituto Caro y Cuervo, Seccion de Publicaciones, Apartado Aereo 51502, Bogota, Cund, Colombia. carocuer@apenway.cam.co.

B

▼ new title ➤ refereed ✶ unverified ♦ full entry avail.

011 ESP
INSTITUTO NACIONAL DE ADMINISTRACION PUBLICA. SERVICIO DE BIBLIOTECA Y DOCUMENTACION. BOLETIN DE INFORMACION BIBLIOGRAFICA. Text in Spanish. 1959. m. free. **Document type:** *Bulletin, Government.*
Former titles: Instituto Nacional de Administracion Publica. Biblioteca. Boletin Informativo; (until 1977): Antigua Universidad de Cisneros. Instituto Nacional de Administracion Publica. Biblioteca. Boletin Informativo
Published by: (Servicio de Biblioteca y Documentacion), Instituto Nacional de Administracion Publica, Atocha 106, Madrid, 28012, Spain. TEL 34-91-2739100, FAX 34-91-2739270, publicaciones@inap.map.es, http://www.inap.map.es/. Ed. Enrique Orduna Rebollo.

011 DOM
INSTITUTO TECNOLOGICO DE SANTO DOMINGO. BIBLIOTECA. BOLETIN DE ADQUISICIONES. Text in Spanish. q. **Document type:** *Bibliography.*
Published by: (Biblioteca), Instituto Tecnologico de Santo Domingo, Apdo Postal 342-9, Santo Domingo, Dominican Republic. Ed. Lucero Arboleda de Roa.

B

800 015 ESP ISSN 0020-4536
Z1007
INSULA; revista de letras y ciencias humanas. Text in Spanish. 1946. m. EUR 52.20 domestic; EUR 72.90 in Europe; EUR 84.33 in the Americas (effective 2004). adv. bk.rev. bibl.; illus. cum.index: 1946-1980. 32 p./no.; back issues avail.; reprint service avail. from PQC. **Document type:** *Journal, Consumer.*
Related titles: Microfilm ed.: (from BHP, PQC).
Indexed: ASCA, AmH&L, ArtHuCI, BibInd, BiolAb, ChPerI, CurCont, HAPI, HistAb, IBR, MLA, MLA-IB, PCI, RASB, RILM, SFA, SSCI.
—CINDOC. **CCC.**
Published by: Insula: Libreria Ediciones y Publicaciones, S.A., Complejo Atica Edif. 4, Via de las Dos Casillas, 33, Madrid, 28224, Spain. TEL 34-91-7848200, FAX 34-91-3589505, insula@espasa.es. Ed. V Garcia de la Concha. Circ: 6,000.
Dist. by: Asociacion de Revistas Culturales de Espana, Hortaleza, 75, Madrid 28004, Spain. TEL 34-91-3086066, FAX 34-91-3199267, info@arce.es, http://www.arce.es.

960 015 DEU ISSN 0020-5877
Z3501
INTERNATIONAL AFRICAN BIBLIOGRAPHY; current books, articles and papers in African studies. Text in English. 1971. q. EUR 320; EUR 87 newsstand/cover (effective 2006). adv. illus. index. reprints avail. **Document type:** *Journal, Bibliography.* **Description:** Indexes the latest periodical articles, books and papers published internationally on Africa. Details more than 4000 publications, and articles from 1150 periodicals, 250 of which are African.
Indexed: AICP, CCA, PopulInd, RASB.
Published by: (Centre of African Studies GBR), K.G. Saur Verlag GmbH (Subsidiary of: Gale Group), Ortlerstr 8, Munchen, 81373, Germany. TEL 49-89-769020, FAX 49-89-76902150, info@saur.de, http://www.saur.de.

011 DEU ISSN 0724-2298
INTERNATIONAL ANNUAL BIBLIOGRAPHY OF FESTSCHRIFTEN. Short title: I J B F. Text in Multiple languages. 1980. a. (in 4 vols.). EUR 749 (effective 2003). **Document type:** *Bibliography.*
Related titles: CD-ROM ed.: EUR 725 (effective 2003).
Indexed: RASB.
Published by: K.G. Saur Verlag GmbH (Subsidiary of: Gale Group), Hirschberger Str. 17b, Osnabrueck, 49086, Germany. TEL 49-541-404590, FAX 49-541-41255, g.hochgeladen@saur.de, http://www.saur.de.

INTERNATIONAL BIBLIOGRAPHY OF HISTORICAL DEMOGRAPHY/BIBLIOGRAPHIE INTERNATIONALE DE LA DEMOGRAPHIE HISTORIQUE. see *POPULATION STUDIES—Abstracting, Bibliographies, Statistics*

INTERNATIONAL BIBLIOGRAPHY OF THE SOCIAL SCIENCES. ANTHROPOLOGY. see *ANTHROPOLOGY—Abstracting, Bibliographies, Statistics*

INTERNATIONAL BIBLIOGRAPHY OF THE SOCIAL SCIENCES. POLITICAL SCIENCE/BIBLIOGRAPHIE INTERNATIONALE DE SCIENCE POLITIQUE. see *POLITICAL SCIENCE—Abstracting, Bibliographies, Statistics*

INTERNATIONAL BIBLIOGRAPHY OF THE SOCIAL SCIENCES. SOCIOLOGY/BIBLIOGRAPHIE INTERNATIONALE DE SOCIOLOGIE. see *SOCIOLOGY—Abstracting, Bibliographies, Statistics*

016 327 GBR ISSN 0000-0477
Z6482
INTERNATIONAL BIBLIOGRAPHY: PUBLICATIONS OF INTERGOVERNMENTAL ORGANIZATIONS. Text in English. 1973. q. USD 100 (effective 2000). adv. index. **Document type:** *Bibliography.* **Description:** Current coverage of specialized information published by the United Nations system and related governmental organizations.
Formerly (until 1983): I B I D (International Bibliography, Information, Documentation) (0000-0329)
Indexed: RASB.
Published by: Marston Book Services Ltd., PO Box 269, Abingdon, Oxon OX14 4YN, United Kingdom. Circ: 1,200.

011 DEU ISSN 0170-9348
Z2005
INTERNATIONAL BOOKS IN PRINT; a listing of English-language titles published in Africa, Asia, Australia, Canada, Continental Europe, Latin America, New Zealand, Oceania, and the Republic of Ireland. Text in German. 1979. a. (in 4 vols.). USD 445 (effective 2000). **Document type:** *Directory, Bibliography.* **Description:** Covers English-language fiction and nonfiction books, pamphlets and microforms. Provides prices and detailed publisher and distributor information.
Related titles: CD-ROM ed.; Online - full text ed.: ISSN 1439-3980.
—BLDSC (4537.390000), CISTI.
Published by: K.G. Saur Verlag GmbH (Subsidiary of: Gale Group), Ortlerstr 8, Munchen, 81373, Germany. TEL 49-89-769020, FAX 49-89-76902150, info@saur.de, http://www.saur.de.

011 DEU
INTERNATIONAL BOOKS IN PRINT PLUS. Text in German. a. USD 1,303 standalone; USD 1,703 network ed. (effective 2000). **Document type:** *Directory.* **Description:** Provides access to more than 260,000 English-language titles published outside the US and the UK.
Formerly: International Books in Print on CD-ROM
Media: CD-ROM.
Published by: K.G. Saur Verlag GmbH (Subsidiary of: Gale Group), Ortlerstr 8, Munchen, 81373, Germany. TEL 49-89-769020, FAX 49-89-76902150, info@saur.de, http://www.saur.de.

INTERNATIONAL BULLETIN OF BIBLIOGRAPHY ON EDUCATION/BOLETIM INTERNACIONAL DE BIBLIOGRAFIA SOBRE EDUCACAO/BOLETIN INTERNACIONAL DE BIBLIOGRAFIA SOBRE EDUCACION/BULLETIN INTERNATIONAL DE BIBLIOGRAPHIE SUR L'EDUCATION/INTERNATIONALE BIBLIOGRAPHIE ZU DEN ERZIEHUNGSWISSENSCHAFTEN/SERVIZIO INTERNAZIONALE DI BIBLIOGRAFIA SULL'EDUCAZIONE. see *EDUCATION—Abstracting, Bibliographies, Statistics*

INTERNATIONAL DAIRY FEDERATION. CATALOGUE OF I D F PUBLICATIONS/FEDERATION INTERNATIONALE LAITIERE. CATALOGUE DES PUBLICATIONS. see *AGRICULTURE—Abstracting, Bibliographies, Statistics*

INTERNATIONAL DIRECTORY OF LITTLE MAGAZINES AND SMALL PRESSES. see *PUBLISHING AND BOOK TRADE—Abstracting, Bibliographies, Statistics*

016 DEU
INTERNATIONAL GUIDE TO MICROFORM MASTERS. Text in German. a. USD 1,595 (effective 2001). **Document type:** *Directory, Academic/Scholarly.* **Description:** Provides access to the microform collections of over 200 libraries and research institutes in the US, Canada and Europe.
Media: CD-ROM (from K. G. Saur Verlag GmbH & Co.).
Published by: K.G. Saur Verlag GmbH (Subsidiary of: Gale Group), Ortlerstr 8, Munchen, 81373, Germany. TEL 49-89-76902-0, FAX 49-89-76901250, customerservice_saur@csi.com, http://www.saur.de.

INTERNATIONAL INSTITUTE FOR LAND RECLAMATION AND IMPROVEMENT. BIBLIOGRAPHY. see *AGRICULTURE—Abstracting, Bibliographies, Statistics*

INTERNATIONAL MEDIA GUIDE. BUSINESS - PROFESSIONAL. EUROPE. see *ADVERTISING AND PUBLIC RELATIONS—Abstracting, Bibliographies, Statistics*

INTERNATIONAL MEDIA GUIDE. CONSUMER MAGAZINES WORLDWIDE. see *ADVERTISING AND PUBLIC RELATIONS—Abstracting, Bibliographies, Statistics*

INTERNATIONAL MEDIA GUIDE. NEWSPAPERS WORLDWIDE. see *ADVERTISING AND PUBLIC RELATIONS—Abstracting, Bibliographies, Statistics*

INTERNATIONAL MEDIEVAL BIBLIOGRAPHY; bibliography for the study of the European Middle Ages (450-1500). see *HISTORY—Abstracting, Bibliographies, Statistics*

INTERNATIONAL TELECOMMUNICATION UNION. CENTRAL LIBRARY. LIST OF PERIODICALS/UNION INTERNACIONAL DE TELECOMMUNICACIONES. BIBLIOTECA CENTRAL. LISTA DE REVISTAS/UNION INTERNATIONALE DES TELECOMMUNICATIONS. BIBLIOTHEQUE CENTRALE. LISTE DES PERIODIQUES. see *COMMUNICATIONS—Abstracting, Bibliographies, Statistics*

INTERNATIONAL TELECOMMUNICATION UNION. CENTRAL LIBRARY. LIST OF RECENT ACQUISITIONS/UNION INTERNACIONAL DE TELECOMUNICACIONES. BIBLIOTECA CENTRAL. LISTA DE ADQUISICIONES RECIENTES/UNION INTERNATIONALE DES TELECOMMUNICATIONS. BIBLIOTHEQUE CENTRALE. LISTE DES ACQUISITIONS RECENTES. see *COMMUNICATIONS—Abstracting, Bibliographies, Statistics*

INTERNATIONAL TELECOMMUNICATION UNION. LIST OF ANNUALS/UNION INTERNACIONAL DE TELECOMUNICACIONES. LISTA DE PUBLICACIONES ANUALES/UNION INTERNATIONALE DES TELECOMMUNICATIONS. LISTES DES PUBLICATIONS ANNUELLES. see *COMMUNICATIONS—Abstracting, Bibliographies, Statistics*

INTERNATIONAL TRADE RESOURCES; an internet miniguide. see *BUSINESS AND ECONOMICS—Abstracting, Bibliographies, Statistics*

011 DEU ISSN 0323-5734
Z2233
INTERNATIONALE BIBLIOGRAPHIE ZUR DEUTSCHEN KLASSIK 1750-1850. Text in German. 1960. a. adv. bk.rev. index. back issues avail. **Document type:** *Bibliography.* **Description:** Covers German literature and literary criticism, both books and articles. Includes index of reviews. In 2 sections: collections and general works; and individual writers.
Published by: K.G. Saur Verlag GmbH (Subsidiary of: Gale Group), Ortlerstr 8, Munchen, 81373, Germany. TEL 49-89-76902464, FAX 49-89-76902150, customerservice_saur@csi.com, http://www.saur.de. Ed. Heidi Zeilinger. Adv. contact Romana Kimmel.

INTERNATIONALE JAHRESBIBLIOGRAPHIE DER KONGRESSBERICHTE/INTERNATIONAL ANNUAL BIBLIOGRAPHY OF CONGRESS PROCEEDINGS. see *MEETINGS AND CONGRESSES—Abstracting, Bibliographies, Statistics*

011 USA
INTERNET BOOKWATCH. Text in English. m. back issues avail. **Document type:** *Newsletter, Trade.*
Media: Online - full content.
Published by: Midwest Book Review, 278 Orchard Dr, Oregon, WI 53575. TEL 608-835-7937, mbr@execpc.com, mwbookrevw@aol.com Ed. James A Cox.

016 020 DEU ISSN 0535-5079
INVENTARE NICHTSTAATLICHER ARCHIVE. Text in German. 1952. irreg., latest vol.39, 1997. price varies. **Document type:** *Monographic series, Academic/Scholarly.*
Published by: (Landschaftsverband Rheinland, Rheinisches Archiv- und Museumsamt), Rheinland Verlag GmbH, Abtei Brauweiler, Postfach 2140, Pulheim, 50250, Germany. TEL 49-2234-9854265, FAX 49-2234-82503. **Dist. by:** Dr. Rudolf Habelt GmbH, Am Buchenhang 1, Bonn 53115, Germany. TEL 49-228-9238322, FAX 49-228-232017.

011 332.6 IND
INVESTMENT PLANNING AND PROJECT EVALUATION BIBLIOGRAPHY. Text in English. irreg. **Document type:** *Bibliography.*
Published by: Institute of Economic Growth, University of Enclave, New Delhi, 110 007, India. TEL 7257101.

015 IRN ISSN 0075-0522
Z3366
IRANIAN NATIONAL BIBLIOGRAPHY/KETAB SHENASI-YE MELLI-YE IRAN. Text in Persian, Modern. 1963. q. price varies. **Document type:** *Bibliography.* **Description:** Contains bibliographic information on all books, pamphlets and talking books (sound recordings) published in Iran.
Related titles: CD-ROM ed.
Published by: National Library of Iran, Shahid Bahonar St., Tehran, 19548, Iran. TEL 98-21-2280937, FAX 98-21-2288680. Circ: 2,000.

ISRAEL. CENTRAL BUREAU OF STATISTICS. NEW STATISTICAL PROJECTS AND PUBLICATIONS IN ISRAEL. see *STATISTICS*

ISRAEL. GEOLOGICAL SURVEY. BIBLIOGRAPHY SERIES. see *EARTH SCIENCES—Abstracting, Bibliographies, Statistics*

ISTORIYA. ISTORYCHNI NAUKY. see *HISTORY—Abstracting, Bibliographies, Statistics*

ISTORIYA SIBIRI I DAL'NEGO VOSTOKA; tekushchii ukazatel' literatury. see *HISTORY—Abstracting, Bibliographies, Statistics*

J A E R I REPORT. (Japan Atomic Energy Research Institute) see *ENERGY—Nuclear Energy*

011 USA ISSN 1066-8454
J I S COMPUTERIZED BIBLIOGRAPHY; 1989-2002. Text in English. 1991. a. USD 25 (effective 2003). cum.index: 1989-2002. 162 p./no. 1 cols./p.; **Document type:** *Bibliography.*
Related titles: Diskette ed.: USD 25; Online - full text ed.

Published by: Institute for Interdisciplinary Research, 1065 Pine Bluff Dr, Pasadena, CA 91107-1751. TEL 626-351-0419, og@jis3.org, http://www.jis3.org. Ed., Pub. Oskar Gruenwald.

JAHRBUCH FUER WIRTSCHAFTSWISSENSCHAFTEN; review of economics. see *BUSINESS AND ECONOMICS—Abstracting, Bibliographies, Statistics*

015 JAM ISSN 0075-2991
JAMAICAN NATIONAL BIBLIOGRAPHY. Text in English. 1964. q. USD 20 (effective 1999). reprint service avail. from PQC. **Document type:** *Bibliography.*
Formerly: Institute of Jamaica, Kingston. West Indian Reference Library. Jamaica Accessions
Indexed: RASB.
Published by: National Library of Jamaica, 12 East St., P.O. Box 823, Kingston, Jamaica. TEL 876-967-1526, FAX 809-92-25567, TELEX 596, nlj@infochan.com. Ed. June Vernon. Circ: 200.

011 JPN ISSN 0910-7908
Z3301
JAPAN ENGLISH PUBLICATIONS IN PRINT. Text in English. 1985. irreg., latest vol.2, 1993. JPY 27,000, USD 270. adv. bibl. **Document type:** *Directory.* **Description:** Provides a complete listing of useful directories and information sources.
Incorporates (1987-1993): Japan Publishers Directory; Formed by the merger of: Japan English Magazine Directory (0387-3935); Japan English Books in Print (0388-4201)
Related titles: Diskette ed.
—CCC.
Published by: Japan Publications Guide Service, 5-5-13 Matsushiro, Tsukuba-shi, Ibaraki-ken 305-0035, Japan. FAX 81-3-3667-9646. Ed. W E Ball. Circ: 1,000. **Subscr. to:** Intercontinental Marketing Corp., IPO Box 5056, Tokyo 100-30, Japan.

015 JPN
JAPANESE BOOKS IN PRINT (YEAR). Text in Japanese. 1977. a. JPY 69,000 (effective 2001). **Document type:** *Bibliography.*
Related titles: CD-ROM ed.
Published by: Japan Book Publishers Association/Nihon Shoseki Shuppan Kyokai, 6 Fukuro-Machi, Shinjuku-ku, Tokyo, 162-0828, Japan. TEL 81-3-3268-1301, FAX 81-3-3268-1196, onuki@jbpa.or.jp, http://www.books.or.jp. Ed. Takao Watanabe. Circ: 4,000.

JAPANESE MILITARY AIRCRAFT SERIALS. see *MILITARY—Abstracting, Bibliographies, Statistics*

JEWISH BOOK WORLD. see *RELIGIONS AND THEOLOGY—Abstracting, Bibliographies, Statistics*

956.96 016 JOR
JORDANIAN NATIONAL BIBLIOGRAPHY; annual register of book production in Jordan. Text in Arabic, English. 1979. a. USD 20.
Published by: Jordan Library Association, P O Box 6289, Amman, Jordan. TEL 629-412.

JOURNAL OF SPICES AND AROMATIC CROPS. see *BIOLOGY*

JOURNALS OF DISSENT AND SOCIAL CHANGE; a bibliography of titles in the California State University, Sacramento, library. see *SOCIOLOGY—Abstracting, Bibliographies, Statistics*

JUDAICA BOOK NEWS. see *RELIGIONS AND THEOLOGY—Abstracting, Bibliographies, Statistics*

015.4 GBR ISSN 1353-7806
Z7165.E8
JUSTIS EUROPEAN REFERENCES. Text in English. q. GBP 700. **Description:** Contains references to over 2000 publications on EC legislation, EC publications and worldwide journal articles.
Media: CD-ROM (from Context Ltd.).
Published by: Context Ltd., Grand Union House, 20 Kentish Town Rd., London, NW1 9NR, United Kingdom. TEL 44-20-72848080, FAX 44-20-72671133, http://www.justis.com.

KARTOGRAFICHESKAYA LETOPIS'. see *GEOGRAPHY—Abstracting, Bibliographies, Statistics*

KATALOG FOR SKOLEBIBLIOTEKER. ELEVERNE. see *EDUCATION—Abstracting, Bibliographies, Statistics*

KATALOG FOR SKOLEBIBLIOTEKER. SKOLEBIBLIOTEKAREN. see *EDUCATION—Abstracting, Bibliographies, Statistics*

015 SCG
KATALOG KNJIGA JUGOSLOVENSKIH IZDAVACA. Text in Serbian. 1956. a. USD 35 domestic; USD 70 foreign (effective 2000 - 2001). adv. back issues avail. **Document type:** *Catalog.* **Description:** Lists available domestic book titles by publisher, title, and author. Also lists main public libraries in Serbia and Montenegro.
Published by: Udruzenje Izdavaca i Kinjizara Jugoslavije/ Association of Yugoslav Publishers and Booksellers, Kneza Milosa 25, Belgrade, 11000. TEL 38111-642-533, FAX 38111-646-339, ognjenl@eunet.yu. Ed. Ognjen Lakicevic. Pub. Mirjana Popovic. Circ: 500.

016.05 POL ISSN 1426-1480
KATALOG MEDIOW POLSKICH. Text in Polish; Summaries in English. 1992. a. PLZ 160 domestic; USD 160 foreign (effective 2003). adv. 500 p./no.; **Document type:** *Catalog, Bibliography.* **Description:** Lists 6000 newspapers, periodicals, and radio/TV stations in Poland.
Formerly (until 1994): Katalog Prasy Polskiej (1232-0323)
Related titles: CD-ROM ed.; Diskette ed.; Online - full text ed.
Published by: (Uniwersytet Jagiellonski, Osrodek Badan Prasoznawczych/Jagiellonian University, Press Research Center), Wydawnictwo Uniwersytetu Jagiellonskiego/ Jagiellonian University Press, ul Grodzka 26, Krakow, 31044, Poland. TEL 48-12-4312364, FAX 48-12-4301995, w.chorazki@pp.com.pl, wydaw@if.uj.edu.pl, http://www.obp.pl/katalog_pl.htm, http://www.wuj.pl. Ed. Wlodzimierz Chorazki. Pub. Stanislaw Nowicki. R&P, Adv. contact Pavel Planeta. B&W page USD 300, color page USD 650; trim 175 x 270. Circ: 1,000 (paid).

015 SCG ISSN 0352-132X
Z6945
KATALOG STRANIH SERIJSKIH PUBLIKACIJA U BIBLIOTEKAMA JUGOSLAVIJE. Text in Serbo-Croatian. 1957. irreg. (in 2 vols.), latest covers 1988. 350 p./no. 2 cols./p.; back issues avail. **Document type:** *Bulletin, Bibliography.* **Description:** Bibliography of foreign serials in Yugoslav libraries.
Formerly (until 1978): Katalog Tekucih Stranih Publikacija u Bibliotekama Jugoslavije (0350-0411)
Indexed: RASB.
Published by: Jugoslovenski Bibliografsko-Informacijski Institut (YUBIN)/Yugoslav Institute for Bibliography and Information, Terazije 26, Belgrade. FAX 381-11-687760, yubin@jbi.bg.ac.yu, http://www.yugoslavia.com/culture/yubin. Ed. Radomir Glavicki. Adv. contact Tanja Ostojic. Circ: 350.

015 USA ISSN 1054-2841
Z1223.5.K4
KENTUCKY CHECKLIST OF STATE PUBLICATIONS. Text in English. 1962. q. free. **Description:** A list of publications generated through the Public Records Division by the departments, commissions, societies, councils, and cabinets of the state.
Former titles: Kentucky Monthly Checklist; Monthly Checklist of Kentucky State Publications (0091-5653)
Media: Duplicated (not offset). **Related titles:** Microfiche ed.
Published by: Department for Libraries and Archives, Public Records Division, PO Box 537, Frankfort, KY 40602-0537. TEL 502-875-7000, FAX 502-564-5773. Ed. William C Richardson. Circ: 500.

015 KEN
KENYA. GOVERNMENT PRINTING AND STATIONERY DEPARTMENT. CATALOGUE OF GOVERNMENT PUBLICATIONS. Text in English. irreg. (approx. a.). **Document type:** *Government.*
Published by: Government Printing and Stationery Department, PO Box 30128, Nairobi, Kenya.

THE KEY GUIDE SERIES. see *LIBRARY AND INFORMATION SCIENCES—Abstracting, Bibliographies, Statistics*

KEY GUIDE TO ELECTRONIC RESOURCE: ENGINEERING. see *ENGINEERING—Abstracting, Bibliographies, Statistics*

KEY GUIDE TO ELECTRONIC RESOURCES: AGRICULTURE. see *AGRICULTURE—Abstracting, Bibliographies, Statistics*

KEY GUIDE TO ELECTRONIC RESOURCES: ART AND ART HISTORY. see *ART—Abstracting, Bibliographies, Statistics*

KEY GUIDE TO ELECTRONIC RESOURCES: LANGUAGE AND LITERATURE. see *LINGUISTICS—Abstracting, Bibliographies, Statistics*

011 SDN
KHARTOUM UNIVERSITY PRESS. CLASSIFIED LIST OF PUBLICATIONS. Text in Arabic, English. a. free. **Description:** Lists all publications available from Khartoum University Press.
Published by: Khartoum University Press, P O Box 321, Khartoum, Sudan. TEL 80558, TELEX 22738 KUP SD.

016.968 ZAF
KILLIE CAMPBELL AFRICANA LIBRARY. BIBLIOGRAPHIC SERIES. Text in English. 1993. irreg., latest vol.2, 1994. back issues avail. **Document type:** *Bibliography.*
Published by: Killie Campbell Africana Library, 220 Marriott Rd, Durban, KwaZulu-Natal 4001, South Africa.

KIRYAT SEFER; bibliographical quarterly. see *RELIGIONS AND THEOLOGY—Abstracting, Bibliographies, Statistics*

840 011 DEU ISSN 0453-9834
KLASSISCHE TEXTE DES ROMANISCHEN MITTELALTERSZWEISPRACHIGEN AUSGABEN. Text in German. 1962. irreg., latest vol.30. **Document type:** *Monographic series.*
Published by: Wilhelm Fink Verlag, Ohmstr 5, Munich, 80802, Germany. TEL 49-89-348017, FAX 49-89-341378, http://www.fink.de. R&P Marlene Braun.

011 DEU ISSN 0941-6617
KLEINE BIBLIOGRAPHISCHE REIHE. Text in German. irreg. **Document type:** *Monographic series, Bibliography.*
Published by: Laurentius Verlag, Kirchroeder Str 44F, Hannover, 30625, Germany. TEL 49-511-5353374, FAX 49-511-5353374, dehmlow@bigfoot.com, http://www.laurentius-verlag.de. Ed. Raimund Dehmlow.

015 BLR
KNIGI BELARUSI/BYELORUSSIAN BOOKS. Text in Belorussian, Russian. 1984. a. **Description:** State bibliographic directory containing information on books in all fields.
Formerly: Knigi Belorusskoi S.S.R. (0235-3393)
Indexed: RASB.
Published by: Natsiyanal'naya Knizhnaya Palata Belarusi/National Book Chamber of Belarus, Vul V Kharuzhai 31-a, Minsk, 220002, Belarus. Ed. L N Nekhaichik. Circ: 250. **US dist. addr.:** East View Information Services, 3020 Harbor Ln. N., Minneapolis, MN 55447. TEL 612-550-0961.

B

011 RUS ISSN 0201-6354
KNIGI ROSSISKOI FEDERATSII. Text in Russian. 1927. a. (in 11 vols.), latest 2003. USD 300 foreign for annual issue of 11 vols. (effective 2004). index. 590 p./no. 2 cols./p.; back issues avail. **Document type:** *Bibliography.* **Description:** Informs readers about books and booklets published in Russia in all languages.
Formerly (until 1994): Ezhegodnik Knigi Rossiskoi Federatsii
Related titles: CD-ROM ed.; Diskette ed.; E-mail ed.
—Linda Hall.
Published by: Rossiiskaya Knizhnaya Palata/Book Chamber International, Ostozhenka 4, Moscow, 119034, Russian Federation. TEL 7-095-2911278, FAX 7-095-2919630, bookch@postman.ru, http://www.bookchamber.ru/international/rf_books_yearly.html. Ed. E Belaeva. Circ: 1,000 (controlled).

011 RUS
KNIGI V NALICHII I PECHATI/RUSSIAN BOOKS IN PRINT. Text in Russian. 1996. s-a. RUR 7,700 domestic; USD 180 foreign (effective 2004). **Document type:** *Bibliography.* **Description:** Contains information on books that have just been published, publishing houses and other book-selling organizations.
Related titles: CD-ROM ed.; Diskette ed.; E-mail ed.; Online - full content ed.
Published by: Rossiiskaya Knizhnaya Palata/Book Chamber International, Ostozhenka 4, Moscow, 119034, Russian Federation. TEL 7-095-2911278, FAX 7-095-2919630, bookch@postman.ru, http://www.bookchamber.ru.

011 RUS ISSN 0869-5962
Z2491
KNIZHNAYA LETOPIS'. Text in Russian. 1907. w. RUR 10,065, USD 350 for 6 mos. foreign (effective 2004). q. and a. index. 168 p./no. 1 cols./p.; back issues avail. **Document type:** *Bibliography.* **Description:** Contains information on all books and booklets published in Russia in all languages.
Related titles: CD-ROM ed.; Microfiche ed.: (from EVP, IDC); Online - full text ed.: (from East View Information Services).
Indexed: MathSciNet, RASB.
—East View.
Published by: Rossiiskaya Knizhnaya Palata/Book Chamber International, Ostozhenka 4, Moscow, 119034, Russian Federation. TEL 7-095-2911278, FAX 7-095-2919630, bookch@postman.ru, http://www.bookchamber.ru/international/letopis_books.html. Circ: 1,000 (controlled).

020 DNK ISSN 0105-8215
KONGELIGE BIBLIOTEK. SPECIALHJAELPEMIDLER. Text in Danish. 1978. irreg., latest vol.37, 1999.
Published by: Kongelige Bibliotek, Christians Brygge, PO Box 2149, Copenhagen K, 1016, Denmark.

KONINKLIJK INSTITUUT VOOR DE TROPEN. CRITICAL REVIEWS AND ANNOTATED BIBLIOGRAPHIES. see *AGRICULTURE—Abstracting, Bibliographies, Statistics*

KONINKLIJK INSTITUUT VOOR TAAL-, LAND- EN VOLKENKUNDE. BIBLIOGRAPHICAL SERIES. see *ANTHROPOLOGY—Abstracting, Bibliographies, Statistics*

KONINKLIJK NEDERLANDS HISTORISCH GENOOTSCHAP. KRONIEK; lijst van de voornaamste in...verschenen boeken en artikelen op het van de Nederlandse geschiedenis. see *HISTORY—History Of Europe*

010 IND ISSN 0075-6970
KOTHARI'S WORLD OF REFERENCE WORKS. Text in English. 1963. irreg. USD 10 (effective 2000). adv. **Description:** Lists international reference works and directories worldwide. Names of publishers, addresses and prices.
Published by: Kothari Publications, 12 India Exchange Pl., Kolkata, West Bengal 700 001, India. TEL 91-33-220-9563. Ed. H Kothari.

KUERSCHNERS DEUTSCHER GELEHRTEN-KALENDER. see *BIOGRAPHY*

015 DEU ISSN 0343-0936
KUERSCHNERS DEUTSCHER LITERATUR-KALENDER. Text in German. 1903. a. (in 2 vols.). EUR 348 (effective 2004). **Document type:** *Directory, Academic/Scholarly.* **Description:** Contains bibliographical and biographical documentation of contemporary German literature.
Published by: K.G. Saur Verlag GmbH (Subsidiary of: Gale Group), Ortlerstr 8, Munchen, 81373, Germany. TEL 49-89-769020, FAX 49-89-76902150, info@saur.de, http://www.saur.de. Ed. Andreas Klimt.

011 SWE ISSN 0280-0799
Z2646.C55
KULTURTIDSKRIFTEN (YEAR); katalogen oever Sveriges kulturtidskrifter. Text in Swedish. 1981. a. free. 66 p./no.; **Document type:** *Bibliography.* **Description:** Information about cultural magazines published in Sweden.
Related titles: Online - full text ed.
Indexed: MLA-IB.
Published by: Statens Kulturraad/Swedish National Council for Cultural Affairs, Laanger Raden 4, Skeppsholmen, P O Box 7843, Stockholm, 10398, Sweden. TEL 46-08-519 264 00, FAX 46-08-519 164 99, statens.kulturrad@kur.se, http://www.tidskrift.nu. Eds. Maria Oestling, Bo Pettersson. **Dist. by:** Kulturraadets Distribution.

B

L E I - DRAAD. see *AGRICULTURE—Abstracting, Bibliographies, Statistics*

L I L A C S - CD-ROM. (Literatura Latinoamericana y del Caribe en Ciencias de la Salud) see *MEDICAL SCIENCES—Abstracting, Bibliographies, Statistics*

015 USA ISSN 0732-6084
HD5725.O7
LABOR MARKET INFORMATION DIRECTORY. Variant title: Oregon Labor Market Information Directory. Text in English. 197?. a. free. **Document type:** *Catalog, Government.* **Description:** Contains a list of publications produced by the research section of the Oregon Employment Department.
Published by: Oregon Employment Dept., 875 Union St N E, Salem, OR 97311. TEL 503-947-1266, FAX 503-947-1210, kathi.r.riddell@state.or.us. Ed. Kathi Riddell. Circ: 10,000.

LATIN AMERICAN AND CARIBBEAN STUDIES IN THE HUMANITIES AND SOCIAL SCIENCES IN THE UNIVERSITIES OF THE UNITED KINGDOM. see *HISTORY—Abstracting, Bibliographies, Statistics*

LATIN AMERICAN BOOKS NEWSLETTER. see *PUBLISHING AND BOOK TRADE—Abstracting, Bibliographies, Statistics*

016.05 LVA ISSN 1407-0049
Z375.L3
LATVIJAS PRESE (YEAR). Text in Latvian. 1957. a. USD 9 (effective 2001). **Document type:** *Yearbook, Bibliography.*
Formerly (until 1990): Latvijas PSR Prese (1407-0456)
Published by: Latvijas Nacionalas Bibliotekas, Bibliografijas Instituts, Anglikanu iela 5, Riga, 1816, Latvia. TEL 371-7212668, 371-7225135, anitag@lbi.lnb.lv, http://vip.latnet.lv/lnb. Ed. Sk Rozenbaha. Circ: 150.

016.05 LVA ISSN 1017-7604
Z2535
LATVIJAS PRESES HRONIKA. Text in Latvian. 1957. m. USD 53 (effective 2001). **Document type:** *Bibliography.*
Formerly (until 1990): Latvijas P.S.R. Preses Hronika (0130-9226)
Indexed: ForAb.
Published by: Latvijas Nacionalas Bibliotekas, Bibliografijas Instituts, Anglikanu iela 5, Riga, 1816, Latvia. TEL 371-7225135, lnb@latnet.lv, anitag@lbi.lnb.lv, http://vip.latnet.lv/lnb. Eds. Gundega Bligzne, Ilona Dukure. Pub. Gundega Bligzne. Circ: 200. **Dist. by:** National Library of Latvia, Kr Barona iela 14, Riga 1423, Latvia. TEL 371-728-9874, FAX 371-728-0851; **US dist. addr.:** East View Information Services, 3020 Harbor Ln. N., Minneapolis, MN 55447. TEL 612-550-0961.

LAW BOOKS AND SERIALS IN PRINT; a multimedia sourcebook. see *LAW—Abstracting, Bibliographies, Statistics*

LAW BOOKS IN PRINT; law books in English published throughout the world. see *LAW—Abstracting, Bibliographies, Statistics*

LAW BOOKS PUBLISHED. see *LAW—Abstracting, Bibliographies, Statistics*

LEGAL LOOSELEAFS IN PRINT. see *LAW—Abstracting, Bibliographies, Statistics*

LEGAL NEWSLETTERS IN PRINT (YEAR). see *LAW—Abstracting, Bibliographies, Statistics*

THE LEGAL PUBLISHER. see *LAW*

LEGAL RESOURCES; an internet miniguide. see *LAW—Abstracting, Bibliographies, Statistics*

LESBIAN HERSTORY ARCHIVES NEWSLETTER. see *HOMOSEXUALITY*

011 BLR
Z2514.W5
LETAPIS DRUKU BELARUSI. KNIZHNY LETAPIS. Text in Belorussian, Russian. 1924. m. USD 194 foreign (effective 2003). **Description:** State bibliographical guide, containing information on all types of publications: books, periodicals, newspapers.
Supersedes in part: Letopis' Pechati Belarusi; Which was formerly: Letopis' Pechati B.S.S.R. (0130-9218); Incorporates (1946-1992): Belaruskaya S.S.R. v Pechati S.S.S.R. i Zarubezhnykh Stran (0868-524X); Which was formerly (until 1990): Belaruskaya S.S.R. v Pechati S.S.S.R. i Zarubezhnykh Socialisticheskikh Stran (0207-9003)
Published by: Natsiyanal'naya Knizhnaya Palata Belarusi/National Book Chamber of Belarus, Vul V Kharuzhai 31-a, Minsk, 220002, Belarus. palata@palata.belpak.minsk.by. Eds. I A Panferova, S M Tel'nova. Circ: 380. **Dist. by:** M K - Periodica, ul Gilyarovskogo 39, Moscow 129110, Russian Federation. TEL 7-095-2845008, FAX 7-095-2813798, info@periodicals.ru, http://www.mkniga.ru; **US dist. addr.:** East View Information Services, 3020 Harbor Ln. N., Minneapolis, MN 55447. TEL 612-550-0961.

011 BLR ISSN 1561-3496
LETAPIS DRUKU BELARUSI. LETAPIS CHASOPISNYKH ARTYKULAU. Text in Belorussian, Russian. 1924. m. USD 162 foreign (effective 2003).
Supersedes in part: Letopis' Pechati Belarusi; Which was formerly: Letopis' Pechati B.S.S.R. (0130-9218); Incorporates (in 1992): Belaruskaya S.S.R. v Pechati S.S.S.R. i Zarubezhnykh Stran (0868-524X); Which was formerly (1946-1990): Belaruskaya S.S.R. v Pechati S.S.S.R. i Zarubezhnykh Socialisticheskikh Stran (0207-9003)
Published by: Natsiyanal'naya Knizhnaya Palata Belarusi/National Book Chamber of Belarus, Vul V Kharuzhai 31-a, Minsk, 220002, Belarus. palata@palata.belpak.minsk.by. Ed. I A Panferova. **Dist. by:** M K - Periodica, ul Gilyarovskogo 39, Moscow 129110, Russian Federation. TEL 7-095-2845008, FAX 7-095-2813798, info@periodicals.ru, http://www.mkniga.ru.

011 BLR ISSN 1561-350X
LETAPIS DRUKU BELARUSI. LETAPIS GAZETNYKH ARTYKULAU. Text in Belorussian, Russian. 1924. 24/yr. USD 240 foreign (effective 2003).
Supersedes in part: Letopis' Pechati Belarusi; Which was formerly: Letopis' Pechati B.S.S.R. (0130-9218); Incorporates (in 1992): Belaruskaya S.S.R. v Pechati S.S.S.R. i Zarubezhnykh Stran (0868-524X); Which was formerly (1946-1990): Belaruskaya S.S.R. v Pechati S.S.S.R. i Zarubezhnykh Socialisticheskikh Stran (0207-9003)
Published by: Natsiyanal'naya Knizhnaya Palata Belarusi/National Book Chamber of Belarus, Vul V Kharuzhai 31-a, Minsk, 220002, Belarus. palata@palata.belpak.minsk.by. Ed. M Ju Goljas. **Dist. by:** M K - Periodica, ul Gilyarovskogo 39, Moscow 129110, Russian Federation. TEL 7-095-2845008, FAX 7-095-2813798, info@periodicals.ru, http://www.mkniga.ru.

015.47 RUS ISSN 0869-5954
Z2495
LETOPIS' AVTOREFERATOV DISSERTATSII. Text in Russian. 1981. m. RUR 4,785 for 6 mos. domestic; USD 155 for 6 mos. foreign (effective 2004). index. 70 p./no. 1 cols./p.; back issues avail. **Document type:** *Bibliography.* **Description:** Informs readers of author's abstracts of dissertations in all fields.
Formerly: Knizhnaya Letopis'. Dopolnitelhyi Vypusk. Autoreferaty Dissertatsii
Media: Large Type. **Related titles:** CD-ROM ed.; Diskette ed.; E-mail ed.; Microfiche ed.: (from EVP); Online - full text ed.: (from East View Information Services).
Indexed: RASB.
—East View.
Published by: Rossiiskaya Knizhnaya Palata/Book Chamber International, Ostozhenka 4, Moscow, 119034, Russian Federation. TEL 7-095-2911278, FAX 7-095-2919630, bookch@postman.ru, http://www.bookchamber.ru/international/letopis_referats.html. Ed. E Belaeva. Circ: 1,000.

015.47 RUS ISSN 0024-1172
AI15
LETOPIS' GAZETNYKH STATEI. Text in Russian. 1936. w. RUR 7,722 for 6 mos. domestic; USD 250 for 6 mos. foreign (effective 2004). 48 p./no.; back issues avail. **Document type:** *Bibliography.* **Description:** Informs about newspaper articles published in Russia.
Related titles: Diskette ed.; E-mail ed.; Microfiche ed.: (from EVP); Online - full text ed.: (from East View Information Services).
Indexed: RASB.
—East View.
Published by: Rossiiskaya Knizhnaya Palata/Book Chamber International, Ostozhenka 4, Moscow, 119034, Russian Federation. TEL 7-095-2911278, FAX 7-095-2919630, bookch@postman.ru, http://www.bookchamber.ru/international/letopis_papers.html. Ed. E Belaeva. Circ: 1,000.

011 RUS ISSN 0134-8388
LETOPIS' IZOIZDANII. Text in Russian. 1934. q. RUR 2,255 for 6 mos. domestic; USD 80 for 6 mos. foreign (effective 2004). bibl. index. 40 p./no.; back issues avail. **Document type:** *Bibliography.* **Description:** Informs readers about posters, reproductions, prints, and albums published in Russia in all languages.
Formerly: Letopis' Pechatnykh Proizvedenii Izobrazitel'nogo Iskusstva (0024-1199)
Related titles: Diskette ed.; E-mail ed.; Microfiche ed.: (from EVP); Online - full text ed.: (from East View Information Services).
Indexed: RASB.
—East View.
Published by: Rossiiskaya Knizhnaya Palata/Book Chamber International, Ostozhenka 4, Moscow, 119034, Russian Federation. TEL 7-095-2911278, FAX 7-095-2919630, bookch@postman.ru, http://www.bookchamber.ru. Ed. E Belaeva. Circ: 500.

057 016 BGR ISSN 0324-0398
AI15
LETOPIS NA STATIITE OT BULGARSKITE SPISANIIA I SBORNITSI/ARTICLES FROM BULGARIAN JOURNALS AND COLLECTIONS. Text in Bulgarian. 1952. m. BGL 1.65 (effective 2003). bk.rev. **Document type:** *Bulletin, Bibliography.*
Supersedes in part: Letopis na Periodichna Pechat (0024-1180)
Related titles: Diskette ed.; E-mail ed.
Indexed: RASB.
Published by: Narodna Biblioteka Sv. sv. Kiril i Metodii/Cyril and Methodius National Library, 88 Levski Blvd, Sofia, 1504, Bulgaria. TEL 359-2-9881600, FAX 359-2-435495, nbkm@nl.otel.net. Ed., R&P L Kostova TEL 359-2-9882811 ext 275. Circ: 420.

016 276 BGR ISSN 0324-0347
AI15
LETOPIS NA STATIITE OT BULGARSKITE VESTNITSI/ARTICLES FROM BULGARIAN NEWSPAPERS; mesechen biuletin. Text in Bulgarian. 1952. m. BGL 0.80 (effective 2003). illus.; stat. **Document type:** *Bulletin, Bibliography.*
Supersedes in part: Letopis na Periodichna Pechat (0024-1180)
Related titles: Diskette ed.; E-mail ed.
Indexed: RASB.
Published by: Narodna Biblioteka Sv. sv. Kiril i Metodii/Cyril and Methodius National Library, 88 Levski Blvd, Sofia, 1504, Bulgaria. TEL 359-2-9881600, FAX 359-2-435495, nbkm@nl.otel.net. Ed., R&P M Gavrilova TEL 359-2-9882811 ext 294. Circ: 375.

015.47 RUS ISSN 0201-6265
Z6956.R9
LETOPIS' PERIODICHESKIKH I PRODOLZHAYUSHCHIKHSYA IZDANII. Text in Russian. 1933. a. USD 30 per issue (effective 2004). 145 p./no.; back issues avail. **Document type:** *Bibliography.* **Description:** Informs readers about magazines and newspapers which have just appeared, changed their titles, or stopped being published in Russia, as well as other bibliographic changes in periodicals. Includes a number of subsidiary indexes.
Related titles: Diskette ed.; E-mail ed.
—Linda Hall.
Published by: Rossiiskaya Knizhnaya Palata/Book Chamber International, Ostozhenka 4, Moscow, 119034, Russian Federation. TEL 7-095-2911278, FAX 7-095-2919630, bookch@postman.ru, http://www.bookchamber.ru/international/letopis_serial.html. Ed. N Shirina. Circ: 500 (controlled).

016.8 RUS ISSN 0130-9242
Z2495
LETOPIS' RETSENZII. Text in Russian. 1935. m. RUR 3,190 for 6 mos. domestic; USD 110 for 6 mos. foreign (effective 2004). index. back issues avail. **Document type:** *Bibliography.* **Description:** Informs about reviews and critical essays on editions published in Russia and abroad.
Related titles: Diskette ed.; E-mail ed.; Microfiche ed.: (from EVP); Online - full text ed.: (from East View Information Services).
Indexed: RASB.
—East View.
Published by: Rossiiskaya Knizhnaya Palata/Book Chamber International, Ostozhenka 4, Moscow, 119034, Russian Federation. TEL 7-095-2911278, FAX 7-095-2919630, bookch@postman.ru, http://www.bookchamber.ru/international/letopis_reviews.html. Ed. N Shirina. Circ: 1,000 (controlled).

015.47 RUS ISSN 0024-1202
AI15
LETOPIS' ZHURNAL'NYKH STATEI. Text in Russian. 1926. w. RUR 10,978 for 6 mos. domestic; USD 390 for 6 mos. foreign (effective 2004). 152 p./no.; back issues avail.; reprints avail. **Document type:** *Bibliography.* **Description:** Contains bibliographic information on all jounal articles published in the Russian Federation.
Related titles: Diskette ed.; E-mail ed.; Microfiche ed.: (from EVP); Online - full text ed.: (from East View Information Services).
Indexed: RASB.
—East View.

Published by: Rossiiskaya Knizhnaya Palata/Book Chamber International, Ostozhenka 4, Moscow, 119034, Russian Federation. TEL 7-095-2911278, FAX 7-095-2919630, bookch@postman.ru, http://www.bookchamber.ru/international/letopis_magazines.html. Ed. E Belaeva. Circ: 1,000.

015 ITA ISSN 1122-5521
Z2341.A1
I LIBRI; bimestrale di bibliografia italiana. Text in Italian. 1994. bi-m. adv. index. **Document type:** *Bibliography.* **Description:** Contains complete bibliographical records for works which have appeared in Italy in the previous 2 months. Covers all subject areas and includes indices.
Indexed: ArtHuCI, CMCI.
Published by: Casalini Libri, Via Benedetto da Maiano 3, Fiesole, FI 50014, Italy. TEL 39-055-50181, FAX 39-055-5018201, info@casalini.it, http://www.casalini.it. Pub. Barbara Casalini.

015 CHL
LIBRO CHILENO EN VENTA. Text in Spanish. 1975. biennial. USD 108 (effective 2001). back issues avail. **Document type:** *Bibliography.*
Published by: Servicio de Extension de Cultura Chilena, Casilla 58-22, Santiago, Santiago, Chile. TEL 56-2-3434214, FAX 56-2-2395333, serec@terra.cl. Ed. Marta Dominguez Diaz.

011 PRI ISSN 1093-3689
Z1601
LIBROS EN VENTA EN HISPANOAMERICA Y ESPANA/SPANISH BOOKS IN PRINT; guia bibliografica de libros disponibles en espanol. Text in Spanish. 1964. a. (in 3 vols.). USD 540. **Document type:** *Directory, Bibliography.* **Description:** Lists Spanish-language books in print in 36 countries.
Related titles: CD-ROM ed.: 1964. USD 1,195 (from National Information Services Corp. (N I S C)); Online - full text ed.: 1964 (from National Information Services Corp. (N I S C)).
Published by: N I S C Puerto Rico, Edificio Center Building, Av. de Diego 312, Of. 601, San Juan, 00909, Puerto Rico. TEL 787-724-1352, FAX 787-724-2886, nisc@caribe.net, http://www.nisc.com.mx/productos/lev.html. **Affiliate:** N I S C USA.

011 ESP ISSN 0214-6304
Z2683
LIBROS ESPANOLES EN VENTA. Text in Spanish. 1973. m. **Document type:** *Bibliography.*
Former titles (until 1986): Libros Espanoles en Venta I S B N (0213-1099); (until 1982): Libros Espanoles I S B N (0377-0974); (until 1973): Libros Espanoles. Catalogo I S B N (0302-4652)
Related titles: CD-ROM ed.: ESP 55,000; Online - full text ed.
Indexed: RASB.
—Linda Hall.
Published by: (Spain. Agencia Espanola I S B N), Ministerio Educacion y Cultura, Subd. Gral. Promocion del Libro, Santiago Rusinol, 8, Madrid, 28040, Spain. TEL 536-88-30, FAX 553-99-90, agencia.isbn@cll.mcu.es, http://www.mcu.es. Circ: 1,000 (paid).

LIFE SCIENCE BOOK REVIEW. see *BIOLOGY—Abstracting, Bibliographies, Statistics*

LIGHT'S LIST OF LITERARY MAGAZINES. see *LITERARY AND POLITICAL REVIEWS—Abstracting, Bibliographies, Statistics*

LINGUISTIC BIBLIOGRAPHY/BIBLIOGRAPHIE LINGUISTIQUE. see *LINGUISTICS—Abstracting, Bibliographies, Statistics*

LIST OF BOOKS AND ARTICLES CATALOGUED. see *PUBLIC ADMINISTRATION—Abstracting, Bibliographies, Statistics*

LIST OF CLASSES OF UNITED STATES GOVERNMENT PUBLICATIONS AVAILABLE FOR SELECTION BY DEPOSITORY LIBRARIES. see *LIBRARY AND INFORMATION SCIENCES—Abstracting, Bibliographies, Statistics*

011 FRA ISSN 1726-9032
CODEN: LMTTAJ
LISTE D'ABREVIATIONS DE MOTS DE TITRES. TITRES DE PUBLICATIONS EN SERIE ET AUTRES RESSOURCES EN CONTINU. Text in French. irreg., latest 1998. FRF 650 (effective 1999). **Description:** Contains the key words of the titles of serials processed by the ISSN network and their abbreviations.
Formerly (until 2002): List of Serial Title Word Abbreviations (0259-000X)
Related titles: Diskette ed.: ISSN 1018-810X.
—KNAW.
Published by: International Centre for the Registration of Serials, I S S N International Centre/Centre International d'Enregistrement des Publications en Serie, 20 rue Bachaumont, Paris, 75002, France. TEL 33-1-44882220, FAX 33-1-40263243, issnic@issn.org, portal@issn.org, http://www.issn.org.

015 RUS
LITERATURA O SAKHALINSKOI OBLASTI. Text in Russian. 1968. a.
Published by: (Sakhalinskaya Oblastnaya Biblioteka), Dal'nevostochnoe Knizhnoe Izdatel'stvo, Sakhalinskoe Otdelenie, Ul Dzerzhinskogo 34, Yuzhno Sakhalinsk, Russian Federation.

LITERATURE OF AMERICAN LABOR SERIES. see *BUSINESS AND ECONOMICS—Abstracting, Bibliographies, Statistics*

LITERATURINFORMATIONEN AUS DER BILDUNGSFORSCHUNG. see *EDUCATION—Abstracting, Bibliographies, Statistics*

LITOPYS AVTOREFERATIV DYSSERTATSII. see *SCIENCES: COMPREHENSIVE WORKS—Abstracting, Bibliographies, Statistics*

LITOPYS HAZETNYKH STATEI; derzhavnyi bibliografichnyi pokazhchyk Ukrainy. see *JOURNALISM—Abstracting, Bibliographies, Statistics*

LITOPYS KARTOHRAFICHNYKH VYDAN'. see *GEOGRAPHY—Abstracting, Bibliographies, Statistics*

LITOPYS KNYH; derzhavnyi bibliografichnyi pokazhchyk Ukrainy. see *PUBLISHING AND BOOK TRADE—Abstracting, Bibliographies, Statistics*

LITOPYS NOT. see *PUBLISHING AND BOOK TRADE—Abstracting, Bibliographies, Statistics*

LITOPYS OBRAZOTVORCHYKH VYDAN'. see *PUBLISHING AND BOOK TRADE—Abstracting, Bibliographies, Statistics*

LITOPYS RETSENZII/REVIEWS CHRONICLE. see *LITERATURE—Abstracting, Bibliographies, Statistics*

LITOPYS ZHURNAL'NYKH STATEI; derzhavnyi bibliografichnyi pokazhchyk Ukrainy. see *JOURNALISM—Abstracting, Bibliographies, Statistics*

016 FRA ISSN 0240-6608
LIVRES DISPONIBLES. Text in French. 1972. a. (in 6 vols.). **Document type:** *Bibliography.*
Formed by the merger of: Catalogue de l'Edition Francaise (0069-1089); Repertoire des Livres de Langue Francaise Disponibles (0080-1003)
Related titles: CD-ROM ed.; Microfiche ed.
—BLDSC (5284.250000), Linda Hall.
Published by: Electre - Editions du Cercle de la Librairie, 35 rue Gregoire de Tours, Paris, 75006, France. TEL 33-1-44412800, FAX 33-1-43296895. Ed. Pascal Fouche.

LIVRES HEBDO. see *PUBLISHING AND BOOK TRADE—Abstracting, Bibliographies, Statistics*

015 PRT ISSN 0870-6093
Z2715
LIVROS DISPONIVEIS (YEAR). Text in Portuguese. a. **Document type:** *Catalog.*
Formerly (until 1987): Catalogo dos Livros Disponiveis (0871-0503)
Published by: Associacao Portuguesa de Editores e Livreiros, Avenida dos Estados Unidos da America, 97 6o Esq, Lisbon, 1700, Portugal. TEL 351-1-8435180, FAX 351-1-8489377.

011 USA
LOOMPANICS UNLIMITED CATALOG. Text in English. 1973. a. USD 5 (effective 2000). bk.rev. illus.; tr.lit. index. **Document type:** *Catalog, Bibliography.* **Description:** Champions the First Amendment with books on revenge, drugs, underground economy, survival, self-sufficiency, and sex.
Related titles: Online - full text ed.
Published by: Loompanics Unlimited, PO Box 1197, Port Townsend, WA 98368. TEL 360-385-2230, FAX 360-385-7785, loompanics@olympus.net, http://www.loompanics.com. Ed. Gia Cosindas. Pub. Michael Hoy. Circ: 75,000 (paid).

LYELL LECTURES IN BIBLIOGRAPHY. see *LITERATURE*

M L A INTERNATIONAL BIBLIOGRAPHY OF BOOKS AND ARTICLES ON THE MODERN LANGUAGES AND LITERATURES. see *LITERATURE—Abstracting, Bibliographies, Statistics*

M P Z PUBLIK. see *MUSEUMS AND ART GALLERIES—Abstracting, Bibliographies, Statistics*

MABUA/FOUNTAIN; religious creation in literature, society and thought. see *LITERATURE*

011 MAC
MACAO. DIRECCAO DOS SERVICOS DE ESTATISTICA E CENSOS. BOLETIM BIBLIOGRAFICO/MACAO. CENSUS AND STATISTICS DEPARTMENT. BIBLIOGRAPHY BULLETIN. Text in Portuguese, English. 1984. q. free. **Document type:** *Government.* **Description:** Contains the information of publications received from external sources.
Published by: Direccao dos Servicos de Estatistica e Censos, Rua Inacio Baptista, No. 4-6, P.O. Box 3022, Macau. TEL 853-3995311, FAX 853-307825, info@dsec.gov.mo, http://www.dsec.gov.mo/.

011.3 JPN ISSN 0918-8002
MACINTOSH CD-ROM GUIDE. Text in Japanese. 1993. a. JPY 3,000. **Description:** Contains 1,100 Japanese CD-ROM titles for Macintosh and 1,000 foreign titles.
Published by: PenLogue Publishing Corp., Futaba Building, 3-4-18 Mita, Minato-ku, Tokyo, 108-0073, Japan. TEL 03-3452-8080, FAX 03-3452-5728.

MADHYA PRADESH WHO'S WHO. see *BIOGRAPHY*

011 USA ISSN 0000-0914
Z6941
MAGAZINES FOR LIBRARIES; for the general reader and school, junior college, university and public libraries. Text in English. 1969 (1st ed.). a. ((irreg. until 2004)), latest 13th ed. USD 225 (effective 2004); USD 240 (effective 2005). **Document type:** *Directory, Bibliography.* **Description:** Profiles over 7,000 top-rated periodicals, including general-interest magazines, research journals, and high-quality commercial publications suitable for a range of libraries in public, academic, special, government, and school settings.
Indexed: BRI, CBRI.
Published by: R.R. Bowker LLC (Subsidiary of: Cambridge Information Group), 630 Central Ave., New Providence, NJ 07974. TEL 908-286-1090, 800-526-9537, FAX 908-219-0098, info@bowker.com, http://www.bowker.com. Eds. Bill Katz, Cheryl LaGuardia, Linda Sternberg Katz. **Subscr. to:** Order Dept., PO Box 32, New Providence, NJ 07974-9903. TEL 800-521-8110.

MAGAZINES IN SPECIAL MEDIA. see *HANDICAPPED—Abstracting, Bibliographies, Statistics*

015 HUN ISSN 1218-5604
MAGYAR KONYVESZET. Text in Hungarian. 1994. a. USD 150. **Document type:** *Bibliography.* **Description:** Lists books, brochures, official publications, first issues and title changes of serials published in Hungary from 1976 and officially deposited in the library.
Media: CD-ROM.
Indexed: HistAb.
Published by: Orszagos Szechenyi Konyvtar/National Szechenyi Library, Budavari Palota F epulet, Budapest, 1827, Hungary. TEL 36-1-224-3741, FAX 36-1-2020804, pr@oszk.hu. **Subscr. to:** Nemzetkozi es Kulturalis Kapcsolatok Irodaja - Public Relations and Cultural Affairs, Budavari Palota F epulet, Budapest 1827, Hungary.

MAGYAR KONYVTARI SZAKIRODALOM BIBLIOGRAFIAJA/BIBLIOGRAPHY ON HUNGARIAN LIBRARY LITERATURE. see *COMPUTERS—Abstracting, Bibliographies, Statistics*

MAGYAR MEZOGAZDASAGI BIBLIOGRAFIA. see *AGRICULTURE—Abstracting, Bibliographies, Statistics*

016 HUN ISSN 0231-4592
Z6956.H8
MAGYAR NEMZETI BIBLIOGRAFIA. IDOSZAKI KIADVANYOK BIBLIOGRAFIAJA. Text in Hungarian. 1946. a. price varies. **Document type:** *Bibliography.* **Description:** Bibliography of Hungarian periodicals officially deposited in the National Szechenyi Library.
Formerly (until 1980): Kurrens Idoszaki Kiadvanyok (0134-0247); Which supersedes in part (in 1977): Magyar Nemzeti Bibliografia (0373-1766)
Media: CD-ROM.
Indexed: RASB.
Published by: Orszagos Szechenyi Konyvtar/National Szechenyi Library, Budavari Palota F epulet, Budapest, 1827, Hungary. TEL 36-1-156-9378, FAX 36-1-2020804, vili@oszk.hu. Ed. Aniko Nagy. Circ: 620. **Subscr. to:** Nemzetkozi es Kulturalis Kapcsolatok Irodaja, Public Relations and Cultural Affairs, Budavari Palota F epulet, Budapest 1827, Hungary.

MAGYAR NEMZETI BIBLIOGRAFIA. IDOSZAKI KIADVANYOK REPERTORIUMA; tarsadalomtudomanyok, termeszettudomanyok. see *SOCIAL SCIENCES: COMPREHENSIVE WORKS—Abstracting, Bibliographies, Statistics*

015 HUN ISSN 1218-2192
MAGYAR NEMZETI BIBLIOGRAFIA. KONYVEK/HUNGARIAN NATIONAL BIBLIOGRAPHY. BOOKS. Text in Hungarian. 1994. s-a. USD 700. **Document type:** *Bibliography.* **Description:** Lists books, brochures, official publications, first issues and title changes of serials published in Hungary from 1976 deposited in the library.
Media: CD-ROM.
Published by: Orszagos Szechenyi Konyvtar/National Szechenyi Library, Budavari Palota F epulet, Budapest, 1827, Hungary. TEL 36-1-224-3741, FAX 36-1-2020804, pr@oszk.hu. Ed. Rozalia Szalai. **Subscr. to:** Nemzetkozi es Kulturalis Kapcsolatok Irodaja - Public Relations and Cultural Affairs, Budavari Palota F epulet, Budapest 1827, Hungary.

B

▼ new title ➤ refereed ✶ unverified ♦ full entry avail.

016 HUN ISSN 0133-6843
Z2141
MAGYAR NEMZETI BIBLIOGRAFIA. KONYVEK BIBLIOGRAFIAJA. Text in Hungarian. 1946. s-m. HUF 6,000, USD 100. **Document type:** *Bibliography.* **Description:** Bibliography of books, brochures, official publications, first issues and title changes of serials published in Hungary and officially deposited in the National Szechenyi Library.
Supersedes in part (in 1977): Magyar Nemzeti Bibliografia (0373-1766)
Related titles: CD-ROM ed.; ♦ Supplement(s): Magyar Nemzeti Bibliografia. Uj Periodikumok. ISSN 1219-6835.
Indexed: RASB.
Published by: Orszagos Szechenyi Konyvtar/National Szechenyi Library, Budavari Palota F epulet, Budapest, 1827, Hungary. TEL 36-1-224-3741, FAX 36-1-2020804, pr@oszk.hu, http://www.oszk.hu.mnbkb. Ed. Rozalia Szalai. Circ: 800. **Subscr. to:** Nemzetkozi es Kulturalis Kapcsolatok Irodaja, Public Relations and Cultural Affairs, Budavari Palota F epulet, Budapest 1827, Hungary.

015 HUN ISSN 1416-5414
MAGYAR NEMZETI BIBLIOGRAFIA. PERIODIKUMOK/ HUNGARIAN NATIONAL BIBLIOGRAPHY. SERIALS. Text in Hungarian. 1996. s-a. USD 700; USD 800 for multi users. **Document type:** *Bibliography.* **Description:** Lists periodicals, first issues and title changes, published in Hungary and officially deposited in the library from 1986.
Media: CD-ROM.
Published by: Orszagos Szechenyi Konyvtar/National Szechenyi Library, Budavari Palota F epulet, Budapest, 1827, Hungary. TEL 36-1-224-3763, FAX 36-1-2020804, aniko@oszk.hu. Ed. Aniko Nagy. **Subscr. to:** Nemzetkozi es Kulturalis Kapcsolatok Irodaja - Public Relations and Cultural Affairs, Budavari Palota F epulet, Budapest 1827, Hungary.

015 HUN ISSN 1419-1903
MAGYAR NEMZETI BIBLIOGRAFIA. SAJTOREPERTORIUM/ HUNGARIAN NATIONAL BIBLIOGRAPHY. REPERTORY OF SERIALS. Text in Hungarian. 1998. s-a. USD 700. **Document type:** *Bibliography.* **Description:** Bibliography of component parts of serials published in Hungary and deposited at the National Szechenyi Library through legal deposit from 1993 in the fields of social and natural sciences.
Related titles: CD-ROM ed.
Published by: Orszagos Szechenyi Konyvtar/National Szechenyi Library, Budavari Palota F epulet, Budapest, 1827, Hungary. TEL 36-1-224-3573, FAX 36-1-2020804, iker@oszk.hu. Ed. Magda Wolf.

015 HUN ISSN 1219-6835
Z6956.H8
MAGYAR NEMZETI BIBLIOGRAFIA. UJ PERIODIKUMOK. Text in Hungarian. 1991. m. HUF 1,500 (effective 1999). **Document type:** *Bibliography.* **Description:** Bibliography of new periodicals and title changes published in Hungary and deposited at the National Szechenyi Library through legal deposit acquired from other sources.
Related titles: ♦ Supplement to: Magyar Nemzeti Bibliografia. Konyvek Bibliografiaja. ISSN 0133-6843.
Published by: Orszagos Szechenyi Konyvtar/National Szechenyi Library, Budavari Palota F epulet, Budapest, 1827, Hungary. TEL 36-1-224-3763, FAX 36-1-2020804, pr@oszk.hu. Ed. Aniko Nagy.

MAGYAR NEMZETI BIBLIOGRAFIA. ZENEMUVEK BIBLIOGRAFIAJA. see *MUSIC—Abstracting, Bibliographies, Statistics*

015 HUN ISSN 0541-9492
MAGYAR TUDOMANYOS AKADEMIA KONYVTARA KEZIRATTARANAK KATALOGUSAI/CATALOGI COLLECTIONIS MANUSCRIPTORUM BIBLIOTHECAE ACADEMIAE SCIENTIARUM HUNGARICAE. Text in Hungarian; Summaries in English, French, German. 1966. irreg. price varies. **Document type:** *Bibliography.* **Description:** Information on the library's manuscripts, with catalogues of outstanding bequests.
Published by: Magyar Tudomanyos Akademia, Konyvtara, Arany Janos utca 1, PO Box 1002, Budapest, 1245, Hungary. TEL 36-1-3338-2344, FAX 36-1-331-6954. Ed. M Rozsondai.

MAJOR AUTHORS AND ILLUSTRATORS FOR CHILDREN AND YOUNG ADULTS. see *LITERATURE*

015 IND ISSN 0971-4669
Z3203
MAJOR INDIAN WORKS ANNUAL. Abbreviated title: M I W A. Text in English. 1980. a. USD 10 (effective 2003). bk.rev. bibl. back issues avail. **Document type:** *Bibliography.* **Description:** Contains an annual bibliography of the latest significant works published in India. Aims at librarians and scholars interested in the Indian publishing scene.
Published by: D.K. Agencies Pvt. Ltd., A-15-17, D K Ave, Mohan Garden, Najaf Garh Rd., New Delhi, 110 059, India. TEL 91-11-535-7104, FAX 91-11-535-7103, custserv@dkagencies.com, http://www.dkagencies.com. Ed. R K Mittal. Pub., R&P R.K. Mittal. Circ: 2,000.

027 011 UGA ISSN 0047-3138
MAKERERE UNIVERSITY. LIBRARY. LIBRARY BULLETIN AND ACCESSIONS LIST. Text in English. 1954. q. UGX 70, USD 10.
Published by: Makerere University, Library, PO Box 16002, Kampala, Uganda. Ed. Margaret M Barlow. Circ: 300.

MALAWI. GOVERNMENT PRINTER. CATALOGUE OF PUBLICATIONS. see *PUBLIC ADMINISTRATION—Abstracting, Bibliographies, Statistics*

011 MWI
MALAWI NATIONAL BIBLIOGRAPHY; list of publications deposited in the library of the National Archives. Text in English. 1963-1983; resumed 1994. every 5 yrs., latest 1997-2001. back issues avail. **Document type:** *Directory, Bibliography.* **Description:** A general list of publications deposited in the library of the National Archives under legal deposit.
Formerly (until 1967): Malawi. List of Publications Deposited in the Library of the National Archives
Related titles: Online - full content ed.
Published by: National Archives of Malawi, Library, Mkulichi Rd., PO Box 62, Zomba, Malawi. archives@sdnp.org.mw, http://chambo.sdnp.org.mw/ruleoflaw/archives/index.htm. Circ: 200 (controlled).

011 MYS ISSN 1394-5602
Z3246
MALAYSIAN NATIONAL BIBLIOGRAPHY (CD-ROM EDITION). Text in Chinese, English, Tamil, Malay. 1996. irreg. MYR 300 (effective 2000). **Document type:** *Bibliography.* **Description:** Contains all titles of materials received under Preservation of Books Act 1966 and Deposit of Library Matieral Act 1986.
Media: CD-ROM. **Related titles:** ♦ Online - full content ed.: Malaysian National Bibliography (Online Edition).
Published by: Perpustakaan Negara Malaysia/National Library of Malaysia, 232 Jalan Tun Razak, Kuala Lumpur, 50572, Malaysia. TEL 60-3-2943488, FAX 60-3-2929767, pnn@pnm.my, http://www.pnm.my. Ed. Ruzilah Ehsan. **Subscr. to:** Parry's Book Center Sdn. Bhd., 60 Jalan Negara, Taman Melawati 53100, Malaysia.

011 MYS
MALAYSIAN NATIONAL BIBLIOGRAPHY (ONLINE EDITION). Text in Chinese, English, Malay, Tamil. irreg. bibl.
Media: Online - full content. **Related titles:** ♦ CD-ROM ed.: Malaysian National Bibliography (CD-ROM Edition). ISSN 1394-5602.
Published by: Perpustakaan Negara Malaysia/National Library of Malaysia, 232 Jalan Tun Razak, Kuala Lumpur, 50572, Malaysia. TEL 60-3-2943488, FAX 60-3-2929767, pnn@pnm.my, telnet://opac.pnm.my, http://www.pnm.my.

015 MLT ISSN 0258-669X
MALTA NATIONAL BIBLIOGRAPHY/BIBLIOGRAFIJA NAZZJONALITA MALTA. Text in English. 1983. a. USD 15 (effective 2000). **Document type:** *Bibliography.*
—BLDSC (5356.347000).
Published by: National Library of Malta, 36 Old Treasury St., Valletta, Malta. TEL 356-224338, FAX 356-235992. R&P Moira Borg. Circ: 500.

MARKAZ AL-MALIK FAISAL LIL-BUHUTH WAL-DIRASAT AL-ISLAMIYYAH. FIHRIS AL-MAKHTUTAT/KING FAISAL CENTER FOR RESEARCH AND ISLAMIC STUDIES. MANUSCRIPT CATALOGUE. see *ASIAN STUDIES—Abstracting, Bibliographies, Statistics*

MARKETSEARCH. see *BUSINESS AND ECONOMICS—Abstracting, Bibliographies, Statistics*

MASTERS THESES IN THE PURE AND APPLIED SCIENCES ACCEPTED BY COLLEGES AND UNIVERSITIES OF THE UNITED STATES AND CANADA. see *EDUCATION—Abstracting, Bibliographies, Statistics*

A MATTER OF FACT: STATEMENTS CONTAINING STATISTICS ON CURRENT SOCIAL, ECONOMIC AND POLITICAL ISSUES. see *HISTORY*

MEDIA-DATEN (ZURICH); directory of Swiss media. see *ADVERTISING AND PUBLIC RELATIONS—Abstracting, Bibliographies, Statistics*

MEDIA-DATEN: ZEITUNGEN - ANZEIGENBLAETTER. see *ADVERTISING AND PUBLIC RELATIONS—Abstracting, Bibliographies, Statistics*

MEDICAL AND HEALTH CARE BOOKS AND SERIALS IN PRINT; an index to literature in health sciences. see *MEDICAL SCIENCES—Abstracting, Bibliographies, Statistics*

011 940 USA
MEDIEVAL BOOK. Text in English. 1993. irreg. **Document type:** *Monographic series.*
Published by: University of Notre Dame Press, 310 Flanner Hall, Notre Dame, IN 46556. TEL 219-631-6346, FAX 219-631-8148, undpress1@nd.edu, undpress.1@nd.edu, http://www.undpress.nd.edu. R&P Ann Bromley. **Dist. overseas by:** Eurospan University Press Group, Order Dept, 3 Henrietta St, London WC2E 8LU, United Kingdom. TEL 44-20-7240-0856, FAX 44-20-7379-0609, http://www.eurospan.co.uk.

MELLEN BIBLIOGRAPHIES FOR BIBLICAL RESEARCH. NEW TESTAMENT SERIES. see *RELIGIONS AND THEOLOGY—Abstracting, Bibliographies, Statistics*

MELLEN BIBLIOGRAPHIES FOR BIBLICAL RESEARCH. OLD TESTAMENT SERIES. see *RELIGIONS AND THEOLOGY—Abstracting, Bibliographies, Statistics*

MELLEN BIBLIOGRAPHIES FOR BIBLICAL RESEARCH. PERIODIC LITERATURE FOR THE STUDY OF THE NEW TESTAMENT. see *RELIGIONS AND THEOLOGY—Abstracting, Bibliographies, Statistics*

MELLEN BIBLIOGRAPHIES FOR BIBLICAL RESEARCH. PERIODIC LITERATURE FOR THE STUDY OF THE OLD TESTAMENT. see *RELIGIONS AND THEOLOGY—Abstracting, Bibliographies, Statistics*

MELLEN BIBLIOGRAPHIES FOR BIBLICAL RESEARCH. SUPPLEMENTAL SERIES. see *RELIGIONS AND THEOLOGY—Abstracting, Bibliographies, Statistics*

MEMOIRE DE TRAME; le bimensuel des ecrits sur la communication. see *COMMUNICATIONS—Abstracting, Bibliographies, Statistics*

011 MUS
MEMORANDUM OF BOOKS PRINTED IN MAURITIUS AND REGISTERED IN THE ARCHIVES OFFICE. Text in English; Summaries in English, French. 1894. q. free.
Published by: Archives Department, Development Bank of Mauritius Complex, Petite Riviere, Mauritius.

011 MEX
MEXICO. CENTRO DE INFORMACION TECNICA Y DOCUMENTACION. INDICE BIBLIOGRAFICO. Text in Spanish. 1972. q. MXP 80, USD 5. cum.index.
Related titles: Microfilm ed.
Published by: (Mexico. Centro de Informacion Tecnica y Documentacion), Instituto Nacional de Productividad, Calzada Atzcapotzalco-la Villa 209, Col Santa Catarina, Mexico City, DF 02250, Mexico. Ed. Marco A Tapia. Circ: 2,500.

011 USA ISSN 0270-8523
Z1033.M5
MICROFORMS ANNUAL✶. Text in English. 1973. biennial. USD 15. adv.
Formerly: M I M C Microforms Annual (0362-4552)
Published by: Microforms International (Subsidiary of: Pergamon Press, Inc.), Elsevier Science, Box 945, Madison Sq Sta, New York, NY 10159-0945. TEL 914-592-7700. Circ: 15,000.

MISSOURI STATE GOVERNMENT PUBLICATIONS. see *PUBLIC ADMINISTRATION—Abstracting, Bibliographies, Statistics*

MONTHLY CATALOG OF UNITED STATES GOVERNMENT PUBLICATIONS. see *PUBLIC ADMINISTRATION—Abstracting, Bibliographies, Statistics*

016 BEL ISSN 0773-8560
MUSEE ROYAL DE L'AFRIQUE CENTRALE. CATALOGUE DES EDITIONS/KONINKLIJK MUSEUM VOOR MIDDEN-AFRIKA. CATALOGUS DER UITGAVEN. Text in Dutch, French. 1965. a. **Document type:** *Catalog.*
Formerly (until 1970): Musee Royal de l'Afrique Centrale. Publications (0082-2906)
Published by: Musee Royal de l'Afrique Centrale/Koninklijk Museum voor Midden-Afrika, Steenweg op Leuven 13, Tervuren, 3080, Belgium. TEL 32-2-7695299, FAX 32-2-767-0242.

011 IND
N A S S D O C RESEARCH INFORMATION SERIES. BIBLIOGRAPHIC REPRINTS. (N A S S D O C Research Information Series) Text in English. irreg. INR 50 (effective 2001). bibl. **Document type:** *Bulletin, Bibliography.* **Description:** Contains short bibliographies compiled for scholars on different social science topics.
Related titles: Duplicated (not offset) ed.
Published by: (National Social Science Documentation Centre), Indian Council of Social Science Research, 35 Ferozshah Rd., New Delhi, 110 001, India. TEL 91-11-6179832, FAX 91-11-6179836, info@icssr.org, http://www.icssr.org. Ed. Savitri Devi. Circ: 100.

017 NOR ISSN 0805-7575
N O S P ADRESSELISTE TIL NORDISKE BIBLIOTHEK. Text in Norwegian. 1981. a. NOK 250 (effective 2000). **Document type:** *Bibliography.*
Formerly (until 1994): N O S P Mikro. Foerteckning Oeveri N O S P Representerade Bibliothek (0783-4020)
Related titles: ♦ Online - full content ed.: N O S P on Web.

Published by: University of Oslo Library, N O S P - Centre, Postboks 2674, Solli, Oslo, 0203, Norway. TEL 47-23-27-61-10, FAX 47-23-27-60-10, nosp@nb.no, http://www.nb.no/nosp.

011 NOR
N O S P ON WEB. Text in English. q. NOK 500 for ordering 1-100 copies (effective 2000). abstr.; bibl. **Document type:** *Directory.* **Description:** Contains bibliographic listings of 160,000 serials.
Media: Online - full content. **Related titles:** ♦ Print ed.: N O S P Adresseliste til Nordiske Bibliothek. ISSN 0805-7575.
Published by: The NOSP-Centre, National Library of Norway, Oslo Division, P.O.Box 2674 Solli, Oslo, N-0203 , Norway. TEL 47-2-3276110, FAX 47-2-3276010, nosp@nb.no.

015 PNG
N R I BIBLIOGRAPHIES. Text in English. 1976. irreg. price varies. **Document type:** *Bibliography.*
Published by: National Research Institute, PO Box 5854, Boroko, Papua New Guinea. TEL 675-26-0300, FAX 675-26-0213. Ed. Jim Robbins.

N T I S DATA BASE. see *SCIENCES: COMPREHENSIVE WORKS—Abstracting, Bibliographies, Statistics*

011 AUS
N U C O S ON DISK. Text in English. 3/yr.
Media: CD-ROM (from R M I T Publishing).
Published by: National Library of Australia, Publications Section, Cultural and Educational Services Division, Canberra, ACT 2600, Australia. TEL 61-6-262-1365, FAX 61-6-2734493, http://www.nla.gov.au.

NAMES OF PERSONS; national usages for entry in catalogues. see *LIBRARY AND INFORMATION SCIENCES*

NARODNI BIBLIOGRAFIE CESKE REPUBLIKY. MAPY (CD-ROM EDITION). see *GEOGRAPHY—Abstracting, Bibliographies, Statistics*

NATIONAL AEROSPACE LABORATORIES. COMBINED AEROSPACE BOOK ADDITIONS. see *AERONAUTICS AND SPACE FLIGHT—Abstracting, Bibliographies, Statistics*

NATIONAL ASSOCIATION OF ELEMENTARY SCHOOL PRINCIPALS. PROFESSIONAL RESOURCES CATALOG. see *EDUCATION—School Organization And Administration*

015 BRB ISSN 0256-7709
Z1502.B35
NATIONAL BIBLIOGRAPHY OF BARBADOS. Text in English. 1975. s-a. USD 10. **Document type:** *Bibliography.*
Description: Lists works deposited with the National Library Service in compliance with the Publications Act and works of Barbadian authorship printed abroad.
Related titles: Online - full text ed.
Published by: National Library Service, Culloden Farm, Culloden Rd., St Michael, Barbados. TEL 246-429-5716, FAX 246-436-1501, TELEX WB 2222. Circ: 100.

NATIONAL BIBLIOGRAPHY OF BOTSWANA. see *PUBLISHING AND BOOK TRADE—Abstracting, Bibliographies, Statistics*

015 NGA ISSN 0331-0019
Z3553.N5
NATIONAL BIBLIOGRAPHY OF NIGERIA. Text in English. 1951. m. (plus s-a. & a. cumulations). **Document type:** *Bibliography.*
Former titles: Nigerian Publications; Nigerian publications: Current National Bibliography (0078-0812)
—Linda Hall.
Published by: National Library of Nigeria, 4 Wesley St, PMB 12626, Lagos, Nigeria. TEL 234-1-634704.

011 ZMB ISSN 0377-1636
Z3573.Z3
NATIONAL BIBLIOGRAPHY OF ZAMBIA. Text in English. a. looseleaf. ZMK 500. back issues avail. **Document type:** *Bibliography.*
Published by: National Archives, Ridgeway, PO Box RW 50010, Lusaka, Zambia. Ed. Christine Kamwana. Circ: 500.

015 USA ISSN 1050-5830
HF5466
NATIONAL DIRECTORY OF CATALOGS. Text in English. 1990. a. USD 645; USD 895 CD-ROM ed.; USD 1,195 combined subscription print & CD-ROM eds. (effective 2004). adv.
Document type: *Directory, Trade.* **Description:** Lists more than 8,000 catalogs with comprehensive business information.
Related titles: CD-ROM ed.; Online - full text ed.
Published by: Oxbridge Communications, Inc., 186 Fifth Ave., New York, NY 10010. TEL 212-741-0231, 800-955-0231, FAX 212-633-2938, info@mediafinder.com, http://www.mediafinder.com. Pub. Patricia Hagood. R&P Kerry Murphy. Adv. contacts Deborah Striplin, Johanna Barwick.

011 USA
Z6951
NATIONAL DIRECTORY OF COMMUNITY NEWSPAPERS. Text in English. 1923. a. USD 105 (effective 2000). adv. **Document type:** *Directory.*
Formerly: Directory of Community Newspapers (1045-1102)
Published by: American Newspaper Representatives, Inc., 2075 W. Big Beaver Rd., Ste. 310, Troy, MI 48084-3439. TEL 800-550-7557, FAX 248-643-0606, rsontag@anrinc.net. Ed., Pub., R&P, Adv. contact Robert Sontag. Circ: 1,000.

016.05 USA ISSN 0895-4321
Z6941
NATIONAL DIRECTORY OF MAGAZINES. Text in English. 1987. a. USD 895; USD 995 CD-ROM ed.; USD 1,695 combined subscription print & CD-ROM eds. (effective 2004). adv.
Document type: *Directory, Trade.* **Description:** Provides publishers with comprehensive information on the state of the magazine industry with more than 25,000 listings.
Related titles: CD-ROM ed.; Online - full text ed.
Published by: Oxbridge Communications, Inc., 186 Fifth Ave., New York, NY 10010. TEL 212-741-0231, 800-955-0231, FAX 212-633-2938, info@mediafinder.com, http://www.mediafinder.com. Pub. Patricia Hagood. R&P Kerry Murphy. Adv. contacts Deborah Striplin, Johanna Barwick.

NATIONAL ENGLISH LITERARY MUSEUM. BIBLIOGRAPHIC SERIES. see *LITERATURE—Abstracting, Bibliographies, Statistics*

NATIONAL ENGLISH LITERARY MUSEUM. INTRODUCTION SERIES. see *LITERATURE—Abstracting, Bibliographies, Statistics*

NATIONAL RESEARCH COUNCIL. TRANSPORTATION RESEARCH BOARD. BIBLIOGRAPHY. see *TRANSPORTATION—Abstracting, Bibliographies, Statistics*

015.485 SWE
Z2625
NATIONALBIBLIOGRAFIN - BOECKER/SWEDISH NATIONAL BIBLIOGRAPHY. Text in Swedish. 1861. w. back issues avail. **Document type:** *Bibliography.*
Former titles (until 2004): Svensk Bokfoerteckning (Print edition) (0039-6443); (until 1953): Aarskatalog foer Svenska Bokhandeln (0349-442X)
Media: Online - full content.
Indexed: BEL&L, RASB.
—Linda Hall.
Published by: Kungliga Biblioteket, Nationalbibliografin. Monografienheten/National Library of Sweden. National Bibliography, Humlegaarden, PO Box 5039, Stockholm, 10241, Sweden. TEL 46-8-4634433, bibliogr@kb.se, http://www.kb.se/nbm/nbb.htm.

NATURAL HAZARDS CENTER. TOPICAL BIBLIOGRAPHIES. see *CIVIL DEFENSE—Abstracting, Bibliographies, Statistics*

016.05 USA
THE NAVIGATOR (BRIDGEWATER). Text in English. q.
Document type: *Journal, Trade.* **Description:** Keeps Baker & Taylor customers informed about current and forthcoming series and serials.
Published by: Baker & Taylor, PO Box 6885, Bridgewater, NJ 08807-0885. TEL 800-775-1800, FAX 704-329-8989, btinfo@btol.com, http://www.btol.com.

NESTOR. see *ARCHAEOLOGY—Abstracting, Bibliographies, Statistics*

NETHERLANDS. MINISTERIE VAN ONDERWIJS EN WETENSCHAPPEN. PEDAGOGISCHE BIBLIOGRAFIE. see *EDUCATION—Abstracting, Bibliographies, Statistics*

011 DEU ISSN 0028-3533
DIE NEUEN BUECHER. Text in German. 1962. q. adv. bk.rev. bibl.; illus.; tr.lit. **Document type:** *Magazine, Consumer.*
Published by: Rossipaul Kommunikation GmbH, Menzinger Str 37, Munich, 80638, Germany. TEL 49-89-179106-0, FAX 49-89-17910622, info@rossipaul.de, http://www.rossipaul.de/dieneuenbuecher.html. adv.: page EUR 3,290. Circ: 500,000 (controlled).

011 ETH ISSN 0255-5190
NEW ACQUISITIONS IN THE U N E C A LIBRARY. Text in English. 1962. bi-m. per issue exchange basis.
Media: Duplicated (not offset).
Published by: United Nations Economic Commission for Africa, Documents & Publishing Services Unit, PO Box 3001, Addis Ababa, Ethiopia.

NEW BOOKS QUARTERLY ON ISLAM & THE MUSLIM WORLD. see *RELIGIONS AND THEOLOGY—Abstracting, Bibliographies, Statistics*

NEW BOOKS RECEIVED BY THE FACULTY LIBRARY. see *AERONAUTICS AND SPACE FLIGHT—Abstracting, Bibliographies, Statistics*

490 016 DEU ISSN 0173-6388
Z7043
NEW CONTENTS SLAVISTICS. Text in Slavic, Multiple languages. 1976. q. EUR 40.90 (effective 2003). back issues avail. **Document type:** *Journal, Academic/Scholarly.*
Description: Tables of contents of Slavistic periodicals.
Formerly (until 1980): Inhaltsverzeichnisse Slavistischer Zeitschriften (0173-6442)
Published by: (Berlin. Staatsbibliothek), Verlag Otto Sagner, Hessstr. 39-41, Munich, 80798, Germany. TEL 49-89-54218740, FAX 49-89-54218218, postmaster@kubon-sagner.de, http://www.kubon-sagner.de. Circ: 200.

NEW HOPE INTERNATIONAL REVIEW. see *LITERATURE—Abstracting, Bibliographies, Statistics*

011 USA ISSN 1528-0551
THE NEW INFORMATION REPORT. Text in English. 1985. m. looseleaf. USD 160 (effective 1999). bk.rev. s-a index, cum.index. back issues avail. **Document type:** *Newsletter.*
Description: Keeps managers current on the best sources of critical data and analysis on such topics as the strong overseas competition, political risks, export markets, and global demographics.
Formerly (until 1999): The International Information Report (0748-206X)
Related titles: Online - full text ed.
Published by: Washington Researchers, Ltd., 1655 Fort Myer Dr., Ste. 800, Arlington, VA 22209-3119. TEL 703-312-2863, FAX 703-527-4586, research@researchers.com, http://www.researchers.com, http://www.washingtonresearchers.com. Ed. Laurie Schlagel. R&P Ellen O'Kane.

NEW LITERATURE ON OLD AGE. see *GERONTOLOGY AND GERIATRICS—Abstracting, Bibliographies, Statistics*

NEW LITERATURE ON VISUAL IMPAIRMENT. see *HANDICAPPED—Abstracting, Bibliographies, Statistics*

011 ISR ISSN 0334-5262
Z1035.1
NEW REFERENCE BOOKS. Text in English, Hebrew. 1973. a. free. bibl. **Document type:** *Bibliography.* **Description:** Listing of new reference books in libraries of the Hebrew University and the National Library.
Published by: (Reference Service), Jewish National and University Library, Jewish National and University Library, PO Box 34165, Jerusalem, Israel. TEL 972-2-6585027, FAX 972-2-651-1771, TELEX 25367, nirai@vms.huji.ac.il, http://sites.huji.ac.il/jnul. Ed. Lira Ilsar. Circ: 600.

NEW RESOURCES. see *PUBLIC ADMINISTRATION—Abstracting, Bibliographies, Statistics*

011 USA
NEW SCHOLARLY BOOKS IN AMERICA✶ . Text in English. 1972. q. USD 8. bk.rev.
Published by: Beverly Books Inc., 29 Race St, Frenchtown, NJ 08825-1011. Ed. Norman Perle. Circ: 10,000.

NEW TECHNICAL BOOKS; a selective list with descriptive annotations. see *SCIENCES: COMPREHENSIVE WORKS—Abstracting, Bibliographies, Statistics*

NEW UNESCO DOCUMENTS AND PUBLICATIONS. see *EDUCATION—Abstracting, Bibliographies, Statistics*

011 USA
THE NEW YORK TIMES SCHOOL MICROFILM COLLECTION INDEX. Text in English. irreg. illus. **Document type:** *Abstract/Index.*
Formerly: New York Times School Microfilm Collection Index by Reels (0095-5663)
Published by: (New York Times Company), ProQuest Information & Learning, 300 N Zeeb Rd., PO Box 1346, Ann Arbor, MI 48106-1346. TEL 313-761-4700, 800-521-0600, FAX 800-864-0019.

011 AUS ISSN 0157-7662
NEW ZEALAND BOOKS IN PRINT. Text in English. 1964. a. USD 59 (effective 2003). **Document type:** *Directory, Bibliography.* **Description:** Provides bibliographic information on more than 6,000 titles. Entries are indexed by title, publishers and subject; includes a book trade directory.
Indexed: BEL&L, INZP.
—CCC.
Published by: Thorpe - Bowker (Subsidiary of: R.R. Bowker LLC), Bldg C3, 85 Turner St, Port Melbourne, VIC 3207, Australia. TEL 61-3-9245-7370, FAX 61-3-9245-7395, customer.service@thorpe.com.au, subscriptions@thorpe.com.au, http://www.thorpe.com.au. Ed. Frances Kinnaird. Pub. Paulene Morey. Circ: 2,000. **N. America subscr. to:** R.R. Bowker LLC, Order Dept., PO Box 32, New Providence, NJ 07974-9903. TEL 800-521-8110.

015 NZL
NEW ZEALAND NATIONAL BIBLIOGRAPHY/TE RARANGI PUKAPUKA MATUA O AOTEAROA. Text in English. 1966. m. back issues avail. **Document type:** *Bibliography.*
Description: Bibliographic citations for New Zealand publications (including non-books) published in the current and preceding five years. Includes works written by New Zealanders or about New Zealand published overseas.
Supersedes: New Zealand National Bibliography (Microfiche Edition); Which superseded (in 1983): New Zealand National Bibliography (Print Edition) (0028-8497)

Media: Online - full content. **Related titles:** ◆ CD-ROM ed.: Te Puna CD-ROM. ISSN 1175-1371.
Indexed: RASB.
—BLDSC (6096.300000). **CCC.**
Published by: National Library of New Zealand, PO Box 1467, Wellington, 6001, New Zealand. TEL 64-4-4743000, FAX 64-4-4743035, nznb@natlib.govt.nz, http://www.natlib.govt.nz/.

016.028   USA
NEWBERRY (YEAR) MEDAL BOOKS. Text in English. a. USD 18 for package of 50. **Document type:** Bibliography.
Description: Lists the current Newberry medal and honor books, as well as all the children's and young adult books that earned the prestigious award from 1922 on.
Published by: (American Library Association, Association for Library Service to Children), American Library Association, 50 E Huron St, Chicago, IL 60611-2795. TEL 800-545-2433, http://www.ala.org. **Subscr. to:** PO Box 932501, Atlanta, GA 31193-2501. TEL 866-746-7252, FAX 770-442-9742, ala-orders@pbd.com.

011   USA   ISSN 0899-0425
Z6941
NEWSLETTERS IN PRINT; a descriptive guide to more than 11,500 subscription, membership, and free newsletters, bulletins, digests, updates, and similar serial publications issued in the United States or Canada and available in print or online. Text in English. 1966. a., latest 2004, 18th ed. USD 315 (effective 2004). **Description:** Updating on newsletters available in the U.S. and Canada.
Former titles: Newsletter Directory (0893-7656); National Directory of Newsletters and Reporting Services (0547-6232)
Related titles: CD-ROM ed.; Online - full text ed.
Published by: Gale Group (Subsidiary of: Thomson Corporation), 27500 Drake Rd, Farmington Hills, MI 48331-3535. TEL 248-699-8061, 800-877-4253, FAX 248-699-4253, galeord@gale.com, http://www.gale.com. Ed. Jan Klisz.

015   NGA   ISSN 0078-0693
NIGERIAN BOOKS IN PRINT. Text in English. 1968. a. USD 5. **Document type:** Bibliography.
Published by: National Library of Nigeria, 4 Wesley St, PMB 12626, Lagos, Nigeria. TEL 234-1-634704.

NIGERIAN INSTITUTE OF SOCIAL AND ECONOMIC RESEARCH. LIBRARY. LIST OF ACCESSIONS. see SOCIAL SCIENCES: COMPREHENSIVE WORKS—Abstracting, Bibliographies, Statistics

016   JPN
NIHON HAKUSHIROKU. Text in Japanese. 1955. irreg. JPY 5,800. bibl.
Published by: Kojunsha, 2-9 Kitaka-Rasuyama, Setagaya-ku, Tokyo, 157-0061, Japan.

NIHON KAGAKU GIJUTSU KANKEI CHIKUJI KANKOBUTSU SORAN (ONLINE EDITION)/DIRECTORY OF JAPANESE SCIENTIFIC PERIODICALS (ONLINE EDITION). see PUBLISHING AND BOOK TRADE—Abstracting, Bibliographies, Statistics

015.52   JPN   ISSN 0389-4002
            CODEN: NZSHER
NIHON ZENKOKU SHOSHI/JAPANESE NATIONAL BIBLIOGRAPHY WEEKLY LIST. Text in Japanese. 1955. w. JPY 735 per issue (effective 1999). **Document type:** Bibliography.
Formerly (until 1981): Nuohon Shuuhuo - Current Publications (0385-3292)
Related titles: CD-ROM ed.: J - B I S C; Magnetic Tape ed.; Online - full content ed.: ISSN 1347-0000. free.
Published by: (National Diet Library/Kokuritsu Kokkai Toshokan), Kokuritsu Insatsukyoku/National Printing Bureau, 2-2-4 Toranomon, Minato-Ku, Tokyo, 105-8445, Japan. TEL 81-3-3587-4283, http://npg.go.jp, http://www.npb.go.jp/. Circ: 1,000.

NIJHOFF INFORMATION, NEW PUBLICATIONS FROM CONTINENTAL EUROPE. see PUBLISHING AND BOOK TRADE—Abstracting, Bibliographies, Statistics

NIJHOFF INFORMATION, NEW PUBLICATIONS FROM THE NETHERLANDS. see PUBLISHING AND BOOK TRADE—Abstracting, Bibliographies, Statistics

016.8   USA   ISSN 1353-1980
AP4
NINETEENTH CENTURY BIBLIOGRAPHIC RECORDS. Text in English. 1994. a. **Document type:** Bibliography. **Description:** Presents bibliographic data on English-language books and pamphlets of permanent research value republished in the Nineteenth Century microfiche program.
Media: CD-ROM (from Chadwyck-Healey Inc.). **Related titles:** Microfiche ed.: (from PQC).
Published by: ProQuest Information & Learning, 300 N Zeeb Rd., PO Box 1346, Ann Arbor, MI 48106-1346. FAX 703-683-7589, info@il.proquest.com, http://www.chadwyck.com.

NORMAN PATERSON SCHOOL OF INTERNATIONAL AFFAIRS. BIBLIOGRAPHY SERIES. see POLITICAL SCIENCE—Abstracting, Bibliographies, Statistics

015.481   NOR   ISSN 0029-1870
Z2591
NORSK BOKFORTEGNELSE. AARSKATALOG. Text in Norwegian. 1903. a. (in 3 vols.). NOK 1,100 (effective 2001). **Document type:** Bibliography.
Former titles (until 1952): Aarskatalog over Norsk Litteratur (0805-7001); (until 1903): Kvartalskatalog over Norsk Litteratur (0805-9357)
Related titles: Online - full content ed.: free.
Indexed: BEL&L.
Published by: National Library of Norway, Bibliographic Services Department, Solli, PO Box 2674, Oslo, 0203, Norway. TEL 47-23-27-61-19, FAX 47-23-27-60-50, unni.knutsen@nb.no, http://www.nb.no/baser.

015.481   NOR   ISSN 0805-6978
Z2595
NORSK BOKFORTEGNELSE. NYHETSLISTE/NORWEGIAN NATIONAL BIBLIOGRAPHY. LIST OF NEW BOOKS. Text in Norwegian. 1972. fortn. NOK 960 (effective 2000). **Document type:** Bibliography.
Formerly (until 1994): Norsk Bokfortegnelse (0805-6986)
Indexed: RASB.
Published by: (Bibliographic Services Department), National Library of Norway, Oslo Division, Oslo, 0203, Norway. FAX 47-23-27-60-50, r.v.gausla@nb.no, http://www.nb.no/baser/norbok. Ed. Unni Knutsen.

NORSK MUSIKKFORTEGNELSE. LYDFESTINGER/NORWEGIAN NATIONAL DISCOGRAPHY. see MUSIC—Abstracting, Bibliographies, Statistics

NORSK MUSIKKFORTEGNELSE. NOTETRYKK/NORWEGIAN NATIONAL BIBLIOGRAPHY OF PRINTED MUSIC. see MUSIC—Abstracting, Bibliographies, Statistics

015.481   NOR
Z6956.N8
NORSK PERIODIKAFORTEGNELSE/NORWEGIAN LIST OF SERIALS. Text in Norwegian. d. free. **Document type:** Bibliography.
Media: Online - full text.
Published by: National Library of Norway, Bibliographic Services Department, Solli, PO Box 2674, Oslo, 0203, Norway. TEL 47-23-27-61-19, FAX 47-23-27-60-50, unni.knutsen@nb.no, http://www.nb.no/baser/norper/english.html.

NOTABLE SOCIAL STUDIES TRADE BOOKS FOR YOUNG PEOPLE. see SOCIAL SCIENCES: COMPREHENSIVE WORKS—Abstracting, Bibliographies, Statistics

NOTICIAS DEL PUERTO DE MONTEREY. see HISTORY—History Of North And South America

NOTNAYA LETOPIS'. see MUSIC—Abstracting, Bibliographies, Statistics

NOVAYA LITERATURA PO SOTSIAL'NYM I GUMANITARNYM NAUKAM. EKONOMIKA; bibliograficheskii ukazatel'. see BUSINESS AND ECONOMICS—Abstracting, Bibliographies, Statistics

NOVAYA LITERATURA PO SOTSIAL'NYM I GUMANITARNYM NAUKAM. FILOSOFIYA I SOTSIOLOGIYA; bibliograficheskii ukazatel'. see PHILOSOPHY—Abstracting, Bibliographies, Statistics

NOVAYA LITERATURA PO SOTSIAL'NYM I GUMANITARNYM NAUKAM. LITERATUROVEDENIE; bibliograficheskii ukazatel'. see LITERATURE—Abstracting, Bibliographies, Statistics

NOVAYA LITERATURA PO SOTSIAL'NYM I GUMANITARNYM NAUKAM. NAUKOVEDENIE; bibliograficheskii ukazatel'. see SCIENCES: COMPREHENSIVE WORKS—Abstracting, Bibliographies, Statistics

NOVAYA LITERATURA PO SOTSIAL'NYM I GUMANITARNYM NAUKAM. PRAVOVEDENIE. POLITOLIGIYA; bibliograficheskii ukazatel'. see LAW—Abstracting, Bibliographies, Statistics

NOVAYA LITERATURA PO SOTSIAL'NYM I GUMANITARNYM NAUKAM. RELIGIOVEDENIE; bibliograficheskii ukazatel'. see RELIGIONS AND THEOLOGY—Abstracting, Bibliographies, Statistics

NOVAYA LITERATURA PO SOTSIAL'NYM I GUMANITARNYM NAUKAM. YAZYKOZNANIE; bibliograficheskii ukazatel'. see LINGUISTICS—Abstracting, Bibliographies, Statistics

011   ESP
NOVEDADES; servicio de informacion bibliografica. Text in Spanish. m. illus.
Published by: Editorial Planeta S.A., Corsega, 273-277, Barcelona, 08008, Spain.

015   ARG   ISSN 0327-9979
NOVEDADES BIBLIOGRAFICAS. Text in Spanish. 1993. 3/yr. per issue exchange basis. **Document type:** Catalog.

Published by: Congreso de la Nacion, Biblioteca, Avda. Rivadavia, 1850, Capital Federal, Buenos Aires 1033, Argentina.

NOVELLEREGISTER; titel- og forfatterindeks til novellesamlinger og antologier. see LITERATURE

NOVI VYDANNYA UKRAINY. see PUBLISHING AND BOOK TRADE—Abstracting, Bibliographies, Statistics

NOVINKY LITERATURY. ZDRAVOTNICTVI-PRIRUSTKY FONDU NARODNI LEKARSKE KNIHOVNY. see MEDICAL SCIENCES—Abstracting, Bibliographies, Statistics

005   RUS
NOVYE KNIGI ROSSII. Text in Russian. 2000. w. RUR 11,800 domestic; USD 400 foreign (effective 2004). **Document type:** Bibliography. **Description:** Contains quick information on new books and booklets published in Russia in all languages.
Related titles: Diskette ed.; Online - full text ed.
Published by: Rossiiskaya Knizhnaya Palata/Book Chamber International, Ostozhenka 4, Moscow, 119034, Russian Federation. TEL 7-095-2911278, FAX 7-095-2919630, bookch@postman.ru, http://www.bookchamber.ru.

011   POL   ISSN 0867-2202
NOWOSCI KSIEGARSKIE∗ . Text in Polish. 1951. w. PLZ 15,600, USD 33.80. bk.rev. bibl. **Document type:** Bibliography.
Former titles (until 1990): Kartkowy Katalog Nowosci (0324-8003); (until 1952): Biuletyn Nowosci (0137-6837)
Published by: Panstwowe Przedsiebiorstwo Skladnica Ksiegarska, c/o Ars Polona,, Krakowskie Przedmiescie 7, PO Box 1001, Warsaw, 00068, Poland. Ed. Barbara Napierzynska. Circ: 5,000. **Dist. by:** Ars Polona, Krakowskie Przedmiescie 7, Warsaw, Poland.

NUMISMATIC BOOKS IN PRINT. see NUMISMATICS—Abstracting, Bibliographies, Statistics

010   ITA
NUOVA INFORMAZIONE BIBLIOGRAFICA; trimestrale di analisi della produzione libraria italiana. Text in Italian. 1975. q. EUR 48 domestic to individuals; EUR 85 foreign to individuals; EUR 65 combined subscription domestic print & online eds.; EUR 102 combined subscription foreign print & online eds. (effective 2005). index. back issues avail. **Document type:** Academic/Scholarly.
Formerly (until 2003): L' Informazione Bibliografica (0391-6812)
Related titles: Online - full text ed.
Published by: (Consorzio Provinciale per la Pubblica Lettura), Societa Editrice Il Mulino, Strada Maggiore 37, Bologna, 40125, Italy. TEL 39-051-256011, FAX 39-051-256034, riviste@mulino.it, http://www.mulino.it/edizioni/riviste/scheda_rivista.php?issn=1824-0771. Eds. Giuseppe Ulianich, Pasquale Petrucci. Circ: 4,000.

NY LITTERATUR OM KVINNOR/NEW LITERATURE ON WOMEN; en bibliografi. see WOMEN'S STUDIES—Abstracting, Bibliographies, Statistics

NY LITTERATUR OM KVINNOR. SUPPLEMENT. see WOMEN'S STUDIES—Abstracting, Bibliographies, Statistics

330 016   FRA   ISSN 0474-5086
O E C D CATALOGUE OF PUBLICATIONS. Text in French. a. free. **Document type:** Catalog, Government.
Published by: Organization for Economic Cooperation and Development, 2 Rue Andre Pascal, Paris, 75775 Cedex 16, France. TEL 33-1-45248200, FAX 33-1-45248500, http://www.oecd.org.

O E C D LIBRARY SPECIAL ANNOTATED BIBLIOGRAPHY: AUTOMATION/O C D E BIBLIOTHEQUE BIBLIOGRAPHIE SPECIALE ANALYTIQUE: AUTOMATION. see COMPUTERS—Abstracting, Bibliographies, Statistics

O E C S SELECT BIBLIOGRAPHY. see BUSINESS AND ECONOMICS—Economic Situation And Conditions

OCCULT PUBLICATIONS DIRECTORY. see PARAPSYCHOLOGY AND OCCULTISM—Abstracting, Bibliographies, Statistics

OESTERREICHISCHE BIBLIOGRAPHIE. REIHE A: VERZEICHNIS DER OESTERREICHISCHEN NEUERSCHEINUNGEN (ONLINE EDITION). see PUBLISHING AND BOOK TRADE—Abstracting, Bibliographies, Statistics

OESTERREICHISCHE BIBLIOGRAPHIE. REIHE B: VERZEICHNIS DER OESTERREICHISCHEN HOCHSCHULSCHRIFTEN. see PUBLISHING AND BOOK TRADE—Abstracting, Bibliographies, Statistics

OESTERREICHISCHE BIBLIOGRAPHIE. REIHE C: NEUERE AUSLAENDISCHE AUSTRIACA. see PUBLISHING AND BOOK TRADE—Abstracting, Bibliographies, Statistics

B

OESTERREICHISCHE FORSCHUNGSSTIFTUNG FUER ENTWICKLUNGSHILFE. ANNOTIERTE BIBLIOGRAPHIE; ausgewaehlte neue Literatur zur Entwicklungspolitik. see *BUSINESS AND ECONOMICS—Abstracting, Bibliographies, Statistics*

OESTERREICHISCHE VOLKSKUNDLICHE BIBLIOGRAPHIE. see *ANTHROPOLOGY—Abstracting, Bibliographies, Statistics*

OESTERREICHISCHES MUSEUM FUER VOLKSKUNDE. KATALOGE. see *MUSEUMS AND ART GALLERIES—Abstracting, Bibliographies, Statistics*

011 USA ISSN 0147-2542
Z1223.5.O4
OHIO DOCUMENTS. Text in English. 1971. q. **Document type:** *Government.*
Published by: Ohio State Library Board, 65 S Front St, Columbus, OH 43215-4163. TEL 614-644-7051, FAX 614-752-9178, http://winslo.state.oh.us.

015 CZE ISSN 1210-4566
Z2133
OHLASENE KNIHY. Short title: O.K. Text in Czech. 1993. bi-m. CZK 360 domestic; USD 20 foreign (effective 2003). bk.rev. index. **Document type:** *Bibliography.* **Description:** Lists Czech books to be published.
Related titles: Online - full content ed.: 1999.
Published by: Narodni Knihovna Ceske Republiky/National Library of the Czech Republic, Klementinum 190, Prague, 11001, Czech Republic. TEL 420-2-221663262, FAX 420-2-281013333, public.ur@nkp.cz, sekret.ur@nkp.cz, http://www.nkp.cz. Ed. Antonin Jerabek. R&P Adolf Knoll.

011 USA
OMNIBUS✶ . Text in English. 1990. 3/yr. bk.rev. **Document type:** *Bibliography.* **Description:** Reviews of books, videos, cassettes, compact discs, government documents, and periodicals in the KCLS collection for all ages.
Published by: King County Library System, 960 Newport Way NW, Issaquah, WA 98027-2702. TEL 206-684-6650, FAX 206-684-6690. Ed. Marsha Iverson. Circ: 10,000.

ONLINE JOURNAL OF CLINICAL INNOVATIONS. see *MEDICAL SCIENCES—Nurses And Nursing*

540 016 NLD
ORGANIC AND ORGANOMETALLIC CRYSTAL STRUCTURES; BIBLIOGRAPHY. Text in Dutch. 1971. irreg. price varies. **Document type:** *Bibliography.*
Related titles: ♦ Series of: Molecular Structures and Dimensions. Bibliography. ISSN 0377-2012.
Published by: Springer-Verlag Dordrecht (Subsidiary of: Springer Science+Business Media), Van Godewijckstraat 30, Dordrecht, 3311 GX, Netherlands. TEL 31-78-6576050, FAX 31-78-6576474, http://www.springeronline.com.

OUTSTANDING SCIENCE TRADE BOOKS FOR CHILDREN. see *CHILDREN AND YOUTH—Abstracting, Bibliographies, Statistics*

010 GBR ISSN 0078-7124
OVERSEAS DIRECTORIES, WHO'S WHO, PRESS GUIDES, YEAR BOOKS AND OVERSEAS PERIODICAL SUBSCRIPTIONS. Text in English. 1947. biennial. GBP 18, USD 55. adv.
Related titles: Microfilm ed.: (from PQC).
Published by: New Product Newsletter Co. Ltd., 1a Chesterfield St, London, W1X 7HF, United Kingdom. Ed. H R Vaughan. Circ: 5,000.

016.05 USA ISSN 0163-7010
Z6944.N44
OXBRIDGE DIRECTORY OF NEWSLETTERS. Text in English. 1979. a. USD 895; USD 995 CD-ROM ed.; USD 1,695 combined subscription print & CD-ROM eds. (effective 2004). adv. **Document type:** *Directory, Trade.* **Description:** Lists over 15,000 newsletters published in the U.S. and Canada, arranged by major subject categories.
Related titles: CD-ROM ed.; Online - full text ed.
Published by: Oxbridge Communications, Inc., 186 Fifth Ave., New York, NY 10010. TEL 212-741-0231, FAX 212-633-2938, http://www.mediafinder.com. Pub. Patricia Hagood. Adv. contact Kerry Murphy.

P A I S INTERNATIONAL - JOURNALS INDEXED IN (YEAR). (Public Affairs Information Service, Inc.) see *SOCIAL SCIENCES: COMPREHENSIVE WORKS*

011 IND
PACIFIC ISLANDS BOOKS NEWS LETTERS. Text in English. 1981. m. INR 352, USD 71 (effective 2000). **Document type:** *Newsletter.*
Published by: K.K. Roy (Private) Ltd., 55 Gariahat Rd., P O Box 10210, Kolkata, West Bengal 700 019, India. R&P M Misra TEL 91-33-475-4872.

015.45 ITA ISSN 1594-9613
PAGINE APERTE; mensile bibliografico. Text in Italian. 1962. m. free. adv. bk.rev. **Document type:** *Bibliography.* **Description:** Reviews books.
Formerly: Edizioni Nostre (0013-0982)
Published by: Edizioni San Paolo, Piazza Soncino 5, Cinisello Balsamo, CN 20092, Italy. TEL 39-02-660751, FAX 39-02-66075211, sanpaoloedizioni@stpauls.it, http://www.edizionisanpaolo.it. Circ: 80,000.

PAKISTAN'S BOOKS & LIBRARIES; the only monthly magazine of its kind. see *PUBLISHING AND BOOK TRADE*

015.953 PNG ISSN 0252-8347
Z4811
PAPUA NEW GUINEA NATIONAL BIBLIOGRAPHY. Text in English. 1981. s-a. PGK 36 (effective 1996). index. back issues avail. **Document type:** *Bibliography.*
Published by: National Library Service, Office of Libraries and Archives, PO Box 734, Waigani, NCD, Papua New Guinea. FAX 675-3251331. Ed. Karina Sereva. Circ: 280 (controlled).

011 PRY ISSN 0257-7070
Z1821
PARAGUAY; un ano de bibliografia. Text in Spanish. 1980. a. USD 25. bk.rev. bibl.
Published by: Distribuidor Internacional Publicaciones Paraguayas, Ayoreos e-4a y 5a, PO Box 2507, Asuncion, Paraguay. TEL 595-21-495367, FAX 595-21-447460. Ed. Margarita Kallsen. Circ: 1,000.

011 IND
PATRIKAPANJEE. Text in Bengali. 1982. a., latest 2000. INR 50 (effective 2001). bibl. 200 p./no.; **Document type:** *Yearbook, Bibliography.*
Published by: Bangla Bhasa Sahitya-o-Samskriti Gabesane Samastha, c/o Little Magazine Stall & Bektigata Prakashani, 6 B Ramanath Mazumder St., Kolkata, West Bengal 700 009, India. TEL 03212-59622. Ed. Asok Kumar Kundu. Circ: 1,100.

015 USA
▼ **PATRON BOOKS IN PRINT.** Text in English. 2004. w.
Media: Online - full text.
Published by: R.R. Bowker LLC (Subsidiary of: Cambridge Information Group), 630 Central Ave., New Providence, NJ 07974. TEL 908-286-1090, 888-269-5372, FAX 908-219-0098, info@bowker.com, http://www.bowker.com. **Subscr. to:** Order Dept., PO Box 32, New Providence, NJ 07974-9903.

PERIODICALS IN CANADIAN LAW LIBRARIES. see *LAW—Abstracting, Bibliographies, Statistics*

011 AUS ISSN 1322-3895
Z6961
PERIODICALS IN PRINT: AUSTRALIA, NEW ZEALAND & THE SOUTH PACIFIC (YEAR). Text in English. 1981. a., latest vol.14, 1997. AUD 149 domestic; AUD 184 foreign (effective 2000). **Document type:** *Directory, Bibliography.* **Description:** Lists some 13,000 periodicals published in Australia, New Zealand and the Pacific Islands; includes magazines, directories, yearbooks carrying ISSNs, newspapers, proceedings, and trade publications. Government publications - with the exception of major serials - are excluded. Entries are indexed by title, publisher, and subject.
Former titles (until 1994): Australian Periodicals in Print (1030-2476); Australian Serials in Print (0725-5462)
—BLDSC (6426.123000). **CCC.**
Published by: Bookman Press Pty Ltd, Lu 10, 227 Collins St, Melbourne, VIC 3000, Australia. TEL 61-3-96542000, FAX 61-3-96542290, bookman@bookman.com.au, http://www.bookman.com.au. Circ: 2,000 (paid).

015 HUN ISSN 0209-9500
PETOFI IRODALMI MUZEUM BIBLIOGRAFIAI FUZETEI/BIBLIOGRAPHICAL UNITS OF THE LITERARY MUSEUM. Text in Hungarian. 1972. irreg. HUF 800. **Document type:** *Bibliography.* **Description:** Provides annotated bibliographies of Hungarian literary periodicals, journals and first editions.
Published by: Magyar Irodalmi Muzeum/Musuem of Hungarian Literature, Karolyi Mihaly utca 16, Budapest 5, 1053, Hungary. TEL 36-1-3171722, FAX 36-1-3171722. Ed. Ferenc Botka.

015.599 PHL ISSN 0303-190X
Z3296 CODEN: PNBIDI
PHILIPPINE NATIONAL BIBLIOGRAPHY. Text in English. 1974. q. (plus a. cumulations). price varies. **Document type:** *Bibliography.* **Description:** Lists current works of research value published or printed in the Philippines by Filipino authors, or about the Philippines.
Related titles: ♦ Supplement(s): Philippine National Bibliography. Part 2: Theses and Dissertations. ISSN 0116-2705.
—CASDDS.
Published by: National Library, T.M. Kalaw St, Manila, Philippines. TEL 02-524-1011, FAX 02-524-2329. Ed. Leonila D Tominez. Circ: 2,500.

015.599 PHL ISSN 0116-2705
PHILIPPINE NATIONAL BIBLIOGRAPHY. PART 2: THESES AND DISSERTATIONS. Text in English. 1985. a. price varies. **Document type:** *Bibliography.*
Related titles: ♦ Supplement to: Philippine National Bibliography. ISSN 0303-190X.
Published by: National Library, T.M. Kalaw St, Manila, Philippines. TEL 63-2-524-1011, FAX 63-2-524-2329. Ed. Leonila D Tominez.

015 PHL ISSN 0115-7213
PHILIPPINES. NATIONAL LIBRARY. T N L RESEARCH GUIDE SERIES. Short title: T N L Research Guide Series. Text in English. 1971. irreg. (approx. 2/yr). per issue exchange basis.
Media: Duplicated (not offset).
Published by: (Bibliography Division), National Library, T.M. Kalaw St, Manila, Philippines. TEL 63-2-524-1011, FAX 63-2-524-2329. Ed. Leonila D Tominez. Circ: 300.

PHILOSOPHICAL BOOKS. see *PHILOSOPHY—Abstracting, Bibliographies, Statistics*

PHONOLOG REPORTER; all-in-one-reporter. see *MUSIC—Abstracting, Bibliographies, Statistics*

PICTURE BOOKS FOR CHILDREN. see *CHILDREN AND YOUTH—Abstracting, Bibliographies, Statistics*

011 070 GBR ISSN 0957-6916
PIMS EUROPEAN CONSUMER DIRECTORY. Text in English. 1989. s-a. GBP 185 (effective 1997). **Document type:** *Directory.* **Description:** Consumer publications listed by subject area - country.
Published by: P I M S (UK) Ltd., PIMS House, Mildmay Ave, London, N1 4RS, United Kingdom. TEL 44-20-7226-1000, FAX 44-20-7354-7053.

011 070 GBR ISSN 0955-1581
PIMS EUROPEAN NEWSPAPERS DIRECTORY. Text in English. 1989. 2/yr. GBP 185 (effective 1997). **Document type:** *Directory.* **Description:** Contacts in 80 subject areas for major European daily and Sunday newspapers.
Published by: P I M S (UK) Ltd., PIMS House, Mildmay Ave, London, N1 4RS, United Kingdom. TEL 44-20-7226-1000, FAX 44-20-7354-7053.

011 070 GBR ISSN 0957-6908
PIMS U S A CONSUMER DIRECTORY. Text in English. 1989. 2/yr. GBP 179 (effective 1997). **Document type:** *Directory.* **Description:** Consumer publications listed by subject area.
Published by: P I M S (UK) Ltd., PIMS House, Mildmay Ave, London, N1 4RS, United Kingdom. TEL 44-20-7226-1000, FAX 44-20-7354-7053.

011 070 GBR ISSN 0955-8675
PIMS U S A NEWSPAPER DIRECTORY. Text in English. 1989. s-a. GBP 179 (effective 1997). **Document type:** *Directory.* **Description:** Contacts in over 30 subject areas for US daily newspapers.
Published by: P I M S (UK) Ltd., PIMS House, Mildmay Ave, London, N1 4RS, United Kingdom. TEL 44-20-7226-1000, FAX 44-20-7354-7053.

011 070 GBR ISSN 0954-6138
PIMS U S A TRADE & TECHNICAL DIRECTORY. Text in English. 1988. 2/yr. GBP 179 (effective 1997). **Document type:** *Directory.* **Description:** Trade and technical publications listed by subject area.
Published by: P I M S (UK) Ltd., PIMS House, Mildmay Ave, London, N1 4RS, United Kingdom. TEL 44-20-7226-1000, FAX 44-20-7354-7053.

PIMSLEUR'S CHECKLIST OF BASIC AMERICAN LEGAL PUBLICATIONS. see *LAW—Abstracting, Bibliographies, Statistics*

PLAYWRIGHTS UNION OF CANADA CATALOGUE OF CANADIAN PLAYS. see *THEATER—Abstracting, Bibliographies, Statistics*

POLITYKA. POLITYCHNI NAUKY. see *POLITICAL SCIENCE—Abstracting, Bibliographies, Statistics*

361 300 ITA
POLLICINO; banca dati su emarginazione disagio giovanile professioni e politiche sociali. Text in Italian. base vol. plus q. updates. **Document type:** *Bibliography.* **Description:** Contains bibliographic data on such social issues as addiction, problems of youth and adolescents, crime and encarceration, homosexuality, prostitution, AIDS, and immigration problems, as well as conflict resolution.
Media: CD-ROM.
Published by: Edizioni Gruppo Abele, Corso Trapani 95, Turin, TO 10141, Italy. TEL 39-011-3841011, FAX 39-011-3841031, segreteria@gruppoabele.org, http://www.gruppoabele.org.

011 POL ISSN 0554-5625
Z2523
POLONICA ZAGRANICZNE. BIBLIOGRAFIA. Text in Polish. 1960. a., latest 1995. PLZ 25 domestic; USD 16.66 foreign (effective 2001). **Document type:** *Bibliography.* **Description:** Covers books, maps and printed music, etchings, and first issues of foreign serials in Polish language or fully devoted to Poland and Poles.
Published by: Biblioteka Narodowa, Instytut Bibliograficzny, Al Niepodleglosci 213, Warsaw, 02086, Poland. TEL 48-22-6082408, FAX 48-22-8255251, polonica@bn.org.pl, http://www.bn.org.pl. Ed. Danuta Bilikiewicz Blanc. **Dist. by:** P.P. CHZ Ars Polona, Krakowskie Przedmiescie 7, Warsaw 00068, Poland.

B

▼ *new title* ➤ *refereed* ✶ *unverified* ♦ *full entry avail.*

POLSKA AKADEMIA NAUK. ODDZIAL W KRAKOWIE. KOMISJA HISTORYCZNA. PRACE. see *HISTORY—Abstracting, Bibliographies, Statistics*

POLSKA BIBLIOGRAFIA BIBLIOLOGICZNA/POLISH BIBLIOGRAPHY OF LIBRARY SCIENCE. see *LIBRARY AND INFORMATION SCIENCES—Abstracting, Bibliographies, Statistics*

POPULATION EDUCATION ACCESSIONS LIST. see *EDUCATION—Abstracting, Bibliographies, Statistics*

PREHLED PEDAGOGICKE LITERATURY. RADA A. see *EDUCATION—Abstracting, Bibliographies, Statistics*

PREHLED PEDAGOGICKE LITERATURY. RADA B. see *EDUCATION—Abstracting, Bibliographies, Statistics*

070 015 IND ISSN 0445-6653
PRESS IN INDIA. Text in English. 1957. a. (in 2 vols.), latest 1990. USD 95.40. title index.
Published by: Controller of Publications, Civil Lines, New Delhi, 110 006, India. Circ: 1,000.

017.8 DEU ISSN 0176-5248
PRESSE-PORTRAETS; das Angebot des Pressehandels. Text in German. 1978. s-a. EUR 44; EUR 26 newsstand/cover (effective 2005). adv. index. **Document type:** *Magazine, Trade.* **Description:** Catalog for the trade and the consumer of newspapers, magazines, comic books, and paperback books, with publishing information and short descriptions.
Related titles: ◆ Supplement to: Presse Report. ISSN 0341-8073.
Published by: Presse Fachverlag GmbH & Co. KG, Eidelstedter Weg 22, Hamburg, 20255, Germany. TEL 49-40-6090090, FAX 49-40-60900915, info@presse-fachverlag.de, http://www.presse-portraets.de, http://www.presse-fachverlag.de. Circ: 35,000 (paid and controlled).

011 DNK ISSN 0108-1594
PRIMA VISTA; udvalg af nye boeger og tidsskriftartikler. Text in Danish. 1981. 6/yr. free. back issues avail. **Document type:** *Newsletter.*
Related titles: Online - full content ed.: Net Prima Vista. ISSN 1398-0459. 1997.
Published by: Det Administrative Bibliotek, Slotsholmsgade 12, Copenhagen K, 1216, Denmark. TEL 45-33-924691, 45-33-924695, FAX 45-33-910629, dab@dab.dkg, http://www.dab.dk/indhfrm.htm?om/om.htm, http://www.dab.dkg. Eds. Suzanne Weimann TEL 45-33-924648, Winnie Henriksen TEL 45-33-924742.

011 GBR ISSN 0079-5402
PRIVATE PRESS BOOKS; a checklist of books issued by private presses in the past year. Text in English. 1960. a., latest 1994-8. GBP 20, USD 40 to non-members (effective 2001). index. cum.index. 100 p./no. 1 cols./p.; back issues avail. **Document type:** *Bibliography.*
Published by: Private Libraries Association, Ravelston, South View Rd, Pinner, Mddx HA5 3YD, United Kingdom. Ed. Paul Nash. R&P David Chambers. Circ: 400.

016 947 RUS ISSN 0555-2982
CODEN: PBYSA8
PROBLEMY SEVERA; tekushchii ukazatel' literatury. Text in English, Russian, Multiple languages. 1968. 3/yr. USD 96 foreign (effective 1999). **Description:** Covers books, articles, summaries and reports on ecological, economical, social, medical and biological, agricultural problems encountered in the developing Russian north and other countries of the far north.
Indexed: MEDLINE, RASB.
—CISTI, GNLM, Linda Hall.
Published by: Rossiiskaya Akademiya Nauk, Sibirskoe Otdelenie, Gosudarstvennaya Publichnaya Nauchno-tekhnicheskaya Biblioteka/State Public Scientific and Technical Library of the Siberian Branch of the Russian Academy of Sciences, Ul Voskhod 15, Novosibirsk, 630200, Russian Federation. TEL 7-3832-661367, FAX 7-3832-663365, TELEX 133220, onb@spsl.nsc.ru, root@libr.nsk.su. Eds. S S Guzner, S V Vasiliev.

PRODUCTION PLANNING SYSTEM. see *ADVERTISING AND PUBLIC RELATIONS—Abstracting, Bibliographies, Statistics*

PROVIDENT BOOK FINDER. see *RELIGIONS AND THEOLOGY—Abstracting, Bibliographies, Statistics*

015 CAN ISSN 0550-1792
PROVINCE OF NOVA SCOTIA. PUBLICATIONS. Text in English. 1967. a.
Published by: (Nova Scotia Legislative Library), Queen's Printer, Nova Scotia, PO Box 637, Halifax, NS B3J 2T3, Canada. TEL 902-424-7580, FAX 902-424-7161, publications@gov.ns.ca, http://www.gov.ns.ca/.

011 POL ISSN 0033-2518
Z2523 CODEN: PRBIBA
PRZEWODNIK BIBLIOGRAFICZNY; urzedowy wykaz drukow wydanych w Rzeczypospolitej Polskiej. Text in Polish. 1944. w. PLZ 16 domestic; PLZ 3 per issue domestic; USD 2 per issue foreign (effective 2001). **Document type:** *Bibliography.* **Description:** Covers books, maps and printed music, in classified order by UDC.
Related titles: CD-ROM ed.: ISSN 1505-7895; Online - full text ed.: Czasopisma Polskie Nowe; ◆ Supplement(s): Bibliografia Wydawnictw Ciaglych Nowych, Zawieszonych i Zmieniajacych Tytul. ISSN 0239-5606.
Indexed: IBR, IBZ, RASB.
—CASDDS.
Published by: Biblioteka Narodowa, Instytut Bibliograficzny, Al Niepodleglosci 213, Warsaw, 02086, Poland. TEL 48-22-6082426, FAX 48-22-6082424, polonica@bn.org.pl, http://www.bn.org.pl. Ed. Ewa Zalewska-Macik. **Dist. by:** P.P. CHZ Ars Polona, Krakowskie Przedmiescie 7, Warsaw 00068, Poland.

PUBLIC INTERNATIONAL LAW; a current bibliography of books and articles. see *LAW—Abstracting, Bibliographies, Statistics*

015 ROM
PUBLICATII DIN ROMANIA. Text in Romanian. s-a.
Published by: Agentia Nationala de Presa Rompres, Piata Presei Libere 1, Bucharest, Romania. TEL 17-60-10, FAX 17-04-87.

PUBLICATIONS IN EDUCATION AND THE SOCIAL SCIENCES IN ISRAEL. see *SOCIOLOGY—Abstracting, Bibliographies, Statistics*

QUANGUO XIN SHUMU/NEW BOOKS CATALOG OF P R C. see *PUBLISHING AND BOOK TRADE—Abstracting, Bibliographies, Statistics*

011 CHN
QUANGUO XINSHU MU/NATIONAL NEW BOOKS. Text in Chinese. 1951. m. **Document type:** *Academic/Scholarly.* **Description:** Provides news and information on new books published in China.
Contact Dist.: China International Book Trading Corp/Zhongguo Guoji Tushu Maoyi Zonggongsi, 35 Chegongzhuang Xilu, Haidian District, PO Box 399, Beijing, 100044, China. TEL 86-10-68412045, FAX 86-10-68412023, cibtc@mail.cibtc.com.cn, http://www.cibtc.com.cn.

011 TWN ISSN 1560-6708
Z3113
QUANGUO XINSHU ZIXUN YUEKAN/NEW BOOKS: RECENT AND FORTHCOMING PUBLICATIONS IN TAIWAN, ROC. Text in Chinese. 1990. m. bk.rev. **Document type:** *Directory, Bibliography.*
Formerly (until 1996): Guoji Biaozhun Shuhao Zhongxin Tongxun/I S B N Newsletter (1016-6246)
Published by: Guoli Zhongyang Tushuguan/National Central Library, 20 Chung Shan S. Rd, Taipei, 100-01, Taiwan. shiny@msg.ncl.edu.tw.

011 CAN
QUEBEC (PROVINCE). SERVICES DOCUMENTAIRES MULTIMEDIA. CHOIX: DOCUMENTATION IMPRIMEE. Text in French. 1965. m. CND 160, USD 180.
Formerly: Quebec (Province). Centrale des Bibliotheques. Choix: Documentation Imprimee (0706-2249)
Related titles: CD-ROM ed.; Microfiche ed.; Online - full text ed.
Published by: Services Documentaires Multimedia Inc., 75 Port Royal E, bureau 300, Montreal, PQ H3L 3T1, Canada. TEL 514-382-0895, FAX 514-384-9139, info@sdm.qc.ca, http://www.sdm.qc.ca. Circ: 800.

011.37 CAN
QUEBEC (PROVINCE). SERVICES DOCUMENTAIRES MULTIMEDIA. D A V I D: DOCUMENTATION AUDIOVISUELLE. Text in French. 1971. 6/yr. (plus a. cumulation). CND 53, USD 68.
Former titles: Quebec (Province). Centrale des Bibliotheques. Choix. Documentation Audiovisuelle (0706-2257); Quebec (Province). Centrale des Bibliotheques. Choix Jeunes: Documentation Audiovisuelle (0706-2273)
Related titles: CD-ROM ed.; Microfiche ed.; Online - full text ed.
Published by: Services Documentaires Multimedia Inc., 75 Port Royal E, bureau 300, Montreal, PQ H3L 3T1, Canada. TEL 514-382-0895, FAX 514-384-9139, info@sdm.qc.ca, http://www.sdm.qc.ca. Circ: 400.

011.62 CAN
QUEBEC (PROVINCE). SERVICES DOCUMENTATION MULTIMEDIA. CHOIX JEUNESSE: DOCUMENTATION IMPRIMEE. Text in French. 1978. 10/yr. CND 55, USD 68.
Formerly: Quebec (Province). Centrale des Bibliotheques. Choix Jeunesse: Documentation Imprimee (0706-2265)
Related titles: CD-ROM ed.; Microfiche ed.; Online - full text ed.
Published by: Services Documentaires Multimedia Inc., 75 Port Royal E, bureau 300, Montreal, PQ H3L 3T1, Canada. TEL 514-382-0895, FAX 514-384-9139, info@sdm.qc.ca, http://www.sdm.qc.ca.

016.05 USA ISSN 1057-8188
CODEN: INBOES
R S A P NEWSLETTER. Text in English. 1991. 2/yr. looseleaf. USD 5 with American Periodicals; free American Periodicals (effective 2000). adv. **Document type:** *Newsletter.* **Description:** Covers the Society's activities and conferences, and recent publications in the field of periodicals research.
Related titles: ◆ Supplement to: American Periodicals. ISSN 1054-7479.
Published by: (Research Society for American Periodicals), University of North Texas, Department of English, PO BOX 305098, UNT STA, Denton, TX 76203-5098. TEL 940-565-2134, FAX 940-369-8770, jamest@unt.edu. Ed. James T F Tanner TEL 940-565-2117. Circ: 300.

R S O A S PRINT NEWS. see *ASIAN STUDIES—Abstracting, Bibliographies, Statistics*

015 IND
RECENT INDIAN BOOKS✶. Text in English. 1975. q. free. adv. bk.rev. index.
Indexed: RASB.
Published by: Federation of Indian Publishers and Booksellers Associations, Federation H S C, 18/1-C Institutional Area, Aruna Asif Ali Marg, New Delhi, 110 067, India. Ed. J C Mehta. Circ: 2,000.

RECENT PUBLICATIONS ON THE EUROPEAN UNION RECEIVED BY THE LIBRARY/NEUERSCHEINUNGEN UEBER DIE EUROPAEISCHE UNION EINGEGANGEN IN DER BIBLIOTHEK/NYE PUBLIKATIONER OM DEN EUROPAEISKE UNION MODTAGET AF BIBLIOTEKET/ PUBBLICAZIONI RECENTI SULL'UNIONE EUROPEA RECEVUTE DALLA BIBLIOTECA/PUBLICACIONES RECIENTES SOBRE LA UNION EUROPEA RECIBIDAS POR LA BIBLIOTECA/PUBLICATIONS RECENTES SUR L'UNION EUROPEENNE RECUES PAR LA BIBLIOTHEQUE. see *POLITICAL SCIENCE—Abstracting, Bibliographies, Statistics*

015 ESP ISSN 1132-6840
RED DE BIBLIOTECAS UNIVERSITARIAS; catalogo colectivo. Short title: Rebiun. Text in Spanish. 1992. s-a. **Document type:** *Bibliography.*
—CINDOC.
Published by: D O C 6 S.A., Mallorca, 272, Barcelona, 08015, Spain. TEL 34-3-2154313, FAX 34-3-4883621, mail@doc6.es.

020 USA ISSN 0887-3763
Z1035.1
REFERENCE AND RESEARCH BOOK NEWS; annotations and reviews of new books for libraries. Text in English. 1986. q. USD 130 in US & Canada to individuals; USD 180 foreign to individuals; USD 175 domestic to institutions; USD 225 foreign to institutions (effective 2005). adv. bk.rev. illus. back issues avail.; reprints avail. **Document type:** *Magazine, Abstract/Index.* **Description:** Presents concise, subject-arranged reviews of new scholarly and reference books appropriate for academic and public libraries and librarians. Over 2,500 reviews in each issue.
Incorporates (1989-1992): University Press Book News (1040-8991)
Related titles: Online - full text ed.: (from EBSCO Publishing).
Indexed: BRI, CBRI.
—Linda Hall.
Published by: Book News, Inc. (Portland), 5739 N E Sumner St, Portland, OR 97218. BookNews@BookNews.com, http://www.booknews.com. Ed. Jane Erskine. Pub. Fred Gullette. Circ: 1,700.

011 USA ISSN 0272-1988
Z1035.1
REFERENCE BOOK REVIEW. Text in English. 1976. 2/yr. USD 11 (effective 1999). bk.rev. index. back issues avail. **Document type:** *Trade.*
Indexed: BRI, CBRI.
Address: PO Box 50246, Baltimore, MD 21211-4246. FAX 214-479-1038. Eds. Cameron Northouse, Donna Northouse. Circ: 1,000.

REFERENCE SOURCES FOR SMALL AND MEDIUM-SIZED LIBRARIES. see *LIBRARY AND INFORMATION SCIENCES—Abstracting, Bibliographies, Statistics*

015 CHL ISSN 0716-1778
Z1701
REFERENCIAS CRITICAS SOBRE AUTORES CHILENOS. Text in Spanish. 1968. a., latest 1987. **Document type:** *Bibliography.* **Description:** Contains data on literary criticism of Chilean authors and some coverage of Spanish and Ibero-American authors.
Published by: Direccion de Bibliotecas Archivos y Museos, Biblioteca Nacional, Alameda, 651, Santiago, Chile. TEL 6380461, FAX 6381975.

016 GBR ISSN 0305-960X
CODEN: DYSPE2
RELIGIOUS BOOKS IN PRINT. Text in English. 1974. a. GBP 65 domestic; GBP 70 foreign (effective 1999). adv. **Document type:** *Bibliography.*

Published by: Whitaker Ltd., Woolmead House W., Bear Ln, Farnham, Surrey GU9 7LG, United Kingdom. TEL 44-1252-742525, FAX 44-1252-742526, custserv@whitaker.co.uk.

RELIGIOUS STUDIES REVIEW; a quarterly review of publications in the field of religion and related disciplines. see *RELIGIONS AND THEOLOGY—Abstracting, Bibliographies, Statistics*

610 016   MEX   ISSN 0304-1840
REMEDIA. Variant title: Referencias Medicas de Informacion Actualizada. Text in Spanish. 1974. bi-m.
Published by: Instituto Mexicano del Seguro Social, Division de Bibliotecas y Documentacion Biomedica, Apdo. Postal 12976, Mexico City, DF 03001, Mexico. Circ: 2,000.

REPERTOIRE BIBLIOGRAPHIQUE DE LA PHILOSOPHIE/ BIBLIOGRAFISCH REPERTORIUM VAN DE WIJSBEGEERTE/INTERNATIONAL PHILOSOPHICAL BIBLIOGRAPHY. see *PHILOSOPHY—Abstracting, Bibliographies, Statistics*

016   DEU   ISSN 0085-5499
➤ **REPERTOIRE BIBLIOGRAPHIQUE DES LIVRES IMPRIMES EN FRANCE.** Text in French. 1968. irreg., latest vol.25, 2000. price varies. bibl. back issues avail. **Document type:** *Monographic series, Academic/Scholarly.* **Description:** Bibliography of all books printed in France during the 16th, 17th and 18th centuries.
Published by: Verlag Valentin Koerner GmbH, Postfach 100164, Baden-Baden, 76482, Germany. TEL 49-7221-22423, FAX 49-7221-38697, valentin.koerner@t-online.de, http://www.koernerverlag.de.

010   FRA
REPERTOIRE DES ANNUAIRES. Text in French. 1936. a. adv. **Document type:** *Directory.*
Formerly: Annuaire des Annuaires (0066-2720)
Published by: Syndicat Professionnel Annuaire Telematique Communication (ATC), 35 rue Gregoire de Tours, Paris, 75006, France. Adv. contact Jean Raoul Guillerot.

REPERTORIO CRONOLOGICO DE LEGISLACION. INDICES AUXILIARES. see *LAW—Abstracting, Bibliographies, Statistics*

REPERTORIO DE JURISPRUDENCIA. INDICES AUXILIARES. see *LAW—Abstracting, Bibliographies, Statistics*

016.05   ROM   ISSN 1221-6860
REPERTORIUL COLECTIV AL PERIODICELOR STRAINE INTRATE IN BIBLIOTECILE DIN ROMANIA. Text in Romanian. 1958. a., latest 2001. ROL 70,000 (effective 2003). 350 p./no.; back issues avail. **Document type:** *Yearbook, Bibliography.*
Published by: Biblioteca Nationala a Romaniei, Str. Ion Ghica 4, Sector 3, Bucharest, 79708, Romania. TEL 40-21-3157063, FAX 40-21-3123381, go@bibnat.ro, http://www.bibnat.ro. Eds. Alexandra Crasneanu, Marina Iliescu.

REPUBLICKI ZAVOD ZA UNAPREDJIVANJE VASPITANJA I OBRAZOVANJA. BIBLIOGRAFIJA; lista bibliografskih podataka novonabavljenih knjiga i clanaka iz domace i inostrane pedagoske literature. see *EDUCATION—Abstracting, Bibliographies, Statistics*

RESIDUOS. see *ENVIRONMENTAL STUDIES—Waste Management*

016.362   USA   ISSN 1047-1286
Z7164.C4
RESOURCES (NEW YORK); a directory of New York City directories. Text in English. 1988. irreg., latest 1996. USD 9 (effective 2000). **Document type:** *Directory.*
Published by: Community Service Society, Office of Information, 105 E 22nd St, New York, NY 10010. TEL 212-254-8900, http://www.cssny.org. Eds. Patricia Friedland, Rabina Naraine.

THE REVIEW OF EDUCATION - PEDAGOGY - CULTURAL STUDIES. see *EDUCATION—Abstracting, Bibliographies, Statistics*

011   USA
REVIEWER'S BOOKWATCH. Text in English. m. USD 12 (effective 2000). back issues avail. **Document type:** *Newsletter, Trade.*
Published by: Midwest Book Review, 278 Orchard Dr, Oregon, WI 53575. TEL 608-835-7937, mbr@execpc.com, mwbookrevw@aol.com, http://www.execpc.com/~mbr/ bookwatch, http://www.execpc.com/~mbr/bookwatch/mbr. Ed. James A Cox.

REVISTA BRASILEIRA DE INFORMACAO BIBLIOGRAFICA EM CIENCIAS SOCIAIS. see *SOCIAL SCIENCES: COMPREHENSIVE WORKS—Abstracting, Bibliographies, Statistics*

015   CHL
REVISTA CHILENA EN VENTA. Text in Spanish. 1974. irreg., latest 1994. USD 80 (effective 2001). back issues avail. **Document type:** *Bibliography.*
Media: Duplicated (not offset).

Published by: Servicio de Extension de Cultura Chilena, Casilla 58-22, Santiago, Santiago, Chile. TEL 56-2-3434214, FAX 56-2-2395333, serec@terra.cl. Ed. Marta Dominguez Diaz.

REVISTA DE PUBLICACIONES NAVALES. see *MILITARY—Abstracting, Bibliographies, Statistics*

011   MEX
REVISTA DE REVISTAS. Text in Spanish. w. USD 85. adv.
Indexed: RASB.
Published by: Compania Editorial Excelsior S.C.L., Reforma 18, 1er piso, Delegacion Cuauhtemoc, Mexico City, DF 06600, Mexico. Ed. Gustavo Duran de Huerta. Circ: 30,000.

015   USA   ISSN 0085-5642
Z6953.8
REVISTERO✷ ; el mas completo informe sobre las publicaciones periodicas de America Latina. Text in English. 1972. a. USD 60.
Published by: E. Darino, Ed. & Pub., 222 Park Ave S, Apt 2A, New York, NY 10003. Circ: 1,000.

REVUE BIBLIOGRAPHIQUE DE SINOLOGIE. see *SOCIAL SCIENCES: COMPREHENSIVE WORKS—Abstracting, Bibliographies, Statistics*

015   BRA
RIO DE JANEIRO, BRAZIL (STATE). INSTITUTO ESTADUAL DO LIVRO. DIVISAO DE BIBLIOTECAS. BOLETIM BIBLIOGRAFICO. Text in Portuguese. 1977. irreg.
Published by: Instituto Estadual do Livro, Divisao de Bibliotecas, Av Presidente Vargas, 1261, Centro, Rio De Janeiro, RJ 20071-004, Brazil. Circ: 1,000.

016.65   ITA   ISSN 1590-301X
LE RIVISTE DATABASE. Text in Multiple languages. 2000. w. **Document type:** *Catalog, Bibliography.*
Media: Online - full text.
Published by: Casalini Libri, Via Benedetto da Maiano 3, Fiesole, FI 50014, Italy. TEL 39-055-50181, FAX 39-055-5018201, info@casalini.it, http://www.casalini.it.

011   RUS
ROSSIISKAYA AKADEMIYA NAUK. BIBLIOGRAFIYA IZDANII. Cover title: Bibliografiya Izdanii Akademii Nauk. Text in Russian. 1982. a.
Formerly (until 1992): Bibliografiya Izdanii Akademii Nauk S.S.S.R. (0234-4343)
Indexed: RASB.
Published by: Rossiiskaya Akademiya Nauk, Biblioteka, Birzhevaya liniya 1, St Petersburg, 199034, Russian Federation. Ed. V P Leonov.

ROYAL HISTORICAL SOCIETY. ANNUAL BIBLIOGRAPHY OF BRITISH AND IRISH HISTORY. see *HISTORY—Abstracting, Bibliographies, Statistics*

ROYAL PHILATELIC SOCIETY OF NEW ZEALAND. BIBLIOGRAPHIC SERIES. see *PHILATELY—Abstracting, Bibliographies, Statistics*

RUCH WYDAWNICZY W LICZBACH/POLISH PUBLISHING IN FIGURES. see *PUBLISHING AND BOOK TRADE— Abstracting, Bibliographies, Statistics*

RUDOLF STEINER PUBLICATIONS. see *PHILOSOPHY— Abstracting, Bibliographies, Statistics*

015   DEU
RUSSIAN NATIONAL BIBLIOGRAPHY. Text in English, German. a. **Document type:** *Catalog, Abstract/Index.*
Media: CD-ROM (from K. G. Saur Verlag GmbH & Co.).
Published by: K.G. Saur Verlag GmbH (Subsidiary of: Gale Group), Örtlerstr 8, Munchen, 81373, Germany. TEL 49-89-76902232, FAX 49-89-76902150, customerservice_saur@csi.com, http://www.saur.de.

S A L A L M BIBLIOGRAPHY AND REFERENCE SERIES. see *LIBRARY AND INFORMATION SCIENCES—Abstracting, Bibliographies, Statistics*

020 016   USA   ISSN 0098-6275
Z689
S A L A L M NEWSLETTER. Text in English. 1973. bi-m. USD 25 to non-members. bk.rev. bibl. **Document type:** *Newsletter.*
Indexed: CALL.
Published by: Seminar on the Acquisition of Latin American Library Materials, Benson Latin American Collection, University of Texas at Austin, Sid Richardson Hall 1 109, Austin, TX 78713-8916. TEL 512-495-4471, FAX 512-495-4488. Ed. Nancy Hallock.

S A L G NEWSLETTER. see *LIBRARY AND INFORMATION SCIENCES—Abstracting, Bibliographies, Statistics*

S I L - A A I B BIBLIOGRAPHY. see *LINGUISTICS—Abstracting, Bibliographies, Statistics*

S I O REFERENCE SERIES. BIBLIOGRAPHY. (Scripps Institution of Oceanography) see *EARTH SCIENCES—Oceanography*

S R D S BUSINESS PUBLICATION ADVERTISING SOURCE. see *ADVERTISING AND PUBLIC RELATIONS—Abstracting, Bibliographies, Statistics*

S R D S COMMUNITY PUBLICATION ADVERTISING SOURCE. see *ADVERTISING AND PUBLIC RELATIONS—Abstracting, Bibliographies, Statistics*

S R D S CONSUMER MAGAZINE ADVERTISING SOURCE. see *ADVERTISING AND PUBLIC RELATIONS—Abstracting, Bibliographies, Statistics*

S R D S DIRECT MARKETING LIST SOURCE. see *ADVERTISING AND PUBLIC RELATIONS—Abstracting, Bibliographies, Statistics*

S R D S MEXICAN AUDIOVISUAL MEDIA RATES & DATA. see *ADVERTISING AND PUBLIC RELATIONS—Abstracting, Bibliographies, Statistics*

S R D S MEXICAN PRINT MEDIA RATES & DATA. see *ADVERTISING AND PUBLIC RELATIONS—Abstracting, Bibliographies, Statistics*

S R D S NEWSPAPER ADVERTISING SOURCE. see *ADVERTISING AND PUBLIC RELATIONS—Abstracting, Bibliographies, Statistics*

S R D S PRINT MEDIA PRODUCTION SOURCE. see *ADVERTISING AND PUBLIC RELATIONS—Abstracting, Bibliographies, Statistics*

S R D S RADIO ADVERTISING SOURCE. see *ADVERTISING AND PUBLIC RELATIONS—Abstracting, Bibliographies, Statistics*

S R D S TECHNOLOGY MEDIA SOURCE. see *ADVERTISING AND PUBLIC RELATIONS—Abstracting, Bibliographies, Statistics*

011   DEU   ISSN 0419-7305
SAECHSISCHE BIBLIOGRAPHIE. Text in German. 1961. a. EUR 38 (effective 2001). **Document type:** *Bibliography.*
Published by: Saechsische Landesbibliothek, Staats- und Universitaetsbibliothek Dresden, Dresden, 01054, Germany. TEL 49-351-8130-0, FAX 49-351-8130200. Ed. Ulrich Voigt.

SANKO SHOSHI KENKYU/REFERENCE SERVICE AND BIBLIOGRAPHY. see *LIBRARY AND INFORMATION SCIENCES*

011   USA
SCARECROW AUTHOR BIBLIOGRAPHIES. Text in English. 1969. irreg., latest vol.104. price varies. **Document type:** *Bibliography.*
—BLDSC (8087.760000), ingenta.
Published by: Scarecrow Press, Inc. (Subsidiary of: Rowman & Littlefield Publishers, Inc.), 4501 Forbes Blvd., Suite 200, Lanham, MD 20706. TEL 301-459-3366, 800-462-6420, FAX 301-429-5748, 800-338-4550, custserv@rowman.com, http://www.scarecrowpress.com.

SCHWANN BEST RATED C DS - CLASSICAL. see *MUSIC—Abstracting, Bibliographies, Statistics*

SCHWANN BEST RATED C DS - JAZZ, POPULAR, ETC. see *MUSIC—Abstracting, Bibliographies, Statistics*

SCIENCE AND TECHNOLOGY (PITTSBURGH, ONLINE EDITION); a purchase guide for libraries. see *SCIENCES: COMPREHENSIVE WORKS—Abstracting, Bibliographies, Statistics*

SCIENCE REFERENCE AND INFORMATION SERVICE CATALOGUE. see *SCIENCES: COMPREHENSIVE WORKS—Abstracting, Bibliographies, Statistics*

SCIENTIFIC SERIALS IN THAI LIBRARIES. see *SCIENCES: COMPREHENSIVE WORKS—Abstracting, Bibliographies, Statistics*

011 300 600   USA   ISSN 0196-6006
SCITECH BOOK NEWS; an annotated bibliography of new books in science, technology, & medicine. Text in English. 1977. q. USD 130 in US & Canada to individuals; USD 180 elsewhere to individuals; USD 175 in US & Canada to institutions; USD 225 elsewhere to institutions (effective 2005). bk.rev. abstr.; bibl. back issues avail. **Document type:** *Magazine, Bibliography.* **Description:** Presents concise reviews of newhigh-level books in science, technology, medicine, agriculture and engineering. Over 1,500 reviews in each issue.
Related titles: Online - full text ed.: (from EBSCO Publishing).
Indexed: BRI, CBRI.
—Linda Hall.
Published by: Book News, Inc. (Portland), 5739 N E Sumner St, Portland, OR 97218. booknews@booknews.com, http://www.booknews.com. Ed., Adv. contact Jane Erskine. Pub. Fred Gullette. Circ: 2,200 (paid).

▼ *new title*   ➤ *refereed*   ✷ *unverified*   ◆ *full entry avail.*

010 USA ISSN 1542-5843
▼ **THE SCOTS RECORD.** Text in English. 2003. a.
Media: Online - full content.
Published by: Edinboro University of Pennsylvania, Highlands Center for Faculty Initiatives, 135 McNerney Hall, Edinboro, PA 16444. http://www.edinboro.edu/cwis/highlands/HighlandsWebSite/SCOTSRECORDWEB/TITLE.HTML, http://www.edinboro.edu/cwis/highlands/HighlandsWebSite/HighlandsWelcome.html.edu. Ed. Jack Widner.

SCOTTISH BIBLIOGRAPHIES ONLINE; bibliography of Scotland - bibliography of Scottish Gaelic. see *LITERATURE—Abstracting, Bibliographies, Statistics*

011.3 JPN ISSN 0915-9088
SEKAI CD-ROM SORAN. Text in Japanese. 1988. a. JPY 23,000.
Description: Contains 3,500 Japanese CD-ROM titles and 2,400 foreign titles.
Published by: PenLogue Publishing Corp., Futaba Building, 3-4-18 Mita, Minato-ku, Tokyo, 108-0073, Japan. TEL 81-3-3452-8080, FAX 81-3-3452-5728, pdb01343@nifty-serve.com.

B

SELECTED BIBLIOGRAPHIES ON AGEING. see *GERONTOLOGY AND GERIATRICS—Abstracting, Bibliographies, Statistics*

016 ARG ISSN 0327-0688
Z1007
SENALES✱; revista bibliografica. Text in Spanish. 1943. q. ARS 50, USD 18. adv. bk.rev. bibl.
Address: Casilla de Correo 2484, Buenos Aires, 1000, Argentina. Ed. Amy Dominguez Murray. Circ: 2,000.

SEQUELS; an annotated guide to novels in series. see *LIBRARY AND INFORMATION SCIENCES—Abstracting, Bibliographies, Statistics*

016.05 USA
Z6941
SERIALS DIRECTORY; an international reference book. Text in English. q. USD 339 domestic; USD 369 in Canada & Mexico; USD 389 elsewhere. **Document type:** *Directory.* **Description:** Includes information on over 150,000 international titles (journals, newspapers and monographic series).
Media: Online - full content. **Related titles:** CD-ROM ed.: ISSN 1066-7490.
Published by: EBSCO Publishing (Subsidiary of: EBSCO Industries, Inc.), 10 Estes St, PO Box 682, Ipswich, MA 01938-0682. TEL 978-356-6500, 800-653-2726, FAX 978-356-6565, ep@epnet.com, http://www.epnet.com. **Subscr. to:** Subscription Services, PO Box 1943, Birmingham, AL 35201-1943. TEL 205-991-6600, FAX 205-995-1518.

016.05 CAN ISSN 0709-0536
SERIALS HOLDINGS IN NEWFOUNDLAND LIBRARIES. Text in English. 1974. irreg. price varies.
Former titles (until 1979): Serials Holdings in the Libraries of Memorial University of Newfoundland, St. John's Public Library and College of Trades and Technology (0316-6597); Memorial University of Newfoundland. Library. Serials Holdings in the Libraries of Memorial University of Newfoundland and St. John's Public Library (0316-6600)
Related titles: Microfiche ed.
Published by: Memorial University of Newfoundland Library, Periodicals Division, St. John's, NF A1C 5S7, Canada. TEL 709-753-8425, FAX 709-737-4569, TELEX 016-4101. Ed. S Ellison. Circ: (controlled).

SERIALS IN THE BRITISH LIBRARY. see *LIBRARY AND INFORMATION SCIENCES—Abstracting, Bibliographies, Statistics*

016 NLD
SERIALS IN WESTERN LANGUAGES; research collections on microfiche. Text in English. irreg., latest vol.3, 1993. free. illus. **Document type:** *Catalog.* **Description:** Presents information on microform availability of more than 1900 serials and newspapers in Western languages.
Published by: I D C Publishers, PO Box 11205, Leiden, 2301 EE, Netherlands. TEL 31-71-5142700, FAX 31-71-5131721, info@idc.nl, http://www.idc.nl.

011 ZWE ISSN 0037-3494
Z858.N348
SHELFMARK. Text in English. 1966. q. ZWD 1. bk.rev. abstr.; bibl.
Published by: National Library and Documentation Service, PO Box 1773, Bulawayo, Zimbabwe. Circ: 300.

SIERRA LEONE PUBLICATIONS. see *LIBRARY AND INFORMATION SCIENCES—Abstracting, Bibliographies, Statistics*

070.5 BRA ISSN 0103-8834
SINDICATO NACIONAL DOS EDITORES DE LIVROS. INFORMATIVO BIBLIOGRAFICO. Text in Portuguese. 1968. a. bibl.; stat. **Document type:** *Bibliography.*
Former titles (until 1976): Sindicato Nacional dos Editores de Livros. Centro de Bibliotecnia. Resumo Bibliografica; (until 1972): Sindicato Nacional dos Editores de Livros. Centro de Bibliotecnia. Resenha Bibliografica
Published by: (Centro de Bibliotecnia), Sindicato Nacional dos Editores de Livros, Av Rio Branco, 37 Andar 15 s-1503-06, Centro, Rio De Janeiro, RJ 20090-003, Brazil. TEL 55-21-2336481, FAX 55-21-2538502, TELEX 21-37063. Ed. Nilson Lopes da Silva.

011 SWE ISSN 0037-6469
SKOLANS ARTIKELSERVICE; register och kopior av tidningsartiklar valda i anslutning till laeroplanerna foer grundskolans hoegstadium och gymnasieskolan. Text in Swedish. 1961. 12/yr. SEK 12,850 (effective 2003). bibl. index. **Document type:** *Bibliography.*
Formerly (until 1961): Skolans Artikelregister
Published by: Bibliotekstjaenst AB, Traktorvaegen 11, Lund, 22182, Sweden. TEL 46-18-00-00, FAX 46-18-04-41. Ed. Irja Heino.

015 SVN ISSN 0353-1724
Z2957.S6
SLOVENSKA BIBLIOGRAFIJA. A. SERIJSKE PUBLIKACIJE. Text in Slovenian. 1978. a. SIT 5,500 (effective 2001). **Document type:** *Bibliography.*
Supersedes in part (in 1978): Slovenska Bibliografija (0350-3585)
Related titles: ◆ Print ed.: Slovenska Bibliografija. Knjige. ISSN 0353-1716.
Indexed: RASB.
Published by: Narodna in Univerzitetna Knjiznica, Turjaska 1, Ljubljana, 1001, Slovenia. TEL 386-1-2001-100, lidija.wagner@nuk.uni-lj.si. Ed., Adv. contact Lidija Wagner TEL 386-1-2001-115. Circ: 400 (controlled).

011 SVN ISSN 0353-1716
Z2957.S6
SLOVENSKA BIBLIOGRAFIJA. KNJIGE. Text in Slovenian. 1945. q. SIT 22,000 (effective 2001).
Formerly (until 1985): Slovenska Bibliografija. B, Knjige (1318-0479); Supersedes in part (in 1978): Slovenska Bibliografija (0350-3585)
Related titles: ◆ Print ed.: Slovenska Bibliografija. A. Serijske Publikacije. ISSN 0353-1724.
Indexed: RASB.
Published by: Narodna in Univerzitetna Knjiznica, Turjaska 1, Ljubljana, 1001, Slovenia. TEL 386-1-2001-100, FAX 386-1-4257-293. Ed., Adv. contact Lidija Wagner TEL 386-1-2001-115. Circ: 350 (paid).

016 SVK ISSN 1335-2202
Z2151
SLOVENSKA NARODNA BIBLIOGRAFIA. Text in Slovak. 1997. q.
Incorporates (in 1999): Slovenska Narodna Bibliografia. Rozpisovy Rad Clanky
Media: CD-ROM. **Related titles:** ◆ Print ed.: Slovenska Narodna Bibliografia Seria A: Knihy. ISSN 0231-9780; ◆ Slovenska Narodna Bibliografia: Serie B-S. ISSN 0231-973X.
Published by: Slovenska Narodna Kniznica, Martin, Nam J C Hronskeho 1, Martin, 03601, Slovakia. http://www.snk.sk.

016 SVK ISSN 0231-9780
Z2124.S56
SLOVENSKA NARODNA BIBLIOGRAFIA SERIA A: KNIHY. Text in Slovak. 1949. 13/yr. USD 111 (effective 2000). **Document type:** *Bibliography.*
Former titles (until 1970): Bibliograficky Katalog C S S R. Slovenske Knihy (0583-6204); (until 1955): Bibliograficky Katalog C S R. Slovenska Kniha (0231-5459)
Related titles: ◆ CD-ROM ed.: Slovenska Narodna Bibliografia. ISSN 1335-2202.
Indexed: RASB.
Published by: Slovenska Narodna Kniznica, Martin, Nam J C Hronskeho 1, Martin, 03601, Slovakia. TEL 421-43-4132993, 421-43-4131372, FAX 421-43-4224983, TELEX 075-331, jahnatkova@snk.sk. Ed. Marta Jahnatkova.

015 SVK ISSN 0231-973X
Z2137.S6
SLOVENSKA NARODNA BIBLIOGRAFIA: SERIE B-S. Text in Slovak. 1981. q. SKK 80 (effective 2001). back issues avail. **Document type:** *Catalog, Bibliography.*
Related titles: ◆ CD-ROM ed.: Slovenska Narodna Bibliografia. ISSN 1335-2202.
Published by: Slovenska Narodna Kniznica, Martin, Nam J C Hronskeho 1, Martin, 03601, Slovakia. risian@snk.sk, http://www.snk.sk. Ed. Emil Risian.

SMALL PRESS RECORD OF BOOKS IN PRINT. see *PUBLISHING AND BOOK TRADE—Abstracting, Bibliographies, Statistics*

SOCIAL THEORY: A BIBLIOGRAPHIC SERIES. see *SOCIOLOGY—Abstracting, Bibliographies, Statistics*

SOCIETE RENCESVALS. BULLETIN BIBLIOGRAPHIQUE. see *LITERATURE—Abstracting, Bibliographies, Statistics*

SOFTWARE ENCYCLOPEDIA; a guide for personal, professional, and business users. see *COMPUTERS—Software*

SOHO BIBLIOGRAPHIES. see *LITERATURE—Abstracting, Bibliographies, Statistics*

015 POL ISSN 0239-0345
Z2523 CODEN: SOAPE7
SOON TO APPEAR...; forthcoming Polish books. Text in English. 1953. m. USD 14.30. adv. bk.rev. illus. index.
Formerly: New Polish Publications (0028-6486)
Related titles: German ed.: In Kurze Erscheinen. ISSN 0209-0376; Russian ed.: Vychodjat iz Pecati.... ISSN 0239-0299; French ed.: Bientot en Librairie. ISSN 0239-0396.
Published by: AGPOL - Polexportpress, Ul Kierbedzia 4, Warsaw, 00957, Poland. Ed. Ryszard Salinger. Circ: 6,000.
Dist. by: Ars Polona, Krakowskie Przedmiescie 7, Warsaw, Poland.

011 ZAF
SOUTH AFRICAN NATIONAL BIBLIOGRAPHY (ONLINE EDITION). (National Library of South Africa (NLSA) was formed by the merger of State Library and South African Library.) Text in English. irreg.
Media: Online - full text. **Related titles:** CD-ROM ed.: (from National Information Services Corp. (N I S C)); Microfiche ed.: ISSN 1024-6045 (from PSL).
Published by: National Library of South Africa, PO Box 496, Cape Town, 8000, South Africa. TEL 27-21-4246320, FAX 27-21-4233359, http://www.nlsa.ac.za.

015 IND ISSN 0971-9695
Z3185
➤ **SOUTH ASIAN BIBLIOGRAPHER.** Text in English. 1998. bi-m. USD 320; USD 47 newsstand/cover (effective 2004). adv. index. back issues avail. **Document type:** *Journal, Academic/Scholarly.* **Description:** Provides a comprehensive bibliography of current publications from all countries of South Asia. All major languages from the region, all subjects and areas of human endeavour and all sources of publications are covered.
Published by: (Library of Congress, New Delhi Office), Sage Publications India Pvt. Ltd. (Subsidiary of: Sage Publications, Inc.), M-32 Market, Greater Kailash-I, PO Box 4215, New Delhi, 110 048, India. TEL 91-11-6444958, FAX 91-11-6472426, http://www.sagepub.com/JournalSubscribe.aspx?pid=260, http://www.indiasage.com/. Pub. Tejeshwar Singh. Adv. contact Sunanda Ghosh. page USD 75. Circ: 1,000. **Subscr. in Europe to:** Sage Publications Ltd., 1 Oliver's Yard, 55 City Rd, London EC1 1SP, United Kingdom. TEL 44-20-73740645, FAX 44-20-73748741, subscription@sagepub.co.uk; **Subscr. in N America to:** Sage Publications, Inc., 2455 Teller Rd, Thousand Oaks, CA 91320. TEL 805-499-0721, FAX 805-499-0871.

015.96 FJI ISSN 0257-9146
Z4001
SOUTH PACIFIC BIBLIOGRAPHY. Text in English. 1981. biennial. FJD 30 (effective 2001). **Document type:** *Bibliography.* **Description:** Lists works published in the South Pacific and overseas relating wholly or in part to the region.
Supersedes: University of the South Pacific. Library. Pacific Collection. Accession List; Incorporates: University of the South Pacific. Library. Legal Deposit Accessions
Related titles: Microform ed.
Published by: Pacific Information Centre, University of the South Pacific Library, Suva, Fiji. TEL 679-313900, FAX 679-300830, mamtora_j@usp.ac.fj, http://www.usp.ac.fj/~library. Ed., R&P Jayshree Mamtora TEL 679-212375. Circ: 400.

996 FJI ISSN 1011-5145
SOUTH PACIFIC RESEARCH REGISTER. Text in English. 1982. biennial. FJD 10 (effective 2001). **Document type:** *Bibliography.* **Description:** Directory of international researchers on subjects with a direct South Pacific interest.
Supersedes: Fiji Register of Research and Investigations
Related titles: Microform ed.
Published by: Pacific Information Centre, University of the South Pacific Library, Suva, Fiji. TEL 679-313900, FAX 679-300830, mamtora_j@usp.ac.fj, http://www.usp.ac.fj/~library. R&P Jayshree Mamtora TEL 679-212375.

SOUTHEAST ASIAN MINISTERS OF EDUCATION ORGANISATION. REGIONAL CENTRE FOR EDUCATION IN SCIENCE AND MATHEMATICS. LIBRARY ACCESSION LIST. see *EDUCATION—Abstracting, Bibliographies, Statistics*

015.68 ZAF
SOUTHERN AFRICAN BOOKS IN PRINT. Text in English. 1993. a. ZAR 760. **Document type:** *Bibliography.* **Description:** Lists more than 34,300 books in 31 languages published and sold in Southern Africa.
Related titles: CD-ROM ed.: Southern African Books in Print on CD-ROM. ISSN 1024-039X; Microfiche ed.
Published by: Books in Print Information Services, PO Box 15129, Vlaeberg, Cape Town 8018, South Africa. FAX 27-21-4615467, sabip@iafrica.com.

010 USA
SOUTHERN ILLINOIS UNIVERSITY AT CARBONDALE. LIBRARY. BIBLIOGRAPHIC CONTRIBUTIONS. Text in English. 1964. irreg. price varies. **Document type:** *Bibliography.*

Formerly: Southern Illinois University, Carbondale. University Libraries. Bibliographic Contributions (0073-4977)
Published by: Southern Illinois University at Carbondale, Library Affairs, Carbondale, IL 62901. TEL 618-453-2522. Ed. Carolyn A Snyder. Circ: 600.

SPANISH LANGUAGE BOOKS FOR CHILDREN & YOUNG ADULTS. see *PUBLISHING AND BOOK TRADE—Abstracting, Bibliographies, Statistics*

SPIRIT OF BOOKS. see *RELIGIONS AND THEOLOGY—Abstracting, Bibliographies, Statistics*

SPRINGER BOOKS ON PROFESSIONAL COMPUTING. see *COMPUTERS*

SRI LANKA NATIONAL BIBLIOGRAPHY. see *PUBLISHING AND BOOK TRADE—Abstracting, Bibliographies, Statistics*

STADT MANNHEIM. VIERTELJAHRESBERICHT. see *PUBLIC ADMINISTRATION—Abstracting, Bibliographies, Statistics*

016 DEU ISSN 0942-3869
Z6956.G3
STAMM; Presse- und Medien Handbuch. Text in German. 1947. a. EUR 125 (effective 2003). adv. **Document type:** *Directory, Trade.* **Description:** Provides lists and descriptions of periodical publications, broadcasting stations and advertising possibilities in Germany as well as information on important newspapers and magazines from throughout the world.
Former titles (until 1991): Stamm. Leitfaden Durch Presse und Werbung (0341-7093); (until 1972): Leitfaden fuer Presse und Werbung (0075-8728)
—GNLM.
Published by: Stamm Verlag GmbH, Goldammerweg 16, Essen, 45134, Germany. TEL 49-201-84300-0, FAX 49-201-472590, info@stamm.de, anzeigen@stamm.de, http://www.stamm.de. Ed. Ulrich Tewes. adv.: B&W page EUR 990; trim 146 x 222. Circ: 5,000.

050 USA ISSN 0085-6630
Z6951
STANDARD PERIODICAL DIRECTORY. Text in English. 1963. a. USD 1,395; USD 2,495 combined subscription print & CD-ROM eds. (effective 2004). adv. **Document type:** *Directory, Trade.* **Description:** Contains circulation, advertising, production and list rental data for more than 75,000 North American periodicals.
Related titles: CD-ROM ed.: USD 1,495 (effective 2004); Online - full text ed.
—BLDSC (8430.276000), Linda Hall.
Published by: Oxbridge Communications, Inc., 186 Fifth Ave., New York, NY 10010. TEL 212-741-0231, 800-955-0231, FAX 212-633-2938, info@mediafinder.com, http://www.mediafinder.com. Pub. Fay Shapiro. Adv. contacts Deborah Striplin, Johanna Barwick.

011 GBR ISSN 1367-5184
Z2009
STATIONERY OFFICE MONTHLY CATALOGUE. Variant title: Great Britain. H.M.S.O. Government Publications (Monthly). Text in English. m. **Document type:** *Catalog, Government.* **Description:** Lists all titles published by H.M.S.O. during the previous month, excluding Statutory Instruments.
Former titles (until 1996): H M S O Monthly Catalogue (1367-5176); Great Britain. H.M.S.O. Monthly Catalogue (0263-7197)
Related titles: Online - full text ed.: (from The Dialog Corporation).
Indexed: RASB.
—BLDSC (8447.295000), CISTI.
Published by: H.M.S.O. Books, 51 Nine Elms Ln, London, SW8 5DA, United Kingdom. TEL 44-20-7873-0011, FAX 44-20-7873-8247. **Subscr. to:** PO Box 276, London SW8 5DJ, United Kingdom. TEL 44-20-7873-8499, FAX 44-20-7873-8222.

011 310 IND
STATISTICAL ANNUALS: LIST OF I E G LIBRARY HOLDINGS. Text in English. a. **Document type:** *Bibliography.*
Published by: Institute of Economic Growth, University of Enclave, New Delhi, 110 007, India. TEL 7257101.

011 AUT
STEIERMAERKISCHE LANDESBIBLIOTHEK. ARBEITEN. Text in German. irreg., latest vol.22. **Document type:** *Monographic series, Academic/Scholarly.*
Published by: Steiermaerkische Landesbibliothek, Kalchberggasse 2, Graz, St 8011, Austria. TEL 43-8016-4600, FAX 43-8016-4633.

STIFTUNG LESEN. LESE-EMPFEHLUNGEN. see *CHILDREN AND YOUTH—For*

STORIES: A LIST OF STORIES TO TELL AND TO READ ALOUD. see *CHILDREN AND YOUTH—Abstracting, Bibliographies, Statistics*

010 USA ISSN 0081-7600
Z1008
➤ **STUDIES IN BIBLIOGRAPHY.** Text in English. 1948. a. USD 55 per issue domestic (effective 2005). illus. reprints avail. **Document type:** *Journal, Academic/Scholarly.* **Description:** Scholarly articles on analytical and descriptive bibliography, textual criticism, scholarly editing, and book history.
Indexed: ASCA, ArtHuCI, DIP, IBR, IBZ, MLA, MLA-IB, PCI.
—Linda Hall.
Published by: (Bibliographical Society of the University of Virginia), University Press of Virginia, PO Box 400318, Charlottesville, VA 22904-4318. TEL 800-831-3406, FAX 877-288-6400, bibsoc@virginia.edu, upressva@virginia.edu, http://www.upress.virginia.edu. Ed., R&P Dr. David L Vander Meulen. Circ: 1,000.

016 USA ISSN 0000-0159
Z1215
SUBJECT GUIDE TO BOOKS IN PRINT. Text in English. 1956. a. (in 7 vols.). USD 525 (effective 2004); USD 550 (effective 2005). **Document type:** *Directory, Bibliography.* **Description:** Indexes all 178,000 nonfiction titles in Books in Print, thoroughly updated, under 57,000 U.S. Library of Congress subject headings. Includes a subject thesaurus and publisher information.
Related titles: Magnetic Tape ed.; Microfiche ed.; Online - full text ed.
—CISTI, Linda Hall. **CCC.**
Published by: R.R. Bowker LLC (Subsidiary of: Cambridge Information Group), 630 Central Ave., New Providence, NJ 07974. TEL 908-286-1090, 800-526-9537, FAX 908-219-0098, info@bowker.com, http://www.bowker.com. Ed. Elsa Meyers. Pub. Marin Mixon. **Subscr. to:** Order Dept., PO Box 32, New Providence, NJ 07974-9903. TEL 800-521-8110.

016 USA ISSN 0000-0167
Z1037.A1
SUBJECT GUIDE TO CHILDREN'S BOOKS IN PRINT. Text in English. 1971. a. USD 225 (effective 2004); USD 250 (effective 2005). **Document type:** *Directory, Bibliography.* **Description:** Indexes children's fiction and nonfiction books under Sears and US Library of Congress headings. Includes publisher information.
Related titles: Magnetic Tape ed.; Online - full text ed.
—CCC.
Published by: R.R. Bowker LLC (Subsidiary of: Cambridge Information Group), 630 Central Ave., New Providence, NJ 07974. TEL 908-286-1090, 800-526-9537, FAX 908-219-0098, info@bowker.com, http://www.bowker.com. **Subscr. to:** Order Dept., PO Box 32, New Providence, NJ 07974-9903. TEL 800-521-8110.

016 949.6 DEU ISSN 0081-9131
SUEDOSTEUROPA - BIBLIOGRAPHIE. Text in Multiple languages. 1956. irreg. price varies. **Document type:** *Bibliography.*
Published by: (Suedost-Institut), Oldenbourg Wissenschaftsverlag GmbH, Rosenheimer Str 145, Munich, 81671, Germany. TEL 49-89-450510, FAX 49-89-45051333, vertrieb-zs@verlag.oldenbourg.de, http://www.oldenbourg.de. Eds. Gerhard Seewann, Gertrud Krallert.

SUOMEN SANOMALEHTIEN MIKROFILMIT/MICROFILMED NEWSPAPERS OF FINLAND. see *JOURNALISM—Abstracting, Bibliographies, Statistics*

SUSSIDI ERUDITI. see *HISTORY—Abstracting, Bibliographies, Statistics*

016.05 SWE ISSN 0491-6522
SVENSK ANNONSTAXA. Text in Swedish. 1924. a. SEK 1,700 Paper edition; SEK 2,000 Online edition (effective 2003). **Document type:** *Directory, Trade.* **Description:** Contains advertising rates, publication schedules, technical information, circulation figures, contact names and addresses, and other essential information for newspapers and periodicals.
Related titles: ♦ Online - full content ed.: Svensk Annonstaxa Online.
Published by: Tidningsstatistik AB, Linnegatan 87, Stockholm, 11478, Sweden. TEL 46-8-50742400, FAX 46-8-50742401, tidningsstatistik@ts.se, http://www.ts.se.

SVENSK ANNONSTAXA ONLINE. see *PUBLISHING AND BOOK TRADE—Abstracting, Bibliographies, Statistics*

015.485 SWE
Z2625
SVENSK PERIODICAFOERTECKNING. (ONLINE)/CURRENT SWEDISH PERIODICALS; tidskrifter, aarsboecker, dagstidningar och rapportserier. Text in Swedish. 1953. irreg. **Document type:** *Bibliography.*
Former titles (until 2003): Svensk Periodicafoerteckning (Print edition) (1104-1102); (until 1994): Svensk Tidskriftsfoerteckning (0586-0431)
Media: Online - full content.
Published by: Kungliga Biblioteket, Nationalbibliografin. Periodicaenheten, Humlegaarden, PO Box 5039, Stockholm, 10241, Sweden. http://www.kb.se/nbp/nysvp.htm. Ed. Eva Crantz.

016.05 SWE ISSN 0282-0919
SVENSK REKLAMTAXA. Text in Swedish. 1957. a. SEK 950 Paper edition; SEK 1,200 Online edition (effective 2003). **Document type:** *Directory, Trade.* **Description:** Contains base information on free newspapers and periodicals, advertising sheets, target group oriented publications, pace-setting media and direct advertising.
Related titles: ♦ Online - full content ed.: Svensk Reklamtaxa Online.
Published by: Tidningsstatistik AB, Linnegatan 87, Stockholm, 11478, Sweden. TEL 46-8-50742400, FAX 46-8-50742401, tidningsstatistik@ts.se, http://www.ts.se.

SVENSK REKLAMTAXA ONLINE. see *PUBLISHING AND BOOK TRADE—Abstracting, Bibliographies, Statistics*

SWAZILAND NATIONAL BIBLIOGRAPHY. see *PUBLISHING AND BOOK TRADE—Abstracting, Bibliographies, Statistics*

SWEDEN. STATISTISKA CENTRALBYRAANS BIBLIOTEK. STATISTIK FRAAN INTERNATIONELLA ORGAN. see *STATISTICS*

SZLADITS BIBLIOGRAPHY ON FOREIGN AND COMPARATIVE LAW; books and articles in English. see *LAW—Abstracting, Bibliographies, Statistics*

SZOCIOLOGIAI INFORMACIO/SOCIOLOGICAL INFORMATION; a magyar nyelvu es magyar vonatkozasu szakirodalom valogatott bibliografiaja. see *SOCIOLOGY—Abstracting, Bibliographies, Statistics*

T V & CABLE SOURCE. see *ADVERTISING AND PUBLIC RELATIONS—Abstracting, Bibliographies, Statistics*

015.678 TZA ISSN 0856-003X
Z3588
TANZANIA NATIONAL BIBLIOGRAPHY. Text in English. 1970. a. TZS 9,520 domestic; USD 90 foreign. **Document type:** *Bibliography.* **Description:** Lists new books and other publications produced in Tanzania and deposited at the National Bibliographic Agency. Includes books, reports, dissertations, other mimeographed documents, and the first issue of new serial titles.
Formerly (until 1982): Printed in Tanzania
Published by: Library Services Board, National Bibliographic Agency, PO Box 9283, Dar Es Salaam, Tanzania. TEL 255-51-150048, tlsb@africaonline.co.tz. Ed. Irene Minja. Circ: 250.

011 DEU
TASCHENBUCH DER AUKTIONSPREISE ALTER BUECHER. Text in German. 1975. a. adv. **Document type:** *Catalog.*
Published by: Verlag fuer Buechersammler, Postfach 101756, Aachen, 52019, Germany. FAX 49-241-601912. Ed. F Radtke.

TASCHENBUCH DES OEFFENTLICHEN LEBENS; Deutschland. see *PUBLIC ADMINISTRATION—Abstracting, Bibliographies, Statistics*

TASCHENBUCH DES OEFFENTLICHEN LEBENS. EUROPA UND INTERNATIONALE ZUSAMMENSCHLUESE. see *PUBLIC ADMINISTRATION—Abstracting, Bibliographies, Statistics*

TAYLOR TALK; the yearbook magazine. see *PUBLISHING AND BOOK TRADE—Abstracting, Bibliographies, Statistics*

TEACHERS' CHOICES. see *CHILDREN AND YOUTH—Abstracting, Bibliographies, Statistics*

620 016 HUN ISSN 0040-1110
TECHNIKA. Text in Russian. 1957. m. USD 30.50. adv. bk.rev. abstr.; charts; illus.; pat.; stat.; tr.mk.
Related titles: German ed.; Russian ed.
Indexed: INIS AtomInd, RefZh.
Published by: (Hungarian Technical Information Center and Library), Nepszava Lapkiado Vallalat, Rakoczi ut 54, Budapest, 1964, Hungary. TEL 224-810. Ed. Emil Szluka. Circ: 15,000. **Subscr. to:** Kultura, PO Box 149, Budapest 1389, Hungary.

620.16 NLD ISSN 0929-0567
TECHNISCHE UNIVERSITEIT TE DELFT. BIBLIOTHEEK. LIJST VAN LOPENDE SERIELE PUBLIKATIES. Cover title: Lijst van Lopende Seriele Publikaties - List of Current Serial Publications. Text in Dutch. 1967. a. index. **Document type:** *Catalog.* **Description:** Lists current serial and periodical subscriptions of the library.
Former titles (until 1993): Technische Universiteit te Delft. Bibliotheek. Lijst van Lopende Tijdschriftabonnementen (0923-8689); Technische Hogeschool te Delft. Bibliotheek. Lijst van Lopende Tijdschriftabonnementen
—KNAW.
Published by: Technische Universiteit Delft, Bibliotheek/Delft University of Technology, PO Box 98, Delft, 2600 MG, Netherlands. TEL 31-15-2782054, FAX 31-15-2572060. Circ: 1,000.

▼ new title ➤ refereed ✶ unverified ♦ full entry avail.

011 USA ISSN 0739-3202
F381
TEXAS BOOKS IN REVIEW. Text in English. 1981. q. USD 14; USD 18 foreign (effective 1999). adv. bk.rev. **Document type:** *Academic/Scholarly.* **Description:** Publishes reviews of books by and about Texans or Texas. Includes regional articles about the literary scene around the state.
Related titles: Online - full text ed.: (from EBSCO Publishing).
Indexed: AmHI.
Address: Center for the Study of the Southwest, San Marcos, TX 78666. TEL 512-245-2232, FAX 512-245-7462, MBB@SWT.edu, http://www.english.swt.edu/css/cssindex.htm. Ed. Dick Heaberlin. R&P, Adv. contact Mark Busby. Circ: 500.

011 SWE ISSN 0345-0112
TEXT; svensk tidskrift foer bibliografi. Text in English, Swedish. 1974. irreg. (approx. 1/yr.). SEK 480 per vol. (effective 2000). adv. bk.rev. **Document type:** *Magazine, Academic/Scholarly.*
Published by: (Center for Bibliographical Studies, Uppsala), Dahlia Books International Publishers and Booksellers, Fack 1025, Uppsala, 75140, Sweden. TEL 46-18-101098, FAX 46-8-100525, dahlia@telia.com. Ed. Rolf E Du Rietz. Circ: 200.

B

THAILAND. NATIONAL STATISTICAL OFFICE. ANNOTATED STATISTICAL BIBLIOGRAPHY. see *STATISTICS*

015.48513075 DNK ISSN 1603-0338
▼ **THESES AND OTHER PUBLICATIONS OF THE UNIVERSITY OF COPENHAGEN.** Text in English. 2003. bi-w.
Media: Online - full content.
Published by: Danish National Library of Science and Medicine, Noerre Alle 49, Copenhagen N, 2200, Denmark. TEL 45-31-39-65-23, FAX 45-31-39-85-33, HF@dnlb.dk.

011 AUS ISSN 1038-3395
THORPE - R O M; Australian & New Zealand books in print, plus annotations, on CD-ROM. Text in English. 1992. m. AUD 920 (effective 1999). **Description:** Includes more than 100,000 Australian, New Zealand and Pacific Island books in print (all Australian titles published since 1990 fully annotated), over 4,000 publishers and distributors, as well as full agency and imprint information.
Media: CD-ROM.
Published by: Thorpe - Bowker (Subsidiary of: R.R. Bowker LLC), Bldg C3, 85 Turner St, Port Melbourne, VIC 3207, Australia. TEL 61-3-9245-7370, FAX 61-3-9245-7395, customer.service@thorpe.com.au, subscriptions@thorpe.com.au, http://www.thorpe.com.au.

015 NZL ISSN 1170-800X
Z4124.T65
TOKELAU NATIONAL BIBLIOGRAPHY. Text in English. 1992. irreg., latest 2002, 2nd Ed. incl. in New Zealand National Bibliography. **Document type:** *Bibliography.* **Description:** Provides a comprehensive list of Tokelau publications, including non-books.
Related titles: Online - full text ed.
Published by: National Library of New Zealand, PO Box 1467, Wellington, 6001, New Zealand. TEL 64-4-4743000, FAX 64-4-4743035, nznb@natlib.govt.nz, http://www.natlib.govt.nz/.

TOKYO SHIKA DAIGAKU SEIRIGAKU KYOSHITSU GYOSEKISHU/TOKYO DENTAL COLLEGE. DEPARTMENT OF PHYSIOLOGY. BIBLIOGRAPHY. see *BIOLOGY—Abstracting, Bibliographies, Statistics*

TOPICS IN RELIGION: A BIBLIOGRAPHIC SERIES. see *RELIGIONS AND THEOLOGY—Abstracting, Bibliographies, Statistics*

TRAVAUX. see *ENGINEERING—Abstracting, Bibliographies, Statistics*

TRAVEL BOOKS WORLDWIDE; the travel book review. see *TRAVEL AND TOURISM*

TS-BOKEN. see *PUBLISHING AND BOOK TRADE—Abstracting, Bibliographies, Statistics*

TS-BOKEN ONLINE. see *PUBLISHING AND BOOK TRADE—Abstracting, Bibliographies, Statistics*

TS-TIDNINGEN. see *PUBLISHING AND BOOK TRADE—Abstracting, Bibliographies, Statistics*

015.561 TUR ISSN 0041-4328
Z2835
TURKISH NATIONAL BIBLIOGRAPHY/TURKIYE BIBLIYOGRAFYASI. Text in Turkish. 1928. m. USD 60 (effective 2001). bibl. index. **Document type:** *Catalog, Bibliography.* **Description:** Contains annual indexes of personal authors, titles of books and periodicals.
Related titles: Online - full text ed.
Indexed: RASB.
Published by: Milli Kutuphane Baskanligi, Bibliografya Hazirlama Sube Mudurlugu/National Library, Bibliography Preparation Department, Bahcelievler, Ankara, 06490, Turkey. TEL 90-312-2224768, FAX 90-312-2230451, katalog@mkutup.gov.tr, http://www.mkutup.gov.tr. Circ: 1,000.
Subscr. to: Kultur Bakanligi, Doner Sermaye Isletmeleri Merkez, Mudurlugu Cumhuriyet Bulvari, Fevzi Pasa Mah. 4, Ulus - Ankara, Turkey.

015.561 TUR ISSN 0041-4344
TURKIYE MAKALELER BIBLIYOGRAFYASI/BIBLIOGRAPHY OF ARTICLES IN TURKISH PERIODICALS. Text in Turkish. 1952. m. USD 50 (effective 2001). index. **Document type:** *Catalog, Bibliography.* **Description:** Covers selected articles in scholarly and cultural periodicals which are sent to the National Library.
Indexed: RASB.
Published by: Milli Kutuphane Baskanligi, Bibliografya Hazirlama Sube Mudurlugu/National Library, Bibliography Preparation Department, Bahcelievler, Ankara, 06490, Turkey. TEL 90-312-3094953, FAX 90-312-3118233, bibliyografya@mkutup.gov.tr, katalog@mkutup.gov.tr, http://www.mkutup.gov.tr. Circ: 1,000. **Subscr. to:** Kultur Bakanligi, Doner Sermaye Isletmeleri Merkez, Mudurlugu Cumhuriyet Bulvari, Fevzi Pasa Mah. 4, Ulus - Ankara, Turkey.

U K CONSUMER DIRECTORY. see *PUBLISHING AND BOOK TRADE—Abstracting, Bibliographies, Statistics*

U K O P; the catalogue of United Kingdom official publications on CD-ROM. (United Kingdom Official Publications) see *PUBLIC ADMINISTRATION—Abstracting, Bibliographies, Statistics*

U N I M A R C MANUAL - BIBLIOGRAPHIC FORMAT. see *LIBRARY AND INFORMATION SCIENCES*

U.S. DEPARTMENT OF STATE. LIBRARY. COMMERCIAL LIBRARY PROGRAM. PUBLICATIONS LIST. see *POLITICAL SCIENCE—Abstracting, Bibliographies, Statistics*

011 332 USA ISSN 0145-0301
Z7164.F5
U.S. FEDERAL RESERVE SYSTEM. RESEARCH LIBRARY - RECENT ACQUISITIONS. Text in English. m. free. **Document type:** *Government.*
Published by: U.S. Federal Reserve System, Board of Governors, Publications Services, Rm MS 123, Washington, DC 20551. TEL 202-452-3244, FAX 202-728-5886.

015.942 025.3 USA
U.S. GOVERNMENT PRINTING OFFICE. CATALOGING FILE. Text in English. m. USD 1,920 in North America; USD 2,270 elsewhere. **Document type:** *Bibliography.* **Description:** Compiles MARC records for books, serials, maps, audiovisual materials, and computer files cataloged by the U.S. Government Printing Office on OCLC.
Media: Duplicated (not offset).
Published by: U.S. Library of Congress, Cataloging Distribution Service, 101 Independence Ave, S E, Washington, DC 20541-4912. TEL 202-707-6100, 800-255-3666, FAX 202-707-1334, cdsinfo@mail.loc.gov, cdsinfo@loc.gov.

016.5 KEN ISSN 1527-5396
CODEN: ALEAEZ
U.S. LIBRARY OF CONGRESS. ACCESSIONS LIST OF THE LIBRARY OF CONGRESS OFFICE, NAIROBI, KENYA. Text in English. 1968. bi-m. free to libraries. **Document type:** *Government.* **Description:** Lists monographs and serials acquired for the Library of Congress from commercial publishers, governmental, nongovernmental and international organizations located in 28 African countries.
Former titles: U.S. Library of Congress. Accessions List: Eastern and Southern Africa (1070-2717); U.S. Library of Congress. Accessions List: Eastern Africa (0090-371X)
Related titles: ◆ Supplement(s): U.S. Library of Congress. Accessions List of the Library of Congress Office, Nairobi, Kenya. Serial Supplement. ISSN 1527-537X; ◆ U.S. Library of Congress. Accessions List of the Library of Congress Office, Nairobi, Kenya. Annual Publishers Directory, Monographs and Serials. ISSN 1527-540X.
Indexed: PopulInd.
Published by: U.S. Library of Congress Office, Embassy of the United States of America, PO Box 30598, Nairobi, Kenya. TEL 254-2-442321, FAX 254-2-445580, nairobi@libcon-kenya.org, http://www.icipe.org/locnairobi.

016.5 KEN ISSN 1527-540X
Z465.5
U.S. LIBRARY OF CONGRESS. ACCESSIONS LIST OF THE LIBRARY OF CONGRESS OFFICE, NAIROBI, KENYA. ANNUAL PUBLISHERS DIRECTORY, MONOGRAPHS AND SERIALS. Text in English. 1976. a. free. **Document type:** *Directory, Government.*
Formerly: U.S. Library of Congress. Accessions List: Eastern and Southern Africa. Annual Publishers' Directory, Monographs and Serials (1074-3839)
Related titles: ◆ Supplement to: U.S. Library of Congress. Accessions List of the Library of Congress Office, Nairobi, Kenya. ISSN 1527-5396.
Published by: U.S. Library of Congress Office, Embassy of the United States of America, PO Box 30598, Nairobi, Kenya. TEL 254-2-442321, FAX 254-2-445580, nairobi@libcon-kenya.org, http://www.icipe.org/locnairobi.

016.5 KEN ISSN 1527-537X
Z6959.Z9
U.S. LIBRARY OF CONGRESS. ACCESSIONS LIST OF THE LIBRARY OF CONGRESS OFFICE, NAIROBI, KENYA. SERIAL SUPPLEMENT. Text in English. 1968. s-a. **Document type:** *Government.* **Description:** Lists all serial titles currently received by the Nairobi Office, covering 28 African countries.
Former titles: U.S. Library of Congress. Accessions List: Eastern and Southern Africa. Serial Supplement (1074-3820); (until 1995): U.S. Library of Congress. Annual Serial Supplement (0192-7388)
Related titles: ◆ Supplement to: U.S. Library of Congress. Accessions List of the Library of Congress Office, Nairobi, Kenya. ISSN 1527-5396.
Published by: U.S. Library of Congress Office, Embassy of the United States of America, PO Box 30598, Nairobi, Kenya. TEL 254-2-442321, FAX 254-2-445580, nairobi@libcon-kenya.org, http://www.icipe.org/locnairobi.

015.73 025.3 USA
U.S. LIBRARY OF CONGRESS. AUTHORITY FILES - NAME AUTHORITIES. Text in English. 1977. w. USD 12,595. **Document type:** *Bibliography.* **Description:** Compiles MARC records for personal, corporate, conference, and geographical name headings, uniform titles, and series.
Media: Online - full text.
Published by: (Customer Service Section), U.S. Library of Congress, Cataloging Distribution Service, 101 Independence Ave, S E, Washington, DC 20541-4912. TEL 202-707-6100, 800-255-3666, FAX 202-707-1334, cdsinfo@loc.gov.

011.295 USA
U.S. LIBRARY OF CONGRESS. BOOKS C J K. (Chinese, Japanese, Korean) Text in English. 1987. w. USD 1,555. **Document type:** *Bibliography.* **Description:** Compiles MARC records for Chinese-, Japanese-, and Korean-language monographs cataloged by the US Library of Congress.
Media: Online - full text.
Published by: (Customer Service Section), U.S. Library of Congress, Cataloging Distribution Service, 101 Independence Ave, S E, Washington, DC 20541-4912. TEL 202-707-6100, 800-255-3666, FAX 202-707-1334, cdsinfo@loc.gov.

011 025.3 USA ISSN 1073-4929
Z693
U.S. LIBRARY OF CONGRESS. CATALOGER'S DESKTOP. Text in English. 1994. q. USD 690. **Document type:** *Government.* **Description:** Comprises the most popular US Library of Congress cataloging publications, including LOC Rule Interpretations; Subject Cataloging Manual: Subject Headings; Subject Cataloging Manual: Classification; USMARC Concise Formats; USMARC Format for Bibliographic Data; USMARC Format for Authority Data; and the entire set of USMARC Code Lists.
Media: CD-ROM. **Related titles:** Online - full content ed.: ISSN 1551-2185.
Published by: (Customer Service Section), U.S. Library of Congress, Cataloging Distribution Service, 101 Independence Ave, S E, Washington, DC 20541-4912. TEL 202-707-6100, 800-255-3666, FAX 202-707-1334, cdsinfo@loc.gov.

011.1 025.3 USA
U.S. LIBRARY OF CONGRESS. CATALOGING FILES - BOOKS ALL. Text in English. 1968. w. USD 15,280 in North America; USD 16,410 elsewhere. **Document type:** *Bibliography.* **Description:** Compiles the entire U.S. Library of Congress MARC bibliography for books in all languages.
Media: Duplicated (not offset).
Published by: (Customer Service Section), U.S. Library of Congress, Cataloging Distribution Service, 101 Independence Ave, S E, Washington, DC 20541-4912. TEL 202-707-6100, 800-255-3666, FAX 202-707-1334, cdsinfo@mail.loc.gov, cdsinfo@loc.gov.

015.942 025.3 USA
U.S. LIBRARY OF CONGRESS. CATALOGING FILES - BOOKS ENGLISH. Text in English. 1968. w. USD 13,525 in North America; USD 14,405 elsewhere. **Document type:** *Bibliography.* **Description:** Compiles the entire U.S. Library of Congress MARC database for all books published in English.
Media: Duplicated (not offset).
Published by: (Customer Service Section), U.S. Library of Congress, Cataloging Distribution Service, 101 Independence Ave, S E, Washington, DC 20541-4912. TEL 202-707-6100, 800-255-3666, FAX 202-707-1334, cdsinfo@mail.loc.gov, cdsinfo@loc.gov.

015.73 025.3 USA
U.S. LIBRARY OF CONGRESS. CATALOGING FILES - BOOKS U S. Text in English. 1968. w. USD 8,650 in North America; USD 9,125 elsewhere. **Document type:** *Bibliography.* **Description:** Compiles all U.S. Library of Congress MARC bibliographic records for books printed in the US.

Published by: (Customer Service Section), U.S. Library of Congress, Cataloging Distribution Service, 101 Independence Ave, S E, Washington, DC 20541-4912. TEL 202-707-6100, 800-255-3666, FAX 202-707-1334, cdsinfo@loc.gov.

011.1 025.3 USA
U.S. LIBRARY OF CONGRESS. CATALOGING FILES - COMPLETE SERVICE. Text in English. 1968. w. USD 22,325. **Document type:** *Bibliography.* **Description:** Compiles the entire U.S. Library of Congress MARC bibliography.
Media: Online - full text.
Published by: (Customer Service Section), U.S. Library of Congress, Cataloging Distribution Service, 101 Independence Ave, S E, Washington, DC 20541-4912. TEL 202-707-6100, 800-255-3666, FAX 202-707-1334, cdsinfo@loc.gov.

016.912 025.3 USA
U.S. LIBRARY OF CONGRESS. CATALOGING FILES - MAPS. Text in English. 1973. w. USD 1,465. **Document type:** *Bibliography.* **Description:** Compiles U.S. Library of Congress MARC21 bibliographic records for all single- and multi-sheet maps, map sets, and maps treated as serials.
Media: Online - full text.
Published by: (Customer Service Section), U.S. Library of Congress, Cataloging Distribution Service, 101 Independence Ave, S E, Washington, DC 20541-4912. TEL 202-707-6100, 800-255-3666, FAX 202-707-1334, cdsinfo@loc.gov.

016.78 USA
U.S. LIBRARY OF CONGRESS. CATALOGING FILES - MUSIC. Text in English. 1984. w. USD 1,750. **Document type:** *Bibliography.* **Description:** Compiles U.S. Library of Congress MARC21 bibliographic records for printed and manuscript music and for music and nonmusic sound recordings.
Media: Online - full text.
Published by: (Customer Service Section), U.S. Library of Congress, Cataloging Distribution Service, 101 Independence Ave, S E, Washington, DC 20541-4912. TEL 202-707-6100, 800-255-3666, FAX 202-707-1334, cdsinfo@loc.gov.

016.05 USA
U.S. LIBRARY OF CONGRESS. CATALOGING FILES - SERIALS. Text in English. 1973. w. USD 6,640. **Document type:** *Bibliography.* **Description:** Compiles U.S. Library of Congress MARC21 records for serial publications cataloged or processed by the Cooperative Online Serials Program (CONSER).
Media: Online - full text.
Published by: (Customer Service Section), U.S. Library of Congress, Cataloging Distribution Service, 101 Independence Ave, S E, Washington, DC 20541-4912. TEL 202-707-1334, 800-255-3666, FAX 202-707-1334, cdsinfo@loc.gov.

011.37 USA
U.S. LIBRARY OF CONGRESS. CATALOGING FILES - VISUAL MATERIALS. Text in English. 1972. w. USD 1,465. **Document type:** *Bibliography.* **Description:** Compiles all U.S. Library of Congress MARC bibliographic records for motion pictures, video recordings, filmstrips, transparencies, slides, and nonprojectable graphics.
Media: Online - full text.
Published by: (Customer Service Section), U.S. Library of Congress, Cataloging Distribution Service, 101 Independence Ave, S E, Washington, DC 20541-4912. TEL 202-707-6100, 800-255-3666, FAX 202-707-1334, cdsinfo@loc.gov.

011 025.3 USA ISSN 1052-1445
Z696.U4
U.S. LIBRARY OF CONGRESS. FREE - FLOATING SUBDIVISIONS: AN ALPHABETIC INDEX. Text in English. 1989. a., latest 2005, 17th ed. USD 35 in North America; USD 40 elsewhere (effective 2005). **Document type:** *Catalog, Abstract/Index.* **Description:** Lists US Library of Congress subject subdivisions assigned by the subject cataloger under designated subjects without the usage being established editorially and, therefore, without the usage appearing in the subject authority file under each individual subject heading.
Published by: (Customer Service Section), U.S. Library of Congress, Cataloging Distribution Service, 101 Independence Ave, S E, Washington, DC 20541-4912. TEL 202-707-6100, 800-255-3666, FAX 202-707-1334, cdsinfo@loc.gov, http://www.loc.gov/cds.

011.24927 USA
U.S. LIBRARY OF CONGRESS. NON-ROMAN CATALOGING FILES - BOOKS. ARABIC. Text in English. 1991. q. USD 4,060 in North America; USD 4,100 elsewhere. **Document type:** *Bibliography.* **Description:** Compiles MARC records for Arabic- and Persian-language monographs cataloged by the US Library of Congress.
Media: Duplicated (not offset).
Published by: (Customer Service Section), U.S. Library of Congress, Cataloging Distribution Service, 101 Independence Ave, S E, Washington, DC 20541-4912. TEL 202-707-6100, 800-255-3666, FAX 202-707-1334, cdsinfo@mail.loc.gov, cdsinfo@loc.gov.

U.S. LIBRARY OF CONGRESS. NON-ROMAN CATALOGING FILES. HEBREW. see *LINGUISTICS—Abstracting, Bibliographies, Statistics*

011 025.3 USA ISSN 1541-2997
Z733.U58
U.S. LIBRARY OF CONGRESS. PRODUCT CATALOG. Text in English. a. free. **Document type:** *Catalog, Government.* **Description:** Provides lists and annotations of all Cataloging Distribution Service serials, books, and databases available.
Former titles (until 2001): U.S. Library of Congress. Bibliographic Products & Services (1541-2989); (until 1998): U.S. Library of Congress. Catalog of Bibliographic Products and Services (1090-6185); (until 1997): U.S. Library of Congress. Complete Catalog of Bibliographic Products and Services (1058-5257); (until 1991): Access C D S (1058-5249); (until 1990): Library of Congress. Catalogs and Technical Publications (0743-6181)
Published by: (Customer Service Section), U.S. Library of Congress, Cataloging Distribution Service, 101 Independence Ave, S E, Washington, DC 20541-4912. TEL 202-707-6100, 800-255-3666, FAX 202-707-1334, cdsinfo@loc.gov, http://www.loc.gov/cds.

016.328 USA
U.S. LIBRARY OF CONGRESS. REFERENCE FILES - INDEX TO HISPANIC LEGISLATION. Text in English. 1976. q. USD 3,500 in North America; USD 3,600 elsewhere. **Document type:** *Abstract/Index.* **Description:** Provides hard-to-find information on the legislation of countries studied by the US Library of Congress Hispanic Law Division Law Library.
Media: Duplicated (not offset). **Related titles:** Online - full text ed.: (from Research Libraries Group).
Published by: (Customer Service Section), U.S. Library of Congress, Cataloging Distribution Service, 101 Independence Ave, S E, Washington, DC 20541-4912. TEL 202-707-6100, 800-255-3666, FAX 202-707-1334, cdsinfo@mail.loc.gov, cdsinfo@loc.gov.

011.31 USA
U.S. LIBRARY OF CONGRESS. REFERENCE FILES - NATIONAL UNION CATALOG OF MANUSCRIPT COLLECTIONS. Text in English. 1989. q. USD 1,050 in North America; USD 1,185 elsewhere. **Document type:** *Bibliography.* **Description:** Compiles MARC records for collections of personal and family papers, business records, and other manuscripts of historical and research importance.
Media: Duplicated (not offset).
Published by: (Customer Service Section), U.S. Library of Congress, Cataloging Distribution Service, 101 Independence Ave, S E, Washington, DC 20541-4912. TEL 202-707-6100, 800-255-3666, FAX 202-707-1334, cdsinfo@mail.loc.gov, cdsinfo@loc.gov.

U.S. NATIONAL AERONAUTICS AND SPACE ADMINISTRATION. VIDEO CATALOG. see *AERONAUTICS AND SPACE FLIGHT—Abstracting, Bibliographies, Statistics*

UDDANNELSE OG ERHVER. MATERIALER. see *MOTION PICTURES—Abstracting, Bibliographies, Statistics*

015 HUN ISSN 0049-5069
Z1035.6
UJ KONYVEK. Text in Hungarian. 1964. s-m. HUF 300, USD 8. bk.rev. bibl. **Description:** Lists Hungarian books commercially available in the country.
Indexed: RASB.
Published by: (Orszagos Szechenyi Konyvtar/National Szechenyi Library, Konyvtartudomanyi es Modszertani Kozpont/Center for Library Science and Methodology), Konyvertekesito Vallalat, Vaci utca 19, Budapest, 1134, Hungary. FAX 36-1-20-20-804, TELEX 224226 BIBLN H. Ed. E Gyori. Circ: 8,500. **Subscr. to:** Kultura, PO Box 149, Budapest 1389, Hungary.

015 BLR
UKAZATEL BIBLIOGRAFICHESKIKH POSOBYI. Text in Belorussian, Russian. 1978. a. BYB 45. **Description:** Contains bibliographies on books in all fields.
Formerly: Bibliograficheskie Posobiya Belorusskoi S.S.R. (0203-3941)
Indexed: RASB.
Published by: Natsiyanal'naya Knizhnaya Palata Belarusi/National Book Chamber of Belarus, Pr Masherava 11, Minsk, 220600, Belarus. TEL 23-08-396. Ed. L N Nekhaichik. Circ: 300.

016.05 USA ISSN 0000-1724
Z6941
ULRICH'S ON DISC. Text in English. 1986. q. USD 1,175 single user (effective 2005). **Document type:** *Directory, Bibliography.* **Description:** Includes magazines, journals, newsletters, newspapers, annuals and irregular serials published worldwide. Entries include title, circulation, frequency, complete publisher address, telephone, fax, email and URL, description, subscription price, with subscription and distribution addresses, telephone and fax information. Also includes bibliographic classification (LC, DDC and CODEN), abstracting and indexing information, document type notations, online and CD-ROM availability, document delivery service availability, advertising rates and contact name, among other data.
Formerly (until 1998): Ulrich's Plus (1068-0500)
Media: CD-ROM (from R.R. Bowker LLC). **Related titles:** ◆ Online - full text ed.: Ulrichsweb.com; ◆ Print ed.: Ulrich's Periodicals Directory. ISSN 0000-2100.
—CINDOC, CISTI, KNAW.

Published by: R.R. Bowker LLC (Subsidiary of: Cambridge Information Group), 630 Central Ave., New Providence, NJ 07974. TEL 908-286-1090, 800-526-9537, FAX 908-219-0098, info@bowker.com, http://www.ulrichsweb.com, http://www.bowker.com. Ed. Laurie Kaplan. **Subscr. in N. America to:** Order Dept., PO Box 32, New Providence, NJ 07974-9903. TEL 800-521-8110.

016.05 USA ISSN 0000-2100
Z6941 CODEN: UPDLB2
ULRICH'S PERIODICALS DIRECTORY; international periodicals information since 1932. Text in English. 1932. a. (since 1980; previously biennial) (in 4 vols.). USD 850 (effective 2006). index. **Document type:** *Directory, Bibliography.* **Description:** Arranged by subject classification, includes magazines, journals, newsletters, newspapers, annuals and irregular serials published worldwide. Separate indices list refereed serials, serials available on CD-ROM, CD-ROM producers, serials available online, online services, cessations, publications of international organizations, International Standard Serial Numbers, and titles. Entries include title, circulation, frequency, complete publisher address, telephone, fax, email and URL, description, subscription price, with subscription and distribution addresses, telephone and fax information. Also includes bibliographic classification (LC, DDC and CODEN), abstracting and indexing information, document type notations, document delivery service availability, advertising rates and contact name, among other data.
Former titles (until 2000): Ulrich's International Periodicals Directory (0000-0175); (until 1965): Ulrich's Periodicals Directory; Incorporates (1967-1987): Irregular Serials and Annuals (0000-0043)
Related titles: ◆ CD-ROM ed.: Ulrich's On Disc. ISSN 0000-1724; Ulrich's International Periodicals Directory (ERL). USD 936 (effective 1999) (from SilverPlatter Information, Inc.); ◆ Online - full text ed.: Ulrichsweb.com; Ulrich's Online (from SilverPlatter Information, Inc.).
Indexed: RASB.
—CINDOC, CISTI. **CCC.**
Published by: R.R. Bowker LLC (Subsidiary of: Cambridge Information Group), 630 Central Ave., New Providence, NJ 07974. TEL 908-286-1090, 800-526-9537, 800-346-6049, FAX 908-219-0098, 908-219-0182, ulrichs@bowker.com, info@bowker.com, http://www.ulrichsweb.com, http://www.bowker.com. Ed. Laurie Kaplan. **US & Canada subscr. to:** Order Dept., PO Box 32, New Providence, NJ 07974-9903. TEL 800-521-8110.

ULRICHSWEB.COM. see *PUBLISHING AND BOOK TRADE—Abstracting, Bibliographies, Statistics*

011 FRA ISSN 1020-0223
AS4.U8
UNESCO DATABASES. Text in English, French, Spanish. a. EUR 45.73 (effective 2003). **Document type:** *Database, Abstract/Index.* **Description:** Bibliographical references of all UNESCO documents and publications. International specialized bibliographies in every area of education, museums, monuments and sites. Names, addresses and activities of 10,000 research, training and documentation institutions in the social sciences. Also includes the UNESCO and the International Bureau of Education thesauri.
Media: CD-ROM.
—CINDOC.
Published by: UNESCO Publishing, 7 place de Fontenoy, Paris, 75352, France. TEL 33-1-45684300, FAX 33-1-45685737, http://www.unesco.org/publications. **Dist. in US by:** Bernan Associates, Bernan, 4611-F Assembly Dr., Lanham, MD 20706-4391. TEL 800-274-4447, FAX 800-865-3450.

016.912 FRA
UNESCO SCIENTIFIC MAPS AND ATLASES AND OTHER RELATED PUBLICATIONS. Text in French. irreg. bibl.; illus.
Published by: UNESCO Publishing, 7 place de Fontenoy, Paris, 75352, France. TEL 33-1-45684300, FAX 33-1-45685737, http://www.unesco.org/publications. **Dist. in the U.S. by:** Bernan Associates, Bernan, 4611-F Assembly Dr., Lanham, MD 20706-4391. TEL 800-274-4447, FAX 800-865-3450.

UNGDOMS- OG VOKSENUNDERVISNING. see *EDUCATION—Abstracting, Bibliographies, Statistics*

011 500 ZMB
UNION LIST OF SCIENTIFIC AND TECHNICAL PERIODICALS IN ZAMBIA. Text in English. 1980. irreg. ZMK 4.50.
Published by: National Council for Scientific Research, Chelston, PO Box CH 158, Lusaka, Zambia. Eds. J C Michello, W C Muship.

500 016.05 ISR ISSN 0333-5321
Z6945
UNION LIST OF SERIALS IN ISRAEL LIBRARIES. Key Title: U L S - Israel. Text in English. 1955. a. USD 85 (effective 1998). **Document type:** *Bibliography.*
Formerly (until 1980): Union List of Serials in Israel Libraries (0082-7665)
Media: Online - full text.
Published by: Jewish National and University Library, Jewish National and University Library, PO Box 34165, Jerusalem, Israel. TEL 972-2-6585028, FAX 972-2-651-1771. Ed. Simona Anner. Circ: 120.

▼ new title ➤ refereed ✶ unverified ◆ full entry avail.

UNION NATIONALE CULTURE ET BIBLIOTHEQUES POUR TOUS. NOTES BIBLIOGRAPHIQUES. see *LIBRARY AND INFORMATION SCIENCES—Abstracting, Bibliographies, Statistics*

UNITED NATIONS CENTRE FOR HUMAN SETTLEMENTS. BIBLIOGRAPHIC NOTES. see *HOUSING AND URBAN PLANNING—Abstracting, Bibliographies, Statistics*

016 USA
UNITED NATIONS DOCUMENTS AND PUBLICATIONS. Text in English. 1946. q. (plus a. cumulation). index. **Document type:** *Abstract/Index.* **Description:** Makes accessible invaluable documents for researchers, academics, and graduate and undergraduate students.
Former titles: United Nations Documents and Publications. Checklist; United Nations Documents (0191-8087); Readex Microprint Publications (0079-984X)
Media: CD-ROM. **Related titles:** Microfiche ed.
Published by: Newsbank, Inc., 58 Pine St, New Canaan, CT 06840-5426. TEL 203-966-1100, 800-762-8182, FAX 203-966-6254, Cust.Serv@newsbank.com, http://www.newsbank.com. Circ: 6,975.

B

UNITED NATIONS LIBRARY. MONTHLY BIBLIOGRAPHY. PART 1: BOOKS, OFFICIAL DOCUMENTS, SERIALS. see *POLITICAL SCIENCE—Abstracting, Bibliographies, Statistics*

UNITED NATIONS LIBRARY. MONTHLY BIBLIOGRAPHY. PART 2: SELECTED ARTICLES. see *POLITICAL SCIENCE—Abstracting, Bibliographies, Statistics*

015 DOM ISSN 0041-8277
UNIVERSIDAD AUTONOMA DE SANTO DOMINGO. BIBLIOTECA CENTRAL. BOLETIN DE ADQUISICIONES✶. Text in Spanish. 1969. bi-m. free. bk.rev. bibl.
Published by: Universidad Autonoma de Santo Domingo, Biblioteca Central, Santo Domingo, Dominican Republic. Circ: (controlled).

015 ECU
UNIVERSIDAD CENTRAL DEL ECUADOR. BIBLIOTECA GENERAL. BIBLIOGRAFIA ECUATORIANA. Text in Spanish. 1975. bi-m.
Published by: (Biblioteca General), Universidad Central del Ecuador, Apdo 3291, Quito, Pichincha, Ecuador.

011 VEN
UNIVERSIDAD DE LOS ANDES. INSTITUTO DE INVESTIGACIONES LITERARIAS. SERIE ENSAYO Y CRITICA LITERARIA✶. Text in Spanish. 1981. irreg. free.
Supersedes (1977-1978): Universidad de Los Andes. Instituto de Investigaciones Literarias. Serie Bibliografico; Which was formerly (1971-1977): Universidad de Los Andes. Centro de Investigaciones Literarias. Serie Bibliografico
Published by: Universidad de Los Andes, Instituto de Investigaciones Literarias, Via los Chorras de Milla, Merida, 5101, Venezuela. Circ: 500.

011 ESP
UNIVERSIDAD DE NAVARRA. COLECCION BIBLIOGRAFIA. Text in Spanish. 1977. irreg.
Published by: (Universidad de Navarra, Facultad de Filosofia y Letras), Ediciones Universidad de Navarra S.A., Pza. Los Sauces, 1-2, Baranain, (Navarra) 31010, Spain. TEL 34-948-256850, FAX 34-948-256854, http://www.eunsa.es.

UNIVERSIDAD DE SEVILLA. INSTITUTO GARCIA OVIEDO. PUBLICACIONES. see *LAW—Abstracting, Bibliographies, Statistics*

011 ESP
UNIVERSIDAD DE SEVILLA. SERIE: BIBLIOTECA UNIVERSITARIA. Text in Spanish. irreg., latest vol.16, 1999. price varies. **Document type:** *Monographic series, Academic/Scholarly.*
Published by: Universidad de Sevilla, Secretariado de Publicaciones, Porvenir 27, Sevilla, 41013, Spain. TEL 34-95-4487444, FAX 34-95-4487443, secpub10@us.es, http://www.us.es/publius/inicio.html.

011 MEX ISSN 0006-1719
Z1007
UNIVERSIDAD NACIONAL AUTONOMA DE MEXICO. INSTITUTO DE INVESTIGACIONES BIBLIOGRAFICAS. BOLETIN. Text in Spanish. 1969. s-a. MXP 300, USD 90 (effective 2000). bibl.; illus. **Document type:** *Academic/Scholarly.*
Supersedes: Biblioteca Nacional. Boletin
Indexed: AmH&L, BAS, BHA, HAPI, HistAb.
Published by: Universidad Nacional Autonoma de Mexico, Instituto de Investigaciones Bibliograficas, Ciudad Universitaria, Coyoacan, Mexico City, DF 04510, Mexico. TEL 52-5-6226807, FAX 52-5-6650951, libros@biblional.biblig.unam.mx. Ed. Jose G Moreno de Alba.
Co-sponsor: Biblioteca Nacional.

010 MEX ISSN 0076-7468
UNIVERSIDAD NACIONAL AUTONOMA DE MEXICO. SEMINARIO DE INVESTIGACIONES BIBLIOTECOLOGICA. PUBLICACIONES. SERIE B. BIBLIOGRAFIA✶. Text in Spanish. 1960. irreg., latest vol.4, 1967.
Published by: Universidad Nacional Autonoma de Mexico, Seminario de Investigaciones Bibliotecologicas, Cuidad Universitaria, Mexico City, DF 04510, Mexico. Ed. Dr. Alicia Perales de Mercado. Circ: (controlled).

UNIVERSIDADE DE SAO PAULO. DEPARTAMENTO DE SOCIOLOGIA. SERIE BIBLIOGRAFIA. see *SOCIOLOGY—Abstracting, Bibliographies, Statistics*

010 BRA
UNIVERSIDADE DE SAO PAULO. FACULDADE DE ECONOMIA E ADMINISTRACAO. BIBLIOTECA. BOLETIM. Text in Portuguese. 1965. irreg. per issue exchange basis. bk.rev.
Formerly: Universidade de Sao Paulo. Faculdade de Ciencias Economicas e Administrativas. Biblioteca. Boletim
Published by: (Biblioteca), Universidade de Sao Paulo, Faculdade de Economia e Administracao, Cidade Universitaria Armando de Salles Oliveira, Pinheiros, Caixa Postal 11498, Sao Paulo, RS 05422-970, Brazil. Circ: 250.

011 DEU ISSN 0080-5173
UNIVERSITAET DES SAARLANDES. JAHRESBIBLIOGRAPHIE. Text in German. 1968. a. exchange basis. **Document type:** *Bibliography.* **Description:** Lists books and articles published by members of the University of the Saarland..
Related titles: Online - full text ed.
Published by: Universitaet des Saarlandes, Universitaetsbibliothek, Saarbruecken, 66123, Germany. TEL 49-681-3023010, FAX 49-681-3022796, ubswk@rz.uni-sb.de, http://www.uni-sb.de/z-einr/ub/uni-veroeff/jbpub.html. Ed. Wolfgang Kowalk. Circ: 530.

UNIVERSITY OF CALIFORNIA. INSTITUTE OF GOVERNMENTAL STUDIES LIBRARY. ACCESSIONS LIST. see *PUBLIC ADMINISTRATION—Abstracting, Bibliographies, Statistics*

011 USA
UNIVERSITY OF CALIFORNIA PUBLICATIONS IN CATALOGS & BIBLIOGRAPHIES. Text in English. 1986. irreg., latest vol.13, 1997. price varies. back issues avail. **Document type:** *Bibliography.* **Description:** Lists publications and catalogs available in the University of California libraries.
Published by: University of California Press, Journals Division, 2000 Center St, Ste 303, Berkeley, CA 94704-1223. TEL 510-643-7154, FAX 510-642-9917, journals@ucpress.edu, http://www.ucpress.edu/journals. **Orders to:** California - Princeton Fulfillment Services, 1445 Lower Ferry Rd, Ewing, NJ 08618. TEL 800-777-4726, FAX 800-999-1958.

UNIVERSITY OF GUELPH LIBRARY. COLLECTION UPDATE. see *LIBRARY AND INFORMATION SCIENCES*

011 020 GBR ISSN 0140-7260
UNIVERSITY OF LONDON. SCHOOL OF SLAVONIC AND EAST EUROPEAN STUDIES. LIBRARY. BIBLIOGRAPHICAL GUIDES. Text in English. 1977. irreg. price varies. back issues avail. **Description:** Guides to, or check-lists of, material held in the library.
Published by: University of London, School of Slavonic and East European Studies (Subsidiary of: University of London), Senate House, Malet St, London, WCIE 7HU, United Kingdom. TEL 44-20-76368000, FAX 44-20-78628640, http://www.ssees.ac.uk/.

011 USA
UNIVERSITY OF MAINE. COOPERATIVE EXTENSION. PUBLICATIONS CATALOG. Text in English. a. free. **Document type:** *Catalog, Government.* **Description:** Lists a wide variety of general-interest titles available to the public.
Published by: University of Maine, Cooperative Extension, 5741 Libby Hall, Orono, ME 04469-5741. TEL 207-581-3185, 800-287-0274, FAX 207-581-1387, mspencer@umce.umext.maine.edu, http://www.umext.maine.edu. Ed. Melanie Spencer.

996 FJI ISSN 1011-5129
UNIVERSITY OF THE SOUTH PACIFIC. PUBLICATIONS. Text in English. 1981. a. FJD 20 (effective 2000). **Document type:** *Academic/Scholarly.* **Description:** Includes works written, published, authorized and sponsored by the University of the South Pacific or individuals associated with it.
Published by: Pacific Information Centre, University of the South Pacific Library, Suva, Fiji. TEL 679-313900, FAX 679-300830, TELEX 2276 USPFJ, mamtora_j@usp.ac.fj, http://www.usp.ac.fj/~library. Ed., R&P Jayshree Mamtora TEL 679-212375.

UNIVERSITY OF WATERLOO BIBLIOGRAPHY SERIES. see *LIBRARY AND INFORMATION SCIENCES—Abstracting, Bibliographies, Statistics*

011 DEU
V V B - VERZEICHNIS VERGRIFFENER BUECHER CD-ROM. Text in German. a. **Document type:** *Bibliography.*
Media: CD-ROM.
Published by: M V B - Marketing- und Verlagsservice des Buchhandels GmbH, Postfach 100442, Frankfurt Am Main, 60004, Germany. TEL 49-69-1306-243, FAX 49-69-1306255, info@mvb-online.de, http://www.buchhaendler-vereinigung.de.
Dist. by: K.G. Saur Verlag GmbH. TEL 49-89-76902-0, FAX 49-89-76901250.

016 SWE ISSN 0042-2150
VAESTGOETALITTERATUR. Text in Swedish. 1963. a. SEK 100 (effective 1994). bk.rev. bibl.; illus.
Published by: Foereningen foer Vaestgoetalitteratur, Fack 325, Skara, 53224, Sweden. Ed. W Aengermark. Circ: 1,700.

VENEZUELAN FORESTRY BIBLIOGRAPHY. see *FORESTS AND FORESTRY—Abstracting, Bibliographies, Statistics*

015 DEU ISSN 0948-7697
VERLAGE - VERTRETUNGEN - AUSLIEFERUNGEN (YEAR). Variant title: Banger. Verlage - Vertretungen - Auslieferungen (Year). Text in German. 1995. a. EUR 220 (effective 2002). **Document type:** *Directory, Bibliography.*
Media: CD-ROM.
Published by: Verlag der Schillerbuchhandlung Hans Banger, Guldenbachstr 1, Cologne, 50935, Germany. TEL 49-221-46014-0, FAX 49-221-46014-25, banger@banger.de, http://www.banger.de.

015 DEU ISSN 0945-473X
Z317
VERLAGSAUSLIEFERUNGEN. Text in German. 1994. a. EUR 30 (effective 2002). **Document type:** *Directory, Bibliography.*
Published by: Verlag der Schillerbuchhandlung Hans Banger, Guldenbachstr 1, Cologne, 50935, Germany. TEL 49-221-46014-0, FAX 49-221-46014-25, banger@banger.de, http://www.banger.de.

015 DEU ISSN 0944-3754
Z317
VERLAGSVERTRETUNGEN. Text in German. 1993. a. EUR 44 (effective 2002). **Document type:** *Directory, Bibliography.*
Published by: Verlag der Schillerbuchhandlung Hans Banger, Guldenbachstr 1, Cologne, 50935, Germany. TEL 49-221-46014-0, FAX 49-221-46014-25, banger@banger.de, http://www.banger.de.

015 DEU ISSN 0067-8899
Z2221
VERZEICHNIS LIEFERBARER BUECHER/GERMAN BOOKS IN PRINT. Short title: V L B. (Consists of five sections: Authors-Titles-Catchword (in eight vols., 29th ed., 2000); ISBN Index to German Books in Print (in one vol., 29th ed., 2000); Subject Guide to German Books in Print (in seven vols., 22nd ed., 2000); Supplement (in one vol., 29th ed., 2001); ISBN Index to Supplement (in one vol., 29th ed., 2001)) Text in German. 1971. a. EUR 722.25 (effective 2005). index. **Document type:** *Directory, Bibliography.* **Description:** Lists every book available in the German language. Includes listings of series, publishers, and ISBNs.
Related titles: CD-ROM ed.: (from K. G. Saur Verlag GmbH & Co.).
—BLDSC (9218.260000), Linda Hall.
Published by: M V B - Marketing- und Verlagsservice des Buchhandels GmbH, Postfach 100442, Frankfurt Am Main, 60004, Germany. TEL 49-69-13060, FAX 49-69-1306201, info@mvb-online.de, http://www.mvb-vlb.de, http://www.buchhaendler-vereinigung.de.

015 DEU
VERZEICHNIS LIEFERBARER BUECHER - CD-ROM/GERMAN BOOKS IN PRINT ON CD-ROM. Text in English, French, German. m. USD 1,440 (effective 2001). **Document type:** *Bibliography.* **Description:** Contains more than 600,000 books, audiocassettes, videos, software, and bibles found in the hardcopy edition of German Books in Print. Features the complete contents of L.I.B.R.I. (the database of wholesalers in Hamburg and Frankfurt) and S.B.Z. (the database of the Swiss Book Center).
Media: CD-ROM (from K. G. Saur Verlag GmbH & Co.). **Related titles:** ◆ Supplement(s): German Books Out of Print on CD-ROM.
Published by: (M V B - Marketing- und Verlagsservice des Buchhandels GmbH), K.G. Saur Verlag GmbH (Subsidiary of: Gale Group), Ortlerstr 8, Munchen, 81373, Germany. TEL 49-89-76902-0, FAX 49-89-76901250, customerservice_saur@csi.com, http://www.saur.de.

VICTORIAN FICTION RESEARCH GUIDES. see *LITERATURE—Abstracting, Bibliographies, Statistics*

011 AUS ISSN 0313-2463
VICTORIAN GOVERNMENT PUBLICATIONS. Text in English. 1976. m. AUD 50 (effective 1999). adv. back issues avail. **Document type:** *Government.* **Description:** Comprehensive record of Victorian government publishing from both state and local government sources.
Published by: Government Publications Librarian, State Library of Victoria, 328 Swanston St, Melbourne, VIC 3000, Australia. TEL 61-3-96699920, FAX 61-3-96631480, dianneb@slv.vic.gov.au, http://www.cf.vicnet.net.au/vgp. Ed. Dianne Beaumont. Circ: 70 (paid).

B

015 USA
VIRGINIA STATE DOCUMENTS. Text in English. 1991. a.
Document type: *Bibliography.* **Description:** Lists all
publications issued by Virginia state government agencies
currently in print.
Formed by the merger of (1926-1991): Check-List of Virginia
State Publications (0364-7293); Virginia State Publications in
Print (0507-102X)
Published by: Library of Virginia, Publications, 800 E Broad St,
Richmond, VA 23219-8000. TEL 804-692-3754, FAX
804-692-3814, mclark@lva.lib.va.us, http://www.lva.lib.va.us/
whatwehave/gov/vsd/, http://lva.lib.us.va. Ed., R&P Mary Clark.
Circ: 600.

015 RUS
VOLOGODSKAYA BIBLIOTEKA IM. BABUSHKINA.
LITERATURA O VOLOGODSKOI OBLASTI. Text in Russian.
1961. a. RUR 2,000. **Document type:** *Bibliography.*
Description: Publishes brief annotated bibliographical list of
books and articles from local and center press.
Published by: Vologodskaya Oblastnaya Universalnaya
Nauchnaya Biblioteka, Otdel Kraevedcheskoi Bibliografii, Ul
Ul'yanovoi 1, Vologda, 160000, Russian Federation. TEL
7-8172-721103, FAX 7-8172-251769, bibln@vcom.ru. Ed. E A
Volkova. Circ: 500.

VYBER KULTURNICH VYROCI. see *HUMANITIES:*
COMPREHENSIVE WORKS—Abstracting, Bibliographies,
Statistics

011 GBR
WALFORD'S GUIDE TO REFERENCE MATERIAL. Text in
English. 1959. triennial (in 3 vols.). price varies. index.
Document type: *Bibliography.*
Formerly: Guide to Reference Material (0072-8640)
Published by: Facet Publishing, 7 Ridgmount St, London, WC1E
7AE, United Kingdom. TEL 44-20-7255-0590, FAX
44-20-7255-0591. Ed. A J Walford. Dist. in U.S. by: Bernan
Associates, Bernan, 4611-F Assembly Dr., Lanham, MD
20706-4391, TEL 800-274-4447, FAX 800-865-3450.

WELLCOME UNIT FOR THE HISTORY OF MEDICINE.
RESEARCH PUBLICATIONS. see *MEDICAL SCIENCES*

015 CHN ISSN 1000-0437
AP95.C4
WENXIAN/DOCUMENTS. Text in Chinese. 1979. q. CNY 10
newsstand/cover (effective 2005). **Document type:** *Journal,*
Academic/Scholarly. **Description:** Covers documents and
research results on ancient and contemporary Chinese
literature and history from the collections of Beijing Library
and other libraries at home and abroad.
Indexed: AmH&L, HistAb, RASB.
—BLDSC (9295.215500).
Published by: (Beijing Tushuguan/Beijing Library), Zhongguo
Guojia Tushuguan, 33 Zhongguancun Nandajie, Beijing,
100081, China. TEL 86-10-68415566 ext 5562,
wanghan@publicf.nlc.gov.cn, http://wenx.periodicals.net.cn/,
http://www.nlc.gov.cn/. Circ: 6,000. **Dist. in US by:** China
Books & Periodicals Inc, 360 Swift Ave., Ste. 48, S San Fran,
CA 94080-6220; **Dist. outside China by:** China International
Book Trading Corp, 35 Chegongzhuang Xilu, Haidian District,
PO Box 399, Beijing 100044, China.

010 USA ISSN 0512-4743
Z6945
WEST VIRGINIA UNION LIST OF SERIALS. Text in English.
1962. a. USD 62. **Document type:** *Bibliography.* **Description:**
Computer-based listing of major serials for forty-five libraries
in West Virginia as well as all of the West Virginia University
libraries.
Published by: West Virginia University, Charles C. Wise, Jr.
Library, Main Office, Box 6069, Morgantown, WV 26506-6069.
TEL 304-293-5395, FAX 304-293-6638. Ed. Mildred Moyers.

011 USA ISSN 1052-2212
PN3427
WHAT DO I READ NEXT?. Text in English. 1991. a. (in 2 vols.),
latest 2004. USD 155 per vol. (effective 2004). **Description:**
Points out the similarities between various works of fiction for
librarians to help readers make on-the-spot decisions about
the fiction they want to read next.
Published by: Gale Group (Subsidiary of: Thomson Corporation),
27500 Drake Rd, Farmington Hills, MI 48331-3535. TEL
248-699-8061, FAX 248-699-4253, galeord@gale.com,
http://www.gale.com.

WHAT WORKS: AN ANNOTATED BIBLIOGRAPHY OF CASE
STUDIES OF SUSTAINABLE DEVELOPMENT. see
ENVIRONMENTAL STUDIES—Abstracting, Bibliographies,
Statistics

WHAT'S NEW IN ADVERTISING AND MARKETING. see
ADVERTISING AND PUBLIC RELATIONS—Abstracting,
Bibliographies, Statistics

WHAT'S NEW IN W W W SOCIAL SCIENCES NEWSLETTER.
(World Wide Web) see *HUMANITIES: COMPREHENSIVE*
WORKS—Abstracting, Bibliographies, Statistics

015 AUS
THE WHOLE STORY; 3000 years of series and sequels. Text in
English. irreg., latest vol.2, 1999. USD 150 (effective 2005).
Document type: *Bibliography.* **Description:** Lists every book
sequence ever published or translated into English, from
Homer's epics to the latest bestsellers. Indexes more than
100,000 titles and 16,500 writers.
Related titles: CD-ROM ed.: (from R M I T Publishing).
Published by: Thorpe - Bowker (Subsidiary of: R.R. Bowker
LLC), Bldg C3, 85 Turner St, Port Melbourne, VIC 3207,
Australia. TEL 61-3-9245-7370, FAX 61-3-9245-7395,
subscriptions@thorpe.com.au, http://www.thorpe.com.au. Ed.
John E Simkin. **Subscr. in N. America to:** R.R. Bowker LLC,
Order Dept., PO Box 32, New Providence, NJ 07974-9903.
TEL 800-521-8110.

WINTERGREEN; a directory of progressive periodicals. see
LITERARY AND POLITICAL REVIEWS—Abstracting,
Bibliographies, Statistics

011 USA
WISCONSIN BOOKWATCH. Text in English. m. back issues avail.
Document type: *Journal, Trade.*
Published by: Midwest Book Review, 278 Orchard Dr, Oregon,
WI 53575. TEL 608-835-7937, mbr@execpc.com,
mwbookrevw@aol.com, Ed. James A Cox.

WISCONSIN PUBLIC DOCUMENTS. see *PUBLIC*
ADMINISTRATION—Abstracting, Bibliographies, Statistics

WORK IN AMERICA INSTITUTE: HIGHLIGHTS OF THE
LITERATURE. see *BUSINESS AND ECONOMICS—*
Abstracting, Bibliographies, Statistics

WORK IN AMERICA INSTITUTE STUDIES IN PRODUCTIVITY.
see *BUSINESS AND ECONOMICS—Abstracting,*
Bibliographies, Statistics

WORLD BANK. PUBLICATIONS UPDATE. see *BUSINESS AND*
ECONOMICS—International Development And Assistance

011 AUS
WORLD BIBLIOGRAPHY OF BIBLIOGRAPHIES OF
BIBLIOGRAPHIES. Text in English. 1987. irreg. price varies.
back issues avail. **Document type:** *Bibliography.*
Published by: Noyce Publishing, GPO Box 2222 T, Melbourne,
VIC 3001, Australia. noycepublishing@hotmail.com.

WORLD DATABASE OF BUSINESS INFORMATION SOURCES.
see *BUSINESS AND ECONOMICS—Abstracting,*
Bibliographies, Statistics

WORLD GUIDE TO SCIENTIFIC ASSOCIATIONS AND
LEARNED SOCIETIES. see *SCIENCES: COMPREHENSIVE*
WORKS

WORLD GUIDE TO SPECIAL LIBRARIES. see *LIBRARY AND*
INFORMATION SCIENCES

WRITINGS ON IRISH HISTORY. see *HISTORY—Abstracting,*
Bibliographies, Statistics

YEAR'S WORK IN MODERN LANGUAGE STUDIES. see
LINGUISTICS—Abstracting, Bibliographies, Statistics

YEMEN BIBLIOGRAPHY SERIES. see *GENERAL INTEREST*
PERIODICALS—Yemen, Republic Of

YEMEN DEVELOPMENT SERIES. see *GENERAL INTEREST*
PERIODICALS—Yemen, Republic Of

YOUNG ADULTS' CHOICES. see *CHILDREN AND*
YOUTH—Abstracting, Bibliographies, Statistics

ZAMBIA. NATIONAL COUNCIL FOR SCIENTIFIC RESEARCH.
N C S R BIBLIOGRAPHY. see *SCIENCES:*
COMPREHENSIVE WORKS—Abstracting, Bibliographies,
Statistics

ZEITSCHRIFT FUER BIBLIOTHEKSWESEN UND
BIBLIOGRAPHIE. see *LIBRARY AND INFORMATION*
SCIENCES

ZEITSCHRIFT FUER BIBLIOTHEKSWESEN UND
BIBLIOGRAPHIE. SONDERHEFTE. see *LIBRARY AND*
INFORMATION SCIENCES

053 015 DEU ISSN 1439-0728
Z6956.G3 CODEN: ZDOSBF
ZEITSCHRIFTEN (YEAR). Text in German. 1956. a. EUR 86
(effective 2002). **Document type:** *Directory, Trade.*
Former titles: Deutschsprachige Zeitschriften; Deutschsprachige
Zeitschriften Deutschland - Oesterreich - Schweiz
(0419-005X); Anschriften Deutschsprachiger Zeitschriften
(0066-460X)
Indexed: RASB.
—BLDSC (9497.155000), CASDDS, GNLM, Linda Hall.

Published by: Verlag der Schillerbuchhandlung Hans Banger,
Guldenbachstr 1, Cologne, 50935, Germany. TEL
49-221-46014-0, FAX 49-221-46014-25, banger@banger.de,
http://www.banger.de.

015 DEU ISSN 0949-863X
ZEITSCHRIFTEN - LOSEBLATTWERKE - JAHRBUECHER
(YEAR). Variant title: Banger. Zeitschriften - Loseblattwerke -
Jahrbuecher (Year). Text in German. a. EUR 220 (effective
2002). **Document type:** *Directory, Bibliography.*
Media: CD-ROM.
Published by: Verlag der Schillerbuchhandlung Hans Banger,
Guldenbachstr 1, Cologne, 50935, Germany. TEL
49-221-46014-0, FAX 49-221-46014-25, banger@banger.de,
http://www.banger.de.

ZEITSCHRIFTENBIBLIOGRAPHIE GERONTOLOGIE. see
GERONTOLOGY AND GERIATRICS—Abstracting,
Bibliographies, Statistics

015 ZWE
ZIMBABWE NATIONAL BIBLIOGRAPHY. Text in English. 1961.
a., latest 1997. ZWD 116 domestic; USD 15 foreign. index.
Document type: *Bibliography.*
Former titles (until 1978): Rhodesia National Bibliography
(0085-5677); (until 1966): Publications Deposited in the
National Archives
Published by: National Archives, Causeway, Private Bag 7729,
Harare, Zimbabwe. TEL 263-4-792741, 263-04-79274113, FAX
263-4-792398, 263-04-792398, gpsdept@samara.co.zw,
archives@gta.gov.zw. Ed., R&P Obert Wutete. Circ: 400.

015 ZWE
ZIMBABWEAN PERIODICALS. Text in English. 1988. irreg.,
latest 1997. ZWD 30 (effective 2002). **Document type:**
Bibliography.
Published by: National Archives, Causeway, Private Bag 7729,
Harare, Zimbabwe. TEL 263-4-792741, 263-04-79274113, FAX
263-4-792398, 263-04-792398, archives@gta.gov.zw. Ed.,
R&P Obert Wutete.

ZIMPEL. TEIL 2: PUBLIKUMSZEITSCHRIFTEN. see
PUBLISHING AND BOOK TRADE—Abstracting,
Bibliographies, Statistics

50 TITRES SUR... see *POPULATION STUDIES—Abstracting,*
Bibliographies, Statistics

BICYCLES AND MOTORCYCLES

see SPORTS AND GAMES—Bicycles And Motorcycles

BIOENGINEERING

see BIOLOGY—Bioengineering

BIOGRAPHY

920 USA ISSN 0737-1446
BF30
A P A. MEMBERSHIP REGISTER. (Supplement to: American
Psychological Association Biographical Directory) Text in
English. 1967. a. **Document type:** *Directory, Trade.*
Formerly (until 1982): American Psychological Association.
Membership Register (0569-714X)
Published by: American Psychological Association, 12884 Harbor
Dr., Woodbridge, VA 22192-2921. http://www.apa.org. Ed.
John A Lazo.

A S C A P BIOGRAPHICAL DICTIONARY. see *MUSIC*

AARDVARK ENTREPRISES. CATALOGUE OF PUBLICATIONS.
see *LITERATURE*

920 BEL ISSN 0065-0609
ACADEMIE ROYALE DES SCIENCES, DES LETTRES ET DES
BEAUX-ARTS DE BELGIQUE. INDEX BIOGRAPHIQUE DES
MEMBRES, CORRESPONDANTS ET ASSOCIES. Text in
French. 1948. irreg., latest vol.4, 1995. EUR 15 (effective
2003). 209 p./no. 2 cols./p.; **Document type:** *Directory.*
Published by: Academie Royale des Sciences des Lettres et des
Beaux-Arts de Belgique, Palais des Academies, Rue Ducale
1, Brussels, 1000, Belgium. TEL 32-2-5502211, FAX
32-2-25502205, arb@cjwb.be, http://www.arb.cjwb.be. Ed. Leo
Houziaux. Adv. contact Beatrice Denuit TEL 32-2-5502221.
Circ: 350. **Subscr. to:** Academie Royale de Belgique,
Departement Publications, 1 Rue Ducale, Brussels 1000,
Belgium. TEL 32-2-5502, FAX 32-2-5502205,
luc.moreau@cfwb.be, http://www.arb.cfwb.be.

920 USA ISSN 1040-127X
CT104
ALMANAC OF FAMOUS PEOPLE; a comprehensive reference guide to more than 30,000 famous and infamous newsmakers from biblical times to the present. Text in English. 1981. irreg., latest 7th, 2000 (in 2 vols.). USD 175 (effective 2004).
Description: Provides brief biographical data with citations to over 30,000 biographical sketches appearing in more than 960 sources.
Formerly: Biography Almanac (0738-0097)
Related titles: Online - full text ed.
Published by: Gale Group (Subsidiary of: Thomson Corporation), 27500 Drake Rd, Farmington Hills, MI 48331-3535. TEL 248-699-8061, FAX 248-699-4253, galeord@gale.com, http://www.gale.com. Ed. Frank V Castronova.

ALMANACH DU PEUPLE. see *ENCYCLOPEDIAS AND GENERAL ALMANACS*

509.2 USA ISSN 0000-1287
Q141
AMERICAN MEN AND WOMEN OF SCIENCE; a biographical directory of today's leaders in physical, biological and related sciences. Text in English. 1906. triennial (in 8 vols.), latest vol.22, 2004. USD 1,025 (effective 2005). **Document type:** *Directory, Trade.* **Description:** Capsule biographies of prominent Americans and Canadians, including birthplace and date, scientific field, education, experience, research focus and mailing address. Includes an index by discipline and geographic location.
Formerly (until 1990): American Men and Women of Science. The Physical and Biological Sciences (0192-8570); Which superseded in part (in 1971): American Men of Science (0192-7647)
Related titles: Magnetic Tape ed.; Online - full text ed.: USD 1,045 (effective 2003).
Indexed: CA&I.
Published by: Gale Group (Subsidiary of: Thomson Corporation), 27500 Drake Rd, Farmington Hills, MI 48331-3535. TEL 248-699-4253, 800-347-4253, FAX 248-699-8035, gale.galeord@thomson.com, http://www.galegroup.com.

150 920 USA ISSN 0196-6545
BF11
AMERICAN PSYCHOLOGICAL ASSOCIATION. DIRECTORY. Text in English. 1916. quadrennial. price varies. adv. **Document type:** *Directory, Trade.*
Formerly: American Psychological Association. Biographical Directory (0090-9076)
Published by: American Psychological Association, 12884 Harbor Dr., Woodbridge, VA 22192-2921. TEL 800-374-2721, journals@apa.org, http://www.apa.org. Eds. John Dovidio, Mitch Finegold. Circ: 4,000.

AMIS DE RAMUZ. BULLETIN. see *LITERATURE*

ARGENTINA. DEPARTAMENTO DE ESTUDIOS HISTORICOS NAVALES. SERIE C: BIOGRAFIAS NAVALES ARGENTINAS. see *MILITARY*

920 335 USA
▼ **ARMCHAIR GENERAL.** Text in English. 2004 (Feb.). bi-m. USD 35.70 (effective 2004). **Document type:** *Magazine, Consumer.* **Description:** Covers various battlefield leaderships throughout history, including combat stories, locations and situations.
Published by: Armchair General, LLC, 4165 E Thousand Oaks Blvd Ste 255, Thousand Oaks, CA 91362. http://www.armchairgeneral.com/. Pub. Eric Weider.

ASSOCIATION OF COMMONWEALTH UNIVERSITIES. WHO'S WHO (YEAR). see *EDUCATION—Higher Education*

AUSTIN GENEALOGICAL SOCIETY QUARTERLY. see *GENEALOGY AND HERALDRY*

AUSTRALIAN ART AUCTION RECORDS. see *ART*

AUSTRALIAN CHURCHES OF CHRIST HISTORICAL SOCIETY. DIGEST. see *RELIGIONS AND THEOLOGY*

AUSTRALIAN DIRECTORY OF ACADEMICS; who's who in Australian universities. see *EDUCATION—Higher Education*

AUSTRALIAN PLAYWRIGHTS; a series of monographs and video programmes. see *LITERATURE*

920 GBR ISSN 0967-5507
CT25
➤ **AUTO-BIOGRAPHY**; an international & interdisciplinary journal. Text in English. 1992. 3/yr. GBP 66 in Europe to individuals; USD 108 in North America to individuals; GBP 73 elsewhere to individuals; GBP 162 in Europe to institutions; USD 271 in North America to institutions; GBP 176 elsewhere to institutions; GBP 90 in developing nations; GBP 55 per issue in Europe; USD 100 per issue in North America; GBP 60 per issue elsewhere (effective 2006); subscr. inludes online access. adv. bk.rev. bibl.; illus. 140 p./no. 2 cols./p.; back issues avail. **Document type:** *Journal, Academic/Scholarly.* **Description:** Addresses theoretical, epistemological, and empirical issues relating to autobiographical and biographical research.
Related titles: Online - full text ed.: ISSN 1479-9715 (from EBSCO Publishing, Gale Group, IngentaConnect, O C L C Online Computer Library Center, Inc., Swets Information Services).
—BLDSC (1827.175500). **CCC.**
Published by: Hodder Arnold Journals (Subsidiary of: Hodder Headline plc.), 338 Euston Rd, London, NW1 3BH, United Kingdom. TEL 44-20-78736000, FAX 44-20-78736367, arnoldjournals@hodder.co.uk, http://www.autobiographyjournal.com, http://www.hodderarnoldjournals.com/. Ed. Andrew Sparkes. adv.: B&W page GBP 370; trim 156 x 234. Circ: 200 (paid).
Co-sponsor: British Sociological Association.

920 USA ISSN 0898-9575
CT25
➤ **AUTO/BIOGRAPHY STUDIES.** Abbreviated title: A/B. Text in English. 1986. s-a. USD 20 in US & Canada to individuals; USD 25 elsewhere to individuals; USD 35 in US & Canada to institutions; USD 40 elsewhere to institutions (effective 2003). bk.rev. bibl.; illus. cum.index: 1985-1999. reprints avail. **Document type:** *Journal, Academic/Scholarly.* **Description:** Serves as a forum for interdisciplinary scholarship and criticism on all forms of lifewriting. Covers autobiography, biography, diaries, and letters as well as the relationships between lifewriting and other discourse. Emphasizes work that deals with diverse ethnic and national topics.
Related titles: Online - full text ed.: (from ProQuest Information & Learning).
Indexed: BibInd, MLA-IB.
—BLDSC (0537.005900), IE, ingenta.
Published by: University of North Carolina at Chapel Hill, Department of English, Greenlaw Hall CB 3520, Chapel Hill, NC 27599-3520. TEL 919-962-8482, FAX 919-962-3520, a/b@unc.edu, jclem@email.unc.edu, http://english.unc.edu/journals/ab/. Eds. Joseph Hogan, Rebecca Hogan. R&P, Adv. contact Alex Vernon.

920 DEU
BADEN-WUERTTEMBERGISCHE BIOGRAPHIEN. Text in German. 1994. irreg. EUR 27 per vol. (effective 2003). **Document type:** *Monographic series, Academic/Scholarly.* **Description:** Short biographies of people connected with the state of Baden-Wuerttemberg who died after 1952.
Published by: Kommission fuer geschichtliche Landeskunde in Baden-Wuerttemberg, Eugenstr 7, Stuttgart, 70182, Germany. TEL 49-711-212-4266, FAX 49-711-212-4269, poststelle@kommission.belwue.de. Eds. Bernd Ottnad, Fred Sepaintner.

BAPTIST QUARTERLY. see *RELIGIONS AND THEOLOGY—Protestant*

BEAN HOME NEWSLETTER. see *LITERATURE*

BELCHER BULLETIN. see *GENEALOGY AND HERALDRY*

BESZELO TARGYAK/TALKING THINGS. see *LITERATURE*

920 USA
▼ **BIOGRAFIAS HOY/BIOGRAPHY TODAY IN SPANISH.** Text in Spanish; Index in English, Spanish. 2003. s-a. (in 2 vols.). USD 39 per vol. (effective 2003). Index. 227 p./no.; back issues avail. **Document type:** *Bibliography.*
Published by: Omnigraphics, Inc., 615 Griswold St, Detroit, MI 48226. TEL 313-961-1340, 800-234-1340, FAX 313-961-1383, 800-875-1340, info@omnigraphics.com, http://www.omnigraphics.com/category_view.php?ID=41.

920 SVK ISSN 0067-8724
BIOGRAFICKE STUDIE. Text in Slovak; Summaries in German; Text occasionally in Russian. 1970. a. price varies. bk.rev. **Document type:** *Monographic series, Bibliography.* **Description:** Contains studies of the lives and genealogies of Slovak writers. Also includes documents, bibliographies and other biographical sources.
Indexed: RASB.
Published by: (Biograficky Ustav), Matica Slovenska, Pamatnik Slovenskej Literatury, Namestie JC Hronskeho 1, Martin, 03652, Slovakia. TEL 421-842-4138706, FAX 421-842-4132454. Ed., R&P, Adv. contact Augustin Matovcik. Circ: 350.

920 ITA
BIOGRAFIE. Text in Italian. 1994. irreg., latest vol.4, 1998. price varies. **Document type:** *Monographic series.*
Published by: Liguori Editore srl, Via Posillipo 394, Naples, 80123, Italy. TEL 69-08-17206111, 39-081-7206111, http://www.liguori.it. Pub. Guido Liguori. Adv. contact Maria Liguori.

920 USA ISSN 0162-4962
CT100 CODEN: BGPYE2
➤ **BIOGRAPHY (HONOLULU)**; an interdisciplinary quarterly. Text in English. 1978. q. USD 30 to individuals; USD 50 to institutions (effective 2004). bk.rev. abstr.; bibl.; illus. index, cum.index. back issues avail.; reprint service avail. from PQC,ISI,PSC. **Document type:** *Journal, Academic/Scholarly.* **Description:** Focuses on life-writing and biographical theory.
Related titles: Online - full text ed.: ISSN 1529-1456. 2000 (from bigchalk, Chadwyck-Healey Inc., EBSCO Publishing, Florida Center for Library Automation, Gale Group, O C L C Online Computer Library Center, Inc., Project MUSE, ProQuest Information & Learning, Swets Information Services).
Indexed: ASCA, AmH&L, ArtHuCI, BRI, BibInd, CBRI, CurCont, DIP, GSS&RPL, HistAb, IBR, IBRH, IBSS, IBZ, LIFT, MLA, MLA-IB, SSCI.
—BLDSC (2072.329000), IDS, IE, ingenta. **CCC.**
Published by: (Biographical Research Center), University of Hawaii Press, Journals Department, 2840 Kolowalu St, Honolulu, HI 96822-1888. TEL 808-956-8833, FAX 808-988-6052, biograph@hawaii.edu, uhpjourn@hawaii.edu, http://www.uhpress.hawaii.edu/journals/bio/index.html. Ed. Craig Howes. R&P Stan Schab. Adv. contact Norman Kaneshiro. Circ: 450.

920 USA ISSN 1075-3451
CT21
➤ **BIOGRAPHY AND SOURCE STUDIES.** Text in English. 1994. a. USD 67.50 (effective 2002). bk.rev. bibl. Index. 300 p./no.; back issues avail. **Document type:** *Academic/Scholarly.* **Description:** Aspects, criticisms and techniques pertaining to the writing of biographies.
Published by: A M S Press, Inc., 63 Flushing Ave., # 417, Brooklyn, NY 11205-1005. TEL 212-777-4700, FAX 212-995-5413, amserve@earthlink.net. Ed. Frederick R Karl.

920 USA ISSN 1081-4973
CT107
BIOGRAPHY FOR BEGINNERS; sketches for early readers. Text in English. 1995. s-a. USD 40 (effective 2005). illus. index. 150 p./no.; back issues avail.; reprints avail. **Document type:** *Magazine, Consumer.* **Description:** Includes 15 biographies of notable world figures, authors, artists, cartoonists, TV and film stars and sports stars for young readers ages 6-9.
Media: Large Type (14 pt.).
Published by: Favorable Impressions, PO Box 69018, Pleasant Ridge, MI 48069. TEL 248-544-2421, FAX 248-582-0912, danh@favimp.com, http://www.favimp.com/Bio%20Beginners.html. Ed., Pub., R&P Laurie Harris. Adv. contact Dan Harris. Circ: 4,000.

920 USA ISSN 1071-4987
CT107
BIOGRAPHY TODAY (ANNUAL); profiles of people of interest to young readers. Text in English. 1992. a., latest 2004. USD 62 per vol. (effective 2004). illus. back issues avail. **Document type:** *Bibliography.* **Description:** Cumulation of all profiles found in the three softcover issues for 2000. Twenty-eight profiles are arranged in alphabetical sequence. Cumulative indexes include General Name Index. Places of Birth Index, and Birthday Index.
Indexed: ICM, RGYP.
Published by: Omnigraphics, Inc., 615 Griswold St, Detroit, MI 48226. TEL 313-961-1340, 800-234-1340, FAX 313-961-1383, 800-875-1340, info@omnigraphics.com, http://www.omnigraphics.com. Ed., R&P Cherie D. Abbey. Pub. Frederick G Ruffner Jr.

920 USA ISSN 1058-2347
CT107
BIOGRAPHY TODAY (GENERAL SERIES); profiles of people of interest to young readers. Text in English. 1992. 3/yr. USD 60 (effective 2004). illus. index. back issues avail.; reprints avail. **Document type:** *Bibliography.* **Description:** Each issue contains 10-12 biographies of persons of interest to young readers, with the individual's full name and birth date, and a narrative sketch highlighting information on birth, growing up, education, family, career highlights, and honors and awards. For ages 9 and up.
Indexed: ICM, RGYP.
Published by: Omnigraphics, Inc., 615 Griswold St, Detroit, MI 48226. TEL 313-961-1340, 800-234-1340, FAX 313-961-1383, 800-875-1340, info@omnigraphics.com, http://www.omnigraphics.com. Ed., R&P Cherie D. Abbey. Pub. Frederick G Ruffner Jr. Circ: 12,000.

920 700 USA ISSN 1091-3947
BIOGRAPHY TODAY ARTISTS SERIES. Text in English. 1996. biennial, latest vol.1. USD 39 per vol. (effective 2004). bibl.; illus. index. 200 p./no.; back issues avail. **Document type:** *Bibliography.* **Description:** Profiles artists who would be of interest to young readers, ages 9 and older.
Indexed: ICM.

Published by: Omnigraphics, Inc., 615 Griswold St, Detroit, MI 48226. TEL 313-961-1340, 800-234-1340, FAX 313-961-1383, 800-875-1340, info@omnigraphics.com, http://www.omnigraphics.com/category_view.php?ID=12. Ed., R&P Cherie D. Abbey. Pub. Frederick G Ruffner Jr.

920   USA   ISSN 1082-9989
PS490
BIOGRAPHY TODAY AUTHOR SERIES. Text in English. 1995. irreg., latest vol.16, 2004. USD 39 per vol. (effective 2004). bibl.; illus. index. 200 p./no.; back issues avail. **Document type:** *Bibliography*. **Description:** Offers detailed biographical information on authors of interest to young readers ages 9 and older.
Indexed: ICM.
Published by: Omnigraphics, Inc., 615 Griswold St, Detroit, MI 48226. TEL 313-961-1340, 800-234-1340, FAX 313-961-1383, 800-875-1340, info@omnigraphics.com, http://www.omnigraphics.com. Ed., R&P Cherie D. Abbey. Pub. Frederick G Ruffner Jr.

920   USA
▼ **BIOGRAPHY TODAY PERFORMING ARTISTS SERIES.** Text in English. 2003. s-a. (in 2 vols.). USD 39 per vol. (effective 2004). **Document type:** *Bibliography*.
Published by: Omnigraphics, Inc., 615 Griswold St, Detroit, MI 48226. TEL 313-961-1340, 800-234-1340, FAX 313-961-1383, 800-875-1340, info@omnigraphics.com, http://www.omnigraphics.com/category_view.php?ID=40.

920   USA   ISSN 1091-3939
Q141
BIOGRAPHY TODAY SCIENTISTS & INVENTORS SERIES; profiles of people of interest to young readers. Text in English. 1997. s-a. (in 2 vols.). USD 39 per vol. (effective 2004). bibl.; illus. Index. 200 p./no.; back issues avail. **Document type:** *Bibliography*. **Description:** Profiles of scientists and inventors specifically in the area of computer science that are of interest to readers ages 9 and above. Approximately fifteen entries describe the individual's life and the most memorable accomplishments. Cumulative General, Places of Birth, and Birthday Indexes. No duplication between profiles in the Regular Series of Biography Today.
Published by: Omnigraphics, Inc., 615 Griswold St, Detroit, MI 48226. TEL 313-961-1340, 800-234-1340, FAX 313-961-1383, 800-875-1340, info@omnigraphics.com, http://www.omnigraphics.com. Ed., R&P Laurie Lanzen Harris. Pub. Frederick G Ruffner Jr.

920 790.1   USA   ISSN 1529-3742
GV697.A1
BIOGRAPHY TODAY SPORTS SERIES; profiles of people of interest to young readers. Text in English. 1996. a. USD 39 per vol. (effective 2004). bibl.; illus. Index. 200 p./no.; back issues avail. **Document type:** *Bibliography*. **Description:** Profiles of authors of interest to readers ages 9 and above. Approximately fifteen entries describe the individual's life and most memorable accomplishments. Cumulative General, Places of Birth, and Birthday Indexes. No duplication between profiles in the Regular Series of Biography Today.
Indexed: ICM.
Published by: Omnigraphics, Inc., 615 Griswold St, Detroit, MI 48226. TEL 313-961-1341, 800-234-1340, FAX 313-961-1383, 800-875-1340, info@omnigraphics.com, http://www.omnigraphics.com/category_view.php?ID=15. Ed., R&P Cherie D. Abbey. Pub. Frederick G Ruffner Jr.

920   USA   ISSN 1094-2823
GE55
BIOGRAPHY TODAY WORLD LEADERS SERIES. Text in English. 1997. irreg., latest vol.3, 2000. USD 39 per vol. (effective 2004). bibl.; illus. 200 p./no.; back issues avail. **Document type:** *Bibliography*. **Description:** Profiles notable leaders from all around the world, role models of interest to young readers ages 9 and older.
Indexed: ICM.
Published by: Omnigraphics, Inc., 615 Griswold St, Detroit, MI 48226. TEL 313-961-1340, 800-234-1340, FAX 313-961-1383, 800-875-1340, info@omnigraphics.com, http://www.omnigraphics.com/category_view.php?ID=16. Ed., R&P Cherie D. Abbey. Pub. Frederick G Ruffner Jr.

920   DEU   ISSN 0933-5315
CT21
➤ **BIOS;** Zeitschrift fuer Biographieforschung und Oral History. Text in German. 1988. 2/yr. EUR 42 domestic; EUR 46 foreign; EUR 24.20 newsstand/cover (effective 2004). **Document type:** *Journal, Academic/Scholarly*.
Indexed: AmH&L, BibInd, DIP, HistAb, IBR, IBSS, IBZ.
Published by: V S - Verlag fuer Sozialwissenschaften (Subsidiary of: Springer Science+Business Media), Abraham-Lincoln-Str 46, Wiesbaden, 65189, Germany. TEL 49-611-78780, FAX 49-611-7878400, info@vs-verlag.de, http://www.vs-verlag.de.

920   GBR
BIRMINGHAM POST AND MAIL YEAR BOOK AND WHO'S WHO ∗ . Text in English. 1949. a. GBP 30 (effective 1998). **Document type:** *Directory*.
Former titles: Birmingham Post Year Book and Who's Who; Birmingham Post and Mail Year Book and Who's Who; (until 1985): Birmingham Post Year Book and Who's Who

Published by: Kingslea Press Ltd., 137 Newhall St., Birmingham, West Midlands B3 1SF, United Kingdom. TEL 44-1902-771134, FAX 44-1902-771195. Ed. Arthur Smith. R&P Phil Walder. Circ: 1,700.

920 910.03 USA   ISSN 1060-9148
BLACK AUTHORS & PUBLISHED WRITERS DIRECTORY. Text in English. 1993. a. USD 69.95 (effective 1999). adv. **Document type:** *Directory*. **Description:** For free-lance writers, established authors, and groups interested in Black talent, Black literature, marketplace. Includes profiles of writers, authors, agents, print and broadcast media and libraries.
Related titles: ◆ Supplement(s): Black Literary Players. ISSN 1066-9396.
Published by: Grace Publishing Co., 829 Langdon Ct, Rochester, MI 48307-2921. TEL 248-868-5994. Ed. Grace Adams.

920 910.03 USA   ISSN 1066-9396
BLACK LITERARY PLAYERS. Text in English. 1993. m. USD 146 (effective 1999). bk.rev. back issues avail. **Document type:** *Newsletter*. **Description:** Contains Black publishing and entertainment industry news, reviews and subscriber views.
Related titles: ◆ Supplement to: Black Authors & Published Writers Directory. ISSN 1060-9148.
Published by: Grace Publishing Co., 829 Langdon Ct, Rochester, MI 48307-2921. TEL 248-556-7335. Ed. Grace Adams. adv.: B&W page USD 225. Circ: 1,400 (paid).

920   USA   ISSN 1040-7405
PS1029.A3
BOOTBLACK; the Horatio Alger annual. Text in English. 1989. a. USD 50 (effective 1998).
Address: 1001 S W 5th Court, Boynton Beach, FL 33426. TEL 561-736-2340.

920   FRA   ISSN 1268-7057
BOTTIN MONDAIN; Tout Paris-Toute la France. Text in French. 1903. a. EUR 120 to members; EUR 190 to non-members (effective 2006). bibl.; maps. **Document type:** *Directory*.
Related titles: E-mail ed.
Published by: Societe du Bottin Mondain, 15 place de la Madeleine, Paris, 75008, France. TEL 33-1-44511313, FAX 33-1-42666901, http://www.bottin-mondain.fr/, http://www.bottin-mondain.com. Ed., R&P Blanche de Kersaint. Pub. Laurent Parquet. Adv. contact Isabelle Acker.

920   GBR
BRITAIN'S RICHEST ASIAN 200. Text in English. a. **Document type:** *Consumer*.
Published by: Ethnic Media Group, 65 Whitechapel Rd, London, E1 1DU, United Kingdom. TEL 44-20-76502000, FAX 44-20-76502001, http://www.ethnicmedia.co.uk/.

BUILDERS OF INDIAN ANTHROPOLOGY. see *SOCIAL SCIENCES: COMPREHENSIVE WORKS*

920   USA   ISSN 1520-9296
BUSINESS LEADER PROFILES FOR STUDENTS. Text in English. 199?. biennial (in 2 vols.). **Document type:** *Monographic series, Academic/Scholarly*. **Description:** Focuses on prominent individuals who have made significant contributions to business and industry.
Related titles: Online - full content ed.
Published by: Gale Group (Subsidiary of: Thomson Corporation), 27500 Drake Rd, Farmington Hills, MI 48331-3535. TEL 248-699-4253, 800-877-4253, FAX 248-699-8035, 800-414-5043, galeord@gale.com, http://www.gale.com/servlet/BrowseSeriesServlet?region=9&imprint=000&titleCode=BLFS&edition=, http://www.galegroup.com.

LES CAHIERS ALEXANDRE DUMAS. see *LITERATURE*

CANADIAN PLAINS REFERENCE WORKS. see *SCIENCES: COMPREHENSIVE WORKS*

920   CAN   ISSN 0068-9963
F1033
CANADIAN WHO'S WHO. Text in English; Text occasionally in French. 1910. a. CND 195 per issue (effective 2005). **Document type:** *Directory, Consumer*. **Description:** Contains biographies of 14,000 notable Canadians, including education, career, awards and contact information.
Formerly: Who's Who, The Canadian
Related titles: CD-ROM ed.
Indexed: CA&I, RASB.
—CISTI. **CCC.**
Published by: University of Toronto Press, Reference Division, 10 St Mary St, Ste 700, Toronto, ON M4Y 2W8, Canada. TEL 416-978-2239, FAX 416-978-4738, utpbooks@utpress.utoronto.ca, http://www.utpress.utoronto.ca. Ed. Elizabeth Lumley. Circ: 5,000.

920   CAN
F1033
CANADIAN WHO'S WHO (YEAR). Text in English. 1911. a. CND 185 (effective 2003). **Document type:** *Directory, Consumer*. **Description:** Provides biographies on prominent Canadian business, social, and government leaders.

Former titles: Who's Who in Canada (Year) (0083-9450); (until 1922): Who's Who and Why (0316-0971); Who's Who in Western Canada
Related titles: CD-ROM ed.: CND 195 (effective 2003).
Indexed: CA&I.
—CISTI.
Published by: International Press Publications Inc, 90 Nolan Ct, Ste 21, Markham, ON L3R 4L9, Canada. TEL 905-946-9588, 800-679-2514, FAX 905-946-9590, ipp@interlog.com, http://www.interlog.com/~ipp. Ed. Jack Kohane.

920 800   CAN   ISSN 1074-2670
PR4432
CARLYLE STUDIES ANNUAL; essays on Thomas and Jane Carlyle and their circle. Text in English. 1979. a. USD 12 to individuals; USD 15 to institutions (effective 2005). illus. back issues avail. **Document type:** *Journal, Academic/Scholarly*.
Former titles (until 1993): Carlyle Annual (1050-3099); (until 1989): Carlyle Newsletter (0269-8226)
Indexed: MLA, MLA-IB.
Address: c/o Mark Cumming, Editor, Memorial University of Newfoundland, St. John's, NF A1C 5S7, Canada. R&P Rodger L Tarr. Circ: 250.

920   GBR   ISSN 0045-6020
CELEBRITY BULLETIN. Text in English. 1952. s-w. GBP 720 (effective 1999). **Document type:** *Bulletin*.
Published by: Celebrity Service Ltd., 93 Regent St, London, W1R 7TA, United Kingdom. TEL 44-171-439-9840, FAX 44-171-494-3500. Ed. Diane F Oliver.

CENTENNIAL BIOGRAPHICAL DIRECTORY OF MEMBERS. see *POLITICAL SCIENCE*

CHEMISTS AND CHEMISTRY. see *CHEMISTRY*

CHI E CHI DEL GIORNALISMO DELL'AUTO. see *JOURNALISM*

CHI E CHI DEL GIORNALISMO E DELLA MODA. see *CLOTHING TRADE—Fashions*

CHI E CHI DELL'AERONAUTICA E DELLO SPAZIO. see *AERONAUTICS AND SPACE FLIGHT*

CHI E CHI NEWS. see *JOURNALISM*

CHI E CHI SANITA E SALUTE. see *PHARMACY AND PHARMACOLOGY*

CHIROPRACTIC HISTORY. see *MEDICAL SCIENCES— Chiropractic, Homeopathy, Osteopathy*

920   VEN   ISSN 0069-5033
COLECCION "ANIVERSARIOS CULTURALES". Text in Spanish. 1965. irreg., latest vol.4, 1968.
Published by: Universidad Central de Venezuela, Direccion de Cultura, Biblioteca, Piso 10, Ciudad Universitaria, Caracas, Venezuela.

COLLECTION MONOGRAPHIQUE RODOPI EN LITTERATURE FRANCAISE CONTEMPORAINE. see *LITERATURE*

920   USA
THE COMPLETE MARQUIS WHO'S WHO ON CD-ROM. Text in English. a. (plus s-a. updates). USD 1,010 (effective 1999). **Description:** Includes all the entries from the renowned Who's Who in America, and Who's Who in the World, as well as 16 other Marquis print volumes, covering the whole range of human endeavour and achievement - from the arts to business, from government to religion, and law to science.
Media: CD-ROM.
Published by: Marquis Who's Who, 562 Central Ave, New Providence, NJ 07964. TEL 800-621-9669, FAX 908-665-6688, info@marquiswhoswho.com, http://www.marquiswhoswho.com.

COMPOSERS OF THE AMERICAS/COMPOSITORES DE AMERICA. see *MUSIC*

CONFLUENCE (WENATCHEE). see *MUSEUMS AND ART GALLERIES*

CONGRESSIONAL YELLOW BOOK; who's who in Congress, including committees and key staff. see *PUBLIC ADMINISTRATION*

920   USA   ISSN 0010-7468
Z1224
CONTEMPORARY AUTHORS. Text in English. 1962. irreg., latest vol.230, 2004. USD 195 (effective 2004). bibl. cum.index. reprints avail. **Document type:** *Academic/Scholarly*. **Description:** Biographies and descriptions of contemporary authors.
Incorporates (1984-1999): Contemporary Authors Autobiography Series (0748-0636)
Related titles: Online - full text ed.; Cumulative ed(s).: Contemporary Authors Culumative Index. ISSN 0196-0245.
Indexed: CA&I, RASB.

▼ *new title*   ➤ *refereed*   ∗ *unverified*   ◆ *full entry avail.*

Published by: Gale Group (Subsidiary of: Thomson Corporation), 27500 Drake Rd, Farmington Hills, MI 48331-3535. TEL 248-699-8061, 800-877-4253, FAX 248-699-4253, galeord@gale.com, http://www.gale.com. Ed. Terri Rooney.

920 800 USA ISSN 0275-7176
Z1224
CONTEMPORARY AUTHORS. NEW REVISION SERIES. Text in English. 1981. irreg., latest vol.143, 2005. price varies. **Document type:** *Monographic series, Trade.* **Description:** Contains the most recent data on the world's most-popular authors.
Published by: Gale Research Co. (Subsidiary of: Gale Group), 27500 Drake Rd, Farmington, MI 48331-3535. TEL 248-699-4253, 800-877-4253, gale.galeord@thomson.com, http://www.gale.com.

920 910.03 USA ISSN 1058-1316
E185.96
CONTEMPORARY BLACK BIOGRAPHY; profiles from the international black community. Text in English. 1991. 3/yr., latest vol.49, 2002. USD 99 per issue (effective 2004). **Description:** Provides about 70 biographical entries per volume about prominent black individuals.
Published by: Gale Group (Subsidiary of: Thomson Corporation), 27500 Drake Rd, Farmington Hills, MI 48331-3535. TEL 248-699-8061, 800-877-4253, FAX 248-699-4253, galeord@gale.com, http://www.gale.com. Ed. Shirelle Phelps.

920 USA
CONTEMPORARY HEROES AND HEROINES; a biographical guide to heroic figures of the twentieth century. Text in English. 1990. irreg., latest vol.4, 2000. USD 95 per vol. (effective 2004). back issues avail. **Document type:** *Monographic series, Consumer.* **Description:** Discusses the lives and the aspirations and motivations of noteworthy individuals to inspire young adults.
Related titles: Online - full text ed.
Published by: Gale Group (Subsidiary of: Thomson Corporation), 27500 Drake Rd, Farmington Hills, MI 48331-3535. TEL 248-699-8061, 800-877-4253, FAX 248-699-4253, galeord@gale.com, http://www.gale.com.

920.0092 305.868 USA ISSN 1541-1524
F1407
CONTEMPORARY HISPANIC BIOGRAPHY; profiles from the international hispanic community. Text in English. 2002. irreg., latest vol.4, 2004. USD 99 per vol. (effective 2004).
Published by: Gale Group (Subsidiary of: Thomson Corporation), 27500 Drake Rd, Farmington Hills, MI 48331-3535. TEL 248-699-4253, 800-347-4253, FAX 248-699-8035, http://www.gale.com. Ed. Ashyia N. Henderson.

CONTEMPORARY MUSICIANS; profiles of the people in music. see *MUSIC*

920 USA ISSN 0749-064X
PN2285
CONTEMPORARY THEATRE, FILM & TELEVISION. Text in English. 1984. irreg., latest vol.61, 2004. USD 195 (effective 2004). cum.index. back issues avail. **Document type:** *Directory.* **Description:** Biographies of workers in theatre, film and television industries.
Incorporating (1912-1981): Who's Who in the Theatre (0083-9833)
Indexed: CA&I, PABMI.
—BLDSC (3425.307700).
Published by: Gale Group (Subsidiary of: Thomson Corporation), 27500 Drake Rd, Farmington Hills, MI 48331-3535. TEL 248-699-8061, 800-877-4253, FAX 248-699-4253, galeord@gale.com, http://www.gale.com. Ed. Emily J McMurray.

COOPER SOCIETY NEWSLETTER. see *LITERATURE*

CORPORATE REGISTER. see *BUSINESS AND ECONOMICS*

920 USA ISSN 0011-3344
CT100
CURRENT BIOGRAPHY. Text in English. 1940. 11/yr. USD 140 in US & Canada; USD 165 elsewhere; USD 35 per issue (effective 2006). bibl.; illus. index, cum.index 1940-1995. reprints avail. **Document type:** *Magazine, Consumer.* **Description:** Contains accurate, up-to-date biographies of the men and women who make today's headlines and tomorrow's history. Draws information from newspaper and magazine articles, books, and occasionally personal interviews or questionnaires completed by the subjects. This resource presents biographical information in a lively style that makes for entertaining as well as informative reading.
Related titles: CD-ROM ed.: (from H.W. Wilson, SilverPlatter Information, Inc.); Online - full text ed.: USD 670 in US & Canada (effective 2006) (from The Dialog Corporation).
Indexed: ARG, Acal, CPerI, DAAI, IDP, IIPA, IPARL, LRI, LibLit, MagInd, RASB, RGAb, RGPR, RGYP, RILM, TOM.
Published by: H.W. Wilson Co., 950 University Ave, Bronx, NY 10452-4224. TEL 718-588-8400, 800-367-6770, FAX 718-590-1617, 800-590-1617, bottervik@hwwilson.com, custserv@hwwilson.com, http://www.hwwilson.com/currentbio/curbio.html. Eds. Clifford Thompson, Eileen Sutter. Adv. contact Jessie Clark. Circ: 20,000 (paid).

920 USA ISSN 1538-3296
CT120
CURRENT BIOGRAPHY INTERNATIONAL YEARBOOK. Text in English. 2002. a. USD 140 per issue in US & Canada; USD 165 per issue elsewhere (effective 2006). **Document type:** *Directory, Consumer.* **Description:** Presents biographical profiles of people making international news and history.
Published by: H.W. Wilson Co., 950 University Ave, Bronx, NY 10452-4224. TEL 718-588-8400, 800-367-6770, FAX 718-590-1617, 800-590-1617, custserv@hwwilson.com, http://www.hwwilson.com.

920 USA ISSN 0084-9499
CT100
CURRENT BIOGRAPHY YEARBOOK. Text in English. 1940. a. USD 140 per issue in US & Canada; USD 165 per issue elsewhere (effective 2006). bibl. index, cum.index: 1940-1995. 683 p./no.; back issues avail. **Document type:** *Yearbook, Academic/Scholarly.* **Description:** Includes a complete cumulation of the year's obituaries, a cumulated index for articles and obituaries published in the current decade, and a classification of the subjects of articles by their professions. A sturdy library binding and acid-free paper make this investment last.
Related titles: CD-ROM ed.: (from H.W. Wilson).
Indexed: ABS&EES, CA&I, IDP.
Published by: H.W. Wilson Co., 950 University Ave, Bronx, NY 10452-4224. TEL 718-588-8400, 800-367-6770, FAX 718-590-1617, 800-590-1617, custserv@hwwilson.com, http://www.hwwilson.com/print/cbyrbook.htm. Ed. Clifford Thompson.

929.72 GBR ISSN 1356-7802
CT770
DEBRETT'S PEOPLE OF TODAY. Key Title: People of Today. Text in English. 1982. a. GBP 100 domestic; GBP 113 foreign. **Document type:** *Directory.*
Former titles (until 1991): Debrett's Distinguished People of Today (0957-0284); (until 1988): Debrett's Handbook (0264-2581)
—BLDSC (3535.979505).
Published by: Debrett's Peerage Ltd., 73-77 Britannia Rd, Fulham, London, SW6 2JA, United Kingdom. TEL 44-171-736-6524, FAX 44-171-731-7768, people@debretts.co.uk, http://www.debrett's.co.uk. Ed. Jonathan Parker.

920 DEU ISSN 0341-6771
DEIKE GEDENKTAGE. Text in German. 1923. m. CHF 45. **Document type:** *Bulletin.*
—CCC.
Published by: Verlag Horst Deike KG, Postfach 100452, Konstanz, 78404, Germany. TEL 07531-8155-0, FAX 07531-815581.

920 CAN ISSN 0070-4717
F1005
DICTIONARY OF CANADIAN BIOGRAPHY/DICTIONNAIRE BIBLIOGRAPHIQUE DU CANADA. Text in English. 1966. irreg. **Document type:** *Academic/Scholarly.*
—CISTI.
Published by: University of Toronto Press, 130 St George St, 14th Fl, Toronto, ON M5S 3H1, Canada. TEL 416-978-2244, FAX 416-978-2611, robert.fraser@utoronto.ca. Ed. Ramsay Cook. **Co-publisher:** Universite Laval.

920 GBR ISSN 0419-1137
CT101
DICTIONARY OF INTERNATIONAL BIOGRAPHY. Text in English. 1963. a., latest 29th Ed. GBP 135, USD 245 per vol. (effective 2001). **Document type:** *Directory.* **Description:** Contains approximately 5,000 biographical entries of leaders in all fields.
—BLDSC (3580.295000).
Published by: Melrose Press Ltd., St Thomas Pl, Ely, Cambs CB7 4GG, United Kingdom. TEL 44-1353-646600, FAX 44-1353-646601, tradesales@melrosepress.co.uk, http://www.melrosepress.co.uk. Ed. Jon Gifford. Pub. Nicholas Law. **Dist. in US by:** Taylor & Francis Inc., 7625 Empire Dr., Florence, KY 41042-2919. cserve@routledge-ny.com.

920 800 USA ISSN 1096-8547
DICTIONARY OF LITERARY BIOGRAPHY. Text in English. 1978. irreg., latest vol.312, 2004. USD 205 per vol. (effective 2004). **Document type:** *Monographic series, Academic/Scholarly.* **Description:** Provides biographical and analytical coverage on some 7,000 prominent literary figures.
Related titles: Online - full text ed.
Indexed: CA&I, MLA, MLA-IB, PABMI.
Published by: Gale Group (Subsidiary of: Thomson Corporation), 27500 Drake Rd, Farmington Hills, MI 48331-3535. TEL 248-699-8061, FAX 248-699-4253, galeord@gale.com, http://www.gale.com. Ed. Matthew J Bruccoli.

920 800 USA
DICTIONARY OF LITERARY BIOGRAPHY: DOCUMENTARY SERIES. Text in English. irreg., latest vol.19, 1998. USD 205 per vol. (effective 2004). illus. back issues avail. **Document type:** *Monographic series, Academic/Scholarly.* **Description:** Concentrates on the major figures of a particular literary period, movement or genre in each volume.
Published by: Gale Group (Subsidiary of: Thomson Corporation), 27500 Drake Rd, Farmington Hills, MI 48331-3535. TEL 248-699-8061, 800-877-4253, FAX 248-699-4253, galeord@gale.com, http://www.gale.com. Eds. Matthew J Bruccoli, Richard Layman.

920 800 USA ISSN 0731-7867
PS221
DICTIONARY OF LITERARY BIOGRAPHY YEARBOOK. Text in English. 1981. a., latest 2002. USD 205 (effective 2004). back issues avail. **Document type:** *Monographic series, Academic/Scholarly.* **Description:** Provides an annual reference on works of literary biography.
Published by: Gale Group (Subsidiary of: Thomson Corporation), 27500 Drake Rd, Farmington Hills, MI 48331-3535. TEL 248-699-8061, 800-877-4253, FAX 248-699-4253, galeord@gale.com, http://www.gale.com. Eds. Matthew J Bruccoli, Richard Layman.

920 967 MUS ISSN 1025-367X
DICTIONNAIRE DE BIOGRAPHIE MAURICIENNE/DICTIONARY OF MAURITIAN BIOGRAPHY. Text in English, French. 1941. irreg. USD 8.
Published by: Societe de l'Histoire de l'Ile Maurice, Rue de Froberville, Curepipe Rd, Port Louis, Mauritius.

920 658 IND ISSN 0070-542X
DIRECTORY OF DIRECTORS. Text in English. 1966. irreg. INR 30, USD 9 (effective 2000). adv. **Document type:** *Directory.* **Description:** Lists about 2500 names, addresses and ages of leading Indian company directors.
Published by: Kothari Publications, 12 India Exchange Pl., Kolkata, West Bengal 700 001, India. TEL 91-33-220-9563. Ed. H Kothari.

354.438 USA ISSN 0090-9955
JN6757
DIRECTORY OF POLISH OFFICIALS. Text in English. irreg. USD 20.95; USD 41.90 foreign (effective 1999). **Document type:** *Directory, Government.*
Published by: U.S. Central Intelligence Agency, c/o U S National Technical Information Service, U S Department of Commerce, 5285 Port Royal Rd, Springfield, VA 22161. TEL 703-605-6000, 800-553-6847, http://www.ntis.gov. **Dist. to Non-U.S. Government users by:** Document Expediting (DOCEX) Project, Library of Congress, Washington, DC 20540.

920 942 GBR ISSN 0070-7120
DORSET WORTHIES. Text in English. 1962. irreg., latest vol.23, 1998. **Document type:** *Monographic series.*
Published by: Dorset County Museum, Dorchester, Dorset, United Kingdom. TEL 44-1305-262735, dorsetcountymuseum@dor-mus.demon.co.uk, http://www.dorset.museum.clara.net. Ed. Peter Lock. R&P R Depeyer.

920 949.2 NLD ISSN 0929-9807
EGODOCUMENTEN. Text in Dutch. 1988. s-a. price varies. illus. back issues avail. **Document type:** *Monographic series.* **Description:** Publishes scholarly editions of autobiographies, journals and correspondence from the period 1500 to 1850.
Published by: (Stichting Egodocument), Uitgeverij Verloren, PO Box 1741, Hilversum, 1200 BS, Netherlands. TEL 31-35-685-9856, FAX 31-35-683-6557, http://www.verloren.nl. Ed. R M Dekker.

920 USA ISSN 1520-3239
ENCYCLOPEDIA OF WORLD BIOGRAPHY (EBOOK EDITION). Text in English. 1973. irreg. (in 17 vols.), latest vol.24, 2004. price varies. Supplement avail. **Document type:** *Academic/Scholarly.* **Description:** Contains almost 7,000 biographies with high resolution photographs and facts.
Media: Online - full content. **Related titles:** CD-ROM ed.: USD 995 (effective 2004); Print ed.: 1973; Abridged ed.: Abridged Encyclopedia of World Biography. USD 595 (effective 2004).
Published by: Gale Group (Subsidiary of: Thomson Corporation), 27500 Drake Rd, Farmington Hills, MI 48331-3535. TEL 248-699-4253, 800-877-4253, FAX 248-699-8035, 800-414-5043, gale.galeord@thomson.com, http://www.galegroup.com.

382.029 BEL ISSN 1370-6454
EURO - WHO'S WHO; who is who in the institutions of the European Union and in the other European organizations. Text in English, French, German. 1978. triennial, latest 2004, 6th ed. USD 240 per vol. (effective 2005). adv. 320 p./no.; **Document type:** *Directory.* **Description:** Includes the biographies of the senior civil servants currently working within the institutions of the European Union and within more than 20 other European organizations, and the chairmen and secretaries of more than 1,500 non-governmental organizations.
Formerly (until 1991): European Communities and Other European Organizations Who's Who (0771-7911)
Published by: Editions Delta, Rue Scailquin 55, Brussels, 1210, Belgium. TEL 32-2-217-5555, FAX 32-2-217-9393, editions.delta@skynet.be. Ed. Georges Francis Seingry. Circ: 6,000. **Dist. in US by:** Berman Associates, Berman, 4611-F Assembly Dr., Lanham, MD 20706-4391.

EUROPEAN JOYCE STUDIES. see *LITERATURE*

FAULKNER NEWSLETTER & YOKNAPATAWPHA REVIEW. see *LITERATURE*

FEDERAL REGIONAL YELLOW BOOK; who's who in the federal government's departments, agencies, diplomatic missions, military installations and service academies outside of Washington, DC. see *PUBLIC ADMINISTRATION*

FINEST HOUR. see *HISTORY*

920 USA ISSN 1087-3996
CT120
FIVE HUNDRED LEADERS OF INFLUENCE. Text in English. 1993. a. USD 175 (effective 2000). illus. **Document type:** *Directory.* **Description:** Includes biographies of an elite group who have helped mold international societies during this century.
Published by: American Biographical Institute, Inc., Governing Board of Editors, 5126 Bur Oak Circle, Box 31226, Raleigh, NC 27622. TEL 919-781-8710, FAX 919-781-8712.

920 USA ISSN 1087-3953
CT120
FIVE THOUSAND PERSONALITIES OF THE WORLD. Text in English. 1986. biennial. USD 99.50 (effective 2000). **Document type:** *Directory.* **Description:** Recognizes distinguished leaders.
Published by: American Biographical Institute, Inc., Governing Board of Editors, 5126 Bur Oak Circle, Box 31226, Raleigh, NC 27622. TEL 919-781-8710, FAX 919-781-8712.

FOTOTEKA. see *PHOTOGRAPHY*

920 USA ISSN 1060-5312
FRANKLIN PIERCE TIMES. Text in English. 1992. q. USD 11.50 (effective 1998). bk.rev. back issues avail. **Document type:** *Newsletter.* **Description:** Biography of the 14th U.S. president, including all his available letters. Contains commentary and news of efforts to obtain greater interest in the life and achievements of Franklin Pierce.
Address: 79 Elm St, Springfield, VT 05156. Ed., Pub. Irving Bell. Circ: 200 (paid).

920 943 DEU ISSN 0949-2097
GEDENKTAGE. Text in German. 1958. a. back issues avail. **Document type:** *Journal, Academic/Scholarly.*
Formerly (until 1994): Gedenktage des Mitteldeutschen Raumes (0341-0749)
Published by: (Stiftung Mitteldeutscher Kulturrat), Boehlau Verlag GmbH & Cie, Ursulaplatz 1, Cologne, 50668, Germany. TEL 49-221-913900, FAX 49-221-9139011, vertrieb@boehlau.de, http://www.boehlau.de.

920 USA ISSN 1065-9552
JK2447
GOVERNORS OF AMERICAN STATES, COMMONWEALTHS, AND TERRITORIES. Text in English. a. USD 8.95. **Document type:** *Directory.* **Description:** Biographical information of American governors.
Former titles (until 1991): Directory of Governors of the American States, Commonwealths, and Territories (0898-3291); (until 1988): Governors of the American States, Commonwealths, and Territories (0196-4348)
Published by: National Governors' Association, 444 N Capitol St, Washington, DC 20001. TEL 202-624-5330. Ed. Alicia Albergold.

920 968 ZAF
GRAHAM'S TOWN SERIES. Text in English. 1971. irreg., latest vol.7, 1984. price varies. **Document type:** *Monographic series.* **Description:** Publishes historical material relating to the Eastern Cape in the nineteenth century, including diaries and collections of letters.
Published by: (Rhodes University), Grahamstown Publicity Association, 63 High St, Grahamstown, East Cape 6140, South Africa. Eds. Guy Butler, Winnie Maxwell.

920 FRA
GRANDS NOTABLES DU PREMIER EMPIRE. Text in French. irreg. price varies. adv. bk.rev. index.
Published by: C N R S Editions, 15 Rue Malebranche, Paris, 75005, France. TEL 33-1-53102700, FAX 33-1-53102727, http://www.cnrseditions.fr. Circ: 1,500 (controlled).

920 USA ISSN 1540-4900
▼ **GREENWOOD PRESS BIOGRAPHY SERIES.** Text in English. 2003. irreg.
Published by: Greenwood Publishing Group Inc. (Subsidiary of: Harcourt International), 88 Post Rd W, PO Box 5007, Westport, CT 06881. TEL 203-226-3571, FAX 203-226-1502, info@greenwoodpublishing.com, http://www.greenwood.com.

920 CHN ISSN 1003-7225
➤ **GUO MORUO XUEKAN.** Text in Chinese. 1987. q. CNY 5.60. adv. **Document type:** *Academic/Scholarly.* **Description:** Studies the literary life, theory and works of Guo Moruo, a distinguished writer, scientist and social activist in modern Chinese history.
Related titles: Online - full text ed.: (from East View Information Services).
Published by: (Sichuan Guo Moruo Study Institute), Guo Moruo Xuekan Qikanshe, Dafo Si Nei, Leshan, Sichuan 614003, China. TEL 86-833-2139721. Eds. Wang Jinhou, Zhang Hao. Adv. contact Anna Tang. Circ: 3,000. **Dist. overseas by:** Jiangsu Publications Import & Export Corp., 56 Gao Yun Ling, Nanjing, Jiangsu, China.

➤ **HANS - PFITZNER - GESELLSCHAFT. MITTEILUNGEN.** see *MUSIC*

➤ **HAYDN - STUDIEN.** see *MUSIC*

920 820 AUS ISSN 0729-2449
HERMIT PRESS PAMPHLETS. Text in English. 1982. irreg. **Document type:** *Monographic series, Academic/Scholarly.* **Description:** Presents biographical studies of neglected writers for academic and general readership.
Published by: Pioneer Books, PO Box 57, Oaklands Park, SA 5046, Australia. TEL 61-8-82984645, FAX 61-8-83772355, pioneer@dezzanet.net.au, http://www.pioneerbooks.com.au. Ed., R&P Paul Depasquale. **Co-publisher:** Hermit Press.

920 FRA ISSN 1251-5132
HISTOIRE ECONOMIQUE ET FINANCIERE DE LA FRANCE. MEMOIRE. Text in French. 1990. irreg. Price varies. **Document type:** *Monographic series.*
Published by: Ministere de l'Economie, des Finances et de l'Industrie, Comite pour l'Histoire Economique et Financiere de la France, 6 av. de l'Opera, 2eme Etage, Paris, 75001, France. TEL 33-1-44775264, FAX 33-1-44775298, http://www.minefi.gouv.fr/DICOM/cheff.

HISTORIC GUELPH; the royal city. see *HISTORY—History Of North And South America*

920 800 USA
HISTORICAL GUIDES TO AMERICAN AUTHORS. Text in English. 2000. irreg., latest 2003, Dec. price varies. **Document type:** *Monographic series, Academic/Scholarly.*
Indexed: MLA-IB.
Published by: Oxford University Press (Subsidiary of: Oxford University Press), 2001 Evans Rd, Cary, NC 27513. TEL 919-677-0977, 800-852-7323, FAX 919-677-1714, http://www.oup-usa.org/catalogs/general/series/Historical_Guides_to_American_Authors.html, http://www.us.oup.com.

HISTORICAL SOCIETY OF LOUDOUN COUNTY, VIRGINIA. BULLETIN; 1997 Annual. see *HISTORY—History Of North And South America*

920 CHN
HUAXIA MINGREN/CHINA'S FAMOUS PEOPLE. Text in Chinese. bi-m. USD 18.50.
Contact Dist.: China Books & Periodicals Inc TEL 415-282-2994.

920 USA ISSN 0899-1138
IMAGES OF EXCELLENCE. Text in English. 1986. bi-m. USD 6.
Published by: Images of Excellence Foundation, PO Box 1131, Boiling Springs, NC 28017. Ed. Robert Detjen.

920 DEU ISSN 1614-4449
▼ **IMAGO VITAE.** Text in German. 2004. irreg., latest vol.2, 2004. price varies. **Document type:** *Monographic series, Academic/Scholarly.*
Published by: Verlag Dr. Kovac, Arnoldstr 49, Hamburg, 22763, Germany. TEL 49-40-3988800, FAX 49-40-39888055, info@verlagdrkovac.de, http://www.verlagdrkovac.de/10-5.htm.

920 954 IND ISSN 0073-6244
INDIA WHO'S WHO. Text in English. 1969. a. USD 100 (effective 2000). adv. **Document type:** *Directory.* **Description:** Profiles of 5,000 influential men and women.
Indexed: RASB.
Published by: (India News and Feature Alliance), I N F A Publications, Jeevan Deep Bldg. Parliament St., New Delhi, 110 001, India. TEL 91-11-3733330, FAX 91-11-3746788. Ed. Mr. Inderjit. Pub. Poonam I Kaushik. Adv. contact Anand Kumar. Circ: 5,000.

920 IND
INDIAN BIOGRAPHY. Text in English. 1976-19??; resumed 1990. irreg. INR 25 (effective 2001). **Description:** Presents concise biographical notices of eminent people in South Asia and Indologists throughout the world.
Published by: Centre for Asian Dokumentation, K-15, CIT Bldg., Christopher Rd., Kolkata, West Bengal 700 014, India. TEL 2461185. Ed. S Chaudhuri. **Dist. by:** Punthi Pustak, 136 4B Bidhan Sarani, Calcutta, West Bengal 700 004, India.

509 IND
INDIAN NATIONAL SCIENCE ACADEMY. BIOGRAPHICAL MEMOIRS OF FELLOWS. Text in English. irreg. price varies. bibl.
Formerly: National Institute of Sciences of India. Biographical Memoirs of Fellows (0547-7557)
Published by: Indian National Science Academy, 1 Bahadur Shah Zafar Marg, New Delhi, 110 002, India. TEL 91-11-323-2066, FAX 91-11-3235648, TELEX 31-61835 INSA IN.

800 GBR ISSN 0143-8263
Z1010
INTERNATIONAL AUTHORS AND WRITERS WHO'S WHO. Text in English. 1934. a. (19th ed.), latest 2004. USD 240 per vol. (effective 2004). **Document type:** *Directory.* **Description:** Biographical profiles on leading authors, novelists, playwrights, journalists, editors, critics and columnists worldwide.
Formerly: Author's and Writer's Who's Who (0067-2386)
Indexed: CA&I.
Published by: Europa Publications Limited (Subsidiary of: Taylor & Francis Group), 11 New Fetter Ln, London, EC4P 4EE, United Kingdom. TEL 44-20-7822-4300, FAX 44-20-7842-4319, sales.europa@tandf.co.uk, http://www.europapublications.com. **Subsc. addr. in N. America:** Taylor & Francis Inc.; **Subscr. to:** Taylor & Francis Ltd. enquiry@tandf.co.uk.

INTERNATIONAL BIBLIOGRAPHY OF HISTORICAL SCIENCES. see *HISTORY—Abstracting, Bibliographies, Statistics*

920 200 DEU
INTERNATIONAL BIOGRAPHICAL DICTIONARY OF RELIGION; an encyclopedia of more than 4000 leading personalities. Text in English. a. USD 420 in North America (effective 2001). **Document type:** *Directory, Academic/Scholarly.* **Description:** Lists over 4,000 key religious leaders of the major religions of the world, including hierarchies from Christianity, Islam, Buddhism, Hinduism, Sikhism, Baha'i, Confucianism, Jainism, Shintoism, and Judaism. Theologians and other academics, spiritual leaders, administrators, pastors, priests, rabbis, imams, monks, and nuns are included.
Formerly: International Biographical Dictionary of the Religious World (Year)
Published by: (Union of International Associations/Union des Associations Internationales BEL), K.G. Saur Verlag GmbH (Subsidiary of: Gale Group), Ortlerstr 8, Munchen, 81373, Germany. TEL 49-89-76902-0, FAX 49-89-76902150, customerservice_saur@csi.com, http://www.saur.de. Eds. Cecile Vanden Bloock, Jon C Jenkins.

B

920 USA ISSN 1087-397X
CT120
INTERNATIONAL BOOK OF HONOR. Text in English. 1985. biennial. USD 150 (effective 2000). illus. **Document type:** *Directory.* **Description:** Recognizes outstanding men and women around the globe, an average of 100 countries.
Published by: American Biographical Institute, Inc., Governing Board of Editors, 5126 Bur Oak Circle, Box 31226, Raleigh, NC 27622. TEL 919-781-8710, FAX 919-781-8712.

012 USA ISSN 1087-3988
CT120
INTERNATIONAL DIRECTORY OF DISTINGUISHED LEADERSHIP. Text in English. 1968. a. USD 150 (effective 2002). **Document type:** *Directory, Trade.* **Description:** Contains a list of distinguished community leaders.
Former titles (until 1986): Community Leaders of America (0741-4161); Community Leaders and Noteworthy Americans (0094-5587)
Published by: American Biographical Institute, Inc., Governing Board of Editors, 5126 Bur Oak Circle, Box 31226, Raleigh, NC 27622. TEL 919-781-8710, FAX 919-781-8712. Ed., Pub. Janet M Evans. Circ: 5,000.

920 020 USA
INTERNATIONAL DIRECTORY OF SERIALS SPECIALISTS. Text in English. 1995. irreg. USD 69.95 (effective 2001). **Document type:** *Directory, Trade.*
Published by: Haworth Press, Inc., 10 Alice St, Binghamton, NY 13904-1580. TEL 607-722-5857, 800-429-6784, FAX 607-722-1424, getinfo@haworthpressinc.com, getinfo@haworthpress.com, http://www.haworthpress.com. Ed. Jean Whiffin. Pub. William Cohen. R&P Ruth Ann Heath TEL 607-722-5857 ext 316. Adv. contact Rebecca Miller-Baum TEL 607-722-5857 ext 337.

920 GBR ISSN 0074-9613
CT120
INTERNATIONAL WHO'S WHO (YEAR). Text in English. 1935. a., latest 2005, 68th Ed. GBP 310 per vol. includes online access (effective 2005). 2040 p./no.; **Document type:** *Directory.* **Description:** Covers the world's leading men and women, both the famous and the less well known. Biographical information about important figures from a wide variety of fields. Each entry gives nationality, date and place of birth, education, career details, present position, honours, awards, publications, current address, and, wherever possible, personal interests.
Related titles: CD-ROM ed.: free with subscr. to print edition.; Online - full text ed.
Indexed: CA&I, RASB.
—BLDSC (4552.100000), CISTI. **CCC.**
Published by: Europa Publications Limited (Subsidiary of: Taylor & Francis Group), 11 New Fetter Ln, London, EC4P 4EE, United Kingdom. TEL 44-20-7822-4300, FAX 44-20-7842-2249, 44-20-7842-4319, sales.europa@tandf.co.uk, http://www.europapublications.com. Ed. Elizabeth Sleeman. Circ: 5,500.

▼ new title ➤ refereed ✶ unverified ♦ full entry avail.

520 GBR
PS324
INTERNATIONAL WHO'S WHO IN POETRY AND POETS' ENCYCLOPAEDIA. Text in English. 1957. biennial. GBP 105, USD 180 per vol. (effective 2001). **Document type:** *Directory.* **Description:** Biographies and bibliographies of approximately 4,000 established and emerging poets from around the world.
Formerly: International Who's Who in Poetry (0539-1342)
Published by: Melrose Press Ltd., St Thomas Pl, Ely, Cambs CB7 4GG, United Kingdom. TEL 44-1353-646600, FAX 44-1353-646601, tradesales@melrosepress.co.uk, http://www.melrosepress.co.uk. Eds. David Cummings, Dennis McIntire. Pub. Nicholas Law. **Dist. in US by:** Taylor & Francis Inc., 7625 Empire Dr., Florence, KY 41042-2919. cserve@routledge-ny.com.

920 USA ISSN 1073-9734
CT120
INTERNATIONAL WHO'S WHO OF CONTEMPORARY ACHIEVEMENT. Text in English. 1989. biennial. USD 95 (effective 2000). **Document type:** *Directory.* **Description:** Focuses on prevailing achievements. Includes accomplished men and women of all ages, cultures, geographical locations, and professions.
Published by: American Biographical Institute, Inc., Governing Board of Editors, 5126 Bur Oak Circle, Box 31226, Raleigh, NC 27622. TEL 919-781-8710, FAX 919-781-8712.

B

920 GBR
INTERNATIONAL WHO'S WHO OF INTELLECTUALS. Text in English. 1978. biennial. GBP 175, USD 295 (effective 2000). back issues avail. **Document type:** *Directory.* **Description:** Contains essays detailing the lives and achievements of approximately 1,500 men and women.
Published by: Melrose Press Ltd., St Thomas Pl, Ely, Cambs CB7 4GG, United Kingdom. TEL 44-1353-721091, FAX 44-1353-721839, tradesales@melrosepress.co.uk. Ed. Jon Gifford. Pub. Nicholas Law. **Dist. in US by:** Taylor & Francis Inc., 7625 Empire Dr., Florence, KY 41042-2919. cserve@routledge-ny.com.

920 USA ISSN 0959-1680
HD6054
INTERNATIONAL WHO'S WHO OF PROFESSIONAL AND BUSINESS WOMEN. Text in English. 1989. biennial. USD 110 (effective 2000). **Document type:** *Directory.* **Description:** Contains a tribute to the women whose accomplishments serve as a model for other women as well as future generations.
Published by: American Biographical Institute, Inc., Governing Board of Editors, 5126 Bur Oak Circle, Box 31226, Raleigh, NC 27622. TEL 919-781-8710, FAX 919-781-8712.

INTERNATIONAL WHO'S WHO OF WOMEN (YEAR). see *WOMEN'S STUDIES*

320.9 GBR ISSN 0074-9621
JA51
INTERNATIONAL YEAR BOOK AND STATESMEN'S WHO'S WHO. Text in English. 1953. a. GBP 230 (effective 2002). 1400 p./no.; **Document type:** *Directory.* **Description:** Provides information on the structure and function of the world's major international and national organizations. Also contains career details of politicians - the attainments of leading diplomats, heads of state, judges, bankers, influential industrialists.
—CISTI.
Published by: Reed Business Information Ltd. (Subsidiary of: Reed Business), Windsor Ct., East Grinstead, W Sussex RH19 1XA, United Kingdom. TEL 44-1342-330100, FAX 44-1342-330195. Circ: 1,500.

INTERNATIONALE SCHOENBERG-GESELLSCHAFT. PUBLIKATIONEN. see *MUSIC*

920 DEU
INTERNATIONALES BIOGRAPHISCHES ARCHIV - PERSONEN AKTUELL. Text in German. 1913. w. adv. **Document type:** *Newsletter, Consumer.*
Formerly: Internationales Biographisches Archiv (0020-9457)
Published by: Munzinger Archiv GmbH, Albersfelder Str 34, Ravensburg, 88213, Germany. TEL 49-751-76931-0, FAX 49-751-652424, box@munzinger.de, http://www.munzinger.de. Ed. Dr. Ludwig Munzinger. adv.: B&W page EUR 600. Circ: 1,200 (controlled).

920 ESP ISSN 0329-3416
F2805
INTRAMUROS. Text in Spanish. 1995. s-a. EUR 13.52 domestic; USD 15 in Europe; USD 20 in the Americas (effective 2003). 40 p./no.; **Document type:** *Magazine, Consumer.* **Description:** Tends to construct a net to preserve the memorial patrimony of the linguistic community of those who feel and write in Spanish and to spread biographies and autobiographies.
Indexed: DAAI.
Published by: Maria Sheila Cremaschi, Ruiz de Alarcon 25, 8 Dcha, Madrid, 28014, Spain. TEL 34-91-4202060, FAX 34-91-4263869, editoramshc@grupointramuros.com. Ed. Beltran Gambier.

920 IRN
IRAN WHO'S WHO. Text in English. irreg. **Document type:** *Directory, Consumer.* **Description:** Includes biographies of famous Iranian personalities including government members, Majlis deputies, officials of organs and foundations, university professors and writers, artists and sport heroes, etc. It contains biographies on approximately 1,800 persons.
Address: No.4 Hourtab Alley, Hafez Ave, P O Box 14155-1168, Tehran, Iran. TEL 98-21-6468114, FAX 98-21-6464790.

011 JPN
J I C S T HOLDING LIST OF SERIALS: A LIST. (Japan Information Center for Science and Technology) Text in Japanese. triennial.
Formerly: J I C S T Holding List of Serials and Proceedings: A List
Published by: Japan Science and Technology Corporation, Information Center for Science and Technology/Kagaku Gijutsu Shinko Jigyodan, 5-3 Yonban-cho, Chiyoda-ku, Tokyo, 102-0081, Japan. TEL 81-3-5214-8413, FAX 81-3-5214-8410.

JAMES DICKEY NEWSLETTER. see *LITERATURE*

920 CHN ISSN 1005-3786
JINRI MINGLIU/CONTEMPORARY CELEBRITIES. Text in Chinese. 1994. m. CNY 8 newsstand/cover (effective 2005). **Document type:** *Magazine, Consumer.*
Related titles: Online - full text ed.: (from WanFang Data Corp.).
Address: Wuchang-qu, 417, Donghu Lu, Wuhan, 430077, China. TEL 86-27-86781962, FAX 86-27-86795479, jrmlb@public.wh.hb.cn, http://jrml.periodicals.net.cn/.

920 610 GBR ISSN 0967-7720
R134
➤ **JOURNAL OF MEDICAL BIOGRAPHY.** Text in English. 1993. q. GBP 61 in Europe to individuals; USD 110 in United States to individuals; GBP 65 elsewhere to individuals; GBP 111 in Europe to institutions; USD 197 in United States to institutions; GBP 115 elsewhere to institutions (effective 2005). **Document type:** *Journal, Academic/Scholarly.* **Description:** Aimed at a wide audience among both the medical and non-medical community, including clinicians, scientists, historians, archivists, librarians, and others with an interest in biographical aspects of medical history. It focuses on the lives of those in and associated with medicine and their significance in various contexts.
Related titles: Online - full text ed.: (from bigchalk, ProQuest Information & Learning).
Indexed: AmH&L, HistAb, IndMed, MEDLINE, RILM.
—BLDSC (5017.049000), GNLM, IE, Infotrieve, ingenta. **CCC.**
Published by: Royal Society of Medicine Press Ltd., 1 Wimpole St, London, W1M 8AE, United Kingdom. TEL 44-20-72902921, FAX 44-20-72902929, publishing@rsm.ac.uk, http://www.rsmpress.co.uk/jmb.htm, http://www.roysocmed.ac.uk. Ed. J M H Moll. R&P Caroline McLaughlin. **Subscr. addr.:** PO Box 9002, London W1A 0ZA, United Kingdom. TEL 44-20-7290-2927, 44-20-7290-2928, FAX 44-20-7290-2929, rsmjournals@rsm.ac.uk.

➤ **JOURNAL OF SEVENTEENTH CENTURY MUSIC.** see *MUSIC*

920 GBR
AS122
➤ **THE JOURNAL OF WILLIAM MORRIS STUDIES.** Text in English. 1961. 2/yr. USD 30 in United States to individual members (effective 2005); CND 40 in Canada to individual members; GBP 18 elsewhere to individual members (effective 2003). adv. bk.rev. back issues avail. **Document type:** *Journal, Academic/Scholarly.*
Formerly (until 200?): William Morris Society. Journal (0084-0254)
Indexed: BibInd, DAAI, IBRH, MLA-IB.
Published by: William Morris Society, Kelmscott House, 26 Upper Mall, London, W6 9TA, United Kingdom. TEL 44-20-87413735, FAX 44-20-87485207, uk@morrissociety.org, http://www.morrissociety.org/jwms.html. Ed. Rosie Miles. Circ: 2,200.

920 808.068 USA
JUNIOR AUTHORS AND ILLUSTRATORS SERIES. Text in English. 1951. q. USD 325 in US & Canada (effective 2006). illus. index. back issues avail. **Document type:** *Monographic series, Bibliography.* **Description:** Contains biographical sketches of outstanding creators of children's literature.
Related titles: Online - full content ed.
Published by: H.W. Wilson Co., 950 University Ave, Bronx, NY 10452-4224. TEL 718-588-8400, 800-367-6770, FAX 718-590-1617, 800-590-1617, custserv@hwwilson.com, http://www.hwwilson.com/print/jrauthorseries.htm. Ed. Sally Holmes Holtze.

KATERI; Lily of the Mohawks. see *RELIGIONS AND THEOLOGY—Roman Catholic*

920 GBR ISSN 0075-6083
KINGS OF TOMORROW SERIES. Text in English. 1967. irreg. price varies.
Published by: Monarchist Press Association, 7 Sutherland Rd, West Ealing, London, W13 0DX, United Kingdom. Circ: 3,500.

920 DEU ISSN 0454-1383
KOEPFE DES 20. JAHRHUNDERTS✶. Text in German. 1957. irreg. **Document type:** *Monographic series, Academic/Scholarly.*
Published by: Edition Colloquium, Gneisenaustr 33, Berlin, 10961, Germany. TEL 49-30-6917073, FAX 49-30-6914067, info@spiess-verlage.de, http://www.spiess-verlage.de/html/edition_colloquium.html. Circ: 3,000.

KOMPONISTEN UNSERER ZEIT. see *MUSIC*

920 DEU ISSN 1616-8399
KUERSCHNERS DEUTSCHER GELEHRTEN-KALENDER. Text in German. 2001. irreg. (in 3 vols.), latest vol.19, 2003. EUR 698 per vol. (effective 2005). **Document type:** *Directory, Bibliography.* **Description:** Presents biographical and bibliographical information on academics working at German-speaking universities and other scientific and scholarly institutions.
Formed by the merger of (1925-2001): Kuerschners Deutscher Gelehrten-Kalender. Geistes- und Sozialwissenschaften (1433-9161); (1925-2001): Kuerschners Deutscher Gelehrten-Kalender. Medizin, Naturwissenschaften, Technik (1433-917X); Both of which superseded in part (in 1991): Kuerschners Deutscher Gelehrten-Kalender (0341-8049)
Published by: K.G. Saur Verlag GmbH (Subsidiary of: Gale Group), Ortlerstr 8, Munchen, 81373, Germany. TEL 49-89-769020, FAX 49-89-76902150, info@saur.de, http://www.saur.de.

KUERSCHNERS DEUTSCHER LITERATUR-KALENDER. see *BIBLIOGRAPHIES*

920 DEU
KUERSCHNERS DEUTSCHER MUSIK-KALENDER. Text in German. irreg., latest vol.4, 2004. EUR 248 per vol. (effective 2004). **Document type:** *Directory, Bibliography.* **Description:** Contains information on over 12,000 living, creative music professionals from the world of serious music, who work predominantly within the German-language area.
Published by: K.G. Saur Verlag GmbH (Subsidiary of: Gale Group), Ortlerstr 8, Munchen, 81373, Germany. TEL 49-89-769020, FAX 49-89-76902150, info@saur.de, http://www.saur.de.

920 DEU
KUERSCHNERS DEUTSCHER SACHBUCH-KALENDER. Text in German. 2001. biennial, latest vol.2, 2003. EUR 298 per vol. (effective 2004). **Document type:** *Directory, Bibliography.* **Description:** Contains biographical entries on over 8,500 German-speaking authors of non-fiction with bibliographic references to some 86,000 publications.
Published by: K.G. Saur Verlag GmbH (Subsidiary of: Gale Group), Ortlerstr 8, Munchen, 81373, Germany. TEL 49-89-769020, FAX 49-89-76902150, info@saur.de, http://www.saur.de.

920 FIN ISSN 1237-7570
CT1220
KUKA KUKIN ON/WHO'S WHO IN FINLAND. Text in Finnish. 1909. biennial. **Document type:** *Directory.*
Related titles: CD-ROM ed.: 1998. FIM 1,000 (effective 2001).
Published by: Kustannusosakeyhtio Otava/Otava Publishing Company, Uudenmaankatu 10, Helsinki, 00120, Finland. TEL 358-9-19961, FAX 368-9-1996477, http://www.otava.fi. Ed. Risto Rantala. Circ: 5,000.

920 980 NLD ISSN 1384-5799
LATINOAMERICANISTAS EN EUROPA (YEAR); registro bio-bibliografico. Text in Spanish. 1995 (7th ed.). irreg., latest 7th ed. EUR 40, USD 40 per issue (effective 2004). **Document type:** *Directory, Academic/Scholarly.* **Description:** Contains biographical and bibliographical information on some 500 researchers in Latin American studies (social sciences and humanities) who are resident in Europe.
Indexed: PAIS, PSA, SOPODA, SSA, SociolAb.
Published by: Centrum voor Studie en Documentatie van Latijns Amerika/Center for Latin American Research and Documentation - Centro de Estudios y Documentacion Latinoamericanos, Keizersgracht 395-397, Amsterdam, 1016 EK, Netherlands. TEL 31-20-525-3498, FAX 31-20-625-5127, CEDLApublications@cedla.uva.nl.

LEAD BELLY LETTER; to appreciate and celebrate Lead Belly music. see *MUSIC*

920 943 DEU
LEBENSBILDER AUS BADEN-WUERTTEMBERG. Text in German. 1940. irreg. EUR 28.50 per vol. (effective 2003). **Document type:** *Monographic series, Academic/Scholarly.* **Description:** Essays on important men and women in the history of ancient Bade and Wuerttemberg.
Formerly: Lebensbilder aus Schwaben und Franken
Published by: Kommission fuer geschichtliche Landeskunde in Baden-Wuerttemberg, Eugenstr 7, Stuttgart, 70182, Germany. TEL 49-711-212-4266, FAX 49-711-212-4269, poststelle@kommission.belwue.de. Eds. Gerhard Taddey, Joachim Fischer.

LEITENDE MAENNER UND FRAUEN DER WIRTSCHAFT. see *BUSINESS AND ECONOMICS—Management*

920 800 100 530 DEU ISSN 0936-4242
B2681.L44
LICHTENBERG-JAHRBUCH. Text in German. 1979. a. adv. bk.rev. bibl.; illus. back issues avail. **Document type:** *Academic/Scholarly.*
Formerly: Photorin (0172-0015)
Indexed: DIP, IBR, IBZ, PhilInd.
Published by: (Lichtenberg-Gesellschaft e.V.), Saarbruecker Druckerei und Verlag GmbH, Halbergstr 3, Saarbruecken, 66121, Germany. TEL 49-681-66501-0, FAX 49-681-6650110. Circ: 500.

LINCOLN MEMORIAL ASSOCIATION NEWSLETTER. see *HISTORY—History Of North And South America*

920 895.1 CHN ISSN 1003-0638
➤ **LU XUN YANJIU YUEKAN/LU XUN STUDIES MONTHLY.** Text in Chinese. 1984. m. USD 49.50; CNY 5 per issue (effective 2003). adv. bk.rev. **Document type:** *Academic/Scholarly.*
Related titles: Online - full text ed.: (from East View Information Services).
Published by: Beijing Lu Xun Bowuguan, Beijing, 100034, China. TEL 86-1-66165648, FAX 86-1-66165647, lxyjyk@vip.sina.com. Eds. Qiaosheng Huang, Sun Yu. R&P, Adv. contact Qiaosheng Huang. Circ: 2,000. **Dist. in US by:** China Books & Periodicals Inc, 360 Swift Ave., Ste. 48, S San Fran, CA 94080-6220. TEL 415-282-2994.

➤ **MABUA/FOUNTAIN**; religious creation in literature, society and thought. see *LITERATURE*

015 IND
MADHYA PRADESH WHO'S WHO. Text in English. 1978. a. INR 30.
Published by: New Era Publication, S.N.6 Char Bungalow Rd., Professor Colony, Bhopal, Madhya Pradesh 462 001, India.

340 USA
MARTINDALE-HUBBELL PREMIER ACCOUNT NEWS. Text in English. 1992. 4/yr. free to qualified personnel. **Document type:** *Consumer.*
Published by: Martindale-Hubbell (Subsidiary of: LexisNexis North America), 121 Chanlon Rd, New Providence, NJ 07974. TEL 800-526-4902, FAX 908-464-3553, info@martindale.com, http://www.martindale.com.

012 USA
MEN AND WOMEN OF HAWAII✶. Variant title: Who's Who in Hawaii. Text in English. 1918. irreg., latest 1972. USD 25.
Published by: S B Printers, Inc., PO Box 100, Honolulu, HI 96810-0100. TEL 808-537-5353. Ed. Betty Buker. Circ: 3,000.

920 USA ISSN 1098-3171
CT120
MILLENNIUM HALL OF FAME. Text in English. 1998. a. USD 295 (effective 2000). illus. **Document type:** *Directory.* **Description:** Features men and women who have achieved greatness during the twentieth century.
Published by: American Biographical Institute, Inc., Governing Board of Editors, 5126 Bur Oak Circle, Box 31226, Raleigh, NC 27622. TEL 919-781-8710, FAX 919-781-8712.

920 CHN ISSN 1002-6282
CT203.C5
MINGREN ZHUANJI. Text in Chinese. 1985. m. CNY 36 (effective 1994). adv. **Document type:** *Bibliography.* **Description:** Provides literary biographies of great names in all times all over the world.
Published by: Henan People's Publishing House, Mingren Zhuanji Editorial Department, No 73 Nongye Lu, Zhengzhou, Henan, 450002, China. TEL 5951756, FAX 544757. Ed. Deng Zhigang. Adv. contact Ruixiang Song. page CNY 10,000. Circ: 190,000. **Dist. overseas by:** China International Book Trading Corp, 35 Chegongzhuang Xilu, Haidian District, PO Box 399, Beijing 100044, China.

920.02 USA ISSN 1073-788X
CT120
MOST ADMIRED MEN AND WOMEN OF THE YEAR. Text in English. 1993. a. USD 95 (effective 2000). **Document type:** *Directory.* **Description:** Covers the results of the institute's voting.
Published by: American Biographical Institute, Inc., Governing Board of Editors, 5126 Bur Oak Circle, Box 31226, Raleigh, NC 27622. TEL 919-781-8710, FAX 919-781-8712.

920 USA ISSN 0077-2933
CODEN: BMNSAC
NATIONAL ACADEMY OF SCIENCES. BIOGRAPHICAL MEMOIRS. Text in English. 1953. irreg. price varies. adv. **Document type:** *Monographic series.*
Indexed: BIOSIS Prev, BiolAb, RASB.
—CASDDS, CISTI, Linda Hall. **CCC.**
Published by: (National Academy of Sciences), National Academy Press, 2101 Constitution Ave, N W, Lockbox 285, Washington, DC 20055. TEL 202-334-3335, 202-334-3313, 888-624-8373, FAX 202-334-2451. Ed. Stephen Mauter. R&P Dick Morris. Adv. contact Mona Neff.

920 USA ISSN 0077-5371
NATIONAL REGISTER OF PROMINENT AMERICANS AND INTERNATIONAL NOTABLES. Text in English. 1966. biennial. USD 125 (effective 2001). bk.rev. reprint service avail. from PQC.
Related titles: Microform ed.: (from PQC).
Indexed: ChemAb, ChemTitl.
Published by: National Register of Prominent Americans, Drawer 1375, Washington, DC 20013-1375. Ed. William Smith.

NEW YORK GENEALOGICAL AND BIOGRAPHICAL RECORD. see *GENEALOGY AND HERALDRY*

920 USA ISSN 0161-2433
CT120
THE NEW YORK TIMES BIOGRAPHICAL SERVICE. Text in English. 1969. m. looseleaf. index. **Document type:** *Bibliography.*
Formerly: New York Times Biographical Edition (0048-0088)
Indexed: CA&I, RILM.
Published by: (New York Times Company), ProQuest Information & Learning, 300 N Zeeb Rd., PO Box 1346, Ann Arbor, MI 48106-1346. TEL 313-761-4700, 800-521-0600, FAX 800-864-0019. Circ: 750.

NEW ZEALAND BUSINESS WHO'S WHO. see *BUSINESS AND ECONOMICS—Trade And Industrial Directories*

920 USA ISSN 0028-9396
NEWSBOY. Text in English. 1962. 6/yr. USD 25 domestic; USD 30 foreign; USD 3 newsstand/cover (effective 1999). adv. bk.rev. back issues avail. **Document type:** *Newsletter.*
Formerly: Horatio Alger Newsboy (0018-4918)
Indexed: MLA, MLA-IB.
Published by: Horatio Alger Society, 23726 N Overhill Dr, Lake Zurich, IL 60047-8044. TEL 847-726-8946, rkasper@hotmail.com, http://www.ihot.com/~has/. Ed., Pub., R&P William R Gowen. Adv. contact William Gowen. B&W page USD 32. Circ: 230 (paid); 20 (controlled). **Subscr. to:** P O Box 70361, Richmond, VA 23255.

920 USA ISSN 0899-0417
CT120
NEWSMAKERS; the people behind today's headlines. Text in English. 1990. 3/yr. (plus a. cumulation). USD 180 (effective 2004). illus. Index. back issues avail.; reprints avail. **Description:** Contains biographical facts on about 50 prominent personalities in each issue.
Formerly (until 1988): Contemporary Newsmakers (0883-1564)
Related titles: Diskette ed.; Magnetic Tape ed.
Published by: Gale Group (Subsidiary of: Thomson Corporation), 27500 Drake Rd, Farmington Hills, MI 48331-3535. TEL 248-699-8061, FAX 248-699-4253, galeord@gale.com, http://www.gale.com. Ed. Louise Mooney.

NORTH KOREA DIRECTORY (YEAR); comprehensive guide to North Korean organizations and leadership. see *PUBLIC ADMINISTRATION*

NOTABLE HISPANIC AMERICAN WOMEN. see *WOMEN'S STUDIES*

NOUVELLE BIBLIOTHEQUE NERVALIENNE. see *LITERATURE*

OFFICIAL A B M S DIRECTORY OF BOARD CERTIFIED MEDICAL SPECIALISTS. see *MEDICAL SCIENCES*

791.450 369 USA
THE OFFICIAL MCCALLUM OBSERVER PRINT JOURNAL. Text in English. 1985 (Oct.). q. USD 12 in US & Canada membership; USD 14 elsewhere membership (effective 2004). adv. bk.rev.; film rev.; play rev.; rec.rev.; tel.rev.; video rev. 28 p./no.; back issues avail. **Document type:** *Journal, Consumer.* **Description:** Publication devoted to the acting career of David McCallum (aka Illya Kuryakin & Dr. Ducky Mallard).
Former titles: The Official McCallum Observer; (until 1999): McCallum Observer (1083-2327)
Related titles: Online - full text ed.
Published by: Official McCallum Observer Print Journal, PO Box 313, Lansing, IL 60438-0313. TEL 708-895-0736, davidmccallum@fan.com, http://www.davidmccallum.org. Ed., R&P L S Mendoza. Circ: 200.

920.4 976 USA
OKLAHOMA WESTERN BIOGRAPHIES. Text in English. 1988. irreg. price varies. **Document type:** *Academic/Scholarly.*
Published by: University of Oklahoma Press, 1005 Asp Ave, Norman, OK 73019. TEL 405-325-2000, FAX 405-364-5798.

OLD NEWS. see *HISTORY*

920 USA
PENGUIN LIVES. Text in English. irreg. price varies. **Document type:** *Monographic series.*
Indexed: MLA-IB.
Published by: Penguin Books U S A, Inc., 375 Hudson St, New York, NY 10014. http://www.penguinputnam.com/static/packages/us/penguinlives/. **Dist. by:** Penguin Group (USA) Inc, 405 Murray Hill Pkwy, East Rutherford, NJ 07073-2136. TEL 800-788-6262, FAX 201-256-0017, 800-227-9604.

PENNSYLVANIA MAGAZINE OF HISTORY AND BIOGRAPHY. see *HISTORY—History Of North And South America*

920 GBR ISSN 0079-0729
PEOPLE FROM THE PAST SERIES. Text in English. 1964. irreg., latest vol.15, 1977. GBP 4.95. **Document type:** *Monographic series.*
Published by: Dennis Dobson Books Ltd., 80 Kensington Church St, London, W8 4BY, United Kingdom. Ed. Egon Larsen.

920 USA
PEOPLE PROFILES. Text in English. 1999. m. USD 4.99 newsstand/cover. back issues avail. **Document type:** *Consumer.* **Description:** Each volume profiles a well-known celebrity in detail.
Published by: Time, Inc (Subsidiary of: Time Warner, Inc.), Time & Life Bldg,, Rockefeller Center, 29th Fl, 1271 Ave of the Americas, New York, NY 10020-1393. TEL 212-522-1212, http://www.pathfinder.com/people/web/profiles.html.

920 ARG
PERFILES CONTEMPORANEOS. Text in Spanish. 1976 (no.2). irreg.
Published by: Editorial Plus Ultra, Avda. Callao, 575, Capital Federal, Buenos Aires 1022, Argentina. Ed. Jose Isaacson.

920 981 BRA
PERFIS PARLAMENTARES. Text in Portuguese. 1967. irreg., latest vol.44, 1997. BRL 10 domestic; USD 8 foreign (effective 1998). **Document type:** *Government.* **Description:** Each monograph includes biographical data concerned with the parliamentary life of a respected deputy.
Published by: Camara dos Deputados, Coordenacao de Publicacoes, Brasilia, DF, Brazil. TEL 55-61-3186865, FAX 55-61-3182190, publicacoes@cedi.camara.gov.br, http://www.camara.gov.br. Ed., R&P Nelda Mendonca Raulino.

PERSONALHISTORISK TIDSSKRIFT. see *GENEALOGY AND HERALDRY*

920 DOM
PERSONALIDADES DOMINICANAS. Text in Spanish. a.
Published by: Molina Morillo y Asociados, c/o Editora de Colores, Arroyo Hondo, C Juan Tomas Mejia y Cotes 8, Santo Domingo, Dominican Republic. TEL 767-567-3214.

929 SWE ISSN 0031-5699
CT1310
➤ **PERSONHISTORISK TIDSKRIFT.** Text in Swedish. 1879. s-a. SEK 180 in Scandinavia; SEK 200 in Europe; SEK 220 elsewhere (effective 2003). bk.rev. charts; illus. index. 100 p./no.; back issues avail. **Document type:** *Journal, Academic/Scholarly.* **Description:** Constitutes an important tool for biographical research, especially concerning Sweden from 1200 AD to the present.
Formerly (until 1898): Svenska Autografsaellskapets Tidskrift
Indexed: ABM, AmH&L, HistAb, MLA, MLA-IB, RASB.
Published by: Personhistoriska Samfundet/Swedish Society for Personal History, c/o Irma Ridbaeck, Riksarkivet, PO Box 12541, Stockholm, 10229, Sweden. TEL 46-8-7376378, FAX 46-8-7376374, irma.ridbeck@riksarkivet.ra.se, http://www.ra.se/PHS/. Ed. Olof Haegerstrand. Circ: 500.

920 PER
PERU REPORT'S GUIDE TO TOP PEOPLE IN PERU; quien es quien?. Text in Spanish. 1992. irreg., latest 1997. USD 65. adv. **Description:** Guide to the top professionals in 70 areas.
Published by: Peru Reporting E.I.R.L., Francisco Grana, 319, Magdalena, Lima 17, Peru. TEL 5114-617416, FAX 5114-634466, postmast@perurep.com.pe. Ed. Jonathan Cavanagh. Circ: 1,500 (paid).

PLANTAGENET PRODUCTIONS; libraries of spoken word recordings, of stagescripts, and of family papers. see *LITERATURE*

POPE JOHN PAUL II CENTER NEWSLETTER. see *RELIGIONS AND THEOLOGY—Roman Catholic*

PROFILES OF WORLDWIDE GOVERNMENT LEADERS. see *POLITICAL SCIENCE*

920 USA ISSN 0898-9745
E872
THE REAL CALVIN COOLIDGE. Text in English. 1983. a. USD 2.95 to non-members; free to members. bk.rev. back issues avail. **Document type:** *Newsletter.* **Description:** Articles of original Coolidge research of interest to Coolidge buffs, researchers, and historians.
Published by: Calvin Coolidge Memorial Foundation, Inc., PO Box 97, Plymouth, VT 05056. TEL 802-672-3389. Ed. Robert H Ferrell. Circ: 700.

920 USA ISSN 1040-9335
REAL PEOPLE. Text in English. 1988. bi-m. USD 24 (effective 1999). adv. bk.rev. illus. **Document type:** *Consumer.* **Description:** Covers celebrities and other interesting people.
Formerly (until 1988): Family Digest (0894-5586)

B

Published by: Main Street Publishing Co., Inc., 450 Fashion Ave, Ste 1701, New York, NY 10123-1799. TEL 212-244-2351, FAX 212-244-2367. Ed. Alex Polner. Pub., R&P Suzanne Hochman. Adv. contact Bob Millar. Circ: 100,000. **Subscr. to:** PO Box 7851, Red Oak, IA 51591-0581.

RELIGIOUS LEADERS OF AMERICA. see *RELIGIONS AND THEOLOGY*

920 951   CHN
RENMIN/PEOPLE. Text in Chinese. 1980. bi-m. CNY 2.40. bk.rev. index. back issues avail. **Description:** Introduces Chinese and other personalities in modern history.
Published by: Renmin Chubanshe, Qikan Bu/People's Publishing House, 166 Chaonei Dajie, Beijing, 100706, China. TEL 55-0415. Ed. Wu Chengwan. Circ: 70,000.

920   CHN   ISSN 1001-6635
DS778.A1
RENWU. Text in Chinese; Contents page in English. bi-m. CNY 1.80, USD 33.80. **Description:** Contains biographies and reminiscences of Chinese and other personalities in modern history.
Indexed: RASB.
Published by: Renmin Chubanshe, Qikan Bu/People's Publishing House, 166 Chaonei Dajie, Beijing, 100706, China. TEL 55-0415. Ed. Wu Chengwan. **Dist. in US by:** China Books & Periodicals Inc, 360 Swift Ave., Ste. 48, S San Fran, CA 94080-6220. TEL 415-282-2994; **Dist. outside China by:** China International Book Trading Corp, 35 Chegongzhuang Xilu, Haidian District, PO Box 399, Beijing 100044, China. TEL 86-10-68412045, FAX 86-10-68412023, cibtc@mail.cibtc.com.cn, http://www.cibtc.com.cn.

920 362.4   USA
RESOURCE DIRECTORY OF SCIENTISTS AND ENGINEERS WITH DISABILITIES. Text in English. 1982. irreg., latest vol.3, 1995. USD 20. **Description:** Source of role models for disabled youth and mid-career scientists and engineers. Lists 950 scientists and engineers with an address, phone number, discipline and degree(s), position, nature of and age of disability.
Published by: (Project on Science, Technology and Disability), American Association for the Advancement of Science, 1200 New York Ave, NW, Washington, DC 20005. TEL 202-326-6649, FAX 202-371-9849, 1summers@aaas.org. Eds. Laureen Summers, Virginia W Stern.

920 943   DEU   ISSN 0080-2670
RHEINISCHE LEBENSBILDER. Text in German. 1961. irreg., latest vol.18, 1999. price varies. **Document type:** *Monographic series, Academic/Scholarly.*
Published by: (Gesellschaft fuer Rheinische Geschichtskunde), Rheinland Verlag GmbH, Abtei Brauweiler, Postfach 2140, Pulheim, 50250, Germany. TEL 49-2234-9854265, FAX 49-2234-82503. **Dist. by:** Dr. Rudolf Habelt GmbH, Am Buchenhang 1, Bonn 53115, Germany. TEL 49-228-9238322, FAX 49-228-232017.

RICHARD STRAUSS BLAETTER; neue Folge. see *MUSIC*

RICHARD WAGNER BLAETTER. see *MUSIC*

RIVISTA DALMATICA. see *HISTORY—History Of Europe*

ROMANSERIER OG SELVBIOGRAFISKE SERIER. see *LITERATURE*

920   RUS
ROSSIISKII KTO EST' KTO. Text in Russian. q. USD 85 in United States.
Published by: Russkii Biograficheskii Institut, Ul Baumanskaya 43-1, ofis 627, Moscow, 107005, Russian Federation. TEL 7-095-2076574. **US dist. addr.:** East View Information Services, 3020 Harbor Ln. N., Minneapolis, MN 55447. TEL 612-550-0961. **Co-sponsor:** Natsional'noe Agentsvo Delovoi i Politicheskoi Informatsii.

920   USA
ROYAL BOOK NEWS. Text in English. 1984. bi-m. USD 25 (effective 2004). adv. bk.rev. back issues avail. **Document type:** *Newsletter, Consumer.* **Description:** News and reviews of books on British and European royalty from the U.S. and around the world.
Published by: Marlene Koenig Royal Book News, 5590 Jowett Ct, Alexandria, VA 22315-5542. TEL 703-313-0160, marlenekoenig@aol.com. Ed., Pub. Marlene Koenig.

920 500   GBR   ISSN 0080-4606
Q41   CODEN: BMFRA3
ROYAL SOCIETY OF LONDON. BIOGRAPHICAL MEMOIRS OF FELLOWS OF THE ROYAL SOCIETY. Text in English. 1932. a. GBP 130 per vol. in Europe; GBP 135 per vol. in US & Canada (effective 2003). bibl.; illus. index. back issues avail.; reprint service avail. from ISI. **Document type:** *Academic/Scholarly.*
Supersedes (in 1954): Obituary Notices of Fellows of the Royal Society (1479-571X)
Related titles: Online - full text ed.: (from JSTOR (Web-based Journal Archive)).

—BLDSC (2072.300000), CASDDS, CISTI, GNLM, IE, Infotrieve, ingenta. **CCC.**
Published by: Royal Society of London, 6-9 Carlton House Terr, London, SW1Y 5AG, United Kingdom. TEL 44-207-8395561, FAX 44-207-9761837, sales@royalsoc.ac.uk, jackie.knapp@royalsoc.ac.uk, http://www.pubs.royalsoc.ac.uk, http://www.royalsoc.ac.uk. Ed. John Enderby, FRS. R&P Charles Lusty. Circ: 1,343.

920   DEU   ISSN 0945-9960
SCHMITTIANA; Beitraege zu Leben und Werk Carl Schmitts. Text in German. 1988. irreg., latest vol.8, 2003. price varies. **Document type:** *Monographic series, Academic/Scholarly.*
Published by: Duncker und Humblot GmbH, Carl-Heinrich-Becker-Weg 9, Berlin, 12165, Germany. TEL 49-30-7900060, FAX 49-30-79000631, info@duncker-humblot.de, http://www.duncker-humblot.de.

920 780   DEU
SCHUBERT DURCH DIE BRILLE. Text in German, English. 1991. s-a. **Document type:** *Journal, Academic/Scholarly.*
Indexed: RILM.
Published by: (Internationales Franz Schubert Institut), Verlag Dr. Hans Schneider GmbH, Mozartstr 6, Tutzing, 82323, Germany. TEL 08158-3050, FAX 08158-7636.

SEVENTEENTH CENTURY MUSIC. see *MUSIC*

SLOWNIK BIOGRAFICZNY POLSKICH NAUK MEDYCZNYCH XX WIEKU. see *MEDICAL SCIENCES*

SOLDIERS OF THE QUEEN. see *MILITARY*

SOMETHING ABOUT THE AUTHOR. see *LITERATURE*

SOUTHWESTERN STUDIES. MONOGRAPHS. see *HISTORY—History Of North And South America*

920 914.706   USA
SOVIET BIOGRAPHICAL SERVICE. Text in English. 1985. q. looseleaf. USD 100 (effective 2001). index. **Document type:** *Academic/Scholarly.* **Description:** Provides biographies of leaders in the former Soviet republics.
Published by: J.L. Scherer, Ed. & Pub., 4900 18th Ave S, Minneapolis, MN 55417. TEL 612-722-1947.

778.53   ITA
STELLE FILANTI. Text in Italian. 1978. irreg.
Published by: Gremese Editore S.r.l., Via Virginia Agnelli, 88, Rome, RM 00151, Italy. Eds. Claudio G Fava, Orio Caldiron.

920   DEU
STERN SPEZIAL BIOGRAFIE. Text in German. 2002. 2/yr. **Document type:** *Magazine, Consumer.* **Description:** Contains biographies on a wide variety of famous, important and interesting people.
Published by: Gruner und Jahr AG & Co., Am Baumwall 11, Hamburg, 20459, Germany. TEL 49-40-3703-0, FAX 49-40-37036000, ksc@guj.de, http://www.guj.de. Circ: 230,000 (controlled).

STOVALL JOURNAL. see *GENEALOGY AND HERALDRY*

920 780   ITA   ISSN 1594-0012
ML410.V82
STUDI VIVALDIANI. Text in English, French, German, Italian; Summaries in English, Italian. 1980. a. bk.rev. illus. **Document type:** *Bulletin.*
Formerly (until 2001): Informazioni e Studi Vivaldiani (0393-2915)
Indexed: IIMP, MusicInd, RILM.
—BLDSC (4496.957000).
Published by: (Istituto Italiano Antonio Vivaldi), B M G Ricordi SpA, Via Giovanni Berchet, 2, Milan, MI 20121, Italy. TEL 39-02-88811, FAX 39-02-88814288, TELEX 325217 RICOR I. Ed. Francesco Fanna. Circ: 1,300.

SUOMEN SUKUTUTKIMUSSEURA. JULKAISUJA/ GENEALOGISKA SAMFUNDET I FINLAND. SKRIFTER. see *HISTORY—History Of Europe*

SUZI DEVERAUX INTERNATIONAL FAN CLUB. see *MUSIC*

SVERIGES FOERFATTARFOERBUND. MEDLEMSFOERTECKNING/SWEDISH WRITERS UNION. MEMBERSHIP ROLL. see *LITERATURE*

920   SWE
SWEDEN. RIKSMARSKALKSAAMBETET. KUNGLIGA HOVSTATERNA✱ . Text in Swedish. a.
Published by: (Riksmarskalksaambetet), A W I International AB, PO Box 4627, Stockholm, 11691, Sweden. TEL 46-8-7282500, FAX 46-8-338707.

920   CHE
SWISS BIOGRAPHICAL INDEX OF PROMINENT PERSONS/ANNUAIRE SUISSE DU MONDE ET DES AFFAIRES/CHI E CHI IN SVIZZERA?/WER IST WER IN DER SCHWEIZ UND IM FUERSTENSTUM LIECHTENSTEIN?. Text in German, English, French. 1972. biennial. CHF 220, USD 150 (effective 2001). adv. **Document type:** *Directory, Consumer.*
Published by: Editions Who's Who International S.A., 23 Chemin du Levant, Lausanne, 1005, Switzerland. TEL 41-21-3114470, FAX 41-21-3114470, http://www.who-s-who.com. Ed. Louis Marc Servien. Circ: 3,000.

920   POL   ISSN 1230-4328
SYLWETKI LODZKICH UCZONYCH. Text in Polish. 1992. 5/yr., latest vol.62. USD 9 (effective 2000). **Document type:** *Bulletin.*
Published by: Lodzkie Towarzystwo Naukowe/Lodz Scientific Society, ul. M. Sklodowskiej-Curie 11, Lodz, 90-505, Poland. TEL 48-42-6361026, FAX 48-42-6361995. Ed. Edward Karasinski. **Dist. by:** Ars Polona, Krakowskie Przedmiescie 7, Warsaw, Poland.

820 920   USA   ISSN 1054-514X
T E NOTES. Variant title: Thomas Edward Lawrence Notes. Text in English. 1990. s-a. USD 20 domestic; USD 25 foreign (effective 2003). back issues avail. **Document type:** *Newsletter.* **Description:** Publishes articles covering all periods of Lawrence's life.
Indexed: MLA-IB.
Address: 17 Shadow Rd, Melrose, MA 02176-5109. TENotes@aol.com, http://www.denismcd.com/tenotes.htm. Eds. Elaine Steblecki, Suellen J Miller. Pub. Denis McDonnell.

THE TEXAS GULF HISTORICAL & BIOGRAPHICAL RECORD. see *HISTORY—History Of North And South America*

920 970   USA   ISSN 0161-8423
E757.2
THEODORE ROOSEVELT ASSOCIATION JOURNAL. Text in English. 1975. q. USD 35 (effective 2001). adv. bk.rev. bibl.; illus. **Document type:** *Journal, Academic/Scholarly.* **Description:** Contains historical articles and reviews on the life and works of Theodore Roosevelt.
Indexed: ABS&EES, AmH&L, HistAb.
Published by: Theodore Roosevelt Association, PO Box 719, Oyster Bay, NY 11771. TEL 516-921-6319, FAX 516-921-6481, http://www.theodoreroosevelt.org. Ed. John A Gable. Circ: 2,100 (paid).

TONIC. see *MUSIC*

TOP MANAGEMENT & FINANCE LUXEMBOURG. see *BUSINESS AND ECONOMICS—Management*

TOP MANAGEMENT BELGIUM. see *BUSINESS AND ECONOMICS—Management*

TOP MANAGEMENT FRANCE. see *BUSINESS AND ECONOMICS—Management*

TWAYNE'S UNITED STATES AUTHORS SERIES. see *LITERATURE*

920   USA
TWO THOUSAND NOTABLE AMERICAN MEN. Text in English. 1992. a. USD 150 (effective 2000). **Document type:** *Directory.* **Description:** Includes men who have demonstrated professional skills and advancements in addition to outstanding community service.
Published by: American Biographical Institute, Inc., Governing Board of Editors, 5126 Bur Oak Circle, Box 31226, Raleigh, NC 27622. TEL 919-781-8710, FAX 919-781-8712.

920   USA   ISSN 1087-3961
CT3235
TWO THOUSAND NOTABLE AMERICAN WOMEN. Text in English. 1989. a. USD 150 (effective 2000). **Document type:** *Directory.* **Description:** Includes outstanding American women of the 1980's and 1990's.
Published by: American Biographical Institute, Inc., Governing Board of Editors, 5126 Bur Oak Circle, Box 31226, Raleigh, NC 27622. TEL 919-781-8710, FAX 919-781-8712.

920 940   ITA
UOMINI E DOTTRINE. Text in Multiple languages. irreg., latest vol.40, 2003. price varies. **Document type:** *Monographic series, Academic/Scholarly.*
Published by: Edizioni di Storia e Letteratura, Via Lancellotti 18, Rome, 00186, Italy. TEL 39-06-68806556, FAX 39-06-68800640, edi.storialett@tiscalinet.it, http://www.weeb.it/edistorialett.

VERDI NEWSLETTER. see *MUSIC*

920 914.3   NLD   ISSN 0924-624X
➤ **VIENNA CIRCLE COLLECTION.** Text in Dutch. 1973. irreg., latest vol.23, 2004. price varies. **Document type:** *Monographic series, Academic/Scholarly.*
—BLDSC (9235.585000).

B

Published by: Springer-Verlag Dordrecht (Subsidiary of: Springer Science+Business Media), Van Godewijckstraat 30, Dordrecht, 3311 GX, Netherlands. TEL 31-78-6576050, FAX 31-78-6576474, http://www.springeronline.com. Eds. R S Cohen, T E Uebel.

➤ **VIRGINIA MAGAZINE OF HISTORY AND BIOGRAPHY.** see *HISTORY—History Of North And South America*

920.007 USA ISSN 0735-1909
LB1029.B55
➤ **VITAE SCHOLASTICAE;** the journal of educational biography. Text in English. 1982. s-a. USD 40 domestic to individuals; USD 60 foreign to institutions (effective 2003). adv. bk.rev. bibl.; illus. Index. 96 p./no. 1 cols./p.; back issues avail.; reprints avail. **Document type:** *Journal, Academic/Scholarly.*
Indexed: AmH&L, CPE, DIP, ERA, ETA, HistAb, IBR, IBZ, MEA, RHEA, SEA, SENA, SOMA, TEA.
Published by: (International Society for Educational Biography), Caddo Gap Press, 3145 Geary Blvd., PMB 275, San Francisco, CA 94118. TEL 415-922-1911, FAX 415-440-4870, caddogap@aol.com. Ed. Lucy F Townsend. Pub., R&P Alan H Jones. adv.: page USD 200; 4.5 x 7. Circ: 150 (paid).

➤ **VOODOO CHILD.** see *MUSIC*

➤ **VSPOMOGATEL'NYE ISTORICHESKIE DISTSIPLINY.** see *HISTORY—History Of Europe*

➤ **WAGNER.** see *MUSIC*

➤ **WAGNER NEWS.** see *MUSIC*

920 DEU ISSN 0172-911X
WER IST WER?; das deutsche who's who. Text in German. 1995. a. EUR 210 (effective 2005). **Document type:** *Directory, Consumer.*
Related titles: CD-ROM ed.: EUR 190 (effective 2005).
Indexed: RASB.
Published by: Schmidt-Roemhild Verlag, Mengstr 16, Luebeck, 23552, Germany. TEL 49-451-7031-01, FAX 49-451-7031253, eickershoff@beleke.de, http://www.beleke.de/outsites/ind_wiw.html, http://www.schmidt-roemhild.de. Circ: 5,000 (controlled).

920 USA ISSN 0146-8081
E176
WHO WAS WHO IN AMERICA. Text in English. 1896. irreg., latest vol.14, 2002. USD 899.95 for 16-vol. set; USD 149.95 per vol. (effective 2003). **Document type:** *Directory, Trade.* **Description:** Profiles over 127,000 notable figures in American history, from the first Jamestown settlement to current times.
Related titles: Magnetic Tape ed.
Published by: Marquis Who's Who, 562 Central Ave, New Providence, NJ 07964. TEL 908-673-1000, 800-621-9669, FAX 908-673-1179, marquisinfo@renp.com, http://www.marquiswhoswho.com/products/wwa_wn.asp.

920 USA ISSN 1053-9395
DA28
➤ **WHO'S WHO (YEAR);** an annual biographical dictionary. Text in English. a. USD 240 (effective 1999). adv. **Document type:** *Academic/Scholarly.*
Published by: St. Martin's Press, Scholarly and Reference Division (Subsidiary of: Holtzbrink Publishers), 175 Fifth Ave, New York, NY 10010. TEL 212-982-3900, FAX 212-777-6359. Ed. Garrett Kiely. R&P Ellen Dowling. Adv. contact Valerie Burton.

920.01 GBR ISSN 0083-937X
DA28
WHO'S WHO (YEAR); an annual biographical dictionary. Text in English. 1849. a. GBP 110 (effective 1999). **Document type:** *Directory.* **Description:** With more than 29,000 entries, provides an overview of international people from all walks of life.
—BLDSC (9312.000000). **CCC.**
Published by: A. & C. Black (Publishers) Ltd., Eaton Socon, Howard Rd, St Neots, Huntingdon, Cambs PE19 3EZ, United Kingdom. TEL 44-1480-212666, FAX 44-1480-405014. **Dist. in the U.S. by:** St. Martin's Press, 175 Fifth Ave, New York, NY 10010. TEL 800-221-7945.

920 USA ISSN 1081-1400
E185.96
WHO'S WHO AMONG AFRICAN AMERICANS. Text in English. 1976. irreg., latest vol.17, 2004. USD 225 per vol. (effective 2004). **Document type:** *Directory, Trade.* **Description:** Documents the lives of over 17,000 American blacks who have emerged as leaders and policymakers in their chosen fields.
Formerly (until 1997): Who's Who Among Black Americans (0362-5753)
Published by: Gale Group (Subsidiary of: Thomson Corporation), 27500 Drake Rd, Farmington Hills, MI 48331-3535. TEL 248-699-8061, 800-877-4253, FAX 248-699-4253, galeord@gale.com, http://www.gale.com.

920 USA ISSN 1052-7354
E184.S75
WHO'S WHO AMONG HISPANIC AMERICANS. Text in English. 1990. biennial, latest 1994, 3rd ed. USD 145 (effective 2004). **Document type:** *Directory.* **Description:** Contains biographical data on more than 11,000 contemporary Hispanic Americans. Arranged alphabetically, with occupation, geographic location, and country of descent indexes.
Related titles: Online - full text ed.
Published by: Gale Group (Subsidiary of: Thomson Corporation), 27500 Drake Rd, Farmington Hills, MI 48331-3535. TEL 248-699-8061, 800-877-4253, FAX 248-699-4253, galeord@gale.com, http://www.gale.com. Eds. Amy L Unterburger, Jane L Delgado.

WHO'S WHO AMONG STUDENTS IN AMERICAN JUNIOR COLLEGES. see *EDUCATION—Higher Education*

WHO'S WHO AMONG STUDENTS IN AMERICAN UNIVERSITIES AND COLLEGES. see *EDUCATION—Higher Education*

920 USA ISSN 0083-9396
E176
WHO'S WHO IN AMERICA. Text in English. 1899. a. (in 2 vols.), latest vol.59, 2005. USD 749 per issue (effective 2005). reprints avail. **Document type:** *Directory, Trade.* **Description:** Biographical resource on leading and influential Americans. Lists over 105,000 leaders, decision-makers, and innovators from every important field, along with more than 15,000 emerging figures profiled for the first time.
Related titles: CD-ROM ed.; Magnetic Tape ed.; Online - full text ed.: (from SilverPlatter Information, Inc.).
Indexed: CA&I.
—BLDSC (9312.050000), CISTI.
Published by: Marquis Who's Who, 562 Central Ave, New Providence, NJ 07964. TEL 908-673-1001, 800-473-7020, FAX 908-673-1189, info@marquiswhoswho.com, http://www.marquiswhoswho.com/products/WAprodinfo.asp. Ed. Fred Marks. Pub. Randy Mysel.

700.92 USA ISSN 0000-0191
N6536
WHO'S WHO IN AMERICAN ART. Text in English. 1936. biennial. USD 275 (effective 2003). index. **Document type:** *Directory, Trade.* **Description:** Profiles artists, critics, curators, collectors, dealers, administrators involved in the usual arts in the U.S. and Canada, with brief biographies and mailing addresses.
Related titles: Magnetic Tape ed.; Online - full text ed.
Indexed: CA&I.
Published by: Marquis Who's Who, 562 Central Ave, New Providence, NJ 07964. TEL 908-673-1000, 800-621-9669, FAX 908-673-1179, marquisinfo@renp.com, http://www.marquiswhoswho.com/products/wwpp_aa.asp. Ed. Patricia Flinsch Rodrigues.

370.92 USA ISSN 1046-7203
LA2311
WHO'S WHO IN AMERICAN EDUCATION. Text in English. 1988. irreg., latest vol.6, 2004. USD 235 per vol. (effective 2004). **Document type:** *Directory, Trade.* **Description:** Provides information on over 27,000 achievers in the field of education - from elementary school teachers to university professors, and from local school board members to US Department of Education administrators.
Related titles: CD-ROM ed.; Magnetic Tape ed.
Published by: Marquis Who's Who, 562 Central Ave, New Providence, NJ 07964. TEL 908-673-1001, 800-473-7020, FAX 908-673-1189, info@marquiswhoswho.com, http://www.marquiswhoswho.com/products/EDprodinfo.asp.

WHO'S WHO IN AMERICAN LAW. see *LAW*

320.092 USA ISSN 0000-0205
E176
WHO'S WHO IN AMERICAN POLITICS. Text in English. 1967. biennial. USD 324.99 (effective 2003). stat. index. **Document type:** *Directory, Trade.* **Description:** Comprises capsule biographies of political decision-makers from President to local town officials.
Related titles: Magnetic Tape ed.; Online - full text ed.
Published by: Marquis Who's Who, 562 Central Ave, New Providence, NJ 07964. TEL 908-673-1000, 800-621-9669, FAX 908-673-1179, marquisinfo@renp.com, http://www.marquiswhoswho.com/products/ameripol.html.

920 700 GBR
WHO'S WHO IN ART. Text in English. 1927. biennial. GBP 39.50 (effective 2000). **Document type:** *Directory.* **Description:** Lists prominent persons in the art world.
Published by: Art Trade Press, 9 Brockhampton Rd, Havant, Hants PO9 1NU, United Kingdom. TEL 44-2392-484943, FAX 44-2392-484943.

920 GBR
WHO'S WHO IN ASIA AND THE PACIFIC NATIONS. Text in English. 1989. irreg., latest 4th Ed. GBP 95, USD 165 per vol. (effective 2001). **Document type:** *Directory.* **Description:** Contains 4,000 biographical profiles detailing the achievements of leading figures in all areas of interest.
Former titles: Who's Who in Australasia and the Pacific Nations; Who's Who in Australasia and the Far East
Published by: Melrose Press Ltd., St Thomas Pl, Ely, Cambs CB7 4GG, United Kingdom. TEL 44-1353-646600, FAX 44-1353-646601, tradesales@melrosepress.co.uk. Eds. Ben Kay, Cara Bootman, Jon Gifford. Pub. Nicholas Law. **Dist. in US by:** Taylor & Francis Inc., 7625 Empire Dr., Florence, KY 41042-2919. cserve@routledge-ny.com.

920 USA ISSN 0511-8948
F860
WHO'S WHO IN CALIFORNIA. Text in English. 1928. biennial (27th ed. 1998-1999). back issues avail. **Document type:** *Directory.* **Description:** Lists the biographies of over 4,500 eminent Californians from the arts, science, medicine, education, religion, business, law, and government.
Published by: Who's Who Historical Society, 2533 N Carson St, Ste 1147, Carson City, NV 89706. TEL 775-882-0412, FAX 775-883-2384. Ed., R&P Edna L Barrett. Circ: 5,000.

791.43025 CAN ISSN 0831-6309
WHO'S WHO IN CANADIAN FILM AND TELEVISION (YEAR)/QUI EST QUI AU CINEMA ET A LA TELEVISION AU CANADA. Text in English, French. 1985. irreg. CND 59.95. adv. **Document type:** *Directory.* **Description:** Guide to industry members working behind the scenes in Canadian film and television.
Published by: (Academy of Canadian Cinema & Television/Academie Canadienne du Cinema et de la Television), Global Press, 99 Yorkville Ave Ste 400, Toronto, ON M5K 3K5, Canada. TEL 416-963-8830, FAX 416-923-4821, http://www.academy.ca, httP//www.academy.ca. Ed. And Pub Susan Ritcey. Circ: 3,000.

920 USA ISSN 0147-8265
RZ231
WHO'S WHO IN CHIROPRACTIC, INTERNATIONAL ✶. Text in English. 1977. biennial. USD 49.50.
Published by: Who's Who in Chiropractic, International Publishing Co., Inc., Box 150098, Lakewood, Littleton, CO 80215-0098. Ed. Fern L Dzaman.

920 330.9 USA
WHO'S WHO IN ECONOMIC DEVELOPMENT. Text in English. a. **Document type:** *Directory.*
Published by: American Economic Development Council, 734 15th St NW., Ste 900, Washington, DC 20005-1013. TEL 202-223-7800, FAX 202-223-4745, aedc@interacess.com, aedc@aedc.com, http://www.aedc.org/hqtrs, http://www.iedconline.org. Ed. Marion Morgan. adv.: page USD 800; trim 10.88 x 8.38. Circ: 2,700 (controlled).

620 USA ISSN 0149-7537
TA139
WHO'S WHO IN ENGINEERING. Text in English. 1970. triennial. USD 250 to non-members; USD 150 to members (effective 2000). **Document type:** *Directory.* **Description:** Lists more than 14,000 of the world's top engineers, recognizing them for their achievements.
Formerly: Engineers of Distinction (0149-7545)
—CISTI, Linda Hall.
Published by: American Association of Engineering Societies, 1111 19th St, N W, Ste 403, Washington, DC 20036-3690. TEL 202-296-2237, 888-400-2237, FAX 202-296-1151, aaes@access.digex.net, http://www.aaes.org/ewc.

920 330 USA
WHO'S WHO IN EUROPEAN BUSINESS. Text in English. 1993. irreg. GBP 110 (effective 1999). **Document type:** *Directory.* **Description:** Biographies of the top 5,000 business leaders in both Eastern and Western Europe. Profiles the leading executives from Europe's top companies, as well as from the largest companies in each country.
Published by: Marquis Who's Who, 562 Central Ave, New Providence, NJ 07964. TEL 800-621-9669, FAX 908-665-6688, info@marquiswhoswho.com, http://www.marquiswhoswho.com.

920 600 DEU
WHO'S WHO IN EUROPEAN RESEARCH AND DEVELOPMENT. Text in English. a. GBP 275. 1150 p./no.; **Document type:** *Directory.* **Description:** Contains detailed biographies of 13,000 senior research professionals, indexed by field of research and country.
Formerly: Who's Who in Research and Development
Related titles: CD-ROM ed.
Published by: K.G. Saur Verlag GmbH (Subsidiary of: Gale Group), Ortlerstr 8, Munchen, 81373, Germany. TEL 49-89-769020, FAX 49-89-76902150, saur.info@thomson.com, http://www.saur.de.

920 330 USA ISSN 0083-9523
HC29
WHO'S WHO IN FINANCE AND INDUSTRY. Text in English. 1936. biennial. USD 325 (effective 2003). **Document type:** *Directory, Trade.* **Description:** Provides biographical coverage of more than 22,400 principal decision-makers and leaders in the industrial and financial markets.
Former titles (until 1972): World Who's Who in Finance and Industry (0190-5058); (until 1971): World Who's Who in Commerce and Industry (0190-2806)
Related titles: CD-ROM ed.; Magnetic Tape ed.
—CISTI.

B

Published by: Marquis Who's Who, 562 Central Ave, New Providence, NJ 07964. TEL 908-673-1000, 800-621-9669, FAX 908-673-1179, marquisinfo@renp.com, http://www.marquiswhoswho.com.

920 FRA ISSN 0083-9531
WHO'S WHO IN FRANCE/QUI EST QUI EN FRANCE. Text in French. 1953. a. adv. **Document type:** *Directory.*
Published by: Editions Jacques Lafitte, 16 rue Camille Pelletan, Levallois Perret, 92300, France. FAX 33-1-41-27-28-40. Ed. Eleonore de Dampierre. Circ: 10,000.

920 IND ISSN 0301-5106
WHO'S WHO IN INDIA (CALCUTTA). Text in English. 1973. irreg. INR 50, USD 15 (effective 2000). adv. **Document type:** *Directory.* **Description:** Biographical roster of leading personalities in India.
Published by: Kothari Publications, 12 India Exchange Pl., Kolkata, West Bengal 700 001, India. TEL 91-33-220-9563. Ed. H Kothari.

920 600 IND ISSN 0083-9558
WHO'S WHO IN INDIAN ENGINEERING AND INDUSTRY. Text in English. 1962. irreg. INR 30, USD 9 (effective 2000). adv. **Document type:** *Directory.* **Description:** Guide to prominent people and organizations in all branches of Indian engineering and industry.
Published by: Kothari Publications, 12 India Exchange Pl., Kolkata, West Bengal 700 001, India. TEL 91-33-220-9563. Ed. H Kothari.

500 IND ISSN 0083-9566
WHO'S WHO IN INDIAN SCIENCE. Text in English. 1964. irreg., latest 1969. INR 20, USD 20 (effective 2000). **Document type:** *Directory.* **Description:** Lists biographical information about leading Indian scientists, doctors, engineers and scientific organizations.
Published by: Kothari Publications, 12 India Exchange Pl., Kolkata, West Bengal 700 001, India. TEL 91-33-220-9563. Ed. H Kothari.

920 332 GBR ISSN 0958-7357
WHO'S WHO IN INTERNATIONAL BANKING. Text in English. irreg., latest vol.6, 1992. GBP 177 (effective 1999). **Document type:** *Directory.* **Description:** Provides concise biographical and contact information on some 4,000 of today's leading bankers, including details about the entrant's education, career, civic interests, business and professional memberships, honors and awards, publications.
Published by: International Insider Publishing Company Ltd., I B C Business Publishing (Subsidiary of: I B C Group Plc), Ludgate House, 107 Fleet St, London, EC4A 2AB, United Kingdom. TEL 44-171-535-7314, FAX 44-171-353-0017. **Orders to:** World Wide Subscription Service Ltd., Unit 4, Gibbs Reed Farm, Ticehurst, E Sussex TN5 7HE, United Kingdom. TEL 44-1580-200657, FAX 44-1580-200616.

920 DEU
WHO'S WHO IN INTERNATIONAL ORGANIZATIONS; a biographical encyclopedia of more than 13,000 leading personalities. Text in German. irreg., latest 1999, 3rd (in 3 vols.). back issues avail. **Document type:** *Directory, Trade.* **Description:** Contains 12,000 biographies covering prominent individuals in 7,000 organizations, focusing on every field of human endeavor.
Published by: (Union of International Associations/Union des Associations Internationales BEL), K.G. Saur Verlag GmbH (Subsidiary of: Gale Group), Ortlerstr 8, Munchen, 81373, Germany. TEL 49-89-76902-0, FAX 49-89-76902150, customerservice_saur@csi.com, http://www.saur.de. Eds. Jacqueline Nebel, Jon J Jenkins.

920 DEU ISSN 0083-9612
DS80.75
WHO'S WHO IN LEBANON. Text in English. 1963. biennial. adv. 498 p./no.; **Document type:** *Directory.* **Description:** Describes 1,000 of the most prominent persons in Lebanon.
Published by: K.G. Saur Verlag GmbH (Subsidiary of: Gale Group), Ortlerstr 8, Munchen, 81373, Germany. customerservice_saur@csi.com, http://www.saur.de. Ed. Charles G Gedeon. Circ: 3,000.

WHO'S WHO IN MEDICINE AND HEALTHCARE. see *MEDICAL SCIENCES*

598.0922 GBR
WHO'S WHO IN ORNITHOLOGY. Text in English. 1997. irreg. GBP 29.95 (effective 1999). **Document type:** *Academic/Scholarly.* **Description:** Contains over 1,000 biographical entries.
Published by: Buckingham Press, 55 Thorpe Park Road, Peterborough, Cambridgeshire PE3 6LJ, United Kingdom. TEL 44-1733-561739. Ed. John E Pemberton.

659.2 920 USA ISSN 0511-9022
HM263
WHO'S WHO IN PUBLIC RELATIONS (INTERNATIONAL). Text in English. 1959. irreg., latest vol.6, 1992. **Document type:** *Directory.*
Published by: P R Publishing Co., Inc., PO Box 600, Exeter, NH 03833-0600. TEL 603-778-0514, FAX 603-778-1741, prr@prpublishing.com.

920 790.1 USA
WHO'S WHO IN RECREATION. Text in English. 1989. a. USD 69.95 to members (effective 2000). adv. **Document type:** *Directory.*
Published by: Society of Recreation Executives, PO Box 520, Gonzalez, FL 32560-0520. TEL 850-944-7992, FAX 850-968-1944, nrvockws@spydee.net. Ed. Debbie A Eckert. Pub. K W Stephens. Circ: 4,100 (controlled).

920 USA ISSN 1063-5599
Q141
WHO'S WHO IN SCIENCE AND ENGINEERING. Text in English. 1992. biennial (8th ed., 2005-2006). USD 335 per issue (effective 2005). 1400 p./no.; **Document type:** *Directory, Trade.* **Description:** Profiles 26,000 leading international figures, each selected for achievements in aerospace, microcircuitry, lasers, genetics, biotechnology, and all disciplines of science and engineering.
Related titles: CD-ROM ed.; Magnetic Tape ed.
—Linda Hall.
Published by: Marquis Who's Who, 562 Central Ave, New Providence, NJ 07964. TEL 908-673-1001, 800-473-7020, FAX 908-673-1189, info@marquiswhoswho.com, http://www.marquiswhoswho.com/products/SCprodinfo.asp.

920 GBR ISSN 0269-1736
WHO'S WHO IN SCOTLAND. Text in English. 1986. a. GBP 50 (effective 2002). adv. **Document type:** *Directory.* **Description:** Biographies of approximately 5,000 people prominent in Scottish public life.
Published by: Carrick Media, 1-4 Galt House, 31 Bank St, Irvine, KA12 0LL, United Kingdom. carrickmedia.demon.co.uk.

320.092 DEU
WHO'S WHO IN SOUTH AFRICAN POLITICS. Text in English. irreg., latest vol.4, 1993. GBP 75 (effective 1999). **Document type:** *Directory.* **Description:** Provides biographies on over 150 prominent political figures.
Published by: K.G. Saur Verlag GmbH (Subsidiary of: Gale Group), Ortlerstr 8, Munchen, 81373, Germany. TEL 49-89-769020, FAX 49-89-76902150, info@saur.de, http://www.saur.de. **Orders to:** World Wide Subscription Service Ltd., Unit 4, Gibbs Reed Farm, Ticehurst, E Sussex TN5 7HE, United Kingdom. TEL 44-1580-200657, FAX 44-1580-200616.

920 CHE ISSN 0083-9736
DQ52
WHO'S WHO IN SWITZERLAND. Text in German. 1951. biennial. CHF 128 (effective 2000). **Document type:** *Directory, Trade.*
Published by: Orell Fuessli Verlag, Dietzingerstr 3, Zuerich, 8036, Switzerland. TEL 41-1-4667711, FAX 41-1-4667412. Ed. A Spillmann. R&P P Hiefner. Circ: 2,000.

920.0593 THA ISSN 0125-1694
DS570.5
WHO'S WHO IN THAILAND★ . Text in Thai. 1973. m. USD 6.92. illus.
Published by: International Publishing and Marketing Co., B.O.A.C. Bldg, 5th Fl, Rajaprasong Corner, Bangkok, Thailand.

920 LBN ISSN 0083-9752
D198.3
WHO'S WHO IN THE ARAB WORLD. Text in English. 1965. biennial. USD 400 (effective 2000). bibl. **Document type:** *Bibliography.* **Description:** Profiles 6,000 eminent individuals in every area of Arab life, from each of the 19 Arab states.
Indexed: RASB.
Published by: Publitec Publications, Gedeon House, Jisr el Bacha, John F Kennedy St 139-141, P O Box 11-5936, Beirut, Lebanon. Ed. Charles G Gedeon. Circ: 5,000. **Orders in Europe to:** K.G. Saur Verlag GmbH, Postfach 701620, Munich 81316, Germany. TEL 49-89-76902-232, FAX 49-89-76902-250.

920 USA ISSN 0083-9760
E176
WHO'S WHO IN THE EAST. Text in English. 1945. biennial. USD 299.99 (effective 2003). **Document type:** *Directory, Trade.* **Description:** Lists over 25,700 biographies of prominent people living in Connecticut, Delaware, District of Columbia, Maine, Maryland, Massachusetts, New Hampshire, New Jersey, New York, Pennsylvania, Rhode Island, and Vermont, as well as New Brunswick, Newfoundland, Nova Scotia, Prince Edward Island, Quebec, and eastern Ontario in Canada.
Related titles: CD-ROM ed.; Magnetic Tape ed.
Published by: Marquis Who's Who, 562 Central Ave, New Providence, NJ 07964. TEL 908-673-1000, 800-621-9669, FAX 908-673-1179, marquisinfo@renp.com, http://www.marquiswhoswho.com.

920 LUX ISSN 1680-3698
WHO'S WHO IN THE EUROPEAN UNION; interinstitutional directory. Text in English. a. **Document type:** *Directory.* **Description:** Comprises the directories of the various European Union institutions, with listings by individual name, organizational entity, and hierarchical ranking.
Related titles: Online - full text ed.: I D E A; Dutch ed.; Danish ed.; French ed.; Finnish ed.; German ed.; Greek ed.; Italian ed.; Portuguese ed.; Spanish ed.; Swedish ed.
—BLDSC (9312.367460).
Published by: European Commission, Office for Official Publications of the European Union, 2 Rue Mercier, Luxembourg, L-2985, Luxembourg. TEL 352-29291, FAX 352-2929-44637, TELEX PUBOF LU 1324 B, idea@opoce.cec.be, http://europa.eu.int.

920 USA ISSN 0083-9787
E176
WHO'S WHO IN THE MIDWEST. Text in English. 1946. biennial. USD 285 (effective 2003). **Document type:** *Directory, Trade.* **Description:** Lists some 16,000 biographies of prominent people living in Illinois, Indiana, Iowa, Kansas, Michigan, Minnesota, Missouri, Nebraska, North Dakota, Ohio, South Dakota, and Wisconsin, as well as Manitoba, and western Ontario in Canada.
Related titles: CD-ROM ed.; Magnetic Tape ed.
Indexed: CA&I.
Published by: Marquis Who's Who, 562 Central Ave, New Providence, NJ 07964. TEL 908-673-1000, 800-621-9669, FAX 908-673-1179, marquisinfo@renp.com, http://www.marquiswhoswho.com.

920 DEU
WHO'S WHO IN THE PEOPLE'S REPUBLIC OF CHINA. Text in German. irreg., latest 1997, in 2 vols. USD 350 per vol. (effective 2001). illus. **Document type:** *Directory, Government.* **Description:** Profiles more than 4,100 of China's most influential current and political leaders.
Published by: K.G. Saur Verlag GmbH (Subsidiary of: Gale Group), Ortlerstr 8, Munchen, 81373, Germany. TEL 49-89-76902-0, FAX 49-89-76902150, customerservice_saur@csi.com, http://www.saur.de. Ed. Wolfgang Bartke.

920 USA ISSN 0083-9809
E176
WHO'S WHO IN THE SOUTH AND SOUTHWEST. Text in English. 1946. biennial. USD 285 (effective 2003). **Document type:** *Directory, Trade.* **Description:** Lists nearly 19,500 biographies of prominent people living in Alabama, Arkansas, Florida, Georgia, Kentucky, Louisiana, Mississippi, North Carolina, Oklahoma, South Carolina, Tennessee, Texas, Virginia, West Virginia, Puerto Rico, the Virgin Islands, and Mexico.
Related titles: CD-ROM ed.; Magnetic Tape ed.
Indexed: CA&I.
Published by: Marquis Who's Who, 562 Central Ave, New Providence, NJ 07964. TEL 908-673-1000, 800-621-9669, FAX 908-673-1179, marquisinfo@renp.com, http://www.marquiswhoswho.com/products/SWprodinfo.asp.

WHO'S WHO IN THE U K INFORMATION WORLD. see *LIBRARY AND INFORMATION SCIENCES*

920 USA ISSN 0083-9817
E176
WHO'S WHO IN THE WEST. Text in English. 1946. biennial. USD 285 (effective 2003). **Document type:** *Directory, Trade.* **Description:** Lists over 19,500 biographies of prominent people living in Alaska, Arizona, California, Colorado, Hawaii, Idaho, Montana, Nevada, New Mexico, Oregon, Utah, Washington, and Wyoming, as well as Alberta, British Columbia, and Saskatchewan in Canada.
Related titles: CD-ROM ed.; Magnetic Tape ed.
Published by: Marquis Who's Who, 562 Central Ave, New Providence, NJ 07964. TEL 908-673-1000, 800-621-9669, FAX 908-673-1179, marquisinfo@renp.com, http://www.marquiswhoswho.com/products/WPprodinfo.asp.

920 USA ISSN 0083-9825
CT120
WHO'S WHO IN THE WORLD. Text in English. 1971. a., latest vol.20, 2003. USD 475 (effective 2003). **Document type:** *Directory, Trade.* **Description:** Profiles over 45,000 individual biographies of the people whose activities are shaping today's world. Includes prominent government figures, high-ranking military officers, leaders of the largest corporations in each country, heads of religious organizations, pioneers in science and the arts, and more.
Related titles: CD-ROM ed.; Magnetic Tape ed.
Indexed: RASB.
—BLDSC (9312.558500), CISTI.
Published by: Marquis Who's Who, 562 Central Ave, New Providence, NJ 07964. TEL 908-673-1000, 800-621-9669, FAX 908-673-1179, marquisinfo@renp.com, http://www.marquiswhoswho.com/products/WOprodinfo.asp.

WHO'S WHO IN TRAINING AND DEVELOPMENT. see *BUSINESS AND ECONOMICS—Management*

920 360 USA ISSN 1076-4755
WHO'S WHO IN WASHINGTON NONPROFIT GROUPS. Text in English. 1994. a.
Published by: C Q Press, Inc. (Subsidiary of: Congressional Quarterly, Inc.), 1255 22nd St., N.W., Ste. 400, Washington, DC 20037. TEL 800-432-2250, FAX 202-729-1800, customerservice@cq.com, http://www.cqpress.com/gethome.asp. Ed. Jerry A Orvedahl.

WHO'S WHO IN WORLD BIOTECHNOLOGY (YEAR). see *BIOLOGY—Biotechnology*

920 USA ISSN 0083-9841
E176
WHO'S WHO OF AMERICAN WOMEN. Text in English. 1958. biennial (23rd ed., 2002-2003). USD 279 (effective 2003). **Document type:** *Directory, Trade.* **Description:** Contains vital and insightful biographical facts on more than 33,000 achievers. Covers a wide range of disciplines and professions including government, business, the arts, and medicine.
Former titles (until 1969): Who's Who of American Women and Women of Canada (0270-2800); (until 1967): Who's Who of American Women (0270-2940)
Related titles: CD-ROM ed.; Magnetic Tape ed.
—CISTI.
Published by: Marquis Who's Who, 562 Central Ave, New Providence, NJ 07964. TEL 908-673-1000, 800-621-9669, FAX 908-673-1179, marquisinfo@renp.com, http://www.marquiswhoswho.com/products/AWprodinfo.asp.

920 808.02 DEU
WHO'S WHO OF AUSTRALIAN WRITERS. Text in English. irreg., latest vol.2, 1995. GBP 52 (effective 1999). **Document type:** *Directory.* **Description:** Includes approximately 5,000 entries on living writers of fiction, poetry, plays, radio and TV scripts.
Published by: (Australia Council AUS), K.G. Saur Verlag GmbH (Subsidiary of: Gale Group), Ortlerstr 8, Munchen, 81373, Germany. TEL 49-89-769020, FAX 49-89-76902150, info@saur.de, http://www.saur.de. **Orders to:** World Wide Subscription Service Ltd., Unit 4, Gibbs Reed Farm, Ticehurst, E Sussex TN5 7HE, United Kingdom. TEL 44-1580-200657, FAX 44-1580-200616. **Co-sponsor:** Monash University, National Center for Australian Studies.

920 ZAF
WHO'S WHO OF SOUTHERN AFRICA INCLUDING MAURITIUS, NAMIBIA, ZIMBABWE, BOTSWANA, SWAZILAND AND NEIGHBORING COUNTRIES. Text in English. 1907. a. ZAR 375 (effective 2003). adv. **Document type:** *Bibliography.*
Former titles: Who's Who of Southern Africa Including Mauritius, South West Africa, Zimbabwe and Neighboring Countries; Who's Who of Southern Africa Including Mauritius, South West Africa, Zimbabwe-Rhodesia and Neighboring Countries; Who's Who of Southern Africa Including Mauritius, South West Africa, Rhodesia and Neighboring Countries; Who's Who of Southern Africa (0083-9876); Incorporates: Who's Who of Rhodesia, Mauritius, Central and East Africa (0083-9868)
Indexed: RASB.
Published by: Jonathan Ball Publishers, PO Box 33977, Jeppestown, 2043, South Africa. TEL 27-11-6222900, FAX 27-11-6223553, orders@jonathanball.co.za, http://www.nasboek.co.za. Ed., R&P, Adv. contact Sandra Hayes. Pub. Jonathan Ball. Circ: 4,000 (paid).

320.082 DEU
WHO'S WHO OF WOMEN IN WORLD POLITICS; biographies of women currently in government legislatures worldwide. Text in English. 1991. irreg. GBP 91 (effective 1999). **Document type:** *Directory.* **Description:** Features more than 1,500 biographies organized by country, and in alphabetical order, of prominent female politicians from over 100 countries.
Published by: K.G. Saur Verlag GmbH (Subsidiary of: Gale Group), Ortlerstr 8, Munchen, 81373, Germany. TEL 49-89-769020, FAX 49-89-76902150, info@saur.de, http://www.saur.de. **Orders to:** World Wide Subscription Service, Unit 4, Gibbs Reed Farm, Ticehurst, E Sussex TN4 7HE, United Kingdom. TEL 44-1580-200657, FAX 44-1580-200616.

WINE PRESS. see *GENEALOGY AND HERALDRY*

WINESBURG EAGLE. see *LITERATURE*

WOMEN OF ACHIEVEMENT AND HERSTORY. see *WOMEN'S INTERESTS*

WORLD LEADER UPDATE. see *POLITICAL SCIENCE*

920 USA ISSN 1532-7353
CT103
WORLD'S GREATEST BIOGRAPHIES. Text in English. 2001. bi-m.
Published by: Reader's Digest Association, Inc, Reader's Digest Rd, Pleasantville, NY 10570-7000. TEL 914-238-1000, http://www.readersdigest.com/corporate.

ZHONGGUO ZUOJIA; daxing wenxue shuangyuekan. see *LITERATURE*

920 CHN ISSN 1003-0557
ZHONGHUA ERNU. Text in Chinese. 1988. bi-m. **Document type:** *Consumer.* **Description:** Contains biographies of Chinese officials, entrepreneurs, artists, writers and other prominent figures.
Published by: (Zhonghua Quanguo Qingnian Lianhehui), Zhongguo Qingnian Chubanshe, 10 Dong Dajie, Qianmen, Beijing, 100051, China. TEL 86-10-7012288.

920 CHN ISSN 1005-2151
ZHONGHUA ERNU (HAIWAIBAN). Text in Chinese. m. 80 p./no.; **Document type:** *Consumer.* **Description:** For overseas Chinese. Contains biographies of Chinese officials, entrepreneurs, writers, artists and other prominent features.
Related titles: Online - full text ed.: (from East View Information Services).
Published by: (Zhonghua Quanguo Qingnian Lianhehui), Zhongguo Qingnian Chubanshe, 10 Dong Dajie, Qianmen, Beijing, 100051, China. TEL 86-10-7012288. **Dist. overseas by:** China International Book Trading Corp, 35 Chegongzhuang Xilu, Haidian District, PO Box 399, Beijing 100044, China. TEL 86-10-68412045, FAX 86-10-68412023, cibtc@mail.cibtc.com.cn, http://www.cibtc.com.cn.

920 USA ISSN 1098-3163
CT3235
500 NOTABLE WOMEN. Text in English. 1998. a. USD 195 (effective 2000). illus. **Document type:** *Directory.* **Description:** Includes profiles on women in this century.
Published by: American Biographical Institute, Inc., Governing Board of Editors, 5126 Bur Oak Circle, Box 31226, Raleigh, NC 27622. TEL 919-781-8710, FAX 919-781-8712.

BIOGRAPHY—Abstracting, Bibliographies, Statistics

016.929 USA
ABRIDGED BIOGRAPHY AND GENEALOGY MASTER INDEX. Text in English. irreg. (in 3 vols.). USD 495 (effective 2003). **Document type:** *Abstract/Index.* **Description:** Indexes selected biographical and genealogical information found in biographical dictionaries and Who's Who directories.
Published by: Gale Group (Subsidiary of: Thomson Corporation), 27500 Drake Rd, Farmington Hills, MI 48331-3535. TEL 248-699-8061, 800-877-4253, FAX 248-699-4253, galeord@gale.com, http://www.gale.com. Ed. Geri Speace.

920 USA ISSN 0741-8655
Z5304.A8
AUTHOR BIOGRAPHIES MASTER INDEX. Text in English. 1978. irreg., latest 1997, 5th ed., (in 2 vols.). USD 325 (effective 2003). **Description:** Indexes biographies of more than 1,140,000 literary figures.
Published by: Gale Group (Subsidiary of: Thomson Corporation), 27500 Drake Rd, Farmington Hills, MI 48331-3535. TEL 248-699-8061, FAX 248-699-4253, galeord@gale.com, http://www.gale.com. Ed. Geri Speace.

016.929 USA ISSN 0730-1316
Z5305.U5
BIOGRAPHY AND GENEALOGY MASTER INDEX. Text in English. 1975. a. (in 2 vols.). USD 280 per vol. (effective 2003). illus. reprints avail. **Document type:** *Abstract/Index.* **Description:** Indexes biographical and genealogical information found in biographical dictionaries and Who's Who directories.
Formerly: Biographical Dictionaries Master Index
Related titles: CD-ROM ed.: USD 565 (effective 2000); Microfiche ed.: Bio-Base. ISSN 0742-2318; Online - full text ed.: USD 275 (effective 1999).
Published by: Gale Group (Subsidiary of: Thomson Corporation), 27500 Drake Rd, Farmington Hills, MI 48331-3535. TEL 248-699-8061, FAX 248-699-4253, galeord@gale.com, http://www.gale.com. Ed. Geri Speace.

016.92 920 USA ISSN 0006-3053
Z5301
BIOGRAPHY INDEX; a quarterly index to biographical material in books and magazines. Text in English. 1946. q. (plus a. cumulation). USD 295 in US & Canada (effective 2006). **Document type:** *Abstract/Index.* **Description:** Indexes biographical material in books and magazines.
Related titles: CD-ROM ed.: ISSN 1063-3286. 198? (from H.W. Wilson, SilverPlatter Information, Inc.); Magnetic Tape ed.; Online - full text ed.: USD 1,700 in US & Canada (effective 2006).
Indexed: RASB.
—BLDSC (2072.330000), Linda Hall.
Published by: H.W. Wilson Co., 950 University Ave, Bronx, NY 10452-4224. TEL 718-588-8400, 800-367-6770, FAX 718-590-1617, 800-590-1617, custserv@hwwilson.com, http://www.hwwilson.com/Databases/bioind.htm. Ed. Charles Cornell.

920 944 FRA
DICTIONNAIRE DE BIOGRAPHIE FRANCAISE. Text in French. irreg., latest vol.19, 1998. back issues avail. **Description:** Provides biographies on the men and women who played an important role in French history.
Published by: Letouzey et Ane Editeurs, 87 bd. Raspail, Paris, 75006, France. TEL 33-1-45488014, FAX 33-1-45490343. R&P Florence Letouzey.

920 071 USA ISSN 1058-5648
F614.C8
OBITUARIES INDEX. Text in English. 1989. irreg.
Published by: University of Minnesota at Crookston, 2900 University Ave, Crookston, MN 56716-5001.

920 CAN ISSN 0827-6307
PG3809.R8
RUDNYCKIANA✶. Text in English. 1985. a. CND 10. **Document type:** *Academic/Scholarly.*
Published by: Bureau of Ukrainian Information, 665 Terrace du Ruisseau, Apt 102, Lachine, PQ H8T 3L7, Canada.

016.92 USA ISSN 1099-2235
WILSON BIOGRAPHIES. Text in English. 1997. d. USD 1,170 in US & Canada (effective 2006). **Document type:** *Abstract/Index.*
Media: Online - full content.
Published by: H.W. Wilson Co., 950 University Ave, Bronx, NY 10452-4224. TEL 718-588-8400, 800-367-6770, FAX 718-590-1617, 800-590-1617, custserv@hwwilson.com, http://www.hwwilson.com.

920 DEU
WORLD BIOGRAPHICAL INDEX/INTERNATIONALER BIOGRAPHISCHER INDEX. Text in English, German. a. **Document type:** *Catalog, Abstract/Index.* **Description:** Provides an electronic index to numerous biographical articles and reference works in different languages.
Media: CD-ROM (from K. G. Saur Verlag GmbH & Co.).
Published by: K.G. Saur Verlag GmbH (Subsidiary of: Gale Group), Ortlerstr 8, Munchen, 81373, Germany. TEL 49-89-76902232, FAX 49-89-76902150, customerservice_saur@csi.com, http://www.saur.de.

BIOCHEMISTRY

see BIOLOGY—Biochemistry

BIOLOGY

see also BIOLOGY—Biochemistry ; BIOLOGY—Bioengineering ; BIOLOGY—Biophysics ; BIOLOGY—Biotechnology ; BIOLOGY—Botany ; BIOLOGY—Computer Applications ; BIOLOGY—Cytology And Histology ; BIOLOGY—Entomology ; BIOLOGY—Genetics ; BIOLOGY—Microbiology ; BIOLOGY—Microscopy ; BIOLOGY—Ornithology ; BIOLOGY—Physiology ; BIOLOGY—Zoology ; MEDICAL SCIENCES ; PHARMACY AND PHARMACOLOGY

571.9 610 DNK ISSN 0903-4641
R81 CODEN: APMSEL
➤ **A P M I S.** (Acta Pathologica Microbiologica et Immunologica Scandinavica) Text and summaries in English. 1926. m. GBP 546 combined subscription elsewhere to institutions print & online eds.; USD 917 combined subscription in the Americas to institutions & Caribbean (print & online eds.) (effective 2006). bk.rev. Supplement avail.; back issues avail.; reprint service avail. from ISI,PSC. **Document type:** *Journal, Academic/Scholarly.*
Formed by the 1988 merger of: Acta Pathologica, Microbiologica et Immunologica Scandinavica. Section A. Pathology (0108-0164); Which was formerly (1970-1982): Acta Pathologica et Microbiologica Scandinavica. Section A. Pathology (0365-4184); Acta Pathologica, Microbiologica et Immunologica Scandinavic. Section B. Microbiology (0108-0180); Which was formerly (1975-1982): Acta Pathologica et Microbiologica Scandinavica. Section B. Microbiology (0304-131X); Acta Pathologica, Microbiologica et Immunologica Scandinavic. Section C. Immunology (0108-0202); Which was formerly (1975-1982): Acta Pathologica et Microbiologica Scandinavica. Section C. Immunology (0304-1328); Section B & C superseded in part (1970-1975): Acta Pathologica et Microbiologica Scandinavica. Section B. Microbiology and Immunology (0365-5563); Section A & B superseded in part (1924-1970): Acta Pathologica et Microbiologica Scandinavica (0365-5555)
Related titles: Online - full text ed.: ISSN 1600-0463. GBP 519 elsewhere to institutions; USD 872 in the Americas to institutions & Caribbean (effective 2006) (from Blackwell Synergy, EBSCO Publishing, Gale Group, IngentaConnect, O C L C Online Computer Library Center, Inc., Swets Information Services); ♦ Supplement(s): A P M I S Supplementum. ISSN 0903-465X.
Indexed: ASCA, AbHyg, AgBio, AnBrAb, BIOBASE, BIOSIS Prev, BiolAb, ChemAb, CurCont, DBA, DSA, DentInd, ESPM, ExcerpMed, HelmAb, HerbAb, HortAb, IABS, ISR, IndMed, IndVet, Inpharma, MBA, MEDLINE, MS&D, NRN, NutrAb, PN&I, PoultAb, ProtozoAb, RA&MP, RDA, RM&VM, RPP, Reac, RevApplEntom, S&F, SAA, SCI, SoyAb, TDB, VetBull, WAE&RSA, WildRev.
—BLDSC (1568.740000), CASDDS, CISTI, GNLM, IDS, IE, Infotrieve, ingenta, KNAW. **CCC.**
Published by: (/A P M I S), Blackwell Munksgaard (Subsidiary of: Blackwell Publishing Ltd.), Rosenoerns Alle 1, PO Box 227, Copenhagen V, 1502, Denmark. TEL 45-77-333333, FAX 45-77-333377, info@mks.blackwellpublishing.com, http://www.blackwellpublishing.com/journals/APMIS, http://www.blackwellmunksgaard.com. Eds. B. Norrild, E. Ralfkjaer. Circ: 800.

B

▼ new title ➤ refereed ✶ unverified ♦ full entry avail.

610 576 DNK ISSN 0903-465X
R81 CODEN: AISSE2

➤ **A P M I S SUPPLEMENTUM.** (Acta Pathologica, Microbiologica et Immunologica Scandinavica) Text in English. 1926. irreg., latest vol.114, 2003. Free with subscription to APMIS. back issues avail.; reprint service avail. from ISI,PSC. **Document type:** *Monographic series, Academic/Scholarly.*

Formed by the 1988 merger of: Acta Pathologica, Microbiologica et Immunologica Scandinavica. Section A. Supplement (0108-0172); Which was formerly (until 1982): Acta Pathologica et Microbiologica Scandinavica. Section A. Supplement (0365-5571); Acta Pathologica, Microbiologica et Immunologica Scandinavica. Section C. Supplement (0108-0210); Which was formerly (until 1981): Acta Pathologica et Microbiologica Scandinavica. Section C. Supplement (0105-8703); Superseded in part (in 1970): Acta Pathologica et Microbiologica Scandinavica. Supplementum (0065-1486)

Related titles: Microfilm ed.: (from PMC); Online - full text ed.: ISSN 1600-5503; ♦ Supplement to: A P M I S. ISSN 0903-4641.

Indexed: BIOBASE, BiolAb, ChemAb, CurCont, DentInd, ExcerpMed, IABS, ISR, IndMed, MEDLINE, TDB.

—BLDSC (1568.750000), CASDDS, CISTI, IE, Infotrieve, ingenta, KNAW. **CCC.**

Published by: Blackwell Munksgaard (Subsidiary of: Blackwell Publishing Ltd.), Rosenoerns Alle 1, PO Box 227, Copenhagen V, 1502, Denmark. TEL 45-77-333333, FAX 45-77-333377, info@mks.blackwellpublishing.com, http://www.blackwellmunksgaard.com. Eds. B. Norrild, E. Ralfkjaer.

570.752 USA

A T C C PRESERVATION METHODS: FREEZING & FREEZE-DRYING. Text in English. 1991. irreg. USD 45; USD 50 foreign.

Published by: American Type Culture Collection, 10801 University Blvd, Manassas, VA 20110. TEL 800-638-6597, FAX 301-816-4361. Eds. E M Brown, F P Simione.

577 GBR ISSN 0951-5674

➤ **ABERDEEN LETTERS IN ECOLOGY.** Text in English. 1987. a. GBP 10. **Document type:** *Academic/Scholarly.*

Description: Brief reports of current research work.

Published by: University of Aberdeen, Department of Agriculture, MacRobert Bldg, 581 King St, Aberdeen, AB24 5UA, United Kingdom. TEL 44-1224-274122, FAX 44-1224-273731, agrisec@aberdeen.ac.uk. Ed. Robert Naylor. Circ: 250 (paid).

570 540 MDA ISSN 1019-5289
CODEN: IMBKB6

ACADEMIA DE STIINTE A REPUBLICII MOLDOVA. BULETINUL. STIINTE BIOLOGICE SI CHIMICE/AKADEMIYA NAUK RESPUBLIKI MOLDOVA. IZVESTIYA. BIOLOGICHESKIE I KHIMICHESKIE NAUKI. Text in Romanian, Russian. bi-m. USD 50.

Formerly: Akademiya Nauk Moldovskoi S.S.R. Izvestiya. Biologicheskie i Khimicheskie Nauki (0568-5192)

Indexed: BiolAb, CIN, CPA, ChemAb, ChemTitl, DSA, FCA, HortAb, NemAb, NutrAb, PBA, PGrRegA, RPP, SeedAb, SoyAb, TriticAb.

—CASDDS, CISTI, Linda Hall.

Published by: Academia de Stiinte a Moldovej, Biblioteca Stiintifica Centrala, Bd Stefan cel Mare 1, Chisinau, 2001, Moldova. TEL 373-2-274279, http://www.asm.md/altstruc/library.

570 FRA ISSN 1631-0691
Q2 CODEN: CRBOCM

➤ **ACADEMIE DES SCIENCES. COMPTES RENDUS. BIOLOGIES.** Text and summaries in English, French; Abstracts in French, English. 1835. 12/yr. EUR 639.57 domestic to institutions; EUR 779 in Europe to institutions; JPY 87,900 in Japan to institutions; USD 974 elsewhere to institutions (effective 2006). charts; illus. index. **Document type:** *Journal, Academic/Scholarly.* **Description:** Contains information on theoretical biology, molecular biology, genetics, marine biology, general ecology, anthropology, animal nutrition and botany.

Former titles (until 2001): Academie des Sciences. Comptes Rendus. Serie 3: Sciences de la Vie (0764-4469); (until 1984): Academie des Sciences. Comptes Rendus des Seances. Serie 3: Sciences de la Vie (0249-6313); (until 1981): Academie des Sciences. Comptes Rendus Hebdomadaires des Seances. Series D: Sciences Naturelles (0567-655X)

Related titles: Microform ed.: (from PMC); Online - full text ed.: (from EBSCO Publishing, Gale Group, IngentaConnect, ScienceDirect, Swets Information Services).

Indexed: ASCA, ASFA, AbHyg, AgBio, AgrForAb, AnBeAb, AnBrAb, ApEcolAb, ApMecR, BIOBASE, BIOSIS Prev, BioCN&I, BiolAb, BrGeoL, CIN, CPA, ChemAb, ChemTitl, CurCont, DBA, DSA, ESPM, EngInd, EntAb, ExcerpMed, FCA, FPA, FS&TA, ForAb, GEOBASE, GenetAb, HGA, HelmAb, HerbAb, HortAb, I&DA, IABS, INIS AtomInd, ISR, IndMed, IndVet, MEDLINE, MaizeAb, MathR, NemAb, NutrAb, OrnHort, PBA, PGegResA, PGrRegA, PHN&I, PN&I, PotatoAb, PoultAb, ProtozoAb, RA&MP, RM&VM, RPP, RefZh, RevApplEntom, RiceAb, S&F, SCI, SFA, SIA, SPPI, SeedAb, SoyAb, TDB, TriticAb, VITIS, VetBull, WAE&RSA, WeedAb, WildRev, ZooRec.

—BLDSC (3384.515500), CASDDS, CISTI, Ei, GNLM, IDS, IE, ingenta, KNAW, Linda Hall, PADDS. **CCC.**

Published by: (Academie des Sciences), Elsevier France, Editions Scientifiques et Medicales (Subsidiary of: Elsevier Science & Technology), 23 Rue Linois, Paris, 75724, France. TEL 33-1-71724600, FAX 33-1-71724650, http://www.elsevier.com/locate/crvi, http://www.elsevier.fr. Ed. N Le Douarin. Circ: 3,200. **Subscr. to:** Elsevier BV, PO Box 211, Amsterdam 1000 AE, Netherlands. TEL 31-20-485-3757, FAX 31-20-485-3432, http://www.elsevier.nl.

➤ **ACADEMIE SERBE DES SCIENCES ET DES ARTS. CLASSE DES SCIENCES MATHEMATIQUES ET NATURELLES. BULLETIN SCIENCES NATURELLES.** see *SCIENCES: COMPREHENSIVE WORKS*

➤ **ACTA ALBERTINA RATISBONENSIA.** see *EARTH SCIENCES*

570 HRV ISSN 0448-0147
QH178.Y8 CODEN: ACBLDN

ACTA BIOLOGICA. Text and summaries in Croatian, English, French, German, Russian. 1913. biennial. USD 10. back issues avail. **Document type:** *Academic/Scholarly.*

Indexed: BiolAb, ZooRec.

—KNAW, Linda Hall.

Published by: Hrvatska Akademija Znanosti i Umjetnosti/Croatian Academy of Sciences and Arts, Zrinski trg 11, Zagreb, 41000, Croatia. TEL 385-1-4819982, FAX 385-1-4819979. Ed. Zvonimir Devide. Circ: 800.

570 POL ISSN 0137-9623

ACTA BIOLOGICA. Text in Polish. 1957. irreg., latest vol.9, 2002. price varies. **Document type:** *Monographic series, Academic/Scholarly.*

Supersedes in part (in 1976): Acta Biologica et Medica (0065-1087)

Indexed: AgrLib.

—Linda Hall.

Published by: Gdanskie Towarzystwo Naukowe/Gdansk Scientific Society, Ul Grodzka 12, Gdansk, 80841, Poland. TEL 48-58-3012124, FAX 48-58-3058131, gtn@3net.pl.

615.532 DEU ISSN 0722-4192

ACTA BIOLOGICA; Zeitschrift fuer angewandte Homoeo-Phytotherapie, Ganzheitsbehandlungen und Sondermethoden der Medizin. Text in German. 1962. s-a. **Document type:** *Academic/Scholarly.*

—GNLM.

Published by: Pascoe Pharmazeutische Praeparate GmbH, Schiffenberger Weg 55, Giessen, 35394, Germany. TEL 0641-7960-0, FAX 0641-77333. Circ: 7,500.

570 HUN ISSN 0567-7327
QH301 CODEN: ABIDAO

ACTA BIOLOGICA DEBRECINA✶. Text in English, German, Hungarian, Russian. 1962. irreg. bibl.; illus. **Document type:** *Academic/Scholarly.*

Indexed: BiolAb, ChemAb, ZooRec.

—CASDDS, Linda Hall.

Published by: (Novenytani Tanszek), Kossuth Lajos Tudomanyegyetem, PF 37, Debrecen, 4010, Hungary. Circ: 450.

570 610 POL ISSN 0065-1087
QH301 CODEN: ACBMAN

ACTA BIOLOGICA ET MEDICA. Text in Polish. 1957. irreg., latest vol.20, 2002. price varies. **Document type:** *Monographic series, Academic/Scholarly.*

Indexed: AgrLib, MEDLINE.

—CISTI, GNLM.

Published by: Gdanskie Towarzystwo Naukowe/Gdansk Scientific Society, Ul Grodzka 12, Gdansk, 80841, Poland. TEL 48-58-3012124, FAX 48-58-3058131, gtn@3net.pl.

570 HUN ISSN 0236-5383
QH301 CODEN: ABAHAU

➤ **ACTA BIOLOGICA HUNGARICA.** Text in English. 1948. q. USD 320 (effective 2006). adv. bk.rev. bibl.; charts; illus.; abstr. index. 120 p./no.; **Document type:** *Journal, Academic/Scholarly.* **Description:** Provides a forum for original research in the field of experimental biology. Covers cytology, morphology, embryology, genetics, endocrinology, radiation biology, cellular level of biological regulation, ethology and environmental biology.

Former titles (until 1983): Academiae Scientiarum Hungaricae. Acta Biologica (0001-5288); (until 1950): Acta Biologica Hungarica (0367-6390)

Related titles: Online - full text ed.: ISSN 1588-256X (from EBSCO Publishing, Swets Information Services).

Indexed: ASCA, ASFA, AbHyg, AgBio, AnBrAb, ApicAb, BIOBASE, BIOSIS Prev, BioCN&I, BiolAb, CIN, CPA, ChemAb, ChemTitl, CurCont, DSA, EntAb, ExcerpMed, FCA, FPA, ForAb, HelmAb, HerbAb, HortAb, ISR, IndMed, IndVet, MEDLINE, NSCI, NemAb, NutrAb, OrnHort, PBA, PGegResA, PGrRegA, PN&I, PotatoAb, PoultAb, RA&MP, RM&VM, RPP, RefZh, RevApplEntom, S&F, SCI, SIA, SeedAb, TriticAb, VITIS, VetBull, WeedAb, ZooRec.

—BLDSC (0602.874000), CASDDS, CISTI, GNLM, IDS, IE, Infotrieve, ingenta, KNAW, Linda Hall. **CCC.**

Published by: (Magyar Tudomanyos Akademia/Hungarian Academy of Sciences), Akademiai Kiado Rt. (Subsidiary of: Wolters Kluwer N.V.), Prielle Kornelia U. 19, Budapest, 1117, Hungary. TEL 36-1-4648282, FAX 36-1-4648221, journals@akkrt.hu, http://www.akkrt.hu. Ed. Janos Salanki.

577 SCG ISSN 0531-9110

ACTA BIOLOGICA IUGOSLAVICA. SERIJA D: EKOLOGIJA. Key Title: Ekologija. Text in Serbo-Croatian. 1966. s-a. price varies. **Document type:** *Journal, Academic/Scholarly.* **Description:** Focuses on ecological issues.

—Linda Hall.

Published by: Drustvo Ekologa Srbije, c/o Dr Dmitar Lakusic, Secr., Institut za Botaniku i Botanicka Basta Jevremovac, Bioloski Fakultet Univerziteta u Beogradu, Takovska 43, Belgrade, 11000. TEL 381-11-767988, FAX 381-11-769903, juca@ibiss.bg.ac.yu, http://www.des.org.yu/ekologija, http://www.des.org.yu/archive/izlog/sbd.html.

570 BRA ISSN 0101-5354
QH301 CODEN: ABLEEC

ACTA BIOLOGICA LEOPOLDENSIA. Text in Portuguese. 1979. s-a. USD 24; or exchange basis. bibl.; charts; illus. **Document type:** *Academic/Scholarly.*

Indexed: BiolAb, ZooRec.

—CISTI.

Published by: (Universidade do Vale do Rio dos Sinos), Unisinos, Av Unisinos, 950, Sao Leopoldo, RS 93022-000, Brazil. TEL 55-51-590-8239, ext. 1951, FAX 55-51-592-8238. Ed. Elena Diehl.

570 BRA ISSN 0301-2123
QH301 CODEN: ACBPAW

➤ **ACTA BIOLOGICA PARANAENSE.** Text in Portuguese; Summaries in English, French. 1960. a. free. bk.rev. index. **Document type:** *Academic/Scholarly.*

Supersedes in part: Universidade Federal do Parana. Departamento de Botanica. Boletim; Zoologia (0044-5053); Formerly: Universidade do Parana. Departamento do Botanica e Farmacognosia. Boletim (0041-8900)

Indexed: BIOSIS Prev, BiolAb, CurCont, ZooRec.

—CASDDS, CISTI, KNAW.

Published by: Universidade Federal do Parana, Setor de Ciencias Biologicas, Jd Americas, Caixa Postal 19020, Curitiba, PR 81531-990, Brazil. TEL 55-41-3663144 ext. 165, FAX 55-41-2662042, TELEX 415100, slaroca@netpar.com.br. Ed. Dr. Sebastiao Laroca. Circ: 1,000.

570 HUN ISSN 1588-385X
QH7 CODEN: AUSGAC

ACTA BIOLOGICA SZEGEDIENSIS. Variant title: Acta Universitatis Szegediensis: Acta Biologica. Text in English. 1947; N.S. 1955. a., latest vol.47, 2003. price varies. **Document type:** *Journal, Academic/Scholarly.* **Description:** Journal of animal and plant taxonomy and physiology, physical anthropology and ecology.

Formerly (until 2000): Acta Universitatis de Attila Jozsef Nominatae. Acta Biologica (0563-0592)

Related titles: Online - full content ed.: ISSN 1588-4082. 2000.

Indexed: AnthLit, BIOBASE, ExcerpMed.

—CASDDS, CISTI, Linda Hall.

Published by: (Szegedi Tudomanyegyetem, Termeszettudomanyi Kar/University of Szeged, Faculty of Science), Szegedi Tudomanyegyetem/University of Szeged, c/o E Szabo, Exchange Librarian, Dugonics ter 13, PO Box 393, Szeged, 6701, Hungary. TEL 36-62-544009, FAX 36-62-420895, gulyak@bio.u-szeged.hu, Eneh.Szabo@bibl.u-szeged.hu, http://ttkde4.sci.u-szeged.hu/ABS/, http://www.u-szeged.hu. Ed. Karoly Gulya TEL 36-62-544048. Circ: 400.

ACTA BIOLOGICA UNIVERSITATIS DAUGAVPILIENSIS. see *BIOLOGY—Botany*

570 VEN ISSN 0001-5326
QH7 CODEN: ABVEAO

➤ **ACTA BIOLOGICA VENEZUELICA.** Text in English, Portuguese, Spanish. 1951. q. VEB 16,000 per issue domestic; USD 10 per issue foreign (effective 2005). bk.rev. bibl.; charts; illus. index. back issues avail. **Document type:** *Journal, Academic/Scholarly.* **Description:** Publishes original contributions to systematics, ecology, physiology, parasitology and related biological disciplines. Includes short notes on methodological innovations and recent advances. Aimed at upper undergraduate, graduate students and professional staff.

Indexed: ASFA, AnBrAb, BiolAb, CPA, ChemAb, ESPM, FCA, ForAb, HelmAb, HerbAb, HortAb, I&DA, IndVet, MaizeAb, NutrAb, PBA, PGegResA, PN&I, PoultAb, ProtozoAb, RDA, RPP, RRTA, RevApplEntom, S&F, SFA, SeedAb, TDB, VetBull, WAE&RSA, WeedAb, WildRev, ZooRec.

—Linda Hall.

Published by: Universidad Central de Venezuela, Instituto de Zoologia Tropical, Facultad de Ciencias-UCV, Apartado 47058, Caracas, DF 1041-A, Venezuela. TEL 58-212-6051424, FAX 58-212-6051204, lmorales@ciens.ucv.ve, http://strix.ciens.ucv.ve/~instzool/actaBV.html. Ed., R&P Luis Gonzalo Morales. Circ: 700 (controlled).

570 NLD ISSN 0001-5342
QH301 CODEN: ABIOAN

➤ **ACTA BIOTHEORETICA.** Text in English. 1935. q. EUR 342, USD 342, GBP 214 combined subscription to institutions print & online eds. (effective 2005). bibl.; charts; illus. back issues avail.; reprint service avail. from PSC. **Document type:** *Journal, Academic/Scholarly.* **Description:** Promotes theoretical biology and publishes papers on the subject, including the philosophy of biology and biomathematics.
Incorporates (in 1978): Folia Biotheoretica (0920-2676)
Related titles: Microform ed.: (from PQC); Online - full text ed.: ISSN 1572-8358. USD 342 (effective 2005) (from EBSCO Publishing, Gale Group, IngentaConnect, Kluwer Online, O C L C Online Computer Library Center, Inc., Ovid Technologies, Inc., Springer LINK, Swets Information Services).
Indexed: ASCA, AbHyg, AgBio, AgrForAb, AnBrAb, ArtHuCI, BIOBASE, BIOSIS Prev, BibLing, BioCN&I, BiolAb, CPA, ChemAb, CurCont, ExcerpMed, FCA, ForAb, GEOBASE, HerbAb, HortAb, IABS, ISR, IndMed, IndVet, MEDLINE, NutrAb, OrnHort, PBA, PGegResA, PN&I, ProtozoAb, RPP, RefZh, RevApplEntom, S&F, SCI, TDB, VetBull, ZooRec.
—BLDSC (0604.000000), CASDDS, CISTI, IDS, IE, Infotrieve, ingenta, Linda Hall. **CCC.**
Published by: (Prof. Dr. Jan van der Hoeven Foundation for Theoretical Biology), Springer-Verlag Dordrecht (Subsidiary of: Springer Science+Business Media), Van Godewijckstraat 30, Dordrecht, 3311 GX, Netherlands. TEL 31-78-6576050, FAX 31-78-6576474, http://springerlink.metapress.com/openurl.asp?genre=journal&issn=0001-5342, http://www.springeronline.com.

➤ **ACTA ECOLOGICA.** see *ENVIRONMENTAL STUDIES*

571.9 DEU ISSN 1437-9546
QL750

➤ **ACTA ETHOLOGICA ONLINE.** Text in English. 2/yr. **Document type:** *Journal, Academic/Scholarly.*
Media: Online - full text (from EBSCO Publishing, ProQuest Information & Learning, Springer LINK, Swets Information Services). **Related titles:** Microform ed.; ♦ Print ed.: Acta Ethologica. ISSN 0873-9749.
—**CCC.**
Published by: (Instituto Superior de Psicologia Aplicada PRT), Springer-Verlag (Subsidiary of: Springer Science+Business Media), Haber Str 7, Heidelberg, 69126, Germany. TEL 49-6221-3450, FAX 49-6221-229, service@springer.de, http://www.springer.de.

➤ **ACTA FACULTATIS MEDICAE UNIVERSITATIS BRUNENSIS.** see *MEDICAL SCIENCES*

570 910.02 SVK

➤ **ACTA FACULTATIS STUDIORUM HUMANITATIS ET NATURAE UNIVERSITATIS PRESOVIENSIS;** folia geographica. Text in English, Slovak; Summaries in English, German. 1959. s-a. per issue exchange basis. bibl.; charts; illus.; maps; stat. back issues avail. **Document type:** *Academic/Scholarly.* **Description:** Looks to inform teachers and scientists in a variety of geography disciplines results of research in physical geography, human geography, and regional geography.
Former titles (until 1997): Presovska Univerzita. Fakulta Humanitnych a Prirodnych Vied. Prirodne Vedy. Biologia - Geografia - Chemia; Univerzita P.J. Safarika v Kosiciach. Pedagogicka Fakulta v Presove. Zbornik. Prirodne Vedy (0139-5076)
Published by: Presovska Univerzita, Fakulta Humanitnych a Prirodnych Vied, Ul 17 Novembra 1, Presov, 08116, Slovakia. TEL 421-91-722577, FAX 421-91-722547, matlren@unipo.sk. Ed. Rene Matlovic. Circ: 500.

➤ **ACTA MEDICA ET BIOLOGICA/IGAKU SEIBUTSUGAKU KENKYU KIYO.** see *MEDICAL SCIENCES*

➤ **ACTA MEDICA ROMANA.** see *MEDICAL SCIENCES*

570 MKD ISSN 0583-4988
QH7 CODEN: AMMSBV

ACTA MUSEI MACEDONICI SCIENTIARUM NATURALIUM. Text in Macedonian. 1953. irreg. **Document type:** *Monographic series, Academic/Scholarly.*
Indexed: BIOSIS Prev, BiolAb, ESPM, ZooRec.
Published by: Prirodonaucen Muzej na Makedonija, Bulevar Ilinden 86, Skopje, 91000, Macedonia.

570 CZE ISSN 1211-8788
AS142

ACTA MUSEI MORAVIAE. SCIENTIAE BIOLOGICAE/ MORAVSKE ZEMSKE MUZEUM. CASOPIS. VEDY BIOLOGICKE. Text in Czech, English, French, German; Summaries in English, German. 1901. s-a. exchange basis. bk.rev. **Document type:** *Journal, Academic/Scholarly.* **Description:** Brings original papers, reviews and short notes, such as faunistic records, biographies and book reviews.
Supersedes in part (in 1997): Moravske Zemske Muzeum. Casopis. Vedy Prirodni (Acta Musei Moraviae - Scientiae Naturales) (0521-2359); Which superseded in part (in 1950): Moravskeho Musea v Brne. Casopis (1212-1967); Which was formerly (until 1949): Zemskeho Musea v Brne. Casopis (1212-1959); (until 1947): Moravskeho Musea Zemskeho. Casopis (1212-1940)
Related titles: ♦ Supplement(s): Acta Musei Moraviae. Supplementum: Folia Mendeliana. ISSN 0085-0748; ♦ Acta Musei Moraviae. Scientiae Geologicae. ISSN 1211-8796.
Indexed: ZooRec.
Published by: Moravske Zemske Muzeum, Zelny trh 6, Brno, 65937, Czech Republic. TEL 420-5-42321205, FAX 420-5-42212792, ento.kol@volny.cz, mzm@mzm.cz, http://www.mzm.cz/engmzm/ento/uvod-acta.htm. Ed. Jiri Kolibac.

ACTA NEUROBIOLOGIAE EXPERIMENTALIS. see *MEDICAL SCIENCES—Psychiatry And Neurology*

577 FRA ISSN 1146-609X
QH540 CODEN: ACOEEY

➤ **ACTA OECOLOGICA.** Text in English; Abstracts in English, French. 1981. 6/yr. EUR 400 in Europe to institutions; JPY 53,000 in Japan to institutions; USD 448 elsewhere to institutions (effective 2006). bk.rev. charts. back issues avail. **Document type:** *Journal, Academic/Scholarly.* **Description:** Publishes research articles and reviews in ecology, including studies in behavioural ecology, community ecology, conservation biology, evolutionary ecology, physiological ecology and population ecology.
Formed by the merger of (1980-1990): Oecologia Applicata (0243-7678); (1980-1990): Oecologia Generalis (0243-766X); (1966-1990): Acta Oecologica. Oecologia Plantarum (0243-7651); Which was formerly (until 1980): Oecologia Plantarum (0029-8557)
Related titles: Microform ed.: (from MIM, PQC); Online - full text ed.: (from EBSCO Publishing, Gale Group, IngentaConnect, ScienceDirect, Swets Information Services).
Indexed: AEA, ASCA, ASFA, AgrForAb, AnBrAb, ApEcolAb, B&BAb, BIOBASE, BIOSIS Prev, BioCN&I, BiolAb, BrCerAb, C&ISA, CPA, CerAb, ChemAb, CorrAb, CurCont, E&CAJ, EMA, ESPM, EntAb, ExcerpMed, FCA, FPA, ForAb, GEOBASE, HGA, HelmAb, HerbAb, HortAb, I&DA, IAA, IBR, ISR, IndVet, KWIWR, M&TEA, MBF, METADEX, NemAb, NutrAb, OceAb, OrnHort, PBA, PGegResA, PGrRegA, PN&I, PlantSci, PoultAb, RA&MP, RM&VM, RPP, RevApplEntom, S&F, SCI, SFA, SIA, SSCI, SWRA, SeedAb, SolStAb, SoyAb, TriticAb, VetBull, WAA, WAE&RSA, WeedAb, WildRev, ZooRec.
—BLDSC (0641.655000), CASDDS, CISTI, IDS, IE, Infotrieve, ingenta, Linda Hall. **CCC.**
Published by: Elsevier France, Editions Scientifiques et Medicales (Subsidiary of: Elsevier Science & Technology), 23 Rue Linois, Paris, 75724, France. TEL 33-1-71724600, FAX 33-1-71724650, acta.oecologica@inapg.fr, academic@elsevier-fr.com, http://www.elsevier.com/locate/actao. Ed. R. Arditi. Circ: 1,000. **Subscr. to:** Elsevier BV, PO Box 211, Amsterdam 1000 AE, Netherlands. TEL 31-20-485-3757, FAX 31-20-485-3432, nlinfo-f@elsevier.nl, http://www.elsevier.nl. **Co-sponsor:** INRA, CNRS, ORSTOM.

570 610 SWE ISSN 1101-8429

ACTA REGIAE SOCIETATIS SCIENTIARUM ET LITTERARUM GOTHOBURGENSIS. BIOMEDICA. Text in English. 1991. irreg. SEK 100 (effective 2003). **Document type:** *Monographic series, Academic/Scholarly.*
Published by: Kungliga Vetenskaps- och Vitterhets-Samhaelle, c/o Goeteborgs Universitetsbibliotek, PO Box 222, Goeteborg, 40530, Sweden. TEL 46-31-7731733, FAX 46-31-163797.

570.711 BRA ISSN 1415-6814
AS80.U54 CODEN: ASCCCA

➤ **ACTA SCIENTIARUM.** Text in Portuguese, English; Summaries in English, Portuguese. 1974. bi-m. (in 6 vols.). bk.rev. abstr.; bibl.; illus. **Document type:** *Academic/Scholarly.* **Description:** Covers all areas of knowledge. Is subdivided into six parts: Human and Social Sciences (published in February,) Biology (April,) Health (June,) Zoology (August,) Agronomy (October) and Sciences and Technology (December).
Formerly (until 1998): Revista UniMar (0100-9354)
Indexed: AEA, ASFA, AbHyg, AgBio, AgrForAb, AnBrAb, BIOBASE, BIOSIS Prev, BioCN&I, BiolAb, CPA, DSA, ESPM, ExcerpMed, FCA, FPA, ForAb, HelmAb, HerbAb, HortAb, I&DA, IndMed, IndVet, L&LBA, MBA, MLA, MaizeAb, NemAb, NutrAb, OrnHort, PBA, PGegResA, PGrRegA, PHN&I, PN&I, PSA, PoultAb, ProtozoAb, RA&MP, RDA, RPP, RRTA, RefZh, RevApplEntom, RiceAb, S&F, SIA, SOPODA, SSA, SeedAb, SoyAb, TDB, TriticAb, VetBull, WAE&RSA, WeedAb, ZooRec.
Published by: (Universidade Estadual de Maringa, Pro-Reitoria de Pesquisa e Pos-Graduacao), Universidade Estadual de Maringa, Av. Colombo, 5.790, Maringa, Parana 87020-900, Brazil. TEL 55-44-2614253, FAX 55-44-2222754, http://www.uem.br. Ed., R&P Fabio Amodeo Lansac-Toha. Pub. Gilberto Cesar Pavanelli. Circ: 700.

570 CZE ISSN 0001-7124
CODEN: ACBIBC

ACTA UNIVERSITATIS CAROLINAE: BIOLOGICA. Text in English. 1954. q. USD 80 (effective 1999). bk.rev. bibl.; charts; illus.; stat. index. **Document type:** *Academic/Scholarly.* **Description:** Covers cooperative research projects in the field of zoology, anthropology and botany.
Indexed: ASFA, ApicAb, BIOSIS Prev, BiolAb, EntAb, ExcerpMed, PBA, RefZh, S&F, SFA, VITIS, WildRev, ZooRec.
—BLDSC (0584.500000), CASDDS, CISTI, IE, ingenta, Linda Hall.
Published by: (Univerzita Karlova, Prirodovedecka Fakulta), Vydavatelstvi Karolinum, Celetna 18, Prague 1, 116 36, Czech Republic. TEL 420-2-24491111, FAX 420-2-24212041, edice@cuni.cz, kinkorov@mail.natur.cuni. Ed. Milan Chvala. Circ: 650. **Subscr. to:** Vinicna 7, Prague 128 44, Czech Republic.

570 POL ISSN 0208-4449

ACTA UNIVERSITATIS NICOLAI COPERNICI. BIOLOGIA. Text in Polish. 1956. irreg. price varies. **Document type:** *Academic/Scholarly.*
Formerly: Uniwersytet Mikolaja Kopernika, Torun. Nauki Matematyczno-Przyrodnicze. Biologia (0083-4521)
Indexed: AgrAg, AgrLib, BIOSIS Prev, BiolAb, RefZh, ZooRec.
Published by: Uniwersytet Mikolaja Kopernika/Nicolaus Copernicus University, Wydawnictwo, ul Gagarina 39, Torun, 87100, Poland. TEL 48-56-14295. **Dist. by:** Osrodek Rozpowszechniania Wydawnictw Naukowych PAN, Palac Kultury i Nauki, Warsaw 00901, Poland.

570 CZE ISSN 0231-8121
QH301

ACTA UNIVERSITATIS PALACKIANAE OLOMUCENSIS. FACULTAS RERUM NATURALIUM. BIOLOGICA. Text in Multiple languages. 1960. irreg.
Formerly (until 1983): Univerzita Palackeho v Olomouci. Prirodovedecka Fakulta. Sbornik Praci. Biologie (0474-1110)
Indexed: RefZh, ZooRec.
—Linda Hall.
Published by: Univerzita Palackeho v Olomouci, Prirodovedecka Fakulta, tr Svobody 26, c.p.686, Olomouc, 77146, Czech Republic. TEL 420-68-5634060, FAX 420-68-5225737, dekanprf@risc.upd.cz, http://www.upd.cz.

570 LTU ISSN 1392-1657
QL298.L58 CODEN: AZLIFN

➤ **ACTA ZOOLOGICA LITUANICA;** ornithologia, hydrobiologia, entomologia, theriologia, parasitologia, biodiversity. Text in English; Summaries in Lithuanian. 1989. q. EUR 120; EUR 30 per issue (effective 2004). bk.rev. **Document type:** *Journal, Academic/Scholarly.* **Description:** Contains original research articles on theoretical, experimental and methodical study in the field of zoology and animal ecology.
Formerly (until 1995): Acta Ornithologica Lituanica (0135-3861)
Related titles: Online - full text ed.: (from EBSCO Publishing).
Indexed: ESPM, FCA, RevApplEntom, SFA, WildRev, ZooRec.
—BLDSC (0674.200000), IE, ingenta, KNAW, Linda Hall.
Published by: Vilniaus Universiteto, Ekologijos Institutas/Vilnius University, Institute of Ecology, Akademijos 2, Vilnius, 2600, Lithuania. ekoi@ekoi.lt, http://server.ekoi.lt/library/, http://www.ekoi.lt. Ed. Juozas Virbickas. Circ: 500.
Co-sponsor: Lithuanian Scientific Council.

570 COL ISSN 0304-3584
QH301 CODEN: ACBIEF

➤ **ACTUALIDADES BIOLOGICAS.** Text in English, Portuguese, Spanish; Summaries in English, Spanish. 1972-1987; resumed 1988 (vol.20, no.68). s-a. COP 20,000 domestic; USD 25 in the Americas; USD 30 elsewhere (effective 2004). bk.rev. illus. back issues avail. **Document type:** *Journal, Academic/Scholarly.* **Description:** Presents results of investigations in all fields of biology, most of which take place in Colombia.
Indexed: ASFA, BIOSIS Prev, BiolAb, ChemAb, ESPM, ZooRec.
—CASDDS, CISTI.
Published by: Universidad de Antioquia, Instituto de Biologia, Apdo Aereo 1226, Medellin, Colombia. TEL 574-210-5146, FAX 574-211-6939, actubiol@matematicas.udea.edu.co, http://matematicas.udea.edu.co/cen/revista/actbiol.html. Ed. Daniel Aldana. Circ: 700.

570 FRA ISSN 0753-3918

ACTUALITES BIOLOGIQUES. Text in French. m. adv. **Document type:** *Trade.* **Description:** For professionals and administrators of biological analysis laboratories.
Published by: Centre National des Biologistes, 80 av. du Maine, Paris, 75014, France. TEL 33-1-43229770, FAX 33-1-43217312. Pub. Jean Benoit. Adv. contact Jeanne Berga.

ADRESBOEK VOOR BIOLOGEN. see *BUSINESS AND ECONOMICS—Trade And Industrial Directories*

570 SCG ISSN 0354-5547
DE1

ADRIATICO. Text in English. 1994. a. illus. back issues avail. **Document type:** *Academic/Scholarly.* **Description:** Regional cooperation in the Mediterranean.
Published by: Ministry of Foreign Affairs of the Republic of Montenegro, Center for Mediterranean Studies, Stanka Dragojevica 2, Podgorica, 81000. TEL 381-81-241-334, FAX 381-81-245-752, mip@cg.yu. Ed. Sanja Elezovic. Circ: 500.

ADVANCED DRUG DELIVERY REVIEWS. see *PHARMACY AND PHARMACOLOGY*

B

570 USA ISSN 0301-5556
QL801
➤ **ADVANCES IN ANATOMY, EMBRYOLOGY AND CELL BIOLOGY.** Text in English. 1891. irreg., latest vol.177, 2004. price varies. reprint service avail. from ISI. **Document type:** *Monographic series, Academic/Scholarly.* **Description:** Presents critical reviews on all topical fields of normal and experimental anatomy including cell biology.
Formerly (until 1973): Ergebnisse der Anatomie und Entwicklungsgeschichte (0071-1098)
Indexed: ASCA, BIOSIS Prev, BiolAb, ISR, IndMed, IndVet, MEDLINE, SCI, VetBull, ZooRec.
—BLDSC (0698.800000), CISTI, GNLM, IE, Infotrieve, ingenta, KNAW. **CCC.**
Published by: Springer-Verlag New York, Inc. (Subsidiary of: Springer Science+Business Media), 233 Spring St, New York, NY 10013. TEL 212-460-1500, 800-777-4643, FAX 212-473-6272, http://www.springer-ny.com.

➤ **ADVANCES IN BEHAVIORAL BIOLOGY.** see *PSYCHOLOGY*

➤ **ADVANCES IN BIOETHICS.** see *PHILOSOPHY*

➤ **ADVANCES IN COLLOID AND INTERFACE SCIENCE.** see *CHEMISTRY—Physical Chemistry*

571 572 NLD ISSN 1569-1799
CODEN: ADBBCX
ADVANCES IN DEVELOPMENTAL BIOLOGY AND BIOCHEMISTRY. Text in English. 2002. s-a. price varies. back issues avail. **Document type:** *Monographic series, Academic/Scholarly.* **Description:** Represents an attempt to consider timely issues in developmental biology and biochemistry research. It provides annual reviews of selected topics, written from the perspectives of leading investigators in the field of development.
Formed by the merger of (1992-2002): Advances in Developmental Biochemistry (1064-2722); Advances in Developmental Biology (1566-3116)
Related titles: Online - full text ed.: (from ScienceDirect).
—BLDSC (0704.243820), CISTI.
Published by: Elsevier BV (Subsidiary of: Elsevier Science & Technology), Radarweg 29, Amsterdam, 1043 NX, Netherlands. TEL 31-20-4853911, FAX 31-20-4852457, nlinfo-f@elsevier.nl, http://www.elsevier.nl. Ed. Paul Wassarman TEL 212-241-8616. Pub. Hendrik van Leusen TEL 31-20-4853852.

ADVANCES IN ECOLOGICAL RESEARCH. see *ENVIRONMENTAL STUDIES*

ADVANCES IN ECOLOGICAL SCIENCES. see *ENVIRONMENTAL STUDIES*

ADVANCES IN FISH BIOLOGY AND FISHERIES. see *FISH AND FISHERIES*

570 CHE
➤ **ADVANCES IN LIFE SCIENCES.** Text in English. irreg. price varies. **Document type:** *Monographic series, Academic/Scholarly.*
Published by: Birkhaeuser Verlag AG (Subsidiary of: Springer Science+Business Media), Viaduktstr 42, Postfach 133, Basel, 4051, Switzerland. TEL 41-61-2050707, FAX 41-61-2050792, orders@birkhauser.ch, birkhauser@springer.de, http://www.birkhauser.ch.

➤ **ADVANCES IN LIMNOLOGY**; archiv fur hydrobiologie, special issues. see *EARTH SCIENCES—Hydrology*

578.77 USA ISSN 0065-2881
QH91.A1 CODEN: AMBYAR
➤ **ADVANCES IN MARINE BIOLOGY.** Text in English. 1963. irreg., latest vol.44. USD 149.95 per vol. vol.45 (effective 2004). index. reprint service avail. from ISI. **Document type:** *Monographic series, Academic/Scholarly.* **Description:** Provides in-depth and up-to-date reviews on all aspects of Marine Biology.
Related titles: Online - full text ed.: (from ScienceDirect).
Indexed: ASCA, ASFA, B&AI, BIOSIS Prev, BiolAb, ChemAb, ESPM, GEOBASE, ISR, OceAb, SCI, SFA, WildRev, ZooRec.
—BLDSC (0709.340000), CASDDS, CISTI, IE, ingenta, KNAW, Linda Hall. **CCC.**
Published by: Academic Press (Subsidiary of: Elsevier Science & Technology), 525 B St, Ste 1900, San Diego, CA 92101-4495. TEL 619-231-6616, 800-894-3434, apsubs@acad.com, http://www.academicpress.com. Eds. F S Russell, J H S Blaxter.

570 USA ISSN 1554-4516
▼ **ADVANCES IN PLANAR LIPID BILAYERS AND LIPOSOMES.** Text in English. 2005 (June). m. **Document type:** *Journal, Academic/Scholarly.*
Published by: Elsevier Inc. (Subsidiary of: Elsevier Science & Technology), 525 B St. Ste. 1900, San Diego, CA 92101-4495. TEL 619-231-6616, FAX 619-699-6422, usinfo-f@elsevier.com, http://www.elsevier.com.

570 USA ISSN 1064-6000
QH573 CODEN: ASBIEP
ADVANCES IN STRUCTURAL BIOLOGY. Text in English. 1991. irreg., latest vol.6, 2002. price varies. back issues avail. **Document type:** *Monographic series, Academic/Scholarly.*
Indexed: BIOSIS Prev, ZooRec.
—BLDSC (0711.584700), CISTI, IE, ingenta. **CCC.**
Published by: J A I Press Inc. (Subsidiary of: Elsevier Science & Technology), 360 Park Ave S, New York, NY 10010-1710. TEL 212-989-5800, FAX 212-633-3990, usinfo-f@elsevier.com, http://www.elsevier.com/wps/find/bookdescription.cws_home/BS_ASB/description#description. Ed. S K Malhotra.

363.7 NLD ISSN 0393-5965
QR101 CODEN: AROBFT
➤ **AEROBIOLOGIA**; international journal of aerobiology. Text in English. 1985. q. EUR 357, USD 356, GBP 235 combined subscription to institutions print & online eds. (effective 2005). **Document type:** *Journal, Academic/Scholarly.* **Description:** Publishes original research and review papers in the interdisciplinary fields of aerobiology and biosphere-atmosphere interaction, including airborne microbiology, biometeorology, climatology, and related issues such as respiratory allergology, indoor air quality and biological weathering.
Formerly (until 1994): European Journal of Aerobiology
Related titles: Online - full text ed.: ISSN 1573-3025 (from EBSCO Publishing, Gale Group, IngentaConnect, Kluwer Online, O C L C Online Computer Library Center, Inc., ScienceDirect, Springer LINK, Swets Information Services).
Indexed: AbHyg, B&BAb, BIOBASE, BIOSIS Prev, BibLing, BiolAb, ESPM, EnvEAb, ExcerpMed, ForAb, H&SSA, M&GPA, MBA, PollutAb, RM&VM, RefZh, ToxAb, WeedAb.
—BLDSC (0721.350000), CISTI, IE, Infotrieve, ingenta. **CCC.**
Published by: (Italian Association for Aerobiology/Associazzione Italiana di Aerobiologia ITA), Springer-Verlag Dordrecht (Subsidiary of: Springer Science+Business Media), Van Godewijckstraat 30, Dordrecht, 3311 GX, Netherlands. TEL 31-78-6576050, FAX 31-78-6576474, http://springerlink.metapress.com/openurl.asp?genre=journal&issn=0393-5965, http://www.springeronline.com.

551.48 ZAF ISSN 1608-5914
QH90.A1 CODEN: AJASBI
➤ **AFRICAN JOURNAL OF AQUATIC SCIENCE**; official journal of the Southern African Society of Aquatic Scientists. Text and summaries in English. 1915. s-a., latest vol.26, no.2, 2001. ZAR 342 domestic to individuals; ZAR 380 in Africa to individuals; USD 145 elsewhere to individuals; ZAR 495 elsewhere to institutions; ZAR 495 in Africa to institutions; USD 220 elsewhere to institutions (effective 2004). adv. bk.rev. charts; illus. cum.index: 1975-1985. back issues avail. **Document type:** *Academic/Scholarly.* **Description:** Research papers on the aquatic sciences, with emphasis on Southern African issues and circumstances.
Former titles (until Mar. 2001): Southern African Journal of Aquatic Sciences (1018-3469); (until 1988): Limnological Society of Southern Africa. Journal (0377-9688); (until 1964): Limnological Society of Southern Africa. Newsletter (0024-3582)
Related titles: Microfiche ed.: 1964; Online - full text ed.: ISSN 1727-9364 (from EBSCO Publishing, Gale Group, IngentaConnect, International Network for the Availability of Scientific Publications, African Journals Online).
Indexed: ASFA, AgrForAb, AnBrAb, BIOSIS Prev, BioCN&I, BiolAb, CIN, CTO, ChemAb, ChemTitl, DIP, ESPM, EntAb, EnvEAb, HelmAb, HerbAb, I&DA, IBR, IBZ, ISAP, IndVet, PN&I, PollutAb, RDA, RRTA, S&F, SCI, SFA, SJW, SWRA, TDB, VetBull, WAE&RSA, WRCInf, WeedAb, WildRev, ZooRec.
—BLDSC (0732.515700), CASDDS, CISTI, Linda Hall. **CCC.**
Published by: (Southern African Society of Aquatic Scientists), National Inquiry Services Centre (Pty) Ltd (Subsidiary of: N I S C USA), PO Box 377, Grahamstown, 6140, South Africa. TEL 27-46-622-9698, 27-33-344-2789, FAX 27-46-622-9550, journals@nisc.co.za, info@nisc.co.za, http://www.dwaf.pwv.gov.za/iwqs/sasaqs; http://www.inasp.info/ajol/journals/ajas/about.html, http://www.nisc.co.za. Ed. Mike Coke TEL 27-33-344-2789. Pub., Adv. contact Georgina Jones. R&P Margaret Crampton. B&W page USD 300; 175 x 245. Circ: 400.

577 GBR ISSN 0141-6707
QL337.E25 CODEN: AJOEDE
➤ **AFRICAN JOURNAL OF ECOLOGY.** Text in English. 1962. q. USD 1,006 combined subscription in the Americas to institutions & Caribbean, print & online eds.; GBP 545 combined subscription in Europe to institutions print & online eds.; GBP 599 combined subscription elsewhere to institutions print & online eds. (effective 2006). adv. bk.rev. illus. cum.index. back issues avail.; reprint service avail. from ISI,PSC. **Document type:** *Journal, Academic/Scholarly.* **Description:** Publishes original scientific research into the ecology of the animals and plants of Africa.
Formerly: East African Wildlife Journal (0070-8038)
Related titles: Microform ed.: (from PQC); ◆ Online - full text ed.: African Journal of Ecology Online. ISSN 1365-2028.
Indexed: AEA, ASCA, ASFA, AbAn, AgrForAb, AnBrAb, ApEcolAb, BIOBASE, BIOSIS Prev, BioCN&I, BiolAb, CPA, CRFR, CurCont, DSA, EPB, ESPM, EntAb, FCA, FPA, ForAb, GEOBASE, HelmAb, HerbAb, HortAb, I&DA, IABS, ISR, IndVet, MaizeAb, NutrAb, PBA, PGegResA, PN&I, PlantSci, PoultAb, ProtozoAb, RA&MP, RM&VM, RPP, RRTA, RevApplEntom, RiceAb, S&F, SCI, SFA, SWRA, SeedAb, SoyAb, TDB, VetBull, WAE&RSA, WLR, WeedAb, WildRev, ZooRec.
—BLDSC (0732.519000), IDS, IE, Infotrieve, ingenta, Linda Hall. **CCC.**
Published by: (East African Wild Life Society), Blackwell Publishing Ltd., 9600 Garsington Rd, Oxford, OX4 2ZG, United Kingdom. TEL 44-1865-776868, FAX 44-1865-714591, customerservices@oxon.blackwellpublishing.com, http://www.blackwellpublishing.com/journals/AJE. Ed. F I B Kayanja. Pub. Sue Hewitt. R&P Sophie Savage. Adv. contact Jenny Applin. Circ: 380.

577 GBR ISSN 1365-2028
QL337.E25
AFRICAN JOURNAL OF ECOLOGY ONLINE. Text in English. q. USD 956 in the Americas to institutions & Caribbean; GBP 519 in Europe to institutions; GBP 569 elsewhere to institutions (effective 2006). **Document type:** *Academic/Scholarly.*
Media: Online - full text (from Blackwell Synergy, EBSCO Publishing, Gale Group, IngentaConnect, O C L C Online Computer Library Center, Inc., Swets Information Services).
Related titles: Microform ed.: (from PQC); ◆ Print ed.: African Journal of Ecology. ISSN 0141-6707.
Published by: Blackwell Publishing Ltd., 9600 Garsington Rd, Oxford, OX4 2ZG, United Kingdom. TEL 44-1865-776868, FAX 44-1865-714591, customerservices@oxon.blackwellpublishing.com, http://www.blackwellpublishing.com.

AFRICAN JOURNAL OF TROPICAL HYDROBIOLOGY AND FISHERIES. see *FISH AND FISHERIES*

THE AG BIOETHICS FORUM. see *AGRICULTURE*

570 JPN
AGEHA/SWALLOW-TAIL. Text in Japanese. 1949. biennial.
Published by: Aichi Kenritsu Kariya Koto Gakko, Seibutsu Kurabu O B Agehakai/Aichi Prefectural Kariya Senior High School, Agehakai in Alumnus of Biological Club, c/o Mr Masami Sugiura, 5-25 Yahatamachi, Kariya-shi, Aichi-ken 448-0000, Japan.

AGRICULTURAL AND BIOLOGICAL RESEARCH. see *AGRICULTURE*

AGRO SUR. see *AGRICULTURE*

AGROCIENCIA. see *AGRICULTURE*

577 ITA ISSN 1124-8343
AIRONE. Text in Italian. 1981. m. adv. bk.rev. charts; illus. **Document type:** *Magazine, Consumer.* **Description:** Features items on ecology, nature and civilization.
Published by: Editoriale Giorgio Mondadori SpA (Subsidiary of: Cairo Communication SpA), Via Tucidide 56, Torre 3, Milan, 20134, Italy. TEL 39-02-748111, FAX 39-02-70100102, info@cairocommunication.it, http://www.cairocommunication.it. Ed. Nicoletta Salvatori. Circ: 100,000.

570 JPN ISSN 0912-5949
AIZU SEIBUTSU DOKOKAISHI/AIZU BIOLOGICAL CIRCLE. JOURNAL. Text in Japanese. 1962. a.
Published by: Aizu Seibutsu Dokokai/Aizu Biological Circle, 8-1 Hanaharu-Machi, Aizuwakamatsu-shi, Fukushima-ken 965-0804, Japan.

570 ARM ISSN 0002-2918
QH301 CODEN: BZARAZ
➤ **AJASTAN KENSABANAKAN HANDES/BIOLOGICAL JOURNAL OF ARMENIA/BIOLOGICHESKII ZHURNAL ARMENII.** Text in Armenian, Russian, English. 1948. q. USD 40 foreign (effective 2003). abstr.; illus.; bibl.; charts. 75 p./no. 1 cols./p.; back issues avail. **Document type:** *Journal, Academic/Scholarly.* **Description:** Publishes original papers in botany, zoology, physiology, boichemistry, biophysics, microbiology, boitechnology, genetics.
Related titles: CD-ROM ed.; Diskette ed.
Indexed: AnBrAb, BioDAb, BiolAb, CIN, CPA, ChemAb, ChemTitl, DSA, FCA, FS&TA, ForAb, HerbAb, HortAb, INIS AtomInd, MaizeAb, PBA, PoultAb, RPP, S&F, SeedAb, TriticAb, VITIS, VetBull.
—CISTI, Linda Hall.
Published by: (Hayastany Guitoutyunnery Azgayin Academia, Manrenery Avandadrman Hanrapetakan Kentron/National Academy of Sciences of Armenia, State Microbial Depository Centre), Edit Print, Tumanyan St 12-3, Yerevan 1, Armenia. microbio@pnas.sci.am. Ed. Dr. Evrik Afrikian.

570 KAZ
QH301 CODEN: IKABAR
AKADEMIYA NAUK KAZAKHSTANA. IZVESTIYA. SERIYA BIOLOGICHESKAYA. Text in Russian. 1955. bi-m. charts; illus. index. **Document type:** *Academic/Scholarly.*

Formerly (until 1992): Akademiya Nauk Kazakhskoi S.S.R. Izvestiya. Seriya Biologicheskaya (0002-3183)
Indexed: AnBrAb, BiolAb, CPA, ChemAb, DSA, FCA, HerbAb, HortAb, IndVet, PBA, ProtozoAb, RPP, S&F, SeedAb, TriticAb, VetBull, WeedAb.
—CASDDS, CISTI, KNAW, Linda Hall.
Published by: (Kazakstan Respublikasy Ulttyk Gylym Akademiasy/National Academy of Sciences of the Republic of Kazakhstan), Gylym, Pushkina 111-113, Almaty, 480100, Kazakstan. TEL 3272-611877. Ed. K T Tashenov. **Subscr. to:** G.R. Kondubayeva, Ul Shevchenko 28, Almaty 480021, Kazakstan.

570 TKM CODEN: ITUBAK
AKADEMIYA NAUK TURKMENISTANA. IZVESTIYA. SERIYA BIOLOGICHESKIKH NAUK. Text in Russian. 1960. bi-m. charts; illus. index.
Formerly (until 1992): Akademiya Nauk Turkmenskoi S.S.R. Izvestiya. Seriya Biologicheskikh Nauk (0321-1746)
Indexed: BioCN&I, BiolAb, ChemAb, HortAb, OrnHort, VetBull, WeedAb, ZooRec.
—CASDDS, CISTI, Linda Hall. **CCC.**
Published by: Akademiya Nauk Turkmenistana, Gogolya ul 15, Ashkhabad, 744000, Turkmenistan. Circ: 500.

578.77 USA ISSN 0271-7069
ALASKA SEA GRANT REPORT. Text in English. irreg. **Document type:** *Monographic series.*
Indexed: BIOSIS Prev, ZooRec.
Published by: University of Alaska Sea Grant College Program, PO Box 755040-INT, Fairbanks, AK 99775-5040. TEL 907-474-6707, 888-789-0090, FAX 907-474-6285, fygrant@uaf.edu, http://www.uaf.edu/seagrant/.

579.8 DEU ISSN 0342-1120
QK564
ALGOLOGICAL STUDIES; Archiv fur Hydrobiologie, Supplementbaende. Text in English, French, German. 1970. irreg. EUR 122 per vol. domestic (effective 2005). bk.rev. **Document type:** *Monographic series, Academic/Scholarly.*
Related titles: ♦ Supplement to: Archiv fuer Hydrobiologie. ISSN 0003-9136.
Indexed: ASFA, BiolAb, ESPM, IABS, SFA, WildRev, ZooRec.
—BLDSC (1613.001000), CISTI, IE, ingenta, Linda Hall. **CCC.**
Published by: E. Schweizerbart'sche Verlagsbuchhandlung, Johannesstr 3A, Stuttgart, 70176, Germany. TEL 49-711-3514560, FAX 49-711-35145699, algolstud@butbn.cas.cz, mail@schweizerbart.de, http://www.schweizerbart.de/j/algological-studies/. Ed. O Lhotsky.

ALMANAK NUKLIR BIOLOGI DAN KIMIA. see *ENERGY—Nuclear Energy*

570 ISR ISSN 0333-9815
ALON LEMOREH HABIOLOGIA/PAMPHLET FOR BIOLOGY TEACHERS. Text in Hebrew. 1969. q. USD 20. bk.rev. index. back issues avail. **Document type:** *Trade.* **Description:** Provides biology teachers with ideas and activities for classroom enrichment. Discusses current information in the biological sciences and problems and issues in biology education.
Indexed: IHP.
Published by: Hebrew University of Jerusalem, Amos De Shalit Science Teaching Centre, Jerusalem, Israel. TEL 972-2-585365. Ed. Talmona Oryan. Circ: 700.

570 551 560 DEU ISSN 0232-5381
ALTENBURGER NATURWISSENSCHAFTLICHE FORSCHUNGEN. Text in German; Summaries in English, German. 1981. a. price varies. bk.rev. back issues avail. **Document type:** *Journal, Academic/Scholarly.*
Indexed: RefZh, ZooRec.
—Linda Hall.
Published by: Naturkundliches Museum Mauritianum, Postfach 1644, Altenburg, 04590, Germany. direktion@mauritianum.de, http://www.mauritianum.de. Ed. Norbert Hoeser. Circ: 1,200.

570 JPN ISSN 0065-6682
QH91.Al CODEN: ARJPB8
AMAKUSA MARINE BIOLOGICAL LABORATORY. PUBLICATIONS. Text and summaries in English. 1966. a. per issue exchange basis. **Document type:** *Academic/Scholarly.* **Description:** Publishes mainly achievements of laboratory staff and visiting scientists. Also contains ecological and taxonomic studies of benthic invertebrates in the littoral and shallow sea.
Indexed: ASFA, BiolAb, ESPM, SFA, ZooRec.
—Linda Hall.
Published by: Kyushu University, Amakusa Marine Biological Laboratory/Kyushu Daigaku Rigakubu Fuzoku Amakusa Rinkai Jikkensho, 2231 Tomioka, Amakusa-gun, Reihoku Cho, Kumamoto ken 8632507, Japan. TEL 81-969-35-0003, FAX 81-969-35-2413. R&P Taiji Kikuchi. Circ: 450.

577 DEU ISSN 0065-6755
QH117 CODEN: AMAZAP
➤ **AMAZONIANA.** Text in Multiple languages. 1965. a. (2 nos./vol.). **Document type:** *Journal, Academic/Scholarly.*
Indexed: ASCA, ASFA, ApEcolAb, BIOSIS Prev, BiolAb, CurCont, ESPM, EntAb, FPA, ForAb, GEOBASE, PollutAb, RefZh, RevApplEntom, S&F, SWRA, ZooRec.
—IDS. **CCC.**
Published by: Universitaetsbuchhandlung Muehlau, Holtenauer Str 116, Kiel, 24105, Germany. TEL 49-431-800900, FAX 49-431-8009050, http://www.muehlau.de. Eds. Djalma Batista, Harald Sioli.

577 ARG
AMBIENTE ECOLOGICO. Text in Spanish. m.
Media: Online - full text.
Published by: Multimedios Ambiente Ecologico, Ave General Urquiza 4750, Buenos Aires, Caseros 1678, Argentina. TEL 54-11-4750-9628, info@ambiente-ecologico.com, http://www.ambiente-ecologico.com. Ed. Alejandro Rodolfo Malpartida.

570 SWE ISSN 0301-0325
CODEN: AOSRB4
AMBIO SPECIAL REPORT. Text in English. 1972. irreg. back issues avail. **Document type:** *Monographic series, Academic/Scholarly.*
Related titles: ♦ Supplement to: Ambio. ISSN 0044-7447.
Indexed: BIOSIS Prev, BiolAb, ZooRec.
—BLDSC (0808.950000), CISTI, Linda Hall.
Published by: Kungliga Vetenskapsakademien/Royal Swedish Academy of Sciences, PO Box 50005, Stockholm, 10405, Sweden. TEL 46-8-6739551, FAX 46-8-166251, http://www.kva.se.

570 590 AUT ISSN 1028-2831
➤ **AMEMBOA**; news and results on Thai heteroptera. Text and summaries in English, German. 1996. irreg. price varies. illus.; maps. back issues avail. **Document type:** *Journal, Academic/Scholarly.* **Description:** Presents news and results connected with the international research project "Heteroptera of Thailand.".
Indexed: BIOSIS Prev, BiolAb, ZooRec.
Published by: Naturhistorisches Museum in Wien, Burgring 7, Postfach 417, Vienna, W 1014, Austria. TEL 43-1-52177-497, herbert.zettel@nhm-wien.ac.at, http://www.nhm-wien.ac.at. Ed. Herbert Zettel.

570.711 USA ISSN 0002-7685
QH1
➤ **THE AMERICAN BIOLOGY TEACHER.** Text in English. 1938. m. (during school year). USD 90 domestic membership; USD 125 foreign membership (effective 2005). adv. bk.rev.; film rev.; software rev. charts; illus.; stat. Index. back issues avail.; reprints avail. **Document type:** *Magazine, Academic/Scholarly.* **Description:** Includes updates on biological research, educational strategies and technologies, suggestions for laboratory and classroom exercises, and audio-visual reviews.
Related titles: Microfilm ed.: (from PQC); Online - full text ed.: (from bigchalk, BioOne, C S A, O C L C Online Computer Library Center, Inc., ProQuest Information & Learning).
Indexed: ABIn, ABS&EES, ASCA, AbHyg, AgBio, Agr, AnBrAb, BRI, BioCN&I, BiolAb, BiolDig, CIJE, CPE, CurCont, DSA, EduInd, EnvAb, FCA, ForAb, GSI, GardL, HortAb, IndVet, MRD, MaizeAb, NutrAb, PBA, PHN&I, ProtozoAb, RASB, RILM, RPP, RefZh, S&F, SSCI, SeedAb, Telegen, VetBull, WeedAb, WildRev.
—BLDSC (0810.800000), CIS, CISTI, IDS, IE, Infotrieve, ingenta, Linda Hall.
Published by: National Association of Biology Teachers, Inc., 12030 Sunrise Valley Dr, 110, Reston, VA 20191. TEL 703-264-9696, FAX 703-264-7778, nabter@aol.com, http://www.nabt.org. Ed. Ann Haley Mackenzie. Pub. Wayne Carley. Circ: 12,000 (paid).

➤ **AMERICAN JOURNAL OF CLINICAL PATHOLOGY.** see *MEDICAL SCIENCES*

570 USA ISSN 1042-0533
QP1 CODEN: AJHUES
➤ **AMERICAN JOURNAL OF HUMAN BIOLOGY.** Text in English. 1989. bi-m. USD 1,140 domestic to institutions; USD 1,212 in Canada & Mexico to institutions; USD 1,254 elsewhere to institutions; USD 1,254 combined subscription domestic to institutions print & online eds.; USD 1,326 combined subscription in Canada & Mexico to institutions print & online eds.; USD 1,368 combined subscription elsewhere to institutions print & online eds. (effective 2006). adv. back issues avail. **Document type:** *Journal, Academic/Scholarly.* **Description:** Provides a forum for research in human biology. For scientists and professionals interested in understanding individual and population variations in health and disease. Covers a wide range of topics in such areas as genetic variation, anatomy and physiology, growth and aging, physical performance and evolution.
Formerly: Human Biology (New York)
Related titles: Microform ed.: (from PQC); Online - full text ed.: ISSN 1520-6300. USD 1,140 to institutions (effective 2006) (from EBSCO Publishing, Swets Information Services, Wiley InterScience).
Indexed: AICP, ASCA, AbHyg, AgeL, AnBrAb, AnthLit, ArtHuCI, BIOBASE, BIOSIS Prev, BiolAb, BiolDig, CIS, CTA, CurCont, DSA, ExcerpMed, FamI, GSI, HelmAb, HortAb, Inpharma, NRN, NutrAb, PE&ON, PEI, PopulInd, ProtozoAb, RDA, RRTA, Reac, RefZh, RevApplEntom, RiceAb, SSCI, TDB, WAE&RSA.
—BLDSC (0824.900000), CISTI, GNLM, IDS, IE, Infotrieve, ingenta, KNAW. **CCC.**
Published by: (Human Biology Council), John Wiley & Sons, Inc., 111 River St, Hoboken, NJ 07030-5774. TEL 201-748-6000, FAX 201-748-5915, uscs-wis@wiley.com, http://www.interscience.wiley.com/jpages/1042-0533/, http://www.wiley.com. Ed. Peter Ellison. adv.: B&W page GBP 640, color page GBP 1,515; trim 174 x 254. Circ: 800. **Subscr. outside the Americas to:** John Wiley & Sons Ltd., The Atrium, Southern Gate, Chichester, West Sussex PO19 8SQ, United Kingdom. TEL 44-1243-843335, 0800-243407, FAX 44-1243-843232, cs-journals@wiley.co.uk.

577 USA ISSN 0003-0147
CODEN: AMNTA4
➤ **THE AMERICAN NATURALIST.** Text in English. 1867. m. USD 75 combined subscription to individuals print & online eds.; USD 499 combined subscription to institutions print & online eds.; USD 11 per issue to individuals; USD 49 per issue to institutions (effective 2006). adv. illus. Index. 145 p./no.; reprints avail. **Document type:** *Journal, Academic/Scholarly.* **Description:** Addresses ecology and evolutionary biology; devoted to the conceptual unification of the biological sciences.
Related titles: Microform ed.: (from IDC, PMC, PQC); Online - full text ed.: ISSN 1537-5323. USD 51 to individual members (effective 2006) (from EBSCO Publishing, Florida Center for Library Automation, Gale Group, JSTOR (Web-based Journal Archive), ProQuest Information & Learning).
Indexed: AEA, APD, ASCA, ASFA, AbHyg, AgBio, Agr, AnBeAb, AnBrAb, ApEcolAb, ApicAb, B&AI, B&BAb, BIOBASE, BIOSIS Prev, BioCN&I, BiolAb, BiolDig, CIS, CPA, CRFR, ChemAb, CurCont, DSA, EPB, ESPM, EngInd, EntAb, FCA, ForAb, GEOBASE, GSI, GardL, GenetAb, HelmAb, HerbAb, HortAb, I&DA, IABS, IAOP, ISR, IndVet, KWIWR, MEDLINE, MathR, NemAb, NutrAb, OceAb, OrnHort, PBA, PGegResA, PGrRegA, PHN&I, PlantSci, PoultAb, ProtozoAb, RA&MP, RASB, RM&VM, RPP, RefZh, RevApplEntom, RiceAb, S&F, SCI, SFA, SIA, SSCI, SeedAb, SoyAb, TDB, VetBull, WeedAb, WildRev, ZooRec.
—BLDSC (0846.000000), CASDDS, CISTI, Ei, IDS, IE, Infotrieve, ingenta, Linda Hall. **CCC.**
Published by: (American Society of Naturalists), University of Chicago Press, Journals Division, 1111 E. 60th St, Chicago, IL 60637. TEL 773-753-3347, FAX 773-753-0811, subscriptions@press.uchicago.edu, http://www.journals.uchicago.edu/AN. Eds. Jonathan Losos, Michael C Whitlock. Adv. contact Cheryl Jones. page USD 545; trim 8.25 x 10.875. Circ: 2,600 (paid).

372.357 NLD ISSN 0926-3543
AMOEBA. Text in Dutch. 1926. 5/yr. EUR 12.50 to members (effective 2005). charts; illus.; stat. **Document type:** *Bulletin.* **Description:** Presents environmental studies to young people and discusses botany, entomology, ornithology, zoology, and nature conservation. Includes lists of local, regional, and national events of relevance to members.
Indexed: ZooRec.
Published by: Nederlands Jeugdbond voor Natuurstudie/Netherlands Youth Organization for Natural Studies, Postbus 9955, 's Graveland, 1243 ZS, Netherlands. TEL 31-35-6559848, amoeba@njn.nl, info@njn.nl, http://www.njn.nl. Circ: 1,200.

570 CHL ISSN 0716-6486
QH119
ANALES DE LA PATAGONIA. SERIE CIENCIAS NATURALES. Text in Spanish. 1970. a.
Supersedes in part (in 1984): Anales del Instituto de la Patagonia (0085-1922)
Indexed: BiolAb, ZooRec.
Published by: Universidad de Magallanes, Instituto de la Patagonia, Casilla de Correos 113 D, Punta Arenas, Magallanes, Chile. TEL 56-91-207061, FAX 56-61-212973, xsilva@aoniken.fc.umag.cl.

570 560 VEN ISSN 1315-642X
ANARTIA. Text in Spanish. 1989. q. **Document type:** *Monographic series.*
Indexed: ASFA, GEOBASE, ZooRec.
Published by: Universidad del Zulia, Museo de Biologia, Edificio A-1, Grano de Oro, Aptdo 526, Maracaibo, 4011, Venezuela. TEL 261-7519795, FAX 261-7524310.

571.3 611 USA ISSN 1552-4884
QL801
➤ **THE ANATOMICAL RECORD. PART A: DISCOVERIES IN MOLECULAR, CELLULAR, AND EVOLUTIONARY BIOLOGY.** Text in English. 1906. 12/yr. USD 5,795 domestic to institutions; USD 5,975 in Canada & Mexico to institutions; USD 6,128 elsewhere to institutions; USD 6,375 combined subscription domestic to institutions print & online eds.; USD 6,555 combined subscription in Canada & Mexico to institutions print & online eds.; USD 6,708 combined subscription elsewhere to institutions print & online eds. (effective 2006); includes Part B. adv. bk.rev. abstr.; bibl.; charts; illus. index. back issues avail.; reprints avail. **Document type:** *Journal, Academic/Scholarly.* **Description:** Focuses upon major new findings in the anatomical consequences of gene disruption, activation, or over expression upon cell, tissue, or organ architecture.

Supersedes in part (in 2003): The Anatomical Record (0003-276X)
Related titles: Microfilm ed.: (from PMC); Microform ed.: (from PQC); Online - full content ed.: ISSN 1552-4892. USD 5,795 to institutions (effective 2006); Online - full text ed.: (from EBSCO Publishing, Swets Information Services, Wiley InterScience).
Indexed: ASCA, ASFA, AbAn, AnBrAb, B&AI, BiolAb, CIN, CTD, ChemAb, ChemTitl, CurCont, DentInd, ExcerpMed, FoVS&M, IABS, ISR, IndMed, IndVet, Inpharma, NSCI, NutrAb, PE&ON, Reac, RefZh, SCI, SFA, THA, VetBull, WildRev, ZooRec.
—BLDSC (0898.020000), CASDDS, CISTI, GNLM, IDS, IE, Infotrieve, KNAW, Linda Hall.
Published by: (American Association of Anatomists), John Wiley & Sons, Inc., 111 River St, Hoboken, NJ 07030-5774. TEL 201-748-6000, FAX 201-748-5915, uscs-wis@wiley.com, http://www3.interscience.wiley.com/cgi-bin/jhome/28243, http://www.wiley.com. Ed. Aaron J Ladman. adv.: B&W page USD 1,080, color page USD 2,420; trim 8.25 x 11. Circ: 1,200 (paid). **Subscr. outside the Americas to:** John Wiley & Sons Ltd., The Atrium, Southern Gate, Chichester, West Sussex PO19 8SQ, United Kingdom. TEL 44-1243-779777, FAX 44-1243-775878, cs-journals@wiley.co.uk.

571.3 611 USA ISSN 1552-4906
QL801
➤ **THE ANATOMICAL RECORD. PART B: THE NEW ANATOMIST.** Text in English. 1906. 6/yr. USD 5,795 domestic to institutions; USD 5,975 in Canada & Mexico to institutions; USD 6,128 elsewhere to institutions; USD 6,375 combined subscription domestic to institutions print & online eds.; USD 6,555 combined subscription in Canada & Mexico to institutions print & online eds.; USD 6,708 combined subscription elsewhere to institutions print & online eds. (effective 2006); includes Part A. back issues avail. **Document type:** *Journal, Academic/Scholarly.*
Supersedes in part (in 2003): The Anatomical Record (0003-276X)
Related titles: Online - full text ed.: ISSN 1552-4914. USD 5,795 to institutions (effective 2006) (from EBSCO Publishing, Swets Information Services, Wiley InterScience).
—BLDSC (0898.030000), CISTI, IE.
Published by: John Wiley & Sons, Inc., 111 River St, Hoboken, NJ 07030-5774. TEL 201-748-6000, FAX 201-748-5915, uscs-wis@wiley.com, http://www3.interscience.wiley.com/cgi-bin/jhome/101521780, http://www.wiley.com.

571.3 AUS ISSN 1447-6959
CODEN: KAIZAN
➤ **ANATOMICAL SCIENCE INTERNATIONAL.** Text in English, Japanese; Summaries in English, German. 1893. q. USD 161 combined subscription in the Americas to individuals & Caribbean, print & online eds.; EUR 149 combined subscription in Europe to individuals print & online eds.; GBP 99 combined subscription elsewhere to individuals print & online eds.; USD 303 combined subscription in the Americas to institutions & Caribbean; GBP 186 combined subscription elsewhere to institutions print & online eds. (effective 2006). adv. bk.rev. abstr.; bibl. Index. **Document type:** *Journal, Academic/Scholarly.* **Description:** Publishes original research articles dealing with morphological sciences, including molecular, cellular, histological, and gross anatomical studies on normal and experimental animals and humans.
Formerly (until 2002): Kaibogaku Zasshi (0022-7722)
Related titles: Online - full text ed.: ISSN 1447-073X. GBP 288 in the Americas to institutions & Caribbean; USD 177 elsewhere to institutions (effective 2006) (from Blackwell Synergy, EBSCO Publishing, Gale Group, IngentaConnect, O C L C Online Computer Library Center, Inc., Ovid Technologies, Inc., Swets Information Services).
Indexed: BIOSIS Prev, BiolAb, ChemAb, DentInd, ExcerpMed, IndMed, IndVet, MEDLINE, SFA, VetBull, ZooRec.
—BLDSC (0898.050000), CISTI, GNLM, IE. **CCC.**
Published by: (Japanese Association of Anatomists JPN), Blackwell Publishing Asia (Subsidiary of: Blackwell Publishing Ltd.), 550 Swanston St, Carlton South, VIC 3053, Australia. TEL 61-383591011, FAX 61-383591120, subs@blackwellpublishingasia.com, http://www.blackwellpublishing.com/journals/ASI. Ed. Shohei Yamashina. Circ: 1,950.

571.3 611 IND ISSN 0003-2778
QM1 CODEN: JAINAA
➤ **ANATOMICAL SOCIETY OF INDIA. JOURNAL.** Text in English. 1951. s-a. adv. bk.rev. charts; illus.; abstr. index. 100 p./no. 2 cols./p.; back issues avail. **Document type:** *Journal, Academic/Scholarly.* **Description:** Covers anatomy, anthropology, cytology, histology, genetics and clinical applied medicine.
Related titles: Online - full text ed.: free (effective 2005).
Indexed: BiolAb, ChemAb, ExcerpMed, IndVet, MEDLINE, NutrAb, VetBull.
—CASDDS, CISTI.
Published by: Anatomical Society of India, Department of Anatomy, M.L.B. Medical College, Jhansi, Uttar Pradesh 284 128, India. TEL 0517-320032, editorjasi@rediffmail.com, secasi@yahoo.com, http://medind.nic.in/jae/jaem.shtml. Ed. GopiChand V.V. Patnaik. adv.: page INR 1,200. Circ: 550.

➤ **ANGEIOLOGIE.** see *MEDICAL SCIENCES—Cardiovascular Diseases*

570 610 FRA ISSN 0003-3898
RB1 CODEN: ABCLAI
➤ **ANNALES DE BIOLOGIE CLINIQUE.** Text in French; Summaries in English, French. 1943. 6/yr. EUR 146 combined subscription domestic to individuals print & online eds.; EUR 166 combined subscription in the European Union to individuals print & online eds.; EUR 177 combined subscription elsewhere to individuals print & online eds.; EUR 255 combined subscription domestic to institutions print & online eds.; EUR 276 combined subscription in the European Union to institutions print & online eds.; EUR 286 combined subscription elsewhere to institutions print & online eds. (effective 2006). adv. bk.rev. charts; illus. index. **Document type:** *Journal, Academic/Scholarly.* **Description:** Covers all aspects of clinical biology, from instrumentation and methodology to laboratory applications, clinical investigations, animal experimentation, human pathology and evaluations of apparatus or reagents.
Related titles: Online - full text ed.: FRF 750 to individuals; FRF 1,550 to institutions (effective 2001) (from EBSCO Publishing).
Indexed: ASCA, BIOBASE, BIOSIS Prev, BiolAb, CCI, CIN, CISA, ChemAb, ChemTitl, CurCont, ExcerpMed, FS&TA, IABS, INI, ISR, IndMed, IndVet, MEDLINE, MSB, NutrAb, PN&I, ProtozoAb, RM&VM, SCI, VetBull.
—BLDSC (0967.730000), CASDDS, CISTI, GNLM, IDS, IE, Infotrieve, ingenta, KNAW. **CCC.**
Published by: (Societe Francaise de Biologie Clinique), John Libbey Eurotext, 127 Avenue de la Republique, Montrouge, 92120, France. TEL 33-1-46730660, FAX 33-1-40840999, contact@jle.com, http://www.john-libbey-eurotext.fr. Ed. Jean Louis Dhondt. Circ: 3,000. **Subscr. to:** A T E I, 3 av. Pierre Kerautret, Romainville 92230, France. TEL 33-1-48408686, FAX 33-1-48400731, atei@club-internet.fr.

571.9 616.07 FRA ISSN 0242-6498
CODEN: ASPAD2
➤ **ANNALES DE PATHOLOGIE.** Text in French; Summaries in English, French. 1924. 6/yr. EUR 230 domestic to individuals; EUR 277 domestic to institutions; EUR 312 in the European Union to institutions; EUR 342 elsewhere to institutions (effective 2004). bk.rev. bibl.; illus. index. reprint service avail. from ISI. **Document type:** *Academic/Scholarly.* **Description:** Publishes observations and works of a morphological order, reflecting the achievements of French-speaking anatomopathologists.
Formerly (until 1981): Annales d'Anatomie Pathologique (0003-3871); Incorporates (in 1999): Clinical and Experimental Pathology (1292-7953); Which was formerly (until 1998): Archives d'Anatomie et de Cytologie Pathologiques (0395-501X); (1953-1976): Archives d'Anatomie Pathologique (0003-9608)
Related titles: Microform ed.: (from PQC); Online - full text ed.: (from EBSCO Publishing).
Indexed: ASCA, ASFA, AbHyg, BiolAb, ChemAb, CurCont, DentInd, ESPM, ExcerpMed, HelmAb, ISR, IndMed, IndVet, Inpharma, MEDLINE, PE&ON, PN&I, ProtozoAb, RM&VM, Reac, SCI, TDB, VetBull.
—BLDSC (0991.300000), CASDDS, CISTI, GNLM, IDS, IE, Infotrieve, ingenta, KNAW. **CCC.**
Published by: (Societe Francaise de Pathologie), Masson Editeur (Subsidiary of: Groupe Medimedia France), 21 Rue Camille Desmoulins, Issy les Moulineaux, 92789 Cedex 9, France. TEL 33-1-73281634, FAX 33-1-73281649, infos@masson.fr, http://www.masson.fr. Ed. D Henin. Circ: 1,400. **Subscr. to:** Societe de Periodiques Specialises, BP 22, Vineuil Cedex 41354, France. TEL 33-2-54504612, FAX 33-2-54504611.

570 POL ISSN 0066-2232
QH301.L8 CODEN: AUCBAJ
ANNALES UNIVERSITATIS MARIAE CURIE-SKLODOWSKA. SECTIO C. BIOLOGIA. Text in English, Polish; Summaries in English, French, German. 1946. a. price varies. **Document type:** *Academic/Scholarly.*
Indexed: AICP, AgrAg, AgrLib, BiolAb, ChemAb, FCA, FPA, ForAb, HerbAb, HortAb, IABS, PBA, RevApplEntom, ZooRec.
—CASDDS, CISTI, Linda Hall.
Published by: Uniwersytet Marii Curie-Sklodowskiej w Lublinie, Wydawnictwo, pl M Curie Sklodowskiej 5, Lublin, 20031, Poland. TEL 48-31-375304, FAX 48-81-336699, TELEX 0643223. Ed. Zbigniew Lorkiewicz. Circ: 950.

ANNALS OF AGRI BIO RESEARCH; an international journal of basic and applied agriculture and biology. see *AGRICULTURE*

ANNALS OF ANATOMY. see *MEDICAL SCIENCES*

570 GBR ISSN 0003-4746
QH301 CODEN: AABIAV
➤ **ANNALS OF APPLIED BIOLOGY.** Text in English. 1914. bi-m. (in 2 vols.). USD 633 combined subscription in the Americas to institutions & the Caribbean (print & online eds.); GBP 343 combined subscription in Europe to institutions; GBP 377 combined subscription elsewhere to institutions (effective 2006). adv. illus. cum.index: 1914-1978, 1979-1985. **Document type:** *Journal, Academic/Scholarly.* **Description:** Publishes original research papers on all aspects of applied research on crop production, crop protection and the cropping ecosystem.
Related titles: Online - full text ed.: ISSN 1744-7348. GBP 326 in Europe to institutions; USD 601 in the Americas to institutions & Caribbean; GBP 358 elsewhere to institutions (effective 2006) (from Blackwell Synergy, EBSCO Publishing, Gale Group, H.W. Wilson, IngentaConnect, O C L C Online Computer Library Center, Inc., Swets Information Services); ♦ Supplement(s): Tests of Agrochemicals and Cultivars. ISSN 0951-4309.
Indexed: AEA, ASCA, ASFA, AgBio, Agr, AgrForAb, B&AI, B&BAb, BIOBASE, BIOSIS Prev, BioCN&I, BioDAb, BiolAb, CBTA, CIN, CPA, ChemAb, ChemTitl, CurCont, DBA, DSA, ESPM, EntAb, ExcerpMed, FCA, FPA, FS&TA, FaBeAb, ForAb, GEOBASE, HGA, HelmAb, HerbAb, HortAb, I&DA, IABS, ISR, IndMed, IndVet, MBA, MEDLINE, MaizeAb, NemAb, NutrAb, OrnHort, PBA, PGegResA, PGrRegA, PHN&I, PlantSci, PotatoAb, PoultAb, ProtozoAb, RA&MP, RM&VM, RPP, RefZh, RevApplEntom, RiceAb, S&F, S&MA, SCI, SFA, SIA, SeedAb, SoyAb, TOSA, TriticAb, VITIS, VetBull, WAE&RSA, WeedAb, WildRev, ZooRec.
—BLDSC (1038.000000), CASDDS, CISTI, GNLM, IE, Infotrieve, ingenta, Linda Hall. **CCC.**
Published by: (Association of Applied Biologists, Horticultural Research International), Blackwell Publishing Ltd., 9600 Garsington Rd, Oxford, OX4 2ZG, United Kingdom. http://www.blackwellpublishing.com/journals/AAB. Ed. Martin A J Parry. Circ: 1,000.

➤ **ANNALS OF BANGLADESH AGRICULTURE.** see *AGRICULTURE*

570 IND ISSN 0970-0153
CODEN: ANBIEO
ANNALS OF BIOLOGY; an international journal of basic and applied biology. Text in English. 1985. s-a. INR 600, USD 60 (effective 2003). adv. bk.rev. **Document type:** *Academic/Scholarly.*
Indexed: AEA, ASFA, AgBio, AgrForAb, Agrind, AnBrAb, BIOSIS Prev, BioCN&I, BiolAb, CPA, DSA, ESPM, EntAb, FCA, FPA, FS&TA, ForAb, GEOBASE, GenetAb, HerbAb, HortAb, I&DA, ISA, IndVet, MBA, MaizeAb, NemAb, NutrAb, OceAb, OrnHort, PBA, PGegResA, PGrRegA, PHN&I, PoultAb, RA&MP, RDA, RM&VM, RPP, RevApplEntom, RiceAb, S&F, S&MA, SIA, SWRA, SeedAb, SoyAb, TOSA, TriticAb, WAE&RSA, WeedAb, ZooRec.
—BLDSC (1039.300000), CASDDS, CISTI, IE, Infotrieve, ingenta.
Published by: Agri Bio Research Publishers, 121 Mohalla Chaudharian, Hisar, 125 001, India. TEL 91-1662-37530, bajdasch@nde.vsnl.com. Eds. Dr. Manjit S Dhindsa, Dr. R K Behl. Circ: 500.

ANNALS OF BIOMEDICAL RESEARCH AND EDUCATION. see *MEDICAL SCIENCES*

ANNALS OF CONTEMPORARY DIAGNOSTIC PATHOLOGY. see *MEDICAL SCIENCES*

ANNALS OF DIAGNOSTIC PATHOLOGY. see *MEDICAL SCIENCES*

570 GBR ISSN 0301-4460
QP34.5 CODEN: AHUBBJ
➤ **ANNALS OF HUMAN BIOLOGY.** Text in English; Summaries in French, German. 1974. bi-m. GBP 814, USD 1,343 combined subscription to institutions print & online eds. (effective 2006). bk.rev. bibl.; charts; stat. index. reprint service avail. from PSC. **Document type:** *Journal, Academic/Scholarly.* **Description:** Publishes papers concerning research into biological aspects of human populations with regard to their ecology, demography, genetics, evolution, and the growth, physiology, disease patterns and behavior of the individuals composing them.
Related titles: Microform ed.: 1974; Online - full text ed.: ISSN 1464-5033. 1974. GBP 773, USD 1,276 to institutions (effective 2006) (from EBSCO Publishing, Gale Group, IngentaConnect, O C L C Online Computer Library Center, Inc., Swets Information Services).
Indexed: AICP, ASCA, AbAn, AbHyg, AnthLit, BDM&CN, BIOBASE, BIOSIS Prev, BiolAb, ChemAb, CurCont, DSA, DentInd, ErgAb, ExcerpMed, FLUIDEX, GEOBASE, HelmAb, IBSS, ISR, IndMed, Inpharma, MEDLINE, NRN, NutrAb, PopulInd, ProtozoAb, RDA, RRTA, Reac, SCI, SSCI, TDB.
—BLDSC (1040.900000), CASDDS, CISTI, GNLM, IDS, IE, Infotrieve, ingenta, Linda Hall. **CCC.**
Published by: (Society for the Study of Human Biology), Taylor & Francis Ltd (Subsidiary of: Taylor & Francis Group), 4 Park Sq, Milton Park, Abingdon, OX14 4RN, United Kingdom. TEL 44-1235-828600, FAX 44-1235-829000, info@tandf.co.uk, http://www.tandf.co.uk/journals/titles/03014460.html. Eds. N G Norgan, R Hauspie. **Subscr. in N. America to:** Taylor & Francis Inc., Customer Services Dept, 325 Chestnut St, 8th Fl, Philadelphia, PA 19106. TEL 800-354-1420, FAX 215-625-8914; **Subscr. to:** Journals Customer Service, Rankine Rd, Basingstoke, Hants RG24 8PR, United Kingdom. TEL 44-1256-813000, FAX 44-1256-330245, enquiry@tandf.co.uk.

610 FRA ISSN 1157-4135
ANNUAIRE DE LA RECHERCHE BIO-MEDICALE. Short title: A R B M. Text in French. 1989. a., latest vol.5, 1995. price varies. **Document type:** *Directory, Academic/Scholarly.*
Description: Covers all public and semi-public biomedical research centers in France, including INSERM, CEA, CNRS, ORSTOM, medical schools, science faculties, Pasteur Institutes, and centers for cancer research.
Published by: Elsevier France, Editions Scientifiques et Medicales (Subsidiary of: Elsevier Science & Technology), 23 Rue Linois, Paris, 75724, France. TEL 33-1-71724600, FAX 33-1-71724650, http://www.elsevier.fr.

573.6 306.7 USA ISSN 1091-9961
HQ21
➤ **ANNUAL EDITIONS: HUMAN SEXUALITY.** Text in English. 1975. a., latest 2002, 28th ed. USD 20.31 per vol. (effective 2004). illus. **Document type:** *Academic/Scholarly.*
Description: Contains a compilation of articles selected from magazines, newspapers, and journals, relating to issues dealing with sexuality and society, sexual biology, reproduction, and interpersonal relationships.
Former titles: Annual Editions: Readings in Human Sexuality (0163-836X); Focus: Human Sexuality (0147-0655)
Indexed: e-psyche.
Published by: McGraw-Hill - Dushkin (Subsidiary of: McGraw-Hill Higher Education), 2460 Kerper Blvd, Dubuque, IA 52001. TEL 800-243-6532, customer.service@mcgraw-hill.com, http://www.dushkin.com/text-data/catalog/0072548541.mhtml. Ed. Susan Bunting. Pub. Ian Nielsen. R&P Cheryl Greenleaf.

660.6 USA ISSN 1523-9829
R856.A1 CODEN: ARBEF7
ANNUAL REVIEW OF BIOMEDICAL ENGINEERING. Text in English. 1999. a., latest vol.6, 2004. USD 175 to institutions print or online ed.; USD 210 combined subscription to institutions print & online eds. (effective 2006). abstr.; charts; bibl. back issues avail.; reprints avail. **Document type:** *Academic/Scholarly.* **Description:** Contains full text articles about biological engineering, including biotechnology.
Related titles: Online - full content ed.: ISSN 1545-4274. USD 173 (effective 2005); Online - full text ed.: (from EBSCO Publishing, Swets Information Services).
Indexed: B&BAb, BIOSIS Prev, BioEngAb, ChemAb, CurCont, ExcerpMed, ISR, M&PBA, SCI.
—BLDSC (1522.025000), CISTI, IE, Infotrieve, ingenta. **CCC.**
Published by: Annual Reviews, 4139 El Camino Way, Palo Alto, CA 94303-0139. TEL 650-493-4400, 800-523-8635, FAX 650-424-0910, service@annualreviews.org, http://arjournals.annualreviews.org/loi/bioeng, http://www.annualreviews.org. Ed. Martin Yarmush. R&P Laura Folkner.

ANNUAL REVIEW OF ECOLOGY, EVOLUTION AND SYSTEMATICS. see *ENVIRONMENTAL STUDIES*

559.89 570 GBR ISSN 0954-1020
Q127.A48 CODEN: ANTSE8
➤ **ANTARCTIC SCIENCE.** Text in English. q. USD 483 in North America to institutions; GBP 292 elsewhere to institutions; USD 528 combined subscription in North America to institutions print & online eds.; GBP 328 combined subscription elsewhere to institutions print & online eds. (effective 2006). adv. bk.rev. illus. index. back issues avail.
Document type: *Journal, Academic/Scholarly.* **Description:** Contains both review and data papers, short notes on technical developments and recent discoveries, reports on key Antarctic meetings, book reviews, and a diary of forthcoming events.
Related titles: Microform ed.: (from PQC); Online - full text ed.: ISSN 1365-2079. USD 463 in North America to institutions; GBP 279 elsewhere to institutions (effective 2006) (from EBSCO Publishing, O C L C Online Computer Library Center, Inc., Swets Information Services).
Indexed: ASCA, ASFA, BIOBASE, BIOSIS Prev, BiolAb, CurCont, EPB, ESPM, EngInd, EnvAb, GEOBASE, I&DA, IABS, ISR, M&GPA, MBA, MinerAb, NemAb, RefZh, S&F, SCI, SFA, SWRA, WildRev, ZooRec.
—BLDSC (1542.130500), CISTI, Ei, IDS, IE, Infotrieve, ingenta, Linda Hall. **CCC.**
Published by: (British Antarctic Survey), Cambridge University Press, The Edinburgh Bldg, Shaftesbury Rd, Cambridge, CB2 2RU, United Kingdom. TEL 44-1223-312393, FAX 44-1223-315052, journals@cambridge.org, http://titles.cambridge.org/journals/journal_catalogue.asp?mnemonic=ans, http://uk.cambridge.org/journals. Eds. Alan P.M. Vaughan, David W.H. Walton, Michiel R Van Den Broeke. Adv. contact Martine Cariou Keen. Circ: 455. **Subscr. to:** Cambridge University Press, 100 Brook Hill Dr, West Nyack, NY 10994. TEL 845-353-7500, FAX 845-353-4141, journals_subscriptions@cup.org

570 JPN ISSN 0286-4444
AOMORIKEN SEIBUTSU GAKKAISHI/AOMORIKEN BIOLOGICAL SOCIETY. JOURNAL. Text in Japanese; Summaries in English. 1956. a.
Published by: Aomoriken Seibutsu Gakkai/Aomoriken Biological Society, Hirosaki Daigaku Rigakubu Seibutsugaku Kyoshitsu, 3 Bunkyo-cho, Hirosaki-shi, Aomori-ken 036-8224, Japan.

APPLIED SOIL ECOLOGY. see *AGRICULTURE—Crop Production And Soil*

631 USA ISSN 1552-5821
➤ **APPLIED TURFGRASS SCIENCE.** Text in English. irreg. free to members. **Document type:** *Journal, Academic/Scholarly.*
Description: Provides a forum for turfgrass professionals to exchange ideas, promote new products, and discuss new initiatives, developments, and issues that face the turfgrass industry.
Media: Online - full content.
Published by: Plant Management Network, 3340 Pilot Knob Rd, St Paul, MN 55121-2097. TEL 651-454-7250, 800-328-7590, FAX 651-454-0766, editorialoffice@plantmanagementnetwork.org, http://www.plantmanagementnetwork.org/ats/. Ed. Mike Richardson.

578.77 597 ITA ISSN 0945-9871
AQUA; journal of ichthyology & aquatic biology. Text in German. 1994. q. EUR 40 (effective 2004). **Document type:** *Journal.*
Description: Covers the fields of fish, amphibians, aquatic invertebrates, and aquatic plants.
Related titles: ◆ Supplement to: Aqua Geographia (Italian Edition). ISSN 0937-7131.
Indexed: ASFA, ESPM, OceAb.
—BLDSC (1581.860500).
Published by: Aquapress Publishing, Via G Falcone 11, Miradolo Terme (Pavia), 27010, Italy. TEL 39-0382-754707, FAX 39-0382-754129, heiko@pmp.it, http://www.aquageo.com.

AQUATIC CONSERVATION; marine and freshwater ecosystems. see *CONSERVATION*

570 NLD ISSN 1386-2588
QH90.A1 CODEN: AQECF9
➤ **AQUATIC ECOLOGY;** a multidisciplinary journal relating to processes and structures at different organizational levels. Text in English. 1975 (vol.9). q. EUR 311, USD 311, GBP 205 combined subscription to institutions print & online eds. (effective 2005). bk.rev. reprint service avail. from PSC.
Document type: *Journal, Academic/Scholarly.* **Description:** Publishes fundamental and applied research on the ecology of fresh, brackish, estuarine, and marine environments.
Former titles (until 1997): Netherlands Journal of Aquatic Ecology (1380-8427); (until 1992): Hydrobiological Bulletin (0165-1404); (until 1973): Hydrobiologische Vereniging. Mededelingen
Related titles: Online - full text ed.: ISSN 1573-5125. USD 311 to institutions (effective 2005) (from EBSCO Publishing, Gale Group, IngentaConnect, Kluwer Online, O C L C Online Computer Library Center, Inc., Springer LINK, Swets Information Services).
Indexed: ASFA, ApEcolAb, BIOBASE, BIOSIS Prev, BibLing, BiolAb, CIN, ChemAb, ChemTitl, CurCont, ESPM, ExcerpMed, GEOBASE, HGA, M&TEA, OceAb, PollutAb, RefZh, SFA, SWRA, ZooRec.
—BLDSC (1582.372500), CASDDS, CISTI, IE, Infotrieve, ingenta, Linda Hall. **CCC.**
Published by: (Nederlandse Vereniging voor Aquatische Ecologie), Springer-Verlag Dordrecht (Subsidiary of: Springer Science+Business Media), Van Godewijckstraat 30, Dordrecht, 3311 GX, Netherlands. TEL 31-78-6576050, FAX 31-78-6576474, http://springerlink.metapress.com/openurl.asp?genre=journal&issn=1386-2588, http://www.springeronline.com. Ed. Ramesh D Gulati.

➤ **AQUATIC ENVIRONMENT MONITORING REPORT.** see *ENVIRONMENTAL STUDIES*

578.77 DEU ISSN 0003-9136
QH301 CODEN: AHYBA4
➤ **ARCHIV FUER HYDROBIOLOGIE;** Official journal of the International Association of Theoretical and Applied Limnology. Text in English, French, German. 1906. m. EUR 86 per issue domestic for print & online eds.; EUR 90 per issue foreign for print & online eds. (effective 2005). adv. bk.rev. bibl.; charts; illus. reprints avail. **Document type:** *Journal, Academic/Scholarly.* **Description:** Contains information on freshwater research, including problems of marine biology and brackish water research.
Related titles: Online - full text ed.: (from EBSCO Publishing, Gale Group, IngentaConnect, Swets Information Services); ◆ Supplement(s): Algological Studies. ISSN 0342-1120; ◆ Advances in Limnology. ISSN 1612-166X; ◆ Archiv fuer Hydrobiologie. Supplement-Band: Large Rivers. ISSN 0945-3784; ◆ Archiv fuer Hydrobiologie. Supplement-Band: Untersuchungen des Elbe-Aestuars. ISSN 0342-1066.
Indexed: ASCA, ASFA, AgrForAb, AnBrAb, ApEcolAb, BIOBASE, BIOSIS Prev, BiolAb, CIN, ChemAb, ChemTitl, CivEngAb, CurCont, ESPM, EntAb, EnvEAb, ExcerpMed, ForAb, GEOBASE, HelmAb, HerbAb, I&DA, IBR, ISR, M&TEA, NemAb, NutrAb, PollutAb, ProtozoAb, RM&VM, RPP, RefZh, RevApplEntom, RiceAb, S&F, SCI, SFA, SIA, SPPI, SSCI, SWRA, SeedAb, WRCInf, WeedAb, WildRev, ZooRec.
—BLDSC (1613.000000), CASDDS, CISTI, IDS, IE, Infotrieve, ingenta, Linda Hall. **CCC.**
Published by: (International Association for Theoretical and Applied Limnology), E. Schweizerbart'sche Verlagsbuchhandlung, Johannesstr 3A, Stuttgart, 70176, Germany. TEL 49-711-3514560, FAX 49-711-35145699, mail@schweizerbart.de, http://www.schweizerbart.de/j/archiv-hydrobiologie. Ed. W Lampert.

578.77 DEU ISSN 0945-3784
ARCHIV FUER HYDROBIOLOGIE. SUPPLEMENT-BAND: LARGE RIVERS. Text in German. irreg. EUR 98 per issue domestic; EUR 102 per issue foreign (effective 2005).
Document type: *Monographic series, Academic/Scholarly.*
Related titles: ◆ Supplement to: Archiv fuer Hydrobiologie. ISSN 0003-9136.
Indexed: ASFA, ESPM.
—CISTI.
Published by: E. Schweizerbart'sche Verlagsbuchhandlung, Johannesstr 3A, Stuttgart, 70176, Germany. TEL 49-711-3514560, FAX 49-711-35145699, mail@schweizerbart.de, http://www.schweizerbart.de.

578.77 DEU ISSN 0342-1066
ARCHIV FUER HYDROBIOLOGIE. SUPPLEMENT-BAND: UNTERSUCHUNGEN DES ELBE-AESTUARS. Text in German. 1961. irreg. EUR 88 per issue domestic; EUR 92 per issue foreign (effective 2005). **Document type:** *Monographic series, Academic/Scholarly.*
Related titles: ◆ Supplement to: Archiv fuer Hydrobiologie. ISSN 0003-9136.
Indexed: ASFA, ESPM.
Published by: E. Schweizerbart'sche Verlagsbuchhandlung, Johannesstr 3A, Stuttgart, 70176, Germany. TEL 49-711-3514560, FAX 49-711-35145699, mail@schweizerbart.de, http://www.schweizerbart.de/j/archiv-hydrobiologie.

B

578.77 DEU ISSN 1435-6406
QH301 CODEN: AHBSA8
ARCHIV FUER HYDROBIOLOGIE. SUPPLEMENT VOLUMES, MONOGRAPHIC STUDIES. Text in German, English. 1911. irreg. EUR 94 per issue domestic; EUR 98 per issue foreign (effective 2005). **Document type:** *Monographic series, Academic/Scholarly.*
Former titles (until 1995): Archiv fuer Hydrobiologie. Supplement-Band, Monographische Beitrage (0341-2881); (until 1967): Archiv fuer Hydrobiologie. Supplement-Band (0365-284X); Archiv fuer Hydrobiologie und Planktonkunde. Supplement-Band (0931-6256)
Indexed: ASFA, ESPM, ZooRec.
—CASDDS, CISTI, Linda Hall. **CCC.**
Published by: E. Schweizerbart'sche Verlagsbuchhandlung, Johannesstr 3A, Stuttgart, 70176, Germany. TEL 49-711-3514560, FAX 49-711-35145699, mail@schweizerbart.de, http://www.schweizerbart.de/j/archiv-hydrobiologie.

570 SCG ISSN 0354-4664
ARCHIVES OF BIOLOGICAL SCIENCES. Text in English. 1949. q.?.
Formerly (until 1993): Arhiv Bioloskih Nauka (0375-8575)
Indexed: INIS AtomInd.
—CISTI.
Published by: Institut za Bioloska Istrazivanja "Sinisa Stankovic", 29 novembra 142, Belgrade, 11060. Ed. Maksim Todorovic.

570 ARG ISSN 0004-0401
ARCHIVO DE CIENCIAS BIOLOGICAS Y NATURALES, TEORICAS Y APLICADAS✶. Text in Spanish. 1956. 2/yr. USD 1.
—Linda Hall.
Published by: Librart s.r.l., Departamento de Publicaciones Cientificas Argentinas, Avda. Corrientes 127, Casilla Correo Central 5047, Buenos Aires, Argentina. Ed. A Silvia Colla.

571.3 ESP ISSN 0004-0436
ARCHIVO ESPANOL DE MORFOLOGIA. Text in English, Spanish. 1941; N.S. 1996. 3/yr. **Document type:** *Monographic series.*
Indexed: MEDLINE.
—GNLM.
Published by: Morphos Ediciones S.L., C PASOS, 3, Alcantarilla, Murcia 30820, Spain. FAX 34-968-8953912, morphos@distrito.com. Ed. Andres Martinez Almagro.

570 PER ISSN 0250-5037
QP82.2.A4 CODEN: ABANDH
ARCHIVOS DE BIOLOGIA ANDINA. Text in Spanish; Text occasionally in English; Summaries in English. 1965. s-a. free. abstr.; bibl.; charts; stat.
Formerly (until 1977): Universidad Nacional Mayor de San Marcos. Instituto de Biologia Andina. Archivos (0020-3750)
Indexed: AICP, BiolAb, ChemAb, IndMed, MEDLINE, RPP, SCI.
—CASDDS.
Published by: Universidad Nacional Mayor de San Marcos, Instituto de Biologia Andina, c/o Centro de Investigacion, Apdo. 5073, Lima, Peru. Ed. Dr. E Picon Reategui. Circ: 1,000.

ARCTIC, ANTARCTIC, AND ALPINE RESEARCH. see *SCIENCES: COMPREHENSIVE WORKS*

570 560 ARG ISSN 0325-3856
➤ **ARGENTINA. MUSEO PROVINCIAL DE CIENCIAS NATURALES. COMUNICACIONES.** Text in Spanish; Summaries in English. 1967; N.S. 1983. a. bibl.; illus.; maps; stat. back issues avail. **Document type:** *Monographic series, Academic/Scholarly.* **Description:** Covers natural resources of the Santa Fe region, with emphasis on how to care for them within the ecological balance of nature.

▼ new title ➤ refereed ✶ unverified ◆ full entry avail.

—Linda Hall.
Published by: Ministerio de Educacion y Cultura, Museo Provincial de Ciencias Naturales "Florentino Ameghino", Primera Junta, 2859, Santa Fe, 3000, Argentina. htpp://www.unl.edu.ar/SantaFe/museocn.htm. Ed., R&P Carlos Alberto Virasoro. Circ: 800.

570.72 ZWE ISSN 0250-6386
AS622 CODEN: AZIMDI
ARNOLDIA ZIMBABWE. Text in English. 1964. irreg. price varies. illus. index. **Document type:** *Academic/Scholarly.*
Description: Results of research in the natural sciences in southern Africa.
Former titles: Arnoldia Zimbabwe Rhodesia; Arnoldia Rhodesia (0066-7781)
Indexed: ASFA, BIOSIS Prev, BiolAb, ESPM, PLESA, RevApplEntom, SFA, WildRev, ZooRec.
—BLDSC (1684.105000).
Published by: National Museums and Monuments of Zimbabwe, PO Box 240, Bulawayo, Zimbabwe. TEL 60045. Ed. A Kumirai. Circ: 400.

B

578.77 PRT ISSN 0873-4704
ARQUIPELAGO - LIFE AND MARINE SCIENCES. SUPPLEMENT. Text in English, Portuguese. a. **Document type:** *Bulletin.* **Description:** Covers the natural environment of the archipelago of the Azores and the surrounding regions.
Related titles: ◆ Supplement to: Arquipelago. Serie Ciencias da Natureza. ISSN 0870-6581.
Indexed: BIOSIS Prev, BiolAb, VITIS, ZooRec.
Published by: Universidade dos Acores/University of the Azores, Rua da Mae de Deus, Ponta Delgada, 9500, Portugal. Ed. Helen Rost Martins.

570 DEU ISSN 0171-4090
➤ **ARTICULATA;** Zeitschrift fuer Biologie, Systematik und Neubeschreibung von Orthopteren. Text in English, French, German. 1975. s-a. EUR 25 (effective 2001). bk.rev. index. back issues avail. **Document type:** *Journal, Academic/Scholarly.*
Indexed: RefZh, ZooRec.
Published by: Deutsche Gesellschaft fuer Orthopterologie e.V., c/o Georg Waeber, Fliederstr 21, Rednitzhembach, 91126, Germany. TEL 49-9122-76717, g.waeber@net24.de. Ed., Adv. contact Georg Waeber. Circ: 650.

➤ **ARTIFICIAL LIFE.** see *COMPUTERS—Artificial Intelligence*

570 PHL ISSN 0117-3375
CODEN: ALSCE9
➤ **ASIA LIFE SCIENCES;** the Asian international journal of life sciences. Text in English. 1992. s-a. PHP 500 domestic to individuals; USD 70 foreign to individuals; PHP 1,000 domestic to institutions; USD 100 foreign to institutions (effective 2003). adv. bk.rev. illus. index. 100 p./no.; back issues avail. **Document type:** *Journal, Academic/Scholarly.*
Indexed: BIOSIS Prev, BiolAb, ZooRec.
Published by: (University of the Philippines at Los Banos), Rushing Water Publishers Ltd., 81 Gov F T Sam Luis Ave, Diamond Jubileeville, Masaya Bay, Laguna 4033, Philippines. TEL 63-916-430-8764, FAX 63-49-536-2517. Ed. William Sm Gruezo. R&P, Adv. contact William Sm. Gruezo TEL 63-918-804-6279. Circ: 1,000 (controlled). **Subscr. to:** Asia Life Sciences, D-206 Biological Sciences Bldg, University of the Los Banos, College, Laguna 4031, Philippines.

578.77 HKG ISSN 1011-4041
QH179 CODEN: AMABEP
➤ **ASIAN MARINE BIOLOGY.** Text in English. 1985. a., latest vol.18, 2001. HKD 150, USD 27.50 (effective 2003). illus.; abstr.; bibl. 160 p./no.; back issues avail. **Document type:** *Academic/Scholarly.* **Description:** Research on marine biology in Asian region.
Indexed: BIOSIS Prev, BiolAb, ZooRec.
Published by: Marine Biological Association of Hong Kong, c/o The Swire Institute of Marine Science, Cape d Aguilar Rd, Shek O, Hong Kong, Hong Kong. TEL 852-2552-2703, FAX 852-2875-0734, hkupress@hkucc.hku.hk, http://www.hkupress.org. Ed. Brian Morton. **Dist. in Europe by:** Eurospan University Press Group, Order Dept, 3 Henrietta St, London WC2E 8LU, United Kingdom. TEL 44-20-7240-0856, FAX 44-20-7379-0609, http://www.eurospan.co.uk; **Dist. in rest of the world by:** Hong Kong University Press, 14-F, Hing Wai Centre, 7 Tin Wan Praya Rd, Aberdeen, Hong Kong. TEL 852-2550-2703, 852-2875-0734, hkupress@hkucc.hk.hk, http://www.hkupress.org.

➤ **ASSOCIATION BELGE DES TECHNOLOGUES DE LABORATOIRE. REVUE/BELGISCHE VERENIGING VAN LABORATORIUM TECHNOLOGEN. TIJDSCHRIFT.** see *CHEMISTRY*

➤ **ASSOCIATION OF MARINE LABORATORIES OF THE CARIBBEAN. NEWSLETTER.** see *EARTH SCIENCES—Oceanography*

➤ **ASSOCIATION OF MARINE LABORATORIES OF THE CARIBBEAN. PROCEEDINGS.** see *EARTH SCIENCES—Oceanography*

570 USA ISSN 1531-1074
QH327 CODEN: ASTRC4
➤ **ASTROBIOLOGY.** Text in English. 2001. bi-m. USD 366 domestic to institutions; USD 403 foreign to institutions; USD 433 combined subscription domestic to institutions print & online eds.; USD 487 combined subscription foreign to institutions print & online eds. (effective 2006). adv. reprint service avail. from PSC. **Document type:** *Journal, Academic/Scholarly.* **Description:** Provides a forum for scientists who define the future of astrobiology, including meteoritics, cosmochemistry, gravitational biology, and planetary geology.
Related titles: Online - full text ed.: ISSN 1557-8070. USD 316 to institutions (effective 2006) (from EBSCO Publishing, Gale Group, O C L C Online Computer Library Center, Inc., Swets Information Services).
Indexed: ASFA, BiolAb, CurCont, M&GPA.
—BLDSC (1747.892500), CISTI, IE, Infotrieve, Linda Hall. **CCC.**
Published by: Mary Ann Liebert, Inc. Publishers, 140 Huguenot St 3rd Fl, New Rochelle, NY 10801-5215. TEL 914-740-2100, FAX 914-740-2101, 800-654-3237, info@liebertpub.com, http://www.liebertpub.com/ast. Ed. Sherry Cady. R&P Esther Bicovany. Adv. contact Harriet Matysko. B&W page USD 1,215; trim 8.5 x 11. Circ: 1,500 (paid).

➤ **ATELIERS.** see *CHILDREN AND YOUTH—For*

➤ **ATENEO PARMENSE. ACTA BIO MEDICA.** see *MEDICAL SCIENCES*

578.77 591.35 CAN
ATLANTIC SALMON FEDERATION. SALMON GENETICS RESEARCH PROGRAM. REPORT SERIES. Text in English. irreg. **Description:** Publishes previously unpublished scientific materials, reprints of primary scientific publications, and administrative reports and newsletters of the program.
Published by: (Atlantic Salmon Federation, Salmon Genetics Research Program), Atlantic Salmon Federation, PO Box 5200, St Andrews, NB E5B 3S8, Canada. http://www.asf.ca/Research/resrch17.htm.

577 AUS ISSN 1442-9985
QH197 CODEN: AUECF3
➤ **AUSTRAL ECOLOGY;** a journal of ecology in the Southern Hemisphere. Text in English. 1976. 8/yr. AUD 252 combined subscription in Australia & New Zealand to individuals print & online eds.; EUR 206 combined subscription in Europe to individuals print & online eds.; USD 205 combined subscription in the Americas to individuals print & online eds.; GBP 137 combined subscription elsewhere to individuals print & online eds.; AUD 377 combined subscription in Australia & New Zealand to institutions print & online eds.; USD 984 combined subscription in the Americas to institutions print & online eds.; GBP 609 combined subscription elsewhere to institutions print & online eds. (effective 2006). adv. bk.rev. Index. back issues avail.; reprint service avail. from PQC. **Document type:** *Journal, Academic/Scholarly.* **Description:** Publishes original papers describing experimental, comprehensive, observational or theoretical studies on terrestrial, marine or freshwater systems.
Formerly (until 2000): Australian Journal of Ecology (0307-692X)
Related titles: Online - full text ed.: ISSN 1442-9993. GBP 358 in Australia & New Zealand to institutions; USD 935 in the Americas to institutions & Caribbean; GBP 579 elsewhere to institutions (effective 2006) (from Blackwell Synergy, EBSCO Publishing, Gale Group, IngentaConnect, O C L C Online Computer Library Center, Inc., Swets Information Services).
Indexed: AESIS, ASCA, ASFA, AbAn, Agr, AgrForAb, AnBeAb, AnBrAb, ApEcolAb, ApicAb, BIOBASE, BIOSIS Prev, BibAg, BioCN&I, BiolAb, CPA, CRFR, ChemAb, CurCont, EPB, ESPM, EngInd, EntAb, FCA, FPA, ForAb, GEOBASE, HerbAb, HortAb, I&DA, INIS AtomInd, ISR, IndVet, KWIWR, M&GPA, OceAb, OrnHort, PBA, PGegResA, PN&I, PlantSci, PollutAb, PoultAb, RM&VM, RPP, RRTA, RefZh, RevApplEntom, S&F, SCI, SFA, SSCI, SWRA, SeedAb, TDB, WAE&RSA, WeedAb, ZooRec.
—BLDSC (1793.105000), CASDDS, CISTI, Ei, IDS, IE, Infotrieve, ingenta, Linda Hall. **CCC.**
Published by: (Flinders University of South Australia, School of Biological Sciences, Ecological Society of Australia), Blackwell Publishing Asia (Subsidiary of: Blackwell Publishing Ltd.), 550 Swanston St, Carlton South, VIC 3053, Australia. TEL 61-383591011, FAX 61-383591120, subs@blackwellpublishingasia.com, http://www.blackwellpublishing.com/journals/AEC. adv.: B&W page AUD 935, color page AUD 1,950; trim 210 x 275. Circ: 1,650.

574.05 AUS ISSN 1030-6234
➤ **AUSTRALIAN BIOLOGIST.** Text in English. 1988. 2/yr. AUD 32 domestic; AUD 40 foreign (effective 2004). adv. **Document type:** *Journal, Academic/Scholarly.* **Description:** Keeps society members informed of new developments in biology and provides a forum for the views and opinions of Australian biologists on current affairs in biology and biological education.
Published by: Australian Institute of Biology, c/o The Royal Geographical Society of Queensland, 237 Milton Rd, Milton, QLD 4064, Australia. TEL 61-7-33682066, FAX 61-7-33671011, rgsq@gil.com.au, http://www.aibiol.org.au. Adv. contact R.S. Hill. page AUD 95.

572.8 USA ISSN 1554-8627
▼ ➤ **AUTOPHAGY.** Text in English. 2005 (Apr.). q. USD 80 in US & Canada to individuals; USD 130 elsewhere to individuals; USD 350 in US & Canada to institutions; USD 400 elsewhere to institutions; USD 45 per issue (effective 2005). **Document type:** *Journal, Academic/Scholarly.*
Related titles: Online - full text ed.: ISSN 1554-8635.
Published by: Landes Bioscience, 810 S Church St, Georgetown, TX 78626. TEL 512-863-7762, 800-736-9948, FAX 512-863-0081, info@landesbioscience.com, http://www.landesbioscience.com/journals/autophagy/index.php.

570 RUS ISSN 1561-9958
AVIAN ECOLOGY AND BEHAVIOUR. Text in English. 1998. s-a.
Related titles: Supplement(s): Avian Ecology and Behaviour Supplement.
Indexed: ZooRec.
—Linda Hall.
Published by: Rossiiskaya Akademiya Nauk, Zoologicheskii Institut/Russian Academy of Sciences, Zoological Institute, Universitetskaya nab 1, St Petersburg, 199034, Russian Federation. TEL 7-812-3280011, FAX 7-812-3282941, admin@zin.ru, http://www.zin.ru.

590 ESP ISSN 1134-1785
QL229.A2
AVICENNIA. Text in Spanish. 1994. a.
Related titles: Supplement(s): Avicennia Suplemento. ISSN 1138-6541. 1996.
Indexed: ZooRec.
Published by: Universidad de Oviedo, Facultad de Biologia, c/o Carlos Lastra, Redactor, Departamento de Zoologia, Oviedo, 33071, Spain.

570 JPN ISSN 0917-866X
AZABU DAIGAKU SEIBUTSU KAGAKU SOGO KENKYUJO KIYO/AZABU UNIVERSITY. RESEARCH INSTITUTE OF BIOSCIENCES. REPORT. Text in Japanese. 1991. a.
Published by: Azabu Daigaku, Seibutsu Kagaku Sogo Kenkyujo/Azabu University, Research Institute of Biosciences, 17-71 Fuchinobe 1-chome, Sagamihara-shi, Kanagawa-ken 229-0006, Japan.

B B A - BIOENERGETICS. (Biochimica et Biophysica Acta) see *BIOLOGY—Botany*

570 GBR ISSN 1741-7007
▼ ➤ **B M C BIOLOGY.** (BioMed Central) Text in English. 2003. irreg. free (effective 2006). back issues avail. **Document type:** *Journal, Academic/Scholarly.* **Description:** Publishes original research articles and methodology articles in any area of biology but with a focus on the biomedical sciences, including biochemistry, cell biology, chemical biology, computational biology, developmental biology, ecology, evolutionary biology, genetics, genomics, immunology, microbiology, molecular biology, neurobiology, pharmacology, physiology, plant biology and structural biology.
Media: Online - full content (from EBSCO Publishing, National Library of Medicine).
Indexed: ExcerpMed.
Published by: BioMed Central Ltd. (Subsidiary of: Current Science Ltd), Middlesex House, 34-42 Cleveland St, London, W1T 4LB, United Kingdom. TEL 44-20-76319131, FAX 44-20-76319923, info@biomedcentral.com, http://www.biomedcentral.com/bmcbiol/.

570 GBR ISSN 1471-213X
QH491 CODEN: BDBMA7
➤ **B M C DEVELOPMENTAL BIOLOGY.** (BioMed Central) Text in English. 2001. m. free (effective 2006). adv. **Document type:** *Journal, Academic/Scholarly.* **Description:** Publishes original research articles in all aspects of cellular, tissue-level and organismal aspects of development.
Media: Online - full content (from EBSCO Publishing, National Library of Medicine).
Indexed: BIOSIS Prev, BiolAb, MEDLINE, ZooRec.
—Infotrieve. **CCC.**
Published by: BioMed Central Ltd. (Subsidiary of: Current Science Ltd), Middlesex House, 34-42 Cleveland St, London, W1T 4LB, United Kingdom. TEL 44-20-76319131, FAX 44-20-76319923, info@biomedcentral.com, http://www.biomedcentral.com/bmcdevbiol/. Ed. Peter Newmark. Adv. contact Deborah Cockerill.

577 GBR ISSN 1472-6785
QH540 CODEN: BEMCB6
➤ **B M C ECOLOGY.** (BioMed Central) Text in English. 2001. m. free (effective 2006). adv. **Document type:** *Journal, Academic/Scholarly.* **Description:** Publishes original research articles in environmental and population ecology of plants, animals, and microbes.
Media: Online - full content (from EBSCO Publishing, National Library of Medicine).
Indexed: BIOSIS Prev, BiolAb, ZooRec.
—Infotrieve. **CCC.**
Published by: BioMed Central Ltd. (Subsidiary of: Current Science Ltd), Middlesex House, 34-42 Cleveland St, London, W1T 4LB, United Kingdom. TEL 44-20-76319131, FAX 44-20-76319923, info@biomedcentral.com, http://www.biomedcentral.com/bmcecol/. Ed. Peter Newmark. Adv. contact Deborah Cockerill.

➤ **B M C IMMUNOLOGY.** (BioMed Central) see *MEDICAL SCIENCES—Allergology And Immunology*

572.8 GBR ISSN 1471-2199
QH506 CODEN: BMBMC4
➤ **B M C MOLECULAR BIOLOGY.** (BioMed Central) Text in English. 2000. m. free (effective 2006). adv. **Document type:** *Journal, Academic/Scholarly.* **Description:** Publishes original research articles in all aspects of DNA and RNA in a cellular context, encompassing investigations of transcription, mRNA processing, translation, replication, recombination, mutation, and repair.
Media: Online - full content (from EBSCO Publishing, National Library of Medicine).
Indexed: BCI, BIOSIS Prev, BiolAb, ExcerpMed, MEDLINE.
—Infotrieve. **CCC.**
Published by: BioMed Central Ltd. (Subsidiary of: Current Science Ltd), Middlesex House, 34-42 Cleveland St, London, W1T 4LB, United Kingdom. TEL 44-20-76319131, FAX 44-20-76319923, info@biomedcentral.com, http://www.biomedcentral.com/bmcmolbiol/. Ed. Peter Newmark. Adv. contact Deborah Cockerill.

572.8 GBR ISSN 1472-6807
QH506 CODEN: BSBMBB
➤ **B M C STRUCTURAL BIOLOGY.** Text in English. 2001. m. free (effective 2006). adv. **Document type:** *Journal, Academic/Scholarly.* **Description:** Publishes original research articles in investigations into the structure and function of biological macromolecules.
Media: Online - full content (from EBSCO Publishing, National Library of Medicine).
Indexed: BIOSIS Prev, BiolAb, ExcerpMed.
—Infotrieve. **CCC.**
Published by: BioMed Central Ltd. (Subsidiary of: Current Science Ltd), Middlesex House, 34-42 Cleveland St, London, W1T 4LB, United Kingdom. TEL 44-20-76319131, FAX 44-20-76319923, info@biomedcentral.com, http://www.biomedcentral.com/bmcstructbiol/. Ed. Peter Newmark. Adv. contact Deborah Cockerill.

570.71 USA
QH315
B S C S: THE NATURAL SELECTION; innovative science education. Text in English. 1958. 3/yr. free. adv. bk.rev. bibl.; illus. **Document type:** *Newsletter, Academic/Scholarly.* **Description:** Prepares and implements innovative college science programs. Informs educators about BSCS programs and other advances in science education.
Former titles (until 1981): B S C S Journal (0162-3613); (until 1979): Biological Sciences Curriculum Study Journal; (until 1978): B S C S Newsletter (0005-3295)
Related titles: Microform ed.: (from PQC).
—CISTI, GNLM.
Published by: Biological Sciences Curriculum Study, Pikes Peak Research Park, 5415 Mark Dabling Blvd, Colorado Springs, CO 80918. TEL 719-531-5550, FAX 719-531-9104, lengleman@bscs.org, http://www.bscs.org. Ed., R&P Laura Engleman. Circ: 10,000.

570 DEU ISSN 0067-2858
BADISCHER LANDESVEREIN FUER NATURKUNDE UND NATURSCHUTZ, FREIBURG. MITTEILUNGEN. NEUE FOLGE. Text in German. 1919. a. EUR 26 (effective 2003). bk.rev. **Document type:** *Journal, Academic/Scholarly.* **Description:** Publications on biology, geology and mineralogy.
Indexed: BiolAb, ZooRec.
Published by: Badischer Landesverein fuer Naturkunde und Naturschutz e.V., Gerberau 32, Freiburg Im Breisgau, 79098, Germany. TEL 49-761-2012561, FAX 49-761-2012563, http://www.blnn.de. Ed. H Koerner. Circ: 2,500.

570 JPN ISSN 1347-7080
BAIOMATERIARU/JAPANESE SOCIETY FOR BIOMATERIALS. JOURNAL. Text in Japanese. 1983. bi-m. **Document type:** *Journal, Academic/Scholarly.*
Formerly (until 2002): Seitai Zairyo (0910-304X)
—BLDSC (4809.416000), IE. **CCC.**
Published by: Nihon Baiomateriaru Gakkai/Japanese Society for Biomaterials, c/o Business Center for Academic Societies, Japan Sumitomo Fudosan Hongo Bldg., 7th Fl, 3-22-5 Hongo, Tokyo, 113-8531, Japan. TEL 81-3-58145801, FAX 81-3-58145825, http://wwwsoc.nii.ac.jp/jsbm/seitai.html.

570 JPN ISSN 0915-4531
BAIOTORENDO/BIOTRENDS. Text in Japanese. 1989. q. JPY 2,400 per issue.
Published by: Maruzen Co., Ltd./Maruzen Kabushikikaisha, 3-10 Nihonbashi 2-chome, Chuo-ku, Tokyo, 103-0027, Japan. TEL 81-3-3272-7211, FAX 81-3-3278-1937.

578.77 SWE ISSN 0282-8839
BALTIC MARINE BIOLOGISTS. PUBLICATION. Text in English. 1975. irreg. price varies. back issues avail. **Document type:** *Monographic series, Academic/Scholarly.*
Published by: Baltic Marine Biologists, c/o Pauli Snoeijs, Deptment of Evolutionary Biology-Plant Ecology, Villavaegen 14, Uppsala, 752 36, Sweden. FAX 46-18-553419, pauli.snoeijs@ebc.uu.se, http://www.smf.su.se/bmb/publicat.htm.

570 USA ISSN 0198-0068
CODEN: BANRDU
BANBURY REPORTS. Variant title: Banbury Reports Series. Text in English. 1979. irreg., latest vol.35, 1991. price varies. **Document type:** *Monographic series, Academic/Scholarly.* **Description:** Devoted to risk assessments including topics pertaining to human diseases.
Indexed: BiolAb, ChemAb.
—CASDDS, CISTI. **CCC.**
Published by: Cold Spring Harbor Laboratory Press, Publications Department, 500 Sunnyside Blvd., Woodbury, NY 11797-2924. TEL 516-422-4100, 800-843-4388, FAX 516-422-4097, cshpress@cshl.edu, http://www.cshl.org. Ed. John Inglis.

570 630 BGD ISSN 1016-4057
BANGLADESH JOURNAL OF BIOLOGICAL SCIENCES. Text in English. 1955. s-a. BDT 30, USD 5. bk.rev. back issues avail.
Former titles: Bangladesh Journal of Biological and Agricultural Sciences (0045-1428); Pakistan Journal of Biological and Agricultural Sciences (0078-8244)
Indexed: BiolAb, ChemAb, DSA, FCA, HerbAb, PBA, ZooRec.
—CISTI, Linda Hall.
Published by: Bangladesh Society for Biological and Agricultural Sciences, Dept. of Biochemistry, University of Dhaka, Ramna, Dhaka, 2, Bangladesh. Ed. Kamaluddin Ahmad. Circ: 500.

BANGLADESH JOURNAL OF SOIL SCIENCE. see *AGRICULTURE—Crop Production And Soil*

570 GBR ISSN 0408-5655
BARDSEY OBSERVATORY REPORT. Text in English. 1953. a. GBP 5. back issues avail. **Document type:** *Academic/Scholarly.* **Description:** Reports on activities and research concerning Bardsey Island, a national nature reserve off the northwestern coast of Wales.
Indexed: BiolAb.
Published by: Bardsey Bird & Field Observatory, c/o L. Richardson, 33 Doveridge Rd, Hall Green, Birmingham, B28 0LT, United Kingdom. TEL 44-121-745-8881, FAX 44-121-200-2454. Ed. P Hope Jones. Circ: 300.

BASIC AND APPLIED ECOLOGY. see *ENVIRONMENTAL STUDIES*

611.018 ITA ISSN 1120-9992
➤ **BASIC AND APPLIED MYOLOGY.** Short title: B A M. Text in Italian. 1991. bi-m. USD 150. back issues avail. **Document type:** *Academic/Scholarly.* **Description:** Cover skeletal muscle basic research and its applications.
Related titles: Online - full text ed.: free (effective 2005).
—BLDSC (1861.468000), GNLM, IDS, IE, Infotrieve, ingenta.
Published by: (Universita degli Studi di Padova, Department of Biomedical Sciences), Unipress s.a.s., Via Cesare Battisti 231, Padua, PD 35121, Italy. unipress2001@libero.it, http://www.bio.unipd.it/~bam/bam.html. Ed. Ugo Carraro. Circ: 100.

570 USA ISSN 0090-5542
CODEN: BLFSBY
➤ **BASIC LIFE SCIENCES.** Text in English. 1973. irreg., latest vol.66, 2000. EUR 396, USD 436, GBP 273 per vol. (effective 2004); for vol.66. **Document type:** *Monographic series, Academic/Scholarly.*
Indexed: BIOSIS Prev, BiolAb, CIN, ChemAb, ChemTitl, DBA, IndMed, MEDLINE.
—BLDSC (1863.980000), CASDDS, CISTI, GNLM, Infotrieve, ingenta, KNAW. **CCC.**
Published by: Springer-Verlag New York, Inc. (Subsidiary of: Springer Science+Business Media), 233 Spring St, New York, NY 10013. TEL 212-460-1500, FAX 212-460-1575, service@springer-ny.com, http://www.springer-ny.com.

➤ **BASLER VEROEFFENTLICHUNGEN ZUR GESCHICHTE DER MEDIZIN UND DER BIOLOGIE. NEUE FOLGE.** see *MEDICAL SCIENCES*

338 USA
BAYER ALKALIZER. Text in English. 1936. q. free. back issues avail. **Description:** Employee news of research-based healthcare products manufacturer.
Former titles: Miles Alkalizer; (until 1989): Alkalizer
Published by: Bayer Corp., 1884 Miles Ave, Elkhart, IN 46514. TEL 219-264-8111, FAX 219-262-7209, http://www.bayerus.com. Ed. Catherine Wells Bentz. Circ: 6,500 (controlled).

570 GBR ISSN 0951-8959
BEDFORDSHIRE NATURALIST. Text in English. 1948. a.
Indexed: ZooRec.
Published by: Bedfordshire Natural History Society, 46 Mallard Hill, Bedford, MK41 7QS, United Kingdom. TEL 01234-211941, journal@bnhs.org.uk, http://www.bedfordshirenaturalhistorysociety.org.uk/. Ed. Rosemary Brind.

BEHAVIORAL AND BRAIN SCIENCES; an international journal of current research and theory with open peer commentary. see *PSYCHOLOGY*

591.7 USA ISSN 1045-2249
QL750 CODEN: BEECE3
➤ **BEHAVIORAL ECOLOGY.** Text in English. 1990. bi-m. GBP 321, USD 562, EUR 482 to institutions; GBP 338, USD 592, EUR 507 combined subscription to institutions print & online eds. (effective 2006). adv. back issues avail.; reprint service avail. from PSC. **Document type:** *Journal, Academic/Scholarly.* **Description:** Publishes research on environmental influences on the evolution and adaptation of animal behavior.
Related titles: Online - full text ed.: ISSN 1465-7279. GBP 304, USD 532, EUR 456 to institutions (effective 2006) (from EBSCO Publishing, Gale Group, HighWire Press, IngentaConnect, O C L C Online Computer Library Center, Inc., Ovid Technologies, Inc., Oxford University Press Online Journals, ProQuest Information & Learning, Swets Information Services).
Indexed: ASCA, ASFA, AbHyg, AgBio, AnBeAb, AnBrAb, ApEcolAb, ApicAb, B&BAb, BIOBASE, BIOSIS Prev, BioCN&I, BiolAb, CurCont, DSA, EPB, ESPM, EntAb, FCA, ForAb, GEOBASE, GenetAb, HGA, HelmAb, HortAb, IABS, ISR, IndVet, Inpharma, KWIWR, NutrAb, OrnHort, PBA, PE&ON, PGegResA, PHN&I, PoultAb, ProtozoAb, PsycInfo, PsycholAb, RM&VM, Reac, RevApplEntom, SCI, SFA, SIA, SeedAb, VetBull, WildRev, ZooRec, e-psyche.
—BLDSC (1877.390000), IDS, IE, Infotrieve, ingenta. **CCC.**
Published by: (International Society for Behavioral Ecology), Oxford University Press (Subsidiary of: Oxford University Press), 2001 Evans Rd, Cary, NC 27513. TEL 919-677-0977, 800-852-7323, FAX 919-677-1714, jnlorders@oup-usa.org, http://beheco.oxfordjournals.org/, http://www.us.oup.com. Eds. Dr. Andrew Bourke, Dr. Ian Owens. adv.: B&W page GBP 315, B&W page USD 565; trim 190 x 245. Circ: 1,366.

B

➤ **BEHAVIORAL ECOLOGY AND SOCIOBIOLOGY.** see *ENVIRONMENTAL STUDIES*

570 DEU ISSN 0721-3468
BEITRAEGE ZUR NATURKUNDE DER WETTERAU✶. Text in German; Summaries in English, German. 1981. a. adv. bk.rev. back issues avail.
Related titles: Microfiche ed.: 1981.
Published by: Naturkundlicher Arbeitskreis Wetterau, Fuhrstr 5, Rosbach, 61191, Germany. Circ: 800.

570 550 DEU ISSN 0342-5452
BEITRAEGE ZUR NATURKUNDE IN OSTHESSEN. Text in German. 1969. irreg., latest vol.34, 1998. bk.rev. **Document type:** *Monographic series.*
Indexed: ZooRec.
Published by: (Verein fuer Naturkunde in Osthessen e.V.), Verlag Parzeller GmbH & Co. KG, Postfach 409, Fulda, 36004, Germany. TEL 49-661-280-0, FAX 49-661-280-285, verlag@parzeller.de. Circ: 500.

500.9 DEU ISSN 0340-4277
QH5 CODEN: BNNIDQ
BEITRAEGE ZUR NATURKUNDE NIEDERSACHSENS. Text in German. 1948. q. adv. bk.rev. abstr.; charts; illus.; stat. index. back issues avail. **Document type:** *Journal, Academic/Scholarly.* **Description:** Covers general biology as related to the federal state of Lower Saxony and Bremen in Germany.
Formerly (until 1974): Natur, Kultur und Jagd (0028-0577)
Indexed: BiolAb, ForAb, KWIWR, RefZh, ZooRec.
Address: Kastanienallee 13, Peine, 31224, Germany. TEL 49-5171-12233, FAX 49-5171-48283, hans.oelke@t-online.de. Ed., Pub. Dr. Hans Oelke. Circ: 700. **Subscr. to:** J. Streichert, Bergweg 6, Ilsede 31241, Germany. TEL 49-5172-4530.

570 AUT ISSN 1025-3262
BEITRAEGE ZUR NATURKUNDE OBEROESTERREICHS. Text in German; Summaries in English. 1993. a. price varies. back issues avail. **Document type:** *Journal, Academic/Scholarly.* **Description:** Contains scientific contributions in biology.
Indexed: ZooRec.
Published by: Oberoesterreichisches Landesmuseum, Biologiezentrum, J.-W.-Klein-Str 73, Linz, 4040, Austria. TEL 43-732-759733, FAX 43-732-75973399, bio-linz@landesmuseum-linz.ac.at, http://www.biologiezentrum.at. R&P Gerhard Aubrecht. Circ: 500 (paid).

BEITRAEGE ZUR RHEINKUNDE. see *HISTORY—History Of Europe*

BERLIN - BRANDENBURGER NATURMAGAZIN; Naturschutz in Berlin und Brandenburg. see *CONSERVATION*

577 DEU ISSN 0173-7074
➤ **BERLINER NATURSCHUTZBLAETTER**; Zeitschrift fuer Berlin und Brandenburg. Text in German. 1922. q. USD 37 (effective 1999). adv. bk.rev. index. back issues avail. **Document type:** *Journal, Academic/Scholarly.* **Description:** Publication covering pollution, preservation and protection of nature in Berlin, Germnay and worldwide. Features forests, lakes, land, wildlife, ecology, ecotoxicological research, and environmental education. Includes personalities, association news, events and scientific research.
Indexed: IBR, ZooRec.

▼ new title ➤ refereed ✶ unverified ♦ full entry avail.

Published by: Volksbund Naturschutz e.V., Koenigin-Luise-Str 6-8, Berlin, 14195, Germany. TEL 49-30-84107131, FAX 49-30-84107131, vbn@vbcv.de. Ed. Kurt Hoegerle. Adv. contact Reginald Brauch. Circ: 20,000.

➤ **BERMUDA BIOLOGICAL STATION FOR RESEARCH. ANNUAL REPORT.** see *ENVIRONMENTAL STUDIES*

➤ **BERMUDA. BIOLOGICAL STATION FOR RESEARCH. SPECIAL PUBLICATIONS.** see *ENVIRONMENTAL STUDIES*

➤ **DIE BINNENGEWAESSER**; Einzeldarstellungen aus der Limnologie und ihren Grenzgebieten. see *EARTH SCIENCES—Hydrology*

➤ **BIO MED.** see *MEDICAL SCIENCES*

570 IND ISSN 0970-0889
CODEN: BSRB

➤ **BIO-SCIENCE RESEARCH BULLETIN.** Text in English. 1985. 2/yr. INR 300, USD 50, GBP 30 (effective 2005). adv. bk.rev. 110 p./no. 1 cols./p.; back issues avail.; reprints avail. **Document type:** *Journal, Academic/Scholarly.* **Description:** Research papers related with Biological Science and Life Science.
Media: Large Type (11 pt.).
Indexed: ZooRec.
—CCC.
Published by: A.K. Sharma, Ed. & Pub., 19-A, D D A Flats, Mansarover Park, Shahdara, New Delhi, 110 032, India. TEL 91-11-2117408, bulletin@mantraonline.com, ajaykumarsharma1955@yahoo.com. R&P, Adv. contact A K Sharma. B&W page INR 1,000, B&W page USD 50, color page INR 2,000, color page USD 100. Circ: 600.

573 BRA ISSN 0104-3455
QH117
BIOCIENCIAS. Text in Portuguese. 1993. irreg., latest vol.10, no.1, 2002, Jun.
Indexed: ASFA, AgrForAb, BIOSIS Prev, BioCN&I, BiolAb, CPA, ESPM, EntAb, FCA, ForAb, GenetAb, HortAb, IndVet, PBA, PGegResA, ProtozoAb, S&F, SWRA, SeedAb, ZooRec.
—CISTI.
Published by: (Pontificia Universidade Catolica do Rio Grande do Sul, Faculdade de Biociencias), Editora da P U C R S, c/o Antoninho M. Naime, Partenon, Caixa Postal 12001, Porto Alegre, RGS 90651-970, Brazil. gervasio@pucrs.br.

570 JPN ISSN 1342-4815
QR51 CODEN: BISCFY
BIOCONTROL SCIENCE. Text in English. 1996. s-a. subscr. incld. with membership. adv. **Document type:** *Journal, Academic/Scholarly.* **Description:** Provides a medium for the publication of original articles, concise notes, and review articles on all aspects of science & technology of biocontrol.
Indexed: AEBA, ASFA, BIOSIS Prev, BiolAb, ESPM, EngInd, ExcerpMed, FS&TA, MBA, SWRA.
—BLDSC (2071.120000), CASDDS, CISTI, IE, ingenta. **CCC.**
Published by: Nihon Bokin Bobai Gakkai/Society for Antibacterial and Antifungal Agents, Japan, 9th Fl, Shin-Kousan Bldg, 1-13-38, Nishimotocho, Nishi-ku, Osaka-shi, 550-0005, Japan. TEL 81-6-65382166, FAX 81-6-65382169, ttsuchi@ipcku.kansai-u.ac.jp, boukin@nifty.com, http://wwwsoc.nii.ac.jp/saaaj/. Ed. Tetsuaki Tsuchido. R&P K Arai TEL 81-6-6538-2166. Adv. contact Iwao Yamamoto.

570 ESP
BIODATOS BASICOS. Text in Spanish. 1989. irreg., latest vol.5, 1992. price varies.
Related titles: ♦ Supplement to: Universidad de Oviedo. Revista de Biologia. ISSN 0212-8977.
Published by: Universidad de Oviedo, Jesus Arias de Velasco, S/N, Oviedo, 33005, Spain. Ed. Julian Rubio Cardiel.

BIODEGRADATION. see *ENVIRONMENTAL STUDIES—Waste Management*

BIODIVERSITY AND CONSERVATION. see *CONSERVATION*

570 USA ISSN 1546-9735
▼ ➤ **BIODIVERSITY INFORMATICS.** Text in English. 2004. irreg. free (effective 2005). **Document type:** *Journal, Academic/Scholarly.* **Description:** Focuses on the emerging field of biodiversity informatics, the creation, integration, analysis and understanding of information regarding biological diversity.
Media: Online - full text.
Published by: University of Kansas, Informatics Biodiversity Research Center, 1345 Jayhawk Blvd, Lawrence, KS 66045-7561. TEL 785-864-3926, FAX 785-864-5335, http://jbi.nhm.ku.edu/index.php.

333.72 570 GBR ISSN 1360-1164
BIODIVERSITY NEWS; the newsletter for biodiversity action planners. Text in English. 1994. q. **Document type:** *Newsletter.*
Related titles: Online - full content ed.
—BLDSC (2071.830100).
Published by: U K Biodiversity Action Plan, Biodiversity Policy Unit, Kite Zone, Temple Quay House, 2 The Square, Temple Quay, Bristol, BS1 6EB, United Kingdom. TEL 44-117-3726276, ruth.peacey@defra.gsi.gov.uk, http://www.ukbap.org.uk/Library/library_3.htm. Ed. Peacey Ruth.

570 GBR ISSN 0265-9247
QH506 CODEN: BIOEEJ
➤ **BIOESSAYS**; advances in molecular, cellular and developmental biology. Text in English. 1984. m. USD 1,149 domestic to institutions; USD 1,293 in Canada & Mexico to institutions; USD 1,377 elsewhere to institutions; USD 1,264 combined subscription domestic to institutions print & online eds.; USD 1,408 combined subscription in Canada & Mexico to institutions print & online eds.; USD 1,492 combined subscription elsewhere to institutions print & online eds. (effective 2006). adv. reprints avail. **Document type:** *Journal, Academic/Scholarly.* **Description:** Current-awareness journal reviewing advances in molecular, cellular and developmental biology.
Related titles: Online - full content ed.: ISSN 1521-1878. USD 1,149 to institutions (effective 2006); Online - full text ed.: (from EBSCO Publishing, Swets Information Services, Wiley InterScience).
Indexed: ASCA, ASFA, AbHyg, AgBio, AgrForAb, AnBrAb, BBCI, BIOBASE, BIOSIS Prev, BioCN&I, CBTA, CEABA, CIN, CPA, CTA, ChemAb, ChemTitl, CurCont, DSA, ESPM, ExcerpMed, FCA, GenetAb, HGA, HelmAb, HortAb, IABS, ISR, IndMed, IndVet, Inpharma, MEDLINE, MaizeAb, NSA, NSCI, NemAb, NucAcAb, NutrAb, PBA, PGegResA, PGrRegA, PotatoAb, ProtozoAb, RA&MP, RM&VM, RPP, Reac, RefZh, RevApplEntom, S&F, SCI, SFA, SoyAb, TDB, Telegen, TriticAb, VetBull, WeedAb, WildRev, ZooRec.
—BLDSC (2072.118000), CASDDS, CISTI, GNLM, IE, Infotrieve, ingenta, Linda Hall. **CCC.**
Published by: John Wiley & Sons Ltd. (Subsidiary of: John Wiley & Sons, Inc.), The Atrium, Southern Gate, Chichester, West Sussex PO19 8SQ, United Kingdom. TEL 44-1243-779777, FAX 44-1243-775878, customer@wiley.co.uk, http://www.interscience.wiley.com/jpages/0265-9247/, http://www.wiley.co.uk. Ed. Adam S Wilkins. R&P Chris Sheridan. Adv. contact Susan Levey. **Subscr. outside the Americas to:** John Wiley & Sons, Inc., 111 River St, Hoboken, NJ 07030-5774. TEL 201-748-6645, 800-225-5945, subinfo@wiley.com.

➤ **BIOETHICS.** see *PHILOSOPHY*

174.957 ITA ISSN 1122-2344
BIOETICA; Rivista interdisciplinare. Text in Italian. 1993. q. EUR 47 domestic to individuals; EUR 67.14 foreign to individuals; EUR 62.49 domestic to institutions; EUR 77.98 foreign to institutions (effective 2004). 200 p./no.; **Document type:** *Magazine.*
Indexed: DIP.
Published by: (Consulta di Bioetica), Zadig s.r.l., Via Calzecchi 10, Milan, 20133, Italy. TEL 39-02-7526131, FAX 39-02-76113040, segreteria@zadig.it, http://www.bioetica.it, http://www.zadig.it. Ed. Maurizio Mori.

570 USA ISSN 1060-2488
BIOFEEDBACK (CINCINNATI). Text in English. q. USD 105 with S.L.A. membership. adv. bk.rev. bibl. **Document type:** *Newsletter.* **Description:** Contains Division news, announcements, and information of interest to biological science librarians.
—CISTI.
Published by: Special Libraries Association, Biological Sciences Division, c/o John Tebo, Ed, Chemistry Biology Lab, University of Cincinnati, 503 Rieveschel Hall, Mail Location 0151, Cincinnati, OH 45221-0151. TEL 513-556-1494, FAX 513-556-1103, tebo@ucbeh.san.uc.edu. R&P Adam Schiff. Adv. contact Lawrence Kelland. Circ: 600 (paid).

570 GBR ISSN 1479-0505
▼ **BIOFILMS.** Text in English. 2003. q. USD 328 in North America to institutions; GBP 205 elsewhere to institutions; USD 358 combined subscription in North America to institutions print & online eds.; GBP 224 combined subscription elsewhere to institutions print & online eds. (effective 2006). **Document type:** *Journal, Academic/Scholarly.*
Related titles: Online - full text ed.: ISSN 1479-0513. 2004. USD 304 in North America to institutions; GBP 190 elsewhere to institutions (effective 2006) (from EBSCO Publishing, O C L C Online Computer Library Center, Inc., Swets Information Services).
Indexed: ExcerpMed.
—BLDSC (2072.144000), CISTI.
Published by: Cambridge University Press, The Edinburgh Bldg, Shaftesbury Rd, Cambridge, CB2 2RU, United Kingdom. TEL 44-1223-312393, FAX 44-1223-315052, biofilms@cambridge.org, journals@cambridge.org, http://titles.cambridge.org/journals/journal_catalogue.asp?mnemonic=bfm, http://www.cup.cam.ac.uk/. Ed. Michael Wilson. **Subscr. to:** Cambridge University Press, 100 Brook Hill Dr, West Nyack, NY 10994. TEL 845-353-7500, FAX 845-353-4141, journals_subscriptions@cup.org

572.8 579 DEU ISSN 0940-0079
CODEN: BFRME3
BIOFORUM; Forschung & Entwicklung. Text in German. 1991. 10/yr. EUR 98 in Europe to institutions; USD 118 elsewhere to institutions (effective 2006). adv. **Document type:** *Magazine, Trade.*
Formed by the merger of (1978-1991): Forum Mikrobiologie (0170-8244); (1987-1991): G U M (0931-945X)
Indexed: CEABA, CIN, ChemAb, ChemTitl, VITIS.
—CASDDS, GNLM, IE. **CCC.**
Published by: G I T Verlag GmbH (Subsidiary of: Wiley - V C H Verlag GmbH & Co. KGaA), Roesslerstr 90, Darmstadt, 64293, Germany. TEL 49-6151-80900, FAX 49-6151-8090144, info@gitverlag.com, service@wiley-vch.de, http://www.gitverlag.com. Ed. Dr. Birgit Washburn. adv.: B&W page EUR 4,510, color page EUR 5,990; trim 185 x 260. Circ: 14,198 (paid and controlled).

572.8 DEU ISSN 1611-597X
BIOFORUM EUROPE. Text in English. 1997. bi-m. EUR 60 in Europe to institutions; USD 74 elsewhere to institutions (effective 2006). adv. **Document type:** *Magazine, Trade.* **Description:** Aims to anticipate and communicate trends in the biotechnology sector in Europe.
Formerly (until 2003): Bioforum International (1434-2693)
—BLDSC (2072.146350).
Published by: G I T Verlag GmbH (Subsidiary of: Wiley - V C H Verlag GmbH & Co. KGaA), Roesslerstr 90, Darmstadt, 64293, Germany. TEL 49-6151-80900, FAX 49-6151-8090144, info@gitverlag.com, service@wiley-vch.de, http://www.gitverlag.com/index.html?content=%2Fwj%2Fengine%2Fde%2Fpub%2Fmag%2Fsep. Ed. Dr. Birgit Washburn. adv.: B&W page EUR 5,100, color page EUR 6,580; trim 185 x 260. Circ: 27,000 (paid).

660.6 DEU ISSN 1619-7682
BIOFORUM FRANCE. Text in French. 2002. 3/yr. EUR 24 in Europe to institutions; USD 28 elsewhere to institutions (effective 2006). **Document type:** *Journal, Academic/Scholarly.*
Published by: G I T Verlag GmbH (Subsidiary of: Wiley - V C H Verlag GmbH & Co. KGaA), Roesslerstr 90, Darmstadt, 64293, Germany. TEL 49-6151-80900, info@gitverlag.com, service@wiley-vch.de, http://en.media.gitverlag.com/html/bio_edf_2003, http://www.gitverlag.com. Ed. Dr. Birgit Washburn. Circ: 4,000.

570 FRA ISSN 1165-6638
BIOGEOGRAPHICA. Text in English, French, Spanish. 1924. q. bk.rev. charts; illus. **Document type:** *Bulletin.*
Former titles (until 1992): Societe de Biogeographe. Compte Rendu des Seances (0037-9018); (until 1969): Societe de Biogeographie. Compte-Rendu Sommaire des Seances (1153-320X)
Indexed: ASFA, BIOSIS Prev, BiolAb, IndMed, ZooRec.
—BLDSC (2072.169000), IE, ingenta.
Published by: Societe de Biogeographie, 57 rue Cuvier, Paris, Cedex 5 75231, France. Ed. W R Lourenco. Circ: 550.

570 910.02 JPN ISSN 1345-0662
BIOGEOGRAPHY✶; international journal of biogeography, phylogeny, taxonomy, ecology, biodiversity, evolution, and conservation biology. Text in English. 1999. a. **Document type:** *Academic/Scholarly.*
Indexed: AgrForAb, BIOSIS Prev, BiolAb, ForAb, HelmAb, HortAb, IndVet, NemAb, S&F, VetBull, ZooRec.
Published by: Biogeographical Society of Japan/Nippon Seibutsu Chiri Gakkai, Gifu University, Faculty Of Regional Studies, Yanagido 1-1, Gifu, 501-1193, Japan. TEL 81-58-2933027, FAX 81-58-2933008, biogeo-mukai@nifty.com, http://wwwsoc.nii.ac.jp/tbsj/pubrication/Biogeo01.htm.

550 DEU ISSN 1726-4170
QH343.7
▼ ➤ **BIOGEOSCIENCES.** Text in English. 2003. irreg. **Document type:** *Journal, Academic/Scholarly.*
Related titles: Online - full text ed.: ISSN 1726-4189. free (effective 2005).
Indexed: ASFA.
Published by: (European Geosciences Union), Copernicus GmbH, Max-Planck Str 13, Katlenburg-Lindau, 37191, Germany. TEL 49-5556-91099, info@copernicus.org, http://www.copernicus.org/site/EGU/bg/.

550 DEU ISSN 1810-6277
▼ ➤ **BIOGEOSCIENCES DISCUSSIONS.** Text in English. 2003. irreg. **Document type:** *Journal, Academic/Scholarly.*
Related titles: Online - full text ed.: ISSN 1810-6285. free (effective 2005).
Published by: (European Geosciences Union), Copernicus GmbH, Max-Planck Str 13, Katlenburg-Lindau, 37191, Germany. TEL 49-5556-91099, info@copernicus.org, http://www.copernicus.org/site/EGU/bg/.

➤ **BIOGERONTOLOGY.** see *GERONTOLOGY AND GERIATRICS*

570 BRA ISSN 0102-9568
QH301
BIOIKOS; revista do instituto de ciencias biologicas e quimica. Text in Portuguese, English, Spanish; Summaries in English. 1987. 2/yr., latest vol.12, no.1, 1998. BRL 20 domestic; USD 5 foreign (effective 2002). **Document type:** *Magazine, Academic/Scholarly.*
Related titles: Fax ed.
Indexed: ZooRec.
Published by: Pontificia Universidade Catolica de Campinas, Instituto de Ciencias Biologicas e Quimica, Av. John Boyd Dunlop, s/no, Campinas, SP 13020-904, Brazil. TEL 55-19-7298360, FAX 55-19-7298517, lzoobot@puc-campinas.br, icbq@puc-campinas.br. Ed. Jose Merciano Filho.

570.25 USA ISSN 1533-2179
BIOINFORM NEWS SERVICES; the integrated informatic news. Text in English. irreg. USD 95 (effective 2003). adv. back issues avail.
Related titles: Online - full text ed.
Published by: GenomeWeb, LLC, PO Box 998, Peck Slip Stn., New York, NY 10272-0998. TEL 212-269-4747, FAX 212-269-3686, http://www.bioinform.com/, http://www.genome.com.

570 IND ISSN 0970-9444
➤ **BIOJOURNAL.** Text in English. 1989. s-a. INR 150 domestic to individuals; USD 30 foreign to individuals; INR 250 domestic to institutions; USD 80 foreign to institutions (effective 2003). **Document type:** *Academic/Scholarly.* **Description:** Contains original research articles on all aspects of life sciences.
—BLDSC (2072.390000).
Published by: Bihar Biological Research Society, c/o Prof. Akhileshwar Sharma, Kalamanch, Bakerganj, Patna, Bihar 800 004, India. TEL 91-612-686938. Eds. Arun Kumar Thakur, Akhileshwar Sharma. Pub., R&P, Adv. contact Akhileshwar Sharma.

570 SWE ISSN 0345-1127
BIOLOGEN. Text in Swedish. 1933. q. SEK 100 (effective 2001). adv. bk.rev. 2 cols./p.; **Document type:** *Journal, Academic/Scholarly.*
Formerly (until 1965): Medlemsblad foer Biologilaerarnas Foerening
Published by: Biologilaerarnas Foerening, c/o Inger Rosen-Larsson, Galonstigen 31, Bromma, 16873, Sweden. Ed. Lars Ljunggren. Pub. Vega Otterland. Adv. contact Magnus Vonkrusenstierna TEL 46-8-500 277 45.

570 ITA ISSN 0392-2510
➤ **BIOLOGI ITALIANI.** Text in Italian. 1971. m. (11/yr.). free to members. adv. bk.rev. **Document type:** *Journal, Academic/Scholarly.* **Description:** Covers clinical biology, environment, biotechnology, didactic of biology.
Indexed: ProtozoAb, RefZh, WeedAb.
—BLDSC (2072.680000), IE, ingenta.
Published by: Ordine Nazionale dei Biologi, Via Icilio 7, Rome, 00153, Italy. TEL 39-06-57090225, FAX 39-06-57090234, http://www.onb.it/BiologiItaliani/BI_LaRivista.htm. Ed. Ernesto Landi. R&P Federico Santini. Adv. contact Federico Santico. Circ: 42,000.

570 PAK ISSN 0006-3096
QH301 CODEN: BILGA6
BIOLOGIA. Text in English, French, German. 1955. s-a. PKR 400, USD 50; or exchange basis. bk.rev. bibl.; charts; illus. index. Supplement avail. **Document type:** *Academic/Scholarly.*
Indexed: ASFA, BiolAb, ChemAb, ESPM, FCA, HerbAb, HortAb, RA&MP, RPP, S&F, SCI, ZooRec.
—BLDSC (2072.750000), CASDDS, CISTI, Infotrieve, KNAW, Linda Hall. **CCC.**
Published by: Biological Society of Pakistan, Biological Laboratories, Government College University, Lahore, Pakistan. Ed. Dr. M S Mahoon. Circ: 200.

570 MEX ISSN 0185-2000
BIOLOGIA. Text in Spanish. 1970. q. price varies. adv. bk.rev. charts; bibl.; illus. cum.index: 1970-1975.
Published by: Consejo Nacional para la Ensenanza de la Biologia, Calejon de Pino 18, Chimalistac San Angel, C.P. 01070, Mexico City, DF, Mexico. Ed. Lopez de la Rosa. Circ: 1,500.

578.7 ARG ISSN 0326-1638
CODEN: BIACEB
➤ **BIOLOGIA ACUATICA.** Text in English, Spanish; Summaries in English, Spanish. 1981. irreg. (1-2/yr.). USD 10; USD 15 foreign. **Document type:** *Academic/Scholarly.* **Description:** Includes papers and research on freshwater biology.
Indexed: ASFA, ESPM, SFA, WildRev, ZooRec.
Published by: Instituto de Limnologia "Dr. Raul A. Ringuelet", Casilla de Correos 712, La Plata, BA 1900, Argentina. TEL 54-1-2375864, FAX 54-1-2377799, postmaster@ilpla.edu.ar. Ed. Hugo L Lopez.

570 ITA
BIOLOGIA E ETOLOGIA. Text in Italian. 1986. irreg., latest vol.4, 1992. price varies. adv. **Document type:** *Monographic series.*
Published by: Liguori Editore srl, Via Posillipo 394, Naples, 80123, Italy. TEL 39-81-7206111, FAX 39-81-7206244, http://www.liguori.it. Ed. Bruno D'Udine. Pub. Guido Liguori. Adv. contact Maria Liguori.

570 371.3 POL ISSN 0137-8031
BIOLOGIA W SZKOLE. Text in Polish. 1948. 5/yr. EUR 25 foreign (effective 2005). bk.rev.; software rev.; Website rev. bibl.; illus. 64 p./no.; back issues avail. **Document type:** *Journal, Academic/Scholarly.* **Description:** For biology teachers at all levels and for students in teacher training colleges and universities. Discusses developments in the biological sciences and recent achievements in the methodology of teaching biology, with articles to improve teachers' knowledge, and comments on teaching syllabi and school textbooks.
Indexed: AgrLib.
Published by: (Poland. Ministerstwo Edukacji Narodowej), Wydawnictwa Szkolne i Pedagogiczne, Pl Dabrowskiego 8, Warsaw, 00950, Poland. TEL 48-22-8279280, wsip@wsip.com.pl, http://www.wsip.com.pl. Ed. Krzystof Spalik. Adv. contact Maria Podstolska. **Dist. by:** Ars Polona, Krakowskie Przedmiescie 7, Warsaw, Poland. TEL 48-22-9263914, FAX 48-22-9265334, arspolona@arspolona.com.pl, http://www.arspolona.com.pl.

BIOLOGICAL ABSTRACTS CUMULATIVE INDEXES. see *BIOLOGY—Abstracting, Bibliographies, Statistics*

BIOLOGICAL ABSTRACTS - R R M (ONLINE EDITION); references and indexes to the world's life science reports, reviews, and meeting literature. (Reports, Reviews, Meetings) see *BIOLOGY—Abstracting, Bibliographies, Statistics*

BIOLOGICAL ABSTRACTS - R R M CUMULATIVE INDEX. (Reports, Reviews, and Meetings) see *BIOLOGY—Abstracting, Bibliographies, Statistics*

570 TWN ISSN 1026-3829
BIOLOGICAL BULLETIN. Text in Chinese, English. irreg., latest 1996. price varies. **Document type:** *Monographic series, Academic/Scholarly.*
Indexed: ZooRec.
Published by: Tunghai University, College of Science, Department of Biology, Box 851, No 181 Section 3, Taichung-Kan Road, Taichung, 407-04, Taiwan. TEL 886-4-23590121 ext 3240, FAX 886-4-23590296, biology@mail.thu.edu.tw, http://www2.thu.edu.tw/~biology/welcome.html.

593 USA ISSN 0006-3185
CODEN: BIBUBX
➤ **BIOLOGICAL BULLETIN.** Text in English. 1897. bi-m. USD 120 to individuals; USD 360 to institutions; USD 25 newsstand/cover to individuals; USD 75 newsstand/cover to institutions (effective 2004). adv. illus. s-a. index, cum.index (approx. every 10 yrs.). back issues avail.; reprints avail. **Document type:** *Journal, Academic/Scholarly.* **Description:** Publishes original research reports of general interest to biologists worldwide.
Formerly (until 1899): Zoological Bulletin (0898-1051)
Related titles: E-mail ed.; Microfilm ed.: (from PMC, PQC); Online - full text ed.: (from bigchalk, EBSCO Publishing, Florida Center for Library Automation, Gale Group, HighWire Press, Northern Light Technology, Inc., O C L C Online Computer Library Center, Inc., ProQuest Information & Learning).
Indexed: AEA, ASFA, AgBio, AnBeAb, AnBrAb, ApEcolAb, B&AI, B&BAb, BIOBASE, BIOSIS Prev, BioCN&I, BiolAb, BiolDig, ChemAb, CurCont, ESPM, ForAb, GEOBASE, GSI, GenetAb, HGA, HelmAb, HerbAb, I&DA, IAA, IABS, ISR, IndMed, IndVet, Inpharma, MEDLINE, NSCI, NemAb, NutrAb, OceAb, ProtozoAb, PsycholAb, RM&VM, Reac, RefZh, RevApplEntom, S&F, SCI, SFA, VetBull, WildRev, ZooRec.
—BLDSC (2075.000000), CASDDS, CISTI, IDS, IE, Infotrieve, ingenta, Linda Hall.
Published by: Marine Biological Laboratory, 7 MBL St, Woods Hole, MA 02543-1015. TEL 508-289-7402, lreuter@mbl.edu, http://www.biolbull.org, http://www.mbl.edu. Ed. Michael J Greenberg. R&P Ms. Carol Schachinger TEL 508-289-7149. Adv. contacts Ms. Carol Schachinger TEL 508-289-7149, Ms. Laura Reuter TEL 508-289-7402. Circ: 1,850. **Subscr. to:** Patty Burns. TEL 504-289-7402, FAX 508-289-7922.

➤ **BIOLOGICAL CONSERVATION.** see *CONSERVATION*

➤ **BIOLOGICAL CONSERVATION, RESTORATION AND SUSTAINABILITY.** see *CONSERVATION*

570 USA ISSN 1049-9644
SB925 CODEN: BCIOEB
➤ **BIOLOGICAL CONTROL.** Text in English. 1991. 12/yr. EUR 380 in Europe to individuals; JPY 39,600 in Japan to individuals; USD 293 elsewhere to individuals; EUR 789 in Europe to institutions; JPY 82,400 in Japan to institutions; USD 613 elsewhere to institutions; EUR 121 in Europe to students; JPY 12,600 in Japan to students; USD 105 elsewhere to students (effective 2006). **Document type:** *Journal, Academic/Scholarly.* **Description:** Promotes the science and technology of biological control and includes articles on entomology, plant pathology, nematology, and weed science.
Related titles: Online - full text ed.: ISSN 1090-2112. USD 587 (effective 2002) (from EBSCO Publishing, Gale Group, IngentaConnect, O C L C Online Computer Library Center, Inc., ScienceDirect, Swets Information Services).
Indexed: AEA, ASCA, AgBio, Agr, AgrForAb, BCI, BIOBASE, BIOSIS Prev, BibAg, BioCN&I, BiolAb, CPA, CurCont, DBA, DSA, FCA, FPA, FS&TA, ForAb, HelmAb, HerbAb, HortAb, IABS, ISR, IndVet, MEDLINE, MaizeAb, NemAb, NutrAb, OrnHort, PBA, PGrRegA, PHN&I, PN&I, PlantSci, PotatoAb, PoultAb, ProtozoAb, RA&MP, RDA, RM&VM, RPP, RRTA, RevApplEntom, RiceAb, S&F, SCI, SIA, SeedAb, SoyAb, TDB, TriticAb, VITIS, VetBull, WAE&RSA, WeedAb, WildRev, ZooRec.
—BLDSC (2075.130000), CISTI, IDS, IE, Infotrieve, ingenta. **CCC.**
Published by: Academic Press (Subsidiary of: Elsevier Science & Technology), 525 B St, Ste 1900, San Diego, CA 92101-4495. TEL 619-231-6616, 800-894-3434, FAX 619-699-6422, apsubs@acad.com, http://www.elsevier.com/locate/ybcon, http://www.academicpress.com. Eds. G. E. Heimpel, M. Coll, R. Charudattan.

➤ **BIOLOGICAL CONTROL NEWS.** see *AGRICULTURE—Crop Production And Soil*

570 NLD ISSN 1387-3547
QH353 CODEN: BLINF4
BIOLOGICAL INVASIONS. Text in Dutch. 1999. bi-m. EUR 331, USD 331, GBP 218 combined subscription to institutions print & online eds. (effective 2005). back issues avail.; reprint service avail. from PSC. **Document type:** *Journal, Academic/Scholarly.* **Description:** Publishes research papers on the patterns and processes of biological invasions (both human-mediated introductions and natural range expansions) in terrestrial, freshwater, and marine (including brackish) ecosystems.
Related titles: Online - full text ed.: ISSN 1573-1464 (from EBSCO Publishing, Gale Group, IngentaConnect, Kluwer Online, O C L C Online Computer Library Center, Inc., Springer LINK, Swets Information Services).
Indexed: ASFA, AgBio, Agr, ApEcolAb, BIOBASE, BIOSIS Prev, BibLing, BiolAb, CurCont, ESPM, GEOBASE, OceAb, RM&VM, RefZh, RevApplEntom, SWRA, WeedAb, ZooRec.
—BLDSC (2075.400000), CISTI, IE, Infotrieve, ingenta, Linda Hall. **CCC.**
Published by: Springer-Verlag Dordrecht (Subsidiary of: Springer Science+Business Media), Van Godewijckstraat 30, Dordrecht, 3311 GX, Netherlands. TEL 31-78-6576050, FAX 31-78-6576474, http://springerlink.metapress.com/openurl.asp?genre=journal&issn=1387-3547, http://www.springeronline.com. Ed. James A Drake.

570 POL ISSN 1644-7700
QH301 CODEN: BLIEA6
➤ **BIOLOGICAL LETTERS.** Text in English, French, German. 1960. s-a. price varies. bibl.; charts; illus. **Document type:** *Bulletin, Academic/Scholarly.*
Former titles (until 2001): Biological Bulletin of Poznan (1426-5656); (until 1994): Societe des Amis des Sciences et des Lettres de Panan. Bulletin. Serie D: Sciences Biologiques (0079-4570)
Indexed: AgrAg, AnBeAb, ApEcolAb, BIOSIS Prev, BiolAb, CIN, ChemAb, ChemTitl, ESPM, EntAb, ZooRec.
—CASDDS, CISTI.
Published by: (Poznanskie Towarzystwo Przyjaciol Nauk, Wydzial Matematyczno-Przyrodniczy), Poznanskie Towarzystwo Przyjaciol Nauk/Poznan Society for the Advancement of the Arts and Sciences, ul Sew Mielzynskiego 27-29, Poznan, 61725, Poland. TEL 48-61-8527441, FAX 48-61-8522205, sekretariat@ptpn.poznan.pl, wydawnictwo@ptpn.poznan.pl, http://www.ptpn.poznan.pl. Ed. Adrzej Lesicki. Circ: 300. **Dist. by:** Ars Polona, Krakowskie Przedmiescie 7, Warsaw, Poland. TEL 48-22-9263914, FAX 48-22-9265334, arspolona@arspolona.com.pl, http://www.arspolona.com.pl.

➤ **BIOLOGICAL PSYCHIATRY.** see *MEDICAL SCIENCES—Psychiatry And Neurology*

➤ **BIOLOGICAL PSYCHOLOGY.** see *PSYCHOLOGY*

570 616.027 CHL ISSN 0716-9760
QH301 CODEN: ABMXA2
➤ **BIOLOGICAL RESEARCH.** Text in English. 1964. q. USD 100 (effective 2004). adv. bk.rev. **Document type:** *Academic/Scholarly.* **Description:** Publishes original works in the different fields of the biological sciences.
Formerly (until 1992): Archivos de Biologia y Medicina Experimentales (0004-0533)
Related titles: Microfiche ed.: (from PQC); Online - full text ed.: ISSN 0717-6287. 1999. free (effective 2005) (from SciELO).
Indexed: ASFA, BIOBASE, BIOSIS Prev, BiolAb, CIN, ChemAb, ChemTitl, CurCont, ESPM, ExcerpMed, IABS, INIS AtomInd, ISR, IndMed, MEDLINE, SCI, SFA, VITIS, ZooRec.
—BLDSC (2077.675000), CASDDS, GNLM, IDS, IE, Infotrieve, ingenta, KNAW, Linda Hall.
Published by: Sociedad de Biologia de Chile, Canada 253, Piso 3, Depto F, Casilla 16169, Santiago, Providencia 9, Chile. TEL 56-2-2093503, FAX 56-2-2258427, pzapata@genes.bio.puc.cl, http://www.scielo.cl/scielo.php?script=sci_serial&pid=0716-9760&lng=en&nrm=iso. Ed. Patricio Zapata. Circ: 1,250.

B

▼ *new title* ➤ *refereed* ✶ *unverified* ♦ *full entry avail.*

570 FIN ISSN 0356-1062
QH301
BIOLOGICAL RESEARCH REPORTS FROM THE UNIVERSITY OF JYVASKYLA. Text in Finnish. 1975. irreg. per issue exchange basis. **Document type:** *Monographic series.*
Indexed: ZooRec.
Published by: Jyvaskylan Yliopisto/University of Jyvaskyla, PO Box 35, Jyvaeskylae, 40014, Finland. TEL 941-601-211, FAX 603-371. Eds. Jukka Saerkkae, Markku Kuitunen. Circ: 450.

570 GBR ISSN 1464-7931
QH301 CODEN: BRCPAH
➤ **BIOLOGICAL REVIEWS.** Text in English. 1923. q. USD 234 in North America to institutions; GBP 138 elsewhere to institutions; USD 262 combined subscription in North America to institutions print & online eds.; GBP 154 combined subscription elsewhere to institutions print & online eds. (effective 2005). bibl.; charts; illus. index. back issues avail.; reprints avail. **Document type:** *Journal, Academic/Scholarly.*
Description: Covers all aspects of biological science. Although scholarly and with extensive bibliographies, the articles are aimed at non-specialist biologists as well as researchers in the field.
Former titles (until 1997): Cambridge Philosophical Society. Biological Reviews (0006-3231); (until 1937): Cambridge Philosophical Society. Biological Reviews and Biological Proceedings (0301-7699); (until 1926): Cambridge Philosophical Society. Proceedings. Biological Sciences
Related titles: Microfiche ed.: (from IDC); Microform ed.: (from PQC); Online - full text ed.: ISSN 1469-185X. USD 220 in North America to institutions; GBP 130 elsewhere to institutions (effective 2005) (from EBSCO Publishing, O C L C Online Computer Library Center, Inc., Swets Information Services).
Indexed: ASCA, ASFA, AbHyg, AgBio, Agr, AgrForAb, AnBeAb, AnBrAb, ApEcolAb, B&AI, BIOBASE, BIOSIS Prev, BioCN&I, BiolAb, ChemAb, CurCont, ESPM, EntAb, ExcerpMed, FCA, FPA, ForAb, GSI, HerbAb, HortAb, IABS, ISR, IndMed, IndVet, Inpharma, MEDLINE, MaizeAb, NemAb, NutrAb, PBA, PGegResA, PGrRegA, PoultAb, ProtozoAb, RASB, RM&VM, RPP, Reac, RefZh, RevApplEntom, S&F, SCI, SFA, SSCI, SeedAb, VetBull, WeedAb, WildRev, ZooRec.
—BLDSC (2079.000000), CASDDS, CISTI, IDS, IE, Infotrieve, ingenta, Linda Hall. **CCC.**
Published by: (Cambridge Philosophical Society), Cambridge University Press, The Edinburgh Bldg, Shaftesbury Rd, Cambridge, CB2 2RU, United Kingdom. TEL 44-1223-312393, FAX 44-1223-315052, journals@cambridge.org, http://www.cambridge.org/uk/journals/journal_catalogue.asp?historylinks=ALPHA&mnemonic=BRE, http://uk.cambridge.org/journals. Ed. W A Foster. R&P Linda Nicol TEL 44-1223-325757. **Subscr. to:** Cambridge University Press, 100 Brook Hill Dr, West Nyack, NY 10994. TEL 845-353-7500, FAX 845-353-4141, journals_subscriptions@cup.org

570 NLD ISSN 0929-1016
QH527 CODEN: BRHREI
➤ **BIOLOGICAL RHYTHM RESEARCH.** Text in English. 1970. bi-m. GBP 506, USD 837 combined subscription to institutions print & online eds. (effective 2006). adv. bk.rev. charts; illus. reprint service avail. from PSC. **Document type:** *Journal, Academic/Scholarly.* **Description:** Publishes original scientific research results and reviews of biological rhythm research.
Formerly (until 1994): Journal of Interdisciplinary Cycle Research (0022-1945)
Related titles: Microform ed.: (from SWZ); Online - full text ed.: GBP 481, USD 795 to institutions (effective 2006) (from EBSCO Publishing, Gale Group, IngentaConnect, O C L C Online Computer Library Center, Inc., Swets Information Services).
Indexed: ASCA, ASFA, AbHyg, AgBio, AnBeAb, AnBrAb, BIOBASE, BIOSIS Prev, BiolAb, CIN, CPA, ChemAb, ChemTitl, CurCont, DSA, EntAb, ErgAb, ExcerpMed, ForAb, GEOBASE, HelmAb, HerbAb, HortAb, IABS, IPsyAb, ISR, IndVet, Inpharma, MaizeAb, NSA, NSCI, NemAb, NutrAb, OrnHort, PBA, PE&ON, PGrRegA, PoultAb, ProtozoAb, PsycInfo, PsycholAb, RASB, RM&VM, Reac, RefZh, RevApplEntom, S&F, SAA, SCI, SFA, SSCI, TDB, VetBull, WildRev, ZooRec, e-psyche.
—BLDSC (2079.590000), CASDDS, CISTI, GNLM, IDS, IE, Infotrieve, ingenta, Linda Hall. **CCC.**
Published by: (European Society for Chronobiology), Taylor & Francis The Netherlands (Subsidiary of: Taylor & Francis Group), Schipolweg 107 C, PO Box 447, Leiden, 2316 XC, Netherlands. TEL 31-715-243080, FAX 31-715-234571, pub@swets.nl, infoho@swets.nl, http://www.tandf.co.uk/journals/titles/09291016.asp, http://www.tandf.co.uk/swets.asp. Ed. W J Rietveld. R&P J van der Valk. adv.: page EUR 300; trim 120 x 196. Circ: 600.

570 JPN ISSN 0045-2033
QH301 CODEN: SBTKAQ
BIOLOGICAL SCIENCE/SEIBUTSU KAGAKU. Text in Japanese. 1949. q. JPY 950 per issue.
Indexed: ChemAb, JPI, ZooRec.
—Linda Hall.
Published by: (Japanese Society of Biological Scientists/Nihon Seibutsu Kagakusha Kyokai), Iwanami Shoten, Publishers, 2-5-5 Hitotsubashi, Chiyoda-ku, Tokyo, 101-0003, Japan. FAX 81-3-239-9618. Ed. K Nagano. **Dist. overseas by:** Japan Publications Trading Co., Ltd., Book Export II Dept, PO Box 5030, Tokyo International, Tokyo 101-3191, Japan. TEL 81-3-32923753, FAX 81-3-32920410, infoserials@jptco.co.jp, http://www.jptco.co.jp.

570 USA ISSN 1081-292X
CODEN: USFODA
➤ **BIOLOGICAL SCIENCE REPORT.** Text in English. 1995. irreg. **Document type:** *Monographic series, Government.*
Description: Publishes original scientific research, reviews, inventories and reports.
Supersedes: U.S. Fish and Wildlife Service. Biological Report (0895-1926); Which was formerly (1976-1984): F W S - O B S (0197-6087)
Related titles: Microform ed.: 1995 (from NTI); Online - full text ed.: 1995; ♦ Series: North American Fauna. ISSN 0078-1304.
Indexed: ASFA, ESPM, MBA, OceAb, SFA, ZooRec.
—CASDDS, CISTI, Linda Hall.
Published by: U.S. Department of the Interior, National Biological Service, C St between 18th & 19th Sts N W, Washington, DC 20240. **Orders to:** U.S. Fish and Wildlife Service, Publications Unit, MS 130, Webb Bldg, 4401 N Fairfax Dr, Arlington, VA 22203.

570 GBR ISSN 0953-5365
➤ **BIOLOGICAL SCIENCES REVIEW.** Text in English. 4/yr. GBP 23.95 domestic; GBP 30 in Europe; GBP 35 elsewhere (effective Sep. 2002). adv. illus. back issues avail. **Document type:** *Magazine, Academic/Scholarly.* **Description:** Focus on the core topics, from a fresh, up-to-date perspective, and feature memorable diagrams and photographs to illustrate important concepts in biology.
Related titles: Online - full text ed.: (from Gale Group).
Indexed: BrHumI, BrTechI.
—BLDSC (2080.455000), IE, ingenta.
Published by: (University of Manchester, School of Biology), Philip Allan Updates, Market Pl, Deddington, Banbury, Oxon OX15 0SE, United Kingdom. TEL 44-1869-338652, FAX 44-1869-338803, sales@philipallan.co.uk, http://www.philipallan.co.uk. Ed. Shiela Tarrant. R&P Robert Pinkeiro. Circ: 24,000.

570 USA ISSN 0097-0298
QH105.D6 CODEN: BBSWA6
BIOLOGICAL SOCIETY OF WASHINGTON. BULLETIN. Text in English. 1918. irreg. **Document type:** *Monographic series, Academic/Scholarly.*
Indexed: BIOSIS Prev, BiolAb, ZooRec.
—BLDSC (2411.670000), CISTI, Linda Hall.
Published by: Biological Society of Washington, National Museum of Natural History, Smithsonian Institution, Washington, DC 20560. http://www.biolsocwash.org.

570 USA ISSN 0006-324X
QH1 CODEN: PBSWAO
➤ **BIOLOGICAL SOCIETY OF WASHINGTON. PROCEEDINGS.** Text in English. 1880. q. USD 40. charts; illus. index, cum.index: 1881-1922, 1923-1961. back issues avail. **Document type:** *Academic/Scholarly.* **Description:** Journal of international scope for publication of papers bearing on systematics in the biological sciences (both botany and zoology, including paleontology).
Indexed: A&ATA, ASCA, ASFA, AgrForAb, BIOSIS Prev, BiolAb, CurCont, ESPM, EntAb, GEOBASE, HelmAb, ISR, IndVet, OceAb, PBA, PGegResA, RM&VM, RevApplEntom, SCI, SFA, SPPI, VetBull, WildRev, ZooRec.
—BLDSC (6661.000000), CISTI, IDS, IE, ingenta, Linda Hall.
Published by: Biological Society of Washington, National Museum of Natural History, Smithsonian Institution, Washington, DC 20560. TEL 202-786-2550, pbsw@allenpress.com, http://www.allenpress.com. Ed. Brian Robbins. Circ: 900. **Subscr. to:** Allen Press Inc., PO Box 1897, Lawrence, KS 66044.

570 USA ISSN 1555-5542
▼ **BIOLOGICAL THEORY:** integrating development, evolution & cognition. Text in English. forthcoming 2006 (Jan.). q. USD 65 combined subscription in US & Canada to individuals print & online eds.; USD 90 combined subscription elsewhere to individuals print & online eds.; USD 190 combined subscription in US & Canada to institutions print & online eds.; USD 225 combined subscription elsewhere to institutions print & online eds. (effective 2006).
Related titles: Online - full text ed.: ISSN 1555-5550. forthcoming 2006 (Jan.). USD 58.50 to individuals; USD 171 to institutions (effective 2006).
Published by: M I T Press, 55 Hayward St, Cambridge, MA 02142-1493. TEL 617-253-5646, FAX 617-258-6779, journals-info@mit.edu, http://mitpress.mit.edu/biot. Ed. Werner Callebaut.

570 GBR ISSN 1045-1056
RA401.A1 CODEN: BILSEC
➤ **BIOLOGICALS.** Text in English. 1973. 4/yr. EUR 469 in Europe to institutions; JPY 50,700 in Japan to institutions; USD 418 elsewhere to institutions (effective 2006). adv. reprints avail. **Document type:** *Journal, Academic/Scholarly.*
Description: Devoted to the timely publication of broad ranging reports relevant to the development, preparation, and quality control of biologicals used in human and veterinary medicine.
Formerly: Journal of Biological Standardization (0092-1157)
Related titles: Online - full text ed.: ISSN 1095-8320. USD 442 (effective 2002) (from EBSCO Publishing, Gale Group, IngentaConnect, O C L C Online Computer Library Center, Inc., ScienceDirect, Swets Information Services).
Indexed: ASCA, ASFA, AbHyg, AgBio, Agr, BIOBASE, BIOSIS Prev, BioEngAb, BiolAb, CIN, ChemAb, ChemTitl, CurCont, DBA, DSA, DokArb, ESPM, ExcerpMed, HelmAb, IABS, ISR, IndMed, IndVet, Inpharma, JDDR, M&PBA, MBA, MEDLINE, NutrAb, PE&ON, PN&I, PoultAb, ProtozoAb, RM&VM, Reac, RevApplEntom, SCI, SIA, TDB, VetBull, WAE&RSA.
—BLDSC (2081.670000), CASDDS, CISTI, GNLM, IDS, IE, Infotrieve, ingenta, KNAW, Linda Hall. **CCC.**
Published by: (International Association for Biologicals CHE), Academic Press (Subsidiary of: Elsevier Science & Technology), 24-28 Oval Rd, London, NW1 7DX, United Kingdom. TEL 44-20-72674466, FAX 44-20-74822293, apsubs@acad.com, http://www.elsevier.com/locate/biologicals. Ed. D. Espeseth. **Subscr. to:** Harcourt Publishers Ltd., Foots Cray High St, Sidcup, Kent DA14 5HP, United Kingdom. TEL 44-20-300-3322, FAX 44-20-8309-0807.

570 RUS ISSN 1028-0057
BIOLOGICHESKIE NAUKI. Text in Russian. 1958. m. **Document type:** *Journal, Academic/Scholarly.*
Formerly (until 1992): Vysshaya Shkola. Nauchnye Doklady. Biologicheskie Nauki (0470-4606)
—CISTI. **CCC.**
Published by: Izdatel'stvo Vysshaya Shkola, Neglinnaya ul 29-14, Moscow, 127994, Russian Federation. TEL 7-095-2000456, FAX 7-095-2000301, info@v-shkola.ru, http://www.v-shkola.ru.

570 CZE ISSN 0366-0486
QH301 CODEN: BILIAC
➤ **BIOLOGICKE LISTY/BIOLOGICAL LETTERS.** Text in Czech, Slovak; Summaries in English. 1912. q. CZK 320 (effective 2003). bk.rev. illus. 80 p./no. 1 cols./p.; back issues avail.; reprints avail. **Document type:** *Journal, Academic/Scholarly.*
Description: Papers and reviews dealing with all fields of biology.
Indexed: AnBrAb, BiolAb, CIN, CTO, ChemAb, ChemTitl, RefZh.
—BLDSC (2081.700000), CASDDS, CISTI.
Published by: Akademie Ved Ceske Republiky, Ustav Molekularni Genetiky/Academy of Sciences of the Czech Republic, Institute of Molecular Genetics, Flemingovo n 2, Prague, 16637, Czech Republic. TEL 42-2-24310234, FAX 42-2-24310955, office@img.cas.cz, http://www.img.cas.cz/bl/. Ed. S Zadrazil. **Dist. in Western countries by:** Kubon & Sagner Buchexport - Import GmbH, Postfach 24, Munich 34 8000, Germany.

570 DEU ISSN 0045-205X
CODEN: BLUZAR
BIOLOGIE IN UNSERER ZEIT. Abbreviated title: B I U Z. Text in German. 1971. bi-m. EUR 188 in Europe; CHF 298 in Switzerland & Liechtenstein; USD 208 elsewhere; EUR 207 combined subscription in Europe print & online eds.; CHF 328 combined subscription in Switzerland & Liechtenstein for print & online eds.; USD 229 combined subscription elsewhere print & online eds. (effective 2006). adv. bk.rev.; software rev.; Website rev. charts; illus.; maps. index. reprint service avail. from ISI. **Document type:** *Journal, Academic/Scholarly.*
Description: Presents current developments in all areas of biology.
Related titles: Online - full text ed.: ISSN 1521-415X. EUR 188 in Europe to institutions; CHF 298 to institutions in Switzerland & Liechtenstein; USD 208 elsewhere to institutions (effective 2006) (from EBSCO Publishing, Swets Information Services, Wiley InterScience).
Indexed: BiolAb, CIN, ChemAb, ChemTitl, ExcerpMed, RefZh, ZooRec.
—CASDDS, CISTI, IE, Infotrieve, Linda Hall. **CCC.**
Published by: Wiley - V C H Verlag GmbH & Co. KGaA (Subsidiary of: John Wiley & Sons, Inc.), Boschstr 12, Weinheim, 69469, Germany. TEL 49-6201-606-147, FAX 49-6201-606-117, subservice@wiley-vch.de, http://www.wiley-vch.de/home/biuz. Ed. Claudia Von See. R&P Claudia Rutz. Adv. contact Marion Schulz TEL 49-6201-606565. B&W page EUR 2,600, color page EUR 3,900. Circ: 9,610. **Subscr. in the Americas to:** John Wiley & Sons, Inc.. TEL 201-748-6645, FAX 201-748-6088, subinfo@wiley.com; **Subscr. outside Germany, Austria & Switzerland to:** John Wiley & Sons Ltd., The Atrium, Southern Gate, Chichester, West Sussex PO19 8SQ, United Kingdom. TEL 44-1243-779777, FAX 44-1243-775878.

570 LTU ISSN 1392-0146
QH301 CODEN: BOLOE8
BIOLOGIJA. Text in Multiple languages. 1993. q. USD 80 foreign. adv. **Document type:** *Academic/Scholarly.*

B

Formed by the merger of (1961-1993): Lietuvos T.S.R. Aukstuju Mokyklu Mokslu Darbai. Biologija (0459-3383); (1990-1993): Lietuvos Mokslu Akademija. Eksperimentine Biologija (0235-7232); Which superseded in part (in 1990): Lietuvos T.S.R. Mokslu Akademijos Darbai. C Serija. Biologijos Mosklai (0131-3851)
Indexed: AEA, ASFA, AgBio, AnBrAb, CIN, CPA, ChemAb, ChemTitl, ESPM, FCA, FPA, ForAb, HerbAb, HortAb, INIS AtomInd, IndVet, MaizeAb, OrnHort, PBA, PGegResA, PGrRegA, PN&I, PotatoAb, PoultAb, RA&MP, RPP, S&F, SeedAb, SoyAb, TriticAb, VetBull, WeedAb, ZooRec.
—BLDSC (2082.490000), CASDDS, CISTI, KNAW, Linda Hall.
Published by: (Lietuvos Mokslu Akademija/Lithuanian Academy of Sciences), Leidykla Academia, A Gostauto 12, Vilnius, 2000, Lithuania. TEL 370-2-626851. Ed. A Merkys. R&P A Garliauskas. Adv. contact A. Garliauskas. **Co-sponsor:** Lietuvos Aukstosios Mokyklos.

570 DEU ISSN 0406-3333
BIOLOGISCHE ARBEITSBUECHER. Text in German. 1958. irreg., latest vol.52, 2000. price varies. **Document type:** *Monographic series, Academic/Scholarly.*
Published by: Quelle und Meyer Verlag, Industriepark 3, Wiebelsheim, 56291, Germany. TEL 49-6766-903200, FAX 49-6766-903320.

BIOLOGISCHE TIERMEDIZIN. see *VETERINARY SCIENCE*

570 GBR ISSN 0006-3347
QH1 CODEN: BLGTB8
BIOLOGIST. Text in English. 1953. 5/yr. free membership (effective 2004). adv. bk.rev.; software rev. illus. **Document type:** *Journal, Academic/Scholarly.* **Description:** Overview articles, news, reviews for professional biologists in the areas of biomedical, environmental, agricultural, and educational biology.
Related titles: Online - full text ed.: (from EBSCO Publishing).
Indexed: ASFA, AbHyg, AgBio, AgrForAb, AnBeAb, ApEcolAb, BIOBASE, BioCN&I, BrArAb, CPA, CPE, DSA, ESPM, EntAb, EnvAb, FCA, FPA, FS&TA, ForAb, HelmAb, HortAb, IndMed, IndVet, MEDLINE, NemAb, NutrAb, OrnHort, PBA, PGegResA, ProtozoAb, RA&MP, RDA, RPP, RevApplEntom, S&F, SFA, SIA, SWRA, SeedAb, TriticAb, VetBull, WAE&RSA, WeedAb, WildRev, ZooRec.
—BLDSC (2086.200000), CASDDS, CISTI, IE, Infotrieve, ingenta, Linda Hall. **CCC.**
Published by: Institute of Biology, 20-22 Queensberry Pl, London, SW7 2DZ, United Kingdom. TEL 44-20-7581-8333, FAX 44-20-7823-9409, info@iob.org, http://www.iob.org/default.asp?edname=213.htm&cont_id=9&n=7. Ed. Alison Bailey. Circ: 15,500.

578.77 551.46 RUS ISSN 0134-3475
QH91.A1 CODEN: BIMOD4
BIOLOGIYA MORYA/MARINE BIOLOGY. Text in Russian. 1975. bi-m. RUR 1,050 for 6 mos. domestic (effective 2004). illus. **Document type:** *Journal, Academic/Scholarly.* **Description:** Publishes papers on marine organisms and their activities, various biological studies conducted on marine objects; practical problems of preservation, rational utilization of biological resources of the sea and limitation of activity of some harmful sea organisms.
Related titles: ♦ English Translation: Russian Journal of Marine Biology. ISSN 1063-0740.
Indexed: ASFA, AnBrAb, BIOSIS Prev, BiolAb, CIN, ChemAb, ChemTitl, CurCont, ESPM, FS&TA, ISR, RefZh, SCI, SFA, WildRev, ZooRec.
—CASDDS, CISTI, East View, KNAW, Linda Hall. **CCC.**
Published by: (Rossiiskaya Akademiya Nauk, Otdelenie Obshchei Biologii), Izdatel'stvo Nauka, Profsoyuznaya ul 90, Moscow, 117864, Russian Federation. TEL 7-095-3347151, FAX 7-095-4202220, secret@naukaran.ru, http://www.naukaran.ru. Circ: 1,200. **Co-sponsor:** Rossiiskaya Akademiya Nauk, Dal'nevostochnyi Nauchnyi Tsentr.

570 RUS ISSN 0320-9660
BIOLOGIYA V SHKOLE. Text in Russian. bi-m. USD 53 foreign (effective 2000). **Document type:** *Academic/Scholarly.*
Indexed: RefZh.
—CISTI, East View.
Published by: Izdatel'stvo Shkola Press, Rustaveli ul 10-3, Moscow, 127254, Russian Federation. TEL 7-095-2198380, FAX 7-095-2195289. Ed. L V Rebrova. **US dist. addr.:** East View Information Services, 3020 Harbor Ln. N., Minneapolis, MN 55447. TEL 612-550-0961.

BIOLOGIYA ZHENE KHIMIYA. see *CHEMISTRY*

570 AUS ISSN 0814-8880
BIOLOGUE. Text in English. 1983. s-a. **Document type:** *Newsletter.*
Media: Online - full content.
Indexed: EnvAb.
Published by: Australian National Botanical Gardens, GPO Box 1777, Canberra, ACT 2601, Australia. TEL 61-2-6250-9450, FAX 61-2-6250-9555, anbg-info@anbg.gov.au, http://www.anbg.gov.au/.

570 IRL ISSN 0791-7945
QH301 CODEN: BENVE3
➤ **BIOLOGY AND ENVIRONMENT**; proceedings of the Royal Irish Academy. Text in English. 1836. 3/yr. EUR 30 to individuals; EUR 115 to institutions (effective 2005). charts; illus. index, cum.index. **Document type:** *Proceedings, Academic/Scholarly.*
Formerly (until 1993): Royal Irish Academy. Proceedings. Section B: Biological, Geological and Chemical Sciences (0035-8983); Which superseded in part (in 1902): Royal Irish Academy. Proceedings (0301-7400)
Related titles: Microform ed.: (from PMC); Online - full text ed.: (from EBSCO Publishing).
Indexed: ASCA, ASFA, AgrForAb, BHA, BIOBASE, BIOSIS Prev, BioCN&I, BiolAb, BrGeoL, CPA, ChemAb, CurCont, ESPM, EnvAb, ExcerpMed, FCA, ForAb, HelmAb, HerbAb, I&DA, IndMed, IndVet, Inspec, MEDLINE, PBA, PGegResA, PHN&I, PhysBer, RPP, RevApplEntom, RiceAb, S&F, SCI, SIA, SeedAb, TriticAb, VetBull, WAE&RSA, ZooRec.
—BLDSC (2086.996500), CASDDS, CISTI, GNLM, IE, ingenta, KNAW, Linda Hall. **CCC.**
Published by: Royal Irish Academy, 19 Dawson St., Dublin, 2, Ireland. TEL 353-1-6762570, FAX 353-1-6762346, h.shiels@ria.ie, publications@ria.ie, http://www.ria.ie/publications/journals/procbi/procbi.html. Eds. Ian Montgomery, Michael Jones. Circ: 600. **Dist. by:** International Specialized Book Services Inc., 5804 N E Hassalo St, Portland, OR 97213-3644. TEL 503-287-3093, 800-944-6190, FAX 503-280-8832, sales@isbs.com.

➤ **BIOLOGY AND FERTILITY OF SOILS.** see *AGRICULTURE—Crop Production And Soil*

570 NLD ISSN 0169-3867
QH331 CODEN: BIOPEI
➤ **BIOLOGY AND PHILOSOPHY.** Text in English. 1986. 5/yr. EUR 498, USD 508, GBP 315 combined subscription to institutions print & online eds. (effective 2005). adv. bk.rev. illus. index. back issues avail.; reprint service avail. from PSC. **Document type:** *Journal, Academic/Scholarly.* **Description:** Publishes discussions of the philosophical implications of biological research, as well as the social implications of recent advances and developments in the biological sciences.
Related titles: Microform ed.: (from PQC); Online - full text ed.: ISSN 1572-8404 (from EBSCO Publishing, Gale Group, IngentaConnect, Kluwer Online, O C L C Online Computer Library Center, Inc., Springer LINK, Swets Information Services).
Indexed: ASCA, ArtHuCI, BIOSIS Prev, BibLing, BiolAb, CurCont, DIP, GEOBASE, IBR, IBZ, IPB, ISR, IndMed, PCI, PhilInd, RASB, RefZh, SCI, SFA, SSCI, WildRev, ZooRec.
—BLDSC (2087.002000), CISTI, IDS, IE, Infotrieve, ingenta, Linda Hall. **CCC.**
Published by: Springer-Verlag Dordrecht (Subsidiary of: Springer Science+Business Media), Van Godewijckstraat 30, Dordrecht, 3311 GX, Netherlands. TEL 31-78-6576050, FAX 31-78-6576474, http://springerlink.metapress.com/openurl.asp?genre=journal&issn=0169-3867, http://www.springeronline.com. Ed. Kim Sterelny. Circ: 500.

578.074 GBR ISSN 1355-8331
THE BIOLOGY CURATOR. Text in English. 1975. q. GBP 8 (effective 2000). adv. bk.rev. **Document type:** *Academic/Scholarly.* **Description:** Provides a forum for persons concerned with the collection of biological specimens and records, along with their interpretation and conservation.
Formed by the merger of (1989-1994): Journal of Biological Curation (0958-7608); (1975-1994): B C G Newsletter (0144-588X)
Indexed: ZooRec.
—BLDSC (2087.052000).
Published by: (Biology Curators Group), Northern Whig Ltd, 107 Limestone Rd, Belfast, BT15 3AH, United Kingdom. TEL 44-1232-352233, 44-1204-332197, FAX 44-1232-352181, 44-1204-332241, bolnathist@gn.apc.org. Eds. K Berry, Kathryn Berry, P Francis, Patricia Francis. Circ: 380. **Subscr. to:** Biology Curators Group, c/o Ms. K. Way, Dept of Zoology, Natural History Museum, Cromwell Rd, London SW7 5BD, United Kingdom.

BIOLOGY DIGEST. see *BIOLOGY—Abstracting, Bibliographies, Statistics*

570.7 IND ISSN 0970-5961
BIOLOGY EDUCATION. Text in English. 1984. q. INR 120, USD 40. **Document type:** *Academic/Scholarly.*
Published by: (India. University Grants Commission), New Age International Pvt. Ltd., Journals Division, 4835-24 Ansari Rd., Darya Ganj, New Delhi, 110 002, India. TEL 91-11-326-1487, FAX 91-11-326-7437. Circ: 1,000.

570 FRA ISSN 0253-2069
QH301 CODEN: BYILDJ
BIOLOGY INTERNATIONAL: I U B S NEWSMAGAZINE. Text in French. s-a. USD 40. **Document type:** *Newsletter, Academic/Scholarly.*
Former titles: I U B S Newsmagazine; I U B S Newsletter
Indexed: BIOSIS Prev, BiolAb, IndVet, NutrAb, PBA, PGegResA, RefZh, S&F, SFA, VITIS.
—CASDDS, CISTI.
Published by: International Union of Biological Sciences, 51 bd. de Montmorency, Paris, 75016, France. TEL 45-25-00-09.

570 GBR ISSN 1744-9561
QH301
▼ ➤ **BIOLOGY LETTERS.** Text in English. 2003. q. GBP 520, USD 885 combined subscription in Europe print & online eds.; GBP 540, USD 920 combined subscription in North America print & online eds.; GBP 565, USD 960 combined subscription elsewhere print & online eds. (effective 2005). **Document type:** *Journal, Academic/Scholarly.* **Description:** Provides rapid publication of shorter articles in the life sciences.
Related titles: Online - full content ed.: ISSN 1744-957X.
Indexed: AnBeAb, ApEcolAb, ESPM, EntAb.
—BLDSC (2087.087000). **CCC.**
Published by: Royal Society of London, 6-9 Carlton House Terr, London, SW1Y 5AG, United Kingdom. TEL 44-20-74512585, FAX 44-20-74512692, sales@royalsoc.ac.uk, http://www.pubs.royalsoc.ac.uk/biologyletters.shtml, http://www.royalsoc.ac.uk. Ed. Brian Charlesworth.

573.6 USA ISSN 0006-3363
QP251.A1 CODEN: BIREBV
➤ **BIOLOGY OF REPRODUCTION.** Text in English. 1969. m. (in 2 vols.). USD 575 combined subscription domestic print & online eds.; USD 625 combined subscription foreign print & online eds. (effective 2006). adv. abstr.; bibl.; charts; illus. s-a. index. 350 p./no. 2 cols./p.; back issues avail. **Document type:** *Journal, Academic/Scholarly.* **Description:** Publishes original research on a variety of topics in the field of reproductive biology, as well as review articles on topics of importance or controversy.
Related titles: Online - full text ed.: ISSN 1529-7268. 1998 (from BioOne, C S A, EBSCO Publishing, HighWire Press, O C L C Online Computer Library Center, Inc.); ♦ Supplement(s): Biology of Reproduction. Supplement. ISSN 0523-6754.
Indexed: AEA, ASCA, ASFA, AbAn, AbHyg, AgBio, Agr, AgrForAb, AnBrAb, B&BAb, BIOBASE, BIOSIS Prev, BibAg, BiolAb, CIN, ChemAb, ChemTitl, CurCont, DSA, ExcerpMed, FoVS&M, GenetAb, HGA, IABS, ISR, IndMed, IndVet, Inpharma, MEDLINE, MaizeAb, NSCI, NucAcAb, NutrAb, PE&ON, PN&I, PoultAb, RA&MP, RM&VM, RPP, Reac, RefZh, SAA, SCI, SFA, SIA, SoyAb, VetBull, WildRev, ZooRec.
—BLDSC (2087.220000), CASDDS, CISTI, GNLM, IDS, IE, Infotrieve, ingenta, Linda Hall. **CCC.**
Published by: Society for the Study of Reproduction, 1619 Monroe St., Madison, WI 53711-2063. TEL 608-256-2777, FAX 608-256-4610, ssr@ssr.org, http://www.biolreprod.org/, http://www.ssr.org. Eds. John Eppig, Mary Ann Handel. R&P, Adv. contact Judith Jansen TEL 608-256-2777. Circ: 3,750 (paid).

573.6 USA
BIOLOGY OF REPRODUCTION MONOGRAPH SERIES. Text in English. 1995. irreg. price varies. **Document type:** *Monographic series.* **Description:** Covers various aspects of the biology of reproduction.
Related titles: ♦ Series of: Equine Reproduction (No.).
Published by: Society for the Study of Reproduction, 1619 Monroe St., Madison, WI 53711-2063. TEL 608-256-2777, FAX 608-256-4610, ssr@ssr.org, http://www.ssr.org.

BIOLOGY OF THE NEONATE; foetal and neonatal research. see *MEDICAL SCIENCES—Obstetrics And Gynecology*

570.7 CHN ISSN 1004-7549
BIOLOGY TEACHING/SHENGWUXUE JIAOXUE. Text in Chinese. 1958. m. USD 19.80. **Document type:** *Academic/Scholarly.* **Description:** Introduces modern biological science and biology teaching experiences.
Related titles: Online - full text ed.: (from East View Information Services).
Published by: (Shengwu Xi), Huadong Shifan Daxue/East China Normal University, 3663 Zhongshan Beilu, Shanghai, 200062, China. TEL 86-21-2577577, http://www.ecnu.edu.cn. Ed. Ma Weiliang. adv.: page USD 1,000. Circ: 30,000. **Subscr. overseas to:** China National Publishing Industry Co., Shanghai Branch, 380 Bei Suzhou Lu, Shanghai, China.

570 540 371.3 UKR
BIOLOHIYA I KHIMIYA V SHKOLI. Text in Ukrainian. 1996. bi-m. USD 16.80 (effective 2000). **Document type:** *Academic/Scholarly.*
Published by: Vydavnytstvo Pedahohichna Presa, Baseina vul 1/2-a, Kiev, 01004, Ukraine. TEL 380-44-2244187, FAX 380-44-2467144. Ed. L Velychko. R&P Y Kuznetsov TEL 38-044-2244187. Adv. contact O Kestenko. **US dist. addr.:** East View Information Services, 3020 Harbor Ln. N., Minneapolis, MN 55447. TEL 612-550-096.

BIOMARKERS. see *MEDICAL SCIENCES*

570 USA ISSN 0067-8821
CODEN: BMATBJ
BIOMATHEMATICS. Text in English. 1970. irreg. price varies. reprint service avail. from ISI. **Document type:** *Academic/Scholarly.*
Indexed: MathR, SCI, ZentMath.
—CISTI. **CCC.**
Published by: Springer-Verlag New York, Inc. (Subsidiary of: Springer Science+Business Media), 233 Spring St, New York, NY 10013. TEL 212-460-1500, FAX 212-473-6272.

▼ new title ➤ refereed ✶ unverified ♦ full entry avail.

570 DEU
BIOMAX; Neugierig auf Wissenschaft. Text in German. 1995. 2/yr. **Document type:** *Newsletter, Academic/Scholarly.*
Published by: Max-Planck-Gesellschaft zur Foerderung der Wissenschaften, Hofgartenstr 8, Munich, 80539, Germany. TEL 49-89-21081232, FAX 49-89-21081405, presse@mpg-gv.mpg.de, http://www.mpg.de/deutsch/aktuell/biogeo.html, http://www.maxplanck.de. Ed., R&P Christina Beck.

610 COL ISSN 0120-4157
BIOMEDICA. Text in Spanish. 1981. q. **Document type:** *Journal, Academic/Scholarly.*
Published by: Instituto Nacional de Salud, Avenida Calle 26 No.51-60, Bogota, D.C., Zona 6, Colombia. http://www.ins.gov.co/biomedica/index.php?id=14.

BIOMEDICAL MEETINGS INDEX. see *MEETINGS AND CONGRESSES*

BIOMEDICAL RESEARCH; an interdisciplinary journal for the biomedical sciences. see *MEDICAL SCIENCES*

BIOMEDICAL RESEARCH. see *MEDICAL SCIENCES*

BIOMEDICAL TECHNOLOGY RESEARCH RESOURCES; a research resources directory. see *MEDICAL SCIENCES*

570 MEX ISSN 1607-6788
BIOMEDICAS. Variant title: Gaceta Biomedicas. Text in Spanish. 1996. m. **Document type:** *Academic/Scholarly.*
Formerly: Instituto de Investigaciones Biomedicas. Informe (0076-7220)
Related titles: Online - full text ed.: ISSN 1606-8378.
Published by: Universidad Nacional Autonoma de Mexico, Instituto de Investigaciones Biomedicas, Circuito Interior, Ciudad Universitaria, Mexico D.F., 04510 , Mexico. TEL 52-5-6226807, FAX 52-5-6650951, namihira@servidor.unam.mx, http://www.biomedicas.unam.mx/gaceta.asp. Ed. Rosalba Namihira. Circ: 2,000.

570 610 615 GBR
BIOMEDNET MAGAZINE. Text in English. bi-w. free (effective 2003). adv. back issues avail. **Document type:** *Magazine, Academic/Scholarly.* **Description:** Provides exciting reviews, news and comment, and primary research from the journals Trends, Current Opinion, Cell Press, Drug Discovery Today, BioMedNet Conference Reporter and BioMedNet News.
Formerly (until Mar. 2002): H M S Beagle
Media: Online - full text.
Published by: BioMedNet Ltd. (Subsidiary of: Elsevier Science & Technology), 84 Theobald's Rd, London, WC1X 8RR, United Kingdom. TEL 44-20-7323-5348, FAX 44-20-7631-0819, magazine@bmn.com, info@biomed.net, http://news.bmn.com/magazine, http://www.biomednet.com/hmsbeagle. Pub. Berlinda Kerkhof. Adv. contact Stacy Barrett.

BIOMETEOROLOGY; proceedings of the International Congress of Biometeorology. see *METEOROLOGY*

BIOMETEOROLOGY BULLETIN. see *METEOROLOGY*

BIOMETRIC BULLETIN. see *STATISTICS*

570 DEU ISSN 0323-3847
QH323.5 CODEN: BIJODN
➤ **BIOMETRICAL JOURNAL**; journal of mathematical methods in biosciences. Text in English. 1959. bi-m. EUR 1,224 in Europe; CHF 1,908 in Switzerland & Liechtenstein; USD 1,574 elsewhere; EUR 1,224 combined subscription in Europe print & online eds.; CHF 2,099 combined subscription in Switzerland & Liechtenstein for print & online eds.; USD 1,732 combined subscription elsewhere print & online eds. (effective 2006). adv. bk.rev. abstr.; bibl.; charts; illus.; stat. index. back issues avail.; reprints avail. **Document type:** *Journal, Academic/Scholarly.* **Description:** Promotes new contributions to the mathematical and statistical theory as well as interesting and original applications of known theoretical methods in the field of biosciences.
Formerly (until 1977): Biometrische Zeitschrift (0006-3452)
Related titles: Online - full text ed.: ISSN 1521-4036. EUR 1,224 in Europe to institutions; CHF 1,908 to institutions in Switzerland & Liechtenstein; USD 1,574 elsewhere to institutions (effective 2006) (from EBSCO Publishing, Swets Information Services, Wiley InterScience).
Indexed: ASCA, AnBrAb, BiolAb, Biostat, CCMJ, CIS, CMCI, CurCont, ExcerpMed, JCQM, MathR, MathSciNet, ORMS, PBA, QC&AS, RefZh, RiceAb, SFA, SSCI, ST&MA, VITIS, WildRev, ZentMath, ZooRec.
—BLDSC (2087.990000), CISTI, IDS, IE, Infotrieve, ingenta, Linda Hall. **CCC.**
Published by: Wiley - V C H Verlag GmbH & Co. KGaA (Subsidiary of: John Wiley & Sons, Inc.), Boschstr 12, Weinheim, 69469, Germany. FAX 49-6201-606-117, biomj@ams.med.uni-goettingen.de, subservice@wiley-vch.de, http://www.interscience.wiley.com/biometricaljournal, http://www.wiley-vch.de. Ed. Peter Bauer. R&P Claudia Rutz.
Subscr. in the Americas to: John Wiley & Sons, Inc.. TEL 201-748-6645, FAX 201-748-6088, subinfo@wiley.com; **Subscr. outside Germany, Austria & Switzerland to:** John Wiley & Sons Ltd., The Atrium, Southern Gate, Chichester, West Sussex PO19 8SQ, United Kingdom. TEL 44-1243-779777, FAX 44-1243-775878.

➤ **BIOMETRICS.** see *STATISTICS*

➤ **BIOMETRIKA.** see *BIOLOGY—Abstracting, Bibliographies, Statistics*

570 IND ISSN 0970-9835
QH301
BIONATURE. Text in English. 1981. s-a. USD 50 (effective 2000). **Document type:** *Academic/Scholarly.*
Indexed: BIOSIS Prev, BiolAb, ZooRec.
—CISTI, Linda Hall.
Published by: (Society of Bionaturalists), H P C Publishers Distributors Pvt. Ltd., 4805 Bharat Ram Rd, 24 Darya Ganj, New Delhi, 110 002, India. TEL 91-11-3254401, FAX 91-11-619-3511, hpcpd@nda.vsnl.net.in, hpcpd@hpc.cc, http://www.hpc.cc, http://www.bizdelhi.com/publisher/hpc, http://www.indianindustry.com.

570 NLD ISSN 0924-7734
QH301
BIONIEUWS. Text in Dutch. 1991. 20/yr. EUR 80 domestic; EUR 130 foreign; EUR 4.50 newsstand/cover (effective 2005). adv. bk.rev. illus. index. 8 p./no.; **Document type:** *Trade.* **Description:** Covers developments in biology and labor conditions affecting the biologist, including scientific policy, education, economic, ethical and environmental topics.
Formed by the merger of (1983-1991): Biotechnologie in Nederland (0924-7742); (1919-1991): Biovisie (0921-9234); Which was formerly (until 1988): Biovisie Magazine (0921-9242); Vakblad voor Biologen (0042-2215)
Indexed: BiolAb, ExcerpMed, ILP, SFA, ZooRec.
—CISTI.
Published by: Nederlands Instituut voor Biologie, Postbus 19245, Utrecht, 3501 DE, Netherlands. TEL 31-30-2369244, bionieuws@nibi.nl, nibi@nibi.nl, http://www.bionieuws.nl/, http://www.nibi.nl. Ed. Gaby van Caulil. Pub. Leen van den Oever. Circ: 8,000.

577 DNK ISSN 0107-4415
BIONYT/BIO-NEWS; populaer forskning. Text in Danish. 1981. irreg. (4-6/yr.). DKK 289 to individuals; DKK 349 to institutions (effective 2004). bk.rev. index, cum index: 1981-1993. back issues avail. **Document type:** *Newsletter.* **Description:** Contains popular reviews and news of international research in biology, medicine and environment with literature references and list of new books in Danish categorized according to subject.
Published by: Foreningen af Yngre Biologer, c/o Biologisk Forum, Falkonergaardsvej 4, Frederiksberg C, 1959, Denmark. TEL 45-35-376408, FAX 45-35-371255, bio@forskning.dk, http://www.bionyt.dk. Ed. Ole Terney. Circ: 1,000.

BIOPHOENIX DATABASE ON CD-ROM. see *MEDICAL SCIENCES*

570 USA ISSN 1542-6319
RM301.4 CODEN: BIINCE
▼ ➤ **BIOPROCESS INTERNATIONAL.** Text in English. 2003. m. USD 240 (effective 2003). adv. **Document type:** *Journal, Academic/Scholarly.*
Related titles: Online - full text ed.: USD 120 (effective 2003).
—BLDSC (2089.474240).
Published by: Informa Life Sciences Group (Subsidiary of: T & F Informa plc), 1 Research Dr, Ste 400A, P. O. Box 770, Westborough, MA 01581-0770. TEL 508-616-5550, FAX 508-616-5533, http://www.bioprocessintl.com/. Ed. S. Anne Montgomery. Pub. Brian J. Caine.

370 BRA ISSN 0104-4389
H8.S6 CODEN: RLEAFJ
BIOS; caderno do departamento de ciencias biologicas. Text in Portuguese. 1999. a. **Document type:** *Journal, Academic/Scholarly.*
Indexed: ASFA, ESPM, EntAb, ZooRec.
Published by: Pontificia Universidade Catolica de Minas Gerais, Av Dom Jose Gaspar, 500, C Eucaristico, Belo Horizonte, MG 30535-610, Brazil. TEL 55-31-33194271, FAX 55-31-33194129, proex@pucminas.br, http://www.pucminas.br.

570 GRC ISSN 1105-5049
BIOS. Variant title: Scientific Annals of the School of Biology. Text in English, Greek. 1932. a.
Formerly (until 1991): Epistemonike Epeteris tes Sholes ton Fusikon kai Mathematikon Epistemon (0379-539X)
Indexed: ESPM, ZooRec.
—CISTI.
Published by: (Aristotle University of Thessaloniki, School of Biology), Aristotle University of Thessaloniki, Admin Bldg, 6th Flr, Thessaloniki, Greece. http://www.auth.gr/.

570 USA ISSN 0005-3155
ML549.8 CODEN: BIOSAN
BIOS; a quarterly journal of biology. Text in English. 1930. q. USD 15 domestic; USD 17 in Canada & Mexico; USD 23 elsewhere (effective 2005). adv. bk.rev. charts; illus. 44 p./no. 2 cols./p.; reprints avail. **Document type:** *Journal, Academic/Scholarly.* **Description:** Includes undergraduate research papers in biology, and news of the society.
Related titles: Microfilm ed.: (from PQC); Online - full text ed.: (from BioOne, C S A).
Indexed: ASFA, ApEcolAb, BIOSIS Prev, BiolAb, BiolDig, CIN, ChemAb, ChemTitl, ESPM, GenetAb, RefZh, SFA, WildRev, ZooRec.
—BLDSC (2089.600000), CASDDS, CISTI, IE, ingenta, Linda Hall.
Published by: Beta Beta Beta Biological Honor Society, University of North Alabama, UNA Box 5079, Florence, AL 35632. TEL 256-765-6220, FAX 256-765-6221, lori.kelman@montgomerycollege.edu, tribeta@una.edu, http://www.tri-beta.org/bbbnational.html. Circ: 8,500 (paid).

570 371.3 USA ISSN 1539-2422
➤ **BIOSCENE**; journal of college biology teaching. Text in English. 1991. 4/yr. **Document type:** *Journal, Academic/Scholarly.*
Related titles: Online - full text ed.: free (effective 2005).
Indexed: CIJE.
Published by: Association of College and Biology Educators, c/o Ethel Stanley, Dept. of Biology, Beloit College, 700 College St, Beloit, WI 53511. FAX 608-363-2052, http://acube.org/publications/index.html, http://acube.orgg. Eds. Ethel Stanley, Timothy Mulkey.

570 USA ISSN 0006-3568
QH1 CODEN: BISNAS
➤ **BIOSCIENCE.** Text in English. 1951. m. USD 70 to individuals; USD 55 K-12 institutions; USD 294 combined subscription domestic to institutions print & online eds.; USD 353 combined subscription foreign to institutions print & online eds. (effective 2005). adv. bk.rev. bibl.; illus. index. back issues avail.; reprint service avail. from PQC. **Document type:** *Journal, Academic/Scholarly.* **Description:** Contains articles from all areas of biological sciences, including animals, humans, plants, and the environment.
Formerly (until 1963): A I B S Bulletin (0096-7645)
Related titles: Microform ed.: (from PQC); Online - full text ed.: ISSN 1525-3244. USD 265 (effective 2005) (from bigchalk, BioOne, C S A, EBSCO Publishing, Florida Center for Library Automation, Gale Group, H.W. Wilson, IngentaConnect, JSTOR (Web-based Journal Archive), Northern Light Technology, Inc., O C L C Online Computer Library Center, Inc., ProQuest Information & Learning, Swets Information Services).
Indexed: ABIPC, AEA, APD, ASFA, AbHyg, AcaI, AgBio, Agr, AgrForAb, AnBeAb, AnBrAb, ApEcolAb, B&AI, B&BAb, BIOBASE, BIOSIS Prev, BRI, BibAg, BioCN&I, BiolAb, BiolDig, CBRI, CBTA, CEABA, CIJE, CLFP, CPA, CTO, ChemAb, CivEngAb, CurCont, CybAb, DSA, EPB, ESPM, EntAb, EnvAb, EnvEAb, EnvInd, FCA, FPA, ForAb, FutSurv, GSI, GardL, GenetAb, HelmAb, HerbAb, HlthInd, HortAb, I&DA, IABS, ISR, IndVet, KWIWR, M&TEA, MASUSE, MBA, MEDLINE, MagInd, MaizeAb, NutrAb, OrnHort, PBA, PGegResA, PMR, PlantSci, PollutAb, PotatoAb, PoultAb, ProtozoAb, RA&MP, RDA, RGAb, RGPR, RM&VM, RPP, RRTA, RefSour, RefZh, RevApplEntom, RiceAb, S&F, SAA, SCI, SFA, SIA, SSCI, SWRA, SeedAb, TDB, Telegen, TriticAb, VetBull, WAE&RSA, WBA, WMB, WeedAb, WildRev, ZooRec.
—BLDSC (2089.611400), CASDDS, CIS, CISTI, GNLM, IDS, IE, Infotrieve, ingenta, Linda Hall. **CCC.**
Published by: American Institute of Biological Sciences, 1313 Dolley Madison Blvd, Ste 402, McLean, VA 22101. TEL 703-790-1745, 800-992-2427, FAX 703-790-2672, bioscience@aibs.org, admin@aibs.org, http://www.aibs.org. Eds. Rebecca Saxer, Timothy M Beardsley. Pub. Richard T O'Grady. R&P Jennifer A Williams. Adv. contact Carrie Hartin. B&W page USD 1,095, color page USD 1,615. Circ: 6,100 (paid).

570 580 JPN ISSN 1342-1441
CODEN: BIMIFM
BIOSCIENCE AND MICROFLORA. Text in Japanese. 1982. q. JPY 2,500 newsstand/cover domestic; USD 17.50 newsstand/cover foreign (effective 2004). **Document type:** *Journal, Academic/Scholarly.* **Description:** Contains full papers, notes, reviews, and bibliography of the world literature.
Formerly (until 1995): Bifidobacteria and Microflora (0286-9306)
Related titles: Online - full text ed.: ISSN 1349-8355 (from J-Stage).
Indexed: ASFA, AbHyg, AgBio, AgrForAb, B&BAb, DSA, ESPM, HortAb, IndVet, MBA, PHN&I, PN&I, PoultAb, RA&MP, RM&VM, SIA, SoyAb, TDB, WAE&RSA.
—CASDDS, CISTI, GNLM. **CCC.**
Published by: Nihon Bifizusukin Senta/Japan Bifidus Foundation, 1-24-11 Sugamo,Toshima-ku, Tokyo, 170-0002, Japan. TEL 81-3-53959610, FAX 81-3-59784068, 003@ipec-pub.co.jp, http://www.ipec-pub.co.jp/jbf/.

570 GBR ISSN 1479-7860
▼ **BIOSCIENCE EDUCATION ELECTRONIC JOURNAL.** Key Title: Bioscience Education e - Journal. Variant title: B E E - j. Text in English. 2003. s-a. free (effective 2005).
Media: Online - full text.

B

Published by: Learning and Teaching Support Network Centre for Bioscience, Rm 8, 49n, Worsley Bldg, University of Leeds, Leeds, LS2 9JT, United Kingdom. TEL 44-113-3433001, FAX 44-113-3435894, ltsnbioscience@leeds.ac.uk, http://bio.ltsn.ac.uk/journal/.

570 575.1 FRA ISSN 1158-467X CODEN: BIOSER

BIOSCIENCES. Variant title: Biosciences Appliquees. Text and summaries in English, French. 1982. q. adv. bk.rev. index. **Document type:** *Academic/Scholarly.*
Formerly (until 1990): Bio-Sciences (Chateaufort) (0292-8418)
Indexed: ApicAb, BioDAb, CBTA.
—CASDDS, CISTI. **CCC.**
Published by: Dunod, 5 rue Laromiguiere, Paris, 75005, France. TEL 33-1-40463500, FAX 33-1-40464995, infos@dunod.com, http://www.dunod.com. Ed. Christian Doinel. Circ: 1,000.

BIOSIS EVOLUTIONS. see *BIOLOGY—Abstracting, Bibliographies, Statistics*

BIOSIS SEARCH GUIDE (YEARS). see *BIOLOGY—Abstracting, Bibliographies, Statistics*

BIOSIS SERIAL SOURCES. see *BIOLOGY—Abstracting, Bibliographies, Statistics*

570 DEU ISSN 0947-0867 CODEN: BOSPFD

BIOSPEKTRUM. Text in German. 1995. bi-m. EUR 59 to individuals; EUR 119 to institutions; EUR 25 to students; EUR 19 newsstand/cover (effective 2004). adv. **Document type:** *Journal, Academic/Scholarly.*
Indexed: CIN, ChemAb, ChemTitl, MSB, RefZh.
—BLDSC (2089.616800), CASDDS, IE, Infotrieve, ingenta. **CCC.**
Published by: (Vereinigung fuer Allgemeine und Angewandte Mikrobiologie), Spektrum Akademischer Verlag GmbH (Subsidiary of: Elsevier Science & Technology), Slevogtstr. 3-5, Heidelberg, 69126, Germany. TEL 49-6221-9126300, FAX 49-6221-9126338, biospektrum@elsevier.com, verlag@spektrum.com, http://www.biospektrum.de, http://www.spektrumverlag.com. Ed. Dr. Christine Schreiber. Adv. contact Bernd Beutel. B&W page EUR 3,660, color page EUR 4,690. Circ: 12,726 (paid). **Co-sponsor:** Gesellschaft fuer Biologische Chemie.

572.8 USA ISSN 1093-0248

BIOSUPPLYNET SOURCE BOOK. Text in English. 1995. a.
Formerly (until 1997): The Lab Manual Source Book (1079-4875)
Published by: BioSupplyNet, Inc., 5151 McCrimmon Pkwy Ste 216, Morrisville, NC 27560. TEL 919-659-2100, info@biosupplynet.com, http://www.biosupplynet.com.

570 AUT ISSN 1026-4949

BIOSYSTEMATICS AND ECOLOGY. Text in English. irreg., latest vol.17, 2001. price varies. **Document type:** *Monographic series, Academic/Scholarly.*
Indexed: BIOSIS Prev, ZooRec.
Published by: Verlag der Oesterreichischen Akademie der Wissenschaften, Postfach 471, Vienna, W 1011, Austria. TEL 43-1-515813402, FAX 43-1-515813400, verlag@oeaw.ac.at, http://verlag.oeaw.ac.at. Eds. H Winkler, Wilfried Morawetz.

570 IRL ISSN 0303-2647
QH301 CODEN: BSYMBO

➤ **BIOSYSTEMS.** Text in English. 1967. 12/yr. EUR 1,571 in Europe to institutions; JPY 208,900 in Japan to institutions; USD 1,758 to institutions except Europe and Japan; EUR 88 in Europe to qualified personnel; JPY 11,700 in Japan to qualified personnel; USD 99 to qualified personnel except Europe and Japan (effective 2006). bk.rev. charts; illus. index. back issues avail. **Document type:** *Journal, Academic/Scholarly.* **Description:** Devoted to achieving an improved understanding of biological origins and evolution by means of the analysis and modeling of complex biological systems.
Formerly (until 1974): Currents in Modern Biology (0011-4014)
Related titles: Microform ed.: (from PQC); Online - full content ed.; Online - full text ed.: (from EBSCO Publishing, Gale Group, IngentaConnect, ScienceDirect, Swets Information Services).
Indexed: ASCA, ASFA, AgBio, AnBrAb, BIOBASE, BIOSIS Prev, BiolAb, CIN, CMCI, CPA, ChemAb, ChemTitl, CurCont, DSA, ESPM, ExcerpMed, FCA, ForAb, GEOBASE, HelmAb, HortAb, IABS, ISR, IndMed, Inpharma, MEDLINE, NutrAb, PBA, PGegResA, ProtozoAb, RM&VM, Reac, RevApplEntom, SCI, SFA, VITIS, WildRev, ZooRec.
—BLDSC (2089.670000), CASDDS, CISTI, GNLM, IDS, IE, Infotrieve, ingenta, Linda Hall. **CCC.**
Published by: Elsevier Ireland Ltd (Subsidiary of: Elsevier Science & Technology), Elsevier House, Brookvale Plaza, E. Park, Shannon, Co. Clare, Ireland. TEL 353-61-709600, FAX 353-61-709100, http://www.elsevier.com/locate/biosystems. Ed. David B Fogel. R&P Annette Moloney. **Subscr. to:** Elsevier BV, PO Box 211, Amsterdam 1000 AE, Netherlands. TEL 31-20-485-3757, FAX 31-20-485-3432, nlinfo-f@elsevier.nl, http://www.elsevier.nl.

577 SVN ISSN 1580-4208

➤ **BIOTA;** journal for biology and ecology. Text in English, Slovenian. 2000. s-a. SIT 5,000 domestic; EUR 80 in Europe; USD 100 elsewhere (effective 2003). bk.rev. 200 p./no. 2 cols./p.; back issues avail. **Document type:** *Journal, Academic/Scholarly.* **Description:** Covers all fields of biology and ecology.
Indexed: ASFA, EntAb, GEOBASE, ZooRec.
Published by: (Drustva Varuhov Okolja/Environmental Society Radoziv), Drustvo za Proucevanje Ptic in Varstvo Narave/Society of Bird Research and Nature Conservation, Ptujska c 91, Race, 2327s, Slovenia. FAX 386-2-788-30-51, milan.vogrin@guest.arnes.si, http://www.zalec.si/radoziv/biota/. Ed., Adv. contact Milan Vogrin.

570 COL ISSN 0124-5376

➤ **BIOTA COLOMBIANA.** Text in English, Spanish. 2000. s-a. COP 50,000 domestic to individuals; USD 110 foreign to individuals; COP 90,000 domestic to institutions; USD 110 foreign to institutions (effective 2004). bk.rev. bibl. Index. back issues avail. **Document type:** *Journal, Academic/Scholarly.*
Related titles: Online - full text ed.
Published by: Instituto de Investigacion de Recursos Biologicos Alexander von Humboldt, Claustro de San Agustin, Villa de Leyva, Boyaca, Colombia. TEL 57-87-320791, FAX 57-87-320792, biotacol@humboldt.org.co, http://www.humboldt.org.co. Ed. Fernando Fernandez. R&P Daniel Davila Reyes. Circ: 500 (paid and free). **Co-sponsor:** Universidad Nacional de Colombia, Instituto de Ciencias.

570 BRA ISSN 1676-0611

BIOTA NEOTROPICA. Text in Portuguese, Spanish, English. 2001. s-a. free (effective 2005). **Document type:** *Journal, Academic/Scholarly.*
Media: Online - full text.
Published by: Centro de Referencia em Informacao Ambiental, Av Romeo Tortima 388, Barao Geraldo, Campinas, SP 13083-885, Brazil. TEL 55-19-32880466, FAX 55-19-32490960, http://www.biotaneotropica.org.br/v3n2/en/, http://www.cria.org.br.

570 USA ISSN 1529-2193

➤ **BIOTA OF SOUTH CAROLINA.** Text in English. 2000. a. **Document type:** *Monographic series, Academic/Scholarly.*
Published by: Clemson University, College of Agriculture, Forestry and Life Sciences, c/o Dept. of Entomology, Clemson University, Clemson, SC 29634-0365. awhlr@clemson.edu, http://cufan.clemson.edu/olos/. Ed. Alfred G. Wheeler. **Subscr. to:** Public Service Bulletin Rm., 82 Poole Agricultural Center, Clemson, SC 29634-0311.

570 SWE ISSN 1651-324X

BIOTECH SWEDEN. Text in Swedish. 2002. 11/yr. SEK 695 (effective 2003). adv. **Document type:** *Magazine, Trade.*
Incorporates (in 2002): Biotechwaerlden (1651-1522)
Related titles: Online - full text ed.
Published by: I D G AB (Subsidiary of: I D G Communications Inc.), Sturegatan 11, Stockholm, 10678, Sweden. TEL 46-8-453-60-00, FAX 46-8-453-60-05, http://www.biotech.idg.se. Ed. Fredrik Bernsel TEL 46-8-4536230. Adv. contact Ida Hasselrot TEL 46-8-453-61-03. color page SEK 37,000; 252 x 358. Circ: 20,000.

BIOTECHNOLOGY GUIDE U.S.A. see *BIOLOGY—Biotechnology*

660.6 570 USA

BIOTECHNOLOGY INDUSTRY GUIDE. Text in English. 1996. biennial. USD 49.99; USD 59.95 foreign (effective 1998). **Document type:** *Trade.* **Description:** Contains contact information for over 950 companies throughout the United States, including biotechnology firms from all sectors of the industry and other large corporations active in pharmaceuticals, diagnostics and agriculture.
Published by: Institute for Biotechnology Information, c/o Mark Dibner, Pres., Box 14569, Research Triangle Park, NC 27709-4569. TEL 919-544-5111, FAX 919-544-5401, ibi@mindspring.com, http://www.bitechinfo.com.

▼ **BIOTECHNOLOGY MANAGEMENT PRACTICES.** see *BUSINESS AND ECONOMICS—Management*

570 BRA ISSN 0103-1643

➤ **BIOTEMAS.** Text in English, Spanish, Portuguese. 1988. s-a. **Document type:** *Journal, Academic/Scholarly.* **Description:** Publishes articles in all areas of the biological sciences.
Related titles: Online - full text ed.: 2004. free (effective 2005).
Published by: Universidade Federal de Santa Caterina, Centro de Ciencias Biologicas, Campus Universitario - Trindade, Florianopolis, 88040-900, Brazil. biotemas@ccb.ufsc.br, http://www.biotemas.ufsc.br.

➤ **BIOTERRORISM WEEK.** see *POLITICAL SCIENCE—International Relations*

571.3 GBR ISSN 1352-2396

BIOTRANSFORMATIONS (CAMBRIDGE); a survey of the biotransformations of drugs and chemicals in animals. Text in English. 1989. irreg., latest vol.7, 1996. price varies. 486 p./no.; back issues avail. **Document type:** *Monographic series, Academic/Scholarly.* **Description:** Surveys the literature on biotransformations in animals.
Indexed: BIOSIS Prev.
—GNLM. **CCC.**
Published by: Royal Society of Chemistry, Thomas Graham House, Science Park, Milton Rd, Cambridge, CB4 0WF, United Kingdom. TEL 44-1223-420066, FAX 44-1223-423623, sales@rsc.org, http://www.rsc.org. Ed. D R Hawkins.

570 GBR ISSN 1359-2963

BIOTRANSFORMATIONS (LONDON). Text in English. 1996. s-a. GBP 4,000; GBP 800 renewals. **Description:** Provides data on new and established methods for preparative biosynthetic reactions. Contains both archival and current material from Professor Dr. Klaus Kieslich's Databank of Biotransformations and the Warwick Biotransformation Club.
Media: CD-ROM.
Published by: Chapman & Hall, Electronic Publishing Division, Chapman & Hall, 2-6 Boundary Row, London, SE1 8HN, United Kingdom. TEL 44-20-7865-0066, FAX 44-20-7522-0101, cust.serv@chall.co.uk, http://epd.chapmanhall.com. **Dist. by:** Cheriton House, North Way, Andover, Hamps SP10 5BE, United Kingdom. TEL 44-1264-332424, FAX 44-1264-342787.

BIOTRONICS; environment control and environmental biology. see *ENVIRONMENTAL STUDIES*

B

570 IDN ISSN 0215-6334
SD235.S67 CODEN: BITREF

BIOTROPIA. Text in English. 1988. s-a. USD 15. **Document type:** *Academic/Scholarly.* **Description:** Contains scientific articles on research findings in the fields of tropical forest biology, tropical agricultural pest biology and tropical aquatic biology.
Formed by the merger of: Seameo Biotrop Newsletter; Biotrop Bulletin in Tropical Biology; Biotrop Technical Bulletin
Indexed: AgrForAb, AnBrAb, BioCN&I, FPA, ForAb, HortAb, IndVet, MaizeAb, PBA, PGegResA, PHN&I, RA&MP, RPP, RevApplEntom, RiceAb, S&F, SeedAb, VetBull, WeedAb, ZooRec.
—BLDSC (2089.899000), IE, ingenta.
Published by: Seameo Biotrop - Southeast Asian Regional Centre for Tropical Biology, PO Box 116, Bogor, 16001, Indonesia. TEL 62-251-323848, FAX 62-251-326851. Ed. Sitanala Arsyad.

578.0913 USA ISSN 0006-3606
QH1 CODEN: BTROAZ

➤ **BIOTROPICA.** Text in English. 1969. q. free to members (effective 2005); USD 244 combined subscription in the Americas to institutions & Caribbean, print & online eds.; GBP 75 combined subscription in Europe to institutions print & online eds.; GBP 149 combined subscription elsewhere to institutions print & online eds. (effective 2006). adv. back issues avail.; reprint service avail. from PQC. **Document type:** *Journal, Academic/Scholarly.* **Description:** Publishes articles dealing with any phase of tropical biology with related subjects, as long as the primary emphasis is tropical and biological.
Formerly: Association for Tropical Biology. Bulletin
Related titles: Microfilm ed.: (from PQC); Online - full text ed.: ISSN 1744-7429. USD 240 in the Americas to institutions & Caribbean; USD 123 in Canada & Mexico to institutions; GBP 188 elsewhere to institutions (effective 2006) (from BioOne, Blackwell Synergy, C S A, EBSCO Publishing, IngentaConnect, JSTOR (Web-based Journal Archive), O C L C Online Computer Library Center, Inc.).
Indexed: AEA, ASCA, ASFA, AgBio, Agr, AgrForAb, AnBeAb, AnBrAb, ApEcolAb, ApicAb, BIOBASE, BIOSIS Prev, BioCN&I, BiolAb, CPA, CurCont, ESPM, EntAb, ExcerpMed, FCA, FPA, ForAb, GEOBASE, HerbAb, HortAb, I&DA, ISR, KWIWR, M&GPA, MBA, MaizeAb, NutrAb, OrnHort, PBA, PGegResA, PN&I, PoultAb, ProtozoAb, RA&MP, RDA, RPP, RevApplEntom, S&F, SCI, SFA, SIA, SPPI, SWRA, SeedAb, WeedAb, WildRev, ZooRec.
—BLDSC (2089.900000), CISTI, IDS, IE, Infotrieve, ingenta, Linda Hall. **CCC.**
Published by: (Association for Tropical Biology and Conservation), Blackwell Publishing, Inc. (Subsidiary of: Blackwell Publishing Ltd.), Commerce Place, 350 Main St, Malden, MA 02148. TEL 781-388-8206, FAX 781-388-8232, eeb.biotropica@uconn.edu, http://www.atbio.org/biotropica.html#ed, http://www.blackwellpublishing.com. Ed. Robin L Chazdon. R&P W John Kress TEL 202-357-2534. Circ: 1,600 (paid).

570 IND ISSN 0971-0108 CODEN: BIOVE2

BIOVED. Text in English. 1990. bi-m. INR 200 domestic to individuals; USD 100 foreign to individuals; INR 1,000 domestic to institutions; USD 200 foreign to institutions (effective 2003). adv. **Document type:** *Academic/Scholarly.* **Description:** Discusses new research in the life sciences.
Indexed: AEA, AgBio, AgrForAb, AnBrAb, BioCN&I, CIN, CPA, ChemAb, ChemTitl, DSA, FCA, FPA, ForAb, HelmAb, HortAb, I&DA, IndVet, MaizeAb, NutrAb, OrnHort, PBA, PGegResA, PGrRegA, PHN&I, PotatoAb, PoultAb, ProtozoAb, RA&MP, RDA, RM&VM, RPP, RiceAb, S&F, SIA, SeedAb, SoyAb, TriticAb, VetBull, WAE&RSA, WeedAb, ZooRec.
—BLDSC (2090.050000), CASDDS. **CCC.**

Published by: Bioved Research Society, c/o Brijesh K. Dwivedi General Secretary, Teliarganj, U.P., 133/42, MLN Rd, Allahabad, Uttar Pradesh 211 002, India. bioved2003@yahoo.com. Ed. B K Dwivedi. adv.: page INR 3,000.

577 332 USA ISSN 1541-0579
BIOWORLD FINANCIAL WATCH. Text in English. w. (Mon.). USD 1,247 (effective 2006). **Document type:** *Newsletter, Trade.* **Description:** Covers the business side of biotechnology and business opportunities available in this dynamic industry.
Media: Fax. **Related titles:** Online - full text ed.: USD 1,197 (effective 2005) (from Florida Center for Library Automation).
Published by: Thomson American Health Consultants, Inc. (Subsidiary of: Thomson Corporation, Healthcare Information Group), 3525 Piedmont Rd, N E, Bldg 6, Ste 400, Atlanta, GA 30305. TEL 404-262-5511, 800-688-2421, FAX 404-262-7837, customerservice@ahcpub.com, http://www.bioworld.com/servlet/com.accumedia.web.Dispatcher?next=bioWorldFinancial, http://www.ahcpub.com. Pub. Donald R Johnston. Circ: 10,000 (paid).

570 USA ISSN 1541-0587
BIOWORLD INTERNATIONAL. Text in English. w. USD 1,247 for fax or online eds.; USD 48 newsstand/cover (effective 2006). **Document type:** *Newsletter, Trade.*
Media: Fax. **Related titles:** Online - full text ed.
Published by: Thomson American Health Consultants, Inc. (Subsidiary of: Thomson Corporation, Healthcare Information Group), 3525 Piedmont Rd, N E, Bldg 6, Ste 400, Atlanta, GA 30305. TEL 404-262-5511, FAX 404-262-7837, customerservice@ahcpub.com, http://www.bioworld.com/servlet/com.accumedia.web.Dispatcher?next=bioWorldInternational, http://www.ahcpub.com.

570 USA ISSN 1541-0595
BIOWORLD TODAY. Text in English. d. (Mon.-Fri.). USD 2,295 for print or fax or online eds.; USD 18 newsstand/cover (effective 2006). **Document type:** *Newspaper, Consumer.*
Related titles: Fax ed.; Online - full text ed.: USD 2,997 archive access; USD 4,659 archive access & current (effective 2006) (from Gale Group).
Indexed: Inpharma, Reac.
—**CCC.**
Published by: Thomson American Health Consultants, Inc. (Subsidiary of: Thomson Corporation, Healthcare Information Group), 3525 Piedmont Rd, N E, Bldg 6, Ste 400, Atlanta, GA 30305. TEL 404-262-5511, 800-688-2421, FAX 404-262-7837, bioworld.customerservive@thomson.com, customerservice@ahcpub.com, http://www.bioworld.com/servlet/com.accumedia.web.Dispatcher?next=bioWorldToday, http://www.ahcpub.com. Pub. Donald R Johnston.

577 USA
BIOWORLD WEEK. Text in English. w. (Mondays). USD 927; USD 36 newsstand/cover (effective 2006). 5 p./no.; **Document type:** *Newsletter, Trade.* **Description:** Contains abridged biotech news intelligence service as reported in BioWorld Today.
Media: Fax.
Published by: Thomson American Health Consultants, Inc. (Subsidiary of: Thomson Corporation, Healthcare Information Group), 3525 Piedmont Rd, N E, Bldg 6, Ste 400, Atlanta, GA 30305. TEL 404-262-5511, FAX 404-262-7837, customerservice@ahcpub.com, http://www.ahcpub.com/ahc_root_html/products/newsletters/bww.html.

570 JPN ISSN 0913-5219
BIRDER/BADA. Text in Japanese. 1987. m. JPY 10,800 (effective 1998). bk.rev. **Document type:** *Trade.* **Description:** Serves as a magazine for bird watchers.
Published by: Bun'ichi Sogo Shuppan Co. Ltd., 13-10 Nishi-Goken-cho, Shinjuku-ku, Tokyo, 162-0812, Japan. TEL 81-3-3235-7341, FAX 81-3-3269-1402, bunichi@vinet.or.jp, http://www.vinet.or.jp/~bunichi/. Ed., R&P Masayuki Harada. Pub. Takeshi Okumura. Circ: 36,000.

571.976 USA ISSN 1542-0752
QM691 CODEN: BDRPBT
➤ **BIRTH DEFECTS RESEARCH. PART A: CLINICAL AND MOLECULAR TERATOLOGY.** Text in English. 1968. m. USD 5,300 domestic to institutions; USD 5,564 in Canada & Mexico to institutions; USD 5,718 elsewhere to institutions; USD 5,830 combined subscription domestic to institutions print & online eds.; USD 6,094 combined subscription in Canada & Mexico to institutions print & online eds.; USD 6,248 combined subscription elsewhere to institutions includes Part B & C. adv. bk.rev. bibl.; charts; illus. index. back issues avail.; reprints avail. **Document type:** *Journal, Academic/Scholarly.* **Description:** Investigates abnormal fetal development in humans and in experimental animal models.
Formerly (until 2003): Teratology (0040-3709)
Related titles: Microform ed.: (from PQC, SWZ); Online - full content ed.: ISSN 1542-0760. 1996. USD 5,300 to institutions Parts A, B, & C (effective 2006); Online - full text ed.: (from EBSCO Publishing, Swets Information Services, Wiley InterScience).
Indexed: A&ATA, ASCA, AbHyg, AnBrAb, B&BAb, BDM&CN, BIOSIS Prev, BiolAb, CIN, ChemAb, ChemTitl, CurCont, DBA, DSA, DentInd, ESPM, ExcerpMed, Faml, GenetAb, IPA, ISR, IndMed, IndVet, Inpharma, MEDLINE, NRN, NSCI, NutrAb, PE&ON, PN&I, PoultAb, RM&VM, Reac, RefZh, SCI, SFA, TDB, THA, VetBull, WildRev, ZooRec.
—BLDSC (2094.091250), CASDDS, CISTI, GNLM, IDS, IE, ingenta, KNAW, Linda Hall. **CCC.**
Published by: (Teratology Society), John Wiley & Sons, Inc., 111 River St, Hoboken, NJ 07030-5774. TEL 201-748-6000, FAX 201-748-5915, uscs-wis@wiley.com, http://www3.interscience.wiley.com/cgi-bin/jhome/102526943, http://www.wiley.com. Ed. Philip E Mirkes. adv.: B&W page GBP 640, color page GBP 1,515; trim 210 x 279. Circ: 1,600. **Subscr. outside the Americas to:** John Wiley & Sons Ltd., The Atrium, Southern Gate, Chichester, West Sussex PO19 8SQ, United Kingdom. TEL 44-1243-843335, 0800-243407, FAX 44-1243-843232, cs-journals@wiley.co.uk.

➤ **BIULETIN ZA NOVONABAVENI KNIGI NA CHUZHDI EZITZI. SERIYA B: ESTESTVENI I PRILOZHNI NAUKI. MEDIZINA. TEKHNIKA. SELSKO STOPANSTVO.** see *BIOLOGY—Abstracting, Bibliographies, Statistics*

➤ **BOLETIM C E O.** (Centro de Estudos Ornitologicos) see *ENVIRONMENTAL STUDIES*

578.77 BRA ISSN 0101-4242
QP31.2 CODEN: BFANDM
BOLETIM DE FISIOLOGIA ANIMAL. Text in Portuguese. 1977. a.
Indexed: ESPM.
Published by: Universidade de Sao Paulo, Instituto de Biociencias, Rua do Matao, Travessa 14, 321, Sao Paulo, 05508-900, Brazil. ib@edu.usp.br, http://www.ib.usp.br/.

BOLETIN DE AGRICULTURA BIOLOGICO-DINAMICA. see *AGRICULTURE*

570 ESP ISSN 0211-0326
BOLETIN DE CIENCIAS DE LA NATURALEZA. Text in Spanish. 1960. s-a.
Formerly (until 1979): Instituto de Estudios Asturianos. Boletin. Suplemento de Ciencias (0561-3566)
Indexed: IECT.
—CINDOC.
Published by: Real Instituto de Estudios Asturianos, Plaza Porlier 5, Apdo. 9, Oviedo, 33003, Spain.

BORNEO RESEARCH BULLETIN. see *ANTHROPOLOGY*

BOTANISCHER VEREIN VON BERLIN UND BRANDENBURG. VERHANDLUNGEN. see *BIOLOGY—Botany*

BOUNDARY-LAYER METEOROLOGY; an international journal of physical and biological processes in the atmospheric boundary layer. see *METEOROLOGY*

BRAGANTIA. see *AGRICULTURE*

570 BRA ISSN 1519-6984
QH301 CODEN: RBBIAL
BRAZILIAN JOURNAL OF BIOLOGY. Text in English, French, German, Italian, Portuguese, Spanish. 1941. q. BRL 250 domestic; USD 150 foreign (effective 2003). bk.rev. bibl.; charts; illus. index.
Formerly: Revista Brasileira de Biologia (0034-7108)
Related titles: Online - full text ed.: free (effective 2005) (from SciELO).
Indexed: ASFA, AgBio, AgrForAb, AnBeAb, AnBrAb, ApEcolAb, BIOSIS Prev, BioCN&I, BiolAb, CPA, ChemAb, DSA, DentInd, ESPM, EntAb, FPA, ForAb, HelmAb, HerbAb, HortAb, I&DA, IndMed, IndVet, MEDLINE, NutrAb, OceAb, OrnHort, PBA, PGegResA, PHN&I, PN&I, PoultAb, ProtozoAb, RA&MP, RDA, RM&VM, RPP, RRTA, RevApplEntom, RiceAb, S&F, SFA, SIA, SWRA, SeedAb, SoyAb, TriticAb, VetBull, WAE&RSA, WeedAb, ZooRec.
—BLDSC (2277.401300), CASDDS, GNLM, IE, Infotrieve, ingenta, Linda Hall. **CCC.**
Published by: Instituto Internacional de Ecologia/International Institute of Ecology, Rua Bento Carlos, 759, Centro, Sao Carlos, SP 13560-660, Brazil. iie@iie.com.br, http://www.scielo.br/scielo.php?script=sci_serial&pid=1519-6984&lng=en&nrm=iso. Ed. Dr. Takako Matsumura Tundisi.

BRAZILIAN JOURNAL OF MEDICAL AND BIOLOGICAL RESEARCH. see *MEDICAL SCIENCES*

BRITISH ECOLOGICAL SOCIETY. BULLETIN. see *ENVIRONMENTAL STUDIES*

577 GBR
BRITISH ECOLOGICAL SOCIETY. ECOLOGICAL ISSUES SERIES. Text in English. irreg., latest vol.5, 1994. GBP 20 (effective 1999). **Document type:** *Monographic series.*
—ingenta.
Published by: British Ecological Society, 26 Blades Ct, Putney, London, SW15 2NU, United Kingdom.

BRITISH ECOLOGICAL SOCIETY. SPECIAL SYMPOSIA SERIES. see *ENVIRONMENTAL STUDIES*

BRITISH ECOLOGICAL SOCIETY. SYMPOSIUM. see *ENVIRONMENTAL STUDIES*

570 USA ISSN 0068-2799
CODEN: BSBIAW
➤ **BROOKHAVEN SYMPOSIA IN BIOLOGY.** Text in English. irreg., latest vol.36, 1991. **Document type:** *Proceedings, Academic/Scholarly.*
Indexed: AnBrAb, BiolAb, DSA, ExcerpMed, IndMed, MEDLINE, PBA.
—CASDDS, CISTI, Infotrieve. **CCC.**
Published by: Brookhaven National Laboratory, Biology Department, Bldg. 463, Upton, NY 11973-5000. TEL 631-344-3415, FAX 631-344-6398, folkers@bnl.gov, http://www.biology.bnl.gov/. **Dist. by:** National Technical Information Service, Government Research Center, 5285 Port Royal Rd, Springfield, VA 22161. TEL 703-605-6060, 800-363-2068, http://www.ntis.gov.

570 USA ISSN 1554-7647
▼ **BULLETIN OF BIOLOGICAL SCIENCES.** Text in English. forthcoming 2006. q. **Document type:** *Bulletin, Academic/Scholarly.*
Published by: Rochester Institute of Technology, Department of Biological Sciences, 85 Lomb Memorial Dr, Rochester, NY 14623-5603. TEL 585-475-2496, biology@osfmail.rit.edu, http://www.rit.edu/~672www/index.html. Ed. Gary R Skuse.

570 610 USA ISSN 0007-4888
R850 CODEN: BEXBAN
➤ **BULLETIN OF EXPERIMENTAL BIOLOGY AND MEDICINE.** Text in English. 1956. m. EUR 3,498, USD 3,575, GBP 2,185 combined subscription to institutions print & online eds. (effective 2005). adv. back issues avail. **Document type:** *Journal, Academic/Scholarly.* **Description:** Presents the latest experimental research on key issues in modern biology and medicine, translated from the Russian.
Related titles: Microfilm ed.: (from PQC); Online - full text ed.: ISSN 1573-8221 (from EBSCO Publishing, Gale Group, IngentaConnect, Kluwer Online, O C L C Online Computer Library Center, Inc., Ovid Technologies, Inc., ProQuest Information & Learning, Springer LINK, Swets Information Services); ♦ Translation of: Byulleten' Eksperimental'noi Biologii i Meditsiny. ISSN 0365-9615.
Indexed: ASCA, AbHyg, AnBrAb, BibLing, BiolAb, ChemTitl, CurCont, ExcerpMed, FPA, ForAb, IABS, ISR, IndMed, MEDLINE, NSCI, ProtozoAb, RA&MP, SCI, SSCI, TDB.
—BLDSC (0409.500000), CASDDS, CISTI, IDS, IE, Infotrieve, ingenta. **CCC.**
Published by: (Akademiya Meditsinskikh Nauk Rossii/Russian Academy of Medical Sciences RUS), Consultants Bureau (Subsidiary of: Springer-Verlag New York, Inc.), 233 Spring St, New York, NY 10013. TEL 212-460-1500, FAX 212-460-1575, service@springer-ny.com, http://springerlink.metapress.com/openurl.asp?genre=journal&issn=0007-4888, http://www.springeronline.com. Ed. Vladimir N Yarigin. **Subscr. to:** Springer-Verlag New York, Inc., Journal Fulfillment, PO Box 2485, Secaucus, NJ 07096-2485. TEL 201-348-4033, FAX 201-348-4505, journals@springer-ny.com; Springer-Verlag Dordrecht, Journals Department, PO Box 322, Dordrecht, Netherlands. TEL 31-78-6576392, FAX 31-78-6576474.

➤ **BULLETIN OF MARINE SCIENCE.** see *EARTH SCIENCES—Oceanography*

570 GBR ISSN 0092-8240
QH505.A1 CODEN: BMTBAP
➤ **BULLETIN OF MATHEMATICAL BIOLOGY.** Text in English. 1939. bi-m. EUR 1,029 in Europe to institutions; JPY 111,200 in Japan to institutions; USD 915 to institutions except Europe and Japan (effective 2005). adv. bk.rev.; software rev. reprints avail. **Document type:** *Bulletin, Academic/Scholarly.* **Description:** Devoted to research at the junction of computational, theoretical and experimental biology.
Formerly: Bulletin of Mathematical Biophysics (0007-4985)
Related titles: Microfilm ed.: (from PQC); Online - full text ed.: ISSN 1522-9602. USD 1,043 (effective 2002) (from EBSCO Publishing, Gale Group, IngentaConnect, O C L C Online Computer Library Center, Inc., ScienceDirect, Swets Information Services).
Indexed: ASCA, ASFA, AbHyg, AcoustA, AgBio, Agr, AnBrAb, ApEcolAb, ApMecR, BIOBASE, BIOSIS Prev, BibAg, BioCN&I, BiolAb, Biostat, CIN, CIS, CMCI, ChemAb, ChemTitl, CurCont, ESPM, EntAb, ExcerpMed, FCA, ForAb, HelmAb, HerbAb, IABS, ISR, IndMed, IndVet, Inpharma, Inspec, MEDLINE, MathR, NutrAb, PBA, PE&ON, PHN&I, ProtozoAb, RPP, RRTA, Reac, RevApplEntom, SCI, SFA, TDB, VetBull, WeedAb, WildRev, ZentMath, ZooRec.
—BLDSC (2867.970000), CASDDS, CISTI, GNLM, IDS, IE, Infotrieve, ingenta, Linda Hall. **CCC.**
Published by: (Society for Mathematical Biology), Academic Press (Subsidiary of: Elsevier Science & Technology), 24-28 Oval Rd, London, NW1 7DX, United Kingdom. apsubs@acad.com, http://www.academicpress.com/bmb, http://www.elsevier.com/. Ed. Dr. P.K. Maini. Circ: 1,250. **Subscr. to:** Elsevier BV, PO Box 211, Amsterdam 1000 AE, Netherlands. TEL 31-20-485-3757, FAX 31-20-485-3432, nlinfo-f@elsevier.nl, http://www.elsevier.nl.

611.01816 ITA ISSN 0391-481X
CODEN: BMBMD5
BULLETIN OF MOLECULAR BIOLOGY AND MEDICINE; a journal for the rapid publication of reports in the field of biochemical sciences. Text in English. 1975. q. USD 150 (effective 1999). abstr.; charts; stat. **Description:** Contains topics about molecular biology and medicine.
Indexed: CIN, ChemAb, ChemTitl, DBA, ExcerpMed.
—BLDSC (2881.370000), CASDDS, CISTI, GNLM.
Published by: Casa Editrice Idelson Gnocchi, Via Michele Pietravalle 85, Naples, NA 80131, Italy. TEL 39-081-5524733, FAX 39-081-5518295, idelgno@tin.it, informazioni@idelson-gnocchi.com, http://www.idelson-gnocchi.com. Eds. Ernesto Quagliariello, Francesco Salvatore.

BUNDESAMT FUER SERA UND IMPFSTOFFE. PAUL-EHRLICH-INSTITUT. ARBEITEN. see *MEDICAL SCIENCES*

570 610 RUS ISSN 0365-9615
CODEN: BEBMAE
➤ **BYULLETEN' EKSPERIMENTAL'NOI BIOLOGII I MEDITSINY.** Text in Russian. 1936. m. USD 605 foreign (effective 2005). adv. **Document type:** *Journal, Academic/Scholarly.* **Description:** Publishes brief accounts of original experimental research devoted to urgent problems of biology and medicine by members of the Academy of Medical Sciences in their particular fields.
Related titles: ♦ English Translation: Bulletin of Experimental Biology and Medicine. ISSN 0007-4888.
Indexed: ASFA, AnBrAb, CIN, ChemAb, ChemTitl, DBA, DSA, DentInd, ExcerpMed, IndMed, MEDLINE, RM&VM, RefZh.
—BLDSC (0025.000000), CASDDS, CISTI, East View, GNLM. **CCC.**
Published by: Akademiya Meditsinskikh Nauk Rossii/Russian Academy of Medical Sciences, ul Solyanka 14, Moscow, 109801, Russian Federation. TEL 7-095-2982048, FAX 7-095-2982111, http://medi.ru/bbm/bbmeng.htm. Ed. D S Sarkisov. Adv. contact K V Movsesyan. **US dist. addr.:** East View Information Services, 3020 Harbor Ln. N., Minneapolis, MN 55447. TEL 763-550-0961, FAX 763-559-2931, eastview@eastview.com, http://www.eastview.com.

➤ **C A P TODAY.** see *MEDICAL SCIENCES*

➤ **C A SELECTS. PSYCHOBIOCHEMISTRY.** see *BIOLOGY—Abstracting, Bibliographies, Statistics*

570 363.7 CAN ISSN 1020-9018
C B D NEWS. (Convention on Biological Diversity) Text in English. 2001. 3/yr. **Document type:** *Newsletter.*
Related titles: Online - full content ed.: ISSN 1020-9050.
Published by: Secretariat of the Convention on Biological Diversity, World Trade Centre, 393 St Jacques St, Office 300, Montreal, PQ H2Y 1N9, Canada. TEL 514-288-2220, FAX 514-288-6588, secretariat@biodiv.org, http://www.biodiv.org/doc/newsletters.

C B E VIEWS. (Council of Biology Editors) see *PUBLISHING AND BOOK TRADE*

577 614.7 GBR
C E E NEWSLETTER. (Center for Ecology & Evolution) Text in English. q. back issues avail. **Document type:** *Newsletter, Academic/Scholarly.*
Published by: University College London, Centre for Ecology & Evolution, Galton Laboratory, Rm 5l9, Wolfson House, 4 Stephenson Way, London, NW1 2HE, United Kingdom. l.feldman@ucl.ac.uk, http://www.gene.ucl.ac.uk/cee/letter.html.

577 JPN ISSN 0915-4353
C E L S S JOURNAL/C E L S S GAKKAISHI. Text in Japanese; Summaries in English. 1989. s-a. JPY 5,000. **Document type:** *Proceedings.*
—**CCC.**
Published by: Japan Society for Controlled Ecological and Life Support Systems, Institute for Future Technology, 2-6-11 Tomiokabashi Bldg, Fukagawa, Koto-ku, Tokyo, 135-0033, Japan. FAX 81-3-5245-1061.

577 JPN ISSN 0917-4869
C E L S S NEWS. Text in Japanese. 1988. 4/yr. **Document type:** *Newsletter.*
Published by: Japan Society for Controlled Ecological and Life Support Systems, Institute for Future Technology, 2-6-11 Tomiokabashi Bldg, Fukagawa, Koto-ku, Tokyo, 135-0033, Japan. FAX 81-3-5245-1061.

C F S; Courier Forschungsergebnisse Senckenberg. (Courier Forschungsinstitut Senckenberg) see *SCIENCES: COMPREHENSIVE WORKS*

C M A S BULLETIN D'INFORMATION/C M A S NEWSLETTER. (Confederation Mondiale des Activites) see *EARTH SCIENCES—Oceanography*

570 ESP ISSN 0214-848X
CADERNOS DA AREA DE CIENCIAS BIOLOXICAS. INVENTARIOS. Text in Spanish. 1988. irreg. **Document type:** *Monographic series.*
Indexed: IECT.
—CINDOC.
Published by: Seminario de Estudos Galegos, El Castro, Sada, (La Coruna) 15168, Spain.

578.77 FRA ISSN 0007-9723
QH90 CODEN: CBIMA5
➤ **CAHIERS DE BIOLOGIE MARINE.** Text in English, French. 1960. q. EUR 226.89 domestic; EUR 222.22 foreign (effective 2002). adv. bk.rev. bibl.; charts; illus. 100 p./no.; back issues avail. **Document type:** *Academic/Scholarly.* **Description:** Contains papers and short notes concerning marine biology, reproduction, life cycles, developmental biology, morphogenesis, genetics, population dynamics, ecophysiology, plankton, benthos and algology.
Related titles: Online - full text ed.: (from EBSCO Publishing).
Indexed: ASCA, ASFA, AgBio, AnBrAb, BIOSIS Prev, BiolAb, CPA, ChemAb, CurCont, ESPM, GEOBASE, HelmAb, HortAb, ISR, NemAb, PBA, PGegResA, PollutAb, RPP, RefZh, RevApplEntom, S&F, SCI, SFA, SIA, SWRA, SeedAb, WAE&RSA, WeedAb, WildRev, ZooRec.
—BLDSC (2948.650000), CASDDS, CISTI, IDS, IE, Infotrieve, ingenta, Linda Hall.
Published by: Station Biologique de Roscoff, Place Georges Teissier, BP 74, Roscoff, Cedex 29682, France. TEL 33-2-98292302, FAX 33-2-98292380, jouin@sb-roscoff.fr, http://www.sb-roscoff.fr/cbmintro_eng.html. Pub. Andre Toulmond. Adv. contact Claude Jouin Toulmond. Circ: 400.

570 551.46 JPN ISSN 0288-6243
QH91.A1
CALANUS. Text in English, Japanese; Summaries in Japanese. 1968. a.
Indexed: ASFA.
Published by: (Fuzoku Aitsu Rinkai Jikkenjo), Kumamoto Daigaku, Rigakubu/Kumamoto University, Faculty of Science, Aitsu Marine Biological Station, Aitsu, Amakusa-gun, Matsushima-machi, Kumamoto-ken 861-6102, Japan.

570 USA ISSN 0885-4629
Q11 CODEN: CFAMBS
➤ **CALIFORNIA ACADEMY OF SCIENCES. MEMOIRS.** Text in English. 1868. irreg., latest vol.27. price varies. back issues avail. **Document type:** *Monographic series, Academic/Scholarly.* **Description:** Produces two series of publications containing the results of original research conducted by the scientific staff and research associates of the institution and others.
Indexed: ZooRec.
—BLDSC (5580.300000), Linda Hall. **CCC.**
Published by: California Academy of Sciences, Golden Gate Park, San Francisco, CA 94118. TEL 415-750-7243, FAX 415-750-7090, scipubs@cas.calacademy.org, http://www.calacademy.org.

570 USA ISSN 0068-547X
Q11 CODEN: PCASAV
➤ **CALIFORNIA ACADEMY OF SCIENCES. PROCEEDINGS.** Text in English. 1907. irreg., latest vol.53, 2002. USD 40 (effective 2004). index. back issues avail. **Document type:** *Proceedings, Academic/Scholarly.* **Description:** Contains the results of original research in the areas of taxonomy, systematics, biogeography and natural history . Subject areas include fish, nudibranchs, plants, frogs, soft corals, and others.
Related titles: Microform ed.: (from PQC).
Indexed: ASFA, Agr, BIOSIS Prev, BiolAb, ESPM, ForAb, HortAb, IndVet, KWIWR, OceAb, OrnHort, PBA, PGegResA, RefZh, RevApplEntom, SFA, WildRev, ZooRec.
—BLDSC (6671.000000), CISTI, IE, ingenta, KNAW, Linda Hall. **CCC.**
Published by: California Academy of Sciences, 875 Howard St, San Francisco, CA 94103. TEL 415-221-5100, scipubs@cas.calacademy.org, info@calacademy.org, http://www.calacademy.org. Ed. Alan E Leviton. R&P Katie Martin. Circ: 1,000.

570 USA
CALIFORNIA EDUCATIONAL LINKAGES IN THE LIFE SCIENCES. Abbreviated title: C E L L S. Text in English. 1990. s-a. free. **Document type:** *Newsletter.* **Description:** Aims to promote development of collaborative programs for bringing recent biological science advances into the classroom through various resources.
Related titles: Issued with: California Science Teachers Association Newspaper.
Published by: University of California at Berkeley, Lawrence Hall of Science, Centennial Dr, Berkeley, CA 94720. TEL 510-643-5537, FAX 510-642-1055. Circ: 25,000.

570.9 USA ISSN 0068-5755
CALIFORNIA NATURAL HISTORY GUIDES. Text in English. 1959 (no.4). irreg., latest vol.58, 1994. price varies. back issues avail. **Document type:** *Monographic series.* **Description:** Describes the fauna, flora, and geology of various regions of California.
Indexed: BIOSIS Prev, ZooRec.
—BLDSC (3015.080000). **CCC.**
Published by: University of California Press, Book Series, 2120 Berkeley Way, Berkeley, CA 94720. TEL 510-642-4247, FAX 510-643-7127, askucp@ucpress.edu, http://www.ucpress.edu/books/CNHG.ser.html, http://www.ucpress.edu/books/series.html. **Orders to:** California - Princeton Fulfillment Services, 1445 Lower Ferry Rd, Ewing, NJ 08618. TEL 800-777-4726, FAX 800-999-1958.

CALIFORNIA SEA GRANT COLLEGE PROGRAM. REPORT SERIES. see *EARTH SCIENCES—Oceanography*

CAMBRIDGE PALEOBIOLOGY SERIES. see *PALEONTOLOGY*

570 301 GBR
CODEN: CSBAEN
CAMBRIDGE STUDIES IN BIOLOGICAL AND EVOLUTIONARY ANTHROPOLOGY. Text in English. 1958. irreg. price varies. **Document type:** *Monographic series.*
Formerly: Cambridge Studies in Biological Anthropology (0957-0306)
Indexed: AnthLit, BIOSIS Prev, BrArAb, ZooRec.
—BLDSC (3015.992300), ingenta, KNAW.
Published by: Cambridge University Press, The Edinburgh Bldg, Shaftesbury Rd, Cambridge, CB2 2RU, United Kingdom. TEL 44-1223-312393, FAX 44-1223-315052, information@cambridge.org, http://publishing.cambridge.org/series/csba. R&P Linda Nicol TEL 44-1223-325757.

B

570 577 GBR ISSN 0957-0764
CODEN: CSECEA
CAMBRIDGE STUDIES IN ECOLOGY. Text in English. 1982. irreg. price varies. **Document type:** *Monographic series.*
Published by: Cambridge University Press, The Edinburgh Bldg, Shaftesbury Rd, Cambridge, CB2 2RU, United Kingdom. TEL 44-1223-312393, FAX 44-1223-315052, information@cambridge.org, http://publishing.cambridge.org/series/cse. R&P Linda Nicol TEL 44-1223-325757.

570 510 GBR ISSN 0263-9424
CODEN: CSMBDC
CAMBRIDGE STUDIES IN MATHEMATICAL BIOLOGY. Text in English. 1980. irreg. price varies. **Document type:** *Monographic series.*
Indexed: BIOSIS Prev, BiolAb, CCMJ, MathR, ZentMath, ZooRec.
—BLDSC (3015.994600), CISTI.
Published by: Cambridge University Press, The Edinburgh Bldg, Shaftesbury Rd, Cambridge, CB2 2RU, United Kingdom. TEL 44-1223-312393, FAX 44-1223-315052, information@cambridge.org, http://publishing.cambridge.org/series/csmb, http://www.cup.cam.ac.uk/. R&P Linda Nicol TEL 44-1223-325757.

CANADIAN BIOETHICS REPORT. see *PHILOSOPHY*

CANADIAN BULLETIN OF FISHERIES AND AQUATIC SCIENCES. see *FISH AND FISHERIES*

578.77 CAN ISSN 0706-6465
CODEN: CDRSDH
CANADIAN DATA REPORT OF FISHERIES AND AQUATIC SCIENCES. Text in English, French. 1977. irreg. **Document type:** *Monographic series.*
Formerly (until 1979): Fisheries and Marine Service. Data Report (0701-7634)
Indexed: BIOSIS Prev, BiolAb, ESPM.
—CISTI. **CCC.**
Published by: (Canada. Department of Fisheries and Oceans, Fisheries and Marine Service), Department of Fisheries and Oceans, Communications Directorate, 200 Kent St, 13th Fl, Sta 13228, Ottawa, ON K1A 0E6, Canada. TEL 613-993-0999, FAX 613-990-1866, info@dfo-mpo.gc.ca, http://www.ncr.dfo.ca.

570 CAN ISSN 0845-5066
QH301.C246
CANADIAN FEDERATION OF BIOLOGICAL SOCIETIES. ANNUAL MEETING. PROGRAMME, PROCEEDINGS. Text in English. 1987. a. USD 10. adv. author index. **Document type:** *Proceedings.* **Description:** Contains summaries and descriptions of papers, posters and symposia presented at the annual meeting of the federation.
Formed by the 1987 merger of: Programme - Canadian Federation of Biological Societies. Annual Meeting (0845-5058); Canadian Federation of Biological Societies. Annual Meeting. Proceedings (0714-8577); Which continues in part: Canadian Federation of Biological Societies. Programme and Proceedings of the Annual Meeting (0709-1265); Which was formed by the merger of: Canadian Federation of Biological Societies. Programme of the Annual Meeting (0068-8703); Canadian Federation of Biological Societies. Annual Meeting. Proceedings (0068-869X)
Indexed: BiolAb.
—BLDSC (1087.691500), CISTI. **CCC.**
Published by: Canadian Federation of Biological Societies, 104 1750 Courtwood Cres, Ottawa, ON K2C 2B5, Canada. TEL 613-225-8889, FAX 613-225-9621. R&P Paul Hough. Adv. contact Natalie Lamarche.

570 CAN ISSN 0068-8681
CANADIAN FEDERATION OF BIOLOGICAL SOCIETIES. NEWSLETTER. Text in English, French. 1959. s-a. adv. **Document type:** *Newspaper.* **Description:** Reports about science projects, funding, and new developments in biological sciences.
Related titles: Online - full text ed.
Published by: Canadian Federation of Biological Societies, 104 1750 Courtwood Cres, Ottawa, ON K2C 2B5, Canada. TEL 613-225-8889, FAX 613-225-9621, http://www.fermentas.com/cfbs. R&P Paul Hough. Adv. contact Natalie Lamarche.

CANADIAN SOCIETY OF ENVIRONMENTAL BIOLOGISTS NEWSLETTER. see *ENVIRONMENTAL STUDIES*

CANADIAN SPECIAL PUBLICATION OF FISHERIES AND AQUATIC SCIENCES. see *FISH AND FISHERIES*

CANADIAN TECHNICAL REPORT OF FISHERIES AND AQUATIC SCIENCES. see *FISH AND FISHERIES*

578.77 CAN ISSN 0704-3716
CANADIAN TRANSLATION OF FISHERIES AND AQUATIC SCIENCES. Text in English. irreg. **Document type:** *Monographic series.*
Former titles (until 1979): Fisheries and Marine Service. Translation Series (0226-2215); (until 1974): Fisheries Research Board of Canada. Translation Series (0527-7590)
Indexed: ESPM.
—BLDSC (3046.013000), CISTI. **CCC.**
Published by: (Canada. Department of Fisheries and Oceans, Fisheries and Marine Service), Department of Fisheries and Oceans, Communications Directorate, 200 Kent St, 13th Fl, Sta 13228, Ottawa, ON K1A 0E6, Canada. TEL 613-993-0999, FAX 613-990-1866, info@dfo-mpo.gc.ca, http://www.ncr.dfo.ca.

570 PRI ISSN 0008-6452
Q1 CODEN: CRJSA4
➤ **CARIBBEAN JOURNAL OF SCIENCE.** Text in English. 1961. 3/yr. USD 25 to individuals; USD 45 to institutions (effective 2005). bk.rev. cum.index: vol.1-15, vol.16-27. 125 p./no.; back issues avail. **Document type:** *Journal, Academic/Scholarly.* **Description:** Contains natural history papers pertinent to the Caribbean. Papers are technical, most in the area of botany, zoology, ecology and geology.
Related titles: CD-ROM ed.: USD 20 per issue (effective 2004); Online - full text ed.: 2001. free (effective 2005).
Indexed: ASFA, AgrForAb, AnBeAb, AnBrAb, ApEcolAb, BIOSIS Prev, BioCN&I, BiolAb, BiolDig, CPA, CurCont, ESPM, EntAb, ForAb, GEOBASE, HelmAb, HerbAb, HortAb, I&DA, IndVet, M&GPA, NutrAb, OceAb, PBA, ProtozoAb, S&F, SFA, SeedAb, TDB, VetBull, WAE&RSA, WildRev, ZooRec.
—BLDSC (3053.100000), CISTI, IE, ingenta, Linda Hall.
Published by: University of Puerto Rico at Mayaguez, College of Arts and Sciences, PO Box 9280, Mayaguez, 00681-9280, Puerto Rico. TEL 787-832-4040, FAX 425-699-0198, 801-469-7143, editor@caribjsci.org, http://www.caribjsci.org/index.html, http://mayaweb.upr.clu.edu/artssciences/cjs. Ed. Ines Sastre de Jesus. Circ: 500 (paid).

578.77 577 TTO ISSN 1017-7450
➤ **CARIBBEAN MARINE STUDIES.** Text in English. 1990. a. USD 20 to individuals; USD 30 to institutions (effective 2002). illus. **Document type:** *Academic/Scholarly.* **Description:** Publishes research on marine and environmental issues of the Wider Caribbean Region.
Indexed: ESPM, ZooRec.
Published by: Institute of Marine Affairs, Hilltop Lane, Chaguaramas, PO Box 3160, Carenage, Trinidad & Tobago. TEL 809-634-4291, FAX 809-634-4433, journal@ima.gov.tt, director@ima.gov.tt, http://www.ima.gov.tt/marinejournal.htm. Eds. Peter Bacon, Ramsay Saunders.

➤ **CARIBBEAN RESEARCH INSTITUTE. REPORT.** see *HISTORY—History Of North And South America*

➤ **CARNEGIE MUSEUM OF NATURAL HISTORY. ANNALS.** see *SCIENCES: COMPREHENSIVE WORKS*

➤ **CARNEGIE MUSEUM OF NATURAL HISTORY. BULLETIN.** see *SCIENCES: COMPREHENSIVE WORKS*

570.71 USA ISSN 0045-5865
CAROLINA TIPS. Text in English. 1938. 4/yr. free to qualified personnel. adv. bk.rev. illus. index. back issues avail. **Document type:** *Newsletter, Academic/Scholarly.*
Related titles: Online - full text ed.
Indexed: BiolAb.
Published by: Carolina Biological Supply Co., 2700 York Rd, Burlington, NC 27215-3398. TEL 336-584-0381, 800-334-5551, FAX 800-222-7112, carolina@carolina.com, http://www.carolina.com/tips/Default.asp. R&P Gwen W Oakley TEL 336-538-6233. Adv. contact Harry Shoffner TEL 336-222-6438. Circ: 100,000.

CEIBA. see *AGRICULTURE*

570 USA ISSN 1541-9061
CODEN: CADCEF
➤ **CELL COMMUNICATION & ADHESION.** Variant title: Cell Communication & Adhesion. Text in English. 1993. bi-m. GBP 638, USD 969 combined subscription to institutions print & online eds. (effective 2006). reprint service avail. from PSC. **Document type:** *Journal, Academic/Scholarly.* **Description:** Presents research, short communications, and reviews on all families of adhesion receptors and counterreceptors from diverse biological systems.
Formerly (until 2000): Cell Adhesion and Communication (1061-5385)
Related titles: CD-ROM ed.: ISSN 1026-7883; Microform ed.; Online - full text ed.: ISSN 1029-2314. GBP 606, USD 921 to institutions (effective 2006) (from EBSCO Publishing, Gale Group, IngentaConnect, O C L C Online Computer Library Center, Inc., Swets Information Services).
Indexed: ASCA, ASFA, BBCI, BIOBASE, CurCont, ExcerpMed, IABS, ISR, IndMed, Inpharma, MEDLINE, ProtozoAb, Reac, SCI.
—BLDSC (3097.735000), CISTI, GNLM, IE, Infotrieve, ingenta. **CCC.**
Published by: Taylor & Francis Inc. (Subsidiary of: Taylor & Francis Group), 325 Chestnut St, Ste 800, Philadelphia, PA 19016. TEL 215-625-8900, FAX 215-625-2940, info@taylorandfrancis.com, http://www.tandf.co.uk/journals/titles/15419061.asp, http://www.taylorandfrancis.com.

570 GBR ISSN 1478-811X
▼ ➤ **CELL COMMUNICATION AND SIGNALING.** Text in English. 2003. irreg. free (effective 2006). adv. **Document type:** *Journal, Academic/Scholarly.* **Description:** Covers all aspects of the identification and function of receptors, ligands, and other biomolecules participating in the outward and inward cellular signaling pathways in normal and pathological conditions.
Media: Online - full content (from EBSCO Publishing, National Library of Medicine).
Published by: BioMed Central Ltd. (Subsidiary of: Current Science Ltd), Middlesex House, 34-42 Cleveland St, London, W1T 4LB, United Kingdom. TEL 44-20-76319131, 44-20-73230323, FAX 44-20-76319923, info@biomedcentral.com, http://www.biosignaling.com/home/, http://www.biomedcentral.com. Ed. Bernard Perbal.

570 CHN ISSN 1001-0602
CODEN: CREEB6
➤ **CELL RESEARCH/XIBAO YANJIU.** Text in English. 1990. m. (s-a. until 1997, q. until 2001, bi-m. until 2004). USD 150 to individuals; USD 300 to institutions (effective 2005). 104 p./no.; **Document type:** *Journal, Academic/Scholarly.* **Description:** Publishes original articles, reviews, commentaries and rapid/brief communications in different fields of cell biology and molecular cell biology.
Related titles: Online - full text ed.: free (effective 2005) (from East View Information Services).
Indexed: B&BAb, BCI, BIOSIS Prev, BiolAb, CurCont, GenetAb, ISR, IndMed, MEDLINE, RefZh, SCI.
—BLDSC (3097.858000), CISTI, IE, Infotrieve, ingenta.
Published by: Chinese Academy of Sciences, Shanghai Institutes for Biological Sciences/Zhongguo Kexueyuan, Shanghai Xibaoxue Yanjiusuo, Bldg 23 Rm 308, 320 Yueyang Rd, Shanghai, 200031, China. TEL 86-21-54920958, FAX 86-21-54920952, cellres@sibs.ac.cn; cellres@sunm.shcnc.ac.cn, http://www.cell-research.com/. Ed. Zhen Yao TEL 86-21-54921368. **Dist. by:** China International Book Trading Corp, 35 Chegongzhuang Xilu, Haidian District, PO Box 399, Beijing 100044, China. TEL 86-10-68412045, cibtc@mail.cibtc.com.cn, http://www.cibtc.com.cn.

➤ **CELL STRESS & CHAPERONES.** see *MEDICAL SCIENCES*

570 USA ISSN 1742-8130
CELLSCIENCE REVIEWS. Text in English. q. free. **Document type:** *Journal, Academic/Scholarly.* **Description:** Covers all aspects of cellular science, from molecular aspects of cell function to cellular systems and signaling.
Media: Online - full content.
Published by: Cellscience TEL 44-7980-748526, http://www.cellscience.com/journal/journalindex.asp, http://cellscience.com/.

572.8 FRA ISSN 0145-5680
QH611 CODEN: CMBID4
➤ **CELLULAR AND MOLECULAR BIOLOGY.** Text in English; Summaries in English. 1977. 8/yr. EUR 475, USD 605.88 print & online eds. (effective 2005). adv. bk.rev. index. 150 p./no.; Supplement avail.; back issues avail. **Document type:** *Journal, Academic/Scholarly.* **Description:** Covers all relevant areas of the life sciences. Analyzes the relationship between structure and chemical and/or physical content.
Formerly (until 1977): Annales d'Histochimie (0003-4355); Incorporates: Cyto-Enzymology
Related titles: Online - full content ed.: ISSN 1165-158X. 2001. EUR 450, USD 538.15 (effective 2004).
Indexed: ASCA, ASFA, AbHyg, AgBio, AnBrAb, B&BAb, BBCI, BCI, BIOSIS Prev, BioCN&I, BiolAb, CIN, CPA, ChemAb, ChemTitl, CurCont, DSA, ExcerpMed, FCA, FPA, ForAb, GenetAb, HelmAb, HortAb, INIS AtomInd, ISR, IndMed, IndVet, Inpharma, MEDLINE, MaizeAb, NSA, NemAb, NutrAb, PBA, PE&ON, PHN&I, PN&I, PotatoAb, PoultAb, ProtozoAb, RA&MP, RDA, RM&VM, RPP, Reac, RevApplEntom, RiceAb, S&F, SCI, SeedAb, SoyAb, TDB, VetBull.
—BLDSC (3097.921000), CASDDS, CISTI, GNLM, IE, Infotrieve, ingenta, KNAW, Linda Hall. **CCC.**
Published by: C M B Association, 2 Rue de Rouhling, Sarreguemines, 57200, France. TEL 33-3-87029962, FAX 33-3-87025805, cellmolbiol@wanadoo.fr, cmb-ass@wanadoo.fr, http://www.cellmolbiol.com. Ed. Richard F Ochillo. R&P Raymond Wegmann. Adv. contact Mieke Wegmann. B&W page EUR 457.35, color page EUR 762.25; 17.5 x 23. Circ: 750.

571 POL ISSN 1425-8153
QH573 CODEN: CMBLFF
➤ **CELLULAR & MOLECULAR BIOLOGY LETTERS**; an international journal. Text in English. 1996. q. EUR 136 foreign (effective 2005). back issues avail. **Document type:** *Journal, Academic/Scholarly.* **Description:** Publishes accelerated papers on biochemistry, molecular biology, cellural biology, physiology and biophysics as well as general and applied biotechnology.
Related titles: E-mail ed.; Online - full text ed.: ISSN 1689-1392. free (effective 2005).
Indexed: AgrAg, B&BAb, BBCI, BIOBASE, BIOSIS Prev, BiolAb, ChemAb, ExcerpMed, FCA, GenetAb, IABS, INIS AtomInd, NucAcAb, RefZh, SCI.
—BLDSC (3097.921500), CISTI, IE, Infotrieve, ingenta.
Published by: (Polskie Towarzystwo Biologii Komorki/Polish Society for Cell Biology), Uniwersytet Wroclawski, Instytut Biochemii, Zaklad Biochemii Genetycznej/University of Wroclaw, Institute of Biochemistry, Department of Genetic Biochemistry, ul Przybyszewskiego 63-77, Wroclaw, 51-148, Poland. TEL 48-71-3247208, FAX 48-71-3756208, cmbl@cmbl.org.pl, http://www.cmbl.org.pl. Eds. Aleksander F Sikorski, Arkadiusz Kozubek, Jan Szopa. **Dist. by:** Ars Polona, Krakowskie Przedmiescie 7, Warsaw, Poland. TEL 48-22-9263914, FAX 48-22-9265334, arspolona@arspolona.com.pl, http://www.arspolona.com.pl.

509 CHE ISSN 1420-682X
Q1.A1 CODEN: CMLSFI
➤ **CELLULAR AND MOLECULAR LIFE SCIENCES.** Text in English. 1945. s-m. EUR 2,548 combined subscription to institutions print & online eds. (effective 2005). adv. charts; illus. index. back issues avail. **Document type:** *Journal, Academic/Scholarly.* **Description:** Contains research articles covering the latest aspects of biological and biomedical research with contributions focusing on molecular and cellular aspects of biomedicine, cell biology, immunology, molecular genetics, neuroscience, biochemistry, pharmacology and physiology related to pharmacology.
Formerly (until 1997): Experientia (0014-4754)
Related titles: Online - full text ed.: ISSN 1420-9071 (from EBSCO Publishing, Springer LINK, Swets Information Services); ♦ Supplement(s): E X S. ISSN 1023-294X.
Indexed: AEA, ASCA, ASFA, AbHyg, AgBio, Agr, AnBrAb, ApicAb, ArtHuCI, B&BAb, BIOBASE, BIOSIS Prev, BioCN&I, BioDAb, BiolAb, CCI, CPA, CTA, CTFA, ChemAb, ChemInfo, CurCR, CurCont, DBA, DSA, DentInd, DokArb, ESPM, EntAb, ExcerpMed, FCA, FPA, FS&TA, ForAb, GenetAb, HelmAb, HerbAb, HortAb, I&DA, IABS, ISR, IndChem, IndMed, IndVet, Inspec, LHB, MBA, MEDLINE, MSB, MaizeAb, NPU, NRN, NSA, NSCI, NemAb, NutrAb, OrnHort, PBA, PGegResA, PGrRegA, PN&I, PoultAb, ProtozoAb, PsycholAb, RA&MP, RCI, RM&VM, RPP, RefZh, RevApplEntom, S&F, SCI, SFA, SIA, SSCI, SWRA, SeedAb, SoyAb, TDB, THA, ToxAb, TriticAb, VITIS, VetBull, WeedAb, WildRev, ZooRec.
—BLDSC (3097.923800), CASDDS, CINDOC, CISTI, GNLM, IDS, IE, Infotrieve, ingenta, Linda Hall. **CCC.**
Published by: Birkhaeuser Verlag AG (Subsidiary of: Springer Science+Business Media), Viaduktstr 42, Postfach 133, Basel, 4051, Switzerland. TEL 41-61-2050707, FAX 41-61-2050799, CMLSedit@birkhauser.ch, info@birkhauser.ch, http://link.springer.de/link/service/journals/00018/index.htm, http://www.birkhauser.ch/journals. Ed. Dr. Pierre Jolles TEL 33-1-44275072. **Subscr. in the Americas to:** Springer-Verlag New York, Inc., Journal Fulfillment, PO Box 2485, Secaucus, NJ 07096-2485. TEL 800-777-4643, 201-348-4033, FAX 201-348-4505, journals@birkhauser.com; **Subscr. to:** Springer GmbH Auslieferungsgesellschaft, Haberstr 7, Heidelberg 69126, Germany. TEL 49-6221-345-0, FAX 49-6221-345-4229, birkhauser@springer.de.

617.22 570.22 USA ISSN 1052-5882
CODEN: CMMIEQ
CELLULAR AND MOLECULAR MECHANISMS OF INFLAMMATION; receptors of inflammatory cells: structure-function relationships. Text in English. 1990. irreg., latest vol.5, 1999.
Indexed: BIOSIS Prev, CIN, ChemAb, ChemTitl.
—CASDDS, CISTI, GNLM, KNAW. **CCC.**
Published by: Academic Press (Subsidiary of: Elsevier Science & Technology), 525 B St, Ste 1900, San Diego, CA 92101-4495. apsubs@acad.com, http://www.academicpress.com. Eds. Charles G Cochrane, Michael A Gimbrone Jr.

570 POL ISSN 1644-3632
▼ ➤ **CENTRAL EUROPEAN JOURNAL OF BIOLOGY.** Text in English. 2006. q. USD 249, EUR 199 to individuals; USD 1,000, EUR 800 to institutions (effective 2006). **Document type:** *Journal, Academic/Scholarly.* **Description:** Aims to publish research results of wide interest in all fields of biology.
Media: Online - full content.

Published by: Central European Science Journals, 8, Mariensztat St, Warsaw, 00-302, Poland. TEL 48-22-8286020, FAX 48-22-8286024, gm@cesj.com, http://www.cesj.com/. Ed. Mariusz Ratajczak.

570 MDG
CENTRE D'INFORMATION ET DE DOCUMENTATION SCIENTIFIQUE ET TECHNIQUE. RECHERCHES POUR LE DEVELOPPEMENT. SERIE SCIENCES BIOLOGIQUE. Text in French; Summaries in English, French. 1985. s-a. MGF 60, USD 10. abstr.; bibl.; charts; illus.; stat. back issues avail.
Indexed: ZooRec.
Published by: Centre d'Information et de Documentation Scientifique et Technique, BP 6224, Antananarivo, 101, Madagascar. TEL 261-2-33288. Circ: 1,000.

595.6 592.74 FRA ISSN 1161-2398
CENTRE INTERNATIONAL DE MYRIAPODOLOGIE. BULLETIN. Text in English, French. 1969. a. bk.rev. bibl. back issues avail.
Related titles: E-mail ed.
Indexed: ZooRec.
Published by: Centre International de Myriapodologie, MNHN, Zoologie-Arthropodes, 61, rue Buffon, Paris, 75005, France. TEL 33-1-40793582, FAX 33-1-40793863, millicim@mnhn.fr, http://www.mnhn.fr/assoc/myriapoda.index.htm. Pub. Jean Jacques Geoffroy.

570 ECU
CENTRO DE BIODIVERSIDAD Y AMBIENTE. MUSEO DE ZOOLOGIA. PUBLICACION ESPECIAL. Text in Spanish. irreg.
Indexed: ZooRec.
Published by: Pontificia Universidad Catolica del Ecuador, Departamento de Ciencias Biologicas, Centro de Biodiversidad y Ambiente, Museo de Zoologia, Quito, Ecuador. TEL 593-2-2565627, http://www.puce.edu.ec/zoologia/.

577 ARG
CENTRO DE ECOLOGIA APLICADA DEL NEUQUEN. INFORME TECNICO. Text in Spanish. irreg.
Published by: Centro de Ecologia Aplicada del Neuquen, Ruta Prov 61, Km 3, Valle San Cabao, CC 7, Junin de los Andes, 8371, Argentina. cean@jandes.com.ar, http://www.neuquen.gov.ar/org/cean/cean.htm.

570 ESP
➤ **CENTRO DE INVESTIGACIONES BIOLOGICAS. MEMORIA CIENTIFICA.** Text in Spanish. 1963. biennial, latest 1999. free. **Document type:** *Academic/Scholarly.* **Description:** Reports on the current projects of the institution, as well as on the scientific production of the different groups.
Formerly: Centro de Investigaciones Biologicas. Memoria
—BLDSC (5669.575700), CINDOC.
Published by: Centro de Investigaciones Biologicas, Velazquez 144, Madrid, 28006, Spain. TEL 34-91-5611800, FAX 34-91-5627518, http://www.cib.csic.es.

616.96 CZE
CESKA PARAZITOLOGICKA SPOLECNOST. ZPRAVY/CZECH PARASITOLOGY SOCIETY. REPORTS. Text in Czech. q. bk.rev. **Document type:** *Academic/Scholarly.* **Description:** Contains news of recent society activities and a calendar of related events within the Czech Republic and abroad.
Published by: Akademie Ved Ceske Republiky, Parazitologicky Ustav/Academy of Sciences of the Czech Republic, Institute of Parasitology, Branisovska 31, Ceske Budejovice, 37005, Czech Republic. TEL 420-387-775403, FAX 420-385-310388, oleg@paru.cas.cz, http://www.paru.cas.cz. Ed. Oleg Ditrich.

578.77 CZE
CESKE AKADEMIE VED. HYDROBIOLOGICKY USTAV. ANNUAL REPORT. Text in English. 1960. a. per issue exchange basis only. back issues avail. **Document type:** *Academic/Scholarly.* **Description:** Contains brief description of scientific results and other activities of the institute during a given year.
Former titles: Academy of Sciences of the Czech Republic. Hydrobiological Institute. Annual Report (1210-9649); (until 1991): Czechoslovak Academy of Sciences. Institute of Landscape Ecology. Section of Hydrobiology. Annual Report (0232-0533); (until 1983): Czechoslovak Academy of Sciences. Institute of Landscape Ecology. Hydrobiological Laboratory. Annual Report (1210-1338); (until 1980): Czechoslovak Academy of Sciences. Hydrobiological Laboratory. Annual Report (0139-8024)
Related titles: Online - full text ed.
Indexed: BiolAb.
Published by: Akademie Ved Ceske Republiky, Hydrobiologicky Ustav, Na Sadkach 7, Ceske Budejovice, 37005, Czech Republic. TEL 420-38-7775819, FAX 420-38-45718, TELEX 144 406 CSAC C, hbu@hbu.cas.cz, http://www.jcu.cz/~hbu. Ed. V Straskrabova. Circ: 750.

CESKO-SLOVENSKA PATOLOGIE A SOUDNI LEKARSTVI. see *MEDICAL SCIENCES*

570 LKA ISSN 0069-2379
CODEN: CYJBA2
➤ **CEYLON JOURNAL OF SCIENCE. BIOLOGICAL SCIENCES.** Text in English. 1957. a., latest vol.30. LKR 150, USD 16 (effective 2003). bk.rev. charts; illus. 70 p./no.; back issues avail.; reprints avail. **Document type:** *Journal, Academic/Scholarly.*
Media: Large Type.
Indexed: ASFA, AgBio, AgrForAb, BioCN&I, BiolAb, CPA, FCA, ForAb, HerbAb, HortAb, I&DA, IBR, IndVet, MLA-IB, MaizeAb, NutrAb, OrnHort, PBA, PGegResA, PGrRegA, PHN&I, ProtozoAb, RA&MP, RDA, RM&VM, RPP, RevApplEntom, RiceAb, S&F, SLSI, SoyAb, TriticAb, VetBull, WAE&RSA, WeedAb, ZooRec.
—CISTI, Linda Hall.
Published by: University of Peradeniya, P.O. Box 35, Peradeniya, Sri Lanka. librarian@pdn.ac.lk, http://www.pdn.ac.lk. Ed. N K B Adikaram. Circ: 300.

➤ **CHEM-BIO INFORMATICS JOURNAL.** see *CHEMISTRY—Computer Applications*

➤ **CHEMICAL BIOLOGY VIRTUAL JOURNAL.** see *CHEMISTRY*

➤ **CHEMICO-BIOLOGICAL INTERACTIONS.** see *ENVIRONMENTAL STUDIES—Toxicology And Environmental Safety*

▼ ➤ **CHEMISTRY & BIODIVERSITY.** see *CHEMISTRY*

➤ **CHEMISTRY & BIOLOGY.** see *CHEMISTRY*

➤ **CHEMISTRY AND ECOLOGY.** see *CHEMISTRY*

➤ **CHEMOECOLOGY;** evolutionary, mechanistic and environmental approaches to chemically-mediated interactions. see *CHEMISTRY—Organic Chemistry*

570 JPN ISSN 0385-0986
CHIBA SEIBUTSUSHI/BIOLOGICAL SOCIETY OF CHIBA. BULLETIN. Text in Japanese; Summaries in English, Japanese. 1948. s-a.
Published by: Chibaken Seibutsu Gakkai/Biological Society of Chiba, Chiba Daigaku Rigakubu, 1-33 Yayoi-cho, Inage-ku, Chiba-shi, 263-0022, Japan.

577 JPN ISSN 1345-4986
CHIBA UNIVERSITY. MARINE BIOSYSTEMS RESEARCH CENTER. ANNUAL REPORT. Text in Japanese. 1990. a. **Document type:** *Bulletin, Academic/Scholarly.*
Formerly (until 2000): Chiba Daigaku Rigakubu Kaiyo Seitaikei Kenkyu Senta Nenpo (0916-6025)
Indexed: ZooRec.
Published by: (Kaiyo Seitaikei Kenkyu Senta), Chiba Daigaku, Rigakubu/Chiba University, Marine Ecosystem Research Center, Amatsu-Kominato, Awa-gun, Chiba-shi, 299-5502, Japan. Circ: 300.

CHIHUAHUAN DESERT DISCOVERY. see *EARTH SCIENCES*

CHIHUAHUAN DESERT NEWSBRIEFS. see *EARTH SCIENCES*

CHINESE MEDICAL SCIENCES JOURNAL. see *MEDICAL SCIENCES*

570 ITA ISSN 0390-0037
QP84.6 CODEN: CBLGA2
CHRONOBIOLOGIA. Text in English. 1974. q. USD 180. bk.rev. abstr.; bibl.; illus. index. **Document type:** *Journal, Academic/Scholarly.*
Related titles: Microfiche ed.: (from PQC).
Indexed: ASFA, ApicAb, BiolAb, CIN, ChemAb, ChemTitl, CurCont, ExcerpMed, GenetAb, HGA, IndMed, MEDLINE, PsycholAb.
—CASDDS, GNLM, Infotrieve, KNAW, Linda Hall.
Published by: (International Society for Chronobiology USA), Casa Editrice Il Ponte, 17 Via de' Griffoni, Bologna, 40123, Italy. TEL 39-051-2968700, FAX 39-051-580919, ilponte@editriceilponte.com, http://www.editriceilponte.com. Circ: 6,000.

570 USA ISSN 0742-0528
QH527 CODEN: CHBIE4
➤ **CHRONOBIOLOGY INTERNATIONAL;** the journal of biological and medical rhythm research. Text in English. 1984. bi-m. GBP 624, USD 1,030 combined subscription to institutions print & online eds. (effective 2006). adv. charts; illus. reprint service avail. from PQC,PSC. **Document type:** *Journal, Academic/Scholarly.* **Description:** Publishes original research investigations, short communications, and commentaries in chronobiology and related disciplines.
Incorporates: Annual Review of Chronopharmacology. (0743-9539)
Related titles: Online - full text ed.: ISSN 1525-6073. GBP 593, USD 979 to institutions (effective 2006) (from EBSCO Publishing, O C L C Online Computer Library Center, Inc., Swets Information Services).
Indexed: AEA, ASCA, ASFA, AbHyg, AgBio, AnBeAb, AnBrAb, BIOBASE, BIOSIS Prev, BiolAb, CIN, CPA, ChemAb, ChemTitl, CurCont, DBA, DSA, EPB, EntAb, ExcerpMed, FCA, HortAb, IABS, ISR, IndMed, IndVet, Inpharma, MEDLINE, NSA, NucAcAb, NutrAb, PBA, PE&ON, PoultAb, ProtozoAb, PsycholAb, RA&MP, RPP, Reac, RefZh, RiceAb, SCI, SSCI, VetBull, WeedAb, ZooRec, e-psyche.
—BLDSC (3188.320000), CASDDS, CISTI, GNLM, IDS, IE, Infotrieve, ingenta, KNAW. **CCC.**
Published by: (International Society for Chronobiology), Taylor & Francis Inc. (Subsidiary of: Taylor & Francis Group), 325 Chestnut St, Ste 800, Philadelphia, PA 19016. TEL 215-625-8900, 800-354-1420, FAX 215-625-2940, info@taylorandfrancis.com, http://www.tandf.co.uk/journals/titles/07420528.asp, http://www.taylorandfrancis.com. Eds. Dr. Ludger Rensing, Dr. Michael H Slomensky. R&P Elaine Inverso. Adv. contact Mary Drabot. B&W page USD 600. Circ: 650.

B

570 BRA ISSN 1516-4993
QH301
CIENCIAS BIOLOGICAS E DO AMBIENTE. Text in Portuguese. 1999. q.
Indexed: ASFA, M&GPA.
Published by: Pontificia Universidade Catolica de Sao Paulo, Faculdade de Ciencias Biologicas, Rua Monte Alegre 984, Perdizes, Sao Paulo, Sao Paulo 05014-901, Brazil. TEL 55-11-36708000, http://www.pucsp.br.

CIMBEBASIA. MEMOIR. see *SCIENCES: COMPREHENSIVE WORKS*

578.77 ITA
CIVICA STAZIONE IDROBIOLOGICA DI MILANO. QUADERNI. Text in Italian; Summaries in English. 1970. irreg. free to researchers. bibl.; charts; illus. **Document type:** *Academic/Scholarly.*
Indexed: SFA, ZooRec.
Published by: Civica Stazione Idrobiologica di Milano, Via Gerolamo Gadio, 2, Milan, MI 20121, Italy. TEL 39-2-86462051, FAX 39-2-8690719, IATOMI@tin.it. Ed. Mauro Mariani. R&P Cristina Gilardi.

570 GBR ISSN 0748-3007
QH83 CODEN: CLADEC
➤ **CLADISTICS;** the international journal of the Willi Hennig Society. Text in English. 1986. bi-m. GBP 287 combined subscription in Europe to institutions print & online eds.; USD 531 combined subscription in the Americas to institutions & Caribbean (print & online eds.); GBP 316 combined subscription elsewhere to institutions print & online eds. (effective 2006). adv. reprints avail. **Document type:** *Journal, Academic/Scholarly.* **Description:** Covers theory, method, the philosophical aspects of systematics, and the role of systematic and evolutionary studies in the investigation of biogeographical and other general biological phenomena.
Related titles: Online - full text ed.: ISSN 1096-0031. GBP 273 in Europe to institutions; USD 504 in the Americas to institutions & Caribbean; GBP 300 elsewhere to institutions (effective 2006) (from Blackwell Synergy, EBSCO Publishing, Gale Group, IngentaConnect, O C L C Online Computer Library Center, Inc., ScienceDirect, Swets Information Services).
Indexed: ASCA, AgBio, Agr, B&BAb, BIOBASE, BIOSIS Prev, BiolAb, CurCont, EntAb, GEOBASE, GenetAb, HelmAb, HerbAb, ISR, PBA, PGegResA, ProtozoAb, RPP, RevApplEntom, SCI, SFA, ZooRec.
—BLDSC (3274.292500), CISTI, IDS, IE, Infotrieve, ingenta, Linda Hall. **CCC.**
Published by: (Willi Hennig Society), Blackwell Publishing Ltd., 9600 Garsington Rd, Oxford, OX4 2ZG, United Kingdom. TEL 44-1865-776868, FAX 44-1865-714591, customerservices@oxon.blackwellpublishing.com, http://www.blackwellpublishing.com/journals/CLA. Ed. Dr. James M Carpenter TEL 212-769-5611. Circ: 800.

➤ **CLINICAL ANATOMY.** see *MEDICAL SCIENCES*

571.3 USA ISSN 0962-8827
CODEN: CDYSEJ
➤ **CLINICAL DYSMORPHOLOGY.** Text in English. 1992. q. USD 206 to individuals; USD 685 to institutions (effective 2006). adv. bk.rev. illus. reprints avail. **Document type:** *Journal, Academic/Scholarly.* **Description:** Devoted to publishing reports of multiple congenital anomaly syndromes, original studies and review articles on etiology, clinical delineation, genetic mapping, and molecular embryology of birth defects.
Related titles: Online - full text ed.: (from EBSCO Publishing, O C L C Online Computer Library Center, Inc., Ovid Technologies, Inc., Swets Information Services).
Indexed: ASCA, BCI, CurCont, ExcerpMed, IndMed, Inpharma, MEDLINE, NSCI, PE&ON, Reac.
—BLDSC (3286.273700), CISTI, GNLM, IDS, IE, Infotrieve, ingenta, KNAW. **CCC.**
Published by: Lippincott Williams & Wilkins (Subsidiary of: Wolters Kluwer N.V.), 530 Walnut St, Philadelphia, PA 19106-3621. TEL 215-521-8300, FAX 215-521-8902, http://www.lww.com/product/?0962-8827. Eds. Dian Donnai, Jill Clayton-Smith, Michael Baraitser. Circ: 296. **Subscr. to:** PO Box 1620, Hagerstown, MD 21741. TEL 800-777-2295, FAX 301-824-7390.

B

➤ CLINICAL INVESTIGATOR NEWS. see *PHARMACY AND PHARMACOLOGY*

➤ CLINICAL SCIENCE. see *MEDICAL SCIENCES*

016.574   USA   ISSN 0084-8824
COLD SPRING HARBOR LABORATORY. ABSTRACTS OF
PAPERS PRESENTED AT MEETINGS. Text in English. irreg.
(8-13/yr.). price varies. **Document type:** *Abstract/Index.*
—BLDSC (0566.578000). **CCC.**
Published by: Cold Spring Harbor Laboratory Press, Publications
Department, 500 Sunnyside Blvd., Woodbury, NY 11797-2924.
TEL 516-422-4100, 800-843-4388, FAX 516-422-4097,
cshpress@cshl.edu, http://www.cshl.org. Circ: (controlled)

016.524   USA
COLD SPRING HARBOR LABORATORY. ABSTRACTS OF
PAPERS PRESENTED AT THE MEETING ON
PROTEOLYSIS & BIOLOGICAL CONTROL. Text in English.
irreg. **Document type:** *Abstract/Index.*
—BLDSC (0566.578773).
Published by: Cold Spring Harbor Laboratory Press, Publications
Department, 500 Sunnyside Blvd., Woodbury, NY 11797-2924.
TEL 516-422-4100, 800-843-4388, FAX 516-422-4097,
cshpress@cshl.edu, http://www.cshl.org.

570   USA   ISSN 0069-5009
COLD SPRING HARBOR LABORATORY. ANNUAL REPORT.
Text in English. 1924. a. **Document type:** *Corporate.*
Indexed: EnvAb.
Published by: Cold Spring Harbor Laboratory Press, Publications
Department, 500 Sunnyside Blvd., Woodbury, NY 11797-2924.
TEL 516-422-4100, 800-843-4388, FAX 516-422-4097,
cshpress@cshl.edu, http://www.cshl.org. Circ: (controlled).

570   USA   ISSN 0091-7451
QH301   CODEN: CSHSAZ
➤ COLD SPRING HARBOR LABORATORY. SYMPOSIA ON
QUANTITATIVE BIOLOGY. Text in English. 1933. a. price
varies. back issues avail. **Document type:** *Proceedings,
Academic/Scholarly.*
Indexed: ASCA, ASFA, AgBio, Agr, AnBrAb, B&AI, BBCI,
BIOBASE, BIOSIS Prev, BiolAb, CIN, ChemAb, ChemTitl,
CurCont, DentInd, ESPM, ExcerpMed, GenetAb, IABS, ISR,
IndMed, Inpharma, MEDLINE, MaizeAb, NemAb, PBA,
PE&ON, PollutAb, Reac, SCI, SFA, ZooRec.
—BLDSC (3296.000000), CASDDS, CISTI, GNLM, IDS, IE,
Infotrieve, ingenta, KNAW, Linda Hall. **CCC.**
Published by: Cold Spring Harbor Laboratory Press, Publications
Department, 500 Sunnyside Blvd., Woodbury, NY 11797-2924.
TEL 516-422-4100, 800-843-4388, FAX 516-422-4097,
cshpress@cshl.edu, http://www.cshl.org.

570   USA   ISSN 0270-1847
                                 CODEN: CHMSDK
COLD SPRING HARBOR MONOGRAPH SERIES. Text in
English. 1970. irreg. price varies. illus. index. **Document type:**
Monographic series, Academic/Scholarly.
Indexed: ASFA, BIOSIS Prev, BiolAb, CIN, ChemAb, ChemTitl,
ESPM, SCI.
—BLDSC (3295.855000), CASDDS, CISTI, IE, ingenta, KNAW.
CCC.
Published by: Cold Spring Harbor Laboratory Press, Publications
Department, 500 Sunnyside Blvd., Woodbury, NY 11797-2924.
TEL 516-422-4100, 800-843-4388, FAX 516-422-4097,
cshpress@cshl.edu, http://www.cshl.org.

570   ESP
COLECCION CIENCIAS BIOLOGICAS. Text in Spanish. 1974.
irreg. price varies. **Document type:** *Academic/Scholarly.*
Published by: (Universidad de Navarra, Facultad de Ciencias,
Universidad de Navarra), Ediciones Universidad de Navarra
S.A., Pza. Los Sauces, 1-2, Baranain, (Navarra) 31010,
Spain. TEL 34-948-256850, FAX 34-948-256854,
ensaidi@abc.ibernet.com, http://www.unav.es.

570   FRA   ISSN 0338-263X
COLLECTION DE BIOLOGIE EVOLUTIVE. Text in French. 1973.
irreg. **Document type:** *Monographic series,
Academic/Scholarly.*
Indexed: BIOSIS Prev.
—CISTI.
Published by: Masson Editeur (Subsidiary of: Groupe Medimedia
France), 21 Rue Camille Desmoulins, Issy les Moulineaux,
92789 Cedex 9, France. TEL 33-1-73281634, FAX
33-1-73281649, infos@masson.fr, http://www.masson.fr.

570   USA   ISSN 0069-6285
➤ COLUMBIA BIOLOGICAL SERIES. Text in English. 1910.
irreg., latest vol.24, 1968. **Document type:** *Monographic
series, Academic/Scholarly.*
Published by: Columbia University Press, 61 W 62nd St, New
York, NY 10023. TEL 212-666-1000. Ed. Kate Witterberg.
R&P Lisa Simmars.

572.8   USA   ISSN 1549-2524
➤ COLUMBIA SERIES IN MOLECULAR BIOLOGY. Text in
English. irreg., latest 1976. price varies. **Document type:**
Monographic series, Academic/Scholarly.

Published by: Columbia University Press, 61 W 62nd St, New
York, NY 10023. TEL 212-666-1000. Ed. Kate Witterberg.
R&P Lisa Simmars.

➤ COMMENT; a funding first publication. see *MEDICAL
SCIENCES*

578.77   MCO   ISSN 0373-434X
                                 CODEN: CIRPB7
COMMISSION INTERNATIONALE POUR L'EXPLOITATION
SCIENTIFIQUE DE LA MER MEDITERRANEE. RAPPORT
DU CONGRES. Text in French, English. irreg.
Indexed: ASFA, ESPM, OceAb, PollutAb, ZooRec.
Published by: International Commission for the Scientific
Exploration of the Mediterranean Sea/Commission
Internationale pour l'Exploitation Scientifique de la Mer
Mediterranee, 16 Boulevard de Suisse, Monte Carlo, 98000,
Monaco.

COMMUNITY PLANT VARIETY OFFICE. ANNUAL REPORT. see
ENVIRONMENTAL STUDIES

570   CHE   ISSN 1424-8492
                                 CODEN: COMPCP
▼ ➤ COMPLEXUS; modelling and understanding functional
interactions in life sciences. Text in English. 2003. q. CHF 907
in Europe to institutions; CHF 920.60 elsewhere to institutions;
CHF 977 combined subscription in Europe to institutions print
& online eds.; CHF 990.60 combined subscription elsewhere
to institutions print & online eds. (effective 2006). adv.
Document type: *Journal, Academic/Scholarly.* **Description:**
Aims to catalyze scientific collaboration toward greater
understanding of complex biological systems in the
post-genome era.
Related titles: Online - full text ed.: ISSN 1424-8506. 2003. CHF
879 to institutions (effective 2006) (from EBSCO Publishing; O
C L C Online Computer Library Center, Inc., Swets
Information Services).
Indexed: BiolAb, ExcerpMed.
—BLDSC (3364.585820), CISTI, IE, Infotrieve, ingenta, Linda
Hall. **CCC.**
Published by: S. Karger AG, Allschwilerstr 10, Basel, 4009,
Switzerland. TEL 41-61-3061111, FAX 41-61-3061234,
complexus@karger.ch, karger@karger.ch, http://
www.karger.com/CPU, http://www.karger.ch. Ed. H. Atlan. adv.:
page USD 1,185.

570   NLD   ISSN 1574-0404
COMPUTING LETTERS. Text in English. q. USD 281 in the
Americas to institutions; EUR 225 elsewhere to institutions
(effective 2006).
Media: Online - full content. **Related titles:** Online - full text ed.:
(from Gale Group, IngentaConnect).
—IE.
Published by: V S P (Subsidiary of: Brill Academic Publishers),
Brill Academic Publishers, PO Box 9000, Leiden, 2300 PA,
Netherlands. TEL 31-71-5353500, FAX 31-71-5317532,
http://www.brill.nl/m_catalogue_sub6_id23019.htm,
http://www.vsppub.com. Ed. T E Simos. **Dist. by:** Extenza -
Turpin, Pegasus Dr, Stratton Business Park, Biggleswade,
Beds SG18 8TQ, United Kingdom. TEL 44-1767-604954, FAX
44-1767-601640, marketing@extenza-turpin.com,
http://www.extenza-turpin.com.

594   GBR   ISSN 0144-9826
CONCHOLOGICAL SOCIETY SPECIAL PUBLICATION. Text in
English. 1980. irreg., latest vol.2, 1998. price varies.
Document type: *Monographic series, Academic/Scholarly.*
Published by: Conchological Society of Great Britain and Ireland,
c/o Mr. M.D. Weideli, 35 Bartlemy Rd, Newbury, Berks RG14
6LD, United Kingdom. TEL 44-1635-42190, FAX
44-1635-820904, membership@conchsoc.org,
Mike_Weideli@compuserve.com, http://www.conchsoc.org. Ed.
P G Oliver.

CONSEQUENCES; the nature and implications of environmental
change. see *ENVIRONMENTAL STUDIES*

CONSERVATION BIOLOGY. see *CONSERVATION*

CONSERVATION BIOLOGY SERIES. see *CONSERVATION*

CONSERVATION IN PRACTICE. see *CONSERVATION*

CONSERVATION SCIENCE WESTERN AUSTRALIA. see
CONSERVATION

570   USA   ISSN 0160-5313
QH301   CODEN: CBGMDW
CONTRIBUTIONS IN BIOLOGY AND GEOLOGY. Text in English.
1974. irreg. (approx. 3/yr.).
Indexed: BIOSIS Prev, BiolAb, SFA, WildRev, ZooRec.
—CISTI, Linda Hall.
Published by: Milwaukee Public Museum, 800 W Wells St,
Milwaukee, WI 53233. TEL 414-278-2710, FAX 414-223-1396.
Ed. Rodney M Watkins. Circ: 1,500.

551.46   USA   ISSN 0082-3449
                                 CODEN: CMSCAY
➤ CONTRIBUTIONS IN MARINE SCIENCE. Text in English.
1945. a. USD 30 to individuals; USD 80 to libraries (effective
2000). back issues avail. **Document type:** *Monographic
series, Academic/Scholarly.* **Description:** Focuses on
monographs, reviews, and lengthy taxonomic keys relevant to
the Gulf of Mexico. These lengthy documents are often
difficult to publish but serve a valuable scientific role. A unique
publication for the Gulf of Mexico and Southern United States.
Formerly (until 1967): University of Texas. Institute of Marine
Science. Publications (0096-431X)
Indexed: ASFA, B&AI, BIOSIS Prev, BiolAb, ChemAb, ESPM,
ExcerpMed, ISR, NutrAb, OceAb, SCI, SFA, WildRev, ZooRec.
—CASDDS, CISTI, Linda Hall.
Published by: University of Texas at Austin, Marine Science
Institute, 750 Channelview Dr, Port Aransas, TX 78373-5015.
TEL 361-749-6711, FAX 361-749-6777,
cms@utmsi.utexas.edu, http://www.utmsi.utexas.edu. Eds.
Barbara Dorf TEL 361-749-6732, Tracy Villareal. Circ: 1,200
(controlled).

333.9   AUS   ISSN 1446-7852
COOPERATIVE RESEARCH CENTRE FOR FRESHWATER
ECOLOGY. IDENTIFICATION AND ECOLOGY GUIDE. Text
in English. 1994. irreg.
Formerly (until 2002): Cooperative Research Centre for
Freshwater Ecology. Identification Guide (1321-280X)
Indexed: ZooRec.
Published by: Cooperative Research Centre for Freshwater
Ecology, University of Canberra, Canberra, ACT, Australia.

CORNELL FOCUS. see *AGRICULTURE*

CORNELL UNIVERSITY. NEW YORK STATE COLLEGE OF
AGRICULTURE AND LIFE SCIENCES. BIOMETRICS UNIT.
ANNUAL REPORT. see *BIOLOGY—Abstracting,
Bibliographies, Statistics*

CREATION; journal of the creation science movement. see
RELIGIONS AND THEOLOGY

CRITICAL REVIEWS IN NEUROBIOLOGY. see *MEDICAL
SCIENCES—Psychiatry And Neurology*

570   ESP   ISSN 0211-5700
QH301
CUADERNOS DE INVESTIGACION BIOLOGICA. Text in
Spanish. 1979. a. **Document type:** *Academic/Scholarly.*
Indexed: IECT, ZooRec.
—CINDOC, CISTI.
Published by: (Laboratorio de Citologia e Histologia), Universidad
del Pais Vasco, Facultad de Ciencias, Apartado 1397, Bilbao,
Vizcaya 48080, Spain. TEL 34-4-4647700 ext. 2148, FAX
34-4-4801314, luzedito@lg.ehu.es. Ed. Jesus Moya. Pub.
Juan J Rodriguez.

CURRENT AWARENESS IN BIOLOGICAL SCIENCES. see
BIOLOGY—Abstracting, Bibliographies, Statistics

CURRENT BIBLIOGRAPHIES ON SCIENCE AND
TECHNOLOGY: BIOLOGY, PHARMACY AND FOOD
SCIENCE. see *BIOLOGY—Abstracting, Bibliographies,
Statistics*

CURRENT BIBLIOGRAPHY ON SCIENCE AND TECHNOLOGY:
LIFE SCIENCES/KAGAKU GIJUTSU BUNKEN SOKUHO.
RAIFUSAIENSU HEN. see *BIOLOGY—Abstracting,
Bibliographies, Statistics*

CURRENT BIOLOGY. see *BIOLOGY—Abstracting, Bibliographies,
Statistics*

CURRENT CONTENTS: LIFE SCIENCES. see
BIOLOGY—Abstracting, Bibliographies, Statistics

572.8   USA
CURRENT PROTOCOLS IN MOLECULAR BIOLOGY. Text in
English. 4 base vols. plus q. updates. USD 845 combined
subscription to institutions base vol. & updates; USD 465
renewals to institutions (effective 2006). **Document type:**
Academic/Scholarly.
Related titles: CD-ROM ed.: USD 820 combined subscription to
institutions base vol. & updates; USD 450 renewals to
institutions (effective 2006).
—BLDSC (3501.540000).
Published by: John Wiley & Sons, Inc., 111 River St, Hoboken,
NJ 07030-5774. TEL 201-748-6000, 800-825-7550, FAX
201-748-5915, protocol@wiley.com, http://www.does.org/
masterli/cpmb.html, http://www.wiley.com. **Subscr. to:** John
Wiley & Sons Ltd., The Atrium, Southern Gate, Chichester,
West Sussex PO19 8SQ, United Kingdom. TEL
44-1243-779777, FAX 44-1243-775878,
cs-journals@wiley.co.uk.

CURRENT RESEARCH IN BRITAIN. BIOLOGICAL SCIENCES.
see *BIOLOGY—Abstracting, Bibliographies, Statistics*

570   USA   ISSN 0070-2137
QH573   CODEN: CTCRAE
➤ **CURRENT TOPICS IN CELLULAR REGULATION.** Text in English. 1969. irreg., latest vol.36, 2000. USD 139.95 per vol. vol.36 (effective 2004). reprint service avail. from ISI. **Document type:** *Academic/Scholarly.* **Description:** Reviews the progress being made in those specialized areas of study that have undergone substantial development.
Indexed: ASCA, BIOSIS Prev, BiolAb, CIN, ChemAb, ChemTitl, ISR, IndMed, MEDLINE, SCI.
—BLDSC (3504.875000), CASDDS, CISTI, GNLM, IE, ingenta, Linda Hall. **CCC.**
Published by: Academic Press (Subsidiary of: Elsevier Science & Technology), 525 B St, Ste 1900, San Diego, CA 92101-4495. TEL 619-231-6616, 800-894-3434, apsubs@acad.com, http://www.academicpress.com. Eds. Bernard L Horecker, Earl R Stadtman.

570   USA   ISSN 0070-2153
QL951   CODEN: CTDBA5
➤ **CURRENT TOPICS IN DEVELOPMENTAL BIOLOGY.** Text in English. 1966. irreg., latest vol.54, 2003. USD 149.95 vol.60 (effective 2004). reprint service avail. from ISI. **Document type:** *Monographic series, Academic/Scholarly.* **Description:** Provides a comprehensive survey of the major topics in the field of developmental biology.
Related titles: Online - full text ed.: ISSN 1557-8933 (from ScienceDirect).
Indexed: ASCA, ASFA, AnBrAb, BBCI, BIOSIS Prev, BiolAb, CIN, CPA, ChemAb, ChemTitl, ESPM, ISR, IndMed, MEDLINE, NutrAb, PBA, PoultAb, SCI, SFA, SeedAb, WildRev, ZooRec.
—BLDSC (3504.880000), CASDDS, CISTI, GNLM, IE, Infotrieve, ingenta, Linda Hall. **CCC.**
Published by: Academic Press (Subsidiary of: Elsevier Science & Technology), 525 B St, Ste 1900, San Diego, CA 92101-4495. apsubs@acad.com, http://www.academicpress.com. Ed. A A Moscona.

➤ **CURRENT TOPICS IN PATHOLOGY.** see *MEDICAL SCIENCES*

570   IND   ISSN 0378-7540
     CODEN: CTSCDI
CURRENT TRENDS IN LIFE SCIENCES; recent researches in cold water fisheries. Text in English. irreg., latest vol.21, 1996. price varies. **Document type:** *Monographic series.*
Indexed: BiolAb, CIN, ChemAb, ChemTitl, CurCont, ZooRec.
—BLDSC (3504.945000), CASDDS, CISTI. **CCC.**
Published by: Today and Tomorrow's Printers & Publishers, 24 B-5 Desh Bandhu Gupta Rd., Karol Bagh, New Delhi, 110 005, India. TEL 5721928. Ed. K L Sehgal. **Dist. in U.S. by:** Scholarly Publications, 2825 Wilcrest Dr, Ste 255, Houston, TX 77042. TEL 713-781-0070.

577   AUS
➤ **CURTIN UNIVERSITY. SCHOOL OF ENVIRONMENTAL BIOLOGY. BULLETIN.** Text in English. 1980. irreg., latest vol.22, 2002. free (effective 2003). back issues avail. **Document type:** *Bulletin, Academic/Scholarly.*
Former titles: Curtin University. School of Biology. Bulletin; (until 1981): Western Australian Institute of Technology. Department of Biology. Bulletin (0158-3301)
Indexed: ASFA, ZooRec.
Published by: Curtin University, Department of Environmental Biology, Bentley, W.A., Australia. TEL 61-8-92667041, FAX 61-8-92662495. Ed., R&P Jonathan D Majer. Circ: 150.

578.77   CAN
DALHOUSIE UNIVERSITY. AQUATRON LABORATORY. BIENNIAL REPORT. Text in English. biennial.
Published by: Dalhousie University, Aquatron Laboratory, Life Sciences Centre, Halifax, NS B3H 4J1, Canada. TEL 902-494-3874, aquatron@dal.ca, http://www.dal.ca/~aquatron/pages/mainpage.htm.

DANESHMAND. see *ENGINEERING*

550 570   DEU   ISSN 0366-872X
     CODEN: DCNNAH
DECHENIANA. Text in English, German. 1943. a. price varies. **Document type:** *Monographic series, Academic/Scholarly.*
Formed by the merger of (1937-1943): Decheniana. A. Geologische Abteilung (0724-4541); (1937-1943): Decheniana. B. Biologische Abteilung (0724-455X)
Related titles: ♦ Supplement(s): Decheniana-Beihefte (Bonn). ISSN 0416-833X.
Indexed: ESPM, ZooRec.
—Linda Hall.
Published by: Naturhistorischer Verein, Nussallee 15A, Bonn, 53115, Germany. TEL 49-228-735525, FAX 49-228-692377, nhv@uni-bonn.de, http://www.nhv.uni-bonn.de/publik/jahrband.htm.

570 550   DEU   ISSN 0416-833X
     CODEN: DEBEAC
DECHENIANA-BEIHEFTE (BONN). Text in German; Summaries in English. 1955. irreg., latest vol.38, 1999. price varies. back issues avail. **Document type:** *Monographic series, Academic/Scholarly.*
Related titles: ♦ Supplement to: Decheniana. ISSN 0366-872X.
Indexed: ASFA, ZooRec.
—CISTI, Linda Hall.

Published by: Naturhistorischer Verein, Nussallee 15A, Bonn, 53115, Germany. TEL 49-228-735525. Ed., R&P Bodo Moeseler.

DEEP-SEA RESEARCH. PART 1: OCEANOGRAPHIC RESEARCH PAPERS. see *EARTH SCIENCES— Oceanography*

570   ITA   ISSN 0416-928X
     CODEN: DLPNAM
DELPINOA. Text in Italian; Summaries in English. 1959. irreg. per issue exchange basis. bibl.; charts; illus.
Indexed: BiolAb.
Published by: Universita degli Studi di Napoli, Dipartimento di Biologia Vegetale, Via Foria, 223, Naples, NA 80139, Italy. Ed. Giuseppe Caputo. Circ: 650.

570   AUT   ISSN 1608-8700
QL1
DENISIA. Text in English, German; Summaries in English. 2001. irreg., latest vol.7, 2003. price varies. charts; illus. Index. back issues avail. **Document type:** *Monographic series, Academic/Scholarly.* **Description:** Contains biological monographs, proceedings, articles and exhibition descriptions.
Indexed: BiolAb, ZooRec.
Published by: Oberoesterreichisches Landesmuseum, Biologiezentrum, J.-W.-Klein-Str 73, Linz, 4040, Austria. TEL 43-732-759733, FAX 43-732-75973399, bio-linz@landesmuseum-linz.ac.at, http://www.biologiezentrum.at. R&P Gerhard Aubrecht. Circ: 500 (controlled).

DENMARK. MINISTERIET FOR FOEDEVARER, LANDBRUG OG FISKERI. DANMARKS FISKERIUNDERSOEGELSER. AARSBERETNING. see *FISH AND FISHERIES*

570   DNK   ISSN 1602-0103
DENMARK. RISOE NATIONAL LABORATORY. PLANT RESEARCH DEPARTMENT. ANNUAL REPORT. Text in English. 1991. a. free (effective 2003). **Document type:** *Academic/Scholarly.*
Former titles (until 2002): Denmark. Risoe National Laboratory. Plant Biology and Biogeochemistry Department. Annual Report (1397-8977); (until 1997): Denmark. Risoe National Laboratory. Environmental Science and Technology Department. Annual Report (0906-8090)
Related titles: Online - full content ed.; ♦ Series of: Denmark. Forskningscenter Risoe. Risoe-R. ISSN 0106-2840.
Published by: Forskningscenter Risoe/Risoe National Laboratory, Frederiksborgvej 399, PO Box 49, Roskilde, 4000, Denmark. TEL 45-46-774677, FAX 45-46-775688, risoe@risoe.dk, http://www.risoe.dk/rispubl/PBK/plant.htm.

DEUTSCHE GESELLSCHAFT FUER PATHOLOGIE. VERHANDLUNGEN. see *MEDICAL SCIENCES*

DEVELOPING WORLD BIOETHICS. see *PHILOSOPHY*

571.3   GBR   ISSN 0950-1991
QL951   CODEN: DEVPED
➤ **DEVELOPMENT (CAMBRIDGE).** Text in English. 1953. s-m. USD 555 in North America to individuals; EUR 498 in Europe to individuals eurozone; GBP 327 to individuals in the UK & elsewhere; USD 2,695 in North America to institutions; EUR 2,440 in Europe to institutions eurozone; GBP 1,605 to institutions in the UK & elsewhere; USD 700 combined subscription in North America to individuals print & online; EUR 632 combined subscription in Europe to individuals eurozone; print & online; GBP 415 combined subscription to individuals in the UK & elsewhere; print & online; USD 3,130 combined subscription in North America to institutions print & online; EUR 2,840 combined subscription in Europe to institutions eurozone; print & online; GBP 1,865 combined subscription to institutions in the UK & elsewhere; print & online (effective 2005). adv. abstr.; bibl.; illus. index. back issues avail.; reprints avail. **Document type:** *Journal, Academic/Scholarly.* **Description:** Focuses on experimental studies of genetic, molecular and cellular aspects of animal and plant development.
Formerly (until 1986): Journal of Embryology and Experimental Morphology (0022-0752)
Related titles: Online - full text ed.: ISSN 1477-9129. USD 150 in North America to individuals; EUR 134 in Europe to individuals eurozone; GBP 89 to individuals in the UK & elsewhere; USD 2,375 in North America to institutions; EUR 2,152 in Europe to institutions eurozone; GBP 1,415 to institutions in the UK & elsewhere (effective 2005) (from EBSCO Publishing, HighWire Press); Supplement(s): Development. Supplement. ISSN 1351-6531. 1990.
Indexed: ASFA, AbHyg, AgBio, AnBrAb, B&AI, B&BAb, BIOBASE, BIOSIS Prev, BiolAb, CIN, CPA, CTA, ChemAb, ChemTitl, CurCont, DSA, DentInd, EntAb, ExcerpMed, FCA, ForAb, GenetAb, HGA, HelmAb, HortAb, IABS, ISR, IndMed, IndVet, MEDLINE, MaizeAb, NSA, NemAb, PBA, PGegResA, PGrRegA, RevApplEntom, RiceAb, S&F, SCI, SFA, SeedAb, VetBull, WeedAb, WildRev, ZooRec.
—BLDSC (3578.598000), CASDDS, CISTI, GNLM, IE, Infotrieve, ingenta, Linda Hall.

Published by: The Company of Biologists Ltd., Bidder Building, 140 Cowley Rd, Cambridge, CB4 4DL, United Kingdom. TEL 44-1223-426164, FAX 44-1223-423353, sales@biologists.com, http://dev.biologists.org, http://www.biologists.com/development. Ed. Dr. Jim Smith. R&P Dr. Jane Alfred. Adv. contact Miss Amanda Sheppardson. Circ: 2,700.

571.3   DEU   ISSN 0949-944X
QL951   CODEN: DGEVFT
➤ **DEVELOPMENT, GENES AND EVOLUTION.** Text in English. 1894. m. EUR 778 combined subscription to institutions print & online eds. (effective 2005). adv. bibl.; charts; illus. index. back issues avail.; reprint service avail. from ISI. **Document type:** *Journal, Academic/Scholarly.* **Description:** Reports on experimental work at the systemic, cellular and molecular levels in the field of animal and plant systems.
Former titles (until 1996): Roux's Archives of Developmental Biology (0930-035X); (until 1986): Wilhelm Roux's Archives of Developmental Biology (0340-0794); Roux' Archiv fuer Entwicklungsmechanik der Organismen (0043-5546)
Related titles: Microform ed.: (from PQC); Online - full text ed.: ISSN 1432-041X (from EBSCO Publishing, Springer LINK, Swets Information Services).
Indexed: ASCA, ASFA, AgBio, AnBrAb, B&BAb, BIOBASE, BIOSIS Prev, BioCN&I, BiolAb, CIN, CPA, CTA, ChemAb, ChemTitl, CurCont, ESPM, EntAb, ExcerpMed, GenetAb, HGA, HelmAb, HortAb, ISR, IndMed, IndVet, Inpharma, MBA, MEDLINE, MaizeAb, NSCI, NemAb, OrnHort, PBA, PE&ON, PGegResA, PHN&I, PoultAb, ProtozoAb, Reac, RevApplEntom, RiceAb, SCI, SFA, SeedAb, SoyAb, WeedAb, WildRev, ZooRec.
—BLDSC (3579.034000), CASDDS, CISTI, GNLM, IDS, IE, Infotrieve, ingenta, Linda Hall. **CCC.**
Published by: (European Developmental Biology Organization, Executive Board), Springer-Verlag (Subsidiary of: Springer Science+Business Media), Tiergartenstr 17, Heidelberg, 69121, Germany. TEL 49-6221-3450, FAX 49-6221-345229, http://link.springer.de/link/service/journals/00427/. Ed. Dr. Diethard Tautz TEL 49-221-4702465. Adv. contact Stephan Kroeck TEL 49-30-827875739. **Subscr. in the Americas to:** Springer-Verlag New York, Inc., Journal Fulfillment, PO Box 2485, Secaucus, NJ 07096-2485. TEL 800-777-4643, 201-348-4033, FAX 201-348-4505, journals@springer-ny.com, http://www.springer-ny.com; **Subscr. to:** Springer GmbH Auslieferungsgesellschaft, Haberstr 7, Heidelberg 69126, Germany. TEL 49-6221-345-0, FAX 49-6221-345-4229, subscriptions@springer.de.

570   AUS   ISSN 0012-1592
     CODEN: DGDFA5
➤ **DEVELOPMENT, GROWTH AND DIFFERENTIATION/ HASSEI, SEICHO, BUNKA.** Text in English. 1950. 9/yr. USD 291 combined subscription in the Americas to individuals in Caribbean, print & online eds.; EUR 270 combined subscription in Europe to individuals print & online eds.; GBP 180 combined subscription elsewhere to individuals print & online eds.; USD 1,079 combined subscription in the Americas to institutions & Caribbean, print & online eds.; GBP 666 combined subscription elsewhere to institutions print & online eds. (effective 2006). adv. bibl.; charts; illus. back issues avail. **Document type:** *Journal, Academic/Scholarly.* **Description:** Covers developmental phenomena for all types of organisms, including plants and microorganisms. Focus is biochemical and analytical.
Formerly (until 1959): Embryologia
Related titles: Online - full text ed.: ISSN 1440-169X. USD 1,025 in the Americas to institutions & Caribbean; GBP 633 elsewhere to institutions (effective 2006) (from Blackwell Synergy, EBSCO Publishing, Gale Group, IngentaConnect, O C L C Online Computer Library Center, Inc., Swets Information Services).
Indexed: ASCA, ASFA, AgBio, Agr, AnBrAb, B&BAb, BIOBASE, BIOSIS Prev, BiolAb, CIN, ChemAb, ChemTitl, CurCont, DSA, EntAb, ExcerpMed, GenetAb, HGA, INIS AtomInd, ISR, IndMed, Inpharma, MEDLINE, NSA, NemAb, PE&ON, PoultAb, Reac, RefZh, RevApplEntom, SCI, SFA, ZooRec.
—BLDSC (3579.035000), CASDDS, CISTI, GNLM, IDS, IE, Infotrieve, ingenta, Linda Hall. **CCC.**
Published by: (Japanese Society of Developmental Biologists JPN), Blackwell Publishing Asia (Subsidiary of: Blackwell Publishing Ltd.), 550 Swanston St, Carlton South, VIC 3053, Australia. TEL 61-383591011, FAX 61-383591120, http://www.blackwellpublishing.com/journals/DGD. Ed. Sadao Yasugi. adv.: B&W page AUD 1,243, color page AUD 2,497; 210 x 275. Circ: 1,850. **Subscr. to:** PO Box 378, Carlton South, VIC 3053, Australia.

574   CHN   ISSN 1004-6453
DEVELOPMENTAL & REPRODUCTIVE BIOLOGY. Text in English. 1992. s-a. **Document type:** *Journal, Academic/Scholarly.*
Related titles: Online - full text ed.: (from East View Information Services); Print ed.: (from WanFang Data Corp.).
Published by: Zhongguo Kexueyuan, Yichuan yu Fayu Shengwu Yangjiusuo/Chinese Academy of Sciences, Institute of Genetics and Developmental Biology, 917 Building, Datun Road, Andingmenwai, Beijing, 100101, China. TEL 86-10-64889776, wangwx@263.net, yphuang@genetics.ac.cn, http://fyyszswxxb-e.periodicals.net.cn/default.html, http://www.genetics.ac.cn/.

B

570 USA ISSN 0012-1606
QL951 CODEN: DEBIAO
➤ **DEVELOPMENTAL BIOLOGY.** Text in English. 1959. 24/yr. EUR 534 in Europe to individuals; JPY 55,600 in Japan to individuals; USD 463 to individuals except Europe and Japan; EUR 7,835 in Europe to institutions; JPY 818,200 in Japan to institutions; USD 5,979 to institutions except Europe and Japan; EUR 438 in Europe to students; JPY 45,700 in Japan to students; USD 381 to students except Europe and Japan (effective 2006). adv. charts; illus. index every 6 mos. back issues avail.; reprints avail. **Document type:** *Journal, Academic/Scholarly.* **Description:** Publishes original analytical research on mechanisms of development, differentiation, growth, regulation, and tissue repair in plants and animals at the molecular, cellular, and genetic levels.
Related titles: Online - full text ed.: ISSN 1095-564X. USD 6,308 (effective 2002) (from EBSCO Publishing, Gale Group, IngentaConnect, O C L C Online Computer Library Center, Inc., ScienceDirect, Swets Information Services).
Indexed: ASCA, ASFA, AgBio, Agr, AnBrAb, B&AI, B&BAb, BIOBASE, BIOSIS Prev, BibAg, BiolAb, CIN, CPA, CTA, ChemAb, ChemTitl, ChemoAb, CurCont, DSA, DentInd, EntAb, ExcerpMed, FCA, GSI, GenetAb, HGA, HelmAb, HortAb, IABS, ISR, IndMed, IndVet, Inpharma, MBA, MEDLINE, MaizeAb, NSA, NSCI, NemAb, NutrAb, OrnHort, PBA, PGegResA, PGrRegA, PN&I, PoultAb, RA&MP, RM&VM, Reac, RefZh, RevApplEntom, RiceAb, S&F, SCI, SFA, SeedAb, SoyAb, TriticAb, VetBull, WeedAb, WildRev, ZooRec.
—BLDSC (3579.051900), CASDDS, CISTI, GNLM, IDS, IE, Infotrieve, ingenta, Linda Hall. **CCC.**
Published by: Academic Press (Subsidiary of: Elsevier Science & Technology), 525 B St, Ste 1900, San Diego, CA 92101-4495. TEL 619-231-6616, 800-894-3434, apsubs@acad.com, http://www.elsevier.com/locate/ydbio, http://www.academicpress.com. Ed. Dr. Eric N Olson.

571.8 611 USA ISSN 1058-8388
QL801 CODEN: DEDYEI
➤ **DEVELOPMENTAL DYNAMICS.** Text in English. 1901. m. USD 4,395 domestic to institutions; USD 4,539 in Canada & Mexico to institutions; USD 4,623 elsewhere to institutions; USD 4,835 combined subscription domestic to institutions print & online eds.; USD 4,979 combined subscription in Canada & Mexico to institutions print & online eds.; USD 5,063 combined subscription elsewhere to institutions print & online eds. (effective 2006). adv. bk.rev. abstr.; bibl.; charts; illus. back issues avail.; reprints avail. **Document type:** *Journal, Academic/Scholarly.* **Description:** Provides a focus for communication among developmental biologists who study the emergence of form during animal development.
Formerly: American Journal of Anatomy (0002-9106)
Related titles: Microfiche ed.: (from IDC); Microform ed.: (from PMC, PQC, SWZ); Online - full content ed.: ISSN 1097-0177. USD 4,395 to institutions (effective 2006); Online - full text ed.: (from EBSCO Publishing, Swets Information Services, Wiley InterScience).
Indexed: ASCA, AbAn, AgBio, AnBrAb, BIOBASE, BIOSIS Prev, BiolAb, CIN, ChemAb, ChemTitl, CurCont, DSA, DentInd, ESPM, ExcerpMed, FoVS&M, GenetAb, IABS, ISR, IndMed, IndVet, Inpharma, MEDLINE, NSCI, NemAb, NutrAb, PN&I, PoultAb, Reac, RefZh, S&F, SAA, SCI, SFA, SeedAb, VetBull, WildRev, ZooRec.
—BLDSC (3579.054470), CASDDS, CISTI, GNLM, IDS, IE, Infotrieve, ingenta, Linda Hall. **CCC.**
Published by: John Wiley & Sons, Inc., 111 River St, Hoboken, NJ 07030-5774. TEL 201-748-6000, FAX 201-748-5915, uscs-wis@wiley.com, http://www3.interscience.wiley.com/cgi-bin/jhome/38417, http://www.wiley.com. Ed. Gary C Schoenwolf. adv.: B&W page GBP 640, color page GBP 1,515; trim 210 x 279. Circ: 1,250. **Subscr. outside N. America to:** John Wiley & Sons Ltd., The Atrium, Southern Gate, Chichester, West Sussex PO19 8SQ, United Kingdom. TEL 44-1243-843335, 0800-243407, FAX 44-1243-843232, cs-journals@wiley.co.uk.

573.8 612.8 USA ISSN 0012-1630
QL750 CODEN: DEPBA5
➤ **DEVELOPMENTAL PSYCHOBIOLOGY.** Text in English. 1967. 8/yr. USD 1,975 domestic to institutions; USD 2,071 in Canada & Mexico to institutions; USD 2,127 elsewhere to institutions; USD 2,173 combined subscription domestic to institutions print & online eds.; USD 2,269 combined subscription in Canada & Mexico to institutions print & online eds.; USD 2,325 combined subscription elsewhere to institutions print & online eds. (effective 2006). adv. bk.rev. index. back issues avail.; reprint service avail. from PQC. **Document type:** *Journal, Academic/Scholarly.* **Description:** Presents original research reports that contribute to the understanding of behaviorally related processes, whether in the embryo, fetus, neonate, or juvenile.
Related titles: Microform ed.: (from PQC); Online - full content ed.: ISSN 1098-2302. USD 1,975 to institutions (effective 2006); Online - full text ed.: (from EBSCO Publishing, Swets Information Services, Wiley InterScience).
Indexed: ASCA, ASFA, AbAn, AnBeAb, AnBrAb, BIOSIS Prev, BibInd, BiolAb, CDA, CIN, ChemAb, ChemTitl, CurCont, DSA, ExcerpMed, FamI, ISR, IndMed, IndVet, Inpharma, MEDLINE, NSCI, NemAb, NutrAb, PE&ON, PoultAb, PsycInfo, PsycholAb, PsycholRG, Reac, SCI, SIA, SSCI, VetBull, ZooRec, e-psyche.
—BLDSC (3579.058000), CASDDS, CISTI, GNLM, IDS, IE, Infotrieve, ingenta. **CCC.**
Published by: (International Society for Developmental Psychology), John Wiley & Sons, Inc., 111 River St, Hoboken, NJ 07030-5774. TEL 201-748-6000, FAX 201-748-5915, uscs-wis@wiley.com, http://www.interscience.wiley.com/jpages/0012-1630/, http://www.wiley.com. Ed. George F Michel. adv.: B&W page GBP 640, color page GBP 1,515; trim 165 x 254. Circ: 800. **Subscr. outside the Americas to:** John Wiley & Sons Ltd., The Atrium, Southern Gate, Chichester, West Sussex PO19 8SQ, United Kingdom. TEL 44-1243-843335, 0800-243407, FAX 44-1243-843232, cs-journals@wiley.co.uk.

➤ **DEVELOPMENTS IN BIOGEOCHEMISTRY.** see *EARTH SCIENCES*

➤ **DEVELOPMENTS IN BIOLOGICALS.** see *METROLOGY AND STANDARDIZATION*

578.77 551.4 NLD ISSN 0167-8418
CODEN: DEHYD3
➤ **DEVELOPMENTS IN HYDROBIOLOGY.** Text in English. 1981. irreg., latest vol.178, 2004. price varies. **Document type:** *Monographic series, Academic/Scholarly.*
Indexed: ASFA, BIOSIS Prev, BiolAb, ChemAb, ESPM, MBA, OceAb, PollutAb, SWRA, ZooRec.
—CASDDS, CISTI. **CCC.**
Published by: Springer-Verlag Dordrecht (Subsidiary of: Springer Science+Business Media), Van Godewijckstraat 30, Dordrecht, 3311 GX, Netherlands. TEL 31-78-6576050, FAX 31-78-6576474, http://www.springeronline.com. Ed. Koen Martens.

570.72 GBR ISSN 1467-4912
DEVELOPMENTS IN LIFE SCIENCES; the journal of pharmaceutical, agrochemical and chemical research. Text in English. 1999. q.
—BLDSC (3579.084100).
Published by: Huntingdon Life Sciences, Woolley Rd, Alconbury, Huntingdon, Cambs, PE17 5HS, United Kingdom. TEL 44-1480-892000, sales@ukorg.huntingdon.com, http://www.huntingdon.com.

DEVELOPMENTS IN MARINE BIOLOGY. see *EARTH SCIENCES—Oceanography*

DI SI JUNYI DAXUE XUEBAO/FOURTH MILITARY MEDICAL UNIVERSITY. JOURNAL. see *MEDICAL SCIENCES*

DIAGNOSTIC INSIGHT. see *MEDICAL SCIENCES*

570 GBR ISSN 0301-4681
QH573 CODEN: DFFNAW
➤ **DIFFERENTIATION**; ontogeny, neoplasia and differentiation therapy. Text in English. 1973. 10/yr. USD 1,755 combined subscription in the Americas to institutions & Caribbean (print & online eds.); GBP 1,218 elsewhere to institutions print & online eds. (effective 2006). back issues avail.; reprint service avail. from ISI. **Document type:** *Journal, Academic/Scholarly.* **Description:** Reports on the most up-to-date research results on problems of biological diversification in plants and animals.
Related titles: Online - full text ed.: ISSN 1432-0436. USD 1,667 in the Americas to institutions & Caribbean; GBP 1,157 elsewhere to institutions (effective 2006) (from Blackwell Synergy, EBSCO Publishing, Gale Group, IngentaConnect, O C L C Online Computer Library Center, Inc., Ovid Technologies, Inc., Swets Information Services).
Indexed: ASCA, ASFA, AbHyg, AgBio, AnBrAb, B&BAb, BIOBASE, BIOSIS Prev, BiolAb, CIN, ChemAb, ChemTitl, CurCont, DSA, DentInd, EntAb, ExcerpMed, FS&TA, GenetAb, HortAb, IABS, ISR, IndMed, IndVet, Inpharma, MEDLINE, MaizeAb, NemAb, PBA, PGrRegA, PoultAb, ProtozoAb, RA&MP, Reac, SCI, VetBull, WeedAb, ZooRec.
—BLDSC (3584.240000), CASDDS, CISTI, GNLM, IDS, IE, Infotrieve, ingenta, Linda Hall. **CCC.**
Published by: (International Society of Differentiation USA), Blackwell Publishing Ltd., 9600 Garsington Rd, Oxford, OX4 2ZG, United Kingdom. TEL 44-1865-776868, FAX 44-1865-714591, customerservices@oxon.blackwellpublishing.com, http://www.blackwellpublishing.com/journals/DIF. Ed. Eero Lehtonen.

➤ **DIRASAT. MEDICAL AND BIOLOGICAL SCIENCES.** see *MEDICAL SCIENCES*

➤ **DIRECTORY OF BIOTECHNOLOGY CENTERS.** see *BIOLOGY—Biotechnology*

➤ **DIRECTORY OF PATHOLOGY TRAINING PROGRAMS (YEAR).** see *EDUCATION—Higher Education*

➤ **DISCOVERY.** see *SCIENCES: COMPREHENSIVE WORKS*

577 GBR ISSN 1366-9516
QH75.A1 CODEN: DIDIFX
DIVERSITY AND DISTRIBUTIONS; a journal of conservation biogeography. Text in English. 1993. bi-m. GBP 211 combined subscription in Europe to individuals non Eurozone (print & online eds.); EUR 317 combined subscription in Europe to individuals Eurozone (print & online eds.); USD 391 combined subscription in North America to individuals & the Caribbean (print & online eds.); GBP 233 combined subscription elsewhere to individuals print & online eds.; GBP 1,997 combined subscription in Europe to institutions print & online eds.; USD 3,691 combined subscription in North America to institutions & the Caribbean (print & online eds.); GBP 2,197 combined subscription elsewhere to institutions print & online eds. (effective 2005); includes Journal of Biogeography & Global Ecology and Biogeography. adv. reprint service avail. from PSC. **Document type:** *Journal, Academic/Scholarly.* **Description:** Covers all aspects of the ecology of biodiversity and the distribution of organisms.
Formerly (until 1999): Biodiversity Letters (0967-9952)
Related titles: Online - full text ed.: ISSN 1472-4642. GBP 1,898 in Europe to institutions; USD 3,506 in the Americas to institutions; GBP 2,087 elsewhere to institutions (effective 2005) (from Blackwell Synergy, EBSCO Publishing, Gale Group, IngentaConnect, JSTOR (Web-based Journal Archive), O C L C Online Computer Library Center, Inc., Swets Information Services); ♦ Series of: Journal of Biogeography. ISSN 0305-0270.
Indexed: ASFA, AgBio, AgrForAb, ApEcolAb, BIOBASE, BIOSIS Prev, BioCN&I, BiolAb, CPA, CurCont, EPB, ESPM, EnvAb, FPA, ForAb, GEOBASE, HelmAb, HerbAb, HortAb, I&DA, IndVet, OrnHort, PBA, PGegResA, PotatoAb, PoultAb, RA&MP, RDA, RM&VM, RefZh, RevApplEntom, S&F, SWRA, SeedAb, VetBull, WeedAb, WildRev, ZooRec.
—BLDSC (3604.271107), CISTI, IE, Infotrieve, ingenta, Linda Hall. **CCC.**
Published by: Blackwell Publishing Ltd., 9600 Garsington Rd, Oxford, OX4 2ZG, United Kingdom. TEL 44-1865-776868, FAX 44-1865-714591, customerservices@oxon.blackwellpublishing.com, http://www.blackwellpublishing.com/journal.asp?ref=1366-9516&site=1. Ed. David M Richardson. Pub. Sue Hewitt. R&P Sophie Savage. Adv. contact Jenny Applin.

595 RUS ISSN 0012-4966
QH505 CODEN: DKBSAS
➤ **DOKLADY BIOLOGICAL SCIENCES.** Text in English. 1933. bi-m. EUR 2,725, USD 2,428, GBP 1,698 combined subscription to institutions print & online eds. (effective 2005). index. back issues avail. **Document type:** *Journal, Academic/Scholarly.* **Description:** Disseminates the most noteworthy research in the biological sciences, translated from the Russian into English.
Supersedes in part (in 1963): Doklady. Biological Science Sections (0886-7534); Incorporates (1958-1962): Doklady. Biochemistry Section (0097-6466)
Related titles: Microfilm ed.: (from PQC); Online - full content ed.: ISSN 1608-3105; Online - full text ed.: (from EBSCO Publishing, Gale Group, IngentaConnect, Kluwer Online, O C L C Online Computer Library Center, Inc., Ovid Technologies, Inc., Springer LINK, Swets Information Services); ♦ Partial translation of: Rossiiskaya Akademiya Nauk. Doklady. ISSN 0869-5652.
Indexed: AEA, AbHyg, AgBio, AgrForAb, AnBrAb, BibLing, BioCN&I, BiolAb, CPA, ChemTitl, DSA, EnerRA, ExcerpMed, FCA, FPA, ForAb, HelmAb, HerbAb, HortAb, I&DA, IABS, IndMed, IndVet, MEDLINE, MaizeAb, NemAb, NutrAb, OrnHort, PBA, PGegResA, PGrRegA, PN&I, PotatoAb, PoultAb, ProtozoAb, RA&MP, RM&VM, RPP, RRTA, RevApplEntom, RiceAb, S&F, SFA, SIA, SeedAb, TDB, TriticAb, VetBull, WeedAb, WildRev, ZooRec.
—BLDSC (0411.200000), CISTI, IE, Infotrieve, ingenta. **CCC.**
Published by: (Rossiiskaya Akademiya Nauk/Russian Academy of Sciences), M A I K Nauka - Interperiodica, Profsoyuznaya ul 90, Moscow, 117997, Russian Federation. TEL 7-095-3347420, FAX 7-095-3360666, compmg@maik.ru, http://www.maik.ru. Ed. Victor A. Kabanov. **Subscr. to:** Springer-Verlag Dordrecht, Journals Department, PO Box 322, Dordrecht, Netherlands. TEL 31-78-6576392, FAX 31-78-6576474.

➤ **LES DONNEES DE L'ENVIRONNEMENT.** see *ENVIRONMENTAL STUDIES*

577 550 DEU ISSN 0340-3947
DORTMUNDER BEITRAEGE ZUR LANDESKUNDE. Text in English, German. 1967. a. bk.rev. back issues avail. **Document type:** *Journal, Academic/Scholarly.*
Indexed: ZooRec.
Published by: Museum fuer Naturkunde, Muensterstr 271, Dortmund, 44122, Germany. TEL 49-231-5024850, FAX 49-231-5024852, naturkundemuseum@stadtdortmund.de, http://www.museendortmund.de. Circ: 600.

570 DEU ISSN 0341-406X
CODEN: DRSRDQ
DROSERA; Naturkundliche Mitteilungen aus Nordwestdeutschland. Text in German; Summaries in English. 1976. s-a. **Document type:** *Academic/Scholarly.*
Indexed: ASFA, BIOSIS Prev, BiolAb, EntAb, GenetAb, HGA, RefZh, ZooRec.
—CCC.

Published by: Landesmuseum fuer Natur und Mensch, Damm 38-44, Oldenburg, 26135, Germany. TEL 49-441-9244300, FAX 49-441-9244399. Ed., R&P Ulf Beichle.

570 KEN ISSN 0374-7387
QH195.A23 CODEN: EANHAU
E A N H S BULLETIN. Text in English. 2/yr. USD 36 to members. bk.rev. bibl. **Document type:** *Bulletin, Academic/Scholarly.* **Description:** Contains information about natural history subjects and related correspondence.
Formerly (until 1971): E A N H S Newsletter (0252-807X)
Indexed: AICP, BiolAb, KWIWR, RevApplEntom, SFA, WildRev, ZooRec.
—Linda Hall.
Published by: East Africa Natural History Society, PO Box 44486, Nairobi, 00100, Kenya. TEL 254-2-749957, FAX 254-2-741049, eanhs@africaonline.co.ke, office@naturekenya.org, http://www.naturekenya.org/EANHSbulletin.htm. Ed. Catherine Ngarachu.

E U R. (Europe) see *MEDICAL SCIENCES*

570 610 CHE ISSN 1023-294X
CODEN: EXPSAU
➤ **E X S.** Text in English, German. 1953. irreg., latest vol.94, 2004. price varies. **Document type:** *Monographic series, Academic/Scholarly.* **Description:** Covers new research in medical biology.
Formerly (until 1992): Experientia. Supplementum (0071-335X)
Related titles: ♦ Supplement to: Cellular and Molecular Life Sciences. ISSN 1420-682X.
Indexed: BIOSIS Prev, BioCN&I, BiolAb, ChemAb, IndMed, MEDLINE, TriticAb, ZooRec.
—BLDSC (3843.451400), CASDDS, CINDOC, CISTI, GNLM, IE, Infotrieve, ingenta. **CCC.**
Published by: Birkhaeuser Verlag AG (Subsidiary of: Springer Science+Business Media), Viaduktstr 42, Postfach 133, Basel, 4051, Switzerland. TEL 41-61-2050707, FAX 41-61-2050792, birkhauser@springer.de, http://www.birkhauser.ch.

500 THA ISSN 1513-489X
CODEN: JSFUD9
➤ **EAST-WEST JOURNAL OF MATHEMATICS.** Text in English. 1974. s-a. THB 200 domestic to institutions; USD 25 foreign to institutions (effective 2000). back issues avail. **Document type:** *Academic/Scholarly.* **Description:** Publishes research papers, survey papers, or research announcements in pure and applied mathematics.
Formerly (until 1998): Science Faculty of Chiang Mai University. Journal (0125-2526)
Related titles: Fax ed.; Online - full content ed.
Indexed: MathR, MathSciNet, ZentMath.
Published by: Chiang Mai University, Faculty of Science, 239 Huay Kaew Rd, Chiang Mai, 50200, Thailand. TEL 66-53-943327, FAX 66-53-892280, g4365178@cm.edu, vansanh@kku.ac.th, http://math.chiangmai.ac.th. Ed. Surin Khanabsakdi. Circ: 50 (paid); 300 (controlled).

➤ **ECOGRAPHY;** pattern and diversity in ecology. see *ENVIRONMENTAL STUDIES*

▼ ➤ **ECOHEALTH.** see *ENVIRONMENTAL STUDIES*

➤ **ECOHYDROLOGY & HYDROBIOLOGY.** see *EARTH SCIENCES—Hydrology*

577 ESP ISSN 0214-0896
QH171 CODEN: ECOLEV
➤ **ECOLOGIA.** Text in English, Spanish; Summaries in English. 1972. a., latest vol.4, 2000. bk.rev. bibl.; charts; illus.; stat. back issues avail. **Document type:** *Yearbook, Academic/Scholarly.* **Description:** Provides original papers relating to the various aspects of environmental science.
Formerly (until 1987): Estacion Central de Ecologia. Boletin (0210-2536)
Indexed: AEA, ASFA, AgrForAb, AnBrAb, BIOBASE, BioCN&I, BiolAb, CPA, ChemAb, CurCont, FCA, FPA, ForAb, HelmAb, HerbAb, I&DA, IECT, IndVet, NutrAb, PBA, PGegResA, PoultAb, ProtozoAb, RA&MP, RPP, RevApplEntom, S&F, SFA, SeedAb, TriticAb, VetBull, WAE&RSA, WLR, WeedAb, WildRev, ZooRec.
—CINDOC, CISTI.
Published by: Direccion General de Conservacion de la Naturaleza, Gran Via de San Francisco, 4, Madrid, 28005, Spain. TEL 34-91-59755639, FAX 34-91-5975566, beningno.asensio@gvsf.mma.es, http://www.mma.es/. Ed. Benigno Asensio. Circ: 3,000.

577 ARG ISSN 0327-5477
ECOLOGIA AUSTRAL. Text in English, Portuguese, Spanish. 1973. s-a. **Document type:** *Journal.*
Formerly (until 1991): Ecologia (0325-8564)
Related titles: Online - full text ed.: ISSN 1667-782X; ISSN 1667-7838.
Indexed: ASFA, AgrForAb, AnBrAb, ApEcolAb, CPA, ESPM, EntAb, FCA, ForAb, GEOBASE, HerbAb, I&DA, MaizeAb, PBA, S&F, SeedAb, SoyAb, TDB, TriticAb, WeedAb, ZooRec.
Published by: Asociacion Argentina de Ecologia, c/o Enrique Chaneton, IFEVA, Facultad de Agronomia, Universidad de Buenos Aires, Av. San Martin 4453, Buenos Aires, 1417, Argentina. asae@cenpat.edu.ar, http://ecologiaaustral.dnsart.com/presentacion.php, http://www.ifeva.edu.ar/asae/. Ed. Jorge Rabinovich.

ECOLOGIA E DESENVOLVIMENTO; revista mensal brasileira de ecologia e meio ambiente. see *ENVIRONMENTAL STUDIES*

577 550 BOL
CODEN: ECBOE9
➤ **ECOLOGIA EN BOLIVIA.** Text in Spanish; Abstracts in English, German. 1982. 3/yr. USD 30 (effective 1998 & 1999). bk.rev. back issues avail. **Document type:** *Bulletin, Academic/Scholarly.* **Description:** Publishes scientific work on ecology and biodiversity in Bolivia.
Indexed: CPA, FPA, ForAb, HerbAb, HortAb, NutrAb, RA&MP, RevApplEntom, S&F, SFA, SeedAb, WeedAb, WildRev, ZooRec.
Published by: Instituto de Ecologia, Casilla 10077, La Paz, Bolivia. TEL 591-2-792582, FAX 591-2-797511, insteco@ie.rds.org.bo. Ed., R&P Cecile de Morales. Circ: 1,000.

577 182 FRA ISSN 0153-8756
QK314.5 CODEN: EMEDDQ
ECOLOGIA MEDITERRANEA; revue internationale d'ecologie mediterraneenne. Text in French, English, Italian, Spanish. 1975. s-a. EUR 61 (effective 2003). bk.rev. 160 p./no.; **Document type:** *Journal.*
Indexed: BIOSIS Prev, BiolAb, ZooRec.
—CCC.
Published by: Edisud, 3120 route d'Avignon - La Calde, Aix-en-Provence, 13090, France. TEL 33-442216144, FAX 33-442215620, http://www.edisud.com.

ECOLOGIA POLITICA. see *ENVIRONMENTAL STUDIES*

577 PER
ECOLOGIA Y DESARROLLO. Text in Spanish. 1985. irreg., latest 1993. price varies. **Document type:** *Monographic series.*
Published by: Centro de Estudios Regionales Andinos "Bartolome de Las Casas", Apdo Postal 14087, Lima, 14, Peru. TEL 51-14-429992, FAX 51-14-427894, cbcimpta@apu.cbc.org.pe. Pub. Andres Chirinos Rivera.

ECOLOGICAL ABSTRACTS. see *BIOLOGY—Abstracting, Bibliographies, Statistics*

ECOLOGICAL APPLICATIONS. see *ENVIRONMENTAL STUDIES*

ECOLOGICAL BULLETINS. see *ENVIRONMENTAL STUDIES*

ECOLOGICAL MANAGEMENT & RESTORATION. see *ENVIRONMENTAL STUDIES*

ECOLOGICAL MANAGEMENT & RESTORATION ONLINE. see *ENVIRONMENTAL STUDIES*

ECOLOGICAL MONOGRAPHS. see *ENVIRONMENTAL STUDIES*

577 JPN ISSN 0912-3814
QH540 CODEN: ECRSEX
➤ **ECOLOGICAL RESEARCH.** Text in English. 1986. bi-m. EUR 488 combined subscription to institutions print & online eds. (effective 2005). adv. bk.rev. charts; illus. Index. **Document type:** *Journal, Academic/Scholarly.* **Description:** Publishes research papers on all aspects of ecology: aquatic, terrestrial, and marine.
Related titles: Online - full text ed.: ISSN 1440-1703. GBP 355 in Japan to institutions; USD 497 in the Americas to institutions; GBP 307 elsewhere to institutions (effective 2004) (from Blackwell Synergy, EBSCO Publishing, Gale Group, IngentaConnect, O C L C Online Computer Library Center, Inc., Springer LINK, Swets Information Services).
Indexed: AEA, ASCA, ASFA, AgBio, AgrForAb, AnBeAb, AnBrAb, ApEcolAb, B&BAb, BIOBASE, BIOSIS Prev, BioCN&I, BiolAb, CIN, CPA, ChemAb, ChemTitl, CurCont, EPB, ESPM, EntAb, FCA, FPA, FS&TA, ForAb, GEOBASE, GardL, GenetAb, HGA, HerbAb, HortAb, I&DA, IABS, ISR, IndVet, M&GPA, MBA, NemAb, NutrAb, OrnHort, PBA, PGegResA, PHN&I, PlantSci, PoultAb, RA&MP, RPP, RRTA, RefZh, RevApplEntom, RiceAb, S&F, SCI, SFA, SWRA, SeedAb, SoyAb, VetBull, WAE&RSA, WeedAb, WildRev, ZooRec.
—BLDSC (3649.100000), CASDDS, CISTI, IDS, IE, Infotrieve, ingenta, Linda Hall. **CCC.**
Published by: (Ecological Society of Japan), Springer-Verlag Tokyo (Subsidiary of: Springer Science+Business Media), 3-13 Hongo 3-chome, Bunkyo-ku, Tokyo, 113-0033, Japan. TEL 81-3-38120331, FAX 81-3-38187454, orders@svt-ebs.co.jp, http://www.blackwellpublishing.com/journal.asp?ref=0912-3814&site=1, http://www.springer-tokyo.co.jp/. Adv. contact Stephan Kroeck TEL 49-30-827875739. B&W page AUD 935, color page AUD 1,958; trim 275 x 210. Circ: 3,550.

➤ **ECOLOGICAL RESTORATION.** see *CONSERVATION*

570 JPN ISSN 0371-0548
QK900
ECOLOGICAL REVIEW/SEITAIGAKU KENKYU. Text in English. 1935. a. **Document type:** *Academic/Scholarly.*
Indexed: ASFA, Agr, ApEcolAb, BAS, ESPM, GenetAb, HGA, SeedAb, WeedAb.
—Linda Hall.
Published by: Tohoku University, Mt. Hakkoda Botanical Laboratory/Tohoku Daigaku Hakkodasan Shokubutsu Jikkenjo, c/o Botanical Garden, Tohoku University, Kawauchi, Aoba-ku, Sendai-shi, Miyagi-ken 980-0862, Japan. TEL 81-22-217-6765, FAX 81-22-217-6766, 050842@cctu.cc.tohoku.ac.jp. Ed. Tadaki Hirose.

ECOLOGICAL SOCIETY OF AMERICA. BULLETIN. see *ENVIRONMENTAL STUDIES*

577 USA ISSN 0070-8356
CODEN: ESASAM
ECOLOGICAL STUDIES: ANALYSIS AND SYNTHESIS. Text in English. 1970. irreg., latest vol.119, 1996. price varies. reprint service avail. from ISI. **Document type:** *Monographic series.*
Indexed: ASFA, Agr, BIOSIS Prev, BibAg, BiolAb, ChemAb, ESPM, EngInd, ForAb, ZooRec.
—BLDSC (3649.300000), CASDDS, CISTI, Ei, IE, ingenta. **CCC.**
Published by: Springer-Verlag New York, Inc. (Subsidiary of: Springer Science+Business Media), 233 Spring St, New York, NY 10013. TEL 212-460-1500, FAX 212-473-6272.

B

577 IND
THE ECOLOGIST ASIA. Text in English. q.
—ingenta.
Published by: The Ecologist Asia, 602 Maker Chambers V, Nariman Point, Mumbai, Maharastra 400 021, India. TEL 91-22-22830061, FAX 91-22-22874380.

577 IND
THE ECOLOGISTS. Text in English. bi-m. USD 40 (effective 2000). **Document type:** *Academic/Scholarly.*
Published by: H P C Publishers Distributors Pvt. Ltd., 4805 Bharat Ram Rd, 24 Darya Ganj, New Delhi, 110 002, India. TEL 91-11-3254401, FAX 91-11-619-3511, hpcpd@nda.vsnl.net.in, hpcpd@hpc.cc, http://www.hpc.cc, http://www.bizdelhi.com/publisher/hpc, http://www.indianindustry.com. **Co-publisher:** The Ecologist Asia.

ECOLOGY. see *ENVIRONMENTAL STUDIES*

ECOLOGY & ENVIRONMENT. see *ENVIRONMENTAL STUDIES*

ECOLOGY DIGEST. see *ENVIRONMENTAL STUDIES*

577 363.7 333.72 344.046 IND ISSN 0971-765X
QH183
ECOLOGY, ENVIRONMENT AND CONSERVATION. Text in English. 1995. q. USD 200 to institutions (effective 2003). adv. bk.rev. **Document type:** *Academic/Scholarly.* **Description:** Contains research papers, technical articles, news and other relevant information on all aspects of ecology, environment, pollution and nature conservation.
Indexed: ASFA, CIN, ChemAb, ChemTitl, ESPM, GEOBASE, SWRA, WRCInf, ZooRec.
—BLDSC (3650.042500), IE, ingenta.
Published by: Enviro Media, 2nd Fl. Rohan Heights, P O Box 90, Karad, 415 110, India. Ed., R&P Rakesh Kumar Trivedy. Pub., Adv. contact Sukhada Trivedy. **Subscr. to:** Scientific Publishers, 5-A New Pali Rd., Near Hotel Taj Hari Mahal, PO Box 91, Jodhpur, Rajasthan 342 003, India. TEL 91-291-2433323, FAX 91-291-2512580, info@scientificpub.com, http://www.scientificpub.com.

577 GBR ISSN 1461-023X
QH540 CODEN: ECLEFU
➤ **ECOLOGY LETTERS.** Text in English. 1998. m. GBP 109, EUR 164 combined subscription in Europe to individuals print & online eds.; USD 202 combined subscription in the Americas to individuals & Caribbean (print & online eds.); GBP 120 combined subscription elsewhere to individuals print & online eds.; GBP 937 combined subscription in Europe to institutions print & online eds.; USD 1,730 combined subscription in the Americas to institutions & Caribbean (print & online eds.); GBP 1,030 combined subscription elsewhere to institutions print & online eds. (effective 2006). adv. **Document type:** *Journal, Academic/Scholarly.* **Description:** Publishes articles dealing with current discoveries, issues and information in ecology.
Related titles: Online - full text ed.: ISSN 1461-0248. GBP 890 in Europe to institutions; USD 1,645 in the Americas to institutions & Caribbean; GBP 979 elsewhere to institutions (effective 2006) (from Blackwell Synergy, EBSCO Publishing, Gale Group, IngentaConnect, O C L C Online Computer Library Center, Inc., Swets Information Services).
Indexed: AIDS&CR, ASFA, AbHyg, AgBio, AgrForAb, AnBrAb, ApEcolAb, BIOBASE, BIOSIS Prev, BioCN&I, BiolAb, CPA, CurCont, DSA, EPB, ESPM, EntAb, FCA, FPA, ForAb, GEOBASE, HelmAb, HerbAb, HortAb, I&DA, ISR, IndVet, MBA, MaizeAb, NemAb, NutrAb, OrnHort, PBA, PGegResA, PGrRegA, PHN&I, PN&I, PoultAb, ProtozoAb, RA&MP, RM&VM, RPP, RefZh, RevApplEntom, RiceAb, S&F, SCI, SeedAb, VetBull, VirolAbstr, WAE&RSA, WeedAb, ZooRec.

—BLDSC (3650.044200), CISTI, IDS, IE, Infotrieve, ingenta, Linda Hall. **CCC.**

Published by: Blackwell Publishing Ltd., 9600 Garsington Rd, Oxford, OX4 2ZG, United Kingdom. TEL 44-1865-776868, FAX 44-1865-714591, customerservices@oxon.blackwellpublishing.com, http://www.blackwellpublishing.com/journals/ELE. Ed. Michael Hochberg. Pub. Aileen Boyd Squires. R&P Sophie Savage. Adv. contact Jenny Applin. Circ: 800. **Co-sponsor:** Centre National de la Recherche Scientifique.

➤ **ECOLOGY U S A.** see *ENVIRONMENTAL STUDIES*

▼ ➤ **ECONOMICS AND HUMAN BIOLOGY.** see *SOCIAL SCIENCES: COMPREHENSIVE WORKS*

➤ **ECOSYSTEMS OF THE WORLD.** see *ENVIRONMENTAL STUDIES*

➤ **ECOTROPICA. ECOSISTEMAS TROPICALES.** see *EARTH SCIENCES—Oceanography*

570 VEN ISSN 1012-1692
QH130

ECOTROPICOS; revista de la Sociedad Venezolana de Ecologia. Text in Multiple languages. 1988. s-a. **Document type:** *Journal, Academic/Scholarly.* **Description:** Intends to contribute to the knowledge of the ecosystems of Venezuela and of the tropics in general.

Related titles: Online - full text ed.: free (effective 2005).

Indexed: ASFA, ApEcolAb, BIOSIS Prev, BiolAb, ESPM, EntAb, ZooRec.

Published by: (Sociedad Venezolano de Ecologia), Universidad de los Andes, Facultad de Ciencias, La Hechicera, Apartado Postal 5, Merida, 5101, Venezuela. TEL 58-274-2401255, ecotrop@ula.ve, http://ecotropicos.saber.ula.ve/, http://www.ula.ve. Ed. Michelle Ataroff.

570 EST ISSN 0135-2431

EESTI LOODUSEUURIJATE SELTSI. AASTARAAMAT/ ESTONIAN NATURALISTS' SOCIETY. YEARBOOK/ ESTONSKOYE OBSHCHESTVO ESTESTVOISPYTATELEI. EZHEGODNIK. Text in English, Estonian. 1955. irreg.

Formerly (until 1976): Loodusuurijate Seltsi. Aastaraamat (0320-6688)

Indexed: ESPM, ZooRec.

—Linda Hall.

Published by: (Eesti Looduseuurijate Selts/Estonian Naturalists' Society, Eesti Teaduste Akadeemia), Teaduste Akadeemia Kirjastus/Estonian Academy Publishers, Kohtu 6, Tallinn, 10130, Estonia. TEL 372-6-454504, FAX 372-6-466026, niine@kirj.ee, http://www.kirj.ee.

578.77 639.2 EGY ISSN 1110-6131

EGYPTIAN JOURNAL OF AQUATIC BIOLOGY AND FISHERIES/AL-MAGALLAT AL-MISRIYYAT LIL-BAYULUGIYA AL-MAIYYAT WA-ALMASA. Text in English. 1997. q. **Document type:** *Journal, Academic/Scholarly.*

Published by: The Egyptian Society for the Development of Fisheries and Human Health, Zoology Department, Faculty of Science, Ain Shams University, Cairo, Egypt. TEL 20-2-4821096, FAX 20-2-4821031, http://derp.sti.sci.eg/data/0214.htm. Ed. Abd-Allah Ebrahim.

570 EGY ISSN 1110-6859

➤ **EGYPTIAN JOURNAL OF BIOLOGY.** Text in English. 1999. a. **Document type:** *Journal, Academic/Scholarly.* **Description:** Publishes standard scientific contributions and reviews from all aspects of the biological sciences.

Related titles: Online - full text ed.: free (effective 2005) (from International Network for the Availability of Scientific Publications, African Journals Online).

Indexed: BiolAb, FCA, ZooRec.

Published by: Egyptian-English Society for Biological Sciences, Suez Canal University, Faculty of Science, Ismailia, Egypt. http://www.nottingham.ac.uk/~plzfg/EBBSoc/ejb.html. Ed. Sami Zalatt.

➤ **EGYPTIAN JOURNAL OF COMPARATIVE PATHOLOGY AND CLINICAL PATHOLOGY/AL-MAGALLAT AL-MISRIYYAT LIL-PATHOLOGIA WA AL-PATHOLOGIA AL-'IKLINIKIAT AL MOQAARANAT.** see *MEDICAL SCIENCES*

577 EGY ISSN 1110-6867

EGYPTIAN JOURNAL OF NATURAL HISTORY. Text in English. 1999. a. **Document type:** *Journal, Academic/Scholarly.*

Related titles: Online - full text ed.: (from International Network for the Availability of Scientific Publications, African Journals Online).

Indexed: BiolAb, ZooRec.

Published by: Egyptian-English Society for Biological Sciences, Suez Canal University, Faculty of Science, Ismailia, Egypt. http://derp.sti.sci.eg/data/0327.htm.

570 610 USA CODEN: EQJMD4

➤ **EINSTEIN JOURNAL OF BIOLOGY AND MEDICINE.** Abbreviated title: E J B M. Text in English. 1984. q. adv. reprint service avail. from ISI. **Document type:** *Journal, Academic/Scholarly.* **Description:** Serves as an intellectual forum for the medical scientific community, and encourages the publication of a wide range of scholarly material by students, fellows, residents, faculty, and alumni.

Formerly: Einstein Quarterly Journal of Biology and Medicine (0724-6706)

Related titles: Microform ed.: (from PQC); Online - full text ed.: (from EBSCO Publishing).

Indexed: BIOSIS Prev, BiolAb, CIN, ChemAb, ChemTitl, ExcerpMed.

—BLDSC (3665.635000), CASDDS, CISTI, GNLM, Infotrieve.

Published by: Albert Einstein College of Medicine (Subsidiary of: Yeshiva University), Jack and Pearl Resnick Campus, 1300 Morris Park Ave, Forchheimer Bldg, Rm 306, Bronx, NY 10461. TEL 718-430-8768, FAX 718-430-3073, http://www.aecom.yu.edu/home/ejbm/. Ed. Joseph J Abrajano.

577 CZE ISSN 1210-4728
CODEN: EESPFA

EKO. EKOLOGIE A SPOLECNOST. Text in Czech. 1990. bi-m. CZK 268; CZK 30 per issue (effective 2004). adv. **Document type:** *Magazine, Trade.*

Indexed: INIS AtomInd.

Published by: Ceske Nakladatelstvi Technicke Literatury s.r.o., Jezkova 1, Prague, 130 00, Czech Republic. TEL 420-2-22721164, FAX 420-2-22722380, cntl@cntl.cz, http://www.cntl.cz/eko.html.

577 SVK ISSN 1335-342X

➤ **EKOLOGIA/ECOLOGY.** Text in English. 1982. q. USD 148 foreign (effective 2005). **Document type:** *Journal, Academic/Scholarly.* **Description:** Presents papers that deal with theoretical and practical problems of landscape preservation and planning with the main emphasis on complex characteristics of ecosystems.

Related titles: Online - full text ed.: (from ProQuest Information & Learning).

Indexed: ASCA, ASFA, AgBio, AgrForAb, ApEcolAb, BIOBASE, BIOSIS Prev, BioCN&I, BiolAb, CDSP, CIN, CPA, ChemAb, ChemTitl, CurCont, EIP, ESPM, EntAb, ExcerpMed, FCA, FPA, ForAb, GEOBASE, HerbAb, HortAb, I&DA, IABS, MBA, MaizeAb, NemAb, NutrAb, OrnHort, PBA, PGegResA, PHN&I, PN&I, PlantSci, PotatoAb, PoultAb, RA&MP, RPP, RRTA, RefZh, RevApplEntom, S&F, SSCI, SWRA, SeedAb, WAE&RSA, WeedAb, ZooRec.

—BLDSC (3649.800000), IE, ingenta.

Published by: (Slovenska Akademia Vied, Ustav Krajinnej Ekologie/Slovak Academy of Sciences, Institute of Landscape Ecology), Slovak Academic Press Ltd., Nam Slobody 6, PO Box 57, Bratislava, 81005, Slovakia. sap@sappress.sk, http://www.sappress.sk. **Dist. by:** Slovart G.T.G. s.r.o., Krupinska 4, PO Box 152, Bratislava 85299, Slovakia. TEL 421-2-63839472, FAX 421-2-63839485, http://www.slovart-gtg.sk. **Co-publisher:** Akademie Ved Ceske Republiky, Ustav Ekologii Krajiny.

577 RUS

EKOLOGICHESKII VESTNIK MOSKVY; ezhemesyachnyi sbornik informatsionno-spravochnykh materialov. Text in Russian. m.

Published by: Moskovskii Gorodskii Komitet Okhrany Okruzhayushchei Sredy i Prirodnykh Resursov, Novyi Arbat 11, Moscow, Russian Federation. TEL 7-095-2918826. Ed. A G Ishkov. **Co-sponsor:** Moskovskii Gorodskoi Ekologicheskii Fond.

EKOLOGIYA. see *ENVIRONMENTAL STUDIES*

577 UKR ISSN 0203-4646
QH541.5.S3 CODEN: EKMODH

EKOLOGIYA MORYA; respublikanskii mezhvedomstvennyi sbornik nauchnykh trudov. Text in Russian; Summaries in English, Russian. 1980. q. **Document type:** *Academic/Scholarly.*

Formerly: Biologiya Morya (0320-9695)

Indexed: ASFA, ChemAb, ESPM, SPPI, ZooRec.

—CASDDS, CISTI, Linda Hall. **CCC.**

Published by: (Natsional'na Akademiya Nauk Ukrainy, Instytut Biolohii Pivdennykh Moriv im. A.O. Kovalevskoho), Natsional'na Akademiya Nauk Ukrainy, vul Volodymyrs'ka 54, Kyiv, 01601, Ukraine. TEL 380-44-2352239, FAX 380-44-2343243, prez@nas.gov.ua, http://www.nas.gov.ua.

570 FRA

ELECTRICITE DE FRANCE. DIRECTION DES ETUDES ET RECHERCHES. COLLECTION DE NOTES INTERNES. BIOLOGIE, SCIENCES DE LA TERRE ET ENVIRONNEMENT. Text in French. 1992. irreg.

Indexed: CIN, ChemAb, ChemTitl.

Published by: Electricite de France, Direction des Etudes et Recherches, 1 av. du General de Gaulle, Clamart, Cedex 92141, France. TEL 33-1-47654158, FAX 33-1-47653124.

570 ESP ISSN 1134-8496

ENCUENTROS EN LA BIOLOGIA. Text in Spanish. q. back issues avail.

Related titles: Online - full text ed.

Published by: Universidad de Malaga, Departamento de Biologia Celular, Campus de Teatinos, Malaga, 29071, Spain. TEL 34-95-2131961, FAX 34-95-2132000, http://www.ciencias.unam.es/publicaciones/encuentros/, http://www.ciencias.uma.es/. Ed. Salvador Guirado.

ENDANGERED SPECIES UPDATE; science, policy & emerging issues. see *CONSERVATION*

570 USA ISSN 1062-3329
QP88.45 CODEN: ENDTE9

➤ **ENDOTHELIUM**; journal of endothelial cell research. Text in English. 1993. bi-m. GBP 498, USD 745 combined subscription to institutions print & online eds. (effective 2006). back issues avail.; reprint service avail. from PSC. **Document type:** *Journal, Academic/Scholarly.* **Description:** Dedicated to the rapid turnaround of significant basic and clinical research on the endothelium, including endothelial-derived biologically active factors involved in the regulation of vascular tone and structure in haemostasis, fibrinolysis, inflamation and immune responses.

Related titles: CD-ROM ed.: ISSN 1026-793X; Online - full text ed.: ISSN 1029-2373. GBP 473, USD 708 to institutions (effective 2006) (from EBSCO Publishing, Gale Group, IngentaConnect, O C L C Online Computer Library Center, Inc., Swets Information Services).

Indexed: BBCI, BIOBASE, CurCont, ExcerpMed, IABS, ISR, IndMed, MEDLINE, SCI.

—BLDSC (3743.651000), CISTI, GNLM, IE, Infotrieve, ingenta, KNAW. **CCC.**

Published by: Taylor & Francis Inc. (Subsidiary of: Taylor & Francis Group), 325 Chestnut St, Ste 800, Philadelphia, PA 19016. TEL 215-625-8900, 800-354-1420, FAX 215-625-2940, 215-625-8914, info@taylorandfrancis.com, http://www.tandf.co.uk/journals/titles/10623329.asp, http://www.taylorandfrancis.com. Ed. Peter I Lelkes. **Subscr. outside N. America to:** Taylor & Francis Ltd, Journals Customer Service, Rankine Rd, Basingstoke, Hants RG24 8PR, United Kingdom. TEL 44-1256-813000, FAX 44-1256-330245, enquiry@tandf.co.uk.

➤ **ENVIROFICHE.** see *BIOLOGY—Abstracting, Bibliographies, Statistics*

▼ ➤ **ENVIRONMENTAL BIOINDICATORS.** see *ENVIRONMENTAL STUDIES*

➤ **ENVIRONMENTAL BIOLOGY.** see *ENVIRONMENTAL STUDIES*

➤ **ENVIRONMENTAL GEOSCIENCES.** see *ENVIRONMENTAL STUDIES*

➤ **ENVIRONMENTAL SCIENCE RESEARCH.** see *ENVIRONMENTAL STUDIES*

570 BEL ISSN 0773-9400

L'ERABLE. Text in French. 1977. q.

Indexed: RefZh.

Published by: Cercles des Naturalistes de Belgique, 21 Rue des Ecoles, Vierves-sur-Viron, 5670, Belgium. TEL 32-60-399878, FAX 32-60-399436.

570 CZE ISSN 1210-065X

ERICA. Text in Czech; Summaries in German, English. 1992. a. back issues avail. **Document type:** *Academic/Scholarly.*

Indexed: AnBrAb, ForAb, HerbAb, IndVet, PGegResA, PoultAb, RA&MP, RPP, RevApplEntom, S&F, WeedAb, ZooRec.

Published by: Zapadoceske Muzeum, Kopeckeho sady 2, Plzen, 30135, Czech Republic. TEL 42-19-7236541, FAX 42-19-7236541, zpcm@pm.cesnet.cz. Ed. Jaroslava Nesvadbova.

ERLANGER FORSCHUNGEN. REIHE B: NATURWISSENSCHAFTEN UND MEDIZIN. see *MEDICAL SCIENCES*

ESCUELA TECNICA SUPERIOR DE INGENIEROS DE MONTES. BIBLIOTECA. BOLETIN BIBLIOGRAFICO Y DOCUMENTAL. INFORMACION FORESTAL. SERIE A: MONOGRAFIAS. see *FORESTS AND FORESTRY—Abstracting, Bibliographies, Statistics*

ESCUELA TECNICA SUPERIOR DE INGENIEROS DE MONTES. BIBLIOTECA. BOLETIN BIBLIOGRAFICO Y DOCUMENTAL. INFORMACION FORESTAL. SERIE B: PUBLICACIONES PERIODICAS. see *FORESTS AND FORESTRY—Abstracting, Bibliographies, Statistics*

577 EST ISSN 1406-0914
QH301 CODEN: PEABFX

➤ **ESTONIAN ACADEMY OF SCIENCES. PROCEEDINGS. BIOLOGY. ECOLOGY/EESTI TEADUSTE AKADEEMIA TOIMETISED. BIOLOOGIA. OKOLOOGIA.** Text in English; Summaries in English, Estonian. 1997. q. EUR 85 foreign (effective 2004). adv. illus.; abstr.; charts; maps. 80 p./no.; back issues avail. **Document type:** *Journal, Academic/Scholarly.*

Formed by the merger of (1991-1997): Eesti Teaduste Akadeemia. Toimetised. Okoloogia (0868-5894); (1990-1997): Eesti Teaduste Akadeemia. Toimetised. Bioloogia (1018-7642); Which was formerly (1956-1990): Akademiya Nauk Estonskoi S.S.R. Izvestiya. Biologiya (0013-2144)
Related titles: Online - full text ed.: (from EBSCO Publishing).
Indexed: ASFA, AgBio, AnBrAb, ApEcolAb, BIOSIS Prev, BiolAb, CIN, CPA, ChemAb, ChemTitl, DSA, ESPM, EntAb, FCA, FPA, ForAb, HelmAb, HerbAb, HortAb, I&DA, IAA, INIS AtomInd, IndVet, M&TEA, NAA, NemAb, NutrAb, OrnHort, PBA, PGegResA, PGrRegA, PollutAb, PotatoAb, PoultAb, ProtozoAb, RPP, RevApplEntom, S&F, SIA, SWRA, TriticAb, VetBull, WeedAb, ZooRec.
—CASDDS, CISTI, KNAW, Linda Hall. **CCC.**
Published by: (Eesti Teaduste Akadeemia), Teaduste Akadeemia Kirjastus/Estonian Academy Publishers, Kohtu 6, Tallinn, 10130, Estonia. TEL 372-6-454504, FAX 372-6-466026, niine@kirj.ee, http://www.kirj.ee. Ed. Hillar Aben. Pub. Ylo Niine. R&P Asta Tikerpae TEL 373-6-454504. Adv. contact Asta Tikerpae TEL 373-6-454106. Circ: 550.

551.4609 USA ISSN 0160-8347
S932.C47 CODEN: ESTUDO
➤ **ESTUARIES**; a journal of research on any aspect of natural science and management applied to estuaries. Text in English. 1978. bi-m. USD 360 in North America; USD 375 elsewhere (effective 2001). adv. bk.rev. abstr.; bibl.; charts; illus.; maps; stat. index. back issues avail.; reprint service avail. from PQC. **Document type:** *Journal, Academic/Scholarly.* **Description:** It is devoted to publishing original papers based on research in any aspect of natural science or management of estuaries and the coastal zone, including selected interpretive review papers that lead to new and important generalizations.
Formerly: Chesapeake Science (0009-3262)
Related titles: Microform ed.: (from MIM, PMC, PQC); Online - full text ed.: (from EBSCO Publishing, JSTOR (Web-based Journal Archive)).
Indexed: ABIPC, ASCA, ASFA, AgBio, Agr, AnBeAb, AnBrAb, ApEcolAb, BIOBASE, BIOSIS Prev, BioDAb, BiolAb, CIN, CTO, ChemAb, ChemTitl, CivEngAb, CurCont, EPB, ESPM, EntAb, ExcerpMed, FLUIDEX, ForAb, GEOBASE, HelmAb, HerbAb, I&DA, IABS, ISR, M&GPA, M&TEA, NutrAb, OceAb, PN&I, PollutAb, RRTA, RefZh, RevApplEntom, S&F, SCI, SFA, SWRA, SeedAb, TDB, WAE&RSA, WRCInf, WeedAb, WildRev, ZooRec.
—BLDSC (3812.593700), CASDDS, CISTI, IDS, IE, Infotrieve, ingenta, Linda Hall. **CCC.**
Published by: Estuarine Research Federation, 2018 Daffodil, PO Box 510, Port Republic, MD 20676. TEL 410-586-0997, FAX 410-586-9226, stt@estuaries-olemiss.edu, http://erf.org/journal/journal.html, http://erf.org/journal.html. R&P Harold Stevenson. Adv. contact Joy Bartholonnew. Circ: 1,800.
Subscr. to: Allen Press Inc., PO Box 1897, Lawrence, KS 66044. TEL 785-843-1235, FAX 785-843-1274, estuaries@allenpress.com.

➤ **ESTUARINE, COASTAL AND SHELF SCIENCE.** see *EARTH SCIENCES—Oceanography*

➤ **ESTUDIOS DE ANTROPOLOGIA BIOLOGICA.** see *ANTHROPOLOGY*

174.957 JPN ISSN 1173-2571
➤ **EUBIOS JOURNAL OF ASIAN AND INTERNATIONAL BIOETHICS.** Text in English. 1991. bi-m. JPY 3,500, USD 35, NZD 60 (effective 2003). adv. bk.rev. 40 p./no.; back issues avail. **Document type:** *Journal, Academic/Scholarly.* **Description:** Aims to review and update news and trends in bioethics from around the world.
Formerly (until 1995): Eubios Ethics Institute Newsletter (1170-5485)
Related titles: Online - full text ed.: free (effective 2005).
Published by: Eubios Ethics Institute, PO Box 125, Tsukuba Science City, 305-8591, Japan. TEL 81-298-534662, FAX 81-298-536614, macer@sakura.cc.tsukuba.ac.jp, http://www.biol.tsukuba.ac.jp/~macer/EJAIB.html. Ed., R&P, Adv. contact Darryl Macer. Circ: 500 (paid and controlled).

➤ **EUPOLIS**; rivista critica di ecologia territoriale. see *ENVIRONMENTAL STUDIES*

570 USA ISSN 1548-0488
▼ **EUREKAH BIOSCIENCE.** Text in English. 2004. m. USD 150 domestic to individuals; USD 250 foreign to individuals; USD 700 domestic to institutions; USD 800 foreign to institutions; USD 35 per issue (effective 2004).
Published by: Landes Bioscience, 810 S Church St, Georgetown, TX 78626. TEL 512-863-7762, FAX 512-863-0081, http://www.landesbioscience.com/.

570 FRA ISSN 0999-5749
RB37.A1 CODEN: BIOLE6
➤ **EUROBIOLOGISTE.** Text in French. 1955. bi-m. adv. bk.rev. **Document type:** *Academic/Scholarly.* **Description:** Scholarly articles focusing on research findings in the biological sciences.
Former titles: Biologiste (0981-6003); Pharmacien Biologiste (0553-9323)
Related titles: Online - full text ed.
Indexed: BiolAb, ChemAb, ExcerpMed, IPA, RefZh.
—CASDDS, Linda Hall. **CCC.**
Published by: Centre National des Biologistes, 80 av. du Maine, Paris, 75014, France. TEL 33-1-43229770, FAX 33-1-43217312. Pub. Jean Benoit. Adv. contact Jeanne Berga. Circ: 3,200.

571.3 NLD ISSN 0924-3860
QL799 CODEN: EJMOEB
➤ **EUROPEAN JOURNAL OF MORPHOLOGY**; incorporating European archives & biology. Text in English. 1938. 5/yr. GBP 425, USD 700 combined subscription to institutions print & online eds. (effective 2006). adv. bk.rev. bibl.; charts. index. back issues avail.; reprint service avail. from PSC. **Document type:** *Journal, Academic/Scholarly.* **Description:** Publishes research and commentary in all areas of vertabrate morphology, especially human embryology and anatomy.
Incorporates (in 1995): European Archives of Biology (0777-0553); Which was formerly (1886-1989): Archives de Biologie (0003-9624); Former titles (until 1989): Acta Morphologica Neerlando-Scandinavica (0001-6225); (until 1956): Acta Nederlandica Morphologiae Narmalis et Pathologicae (0365-4907)
Related titles: Microfiche ed.: (from BHP); Online - full text ed.: ISSN 1744-4241. GBP 404, USD 700 to institutions (effective 2006) (from EBSCO Publishing, Gale Group, IngentaConnect, O C L C Online Computer Library Center, Inc., Swets Information Services).
Indexed: ASCA, ASFA, AgBio, AnBrAb, BIOBASE, BIOSIS Prev, BiolAb, ChemAb, CurCont, DSA, DentInd, ESPM, ExcerpMed, IABS, ISR, IndMed, IndVet, Inpharma, MEDLINE, NutrAb, PE&ON, PN&I, PollutAb, PoultAb, Reac, RefZh, SCI, SFA, VetBull, WildRev, ZooRec.
—BLDSC (3829.731660), CASDDS, CISTI, GNLM, IDS, IE, Infotrieve, ingenta, Linda Hall. **CCC.**
Published by: Taylor & Francis The Netherlands (Subsidiary of: Taylor & Francis Group), Schipolweg 107 C, PO Box 447, Leiden, 2316 XC, Netherlands. TEL 31-715-243080, FAX 31-715-234571, pub@swets.nl, http://www.tandf.co.uk/journals/titles/09243860.asp, http://www.tandf.co.uk/swets.asp. Eds. Benjamin M, Hillen B. R&P J van der Valk. Adv. contact Miranda Mauritz. page EUR 300; trim 210 x 297. Circ: 600.

577 FRA ISSN 1164-5563
QH84.8 CODEN: EJSBE2
➤ **EUROPEAN JOURNAL OF SOIL BIOLOGY.** Text in English; Summaries in French, English. 1964. 4/yr. EUR 275 in Europe to institutions; JPY 36,400 in Japan to institutions; USD 308 to institutions except Europe and Japan (effective 2006). adv. bk.rev. bibl.; charts; illus. index. back issues avail. **Document type:** *Journal, Academic/Scholarly.* **Description:** Examines biology and ecology of the soil. Also focuses on interactions of soil organisms and the ecosystem balance.
Formerly: Revue d'Ecologie et de Biologie du Sol (0035-1822)
Related titles: Microform ed.: (from PQC); Online - full text ed.: (from EBSCO Publishing, Gale Group, IngentaConnect, ScienceDirect, Swets Information Services).
Indexed: AEA, ASCA, AbHyg, AgBio, AgrForAb, AnBrAb, BIOBASE, BIOSIS Prev, BioCN&I, BiolAb, CIN, CPA, ChemAb, ChemTitl, CurCont, EIA, EnerInd, EngInd, ExcerpMed, FCA, FPA, ForAb, HerbAb, HortAb, I&DA, MaizeAb, NemAb, NutrAb, PN&I, PlantSci, PotatoAb, PoultAb, ProtozoAb, RA&MP, RPP, RevApplEntom, RiceAb, S&F, SCI, SFA, SIA, SeedAb, SoyAb, TriticAb, WeedAb, WildRev, ZooRec.
—BLDSC (3829.741000), CASDDS, CISTI, Ei, IDS, IE, Infotrieve, ingenta, Linda Hall. **CCC.**
Published by: Elsevier France, Editions Scientifiques et Medicales (Subsidiary of: Elsevier Science & Technology), 23 Rue Linois, Paris, 75724, France. TEL 33-1-71724600, FAX 33-1-71724650, academic@elsevier-fr.com, http://www.elsevier.com/locate/ejsobi. Ed. T Vogel. Circ: 1,000.
Subscr. to: Elsevier BV, PO Box 211, Amsterdam 1000 AE, Netherlands. nlinfo-f@elsevier.nl, http://www.elsevier.nl.

➤ **EUROPEAN JOURNAL OF ULTRASOUND.** see *MEDICAL SCIENCES—Radiology And Nuclear Medicine*

➤ **EVOLUTION AND COGNITION.** see *PSYCHOLOGY*

571.3 USA ISSN 1520-541X
QH359 CODEN: ELDMF9
➤ **EVOLUTION & DEVELOPMENT.** Text in English. 1999. bi-m. USD 138 combined subscription in the Americas to individuals & Caribbean (print & online eds.); USD 149 combined subscription in Canada & Mexico to individuals print & online eds.; GBP 119 combined subscription elsewhere to individuals print & online eds.; USD 340 combined subscription in the Americas to institutions & Caribbean (print & online eds.); USD 353 combined subscription in Canada & Mexico to institutions print & online eds.; GBP 254 combined subscription elsewhere to institutions print & online eds. (effective 2006). adv. bk.rev. reprints avail. **Document type:** *Journal, Academic/Scholarly.* **Description:** Publishes research papers and review articles reflecting the rapid growth in research where the fields of evolutionary and developmental biology have, after some 50 years, become reintegrated.
Related titles: ♦ Online - full text ed.: Evolution & Development Online. ISSN 1525-142X.
Indexed: BIOBASE, CurCont, EntAb, GEOBASE, ISR, MEDLINE, SCI, ZooRec.
—BLDSC (3834.215000), CISTI, IE, Infotrieve, ingenta. **CCC.**
Published by: (Society for Integrative and Comparative Biology), Blackwell Publishing, Inc. (Subsidiary of: Blackwell Publishing Ltd.), Commerce Place, 350 Main St, Malden, MA 02148. TEL 781-388-8206, FAX 781-388-8232, subscrip@blackwellpub.com, http://www.blackwellpublishing.com/journals/EDE. Ed. Rudolf A Raff. R&P Tracey Davies. Adv. contact Jenny Applin.

571.3 USA ISSN 1525-142X
EVOLUTION & DEVELOPMENT ONLINE. Text in English. bi-m. USD 323 in the Americas to institutions & Caribbean; USD 335 in Canada & Mexico to institutions; GBP 241 elsewhere to institutions (effective 2006). **Document type:** *Academic/Scholarly.*
Media: Online - full text (from Blackwell Synergy, EBSCO Publishing, Gale Group, IngentaConnect, O C L C Online Computer Library Center, Inc., Swets Information Services).
Related titles: ♦ Print ed.: Evolution & Development. ISSN 1520-541X.
Published by: Blackwell Publishing, Inc. (Subsidiary of: Blackwell Publishing Ltd.), Commerce Place, 350 Main St, Malden, MA 02148. TEL 781-388-8206, FAX 781-388-8232, website@blacksci.com, subscrip@blackwellpub.com, http://www.blackwell-science.com/~cgilib/bsinc.bin?Journal=geoscience, http://www.blackwellpublishing.com.

EVOLUTIONARY ECOLOGY. see *ENVIRONMENTAL STUDIES*

EVOLUTIONARY ECOLOGY RESEARCH. see *ENVIRONMENTAL STUDIES*

599.9 USA ISSN 0272-0809
➤ **EVOLUTIONARY MONOGRAPHS.** Text in English. 1979. irreg. price varies. **Document type:** *Monographic series, Academic/Scholarly.* **Description:** Publishes long papers and other nonstandard items in the evolutionary half of biology and historical geology.
Indexed: BiolAb.
—BLDSC (3834.452000).
Published by: University of Chicago, Department of Ecology and Evolution, 1101 E 57th St, Chicago, IL 60637. TEL 312-702-9475. Ed. Leigh M Van Valen. Circ: 200 (paid).

570 USA ISSN 1528-2619
QH359 CODEN: EVTHB4
➤ **EVOLUTIONARY THEORY & REVIEW**; an international journal of fact and interpretation. Text in English. 1973. irreg. USD 28. bk.rev. **Document type:** *Academic/Scholarly.* **Description:** Publishes factual and theoretical papers and reviews on topics in evolutionary biology.
Formerly (until 1991): Evolutionary Theory (0093-4755)
Indexed: AnBrAb, BIOSIS Prev, BiolAb, Biostat, CIS, CurCont, SFA, ZooRec.
—Linda Hall.
Published by: University of Chicago, Department of Ecology and Evolution, 1101 E 57th St, Chicago, IL 60637. TEL 312-702-9475. Eds. Leigh M Van Valen, Virginia C Maiorana. Circ: 650 (paid).

570 ARG ISSN 1514-920X
EXACTAMENTE. Text in Spanish. 1994. 3/yr. back issues avail. **Document type:** *Academic/Scholarly.*
Related titles: Online - full text ed.
Published by: Universidad de Buenos Aires, Facultad de Ciencias Exactas y Naturales, Cuidad Universitaria, Nunez - Pabellon 2, Buenos Aires, 1428, Argentina. TEL 54-11-4573300, revista@de.fcen.uba.ar, info@fcen.uba.ar, http://www.fcen.uba.ar/publicac/revexact/revindex.htm, http://fcen.uba.ar/. Ed. Dr. Julio Rey Pastor.

EXCERPTA MEDICA. SECTION 5: GENERAL PATHOLOGY AND PATHOLOGICAL ANATOMY. see *BIOLOGY—Abstracting, Bibliographies, Statistics*

570 GBR
EXMOOR NATIONAL PARK AUTHORITY. ANNUAL REPORT. Text in English. a.
Published by: Exmoor National Park Authority, Exmoor House, Dulverton, Somerset, TA22 9HL, United Kingdom. TEL 01398-323665, FAX 01398-323150.

570 GBR ISSN 1367-7047
EXMOOR NATURALIST. Text in English. irreg.
Indexed: ZooRec.
Published by: Exmoor National Park Authority, Exmoor House, Dulverton, Somerset, TA22 9HL, United Kingdom. TEL 01398-323665, FAX 01398-323150.

570 610 USA ISSN 1535-3702
QP1 CODEN: EBMMBE
➤ **EXPERIMENTAL BIOLOGY AND MEDICINE (MAYWOOD).** Text in English. 1903. 11/yr. membership dues include a subscription to print & online eds. adv. abstr.; bibl.; illus. index. back issues avail.; reprints avail. **Document type:** *Academic/Scholarly.* **Description:** Attempts to promote investigation in the biomedical sciences by encouraging and facilitating the interchange of scientific information among disciplines. Presents original articles, minireviews, and symposia.
Formerly (until 2001): Society for Experimental Biology and Medicine. Proceedings (0037-9727)

B

Related titles: Microfilm ed.: (from PMC, WWS); Online - full text ed.: ISSN 1535-3699 (from Blackwell Synergy, EBSCO Publishing, Gale Group, HighWire Press, IngentaConnect, O C L C Online Computer Library Center, Inc., Swets Information Services).
Indexed: ASCA, ASFA, AbHyg, AgBio, Agr, AnBrAb, BBCI, BIOBASE, BIOSIS Prev, BibAg, BiolAb, CPA, ChemAb, ChemTitl, CurCont, DBA, DSA, DentInd, ExcerpMed, FS&TA, HortAb, IABS, ISR, IndMed, IndVet, Inpharma, MEDLINE, MaizeAb, NutrAb, PBA, PE&ON, PHN&I, PN&I, PoultAb, ProtozoAb, RA&MP, RM&VM, RPP, Reac, RevApplEntom, SAA, SCI, SFA, SIA, SoyAb, TDB, THA, TriticAb, VetBull, WeedAb, WildRev, ZooRec.
—BLDSC (3838.750700), CASDDS, CISTI, GNLM, IDS, IE, ingenta, KNAW, Linda Hall. **CCC.**
Published by: Society for Experimental Biology and Medicine, 195 W. Spring Valley Ave., Maywood, NJ 07607-1727. TEL 201-291-9080, FAX 201-291-2988, sebm@inch.com, http://www.ebmonline.org/. Ed. Andrzej Bartke. Circ: 3,200.

➤ **EXPERIMENTAL PARASITOLOGY.** see *MEDICAL SCIENCES—Communicable Diseases*

➤ **EXPRESS BULLETINS**; a series of current awareness bulletins for researchers in biology and medicine. see *BIOLOGY—Abstracting, Bibliographies, Statistics*

570 540 510 530 ARG ISSN 0325-4216
QH113 CODEN: FACEDE
F A C E N A. Text in English, Portuguese, Spanish; Summaries in English, Spanish. 1980. a. USD 20 (effective 2000). adv. bk.rev. index. back issues avail. **Document type:** *Bulletin, Academic/Scholarly.* **Description:** Publishes original scientific papers, communications or short notes and critical reviews related to basic investigation and-or technological development in biology, chemistry, mathematics and physics.
Indexed: BiolAb, ChemAb.
—CASDDS.
Published by: Universidad Nacional del Nordeste, Facultad de Ciencias Exactas y Naturales y Agrimensura, Avenida Libertad 5450, Corrientes, 3400, Argentina. TEL 54-3783-473930, FAX 54-3783-473930, balvarez@exa.unne.edu.ar. Adv. contact Blanca Beatriz Alvarez de Avanza. Circ: 200.

570 USA ISSN 0892-6638
QH301 CODEN: FAJOEC
➤ **THE F A S E B JOURNAL.** Text in English. 1987. 14/yr. ((monthly excep. 3 times in Mar.)). USD 182 combined subscription domestic to individuals print & online eds.; USD 206 combined subscription in Canada & Mexico to individuals print & online eds.; USD 278 combined subscription elsewhere to individuals print & online eds.; USD 798 combined subscription domestic to institutions print & online eds.; USD 822 combined subscription in Canada & Mexico to institutions print & online eds.; USD 894 combined subscription elsewhere to institutions print & online eds.; USD 106 combined subscription domestic to members print & online eds.; USD 130 combined subscription in Canada & Mexico to members print & online eds.; USD 202 combined subscription elsewhere to members print & online eds. (effective 2005). adv. abstr.; charts; illus. index. back issues avail.; reprint service avail. from PQC. **Document type:** *Journal, Academic/Scholarly.* **Description:** Presents scholarly papers and reviews of research in experimental biology, encompassing physiology, biological chemistry, pharmacology, experimental therapeutics, immunology, nutrition, and cell biology.
Supersedes (in 1987): Federation of American Societies for Experimental Biology. Federation Proceedings (0014-9446)
Related titles: Microform ed.; Online - full text ed.: ISSN 1530-6860. USD 540 (effective 2001) (from EBSCO Publishing, HighWire Press); Supplement(s): Experimental Biology (Year) Abstracts.
Indexed: ASCA, ASFA, AbHyg, AgBio, Agr, AnBrAb, B&AI, BIOBASE, BIOSIS Prev, BibAg, BiolAb, BiolDig, CCI, CIN, CPA, CTA, ChemAb, ChemTitl, CurCont, DBA, DSA, ESPM, ExcerpMed, FCA, FS&TA, ForAb, GenetAb, HGA, HelmAb, HortAb, IABS, ISR, IndMed, IndVet, Inpharma, MEDLINE, MS&D, NRN, NSA, NemAb, NucAcAb, NutrAb, PBA, PE&ON, PGegResA, PGrRegA, PN&I, PoultAb, ProtozoAb, RA&MP, RM&VM, RPP, Reac, RevApplEntom, S&F, SCI, SFA, SSCI, SoyAb, TDB, THA, TriticAb, VetBull, WeedAb, WildRev, ZooRec.
—BLDSC (3896.579700), CASDDS, CISTI, GNLM, IDS, IE, Infotrieve, ingenta, Linda Hall. **CCC.**
Published by: Federation of American Societies for Experimental Biology, 9650 Rockville Pike, Rm L-2407A, Bethesda, MD 20814-3998. TEL 301-634-7029, FAX 301-634-7809, staff@faseb.org, http://www.faseb.org. Ed. Vincent T Marchesi. R&P S. Jacobson. Adv. contact Susan Mergenhagen. B&W page USD 1,950, color page USD 3,045; trim 7 x 10. Circ: 6,000 (paid).

570 USA
F A S E B NEWS. Text in English. bi-m. adv. **Document type:** *Newsletter.*
Published by: Federation of American Societies for Experimental Biology, 9650 Rockville Pike, Rm L-2407A, Bethesda, MD 20814-3998. TEL 301-634-7100, FAX 301-634-7153, http://www.faseb.org/opa/fnews.html. Adv. contact Susan Mergenhagen. B&W page USD 2,495; trim 8.5 x 11.

578.77 USA ISSN 1092-194X
SH222.F6
F M R I TECHNICAL REPORTS. (Florida Marine Research Institute) Text in English. 1995. irreg.
Indexed: ASFA, ZooRec.
Published by: Florida Marine Research Institute, Department of Environmental Protection, 100 8th Ave. S.E., St. Petersburg, FL 33701. FAX 813-823-0166.

FACHBUCHVERZEICHNIS NATURWISSENSCHAFTEN. see *BIOLOGY—Abstracting, Bibliographies, Statistics*

FACTA UNIVERSITATIS. SERIES MEDICINE AND BIOLOGY. see *MEDICAL SCIENCES*

578.77 COL ISSN 0120-9000
FACULTAD DE BIOLOGIA MARINA. BOLETIN. Text in Spanish. 1983. s-a.
Indexed: ESPM.
Published by: Fundacion Universidad de Bogota Jorge Tadeo Lozano, Facultad de Biologia Marina, Carrera 4 No 22-61, Sector A, Modulo 1, Oficina 434, Bogota, Colombia. TEL 57-1-3341777, FAX 57-1-2826197, biologia.marina@utadeo.edu.co, http://www.utadeo.edu.co.

FACULTAD NACIONAL DE AGRONOMIA MEDELLIN. REVISTA. see *AGRICULTURE*

570 GBR ISSN 1740-4118
▼ **FACULTY OF 1000 BIOLOGY.** Variant title: Faculty of One Thousand Biology. Text in English. 2003. m. GBP 1,000, USD 1,755, EUR 1,456 to institutions 1-20 users; GBP 297, USD 535, EUR 430 academic institutions, 1-20 users (effective 2006). **Document type:** *Academic/Scholarly.* **Description:** Online research tool that highlights the most interesting papers in biology, based on the recommendations of over 1000 leading scientists.
Formerly (until 2005): Faculty of 1000 (1474-2276)
Media: Online - full content.
Published by: BioMed Central Ltd. (Subsidiary of: Current Science Ltd), Middlesex House, 34-42 Cleveland St, London, W1T 4LB, United Kingdom. TEL 44-20-76319131, FAX 44-20-76319923, info@biomedcentral.com, http://www.facultyof1000.com/, http://www.biomedcentral.com.

FAELTBIOLOGEN. see *ENVIRONMENTAL STUDIES*

570 FRA ISSN 0428-2779
CODEN: FBIOAA
FEUILLETS DE BIOLOGIE; le repertoire medical pratique. Text in French. 1960. bi-m. adv. bk.rev. bibl.; charts; illus.
Indexed: BIOBASE, BiolAb, ChemAb, ExcerpMed, IABS, RM&VM.
—BLDSC (3913.600000), CASDDS, GNLM, IE, Infotrieve, ingenta. **CCC.**
Published by: Editions Orion, 9 av. du Bel Air, Bezons, 95870, France. TEL 33-1-39472260, FAX 33-1-30762212. Ed. Dr. Bernard Bousquet. Circ: 4,000.

570 JPN ISSN 0917-4850
➤ **FIRUDO BAIOROJISUTO/FIELD BIOLOGIST.** Text in Japanese. 1991. s-a. JPY 5,000. bk.rev. **Document type:** *Academic/Scholarly.* **Description:** Covers ecology, systematics, biogeography, and natural environment.
Published by: Gunma Yagai Seibutsu Gakkai/Field Biologist's Society of Gunma, c/o Mr S. Saito, Gunma Pref. Women's University, 1395 Kami-Note, Sawa-gun, Tamamura-machi, Gunma-ken 370-1127, Japan. TEL 0270-65-8511, FAX 0270-65-9538. Ed. Yukio Shishida. Circ: 500 (controlled).

578.77 GBR ISSN 1050-4648
QL638.97 CODEN: FSIMEP
➤ **FISH AND SHELLFISH IMMUNOLOGY.** Text in English. 1991. 10/yr. EUR 828 in Europe to institutions; JPY 89,400 in Japan to institutions; USD 737 to institutions except Europe and Japan (effective 2006). adv. illus. Index. reprints avail. **Document type:** *Journal, Academic/Scholarly.* **Description:** Presents studies on the basic mechanisms of both the specific and nonspecific defense systems, the cells, tissues, and hormonal factors involved, their dependence on environmental and intrinsic factors, response to pathogens, response to vaccination, and applied studies on the development of specific vaccines for use in the aquaculture industry.
Related titles: Online - full text ed.: ISSN 1095-9947. USD 777 (effective 2002) (from EBSCO Publishing, Gale Group, IngentaConnect, O C L C Online Computer Library Center, Inc., ScienceDirect, Swets Information Services).
Indexed: AIDS&CR, ASCA, ASFA, AgBio, AnBrAb, B&BAb, BIOSIS Prev, BiolAb, CurCont, DSA, ESPM, FoVS&M, HelmAb, ISR, ImmunAb, IndMed, IndVet, MEDLINE, NutrAb, OceAb, PBA, ProtozoAb, RM&VM, SCI, SFA, SoyAb, TDB, VetBull, WildRev, ZooRec.
—BLDSC (3934.880000), CINDOC, CISTI, IDS, IE, Infotrieve, ingenta. **CCC.**
Published by: Academic Press (Subsidiary of: Elsevier Science & Technology), Harcourt Pl, 32 Jamestown Rd, London, NW1 7BY, United Kingdom. TEL 44-20-7424-4200, FAX 44-20-7483-2293, apsubs@acad.com, http://www.elsevier.com/locate/fsi. Eds. A E Ellis, C Secombes. R&P Catherine John. Adv. contact Nik Screen.

571.96 USA
FISH IMMUNOLOGY - TECHNICAL COMMUNICATIONS. Text in English. irreg. **Document type:** *Monographic series, Academic/Scholarly.*
Published by: SOS Publications, 43 DeNormadie Ave, Fair Haven, NJ 07704-3303. TEL 732-530-3199, FAX 732-530-5896, sosjs@netlabs.net, http://netlabs.net/hp/sosjs. Eds. J.S. Stolen, T.C. Fletcher.

578.77 TON ISSN 1173-3012
FISHERIES RESEARCH BULLETING OF TONGA. Text in English. 199?. irreg.
Published by: Tonga. Ministry of Fisheries, PO Box 871, Nukualofa, Tonga. TEL 676-21399, FAX 676-23891, mofish01@kalianet.to.

578.77 USA
FISHES OF THE WESTERN NORTH ATLANTIC. MEMOIRS. Text in English. 1948. irreg., latest vol.1, 1989, part 9. price varies. back issues avail. **Document type:** *Monographic series.*
Published by: Sears Foundation for Marine Research, Kline Geology Laboratory, Yale University, Box 208109, New Haven, CT 06520-8109. FAX 203-432-3760. Ed. Dr. Leo Buss.

578.77 USA ISSN 0095-0157
CODEN: FMPUA4
FLORIDA MARINE RESEARCH PUBLICATIONS. Text in English. 1973. irreg. per issue exchange basis. charts; illus. **Document type:** *Academic/Scholarly.*
Formed by the merger of: Florida Marine Research Institute. Educational Series (0094-2693); Florida Marine Research Institute. Leaflet Series; Florida Marine Research Institute. Professional Papers Series (0160-4473); Florida Marine Research Institute. Saltwater Fishery Leaflets; Florida Marine Research Institute. Special Scientific Report; Florida Marine Research Institute. Technical Series (0149-4015)
Indexed: ASFA, BIOSIS Prev, BiolAb, ESPM, OceAb, SFA, WildRev, ZooRec.
—CISTI, Linda Hall.
Published by: Florida Marine Research Institute, Department of Environmental Protection, 100 8th Ave. S.E., St. Petersburg, FL 33701. FAX 813-823-0166. Ed. K A Steidinger. Circ: 1,000.

508 USA
QH1 CODEN: BFMSEU
➤ **FLORIDA MUSEUM OF NATURAL HISTORY. BULLETIN.** Summaries in English, Spanish. 1956. irreg. price varies. abstr.; bibl.; charts; illus.; stat. cum.index. back issues avail.; reprints avail. **Document type:** *Journal, Academic/Scholarly.* **Description:** Presents the results of research in the natural sciences, emphasizing the circum-Caribbean region.
Former titles: Florida Museum of Natural History. Bulletin. Biological Sciences (1052-3669); (until 1990): Florida State Museum. Bulletin. Biological Sciences (0071-6154)
Indexed: ASFA, BIOSIS Prev, BiolAb, ESPM, SFA, WildRev, ZooRec.
—CISTI, Linda Hall.
Published by: Florida Museum of Natural History, University of Florida, Box 117800, Gainesville, FL 32611-7800. TEL 352-392-1721, FAX 352-846-0287, mjoyner@flmnh.ufl.edu, http://www.flmnh.edu/admin/bulletin.htm. Eds. John F Eisenberg, Richard Franz. R&P Margaret E.B. Joyner. Circ: 700.

➤ **FLORIDA SEA GRANT COLLEGE PROGRAM. EXTENSION BULLETIN.** see *FISH AND FISHERIES*

570 USA ISSN 0533-1242
➤ **FOCUS (ROCKVILLE).** Text in English. 1979. q. free. index, cum.index: vols.1-21. back issues avail. **Document type:** *Newsletter, Academic/Scholarly.* **Description:** Describes novel techniques, improvements of common techniques, simplified protocols, and trouble shooting of life science techniques.
Related titles: Online - full text ed.: (from East View Information Services).
Indexed: ASFA, ESPM, H&SSA.
Published by: Life Technologies, Inc., PO Box 6482, Rockville, MD 20849-6482. TEL 301-610-8000, http://www.lifetech.com. Ed., R&P Doreen Cupo. Circ: 40,000.

➤ **FOLIA BIOCHIMICA ET BIOLOGICA GRAECA.** see *BIOLOGY—Biochemistry*

570 POL ISSN 0015-5497
CODEN: FOBGA8
➤ **FOLIA BIOLOGICA**; international journal of biological research. Text and summaries in English. 1953. q. EUR 69 foreign (effective 2005). adv. bk.rev. abstr.; bibl.; charts; illus. index. back issues avail. **Document type:** *Journal, Academic/Scholarly.* **Description:** Publishes papers concerning various aspects of experimental zoology, nuclear and chromosome research and ultrastructural studies.
Related titles: E-mail ed.; Fax ed.; Online - full text ed.: (from IngentaConnect).
Indexed: ASFA, AbHyg, AgBio, AgrAg, AgrForAb, AnBrAb, BIOBASE, BIOSIS Prev, BioCN&I, BiolAb, CIN, ChemAb, ChemTitl, CurCont, DSA, DentInd, ESPM, EntAb, ExcerpMed, ForAb, IABS, ISR, IndMed, IndVet, MEDLINE, NemAb, NutrAb, PBA, PN&I, PoultAb, ProtozoAb, RPP, TDB, VetBull, ZooRec.
—BLDSC (3966.900000), CASDDS, CISTI, GNLM, IDS, IE, Infotrieve, ingenta, Linda Hall.

Published by: Polska Akademia Nauk, Instytut Systematyki i Ewolucji Zwierzat/Polish Academy of Sciences, Institute of Systematics and Evolution of Animals, ul Slawkowska 17, Krakow, 31-016, Poland. TEL 48-12-4221901, FAX 48-12-4224294, folia@isez.pan.krakow.pl, http://www.isez.pan.krakow.pl. Ed., R&P Halina Kosciuszko. Adv. contact Ewa Zychowska. Circ: 350. **Dist. by:** Ars Polona, Krakowskie Przedmiescie 7, Warsaw, Poland. TEL 48-22-9263914, FAX 48-22-9265334, arspolona@arspolona.com.pl, http://www.arspolona.com.pl.

570 CZE ISSN 0015-5500
QH301 CODEN: FOBLAN

➤ **FOLIA BIOLOGICA**; journal of cellular and molecular biology. Text and summaries in English. 1952. bi-m. EUR 260 in Europe; USD 275 elsewhere (effective 2005). adv. bk.rev. abstr.; charts; illus. index. back issues avail. **Document type:** *Journal, Academic/Scholarly.* **Description:** Publishes reports on the results of original research in the field of molecular and cellular biology.
Supersedes in part (in 1959): Ceskoslovenska Biologie (0411-6038)
Related titles: Online - full text ed.: 2000 (from ProQuest Information & Learning).
Indexed: ASFA, AbHyg, AgBio, AgrLib, AnBrAb, BIOBASE, BIOSIS Prev, BiolAb, CIN, CISA, ChemAb, ChemTitl, CurCont, DSA, ExcerpMed, HortAb, IABS, INIS AtomInd, ISR, IndMed, IndVet, Inpharma, MEDLINE, NutrAb, PBA, PN&I, PoultAb, ProtozoAb, RM&VM, Reac, SCI, SeedAb, TDB, VetBull.
—BLDSC (3967.000000), CASDDS, CISTI, GNLM, IDS, IE, Infotrieve, ingenta, Linda Hall. **CCC.**
Published by: Akademie Ved Ceske Republiky, Ustav Molekularni Genetiky/Academy of Sciences of the Czech Republic, Institute of Molecular Genetics, Flemingovo n 2, Prague, 16637, Czech Republic. TEL 42-2-24310234, FAX 42-2-24310955, folia@img.cas.cz, office@img.cas.cz, http://www.img.cas.cz/fb/. Ed. J Svoboda. R&P Catherine John. Adv. contact Nik Screen. Circ: 950. **Subscr. to:** Myris Trade, V Stihlach 1311, PO Box 2, Prague 4 14201, Czech Republic. TEL 420-2-34035200, FAX 420-2-34035207, myris@myris.cz, http://www.myris.cz.

➤ **FOLIA DENDROLOGICA.** see *FORESTS AND FORESTRY*

570 CZE ISSN 1211-3662
CODEN: FFUBAP

FOLIA FACULTATIS SCIENTIARUM NATURALIUM UNIVERSITATIS MASARYKIANAE BRUNENSIS. BIOLOGIA. Text in Czech. a. price varies. **Document type:** *Monographic series, Academic/Scholarly.*
Formerly (until 1992): Folia Facultatis Scientiarum Naturalium Universitatis Purkynianae Brunensis: Biologia (0323-0082)
Indexed: BiolAb, ChemAb, RefZh, ZooRec.
—CASDDS, CISTI, Linda Hall.
Published by: Masarykova Universita, Prirodovedecka Fakulta/Masaryk University, Faculty of Sciences, Kotlarska 2, Brno, 61137, Czech Republic. Ed. Jaromir Vanhara.

571.3 POL ISSN 0015-5659
QL799 CODEN: FOMOAJ

➤ **FOLIA MORPHOLOGICA.** Text in English. 1929. q. (in 1 vol., 4 nos./vol.). EUR 84 foreign (effective 2005). adv. bk.rev. charts; illus. index. 85 p./no. 2 cols./p.; back issues avail.; reprints avail. **Document type:** *Journal, Academic/Scholarly.* **Description:** An international multidisciplinary journal devoted to fundamental research in the morphological sciences (anatomy, cytology, embryology, histology and histochemistry).
Related titles: Online - full content ed.
Indexed: BIOBASE, BiolAb, ChemAb, DentInd, ExcerpMed, IndMed, MEDLINE, SFA, VetBull, ZooRec.
—BLDSC (3971.610000), CASDDS, CISTI, GNLM, IE, Infotrieve, ingenta, KNAW, Linda Hall.
Published by: (Polskie Towarzystwo Anatomiczne/Polish Anatomical Society), Wydawnictwo Via Medica, ul Swietokrzyska 73, Gdansk, 80180, Poland. TEL 48-58-3209494, FAX 48-58-3209460, redakcja@viamedica.pl, http://www.fm.viamedica.pl. Ed. Janusz Morys. Circ: 870. **Dist. by:** Ars Polona, Krakowskie Przedmiescie 7, Warsaw, Poland. TEL 48-22-9263914, FAX 48-22-9265334, arspolona@arspolona.com.pl, http://www.arspolona.com.pl.

616.079 GBR ISSN 0954-0105
CODEN: FAIMEZ

➤ **FOOD AND AGRICULTURAL IMMUNOLOGY.** Text in English. 1989. q. GBP 754, USD 1,239 combined subscription to institutions print & online eds. (effective 2006). reprint service avail. from PSC. **Document type:** *Journal, Academic/Scholarly.* **Description:** Features original immunological research with food, agricultural, environmental and veterinary applications.
Related titles: Online - full text ed.: ISSN 1465-3443. GBP 716, USD 1,177 to institutions (effective 2006) (from EBSCO Publishing, Gale Group, IngentaConnect, O C L C Online Computer Library Center, Inc., ProQuest Information & Learning, Swets Information Services).
Indexed: AEBA, AIDS&CR, ASCA, ASFA, AbHyg, AgBio, Agr, AgrForAb, AnBrAb, AnalAb, B&BAb, BIOBASE, BIOSIS Prev, BioDAb, BioEngAb, BiolAb, CIN, CPA, ChemAb, ChemTitl, CurCont, DSA, EPB, ESPM, FCA, FPA, FS&TA, ForAb, HelmAb, HerbAb, HortAb, IABS, ImmunAb, IndVet, MBA, MaizeAb, NutrAb, OrnHort, PBA, PGegResA, PHN&I, PN&I, PotatoAb, PoultAb, RM&VM, RPP, RefZh, RevApplEntom, RiceAb, S&F, SIA, SeedAb, SoyAb, TDB, TriticAb, VITIS, VetBull, WeedAb.
—BLDSC (3977.004500), CASDDS, CISTI, IDS, IE, Infotrieve, ingenta. **CCC.**
Published by: Taylor & Francis Ltd (Subsidiary of: Taylor & Francis Group), 4 Park Sq, Milton Park, Abingdon, OX14 4RN, United Kingdom. TEL 44-1235-828600, FAX 44-1235-829000, info@tandf.co.uk, http://www.tandf.co.uk/journals/titles/09540105.asp. Ed. Chris Smith. **Subscr. in N. America to:** Taylor & Francis Inc., Customer Services Dept, 325 Chestnut St, 8th Fl, Philadelphia, PA 19106. TEL 215-625-8900, 800-354-1420, FAX 215-625-8914, customerservice@taylorandfrancis.com; **Subscr. to:** Journals Customer Service, Rankine Rd, Basingstoke, Hants RG24 8PR, United Kingdom. TEL 44-1256-813000, FAX 44-1256-330245, enquiry@tandf.co.uk.

➤ **FOREST ECOLOGY AND MANAGEMENT.** see *FORESTS AND FORESTRY*

➤ **FOREST POLICY AND ECONOMICS.** see *FORESTS AND FORESTRY*

610 DEU ISSN 1433-5549

FORSCHUNGSZENTRUM JUELICH. SCHRIFTEN. REIHE LEBENSWISSENSCHAFTEN. Text in German, English. 1998. irreg., latest vol.4, 2000. **Document type:** *Monographic series, Academic/Scholarly.*
Published by: Forschungszentrum Juelich GmbH, Leo-Brandt-Str, Juelich, 52428, Germany. TEL 49-2461-615220, FAX 49-2461-616103, fzj@fz-juelich.de, http://www.fz-juelich.de/zb/text/publikation/l_wiss.html.

570 550 NLD ISSN 1381-2491
QH7

FOUNDATION FOR SCIENTIFIC RESEARCH IN THE CARIBBEAN REGION. PUBLICATION. Text in English. 1946. irreg., latest vol.137, 1996. price varies. back issues avail. **Document type:** *Monographic series.*
Formerly (until 1990): Natuurwetenschappelijke Studiekring voor Suriname en de Nederlandse Antillen. Uitgaven (0300-5534)
Indexed: BIOSIS Prev, BiolAb, ZooRec.
Published by: Foundation for Scientific Research in the Caribbean Region/Natuurwetenschappelijke Studiekring voor het Caraibische Gebied, Instituut voor Taxonomische Zoologie, Plantage Middenlaan 45, Amsterdam, 1018 DC, Netherlands. TEL 31-20-5255926, FAX 31-20-5256612. Ed. Louise J van der Steen. R&P Louise J Westermann.

FRANC - VERT. see *CONSERVATION*

570 USA ISSN 0891-5849
QP527 CODEN: FRBMEH

➤ **FREE RADICAL BIOLOGY & MEDICINE.** Text in English. 1987. 24/yr. EUR 2,594 in Europe to institutions; JPY 344,500 in Japan to institutions; USD 2,901 to institutions except Europe and Japan; EUR 506 in Europe to qualified personnel; JPY 67,400 in Japan to qualified personnel; USD 567 to qualified personnel except Europe and Japan (effective 2006). adv. back issues avail. **Document type:** *Journal, Academic/Scholarly.* **Description:** Encompasses chemical, biochemical, physiological, pathological, pharmacological, toxicological and medical approaches to free-radical research.
Formed by the merger of (1985-1987): Advances in Free Radical Biology and Medicine (8755-9668); (1985-1987): Journal of Free Radicals in Biology and Medicine (0748-5514)
Related titles: Microfilm ed.: (from PQC); Online - full text ed.: (from EBSCO Publishing, Gale Group, IngentaConnect, ScienceDirect, Swets Information Services).
Indexed: ASCA, B&BAb, BBCI, BIOBASE, BIOSIS Prev, BiolAb, CCI, CIN, ChemAb, ChemTitl, CurCont, ESPM, ExcerpMed, FPA, ForAb, GenetAb, HGA, IABS, INIS AtomInd, ISR, IndMed, Inpharma, MEDLINE, MSB, NRN, NSCI, NucAcAb, PE&ON, RA&MP, Reac, RefZh, SCI, THA, ToxAb, VITIS.
—BLDSC (4033.326480), CASDDS, CISTI, GNLM, IDS, IE, Infotrieve, ingenta, KNAW, Linda Hall. **CCC.**
Published by: (Oxygen Society), Elsevier Inc. (Subsidiary of: Elsevier Science & Technology), 360 Park Ave. S, New York, NY 10010-1710. TEL 212-633-3730, 888-437-4636, FAX 212-633-3140, m.targowski@elsevier.com, usinfo-f@elsevier.com, http://www.elsevier.com/locate/freeradbiomed. Eds. Kelvin J A Davies, William A Pryor. Adv. contact Michael Targowski. B&W page USD 1,075, color page USD 1,285.

577 IND

FRENCH INSTITUTE, PONDICHERRY. PONDY PAPERS IN ECOLOGY. Text in English; Summaries in French. 1997. irreg. (approx. 3/yr.). price varies.
Published by: Institut Francais de Pondichery/French Institute of Pondicherry, P O Box 33, Pondicherry, Tamil Nadu 605 001, India. TEL 91-413-34-170, FAX 91-413-39-534, instran@giasmd01.vsnl.net.in. Ed. F Houllier. Circ: 250.

FRESENIUS ENVIRONMENTAL BULLETIN. see *ENVIRONMENTAL STUDIES*

578.77 GBR ISSN 0308-6739
CODEN: OPFAEI

FRESHWATER BIOLOGICAL ASSOCIATION. OCCASIONAL PUBLICATIONS. Text in English. 1976. irreg. price varies. back issues avail. **Document type:** *Monographic series, Academic/Scholarly.*
Related titles: Microfiche ed.
Indexed: ASFA, ESPM, ForAb, MathR, S&F, ZooRec.
—BLDSC (6225.650000), Linda Hall. **CCC.**
Published by: Freshwater Biological Association, The Ferry House, Ambleside, Cumbria LA22 0LP, United Kingdom. TEL 44-1539-442468, FAX 44-1539-446914, info@fba.org.uk, http://www.fba.org.uk. Ed. D W Sutcliffe. Circ: 400.

578.77 GBR ISSN 0367-1887
QH96.A1 CODEN: FBSPAT

FRESHWATER BIOLOGICAL ASSOCIATION. SCIENTIFIC PUBLICATIONS. Text in English. a. price varies. back issues avail. **Document type:** *Academic/Scholarly.*
Related titles: Microfiche ed.
Indexed: ASFA, BIOSIS Prev, BiolAb, ESPM, SFA, WildRev, ZooRec.
—BLDSC (8191.000000), CISTI. **CCC.**
Published by: Freshwater Biological Association, The Ferry House, Ambleside, Cumbria LA22 0LP, United Kingdom. TEL 44-1539-442468, FAX 44-1539-446914, info@fba.org.uk, http://www.fba.org.uk. Eds. D W Sutcliffe, J M Elliott. Circ: 2,500.

B

578.77 GBR

FRESHWATER BIOLOGICAL ASSOCIATION. SPECIAL PUBLICATIONS. Text in English. irreg.
Indexed: ZooRec.
Published by: Freshwater Biological Association, The Ferry House, Ambleside, Cumbria LA22 0LP, United Kingdom. TEL 44-1539-442468, FAX 44-1539-446914, info@fba.org.uk, http://www.fba.org.uk.

578.77 GBR ISSN 0046-5070
QH96.A1 CODEN: FWBLAB

➤ **FRESHWATER BIOLOGY.** Text in English. 1971. m. (in 3 vols.). GBP 156, EUR 234 combined subscription in Europe to individuals print & online eds.; USD 289 combined subscription in the Americas to individuals & Caribbean (print & online eds.); GBP 172 combined subscription elsewhere to individuals print & online eds.; GBP 2,113 combined subscription in Europe to institutions print & online eds.; USD 3,904 combined subscription in the Americas to institutions & Caribbean (print & online eds.); GBP 2,324 combined subscription elsewhere to institutions print & online eds. (effective 2006). bk.rev. abstr.; charts; illus.; stat. index. back issues avail.; reprint service avail. from ISI. **Document type:** *Journal, Academic/Scholarly.*
Related titles: Microform ed.: (from PQC); ♦ Online - full text ed.: Freshwater Biology Online. ISSN 1365-2427.
Indexed: ABIPC, AEA, APD, ASCA, ASFA, AgBio, AgrForAb, AnBrAb, ApEcolAb, B&AI, BIOBASE, BIOSIS Prev, BioCN&I, BiolAb, BiolDig, CIN, CPA, CRFR, ChemAb, ChemTitl, CurCont, EPB, ESPM, EntAb, EnvAb, ExcerpMed, FPA, ForAb, GEOBASE, HelmAb, HerbAb, HortAb, I&DA, IABS, ISR, IndVet, MBA, NemAb, NutrAb, PBA, PGegResA, PlantSci, PollutAb, ProtozoAb, RM&VM, RRTA, RefZh, RevApplEntom, S&F, SCI, SFA, SJW, SWRA, SeedAb, VetBull, WAE&RSA, WRCInf, WeedAb, WildRev, ZooRec.
—BLDSC (4037.200000), CASDDS, CISTI, IDS, IE, Infotrieve, ingenta, Linda Hall. **CCC.**
Published by: Blackwell Publishing Ltd., 9600 Garsington Rd, Oxford, OX4 2ZG, United Kingdom. TEL 44-1865-776868, FAX 44-1865-714591, customerservices@oxon.blackwellpublishing.com, http://www.blackwellpublishing.com/journals/FWB. Eds. Dr. Alan G. Hildrew, Dr. Colin R. Townsend. Pub. Sue Hewitt. R&P Sophie Savage. Adv. contact Jenny Applin. Circ: 840.

578.77 GBR ISSN 1365-2427
QH96.A1

➤ **FRESHWATER BIOLOGY ONLINE.** Text in English. 1998. m. GBP 2,007 in Europe to institutions; USD 3,708 in the Americas to institutions & Caribbean; GBP 2,207 elsewhere to institutions (effective 2006). **Document type:** *Academic/Scholarly.*
Media: Online - full text (from Blackwell Synergy, EBSCO Publishing, Gale Group, IngentaConnect, O C L C Online Computer Library Center, Inc., Swets Information Services).
Related titles: Microform ed.: (from PQC); ♦ Print ed.: Freshwater Biology. ISSN 0046-5070.
Published by: Blackwell Publishing Ltd., 9600 Garsington Rd, Oxford, OX4 2ZG, United Kingdom. TEL 44-1865-776868, FAX 44-1865-714591, customerservices@oxon.blackwellpublishing.com, http://www.blackwellpublishing.com.

578.77 GBR ISSN 0961-4664
QH96.A1 CODEN: FRFOE9

FRESHWATER FORUM. Text in English. 1930. a. GBP 30 per issue to individuals membership; GBP 250 per issue to corporations membership; GBP 15 per issue to students membership (effective 2003). back issues avail. **Document type:** *Academic/Scholarly.*

Formerly (until 1990): Freshwater Biological Association. Annual Report (0374-7646)
Indexed: BiolAb, ESPM, SFA, ZooRec.
—BLDSC (4037.325000), CASDDS, IE, ingenta, Linda Hall. **CCC.**
Published by: Freshwater Biological Association, The Ferry House, Ambleside, Cumbria LA22 0LP, United Kingdom. TEL 44-1539-442468, FAX 44-1539-446914, info@fba.org.uk, http://www.fba.org.uk. Ed. K J Rouen. Circ: 2,400.

570 610.9 USA ISSN 1541-8766
FRONTIERS IN BIOMEDICAL SCIENCE AND TECHNOLOGY. SERIES. Text in English. 2002 (Nov.). irreg. USD 55 per vol. (effective 2003). **Document type:** *Monographic series, Academic/Scholarly.* **Description:** Covers all aspects of biomedicine and bioscience.
Published by: Stefan University Press, PO Box 2946, La Jolla, CA 92038-2946. TEL 858-245-6674, FAX 858-395-6768, wisdom@stefan-university.edu, http://www.stefan-university-terramedia.com. Ed., Pub. Vladislav Stefan. R&P, Adv. contact Chris Nielsen.

FRONTIERS IN BIOSCIENCE. see *MEDICAL SCIENCES*

B

577 USA ISSN 1540-9295
QH540
▼ **FRONTIERS IN ECOLOGY AND THE ENVIRONMENT.** Text in English. 2003 (Feb.). 10/yr. USD 215 to institutions; USD 265 combined subscription to institutions small, under 2500 FTE enrollment; USD 315 combined subscription to institutions medium, over 2500 FTE enrollment; USD 400 combined subscription to institutions large, research institution per campus (effective 2005). adv. **Description:** Focuses on current ecological issues and environmental challenges.
Related titles: Online - full text ed.: ISSN 1540-9309 (from EBSCO Publishing).
Indexed: ApEcolAb, CurCont, ESPM, GardL.
—BLDSC (4042.003500), CISTI, IE.
Published by: Ecological Society of America, 1707 H St, N W, Ste 400, Washington, DC 20006. TEL 202-833-8773, FAX 202-833-8775, esahq@esa.org, http://www.frontiersinecology.org/, http://www.esa.org. Ed. Sue Silver. Adv. contact Jacqueline L. M. Byrd.

570 JPN ISSN 1346-1389
FUJI JOSHI DAIGAKU KIYOU. DAI 2-BU/FUJI WOMEN'S COLLEGE. BULLETIN. SERIES 2. Text in Japanese, English. 1967. a.
Formerly (until 1999): Fuji Joshi Daigaku, Fuji Joshi Tanki Daigaku kiyo. Dai 2-bu (0286-9470); Which superseded in part (in 1968): Fuji Joshi Daigaku, Fuji Joshi Tanki Daigaku Kiyo (0286-9942); Which was formed by the merger of (1962-1967): Fuji Joshi Daigaku Bungakubu Kiyo (0286-9926); (1956-1967): Fuji Joshi Tanki Daigaku Kiyo (0286-9934)
Indexed: ZooRec.
Published by: Masaharu Kawakatsu Ed.&Publ, 9-jo, 9-chome 1-8, Kita-ku, Sapporo, Hokkaido 001-0909, Japan. TEL 81-11-7624450, FAX 81-11-7624450, dqao1524@nifty.ne.jp.

570 JPN ISSN 0912-0300
FUKUSHIMA SEIBUTSU/FUKUSHIMA BIOLOGICAL SOCIETY. JOURNAL. Text in Japanese. 1958. a.
Published by: Fukushimaken Seibutsu Dokokai/Fukushima Biological Society, Fukushima Daigaku Kyoikugakubu Seibutsugaku Kyoshitsu, 2 Naomichi, Asakawa, Matsukawamachi, Fukushima-shi, Fukushima-ken 960-12, Japan.

FUKUYAMA DAIGAKU FUZOKU NAIKAI SEIBUTSU SHIGEN KENKYUJO HOKOKU/FUKUYAMA UNIVERSITY. RESEARCH INSTITUTE OF MARINE BIORESOURCES. REPORT. see *EARTH SCIENCES—Oceanography*

FUNCTIONAL ECOLOGY. see *CONSERVATION*

573.6 USA ISSN 0895-1942
QK623.S73 CODEN: FGNEEA
FUNGAL GENETICS NEWSLETTER. Text in English. 1962. a. USD 20 (effective 2004). back issues avail. **Document type:** *Newsletter.* **Description:** Publishes articles, bibliographies and addresses for researches in fungal genetics.
Formerly: Neurospora Newsletter (0028-3975)
Related titles: Online - full text ed.: ISSN 1556-1275. free.
Indexed: BiolAb, RPP.
—BLDSC (4056.650000), CISTI, IE, ingenta.
Published by: Fungal Genetics Stock Center, University of Kansas Medical School, Department of Microbiology, Kansas City, KS 66160-7420. TEL 913-588-7044, FAX 913-588-7295, fgsc@kuhub.cc.ukans.edu, http://www.fgsc.net/newslet.html. Ed. Peter J Russell. R&P Kevin McCluskey. Circ: 1,000.

GALVESTON BAY NATIONAL ESTUARY PROGRAM. PUBLICATIONS. see *ENVIRONMENTAL STUDIES*

GARCIA DE ORTA: SERIE DE ANTROPOBIOLOGIA. see *ANTHROPOLOGY*

GEELONG NATURALIST. see *SCIENCES: COMPREHENSIVE WORKS*

572.8 171.7 GBR ISSN 1474-760X
➤ **GENOME BIOLOGY (ONLINE EDITION).** Text in English. 2000. m. GBP 288, USD 482, EUR 432 to institutions; GBP 144, USD 241, EUR 216 academic institutions (effective 2006). **Document type:** *Journal, Academic/Scholarly.* **Description:** Aims to help researchers respond to the increasing impact of genomic and genome-scale information on biological research. Publishes research, reports, commentaries and reviews on all areas of biology informed by genomics.
Formerly (until 2001): GenomeBiology.com (1465-6914)
Media: Online - full text (from EBSCO Publishing, National Library of Medicine, Swets Information Services).
Indexed: BCI.
—CCC.
Published by: BioMed Central Ltd. (Subsidiary of: Current Science Ltd), Middlesex House, 34-42 Cleveland St, London, W1T 4LB, United Kingdom. TEL 44-20-76319131, 44-20-73230323, info@genomebiology.com, info@biomedcentral.com, http://www.genomebiology.com, http://www.biomedcentral.com.

577 BEL ISSN 1370-6071
GEO-ECO-TROP. Text in English, French. q. **Description:** Publishes papers on tropical ecology and geography.
Indexed: GEOBASE.
Address: Universite de Liege, Institut de Geographie, Allee du 6 Aout, B11, Liege, 4000, Belgium. Ed. J. Alexandre.

GEOBIOLOGY. see *EARTH SCIENCES—Geology*

570 550 IND ISSN 0251-1223
QH301 CODEN: GBOSBU
➤ **GEOBIOS**; an international journal of life sciences on earth. Text in English. 1974. q. USD 80 to institutions (effective 2006). adv. bk.rev. 64 p./no. 2 cols./p.; back issues avail.; reprints avail. **Document type:** *Journal, Academic/Scholarly.*
Indexed: BIOSIS Prev, BiolAb, BrGeoL, CIN, ChemAb, ChemTitl, ExcerpMed, HortAb, ZooRec.
—BLDSC (4116.901500), CASDDS, CISTI, IE, ingenta, Linda Hall.
Published by: Geobios Zion, 41B/ Bi / A- PWD Colony, P O Box 14, Zion, Jodhpur, Rajasthan 342 001, India. TEL 91-291-2431726, profdnsen@rediffmail.com, http://www.scientificpub.com/bookdetails.php?booktransid=477&bookid=473. Ed. David Navin Sen. **Subscr. to:** Scientific Publishers, 5-A New Pali Rd., Near Hotel Taj Hari Mahal, PO Box 91, Jodhpur, Rajasthan 342 003, India. TEL 91-291-2433323, FAX 91-291-2512580, http://www.scientificpub.com.

570 550 IND ISSN 0253-3340
QH301
GEOBIOS NEW REPORTS; biannual journal of life sciences. Text in English. 1982. biennial. INR 100, USD 35 to individuals; INR 350, USD 70 to institutions (effective 1999). bk.rev. reprints avail. **Document type:** *Academic/Scholarly.* **Description:** Publishes research reports in the life sciences.
Indexed: ZooRec.
—Linda Hall.
Published by: Geobios Zion, 41B/ Bi / A- PWD Colony, P O Box 14, Zion, Jodhpur, Rajasthan 342 001, India. TEL 91-291-2431726, profdnsen@rediffmail.com. Ed. David Navin Sen.

578.77 USA ISSN 0275-6269
GEORGIA MARINE SCIENCE CENTER. TECHNICAL REPORT SERIES. Text in English. 1971. irreg. free. **Document type:** *Monographic series.*
Published by: (University of Georgia, Georgia Sea Grant), University of Georgia, Marine Extension Service, 20 Ocean Science Circle, Savannah, GA 31411-1011. TEL 912-598-2348, FAX 912-598-2399, http://www.uga.edu/mariculture/.

GEORGIAN MEDICAL NEWS; monthly scientific bulletin. see *MEDICAL SCIENCES*

570 DEU ISSN 0368-2307
QH5 CODEN: JGNWA2
GESELLSCHAFT FUER NATURKUNDE IN WUERTTEMBERG. JAHRESHEFTE. Text in German. 1845. a. **Document type:** *Proceedings, Academic/Scholarly.*
Formerly (until 1969): Verein fuer Vaterlaendische Naturkunde in Wuerttemberg. Jahresheft (0368-4717)
Indexed: BIOSIS Prev, BiolAb, RefZh, ZooRec.
—Linda Hall.
Published by: Gesellschaft fuer Naturkunde in Wuerttemberg e.V., Rosensteinstr 1, Stuttgart, 70191, Germany. TEL 49-711-8936146, http://www.ges-naturkde-wuertt.de/gesellschaft-naturkunde-800x600.html. Ed. Siegmund Seybold. Circ: 1,100.

577 DEU ISSN 0171-1113
GESELLSCHAFT FUER OEKOLOGIE. VERHANDLUNGEN. Text in Multiple languages. 1973. a. **Document type:** *Journal, Academic/Scholarly.*
Indexed: ASFA, AgBio, BIOBASE, ForAb, GEOBASE, HerbAb, HortAb, I&DA, IndVet, MaizeAb, NemAb, PBA, PotatoAb, RPP, S&F, SeedAb, TriticAb, WAE&RSA, WeedAb.
—CISTI. **CCC.**
Published by: (Gesellschaft fuer Oekologie), Elsevier GmbH, Urban & Fischer Verlag (Subsidiary of: Elsevier Science & Technology), Loebdergraben 14a, Jena, 07743, Germany. TEL 49-3641-626444, FAX 49-3641-626500, http://www.uni-giessen.de/gfoe/verh-bst.htm, http://www.urbanfischer.de.

GESTION AMBIENTAL. see *ENVIRONMENTAL STUDIES*

570 UKR ISSN 0375-8990
CODEN: GBZUAM
➤ **GIDROBIOLOGICHESKII ZHURNAL/HIDROBIOLOHICHNYI ZHURNAL**; nauchnyi zhurnal. Text in Russian, Ukrainian; Summaries in English, Ukrainian. 1965. bi-m. UAK 53.40 domestic; USD 141 foreign (effective 2005). **Document type:** *Journal, Academic/Scholarly.* **Description:** Covers general hydrobiology, sanitary hydrobiology, ecological physiology and biochemistry of aquatic plants and animals, aquatic toxicology, aquatic radioecology.
Related titles: ♦ English Translation: Hydrobiological Journal. ISSN 0018-8166.
Indexed: ASFA, BiolAb, CIN, ChemAb, ChemTitl, ESPM, INIS AtomInd, ProtozoAb, RefZh, SFA, WildRev, ZooRec.
—CASDDS, CISTI, East View, KNAW, Linda Hall. **CCC.**
Published by: Natsional'na Akademiya Nauk Ukrainy, Viddil Zahal'noyi Biolohii, Instytut Hidrobiolohii/National Academy of Sciences of Ukraine, Department of General Biology, Institute of Hydrobiology, 12, Heroyiv Stalingradu Ave, Kyiv, 04210, Ukraine. TEL 380-44-4193981, FAX 380-44-4182232, hydrobiol@igb.ibc.com.ua. Ed. Viktor D Romanenko. **Dist. by:** M K - Periodica, ul Gilyarovskogo 39, Moscow 129110, Russian Federation. TEL 7-095-2845008, FAX 7-095-2813798, info@periodicals.ru, http://www.mkniga.ru.

577 ITA ISSN 1121-8487
GIORNALE DELLA NATURA; mensile delle alternative del vivere ecologico. Key Title: Giornale della Natura Illustrato. Text in Italian. 1986. m. USD 40. adv. **Document type:** *Consumer.* **Description:** Covers ecology-friendly products, organic agriculture and environment-conscious ways of living.
Published by: Stampa Natura Solidarieta SpA, Via Antonio Bazzini, 40, Milan, MI 20131, Italy. TEL 39-02-26680654, FAX 39-02-26680664. Circ: 30,000 (paid).

570 500 GBR ISSN 0373-241X
CODEN: GGNTAS
➤ **GLASGOW NATURALIST.** Text in English. 1908. a. GBP 3 domestic; GBP 6 foreign (effective 2001). adv. bk.rev. charts; illus. cum.index every 5 yrs. **Document type:** *Academic/Scholarly.* **Description:** Contains general articles, papers, and short notes on natural history of Scotland.
Related titles: Microfilm ed.: (from PMC).
Indexed: BIOSIS Prev, BiolAb, SFA, ZooRec.
—BLDSC (4184.000000), IE, ingenta.
Published by: Glasgow Natural History Society, c/o Dr. J.R. Downie, Ed, Graham Kerr (Zoology) Bldg, University of Glasgow, Glasgow, Lanarkshire G12 8QQ, United Kingdom. TEL 44-141-330-5157, FAX 44-141-330-5971, j.r.downie@bio.gla.ac.uk. Ed., R&P J R Downie. Circ: 500.

570 170 ITA ISSN 1128-7462
QH332
GLOBAL BIOETHICS. Text in English. 1992. q. EUR 110 to individuals print & online eds.; EUR 128 to institutions print & online eds. (effective 2005). bk.rev. abstr. back issues avail. **Document type:** *Academic/Scholarly.* **Description:** Forum for reflection and debate on all questions inherent in the generally-defined boundaries of bio-ethics, medical ethics and environmental ethics.
Formerly (until 1991): Problemi di Bioetica
Related titles: Online - full text ed.: ISSN 1591-7398. 2001.
—BLDSC (4195.351750).
Published by: (International Institute for the Study of Man), Angelo Pontecorboli Editore, Via Carrand 22, Florence, 50133, Italy. TEL 39-055-5520903, FAX 39-055-5528456, angelo@pontecorboli.it, http://www.pontecorboli.it. Ed. A B Chiarelli. Circ: 100.

577 GBR ISSN 1354-1013
QC981.8.C5
➤ **GLOBAL CHANGE BIOLOGY.** Text in English. 1995. m. GBP 171, EUR 257 combined subscription in Europe to individuals print & online eds.; USD 316 combined subscription in the Americas to individuals & Caribbean (print & online eds.); GBP 188 combined subscription elsewhere to individuals print & online eds.; GBP 1,552 combined subscription in Europe to institutions print & online eds.; USD 2,868 combined subscription in the Americas to institutions & Caribbean (print & online eds.); GBP 1,707 combined subscription elsewhere to institutions print & online eds. (effective 2006). adv. back issues avail.; reprint service avail. from PSC. **Document type:** *Journal, Academic/Scholarly.* **Description:** Disseminates the latest research on the connection between current environmental change and biological systems.
Related titles: Online - full text ed.: ISSN 1365-2486. GBP 1,474 in Europe to institutions; USD 2,725 in the Americas to institutions & Caribbean; GBP 1,622 elsewhere to institutions (effective 2006) (from Blackwell Synergy, EBSCO Publishing, Gale Group, IngentaConnect, O C L C Online Computer Library Center, Inc., Swets Information Services).

Indexed: AEA, ASCA, ASFA, AgBio, Agr, AgrForAb, AnBrAb, ApEcolAb, BioCN&I, CPA, CurCont, DSA, EPB, ESPM, EnvAb, FCA, FPA, FS&TA, ForAb, GEOBASE, HerbAb, HortAb, I&DA, ISR, IndVet, M&GPA, MaizeAb, NemAb, NutrAb, OrnHort, PBA, PGegResA, PHN&I, PN&I, PollutAb, PotatoAb, PoultAb, RA&MP, RPP, RefZh, RevApplEntom, RiceAb, S&F, SCI, SFA, SIA, SWRA, SeedAb, SoyAb, TriticAb, VITIS, VetBull, WeedAb, WildRev, ZooRec.
—BLDSC (4195.358330), CISTI, IDS, IE, Infotrieve, ingenta, Linda Hall. **CCC.**
Published by: Blackwell Publishing Ltd., 9600 Garsington Rd, Oxford, OX4 2ZG, United Kingdom. TEL 44-1865-776868, FAX 44-1865-714591, customerservices@oxon.blackwellpublishing.com, http://www.blackwellpublishing.com/journals/GCB. Ed. Steve Long. Pub. Sue Hewitt. R&P Sophie Savage. Adv. contact Jenny Applin. Circ: 425.

➤ **GLOBAL CONNECTIONS (ROCHESTER).** see *LIBRARY AND INFORMATION SCIENCES*

➤ **GORTANIA**; atti del Museo Friulano di Storia Naturale. see *SCIENCES: COMPREHENSIVE WORKS*

570 590 ESP ISSN 0367-5041
QL461 CODEN: GRAEAT
➤ **GRAELLSIA**; revista de zoologia. Text and summaries in English, Spanish. 1943. a. price varies. bk.rev. Supplement avail.; back issues avail. **Document type:** *Journal, Academic/Scholarly.* **Description:** Covers contributions to the advancement of knowledge in zoological biodiversity, including taxonomy, fauna, biogeography and evolution and conservation studies.
Indexed: BIOSIS Prev, BiolAb, IECT, RevApplEntom, ZooRec.
—CINDOC.
Published by: Museo Nacional de Ciencias Naturales, Jose Gutierrez Abascal, 2, Madrid, 28006, Spain. TEL 34-1-4111328, FAX 34-1-5645078, graellsia@mncn.csic.es. Eds. Ana I Camacho, M Angeles Ramos. Circ: 400.

➤ **GRAVITATIONAL AND SPACE BIOLOGY BULLETIN.** see *AERONAUTICS AND SPACE FLIGHT*

578.77 AUS ISSN 0155-8072
J905
GREAT BARRIER REEF MARINE PARK AUTHORITY. ANNUAL REPORT. Text in English. 1978. a.
Indexed: ESPM.
Published by: Great Barrier Reef Marine Park Authority, 2-68 Flinders St, PO Box 1379, Townsville, QLD 4810, Australia. TEL 61-7-47500700, FAX 61-7-47726093, http://www.gbrmpa.gov.au/corp_site/info_services/publications/annual_reports/index.html.

578.77 551.46 AUS ISSN 1037-1508
➤ **GREAT BARRIER REEF MARINE PARK AUTHORITY RESEARCH PUBLICATION SERIES.** Text and summaries in English. 1979. irreg., latest no.60, 2000. price varies. back issues avail. **Document type:** *Monographic series, Academic/Scholarly.* **Description:** Contains information on the research and monitoring related to the management of the Great Barrier Reef Marine Park.
Indexed: ASFA, SFA, ZooRec.
Published by: Great Barrier Reef Marine Park Authority, 2-68 Flinders St, PO Box 1379, Townsville, QLD 4810, Australia. TEL 61-7-47500700, FAX 61-7-47726093, registry@gbrmpa.gov.au, http://www.gbrmpa.gov.au. Circ: 350.

578.77 551.46 AUS ISSN 0817-6094
➤ **GREAT BARRIER REEF MARINE PARK AUTHORITY TECHNICAL MEMORANDUM.** Text in English. 1978. irreg., latest 1993, TM-24. price varies. **Document type:** *Monographic series, Academic/Scholarly.*
Published by: Great Barrier Reef Marine Park Authority, 2-68 Flinders St, PO Box 1379, Townsville, QLD 4810, Australia. TEL 61-7-47500700, FAX 61-7-47726093, registry@gbrmpa.gov.au, http://www.gbrmpa.gov.au.

➤ **GREAT BARRIER REEF MARINE PARK AUTHORITY WORKSHOP SERIES.** see *EARTH SCIENCES—Oceanography*

577 GBR ISSN 0141-6464
GREAT BRITAIN. INSTITUTE OF TERRESTRIAL ECOLOGY. STATISTICAL CHECKLIST. Text in English. 1978. irreg. GBP 0.30.
Published by: Centre for Ecology & Hydrology, CEH Publication Sales, Monks Wood, Abbots Ripton, Huntingdon, Cambs. PE28 2LS, United Kingdom. TEL 44-1487-772400, FAX 44-1487-773590, rmt@ceh.ac.uk, http://www.ceh.ac.uk.

612.67 USA ISSN 1041-1232
QH511.A1 CODEN: GDAGE9
➤ **GROWTH, DEVELOPMENT & AGING.** Text in English. 1937. s-a. USD 45 domestic to non-members; USD 55 foreign to non-members; USD 20 domestic to members; USD 25 foreign to members (effective 2004). adv. bk.rev. bibl.; charts; illus. index. reprint service avail. from PQC,ISI. **Document type:** *Journal, Academic/Scholarly.* **Description:** Devoted to problems of normal and abnormal growth patterns; relationship among growth, development and aging; and mathematical models related to these areas.
Formerly (until 1988): Growth (0017-4793)
Related titles: Microform ed.: (from PMC, PQC); Online - full text ed.: (from H.W. Wilson, O C L C Online Computer Library Center, Inc.).
Indexed: ASCA, ASFA, ASG, AbAn, AbHyg, AgBio, Agr, AnBrAb, B&AI, B&BAb, BIOBASE, BIOSIS Prev, BiolAb, CIN, ChemAb, ChemTitl, CurCont, DSA, DentInd, ExcerpMed, GenetAb, IABS, ISR, IndMed, IndVet, Inpharma, MEA&I, MEDLINE, NRN, NutrAb, PE&ON, PN&I, PoultAb, Reac, RefZh, SCI, SFSA, THA, VetBull, ZooRec.
—BLDSC (4223.032500), CASDDS, CISTI, GNLM, IDS, IE, Infotrieve, ingenta, Linda Hall.
Published by: Growth Publishing Co., Inc., PO Box 205, Hulls Cove, ME 04644-0205. FAX 207-288-6079, deh@jax.org, http://www.growthdevelaging.org. Ed., R&P Dr. David E Harrison TEL 207-288-6357. Circ: 625.

➤ **GRUENSTIFT (BERLIN)**; das regionale Umweltmagazin fuer Berlin und Brandenburg. see *CONSERVATION*

570 NOR ISSN 0332-8554
QH168 CODEN: KNVGDN
➤ **GUNNERIA.** Text and summaries in English, German, Norwegian. 1971. irreg., latest vol.76, 1999. **Document type:** *Academic/Scholarly.*
Formerly (until no.26, 1977): Kongelige Norske Videnskabers Selskab. Museet. Miscellanea (0332-8430)
Indexed: ASFA, BIOSIS Prev, BiolAb, ChemAb, ESPM, ForAb, HerbAb, NAA, PGegResA, S&F, ZooRec.
—CCC.
Published by: Norges Teknisk-Naturvitenskapelige Universitet, Vitenskapmuseet/Norwegian University of Science and Technology, Museum of Natural History and Archaeology, Trondheim, 7491, Norway. TEL 47-73-59-21-45, FAX 47-73-59-22-23, ase.vanvik@vm.ntnu.no. Ed. Astrid Langvath. Circ: 500.

➤ **HABITATS**; revista del Centre de Biodiversitat. see *CONSERVATION*

570 TUR ISSN 1303-5002
CODEN: HFMBDA
➤ **HACETTEPE JOURNAL OF BIOLOGY AND CHEMISTRY/HACETTEPE BULLETIN OF NATURAL SCIENCES AND ENGINEERING. SERIES A: BIOLOGY AND CHEMISTRY.** Text in English. 1971. a. free (effective 2003). 200 p./no.; **Document type:** *Journal, Academic/Scholarly.* **Description:** Publishes short to medium length research papers.
Formerly (until 2003): Hacettepe Fen ve Muhendislik Bilimleri Dergisi. Seri A: Biyoloji ve Kimya (0072-9221); Which was formed by the merger of: Hacettepe Bulletin of Natural Sciences and Engineering. Series A: Biology; Hacettepe Bulletin of Natural Sciences and Engineering. Series C: Chemistry, Physics and Engineering
Related titles: Online - full text ed.: (from EBSCO Publishing).
Indexed: ASFA, AgBio, B&BAb, CPA, ESPM, FCA, ForAb, HortAb, INIS AtomInd, MBA, OrnHort, PBA, PGegResA, PGrRegA, RA&MP, RPP, RefZh, RiceAb, S&F, SWRA, TDB, WeedAb, ZooRec.
—CASDDS, KNAW.
Published by: Hacettepe Universitesi, Fen Fakultesi/Hacettepe University, Faculty of Science, 06532 Beytepe, Ankara, Turkey. TEL 90-312-2976850, FAX 90-312-2992093, akalay@hacettepe.edu.tr, http://yunus.hacettepe.edu.tr. Ed. Gurol Okay. R&P Ali Kalaycioglu.

➤ **HAIYANG KEXUE JIKAN/STUDIA MARINA SINICA.** see *EARTH SCIENCES—Oceanography*

➤ **HANDBOOK OF BEHAVIORAL NEUROBIOLOGY.** see *MEDICAL SCIENCES—Psychiatry And Neurology*

579.8 551.46 FRA ISSN 1020-2706
HARMFUL ALGAE NEWS. Text in English. 1992. irreg., latest vol.25, 2004. **Document type:** *Newsletter.*
Published by: (Intergovernmental Oceanographic Commission USA), UNESCO Publishing, 7 place de Fontenoy, Paris, 75352, France. http://ioc.unesco.org/hab/news.htm. Ed. Tim Wyatt.

THE HARVARD FOREST. see *ENVIRONMENTAL STUDIES*

HASTINGS CENTER REPORT. see *MEDICAL SCIENCES*

570 USA ISSN 0073-1331
QH91.A1
➤ **HAWAII INSTITUTE OF MARINE BIOLOGY. TECHNICAL REPORTS.** Text in English. 1964. irreg., latest vol.39, 1988. price varies. **Document type:** *Academic/Scholarly.*
Published by: Hawaii Institute of Marine Biology, PO Box 1346, Kaneohe, HI 96744. TEL 808-237-7401, FAX 808-247-6634. Ed. Philip Helfrich. Circ: 200.

➤ **HELICOBACTER.** see *BIOLOGY—Abstracting, Bibliographies, Statistics*

578.77 MEX ISSN 0188-8897
QH107
HIDROBIOLOGICA. Text in Spanish. 1991. s-a.
Indexed: ESPM.
Published by: Universidad Autonoma Metropolitana - Iztapalapa, Departamento de Hidrobiologia, Ave Michoacan y la Purisma, Col Vicentina, Mexico City, DF 09340, Mexico. TEL 52-5724-4737, FAX 52-5724-4728.

HIGH ALTITUDE MEDICINE AND BIOLOGY. see *MEDICAL SCIENCES*

HIROSAKI DAIGAKU RIGAKUBU FUZOKU FUKAURA RINKAI JISSHUJO HOKOKU/HIROSAKI UNIVERSITY. FUKAURA MARINE BIOLOGICAL LABORATORY. REPORT. see *EARTH SCIENCES—Oceanography*

HIROSAKI IGAKU/HIROSAKI MEDICAL JOURNAL. see *MEDICAL SCIENCES*

570 JPN ISSN 0367-5912
QH301 CODEN: HIRKAC
HIROSHIMA DAIGAKU SEIBUTSU GAKKAISHI/BIOLOGICAL SOCIETY OF HIROSHIMA UNIVERSITY. BULLETIN. Text in English, Japanese. 1934. a.
Indexed: JPI.
—CASDDS.
Published by: Hiroshima Daigaku Seibutsu Gakkai/Biological Society of Hiroshima University, Hiroshima Daigaku Rigakubu, 1-89 Higashisendacho 1-chome, Naka-ku, Hiroshima-shi, 730, Japan.

HIROSHIMA UNIVERSITY. MUKAISHIMA MARINE BIOLOGICAL STATION. CONTRIBUTIONS. see *EARTH SCIENCES—Oceanography*

HISTORIA NATURAL. see *SCIENCES: COMPREHENSIVE WORKS*

HISTORICAL BIOLOGY; an international journal of paleobiology. see *PALEONTOLOGY*

HISTORICAL STUDIES IN THE PHYSICAL AND BIOLOGICAL SCIENCES. see *SCIENCES: COMPREHENSIVE WORKS*

570 GBR ISSN 0391-9714
QH305 CODEN: HPLSDO
➤ **HISTORY AND PHILOSOPHY OF THE LIFE SCIENCES.** Text in English. 1916. q. GBP 294, USD 487 combined subscription to institutions print & online eds. (effective 2006). adv. bk.rev. back issues avail.; reprint service avail. from PSC. **Document type:** *Journal, Academic/Scholarly.* **Description:** Explores the historical development of the life sciences and the social and epistemological implications.
Supersedes in part (in 1979): Stazione Zoologica di Napoli. Pubblicazioni (0039-081X)
Related titles: Online - full text ed.: ISSN 1742-6316. GBP 279, USD 463 to institutions (effective 2006) (from EBSCO Publishing, Gale Group, IngentaConnect, O C L C Online Computer Library Center, Inc., Swets Information Services).
Indexed: ASCA, AmH&L, ArtHuCI, CurCont, DIP, HistAb, IBR, IBZ, IPB, IndMed, MEDLINE, PhilInd, RASB, RefZh, SSCI, ZooRec.
—BLDSC (4317.820000), CISTI, IDS, IE, Infotrieve, ingenta, Linda Hall. **CCC.**
Published by: (Stazione Zoologica di Napoli ITA), Taylor & Francis Ltd (Subsidiary of: Taylor & Francis Group), 4 Park Sq, Milton Park, Abingdon, OX14 4RN, United Kingdom. TEL 44-1235-828600, FAX 44-1235-829000, info@tandf.co.uk, http://www.tandf.co.uk/journals/titles/03919714.asp. Ed. Bernardino Fantini. **Subscr. in N. America to:** Taylor & Francis Inc., Customer Services Dept, 325 Chestnut St, 8th Fl, Philadelphia, PA 19106. TEL 215-625-8900, 800-354-1420, FAX 215-625-8914, customerservice@taylorandfrancis.com; **Subscr. to:** Journals Customer Service, Rankine Rd, Basingstoke, Hants RG24 8PR, United Kingdom. TEL 44-1256-813000, FAX 44-1256-330245, enquiry@tandf.co.uk.

570 JPN ISSN 0018-3393
QH301 CODEN: HKDSBF
HOKKAIDO KYOIKU DAIGAKU KIYO. DAI-2-BU, B. SEIBUTSUGAKU, CHIGAKU, NOGAKU-HEN/HOKKAIDO UNIVERSITY OF EDUCATION. JOURNAL. SECTION 2 B. BIOLOGY, GEOLOGY, AND AGRICULTURE. Text in English, French, Japanese; Summaries in English. 1982 (vol.32). s-a. per issue exchange basis. **Document type:** *Bulletin.*
Indexed: BiolAb, ChemAb, ZooRec.
Published by: Hokkaido University of Education/Hokkaido Kyoiku Daigaku, Ainosato 5-jo, 3-chome, Kita-ku, Sapporo-shi, Hokkaido 002, Japan. Circ: 500.

570 IND ISSN 0441-2370
HORNBILL. Text in English. 1976. q. USD 30 to members (effective 2001). adv. bk.rev. back issues avail. **Document type:** *Newsletter, Academic/Scholarly.*
Indexed: BiolAb, ForAb, KWIWR.
Published by: Bombay Natural History Society, Hornbill House, Shaheed Bhagat Singh Rd., Mumbai, Maharashtra 400 023, India. TEL 91-22-282-1811, FAX 91-22-283-7615, bnhs@bom4.vsnl.net.in, http://www.bnhs.org. Circ: 3,000.

B

▼ new title ➤ refereed ✶ unverified ♦ full entry avail.

570   **HRV**
HRVATSKA AKADEMIJA ZNANOSTI I UMJETNOSTI. RAZRED ZA PRIRODNE ZNANOSTI. RAD. Text and summaries in Croatian, English, French, German. 1866. a. USD 30. **Document type:** *Academic/Scholarly.*
Formerly: Jugoslavenska Akademija Znanosti i Umjetnosti. Razred za Prirodne Znanosti. Rad. (0351-3297)
Indexed: BiolAb, ConcrAb.
—Linda Hall.
Published by: Hrvatska Akademija Znanosti i Umjetnosti, Razred za Prirodne Znanosti, Zrinski trg 11, Zagreb, 10000, Croatia. TEL 385-1-4813344, FAX 385-1-4819979.

HUMAN ECOLOGY REVIEW. see *SOCIOLOGY*

HUMAN ETHOLOGY BULLETIN. see *PSYCHOLOGY*

HUMAN EVOLUTION; international journal. see *ANTHROPOLOGY*

HUMAN NATURE; an interdisciplinary biosocial perspective. see *SOCIAL SCIENCES: COMPREHENSIVE WORKS*

599.9 573.6 170   **GBR**   **ISSN 1028-7825**
➤ **HUMAN REPRODUCTION AND GENETIC ETHICS;** an international journal. Text in English. 1995. s-a. GBP 12.50 to individuals (effective 2004); EUR 25 to individuals (effective 2003); USD 28 to individuals; GBP 21, EUR 36, USD 40 to institutions (effective 2004). adv. bk.rev.; film rev.; play rev. back issues avail. **Document type:** *Journal, Academic/Scholarly.* **Description:** Publishes contributions on ethical perspectives of genetics and human reproduction across all disciplines. Themes include human genome analysis, artificial fecundation and reproduction, sex selection, privacy of genetic data and screening, human gene therapy, eugenics, biotechnology, and cloning.
Formerly: (until 1998): European Journal of Genetics in Society (1023-9022)
Indexed: RefZh.
—BLDSC (4336.431200), GNLM, IE, ingenta. **CCC.**
Published by: European Bioethical Research, 191 Leith Walk, Edinburgh, Midlothian EH6 8NX, United Kingdom. TEL 44-131-5548869, bioethics@europe.com, http://www.bioethics.org.uk/journal.htm. Ed., R&P Dr. Calum MacKellar TEL 44-131-5548869.

➤ **HUMBOLDT SOCIETY NEWSLETTER;** lesbian and gay naturalists of philadelphia. see *HOMOSEXUALITY*

578.77   **NLD**   **ISSN 0018-8158**
QH90   **CODEN: HYDRB8**
➤ **HYDROBIOLOGIA;** the international journal on limnology and marine sciences. Text in English. 1948. 21/yr. EUR 7,998, USD 8,068, GBP 5,265 combined subscription to institutions print & online eds. (effective 2005). bk.rev. bibl. reprint service avail. from PSC. **Document type:** *Journal, Academic/Scholarly.* **Description:** Publishes original articles in the fields of fundamental limnology and marine biology.
Incorporates (in 2003): Journal of Aquatic Ecosystem Stress and Recovery (1386-1980); Which was formerly (1991-1997): Journal of Aquatic Ecosystem Health (0925-1014); Incorporated (1992-2000): International Journal of Salt Lake Research (1037-0544)
Related titles: Microform ed.: (from PQC); Online - full text ed.: ISSN 1573-5117 (from EBSCO Publishing, Gale Group, IngentaConnect, Kluwer Online, O C L C Online Computer Library Center, Inc., Springer LINK, Swets Information Services); ◆ Supplement(s): Journal of Applied Phycology. ISSN 0921-8971.
Indexed: AEA, APD, ASCA, ASFA, AbHyg, AgBio, AgrForAb, AnBeAb, AnBrAb, ApEcolAb, B&BAb, BIOBASE, BIOSIS Prev, BibLing, BioCN&I, BiolAb, CCI, CIN, CPA, CRFR, Cadscan, ChemAb, ChemTitl, CivEngAb, CurCont, DSA, EPB, ESPM, EngInd, EntAb, EnvAb, EnvEAb, EnvInd, ExcerpMed, FCA, FPA, FS&TA, ForAb, GEOBASE, GenetAb, HGA, HelmAb, HerbAb, HortAb, I&DA, IABS, ISR, IndVet, LeadAb, M&TEA, MBA, MSB, NemAb, NutrAb, OceAb, PBA, PGegResA, PGrRegA, PN&I, PollutAb, PoultAb, ProtozoAb, RDA, RM&VM, RPP, RRTA, RefZh, RevApplEntom, RiceAb, S&F, SCI, SFA, SIA, SJW, SPPI, SSCI, SWRA, SeedAb, SoyAb, TDB, TriticAb, VetBull, WAE&RSA, WRCInf, WeedAb, WildRev, Zincscan, ZooRec.
—BLDSC (4343.000000), CASDDS, CINDOC, CIS, CISTI, Ei, IDS, IE, Infotrieve, ingenta, Linda Hall. **CCC.**
Published by: Springer-Verlag Dordrecht (Subsidiary of: Springer Science+Business Media), Van Godewijckstraat 30, Dordrecht, 3311 GX, Netherlands. TEL 31-78-6576050, FAX 31-78-6576474, http://springerlink.metapress.com/openurl.asp?genre=journal&issn=0018-8158, http://www.springeronline.com. Ed. Koen Martens. Circ: 1,000.

578.77 551.48   **USA**   **ISSN 0018-8166**
QH91.A1   **CODEN: HYBJA**
HYDROBIOLOGICAL JOURNAL. Text in English. 1970. bi-m. USD 1,847 to institutions (effective 2005). adv. bk.rev. charts; illus. index. **Document type:** *Journal, Academic/Scholarly.* **Description:** Covers areas of physiology, biochemistry, systematics, ecology and conservation of freshwater fish, invertebrates, vascular plants, zoo- and phytoplankton, as well as freshwater quality and toxicology.

Related titles: Microform ed.: (from PQC); Online - full text ed.: (from EBSCO Publishing); ◆ Translation of: Gidrobiologicheskii Zhurnal. ISSN 0375-8990.
Indexed: ASFA, BiolAb, CTO, ESPM, EngInd, ExcerpMed, F&EA, FLUIDEX, GEOBASE, MBA, PollutAb, S&F, SFA, SJW, SWRA, WeedAb, WildRev, ZooRec.
—BLDSC (0412.088600), CISTI, Ei, IE, Infotrieve, ingenta. **CCC.**
Published by: (Natsional'na Akademiya Nauk Ukrainy, Viddil Zahal'noyi Biolohii, Instytut Hidrobiolohii/National Academy of Sciences of Ukraine, Department of General Biology, Institute of Hydrobiology UKR), Begell House Inc., 145 Madison Ave, New York, NY 10016-6717. TEL 212-725-1999, FAX 212-213-8368, orders@begellhouse.com, http://www.begellhouse.com/hj/hj.html. Ed. Viktor D Romanenko. Circ: 275 (paid).

578.77   **BGR**   **ISSN 0324-0924**
QH90.A1   **CODEN: KHIDD9**
HYDROBIOLOGY. Text in Bulgarian, English, French, Russian. 1975. irreg. BGL 1.32 per issue. bibl.; illus. reprint service avail. from IRC.
—CASDDS, CISTI, KNAW, Linda Hall.
Published by: (Bulgarska Akademiya na Naukite/Bulgarian Academy of Sciences), Universitetsko Izdatelstvo Sv. Kliment Okhridski/Publishing House of the Sofia University St. Kliment Ohridski, Akad G Bonchev 6, Sofia, 1113, Bulgaria. Circ: 430.
Dist. by: Hemus, 6 Rouski Blvd., Sofia 1000, Bulgaria.

570.71   **JPN**   **ISSN 0911-6230**
                             CODEN: HKDKES
HYOGO KYOIKU DAIGAKU KENKYU KIYO. DAI-3-BUNSATSU. SHIZENKEI KYOIKU, SEIKATSU KENKOKEI KYOIKU/HYOGO UNIVERSITY OF TEACHER EDUCATION JOURNAL. SERIES 3: NATURAL SCIENCE, PRACTICAL LIFE STUDIES. Text in English, Japanese; Summaries in English. a. abstr.
Indexed: IBSS, RILM.
Published by: Hyogo University of Teacher Education/Hyogo Kyoiku Daigaku, 942-1 Shimo-Kume, Yashiro-cho, Kato-gun, Hyogo-ken 673-1415, Japan.

570   **JPN**   **ISSN 0914-6660**
HYOGO RIKUSUI SEIBUTSU/HYOGO FRESH-WATER BIOLOGY. Text in Japanese. 1981. 3/yr.
Published by: Hyogo Rikusui Seibutsu Kenkyukai/Hyogo Fresh-Water Biological Society, c/o Mr Noboru Nishimura, 1841 Sekinomiya, Yabu-gun, Sekinomiya-cho, Hyogo-ken 667-1105, Japan.

570   **JPN**   **ISSN 0914-8973**
HYUMAN SAIENSU✳/JOURNAL OF HUMAN SCIENCES. Text in Japanese. 1990. bi-m. JPY 800 per issue.
—BLDSC (5003.432800).
Published by: Hyuman Saiensu Shinko Zaidan/Japan Health Science Foundation, c/o Japan Public Health Association, Koei Bldg, 29-8 Shinjuku 1-chome, Shinjuku-ku, Tokyo, 160-0022, Japan.

I-BUNPI KENKYUKAISHI/JAPANESE SOCIETY OF GASTRIC SECRETION RESEARCH. PROCEEDINGS. see *MEDICAL SCIENCES—Endocrinology*

I C E S IDENTIFICATION LEAFLETS FOR PLANKTON/FICHES D'IDENTIFICATION DU PLANCTON. (International Council for the Exploration of the Sea) see *ENVIRONMENTAL STUDIES*

578.77   **DNK**   **ISSN 0903-2606**
GC1080   **CODEN: TMESEX**
I C E S TECHNIQUES IN MARINE ENVIRONMENTAL SCIENCES. Text in English. 1987. irreg. latest vol.31, 2002. price varies. back issues avail. **Document type:** *Monographic series, Academic/Scholarly.*
Indexed: ASFA, CIN, ChemAb, ChemTitl, ESPM, EnvEAb, PollutAb, RefZh, ZooRec.
—BLDSC (4361.511700), CASDDS.
Published by: International Council for the Exploration of the Sea, H. C. Andersens Boulevard 44-46, Copenhagen K, 1553, Denmark. TEL 45-33-386700, FAX 45-33-934215, info@ices.dk, http://www.ices.dk/products/techniques.asp. Ed. J Pawlak. Circ: 500.

I E E E - E M B S CONFERENCE ON INFORMATION TECHNOLOGY APPLICATIONS IN BIOMEDICINE. PROCEEDINGS. (Institute of Electrical and Electronics Engineers - Engineering in Medicine and Biology Society) see *COMPUTERS*

I F M RAPPORT. (Institutt for Fiskeri- og Marinbiologi) see *FISH AND FISHERIES*

577 590   **DEU**   **ISSN 1432-508X**
I G B BERICHTE. Text in English, German. irreg. **Document type:** *Monographic series, Academic/Scholarly.*
Published by: Leibniz-Institut fuer Gewaesseroekologie und Binnenfischerei/Leibniz-Institute of Freshwater Ecology and Inland Fisheries, Mueggelseedamm 310, Berlin, 12587, Germany. TEL 49-30-641815, FAX 49-30-64181600, http://www.igb-berlin.de.

I G B P SCIENCE. (International Geosphere - Biosphere Programme) see *SOCIAL SCIENCES: COMPREHENSIVE WORKS*

571.9   **GBR**
                           CODEN: CMIFAR
I M I DESCRIPTIONS OF FUNGI AND BACTERIA. (International Mycological Institute) (Former name of issuing body: Commonwealth Mycological Institute (C M I)) Text in English. 1964. q. looseleaf. GBP 210, USD 370 (effective 2004). charts; illus. cum.index. **Document type:** *Monographic series, Academic/Scholarly.* **Description:** Provides descriptions of pathogens for use by plant pathologists and medical mycologists.
Formerly: C M I Descriptions of Pathogenic Fungi and Bacteria (0009-9716)
Indexed: AbHyg, BIOSIS Prev, BioCN&I, BiolAb, FCA, FPA, ForAb, HerbAb, HortAb, MaizeAb, PBA, RM&VM, RPP, RevApplEntom, S&F.
—CISTI. **CCC.**
Published by: (International Mycological Institute), CABI Publishing (Subsidiary of: CAB International), CAB International, Wallingford, Oxfordshire OX10 8DE, United Kingdom. TEL 44-1491-832111, FAX 44-1491-833508, j.david@cabi.org, cabi@cabi.org, http://pest.cabweb.org/Descriptions/Descriptions/IMIDSTAT.HTM, http://www.cabi-publishing.org/. Ed. Dr. John David TEL 44-1784-470111.

I M S NEWSLETTER. (International Marine Science) see *EARTH SCIENCES—Oceanography*

570   **GBR**   **ISSN 0952-2204**
                           CODEN: IMSEE8
I U B S MONOGRAPH SERIES. Text in English. 1985. irreg., latest vol.8, 1992. price varies. **Document type:** *Monographic series.*
Indexed: BiolAb, ZooRec.
—BLDSC (4588.827000).
Published by: (International Union of Biological Sciences FRA), I R L Press Ltd. (Subsidiary of: Oxford University Press), Pinkhill House, Southfield Rd, Eynsham, Oxfords OX8 1JJ, United Kingdom. TEL 44-865-882283, FAX 44-865-882890. **Subscr. to:** IUBS Secretariat, 51 bd. de Montmorency, Paris 75016, France; **U.S. subscr. to:** I R L Press, PO Box Q, Mclean, VA 22101.

IGAKU TO SEIBUTSUGAKU/MEDICINE AND BIOLOGY. see *MEDICAL SCIENCES*

573.6   **JPN**   **ISSN 1344-7629**
➤ **IKUSHUGAKU KENKYU/BREEDING RESEARCH.** Text in Japanese. 1951. q. JPY 8,000 membership (effective 2004). back issues avail. **Document type:** *Journal, Academic/Scholarly.*
Supersedes in part (in 1998): Ikushugaku Zasshi/Japanese Journal of Breeding (0536-3683)
Related titles: Online - full content ed.: ISSN 1348-1290. 2002. free (effective 2005); Online - full text ed.: (from J-Stage).
—BLDSC (2277.715200), CISTI.
Published by: Nihon Ikushu Gakkai/Japanese Society of Breeding, c/o Nakanishi Printing Co., Ltd., Shimotachiuri Ogawa-Higashi, Kamikyo-ku, Kyoto, 602-8048, Japan. TEL 81-75-4153661, morikawa@plant.osakafu-u.ac.jp, jsb@nacos.com, http://www.nacos.com/jsb/ikushu.html#ikuzatsu. Ed. Masahiro Nakagahra.

570   **USA**   **ISSN 0073-4748**
                           CODEN: ILBMA4
➤ **ILLINOIS BIOLOGICAL MONOGRAPHS SERIES.** Text in English. 1914. irreg. price varies. reprint service avail. from PQC. **Document type:** *Monographic series, Academic/Scholarly.*
Related titles: Microform ed.: (from PQC).
Indexed: ASFA, BiolAb, ESPM, RevApplEntom, SFA, ZooRec.
—BLDSC (4365.000000), CISTI, Linda Hall. **CCC.**
Published by: University of Illinois Press, 1325 S Oak St, Champaign, IL 61820-6903. TEL 217-333-0950.

570 551.46   **USA**
ILLINOIS-INDIANA SEA GRANT COLLEGE PROGRAM. REPORT. Text in English. irreg.
Published by: Illinois-Indiana Sea Grant College Program, University of Illinois, 350 National Soybean Research Center, MC-635, 1101 W Peabody Dr, Urbana, IL 61801. TEL 217-333-6444, http://www.iisgcp.org.

570   **USA**   **ISSN 1076-4712**
QH9   **CODEN: INHNAH**
➤ **ILLINOIS NATURAL HISTORY SURVEY. BIOLOGICAL NOTES.** Text in English. 1933. irreg., latest vol.140, 1997. USD 4 per issue (effective 2003). back issues avail. **Document type:** *Monographic series, Academic/Scholarly.* **Description:** Reports of research results and techniques; faunistic surveys with emphasis on Illinois species.
Formerly: (until 1988): Biological Notes (0073-490X)
Indexed: ASFA, BIOSIS Prev, BiolAb, RPP, SFA, WLR, WildRev, ZooRec.
—CISTI, Linda Hall.

Published by: Illinois Natural History Survey, Natural Resources Bldg, 607 E Peabody Dr, Champaign, IL 61820. TEL 217-244-2115, FAX 217-333-4949, rjohnson@inhs.uiuc.edu, http://www.inhs.uiuc.edu/chf/pub/sort-pubtype.html#bionotes. Ed. Charles Warwick. Circ: 1,500.

570 USA ISSN 0073-4918
QH1 CODEN: INHBAF
➤ **ILLINOIS NATURAL HISTORY SURVEY. BULLETIN.** Text in English. 1876. irreg., latest vol.36, no.5, 2003. USD 10 per issue (effective 2004). bibl.; illus. **Document type:** *Journal, Academic/Scholarly.* **Description:** Reports of research results and biological data with emphasis on Illinois.
Indexed: BIOSIS Prev, BiolAb, ForAb, IndVet, PoultAb, RPP, RefZh, SFA, VetBull, WLR, WildRev, ZooRec.
—BLDSC (2558.000000), CISTI, Linda Hall.
Published by: Illinois Natural History Survey, Natural Resources Bldg, 607 E Peabody Dr, Champaign, IL 61820. TEL 217-244-2115, FAX 217-333-4949, rjohnson@inhs.uiuc.edu, http://www.inhs.uiuc.edu/chf/pub/sort-pubtype.html#bulletin.

508 USA ISSN 0888-9546
QH105.I3
ILLINOIS. NATURAL HISTORY SURVEY. SPECIAL PUBLICATION. Text in English. 1976. irreg., latest vol.23, 2002. price varies. bibl.; illus. **Document type:** *Academic/Scholarly.* **Description:** Covers a range of topics related to the biological resources of Illinois.
Indexed: ASFA, BiolAb, RPP, SFA, WLR, WildRev, ZooRec.
—BLDSC (4365.423000), CISTI, Linda Hall.
Published by: Illinois Natural History Survey, Natural Resources Bldg, 607 E Peabody Dr, Champaign, IL 61820. TEL 217-244-2115, FAX 217-333-4949, rjohnson@inhs.uiuc.edu, http://www.inhs.uiuc.edu/chf/pub/sort-pubtype.html#specpubs. R&P Charles Warwick.

ILLINOIS. STATE MUSEUM. SCIENTIFIC PAPERS SERIES. see *SCIENCES: COMPREHENSIVE WORKS*

ILLINOIS STEWARD. see *CONSERVATION*

570 510 SVN ISSN 1580-3139
CODEN: IASMCE
➤ **IMAGE ANALYSIS AND STEREOLOGY.** Text in English. 1982. 3/yr. EUR 76 in Europe; EUR 97 elsewhere (effective 2005). adv. bk.rev.; software rev.; Website rev. Index. 70 p./no. 2 cols./p.; back issues avail.; reprints avail. **Document type:** *Journal, Academic/Scholarly.* **Description:** Promotes the exchange of scientific, technical, organizational and other information among scientists interested in the quantitative analysis of populations having a geometrical structure. Includes stereology, image analysis, image processing, mathematical morphology, stochastic geometry, pattern recognition, and related topics.
Formerly (until 2000): Acta Stereologica (0351-580X)
Related titles: CD-ROM ed.; Online - full content ed.
Indexed: BiolAb, BrCerAb, C&ISA, CIN, CerAb, ChemAb, ChemTitl, CorrAb, E&CAJ, EMA, ExcerpMed, IAA, Inspec, M&TEA, MBF, METADEX, MathR, MathSciNet, RefZh, SolStAb, WAA, ZentMath.
—BLDSC (4368.991220), CASDDS, CISTI, Linda Hall.
Published by: International Society for Stereology, Institute of Anatomy, Medical Faculty, Korytkova 2, Ljubljana, SI-1000, Slovenia. TEL 386-1-5437300, FAX 386-1-5437301, IAS@mf.uni-lj.si, iss@cmm.ensmp.fr, http://www.wise-t.com/ias/, http://www.stereologysociety.org/ias.html. Ed. IDA Erzen. adv.: page SIT 110,000, page USD 600. Circ: 500.

571.974 FRA ISSN 0923-2532
CODEN: IBSPE
➤ **IMMUNOANALYSE ET BIOLOGIE SPECIALISEE.** Abbreviated title: I B S. Text in French. 1986. 6/yr. EUR 252.69 domestic to individuals; EUR 289 in Europe to individuals; JPY 38,500 in Japan to individuals; USD 367 elsewhere to individuals; EUR 268.36 domestic to institutions; EUR 302 in Europe to institutions; JPY 35,800 in Japan to institutions; USD 383 elsewhere to institutions (effective 2006). adv. bk.rev. **Document type:** *Journal, Academic/Scholarly.* **Description:** Covers research and application of clinical biology as in immunology, molecular biology, cell biology, and analyses involving probes and receptors.
Formerly (until 1989): Trait-d'Union (0980-9090)
Related titles: Online - full text ed.: (from EBSCO Publishing, IngentaConnect, ScienceDirect, Swets Information Services).
Indexed: BIOBASE, ExcerpMed, IABS.
—BLDSC (4369.654800), CISTI, GNLM, IE, Infotrieve, ingenta. **CCC.**
Published by: (Societe Francaise de Biophysique et de Medecine Nucleaire), Elsevier France, Editions Scientifiques et Medicales (Subsidiary of: Elsevier Science & Technology), 23 Rue Linois, Paris, 75724, France. TEL 33-1-71724600, FAX 33-1-71724650, labm@elsevier-fr.com, http://www.elsevier.com/locate/immbio. Ed. B. Poggi. Circ: 2,000.
Subscr. to: Elsevier BV. nlinfo-f@elsevier.nl, http://www.elsevier.nl.

➤ **IMMUNOLOGY AND CELL BIOLOGY.** see *MEDICAL SCIENCES—Allergology And Immunology*

615 570 USA ISSN 1539-4921
IN VIVO EUROPE RX. Text in English. 2002. m. USD 850 (effective 2004). **Document type:** *Journal, Trade.* **Description:** An insider's view on Europe's most interesting pharmaceutical and biotech companies.
Media: Online - full text.
Published by: Windhover Information, Inc., 10 Hoyt St, Norwalk, CT 06851. TEL 203-838-4401, ext 232, FAX 203-838-3214, custserv@windhover.com, http://www.windhover.com.

570 GBR
INDEX FILICUM. Text in English. 1906. irreg. price varies. **Document type:** *Academic/Scholarly.*
Contact Corp. Auth.: Royal Botanic Gardens, Kew, Richmond, Surrey TW9 3AB, United Kingdom. TEL 44-20-83325000, info@kew.org. Ed. B S Parris.

570 IND ISSN 0302-7554
QH301 CODEN: INBID9
INDIAN BIOLOGIST. Text in English. 1968. s-a. USD 30 (effective 1999). adv. bk.rev.
Indexed: BiolAb, CIN, ChemAb, ChemTitl, CurCont, ExcerpMed, ZooRec.
—CASDDS, CISTI, Linda Hall.
Published by: Indian Association of Biological Sciences, c/o Life Science Centre, University of Calcutta, 35 Ballygunge Circular Rd., Calcutta, West Bengal 700 019, India. Ed. T M Das. Circ: 1,000.

INDIAN JOURNAL OF DAIRY & BIOSCIENCES. see *AGRICULTURE—Dairying And Dairy Products*

INDIAN JOURNAL OF ECOLOGY. see *ENVIRONMENTAL STUDIES*

570 IND ISSN 0019-5189
QH301 CODEN: IJEBA6
INDIAN JOURNAL OF EXPERIMENTAL BIOLOGY. Text in English. 1963. m. USD 550 to institutions (effective 2006). bk.rev. bibl.; charts; illus. index. back issues avail. **Document type:** *Academic/Scholarly.* **Description:** Covers research in the fields of experimental botany, zoology, micrology, pharmacology and nutrition.
Indexed: ASFA, AbAn, AbHyg, AgBio, AgrForAb, AnBrAb, AnalAb, BIOBASE, BIOSIS Prev, BioCN&I, BiolAb, CIN, CLL, CPA, CTA, ChemAb, ChemTitl, CurCont, DBA, DSA, ESPM, EngInd, ExcerpMed, FCA, FPA, FS&TA, ForAb, HelmAb, HerbAb, HortAb, I&DA, INIS AtomInd, ISR, IndMed, IndVet, Inspec, JDDR, MEDLINE, MaizeAb, NemAb, NutrAb, OrnHort, PBA, PGegResA, PGrRegA, PHN&I, PN&I, PotatoAb, PoultAb, ProtozoAb, RA&MP, RM&VM, RPP, RefZh, RevApplEntom, RiceAb, S&F, SCI, SFA, SIA, SeedAb, SoyAb, TDB, TTI, TriticAb, VetBull, WeedAb, WildRev, ZooRec.
—BLDSC (4412.200000), CASDDS, CISTI, Ei, GNLM, IDS, IE, Infotrieve, ingenta, KNAW, Linda Hall.
Published by: (India. Council of Scientific and Industrial Research, India. Publications & Information Directorate), Scientific Publishers, 5-A New Pali Rd., Near Hotel Taj Hari Mahal, PO Box 91, Jodhpur, Rajasthan 342 003, India. TEL 91-291-2433323, FAX 91-291-2512580, info@scientificpub.com, http://www.scientificpub.com/bookdetails.php?booktransid=319&bookid=315. Ed. K Satayanarayana. Circ: 1,200.

INDIAN JOURNAL OF LANDSCAPE SYSTEMS AND ECOLOGICAL STUDIES. see *ENVIRONMENTAL STUDIES*

INDIAN JOURNAL OF MARINE SCIENCES. see *EARTH SCIENCES—Oceanography*

INDIAN JOURNAL OF MEDICAL PHOTOGRAPHY. see *PHOTOGRAPHY*

THE INDIAN JOURNAL OF MEDICAL RESEARCH. see *MEDICAL SCIENCES*

INDONESIAN BIOLOGICAL AND AGRICULTURAL INDEX/INDEKS BIOLOGI DAN PERTANIAN DE INDONESIA. see *AGRICULTURE—Abstracting, Bibliographies, Statistics*

INDONESIAN JOURNAL OF BIOANTHROPOLOGY/BERKALA BIOANTHROPOLOGI INDONESIA. see *ANTHROPOLOGY*

INFORMATIK, BIOMETRIE UND EPIDEMIOLOGIE; in Medizin und Biologie. see *MEDICAL SCIENCES*

INFORMATION PLUS REFERENCE SERIES. ENDANGERED SPECIES; must they disappear?. see *ENVIRONMENTAL STUDIES*

570 DEU
INFORMATION SOURCES IN THE LIFE SCIENCES. Text in English. irreg., latest vol.4, 1997. bibl. **Document type:** *Directory, Bibliography.* **Description:** Enables information professionals and librarians to evaluate information sources in life sciences.
Related titles: ◆ Series: Information Sources for the Press and Broadcast Media; ◆ Information Sources in Chemistry; ◆ Information Sources in Finance and Banking; ◆ Information Sources in Grey Literature; ◆ Information Sources in Physics; ◆ Guides to Information Sources Series; ◆ Information Sources in Architecture and Construction; ◆ Information Sources in Development Studies; ◆ Information Sources in Engineering; ◆ Information Sources in Environmental Protection; ◆ Information Sources in Law; ◆ Information Sources in Official Publications.
Published by: K.G. Saur Verlag GmbH (Subsidiary of: Gale Group), Ortlerstr 8, Munchen, 81373, Germany. TEL 49-89-769020, FAX 49-89-76902150, info@saur.de, http://www.saur.de. Ed. H V Wyatt.

570 551 USA ISSN 1548-4041
▼ ➤ **INSIGHT (MILWAUKEE).** Text in English. 2003 (Sept.). irreg. free (effective 2004). **Document type:** *Academic/Scholarly.*
Media: Online - full content.
Published by: Milwaukee Public Museum, 800 W Wells St, Milwaukee, WI 53233. TEL 414-278-2700, FAX 414-278-6100, http://mpm.edu/cr/insight/insighthome.html, http://www.mpm.edu. Ed. Gerald R. Noonan.

B

578.77 NCL
INSTITUT DE RECHERCHE POUR LE DEVELOPPEMENT. CENTRE DE NOUMEA. SCIENCES DE LA MER: BIOLOGIE MARINE. CONVENTIONS. Text in French. irreg.
Published by: Institut de Recherche pour le Developpement, Centre de Noumea, 101 Promenade Roger Laroque - Anse Vata, Noumea, BP A5 - 98848, New Caledonia. TEL 687 26 10 00, FAX 687 26 43 26, http://www.ird.nc.

INSTITUT PASTEUR DE TUNIS. ARCHIVES. see *MEDICAL SCIENCES*

577 BEL ISSN 0374-6429
QH301 CODEN: BNBBAA
➤ **INSTITUT ROYAL DES SCIENCES NATURELLES DE BELGIQUE. BULLETIN. SERIE BIOLOGIE.** Text in English. 1930. a., latest vol.72, 2002. EUR 33.47 (effective 2003). abstr.; bibl.; charts; illus. cum.index. 200 p./no.; back issues avail. **Document type:** *Bulletin, Academic/Scholarly.*
Indexed: ASFA, BIOSIS Prev, BiolAb, ESPM, EntAb, ForAb, NemAb, OceAb, RefZh, SFA, SWRA, WildRev, ZooRec.
—Linda Hall.
Published by: Koninklijk Belgisch Instituut voor Natuurwetenschappen/Institut Royal des Sciences Naturelles de Belgique, Vautierstraat 29, Brussels, 1000, Belgium. TEL 32-2-6274211, FAX 32-2-6274113, karel.wouters@naturalsciences.be, bib@naturalsciences.be. Ed. Karel Wouters. Circ: 1,500.

570 MAR
INSTITUT SCIENTIFIQUE. BULLETIN. SECTION SCIENCES DE LA VIE. Text in French. a.
Indexed: ZooRec.
Published by: Universite Mohammed V, Institut Scientifique, Ave Ibn Batouta, BP 703, Rabat-Agdal, Rabat, 10106, Morocco. TEL 212-37-774548, FAX 212-37-774540.

INSTITUTE OF ENVIRONMENTAL SCIENCES AND TECHNOLOGY. ANNUAL TECHNICAL MEETING. PROCEEDINGS. see *ENVIRONMENTAL STUDIES*

INSTITUTE OF ENVIRONMENTAL SCIENCES AND TECHNOLOGY. TUTORIAL SERIES. see *ENVIRONMENTAL STUDIES*

570 BRA ISSN 0020-3661
CODEN: BBIBAT
INSTITUTO BIOLOGICO DA BAHIA. BOLETIM. Summaries in English, Portuguese. 1954. irreg. bibl.; charts; illus.
Indexed: BiolAb, ChemAb.
—CASDDS.
Published by: Instituto Biologico da Bahia, Ave. ADHEMAR DE BARROS-ONDINA, Comercio, Caixa Postal 553, Salvador, BA 40001-970, Brazil. Ed. Antonio A J da Silva.

578.0913 PRT ISSN 0871-1755
INSTITUTO DE INVESTIGACAO CIENTIFICA TROPICAL. COMUNICACOES. SERIE DE CIENCIAS BIOLOGICAS. Text in Portuguese. 1989. irreg. price varies. back issues avail. **Document type:** *Monographic series.*
Indexed: ZooRec.
Published by: Instituto de Investigacao Cientifica Tropical, Rua da Junqueira, 30, Lisbon, 1349-007, Portugal. TEL 351-21-3622621, FAX 351-21-3631460, iict@iict.pt. Circ: 1,000. **Subscr. to:** Centro de Documentacao e Informacao, Rua de Jau, 47, Lisbon 1300, Portugal. TEL 351-21-3644846, FAX 351-21-3628218.

578.77 PER
INSTITUTO DEL MAR DEL PERU. INFORME PROGRESIVO. Text in Spanish. m.
Published by: Instituto del Mar del Peru, Apdo Postal 22, Callao, Peru. http://www.imarpe.gob.pe.

570 610 BRA ISSN 0074-0276
R108 CODEN: MIOCAS
➤ **INSTITUTO OSWALDO CRUZ, RIO DE JANEIRO. MEMORIAS.** Text in English. 1909. bi-m. BRL 35 domestic to individuals; BRL 45 in South America to individuals; BRL 60 elsewhere to individuals; BRL 70 domestic to institutions; BRL 80 in South America to institutions; BRL 120 elsewhere to institutions (effective 1999). adv. bk.rev. back issues avail. **Document type:** *Academic/Scholarly.*
Related titles: Microform ed.: (from PMC); Online - full text ed.: ISSN 1678-8060. free (effective 2005).
Indexed: ASCA, ASFA, AbHyg, AgBio, AgrForAb, BIOSIS Prev, BioCN&I, BiolAb, CurCont, DSA, ESPM, EntAb, FPA, ForAb, H&SSA, HelmAb, HerbAb, HortAb, INIS AtomInd, ISR, IndMed, IndVet, Inpharma, MBA, MEDLINE, NemAb, NutrAb, PBA, PE&ON, PGegResA, PN&I, PoultAb, ProtozoAb, RA&MP, RDA, RM&VM, RPP, RRTA, Reac, RefZh, RevApplEntom, RiceAb, S&F, SCI, SFA, SIA, SWRA, SoyAb, TDB, VetBull, VirolAbstr, WeedAb, WildRev, ZooRec.
—BLDSC (5661.000000), CISTI, GNLM, IDS, IE, Infotrieve, ingenta, KNAW, Linda Hall.
Published by: Fundacao Oswaldo Cruz, Avda. Brasil 4365, Rio de Janeiro, RJ 21045-900, Brazil. TEL 55-21-25984242, FAX 55-21-2805048, memorias@pobox.com, http://www.bioline.org.br/oc, http://www.fiocruz.br. Ed. Hooman Momen. Adv. contact Luciane Dec B Soares. Circ: 1,400.

B

570 ESP
INSTITUTO PIRENAICO DE ECOLOGIA. MONOGRAFIAS. Text in Spanish. 1987. irreg., latest vol.6, 1992. price varies. **Document type:** *Monographic series.*
Published by: Consejo Superior de Investigaciones Cientificas, Instituto Pirenaico de Ecologia, Avda. Regimento de Galicia, s-n, Jaca, Huesca 22700, Spain. TEL 974-361441, ipjaca@pinar1.csic.es. Ed. Juan Pablo Martinez Rica.

570 MEX ISSN 0365-1932
QH301 CODEN: AENBAU
➤ **INSTITUTO POLITECNICO NACIONAL. ESCUELA NACIONAL DE CIENCIAS BIOLOGICAS. ANALES.** Key Title: Anales de la Escuela Nacional de Ciencias Biologicas (Mexico). Text in Spanish; Summaries in English, Spanish. 1938. a. MXP 150, USD 50 (effective 1997). charts; illus.; stat. **Document type:** *Academic/Scholarly.* **Description:** Presents original research in the biological sciences: zoology, botany, morphology, ecology.
Indexed: SFA, VITIS, WildRev, ZooRec.
—CISTI, Linda Hall.
Published by: Instituto Politecnico Nacional, Escuela Nacional de Ciencias Biologicas, Carpio y Plan de Ayala,, Col Santa Tomas, Apartado Postal 42 186, Mexico City, DF 11340, Mexico. FAX 52-5-3963503. Ed. Dr. Fernando de la Jara Alcocer. Pub. Paul Vallejo de Aquino. Circ: 1,000 (controlled).

➤ **INSTITUTO PORTUGUES DE INVESTIGACAO MARITIMA. RELATORIOS CIENTIFICOS E TECNICOS.** see *SCIENCES: COMPREHENSIVE WORKS*

570 ROM
INSTITUTUL DE SUBINGINERI ORADEA. LUCRARI STIINTIFICE: SERIA BIOLOGIC. Text in Romanian; Text occasionally in English, French; Summaries in English, French, German, Romanian. 1967. a. **Document type:** *Journal, Abstract/Index.*
Formerly: Institutul Pedagogic Oradea. Lucrari Stiintifice Seria Biologic; Which superseded in part (in 1973): Institutul Pedagogic Oradea. Lucrari Stiintifice: Seria Educatie Fizica, Biologie, Stiinte Medicale; Which superseded in part (in 1971): Institutul Pedagogic Oradea. Lucraria Stiintifice: Seria A and Seria B; Which was formerly (until 1969): Institutul Pedagogic Oradea. Lucrari Stiintifice
Published by: Institutul de Subingineri Oradea, Calea Armatei Rosii 5, Oradea, 3700, Romania.

578.77 577 FRA ISSN 1014-9538
INTERGOVERNMENTAL OCEANOGRAPHIC COMMISSION. REPORT OF MEETINGS OF EXPERTS AND EQUIVALENT BODIES. Text in English. irreg.
Published by: (Intergovernmental Oceanographic Commission USA), UNESCO Publishing, 7 place de Fontenoy, Paris, 75352, France. FAX 33-1-45685737, http://ioc.unesco.org/iocweb/IOCpub/elibexp.htm, http://www.unesco.org/publishing.

INTERMOUNTAIN JOURNAL OF SCIENCES. see *SCIENCES: COMPREHENSIVE WORKS*

INTERNATIONAL ASSOCIATION OF THEORETICAL AND APPLIED LIMNOLOGY. COMMUNICATIONS/ INTERNATIONALE VEREINIGUNG FUER THEORETISCHE UND ANGEWANDTE LIMNOLOGIE. MITTEILUNGEN. see *EARTH SCIENCES—Hydrology*

INTERNATIONAL ASSOCIATION OF THEORETICAL AND APPLIED LIMNOLOGY. PROCEEDINGS/INTERNATIONALE VEREINIGUNG FUER THEORETISCHE UND ANGEWANDTE LIMNOLOGIE. VERHANDLUNGEN. see *EARTH SCIENCES—Hydrology*

578.77 POL
INTERNATIONAL BALTIC SEA FISHERY COMMISSION. PROCEEDINGS. Text in English. 1974. a.
Published by: International Baltic Sea Fishery Commission, 20, Hozastr., Warsaw, 00-528, Poland. TEL 48-22-6288647, FAX 48-22-6253372, ibsfc@polbox.pl, http://www.ibsfc.org.

570 GBR ISSN 0962-5968
INTERNATIONAL BIOLOGICAL PROGRAMME SERIES. Text in English. 1975. irreg., latest vol.26, 1981. price varies. **Document type:** *Monographic series.*
Indexed: BiolAb.
—CISTI.
Published by: Cambridge University Press, The Edinburgh Bldg, Shaftesbury Rd, Cambridge, CB2 2RU, United Kingdom. TEL 44-1223-312393, FAX 44-1223-315052, information@cambridge.org, http://www.cup.cam.ac.uk/, http://publishing.cambridge.org/series. R&P Linda Nicol TEL 44-1223-325757.

572.8 USA
INTERNATIONAL CONFERENCE ON COMPUTATIONAL MOLECULAR BIOLOGY. ANNUAL. PROCEEDINGS. Text in English. a. **Document type:** *Proceedings, Academic/Scholarly.*
Published by: Association for Computing Machinery, Inc., 1515 Broadway, 17th Fl, New York, NY 10036-5701. TEL 212-626-0500, 800-342-6626, FAX 212-869-0481, http://www.acm.org.

INTERNATIONAL CONFERENCE ON ECOLOGICAL AGRICULTURE: PROCEEDINGS: TOWARDS SUSTAINABLE AGRICULTURE. see *ENVIRONMENTAL STUDIES*

INTERNATIONAL JOURNAL OF AGRICULTURE AND BIOLOGY. see *AGRICULTURE*

570 GBR ISSN 1473-5504
QH325 CODEN: IJANFR
INTERNATIONAL JOURNAL OF ASTROBIOLOGY. Text in English. 2002. q. GBP 160 to institutions; USD 250 in North America to institutions; GBP 172 combined subscription to institutions print & online eds.; USD 268 combined subscription in North America to institutions print & online eds. (effective 2006). abstr. reprint service avail. from PSC. **Description:** Includes cosmic prebiotic chemistry, planetary evolution, the search the planetary systems and habitable zones, extremophile biology and experimental simulation of extraterrestrial environments.
Related titles: Online - full text ed.: ISSN 1475-3006. GBP 145 to institutions; USD 230 in North America to institutions (effective 2006) (from EBSCO Publishing, O C L C Online Computer Library Center, Inc., Swets Information Services).
Indexed: RefZh.
—BLDSC (4542.108000), IE, Infotrieve, ingenta. **CCC.**
Published by: Cambridge University Press, The Edinburgh Bldg, Shaftesbury Rd, Cambridge, CB2 2RU, United Kingdom. TEL 44-1223-312393, FAX 44-1223-315052, journals@cambridge.org, http://titles.cambridge.org/journals/journal_catalogue.asp?historylinks=ALPHA&mnemonic=IJA, http://www.cup.cam.ac.uk/. **Subscr. to:** Cambridge University Press, 100 Brook Hill Dr, West Nyack, NY 10994. TEL 845-353-7500, FAX 845-353-4141, journals_subscriptions@cup.org

616 ITA ISSN 0393-6155
CODEN: IBMAEP
➤ **INTERNATIONAL JOURNAL OF BIOLOGICAL MARKERS.** Text in English. 1986. q. EUR 179.50 in Europe to individuals; USD 197 elsewhere to individuals; EUR 235.50 in Europe to institutions; USD 253 elsewhere to institutions; USD 107.50 in Europe residents; USD 125 elsewhere residents (effective 2004). adv. abstr.; bibl.; charts; illus. Index. 64 p./no.; back issues avail.; reprints avail. **Document type:** *Journal, Academic/Scholarly.*
Related titles: Online - full text ed.: (from EBSCO Publishing).
Indexed: ASCA, BBCI, BCI, BIOSIS Prev, BiolAb, CIN, ChemAb, ChemTitl, CurCont, ExcerpMed, IndMed, Inpharma, MEDLINE, PE&ON, Reac, RefZh.
—BLDSC (4542.151100), CASDDS, CISTI, GNLM, IDS, IE, Infotrieve, ingenta, KNAW. **CCC.**
Published by: Wichtig Editore s.r.l., Via Friuli 72, Milan, MI 20135, Italy. TEL 39-02-55195443, FAX 39-02-55195971, info@wichtig-publisher.com, http://www.biological-markers.com, http://www.wichtig-publisher.com. Pub. Dr. Diego Brancaccio. adv.: color page USD 1,350; trim 21 x 28. Circ: 1,500 (controlled).

570 660.6 572 AUS ISSN 1449-2288
▼ ➤ **INTERNATIONAL JOURNAL OF BIOLOGICAL SCIENCES.** Text in English. 2005. irreg. free (effective 2005). **Document type:** *Journal, Academic/Scholarly.* **Description:** Publishes scientific papers of significance in all areas of biological sciences.
Media: Online - full text (from National Library of Medicine).
Published by: Ivyspring International Publisher, PO Box 4546, Lake Haven, NSW, Australia. FAX 61-2-43905660, http://www.biolsci.org/index.htm, http://www.ivyspring.com.

➤ **INTERNATIONAL JOURNAL OF BIOMETEOROLOGY**; the description, causes, and implications of climatic change. see *METEOROLOGY*

570.15195 USA ISSN 1557-4679
▼ ➤ **THE INTERNATIONAL JOURNAL OF BIOSTATISTICS.** Text in English. 2005. irreg. USD 35 to individuals; USD 365 to institutions (effective 2006). **Document type:** *Journal, Academic/Scholarly.*
Media: Online - full content.
Published by: Berkeley Electronic Press, 2809 Telegraph Ave., Ste 202, Berkeley, CA 94705. TEL 510-665-1200, FAX 510-665-1201, info@bepress.com, http://www.bepress.com/ijb/.

▼ ➤ **INTERNATIONAL JOURNAL OF COMPUTATIONAL METHODS.** see *MATHEMATICS*

570 ESP ISSN 0214-6282
QH491 CODEN: IJDBE5
➤ **THE INTERNATIONAL JOURNAL OF DEVELOPMENTAL BIOLOGY.** Text in English. 1952. 8/yr. USD 280 combined subscription in US & Canada to individuals print & online eds.; EUR 180 combined subscription elsewhere to individuals print & online eds.; USD 900 combined subscription in US & Canada to institutions print & online eds.; EUR 550 combined subscription elsewhere to institutions print & online eds. (effective 2005). bk.rev. abstr. Index. back issues avail. **Document type:** *Journal, Academic/Scholarly.* **Description:** Reports substantial and original findings in biological development, molecular studies on animal and vegetable organisms, developmental genetics, cell differentiation, morphogenesis and growth, pathological phenomena.
Formerly (until 1989): Anales del Desarrollo (0569-9908); Supersedes in part: Anales de Anatomia (0569-9894)
Related titles: Online - full text ed.: ISSN 1696-3547. 1997. USD 225 in US & Canada to individuals; EUR 100 elsewhere to individuals; USD 750 in US & Canada to institutions; EUR 460 elsewhere to institutions (effective 2004) (from EBSCO Publishing).
Indexed: ASCA, ASFA, AgBio, AnBrAb, BIOBASE, BIOSIS Prev, BiolAb, ChemAb, ChemTitl, CurCont, DSA, ESPM, ExcerpMed, GenetAb, HGA, HelmAb, IABS, IECT, IME, ISR, IndMed, Inpharma, MEDLINE, NucAcAb, NutrAb, PN&I, PoultAb, Reac, RefZh, SCI, ZooRec.
—BLDSC (4542.185090), CASDDS, CINDOC, CISTI, GNLM, IDS, IE, Infotrieve, ingenta, KNAW. **CCC.**
Published by: Universidad del Pais Vasco, Servicio Editorial, Apartado 1397, Bilbao, 48080, Spain. TEL 34-94-6015126, FAX 34-94-4801314, ijdb@lg.ehu.es, http://www.ijdb.ehu.es/, http://www.ehu.es/servicios/se_az/. Ed. Juan M Arechage. Circ: 1,000.

➤ **INTERNATIONAL JOURNAL OF FERTILITY AND WOMEN'S MEDICINE.** see *MEDICAL SCIENCES*

570 USA ISSN 1094-2912
TX541 CODEN: IJFPFO
INTERNATIONAL JOURNAL OF FOOD PROPERTIES. Text in English. 1998. 4/yr. USD 947, GBP 575 combined subscription to institutions print & online eds. (effective 2006). adv. reprint service avail. from PSC. **Document type:** *Journal, Academic/Scholarly.* **Description:** Publishes original research papers devoted to all scientific and applied aspects of food properties, with an emphasis on measurement methods, development of standard materials, and data on food properties, predictions, and applications.
Related titles: Online - full text ed.: ISSN 1532-2386. USD 900, GBP 546 to institutions (effective 2006) (from EBSCO Publishing, O C L C Online Computer Library Center, Inc., Swets Information Services).
Indexed: AEA, ASFA, Agr, AgrForAb, B&BAb, ChemoAb, CurCont, DSA, EngInd, FCA, FS&TA, HortAb, MaizeAb, NutrAb, PBA, PHN&I, PN&I, PotatoAb, RefZh, RiceAb, SIA, SeedAb, SoyAb, TriticAb, VITIS.
—BLDSC (4542.253100), CISTI, IE, Infotrieve, ingenta. **CCC.**
Published by: Taylor & Francis Inc. (Subsidiary of: Taylor & Francis Group), 325 Chestnut St, Ste 800, Philadelphia, PA 19016. TEL 215-625-8900, 800-354-1420, FAX 215-625-2940, info@taylorandfrancis.com, http://www.tandf.co.uk/journals/titles/10942912.asp, http://www.taylorandfrancis.com. Ed. M Shafiur Rahman. R&P Elaine Inverso. Adv. contact Mary Drabot. B&W page USD 600. Circ: 250.

INTERNATIONAL JOURNAL OF MEDICAL AND BIOLOGICAL FRONTIERS. see *MEDICAL SCIENCES*

INTERNATIONAL JOURNAL OF MORPHOLOGY. see *MEDICAL SCIENCES*

578.77 DEU ISSN 1434-2944
QH301 CODEN: IRHYFF
➤ **INTERNATIONAL REVIEW OF HYDROBIOLOGY**; a journal covering all aspects of limnology and marine biology. Text in English, French, German. 1908. bi-m. EUR 978 in Europe; CHF 1,548 in Switzerland & Liechtenstein; USD 1,298 elsewhere; EUR 1,076 combined subscription in Europe print & online eds.; CHF 1,703 combined subscription in Switzerland & Liechtenstein for print & online eds.; USD 1,428 combined subscription elsewhere print & online eds. (effective 2006). adv. charts; illus. index. **Document type:** *Journal, Academic/Scholarly.* **Description:** Covers the analysis and assessment of biological structures in water in their interconnection with the internal and external cycle of materials.
Formerly: Internationale Revue der Gesamten Hydrobiologie (0020-9309)

Related titles: Online - full text ed.: ISSN 1522-2632. EUR 978 in Europe; CHF 1,548 in Switzerland & Liechtenstein; USD 1,298 elsewhere (effective 2006) (from EBSCO Publishing, Swets Information Services, Wiley InterScience).
Indexed: ASCA, ASFA, AgBio, AgrForAb, AnBrAb, ApEcolAb, BIOBASE, BiolAb, CIN, CPA, ChemAb, ChemTitl, CurCont, ESPM, EntAb, ExcerpMed, FLUIDEX, FPA, ForAb, GEOBASE, HelmAb, HerbAb, I&DA, IABS, ISR, IndVet, NemAb, NutrAb, PGegResA, PollutAb, ProtozoAb, RM&VM, RPP, RefZh, S&F, SCI, SFA, SIA, SWRA, SoyAb, WAE&RSA, ZooRec.
—BLDSC (4547.300000), CASDDS, CISTI, IDS, IE, Infotrieve, ingenta, Linda Hall. **CCC.**
Published by: Wiley - V C H Verlag GmbH & Co. KGaA (Subsidiary of: John Wiley & Sons, Inc.), Boschstr 12, Weinheim, 69469, Germany. FAX 49-6201-606-117, subservice@wiley-vch.de, http://www.wiley-vch.de. Ed. U Walz. R&P Claudia Rutz. Adv. contact Aenne Anders TEL 49-6201-606552. **Subscr. in the Americas to:** John Wiley & Sons, Inc.. TEL 201-748-6645, FAX 201-748-6088, subinfo@wiley.com; **Subscr. outside Germany, Austria & Switzerland to:** John Wiley & Sons Ltd., The Atrium, Southern Gate, Chichester, West Sussex PO19 8SQ, United Kingdom. TEL 44-1243-779777, FAX 44-1243-775878.

570 IND ISSN 0379-8097
CODEN: BMEMDK
INTERNATIONAL SOCIETY OF APPLIED BIOLOGY. BIOLOGICAL MEMOIRS. Text in English. 1977. s-a. INR 500, USD 60. adv. bk.rev. **Description:** Covers various classical and applied aspects of life sciences.
Indexed: BIOSIS Prev, BiolAb, CIN, ChemAb, ChemTitl, ZooRec.
—CASDDS, CISTI, Linda Hall.
Published by: International Society of Applied Biology, Division of Biochemistry, Central Drug Research Institute, Lucknow, Uttar Pradesh 226 001, India. FAX 91-5222-293405, root@ren.nic.in. Ed. O P Shkula. R&P, Adv. contact Anil Roy Chowdhury.

570 FRA ISSN 0445-1333
INTERNATIONAL UNION OF BIOLOGICAL SCIENCES. GENERAL ASSEMBLIES. PROCEEDINGS. Text in French. triennial. **Document type:** *Proceedings.*
Formerly: International Union of Biological Sciences. Reports of General Assemblies (0074-9362)
Published by: International Union of Biological Sciences, 51 bd. de Montmorency, Paris, 75016, France. TEL 45-25-00-09.

IRANIAN BIOMEDICAL JOURNAL. see *MEDICAL SCIENCES*

IRISH BIOGEOGRAPHICAL SOCIETY. BULLETIN. see *GEOGRAPHY*

IRISH FISHERIES INVESTIGATIONS. SERIES A: FRESHWATER. see *FISH AND FISHERIES*

IRISH FISHERIES INVESTIGATIONS. SERIES B: MARINE. see *FISH AND FISHERIES*

570 ISR
ISRAEL INSTITUTE FOR BIOLOGICAL RESEARCH. PUBLICATIONS. Text in English. 1970. a. free. **Document type:** *Bibliography.*
Formerly (until 1993): Israel Institute for Biological Research. Scientific Activities
Published by: Israel Institute for Biological Research, P O Box 19, Ness-ziona, 74100, Israel. TEL 972-8-9381595, FAX 972-8-9401404, mambi@iibr.gov.il.

ISSUES IN ECOLOGY. see *ENVIRONMENTAL STUDIES*

570 611 ITA ISSN 1122-6714
CODEN: AIAEA2
ITALIAN JOURNAL OF ANATOMY AND EMBRYOLOGY. Text in Italian; Summaries in English, French, German. 1902. q. adv. bk.rev. charts; illus. index.
Formerly (until 1991): Archivio Italiano di Anatomia e di Embriologia (0004-0223)
Indexed: BIOSIS Prev, BiolAb, ChemAb, DentInd, ExcerpMed, IndMed, IndVet, MEDLINE, VetBull.
—BLDSC (4588.339500), CASDDS, CISTI, GNLM, IE, Infotrieve, ingenta, KNAW.
Published by: Editrice Il Sedicesimo, Via Mannelli, 29, Florence, FI 50136, Italy. TEL 39-055-2476781, FAX 39-055-2478568. Ed. Enzo Brizzi. Circ: 600.

ITINERARIUM; rivista multidisciplinare dell'Istituto Teologico "S. Tommaso" Messina. see *RELIGIONS AND THEOLOGY*

578.77 ESP ISSN 1136-4963
V88.P35
ITSAS MEMORIA; revista de estudios maritimos del Pais Vasco. Text in Spanish. 1996. s-a.
—CINDOC.
Published by: Museo Naval, P. del Muelle, 24, Donostia - San Sebastian, 20003, Spain.

570 DEU ISSN 0944-3266
QH305
JAHRBUCH FUER GESCHICHTE UND THEORIE DER BIOLOGIE. Text in German. a. EUR 20 (effective 2002). back issues avail. **Document type:** *Journal, Academic/Scholarly.* **Description:** Presents articles about various themes of the history of biology.
Indexed: DIP, IBR, IBZ.
Published by: (Deutsche Gesellschaft fuer Geschichte und Theorie der Biologie), V W B - Verlag fuer Wissenschaft und Bildung, Zossener Str 55, Berlin, 10961, Germany. TEL 49-30-2510415, FAX 49-30-2511136, 100615.1565@compuserve.com, http://www.vwb-verlag.com. Eds. Hans Joerg Rheinberger, Michael Weingarten.

JAMAICA NATURALIST. see *CONSERVATION*

JANGAL VA MARTA'. see *ENVIRONMENTAL STUDIES*

JAPAN MATRIX (COLLAGEN) CLUB. PROCEEDINGS OF THE ANNUAL MEETING OF JAPAN MATRIX CLUB. see *MEDICAL SCIENCES*

JAPAN SOCIETY FOR COMPARATIVE ENDOCRINOLOGY. PROCEEDINGS. see *MEDICAL SCIENCES—Endocrinology*

750 JPN ISSN 0918-4430
➤ **JAPANESE JOURNAL OF BIOMETRICS.** Text in English, Japanese. 1980. s-a. JPY 10,000 (effective 2003). adv. **Document type:** *Academic/Scholarly.*
Indexed: CIS, CurCont, ST&MA.
Published by: Nihon Keiryo Seibutsu Gakkai/Biometric Society of Japan, c/o Sinfonica, Mainami-Aoyama 6-3-9, Minato, Tokyo, 107-0062, Japan. TEL 81-3-5467-0481, FAX 81-3-5467-0482, biometrics@sinfonica.or.jp, http://wwwsoc.nii.ac.jp/jbs/index.html. Ed., R&P Toshiya Sato. Adv. contact Hideki Origasa.

615 577 JPN ISSN 0368-9395
JAPANESE JOURNAL OF HEALTH AND HUMAN ECOLOGY. Text and summaries in English, Japanese. 1935. bi-m. JPY 17,000. **Document type:** *Academic/Scholarly.*
Indexed: BIOSIS Prev, BiolAb.
—CCC.
Published by: Kyorin Shoin, 4-2-1 Yushima, Bunkyo-ku, Tokyo, 113-0034, Japan. TEL 81-3-811-4887. Ed. M Uematsu.

JAPANESE JOURNAL OF INFECTIOUS DISEASES. see *MEDICAL SCIENCES*

570 JPN
JAPANESE SOCIETY OF DEVELOPMENTAL BIOLOGISTS. PROCEEDINGS OF ANNUAL MEETING/NIHON HASSEI SEIBUTSU GAKKAI TAIKAI HAPPYO YOSHISHU. Text in Japanese. a. **Document type:** *Proceedings.*
Published by: Japanese Society of Developmental Biologists, Daigaku Rigakubu Dobutsugaku Kyoshitsu, 3-1 Hongo 7-chome, Bunkyo-ku, Tokyo, 113-0033, Japan.

570 CHN ISSN 1001-1633
JIEPOUXUE ZAZHI/JOURNAL OF ANATOMY. Text in Chinese. 1964. bi-m. CNY 30 domestic; USD 25.20 foreign (effective 2005). **Document type:** *Journal, Academic/Scholarly.*
Related titles: Online - full text ed.: (from East View Information Services).
Indexed: RefZh.
Published by: Zhongguo Jiepou Xuehui, 800, Xiangyin Lu, Dier Junyi Daxue, Shanghai, 200433, China. jpxzz@yahoo.com.cn, http://jpxzz.periodicals.net.cn/. **Dist. by:** China International Book Trading Corp, 35 Chegongzhuang Xilu, Haidian District, PO Box 399, Beijing 100044, China. TEL 86-10-68412045, FAX 86-10-68412023, cibtc@mail.cibtc.com.cn, http://www.cibtc.com.cn.

JINRUI DOTAI GAKKAI KAIHO/HUMAN ERGOLOGY SOCIETY. NEWSLETTER. see *PHYSICS*

JOURNAL INTERNATIONAL DE BIOETHIQUE/INTERNATIONAL JOURNAL OF BIOETHICS. see *PHILOSOPHY*

570 IND
JOURNAL OF ADVANCES IN BIOSCIENCE. Text in English. s-a. USD 35 (effective 2000). **Document type:** *Academic/Scholarly.*
Published by: H P C Publishers Distributors Pvt. Ltd., 4805 Bharat Ram Rd, 24 Darya Ganj, New Delhi, 110 002, India. TEL 91-11-3254401, FAX 91-11-619-3511, hpcpd@nda.vsnl.net.in, hpcpd@hpc.cc, http://www.bizdelhi.com/publisher/hpc, http://www.indianindustry.com.
Co-publisher: Society of Bio-Sciences.

571.3 611 GBR ISSN 0021-8782
QL801 CODEN: JOANAY
➤ **JOURNAL OF ANATOMY;** molecular, cellular and experimental morphology. Text in English. m. GBP 166, EUR 249 combined subscription in Europe to individuals print & online eds.; USD 306 combined subscription in the Americas to individuals & Caribbean, print & online eds.; GBP 182 combined subscription elsewhere to individuals print & online eds.; GBP 906 combined subscription in Europe to institutions print & online eds.; USD 1,676 combined subscription in the Americas to institutions & Caribbean, print & online eds.; GBP 997 combined subscription elsewhere to institutions print & online eds. (effective 2006). adv. bk.rev. bibl.; charts; illus. index. cum.index: 1866-1966. back issues avail.; reprints avail. **Document type:** *Journal, Academic/Scholarly.* **Description:** Presents articles and reviews covering normal human and comparative anatomy, including applied anatomy, physical anthropology, neurology, endocrinology, embryology.
Related titles: Microfilm ed.: (from BHP); Microform ed.: (from PQC); Online - full text ed.: ISSN 1469-7580. GBP 861 in Europe to institutions; USD 1,591 in the Americas to institutions & Caribbean; GBP 947 elsewhere to institutions (effective 2006) (from Blackwell Synergy, EBSCO Publishing, Gale Group, IngentaConnect, O C L C Online Computer Library Center, Inc., Ovid Technologies, Inc., Swets Information Services).
Indexed: ASCA, AbAn, AbHyg, AgBio, AnBrAb, BIOBASE, BIOSIS Prev, BiolAb, CIN, ChemAb, ChemTitl, CurCont, DSA, DentInd, ExcerpMed, IABS, ISR, IndMed, IndVet, Inpharma, MEDLINE, NSCI, NemAb, NutrAb, PBA, PN&I, PoultAb, Reac, RefZh, SCI, SFA, SoyAb, VetBull, WildRev, ZooRec.
—BLDSC (4929.000000), CASDDS, CISTI, GNLM, IDS, IE, Infotrieve, ingenta, KNAW, Linda Hall. **CCC.**
Published by: (Anatomical Society of Great Britain and Ireland), Blackwell Publishing Ltd., 9600 Garsington Rd, Oxford, OX4 2ZG, United Kingdom. TEL 44-1865-776868, FAX 44-1865-714591, customerservices@oxon.blackwellpublishing.com, http://www.blackwellpublishing.com/journals/JOA. Ed. Gillian Morriss-Kay. R&P Sophie Savage. Adv. contact Jenny Applin.

591.7 GBR ISSN 0021-8790
QL750 CODEN: JAECAP
➤ **JOURNAL OF ANIMAL ECOLOGY.** Text in English. 1932. bi-m. GBP 518 combined subscription in Europe to institutions print & online eds.; USD 956 combined subscription in the Americas to institutions & Caribbean (print & online eds.); GBP 569 combined subscription elsewhere to institutions print & online eds. (effective 2006). adv. bk.rev. bibl.; illus. index. back issues avail.; reprint service avail. from ISI,PSC. **Document type:** *Journal, Academic/Scholarly.* **Description:** Publishes original research papers on most aspects of animal ecology, plus reviews that shed light on subjects central to animal ecology, including theoretical analyses of specific topics.
Related titles: Microform ed.: (from PQC); Online - full text ed.: ISSN 1365-2656. GBP 492 in Europe to institutions; USD 909 in the Americas to institutions & Caribbean; GBP 541 elsewhere to institutions (effective 2006) (from Blackwell Synergy, EBSCO Publishing, Gale Group, IngentaConnect, JSTOR (Web-based Journal Archive), O C L C Online Computer Library Center, Inc., Swets Information Services).
Indexed: ASCA, ASFA, AbAn, AbHyg, AgrForAb, AnBeAb, AnBrAb, ApEcolAb, B&AI, B&BAb, BIOBASE, BIOSIS Prev, BioCN&I, BiolAb, CIS, CPA, CRFR, ChemAb, CurCont, EPB, ESPM, EntAb, FCA, FS&TA, ForAb, GEOBASE, GenetAb, HGA, HelmAb, HerbAb, HortAb, IABS, ISR, IndVet, KWIWR, MathR, NutrAb, OrnHort, PBA, PCI, PGrRegA, PHN&I, PN&I, PoultAb, ProtozoAb, RA&MP, RM&VM, RPP, RefZh, RevApplEntom, S&F, SCI, SFA, SWRA, SeedAb, TDB, TriticAb, VetBull, WeedAb, WildRev, ZooRec.
—BLDSC (4936.000000), CISTI, IDS, IE, Infotrieve, ingenta, Linda Hall. **CCC.**
Published by: (British Ecological Society), Blackwell Publishing Ltd., 9600 Garsington Rd, Oxford, OX4 2ZG, United Kingdom. TEL 44-1865-776868, FAX 44-1865-714591, customerservices@oxon.blackwellpublishing.com, http://www.blackwellpublishing.com/journals/JAE. Eds. Dave Raffaelli, Kevin McCann, Rob Smith. Pub. Sue Hewitt. R&P Sophie Savage. Adv. contact Jenny Applin. Circ: 2,715.

571.3 IND ISSN 0021-8804
QL801 CODEN: JAMPA2
JOURNAL OF ANIMAL MORPHOLOGY AND PHYSIOLOGY. Text in English. 1954. s-a. INR 125; USD 35 foreign. adv. bk.rev. charts; illus. index. **Document type:** *Academic/Scholarly.*
Indexed: ASFA, AnBrAb, BIOSIS Prev, BiolAb, CIN, ChemAb, ChemTitl, ESPM, EntAb, ExcerpMed, GenetAb, HGA, IndVet, VetBull, ZooRec.
—CASDDS, CISTI, IE, Linda Hall.
Published by: Society of Animal Morphologists & Physiologists, c/o Maharaja Sayajirao University of Baroda, Dept. of Zoology, Faculty of Science, Baroda, Gujarat 390 002, India. TEL 91-265-336492. Ed., Adv. contact Bonny Pilo. Circ: 300.

JOURNAL OF APPLIED AQUACULTURE. see *FISH AND FISHERIES*

B

577 GBR ISSN 0021-8901
S3 CODEN: JAPEAI
➤ **JOURNAL OF APPLIED ECOLOGY.** Text in English. 1964. bi-m. GBP 518 combined subscription in Europe to institutions print & online eds.; USD 956 combined subscription in the Americas to institutions & Caribbean (print & online eds.); GBP 569 combined subscription elsewhere to institutions print & online eds. (effective 2006). adv. bk.rev. bibl.; charts; illus. index. back issues avail.; reprint service avail. from ISI,PSC. **Document type:** *Journal, Academic/Scholarly.* **Description:** Publishes papers that discuss the application of ecological ideas, theories, and methods to the use of biological resources in the widest sense.
Related titles: Microform ed.: (from PQC); Online - full text ed.: ISSN 1365-2664. 1999. GBP 492 in Europe to institutions; USD 909 in the Americas to institutions & Caribbean; GBP 541 elsewhere to institutions (effective 2006) (from Blackwell Synergy, EBSCO Publishing, Gale Group, IngentaConnect, JSTOR (Web-based Journal Archive), O C L C Online Computer Library Center, Inc., Swets Information Services).
Indexed: AEA, AESIS, ASCA, ASFA, AbHyg, AgBio, Agr, AgrForAb, AnBrAb, ApEcolAb, B&AI, B&BAb, BIOBASE, BIOSIS Prev, BioCN&I, BiolAb, Biostat, CIN, CIS, CPA, CTFA, ChemAb, ChemTitl, CurCont, DBA, DSA, EIA, EPB, ESPM, EnerInd, EngInd, EntAb, EnvAb, ExcerpMed, FCA, FPA, ForAb, GEOBASE, GardL, GenetAb, HGA, HelmAb, HerbAb, HortAb, I&DA, IABS, ISR, IndVet, KWIWR, MaizeAb, NemAb, NutrAb, OceAb, OrnHort, PBA, PGegResA, PHN&I, PN&I, PollutAb, PotatoAb, PoultAb, ProtozoAb, RA&MP, RDA, RM&VM, RPP, RRTA, RefZh, RevApplEntom, RiceAb, S&F, SAA, SCI, SFA, SIA, SWRA, SeedAb, SoyAb, TDB, ToxAb, TriticAb, VITIS, VetBull, WAE&RSA, WRCInf, WeedAb, WildRev, ZooRec.
—BLDSC (4942.500000), CASDDS, CISTI, Ei, IDS, IE, Infotrieve, ingenta, Linda Hall. **CCC.**
Published by: (British Ecological Society), Blackwell Publishing Ltd., 9600 Garsington Rd, Oxford, OX4 2ZG, United Kingdom. TEL 44-1865-776868, FAX 44-1865-714591, customerservices@oxon.blackwellpublishing.com, http://www.blackwellpublishing.com/journals/JPE. Pub. Sue Hewitt. Circ: 2,690.

578.77 333.91 USA ISSN 0733-2076
SH151 CODEN: JAQSDY
➤ **JOURNAL OF AQUARICULTURE AND AQUATIC SCIENCES.** Text in English. 1980. irreg. price varies. adv. bk.rev. abstr.; bibl.; charts; illus. index. back issues avail.; reprints avail. **Document type:** *Journal, Academic/Scholarly.* **Description:** Publishes original scientific research and correspondence pertaining to aquariculture, the art or science of cultivating living aquatic animals in artificial ponds or tanks. Also covers related aquatic sciences.
Formerly (until 1982): Journal of Aquariculture
Related titles: Online - full text ed.: (from CompuServe Inc.).
Indexed: ASFA, B&BAb, BIOSIS Prev, BiolAb, CurCont, ESPM, MBA, PollutAb, RefZh, SFA, SWRA, WildRev, ZooRec.
—CASDDS, Linda Hall. **CCC.**
Published by: The Written Word, 7601 E. Forest Lake Dr., N.W., Parkville, MO 64152. TEL 816-891-6671, FAX 816-474-6486, http://aquascienceresearch.com/Associates/JAAS/JAAS.htm. Ed., Pub. John Farrell Kuhns. Adv. contact Carol L Kuhns. Circ: 800 (paid).

571.95 USA ISSN 1095-6670
RA1190 CODEN: JBMTFQ
JOURNAL OF BIOCHEMICAL AND MOLECULAR TOXICOLOGY. Text in English. 1986. bi-m. USD 758 domestic to institutions; USD 830 in Canada & Mexico to institutions; USD 872 elsewhere to institutions; USD 834 combined subscription domestic to institutions print & online eds.; USD 906 combined subscription in Canada & Mexico to institutions print & online eds.; USD 948 combined subscription elsewhere to institutions print & online eds. (effective 2006). adv. **Document type:** *Journal, Academic/Scholarly.* **Description:** Focuses on the molecular mechanism of action and detoxication of exogenous and endogenous chemical toxic agents. Includes effects on the organisms at all stages of development.
Formerly (until vol. 11, no. 6, 1996): Journal of Biochemical Toxicology (0887-2082)
Related titles: Microform ed.; Online - full content ed.: ISSN 1099-0461. 1998. USD 758 to institutions (effective 2006); Online - full text ed.: ISSN 1522-7146 (from EBSCO Publishing, Swets Information Services, Wiley InterScience).
Indexed: ASCA, BBCI, BIOBASE, BIOSIS Prev, BiolAb, CIN, ChemAb, ChemTitl, CurCont, ESPM, ExcerpMed, IndMed, Inpharma, MEDLINE, PE&ON, Reac, SCI, ZooRec.
—BLDSC (4951.650000), CASDDS, CISTI, GNLM, IDS, IE, Infotrieve, ingenta, Linda Hall. **CCC.**
Published by: John Wiley & Sons, Inc., 111 River St, Hoboken, NJ 07030-5774. TEL 201-748-6000, FAX 201-748-5915, uscs-wis@wiley.com, http://www3.interscience.wiley.com/cgi-bin/jhome/38998, http://www.wiley.com. Ed. Ernest Hodgson. adv.: B&W page GBP 640, color page GBP 1,515; trim 210 x 279. Circ: 855. **Subscr. outside the Americas to:** John Wiley & Sons Ltd., The Atrium, Southern Gate, Chichester, West Sussex PO19 8SQ, United Kingdom. TEL 44-1243-843335, 0800-243407, FAX 44-1243-843232, cs-journals@wiley.co.uk.

570 330.1 USA ISSN 1387-6996
QH705
JOURNAL OF BIOECONOMICS. Text in English. 1999. 3/yr. EUR 275, USD 275, GBP 171 combined subscription to institutions print & online eds. (effective 2005). bk.rev. back issues avail.; reprint service avail. from PSC. **Document type:** *Journal, Academic/Scholarly.* **Description:** Covers various paradigms and schools of thought in biology, including game theory, evolutionary economics, institutional economics, public choice theory, behavioral and ecological economics, and feminist economics, along with evolutionary biology, systematic biology, behavioral ecology, ethology, paleobiology, paleontology, and sociobiology.
Related titles: Online - full text ed.: ISSN 1573-6989 (from EBSCO Publishing, Gale Group, IngentaConnect, Kluwer Online, O C L C Online Computer Library Center, Inc., ProQuest Information & Learning, Springer LINK, Swets Information Services).
Indexed: ABIn, ASFA, BibLing, GEOBASE, Inspec, JEL, RefZh, ZooRec.
—BLDSC (4952.415000), IE, Infotrieve, ingenta. **CCC.**
Published by: Springer-Verlag New York, Inc. (Subsidiary of: Springer Science+Business Media), 233 Spring St, New York, NY 10013. TEL 212-460-1500, FAX 212-460-1575, service@springer-ny.com, http://springerlink.metapress.com/openurl.asp?genre=journal&issn=1387-6996, http://www.springer-ny.com. Ed. Janet T Landa. **Subscr. to:** Journal Fulfillment, PO Box 2485, Secaucus, NJ 07096-2485. TEL 201-348-4033, FAX 201-348-4505, journals@springer-ny.com.

JOURNAL OF BIOGEOGRAPHY. see *GEOGRAPHY*

570 610 GBR ISSN 0219-7200
QH507 CODEN: JBCBBK
▼ **JOURNAL OF BIOINFORMATICS AND COMPUTATIONAL BIOLOGY.** Text in English. 2003. 6/yr. SGD 260, USD 153, EUR 139 to individuals; SGD 649, USD 382, EUR 347 combined subscription to institutions print & online eds. (effective 2006). back issues avail. **Document type:** *Journal, Academic/Scholarly.* **Description:** Publishes original research articles, expository tutorial papers and review papers as well as short, critical comments on technical issues associated with the analysis of cellular information and the use of such information in biomedicine.
Related titles: Online - full text ed.: (from EBSCO Publishing, O C L C Online Computer Library Center, Inc., Swets Information Services).
Indexed: B&BAb, BioEngAb, ExcerpMed.
—BLDSC (4952.925000), CISTI, IE, Linda Hall.
Published by: Imperial College Press (Subsidiary of: World Scientific Publishing Co. Pte. Ltd.), 57 Shelton St, London, WC2H 9HE, United Kingdom. TEL 44-20-7836-3954, FAX 44-20-7836-2002, edit@icpress.co.uk, geetha@icpress.co.uk, http://www.worldscinet.com/jbcb/jbcb.shtml, http://www.icpress.co.uk/. Eds. John Wooley, Ming Li, Wong Limsoon. **Dist. by:** World Scientific Publishing Co., Inc., 1060 Main St, River Edge, NJ 07661. TEL 201-487-9655, 800-227-7562, FAX 201-487-9656, 888-977-2665.

570 GBR ISSN 0021-9266
QH315 CODEN: JBIEAO
➤ **JOURNAL OF BIOLOGICAL EDUCATION.** Text in English. 1966. 4/yr. GBP 53 domestic to individuals; GBP 67 foreign to individuals; GBP 94 domestic to institutions; GBP 108 foreign to institutions (effective 2004). adv. bk.rev. illus. index. 48 p./no.; back issues avail.; reprints avail. **Document type:** *Journal, Academic/Scholarly.* **Description:** Presents articles on practical work, curricular matters, and teaching methods in biology.
Related titles: Online - full text ed.: (from EBSCO Publishing, H.W. Wilson, O C L C Online Computer Library Center, Inc.).
Indexed: ABIn, AEA, ASCA, ASFA, AgBio, AgrForAb, BIOSIS Prev, BioCN&I, BiolAb, BrEdI, CIJE, CPA, CPE, ChemAb, CurCont, DSA, ERA, ESPM, ETA, EduInd, EnvAb, FCA, ForAb, HECAB, HelmAb, HortAb, IBR, IBZ, IndVet, MEA, MRD, MaizeAb, OrnHort, PBA, PHN&I, PotatoAb, RASB, RHEA, RPP, RRTA, RefZh, S&F, SEA, SENA, SOMA, SSCI, SeedAb, SoyAb, TEA, Telegen, WAE&RSA, ZooRec.
—BLDSC (4953.100000), CIS, CISTI, IDS, IE, Infotrieve, ingenta, Linda Hall. **CCC.**
Published by: Institute of Biology, 20-22 Queensberry Pl, London, SW7 2DZ, United Kingdom. TEL 44-20-7581-8333, FAX 44-20-7823-9409, jbe@iob.org, info@iob.org, http://www.iob.org/default.asp?edname=457.htm&cont_id=13&n=7. Ed. David R Slingsby. Adv. contact Natalie P Partridge. Circ: 2,300 (paid).

570 ITA ISSN 0393-974X
CODEN: JBRAER
➤ **JOURNAL OF BIOLOGICAL REGULATORS AND HOMEOSTATIC AGENTS.** Text in English. 1987. q. EUR 179.50 in Europe to individuals; EUR 197 elsewhere to individuals; EUR 235.50 in Europe to institutions; EUR 253 elsewhere to institutions; EUR 107.50 in Europe residents; EUR 125 elsewhere residents (effective 2004). adv. abstr.; bibl.; charts. 64 p./no.; back issues avail.; reprints avail. **Document type:** *Journal, Academic/Scholarly.*
Indexed: ASCA, AbHyg, AgBio, BIOBASE, BIOSIS Prev, BiolAb, CIN, ChemAb, ChemTitl, CurCont, DBA, ExcerpMed, IABS, IndMed, Inpharma, MEDLINE, PE&ON, RM&VM, RRTA, Reac, RefZh, TDB.
—BLDSC (4953.220000), CASDDS, CISTI, GNLM, IDS, IE, Infotrieve, ingenta, KNAW. **CCC.**
Published by: Wichtig Editore s.r.l., Via Friuli 72, Milan, MI 20135, Italy. TEL 39-02-55195443, FAX 39-02-55195971, info@wichtig-publisher.com, http://www.jbrha.com, http://www.wichtig-publisher.com. Eds. F Dianzani, F Mandelli. Pub. Dr. Diego Brancaccio. Adv. contact Nella Bini. color page AED 1,450; trim 21 x 28. Circ: 1,500 (controlled).

570 GRC ISSN 1790-045X
▼ **JOURNAL OF BIOLOGICAL RESEARCH.** Text in English. 2004. s-a. free (effective 2005). **Document type:** *Journal, Academic/Scholarly.*
Media: Online - full text.
Published by: (Aristotle University of Thessaloniki, School of Biology), Aristotle University of Thessaloniki, Admin Bldg, 6th Flr, Thessaloniki, Greece. http://www.auth.gr/jbr/main/index.htm. Ed. A M Basabalidis.

570 PAK ISSN 1727-3048
➤ **JOURNAL OF BIOLOGICAL SCIENCES.** Text in English. 2000. m. USD 1,200 to corporations (effective 2005). **Document type:** *Journal, Academic/Scholarly.* **Description:** Publishes articles, reviews and short communications in the biological sciences.
Related titles: Online - full text ed.: ISSN 1812-5719. free (effective 2005).
Published by: Asian Network for Scientific Information, 308-Lasani Town, Sargodha Rd, Faislabad, 38090, Pakistan. TEL 92-41-2001145, http://www.ansinet.org/c4p.php?j_id=jbs, http://www.ansinet.net.

570 IND ISSN 0021-9282
QH1 CODEN: JBSBAV
JOURNAL OF BIOLOGICAL SCIENCES. Text in English. 1958. s-a. INR 30, USD 8. adv. bk.rev. charts; illus. index. reprint service avail. from PQC.
Related titles: Microfilm ed.: (from PQC).
Indexed: BiolAb, ChemAb, ISA, SeedAb, VetBull.
—CASDDS, CISTI, Linda Hall.
Published by: Bombay Biological Association, c/o Biology Dept., R. J. College, Ghatkopar, Mumbai, Maharashtra 400 086, India. Eds. K P Dhage, S M Karmarkar. Circ: 250.

570 SGP ISSN 0218-3390
QH323.5 CODEN: JBSYE2
➤ **JOURNAL OF BIOLOGICAL SYSTEMS.** Text in English. 1993. q. SGD 272, USD 155, EUR 150 to individuals; SGD 748, USD 427, EUR 411 combined subscription to institutions print & online eds.; SGD 455, USD 261, EUR 250 combined subscription in developing nations to institutions print & online eds. (effective 2006). back issues avail. **Document type:** *Journal, Academic/Scholarly.* **Description:** Promotes interdisciplinary approaches in biology and in medicine, including mathematical methods and general systems theory as they contribute to the study of biological situations.
Related titles: Online - full text ed.: (from EBSCO Publishing, O C L C Online Computer Library Center, Inc., Swets Information Services).
Indexed: ASFA, BIOSIS Prev, BiolAb, EPB, ESPM, GenetAb, PollutAb, ZooRec.
—BLDSC (4953.420000), CISTI, IE, ingenta. **CCC.**
Published by: World Scientific Publishing Co. Pte. Ltd., 5 Toh Tuck Link, Singapore, 596224, Singapore. TEL 65-466-5775, FAX 65-467-7667, wspc@wspc.com.sg, http://www.worldscinet.com/jbs/jbs.shtml, http://www.worldscientific.com. Ed. R V Jean. **Subscr. to:** Farrer Rd, PO Box 128, Singapore 912805, Singapore. sales@wspc.com.sg. **Dist. by:** World Scientific Publishing Co., Inc., 1060 Main St, River Edge, NJ 07661. TEL 201-487-9655, 800-227-7562, FAX 201-487-9656, 888-977-2665.; World Scientific Publishing Ltd., 57 Shelton St, London WC2H 9HE, United Kingdom. TEL 44-20-78360888, FAX 44-20-78362020, sales@wspc.co.uk.

570 GBR ISSN 1478-5854
QH301 CODEN: JBOIAW
➤ **JOURNAL OF BIOLOGY.** Text in English. 2002. irreg. (avail. immediately on publication). free (effective 2006). **Document type:** *Journal, Academic/Scholarly.* **Description:** Publishes biological research articles of exceptional interest, together with associated commentary.
Related titles: Online - full text ed.: ISSN 1475-4924. 2002. free (effective 2005) (from EBSCO Publishing, National Library of Medicine, Swets Information Services).
Indexed: ASFA, ESPM, EntAb, GenetAb.
—BLDSC (4953.497750), IE. **CCC.**
Published by: BioMed Central Ltd. (Subsidiary of: Current Science Ltd), Middlesex House, 34-42 Cleveland St, London, W1T 4LB, United Kingdom. TEL 44-20-73230323, FAX 44-20-76319923, editorial@jbiol.com, info@biomedcentral.com, http://www.jbiol.com/, http://www.biomedcentral.com. Ed. Martin Raff.

➤ **JOURNAL OF BIOMEDICAL OPTICS.** see *PHYSICS—Optics*

➤ **JOURNAL OF BIOMEDICAL SCIENCE.** see *MEDICAL SCIENCES*

578.77 MYS ISSN 0128-4541
JOURNAL OF BIOSCIENCE (PENANG); jurnal biosains. Text in English. s-a.

B

Indexed: ASFA, B&BAb, ESPM, OceAb, SWRA.
Published by: Universiti Sains Malaysia, School of Biological Sciences, Minden, Penang 11800, Malaysia. Ed. Yap Han Heng.

570 IND ISSN 0250-5991
CODEN: JOBSDN
➤ **JOURNAL OF BIOSCIENCES.** Text in English. 1979. irreg. (4-6/yr.), latest vol.24, 2000. INR 125 domestic to individuals; USD 30 foreign to individuals; INR 200 domestic to institutions; USD 100 foreign to institutions (effective 2003). 120 p./no. 2 cols./p.; back issues avail.; reprint service avail. from ISI. **Document type:** *Journal, Academic/Scholarly.* **Description:** Covers all areas of biology and is the premier journal in the country within its scope.
Incorporates (1934-1991): Indian Academy of Sciences. Proceedings. Animal Sciences (0253-4118); Indian Academy of Sciences. Proceedings. Plant Sciences (0253-410X)
Related titles: Online - full text ed.: free (effective 2005).
Indexed: ASCA, ASFA, AbHyg, AgBio, AgrForAb, AnBrAb, ApicAb, B&BAb, BIOBASE, BIOSIS Prev, BioCN&I, BiolAb, CIN, CPA, ChemAb, ChemTitl, CurCont, DSA, ESPM, EnvAb, ExcerpMed, FCA, FPA, ForAb, GEOBASE, HelmAb, HerbAb, HortAb, IABS, INIS AtomInd, ISR, IndMed, IndVet, Inpharma, MEDLINE, MaizeAb, NemAb, NutrAb, OrnHort, PBA, PGegResA, PGrRegA, PHN&I, PotatoAb, ProtozoAb, RA&MP, RDA, RM&VM, RPP, RRTA, Reac, RefZh, RevApplEntom, RiceAb, S&F, S&MA, SCI, SFA, SIA, SeedAb, SoyAb, TDB, TOSA, Telegen, TriticAb, VITIS, VetBull, WAE&RSA, WeedAb, ZooRec.
—BLDSC (4954.070000), CASDDS, CIS, CISTI, GNLM, IDS, IE, Infotrieve, ingenta, KNAW, Linda Hall.
Published by: Indian Academy of Sciences, C.V. Raman Ave., Sadashivanagar, P O Box 8005, Bangalore, Karnataka 560 080, India. TEL 91-80-23612546, FAX 91-80-23616094, jbiosci@ias.ernet.in, http://www.ias.ac.in/jbiosci. Ed. V Nanjundiah. Circ: 1,500.

▼ ➤ **JOURNAL OF CIRCADIAN RHYTHMS.** see *MEDICAL SCIENCES*

616.079 571.9 GBR ISSN 0021-9975
CODEN: JCVPAR
➤ **JOURNAL OF COMPARATIVE PATHOLOGY.** Text in English. 1888. 8/yr. EUR 438 in Europe to individuals; JPY 47,200 in Japan to individuals; USD 389 to individuals except Europe and Japan; EUR 922 in Europe to institutions; JPY 99,500 in Japan to institutions; USD 819 to institutions except Europe and Japan (effective 2006). adv. bibl.; charts; illus. index. reprints avail. **Document type:** *Academic/Scholarly.* **Description:** Directed to workers in veterinary and medical science who investigate diseases of all vertebrate animals, including domesticated zoo, wild and marine species, and man.
Related titles: Online - full text ed.: (from EBSCO Publishing, O C L C Online Computer Library Center, Inc., ScienceDirect, Swets Information Services).
Indexed: ASCA, AbHyg, AgBio, Agr, AnBrAb, BIOSIS Prev, BioCN&I, BiolAb, CIN, CRFR, ChemAb, ChemTitl, CurCont, DBA, DSA, DentInd, ExcerpMed, FoVS&M, HelmAb, ISR, IndMed, IndVet, Inpharma, MEDLINE, NSCI, NutrAb, PBA, PN&I, PoultAb, ProtozoAb, RM&VM, RPP, Reac, RevApplEntom, SAA, SCI, SFA, SoyAb, TDB, VetBull, WeedAb, WildRev, ZooRec.
—BLDSC (4962.800000), CASDDS, CISTI, GNLM, IDS, IE, Infotrieve, ingenta, KNAW. **CCC.**
Published by: W.B. Saunders Co. Ltd. (Subsidiary of: Elsevier Health Sciences), 32 Jamestown Rd, London, NW1 7BY, United Kingdom. TEL 44-20-7424-4200, FAX 44-20-7485-4752, http://www.elsevier.com/locate/jcpa.

570.285 USA ISSN 1066-5277
QH506 CODEN: JCOBEM
➤ **JOURNAL OF COMPUTATIONAL BIOLOGY**; a journal of computational molecular cell biology. Text in English. 1994. bi-m. (10/yr.). USD 1,011 domestic to institutions; USD 1,242 foreign to institutions; USD 1,209 combined subscription domestic to institutions print & online eds.; USD 1,432 combined subscription foreign to institutions print & online eds. (effective 2006). adv. back issues avail.; reprint service avail. from PSC. **Document type:** *Journal, Academic/Scholarly.* **Description:** Provides a forum for scientific and technical issues associated with the analysis and management of biological information at the molecular level.
Related titles: Online - full text ed.: ISSN 1557-8666. USD 938 to institutions (effective 2006) (from EBSCO Publishing, Gale Group, O C L C Online Computer Library Center, Inc., Swets Information Services).
Indexed: ASFA, BBCI, BCI, BIOBASE, BIOSIS Prev, BioEngAb, BiolAb, CIN, CMCI, ChemAb, ChemTitl, CurCont, ExcerpMed, IABS, IndMed, Inpharma, MEDLINE, Reac.
—BLDSC (4963.455000), CASDDS, CISTI, IDS, IE, Infotrieve, ingenta, Linda Hall. **CCC.**
Published by: Mary Ann Liebert, Inc. Publishers, 140 Huguenot St 3rd Fl, New Rochelle, NY 10801-5215. TEL 914-740-2100, FAX 914-740-2101, 800-654-3237, info@liebertpub.com, http://www.liebertpub.com/cmb. Eds. Dr. Michael S Waterman, Dr. Sorin Istrail. adv.: B&W page USD 1,150; trim 8.5 x 11. Circ: 1,526 (paid).

508.676 KEN ISSN 1026-1613
QH1
➤ **JOURNAL OF EAST AFRICA NATURAL HISTORY.** Text in English. 1995. 2/yr. USD 25 per vol. (effective 2002). bk.rev. **Document type:** *Academic/Scholarly.* **Description:** Contains information about natural history or conservation of the natural environment.
Formed by the merger of (1988-1994): Utafiti (1015-8707); (1909-1994): Journal of the East Africa Natural History Society and National Museum (0012-8317)
Indexed: ASFA, HortAb, SFA, WeedAb, ZooRec.
—CISTI, Linda Hall.
Published by: East Africa Natural History Society, PO Box 44486, Nairobi, 00100, Kenya. TEL 254-2-749957, FAX 254-2-741049, eanhs@africaonline.co.ke, office@naturekenya.org, http://www.naturekenya.org. Eds. Benny Bytebier, Lorna Depew. R&P Catherine Ngarachu. Circ: 1,035. **Co-sponsor:** National Museums of Kenya.

570 IND ISSN 0970-9037
QH183 CODEN: JECBEA
➤ **JOURNAL OF ECOBIOLOGY**; international journal of scientific research on environmental biology and inter-relations. Text in English. 1989. q. USD 500 to institutions (effective 2006). adv. bk.rev. charts; illus.; abstr. indexed in many leading indexing/abstract. 80 p./no. 1 cols./p.; back issues avail.; reprints avail. **Document type:** *Journal, Academic/Scholarly.*
Indexed: ASFA, AgBio, AgrForAb, AnBrAb, ApEcolAb, B&BAb, BioCN&I, CPA, ESPM, EntAb, FCA, FPA, ForAb, HelmAb, HerbAb, HortAb, I&DA, IndVet, MaizeAb, NemAb, NutrAb, OrnHort, PBA, PGegResA, PGrRegA, PHN&I, PoultAb, ProtozoAb, RA&MP, RDA, RM&VM, RPP, RefZh, RevApplEntom, RiceAb, S&F, SIA, SWRA, SeedAb, SoyAb, TDB, TriticAb, VetBull, WAE&RSA, WeedAb, ZooRec.
—BLDSC (4971.850000), CASDDS, IE, ingenta. **CCC.**
Published by: Palani Paramount Publications, 57, Anna Nagar, Palani, Tamil Nadu 624 602, India. TEL 91-04545-42332, FAX 91-04545-45919, spalani1@md4.vsnl.net.in, http://www.scientificpub.com/bookdetails.php?booktransid=453&bookid=449. Ed., R&P S Palanichamy. Adv. contact P Sarojini. page USD 125. Circ: 400. **Subscr. to:** Scientific Publishers, 5-A New Pali Rd., Near Hotel Taj Hari Mahal, PO Box 91, Jodhpur, Rajasthan 342 003, India.

577 GBR ISSN 0022-0477
QH540 CODEN: JECOAB
➤ **JOURNAL OF ECOLOGY.** Text in English. 1913. bi-m. GBP 545 combined subscription in Europe to institutions print & online eds.; USD 1,006 combined subscription in the Americas to institutions & Caribbean (print & online eds.); GBP 599 combined subscription elsewhere to institutions print & online eds. (effective 2006). adv. bk.rev. abstr.; bibl.; charts; illus.; maps. index, cum.index: vols.1-20 (1913-1932), vols.21-50 (1933-1982). back issues avail.; reprint service avail. from PSC,ISI. **Document type:** *Journal, Academic/Scholarly.*
Related titles: Microform ed.: (from PQC); Online - full text ed.: ISSN 1365-2745. GBP 518 in Europe to institutions; USD 956 in the Americas to institutions & Caribbean; GBP 569 elsewhere to institutions (effective 2006) (from Blackwell Synergy, EBSCO Publishing, Gale Group, IngentaConnect, JSTOR (Web-based Journal Archive), O C L C Online Computer Library Center, Inc., Swets Information Services).
Indexed: ASCA, ASFA, AgBio, Agr, AgrForAb, AnBeAb, ApEcolAb, B&AI, B&BAb, BIOBASE, BIOSIS Prev, BibAg, BioCN&I, BiolAb, Biostat, BrArAb, BrGeoL, CIN, CIS, CPA, CRFR, ChemAb, ChemTitl, CurCont, EPB, ESPM, EnerRev, EntAb, EnvAb, ExcerpMed, FCA, FPA, ForAb, GEOBASE, GSI, GardL, GenetAb, HGA, HerbAb, HortAb, I&DA, IABS, IBR, ISR, KWIWR, MBA, MaizeAb, NemAb, NutrAb, OceAb, OrnHort, PBA, PCI, PGegResA, PGrRegA, PN&I, PlantSci, PoultAb, RA&MP, RPP, RRTA, RefZh, RevApplEntom, S&F, SCI, SFA, SWRA, SeedAb, SoyAb, TriticAb, WRCInf, WeedAb, WildRev, ZooRec.
—BLDSC (4972.000000), CASDDS, CISTI, IDS, IE, Infotrieve, ingenta, Linda Hall. **CCC.**
Published by: (British Ecological Society), Blackwell Publishing Ltd., 9600 Garsington Rd, Oxford, OX4 2ZG, United Kingdom. TEL 44-1865-776868, FAX 44-1865-714591, customerservices@oxon.blackwellpublishing.com, http://www.blackwellpublishing.com/journals/JEC. Eds. David J Gibson, Malcolm C Press, Michael J Hutchings. Pub. Sue Hewitt. R&P Sophie Savage. Adv. contact Jenny Applin. Circ: 3,190.

573.6 IND
CODEN: JRBED2
JOURNAL OF ENDOCRINOLOGY & REPRODUCTION. Text in English. 1981. s-a. USD 60 (effective 2000). **Document type:** *Academic/Scholarly.*
Formerly: Journal of Reproductive Biology and Comparative Endocrinology (0254-3583)
Indexed: BIOSIS Prev, BiolAb, CIN, ChemAb, ChemTitl.
—CASDDS, CISTI.
Published by: (Society for Reproductive Biology and Comparative Endocrinology), H P C Publishers Distributors Pvt. Ltd., 4805 Bharat Ram Rd, 24 Darya Ganj, New Delhi, 110 002, India. TEL 91-11-3254401, FAX 91-11-619-3511, hpcpd@nda.vsnl.net.in, hpcpd@hpc.cc, http://www.hpc.cc, http://www.bizdelhi.com/publisher/hpc, http://www.indianindustry.com.

JOURNAL OF ENVIRONMENTAL BIOLOGY; an international research journal of environmental sciences & toxicology. see *ENVIRONMENTAL STUDIES*

JOURNAL OF ENVIRONMENTAL MONITORING AND RESTORATION. see *ENVIRONMENTAL STUDIES*

570 GBR ISSN 0022-0949
QH301 CODEN: JEBIAM
➤ **THE JOURNAL OF EXPERIMENTAL BIOLOGY.** Text in English. 1923. bi-m. USD 405 in North America to individuals; EUR 363 in Europe to individuals eurozone; GBP 238 to individuals in the UK & elsewhere; USD 2,245 in North America to institutions; EUR 2,040 in Europe to institutions eurozone; GBP 1,345 to institutions in the UK & elsewhere; USD 485 combined subscription in North America to individuals print & online; EUR 435 combined subscription in Europe to individuals eurozone; print & online; GBP 290 combined subscription to individuals in the UK & elsewhere; print & online; USD 2,590 combined subscription in North America to institutions print & online; EUR 2,360 combined subscription in Europe to institutions eurozone; print & online; GBP 1,555 combined subscription to institutions in the UK & elsewhere; print & online (effective 2005). adv. charts; illus. index; cum.index. back issues avail.; reprints avail. **Document type:** *Journal, Academic/Scholarly.* **Description:** Covers integrative biology from the molecular and sub-cellular to the whole animal.
Formerly (until 1925): British Journal of Experimental Biology (0366-0788)
Related titles: Online - full text ed.: ISSN 1477-9145. USD 110 in North America to individuals; EUR 101 in Europe to individuals eurozone; GBP 66 to individuals in the UK & elsewhere; USD 1,965 in North America to institutions; EUR 1,784 in Europe to institutions eurozone; GBP 1,175 to institutions in the UK & elsewhere (effective 2005) (from EBSCO Publishing, HighWire Press).
Indexed: AEA, ASCA, ASFA, AbHyg, AgBio, AgrForAb, AnBeAb, AnBrAb, ApicAb, B&AI, B&BAb, BBCI, BIOBASE, BIOSIS Prev, BioCN&I, BiolAb, CCI, CIN, CPA, CRFR, ChemAb, ChemTitl, CurCont, DSA, DentInd, ESPM, EntAb, ExcerpMed, ForAb, GSI, GenetAb, HelmAb, HerbAb, HortAb, IABS, ISR, IndMed, IndVet, Inpharma, KWIWR, MEDLINE, MS&D, NSCI, NemAb, NutrAb, OrnHort, PHN&I, PN&I, PotatoAb, PoultAb, ProtozoAb, PsycholAb, RA&MP, RM&VM, Reac, RefZh, RevApplEntom, S&F, SCI, SFA, SIA, SSCI, SoyAb, TDB, ToxAb, VetBull, WeedAb, WildRev, ZooRec.
—BLDSC (4980.000000), CASDDS, CISTI, GNLM, IE, Infotrieve, ingenta, Linda Hall.
Published by: The Company of Biologists Ltd., Bidder Building, 140 Cowley Rd, Cambridge, CB4 4DL, United Kingdom. TEL 44-1223-426164, FAX 44-1223-423353, sales@thecob.demon.co.uk, http://jeb.biologists.org, http://www.biologists.com. Ed. Dr. H Hoppeler. R&P Dr. Katheryn Phillips. Adv. contact Miss Amanda Sheppardson. Circ: 1,250.

578.77 NLD ISSN 0022-0981
QH91.A1 CODEN: JEMBAM
➤ **JOURNAL OF EXPERIMENTAL MARINE BIOLOGY AND ECOLOGY.** Text in Dutch. 1967. 28/yr. EUR 4,227 in Europe to institutions; JPY 561,100 in Japan to institutions; USD 4,729 elsewhere to institutions (effective 2006). adv. bk.rev. illus. Index. back issues avail.; reprint service avail. from ISI. **Document type:** *Journal, Academic/Scholarly.* **Description:** Provides a forum for work in the biochemistry, physiology, behavior, and genetics of marine plants and animals in relation to their ecology.
Related titles: Microform ed.: (from PQC); Online - full text ed.: (from EBSCO Publishing, Gale Group, IngentaConnect, ScienceDirect, Swets Information Services).
Indexed: AEA, ASCA, ASFA, AgBio, AnBrAb, ApEcolAb, B&AI, B&BAb, BIOBASE, BIOSIS Prev, BioCN&I, BiolAb, CIN, CPA, CRFR, ChemAb, ChemTitl, CurCont, EIA, EPB, ESPM, EnerInd, EnvAb, EnvEAb, ExcerpMed, ForAb, GEOBASE, GenetAb, HGA, HelmAb, HortAb, IABS, ISR, IndVet, MBA, MEDLINE, MSCT, NemAb, NutrAb, OceAb, PlantSci, PollutAb, ProtozoAb, RM&VM, RefZh, S&F, SCI, SFA, SIA, SSCI, SWRA, TriticAb, VetBull, WeedAb, WildRev, ZooRec.
—BLDSC (4981.600000), CASDDS, CISTI, IDS, IE, Infotrieve, ingenta, Linda Hall. **CCC.**
Published by: Elsevier BV (Subsidiary of: Elsevier Science & Technology), Radarweg 29, Amsterdam, 1043 NX, Netherlands. TEL 31-20-4853911, FAX 31-20-4852457, jembe@wpo.nerc.ac.uk, nlinfo-f@elsevier.nl, http://www.elsevier.com/locate/jembe, http://www.elsevier.nl. Eds. Dr. P M J Herman, R Hughes, Dr. Sandra E. Shumway. **Subscr. in the Americas to:** Elsevier, Subscription Customer Service, 6277 Sea Harbor Dr, Orlando, FL 32887-4800. TEL 407-345-4020, 877-839-7126, FAX 407-363-1354.

578.7 IND ISSN 0970-3594
QH90.A1 CODEN: JOHYE4
JOURNAL OF HYDROBIOLOGY. Text in English. 1985. s-a. INR 750, USD 20. adv. bk.rev.
Indexed: BiolAb, ZooRec.
—CISTI.
Published by: Vikram University, School of Studies in Zoology, P O Box 233, Ujjain, 456 010, India. Ed. K S Rao.

B

570 USA ISSN 0883-1394
CODEN: JIDBE9

JOURNAL OF INFERENTIAL AND DEDUCTIVE BIOLOGY∗ . Text in English. 1985. irreg. USD 188. adv. bk.rev. —CASDDS.
Published by: Danielli Associates, c/o Richard F. Danielli, 667 Washington St Apt 223, Auburn, MA 01501-2789. Eds. Alejandro B Engel, Roger V Jean.

570 USA ISSN 0741-5400
QP185 CODEN: JLBIE7

➤ **JOURNAL OF LEUKOCYTE BIOLOGY.** Text in English. 1967. m. (2 vols./yr.). USD 105 combined subscription domestic to individuals print & online eds.; USD 125 combined subscription in Canada & Mexico to individuals print & online eds.; USD 153 combined subscription elsewhere to individuals print & online eds.; USD 849 combined subscription domestic to institutions print & online eds.; USD 869 combined subscription in Canada & Mexico to institutions print & online eds.; USD 899 combined subscription elsewhere to institutions print & online eds. (effective 2005). adv. charts; illus. index. back issues avail. **Document type:** *Journal, Academic/Scholarly.* **Description:** Presents manuscripts of original investigations on the origins, developmental biology, and functions of granulocytes, lymphocytes, and mononuclear phagocytes.
Formerly (until 1984): R E S. Reticuloendothelial Society. Journal (0033-6890)
Related titles: Online - full text ed.: (from EBSCO Publishing, HighWire Press).
Indexed: AIDS&Cr, ASCA, BIOSIS Prev, BiolAb, ChemAb, ChemTitl, CurCont, DSA, DentInd, ExcerpMed, IAA, ISR, ImmunAb, IndMed, IndVet, Inpharma, MEDLINE, NSCI, PE&ON, PN&I, ProtozoAb, RM&VM, Reac, SAA, SCI, SSCI, VetBull.
—BLDSC (5010.305000), CASDDS, CISTI, GNLM, IDS, IE, Infotrieve, ingenta, KNAW, Linda Hall. **CCC.**
Published by: (Society for Leukocyte Biology), Federation of American Societies for Experimental Biology, 9650 Rockville Pike, Rm L-2407A, Bethesda, MD 20814-3998. TEL 301-634-7029, FAX 301-634-7809, staff@faseb.org, http://www.jleukbio.org/, http://www.faseb.org. Ed. Joost J Oppenheim. R&P S. Jacobson. Adv. contact Susan Mergenhagen. B&W page USD 840; trim 8.25 x 11. Circ: 2,000 (paid).

578.77 ITA ISSN 1129-5767
QH96 CODEN: MIIMAS

JOURNAL OF LIMNOLOGY. Text in English. 1942. s-a. per issue exchange basis. **Document type:** *Academic/Scholarly.*
Description: Publishes peer-reviewed original papers, review papers, and notes in the field of limnology, including hydrochemistry, lake physics, methodology, taxonomy, all aspects of ecology, biogeography and pollution.
Formed by the merger of (1942-1998): Istituto Italiano di Idrobiologia. Memorie (0374-9118); (1984-1988): Istituto Italiano di Idrobiologia. Documenta (0393-8395)
Indexed: ASFA, BIOSIS Prev, BiolAb, ESPM, GEOBASE, RefZh, SFA, WatResAb, WildRev, ZooRec.
—BLDSC (5010.474600), CASDDS, CISTI, IE, ingenta, Linda Hall.
Published by: Istituto Italiano di Idrobiologia, Largo Vittorio Tonolli, 50, Verbania Pallanza, VB 28922, Italy. TEL 39-0323-518300, FAX 39-0323-556513, g.giussani@iii.to.cnr.it, http://www.iii.to.cnr.it/pubblicaz/jour_lim.htm. Ed. Riccardo de Bernardi. Circ: 800.

570 DEU ISSN 0303-6812
QH323.5 CODEN: JMBLAJ

➤ **JOURNAL OF MATHEMATICAL BIOLOGY.** Text in English. m. EUR 1,098 combined subscription to institutions print & online eds. (effective 2005). adv. back issues avail.; reprint service avail. from PSC,ISI. **Document type:** *Journal, Academic/Scholarly.* **Description:** Includes the fields of genetics, demography, ecology, neurobiology, epidemiology, morphogenesis, and cell biology.
Related titles: Microform ed.: (from PQC); Online - full text ed.: ISSN 1432-1416 (from EBSCO Publishing, Springer LINK, Swets Information Services).
Indexed: ASCA, ASFA, AnBrAb, ApEcolAb, BIOSIS Prev, BiolAb, Biostat, CCMJ, CIS, CMCI, CompAb, CurCont, ESPM, ExcerpMed, ISR, IndMed, Inpharma, Inspec, MEDLINE, MathR, MathSciNet, PBA, PHN&I, Reac, SCI, SFA, ST&MA, WildRev, ZentMath, ZooRec.
—BLDSC (5012.375000), AskIEEE, CISTI, GNLM, IDS, IE, Infotrieve, ingenta, Linda Hall. **CCC.**
Published by: Springer-Verlag (Subsidiary of: Springer Science+Business Media), Tiergartenstr 17, Heidelberg, 69121, Germany. TEL 49-6221-3450, FAX 49-6221-345229, http://link.springer.de/link/service/journals/00285/index.htm. Eds. A Hastings TEL 530-752-8116, O Diekmann. Adv. contact Stephan Kroeck TEL 49-30-827875739. **Subscr. in the Americas to:** Springer-Verlag New York, Inc., Journal Fulfillment, PO Box 2485, Secaucus, NJ 07096-2485. TEL 800-777-4643, 201-348-4033, FAX 201-348-4505, journals@springer-ny.com, http://www.springer-ny.com. **Subscr. to:** Springer GmbH Auslieferungsgesellschaft, Haberstr 7, Heidelberg 69126, Germany. TEL 49-6221-345-0, FAX 49-6221-345-4229, subscriptions@springer.de.

570 610 SGP ISSN 0219-5194
QH513 CODEN: JMMBBB

➤ **JOURNAL OF MECHANICS IN MEDICINE AND BIOLOGY.** Text in English. 2001. q. SGD 188, USD 108, EUR 104 to individuals; SGD 469, USD 269, EUR 258 combined subscription to institutions print & online eds.; SGD 282, USD 161, EUR 155 combined subscription in developing nations to institutions print & online eds. (effective 2006). back issues avail. **Document type:** *Journal, Academic/Scholarly.*
Description: Publishes original papers covering biomedical science subjects ranging from nano to macro scale, and the applied technology of the methods and techniques of medical and clinical treatment.
Related titles: Online - full content ed.; Online - full text ed.: (from EBSCO Publishing, O C L C Online Computer Library Center, Inc., Swets Information Services).
Indexed: B&BAb, BioEngAb, IAA, Inspec, PEI.
—BLDSC (5016.200000), IE. **CCC.**
Published by: World Scientific Publishing Co. Pte. Ltd., 5 Toh Tuck Link, Singapore, 596224, Singapore. TEL 65-466-5775, FAX 65-467-7667, http://www.worldscinet.com/jmmb/jmmb.shtml, http://www.worldscientific.com. Ed. Wen-Jei Yang TEL 734-764-9910. **Subscr. to:** Farrer Rd, PO Box 128, Singapore 912805, Singapore. sales@wspc.com.sg. **Dist. in the US by:** World Scientific Publishing Co., Inc., 1060 Main St, River Edge, NJ 07661. TEL 201-487-9655, 800-227-7562, FAX 201-487-9656, 888-977-2665, wspc@wspc.com.; **Dist. by:** World Scientific Publishing Ltd., 57 Shelton St, London WC2H 9HE, United Kingdom. TEL 44-20-78360888, FAX 44-20-78362020, sales@wspc.co.uk.

571.86 612.64 ROM ISSN 1582-4918
CODEN: RRMEEA

JOURNAL OF MOLECULAR AND CELLULAR PATHOLOGY/REVUE ROUMAINE DE MORPHOLOGIE ET EMBRYOLOGIE. Text in English, French, German, Russian, Spanish. 1974. q. bk.rev. charts; illus. index. **Document type:** *Journal, Academic/Scholarly.*
Former titles (until 2001): Romanian Journal of Morphology and Embryology (1220-0522); (until 1990): Morphologie et Embryologie (0377-5038); Which superseded in part (in 1975): Revue Roumaine de Morphologie et de Physiologie (0377-4953); Which was formed by the merger of (1954-1974): Revue Roumaine de Physiologie (0035-399X); (1974-1974): Revue Roumaine de Morphologie et d'Embryologie (0377-4945); Which was formed by the merger of (1953-1974): Morfologia Normala si Patologica (0027-1063); (1953-1974): Revue Roumaine d'Embryologie et de Cytologie. Serie de Cytologie (0556-8056); (1953-1974): Revue Roumaine d'Embryologie (0300-063X); Which was formerly (until 1972): Revue Roumaine d'Embryologie et de Cytologie. Serie d'Embryologie (0035-4007); All of which superseded in part (in 1963): Revue des Sciences Medicales (0484-8632); Which superseded in part (in 1954): La Science dans la Republique Populaire Roumaine (1220-4757)
Related titles: Online - full text ed.: ISSN 1582-4926.
Indexed: BiolAb, CIN, ChemAb, ChemTitl, ExcerpMed, IndMed, MEDLINE, NutrAb.
—BLDSC (8019.636500), CASDDS, CISTI, GNLM, KNAW, Linda Hall.
Published by: (Academia de Stiinte Medicale), Editura Academiei Romane/Publishing House of the Romanian Academy, Calea 13 Septembrie 13, Sector 5, Bucharest, 76117, Romania. TEL 40-21-4119008, FAX 40-21-4103983, edacad@ear.ro, http://www.ear.ro. Ed. V D Marza. **Dist. by:** Rodipet S.A., Piata Presei Libere 1, sector 1, PO Box 33-57, Bucharest 3, Romania. TEL 40-21-2224126, 40-21-2226407, rodipet@rodipet.ro.

571.3 USA ISSN 0362-2525
QL801 CODEN: JOMOAT

➤ **JOURNAL OF MORPHOLOGY.** Text in English. 1887. m. USD 4,795 domestic to institutions; USD 4,939 in Canada & Mexico to institutions; USD 5,023 elsewhere to institutions; USD 5,275 combined subscription domestic to institutions print & online eds.; USD 5,419 combined subscription in Canada & Mexico to institutions print & online eds.; USD 5,503 combined subscription elsewhere to institutions print & online eds. (effective 2006). adv. abstr.; bibl.; charts; illus. index. back issues avail.; reprints avail. **Document type:** *Journal, Academic/Scholarly.* **Description:** Publishes original research in morphology including cytology, protozoology, developmental biology, and general and functional morphology.
Former titles (until 1930): Journal of Morphology and Physiology (0095-9626); (until 1923): Journal of Morphology (0022-2887)
Related titles: Microform ed.: (from PMC, PQC, SWZ); Online - full text ed.: ISSN 1097-4687. USD 4,795 to institutions (effective 2006) (from EBSCO Publishing, Swets Information Services, Wiley InterScience).
Indexed: ASCA, ASFA, Agr, AnBrAb, BIOBASE, BIOSIS Prev, BiolAb, CIN, ChemAb, ChemTitl, CurCont, DentInd, ESPM, EntAb, ExcerpMed, IABS, ISR, IndMed, IndVet, Inpharma, MEDLINE, NSCI, PollutAb, PoultAb, Reac, RefZh, RevApplEntom, SCI, SFA, SSCI, VetBull, WildRev, ZooRec.
—BLDSC (5021.000000), CASDDS, CISTI, GNLM, IDS, IE, Infotrieve, ingenta, Linda Hall. **CCC.**

Published by: John Wiley & Sons, Inc., 111 River St, Hoboken, NJ 07030-5774. TEL 201-748-6000, FAX 201-748-5915, uscs-wis@wiley.com, http://www3.interscience.wiley.com/cgi-bin/jhome/35280, http://www.wiley.com. Ed. Frederick W Harrison. adv.: B&W page GBP 640, color page GBP 1,515; trim 174 x 254. Circ: 900. **Subscr. outside the Americas to:** John Wiley & Sons Ltd., The Atrium, Southern Gate, Chichester, West Sussex PO19 8SQ, United Kingdom. TEL 44-1243-843335, 0800-243407, FAX 44-1243-843232, cs-journals@wiley.co.uk.

➤ **JOURNAL OF MOUNTAIN ECOLOGY.** see *ENVIRONMENTAL STUDIES*

570 GBR ISSN 0022-2933
QH1 CODEN: JNAHA9

➤ **JOURNAL OF NATURAL HISTORY.** Text in English. 1841. 48/yr. GBP 4,449, USD 7,341 combined subscription to institutions print & online eds. (effective 2006). adv. bk.rev. reprint service avail. from PSC. **Document type:** *Journal, Academic/Scholarly.* **Description:** Contains original research and reviews in systematics and evolutionary and general biology.
Formerly (until 1967): Annals and Magazine of Natural History (0374-5481)
Related titles: Microform ed.; Online - full text ed.: ISSN 1464-5262. 199?. GBP 4,227, USD 6,974 (effective 2006) (from EBSCO Publishing, Gale Group, IngentaConnect, O C L C Online Computer Library Center, Inc., Swets Information Services).
Indexed: ASCA, ASFA, AgBio, AgrForAb, AnBeAb, AnBrAb, ApEcolAb, ApicAb, BIOBASE, BIOSIS Prev, BioCN&I, BiolAb, CPA, CRFR, CTO, CurCont, EPB, ESPM, EntAb, ForAb, GEOBASE, HelmAb, HerbAb, HortAb, IABS, IBR, ISR, IndVet, NemAb, NutrAb, OrnHort, PBA, PGegResA, PoultAb, ProtozoAb, RA&MP, RM&VM, RPP, RefSour, RevApplEntom, S&F, SCI, SFA, SPPI, SeedAb, SoyAb, TDB, TriticAb, VetBull, WeedAb, WildRev, ZooRec.
—BLDSC (5021.200000), CISTI, IDS, IE, Infotrieve, ingenta, Linda Hall. **CCC.**
Published by: Taylor & Francis Ltd (Subsidiary of: Taylor & Francis Group), 4 Park Sq, Milton Park, Abingdon, OX14 4RN, United Kingdom. TEL 44-1235-828600, FAX 44-1235-829000, info@tandf.co.uk, http://www.tandf.co.uk/journals/titles/00222933.asp. Eds. A Polaszek, P J Hayward. **Subscr. in N. America to:** Taylor & Francis Inc., Customer Services Dept, 325 Chestnut St, 8th Fl, Philadelphia, PA 19106. TEL 800-354-1420, FAX 215-625-8914; **Subscr. to:** Journals Customer Service, Rankine Rd, Basingstoke, Hants RG24 8PR, United Kingdom. TEL 44-1256-813000, FAX 44-1256-330245, enquiry@tandf.co.uk.

570.71 USA ISSN 1059-9053
S530 CODEN: JRLEEJ

➤ **JOURNAL OF NATURAL RESOURCES AND LIFE SCIENCES EDUCATION;** an international journal. Text in English. 1972. a. USD 100 domestic to non-members; USD 110 foreign to non-members; USD 35 domestic to members; USD 45 foreign to members (effective 2005). adv. bk.rev.; software rev.; video rev. charts; illus. back issues avail. **Document type:** *Journal, Academic/Scholarly.* **Description:** Designed for educators in universities, extension, and industry. Presents innovative concepts and techniques for improving education programs.
Formerly (until 1992): Journal of Agronomic Education (0094-2391)
Related titles: Online - full content ed.: ISSN 1539-1582; Online - full text ed.: (from bigchalk, EBSCO Publishing, ProQuest Information & Learning).
Indexed: ABIn, AEA, AbHyg, AgBio, Agr, BIOSIS Prev, BibAg, BiolAb, CIJE, CPA, DSA, EduInd, EnvAb, FCA, FPA, ForAb, GardL, HerbAb, HortAb, I&DA, IndVet, MaizeAb, NutrAb, OrnHort, PBA, PN&I, PotatoAb, PoultAb, RDA, RM&VM, RPP, RRTA, RefZh, RevApplEntom, S&F, TriticAb, WAE&RSA, WeedAb.
—BLDSC (5021.227000), CASDDS, CISTI, Ei, IE, Infotrieve, ingenta. **CCC.**
Published by: American Society of Agronomy, Inc., 677 S Segoe Rd, Madison, WI 53711. TEL 608-273-8080, FAX 608-273-2021, http://www.jnrlse.org/. Eds. John Greveel, J L Hatfield. Adv. contacts Keith R Schlesinger, Betsy Ahner. B&W page USD 360. Circ: 1,000 (paid).

611 GBR ISSN 1477-5751

➤ **JOURNAL OF NEGATIVE RESULTS IN BIOMEDICINE.** Text in English. 2002. irreg. free (effective 2006). **Document type:** *Journal, Academic/Scholarly.* **Description:** Provides a forum for promoting science and medical practice by publishing well documented results/conclusions that are unexpected, controversial, provocative and/or negative in the context of current tenets, providing scientists and physicians with responsible and balanced information to support informed experimental and clinical decisions.
Media: Online - full content (from EBSCO Publishing, National Library of Medicine).
Indexed: ExcerpMed.
—**CCC.**
Published by: BioMed Central Ltd. (Subsidiary of: Current Science Ltd), Middlesex House, 34-42 Cleveland St, London, W1T 4LB, United Kingdom. TEL 44-20-76319131, FAX 44-20-76319923, info@biomedcentral.com, http://www.jnrbm.com, http://www.biomedcentral.com. Ed. Bjorn R. Olsen.

571.3 ESP ISSN 1139-5192
QL391.N4
JOURNAL OF NEMATODE MORPHOLOGY AND SYSTEMATICS. Text in Spanish, English. 1998. s-a. **Document type:** *Journal, Academic/Scholarly.*
Indexed: AgBio, BioCN&I, ForAb, IECT, NemAb, S&F, ZooRec.
—BLDSC (5021.398000).
Published by: Universidad de Jaen, Departamento de Biologia Animal, Biologia Vegetal y Ecologia, Paraje Las Lagunillas, s-n, Edificio No 5, Jaen, 23071, Spain. TEL 34-53-012143, http://www.ujaen.es/dep/bioani/.

▼ **JOURNAL OF NEURAL ENGINEERING.** see *COMPUTERS—Artificial Intelligence*

JOURNAL OF NUCLEAR AGRICULTURE AND BIOLOGY. see *AGRICULTURE—Crop Production And Soil*

JOURNAL OF OIL PALM RESEARCH. see *AGRICULTURE*

JOURNAL OF PALEOLIMNOLOGY. see *PALEONTOLOGY*

578.77 GBR ISSN 0142-7873
QH90.8.P5 CODEN: JPLRD9
➤ **JOURNAL OF PLANKTON RESEARCH.** Text in English. 1979. 13/yr. GBP 510, USD 867, EUR 765 to institutions; GBP 537, USD 913, EUR 806 combined subscription to institutions print & online eds. (effective 2006). adv. bk.rev. illus. index. back issues avail.; reprint service avail. from PSC. **Document type:** *Academic/Scholarly.* **Description:** A forum for international papers covering zooplankton and phytoplankton in three main areas: ecology (including model studies); physiology; distribution, life and taxonomy.
Related titles: Online - full text ed.: ISSN 1464-3774. GBP 483, USD 821, EUR 725 to institutions (effective 2006) (from EBSCO Publishing, Gale Group, HighWire Press, IngentaConnect, O C L C Online Computer Library Center, Inc., Ovid Technologies, Inc., Oxford University Press Online Journals, ProQuest Information & Learning, Swets Information Services).
Indexed: ASCA, ASFA, AnBeAb, ApEcolAb, ArtHuCI, B&BAb, BIOBASE, BIOSIS Prev, BiolAb, CIN, ChemAb, ChemTitl, CurCont, ESPM, FPA, ForAb, GEOBASE, HelmAb, I&DA, IABS, ISR, IndVet, MBA, OceAb, PlantSci, PollutAb, ProtozoAb, RevApplEntom, S&F, SCI, SFA, SWRA, ZooRec.
—BLDSC (5040.350000), CASDDS, CINDOC, CISTI, IDS, IE, Infotrieve, ingenta, Linda Hall. **CCC.**
Published by: Oxford University Press, Great Clarendon St, Oxford, OX2 6DP, United Kingdom. TEL 44-1865-556767, FAX 44-1865-556646, jnl.orders@oup.co.uk, http://plankt.oxfordjournals.org/, http://www.oxfordjournals.org/. Ed. Kevin J Flynn. Pub. Cathy Kennedy. R&P Fiona Bennett. adv.: B&W page GBP 230, B&W page USD 415; trim 216 x 279. Circ: 620.

577 GBR ISSN 1354-0270
JOURNAL OF PRACTICAL ECOLOGY & CONSERVATION. Text in English. 1995. q. GBP 12 per issue to individuals; GBP 22 per issue to institutions; GBP 26 per issue foreign to institutions (effective 2000). bk.rev. **Document type:** *Academic/Scholarly.* **Description:** A journal for professional ecologists and conservation managers.
Related titles: ♦ Supplement(s): Journal of Practical Ecology & Conservation. Special Publication. ISSN 1368-9355.
Indexed: ZooRec.
—BLDSC (5041.535000), IE, ingenta.
Published by: Wildtrack Publishing, Wildtrack Publishing, PO Box 1142, Sheffield, S Yorks S1 1SZ, United Kingdom. Ed. Ian Rotherham.

577 GBR ISSN 1368-9355
JOURNAL OF PRACTICAL ECOLOGY & CONSERVATION. SPECIAL PUBLICATION. Text in English. 1996. irreg. GBP 11 per vol. (effective 2000). **Document type:** *Monographic series, Academic/Scholarly.*
Related titles: ♦ Supplement to: Journal of Practical Ecology & Conservation. ISSN 1354-0270.
Indexed: ZooRec.
Published by: Wildtrack Publishing, Wildtrack Publishing, PO Box 1142, Sheffield, S Yorks S1 1SZ, United Kingdom.

616.93601 JPN ISSN 0917-4427
JOURNAL OF PROTOZOOLOGY RESEARCH. Text in English. 1991. q. **Document type:** *Journal, Academic/Scholarly.* **Description:** Publishes original research, invited review and mini-review articles, and short communications in the fields of protozoology and tropical biology.
Indexed: AgBio, DSA, IndVet, PN&I, PoultAb, ProtozoAb, TDB.
Published by: National Research Center for Protozoan Diseases, Nishi 2-13, Inada-cho, Obihiro, Hokkaido 080-8555, Japan. protozoa@obihiro.ac.jp, http://www.obihiro.ac.jp/~protozoa/text/Journal.htm.

JOURNAL OF QUATERNARY SCIENCE. see *EARTH SCIENCES—Geology*

570 USA
QH603.C43 CODEN: JRETET
➤ **JOURNAL OF RECEPTORS AND SIGNAL TRANSDUCTION.** Text in English. 1975. bi-m. GBP 1,772, USD 2,925 combined subscription to institutions print & online eds. (effective 2006). adv. bk.rev. charts; illus. Index. back issues avail.; reprint service avail. from PSC. **Document type:** *Journal, Academic/Scholarly.* **Description:** Presents a forum for the rapid publication of laboratory and clinical research on biological receptors and associated signal transduction pathways for hormones, growth factors, drugs, and ligands involved in the immune response.
Formerly (until 2002): Journal of Receptor and Signal Transduction Research (1079-9893); Which was formed by the merger of (1980-1994): Journal of Receptor Research (0197-5110); (1988-1993): Second Messengers and Phosphoproteins (0895-7479); Which was formerly (1983-1988): Journal of Cyclic Nucleotide and Protein Phosphorylation Research (0746-3898); (1975-1983): Journal of Cyclic Nucleotide Research (0095-1544)
Related titles: Microform ed.: (from RPI); Online - full text ed.: ISSN 1532-4281. GBP 1,683, USD 2,779 to institutions (effective 2006) (from EBSCO Publishing, O C L C Online Computer Library Center, Inc., Swets Information Services).
Indexed: ASCA, AbHyg, AgBio, AnBrAb, BBCI, BIOBASE, BiolAb, CIN, CTA, ChemAb, ChemTitl, CurCont, DBA, DSA, ExcerpMed, ForAb, HortAb, IABS, ISR, IndMed, Inpharma, MEDLINE, MSB, NSA, NucAcAb, NutrAb, OrnHort, PGrRegA, ProtozoAb, RA&MP, RM&VM, Reac, RefZh, SCI.
—BLDSC (5047.849000), CASDDS, CISTI, GNLM, IDS, IE, ingenta, Linda Hall. **CCC.**
Published by: Taylor & Francis Inc. (Subsidiary of: Taylor & Francis Group), 325 Chestnut St, Ste 800, Philadelphia, PA 19016. TEL 215-625-8900, 800-354-1420, FAX 215-625-8914, info@taylorandfrancis.com, http://www.tandf.co.uk/journals/titles/10799893.asp, http://www.taylorandfrancis.com. Ed. Dr. Alex N Eberle. R&P Elaine Inverso. Adv. contact Mary Drabot. page USD 600. Circ: 525 (paid).

612 573.6 IND
JOURNAL OF REPRODUCTION AND FERTILITY. Text in English. q.
Related titles: Microfilm ed.: (from PMC).
Indexed: B&AI, BiolAb, CIN, ChemAb, ChemTitl, CurCont, DSA, SAA, VetBull.
Published by: Indian Society for the Study of Reproduction and Endocrinology, c/o Department of Zoology, University of Delhi, New Delhi, 110 007, India.

JOURNAL OF RUBBER RESEARCH. see *RUBBER*

JOURNAL OF SEA RESEARCH. see *EARTH SCIENCES—Oceanography*

578.757 IND ISSN 0970-1370
QH183
➤ **JOURNAL OF SOIL BIOLOGY AND ECOLOGY.** Text and summaries in English. 1981. s-a. INR 400, USD 60 (effective 1997). adv. back issues avail. **Document type:** *Journal, Academic/Scholarly.*
Related titles: CD-ROM ed.
Indexed: BiolAb, S&F, S&MA, ZooRec.
—BLDSC (5064.955000), CISTI.
Published by: Indian Society of Soil Biology and Ecology, University of Agricultural Sciences, Department of Entomology, Hebbal, Bangalore, Karnataka 560 024, India. TEL 91-80-3330153, FAX 91-80-3330277. Ed. G K Veeresh. Circ: 350.

570 011 IND ISSN 0971-3328
➤ **JOURNAL OF SPICES AND AROMATIC CROPS.** Text in English. 1992. q. USD 50 to institutions (effective 2006). adv. bk.rev. bibl. **Document type:** *Journal, Academic/Scholarly.* **Description:** Devoted to the advancement of research on spices, aromatic, medicinal and related plants.
Indexed: AEA, AgBio, AgrForAb, BioCN&I, CPA, FCA, FPA, FS&TA, ForAb, HerbAb, HortAb, I&DA, MaizeAb, NemAb, OrnHort, PBA, PGegResA, PGrRegA, PHN&I, RA&MP, RDA, RM&VM, RPP, RevApplEntom, RiceAb, S&F, SIA, SeedAb, TriticAb, WAE&RSA, WeedAb.
—BLDSC (5066.181000).
Published by: (Indian Society for Spices), Scientific Publishers, 5-A New Pali Rd., Near Hotel Taj Hari Mahal, PO Box 91, Jodhpur, Rajasthan 342 003, India. TEL 91-291-2433323, FAX 91-291-2512580, josac@iisr.org, journals@scientificpub.com, http://www.scientificpub.com/bookdetails.php?booktransid=458&bookid=454. Ed. Santhosh Eapen. adv.: B&W page INR 2,000. Circ: 400 (paid).

570 USA ISSN 1047-8477
QH573 CODEN: JSBIEM
➤ **JOURNAL OF STRUCTURAL BIOLOGY.** Text in Multiple languages. 1957. 12/yr. EUR 649 in Europe to individuals; JPY 67,700 in Japan to individuals; USD 494 elsewhere to individuals; EUR 1,366 in Europe to institutions; JPY 142,700 in Japan to institutions; USD 1,039 elsewhere to institutions; EUR 88 in Europe to students; JPY 9,200 in Japan to students; USD 78 elsewhere to students (effective 2006). adv. bibl.; charts; illus. index. **Document type:** *Academic/Scholarly.* **Description:** Deals with the structural analysis of biological matter at all levels of organization by means of light and electron microscopy, x-ray diffraction, nuclear magnetic resonance, as well as other imaging, diffraction, spectroscopic, or scanning probe techniques yielding structural information.
Former titles: Journal of Ultrastructure and Molecular Structure Research (0889-1605); Journal of Ultrastructure Research (0022-5320)
Related titles: Online - full text ed.: ISSN 1095-8657. USD 1,099 (effective 2002) (from EBSCO Publishing, Gale Group, IngentaConnect, O C L C Online Computer Library Center, Inc., ScienceDirect, Swets Information Services).
Indexed: ABIPC, ASCA, ASFA, AbHyg, Agr, AnBrAb, BBCI, BIOSIS Prev, BibAg, BiolAb, CIN, ChemAb, ChemTitl, CurCont, DSA, ESPM, ExcerpMed, FCA, HerbAb, ISR, IndMed, IndVet, Inpharma, Inspec, MEDLINE, NutrAb, PN&I, PoultAb, ProtozoAb, RPP, Reac, S&F, SCI, SFA, TDB, VetBull, WildRev, ZooRec.
—BLDSC (5066.874500), CASDDS, CISTI, GNLM, IDS, IE, Infotrieve, ingenta, Linda Hall. **CCC.**
Published by: Academic Press (Subsidiary of: Elsevier Science & Technology), 525 B St, Ste 1900, San Diego, CA 92101-4495. TEL 619-231-6616, 800-894-3434, FAX 619-699-6422, apsubs@acad.com, http://www.elsevier.com/locate/yjsbi, http://www.academicpress.com. Eds. Alasdair C Steven, W. Baumeister.

570 NLD ISSN 0022-5010
QH305 CODEN: JHBIA9
➤ **JOURNAL OF THE HISTORY OF BIOLOGY.** Text in English. 1968. 3/yr. EUR 368, USD 378, GBP 235 combined subscription to institutions print & online eds. (effective 2005). adv. bk.rev. charts; illus. index. reprint service avail. from PSC. **Document type:** *Journal, Academic/Scholarly.* **Description:** Publishes research on the history of the biological sciences, with particular emphasis on developments of the 19th and 20th centuries, including philosophical issues.
Related titles: Microform ed.: (from PQC); Online - full text ed.: ISSN 1573-0387 (from EBSCO Publishing, Gale Group, IngentaConnect, Kluwer Online, O C L C Online Computer Library Center, Inc., Springer LINK, Swets Information Services); ♦ French ed.: Revue de l'Histoire de Biologie.
Indexed: ABS&EES, ASCA, AmH&L, ArtHuCI, B&AI, BIOBASE, BIOSIS Prev, BibLing, BiolAb, CurCont, DIP, GSI, HistAb, IBR, IBZ, ISR, IndMed, MaizeAb, PBA, PGrRegA, PhilInd, ProtozoAb, RASB, RM&VM, RefZh, SCI, SFA, SSCI, ZooRec.
—BLDSC (5000.700000), CISTI, IDS, IE, Infotrieve, ingenta, Linda Hall. **CCC.**
Published by: Springer-Verlag Dordrecht (Subsidiary of: Springer Science+Business Media), Van Godewijckstraat 30, Dordrecht, 3311 GX, Netherlands. TEL 31-78-6576050, FAX 31-78-6576474, http://springerlink.metapress.com/openurl.asp?genre=journal&issn=0022-5010, http://www.springeronline.com. Eds. Garland E Allen, Jane Maienschein.

➤ **JOURNAL OF THE PERIPHERAL NERVOUS SYSTEM.** see *MEDICAL SCIENCES—Psychiatry And Neurology*

➤ **JOURNAL OF THE PERIPHERAL NERVOUS SYSTEM ONLINE.** see *MEDICAL SCIENCES—Psychiatry And Neurology*

570 GBR ISSN 0022-5193
QH301 CODEN: JTBIAP
➤ **JOURNAL OF THEORETICAL BIOLOGY.** Text in English. 1961. 24/yr. EUR 4,596 in Europe to institutions; JPY 496,500 in Japan to institutions; USD 4,085 elsewhere to institutions (effective 2006). bibl.; charts; illus. index. reprints avail. **Document type:** *Academic/Scholarly.* **Description:** Provides a forum for theoretical papers that give insight into biological processes.
Related titles: Online - full text ed.: ISSN 1095-8541. USD 4,307 (effective 2002) (from EBSCO Publishing, Gale Group, IngentaConnect, O C L C Online Computer Library Center, Inc., ScienceDirect, Swets Information Services).
Indexed: ASCA, ASFA, AbAn, Agr, AnBeAb, ApEcolAb, ApicAb, BIOBASE, BIOSIS Prev, BibAg, BiolAb, Biostat, CCI, CIN, CIS, CMCI, ChemAb, ChemTitl, CurCont, DSA, DentInd, ESPM, EntAb, ExcerpMed, FCA, FLUIDEX, GEOBASE, GenetAb, HGA, HerbAb, IAA, IABS, ISR, IndMed, IndVet, Inpharma, KWIWR, MBA, MEDLINE, MathR, MathSciNet, NSCI, NutrAb, ProtozoAb, Reac, RefZh, SCI, SFA, SSCI, VetBull, WeedAb, WildRev, ZooRec.
—BLDSC (5069.075000), CASDDS, CISTI, GNLM, IDS, IE, Infotrieve, ingenta, Linda Hall. **CCC.**
Published by: Academic Press (Subsidiary of: Elsevier Science & Technology), 24-28 Oval Rd, London, NW1 7DX, United Kingdom. apsubs@acad.com, http://www.elsevier.com/locate/yjtbi. Eds. D Kirschner, L Wolpert, Y Iwasa. **Subscr. to:** Harcourt Publishers Ltd., Foots Cray High St, Sidcup, Kent DA14 5HP, United Kingdom. TEL 44-208-3085700, FAX 44-20-83090807.

B

➤ **JOURNAL OF TOXICOLOGY AND PUBLIC HEALTH.** see *ENVIRONMENTAL STUDIES*

570 DEU ISSN 0946-672X
CODEN: JTEBFO

➤ **JOURNAL OF TRACE ELEMENTS IN MEDICINE AND BIOLOGY.** Text in English. 1987. 4/yr. EUR 209 in Europe to individuals; JPY 26,000 in Japan to individuals; USD 204 to individuals except Europe and Japan; EUR 510 in Europe to institutions; JPY 65,800 in Japan to institutions; USD 573 to institutions except Europe and Japan (effective 2006). adv. index. back issues avail. **Document type:** *Journal, Academic/Scholarly.* **Description:** Contains research papers and articles on theoretical and applied aspects of trace elements in medicine and biology.
Formerly (until 1994): Journal of Trace Elements and Electrolytes in Health and Disease (0931-2838)
Related titles: Online - full text ed.: (from bigchalk, EBSCO Publishing, ProQuest Information & Learning, ScienceDirect).
Indexed: ASCA, AnalAb, BBCI, BIOSIS Prev, BiolAb, ChemAb, ChemTitl, CurCont, DSA, ExcerpMed, ISR, IndMed, Inpharma, MEDLINE, MSB, NutrAb, PE&ON, Reac, SCI, TriticAb.
—BLDSC (5069.744400), CASDDS, CISTI, GNLM, IDS, IE, Infotrieve, ingenta. **CCC.**
Published by: (Federation of European Societies on Trace Elements and Minerals FRA, Society for Minerals and Trace Elements), Elsevier GmbH, Urban & Fischer Verlag (Subsidiary of: Elsevier Science & Technology), Loebdergraben 14a, Jena, 07743, Germany. TEL 49-3641-626430, FAX 49-3641-626432, marketing.journals@urbanfischer.de, http://www.elsevier.com/locate/jtraceelm, http://www.urbanfischer.de/journals. Ed. Virginia Negretti de Braetter. R&Ps Kerstin Schumann TEL 49-3641-626444, Martin Huber TEL 49-3641-626430. Adv. contact Sabine Schroeter TEL 49-3641-626445. B&W page EUR 400, color page EUR 1,345; 210 x 280. Circ: 375 (paid and controlled). **Subscr. to:** Nature Publishing Group, Brunel Rd, Houndmills, Basingstoke, Hamps RG21 6XS, United Kingdom. TEL 44-1256-302629, FAX 44-1256-476117, subscriptions@nature.com.

➤ **JOURNAL OF TROPICAL ECOLOGY.** see *ENVIRONMENTAL STUDIES*

571.986 USA ISSN 1081-1710
RA639 CODEN: BSVEDL

➤ **JOURNAL OF VECTOR ECOLOGY.** Text in English. 1974. s-a. free to members. adv. bk.rev. **Document type:** *Journal, Academic/Scholarly.* **Description:** Contains public health related research papers and proceedings from national and international conferences. Also provides members and selected nonmembers worldwide with updated information regarding disease vector-control information.
Former titles (until Jun. 1995): Society for Vector Ecology. Bulletin; Society of Vector Ecologists. Bulletin (0146-6429)
Indexed: ASCA, AbHyg, Agr, AgrForAb, AnBrAb, BIOSIS Prev, BioCN&I, BiolAb, ChemAb, CurCont, DSA, ForAb, HelmAb, HortAb, ISR, IndMed, IndVet, MEDLINE, NutrAb, PN&I, PoultAb, ProtozoAb, RA&MP, RM&VM, RevApplEntom, RiceAb, SCI, TDB, VetBull, ZooRec.
—BLDSC (5072.273000), CASDDS, CISTI, IDS, IE, Infotrieve, ingenta, KNAW. **CCC.**
Published by: Society for Vector Ecology, 1966 Compton Ave, Corona, CA 91719. TEL 714-971-2421, FAX 714-971-3940, mklowden@marvin.ag.uidaho.edu. Ed. Marc J Klowden. R&P Major S Dhillon TEL 909-340-9792. Adv. contact Dan Abiaz. page USD 150; trim 11 x 8.5. Circ: 860 (paid).

➤ **JURNAL BIOTEKNOLOGI PERTANIAN**; Indonesian Agricultural Biotechnology. see *AGRICULTURE*

570 JPN ISSN 0287-6531
KAGAWA SEIBUTSU/BIOLOGICAL SOCIETY OF KAGAWA. BULLETIN. Text in Japanese; Summaries in English, Japanese. 1953. a. JPY 2,000.
Published by: Kagawa Seibutsu Gakkai/Biological Society of Kagawa, Kagawa Daigaku Kyoikugakubu Seibutsugaku Kyoshitsu, 1-1 Saiwai-cho, Takamatsu-shi, Kagawa-ken 760-0016, Japan.

570 551.46 JPN
KAIYO SEIBUTSU KANKYO KENKYUJO KENKYU HOKOKU/MARINE ECOLOGY RESEARCH INSTITUTE. REPORT. Text in Japanese; Summaries in English, Japanese. irreg.
Published by: Kaiyo Seibutsu Kankyo Kenkyujo, Chuo Kenkyujo/Marine Ecology Research Institute, Central Laboratory, 300 Iwawada, Isumi-gun, Onjuku-machi, Chiba-ken 299-5105, Japan.

KANAZAWA DAIGAKU RIGAKUBU FUZOKU NOTO RINKAI JIKKENJO KENKYU GAIYO NENJI HOKOKU/KANAZAWA UNIVERSITY. NOTO MARINE LABORATORY. ANNUAL PROGRESS REPORTS. see *EARTH SCIENCES—Oceanography*

570.7 USA ISSN 1064-105X
➤ **KANSAS BIOLOGY TEACHER.** Text in English. 1991. irreg. (1-2/yr.). USD 10 to members. back issues avail. **Document type:** *Journal, Academic/Scholarly.* **Description:** Covers biology education, science education and teacher training.
Indexed: WildRev.
Published by: (Emporia State University, Division of Biology), Emporia State University Press, 1200 Commercial, Emporia, KS 66801-5087. TEL 316-341-5614. Ed. John Richard Schrock. Circ: 200. **Co-sponsor:** Kansas Association of Biology Teachers.

➤ **KARUSHUMU SHINPOJUMU KOEN YOSHI/ABSTRACTS OF CALCIUM SYMPOSIUM.** see *BIOLOGY—Abstracting, Bibliographies, Statistics*

570 JPN ISSN 1348-3412
KAWAKATSU & SASAKI'S WEBPAGES ON PLANARIANS, SAPPORO AND TOKYO (ONLINE). Text in English. 1970. irreg., latest vol.34, 2000, Jun.15th. free to qualified personnel. adv. **Document type:** *Newsletter, Academic/Scholarly.* **Description:** Reports the results of turbellarian studies (Plathelminthes, Turbellaria) conducted by the editor and his co-authors.
Formerly (until 2000): Fuji Women's College. Biological Laboratory. Occasional Publications (Print) (0917-4362)
Media: Online - full content.
Indexed: ZooRec.
Published by: Masaharu Kawakatsu Ed.&Publ, 9-jo, 9-chome 1-8, Kita-ku, Sapporo, Hokkaido 001-0909, Japan. TEL 81-11-7624450, FAX 81-11-7624450, dqao1524@nifty.ne.jp, http://planarian.net/kswp/index.html. R&P, Adv. contact Masaharu Kawakatsu.

KEIO UNIVERSITY. INTERNATIONAL SYMPOSIA FOR LIFE SCIENCES AND MEDICINE. see *MEDICAL SCIENCES*

570 KEN
CODEN: KSTSDG
KENYA JOURNAL OF SCIENCES. SERIES B: BIOLOGICAL SCIENCES. Text and summaries in English. 1966. s-a. USD 140 domestic; USD 70 foreign (effective 1999). **Document type:** *Academic/Scholarly.*
Formerly: Kenya Journal of Science and Technology. Series B: Biological Sciences (0250-8257)
Indexed: ASFA, BiolAb, ChemAb, DSA, ESPM, FCA, FS&TA, HerbAb.
—CASDDS, Linda Hall.
Published by: Kenya National Academy of Sciences, PO Box 39450, Nairobi, Kenya. TEL 254-2-721345, FAX 254-2-721138, knas@1connect.co.ke. Ed. F N Onyango. Circ: 500 (paid).

570 IND ISSN 0374-860X
KERALA ACADEMY OF BIOLOGY. JOURNAL✱. Text in Malayalam; Summaries in English. s-a. INR 15.
Indexed: BiolAb.
Published by: Kerala Academy of Biology, Thiruvananthapuram, Kerala, India.

570 FIN ISSN 0356-861X
KEVO NOTES. Text in English, Finnish. 1975. irreg., latest vol.11, 1996. price varies. maps. back issues avail. **Document type:** *Magazine, Academic/Scholarly.* **Description:** Scientific report of the flora and fauna mapping of Inari Lapland, Finland.
Indexed: ForAb, HerbAb, S&F, WeedAb.
—CISTI.
Published by: University of Turku, Kevo Subarctic Research Institute, Turku, 20014, Finland. TEL 358-2-3335913, FAX 358-2-3335960, http://www.utu.fi/erill/kevo. Ed. Lasse Iso-Iivari TEL 358-2-3335932. Circ: 400.

570 FIN ISSN 0453-7831
AS262.T84
➤ **KEVO SUBARCTIC RESEARCH INSTITUTE. REPORTS.** Text in English, German; Summaries in English. 1964. irreg., latest vol.22, 1998. price varies. bk.rev. back issues avail.; reprints avail. **Document type:** *Journal, Academic/Scholarly.* **Description:** Studies on the nature of subarctic areas.
Indexed: BioCN&I, BiolAb, CurCont, ForAb, GEOBASE, RPP, RevApplEntom, ZooRec.
—CISTI.
Published by: University of Turku, Kevo Subarctic Research Institute, Turku, 20014, Finland. TEL 358-2-3335913, FAX 358-2-3335960, http://www.utu.fi/erill/kevo. Ed. Seppo Neuvonen TEL 358-2-3335930. Circ: 400.

578.77 SAU ISSN 1012-8840
GC1 CODEN: JFMSDF
KING ABDUL AZIZ UNIVERSITY. FACULTY OF MARINE SCIENCE. JOURNAL. Text in Arabic, English. 1981. a. USD 5. illus. **Description:** Promotes research in the field of marine science.
Published by: King Abdul Aziz University, Faculty of Marine Science, P O Box 1540, Jeddah, 21441, Saudi Arabia. TEL 6952386, FAX 6952381, TELEX 601141 KAUNI SJ. Ed. A K Behairy.

570 JPN
KINKI DAIGAKU RAIFU SAIENSU KENKYU HOKOKU/KINKI UNIVERSITY. LIFE SCIENCE INSTITUTE. REPORT OF STUDIES. Text in Japanese. 1976. a.
Published by: Kinki Daigaku, Raifu Saiensu Kenkyujo/Kinki University, Life Science Institute, 377-2 Ono-Higashi, Osakasayama-shi, Osaka-fu 589-0014, Japan.

KOBE UNIVERSITY. FACULTY OF AGRICULTURE. SCIENCE REPORTS. see *AGRICULTURE*

KOCHI DAIGAKU GAKUJUTSU KENKYU HOKOKU. NOGAKU/KOCHI UNIVERSITY. AGRICULTURAL SCIENCE. RESEARCH REPORTS. see *AGRICULTURE*

570 JPN ISSN 0389-0287
KOCHI UNIVERSITY. FACULTY OF SCIENCE. MEMOIRS. SERIES D, BIOLOGY/KOCHI DAIGAKU RIGAKUBU KIYO. SEIBUTSUGAKU. Text in English. 1980. a.
Indexed: BIOSIS Prev, BiolAb, ForAb, HerbAb, MaizeAb, PGegResA, S&F, WeedAb, ZooRec.
—BLDSC (5597.836000), CISTI.
Published by: Kochi University, Faculty of Science/Kochi Daigaku Rigakubu, 5-1 Akebono-cho 2-chome, Kochi-shi, 780-8072, Japan.

570 AUT ISSN 0075-6547
QL571 CODEN: KLRUAS
➤ **KOLEOPTEROLOGISCHE RUNDSCHAU.** Text in German; Abstracts in English. 1912. a. EUR 50 (effective 2003). illus.; abstr.; maps. **Document type:** *Journal, Academic/Scholarly.*
Indexed: ASFA, BioCN&I, BiolAb, ForAb, IBR, RefZh, RevApplEntom, ZooRec.
—Linda Hall.
Published by: Zoologisch-Botanische Gesellschaft in Oesterreich, Althanstr. 14, Postfach 267, Vienna, 1091, Austria. TEL 43-1-427754313, FAX 43-1-42779542, wolfgang.punz@univie.ac.at, http://www.univie.ac.at/zoobot. Circ: 180.

570 DNK ISSN 0366-3612
QH7 CODEN: BSVSAQ
KONGELIGE DANSKE VIDENSKABERNES SELSKAB. BIOLOGISKE SKRIFTER. Text mainly in English. 1941. irreg., latest vol.54, 2002. price varies. bibl.; illus. back issues avail. **Document type:** *Monographic series, Academic/Scholarly.*
Indexed: ASFA, BIOSIS Prev, BiolAb, RefZh, SeedAb, ZooRec.
—CISTI, KNAW, Linda Hall. **CCC.**
Published by: Kongelige Danske Videnskabernes Selskab/Royal Danish Academy of Sciences and Letters, H. C. Andersens Boulevard 35, Copenhagen V, 1553, Denmark. TEL 45-33-435300, FAX 45-33-435301, email@royalacademy.dk, http://www.royalacademy.dk/pubs.htm. Ed. Flemming Lundgreen Nielsen. **Subscr. to:** C.A. Reitzels Boghandel & Forlag A/S, Noerregade 20, Copenhagen K 1165, Denmark. TEL 45-33-122300, FAX 45-33-140270, info@careitzel.com, http://www.careitzel.com.

570 BEL ISSN 0777-0111
KONINKLIJK BELGISCH INSTITUUT VOOR NATUURWETENSCHAPPEN. STUDIEDOCUMENTEN/INSTITUT ROYAL DES SCIENCES NATURELLES DE BELGIQUE. DOCUMENTS DE TRAVAIL. Text in Dutch, English, French. 1963. irreg., latest vol.93, 1998. price varies. bibl.; charts; illus. back issues avail.
Indexed: RefZh, ZooRec.
Published by: Koninklijk Belgisch Instituut voor Natuurwetenschappen/Institut Royal des Sciences Naturelles de Belgique, Vautierstraat 29, Brussels, 1000, Belgium. TEL 32-2-6274211, FAX 32-2-6274113, jackie.vangoethem@naturalsciences.be, bib@naturalsciences.be. Eds. D Cahen, Jackie Van Goethem.

570 POL ISSN 0023-4249
CODEN: KOSMEY
➤ **KOSMOS**; problemy nauk biologicznych. Variant title: Kosmos. Series A. Biologia. Text in Polish; Contents page in English. 1876. q. EUR 37 foreign (effective 2005). bk.rev. charts; illus. index. back issues avail.; reprints avail. **Document type:** *Journal, Academic/Scholarly.* **Description:** Devoted to dissemination of knowledge in biological sciences, addressed to scientists, university and middle school teachers, and students.
Indexed: AgrLib, BiolAb, CIN, ChemAb, ChemTitl, FCA, HerbAb, ProtozoAb.
—CASDDS, CISTI, Linda Hall.
Published by: (Polska Akademia Nauk, Instytut Biochemii i Biofizyki), Polskie Towarzystwo Przyrodnikow im. Kopernika/Polish Copernicus Society of Naturalists, Podwale 1, Krakow, 31118, Poland. klw@ibb.waw.pl, ginkgo@wp.pl, http://kosmos.icm.edu.pl, http://darwin.iz.uj.edu.pl/iz/ptp. Ed. Kazimierz Wierzshowski. Adv. contact Jerzy Vetulani. Circ: 500. **Dist. by:** Ars Polona, Krakowskie Przedmiescie 7, Warsaw, Poland. TEL 48-22-9263914, FAX 48-22-9265334, arspolona@arspolona.com.pl, http://www.arspolona.com.pl.

578.77 KWT ISSN 0250-362X
CODEN: KBMSDW
KUWAIT BULLETIN OF MARINE SCIENCE. Text and summaries in Arabic, English. 1979-1990; resumed 1996. irreg. free. charts; illus.; stat. cum.index. back issues avail. **Document type:** *Academic/Scholarly.* **Description:** General marine science with a regional focus.
Indexed: ASFA, BiolAb, ESPM, SFA, WildRev, ZooRec.
Published by: (Library), Kuwait Institute for Scientific Research, Mariculture and Fisheries Department, P O Box 1638, Salmiya, Kuwait. TEL 965-575-1984, FAX 965-571-1293, TELEX 22299 KISR KT. Ed. M S Abdulla. Circ: 700 (controlled).

KYOKUIKI SEIBUTSU SHINPOJUMU KOEN YOSHISHU/ABSTRACTS OF THE SYMPOSIUM ON POLAR BIOLOGY. see *BIOLOGY—Abstracting, Bibliographies, Statistics*

KYOTO DAIGAKU. REICHORUI KENKYUJO NENPO/KYOTO UNIVERSITY. PRIMATE RESEARCH INSTITUTE. ANNUAL REPORTS. see *ANTHROPOLOGY*

570 JPN ISSN 0452-9987
CODEN: CBLKAE
➤ **KYOTO UNIVERSITY. BIOLOGICAL LABORATORY. CONTRIBUTIONS.** Text in English. 1955. a. adv. **Document type:** *Proceedings, Academic/Scholarly.*
Indexed: ApicAb, BIOSIS Prev, BiolAb, ZooRec.
Published by: (Biological Laboratory), Kyoto University, Faculty of General Education/Kyoto Daigaku Kyoyobu Seibutsugaku Kyoshitsu, Yoshidanihonmatsu-cho, Sakyo-ku, Kyoto-shi, 606-8316, Japan. TEL 81-75-753-6849, FAX 81-75-753-6864. Ed., R&P, Adv. contact Makoto Kato.

570 551.48 JPN
KYOTO UNIVERSITY. CENTER FOR ECOLOGICAL RESEARCH. COLLECTED PAPERS✶. Text in Japanese, English. a. **Document type:** *Academic/Scholarly.*
Formerly: Kyoto University. Otsu Hydrobiological Station. Collected Papers
Published by: Kyoto Daigaku, Rigakubu Fuzoku Otsu Rinko Jikkenjo/Kyoto University, Center for Ecological Research, Kamitanakami Hiranocho, Otsu, Shiga 520-2113, Japan. TEL 81-77-5498200, FAX 81-77-5498201, http://www.ecology.kyoto-u.ac.jp/.

570 JPN ISSN 0454-7802
QH301 CODEN: MFKBBJ
KYOTO UNIVERSITY. FACULTY OF SCIENCE. MEMOIRS. SERIES OF BIOLOGY. Text in English. 1924; N.S. 1967. s-a. per issue exchange basis. back issues avail.
Indexed: BIOSIS Prev, BiolAb, ChemAb, FCA, HerbAb, INIS AtomInd, RefZh, ZooRec.
—CISTI, KNAW, Linda Hall.
Published by: Kyoto University, Faculty of Science/Kyoto Daigaku Rigakubu, Kita-Shirakawaoiwake-cho, Sakyo-ku, Kyoto-shi, 606-8224, Japan.

LAB ON A CHIP; miniaturisation for chemistry and biology. see *CHEMISTRY*

LABORATORY TECHNIQUES IN BIOCHEMISTRY AND MOLECULAR BIOLOGY. see *BIOLOGY—Biochemistry*

570 363.7 NZL
LANDCARE RESEARCH SCIENCE SERIES. Text in English. 1993. irreg., latest vol.23, 2001. price varies. back issues avail. **Document type:** *Monographic series, Academic/Scholarly.* **Description:** Covers a variety of specialist topics based on the work of Landcare Research New Zealand.
Indexed: BIOSIS Prev.
Published by: (Landcare Research New Zealand), Manaaki Whenua Press, 40, Lincoln, 8152, New Zealand. TEL 64-3-3256700, FAX 64-3-3252127, mwpress@landcare.cri.nz, http://www.mwpress.co.nz. Pub., R&P Greg Comfort TEL 64-3-3256700.

570 DEU
LANDESMUSEUM FUER NATUR UND MENSCH. SCHRIFTENREIHE. Text in German. 1997. irreg., latest vol.16, 2000. **Document type:** *Monographic series, Academic/Scholarly.*
Formerly: Staatliches Museum fuer Naturkunde und Vorgeschichte. Schriftenreihe
Indexed: ZooRec.
Published by: (Landesmuseum fuer Natur und Mensch), Isensee Verlag, Haarenstr 20, Oldenburg, 26122, Germany. TEL 49-441-25388, FAX 49-441-17872, verlag@isensee.de, http://www.isensee.de.

LANDSCAPE ECOLOGY. see *ENVIRONMENTAL STUDIES*

LATVIJAS ZINATNU AKADEMIJAS VETIS. B DALA. DABASZINATNES/LATVIAN ACADEMY OF SCIENCES. SECTION B. NATURAL SCIENCES. PROCEEDINGS. see *SCIENCES: COMPREHENSIVE WORKS*

591.9 DEU ISSN 0935-333X
➤ **LAUTERBORNIA**; Zeitschrift fuer Faunistik und Floristik des Suesswassers. Text in German. 1989. irreg. (3-4/yr.). EUR 45 (effective 2003). adv. bk.rev. back issues avail. **Document type:** *Journal, Academic/Scholarly.*
Indexed: ASFA, ZooRec.
—BLDSC (5160.816000).
Published by: Erik Mauch Verlag, Muehlangerstr. 11, Dinkelscherben, 86424, Germany. TEL 49-8292-2212, FAX 49-8292-950778, erik.mauch.verlag@t-online.de, http://www.lauterbornia.de. Ed., Pub. Erik Mauch. Circ: 350 (paid).

570 340 GBR ISSN 1475-5335
K9
➤ **LAW, SCIENCE AND POLICY**; an international journal. Text in English. 1996. 4/yr. GBP 129, USD 219 (effective 2004). bk.rev. back issues avail. **Document type:** *Journal, Academic/Scholarly.* **Description:** Provides analyses of both legal and scientific issues related to the environment; the regulation of medical, agricultural and environmental biotechnology; public health; agriculture and fisheries; food and water quality and safety. Emphasis is on furthering understanding and communication between lawyers and scientists.
Formerly: International Journal of Biosciences and the Law (1353-274X)
Indexed: AIDS&CR, ASFA, ESPM, H&SSA, RiskAb, ToxAb, VirolAbstr.
—BLDSC (5010.197000), IE, ingenta.
Published by: A B Academic Publishers, PO Box 42, Bicester, Oxon OX26 6NW, United Kingdom. jrnls@abapubl.demon.co.uk.

570 JPN
LEBEN/KAGOSHIMA DAIGAKU SEIBUTSU KENKYUKAI KAISHI. Text in Japanese. a.
Published by: Kagoshima Daigaku, Seibutsu Kenkyukai/Biological Society of Kagoshima University, Kagoshima Daigaku Gakuyukai, 21-24 Korimo-To 1-chome, Kagoshima-shi, 890-0065, Japan.

LEBENDIGE ERDE; Biologisch-Dynamische Landwirtschaft, Ernaehrung, Kultur. see *AGRICULTURE*

LECTURES ON MATHEMATICS IN THE LIFE SCIENCES. see *MATHEMATICS*

577 BEL ISSN 0772-1110
LEEFMILIEU. Text in Dutch. 1978. bi-m.
Indexed: RefZh.
Published by: Argus vzw, Elemarkt 8, Antwerp, 2000, Belgium. http://www.argusmilieu.be.

LIBELLULA. see *BIOLOGY—Entomology*

LIDIA (AS). see *AGRICULTURE*

580 590 LIE
LIECHTENSTEIN. BOTANISCH-ZOOLOGISCHE GESELLSCHAFT LIECHTENSTEIN SARGANS-WERDENBERG. BERICHT. Text in German. 1972. a. USD 30 (effective 2000). adv. bk.rev. bibl.; illus. **Document type:** *Proceedings, Academic/Scholarly.*
Indexed: ZooRec.
Published by: Botanisch-Zoologische Gesellschaft Liechtenstein-Sargans-Werdenberg, Im Bretscha 22, Schaan, 9494, Liechtenstein. Ed. Rudolf Staub. Circ: 1,000.

577 LTU ISSN 0235-7224
QH540 CODEN: EKOLEJ
LIETUVOS MOKSLU AKADEMIJA. EKOLOGIJA. Text in English, Lithuanian, Russian; Summaries in Lithuanian, Russian. 1955. q. USD 80 foreign (effective 2003). adv. **Document type:** *Academic/Scholarly.*
Supersedes in part (in 1990): Lietuvos T.S.R. Mokslu Akademijos Darbai. C Serija. Biologijos Mokslai (0131-3851)
Indexed: ASFA, ChemAb, ESPM, FPA, ForAb, HerbAb, HortAb, INIS AtomInd, IndVet, NutrAb, PoultAb, RRTA, VetBull, ZooRec.
—BLDSC (0397.597950), CASDDS, CISTI, KNAW, Linda Hall.
Published by: (Lietuvos Mokslu Akademija/Lithuanian Academy of Sciences), Lietuvos Mokslu Akademijos Leidykla, Gedimino pr 3, Vilnius, 2600, Lithuania. TEL 370-2-2626851, FAX 370-2-2126351, lmokal@aiva.lt, http://www.maleidykla.katalogas.lt. Circ: 283.

LIFE SCIENCE BOOK REVIEW. see *BIOLOGY—Abstracting, Bibliographies, Statistics*

570 USA
LIFE SCIENCE QUARTERLY. Text in English. 2000 (Jul.). q. free to qualified personnel. **Document type:** *Newsletter, Trade.*
Related titles: Online - full content ed.
Published by: Sigma-Aldrich Co., 3050 Spruce St, St. Louis, MO 63103. TEL 800-521-8956, http://www.sigmaaldrich.com/Area_of_Interest/Life_Science/Life_Science_Quarterly.html.

571.3 GBR ISSN 0950-1096
THE LINNEAN; newsletter and proceedings of the Linnean Society of London. Text in English. 1984. q. membership. bk.rev. charts; illus. **Document type:** *Newsletter, Academic/Scholarly.* **Description:** Provides topical updates on recent Linnean Society activities and events, along with articles on the history, science, and personalities behind the society.
Indexed: ZooRec.
Published by: Linnean Society of London, Burlington House, Piccadilly, London, W1V 0LQ, United Kingdom. TEL 44-20-74344479, FAX 44-20-72879364, john@linnean.org, http://www.linnean.org/html/publications/publications_linnean_newsletter.htm.

570 GBR ISSN 0024-4066
QH1 CODEN: BJLSBG
➤ **LINNEAN SOCIETY. BIOLOGICAL JOURNAL**; a journal of evolution. Text in English. 1791. m. GBP 1,922 combined subscription in Europe to institutions print & online eds.; USD 3,552 combined subscription in the Americas to institutions & Caribbean (print & online eds.); GBP 1,922 combined subscription elsewhere to institutions print & online eds. (effective 2006). adv. bk.rev. bibl.; illus. index per vol. reprints avail. **Document type:** *Journal, Academic/Scholarly.* **Description:** Examines the process of organic evolution, with particular emphasis on theoretical and empirical contributions illustrating unifying concepts of evolutionary biology.
Formerly (until 1969): Linnean Society of London. Proceedings
Related titles: Microfilm ed.: (from BHP); Online - full text ed.: ISSN 1095-8312. GBP 1,826 in Europe to institutions; USD 3,375 in the Americas to institutions & Caribbean; GBP 2,009 elsewhere to institutions (effective 2006) (from Blackwell Synergy, EBSCO Publishing, Gale Group, IngentaConnect, O C L C Online Computer Library Center, Inc., ScienceDirect, Swets Information Services).
Indexed: AEA, ASCA, ASFA, AgBio, Agr, AgrForAb, AnBeAb, AnBrAb, ApEcolAb, ApicAb, B&BAb, BIOBASE, BIOSIS Prev, BibAg, BioCN&I, BiolAb, BiolDig, CPA, CurCont, ESPM, EntAb, FCA, ForAb, GEOBASE, GenetAb, HelmAb, HerbAb, HortAb, IABS, ISR, IndVet, KWIWR, MEDLINE, NemAb, NutrAb, OrnHort, PBA, PGegResA, PlantSci, PotatoAb, PoultAb, ProtozoAb, RM&VM, RPP, RefZh, RevApplEntom, S&F, SCI, SFA, SeedAb, TDB, TriticAb, VetBull, WeedAb, WildRev, ZooRec.
—BLDSC (2075.460000), CISTI, IDS, IE, Infotrieve, ingenta, Linda Hall. **CCC.**
Published by: (Linnean Society of London), Blackwell Publishing Ltd., 9600 Garsington Rd, Oxford, OX4 2ZG, United Kingdom. TEL 44-1865-776868, FAX 44-1865-714591, customerservices@oxon.blackwellpublishing.com, http://www.blackwellpublishing.com/journals/BIJ. Ed. J A Allen.

570 USA ISSN 0161-6366
CODEN: LSSSDM
LINNEAN SOCIETY. SYMPOSIA SERIES. Text in English. 1976. irreg., latest vol.18, 1996. price varies. back issues avail.; reprint service avail. from ISI. **Document type:** *Proceedings.* **Description:** Publishes scholarly papers read at the Linnean Society's symposia but not included in one of its three journals.
Indexed: BIOSIS Prev, BiolAb, CIN, ChemAb, ChemTitl, ZooRec.
—BLDSC (5221.493000), CASDDS, CISTI, IE, ingenta. **CCC.**
Published by: (Linnaean Society of London), Academic Press (Subsidiary of: Elsevier Science & Technology), 525 B St, Ste 1900, San Diego, CA 92101-4495. john@linnean.org, apsubs@acad.com, http://www.linnean.org/html/publications/publications_symposia.htm, http://www.academicpress.com.

570 AUT ISSN 0253-116X
LINZER BIOLOGISCHE BEITRAEGE. Text in English, German; Summaries in English. 1969. s-a. price varies. 800 p./no.; back issues avail. **Document type:** *Journal, Academic/Scholarly.* **Description:** Contains contributions on various areas of biology.
Formerly (until 1975): Oberoesterreichisches Landesmuseum. Botanistische Arbeitsgemeinschaft. Mitteilungen (0257-2737)
Indexed: BIOSIS Prev, BiolAb, ZooRec.
—BLDSC (5221.680000).
Published by: Oberoesterreichisches Landesmuseum, Biologiezentrum, J.-W.-Klein-Str 73, Linz, 4040, Austria. TEL 43-732-759733, FAX 43-732-75973399, bio-linz@landesmuseum-linz.ac.at, http://www.biologiezentrum.at. R&P Gerhard Aubrecht. Circ: 500 (controlled).

572.8 USA
LIPPINCOTT-RAVEN PRESS SERIES ON MOLECULAR AND CELLULAR BIOLOGY✶. Text in English. 1992. irreg. price varies. **Document type:** *Proceedings.*
Formerly: Raven Press Series on Molecular and Cellular Biology (1066-8330)
Indexed: BIOSIS Prev.
—CISTI.
Published by: Lippincott Williams & Wilkins (Subsidiary of: Wolters Kluwer N.V.), 530 Walnut St, Philadelphia, PA 19106-3621. TEL 215-521-8300, FAX 215-521-8902, custserv@lww.com, http://www.lww.com. **Subscr. to:** PO Box 1620, Hagerstown, MD 21741. TEL 301-223-2300, 800-638-3030, FAX 301-223-2365.

570.15195 POL ISSN 0458-0036
➤ **LISTY BIOMETRYCZNE/BIOMETRICAL LETTERS.** Text and summaries in English, Polish. 1964. 2/yr. USD 10 (effective 1999). adv. bk.rev. back issues avail. **Document type:** *Academic/Scholarly.* **Description:** Publishes papers concerned with different aspects of the analysis and interpretation of results obtained from biometrical experiments, using statistical methods.
Indexed: CIS.
Published by: Polskie Towarzystwo Biometryczne/Polish Biometric Society, c/o Akademia Rolnicza w Poznaniu, Dept. Metod Matematyczno-Statystycznych, Wojska Polskiego 28, Poznan, 60637, Poland. TEL 48-61-8487140, FAX 48-61-8487146, smejza@au.poznan.pl, pkra@igr.poznan.pl, http://www.igr.poznan.pl. Ed. Zygmunt Kaczmarek. Pub. Stanisław Mejza. R&P, Adv. contact Pawel Krajewski TEL 48-61-233511. Circ: 100 (paid); 300 (controlled).

570.9 GBR ISSN 0076-0579
CODEN: LONAAE
LONDON NATURALIST. Text in English. 1915. a. GBP 6 (effective 2001). bk.rev. back issues avail. **Document type:** *Bulletin.*
Indexed: BIOSIS Prev, BiolAb, WildRev, ZooRec.
—BLDSC (5294.000000), IE, ingenta.
Published by: London Natural History Society, 4 Falkland Ave, London, N3 1QR, United Kingdom. TEL 44-20-8346-4359, http://www.users.globalnet.co.uk/~inhsweb, http://www.users.globalnet.co.uk/~lnhsweb. Ed. K.H. Hyatt. R&P K H Hyatt. Circ: 1,200.

570 ESP ISSN 0214-8315
LUCAS MALLADA; revista de ciencias. Text in Spanish. 1989. a.
Indexed: IECT, ZooRec.
—CINDOC.
Published by: Instituto de Estudios Altoaragoneses, Ave. del Parque, 10, Huesca, 22002, Spain. TEL 34-974-294120, FAX 34-974-294122, iea@iea.es, http://www.pirenaicasoft.com/tres/index.php3.

B

910 SWE ISSN 1400-1144
GF1
LUND STUDIES IN GEOGRAPHY. Text in English. 1949. irreg. price varies. index. cum.index every 4 yrs. **Document type:** *Monographic series, Academic/Scholarly.*
Formerly (until 1994): Lund Studies in Geography. Series B. Human Geography (0076-1478)
—CISTI.
Published by: Lunds Universitet, Department of Social and Economic Geography/Lund University, Soelvegatan 13, Lund, 22362, Sweden. TEL 46-46-2220000, FAX 46-46-2228401, kulekgeo@kulekgeo.lu.se, http://www1.ldc.lu.se/kulekgeo.

570 BRA ISSN 1676-6180
LUNDIANA; international journal of biodiversity. Text in English, Portuguese, Spanish. 1980. s-a. BRL 35 to individuals; BRL 60 to institutions; BRL 25 to students (effective 2004). **Document type:** *Journal.* **Description:** Publishes scientific research in the areas of biogeography, conservation, ecology, evolution, and taxonomy, mainly from the Neotropical region.
Incorporates (in 2003): International Journal of Ornithology (1519-888X)
Indexed: AgrForAb, AnBrAb, ForAb, GEOBASE, HelmAb, HerbAb, PBA, PGegResA, PoultAb, S&F, TDB.
Published by: Universidade Federal de Minas Gerais, Instituto de Ciencias Biologicas, CP 486, Belo Horizonte, MG 31270-901, Brazil. TEL 55-31-34992857, FAX 55-31-34992870, http://www.icb.ufmg.br/~lundiana/. Ed. Alan Lane de Melo.

570 FIN ISSN 0024-7383
QH7 CODEN: LUTUAA
LUONNON TUTKIJA/NATURALIST. Text in Finnish. 1897. 5/yr. EUR 25 (effective 2003). adv. bk.rev. charts; illus. cum.index: 1897-1910, 1911-1930. **Document type:** *Academic/Scholarly.*
Formerly (until 1947): Luonnen Ystava (0788-6926)
Indexed: BiolAb, RefZh.
—BLDSC (5307.350000), IE, ingenta.
Published by: Societas Biologica Fennica Vanamo, Unioninkatu 44, PO Box 7, Helsinki, 00014, Finland. TEL 358-40-8416377, FAX 358-9-19150058, http://www.vanamo.fi. Ed. Juhani Manttari. Circ: 2,200.

M B I. (Medico-Biologic Information) see *MEDICAL SCIENCES*

MADOQUA; journal of arid zone biology and nature conservation research. see *CONSERVATION*

MAINE AGRICULTURAL AND FOREST EXPERIMENT STATION. ANNUAL REPORT. see *AGRICULTURE*

MAINE ENVIRONNEWS. see *ENVIRONMENTAL STUDIES*

570 610 MKD ISSN 0351-3254
R91 CODEN: PANND2
MAKEDONSKA AKADEMIJA NA NAUKITE I UMETNOSTITE. ODDELENIE ZA BIOLOSKI I MEDICINSKI NAUKI. PRILOZI/MACEDONIAN ACADEMY OF SCIENCES AND ARTS. SECTION OF BIOLOGICAL AND MEDICAL SCIENCES. CONTRIBUTIONS. Text in Macedonian. 1980. s-a. **Description:** Presents research reports in botany, zoology, biochemistry, medicine and pharmacology, genetics, and agriculture.
Indexed: ChemAb, INIS AtomInd, ZooRec.
—CASDDS, KNAW, Linda Hall.
Published by: (Oddelenie za Bioloski i Medicinski Nauki), Makedonska Akademija na Naukite i Umetnostite, Bulevar Krste Misirkov 2, PO Box 428, Skopje, 91000, Macedonia. TEL 398-02-114200, FAX 389-02-115903, makakad@manu.edu.mk, http://www.manu.edu.mk. Ed. Georgi Efremov.

MALAYSIAN APPLIED BIOLOGY JOURNAL. see *AGRICULTURE*

570 MYS ISSN 1394-1712
QH301 CODEN: MLJSA4
➤ **MALAYSIAN JOURNAL OF SCIENCE. SERIES A: LIFE SCIENCES.** Text in English. 1971. 2/yr. adv. bk.rev. **Document type:** *Academic/Scholarly.* **Description:** Covers original research, communications, and reviews in the field of life sciences.
Supersedes in part (in 1994): Malaysian Journal of Science (0126-7906)
Indexed: BiolAb, ChemAb, ChemTitl, EnvAb, FPA, ForAb, INIS AtomInd, RevApplEntom, ZooRec.
—CASDDS, Linda Hall.
Published by: (University of Malaya, Faculty of Science), University of Malaya/Perpustakaan Universiti Malaya, Lembah Pantai, Kuala Lumpur, 59100, Malaysia. http://www.um.edu.my. Ed. Dr. Yong Hoi Sen. Circ: 1,000.

➤ **MANAB MON**; a journal depicting the modern trends in psychology, biology, and sociology. see *PSYCHOLOGY*

570 EGY ISSN 1110-4570
MANSOURA SCIENCE BULLETIN. B, BIOLOGY/NASHRAT KOLIYYAT AL-'LUM B BAIULUGI. Text in English. 1976. bi-m. **Document type:** *Bulletin, Academic/Scholarly.*
Published by: Mansoura University, Faculty of Science, PO Box 35516, Mansoura - Dakahlia, Egypt. TEL 20-50-2247055, FAX 20-50-2247330, http://derp.sti.sci.eg/data/0290.htm, http-://www.mans.edu.eg.

MANUAL OF BIOLOGICAL MARKERS OF DISEASE. see *MEDICAL SCIENCES—Allergology And Immunology*

570 610 SGP ISSN 1793-1894
MANUALS IN BIOMEDICAL RESEARCH. Text in English. irreg., latest vol.2. price varies. **Document type:** *Monographic series, Academic/Scholarly.*
Published by: World Scientific Publishing Co. Pte. Ltd., 5 Toh Tuck Link, Singapore, 596224, Singapore. TEL 65-466-5775, FAX 65-467-7667, wspc@wspc.com.sg, http://www.worldscibooks.com/series/mbr_series.shtml, http://www.worldscientific.com. **Subscr. to:** Farrer Rd, PO Box 128, Singapore 912805, Singapore. TEL 65-382-5663, FAX 65-382-5919. **Dist. by:** World Scientific Publishing Co., Inc., 1060 Main St, River Edge, NJ 07661. TEL 201-487-9655, 800-227-7562, FAX 201-487-9656, 888-977-2665, wspc@wspc.com.

578.77 GBR ISSN 1023-6244
QL121 CODEN: MBPHAX
➤ **MARINE AND FRESHWATER BEHAVIOUR AND PHYSIOLOGY.** Text in French. 1973. q. GBP 697, USD 1,043 combined subscription to institutions print & online eds. (effective 2006). adv. bk.rev. charts; illus. index. back issues avail.; reprint service avail. from PSC. **Document type:** *Journal, Academic/Scholarly.* **Description:** Publishes papers on research into the physiology o marine and freshwater animals. Includes all fields of physiology as well as behavioural and neurobiological matters.
Formerly (until vol.25, 1995): Marine Behaviour and Physiology (0091-181X)
Related titles: CD-ROM ed.; Microform ed.; Online - full text ed.: ISSN 1029-0362. GBP 662, USD 991 to institutions (effective 2006) (from EBSCO Publishing, Gale Group, IngentaConnect, O C L C Online Computer Library Center, Inc., Swets Information Services).
Indexed: ASCA, ASFA, AnBeAb, AnBrAb, BiolAb, CRFR, ChemAb, CurCont, EPB, FS&TA, GEOBASE, HortAb, ISR, IndVet, Inspec, OceAb, ProtozoAb, PsycInfo, PsycholAb, SCI, SFA, VetBull, ZooRec, e-psyche.
—BLDSC (5373.625300), CISTI, IE, Infotrieve, ingenta, Linda Hall. **CCC.**
Published by: Taylor & Francis Ltd (Subsidiary of: Taylor & Francis Group), 4 Park Sq, Milton Park, Abingdon, OX14 4RN, United Kingdom. TEL 44-1235-828600, FAX 44-1235-829000, info@tandf.co.uk, http://www.tandf.co.uk/journals/titles/10236244.asp. Ed. David L MacMillan. **Subscr. to:** Journals Customer Service, Rankine Rd, Basingstoke, Hants RG24 8PR, United Kingdom. TEL 44-1256-813000, FAX 44-1256-330245, enquiry@tandf.co.uk.

➤ **MARINE AND FRESHWATER RESEARCH.** see *EARTH SCIENCES—Oceanography*

578.77 IND ISSN 0025-3146
CODEN: JMBIAA
MARINE BIOLOGICAL ASSOCIATION OF INDIA. JOURNAL. Text mainly in English; Text occasionally in French, German, Spanish. 1959. a., latest vol.43, no.2, 2001. USD 90 (effective 2001). adv. bk.rev. charts; illus. index. **Document type:** *Journal, Academic/Scholarly.* **Description:** Contains original contributions about marine biology. Covers plankton, coral, ecosystems, population dynamics, propagation of cultivable species, biology of fishes, marine reptiles, sea birds, mammals and pollution.
Indexed: ASFA, BiolAb, ESPM, S&F, SFA, ZooRec.
—CASDDS, CISTI.
Published by: (Marine Biological Association of India), Scientific Publishers, 5-A New Pali Rd., Near Hotel Taj Hari Mahal, PO Box 91, Jodhpur, Rajasthan 342 003, India. TEL 91-291-2433323, FAX 91-291-2512580, info@scientificpub.com, http://www.scientificpub.com. Ed. K Rengarajan. Circ: 700.

578.77 GBR
MARINE BIOLOGICAL ASSOCIATION OF THE UNITED KINGDOM. ANNUAL REPORT. Text in English. a. **Description:** Emphasizes research conducted by the association during the previous year.
Published by: Marine Biological Association of the United Kingdom, Citadel Hill, Plymouth, PL1 2PB, United Kingdom. TEL 44-1752-633207, FAX 44-1752-633102, http://www.mba.ac.uk/journal/publications.htm.

578.77 GBR ISSN 0025-3154
QH301 CODEN: JMBAAK
➤ **MARINE BIOLOGICAL ASSOCIATION OF THE UNITED KINGDOM. JOURNAL.** Short title: J M B A. Text in English. 1887. bi-m. GBP 445 to institutions; USD 720 in North America to institutions; GBP 494 combined subscription to institutions print & online eds.; USD 795 combined subscription in North America to institutions print & online eds. (effective 2006). adv. bk.rev. illus. Index. back issues avail.; reprints avail. **Document type:** *Journal, Academic/Scholarly.* **Description:** Publishes original research on all aspects of marine biology.
Related titles: Microfilm ed.: (from BHP); Microform ed.: (from PQC); Online - full text ed.: ISSN 1469-7769. GBP 410 to institutions; USD 655 in North America to institutions (effective 2006) (from EBSCO Publishing, O C L C Online Computer Library Center, Inc., Swets Information Services).
Indexed: ASCA, ASFA, AgBio, AnBrAb, B&AI, BIOBASE, BIOSIS Prev, BioCN&I, BiolAb, CIN, CTO, Cadscan, ChemAb, ChemTitl, CurCont, EPB, ESPM, ForAb, GEOBASE, HelmAb, IABS, ISR, IndVet, LeadAb, NemAb, NutrAb, PGegResA, PollutAb, ProtozoAb, RM&VM, RefZh, RevApplEntom, S&F, SCI, SFA, VetBull, WRCInf, WeedAb, WildRev, Zincscan, ZooRec.
—BLDSC (4821.000000), CASDDS, CISTI, IDS, IE, Infotrieve, ingenta, Linda Hall. **CCC.**
Published by: (Marine Biological Association of the United Kingdom), Cambridge University Press, The Edinburgh Bldg, Shaftesbury Rd, Cambridge, CB2 2RU, United Kingdom. TEL 44-1223-312393, FAX 44-1223-315052, journals@cambridge.org, http://uk.cambridge.org/journals/mbi/. Eds. John A Raven, P E Gibbs, P.A. Tyler, R. Seed. R&P Linda Nicol TEL 44-1223-325757. Adv. contact Rebecca Curtis TEL 44-1223-325757. **Subscr. to:** Cambridge University Press, 100 Brook Hill Dr, West Nyack, NY 10994. TEL 845-353-7500, FAX 845-353-4141, journals_subscriptions@cup.org

578.77 GBR ISSN 0260-2784
➤ **MARINE BIOLOGICAL ASSOCIATION OF THE UNITED KINGDOM. OCCASIONAL PUBLICATIONS.** Text in English. 1980. irreg. price varies. bk.rev. **Document type:** *Monographic series, Academic/Scholarly.*
Indexed: ASFA, ESPM, ZooRec.
—CISTI.
Published by: Marine Biological Association of the United Kingdom, Citadel Hill, Plymouth, PL1 2PB, United Kingdom. TEL 44-1752-633334, FAX 44-1752-633102. Ed. Ann Pulsford. Circ: 500.

578.77 DEU ISSN 0025-3162
QH91.A1 CODEN: MBIOAJ
➤ **MARINE BIOLOGY**; international journal on life in oceans and coastal waters. Text in English. 1967. m. EUR 4,598 combined subscription to institutions print & online eds. (effective 2005). adv. charts; illus. back issues avail.; reprint service avail. from ISI. **Document type:** *Journal, Academic/Scholarly.* **Description:** Reports on plankton research, theoretical biology related to the marine environment, apparatus and techniques, and underwater exploration and experimentation.
Related titles: Microform ed.: (from PQC); Online - full text ed.: ISSN 1432-1793 (from EBSCO Publishing, Springer LINK, Swets Information Services).
Indexed: AESIS, ASCA, ASFA, AgBio, AnBeAb, AnBrAb, ApEcolAb, B&AI, B&BAb, BIOBASE, BIOSIS Prev, BiolAb, CPA, CRFR, Cadscan, ChemAb, ChemTitl, CurCont, DSA, EPB, ESPM, EnvAb, ExcerpMed, F&EA, FS&TA, ForAb, GEOBASE, GenetAb, HGA, HelmAb, HortAb, IABS, IBR, ISR, IndVet, LeadAb, MBA, NemAb, NutrAb, OceAb, PBA, PGegResA, PlantSci, ProtozoAb, RM&VM, RPP, RefZh, S&F, SCI, SFA, SWRA, SoyAb, TDB, VetBull, Zincscan, ZooRec.
—BLDSC (5373.700000), CASDDS, CINDOC, CISTI, IDS, IE, Infotrieve, ingenta, Linda Hall. **CCC.**
Published by: Springer-Verlag (Subsidiary of: Springer Science+Business Media), Tiergartenstr 17, Heidelberg, 69121, Germany. TEL 49-6221-3450, FAX 49-6221-345229, http://link.springer.de/link/service/journals/00227/index.htm. Ed. Otto Kinne TEL 49-41-328883 49 41 32/88 83. Adv. contact Stephan Kroeck TEL 49-30-827875739. **Subscr. in the Americas to:** Springer-Verlag New York, Inc., Journal Fulfillment, PO Box 2485, Secaucus, NJ 07096-2485. TEL 800-777-4643, 201-348-4033, FAX 201-348-4505, journals@springer-ny.com, http://www.springer-ny.com; **Subscr. to:** Springer GmbH Auslieferungsgesellschaft, Haberstr 7, Heidelberg 69126, Germany. TEL 49-6221-345-0, FAX 49-6221-345-4229, subscriptions@springer.de.

578.77 GBR ISSN 1745-1000
QH91.A1
▼ **MARINE BIOLOGY RESEARCH.** Text in English. 2005. bi-m. GBP 194, USD 320 combined subscription to institutions print & online eds. (effective 2006). **Document type:** *Journal, Academic/Scholarly.* **Description:** Aims to provide practitioners and academics with a forum for ideas and discussion on all areas of marine biology and oceanography.
Formed by the merger of (1961-2005): Sarsia (0036-4827); (1964-2005): Ophelia (0078-5326)
Related titles: Online - full text ed.: ISSN 1745-1019. GBP 184, USD 304 to institutions (effective 2006) (from EBSCO Publishing).
Indexed: ASFA, ApEcolAb, ESPM, OceAb.
Published by: (Institute of Marine Research NOR, University of Bergen, Department of Biology NOR), Taylor & Francis Ltd (Subsidiary of: Taylor & Francis Group), 4 Park Sq, Milton Park, Abingdon, OX14 4RN, United Kingdom. TEL 44-1235-828600, FAX 44-1235-829000, info@tandf.co.uk, http://www.tandf.co.uk/journals/titles/17451000.asp. Eds. Tore Hoisaeter, Tom Fenchel.

578.77 GBR ISSN 0268-7666
MARINE CONSERVATION. Text in English. q. GBP 20 domestic; GBP 30 foreign (effective 2001). adv. **Document type:** *Newsletter, Consumer.* **Description:** Provides current information and articles on marine biology and conservation.
Formerly (until 1985): Sea
Indexed: SFA.
Published by: Marine Conservation Society, 9 Gloucester Rd, Ross-on-Wye, Herefordshire HR9 5BU, United Kingdom. TEL 44-1989-566017, FAX 44-1989-567815, http://www.mcsuk.org. Ed., R&P Richard Harrington. Circ: 6,000 (paid).

MARINE CONSERVATION AND DEVELOPMENT REPORT. see *CONSERVATION*

577.7 DEU ISSN 0173-9565
QH541.5.S3 CODEN: MAECDR
➤ **MARINE ECOLOGY.** Text in English. 1879. q. EUR 174 combined subscription in Europe to individuals print & online eds.; USD 188 combined subscription in the Americas to individuals & Caribbean, print & online eds.; GBP 116 combined subscription elsewhere to individuals print & online eds.; GBP 421 combined subscription in Europe to institutions print & online eds.; USD 708 combined subscription in the Americas to institutions & Caribbean, print & online eds.; GBP 463 combined subscription elsewhere to institutions print & online eds. (effective 2006). reprint service avail. from PSC. **Document type:** *Journal, Academic/Scholarly.* **Description:** Covers biological and ecological topics regarding the Mediterranean and other seas.
Supersedes in part (in 1979): Stazione Zoologica di Napoli. Pubblicazioni (0039-081X); Which was formerly (until 1916): Zoologische Station zu Neapel. Mitteilungen (0390-5373)
Related titles: Online - full text ed.: ISSN 1439-0485. USD 673 in the Americas to institutions & Caribbean; GBP 400 elsewhere to institutions (effective 2006) (from Blackwell Synergy, EBSCO Publishing, Gale Group, IngentaConnect, O C L C Online Computer Library Center, Inc., Swets Information Services).
Indexed: ASFA, AnBrAb, ApEcolAb, B&BAb, BIOSIS Prev, BiolAb, CTO, ChemAb, ChemTitl, CurCont, EPB, ESPM, GEOBASE, GenetAb, HGA, IBR, ISR, NemAb, NutrAb, OceAb, RefZh, SCI, SFA, SWRA, WildRev, ZooRec.
—BLDSC (5373.850000), CASDDS, CISTI, IDS, IE, Infotrieve, ingenta, Linda Hall. **CCC.**
Published by: (Stazione Zoologica di Napoli ITA), Blackwell Verlag GmbH (Subsidiary of: Blackwell Publishing Ltd.), Kurfuerstendamm 57, Berlin, 10707, Germany. TEL 49-30-32790634, FAX 49-30-32790610, verlag@blackwell.de, http://www.blackwellpublishing.com/journals/MAE, http://www.blackwell.de. Eds. D Marino, J Ott. Circ: 560.

577.78 DEU ISSN 0171-8630
QH541.5.S3 CODEN: MESEDT
➤ **MARINE ECOLOGY - PROGRESS SERIES.** Text in English. 1979. 20/yr. EUR 3,949 domestic; EUR 4,025 Sat. foreign (effective 2006). adv. illus. Index. back issues avail.; reprints avail. **Document type:** *Journal, Academic/Scholarly.* **Description:** Presents original papers, short notes and reviews in environmental factors, physiological mechanisms, cultivation, dynamics and ocean management.
Related titles: ♦ Online - full text ed.: Marine Ecology - Progress Series Online. ISSN 1616-1599.
Indexed: ASCA, ASFA, AbHyg, AgBio, AnBeAb, AnBrAb, ApEcolAb, BIOBASE, BIOSIS Prev, BiolAb, CIN, CPA, Cadscan, ChemAb, ChemTitl, CivEngAb, CurCont, DSA, ESPM, ForAb, GEOBASE, HGA, HelmAb, HerbAb, HortAb, I&DA, IABS, IBR, ISR, IndVet, LeadAb, M&GPA, M&TEA, MBA, NemAb, NutrAb, OceAb, PBA, PGegResA, PN&I, PollutAb, ProtozoAb, RA&MP, RM&VM, S&F, SCI, SFA, SWRA, TDB, VetBull, WeedAb, WildRev, Zincscan, ZooRec.
—BLDSC (5373.904000), CASDDS, CISTI, IE, Infotrieve, ingenta, Linda Hall.
Published by: Inter-Research, Nordbuente 23, Oldendorf, 21385, Germany. TEL 49-4132-7127, FAX 49-4132-8883, ir@int-res.com, http://www.int-res.com/journals/meps/index.html. Ed. Otto Kinne. Adv. contact H Witt. Circ: 1,000.

577.78 DEU ISSN 1616-1599
➤ **MARINE ECOLOGY - PROGRESS SERIES ONLINE.** Text in English. 18/yr. EUR 3,150 (effective 2006). **Document type:** *Academic/Scholarly.*
Media: Online - full text (from EBSCO Publishing). **Related titles:** ♦ Print ed.: Marine Ecology - Progress Series. ISSN 0171-8630.
Published by: Inter-Research, Nordbuente 23, Oldendorf, 21385, Germany. TEL 49-4132-7127, FAX 49-4132-8883, webmaster@int-res.com, ir@int-res.com, http://www.int-res.com/journals/meps/index.html.

➤ **MARINE ENVIRONMENTAL RESEARCH.** see *ENVIRONMENTAL STUDIES—Pollution*

➤ **MARINE ISSUES COMMITTEE. SPECIAL PUBLICATION.** see *CONSERVATION*

578.77 USA
➤ **MARINE MODELS ELECTRONIC RECORD.** Text in English. irreg. free (effective 2004). **Document type:** *Journal, Academic/Scholarly.*
Media: Online - full content.
Published by: Marine Biological Laboratory, 7 MBL St, Woods Hole, MA 02543-1015. TEL 508-289-7149, FAX 508-289-7922, cschachi@mbl.edu, http://www.mbl.edu/BiologicalBulletin/mmer.html. Ed. William D Cohen.

➤ **MARINE SCIENTIST.** see *EARTH SCIENCES—Oceanography*

➤ **MARYLAND ESSAYS IN HUMAN BIODIVERSITY.** see *ANTHROPOLOGY*

570 CZE
MASARYK UNIVERSITY. FACULTY OF SCIENCES. SCRIPTA BIOLOGIA/SCRIPTA FACULTATIS SCIENTIARUM NATURALIUM UNIVERSITATIS MASARYKIANAE BRUNENSIS. BIOLOGIA. Text in English, French, Russian. a. price varies. bibl. **Document type:** *Academic/Scholarly.*
Former titles: Scripta Facultatis Scientiarum Naturalium Universitatis Purkynianae Brunensis. Biologia (0231-5777); Supersedes in part (in 1970): Universita J.E. Purkyne. Prirodovedecka Fakulta. Spisy
Indexed: BiolAb, CIN, ChemAb, ChemTitl, FCA, HerbAb, PGrRegA, RefZh.
—CISTI.
Published by: Masarykova Universita, Prirodovedecka Fakulta/Masaryk University, Faculty of Sciences, Kotlarska 2, Brno, 61137, Czech Republic. Ed. Jiri Gaisler.

MASSACHUSETTS WILDLIFE. see *CONSERVATION*

MATHEMATICAL BIOSCIENCES. see *MATHEMATICS*

▼ **MATHEMATICAL BIOSCIENCES AND ENGINEERING.** see *MATHEMATICS*

MATHEMATICAL MEDICINE AND BIOLOGY; a journal of the I M A. see *MATHEMATICS*

400 617.6 JPN ISSN 0385-1613
CODEN: MATSDE
➤ **MATSUMOTO SHIGAKU/MATSUMOTO DENTAL UNIVERSITY SOCIETY. JOURNAL.** Text in Japanese; Summaries in English. 1975. 3/yr. JPY 3,500 domestic; USD 30 foreign (effective 2002). adv. back issues avail. **Document type:** *Journal, Academic/Scholarly.*
Related titles: CD-ROM ed.; Fax ed.
Indexed: ChemAb, ChemTitl.
—BLDSC (5413.245000), CASDDS.
Published by: Matsumoto Dental University Society/Matsumoto Shika Daigaku Gakkai, 1780 Gobara-Hiroka, shiojiri-shi, Nagano-ken 399-0700, Japan. TEL 81-263-523100, FAX 81-263-533456, yamaoka@po.mdu.ac.jp. Ed. Eiko Sairenji. R&P, Adv. contact Minoru Yamaoka TEL 81-263-51-2075. B&W page JPY 90,000; trim 232 x 160. Circ: 1,800.

570 DNK ISSN 0106-1054
QH132.G73
MEDDELELSER OM GROENLAND, BIOSCIENCE. Variant title: Greenland Bioscience. Text in Danish. 1878. irreg., latest vol.53, 2001. price varies. charts; illus. back issues avail. **Document type:** *Monographic series, Academic/Scholarly.*
Supersedes in part (in 1979): Meddelelser om Groenland (0025-6676)
Indexed: BiolAb, ChemAb, ZooRec.
—CISTI, Linda Hall. **CCC.**
Published by: Dansk Polarcenter/Danish Polar Center, Strandgade 100 H, Copenhagen K, 1401, Denmark. TEL 45-32-880100, FAX 45-32-880101, dpc@dpc.dk, http://www.dpc.dk/polarpubs/. Ed. Erik Born.

MEDICINAL CHEMISTRY RESEARCH; an international journal for rapid communications on design and mechanisms of action of biologically active agents. see *MEDICAL SCIENCES*

MEDICINE ON THE MIDWAY. see *COLLEGE AND ALUMNI*

MEDICINSKI RAZGLEDI. see *MEDICAL SCIENCES*

577 ESP ISSN 0210-5004
CODEN: MDTRDW
MEDITERRANEA. SERIE DE ESTUDIOS BIOLOGICOS. Text in Spanish; Summaries in English. 1976. a. **Document type:** *Monographic series.* **Description:** Publishes scientific works on land ecology of the Mediterranean climate.
Indexed: BiolAb, IECT, SFA, WildRev, ZooRec.
—CINDOC.
Published by: Universidad de Alicante, Facultad de Ciencias, Apartado 99, Alicante, 03080, Spain. TEL 96-590-3400, FAX 96-590-3464, TELEX 66616. Circ: 600 (controlled).

551.46 USA ISSN 0085-0683
QH92.3 CODEN: MHGCBG
MEMOIRS OF THE HOURGLASS CRUISES. Text in English. 1969. irreg. per issue exchange basis. charts; illus. back issues avail.
Indexed: ASFA, BIOSIS Prev, BiolAb, ESPM, OceAb, SFA, WildRev, ZooRec.
—Linda Hall.
Published by: Florida Marine Research Institute, Department of Environmental Protection, 100 8th Ave. S.E., St. Petersburg, FL 33701. FAX 813-823-0166. Ed. K A Steidinger. Circ: 1,000.

B

570 IND
MEMOIRS ON INDIAN ANIMAL TYPES. Text in English. 1983. irreg., latest 1995. price varies. **Document type:** *Monographic series, Academic/Scholarly.*
Published by: Hindustan Publishing Corporation (India), 4805-24, Bharat Ram Rd., 1st Fl., Flats 1 & 2, Darya Ganj, New Delhi, 110 002, India. TEL 91-11-325-4401, FAX 91-11-6193511, hpcpd@nda.vsnl.net.in, hpcpd@hpc.cc, http://www.bizdelhi.com/publisher/hpc, http://www.hpc.cc. Ed. M L Bhatia.

MEMORIE DI BIOLOGIA MARINA E DI OCEANOGRAFIA. see *EARTH SCIENCES—Oceanography*

578.77 540 550 JPN ISSN 0503-1540
GC1 CODEN: MERSBU
➤ **LA MER/UMI.** Text in English, Japanese, French. 1963. q. Subscr. incld. with membership. adv. bk.rev. back issues avail. **Document type:** *Journal, Academic/Scholarly.* **Description:** Original articles, short contributions, reviews, book reviews, and information in oceanography.
Indexed: ASCA, ASFA, BIOSIS Prev, BiolAb, ChemAb, FLUIDEX, GEOBASE, JPI, RefZh, SFA, ZooRec.
—CASDDS, Linda Hall. **CCC.**
Published by: Societe Franco-Japonaise d'Oceanographie/Japanese-French Oceanographic Society, c/o Jiro Yoshida, Tokyo Univ of Marine Science&Techno, Dept of Ocean Sciences, 4-5-7, Konan, Minato-ku, Tokyo, 108-8477, Japan. jiroy@tokyo-u-fish.ac.jp, http://wwwsoc.nii.ac.jp/sfjo/en/journal.html. Ed. Jiro Yoshida. Circ: 600 (controlled).

➤ **METABOLISM;** clinical and experimental. see *MEDICAL SCIENCES—Endocrinology*

570 610 CHE
METHODS AND TOOLS IN BIOSCIENCES AND MEDICINE. Text in English. 1987. irreg., latest 2002. **Document type:** *Monographic series, Academic/Scholarly.* **Description:** Emphasizes important developments in methodology and research tools and their potential for application to human and other biologic systems.
Formerly (until 1999): Biomethods Series (1018-6255)
Indexed: BIOSIS Prev.
—CISTI. **CCC.**
Published by: Birkhaeuser Verlag AG (Subsidiary of: Springer Science+Business Media), Viaduktstr 42, Postfach 133, Basel, 4051, Switzerland. TEL 41-61-2050707, FAX 41-61-2050799, info@birkhauser.ch, http://www.birkhauser.ch/books/biosc/mtbm/index.html. Ed. Beatrice Menz.

572.8 USA ISSN 1064-3745
CODEN: MMBIED
METHODS IN MOLECULAR BIOLOGY. Text in English. 1984. irreg., latest vol.308, 2005. price varies. back issues avail. **Document type:** *Journal, Academic/Scholarly.* **Description:** Offers the latest molecular biology and biochemistry laboratory methods and protocols.
Indexed: BIOSIS Prev, CIN, ChemAb, ChemTitl, IndMed, MEDLINE, MSB.
—BLDSC (5748.201800), CASDDS, CISTI, IE, Infotrieve, ingenta. **CCC.**
Published by: Humana Press, Inc., 999 Riverview Dr, Ste 208, Totowa, NJ 07512. TEL 973-256-1699, FAX 973-256-8341, humana@humanapr.com, http://humanapress.com/journals.pasp. Ed. John M Walker. R&P Richard Hruska.

578.77 551.46 USA
MICHIGAN SEA GRANT COLLEGE PROGRAM. TECHNICAL REPORT. Text in English. irreg.
Published by: Michigan Sea Grant College Program, 401 E Liberty, Ste 330, Ann Arbor, MI 48104-2298. TEL 734-764-1118, FAX 734-647-0768, msgpubs@umich.edu, http://www.miseagrant.umich.edu.

570 USA ISSN 0076-8227
QH1 CODEN: PMUBAE
MICHIGAN STATE UNIVERSITY. MUSEUM PUBLICATIONS. BIOLOGICAL SERIES. Text in English; Abstracts occasionally in German. 1957. irreg. (approx. 1-2/yr.). price varies.
Document type: *Monographic series, Academic/Scholarly.*
Indexed: BiolAb.
—CISTI, Linda Hall.
Published by: Michigan State University, Museum, MSU Library, East Lansing, MI 48824. TEL 517-355-2370. Circ: 1,850.

MICRONESICA; a journal of the University of Guam. see *ANTHROPOLOGY*

380 ARG
MICROSEMANARIO. Text in Spanish. 1990. w. back issues avail.
Document type: *Academic/Scholarly.*
Media: Online - full text. **Related titles:** E-mail ed.
Published by: Universidad de Buenos Aires, Facultad de Ciencias Exactas y Naturales, Cuidad Universitaria, Nunez - Pabellon 2, Buenos Aires, 1428, Argentina. TEL 54-11-4573300, info@fcen.uba.ar, http://www.fcen.uba.ar/prensa/microcol.htm, http://fcen.uba.ar/.

570 JPN ISSN 0914-7357
MIE SEIBUTSU/MIE BIOLOGICAL SOCIETY. JOURNAL. Text in Japanese. 1950. a.
Published by: Mie Seibutsu Kyoikukai/Mie Biological Society, c/o Mr Akira Aoyama, Mie Kenritsu Yokkaichi Koto Gakko, Tomida, Yokkaichi-shi, Mie-ken 510-8014, Japan.

570 JPN
➤ **MITSUBISHI KAGAKU INSTITUTE OF LIFE SCIENCES. ANNUAL REPORT.** Text in English. 1971. a., latest no.29, 2000. **Document type:** *Yearbook, Academic/Scholarly.*
Description: Outlines the scientific achievements of the Institute's research activities in neuroscience, immunology, development-gerontology, and other major fields in the life sciences.
Formerly: Mitsubishi Kasei Institute of Life Sciences. Annual Report (0910-2523)
—GNLM, KNAW. **CCC.**
Published by: Mitsubishi Kagaku Institute of Life Sciences/Mitsubishi Kagaku Seimei Kagaku Kenkyujo, 11 Minami-Oya, Machida-shi, Tokyo-to 194-8511, Japan. TEL 81-427-24-6202, FAX 81-427-29-1252, mats@libra.ls.m-kagaku.co.jp. Circ: 1,000.

570 USA ISSN 1549-1692
➤ **MODERN BIOLOGY SERIES.** Text in English. irreg. price varies. **Document type:** *Academic/Scholarly.*
Published by: Holt, Rinehart and Winston, Inc., c/o Harcourt Brace Jovanovich, 6277 Sea Harbor Dr, Orlando, FL 32887. TEL 407-345-2500. Ed. Bob Todd.

➤ **MODERN PATHOLOGY**; published on behalf of the United States & Canadian Academy of Pathology. see *MEDICAL SCIENCES*

578.77 SGP ISSN 0219-9777
MOLECULAR ASPECTS OF FISH & MARINE BIOLOGY. Text in English. 2002. irreg., latest vol.4. price varies. **Document type:** *Monographic series, Academic/Scholarly.*
Published by: World Scientific Publishing Co. Pte. Ltd., 5 Toh Tuck Link, Singapore, 596224, Singapore. TEL 65-466-5775, FAX 65-467-7667, wspc@wspc.com.sg, series@wspc.com.sg, wspc@wspc.com.sg, http://www.wspc.com.sg/books/series/mafmb_series.shtml, http://www.worldscientific.com. Eds. Choy Leong Hew, Kathryn Vanya Ewart. **Dist. by:** World Scientific Publishing Co., Inc., 1060 Main St, River Edge, NJ 07661. TEL 201-487-9655, 800-227-7562, FAX 201-487-9656, 888-977-2665; World Scientific Publishing Ltd., 57 Shelton St, London WC2H 9HE, United Kingdom. TEL 44-20-78360888, FAX 44-20-78362020, sales@wspc.co.uk.

572.8 USA ISSN 0737-4038
QH506 CODEN: MBEVEO
➤ **MOLECULAR BIOLOGY AND EVOLUTION.** Text in English. 1983. m. GBP 355, USD 586, EUR 533 to institutions; GBP 374, USD 617, EUR 561 combined subscription to institutions print & online eds. (effective 2006). adv. illus. Index. reprint service avail. from PQC,ISI,PSC. **Document type:** *Journal, Academic/Scholarly.* **Description:** Includes research at the interface between molecular and evolutionary biology. This includes investigations of molecular evolutionary patterns and processes; tests of evolutionary hypotheses that use molecular data.
Related titles: Microform ed.: (from PMC, PQC); Online - full text ed.: ISSN 1537-1719. GBP 337, USD 556, EUR 506 to institutions (effective 2006) (from EBSCO Publishing, Gale Group, HighWire Press, IngentaConnect, O C L C Online Computer Library Center, Inc., Oxford University Press Online Journals, Swets Information Services).
Indexed: ASCA, ASFA, AbAn, AbHyg, AgBio, AgrForAb, AnBrAb, B&BAb, BBCI, BCI, BIOBASE, BIOSIS Prev, BioCN&I, BiolAb, CIN, CIS, ChemAb, ChemTitl, CurCont, DSA, EntAb, ExcerpMed, FCA, ForAb, GenetAb, HGA, HelmAb, HerbAb, HortAb, IABS, ISR, IndMed, IndVet, Inpharma, MEDLINE, MaizeAb, NemAb, NutrAb, PBA, PGegResA, PotatoAb, PoultAb, ProtozoAb, RA&MP, RM&VM, RPP, Reac, RevApplEntom, RiceAb, S&F, SCI, SFA, SeedAb, SoyAb, TDB, TriticAb, VetBull, WeedAb, WildRev, ZooRec.
—BLDSC (5900.782000), CASDDS, CISTI, GNLM, IDS, IE, Infotrieve, ingenta, KNAW, Linda Hall. **CCC.**
Published by: (Australian National University, The John Curtin School of Medical Research AUS), Oxford University Press (Subsidiary of: Oxford University Press), 2001 Evans Rd, Cary, NC 27513. TEL 919-677-0977, FAX 919-677-1714, mbe@anu.edu.au, jnlorders@oup-usa.org, http://mbe.oxfordjournals.org/, http://www.us.oup.com. Ed. William Martin. Circ: 918 (paid).

570 540 GBR ISSN 1742-206X
▼ **MOLECULAR BIOSYSTEMS.** Text in English. 2005. m. GBP 751, USD 1,374 combined subscription print & online eds. (effective 2006). **Document type:** *Journal, Academic/Scholarly.* **Description:** Publishes research in chemical biology with a particular focus on the interface between chemistry and the -omic sciences and systems biology.
Related titles: Online - full text ed.: ISSN 1742-2051. GBP 676, USD 1,237 (effective 2006) (from EBSCO Publishing); ♦ Issued with: Chemical Communications. ISSN 1359-7345.
Indexed: AnalAb, MSB.
—**CCC.**
Published by: Royal Society of Chemistry, Thomas Graham House, Science Park, Milton Rd, Cambridge, CB4 0WF, United Kingdom. TEL 44-1223-420066, FAX 44-1223-423623, sales@rsc.org, http://www.rsc.org/is/journals/current/mbs/mbspub.htm. Ed. Dr. Caroline Evans.

MOLECULAR BRAIN RESEARCH. see *MEDICAL SCIENCES—Psychiatry And Neurology*

MOLECULAR HUMAN REPRODUCTION. see *MEDICAL SCIENCES—Obstetrics And Gynecology*

MOLECULAR PSYCHIATRY. see *MEDICAL SCIENCES—Psychiatry And Neurology*

570 GBR ISSN 1744-4292
▼ ➤ **MOLECULAR SYSTEMS BIOLOGY.** Text in English. 2005. irreg. free (effective 2005). **Document type:** *Journal, Academic/Scholarly.* **Description:** Publishes full-length papers and accompanying synopses describing original research in the field of molecular systems biology; it focuses on the analysis, integration and modeling of molecular and cellular phenomena.
Media: Online - full text.
Published by: (European Molecular Biology Organization), Nature Publishing Group (Subsidiary of: Macmillan Publishers Ltd.), The MacMillan Building, 4 Crinan St, London, N1 9XW, United Kingdom. TEL 44-20-78334000, FAX 44-20-78434596, http://www.nature.com/msb/index.html.

572.8 CHE
MOLECULES (PRINT ARCHIVE EDITION). Text in English. 1996. a.
Related titles: ♦ Special ed. of: Molecules. ISSN 1420-3049.
—CISTI.
Published by: Molecular Diversity Preservation International, MDPI Center, Matthaeusstr 11, Basel, 4057, Switzerland.

570 KOR ISSN 1016-8478
QH506 CODEN: MOCEEK
➤ **MOLECULES AND CELLS.** Text in English. 1992. bi-m. (in 2 vols., 3 nos./vol.). USD 380 to institutions (effective 2005). 150 p./no.; **Document type:** *Journal, Academic/Scholarly.*
Description: Devoted to the advancement and dissemination of fundamental knowledge concerning the molecular biology of cells.
Related titles: Online - full text ed.: ISSN 0219-1032 (from EBSCO Publishing, Springer LINK).
Indexed: ASCA, AbHyg, AgBio, AnBrAb, BBCI, BIOBASE, BIOSIS Prev, BioCN&I, BiolAb, CIN, CPA, ChemAb, ChemTitl, CurCont, DSA, ExcerpMed, FCA, ForAb, HelmAb, HerbAb, HortAb, ISR, IndMed, IndVet, Inpharma, MEDLINE, MaizeAb, NemAb, NutrAb, OrnHort, PBA, PE&ON, PGegResA, PGrRegA, PHN&I, PN&I, PotatoAb, PoultAb, ProtozoAb, RA&MP, RM&VM, RPP, Reac, RevApplEntom, RiceAb, S&F, SCI, SIA, SeedAb, SoyAb, TDB, WeedAb, ZooRec.
—BLDSC (5900.857500), CASDDS, CISTI, GNLM, IDS, IE, Infotrieve, ingenta, Linda Hall. **CCC.**
Published by: Korean Society for Molecular Biology, Korea Science and Technology Center, Rm. 815, 635-4. Yeogsam-dong, Kangnam-gu, Seoul, 135-703, Korea, S. TEL 82-2-5684490, FAX 82-2-5580131, home@ksmb.or.kr, http://ksmb.or.kr/home/journal/, http://ksmb.or.kr/default.htm. Ed. Chin Ha Chung.

570 ARG ISSN 0328-1620
➤ **MONOGRAFIAS DE L.O.L.A.** (Literature of Latin America) Text in English, Spanish. 1994. irreg. price varies. adv. illus. back issues avail. **Document type:** *Monographic series, Academic/Scholarly.* **Description:** Includes articles on biology.
Indexed: ZooRec.
Address: Pena Rodriguez, 115 2o, Capital Federal, Buenos Aires 1020, Argentina. TEL 54-114-3720518, FAX 54-114-3722787, csharp@ba.net, http://www.thebookplace.com/lola. Ed. Colin Sharp.

570 ITA ISSN 0390-6639
MONOGRAFIE DI NATURA BRESCIANA. Text in Italian. 1969. irreg. **Document type:** *Monographic series.*
Indexed: BIOSIS Prev, BiolAb, RefZh, ZooRec.
Published by: Museo Civico di Storia Naturale di Brescia, Via Ozanam 4, Brescia, Italy. TEL 39-030-2978672.

570.9 NLD ISSN 0077-0639
QH301 CODEN: MOBIAN
➤ **MONOGRAPHIAE BIOLOGICAE.** Text in English. 1957. irreg., latest vol.80, 2002. price varies. **Document type:** *Monographic series, Academic/Scholarly.*
Indexed: ASFA, BIOSIS Prev, BiolAb, ESPM, SFA, WildRev, ZooRec.
—BLDSC (5917.783000), CASDDS, CISTI, ingenta. **CCC.**
Published by: Springer-Verlag Dordrecht (Subsidiary of: Springer Science+Business Media), Van Godewijckstraat 30, Dordrecht, 3311 GX, Netherlands. TEL 31-78-6576050, FAX 31-78-6576474, http://www.springeronline.com. Eds. Henri J Dumont, M J A Werger.

570 USA
MONOGRAPHS IN BEHAVIOR AND ECOLOGY. Text in English. 1986. irreg., latest 2002. price varies. charts; illus. back issues avail. **Document type:** *Monographic series, Academic/Scholarly.* **Description:** Explores issues of animal behavior from an ecological perspective.
Published by: Princeton University Press, 41 William St, Princeton, NJ 08540-5237. TEL 609-258-4900, 800-777-4726, FAX 609-258-6305, Orders@cpfs.pupress.princeton.edu, http://pup.princeton.edu/catalogs/series/mbe.html. Eds. John Krebs, T H Clutton-Brock. **Subscr. addr. in US:** California - Princeton Fulfillment Services, 1445 Lower Ferry Rd, Ewing, NJ 08618. FAX 800-999-1958, orders@cpfs.pupress.princeton.edu. **Dist. addr. in Canada:** University Press Group, 164 Hillsdale Ave E, Toronto, ON M4S 1T5, Canada.; **Dist. addr. in UK:** John Wiley & Sons Ltd., The Atrium, Southern Gate, Chichester, West Sussex PO19 8SQ, United Kingdom.

MONOGRAPHS IN EPIDEMIOLOGY AND BIOSTATISTICS. see *PUBLIC HEALTH AND SAFETY*

570 USA ISSN 0077-0930
CODEN: MPOBA6
MONOGRAPHS IN POPULATION BIOLOGY. Text in English. 1967. irreg., latest 2002. price varies. charts; illus. back issues avail.; reprint service avail. from PQC. **Document type:** *Monographic series, Academic/Scholarly.* **Description:** Publishes research findings in the subdiscipline of population biology.
Indexed: BIOSIS Prev, BiolAb, IndMed, MEDLINE, ZooRec.
—BLDSC (5915.960000), CISTI. **CCC.**
Published by: Princeton University Press, 41 William St, Princeton, NJ 08540-5237. TEL 609-258-4900, 800-777-4726, FAX 609-258-6305, http://pup.princeton.edu/catalogs/series/mpb.html. Eds. Henry S Horn, Simon A Levin. **Subscr. to:** California - Princeton Fulfillment Services, 1445 Lower Ferry Rd, Ewing, NJ 08618. FAX 800-999-1958, orders@cpfs.pupress.princeton.edu. **Dist. in Canada, Australia & New Zealand, and Latin America by:** University Press Group, 164 Hillsdale Ave E, Toronto, ON M4S 1T5, Canada.; **Dist. by:** John Wiley & Sons Ltd., The Atrium, Southern Gate, Chichester, West Sussex PO19 8SQ, United Kingdom.

571.3 611 RUS ISSN 1026-3543
CODEN: AAGEAA
➤ **MORFOLOGIYA.** Text in Russian; Summaries in English, Russian. 1916. bi-m. RUR 60, USD 10 (effective 1999). bk.rev. bibl. index. back issues avail. **Document type:** *Academic/Scholarly.* **Description:** Carries original investigations; reviews and discussion of papers on cytology, histology, embryology (normal and topographic), and comparative anatomy and anthropology; methods of morphological investigation; history of morphology; reports on the latest achievements in morphological sciences.
Formerly (until 1992): Arkhiv Anatomii, Gistologii i Embriologii (0004-1947)
Related titles: E-mail ed.; Fax ed.; Online - full text ed.
Indexed: ASFA, BIOSIS Prev, BiolAb, CIN, ChemAb, ChemTitl, DentInd, ESPM, IndMed, MEDLINE, RefZh, ZooRec.
—BLDSC (0118.230000), CASDDS, CISTI, GNLM. **CCC.**
Published by: (Akademiya Meditsinskikh Nauk Rossii/Russian Academy of Medical Sciences), Morfologiya, B Zelem'na 43-A, St Petersburg, 197110, Russian Federation. TEL 7-812-235-3009, FAX 7-812-235-0986, aeseulap@mail.wplus.net, http://www.aeseulap.net. Ed. F V Sudzilovskii. adv.: B&W page USD 600, color page USD 2,000; trim 295 x 210. Circ: 1,000 (paid). **US dist. addr.:** East View Information Services, 3020 Harbor Ln. N., Minneapolis, MN 55447. TEL 612-550-0961. **Co-sponsor:** Vsesoyuznoe Nauchnoe Obshchestvo Anatomov, Gistologov i Embriologov.

➤ **MORPHOLOGIE.** see *MEDICAL SCIENCES*

570 USA ISSN 0096-3925
QH301 CODEN: MUBBDD
➤ **MOSCOW STATE UNIVERSITY BIOLOGICAL SCIENCES BULLETIN.** Text in English. 1974. q. USD 1,880 per vol. in US & Canada; USD 2,160 per vol. elsewhere (effective 2006). bibl.; charts; illus.; abstr. index. back issues avail. **Document type:** *Journal, Academic/Scholarly.* **Description:** Covers human, animal and plant physiology, genetics, flora and fauna, biochemistry and biophysics, and cell physiology.

Related titles: ♦ Russian ed.: Moskovskii Gosudarstvennyi Universitet. Vestnik. Seriya 16: Biologiya. ISSN 0137-0952; ♦ Translation of: Moskovskii Gosudarstvennyi Universitet. Vestnik. Seriya 17: Pochvovedenie. ISSN 0137-0944; ♦ Partial translation of: Moskovskii Gosudarstvennyi Universitet. Vestnik. Seriya 16: Biologiya. ISSN 0137-0952.
Indexed: AnBrAb, BiolAb, CPA, ExcerpMed, FCA, ForAb, HerbAb, HortAb, NutrAb, OrnHort, PGrRegA, PotatoAb, ProtozoAb, RPP, RevApplEntom, S&F, SFA, WeedAb, WildRev, ZooRec.
—BLDSC (0416.237000), CISTI, IE, ingenta. **CCC.**
Published by: (Moskovskii Gosudarstvennyi Universitet im. M.V. Lomonosova/M.V. Lomonosov Moscow State University RUS), Allerton Press, Inc., 18 W 27th St, New York, NY 10001. TEL 646-424-9686, FAX 646-424-9695, journals@allertonpress.com, http://www.allertonpress.com/journals/mub.htm. Ed. Mikhail V Gusev.

570 RUS ISSN 0137-0952
QH301 CODEN: VMUBDF
MOSKOVSKII GOSUDARSTVENNYI UNIVERSITET. VESTNIK. SERIYA 16: BIOLOGIYA. Text in Russian; Contents page in English. 1960. irreg. USD 28 foreign (effective 2004). bk.rev. bibl. index. **Document type:** *Journal, Academic/Scholarly.*
Formerly (until 1977): Moskovskii Gosudarstvennyi Universitet. Vestnik. Seriya 6: Biologiya, Pochvovedenie (0579-9422)
Related titles: ♦ English ed.: Moscow State University Biological Sciences Bulletin. ISSN 0096-3925; ♦ English Translation: Moscow State University Soil Science Bulletin. ISSN 0147-6874; ♦ Partial English translation(s): Moscow State University Biological Sciences Bulletin. ISSN 0096-3925.
Indexed: ASFA, BIOSIS Prev, BiolAb, CIN, ChemAb, ESPM, FCA, PGrRegA, RASB, RefZh, ZooRec.
—CASDDS, CISTI, East View, Linda Hall.
Published by: (Moskovskii Gosudarstvennyi Universitet im. M.V. Lomonosova, Biologicheskii Fakul'tet/M.V. Lomonosov Moscow State University, Department of Biology), Izdatel'stvo Moskovskogo Gosudarstvennogo Universiteta im. M. V. Lomonosova/Publishing House of Moscow State University, B Nikitskaya 5/7, Moscow, 103009, Russian Federation. TEL 7-095-2295091, FAX 7-095-2036671, kd_mgu@rambler.ru, http://www.msu.ru/depts/MSUPubl. **Dist. by:** M K - Periodica, ul Gilyarovskogo 39, Moscow 129110, Russian Federation. TEL 7-095-2845008, FAX 7-095-2813798, info@periodicals.ru, http://www.mkniga.ru.

570 RUS ISSN 0027-1403
Q60 CODEN: BYMOAB
MOSKOVSKOE OBSHCHESTVO ISPYTATELEI PRIRODY. BIOLOGICHESKII OTDEL. BYULLETEN/MOSCOW SOCIETY OF NATURALISTS. BIOLOGICAL SERIES. BULLETIN. Text in Russian; Summaries in English. 1829. bi-m. USD 84 foreign (effective 2004). bk.rev. abstr.; bibl.; charts; illus. **Document type:** *Journal, Academic/Scholarly.*
Formerly (1829-1917): Moskovskoe Obshchestvo Ispytatelei Prirody. Byulleten' (0007-7682)
Related titles: Microfiche ed.: (from IDC).
Indexed: ASFA, BIOSIS Prev, BioCN&I, BiolAb, ESPM, ForAb, HerbAb, KWIWR, RASB, RefZh, RevApplEntom, SFA, TriticAb, ZooRec.
—BLDSC (0022.000000), CISTI, East View, KNAW, Linda Hall.
Published by: (Moskovskoe Obshchestvo Ispytatelei Pripody, Biologicheskii Otdel/Moscow Society of Naturalists, Biological Section), Izdatel'stvo Moskovskogo Gosudarstvennogo Universiteta im. M. V. Lomonosova/Publishing House of Moscow State University, B Nikitskaya 5/7, Moscow, 103009, Russian Federation. TEL 7-095-2295091, FAX 7-095-2036671, kd_mgu@rambler.ru, http://herba.msu.ru/journals/bmsn/, http://www.msu.ru/depts/MSUPubl. Ed. A S Severtsov. Circ: 1,635. **Dist. by:** M K - Periodica, ul Gilyarovskogo 39, Moscow 129110, Russian Federation. TEL 7-095-2845008, FAX 7-095-2813798, info@periodicals.ru, http://www.mkniga.ru.

570 USA ISSN 0097-0883
QH323 CODEN: BMDIAY
➤ **MOUNT DESERT ISLAND BIOLOGICAL LABORATORY. BULLETIN.** Text in English. 1960. a. USD 10 to non-members (effective 2000). charts; illus. index. **Document type:** *Bulletin, Academic/Scholarly.*
Indexed: ASFA, BiolAb, CurCont, SFA, WildRev, ZooRec.
—BLDSC (2622.000000), Linda Hall.
Published by: Mount Desert Island Biological Laboratory, Old Bar Harbor Rd, PO Box 35, Salsbury Cove, ME 04672. TEL 207-288-3605, mmckernan@mdibl.org, http://www.mdibl.org. Ed. David Miller. Circ: 1,000.

570 JPN ISSN 0910-0903
MUKIN SEIBUTSU/JOURNAL OF GERMFREE LIFE AND GNOTOBIOLOGY. Text in English, Japanese. 1971. s-a.
Published by: Nihon Mukin Seibutsu Noto Baioroji Gakkai/Japanese Association of Germfree Life and Gnotobiology, c/o Ms. Kazuko Adachi, Kobe Gakuin Daigaku Eiyogakubu, Arise, Ikawadanicho, Nishi-ku, Kobe-shi, Hyogo-ken 673, Japan.

570 NLD ISSN 1573-6105
▼ **MULTIDISCIPLINE MODELING IN MATERIALS AND STRUCTURES.** Text in English. 2005. q. USD 313 combined subscription in the Americas to institutions print & online eds.; EUR 250 combined subscription elsewhere to institutions print & online eds. (effective 2006). back issues avail. **Document type:** *Journal, Academic/Scholarly.*
Related titles: Online - full text ed.: ISSN 1573-6113. USD 282 in the Americas to institutions; EUR 225 elsewhere to institutions (effective 2006) (from IngentaConnect).
Published by: V S P (Subsidiary of: Brill Academic Publishers), Brill Academic Publishers, PO Box 9000, Leiden, 2300 PA, Netherlands. TEL 31-71-5353500, FAX 31-71-5317532, http://www.brill.nl/m_catalogue_sub6_id22737.htm, http://www.vsppub.com. Ed. Zhufeng Yue. **Dist. by:** Extenza - Turpin, Pegasus Dr, Stratton Business Park, Biggleswade, Beds SG18 8TQ, United Kingdom. TEL 44-1767-604954, FAX 44-1767-601640, marketing@extenza-turpin.com, http://www.extenza-turpin.com.

THE MUNDI CLUB. SPECIAL PUBLICATIONS. see *ENVIRONMENTAL STUDIES*

570 GBR
MUNTJAC; the newsletter of the Bedfordshire Natural History Society. Text in English. m.
Published by: Bedfordshire Natural History Society, 46 Mallard Hill, Bedford, MK41 7QS, United Kingdom. TEL 01234-211941, journal@bnhs.org.uk, http://www.bedfordshirenaturalhistorysociety.org.uk/.

570 550 ITA ISSN 0505-205X
QH7 CODEN: BMSNA
➤ **MUSEO CIVICO DI STORIA NATURALE DI VENEZIA. BOLLETTINO.** Text in English, French, German, Italian, Spanish; Summaries in English, Italian. 1932. a., latest vol.5, 1999. per issue exchange basis. index. **Document type:** *Bulletin, Academic/Scholarly.* **Description:** Covers taxonomy, biogeography, ecology, and the flora and fauna of the lagoon of Venice.
Former titles (until 1954): Bollettino della Societa Veneziana di Storia Naturale del Museo Civico di Storia Naturale; (until 1940): Societa Veneziana di Storia Naturale. Bollettino
Indexed: AnBrAb, BIOSIS Prev, BioCN&I, BiolAb, FCA, FPA, ForAb, HerbAb, HortAb, I&DA, IndVet, NemAb, PoultAb, RM&VM, RPP, RefZh, RevApplEntom, S&F, VetBull, WeedAb, ZooRec.
—CISTI.
Published by: Museo Civico di Storia Naturale di Venezia, Fontego dei Turchi, S. Croce 1730, Venice, VE 30135, Italy. TEL 39-041-2750206, FAX 39-041-721000, nat.mus.ve@iol.it. Circ: 1,000 (controlled).

570 550 ITA
MUSEO CIVICO DI STORIA NATURALE DI VENEZIA. QUADERNI. Text in English, French, German, Italian, Spanish; Summaries in English, Italian. 1980. irreg., latest vol.5, 1999. per issue exchange basis. back issues avail. **Document type:** *Monographic series.* **Description:** Covers taxonomy, biogeography, ecology, and the flora and fauna of the lagoon of Venice.
Indexed: ZooRec.
Published by: Museo Civico di Storia Naturale di Venezia, Fontego dei Turchi, S. Croce 1730, Venice, VE 30135, Italy. TEL 39-041-2750206, FAX 39-041-721000, nat.mus.ve@iol.it. Circ: 800.

508 ITA
MUSEO CIVICO DI STORIA NATURALE DI VERONA. MEMORIE. SERIE 2, SEZIONE A: SCIENZE DELLA VITA. Text in Italian. 1977. irreg., latest vol.13, 1998. price varies. **Document type:** *Monographic series.*
Formerly: Museo Civico di Storia Naturale di Verona. Memorie. Serie 2, Part 1: Biologia
Indexed: ZooRec.
Published by: Museo Civico di Storia Naturale di Verona, Lungadige Porta Vittoria 9, Verona, VR 37129, Italy. TEL 39-045-8079400, FAX 39-045-8035639, mcsnat@comune.verona.it, http://www.museostorianaturaleverona.it.

570 560 ITA ISSN 1126-0882
MUSEO DI STORIA NATURALE DELLA MAREMMA. ATTI. Text in Italian, English. 1983. a., latest vol.19, 2001. bk.rev. abstr. 200 p./no.; back issues avail. **Document type:** *Bulletin, Academic/Scholarly.*
Formerly (until 1997): Museo Civico di Storia Naturale di Grosseto. Atti (0393-6015)
Indexed: ForAb, HerbAb, HortAb, OrnHort, PGegResA, RA&MP, RevApplEntom, S&F, ZooRec.
Published by: Museo di Storia Naturale della Maremma, Strada Corsini 5, Grosseto, GR 58100, Italy. TEL 39-0564-414701, FAX 39-0564-488811, msnmare@gol.grosseto.it. Circ: 350.

570 ITA ISSN 0392-758X
➤ **MUSEO REGIONALE DI SCIENZE NATURALI, TORINO. BOLLETTINO.** Text in English, French, Italian, Spanish; Summaries in English. 1983. s-a. EUR 26 (effective 2003). back issues avail. **Document type:** *Bulletin, Academic/Scholarly.* **Description:** Features readings on natural sciences, including paleontology, botany, mineralogy, geology and zoology.
Indexed: BIOSIS Prev, BiolAb, RefZh, ZooRec.
—BLDSC (2227.600000), IE.
Published by: Museo Regionale di Scienze Naturali Torino, Redazione, Via Giovanni Giolitti, 36, Turin, TO 10123, Italy. TEL 39-011-4323063, FAX 39-011-4323331, redazione.mrsn@regione.piemonte.it, http://www.regione.piemonte.it/museodiscienzenaturali/museodiscienzenaturali.htm. Ed. Giulia Bottero. Circ: 700.

570 BRA ISSN 0103-9121
QH117
MUSEU DE BIOLOGIA MELLO LEITAO. BOLETIM. Text in English, Portuguese. 1992. q. **Document type:** *Monographic series.*
Indexed: ASFA, AgrForAb, AnBrAb, BioCN&I, CPA, ForAb, HortAb, NutrAb, OrnHort, PBA, PGegResA, PGrRegA, PN&I, RefZh, S&F, SeedAb, ZooRec.
Published by: Instituto Brasileiro do Patrimonio Cultural, Museu de Biologia Mello Leitao, Av Jose Ruschi, 4, Santa Teresa, ES 29650-000, Brazil. TEL 55-27-259-1182, FAX 55-27-259-1182.

MUSEU MUNICIPAL DO FUNCHAL. BOLETIM. see *BIOLOGY—Zoology*

570.74 ROM ISSN 1223-2254
QH1 CODEN: TMNAAK
➤ **MUSEUM NATIONAL D'HISTOIRE NATURELLE "GRIGORE ANTIPA". TRAVAUX/MUZEUL NATIONAL DE ISTORIE NATURALA "GRIGORE ANTIPA". TRAVAUX.** Text in English, French, German; Summaries in Romanian; Abstracts in English, French. 1957. a., latest vol.44. price varies. adv. bk.rev. index. back issues avail. **Document type:** *Bulletin, Academic/Scholarly.*
Formerly (until 1995): Museum d'Histoire Naturelle "Grigore Antipa." Travaux (0068-3078)
Indexed: BioCN&I, ForAb, HelmAb, RevApplEntom, SFA, ZooRec.
—BLDSC (9039.500000), CISTI, Linda Hall.
Published by: Muzeul National de Istorie Naturala "Grigore Antipa", Sos. Kiseleff 1, Bucharest, 79744, Romania. TEL 40-21-3128826, FAX 40-21-3128863, dmurariu@antipa.ro, http://www.antipa.ro. Ed., R&P Dumitru Murariu TEL 40-21-3128886. Adv. contact Elena Cursaru. Circ: 900.

➤ **MUSEUM NATIONAL D'HISTOIRE NATURELLE. MEMOIRES.** see *SCIENCES: COMPREHENSIVE WORKS*

570 POL ISSN 0068-466X
CODEN: ASMHE9
MUZEUM GORNOSLASKIE W BYTOMIU. ROCZNIK. SERIA PRZYRODA. Text and summaries in English, Polish. 1962. irreg. USD 15. **Document type:** *Proceedings.*
Indexed: ASFA, AgrLib, ZooRec.
Published by: Muzeum Gornoslaskie w Bytomiu/The Museum of Upper Silesia, Pl Jana III Sobieskiego 2, Bytom, 41902, Poland. TEL 48-32-28182941, dobosz@us.edu.pl, mgbytom@us.edu.pl.

570 ESP ISSN 1130-9717
QH301 CODEN: PAPOFH
➤ **N A C C BIOLOXIA.** (Nova Acta Cientifica Compostelana) Text in Spanish, Gallegan; Summaries in English, Spanish. 1990. a. EUR 19.23 (effective 2005). bk.rev. charts; illus. back issues avail. **Document type:** *Journal, Academic/Scholarly.*
Supersedes (1971-1986): Trabajos Compostelanos de Biologia (0211-0733)
Indexed: ASFA, ESPM, EntAb, IECT, PollutAb, SWRA, ZooRec.
—CINDOC.
Published by: Universidad de Santiago de Compostela, Servicio de Publicacions, Campus Universitario Sur, Santiago de Compostela, 15782, Spain. TEL 34-981-593500, FAX 34-981-593963, spublic@usc.es, http://www.usc.es/spubl/revnacc.htm. Ed. Jose Luis Perez Cirera. Circ: 500.

➤ **N A P R A L E R T.** (Natural Products Alert) see *PHARMACY AND PHARMACOLOGY*

➤ **N B I A NEWSLETTER.** see *AGRICULTURE*

➤ **N C R R REPORTER.** (National Center for Research Resources) see *MEDICAL SCIENCES*

570 NZL ISSN 1174-0043
➤ **N I W A BIODIVERSITY MEMOIR.** Text in English. 1955. irreg., latest vol.118, 2002. price varies. abstr.; bibl.; illus. back issues avail. **Document type:** *Monographic series, Academic/Scholarly.*
Formerly (until 1996): New Zealand Oceanographic Institute Memoir (0083-7903)
Indexed: ASFA, BIOSIS Prev, BiolAb, RefZh, ZooRec.
—CISTI, Linda Hall.
Published by: National Institute of Water and Atmospheric Research Ltd., PO Box 14-901, Kilbirnie, Wellington, New Zealand. TEL 64-4-3860300, FAX 64-4-3862153, d.gordon@niwa.co.nz, http://www.niwa.co.nz. Ed. Dennis P Gordon. R&P Dennis Gordon. Circ: 500.

578.77 JPN ISSN 0547-1427
SH1 CODEN: NADKAK
NAGASAKI DAIGAKU SUISANGAKUBU. KENKYU HOKOKU/NAGASAKI UNIVERSITY. FACULTY OF FISHERIES. BULLETIN. Text in English, Japanese. 1953. a.
Indexed: ESPM, ZooRec.
—BLDSC (2508.380000), CISTI, IE, ingenta.

B

Published by: Nagasaki Daigaku, Suisangakubu/Nagasaki University, Faculty of Fisheries, 1-14 Bunkyou-machi, Nagasaki, 852-8521, Japan. TEL 81-95-847-1111, FAX 81-95-844-3516, http://www.lb.nagasaki-u.ac.jp/kiyo/fish/, http://www.fish.nagasaki-u.ac.jp/.

570 JPN ISSN 0387-4249
NAGASAKIKEN SEIBUTSU GAKKAISHI/NAGASAKI BIOLOGICAL SOCIETY. TRANSACTIONS. Text in English, Japanese. 1971. s-a. JPY 2,000 per issue.
Published by: Nagasakiken Seibutsu Gakkai/Nagasaki Biological Society, Nagasaki Daigaku Kyoyobu Seibutsugaku Kyoshitsu, 1-14 Bunkyo-Machi, Nagasaki-shi, 852-8131, Japan.

▼ **NANOTOXICOLOGY.** see *MEDICAL SCIENCES—Radiology And Nuclear Medicine*

570 JPN ISSN 0912-0114
NAN'YO SEIBUTSU/NAN'YO BIOLOGICAL SOCIETY. REPORTS. Text in Japanese. 1985. a. JPY 3,000 membership. **Document type:** *Bulletin.*
Published by: Nan'yo Seibutsu Kenkyukai/Nan'yo Biological Society, c/o Mr Kiyokazu Hashigoe, 1-1-43 Nagabori, Uwajima-shi, Ehime-ken 789-0082, Japan. TEL 81-895-22-1610, FAX 81-895-22-1610. Eds. Kiyokazu Hashigoe, Koichi Tsuji. Pub. Koichi Tsuji.

B

570.74 ZAF ISSN 0067-9208
GN656 CODEN: NVNMAJ
➤ **NASIONALE MUSEUM, BLOEMFONTEIN. NAVORSINGE/NATIONAL MUSEUM, BLOEMFONTEIN. RESEARCHES.** Key Title: Navorsinge van die Nasionale Museum. Text and summaries in Afrikaans, English. 1952. irreg. (1 vol./yr. in 10-14 parts), latest vol.18, no.8, 2003. price varies. abstr.; bibl.; charts; illus.; stat. index. back issues avail. **Document type:** *Monographic series, Academic/Scholarly.* **Description:** Publishes original research papers in natural science and the human sciences, with particular emphasis on the research disciplines of the National Museum, studies relating to collections of the Museum, local ecology, fauna and history.
Incorporates (after vol.25, 1989): National Museum, Bloemfontein. Memoirs (0374-9665)
Indexed: BIOSIS Prev, BiolAb, EntAb, ISAP, RASB, SFA, WildRev, ZooRec.
—BLDSC (7776.000000), IE, ingenta, KNAW.
Published by: Nasionale Museum Bloemfontein/National Museum, Bloemfontein, PO Box 266, Bloemfontein, 9300, South Africa. TEL 27-51-447-9609, FAX 27-51-447-6273, library@nasmus.co.za. Ed. J Haasbroek. Circ: 500.

570 IND ISSN 0369-8211
Q73 CODEN: PAIBA6
NATIONAL ACADEMY OF SCIENCES, INDIA. PROCEEDINGS. SECTION B. BIOLOGICAL SCIENCES. Text in English. 1930. q. INR 250, USD 100; USD 200 Includes Section A & B (effective 2000). bk.rev. bibl.; charts; illus.; stat. **Document type:** *Proceedings.*
Indexed: ASFA, AbHyg, AgBio, AgrForAb, AnBrAb, BIOSIS Prev, BioCN&I, BiolAb, CCMJ, CIN, CPA, ChemAb, ChemTitl, CurCont, ESPM, FCA, FS&TA, ForAb, HelmAb, HortAb, I&DA, INIS AtomInd, IndVet, Inspec, MaizeAb, MathR, MathSciNet, NemAb, NutrAb, OrnHort, PBA, PGegResA, PGrRegA, PHN&I, ProtozoAb, RA&MP, RM&VM, RPP, RefZh, RevApplEntom, RiceAb, S&F, S&MA, SIA, SeedAb, SoyAb, TDB, TriticAb, VetBull, WAE&RSA, WeedAb, ZooRec.
—BLDSC (6761.901000), CASDDS, CISTI, IE, ingenta, Linda Hall.
Published by: National Academy of Sciences, 5 Lajpatrai Rd., Allahabad, Uttar Pradesh 211 002, India. FAX 91-532-641183, nasi@nde.vsnl.net.in, http://www4.nationalacademies.org/nas/nashome.nsf. Ed. K Swarup. Circ: 500.

NATIONAL AQUATIC RESOURCES RESEARCH AND DEVELOPMENT AGENCY. JOURNAL. see *CONSERVATION*

570.71 USA
NATIONAL ASSOCIATION OF BIOLOGY TEACHERS. NEWS AND VIEWS; issues, events, professional development for biology teachers. Text in English. 4/yr. looseleaf. membership. **Document type:** *Newsletter.*
Published by: National Association of Biology Teachers, Inc., 12030 Sunrise Valley Dr, 110, Reston, VA 20191. TEL 703-264-9696, FAX 703-264-7778, NABTer@aol.com, http://www.nabt.org. Pub. Wayne Carley. R&P Christine Chantry. Circ: 8,000.

578.77 540 639.2 KOR ISSN 1225-2751
CODEN: PTHPD9
NATIONAL FISHERIES UNIVERSITY OF PUSAN. INSTITUTE OF MARINE SCIENCES. CONTRIBUTIONS. Text in Korean; Summaries in English. 1968. a. KRW 12,000, USD 16. back issues avail. **Description:** Covers physical oceanography, chemical oceanography, marine geology, and marine biology.
Formerly (until 1983): National Fisheries University of Pusan. Institute of Marine Sciences. Publications (0250-3387)
Indexed: ASFA, ESPM.
—CASDDS, Linda Hall.
Published by: National Fisheries University of Pusan, Institute of Marine Sciences, Haewundae, Pusan, 612021, Korea, S. TEL 51-742-0475. Ed. Chung Gil Park. Circ: 800.

NATIONAL INSTITUTE FOR AGRO-ENVIRONMENTAL SCIENCES. ANNUAL REPORT. see *AGRICULTURE*

570 JPN ISSN 0912-1315
S494.5.B563
NATIONAL INSTITUTE OF AGROBIOLOGICAL RESOURCES. ANNUAL REPORT. Text in English. 1985. a.
Indexed: VITIS.
—BLDSC (1364.620000), Linda Hall.
Published by: Norin Suisansho, Nogyo Seibutsu Shigen Kenkyujo/Ministry of Agriculture, Forestry and Fisheries, National Institute of Agrobiological Resources, 2-1-2 Kannondai, Tsukuba-shi, Ibaraki-ken 305-0856, Japan.

570 610 JPN ISSN 0386-5541
➤ **NATIONAL INSTITUTE OF POLAR RESEARCH. MEMOIRS. SERIES E: BIOLOGY AND MEDICAL SCIENCE.** Text and summaries in English. 1959. irreg., latest vol.39, 1996. per issue exchange basis. **Document type:** *Monographic series, Academic/Scholarly.*
Supersedes: Japanese Antarctic Research Expedition, 1956-1962. Scientific Reports. Series E. Biology (0075-3394)
Indexed: ASFA, BIOSIS Prev, BiolAb, SFA, ZooRec.
—BLDSC (5626.812000), Linda Hall.
Published by: National Institute of Polar Research/Kokuritsu Kyokuchi Kenkyujo, Publications, 9-10, Kiga 1-chome, Itabashi-ku, Tokyo, 173, Japan. TEL 81-3-3962-2214, FAX 81-3-3962-2225, TELEX 272-2515 POLRSCJ, publication@nipr.ac.jp. Ed. Okitsugu Watanabe. Circ: 1,000.

➤ **NATIONAL TOXICOLOGY PROGRAM TECHNICAL REPORT SERIES.** see *ENVIRONMENTAL STUDIES*

570 KAZ
NATSIONALNAYA AKADEMIYA NAUK RESPUBLIKI KAZAKHSTAN. IZVESTIYA. SERIYA BIOLOGICHESKAYA. Text in Russian. bi-m. USD 245 in North America (effective 2000).
Indexed: ZooRec.
Published by: Academy of Sciences of Kazakhstan, Ul Kabanbai Batyra 69-a, Almaty, 480100, Kazakstan. TEL 7-3732-615608, FAX 7-3272-615314, adm@geol.academ.alma-ata.su. **Dist. by:** East View Information Services, 3020 Harbor Ln. N., Minneapolis, MN 55447. TEL 763-550-0961, FAX 763-559-2931.

570 BLR ISSN 1029-8940
CODEN: VABBA3
➤ **NATSIYANAL'NAYA AKADEMIYA NAVUK BELARUSI. VESTSI. SERYYA BIYALAGICHNYKH NAVUK/NATIONAL ACADEMY OF SCIENCES OF BELARUS. PROCEEDINGS. SERIES OF BIOLOGICAL SCIENCES.** Text in Belorussian, Russian; Summaries in English. 1956. q. USD 115 foreign (effective 2003). bibl.; charts; illus. index. **Document type:** *Journal, Academic/Scholarly.* **Description:** Publishes the original results of experimental and theoretical investigations in the field of general biology, ecology, botany and zoology, hydrobiology, biological foundations of rational use, transformation and protection of plant and animal world, radiobiology, biochemistry, etc.
Former titles (until 1998): Akademiya Navuk Belarusi. Vestsi. Seryya Biyalagichnykh Navuk (1023-6279); (until 1992): Akademiya Navuk Belarusskai S.S.R. Vestsi. Seryya Biyalagichnykh Navuk (0002-3558)
Indexed: AEA, AbHyg, AgBio, AgrForAb, AnBrAb, BioCN&I, BiolAb, CPA, DSA, FCA, FPA, ForAb, HelmAb, HerbAb, HortAb, I&DA, INIS AtomInd, IndVet, MaizeAb, NutrAb, OrnHort, PBA, PGegResA, PGrRegA, PHN&I, PN&I, PotatoAb, ProtozoAb, RA&MP, RM&VM, RPP, RRTA, RefZh, RevApplEntom, S&F, SIA, SeedAb, SoyAb, TriticAb, VITIS, VetBull, WAE&RSA, WeedAb, ZooRec.
—CASDDS, CISTI, KNAW, Linda Hall.
Published by: (Natsiyanal'naya Akademiya Navuk Belarusi/National Academy of Sciences of Belarus), Vydavetstvo Belaruskaya Navuka/Publishing House Belaruskaya Navuka, 18 Academician V F Kuprevich St, Minsk, 220141, Belarus. TEL 375-172-284-2821, 375-17-2632327, FAX 375-17-2637618, biology@presidium.bas-net.by, belnauka@infonet.by, http://ns1.hmti.ac.by/publications/vesti/vestib.html. Ed. A G Lobanok. Circ: 300. **Dist. by:** M K - Periodica, ul Gilyarovskogo 39, Moscow 129110, Russian Federation. TEL 7-095-2845008, FAX 7-095-2813798, info@periodicals.ru, http://www.mkniga.ru.

➤ **NATSIYANAL'NAYA AKADEMIYA NAVUK BELARUSI. VESTSI. SERYYA MEDYKA-BIYALAGICHNYKH NAVUK/NATIONAL ACADEMY OF SCIENCES OF BELARUS. PROCEEDINGS. SERIES OF MEDICAL-BIOLOGICAL SCIENCES.** see *MEDICAL SCIENCES*

➤ **NATUR - DAS KINDERWEB.** see *CHILDREN AND YOUTH—For*

➤ **NATUR UND KOSMOS.** see *ENVIRONMENTAL STUDIES*

570 930 DEU ISSN 0077-6025
NATUR UND MENSCH. Text in German. 1965. a. price varies. **Document type:** *Yearbook, Academic/Scholarly.*
Former titles (until 1975): Naturhistorische Gesellschaft Nuernberg. Jahresmitteilungen (0170-012X); (until 1969): Naturhistorische Gesellschaft Nuernberg. Mitteilungen und Jahresbericht (0174-920X)
Indexed: BiolAb, KWIWR, RefZh, ZooRec.
Published by: Naturhistorische Gesellschaft Nuernberg e.V., Norishalle, Marientorgraben 8, Nuernberg, 90402, Germany. TEL 49-911-227970, FAX 49-911-2447441, nhgnbg@t-online.de, http://www.nhg-nuernberg.de. Circ: 2,500.

570 BRA
NATURA. Text in Portuguese. 1975. s-a. free.
Published by: Universidade Federal da Bahia, Instituto de Biologia, Rua Barao de Geremoabo-Ondina, Salvador, Bahia 40000, Brazil. Ed. Antonio Pedreira. Circ: 1,500. **Co-sponsor:** Instituto de Ciencias da Saude.

333.72 ITA ISSN 0028-0658
NATURA & MONTAGNA; rivista semestrale di divulgazione naturalistica. Text in Italian. 1954. s-a. EUR 30 domestic; EUR 45 foreign (effective 2005). back issues avail. **Document type:** *Magazine, Consumer.* **Description:** Provides readers with top-quality news and articles on the natural world, along with scientific observations and updates on environmental legislation in Italy.
Published by: (Unione Bolognesi Naturalisti), Patron Editore, Via Badini 12, Quarto Inferiore, BO 40050, Italy. TEL 39-051-767003, FAX 39-051-768252, info@patroneditore.com, http://www.patroneditore.com. Ed. Francesco Corbetta.

591.9 HRV ISSN 1330-3430
NATURA CROATICA. SUPPLEMENTUM. Text in English. 1992. irreg.
Related titles: ♦ Supplement to: Natura Croatica. ISSN 1330-0520.
Indexed: ASFA, EntAb, RefZh.
Published by: Hrvatski Prirodoslovni Muzej/Croatian Natural History Museum, Demetrova 1, Zagreb, 10000, Croatia. TEL 385-1-4851700, FAX 385-1-4851644, natura.croatica@hpm.hr, http://mahpm.hpm.hr/natura.htm.

570 DNK ISSN 0077-6033
QH7 CODEN: NAJUAC
NATURA JUTLANDICA. Text in English. 1947. irreg. DKK 100, USD 17. illus. **Document type:** *Academic/Scholarly.*
Indexed: ASFA, BiolAb, KWIWR, SFA, WildRev, ZooRec.
—CISTI, Linda Hall.
Published by: Naturhistorisk Museum, Universitetsparken, Bygning 210, Aarhus C, 8000, Denmark. TEL 86-12-97-77, FAX 86-13-08-82, nm@nathist.aau.dk, http://www.naturhistoriskmuseum.dk. Ed. Thomas Secher Jensen. Circ: 1,000.

577 GBR
NATURAL ENVIRONMENT RESEARCH COUNCIL. INSTITUTE OF TERRESTRIAL ECOLOGY. SCIENTIFIC REPORT. Text in English. irreg.
Published by: Natural Environment Research Council, Institute of Terrestrial Ecology, Monks Wood, Abbots Ripton, Huntingdon, Cambs PE26 2LS, United Kingdom. TEL 44-1487-772400, FAX 44-1487-773590, rmt@ceh.ac.uk, http://www.ceh.ac.uk.

570 560 CAN ISSN 0707-3887
NATURAL HISTORY CONTRIBUTIONS. Text in English. 1978. irreg., latest vol.11, 1992. free. back issues avail. **Document type:** *Monographic series.*
Published by: Royal Saskatchewan Museum, 2340 Albert St, Regina, SK S4P 3V7, Canada. TEL 306-787-2801, FAX 306-787-2645. Ed. Keith Roney. Circ: 300.

570 550 JPN ISSN 1340-2684
➤ **NATURAL HISTORY MUSEUM AND INSTITUTE, CHIBA. JOURNAL. SPECIAL ISSUE.** Text in English, Japanese. 1994. irreg. per issue exchange basis. back issues avail. **Document type:** *Monographic series, Academic/Scholarly.* **Description:** Contains original articles and reviews on natural history.
Indexed: RefZh, ZooRec.
Published by: Natural History Museum and Institute Chiba, 955-2 Aoba-cho, Chuo-ku, Chiba-shi, 260-0852, Japan. TEL 81-43-265-3111, FAX 81-43-266-2481. Circ: 1,500 (controlled).

➤ **NATURAL HISTORY RESEARCH CENTER. PUBLICATION.** see *SCIENCES: COMPREHENSIVE WORKS*

570 550 JPN ISSN 1340-2692
QH1
➤ **NATURAL HISTORY RESEARCH. SPECIAL ISSUE.** Text in English. 1994. irreg. per issue exchange basis. back issues avail. **Document type:** *Monographic series, Academic/Scholarly.* **Description:** Contain original articles and reviews on natural history.
Indexed: RefZh, ZooRec.
Published by: Natural History Museum and Institute Chiba, 955-2 Aoba-cho, Chuo-ku, Chiba-shi, 260-0852, Japan. TEL 81-43-265-3111, FAX 81-43-266-2481. Circ: 1,500 (controlled).

570 BRA ISSN 0101-1944
QH7 CODEN: NTRLDP
➤ **NATURALIA.** Text in Portuguese; Summaries in English, Portuguese. 1975-1979; N.S. 1980. a., latest vol.26, 2001. USD 30 per vol. (effective 2005); or exchange basis. charts; illus.; stat.; abstr.; bibl. back issues avail. **Document type:** *Journal, Academic/Scholarly.* **Description:** Publishes original contributions on biological sciences.
Indexed: ASFA, AbAn, AgBio, AgrForAb, ApicAb, BIOSIS Prev, BioCN&I, BiolAb, CPA, ESPM, EntAb, ForAb, HelmAb, HerbAb, HortAb, MathR, NutrAb, OrnHort, PBA, PGegResA, PollutAb, ProtozoAb, RA&MP, RDA, RM&VM, RPP, RefZh, RevApplEntom, S&F, SeedAb, WeedAb, ZooRec.
—BLDSC (6041.910000), CASDDS, CISTI, IE, ingenta, KNAW, Linda Hall.
Published by: Fundacao Editora U N E S P, Praca da Se 108, Sao Paulo, SP 01001-900, Brazil. TEL 55-11-32427171, cgb@marilia.unesp.br, http://www.unesp.br. Ed. Flavio Henrique Caetano. Circ: 1,000.

570 ARG ISSN 0327-8050
QH305.2.P33
➤ **NATURALIA PATAGONICA. SERIE CIENCIAS BIOLOGICAS.** Text in Spanish; Summaries in English. 1993. a. ARS 10 (effective 2001). charts; illus.; maps; stat. back issues avail. **Document type:** *Academic/Scholarly.* **Description:** Devoted to biological and ecological studies and their application in Patagonia.
Indexed: ASFA, ZooRec.
Published by: Universidad Nacional de la Patagonia San Juan Bosco, Facultad de Ciencias Naturales, Ciudad Universitaria Km 4, Comodoro Rivadavia, Chubut 9005, Argentina. uvin@unpata.edu.ar, http://www.unp.edu.ar. Ed. Hector E Zaixso. Circ: 300.

570 ARG ISSN 0327-9510
NATURALIA PATAGONICA. SERIE REPORTES TECNICOS. Text in Spanish. 1993. a. **Document type:** *Monographic series.*
Indexed: ASFA, ESPM, PollutAb, ZooRec.
Published by: Universidad Nacional de la Patagonia San Juan Bosco, Facultad de Ciencias Naturales, Ciudad Universitaria Km 4, Comodoro Rivadavia, Chubut 9005, Argentina. uvin@unpata.edu.ar, http://www.unp.edu.ar.

570 508 GBR ISSN 0028-0771
QH1 CODEN: NTRLAM
➤ **THE NATURALIST.** Text in English. 1875. q. GBP 20 (effective 2001). adv. bk.rev. index. reprint service avail. from PQC. **Document type:** *Academic/Scholarly.*
Related titles: Microfilm ed.: (from PQC).
Indexed: ASFA, BIOSIS Prev, BiolAb, ChemAb, EPB, IBR, IBZ, RPP, ZooRec.
—BLDSC (6042.000000). **CCC.**
Published by: Yorkshire Naturalists' Union, University of Bradford, Bradford, W Yorks BD7 1DP, United Kingdom. TEL 44-1274-234212, FAX 44-1274-234231, m.r.d.seaward@bradford.ac.uk. Ed. M R D Seaward. Circ: 3,600.

570 551 ITA ISSN 1120-6519
➤ **IL NATURALISTA VALTELLINESE**; atti del Museo Civico di Storia Naturale di Morbegno. Variant title: Museo Civico di Storia Naturale di Morbegno. Atti. Text in Italian, English, French, German. 1990. a., latest vol.12, 2002. EUR 5 (effective 2003). 190 p./no.; back issues avail. **Document type:** *Academic/Scholarly.* **Description:** Publishes papers dealing with all the branches of natural sciences, giving priority to papers on the Province of Sondrio and the Central Alps region, and to collections and researches of the Museum of Natural History of Morbegno.
Indexed: ZooRec.
Published by: Museo Civico di Storia Naturale di Morbegno, Via Cortivacci 2, Morbegno, SO 23017, Italy. TEL 39-0342-612451, FAX 39-0342-615528, museo.morbegno@provincia.so.it, http://fc.provincia.so.it/~museo.morbegno/page8.html. Pub. Fabio Penati. Circ: 500.

500.9 BEL ISSN 0028-0801
QH3 CODEN: NTUBA7
LES NATURALISTES BELGES. Text in French. 1920. q. bk.rev. charts; illus. index. **Document type:** *Bulletin.*
Indexed: BIOSIS Prev, BiolAb, RefZh, ZooRec.
Published by: Naturalistes Belges a.s.b.l., Rue Vautier 29, Bruxelles, 1000, Belgium. TEL 32-2-627-4239, FAX 32-2-646 4466. Ed. Alain Quintart.

570 USA ISSN 0277-609X
THE NATURALISTS' DIRECTORY AND ALMANAC INTERNATIONAL. Text in English. 1877. irreg., latest vol.48, 1998. USD 35 domestic; USD 38 foreign (effective 2000). adv. bk.rev. bibl. back issues avail. **Document type:** *Directory.* **Description:** Source for access to the world's leading natural science professionals.
Formerly: Naturalists' Directory International
Published by: Naturalists' Directory and Almanac International, PO Box 382595, Cambridge, MA 02238-2595. TEL 978-658-2271, FAX 978-658-2271, nature@ma.ultranet.com, http://www.ultranet.com/~nature. Ed., R&P, Adv. contact Philip West Mallard. Circ: 2,500.

NATURE ALBERTA. see *CONSERVATION*

NATURE MEDICINE. see *MEDICAL SCIENCES*

570 USA ISSN 1545-9993
QH506 CODEN: NSMBCU
➤ **NATURE STRUCTURAL AND MOLECULAR BIOLOGY.** Text in English. 1994. m. EUR 1,240 in Europe to institutions Eurozone; USD 1,440 in the Americas to institutions; GBP 800 to institutions in the UK & elsewhere; EUR 271 combined subscription in Europe to individuals Eurozone; print & online; USD 199 combined subscription in the Americas to individuals print & online; GBP 175 combined subscription to individuals in the UK & elsewhere; print & online (effective 2006). adv. illus. index. back issues avail. **Document type:** *Journal, Academic/Scholarly.* **Description:** Publishes biomedical research results in structural biology, including applications of new technologies and techniques.
Formerly (until 2004): Nature Structural Biology (1072-8368)
Related titles: Online - full text ed.: ISSN 1545-9985 (from EBSCO Publishing, Swets Information Services).
Indexed: AEBA, AIDS&CR, ASCA, ASFA, AgBio, AnBrAb, BBCI, BIOBASE, BIOSIS Prev, BioCN&I, BiolAb, CIN, CPA, CTA, ChemAb, ChemTitl, ChemoAb, CurCont, DSA, ESPM, EntAb, ExcerpMed, FCA, FS&TA, GenetAb, HGA, HelmAb, HerbAb, HortAb, IABS, INIS AtomInd, ISR, IndMed, IndVet, Inpharma, Inspec, M&PBA, MBA, MEDLINE, MaizeAb, NSA, NucAcAb, NutrAb, OGFA, OrnHort, PBA, PN&I, ProtozoAb, RA&MP, RM&VM, RPP, Reac, RefZh, RevApplEntom, SCI, SIA, TriticAb, VetBull, WAE&RSA.
—BLDSC (6047.372500), CASDDS, CISTI, GNLM, IDS, IE, Infotrieve, ingenta, Linda Hall. **CCC.**
Published by: Nature Publishing Group (Subsidiary of: Macmillan Publishers Ltd.), 345 Park Ave S, 10th Fl, New York, NY 10010. TEL 212-726-9200, FAX 212-696-9635, nsmb@natureny.com, http://www.nature.com/nsmb/. Ed. Boyana Konforti. Pub. Beatrice Renault. **Subscr. in Asia to:** Nature Japan KK, MG Ichigaya Bldg. 5F, 19-1 Haraikatamachi, Shinjuku-ku, Tokyo 162-0841, Japan. TEL 81-3-3267-8751, FAX 81-3 3267-8746, subscriptions@naturejpn.com; **Subscr. in the Americas to:** PO Box 5161, Brentwood, TN 37024-5161. TEL 615-850-5315, 800-524-0384, FAX 615-377-0525, subscriptions@natureny.com; **Subscr. to:** Nature Publishing Group, Brunel Rd, Houndmills, Basingstoke, Hamps RG21 6XS, United Kingdom. TEL 44-1256-329242, FAX 44-1256-812358, subscriptions@nature.com, http://www.nature.com.

570 550 DEU ISSN 0374-6054
QH5 CODEN: BBNGAZ
NATURHISTORISCHE GESELLSCHAFT HANNOVER. BEIHEFTE ZU DEN BERICHTEN. Text in German; Summaries in English, German. 1928. irreg. price varies. bibl.; charts; illus. **Document type:** *Monographic series, Academic/Scholarly.*
Published by: Naturhistorische Gesellschaft Hannover, Willy-Brandt-Allee 5, Hannover, 30169, Germany. TEL 49-511-9807-860, FAX 49-511-9807-880. Circ: 850.

NATURHISTORISCHE GESELLSCHAFT NUERNBERG. ABHANDLUNGEN. see *ARCHAEOLOGY*

570 610 AUT ISSN 0379-1416
Q44 CODEN: BNMVAN
➤ **NATURWISSENSCHAFTLICH - MEDIZINISCHEN VEREINS IN INNSBRUCK. BERICHTE.** Text in English, German; Summaries in English, French, German, Italian. 1870. a. EUR 36.50. bk.rev. abstr. back issues avail. **Document type:** *Journal, Academic/Scholarly.* **Description:** Covers biological, faunistic, floristic, environmental and medical sciences. Accentuates the problems of the Alps, other high mountain groups and the Mediterranean basin.
Related titles: Supplement(s): Naturwissenschaftlich - Medizinischen Vereins in Innsbruck. Berichte. Supplementum. ISSN 1727-2483. 1984.
Indexed: ASFA, BIOSIS Prev, BiolAb, EntAb, RefZh, ZooRec.
—BLDSC (1923.300000), IE, ingenta.
Published by: Naturwissenschaftlich - Medizinischen Verein in Innsbruck, Technikerstr 25, Innsbruck, T 6020, Austria. TEL 43-512-5076142, FAX 43-512-5072930, erwin.meyer@uibk.ac.at. Ed. Dr. Erwin Meyer. Circ: 500.

570 550 DEU ISSN 0932-9447
NATURWISSENSCHAFTLICHE ZEITSCHRIFT FUER NIEDERBAYERN. Text in German. 1864. triennial. adv. bk.rev. **Document type:** *Proceedings, Academic/Scholarly.*
Published by: Naturwissenschaftlicher Verein fuer Niederbayern, Bachstr. 51 (Stadtarchiv), Landshut, 84036, Germany. TEL 49-871-43364, FAX 49-871-9454934. Ed., R&P, Adv. contact Georg Spitzlberger TEL 0871-42266.

570 DEU ISSN 0720-3705
NATURWISSENSCHAFTLICHER VEREIN FUER SCHWABEN. BERICHTE. Text in German. 1848. a. EUR 25 (effective 2001). bk.rev. 112 p./no.; back issues avail. **Document type:** *Yearbook, Academic/Scholarly.*
Formerly (until 1885): Naturhistorischer Verein Augsburg. Bericht (0340-3734)
Indexed: IBR, IBZ, ZooRec.
Published by: Naturwissenschaftlicher Verein fuer Schwaben e.V., Im Thaele 3, Augsburg, 86152, Germany. TEL 49-821-3246730, FAX 49-821-3246741. Eds. Hermann Oblinger, Otto Mair. Circ: 1,000.

370 550 DEU ISSN 0547-9770
CODEN: NWVAAU
➤ **NATURWISSENSCHAFTLICHER VEREIN WUERZBURG. ABHANDLUNGEN.** Text in German; Summaries in English, German. 1956. a. illus.; maps; stat. back issues avail. **Document type:** *Journal, Academic/Scholarly.* **Description:** Contains various scientific articles on biology, the earth sciences, and paleontology.
Indexed: ZooRec.
Published by: Naturwissenschaftlicher Verein Wuerzburg e.V., Crevennastr 10, Wuerzburg, 97072, Germany. TEL 49-931-56814, FAX 49-931-56814. Ed., R&P Joachim Raftopoulo. Circ: 500 (controlled). **Subscr. to:** Otto Hahn Str 35, Gerbrunn 97218, Germany.

370 550 DEU ISSN 0340-3718
Q3 CODEN: ANVBAV
➤ **NATURWISSENSCHAFTLICHER VEREIN ZU BREMEN. ABHANDLUNGEN.** Text in German. 1886. irreg., latest vol.44, 1999. **Document type:** *Journal, Academic/Scholarly.* **Description:** Presents articles and research concerning all fields of the natural sciences.
Indexed: ASFA, BIOSIS Prev, BiolAb, DIP, ESPM, IBZ, RefZh, ZooRec.
—CISTI, Linda Hall.
Published by: Naturwissenschaftlicher Verein zu Bremen, Bahnhofsplatz 13, Bremen, 28195, Germany. TEL 49-421-36111998, nwv.bremen@lycosmail.com, http://www.bremen.de/info/nwv/publikat.htm.

B

570 ESP ISSN 1137-8603
QH171
NATURZALE. Text in Spanish. 1983. irreg. price varies. **Document type:** *Monographic series, Academic/Scholarly.*
Formerly (until 1997): Sociedad de Estudios Vascos. Cuadernos de Seccion. Ciencias Naturales (0212-4173)
Indexed: FPA, ForAb, PGegResA, S&F, WAE&RSA, WeedAb.
Published by: Eusko Ikaskuntza/Sociedad de Estudios Vascos, Palacio Miramar, Miraconcha 48, Donostia, San Sebastian 20007, Spain. TEL 34-943-310855, FAX 34-943-213956, ei-sev@sc.ehu.es, http://www.eusko-ikaskuntza.org/.

570 560 NLD ISSN 0374-955X
NATUURHISTORISCH GENOOTSCHAP IN LIMBURG. PUBLICATIES. Text in Dutch, English; Summaries in English. 1948. irreg. (1-2/yr.), latest vol.44, 2003. price varies. back issues avail. **Document type:** *Monographic series, Academic/Scholarly.* **Description:** Covers the biological, geological, and paleontological research of Limburg.
Indexed: BIOSIS Prev, BiolAb, RevApplEntom, ZooRec.
—CISTI.
Published by: (Natuurhistorisch Genootschap in Limburg), Publicatie Bureau N H G, Groenstraat 106, Melick, 6074 EL, Netherlands. TEL 31-475-537095. R&P A Lenders. Circ: 1,000.

NAUKOVE TOVARYSTVO IMENI SHEVCHENKA. PROCEEDINGS OF THE SECTION OF CHEMISTRY, BIOLOGY AND MEDICINE. see *CHEMISTRY*

NEUROBIOLOGICAL RESEARCH. see *MEDICAL SCIENCES—Psychiatry And Neurology*

NEUROBIOLOGY OF LEARNING AND MEMORY. see *MEDICAL SCIENCES—Psychiatry And Neurology*

▼ **NEURODEGENERATIVE DISEASES.** see *MEDICAL SCIENCES—Gastroenterology*

NEURON. see *MEDICAL SCIENCES—Psychiatry And Neurology*

▼ **NEURON GLIA BIOLOGY.** see *MEDICAL SCIENCES—Psychiatry And Neurology*

NEW DEVELOPMENTS IN BIOSCIENCES. see *MEDICAL SCIENCES*

578.77 551.46 USA
NEW YORK SEA GRANT INSTITUTE. REPORT SERIES. Text in English. irreg.
Published by: New York Sea Grant Institute, 121 Discovery Hall, State University of New York at Stony Brook, Stony Brook, NY 11794-5001. TEL 516-632-9124, FAX 631-632-6917, nyseagrant@stonybrook.edu, http://www.seagrant.sunysb.edu/.

577 NZL ISSN 0110-6465
QH540 CODEN: NZJED6
➤ **NEW ZEALAND JOURNAL OF ECOLOGY.** Text in English. 1953. s-a. free to members. adv. bk.rev. 21 year cum.index. back issues avail. **Document type:** *Journal, Academic/Scholarly.* **Description:** Publishes scientific studies of ecology in, or relevant to, New Zealand.
Formerly: New Zealand Ecological Society. Proceedings (0077-9946)
Related titles: Microfiche ed.: (from IDC).

▼ new title ➤ refereed ✶ unverified ◆ full entry avail.

Indexed: ASCA, ASFA, ApEcolAb, ApicAb, B&BAb, BIOSIS Prev, BioCN&I, BiolAb, CPA, CRFR, ChemAb, CurCont, DSA, ESPM, EntAb, ExcerpMed, FCA, FPA, ForAb, GEOBASE, GenetAb, HGA, HerbAb, HortAb, ISR, IndVet, NemAb, NutrAb, PGegResA, PN&I, PollutAb, PoultAb, RPP, RRTA, RevApplEntom, S&F, SCI, SFA, SWRA, SeedAb, VetBull, WeedAb, WildRev, ZooRec.
—BLDSC (6093.530000), CASDDS, CISTI, IDS, IE, ingenta, Linda Hall. **CCC.**
Published by: New Zealand Ecological Society, Inc., PO Box 25 178, Christchurch, New Zealand. info@nzes.org.nz, http://www.nzes.org.nz/nzje/. Eds. Duane Peltzer, Peter Bellingham. adv.: page NZD 200. Circ: 700.

➤ **NEW ZEALAND JOURNAL OF MARINE AND FRESHWATER RESEARCH.** see *EARTH SCIENCES—Oceanography*

B

578.77 NZL ISSN 1170-8352
NEW ZEALAND MARINE SCIENCES SOCIETY REVIEW. Text in English. 1961. a. NZD 45 membership (effective 2005). adv. bk.rev. bibl. **Document type:** *Academic/Scholarly.*
Former titles (until no.33, 1991): New Zealand Marine Sciences Society News (0112-8396); New Zealand Marine Sciences Newsletter (0028-842X)
Related titles: Online - full content ed.
Indexed: SFA.
Published by: New Zealand Marine Sciences Society, c/o Alison MacDiarmid, NIWA, PO Box 14-901, Wellington, New Zealand. secretary@nzmss.rsnz.org, http://nzmss.rsnz.org/. Circ: 300 (controlled). **Subscr. to:** c/o Brian Paavo, NZMSS Membership, Portobello Marine Laboratory, Portobello, P.O.Box 8, Dunedin, New Zealand. paavo@wormguy.com.

570 NZL ISSN 0113-7492
CODEN: NZNSEZ
➤ **NEW ZEALAND NATURAL SCIENCES.** Text in English. 1973. a. NZD 18 to individuals; NZD 25 to libraries; USD 20 foreign (effective 2005). bk.rev. **Document type:** *Journal, Academic/Scholarly.* **Description:** Documents scientific research in the earth, life and environmental sciences relevant to New Zealand or Antarctica.
Formerly (until 1988): Mauri Ora (0302-086X)
Indexed: BIOSIS Prev, BiolAb, ExcerpMed, MinerAb, SFA, WildRev, ZooRec.
—BLDSC (6096.315000), CASDDS, CISTI, IE, ingenta, Linda Hall. **CCC.**
Published by: University of Canterbury, School of Biological Sciences, Private Bag 4800, Christchurch, New Zealand. TEL 64-3-3642860, FAX 64-3-3642024, natsci@zool.canterbury.ac.nz. Ed. Tanya Blakely. Circ: 260.

➤ **NEWS FROM HUDSONIA.** see *ENVIRONMENTAL STUDIES*

570.7 NLD ISSN 1389-9082
NICHE - BULLETIN VOOR NET ANDER WIJS IN DE BIOLOGIE. Text in Dutch. 1969. bi-m. EUR 40 (effective 2005). adv. **Document type:** *Bulletin.*
Former titles (until 1999): Bulletin voor het Onderwijs in de Biologie (0166-512X); (until 1979): Bulletin voor Docenten in de Biologie (0921-5530)
Published by: Nederlands Instituut voor Biologie, Postbus 19245, Utrecht, 3501 DE, Netherlands. TEL 31-30-2369244, niche@nibi.nl, nibi@nibi.nl, http://www.nibi.nl. Ed. Jaap Rodenburg.

570 JPN
NICHII SEIBUTSUGAKU KYOKAI KAIHO/ASSOCIAZIONE BIOLOGICA ITALO-GIAPPONESE BOLLETTINO. Text in English, Japanese. 1979. a.
Published by: Nichii Seibutsugaku Kyokai/Associazione Biologica Italo-Giapponese, Nagoya Daigaku Rigakubu Rinkai Jikkenjo, Furo-cho, Chikusa-ku, Nagoya-shi, Aichi-ken 464-0814, Japan.

NIHON BAIOREORIJI GAKKAI NENKAI SHOROKUSHU/JAPANESE SOCIETY OF BIORHEOLOGY. ABSTRACTS OF THE ANNUAL MEETING. see *BIOLOGY—Abstracting, Bibliographies, Statistics*

NIHON BENTOSU GAKKAI TAIKAI/JAPANESE ASSOCIATION OF BENTHOLOGY. ABSTRACTS OF ANNUAL MEETING. see *BIOLOGY—Abstracting, Bibliographies, Statistics*

570 JPN ISSN 0289-4548
NIHON BENTOSU GAKKAISHI/BENTHOS RESEARCH. Text in English, Japanese; Summaries in English. 1970. s-a. JPY 4,000 to individuals; JPY 8,000 to institutions. **Description:** Contains research articles related to benthic biologies, such as ecology, taxonomy, fisheries and conservation biology.
Indexed: ZooRec.
—BLDSC (1892.075000), IE, ingenta.
Published by: Nihon Bentosu Gakkai/Japanese Association of Benthology, Ocean Research Institute, University of, Minami-Dai, Nakano-ku, Tokyo, 164-0014, Japan. TEL 81-3-5351-6469, FAX 81-3-3375-6716, sirayama@ori.u-tokyo.ac.jp. Circ: 500 (paid).

570.88 JPN
NIHON BUNSHI SEIBUTSU GAKKAI KAIHO/BIOLOGY MOLECULAR SOCIETY OF JAPAN. BULLETIN. Text in Japanese. 3/yr.
Related titles: Online - full content ed.
Published by: Nihon Bunshi Seibutsu Gakkai/Biology Molecular Society of Japan, Nihon Gakkai Jimu Senta, 5-16-9 Hon-Komagome, Bunkyo-ku, Tokyo, 113-8622, Japan. TEL 81-3-5814-5810, FAX 81-3-5814-5825, mbsj-mem@bcasj.or.jp, http://wwwsoc.nii.ac.jp/mbsj/index.html.

578.77 JPN ISSN 0387-8961
NIHON PURANKUTON GAKKAIHO/PLANKTON SOCIETY OF JAPAN. BULLETIN. Text in Japanese. 1953. s-a. JPY 6,000 membership (effective 2004). adv. bk.rev. **Document type:** *Bulletin, Academic/Scholarly.* **Description:** Covers all aspects of zoo- and phytoplankton in marine, freshwater, brackish and airborne environments.
Formerly (until 1967): Nihon Purankuton Kenkyu Renrakukaiho (0549-4109)
Indexed: ASFA, Agrind, BiolAb, ESPM, GEOBASE, JPI, RefZh, SWRA, ZooRec.
—BLDSC (2684.150000), CISTI. **CCC.**
Published by: Plankton Society of Japan/Nihon Purankuton Gakkai, c/o Tokyo University of Marine Science and Technology, 4-5-7 Kounan, Minato-ku, Tokyo, 108-8477, Japan. plankton@s.kaiyodai.ac.jp, http://www.plankton.jp/sub07.html. Circ: 700.

570.9 JPN ISSN 0067-8716
NIHON SEIBUTSU CHIRI GAKKAI KAIHO/BIOGEOGRAPHICAL SOCIETY OF JAPAN. BULLETIN. Text in English, Japanese; Summaries in English. 1928. a. JPY 4,000 newsstand/cover (effective 2005). **Document type:** *Bulletin, Academic/Scholarly.*
Indexed: AbHyg, ApicAb, BIOSIS Prev, BioCN&I, BiolAb, ForAb, HelmAb, HortAb, IndVet, OrnHort, S&F, TDB, ZooRec.
—CCC.
Published by: Biogeographical Society of Japan/Nippon Seibutsu Chiri Gakkai, Gifu University, Faculty Of Regional Studies, Yanagido 1-1, Gifu, 501-1193, Japan. TEL 81-58-2933027, FAX 81-58-2933008, biogeo-mukai@nifty.com, http://wwwsoc.nii.ac.jp/tbsj/publication/bulBSJ01.htm. Ed. Seiroku Sakai.

577 JPN ISSN 0289-2421
NIHON SEITAI GAKKAI KANTO CHIKUKAI KAIHO/ECOLOGICAL SOCIETY OF JAPAN. KANTO BRANCH. NEWS. Text in Japanese. 1961. a.
Published by: Nihon Seitai Gakkai, Kanto Chikukai/Ecological Society of Japan, Kanto Branch, Tukuba Norin Kenkyu, Danchinai Yubinkyoku Shishobako, P.O. Box 16, Norin Suisansho, 305, Japan.

577 JPN
NIHON SEITAI GAKKAI KYUSHU CHIKUKAI KAIHO/ECOLOGICAL SOCIETY OF JAPAN. KYUSHU BRANCH. BULLETIN. Text in Japanese. q.
Published by: Nihon Seitai Gakkai Kyushu Chikukai/Ecological Society of Japan, Kyushu Branch, Kyushu Daigaku Rigakubu Fuzoku Amakusa Rinkai Jikkenjo, 2331 Tomioka, Amakusa-gun, Reihoku-machi, Kumamoto-ken 863-2507, Japan.

577 JPN
NIHON SEITAI GAKKAI TOHOKU CHIKUKAI KAIHO/ECOLOGICAL SOCIETY OF JAPAN. TOHOKU BRANCH. NEWS. Text in Japanese. 1931. a. **Document type:** *Newspaper.*
Published by: Nihon Seitai Gakkai, Tohoku Chikukai/Ecological Society of Japan, Tohoku Branch, Tohoku Daigaku Rigakubu Seibutsugaku Kyoshitsu, Aoba, Aramaki, Aoba-ku, Sendai-shi, Miyagi-ken 981-0945, Japan. Ed. Moritaka Nishihra. Circ: 220.

571.7 JPN ISSN 0916-958X
NIHON SHOKUBUTSU BYORI GAKKAI BAIOKONTORORU KENKYUKAI KOEN YOSHI/PHYTOPATHOLOGICAL SOCIETY OF JAPAN. ABSTRACTS OF THE MEETING OF BIOCONTROL. Text in Japanese. 1989. a. JPY 1,000. **Document type:** *Abstract/Index.*
Published by: Nihon Shokubutsu Byori Gakkai, Baiokontororu Kenkyukai/Phytopathological Society of Japan, Research Group for Biocontrol, c/o Shokubo Bldg, 1-43-11 Komagome, Toshima-ku, Tokyo, 170-0003, Japan. TEL 03-3943-6021. Circ: 400.

570 JPN ISSN 0387-8236
CODEN: NDRHE4
NIIGATA DAIGAKU RIGAKUBU FUZOKU SADO RINKAI JIKKENJO TOKUBETSU HOKOKU/NIIGATA UNIVERSITY. SADO MARINE BIOLOGICAL STATION. SPECIAL PUBLICATION. Text in Japanese; Summaries in English, Japanese. 1978. irreg.
Indexed: ASFA, BIOSIS Prev, BiolAb, ESPM, SFA.
Published by: (Fuzoku Sado Rinkai Jikkenjo), Niigata Daigaku, Rigakubu/Niigata University, Faculty of Science, 8050 Igarashi Nino-cho, Niigata-shi, Nigata-ken 950-21, Japan.

570 JPN ISSN 1343-1633
QH91.A1 CODEN: NRFHE8
➤ **NIIGATA UNIVERSITY. SADO MARINE BIOLOGICAL STATION. ANNUAL ACTIVITY REPORT/NIIGATA DAIGAKU RIGAKUBU FUZOKU SADO RINKAI JIKKENJO KENKYU HOKOKU.** Text and summaries in English. 1971. a. per issue exchange basis. bibl. **Document type:** *Academic/Scholarly.*
Former titles (until 1997): Niigata University. Sado Marine Biological Station. Report (0289-6389); (until 1984): Sado Marine Biological Station. Annual Report (0388-0117)
Related titles: CD-ROM ed.; Online - full text ed.
Indexed: ASFA, BiolAb, ESPM, SFA, ZooRec.
Published by: Niigata Daigaku, Rigakubu Fuzoku Sado Rinkai Jikkenjo/Niigata University, Sado Marine Biological Station, 2-8050 Igarashi, Niigata, 950-21, Japan. TEL 0259-75-2012, FAX 0259-75-2012. Ed. Yoshiharu Honma. Circ: 600 (controlled).

570.7 JPN ISSN 0388-7154
➤ **NIIGATAKEN SEIBUTSU KYOIKU KENKYUKAISHI/NIIGATA PREFECTURAL BIOLOGICAL SOCIETY FOR EDUCATION. BULLETIN.** Text in Japanese. 1964. a. JPY 4,500; USD 40 foreign. bibl.; charts; illus. back issues avail. **Document type:** *Bulletin, Academic/Scholarly.* **Description:** Articles in general biology, botany, zoology, natural history, particularly local oruganismus, letters and communications.
Published by: Niigataken Seibutsu Kyoiku Kenkyukai, c/o Mr Akiyama, Niigata Kenritsu Niigata Chuo Koto Gakko, 5314-1, Gakkocho Dori Nibancho, Niigata-shi, Niigata-ken 951, Japan. TEL 025-266-5161, FAX 025-265-0235. Ed. Yoshiharu Honma. Pub. Hiroshi Matsui. Circ: 350 (paid).

570 JPN ISSN 0911-6788
NIPPON BISEIBUTSU KABU HOZON RENMEI KAISHI/JAPAN FEDERATION FOR CULTURE COLLECTIONS. BULLETIN. Text in English, Japanese. 1985. s-a.
Published by: Nippon Biseibutsu Kabu Hozon Renmei/Japan Federation for Culture Collections, Nogyo Daigaku Sogo Kenkyujo, Kinkabu Hozonshitsu, 1-1 Sakuragaoka 1-chome, Setagaya-ku, Tokyo, 156-0054, Japan. TEL 03-420-2131.

NIPPON SEITAI GAKKAISHI/JAPANESE JOURNAL OF ECOLOGY. see *ENVIRONMENTAL STUDIES*

570 JPN ISSN 0029-0750
NISSEIKEN TAYORI/NIPPON INSTITUTE FOR BIOLOGICAL SCIENCE. JOURNAL. Text in Japanese. 1955. m. looseleaf. free. bk.rev. charts; illus. cum.index. **Document type:** *Newsletter.* **Description:** Summary of research activities in the institute; articles for technical extension; and records of the semi-annual seminar held by the Pathology Division of the Japanese Society for Veterinary Science.
Published by: Nippon Seibutsu Kagaku Kenkyujo/Nippon Institute for Biological Science, 2221-1 Shin-Machi, Ome-shi, Tokyo-to 198-0024, Japan. TEL 81-428-33-1001, FAX 81-429-31-6166, nibs@group.lin.go.jp, http://group.lin.go.jp/nibs/. Ed. Hiromasa Tanaka. Circ: 1,600.

NOGYO KANKYO GIJUTSU KENKYUSHO HOKOKU/NATIONAL INSTITUTE FOR AGRO-ENVIRONMENTAL SCIENCES. BULLETIN. see *AGRICULTURE*

570 JPN ISSN 0911-6575
CODEN: NSSHEC
NOGYO SEIBUTSU SHIGEN KENKYUJO KENKYU HOKOKU/NATIONAL INSTITUTE OF AGROBIOLOGICAL RESOURCES. BULLETIN. Text in English, Japanese. 1985. a. per issue exchange basis. **Document type:** *Bulletin.*
Indexed: AgBio, Agrind, AnBrAb, BioCN&I, BiolAb, CIN, CPA, ChemAb, ChemTitl, FCA, FaBeAb, HortAb, MaizeAb, NutrAb, PBA, PGegResA, PN&I, PoultAb, RA&MP, RPP, RefZh, RevApplEntom, RiceAb, S&F, SeedAb, SoyAb, TriticAb, VITIS, VetBull.
—BLDSC (2640.010000), CASDDS, CISTI, IE, Linda Hall.
Published by: Norin Suisansho, Nogyo Seibutsu Shigen Kenkyujo/Ministry of Agriculture, Forestry and Fisheries, National Institute of Agrobiological Resources, 2-1-2 Kannondai, Tsukuba-shi, Ibaraki-ken 305-0856, Japan. TEL 0298-38-7004, FAX 0298-38-7408. Ed. Kenji Takayanagi.

570 JPN ISSN 0915-6836
S494.5.B563
NOGYO SEIBUTSU SHIGEN KENKYUJO KENKYU SHIRYO/NATIONAL INSTITUTE OF AGROBIOLOGICAL RESOURCES. MISCELLANEOUS PUBLICATION. Text in English, Japanese. 1989. irreg.
Published by: Norin Suisansho, Nogyo Seibutsu Shigen Kenkyujo/Ministry of Agriculture, Forestry and Fisheries, National Institute of Agrobiological Resources, 2-1-2 Kannondai, Tsukuba-shi, Ibaraki-ken 305-0856, Japan.

570 JPN ISSN 0911-9590
S494.5.B563
NOGYO SEIBUTSU SHIGEN KENKYUJO NENPO/NATIONAL INSTITUTE OF AGROBIOLOGICAL RESOURCES. ANNUAL REPORT. Text in Japanese. a.
Published by: Norin Suisansho, Nogyo Seibutsu Shigen Kenkyujo/Ministry of Agriculture, Forestry and Fisheries, National Institute of Agrobiological Resources, 2-1-2 Kannondai, Tsukuba-shi, Ibaraki-ken 305-0856, Japan.

570 JPN ISSN 0289-9248
NOGYO SEIBUTSU SHIGEN KENKYUJO NYUSU/NATIONAL INSTITUTE OF AGROBIOLOGICAL RESOURCES. NEWS. Text in Japanese. 1984. q.
Published by: Norin Suisansho, Nogyo Seibutsu Shigen Kenkyujo/Ministry of Agriculture, Forestry and Fisheries, National Institute of Agrobiological Resources, 2-1-2 Kannondai, Tsukuba-shi, Ibaraki-ken 305-0856, Japan.

NONLINEAR DYNAMICS, PSYCHOLOGY, AND LIFE SCIENCES. see *PSYCHOLOGY*

570 910 FIN ISSN 0356-0910
AS262
NORDENSKIOLD-SAMFUNDETS TIDSKRIFT. Text in Swedish. 1941. a. EUR 20. bk.rev. Index. **Document type:** *Academic/Scholarly.* **Description:** Deals with the natural sciences regarding the coastal areas and archipelagoes of Finland, the Baltic Sea and the arctic areas.
Published by: Nordenskiold-Samfundet i Finland, c/o Department of Ecology and Systematics, Unionsgatan 44, University of Helsinki, PL 7, Helsinki, 00014, Finland. TEL 358-9-191-86-01, FAX 358-9-191-86-56, carl-adam.haeggstrom@helsinki.fi. Ed. Carl Adam Haeggstrom. Circ: 400.

578.777 CAN
NORTH AMERICAN BENTHOLOGICAL SOCIETY. BULLETIN. Text in English. 1984. 3/yr. USD 35. adv. bk.rev. abstr.; bibl. index. **Document type:** *Bulletin, Academic/Scholarly.* **Description:** Promotes better understanding of the benthic biological community and its role in aquatics ecosystems. Communicates information about society functions and activities, including abstracts of meetings.
Published by: North American Benthological Society, c/o Donna Giberson, Sec, Dept of Biology, University of Prince Edward Island, Charlottetown, PE C1A 4P3, Canada. TEL 902-566-0797, FAX 902-566-0740. Ed. Steven Canton. **Subscr. to:** NABS, PO Box 1897, Lawrence, KS 66044-8897. TEL 800-627-0629.

578.777 CAN ISSN 0887-3593
QL141 CODEN: JNASEC
➤ **NORTH AMERICAN BENTHOLOGICAL SOCIETY. JOURNAL.** Text in English. 1982. q. USD 125; USD 180 combined subscription print & online eds (effective 2004). back issues avail. **Document type:** *Journal, Academic/Scholarly.* **Description:** Promotes better understanding of the biotic communities of lake and stream bottoms and their role in aquatic ecosystems.
Formerly (until 1986): Freshwater Invertebrate Biology (0738-2189)
Related titles: Online - full text ed.: (from BioOne, C S A, EBSCO Publishing).
Indexed: ASCA, ASFA, AnBeAb, AnBrAb, ApEcolAb, BIOBASE, BIOSIS Prev, BiolAb, BiolDig, CivEngAb, CurCont, ESPM, EntAb, FPA, ForAb, GEOBASE, HelmAb, HerbAb, I&DA, IABS, ISR, NutrAb, PollutAb, RM&VM, RRTA, RevApplEntom, S&F, SCI, SFA, SWRA, WeedAb, WildRev, ZooRec.
—BLDSC (4833.740000), IE, Infotrieve, ingenta, Linda Hall. **CCC.**
Published by: North American Benthological Society, c/o Donna Giberson, Sec, Dept of Biology, University of Prince Edward Island, Charlottetown, PE C1A 4P3, Canada. TEL 902-566-0797, FAX 902-566-0740, orders@allenpress.com, http://www.benthos.org, http://www.allenpress.com. Ed. David Rosenberg. **Subscr. in US to:** Allen Press Inc., PO Box 1897, Lawrence, KS 66044.

➤ **NOTICIAS DE GALAPAGOS.** see *SCIENCES: COMPREHENSIVE WORKS*

570 CUB
NOTICIERO CIENTIFICO. SERIE: BIOLOGIA. Text in Spanish. forth.
Published by: Academia de Ciencias, Instituto de Documentacion e Informacion Cientifico-Tecnica (I D I C T), Capitolio Nacional, Prado y San Jose, Habana, 2, Cuba.

570 NLD ISSN 0166-6584
QL520 CODEN: NOODDJ
NOTULAE ODONATOLOGICAE. Text in English, French, German, Italian, Spanish. 1978. s-a. bk.rev. charts. **Document type:** *Bulletin.*
Indexed: ASFA, BIOSIS Prev, BiolAb, ESPM, ZooRec.
—BLDSC (6176.010000).
Published by: Societas Internationalis Odonatologica/International Odonatological Foundation, c/o Mrs. M.Kiauta, PO Box 256, Bilthoven, 3720 AG, Netherlands. Circ: 500.

NOVA THALASSIA. see *EARTH SCIENCES—Oceanography*

NUCLEAR MEDICINE AND BIOLOGY. see *MEDICAL SCIENCES—Radiology And Nuclear Medicine*

572.8 GBR ISSN 1478-1336
▼ ➤ **NUCLEAR RECEPTOR.** Text in English. 2003. m. free (effective 2006). **Document type:** *Journal, Academic/Scholarly.* **Description:** Aims to integrate knowledge regarding nuclear receptor signalling molecules from a wide range of sources.
Media: Online - full content (from EBSCO Publishing, National Library of Medicine).
Indexed: ExcerpMed.
—**CCC.**
Published by: BioMed Central Ltd. (Subsidiary of: Current Science Ltd), Middlesex House, 34-42 Cleveland St, London, W1T 4LB, United Kingdom. TEL 44-20-76319131, FAX 44-20-76319923, info@biomedcentral.com, http://www.nuclear-receptor.com, http://www.biomedcentral.com. Ed. Colin Palmer.

➤ **NUKADA INSTITUTE FOR MEDICAL AND BIOLOGICAL RESEARCH. REPORTS.** see *MEDICAL SCIENCES*

➤ **LA NUOVA ECOLOGIA**; il mensile dei verdi e dei consumatori. see *ENVIRONMENTAL STUDIES*

571.9 BGR ISSN 0324-1998
CODEN: OSPADK
OBSTA I SRAVNITELNA PATOLOGIIA. Text in Multiple languages. 1976. s-a. price varies. reprint service avail. from IRC.
Indexed: ABSML, BSLBiol, BiolAb, ChemAb, ExcerpMed, IndVet, PoultAb, VetBull.
—CASDDS, GNLM, KNAW. **CCC.**
Published by: (Bulgarska Akademiya na Naukite/Bulgarian Academy of Sciences), Universitetsko Izdatelstvo Sv. Kliment Okhridski/Publishing House of the Sofia University St. Kliment Ohridski, Akad G Bonchev 6, Sofia, 1113, Bulgaria. Circ: 500.

OCEAN BIOCOENOSIS SERIES. see *EARTH SCIENCES—Oceanography*

578.77 USA
OCEANIC INSTITUTE. ANNUAL REPORT. Text in English. a.
Published by: Oceanic Institute, 41-202 Kalanianaole Hwy, Waimanalo, HI 96795. FAX 808-259-5971, http://www.oceanicinstitute.org.

OCEANIDES. see *EARTH SCIENCES—Oceanography*

578.77 ZAF ISSN 0078-320X
GC1 CODEN: ORIIAX
➤ **OCEANOGRAPHIC RESEARCH INSTITUTE. INVESTIGATIONAL REPORT.** Text in English. 1961. irreg., latest vol.71, 1997. per issue exchange basis. back issues avail. **Document type:** *Academic/Scholarly.* **Description:** Presents detailed results of current marine biological research.
Indexed: ASFA, BiolAb, ESPM, SFA, ZooRec.
—BLDSC (4560.120000).
Published by: Oceanographic Research Institute, Marine Parade, PO Box 10712, Durban, KwaZulu-Natal 4056, South Africa. TEL 27-31-3373536, FAX 27-31-3372132, ori@ori.org.za, http://www.ori.org.za. Ed. R. P. Van der Elst. R&P R P Van der Elst. Circ: 400 (controlled). **Co-sponsor:** South African Association for Marine Biological Research.

➤ **OCEANOGRAPHY AND MARINE BIOLOGY**; an annual review. see *EARTH SCIENCES—Oceanography*

➤ **OCHANOMIZU UNIVERSITY. TATEYAMA MARINE LABORATORY. CONTRIBUTIONS.** see *EARTH SCIENCES—Oceanography*

➤ **OCROTIREA NATURII SI A MEDIULUI INCONJURATOR.** see *SCIENCES: COMPREHENSIVE WORKS*

570 NLD ISSN 0375-0183
QL520 CODEN: ODTGAI
ODONATOLOGICA. Text in English, French, German. 1972. q. bk.rev. charts. **Document type:** *Journal, Academic/Scholarly.*
Indexed: ASFA, AnBeAb, BIOSIS Prev, BiolAb, CurCont, EntAb, GEOBASE, ZooRec.
Published by: Societas Internationalis Odonatologica/International Odonatological Foundation, c/o Mrs. M.Kiauta, PO Box 256, Bilthoven, 3720 AG, Netherlands. http://www.afn.org/~iori/siointro.html. Circ: 500.

577 DEU ISSN 0029-8549
QH540 CODEN: OECOBX
➤ **OECOLOGIA.** Text in English. 1924. 16/yr. EUR 3,898 combined subscription to institutions print & online eds. (effective 2005). adv. bibl.; illus. index. back issues avail.; reprint service avail. from PSC,ISI. **Document type:** *Journal, Academic/Scholarly.* **Description:** Presents articles on research developments in the functional relationships between plant and animal organisms and their environment.
Formerly: Zeitschrift fuer Morphologie und Oekologie der Tiere
Related titles: Microform ed.: (from PQC); Online - full text ed.: ISSN 1432-1939 (from EBSCO Publishing, Springer LINK, Swets Information Services).
Indexed: AEA, ASCA, ASFA, AgBio, Agr, AgrForAb, AnBeAb, AnBrAb, ApEcolAb, ApicAb, B&AI, BIOBASE, BIOSIS Prev, BibAg, BioCN&I, BiolAb, CPA, CRFR, CurCont, DSA, ESPM, EntAb, ExcerpMed, FCA, FPA, ForAb, GEOBASE, GenetAb, HGA, HelmAb, HerbAb, HortAb, I&DA, IABS, ISR, IndVet, KWIWR, MBA, MaizeAb, NemAb, NutrAb, OceAb, OrnHort, PBA, PGegResA, PGrRegA, PHN&I, PN&I, PlantSci, PoultAb, ProtozoAb, RA&MP, RM&VM, RPP, RefZh, RevApplEntom, RiceAb, S&F, SCI, SFA, SIA, SWRA, SeedAb, SoyAb, TriticAb, VITIS, VetBull, WAE&RSA, WeedAb, WildRev, ZooRec.
—BLDSC (6235.262600), CISTI, IDS, IE, Infotrieve, ingenta, Linda Hall. **CCC.**
Published by: (International Association for Ecology, (Intecol) NLD), Springer-Verlag (Subsidiary of: Springer Science+Business Media), Tiergartenstr 17, Heidelberg, 69121, Germany. TEL 49-6221-3450, FAX 49-6221-345229, http://link.springer.de/link/service/journals/00442/index.htm. Eds. Christian Koerner, Craig W Osenberg, James R Ehleringer, Roland Brandl. Adv. contact Stephan Kroeck TEL 49-30-827875739. **Subscr. in the Americas to:** Springer-Verlag New York, Inc., Journal Fulfillment, PO Box 2485, Secaucus, NJ 07096-2485. TEL 800-777-4643, 201-348-4033, FAX 201-348-4505, journals@springer-ny.com, http://www.springer-ny.com; **Subscr. to:** Springer GmbH Auslieferungsgesellschaft, Haberstr 7, Heidelberg 69126, Germany. TEL 49-6221-345-0, FAX 49-6221-345-4229, subscriptions@springer.de.

502.7 581.5 SVK ISSN 1210-3209
OECOLOGIA MONTANA. Text in English. 1992. s-a.
Indexed: ASFA, AgrForAb, ApEcolAb, BIOSIS Prev, BiolAb, CPA, ESPM, EntAb, ForAb, HerbAb, PollutAb, PoultAb, S&F, SWRA, WAE&RSA.
Published by: (Tatransky Narodny Park/High Tatras National Park), Prunella Publishers, Jarmocna 1298/16, Poprad, 05801, Slovakia. kpl@vsld.tuzvo.cs. Eds. Marian Janiga, R Soltes.

578.77 AUT ISSN 0257-3113
OESTERREICHISCHE AKADEMIE DER WISSENSCHAFT. INSTITUT FUER LIMNOLOGIE. BIOLOGISCHE STATION LUNZ. JAHRESBERICHT. Text in German. 1978. a. **Document type:** *Yearbook, Academic/Scholarly.*
Indexed: ESPM.
Published by: Oesterreichische Akademie der Wissenschaft, Institut fuer Limnologie, Biologische Station Lunz, Seehof 4, Lunz am See, 3293, Austria. TEL 43-7486-8095, FAX 43-7486-809531, office.bsl@oeaw.ac.at, http://www.bsl.oeaw.ac.at/station/index.htm.

B

548 AUT ISSN 0723-791X
OESTERREICHISCHE AKADEMIE DER WISSENSCHAFTEN. ABTEILUNG 1: BIOLOGISCHE WISSENSCHAFTEN UND ERDWISSENSCHAFTEN. SITZUNGSBERICHTE UND ANZEIGER. Text in German. 1861. irreg. price varies. **Document type:** *Monographic series, Academic/Scholarly.*
Former titles: Oesterreichische Akademie der Wissenschaften. Mathematisch - Naturwissenschaftliche Klasse. Abteilung 1: Biologie, Mineralogie, Erdkunde und Verwandte Wissenschaften. Sitzungsberichte (0029-8808); (until 1946): Akademie der Wissenschaften in Wien. Mathematisch - Naturwissenschaftliche Klasse. Abteilung 1: Mineralogie, Biologie, Erdkunde. Sitzungsberichte (0371-4810)
Related titles: Online - full text ed.: ISSN 1728-0540 (from Swets Information Services).
Indexed: ZooRec.
—CISTI, Linda Hall. **CCC.**
Published by: Verlag der Oesterreichischen Akademie der Wissenschaften, Postgasse 7/4, Vienna, W 1011, Austria. TEL 43-1-515813402, FAX 43-1-515813400, verlag@oeaw.ac.at, http://verlag.oeaw.ac.at.

570 USA ISSN 0078-3994
QH105.O3 CODEN: BOBNAJ
➤ **OHIO BIOLOGICAL SURVEY. BULLETIN. NEW SERIES.** Text in English. 1913; N.S. 1959. irreg., latest vol.13, no.1, 1998. price varies. **Document type:** *Monographic series, Academic/Scholarly.*
Indexed: BIOSIS Prev, BiolAb, SFA, WildRev, ZooRec.
—CISTI, Linda Hall.
Published by: Ohio Biological Survey, 5530 Olentangy River Rd., Columbus, OH 43235-3444. TEL 614-292-9645, FAX 614-688-4322. Ed. Veda M Cafazzo. Circ: 1,000.

570 USA ISSN 1074-9233
➤ **OHIO BIOLOGICAL SURVEY. MISCELLANEOUS CONTRIBUTIONS.** Text in English. 1994. irreg., latest vol.4, 1998. price varies. **Document type:** *Monographic series, Academic/Scholarly.*
Indexed: ZooRec.
Published by: Ohio Biological Survey, 5530 Olentangy River Rd., Columbus, OH 43235-3444. TEL 614-292-9645, FAX 614-688-4322. Ed. Veda M Cafazzo. Circ: 1,000.

570 USA ISSN 1097-1904
➤ **OHIO BIOLOGICAL SURVEY NOTES.** Text in English. 1998. irreg. (1-2/yr.). USD 5 per issue. charts; illus.; maps; stat. **Document type:** *Academic/Scholarly.*
Published by: Ohio Biological Survey, 5530 Olentangy River Rd., Columbus, OH 43235-3444. TEL 614-292-9645, FAX 614-688-4322, http://www.obs.biosci.ohio-state.edu. Pub. Brian J Armitage. R&P Veda M Catazzo. Circ: 1,000.

➤ **OHIO SEA GRANT COLLEGE PROGRAM. TECHNICAL SUMMARY.** see *FISH AND FISHERIES*

➤ **OIKOS**; a journal of ecology. see *ENVIRONMENTAL STUDIES*

570 JPN ISSN 0030-154X
QL801 CODEN: OFAJAE
➤ **OKAJIMA'S FOLIA ANATOMICA JAPONICA/OKAJIMA FORIA ANATOMIKA YAPONIKA.** Text in English. 1922. 5/yr. (May, Aug, Oct, Dec., March; no.2 & 3 combined). JPY 18,000. bk.rev. bibl.; illus. index. reprints avail. **Document type:** *Academic/Scholarly.* **Description:** Publishes original papers in all the fields of anatomical science, macroscopic anatomy, embryology, experimental morphology, physical anthropology, and macroscopic research methods.
Indexed: BIOSIS Prev, BiolAb, ChemAb, ChemTitl, DentInd, ExcerpMed, INIS AtomInd, IndMed, MEDLINE, ZooRec.
—BLDSC (6252.800000), CASDDS, GNLM, IE, Infotrieve, ingenta, Linda Hall.

Published by: Okajima Foria Anatomica Yaponika Henshubu, c/o Keio University, School of Medicine Dept of Anatomy, 35 Shinano-Machi, Shinjuku-ku, Tokyo, 160-8582, Japan. TEL 81-3-3353-1211, FAX 81-3-5360-1524. Ed. Sadakazu Aiso. Circ: 400. **Dist. by:** Japan Publications Trading Co., Ltd., Book Export II Dept, PO Box 5030, Tokyo International, Tokyo 101-3191, Japan. TEL 81-3-32923753, FAX 81-3-32920410, infoserials@jptco.co.jp, http://www.jptco.co.jp.

570 JPN ISSN 0916-930X
QH301 CODEN: OSSHEN
OKAYAMA DAIGAKU SHIGEN SEIBUTSU KAGAKU KENKYUJO HOKOKU/OKAYAMA UNIVERSITY. RESEARCH INSTITUTE FOR BIORESOURCES. BULLETIN. Text in English, Japanese. 1990. q. per issue exchange basis.
Formed by the merger of (1916-1990): Okayama Universitaet. Berichte des Ohara Instituts fuer Landwirtschaftliche Biologie (0365-9860); Which was formerly (until 1954): Okayama Universitaet. Berichte des Ohara Instituts fuer Landwirtschaftliche Forschungen (0365-9879); (1924-1990): Nogaku Kenkyu - Ohara Institute for Agricultural Biology. Report (0029-0874); Which was formerly: Nogaku Koenshu
Indexed: AgBio, Agr, BIOSIS Prev, BiolAb, CIN, CPA, ChemAb, ChemTitl, FCA, HortAb, MaizeAb, PBA, RPP, RefZh, RevApplEntom, RiceAb, SeedAb, SoyAb, TriticAb.
—CASDDS, CISTI, Linda Hall.
Published by: Okayama Daigaku, Shigen Seibutsu Kagaku Kenkyujo/Okayama University, Research Institute for Bioresources, 20-1 Chuo 2-chome, Kurashiki-shi, Okayama-ken 710-0046, Japan. Ed. Isao Aoyama. Circ: 875.

570 JPN ISSN 0917-5911
OKAZAKI KOKURITSU KYODO KENKYU KIKO KISO SEIBUTSUGAKU KENKYUJO KYODO KENKYU HOKOKUSHO/NATIONAL INSTITUTE FOR BASIC BIOLOGY, OKAZAKI NATIONAL RESEARCH INSTITUTES. JOINT RESEARCH REPORT. Text in Japanese. 1988. biennial.
Published by: Okazaki Kokuritsu Kyodo Kenkyu Kiko Kiso Seibutsugaku Kenkyujo/National Institute for Basic Biology, Okazaki National Research Institutes, 38 Saigonaka-Myodaijicho, Okazaki-shi, Aichi-ken 444-0000, Japan.

570 JPN
OKINAWA SEIBUTSU GAKKAI TSUSHIN/BIOLOGICAL SOCIETY OF OKINAWA NEWS. Text in Japanese. 1967. 2/yr. **Document type:** *Newsletter.*
Published by: Okinawa Seibutsu Gakkai/Biological Society of Okinawa, Ryukyu Daigaku Rigakubu, 1 Senbaru, Nakagami-gun, Nishihara-cho, Okinawa-ken 903-0129, Japan. FAX 81-98-895-5376. Ed. Michio Hidaka.

570 JPN ISSN 0474-0394
➤ **OKINAWA SEIBUTSU GAKKAISHI/BIOLOGICAL MAGAZINE OKINAWA.** Text in English, Japanese. 1964. a. JPY 4,000. **Document type:** *Bulletin, Academic/Scholarly.*
Indexed: JPI, ZooRec.
Published by: Okinawa Seibutsu Gakkai/Biological Society of Okinawa, Ryukyu Daigaku Rigakubu, 1 Senbaru, Nakagami-gun, Nishihara-cho, Okinawa-ken 903-0129, Japan. FAX 81-98-895-5376. Ed. Eishin Isa. Circ: 600.

➤ **OKINAWA TOSHO KENKYU/ISLAND STUDIES IN OKINAWA.** see *EARTH SCIENCES*

570 RUS ISSN 0475-1450
QH491 CODEN: ONGZAC
➤ **ONTOGENEZ.** Text in Russian. 1970. bi-m. RUR 770 for 6 mos. domestic (effective 2004). back issues avail. **Document type:** *Journal, Academic/Scholarly.* **Description:** Publishes fundamental and applied research papers and reviews on development, regeneration, and carcinogenesis at the molecular, cellular, and organismic levels.
Related titles: Microfilm ed.: (from PQC); Online - full text ed.; ◆ English Translation: Russian Journal of Developmental Biology. ISSN 1062-3604.
Indexed: BIOSIS Prev, BiolAb, ChemAb, ChemTitl, IndMed, MEDLINE, RefZh, ZooRec.
—BLDSC (0127.452000), CASDDS, CISTI, East View, GNLM, IE, Infotrieve, ingenta, KNAW, Linda Hall. **CCC.**
Published by: (Rossiiskaya Akademiya Nauk/Russian Academy of Sciences), Izdatel'stvo Nauka, Profsoyuznaya ul 90, Moscow, 117864, Russian Federation. TEL 7-095-3347151, FAX 7-095-4202220, secret@naukaran.ru, http://www.maik.rssi.ru/cgi-bin/list.pl?page=ont, http://www.naukaran.ru.

570 610 FRA ISSN 0992-5945
➤ **OPTION / BIO.** Text in French. 1989. 20/yr. EUR 127.33 domestic to individuals; EUR 152 in Europe to individuals; JPY 20,200 in Japan to individuals; USD 187 elsewhere to individuals; EUR 129.29 domestic to institutions; EUR 154 in Europe to institutions; JPY 17,200 in Japan to institutions; USD 186 elsewhere to institutions; EUR 74 in Europe to students; JPY 8,200 in Japan to students; USD 89 elsewhere to students (effective 2006). adv. back issues avail. **Document type:** *Academic/Scholarly.* **Description:** Provides day-to-day news, scientific information in the medical and biological areas, diagnostic approaches and technical viewpoints.
—IE. **CCC.**
Published by: Elsevier France, Editions Scientifiques et Medicales (Subsidiary of: Elsevier Science & Technology), 23 Rue Linois, Paris, 75724, France. TEL 33-1-71724600, FAX 33-1-71724650, http://www.elsevier.com/locate/optbio, http://www.elsevier.fr. Ed. Lylia Belloul. Circ: 6,800. **Subscr. to:** Elsevier BV, PO Box 211, Amsterdam 1000 AE, Netherlands. TEL 31-20-485-3757, FAX 31-20-485-3432.

➤ **OREGON STATE UNIVERSITY. SEA GRANT COLLEGE PROGRAM. PUBLICATIONS.** see *FISH AND FISHERIES*

571.3 DEU ISSN 1439-6092
QH301 CODEN: ODERAA
➤ **ORGANISMS DIVERSITY & EVOLUTION.** Text in English. 2001. 4/yr. EUR 131 in Europe to individuals; JPY 16,600 in Japan to individuals; USD 129 to individuals except Europe and Japan; EUR 302 to institutions; EUR 322 in Europe to institutions; JPY 43,000 in Japan to institutions; USD 347 to institutions except Europe and Japan (effective 2006). adv. **Document type:** *Journal, Academic/Scholarly.* **Description:** Devoted to the understanding of organismal diversity.
Related titles: Online - full text ed.: (from EBSCO Publishing, Gale Group, IngentaConnect, O C L C Online Computer Library Center, Inc., ScienceDirect, Swets Information Services).
Indexed: ASFA, ApEcolAb, B&BAb, BIOBASE, BIOSIS Prev, BiolAb, CurCont, ESPM, EntAb, GEOBASE, GenetAb, RefZh, ZooRec.
—BLDSC (6289.860000), CISTI, IE, Infotrieve, ingenta. **CCC.**
Published by: (Gesellschaft fuer Biologische Systematik), Elsevier GmbH, Urban & Fischer Verlag (Subsidiary of: Elsevier Science & Technology), Loebdergraben 14a, Jena, 07743, Germany. TEL 49-3641-626430, FAX 49-3641-626432, info@urbanfischer.de, http://www.elsevier.com/locate/ode, http://www.urbanfischer.de/journals. Eds. Gerhard Haszprunar, J.Wolfgang Waegele. R&P Martin Huber TEL 49-3641-626430. Adv. contact Sabine Schroeter TEL 49-3641-626445. B&W page EUR 485, color page EUR 1,430; 210 x 280. Circ: 650 (paid and controlled). **Non-German speaking countries subscr. to:** Nature Publishing Group, Brunel Rd, Houndmills, Basingstoke, Hamps RG21 6XS, United Kingdom. TEL 44-1256-302629, FAX 44-1256-476117

570 USA ISSN 0553-0342
ORGANIZATION OF AMERICAN STATES. DEPARTMENT OF SCIENTIFIC AFFAIRS. SERIE DE BIOLOGIA: MONOGRAFIAS. Text in Spanish. 1965. irreg., latest vol.20, 1978. USD 3.50 per issue. **Document type:** *Monographic series.*
Published by: Organization of American States/Organizacion de los Estados Americanos, Department of Publications, 1889 F St, N W, Washington, DC 20006. TEL 703-941-1617. Circ: 3,000.

572.38 578 NLD ISSN 0169-6149
QH325
➤ **ORIGINS OF LIFE AND EVOLUTION OF THE BIOSPHERE.** Text in Dutch. 1968. bi-m. EUR 588, USD 598, GBP 388 combined subscription to institutions print & online eds. (effective 2005). adv. bk.rev. bibl.; illus. reprint service avail. from PSC. **Document type:** *Journal, Academic/Scholarly.* **Description:** Publishes experimental and theoretical studies of chemical evolution, including evolution of planetary atmospheres, prebiotic chemistry and biochemical evolution.
Former titles: Origins of Life (0302-1688); (until 1974): Space Life Sciences (0038-6286)
Related titles: Microform ed.: (from PQC); Online - full text ed.: ISSN 1573-0875 (from EBSCO Publishing, Gale Group, IngentaConnect, Kluwer Online, O C L C Online Computer Library Center, Inc., Springer LINK, Swets Information Services).
Indexed: A&AAb, ASCA, ApMecR, BIOBASE, BIOSIS Prev, BibLing, BiolAb, ChemAb, ChemTitl, CurCont, EPB, ExcerpMed, GEOBASE, IAA, IBR, IBZ, ISR, IndMed, Inpharma, Inspec, M&GPA, MEDLINE, MSB, PhysBer, Reac, RefZh, SCI.
—BLDSC (6291.265100), AskIEEE, CASDDS, CISTI, GNLM, IDS, IE, Infotrieve, ingenta, Linda Hall. **CCC.**
Published by: (International Society for the Study of the Origins of Life), Springer-Verlag Dordrecht (Subsidiary of: Springer Science+Business Media), Van Godewijckstraat 30, Dordrecht, 3311 GX, Netherlands. TEL 31-78-6576050, FAX 31-78-6576474, http://springerlink.metapress.com/openurl.asp?genre=journal&issn=0169-6149, http://www.springeronline.com. Ed. Alan W Schwartz.

570 ESP ISSN 0213-4039
➤ **ORSIS.** Variant title: Organismes i Sistemes. Text in Catalan, English, French, Spanish. 1985. a. EUR 13.22 per issue (effective 2005). **Document type:** *Journal, Academic/Scholarly.* **Description:** Publishes original works and review articles on botany, zoology and ecology.
Indexed: BIOSIS Prev, BiolAb, IECT, ZooRec.
—CINDOC, KNAW.
Published by: (Universitat Autonoma de Barcelona, Facultat de Ciencies), Universitat Autonoma de Barcelona, Servei de Publicacions, Edifici A, Bellaterra, Cardanyola del Valles, 08193, Spain. TEL 34-93-5811022, FAX 34-93-5813239, sp@uab.es, http://www.uab.es/publicacions/.

➤ **ORYZA.** see *AGRICULTURE—Crop Production And Soil*

570 JPN ISSN 0389-9047
OSAKA-SHIRITSU SHIZENSHI HAKUBUTSUKAN SHUZO SHIRYO MOKUROKU/OSAKA MUSEUM OF NATURAL HISTORY. SPECIAL PUBLICATIONS. Text in Japanese. 1969. a. price varies; also avail. on exchange basis. **Document type:** *Catalog.*
Indexed: ZooRec.
—BLDSC (8379.670000).
Published by: Osaka-shiritsu Shizenshi Hakubutsukan/Osaka Museum of Natural History, 1-23 Nagaikoen, Higashisumiyoshi-ku, Osaka-shi, 546-0034, Japan. TEL 81-6-6697-6221, FAX 81-6-6697-6225, library@mus-nh.city.osaka.jp, http://www.mus-nh.city.osaka.jp. Ed. Takayoshi Nasu. Circ: 1,000.

570 GBR
OXFORD SERIES IN ECOLOGY AND EVOLUTION. Text in English. irreg., latest 2003. price varies. illus. **Document type:** *Monographic series.*
Published by: Oxford University Press, Great Clarendon St, Oxford, OX2 6DP, United Kingdom. TEL 44-1865-556767, FAX 44-1865-556646, enquiry@oup.co.uk, http://www.oup-usa.org/catalogs/general/series/Oxford_Series_in_Ecology_and_Evolution.html, http://www.oup.co.uk/. **Orders in N. America to:** Oxford University Press, 2001 Evans Rd, Cary, NC 27513. jnlorders@oup-usa.org.

570 USA ISSN 1544-9173
▼ ➤ **P L O S BIOLOGY.** Text in English. 2003 (Oct.). m. USD 160 (effective 2005). **Document type:** *Journal, Academic/Scholarly.* **Description:** Contains works of significance in all areas of biological science, from molecules to ecosystems, including works at the interface with other disciplines.
Related titles: Online - full text ed.: ISSN 1545-7885. free (effective 2005) (from EBSCO Publishing, National Library of Medicine).
Indexed: ASFA, AnBeAb, ApEcolAb, B&BAb, BCI, CurCont, ESPM, EntAb, ExcerpMed, GenetAb, RefZh.
—BLDSC (6539.556700), IE, Linda Hall.
Published by: Public Library of Science, 185 Berry St, Ste 1300, San Francisco, CA 94107. TEL 415-624-1200, plos@plos.org, http://www.plosbiology.org/plosonline/?request=index-html, http://www.publiclibraryofscience.org.

578.77 ECU ISSN 0255-4925
SH214.8
PACIFICO SUR. Variant title: Revista de la Comision Permanente del Pacifico Sur. Text in Spanish. 1971. irreg. free. back issues avail.
Published by: Comision Permanente del Pacifico Sur, Edificio Inmaral 1er Piso, Av Carlos Julio Arosemena, Km 3, Guayaquil, Ecuador. TEL 593-4-2221-202, FAX 593-4-2221-201, contact@cpps-int.org, http://www.cpps-int.org/. Circ: 1,000.

570 PAK ISSN 1028-8880
➤ **PAKISTAN JOURNAL OF BIOLOGICAL SCIENCES.** Text in English. 1998. m. **Document type:** *Journal, Academic/Scholarly.* **Description:** Subjects covered include: animal science, bacteriology, biological chemistry, forestry, genetics and molecular, biology, immunology and microbiology, plant and soil science, pharmacology and toxicology, virology, zoology and fisheries.
Related titles: Online - full text ed.: ISSN 1812-5735. free (effective 2005).
Indexed: FCA.
Published by: Asian Network for Scientific Information, 308-Lasani Town, Sargodha Rd, Faislabad, 38090, Pakistan. TEL 92-41-2001145, FAX 92-41-731433, http://www.ansinet.org/c4p.php?j_id=pjbs, http://www.ansinet.net.

578.77 PAK ISSN 1562-1286
QH91.A1 CODEN: PJMBFQ
PAKISTAN JOURNAL OF MARINE BIOLOGY. Text in English. 1992. s-a.
Formerly (until 1999): Marine Research (1021-5654)
Indexed: ESPM.
Published by: University of Karachi, Centre of Excellence in Marine Biology, Karachi, Pakistan. http://www.ku.edu.pk/research/cemb/.

PALAEOHISTORIA; acta et communicationes instituti bioarchaeologici universitatis groningianae. see *ARCHAEOLOGY*

PARASITE IMMUNOLOGY. see *MEDICAL SCIENCES—Communicable Diseases*

577 595.7 BEL ISSN 0031-1812
SB599 CODEN: PARGAW
➤ **PARASITICA.** Text in Dutch, English, French, German. 1945. q. EUR 130 domestic; EUR 230 foreign (effective 2003). adv. bk.rev. charts; illus. index. back issues avail. **Document type:** *Bulletin, Academic/Scholarly.*
Related titles: Microform ed.: (from PMC).

Indexed: AEA, ASFA, B&BAb, BioCN&I, BiolAb, CPA, ChemAb, CurCont, DBA, ESPM, EntAb, FCA, ForAb, HelmAb, HerbAb, HortAb, MBA, MaizeAb, NemAb, OrnHort, PBA, PGegResA, PGrRegA, PHN&I, PotatoAb, ProtozoAb, RA&MP, RPP, RefZh, RevApplEntom, RiceAb, S&F, SIA, SeedAb, TriticAb, WeedAb, ZooRec.
—CASDDS, CISTI, Linda Hall.
Published by: Association pour les Etudes et Recherches de Zoologie Appliquee et de Phytopathologie, Rue du Bordia 11, Gembloux, 5030, Belgium. TEL 32-81-625262, FAX 32-81-625272, galoux@cra.wallonie.be. Ed. R Moens. R&P R. Moens TEL 32-81-625272. Adv. contact M Galoux. B&W page EUR 200. Circ: 550.

➤ **PARKS & HERITAGE SERIES.** see *FORESTS AND FORESTRY*

➤ **PATHOLOGIE ET BIOLOGIE.** see *MEDICAL SCIENCES*

➤ **PATHOLOGY.** see *MEDICAL SCIENCES*

➤ **PATHOLOGY PATTERNS REVIEWS.** see *MEDICAL SCIENCES*

571.9 MEX ISSN 0185-4305
➤ **PATOLOGIA**; revista latinoamericana. Text in Spanish; Summaries in English, Portuguese. 1992. q. adv. bk.rev. charts; illus. index. back issues avail. **Document type:** *Academic/Scholarly.* **Description:** Contains original articles, research reports, review articles, clinical cases and notices related to anatomical pathology.
Formerly (until 1970): Asociacion Mexicana de Patologos. Boletin
Related titles: CD-ROM ed.
Indexed: BiolAb, CurCont, ExcerpMed, SCI.
Published by: (Asociacion Latinoamericana de Patologia), Obsidiana Editores S.A., CZDA DE TLALPAN 2365, Col Ciudad Jardin, Mexico City, DF 04370, Mexico. TEL 52-5-689-9133. Ed. Dr. Luis Benitez Bribiesca. Pub. Jorge Godoy-Gutierrez. Circ: 630 (paid); 1,370 (controlled). **Dist. by:** Distribuidora Editorial de Mexico SA de CV, P.O. Box 76-026, Mexico City, DF 04201, Mexico. TEL 52-5-544-7953, FAX 52-5-689-6545. **Co-sponsor:** Asociacion Mexicana de Patologos.

➤ **PATOLOGICHESKAYA FIZIOLOGIYA I EKSPERIMENTAL'NAYA TERAPIYA/PATHOLOGICAL PHYSIOLOGY AND EXPERIMENTAL THERAPY.** see *MEDICAL SCIENCES*

➤ **PEDOBIOLOGIA.** see *AGRICULTURE—Crop Production And Soil*

➤ **PELAGOS.** see *EARTH SCIENCES—Oceanography*

570 FRA ISSN 0553-4992
PENN AR BED. Text in French. 1953. irreg.
Indexed: ESPM, ZooRec.
Published by: Societe pour l'Etude et la Protection de la Nature en Bretagne, 48 Blvd Magenta, Rennes, 35000, France. TEL 33-299-306464.

PENNSYLVANIA ACADEMY OF SCIENCE. JOURNAL. see *SCIENCES: COMPREHENSIVE WORKS*

573.6 MEX ISSN 0187-5337
PERINATOLOGIA Y REPRODUCCION HUMANA. Text in Spanish. 1987. q. **Document type:** *Journal, Academic/Scholarly.*
Related titles: Online - full content ed.: free (effective 2005); Online - full text ed.: (from EBSCO Publishing).
—CISTI.
Published by: Instituto Nacional de Perinatologia, Montes Urales No. 800, Col. Loma de Virreyes, C.P. 11000, Mexico. http://inper.entornomedico.org/. Ed. Esther Casanueva.

570 610 HRV ISSN 0031-5362
QH301 CODEN: PDBIAD
PERIODICUM BIOLOGORUM. Text in English. 1886. q. USD 50 foreign (effective 2005). bk.rev. index. back issues avail. **Document type:** *Journal, Academic/Scholarly.*
Indexed: AbHyg, AgBio, AgrForAb, AnBrAb, BIOBASE, BIOSIS Prev, BiolAb, CIN, CPA, ChemAb, ChemTitl, CurCont, DSA, ExcerpMed, FCA, ForAb, HelmAb, HerbAb, HortAb, I&DA, IABS, INIS AtomInd, IndVet, MaizeAb, NemAb, NutrAb, OrnHort, PBA, PGegResA, PGrRegA, PHN&I, PN&I, PoultAb, RA&MP, RM&VM, RPP, RRTA, RevApplEntom, S&F, SCI, SFA, SIA, SeedAb, TDB, TriticAb, VetBull, WAE&RSA, WeedAb, WildRev, ZooRec.
—BLDSC (6426.240000), CASDDS, CISTI, GNLM, IDS, IE, ingenta, KNAW, Linda Hall.
Published by: Hrvatsko Prirodoslovno Drustvo/Croatian Society of Natural Sciences, Frankopanska 1, P.O. Box 258, Zagreb, 0001, Croatia. TEL 385-1-4831224, FAX 385-1-4831223, http://mcc.irb.hr/instruct.html. Ed. Branko Vitale TEL 385-1-4680240. Circ: 700.

PERSPECTIVES IN BIOLOGY AND MEDICINE. see *MEDICAL SCIENCES*

599.9 SGP ISSN 1038-5762
QP34.5
➤ **PERSPECTIVES IN HUMAN BIOLOGY.** Text in English. 1992. a., latest vol.3. price varies. bk.rev. **Document type:** *Monographic series, Academic/Scholarly.* **Description:** Publishes within-discipline and across-discipline integrative investigations and reviews which foster an understanding of the complex, holistic nature of the human condition.
Indexed: AICP.
—BLDSC (6428.143180).
Published by: (Centre for Human Biology AUS), World Scientific Publishing Co. Pte. Ltd., 5 Toh Tuck Link, Singapore, 596224, Singapore. TEL 65-466-5775, FAX 65-467-7667, editor@worldscientific.com, wspc@wspc.com.sg, http://www.wspc.com.sg/books/series/phb_series.shtml, http://www.worldscientific.com. Ed. Charles Oxnard. Circ: 200. **Dist. by:** World Scientific Publishing Co., Inc., 1060 Main St, River Edge, NJ 07661; World Scientific Publishing Ltd., 57 Shelton St, London WC2H 9HE, United Kingdom.

➤ **PETERSON'S GRADUATE AND PROFESSIONAL PROGRAMS: THE BIOLOGICAL SCIENCES (YEAR) (BOOK 3).** see *EDUCATION—Guides To Schools And Colleges*

570 550 SYC ISSN 1026-5023
➤ **PHELSUMA.** Text in English. 1993. a. SCR 125 domestic; USD 25 foreign (effective 2001). bibl. 80 p./no. 1 cols./p.; back issues avail. **Document type:** *Journal, Academic/Scholarly.* **Description:** Deals with all aspects of nature (especially biology and the earth Sciences) in the western Indian Ocean, including marine and terrestrial subjects in Seychelles, Comoros, Madagascar, Reunion, Mauritius and Chagos.
Indexed: RPP, ZooRec.
Published by: Nature Protection Trust of Seychelles, PO Box 207, Victoria, Mahe, Seychelles. npts@seychelles.net, http://www.members.aol.com/jstgerlach. Ed. Justin Gerlach. Circ: 100 (paid).

➤ **PHILIPPIA.** see *MUSEUMS AND ART GALLERIES*

570 GBR ISSN 0268-487X
QL691.5 CODEN: PHOEEU
PHOENIX (SOMERSHAM). Text in English. 1985. a. GBP 20 (effective 2000). adv. bk.rev. abstr.; bibl.; illus.; stat.; tr.lit. index. back issues avail. **Document type:** *Newsletter, Academic/Scholarly.* **Description:** Articles and short scientific papers relating to breeding bird biology in the Arabian Peninsula and the Middle East in general.
Indexed: SFA, WildRev, ZooRec.
Address: 1 Warners Farm, Warners Drove, Somersham, Cambs PE17 3HW, United Kingdom. TEL 44-1487-841733, FAX 44-1487-841733, arabian.birds@dial.pipex.com, http://dspace.dial.pipex.com/arabian.birds/. Ed. Michael Jennings. Circ: 750.

PHOTOCHEMICAL & PHOTOBIOLOGICAL SCIENCES. see *CHEMISTRY*

PHOTOCHEMISTRY AND PHOTOBIOLOGY. see *CHEMISTRY—Physical Chemistry*

578.77 THA ISSN 0858-1088
QH193.T46 CODEN: RBPCE9
➤ **PHUKET MARINE BIOLOGICAL CENTER. RESEARCH BULLETIN.** Text in English. 1973. irreg. (1-2/yr.). USD 10 (effective 1993). illus. back issues avail. **Document type:** *Bulletin, Academic/Scholarly.* **Description:** Examines research results carried out at the center; in cooperation with the center; or independent research performed in Thailand and adjacent areas.
Indexed: ASFA, ESPM, SFA, ZooRec.
Published by: Phuket Marine Biological Center, PO Box 60, Phuket, 83000, Thailand. TEL 076-391128, FAX 076-391127. Ed. Samsak Chullasorn. Circ: 500.

570 THA ISSN 0858-3633
PHUKET MARINE BIOLOGICAL CENTER. SPECIAL PUBLICATIONS. Text in English. 1983. irreg. price varies. illus. **Document type:** *Proceedings.* **Description:** Contains papers from the Tropical Marine Mollusc Programme.
Indexed: ASFA, ESPM, SFA, ZooRec.
Published by: Phuket Marine Biological Center, PO Box 60, Phuket, 83000, Thailand. TEL 076-391128, FAX 66-76-391127. Ed. Somsak Chullasorn. Circ: 500.

▼ **PHYSICAL BIOLOGY.** see *PHYSICS*

570 530 NLD ISSN 1571-0645
QH505
▼ ➤ **PHYSICS OF LIFE REVIEWS.** Text in English. 2004. 4/yr. EUR 389 in Europe to institutions; JPY 46,200 in Japan to institutions; USD 389 to institutions except Europe and Japan (effective 2006). **Document type:** *Journal, Academic/Scholarly.* **Description:** Publishes review articles on physics of living systems, complex phenomena in biological systems, and related fields of artificial life, robotics, mathematical biosemiotics, and artificial intelligent systems. Addresses all living systems from molecules to populations and from genetics to mind and artificial systems modeling these phenomena.
Related titles: Online - full content ed.; Online - full text ed.: (from EBSCO Publishing, ScienceDirect, Swets Information Services).
Indexed: Inspec.
—BLDSC (6478.750000), IE. **CCC.**
Published by: Elsevier BV (Subsidiary of: Elsevier Science & Technology), Radarweg 29, Amsterdam, 1043 NX, Netherlands. TEL 31-20-4853911, FAX 31-20-4852457, nlinfo-f@elsevier.nl, http://www.elsevier.com/locate/plrev, http://www.elsevier.nl. Eds. E Di Mauro, L I Perlovsky.

573.4 616.48 IND
PINEAL GLAND: ITS MOLECULAR SIGNALS. Text in English. 1996. irreg. USD 30 per issue (effective 2000). **Document type:** *Monographic series.*
Published by: Hindustan Publishing Corporation (India), 4805-24, Bharat Ram Rd., 1st Fl., Flats 1 & 2, Darya Ganj, New Delhi, 110 002, India. TEL 91-11-325-4401, FAX 91-11-6193511, hpcpd@nda.vsnl.net.in, hpcpd@hpc.cc, http://www.hpc.cc, http://www.bizdelhi.com/publisher/hpc. Ed. Chandana Haldar.

577.73 551.432 577 ESP ISSN 0373-2568
DP302.P8 CODEN: PRNOAJ
➤ **PIRINEOS**; a journal on mountain ecology. Text in English, French, Spanish; Summaries in English, French, German, Spanish. 1945. 2/yr. USD 12 (effective 2000). adv. bk.rev. **Document type:** *Academic/Scholarly.* **Description:** Papers related to the dynamics of mountain ecosystems.
Indexed: AmH&L, BHA, BiolAb, ForAb, GEOBASE, HerbAb, HistAb, I&DA, IECT, IndIslam, KWIWR, S&F, SeedAb, ZooRec.
—CINDOC. **CCC.**
Published by: Consejo Superior de Investigaciones Cientificas, Instituto Pirenaico de Ecologia, Avda. Regimiento de Galicia, s-n, Jaca, Huesca 22700, Spain. TEL 34-74-361441, FAX 34-74-363222, bib_jaca@bib.csic.es. Ed. Juan Pablo Martinez Rica. Circ: 1,000.

578.77 JPN ISSN 1343-0874
QH90.8.P5 CODEN: PBELCP
➤ **PLANKTON BIOLOGY AND ECOLOGY.** Text in English. s-a. JPY 12,000 (effective 2000). **Document type:** *Academic/Scholarly.* **Description:** Publishes papers, reviews, and notes dealing with all aspects of biology; ecology of marine; freshwater plankton; and their interactions with the environments in any aquatic systems.
Indexed: ASFA, B&BAb, BIOSIS Prev, BiolAb, ESPM, GEOBASE, MBA, OceAb, RefZh, ZooRec.
—BLDSC (6508.553855), CISTI.
Published by: Plankton Society of Japan/Nihon Purankuton Gakkai, c/o Tokyo University of Marine Science and Technology, 4-5-7 Kounan, Minato-ku, Tokyo, 108-8477, Japan. plankton@s.kaiyodai.ac.jp, http://www.plankton.jp/. Ed. Shuhei Nishida. R&P Haruto Jshii. Circ: 700.

➤ **PLANT BREEDING AND SEED SCIENCE/HODOWLA ROSLIN I NASIENNICTWO.** see *AGRICULTURE*

581.7 GBR ISSN 0140-7791
QK710 CODEN: PLCEDV
➤ **PLANT, CELL AND ENVIRONMENT.** Text in English. 1978. m. GBP 129, EUR 213 combined subscription in Europe to individuals print & online eds.; USD 239 combined subscription in the Americas to individuals & Caribbean, print & online eds.; GBP 142 combined subscription elsewhere to individuals print & online eds.; GBP 1,794 combined subscription in Europe to institutions print & online eds.; USD 3,315 combined subscription in the Americas to institutions & Caribbean (print & online eds.); GBP 1,973 combined subscription elsewhere to institutions print & online eds. (effective 2006). adv. bk.rev. bibl.; illus. index. reprint service avail. from PSC,ISI. **Document type:** *Magazine, Academic/Scholarly.* **Description:** Publishes original research, either theoretical or experimental, in any field of the physiology of green plants.
Related titles: Microform ed.: (from PQC); Online - full text ed.: ISSN 1365-3040. 1998. GBP 1,704 in Europe to institutions; USD 3,148 in the Americas to institutions & Caribbean; GBP 1,874 elsewhere to institutions (effective 2006) (from Blackwell Synergy, EBSCO Publishing, Gale Group, IngentaConnect, O C L C Online Computer Library Center, Inc., Swets Information Services).
Indexed: AEA, ASCA, ASFA, AgBio, Agr, AgrForAb, BIOBASE, BIOSIS Prev, BibAg, BioCN&I, BiolAb, CCI, CIN, CPA, CTFA, ChemAb, ChemTitl, CurCont, DBA, EPB, ESPM, EnvAb, ExcerpMed, FCA, FPA, FaBeAb, ForAb, GEOBASE, HerbAb, HortAb, I&DA, IABS, IBR, ISR, M&GPA, MSB, MaizeAb, NemAb, NutrAb, OrnHort, PBA, PGegResA, PGrRegA, PHN&I, PlantSci, PollutAb, PotatoAb, RA&MP, RPP, RefZh, RevApplEntom, RiceAb, S&F, SCI, SIA, SWRA, SeedAb, SoyAb, TriticAb, VITIS, WeedAb.
—BLDSC (6514.200000), CASDDS, CISTI, IDS, IE, Infotrieve, ingenta, Linda Hall. **CCC.**
Published by: Blackwell Publishing Ltd., 9600 Garsington Rd, Oxford, OX4 2ZG, United Kingdom. TEL 44-1865-776868, FAX 44-1865-714591, customerservices@oxon.blackwellpublishing.com, http://www.blackwellpublishing.com/journals/PCE. Ed. Keith Mott. Pub. Sue Hewitt. R&P Sophie Savage. Adv. contact Jenny Applin. Circ: 760.

572.8 NLD ISSN 0167-4412
CODEN: PMBIDB

➤ **PLANT MOLECULAR BIOLOGY**; an international journal on molecular biology, biochemistry and genetic engineering. Text in English. 1981. 18/yr. EUR 2,898, USD 2,938, GBP 1,908 combined subscription to institutions print & online eds. (effective 2005). adv. bk.rev. illus. Index. back issues avail.; reprint service avail. from PSC. **Document type:** *Journal, Academic/Scholarly.* **Description:** Publishes research concerned with plant molecular biology, biochemistry and plant molecular genetics, including cyanobacteria and algae.
Related titles: Microform ed.: (from PQC); Online - full text ed.: ISSN 1573-5028 (from EBSCO Publishing, Gale Group, IngentaConnect, Kluwer Online, O C L C Online Computer Library Center, Inc., Ovid Technologies, Inc., Springer LINK, Swets Information Services).
Indexed: AEA, AEBA, ASCA, ASFA, AgBio, Agr, AgrForAb, BBCI, BCI, BIOBASE, BIOSIS Prev, BibAg, BibLing, BioEngAb, BiolAb, CBTA, CPA, CTFA, ChemAb, ChemTitl, CurCont, DBA, DSA, ESPM, EngInd, FCA, FPA, FS&TA, FaBeAb, ForAb, GenetAb, HGA, HerbAb, HortAb, IABS, ISR, IndMed, MBA, MEDLINE, MaizeAb, NPU, NemAb, NucAcAb, NutrAb, OrnHort, PBA, PGegResA, PGrRegA, PHN&I, PN&I, PlantSci, PotatoAb, RA&MP, RM&VM, RPP, RefZh, RevApplEntom, RiceAb, S&F, SCI, SIA, SeedAb, SoyAb, Telegen, TriticAb, VITIS, WeedAb.
—BLDSC (6520.350000), CASDDS, CISTI, GNLM, IDS, IE, Infotrieve, ingenta, Linda Hall. **CCC.**
Published by: (International Society for Plant Molecular Biology), Springer-Verlag Dordrecht (Subsidiary of: Springer Science+Business Media), Van Godewijckstraat 30, Dordrecht, 3311 GX, Netherlands. TEL 31-78-6576050, FAX 31-78-6576474, http://springerlink.metapress.com/openurl.asp?genre=journal&issn=0167-4412, http://www.springeronline.com. Ed. Wilhelm Gruissem.

570 USA ISSN 0147-619X
QH452 CODEN: PLSMDX

➤ **PLASMID.** Text in English. 1977. 6/yr. EUR 317 in Europe to individuals; JPY 33,100 in Japan to individuals; USD 255 to individuals except Europe and Japan; EUR 885 in Europe to institutions; JPY 92,400 in Japan to institutions; USD 703 to institutions except Europe and Japan; EUR 88 in Europe to students; JPY 9,200 in Japan to students; USD 78 to students except Europe and Japan (effective 2006). adv. index. back issues avail. **Document type:** *Academic/Scholarly.* **Description:** Focuses on the biology of extrachromosomal genetic elements in both prokaryotic and eukaryotic systems, including their biological behavior, molecular structure and genetic function, their gene products, and their use as genetic tools.
Related titles: Online - full text ed.: ISSN 1095-9890. USD 727 (effective 2002) (from EBSCO Publishing, Gale Group, IngentaConnect, O C L C Online Computer Library Center, Inc., ScienceDirect, Swets Information Services).
Indexed: ASCA, AbHyg, AgBio, Agr, AnBrAb, BCI, BIOBASE, BIOSIS Prev, BibAg, BioCN&I, BiolAb, CBTA, CEABA, CIN, ChemAb, ChemTitl, CurCont, DBA, DSA, ESPM, ExcerpMed, FCA, FS&TA, GenetAb, HGA, HortAb, IABS, ISR, IndMed, IndVet, Inpharma, MBA, MEDLINE, NucAcAb, PBA, PN&I, PoultAb, RM&VM, RPP, Reac, RefZh, RevApplEntom, S&F, SCI, SoyAb, TDB, Telegen, VITIS, VetBull.
—BLDSC (6528.790000), CASDDS, CISTI, GNLM, IDS, IE, Infotrieve, ingenta, Linda Hall. **CCC.**
Published by: Academic Press (Subsidiary of: Elsevier Science & Technology), 525 B St, Ste 1900, San Diego, CA 92101-4495. TEL 619-231-6616, 800-894-3434, FAX 619-699-6422, apsubs@acad.com, http://www.elsevier.com/locate/yplas, http://www.academicpress.com. Ed. D. K. Chattoraj.

578.77 GBR ISSN 1359-5881

PLYMOUTH MARINE LABORATORY. REPORT. Text in English. 1973-1975; N.S. 1980. a.
Former titles (until 1987): I M E R (0263-4082); (until 1975): Institute for Marine Environmental Research. Report (0301-715X)
Published by: Plymouth Marine Laboratory, Prospect Pl, The Hoe, Plymouth, PL1 3DH, United Kingdom. TEL 44-1752-633100, FAX 44-1752-633101, forinfo@pml.ac.uk, http://www.pml.ac.uk/pml/.

570 DEU ISSN 0722-4060
QL104 CODEN: POBIDP

➤ **POLAR BIOLOGY.** Text in English. 1982. m. EUR 1,828 combined subscription to institutions print & online eds. (effective 2005). adv. back issues avail.; reprint service avail. from ISI. **Document type:** *Journal, Academic/Scholarly.* **Description:** Presents results of all kinds of studies in plants, animals, and microorganisms of marine, limnic and terrestrial habitats of Arctic and Antarctic regions.
Related titles: Microfiche ed.: (from PQC); Online - full text ed.: ISSN 1432-2056 (from EBSCO Publishing, Springer LINK, Swets Information Services).
Indexed: ASCA, ASFA, AnBrAb, BIOBASE, BIOSIS Prev, BioCN&I, BiolAb, ChemAb, CurCont, DSA, ESPM, EntAb, ForAb, GEOBASE, HelmAb, HerbAb, I&DA, IABS, ISR, IndVet, M&GPA, NemAb, NutrAb, OceAb, PBA, PGegResA, PoultAb, ProtozoAb, RM&VM, RPP, RefZh, RevApplEntom, S&F, SCI, SFA, VetBull, ZooRec.
—BLDSC (6541.936500), CASDDS, CISTI, IDS, IE, Infotrieve, ingenta, Linda Hall. **CCC.**
Published by: Springer-Verlag (Subsidiary of: Springer Science+Business Media), Tiergartenstr 17, Heidelberg, 69121, Germany. TEL 49-6221-3450, FAX 49-6221-345229, http://link.springer.de/link/service/journals/00300/index.htm. Adv. contact Stephan Kroeck TEL 49-30-827875739. **Subscr. in the Americas to:** Springer-Verlag New York, Inc., Journal Fulfillment, PO Box 2485, Secaucus, NJ 07096-2485. TEL 800-777-4643, 201-348-4033, FAX 201-348-4505, journals@springer-ny.com, http://www.springer-ny.com; **Subscr. to:** Springer GmbH Auslieferungsgesellschaft, Haberstr 7, Heidelberg 69126, Germany. TEL 49-6221-345-0, FAX 49-6221-345-4229, subscriptions@springer.de.

570.11 JPN ISSN 1344-6231
QH95.58 CODEN: PNSBEF

➤ **POLAR BIOSCIENCE.** Text in English. 1967. a., latest vol.16, 2003. per issue exchange basis. **Document type:** *Academic/Scholarly.*
Formerly (until 1998): N I P R Symposium on Polar Biology. Proceedings (0914-563X); Supersedes in part (in 1987): National Institute of Polar Research. Memoirs. Special Issue (0386-0744); Which was formerly (until 1972): Japanese Antarctic Research Expedition Scientific Reports. Special Issue (0386-5452)
Indexed: ASFA, ESPM, RefZh, SFA, WildRev, ZooRec.
—BLDSC (6541.936600), CASDDS, CISTI, IE, ingenta, KNAW.
Published by: National Institute of Polar Research/Kokuritsu Kyokuchi Kenkyujo, Publications, 9-10, Kiga 1-chome, Itabashi-ku, Tokyo, 173, Japan. TEL 81-3-3962-2214, FAX 81-3-3962-2225, publication@nipr.ac.jp. Ed. Okitsugu Watanabe. Circ: 1,000.

571.9 POL ISSN 1233-9687
CODEN: PAPOAC

➤ **POLISH JOURNAL OF PATHOLOGY.** Text in Polish. 1950. q. USD 60 foreign (effective 2000). adv. bk.rev. illus. index. **Document type:** *Academic/Scholarly.* **Description:** Contains papers reporting experimental research in pathology.
Formerly (until 1993): Patologia Polska (0031-3114)
Indexed: BIOSIS Prev, BiolAb, CIN, ChemAb, ChemTitl, ExcerpMed, IndMed, MEDLINE.
—CASDDS, CISTI, GNLM.
Published by: Polskie Towarzystwo Patologow/Polish Society of Pathologists, Ul Grzegorzecka 16, Krakow, 31531, Poland. TEL 48-12-4211564, FAX 48-12-4215210, mpstachu@cyf-kr.edu.pl, jszymas@ampat.amu.edu.pl, http://www.bj.uj.edu.pl/cm/pato. Ed. Jerzy Stachura. Adv. contact Wojciech Dabros. Circ: 700. **Co-sponsor:** International Academy of Pathology, Polish Division.

➤ **POLLICHIA. MITTEILUNGEN.** see *EARTH SCIENCES*

570 PRT ISSN 0874-9035
QK1

PORTUGALIA ACTA BIOLOGICA, SISTEMATICA, ECOLOGIA, BIOGEOGRAFIA PALEONTOLOGIA, MORFOLOGIA, FISIOLOGIA, GENETICA E BIOLOGIA GERAL. Text in Portuguese. irreg. **Document type:** *Academic/Scholarly.*
Formed by the 1994 merger of: Portugaliae Acta Biologica. Serie A: Morfologia, Fisiologia, Genetica e Biologia Geral (0032-5147); Portugaliae Acta Biologica. Serie B: Sistematica, Ecologia, Biogeografia e Paleontologia (0375-0280)
Indexed: AgBio, AgrForAb, CPA, ForAb, HerbAb, HortAb, OrnHort, PBA, PGegResA, RA&MP, RDA, RefZh, S&F, SeedAb, TDB, TriticAb, WeedAb.
—CISTI, Linda Hall.
Published by: Universidade de Lisboa, Museu, Laboratorio e Jardim Botanico, Rua da Escola Politecnica, 58, Lisboa, 1250-102, Portugal. TEL 351-21-3921801, FAX 351-21-3970882, jbbiblio@fc.ul.pt, http://www.jb.ul.pt, http://wwwjb.ul.pt/. R&P F M Catarino TEL 351-21-3921890. Adv. contact Manuel Dos Santos Lopes.

DER PRAEPARATOR. see *CONSERVATION*

577 USA ISSN 0091-0376
QH540 CODEN: PRNTBZ

➤ **THE PRAIRIE NATURALIST.** Text in English. 1968. q. USD 15 to individuals; USD 30 to libraries; USD 10 to students (effective 2005). adv. bk.rev. **Document type:** *Journal, Academic/Scholarly.* **Description:** Presents research on the North American grasslands and their biota.
Indexed: BIOSIS Prev, BiolAb, KWIWR, PBA, RefZh, SFA, SeedAb, WLR, WeedAb, WildRev, ZooRec.
—BLDSC (6598.551000), IE, ingenta.
Published by: Great Plains Natural Science Society, Dept. of Biological Sciences, Fort Hays State Univeristy, 600 Park Ste, Hays, KS 67601. TEL 785-628-5594, prairien@fhsu.edu, http://www.fhsu.edu/biology/pn/prairienat.htm. Ed. Dr. Elmer J Finck. Circ: 600 (paid).

570.71 DEU ISSN 1617-5697

PRAXIS DER NATURWISSENSCHAFTEN - BIOLOGIE IN DER SCHULE. Text in German. 2000. 8/yr. EUR 63.20 domestic to individuals; EUR 72 foreign to individuals; EUR 47.20 domestic to students; EUR 54 foreign to students (effective 2006). bk.rev. **Document type:** *Journal, Academic/Scholarly.*
Formed by the merger of (1951-2000): Biologie in der Schule (0406-3317); (1951-2000): Praxis der Naturwissenschaften Biologie (0177-8382); Which was formerly (until 1980): Praxis der Naturwissenschaften. Biologie im Unterricht der Schulen (0341-8510); (until 1972): Praxis der Naturwissenschaften. Teil 2. Biologie (0032-7050)
—BLDSC (6603.175700), CISTI, IE, ingenta.
Published by: Aulis-Verlag Deubner GmbH und Co. KG, Antwerpener Str 6-12, Cologne, 50672, Germany. TEL 49-221-957454-0, FAX 49-221-518443, info@aulis.de, http://www.aulis.de. R&P Wolfgang Deubner. Adv. contact Ulrike Lennertz. Circ: 5,800 (paid).

174 USA

PRINCETON JOURNAL OF BIOETHICS. Text in English. 1998. q. USD 25; USD 5 to students (effective 2003). **Document type:** *Journal, Academic/Scholarly.* **Description:** Devoted to examining contemporary issues in bioethics including genetic engineering, reproductive rights, stem cell research, and euthanasia, to name a few.
—BLDSC (6612.935350), ingenta.
Published by: Princeton University, BioethicsForum, Dod Hall, Princeton, NJ 08540. bioethic@princeton.edu, http://www.princeton.edu/~bioethic/journal. Ed. Gloria Chiang.

570 HRV ISSN 0351-0662
QH7

PRIRODA. Text in Croatian. 1911. 10/yr.
—BLDSC (6615.800000).
Published by: (Hrvatsko Prirodsovno Drustvo), Vjesnik, Petrova 19, Zagreb, 10000, Croatia. TEL 041-515-555. Ed. Tomislav Krcmar. Circ: 10,000.

577 POL ISSN 1427-3381

PROBLEMY EKOLOGII. Text in Polish. 1997. bi-m. **Description:** Covers the problems of sustainable development.
Indexed: INIS AtomInd.
Published by: (Wyzsza Szkola Ekonomii i Administracji), Gornoslaska Wyzsza Szkola Pedagogiczna im Kardynala Augusta Hlonda, ul Piastow Slaskich 10, Myslowice, 41-408, Poland. TEL 48-32-2253873, FAX 48-32-2253871, problemy.ekologii@wsew.edu.pl, http://www.wsew.edu.pl/pe/. Ed. Jan Gurgul.

570 RUS ISSN 0555-2788
QH327 CODEN: PKBBA7

PROBLEMY KOSMICHESKOI BIOLOGII. Text in Russian. 1962. irreg.
Indexed: IndMed, MEDLINE.
—Linda Hall. **CCC.**
Published by: Izdatel'stvo Nauka, Profsoyuznaya ul 90, Moscow, 117864, Russian Federation.

573.6 RUS ISSN 1025-7217
CODEN: PRRECB

PROBLEMY REPRODUKTSII. Text in English, Russian. 1995. bi-m. RUR 390 for 6 mos. to individuals; RUR 495 for 6 mos. to institutions (effective 2003). charts; bibl.; illus. reprints avail. **Document type:** *Journal, Academic/Scholarly.*
Related titles: E-mail ed.; Online - full content ed.
Indexed: RefZh.
—BLDSC (0133.627000), IE, ingenta.
Published by: Media Sfera, Dmitrovskoe shosse 46, korp 2, etazh 4, P.O. Box 54, Moscow, 127238, Russian Federation. TEL 7-095-4824329, FAX 7-095-4824312, mediashp@mediasphera.ru, http://www.mediasphera.ru/reprod/repr-mn.htm, http://mediasphera.ru. Ed. M B Anshina. R&P S E Bashchinskii TEL 7-095-4886637. Adv. contact Valery Nemtsov TEL 7-095-4886000. Circ: 2,000 (paid). **US dist. addr.:** East View Information Services, 3020 Harbor Ln. N., Minneapolis, MN 55447. TEL 763-550-0961, FAX 763-559-2931, eastview@eastview.com, http://www.eastview.com.

578.77 USA ISSN 0079-6603
CODEN: PNMBAF

➤ **PROGRESS IN NUCLEIC ACID RESEARCH AND MOLECULAR BIOLOGY.** Text in English. 1963. irreg., latest vol.72, 2002. USD 129.95 per vol. (effective 2003). reprint service avail. from ISI. **Document type:** *Monographic series, Academic/Scholarly.*
Formerly (until vol.2): Progress in Nucleic Acid Research (0091-4886)
Related titles: Online - full text ed.: (from ScienceDirect).
Indexed: ASCA, ASFA, AgBio, Agr, AnBrAb, BBCI, BCI, BIOSIS Prev, BiolAb, CCI, ChemAb, ChemTitl, DokArb, GenetAb, HGA, ISR, IndMed, MEDLINE, NucAcAb, NutrAb, SCI.
—BLDSC (6871.210000), CASDDS, CISTI, GNLM, IE, Infotrieve, ingenta, Linda Hall. **CCC.**
Published by: Academic Press (Subsidiary of: Elsevier Science & Technology), 525 B St, Ste 1900, San Diego, CA 92101-4495. apsubs@acad.com, http://www.academicpress.com. Eds. J N Davidson, Waldo E Cohn.

570 DEU ISSN 1434-4610
QL366 CODEN: PROTFA
➤ **PROTIST.** Text in English. 1902. 4/yr. EUR 438 to institutions; EUR 568 in Europe to institutions; JPY 75,600 in Japan to institutions; USD 608 to institutions except Europe and Japan (effective 2006). adv. bk.rev. bibl.; charts; illus. index. cum.index: vols.1-50, 1902-1918 (in 2 vols.). reprint service avail. from ISI. **Document type:** *Journal, Academic/Scholarly.* **Description:** Publishes original papers, short historical perspectives, and news and views in all areas of research on protists.
Formerly (until 1998): Archiv fuer Protistenkunde (0003-9365)
Related titles: Microfilm ed.: (from BHP); Online - full text ed.: (from EBSCO Publishing, Gale Group, IngentaConnect, O C L C Online Computer Library Center, Inc., ProQuest Information & Learning, ScienceDirect, Swets Information Services).
Indexed: ASCA, ASFA, AbHyg, AgBio, BIOBASE, BIOSIS Prev, BioCN&I, BiolAb, ChemAb, CurCont, ESPM, ExcerpMed, HelmAb, HerbAb, HortAb, IABS, ISR, IndMed, IndVet, MBA, MEDLINE, PlantSci, ProtozoAb, RM&VM, RPP, S&F, SCI, TDB, VetBull, ZooRec.
—BLDSC (6936.450000), CISTI, IDS, IE, Infotrieve, ingenta, Linda Hall. **CCC.**
Published by: Elsevier GmbH, Urban & Fischer Verlag (Subsidiary of: Elsevier Science & Technology), Loebdergraben 14a, Jena, 07743, Germany. TEL 49-3641-626430, FAX 49-3641-626432, info@urbanfischer.de, http://www.elsevier.com/locate/protist, http://www.urbanfischer.de. Ed. Dr. Michael Melkonian. R&P Martin Huber TEL 49-3641-626430. Adv. contact Sabine Schroeter TEL 49-3641-626445. B&W page EUR 400, color page EUR 1,345; trim 210 x 280. Circ: 300 (paid and controlled).
Non-German speaking countries subscr. to: Nature Publishing Group, Brunel Rd, Houndmills, Basingstoke, Hamps RG21 6XS, United Kingdom. TEL 44-1256-302629, FAX 44-1256-476117

570 RUS ISSN 1680-0826
➤ **PROTISTOLOGY**; an international journal. Text in English. q. **Document type:** *Journal, Academic/Scholarly.* **Description:** Presents original, substantial and critical papers in any area of investigation of protists.
—BLDSC (6936.520000).
Published by: Sankt-Peterburgskii Gosudarstvennyi Universitet, Biologicheskii Nauchno-Issledovatel'skii Institut/St. Petersburg State University, Biological Research Institute, Stary Petergof, Oranienbaumskoye Sch. 2, St. Petersburg, 191011, Russian Federation. adm@paloma.spbu.ru, http://www.bio.pu.ru/win/bnii/bnii.htm. Ed. Sergey Likhachev.

577 POL ISSN 1230-509X
PRZEGLAD PRZYRODNICZY. Text in Polish. 1990. q. PLZ 20; USD 20 in United States. adv. bk.rev. index. **Document type:** *Monographic series, Academic/Scholarly.* **Description:** Regional forum on nature protection and ecology.
Formerly (until 1993): Lubuski Przeglad Przyrodniczy (0867-0331)
Indexed: AgrLib, ZooRec.
—BLDSC (6944.693000).
Published by: Lubuski Klub Przyrodnikow, Ul 1 Maja 22, Swiebodzin, 66200, Poland. TEL 48-6838-28236. Eds. A Jermaczek, P Pawlaczyk. Adv. contact Robert Stanko. Circ: 1,000 (paid).

PSIQUIATRIA BIOLOGICA. see *MEDICAL SCIENCES—Psychiatry And Neurology*

PUERTO RICO HEALTH SCIENCES JOURNAL. see *MEDICAL SCIENCES*

572.8 NLD ISSN 1573-9538
▼ **PURINERGIC SIGNALLING.** Text in English. 2005. q. USD 278 combined subscription to institutions print & online eds. (effective 2005). bk.rev. **Document type:** *Journal, Academic/Scholarly.* **Description:** Publishes original research articles, short communicatons, reviews, commentaries, 'Hot' topics and controversies, as well as meeting reports and book reviews.
Related titles: Online - full text ed.: ISSN 1573-9546 (from EBSCO Publishing, Kluwer Online, Springer LINK).
—**CCC.**
Published by: Springer-Verlag Dordrecht (Subsidiary of: Springer Science+Business Media), Van Godewijckstraat 30, Dordrecht, 3311 GX, Netherlands. TEL 31-78-6576050, FAX 31-78-6576474, http://springerlink.metapress.com/openurl.asp?genre=journal&issn=1573-9538, http://www.springeronline.com. Ed. G Burnstock.

PYMATUNING SYMPOSIA IN ECOLOGY. see *ENVIRONMENTAL STUDIES*

578.77 ITA
QUADERNI I C R A M. Text in Italian. 1992. irreg.
Published by: Istituto Centrale per la Ricerca Scientifica e Tecnologica Applicata al Mare, Via di Casalotti 300, Rome, 00166, Italy. TEL 39-06-615701, FAX 39-06-61561906, http://www.icram.org/Pubblicazioni.html.

QUADERNS D'ECOLOGIA APLICADA. see *ENVIRONMENTAL STUDIES*

THE QUARTERLY JOURNAL OF NUCLEAR MEDICINE AND MOLECULAR IMAGING. see *MEDICAL SCIENCES—Radiology And Nuclear Medicine*

570 USA ISSN 0033-5770
QH301 CODEN: QRBIAK
➤ **THE QUARTERLY REVIEW OF BIOLOGY.** Text in English. 1926. q. USD 45 combined subscription to individuals print & online eds.; USD 268 combined subscription to institutions print & online eds.; USD 16 per issue to individuals; USD 66 per issue to institutions (effective 2006). adv. bk.rev.; software rev. bibl.; charts; illus. Index. reprints avail. **Document type:** *Journal, Academic/Scholarly.* **Description:** Features recent research and software reviews in the various fields of the biological sciences.
Related titles: Microform ed.: (from PQC); Online - full text ed.: ISSN 1539-7718. USD 241 to institutions (effective 2006) (from EBSCO Publishing, Florida Center for Library Automation, Gale Group, JSTOR (Web-based Journal Archive)).
Indexed: ASCA, ASFA, AbAn, AcaI, AgBio, AnBeAb, AnBrAb, ApEcolAb, B&AI, BIOBASE, BIOSIS Prev, BRI, BioCN&I, BiolAb, BiolDig, CBRI, CIN, CPA, CTA, ChemAb, ChemTitl, ChemoAb, CurCont, DSA, ESPM, EntAb, ExcerpMed, GSI, HelmAb, HortAb, ISR, IndMed, IndVet, KWIWR, MBA, MEDLINE, NRN, NSA, NutrAb, PBA, PGegResA, ProtozoAb, RA&MP, RPP, RefSour, RefZh, RevApplEntom, SCI, SFA, SWRA, TDB, VetBull, WeedAb, WildRev, ZooRec.
—BLDSC (7206.000000), CASDDS, CISTI, IDS, IE, Infotrieve, ingenta, Linda Hall. **CCC.**
Published by: University of Chicago Press, Journals Division, Journals Division, PO Box 37005, Chicago, IL 60637. TEL 773-753-3347, 877-705-1878, FAX 773-753-0811, 877-705-1879, subscriptions@press.uchicago.edu, http://www.journals.uchicago.edu/QRB. Eds. Albert D Carlson, Daniel E Dykhuizen, James D Thomson, Massimo Pigliucci. adv.: page USD 590; trim 6.75 x 10. Circ: 1,700 (paid).

➤ **QUARTERLY REVIEWS OF BIOPHYSICS**; a review journal of biological function, structure and mechanism. see *BIOLOGY—Biophysics*

➤ **QUATERNARY OF SOUTH AMERICA AND ANTARCTIC PENINSULA.** see *EARTH SCIENCES—Geology*

578.77 CAN
CODEN: CIQTDG
QUEBEC (PROVINCE). DIRECTION DE L' INNOVATION ET DES TECHNOLOGIES. CAHIER D'INFORMATION. Text in English. 1960. irreg., latest vol.131, 1992. per issue exchange basis. **Document type:** *Government.*
Former titles (until 1996): Quebec (Province). Direction de la Recherche Scientifique et Technique. Cahier d'Information (0712-0613); Quebec (Province). Direction Generale des Peches Maritimes. Cahier d'Information; Quebec (Province). Marine Biological Station, Grande-Riviere. Cahiers d'Information (0079-8762)
Indexed: ASFA, BIOSIS Prev, BiolAb, SFA, WildRev, ZooRec.
Published by: Ministere de l'Agriculture, des Pecheries et de l'Alimentation, 96 Montee de Sandy Beach, bur. 205, Gaspe, PQ G4X 2V6, Canada. TEL 418-368-7615, FAX 418-360-8211, pcarrier@agr.gouv.qc.ca. Circ: 600.

578.77 CAN
QUEBEC (PROVINCE). DIRECTION DE L'INNOVATION ET DES TECHNOLOGIES. ACTIVITES (YEAR). Text in French. 1953-1979; N.S. 1988. a. free. **Document type:** *Government.*
Formerly (until 1996): Quebec (Province). Direction de la Recherche Scientifique et Technique. Activites (Year); Supersedes (in 1988): Quebec (Province). Direction Generale des Peches Maritimes. Direction de la Recherche. Rapport Annuel (0318-8779); (in 1969): Quebec (Province). Marine Biological Station, Grande-Riviere. Rapport (0079-8754)
Indexed: ASFA, BiolAb.
—CISTI.
Published by: Ministere de l'Agriculture, des Pecheries et de l'Alimentation, 96 Montee de Sandy Beach, bur. 205, Gaspe, PQ G4X 2V6, Canada. TEL 418-368-7615, FAX 418-360-8211, pcarrier@agr.gouv.qc.ca.

509 AUS ISSN 0079-8843
CODEN: QLNAAE
➤ **QUEENSLAND NATURALIST.** Text in English. 1908. s-a. AUD 12. **Document type:** *Academic/Scholarly.* **Description:** Covers natural history and natural science.
Indexed: ASFA, BiolAb, OceAb, SFA, WildRev, ZooRec.
—CISTI, Linda Hall.
Published by: Queensland Naturalists' Club Inc., Brisbane, GPO Box 5663, West End, QLD 4101, Australia. TEL 61-7-33652300, FAX 61-7-33651355, p.woodall@mailbox.uq.edu.au. Ed. Peter Woodall. Circ: 600.

363.7 ESP ISSN 1135-4704
R E A. (Red Espanola de Aerobiologia) Text in Spanish. 1995. a. back issues avail.
Related titles: Online - full text ed.
—CINDOC.
Published by: (Asociacion Espanola de Aerobiologia), Universidad de Malaga, Departamento de Biologia Vegetal, Apdo. de Correos 59, Malaga, Andalucia 29080, Spain. aerox@uma.es, http://www.uma.es/Estudios/Departamentos/BiolVeg/02Aer/00HAer/REA.html.

RADIOBIOLOGY. see *MEDICAL SCIENCES—Radiology And Nuclear Medicine*

570 JPN
RAIFU SAIENSU SHINKO ZAIDAN NENPO/LIFE SCIENCE FOUNDATION OF JAPAN. ANNUALS. Text in Japanese. 1986. a.
Published by: Raifu Saiensu Shinko Zaidan/Life Science Foundation of Japan, 203 Hanzomon Asai Biru, 2-18 Hayabusa-cho, Chiyoda-ku, Tokyo, 102-0092, Japan.

636.0845 USA ISSN 1550-7424
SF85 CODEN: JRMGAQ
➤ **RANGELAND ECOLOGY & MANAGEMENT.** Text in English. 1948. bi-m. USD 120 combined subscription domestic to individuals print & online eds.; USD 140 combined subscription foreign to individuals print & online eds.; USD 360 combined subscription domestic to institutions print & online eds.; USD 390 combined subscription foreign to institutions print & online eds. (effective 2005). adv. bk.rev. bibl.; charts; illus. index. back issues avail.; reprint service avail. from PQC. **Document type:** *Journal, Academic/Scholarly.* **Description:** Offers a forum of technical articles about research in range science and range management.
Formerly (until 2005): Journal of Range Management (0022-409X)
Related titles: Microfilm ed.: (from PQC); Online - full text ed.: ISSN 1551-5028 (from C S A, EBSCO Publishing, ProQuest Information & Learning); Supplement(s): Trail Boss News.
Indexed: AEA, ASCA, AbHyg, Agr, AgrForAb, AnBrAb, ApEcolAb, B&AI, BIOBASE, BibAg, BioCN&I, BiolAb, BiolDig, CIS, CPA, ChemAb, CivEngAb, CurCont, DBA, DSA, EIA, EPB, ESPM, EnerInd, F&GI, FCA, FPA, ForAb, GEOBASE, HerbAb, HortAb, I&DA, IABS, IAOP, INIS AtomInd, ISR, IndVet, MaizeAb, NutrAb, OrnHort, PBA, PGegResA, PGrRegA, PHN&I, PN&I, PlantSci, PoultAb, ProtozoAb, RDA, RM&VM, RPP, RRTA, RefZh, RevApplEntom, S&F, SCI, SFA, SIA, SSCI, SeedAb, SoyAb, TDB, TriticAb, VetBull, WAE&RSA, WeedAb, WildRev, ZooRec.
—BLDSC (7254.417180), CASDDS, CISTI, IDS, IE, Infotrieve, ingenta, Linda Hall. **CCC.**
Published by: Society for Range Management, 445 Union Blvd, Ste 230, Lakewood, CO 80228-1259. TEL 303-986-3309, FAX 303-986-3892, srmden@ix.netcom.com, http://uvalde.tamu.edu/jrm/jrmhome.htm, http://srm.org. Ed. Keith Owens. adv.: B&W page USD 750. Circ: 3,000 (paid).

570 ESP ISSN 0583-7499
REAL SOCIEDAD ESPANOLA DE HISTORIA NATURAL. BOLETIN. ACTAS. Text in Spanish; Summaries in English, French. 1950. a., latest vol.98, 2001. bk.rev. reprints avail. **Document type:** *Bulletin, Academic/Scholarly.*
Supersedes in part (in 1950): Real Sociedad Espanola de Historia Natural. Boletin (0365-9755); Which superseded in part (1872-1903): Sociedad Espanola de Historia Natural. Anales (0210-5160)
Indexed: BiolAb, IECT, RevApplEntom, ZooRec.
—CINDOC, CISTI.
Published by: Real Sociedad Espanola de Historia Natural, Facultades de Biologia y Geologia, Universidad Complutense, Madrid, 28040, Spain. rsehno@eucmax.sim.ucm.es, http://www.ucm.es/info/rsehn/. Ed. Antonio Perejon Rincon. Circ: 900.

570 ESP ISSN 0366-3272
QH301 CODEN: BSHBA7
REAL SOCIEDAD ESPANOLA DE HISTORIA NATURAL. BOLETIN. SECCION BIOLOGICA. Text in Spanish; Summaries in English, French. 1901. a. reprints avail. **Document type:** *Bulletin.*
Supersedes in part (in 1950): Real Sociedad Espanola de Historia Natural. Boletin (0365-9755)
Indexed: ASFA, AgBio, AgrForAb, AnBrAb, BIOSIS Prev, BioCN&I, BiolAb, CPA, EntAb, ForAb, HelmAb, HerbAb, HortAb, I&DA, IECT, IndVet, OrnHort, PBA, PGegResA, PoultAb, ProtozoAb, RM&VM, RPP, RevApplEntom, S&F, SeedAb, VetBull, WeedAb, ZooRec.
—CASDDS, CINDOC, CISTI.
Published by: Real Sociedad Espanola de Historia Natural, Facultades de Biologia y Geologia, Universidad Complutense, Madrid, 28040, Spain. rsehno@eucmax.sim.ucm.es, http://www.ucm.es/info/rsehn/. Ed. Antonio Perejon Rincon.

RECENT ADVANCES IN HISTOPATHOLOGY. see *MEDICAL SCIENCES*

570 SGP
RECENT ADVANCES IN HUMAN BIOLOGY. (vol.4: The Natural History of the Doucs and Snubnosed Moneys) Text in English. irreg., latest vol.10. price varies. **Document type:** *Monographic series, Academic/Scholarly.* **Description:** Provides primatologists, anthropologists and biologist with information on conservation and management of highly endangered Asian primates.
Indexed: ZooRec.
—BLDSC (7303.842500).

Published by: (California Academy of Sciences USA), World Scientific Publishing Co. Pte. Ltd., 5 Toh Tuck Link, Singapore, 596224, Singapore. TEL 65-466-5775, FAX 65-467-7667, wspc@wspc.com.sg, series@wspc.com.sg, http://www.wspc.com.sg/books/series/rahb_series.shtml, http://www.worldscientific.com. Ed. C E Oxnard. **Dist. by:** World Scientific Publishing Co., Inc., 1060 Main St, River Edge, NJ 07661. TEL 201-487-9655, 800-227-7562, FAX 201-487-9656, 888-977-2665; World Scientific Publishing Ltd., 57 Shelton St, London WC2H 9HE, United Kingdom. TEL 44-20-78360888, FAX 44-20-78362020, sales@wspc.co.uk.

570 IND
RECENT RESEARCH DEVELOPMENTS IN LIFE SCIENCES. Text in English. a. **Document type:** *Academic/Scholarly.*
—BLDSC (7305.087425).
Published by: Research Signpost, T.C. 37/661 (2), Fort P.O., Trivandrum, Kerala, India.

577 IND ISSN 0971-1708
HD6515.A8 CODEN: CRPTD6
RECENT RESEARCHES IN ECOLOGY, ENVIRONMENT AND POLLUTION. Text in English. 1988. irreg., latest vol.10, 1993. price varies. **Document type:** *Monographic series.*
Formerly (until 1988): Progress in Ecology (0253-665X)
Indexed: BiolAb, ChemAb, CurCont, ZooRec.
—BLDSC (7305.087900), CASDDS, CISTI. **CCC.**
Published by: Today and Tomorrow's Printers & Publishers, 24 B-5 Desh Bandhu Gupta Rd., Karol Bagh, New Delhi, 110 005, India. TEL 5721928. Ed. Malabika Ray. **Dist. in U.S. by:** Scholarly Publications, 2825 Wilcrest Dr, Ste 255, Houston, TX 77042. TEL 713-781-0070.

REDREAMING THE PLAIN. see *ENVIRONMENTAL STUDIES*

REFERATIVNYI ZHURNAL. BIOLOGIYA. see *BIOLOGY—Abstracting, Bibliographies, Statistics*

REFERATIVNYI ZHURNAL. BIOLOGIYA SEL'SKOKHOZYAISTVENNYKH ZHIVOTNYKH. see *BIOLOGY—Abstracting, Bibliographies, Statistics*

REPORT ON THE ACTIVITIES OF O S P A R. see *ENVIRONMENTAL STUDIES*

573.6 GBR ISSN 1470-1626
QP251 CODEN: RCUKBS
➤ **REPRODUCTION.** Text in English. 2001 (Jan). m. GBP 625, USD 1,100, EUR 1,000 combined subscription to institutions print & online eds. (effective 2005). adv. 180 p./no. 2 cols./p.; back issues avail. **Document type:** *Journal, Academic/Scholarly.* **Description:** Publishes original papers on the molecular biology, biochemistry and physiology of reproduction, including lactation, early embyogenesis in man and other animals and reviews on recent developments in the field.
Formed by the merger of (1996-2000): Reviews of Reproduction (1359-6004); (1960-2000): Journal of Reproduction and Fertility (0022-4251); Which was formerly (1949-1958): Society for the Study of Fertility. Proceedings (0562-4142)
Related titles: Online - full text ed.: ISSN 1741-7899. 2001 (from EBSCO Publishing, HighWire Press, Swets Information Services).
Indexed: ASFA, AbHyg, AgBio, Agr, AnBrAb, B&AI, B&BAb, BIOBASE, BIOSIS Prev, BioCN&I, BiolAb, ChemAb, CurCont, DSA, ExcerpMed, FoVS&M, GenetAb, HortAb, ISR, IndMed, IndVet, Inpharma, MEDLINE, NutrAb, PE&ON, PN&I, PoultAb, RA&MP, RM&VM, Reac, RefZh, SCI, SoyAb, VetBull, ZooRec.
—BLDSC (7713.597800), CISTI, IE, Infotrieve, ingenta. **CCC.**
Published by: (Society for Reproduction and Fertility), BioScientifica Ltd., 22 Apex Court, Woodlands, Bradley Stoke, Bristol, BS32 4JT, United Kingdom. TEL 44-1454-642240, FAX 44-1454-642222, editorial@bioscientifica.com, http://www.reproduction-online.org, http:// www.bioscientifica.com/. Ed. John Carroll. adv.: page GBP 405; trim 170 x 240. **Dist. by & subscr. to:** Portland Press Ltd., Commerce Way, Colchester CO2 8HP, United Kingdom. TEL 44-1206-796-351, FAX 44-1206-799-331, sales@portland-services.com, http://www.portland-services.com.

570 AUS ISSN 1031-3613
QP251 CODEN: RFDEEH
➤ **REPRODUCTION, FERTILITY AND DEVELOPMENT.** Text in English. 1989. 8/yr. AUD 160 combined subscription in Australia & New Zealand to individuals for print & online eds.; USD 160 combined subscription elsewhere to individuals for print & online eds.; AUD 760 combined subscription in Australia & New Zealand to institutions for print & online eds.; USD 655 combined subscription elsewhere to institutions for print & online eds. (effective 2004). adv. charts; illus. Index. back issues avail. **Document type:** *Journal, Academic/Scholarly.* **Description:** Covers reproductive biology, reproductive endocrinology and developmental biology.
Formed by the merger of (1982-1989): Clinical Reproduction and Fertility (0725-556X); (1948-1989): Australian Journal of Biological Sciences (0004-9417)
Related titles: Microform ed.: (from PQC); Online - full text ed.: AUD 135 in Australia & New Zealand to individuals; USD 125 elsewhere to individuals; AUD 680 in Australia & New Zealand to institutions; USD 590 elsewhere to institutions (effective 2004) (from EBSCO Publishing, O C L C Online Computer Library Center, Inc., R M I T Publishing, Swets Information Services).
Indexed: AEBA, ASCA, ASFA, AbHyg, AgBio, Agr, AnBrAb, B&AI, B&BAb, BIOBASE, BIOSIS Prev, BiolAb, CBTA, CIN, CLL, CRFR, ChemAb, ChemTitl, CurCont, DSA, EPB, ExcerpMed, FCA, FPA, FS&TA, Faml, ForAb, GenetAb, HortAb, IABS, ISR, IndMed, IndVet, Inpharma, MEDLINE, NutrAb, OceAb, PBA, PE&ON, PN&I, PoultAb, RASB, RM&VM, RPP, Reac, RevApplEntom, S&F, SCI, SFA, SSCI, SoyAb, TDB, TriticAb, VetBull, WeedAb, WildRev, ZooRec.
—BLDSC (7713.603000), CASDDS, CISTI, GNLM, IDS, IE, Infotrieve, ingenta, Linda Hall. **CCC.**
Published by: (C S I R O Australia), C S I R O Publishing, 150 Oxford St, PO Box 1139, Collingwood, VIC 3066, Australia. TEL 61-3-96627629, FAX 61-3-96627611, camilla.myers@publish.csiro.au, publishing@csiro.au, http://www.publish.csiro.au/journals/rfd. Ed. Sharon Mortimer. Circ: 600.

573.6 FRA ISSN 0926-5287
SF768 CODEN: RNDEE5
➤ **REPRODUCTION, NUTRITION, DEVELOPMENT.** Text in English; Abstracts in English. 1961. bi-m. EUR 417 combined subscription domestic print & online eds.; EUR 485 combined subscription in the European Union print & online eds.; EUR 511 combined subscription elsewhere print & online eds. (effective 2005). adv. charts; illus. index. **Document type:** *Academic/Scholarly.* **Description:** Presents papers about reproduction, development and nutrition in animals.
Former titles (until 1989): Reproduction, Nutrition, Developpement (0181-1916); (until 1980): Annales de Biologie Animale, Biochimie, Biophysique (0003-388X)
Related titles: Online - full text ed.: ISSN 1297-9708 (from EBSCO Publishing, Swets Information Services).
Indexed: AEA, ASCA, ASFA, AbHyg, AgBio, AnBrAb, AnalAb, BIOBASE, BIOSIS Prev, BiolAb, CIN, ChemAb, ChemTitl, CurCont, DBA, DSA, DentInd, ExcerpMed, FCA, FS&TA, FoVS&M, HerbAb, HortAb, IABS, ISR, IndMed, IndVet, Inpharma, MEDLINE, MaizeAb, NutrAb, PGegResA, PN&I, PoultAb, ProtozoAb, RA&MP, RM&VM, Reac, S&F, SCI, SFA, SIA, SoyAb, TriticAb, VetBull.
—BLDSC (7713.630000), CASDDS, CISTI, GNLM, IDS, IE, Infotrieve, ingenta, Linda Hall. **CCC.**
Published by: (France. Institut National de la Recherche Agronomique (INRA)), E D P Sciences, 17 Ave du Hoggar, Parc d'Activites de Courtaboeuf, BP 112, Cedex A, Les Ulis, F-91944, France. TEL 33-1-69187575, FAX 33-1-69860678, subscribers@edpsciences.org, http://www.edpsciences.org. Circ: 2,000.

573.6 PHL
REPRODUCTIONS. Text in English. 1970. irreg. (15-20/yr.). looseleaf. PHP 5, USD 4. bk.rev.
Published by: (University of Santo Tomas), University of Santo Tomas, Institute for the Study of Human Reproduction (Subsidiary of: University of Santo Tomas), Faculty of Medicine, Espana St, Sampaloc, Manila, Philippines. Ed. Dr. Vicente J A Rosales. Circ: 5,000.

570 POL ISSN 1642-431X
REPRODUCTIVE BIOLOGY. Text in English. 2001. 3/yr. USD 30 foreign to individuals; USD 60 foreign to institutions (effective 2005). **Document type:** *Journal, Academic/Scholarly.*
—BLDSC (7713.704300).
Published by: Towarzystwo Biologii Rozrodu/Society for Biology of Reproduction, ul Bydgoska 1/8, Olsztyn, 10243, Poland. reniac@uwm.edu.pl.

570 JPN
RESEARCH INSTITUTE OF EVOLUTIONARY BIOLOGY. PUBLICATIONS. Text in English, French. 1978. irreg. **Document type:** *Monographic series, Academic/Scholarly.*
Published by: Research Institute of Evolutionary Biology/Shinka Seibutsugaku Kenkyujo, 4-28 Kami-Yoga 2-chome, Setagaya-ku, Tokyo, 158-0098, Japan.

RESONANCE (SUMTERVILLE). see *PHYSICS*

577 USA ISSN 1070-4868
S494.5.P47
THE RESOURCES OF INTERNATIONAL PERMACULTURE. Variant title: T R I P. Text in English. 1986. irreg. USD 30 domestic; USD 40 foreign (effective 2000). **Document type:** *Directory.* **Description:** Lists groups allied to the permaculture movement worldwide.
Supersedes in part (in 1990): T I P S Y: International Permaculture Species Yearbook (0896-5781)
Related titles: Diskette ed.
Published by: Yankee Permaculture, Hemenway Permaculture, Box 52, Sparr, FL 32192-0052. permacultur@aol.com. R&P Dan Hemenway.

570 CUB ISSN 0864-3490
QH301
➤ **REVISTA BIOLOGIA.** Text in Spanish, English. 1987. s-a. CUP 30 domestic; USD 30 foreign (effective 2003). back issues avail. **Document type:** *Academic/Scholarly.* **Description:** Includes research in the field of biology and related issues.
Related titles: Online - full text ed.: (from EBSCO Publishing).
Indexed: AgBio, BioCN&I, CPA, DSA, FCA, ForAb, HelmAb, HerbAb, HortAb, I&DA, IndVet, NemAb, NutrAb, OrnHort, PBA, PGegResA, PGrRegA, PHN&I, PoultAb, RDA, RPP, RRTA, RefZh, RevApplEntom, S&F, SIA, SeedAb, SoyAb, TDB, VetBull, ZooRec.
—CISTI.
Published by: Universidad de La Habana, Facultad de Biologia, Calle 25 #455 entre J y I, Vedado, Plaza Municipio, Havana, Cuba. TEL 53-7-8329000, FAX 53-7-8321321, marthap@fbio.uh.cu. Ed. Martha Perez. Circ: 200 (paid); 100 (controlled).

➤ **REVISTA BIOMEDICA.** see *MEDICAL SCIENCES*

➤ **REVISTA BRASILEIRA DE PARASITOLOGIA VETERINARIA/BRAZILIAN JOURNAL OF VETERINARY PARASITOLOGY.** see *VETERINARY SCIENCE*

570 CUB ISSN 0253-5688
QH301 CODEN: RCNCD5
REVISTA C E N I C. CIENCIAS BIOLOGICAS. Text and summaries in English, Spanish. 1969. 3/yr. USD 60 in North America; USD 90 elsewhere (effective 2000). adv. bk.rev. bibl.; charts. back issues avail. **Description:** Presents national and international articles in the biological sciences; covers biotechnology, bioengineering, environmental pollution and pharmacology.
Formerly (until 1986): Revista de Ciencias Biologicas (0258-6002)
Related titles: Online - full text ed.: (from EBSCO Publishing).
Indexed: ASFA, BiolAb, CIN, ChemAb, ChemTitl.
—CASDDS, CINDOC, CISTI.
Published by: (Cuba. Ministerio de Educacion Superior), Centro Nacional de Investigaciones Cientificas, Ave. 25 y 158, Apdo. 6880 y 6990, Havana, 10600, Cuba. TEL 537-218066, FAX 537-330497, TELEX 51-1582 CNIC CU, cnic@reduniv.edu.cu. Ed. Juan J Meitin. Circ: 750.

570 577 CHL ISSN 0716-078X
CODEN: IMTCE7
➤ **REVISTA CHILENA DE HISTORIA NATURAL.** Text in Spanish, English. 1897. q. CLP 40,000 domestic; USD 100 foreign (effective 2005). bk.rev. 150 p./no.; back issues avail.; reprints avail. **Document type:** *Journal, Academic/Scholarly.*
Related titles: Online - full text ed.: ISSN 0717-6317. 2000. free (effective 2005) (from SciELO).
Indexed: AgBio, AgrForAb, BIOSIS Prev, BioCN&I, BiolAb, CPA, CurCont, FCA, FPA, ForAb, HelmAb, HerbAb, HortAb, I&DA, IndVet, NutrAb, OrnHort, PBA, PGegResA, PoultAb, ProtozoAb, RA&MP, RDA, RPP, S&F, SIA, SeedAb, SoyAb, TDB, TriticAb, VetBull, WeedAb, ZooRec.
Published by: Sociedad de Biologia de Chile, Canada 253, Piso 3, Depto F, Casilla 16169, Santiago, Providencia 9, Chile. TEL 56-2-2093503, FAX 56-2-2258427, socbiol@reuna.huelen.cl, http://www.scielo.cl/scielo.php?script=sci_serial&pid=0716-078X&lng=en&nrm=iso. Ed. Luis Edensperger.

611.01816 610 CUB ISSN 0864-0300
REVISTA CUBANA DE INVESTIGACIONES BIOMEDICAS. Text in Spanish; Summaries in English, Spanish. q. USD 30 in North America; USD 32 in South America; USD 34 elsewhere (effective 2005). bibl.; charts; illus. index. **Document type:** *Journal, Academic/Scholarly.*
Related titles: Online - full text ed.: ISSN 1561-3011. 1995. free (effective 2005) (from EBSCO Publishing).
Indexed: IPA.
Published by: (Centro Nacional de Informacion de Ciencias Medicas, Cuba. Ministerio de Salud Publica), Editorial de Ciencias Medicas, O'Reilly No. 4, Habana, Cuba. TEL 809-62-8091, http://scielo.sld.cu/scielo.php?script=sci_serial&pid=0864-0300&lng=en&nrm=iso. Ed. Maura Diaz. Circ: 1,400. **Co-sponsors:** Sociedad Cubana de Ciencias Fisiologicas; Instituto Superior de Ciencias Medicales de La Habana.

573.6 CUB ISSN 0138-6700
REVISTA CUBANA DE REPRODUCCION ANIMAL. Abstracts and contents page in English. 1975. 2/yr. USD 14 in North America; USD 15 in South America; USD 19 in Europe. bibl.; charts; illus.
Indexed: Agrind, AnBrAb, BiolAb, IndVet, PoultAb.
—CINDOC.
Published by: Centro de Informacion y Documentacion Agropecuario, Gaveta Postal 4149, Havana, 4, Cuba. Ed. J R Morales. **Dist. by:** Ediciones Cubanas, Obispo No. 527, Apdo. 605, Havana, Cuba.

570 PRT ISSN 0034-7736
QH301 CODEN: RVBIAP
REVISTA DE BIOLOGIA. Text in English, French, German, Portuguese. 1957. irreg. price varies. adv. bk.rev. charts; illus. reprint service avail. from PQC. **Document type:** *Academic/Scholarly.*
Related titles: Microform ed.: (from PQC).

Indexed: ASFA, AgBio, AgrForAb, BIOSIS Prev, BioCN&I, BiolAb, CPA, ChemAb, FCA, ForAb, HelmAb, HerbAb, HortAb, I&DA, IndVet, OceAb, OrnHort, PBA, PGegResA, PGrRegA, ProtozoAb, RPP, RRTA, RefZh, RevApplEntom, S&F, SeedAb, TriticAb, WAE&RSA, WeedAb, ZooRec.
—BLDSC (7842.750000), CASDDS, CISTI.
Published by: Universidade de Lisboa, Museu, Laboratorio e Jardim Botanico, Rua da Escola Politecnica, 58, Lisboa, 1250-102, Portugal. TEL 351-21-3921801, FAX 351-21-3970882, jbbiblio@fc.ul.pt, http://www.jb.ul.pt, http://wwwjb.ul.pt/. Ed., R&P F M Catarino TEL 351-21-3921890. Adv. contact Manuel Dos Santos Lopes. Circ: 250.

570 URY ISSN 0304-971X
QH305.2.U8 CODEN: RBURDA
REVISTA DE BIOLOGIA DEL URUGUAY. Text in Spanish; Summaries in English. 1973. a. USD 20. illus. index. back issues avail. **Document type:** *Academic/Scholarly.*
Indexed: BiolAb.
—CISTI, Linda Hall.
Published by: Fernando Mane-Garzon, Ed. & Pub., Casilla de Correo 157, Montevideo, Uruguay. Circ: 1,500.

578.77 CHL ISSN 0717-3326
QH91.A1 CODEN: RBIMAY
➤ **REVISTA DE BIOLOGIA MARINA Y OCEANOGRAFIA.** Text in English, Spanish; Summaries in English, Spanish. 1948. s-a. USD 10 domestic to individuals; USD 15 foreign to individuals; USD 20 domestic to institutions; USD 25 foreign to institutions (effective 2005); or exchange basis. cum.index. back issues avail. **Document type:** *Journal, Academic/Scholarly.* **Description:** Presents papers on marine biology, ecology, physical, chemical and biological oceanography, marine geology, and estuarine environment.
Former titles (until 1997): Revista de Biologia Marina (0080-2115); (until 1965): Montemar (0716-2855); (until 1961): Revista de Biologia Marina (0716-2863)
Related titles: Online - full text ed.: ISSN 0718-1957. 2001.
Indexed: ASFA, BIOSIS Prev, BiolAb, ESPM, GEOBASE, MSCT, SFA, WildRev, ZooRec.
—BLDSC (7843.100000), CINDOC, CISTI, IE, ingenta.
Published by: Universidad de Valparaiso, Facultad de Ciencias del Mar, Avenida Borgono, Montemar, Vina del Mar, Chile. TEL 56-32-507820, FAX 56-32-507859, jeanette.santana@uv.cl, http://www.revbiolmar.cl/, http://www.uv.cl. Ed., R&P Bernardita Campos. Circ: 400.

570.909 CRI ISSN 0034-7744
RC960 CODEN: RBTCAP
➤ **REVISTA DE BIOLOGIA TROPICAL.** Text in English, Spanish. 1953. 4/yr. USD 40 (effective 2000). charts; illus. index. back issues avail.; reprint service avail. from PQC. **Document type:** *Academic/Scholarly.*
Related titles: Microform ed.: (from PQC); Online - full text ed.: free (effective 2005) (from Gale Group).
Indexed: ASCA, ASFA, AbHyg, AgBio, AgrForAb, AnBrAb, ApicAb, BIOSIS Prev, BioCN&I, BiolAb, CPA, ChemAb, CurCont, DSA, ESPM, FCA, FPA, ForAb, HelmAb, HerbAb, HortAb, I&DA, INIS AtomInd, IndMed, IndVet, MBA, MEDLINE, MaizeAb, NemAb, NutrAb, OrnHort, PBA, PGegResA, PGrRegA, PHN&I, PN&I, PoultAb, ProtozoAb, RA&MP, RDA, RM&VM, RPP, RRTA, RevApplEntom, RiceAb, S&F, SFA, SWRA, SeedAb, SoyAb, TDB, TriticAb, VetBull, WAE&RSA, WeedAb, WildRev, ZooRec.
—BLDSC (7843.200000), CASDDS, CINDOC, CISTI, IDS, IE, Infotrieve, ingenta, Linda Hall.
Published by: Editorial de la Universidad de Costa Rica, Apdo. 75-2060, Ciudad Universitaria Rodrigo Facio Brenes, San Pedro de Montes de Oca, San Jose, 2050, Costa Rica. TEL 506-207-4000, FAX 506-207-5535, cmmoreno@cariari.ucr.ac.cr, http://rbt.biologia.ucr.ac.cr/. Ed. Julian Monge Najera. R&P Mario Murillo TEL 506-2075003. Circ: 1,000.

570 VEN ISSN 1012-2494
QH106.5 CODEN: RECLEQ
➤ **REVISTA DE ECOLOGIA LATINOAMERICANA/JOURNAL OF LATIN AMERICAN ECOLOGY.** Text in English, Portuguese, Spanish, French; Abstracts in English. 1983. 3/yr. USD 50 (effective 2004). adv. bk.rev. bibl. back issues avail.; reprints avail. **Document type:** *Journal, Academic/Scholarly.*
Formerly (until 1997): Revista de Ecologia, Conservacion y Ornitologia Latinoamericana
Related titles: CD-ROM ed.; E-mail ed.; Online - full text ed.
Indexed: ASFA, ApEcolAb, BIOBASE, BiolAb, ESPM, EntAb, ZooRec.
Published by: Centro de Investigacion y Reproduccion de Especies Silvestres, Apartado Postal 397, Merida, 5101, Venezuela. cires@ciens.ula.ve, http://www.ciens.ula.ve/~cires. Ed. Hector Fernando Aguilar. Adv. contact Lieselotte Hoeger de Aguilar. Circ: 3,000.

578.77 CUB ISSN 0252-1962
QH109.C9 CODEN: RIMAD2
REVISTA DE INVESTIGACIONES MARINAS. Text in Spanish; Summaries in English, Spanish. 1980. 3/yr. CUP 4.50 domestic; USD 24 in North America; USD 25 in South America; USD 26 in Europe.
Indexed: ASFA, ESPM, RefZh, ZooRec.
—CINDOC, CISTI, KNAW, Linda Hall.
Published by: (Universidad de La Habana, Direccion de Informacion Cientifico- Tecnica), Ediciones Cubanas, Obispo No. 527, Apdo. 605, Havana, Cuba.

REVISTA ECUATORIANA DE MEDICINA Y CIENCIAS BIOLOGICAS. see *MEDICAL SCIENCES*

578.77 CHL ISSN 0716-1069
QH91.A1
REVISTA INVESTIGACIONES MARINAS. Key Title: Investigaciones Marinas. Text in Spanish. 1970. s-a. USD 100 (effective 2001). bk.rev. **Document type:** *Academic/Scholarly.*
Related titles: Online - full text ed.: ISSN 0717-7178. 2001. free (effective 2005) (from SciELO).
Indexed: ASFA, BiolAb, ESPM, M&GPA, ZooRec.
Published by: (Universidad Catolica de Valparaiso, Escuela de Ciencias del Mar), Ediciones Universitarias de Valparaiso, Casilla 1415, Valparaiso, Chile. TEL 56-32-273086, FAX 56-32-273429, euvsa@ucv.cl, http://www.ucv.cl/web/euv. Ed. Sergio G Palma. Circ: 250.

570 BRA ISSN 0100-7653
CODEN: RNOBDG
REVISTA NORDESTINA DE BIOLOGIA. Text in Portuguese. 1978. s-a.
Indexed: ESPM, ZooRec.
—CISTI.
Published by: Universidade Federal de Campina Grande, Centro de Ciencias Biologicas e da Saude, Campus Campina Grande, Campina Grande, PB 58109-970, Brazil.

570 PER ISSN 1561-0837
QH301
REVISTA PERUANA DE BIOLOGIA. Text in Spanish. 1974. s-a. **Document type:** *Journal, Academic/Scholarly.* **Description:** All areas of biology with emphasis on biodiversity, biotechnology, the environment, ecology and biomedicine.
Related titles: Online - full text ed.: ISSN 1727-9933. 1998. free (effective 2005).
Published by: Universidad Nacional Mayor de San Marcos, Facultad de Ciencias Biologicas, C P 11-0058, Lima, 11, Peru. TEL 51-1-4524135, 51-1-4524135, FAX 51-1-4649110, 51-1-4649110, http://sisbib.unmsm.edu.pe/BVRevistas/biologia/biologiaNEW.htm. Ed. Leonardo Romero.

570 BRA ISSN 0104-7264
S475.B7
REVISTA UNIVERSIDADE RURAL. SERIE CIENCIAS DA VIDA. Text in Portuguese. 1971. s-a. BRL 24. **Description:** Publishes original works on basic and applied research.
Formerly (until 1995): Universidade Federal Rural do Rio de Janeiro. Arquivos (0100-2481)
Indexed: AnBrAb, BioCN&I, DSA, FCA, IndVet, RefZh, RevApplEntom, ZooRec.
—CISTI.
Published by: Universidade Federal Rural do Rio de Janeiro, Antiga Rodovia Rio, km 47, Sala 102-P1, Seropedica, RJ 23890-000, Brazil. TEL 55-21-6821210, FAX 55-21-6821201, edur@ufrrj.br, http://www.ufrrj.br/. Ed. Suzana Bencke Amato.

REVUE D'ECOLOGIE: LA TERRE ET LA VIE; revue d'ecologie appliquee a la protection de la nature. see *ENVIRONMENTAL STUDIES*

REVUE D'ECOLOGIE. SUPPLEMENT. see *ENVIRONMENTAL STUDIES*

570 FRA ISSN 0373-2851
CODEN: RSNAA6
REVUE DES SCIENCES NATURELLES D'AUVERGNE. Text in French. 1921. a. back issues avail.
Indexed: BIOSIS Prev, BiolAb, RefZh, ZooRec.
Published by: Societe d'Histoire Naturelle d'Auvergne, Faculte de Botanique, 2 rue Ledru, Clermont-Ferrand, 63000, France.

570 FRA ISSN 1773-035X
➤ **REVUE FRANCOPHONE DES LABORATOIRES.** Text in French. 1972. 10/yr. EUR 192.95 domestic to individuals; EUR 197 in Europe to individuals; JPY 25,900 in Japan to individuals; USD 218 to individuals except Europe and Japan; EUR 202.74 domestic to institutions; EUR 207 in Europe to institutions; JPY 27,000 in Japan to institutions; USD 234 to institutions except Europe and Japan (effective 2006). adv. **Document type:** *Journal, Academic/Scholarly.* **Description:** Offers articles concentrating on breaking scientific news - both biological and economical - along with developments in research in the diagnostic fields.
Former titles (until 2005): Revue Francaise des Laboratoires (0338-9898); (until 1975): Revue Francaise des Fournisseurs de Laboratoires (0338-988X)
Related titles: Online - full text ed.: (from EBSCO Publishing, Gale Group, IngentaConnect, ScienceDirect, Swets Information Services).
Indexed: RefZh.
—IE. **CCC.**
Published by: (Labo-France), Elsevier France, Editions Scientifiques et Medicales (Subsidiary of: Elsevier Science & Technology), 23 Rue Linois, Paris, 75724, France. TEL 33-1-71724600, FAX 33-1-71724650, http://www.elsevier.com/locate/rfl, http://www.elsevier.fr. Eds. Ms. Martine Tirouche, P Lafargue. Circ: 7,000. **Subscr. to:** Elsevier BV, PO Box 211, Amsterdam 1000 AE, Netherlands. TEL 31-20-485-3757, FAX 31-20-485-3432, nlinfo-f@elsevier.nl, http://www.elsevier.nl.

570 BEL ISSN 0375-1465
REVUE VERVIETOISE D'HISTOIRE NATURELLE; bulletin trimestriel des Naturalistes Vervietois. Text in French. 1944. q.
Formerly (until 1949): Naturaliste Amateur (0770-0709)
Indexed: ZooRec.
Published by: Imprimerie Hamers J.C., Hameau de Husquet 119, Dison, 4820, Belgium. Ed. J Lambert. Circ: 300. **Subscr. to:** M.L. Phillipe, Rue de Jehanster 89, Verviers 4800, Belgium.

B

570 SGP
▼ **RICE GENOMICS.** Text in English. 2003 (Fall). irreg., latest vol.1. price varies. 200 p./no.; **Document type:** *Monographic series, Academic/Scholarly.*
Published by: World Scientific Publishing Co. Pte. Ltd., 5 Toh Tuck Link, Singapore, 596224, Singapore. TEL 65-466-5775, FAX 65-467-7667, wspc@wspc.com.sg, http://www.wspc.com.sg/books/series/rg_series.shtml, http://www.worldscientific.com. Eds. Huanming Yang, S Ramachandran, Yu Jun. **Dist. by:** World Scientific Publishing Co., Inc., 1060 Main St, River Edge, NJ 07661. TEL 201-487-9655, 800-227-7562, FAX 201-487-9656, 888-977-2665; World Scientific Publishing Ltd., 57 Shelton St, London WC2H 9HE, United Kingdom. TEL 44-20-78360888, FAX 44-20-78362020.

570 JPN ISSN 0286-8172
➤ **RIKUSUI SEIBUTSUGAKUHO/BIOLOGY OF INLAND WATERS.** Text in English, Japanese. 1980. irreg., latest vol.13. JPY 4,000 to members. **Document type:** *Academic/Scholarly.* **Description:** Includes observation notes, comments, and original papers on biology of inland waters, e.g. ecology, taxonomy, physiology and ethology.
Indexed: ZooRec.
Published by: Nara Rikusui Seibutsu Kenkyukai/Nara Scientific Research Society of Inland Water Biology, c/o Nara Joshi Daigaku Rigakubu, Seibutsugaku Kyoshitsu, Kita-Uoyanishi-Machi, Nara-shi, 630-8263, Japan. TEL 81-742-20-3424, ape@cc.nara-wu.ac.jp. Ed. Makoto Nagoshi. Circ: 300.

570 ITA ISSN 0035-6050
QH301 CODEN: RBILAV
➤ **RIVISTA DI BIOLOGIA/BIOLOGY FORUM**; biology forum. Text in English, Italian. 1919. 3/yr. EUR 53 domestic; EUR 74 foreign (effective 2005). bk.rev. index. reprint service avail. from PQC. **Document type:** *Journal, Academic/Scholarly.* **Description:** Features essays, reviews, critiques and comments on biological topics.
Indexed: ASCA, ASFA, AbHyg, AgBio, ArtHuCI, BIOBASE, BiolAb, CTA, ChemAb, ChemoAb, CurCont, EPB, ExcerpMed, IndMed, Inspec, MEDLINE, NutrAb, PBA, PGrRegA, RPP, RevApplEntom, SFA, TriticAb, ZooRec.
—BLDSC (7982.100000), CASDDS, CISTI, GNLM, IDS, IE, Infotrieve, ingenta, Linda Hall.
Published by: Tilgher-Genova, Via Assarotti 31-15, Genoa, GE 16122, Italy. TEL 39-010-8391140, FAX 39-010-870653, tilgher@tilgher.it, http://www.tilgher.it/biologiae.html. Eds. Giuseppe Sermonti, Renzo Morchio, Silvano Scannerini. R&P Lucio Bozzi. Circ: 750.

571.9 ITA ISSN 0391-1551
CODEN: RBNPD3
RIVISTA DI BIOLOGIA NORMALE E PATOLOGICA. Text and summaries in English, Italian. 1975. bi-m. bk.rev. back issues avail.
Indexed: AbHyg, BiolAb, ChemAb, ExcerpMed, IndVet, VetBull.
—CASDDS. **CCC.**
Published by: Universita degli Studi di Messina, Centro Universitario di Ricerca sui Tumori, Via Giacomo Venezian, Messina, ME 98122, Italy. Ed. Carmelo Cavallaro. Circ: 300.

578.77 ITA ISSN 0048-8399
QH96.25.I8 CODEN: RIIDBN
RIVISTA DI IDROBIOLOGIA. Text in Italian; Summaries in English. 1960. q. per issue exchange basis. bk.rev. illus. cum.index. **Document type:** *Monographic series.*
Indexed: ASFA, AnBrAb, BIOSIS Prev, BiolAb, ChemAb, ESPM, ForAb, HelmAb, HerbAb, HortAb, I&DA, IndVet, NutrAb, PGegResA, RefZh, S&F, TDB, VetBull, WeedAb, ZooRec.
—BLDSC (7986.650000), CASDDS, CISTI.
Published by: Universita degli Studi di Perugia, Istituto di Idrobiologia, Via Elce Di Sotto, Perugia, PG 06123, Italy. TEL 39-075-5855705, FAX 39-075-5855709. Ed. Giampaolo Moretti. Circ: 300.

RIVISTA DI NEUROBIOLOGIA. see *MEDICAL SCIENCES—Psychiatry And Neurology*

RIVISTA PIEMONTESE DI STORIA NATURALE. see *EARTH SCIENCES—Geology*

▼ *new title* ➤ *refereed* ✶ *unverified* ♦ *full entry avail.*

ROMANIAN ACADEMY. PROCEEDINGS. SERIES B: CHEMISTRY, LIFE SCIENCES AND GEOSCIENCES. see *CHEMISTRY*

570 RUS ISSN 1026-3470
CODEN: IANBAM

ROSSIISKAYA AKADEMIYA NAUK. IZVESTIYA. SERIYA BIOLOGICHESKAYA. Text in Russian; Summaries in English. 1936. bi-m. RUR 1,160 for 6 mos. domestic (effective 2004). bk.rev. index. **Document type:** *Journal, Academic/Scholarly.* **Description:** Focuses on fundamental studies in the fields of cell biology, biochemistry, zoology, botany, physiology, and ecology.
Formerly (until 1992): Akademiya Nauk S.S.S.R. Izvestiya. Seriya Biologicheskaya (0002-3329)
Related titles: ♦ English Translation: Russian Academy of Sciences. Biology Bulletin. ISSN 1062-3590.
Indexed: ASFA, AbHyg, AgBio, AnBrAb, BIOSIS Prev, BiolAb, CPA, ChemAb, CurCont, ESPM, FCA, FPA, ForAb, HelmAb, HerbAb, HortAb, I&DA, IAA, ISR, IndMed, IndVet, MEDLINE, MaizeAb, NutrAb, OrnHort, PBA, PGegResA, PGrRegA, PotatoAb, ProtozoAb, RA&MP, RPP, RefZh, RevApplEntom, RiceAb, S&F, SCI, SeedAb, SoyAb, TDB, TriticAb, WeedAb, ZooRec.
—BLDSC (0082.301000), CASDDS, CISTI, East View, GNLM, IDS, Linda Hall. **CCC.**
Published by: (Rossiiskaya Akademiya Nauk/Russian Academy of Sciences), Izdatel'stvo Nauka, Profsoyuznaya ul 90, Moscow, 117864, Russian Federation. TEL 7-095-3347151, FAX 7-095-4202220, secret@naukaran.ru, http://www.maik.rssi.ru/cgi-bin/list.pl?page=izvbio, http://www.naukaran.ru.

578.77 DEU ISSN 0943-822X
QH92.7

ROSTOCKER MEERESBIOLOGISCHE BEITRAEGE. Text in German. 1993. irreg. **Document type:** *Monographic series, Academic/Scholarly.*
Indexed: ESPM.
Published by: Universitaet Rostock, Fachbereich Biologie, Meeresbiologie, Albert-Einstein-Str. 3B, Rostock, 18051, Germany. TEL 49-381-498-6060, FAX 49-381-498-6052, wolfgang.wranik@biologie.uni.rostock.de, http://www.biologie.uni-rostock.de/.

570 610 GBR ISSN 0962-8436
QH301 CODEN: PTRBAE

➤ **ROYAL SOCIETY OF LONDON. PHILOSOPHICAL TRANSACTIONS. BIOLOGICAL SCIENCES.** Text in English. 1887. m. GBP 1,190 combined subscription in Europe print & online eds.; USD 1,975 combined subscription in North America print & online eds.; GBP 1,280, USD 2,050 combined subscription elsewhere print & online eds. (effective 2004). back issues avail.; reprint service avail. from PQC. **Document type:** *Proceedings, Academic/Scholarly.* **Description:** Contains full reports of the Society discussion meetings, topical themes and reviews on specific subjects.
Former titles (until 1990): Royal Society of London. Philosophical Transactions. Series B. Biological Sciences (0080-4622); (until 1935): Royal Society of London. Philosophical Transactions. Series B. Containing Papers of a Biological Character (0264-3960); (until 1897): Royal Society of London. Philosophical Transactions. B (0264-3839); Which superseded in part (1665-1887): Royal Society of London. Philosophical Transactions (0261-0523); Which was formerly (until 1682): Royal Society of London. Philosophical Collections (0369-8696); (until 1679): Philosophical Transactions (0370-2316)
Related titles: Microfiche ed.: (from IDC); Microform ed.: (from PMC); Online - full text ed.: ISSN 1471-2970 (from EBSCO Publishing, Gale Group, JSTOR (Web-based Journal Archive), O C L C Online Computer Library Center, Inc., Swets Information Services).
Indexed: AEA, AESIS, ASCA, ASFA, AbHyg, AgBio, AgrForAb, AnBrAb, ApicAb, BIOBASE, BIOSIS Prev, BioCN&I, BiolAb, BrArAb, BrGeoL, CBTA, CMCI, CPA, ChemAb, ChemTitl, CurCont, DSA, DentInd, ESPM, EnvAb, EnvInd, ExcerpMed, FCA, FPA, ForAb, GEOBASE, HelmAb, HerbAb, HortAb, I&DA, IABS, ISR, IndMed, IndVet, Inpharma, M&GPA, MEDLINE, MaizeAb, NemAb, NutrAb, OrnHort, PBA, PGegResA, PGrRegA, PN&I, PetrolAb, PlantSci, PotatoAb, PoultAb, ProtozoAb, RDA, RM&VM, RPP, Reac, RefZh, RevApplEntom, S&F, S&MA, SCI, SFA, SIA, SPPI, SeedAb, SoyAb, TDB, TriticAb, VetBull, WAE&RSA, WeedAb, WildRev, ZooRec.
—BLDSC (6464.000000), CASDDS, CISTI, IDS, IE, Infotrieve, ingenta, Linda Hall, PADDS. **CCC.**
Published by: Royal Society of London, 6-9 Carlton House Terr, London, SW1Y 5AG, United Kingdom. TEL 44-207-8395561, FAX 44-207-9761837, sales@royalsoc.ac.uk, http://www.pubs.royalsoc.ac.uk/phil_trans_bio_homepage.shtml, http://www.royalsoc.ac.uk. Ed. Brian Heap. R&P Phil Hurst. Circ: 590.

570 GBR ISSN 0962-8452
QH301

➤ **ROYAL SOCIETY OF LONDON. PROCEEDINGS. BIOLOGICAL SCIENCES.** Text in English. 1905. bi-m. GBP 700 combined subscription in Europe print & online eds.; USD 1,175 combined subscription in US & Canada print & online eds.; GBP 750, USD 1,200 combined subscription elsewhere print & online eds. (effective 2004). back issues avail.; reprint service avail. from ISI. **Document type:** *Proceedings, Academic/Scholarly.* **Description:** Publishes original papers on all aspects of the biological sciences. Including the latest research.
Former titles (until 1990): Royal Society of London. Proceedings. Series B. Biological Sciences (0080-4649); (until 1934): Royal Society of London. Proceedings. Series B. Containing Papers of a Biological Character (0950-1193); Which superseded in part (1832-1905): Royal Society of London. Proceedings (0370-1662); Which was formerly (until 1855): Royal Society of London. Abstracts of the Papers Communicated (0365-0855); (until 1849): Royal Society of London. Philosophical Transactions. Abstracts of the Papers Printed (0365-5695)
Related titles: Microform ed.: (from PMC); Online - full text ed.: ISSN 1471-2954. 1997 (from EBSCO Publishing, Gale Group, JSTOR (Web-based Journal Archive), O C L C Online Computer Library Center, Inc., Swets Information Services).
Indexed: ASCA, ASFA, AbHyg, AgBio, Agr, AgrForAb, AnBeAb, AnBrAb, ApEcolAb, B&BAb, BIOBASE, BIOSIS Prev, BibAg, BioCN&I, BiolAb, BrArAb, BrGeoL, CMCI, CPA, CTA, ChemAb, ChemTitl, ChemoAb, CompAb, CurCont, DSA, DentInd, ESPM, EngInd, EntAb, ExcerpMed, FCA, FPA, FS&TA, ForAb, GEOBASE, GenetAb, HGA, HelmAb, HerbAb, HortAb, I&DA, IABS, ISR, IndMed, IndVet, Inpharma, MEDLINE, MaizeAb, NRN, NemAb, NutrAb, OceAb, OrnHort, PBA, PE&ON, PGegResA, PHN&I, PN&I, PollutAb, PotatoAb, PoultAb, ProtozoAb, RA&MP, RDA, RM&VM, RPP, Reac, RevApplEntom, RiceAb, S&F, SCI, SFA, SIA, SSCI, SeedAb, TDB, TriticAb, VetBull, WAE&RSA, WeedAb, WildRev, ZooRec.
—BLDSC (6804.600000), CASDDS, CISTI, IDS, IE, Infotrieve, ingenta, Linda Hall. **CCC.**
Published by: Royal Society of London, 6-9 Carlton House Terr, London, SW1Y 5AG, United Kingdom. TEL 44-207-8395561, FAX 44-207-9761837, sales@royalsoc.ac.uk, http://www.pubs.royalsoc.ac.uk/proceedingsb.shtml. Ed. Brian Heap. R&P Phil Hurst. Circ: 1,013.

570 550 DEU ISSN 0863-0844

RUDOLSTAEDTER NATURHISTORISCHE SCHRIFTEN. Text and summaries in English, German. 1988. biennial. bk.rev. abstr.; bibl. index. back issues avail. **Document type:** *Academic/Scholarly.* **Description:** Contains articles and papers on various aspects of biology, paleontology, earth sciences, and the history of science.
Related titles: Supplement(s): Rudolstaedter Naturhistorische Schriften. Supplement. ISSN 0949-8702.
Indexed: ASFA, EntAb, ZooRec.
Published by: Thueringer Landesmuseum Heidecksburg Rudolstadt, Schlossbezirk 1, Rudolstadt, 07407, Germany. TEL 49-3672-429030, FAX 49-3672-429090. Pub. Eberhard Mey.

570 RUS ISSN 1062-3590
QH301 CODEN: BRASEK

➤ **RUSSIAN ACADEMY OF SCIENCES. BIOLOGY BULLETIN.** Key Title: Biology Bulletin of the Russian Academy of Sciences. Text in English. 1936. bi-m. EUR 2,598, USD 2,378, GBP 1,628 to institutions (effective 2005). bibl.; charts; illus. index. back issues avail. **Document type:** *Journal, Academic/Scholarly.* **Description:** Focuses on fundamental studies in different fields of biology: cell biology, genetics, biochemistry, zoology, botany, physiology, ecology, and others.
Formerly (until 1992): Academy of Sciences of the U S S R. Biology Bulletin (0098-2164)
Related titles: Online - full text ed.: ISSN 1608-3059. EUR 2,598, USD 2,378, GBP 1,628 to institutions (effective 2005) (from EBSCO Publishing, Gale Group, IngentaConnect, Kluwer Online, O C L C Online Computer Library Center, Inc., Springer LINK, Swets Information Services); ♦ Translation of: Rossiiskaya Akademiya Nauk. Izvestiya. Seriya Biologicheskaya. ISSN 1026-3470.
Indexed: ASFA, AbHyg, AgBio, AgrForAb, AnBrAb, B&BAb, BIOBASE, BibLing, BioCN&I, BioDAb, BiolAb, CPA, CRFR, ChemTitl, CurCont, ESPM, ExcerpMed, FCA, FPA, ForAb, HelmAb, HerbAb, HortAb, I&DA, IABS, IndMed, IndVet, MEDLINE, MaizeAb, NutrAb, OrnHort, PBA, PGegResA, PGrRegA, PHN&I, PotatoAb, PoultAb, ProtozoAb, RA&MP, RM&VM, RPP, RRTA, RevApplEntom, RiceAb, S&F, SIA, SeedAb, TDB, TriticAb, VetBull, WeedAb.
—BLDSC (0406.045000), CISTI, GNLM, IE, Infotrieve, ingenta. **CCC.**
Published by: (Rossiiskaya Akademiya Nauk/Russian Academy of Sciences), M A I K Nauka - Interperiodica, Profsoyuznaya ul 90, Moscow, 117997, Russian Federation. TEL 7-095-3347420, FAX 7-095-3360666, compmg@maik.ru, http://www.maik.ru/cgi-bin/journal.pl?name=biobull&page=main. Ed. Sergei G Vassetzky. **Subscr. to:** Springer-Verlag Dordrecht, Journals Department, PO Box 322, Dordrecht, Netherlands. TEL 31-78-6576392, FAX 31-78-6576474.

570 RUS ISSN 1062-3604
QL951 CODEN: RJDBE2

➤ **RUSSIAN JOURNAL OF DEVELOPMENTAL BIOLOGY.** Text in English. 1970. bi-m. EUR 2,648, USD 2,418, GBP 1,655 to institutions (effective 2005). back issues avail. **Document type:** *Journal, Academic/Scholarly.* **Description:** Publishes fundamental and applied research papers and reviews on development, regeneration, and carcinogenesis at the molecular, cellular, and organismic levels.
Formerly (until 1993): Soviet Journal of Developmental Biology (0049-173X)
Related titles: Online - full text ed.: ISSN 1608-3326. EUR 2,648, USD 2,418, GBP 1,655 to institutions (effective 2005) (from EBSCO Publishing, Gale Group, IngentaConnect, Kluwer Online, O C L C Online Computer Library Center, Inc., Springer LINK, Swets Information Services); ♦ Translation of: Ontogenez. ISSN 0475-1450.
Indexed: BibLing, BiolAb, IndMed, MEDLINE, PsycholAb.
—BLDSC (0420.760900), CASDDS, CISTI, GNLM, IE, Infotrieve, ingenta. **CCC.**
Published by: (Rossiiskaya Akademiya Nauk/Russian Academy of Sciences), M A I K Nauka - Interperiodica, Profsoyuznaya ul 90, Moscow, 117997, Russian Federation. TEL 7-095-3347420, FAX 7-095-3360666, compmg@maik.ru, http://www.maik.rssi.ru/journals/devbio.htm, http://www.maik.ru. Ed. Sergei G Vassetzky. **Subscr. to:** Springer-Verlag Dordrecht, Journals Department, PO Box 322, Dordrecht, Netherlands. TEL 31-78-6576392, FAX 31-78-6576474.

➤ **RUSSIAN JOURNAL OF ECOLOGY.** see *ENVIRONMENTAL STUDIES*

578.77 RUS ISSN 1063-0740
QH91.A1 CODEN: RJMBED

➤ **RUSSIAN JOURNAL OF MARINE BIOLOGY.** Text in English. 1975. bi-m. (Six issues per year plus annual reviews supplement). EUR 1,988, USD 1,778, GBP 1,238 combined subscription to institutions print & online eds. (effective 2005). back issues avail. **Document type:** *Academic/Scholarly.* **Description:** Covers a range of topics in marine biology and related studies of marine biota and the environment.
Formerly (until 1993): Soviet Journal of Marine Biology (0145-1456)
Related titles: Microfilm ed.: (from PQC); Online - full text ed.: ISSN 1608-3377 (from EBSCO Publishing, Gale Group, IngentaConnect, Kluwer Online, O C L C Online Computer Library Center, Inc., Springer LINK, Swets Information Services); ♦ Translation of: Biologiya Morya. ISSN 0134-3475.
Indexed: ASFA, BibLing, BiolAb, CurCont, ESPM, GEOBASE, IABS, OceAb, PollutAb, SFA.
—BLDSC (0420.761500), CISTI, IE, Infotrieve, ingenta. **CCC.**
Published by: (Rossiiskaya Akademiya Nauk/Russian Academy of Sciences), M A I K Nauka - Interperiodica, Profsoyuznaya ul 90, Moscow, 117997, Russian Federation. TEL 7-095-3347420, FAX 7-095-3360666, compmg@maik.ru, http://www.maik.ru. Ed. Vladimir L Kas'yanov. **Subscr. to:** Springer-Verlag Dordrecht, Journals Department, PO Box 322, Dordrecht, Netherlands. TEL 31-78-6576392, FAX 31-78-6576474.

570 PRK

SAENGMULHAK/BIOLOGY. Text in Korean. q.
Indexed: RefZh.
Published by: Science and Encyclopaedia Publishing House, Pyongyang, Korea, N.

570.7 JPN

SAITAMA SEIBUTSU/SAITAMA BIOLOGICAL SOCIETY OF HIGH SCHOOL TEACHERS. Text in Japanese. 1959. a.
Published by: Saitamaken Koto Gakko Seibutsu Kenkyukai/Saitama Biological Society of High School Teachers, Fukaya Dai 1 Koko, 21 Tokiwa-cho, Fukaya-shi, Saitama-ken 366-0034, Japan.

570 GEO ISSN 1027-555X

SAK'ART'VELOS MEC'NIEREBAT'A AKADEMIIS MAC'NE. BIOLOGIIS SERIA/ACADEMY OF SCIENCES OF GEORGIA. PROCEEDINGS. BIOLOGICAL SERIES/AKADEMIYA NAUK GRUZII. IZVESTIYA. SERIYA BIOLOGICESKAYA. Text in Georgian, Russian. 1975. bi-m.
Formerly (until 1990): Akademiya Nauk Gruzinskoi S.S.R. Izvestiya. Seriya Biologicheskaya (0321-1665)
Indexed: BiolAb, ChemAb, FCA, MaizeAb, NumL, RASB, RefZh, TriticAb.
—CISTI, Linda Hall.
Published by: Georgian Academy of Sciences, Rustaveli pr 52, Tbilisi, 380008, Georgia.

SALUSVITA; revista da area de ciencias biologicas e da saude. see *MEDICAL SCIENCES*

570 RUS

SAMARSKII GOSUDARSTVENNYI UNIVERSITET. VESTNIK. ESTESTVENNONAUCHNAYA SERIYA. BIOLOGIYA/ SAMARA STATE UNIVERSITY. VESTNIK. NATURAL SCIENCE SERIES. BIOLOGY. Text in Russian; Summaries in English. 1995. a., latest 2003. **Document type:** *Journal, Academic/Scholarly.*

Published by: (Samarskii Gosudarstvennyi Universitet), Izdatel'stvo Samarskii Universitet/Publishing House of Samara State University, ul Akademika Pavlova 1, k 209, Samara, 443011, Russian Federation. vestnikNS@ssu.samara.ru, http://www.ssu.samara.ru/~vestnik/content/biole.html. Ed. Dr. Yu N Radaev.

570 RUS ISSN 1025-8604
AS262 CODEN: VLUBB6
SANKT-PETERBURGSKII UNIVERSITET. VESTNIK. SERIYA BIOLOGIYA. Text in Russian; Abstracts and contents page in English. 1946. q. bk.rev. charts; illus. index. **Document type:** *Academic/Scholarly.*
Former titles (until 1992): Leningradskii Universitet. Vestnik. Seriya Biologiya (0321-186X); (until 1955): Vestnik Leningradskogo Universiteta (0132-4624)
Related titles: Microform ed.: (from EVP).
Indexed: ASFA, BioCN&I, BiolAb, CIN, CPA, ChemAb, ChemTitl, ESPM, FCA, ForAb, GEOBASE, HerbAb, HortAb, IAA, IBSS, MEDLINE, MLA-IB, PBA, PGrRegA, RASB, RefZh, ZooRec.
—BLDSC (0032.757100), CASDDS, CISTI, GNLM, Linda Hall. **CCC.**
Published by: Izdatelstvo Sankt-Peterburgskogo Universiteta, Universitetskaya nab 7-9, St Petersburg, 199034, Russian Federation. TEL 812-2189784. Ed. S P Merkur'ev. Circ: 1,330. **Subscr. to:** M K - Periodica, ul Gilyarovskogo 39, Moscow 129110, Russian Federation. TEL 7-095-2845008, FAX 7-095-2813798, info@periodicals.ru, http://www.mkniga.ru; **US dist. addr.:** East View Information Services, 3020 Harbor Ln. N., Minneapolis, MN 55447. TEL 612-550-0961.

570 JPN
SANKYO SEIMEI KAGAKU KENKYU SHINKO ZAIDAN KENKYU HOKOKUSHU/REPORT OF STUDIES SUPPORTED BY SANKYO FOUNDATION OF LIFE SCIENCE. Text in Japanese. 1988. a.
Published by: Sankyo Seimei Kagaku Kenkyu Shinko Zaidan/Sankyo Foundation of Life Science, 12-5 Akasaka 3-chome, Minato-ku, Tokyo, 105-0000, Japan.

591.7 ISL
➤ **SCANDINAVIAN-BALTIC SOCIETY FOR PARASITOLOGY. BULLETIN.** Text in English. 1991. irreg. **Document type:** *Bulletin, Academic/Scholarly.*
Formerly (until 2003): Scandinavian Society for Parasitology. Bulletin (0803-4907)
Indexed: ASFA, AbHyg, ESPM, HelmAb, IndVet, PoultAb, ProtozoAb, VetBull, ZooRec.
—BLDSC (2702.440000), IE, ingenta.
Published by: Scandinavian-Baltic Society for Parasitology, c/o Karl Skirnisson, Institute for Experimental Pathology, University of Iceland, Keldur v/Vesturlandsveg, Reykjavik, 112, Iceland. TEL 354-5674700, FAX 354-5673979, karlsk@hi.is, http://www.hi.is/pub/ssp/.

➤ **SCHRIFTENREIHE UMWELT/CAHIERS DE L'ENVIRONNEMENT.** see *CONSERVATION*

570 CHN ISSN 1006-9305
QH301 CODEN: SCCLFO
➤ **SCIENCE IN CHINA. SERIES C: LIFE SCIENCES.** Text in English. 1952. bi-m. USD 312 to individuals; USD 612 to institutions; USD 1,607 to individuals for full set, series A-G; USD 2,990 to institutions for full set, series A-G (effective 2004). back issues avail. **Document type:** *Journal, Academic/Scholarly.* **Description:** Contains academic papers on scientific work in the field of life sciences.
Supersedes in part (in 1996): Science in China. Series B: Chemistry, Life Sciences and Earth Sciences (1001-652X); Which was formerly (until 1989): Scientia Sinica. Series B: Chemistry, Life Sciences and Earth Sciences (0253-5823); Which superseded in part: Scientia Sinica
Related titles: Online - full content ed.: USD 50 (effective 2004); Online - full text ed.: (from East View Information Services, WanFang Data Corp.); ♦ Chinese ed.: Zhongguo Kexue. C Ji: Shengming Kexue. ISSN 1006-9259.
Indexed: ASFA, AgBio, AgrForAb, AnBrAb, B&BAb, BIOBASE, BIOSIS Prev, BioCN&I, BioEngAb, BiolAb, CPA, CurCont, DSA, EngInd, FCA, ForAb, HerbAb, HortAb, I&DA, ISR, IndMed, IndVet, Inpharma, MEDLINE, MaizeAb, OrnHort, PBA, PE&ON, PGegResA, PGrRegA, PN&I, PotatoAb, PoultAb, ProtozoAb, RA&MP, RM&VM, RPP, RRTA, Reac, RefZh, RiceAb, S&F, SCI, SIA, SeedAb, SoyAb, TDB, TriticAb, VetBull, WeedAb, ZooRec.
—BLDSC (8141.670130), CASDDS, CISTI, GNLM, IDS, IE, Infotrieve, ingenta, KNAW, Linda Hall.
Published by: (Chinese Academy of Sciences/Zhongguo Kexueyuan), Zhongguo Kexue Zazhishe/Science in China Press, 16 Donghuangchenggen North Street, Beijing, 100717, China. TEL 86-10-64019820, FAX 86-10-64031816, sale@scichina.com, http://www.scienceinchina.com/scienceinchina_c_en.htm, http://www.scichina.com/. **Subscr. to:** Maney Publishing, China Journal Distribution Services, Hudson Rd, Leeds LS9 7DI, United Kingdom. TEL 44-113-2497481, FAX 44-113-2486983, subscriptions@maney.co.uk.

➤ **THE SCIENTIFIC WORLD JOURNAL.** see *SCIENCES: COMPREHENSIVE WORKS*

570 551 708.9 SVN ISSN 0351-0077
CODEN: SCSUES
➤ **SCOPOLIA.** Text and summaries in English, Slovenian. 1978. 2/yr. back issues avail. **Document type:** *Bulletin, Academic/Scholarly.*
Related titles: ♦ Supplement(s): Scopolia. Supplementum. ISSN 0354-0138.
Indexed: RefZh, ZooRec.
—Linda Hall.
Published by: Prirodoslovni Muzej Slovenije/Slovenian Museum of Natural History, Presernova 20, Box 290, Ljubljana, 1001, Slovenia. TEL 386-1-2410940, FAX 386-1-2410953, uprava@pms-lj.si, http://www2.pms-lj.si. Ed. Gregori Janez.

570 SVN ISSN 0354-0138
SCOPOLIA. SUPPLEMENTUM. Text in English, Slovenian. 1990. irreg.
Related titles: ♦ Supplement to: Scopolia. ISSN 0351-0077.
Indexed: ZooRec.
Published by: Prirodoslovni Muzej Slovenije/Slovenian Museum of Natural History, Presernova 20, Box 290, Ljubljana, 1001, Slovenia. TEL 386-1-2410940, FAX 386-1-2410953, uprava@pms-lj.si, http://www2.pms-lj.si.

570 GBR ISSN 0268-3385
QK306
THE SCOTTISH NATURALIST. Text in English. 1871. 3/yr. GBP 35 (effective 1999). bk.rev. charts; illus.; maps. back issues avail. **Document type:** *Academic/Scholarly.* **Description:** Covers all aspects of Scottish natural history.
Former titles (until 1982): Western Naturalist (0141-5247); Scottish Naturalist
Indexed: ZooRec.
—BLDSC (8211.000000).
Published by: Scottish Natural History Library, Foremount House, Easwald Bank, Milliken Park, Johnstone, Kilbarchan, Renfrewshire PA10 2EZ, United Kingdom. TEL 44-1505-702419. Ed. J A Gibson. Circ: 1,000.

570 JPN ISSN 0286-7761
SEIBUTSU FUKUOKA/BIOLOGIA FUKUOKA. Text in Japanese; Summaries in English. 1961. a. membership.
Published by: Fukuokaken Koto Gakko Seibutsu Bukai/Biological Society of Fukuokaken High School Teachers, Fukuoka Daigaku Fuzoku Ohori Koto Gakko, 12-1 Ropponmatsu 1-chome, Chuo-ku, Fukuoka-shi, 810-0044, Japan.

570 JPN ISSN 0385-5996
SEIBUTSU KAGAKU NYUSU/BIOLOGICAL SCIENCE NEWS. Text in Japanese. 1971. m. **Document type:** *Newsletter.*
Published by: Zoological Society of Japan/Nihon Dobutsu Gakkai, Toshin Bldg 2F, 2-27-2 Hongo, Bunkyo-ku, Tokyo, 113-0033, Japan. TEL 81-3-38145461, FAX 81-3-38146216.

577 JPN ISSN 0582-4087
➤ **SEIBUTSU KANKYO CHOSETSU/ENVIRONMENT CONTROL IN BIOLOGY.** Text in English, Japanese. 1963. q. membership. bk.rev. 80 p./no.; **Document type:** *Journal, Academic/Scholarly.*
Indexed: AEA, AgBio, AgrForAb, Agrind, BIOSIS Prev, BiolAb, CPA, FCA, FS&TA, ForAb, HerbAb, HortAb, I&DA, JPI, MaizeAb, OrnHort, PBA, PGegResA, PGrRegA, PHN&I, PotatoAb, RA&MP, RPP, RevApplEntom, RiceAb, S&F, SIA, SeedAb, SoyAb, TriticAb, VITIS, WeedAb.
—BLDSC (3791.160000), IE, ingenta. **CCC.**
Published by: Nihon Seibutsu Kankyo Chosetsu Gakkai/Japanese Society of Environment Control in Biology, Ehime University, Department of Biomechanical Systems, aboratory of Physiological Green Systems, 3-5-7 Tarumi, Matsuyama, Ehime 790-8566, Japan. TEL 81-89-9469822, FAX 81-89-9469916, nomami@agr.ehime-u.ac.jp, nishina@agr.ehime-u.ac.jp, http://wwwsoc.nii.ac.jp/seikan/index.html. Ed. H Nonami. Adv. contact Changhoo Chun. Circ: 1,500.

570.7 JPN
SEIBUTSU KENKYU/JAPAN ASSOCIATION OF BIOLOGY EDUCATION. RESEARCH REPORT. Text in Japanese. a.
Published by: Nihon Seibutsu Kyoikukai/Japan Association of Biology Education, c/o Mr Shinpei Ono, Toritsu Fukagawa Koto Gakko, 32-19 Toyo 5-chome, Koto-ku, Tokyo, 135-0016, Japan.

570.7 JPN ISSN 0287-119X
➤ **SEIBUTSU KYOIKU/JAPANESE JOURNAL OF BIOLOGICAL EDUCATION.** Text in Japanese; Summaries in English, Japanese. q. JPY 2,000 per issue (effective 2002). bk.rev. back issues avail. **Document type:** *Academic/Scholarly.*
—**CCC.**
Published by: Nihon Seibutsu Kyoiku Gakkai/Society of Biological Sciences Education of Japan, Department of Biology, Toykyo Gakugei University, Koganei, Tokyo 184-8501, Japan. mikami@staff.miyakyo-u.ac.jp, katayama@u-gakugei.ac.jp. Ed. Megumi Okazaki. Circ: 1,100.

570 JPN ISSN 0917-1606
SEIBUTSU SHIIKU KENKYUKAI KAISHI/AQUARIUM AND TERRARIUM ANIMALS. Text in Japanese. 1989. 4/yr. JPY 1,300 per issue.
Published by: Seibutsu Shiiku Kenkyukai/Aquarium and Terrarium Animals, 31-7 Machiya 4-chome, Arakawa-ku, Tokyo, 116-0001, Japan.

570 JPN ISSN 0913-3763
SEIBUTSU SHIRYO BUNSEKI/JOURNAL OF ANALYTICAL BIO-SCIENCE. Text in Japanese. 1978. q. JPY 7,000 membership (effective 2003). **Document type:** *Journal, Academic/Scholarly.*
—BLDSC (4928.220000).
Published by: Seibutsu Shiryo Bunseki Kagakkai/Society of Analytical Bio-Science, 1-21-1 Mnabigaoka, Tarumi-ku, Kobe, 655-0004, Japan. www-ctr@umin.ac.jp, http://gakkai.umin.ac.jp/gakkai/gakkai/2003/A00879.htm.

570 JPN ISSN 0386-9539
QH305
SEIBUTSUGAKUSHI KENKYU/JAPANESE JOURNAL OF THE HISTORY OF BIOLOGY. Text in Japanese. 1955. s-a. JPY 1,500 per issue. **Document type:** *Academic/Scholarly.*
Indexed: JPI.
—BLDSC (8219.150000).
Published by: Nihon Kagakushi Gakkai, Seibutsugakushi Bunkakai/History of Science Society of Japan, Biology Division, Osaka Kyoiku Daigaku, Kankyo Kagaku Kyoiku Kenkyushitsu, 4-698-1 Asahigaoka, Kashiwara-shi, Osaka-fu 582-0026, Japan.

570 JPN ISSN 0287-7775
SEICHO/JOURNAL OF GROWTH. Text in Japanese; Summaries in English. 1962. s-a. JPY 5,000. bk.rev. index. back issues avail.
Related titles: Online - full text ed.: (from JICST).
Indexed: RefZh, ZooRec.
—Linda Hall.
Published by: Aichi-Gakuin University, Department of Anatomy, 1-100 Kusumoto-cho, Chikusa-ku, Nagoya-shi, Aichi-ken 464-0037, Japan. TEL 052-751-2561, FAX 052-752-5988. Ed. Takeo Miyao. Circ: 250.

570 JPN ISSN 0386-7617
CODEN: KNSKDK
SEICHO KAGAKU KYOKAI KENKYU NENPO* /FOUNDATION FOR GROWTH SCIENCE. ANNUAL RESEARCH REPORTS. Text in English, Japanese; Summaries in English. 1977. a.
Indexed: CIN, ChemAb, ChemTitl.
—CASDDS.
Published by: Seicho Kagaku Kyokai, 9-4 Wakamatsu-cho, Shinjuku-ku, Tokyo, 162-0056, Japan. TEL 81-3-3353-6414, FAX 81-3-3353-5865, http://www.fgs.or.jp/public/index.html.

570 363.7 JPN ISSN 1346-6534
SEIKATSU KANKYOU KAGAKU KENKYUUJO KENKYUU HOUKOKU/INSTITUTE OF LIVING AND ENVIRONMENTAL SCIENCES. ANNUAL REPORT. Text in English, Japanese. 1967. a. **Document type:** *Corporate.*
Formerly (until 1999): Seikatsu Kagaku Kenkyujo Kenkyu Hokoku/Institute of Living Sciences. Annual Report (0386-7536)
—BLDSC (1303.365000), IE, ingenta.
Published by: Miyagi Gakuin Joshi Daigaku, Seikatsu Kankyou Kagaku Kenkyuujo/Miyagi Gakuin Women's College, Institute of Living Environmental Sciences, 9-1-1Sakuragaoka, Aoba-ku, Sendai-shi, 981-8557, Japan. TEL 81-22-279-1311, FAX 81-22-279-7566.

570 JPN ISSN 0288-1578
QH301
SEIMEI KAGAKU KENKYUJO KIYO/SOPHIA LIFE SCIENCE BULLETIN. Text in Japanese; Summaries in English. 1982. a.
Published by: Jochi Daigaku, Seimei Kagaku Kenkyujo/Sophia University, Life Science Institute, 7-1 Kioi-cho, Chiyoda-ku, Tokyo, 102-0094, Japan.

570 JPN ISSN 0370-9531
CODEN: SEKAA6
➤ **SEITAI NO KAGAKU/MEDICAL SCIENCE.** Text in Japanese. 1949. bi-m. JPY 12,830; JPY 1,680 newsstand/cover (effective 2005). bk.rev. 90 p./no.; back issues avail. **Document type:** *Journal, Academic/Scholarly.*
Indexed: CIN, ChemAb, ChemTitl.
—CASDDS, CISTI.
Published by: (Ichiro kanehara Foundation), Igaku-Shoin Ltd., 5-24-3 Hongo, Bunkyo-ku, Tokyo, 113-0033, Japan. TEL 81-3-38175600, FAX 81-3-38157791, seitai@abox9.so-net.ne.jp, info@igaku-shoin.co.jp, http://www.igaku-shoin.co.jp/prd/00135/0013541.html. Circ: 3,000. **Subscr. to:** Foreign Publications Department, 3-24-17 Hongo, Bunkyo-ku, Tokyo 113-8719, Japan. TEL 81-3-38175676, FAX 81-3-38157805, fd@igaku-shoin.co.jp.

570 JPN ISSN 0286-0198
CODEN: SEIKDT
SEITAIGAKUTEKI EIYOGAKU KENKYU/JAPANESE ASSOCIATION FOR ECOLOGICAL NUTRITION RESEARCH. ANNALS. Text in Japanese; Summaries in English, Japanese. 1977. a.
Published by: Seitaigakuteki Eiyogaku Kenkyukai, Matsui Byoin, 7-10 Ikegami 1-chome, Ota-ku, Tokyo, 146-0082, Japan.

SENCKENBERGIANA MARITIMA. see *EARTH SCIENCES—Oceanography*

570 551 DEU ISSN 0365-7000
QH5 CODEN: ASNGA7
SENCKENBERGISCHE NATURFORSCHENDE GESELLSCHAFT. ABHANDLUNGEN. Text in German, English. 1884. irreg., latest vol.559, 2003. EUR 62 per issue domestic; EUR 66.10 per issue foreign (effective 2005). back issues avail. **Document type:** *Monographic series, Academic/Scholarly.* **Description:** Contains extensive papers on zoology, geology, paleontology and botany.
Indexed: BIOSIS Prev, BiolAb, GEOBASE, RefZh, SFA, WildRev, ZooRec.
—CISTI, Linda Hall. **CCC.**
Published by: (Senckenbergische Naturforschende Gesellschaft), E. Schweizerbart'sche Verlagsbuchhandlung, Johannesstr 3A, Stuttgart, 70176, Germany. TEL 49-711-3514560, FAX 49-711-35145699, mail@schweizerbart.de, http://www.schweizerbart.de/j/abhandlungen-senck-nat. Ed. Fritz F Steininger. Circ: 550 (paid).

SENEGAL. CENTRE DE RECHERCHE OCEANOGRAPHIQUE. DOCUMENT SCIENTIFIQUE. see *EARTH SCIENCES—Oceanography*

▼ **SENSORY FORMATIONS.** see *PSYCHOLOGY*

570 KOR ISSN 0377-5232
QH301 CODEN: SNBAAO
SEOUL NATIONAL UNIVERSITY. FACULTY PAPERS. BIOLOGY AND AGRICULTURE SERIES. Text in English. 1971. a. **Document type:** *Monographic series.*
Indexed: ExcerpMed.
—GNLM.
Published by: Seoul National University, San 56-1 Sinlim-dong, Kwanak-ku, Seoul, 151742, Korea, S.

639.967827 TZA
SERENGETI WILDLIFE RESEARCH CENTRE. REPORT. Text in English. 1985. biennial. **Description:** Presents scientific results of research projects.
Published by: Serengeti Wildlife Research Centre, PO Box 661, Arusha, Tanzania. Circ: 500.

570 610 SGP ISSN 1793-1258
SERIES IN MATHEMATICAL BIOLOGY AND MEDICINE. Text in English. 1996. irreg., latest vol.8. price varies. **Document type:** *Monographic series, Academic/Scholarly.* **Description:** Promotes interdisciplinary approaches in biology and in medicine by publishing original textbooks and monographs.
Published by: World Scientific Publishing Co. Pte. Ltd., 5 Toh Tuck Link, Singapore, 596224, Singapore. TEL 65-466-5775, FAX 65-467-7667, wspc@wspc.com.sg, series@wspc.com.sg, http://www.wspc.com.sg/books/series/smbm_series.shtml, http://www.worldscientific.com. Eds. P M Auger, R V Jean. **Dist. by:** World Scientific Publishing Co., Inc., 1060 Main St, River Edge, NJ 07661. TEL 201-487-9655, 800-227-7562, FAX 201-487-9656, 888-977-2665; World Scientific Publishing Ltd., 57 Shelton St, London WC2H 9HE, United Kingdom. TEL 44-20-78360888, FAX 44-20-78362020.

SESSILE ORGANISMS. see *EARTH SCIENCES—Oceanography*

570 JPN ISSN 0913-6002
SETO MARINE BIOLOGICAL LABORATORY. ANNUAL REPORT/SETO RINKAI JIKKENJO NENPO. Text in Japanese. 1987. a.
Published by: (Seto Marine Biological Laboratory), Kyoto University, Field Science Education and Reserach Center, Seto Marine Biological Laboratory/Kyoto Daigaku, Seto Rinkai Jikkenjo, Nishimuro-gun, Shirahama-cho, Wakayama-ken 649-2211, Japan. TEL 81-739-42-3515, FAX 81-739-42-4518, http://www.seto.kyoto-u.ac.jp/.

578.77 JPN ISSN 0037-2870
QH91.A1 CODEN: PSMBAG
➤ **SETO MARINE BIOLOGICAL LABORATORY. PUBLICATIONS/SETO RINKAI JIKKENJO KIYO.** Text in English. 1949. s-a. per issue exchange basis. charts; illus. index. **Document type:** *Journal, Academic/Scholarly.* **Description:** Publishes scientific papers on marine biology related to Japanese and Indo-Pacific waters, especially those on taxonomy, morphology and biology.
Indexed: ASFA, BIOSIS Prev, BiolAb, ESPM, OceAb, SFA, ZooRec.
—BLDSC (7112.000000), IE, ingenta.
Published by: Kyoto University, Field Science Education and Reserach Center, Seto Marine Biological Laboratory/Kyoto Daigaku, Seto Rinkai Jikkenjo, Nishimuro-gun, Shirahama-cho, Wakayama-ken 649-2211, Japan. TEL 81-739-42-3515, FAX 81-739-42-4518, http://www.seto.kyoto-u.ac.jp/shuppan.htm. Ed. Yoshihisa Shirayama. Circ: 460.

578.77 JPN ISSN 0389-6609
➤ **SETO MARINE BIOLOGICAL LABORATORY. SPECIAL PUBLICATION SERIES.** Text in English. 1959. irreg. exchange basis. **Document type:** *Monographic series, Academic/Scholarly.*
Formerly: Seto Marine Biological Laboratory. Special Publications (0080-9098)
Indexed: ASFA, BiolAb.
—Linda Hall.
Published by: Kyoto University, Field Science Education and Reserach Center, Seto Marine Biological Laboratory/Kyoto Daigaku, Seto Rinkai Jikkenjo, Nishimuro-gun, Shirahama-cho, Wakayama-ken 649-2211, Japan. TEL 81-739-42-3515, FAX 81-739-42-4518, http://www.seto.kyoto.u.ac.jp, http://www.seto.kyoto-u.ac.jp/. Ed. Yoshihisa Shirayama. Circ: 460.

➤ **SHANXI YIYAO ZAZHI/SHANXI MEDICAL JOURNAL.** see *PHARMACY AND PHARMACOLOGY*

570 CHN ISSN 1004-0374
SHENGMING KEXUE/CHINESE BULLETIN OF LIFE SCIENCES. Text in Chinese. 1988. bi-m. CNY 9 newsstand/cover (effective 2005). **Document type:** *Bulletin, Academic/Scholarly.*
Related titles: Online - full text ed.: (from East View Information Services, WanFang Data Corp.).
—BLDSC (3180.274120), IE.
Published by: Zhongguo Kexueyuan, Shanghai Wenxian Qingbao Zhongxin/Chinese Academy of Sciences, Shanghai Documentation & Information Center, 319 Yueyang Lu, Shanghai, 200031, China. TEL 86-21-64336678, FAX 86-21-64375762, cbls@sibs.ac.cn, cba@peony.slas.ac.cn, http://smkx.periodicals.net.cn/, http://www.slas.ac.cn.

570 CHN ISSN 1007-7847
SHENGMING KEXUE YANJIU/LIFE SCIENCE RESEARCH. Text in Chinese; Text occasionally in English. 1997. q. CNY 8 per issue (effective 2003). abstr.; bibl.; charts; illus.; mkt.; stat.; tr.lit. 96 p./no.; **Document type:** *Journal, Academic/Scholarly.*
Related titles: Online - full content ed.: (from WanFang Data Corp.); Online - full text ed.: (from East View Information Services).
Indexed: CTA, RefZh.
—BLDSC (5208.929960).
Published by: Hunan Shifan Daxue, Shengming Kexue Xueyuan/Hunan Normal University, College of Life Sciences, Yuelushan, Changsha, 410081, China. TEL 86-731-8872527, FAX 86-731-8883310, mailto:sky@mail.hunnu.edu.cn, http://smkxyj.periodicals.com.cn/default.html, http://www2.hunnu.edu.cn/~biology/. Ed. Song-Ping Liang. **Dist. by:** China National Publishing Industry Trading Corporation, PO Box 782, Beijing 100011, China. TEL 86-1-64215031 ext 3130, 86-1-64266648.

SHENGTAI XUEBAO/ACTA ECOLOGICA SINICA. see *ENVIRONMENTAL STUDIES*

SHENGTAIXUE ZAZHI/CHINESE JOURNAL OF ECOLOGY. see *ENVIRONMENTAL STUDIES*

570 CHN ISSN 1005-0094
SHENGWU DUOYANGXING/CHINESE BIODIVERSITY. Text in Chinese. 1993. bi-m. CNY 28 newsstand/cover (effective 2005). **Document type:** *Journal, Academic/Scholarly.*
Related titles: Online - full text ed.: (from East View Information Services, WanFang Data Corp.).
Published by: (Zhongguo Kexueyuan, Shengwu Duoyang Xingwei Yuanhui), Shengwu Duoyangxing, 20, Xiangshan Nanxincun, Beijing, 100093, China. http://swdyx.periodicals.net.cn/.

570 CHN ISSN 1001-9626
SHENGWU SHUXUE XUEBAO. Text in Chinese. s-a. USD 1 per issue. **Document type:** *Academic/Scholarly.*
Related titles: Online - full text ed.: (from East View Information Services).
Indexed: CCMJ, MathR, MathSciNet, ZentMath.
Published by: Anhui Nongxueyuan/Anhui Agricultural College, 130, Changjiang Xilu, Hefei, Anhui 230036, China. http://www.ahau.edu.cn/. Ed. Shih Tsehua.

570 CHN ISSN 0006-3193
QH301 CODEN: SWHTA4
➤ **SHENGWUXUE TONGBAO/BULLETIN OF BIOLOGY.** Text in Chinese, English. bi-m. CNY 58.80 (effective 2004). charts; illus. **Document type:** *Journal, Academic/Scholarly.*
Related titles: Online - full content ed.: (from WanFang Data Corp.); Online - full text ed.: (from East View Information Services).
Indexed: CIN, ChemAb, ChemTitl.
—CASDDS, Linda Hall.
Published by: (Chinese Society of Zoology), Kexue Chubanshe/Science Press, 16 Donghuang Cheng Genbei Jie, Beijing, 100717, China. TEL 86-10-64000246, FAX 86-10-64030255, SWXT@chinajournal.net.cn, http://swxtb.periodicals.net.cn/default.html. **Dist. by:** China International Book Trading Corp, 35 Chegongzhuang Xilu, Haidian District, PO Box 399, Beijing 100044, China. TEL 86-10-68412045, FAX 86-10-68412023, cibtc@mail.cibtc.com.cn, http://www.cibtc.com.cn.
Co-sponsor: Chinese Botanical Society.

578.77 JPN ISSN 0385-1109
SHIMA MARINELAND. SCIENCE REPORT. Text in English, Japanese. 1972. irreg. per issue exchange basis. adv. **Document type:** *Academic/Scholarly.*
Indexed: BiolAb, SFA.
Published by: Shima Marineland Foundation, Kashikojima, Shima-gun, Ago-cho, Mie 517-05, Japan. TEL 81-5994-3-1225, FAX 81-5994-3-1224. Ed. T Tsujii. R&P Tadashi Tsujii. Adv. contact Shuzo Okubo. Circ: 1,500.

SHINSHU DAIGAKU RIGAKUBU FUZOKU SUWA RINKO JIKKENJO HOKOKU/SHINSHU UNIVERSITY. SUWA HYDROBIOLOGICAL STATION. REPORT. see *EARTH SCIENCES—Hydrology*

570 CHN ISSN 1000-3207
QH90.A1 CODEN: SSXUET
➤ **SHUISHENG SHENGWU XUEBAO/ACTA HYDROBIOLOGICA SINICA.** Text in Chinese; Summaries in English. 1955. bi-m. CNY 60 (effective 2004). adv. **Document type:** *Journal, Academic/Scholarly.* **Description:** Directed to college instructors, students, and researchers; contains research articles, brief reports and reviews about taxonomy, ecology, physiology, pathology, toxicology, disease prevention; genetics and breeding of freshwater fish, algae, and other organisms.
Related titles: Online - full text ed.: (from East View Information Services, WanFang Data Corp.); English ed.: ISSN 0559-9385.
Indexed: AEA, ASFA, AgBio, AnBrAb, BIOSIS Prev, BioCN&I, BiolAb, ESPM, FCA, ForAb, HelmAb, HerbAb, HortAb, I&DA, IndVet, NemAb, NutrAb, OrnHort, PBA, PGegResA, PGrRegA, PotatoAb, PoultAb, ProtozoAb, RA&MP, RM&VM, RPP, RevApplEntom, RiceAb, S&F, SFA, SIA, SeedAb, SoyAb, TriticAb, VetBull, WeedAb, ZooRec.
—BLDSC (0624.500000), CASDDS, CISTI, IE, ingenta.
Published by: (Zhongguo Kexueyuan, Shuisheng Shengwu Yanjiusuo/Chinese Academy of Sciences, Institute of Hydrobiology), Kexue Chubanshe/Science Press, 16 Donghuang Cheng Genbei Jie, Beijing, 100717, China. TEL 86-10-64000246, FAX 86-10-64030255, acta@ihb.ac.cn, http://ssswxb.periodicals.net.cn/default.html, http://www.sciencep.com/. Circ: 6,000. **Dist. by:** China International Book Trading Corp, 35 Chegongzhuang Xilu, Haidian District, PO Box 399, Beijing 100044, China. TEL 86-10-68412045, FAX 86-10-68412023, cibtc@mail.cibtc.com.cn, http://www.cibtc.com.cn.

577 RUS ISSN 0869-8627
QH540 CODEN: ISBNBN
SIBIRSKII EKOLOGICHESKII ZHURNAL. Text in Russian. 1963. 6/yr. RUR 440 for 6 mos. domestic; USD 124 foreign (effective 2005). bk.rev. illus. index. **Document type:** *Journal, Academic/Scholarly.*
Former titles (until 1994): Sibirskii Biologicheskii Zhurnal (0869-1347); (until 1990): Akademiya Nauk S.S.S.R. Sibirskoe Otdelenie. Izvestiya. Seriya Biologicheskikh Nauk (0568-6547)
Related titles: English ed.: Siberian Journal of Ecology.
Indexed: BiolAb, ChemAb, FCA, FPA, ForAb, I&DA, RefZh, S&F, SeedAb, ZooRec.
—CASDDS, CISTI, Linda Hall. **CCC.**
Published by: (Sibirskii Ekologicheskii Zhurnal), Izdatel'stvo Sibirskogo Otdeleniya Rossiiskoi Akademii Nauk/Publishing House of the Russian Academy of Sciences, Siberian Branch, Morskoi pr 2, a/ya 187, Novosibirsk, 630090, Russian Federation. TEL 7-3832-300570, FAX 7-3832-333755, phsb@ad-sbras.nsc.ru, psb@ad-sbras.nsc.ru, http://www-psb.ad-sbras.nsc.ru/secjw.htm. Ed. I Yu Koropachinskii. Circ: 370. **Dist. by:** Informnauka Ltd., Ul Usievicha 20, Moscow 125190, Russian Federation. alfimov@viniti.ru.

SICHUAN DAXUE XUEBAO (YIXUE BAN)/SICHUAN UNIVERSITY. JOURNAL (MEDICAL SCIENCE EDITION). see *MEDICAL SCIENCES*

570 JPN ISSN 0559-9822
CODEN: SIEBA7
SIEBOLDIA ACTA BIOLOGICA/SHIBORUDIA. Text in English, Japanese. 1952. irreg. per issue exchange basis. reprint service avail. from PQC.
Indexed: BiolAb.
—CASDDS.
Published by: (Biological Laboratory), Kyushu University, College of General Education, 4-2-1 Ropponmatsu, Chuo-ku, Fukuoka-shi, 810-0044, Japan. TEL 81-92-731-8745, FAX 81-92-771-4161.

578.77 577 GBR
SIR ALISTER HARDY FOUNDATION FOR OCEAN SCIENCE. ANNUAL REPORT. Text in English. a.
Published by: Sir Alister Hardy Foundation for Ocean Science, The Laboratory, Citadel Hill, Plymouth, PL1 2PB, United Kingdom. TEL 44-1752-600016, FAX 44-1752-600015, sahfos@mail.pml.ac.uk, http://192.171.163.165/publications.htm, http://www.sahfos.org.

SLOVENIAN VETERINARY RESEARCH/SLOVENSKI VETERINARSKI ZBORNIK; Slovenski veterinarski zbornik. see *VETERINARY SCIENCE*

570 SVK ISSN 0037-6930
QH7 CODEN: BLGPAT
SLOVENSKA AKADEMIA VIED. BIOLOGICKE PRACE/SLOVAK ACADEMY OF SCIENCES. TREATISES ON BIOLOGY. Text in English, Slovak; Summaries in English, German, Russian. 1955. irreg. USD 5. charts; illus.

Indexed: BiolAb.
—CISTI, Linda Hall.
Published by: (Slovenska Akademia Vied/Slovak Academy of Sciences), Vydavatel'stvo Slovenskej Akademie Vied Veda/Veda, Publishing House of the Slovak Academy of Sciences, Dubravska cesta 9, Bratislava, 84234, Slovakia. Circ: 500. **Dist. by:** Slovart G.T.G. s.r.o., Krupinska 4, PO Box 152, Bratislava 85299, Slovakia. TEL 421-2-63839472, FAX 421-2-63839485, http://www.slovart-gtg.sk.

570 SVK ISSN 0139-5424
SLOVENSKE NARODNE MUZEUM. ZBORNIK. PRIRODNE VEDY/ACTA RERUM NATURALIUM MUSEI NATIONALIS SLOVENICI BRATISLAVA. Text in Slovak, English, German. 1962. irreg., latest vol.46, 2000. price varies. illus. **Document type:** *Monographic series, Academic/Scholarly.*
Published by: (Slovenske Narodne Muzeum, Prirodovedne Muzeum/Slovak National Museum, Natural History Museum), Slovenske Narodne Muzeum, Narodne Muzejne Centrum, Vajanskeho nabr 2, Bratislava, 81436, Slovakia. TEL 421-2-52961973, FAX 421-2-52966653, nmc@snm.sk. Ed. Branislav Matousek.

570 BOL
SOCIEDAD BOLIVIANA DE HISTORIA NATURAL. REVISTA. Text in Spanish; Abstracts occasionally in English. 1974. irreg. illus.
Indexed: BiolAb.
Published by: Sociedad Boliviana de Historia Natural, Casilla de Correos 538, Cochabamba, Bolivia.

570 CHL ISSN 0037-850X
QH301 CODEN: BOBCAK
SOCIEDAD DE BIOLOGIA DE CONCEPCION. BOLETIN. Summaries in Spanish, English. 1927. s-a. per issue exchange basis. charts; illus. index. back issues avail. **Document type:** *Bulletin, Academic/Scholarly.*
Indexed: ASFA, BIOSIS Prev, BiolAb, ChemAb, ESPM, EntAb, OceAb, RefZh, SFA, ZooRec.
—GNLM, Linda Hall.
Published by: Sociedad de Biologia de Concepcion, Casilla 4006, Concepcion, Chile. Ed. Hugo I Moyano. Circ: 500.

570 ITA ISSN 0366-2047
CODEN: BONNAB
SOCIETA DEI NATURALISTI IN NAPOLI. BOLLETTINO. Text in Italian; Summaries in English. 1887. a. **Document type:** *Bulletin, Academic/Scholarly.*
Indexed: BiolAb, ChemAb.
—CASDDS, Linda Hall.
Published by: (Societa dei Naturalisti in Napoli), Giannini Editore, Via Cisterna dell'Olio 6b, Naples, NA 80134, Italy. http://www.gianninieditore.it.

570 ITA ISSN 0037-8771
QH301 CODEN: BSIBAC
SOCIETA ITALIANA DI BIOLOGIA SPERIMENTALE. BOLLETTINO/JOURNAL OF BIOLOGICAL RESEARCH. Text in English, Italian. 1924. bi-m. USD 200 (effective 1999). adv. charts; illus.; stat. index. **Description:** Features articles and research papers covering a wide variety of topics in experimental biology; includes anatomy, molecular biology, botany, cardiology and clinical chemistry.
Related titles: Microform ed.: (from PMC).
Indexed: AnBrAb, AnalAb, BIOSIS Prev, BiolAb, CIN, ChemAb, ChemTitl, DBA, DSA, DentInd, ExcerpMed, IndMed, IndVet, MEDLINE, NutrAb, PoultAb, VetBull.
—BLDSC (2231.000000), CASDDS, CISTI, GNLM, IE, Infotrieve, ingenta, KNAW, Linda Hall.
Published by: Casa Editrice Idelson Gnocchi, Via Michele Pietravalle 85, Naples, NA 80131, Italy. TEL 39-081-5524733, FAX 39-081-5518295, idelgno@tin.it, informazioni@idelson-gnocchi.com, http://www.idelson-gnocchi.com. Ed. Pietro de Franciscis.

571.9 ITA ISSN 1121-9106
SOCIETA ITALIANA DI PATOLOGIA ITTICA. BOLLETTINO. Text in English, Italian. 1989. 3/yr.
Indexed: ASFA, ESPM, VirolAbstr.
Published by: Societa Italiana di Patologia Ittica, c/o Istituto di Malattie Infettive degli Animali M Compagnucci, Piano d'Accio, Teramo, 62040, Italy. TEL 39-0861-558838, FAX 39-0861-558838, sipi@imi.vet.unite.it.

570 NLD ISSN 0926-3551
SOCIETAS INTERNATIONALIS ODONATOLOGICA. RAPID COMMUNICATIONS. Text in Dutch. 1980. irreg. price varies. bk.rev. charts. **Document type:** *Academic/Scholarly.*
Indexed: BiolAb, ZooRec.
Published by: Societas Internationalis Odonatologica/International Odonatological Foundation, c/o Mrs. M.Kiauta, PO Box 256, Bilthoven, 3720 AG, Netherlands. Circ: 500.

581 591 FIN ISSN 0373-6873
QH7 CODEN: MSFFAS
➤ **SOCIETAS PRO FAUNA ET FLORA FENNICA. MEMORANDA.** Text in English, Finnish, German, Swedish; Summaries in English. 1848. q. EUR 12. adv. bk.rev. back issues avail. **Document type:** *Journal, Academic/Scholarly.*
Former titles (until 1927): Societas pro Fauna et Flora Fennica. Meddellanden (0788-6969); (until 1876): Saelskapet pro Fauna et Flora Fennica. Foerhandlingar. Notiser (1455-8548)
Indexed: BIOSIS Prev, BiolAb, GEOBASE, IBR, RefZh, RevApplEntom, SFA, WeedAb, WildRev, ZooRec.
—BLDSC (5645.000000), CISTI, IE, ingenta, KNAW, Linda Hall.
Published by: Societas pro Fauna et Flora Fennica, University of Helsinki, PL 17, Helsinki, 00014, Finland. Ed. Olof Bistroem. Circ: 1,000.

570 ESP ISSN 0212-3037
QH301
➤ **SOCIETAT CATALANA DE BIOLOGIA. TREBALLS.** Text in Spanish. 1963. a. **Document type:** *Monographic series, Academic/Scholarly.*
Indexed: IECT.
—CINDOC.
Published by: Societat Catalana de Biologia, C/ Carme 47, Barcelona, 08001, Spain. TEL 34-933-248584, FAX 34-933-701180, egorgues@iec.es, scb@iecat.net, http://www.iec.es. Ed. F Vidal. Circ: 150.

570 551 ESP
SOCIETAT D'HISTORIA NATURAL DE LES BALEARS. MONOGRAFIE. Text in Spanish. 1991. irreg., latest vol.5, 1996. price varies. **Document type:** *Monographic series.*
Indexed: ZooRec.
Published by: Societat d'Historia Natural de les Balears, Sant Roc, 4, Palma De Mallorca, Baleares 07001, Spain. TEL 34-971-719667, FAX 34-971-719667. Ed. Guillem Pons I Buades.

570 FRA ISSN 1295-0661
CODEN: CRSBAW
SOCIETE DE BIOLOGIE. JOURNAL. Text in French. 1849. bi-m. EUR 206 domestic; EUR 227 foreign (effective 2004). adv. index. reprint service avail. from ISI. **Document type:** *Journal, Academic/Scholarly.* **Description:** Accounts of meetings of the society and its branches.
Formerly (until 1999): Societe de Biologie et de Ses Filiales. Comptes Rendus des Seances (0037-9026)
Related titles: Microform ed.: (from PMC).
Indexed: ASFA, AbHyg, AgBio, AnBrAb, ApicAb, BIOSIS Prev, BioCN&I, BiolAb, CIN, CPA, ChemAb, ChemTitl, DBA, DSA, ESPM, ExcerpMed, FCA, FPA, FS&TA, ForAb, HelmAb, HerbAb, HortAb, IndMed, IndVet, MEDLINE, MaizeAb, NutrAb, OrnHort, PBA, PoultAb, ProtozoAb, RA&MP, RM&VM, RPP, RefZh, RevApplEntom, RiceAb, S&F, SFA, SeedAb, TDB, VetBull, WeedAb, WildRev, ZooRec.
—BLDSC (4876.800000), CASDDS, CISTI, GNLM, IDS, IE, Infotrieve, ingenta, KNAW, Linda Hall. **CCC.**
Published by: (Societe de Biologie), Masson Editeur (Subsidiary of: Groupe Medimedia France), 21 Rue Camille Desmoulins, Issy les Moulineaux, 92789 Cedex 9, France. TEL 33-1-73281634, FAX 33-1-73281649, infos@masson.fr, http://www.masson.fr. Ed. Miss Faibie. Circ: 1,300. **Subscr. to:** Societe de Periodiques Specialises, BP 22, Vineuil Cedex 41354, France. TEL 33-2-54504612, FAX 33-2-54504611.

570 550 LUX ISSN 0304-9620
CODEN: BNLXAO
SOCIETE DES NATURALISTES LUXEMBOURGEOIS. BULLETIN. Text and summaries in English, French, German. 1890. a. USD 8. bk.rev. back issues avail. **Document type:** *Bulletin.*
Indexed: BIOSIS Prev, BiolAb, ZooRec.
—BLDSC (2747.000000), IE, ingenta, Linda Hall.
Published by: Societe des Naturalistes Luxembourgeois, B P 327, Luxembourg, L-2013, Luxembourg. FAX 352-31-38-19. Ed. Paul Diederich. Circ: 850.

SOCIETE DES SCIENCES NATURELLES DE L'OUEST DE LA FRANCE. BULLETIN. see *BIOLOGY—Zoology*

570 914.402 FRA ISSN 0758-4113
SOCIETE D'HISTOIRE NATURELLE DE TOULOUSE. BULLETIN. Text in French. 1866. q.
Indexed: BIOSIS Prev, BiolAb, ZooRec.
—BLDSC (2744.000000), IE, ingenta, Linda Hall.
Published by: Societe d'Histoire Naturelle de Toulouse, University Paul Sabatier, 118 route Narbo, Toulouse, 31400, France.

570 914.402 FRA ISSN 0373-8442
SOCIETE D'HISTOIRE NATURELLE DES ARDENNES. BULLETIN. Text in French. 1894. a. EUR 24 (effective 2003). illus. back issues avail. **Document type:** *Bulletin, Academic/Scholarly.*
Published by: Societe d' Histoire Naturelle des Ardennes, 2 Rue du Musee, Charleville-Mezieres, 08000, France. TEL 33-3-24321475. Ed. Arnaud Bizot. Circ: 250.

570 JPN ISSN 0081-1106
SOCIETE FRANCO-JAPONAISE DE BIOLOGIE. BULLETIN/NICHIFUTSU SEIBUTSU GAKKAISHI. Text in English, French, Japanese. 1955. a.
Published by: Societe Franco-Japonaise de Biologie/Nichifutsu Seibutsu Gakkai, c/o Mr Sadao Yasugi, Tokyo Toritsu Daigaku Rigakubu Seibutsugakka, 1-1 Minami-Osawa, Hachioji-shi, Tokyo-to 192-0364, Japan.

570 FRA ISSN 0366-1326
CODEN: BMSLAG
SOCIETE LINNEENNE DE LYON. BULLETIN MENSUEL. Text in French; Summaries in English. 1822. 10/yr. EUR 18 to members; EUR 24 to non-members (effective 2005). adv. bk.rev. index. back issues avail. **Document type:** *Bulletin.*
Indexed: AICP, ASFA, BIOSIS Prev, BiolAb, ESPM, RPP, RefZh, ZooRec.
—BLDSC (2875.300000), IE, ingenta, Linda Hall.
Published by: Societe Linneenne de Lyon, 33 rue Bossuet, Lyon, 69006, France. societe.linneenne.lyon@wanadoo.fr, http://www.linneenne-lyon.org. Ed. Paul Berthet. Circ: 1,600.

571.4645 USA ISSN 1069-3610
CODEN: GMFNDF
SOCIETY FOR CRYOBIOLOGY. NEWS NOTES. Text in English. 1979. q. membership only. bk.rev. **Document type:** *Newsletter.* **Description:** News of interest about the society.
Published by: Society for Cryobiology, 8650 Rockville Pike, Bethesda, MD 20814. TEL 706-721-4173, FAX 706-721-2347. Ed. A M Karow. Circ: 500.

570 GBR ISSN 0081-1386
QH302 CODEN: SSEBA9
SOCIETY FOR EXPERIMENTAL BIOLOGY. SYMPOSIA. Text in English. 1947. irreg., latest vol.51, 1998. **Document type:** *Proceedings.*
Indexed: ASCA, BiolAb, CIN, ChemAb, ChemTitl, IndMed, MEDLINE, RPP, SFA, SeedAb, WeedAb, ZooRec.
—BLDSC (8585.000000), CASDDS, CISTI, IE, ingenta, KNAW. **CCC.**
Published by: Society for Experimental Biology, 3 The Carronades, New Road, Southampton, Hants SO14 0AA, United Kingdom. TEL 44-23-80224824, FAX 44-23-80226312, http://www.sebiology.org/.

570 USA ISSN 0361-6525
QH301 CODEN: SOCIDT
➤ **SOCIOBIOLOGY.** Text in English. 1976. irreg. (approx. a.). USD 120 (effective 2005). bk.rev. illus. index. back issues avail. **Document type:** *Academic/Scholarly.* **Description:** Provides research articles and translations of classic papers on various aspects of the biology of social animals.
Indexed: ASCA, ASFA, AgBio, Agr, AgrForAb, AnBeAb, ApEcolAb, B&BAb, BibAg, BioCN&I, BiolAb, CurCont, ESPM, EntAb, FPA, ForAb, GenetAb, HGA, HerbAb, HortAb, ISR, MaizeAb, NemAb, NutrAb, OrnHort, RA&MP, RM&VM, RevApplEntom, S&F, SCI, SFA, SeedAb, SoyAb, TDB, WAE&RSA, WildRev, ZooRec.
—BLDSC (8319.562000), CISTI, IDS, IE, Infotrieve, ingenta, Linda Hall. **CCC.**
Published by: California State University, Chico, Department of Biological Sciences, 400 W First St, Chico, CA 95929. TEL 530-898-5356, dkistner@csuchico.edu, http://www.csuchico.edu/biol/Sociobiology/sociobiologyindex.html, http://www.csuchico.edu/biol/biology.html. Ed., R&P David H Kistner. Circ: 400.

570 BGR ISSN 0204-9910
SOFIISKI UNIVERSITET SV. KLIMENT OHRIDSKI. BIOLOGICHESKI FAKULTET. GODISHNIK. KNIGA 2. BOTANIKA. Text in Bulgarian. 1977. a. price varies. reprint service avail. from IRC.
Formerly (until 1978): Sofiiski Universitet. Biologicheski Fakultet. Godishnik. Kniga 2. Botanika (1310-540X)
Indexed: BiolAb, ChemAb, FCA, RefZh.
—CISTI, Linda Hall.
Published by: (Sofiiski Universitet Sv. Kliment Ohridski, Biologicheski Fakultet/Sofia University St. Kliment Ohridski, Faculty of Biology), Universitetsko Izdatelstvo Sv. Kliment Okhridski/Publishing House of the Sofia University St. Kliment Ohridski, Akad G Bonchev 6, Sofia, 1113, Bulgaria. Ed. I Penev. Circ: 550.

SOURCE O C D E. ENVIRONNEMENT ET DEVELOPPEMENT DURABLE. (Organisation de Cooperation et de Developpement Economiques) see *ENVIRONMENTAL STUDIES*

SOURCE O E C D. ENVIRONMENT & SUSTAINABLE DEVELOPMENT. see *ENVIRONMENTAL STUDIES*

578.77 639.2 ZAF ISSN 0259-0050
CODEN: SMBBBL
➤ **SOUTH AFRICAN ASSOCIATION FOR MARINE BIOLOGICAL RESEARCH. BULLETIN.** Text in English. 1960. a., latest vol.28, 2002. free. **Document type:** *Bulletin, Academic/Scholarly.* **Description:** Reviews the research of the Oceanographic Research Institute and curatorial activities of Sea World, Durban, for a general audience.
Indexed: ASFA, SFA.
—BLDSC (2758.900000).
Published by: South African Association for Marine Biological Research, Marine Parade, PO Box 10712, Durban, KwaZulu-Natal 4056, South Africa. TEL 27-31-373536, FAX 27-31-372132, saambr@saambr.org.za, http://www.seaworld.org.za. Circ: 450 (controlled).

➤ **SOUTH AFRICAN INSTITUTE FOR MEDICAL RESEARCH. PUBLICATION.** see *MEDICAL SCIENCES*

B

B

301   ZAF   ISSN 0303-2515
QH1   CODEN: ASAMAS
➤ **SOUTH AFRICAN MUSEUM. ANNALS/SUID-AFRIKAANSE MUSEUM. ANNALE.** Text in English. 1898. irreg. price varies. illus. back issues avail. **Document type:** *Monographic series, Academic/Scholarly.* **Description:** Publishes research and review articles in the fields of anthropology, archeology, geology, paleontology, entomology, and vertebrate and invertebrate zoology.
Indexed: ASFA, AbAn, BIOSIS Prev, BiolAb, ESPM, EntAb, ISAP, OceAb, RefZh, SFA, SWRA, WildRev, ZooRec.
—BLDSC (1032.000000), CISTI.
Published by: South African Museum, PO Box 61, Cape Town, 8000, South Africa. TEL 27-21-4243330, FAX 27-21-4246716, elouw@samuseum. ac.za. Ed. Elizabeth Louw. R&P E Louw. Circ: 450 (controlled).

➤ **SOUTH CAROLINA SEA GRANT CONSORTIUM. PROCEEDINGS.** see *CONSERVATION*

578.77   GBR
THE SOUTH-WEST IRISH SEA SURVEY. Text in English. irreg. **Document type:** *Monographic series, Academic/Scholarly.*
—BLDSC (2089.270000).
Published by: National Museums & Galleries of Wales/Amgueddfa Genedlaethol Cymru, Cathays Park, Cardiff, CF10 3NP, United Kingdom. biosyb@nmgw.ac.uk, http://www.nmgw.ac.uk.

SOUTHEASTERN ASSOCIATION OF FISH AND WILDLIFE AGENCIES. PROCEEDINGS. see *FISH AND FISHERIES*

570   USA   ISSN 1533-8436
SOUTHEASTERN BIOLOGY. Text in English. 1953. q. USD 25 (effective 2003). bk.rev. abstr.; charts; illus.; stat. 1 cols./p.; back issues avail.; reprint service avail. from PQC. **Document type:** *Bulletin, Academic/Scholarly.*
Formerly (until 2001): A S B Bulletin (0001-2386)
Related titles: Microform ed.: (from PQC).
Indexed: BiolAb, SFA, ZooRec.
—CISTI, Linda Hall.
Published by: Association of Southeastern Biologists, Inc., University of Tennessee, Department of Botony, Knoxville, TN 37996-1100. TEL 865-974-2256, FAX 865-974-2258, jcaponet@utk.edu, http://www.asb.appstate.edu/. Ed. James D Caponetti TEL 865-974-6219. Pub. Tim Atkinson. Circ: 1,300.

611.01816   USA   ISSN 1086-4105
R856.A2
SOUTHERN BIOMEDICAL ENGINEERING CONFERENCE. PROCEEDINGS. Text in English. 1982. irreg. price varies.
Related titles: Online - full text ed.: (from I E E E).
Indexed: EngInd.
—BLDSC (8352.920800). **CCC.**
Published by: Pergamon Press, Inc., Journals Division, 660 White Plains Rd, Tarrytown, NY 10591-5153. TEL 914-524-9200, FAX 914-333-2444.

570 610   FRA   ISSN 0295-1967
      CODEN: SPEBEQ
SPECTRA BIOLOGIE. Text in French. 1982. 7/yr. EUR 84 domestic; EUR 118 foreign (effective 2005). adv. bk.rev. **Document type:** *Academic/Scholarly.* **Description:** Focuses on analytical techniques and instruments routinely used in clinical laboratories. Disseminates information on the growth of the profession and on new concepts, which are expected to greatly affect clinical laboratory practice.
Indexed: CIN, ChemAb, ChemTitl, RefZh.
—BLDSC (8408.690000), CASDDS, CISTI, IE, Infotrieve, ingenta. **CCC.**
Published by: P C I, 176 rue du Temple, Paris, 75003, France. TEL 33-1-44593838, FAX 33-1-44593839, http://www.editions-pci.fr/Biolo.html. Ed. Monique Chevalier. Adv. contact Catherine Leclerq Bourdon. Circ: 4,500.

SPEZIELLE PATHOLOGISCHE ANATOMIE. see *MEDICAL SCIENCES*

570   AUT   ISSN 0252-192X
STAPFIA. Text in English, German; Summaries in English. 1977. irreg., latest vol.80, 2002. price varies. Index. back issues avail. **Document type:** *Monographic series, Academic/Scholarly.* **Description:** Contains monographies, proceedings, articles and exhibition descriptions in various fields of biology.
Indexed: ZooRec.
Published by: Oberoesterreichisches Landesmuseum, Biologiezentrum, J.-W.-Klein-Str 73, Linz, 4040, Austria. TEL 43-732-759733, FAX 43-732-75973399, bio-linz@landesmuseum-linz.ac.at, http://www.biologiezentrum.at. R&P Gerhard Aubrecht. Circ: 500 (controlled).

▼ **STATE OF THE WILD;** a global portrait of wildlife, wild lands, and oceans. see *ENVIRONMENTAL STUDIES*

572.8   USA   ISSN 1066-5099
QH442.2   CODEN: STCEEJ
➤ **STEM CELLS;** the international journal of cell differentiation and proliferation. Text in English. 1983. bi-m. USD 195 combined subscription to individuals print & online eds. (effective 2004). adv. bk.rev. back issues avail.; reprints avail. **Document type:** *Journal, Academic/Scholarly.* **Description:** Publishes investigative papers and concise reviews with significant new information on normal and neoplastic stem and progenitor cell biology and molecular biology, clinical applications of gene manipulation, growth factors and cytokines, peripheral blood stem cell mobilization and transplantation and tumor cell purging.
Formerly (until 1992): International Journal of Cell Cloning (0737-1454)
Related titles: Online - full text ed.: ISSN 1549-4918. USD 180 (effective 2005) (from EBSCO Publishing, HighWire Press).
Indexed: ASCA, B&BAb, BCI, BIOBASE, BIOSIS Prev, BiolAb, BiolDig, CIN, ChemAb, ChemTitl, CurCont, ExcerpMed, GenetAb, HortAb, IABS, IPA, ISR, IndMed, Inpharma, M&PBA, MEDLINE, PE&ON, RA&MP, Reac, RefZh, SCI, Telegen.
—BLDSC (8464.133510), CASDDS, CISTI, GNLM, IDS, IE, Infotrieve, ingenta, KNAW, Linda Hall. **CCC.**
Published by: AlphaMed Press, Inc., 318 Blackwell St., Ste. 260, Durham, NC 27701-2884. TEL 937-291-2021, FAX 937-291-4229, stemcells@alphamedpress.com, alphamedpress@alphamedpress.com, subscribers@alphamedpress.com, http://www.stemcells.com. Ed. Curt I. Civin. Pub. Ann Murphy. R&P Tim Sparling. Adv. contact Susan Hughes Hansen, TEL 856-589-5454, ext.18. B&W page USD 1,100, color page USD 1,550. Circ: 950.

578.77   DEU   ISSN 1618-3703
STIFTUNG ALFRED-WEGENER-INSTITUT FUER POLAR- UND MEERESFORSCHUNG. ZWEIJAHRESBERICHT/ALFRED WEGENER INSTITUTE FOUNDATION FOR POLAR AND MARINE RESEARCH. REPORT. Text in English, German. 1986. biennial.
Formed by the 2000 merger of: Alfred-Wegener-Institut fuer Polar- und Meeresforschung Bremerhaven. Zweijahresbericht (0940-4546); Alfred Wegener Institute for Polar and Marine Research. Report (1433-4100)
Published by: Alfred-Wegener-Stiftung, Foundation for Polar and Marine Research, Postfach 12 0161, Bremerhaven, 27515, Germany. TEL 49-471-48310, FAX 49-471-483111, awi-pr@awi-bremerhaven.de, http://www.awi-bremerhaven.de.

577.7   USA   ISSN 0969-2126
QH506   CODEN: STRUE6
➤ **STRUCTURE.** Cover title: Structure with Folding & Design. Text in English. 1993. 12/yr. EUR 406 in Europe to individuals; JPY 42,200 in Japan to individuals; USD 341 in Canada to individuals; USD 341 in United States to individuals; USD 353 elsewhere to individuals; EUR 1,731 in Europe to institutions; JPY 180,600 in Japan to institutions; USD 1,545 in United States to institutions; USD 1,545 in Canada to institutions; USD 1,507 elsewhere to institutions (effective 2006). adv. reprints avail. **Document type:** *Journal, Academic/Scholarly.* **Description:** Directed toward researchers, educators and students of biology. Features original research and reviews.
Incorporates (1995-1998): Folding and Design (1359-0278)
Related titles: Online - full text ed.: USD 315 to individuals (effective 2004) (from EBSCO Publishing, Gale Group, IngentaConnect, O C L C Online Computer Library Center, Inc., ScienceDirect, Swets Information Services).
Indexed: ASFA, BBCI, BIOBASE, BIOSIS Prev, BiolAb, CIN, ChemAb, ChemTitl, CurCont, DSA, EEA, ESPM, ExcerpMed, FS&TA, ISR, IndMed, MEDLINE, MSB, NucAcAb, SCI.
—BLDSC (8478.677000), CASDDS, CISTI, GNLM, IDS, IE, Infotrieve, ingenta, KNAW. **CCC.**
Published by: Cell Press (Subsidiary of: Elsevier Science & Technology), 1100 Massachusetts Ave, Cambridge, MA 02138. TEL 617-661-7057, FAX 617-661-7061, structure@cell.com, editor@cell.com, http://www.elsevier.com/locate/str, http://www.cellpress.com/. Ed. Christopher Lima. Pub. Lynne Herndon. Adv. contact Sande Giaccone TEL 212-633-3914. B&W page USD 1,050, color page USD 2,405; trim 8.5 x 11. Circ: 734 (paid). **Subscr. to:** Quadrant Subscription Services; **Subscr. to:** 6277 Sea Harbor Dr, Orlando, FL 32887. TEL 407-345-3000, 866-314-2355, FAX 407-363-9661, subs@cell.com. **Dist. by:** Extenza - Turpin.

570   ITA   ISSN 0392-0542
STUDI TRENTINI DI SCIENZE NATURALI. ACTA BIOLOGICA. Text in Italian. 1977. q.
Formerly (until 1976): Studi Trentini di Scienze Naturali. Sezione B, Biologica (0585-5616)
Published by: Museo Tridentino di Scienze Naturali, Via Calepina 14, Trento, TN 38100, Italy. TEL 39-0461-270311, FAX 39-0461.233830, info@mtsn.tn.it, http://www.mtsn.tn.it.

577   ESP   ISSN 0211-4623
QH171   CODEN: STOEEB
STUDIA OECOLOGICA. Text in Spanish. 1981. a. price varies. **Document type:** *Academic/Scholarly.*
Indexed: ASFA, ApicAb, ESPM, I&DA, IECT, RASB, S&F, SWRA, SeedAb.
Published by: Ediciones Universidad de Salamanca, Apartado 325, Salamanca, 37080, Spain. TEL 34-923-294598, FAX 34-923-262579, eus@gugu.usal.es, http://www3.usal.es/~eus/indexsp.htm. Ed. Jose Manuel Gomez Gutierrez.

570   ROM   ISSN 1221-8103
QH301   CODEN: SUBBA8
STUDIA UNIVERSITATIS "BABES-BOLYAI". BIOLOGIA. Text in English, French, German, Romanian; Summaries in German, French. 1958. s-a. per issue exchange basis. bk.rev. abstr.; charts; illus.; bibl. **Document type:** *Academic/Scholarly.*
Formerly (until 1974): Studia Universitatis Babes-Bolyai. Series Biologia (0039-3398)
Indexed: AgBio, BiolAb, CPA, ChemAb, DSA, ExcerpMed, FCA, ForAb, HerbAb, HortAb, MaizeAb, NemAb, OrnHort, PBA, PGegResA, PGrRegA, RA&MP, RPP, RefZh, S&F, SIA, SeedAb, SoyAb, TriticAb, VITIS, WeedAb, ZooRec.
—CISTI.
Published by: Universitatea "Babes-Bolyai", Biblioteca Centrala Universitara/Babes-Bolyai University, Central University Library in Cluj-Napoca, Mihail Kogalniceanu 1B, Cluj-Napoca, 3400, Romania. TEL 40-64-194315, FAX 40-64-191906, staff@staff.ubbcluj.ro, http://www.ubbcluj.ro. Eds. Mihai Dragan Bularda, Stefan Kiss, Alina Vesa.

STUDIES IN FERTILITY AND STERILITY. see *MEDICAL SCIENCES*

570   GBR   ISSN 1369-8486
QH305
STUDIES IN HISTORY AND PHILOSOPHY OF SCIENCE PART C: STUDIES IN HISTORY AND PHILOSOPHY OF BIOLOGICAL AND BIOMEDICAL SCIENCES. Text in English. 4/yr. EUR 346 in Europe to institutions; JPY 46,000 in Japan to institutions; USD 387 to institutions except Europe and Japan; EUR 58 in Europe to qualified personnel; JPY 7,900 in Japan to qualified personnel; USD 63 to qualified personnel except Europe and Japan (effective 2006). reprints avail. **Document type:** *Journal, Academic/Scholarly.*
Description: Covers historical, sociological, philosophical, and ethical aspects of the life sciences.
Related titles: Online - full text ed.: (from EBSCO Publishing, Gale Group, IngentaConnect, ScienceDirect, Swets Information Services).
Indexed: AmH&L, HistAb, IPB, PhilInd.
—BLDSC (8490.651500), CISTI, IE, Infotrieve, ingenta, Linda Hall.
Published by: Pergamon (Subsidiary of: Elsevier Science & Technology), The Boulevard, Langford Ln, East Park, Kidlington, Oxford OX5 1GB, United Kingdom. TEL 44-1865-843000, FAX 44-1865-843010, http://www.elsevier.com/locate/shpsc. Ed. Nicholas Jardine. **Subscr. to:** Elsevier BV, PO Box 211, Amsterdam 1000 AE, Netherlands. TEL 31-20-485-3757, FAX 31-20-485-3432, nlinfo-f@elsevier.nl, http://www.elsevier.nl.

570   SGP   ISSN 1793-1428
STUDIES OF NONLINEAR PHENOMENA IN LIFE SCIENCE. Text in English. 1990. irreg., latest vol.10, 2003, Winter. price varies. **Document type:** *Monographic series, Academic/Scholarly.*
Indexed: CCMJ, ZentMath.
—BLDSC (8491.155930).
Published by: World Scientific Publishing Co. Pte. Ltd., 5 Toh Tuck Link, Singapore, 596224, Singapore. TEL 65-466-5775, FAX 65-467-7667, wspc@wspc.com.sg, series@wspc.com.sg, http://www.wspc.com.sg/books/series/snpls_series.shtml, http://www.worldscientific.com. Ed. B J West. **Dist. by:** World Scientific Publishing Co., Inc., 1060 Main St, River Edge, NJ 07661. TEL 201-487-9655, 800-227-7562, FAX 201-487-9656, 888-977-2665; World Scientific Publishing Ltd., 57 Shelton St, London WC2H 9HE, United Kingdom. TEL 44-20-78360888, FAX 44-20-78362020.

570   DEU   ISSN 0341-0145
QH5   CODEN: SBNAAY
STUTTGARTER BEITRAEGE ZUR NATURKUNDE. SERIE A. BIOLOGIE. Text in German. irreg. **Document type:** *Monographic series, Academic/Scholarly.*
Indexed: BIOSIS Prev, BiolAb, ESPM, EntAb, RefZh, ZooRec.
—BLDSC (8501.505000), CISTI, Linda Hall. **CCC.**
Published by: Staatliches Museum fuer Naturkunde Stuttgart, Rosenstein 1, Stuttgart, 70191, Germany. TEL 49-711-89360, FAX 49-711-8936200.

570   FRA
SUBTERRANEAN BIOLOGY. Text in English, French. 1970. a. EUR 40 (effective 2005). **Document type:** *Journal, Academic/Scholarly.*
Former title (until 2002): Memoires de Biospeologie (0184-0266); (until 1978): Laboratoire Souterrain du Centre National de la Recherche Scientifique. Serie Documents (0398-7973)
Indexed: BIOSIS Prev, BiolAb, ZooRec.
—BLDSC (5573.480000).
Published by: Societe de Biospeologie, Moulis, 09200, France. TEL 33-5-61663126, FAX 33-5-61960851. Ed. Marina Cobolli.

SURFACTANT SCIENCE SERIES. see *CHEMISTRY*

570 550   FRA   ISSN 0395-8957
SYMBIOSES. Text in French. 1969. s-a.
Incorporates (1983-1998): Societe des Amis du Museum de Chartres et des Naturalistes d'Eure et Loir. Bulletin (0760-7334)
Indexed: RefZh.

Published by: Societe des Amis du Museum de Chartres et des Naturalistes d'Eure et Loir, 5 bis Blvd de Courtille, Chartres, 28000, France. samnel@wanadoo.fr, http://www.shnlc.free.fr/remuce.html.

577.85 ISR ISSN 0334-5114
QH548 CODEN: SYMBER
➤ **SYMBIOSIS.** Text in English. 1985. bi-m. USD 135 to individual members; USD 630 to libraries; USD 630 to non-members; USD 115 to students (effective 2005). reprint service avail. from PQC. **Document type:** *Academic/Scholarly.* **Description:** Contains original research in symbiotic interactions at the molecular, cellular and organismic levels.
Indexed: ASCA, ASFA, AgBio, Agr, AgrForAb, ApEcolAb, BIOBASE, BIOSIS Prev, BioCN&I, BiolAb, CIN, CPA, ChemAb, ChemTitl, CurCont, DSA, ESPM, FCA, FPA, FS&TA, FaBeAb, ForAb, GEOBASE, HerbAb, HortAb, I&DA, IABS, ISR, MBA, MaizeAb, NutrAb, OceAb, OrnHort, PBA, PGegResA, PGrRegA, PHN&I, PlantSci, PotatoAb, ProtozoAb, RA&MP, RM&VM, RPP, RevApplEntom, RiceAb, S&F, SCI, SFA, SIA, SeedAb, SoyAb, TriticAb, WeedAb, ZooRec.
—BLDSC (8581.640000), CASDDS, CISTI, IDS, IE, Infotrieve, ingenta, Linda Hall.
Published by: Balaban Publishers, International Science Services, P O Box 2039, Rehovot, 76120, Israel. TEL 972-8-947-6216, FAX 972-8-946-7632, balabanm@netvision.net.il. Ed. Margalith Galun.

570 USA ISSN 1063-5157
QH83 CODEN: SYBIER
➤ **SYSTEMATIC BIOLOGY.** Text in English. 1952. bi-m. USD 202, GBP 123 combined subscription to institutions print & online eds. (effective 2006). bk.rev. charts; illus. index. reprint service avail. from PQC,PSC. **Document type:** *Journal, Academic/Scholarly.*
Formerly (until 1991): Systematic Zoology (0039-7989)
Related titles: Microform ed.: (from PQC); Online - full text ed.: ISSN 1076-836X. USD 192, GBP 117 to institutions (effective 2006) (from bigchalk, EBSCO Publishing, Gale Group, IngentaConnect, JSTOR (Web-based Journal Archive), O C L C Online Computer Library Center, Inc., ProQuest Information & Learning, Swets Information Services).
Indexed: ASCA, ASFA, AgBio, Agr, AnBrAb, B&AI, B&BAb, BIOSIS Prev, BioCN&I, BiolAb, BiolDig, CMCI, CRFR, ChemAb, CurCont, ESPM, EntAb, ForAb, GenetAb, HelmAb, HerbAb, HortAb, ISR, IndMed, IndVet, MEDLINE, OceAb, PBA, PGegResA, PHN&I, PhilInd, PoultAb, RPP, RevApplEntom, S&F, SCI, SFA, SSCI, VetBull, WildRev, ZooRec.
—BLDSC (8589.180700), CISTI, IDS, IE, Infotrieve, ingenta, Linda Hall. **CCC.**
Published by: (Society of Systematic Biologists), Taylor & Francis Inc. (Subsidiary of: Taylor & Francis Group), 325 Chestnut St, Ste 800, Philadelphia, PA 19016. TEL 215-625-8900, FAX 215-625-2940, systbiol@u.washington.edu, info@taylorandfrancis.com, http://www.tandf.co.uk/journals/titles/10635157.asp, http://www.taylorandfrancis.com. Ed. Chris Simon. Circ: 2,800. **Subscr. addr. in Europe:** Taylor & Francis Ltd, Journals Customer Service, Rankine Rd, Basingstoke, Hants RG24 8PR, United Kingdom. TEL 44-1256-813000, FAX 44-1256-330245, enquiry@tandf.co.uk.

570 NLD ISSN 0165-5752
QL757 CODEN: SYPAD4
➤ **SYSTEMATIC PARASITOLOGY.** Text in English. 1979. 9/yr. EUR 1,138, USD 1,148, GBP 748 combined subscription to institutions print & online eds. (effective 2005). illus. Index. back issues avail.; reprint service avail. from PSC. **Document type:** *Journal, Academic/Scholarly.* **Description:** Publishes original papers on the systematics, taxonomy and nomenclature of parasites, including nematodes, arthropods, and other parasitic groups.
Related titles: Microform ed.: (from PQC); Online - full text ed.: ISSN 1573-5192 (from EBSCO Publishing, Gale Group, IngentaConnect, Kluwer Online, O C L C Online Computer Library Center, Inc., Ovid Technologies, Inc., Springer LINK, Swets Information Services).
Indexed: ASCA, ASFA, AbHyg, AgBio, Agr, AnBrAb, BIOBASE, BIOSIS Prev, BibLing, BioCN&I, BiolAb, CurCont, ESPM, EntAb, ForAb, HelmAb, HortAb, IABS, ISR, IndMed, IndVet, MBA, MEDLINE, NemAb, OrnHort, PoultAb, ProtozoAb, RM&VM, RefZh, RevApplEntom, S&F, SCI, SFA, TDB, VITIS, VetBull, ZooRec.
—BLDSC (8589.188000), CISTI, IDS, IE, Infotrieve, ingenta, Linda Hall. **CCC.**
Published by: Springer-Verlag Dordrecht (Subsidiary of: Springer Science+Business Media), Van Godewijckstraat 30, Dordrecht, 3311 GX, Netherlands. TEL 31-78-6576050, FAX 31-78-6576474, http://springerlink.metapress.com/openurl.asp?genre=journal&issn=0165-5752, http://www.springeronline.com. Ed. D I Gibson.

570 GBR ISSN 1477-2000
QH541.15.B56
▼ ➤ **SYSTEMATICS AND BIODIVERSITY.** Text in English. 2003. q. GBP 162 to institutions; USD 266 in North America to institutions; GBP 176 combined subscription to institutions print & online eds.; USD 288 combined subscription in North America to institutions print & online eds. (effective 2006). **Document type:** *Journal, Academic/Scholarly.* **Description:** Devoted to whole-organism biology, especially systematics and taxonomic biodiversity. It emphasizes the importance and multi-disciplinary significance of systematics.
Formed by the merger of (1951-2003): Natural History Museum. Bulletin. Botany Series (0968-0446); Which was formerly (until 1994): British Museum (Natural History). Bulletin. Botany (0068-2292); (1949-2003): Natural History Museum. Bulletin. Entomology Series (0968-0454); Which was formerly (until 1994): British Museum (Natural History) Bulltein. Entomology (0524-6431); (1949-2003): Natural History Museum. Bulletin. Zoology Series (0968-0470); Which was formerly (until 1994): British Museum (Natural History). Bulletin. Zoology (0007-1498)
Related titles: Online - full text ed.: ISSN 1478-0933. GBP 152 to institutions; USD 248 in North America to institutions (effective 2006) (from O C L C Online Computer Library Center, Inc., Swets Information Services).
Indexed: RefZh, S&F.
—BLDSC (8589.232000), CISTI, IE, Linda Hall. **CCC.**
Published by: (Natural History Museum), Cambridge University Press, The Edinburgh Bldg, Shaftesbury Rd, Cambridge, CB2 2RU, United Kingdom. TEL 44-1223-312393, FAX 44-1223-315052, journals@cambridge.org, http://titles.cambridge.org/journals/journal_catalogue.asp?historylinks=ALPHA&mnemonic=SYS, http://uk.cambridge.org/journals. Ed. Brian Rosen. **Subscr. to:** Cambridge University Press, 100 Brook Hill Dr, West Nyack, NY 10994. TEL 845-353-7500, FAX 845-353-4141, journals_subscriptions@cup.org

➤ **TAIWAN SUGAR RESEARCH INSTITUTE. ANNUAL REPORT/TAI-WAN TANG YEH YEN CHIU SO NIEN PAO.** see *AGRICULTURE—Crop Production And Soil*

570 JPN
TAKEDA SCIENCE FOUNDATION SYMPOSIUM ON BIOSCIENCE. PROCEEDINGS. Text in English. 1983. biennial. **Document type:** *Proceedings.*
—BLDSC (6849.666800).
Published by: Takeda Kagaku Shinko Zaidan/Takeda Science Foundation, 17-85 Juso-Hon-Machi 2-chome, Yodogawa-ku, Osaka-shi, 532-0024, Japan.

377 USA ISSN 1076-3635
TALKING LEAVES (EUGENE). Text in English. 198?. q.
Published by: Deep Ecology Education Project, 1430 Willamette St #367, Eugene, OR 97401.

570 AUS ISSN 0819-6826
➤ **TASMANIAN NATURALIST.** Text in English. 1904. a. AUD 15 domestic to individuals; AUD 20 domestic to libraries; AUD 25 foreign (effective 2002). bk.rev. bibl.; illus.; maps. 56 p./no.; back issues avail. **Document type:** *Journal, Academic/Scholarly.* **Description:** Covers natural history of Tasmania, including views on management of natural areas and values.
Indexed: ZooRec.
Published by: Tasmanian Field Naturalist Club Inc., GPO Box 68, Hobart, TAS 7001, Australia. TEL 61-3-6233-4914, juliascott@bigpond.com, http://www.tased.edu.au/tasonline/tasfield/homepage.htm. Ed. Robert Taylor. R&P G Gates TEL 61-3-6227-8638. Circ: 200 (paid).

➤ **TAUCHEN**; internationales Unterwasser-Magazin. see *SPORTS AND GAMES*

540 570 USA ISSN 1043-4658
QH506 CODEN: TCHNEV
TECHNIQUE (SAN DIEGO). Text in English. 1989. bi-m. **Document type:** *Academic/Scholarly.*
Indexed: BiolAb, ChemAb.
—CASDDS, GNLM. **CCC.**
Published by: Academic Press (Subsidiary of: Elsevier Science & Technology), 525 B St, Ste 1900, San Diego, CA 92101-4495. TEL 619-231-6616, 800-894-3434, apsubs@acad.com, http://www.apnet.com, http://www.academicpress.com.

TECHNIQUE ET BIOLOGIE; revue de documentation scientifique et d'information professionnelle. see *MEDICAL SCIENCES—Experimental Medicine, Laboratory Technique*

570 GBR ISSN 0951-4309
TESTS OF AGROCHEMICALS AND CULTIVARS. Text in English. 1980. a.
Related titles: ♦ Supplement to: Annals of Applied Biology. ISSN 0003-4746.
Indexed: Agr, AgrForAb, BIOBASE, BIOSIS Prev, BioCN&I, BiolAb, CPA, FCA, FPA, ForAb, HerbAb, HortAb, I&DA, MaizeAb, NemAb, NutrAb, OrnHort, PBA, PGegResA, PGrRegA, PHN&I, PotatoAb, RA&MP, RPP, RefZh, RevApplEntom, RiceAb, S&F, SIA, SeedAb, SoyAb, TriticAb, WeedAb.
—CISTI, Linda Hall. **CCC.**
Published by: Association of Applied Biologists, Horticultural Research International, c/o Warwick HRI, Wellesbourne, Warwick, CV35 9EF, United Kingdom. FAX 44-1789-470234.

TEXAS SHORES. see *ENVIRONMENTAL STUDIES*

572.8 GBR ISSN 1472-9288
QP383.5 CODEN: TRSHBY
THALAMUS AND RELATED SYSTEMS. Text in English. 2001. q. GBP 154 to institutions; USD 258 in North America to institutions; GBP 160 combined subscription to institutions print & online eds.; USD 268 combined subscription in North America to institutions print & online eds. (effective 2006). abstr. reprint service avail. from PSC. **Document type:** *Journal, Academic/Scholarly.* **Description:** Publishes papers on the structure, organization and chemistry of thalamic neurons, including the development, single-cell electrophysiology and synaptic interactions, molecular biology and genetics, neuropsychology, computational neurobiology, and pathology of the thalamus.
Related titles: Online - full text ed.: ISSN 1744-8107. GBP 140 to institutions; USD 235 in North America to institutions (effective 2006) (from EBSCO Publishing, Gale Group, IngentaConnect, ScienceDirect).
Indexed: BIOBASE, ExcerpMed.
—BLDSC (8814.142000), CISTI, IE, ingenta. **CCC.**
Published by: Cambridge University Press, The Edinburgh Bldg, Shaftesbury Rd, Cambridge, CB2 2RU, United Kingdom. TEL 44-1223-312393, FAX 44-1223-315052, journals@cambridge.org, http://www.cambridge.org/uk/journals/journal_catalogue.asp?historylinks=ALPHA&mnemonic=THL, http://uk.cambridge.org/journals. Ed. Mircea Steriade. **Subscr. to:** Cambridge University Press, 100 Brook Hill Dr, West Nyack, NY 10994. TEL 845-353-7500, FAX 845-353-4141, journals_subscriptions@cup.org

B

570 551.46 ESP ISSN 0212-5919
QH91.A1 CODEN: THALEP
➤ **THALASSAS**; revista de ciencias del mar. Text and summaries in English, Spanish. 1983. a. charts; illus. back issues avail. **Document type:** *Academic/Scholarly.* **Description:** Covers marine geology, biology, chemistry and oceanography.
Indexed: ASFA, ESPM, IECT, SFA, WildRev, ZooRec.
—CCC.
Published by: Universidade de Vigo, Servicio de Publicacions, Rua Oporto 1, Vigo, 36201, Spain. TEL 34-986-812000, informacion@uvigo.es, http://www.uvigo.es. Ed. Federico Vilas Martin. Pub., R&P Manuel Vazquez Vazquez. Circ: 500.

570 HRV ISSN 0495-4025
CODEN: THJUAP
THALASSIA JUGOSLAVICA. Text in Croatian. 1956. q. per issue exchange basis. illus. **Document type:** *Academic/Scholarly.*
Indexed: ASFA.
—CASDDS.
Published by: Rudier Boskovic Institute, Center for Marine Research, PO Box 1016, Zagreb, 41001, Croatia. Ed. Tomo Gamulin.

570 USA ISSN 0082-3945
➤ **THEORETICAL AND EXPERIMENTAL BIOLOGY**; an international series of monographs. Text in English. 1961. irreg., latest vol.6, 1967. reprint service avail. from ISI. **Document type:** *Monographic series, Academic/Scholarly.*
Indexed: BiolAb.
—CISTI, GNLM. **CCC.**
Published by: Academic Press (Subsidiary of: Elsevier Science & Technology), 525 B St, Ste 1900, San Diego, CA 92101-4495. TEL 619-231-6616, 800-894-3434, apsubs@acad.com, http://www.academicpress.com. Ed. J F Danielli.

570 GBR ISSN 1742-4682
▼ ➤ **THEORETICAL BIOLOGY AND MEDICAL MODELLING.** Text in English. 2004. 3/yr. free (effective 2006). **Document type:** *Journal, Academic/Scholarly.* **Description:** Covers all aspects of biology and the conceptual modelling required to understand its complexity.
Media: Online - full text (from EBSCO Publishing, National Library of Medicine).
Indexed: ExcerpMed.
Published by: BioMed Central Ltd. (Subsidiary of: Current Science Ltd), Middlesex House, 34-42 Cleveland St, London, W1T 4LB, United Kingdom. TEL 44-20-76319131, FAX 44-20-76319923, info@biomedcentral.com, http://www.tbiomed.com/home/, http://www.biomedcentral.com. Ed. Pier Paolo Delsanto.

570 USA ISSN 0040-5809
QH301 CODEN: TLPBAQ
➤ **THEORETICAL POPULATION BIOLOGY.** Text in English. 1970. 8/yr. EUR 652 in Europe to individuals; JPY 68,100 in Japan to individuals; USD 494 elsewhere to individuals; EUR 1,375 in Europe to institutions; JPY 143,500 in Japan to institutions; USD 1,039 elsewhere to institutions (effective 2006). **Document type:** *Academic/Scholarly.* **Description:** Covers the theoretical aspects of the biology of populations, particularly in the areas of ecology, genetics, demography, and epidemiology.
Related titles: Online - full text ed.: ISSN 1096-0325. USD 1,103 (effective 2002) (from EBSCO Publishing, Gale Group, IngentaConnect, O C L C Online Computer Library Center, Inc., ScienceDirect, Swets Information Services).

▼ new title ➤ refereed ✶ unverified ♦ full entry avail.

Indexed: ASCA, ASFA, AbHyg, AgBio, AnBrAb, ApEcolAb, B&BAb, BIOBASE, BIOSIS Prev, BioCN&I, BiolAb, CIS, CPA, CurCont, DSA, EPB, ESPM, EntAb, ForAb, GEOBASE, GenetAb, HGA, HelmAb, HerbAb, HortAb, IABS, ISR, IndMed, IndVet, Inpharma, MEDLINE, MathR, NemAb, NutrAb, OrnHort, PBA, PGegResA, PopulInd, ProtozoAb, RDA, RPP, Reac, RevApplEntom, S&F, SCI, SFA, SeedAb, TDB, VetBull, WeedAb, WildRev, ZentMath, ZooRec.
—BLDSC (8814.566000), CISTI, GNLM, IDS, IE, Infotrieve, ingenta, Linda Hall. **CCC.**
Published by: Academic Press (Subsidiary of: Elsevier Science & Technology), 525 B St, Ste 1900, San Diego, CA 92101-4495. TEL 619-231-6616, 800-894-3434, FAX 619-699-6422, apsubs@acad.com, http://www.elsevier.com/locate/tpb, http://www.academicpress.com. Ed. P Chesson.

570 DEU ISSN 1431-7613
QH301 CODEN: THBIFM
➤ **THEORY IN BIOSCIENCES/THEORIE IN DEN BIOWISSENSCHAFTEN.** Text and summaries in English, German. 1881. 4/yr. EUR 263 to institutions Germany, Austria, Switzerland; EUR 303 in Europe to institutions; JPY 40,400 in Japan to institutions; USD 340 elsewhere to institutions (effective 2006). adv. bk.rev. charts; illus. reprint service avail. from PQC. **Document type:** *Journal, Academic/Scholarly.* **Description:** Focuses on new concepts in theoretical biology. It is likewise interested in analytical or modelling approaches and in biophilosophy or history of ideas.
Formerly (until 1997): Biologisches Zentralblatt (0006-3304)
Related titles: Microform ed.: (from PMC, PQC); Online - full text ed.: ISSN 1611-7530. 2002 (from EBSCO Publishing, Gale Group, IngentaConnect, O C L C Online Computer Library Center, Inc., ScienceDirect, Swets Information Services).
Indexed: ASCA, ASFA, AgBio, AnBrAb, BIOBASE, BIOSIS Prev, BiolAb, CIN, ChemAb, ChemTitl, CurCont, ExcerpMed, FCA, FaBeAb, HelmAb, HerbAb, HortAb, IABS, ISR, IndVet, KWIWR, NutrAb, PBA, PGegResA, PGrRegA, PoultAb, RM&VM, RPP, RevApplEntom, RiceAb, SCI, SSCI, SeedAb, VetBull, WAE&RSA, WeedAb, WildRev, ZooRec.
—BLDSC (8814.630200), CASDDS, CISTI, IDS, IE, Infotrieve, ingenta, Linda Hall. **CCC.**
Published by: Elsevier GmbH, Urban & Fischer Verlag (Subsidiary of: Elsevier Science & Technology), Loebdergraben 14a, Jena, 07743, Germany. TEL 49-3641-626430, FAX 49-3641-626432, info@urbanfischer.de, http://www.elsevier.com/locate/theorybiosc, http://www.urbanfischer.de/journals. R&P Martin Huber TEL 49-3641-626430. Adv. contact Sabine Schroeter TEL 49-3641-626445. B&W page EUR 320, color page EUR 1,265; trim 170 x 240. Circ: 225 (paid and controlled).
Non-German speaking countries subscr. to: Nature Publishing Group, Brunel Rd, Houndmills, Basingstoke, Hamps RG21 6XS, United Kingdom. TEL 44-1256-302629, FAX 44-1256-476117

577 HUN ISSN 0563-587X
QH178.H8 CODEN: TSCAB8
TISCIA; an ecological journal. Text in English. 1965. irreg., latest vol.33, 2000. per issue exchange basis. charts; illus. **Document type:** *Journal, Academic/Scholarly.* **Description:** Covers the biology and ecology of ecosystems and the pollution of the environment in and around the Tisza River.
Indexed: ASFA, BIOSIS Prev, BiolAb, ChemAb, ChemTitl, MBA, RASB, ZooRec.
—CASDDS.
Published by: (Szegedi Tudomanyegyetem, Okologiai Tanszek/University of Szeged, Department of Ecology), Szegedi Tudomanyegyetem/University of Szeged, c/o E Szabo, Exchange Librarian, Dugonics ter 13, PO Box 393, Szeged, 6701, Hungary. TEL 36-62-544009, FAX 36-62-420895, kormoczy@sol.cc.u-szeged.hu, Eneh.Szabo@bibl.u-szeged.hu, http://ecol1.bio.u-szeged.hu/tiscia.html, http://www.u-szeged.hu. Ed. Laszlo Galle. Circ: 300. **Co-sponsor:** Tisza Kutato Bizottsag.

TISSUE ANTIGENS. see *MEDICAL SCIENCES*

570 JPN
TOHO DAIGAKU RIGAKUBU SEIBUTSU GAKKA GYOSEKI HOKOKU/TOHO UNIVERSITY. FACULTY OF SCIENCE. DEPARTMENT OF BIOLOGY. RESEARCH REPORT. Text in Japanese. triennial.
Published by: (Seibutsugakka), Toho Daigaku, Rigakubu/Toho University, Faculty of Science, Department of Biology, 2-1 Miyama 2-chome, Funabashi-shi, Chiba-ken 274-0072, Japan.

570 JPN ISSN 0040-8786
Q77.T55 CODEN: STUBAS
TOHOKU UNIVERSITY. SCIENCE REPORTS. SERIES 4: BIOLOGY/TOHOKU DAIGAKU RIKA HOKOKU. DAI-4-SHU, SEIBUTSUGAKU. Text in English. 1924. a. per issue exchange basis. bibl.; charts; illus. index.
Related titles: Microform ed.: (from PMC).
Indexed: ASFA, Agrind, BIOSIS Prev, BiolAb, ChemAb, ESPM, ExcerpMed, ZooRec.
—CASDDS, CISTI.
Published by: Tohoku Daigaku, Rigakubu/Tohoku University, Faculty of Science, Laboratory of Nuclear Science, Aramaki, Aoba-ku, Sendai-shi, Miyagi-ken 981-0945, Japan. Ed. Dr. K Sohma. Circ: 700.

TOKYO DAIGAKU RIGAKUBU FUZOKU RINKAI JIKKENJO NENPO/UNIVERSITY OF TOKYO. MISAKI MARINE BIOLOGICAL STATION. ANNUAL REPORT. see *EARTH SCIENCES—Oceanography*

TOPICS IN GEOBIOLOGY. see *EARTH SCIENCES—Geology*

570 CAN ISSN 0820-683X
TORONTO FIELD NATURALIST. Text in English. 1938. 8/yr. CND 25. bk.rev. **Document type:** *Newsletter.* **Description:** Stimulates public interest in natural history and encourages the preservation of Canada's natural heritage through conservation.
Address: 2 Carlton St No 1519, Toronto, ON M5B 1J3, Canada. TEL 416-593-2656. Ed. Helen Juhola. Circ: 1,500 (paid).

570 JPN ISSN 0287-5632
TOTTORI SEIBUTSU/TOTTORI BIOLOGICAL SOCIETY. JOURNAL. Text in Japanese. 1966. a. membership.
Published by: Tottoriken Seibutsu Gakkai/Tottori Biological Society, Tottori Kenritsu Hakubutsukan, 2-124 Higashi-Machi, Tottori-shi, 680-0011, Japan.

570 JPN ISSN 0389-7494
TOYAMA-KEN SEIBUTSU GAKKAI KAISHI/BIOLOGICAL SOCIETY OF TOYAMA. JOURNAL. Text in Japanese. a.
Published by: Toyamaken Seibutsu Gakkai/Biological Society of Toyama, c/o Mr Honda, 3687 Mitsukaichi, Kurobe-shi, Toyama-ken 938-0000, Japan.

570.7 JPN ISSN 0917-2033
TOYAMAKEN KOTO GAKKO KYOIKU KENKYUKAI SEIBUTSU BUNKAIHO/TOYAMA BIOLOGICAL EDUCATION SOCIETY. REPORT. Text in Japanese. a.
Published by: Toyamaken Koto Gakko Kyoiku Kenkyukai Seibutsu Bukai/Toyama Biological Education Society, Toyama Kenritsu Kureha Koto Gakko, 2070-5 kureha-Machi, Toyama-shi, 930-0138, Japan.

TRANSYLVANIA UNIVERSITY OF BRASOV. BULLETIN. SERIES B; mathematics, economical sciences, philology, medicine, physics, chemistry, sports. see *MATHEMATICS*

577 GBR ISSN 0169-5347
QH540 CODEN: TREEEQ
➤ **TRENDS IN ECOLOGY & EVOLUTION.** Text in English. 1986. 12/yr. EUR 181 in Europe to individuals; JPY 22,000 in Japan to individuals; USD 198 elsewhere to individuals; EUR 1,232 in Europe to institutions; JPY 170,900 in Japan to institutions; USD 1,378 elsewhere to institutions (effective 2006). adv. bk.rev.; software rev. charts; illus. index. back issues avail.; reprints avail. **Document type:** *Academic/Scholarly.* **Description:** Contains reviews, commentaries, discussions and letters in all areas of ecology and evolutionary science.
Related titles: Online - full text ed.: (from EBSCO Publishing, Gale Group, IngentaConnect, ScienceDirect, Swets Information Services).
Indexed: ASCA, ASFA, AbHyg, AgBio, AgrForAb, AnBeAb, AnBrAb, ApEcolAb, ApicAb, ArtHuCI, BIOBASE, BIOSIS Prev, BioCN&I, BiolAb, BiolDig, CPA, CurCont, EPB, ESPM, EntAb, EnvAb, FPA, FS&TA, ForAb, GEOBASE, GenetAb, HGA, HelmAb, HerbAb, HortAb, IABS, IBR, ISR, IndVet, MEDLINE, NemAb, NutrAb, OrnHort, PBA, PGegResA, PHN&I, PoultAb, ProtozoAb, RM&VM, RPP, RRTA, RefZh, RevApplEntom, S&F, SCI, SFA, SSCI, SeedAb, TriticAb, VetBull, WAE&RSA, WeedAb, WildRev, ZooRec.
—BLDSC (9049.569000), CISTI, IDS, IE, Infotrieve, ingenta, Linda Hall. **CCC.**
Published by: Elsevier Ltd., Trends Journals (Subsidiary of: Elsevier Science & Technology), 68 Hills Rd, Cambridge, CB2 1LA, United Kingdom. TEL 44-1865-315961, FAX 44-1233-464430, tree@elsevier.co.uk, http://www.elsevier.com/locate/tree. Eds. Katrina A Lythgoe, Laura Smith, Linsey Stapley. Adv. contact Thelma Reid. Circ: 1,649. **Subscr. to:** Elsevier Current Trends Subscriptions, PO Box 331, Haywards Heath, W Sussex RH16 3FG, United Kingdom. TEL 44-1444-475650, FAX 44-1444-445423.

570 ITA ISSN 1120-4648
TRIBUNA BIOLOGICA E MEDICA. Text in Multiple languages. 1990. q.
—GNLM.
Published by: Medical Systems SpA, Via Rio Torbido 40, Genoa, GE 16165, Italy. TEL 39-010-83401, FAX 39-010-803498, info@Medicalsystems.it, http://medicalsystems.it.

531.62 IDN ISSN 0854-1566
QH77.T78
➤ **TROPICAL BIODIVERSITY.** Text in English. 1992. 3/yr. IDR 30,000, USD 50 to individuals; IDR 45,000, USD 200 to institutions. bk.rev. **Document type:** *Academic/Scholarly.*
Indexed: SFA, ZooRec.
Published by: Indonesian Foundation for the Advancement of Biological Sciences, P O Box 103, Depok, 16401, Indonesia. TEL 62-21-775-1837, FAX 62-21-775-1837, 62-21-775-1837. Ed. Jatna Supriatna. Circ: 250.

➤ **TROPICAL FRESHWATER BIOLOGY.** see *FISH AND FISHERIES*

➤ **TROPICAL JOURNAL OF PHARMACEUTICAL RESEARCH.** see *PHARMACY AND PHARMACOLOGY*

578.77 551.46 BRA
QH91.A1 CODEN: URTBAV
➤ **TROPICAL OCEANOGRAPHY.** Text in Spanish, Portuguese, English. 1960. s-a. BRL 20 domestic; USD 20 foreign (effective 2002). adv. bk.rev. abstr. back issues avail. **Document type:** *Bulletin, Academic/Scholarly.* **Description:** Informs about estuarine, coastal and oceanic oceanography research, mainly in tropical areas.
Former titles (until 2001): Universidade Federal de Pernambuco. Departamento de Oceanografia. Centro de Tecnologia. Trabalhos Oceanograficos (0374-0412); (until 1966): Universidade Federal de Pernambuco. Instituto Oceanografico. Trabalhos (0080-0236); (until 1963): Universidade do Recife. Instituto Oceanografico. Trabalhos; (until 1960): Instituto de Biologia Marinha e Oceanografia. Trabalhos
Related titles: Fax ed.
Indexed: ASFA, BiolAb, SFA.
Published by: (Centro de Tecnologia), Editoria Universitaria U F P E, Departamento de Oceanografia, Campus Universitario, C D U, Recife, PE 50670901, Brazil. TEL 55-81-2718397, FAX 55-81-2718395, TELEX 811267, oceano@npd.ufpe.br. Ed., R&P Jose Zanon Oliveira Passauante TEL 55-81-2718225. adv.: B&W page USD 15, color page USD 30; trim 140 x 200. Circ: 250.

570 JPN ISSN 0917-415X
TROPICS/NETTAI KENKYU. Text in English, Japanese. 1991. q.
Indexed: ApicAb.
—**CCC.**
Published by: Nihon Nettai Seiti Gakkai/Japan Society of Tropical Ecology, c/o Mr Hotta, Kagoshima Daigaku Rigakubu Seibutsugakka, 21-35 Korimo-To 1-chome, Kagoshima-shi, 890-0065, Japan.

TROPINET. see *CONSERVATION*

570 TUR ISSN 1300-0152
QH301 CODEN: TJBIEZ
➤ **TURKISH JOURNAL OF BIOLOGY/TURK BIYOLOJI DERGISI.** Text and summaries in English; Abstracts in Turkish. 1976. 4/yr. USD 100 (effective 2005). **Document type:** *Journal, Academic/Scholarly.*
Formerly (until 1994): Doga Turkish Journal of Biology - Doga Turk Biyoloji Dergisi (1010-7576)
Related titles: Online - full text ed.: ISSN 1303-6092. free (effective 2005) (from EBSCO Publishing).
Indexed: AbHyg, AgBio, AgrForAb, AnBrAb, ApicAb, BIOSIS Prev, BioCN&I, BiolAb, CPA, ChemAb, DSA, FCA, FPA, FS&TA, ForAb, HerbAb, HortAb, IndVet, MaizeAb, NemAb, NutrAb, OrnHort, PBA, PGegResA, PGrRegA, PHN&I, PN&I, PoultAb, ProtozoAb, RA&MP, RM&VM, RPP, RevApplEntom, RiceAb, S&F, SIA, SeedAb, SoyAb, TDB, TriticAb, VITIS, VetBull, WeedAb, ZooRec.
—BLDSC (9072.467000), CASDDS, Linda Hall.
Published by: Scientific and Technical Research Council of Turkey - TUBITAK/Turkiye Bilimsel ve Teknik Arastirma Kurumu, Ataturk Bulvari No. 221, Kavaklidere, Ankara, 06100, Turkey. TEL 90-312-468-5300, FAX 90-312-426-8073, bdym@tubitak.gov.tr, http://journals.tubitak.gov.tr/biology/index.php, http://www.tubitak.gov.tr. Ed. Mustafa Ertan Atakan.

➤ **TURKISH JOURNAL OF MEDICAL & BIOLOGICAL RESEARCH.** see *MEDICAL SCIENCES*

570 FIN ISSN 0082-6979
CODEN: ATYBAK
TURUN YLIOPISTO. JULKAISUJA. SARJA A. II. BIOLOGICA - GEOGRAPHICA - GEOLOGICA/ANNALES UNIVERSITATIS TURKUENSIS. Text in English, Finnish, French, German. 1957. irreg. price varies. **Document type:** *Monographic series, Academic/Scholarly.* **Description:** Studies biology, genetics, geography and geology.
Indexed: BIOSIS Prev, BiolAb, INIS AtomInd.
—CASDDS, CISTI, Linda Hall.
Published by: Turun Yliopiston Kirjasto/University of Turku, Turku, 20500, Finland. FAX 358-2-3335050, annales@utu.fi, http://www.utu.fi/kirjasto.

U.S. CENTERS FOR DISEASE CONTROL. CONGENITAL MALFORMATIONS SURVEILLANCE. see *BIOLOGY—Abstracting, Bibliographies, Statistics*

577 USA ISSN 1052-2468
U.S. ENVIRONMENTAL PROTECTION AGENCY. ECOLOGICAL RESEARCH SERIES. Text in English. 1972. irreg. **Document type:** *Monographic series.*
Published by: (U.S. Environmental Protection Agency, Office of Research and Development), U.S. Environmental Protection Agency, 401 M St, S W, Washington, DC 20460. TEL 202-655-4000, FAX 202-554-5603, http://www.epa.gov/epahome/publications.htm. **Dist. by:** National Service Center for Environmental Publications, PO Box 42419, Cincinnati, OH 45242-0419. TEL 513-489-8190, 800-490-9198, FAX 513-489-8695, ncepimal@one.net, http://www.epa.gov/ncepihom/ordering.htm.

570 JPN ISSN 0914-9201
➤ **UCHU SEIBUTSU KAGAKU/BIOLOGICAL SCIENCES IN SPACE.** Text in English, Japanese; Summaries in English. 1987. q. JPY 5,000 membership (effective 2005). bk.rev. back issues avail. **Document type:** *Journal, Academic/Scholarly.*
Description: Publishes original and review papers dealing with all aspects of biological studies related to space.
Related titles: Online - full text ed.: ISSN 1349-967X (from J-Stage).
—BLDSC (2080.456000), IE, ingenta. **CCC.**
Published by: Nihon Uchu Seibutsu Kagakkai/Japanese Society for Biological Sciences in Space, Uchu Kagaku Kenkyujo, 1-1 Yoshinodai 3-chome, Sagamihara-shi, Kanagawa-ken 229-0022, Japan. TEL 81-42-7598230, FAX 81-42-7598449, jsbss@surc.isas.ac.jp, http://cosmo.ric.u-tokyo.ac.jp/JSBSS/Journal.html, http://wwwsoc.nii.ac.jp/jsbss/. Ed. Kenichi Ijiri. Circ: 500.

570 USA ISSN 0301-5629
RM862.7 CODEN: USMBA3
➤ **ULTRASOUND IN MEDICINE & BIOLOGY.** Text in English. 1974. 12/yr. USD 269 domestic to individuals; USD 269 foreign to individuals; USD 1,456 domestic to institutions; USD 1,456 foreign to institutions (effective 2006). adv. charts; illus. Index. back issues avail. **Document type:** *Journal, Academic/Scholarly.* **Description:** Publishes original contributions on significant advances in clinical diagnostic, interventional and therapeutic applications, new and improved clinical techniques, the physics, engineering and technology of ultrasound in medicine and biology, and the interactions between ultrasound and biological materials.
Related titles: Microfilm ed.: (from PQC); Online - full text ed.: (from EBSCO Publishing, Gale Group, IngentaConnect, ScienceDirect).
Indexed: ASCA, ASFA, AcoustA, ApMecR, BIOSIS Prev, BioEngAb, BiolAb, C&ISA, CTA, CurCont, DentInd, E&CAJ, EngInd, ExcerpMed, IIL, ISMEC, ISR, IndMed, Inpharma, Inspec, MEDLINE, PE&ON, Reac, RefZh, SCI, SolStAb.
—BLDSC (9082.815000), AskIEEE, CISTI, Ei, GNLM, IDS, IE, Infotrieve, ingenta, KNAW, Linda Hall. **CCC.**
Published by: (World Federation for Ultrasound in Medicine and Biology), Elsevier Inc. (Subsidiary of: Elsevier Science & Technology), 360 Park Ave. S, New York, NY 10010-1710. TEL 212-989-5800, 888-437-4636, FAX 212-633-3140, usinfo-f@elsevier.com, http://www.elsevier.com/locate/ultrasmedbio. Ed. Peter N.T. Wells. adv.: B&W page USD 985, color page USD 1,175. Circ: 1,500 (paid).

570 USA
UNDERSTANDING THE PROCESS OF AGING; the roles of mitochondria, free radicals, and antioxidants. Text in English. 1999. irreg., latest vol.2. USD 175 vol.2 (effective 2004). **Document type:** *Monographic series.*
Published by: Marcel Dekker Inc. (Subsidiary of: Taylor & Francis Group), 270 Madison Ave, New York, NY 10016-0602. TEL 212-696-9000, FAX 212-685-4540, http://www.dekker.com. Ed. Enrique Lester.

570 COL ISSN 0120-8063
UNIVERSIDAD DE BOGOTA JORGE TADEO LOZANO. MUSEO DEL MAR. INFORME. Text in Spanish; Summaries in English. 1971. irreg. price varies. bibl. **Document type:** *Monographic series.*
Indexed: ASFA.
Published by: Universidad de Bogota Jorge Tadeo Lozano, Museo del Mar, Carrera 4 No. 22-61, Bogota, CUND, Colombia. TEL 57-1-3426581, FAX 57-1-2826197. Ed. Elvira Maria Alvarado Chacon.

570 URY ISSN 0250-653X
QH301
UNIVERSIDAD DE LA REPUBLICA. FACULTAD DE HUMANIDADES Y CIENCIAS. REVISTA. SERIE CIENCIAS BIOLOGICAS. Text in Spanish. N.S. 1978. irreg. per issue exchange basis.
Formerly: Universidad de la Republica. Facultad de Humanidades y Ciencias. Revista. Serie Ciencias; Supersedes in part: Universidad de la Republica. Facultad de Humanidades y Ciencias. Revista
Published by: Universidad de la Republica, Facultad de Humanidades y Ciencias, c/o Seccion Revista, Dr. Tristan Narvaja, 1674, Montevideo, 11205, Uruguay. Ed. Beatriz Martinez Osorio.

570 ESP ISSN 1138-3399
UNIVERSIDAD DE MURCIA. ANALES DE BIOLOGIA. Text mainly in English, Spanish. 1984. a., latest vol.24, 2002. bk.rev. back issues avail. **Document type:** *Journal, Academic/Scholarly.* **Description:** Contains original advances in the field of the biological sciences.
Formed by the 1989 merger of: Universidad de Murcia. Anales de Biologia. Seccion Biologia Animal (0213-3997); Universidad de Murcia. Anales de Biologia. Seccion Biologia Vegetal (0213-5450); Universidad de Murcia. Anales de Biologia. Seccion Biologia Ambiental (0213-4004); Universidad de Murcia. Anales de Biologia. Seccion Biologia General (0213-5442)
Related titles: ♦ Series: Universidad de Murcia. Anales de Biologia. Seccion Biologia Animal. ISSN 0213-3997; ♦ Universidad de Murcia. Anales de Biologia. Seccion Biologia Ambiental. ISSN 0213-4004; ♦ Universidad de Murcia. Anales de Biologia. Seccion Biologia Molecular y Microbiana; ♦ Universidad de Murcia. Anales de Biologia. Seccion Biologia Vegetal. ISSN 0213-5450.
Indexed: IECT, RM&VM.
Published by: (Universidad de Murcia, Facultad de Biologia), Universidad de Murcia, Servicio de Publicaciones, Edificio Saavedra Fajardo, C/ Actor Isidoro Maiquez 9, Murcia, 30007, Spain. TEL 34-968-363887, FAX 34-968-363414, fagp@um.es, http://www.um.es/analesdebiologia/, http://www.um.es/spumweb. Eds. Juan J. Presa, Juan Guerra. Circ: 606.

572.8 ESP
UNIVERSIDAD DE MURCIA. ANALES DE BIOLOGIA. SECCION BIOLOGIA MOLECULAR Y MICROBIANA. Text mainly in English, Spanish. 1984. irreg., latest vol.22, 1999, for the year 1997. bk.rev. back issues avail. **Document type:** *Academic/Scholarly.*
Formerly: Universidad de Murcia. Anales de Biologia. Seccion Biologia General (0213-5442)
Related titles: ♦ Series of: Universidad de Murcia. Anales de Biologia. ISSN 1138-3399.
Indexed: FCA, HerbAb, PGrRegA.
Published by: Universidad de Murcia, Servicio de Publicaciones, Edificio Saavedra Fajardo, C/ Actor Isidoro Maiquez 9, Murcia, 30007, Spain. TEL 34-968-363887, FAX 34-968-363414, servpubl@um.es, http://www.um.es/spumweb. Ed. Diego Jose Rivera Nunez TEL 34-968-364958. Circ: 500.

570 ESP ISSN 0212-8977
CODEN: RBUOE2
UNIVERSIDAD DE OVIEDO. REVISTA DE BIOLOGIA. Text in Spanish; Abstracts in English, Spanish. 1942. a. **Document type:** *Academic/Scholarly.*
Formerly (until 1981): Universidad de Oviedo. Facultad de Ciencias, Revista. Serie Biologia (0473-6303)
Related titles: ♦ Supplement(s): Biodatos Basicos.
Indexed: BiolAb, IECT, SFA.
—CASDDS, CISTI.
Published by: Universidad de Oviedo, Facultad de Biologia, c/o Carlos Lastra, Redactor, Departamento de Zoologia, Oviedo, 33071, Spain. Circ: 750.

570 VEN ISSN 0375-538X
UNIVERSIDAD DEL ZULIA. CENTRO DE INVESTIGACIONES BIOLOGICAS. BOLETIN. Text in Spanish. 1968. s-a. **Document type:** *Monographic series.* **Description:** Publishes basic or applied research results in the field of biological sciences.
Indexed: ASFA, BIOSIS Prev, BiolAb, ESPM, OceAb, SWRA, ZooRec.
—CISTI.
Published by: Universidad del Zulia, Centro de Investigaciones Biologicas, Av 16 Goajira, Nucleo Humanistico, Maracaibo, 4005, Venezuela. TEL 58-61-596400, FAX 58-61-596401, fached@luz.ve, http://www.luz.ve/.

578.77 BRA ISSN 0100-7068
UNIVERSIDADE FEDERAL DO RIO GRANDE DO NORTE. CENTRO DE BIOCIENCIAS. DEPARTAMENTO DE OCEANOGRAFIA E LIMNOLOGIA. BOLETIM. Text in Portuguese. 1964. irreg., latest vol.8, 1991. per issue exchange basis. **Document type:** *Bulletin.* **Description:** Covers hydrology, marine biology, and aquaculture.
Formerly (until vol.5, 1971): Universidade Federal do Rio Grande do Norte. Instituto de Biologia Marinha. Boletim (0041-8927)
Indexed: BiolAb.
Published by: (Universidade Federal do Rio Grande do Norte, Departamento de Oceanografia e Limnologia), Conselho Editorial, Praia de Mae Luiza, s-n, Natal, RN 59020, Brazil. FAX 842296. Ed. Francisca de Assis de Sousa. Circ: 1,000.

570 BRA ISSN 0102-597X
QH117 CODEN: BOIBEM
➤ **UNIVERSIDADE FEDERAL DO RIO GRANDE DO SUL. INSTITUTO DE BIOCIENCIAS. BOLETIM.** Text in Portuguese; Summaries in English. 1954. irreg. USD 7 per issue (effective 2003). charts; illus. index. **Document type:** *Monographic series, Academic/Scholarly.*
Former titles (until 1977): Universidade Federal do Rio Grande do Sul. Instituto Central de Biociencias. Boletim (0101-0972); (until 1970): Universidade do Rio Grande do Sul. Instituto de Ciencias Naturais. Boletim (0079-4058)
Indexed: BiolAb, CPA, ChemAb, FCA, ForAb, HerbAb, PBA, PGegResA, S&F.
Published by: (Biblioteca), Universidade Federal do Rio Grande do Sul, Instituto de Biociencias, Av. Bento Goncalves, 9500 S106 Pd. 43423, Campus do Vale, Porto Alegre - RS 91509-900, Brazil. bibbio@vortex.ufrgs.br, bibbio@ufrgs.br. R&P Katia V C L da Silva. Circ: 1,000.

570 ITA ISSN 0373-4110
UNIVERSITA DEGLI STUDI DI GENOVA. MUSEI E ISTITUTI BIOLOGICI. BOLLETTINO. Key Title: Bollettino dei Musei e degli Istituti Biologici dell'Universita di Genova. Text in English, Italian; Summaries in English. 1891. a. per issue exchange basis. **Document type:** *Academic/Scholarly.*
Indexed: BiolAb, ZooRec.
Published by: Universita degli Studi di Genova, Istituto di Zoologia, Via Balbi 5, Genoa, 16126, Italy. TEL 39-010-2099454, FAX 39-010-2099323, zoologia@unige.it. Ed. Silvio Spano. Circ: 500.

UNIVERSITA DI FERRARA. ANNALI. SEZIONE 18: ECOLOGIA. see *ENVIRONMENTAL STUDIES*

571.9 640 ITA ISSN 1125-0720
UNIVERSITA DI FERRARA. ANNALI. SEZIONE 2: PATOLOGIA CHIRURGICA. Text in Italian. 1952. a. price varies.
Published by: (Universita degli Studi di Ferrara), Casa Editrice Leo S. Olschki, Viuzzo del Pozzetto 8, Florence, 50126, Italy. TEL 39-055-6530684, FAX 39-055-6530214, celso@olschki.it, http://www.olschki.it.

571.86 ITA ISSN 0373-5907
UNIVERSITA DI FERRARA. ANNALI. SEZIONE 3: BIOLOGIA ANIMALE. Text in Italian. 1951. a. price varies.
Published by: (Universita degli Studi di Ferrara), Casa Editrice Leo S. Olschki, Viuzzo del Pozzetto 8, Florence, 50126, Italy. TEL 39-055-6530684, FAX 39-055-6530214, celso@olschki.it, http://www.olschki.it.

B

570 AUT ISSN 0587-484X
UNIVERSITAET INNSBRUCK. ALPIN-BIOLOGISCHE STUDIEN✶. Text in German. 1970. irreg., latest vol.6, 1974. price varies.
Related titles: Series of: Universitaet Innsbruck. Veroeffentlichungen.
Published by: (Universitaet Innsbruck), Oesterreichische Kommissionsbuchhandlung, Glasmalereistr 6, Innsbruck, T 6020, Austria. TEL 43-512-587039, FAX 43-512-5870394, oekobuch@aon.at, http://www.oekobuch.com. Ed. Heinz Janetschek.

570 ROM ISSN 0041-9133
QH301 CODEN: AUIBAF
UNIVERSITATEA "AL. I. CUZA" DIN IASI. ANALELE STIINTIFICE. SECTIUNEA 2A: BIOLOGIE. Text in French, German, Romanian, Russian. 1955. a. ROL 35. bk.rev. abstr.; charts; illus. **Description:** Contains information on genetics, microbiology, plant anatomy, vegetal taxonomy, entomology, ecology and cellular biology.
Indexed: BiolAb, CIN, ChemAb, ChemTitl, HortAb, MathR, OrnHort, RPP, RefZh, SeedAb.
—CASDDS, CISTI, Linda Hall.
Published by: Universitatea "Al. I. Cuza" din Iasi/"Alexandru Ioan Cuza" University of Iasi, Carol I Boulevard, Iasi, 6600, Romania. Ed. C Toma. Circ: 550. **Subscr. to:** ILEXIM, Str. 13 Decembrie 3, PO Box 136-137, Bucharest 70116, Romania.

570 630 ROM ISSN 0254-7236
CODEN: AUCHD6
UNIVERSITATEA DIN CRAIOVA. ANALE. SERIA: BIOLOGIE, AGRONOMIE, HORTICULTURA. Text in Romanian; Summaries in English, French, German. 1972. a. ROL 80, USD 15.
—CASDDS.
Published by: Universitatea din Craiova/University of Craiova, Str. A.I. Cuza 13, Craiova, 1100, Romania. TEL 40-51-414398, FAX 40-51-411688, relint@central.ucv.ro, http://www.central.ucv.ro. Circ: 300.

570 TGO ISSN 1016-9210
UNIVERSITE DU BENIN. ANNALES. SERIE SCIENCE. Text in French; Summaries in English, French. 1975. a. bk.rev. **Document type:** *Academic/Scholarly.*
Published by: Universite du Benin, BP 1515, Lome, Togo. TEL 25-48-44, FAX 25-87-84, TELEX 52-58 UBTO, gbesson@syfed.tg.refer.org. Ed. Messanvi Gbeassor.

578.77 GBR
UNIVERSITY MARINE BIOLOGICAL STATION MILLPORT. ANNUAL REPORT. Text in English. a.
Published by: University Marine Biological Station Millport, Isle of Cumbrae, KA28 0EG, United Kingdom. TEL 44-1475-530581, FAX 44-1475-530601, http://www.gla.ac.uk/Acad/Marine/.

578.77 GBR
UNIVERSITY MARINE BIOLOGICAL STATION. OCCASIONAL PUBLICATION. Text in English. 1984. q.
Published by: University Marine Biological Station Millport, Isle of Cumbrae, KA28 0EG, United Kingdom. TEL 44-1475-530581, FAX 44-1475-530601, http://www.gla.ac.uk/Acad/Marine/. Circ: 2,500.

570 USA ISSN 0568-8604
QH1
➤ **UNIVERSITY OF ALASKA. BIOLOGICAL PAPERS.** Text in English. 1955. irreg., latest vol.25, 1996. USD 30. bibl.; illus. back issues avail. **Document type:** *Monographic series, Academic/Scholarly.*
Indexed: Agr, BiolAb, SFA, WildRev, ZooRec.
—CISTI, Linda Hall.
Published by: (Library), University of Alaska at Fairbanks, Institute of Arctic Biology, 308 Irving I, PO Box 757000, Fairbanks, AK 99775-7000. TEL 907-474-7658, FAX 907-474-7666. Ed., R&P Jean James. Circ: 500.

▼ *new title* ➤ *refereed* ✶ *unverified* ♦ *full entry avail.*

570 USA ISSN 0161-3243
CODEN: BPURDY
UNIVERSITY OF ALASKA. BIOLOGICAL PAPERS. SPECIAL REPORTS. Text in English. 1975. irreg., latest vol.5, 1992. USD 30. **Document type:** *Monographic series.*
Indexed: ZooRec.
—CASDDS, CISTI.
Published by: (Library), University of Alaska at Fairbanks, Institute of Arctic Biology, 308 Irving I, PO Box 757000, Fairbanks, AK 99775-7000. TEL 907-474-7658, FAX 907-474-7666. Ed. Jean James.

570 USA ISSN 0272-9075
UNIVERSITY OF CALIFORNIA. LAWRENCE BERKELEY LABORATORY. BIOLOGY AND MEDICINE DIVISION. ANNUAL REPORT. Text in English. a.
Published by: (University of California at Berkeley, Lawrence Berkeley Laboratory), U.S. Department of Commerce, National Technical Information Service, 5285 Port Royal Rd, Springfield, VA 22161. TEL 703-605-6000, info@ntis.gov, http://www.ntis.gov.

UNIVERSITY OF COLORADO. INSTITUTE OF ARCTIC AND ALPINE RESEARCH. OCCASIONAL PAPERS. see *SCIENCES: COMPREHENSIVE WORKS*

UNIVERSITY OF GEORGIA. INSTITUTE OF ECOLOGY. ANNUAL REPORT. see *ENVIRONMENTAL STUDIES*

570 500.9 USA ISSN 0272-2658
UNIVERSITY OF KANSAS. MUSEUM OF NATURAL HISTORY. PUBLIC EDUCATION SERIES. Text in English. 1974. irreg., latest vol.12, 1992. price varies. reprints avail.
—Linda Hall.
Published by: University of Kansas, Museum of Natural History, 602 Dyche Hall, Lawrence, KS 66044-2454. Ed. Joseph T Collins.

570 500.9 USA ISSN 0193-7766
➤ **UNIVERSITY OF KANSAS. MUSEUM OF NATURAL HISTORY. SPECIAL PUBLICATIONS.** Text in English. irreg., latest vol.19, 1991. price varies. reprints avail. **Document type:** *Academic/Scholarly.*
Indexed: ZooRec.
—Linda Hall.
Published by: University of Kansas, Museum of Natural History, 602 Dyche Hall, Lawrence, KS 66044-2454. TEL 785-654-4450, FAX 785-864-5335, kunhm@ukans.edu, http://www.nhm.ukans.edu. Ed. William E Duellman.

578.77 SDN ISSN 0379-9611
CODEN: AUKUDH
UNIVERSITY OF KHARTOUM. HYDROBIOLOGICAL RESEARCH UNIT. ANNUAL REPORT. Text in English. a.
Published by: University of Khartoum, Hydrobiological Research Unit, P O Box 321, Khartoum, Sudan.

578.77 USA
UNIVERSITY OF MARYLAND CENTER FOR ENVIRONMENTAL SCIENCE. CHESAPEAKE BIOLOGICAL LABORATORY. REPORT. Text in English. irreg.
Former titles (until 1997): University of Maryland Center for Environmental and Estuarine Studies. Chesapeake Biological Laboratory. Report; (until 1975): University of Maryland. Natural Resources Institute. Report; (until 1961): Chesapeake Biological Laboratory. Report
Published by: University of Maryland Center for Environmental Science, Chesapeake Biological Laboratory, One Williams St, PO Box 38, Solomons, MD 20688. TEL 410-326-4281, http://www.cbl.umces.edu/.

570 560 USA ISSN 0093-6812
Q11
UNIVERSITY OF NEBRASKA STATE MUSEUM. BULLETIN. Text in English. 1924. irreg., latest vol.14, 1997. USD 2 per issue. bibl.; charts; illus.; maps. back issues avail. **Document type:** *Monographic series.* **Description:** Covers plants, animals, and fossils. Focuses mainly on taxonomy.
Related titles: E-mail ed.; Fax ed.
Indexed: BIOSIS Prev, BiolAb, ZooRec.
—CISTI, Linda Hall.
Published by: University of Nebraska State Museum, W436 Nebraska Hall, University of Nebraska, Lincoln, NE 68588-0514. TEL 402-472-2614, FAX 402-472-8939, bcr@unlinfo.unl.edu, littrell@unlinfo.unl.edu. Pub. Brett C Ratcliffe. R&P Brett Ratcliffe.

UNIVERSITY OF OSAKA PREFECTURE. COLLEGE OF AGRICULTURE. SCIENTIFIC REPORT. see *AGRICULTURE*

UNIVERSITY OF RHODE ISLAND. SEA GRANT COLLEGE PROGRAM. PUBLICATIONS. see *FISH AND FISHERIES*

UNIVERSITY OF RHODE ISLAND. SEA GRANT COLLEGE PROGRAM. REPORT. see *FISH AND FISHERIES*

UNIVERSITY OF SANTO TOMAS. GRADUATE SCHOOL. JOURNAL OF GRADUATE RESEARCH. see *SOCIAL SCIENCES: COMPREHENSIVE WORKS*

UNIVERSITY OF SIERRA LEONE. FOURAH BAY COLLEGE. INSTITUTE OF MARINE BIOLOGY AND OCEANOGRAPHY. BULLETIN. see *EARTH SCIENCES—Oceanography*

UNIVERSITY OF SOUTHERN CALIFORNIA SEA GRANT PROGRAM. REPORT. see *EARTH SCIENCES—Oceanography*

578.77 USA
UNIVERSITY OF SOUTHERN CALIFORNIA SEA GRANT PROGRAM. TECHNICAL REPORT. Text in English. irreg. USD 2 per issue (effective 2003).
Published by: University of Southern California, Sea Grant Program, AHF 209, Los Angeles, CA 90089-0373. TEL 213-740-1961, FAX 213-740-5936, http://www.usc.edu/org/seagrant/Publications/publicationpubs.html.

UNIVERSITY OF TSUKUBA. SHIMODA MARINE RESEARCH CENTER. CONTRIBUTIONS. see *EARTH SCIENCES—Oceanography*

UNIVERSITY OF WAIKATO. ANTARCTIC RESEARCH UNIT. REPORT. see *EARTH SCIENCES—Geology*

597 578.77 USA
UNIVERSITY OF WASHINGTON. SCHOOL OF AQUATIC AND FISHERY SCIENCES. TECHNICAL REPORT. Text in English. irreg.
Formerly (until 2000): University of Washington. Fisheries Research Institute. Report
Published by: University of Washington, School of Aquatic and Fishery Sciences, 1122 NE Boat St, PO Box 355020, Seattle, WA 98195-5020. TEL 206-543-4270, FAX 206-685-7471, http://www.fish.washington.edu/Publications/frireps.html.

570 CAN ISSN 0317-3348
UNIVERSITY OF WATERLOO BIOLOGY SERIES. Text in English. 1971. irreg. price varies. **Document type:** *Academic/Scholarly.*
—CISTI.
Published by: University of Waterloo, Department of Biology, 200 University Ave, W, Waterloo, ON N2L 3G1, Canada. TEL 519-885-1211, FAX 519-746-0614. Ed. J C Semple.

570 550 USA
UNIVERSITY OF WISCONSIN-MILWAUKEE. FIELD STATION BULLETIN. Text in English. 1968. s-a. free. back issues avail. **Document type:** *Bulletin.*
Indexed: BiolAb, ZooRec.
Published by: University of Wisconsin at Milwaukee, Field Station, 3095 Blue Goose Rd, Saukville, WI 53080. TEL 414-675-6844, FAX 414-675-0337, jimr@csd.uwm.edu. Ed., R&P James A Reinartz. Circ: 400.

570 POL ISSN 0554-811X
UNIWERSYTET IM. ADAMA MICKIEWICZA. BIOLOGIA. Text in Polish; Summaries in English. 1961. irreg., latest vol.57, 1996. price varies. **Document type:** *Monographic series, Academic/Scholarly.* **Description:** Contains current research results of the university's biologists, their Ph.D. works, monographs and other scientific works. Each volume is devoted to the work of one author.
Formerly: Uniwersytet im. Adama Mickiewicza w Poznaniu. Wydzial Biologii i Nauk o Ziemi. Seria Biologia
Indexed: AgrLib, ZooRec.
—CISTI, Linda Hall.
Published by: (Uniwersytet im. Adama Mickiewicza w Poznaniu/Adam Mickiewicz University), Wydawnictwo Naukowe Uniwersytetu im. Adama Mickiewicza/Adam Mickiewicz University Press, Nowowiejskiego 55, Poznan, 61-734, Poland. TEL 48-61-527380, FAX 48-61-527701. Pub. Maria Jankowska. R&P Malgorzata Bis. Circ: 400.

572.8 POL ISSN 0137-2351
QH506 CODEN: ZNUMDV
UNIWERSYTET JAGIELLONSKI. ZESZYTY NAUKOWE. PRACE Z BIOLOGII MOLEKULARNEJ/UNIVERSITAS IAGELLONICA. ACTA SCIENTIARUM LITTERARUMQUE. SCHEDAE AD BIOLOGIAM MOLECULAREM PERTINENTES. Text in Polish; Summaries in English. 1974. irreg. price varies. bibl.; illus.
Indexed: ChemAb.
—CASDDS, CISTI.
Published by: (Uniwersytet Jagiellonski, Wydzial Biologii i Nauk o Ziemi), Wydawnictwo Uniwersytetu Jagiellonskiego/Jagiellonian University Press, ul Grodzka 26, Krakow, 31044, Poland. TEL 48-12-4312364, FAX 48-12-4301995, wydaw@if.uj.edu.pl, http://www.wuj.pl. Ed. Z Zak. Circ: 420.
Dist. by: Ars Polona, Krakowskie Przedmiescie 7, Warsaw, Poland.

570 POL ISSN 0860-2441
UNIWERSYTET SLASKI W KATOWICACH. PRACE NAUKOWE. ACTA BIOLOGICA SILESIANA. Text in English, Polish; Summaries in English, Polish, Russian. 1975. irreg., latest vol.34, 2000. price varies. **Document type:** *Monographic series, Academic/Scholarly.* **Description:** Covers biochemistry, botany, histology, microbiology, physiology, zoology, morphology, systematics, environmental protection.
Formerly (until 1985): Acta Biologica (0208-5046)
Indexed: AgrAg, AgrLib, BIOSIS Prev, BiolAb, RefZh, TriticAb, ZooRec.
Published by: (Uniwersytet Slaski w Katowicach), Wydawnictwo Uniwersytetu Slaskiego w Katowicach, Ul Bankowa 12B, Katowice, 40007, Poland. TEL 48-32-2596915, FAX 48-32-2582735, TELEX 0315584 uskpl, wydawus@us.edu.pl, http://www.us.edu.pl/uniwersytet/jednostki/ogolne/wydawnictwo. **Dist. by:** CHZ Ars Polona, Biblioteka PAN w Warszawie, PO Box 1001, Warsaw 00950, Poland.

570.71 DEU ISSN 0341-5260
UNTERRICHT BIOLOGIE; Beitraege zur seiner Gestaltung. Text in German. 1965. 10/yr. EUR 90; EUR 10 newsstand/cover (effective 2005). adv. abstr. cum.index. **Document type:** *Journal, Academic/Scholarly.*
Incorporates (1977-1984): Naturwissenschaften im Unterricht Biologie (0342-5487); Formerly: Biologieunterricht (0006-3274)
Indexed: BiolAb, DIP, IBR, IBZ, ZooRec.
—CISTI. **CCC.**
Published by: Erhard Friedrich Verlag GmbH, Im Brande 17, Seelze, 30926, Germany. TEL 49-511-400040, FAX 49-511-40004170, info@friedrich-verlag.de, http://www.friedrich-verlag.de/index.cfm?0F5494527D394F4186A315FEC4E2F0EC. Ed. Barbara Dulitz. adv.: B&W page EUR 1,450, color page EUR 2,180. Circ: 10,688 (paid and controlled).

577 USA ISSN 1541-7115
➤ **URBAN HABITATS.** Text in English. 2002 (Oct.). s-a. free (effective 2005). **Document type:** *Journal, Academic/Scholarly.* **Description:** It focuses on current research on the biology of urban areas.
Media: Online - full content.
Published by: Center for Urban Restoration Ecology, 1 College Farm Rd., New Brunswick, NJ 08901-1582. TEL 732-932-8165, FAX 732-932-2972, cure@aesop.rutgers.edu, http://www.urbanhabitats.org, http://www.i-cure.org. Eds. Janet Marinelli, Steven E. Clemants TEL 718-623-7309.

➤ **URBAN NATURE & ENVIRONMENT.** see *ENVIRONMENTAL STUDIES*

572.8 BGR ISSN 0205-0625
QH506 CODEN: UMBIEX
USPEHI NA MOLECULIARNATA BIOLOGIA/ADVANCES IN MOLECULAR BIOLOGY. Text in Bulgarian. 1975. s-a. BGL 1.36 per issue. reprint service avail. from IRC.
Supersedes: Molekulna Biologiia
—CASDDS, Linda Hall.
Published by: (Bulgarska Akademiya na Naukite/Bulgarian Academy of Sciences), Universitetsko Izdatelstvo Sv. Kliment Okhridski/Publishing House of the Sofia University St. Kliment Ohridski, Akad G Bonchev 6, Sofia, 1113, Bulgaria. Circ: 450.

570 RUS ISSN 0042-1324
QH301 CODEN: USBIA3
USPEKHI SOVREMENNOI BIOLOGII. Text in Russian. 1932. bi-m. RUR 760 for 6 mos. domestic; USD 190 foreign (effective 2004). bk.rev. **Document type:** *Journal, Academic/Scholarly.*
Indexed: ASFA, AbHyg, AgBio, AgrForAb, AnBrAb, BIOSIS Prev, BioCN&I, BiolAb, CIN, CPA, ChemAb, DSA, ESPM, FCA, ForAb, HelmAb, HerbAb, HortAb, I&DA, IAA, IndMed, IndVet, MEDLINE, MaizeAb, NutrAb, PBA, PGegResA, PGrRegA, PoultAb, ProtozoAb, RA&MP, RASB, RM&VM, RPP, RefZh, RevApplEntom, S&F, SIA, SeedAb, TOSA, TriticAb, VetBull, WeedAb, ZooRec.
—CASDDS, CISTI, East View, GNLM, KNAW, Linda Hall.
Published by: (Rossiiskaya Akademiya Nauk/Russian Academy of Sciences), Izdatel'stvo Nauka, Profsoyuznaya ul 90, Moscow, 117864, Russian Federation. TEL 7-095-3347151, FAX 7-095-4202220, secret@naukaran.ru, http://www.maik.ru/cgi-bin/list.pl?page=uspbio, http://www.naukaran.ru. **Dist. by:** M K - Periodica, ul Gilyarovskogo 39, Moscow 129110, Russian Federation. TEL 7-095-2845008, FAX 7-095-2813798, info@periodicals.ru, http://www.mkniga.ru.

570 UZB ISSN 0042-1685
QH301.A3652 CODEN: UZBZAZ
UZBEKSKII BIOLOGICHESKII ZHURNAL/O'ZBEKISTON BIOLOGIYA JURNALI/UZBEK JOURNAL OF BIOLOGY. Text in Russian. 1957. bi-m. USD 226 foreign (effective 2005). charts; illus. **Document type:** *Journal, Academic/Scholarly.* **Description:** Presents research papers on the development of biology in Uzbekistan and the rest of the world.
Indexed: BioCN&I, BiolAb, CPA, ChemAb, DSA, FCA, HerbAb, HortAb, INIS AtomInd, IndVet, PGrRegA, PN&I, RPP, S&MA, VetBull, WeedAb, ZooRec.
—CASDDS, CISTI, Linda Hall. **CCC.**
Published by: (O'zbekiston Respublikasi Fanlar Akademiyasi/Academy of Sciences of Uzbekistan), Izdatel'stvo Fan, Ya Gulyamov ul 70, k 105, Tashkent, 700047, Uzbekistan. **Dist. by:** East View Information Services, 3020 Harbor Ln. N., Minneapolis, MN 55447. TEL 763-550-0961, FAX 763-559-2931, eastview@eastview.com, http://www.eastview.com.

578.77 551.46 AUS
VICTORIA. DEPARTMENT OF NATURAL RESOURCES AND ENVIRONMENT. MARINE AND FRESHWATER RESOURCES INSTITUTE. REPORT. Text in English. 1997. irreg.
Related titles: Online - full text ed.

Published by: (State of Victoria Department of Natural Resources and Environment, Marine and Freshwater Resources Institute), Australia Department of Natural Resources and Environment Victoria, Customer Service Centre, 8 Nicholson St, East Melbourne, VIC 3002, Australia. TEL 61-3-9637-8000, FAX 61-3-9637-8148, customer.service@nre.vic.gov.au, http://www.nre.vic.gov.au.

THE VICTORIAN NATURALIST. see *CONSERVATION*

577   FRA   ISSN 0240-8759
                                    CODEN: VIMID2
➤ VIE ET MILIEU/LIFE AND ENVIRONMENT; periodique d'ecologie generale. Text in English, French. 1980. q. EUR 188 domestic; EUR 192 foreign (effective 2005). adv. bk.rev. charts; illus. index. back issues avail. **Document type:** *Journal, Academic/Scholarly.* **Description:** Journal of general ecology: Organisms, communities and ecosystems biology and ecology; trophic webs, energetics; benthic ecology; pollution; numerical ecology, modelings; evolutionary biology and phylogeny, with emphasis on marine, lagoonar and terrestrial milieus. Includes one special topic issue each year.
Formed by the merger of (1979-1980): Vie et Milieu. Serie A B, Biologie Marine et Oceanographique (0240-8767); Which was formed by the merger of (1950-1979): Vie et Milieu. Serie A, Biologie Marine (0506-8916); (1950-1979): Vie et Milieu. Serie B, Oceanographie (0506-8924); (1950-1980): Vie et Milieu. Serie C, Biologie Terrestre (0506-8932); All three of which superseded in part (in 1965): Vie et Milieu (0042-5516)
Indexed: ASFA, AbHyg, AgrForAb, AnBeAb, AnBrAb, ApEcolAb, B&AI, BIOSIS Prev, BiolAb, CurCont, ESPM, EntAb, ExcerpMed, ForAb, GEOBASE, HelmAb, HortAb, ISR, IndVet, NemAb, NutrAb, PoultAb, RM&VM, RefZh, RevApplEntom, S&F, SCI, SFA, SWRA, VetBull, WildRev, ZooRec.
—BLDSC (9235.000000), CISTI, IDS, IE, Infotrieve, ingenta, Linda Hall. **CCC.**
Published by: Universite de Paris VI (Pierre et Marie Curie), Laboratoire Arago, Banyuls Sur Mer, 66650, France. TEL 33-04-68887327, FAX 33-04-68881699, vimilieu@obs-banyuls.fr, http://www.obs-banyuls.fr/Viemilieu/Viemilieu.htm. Ed. Gilles Boeuf. R&P, Adv. contact Nicole Coineau.

570   ESP   ISSN 0210-945X
VIERAEA; folia scientiarum biologicarum canariensium. Text in Spanish. 1970. a. USD 30 (effective 2001). bk.rev. back issues avail.; reprints avail. **Document type:** *Journal, Academic/Scholarly.*
Indexed: BiolAb, IECT, RefZh, ZooRec.
—CINDOC.
Published by: Museo de Ciencias Naturales de Tenerife, Fuentes Morales, S/N, Santa Cruz De Tenerife, Canary Islands 38003, Spain. FAX 34-22-228753, etome@museoscabtf.rcanaria.es.

571.9 616.07   DEU   ISSN 0945-6317
RB1   CODEN: VARCEM
➤ VIRCHOWS ARCHIV; an international journal of pathology. Text in English. 1994. m. EUR 1,458 combined subscription to institutions print & online eds. (effective 2005). adv. bibl.; charts; illus. index. cum.index: vols.301-325, vols.326-343. back issues avail.; reprint service avail. from ISI. **Document type:** *Journal, Academic/Scholarly.* **Description:** Provides fundamental research on disease and on human pathological anatomy and histology in particular.
Formed by the merger of (1907-1994): Virchows Archiv. Section B: Cell Pathology (0340-6075); Which was formerly (until 1968): Frankfurter Zeitschrift fuer Pathologie (0367-3480); (1847-1994): Virchows Archiv. Section A: Pathological Anatomy and Histopathology (0174-7398); Which was formerly (until 1982): Virchows Archiv. Section A: Pathological Anatomy and Histology. (0340-1227); (until 1973): Virchows Archiv. Abteilung A: Pathologische Anatomie (0042-6423); (until 1968): Virchows Archiv fuer Pathologische Anatomie und Physiologie und fuer Klinische Medizin (0376-0081); (until 1902): Archiv fuer Pathologische Anatomie und Physiologie und fuer Klinische Medizin (0720-8723)
Related titles: Microform ed.: (from PMC, PQC); Online - full text ed.: ISSN 1432-2307 (from EBSCO Publishing, Springer LINK, Swets Information Services).
Indexed: ASCA, AbHyg, BIOBASE, BIOSIS Prev, BiolAb, CIN, ChemAb, CurCont, DSA, DentInd, ESPM, ExcerpMed, HelmAb, IABS, ISR, IndMed, IndVet, Inpharma, MEDLINE, MS&D, NSCI, NutrAb, PE&ON, ProtozoAb, RM&VM, Reac, RefZh, SCI, TDB, VetBull.
—BLDSC (9238.000000), CASDDS, CISTI, GNLM, IDS, IE, Infotrieve, ingenta, KNAW. **CCC.**
Published by: (European Society of Pathology), Springer-Verlag (Subsidiary of: Springer Science+Business Media), Tiergartenstr 17, Heidelberg, 69121, Germany. TEL 49-6221-3450, FAX 49-6221-345229, http://link.springer.de/link/service/journals/00428/index.htm. Ed. Heinz Karl Hoefler. Adv. contact Stephan Kroeck TEL 49-30-827875739. **Subscr. in the Americas to:** Springer-Verlag New York, Inc., Journal Fulfillment, PO Box 2485, Secaucus, NJ 07096-2485. TEL 800-777-4643, 201-348-4033, FAX 201-348-4505, journals@springer-ny.com, http://www.springer-ny.com; **Subscr. to:** Springer GmbH Auslieferungsgesellschaft, Haberstr 7, Heidelberg 69126, Germany. TEL 49-6221-345-0, FAX 49-6221-345-4229, subscriptions@springer.de.

578.77   USA   ISSN 0083-6427
VIRGINIA INSTITUTE OF MARINE SCIENCE, GLOUCESTER POINT. EDUCATIONAL SERIES. Text in English. 1943. irreg., latest 1994. price varies. **Document type:** *Monographic series.*
Published by: Virginia Institute of Marine Science, PO Box 3146, Gloucester, VA 23062. TEL 804-684-7170, FAX 804-684-7161, http://www.vims.edu. Ed., R&P Lee Larkin TEL 804-684-7000.

578.77   USA   ISSN 0083-6435
VIRGINIA INSTITUTE OF MARINE SCIENCE, GLOUCESTER POINT. MARINE RESOURCES ADVISORY SERIES. Text in English. 1970. irreg., latest 1998. price varies. **Document type:** *Monographic series.*
Published by: Virginia Institute of Marine Science, PO Box 3146, Gloucester, VA 23062. TEL 804-684-7170, FAX 804-684-7161, http://www.vims.edu.

578.77   USA   ISSN 0083-6443
VIRGINIA INSTITUTE OF MARINE SCIENCE, GLOUCESTER POINT. SPECIAL SCIENTIFIC REPORT. Text in English. 1948. irreg., latest vol.136, 1998. price varies.
Related titles: Microfiche ed.
Indexed: BiolAb.
Published by: Virginia Institute of Marine Science, PO Box 3146, Gloucester, VA 23062. TEL 804-684-7116, FAX 804-684-7113, http://www.vims.edu. R&P Eugene Burreson TEL 804-684-7000.

VIRTUAL JOURNAL OF BIOLOGICAL PHYSICS RESEARCH; a monthly multijournal compilation of the latest research on biological physics. see *PHYSICS*

570   JPN
VITAE. Text in Japanese. 1957. a.
Published by: Kyushu Daigaku, Seibutsu Kenkyubu/Kyushu University, Bio Researching Club, Kyushu Daigaku Kyoyobu, Kagai Katsudo Kyoyo Shisetsu, Ropponmatsu, Chuo-ku, Fukuoka-shi, 810-0044, Japan.

570   JPN   ISSN 0910-4003
QH325   CODEN: VIORE6
VIVA ORIGINO. Text in English, Japanese. 1971. 3/yr. JPY 4,000.
Indexed: CIN, ChemAb.
—BLDSC (9244.320000), CASDDS.
Published by: Seimei no Kigen Oyobi Shinka Gakkai/Society for the Study of the Origin and Evolution of Life, Osaka Furitsu Daigaku Sogo Kagakubu, Seimei Kagaku Koza, Mozu-Ume-Machi, Sakai-shi, Osaka-fu 591-8032, Japan.

570 610   RUS   ISSN 1560-9596
VOPROSY BIOLOGICHESKOI, MEDITSINSKOI, I FARMATSEVTICHESKOI KHIMII/PROBLEMS OF BIOLOGICAL, MEDICAL AND PHARMACOLOGICAL. Text in Russian. 1998. q. USD 209 foreign (effective 2005). adv. bk.rev.; Website rev. **Document type:** *Journal, Academic/Scholarly.* **Description:** Deals with problems of biological, medical, and pharmocological chemistry.
Indexed: RefZh.
—BLDSC (0041.807500).
Published by: Izdatel'stvo Meditsina/Meditsina Publishers, ul B Pirogovskaya, d 2, str 5, Moscow, 119435, Russian Federation. TEL 7-095-2483324, medizina@mtu-net.ru, http://www.medlit.ru. Ed. Yevgenii S Severin. Pub. A M Stochik. Adv. contact O A Fadeeva TEL 7-095-923-51-40. Circ: 200. **US dist. addr.:** East View Information Services, 3020 Harbor Ln. N., Minneapolis, MN 55447. TEL 763-550-0961, FAX 763-559-2931, eastview@eastview.com, http://www.eastview.com.

VOPROSY RADIOBIOLOGII I BIOLOGICHESKOGO DEISTVIYA TSITOSTATICHESKIKH PREPARATOV. see *MEDICAL SCIENCES—Radiology And Nuclear Medicine*

VORONEZHSKII GOSUDARSTVENNYI UNIVERSITET. VESTI. KHIMIYA, BIOLOGIYA. see *CHEMISTRY*

578.768   GBR
W I PUBLICATION✳ . Text in English. 1990 (no.12). irreg. price varies. back issues avail. **Document type:** *Monographic series, Academic/Scholarly.* **Description:** Covers research on waterfowl and wetland ecosystems.
Formerly (until 1996): I W R B Publication
—BLDSC (4589.131600).
Published by: Wetlands International, 2-3 Wills Rd, Totnes, Devon TQ9 5XN, United Kingdom. nhbs@nhbs.co.uk, http://www.nhbs.com/news/p1052.html.

570 550   JPN   ISSN 0913-0187
WASEDA DAIGAKU KYOIKUGAKUBU GAKUJUTSU KENKYU. SEIBUTSUGAKU, CHIGAKU HEN/WASEDA UNIVERSITY. SCHOOL OF EDUCATION. SCIENTIFIC RESEARCHES: BIOLOGY, GEOLOGY. Text and summaries in English, Japanese. 1952. a. membership.
Indexed: JPI.
Published by: Waseda Daigaku, Kyoikugakubu/Waseda University, School of Education, Shinjuku-ku, Tokyo, 169-50, Japan. TEL 03-3203-4141, FAX 03-3208-1032.

570 631   JPN   ISSN 0511-1978
WASEDA SEIBUTSU/WASEDA BIOLOGY. Text in Japanese. 1953. irreg.
Published by: Waseda Daigaku Seibutsu Dokokai/Waseda Biological Circle, c/o Waseda Daigaku, Ippan Kyoiku Seibutsugaku Kyoshitsu, 6-1 Nishiwaseda 1-chome, Shinjuku-ku, Tokyo, 160-0000, Japan.

570   USA   ISSN 0043-0927
QH1   CODEN: WMJBA2
➤ WASMANN JOURNAL OF BIOLOGY. Text in English. 1937. s-a. USD 6.50. abstr.; bibl.; charts; illus. index. **Document type:** *Academic/Scholarly.*
Indexed: Agr, BiolAb, BiolDig, ChemAb, NutrAb, S&F, SFA, WildRev, ZooRec.
—CISTI, Linda Hall.
Published by: University of San Francisco, Biology Department, San Francisco, CA 94117. TEL 415-666-6381. Ed. Gary L Stevens. Circ: 400.

333.9   AUS   ISSN 1447-1655
WATERSHED. Text in English. 1996. q. (4-6/year). 12 p./no.; back issues avail. **Document type:** *Magazine, Academic/Scholarly.*
Formerly: Watershed Magazine (1322-0446)
Related titles: Online - full content ed.: ISSN 1447-1663.
Published by: Cooperative Research Centre for Freshwater Ecology, University of Canberra, Canberra, ACT, Australia. http://enterprise.canberra.edu.au. Ed. Gary Jones.

WAY NORTH; our natural and cultural heritage. see *ANTHROPOLOGY*

WEED BIOLOGY AND MANAGEMENT. see *AGRICULTURE—Crop Production And Soil*

WENNER - GREN INTERNATIONAL SYMPOSIUM SERIES. see *SCIENCES: COMPREHENSIVE WORKS*

WETLANDS ECOLOGY AND MANAGEMENT. see *WATER RESOURCES*

▼ WETLANDS LAW & REGULATION REPORT. see *ENVIRONMENTAL STUDIES*

WHALEWATCHER. see *CONSERVATION*

577   POL   ISSN 0013-2969
                                    CODEN: WEKLAF
➤ WIADOMOSCI EKOLOGICZNE. Text in Polish; Summaries in English. 1955. q. PLZ 52 domestic; USD 27 foreign (effective 2003). adv. bk.rev. bibl. 100 p./no. 1 cols./p.; back issues avail. **Document type:** *Journal, Academic/Scholarly.* **Description:** Publishes various articles, reports from conferences as well as information on activities of ecological institutions in Poland and other countries.
Formerly: Ekologia Polska. Seria B
Indexed: AgrLib, BIOSIS Prev, BiolAb, FCA, HerbAb, INIS AtomInd, RASB, ZooRec.
—BLDSC (9313.100000).
Published by: Polska Akademia Nauk, Miedzynarodowe Centrum Ekologii/Polish Academy of Sciences, International Centre for Ecology, ul Tylna 3, Lodz, 90364, Poland. sekretariat@mcepan.lodz.pan, http://www.mcepan.lodz.pl. Ed., R&P, Adv. contact Eligiusz Pieczynski. Circ: 450. **Dist. by:** Ars Polona, Krakowskie Przedmiescie 7, Warsaw, Poland. TEL 48-22-9263914, FAX 48-22-9265334, arspolona@arspolona.com.pl, http://www.arspolona.com.pl.

616.96   POL   ISSN 0043-5163
                                    CODEN: WIPAAZ
WIADOMOSCI PARAZYTOLOGICZNE. Text in Polish, English. 1955. bi-m. USD 33. bk.rev. bibl.; charts; illus.; tr.lit. index.
Related titles: ◆ Includes: International Commission on Trichinellosis. Proceedings. ISSN 0074-3356.
Indexed: AbHyg, AgBio, AgrAg, AgrLib, AnBrAb, ApicAb, BIOSIS Prev, BioCN&I, BiolAb, ChemAb, DSA, ExcerpMed, ForAb, HelmAb, IndMed, IndVet, MEDLINE, NemAb, NutrAb, PBA, PN&I, PoultAb, ProtozoAb, RA&MP, RM&VM, RPP, RRTA, RevApplEntom, S&F, SIA, SoyAb, TDB, VetBull, WAE&RSA, ZooRec.
—CASDDS, CISTI, GNLM.
Published by: Polskie Towarzystwo Parazytologiczne/Polish Parasitological Society, Ul Grochowska 272, Warsaw, 03849, Poland. bielecki@matman.wsp.olsztyn.pl. Ed. Aleksander Bielecki. Circ: 1,150.

577   USA   ISSN 0084-0122
WILDLIFE BEHAVIOR AND ECOLOGY. Text in English. 1971. irreg., latest 1995. price varies. reprint service avail. from PQC,ISI.
Published by: University of Chicago, 5801 S Ellis Ave, Chicago, IL 60637. TEL 773-702-7899, sales@press.uchicago.edu, http://www.press.uchicago.edu. Ed. George B Schaller.

WOHNUNG & GESUNDHEIT; Fachzeitschrift fuer oekologisches Bauen & Leben. see *ARCHITECTURE*

WOOLHOPE NATURALISTS' FIELD CLUB, HEREFORDSHIRE. TRANSACTIONS. see *ARCHAEOLOGY*

▼ *new title*   ➤ *refereed*   ✳ *unverified*   ◆ *full entry avail.*

B

578.7 FRA
WORLD BIODIVERSITY DATABASE SERIES. Text in French. 1995. a. price varies.
Media: CD-ROM.
Published by: UNESCO Publishing, 7 place de Fontenoy, Paris, 75352, France. TEL 33-1-45684300, FAX 33-1-45685737, http://www.unesco.org/publications. **Dist. in the U.S. by:** Bernan Associates, Bernan, 4611-F Assembly Dr., Lanham, MD 20706-4391. TEL 800-274-4888, FAX 800-865-3450.

571.864 FRA ISSN 0084-1641
RC889
WORLD CONGRESS ON FERTILITY AND STERILITY. PROCEEDINGS. Text in English. 1953. triennial. **Document type:** *Proceedings.*
Indexed: AnBrAb, BiolAb.
Published by: International Federation of Fertility Societies, CSI c/o Prof. Bernard Hedon, 337 rue de la Combe Caude, Montpellier, 34090, France. TEL 33-4-67635340, FAX 33-4-67419427, algcsi@mnet.fr, bhiffs@mnet.fr. R&P B Hedon. Circ: 3,000.

570 USA
THE WORLD WIDE WEB JOURNAL OF BIOLOGY. Text in English. 1995. a., latest vol.4, 1999. free (effective 2005). back issues avail. **Document type:** *Journal, Academic/Scholarly.*
Media: Online - full text. **Related titles:** CD-ROM ed.
Indexed: ZooRec.
Published by: Epress Inc, 130 Union Terrace Ln, Plymouth, MN 55441. editor@epress.com, http://epress.com/w3jbio/wjbhome.htm. Ed. Lester F Harris.

570 CHN ISSN 1001-4276
QH7 CODEN: WUKEE8
WUYI KEXUE/WUYI SCIENCE. Text in Chinese, English. a. CNY 4.20. **Description:** Covers the new research results in botany, zoology and environmental ecology.
Related titles: Online - full text ed.: (from East View Information Services).
Indexed: AEA, AgBio, BioCN&I, BiolAb, CPA, FS&TA, ForAb, HelmAb, HerbAb, HortAb, MaizeAb, NemAb, OrnHort, PBA, PGegResA, PGrRegA, PHN&I, PotatoAb, PoultAb, RPP, RevApplEntom, RiceAb, S&F, SeedAb, SoyAb, WeedAb, ZooRec.
—BLDSC (9365.401500).
Published by: (Fujian Science Commission), Wuyi Kexue Bianjibu, Shengfangsuo, Fujian Nongxueyuan, Jinshan, Fuzhou, Fujian 350002, China. **Dist. overseas by:** Jiangsu Publications Import & Export Corp., 56 Gao Yun Ling, Nanjing, Jiangsu, China.

570.71 POL
WYZSZA SZKOLA PEDAGOGICZNA IM. KOMISJI EDUKACJI NARODOWEJ W KRAKOWIE. ROCZNIK NAUKOWO-DYDAKTYCZNY. PRACE Z DYDAKTYKI BIOLOGII. Text in Polish. 1964. irreg., latest vol.4, 1990. price varies.
Published by: (Wyzsza Szkola Pedagogiczna im. Komisji Edukacji Narodowej w Krakowie), Wydawnictwo Naukowe W S P, Ul Karmelicka 41, Krakow, 31128, Poland. TEL 33-78-20. **Co-sponsor:** Ministerstwo Edukacji Narodowej.

YALE JOURNAL OF BIOLOGY AND MEDICINE. see *MEDICAL SCIENCES*

570 JPN ISSN 0513-4692
Q4 CODEN: YDKSAH
YAMAGATA DAIGAKU KIYO (SHIZEN KAGAKU)/BULLETIN OF THE YAMAGATA UNIVERSITY (NATURAL SCIENCE). Text mainly in Japanese. 1950. a. **Document type:** *Bulletin, Academic/Scholarly.*
Related titles: Online - full text ed.
Indexed: INIS AtomInd, Inspec, MathR, MathSciNet.
—BLDSC (2821.900000), CISTI.
Published by: Yamagata Daigaku/Yamagata University, Publicatin Committee, Library, Division of Information Processing & Management, 1-4-12, Kojirakawa, Yamagata, Yamagata 990-9585, Japan. TEL 81-23-6285054, FAX 81-23-6285059, http://www.lib.yamagata-u.ac.jp/kiyou/kiyou.html.

570 JPN ISSN 0910-7053
YAMAGUCHI SEIBUTSU/YAMAGUCHI SOCIETY OF BIOLOGY. BULLETIN. Text in Japanese. a.
Published by: Yamaguchi Seibutsu Gakkai/Yamaguchi Society of Biology, c/o Mr Kazumi Hoshiide, Yamaguchi Daigaku Kyoikugakubu Seibutsugakka, 1677-1 Yoshida, Yamaguchi-shi, 753-0841, Japan.

570 JPN ISSN 0914-0085
YAMANASHI SEIBUTSU/YAMANASHI BIOLOGICAL AMATEUR SOCIETY. BULLETIN. Text in Japanese. 1955. a.
Published by: Yamanashi Seibutsu Dokokai/Yamanashi Biological Amateur Society, c/o Mr Shiro Nakagome, 246 Nagazuka, Nakakoma-gun, Shikishima-cho, Yamanashi-ken 400-0125, Japan.

YANBIAN - JIBIAN - TUBIAN/CARCINOGENESIS, TERATOGENESIS AND MUTAGENESIS. see *MEDICAL SCIENCES—Oncology*

YANGZHOU DAXUE XUEBAO (NONGYE YU SHENGMING KEXUE BAN)/JOURNAL OF YANGZHOU UNIVERSITY (AGRICULTURAL & LIFE SCIENCES EDITION). see *AGRICULTURE*

YINGYONG SHENGTAI XUEBAO/CHINESE JOURNAL OF APPLIED ECOLOGY. see *ENVIRONMENTAL STUDIES*

363.7 CHN ISSN 1006-687X
CODEN: YYHXFX
YINGYONG YU HUANJING SHENGWU XUEBAO/CHINESE JOURNAL OF APPLIED & ENVIRONMENTAL BIOLOGY. Text in Chinese. 1995. q.
Related titles: Online - full text ed.: (from East View Information Services).
Indexed: ASFA, AgBio, AgrForAb, AnBrAb, B&BAb, BioCN&I, CPA, DSA, ESPM, FCA, FPA, ForAb, HerbAb, HortAb, I&DA, IndVet, MaizeAb, NemAb, NutrAb, OrnHort, PBA, PGegResA, PGrRegA, PHN&I, PN&I, PollutAb, PoultAb, ProtozoAb, RA&MP, RM&VM, RPP, RefZh, RiceAb, S&F, SIA, SWRA, SeedAb, SoyAb, TriticAb, VetBull, WeedAb, ZooRec.
—BLDSC (3180.293800), CISTI, IE, ingenta.
Published by: Zhongguo Kexueyuan, Chengdu Shengwu Yanjiusuo/Chinese Academy of Sciences, Chengdu Institute of Biology, PO Box 416, Chengdu, 610041, China. TEL 86-28-5220920, FAX 86-28-5222753, biojaeb@public.sc.cninfo.net, cascib@mail.sc.cninfo.net, http://www.cib.ac.cn/.

YOKOHAMA MEDICAL JOURNAL. see *MEDICAL SCIENCES*

570 JPN
YOKOHAMA NATIONAL UNIVERSITY. SCIENCE REPORTS. SECTION 2: BIOLOGICAL AND GEOLOGICAL SCIENCES/YOKOHAMA KOKURITSU DAIGAKU RIKA KIYO, DAI-2-RUI. SEIBUTSUGAKU, CHIGAKU. Text in Multiple languages, Japanese. 1952. a. per issue exchange basis only. illus. **Document type:** *Academic/Scholarly.*
Formerly: Yokohama National University. Science Reports. Section 2: Biological Sciences (0513-5613)
Indexed: BiolAb, FPA, ForAb, JPI, JTA, RPP.
—CISTI, Linda Hall.
Published by: Yokohama Kokuritsu Daigaku, Kyoikugakubu/Yokohama National University, Faculty of Education, 156 Tokiwa-Dai, Hodogaya-ku, Yokohama-shi, Kanagawa-ken 240-0067, Japan.

YUNYI NATURALIST. see *CHILDREN AND YOUTH—For*

570 910.02 DEU
ZEITSCHRIFT FUER ANGEWANDTE GEWASSEROEKOLOGIE. Text in German. 1995. biennial. back issues avail. **Document type:** *Magazine, Academic/Scholarly.*
Related titles: E-mail ed.; Fax ed.
Published by: (Institut zur Angewandte Gewasseroekologie), Natur und Text in Brandenburg GmbH, Friedensallee 21, Rangsdorf, 15834, Germany. TEL 49-708-20432, FAX 49-708-20433, nut-brandenburg@t-online.de. Ed. Jens Meisel.

570 DEU ISSN 1619-1749
ZEITSCHRIFT FUER BIOPOLITIK. Text in German. 2002. q. EUR 60 to individuals; EUR 80 to institutions; EUR 40 to students (effective 2004). adv. **Document type:** *Journal, Trade.*
Published by: Biocom AG, Stralsunder Str 58-59, Berlin, 13355, Germany. TEL 49-30-2649210, FAX 49-30-2649211, service@biocom.de, http://www.biocom.de/zfb/zfb-ausgabe.htm. Ed. Andreas Mietzsch. Adv. contact Oliver Schnell. B&W page EUR 500.

570 DEU ISSN 0939-5075
QH301 CODEN: ZNCBDA
➤ **ZEITSCHRIFT FUER NATURFORSCHUNG. SECTION C: A JOURNAL OF BIOSCIENCES.** Text in English. 1946. bi-m. EUR 512 domestic; EUR 525 foreign (effective 2004). bk.rev. bibl.; charts; illus. index. 150 p./no.; **Document type:** *Journal, Academic/Scholarly.* **Description:** Contains contributions on animal and plant physiology, all aspects of biochemistry, neurobiology, virology, and molecular genetics.
Former titles (until 1986): Zeitschrift fuer Naturforschung. Section C: Biosciences (0341-0382); (until 1974): Zeitschrift fuer Naturforschung. Teil C: Biochemie, Biophysik, Biologie, Virologie (0341-0471)
Indexed: ASCA, ASFA, AbHyg, AgBio, AgrForAb, AnBrAb, ApicAb, BBCI, BIOBASE, BIOSIS Prev, BioCN&I, BiolAb, CCI, CIN, CPA, ChemAb, ChemTitl, CurCont, DBA, DSA, DentInd, ESPM, EntAb, ExcerpMed, FCA, FPA, FaBeAb, ForAb, HerbAb, HortAb, I&DA, IABS, ISR, IndMed, IndVet, Inpharma, MEDLINE, MSB, MaizeAb, NPU, NemAb, NutrAb, OrnHort, PBA, PE&ON, PGegResA, PGrRegA, PHN&I, PN&I, PlantSci, PotatoAb, PoultAb, ProtozoAb, RA&MP, RM&VM, RPP, Reac, RevApplEntom, RiceAb, S&F, SCI, SFA, SIA, SeedAb, SoyAb, TDB, TriticAb, VITIS, VetBull, WeedAb, WildRev, ZooRec.
—BLDSC (9475.010000), CASDDS, CINDOC, CISTI, GNLM, IDS, IE, Infotrieve, ingenta, Linda Hall. **CCC.**
Published by: Verlag der Zeitschrift fuer Naturforschung, Postfach 2645, Tuebingen, 72016, Germany. TEL 49-7071-31555, FAX 49-7071-360571, mail@znaturforsch.com, http://www.znaturforsch.com/c.htm. Ed. P. Boeger. R&P Tamina Greifeld. Adv. contact Anneliese Eipper. Circ: 600 (controlled).

508.54 LKA
➤ **ZEYLANICA.** Text in English. 1993. s-a. USD 50 to individuals; USD 80 to institutions (effective 2002). **Document type:** *Journal, Academic/Scholarly.* **Description:** To publish results of research relating to natural history, biodiversity, and conservation in the Asian countries of the western Indian Ocean.
Formerly: Journal of South Asian Natural History (1022-0828)
Indexed: ASFA, ESPM.
Published by: (The Wildlife Heritage Trust of Sri Lanka), W H T Publications (Pvt) Ltd., 95 Cotta Rd., Colombo 8, Sri Lanka. TEL 94-1-699219, FAX 94-75-338131, http://www.wht.org/publications/serials/jsanh/index.htm.

➤ **ZHONGGUO HAIYANG YAOWU ZAZHI/CHINESE JOURNAL OF MARINE DRUGS.** see *PHARMACY AND PHARMACOLOGY*

➤ **ZHONGGUO JISHENGCHONGBING FANGZHI ZAZHI/CHINESE JOURNAL OF PARASITIC DISEASE CONTROL.** see *MEDICAL SCIENCES—Communicable Diseases*

570 CHN ISSN 1005-9261
➤ **ZHONGGUO SHENGWU FANGZHI/CHINESE JOURNAL OF BIOLOGICAL CONTROL.** Text in Chinese. 1985. q. 48 p./no.; **Document type:** *Academic/Scholarly.* **Description:** Covers research reports and experiments in the field of biological control.
Formerly (until 1995): Shengwu Fangzhi Tongbao (1000-1034)
Related titles: Online - full text ed.: (from East View Information Services).
Indexed: AgBio, AgrForAb, BioCN&I, BioDAb, CPA, DBA, DSA, FCA, FPA, ForAb, HelmAb, HerbAb, HortAb, IndVet, MaizeAb, NemAb, OrnHort, PBA, PHN&I, PotatoAb, PoultAb, ProtozoAb, RA&MP, RM&VM, RPP, RevApplEntom, RiceAb, S&F, SIA, SeedAb, SoyAb, TriticAb, WeedAb, ZooRec.
—BLDSC (3180.296000), CISTI, IE, ingenta.
Published by: (Shengwu Fangzi Yanjiusuo), Zhongguo Nongye Kexueyuan/Chinese Academy of Agricultural Sciences, Chinese Society for Horticultural Science, 30 Baishiqiao Lu, Beijing, 100081, China. TEL 86-10-8314433, FAX 86-10-8323182. Ed. Qiu Shibang.

➤ **ZHONGGUO SHENGWUXUE WENZHAI/CHINESE BIOLOGICAL ABSTRACTS.** see *BIOLOGY—Abstracting, Bibliographies, Statistics*

➤ **ZHONGHUA FENGSHIBINGXUE ZAZHI/CHINESE JOURNAL OF RHEUMATOLOGY.** see *MEDICAL SCIENCES—Rheumatology*

570 RUS ISSN 0044-4596
CODEN: ZOBIAU
➤ **ZHURNAL OBSHCHEI BIOLOGII.** Text in Russian; Summaries in English. 1940. bi-m. RUR 1,070 for 6 mos. domestic; USD 256 foreign (effective 2004). index. **Document type:** *Journal, Academic/Scholarly.*
Indexed: ASCA, ASFA, AbHyg, AgBio, AnBrAb, BIOSIS Prev, BioCN&I, BiolAb, CIN, CPA, ChemAb, ChemTitl, CurCont, DSA, ESPM, ExcerpMed, FCA, ForAb, HerbAb, HortAb, IAA, ISR, IndMed, IndVet, MEDLINE, MaizeAb, NemAb, OrnHort, PBA, PGegResA, PGrRegA, ProtozoAb, RASB, RPP, RefZh, RevApplEntom, S&F, SCI, SIA, TDB, TriticAb, VetBull, WeedAb, ZooRec.
—CASDDS, CISTI, East View, GNLM, IDS, Infotrieve, KNAW, Linda Hall. **CCC.**
Published by: (Rossiiskaya Akademiya Nauk/Russian Academy of Sciences, Rossiiskaya Akademiya Nauk, Otdelenie Obshchei Biologii), Izdatel'stvo Nauka, Profsoyuznaya ul 90, Moscow, 117864, Russian Federation. TEL 7-095-3347151, FAX 7-095-4202220, secret@naukaran.ru, http://www.naukaran.ru. **Dist. by:** M K - Periodica, ul Gilyarovskogo 39, Moscow 129110, Russian Federation. TEL 7-095-2845008, FAX 7-095-2813798, info@periodicals.ru, http://www.mkniga.ru.

570 CZE ISSN 0044-4812
ZIVA/LIVE; casopis pro biologickou praci. Text in Slovak, Czech. 1953. bi-m. CZK 222 (effective 2005). bk.rev. illus. index. **Document type:** *Journal, Academic/Scholarly.* **Description:** Devoted to the popularization of natural sciences, botany, zoology, nature conservation. Also contains information about recent research into biology and new trends in research work.
Indexed: BiolAb, ChemAb, CurCont, RASB, ZooRec.
—CISTI, Linda Hall.
Published by: (Akademie Ved Ceske Republiky), Academia, Nakladatelstvi Akademie Ved Ceske Republiky, Narodni 3, Prague 1, 110 00, Czech Republic. TEL 420-2-24240517, FAX 420-2-24240542, ziva@kav.cas.cz, knihkup_academia@kav.cas.cz, http://www.lib.cas.cz/knav/journals/cz/Ziva.htm, http://www.academia.cz. Ed. Ludmila Krupkova. Circ: 22,000. **Subscr. to:** Artia.

570 333.72 SVN ISSN 1408-533X
➤ **ZNANSTVENO RAZISKOVALNO SREDISCE REPUBLIKE SLOVENIJE. ANNALES. SERIES HISTORIA NATURALIS.** Text in Slovenian, English, Croatian, Italian. 1991. s-a. **Document type:** *Journal, Academic/Scholarly.* **Description:** Publishes original scientific natural science works dealing with nature conservation, ecology and biology.

Supersedes in part (in 1994): Zgodovinsko Drustvo za Juzno Primorsko. Annales (0353-8281)
Indexed: ASFA, BIOSIS Prev, BiolAb, ESPM, M&GPA, ZooRec.
Published by: Znanstveno Raziskovalno Sredisce Republike Slovenije/Scientific and Research Center of the Republic of Slovenia, Univerza na Primorskem, Garibaldijeva 1, Koper, 6000, Slovenia. TEL 386-5-6637700, FAX 386-5-6637710, http://www.zrs-kp.si/indexe.htm.

➤ **ZONES HUMIDES INFOS.** see *ENVIRONMENTAL STUDIES*

571.3 DEU ISSN 0720-213X
QL1 CODEN: ZMPHDI
➤ **ZOOMORPHOLOGY**; an international journal of comparative and functional morphology. Text in English. 1924. q. EUR 1,078 combined subscription to institutions print & online eds. (effective 2005). adv. bibl.; illus. back issues avail.; reprint service avail. from ISI. **Document type:** *Journal, Academic/Scholarly.* **Description:** Reviews research on animal morphology at all levels of ontogeny and organization, including ultrastructure of invertebrates and vertebrates.
Former titles (until 1980): Zoomorphologie (0340-6725); (until 1975): Zeitschrift fuer Morphologie der Tiere (0044-3131); Which superseded in part (in 1967): Zeitschrift fuer Morphologie und Oekologie der Tiere (0372-9389)
Related titles: Microform ed.: (from PQC); Online - full text ed.: ISSN 1432-234X (from EBSCO Publishing, Springer LINK, Swets Information Services).
Indexed: ASCA, ASFA, BIOSIS Prev, BioCN&I, BiolAb, CRFR, CurCont, EntAb, ForAb, HelmAb, ISR, NemAb, NutrAb, RM&VM, RefZh, RevApplEntom, SCI, SFA, WildRev, ZooRec.
—BLDSC (9530.310000), CISTI, IDS, IE, Infotrieve, ingenta, Linda Hall. **CCC.**
Published by: Springer-Verlag (Subsidiary of: Springer Science+Business Media), Tiergartenstr 17, Heidelberg, 69121, Germany. TEL 49-6221-3450, FAX 49-6221-345229, http://link.springer.de/link/service/journals/00435/index.htm. Ed. Thomas Bartolomaeus. Adv. contact Stephan Kroeck TEL 49-30-827875739. **Subscr. in the Americas to:** Springer-Verlag New York, Inc., Journal Fulfillment, PO Box 2485, Secaucus, NJ 07096-2485. TEL 800-777-4643, 201-348-4033, FAX 201-348-4505, journals@springer-ny.com, http://www.springer-ny.com; **Subscr. to:** Springer GmbH Auslieferungsgesellschaft, Haberstr 7, Heidelberg 69126, Germany. TEL 49-6221-345-0, FAX 49-6221-345-4229, subscriptions@springer.de.

577 USA ISSN 0720-1842
CODEN: ZOOPDH
ZOOPHYSIOLOGY. Text in English. 1971. irreg., latest vol.33, 1995. price varies. reprint service avail. from ISI. **Document type:** *Monographic series.*
Formerly (until 1977): Zoophysiology and Ecology (0084-5663)
Indexed: ASFA, BIOSIS Prev, BiolAb, ESPM, ZooRec.
—BLDSC (9531.259000), CISTI, KNAW.
Published by: Springer-Verlag New York, Inc. (Subsidiary of: Springer Science+Business Media), 233 Spring St, New York, NY 10013. TEL 212-460-1500, FAX 212-473-6272. Ed. D S Farne.

BIOLOGY—Abstracting, Bibliographies, Statistics

016.58 BEL ISSN 0066-9784
A E T F A T INDEX; releve des travaux de phanerogamie systematique et des taxons nouveaux concernant l'Afrique au sud du Sahara et Madagascar. Text in English, French. 1953. a. USD 8.50. cum.index: 1953-1985.
Published by: Association pour l'Etude Taxonomique de la Flore d'Afrique Tropicale, Rue de la Hulpe 136, Rosieres, 1331, Belgium. Ed. J Lejoly.

016.6606 USA ISSN 1555-6182
A S F A MARINE BIOTECHNOLOGY ABSTRACTS (ONLINE EDITION). Text in English. m. USD 410 (effective 2006).
Media: Online - full text.
Published by: C S A Journal Division (Subsidiary of: Cambridge Information Group), 7200 Wisconsin Ave, Ste 715, Bethesda, MD 20814. TEL 301-961-6798, 800-843-7751, FAX 301-961-6799, journals@csa.com, http://www.csa.com.

016.612015 GBR ISSN 0261-4553
A T PASES. (Adenosine Triphosphatases) Text in English. s-m. looseleaf. GBP 96 for print ed. or e-mail (effective 2001). adv. back issues avail. **Document type:** *Abstract/Index.* **Description:** Provides a current-awareness service for researchers in clinical and life sciences.
Related titles: E-mail ed.; Online - full text ed.: GBP 108 to individuals (effective 2001).
—**CCC.**
Published by: S U B I S (Subsidiary of: Sheffield Academic Press Ltd), Mansion House, 19 Kingfield Rd, Sheffield, S Yorks S11 9AS, United Kingdom. TEL 44-114-255-4433, FAX 44-114-255-4626, subis@sheffac.demon.co.uk, http://www.shef-ac-press.co.uk/subis. Ed. S Huntridge. Adv. contact C Evans.

016.597 USA ISSN 0001-3579
Z5856 CODEN: AEMYA
ABSTRACTS OF ENTOMOLOGY. Text in English. 1970. m. USD 725 (effective 2005). bk.rev. abstr.; bibl. cum.index. back issues avail. **Document type:** *Magazine, Abstract/Index.* **Description:** Current awareness journal containing abstracts and content summaries in English of pure and applied research involving insects, arachnids and insecticides.
Indexed: RevApplEntom.
—BLDSC (0564.230000).
Published by: Thomson BIOSIS (Subsidiary of: Thomson I S I), 3501 Market St, Philadelphia, PA 19104. TEL 215-386-0100, FAX 215-243-2208, info@biosis.org, http://www.biosis.org/products_services/ento.html. Pub. John Schnepp.

016.5795 USA ISSN 0001-3617
QK600 CODEN: ABMYA5
ABSTRACTS OF MYCOLOGY. Text in English. 1967. m. USD 630 (effective 2005). bk.rev. abstr.; bibl. cum.index. back issues avail. **Document type:** *Abstract/Index.* **Description:** Contains abstracts in English about research involving fungi, lichens, and fungicides.
—BLDSC (0565.430000), CASDDS, CISTI.
Published by: Thomson BIOSIS (Subsidiary of: Thomson I S I), 3501 Market St, Philadelphia, PA 19104. TEL 215-386-0100, FAX 215-243-2208, info@biosis.org, http://www.biosis.org/products_services/myco.html. Pub. John Schnepp.

AEROSPACE MEDICINE AND BIOLOGY; a continuing bibliography. see *MEDICAL SCIENCES—Abstracting, Bibliographies, Statistics*

016.63 GBR ISSN 0954-9897
S494.5.B563
AGBIOTECH NEWS AND INFORMATION. Text in English. 1989. m. USD 2,040 in the Americas to institutions except Canada; GBP 1,165 elsewhere to institutions (effective 2006). adv. back issues avail. **Document type:** *Abstract/Index.* **Description:** Contains a comprehensive selection of abstracts of the world's literature on agricultural biotechnology and some human applications of biotechnology. Focuses on the impact of biotechnology in agriculture and policy issues, as well as the purely scientific ones.
Related titles: Online - full text ed.: AgBiotechNet (from DIMDI, The Dialog Corporation).
Indexed: AnBrAb, DSA, FPA, FS&TA, ForAb, HortAb, NutrAb, PBA, PGegResA, RA&MP, RPP, RevApplEntom, SeedAb, TriticAb, WeedAb.
—BLDSC (0736.034000), CISTI, IE. **CCC.**
Published by: CABI Publishing (Subsidiary of: CAB International), CAB International, Wallingford, Oxfordshire OX10 8DE, United Kingdom. TEL 44-1491-832111, FAX 44-1491-833508, cabi@cabi.org, http://www.agbiotechnet.com, http://www.cabi-publishing.org/. Ed. David Hemming. adv.: B&W page GBP 90, B&W page USD 145; 170 x 267. Circ: 180. **Subscr. in N America:** CABI Publishing North America, 875 Massachusetts Ave, 7th Fl, Cambridge, MA 02139. TEL 617-395-4056, 800-528-4841, FAX 617-354-6875, cabi-nao@cabi.org.

016.579 USA ISSN 1060-2011
QR1
AMERICAN SOCIETY FOR MICROBIOLOGY. ABSTRACTS OF THE GENERAL MEETING. Text in English. 1948. a. index. reprint service avail. from PQC. **Document type:** *Proceedings.*
Former titles: American Society for Microbiology. Abstracts of the Annual Meeting (0094-8519); Bacteriological Proceedings (0067-2777)
Related titles: Online - full text ed.
Indexed: BIOSIS Prev, BiolAb, DBA, DSA, FS&TA, IndVet, NutrAb, S&F, VetBull, WeedAb.
—BLDSC (0564.255000), CISTI, GNLM, Linda Hall. **CCC.**
Published by: American Society for Microbiology, 1752 N St, N W, Washington, DC 20036-2904. asmjournals@asm.org, subscriptions@asmusa.org, http://www.asm.org. Circ: 10,000.

016.58 IND ISSN 0970-2377
APPLIED BOTANY ABSTRACTS. Text in English. 1981. q. USD 150 (effective 2003). **Document type:** *Abstract/Index.*
Formerly (until 1980): Current Literature in Plant Science
Indexed: AgrForAb, CPA, FCA, FPA, ForAb, HortAb, NutrAb, OrnHort, PBA, PGegResA, PGrRegA, PHN&I, RA&MP, RDA, RPP, S&F, SeedAb, TDB, WAE&RSA.
Published by: National Botanical Research Institute, Economic Botany Information Service, Rana Prata Marg, Lucknow, Uttar Pradesh 226 001, India. FAX 91-522205836, TELEX 0535-315. Ed. R Mitra. Circ: 300. **Dist. overseas by:** HPC Publishers' Distributors Pvt. Ltd., 4805-24, 1st Bharat Ram Rd., Darya Ganj, New Delhi 110 002, India. TEL 91-11-325-4401, 91-11-686-3511.

016.571 612 USA ISSN 1080-4757
APSTRACTS. Text in English. w. free (effective 2005). **Document type:** *Academic/Scholarly.* **Description:** Features current articles that are accepted and scheduled to be published in the journals of the American Physiological Society.
Media: Online - full text.
Published by: American Physiological Society, 9650 Rockville Pike, Bethesda, MD 20814-3991. TEL 301-634-7164, FAX 301-634-7241, info@aps.faseb.org, info@the-aps.org, http://www.uth.tmc.edu/apstracts, http://www.the-aps.org. Ed. Dr. Martin Frank.

016.57877 ZAF ISSN 1083-883X
AQUATIC BIOLOGY, AQUACULTURE & FISHERIES RESOURCES. Text in English. 1995. q. ZAR 27,420. **Document type:** *Abstract/Index.* **Description:** Provides access to comprehensive information on the science and management of aquatic organisms and environments.
Media: Online - full content. **Related titles:** CD-ROM ed.: (from National Information Services Corp. (N I S C)).
Published by: National Inquiry Services Centre (Pty) Ltd (Subsidiary of: N I S C USA), PO Box 377, Grahamstown, 6140, South Africa. TEL 27-46-622-9698, FAX 27-46-622-9550, nisc@ru.ac.za, info@nisc.co.za, http://education.nation.co.za/nisc/aquatic.html, http://www.nisc.co.za.

016.5765 AUS
AUSTRALIAN AND NEW ZEALAND DIRECTORY OF GENETICS SUPPORT GROUPS, SERVICES AND INFORMATION. Text in English. 1992. biennial. looseleaf. AUD 35 (effective 1999). **Document type:** *Directory.* **Description:** Provides information about genetic support groups and services for the health professionals, students, teachers, and the general community.
Published by: New South Wales Genetics Education Program, PO Box 317, St Leonards, NSW 2065, Australia. FAX 61-2-9906-7529, gethi@blackburn.med.usyd.edu.au, http://www.genetics.com.au. Ed., R&P Kristine Barlow-Stewart TEL 61-2-9926-7324. Pub. Kristine Barlow Stewart. Circ: 1,500.

016.58 GBR ISSN 0307-2657
B S B I ABSTRACTS; abstracts from literature relating to the vascular plants of the British Isles. Text in English. 1971. a. GBP 20 in United Kingdom membership; GBP 22 elsewhere membership (effective 2001). **Document type:** *Abstract/Index.* **Description:** Contains full details of publication, often with summaries, of books and research papers relating to the distribution and taxonomic classification of UK plants.
Indexed: WeedAb.
—Linda Hall.
Published by: Botanical Society of the British Isles, c/o Department of Botany, The Natural History Museum, Cromwell Rd, London, SW7 5BD, United Kingdom. TEL 44-20-7942-5002, bsbihgs@aol.com. Circ: 3,000.

016.58 POL ISSN 0860-4509
BIBLIOGRAFIE BOTANICZNE/BOTANICAL BIBLIOGRAPHIES. Text in Polish. 1983. irreg., latest vol.7, 2001. price varies. adv. bibl. back issues avail. **Document type:** *Bibliography.* **Description:** Presents a list of publications dealing with all plant groups by Polish botanists as well publications covering territory of Poland by foreign authors.
Published by: Polska Akademia Nauk, Instytut Botaniki im. W. Szafera/Polish Academy of Sciences, W. Szafer Institute of Botany, ul Lubicz 46, Krakow, 31512, Poland. TEL 48-12-4241737, FAX 48-12-4219790, office@ib-pan.krakow.pl. Ed. Jadwiga Sieminska. Pub. Jacek W Wieser. R&P Mirek Zbigniew. Adv. contact Jacek Wieser. Circ: 3,000 (paid).

016.58 DEU
BIBLIOGRAPHIA PHYTOSOCIOLOGICA SYNTAXONOMICA. Text in German. 1971. irreg., latest vol.39, 1986. price varies. **Document type:** *Monographic series, Bibliography.*
Indexed: BiolAb.
Published by: J. Cramer in der Gebrueder Borntraeger Verlagsbuchhandlung, Johannesstr 3A, Stuttgart, 70176, Germany. TEL 49-711-3514560, FAX 49-711-35145699, mail@borntraeger-cramer.de, http://www.schweizerbart.de.

016.5795 GBR ISSN 0006-1573
Z5356.F97
BIBLIOGRAPHY OF SYSTEMATIC MYCOLOGY. Text in English. 1947. s-a. USD 410 in the Americas to institutions except Canada; GBP 235 elsewhere to institutions (effective 2006). bk.rev. reprints avail. **Document type:** *Bibliography.* **Description:** Lists papers and books on all aspects of the taxonomy of fungi each year.
Related titles: CD-ROM ed.: Bibliography of Systematic Mycology on CD-ROM. ISSN 1359-5423. 1995. GBP 850, USD 1,894; Diskette ed.; Online - full text ed.
Indexed: PBA, RPP.
—CISTI. **CCC.**
Published by: CABI Publishing (Subsidiary of: CAB International), CAB International, Wallingford, Oxfordshire OX10 8DE, United Kingdom. TEL 44-1491-832111, FAX 44-1491-833508, cabi@cabi.org, http://www.cabi-publishing.org/. Ed. Ken Hudson.

016.572 USA ISSN 1065-7509
QH345
BIOCHEMISTRY AND BIOPHYSICS CITATION INDEX. Text in English. bi-m. USD 1,480 for CD-ROM (effective 2005). **Document type:** *Academic/Scholarly.* **Description:** Provides bibliographic data, cited references, related records and English-language author abstracts for international scholarly research journals and conference proceedings.

▼ new title ➤ refereed ∗ unverified ♦ full entry avail.

Related titles: CD-ROM ed.: (from Thomson I S I); Magnetic Tape ed.
Published by: Thomson I S I (Subsidiary of: Thomson Corporation), 3501 Market St., Philadelphia, PA 19104. TEL 215-386-0100, 800-336-4474, FAX 215-386-2911, sales@isinet.com, http://scientific.thomson.com/products/bbci/, http://www.isinet.com.

016.61028 USA ISSN 1555-6271
R856.A1
BIOENGINEERING ABSTRACTS (ONLINE EDITION). Text in English. m. USD 845 (effective 2006). bk.rev. abstr. index on CD-ROM. back issues avail.; reprints avail. **Document type:** *Abstract/Index.* **Description:** Covers the world's technological literature in the area of bioengineering and biomedical engineering.
Media: Online - full content.
Published by: C S A Journal Division (Subsidiary of: Cambridge Information Group), 7200 Wisconsin Ave, Ste 715, Bethesda, MD 20814. TEL 301-961-6798, 800-843-7751, FAX 301-961-6799, journals@csa.com, http://www.csa.com/factsheets/bioengineering-set-c.php. Ed. Deborah B Whitman. Pub. Ted Caris. **Co-publisher:** Elsevier Engineering Information, Inc.

B

BIOFUELS ABSTRACTS. see *ENERGY—Abstracting, Bibliographies, Statistics*

016.57 USA ISSN 0006-3169
QH301 CODEN: BIABA4
BIOLOGICAL ABSTRACTS; references, abstracts, and indexes to the world's life sciences research literature. Text in English. 1926. s-m. USD 9,850; USD 16,985 combined subscription print & electronic media; USD 18,185 combined subscription includes print, cumulative indexes & electronic media (effective 2003). abstr.; illus. index, cum.index. reprints avail. **Document type:** *Abstract/Index.*
Formed by the 1926 merger of: Abstracts of Bacteriology (0096-5340); Botanical Abstracts (0096-526X)
Related titles: CD-ROM ed.: ISSN 1058-4129 (from SilverPlatter Information, Inc.); Online - full text ed.: (from Data-Star, DIMDI).
Indexed: PopulInd.
—BLDSC (2074.000000), CASDDS, CISTI, Linda Hall.
Published by: Thomson BIOSIS (Subsidiary of: Thomson I S I), 3501 Market St, Philadelphia, PA 19104. TEL 215-386-0100, 800-336-4474, FAX 215-243-2208, info@biosis.org, http://www.biosis.org/products/ba/.

016.57 USA
BIOLOGICAL ABSTRACTS CUMULATIVE INDEXES. Text in English. 1927. s-a. USD 4,250 combined subscription print or electronic media; USD 18,185 combined subscription includes Indexes with electronic media & Biological Abstracts (effective 2003). **Document type:** *Abstract/Index.*
Related titles: CD-ROM ed.; Microform ed.: (from BIO); Online - full text ed.
—Linda Hall.
Published by: Thomson BIOSIS (Subsidiary of: Thomson I S I), 3501 Market St, Philadelphia, PA 19104. TEL 215-231-7500, 800-523-4806, FAX 215-587-2016, info@biosis.org, http://www.biosis.org/.

016.57 USA
BIOLOGICAL ABSTRACTS - R R M (ONLINE EDITION); references and indexes to the world's life science reports, reviews, and meeting literature. (Reports, Reviews, Meetings) Text in English. q.
Media: Online - full text (from Data-Star, DIMDI). **Related titles:** CD-ROM ed.: ISSN 1058-4137 (from SilverPlatter Information, Inc.); Microfiche ed.
Published by: Thomson BIOSIS (Subsidiary of: Thomson I S I), 3501 Market St, Philadelphia, PA 19104. TEL 215-386-0100, 800-336-4474, FAX 215-243-2208, info@biosis.org, http://www.biosis.org/products/baarm/.

016.57 USA
BIOLOGICAL ABSTRACTS - R R M CUMULATIVE INDEX. (Reports, Reviews, and Meetings) Text in English. 1970. s-a. USD 2,125; USD 9,255 combined subscription print & electronic media (effective 2003). bk.rev. **Document type:** *Abstract/Index.*
Former titles: Cumulative Index to Biological Abstracts R R M; Cumulative Index to Bioresearch Index; Annual Cumulative Index to Bioresearch Index
Related titles: CD-ROM ed.; Microfiche ed.: (from BIO); Online - full text ed.
Published by: Thomson BIOSIS (Subsidiary of: Thomson I S I), 3501 Market St, Philadelphia, PA 19104. TEL 215-231-7500, 800-523-4806, FAX 215-587-2016, info@biosis.org, http://www.biosis.org/products_services/ba_rrm.html.

016.57 USA ISSN 0006-3177
Z5073
BIOLOGICAL & AGRICULTURAL INDEX. Text in English. 1964. m. (except Aug., plus q. & a. cumulations). USD 570 in US & Canada (effective 2006). **Document type:** *Abstract/Index.* **Description:** Provides a cumulative subject index to periodicals in the fields of biology, agriculture and related sciences.
Formerly (until 1964): Agricultural Index (0196-5883)
Related titles: CD-ROM ed.: ISSN 1076-7037 (from H.W. Wilson, SilverPlatter Information, Inc.); Magnetic Tape ed.; Online - full text ed.: 1985. USD 2,380 in US & Canada (effective 2006).
—CISTI, Linda Hall.
Published by: H.W. Wilson Co., 950 University Ave, Bronx, NY 10452-4224. TEL 718-588-8400, 800-367-6770, FAX 718-590-1617, 800-590-1617, custserv@hwwilson.com, http://www.hwwilson.com/Databases/bioag.htm. Ed. Syed Shah.

016.57 GBR ISSN 0142-8004
BIOLOGICAL RHYTHMS. Text in English. 1970. s-m. GBP 120 (effective 2001). adv. **Document type:** *Abstract/Index.* **Description:** Current awareness service for researchers in clinical and life sciences.
Formerly: Circadian Rhythms
Related titles: E-mail ed.: GBP 120 (effective 2001); Online - full text ed.: GBP 108 (effective 2001).
—CCC.
Published by: S U B I S (Subsidiary of: Sheffield Academic Press Ltd), Mansion House, 19 Kingfield Rd, Sheffield, S Yorks S11 9AS, United Kingdom. TEL 44-114-255-4433, FAX 44-114-255-4626, subis@sheffac.demon.co.uk, http://www.shef-ac-press.co.uk/subis. Ed. S Huntridge. Adv. contact C Evans.

016.57 USA ISSN 0095-2958
QH301
BIOLOGY DIGEST. Text in English. 1974. m. (Sep.-May). USD 149 in US & Canada; USD 159 elsewhere (effective 2005). bk.rev. abstr.; bibl.; illus. cum.index. 140 p./no.; back issues avail.; reprints avail. **Document type:** *Journal, Abstract/Index.* **Description:** Contains abstracts of current life science articles and research reports for high school and college students.
Incorporates: Environmental Quality Abstracts (0095-0149)
Related titles: CD-ROM ed.; Microfiche ed.: (from PQC); Online - full text ed.
—BLDSC (2087.058000).
Published by: Plexus Publishing, Inc., 143 Old Marlton Pike, Medford, NJ 08055. TEL 609-654-6500, FAX 609-654-4309, info@plexuspublishing.com, http://www.plexuspublishing.com. Ed. Thomas H Hogan. Circ: 2,000 (paid).

570.15195 GBR ISSN 0006-3444
QH301
➤ **BIOMETRIKA.** Text in English. 1901. q. GBP 95, USD 171, EUR 143 to institutions; GBP 100, USD 180, EUR 150 combined subscription to institutions print & online eds. (effective 2006). charts; illus. author index: vols.1-78, 1901-1991; subject index: vols.1-37, 1901-1950. back issues avail.; reprint service avail. from PQC,PSC. **Document type:** *Journal, Academic/Scholarly.* **Description:** Contains statistics with theoretical papers of direct or potential value in applications.
Related titles: Microform ed.: (from PMC, PQC); Online - full text ed.: ISSN 1464-3510. 199?. GBP 90, USD 162, EUR 135 to institutions (effective 2006) (from EBSCO Publishing, Gale Group, HighWire Press, IngentaConnect, JSTOR (Web-based Journal Archive), O C L C Online Computer Library Center, Inc., Ovid Technologies, Inc., Oxford University Press Online Journals, ProQuest Information & Learning, Swets Information Services).
Indexed: ABIn, AS&TI, ASCA, ASFA, AnBrAb, B&AI, BIOSIS Prev, BiolAb, Biostat, CCMJ, CIS, CISA, CMCI, ChemAb, CurCont, DSA, ESPM, ExcerpMed, HortAb, ISR, Inpharma, Inspec, JCQM, MEDLINE, MathR, MathSciNet, NutrAb, ORMS, PBA, QC&AS, RASB, Reac, RefZh, SCI, SFA, SSCI, ST&MA, WildRev, ZentMath, ZooRec.
—BLDSC (2089.000000), CISTI, GNLM, IE, Infotrieve, ingenta, Linda Hall. **CCC.**
Published by: (Biometrika Trust), Oxford University Press, Great Clarendon St, Oxford, OX2 6DP, United Kingdom. TEL 44-1865-556767, FAX 44-1865-556646, jnl.orders@oup.co.uk, enquiry@oup.co.uk, http://biomet.oxfordjournals.org/, http://www.oxfordjournals.org/. Ed. D. M. Titterington. Pub. Ian McIntosh. R&P Fiona Bennett. Circ: 3,700.

016.5714 USA ISSN 0523-6800
QH505.A1
➤ **BIOPHYSICAL SOCIETY. ANNUAL MEETING. ABSTRACTS.** Text in English. 1958. a., latest vol.82, 2002. USD 1,007 combined subscription domestic print & online eds.; USD 1,137 combined subscription in Canada print & online eds.; USD 1,063 combined subscription elsewhere print & online eds. (effective 2005); includes Biophysical Journal. adv. **Document type:** *Proceedings, Academic/Scholarly.*
Formerly: Biophysical Society. Abstracts (0067-8910); Supersedes: Biophysical Society. Symposium Proceedings (0520-1985)
Related titles: CD-ROM ed.; ◆ Supplement to: Biophysical Journal. ISSN 0006-3495.
Indexed: BiolAb.
—CISTI. **CCC.**
Published by: Biophysical Society, 9650 Rockville Pike, Bethesda, MD 20814. TEL 301-634-7114, FAX 301-634-7133, ckenney@biophysics.org, http://www.biophysics.org/. Ed. Peter Moore. R&P Cathy Kenney. Adv. contact Jeanne Brooksbank.

016.57 USA ISSN 1081-8669
CODEN: BIEVEK
BIOSIS EVOLUTIONS. Text in English. 1994. bi-m. free. back issues avail. **Document type:** *Newsletter.* **Description:** Reports information on BIOSIS's products and services, as well as items of current interest to the users of biological and biomedical information.
Formed by the merger of (1970-1994): BioScene (0090-3337); (1983-1994): BioSearch (1041-8946)
Related titles: Online - full text ed.
Indexed: BiolDig, CIJE.
—CISTI, Linda Hall.
Published by: Biosis, 2001 Market St, Ste 700, Philadelphia, PA 19103-7095. TEL 215-587-4800, 800-523-4806, FAX 215-587-2016, info@mail.biosis.org, http://www.biosis.org. Eds. Christopher D'Lauro, Robert Connor. R&P John Anderson TEL 215-587-4800. Circ: 10,000.

016.57 USA
BIOSIS PREVIEWS; your complete life sciences database. Text in English. base vol. plus w. updates. **Description:** Covers life sciences, from botany to genetic engineering. Abstracts and indexes information from more than 5,500 sources, including: journal articles, meeting and conference reports, books, and patents.
Media: Online - full content.
Published by: Thomson BIOSIS (Subsidiary of: Thomson I S I), 3501 Market St, Philadelphia, PA 19104. TEL 215-231-7500, 800-523-4806, FAX 215-587-2016, info@biosis.org, http://www.biosis.org/.

016.57 USA
Z695.1.B5
BIOSIS SEARCH GUIDE (YEARS). Text in English. 1977. biennial. USD 150 per issue (effective 2003). **Document type:** *Abstract/Index.*
Former titles: BIOSIS Previews Search Guide (Year) (0898-2414); BIOSIS Search Guide
Published by: Thomson BIOSIS (Subsidiary of: Thomson I S I), 3501 Market St, Philadelphia, PA 19104. TEL 215-231-7500, 800-523-4806, FAX 215-587-2016, info@biosis.org, http://www.biosis.org/.

016.57 USA ISSN 1086-2951
Z5321 CODEN: SSBDE4
BIOSIS SERIAL SOURCES. Text in English. 1938. a. USD 170 per issue (effective 2005). **Document type:** *Abstract/Index.*
Former titles (until 1996): Serial Sources for the BIOSIS Previers Database (1044-4297); (until 1989): Serial Sources for the BIOSIS Database (0162-2048); (until 1978): BIOSIS: List of Serials with Coden, Title Abbreviations, New, Changed and Ceased Titles (0067-8937); (until 1969): Biological Abstracts List of Serials with Title Abbreviations (0523-6568)
Related titles: CD-ROM ed.
—BLDSC (2089.612600), CASDDS, CISTI, Linda Hall.
Published by: Thomson BIOSIS (Subsidiary of: Thomson I S I), 3501 Market St, Philadelphia, PA 19104. TEL 215-386-0100, 800-523-4806, FAX 215-243-2208, info@biosis.org, http://www.biosis.org/products_services/bss.html.

016.6606 USA ISSN 1057-607X
TP248.13
BIOTECHNOLOGY CITATION INDEX. Text in English. 1991. bi-m. USD 1,480 for CD-ROM (effective 2005). **Document type:** *Abstract/Index.* **Description:** Provides bibliographic data, cited references, related records and English-language author abstracts from international scholarly research journals and conference proceedings.
Related titles: CD-ROM ed.: (from Thomson I S I); Magnetic Tape ed.
Published by: Thomson I S I (Subsidiary of: Thomson Corporation), 3501 Market St., Philadelphia, PA 19104. TEL 215-386-0100, 800-336-4474, FAX 215-386-2911, sales@isinet.com, http://scientific.thomson.com/products/bci/, http://www.isinet.com.

016.6606 HUN ISSN 0237-0115
BIOTECHNOLOGY INFORMATION. Variant title: Biotech-Info. Text in Hungarian. 1984. m. HUF 3,600. abstr.
Published by: Orszagos Muszaki Informacios Kozpont es Konyvtar/National Technical Information Centre and Library, Muzeum utca 17, PO Box 12, Budapest, 1428, Hungary. Ed. Fazekasne Zsuzsanna Horvath. Circ: 420.

016.579 JPN
BISEIBUTSU KAGAKU BUNRUI KENKYUKAI KOEN YOSHISHU/ABSTRACTS OF ANNUAL MEETING ON MICROBIAL CHEMOTAXONOMY. Text in English, Japanese. 1988. a. **Document type:** *Abstract/Index.*
Published by: Biseibutsu Kagaku Bunrui Kenkyukai/Society of Microbial Chemotaxonomy, Daigaku Oyo Biseibutsu Kenkyujo, 1-1 Yayoi 1-chome, Bunkyo-ku, Tokyo, 113-0032, Japan.

016.57 BGR ISSN 0861-5691
BIULETIN ZA NOVONABAVENI KNIGI NA CHUZHDI EZITZI. SERIYA B: ESTESTVENI I PRILOZHNI NAUKI. MEDIZINA. TEKHNIKA. SELSKO STOPANSTVO. Text in Bulgarian. 1954. m. BGL 16.80 (effective 2003). **Document type:** *Bulletin.* **Description:** Lists newly acquired foreign-language books in the natural sciences.

Published by: Narodna Biblioteka Sv. sv. Kiril i Metodii/Cyril and Methodius National Library, 88 Levski Blvd, Sofia, 1504, Bulgaria. TEL 359-2-9881600, FAX 359-2-435495, nbkm@nl.otel.net. Ed., R&P T Nikolova TEL 359-2-9882811 ext 220. Circ: 40 (paid).

BOTANICAL PESTICIDES ABSTRACTS. see *ENVIRONMENTAL STUDIES—Abstracting, Bibliographies, Statistics*

016.58 DNK ISSN 0900-2367
BOTANISK CENTRALBIBLIOTEK. FORTEGNELSE OVER LOEBENDE PERIODICA VED BOTANISK CENTRALBIBLITEK. Text in Danish. 1977. irreg., latest 1998. free. **Document type:** *Catalog.*
Published by: Botanisk Centralbibliotek, OPG S, Soelvgade 83, Copenhagen K, 1307, Denmark. bcb@bot.ku.dk. Ed. Annelise Hartmann.

016.579 USA ISSN 1047-8167
CODEN: CSATE7
C A SELECTS. ANTIFUNGAL & ANTIMYCOTIC AGENTS. Text in English. 1988. s-w. USD 315 to non-members; USD 95 to members (effective 2005). **Document type:** *Abstract/Index.* **Description:** Covers the antifungal and antimycotic activities of both established and developmental drugs. Includes synthesis, mechanism(s) of action, formulation, and structure-activity relationships.
Formerly (until 1989): BIOSIS CAS Selects: Antifungal Agents
Published by: Chemical Abstracts Service (C A S) (Subsidiary of: American Chemical Society), 2540 Olentangy River Rd., Columbus, OH 43210-0012. TEL 614-447-3600, FAX 614-447-3713, help@cas.com, http://www.cas.org, http://caselects.cas.org. **Subscr. to:** PO Box 3012, Columbus, OH 43210. TEL 800-753-4227, FAX 614-447-3751.

016.572 USA ISSN 0895-5905
CODEN: CAFRE2
C A SELECTS. FREE RADICALS (BIOCHEMICAL ASPECTS). Text in English. 1988. s-w. USD 315 to non-members; USD 95 to members (effective 2005). **Document type:** *Abstract/Index.* **Description:** Covers reactions and interactions of free radicals, including activated oxygen species in biological systems; formation, metabolic aspects, and toxicity of free radicals in intact organs, isolated organs, tissues, cells, and subcellular systems, as well as in model biological systems.
Published by: Chemical Abstracts Service (C A S) (Subsidiary of: American Chemical Society), 2540 Olentangy River Rd., Columbus, OH 43210-0012. TEL 614-447-3600, FAX 614-447-3713, help@cas.com, http://www.cas.org, http://caselects.cas.org. **Subscr. to:** PO Box 3012, Columbus, OH 43210. TEL 800-753-4227, FAX 614-447-3751.

016.57265 USA ISSN 1083-2750
CODEN: CSPPF3
C A SELECTS PLUS. AMINO ACIDS, PEPTIDES AND PROTEINS. Text in English. s-w. USD 315 to non-members; USD 95 to members (effective 2005). **Document type:** *Abstract/Index.* **Description:** Covers chemistry and synthesis of amino acids, peptides, and proteins.
Formerly: C A Selects. Amino Acids, Peptides and Proteins (0275-701X)
Published by: Chemical Abstracts Service (C A S) (Subsidiary of: American Chemical Society), 2540 Olentangy River Rd., Columbus, OH 43210-0012. TEL 614-447-3600, FAX 614-447-3713, help@cas.com, http://www.cas.org, http://caselects.cas.org. **Subscr. to:** PO Box 3012, Columbus, OH 43210. TEL 800-753-4227, FAX 614-447-3751.

016.5719 USA ISSN 0362-9848
CODEN: CASPDQ
C A SELECTS. PSYCHOBIOCHEMISTRY. Text in English. s-w. USD 315 to non-members; USD 95 to members (effective 2005). **Document type:** *Abstract/Index.* **Description:** Covers the pathological and pharmacological aspects of mental function, including human and animal behavior, and emotions.
Published by: Chemical Abstracts Service (C A S) (Subsidiary of: American Chemical Society), 2540 Olentangy River Rd., Columbus, OH 43210-0012. TEL 614-447-3600, FAX 614-447-3713, help@cas.com, http://www.cas.org, http://caselects.cas.org. **Subscr. to:** PO Box 3012, Columbus, OH 43210. TEL 800-753-4227, FAX 614-447-3751.

016.572 USA ISSN 0160-9173
CODEN: CSBSDB
C A SELECTS. STEROIDS (BIOCHEMICAL ASPECTS). Text in English. s-w. USD 315 to non-members; USD 95 to members (effective 2005). **Document type:** *Abstract/Index.* **Description:** Covers pharmacology, toxicology, general biochemistry, and nutritional uses of steroids.
Published by: Chemical Abstracts Service (C A S) (Subsidiary of: American Chemical Society), 2540 Olentangy River Rd., Columbus, OH 43210-0012. TEL 614-447-3600, FAX 614-447-3713, help@cas.com, http://www.cas.org, http://caselects.cas.org. **Subscr. to:** PO Box 3012, Columbus, OH 43210. TEL 800-753-4227, FAX 614-447-3751.

016.5915 USA ISSN 0301-8695
QL750
C S A ANIMAL BEHAVIOR ABSTRACTS. (Cambridge Scientific Abstracts) Text in English. 1972. q. (5 issues). USD 1,015 combined subscription print & online eds. (effective 2006). bk.rev. abstr. index. back issues avail. **Document type:** *Abstract/Index.* **Description:** Covers field and laboratory studies of all aspects of animal behavior.
Formerly (until 1974): Behavioural Biology Abstracts, Section A: Animal Behaviour (0300-5852)
Related titles: CD-ROM ed.; Online - full text ed.: ISSN 1555-6131. USD 760 (effective 2006).
Indexed: RASB.
—BLDSC (0902.960000), CISTI.
Published by: C S A Journal Division (Subsidiary of: Cambridge Information Group), 7200 Wisconsin Ave, Ste 715, Bethesda, MD 20814. TEL 301-961-6798, 800-843-7751, FAX 301-961-6799, journals@csa.com, service@csa.com, http://www.csa.com/factsheets/animal-behavior-set-c.php. Ed. Robert Hilton. Pub. Ted Caris.

016.5792 USA ISSN 0896-5919
QR360
C S A VIROLOGY AND AIDS ABSTRACTS. (Cambridge Scientific Abstracts) Text in English. 1967. m. (except Dec.). USD 1,650 combined subscription print & online eds. (effective 2006). bk.rev. abstr. a index on CD-ROM. back issues avail. **Document type:** *Abstract/Index.* **Description:** Covers viruses of humans, animals and plants, with emphasis on AIDS.
Formerly (until 1988): Virology Abstracts (0042-6830)
Related titles: CD-ROM ed.: (from SilverPlatter Information, Inc.); Online - full text ed.: ISSN 1555-4554. USD 1,240 (effective 2005).
Published by: C S A Journal Division (Subsidiary of: Cambridge Information Group), 7200 Wisconsin Ave, Ste 715, Bethesda, MD 20814. TEL 301-961-6798, 800-843-7751, FAX 301-961-6799, journals@csa.com, http://www.csa.com. Ed. Christine Hong. Pub. Ted Caris.

016.5715 USA ISSN 1555-6298
QP88.2
CALCIUM AND CALCIFIED TISSUE ABSTRACTS (ONLINE EDITION). Text in English. m. USD 725 (effective 2006). adv. bk.rev. abstr. index on CD-ROM. back issues avail. **Document type:** *Abstract/Index.* **Description:** Covers the role of calcium metabolism in maintaining body function, including bone structure and diseases.
Media: Online - full text.
—GNLM.
Published by: C S A Journal Division (Subsidiary of: Cambridge Information Group), 7200 Wisconsin Ave, Ste 715, Bethesda, MD 20814. TEL 301-961-6798, 800-843-7751, FAX 301-961-6799, journals@csa.com, http://www.csa.com/factsheets/calcified-tissue-set-c.php. Ed. Janet L Padgett. Pub. Ted Caris.

016.59 USA
CANADIAN ZOOLOGY ABSTRACTS. Text in English. 1945. q. USD 100 to individuals; USD 175 to libraries; USD 325 universities; USD 475 region; USD 80 to students (effective 2005). cum. index: 1945-2001. **Document type:** *Abstract/Index.* **Description:** Contains citations and abstracts published from 1945 to present in the Canadian Journal of Zoology.
Media: Online - full content. **Related titles:** CD-ROM ed.: USD 149 to individuals; USD 250 to libraries; USD 450 universities; USD 650 region; USD 129 to students (effective 2002).
Published by: ABSEARCH, Inc., 1204 Thatuna Ave, Moscow, ID 83843. TEL 208-883-5544, 800-867-1877, FAX 208-883-5554, custinfo@absearch.com, sales@absearch.com, http://www.absearch.com.

016.5716 GBR ISSN 0263-726X
CELL DIFFERENTIATION. Text in English. 1983. s-m. GBP 96 for print ed. or e-mail (effective 2001). adv. back issues avail. **Document type:** *Abstract/Index.* **Description:** Current awareness service for researchers in clinical and life sciences.
Related titles: E-mail ed.; Online - full text ed.: GBP 108 to individuals (effective 2001).
—CCC.
Published by: S U B I S (Subsidiary of: Sheffield Academic Press Ltd), Mansion House, 19 Kingfield Rd, Sheffield, S Yorks S11 9AS, United Kingdom. TEL 44-114-255-4433, FAX 44-114-255-4626, subis@sheffac.demon.co.uk, http://www.shef-ac-press.co.uk/subis. Ed. S Huntridge. Adv. contact C Evans.

016.572 GBR ISSN 0142-8047
CELL MEMBRANES. Text in English. 1970. s-m. GBP 120 for print or e-mail eds. (effective 2001). adv. **Document type:** *Abstract/Index.* **Description:** Current awareness service for researchers in clinical and life sciences. Covers membrane transport, protein transport, channels, electrical properties, lipids and model systems.
Related titles: E-mail ed.; Online - full text ed.: GBP 108 (effective 2001).
Indexed: CIN, ChemAb, ChemTitl, SCI.
—CCC.

Published by: S U B I S (Subsidiary of: Sheffield Academic Press Ltd), Mansion House, 19 Kingfield Rd, Sheffield, S Yorks S11 9AS, United Kingdom. TEL 44-114-255-4433, FAX 44-114-255-4626, subis@sheffac.demon.co.uk, http://www.shef-ac-press.co.uk/subis. Ed. S Huntridge. Adv. contact C Evans.

016.572 USA ISSN 0009-2304
CODEN: CABSBG
CHEMICAL ABSTRACTS - BIOCHEMISTRY SECTIONS. Abbreviated title: C A B S. Text in English. 1963. s-w. USD 3,355; USD 3,040 to CA subscribers; USD 671 ACS members (effective 2005). charts; pat.; stat. index. **Document type:** *Abstract/Index.*
Related titles: Online - full text ed.
Indexed: DSA, VITIS.
—CASDDS, CISTI.
Published by: Chemical Abstracts Service (C A S) (Subsidiary of: American Chemical Society), 2540 Olentangy River Rd., Columbus, OH 43210-0012. TEL 614-447-3600, FAX 614-447-3713, help@cas.com, http://www.cas.org. Ed. David W Weisgerber. **Subscr. to:** PO Box 3012, Columbus, OH 43210. TEL 800-753-4227, FAX 614-447-3751.

016.5716592 GBR ISSN 0264-9640
CHLOROPLASTS. Text in English. 1984. s-m. looseleaf. GBP 96 for print ed. or e-mail (effective 2001). adv. back issues avail. **Document type:** *Abstract/Index.* **Description:** Current awareness service for researchers in life sciences.
Related titles: E-mail ed.; Online - full text ed.: GBP 108 to individuals (effective 2001).
—CCC.
Published by: S U B I S (Subsidiary of: Sheffield Academic Press Ltd), Mansion House, 19 Kingfield Rd, Sheffield, S Yorks S11 9AS, United Kingdom. TEL 44-114-255-4433, FAX 44-114-255-4626, subis@sheffac.demon.co.uk, http://www.shef-ac-press.co.uk/subis. Ed. S Huntridge. Adv. contact C Evans.

016.5957 JPN
CHOJU KANKEI TOKEI/ANNUAL STATISTICS OF BIRDS AND ANIMALS. Text in Japanese. a. abstr.; maps; stat.
Published by: Kankyocho, Shizen Kankyokyolan/Ministry of the Environment, Nature Conservation Bureau, 2-2 Kasumigaseki 1-chome, Chiyoda-ku, Tokyo, 100-0013, Japan. TEL 81-3-5521-8284, FAX 81-3-3581-7090.

016.57257 GBR ISSN 0964-7597
CHOLESTEROL & LIPOPROTEINS. Text in English. 1992. s-m. GBP 96 for print ed. or e-mail (effective 2001). adv. **Document type:** *Abstract/Index.* **Description:** Current awareness service for researchers in life sciences.
Related titles: E-mail ed.; Online - full text ed.: GBP 108 to individuals (effective 2001).
Published by: S U B I S (Subsidiary of: Sheffield Academic Press Ltd), Mansion House, 19 Kingfield Rd, Sheffield, S Yorks S11 9AS, United Kingdom. TEL 44-114-255-4433, FAX 44-114-255-4626, subis@sheffac.demon.co.uk, http://www.shef-ac-press.co.uk/subis. Ed. S Huntridge. Adv. contact C Evans.

016.5765 GBR ISSN 0260-5872
CLINICAL CYTOGENETICS. Text in English. 1981. s-m. GBP 120 for print or e-mail eds. (effective 2001). adv. **Document type:** *Abstract/Index.* **Description:** Current awareness service for researchers. Covers chromosomal birth defects, banding techniques, DNA cytometry, DNA probes and gene mapping, leukemias and lymphomas, solid tumors, genetic amniocentesis.
Related titles: E-mail ed.; Online - full text ed.: GBP 108 (effective 2001).
—CCC.
Published by: S U B I S (Subsidiary of: Sheffield Academic Press Ltd), Mansion House, 19 Kingfield Rd, Sheffield, S Yorks S11 9AS, United Kingdom. TEL 44-114-255-4433, FAX 44-114-255-4626, subis@sheffac.demon.co.uk, http://www.shef-ac-press.co.uk/subis. Ed. S Huntridge. Adv. contact C Evans.

CONSERVATION BIOLOGY ABSTRACTS. see *CONSERVATION—Abstracting, Bibliographies, Statistics*

016.59 USA
COPEIA ABSTRACTS. Text in English. 1945. q. USD 100 to individuals; USD 175 to libraries; USD 325 universities; USD 475 region; USD 80 to students (effective 2005). **Document type:** *Abstract/Index.* **Description:** Contains 8,900 + records including all citations and abstracts from Copeia (1945-2001).
Formerly: ABSEARCH Ichthyology and Herpetology
Media: Online - full content. **Related titles:** CD-ROM ed.: USD 149 to individuals; USD 250 to libraries; USD 450 universities; USD 650 region; USD 129 to students (effective 2002).
Published by: ABSEARCH, Inc., 1204 Thatuna Ave, Moscow, ID 83843. TEL 208-883-5544, 800-867-1877, FAX 208-883-5554, custinfo@absearch.com, sales@absearch.com, http://www.absearch.com.

570.15195 USA
CORNELL UNIVERSITY. NEW YORK STATE COLLEGE OF AGRICULTURE AND LIFE SCIENCES. BIOMETRICS UNIT. ANNUAL REPORT. Text in English. 1949. a. free. bk.rev. **Document type:** *Corporate.*

B

▼ new title ➤ refereed ✶ unverified ♦ full entry avail.

Published by: New York State College of Agriculture and Life Sciences, Department of Plant Breeding and Biometry, Cornell University, 436 Warren Hall, Ithaca, NY 14853. TEL 607-255-5488, FAX 607-255-4698, biometrics@cornell.edu. Ed. Janet L Breslin. Circ: (controlled).

016.579 NLD ISSN 0964-8712
Z5180
CURRENT ADVANCES IN APPLIED MICROBIOLOGY & BIOTECHNOLOGY. Text in English. 1984. 12/yr. EUR 1,954 in Europe to institutions; JPY 259,000 in Japan to institutions; USD 2,187 to institutions except Europe and Japan; EUR 141 in Europe to qualified personnel; JPY 19,300 in Japan to qualified personnel; USD 159 to qualified personnel except Europe and Japan (effective 2006). adv. back issues avail. **Document type:** *Abstract/Index.* **Description:** Provides current awareness service in the sphere of applied microbiology and biotechnology. Gives listings of titles of microbiological papers published throughout the world classified into 149 main areas and provides a comprehensive listing of review articles.
Formerly (until 1992): Current Advances in Microbiology (0741-1669)
Related titles: Diskette ed.; Microfilm ed.: (from PQC); Online - full text ed.
—BLDSC (3494.060900). **CCC.**
Published by: Elsevier BV (Subsidiary of: Elsevier Science & Technology), Radarweg 29, Amsterdam, 1043 NX, Netherlands. TEL 31-20-4853911, FAX 31-20-4852457, nlinfo-f@elsevier.nl, http://www.elsevier.com/locate/camicrobio, http://www.elsevier.nl.

016.5716 NLD ISSN 0741-1626
Z5322.C3
CURRENT ADVANCES IN CELL & DEVELOPMENTAL BIOLOGY. Text in English. 1984. 12/yr. EUR 2,071 in Europe to institutions; JPY 274,500 in Japan to institutions; USD 2,315 to institutions except Europe and Japan; EUR 141 in Europe to qualified personnel; JPY 19,300 in Japan to qualified personnel; USD 159 to qualified personnel except Europe and Japan (effective 2006). **Document type:** *Abstract/Index.* **Description:** Provides a current awareness service in the sphere of cell and developmental biology. Gives listings of titles of cell and developmental biology papers published throughout the world classified into 76 main areas and provides a comprehensive listing of review articles.
Related titles: Diskette ed.; Microfilm ed.: (from PQC); Online - full text ed.
—BLDSC (3494.062000). **CCC.**
Published by: Elsevier BV (Subsidiary of: Elsevier Science & Technology), Radarweg 29, Amsterdam, 1043 NX, Netherlands. TEL 31-20-4853911, FAX 31-20-4852457, nlinfo-f@elsevier.nl, http://www.elsevier.com/locate/cacell, http://www.elsevier.nl.

016.579 NLD ISSN 0741-1642
Z5322.G4
CURRENT ADVANCES IN GENETICS & MOLECULAR BIOLOGY. Text in English. 1984. 12/yr. EUR 3,080 in Europe to institutions; JPY 408,400 in Japan to institutions; USD 3,448 to institutions except Europe and Japan; EUR 141 in Europe to qualified personnel; JPY 19,300 in Japan to qualified personnel; USD 159 to qualified personnel except Europe and Japan (effective 2006). adv. **Document type:** *Abstract/Index.* **Description:** Provides current awareness service for biologists, ecologists and environmental scientists. Gives listings of titles of ecological papers published throughout the world classified into 61 main areas and provides a comprehensive listing of review articles.
Related titles: Diskette ed.; Microfilm ed.: (from PQC); Online - full text ed.
—BLDSC (3494.064100). **CCC.**
Published by: Elsevier BV (Subsidiary of: Elsevier Science & Technology), Radarweg 29, Amsterdam, 1043 NX, Netherlands. TEL 31-20-4853911, FAX 31-20-4852457, nlinfo-f@elsevier.nl, http://www.elsevier.com/locate/cagene, http://www.elsevier.nl.

016.58 NLD ISSN 0306-4484
Z5353 CODEN: CAPSCJ
CURRENT ADVANCES IN PLANT SCIENCE. Text in English. 1972. 12/yr. EUR 2,614 in Europe to institutions; JPY 346,400 in Japan to institutions; USD 2,923 to institutions except Europe and Japan; EUR 141 in Europe to qualified personnel; JPY 19,300 in Japan to qualified personnel; USD 159 to qualified personnel except Europe and Japan (effective 2006). adv. bk.rev. illus. back issues avail.; reprints avail. **Document type:** *Abstract/Index.* **Description:** Provides current awareness service in the sphere of plant science. Gives listings of titles of plant science papers published throughout the world classified into 48 main areas and provides a comprehensive listing of review articles.
Related titles: Diskette ed.: ISSN 1350-6536; Microfilm ed.: (from PQC); Online - full text ed.
—BLDSC (3494.065000), CISTI, Linda Hall. **CCC.**
Published by: Elsevier BV (Subsidiary of: Elsevier Science & Technology), Radarweg 29, Amsterdam, 1043 NX, Netherlands. TEL 31-20-4853911, FAX 31-20-4852457, nlinfo-f@elsevier.nl, http://www.elsevier.com/locate/caplant, http://www.elsevier.nl. Circ: 1,200.

016.572 NLD ISSN 0965-0504
Z5524.B54
CURRENT ADVANCES IN PROTEIN BIOCHEMISTRY. Text in English. 1984. 12/yr. EUR 1,730 in Europe to institutions; JPY 229,300 in Japan to institutions; USD 1,937 to institutions except Europe and Japan; EUR 141 in Europe to qualified personnel; JPY 19,300 in Japan to qualified personnel; USD 159 to qualified personnel except Europe and Japan (effective 2006). adv. **Document type:** *Abstract/Index.* **Description:** Lists titles of protein biochemistry papers published throughout the world classified into 141 main areas. Also provides a comprehensive listing of review articles.
Formerly (until 1992): Current Advances in Biochemistry (0741-1618)
Related titles: Diskette ed.; Microform ed.: (from PQC); Online - full text ed.
—BLDSC (3494.067000). **CCC.**
Published by: Elsevier BV (Subsidiary of: Elsevier Science & Technology), Radarweg 29, Amsterdam, 1043 NX, Netherlands. TEL 31-20-4853911, FAX 31-20-4852457, nlinfo-f@elsevier.nl, http://www.elsevier.com/locate/caprobio, http://www.elsevier.nl.

016.57 NLD ISSN 0733-4443
QH301
CURRENT AWARENESS IN BIOLOGICAL SCIENCES. (Consists of 12 sections, Current Advances in: Applied Microbiology & Biotechnology; Cancer Research; Cell & Developmental Biology; Clinical Chemistry; Ecological & Environmental Sciences; Endocrinology & Metabolism; Genetics & Molecular Biology; Immunology & Infectious Diseases; Neuroscience; Plant Science; Protein Biochemistry; Toxicology) Text in Dutch. 1954. 144/yr. EUR 10,416 in Europe; JPY 1,380,900 in Japan; USD 11,652 elsewhere (effective 2005); for all 12 sections. adv. back issues avail. **Document type:** *Abstract/Index.* **Description:** Provides comprehensive coverage of recent publications in the entire spectrum of biological sciences, including relevant work in toxicology and the biomedical and environmental sciences.
Formerly (until 1983): International Abstracts of Biological Sciences (0020-5818)
Related titles: Microfilm ed.: (from PQC); Online - full text ed.
—CISTI, GNLM, Linda Hall. **CCC.**
Published by: Elsevier BV (Subsidiary of: Elsevier Science & Technology), Radarweg 29, Amsterdam, 1043 NX, Netherlands. TEL 31-20-4853911, FAX 31-20-4852457, nlinfo-f@elsevier.nl, http://www.elsevier.com/wps/find/bibliographicdatabasedescription.cws_home/600715/description#description, http://www.elsevier.nl. Circ: 1,000.

016.57 KOR
CURRENT BIBLIOGRAPHIES ON SCIENCE AND TECHNOLOGY: BIOLOGY, PHARMACY AND FOOD SCIENCE. Text in Korean. 1962. m. USD 107. reprint service avail. from PQC.
Formerly: Current Index to Journals in Science and Technology: Biology, Agriculture, Pharmacy; Which superseded in part: Current Bibliography on Science and Technology
Published by: Korea Institute for Economics and Technology, 206-9 Cheongryangri-Dong, Dongdaimun-Ku, P.O. Box 205, Seoul, Korea, S. Circ: 300.

016.57 JPN ISSN 0285-5100
CURRENT BIBLIOGRAPHY ON SCIENCE AND TECHNOLOGY: LIFE SCIENCES/KAGAKU GIJUTSU BUNKEN SOKUHO. RAIFUSAIENSU HEN. Text in Japanese. 1981. 3/m. USD 2,500. index. **Document type:** *Bibliography.*
Related titles: CD-ROM ed.; Online - full text ed.: (from JICST).
Published by: Japan Science and Technology Corporation, Information Center for Science and Technology/Kagaku Gijutsu Shinko Jigyodan, 5-3 Yonban-cho, Chiyoda-ku, Tokyo, 102-0081, Japan. TEL 81-3-5214-8413, FAX 81-3-5214-8410. Circ: 600.

016.57 USA ISSN 0960-9822
QH301 CODEN: CUBLE2
➤ **CURRENT BIOLOGY.** Text in English. 1991. 24/yr. EUR 296 in Europe to individuals; JPY 32,400 in Japan to individuals; USD 172 in Canada to individuals; USD 172 in United States to individuals; USD 259 to individuals except Europe and Japan; EUR 1,312 in Europe to institutions; JPY 136,700 in Japan to institutions; USD 1,185 in United States to institutions; USD 1,185 in Canada to institutions; USD 1,143 to institutions except Europe and Japan (effective 2006). adv. illus. back issues avail.; reprints avail. **Document type:** *Journal, Academic/Scholarly.* **Description:** Directed toward researchers, educators and students of biology. Features original research and reviews of the latest developments in the different specializations within the field.
Related titles: Online - full text ed.: USD 159 to individuals (effective 2004) (from EBSCO Publishing, Gale Group, IngentaConnect, O C L C Online Computer Library Center, Inc., ScienceDirect, Swets Information Services).
Indexed: AIDS&CR, ASCA, ASFA, AbHyg, AgBio, AnBeAb, AnBrAb, BBCI, BIOBASE, BIOSIS Prev, BioCN&I, BiolAb, BiolDig, CIN, CPA, CTA, ChemAb, ChemTitl, ChemoAb, CurCont, EntAb, FCA, GenetAb, HGA, HelmAb, HortAb, IABS, ISR, IndMed, IndVet, Inpharma, MEDLINE, MaizeAb, NSA, NSCI, NemAb, NucAcAb, NutrAb, OrnHort, PBA, PGegResA, PGrRegA, PHN&I, PoultAb, ProtozoAb, PsycInfo, PsycholAb, RM&VM, RPP, Reac, RefZh, RevApplEntom, RiceAb, S&F, SCI, SFA, SSCI, SeedAb, TDB, TriticAb, VetBull, WeedAb, WildRev, ZooRec, e-psyche.
—BLDSC (3494.651300), CASDDS, CISTI, GNLM, IDS, IE, Infotrieve, ingenta, Linda Hall. **CCC.**
Published by: Cell Press (Subsidiary of: Elsevier Science & Technology), 1100 Massachusetts Ave, Cambridge, MA 02138. TEL 617-661-7057, FAX 617-661-7061, cbiol@current-biology.com, http://www.elsevier.com/locate/cub, http://www.cellpress.com/. Ed. Geoffrey North. Pub. Lynne Herndon. Adv. contact Sande Giaccone TEL 212-633-3914. B&W page USD 1,050, color page USD 2,405; trim 8.5 x 11. Circ: 2,156 (paid). **Subscr. to:** Elsevier Inc., 6277 Sea Harbor Dr., Orlando, FL 32887-4800. TEL 407-345-4000, FAX 407-363-9661, 800-225-6030.

016.6606 DEU ISSN 0960-5037
TP248.2 CODEN: CUBIER
CURRENT BIOTECHNOLOGY. Text in English. 1983. m. EUR 981 in Europe; EUR 1,472 elsewhere (effective 2005). adv. **Document type:** *Bulletin, Abstract/Index.* **Description:** Reports on the latest scientific, technical and techno-commercial advances in the broad field of biotechnology.
Incorporates (1985-2000): Biotechnology: Apparatus, Plant, and Equipment (0938-5584); Which was formerly (until 1991): Biotechnologie (0178-8108); Formerly (until 1990): Current Biotechnology Abstracts (0264-3391)
Related titles: CD-ROM ed.: (from The Dialog Corporation); Online - full text ed.: (from Data-Star).
Published by: D E C H E M A e.V., Theodor-Heuss-Allee 25, Frankfurt Am Main, 60486, Germany. TEL 49-69-7564345, FAX 49-69-7564418, http://www.dechema.de. **Subscr. to:** Extenza - Turpin, Pegasus Dr, Stratton Business Park, Biggleswade, Beds SG18 8TQ, United Kingdom. TEL 44-1462-672555.

016.57 USA ISSN 0011-3409
Z5321 CODEN: CCLSBC
CURRENT CONTENTS: LIFE SCIENCES. Short title: C C: L S. Text in English. 1958. w. USD 1,015. Index. **Document type:** *Academic/Scholarly.* **Description:** Lists the tables of contents of the world's leading scientific publications in life sciences including biochemistry, biomedical research, experimental medicine, immunology, microbiology, neuroscience, physiology and toxicology.
Formerly: Current Contents, Chemical, Pharmaco-Medical and Life Sciences
Related titles: CD-ROM ed.: (from Thomson I S I); Diskette ed.; Magnetic Tape ed.; Online - full text ed.
Indexed: Inpharma, PE&ON, RASB, Reac.
—BLDSC (3496.170000), CASDDS, GNLM.
Published by: Thomson I S I (Subsidiary of: Thomson Corporation), 3501 Market St., Philadelphia, PA 19104. TEL 215-386-0100, FAX 215-386-2911.

016.5998 USA ISSN 0590-4102
CURRENT PRIMATE REFERENCES. Text in English. 1964. m. USD 89 (effective 2004). adv. **Document type:** *Abstract/Index.* **Description:** Indexes all scholarly publications concerned with nonhuman primates. Includes citations to journal articles, books, book chapters, technical reports, and dissertations.
Published by: Primate Information Center, University of Washington, 1101 Westlake Ave N, Seattle, WA 98109. TEL 206-543-4376, FAX 206-616-1540, pic@u.washington.edu. Ed. Jackie L Pritchard. Circ: 500.

016.57 GBR ISSN 0267-1956
QH320.G7
CURRENT RESEARCH IN BRITAIN. BIOLOGICAL SCIENCES. Text in English. 1980. a. GBP 150. **Document type:** *Abstract/Index.* **Description:** Research guide for those who work in higher education, industry, technology, medicine, science, social sciences, government. Compiles information submitted by over 4,000 departments representing more than 500 institutions.
Formerly (until 1985): Research in British Universities, Polytechnics and Colleges. Vol.2: Biological Sciences (0143-0734)
Related titles: CD-ROM ed.; ♦ Series: Current Research in Britain. Physical Sciences. ISSN 0267-1948; ♦ Current Research in Britain. Social Sciences. ISSN 0267-1964.
Published by: Financial Times Healthcare, Maple House, 149 Tottenham Ct Rd, London, W1P 9LL, United Kingdom. TEL 44-171-896-2066, FAX 44-171-896-2213, lizg@pearson-pro.com. Ed. Mike Bale.

016.5716 GBR ISSN 0268-1625
CYTOSKELETON. Text in English. s-m. GBP 120 for print or e-mail eds. (effective 2001). adv. **Document type:** *Abstract/Index.* **Description:** Current awareness service for researchers. Covers tubulin, microtubules, microfilaments, neurofilaments, cell motility, cilia and flagella.
Formerly: Microfilaments and Microtubules (0142-8209)
Related titles: E-mail ed.; Online - full text ed.: GBP 108 (effective 2001).
—**CCC.**
Published by: S U B I S (Subsidiary of: Sheffield Academic Press Ltd), Mansion House, 19 Kingfield Rd, Sheffield, S Yorks S11 9AS, United Kingdom. TEL 44-114-255-4433, FAX 44-114-255-4626, subis@sheffac.demon.co.uk, http://www.shef-ac-press.co.uk/subis. Ed. S Huntridge. Adv. contact C Evans.

016.57286 GBR ISSN 0266-6308
D N A PROBES. (Deoxyribonucleic Acid) Text in English. 1985. s-m. GBP 120 for print or e-mail eds. (effective 2001). adv. **Document type:** *Abstract/Index.* **Description:** Covers probes for all organisms: RFLPs, DNA fingerprinting, and polymerase chain reaction.
Related titles: E-mail ed.; Online - full text ed.: GBP 108 (effective 2001).
—CCC.
Published by: S U B I S (Subsidiary of: Sheffield Academic Press Ltd), Mansion House, 19 Kingfield Rd, Sheffield, S Yorks S11 9AS, United Kingdom. TEL 44-114-255-4433, FAX 44-114-255-4626, subis@sheffac.demon.co.uk, http://www.shef-ac-press.co.uk/subis. Ed. S Huntridge. Adv. contact C Evans.

016.6606 GBR ISSN 0262-5318
TP248.13
DERWENT BIOTECHNOLOGY ABSTRACTS. Text in English. 1982. fortn. USD 2,142. **Document type:** *Abstract/Index.* **Description:** Covers a broad range of technical aspects of biotechnology, from genetic manipulation and biochemical engineering to fermentation and downstream processing.
Related titles: CD-ROM ed.: ISSN 1358-6009 (from National Information Services Corp. (N I S C)); Online - full text ed.: (from National Information Services Corp. (N I S C), Questel Orbit Inc.).
Published by: Derwent Information (Subsidiary of: Thomson Corporation), 14 Great Queen St., London, WC2B 5DF, United Kingdom. TEL 44-20-73442800, FAX 44-20-73442900, custserv@derwent.co.uk, http://scientific.thomson.com/support/products/biotechnology/, http://www.derwent.com. **US subscr. to:** Derwent Information, 1725 Duke St, Ste 250, Alexandria, VA 22314. TEL 703-706-4220.

016.577 GBR ISSN 0305-196X
QH540 CODEN: ECABFY
ECOLOGICAL ABSTRACTS. Text in English. 1974. 12/yr. EUR 2,593 in Europe to institutions; JPY 343,800 in Japan to institutions; USD 2,903 elsewhere to institutions (effective 2006). index. back issues avail. **Document type:** *Abstract/Index.* **Description:** International abstracting service for ecologists and biologists.
Related titles: Microform ed.: (from PQC); Online - full content ed.: GEOBASE (from The Dialog Corporation).
—BLDSC (3648.850000), Linda Hall. **CCC.**
Published by: Elsevier - Geo Abstracts (Subsidiary of: Elsevier Science & Technology), Duke St., 34, Norwich, NR3 3AP, United Kingdom. TEL 44-1603-626327, FAX 44-1603-667934, geoabs@elsevier.co.uk, http://www.elsevier.com/locate/ecolabs. Circ: 600. **Subscr. to:** Elsevier BV, PO Box 211, Amsterdam 1000 AE, Netherlands. TEL 31-20-485-3757, FAX 31-20-485-3432, http://www.elsevier.nl.

016.58 USA
ECOLOGY ABSTRACTS (MOSCOW). Variant title: Ecology & Plant Science. Text in English. 1945. q. USD 100 to individuals; USD 175 to libraries; USD 325 universities; USD 475 region; USD 80 to students (effective 2005). **Document type:** *Abstract/Index.* **Description:** Contains 14200 + records including all citations and abstracts from Ecology (1945-2001), Ecological Applications (1991-2001), Ecological Monographs (1945-2001), Conservation Ecology (1997-1999), Journal of Vegetation Science (1990-2001), and Applied Vegetation Science (1998-2001).
Formerly: ABSEARCH Ecology & Plant Science
Media: Online - full content. **Related titles:** CD-ROM ed.: USD 149 to individuals; USD 250 to libraries; USD 450 universities; USD 650 region; USD 129 to students (effective 2002).
Published by: ABSEARCH, Inc., 1204 Thatuna Ave, Moscow, ID 83843. TEL 208-883-5544, 800-867-1877, FAX 208-883-5554, custinfo@absearch.com, sales@absearch.com, http://www.absearch.com.

016.57155 GBR ISSN 0957-3518
ENDOTHELIUM. Text in English. 1990. s-m. GBP 120 for print ed. or e-mail (effective 2001). adv. **Document type:** *Abstract/Index.* **Description:** Current awareness service for researchers. Covers all aspects of endothelial structure and function, including endothelins and EDRF.
Related titles: E-mail ed.; Online - full text ed.: GBP 108 (effective 2001).
Published by: S U B I S (Subsidiary of: Sheffield Academic Press Ltd), Mansion House, 19 Kingfield Rd, Sheffield, S Yorks S11 9AS, United Kingdom. TEL 44-114-255-4433, FAX 44-114-255-4626, subis@sheffac.demon.co.uk, http://www.shef-ac-press.co.uk/subis. Ed. S Huntridge. Adv. contact C Evans.

016.5957 USA ISSN 0013-8924
QL461
ENTOMOLOGY ABSTRACTS. Text in English. 1969. m. (except Dec.). USD 1,730 combined subscription print & online eds. (effective 2006). a. index on CD-ROM. back issues avail. **Document type:** *Abstract/Index.* **Description:** Covers insects, arachnids, myriapods, onychophorans, and terrestrial isopods.
Related titles: CD-ROM ed.; Online - full text ed.: ISSN 1555-6581. USD 1,295 (effective 2006) (from National Information Services Corp. (N I S C)).
Published by: C S A Journal Division (Subsidiary of: Cambridge Information Group), 7200 Wisconsin Ave, Ste 715, Bethesda, MD 20814. TEL 301-961-6798, 800-843-7751, FAX 301-961-6799, journals@csa.com, http://www.csa.com/factsheets/entomology-set-c.php. Ed. Robert Hilton. Pub. Ted Caris.

016.572 576.5 USA ISSN 1078-7712
QP625.N89
ENTREZ DOCUMENT RETRIEVAL SYSTEM. Text in English. bi-m. **Document type:** *Abstract/Index, Government.* **Description:** Cites and abstracts papers with molecular sequence data from MEDLINE, as well as nucleotide sequences from GenBank, EMBL, DDBJ, and dbEST and protein sequences from PIR, Swiss-Prot, PDB, and PRF. DNA, protein, and bibliographic records are linked.
Formed by the merger of (1992-1995): Entrez: Sequences (1065-707X); (1992-1995): Entrez: References (1072-3072); Incorporates (in 1995): N C B I - Sequences (1080-7438)
Media: Online - full text.
Published by: U.S. National Center for Biotechnology Information, National Library of Medicine, Bldg 38A, Rm 8N 803, 8600 Rockville Pike, Bethesda, MD 20894. TEL 301-496-2475, FAX 301-480-9241, info@ncbi.nlm.nih.gov, http://www.ncbi.nlm.nih.gov.

016.577 USA
ENVIROFICHE. Text in English. m. USD 14,730 domestic; USD 16,200 foreign (effective 2005). back issues avail. **Document type:** *Abstract/Index.* **Description:** Full text of the vast majority of abstracted articles and proceedings in Environment Abstracts. Items on microfiche are linked to the print and electronic services through the unique accession number.
Media: Microfiche.
Published by: Congressional Information Service, Inc. (Subsidiary of: LexisNexis), 7500 Old Georgetown Rd, Bethesda, MD 20814-6126. TEL 301-654-1550, 800-638-8380, FAX 301-657-3203, academicinfo@lexisnexis.com, http://www.lexisnexis.com/academic/3cis/cisMnu.asp. Ed. Larry Sheridan. R&P Tim Fusco.

016.57965 NLD ISSN 0921-822X
EXCERPTA MEDICA. ABSTRACT JOURNALS. (Consists of 41 Sections) Text in English. 1947. 774/yr. EUR 58,886 in Europe to institutions; JPY 7,936,500 in Japan to institutions; USD 65,873 elsewhere to institutions (effective 2006). illus. index, cum.index. back issues avail.; reprints avail. **Document type:** *Journal, Abstract/Index.* **Description:** Contains forty-one printed current awareness journals, each devoted to a specific biomedical topic or discipline covering the entire range of basic and clinical aspects. Every journal contains bibliographic references and abstracts summarizing original articles from primary research and clinical journals.
Related titles: CD-ROM ed.: EMBASE C D (from SilverPlatter Information, Inc.); ♦ Online - full content ed.: EMBASE. ISSN 0929-3302.
—Linda Hall.
Published by: Excerpta Medica Medical Communications BV (Subsidiary of: Elsevier Health Sciences), Rooseveltweg 15, Almere, 1314 SJ, Netherlands. TEL 31-36-5385600, FAX 31-36-5385650, http://www.elsevier.com/locate/emset, http://www.excerptamedica.com. **Subscr. to:** Elsevier BV, PO Box 211, Amsterdam 1000 AE, Netherlands. TEL 31-20-485-3757, FAX 31-20-485-3432, nlinfo-f@elsevier.nl, http://www.elsevier.nl.

016.61 NLD ISSN 0014-4053
CODEN: AAEHA9
EXCERPTA MEDICA. SECTION 1: ANATOMY, ANTHROPOLOGY, EMBRYOLOGY & HISTOLOGY. Text in English. 1947. 12/yr. EUR 2,231 in Europe to institutions; JPY 295,800 in Japan to institutions; USD 2,497 elsewhere to institutions (effective 2006). adv. cum.index. **Document type:** *Journal, Abstract/Index.* **Description:** Provides a comprehensive current-awareness service for academic and trade articles in the fields of anatomy, anthropology, embryology, and histology.
Related titles: CD-ROM ed.: (from SilverPlatter Information, Inc.); Online - full text ed.: (from Data-Star, DIMDI, JICST, The Dialog Corporation).
—GNLM. **CCC.**
Published by: Excerpta Medica Medical Communications BV (Subsidiary of: Elsevier Health Sciences), Rooseveltweg 15, Almere, 1314 SJ, Netherlands. TEL 31-36-5385600, FAX 31-36-5385650, http://www.elsevier.com/locate/anatomy. **Subscr. to:** Elsevier BV, PO Box 211, Amsterdam 1000 AE, Netherlands. TEL 31-20-485-3757, FAX 31-20-485-3432, nlinfo-f@elsevier.nl, http://www.elsevier.nl.

EXCERPTA MEDICA. SECTION 2: PHYSIOLOGY. see *MEDICAL SCIENCES—Abstracting, Bibliographies, Statistics*

016.612 NLD ISSN 0014-4258
CODEN: DBITA
EXCERPTA MEDICA. SECTION 21: DEVELOPMENTAL BIOLOGY AND TERATOLOGY. Text in English. 1961. 12/yr. EUR 2,708 in Europe to institutions; JPY 359,200 in Japan to institutions; USD 3,031 elsewhere to institutions (effective 2006). adv. index, cum.index. back issues avail. **Document type:** *Abstract/Index.* **Description:** Provides a comprehensive current-awareness service of trade and academic articles covering both the experimental and clinical aspects of embryology and fetal, neonatal development.
Related titles: CD-ROM ed.: (from SilverPlatter Information, Inc.); Online - full text ed.: (from Data-Star, DIMDI, JICST, The Dialog Corporation).
—GNLM, Linda Hall. **CCC.**
Published by: Excerpta Medica Medical Communications BV (Subsidiary of: Elsevier Health Sciences), Rooseveltweg 15, Almere, 1314 SJ, Netherlands. TEL 31-36-5385600, FAX 31-36-5385650, info@excerptamedica.com, http://www.elsevier.com/locate/devbioter, http://www.excerptamedica.com. **Subscr. to:** Elsevier BV, PO Box 211, Amsterdam 1000 AE, Netherlands. TEL 31-20-485-3757, FAX 31-20-485-3432, nlinfo-f@elsevier.nl, http://www.elsevier.nl.

016.5999 NLD ISSN 0014-4266
QH431 CODEN: HUGEA
EXCERPTA MEDICA. SECTION 22: HUMAN GENETICS. Text in English. 1963. 24/yr. EUR 4,397 in Europe to institutions; JPY 582,900 in Japan to institutions; USD 4,919 elsewhere to institutions; EUR 396 in Europe to qualified personnel; JPY 53,600 in Japan to qualified personnel; USD 442 elsewhere to qualified personnel (effective 2006). adv. index, cum.index. **Document type:** *Journal, Abstract/Index.* **Description:** Provides a comprehensive current-awareness service of trade and academic articles covering both the clinical and experimental aspects of human genetics; includes genetics of lower animals when potentially relevant to human medicine; congenital defects and malformations; basic genetics such as DNA synthesis, gene structure and regulation, genetics recombination and mutagenesis.
Related titles: CD-ROM ed.: (from SilverPlatter Information, Inc.); Online - full text ed.: (from Data-Star, DIMDI, JICST, The Dialog Corporation).
—GNLM, Linda Hall. **CCC.**
Published by: Excerpta Medica Medical Communications BV (Subsidiary of: Elsevier Health Sciences), Rooseveltweg 15, Almere, 1314 SJ, Netherlands. TEL 31-36-5385600, FAX 31-36-5385650, http://www.elsevier.com/locate/humgene, http://www.excerptamedica.com. **Subscr. to:** Elsevier BV, PO Box 211, Amsterdam 1000 AE, Netherlands. TEL 31-20-485-3757, FAX 31-20-485-3432, nlinfo-f@elsevier.nl, http://www.elsevier.nl.

016.57145 NLD ISSN 0014-4312
CODEN: BBMIA
EXCERPTA MEDICA. SECTION 27: BIOPHYSICS, BIO-ENGINEERING AND MEDICAL INSTRUMENTATION. Text in English. 1967. 16/yr. EUR 3,036 in Europe to institutions; JPY 402,500 in Japan to institutions; USD 3,396 elsewhere to institutions (effective 2006). adv. index, cum.index. **Document type:** *Journal, Abstract/Index.* **Description:** Provides a comprehensive current-awareness service for articles that cover the application of biophysical principles to the development of instrumentation, the use of automation in biomedicine, biomechanics, and bioengineering.
Related titles: CD-ROM ed.: (from SilverPlatter Information, Inc.); Online - full text ed.: (from Data-Star, DIMDI, JICST, The Dialog Corporation).
—GNLM, Linda Hall. **CCC.**
Published by: Excerpta Medica Medical Communications BV (Subsidiary of: Elsevier Health Sciences), Rooseveltweg 15, Almere, 1314 SJ, Netherlands. TEL 31-36-5385600, FAX 31-36-5385650, http://www.elsevier.com/locate/biomedinstr, http://www.excerptamedica.com. **Subscr. to:** Elsevier BV, PO Box 211, Amsterdam 1000 AE, Netherlands. TEL 31-20-485-3757, FAX 31-20-485-3432, nlinfo-f@elsevier.nl, http://www.elsevier.nl.

016.572 NLD ISSN 0927-278X
EXCERPTA MEDICA. SECTION 29: CLINICAL AND EXPERIMENTAL BIOCHEMISTRY. Text in English. 1948. 40/yr. EUR 5,321 in Europe to institutions; JPY 705,300 in Japan to institutions; USD 5,954 elsewhere to institutions (effective 2006). adv. bk.rev. charts. index, cum.index. **Document type:** *Journal, Abstract/Index.* **Description:** Provides a current-awareness service for articles covering both clinical chemistry and general biochemistry and includes analytical methods, chemical function tests, enzyme assay, enzyme mode of action studies, and biochemical roles in disease,.
Former titles (until 1992): Excerpta Medica. Section 29. Clinical Biochemistry (0300-5372); Excerpta Medica. Section 29: Biochemistry (0014-4339); Which supersedes in part (in 1964): Excerpta Medica. Section 2: Physiology, Biochemistry and Pharmacology (0014-4061)
Related titles: CD-ROM ed.: (from SilverPlatter Information, Inc.); Online - full text ed.: (from Data-Star, DIMDI, JICST, The Dialog Corporation).
—GNLM, Linda Hall. **CCC.**

B

▼ *new title* ➤ *refereed* ✶ *unverified* ♦ *full entry avail.*

Published by: Excerpta Medica Medical Communications BV (Subsidiary of: Elsevier Health Sciences), Rooseveltweg 15, Almere, 1314 SJ, Netherlands. TEL 31-36-5385600, FAX 31-36-5385650, http://www.elsevier.com/locate/clinexpbio. **Subscr. to:** Elsevier BV, PO Box 211, Amsterdam 1000 AE, Netherlands. TEL 31-20-485-3757, FAX 31-20-485-3432, nlinfo-f@elsevier.nl, http://www.elsevier.nl.

016.579 NLD ISSN 0927-2771

EXCERPTA MEDICA. SECTION 4: MICROBIOLOGY: BACTERIOLOGY, MYCOLOGY, PARASITOLOGY AND VIROLOGY. Text in English. 1948. 40/yr. EUR 6,766 in Europe to institutions; JPY 896,900 in Japan to institutions; USD 7,568 elsewhere to institutions (effective 2006). adv. index, cum.index. back issues avail. **Document type:** *Abstract/Index.* **Description:** Covers general aspects of infectious diseases, diagnosis, treatment, epidemiology and prevention of diseases. Includes bacteriology, parasitology, mycology, algae and sexually transmitted diseases.

Incorporates (1971-1991): Excerpta Medica. Section 47: Virology (0031-6520); Former titles (until 1992): Excerpta Medica. Section 4: Microbiology (0167-4285); Excerpta Medica. Section 4: Microbiology: Bacteriology, Mycology and Parasitology (0376-6314)

Related titles: CD-ROM ed.: (from SilverPlatter Information, Inc.); Online - full text ed.: (from Data-Star, DIMDI, JICST, The Dialog Corporation).

—GNLM. **CCC.**

Published by: Excerpta Medica Medical Communications BV (Subsidiary of: Elsevier Health Sciences), Rooseveltweg 15, Almere, 1314 SJ, Netherlands. TEL 31-36-5385600, FAX 31-36-5385650, http://www.elsevier.com/locate/mbmpv, http://www.excerptamedica.com. **Subscr. to:** Elsevier BV, PO Box 211, Amsterdam 1000 AE, Netherlands. TEL 31-20-485-3757, FAX 31-20-485-3432, nlinfo-f@elsevier.nl, http://www.elsevier.nl.

016.5719 NLD ISSN 0014-4096
RB1 CODEN: GPPABB

EXCERPTA MEDICA. SECTION 5: GENERAL PATHOLOGY AND PATHOLOGICAL ANATOMY. Text in English. 1948. 30/yr. EUR 5,176 in Europe to institutions; JPY 686,300 in Japan to institutions; USD 5,791 elsewhere to institutions (effective 2006). adv. index, cum.index. back issues avail. **Document type:** *Journal, Abstract/Index.* **Description:** Provides users with a current-awareness service of clinical and experimental articles in general pathology.

Related titles: CD-ROM ed.: (from SilverPlatter Information, Inc.); Online - full text ed.: (from Data-Star, DIMDI, JICST, The Dialog Corporation).

—GNLM. **CCC.**

Published by: Excerpta Medica Medical Communications BV (Subsidiary of: Elsevier Health Sciences), Rooseveltweg 15, Almere, 1314 SJ, Netherlands. TEL 31-36-5385600, FAX 31-36-5385650, http://www.elsevier.com/locate/genpathana, http://www.excerptamedica.com. **Subscr. to:** Elsevier BV, PO Box 211, Amsterdam 1000 AE, Netherlands. TEL 31-20-485-3757, FAX 31-20-485-3432, nlinfo-f@elsevier.nl, http://www.elsevier.nl.

016.57 016.61 GBR

EXPRESS BULLETINS; a series of current awareness bulletins for researchers in biology and medicine. Text in English. 1967. s-m. GBP 100 (effective 1999); per title online; diskette price varies. **Document type:** *Abstract/Index.*

Media: Diskette. **Related titles:** Online - full text ed.

Published by: S U B I S (Subsidiary of: Sheffield Academic Press Ltd), Mansion House, 19 Kingfield Rd, Sheffield, S Yorks S11 9AS, United Kingdom. TEL 44-114-255-4433, FAX 44-114-255-4626, subis@sheffac.demon.co.uk.

016.57 DEU

FACHBUCHVERZEICHNIS NATURWISSENSCHAFTEN. Text in German. a. **Document type:** *Bibliography.* **Description:** Bibliography of available books in the natural sciences for students.

Formerly: Buecher fuer das Studium - Naturwissenschaften

Published by: Rossipaul Kommunikation GmbH, Menzinger Str 37, Munich, 80638, Germany. TEL 49-89-179106-0, FAX 49-89-17910622. Ed. Angela Sendlinger. Circ: 25,000.

016.597 USA ISSN 1069-9309
SH1

FISH & FISHERIES WORLDWIDE. Text in English. q. ZAR 7,450. **Document type:** *Abstract/Index.* **Description:** Provides a bibliographic index to literature (scientific to popular magazine articles) on all aspects of aquaculture, fisheries, and ichthyology, including management and research.

Supersedes in part: Wildlife and Fish Worldwide (1046-6479)

Media: CD-ROM (from National Information Services Corp. (N I S C)). **Related titles:** Online - full text ed.: (from National Information Services Corp. (N I S C)).

Published by: National Information Services Corp. (N I S C), Ste 6, Wyman Towers, 3100 St Paul St, Baltimore, MD 21218. TEL 410-243-0797, FAX 410-243-0982, sales@nisc.com, http://www.nisc.com.

016.58 CHL ISSN 0016-5301
QK1 CODEN: GBCBAK

GAYANA: BOTANICA. Text in English, Spanish. 1961. a. USD 12 domestic; USD 23.60 foreign (effective 2000). adv. **Document type:** *Academic/Scholarly.* **Description:** Publishes recent advances in all areas of botany, with an emphasis on southern hemisphere temperate ecosystems.

Related titles: Online - full text ed.: ISSN 0717-6643. 2000. free (effective 2005) (from SciELO).

Indexed: ASFA, BIOSIS Prev, BiolAb, ESPM.

Published by: Universidad de Concepcion, Facultad de Ciencias Naturales y Oceanograficas, Casilla 160-C, Concepcion, Chile. TEL 56-41-203059, FAX 56-41-244805, gayana@udec.cl, http://www.udec.cl/~natul/botanica/gayana/gayana.html. Ed. Roberto Rodriguez. Pub., R&P Andres O Angulo. Adv. contact Alberto P Larrain. B&W page USD 20, color page USD 35. Circ: 1,000.

016.5765 GBR ISSN 1356-1308

GENE THERAPY (SHEFFIELD). Text in English. 1995. s-m. GBP 120 for print ed. or e-mail (effective 2001). adv. **Document type:** *Abstract/Index.* **Description:** Current awareness service for researchers in clinical and life sciences.

Related titles: E-mail ed.; Online - full text ed.: GBP 108 (effective 2001).

Indexed: Inpharma, PE&ON, Reac.

Published by: S U B I S (Subsidiary of: Sheffield Academic Press Ltd), Mansion House, 19 Kingfield Rd, Sheffield, S Yorks S11 9AS, United Kingdom. TEL 44-114-255-4433, FAX 44-114-255-4626, subis@sheffac.demon.co.uk, http://www.shef-ac-press.co.uk/subis. Ed. S Huntridge. Adv. contact C Evans.

016.5765 USA ISSN 0016-674X
QH431

GENETICS ABSTRACTS. Text in English. 1968. m. (except Dec.). USD 1,785 combined subscription print & online eds. (effective 2006). bk.rev. abstr. a. index on CD-ROM. back issues avail. **Document type:** *Abstract/Index.* **Description:** Covers all aspects of genetics in humans, animals, and plants, with emphasis on molecular genetics.

Related titles: CD-ROM ed.; Online - full text ed.: ISSN 1555-6603. USD 1,330 (effective 2006).

—BLDSC (4115.050000).

Published by: C S A Journal Division (Subsidiary of: Cambridge Information Group), 7200 Wisconsin Ave, Ste 715, Bethesda, MD 20814. TEL 301-961-6798, 800-843-7751, FAX 301-961-6799, journals@csa.com, http://www.csa.com/factsheets/genetics-set-c.php. Ed. Jennifer A Phillips. Pub. Ted Caris.

016.5765 JPN

➤ **GENETICS SOCIETY OF JAPAN. ABSTRACTS OF THE ANNUAL MEETING/NIHON IDEN GAKKAI TAIKAI PUROGURAMU YOKOSHU.** Text in English. a. membership. bk.rev. **Document type:** *Abstract/Index.*

Published by: Genetics Society of Japan/Nihon Iden Gakkai, Yata 1111, National Institute of Genetics, Mishima, Shizuoka 411-8540, Japan. japgenet@lab.nig.ac.jp, http://wwwsoc.nii.ac.jp/gsj3/index.html. Ed., R&P Hideo Shinagawa.

016.572566 GBR ISSN 1356-1316

GLYCOBIOLOGY RESEARCH. Text in English. 1995. s-m. GBP 120 for print ed. or e-mail (effective 2001). adv. **Document type:** *Abstract/Index.* **Description:** Current awareness service for researchers in clinical and life sciences.

Related titles: E-mail ed.; Online - full text ed.: GBP 108 (effective 2001).

Published by: S U B I S (Subsidiary of: Sheffield Academic Press Ltd), Mansion House, 19 Kingfield Rd, Sheffield, S Yorks S11 9AS, United Kingdom. TEL 44-114-255-4433, FAX 44-114-255-4626, subis@sheffac.demon.co.uk, http://www.shef-ac-press.co.uk/subis. Ed. S Huntridge. Adv. contact C Evans.

016.57 GBR ISSN 1351-5284

HELICOBACTER. Text in English. 1994. s-m. GBP 96 for print or email ed. (effective 2001). adv. **Document type:** *Abstract/Index.* **Description:** Current awareness service for researchers in clinical and life sciences.

Related titles: E-mail ed.; Online - full text ed.: GBP 108 to individuals (effective 2001).

Indexed: Inpharma, PE&ON, Reac.

Published by: S U B I S (Subsidiary of: Sheffield Academic Press Ltd), Mansion House, 19 Kingfield Rd, Sheffield, S Yorks S11 9AS, United Kingdom. TEL 44-114-255-4433, FAX 44-114-255-4626, subis@sheffac.demon.co.uk, http://www.shef-ac-press.co.uk/subis. Ed. S Huntridge. Adv. contact C Evans.

016.5923 GBR ISSN 0957-6789
QL392.A1 CODEN: HEABEC

HELMINTHOLOGICAL ABSTRACTS. Text in English. 1932. bi-m. USD 1,455 in the Americas to institutions except Canada; GBP 830 elsewhere to institutions; USD 1,560 combined subscription in the Americas to institutions except Canada; print & online eds.; GBP 890 combined subscription elsewhere to institutions print & online eds. (effective 2006). adv. bk.rev. abstr. index, cum.index. back issues avail.; reprints avail. **Document type:** *Abstract/Index.* **Description:** Covers the literature on parasitic helminths: gastrointestinal nematodes, liver flukes, hydatid, trichinella, schistosomes, filariids, and taenia. Aspects covered include morphology, taxonomy, immunology, pathology, biochemistry, epidemiology, life history, control, and molecular biology.

Formerly (until 1989): Helminthological Abstracts. Series A: Animal and Human Helminthology (0300-8339); Which superseded in part (in 1970): Helminthological Abstracts (0018-0122)

Related titles: Online - full text ed.: USD 1,235 in the Americas to institutions; GBP 705 elsewhere to institutions (effective 2006) (from DIMDI, The Dialog Corporation).

Indexed: IndVet.

—CISTI, GNLM, Linda Hall. **CCC.**

Published by: CABI Publishing (Subsidiary of: CAB International), CAB International, Wallingford, Oxfordshire OX10 8DE, United Kingdom. TEL 44-1491-832111, FAX 44-1491-833508, cabi@cabi.org, http://www.cabi-publishing.org/. Adv. contact Sarah Harris TEL 44-1491-829310. B&W page GBP 150, B&W page USD 240; 170 x 267. **Subscr. addr. in N America:** CABI Publishing North America, 875 Massachusetts Ave, 7th Fl, Cambridge, MA 02139. TEL 617-395-4056, 800-528-4841, FAX 617-354-6875, cabi-nao@cabi.org.

016.5737 GBR ISSN 1355-4786
Z6663.R4 CODEN: HRUPF8

➤ **HUMAN REPRODUCTION UPDATE.** Text in English. 1963. bi-m. GBP 546, USD 1,000, EUR 819 to institutions; GBP 575, USD 1,053, EUR 863 combined subscription to institutions print & online eds. (effective 2006). adv. bibl. s-a. index. back issues avail.; reprint service avail. from PSC. **Document type:** *Journal, Academic/Scholarly.* **Description:** Comprehensive review service of research within the field of human reproduction.

Formed by the 1995 merger of: Oxford Review of Reproductive Biology (0955-8713); Bibliography of Reproduction (0006-1565)

Related titles: Online - full text ed.: ISSN 1460-2369. 1997. GBP 518, USD 948, EUR 777 to institutions (effective 2006) (from EBSCO Publishing, Gale Group, HighWire Press, IngentaConnect, O C L C Online Computer Library Center, Inc., Ovid Technologies, Inc., Oxford University Press Online Journals, ProQuest Information & Learning, Swets Information Services).

Indexed: AbHyg, AgBio, AnBrAb, BIOSIS Prev, BiolAb, CTA, CurCont, DSA, ExcerpMed, ISR, IndMed, IndVet, Inpharma, MEDLINE, NutrAb, PE&ON, PN&I, Reac, SCI, VetBull.

—BLDSC (4336.431500), CASDDS, CISTI, GNLM, IDS, IE, Infotrieve, ingenta, Linda Hall. **CCC.**

Published by: (European Society of Human Reproduction and Embryology BEL), Oxford University Press, Great Clarendon St, Oxford, OX2 6DP, United Kingdom. TEL 44-1865-556767, FAX 44-1865-556646, editorial@humanreproduction.co.uk, jnl.orders@oup.co.uk, enquiry@oup.co.uk, http://humupd.oxfordjournals.org, http://www.oxfordjournals.org/. Ed. B. C.J.M. Fauser. Pub. Janet Boulin. R&P Fiona Bennett. adv.: B&W page GBP 315, B&W page USD 595, color page GBP 535, color page USD 1,015; trim 216 x 280. Circ: 750.

016.598 USA

IBIS - WILDFOWL ABSTRACTS. Text in English. 1949. q. USD 100 to individuals; USD 175 to libraries; USD 325 universities; USD 475 region; USD 80 to students (effective 2005). **Document type:** *Abstract/Index.* **Description:** Contains 6300 + records including citations and abstracts from the journals Ibis (1955-2001) and Wildfowl (1945-2001). Also includes records from the Wildfowl Trust Report (1949-1967).

Media: Online - full content. **Related titles:** CD-ROM ed.: USD 149 to individuals; USD 250 to libraries; USD 450 universities; USD 650 region; USD 129 to students (effective 2002).

Published by: ABSEARCH, Inc., 1204 Thatuna Ave, Moscow, ID 83843. TEL 208-883-5544, 800-867-1877, FAX 208-883-5554, custinfo@absearch.com, sales@absearch.com, http://www.absearch.com.

016.5715 GBR ISSN 0142-8136

IMMUNOHISTOCHEMISTRY. Text in English. 1970. s-m. GBP 120 for print ed. or e-mail (effective 2001). adv. **Document type:** *Abstract/Index.* **Description:** Current awareness service for researchers. Covers immunocytochemistry, immunohistology and immuno-electron microscopy.

Formerly (until 1973): Ferritin

Related titles: E-mail ed.; Online - full text ed.: USD 108 (effective 2001).

—**CCC.**

Published by: S U B I S (Subsidiary of: Sheffield Academic Press Ltd), Mansion House, 19 Kingfield Rd, Sheffield, S Yorks S11 9AS, United Kingdom. TEL 44-114-255-4433, FAX 44-114-255-4626, subis@sheffac.demon.co.uk, http://www.shef-ac-press.co.uk/subis. Ed. S Huntridge. Adv. contact C Evans.

B

016.5795 GBR ISSN 0019-3895
SB599
INDEX OF FUNGI. Text in English. 1940. a. USD 375 per issue in the Americas to institutions except Canada; GBP 215 per issue elsewhere to institutions (effective 2006). cum.index every 10 yrs. back issues avail. **Document type:** *Abstract/Index.* **Description:** Listing of new and revised names of fungi, including slime and water moulds, lichens and yeasts, at all ranks from family to form, with host-substratum and epithet indexes.
Related titles: Online - full text ed.: GBP 850, USD 1,495 (effective 1999) (from DIMDI, The Dialog Corporation).
Indexed: RPP.
—CISTI, Linda Hall. **CCC.**
Published by: CABI Publishing (Subsidiary of: CAB International), CAB International, Wallingford, Oxfordshire OX10 8DE, United Kingdom. TEL 44-1491-832111, FAX 44-1491-833508, cabi@cabi.org, http://www.cabi-publishing.org/. Ed. Dr. John David TEL 44-1784-470111.

016.58 NLD ISSN 0073-6007
Z5354.C52
INDEX TO PLANT CHROMOSOME NUMBERS. Text in Dutch. 1956. irreg. price varies.
Related titles: ♦ Series of: Regnum Vegetabile. ISSN 0080-0694.
—CISTI.
Published by: (International Association for Plant Taxonomy), Bohn Stafleu van Loghum B.V. (Subsidiary of: Wolters Kluwer N.V.), Postbus 246, Houten, 3990 GA, Netherlands. boekhandels@bsl.nl, http://www.bsl.nl. Ed. R J Moore. Circ: 1,000.

INDONESIAN BIOLOGICAL AND AGRICULTURAL INDEX/INDEKS BIOLOGI DAN PERTANIAN DE INDONESIA. see *AGRICULTURE—Abstracting, Bibliographies, Statistics*

016.5714 USA
INTERNATIONAL BIOPHYSICS CONGRESS. ABSTRACTS. Text in English. 1961. irreg. USD 10. **Document type:** *Proceedings.*
Published by: Massachusetts Institute of Technology, International Biophysics Congress, 77 Massachusetts Ave, Cambridge, MA 02139. Ed. Walter Rosenelith.

016.5738 016.6168 GBR ISSN 0261-4952
INVERTEBRATE NEUROBIOLOGY. Text in English. 1982. s-m. GBP 120 for print ed. or e-mail (effective 2001). adv. **Document type:** *Abstract/Index.* **Description:** Current awareness service for researchers. Examines invertebrate neuroscience: development, structure, physiology, biochemistry, peptides and transmitters.
Related titles: E-mail ed.; Online - full text ed.: GBP 108 (effective 2001).
—CCC.
Published by: S U B I S (Subsidiary of: Sheffield Academic Press Ltd), Mansion House, 19 Kingfield Rd, Sheffield, S Yorks S11 9AS, United Kingdom. TEL 44-114-255-4433, FAX 44-114-255-4626, subis@sheffac.demon.co.uk, http://www.shef-ac-press.co.uk/subis. Ed. S Huntridge. Adv. contact C Evans.

016.5724 GBR ISSN 0142-8152
IRON METABOLISM. Text in English. 1992. s-m. looseleaf. GBP 96 for print ed. or e-mail (effective 2001). adv. back issues avail. **Document type:** *Abstract/Index.* **Description:** Current awareness service for researchers in clinical and life sciences.
Related titles: E-mail ed.; Online - full text ed.: GBP 108 to individuals (effective 2001).
—CCC.
Published by: S U B I S (Subsidiary of: Sheffield Academic Press Ltd), Mansion House, 19 Kingfield Rd, Sheffield, S Yorks S11 9AS, United Kingdom. TEL 44-114-255-4433, FAX 44-114-255-4626, subis@sheffac.demon.co.uk, http://www.shef-ac-press.co.uk/subis. Ed. S Huntridge. Adv. contact C Evans.

580 USA ISSN 1085-7117
S566.55
➤ **JOURNAL OF AGRICULTURAL, BIOLOGICAL, AND ENVIRONMENTAL STATISTICS.** Text in English. 1996. q. USD 48 combined subscription to members print & online eds; USD 86 combined subscription to non-members print & online eds; USD 225 combined subscription to institutions print & online eds; USD 150 to institutions (effective 2005). adv. abstr.; bibl.; charts; illus. back issues avail. **Document type:** *Journal, Academic/Scholarly.* **Description:** Explores statistical methods for persons working with real biological data in today's world.
Related titles: Online - full text ed.: ISSN 1537-2693 (from EBSCO Publishing, Gale Group, IngentaConnect, JSTOR (Web-based Journal Archive)).
Indexed: AEA, ASFA, Agr, AgrForAb, AnBrAb, B&BAb, BIOSIS Prev, BioEngAb, BiolAb, CIS, CMCI, CurCont, DSA, ESPM, EnvEAb, FCA, FPA, FS&TA, ForAb, GEOBASE, HortAb, I&DA, ISR, IndVet, MaizeAb, MathR, MathSciNet, PBA, PGegResA, PHN&I, PollutAb, PotatoAb, ProtozoAb, RM&VM, RPP, RefZh, RevApplEntom, S&F, SCI, ST&MA, SeedAb, SoyAb, TriticAb, VetBull, WAE&RSA, WeedAb, WildRev, ZooRec.
—BLDSC (4920.300000), CISTI, IDS, IE, Infotrieve, ingenta, Linda Hall. **CCC.**
Published by: (International Biometric Society), American Statistical Association, 1429 Duke St, Alexandria, VA 22314-3415. TEL 703-684-1221, 888-231-3473, FAX 703-684-2037, asainfo@amstat.org, http://www.amstat.org/publications/jabes. adv.: B&W page USD 1,000; trim 10 x 6.88. Circ: 3,000. **Subscr. to:** IBS - JABES, 1444 I St, N W, 700, Washington, DC 20005. TEL 202-712-9049, FAX 202-216-9646, http://www.tibs.org/jabes/index/html.

016.58135 DEU ISSN 1436-8730
QK867 CODEN: JNSSFZ
➤ **JOURNAL OF PLANT NUTRITION AND SOIL SCIENCE/ZEITSCHRIFT FUER PFLANZENERNAEHRUNG UND BODENKUNDE.** Text in English, German. 1935. bi-m. EUR 598 in Europe; CHF 988 in Switzerland & Liechtenstein; USD 788 elsewhere; EUR 658 combined subscription in Europe print & online eds.; CHF 1,087 combined subscription in Switzerland & Liechtenstein for print & online eds.; USD 867 combined subscription elsewhere print & online eds. (effective 2006). adv. bk.rev. abstr.; charts; illus. reprint service avail. from ISI. **Document type:** *Journal, Academic/Scholarly.* **Description:** Covers the entire spectrum of plant nutrition and soil science.
Former titles (until 1999): Zeitschrift fuer Pflanzenernaehrung und Bodenkunde (0044-3263); (until 1967): Zeitschrift fuer Pflanzenernaehrung, Duengung, Bodenkunde (0932-6707); (until 1946): Bodenkunde und Pflanzenernaehrung (0366-2136); (until 1936): Zeitschrift fuer Pflanzenernaehrung, Duengung, Bodenkunde (0372-9702); Which was formed by the merger of (1922-1935): Zeitschrift fuer Pflanzenernaehrung, Duengung, Bodenkunde. Teil A: Wissenschaftlicher Teil (0932-6979); Which was formerly (until 1927): Zeitschrift fuer Pflanzenernaehrung und Duengung. Teil A: Wissenschaftlicher Teil (0372-851X); (1922-1935): Zeitschrift fuer Pflanzenernaehrung, Duengung, Bodenkunde. Teil B: Wirtschaftlich-Praktischer Teil (0932-6987); Which was formerly (until 1927): Zeitschrift fuer Pflanzenernaehrung und Duengung. Teil B: Wirtschaftlich-Praktischer Teil (0932-6995)
Related titles: Microfiche ed.; Online - full text ed.: ISSN 1522-2624. EUR 598 in Europe; CHF 988 in Switzerland & Liechtenstein; USD 788 elsewhere (effective 2006) (from EBSCO Publishing, Swets Information Services, Wiley InterScience).
Indexed: AEA, AEBA, ASCA, ASFA, AgBio, Agr, AgrForAb, AnBrAb, B&BAb, BIOBASE, BIOSIS Prev, BiolAb, CIN, CPA, ChemAb, ChemTitl, CurCont, ESPM, EnvEAb, FCA, FPA, FS&TA, ForAb, HerbAb, HortAb, I&DA, IBZ, ISR, IndVet, M&GPA, MaizeAb, NemAb, NutrAb, PBA, PGegResA, PGrRegA, PHN&I, PN&I, PollutAb, PotatoAb, PoultAb, RPP, RevApplEntom, RiceAb, S&F, S&MA, SCI, SIA, SWRA, SeedAb, SoyAb, TriticAb, VITIS, VetBull, WAE&RSA, WeedAb.
—BLDSC (9478.500000), CASDDS, CISTI, IDS, IE, ingenta, Linda Hall. **CCC.**
Published by: (Deutsche Bodenkundliche Gesellschaft), Wiley - V C H Verlag GmbH & Co. KGaA (Subsidiary of: John Wiley & Sons, Inc.), Boschstr 12, Weinheim, 69469, Germany. TEL 49-6201-6060, FAX 49-6201-606328, adsales@wiley-vch.de, subservice@wiley-vch.de, info@wiley-vch.de, http://www.wiley-vch.de. Eds. Franz Wiesler, Karl-Heinz Feger. R&P Claudia Rutz. **Subscr. in the Americas to:** John Wiley & Sons, Inc.. TEL 201-748-6645, FAX 201-748-6088, subinfo@wiley.com; **Subscr. outside Germany, Austria & Switzerland to:** John Wiley & Sons Ltd., The Atrium, Southern Gate, Chichester, West Sussex PO19 8SQ, United Kingdom. TEL 44-1243-779777, FAX 44-1243-775878. **Co-sponsor:** Deutsche Gesellschaft fuer Pflanzenernaehrung.

016.57 JPN
KARUSHUMU SHINPOJUMU KOEN YOSHI/ABSTRACTS OF CALCIUM SYMPOSIUM. Text in Japanese. 1989. s-a. **Document type:** *Abstract/Index.*
Published by: Karushumu Shinpojumu Un'ei Iinkai/Management Committee of Calcium Symposium, Shokuseikatsu Kenkyukai, 12-19 Nishi-Hon-Machi 1-chome, Nishi-ku, Osaka-shi, 550-0005, Japan.

016.578012 GBR ISSN 0307-2835
Z5354.C53
KEW RECORD OF TAXONOMIC LITERATURE RELATING TO VASCULAR PLANTS. Text in English. 1971. q., latest 1990. price varies. **Document type:** *Abstract/Index.* **Description:** Lists references to all publications on the taxonomy of flowering plants, gymnosperms, and ferns.
Indexed: FPA, ForAb.
—BLDSC (5091.140000), Linda Hall.
Published by: (Royal Botanic Gardens, Kew), Stationery Office (Norwich), St Crispins House, Duke St, PO Box 29, Norwich, NR3 1PD, United Kingdom. TEL 44-870-600-5522, FAX 44-870-600-5533, book.orders@theso.co.uk, customer.services@theso.co.uk, http://www.thestationeryoffice.com/. Circ: 300.

016.5765 JPN
KIKAN KEISEI KENKYUKAI KOEN YOSHISHU/JAPANESE SOCIETY FOR BASIC AND APPLIED ORGAN RESEARCH. ABSTRACTS OF THE MEETING. Text in Japanese. s-a.
Published by: Kikan Keisei Kenkyukai, Nagoya Daigaku Igakubu, Koku Gekagaku Kyoshitsu, 65 Tsurumai-cho, Showa-ku, Nagoya-shi, Aichi-ken 466-0065, Japan.

016.57 JPN
KYOKUIKI SEIBUTSU SHINPOJUMU KOEN YOSHISHU/ABSTRACTS OF THE SYMPOSIUM ON POLAR BIOLOGY. Text in English, Japanese. a., latest vol.25, 2002. **Document type:** *Abstract/Index.*
Published by: National Institute of Polar Research/Kokuritsu Kyokuchi Kenkyujo, Publications, 9-10, Kiga 1-chome, Itabashi-ku, Tokyo, 173, Japan.

016.612015 GBR ISSN 0143-4217
LECTINS. Text in English. 1992. s-m. looseleaf. GBP 96 for print ed. or e-mail (effective 2001). adv. back issues avail. **Document type:** *Abstract/Index.* **Description:** Current awareness service for researchers in clinical and life sciences.
Related titles: E-mail ed.; Online - full text ed.: GBP 108 to individuals (effective 2001).
—CCC.
Published by: S U B I S (Subsidiary of: Sheffield Academic Press Ltd), Mansion House, 19 Kingfield Rd, Sheffield, S Yorks S11 9AS, United Kingdom. TEL 44-114-255-4433, FAX 44-114-255-4626, subis@sheffac.demon.co.uk, http://www.shef-ac-press.co.uk/subis. Ed. S Huntridge. Adv. contact C Evans.

LEUCOCYTES. see *MEDICAL SCIENCES—Abstracting, Bibliographies, Statistics*

016.57 USA
LIFE SCIENCE BOOK REVIEW. Text in English. 1991. bi-m. USD 24. **Description:** Covers all areas of the life sciences.
Published by: Carolina Press, PO Box 24906, Winston Salem, NC 27114. TEL 919-768-9180. Ed. Andrew Goliszek.

016.571655 GBR ISSN 1351-5322
LYSOSOMES AND ENDOCYTOSIS. Text in English. 1994. s-m. looseleaf. GBP 96 fo rprint ed. or e-mail (effective 2001). adv. back issues avail. **Document type:** *Abstract/Index.* **Description:** Current awareness service for researchers in clinical and life sciences.
Formerly (until 1993): Lysosomes (0142-8187)
Related titles: E-mail ed.; Online - full text ed.: GBP 108 to individuals (effective 2001).
—CCC.
Published by: S U B I S (Subsidiary of: Sheffield Academic Press Ltd), Mansion House, 19 Kingfield Rd, Sheffield, S Yorks S11 9AS, United Kingdom. TEL 44-114-255-4433, FAX 44-114-255-4626, subis@sheffac.demon.co.uk, http://www.shef-ac-press.co.uk/subis. Ed. S Huntridge. Adv. contact C Evans.

MACROPHAGES. see *MEDICAL SCIENCES—Abstracting, Bibliographies, Statistics*

016.598 USA
MAMMALOGY ABSTRACTS. Text in English. 1950. q. USD 100 to individuals; USD 175 to libraries; USD 325 universities; USD 475 region; USD 80 to students (effective 2005). **Document type:** *Abstract/Index.* **Description:** Contains citations and abstracts published from 1950 to present in the Journal of Mammalogy, Mammalian Species, and ASM Special Publications.
Media: Online - full content. **Related titles:** CD-ROM ed.: USD 149 to individuals; USD 250 to libraries; USD 450 universities; USD 650 region; USD 129 to students (effective 2002).
Published by: ABSEARCH, Inc., 1204 Thatuna Ave, Moscow, ID 83843. TEL 208-883-5544, 800-867-1877, FAX 208-883-5554, custinfo@absearch.com, sales@absearch.com, http://www.absearch.com.

016.573679 016.6181 GBR ISSN 0964-7600
MAMMARY GLAND. Text in English. 1992. s-m. GBP 96 for print ed. or e-mail ed. (effective 2001). adv. **Document type:** *Abstract/Index.* **Description:** Current awareness service for researchers. Covers all aspects of the mammary gland.
Related titles: E-mail ed.; Online - full text ed.: GBP 108 to individuals (effective 2001).
Published by: S U B I S (Subsidiary of: Sheffield Academic Press Ltd), Mansion House, 19 Kingfield Rd, Sheffield, S Yorks S11 9AS, United Kingdom. TEL 44-114-255-4433, FAX 44-114-255-4626, subis@sheffac.demon.co.uk, http://www.shef-ac-press.co.uk/subis. Ed. S Huntridge. Adv. contact C Evans.

016.579 USA ISSN 0300-838X
QR53
MICROBIOLOGY ABSTRACTS: SECTION A. INDUSTRIAL & APPLIED MICROBIOLOGY. Text in English. 1965. m. (except Dec.). USD 1,755 combined subscription print & online eds.; USD 3,365 combined subscription 3 journals set with print & online eds. (effective 2006). bk.rev. a. index on CD-ROM. back issues avail. **Document type:** *Abstract/Index.* **Description:** Covers scientific research and practical applications in pharmaceuticals, foods, and agriculture.
Related titles: CD-ROM ed.: (from National Information Services Corp. (N I S C), SilverPlatter Information, Inc.); Online - full text ed.: ISSN 1555-4473. USD 1,315; USD 2,520 combined subscription 3 journals set (effective 2006).
—BLDSC (5757.770000), GNLM, Linda Hall.

B

Published by: C S A Journal Division (Subsidiary of: Cambridge Information Group), 7200 Wisconsin Ave, Ste 715, Bethesda, MD 20814. TEL 301-961-6798, 800-843-7751, FAX 301-961-6799, journals@csa.com, http://www.csa.com. Ed. Roberta Gardner. Pub. Ted Caris.

016.5793 USA ISSN 0300-8398
QR1
MICROBIOLOGY ABSTRACTS: SECTION B. BACTERIOLOGY. Text in English. 1966. m. (except Dec.). USD 1,765 combined subscription print & online eds.; USD 3,365 combined subscription 3 journals set with print & online eds. (effective 2006). adv. bk.rev. abstr. index on CD-ROM. back issues avail. **Document type:** *Abstract/Index.* **Description:** Covers clinical applications and pure research in all aspects of bacteriology.
Related titles: CD-ROM ed.: (from SilverPlatter Information, Inc.); Online - full text ed.: ISSN 1555-4481. USD 1,320; USD 2,520 combined subscription 3 journals set (effective 2006).
Published by: C S A Journal Division (Subsidiary of: Cambridge Information Group), 7200 Wisconsin Ave, Ste 715, Bethesda, MD 20814. TEL 301-961-6798, 800-843-7751, FAX 301-961-6799, journals@csa.com, http://www.csa.com. Ed. Roberta Gardner. Pub. Ted Caris.

016.579 USA ISSN 0301-2328
QK564
MICROBIOLOGY ABSTRACTS: SECTION C. ALGOLOGY, MYCOLOGY AND PROTOZOOLOGY. Text in English. 1972. m. (except Dec.). USD 1,680 combined subscription print & online eds.; USD 3,365 combined subscription 3 journals set with print & online eds. (effective 2006). bk.rev. abstr. index on CD-ROM. back issues avail. **Document type:** *Abstract/Index.* **Description:** Covers life cycles of algae, fungi, and protozoa, and their interactions with animals and plants.
Related titles: CD-ROM ed.: (from National Information Services Corp. (N I S C), SilverPlatter Information, Inc.); Online - full text ed.: ISSN 1555-449X. USD 1,260; USD 2,520 combined subscription 3 journals set (effective 2006).
Published by: C S A Journal Division (Subsidiary of: Cambridge Information Group), 7200 Wisconsin Ave, Ste 715, Bethesda, MD 20814. TEL 301-961-6798, 800-843-7751, FAX 301-961-6799, journals@csa.com, service@csa.com, http://www.csa.com. Ed. Roberta Gardner. Pub. Ted Caris.

016.571657 GBR ISSN 0142-8217
Z5322.C3
MITOCHONDRIA. Text in English. 1978. s-m. GBP 120 for print ed. or e-mail (effective 2001). adv. **Document type:** *Abstract/Index.* **Description:** Current awareness service for researchers. Covers electron transport, cytochromes, oxidative phosphorylation, TCA cycle, pathology.
Related titles: E-mail ed.; Online - full text ed.: GBP 108 (effective 2001).
—CCC.
Published by: S U B I S (Subsidiary of: Sheffield Academic Press Ltd), Mansion House, 19 Kingfield Rd, Sheffield, S Yorks S11 9AS, United Kingdom. TEL 44-114-255-4433, FAX 44-114-255-4626, subis@sheffac.demon.co.uk, http://www.shef-ac-press.co.uk/subis. Ed. S Huntridge. Adv. contact C Evans.

016.5728 GBR ISSN 1356-1324
MOLECULAR BIOLOGY TECHNIQUES. Text in English. 1995. s-m. GBP 120 for print ed. or e-mail (effective 2001). adv. **Document type:** *Abstract/Index.* **Description:** Current awareness service for researchers in clinical and life sciences. Covers all aspects of investigations in the field of molecular biology.
Related titles: E-mail ed.; Online - full text ed.: GBP 108 (effective 2001).
Published by: S U B I S (Subsidiary of: Sheffield Academic Press Ltd), Mansion House, 19 Kingfield Rd, Sheffield, S Yorks S11 9AS, United Kingdom. TEL 44-114-255-4433, FAX 44-114-255-4626, subis@sheffac.demon.co.uk, http://www.shef-ac-press.co.uk/subis. Ed. S Huntridge. Adv. contact C Evans.

016.5793 GBR ISSN 1351-5292
MYCOBACTERIA. Text in English. 1994. s-m. GBP 96 for print or email ed. (effective 2001). adv. **Document type:** *Abstract/Index.* **Description:** Current awareness service for researchers in clinical and life sciences.
Related titles: E-mail ed.; Online - full text ed.: GBP 108 to individuals (effective 2001).
Indexed: AbHyg.
Published by: S U B I S (Subsidiary of: Sheffield Academic Press Ltd), Mansion House, 19 Kingfield Rd, Sheffield, S Yorks S11 9AS, United Kingdom. TEL 44-114-255-4433, FAX 44-114-255-4626, subis@sheffac.demon.co.uk, http://www.shef-ac-press.co.uk/subis. Ed. S Huntridge. Adv. contact C Evans.

016.59257 GBR ISSN 0957-6797
CODEN: NEABEA
NEMATOLOGICAL ABSTRACTS. Text in English. 1932. q. USD 655 in the Americas to institutions except Canada; GBP 375 elsewhere to institutions; USD 700 combined subscription in the Americas to institutions except Canada; print & online eds.; GBP 400 combined subscription elsewhere to institutions print & online eds. (effective 2006). adv. bk.rev. back issues avail.; reprints avail. **Document type:** *Abstract/Index.* **Description:** Contains abstracts of the world literature on: nematodes parasitic on plants, free-living and marine nematodes, and nematodes parasitic on insects or other invertebrates.
Supersedes: Helminthological Abstracts. Series B: Plant Nematology (0300-8320); Which was Superseded in part (in 1970): Helminthological Abstracts (0018-0122)
Related titles: Online - full text ed.: USD 560 in the Americas to institutions except Canada; GBP 320 elsewhere to institutions (effective 2006) (from DIMDI, The Dialog Corporation).
Indexed: PotatoAb, RevApplEntom.
—CISTI, Linda Hall. **CCC.**
Published by: CABI Publishing (Subsidiary of: CAB International), CAB International, Wallingford, Oxfordshire OX10 8DE, United Kingdom. TEL 44-1491-832111, FAX 44-1491-833508, cabi@cabi.org, http://www.cabi-publishing.org/. adv.: B&W page GBP 85, B&W page USD 135; 170 x 267. Circ: 300. **Subscr. addr. in N America:** CABI Publishing North America, 875 Massachusetts Ave, 7th Fl, Cambridge, MA 02139. TEL 617-395-4056, 800-528-4841, FAX 617-354-6875, cabi-nao@cabi.org.

016.5716 016.6168 GBR ISSN 0142-8225
NERVE CELL BIOLOGY. Text in English. 1972. s-m. GBP 120 for print ed. or e-mail (effective 2001). adv. **Document type:** *Abstract/Index.* **Description:** Current awareness service for researchers. Covers nerve cell biology: development, regeneration, structure, tissue culture, pharmacology, immunology, membranes and sensory receptors.
Related titles: E-mail ed.; Online - full text ed.: GBP 108 (effective 2001).
—CCC.
Published by: S U B I S (Subsidiary of: Sheffield Academic Press Ltd), Mansion House, 19 Kingfield Rd, Sheffield, S Yorks S11 9AS, United Kingdom. TEL 44-114-255-4433, FAX 44-114-255-4626, subis@sheffac.demon.co.uk, http://www.shef-ac-press.co.uk/subis. Ed. S Huntridge. Adv. contact C Evans.

016.5738 016.6168 GBR ISSN 0142-8241
NEUROPHYSIOLOGY. Text in English. 1972. s-m. GBP 120 for print ed. or e-mail (effective 2001). adv. **Document type:** *Abstract/Index.* **Description:** Current awareness service for researchers. Covers the electrophysiology and pharmacology of the vertebrate central, autonomic and peripheral nervous systems.
Related titles: E-mail ed.; Online - full text ed.: GBP 108 (effective 2001).
Indexed: BiolAb, ChemAb, ExcerpMed, ISR, PsycholAb, SCI, e-psyche.
—CCC.
Published by: S U B I S (Subsidiary of: Sheffield Academic Press Ltd), Mansion House, 19 Kingfield Rd, Sheffield, S Yorks S11 9AS, United Kingdom. TEL 44-114-255-4433, FAX 44-114-255-4626, subis@sheffac.demon.co.uk, http://www.shef-ac-press.co.uk/subis. Ed. S Huntridge. Adv. contact C Evans.

016.57 JPN
NIHON BAIOREOROJI GAKKAI NENKAI SHOROKUSHU/ JAPANESE SOCIETY OF BIORHEOLOGY. ABSTRACTS OF THE ANNUAL MEETING. Text in Japanese. a. **Document type:** *Academic/Scholarly.*
Published by: Nihon Baioreoroji Gakkai/Japanese Society of Biorheology, Gunma Prefectural Cardiovascular Center, Kho 3-12, Kameizumi-Machi, Maebashi-shi, Gunma-ken 371-0004, Japan. Pub. Khoichi Taniguchi.

016.57 JPN
NIHON BENTOSU GAKKAI TAIKAI/JAPANESE ASSOCIATION OF BENTHOLOGY. ABSTRACTS OF ANNUAL MEETING. Text in English, Japanese. 1987. a. **Document type:** *Abstract/Index.*
Published by: Nihon Bentosu Gakkai/Japanese Association of Benthology, Ocean Research Institute, University of, Minami-Dai, Nakano-ku, Tokyo, 164-0014, Japan. TEL 81-3-5351-6469, FAX 81-3-3375-6716, sirayama@ori.u-tokyo.ac.jp.

016.579321 JPN
NIHON BOKIN BOBAI GAKKAI. NENJI TAIKAI YOSHISHU/SOCIETY FOR ANTIBACTERIAL AND ANTIFUNGAL AGENTS, JAPAN. ABSTRACTS OF THE MEETING. Text in Japanese. a. JPY 3,000 (effective 2000). adv. **Document type:** *Abstract/Index.*
Published by: Nihon Bokin Bobai Gakkai/Society for Antibacterial and Antifungal Agents, Japan, 9th Fl, Shin-Kousan Bldg, 1-13-38, Nishimotocho, Nishi-ku, Osaka-shi, 550-0005, Japan. Ed. Tetsuaki Tsuchido. R&P K Arai TEL 81-6-6538-2166. Adv. contact Iwao Yamamoto.

016.579 JPN
NIHON DOJO BISEIBUTSU GAKKAI KOEN YOSHISHU/SOIL MICROBIOLOGICAL SOCIETY OF JAPAN. ABSTRACTS OF THE ANNUAL MEETING. Text in Japanese. a. JPY 1,000 (effective 2000). **Document type:** *Proceedings.*
Formerly: Dojo Biseibutsu Kenkyukai Koen Yoshishu
Published by: Nihon Dojo Biseibutsu Gakkai/Japanese Society of Soil Microbiology, 648 Matsundo, Matsudo City, 271-8510, Japan. TEL 81-47-308-8823, FAX 81-47-308-8824, jssm@midori.h.chiba-u.ac.jp. Ed. Masanori Saito.

016.597 JPN
NIHON GYORUI GAKKAI NENKAI KOEN YOSHI/ ICHTHYOLOGY SOCIETY OF JAPAN. ADVANCE ABSTRACTS FOR THE ANNUAL MEETING. Text in English, Japanese. a. **Document type:** *Abstract/Index.*
Published by: Nihon Gyorui Gakkai/Ichthyology Society of Japan, Suisan Daigaku, 5-7 Ko-Unan 4-chome, Minato-ku, Tokyo, 108-0075, Japan.

016.590724 JPN
NIHON JIKKEN DOBUTSU GAKKAI SOKAI KOEN YOSHISHU/JAPANESE ASSOCIATION FOR LABORATORY ANIMAL SCIENCE. ABSTRACTS OF GENERAL MEETING. Text in Japanese. a. **Document type:** *Abstract/Index.*
Published by: Japanese Association for Laboratory Animal Science/Nihon Jikken Dobutsu Gakkai, Akamon Royal Heights, Rm 1103, 5-29-12 Hongo, Bunkyo-ku, Tokyo, 113-0033, Japan. TEL 81-3-38148276, FAX 81-3-38143990, http://wwwsoc.nii.ac.jp/jalas/.

016.5999 JPN
NIHON JINRUI IDEN GAKKAI TAIKAI SHOROKUSHU/JAPAN SOCIETY OF HUMAN GENETICS. ABSTRACTS OF THE ANNUAL MEETING. Text in English, Japanese. a. **Document type:** *Abstract/Index.*
Published by: Nihon Jinrui Iden Gakkai/Japan Society of Human Genetics, Ika Shika Daigaku Jinrui Idengaku Kenkyushitsu, 5-45 Yushima 1-chome, Bunkyo-ku, Tokyo, 113-0034, Japan.

016.5957 JPN
NIHON KONCHU GAKKAI TAIKAI KOEN YOSHI/ ENTOMOLOGICAL SOCIETY OF JAPAN. ABSTRACTS OF ANNUAL MEETING. Text in Japanese. a. JPY 5,000 to members. adv. **Document type:** *Proceedings.*
Related titles: Online - full text ed.
Published by: Entomological Society of Japan/Nihon Konchu Gakkai, c/o Dept of Zoology, National Science Museum (Natl Hist), 3-23-1 Hiyakunin-cho, Shinjuku-ku, Tokyo, 169-0073, Japan. TEL 81-3-3364-7129, FAX 81-3-3364-7104. Ed. Masataka Sato. Adv. contact Hiroshi Kajita.

016.59 JPN
NIHON MUKIN SEIBUTSU NOTO BAIOROJI GAKKAI SOKAI NITTEI TO SHOROKU/JAPANESE ASSOCIATION OF GERMFREE LIFE AND GNOTOBIOLOGY. ABSTRACTS OF MEETING. Text in Japanese. a. **Document type:** *Abstract/Index.*
Published by: Nihon Mukin Seibutsu Noto Baioroji Gakkai/Japanese Association of Germfree Life and Gnotobiology, c/o Ms. Kazuko Adachi, Kobe Gakuin Daigaku Eiyogakubu, Arise, Ikawadanicho, Nishi-ku, Kobe-shi, Hyogo-ken 673, Japan.

016.5716 JPN
NIHON SAIBO SEIBUTSU GAKKAI TAIKAI KOEN YOSHISHU/JAPAN SOCIETY FOR CELL BIOLOGY. ABSTRACTS OF THE MEETING. Text in Japanese. a. JPY 4,000. adv. **Document type:** *Abstract/Index.*
Published by: Nihon Saibo Seibutsu Gakkai/Japan Society for Cell Biology, Ogawa Higashi Iru, Shimodachuri Dori, Kamigyi-ku, Kyoto-shi, 602, Japan. FAX 81-75-415-3662. Ed. Fumio Hanaoka. Pub., R&P, Adv. contact Yoshihiro Yoneda.

016.571 JPN ISSN 1342-3215
➤ **NIHON SEIRI JINRUI GAKKAISHI/JAPANESE JOURNAL OF PHYSIOLOGICAL ANTHROPOLOGY.** Text in Japanese. 1996. a. **Document type:** *Journal, Academic/Scholarly.*
—CCC.
Published by: Nihon Seiri Jinrui Gakkai/Japan Society of Physiological Anthropology, c/o International Academic Printing Co. Ltd., 3-8-8 Tkadanobaba, Shinjyuku-ku, Tokyo, 169-0075, Japan. TEL 81-3-53896218, FAX 81-3-33682822, jspa-post@bunken.co.jp, http://www.jspa.net/journal_j.html.

016.57287 JPN
NIHON SENSHOKUTAI KENSA GAKKAI SHOROKUSHU/ JAPANESE ASSOCIATION FOR CHROMOSOME ANALYSIS. ABSTRACT OF ANNUAL MEETING. Text in English, Japanese. 1988. a. **Document type:** *Abstract/Index.*
Published by: Nihon Senshokutai Kensa Gakkai, c/o Nihon Gene Research Lab's Inc., 3-36 Ogi-Machi 2-chome, Miyagino-ku, Sendai-shi, Miyagi-ken 983-0034, Japan. TEL 81-22-238-070, kgg0250@niftyserve.or.jp.

016.5957 JPN
NIHON SHOKUBUTSU BYORI GAKKAI DOJO DENSENBYO DANWAKAI KOEN YOSHISHU∗ /PHYTOPATHOLOGICAL SOCIETY OF JAPAN. ABSTRACTS OF THE MEETING OF SOIL BORNE DISEASE. Text in Japanese. a. **Document type:** *Abstract/Index.*

Published by: Nihon Shokubutsu Byori Gakkai, Dojo Densenbyo Danwakai/Phytopathological Society of Japan, Meeting of Soil Borne Disease, c/o Nihon Shokubutsu Boeki Kyokai Bldg, 43-11 Komagome 1-chome, Toshima-ku, Tokyo, 170-0003, Japan.

016.5915 JPN ISSN 0917-5725
NIPPON DOBUTSU KODO GAKKAI TAIKAI HAPPYO YOSHISHU/JAPAN ETHOLOGICAL SOCIETY. ABSTRACTS OF MEETING. Text in Japanese. 1983. a. **Document type:** *Abstract/Index.*
Published by: Nippon Dobutsu Kodo Gakkai/Japan Ethological Society, Daigaku Rigakubu Dobutsugaku Kyoshitsu, Kita-Shirakawaoiwake-cho, Sakyo-ku, Kyoto-shi, 606-8224, Japan. Ed. T Kawamura.

016.5738 GBR ISSN 1351-525X
NITRIC OXIDE. Text in English. 1994. s-m. GBP 120 for print ed. or e-mail (effective 2001). adv. **Document type:** *Abstract/Index.* **Description:** Current awareness service for researchers in clinical and life sciences.
Related titles: E-mail ed.; Online - full text ed.: GBP 108 (effective 2001).
Indexed: ChemAb, IndMed.
Published by: S U B I S (Subsidiary of: Sheffield Academic Press Ltd), Mansion House, 19 Kingfield Rd, Sheffield, S Yorks S11 9AS, United Kingdom. TEL 44-114-255-4433, FAX 44-114-255-4626, subis@sheffac.demon.co.uk, http://www.shef-ac-press.co.uk/subis. Ed. S Huntridge. Adv. contact C Evans.

NITRIC OXIDE: BIOLOGY AND CHEMISTRY. see *BIOLOGY—Biochemistry*

016.5738 JPN
NO NO IGAKU SEIBUTSUGAKU KONWAKAI SHOROKU/ABSTRACTS OF CONFERENCE ON MEDICINE AND BIOLOGY OF THE BRAIN. Text in Japanese. 1986. s-a. **Document type:** *Abstract/Index.*
Published by: No no Igaku Seibutsugaku Konwakai, Fujita Gakuen Hoken Eisei Daigaku, Igakubu Seirigaku Kyoshitsu, 1-98 Dengakukubo-kutsukakecho, Toyoake-shi, Aichi-ken 470-1100, Japan.

016.59 USA
NORTH AMERICAN WILDLIFE & NATURAL RESOURCES ABSTRACTS. Text in English. 1936. q. USD 89 to individuals; USD 150 to libraries; USD 250 universities; USD 350 region; USD 69 to students (effective 2002). **Document type:** *Abstract/Index.* **Description:** Contains 4000+ records including citations and abstracts from Transactions of North American Wildlife and Natural Resources Conference (1936-2001).
Media: Online - full content. **Related titles:** CD-ROM ed.: USD 149 to individuals; USD 250 to libraries; USD 450 universities; USD 650 region; USD 129 to students (effective 2002).
Published by: ABSEARCH, Inc., 1204 Thatuna Ave, Moscow, ID 83843. TEL 208-883-5544, 800-867-1877, FAX 208-883-5554, custinfo@absearch.com, sales@absearch.com, http://www.absearch.com.

016.572 USA ISSN 1555-4511
QP551
NUCLEIC ACIDS ABSTRACTS (ONLINE EDITION). Text in English. m. USD 1,100 (effective 2006). bk.rev. abstr. a. index on CD-ROM. **Document type:** *Abstract/Index.* **Description:** Covers physical, chemical, and biological aspects of nucleic acids and nucleoproteins.
Media: Online - full text.
—GNLM.
Published by: C S A Journal Division (Subsidiary of: Cambridge Information Group), 7200 Wisconsin Ave, Ste 715, Bethesda, MD 20814. TEL 301-961-6798, 800-843-7751, FAX 301-961-6799, journals@csa.com, http://www.csa.com/factsheets/nucleic-acids-set-c.php. Ed. Jennifer A Phillips. Pub. Ted Caris.

016.598 USA
ORNITHOLOGY ABSTRACTS. Text in English. 1955. q. USD 100 to individuals; USD 175 to libraries; USD 325 universities; USD 475 region; USD 80 to students (effective 2005). **Document type:** *Abstract/Index.* **Description:** Contains citations and abstracts published from 1955 to present in Auk, Ornithological Monographs, Condor, Studies in Avian Biology, Wilson Bulletin, Journal of Field Ornithology, and Journal of Raptor Research.
Media: Online - full content. **Related titles:** CD-ROM ed.: USD 149 to individuals; USD 250 to libraries; USD 450 universities; USD 650 region; USD 129 to students (effective 2002).
Published by: ABSEARCH, Inc., 1204 Thatuna Ave, Moscow, ID 83843. TEL 208-883-5544, 800-867-1877, FAX 208-883-5554, custinfo@absearch.com, sales@absearch.com, http://www.absearch.com.

016.572 GBR ISSN 0950-057X
OXYGEN RADICALS. Text in English. 1988. s-m. looseleaf. GBP 120 for print ed. or email (effective 2001). adv. bk.rev. back issues avail. **Document type:** *Abstract/Index.* **Description:** Current awareness service for researchers in clinical and life sciences.
Related titles: E-mail ed.; Online - full text ed.: GBP 108 (effective 2001).
—CCC.
Published by: S U B I S (Subsidiary of: Sheffield Academic Press Ltd), Mansion House, 19 Kingfield Rd, Sheffield, S Yorks S11 9AS, United Kingdom. TEL 44-114-255-4433, FAX 44-114-255-4626, subis@sheffac.demon.co.uk, http://www.shef-ac-press.co.uk/subis. Ed. S Huntridge. Adv. contact C Evans.

016.5734 GBR ISSN 0142-825X
PANCREATIC AND SALIVARY SECRETION. Text in English. 1979. s-m. GBP 120 for print ed. or email (effective 2001). adv. **Document type:** *Abstract/Index.* **Description:** Provides a current-awareness service for researchers. Covers the pharmacology, structure and function of the pancreatic and salivary glands.
Related titles: E-mail ed.; Online - full text ed.: GBP 108 (effective 2001).
—CCC.
Published by: S U B I S (Subsidiary of: Sheffield Academic Press Ltd), Mansion House, 19 Kingfield Rd, Sheffield, S Yorks S11 9AS, United Kingdom. TEL 44-114-255-4433, FAX 44-114-255-4626, subis@sheffac.demon.co.uk, http://www.shef-ac-press.co.uk/subis. Ed. S Huntridge. Adv. contact C Evans.

016.57965 GBR ISSN 0964-7570
PARASITOLOGY (SHEFFIELD). Text in English. 1992. s-m. GBP 120 for print ed. or email (effective 2001). adv. **Document type:** *Abstract/Index.* **Description:** Current awareness service for researchers investigating all aspects of parasitology.
Related titles: E-mail ed.; Online - full text ed.: GBP 108 (effective 2001).
Indexed: CurCont, ISR.
Published by: S U B I S (Subsidiary of: Sheffield Academic Press Ltd), Mansion House, 19 Kingfield Rd, Sheffield, S Yorks S11 9AS, United Kingdom. TEL 44-114-255-4433, FAX 44-114-255-4626, subis@sheffac.demon.co.uk, http://www.shef-ac-press.co.uk/subis. Ed. S Huntridge. Adv. contact C Evans.

572.65 JPN ISSN 0385-8847
PEPTIDE INFORMATION. Text in English. 1975. bi-w. USD 290 to individuals; USD 450 to institutions. **Description:** Contains articles related to peptide research in the field of life sciences. Includes amino acid sequence data, data on synthetic peptides, and structure data of proteins.
Related titles: Diskette ed.; Online - full text ed.
Published by: Protein Research Foundation, Peptide Institute/Tanpakushitsu Kenkyu Shoreikai Pepuchido Kenkyujo, 4-1-2 Ina, Mino-shi, Osaka-fu 562-0015, Japan. TEL 81-727-29-4124, query@prf.or.jp, http://www.pfr.or.jp/.

016.58 GBR ISSN 0260-5902
PLANT BIOTECHNOLOGY. Text in English. 1981. s-m. GBP 120 for print ed. or e-mail (effective 2001). adv. bk.rev. **Document type:** *Abstract/Index.* **Description:** Current awareness service for researchers. Covers plant tissue culture, protoplasts, recombinant work, chemostat technology, immobilized enzymes and cells, biomass production and production of primary and secondary products.
Related titles: E-mail ed.; Online - full text ed.: GBP 108 (effective 2001).
Indexed: ABIPC, CIN, ChemAb, ChemTitl, FS&TA.
—BLDSC (6513.770000). **CCC.**
Published by: S U B I S (Subsidiary of: Sheffield Academic Press Ltd), Mansion House, 19 Kingfield Rd, Sheffield, S Yorks S11 9AS, United Kingdom. TEL 44-114-255-4433, FAX 44-114-255-4626, subis@sheffac.demon.co.uk, http://www.shef-ac-press.co.uk/subis. Ed. S Huntridge. Adv. contact C Evans.

016.58135 GBR ISSN 0966-0100
PLANT GENETIC RESOURCES ABSTRACTS. Text in English. 1992. q. USD 900 in the Americas to institutions except Canada; GBP 515 elsewhere to institutions; USD 965 combined subscription in the Americas to institutions except Canada; print & online eds.; GBP 550 combined subscription elsewhere to institutions print & online eds. (effective 2006). adv. back issues avail. **Document type:** *Abstract/Index.* **Description:** Provides the latest information on the genetic resources of all plant species of economic value and their wild relatives.
Related titles: Online - full text ed.: USD 770 in the Americas to institutions except Canada; GBP 440 elsewhere to institutions (effective 2006).
—CCC.
Published by: CABI Publishing (Subsidiary of: CAB International), CAB International, Wallingford, Oxfordshire OX10 8DE, United Kingdom. TEL 44-1491-832111, FAX 44-1491-833508, cabi@cabi.org, http://www.cabi-publishing.org/. adv.: B&W page GBP 60, B&W page USD 95; 170 x 267. Circ: 620. **Subscr. addr. in N America:** CABI Publishing North America, 875 Massachusetts Ave, 7th Fl, Cambridge, MA 02139. TEL 617-395-4056, 800-528-4841, FAX 617-354-6875, cabi-nao@cabi.org.

016.572 GBR ISSN 0952-0406
PROTEINS: POST-TRANSLATIONAL PROCESSING. Text in English. 1976. s-m. GBP 120 for print ed. or e-mail (effective 2001). adv. **Document type:** *Abstract/Index.* **Description:** Current awareness service for researchers. Covers phosphorylation, methylation, acetylation, amidation, sulphation, hydroxylation and glycoslation as well as transport of proteins.
Formerly (until 1987): Protein Phosphorylation (0142-8292)
Related titles: E-mail ed.; Online - full text ed.: GBP 108 (effective 2001).
—CCC.
Published by: S U B I S (Subsidiary of: Sheffield Academic Press Ltd), Mansion House, 19 Kingfield Rd, Sheffield, S Yorks S11 9AS, United Kingdom. TEL 44-114-255-4433, FAX 44-114-255-4626, subis@sheffac.demon.co.uk, http://www.shef-ac-press.co.uk/subis. Ed. S Huntridge. Adv. contact C Evans.

016.59 GBR ISSN 0309-1287
PROTOZOOLOGICAL ABSTRACTS. Text in English. 1977. m. USD 1,665 in the Americas to institutions except Canada; GBP 950 elsewhere to institutions; USD 1,775 combined subscription in the Americas to institutions except Canada; print & online eds.; GBP 1,015 combined subscription elsewhere to institutions print & online (effective 2006). adv. back issues avail. **Document type:** *Abstract/Index.* **Description:** Covers all protozoan diseases, many endemic to the tropics, affecting humans and animals.
Related titles: Online - full text ed.: USD 1,420 in the Americas to institutions except Canada; GBP 810 elsewhere to institutions (effective 2006) (from DIMDI, The Dialog Corporation).
—Linda Hall. **CCC.**
Published by: CABI Publishing (Subsidiary of: CAB International), CAB International, Wallingford, Oxfordshire OX10 8DE, United Kingdom. TEL 44-1491-832111, FAX 44-1491-833508, cabi@cabi.org, http://www.cabi-publishing.org/. Adv. contact Sarah Harris TEL 44-1491-829310. B&W page GBP 75, B&W page USD 120; 170 x 267. Circ: 150. **Subscr. addr. in N America:** CABI Publishing North America, 875 Massachusetts Ave, 7th Fl, Cambridge, MA 02139. TEL 617-395-4056, 800-528-4841, FAX 617-354-6875, cabi-nao@cabi.org.

B

016.5714 RUS ISSN 0131-3541
REFERATIVNYI ZHURNAL. BIOFIZIKA. Text in Russian. 1964. m. USD 793 foreign (effective 2006). **Document type:** *Abstract/Index.*
Related titles: CD-ROM ed.; Online - full text ed.
—BLDSC (0142.164000), East View.
Published by: Vserossiiskii Institut Nauchnoi i Tekhnicheskoi Informatsii (VINITI), Ul Usievicha 20, Moscow, 125190, Russian Federation. TEL 7-095-1526441, FAX 7-095-9430060, dir@viniti.ru, http://www.viniti.ru. **Dist. by:** Informnauka Ltd., Ul Usievicha 20, Moscow 125190, Russian Federation. alfimov@viniti.ru.

016.57 016.912 RUS ISSN 0202-9243
REFERATIVNYI ZHURNAL. BIOGEOGRAFIYA. GEOGRAFIYA POCHV. Text in Russian. 1956. m. USD 330 foreign (effective 2006). **Document type:** *Abstract/Index.*
Related titles: CD-ROM ed.; Online - full text ed.
—East View.
Published by: Vserossiiskii Institut Nauchnoi i Tekhnicheskoi Informatsii (VINITI), Ul Usievicha 20, Moscow, 125190, Russian Federation. TEL 7-095-1526441, FAX 7-095-9430060, dir@viniti.ru, http://www.viniti.ru. **Dist. by:** Informnauka Ltd., Ul Usievicha 20, Moscow 125190, Russian Federation. alfimov@viniti.ru.

016.572 RUS
▼ **REFERATIVNYI ZHURNAL. BIOKHIMIYA.** Text in Russian. 2004. m. USD 917 foreign (effective 2006). **Document type:** *Journal, Abstract/Index.*
Formed by the merger of (1991-2004): Referativnyi Zhurnal. Biokhimiya. Assimiliyatsiya i Metabolizm Azota. Belki. Biosintez i Metabolizm (0320-7633); Referativnyi Zhurnal. Biokhimiya. Biokhimiya Ksenobiotikov (0204-3815); Referativnyi Zhurnal. Biokhimiya. Obshchie Voprosy, Enzimologiya, Nebelkovye Soedineniya, Regulyatsiya Metabolizma
Related titles: CD-ROM ed.; Online - full text ed.
Published by: Vserossiiskii Institut Nauchnoi i Tekhnicheskoi Informatsii (VINITI), Ul Usievicha 20, Moscow, 125190, Russian Federation. TEL 7-095-1526441, FAX 7-095-9430060, dir@viniti.ru, http://www.viniti.ru. **Dist. by:** Informnauka Ltd., Ul Usievicha 20, Moscow 125190, Russian Federation. alfimov@viniti.ru.

016.57 RUS ISSN 0034-2300
QH7 CODEN: RZBLAS
REFERATIVNYI ZHURNAL. BIOLOGIYA. Text in Russian. 1953. m. USD 8,070 foreign (effective 2006). abstr.; bibl. index. **Document type:** *Abstract/Index.*
Formerly: Referativnyi Zhurnal. Biologicheskaya Khimiya (0486-2260)
Related titles: CD-ROM ed.; Online - full text ed.; ◆ Series: Referativnyi Zhurnal. Biologiya. Fiziko-Khimicheskaya Biologiya. ISSN 0869-4095.
Indexed: ApicAb, BiolAb, ChemAb.
—CASDDS, East View, Linda Hall.

▼ new title ➤ refereed ✶ unverified ◆ full entry avail.

Published by: Vserossiiskii Institut Nauchnoi i Tekhnicheskoi Informatsii (VINITI), Ul Usievicha 20, Moscow, 125190, Russian Federation. TEL 7-095-1526441, FAX 7-095-9430060, dir@viniti.ru, http://www.viniti.ru. Ed. Rem Petrov. Circ: 2,930. **Dist. by:** Informnauka Ltd., Ul Usievicha 20, Moscow 125190, Russian Federation. alfimov@viniti.ru.

016.54 016.553 016.57 RUS ISSN 0869-4095
REFERATIVNYI ZHURNAL. BIOLOGIYA. FIZIKO-KHIMICHESKAYA BIOLOGIYA. Text in Russian. 1982. m. USD 2,943 foreign (effective 2006). **Document type:** *Abstract/Index.*
Related titles: CD-ROM ed.; Online - full text ed.; ♦ Series of: Referativnyi Zhurnal. Biologiya. ISSN 0034-2300.
—East View. **CCC.**
Published by: Vserossiiskii Institut Nauchnoi i Tekhnicheskoi Informatsii (VINITI), Ul Usievicha 20, Moscow, 125190, Russian Federation. TEL 7-095-1526441, FAX 7-095-9430060, dir@viniti.ru, http://www.viniti.ru. **Dist. by:** Informnauka Ltd., Ul Usievicha 20, Moscow 125190, Russian Federation. alfimov@viniti.ru.

B

016.571 RUS ISSN 0869-4079
REFERATIVNYI ZHURNAL. BIOLOGIYA. FIZIOLOGIYA I MORFOLOGIYA CHELOVEKA I ZHIVOTNYKH. Text in Russian. 1959. m. USD 2,146 foreign (effective 2006). **Document type:** *Abstract/Index.*
Formerly (until 1992): Referativnyi Zhurnal. Fiziologiya i Morfologiya Cheloveka i Zhivotnykh (0207-141X)
Related titles: CD-ROM ed.; Online - full text ed.; ♦ Cumulative ed. of: Referativnyi Zhurnal. Obshchie Voprosy Patologicheskoi Anatomii; ♦ Cumulative ed. of: Referativnyi Zhurnal. Fiziologiya Cheloveka i Zhivotnykh. Obshchie Problemy, Vozrastnaya Fiziologiya; ♦ Cumulative ed. of: Referativnyi Zhurnal. Fiziologiya Cheloveka i Zhivotnykh. Obmen Veshchestv, Pitanie, Pishchevarenie. ISSN 0208-2853; ♦ Cumulative ed. of: Referativnyi Zhurnal. Fiziologiya Cheloveka i Zhivotnykh. Endokrinnaya Sistema, Razmnozhenie, Laktatsiya. ISSN 0207-1460; ♦ Cumulative ed. of: Referativnyi Zhurnal. Fiziologiya Cheloveka i Zhivotnykh. Krov', Limfa, Krovoobrashchenie, Dykhanie, Pochki. ISSN 0207-1436; ♦ Cumulative ed. of: Referativnyi Zhurnal. Fiziologiya Cheloveka i Zhivotnykh. Neirofiziologiya, Sensornye Sistemy, V N D, Nervno-Myshechnaya Sistema. ISSN 0207-1444; ♦ Cumulative ed. of: Referativnyi Zhurnal. Morfologiya Cheloveka i Zhivotnykh. Antropologiya. ISSN 0207-1428.
Published by: Vserossiiskii Institut Nauchnoi i Tekhnicheskoi Informatsii (VINITI), Ul Usievicha 20, Moscow, 125190, Russian Federation. TEL 7-095-1526441, FAX 7-095-9430060, dir@viniti.ru, http://www.viniti.ru. **Dist. by:** Informnauka Ltd., Ul Usievicha 20, Moscow 125190, Russian Federation. alfimov@viniti.ru.

016.5999 RUS ISSN 0869-4060
REFERATIVNYI ZHURNAL. BIOLOGIYA. GENETIKA: TSITOLOGIYA. Text in Russian. 1964. m. USD 1,258 foreign (effective 2006). **Document type:** *Abstract/Index.*
Related titles: CD-ROM ed.; Online - full text ed.
—BLDSC (0142.035000), East View.
Published by: Vserossiiskii Institut Nauchnoi i Tekhnicheskoi Informatsii (VINITI), Ul Usievicha 20, Moscow, 125190, Russian Federation. TEL 7-095-1526441, FAX 7-095-9430060, dir@viniti.ru, http://www.viniti.ru. Ed. Yurii Arskii. **Dist. by:** Informnauka Ltd., Ul Usievicha 20, Moscow 125190, Russian Federation. alfimov@viniti.ru.

016.670 RUS
REFERATIVNYI ZHURNAL. BIOLOGIYA. OBSHCHIE PROBLEMY BIOLOGII. RAZDEL -TOM. Text in Russian. 1958. m. USD 1,297 foreign (effective 2006). **Document type:** *Abstract/Index.*
Related titles: CD-ROM ed.; Online - full text ed.
—BLDSC (0142.105000).
Published by: Vserossiiskii Institut Nauchnoi i Tekhnicheskoi Informatsii (VINITI), Ul Usievicha 20, Moscow, 125190, Russian Federation. TEL 7-095-1526441, FAX 7-095-9430060, dir@viniti.ru, http://www.viniti.ru. Ed. Rem Petrov. **Dist. by:** Informnauka Ltd., Ul Usievicha 20, Moscow 125190, Russian Federation. alfimov@viniti.ru.

016.670 RUS
REFERATIVNYI ZHURNAL. BIOLOGIYA. OBSHCHIE PROBLEMY BIOLOGII. VYPUSK RAZDELA -TOMA. Text in Russian. 1958. m. USD 225 (effective 2006). **Document type:** *Abstract/Index.*
Related titles: CD-ROM ed.; Online - full text ed.
Published by: Vserossiiskii Institut Nauchnoi i Tekhnicheskoi Informatsii (VINITI), Ul Usievicha 20, Moscow, 125190, Russian Federation. TEL 7-095-1526441, FAX 7-095-9430060, dir@viniti.ru, http://www.viniti.ru. Ed. Yurii Arskii.

016.57 RUS ISSN 0235-3105
REFERATIVNYI ZHURNAL. BIOLOGIYA SEL'SKOKHOZYAISTVENNYKH ZHIVOTNYKH. Text in Russian. 1959. m. USD 632 foreign (effective 2006). **Document type:** *Abstract/Index.*
Formerly: Referativnyi Zhurnal. Zhivotnovodstvo (0206-5533)
Related titles: CD-ROM ed.; Online - full text ed.
Indexed: ChemAb.
Published by: Vserossiiskii Institut Nauchnoi i Tekhnicheskoi Informatsii (VINITI), Ul Usievicha 20, Moscow, 125190, Russian Federation. TEL 7-095-1526441, FAX 7-095-9430060, dir@viniti.ru, http://www.viniti.ru. Ed. Yurii Arskii. **Dist. by:** Informnauka Ltd., Ul Usievicha 20, Moscow 125190, Russian Federation. alfimov@viniti.ru.

016.5714 RUS ISSN 0202-912X
REFERATIVNYI ZHURNAL. BIONIKA. BIOKIBERNETIKA. BIOINZHENERIYA. Text in Russian. 1975. m. USD 547 foreign (effective 2006). **Document type:** *Abstract/Index.*
Related titles: CD-ROM ed.; Online - full text ed.
Published by: Vserossiiskii Institut Nauchnoi i Tekhnicheskoi Informatsii (VINITI), Ul Usievicha 20, Moscow, 125190, Russian Federation. TEL 7-095-1526441, FAX 7-095-9430060, dir@viniti.ru, http://www.viniti.ru. **Dist. by:** Informnauka Ltd., Ul Usievicha 20, Moscow 125190, Russian Federation. alfimov@viniti.ru.

016.61028 RUS ISSN 0869-4125
REFERATIVNYI ZHURNAL. BIOTEKHNOLOGIYA. Text in Russian. 1982. m. USD 845 foreign (effective 2006). **Document type:** *Abstract/Index.*
Related titles: CD-ROM ed.; Online - full text ed.
—East View.
Published by: Vserossiiskii Institut Nauchnoi i Tekhnicheskoi Informatsii (VINITI), Ul Usievicha 20, Moscow, 125190, Russian Federation. TEL 7-095-1526441, FAX 7-095-9430060, dir@viniti.ru, http://www.viniti.ru. Ed. Yurii Arskii. **Dist. by:** Informnauka Ltd., Ul Usievicha 20, Moscow 125190, Russian Federation. alfimov@viniti.ru.

016.58 RUS ISSN 0869-4044
REFERATIVNYI ZHURNAL. BOTANIKA. Text in Russian. 1958. m. USD 1,647 foreign (effective 2006). **Document type:** *Abstract/Index.*
Related titles: CD-ROM ed.; Online - full text ed.
—East View.
Published by: Vserossiiskii Institut Nauchnoi i Tekhnicheskoi Informatsii (VINITI), Ul Usievicha 20, Moscow, 125190, Russian Federation. TEL 7-095-1526441, FAX 7-095-9430060, dir@viniti.ru, http://www.viniti.ru. Ed. Yurii Arskii. **Dist. by:** Informnauka Ltd., Ul Usievicha 20, Moscow 125190, Russian Federation. alfimov@viniti.ru.

016.58 RUS
REFERATIVNYI ZHURNAL. BOTANIKA. VODOROSLI, GRIBY, LISHAINIKI. Text in Russian. 1958. m. USD 229 foreign (effective 2006). **Document type:** *Abstract/Index.*
Related titles: CD-ROM ed.; Online - full text ed.
Published by: Vserossiiskii Institut Nauchnoi i Tekhnicheskoi Informatsii (VINITI), Ul Usievicha 20, Moscow, 125190, Russian Federation. TEL 7-095-1526441, FAX 7-095-9430060, dir@viniti.ru, http://www.viniti.ru. Ed. Yurii Arskii. **Dist. by:** Informnauka Ltd., Ul Usievicha 20, Moscow 125190, Russian Federation. alfimov@viniti.ru.

016.58 RUS
REFERATIVNYI ZHURNAL. BOTANIKA. VYSSHIE RASTENIYA. Text in Russian. 1958. m. USD 328 foreign (effective 2006). **Document type:** *Abstract/Index.*
Related titles: CD-ROM ed.; Online - full text ed.
Published by: Vserossiiskii Institut Nauchnoi i Tekhnicheskoi Informatsii (VINITI), Ul Usievicha 20, Moscow, 125190, Russian Federation. TEL 7-095-1526441, FAX 7-095-9430060, dir@viniti.ru, http://www.viniti.ru. Ed. Yurii Arskii. **Dist. by:** Informnauka Ltd., Ul Usievicha 20, Moscow 125190, Russian Federation. alfimov@viniti.ru.

016.5957 RUS ISSN 0202-9111
REFERATIVNYI ZHURNAL. ENTOMOLOGIYA. Text in Russian. 1963. m. USD 543 foreign (effective 2006). **Document type:** *Abstract/Index.*
Related titles: CD-ROM ed.; Online - full text ed.
Published by: Vserossiiskii Institut Nauchnoi i Tekhnicheskoi Informatsii (VINITI), Ul Usievicha 20, Moscow, 125190, Russian Federation. TEL 7-095-1526441, FAX 7-095-9430060, dir@viniti.ru, http://www.viniti.ru. **Dist. by:** Informnauka Ltd., Ul Usievicha 20, Moscow 125190, Russian Federation. alfimov@viniti.ru.

016.57 RUS ISSN 0202-9235
REFERATIVNYI ZHURNAL. FITOPATOLOGIYA. Text in Russian. 1978. m. USD 251 foreign (effective 2006). **Document type:** *Abstract/Index.*
Related titles: CD-ROM ed.; Online - full text ed.
Published by: Vserossiiskii Institut Nauchnoi i Tekhnicheskoi Informatsii (VINITI), Ul Usievicha 20, Moscow, 125190, Russian Federation. TEL 7-095-1526441, FAX 7-095-9430060, dir@viniti.ru, http://www.viniti.ru. Ed. Yurii Arskii. **Dist. by:** Informnauka Ltd., Ul Usievicha 20, Moscow 125190, Russian Federation. alfimov@viniti.ru.

016.571 RUS ISSN 0207-1460
REFERATIVNYI ZHURNAL. FIZIOLOGIYA CHELOVEKA I ZHIVOTNYKH. ENDOKRINNAYA SISTEMA, RAZMNOZHENIE, LAKTATSIYA. Text in Russian. 1961. m. USD 377 foreign (effective 2006). **Document type:** *Abstract/Index.*
Related titles: CD-ROM ed.; Online - full text ed.; ♦ Cumulative ed(s).: Referativnyi Zhurnal. Biologiya. Fiziologiya i Morfologiya Cheloveka i Zhivotnykh. ISSN 0869-4079.
—East View.
Published by: Vserossiiskii Institut Nauchnoi i Tekhnicheskoi Informatsii (VINITI), Ul Usievicha 20, Moscow, 125190, Russian Federation. TEL 7-095-1526441, FAX 7-095-9430060, dir@viniti.ru, http://www.viniti.ru. **Dist. by:** Informnauka Ltd., Ul Usievicha 20, Moscow 125190, Russian Federation. alfimov@viniti.ru.

016.571 RUS ISSN 0207-1436
REFERATIVNYI ZHURNAL. FIZIOLOGIYA CHELOVEKA I ZHIVOTNYKH. KROV', LIMFA, KROVOOBRASHCHENIE, DYKHANIE, POCHKI. Text in Russian. 1959. m. USD 696 foreign (effective 2006). **Document type:** *Abstract/Index.*
Related titles: CD-ROM ed.; Online - full text ed.; ♦ Cumulative ed(s).: Referativnyi Zhurnal. Biologiya. Fiziologiya i Morfologiya Cheloveka i Zhivotnykh. ISSN 0869-4079.
Published by: Vserossiiskii Institut Nauchnoi i Tekhnicheskoi Informatsii (VINITI), Ul Usievicha 20, Moscow, 125190, Russian Federation. TEL 7-095-1526441, FAX 7-095-9430060, dir@viniti.ru, http://www.viniti.ru. **Dist. by:** Informnauka Ltd., Ul Usievicha 20, Moscow 125190, Russian Federation. alfimov@viniti.ru.

016.571 RUS ISSN 0207-1444
REFERATIVNYI ZHURNAL. FIZIOLOGIYA CHELOVEKA I ZHIVOTNYKH. NEIROFIZIOLOGIYA, SENSORNYE SISTEMY, V N D, NERVNO-MYSHECHNAYA SISTEMA. Text in Russian. 1959. m. USD 477 foreign (effective 2006). **Document type:** *Abstract/Index.*
Related titles: CD-ROM ed.; Online - full text ed.; ♦ Cumulative ed(s).: Referativnyi Zhurnal. Biologiya. Fiziologiya i Morfologiya Cheloveka i Zhivotnykh. ISSN 0869-4079.
—East View.
Published by: Vserossiiskii Institut Nauchnoi i Tekhnicheskoi Informatsii (VINITI), Ul Usievicha 20, Moscow, 125190, Russian Federation. TEL 7-095-1526441, FAX 7-095-9430060, dir@viniti.ru, http://www.viniti.ru. **Dist. by:** Informnauka Ltd., Ul Usievicha 20, Moscow 125190, Russian Federation. alfimov@viniti.ru.

016.571 RUS ISSN 0208-2853
REFERATIVNYI ZHURNAL. FIZIOLOGIYA CHELOVEKA I ZHIVOTNYKH. OBMEN VESHCHESTV, PITANIE, PISHCHEVARENIE. Text in Russian. 1959. m. USD 402 foreign (effective 2006). **Document type:** *Abstract/Index.*
Related titles: CD-ROM ed.; Online - full text ed.; ♦ Cumulative ed(s).: Referativnyi Zhurnal. Biologiya. Fiziologiya i Morfologiya Cheloveka i Zhivotnykh. ISSN 0869-4079.
—East View.
Published by: Vserossiiskii Institut Nauchnoi i Tekhnicheskoi Informatsii (VINITI), Ul Usievicha 20, Moscow, 125190, Russian Federation. TEL 7-095-1526441, FAX 7-095-9430060, dir@viniti.ru, http://www.viniti.ru. **Dist. by:** Informnauka Ltd., Ul Usievicha 20, Moscow 125190, Russian Federation. alfimov@viniti.ru.

016.571 RUS
REFERATIVNYI ZHURNAL. FIZIOLOGIYA CHELOVEKA I ZHIVOTNYKH. OBSHCHIE PROBLEMY, VOZRASTNAYA FIZIOLOGIYA. Text in Russian. m. USD 425 foreign (effective 2006). **Document type:** *Abstract/Index.*
Related titles: CD-ROM ed.; Online - full text ed.; ♦ Cumulative ed(s).: Referativnyi Zhurnal. Biologiya. Fiziologiya i Morfologiya Cheloveka i Zhivotnykh. ISSN 0869-4079.
Indexed: RASB.
Published by: Vserossiiskii Institut Nauchnoi i Tekhnicheskoi Informatsii (VINITI), Ul Usievicha 20, Moscow, 125190, Russian Federation. TEL 7-095-1526441, FAX 7-095-9430060, dir@viniti.ru, http://www.viniti.ru. **Dist. by:** Informnauka Ltd., Ul Usievicha 20, Moscow 125190, Russian Federation. alfimov@viniti.ru.

016.571 016.522 RUS ISSN 0202-4241
REFERATIVNYI ZHURNAL. FIZIOLOGIYA I BIOKHIMIYA RASTENII. Text in Russian. 1961. m. USD 326 foreign (effective 2006). **Document type:** *Abstract/Index.*
Related titles: CD-ROM ed.; Online - full text ed.
—East View.
Published by: Vserossiiskii Institut Nauchnoi i Tekhnicheskoi Informatsii (VINITI), Ul Usievicha 20, Moscow, 125190, Russian Federation. TEL 7-095-1526441, FAX 7-095-9430060, dir@viniti.ru, http://www.viniti.ru. Ed. Yurii Arskii. **Dist. by:** Informnauka Ltd., Ul Usievicha 20, Moscow 125190, Russian Federation. alfimov@viniti.ru.

016.5765 RUS ISSN 0202-9146
REFERATIVNYI ZHURNAL. GENETIKA CHELOVEKA. Text in Russian. 1969. m. USD 430 foreign (effective 2006). **Document type:** *Abstract/Index.*
Related titles: CD-ROM ed.; Online - full text ed.
—East View.
Published by: Vserossiiskii Institut Nauchnoi i Tekhnicheskoi Informatsii (VINITI), Ul Usievicha 20, Moscow, 125190, Russian Federation. TEL 7-095-1526441, FAX 7-095-9430060, dir@viniti.ru, http://www.viniti.ru. Ed. Yurii Arskii. **Dist. by:** Informnauka Ltd., Ul Usievicha 20, Moscow 125190, Russian Federation. alfimov@viniti.ru.

016.5999 RUS ISSN 0235-8913
REFERATIVNYI ZHURNAL. GENETIKA I SELEKTSIYA MIKROORGANIZMOV. Text in Russian. 1991. m. USD 336 foreign (effective 2006). **Document type:** *Journal, Abstract/Index.*
Related titles: CD-ROM ed.; Online - full text ed.
—East View.
Published by: Vserossiiskii Institut Nauchnoi i Tekhnicheskoi Informatsii (VINITI), Ul Usievicha 20, Moscow, 125190, Russian Federation. TEL 7-095-1526441, FAX 7-095-9430060, dir@viniti.ru, http://www.viniti.ru. Ed. Yurii Arskii. **Dist. by:** Informnauka Ltd., Ul Usievicha 20, Moscow 125190, Russian Federation. alfimov@viniti.ru.

016.5999 RUS ISSN 0235-8921
REFERATIVNYI ZHURNAL. GENETIKA I SELEKTSIYA SEL'SKOKHOZYAISTVENNYKH ZHIVOTNYKH. Text in Russian. 1990. m. USD 145 foreign (effective 2006). **Document type:** *Abstract/Index.*
Related titles: CD-ROM ed.; Online - full text ed.
—East View.
Published by: Vserossiiskii Institut Nauchnoi i Tekhnicheskoi Informatsii (VINITI), Ul Usievicha 20, Moscow, 125190, Russian Federation. TEL 7-095-1526441, FAX 7-095-9430060, dir@viniti.ru, http://www.viniti.ru. Ed. Yurii Arskii. **Dist. by:** Informnauka Ltd., Ul Usievicha 20, Moscow 125190, Russian Federation. alfimov@viniti.ru.

016.5765 RUS ISSN 0202-9138
REFERATIVNYI ZHURNAL. GENETIKA I SELEKTSIYA VOZDELYVAEMYKH RASTENII. Text in Russian. 1978. m. USD 405 foreign (effective 2006). **Document type:** *Abstract/Index.*
Related titles: CD-ROM ed.; Online - full text ed.
—East View.
Published by: Vserossiiskii Institut Nauchnoi i Tekhnicheskoi Informatsii (VINITI), Ul Usievicha 20, Moscow, 125190, Russian Federation. TEL 7-095-1526441, FAX 7-095-9430060, dir@viniti.ru, http://www.viniti.ru. Ed. Yurii Arskii. **Dist. by:** Informnauka Ltd., Ul Usievicha 20, Moscow 125190, Russian Federation. alfimov@viniti.ru.

016.590 RUS
REFERATIVNYI ZHURNAL. IKHTIOLOGIYA. Text in Russian. 1979. m. USD 305 foreign (effective 2006). **Document type:** *Journal, Abstract/Index.*
Related titles: CD-ROM ed.; Online - full text ed.
Published by: Vserossiiskii Institut Nauchnoi i Tekhnicheskoi Informatsii (VINITI), Ul Usievicha 20, Moscow, 125190, Russian Federation. TEL 7-095-1526441, FAX 7-095-9430060, dir@viniti.ru, http://www.viniti.ru. **Dist. by:** Informnauka Ltd., Ul Usievicha 20, Moscow 125190, Russian Federation. alfimov@viniti.ru.

016.580 RUS
REFERATIVNYI ZHURNAL. LEKARTSVENNYE RASTENIYA. Text in Russian. 1991. m. USD 102 foreign (effective 2004). **Document type:** *Journal, Abstract/Index.*
Related titles: Online - full text ed.
Published by: Vserossiiskii Institut Nauchnoi i Tekhnicheskoi Informatsii (VINITI), Ul Usievicha 20, Moscow, 125190, Russian Federation. TEL 7-095-1526441, FAX 7-095-9430060, dir@viniti.ru, http://www.viniti.ru. **Dist. by:** Informnauka Ltd., Ul Usievicha 20, Moscow 125190, Russian Federation. alfimov@viniti.ru.

016.579 RUS ISSN 0208-1466
REFERATIVNYI ZHURNAL. MIKROBIOLOGIYA OBSHCHAYA. Text in Russian. 1959. m. USD 327 foreign (effective 2006). **Document type:** *Abstract/Index.*
Related titles: CD-ROM ed.; Online - full text ed.
—East View.
Published by: Vserossiiskii Institut Nauchnoi i Tekhnicheskoi Informatsii (VINITI), Ul Usievicha 20, Moscow, 125190, Russian Federation. TEL 7-095-1526441, FAX 7-095-9430060, dir@viniti.ru, http://www.viniti.ru. Ed. Yurii Arskii. **Dist. by:** Informnauka Ltd., Ul Usievicha 20, Moscow 125190, Russian Federation. alfimov@viniti.ru.

016.579 RUS
REFERATIVNYI ZHURNAL. MIKROBIOLOGIYA PRIKLADNAYA. Text in Russian. 1958. m. USD 305 foreign (effective 2006). **Document type:** *Abstract/Index.*
Related titles: CD-ROM ed.; Online - full text ed.
Published by: Vserossiiskii Institut Nauchnoi i Tekhnicheskoi Informatsii (VINITI), Ul Usievicha 20, Moscow, 125190, Russian Federation. TEL 7-095-1526441, FAX 7-095-9430060, dir@viniti.ru, http://www.viniti.ru. **Dist. by:** Informnauka Ltd., Ul Usievicha 20, Moscow 125190, Russian Federation. alfimov@viniti.ru.

016.579 RUS ISSN 0206-5517
REFERATIVNYI ZHURNAL. MIKROBIOLOGIYA SANITARNAYA I MEDITSINSKAYA. Text in Russian. 1958. m. USD 405 foreign (effective 2006). **Document type:** *Abstract/Index.*
Related titles: CD-ROM ed.; Online - full text ed.
—East View.
Published by: Vserossiiskii Institut Nauchnoi i Tekhnicheskoi Informatsii (VINITI), Ul Usievicha 20, Moscow, 125190, Russian Federation. TEL 7-095-1526441, FAX 7-095-9430060, dir@viniti.ru, http://www.viniti.ru. Ed. Yurii Arskii. **Dist. by:** Informnauka Ltd., Ul Usievicha 20, Moscow 125190, Russian Federation. alfimov@viniti.ru.

016.5728 RUS ISSN 0207-8619
REFERATIVNYI ZHURNAL. MOLEKULYARNAYA BIOLOGIYA. Text in Russian. 1975. m. USD 1,098 foreign (effective 2006). **Document type:** *Abstract/Index.*
Related titles: CD-ROM ed.; Online - full text ed.
—East View.
Published by: Vserossiiskii Institut Nauchnoi i Tekhnicheskoi Informatsii (VINITI), Ul Usievicha 20, Moscow, 125190, Russian Federation. TEL 7-095-1526441, FAX 7-095-9430060, dir@viniti.ru, http://www.viniti.ru. **Dist. by:** Informnauka Ltd., Ul Usievicha 20, Moscow 125190, Russian Federation. alfimov@viniti.ru.

016.577 RUS
REFERATIVNYI ZHURNAL. OBSHCHAYA EKOLOGIYA. BIOTSENOLOGIYA. GIDROBIOLOGIYA. Text in Russian. 1969. m. USD 385 foreign (effective 2006). **Document type:** *Journal, Abstract/Index.*
Related titles: CD-ROM ed.; Online - full text ed.
Published by: Vserossiiskii Institut Nauchnoi i Tekhnicheskoi Informatsii (VINITI), Ul Usievicha 20, Moscow, 125190, Russian Federation. TEL 7-095-1526441, FAX 7-095-9430060, dir@viniti.ru, http://www.viniti.ru. **Dist. by:** Informnauka Ltd., Ul Usievicha 20, Moscow 125190, Russian Federation. alfimov@viniti.ru.

016.5765 RUS
REFERATIVNYI ZHURNAL. OBSHCHAYA GENETIKA. Text in Russian. 1964. m. USD 537 foreign (effective 2006). **Document type:** *Abstract/Index.*
Related titles: CD-ROM ed.; Online - full text ed.
Published by: Vserossiiskii Institut Nauchnoi i Tekhnicheskoi Informatsii (VINITI), Ul Usievicha 20, Moscow, 125190, Russian Federation. TEL 7-095-1526441, FAX 7-095-9430060, dir@viniti.ru, http://www.viniti.ru. Ed. Yurii Arskii. **Dist. by:** Informnauka Ltd., Ul Usievicha 20, Moscow 125190, Russian Federation. alfimov@viniti.ru.

016.5719 RUS
REFERATIVNYI ZHURNAL. OBSHCHIE VOPROSY PATOLOGICHESKOI ANATOMII. Text in Russian. 1976. m. USD 355 foreign (effective 2006). **Document type:** *Abstract/Index.*
Formerly: Referativnyi Zhurnal. Obshchie Voprosy Patologii (0202-9189)
Related titles: CD-ROM ed.; Online - full text ed.; ♦ Cumulative ed(s).: Referativnyi Zhurnal. Biologiya. Fiziologiya i Morfologiya Cheloveka i Zhivotnykh. ISSN 0869-4079.
Published by: Vserossiiskii Institut Nauchnoi i Tekhnicheskoi Informatsii (VINITI), Ul Usievicha 20, Moscow, 125190, Russian Federation. TEL 7-095-1526441, FAX 7-095-9430060, dir@viniti.ru, http://www.viniti.ru. **Subscr. in US to:** East View Information Services; **Dist. by:** Informnauka Ltd., Ul Usievicha 20, Moscow 125190, Russian Federation. alfimov@viniti.ru.

016.5714 RUS ISSN 0131-355X
QH652.A1 CODEN: RZRBDD
REFERATIVNYI ZHURNAL. RADIATSIONNAYA BIOLOGIYA. Text in Russian. 1973. m. USD 506 foreign (effective 2006). **Document type:** *Abstract/Index.*
Related titles: CD-ROM ed.; Online - full text ed.
Indexed: ChemAb.
—CASDDS, Linda Hall.
Published by: Vserossiiskii Institut Nauchnoi i Tekhnicheskoi Informatsii (VINITI), Ul Usievicha 20, Moscow, 125190, Russian Federation. TEL 7-095-1526441, FAX 7-095-9430060, dir@viniti.ru, http://www.viniti.ru. **Dist. by:** Informnauka Ltd., Ul Usievicha 20, Moscow 125190, Russian Federation. alfimov@viniti.ru.

016.57 RUS ISSN 0202-9200
CODEN: RZRAA7
REFERATIVNYI ZHURNAL. RASTENIEVODSTVO (BIOLOGICHESKIE OSNOVY). Text in Russian. 1961. m. USD 673 foreign (effective 2006). **Document type:** *Abstract/Index.*
Related titles: CD-ROM ed.; Online - full text ed.
Indexed: ChemAb.
—Linda Hall.
Published by: Vserossiiskii Institut Nauchnoi i Tekhnicheskoi Informatsii (VINITI), Ul Usievicha 20, Moscow, 125190, Russian Federation. TEL 7-095-1526441, FAX 7-095-9430060, dir@viniti.ru, http://www.viniti.ru. Ed. Yurii Arskii. **Dist. by:** Informnauka Ltd., Ul Usievicha 20, Moscow 125190, Russian Federation. alfimov@viniti.ru.

016.5716 RUS ISSN 0202-9103
REFERATIVNYI ZHURNAL. TSITOLOGIYA. Text in Russian. 1964. m. USD 351 foreign (effective 2006). **Document type:** *Abstract/Index.*
Related titles: CD-ROM ed.; Online - full text ed.
—East View.
Published by: Vserossiiskii Institut Nauchnoi i Tekhnicheskoi Informatsii (VINITI), Ul Usievicha 20, Moscow, 125190, Russian Federation. TEL 7-095-1526441, FAX 7-095-9430060, dir@viniti.ru, http://www.viniti.ru. Ed. Yurii Arskii. **Dist. by:** Informnauka Ltd., Ul Usievicha 20, Moscow 125190, Russian Federation. alfimov@viniti.ru.

016.579 RUS
REFERATIVNYI ZHURNAL. VIRUSOLOGIYA. Text in Russian. 1959. m. USD 509 foreign (effective 2006). **Document type:** *Abstract/Index.*
Related titles: CD-ROM ed.; Online - full text ed.
Published by: Vserossiiskii Institut Nauchnoi i Tekhnicheskoi Informatsii (VINITI), Ul Usievicha 20, Moscow, 125190, Russian Federation. TEL 7-095-1526441, FAX 7-095-9430060, dir@viniti.ru, http://www.viniti.ru. Ed. Yurii Arskii. **Dist. by:** Informnauka Ltd., Ul Usievicha 20, Moscow 125190, Russian Federation. alfimov@viniti.ru.

016.5792 RUS ISSN 0201-5226
REFERATIVNYI ZHURNAL. VIRUSOLOGIYA. MIKROBIOLOGIYA. Text in Russian. 1959. m. USD 1,014 foreign (effective 2006). **Document type:** *Abstract/Index.*
Related titles: CD-ROM ed.; Online - full text ed.
Published by: Vserossiiskii Institut Nauchnoi i Tekhnicheskoi Informatsii (VINITI), Ul Usievicha 20, Moscow, 125190, Russian Federation. TEL 7-095-1526441, FAX 7-095-9430060, dir@viniti.ru, http://www.viniti.ru. Ed. Yurii Arskii. **Dist. by:** Informnauka Ltd., Ul Usievicha 20, Moscow 125190, Russian Federation. alfimov@viniti.ru.

590 RUS ISSN 0869-4052
REFERATIVNYI ZHURNAL. ZOOLOGIYA. Text in Russian. 1958. m. USD 1,470 foreign (effective 2006). **Document type:** *Academic/Scholarly.*
Related titles: CD-ROM ed.; Online - full text ed.
—East View.
Published by: Vserossiiskii Institut Nauchnoi i Tekhnicheskoi Informatsii (VINITI), Ul Usievicha 20, Moscow, 125190, Russian Federation. TEL 7-095-1526441, FAX 7-095-9430060, dir@viniti.ru, http://www.viniti.ru. Ed. Yurii Arskii. **Dist. by:** Informnauka Ltd., Ul Usievicha 20, Moscow 125190, Russian Federation. alfimov@viniti.ru.

REFERATIVNYI ZHURNAL. ZOOLOGIYA NAZEMNYKH POZVONOCHNYKH: OBSHCHIE VOPROSY. GERPETOLOGIYA. see *BIOLOGY—Zoology*

590 RUS
REFERATIVNYI ZHURNAL. ZOOLOGIYA NAZEMNYKH POZVONOCHNYKH: ORNITOLOGIYA. Text in Russian. 1962. m. USD 215 foreign (effective 2006). **Document type:** *Journal, Abstract/Index.*
Related titles: CD-ROM ed.; Online - full text ed.
Published by: Vserossiiskii Institut Nauchnoi i Tekhnicheskoi Informatsii (VINITI), Ul Usievicha 20, Moscow, 125190, Russian Federation. TEL 7-095-1526441, FAX 7-095-9430060, dir@viniti.ru, http://www.viniti.ru. Ed. Yurii Arskii. **Dist. by:** Informnauka Ltd., Ul Usievicha 20, Moscow 125190, Russian Federation. alfimov@viniti.ru.

590 RUS
REFERATIVNYI ZHURNAL. ZOOLOGIYA NAZEMNYKH POZVONOCHNYKH: TERIOLOGIYA, OKHOTOVEDENIE, ZOOPARKI. Text in Russian. 1962. m. USD 215 foreign (effective 2006). **Document type:** *Abstract/Index.*
Related titles: CD-ROM ed.; Online - full text ed.
Published by: Vserossiiskii Institut Nauchnoi i Tekhnicheskoi Informatsii (VINITI), Ul Usievicha 20, Moscow, 125190, Russian Federation. TEL 7-095-1526441, FAX 7-095-9430060, dir@viniti.ru, http://www.viniti.ru. **Dist. by:** Informnauka Ltd., Ul Usievicha 20, Moscow 125190, Russian Federation. alfimov@viniti.ru.

590 RUS
REFERATIVNYI ZHURNAL. ZOOLOGIYA OBSHCHAYA. ZOOLOGIYA BESPOZVONOCHNYKH. Text in Russian. 1962. m. USD 247 foreign (effective 2006). **Document type:** *Abstract/Index.*
Related titles: CD-ROM ed.; Online - full text ed.
Published by: Vserossiiskii Institut Nauchnoi i Tekhnicheskoi Informatsii (VINITI), Ul Usievicha 20, Moscow, 125190, Russian Federation. TEL 7-095-1526441, FAX 7-095-9430060, dir@viniti.ru, http://www.viniti.ru. Ed. Yurii Arskii. **Dist. by:** Informnauka Ltd., Ul Usievicha 20, Moscow 125190, Russian Federation. alfimov@viniti.ru.

590 RUS
REFERATIVNYI ZHURNAL. ZOOPARAZITOLOGIYA. Text in Russian. 1960. m. USD 313 foreign (effective 2006). **Document type:** *Abstract/Index.*
Related titles: CD-ROM ed.; Online - full text ed.
Published by: Vserossiiskii Institut Nauchnoi i Tekhnicheskoi Informatsii (VINITI), Ul Usievicha 20, Moscow, 125190, Russian Federation. TEL 7-095-1526441, FAX 7-095-9430060, dir@viniti.ru, http://www.viniti.ru. Ed. Yurii Arskii. **Dist. by:** Informnauka Ltd., Ul Usievicha 20, Moscow 125190, Russian Federation. alfimov@viniti.ru.

B

▼ *new title* ➤ *refereed* ✶ *unverified* ♦ *full entry avail.*

016.5734 016.6164 GBR ISSN 0143-4284
RENIN, ANGIOTENSIN & KININS. Text in English. 1980. s-m. GBP 120 for print ed. or e-mail (effective 2001). adv. **Document type:** *Abstract/Index.* **Description:** Current awareness service for researchers.
Related titles: E-mail ed.; Online - full text ed.: GBP 108 to individuals (effective 2001).
—CCC.
Published by: S U B I S (Subsidiary of: Sheffield Academic Press Ltd), Mansion House, 19 Kingfield Rd, Sheffield, S Yorks S11 9AS, United Kingdom. TEL 44-114-255-4433, FAX 44-114-255-4626, subis@sheffac.demon.co.uk, http://www.shef-ac-press.co.uk/subis. Ed. S Huntridge. Adv. contact C Evans.

016.5736 GBR ISSN 1476-3990
QP251
REPRODUCTION. ABSTRACT SERIES. Text in English. 1988. irreg., latest vol.29. price varies. adv. 2 cols./p.; back issues avail. **Document type:** *Proceedings, Academic/Scholarly.*
Formerly (until 2001): Journal of Reproduction and Fertility. Abstract Series (0954-0725)
Related titles: ◆ Supplement to: Journal of Reproduction and Fertility. ISSN 0022-4251.
Indexed: AgBio, AnBrAb, BIOSIS Prev, BiolAb, IndMed, IndVet, MEDLINE, PN&I, PoultAb, SFA, VetBull, WildRev.
—BLDSC (7713.597810), CISTI, KNAW, Linda Hall. **CCC.**
Published by: Society for Reproduction and Fertility, 22 Newmarket Rd, Cambridge, CB5 8DT, United Kingdom. TEL 44-1223-351809, FAX 44-1223-359754, reproduction@srf-reproduction-journal.org, http://www.srf-reproduction.org/. Ed. Dr. C A Doberska. Adv. contact Mrs. C H Clarke. **Dist. by:** Portland Press Ltd., Commerce Way, Colchester CO2 8HP, United Kingdom. TEL 44-1206-796-351, FAX 44-1206-799-331, sales@portland-services.com, http://www.portland-services.com.

B

016.581634 GBR ISSN 1356-1421
REVIEW OF AROMATIC AND MEDICINAL PLANTS. Text in English. 1995. bi-m. USD 675 in the Americas to institutions except Canada; GBP 385 elsewhere to institutions; USD 720 combined subscription in the Americas to institutions except Canada; print & online eds.; GBP 410 combined subscription elsewhere to institutions print & online eds. (effective 2006). adv. back issues avail. **Document type:** *Abstract/Index.* **Description:** Series of annotated bibliographies covering medicinal, aromatic and pesticidal plants.
Related titles: Online - full text ed.: USD 570 in the Americas to institutions except Canada; GBP 325 elsewhere to institutions (effective 2006).
Indexed: HortAb, TDB.
—CCC.
Published by: CABI Publishing (Subsidiary of: CAB International), CAB International, Wallingford, Oxfordshire OX10 8DE, United Kingdom. TEL 44-1491-832111, FAX 44-1491-833508, cabi@cabi.org, http://www.cabi-publishing.org/. Ed. Debbie Cousins. Adv. contact Sarah Harris TEL 44-1491-829310. B&W page GBP 120, B&W page USD 190; 170 x 267. Circ: 245. **Subscr. addr. in N America:** CABI Publishing North America, 875 Massachusetts Ave, 7th Fl, Cambridge, MA 02139. TEL 617-395-4056, 800-528-4841, FAX 617-354-6875, cabi-nao@cabi.org.

REVIEW OF MEDICAL AND VETERINARY ENTOMOLOGY. see *MEDICAL SCIENCES—Abstracting, Bibliographies, Statistics*

016.5795 GBR ISSN 0034-6624
REVIEW OF MEDICAL AND VETERINARY MYCOLOGY. Text in English. 1943. q. USD 980 in the Americas to institutions except Canada; GBP 560 elsewhere to institutions; USD 1,050 combined subscription in the Americas to institutions except Canada; print & online eds.; GBP 600 combined subscription elsewhere to institutions print & online eds. (effective 2006). adv. **Document type:** *Journal, Abstract/Index.* **Description:** Covers mycoses of man and domestic, farm, and wild animals, along with allergic disorders associated with fungi and poisoning by fungi or mold-contaminated foods.
Related titles: Online - full text ed.: USD 830 in the Americas to institutions except Canada; GBP 475 elsewhere to institutions (effective 2006) (from DIMDI, The Dialog Corporation).
—CISTI, GNLM. **CCC.**
Published by: CABI Publishing (Subsidiary of: CAB International), CAB International, Wallingford, Oxfordshire OX10 8DE, United Kingdom. TEL 44-1491-832111, FAX 44-1491-833508, cabi@cabi.org, http://www.cabi-publishing.org/. Ed. James A H Brooks. Adv. contact Sarah Harris TEL 44-1491-829310. B&W page GBP 75, B&W page USD 120; 170 x 267. Circ: 200. **Subscr. addr. in N America:** CABI Publishing North America, 875 Massachusetts Ave, 7th Fl, Cambridge, MA 02139. TEL 617-395-4056, 800-528-4841, FAX 617-354-6875, cabi-nao@cabi.org.

016.57192 GBR ISSN 0034-6438
SB599
REVIEW OF PLANT PATHOLOGY; consisting of abstracts and reviews of current literature on plant pathology. Text in English. 1922. m. USD 1,820 in the Americas to institutions except Canada; GBP 1,040 elsewhere to institutions; USD 1,950 combined subscription in the Americas to institutions except Canada; print & online eds.; GBP 1,115 combined subscription elsewhere to institutions print & online eds. (effective 2006). adv. bk.rev. abstr. index. **Document type:** *Journal, Abstract/Index.* **Description:** Covers diseases of crop plants, ornamental plants and forest trees caused by fungi, bacteria, viruses, mycoplasma-like organisms, and nonparasitic factors and their control.
Formerly (until 1970): Review of Applied Mycology (0375-0671)
Related titles: Online - full text ed.: USD 1,550 in the Americas to institutions except Canada; GBP 885 elsewhere to institutions (effective 2006) (from DIMDI, EBSCO Publishing, The Dialog Corporation).
Indexed: TriticAb.
—CISTI, Linda Hall. **CCC.**
Published by: CABI Publishing (Subsidiary of: CAB International), CAB International, Wallingford, Oxfordshire OX10 8DE, United Kingdom. TEL 44-1491-832111, FAX 44-1491-833508, cabi@cabi.org, http://www.cabi-publishing.org/. Adv. contact Sarah Harris TEL 44-1491-829310. B&W page GBP 250, B&W page USD 395; 170 x 267. Circ: 690. **Subscr. addr. in N America:** CABI Publishing North America, 875 Massachusetts Ave, 7th Fl, Cambridge, MA 02139. TEL 617-395-4056, 800-528-4841, FAX 617-354-6875, cabi-nao@cabi.org.

016.571658 GBR ISSN 0952-0414
RIBOSOMES AND TRANSLATION. Text in English. 1970. s-m. GBP 96 for print ed. or email (effective 2001). adv. **Document type:** *Abstract/Index.* **Description:** Current awareness service for researchers in clinical and life sciences.
Formerly (until 1987): Ribosomes (0142-8322)
Related titles: E-mail ed.; Online - full text ed.: GBP 108 to individuals (effective 2001).
—CCC.
Published by: S U B I S (Subsidiary of: Sheffield Academic Press Ltd), Mansion House, 19 Kingfield Rd, Sheffield, S Yorks S11 9AS, United Kingdom. TEL 44-114-255-4433, FAX 44-114-255-4626, subis@sheffac.demon.co.uk, http://www.shef-ac-press.co.uk/subis. Ed. S Huntridge. Adv. contact C Evans.

016.597079 USA ISSN 0887-4220
SEA GRANT ABSTRACTS; publications from the nation's Sea Grant programs. Text in English. 1985. q. free to qualified personnel. bk.rev. back issues avail. **Document type:** *Abstract/Index.* **Description:** Documents and facilitates the acquisition of publications originating from the program.
Related titles: CD-ROM ed.: (from National Information Services Corp. (N I S C)).
Published by: (National Sea Grant Depository), Woods Hole Data Base, Inc., PO Box 712, Woods Hole, MA 02543. TEL 508-548-2743. Eds. Cynthia Murray, Frank Shephard. Circ: 6,000. **Subscr. to:** PO Box 84, Woods Hole, MA 02543.

016.581467 GBR ISSN 0141-0180
SEED ABSTRACTS. Text in English. 1978. m. USD 955 in the Americas to institutions except Canada; GBP 545 elsewhere to institutions; USD 1,025 combined subscription in the Americas to institutions except Canada; print & online eds.; GBP 585 combined subscription elsewhere to institutions print & online eds. (effective 2006). adv. back issues avail. **Document type:** *Abstract/Index.* **Description:** Topics covered include seed morphology and anatomy, seed chemistry, germination, seed storage and longevity, breeding and selection, seed assessment and testing, seed regulations, seed development, seed ecology, seed production, pests and diseases, seed processing, economics, and marketing.
Related titles: Online - full text ed.: USD 815 in the Americas to institutions except Canada; GBP 465 elsewhere to institutions (effective 2006) (from DIMDI, The Dialog Corporation).
—CCC.
Published by: CABI Publishing (Subsidiary of: CAB International), CAB International, Wallingford, Oxfordshire OX10 8DE, United Kingdom. TEL 44-1491-832111, FAX 44-1491-833508, cabi@cabi.org, http://www.cabi-publishing.org/. Adv. contact Sarah Harris TEL 44-1491-829310. B&W page GBP 65, B&W page USD 105; 170 x 267. Circ: 180. **Subscr. addr. in N America:** CABI Publishing North America, 875 Massachusetts Ave, 7th Fl, Cambridge, MA 02139. TEL 617-395-4056, 800-528-4841, FAX 617-354-6875, cabi-nao@cabi.org.

016.58 JPN
SHIDA SHOKUBUTSU BUNKEN MOKUROKU/BIBLIOGRAPHY OF PTERIDOPHYTES BY JAPANESE FERNISTS. Text in Japanese. a. **Document type:** *Bibliography.*
Published by: Nippon Shida no Kai/Nippon Fernist Club, Tokyo Nogyo Daigaku Seibutsugaku Kenkyushitsu, 1-1 Sakuragaoka 1-chome, Setagaya-ku, Tokyo, 157, Japan.

016.58 JPN
SHOKUBUTSU SOSHIKI SAIBOU BUNSHISEIBUTSU GAKKAI TAIKAI SHINPOJUMU KOEN YOSHISHU/JAPANESE SOCIETY FOR PLANT CELL AND MOLECULAR BIOLOGY. ABSTRACTS OF THE MEETING AND SYMPOSIUM. Text in English, Japanese. biennial. **Document type:** *Abstract/Index.*
Formerly: Shokubutsu Soshiki Baiyo Gakkai Taikai Shinpojumu Koen Yoshishu - Japanese Association for Plant Tissue Culture. Abstracts of the Meeting and Symposium
Published by: Nihon Shokubutsu Saibou Bunshiseibutsu Gakkai/Japanese Society for Plant Cell and Molecular Biology, 30-15 Hongo 5-chome, Bunkyo-ku, Tokyo, 113-0033, Japan.

016.572 GBR ISSN 0964-7589
SIGNAL TRANSDUCTION & CYCLIC NUCLEOTIDES. Text in English. 1970. s-m. GBP 120 for print ed. or e-mail (effective 2001). adv. **Document type:** *Abstract/Index.* **Description:** Current awareness service for researchers in clinical and life sciences.
Supersedes: Signal Transduction (0952-0392); Cyclic A M P (0142-8055)
Related titles: E-mail ed.; Online - full text ed.: GBP 108 to individuals (effective 2001).
—CCC.
Published by: S U B I S (Subsidiary of: Sheffield Academic Press Ltd), Mansion House, 19 Kingfield Rd, Sheffield, S Yorks S11 9AS, United Kingdom. TEL 44-114-255-4433, FAX 44-114-255-4626, subis@sheffac.demon.co.uk, http://www.shef-ac-press.co.uk/subis. Ed. S Huntridge. Adv. contact C Evans.

016.58374 GBR
SOYBEAN ABSTRACTS (ONLINE EDITION). Text in English. 1978. w. USD 620 in the Americas to institutions except Canada; GBP 355 elsewhere to institutions (effective 2006). back issues avail. **Document type:** *Abstract/Index.* **Description:** Topics covered include: breeding and selection, agronomy, physiological disorders, nitrogen fixation, physiology and biochemistry, storage and quality, nutrition and utilization, varieties and varietal resistance, fertilizers, pests and diseases, climate and environment, harvesting, food technology, and economics.
Media: Online - full content (from DIMDI, The Dialog Corporation).
Published by: CABI Publishing (Subsidiary of: CAB International), CAB International, Wallingford, Oxfordshire OX10 8DE, United Kingdom. TEL 44-1491-832111, FAX 44-1491-833508, cabi@cabi.org, http://www.cabi-publishing.org/. **Subscr. addr. in N America:** CABI Publishing North America, 875 Massachusetts Ave, 7th Fl, Cambridge, MA 02139. TEL 617-395-4056, 800-528-4841, FAX 617-354-6875, cabi-nao@cabi.org.

016.572579 GBR ISSN 0142-8330
STEROID RECEPTORS. Text in English. 1976. s-m. GBP 120 for print ed. or e-mail (effective 2001). adv. **Document type:** *Abstract/Index.* **Description:** Current awareness service for researchers. Covers receptors for androgens, vitamin D, estrogens, progesterone, corticosteroids.
Related titles: E-mail ed.; Online - full text ed.: GBP 108 to individuals (effective 2001).
—CCC.
Published by: S U B I S (Subsidiary of: Sheffield Academic Press Ltd), Mansion House, 19 Kingfield Rd, Sheffield, S Yorks S11 9AS, United Kingdom. TEL 44-114-255-4433, FAX 44-114-255-4626, subis@sheffac.demon.co.uk, http://www.shef-ac-press.co.uk/subis. Ed. S Huntridge. Adv. contact C Evans.

016.5716 GBR ISSN 0142-8810
TISSUE CULTURE. Text in English. 1981. s-m. adv. **Document type:** *Abstract/Index.* **Description:** Current awareness service for researchers. Focuses on animal cells, especially growth factors tested in vitro, cell growth in vitro, organ culture.
Related titles: E-mail ed.; Online - full text ed.: GBP 108 to individuals (effective 2001).
—CCC.
Published by: S U B I S (Subsidiary of: Sheffield Academic Press Ltd), Mansion House, 19 Kingfield Rd, Sheffield, S Yorks S11 9AS, United Kingdom. TEL 44-114-255-4433, FAX 44-114-255-4626, subis@sheffac.demon.co.uk, http://www.shef-ac-press.co.uk/subis. Ed. S Huntridge. Adv. contact C Evans.

016.571 JPN
TOKYO SHIKA DAIGAKU SEIRIGAKU KYOSHITSU GYOSEKISHU/TOKYO DENTAL COLLEGE. DEPARTMENT OF PHYSIOLOGY. BIBLIOGRAPHY. Text in English, Japanese. 1964. irreg. **Document type:** *Bibliography.*
Published by: (Seirigaku Kyoshitsu), Tokyo Shika Daigaku/Tokyo Dental College, 1-2-2 Masago, Mihama-ku, Chiba-shi, 261-0011, Japan.

016.57179 USA ISSN 0092-5594
RG627
U.S. CENTERS FOR DISEASE CONTROL. CONGENITAL MALFORMATIONS SURVEILLANCE. Key Title: Congenital Malformations Surveillance. Text in English. q. stat. **Document type:** *Government.*
Indexed: CLFP.
Published by: U.S. Department of Health and Human Services, Centers for Disease Control and Prevention, 1600 Clifton Rd, Atlanta, GA 30333. TEL 404-639-3311, 800-311-3435, http://www.cdc.gov.

016.579 JPN ISSN 0082-481X
QR1
UNIVERSITY OF TOKYO. INSTITUTE OF APPLIED MICROBIOLOGY. REPORTS. Text in English. 1961. a. free. author index. **Description:** Contains abstracts of original papers.
Indexed: JTA.
—CISTI.
Published by: University of Tokyo, Institute of Applied Microbiology/Tokyo Daigaku Oyo Biseibutsu Kenkyujo, 1-1-1 Yayoi, Bunkyo-ku, Tokyo, 113-0032, Japan. Ed. Shoji Mizushima. Circ: (controlled).

016.59 USA ISSN 0499-4175
SK351
WILDLIFE ABSTRACTS. Variant title: Wildlife. Text in English. 1937. q. USD 100 to individuals; USD 175 to libraries; USD 325 universities; USD 475 region; USD 80 to students (effective 2005). **Document type:** *Abstract/Index.* **Description:** Contains citations and abstracts published from 1937 to present in the Journal of Wildlife Management, Wildlife Monographs, and the Wildlife Society Bulletin.
Media: Online - full content. **Related titles:** CD-ROM ed.: USD 149 to individuals; USD 250 to libraries; USD 450 universities; USD 650 region; USD 129 to students (effective 2002).
Published by: ABSEARCH, Inc., 1204 Thatuna Ave, Moscow, ID 83843. TEL 208-883-5544, 800-867-1877, FAX 208-883-5554, custinfo@absearch.com, sales@absearch.com, http://www.absearch.com.

016.59 USA ISSN 1070-5007
SK351
WILDLIFE WORLDWIDE. Text in English. 1992. q. USD 895 (effective 2000). adv. **Document type:** *Abstract/Index.* **Description:** Abstracts and indexes literature on wild mammals, birds, reptiles, and amphibians from around the world.
Supersedes in part: Wildlife and Fish Worldwide (1046-6479)
Media: CD-ROM (from National Information Services Corp. (N I S C)). **Related titles:** Online - full text ed.: (from National Information Services Corp. (N I S C)).
Published by: National Information Services Corp. (N I S C), Ste 6, Wyman Towers, 3100 St Paul St, Baltimore, MD 21218. TEL 410-243-0797, FAX 410-243-0982, sales@nisc.com, http://www.nisc.com. Ed., Pub. Fred Durr. Adv. contact Debbie Durr.

016.57 CHN ISSN 1001-1900
ZHONGGUO SHENGWUXUE WENZHAI/CHINESE BIOLOGICAL ABSTRACTS. Text in Chinese, English. 1987. m. CNY 192; USD 250 foreign. index. back issues avail. **Document type:** *Abstract/Index.*
Related titles: CD-ROM ed.; Diskette ed.; Online - full text ed.
Published by: Zhongguo Kexueyuan, Shanghai Wenxian Qingbao Zhongxin/Chinese Academy of Sciences, Shanghai Documentation & Information Center, 319 Yueyang Lu, Shanghai, 200031, China. TEL 86-21-64336650, FAX 86-21-64375762, cba@peony.slas.ac.cn, http://www.slas.ac.cn. Ed. Gong Yitai. Circ: 1,500 (paid). **Co-sponsor:** Biology Documentation and Information Network, Chinese Academy of Sciences.

016.59 USA ISSN 0144-3607
Z7991 CODEN: ZOREAU
ZOOLOGICAL RECORD. (Consists of 27 sections and subsections avail. separately) Text in English. 1864. a. USD 4,825; USD 6,430 combined subscription print & online eds. (effective 2004). illus. index. back issues avail.; reprints avail. **Document type:** *Journal, Abstract/Index.* **Description:** A comprehensive index to worldwide publications covering all areas of zoology and animal science including anatomy, behavior, conservation, distribution, ecology & environment, evolution, nutrition, systematics, veterinary science. Includes author, subject, geographical, palaeontological and systematic indexes.
Related titles: CD-ROM ed.: Zoological Record on Compact Disc. ISSN 1072-1983. 1993 (from SilverPlatter Information, Inc.); Microfiche ed.: (from BHP); Microfilm ed.: (from PQC); Online - full text ed.: USD 5,830 (effective 2004).
—BLDSC (9520.000000), CISTI, IE, Linda Hall.
Published by: (Zoological Society of London GBR), Thomson BIOSIS (Subsidiary of: Thomson I S I), 3501 Market St, Philadelphia, PA 19104. TEL 215-386-0100, 800-336-4474, FAX 215-243-2208, info@biosis.org, http://www.biosis.org/. Ed. Marcia Edwards.

016.59 USA ISSN 1041-4657
Z7991 CODEN: ZRSSEY
ZOOLOGICAL RECORD SERIAL SOURCES. Text in English. 1988. a., latest 2002, 9th edition. USD 85 per issue (effective 2003). **Document type:** *Abstract/Index.* **Description:** List of international serical publications monitored for Zoological Record. Includes biobliographic details and a list of publishers with their addresses.
—BLDSC (9520.030000), Linda Hall.
Published by: Thomson BIOSIS (Subsidiary of: Thomson I S I), 3501 Market St, Philadelphia, PA 19104. TEL 215-231-7500, 800-523-4806, FAX 215-587-2016, zoorec@york.biosis.org, info@biosis.org, http://www.biosis.org/products_services/zrss.html.

BIOLOGY—Bioengineering

A I U M SOUND WAVES. see *MEDICAL SCIENCES—Radiology And Nuclear Medicine*

610.28 POL ISSN 1509-409X
TA164
➤ **ACTA OF BIOENGINEERING AND BIOMECHANICS.** Text and summaries in English. 1999. 2/yr. EUR 19 (effective 2005); price varies. bk.rev. back issues avail. **Document type:** *Journal, Academic/Scholarly.* **Description:** Contains original theoretical and experimental papers dealing with: engineering biomechanics, biomechanics of sport, modelling and investigating biomechanical problems, biomechanics of labour protection, rehabilitation engineering, orthopaedic biomechanics, substitutive systems that assist a therapy, dental biomechanics, biomaterials, biotribology, computer simulation in biomechanics and experimental methods in biomechanics.
Indexed: ApMecR, Inspec.
—BLDSC (0601.150000), IE, ingenta, Linda Hall.
Published by: (Politechnika Wroclawska, Instytut Konstrukcji i Eksploatacji Maszyn/Wroclaw University of Technology, Institute of Machine Design and Operation, Polskie Towarzystwo Biomechaniki/Polish Society of Biomechanics), Oficyna Wydawnicza Politechniki Wroclawskiej, Wybrzeze Wyspianskiego 27, Wroclaw, 50370, Poland. TEL 48-71-3202994, oficwyd@pwr.wroc.pl, http://exbio.ikem.pwr.wroc.pl/acta/index.html, http://www.pwr.wroc.pl/~oficwyd/#OFICYNA. Ed. Romuald Bedzinski. Circ: 300. **Dist. by:** Ars Polona, Krakowskie Przedmiescie 7, Warsaw, Poland. TEL 48-22-9263914, FAX 48-22-9265334, arspolona@arspolona.com.pl, http://www.arspolona.com.pl. **Co-sponsor:** Komitet Badan Naukowych/Committee of Scientific Research.

570.285 610 SGP ISSN 1793-0790
ADVANCED SERIES IN BIOMECHANICS. Text in English. 1997. irreg., latest vol.3, 2004, Fall. price varies. **Document type:** *Monographic series, Academic/Scholarly.*
Published by: World Scientific Publishing Co. Pte. Ltd., 5 Toh Tuck Link, Singapore, 596224, Singapore. TEL 65-466-5775, FAX 65-467-7667, wspc@wspc.com.sg, series@wspc.com.sg, http://www.wspc.com.sg/books/series/asb_series.shtml, http://www.worldscientific.com. Ed. Y C Fung. **Dist. by:** World Scientific Publishing Co., Inc., 1060 Main St, River Edge, NJ 07661. TEL 201-487-9655, FAX 201-487-9656, 888-977-2665; World Scientific Publishing Ltd., 57 Shelton St, London WC2H 9HE, United Kingdom. TEL 44-20-78360888, FAX 44-20-78362020.

ADVANCES IN BIOCHEMICAL ENGINEERING - BIOTECHNOLOGY. see *BIOLOGY—Biotechnology*

571.43 USA ISSN 0360-9960
R856.A1 CODEN: ADBIDL
➤ **ADVANCES IN BIOENGINEERING.** Text in English. a., latest vol.54, 2003. price varies. illus. **Document type:** *Monographic series, Academic/Scholarly.*
Indexed: BiolAb, ChemAb.
—Linda Hall. **CCC.**
Published by: A S M E International, Three Park Ave, New York, NY 10016-5990. infocentral@asme.org, http://www.asme.org. Ed. L Thibault. **Subscr. to:** 22 Law Dr, PO Box 2900, Fairfield, NJ 07007-2900. TEL 973-882-1170, 973-882-1167, 800-843-2763, 95-800-843-2763, FAX 973-882-1717.

571.43 GBR
ADVANCES IN BIOENGINEERING SERIES. Text in English. 1999. irreg., latest vol.4, 2000. **Document type:** *Monographic series, Academic/Scholarly.* **Description:** Covers areas of current interest on active research in the application of computing to analyze numerically biomedical processes and medical data.
Published by: WIT Press, Ashurst Lodge, Ashurst, Southampton, Hants SO40 7AA, United Kingdom. TEL 44-238-029-3223, FAX 44-238-029-2853, marketing@witpress.com, http://www.witpress.com/advbiser.html. **Dist. by:** Computational Mechanics Inc.. marketing@compmech.com, http://www.compmech.com/witpress.

610.28 GBR ISSN 1465-3222
➤ **ADVANCES IN COMPUTATIONAL BIOENGINEERING.** Text in English. irreg., latest vol.6, 2002. **Document type:** *Monographic series, Academic/Scholarly.* **Description:** Covers state-of-the-art advances in the field of biomedical engineering. Contains papers from leading researchers in bioengineering. Each volume covers areas of current interest or active research.
Formerly (until 1999): Advances in Bioengineering
Indexed: B&BAb, BioEngAb.
—BLDSC (0704.103570).
Published by: WIT Press, Ashurst Lodge, Ashurst, Southampton, Hants SO40 7AA, United Kingdom. TEL 44-238-029-3223, FAX 44-238-029-2853, marketing@witpress.com, http://www.witpress.com. Ed. Peter Johnston. **Dist. by:** Computational Mechanics Inc., 25 Bridge St, Billerica, MA 01821-1007. TEL 978-667-5841, FAX 978-667-7582, marketing@compmech.com, http://www.compmech.com/witpress.

610.28 USA
ALTERNATIVES TO THE USE OF LIVE VERTEBRATES IN BIOMEDICAL RESEARCH AND TESTING. Text in English. q. **Document type:** *Academic/Scholarly.* **Description:** Assists in identifying methods and procedures helpful in supporting the development, testing, application, and validation of alternatives to the use of vertebrates in biomedical research and toxicology testing.
Media: Online - full text.
Published by: Oak Ridge National Laboratory, Environmental Science Division, PO Box 2008, Oak Ridge, TN 37831-6144.

572.43 USA
AMERICAN SOCIETY OF MECHANICAL ENGINEERS. BIOENGINEERING DIVISION. NEWSLETTER. Text in English. a. free membership (effective 2003). back issues avail. **Document type:** *Newsletter, Trade.*
Related titles: Online - full text ed.
Published by: A S M E International, Three Park Ave, New York, NY 10016-5990. TEL 212-591-7722, FAX 212-591-7674, infocentral@asme.org, http://www.asme.org/divisions/bed/newsletter/. **Subscr. to:** 22 Law Dr, PO Box 2900, Fairfield, NJ 07007-2900. TEL 973-882-1170, 973-882-1167, 800-843-2763, 95-800-843-2763, FAX 973-882-1717.

ANNALS OF BIOMEDICAL ENGINEERING. see *MEDICAL SCIENCES*

ANNUAL REVIEW OF BIOMEDICAL ENGINEERING. see *BIOLOGY*

621.9 GBR ISSN 1176-2322
▼ ➤ **APPLIED BIONICS AND BIOMECHANICS.** Text in English. 2003 (Oct.). q. GBP 350 domestic; EUR 500 in Europe; USD 630 in the Americas; GBP 350 elsewhere (effective 2005). **Document type:** *Journal, Academic/Scholarly.* **Description:** Covers technological developments based on the science of biological systems and bionics, the application of biological principles and living organisms structure and functions, to the study and design of engineering systems, especially electronic systems.
Related titles: Online - full text ed.: (from EBSCO Publishing, Swets Information Services).
Published by: Woodhead Publishing Ltd., Abington Hall, Abington, Cambridge, CB1 6AH, United Kingdom. TEL 44-1223-891358, FAX 44-1223-893694, wp@woodheadpublishing.com, http://www.woodheadpublishing.com/en/book.aspx?bookID=882. Ed. Jeom Kee Paik. Pub., R&P, Adv. contact Daniel Smith. Circ: 400 (paid and controlled).

577 USA ISSN 1535-6760
RC967
APPLIED BIOSAFETY: JOURNAL OF THE AMERICAN BIOLOGICAL SAFETY ASSOCIATION. Text in English. 1996. m. USD 92 to individuals; USD 122 to institutions; USD 60 to members; USD 28 newsstand/cover to non-members; USD 18 newsstand/cover to members; USD 35 newsstand/cover to institutions (effective 2002). adv. **Document type:** *Journal, Academic/Scholarly.*
Formerly (until 2001): American Biological Safety Association. Journal (1091-3505)
—BLDSC (1571.912000), IE, ingenta.
Published by: American Biological Safety Association, 1202 Allanson Rd, Mundelein, IL 60060-3808. TEL 847-949-1517, FAX 847-566-4580, estygariii@aol.com, http://www.absa.org. adv.: page USD 400; trim 8.5 x 11.

AUSTRALASIAN PHYSICAL & ENGINEERING SCIENCES IN MEDICINE. see *MEDICAL SCIENCES*

570.285 USA ISSN 1521-4613
B E D SERIES. Text in English. 1986. irreg. **Document type:** *Monographic series.*
Published by: American Society of Mechanical Engineers, Bioengineering Division, Mail Stop 22W3, 3 Park Ave, New York, NY 10016-5990. TEL 212-591-7722, FAX 212-591-7674, Infocentral@asme.org, http://divisions.asme.org/bed/. **Orders & Inquiries to:** PO Box 2300, Fairfield, NJ 07007-2300. TEL 973-882-1170, 800-843-2763, FAX 973-882-1717.

610.28 JPN
BAIOENJINIARINGU SHINPOJUMU RONBUNJU/BIOENGINEERING SYMPOSIUM. Text in Japanese; Summaries in English. 1989. a. JPY 5,000.
Published by: Nihon Kikai Gakkai/Japan Society of Mechanical Engineers, Shinanomachi-Rengakan Bldg, Shinanomachi 35, Shinjuku-ku, Tokyo, 160, Japan.

BIO - I T WORLD. see *BIOLOGY—Biotechnology*

610.28 NLD ISSN 0959-2989
R857.M3 CODEN: BMENEO
➤ **BIO-MEDICAL MATERIALS AND ENGINEERING;** an international journal. Text in English. 1991. q. EUR 798, USD 957 combined subscription print & online eds. (effective 2006). back issues avail. **Document type:** *Journal, Academic/Scholarly.* **Description:** Covers materials and engineering for biological and medical systems.

B

Related titles: Microform ed.: (from PQC); Online - full text ed.: (from EBSCO Publishing, Gale Group, IngentaConnect, O C L C Online Computer Library Center, Inc., Swets Information Services).
Indexed: AMED, ASCA, ApMecR, B&BAb, BIOSIS Prev, BioEngAb, BiolAb, BrCerAb, C&ISA, CIN, CTA, CerAb, ChemAb, ChemTitl, CivEngAb, CorrAb, E&CAJ, EMA, ESPM, ExcerpMed, H&SSA, IAA, IndMed, M&PBA, M&TEA, MBF, MEDLINE, METADEX, MSCI, SolStAb, WAA.
—BLDSC (2087.839000), CASDDS, CISTI, GNLM, IDS, IE, Infotrieve, ingenta, Linda Hall. **CCC.**
Published by: I O S Press, Nieuwe Hemweg 6B, Amsterdam, 1013 BG, Netherlands. TEL 31-20-6883355, FAX 31-20-6203419, order@iospress.nl, http://www.iospress.nl/html/09592989.html. Ed. Takeo Yokobori. Circ: 300. **Subscr. to:** I O S Press, Inc, 4502 Rachael Manor Dr., Fairfax, VA 22032-3631. iosbooks@iospress.com; Kinokuniya Co. Ltd., Shinjuku 3-chome, Shinjuku-ku, Tokyo 160-0022, Japan. FAX 81-3-3439-1094, journal@kinokuniya.co.jp, http://www.kinokuniya.co.jp; Globe Publication Pvt. Ltd., C-62 Inderpuri, New Delhi 100 012, India. TEL 91-11-579-3211, 91-11-579-3212, FAX 91-11-579-8876, custserve@globepub.com, http://www.globepub.com.

B

610.28 POL ISSN 0208-5216
BIOCYBERNETICS AND BIOMEDICAL ENGINEERING. Text in English; Summaries in Polish. 1981. irreg., latest vol.19, 1999. price varies. bibl.; illus. **Document type:** *Academic/Scholarly.* **Description:** Publishes original papers on biocybernetics and biomedical engineering.
—BLDSC (2071.215000), GNLM, IE, ingenta.
Published by: (Polska Akademia Nauk/Polish Academy of Sciences, Instytut Biocybernetyki i Inzynierii Biomedycznej), Wydawnictwo Naukowe P W N SA/Polish Scientific Publishers P W N, ul Miodowa 10, Warsaw, 00251, Poland. TEL 48-22-6954181, FAX 48-22-6954288, ksiegarnia@pwn.pl, http://en.pwn.pl. Circ: 300. **Dist. by:** Ars Polona, Krakowskie Przedmiescie 7, Warsaw, Poland. TEL 48-22-9263914, FAX 48-22-9265334, arspolona@arspolona.com.pl, http://www.arspolona.com.pl.

BIOINGENIOEREN; the medical laboratory technologist. see *MEDICAL SCIENCES—Experimental Medicine, Laboratory Technique*

344 610.28 174 USA
BIOLAW: A LEGAL AND ETHICAL REPORTER ON MEDICINE, HEALTH CARE, AND BIOENGINEERING. Text in English. base vol. plus m. updates. looseleaf. USD 495 (effective 1999); for Resource Manual, Monthly Updates, & Special Sections. back issues avail. **Document type:** *Academic/Scholarly.* **Description:** Covers the most recent developments in case law concerning bioethics.
Incorporates (in 1986): Bioethics Reporter
Related titles: Microfiche ed.
Published by: University Publications of America (Subsidiary of: Congressional Information Service Inc.), 4520 East West Hwy Ste 800, Bethesda, MD 20814-3389. TEL 301-654-1550, 800-638-8380, FAX 301-657-3203, cisinfor@lexis-nexis.com, http://www.cispubs.com.

570.285 SGP ISSN 1793-0413
▼ **BIOMATERIALS ENGINEERING AND PROCESSING SERIES.** Text in English. 2004 (Oct.). irreg. **Document type:** *Monographic series, Academic/Scholarly.* **Description:** Provides updated information on engineering and processing aspects of biomaterials. Includes the biocompatibility issues, engineering and biological design philosophy, the interaction between the host tissue and the biomaterials interface, novel tissue engineering methodologies to regenerate tissues and organs, the use of computer-assisted methods, manufacturing details, sterilization techniques and quality control issues. Of importance is the relationship between material properties, processing methods and design.
Published by: World Scientific Publishing Co. Pte. Ltd., 5 Toh Tuck Link, Singapore, 596224, Singapore. TEL 65-466-5775, FAX 65-467-7667, wspc@wspc.com.sg, http://www.worldscibooks.com/series/beps_series.shtml, http://www.worldscientific.com. **Dist. by:** World Scientific Publishing Co., Inc., 1060 Main St, River Edge, NJ 07661. TEL 201-487-9655, 800-227-7562, FAX 201-487-9656, 888-977-2665, wspc@wspc.com.

666 USA ISSN 1075-9662
RD97
BIOMECHANICS. Text in English. 1994. m. free domestic to qualified personnel; USD 42 domestic; USD 47 foreign (effective 2005). **Document type:** *Magazine, Trade.* **Description:** Dedicated to total body movement and medicine.
Related titles: Online - full content ed.; Online - full text ed.: (from Gale Group, H.W. Wilson, O C L C Online Computer Library Center, Inc.).
Indexed: GSI.
—CCC.
Published by: C M P Healthcare Media (Subsidiary of: C M P Media LLC), 600 Harrison St., 4th flr, San Francisco, CA 94107. TEL 415-905-2200, http://www.biomech.com, http://www.cmphealth.com. Ed. Jordana Bieze. Pub. Marcy Holeton. Circ: 37,845 (controlled).

571 621.9 DEU ISSN 1617-7959
QH513 CODEN: BMMICD
➤ **BIOMECHANICS AND MODELING IN MECHANOBIOLOGY.** Text in English. 2002. q. EUR 298 combined subscription to institutions print & online eds. (effective 2005). adv. back issues avail. **Document type:** *Journal, Academic/Scholarly.*
Related titles: Online - full text ed.: ISSN 1617-7940 (from EBSCO Publishing, Springer LINK, Swets Information Services).
Indexed: ApMecR, Inspec.
—BLDSC (2087.750950), CISTI, IE, Linda Hall. **CCC.**
Published by: Springer-Verlag (Subsidiary of: Springer Science+Business Media), Tiergartenstr 17, Heidelberg, 69121, Germany. TEL 49-6221-3450, FAX 49-6221-345229, http://link.springer.de/link/service/journals/10237/. Eds. Gerhard A Holzapfel, Jay D Humphrey. Adv. contact Stephan Kroeck TEL 49-30-827875739. **Subscr. in the Americas to:** Springer-Verlag New York, Inc., Journal Fulfillment, PO Box 2485, Secaucus, NJ 07096-2485. TEL 800-777-4643, 201-348-4033, FAX 201-348-4505, journals@springer-ny.com, http://www.springer-ny.com; **Subscr. to:** Springer GmbH Auslieferungsgesellschaft, Haberstr 7, Heidelberg 69126, Germany. TEL 49-6221-345-0, FAX 49-6221-345-4229, subscriptions@springer.de.

572.43 TWN ISSN 1016-2372
BIOMEDICAL ENGINEERING APPLICATIONS BASIS COMMUNICATIONS. Text in English, Chinese. 1989. m.
Indexed: ExcerpMed, Inspec.
—BLDSC (2087.813000), IE, ingenta.
Published by: National Taiwan University, College of Medicine, No 1 Jen-Ai Rd Sec 1, Taipei, Taiwan.

BIOMEDICAL ENGINEERING ONLINE. see *MEDICAL SCIENCES*

610.28 RUS
BIOMEDITSINSKIE TEKHNOLOGII I RADIOELEKTRONIKA. Text in Russian. 1998. 8/yr. RUR 300 per issue domestic (effective 2004). **Document type:** *Journal, Academic/Scholarly.*
Formerly: Biomeditsinskaya Radioelektronika
Related titles: ◆ English Translation: Critical Reviews in Biomedical Engineering.
Indexed: RefZh.
Published by: Izdatel'stvo Radiotekhnika, Kuznetskii Most 20/6, Moscow, 103031, Russian Federation. iprzhr@online.ru, http://webcenter.ru/~iprzhr/. **Dist. by:** East View Information Services, 3020 Harbor Ln. N., Minneapolis, MN 55447. TEL 763-550-0961, FAX 763-559-2931, eastview@eastview.com, http://www.eastview.com.

BIOTECHNOLOGY ADVANCES. see *BIOLOGY—Biotechnology*

BIOTECHNOLOGY AND BIOENGINEERING. see *BIOLOGY—Biotechnology*

BIOTECHNOLOGY & BIOENGINEERING ABSTRACTS. see *CHEMISTRY—Abstracting, Bibliographies, Statistics*

BIOTECHNOLOGY AND BIOPROCESS ENGINEERING. see *BIOLOGY—Biotechnology*

BIOTECHNOLOGY AND BIOTECHNOLOGICAL EQUIPMENT; international scientific-theoretical and applied publication. see *BIOLOGY—Biotechnology*

BIOTECHNOLOGY AND GENETIC ENGINEERING REVIEWS. see *BIOLOGY—Biotechnology*

BIOTEKHNOLOGIYA. see *BIOLOGY—Biotechnology*

610.28 USA
C R I S P: BIOMEDICAL RESEARCH INFORMATION ON CD-ROM. Text in English. 1972. q. USD 74 domestic; USD 92.50 foreign (effective 2000). back issues avail. **Document type:** *Government.* **Description:** Contains information on research programs supported by PHS. Includes research on extramural projects such as grants, contracts, and agreements conducted primarily by universities, hospitals, and other research institutions.
Formerly (until 1980): CRISP: Biomedical Research Information
Media: CD-ROM.
Published by: U.S. Department of Health and Human Services, Hubert H. Humphrey Bldg., 200 Independence Ave., S.W., Washington, DC 20201. **Subscr. to:** U.S. Government Printing Office, Superintendent of Documents, PO Box 371954, Pittsburgh, PA 15250-7954. TEL 202-512-1800, FAX 202-512-2250, orders@gpo.gov, http://www.access.gpo.gov.

CHEMICAL AND BIOLOGICAL DEFENSE INFORMATION ANALYSIS CENTER. NEWSLETTER. see *ENGINEERING—Chemical Engineering*

CHEMICAL ENGINEERING JOURNAL. see *ENGINEERING—Chemical Engineering*

▼ **CHINESE JOURNAL OF BIOPROCESS ENGINEERING.** see *BIOLOGY—Biotechnology*

610.28 615.82 JPN ISSN 0386-8109
CODEN: CHRYDT
CHIRYOGAKU/BIOMEDICINE & THERAPEUTICS. Text in Japanese. 1978. m. JPY 19,200 per issue; JPY 1,600 newsstand/cover (effective 2004). **Document type:** *Journal, Academic/Scholarly.*
Indexed: CIN, ChemAb, ChemTitl.
—CASDDS.
Published by: Raifu Saiensu Shuppan K.K./Life Science Publishing Co. Ltd., Daisen Bldg, 11-7 Nihonbashikobuna-cho, Chuo-ku, Tokyo, 103-0024, Japan. chiryo@lifescience.co.jp, info@lifescience.co.jp, http://www.lifescience.co.jp/cr/crindex.htm.

610.28 USA
R856.A1 CODEN: CRBEDR
➤ **CRITICAL REVIEWS IN BIOMEDICAL ENGINEERING.** Text in English. 1974. bi-m. USD 210 to individuals; USD 1,080 to institutions (effective 2002). adv. bibl.; charts; illus. back issues avail.; reprints avail. **Document type:** *Journal, Academic/Scholarly.* **Description:** Critically surveys the wide range of research and applied activities in this field.
Former titles: C R C Critical Reviews in Biomedical Engineering (0278-940X); Critical Reviews in Bioengineering (0731-6984); C R C Critical Reviews in Bioengineering (0045-642X)
Related titles: Online - full text ed.: (from EBSCO Publishing); ◆ Translation of: Biomeditsinskie Tekhnologii i Radioelektronika.
Indexed: ASCA, ApMecR, B&BAb, BIOBASE, BIOSIS Prev, BioEngAb, BiolAb, CurCont, ESPM, EngInd, ExcerpMed, H&SSA, IABS, ISR, IndMed, Inpharma, Inspec, MEDLINE, PE&ON, Reac, RefZh, SCI.
—BLDSC (3487.472300), AskIEEE, CISTI, GNLM, IDS, IE, ingenta, Linda Hall. **CCC.**
Published by: Begell House Inc., 145 Madison Ave, New York, NY 10016-6717. TEL 212-725-1999, FAX 212-213-8368, john.bourne@olin.edu, orders@begellhouse.com, http://www.begellhouse.com/crbe/crbe.html. Ed. John R Bourne. R&P Jim Kelly. Adv. contact Jm Kelly. Circ: 680.

➤ **CRITICAL REVIEWS IN CLINICAL LABORATORY SCIENCES.** see *MEDICAL SCIENCES*

➤ **E S E M NEWS.** see *MEDICAL SCIENCES*

577 FRA ISSN 1635-7922
➤ **ENVIRONMENTAL BIOSAFETY RESEARCH.** Text in English. 2002. q. EUR 375 combined subscription in the European Union print & online eds.; EUR 407 combined subscription elsewhere print & online eds. (effective 2006). **Document type:** *Journal, Academic/Scholarly.*
Related titles: Online - full text ed.: ISSN 1635-7930. EUR 312 (effective 2006) (from EBSCO Publishing, Swets Information Services).
Indexed: AEBA, AgBio, B&BAb, BioCN&I, BioEngAb, CPA, DSA, ESPM, EntAb, FCA, H&SSA, HerbAb, HortAb, MaizeAb, PBA, PGegResA, PollutAb, RA&MP, S&F, SIA, SeedAb, SoyAb, WAE&RSA, WeedAb.
—BLDSC (3791.405620).
Published by: (International Society for Biosafety Research), E D P Sciences, 17 Ave du Hoggar, Parc d'Activites de Courtaboeuf, BP 112, Cedex A, Les Ulis, F-91944, France. TEL 33-1-69187575, FAX 33-1-69860678, subscribers@edpsciences.org, http://www.edpsciences.org/journal/index.cfm?edpsname=ebr.

➤ **EUROPEAN BIOPHARMACEUTICAL REVIEW.** see *PHARMACY AND PHARMACOLOGY*

➤ **EUROPEAN SYMPOSIUM ON BIOCHEMICAL ENGINEERING SCIENCE. PROCEEDINGS.** see *ENGINEERING—Chemical Engineering*

➤ **FOLIA MICROBIOLOGICA.** see *BIOLOGY—Biochemistry*

610.28 USA
FOUNDATION FOR BIOMEDICAL RESEARCH. NEWS. Text in English. 1984. bi-m. looseleaf. USD 25. back issues avail. **Document type:** *Newsletter.*
Formerly (until May 1993): Foundation for Biomedical Research. Newsletter
Published by: Foundation for Biomedical Research, 818 Connecticut Ave N W, 3rd Fl, Washington, DC 20006. TEL 202-457-0654, FAX 202-457-0659. Circ: 1,800.

GATTEFOSSE. BULLETIN TECHNIQUE. see *MEDICAL SCIENCES*

GENEWATCH. see *BIOLOGY—Genetics*

570 CHN ISSN 1001-1110
GUOWAI YIXUE (SHENGWU YIXUE GONGCHENG FENCE)/FOREIGN MEDICAL SCIENCES (BIOMEDICAL ENGINEERING). Text in Chinese. 1978. bi-m. CNY 48 domestic; USD 25.20 foreign (effective 2005). **Document type:** *Journal, Academic/Scholarly.*
Related titles: Online - full text ed.: (from East View Information Services, WanFang Data Corp.).

Published by: Zhongguo Yixue Kexueyuan, Shengwu Yixue Gongcheng Yanjiusuo, Nankai-qu, 7, Keyan Dong Lu, Tianjin, 300192, China. gwsw@chinajournal.net.cn, http://gwyxswyxgc.periodicals.net.cn/default.html. **Dist. by:** China International Book Trading Corp, 35 Chegongzhuang Xilu, Haidian District, PO Box 399, Beijing 100044, China. TEL 86-10-68412045, FAX 86-10-68412023, cibtc@mail.cibtc.com.cn, http://www.cibtc.com.cn.

H H M I BULLETIN. see *MEDICAL SCIENCES*

HUAXUE YU SHENGWU GONGCHENG/CHEMISTRY & BIOENGINEERING. see *CHEMISTRY*

610.28 600 USA ISSN 0739-5175
R856.A1 CODEN: IEMBDE
➤ **I E E E ENGINEERING IN MEDICINE AND BIOLOGY MAGAZINE.** Text in English. bi-m. USD 360 (effective 2006). adv. bk.rev. charts; illus.; pat. index. back issues avail. **Document type:** *Journal, Academic/Scholarly.* **Description:** Technical, short items on current technologies and methods used in biomedical and clinical engineering. Includes news items and correspondence.
Formerly (until June 1982): Engineering in Medicine and Biology (0278-0054); Supersedes (1962-19??): I E E E - E M B S Newsletter
Related titles: CD-ROM ed.; Microfiche ed.; Online - full text ed.: (from EBSCO Publishing).
Indexed: AMED, AS&TI, B&BAb, BioEngAb, CurCont, EngInd, ExcerpMed, IndMed, Inpharma, Inspec, MEDLINE, Reac, RefZh, SSCI.
—BLDSC (4362.927800), AskIEEE, CISTI, Ei, GNLM, IDS, IE, Infotrieve, ingenta, Linda Hall. **CCC.**
Published by: Institute of Electrical and Electronics Engineers, Inc., 445 Hoes Ln, Piscataway, NJ 08854-1331. TEL 732-981-0060, 800-701-4333, FAX 732-981-1721, subscription-service@ieee.org, http://www.ieee.org. Ed. Dr. Alvin S Wald. **Subscr. to:** Maruzen Co., Ltd., 3-10 Nihonbashi 2-chome, Chuo-ku, Tokyo 103-0027, Japan. FAX 81-3-3275-0657; Universal Subscription Agency, Pvt. Ltd., 877, Udyog Vihar, V, Gurgoan 122001, India. TEL 91-124-347261, FAX 91-124-342496. **Co-sponsor:** Engineering in Medicine and Biology Society.

610.28 USA ISSN 0018-9294
R895.A1 CODEN: IEBEAX
➤ **I E E E TRANSACTIONS ON BIOMEDICAL ENGINEERING.** Text in English. 1953. m. USD 895 (effective 2006). bk.rev. abstr.; illus. index. **Document type:** *Journal, Academic/Scholarly.* **Description:** Focuses on concepts and methods of the physical and engineering sciences applied in biology and medicine.
Former titles (until 1963): I E E E Transactions on Bio-Medical Electronics (0096-0616); (until 1962): I R E Transactions on Bio-Medical Electronics (0096-1884); (until 1960): I R E Transactions on Medical Electronics (0097-1049); (until 1955): Professional Group on Medical Electronics. Transactions
Related titles: Microform ed.; Online - full text ed.: (from EBSCO Publishing, Swets Information Services).
Indexed: AS&TI, ASCA, ApMecR, B&BAb, BioEngAb, BiolAb, Biostat, C&ISA, CMCI, ChemAb, CivEngAb, CurCont, DentInd, E&CAJ, ESPM, EngInd, ErgAb, ExcerpMed, H&SSA, IAA, INIS AtomInd, ISMEC, ISR, IndMed, Inpharma, Inspec, MEDLINE, MathR, NSCI, PsycholAb, Reac, RefZh, SCI, SSCI, SolStAb.
—BLDSC (4363.152000), AskIEEE, CASDDS, CISTI, Ei, GNLM, IDS, IE, Infotrieve, ingenta, Linda Hall. **CCC.**
Published by: Institute of Electrical and Electronics Engineers, Inc., 445 Hoes Ln, Piscataway, NJ 08854-1331. TEL 732-981-0060, 800-701-4333, FAX 732-981-1721, subscription-service@ieee.org, http://www.ieee.org. Ed. Dr. Jose C Principe. **Subscr. to:** Maruzen Co., Ltd., 3-10 Nihonbashi 2-chome, Chuo-ku, Tokyo 103-0027, Japan. FAX 81-3-3275-0657; Universal Subscription Agency, Pvt. Ltd., 877, Udyog Vihar, V, Gurgoan 122001, India. TEL 91-124-347261, FAX 91-124-342496. **Co-sponsor:** Engineering in Medicine and Biology Society.

570 USA
I E E E TRANSACTIONS ON NANOBIOSCIENCE. Text in English. 2002. q. USD 455; USD 550 combined subscription print & online eds (effective 2006). **Document type:** *Journal, Trade.*
Formerly (until 2003): I E E E Transactions on Molecular, Cellular and Tissue Engineering (1536-1241)
Related titles: Online - full content ed.: USD 440 (effective 2006); Online - full text ed.: (from EBSCO Publishing).
Indexed: Inspec, RefZh.
—BLDSC (4363.206800), CISTI, IE, Linda Hall. **CCC.**
Published by: Institute of Electrical and Electronics Engineers, Inc., 445 Hoes Ln, Piscataway, NJ 08854-1331. TEL 908-981-0060, 800-701-4333, FAX 732-981-9667, subscription-service@ieee.org, http://www.ieee.org. **Subscr. to:** Maruzen Co., Ltd., 3-10 Nihonbashi 2-chome, Chuo-ku, Tokyo 103-0027, Japan. FAX 81-3-3275-0657; Universal Subscription Agency, Pvt. Ltd., 877, Udyog Vihar, V, Gurgoan 122001, India. TEL 91-124-347261, FAX 91-124-342496.

572.43 USA ISSN 1534-4320
RM950 CODEN: ITNSB3
I E E E TRANSACTIONS ON NEURAL SYSTEMS AND REHABILITATION ENGINEERING. Text in English. 1993. q. USD 310 (effective 2006). adv. **Document type:** *Journal, Trade.* **Description:** Covers human performance measurement and analysis, nerve stimulation, motor control and simulation, biomechanics, signal processing, hardware and software for rehabilitation engineering applications.
Formerly (until 2000): I E E E Transactions on Rehabilitation Engineering (1063-6528)
Related titles: CD-ROM ed.; Microfiche ed.; Online - full text ed.: (from EBSCO Publishing, Swets Information Services).
Indexed: AMED, AS&TI, ASCA, B&BAb, BioEngAb, CurCont, EngInd, ExcerpMed, IndMed, Inspec, MEDLINE, RefZh.
—BLDSC (4363.207500), AskIEEE, CISTI, Ei, GNLM, IDS, IE, Infotrieve, ingenta, Linda Hall. **CCC.**
Published by: Institute of Electrical and Electronics Engineers, Inc., 3 Park Ave, 17th Fl, New York, NY 10016-5997. TEL 908-981-0060, 800-701-4333, FAX 908-981-9667, subscription-service@ieee.org, http://www.ieee.org. Ed. Charles J Robinson. **Subscr. to:** Maruzen Co., Ltd., 3-10 Nihonbashi 2-chome, Chuo-ku, Tokyo 103-0027, Japan; Universal Subscription Agency, Pvt. Ltd., 877, Udyog Vihar, V, Gurgoan 122001, India. TEL 91-124-347261, FAX 91-124-342496.

570.285 GBR ISSN 1359-0944
I F M B E NEWS. (International Federation for Medical & Biological Engineering) Text in English. 1977. bi-m. **Document type:** *Newsletter, Academic/Scholarly.*
Formerly (until 1995): M B E C News (0140-0134)
Related titles: ♦ Supplement to: Medical & Biological Engineering & Computing. ISSN 0140-0118.
—BLDSC (4363.315950).
Published by: INSPEC, I.E.E., Michael Faraday House, Six Hills Way, Stevenage, Herts SG1 2AY, United Kingdom. TEL 44-1438-767266, FAX 44-1438-742849, inspec@iee.org.uk, http://ifmbe-news.iee.org, http://www.iee.org.uk. Ed. Peter Rolfe.

▼ **INFORMATION PLUS REFERENCE SERIES. GENETICS AND GENETIC ENGINEERING.** see *BIOLOGY—Genetics*

610.28 GBR ISSN 0954-4119
R856.A1 CODEN: PIHMEQ
➤ **INSTITUTION OF MECHANICAL ENGINEERS. PROCEEDINGS. PART H: JOURNAL OF ENGINEERING IN MEDICINE.** Text in English. 1971. bi-m. GBP 669 (effective 2005). adv. illus. back issues avail.; reprint service avail. from PQC. **Document type:** *Journal, Academic/Scholarly.* **Description:** Publishes scholarly research articles on theoretical and experimental application in joint and bone replacement prosthetics, mechanical coupling, and ambulatory design; with reviews of supplies and medical equipment; and announcements of conferences, seminars, and exhibitions.
Formerly (until 1989): Engineering in Medicine (0046-2039)
Related titles: Microform ed.: (from PQC); Online - full text ed.: (from EBSCO Publishing, Gale Group, IngentaConnect, O C L C Online Computer Library Center, Inc., Swets Information Services); ♦ Series: Institution of Mechanical Engineers. Proceedings.
Indexed: AMED, AS&TI, ASCA, ApMecR, B&BAb, BrCerAb, BrTechI, C&ISA, CerAb, CivEngAb, CorrAb, CurCont, DentInd, E&CAJ, EMA, EngInd, ExcerpMed, FLUIDEX, IAA, ISMEC, ISR, IndMed, Inspec, M&TEA, MBF, MEDLINE, METADEX, SCI, SolStAb, WAA.
—BLDSC (6724.900900), AskIEEE, CISTI, Ei, GNLM, IDS, IE, Infotrieve, ingenta, Linda Hall. **CCC.**
Published by: (Institution of Mechanical Engineers), Professional Engineering Publishing Ltd., Northgate Ave, Bury St Edmunds, Suffolk IP32 6BW, United Kingdom. TEL 44-1284-705271, FAX 44-1284-718692, 44-1284-768219, journals@pepublishing.com, http://www.pepublishing.com/journal2.asp?id=25, http://www.imeche.org.uk. Ed. A Unsworth. Pub. Rosie Grimes. Circ: 800. **Subscr. to:** PO Box 361, Birmingham, AL 35201-0361. TEL 800-633-4931, FAX 205-995-1588.

570.285 GBR ISSN 1743-8241
▼ ➤ **INTERNATIONAL JOURNAL OF MOLECULAR ENGINEERING.** Text in English. forthcoming 2006. q. USD 450 to institutions; USD 545 to institutions print & online eds. (effective 2005). **Document type:** *Journal, Academic/Scholarly.*
Related titles: Online - full text ed.: ISSN 1743-825X. forthcoming 2006. USD 450 to institutions (effective 2005).
Published by: Inderscience Publishers, IEL Editorial Office, PO Box 735, Olney, Bucks MK46 5WB, United Kingdom. TEL 44-1234-240519, FAX 44-1234-240515, ijme@inderscience.com, info@inderscience.com, http://www.inderscience.com/ijme. **Subscr. to:** World Trade Centre Bldg, 29 route de Pre-Bois, Case Postale 896, Geneva 15 1215, Switzerland. FAX 41-22-7910885, subs@inderscience.com.

570.285 USA
▼ ➤ **THE INTERNET JOURNAL OF BIOENGINEERING.** Text in English. 2004. irreg. USD 500 to institutions (effective 2005). **Document type:** *Journal, Academic/Scholarly.*
Media: Online - full content.
Published by: Internet Scientific Publications, L.L.C., 23 Rippling Creek Dr, Sugar Land, TX 77479. TEL 832-443-1193, FAX 281-240-1533, wenker@ispub.com, http://www.ispub.com/ostia/index.php?xmlFilePath=journals/ijbe/front.xml.

➤ **JOURNAL OF BIOMECHANICS.** see *MEDICAL SCIENCES*

660.6 JPN ISSN 1389-1723
QH301 CODEN: JBBIF6
➤ **JOURNAL OF BIOSCIENCE AND BIOENGINEERING.** Text in English. 1923. 12/yr. EUR 1,351 in Europe to institutions; USD 1,511 elsewhere to institutions (effective 2006). adv. index. back issues avail. **Document type:** *Academic/Scholarly.* **Description:** It is devoted to the advancement and dissemination of knowledge concerning general and molecular biology, including genetics, biochemistry, and physiology of microorganisms, plant, and animal cells.
Former titles (until 1999): Journal of Fermentation and Bioengineering (0922-338X); (until 1989): Journal of Fermentation Technology (0385-6380); Which superseded in part (in 1977): Hakkokogaku Zasshi (0367-5963)
Related titles: Online - full text ed.: ISSN 1347-4421. 2000 (from EBSCO Publishing, Gale Group, IngentaConnect, J-Stage, ScienceDirect, Swets Information Services).
Indexed: AEA, AEBA, ASCA, ASFA, AgBio, AgrForAb, AnBrAb, BBCI, BCI, BIOBASE, BIOSIS Prev, BioCN&I, BioEngAb, BiolAb, C&ISA, CBTA, CCI, CEABA, CIN, CMCI, CPA, ChemAb, ChemTitl, CurCont, DBA, DSA, E&CAJ, EIA, ESPM, EnerInd, EngInd, ExcerpMed, FCA, FPA, FS&TA, ForAb, HerbAb, HortAb, I&DA, IABS, ISMEC, ISR, IndVet, Inpharma, JTA, M&PBA, MBA, NemAb, NutrAb, OrnHort, PBA, PGegResA, PGrRegA, PHN&I, PN&I, PollutAb, PotatoAb, PoultAb, RA&MP, RM&VM, RPP, Reac, RevApplEntom, RiceAb, S&F, SCI, SIA, SeedAb, SolStAb, SoyAb, TDB, TriticAb, VITIS, VetBull, WeedAb.
—BLDSC (4954.067000), CASDDS, CISTI, Ei, IDS, IE, Infotrieve, ingenta, Linda Hall. **CCC.**
Published by: Society for Biotechnology, Japan/Seibutsu Kogakkai, c/o Faculty of Engineering, Osaka University, 2-1 Yamadaoka, Suita, Osaka 565-0871, Japan. TEL 81-6-68762731, FAX 81-6-68792034, sbbj@bio.eng.osaka-u.ac.jp, http://www.jstage.jst.go.jp/browse/jbb/_vols/-char/en, http://wwwsoc.nacsis.ac.jp/sfbj. Ed. Kousaku Murata. **Dist. outside Japan by:** Elsevier BV, PO Box 211, Amsterdam 1000 AE, Netherlands. TEL 31-20-485-3757, FAX 31-20-485-3432, nlinfo-f@elsevier.nl, http://www.elsevier.nl.

B

610.28 USA ISSN 0363-8855
R856.A1 CODEN: JCEND7
➤ **JOURNAL OF CLINICAL ENGINEERING.** Text in English. 1976. q. USD 159 domestic to individuals; USD 211 foreign to individuals; USD 306 domestic to institutions; USD 370 foreign to institutions (effective 2006). adv. bk.rev. charts; illus.; tr.lit. Index. back issues avail. **Document type:** *Journal, Academic/Scholarly.* **Description:** Publishes professional papers covering advances in, and practical aspects of, clinical and biomedical engineering.
Related titles: Microform ed.: 1976 (from PQC); Online - full text ed.: ISSN 1550-3275. 1976 (from EBSCO Publishing, Florida Center for Library Automation, Gale Group, Ovid Technologies, Inc.).
Indexed: AHCMS, BIOSIS Prev, BiolAb, C&ISA, E&CAJ, EngInd, ExcerpMed, HospLI, Inspec, MEDLINE, SolStAb.
—BLDSC (4958.420000), AskIEEE, CISTI, Ei, GNLM, IE, Infotrieve, ingenta, Linda Hall. **CCC.**
Published by: Lippincott Williams & Wilkins (Subsidiary of: Wolters Kluwer N.V.), 530 Walnut St, Philadelphia, PA 19106-3621. TEL 410-528-4000, 215-521-8300, FAX 215-521-8902, custserv@lww.com, http://www.lww.com/products/?0363-8855. Eds. Joseph F. Dyro, William H. Hyman. Pub. Kathleen Phelan. adv.: B&W page USD 890, color page USD 1,865. Circ: 1,000 (paid).

➤ **JOURNAL OF MEDICAL AND BIOLOGICAL ENGINEERING/ZHONGHUA YIXUE GONGCHENG XUEKAN.** see *MEDICAL SCIENCES*

➤ **JOURNAL OF MEDICINE AND BIOMEDICAL RESEARCH.** see *MEDICAL SCIENCES*

➤ **JOURNAL OF MICROMECHATRONICS.** see *ENGINEERING—Electrical Engineering*

570.285 572 USA ISSN 1546-2048
QH513
▼ **MECHANICS & CHEMISTRY OF BIOSYSTEMS.** Abbreviated title: M C B. Text in English. 2004. q. USD 750; USD 1,000 combined subscription print & online eds. (effective 2005). **Document type:** *Journal, Academic/Scholarly.* **Description:** Helps to establish a better understanding of the mechanochemical coupling in living cells, to facilitate the studies of the mechanics of biomolecules including proteins and nucleic acids, and to provide a knowledge base for engineering biosystems such as hybrid bio/abio nano- and micro-mechanical systems.
Related titles: Online - full content ed.: ISSN 1546-2056. USD 600 (effective 2005).
Indexed: BrCerAb, C&ISA, CerAb, CorrAb, E&CAJ, EMA, IAA, M&TEA, MBF, METADEX, WAA.
—BLDSC (5413.415500), IE, Linda Hall.

▼ *new title* ➤ *refereed* ✶ *unverified* ♦ *full entry avail.*

Published by: Tech Science Press, 81 E Main St, Forsyth 488, GA 31029 . TEL 478-992-8121, FAX 661-420-8080, sale@techscience.com, http://www.techscience.com/mcb/index.html. Eds. Satya N Atluri TEL 310-206-0942, Gang Bao.

MEDICAL AND BIOMEDICAL ENGINEERING REPORTS. see *ENGINEERING*

572.4 USA ISSN 1096-7176
TP248.3 CODEN: MEENFM
METABOLIC ENGINEERING. Text in English. 1998. 6/yr. EUR 201 in Europe to individuals; JPY 21,000 in Japan to individuals; USD 151 to individuals except Europe and Japan; EUR 422 in Europe to institutions; JPY 44,100 in Japan to institutions; USD 312 to institutions except Europe and Japan (effective 2006). adv. **Document type:** *Academic/Scholarly.* **Description:** Publishes original research on the targeted improvement of cellular properties or metabolite production via manipulation of specific metabolic or signal transduction pathways.
Related titles: Online - full text ed.: ISSN 1096-7184, USD 307 (effective 2002) (from EBSCO Publishing, Gale Group, IngentaConnect, O C L C Online Computer Library Center, Inc., ScienceDirect, Swets Information Services).
Indexed: AEBA, B&BAb, BCI, BIOBASE, BioEngAb, ChemAb, CurCont, ESPM, ExcerpMed, IndMed, M&PBA, MEDLINE.
—BLDSC (5683.269000), CISTI, IE, Infotrieve. **CCC.**
Published by: Academic Press (Subsidiary of: Elsevier Science & Technology), 525 B St, Ste 1900, San Diego, CA 92101-4495. TEL 619-231-6616, 800-894-3434, apsubs@acad.com, http://www.elsevier.com/locate/meteng, http://www.academicpress.com. Ed. G N Stephanopoulos.

METHODS IN BIOTECHNOLOGY. see *BIOLOGY—Biotechnology*

MO KEXUE JISHU/MEMBRANE SCIENCE AND TECHNOLOGY. see *ENGINEERING—Chemical Engineering*

610.28 USA
NATIONAL BIODYNAMICS LABORATORY. REPORT. Text in English. irreg.
Formerly (until 1996): U.S. Naval Biodynamics Laboratory. Report
Published by: National Biodynamics Laboratory, c/o University of New Orleans, College of Engineering, 2000 Lakeshore Dr, Rm 910, New Orleans, LA 70129. TEL 504-257-3918, FAX 504-257-5456, nbdl@uno.edu, http://www.nbdl.org/publications.html.

610.28 USA ISSN 0277-1063
CODEN: BENYDB
NORTHEAST BIOENGINEERING CONFERENCE. PROCEEDINGS. Key Title: Bioengineering. (Conferences prior to 1982 published by Pergamon Press plc; conferences not held 1983-1984) Text in English. 1973. a. USD 151 membership (effective 2005). **Document type:** *Proceedings, Trade.* **Description:** Forum for the exchange of technical and scientific information among engineers, physicians and other scientists interested in research, development and education.
Former titles (until 1979): New England (Northeast) Bioengineering Conference. Proceedings (0270-1820); (until 1978): New England Bioengineering Conference. Proceedings (0163-1896)
Related titles: CD-ROM ed.; Microfiche ed.
Indexed: ASCA.
—BLDSC (6842.154400), CASDDS, IE, ingenta. **CCC.**
Published by: Institute of Electrical and Electronics Engineers, Inc., 3 Park Ave, 17th Fl, New York, NY 10016-5997. TEL 212-419-7900, 800-678-4333, FAX 212-752-4929, customer.service@ieee.org, http://www.ieee.org.

OF VALUE. see *PHILOSOPHY*

610.28 DEU ISSN 1431-8202
PROGRESS IN BIOMEDICAL RESEARCH. Text in English. 1996. bi-m. **Document type:** *Journal, Academic/Scholarly.*
—BLDSC (6865.992500), IE, ingenta. **CCC.**
Published by: Friedrich-Alexander University Erlangen-Nuremberg, Department of Biomedical Engineering, Henkestr 91, Erlangen, 91052, Germany. TEL 49-9131-8525630, FAX 49-9131-8525631, biomed@biomed.uni-erlangen.de, http://progress.biomedical-research.com. Ed. Dr. Bernhard Hensel.

570.285 USA
▼ **PURINERGIC SIGNALING.** Text in English. 2005. q. **Document type:** *Journal, Academic/Scholarly.* **Description:** Addresses the growing interest in purinergic signalling and its wide specrum of signalling functions in both health and disease.
Published by: Springer Publications, 31201 Chicago Rd, Ste B 300, Warren, MI 48093. TEL 586-939-6800, FAX 586-939-5850.

610.28 JPN
RAIOENJINIARINGU BUMON GAKUJUTSU KOENKAI KOEN RONBUNSHU/JAPANESE SOCIETY OF MECHANICAL ENGINEERS. BIOENGINEERING DIVISION CONFERENCE. Text in Japanese; Summaries in English. 1989. a. JPY 6,000.
Published by: Nihon Kikai Gakkai/Japan Society of Mechanical Engineers, Shinanomachi-Rengakan Bldg, Shinanomachi 35, Shinjuku-ku, Tokyo, 160, Japan.

REFERATIVNYI ZHURNAL. BIOTEKHNOLOGIYA. see *BIOLOGY—Abstracting, Bibliographies, Statistics*

SCHERING ANNUAL REPORT (YEAR). see *PHARMACY AND PHARMACOLOGY*

660.6 SGP
SERIES ON BIOENGINEERING & BIOMEDICAL ENGINEERING. Text in English. 1998. irreg., latest vol.4. price varies. **Document type:** *Monographic series, Academic/Scholarly.* **Description:** Presents a publishing forum for established researchers, educators and professionals in the field of Bioengineering and Biomedical Engineering to promote in-depth documentation of new scientific findings, technological advances, and to provide effective teaching tools of the fundamental aspects of the field.
Published by: World Scientific Publishing Co. Pte. Ltd., 5 Toh Tuck Link, Singapore, 596224, Singapore. TEL 65-466-5775, FAX 65-467-7667, wspc@wspc.com.sg, series@wspc.com.sg, http://www.wspc.com/books/series/sbbe_series.shtml, http://www.worldscientific.com. Ed. Dr. John K J Li. **Dist. by:** World Scientific Publishing Co., Inc., 1060 Main St, River Edge, NJ 07661. TEL 201-487-9655, 800-227-7562, FAX 201-487-9656, 888-977-2665; World Scientific Publishing Ltd., 57 Shelton St, London WC2H 9HE, United Kingdom. TEL 44-20-78360888, FAX 44-20-78362020.

570.285 660.6 GBR
▼ **SERIES ON BIOMATERIALS AND BIOENGINEERING.** Text in English. 2004. irreg., latest vol.3, 2004, Oct. price varies. **Document type:** *Monographic series, Academic/Scholarly.*
Published by: Imperial College Press (Subsidiary of: World Scientific Publishing Co. Pte. Ltd.), 57 Shelton St, London, WC2H 9HE, United Kingdom. TEL 44-20-7836-3954, FAX 44-20-7836-2002, edit@icpress.co.uk, http://www.wspc.com/books/series/sbmbe_series.shtml, http://www.icpress.co.uk/. Eds. Andrew W Batchelor, J R Batchelor, Margam Chandrasekaran.

SHENGWU YIXUE GONGCHENG YU LINCHUANG/BIOMEDICAL ENGINEERING & CLINICAL MEDICINE. see *MEDICAL SCIENCES*

TECHNOLOGY AND HEALTH CARE; official journal of the European Society for Engineering and Medicine. see *MEDICAL SCIENCES*

TISSUE ENGINEERING. see *BIOLOGY—Cytology And Histology*

610.28 JPN ISSN 1347-7110
TOKYO WOMEN'S MEDICAL COLLEGE. INSTITUTE OF ADVANCED BIOMEDICAL ENGINEERING & SCIENCE. REPORTS. Text in English, Japanese. 1976. a.
Formerly: Iyo Kogaku Kenkyu Shisetsu Hokoku (0910-1705)
—BLDSC (7520.224300).
Published by: Institute of Advanced Biomedical Engineering & Science, 8-1 Kawada-cho Sinjuku-ku, Tokyo, 162-0054, Japan.

TRANSGENIC RESEARCH. see *BIOLOGY—Genetics*

TRANSGENICS; biological analysis through dna transfer. see *BIOLOGY—Genetics*

572.43 DEU ISSN 1435-5272
TP248.13 CODEN: BENGEQ
TRANSKRIPT. Text in German. 1985. m. EUR 60 to individuals; EUR 120 to institutions; EUR 30 to students (effective 2004). adv. **Document type:** *Magazine, Trade.*
Supersedes in part (in 1995): Bio-Engineering (0178-2029)
Indexed: CEABA.
—CASDDS, CISTI, Ei, GNLM. **CCC.**
Published by: Biocom AG, Stralsunder Str 58-59, Berlin, 13355, Germany. TEL 49-30-2649210, FAX 49-30-26492111, service@biocom.de, http://www.biocom.de. Ed. Andreas Mietzsch. Adv. contact Oliver Schnell. B&W page EUR 2,000. Circ: 6,000.

660.6 IND ISSN 0971-5622
TP248.13
V A T I S UPDATE. BIOTECHNOLOGY. (Value Added Technology Information Service) Text in English. 1993. bi-m. INR 1,000, USD 100 (effective 2005). adv. bk.rev. bibl.; charts; illus.; mkt.; pat.; tr.lit. 20 p./no. 2 cols./p.; back issues avail. **Document type:** *Journal, Trade.* **Description:** Keeps readers up-to-date with the latest technological developments and events in the field of biotechnology. Designed for policy makers, industries and technology transfer intermediaries.
Published by: Asian and Pacific Centre for Transfer of Technology, Adjoining Technology Bhawan, Qutab Institutional Area, P O Box 4575, New Delhi, 110 016, India. TEL 91-11-6856276, 91-11-6966509, FAX 91-11-6856274, TELEX 31-73271 APCT IN, postmaster@apctt.org, http://www.apctt.org. Ed., R&P, Adv. contact Nanjundappa Srinivasan. page INR 3,750, page USD 105; 220 x 280. Circ: 700. **Co-sponsor:** Biotech Consortium India Ltd.

ZAJIAO SHUIDAO/JOURNAL OF HYBRID RICE. see *AGRICULTURE—Crop Production And Soil*

ZHONGGUO SHENGWU YIXUE GONGCHENG XUEBAO/CHINESE JOURNAL OF BIOMEDICAL ENGINEERING. see *MEDICAL SCIENCES*

BIOLOGY—Biochemistry

572.06 GBR ISSN 0959-860X
A C B NATIONAL MEETING HANDBOOK. Text in English. 1985. a. adv. back issues avail. **Document type:** *Bulletin.*
—CCC.
Published by: (Association of Clinical Biochemists), P R C Associates, The Annexe, Fitznells Manor, Chessington Rd, Ewell Village, Epsom, Surrey KT17 1TF, United Kingdom. TEL 44-20-8786-7376, FAX 44-20-8786-7262. Ed. J D Berg. Circ: 4,500.

572.06 GBR ISSN 0959-9029
A C B NATIONAL MEETING PROCEEDINGS✱ . Text in English. 1987. a. GBP 10 in Europe; USD 20 elsewhere. adv. back issues avail. **Document type:** *Proceedings.*
—CCC.
Published by: (Association of Clinical Biochemists), P R C Associates, The Annexe, Fitznells Manor, Chessington Rd, Ewell Village, Epsom, Surrey KT17 1TF, United Kingdom. TEL 44-20-8786-7376, FAX 44-20-8786-7262. Ed. S P Halloran. Circ: 2,500.

572 GBR ISSN 1461-0337
A C B NEWS. Text in English. 1997. m.
—BLDSC (0570.741000).
Published by: Association of Clinical Biochemists, 130-132 Tooley St, London, SE1 2TU, United Kingdom. TEL 44-207-4038001, FAX 44-207-4038006, admin@acb.org.uk, http://www.acb.org.uk.

A D C NEWS. see *MEDICAL SCIENCES—Oncology*

572.8 USA
➤ **A S B M B TODAY.** Variant title: American Society for Biochemistry and Molecular Biology Today. Text in English. m. adv. **Document type:** *Magazine, Academic/Scholarly.*
Formerly (until Apr.2002): A S B M B News
Published by: (American Society for Biochemistry and Molecular Biology, Inc.), Federation of American Societies for Experimental Biology, 9650 Rockville Pike, Rm L-2407A, Bethesda, MD 20814-3998. TEL 301-634-7029, FAX 301-634-7809, http://www.faseb.org. adv.: B&W page USD 1,025; trim 8.5 x 11.

572.86 USA
A T C C CATALOGUE OF RECOMBINANT D N A MATERIALS. Text in English. irreg., latest vol.3, 1993. USD 5. **Document type:** *Catalog.*
Formerly: American Type Culture Collection. Catalogue of Recombinant D N A Collections; Supersedes in part: American Type Culture Collection. Catalogue of Bacteria, Phages, and D N A Vectors; American Type Culture Collection. Catalogue of Strains 1: Algae, Bacteria, Bacteriophages, Plasmids, Fungi, Plant Viruses and Antisera and Protozoa; Former titles: American Type Culture Collection. Catalogue of Strains 1: Algae, Bacteria, Bacteriophages, Fungi, Plant Viruses and Antisera and Protozoa; American Type Culture Collection. Catalogue of Strains: Algae, Bacteria, Bacteriophages, Fungi and Protozoa (0363-2970)
—CISTI. **CCC.**
Published by: American Type Culture Collection, 10801 University Blvd, Manassas, VA 20110. TEL 800-638-6597, FAX 301-816-4361, sales@atcc.org. Eds. D R Maglott, W C Nierman.

A T PASES. (Adenosine Triphosphatases) see *BIOLOGY—Abstracting, Bibliographies, Statistics*

ABSTRACTS OF SYMPOSIUM ON PEPTIDE CHEMISTRY/PEPUCHIDO KAGAKU TORONKAI KOEN YOSHISHU. see *FISH AND FISHERIES—Abstracting, Bibliographies, Statistics*

572 USA ISSN 1672-9145
CODEN: SHWPAU
➤ **ACTA BIOCHIMICA ET BIOPHYSICA SINICA.** Text in English. 1958. m. USD 349 combined subscription in the Americas to institutions print & online eds.; GBP 207 combined subscription elsewhere to institutions print & online eds. (effective 2006). adv. **Document type:** *Journal, Academic/Scholarly.* **Description:** Publishes research papers, short communications and minireviews in biochemistry, molecular biology and biophysics. Research papers and short communications report on original work, with minireviews providing a concise introduction to the subject matter to inform the readers of the latest developments in a certain area.
Former titles (until 2004): Shengwu Huaxue yu Shengwu Wuli Xuebao (0582-9879); (until 1961): Shengwu Huaxue Xuebao
Related titles: Online - full text ed.: ISSN 1745-7270. USD 332 in the Americas to institutions; GBP 197 elsewhere to institutions (effective 2006) (from Blackwell Synergy, East View Information Services, EBSCO Publishing, O C L C Online Computer Library Center, Inc., Swets Information Services).

Indexed: AbAn, AgBio, AnBrAb, BBCI, BIOSIS Prev, BiolAb, CEABA, CIN, CPA, ChemAb, ChemTitl, FCA, HelmAb, HortAb, ISR, IndVet, MSB, MaizeAb, PBA, PGrRegA, PoultAb, RA&MP, RPP, RefZh, RevApplEntom, RiceAb, S&F, SIA, SeedAb, SoyAb, TDB, TriticAb, ZooRec.
—BLDSC (0600.800000), CASDDS, CISTI, IE, Infotrieve, ingenta, Linda Hall. **CCC.**
Published by: (Chinese Academy of Sciences, Shanghai Institute of Biochemistry, Institute of Biochemistry and Cell Biology/Zhongguo Kexueyuan, Shanghai Shengming Kexue Yanjiuyuan, Shengwu Huaxue yu Xibao Shengwuxue Yanjiusuo CHN), Blackwell Publishing, Inc. (Subsidiary of: Blackwell Publishing Ltd.), Commerce Place, 350 Main St, Malden, MA 02148. TEL 781-388-8206, FAX 781-388-8232, subscrip@blackwellpub.com, http://www.blackwellpublishing.com/subs.asp?ref=1672-9145. Ed. You-Shang Zhang. **Subscr. in Europe to:** Blackwell Publishing Ltd., Journal Customer Services, 9600 Garsington Rd, PO Box 1354, Oxford OX4 2XG, United Kingdom. TEL 44-1865-778315, FAX 44-1865-471775.

572 571.4 POL ISSN 0001-527X
QP501 CODEN: ABPLAF
➤ **ACTA BIOCHIMICA POLONICA.** Text and summaries in English. 1954. q. EUR 135 foreign to institutions (effective 2005). adv. bk.rev. charts; illus.; bibl. index. 200 p./no. 2 cols./p.; back issues avail. **Document type:** *Journal, Academic/Scholarly.* **Description:** Covers enzymology and metabolism, membranes and bioenergetics, gene structure and expression, protein, nucleic acid and carbohydrate structure and metabolism.
Related titles: Online - full text ed.: 2000. free (effective 2005).
Indexed: ASCA, ASFA, AbHyg, AgBio, AgrAg, AgrLib, AnBrAb, BBCI, BIOSIS Prev, BiolAb, CIN, CPA, ChemAb, ChemTitl, CurCont, DSA, DentInd, ExcerpMed, FCA, FS&TA, ForAb, HelmAb, HerbAb, HortAb, IABS, INIS AtomInd, ISR, IndMed, IndVet, Inpharma, MEDLINE, MSB, MaizeAb, NemAb, NutrAb, OrnHort, PBA, PE&ON, PGegResA, PGrRegA, PN&I, PotatoAb, RA&MP, RM&VM, RPP, Reac, RefZh, S&F, SCI, SIA, TriticAb, VetBull.
—BLDSC (0600.990000), CASDDS, CINDOC, CISTI, GNLM, IDS, IE, Infotrieve, ingenta, Linda Hall.
Published by: Polskie Towarzystwo Biochemiczne, Ul Pasteura 3, Warsaw, 02093, Poland. TEL 48-22-6686280, FAX 48-22-6582099, abp@nencki.gov.pl, konarska@nencki.gov.pl, http://www.actabp.pl, http://www.ptbioch.edu.pl. Ed. Liliana Konarska. Adv. contact Malgorzata Basaj. B&W page USD 100, color page USD 200. Circ: 2,000. **Dist. by:** Ars Polona, Krakowskie Przedmiescie 7, Warsaw, Poland. TEL 48-22-9263914, FAX 48-22-9265334, arspolona@arspolona.com.pl, http://www.arspolona.com.pl.

▼ ➤ **ACTA BIOMATERIALIA.** see *BIOLOGY—Biotechnology*

➤ **ACTA BIOPHYSICS SINICA.** see *BIOLOGY—Biophysics*

572 ARG ISSN 0325-2957
CODEN: ABCLDL
➤ **ACTA BIOQUIMICA CLINICA LATINOAMERICANA.** Text in Spanish; Summaries in English, Spanish. 1966. q. adv. bk.rev. abstr.; bibl.; charts; illus. index. **Document type:** *Journal, Academic/Scholarly.* **Description:** It aims at publishing original scientific articles about the health sciences.
Formerly: Bioquimica Clinica (0006-3533)
Related titles: Online - full text ed.: 2005. free (effective 2006).
Indexed: ASCA, BBCI, BiolAb, CIN, ChemAb, ChemTitl, ExcerpMed, INIS AtomInd, IndMed.
—BLDSC (0603.500000), CASDDS, CISTI, IDS, IE, ingenta, KNAW.
Published by: Federacion Bioquimica de la Provincia de Buenos Aires, Calle 6, 1344, La Plata, Buenos Aires 1900, Argentina. TEL 54-114-3882142797, FAX 54-114-254224, http://www.scielo.org.ar/scielo.php?script=sci_serial&pid=0325-2957&lng=en&nrm=iso. Ed. Juan M Castagnino. Circ: 3,000 (controlled).

➤ **ACTA CRYSTALLOGRAPHICA. SECTION D: BIOLOGICAL CRYSTALLOGRAPHY/BIOLOGICAL CRYSTALLOGRAPHY.** see *CHEMISTRY—Crystallography*

572 DEU ISSN 0065-1281
CODEN: AHISA9
➤ **ACTA HISTOCHEMICA.** Text in English. 1954. 6/yr. EUR 202 in Europe to individuals; JPY 24,500 in Japan to individuals; USD 193 to individuals except Europe and Japan; EUR 573 to institutions; EUR 615 in Europe to institutions; JPY 81,100 in Japan to institutions; USD 658 to institutions except Europe and Japan (effective 2006). adv. bk.rev. bibl.; charts; illus. index. reprint service avail. from ISI. **Document type:** *Journal, Academic/Scholarly.* **Description:** Covers the structural biochemistry of cells and tissues. Aims to provide a forum for the cytochemical and histochemical research community. Manuscripts reporting on studies of living cells an tissues are particulary welcome.
Related titles: Microform ed.: (from PMC, SWZ); Online - full text ed.: (from EBSCO Publishing, Gale Group, IngentaConnect, O C L C Online Computer Library Center, Inc., ProQuest Information & Learning, ScienceDirect, Swets Information Services).
Indexed: ASCA, AbHyg, AgBio, AnBrAb, BBCI, BiolAb, CIN, ChemAb, ChemTitl, CurCont, DSA, DentInd, EngInd, ExcerpMed, HortAb, ISR, IndMed, IndVet, Inpharma, MEDLINE, NSCI, NutrAb, PE&ON, PN&I, PoultAb, RA&MP, Reac, SCI, SFA, TDB, VetBull, WildRev, ZooRec.
—BLDSC (0624.000000), CASDDS, CISTI, Ei, GNLM, IDS, IE, Infotrieve, ingenta, KNAW, Linda Hall. **CCC.**
Published by: (International Federation of Societies for Histochemistry and Cytochemistry USA), Elsevier GmbH, Urban & Fischer Verlag (Subsidiary of: Elsevier Science & Technology), Loebdergraben 14a, Jena, 07743, Germany. TEL 49-3641-626444, FAX 49-3641-626443, journals@urbanfischer.de, http://www.elsevier.com/locate/actahist, http://www.urbanfischer.de/journals. Eds. Dr. Raymond Coleman TEL 972-4-8295395, Dr. Susan A Brooks. R&P Martin Huber TEL 49-3641-626430. Adv. contact Cora Grotzke. B&W page EUR 400, color page EUR 1,345; trim 135 x 200. Circ: 400. **Non-German speaking countries subscr. to:** Nature Publishing Group, Brunel Rd, Houndmills, Basingstoke, Hamps RG21 6XS, United Kingdom. TEL 44-1256-302629, FAX 44-1256-476117, subscriptions@nature.com.

➤ **ACTA HISTOCHEMICA ET CYTOCHEMICA/NIHON SOSHIKI SAIBO KAGAKKAI GAKKAISHI.** see *BIOLOGY—Cytology And Histology*

572 POL ISSN 0208-614X
QP501 CODEN: AUFBD3
ACTA UNIVERSITATIS LODZIENSIS: FOLIA BIOCHIMICA ET BIOPHYSICA. Text in Polish; Summaries in Multiple languages. 1955; N.S. 1981. irreg. **Document type:** *Academic/Scholarly.* **Description:** Publishes articles devoted to the studies on biochemistry and biophysics.
Supersedes in part: Uniwersytet Lodzki. Zeszyty Naukowe. Seria 2: Nauki Matematyczno-Przyrodnicze (0076-0366)
Indexed: AgrLib, CIN, ChemAb, ChemTitl, RefZh, ZooRec.
—CASDDS, CISTI, KNAW, Linda Hall.
Published by: Wydawnictwo Uniwersytetu Lodzkiego/Lodz University Press, ul Jaracza 34, Lodz, 90262, Poland. TEL 331671. **Dist. by:** Ars Polona, Krakowskie Przedmiescie 7, Warsaw, Poland.

ADVANCES IN ANTIVIRAL DRUG DESIGN. see *PHARMACY AND PHARMACOLOGY*

572.57 USA
ADVANCES IN APPLIED LIPID RESEARCH. Text in English. 1992. irreg., latest 1996. price varies. **Document type:** *Monographic series, Academic/Scholarly.*
Indexed: BIOSIS Prev, CIN, ChemAb, ChemTitl.
Published by: J A I Press Inc. (Subsidiary of: Elsevier Science & Technology), 360 Park Ave S, New York, NY 10010-1710. TEL 212-989-5800, FAX 212-633-3990, usinfo-f@elsevier.com, http://www.elsevier.com. Ed. Fred B Padley.

ADVANCES IN BIOCHEMICAL ENGINEERING - BIOTECHNOLOGY. see *BIOLOGY—Biotechnology*

572 NLD ISSN 0272-3840
CODEN: ABIODQ
➤ **ADVANCES IN BIOMATERIALS.** Text in Dutch. 1983. irreg., latest vol.10, 1992. price varies. **Document type:** *Monographic series, Academic/Scholarly.* **Description:** Chronicles research and development in the field of biomaterials.
Indexed: CIN, ChemAb, ChemTitl.
—CASDDS, CISTI, KNAW. **CCC.**
Published by: (European Society for Biomaterials GBR), Elsevier BV (Subsidiary of: Elsevier Science & Technology), Radarweg 29, Amsterdam, 1043 NX, Netherlands. TEL 31-20-4853911, FAX 31-20-4852457, nlinfo-f@elsevier.nl, http://www.elsevier.nl.

➤ **ADVANCES IN CARBOHYDRATE CHEMISTRY AND BIOCHEMISTRY.** see *MEDICAL SCIENCES*

➤ **ADVANCES IN CLINICAL AND EXPERIMENTAL MEDICINE.** see *BIOLOGY—Biotechnology*

572 USA ISSN 0065-2423
RB1
➤ **ADVANCES IN CLINICAL CHEMISTRY.** Text in English. 1958. irreg., latest vol.36, 2001. USD 169.95 per vol. vol.37 (effective 2004). index, cum.index: vols.1-5 (1958-1962). reprint service avail. from ISI. **Document type:** *Academic/Scholarly.* **Description:** Continues the objective of expanding the intellectual horizon of clinical chemistry. The fields of analytical, anatomical, sub-cellular and molecular sciences are all represented.
Indexed: ASCA, BBCI, BIOSIS Prev, BiolAb, CIN, ChemAb, ChemTitl, ISR, IndMed, JDDR, MEDLINE, SCI.
—BLDSC (0703.900000), CASDDS, CISTI, GNLM, IE, Infotrieve, ingenta, Linda Hall. **CCC.**
Published by: Academic Press (Subsidiary of: Elsevier Science & Technology), 525 B St, Ste 1900, San Diego, CA 92101-4495. TEL 619-231-6616, 800-894-3434, FAX 619-699-6422, apsubs@acad.com, http://www.academicpress.com. Ed. Herbert E Spiegel.

➤ **ADVANCES IN DEVELOPMENTAL BIOLOGY AND BIOCHEMISTRY.** see *BIOLOGY*

572.86 USA ISSN 1067-568X
QP624.7 CODEN: ADNAEO
ADVANCES IN DNA SEQUENCE SPECIFIC AGENTS. Text in English. 1992. irreg., latest vol.4, 2002. price varies. back issues avail. **Document type:** *Monographic series, Academic/Scholarly.* **Description:** Intends to give the reader an up-to-date view of both established and emergent trends, in research involving DNA-interactive agents with an emphasis on sequence specificity.
Indexed: CIN, ChemAb, ChemTitl.
—BLDSC (0704.249000), CASDDS, GNLM. **CCC.**
Published by: J A I Press Inc. (Subsidiary of: Elsevier Science & Technology), 360 Park Ave S, New York, NY 10010-1710. TEL 212-989-5800, FAX 212-633-3990, usinfo-f@elsevier.com, http://www.elsevier.com/wps/find/bookdescription.cws_home/BS_ADNA/description#description. Ed. Graham B Jones TEL 617-373-8619.

572 NLD ISSN 0924-8137
➤ **ADVANCES IN EICOSANOID RESEARCH.** Text in English. 1988. irreg., latest vol.4, 1988. price varies. back issues avail. **Document type:** *Monographic series, Academic/Scholarly.*
Published by: Springer-Verlag Dordrecht (Subsidiary of: Springer Science+Business Media), Van Godewijckstraat 30, Dordrecht, 3311 GX, Netherlands. TEL 31-78-6576050, FAX 31-78-6576474, http://www.springeronline.com.

572.7 GBR ISSN 0065-2571
QP601.A1 CODEN: AEZRA2
➤ **ADVANCES IN ENZYME REGULATION.** Text in English. 1963. a. EUR 891 in Europe to institutions; JPY 118,300 in Japan to institutions; USD 997 to institutions except Europe and Japan (effective 2006). adv. back issues avail. **Document type:** *Proceedings, Academic/Scholarly.* **Description:** Evaluates topics including metabolic regulation, inborn errors of metabolism, metabolic diseases, diabetes, and cancer in the light of new research results.
Related titles: Microform ed.: (from PQC); Online - full text ed.: (from EBSCO Publishing, Gale Group, IngentaConnect, ScienceDirect, Swets Information Services).
Indexed: ASCA, BBCI, BIOBASE, BIOSIS Prev, BiolAb, CIN, ChemAb, ChemTitl, CurCont, IABS, ISR, IndMed, MEDLINE, SCI.
—BLDSC (0705.950000), CASDDS, CISTI, GNLM, IDS, IE, Infotrieve, ingenta. **CCC.**
Published by: Pergamon (Subsidiary of: Elsevier Science & Technology), The Boulevard, Langford Ln, East Park, Kidlington, Oxford OX5 1GB, United Kingdom. TEL 44-1865-843000, FAX 44-1865-843010, http://www.elsevier.com/locate/advenzreg. Ed. George Weber. **Subscr. to:** Elsevier BV, PO Box 211, Amsterdam 1000 AE, Netherlands. nlinfo-f@elsevier.nl, http://www.elsevier.nl.

572.7 GBR ISSN 0065-258X
QP601.A1 CODEN: AERAAD
➤ **ADVANCES IN ENZYMOLOGY AND RELATED SUBJECTS.** Variant title: Advances in Enzymology and Related Subjects of Biochemistry. Text in English. 1942. irreg. (Part B), latest vol.74, 2000. price varies. 392 p./no.; back issues avail. **Document type:** *Monographic series, Academic/Scholarly.*
Indexed: ASCA, Agr, BBCI, BCI, BIOSIS Prev, BiolAb, CBTA, CIN, ChemAb, ChemTitl, DBA, DSA, ISR, IndMed, MEDLINE, SCI, TDB.
—BLDSC (0705.970000), CASDDS, CISTI, GNLM, IDS, IE, Infotrieve, ingenta, Linda Hall. **CCC.**
Published by: John Wiley & Sons Ltd. (Subsidiary of: John Wiley & Sons, Inc.), The Atrium, Southern Gate, Chichester, West Sussex PO19 8SQ, United Kingdom. TEL 44-1243-779777, FAX 44-1243-775878, customer@wiley.co.uk, http://www.wiley.co.uk. Ed. Daniel Purich.

572.57 GBR
ADVANCES IN LIPID METHODOLOGY. Text in English. irreg., latest vol.5, 2003. price varies. **Document type:** *Monographic series, Academic/Scholarly.*
Published by: P.J. Barnes & Associates, PO Box 200, Bridgwater, TA7 0YZ, United Kingdom. TEL 44-1823-698973, FAX 44-1823-698971, sales@pjbarnes.co.uk, http://www.pjbarnes.co.uk/.

573.84 USA ISSN 0098-6089
QP356.3 CODEN: ADNEDZ
➤ **ADVANCES IN NEUROCHEMISTRY.** Text in English. 1975. irreg., latest vol.9, 1999. price varies. **Document type:** *Monographic series, Academic/Scholarly.*
Indexed: BIOSIS Prev, BiolAb, CIN, ChemAb, e-psyche.
—CASDDS, CISTI, GNLM, KNAW. **CCC.**
Published by: Springer-Verlag New York, Inc. (Subsidiary of: Springer Science+Business Media), 233 Spring St, New York, NY 10013. TEL 212-460-1500, FAX 212-460-1575, service@springer-ny.com, http://www.springer-ny.com. Ed. Brian Popko. **Dist. by:** Journal Fulfillment, PO Box 2485, Secaucus, NJ 07096-2485.

B

▼ new title ➤ refereed ✶ unverified ♦ full entry avail.

572.46 NLD ISSN 1572-0233
CODEN: ADPHFM

➤ **ADVANCES IN PHOTOSYNTHESIS AND RESPIRATION.** Text in English. 1995. irreg., latest vol.19, 2004. price varies. back issues avail. **Document type:** *Monographic series, Academic/Scholarly.*
Formerly (until 2001): Advances in Photosynthesis (1382-4252)
Indexed: BIOSIS Prev, CIN, ChemAb, ChemTitl, ZooRec.
—BLDSC (0709.785000), CASDDS, CISTI, ingenta. **CCC.**
Published by: Springer-Verlag Dordrecht (Subsidiary of: Springer Science+Business Media), Van Godewijckstraat 30, Dordrecht, 3311 GX, Netherlands. TEL 31-78-6576050, FAX 31-78-6576474, http://www.springeronline.com.

572.6 USA ISSN 0065-3233
QD431 CODEN: APCHA2

➤ **ADVANCES IN PROTEIN CHEMISTRY.** Text in English. 1944. irreg., latest vol.71, 2005, Aug. USD 149.95, EUR 130, GBP 99.95 per vol. (effective 2005). reprint service avail. from ISI. **Document type:** *Monographic series, Academic/Scholarly.* **Description:** Covers structure and function of all major elements associated with protein transcription.
Related titles: Online - full text ed.: ISSN 1557-8941 (from ScienceDirect).
Indexed: ASCA, AbHyg, BBCI, BIOBASE, BIOSIS Prev, BiolAb, CCI, CIN, ChemAb, ChemTitl, DSA, ExcerpMed, FS&TA, IABS, ISR, IndMed, MEDLINE, NutrAb, SCI, TDB.
—BLDSC (0711.000000), CASDDS, CISTI, GNLM, IE, Infotrieve, ingenta, KNAW, Linda Hall. **CCC.**
Published by: Academic Press (Subsidiary of: Elsevier Science & Technology), 525 B St, Ste 1900, San Diego, CA 92101-4495. TEL 619-231-6616, 800-894-3434, apsubs@acad.com, http://www.academicpress.com. Eds. John T Edsall, M L Anson.

572 USA ISSN 1040-7952
QP625.N89 CODEN: ACNREY

➤ **ADVANCES IN SECOND MESSENGER AND PHOSPHOPROTEIN RESEARCH.** Text in English. 1972. irreg., latest vol.33, 1999. USD 116.95 per vol. vol.33 (effective 2004). reprint service avail. from PQC. **Document type:** *Proceedings, Academic/Scholarly.* **Description:** Reviews brain functioning at the fundamental, molecular level; Describes key systems that control signaling between and within cells; Explains how channels are used to stimulate growth and changes to activity of the nucleus and genome.
Former titles (until 1988): Advances in Cyclic Nucleotide Research and Protein Phosphorylation Research (0747-7767); (until 1984): Advances in Cyclic Nucleotide Research (0084-5930)
Indexed: ASCA, BBCI, BIOSIS Prev, BiolAb, CIN, ChemAb, ChemTitl, CurCont, ISR, IndMed, MEDLINE, SCI.
—BLDSC (0711.383350), CASDDS, CISTI, GNLM, Infotrieve, ingenta, Linda Hall. **CCC.**
Published by: Academic Press (Subsidiary of: Elsevier Science & Technology), 525 B St, Ste 1900, San Diego, CA 92101-4495. TEL 619-231-6616, 800-894-3434, apsubs@acad.com, http://www.academicpress.com. **Subscr. to:** 6277 Sea Harbor Dr, Orlando, FL 32887-4800. TEL 407-345-4040, 800-545-2522, FAX 407-363-9661.

➤ **ALISO;** a journal of taxonomic and evolutionary botany. see *BIOLOGY—Botany*

572.549 547.7 USA ISSN 0735-8210
ALKALOIDS: CHEMICAL AND BIOLOGICAL PERSPECTIVES. Text in English. 1983. irreg., latest vol.8, 1992. USD 250 per vol. (effective 2005). **Document type:** *Monographic series.*
—BLDSC (0788.530000), CISTI. **CCC.**
Published by: Springer-Verlag New York, Inc. (Subsidiary of: Springer Science+Business Media), 233 Spring St, New York, NY 10013. TEL 212-460-1500, FAX 212-460-1575, http://www.springer-ny.com. Ed. S W Pelletier.

572 USA ISSN 1553-3468

▼ ➤ **AMERICAN JOURNAL OF BIOCHEMISTRY AND BIOTECHNOLOGY.** Text in English. 2005. q. USD 600; USD 200 newsstand/cover (effective 2005). adv. **Document type:** *Journal, Academic/Scholarly.* **Description:** Keeps research workers and the scientific community up-to-date with new developments in the life sciences.
Related titles: Online - full text ed.: free (effective 2005).
Published by: Science Publications, Vails Gate Heights Dr, PO Box 879, Vails Gate, NY 12584. scipub@gmail.com, http://ansinet.org/sciencepub/c4p.php?j_id=ajbb, http://www.scipub.org. Ed., R&P Muhammad S Ahmad. adv.: B&W page USD 200, color page USD 500.

➤ **AMERICAN JOURNAL OF PHARMACOGENOMICS.** see *BIOLOGY—Genetics*

➤ **AMERICAN JOURNAL OF PHYSIOLOGY: LUNG CELLULAR AND MOLECULAR PHYSIOLOGY.** see *BIOLOGY—Physiology*

➤ **AMERICAN SOCIETY FOR NEUROCHEMISTRY. TRANSACTIONS.** see *MEDICAL SCIENCES—Psychiatry And Neurology*

572.65 AUT ISSN 0939-4451
QD431.A1 CODEN: AACIE6

➤ **AMINO ACIDS.** Text in English. 1991. 8/yr. EUR 998 combined subscription to institutions print & online eds. (effective 2005). adv. abstr. back issues avail.; reprint service avail. from PSC. **Document type:** *Journal, Academic/Scholarly.* **Description:** Publishes contributions from all fields of amino acids and protein research.
Related titles: Online - full text ed.: ISSN 1438-2199 (from EBSCO Publishing, Springer LINK, Swets Information Services).
Indexed: ASCA, ASFA, AbHyg, AgBio, Agr, BBCI, BIOBASE, BIOSIS Prev, BiolAb, CCI, CIN, CMCI, CPA, ChemAb, ChemTitl, CurCont, ExcerpMed, FCA, HortAb, IABS, ISR, IndMed, IndVet, Inpharma, MEDLINE, MSB, NutrAb, OrnHort, PBA, PE&ON, PGrRegA, PN&I, PoultAb, ProtozoAb, RA&MP, RM&VM, RPP, RRTA, Reac, RefZh, S&F, SCI, SoyAb, TriticAb, VetBull, WeedAb.
—BLDSC (0859.152000), CASDDS, CISTI, GNLM, IDS, IE, Infotrieve, ingenta, KNAW. **CCC.**
Published by: Springer-Verlag Wien (Subsidiary of: Springer Science+Business Media) journals@springer.at, http://www.springer.at/amino_acids. Eds. G Lubec, Mario Herrera-Marschitz. R&P Angela Foessl TEL 43-1-3302415517. Adv. contact Michael Katzenberger TEL 43-1-3302415220. B&W page EUR 1,000; 170 x 250. **Subscr. in the Americas to:** Springer-Verlag New York, Inc., Journal Fulfillment, PO Box 2485, Secaucus, NJ 07096-2485. TEL 800-777-4643, 201-348-4033, FAX 201-348-4505, journals@springer-ny.com, http://www.springer-ny.com.

572.65 GBR ISSN 1361-5904
QD431.A1 CODEN: AACPER

AMINO ACIDS, PEPTIDES AND PROTEINS. Text in English. 1968. a., latest vol.34, 2004. GBP 249.95, USD 459 per vol. (effective 2004). charts; illus. index. back issues avail. **Document type:** *Academic/Scholarly.*
Former titles (until 1994): Amino Acids and Peptides (0269-7521); (until 1985): Amino Acids, Peptides and Proteins (0306-0004)
Indexed: CIN, ChemAb, ChemTitl, FS&TA.
—BLDSC (0859.155000), CASDDS, CISTI, GNLM, IE, ingenta, Linda Hall. **CCC.**
Published by: Royal Society of Chemistry, Thomas Graham House, Science Park, Milton Rd, Cambridge, CB4 0WF, United Kingdom. TEL 44-1223-420066, FAX 44-1223-423623, sales@rsc.org, http://www.rsc.org/spr. Ed. G C Barrett. **Subscr. to:** Extenza - Turpin, Pegasus Dr, Stratton Business Park, Biggleswade, Beds SG18 8TQ, United Kingdom. TEL 44-1462-672555.

AMPHIPACIFICA. see *ENVIRONMENTAL STUDIES—Toxicology And Environmental Safety*

572.579 USA ISSN 1537-5463
ANABOLIC INSIDER. Text in English. 2001. bi-m. USD 29.99 for 12 nos.; USD 3.99 newsstand/cover for 12 nos. (effective 2001). adv. **Document type:** *Magazine, Consumer.* **Description:** Openly and honestly discusses all the facets of anabolic compounds and their use, including pharmaceutical resources, what's out there, counterfeits, how much, how often, what compounds to stack together and which ones not to, new anabolics, new evaluations of old anabolics, and much more.
Published by: Anabolicstore.com, Inc., 1155 S Havana, Ste 11-392, Aurora, CO 80012. TEL 303-750-8844, 888-577-4464, http://www.anabolicinsider.com.

572 USA ISSN 0003-2697
QP501 CODEN: ANBCA2

➤ **ANALYTICAL BIOCHEMISTRY.** Text in English. 1960. 24/yr. EUR 2,836 in Europe to individuals; JPY 296,000 in Japan to individuals; USD 2,243 elsewhere to individuals; EUR 5,974 in Europe to institutions; JPY 624,000 in Japan to institutions; USD 4,726 elsewhere to institutions (effective 2006). adv. bk.rev. charts; illus. index. back issues avail.; reprints avail. **Document type:** *Journal, Academic/Scholarly.* **Description:** Emphasizes methods in the biological and biochemical sciences and all related fields.
Related titles: Online - full text ed.: ISSN 1096-0309. USD 4,892 (effective 2002) (from EBSCO Publishing, Gale Group, IngentaConnect, O C L C Online Computer Library Center, Inc., ScienceDirect, Swets Information Services).
Indexed: ABIPC, AESIS, ASCA, ASFA, AgBio, AnBrAb, AnalAb, ApicAb, BBCI, BIOBASE, BIOSIS Prev, BiolAb, CCI, CIN, CLL, CPA, ChemAb, ChemTitl, ChromAb, CurCont, DBA, DSA, DentInd, ExcerpMed, FCA, FS&TA, HGA, HerbAb, HortAb, IABS, ISR, IndMed, IndVet, Inpharma, MEDLINE, MSB, MaizeAb, NSCI, NucAcAb, NutrAb, OrnHort, PBA, ProtozoAb, RM&VM, Reac, RefZh, RevApplEntom, RiceAb, S&F, SCI, SFA, SIA, SeedAb, SoyAb, THA, VITIS, VetBull, WeedAb.
—BLDSC (0896.500000), CASDDS, CINDOC, CISTI, GNLM, IDS, IE, Infotrieve, ingenta, Linda Hall. **CCC.**
Published by: Academic Press (Subsidiary of: Elsevier Science & Technology), 525 B St, Ste 1900, San Diego, CA 92101-4495. TEL 619-231-6616, 800-894-3434, FAX 619-699-6422, apsubs@acad.com, http://www.elsevier.com/locate/yabio, http://www.academicpress.com. Ed. William B Jakoby.

612.015 GBR ISSN 0004-5632
CODEN: ACBOBU

➤ **ANNALS OF CLINICAL BIOCHEMISTRY.** Text in English. 1960. bi-m. GBP 165 combined subscription in Europe print & online; USD 286 combined subscription in United States print & online; GBP 170 combined subscription elsewhere print & online (effective 2005). adv. bk.rev. illus. index. back issues avail. **Document type:** *Journal, Academic/Scholarly.* **Description:** Presents international papers about clinical biochemistry, especially for the understanding, diagnosis and treatment of human disease.
Formerly (until 1969): Association of Clinical Biochemists. Proceedings (0369-8564)
Related titles: Online - full text ed.: GBP 149, USD 257 (effective 2005) (from bigchalk, EBSCO Publishing, Gale Group, IngentaConnect, O C L C Online Computer Library Center, Inc., ProQuest Information & Learning, Swets Information Services).
Indexed: ASCA, AnalAb, BBCI, BIOBASE, BiolAb, CIN, ChemAb, ChemTitl, CurCont, DentInd, ExcerpMed, IABS, INI, ISR, IndMed, Inpharma, Kidney, MEDLINE, MSB, NutrAb, PE&ON, RM&VM, Reac, RefZh, SCI, SSCI, THA, VetBull.
—BLDSC (1040.230000), CASDDS, CISTI, GNLM, IDS, IE, Infotrieve, ingenta, KNAW. **CCC.**
Published by: (Association of Clinical Biochemists), Royal Society of Medicine Press Ltd., 1 Wimpole St, London, W1M 8AE, United Kingdom. TEL 44-20-72902921, FAX 44-20-72902929, publishing@rsm.ac.uk, http://www.roysocmed.ac.uk/pub/acb.htm. Ed. Julian H Barth. Pub. Delia Siedle. R&P Caroline McLaughlin. Circ: 3,650. **Subscr. to:** PO Box 9002, London W1A 0ZA, United Kingdom. TEL 44-20-7290-2927, 44-20-7290-2928, FAX 44-20-7290-2929, rsmjournals@rsm.ac.uk.

572.8 ITA ISSN 1590-4261
CODEN: AMNIC7

➤ **ANNALS OF MICROBIOLOGY.** Text in English; Abstracts in English. 1940. q. EUR 80 to individuals; EUR 160 to institutions (effective 2005). adv. bk.rev. bibl.; charts; illus. index, cum.index. **Document type:** *Journal, Academic/Scholarly.* **Description:** Covers non-medical microbiology: general, industrial, soil, food, enzymology, fermentation and microbial chemistry.
Former titles (until 2000): Annali di Microbiologia ed Enzimologia (0003-4649); (until 1956): Annali di Microbiologia (0301-5211)
Indexed: ASCA, AbHyg, AgBio, Agr, AgrForAb, BCI, BIOSIS Prev, BioCN&I, BioDAb, BiolAb, CIN, ChemAb, ChemTitl, DSA, ExcerpMed, FCA, FPA, FS&TA, ForAb, HortAb, IABS, IndVet, MaizeAb, NutrAb, PBA, PGrRegA, PHN&I, PN&I, PotatoAb, PoultAb, RA&MP, RM&VM, RPP, RefZh, S&F, SIA, SeedAb, SoyAb, TDB, TriticAb, VITIS, VetBull, WeedAb.
—BLDSC (1043.131500), CASDDS, CISTI, IDS, IE, ingenta, Linda Hall.
Published by: Universita degli Studi di Milano, Dipartimento di Scienze e Tecnologie Alimentari e Microbiologiche, Via Giovanni Celoria, 2, Milan, MI 20133, Italy. TEL 39-02-50316725, FAX 39-02-50316694, annals.microbiology@unimi.it, annali.microbiologia@unimi.it, http://www.annmicro.unimi.it. Ed., Adv. contact C Sorlini. Circ: 500.

572 USA ISSN 1547-6294
QP552.L48

▼ ➤ **ANNEXINS.** Text in English. 2004. q. USD 80 combined subscription in US & Canada to individuals print & online eds.; USD 130 combined subscription elsewhere to individuals print & online eds.; USD 450 combined subscription in US & Canada to institutions print & online eds.; USD 500 combined subscription elsewhere to institutions print & online eds. (effective 2005). **Document type:** *Journal, Academic/Scholarly.*
Related titles: Online - full text ed.: ISSN 1555-8606.
Indexed: ExcerpMed.
Published by: Landes Bioscience, 810 S Church St, Georgetown, TX 78626. TEL 512-863-7762, 800-736-9948, FAX 512-863-0081, info@landesbioscience.com, http://www.landesbioscience.com/journals/annexins/index.php.

572 USA ISSN 0066-4154
QP501 CODEN: ARBOAW

➤ **ANNUAL REVIEW OF BIOCHEMISTRY.** Text in English. 1932. a., latest vol.73, 2004. USD 208 to institutions print or online ed.; USD 250 combined subscription to institutions print & online eds. (effective 2006). bibl.; charts; abstr. index, cum.index. back issues avail.; reprint service avail. from PSC. **Document type:** *Academic/Scholarly.* **Description:** Original critical reviews of the significant primary literature and current developments in biochemistry.
Related titles: Microfilm ed.: (from PQC); Online - full content ed.: ISSN 1545-4509. USD 203 (effective 2005) (from HighWire Press); Online - full text ed.: (from bigchalk, EBSCO Publishing, H.W. Wilson, O C L C Online Computer Library Center, Inc., ProQuest Information & Learning, Swets Information Services).
Indexed: ABIPC, ASCA, ASFA, AgBio, AnBrAb, B&AI, BBCI, BIOBASE, BIOSIS Prev, BiolAb, CCI, CIN, CPA, CTA, ChemAb, ChemTitl, ChemoAb, CurCont, DSA, ESPM, ExcerpMed, FCA, FS&TA, GSI, GenetAb, HGA, HortAb, IABS, ISR, IndMed, IndVet, Inpharma, JDDR, MEDLINE, MRD, NSA, NucAcAb, NutrAb, PBA, PE&ON, PGegResA, ProtozoAb, Reac, S&F, SCI, SSCI, TDB, THA, VITIS, WeedAb.
—BLDSC (1522.000000), CASDDS, CINDOC, CISTI, GNLM, IDS, IE, Infotrieve, ingenta, KNAW, Linda Hall. **CCC.**

Published by: Annual Reviews, 4139 El Camino Way, Palo Alto, CA 94303-0139. TEL 650-493-4400, 800-523-8635, FAX 650-424-0910, service@annualreviews.org, http://arjournals.annualreviews.org/loi/biochem, http://www.annualreviews.org. Ed. Charles C Richardson. R&P Laura Folkner.

➤ **ANNUAL REVIEW OF BIOPHYSICS AND BIOMOLECULAR STRUCTURE.** see *BIOLOGY—Biophysics*

➤ **ANNUAL REVIEW OF GENOMICS AND HUMAN GENETICS.** see *BIOLOGY—Genetics*

➤ **ANTIOXIDANTS & REDOX SIGNALING.** see *MEDICAL SCIENCES*

572 615 616.9 GBR ISSN 0956-3202
CODEN: ACCHEH

➤ **ANTIVIRAL CHEMISTRY AND CHEMOTHERAPY.** Text in English. 1990. bi-m. GBP 72 in Europe to individuals; USD 109 elsewhere to individuals; GBP 272 in Europe to institutions; USD 419 elsewhere to institutions; GBP 65 in Europe to members; USD 99 elsewhere to members (effective 2004). adv. bk.rev. illus. index. back issues avail. **Document type:** *Journal, Academic/Scholarly.* **Description:** Contains original research and reviews of the biochemistry, mode of action, chemistry, pharmacology and virology of antiviral compounds.
Related titles: Microform ed.: (from PQC).
Indexed: AIDS Ab, AIDS&CR, ASCA, AbHyg, AgrForAb, B&BAb, BIOSIS Prev, BioEngAb, BiolAb, CCI, CIN, ChemAb, ChemTitl, CurCont, DBA, DSA, ESPM, EngInd, ExcerpMed, HortAb, ISR, IndMed, IndVet, Inpharma, M&PBA, MBA, MEDLINE, NutrAb, PE&ON, RA&MP, Reac, RevApplEntom, SCI, TDB, VetBull, VirolAbstr.
—BLDSC (1552.828000), CASDDS, CISTI, Ei, GNLM, IDS, IE, Infotrieve, ingenta, KNAW. **CCC.**
Published by: (International Society for Antiviral Research NLD), International Medical Press, 2-4 Idol Ln, London, EC3R 5DD, United Kingdom. TEL 44-20-73980700, FAX 44-20-73980701, info@intmedpress.com, http://www.intmedpress.com/Journals/AVCC/journals_avcc_home.cfm. Eds. Masanori Baba, Michael Otto, Robert W Sidwell, Hugh J Field. adv.: B&W page GBP 643, B&W page USD 1,158, color page GBP 993, color page USD 1,783; trim 210 x 280. Circ: 285.

➤ **ANTIVIRAL THERAPY.** see *MEDICAL SCIENCES—Communicable Diseases*

572 USA ISSN 0273-2289
TP248.3 CODEN: ABIBDL

➤ **APPLIED BIOCHEMISTRY AND BIOTECHNOLOGY.** Abbreviated title: A B A B. Text in English. 1976. 24/yr. USD 565 to individuals; USD 1,455 to institutions; USD 590 combined subscription to individuals print & online eds.; USD 1,585 combined subscription to institutions print & online eds. (effective 2005). adv. bk.rev. bibl.; charts; illus. **Document type:** *Journal, Academic/Scholarly.* **Description:** Presents innovative, practically oriented research articles in the applications of biotechnology covering genetic engineering, enzyme engineering, fermentation technology, proteins and nucleic acids.
Formerly (until vol.5, 1980): Journal of Solid-Phase Biochemistry (0146-0641)
Related titles: Online - full text ed.: USD 535 to individuals; USD 1,385 to institutions (effective 2005) (from EBSCO Publishing, Gale Group, IngentaConnect, O C L C Online Computer Library Center, Inc., Ovid Technologies, Inc., Swets Information Services).
Indexed: AEA, AEBA, AESIS, ASCA, ASFA, AbHyg, AgBio, Agr, AgrForAb, B&BAb, BBCI, BCI, BIOBASE, BIOSIS Prev, BioDAb, BioEngAb, BiolAb, CBTA, CCI, CEABA, CIN, CPA, ChemAb, ChemTitl, CurCont, DBA, DSA, ESPM, EngInd, ExcerpMed, FCA, FPA, FS&TA, ForAb, HerbAb, HortAb, I&DA, INIS AtomInd, ISR, IndMed, Inpharma, M&PBA, MBA, MEDLINE, MSCI, MaizeAb, NutrAb, OrnHort, PBA, PE&ON, PGrRegA, PotatoAb, PoultAb, RA&MP, RCI, RM&VM, RPP, Reac, RevApplEntom, RiceAb, S&F, SCI, SIA, SSCI, SeedAb, SoyAb, Telegen, TriticAb, VITIS, WAE&RSA, WeedAb.
—BLDSC (1571.880000), CASDDS, CISTI, Ei, GNLM, IDS, IE, Infotrieve, ingenta, Linda Hall. **CCC.**
Published by: Humana Press, Inc., 999 Riverview Dr, Ste 208, Totowa, NJ 07512. TEL 973-256-1699, FAX 973-256-8341, humana@humanapr.com, http://humanapress.com/journals.pasp. Ed. Ashok . Mulchandani. Pub., Adv. contact Thomas B. Lanigan Jr. R&P Wendy A. Warren. **Subscr. to:** Maruzen Co., Ltd., 3-10 Nihonbashi, 2-Chome, Chuo-ku, Tokyo 103, Japan. TEL 81-3-3275-8591, FAX 81-3-3275-0657, journal@maruzen.co.jp, http://www.maruzen.co.jp.

572 RUS ISSN 0003-6838
QH345 CODEN: APBMAC

➤ **APPLIED BIOCHEMISTRY AND MICROBIOLOGY.** Text in English. 1965. bi-m. EUR 3,125, USD 2,898, GBP 1,998 combined subscription to institutions print & online eds. (effective 2005). back issues avail. **Document type:** *Journal, Academic/Scholarly.* **Description:** Offers original accounts and reviews of the latest theoretical, experimental, and applied research in the fields of biochemistry, microbiology, and biotechnology.
Related titles: Online - full text ed.: ISSN 1608-3024 (from EBSCO Publishing, Gale Group, IngentaConnect, Kluwer Online, O C L C Online Computer Library Center, Inc., Ovid Technologies, Inc., Springer LINK, Swets Information Services); ♦ Translation of: Prikladnaya Biokhimiya i Mikrobiologiya. ISSN 0555-1099.
Indexed: AEBA, ASCA, ASFA, BBCI, BCI, BibLing, BioEngAb, BiolAb, CBTA, CCI, ChemAb, ChemTitl, ESPM, ExcerpMed, FPA, FS&TA, IndMed, M&PBA, MBA, PollutAb, VITIS.
—BLDSC (0404.670000), CISTI, IDS, IE, Infotrieve, ingenta. **CCC.**
Published by: (Rossiiskaya Akademiya Nauk/Russian Academy of Sciences), M A I K Nauka - Interperiodica, Profsoyuznaya ul 90, Moscow, 117997, Russian Federation. TEL 7-095-3347420, FAX 7-095-3360666, compmg@maik.ru, http://springerlink.metapress.com/openurl.asp?genre=journal&issn=0003-6838, http://www.maik.ru. Ed. Vladimir O Popov. R&P Vladimir I Vasil'ev. **Subscr. to:** Springer-Verlag Dordrecht, Journals Department, PO Box 322, Dordrecht, Netherlands. TEL 31-78-6576392, FAX 31-78-6576474.

572.8 USA ISSN 1541-2016
RB46.6 CODEN: APIMEH

➤ **APPLIED IMMUNOHISTOCHEMISTRY & MOLECULAR MORPHOLOGY.** Text in English. 1993. q. USD 238 to individuals; USD 402 to institutions (effective 2006). adv. bk.rev. illus. index. back issues avail. **Document type:** *Journal, Academic/Scholarly.* **Description:** Original articles on the diagnostic and prognostic applications of immunohistochemistry to human disease.
Formerly: Applied Immunohistochemistry (1062-3345)
Related titles: Online - full text ed.: ISSN 1533-4058. USD 361.40 domestic academic site license; USD 361.40 foreign academic site license; USD 403.10 domestic corporate site license; USD 403.10 foreign corporate site license (effective 2002) (from EBSCO Publishing, Ovid Technologies, Inc., Swets Information Services).
Indexed: ASCA, BIOSIS Prev, BiolAb, CIN, ChemAb, ChemTitl, CurCont, ExcerpMed, ISR, Inpharma, Reac, SCI.
—CASDDS, GNLM, IDS, ingenta, KNAW. **CCC.**
Published by: (Society for Applied Immunohistochemistry), Lippincott Williams & Wilkins (Subsidiary of: Wolters Kluwer N.V.), 530 Walnut St, Philadelphia, PA 19106-3621. TEL 215-521-8300, FAX 215-521-8902, http://www.appliedimmunohist.com, http://www.lww.com. Eds. Dr. Clive R. Taylor, Dr. Jiang Gu. Pub. Frances R. DeStefano. R&P Margaret Becker. Adv. contact Fred Short. B&W page USD 950, color page USD 2,085. Circ: 1,033 (paid). **Subscr. to:** PO Box 1620, Hagerstown, MD 21741. TEL 301-223-2300, 800-638-3030, FAX 301-223-2365.

➤ **AQUA GEOGRAPHIA (ITALIAN EDITION);** journal of ichthyology and aquatic biology. see *ENVIRONMENTAL STUDIES—Toxicology And Environmental Safety*

➤ **AQUATIC TOXICOLOGY.** see *ENVIRONMENTAL STUDIES—Toxicology And Environmental Safety*

572 USA ISSN 0003-9861
QP501 CODEN: ABBIA4

➤ **ARCHIVES OF BIOCHEMISTRY AND BIOPHYSICS.** Text in English. 1942. 24/yr. EUR 589 in Europe to individuals; JPY 61,500 in Japan to individuals; USD 512 elsewhere to individuals; EUR 6,702 in Europe to institutions; JPY 700,000 in Japan to institutions; USD 5,071 elsewhere to institutions; EUR 277 in Europe to students; JPY 28,900 in Japan to students; USD 241 elsewhere to students (effective 2006). adv. bibl.; illus. index. back issues avail. **Document type:** *Journal, Academic/Scholarly.* **Description:** Presents articles in the areas of biochemistry and biophysics, especially those related to molecular biology, cell biology, and developmental biology.
Formerly (until 1951): Archives of Biochemistry (0096-9621)
Related titles: Online - full text ed.: ISSN 1096-0384. USD 5,374 (effective 2002) (from EBSCO Publishing, Gale Group, IngentaConnect, O C L C Online Computer Library Center, Inc., ScienceDirect, Swets Information Services); ♦ Series: Nitric Oxide: Biology and Chemistry. ISSN 1089-8603.
Indexed: ABIPC, AIDS Ab, ASCA, ASFA, AbHyg, AgBio, Agr, AgrForAb, AnBrAb, BBCI, BIOBASE, BIOSIS Prev, BibAg, BioDAb, BiolAb, CCI, CIN, CISA, CPA, ChemAb, ChemTitl, CurCont, DBA, DSA, DentInd, EngInd, EnvAb, ExcerpMed, FCA, FPA, FS&TA, ForAb, HelmAb, HerbAb, HortAb, IABS, ISR, IndMed, IndVet, Inpharma, MBA, MEDLINE, MSB, MaizeAb, NRN, NSCI, NemAb, NutrAb, OrnHort, PBA, PE&ON, PGegResA, PGrRegA, PHN&I, PN&I, PotatoAb, PoultAb, ProtozoAb, RA&MP, RM&VM, RPP, Reac, RefZh, RevApplEntom, RiceAb, S&F, S&MA, SCI, SFA, SIA, SeedAb, SoyAb, TDB, TOSA, TriticAb, VITIS, VetBull, WeedAb, WildRev, ZooRec.
—BLDSC (1633.000000), CASDDS, CINDOC, CISTI, Ei, GNLM, IDS, IE, Infotrieve, ingenta, Linda Hall. **CCC.**
Published by: Academic Press (Subsidiary of: Elsevier Science & Technology), 525 B St, Ste 1900, San Diego, CA 92101-4495. TEL 619-231-6616, 800-894-3434, FAX 619-699-6422, apsubs@acad.com, http://www.elsevier.com/locate/yabbi, http://www.academicpress.com. Eds. A. Scarpa, H. Sies, P. F. Fitzpatrick.

➤ **ARCHIVES OF INSECT BIOCHEMISTRY AND PHYSIOLOGY.** see *BIOLOGY—Entomology*

➤ **ARCHIVES OF MICROBIOLOGY.** see *BIOLOGY—Microbiology*

➤ **ARCHIVES OF PHYSIOLOGY AND BIOCHEMISTRY.** see *BIOLOGY—Physiology*

572 ARG ISSN 0004-4768
QP501 CODEN: RABAAO

ASOCIACION BIOQUIMICA ARGENTINA. REVISTA. Text in Spanish. 1934. q. USD 60. adv. bk.rev. abstr.; charts; illus. index.
Indexed: BiolAb, ChemAb.
—CASDDS, CISTI, Linda Hall.
Published by: Asociacion Bioquimica Argentina, Venezuela, 1823-Piso 3, Capital Federal, Buenos Aires 1096, Argentina. Ed. Raul G Coronato. Circ: 3,000.

572.06 GBR ISSN 0141-8912

ASSOCIATION OF CLINICAL BIOCHEMISTS. NEWS SHEET. Key Title: News Sheet - Association of Biochemists Limited. Cover title: A C B News Sheet. Text in English. 1951. m. membership. adv. bk.rev. **Description:** Focuses on information about developments in laboratory health care in the U.K. and abroad.
—**CCC.**
Published by: Association of Clinical Biochemists, c/o Dr. Jonathan D. Berg, Ed, Department of Clinical Biochemistry, Sandwell District General Hospital, West Bromwich, W Mids B71 4HJ, United Kingdom. TEL 44-1836-635771, FAX 44-121-745-7929. Pub. Peter Carpenter. Circ: 3,600.

B

572 IND

ASSOCIATION OF CLINICAL BIOCHEMISTS OF INDIA. NEWS BULLETIN. Text in English. q. free to members.
Published by: Association of Clinical Biochemists of India, c/o Dr. N.Rao, Professor, Department of Biochemistry, All India Institute of Medical Sciences, Ansari Nagar, New Delhi, 110 029, India. TEL 91-11-26593545, FAX 91-11-26588641, dnrao311@hotmail.com, http://www.acbindia.org.

572.06094 AUS ISSN 1038-2232
QD415.A1 CODEN: PSBBEX

AUSTRALIAN SOCIETY FOR BIOCHEMISTRY AND MOLECULAR BIOLOGY. PROCEEDINGS. Text in English. 1968. a. AUD 89.50 membership (effective 2004). adv. **Document type:** *Monographic series.*
Former titles (until 1991): Australian Biochemical Society. Proceedings (0067-1703); Australian Biochemical Society. Programme and Abstracts
Indexed: BiolAb, CurCont, DSA, INIS AtomInd, NutrAb.
—BLDSC (6656.500000), CASDDS, CISTI, GNLM, Linda Hall.
Published by: Australian Society for Biochemistry and Molecular Biology, PO Box 2331, Kent Town, SA 5071, Australia. TEL 61-8-83620009, FAX 61-8-83620038, asbmb@bigpond.net.au, http://www.asbmb.org.au/. Circ: 1,400. **Co-sponsor:** C S I R O, Division of Human Nutrition.

AUTOIMMUNE DISEASES. see *MEDICAL SCIENCES—Abstracting, Bibliographies, Statistics*

572 NLD ISSN 0304-4165

➤ **B B A - GENERAL SUBJECTS.** Text in Dutch. 1947. 12/yr. EUR 2,474 in Europe to institutions; JPY 328,700 in Japan to institutions; USD 2,767 elsewhere to institutions (effective 2006). **Document type:** *Journal, Academic/Scholarly.* **Description:** Contains a collection of diverse, authoritative papers which complete BBA's comprehensive coverage of the fields of biochemistry and biophysics.
Related titles: Microform ed.: (from PQC); Online - full text ed.: (from EBSCO Publishing, Gale Group, IngentaConnect, ScienceDirect, Swets Information Services); ♦ Series of: Biochimica et Biophysica Acta. ISSN 0006-3002.
Indexed: ASCA, AgBio, AgrForAb, AnBrAb, BBCI, BIOBASE, BioCN&I, BioDAb, CLL, CPA, CurCont, DBA, DSA, ExcerpMed, FCA, FPA, ForAb, HelmAb, HortAb, IABS, ISR, IndVet, Inpharma, MaizeAb, NutrAb, OrnHort, PBA, PGegResA, PGrRegA, PHN&I, PN&I, PhysBer, PotatoAb, PoultAb, ProtozoAb, RA&MP, RM&VM, RPP, Reac, RefZh, RevApplEntom, RiceAb, S&F, SCI, SIA, SeedAb, SoyAb, TDB, TriticAb, VetBull, WeedAb.
—CISTI, IDS, IE. **CCC.**
Published by: Elsevier BV (Subsidiary of: Elsevier Science & Technology), Radarweg 29, Amsterdam, 1043 NX, Netherlands. TEL 31-20-4853911, FAX 31-20-4852457, nlinfo-f@elsevier.nl, http://www.elsevier.com/locate/bbagen, http://www.elsevier.nl.

572.57 NLD ISSN 1388-1981
QD1

➤ **B B A - MOLECULAR AND CELL BIOLOGY OF LIPIDS.** (Biochimica and Biophysica Acta) Text in Dutch. 1963. 12/yr. EUR 2,642 in Europe to institutions; JPY 350,700 in Japan to institutions; USD 2,955 elsewhere to institutions (effective 2006). **Document type:** *Journal, Academic/Scholarly.* **Description:** Focuses on lipid isolation and characterization, lipid biosynthesis and metabolism, phospholipids and phospholipases, glycolipids, fatty acid metabolism, prostaglandins and related substances, sterols and bile acids, and the functions of lipids in health and disease.
Former titles (until 1999): B B A - Lipids and Lipid Metabolism (0005-2760); (until 1965): Biochimica et Biophysica Acta. Lipids and Related Subjects (0926-6542)

Related titles: Microform ed.: (from PQC); Online - full text ed.: (from EBSCO Publishing, Gale Group, IngentaConnect, ScienceDirect, Swets Information Services); ♦ Series of: Biochimica et Biophysica Acta. ISSN 0006-3002.
Indexed: ASCA, AbHyg, AgBio, AnBrAb, BBCI, BIOBASE, CPA, CurCont, DBA, DSA, ExcerpMed, FCA, ForAb, HelmAb, HortAb, ISR, IndVet, Inpharma, MaizeAb, NemAb, NutrAb, PBA, PGrRegA, PN&I, PotatoAb, PoultAb, ProtozoAb, RA&MP, RM&VM, RPP, Reac, RefZh, RevApplEntom, S&F, SCI, SeedAb, SoyAb, TDB, TriticAb, VITIS, VetBull, WeedAb.
—CISTI, GNLM, IDS, IE, Linda Hall. **CCC.**
Published by: Elsevier BV (Subsidiary of: Elsevier Science & Technology), Radarweg 29, Amsterdam, 1043 NX, Netherlands. TEL 31-20-4853911, FAX 31-20-4852457, nlinfo-f@elsevier.nl, http://www.elsevier.com/locate/bbalip, http://www.elsevier.nl.

➤ **B B A - MOLECULAR BASIS OF DISEASE.** see *BIOLOGY—Genetics*

572 NLD ISSN 1570-9639
QD1
➤ **B B A - PROTEINS AND PROTEOMICS.** Text in Dutch. 1967. 12/yr. EUR 3,082 in Europe to institutions; JPY 408,900 in Japan to institutions; USD 3,447 elsewhere to institutions (effective 2006). back issues avail. **Document type:** *Journal, Academic/Scholarly.* **Description:** Focuses on protein structure, protein conformation, metalloproteins, protein spectroscopy, structure in solution, and protein dynamics.
Former titles (until 2002): B B A - Protein Structure and Molecular Enzymology (0167-4838); (until 1982): B B A - Protein Structure (0005-2795)
Related titles: Microform ed.: (from PQC); Online - full text ed.: (from EBSCO Publishing, Gale Group, IngentaConnect, ScienceDirect, Swets Information Services); ♦ Series of: Biochimica et Biophysica Acta. ISSN 0006-3002.
Indexed: AEA, ASCA, ASFA, AbHyg, AgBio, AgrForAb, AnBrAb, BBCI, BIOBASE, BioCN&I, BiolAb, CPA, ChemAb, CurCont, DBA, DSA, ESPM, ExcerpMed, FCA, FPA, ForAb, GenetAb, HelmAb, HortAb, IABS, ISR, IndChem, IndVet, Inpharma, MaizeAb, NemAb, NucAcAb, NutrAb, OrnHort, PBA, PE&ON, PGegResA, PGrRegA, PHN&I, PN&I, PotatoAb, PoultAb, ProtozoAb, RA&MP, RM&VM, RPP, Reac, RefZh, RevApplEntom, RiceAb, S&F, SCI, SIA, SeedAb, SoyAb, TDB, TriticAb, VetBull, WeedAb.
—CISTI, GNLM, IDS, IE. **CCC.**
Published by: Elsevier BV (Subsidiary of: Elsevier Science & Technology), Radarweg 29, Amsterdam, 1043 NX, Netherlands. TEL 31-20-4853911, FAX 31-20-4852457, nlinfo-f@elsevier.nl, http://www.elsevier.com/locate/bbapap, http://www.elsevier.nl.

572 GBR ISSN 1471-2091
➤ **B M C BIOCHEMISTRY.** (BioMed Central) Text in English. 2000. m. free (effective 2006). adv. **Document type:** *Journal, Academic/Scholarly.* **Description:** Publishes original research articles in all aspects of biochemistry, including metabolic pathways, enzyme functions, and small molecular components of cells and tissues.
Formerly: B M C Biochemistry and Structural Biology (1471-2237)
Media: Online - full content (from EBSCO Publishing, National Library of Medicine).
Indexed: BIOSIS Prev, BiolAb, ExcerpMed, ZooRec.
—Infotrieve. **CCC.**
Published by: BioMed Central Ltd. (Subsidiary of: Current Science Ltd), Middlesex House, 34-42 Cleveland St, London, W1T 4LB, United Kingdom. TEL 44-20-76319131, FAX 44-20-76319923, info@biomedcentral.com, http://www.biomedcentral.com/bmcbiochem/. Ed. Peter Newmark. Adv. contact Deborah Cockerill.

572 GBR ISSN 1472-6769
QD415.A1 CODEN: BCBMBZ
➤ **B M C CHEMICAL BIOLOGY.** (BioMed Central) Text in English. 2001. m. free (effective 2006). adv. **Document type:** *Journal, Academic/Scholarly.* **Description:** Publishes original research articles in the application of chemistry to the investigation of biology and drug design.
Media: Online - full content (from EBSCO Publishing, National Library of Medicine).
Indexed: BIOSIS Prev, BiolAb, ExcerpMed.
—Infotrieve. **CCC.**
Published by: BioMed Central Ltd. (Subsidiary of: Current Science Ltd), Middlesex House, 34-42 Cleveland St, London, W1T 4LB, United Kingdom. TEL 44-20-76319131, FAX 44-20-76319923, info@biomedcentral.com, http://www.biomedcentral.com/bmcchembiol/. Ed. Peter Newmark. Adv. contact Deborah Cockerill.

➤ **B M C PHARMACOLOGY.** see *PHARMACY AND PHARMACOLOGY*

➤ **BABRAHAM INSTITUTE. CORPORATE PLAN.** see *BIOLOGY—Physiology*

➤ **BABRAHAM INSTITUTE. REPORT.** see *BIOLOGY—Physiology*

572 660.6 GBR ISSN 1363-9773
BABRAHAM PUBLICATIONS. Text in English. 1996. irreg. price varies. **Description:** Contains summary of publications by members of the Babraham Institute staff.
Published by: Babraham Institute, Babraham Institute, Babraham Hall, Babraham, Cambridge, CB2 4AT, United Kingdom. TEL 44-1223-496000, FAX 44-1223-496020, babraham.contact@bbsrc.ac.uk, http://www.babraham.ac.uk. Eds. Jennifer Maddock, Mary Read. Pub. Caroline Edmonds. Circ: 1,500 (controlled).

572 BGD ISSN 0253-5432
CODEN: BJSRDG
BANGLADESH JOURNAL OF SCIENTIFIC RESEARCH. Text in English. 1978. 2/yr. BDT 80, USD 10. adv. bk.rev.
Indexed: BiolAb, ChemAb, FCA, HerbAb, JDDR, PGrRegA.
—CASDDS, CISTI, Linda Hall.
Published by: Bangladesh Association for the Advancement of Science, Department of Biochemistry, University of Dhaka, Ramna, Dhaka, 2, Bangladesh. Ed. Abdul Mannan. Circ: 2,500.

BEITRAEGE ZUR TABAKFORSCHUNG INTERNATIONAL; contributions to tobacco research. see *TOBACCO*

572 BEL
BELGIUM. STATION DE RECHERCHES FORESTIERES ET HYDROBIOLOGIQUES. TRAVAUX. SERIE D. HYDROBIOLOGIE. Text in Dutch, French. 1941. irreg.
Formerly: Belgium. Administration des Eaux et Forets. Station de Recherche des Eaux et Forets. Travaux. Serie D. Hydrobiologie (0067-5369)
Indexed: ASFA.
Published by: Station de Recherches Forestieres et Hydrobiologiques, Groenendaal, Duboislaan 14, Hoeilaart, 1560, Belgium.

BIOCATALYSIS AND BIOTRANSFORMATION. see *BIOLOGY—Biotechnology*

572 DEU ISSN 0946-1310
CODEN: BIOCFE
BIOCHEMICA. Text in English. 1994. q. free. **Document type:** *Academic/Scholarly.* **Description:** Disseminates information of interest to the research community.
Formed by the merger of (1993-1994): Colloquium (0945-1110); (1993-1994): Biochemica - Information (Internationale Ausgabe) (0945-1102)
Indexed: CIN, ChemAb, ChemTitl, RefZh.
—BLDSC (2066.821000), CASDDS, IE, ingenta.
Published by: Roche Molecular Biochemicals, Sandhofer Str 116, Mannheim, 68305, Germany. TEL 49-621-759-8555, FAX 49-621-759-8830, burkhard_ziebolz@bmg.boehringer-mannheim.com, burkhard.ziebolz@roche.com, http://biochem.boehringer-mannheim.com, http://biochem.roche.com. Ed. Dr. Burkhard Ziebolz.

572 USA ISSN 0006-291X
QH301 CODEN: BBRCA9
➤ **BIOCHEMICAL AND BIOPHYSICAL RESEARCH COMMUNICATIONS.** Text in English. 1959. 52/yr. EUR 4,164 in Europe to individuals; JPY 434,900 in Japan to individuals; USD 3,333 to individuals except Europe and Japan; EUR 6,752 in Europe to institutions; JPY 705,200 in Japan to institutions; USD 5,401 to institutions except Europe and Japan; EUR 2,084 in Europe to students; JPY 217,600 in Japan to students; USD 1,813 to students except Europe and Japan (effective 2006). adv. bibl.; charts; illus. index. cum.index. back issues avail.; reprints avail. **Document type:** *Journal, Academic/Scholarly.* **Description:** Devoted to the rapid dissemination of timely and significant experimental results in the diverse fields of modern biology.
Related titles: Online - full text ed.: ISSN 1090-2104. USD 5,558 (effective 2002) (from EBSCO Publishing, Gale Group, IngentaConnect, O C L C Online Computer Library Center, Inc., ScienceDirect, Swets Information Services).
Indexed: ABIPC, AIDS Ab, ASCA, ASFA, AbHyg, AgBio, Agr, AgrForAb, AnBrAb, ApicAb, B&BAb, BBCI, BIOBASE, BIOSIS Prev, BibAg, BioCN&I, BioDAb, BiolAb, CCI, CIN, CPA, CTA, ChemAb, ChemTitl, ChemoAb, CurCont, DBA, DSA, DentInd, ESPM, ExcerpMed, FCA, FPA, FS&TA, ForAb, GenetAb, HGA, HelmAb, HerbAb, HortAb, IABS, INIS AtomInd, ISR, IndMed, IndVet, Inpharma, MBA, MEDLINE, MSB, MaizeAb, NSA, NSCI, NemAb, NucAcAb, NutrAb, OrnHort, PBA, PE&ON, PGegResA, PGrRegA, PHN&I, PN&I, PotatoAb, PoultAb, ProtozoAb, RA&MP, RCI, RDA, RM&VM, RPP, Reac, RefZh, RevApplEntom, RiceAb, S&F, SCI, SFA, SIA, SeedAb, SoyAb, TDB, THA, TriticAb, VITIS, VetBull, WeedAb, WildRev, ZooRec.
—BLDSC (2066.900000), CASDDS, CINDOC, CISTI, GNLM, IDS, IE, Infotrieve, ingenta, Linda Hall. **CCC.**
Published by: Academic Press (Subsidiary of: Elsevier Science & Technology), 525 B St, Ste 1900, San Diego, CA 92101-4495. TEL 619-231-6616, 800-894-3434, FAX 619-699-6422, apsubs@acad.com, http://www.elsevier.com/locate/ybbrc, http://www.academicpress.com. Ed. W. Baumeister.

572 NLD ISSN 1369-703X
TP248.3 CODEN: BEJOFV
➤ **BIOCHEMICAL ENGINEERING JOURNAL.** Text in Dutch. 1998. 15/yr. EUR 1,200 in Europe to institutions; JPY 159,500 in Japan to institutions; USD 1,344 elsewhere to institutions (effective 2006). back issues avail. **Document type:** *Journal, Academic/Scholarly.* **Description:** Promotes progress in the crucial chemical engineering aspects of the development of biological processes associated with everything from raw materials preparation to product recovery.
Related titles: Online - full text ed.: (from EBSCO Publishing, Gale Group, IngentaConnect, ScienceDirect, Swets Information Services); ♦ Supplement to: Chemical Engineering Journal. ISSN 1385-8947.
Indexed: AEBA, AgBio, B&BAb, BCI, BioEngAb, CurCont, DSA, ESPM, ExcerpMed, HortAb, MEDLINE, RA&MP, RefZh, SIA, VITIS.
—BLDSC (2066.962500), CASDDS, CISTI, IDS, IE, Infotrieve, ingenta, Linda Hall. **CCC.**
Published by: Elsevier BV (Subsidiary of: Elsevier Science & Technology), Radarweg 29, Amsterdam, 1043 NX, Netherlands. TEL 31-20-4853911, FAX 31-20-4852457, nlinfo-f@elsevier.nl, http://www.elsevier.com/locate/bej, http://www.elsevier.nl. Eds. Colin Webb, H. Unno.

➤ **BIOCHEMICAL GENETICS.** see *BIOLOGY—Genetics*

572 GBR ISSN 0264-6021
QP501 CODEN: BIJOAK
➤ **BIOCHEMICAL JOURNAL.** Text in English. 1984. s-m. (in 8 vols., 3 nos./vol.). GBP 1,561.45, USD 2,830, EUR 2,545 combined subscription to institutions print & online (effective 2005). adv. bk.rev. illus. index. back issues avail.; reprints avail. **Document type:** *Journal, Academic/Scholarly.* **Description:** Contains original refereed papers about all aspects of biochemistry.
Formed by the merger of (1906-1984): Biochemical Journal. Part 1: Cellular Aspects (0306-3283); (1906-1984): Biochemical Journal. Part 2: Molecular Aspects (0306-3275); Both of which superseded in part (in 1973): Biochemical Journal (0006-2936)
Related titles: Microfiche ed.; Microfilm ed.: (from PMC, PQC); Online - full text ed.: ISSN 1470-8728. GBP 1,556.88, USD 2,500, EUR 2,250 to institutions (effective 2005) (from EBSCO Publishing, Swets Information Services).
Indexed: ABIPC, ASCA, ASFA, AbHyg, AgBio, Agr, AgrForAb, AnBrAb, AnalAb, BBCI, BIOBASE, BIOSIS Prev, BibAg, BioCN&I, BiolAb, CCI, CIN, CISA, CPA, CTA, ChemAb, ChemTitl, CurCont, DBA, DSA, DentInd, ESPM, EngInd, ExcerpMed, FCA, FS&TA, FaBeAb, ForAb, HGA, HelmAb, HerbAb, HortAb, IABS, ISR, IndMed, IndVet, Inpharma, MBA, MEDLINE, MSB, MaizeAb, NSCI, NemAb, NucAcAb, NutrAb, OrnHort, PBA, PE&ON, PGegResA, PGrRegA, PHN&I, PN&I, PotatoAb, PoultAb, ProtozoAb, RA&MP, RM&VM, RPP, Reac, RefZh, RevApplEntom, RiceAb, S&F, SAA, SCI, SFA, SIA, SPPI, SeedAb, SoyAb, TDB, TriticAb, VITIS, VetBull, WeedAb.
—BLDSC (2067.000000), CASDDS, CINDOC, CISTI, GNLM, IDS, IE, Infotrieve, ingenta, Linda Hall. **CCC.**
Published by: (Biochemical Society), Portland Press Ltd. (Subsidiary of: Biochemical Society), 3rd Fl, Eagle House, 16 Procter St, London, WC1V 6NX, United Kingdom. TEL 44-20-72804110, FAX 44-20-72804169, sales@portland-services.com, editorial@portlandpress.com, http://www.biochemj.org, http://www.portlandpress.com. Pub. Rhonda Oliver. R&P Adam Marshall. Adv. contact Erica Hammond TEL 44-1206-796351. Circ: 2,300. **Subscr. to:** Commerce Way, Colchester CO2 8HP, United Kingdom. TEL 44-1206-796351, FAX 44-1206-799331.

572 GBR ISSN 1356-739X
BIOCHEMICAL JOURNAL REVIEWS. Text in English. 1990. a. **Document type:** *Academic/Scholarly.*
Indexed: BIOSIS Prev.
—CISTI.
Published by: Portland Press Ltd. (Subsidiary of: Biochemical Society), 3rd Fl, Eagle House, 16 Procter St, London, WC1V 6NX, United Kingdom. TEL 44-20-72804110, FAX 44-20-72804169, editorial@portlandpress.com, http://www.biochemj.org/bj/subjects/reviews.htm, http://www.portlandpress.com.

BIOCHEMICAL PHARMACOLOGY. see *PHARMACY AND PHARMACOLOGY*

572 IND ISSN 0365-9429
QP501 CODEN: BCRVA5
BIOCHEMICAL REVIEWS. Text in English. 1972 (vol.43). a.
Indexed: BiolAb, ChemAb.
—CASDDS, CISTI, Linda Hall.
Published by: Society of Biological Chemists, Department of Biochemistry, Indian Institute of Science, Bangalore, Karnataka 560 012, India.

572 GBR ISSN 0067-8694
QH345 CODEN: BSSYAT
➤ **BIOCHEMICAL SOCIETY SYMPOSIUM.** Text in English. 1948. irreg. (vol.70 due July 2003), latest vol.72, 2005, Jan. price varies. back issues avail. **Document type:** *Proceedings, Academic/Scholarly.*
Indexed: ASCA, BBCI, BIOSIS Prev, ISR, IndMed, MEDLINE, SCI.
—BLDSC (2068.150000), CASDDS, CISTI, GNLM, IDS, IE, Infotrieve, ingenta, KNAW, Linda Hall. **CCC.**

Published by: (Biochemical Society), Portland Press Ltd. (Subsidiary of: Biochemical Society), 3rd Fl, Eagle House, 16 Procter St, London, WC1V 6NX, United Kingdom. TEL 44-20-72804110, FAX 44-20-72804169, sales@portland-services.com, http://www.portlandpress.com/pp/books/prod_list.cfm?product_class=PPBS, http://www.portlandpress.com/books/. R&P Adam Marshall. **Subscr. to:** Commerce Way, Colchester CO2 8HP, United Kingdom. TEL 44-1206-796351, FAX 44-1206-799331.

572 GBR ISSN 0300-5127
QH345 CODEN: BCSTB5
➤ **BIOCHEMICAL SOCIETY TRANSACTIONS.** Text in English. 1973. bi-m. GBP 249.46, USD 450, EUR 407 combined subscription to institutions print & online (effective 2005). adv. bk.rev. abstr.; bibl.; charts. index. back issues avail. **Document type:** *Journal, Academic/Scholarly.* **Description:** Contains short reviews from colloquia sponsored by the society.
Related titles: Online - full text ed.: ISSN 1470-8752. 2000. GBP 247.93, USD 400, EUR 360 to institutions print & online (effective 2005) (from EBSCO Publishing, Swets Information Services).
Indexed: ASCA, ASFA, AbHyg, AgBio, Agr, AgrForAb, AnBrAb, AnalAb, ApicAb, BBCI, BIOBASE, BIOSIS Prev, BioCN&I, BiolAb, CCI, CIN, CPA, ChemAb, ChemTitl, CurCont, DBA, DSA, ExcerpMed, FCA, FS&TA, ForAb, HelmAb, HerbAb, HortAb, IABS, ISR, IndMed, IndVet, Inpharma, JDDR, MEDLINE, MSB, MaizeAb, NSCI, NemAb, NucAcAb, NutrAb, OrnHort, PBA, PE&ON, PGegResA, PGrRegA, PHN&I, PN&I, PotatoAb, PoultAb, ProtozoAb, RA&MP, RM&VM, RPP, Reac, RefZh, RevApplEntom, RiceAb, S&F, SCI, SIA, SeedAb, SoyAb, TDB, TriticAb, VITIS, VetBull, WAE&RSA, WeedAb, ZooRec.
—BLDSC (2068.155000), CASDDS, CISTI, GNLM, IDS, IE, Infotrieve, ingenta, Linda Hall. **CCC.**
Published by: (Biochemical Society), Portland Press Ltd. (Subsidiary of: Biochemical Society), 3rd Fl, Eagle House, 16 Procter St, London, WC1V 6NX, United Kingdom. TEL 44-20-72804110, FAX 44-20-72804169, sales@portland-services.com, http://www.biochemsoctrans.org, http://www.portlandpress.com. Ed. David Richardson. R&P Adam Marshall. Circ: 1,200. **Subscr. to:** Commerce Way, Colchester CO2 8HP, United Kingdom. TEL 44-1206-796351, FAX 44-1206-799331.

572 GBR ISSN 0305-1978
QH83 CODEN: BSECBU
➤ **BIOCHEMICAL SYSTEMATICS AND ECOLOGY.** Text in English. 1973. 12/yr. EUR 1,497 in Europe to institutions; JPY 198,800 in Japan to institutions; USD 1,675 elsewhere to institutions; EUR 160 in Europe to qualified personnel; JPY 21,400 in Japan to qualified personnel; USD 179 elsewhere to qualified personnel (effective 2006). adv. bk.rev. abstr. back issues avail. **Document type:** *Journal, Academic/Scholarly.* **Description:** Publishes papers on the application of biochemistry and chemistry to systematic problems in biology, and on the role of biochemistry in interactions between organisms or between organisms and their environments.
Formerly (until 1974): Biochemical Systematics (0045-2025)
Related titles: Microfilm ed.: (from PQC); Online - full text ed.: (from EBSCO Publishing, Gale Group, IngentaConnect, ScienceDirect, Swets Information Services).
Indexed: ASCA, ASFA, AgBio, Agr, AgrForAb, AnBrAb, ApEcolAb, ApicAb, B&BAb, BBCI, BIOBASE, BIOSIS Prev, BibAg, BioCN&I, BioDAb, BiolAb, CIN, CPA, ChemAb, ChemTitl, ChemoAb, CurCont, ESPM, EntAb, ExcerpMed, FCA, FPA, FS&TA, FaBeAb, ForAb, GEOBASE, GenetAb, HGA, HerbAb, HortAb, IABS, ISR, IndVet, MEDLINE, MaizeAb, NemAb, NutrAb, OrnHort, PBA, PGegResA, PGrRegA, PHN&I, PlantSci, RA&MP, RM&VM, RPP, RRTA, RevApplEntom, S&F, S&MA, SCI, SFA, SeedAb, SoyAb, TriticAb, WeedAb, WildRev, ZooRec.
—BLDSC (2068.162000), CASDDS, CISTI, IDS, IE, Infotrieve, ingenta, Linda Hall. **CCC.**
Published by: Pergamon (Subsidiary of: Elsevier Science & Technology), The Boulevard, Langford Ln, East Park, Kidlington, Oxford OX5 1GB, United Kingdom. TEL 44-1865-843000, FAX 44-1865-843010, http://www.elsevier.com/locate/biochemsyseco. Ed. M. S.J. Simmonds. Circ: 1,000. **Subscr. to:** Elsevier BV, PO Box 211, Amsterdam 1000 AE, Netherlands. TEL 31-20-485-3757, FAX 31-20-485-3432, nlinfo-f@elsevier.nl, http://www.elsevier.nl.

572 USA
TP202
BIOCHEMICALS AND REAGENTS FOR LIFE SCIENCE RESEARCH. Text in English. a. free (effective 2005).
Former titles (until 1997): Biochemicals, Organic Compounds and Diagnostic Reagents; (until 1996): Biochemicals Organic Compounds for Research and Diagnostic Reagents (1044-4203)
Published by: Sigma-Aldrich, 3050 Spruce St, St. Louis, MO 63103. TEL 314-771-5765, 800-521-8956, FAX 314-771-5757, http://www.sigmaaldrich.com.

572 GBR ISSN 0954-982X
CODEN: BCHMFZ
➤ **BIOCHEMIST.** Text in English. 1970. bi-m. GBP 120, USD 228, EUR 204 to institutions (effective 2005). adv. **Document type:** *Academic/Scholarly.* **Description:** Contains a mix of feature articles on matters of general scientific interes on biochemistry.
Formerly (until 1988): Biochemical Society. Buletin (0953-4008)
—BLDSC (2069.150000), CISTI, IE, ingenta. **CCC.**
Published by: Biochemical Society, 59 Portland Pl, London, WN 3AJ, United Kingdom. TEL 44-20-7-580-5530, FAX 44-20-7-323-1136, editorial@portlandpress.com, http://www.biochemistry.org. adv.: B&W page GBP 875, color page GBP 1,095. Circ: 8,165.

572 USA ISSN 0006-2960
QP501 CODEN: BICHAW
➤ **BIOCHEMISTRY.** Text in English. 1962. 51/yr. USD 3,701 in North America to institutions; USD 4,236 elsewhere to institutions; USD 627 in North America to members; USD 1,162 elsewhere to members; USD 470 in North America to students; USD 1,005 elsewhere to students (effective 2006). adv. charts; illus. index. back issues avail.; reprints avail. **Document type:** *Journal, Academic/Scholarly.* **Description:** Contains papers on the most current results of original research in all areas of biochemistry. Emphasis is given to the close relationship of chemistry, biochemistry, molecular and cell biology.
Related titles: CD-ROM ed.; Microfiche ed.: USD 2,660 in North America; USD 2,737 elsewhere (effective 2002); Microfilm ed.: USD 2,660 in North America; USD 2,710 elsewhere (effective 2002); Online - full text ed.: ISSN 1520-4995. USD 100 (effective 2006) (from EBSCO Publishing, Swets Information Services).
Indexed: ABIPC, AIDS Ab, AIDS&CR, ASCA, ASFA, AbHyg, AgBio, Agr, AgrForAb, AnBrAb, B&AI, B&BAb, BBCI, BIOBASE, BIOSIS Prev, BPRC&P, BibAg, BioCN&I, BiolAb, CCI, CLL, CPA, CTA, ChemAb, ChemoAb, CurCont, DBA, DSA, DentInd, ESPM, EngInd, EnvAb, ExcerpMed, FCA, FS&TA, ForAb, GSI, GenetAb, HGA, HelmAb, HortAb, IABS, INIS AtomInd, ISR, IndMed, IndVet, MBA, MEDLINE, MSB, MSCI, MaizeAb, NSA, NSCI, NemAb, NucAcAb, NutrAb, OrnHort, PBA, PGegResA, PGrRegA, PN&I, PotatoAb, PoultAb, ProtozoAb, RA&MP, RM&VM, RPP, RefZh, RevApplEntom, RiceAb, S&F, SCI, SFA, SIA, SeedAb, SoyAb, TDB, Telegen, ToxAb, TriticAb, VetBull, VirolAbstr, WeedAb, WildRev, ZooRec.
—BLDSC (2069.200000), CASDDS, CISTI, GNLM, IDS, IE, Infotrieve, ingenta, Linda Hall. **CCC.**
Published by: American Chemical Society, 1155 16th St, N W, Washington, DC 20036. TEL 202-872-4600, 800-227-5558, FAX 202-776-8258, ascproof@acs.org, service@acs.org, http://pubs.acs.org/biochemistry. Ed. Richard N Armstrong. Circ: 6,200. **Subscr. to:** Member & Subscriber Services, PO Box 3337, Columbus, OH 43210. TEL 614-447-3776, 800-333-9511, FAX 614-447-3671.

572 RUS ISSN 0006-2979
QH301 CODEN: BIORAK
➤ **BIOCHEMISTRY (MOSCOW).** Text in English. 1956. m. EUR 3,998, USD 3,568, GBP 2,465 combined subscription to institutions print & online eds. (effective 2005). bk.rev. back issues avail.; reprint service avail. from PSC. **Document type:** *Journal, Academic/Scholarly.* **Description:** Publishes important research in biochemistry, as well as the related fields of molecular biology, bioorganic chemistry, microbiology, immunology, physiology, and the biological sciences, translated into English from the Russian journal Biokhimiya.
Related titles: Online - full text ed.: ISSN 1608-3040 (from EBSCO Publishing, Gale Group, IngentaConnect, Kluwer Online, O C L C Online Computer Library Center, Inc., Ovid Technologies, Inc., Springer LINK, Swets Information Services); ♦ Russian ed.: Biokhimiya. ISSN 0320-9725; ♦ Translation of: Biokhimiya. ISSN 0320-9725.
Indexed: ASFA, AbHyg, AgBio, AnBrAb, ApicAb, BBCI, BIOSIS Prev, BibLing, BiolAb, CIN, CLL, CPA, ChemAb, ChemTitl, CurCont, DSA, ExcerpMed, FCA, FS&TA, HelmAb, HerbAb, HortAb, IABS, ISR, IndMed, IndVet, MEDLINE, MSB, MaizeAb, NutrAb, OrnHort, PBA, PGrRegA, PN&I, PotatoAb, ProtozoAb, RA&MP, RM&VM, RPP, RiceAb, S&F, SCI, SIA, SoyAb, TDB, TriticAb, VITIS, VetBull, WeedAb.
—BLDSC (0406.000000), CASDDS, CISTI, GNLM, IDS, IE, Infotrieve, ingenta, Linda Hall. **CCC.**
Published by: (Rossiiskaya Akademiya Nauk/Russian Academy of Sciences), M A I K Nauka - Interperiodica, Profsoyuznaya ul 90, Moscow, 117997, Russian Federation. TEL 7-095-3347420, FAX 7-095-3360666, compmg@maik.ru, http://www.protein.bio.msu.su/biokhimiya, http://www.maik.ru. Ed. Vladimir P Skulachev. R&P Vladimir I Vasil'ev. **Subscr. to:** Springer-Verlag Dordrecht, Journals Department, PO Box 322, Dordrecht, Netherlands. TEL 31-78-6576392, FAX 31-78-6576474; Interperiodica, PO Box 1831, Birmingham, AL 35201-1831. TEL 205-995-1567, 800-633-4931, FAX 205-995-1588.

➤ **BIOCHEMISTRY AND BIOPHYSICS CITATION INDEX.** see *BIOLOGY—Abstracting, Bibliographies, Statistics*

572 CAN ISSN 0829-8211
QP501 CODEN: BCBIEQ
➤ **BIOCHEMISTRY AND CELL BIOLOGY/BIOCHIMIE ET BIOLOGIE CELLULAIRE.** Text in English; Text occasionally in French. 1929. bi-m. CND 116 domestic to individuals; USD 116 foreign to individuals; CND 350 domestic to institutions; USD 350 foreign to institutions (effective 1999). adv. bibl.; illus. index. reprint service avail. from PQC. **Document type:** *Academic/Scholarly.*
Former titles (until 1986): Canadian Journal of Biochemistry and Cell Biology - Revue Canadien de Biochimie et Biologie Cellulaire (0714-7511); (until 1983): Canadian Journal of Biochemistry (0008-4018); Which supersedes in part (in 1963): Canadian Journal of Biochemistry and Physiology (0576-5544); Which was formerly (until 1954): Canadian Journal of Medical Sciences (0316-4403); (until 1950): Canadian Journal of Research. Section E: Medical Sciences (0366-743X)
Related titles: Microfiche ed.: (from MML); Microform ed.: (from MML, PMC, PQC); Online - full text ed.: ISSN 1208-6002 (from bigchalk, EBSCO Publishing, Gale Group, IngentaConnect, Micromedia ProQuest, O C L C Online Computer Library Center, Inc., ProQuest Information & Learning, Swets Information Services).
Indexed: ABIPC, ASCA, ASFA, AbHyg, AgBio, Agr, AnBrAb, AnalAb, ApicAb, B&AI, B&BAb, BBCI, BIOBASE, BIOSIS Prev, BibAg, BiolAb, CBCARef, CIN, CPA, ChemAb, ChemTitl, CurCont, DBA, DSA, DentInd, EngInd, ExcerpMed, FCA, FS&TA, GenetAb, HGA, HerbAb, HortAb, IABS, ISR, IndMed, IndVet, Inpharma, MEDLINE, MaizeAb, NemAb, NucAcAb, NutrAb, OrnHort, PBA, PGegResA, PN&I, PoultAb, ProtozoAb, RA&MP, RM&VM, RPP, Reac, RefZh, S&F, SCI, SFA, SeedAb, SoyAb, TDB, TriticAb, VetBull, WTA, WeedAb, WildRev, ZooRec.
—BLDSC (2069.474000), CASDDS, CINDOC, CISTI, GNLM, IDS, IE, Infotrieve, ingenta, KNAW, Linda Hall. **CCC.**
Published by: N R C Research Press, Building M 55, Ottawa, ON K1A 0R6, Canada. TEL 613-993-0362, 800-668-1222, FAX 613-952-7656, research.journal@nrc.ca, pubs@nrc-cnrc.gc.ca, http://pubs.nrc-cnrc.gc.ca/cgi-bin/rp/rp2_desc_e?bcb. Ed. Bruce P Dancik. Adv. contact Judy Heyman. B&W page CND 675; trim 11 x 8.5. Circ: 913.

572.3071 USA ISSN 1470-8175
QP518 CODEN: BMBECE
➤ **BIOCHEMISTRY AND MOLECULAR BIOLOGY EDUCATION.** Text in English. 1972. bi-m. USD 135 combined subscription domestic to individuals print & online eds.; USD 165 combined subscription in Canada to individuals print & online eds.; USD 155 combined subscription elsewhere to individuals print & online eds.; USD 360 combined subscription domestic to institutions print & online eds.; USD 406 combined subscription in Canada to institutions print & online eds.; USD 380 combined subscription elsewhere to institutions print & online eds.; USD 110 combined subscription domestic to members ASBMB, print & online eds.; USD 138 combined subscription in Canada to members ASBMB, print & online eds.; USD 130 combined subscription elsewhere to members ASBMB, print & online eds. (effective 2004). adv. bk.rev. abstr. back issues avail.; reprint service avail. from PQC. **Document type:** *Journal, Academic/Scholarly.* **Description:** Assists in the teaching of biochemistry to science and medical students throughout the world.
Formerly (until 2000): Biochemical Education (0307-4412)
Related titles: Microfilm ed.: (from PQC); Online - full text ed.: ISSN 1539-3429. USD 308 (effective 2002) (from EBSCO Publishing, Gale Group, HighWire Press, IngentaConnect, ScienceDirect).
Indexed: ABIn, ASCA, BBCI, CIJE, CIN, CPE, ChemAb, ChemTitl, ERA, ETA, EduInd, ExcerpMed, ISR, MEA, MEDLINE, RHEA, SEA, SENA, SOMA, SSCI, TEA.
—BLDSC (2069.510000), CASDDS, CISTI, IDS, IE, Infotrieve, ingenta. **CCC.**
Published by: (International Union of Biochemistry and Molecular Biology), American Society for Biochemistry and Molecular Biology, Inc., 9650 Rockville Pike, Bethesda, MD 20814-3996. TEL 301-530-7145, FAX 301-571-1824, voet@sas.upenn.edu, asbmb@asbmb.faseb.org, http://www.bambed.org, http://www.asbmb.org. Eds. Donald Voel, Judith Voel. adv.: B&W page USD 830; trim 8.375 x 10.875. Circ: 5,000.

572 USA ISSN 0887-6495
CODEN: BIELEO
➤ **BIOCHEMISTRY OF THE ELEMENTS.** Text in English. 1980. irreg., latest 2000, vol.13B. price varies. back issues avail. **Document type:** *Monographic series, Academic/Scholarly.*
Indexed: CIN, ChemAb, ChemTitl.
—BLDSC (2069.720000), CASDDS, CISTI, KNAW. **CCC.**
Published by: Springer-Verlag New York, Inc. (Subsidiary of: Springer Science+Business Media), 233 Spring St, New York, NY 10013. TEL 212-460-1500, FAX 212-460-1575, service@springer-ny.com, http://www.springer-ny.com. Ed. C T Horovitz. **Dist. by:** Journal Fulfillment, PO Box 2485, Secaucus, NJ 07096-2485.

572 ITA ISSN 0393-0564
BIOCHIMICA CLINICA. Text in Italian. 1978. m.
Formerly (until 1983): Societa Italiana di Biochimica Clinica. Notiziario (0392-7091)
—BLDSC (2069.925000), IE, Infotrieve, ingenta.
Published by: Societa Italiana di Biochimica Clinica/Italian Society of Clinical Biochemistry, Via C. Farini, 81, Milan, 20159, Italy. TEL 39-02-6887556, FAX 39-02-6887026, segrete@sibioc.it, http://www.sibioc.it.

▼ new title ➤ refereed ✶ unverified ♦ full entry avail.

572 NLD ISSN 0006-3002
QD1 CODEN: BBACAQ

➤ **BIOCHIMICA ET BIOPHYSICA ACTA**; international journal of biochemistry and biophysics. Short title: B B A. Text in English. 1947. 100/yr. EUR 14,677 in Europe; JPY 1,951,500 in Japan; USD 16,418 elsewhere (effective 2006); subscr. incld. all 9 sections: Bioenergetics; Biomembranes; General Subjects; Gene Structure and Expression; Molecular and Cell Biology of Lipids; Molecular Basis of Disease; Molecular Cell Research; Proteins and Proteomics; Reviews on Cancer. adv. charts; illus. cum.index. back issues avail.; reprints avail. **Document type:** *Journal, Academic/Scholarly.*

Related titles: Microform ed.: (from PQC); Online - full text ed.: (from EBSCO Publishing, ScienceDirect); ♦ Series: B B A - Bioenergetics. ISSN 0005-2728; ♦ B B A - Biomembranes. ISSN 0005-2736; ♦ B B A - Molecular and Cell Biology of Lipids. ISSN 1388-1981; ♦ B B A - Proteins and Proteomics. ISSN 1570-9639; ♦ B B A - General Subjects. ISSN 0304-4165; ♦ B B A - Reviews on Biomembranes. ISSN 0304-4157; ♦ B B A - Reviews on Cancer. ISSN 0304-419X; ♦ B B A - Gene Structure and Expression. ISSN 0167-4781; ♦ B B A - Molecular Cell Research. ISSN 0167-4889; ♦ B B A - Molecular Basis of Disease. ISSN 0925-4439.

Indexed: AESIS, ASFA, Agr, AnBrAb, AnalAb, ApicAb, BIOSIS Prev, BPRC&P, BibAg, BioCN&I, BiolAb, CCI, CPA, ChemAb, CurCont, DentInd, ExcerpMed, FCA, FS&TA, FaBeAb, HerbAb, IndMed, Inpharma, Kidney, MBA, MEDLINE, MSB, MSCI, MaizeAb, NSCI, NutrAb, PGrRegA, RPP, Reac, RevApplEntom, SeedAb, SoyAb, Telegen, VetBull, WeedAb, WildRev.

—BLDSC (2070.000000), CASDDS, CINDOC, CISTI, GNLM, IDS, IE, Infotrieve, ingenta, Linda Hall. **CCC.**

Published by: Elsevier BV (Subsidiary of: Elsevier Science & Technology), Radarweg 29, Amsterdam, 1043 NX, Netherlands. TEL 31-20-4853911, FAX 31-20-4852457, nlinfo-f@elsevier.nl, http://www.elsevier.com/locate/bba, http://www.elsevier.nl. Circ: 4,500. **Subscr. to:** Elsevier, Subscription Customer Service, 6277 Sea Harbor Dr, Orlando, FL 32887-4800. TEL 407-345-4020, 877-839-7126, FAX 407-363-1354.

572 FRA ISSN 0300-9084
QP501 CODEN: BICMBE

➤ **BIOCHIMIE.** Text and summaries in English. 1914. 12/yr. EUR 908 in Europe to institutions; JPY 120,300 in Japan to institutions; USD 1,016 to institutions except Europe and Japan (effective 2006). adv. bk.rev. bibl.; charts; illus. reprint service avail. from ISI. **Document type:** *Journal, Academic/Scholarly.* **Description:** Publishes original work, review articles and mini-reviews in enzymology, genetics, immunology, microbiology, and the structure of macromolecules.

Formerly (until 1971): Societe de Chimie Biologique. Bulletin (0037-9042)

Related titles: Microform ed.: (from PQC); Online - full text ed.: (from EBSCO Publishing, Gale Group, IngentaConnect, ScienceDirect, Swets Information Services).

Indexed: ASCA, ASFA, AbHyg, AgBio, Agr, AgrForAb, AnBrAb, AnalAb, BBCI, BIOBASE, BIOSIS Prev, BiolAb, CCI, CIN, CPA, ChemAb, ChemTitl, CurCont, DBA, DSA, ESPM, ExcerpMed, FCA, FS&TA, HelmAb, HerbAb, HortAb, IABS, ISR, IndMed, IndVet, Inpharma, MBA, MEDLINE, MSB, MaizeAb, NemAb, NutrAb, PBA, PE&ON, PGegResA, PN&I, PotatoAb, ProtozoAb, RA&MP, RM&VM, RPP, Reac, RefZh, S&F, SCI, SFA, SIA, SeedAb, TDB, TriticAb, VetBull, WeedAb.

—BLDSC (2070.500000), CASDDS, CISTI, GNLM, IDS, IE, Infotrieve, ingenta, Linda Hall. **CCC.**

Published by: (Centre Universitaire des Saints-Peres, Societe Francaise de Biochimie et Biologie Moleculaire), Elsevier France, Editions Scientifiques et Medicales (Subsidiary of: Elsevier Science & Technology), 23 Rue Linois, Paris, 75724, France. TEL 33-1-71724600, FAX 33-1-71724650, academic@elsevier-fr.com, http://www.elsevier.com/locate/biochi. Eds. M Grunberg-Manago, R H Buckingham. Circ: 3,000. **Subscr. to:** Elsevier BV, PO Box 211, Amsterdam 1000 AE, Netherlands. TEL 31-20-485-3757, FAX 31-20-485-3432, nlinfo-f@elsevier.nl, http://www.elsevier.nl.

572 USA ISSN 1043-1802
QP517.B49 CODEN: BCCHES

➤ **BIOCONJUGATE CHEMISTRY.** Text in English. 1990. bi-m. USD 902 in North America to institutions; USD 972 elsewhere to institutions; USD 162 in North America to members; USD 232 elsewhere to members; USD 122 in North America to students; USD 192 elsewhere to students (effective 2006). adv. back issues avail. **Document type:** *Journal, Academic/Scholarly.* **Description:** Emphasizes the joining of two different molecular functions by chemical or biological means.

Related titles: Microform ed.; Online - full text ed.: ISSN 1520-4812. USD 40 (effective 2006) (from EBSCO Publishing, Swets Information Services).

Indexed: ASCA, B&BAb, BBCI, BCI, BIOBASE, BIOSIS Prev, BioEngAb, BiolAb, CCI, CIN, ChemAb, ChemTitl, CurCont, ExcerpMed, IABS, ISR, IndMed, Inpharma, M&PBA, MEDLINE, MSCI, NucAcAb, PE&ON, Reac, RefZh, SCI.

—BLDSC (2071.080000), CASDDS, CISTI, GNLM, IDS, IE, Infotrieve, ingenta, Linda Hall. **CCC.**

Published by: American Chemical Society, 1155 16th St, N W, Washington, DC 20036. TEL 202-872-4600, 800-227-5558, FAX 202-872-3727, service@acs.org, http://pubs.acs.org/bc. Ed. Claude F Meares. adv.: color page USD 1,620. Circ: 1,100. **Subscr. to:** Member & Subscriber Services, PO Box 3337, Columbus, OH 43210. TEL 614-447-3776, 800-333-9511, FAX 614-447-3671.

572 NLD ISSN 1567-5394
QP341 CODEN: BIOEFK

➤ **BIOELECTROCHEMISTRY.** Text in English. 1974. 4/yr. EUR 1,882 in Europe to institutions; JPY 250,000 in Japan to institutions; USD 2,105 to institutions except Europe and Japan (effective 2006). adv. bk.rev. back issues avail. **Document type:** *Journal, Academic/Scholarly.* **Description:** Publishes papers on electrochemical aspects of biology and biological aspects of electrochemistry.

Formerly (until 2000): Bioelectrochemistry and Bioenergetics (0302-4598)

Related titles: Microform ed.: (from PQC); Online - full text ed.: (from EBSCO Publishing, Gale Group, IngentaConnect, ScienceDirect, Swets Information Services).

Indexed: ASCA, ASFA, AgBio, AnBrAb, AnalAb, B&BAb, BBCI, BIOBASE, BioEngAb, BiolAb, CCI, CEABA, CIN, CTE, ChemAb, ChemTitl, CurCont, EngInd, ExcerpMed, IABS, ISR, IndMed, Inpharma, MEDLINE, MSB, PBA, PE&ON, PoultAb, ProtozoAb, Reac, RefZh, SCI, SIA, VITIS.

—BLDSC (2072.007800), CASDDS, CISTI, Ei, GNLM, IDS, IE, ingenta, Linda Hall. **CCC.**

Published by: (Bioelectrochemical Society USA), Elsevier BV (Subsidiary of: Elsevier Science & Technology), Radarweg 29, Amsterdam, 1043 NX, Netherlands. TEL 31-20-4853911, FAX 31-20-4852457, nlinfo-f@elsevier.nl, http://www.elsevier.com/locate/bioelechem, http://www.elsevier.nl.

572 CHE ISSN 1422-4208

➤ **BIOELECTROCHEMISTRY: PRINCIPLES AND PRACTICE.** Text in English. 1994. irreg. price varies. **Document type:** *Monographic series, Academic/Scholarly.* **Description:** Compiles information on all the physiochemical aspects of the different biochemical and physiological processes.

Indexed: CIN, ChemAb, ChemTitl.

—BLDSC (2072.007500). **CCC.**

Published by: Birkhaeuser Verlag AG (Subsidiary of: Springer Science+Business Media), Viaduktstr 42, Postfach 133, Basel, 4051, Switzerland. TEL 41-61-2050707, FAX 41-61-2050792, orders@birkhauser.ch, birkhauser@springer.de, http://www.birkhauser.ch.

572 NLD ISSN 0951-6433
QP771 CODEN: BIFAEU

➤ **BIOFACTORS**; vitamins - autoregulatory substances - trace elements - growth factors. Text in English. 1988. m. EUR 1,021, USD 1,218 combined subscription print & online eds. (effective 2006). index. back issues avail.; reprints avail. **Document type:** *Journal, Academic/Scholarly.* **Description:** Contains papers and short communications aimed at identifying and investigating effects and roles of trace substances required by organisms.

Related titles: Online - full text ed.: (from EBSCO Publishing, Gale Group, IngentaConnect, O C L C Online Computer Library Center, Inc., Swets Information Services).

Indexed: ASFA, AbHyg, AgBio, AnBrAb, BBCI, BIOBASE, BIOSIS Prev, BiolAb, CIN, ChemAb, ChemTitl, CurCont, DSA, EPB, ExcerpMed, FPA, ForAb, HortAb, I&DA, IABS, IndMed, IndVet, MEDLINE, MSCI, NutrAb, OrnHort, PBA, PN&I, ProtozoAb, RA&MP, RPP, RiceAb, S&F, SCI, SIA, SoyAb, TDB, TriticAb, VITIS, VetBull, WeedAb.

—BLDSC (2072.123000), CASDDS, CISTI, GNLM, IDS, IE, Infotrieve, ingenta, Linda Hall. **CCC.**

Published by: (International Union of Biochemistry and Molecular Biology AUS), I O S Press, Nieuwe Hemweg 6B, Amsterdam, 1013 BG, Netherlands. TEL 31-20-6883355, FAX 31-20-6203419, info@iospress.nl, order@iospress.nl, http://www.iospress.nl/html/09516433.php. Eds. L Flohe TEL 49-531-6181-599, W J Whelan. R&P Ms. Carry Koolbergen TEL 31-20-6382189. Adv. contact Ms. Jolijn van Eunen. Circ: 300. **Subscr. to:** I O S Press, Inc, 4502 Rachael Manor Dr., Fairfax, VA 22032-3631. iosbooks@iospress.com; Globe Publication Pvt. Ltd., C-62 Inderpuri, New Delhi 100 012, India. TEL 91-11-579-3211, 91-11-579-3212, FAX 91-11-579-8876, custserve@globepub.com, http://www.globepub.com; Kinokuniya Co. Ltd., Shinjuku 3-chome, Shinjuku-ku, Tokyo 160-0022, Japan. FAX 81-3-3439-1094, journal@kinokuniya.co.jp, http://www.kinokuniya.co.jp.

572.65 NLD ISSN 0168-8561
QP801.B66 CODEN: BIAME7

➤ **BIOGENIC AMINES.** Text in English. 1984. bi-m. EUR 483, USD 604 combined subscription print & online eds. (effective 2005). back issues avail.; reprint service avail. from PSC. **Document type:** *Journal, Academic/Scholarly.* **Description:** Publishes research on all aspects of biogenic amines and amino acid transmitters, related compounds, and interactions.

Related titles: Online - full text ed.: ISSN 1569-3910. EUR 435, USD 544 (effective 2005) (from EBSCO Publishing, Gale Group, IngentaConnect, Kluwer Online, O C L C Online Computer Library Center, Inc., Ovid Technologies, Inc., Springer LINK, Swets Information Services).

Indexed: ASCA, BBCI, BIOSIS Prev, BiolAb, CIN, ChemAb, ChemTitl, CurCont, ExcerpMed, ISR, Inpharma, NSCI, NutrAb, PE&ON, ProtozoAb, Reac, SCI, TDB.

—BLDSC (2072.149000), CASDDS, CISTI, GNLM, IE, Infotrieve, ingenta. **CCC.**

Published by: V S P (Subsidiary of: Brill Academic Publishers), Brill Academic Publishers, PO Box 9000, Leiden, 2300 PA, Netherlands. TEL 31-71-5353500, FAX 31-71-5317532, vsppub@brill.nl, http://www.vsppub.com/journals/jn-BioAmi.html. Ed. S H Parvez. **Dist. by:** Extenza - Turpin, Pegasus Dr, Stratton Business Park, Biggleswade, Beds SG18 8TQ, United Kingdom. TEL 44-1767-604954, FAX 44-1767-601640, marketing@extenza-turpin.com, http://www.extenza-turpin.com.

572 NLD ISSN 0168-2563
QH343.7 CODEN: BIOGEP

➤ **BIOGEOCHEMISTRY**; an international journal. Text and summaries in English. 1984. 15/yr. (in 5 vols.). EUR 1,788, USD 1,818, GBP 1,178 combined subscription to institutions print & online eds. (effective 2005). adv. bk.rev. reprint service avail. from PSC. **Document type:** *Academic/Scholarly.* **Description:** Publishes original papers dealing with biotic controls on the chemistry of the environment or the geochemical control of the structure and function of ecosystems.

Related titles: Microform ed.: (from PQC); Online - full text ed.: ISSN 1573-515X (from EBSCO Publishing, Gale Group, IngentaConnect, Kluwer Online, O C L C Online Computer Library Center, Inc., Ovid Technologies, Inc., Springer LINK, Swets Information Services).

Indexed: AESIS, ASCA, ASFA, Agr, AgrForAb, AnBrAb, BIOBASE, BIOSIS Prev, BibAg, BibLing, BioCN&I, BiolAb, CIN, CPA, ChemAb, ChemTitl, CurCont, EPB, ESPM, EnvEAb, ExcerpMed, FCA, FPA, ForAb, GEOBASE, HerbAb, HortAb, I&DA, IABS, ISR, MBA, MaizeAb, NutrAb, PBA, PlantSci, PollutAb, RA&MP, RPP, RefZh, RiceAb, S&F, SCI, SIA, SWRA, SeedAb, TriticAb, WAE&RSA, WeedAb.

—BLDSC (2072.163000), CASDDS, CISTI, IDS, IE, Infotrieve, ingenta, Linda Hall. **CCC.**

Published by: Springer-Verlag Dordrecht (Subsidiary of: Springer Science+Business Media), Van Godewijckstraat 30, Dordrecht, 3311 GX, Netherlands. TEL 31-78-6576050, FAX 31-78-6576474, http://springerlink.metapress.com/openurl.asp?genre=journal&issn=0168-2563, http://www.springeronline.com. Ed. Katja Lajtha.

572 NGA ISSN 0795-8080

▼ ➤ **BIOKEMISTRI.** Text in English. 2003. irreg. free (effective 2005). **Description:** Devoted to the dissemination of knowledge relating to all aspects of biochemistry.

Media: Online - full content.

Published by: Nigerian Society for Experimental Biology, University of Ilorin, Dept of Biochemistry, PMB 1515, Ilorin, Nigeria. biokemistri@yahoo.com, http://www.bioline.org.br/bk. Ed. J T Ekanem.

572 RUS ISSN 0320-9725
QH301 CODEN: BIOHAO

BIOKHIMIYA. Text in Russian; Summaries in English. 1936. m. RUR 930 for 6 mos. domestic (effective 2004). adv. bk.rev. illus. index, cum.index: 1946-1955. **Document type:** *Journal, Academic/Scholarly.*

Related titles: Online - full text ed.; ♦ English ed.: Biochemistry (Moscow). ISSN 0006-2979; ♦ English Translation: Biochemistry (Moscow). ISSN 0006-2979.

Indexed: ABIPC, ASFA, AnalAb, BiolAb, ChemAb, CurCont, DBA, DSA, ESPM, EngInd, ExcerpMed, FS&TA, IndMed, Inpharma, MEDLINE, NutrAb, Reac, RefZh, S&F, ZooRec.

—BLDSC (0018.100000), CASDDS, CINDOC, CISTI, East View, GNLM, KNAW, Linda Hall. **CCC.**

Published by: (Rossiiskaya Akademiya Nauk/Russian Academy of Sciences), Izdatel'stvo Nauka, Profsoyuznaya ul 90, Moscow, 117864, Russian Federation. TEL 7-095-3347151, FAX 7-095-4202220, biochem@maik.ru, secret@naukaran.ru, http://www.maik.ru/cgi-bin/list.pl?page=biokhimmsc, http://www.naukaran.ru. Circ: 4,230.

572 UKR ISSN 0136-9377
QP1 CODEN: BZCHDI

BIOKHIMIYA ZHIVOTNYKH I CHELOVEKA; respublikanskii mezhvedomstvennyi sbornik nauchnykh trudov. Text in Russian. 1977. a.

Indexed: CIN, ChemAb, ChemTitl.

—CASDDS, Linda Hall.

Published by: Natsional'na Akademiya Nauk Ukrainy, Instytut Biokhimii im. A.V. Palladina, vul N Leontovicha 9, Kyiv, Ukraine. TEL 38-44-2241181, oficer@biochem.freenet.Kiev.ua.

572.8 SVK ISSN 1335-6399
CODEN: BLOAAO

BIOLOGIA. SECTION: CELLULAR AND MOLECULAR BIOLOGY. Text in English. 1946. s-a. USD 138 for 3 sections (effective 2005). adv. bk.rev. charts; illus. index. **Document type:** *Academic/Scholarly.* **Description:** Covers original experimental and theoretical works in basic biological research from molecular and cell biology and biochemistry.

Formerly (until 1994): Biologia. D: Biochemia a Molekularna Biologia (0862-1152); Supersedes in part (in 1969): Biologia (0006-3088)

Related titles: ♦ Series: Biologia. Section Botany. ISSN 1335-6372; ♦ Biologia. Section Zoology. ISSN 1335-6380.

Indexed: BioDAb, BiolAb, ChemAb, CurCont, IndMed, SFA, SoyAb, TriticAb, WildRev, ZooRec.

B

—BLDSC (2072.700000), CASDDS, CISTI, GNLM, IDS, IE, ingenta, KNAW, Linda Hall.
Published by: (Slovenska Akademia Vied, Ustav Mikrobiologie/Slovak Academy of Sciences, Institute of Microbiology), Slovak Academic Press Ltd., Nam Slobody 6, PO Box 57, Bratislava, 81005, Slovakia. Ed. Stefan Janecek.

BIOLOGICAL & PHARMACEUTICAL BULLETIN. see *PHARMACY AND PHARMACOLOGY*

572.8 572.2 DEU ISSN 1431-6730
QP501 CODEN: BICHF3
➤ **BIOLOGICAL CHEMISTRY**; official scientific journal of the GBM. Text and summaries in English. 1877. m. EUR 1,128 to institutions; EUR 1,218 combined subscription to institutions; EUR 134 newsstand/cover to institutions (effective 2006). adv. abstr.; bibl.; charts; illus.; stat. index. back issues avail.; reprint service avail. from PSC. **Document type:** *Journal, Academic/Scholarly.* **Description:** Keeps you up-to-date with all new developments in the molecular life sciences. Areas covered include: general biochemistry, pathobiochemistry, evolutionary biotechnology, structural biology, molecular and cellular biology, molecular medicine, cancer research, virology, immunology, plant molecular biology and biochemistry, and experimental methodologies.
Former titles (until 1996): Biological Chemistry Hoppe-Seyler (0177-3593); (until 1985): Hoppe-Seyler's Zeitschrift fuer Physiologische Chemie (0018-4888); (until 1895): Zeitschrift fuer Physiologische Chemie (0372-9672)
Related titles: Microform ed.: (from PMC, PQC); Online - full text ed.: ISSN 1437-4315. EUR 1,128 to institutions (effective 2006) (from EBSCO Publishing, O C L C Online Computer Library Center, Inc., Ovid Technologies, Inc., Swets Information Services).
Indexed: ASCA, ASFA, Agr, AnBrAb, BBCI, BIOBASE, BIOSIS Prev, BibAg, BioDAb, BiolAb, CCI, CIN, ChemAb, ChemInfo, ChemTitl, CurCont, DBA, DSA, DentInd, ESPM, ExcerpMed, FCA, FS&TA, IABS, ISR, IndMed, IndVet, Inpharma, MEDLINE, MSB, NutrAb, PE&ON, PGegResA, ProtozoAb, RCI, RPP, Reac, RefZh, RevApplEntom, SCI, SFA, THA, VetBull, WildRev, ZooRec.
—BLDSC (2075.070000), CASDDS, CINDOC, CISTI, GNLM, IDS, IE, Infotrieve, ingenta, Linda Hall. **CCC.**
Published by: Walter de Gruyter GmbH & Co. KG, Genthiner Str. 13, Berlin, 10785, Germany. TEL 49-30-26005176, FAX 49-30-26005251, biol.chem.editorial@degruyter.de, wdg-info@degruyter.de, http://www.degruyter.de/journals/bc. Ed. F.-Ulrich Hartl. Adv. contact Mrs. Imke Ridder TEL 49-8191-971105. B&W page EUR 745, color page EUR 1,590; trim 180 x 264. Circ: 6,000 (paid).

➤ **BIOLOGICAL MAGNETIC RESONANCE.** see *PHYSICS*

➤ **BIOLOGICAL PSYCHIATRY.** see *MEDICAL SCIENCES—Psychiatry And Neurology*

572 USA ISSN 0163-4984
QP534 CODEN: BTERDG
➤ **BIOLOGICAL TRACE ELEMENT RESEARCH.** Abbreviated title: B T E R. Text in English. 1979. 18/yr. USD 485 to individuals; USD 1,350 to institutions; USD 495 combined subscription to individuals print & online eds.; USD 1,435 combined subscription to institutions print & online eds. (effective 2005). adv. bk.rev. bibl.; charts; illus. 100 p./no.; back issues avail.; reprints avail. **Document type:** *Journal, Academic/Scholarly.* **Description:** Forum for original papers in biological, environmental and biomedical research on trace elements. Stresses the integrative aspects of trace element research in all relevant fields, especially focusing on nutritional studies in humans and in animals models.
Related titles: Online - full text ed.: USD 460 to individuals; USD 1,290 to institutions (effective 2005) (from EBSCO Publishing, Gale Group, IngentaConnect, O C L C Online Computer Library Center, Inc., Ovid Technologies, Inc., Swets Information Services).
Indexed: ASCA, ASFA, AbHyg, AgBio, Agr, AgrForAb, AnBrAb, BBCI, BIOSIS Prev, BiolAb, CCI, CIN, CPA, CTA, ChemAb, ChemTitl, CurCont, DSA, ESPM, ExcerpMed, FCA, HerbAb, HortAb, I&DA, ISR, IndMed, IndVet, Inpharma, LHB, MEDLINE, MSB, MaizeAb, NutrAb, OrnHort, PBA, PE&ON, PGegResA, PGrRegA, PHN&I, PN&I, PoultAb, ProtozoAb, RA&MP, RDA, Reac, RevApplEntom, RiceAb, S&F, SCI, SFA, SIA, SWRA, SeedAb, SoyAb, TDB, ToxAb, TriticAb, VetBull, WeedAb, WildRev.
—BLDSC (2081.600000), CASDDS, CISTI, GNLM, IDS, IE, Infotrieve, ingenta, Linda Hall. **CCC.**
Published by: (International Association of Bioinorganic Scientists), Humana Press, Inc., 999 Riverview Dr, Ste 208, Totowa, NJ 07512. TEL 973-256-1699, FAX 973-256-8341, humana@humanapr.com, http://humanapress.com/journals.pasp. Ed. Gerhard N Schrauzer. Pub. Thomas B. Lanigan Jr. R&P Wendy A. Warren. Adv. contacts John Chasse, Thomas B. Lanigan Jr. **Subscr. to:** Maruzen Co., Ltd., 3-10 Nihonbashi, 2-Chome, Chuo-ku, Tokyo 103, Japan. TEL 81-3-3275-8591, FAX 81-3-3275-0657, journal@maruzen.co.jp, http://www.maruzen.co.jp.

572.8 GBR ISSN 1477-044X
QH1
▼ ➤ **BIOMAGNETIC RESEARCH AND TECHNOLOGY.** Text in English. 2003. irreg. free (effective 2006). **Document type:** *Journal, Academic/Scholarly.* **Description:** Provides a forum for the disclosure and discussion of the entire spectrum of biomagnetic research and technology.
Media: Online - full content (from EBSCO Publishing, National Library of Medicine).
—**CCC.**
Published by: BioMed Central Ltd. (Subsidiary of: Current Science Ltd), Middlesex House, 34-42 Cleveland St, London, W1T 4LB, United Kingdom. TEL 44-20-76319131, FAX 44-20-76319923, bmrt@uek.cas.cz, info@biomedcentral.com, http://www.biomagres.com, http://www.biomedcentral.com. Eds. Ivo Safarik, Mirka Safarikova.

➤ **BIOMATERIALS.** see *MEDICAL SCIENCES*

572 USA ISSN 1527-6031
R857.M3
BIOMATERIALS FORUM. Text in English. 1996. q. USD 48 (effective 2003). adv. bk.rev. **Document type:** *Consumer.*
Published by: Society for Biomaterials, 17000 Commerce Pkwy., Ste. C, Mount Laurel, NJ 08054-2267. director@biomaterials.org, http://www.biomaterials.org. Ed. Rosealee M Lee. Circ: 2,000.

572 JPN ISSN 0916-717X
CODEN: BRTEE5
BIOMEDICAL RESEARCH ON TRACE ELEMENTS. Text in English, Japanese; Summaries in English. 1990. irreg. (2-4/yr.). membership. **Document type:** *Journal, Academic/Scholarly.*
Related titles: Online - full content ed.: ISSN 1880-1404; Online - full text ed.: (from J-Stage).
Indexed: CIN, ChemAb, ChemTitl.
—BLDSC (2087.875000), CASDDS, GNLM.
Published by: Japan Society for Biomedical Research on Trace Elements/Nihon Biryo Genso Gakkai, Osaka University Graduate School of Medicine, Faculty of Health Sciences, 1-7 Yamadaoka, Suita, Osaka 565-0871, Japan. takagi@sahs.med.osaka-u.ac.jp, http://www.jstage.jst.go.jp/browse/brte/_vols/-char/ja, http://health-info.jp/brte/top.htm. Ed. Yasuyuki Arakawa.

572 RUS
CODEN: VMDKAM
➤ **BIOMEDITSINSKAYA KHIMIYA/PROBLEMS OF MEDICAL CHEMISTRY.** Text in Russian; Summaries in English. 1955. bi-m. USD 96 foreign (effective 2004). bk.rev. index. **Description:** Publishes original experimental works covering various branches of medical chemistry.
Formerly: Voprosy Meditsinskoi Khimii (0042-8809)
Indexed: ASCA, ASFA, B&BAb, BBCI, BIOSIS Prev, BiolAb, CIN, ChemAb, CurCont, DBA, DSA, DentInd, ExcerpMed, IAA, IndMed, MEDLINE, NutrAb, RM&VM, RefZh.
—CASDDS, CISTI, East View, GNLM, IDS, Infotrieve, KNAW, Linda Hall. **CCC.**
Published by: Akademiya Meditsinskikh Nauk Rossii/Russian Academy of Medical Sciences, Pogodinskaya 10, Moscow, 119832, Russian Federation. TEL 7-095-2466584. Ed. A I Archakov. Circ: 3,000. **Dist. by:** M K - Periodica, ul Gilyarovskogo 39, Moscow 129110, Russian Federation. TEL 7-095-2845008, FAX 7-095-2813798, info@periodicals.ru, http://www.mkniga.ru.

572 USA ISSN 0966-0844
QP532 CODEN: BOMEEH
➤ **BIOMETALS.** Text in Dutch. 1988. bi-m. EUR 1,078, USD 1,098, GBP 675 combined subscription to institutions print & online eds. (effective 2005). adv. reprint service avail. from PSC. **Document type:** *Journal, Academic/Scholarly.* **Description:** Provides an international, multidisciplinary forum for new research and clinical results concerning the role of metal ions in biology, biochemistry and medicine.
Formerly: Biology of Metals (0933-5854)
Related titles: Online - full text ed.: ISSN 1572-8773 (from EBSCO Publishing, Gale Group, IngentaConnect, Kluwer Online, O C L C Online Computer Library Center, Inc., Ovid Technologies, Inc., Springer LINK, Swets Information Services).
Indexed: ASCA, AbHyg, AnBrAb, B&BAb, BBCI, BIOBASE, BIOSIS Prev, BibLing, BioCN&I, BioDAb, BioEngAb, BiolAb, CCI, CIN, CPA, ChemAb, ChemTitl, CurCont, DSA, ExcerpMed, FCA, HortAb, IABS, ISR, IndMed, IndVet, Inpharma, MEDLINE, MaizeAb, NemAb, NutrAb, PBA, PGrRegA, PoultAb, ProtozoAb, RM&VM, RPP, Reac, RefZh, RiceAb, S&F, SCI, SoyAb, TDB, VetBull, WeedAb.
—BLDSC (2087.940000), CASDDS, CISTI, GNLM, IDS, IE, Infotrieve, ingenta. **CCC.**
Published by: Plenum US (Subsidiary of: Springer Science+Business Media), 233 Spring St, New York, NY 10013. TEL 212-460-1500, FAX 212-460-1575, service@springer-ny.com, http://springerlink.metapress.com/openurl.asp?genre=journal&issn=0966-0844, http://www.springeronline.com. Ed. Guenther Winkelmann.

➤ **BIOORGANICHESKAYA KHIMIYA.** see *CHEMISTRY—Organic Chemistry*

➤ **BIOPHYSICAL CHEMISTRY.** see *BIOLOGY—Biophysics*

➤ **BIOPROBES.** see *BIOLOGY—Microbiology*

➤ **BIOSCIENCE, BIOTECHNOLOGY, AND BIOCHEMISTRY.** see *BIOLOGY—Biotechnology*

➤ **BIOSCIENCE REPORTS**; molecular and cellular biology of the cell surface. see *BIOLOGY—Cytology And Histology*

➤ **BIOTECHNOLOGY AND APPLIED BIOCHEMISTRY.** see *BIOLOGY—Biotechnology*

➤ **BIOTECHNOLOGY AND BIOENGINEERING.** see *BIOLOGY—Biotechnology*

572 DNK ISSN 1398-0823
BIOZOOM. Text in Danish, English. 1998. q. DKK 200 membership (effective 2004). adv. back issues avail. **Document type:** *Academic/Scholarly.* **Description:** Describes scientific progress, research and education in the field of biochemistry.
Published by: Biokemisk Forening/Danish Society for Biochemistry and Molecular Biology, c/o Klinisk Biokemisk Afdeling, Glostrup Hospital, Glostrup, 2600, Denmark. TEL 45-43-232456, FAX 45-43-233929, http://www.biokemi.org/biozoom. Ed., R&P Steen Gammeltoft TEL 45-43-232455. adv.: B&W page DKK 7,000, color page DKK 13,000; 150 x 190. Circ: 1,400.

572.8 TUR ISSN 0250-4685
RB112.5 CODEN: BIDEDV
➤ **BIYOKIMYA DERGISI/TURKISH JOURNAL OF BIOCHEMISTRY.** Text in Turkish, English. 1976. q. TRL 20,000 domestic; USD 45 foreign (effective 2003). 32 p./no.; **Document type:** *Journal, Academic/Scholarly.* **Description:** Publishes research papers, case reports, technical notes and invited reviews on all aspects of biochemistry, clinical chemistry and molecular biology.
Related titles: Online - full text ed.: ISSN 1303-829X.
Published by: Turk Biyokimya Dernegi'nin Yayin Organidir/Turkish Biochemical Society, Hirfanli Sokak Banu Apt. 9/3, Gaziosmanpasa, Ankara 06700, Turkey. TEL 90-312-4470997, FAX 90-312-4470963, editor@turkjbiochem.com, info@biyokimya.org, http://www.turkjbiochem.com, http://www.biyokimya.org. Ed. Yahya Laleli. Adv. contact Nazmi Ozer.

➤ **BLOOD.** see *MEDICAL SCIENCES—Hematology*

612.015 USA ISSN 1078-0491
QP94 CODEN: BCEBEK
BLOOD CELL BIOCHEMISTRY. Text in English. 1990. irreg., latest vol.8, 1999. price varies. **Document type:** *Monographic series, Academic/Scholarly.*
Supersedes in part (in 1990): SubCellular Biochemistry (0306-0225); Which superseded (in 1975): Journal of Sub-Cellular Biochemistry
Indexed: BIOSIS Prev.
—BLDSC (8501.890000), CASDDS, CISTI, GNLM, IE, ingenta, Linda Hall. **CCC.**
Published by: Springer-Verlag New York, Inc. (Subsidiary of: Springer Science+Business Media), 233 Spring St, New York, NY 10013. TEL 212-460-1500, FAX 212-460-1575, service@springer-ny.com, http://www.springer-ny.com. Ed. J Robin Harris.

C A SELECTS. FREE RADICALS (BIOCHEMICAL ASPECTS). see *BIOLOGY—Abstracting, Bibliographies, Statistics*

C A SELECTS. PHOTOBIOCHEMISTRY. see *CHEMISTRY—Abstracting, Bibliographies, Statistics*

C A SELECTS PLUS. AMINO ACIDS, PEPTIDES AND PROTEINS. see *BIOLOGY—Abstracting, Bibliographies, Statistics*

C A SELECTS. STEROIDS (BIOCHEMICAL ASPECTS). see *BIOLOGY—Abstracting, Bibliographies, Statistics*

572 GBR ISSN 1367-8930
➤ **C P D BULLETIN. CLINICAL BIOCHEMISTRY.** (Continuing Professional Development) Text in English. 1998. 3/yr. GBP 45 domestic to individuals; GBP 60 foreign to individuals; GBP 60 domestic to libraries; GBP 90 foreign to libraries (effective 2005). **Document type:** *Journal, Academic/Scholarly.*
Indexed: ExcerpMed.
—BLDSC (3486.192130), IE, ingenta. **CCC.**
Published by: Rila Publications Ltd., 73 Newman St, London, W1A 4PG, United Kingdom. TEL 44-20-76311299, FAX 44-20-75807166, admin@rila.co.uk, http://www.rila.co.uk. Ed. R Swaminathan TEL 44-20-79554010.

572 USA ISSN 1554-8643
▼ **CALCIUM BINDING PROTEINS.** Text in English. forthcoming 2006 (Jan.). q. USD 80 in US & Canada to individuals; USD 130 elsewhere to individuals; USD 350 in US & Canada to institutions; USD 350 elsewhere to institutions (effective 2005). **Document type:** *Journal, Academic/Scholarly.*
Related titles: Online - full text ed.: ISSN 1554-8651. forthcoming 2005 (July).

B

Published by: Landes Bioscience, 810 S Church St, Georgetown, TX 78626. TEL 512-863-7762, 800-736-9948, FAX 512-863-0081, info@landesbioscience.com, http://www.landesbioscience.com/journals/cbproteins/index.php.

572.8 CAN CODEN: CBCBBB
CANADIAN SOCIETY OF BIOCHEMISTRY, MOLECULAR AND CELLULAR BIOLOGY. BULLETIN. Text mainly in English; Text occasionally in French. s-a. CND 10, USD 10. adv. bk.rev. **Document type:** *Bulletin.* **Description:** Covers news and meetings in Canada's biochemistry field.
Former titles: Canadian Society of Biochemistry and Molecular Biology. Bulletin; Canadian Biochemical Society. Bulletin (0008-302X)
Indexed: RefZh.
—CASDDS, CISTI.
Published by: Canadian Society of Biochemistry, Molecular and Cellular Biology, c/o Dr E R Tustanoff, Sec, Dept of Biochemistry, University of Western Ontario, London, ON N6A 5C1, Canada. TEL 519-471-1961, FAX 519-661-3175. Ed. David Tinker. Circ: 750.

CANCER BIOCHEMISTRY BIOPHYSICS. see *MEDICAL SCIENCES—Oncology*

▼ **CANCER BIOMARKERS**; section of Disease Markers. see *MEDICAL SCIENCES—Oncology*

572.6 611.01816 NLD ISSN 1568-1254
CELL AND MOLECULAR RESPONSES TO STRESS. Text in English. 2000. irreg. price varies. **Document type:** *Monographic series, Academic/Scholarly.*
—BLDSC (3097.673000), CISTI.
Published by: Elsevier BV (Subsidiary of: Elsevier Science & Technology), Radarweg 29, Amsterdam, 1043 NX, Netherlands. TEL 31-20-4853911, FAX 31-20-4852457, nlinfo-f@elsevier.nl, http://www.elsevier.nl.

CELL BIOCHEMISTRY AND BIOPHYSICS. see *BIOLOGY—Cytology And Histology*

571.6 GBR ISSN 0263-6484
QH611 CODEN: CBFUDH
➤ **CELL BIOCHEMISTRY AND FUNCTION.** Text in English. 1983. bi-m. USD 1,995 to institutions; USD 2,195 combined subscription to institutions print & online eds. (effective 2006). adv. bk.rev. abstr.; illus. index. back issues avail.; reprint service avail. from PSC. **Document type:** *Journal, Academic/Scholarly.* **Description:** Provides a forum for reporting and discussing the biochemistry of whole cells and of the link between the biochemistry and the functioning of cells in isolation, in assemblies, and in tissues.
Related titles: Microform ed.: (from PQC); Online - full content ed.: ISSN 1099-0844. USD 1,995 to institutions (effective 2006); Online - full text ed.: (from EBSCO Publishing, Swets Information Services, Wiley InterScience).
Indexed: ASFA, AbHyg, AgBio, AgrForAb, AnBrAb, B&BAb, BBCI, BIOBASE, BIOSIS Prev, BiolAb, CIN, ChemAb, ChemTitl, CurCont, ESPM, ExcerpMed, GenetAb, HortAb, IABS, ISR, IndMed, IndVet, Inpharma, MEDLINE, NemAb, NutrAb, PBA, PE&ON, PoultAb, ProtozoAb, RA&MP, RM&VM, Reac, SCI, SoyAb, TDB, VetBull.
—BLDSC (3097.702000), CASDDS, CISTI, GNLM, IDS, IE, Infotrieve, ingenta, KNAW, Linda Hall. **CCC.**
Published by: John Wiley & Sons Ltd. (Subsidiary of: John Wiley & Sons, Inc.), The Atrium, Southern Gate, Chichester, West Sussex PO19 8SQ, United Kingdom. TEL 44-1243-779777, FAX 44-1243-775878, customer@wiley.co.uk, http://www.interscience.wiley.com/jpages/0263-6484/, http://www.wiley.co.uk. adv.: B&W page GBP 650, color page GBP 1,550; trim 200 x 260. Circ: 300. **Subscr. to:** John Wiley & Sons, Inc., 111 River St, Hoboken, NJ 07030-5774. TEL 201-748-6645, 800-225-5945, subinfo@wiley.com.

➤ **CELL MEMBRANES.** see *BIOLOGY—Abstracting, Bibliographies, Statistics*

➤ **CELLULAR PHYSIOLOGY AND BIOCHEMISTRY**; international journal of experimental cellular physiology, biochemistry and pharmacology. see *BIOLOGY—Cytology And Histology*

572 DEU ISSN 1439-4227
QP501 CODEN: CBCHFX
➤ **CHEMBIOCHEM**; a european journal of chemical biology. Text in English. 2000. m. EUR 1,398 in Europe; CHF 2,158 in Switzerland & Liechtenstein; USD 1,578 elsewhere; EUR 1,538 combined subscription in Europe print & online eds.; CHF 2,374 combined subscription in Switzerland & Liechtenstein for print & online eds.; USD 1,736 combined subscription elsewhere print & online eds. (effective 2006). adv. illus. back issues avail.; reprints avail. **Document type:** *Journal, Academic/Scholarly.* **Description:** Contains papers, communications, reviews, comments, and news on all aspects of chemical biology.
Related titles: Online - full text ed.: ISSN 1439-7633. 2000. EUR 1,398 in Europe to institutions; CHF 2,158 to institutions in Switzerland & Liechtenstein; USD 1,578 elsewhere to institutions (effective 2006) (from EBSCO Publishing, Swets Information Services, Wiley InterScience).
Indexed: BBCI, BIOBASE, CCI, ChemAb, ChemInfo, CurCont, ESPM, ExcerpMed, ISR, Inpharma, NucAcAb, PE&ON, Reac, RefZh, SCI, VirolAbstr.
—BLDSC (3133.490980), CISTI, IE, Infotrieve, ingenta, Linda Hall. **CCC.**
Published by: Wiley - V C H Verlag GmbH & Co. KGaA (Subsidiary of: John Wiley & Sons, Inc.), Boschstr 12, Weinheim, 69469, Germany. TEL 49-6201-606-0, FAX 49-6201-606-328, chembiochem@wiley-vch.de, subservice@wiley-vch.de, http://www.chembiochem.com, http://www.wiley-vch.de. Ed. Peter Goelitz. R&P Claudia Rutz. Adv. contact Aenne Anders TEL 49-6201-606552.

➤ **CHEMICAL ABSTRACTS - BIOCHEMISTRY SECTIONS.** see *BIOLOGY—Abstracting, Bibliographies, Statistics*

572.65 DNK
QD431.A1 CODEN: JPERFA
➤ **CHEMICAL BIOLOGY & DRUG DESIGN.** Text in English. 1997. m. USD 1,185 combined subscription in the Americas to institutions & Caribbean (print & online eds); GBP 641 combined subscription elsewhere to institutions print & online eds. (effective 2006). adv. charts; illus. index. reprint service avail. from ISI,PSC. **Document type:** *Journal, Academic/Scholarly.* **Description:** Dedicated to the advancement of innovative science, technology and medicine with a focus on the multidisciplinary fields of chemical biology and drug design.
Formerly (until 2006): Journal of Peptide Research (1397-002X); Formed by the merger of (1988-1997): Peptide Research (1040-5704); (1968-1997): International Journal of Peptide and Protein Research (0367-8377); Which was formerly: International Journal of Protein Research (0020-7551)
Related titles: Online - full text ed.: ISSN 1747-0285. USD 1,126 in the Americas to institutions & Caribbean; GBP 609 elsewhere to institutions (effective 2006) (from Blackwell Synergy, EBSCO Publishing, Gale Group, IngentaConnect, O C L C Online Computer Library Center, Inc., Ovid Technologies, Inc., Swets Information Services).
Indexed: ASCA, ASFA, AbHyg, AgBio, AnBrAb, BBCI, BIOBASE, BIOSIS Prev, BiolAb, CCI, CIN, ChemAb, ChemTitl, CurCR, CurCont, DBA, DSA, DentInd, EngInd, ExcerpMed, HortAb, IABS, ISR, IndChem, IndMed, IndVet, Inpharma, MEDLINE, MSB, MSCI, ProtozoAb, RA&MP, RCI, RM&VM, RPP, Reac, RiceAb, SCI, SeedAb, SoyAb, TDB, VetBull.
—BLDSC (5030.528000), CASDDS, CISTI, Ei, GNLM, IDS, IE, Infotrieve, ingenta, Linda Hall. **CCC.**
Published by: (American Peptide Society USA), Blackwell Munksgaard (Subsidiary of: Blackwell Publishing Ltd.), Rosenoerns Alle 1, PO Box 227, Copenhagen V, 1502, Denmark. TEL 45-77-333333, FAX 45-77-333377, info@mks.blackwellpublishing.com, http://www.blackwellpublishing.com/cbdd/, http://www.munksgaard.dk/. Ed. TomVictor KJ Sawyer. Adv. contact Alf Anderson. Circ: 1,400.

➤ **CHEMICAL SENSES.** see *BIOLOGY—Physiology*

➤ **CHEMICO-BIOLOGICAL INTERACTIONS.** see *ENVIRONMENTAL STUDIES—Toxicology And Environmental Safety*

➤ **CHEMISTRY AND ECOLOGY.** see *CHEMISTRY*

572.57 IRL ISSN 0009-3084
QP751 CODEN: CPLIA4
➤ **CHEMISTRY AND PHYSICS OF LIPIDS.** Text in English. 1967. 12/yr. EUR 2,800 in Europe to institutions; JPY 372,100 in Japan to institutions; USD 3,132 elsewhere to institutions (effective 2006). illus. index. back issues avail. **Document type:** *Journal, Academic/Scholarly.* **Description:** Publishes papers and review articles in the field of molecular biology which emphasize chemical and biophysical aspects of lipids.
Related titles: Microform ed.: (from PQC); Online - full text ed.: (from EBSCO Publishing, Gale Group, IngentaConnect, ScienceDirect, Swets Information Services).
Indexed: ASCA, AbHyg, AnBrAb, ApicAb, BBCI, BIOBASE, BIOSIS Prev, BiolAb, CCI, CIN, CPA, ChemAb, ChemTitl, CurCont, DSA, EngInd, ExcerpMed, FCA, FPA, HortAb, IABS, ISR, IndMed, IndVet, Inpharma, Inspec, MEDLINE, MSB, NutrAb, OrnHort, PE&ON, RA&MP, RM&VM, Reac, RevApplEntom, S&F, SCI, SIA, SoyAb, TriticAb, VetBull.
—BLDSC (3170.100000), CASDDS, CISTI, Ei, GNLM, IDS, IE, Infotrieve, ingenta, Linda Hall. **CCC.**
Published by: Elsevier Ireland Ltd (Subsidiary of: Elsevier Science & Technology), Elsevier House, Brookvale Plaza, E. Park, Shannon, Co. Clare, Ireland. TEL 353-61-709600, FAX 353-61-709100, http://www.elsevier.com/locate/chemphyslip. **Subscr. to:** Elsevier BV, PO Box 211, Amsterdam 1000 AE, Netherlands. TEL 31-20-485-3757, FAX 31-20-485-3432, nlinfo-f@elsevier.nl, http://www.elsevier.nl.

572 AUT ISSN 1608-2265
CODEN: CMHICX
➤ **CHEMOTAXIS AND MIGRATION.** Text in English. 2000. q. USD 75 domestic; USD 115 foreign; USD 35 newsstand/cover (effective 2001). adv. back issues avail. **Document type:** *Journal, Academic/Scholarly.* **Description:** Publishes articles, case reports, reviews, and letters on improving communications in understanding the multidisciplinary fields of chemotaxis, cell locomotion, and migration.
Related titles: Online - full text ed.
Indexed: BIOBASE, ExcerpMed.
Published by: V I C E R Publishing, PO Box 14, Vienna, A-1097, Austria. TEL 43-676-9568085, FAX 43-676-9568086, vicer@vicer.org, http://www.vicer.org. Ed., R&P Roland Hofbauer. adv.: B&W page USD 1,700, color page USD 2,200. Circ: 1,000 (paid and controlled).

572.8 USA ISSN 0899-0042
QP517.C57 CODEN: CHRLEP
➤ **CHIRALITY**; the pharmacological, biological, and chemical consequences of molecular asymmetry. Text in English. 1989. 10/yr. USD 2,195 domestic to institutions; USD 2,315 in Canada & Mexico to institutions; USD 2,385 elsewhere to institutions; USD 2,415 combined subscription domestic to institutions print & online eds.; USD 2,535 combined subscription in Canada & Mexico to institutions print & online eds.; USD 2,605 combined subscription elsewhere to institutions print & online eds. (effective 2006). adv. bk.rev. back issues avail. **Document type:** *Journal, Academic/Scholarly.* **Description:** Devoted to molecular asymmetry and its relevance in biological or chemical processes.
Related titles: Microform ed.: (from PQC); Online - full content ed.: ISSN 1520-636X. USD 2,195 to institutions (effective 2006); Online - full text ed.: (from EBSCO Publishing, Swets Information Services, Wiley InterScience).
Indexed: ASCA, ASFA, AnalAb, B&BAb, BIOSIS Prev, BioEngAb, BiolAb, CCI, CIN, CPA, ChemAb, ChemTitl, ChromAb, CurCont, ESPM, ExcerpMed, FCA, HortAb, ISR, IndMed, IndVet, Inpharma, MEDLINE, MSB, PE&ON, PN&I, ProtozoAb, RA&MP, RCI, RM&VM, RPP, Reac, RefZh, S&F, SCI, SIA, ToxAb, VetBull, WeedAb.
—BLDSC (3181.124450), CASDDS, CISTI, GNLM, IDS, IE, Infotrieve, ingenta. **CCC.**
Published by: John Wiley & Sons, Inc., 111 River St, Hoboken, NJ 07030-5774. TEL 201-748-6000, FAX 201-748-5915, uscs-wis@wiley.com, http://www.interscience.wiley.com/jpages/0899-0042/, http://www.wiley.com. Eds. Daniel W Armstrong, William F Trager. adv.: B&W page GBP 640, color page GBP 1,515; trim 210 x 279. Circ: 550. **Subscr. outside the Americas to:** John Wiley & Sons Ltd., The Atrium, Southern Gate, Chichester, West Sussex PO19 8SQ, United Kingdom. TEL 44-1243-843335, 0800-243407, FAX 44-1243-843232, cs-journals@wiley.co.uk.

➤ **CHOLESTEROL & LIPOPROTEINS.** see *BIOLOGY—Abstracting, Bibliographies, Statistics*

572.87 NLD ISSN 0967-3849
QH600 CODEN: CRRSEE
➤ **CHROMOSOME RESEARCH**; the international journal for all aspects of chromosome and nuclear biology. Text in Dutch. 1993. 8/yr. EUR 1,348, USD 1,378, GBP 888 combined subscription to institutions print & online eds. (effective 2005). adv. bk.rev. reprint service avail. from PSC. **Document type:** *Journal, Academic/Scholarly.* **Description:** Provides a forum covering the wide area of chromosomology, including its supramolecular, molecular and evolutionary aspects.
Related titles: CD-ROM ed.; Online - full text ed.: ISSN 1573-6849 (from EBSCO Publishing, Gale Group, IngentaConnect, Kluwer Online, O C L C Online Computer Library Center, Inc., Ovid Technologies, Inc., Springer LINK, Swets Information Services).
Indexed: ASCA, AbHyg, AgBio, Agr, AnBrAb, BBCI, BCI, BIOBASE, BIOSIS Prev, BibLing, BiolAb, CIN, CPA, ChemAb, ChemTitl, CurCont, ExcerpMed, HerbAb, HortAb, IABS, ISR, IndMed, IndVet, Inpharma, MEDLINE, MaizeAb, NemAb, OrnHort, PBA, PGegResA, PN&I, PoultAb, ProtozoAb, RM&VM, RPP, Reac, RefZh, RevApplEntom, RiceAb, S&F, SCI, SFA, SIA, SeedAb, TriticAb, VITIS, VetBull, WeedAb, ZooRec.
—BLDSC (3184.250000), CASDDS, CISTI, IDS, IE, Infotrieve, ingenta, KNAW, Linda Hall. **CCC.**
Published by: Springer-Verlag Dordrecht (Subsidiary of: Springer Science+Business Media), Van Godewijckstraat 30, Dordrecht, 3311 GX, Netherlands. TEL 31-78-6576050, FAX 31-78-6576474, http://springerlink.metapress.com/openurl.asp?genre=journal&issn=0967-3849, http://www.springeronline.com. Ed. Herbert C Macgregor.

572.8 PRT ISSN 0378-875X
QH540 CODEN: CBMBEU
CIENCIA BIOLOGICA: BIOLOGIA MOLECULAR E CELULAR. Text in English, French, German, Portuguese. 1934. q. USD 10. bk.rev. charts; illus. index, cum.index. **Document type:** *Academic/Scholarly.*
Former titles (until 1972): Universidade de Coimbra. Museum Zoologico. Memorias e Estudos (0041-8765); Universidade de Coimbra. Departamento de Zoologia. Ciencia Biologica
Indexed: ASFA, BiolAb, ChemAb, DSA, ESPM, FCA, RevApplEntom, SFA, SeedAb, WildRev, ZooRec.
—CASDDS, CISTI.
Published by: Universidade de Coimbra, Departamento de Zoologia, Largo Marques de Pombal, Coimbra, 3004-517, Portugal. TEL 351-39-34729, FAX 351-39-26798. Ed. Arselio Pato de Carvalho. Circ: 600 (controlled).

B

572 AUS ISSN 0159-8090
CODEN: CBREEU
CLINICAL BIOCHEMIST REVIEWS. Text in English. 1980. q. AUD 85 to non-members; free to members (effective 2004). cum.index vol.1-24. **Document type:** *Journal, Academic/Scholarly.* **Description:** Contains reviews of educational, scientific and philosophical topics in clinical biochemistry and bibliographies on specific subjects.
—BLDSC (3286.260800), CASDDS, CISTI, GNLM, IE, ingenta. **CCC.**
Published by: Australasian Association of Clinical Biochemists, PO Box 278, Mt. Lawley, W.A. 6929, Australia. TEL 61-8-93705224, FAX 61-8-93704409, office@aacb.asn.au, http://www.aacb.asn.au/pubs/cbr.htm. Ed. Sam Vasikaran. Circ: 1,600.

572 USA ISSN 0009-9120
RB112.5 CODEN: CLBIAS
➤ **CLINICAL BIOCHEMISTRY.** Text in English, French. 1967. 12/yr. EUR 569 in Europe to institutions; JPY 75,800 in Japan to institutions; USD 640 to institutions except Europe and Japan (effective 2006). adv. charts; illus.; stat. back issues avail. **Document type:** *Journal, Academic/Scholarly.* **Description:** Publishes articles relating to the applications of molecular biology, biochemistry, chemistry and immunology to clinical investigation and to the diagnosis, therapy, and monitoring of human diseases.
Related titles: Microfilm ed.: (from PQC); Online - full text ed.: (from EBSCO Publishing, Gale Group, IngentaConnect, ScienceDirect, Swets Information Services).
Indexed: AbHyg, AgBio, AnalAb, B&BAb, BBCI, BIOBASE, BIOSIS Prev, BiolAb, CIN, CMCI, ChemAb, ChemTitl, CurCont, DBA, DSA, ExcerpMed, GenetAb, HelmAb, HortAb, IABS, ISR, IndMed, IndVet, Inpharma, MEDLINE, MSB, NutrAb, PE&ON, PN&I, ProtozoAb, RA&MP, RPP, Reac, SCI, SIA, TDB, VITIS.
—BLDSC (3286.262000), CASDDS, CISTI, GNLM, IDS, IE, Infotrieve, ingenta, KNAW, Linda Hall. **CCC.**
Published by: (Canadian Society of Clinical Chemists CAN), Elsevier Inc. (Subsidiary of: Elsevier Science & Technology), 360 Park Ave. S, New York, NY 10010-1710. TEL 212-633-3730, 888-437-4636, usinfo-f@elsevier.com, http://www.elsevier.com/locate/clinbiochem. Ed. Dr. Khosrow Adeli. Circ: 1,500. **Subscr. outside the Americas to:** Elsevier BV, PO Box 211, Amsterdam 1000 AE, Netherlands. TEL 31-20-485-3757, FAX 31-20-485-3432. **Co-sponsor:** National Academy of Biochemistry.

572 DEU ISSN 1434-6621
CODEN: CCLMFW
➤ **CLINICAL CHEMISTRY AND LABORATORY MEDICINE;** Associated with FESCC and IFCC. Text in English. 1963. m. EUR 1,070 to institutions; EUR 1,158 combined subscription to institutions print & online eds.; EUR 98 newsstand/cover (effective 2006). adv. bk.rev. charts; illus.; abstr. index. back issues avail.; reprint service avail. from PSC. **Document type:** *Journal, Academic/Scholarly.*
Former titles (until 1998): European Journal of Clinical Chemistry and Clinical Biochemistry (0939-4974); (until 1991): Journal of Clinical Chemistry and Clinical Biochemistry (0340-076X); (until 1976): Zeitschrift fuer Klinische Chemie und Klinische Biochemie (0044-2933); (until 1967): Zeitschrift fuer Klinische Chemie (0372-9184)
Related titles: Online - full text ed.: ISSN 1437-4331. EUR 1,070 to institutions (effective 2006) (from EBSCO Publishing, O C L C Online Computer Library Center, Inc., Ovid Technologies, Inc., Swets Information Services).
Indexed: ASCA, AnalAb, BBCI, BIOBASE, BIOSIS Prev, BiolAb, ChemAb, CurCont, DSA, DentInd, ExcerpMed, IABS, ISR, IndMed, IndVet, Inpharma, MEDLINE, MSB, NutrAb, PE&ON, ProtozoAb, RM&VM, Reac, RefZh, SCI.
—BLDSC (3286.268100), CASDDS, CINDOC, CISTI, GNLM, IDS, IE, Infotrieve, ingenta, KNAW, Linda Hall. **CCC.**
Published by: (Deutsche Vereinte Gesellschaft fuer Klinische Chemie und Laboratoriumsmedizin e.V.), Walter de Gruyter GmbH & Co. KG, Genthiner Str. 13, Berlin, 10785, Germany. TEL 49-30-26005220, FAX 49-30-26005251, cclm.editorial@degruyter.de, wdg-info@degruyter.de, http://www.degruyter.de/journals/cclm. Ed. Gerard Siest. Adv. contact Mrs. Imke Ridder TEL 49-8191-971105. B&W page EUR 645, color page EUR 1,490; trim 180 x 264. Circ: 2,000 (paid and controlled).

573.84 GBR ISSN 0885-7431
CLINICAL NEUROCHEMISTRY. Text in English. 1986. irreg., latest 1997, July. price varies. **Document type:** *Monographic series, Academic/Scholarly.*
—CISTI.
Published by: Academic Press (Subsidiary of: Elsevier Science & Technology), 24-28 Oval Rd, London, NW1 7DX, United Kingdom. TEL 44-20-72674466, FAX 44-20-74822293.

572 USA ISSN 1542-6416
▼ **CLINICAL PROTEOMICS.** Text in English. 2004 (Jan.). q. USD 400 domestic to institutions; USD 415 foreign to institutions; USD 420 combined subscription domestic to institutions print & online eds.; USD 435 combined subscription foreign to institutions print & online eds. (effective 2004). **Document type:** *Journal, Academic/Scholarly.*
Related titles: Online - full text ed.: USD 350 to institutions (effective 2004) (from EBSCO Publishing, Gale Group, IngentaConnect, Ovid Technologies, Inc., Swets Information Services).
Indexed: ExcerpMed.
—BLDSC (3286.339700). **CCC.**
Published by: Humana Press, Inc., 999 Riverview Dr, Ste 208, Totowa, NJ 07512. TEL 973-256-1699, FAX 973-256-8341, humana@humanapr.com, http://humanapress.com. Eds. Emanuel Petricoin, Lance Liotta.

COMPARATIVE BIOCHEMISTRY AND PHYSIOLOGY. PART A: MOLECULAR & INTEGRATIVE PHYSIOLOGY. see *BIOLOGY—Physiology*

572 USA ISSN 1096-4959
QP33 CODEN: CBPBB8
➤ **COMPARATIVE BIOCHEMISTRY AND PHYSIOLOGY. PART B: BIOCHEMISTRY & MOLECULAR BIOLOGY.** Text and summaries in English, French, German. 1961. 12/yr. EUR 4,833 in Europe to institutions; JPY 641,900 in Japan to institutions; USD 5,406 elsewhere to institutions (effective 2006). adv. bk.rev. bibl.; charts; illus. back issues avail. **Document type:** *Journal, Academic/Scholarly.* **Description:** Publishes original research on the biochemistry and physiology of animals.
Formerly (until 1994): Comparative Biochemistry and Physiology. Part B: Comparative Biochemistry (0305-0491)
Related titles: Microfiche ed.: (from MIM); Microfilm ed.: (from PQC); Online - full text ed.: (from EBSCO Publishing, Gale Group, IngentaConnect, ScienceDirect, Swets Information Services).
Indexed: ASCA, ASFA, AbHyg, AgBio, Agr, AnBeAb, AnBrAb, ApicAb, B&BAb, BBCI, BIOBASE, BIOSIS Prev, BioCN&I, BioDAb, BiolAb, CCI, CPA, ChemAb, CurCont, DSA, DentInd, ESPM, EntAb, ExcerpMed, FCA, ForAb, GenetAb, HGA, HelmAb, HerbAb, HortAb, IABS, ISR, IndMed, IndVet, MEDLINE, MSB, MaizeAb, NSCI, NemAb, NucAcAb, NutrAb, OceAb, PHN&I, PN&I, PotatoAb, PoultAb, ProtozoAb, RA&MP, RM&VM, RPP, RefZh, RevApplEntom, RiceAb, S&F, SAA, SCI, SFA, SIA, SSCI, SeedAb, SoyAb, TDB, TriticAb, VetBull, WeedAb, WildRev, ZooRec.
—BLDSC (3363.752000), CASDDS, CISTI, IDS, IE, Infotrieve, ingenta, Linda Hall. **CCC.**
Published by: Elsevier Inc. (Subsidiary of: Elsevier Science & Technology), 360 Park Ave. S, New York, NY 10010-1710. TEL 212-633-3730, 888-437-4636, usinfo-f@elsevier.com, http://www.elsevier.com/locate/cbpb. Eds. Patrick J. Walsh, Thomas P Mommsen. adv.: B&W page USD 550, color page USD 1,350. Circ: 2,000. **Subscr. outside the Americas to:** Elsevier BV, PO Box 211, Amsterdam 1000 AE, Netherlands. TEL 31-20-485-3757, FAX 31-20-485-3432.

615.1 USA ISSN 1532-0456
QP33 CODEN: CBPPFK
➤ **COMPARATIVE BIOCHEMISTRY AND PHYSIOLOGY. PART C: TOXICOLOGY & PHARMACOLOGY.** Text in English, French. 1975. 8/yr. EUR 2,676 in Europe to institutions; JPY 355,500 in Japan to institutions; USD 2,994 elsewhere to institutions (effective 2006). adv. bk.rev. abstr.; charts; illus. index. back issues avail. **Document type:** *Journal, Academic/Scholarly.* **Description:** Publishes research studying the actions of drugs and chemicals on cells, tissues, and whole animals.
Former titles (until 2000): Comparative Biochemistry and Physiology. Part C: Pharmacology, Toxicology & Endocrinology (1367-8280); (until 1994): Comparative Biochemistry and Physiology. Part C: Comparative Pharmacology & Toxicology (0742-8413); (until 1993): Comparative Biochemistry and Physiology. Part C: Comparative Pharmacology (0306-4492); Which superseded in part: Comparative Biochemistry and Physiology (0010-406X)
Related titles: Microfiche ed.: (from MIM); Microfilm ed.: (from PQC); Online - full text ed.: (from EBSCO Publishing, Gale Group, IngentaConnect, ScienceDirect, Swets Information Services).
Indexed: ASCA, ASFA, AbHyg, AgBio, Agr, AgrForAb, AnBeAb, AnBrAb, ApicAb, B&BAb, BBCI, BIOBASE, BIOSIS Prev, BioCN&I, BiolAb, CPA, ChemAb, CurCont, DSA, ESPM, EntAb, ExcerpMed, FCA, FPA, ForAb, GenetAb, HelmAb, HortAb, IABS, INIS AtomInd, ISR, IndMed, IndVet, Inpharma, MEDLINE, MaizeAb, NSCI, NutrAb, OceAb, PE&ON, PGrRegA, PHN&I, PN&I, PotatoAb, PoultAb, ProtozoAb, RA&MP, RM&VM, RPP, Reac, RefZh, RevApplEntom, S&F, SCI, SFA, SIA, SWRA, SeedAb, SoyAb, TDB, VetBull, WeedAb, WildRev, ZooRec.
—BLDSC (3363.752500), CASDDS, CISTI, IDS, IE, Infotrieve, ingenta, Linda Hall. **CCC.**
Published by: Elsevier Inc. (Subsidiary of: Elsevier Science & Technology), 360 Park Ave. S, New York, NY 10010-1710. TEL 212-633-3730, 888-437-4636, FAX 212-633-3680, usinfo-f@elsevier.com, http://www.elsevier.com/locate/cbpc. Eds. Patrick J. Walsh, Thomas P Mommsen. adv.: B&W page USD 550, color page USD 1,350. Circ: 1,500.

572 USA ISSN 1744-117X
▼ **COMPARATIVE BIOCHEMISTRY AND PHYSIOLOGY. PART D: GENOMICS AND PROTEOMICS.** Text in English. 2005. q. EUR 518 in Europe; JPY 68,900 in Japan; USD 580 elsewhere (effective 2006). **Document type:** *Journal, Academic/Scholarly.* **Description:** Covers the broader comprehensive approaches to comparative biochemistry and physiology that can be generally termed as " -omics", e.g., genomics, functional genomics (transcriptomics), proteomics, metabolomics, and underlying bioinformatics.
Related titles: Online - full text ed.: (from ScienceDirect).
Published by: Elsevier Inc. (Subsidiary of: Elsevier Science & Technology), 360 Park Ave. S, New York, NY 10010-1710. TEL 212-633-3730, FAX 212-633-3680, usinfo-f@elsevier.com, http://www.elsevier.com/locate/cbpd. Eds. Patrick J. Walsh, Thomas P Mommsen.

572 NLD ISSN 0069-8032
➤ **COMPREHENSIVE BIOCHEMISTRY.** Text in Dutch. 1962. irreg., latest vol.41, 2000. price varies. **Document type:** *Monographic series, Academic/Scholarly.*
Indexed: BIOSIS Prev, ISR, SCI.
—BLDSC (3366.300000). **CCC.**
Published by: Elsevier BV (Subsidiary of: Elsevier Science & Technology), Radarweg 29, Amsterdam, 1043 NX, Netherlands. TEL 31-20-4853911, FAX 31-20-4852457, nlinfo-f@elsevier.nl, http://www.elsevier.nl. Ed. G. Semenza.

➤ **COMPUTATIONAL BIOLOGY AND CHEMISTRY.** see *CHEMISTRY—Computer Applications*

572 CHL ISSN 0069-8784
CONFERENCIAS DE BIOQUIMICA✶. Text in Spanish. 1967. a. **Document type:** *Proceedings, Academic/Scholarly.*
Published by: Universidad de Chile, Instituto de Quimica Fisiologica y Patologica, Diag. Paraguay, 265, Torre 15, Santiago, Chile.

612.015 572.8 USA
➤ **CONTEMPORARY BIOMEDICINE.** Text in English. 1979. irreg., latest 1997. price varies. illus. back issues avail.; reprints avail. **Document type:** *Monographic series, Academic/Scholarly.* **Description:** Discusses scientific and medical research in biological chemistry.
Formerly (until 1995): Contemporary Issues in Biomedicine, Ethics, and Society
Published by: Humana Press, Inc., 999 Riverview Dr, Ste 208, Totowa, NJ 07512. TEL 973-256-1699, FAX 973-256-8431, humana@humanapr.com, http://humanapress.com/journals.pasp. R&P Richard Hruska.

➤ **CONTEMPORARY NEUROSCIENCE.** see *MEDICAL SCIENCES—Psychiatry And Neurology*

572 USA ISSN 1040-9238
QP501 CODEN: CRBBEJ
➤ **CRITICAL REVIEWS IN BIOCHEMISTRY AND MOLECULAR BIOLOGY.** Text in English. 1971. bi-m. USD 988, GBP 598 combined subscription to institutions print & online eds. (effective 2006). bibl.; charts; illus. back issues avail.; reprint service avail. from PSC. **Document type:** *Journal, Academic/Scholarly.* **Description:** Includes, in each issue, several critical surveys on specific topics of current interest.
Former titles (until 1988): Critical Reviews in Biochemistry (1040-8355); (until 1980): C R C Critical Reviews in Biochemistry (0045-6411)
Related titles: Online - full text ed.: ISSN 1549-7798. USD 939, GBP 568 to institutions (effective 2006) (from EBSCO Publishing, Gale Group, HighWire Press, IngentaConnect, O C L C Online Computer Library Center, Inc., ProQuest Information & Learning, ScienceDirect, Swets Information Services).
Indexed: ASCA, ASFA, AbHyg, AgBio, Agr, AnBrAb, BBCI, BIOBASE, BIOSIS Prev, BiolAb, BrCerAb, C&ISA, CIN, CPA, CTA, CerAb, ChemAb, ChemTitl, ChemoAb, CorrAb, CurCont, DBA, E&CAJ, EMA, EPB, ExcerpMed, FS&TA, GenetAb, HGA, HelmAb, HortAb, IAA, IABS, ISR, IndMed, IndVet, Inpharma, M&TEA, MBF, MEDLINE, METADEX, NSA, NucAcAb, NutrAb, PBA, ProtozoAb, RPP, Reac, SCI, VetBull, WAA, WeedAb.
—BLDSC (3487.471500), CASDDS, CISTI, GNLM, IDS, IE, Infotrieve, ingenta, Linda Hall. **CCC.**
Published by: Taylor & Francis Inc. (Subsidiary of: Taylor & Francis Group), 325 Chestnut St, Ste 800, Philadelphia, PA 19016. TEL 215-625-8900, 800-354-1420, FAX 215-625-2940, info@taylorandfrancis.com, http://www.crbmb.com, http://www.taylorandfrancis.com. Ed. Dr. Michael Cox. Circ: 570.

➤ **CURRENT ADVANCES IN ENDOCRINOLOGY & METABOLISM.** see *MEDICAL SCIENCES—Endocrinology*

➤ **CURRENT ADVANCES IN GENETICS & MOLECULAR BIOLOGY.** see *BIOLOGY—Abstracting, Bibliographies, Statistics*

➤ **CURRENT ADVANCES IN PROTEIN BIOCHEMISTRY.** see *BIOLOGY—Abstracting, Bibliographies, Statistics*

572.8 USA ISSN 1063-8806
CODEN: CCCBEL
CURRENT COMMUNICATIONS IN CELL AND MOLECULAR BIOLOGY SERIES. Text in English. 1983. irreg. price varies. reprints avail. **Document type:** *Monographic series.* **Description:** Examines topics on which the impact of the techniques and concepts of molecular and cell biology is particularly evident.
Formerly (until 1990): Current Communications in Molecular Biology (0737-3708)
Indexed: BIOSIS Prev, CIN, ChemAb, ChemTitl.
—CASDDS, CISTI, KNAW. **CCC.**

Published by: Cold Spring Harbor Laboratory Press, Publications Department, 500 Sunnyside Blvd., Woodbury, NY 11797-2924. TEL 516-422-4100, 800-843-4388, FAX 516-422-4097, cshpress@cshl.edu, http://www.cshl.org. Eds. Jan Witkowski, John Inglis.

CURRENT ISSUES IN MOLECULAR BIOLOGY. see *BIOLOGY—Microbiology*

572.05 GBR ISSN 1367-5931
QP550 CODEN: COCBF4
➤ **CURRENT OPINION IN CHEMICAL BIOLOGY.** Text in English. 1997. 6/yr. EUR 270 in Europe to individuals; JPY 32,800 in Japan to individuals; USD 293 to individuals except Europe and Japan; EUR 1,232 in Europe to institutions; JPY 170,900 in Japan to institutions; USD 1,378 to institutions except Europe and Japan (effective 2006). illus. back issues avail. **Document type:** *Academic/Scholarly.* **Description:** Serves as a review journal covering the application of chemical techniques to biological problems and the chemical manipulation of biological systems. Includes about 90 reviews, and a guide to significant papers published within the past year.
Related titles: Online - full text ed.: USD 227 in North America to individuals; USD 247 in North America to individuals with print ed; GBP 125 elsewhere to individuals; GBP 150 elsewhere to individuals with print ed; USD 822 in North America to institutions includes print ed; GBP 500 elsewhere to institutions includes print ed (effective 1999 & 2000) (from EBSCO Publishing, Gale Group, IngentaConnect, ScienceDirect, Swets Information Services).
Indexed: ASFA, BBCI, BIOSIS Prev, ChemAb, CurCont, ExcerpMed, GenetAb, HGA, ISR, IndMed, Inpharma, M&PBA, MEDLINE, MSB, PE&ON, Reac, SCI.
—BLDSC (3500.773520), CASDDS, CISTI, GNLM, IDS, IE, Infotrieve, ingenta. **CCC.**
Published by: Elsevier Ltd., Current Opinion Journals (Subsidiary of: Elsevier Science & Technology), 84 Theobald's Rd., London, WC1X 8RR, United Kingdom. TEL 44-20-7611-4000, FAX 44-20-7611-4001, 44-20-7611-4468, http://www.elsevier.com/locate/cbi, http://www.current-opinion.com. Eds. Donald Hilvert, Matt Brown TEL 44-20-7611-4139, Steven V. Ley.

572 GBR ISSN 0959-440X
QH506 CODEN: COSBEF
➤ **CURRENT OPINION IN STRUCTURAL BIOLOGY.** Text in English. 1991. 6/yr. EUR 270 in Europe to individuals; JPY 32,800 in Japan to individuals; USD 293 elsewhere to individuals; EUR 1,378 in Europe to institutions; JPY 191,000 in Japan to institutions; USD 1,540 elsewhere to institutions (effective 2006). adv. bibl.; illus. back issues avail. **Document type:** *Academic/Scholarly.* **Description:** Presents review articles, followed by annotated bibliographies of references consulted; includes a "Paper Alert" section, giving brief summaries of relevant papers recently published in other journals.
Related titles: CD-ROM ed.; Online - full text ed.: USD 227 in North America to individuals; USD 90 in North America to students (effective 1999 & 2000) (from EBSCO Publishing, Gale Group, IngentaConnect, O C L C Online Computer Library Center, Inc., ScienceDirect, Swets Information Services).
Indexed: ASCA, ASFA, BBCI, BIOBASE, BIOSIS Prev, CCI, CIN, CTA, ChemAb, ChemTitl, CurCont, ExcerpMed, FS&TA, GenetAb, IABS, ISR, IndMed, Inpharma, MEDLINE, MSB, NSA, NucAcAb, Reac, SCI.
—BLDSC (3500.779000), CASDDS, CISTI, GNLM, IDS, IE, Infotrieve, ingenta. **CCC.**
Published by: Elsevier Ltd., Current Opinion Journals (Subsidiary of: Elsevier Science & Technology), 84 Theobald's Rd., London, WC1X 8RR, United Kingdom. TEL 44-20-7611-4000, FAX 44-20-7611-4001, http://www.elsevier.com/locate/sbi. Eds. Tom L. Blundell, Wayne A. Hendrickson. Circ: 1,800.

572 NLD ISSN 1389-2037
CODEN: CPPSCM
➤ **CURRENT PROTEIN AND PEPTIDE SCIENCE.** Text in English. 2000 (Jun.). 6/yr. EUR 860, USD 860 to institutions (academic), print or online; EUR 1,550, USD 1,550 to corporations print or online; EUR 210, USD 210 combined subscription to individuals print & online; EUR 940, USD 940 combined subscription to institutions (academic), print & online; EUR 1,860, USD 1,860 combined subscription to corporations print & online (effective 2004). adv. **Document type:** *Journal, Academic/Scholarly.* **Description:** Features reviews in protein and peptide science and related areas.
Related titles: Online - full text ed.: (from EBSCO Publishing, Gale Group, IngentaConnect, Swets Information Services).
Indexed: BBCI, BIOBASE, BIOSIS Prev, BioEngAb, ChemAb, ExcerpMed, M&PBA.
—BLDSC (3501.531000), CISTI, IE, Infotrieve, ingenta, Linda Hall. **CCC.**
Published by: Bentham Science Publishers Ltd., PO Box 1673, Hilversum, BR 1200, Netherlands. TEL 31-35-6923800, FAX 31-35-6980150, M.Bentham@inter.nl.net, http://www.bentham.org/cpps. Ed. Ben M Dunn. **Subscr. addr. in the US:** Bentham Science Publishers Ltd., 1400 Pine St, PO Box 640310, San Francisco, CA 94164-0310. FAX 415-775-4503, shidding@worldonline.nl.

572 NLD ISSN 1570-1646
▼ **CURRENT PROTEOMICS**; the journal for current and in-depth reviews on proteomics. Text in English. 2004. q. USD 140 combined subscription to individuals print & online; USD 500 combined subscription to institutions (academic), print & online; USD 970 combined subscription to corporations print & online (effective 2005). bk.rev. **Document type:** *Journal, Academic/Scholarly.* **Description:** Publishes well-timed review articles in this fast-expanding area on topics relevant and significant to the development of proteomics.
Related titles: Online - full content ed.; Online - full text ed.: (from EBSCO Publishing, Gale Group, IngentaConnect, Swets Information Services).
—BLDSC (3501.531300), IE. **CCC.**
Published by: Bentham Science Publishers Ltd., PO Box 1673, Hilversum, BR 1200, Netherlands. TEL 31-35-6923800, FAX 31-35-6980150, M.Bentham@inter.nl.net, http://www.bentham.org/cp/. Ed. Deb N Chakravarti TEL 909-607-0376.

572 USA
CURRENT PROTOCOLS IN NUCLEIC ACID CHEMISTRY. Text in English. base vol. plus q. updates. USD 610 combined subscription to institutions base vol. & updates; USD 355 renewals to institutions (effective 2006). **Document type:** *Academic/Scholarly.*
Related titles: CD-ROM ed.: USD 595 combined subscription to institutions for base vol. & updates; USD 350 renewals to institutions (effective 2006); Online - full text ed.
Published by: John Wiley & Sons, Inc., 111 River St, Hoboken, NJ 07030-5774. TEL 201-748-6000, 800-825-7550, FAX 201-748-5915, protocol@wiley.com, http://www.does.org/masterli/cpnc.html, http://www.wiley.com. **Subscr. addr. outside the Americas:** John Wiley & Sons Ltd., The Atrium, Southern Gate, Chichester, West Sussex PO19 8SQ, United Kingdom. TEL 44-1243-779777, FAX 44-1243-775878; **Subscr. to:** PO Box 5597, Somerset, NJ 08875. TEL 732-650-4630, FAX 732-650-4623.

572 USA
CURRENT PROTOCOLS IN PROTEIN SCIENCE. Text in English. 2 base vols. plus q. updates. USD 710 combined subscription to institutions base vols. & updates; USD 455 renewals to institutions (effective 2006). **Document type:** *Academic/Scholarly.* **Description:** Covers both basic and advanced methods used in protein purification, characterization, and analysis.
Related titles: CD-ROM ed.: USD 695 combined subscription to institutions base vol. & updates; USD 450 renewals to institutions (effective 2006); Online - full text ed.
Published by: John Wiley & Sons, Inc., 111 River St, Hoboken, NJ 07030-5774. TEL 201-748-6000, 800-825-7550, FAX 201-748-5915, http://www.does.org/masterli/cpps.html, http://www.wiley.com. **Subscr. to:** John Wiley & Sons Ltd., The Atrium, Southern Gate, Chichester, West Sussex PO19 8SQ, United Kingdom. TEL 44-1243-779777, FAX 44-1243-775878, cs-journals@wiley.co.uk; PO Box 5597, Somerset, NJ 08875. TEL 732-650-4630, FAX 732-650-4623.

572 USA
CURRENT PROTOCOLS IN TOXICOLOGY. Text in English. base vol. plus q. updates. looseleaf. USD 585 combined subscription to institutions base vol. & updates; USD 325 renewals to institutions (effective 2006). **Document type:** *Academic/Scholarly.* **Description:** Presents step-by-step laboratory procedures for the assessment of toxicity at the level of whole organisms, organs and tissues, cells and biochemical pathways.
Related titles: CD-ROM ed.: USD 570 combined subscription to institutions base vol. & updates; USD 320 renewals to institutions (effective 2006); Online - full content ed.
Published by: John Wiley & Sons, Inc., 111 River St, Hoboken, NJ 07030-5774. TEL 201-748-6000, 800-825-7550, FAX 201-748-5915, kamorgan@ix.netcom.com, protocol@wiley.com, http://www.does.org/masterli/cptx.html, http://www.wiley.com. Ed. Kathy Morgan. **Subscr. to:** PO Box 5597, Somerset, NJ 08875. TEL 732-650-4630, FAX 732-650-4623.

577.1 IND ISSN 0972-4583
CURRENT TOPICS IN BIOCHEMICAL RESEARCH. Text in English. 1999. a.
—BLDSC (3504.868500).
Published by: Research Trends, T.C. 17/250(3), Chadiyara Rd, Poojapura, Trivandrum, Kerala 695 012, India.

572.65 GBR ISSN 1359-6101
QP552.G76 CODEN: CGFRFB
➤ **CYTOKINE & GROWTH FACTOR REVIEWS.** Text in English. 1989. 6/yr. EUR 129 in Europe to individuals; JPY 17,000 in Japan to individuals; USD 142 to individuals except Europe and Japan; EUR 630 in Europe to institutions; JPY 83,600 in Japan to institutions; USD 704 to institutions except Europe and Japan (effective 2006). abstr. back issues avail. **Document type:** *Academic/Scholarly.* **Description:** Features reviews of current research and applications on cytokines, growth factors and related regulatory peptides.
Formerly (until vol.7): Progress in Growth Factor Research (0955-2235)
Related titles: Microfilm ed.: (from PQC); Online - full text ed.: (from EBSCO Publishing, Gale Group, IngentaConnect, ScienceDirect, Swets Information Services).
Indexed: AIDS&CR, BBCI, BIOBASE, BIOSIS Prev, CIN, ChemAb, ChemTitl, CurCont, ExcerpMed, IABS, ISR, ImmunAb, IndMed, MEDLINE, OGFA, RefZh, SCI.
—BLDSC (3506.778500), CASDDS, CISTI, GNLM, IDS, IE, Infotrieve, ingenta, KNAW. **CCC.**
Published by: Pergamon (Subsidiary of: Elsevier Science & Technology), The Boulevard, Langford Ln, East Park, Kidlington, Oxford OX5 1GB, United Kingdom. TEL 44-1865-843000, FAX 44-1865-843010, http://www.elsevier.com/locate/cytogfr. Eds. Dr. J T Vilcek, Dr. M B Sporn. **Subscr. to:** Elsevier BV, PO Box 211, Amsterdam 1000 AE, Netherlands. TEL 31-20-485-3757, FAX 31-20-485-3432, nlinfo-f@elsevier.nl, http://www.elsevier.nl.

572.86 USA ISSN 1044-5498
QH442 CODEN: DCEBE8
➤ **D N A AND CELL BIOLOGY.** Text in English. 1981. m. USD 2,037 domestic to institutions; USD 2,237 foreign to institutions; USD 2,433 combined subscription domestic to institutions print & online eds.; USD 2,631 combined subscription foreign to institutions print & online eds. (effective 2006). adv. back issues avail.; reprint service avail. from PSC. **Document type:** *Journal, Academic/Scholarly.* **Description:** Covers molecular immunology, molecular medicine, gene structure and function, genetic vaccines, cell cycle and apoptosis. Publishes papers relating to all aspects of biochemistry, cell and molecular biology, structural and disease related molecular science.
Former titles: D N A (0198-0238); Recombinant D N A
Related titles: Online - full text ed.: ISSN 1557-7430. USD 1,944 to institutions (effective 2006) (from EBSCO Publishing, Gale Group, O C L C Online Computer Library Center, Inc., Swets Information Services).
Indexed: AEBA, AIDS&CR, ASCA, ASFA, AbAn, AgBio, AnBrAb, BBCI, BCI, BIOBASE, BIOSIS Prev, BiolAb, CBTA, CIN, CPA, ChemAb, ChemTitl, CurCont, DBA, DSA, ESPM, ExcerpMed, FS&TA, GenetAb, HGA, HortAb, IABS, ISR, IndMed, IndVet, Inpharma, M&PBA, MBA, MEDLINE, NemAb, NucAcAb, NutrAb, OGFA, PBA, PE&ON, PN&I, PoultAb, ProtozoAb, RPP, Reac, SCI, SoyAb, TDB, Telegen, VetBull.
—BLDSC (3605.721420), CASDDS, CISTI, GNLM, IDS, IE, Infotrieve, ingenta, Linda Hall. **CCC.**
Published by: Mary Ann Liebert, Inc. Publishers, 140 Huguenot St 3rd Fl, New Rochelle, NY 10801-5215. TEL 914-740-2100, FAX 914-740-2101, 800-654-3237, info@liebertpub.com, http://www.liebertpub.com/dna. Ed. Mark I Greene. Adv. contact Harriet Matysko. B&W page USD 1,150; trim 8.5 x 11. Circ: 1,700 (paid).

➤ **D N A PROBES.** (Deoxyribonucleic Acid) see *BIOLOGY—Abstracting, Bibliographies, Statistics*

572.86 NLD ISSN 1568-7864
QH467 CODEN: DRNEAR
➤ **D N A REPAIR.** Text in Dutch. 1964. 12/yr. EUR 1,380 in Europe to institutions; JPY 182,900 in Japan to institutions; USD 1,543 elsewhere to institutions (effective 2006). back issues avail. **Document type:** *Journal, Academic/Scholarly.* **Description:** Covers comparisons of cell-to-tissues systems, cloned DNA repair genes, and transformation and mutagen testing.
Former titles (until 2001): Mutation Research - D N A Repair (0921-8777); (until 1988): Mutation Research - D N A Repair - Reports (0167-8817); Which superseded in part (in 1983): Mutation Research (0027-5107)
Related titles: Microform ed.: (from PQC); Online - full text ed.: (from EBSCO Publishing, Gale Group, IngentaConnect, ScienceDirect, Swets Information Services); ♦ Series of: Mutation Research. ISSN 0027-5107.
Indexed: ASCA, ASFA, AgBio, AnBrAb, B&BAb, BBCI, BCI, BIOBASE, BIOSIS Prev, BiolAb, ChemAb, CurCont, ExcerpMed, GenetAb, HGA, HortAb, IABS, ISR, IndMed, Inpharma, MBA, NucAcAb, NutrAb, PBA, RA&MP, RASB, Reac, RefZh, SCI, VetBull.
—BLDSC (3605.721700), CISTI, IDS, IE, ingenta, Linda Hall. **CCC.**
Published by: Elsevier BV (Subsidiary of: Elsevier Science & Technology), Radarweg 29, Amsterdam, 1043 NX, Netherlands. TEL 31-20-4853911, FAX 31-20-4852457, nlinfo-f@elsevier.nl, http://www.elsevier.com/locate/dnarepair, http://www.elsevier.nl. Ed. Dr. E C Friedberg.

572.86 GBR ISSN 1340-2838
CODEN: DARSE8
D N A RESEARCH. (Deoxyribonucleic Acid) Text in English. 1994. bi-m. GBP 147, USD 279, EUR 221 to institutions; GBP 155, USD 295, EUR 233 combined subscription to institutions print & online eds. (effective 2006). **Document type:** *Journal, Academic/Scholarly.*
Related titles: Online - full text ed.
Indexed: B&BAb, BBCI, BCI, BIOBASE, ChemAb, CurCont, ExcerpMed, GenetAb, ISR, MEDLINE, SCI.
—BLDSC (3605.723200), CISTI, IE, Infotrieve, ingenta.
Published by: Oxford University Press, Great Clarendon St, Oxford, OX2 6DP, United Kingdom. TEL 44-1865-556767, FAX 44-1865-556646, jnl.orders@oup.co.uk, enquiry@oup.co.uk, http://www.oxfordjournals.org/.

B

572.86   GBR   ISSN 1042-5179
QP624   CODEN: DNSEES
➤ D N A SEQUENCE; journal of DNA mapping, sequencing, and analysis. (Deoxyribonucleic Acid) Text in English. 1990. bi-m. GBP 687, USD 892 combined subscription to institutions print & online eds. (effective 2006). reprint service avail. from PSC. Document type: Journal, Academic/Scholarly. Description: Covers mapping data, full DNA sequences and their analyses, new sequencing procedures, computer methods to analyze sequences, and compilations of DNA and protein motifs.
Related titles: CD-ROM ed.: ISSN 1026-7913. 1995; Microform ed.; Online - full text ed.: ISSN 1029-2365. GBP 653, USD 847 to institutions (effective 2006) (from EBSCO Publishing, Gale Group, IngentaConnect, O C L C Online Computer Library Center, Inc., Swets Information Services).
Indexed: AEA, ASCA, ASFA, AbHyg, AgBio, Agr, AgrForAb, AnBrAb, B&BAb, BCI, BIOBASE, BibAg, BioCN&I, CPA, ChemAb, CurCont, DSA, ESPM, EntAb, ExcerpMed, FCA, FS&TA, ForAb, GenetAb, HelmAb, HerbAb, HortAb, IABS, ISR, IndMed, IndVet, Inpharma, MEDLINE, MaizeAb, NemAb, NucAcAb, NutrAb, PBA, PGegResA, PGrRegA, PHN&I, PN&I, PotatoAb, PoultAb, ProtozoAb, RA&MP, RM&VM, RPP, Reac, RevApplEntom, RiceAb, S&F, SCI, SIA, SeedAb, SoyAb, TDB, TriticAb, VITIS, VetBull, WAE&RSA, WeedAb, ZooRec.
—BLDSC (3605.723500), CISTI, GNLM, IE, Infotrieve, ingenta. CCC.
Published by: Taylor & Francis Ltd (Subsidiary of: Taylor & Francis Group), 4 Park Sq, Milton Park, Abingdon, OX14 4RN, United Kingdom. TEL 44-1235-828600, FAX 44-1235-829000, info@tandf.co.uk, http://www.tandf.co.uk/journals/titles/10425179.asp. Ed. Stephan Beck. Subscr. in N. America to: Taylor & Francis Inc., Customer Services Dept, 325 Chestnut St, 8th Fl, Philadelphia, PA 19106. TEL 215-625-8900, 800-354-1420, FAX 215-625-8914, customerservice@taylorandfrancis.com; Subscr. to: Journals Customer Service, Rankine Rd, Basingstoke, Hants RG24 8PR, United Kingdom. TEL 44-1256-813000, FAX 44-1256-330245, enquiry@tandf.co.uk.

572   NLD   ISSN 0167-4978
CODEN: DLCBDQ
➤ DEVELOPMENTS IN CLINICAL BIOCHEMISTRY. Text in English. 1980. irreg., latest vol.2, 1980. price varies. Document type: Monographic series, Academic/Scholarly.
—CASDDS, CISTI.
Published by: (European Commission BEL), Springer-Verlag Dordrecht (Subsidiary of: Springer Science+Business Media), Van Godewijckstraat 30, Dordrecht, 3311 GX, Netherlands. TEL 31-78-6576050, FAX 31-78-6576474, http://www.springeronline.com.

572.8   NLD   ISSN 0167-9023
CODEN: DMCBDX
➤ DEVELOPMENTS IN MOLECULAR AND CELLULAR BIOCHEMISTRY. Text in English. 1981. irreg., latest vol.43, 2003. price varies. Document type: Monographic series, Academic/Scholarly.
Indexed: BiolAb, ProtozoAb.
—CISTI. CCC.
Published by: Springer-Verlag Dordrecht (Subsidiary of: Springer Science+Business Media), Van Godewijckstraat 30, Dordrecht, 3311 GX, Netherlands. TEL 31-78-6576050, FAX 31-78-6576474, http://www.springeronline.com.

572.014   MEX
DICCIONARIO DE ESPECIALIDADES BIOQUIMICAS. Text in Spanish. 1984. a. MXP 200, USD 100. adv. bk.rev.
Published by: Ediciones P L M S.A. de C.V., San Bernardino 17, Col del Valle, Mexico City, DF 03100, Mexico. TEL 52-5-6871766, FAX 52-5-5365027. Ed. Federico Garcia Ortega. Circ: 6,000.

DOJIN NYUSU/DOJIN NEWS. see CHEMISTRY—Analytical Chemistry

572 571.4   RUS   ISSN 1607-6729
QP501   CODEN: DBBOAL
DOKLADY BIOCHEMISTRY AND BIOPHYSICS. Text in English. 2001. bi-m. EUR 2,488, USD 2,248, GBP 1,558 combined subscription to institutions print & online eds. (effective 2005). Document type: Journal, Academic/Scholarly. Description: Contains English translation of current Russian research from the biochemistry and biophysics sections of the Doklady Akademii Nauk (Proceedings of the Russian Academy of Sciences).
Formed by the merger of (1964-2001): Doklady Biochemistry (0012-4958); (1964-2001): Doklady Biophysics (0012-4974)
Related titles: Online - full text ed.: ISSN 1608-3091 (from EBSCO Publishing, Gale Group, IngentaConnect, Kluwer Online, O C L C Online Computer Library Center, Inc., Ovid Technologies, Inc., Springer LINK, Swets Information Services); ◆ Partial translation of: Rossiiskaya Akademiya Nauk. Doklady. ISSN 0869-5652.
Indexed: AgBio, AgrForAb, AnBrAb, BibLing, CPA, ChemAb, DSA, FCA, ForAb, HortAb, IndVet, Inspec, MaizeAb, OrnHort, PBA, PGegResA, PGrRegA, PHN&I, PotatoAb, PoultAb, ProtozoAb, RA&MP, RM&VM, RPP, S&F, SeedAb, TDB, TriticAb, VetBull, WeedAb.
—BLDSC (0411.099100), CISTI, IE, Infotrieve, ingenta. CCC.

Published by: (Rossiiskaya Akademiya Nauk/Russian Academy of Sciences), M A I K Nauka - Interperiodica, Profsoyuznaya ul 90, Moscow, 117997, Russian Federation. TEL 7-095-3347420, FAX 7-095-3360666, compmg@maik.ru, http://www.maik.ru. Ed. Victor A. Kabanov. R&P Vladimir I Vasil'ev. Subscr. to: Springer-Verlag Dordrecht, Journals Department, PO Box 322, Dordrecht, Netherlands. TEL 31-78-6576392, FAX 31-78-6576474.

▼ DOPING JOURNAL. see PHARMACY AND PHARMACOLOGY

DRUG TARGETING. see PHARMACY AND PHARMACOLOGY— Abstracting, Bibliographies, Statistics

572   GBR   ISSN 0261-4189
QH506   CODEN: EMJODG
➤ THE E M B O JOURNAL. Text in English. 1982. s-m. EUR 276 combined subscription in Europe to individuals print & online eds.; USD 285 combined subscription in the Americas to individuals print & online eds.; GBP 178 combined subscription to individuals in the UK & elsewhere; print & online eds. (effective 2006); Subscr. rates for academic, corporate and government institutions vary. Please contact publisher.. adv. bk.rev. illus. index. back issues avail.; reprints avail. Document type: Journal, Academic/Scholarly. Description: Covers all areas of molecular biology, including immunology, cell biology, molecular genetics, expression, neurobiology, virology, and plant science.
Related titles: Online - full text ed.: ISSN 1460-2075 (from EBSCO Publishing, HighWire Press, IngentaConnect, National Library of Medicine, O C L C Online Computer Library Center, Inc., Swets Information Services).
Indexed: AEBA, AIDS&CR, ASCA, ASFA, AbHyg, AgBio, Agr, AnBrAb, B&AI, BBCI, BCI, BIOBASE, BIOSIS Prev, BibAg, BiolAb, CBTA, CCI, CIN, CPA, CTA, ChemAb, ChemTitl, CurCont, DBA, DSA, ESPM, ExcerpMed, FCA, FS&TA, ForAb, GenetAb, HGA, HortAb, IABS, ISR, ImmunAb, IndMed, IndVet, Inpharma, M&PBA, MBA, MEDLINE, MaizeAb, NSA, NSCI, NemAb, NucAcAb, NutrAb, OGFA, PBA, PGegResA, PGrRegA, PN&I, PotatoAb, PoultAb, ProtozoAb, RA&MP, RM&VM, RPP, Reac, RefZh, RevApplEntom, RiceAb, S&F, SCI, SIA, SeedAb, SoyAb, TDB, Telegen, TriticAb, VetBull, WeedAb, ZooRec.
—BLDSC (3733.085000), CASDDS, CISTI, GNLM, IDS, IE, Infotrieve, ingenta, Linda Hall. CCC.
Published by: (European Molecular Biology Organization), Nature Publishing Group (Subsidiary of: Macmillan Publishers Ltd.), The MacMillan Building, 4 Crinan St, London, N1 9XW, United Kingdom. TEL 44-20-78334000, FAX 44-20-78433601, subscriptions@nature.com, NatureReviews@nature.com, http://www.embojournal.org, http://www.nature.com. Ed. Iain Mattaj. adv.: B&W page GBP 565, B&W page USD 1,015, color page GBP 855, color page USD 1,537; 178 x 255. Circ: 4,200.

572.8   EGY   ISSN 1012-554X
CODEN: EGJBE4
THE EGYPTIAN JOURNAL OF BIOCHEMISTRY/MAGALLAT AL-GAMIEYAT AL-MISSRIYYAT LIL-KIMIYAA AL-HAYAWEYYAT. Cover title: E J B. Text in English. 1983.
Formerly (until Feb. 2002): The Egyptian Journal of Biochemistry & Molecular Biology (1687-1502)
—BLDSC (3664.287100).
Published by: Egyptian Biochemical Society, Biochemistry Department, Faculty of Medicine, Cairo University, Cairo, Egypt. http://derp.sti.sci.eg/data/0225.htm. Ed. Mohamed Farid El-Asmar TEL 202-6859928.

ELECTRONIC JOURNAL OF BIOTECHNOLOGY. see BIOLOGY—Biotechnology

572   CHE
➤ EMERGING BIOCHEMICAL AND BIOPHYSICAL TECHNIQUES. Text in English. 1994. irreg. CHF 188 (effective 2000). Document type: Monographic series, Academic/Scholarly.
Published by: Birkhaeuser Verlag AG (Subsidiary of: Springer Science+Business Media), Viaduktstr 42, Postfach 133, Basel, 4051, Switzerland. TEL 41-61-2050707, FAX 41-61-2050792, orders@birkhauser.ch, birkhauser@springer.de, http://www.birkhauser.ch. Eds. T M Laue, T M Schuster. Dist. by: Springer GmbH Auslieferungsgesellschaft, Haberstr 7, Heidelberg 69126, Germany. TEL 49-6221-3454324, FAX 49-6221-345229.

572.43   DEU   ISSN 0013-7472
ENERGY AND CHARACTER✴; journal of bio-energetic research. Text in German. 1970. 3/yr. adv. bk.rev. index.
Related titles: Microfiche ed.: 1970.
Indexed: AMED, PsycholAb, e-psyche.
—BLDSC (3747.500000), IE, ingenta.
Published by: Deutsches Institut fuer Biosynthese, Hakenweg 17, Jaderberg, 26349, Germany. Ed. Andreas Wehowsky. Circ: 1,000.

ENTREZ DOCUMENT RETRIEVAL SYSTEM. see BIOLOGY—Abstracting, Bibliographies, Statistics

ENVIRONMENTAL AND MOLECULAR MUTAGENESIS. SUPPLEMENT. see BIOLOGY—Genetics

ENVIRONMENTAL TOXICOLOGY AND CHEMISTRY. see ENVIRONMENTAL STUDIES—Toxicology And Environmental Safety

572.7   USA   ISSN 0094-8500
TP248.E5   CODEN: ENENDT
ENZYME ENGINEERING. Text in English. irreg., latest vol.13, 1996. price varies. Document type: Academic/Scholarly.
Indexed: CBTA.
—CASDDS, CISTI. CCC.
Published by: New York Academy of Sciences, 2 E 63rd St, New York, NY 10021. TEL 212-838-0230, 800-843-6927, FAX 212-888-2894, publications@nyas.org, http://www.nyas.org.

572   DEU   ISSN 0947-6075
CODEN: ESRWEL
ERNST SCHERING RESEARCH FOUNDATION WORKSHOP. Text in German. 199?. irreg., latest vol.49, 2004. price varies. Document type: Monographic series, Academic/Scholarly. Description: Aims to support young scientists and to bridge the distance between academic and applied research.
Formerly (until 1994): Schering Foundation Workshop (0945-246X)
Related titles: Supplement(s): Ernst Schering Research Foundation Workshop. Supplement. ISSN 1431-7133. 1994.
Indexed: BIOSIS Prev, CIN, ChemAb, ChemTitl, MEDLINE.
—BLDSC (3810.747600), CASDDS, CISTI.
Published by: (Schering Research Foundation), Springer-Verlag (Subsidiary of: Springer Science+Business Media), Haber Str 7, Heidelberg, 69126, Germany. TEL 49-30-82787-448, subscriptions@springer.de, http://www.springer-sbm.de. Eds. K Chwalisz, R Garfield.

572   GBR   ISSN 0071-1365
QH345   CODEN: ESBIAV
➤ ESSAYS IN BIOCHEMISTRY. Text in English. 1965. a., latest 2004, June. GBP 19 (effective 2004). reprint service avail. from ISI. Document type: Academic/Scholarly.
Indexed: ASCA, AnBrAb, BBCI, BIOSIS Prev, BiolAb, CIN, ChemAb, ChemTitl, ISR, IndMed, MEDLINE, NutrAb, SCI.
—BLDSC (3811.676000), CASDDS, CISTI, GNLM, IE, Infotrieve, ingenta, Linda Hall. CCC.
Published by: (Biochemical Society), Portland Press Ltd. (Subsidiary of: Biochemical Society), 3rd Fl, Eagle House, 16 Procter St, London, WC1V 6NX, United Kingdom. TEL 44-20-72804110, FAX 44-20-72804169, sales@portland-services.com, editorial@portlandpress.com, http://www.portlandpress.com. Ed. Tom J Cotter. R&P Adam Marshall. Subscr. to: Commerce Way, Colchester CO2 8HP, United Kingdom. TEL 44-1206-796351, FAX 44-1206-799331.

➤ EUROPEAN BIOPHARMACEUTICAL REVIEW. see PHARMACY AND PHARMACOLOGY

572   CHE   ISSN 1473-2262
CODEN: ECMUBB
➤ EUROPEAN CELLS & MATERIALS. Text in English. 2001. s-a. free (effective 2005). Document type: Journal, Academic/Scholarly.
Media: Online - full content.
Indexed: BiolAb, ExcerpMed.
Published by: Swiss Society for Biomaterials, AO Research Institute, Clavadelstr, Davos, 7270, Switzerland. TEL 41-81-4142397, info@ecmjournal.org, info@ssb.biomaterials.ch, http://www.ecmjournal.org, http://ssb.biomaterials.ch. Ed. R Geoff Richards.

571.95 572.8   GBR
➤ EUROPEAN JOURNAL OF GENETIC AND MOLECULAR TOXICOLOGY. Text in English. 1997. irreg. Document type: Journal, Academic/Scholarly.
Related titles: Online - full text ed.
Published by: University of Wales Swansea, School of Biological Sciences, Singleton Park, Swansea, SA2 8PP, United Kingdom. http://www.swan.ac.uk/cget/ejgt1.htm. Ed. James M Parry.

572   ITA   ISSN 1121-760X
CODEN: EJHIE2
➤ EUROPEAN JOURNAL OF HISTOCHEMISTRY. Cover title: E J H. Text in English. 1954. q. EUR 160 in Europe; USD 200 elsewhere (effective 2005). adv. bk.rev. Document type: Journal, Academic/Scholarly.
Former titles (until 1991): European Journal of Basic and Applied Histochemistry (1121-4201); (until 1990): Basic and Applied Histochemistry (0391-7258); (until 1979): Rivista di Istochimica Normale e Patologica (0485-2400)
Indexed: ASCA, AgBio, AnBrAb, BBCI, BIOBASE, BIOSIS Prev, BiolAb, CIN, CPA, ChemAb, ChemTitl, CurCont, DSA, ExcerpMed, HortAb, IABS, ISR, IndMed, IndVet, Inpharma, MEDLINE, NSCI, PBA, Reac, RefZh, S&F, SCI, SIA, VetBull, ZooRec.
—BLDSC (3829.729900), CASDDS, CISTI, GNLM, IDS, IE, Infotrieve, ingenta, KNAW.
Published by: (Societa Italiana di Istochimica), Luigi Ponzio e Figlio Editori, Viale Monte Grappa 2/A, Pavia, PV 27100, Italy. TEL 39-0382-576600, FAX 39-0382-574200, ejh@unipv.it, http://www.ejh.it. Ed. Maria G Manfredi Romanini. Circ: 500.

615 FRA ISSN 0223-5234
CODEN: EJMCA5

➤ **EUROPEAN JOURNAL OF MEDICINAL CHEMISTRY.** Text and summaries in English. 1965. 12/yr. EUR 796 in Europe to institutions; JPY 105,600 in Japan to institutions; USD 890 to institutions except Europe and Japan (effective 2006). adv. bk.rev. bibl.; charts. index. back issues avail. **Document type:** *Journal, Academic/Scholarly.* **Description:** Publishes original papers, laboratory notes, short or preliminary communications, and descriptions of new products involving all aspects of medicinal chemistry.
Formerly (until 1973): Chimica Therapeutica (0009-4374)
Related titles: Microform ed.: (from PQC); Online - full text ed.: (from EBSCO Publishing, Gale Group, IngentaConnect, ScienceDirect, Swets Information Services).
Indexed: ASCA, AbHyg, BBCI, BIOSIS Prev, BiolAb, CCI, CIN, ChemAb, ChemInfo, ChemTitl, CurCR, CurCont, DBA, ExcerpMed, HelmAb, IPA, ISR, IndChem, IndMed, IndVet, Inpharma, MEDLINE, NSCI, PE&ON, ProtozoAb, RA&MP, RCI, RM&VM, Reac, RefZh, SCI.
—BLDSC (3829.731500), CASDDS, CISTI, GNLM, IDS, IE, Infotrieve, ingenta, KNAW, Linda Hall. **CCC.**
Published by: (Societe Francaise de Chimie Therapeutique), Elsevier France, Editions Scientifiques et Medicales (Subsidiary of: Elsevier Science & Technology), 23 Rue Linois, Paris, 75724, France. TEL 33-1-71724600, FAX 33-1-71724650, academic@elsevier.fr, http://www.elsevier.com/locate/ejmech, http://www.elsevier.fr. Ed. O Lafont. Circ: 3,000. **Subscr. to:** Elsevier BV, PO Box 211, Amsterdam 1000 AE, Netherlands. TEL 31-20-485-3757, FAX 31-20-485-3432, http://www.elsevier.nl. **Co-sponsor:** European Federation of Medicinal Chemistry.

➤ **EUROPEAN JOURNAL OF NEUROSCIENCE.** see *MEDICAL SCIENCES—Psychiatry And Neurology*

➤ **EUROPEAN JOURNAL OF NEUROSCIENCE. SUPPLEMENT.** see *MEDICAL SCIENCES—Psychiatry And Neurology*

➤ **EXCERPTA MEDICA. SECTION 29: CLINICAL AND EXPERIMENTAL BIOCHEMISTRY.** see *BIOLOGY—Abstracting, Bibliographies, Statistics*

572 KOR ISSN 1226-3613
CODEN: KJBID3

➤ **EXPERIMENTAL AND MOLECULAR MEDICINE.** Text and summaries in English. 1964. q. KRW 30,000 domestic to individuals; USD 40 foreign to individuals; KRW 100,000 domestic to institutions; USD 130 foreign to institutions; KRW 15,000 domestic to students; USD 20 foreign to students (effective 2005). adv. bk.rev. **Document type:** *Academic/Scholarly.* **Description:** Publishes research papers and mini-reviews in the fields of basic and applied molecular biology, and experimental biochemistry in medicine.
Formerly (until 1996): Korean Journal of Biochemistry (0378-8512)
Related titles: Online - full text ed.: free (effective 2005).
Indexed: ASCA, BBCI, BIOSIS Prev, BiolAb, CIN, ChemAb, ChemTitl, ExcerpMed, ISR, IndMed, MEDLINE, SCI.
—BLDSC (3838.690000), CASDDS, CISTI, GNLM, IDS, IE, Infotrieve, ingenta.
Published by: Korean Society of Medical Biochemistry and Molecular Biology, #812 KSTC, 635-4 Yoksam-dong Kangnam-gu, Seoul, 135-703, Korea, S. TEL 82-2-565-1621, FAX 82-2-565-1622, ksmbmb@ksmbmb.or.kr, http://www.e-emm.org/, http://www.ksmbmb.or.kr. Ed., R&P Soo Il Chung. Adv. contact So Young Kang. Circ: 1,500. **Subscr. to:** #812 KOFST, 635-4 Yoksam-dong Kangnam-gu, Seoul 135-703, Korea, S. **Co-sponsor:** Korean Federation of Science and Technology Societies.

➤ **EXPERIMENTAL BIOLOGY AND MEDICINE (TOTOWA).** see *MEDICAL SCIENCES—Experimental Medicine, Laboratory Technique*

➤ **EXPERT OPINION ON BIOLOGICAL THERAPY**; the complete package for informed commentary and analysis in biopharmaceutical R&D. see *MEDICAL SCIENCES*

572.6 GBR ISSN 1478-9450

▼ **EXPERT REVIEW OF PROTEOMICS.** Text in English. 2004 (Jun). bi-m. ((four issues in 2004)). USD 365 to institutions (academic) in US, Canada & Korea; JPY 47,250 in Japan to institutions (academic); EUR 315 elsewhere to institutions (academic); USD 870 to corporations in US, Canada & Korea; JPY 113,100 in Japan to corporations; EUR 750 elsewhere to corporations; USD 470 combined subscription to institutions (academic) in US, Canada & Korea; print & online; JPY 61,100 combined subscription in Japan to institutions (academic) print & online; EUR 405 combined subscription elsewhere to institutions (academic) print & online; USD 1,125 combined subscription to corporations in US, Canada & Korea; print & online; JPY 146,400 combined subscription in Japan to corporations print & online; EUR 970 combined subscription elsewhere to corporations print & online (effective 2004). adv. **Document type:** *Journal, Academic/Scholarly.* **Description:** Seeks to apply technologies, methods and discoveries from the field of proteomics to advance scientific understanding of the many varied roles protein expression plays in human health and disease.
Related titles: Online - full content ed.; Online - full text ed.: (from EBSCO Publishing).
Indexed: ExcerpMed.
—BLDSC (3842.002997). **CCC.**
Published by: Future Drugs Ltd. (Subsidiary of: Ashley Publications Ltd.), 3rd Fl, Unitec House, 2 Albert Pl, Finchley Central, London, N3 1QB, United Kingdom. TEL 44-20-83492033, FAX 44-20-83432313, info@future-drugs.com, http://www.future-drugs.com/publication.asp?publicationid=9. Ed. Simon Teal. Adv. contact John Buse. **Subscr. in Japan to:** Technomics, Inc., c/o Ken Otsuka, Nihonbashi TM Building, 1-8-11 Nihonbashi Horidome-cho, Chuo-ku, Tokyo 103, Japan. TEL 81-03-36662952, FAX 81-03-36662730, ken.otsuka@technomics.co.jp; **Subscr. in Korea to:** Pharma Koreana Ltd., c/o Yoon-Chong Kim, SL Kangnam, PO Box 99, Seoul 135-600, Korea, S.. TEL 82-02-5549592, FAX 82-02-5571290.

EXTREMOPHILES; life under extreme conditions. see *BIOLOGY—Biotechnology*

572 GBR ISSN 1742-464X
QP501 CODEN: EJBCAI

➤ **THE F E B S JOURNAL.** (Federation of European Biochemical Societies) Text in English. 1906. fortn. GBP 2,041 combined subscription in Europe to institutions print & online eds.; USD 3,727 combined subscription in the Americas to institutions & Caribbean (print & online eds.); GBP 2,245 combined subscription elsewhere to institutions print & online eds. (effective 2006). adv. bibl.; charts; illus. index. back issues avail.; reprint service avail. from ISI. **Document type:** *Academic/Scholarly.* **Description:** Covers the entire basic biomedical sciences community, including molecular genetics, enzymology, physical and inorganic chemistry, metabolic regulation, molecular neurobiology, and developmental biochemistry and immunology.
Former titles (until 2004): European Journal of Biochemistry (0014-2956); (until 1967): Biochemische Zeitschrift (0366-0753)
Related titles: Microform ed.: (from PQC); Online - full text ed.: ISSN 1432-1033. GBP 1,796 in Europe to institutions; USD 3,278 in the Americas to institutions & Caribbean; GBP 1,975 elsewhere to institutions (effective 2005) (from Blackwell Synergy, EBSCO Publishing, Gale Group, HighWire Press, IngentaConnect, O C L C Online Computer Library Center, Inc., Ovid Technologies, Inc., Swets Information Services).
Indexed: ASCA, ASFA, AbHyg, AgBio, Agr, AgrForAb, AnBrAb, ApicAb, B&AI, B&BAb, BBCI, BIOBASE, BIOSIS Prev, BibAg, BioCN&I, BiolAb, CCI, CIN, CPA, CRFR, ChemAb, ChemTitl, CurCont, DBA, DSA, DentInd, ESPM, EngInd, ExcerpMed, FCA, FPA, FS&TA, ForAb, GenetAb, HGA, HelmAb, HerbAb, HortAb, IABS, ISR, IndMed, IndVet, Inpharma, MBA, MEDLINE, MSB, MaizeAb, NPU, NSCI, NemAb, NucAcAb, NutrAb, OrnHort, PBA, PE&ON, PGegResA, PGrRegA, PHN&I, PN&I, PotatoAb, PoultAb, ProtozoAb, RA&MP, RM&VM, RPP, Reac, RefZh, RevApplEntom, RiceAb, S&F, SCI, SIA, SeedAb, SoyAb, TDB, TriticAb, VITIS, VetBull, WeedAb, WildRev, ZooRec.
—BLDSC (3901.578500), CASDDS, CINDOC, CISTI, Ei, GNLM, IDS, IE, Infotrieve, ingenta, KNAW, Linda Hall. **CCC.**
Published by: (Federation of European Biochemical Societies DNK), Blackwell Publishing Ltd., 9600 Garsington Rd, Oxford, OX4 2ZG, United Kingdom. TEL 44-1865-776868, FAX 44-1865-714591, customerservices@oxon.blackwellpublishing.com, http://www.blackwellpublishing.com/journals/EJB. Ed. Richard Perham. Pub. Amanda McLean Inglis. R&P Sophie Savage. Adv. contact Jenny Applin. Circ: 1,950.

572 NLD ISSN 0014-5793
QP501 CODEN: FEBLAL

➤ **F E B S LETTERS.** Text in English, French, German; Summaries in English. 1968. 30/yr. EUR 621 in Europe to individuals; JPY 81,100 in Japan to individuals; USD 695 elsewhere to individuals; EUR 4,331 in Europe to institutions; JPY 618,400 in Japan to institutions; USD 4,846 elsewhere to institutions (effective 2006). adv. bk.rev. charts; illus.; stat. cum.index. reprint service avail. from ISI. **Document type:** *Journal, Academic/Scholarly.* **Description:** Publishes short reports of immediate importance to investigators in biochemistry, biophysics and molecular biology.
Related titles: Microform ed.: (from PQC); Online - full text ed.: (from EBSCO Publishing, Gale Group, IngentaConnect, ScienceDirect, Swets Information Services).
Indexed: AIDS Ab, ASCA, ASFA, AbHyg, AgBio, AgrForAb, AnBrAb, ApicAb, BBCI, BIOBASE, BIOSIS Prev, BPRC&P, BioCN&I, BiolAb, CCI, CIN, CPA, CTA, ChemAb, ChemTitl, CurCont, DBA, DSA, DentInd, ESPM, EnvAb, ExcerpMed, FCA, FPA, FS&TA, ForAb, GenetAb, HGA, HelmAb, HerbAb, HortAb, IABS, ISR, IndMed, IndVet, Inpharma, MBA, MEDLINE, MSB, MaizeAb, NSCI, NemAb, NucAcAb, NutrAb, OrnHort, PBA, PE&ON, PGegResA, PGrRegA, PHN&I, PN&I, PotatoAb, PoultAb, ProtozoAb, RA&MP, RCI, RM&VM, RPP, Reac, RefZh, RevApplEntom, RiceAb, S&F, S&MA, SCI, SFA, SIA, SeedAb, SoyAb, TDB, THA, TOSA, Telegen, TriticAb, VITIS, VetBull, WeedAb.
—BLDSC (3901.600000), CASDDS, CISTI, GNLM, IDS, IE, Infotrieve, ingenta, Linda Hall. **CCC.**
Published by: (Federation of European Biochemical Societies DNK), Elsevier BV (Subsidiary of: Elsevier Science & Technology), Radarweg 29, Amsterdam, 1043 NX, Netherlands. TEL 31-20-4853911, FAX 31-20-4852457, fw-febs-letters@uni-hd.de, nlinfo-f@elsevier.nl, http://www.elsevier.com/locate/febslet, http://www.elsevier.nl. Circ: (controlled).

572 662 663.1 GBR ISSN 1478-5765

F.O. LICHT'S WORLD ETHANOL & BIOFUELS REPORT. Text in English. 2002 (Sept.). 24/yr. GBP 817 in Europe; GBP 873 elsewhere (effective 2005). stat. **Document type:** *Trade.* **Description:** Contains news, background analysis and statistics on fuel ethanol, biodiesel, industrial and beverage alcohol markets worldwide. Also includes fermentation products: MSG, lysine, citric acid, yeast.
Published by: Agra Europe (London) Ltd. (Subsidiary of: T & F Informa plc), 80 Calverley Rd, Tunbridge Wells, Kent TN1 2UN, United Kingdom. TEL 44-1892-533813, FAX 44-1892-544895, marketing@agra-net.com, http://www.agra-net.com. **US subscr. addr.:** PO Box 297044, Ft. Worth, TX 76129.

FIZIOLOGIYA I BIOKHIMIYA KUL'TURNYKH RASTENII/ PHYSIOLOGY AND BIOCHEMISTRY OF CULTIVATED PLANTS; nauchno-teoreticheskii zhurnal. see *BIOLOGY—Physiology*

572 GRC ISSN 0015-5489
CODEN: FBBGAJ

FOLIA BIOCHIMICA ET BIOLOGICA GRAECA. Text in English, French, German, Greek. 1964. irreg. (3-4/yr.). per issue exchange basis.
Indexed: BiolAb, ChemAb, ExcerpMed.
—CASDDS, CISTI.
Published by: (Hellenic Society of Marine Molecular Biology), Institute of Marine Molecular Biology, 2 Lampsakou St, Athens, 611, Greece. Ed. A Christomanos.

579 CZE ISSN 0015-5632
CODEN: FOMIAZ

➤ **FOLIA MICROBIOLOGICA.** Text and summaries in English. 1956. bi-m. EUR 325 in Europe; USD 335 elsewhere (effective 2005). adv. bk.rev. abstr.; charts; illus.; mkt. index. **Document type:** *Journal, Academic/Scholarly.* **Description:** A forum for microbiologists and immunologists all over the world. Includes papers and reports from meetings of international nomenclature committees in microbiology and biochemistry.
Formerly (until 1958): Ceskoslovenska Mikrobiologie
Indexed: AEA, ASCA, ASFA, AbHyg, AgBio, AgrForAb, AnBrAb, BCI, BIOSIS Prev, BioCN&I, BiolAb, CBTA, CIN, CPA, ChemAb, ChemTitl, CurCont, DBA, DSA, ESPM, ExcerpMed, FCA, FPA, FS&TA, ForAb, HelmAb, HerbAb, HortAb, I&DA, ISR, IndMed, IndVet, Inpharma, MBA, MEDLINE, MaizeAb, NutrAb, OrnHort, PBA, PE&ON, PGrRegA, PHN&I, PN&I, PotatoAb, PoultAb, ProtozoAb, RA&MP, RM&VM, RPP, Reac, RevApplEntom, RiceAb, S&F, SCI, SIA, SeedAb, SoyAb, TDB, TriticAb, VITIS, VetBull, VirolAbstr, WeedAb.
—BLDSC (3971.500000), CASDDS, CISTI, GNLM, IDS, IE, Infotrieve, ingenta, Linda Hall. **CCC.**
Published by: Akademie Ved Ceske Republiky, Mikrobiologicky Ustav/Czech Academy of Sciences, Institute of Microbiology, Videnska 1083, Prague 4, 142 20, Czech Republic. TEL 420-2-41726994, FAX 420-2-41062622, folia@biomed.cas.cz, http://www.biomed.cas.cz/mbu/folia/index.html. Ed., R&P J Mateju. Circ: 1,200. **Subscr. to:** Myris Trade, V Stihlach 1311, PO Box 2, Prague 4 14201, Czech Republic. TEL 420-2-34035200, FAX 420-2-34035207, myris@myris.cz, http://www.myris.cz. **Co-sponsor:** Ceskoslovenska Spolecnost Mikrobiologicka.

➤ **FOUNDATIONS OF PHYSICS**; an international journal devoted to the conceptual and fundamental theories of modern physics, biophysics, and cosmology. see *PHYSICS*

572 GBR ISSN 1071-5762
CODEN: FRARER

➤ **FREE RADICAL RESEARCH.** Text in English. m. GBP 1,860, USD 2,599 combined subscription to institutions print & online eds. (effective 2006). back issues avail.; reprint service avail. from PSC. **Document type:** *Journal, Academic/Scholarly.* **Description:** Publishes articles on the chemistry of free radicals, the production of free radicals by xenobiotics and biological systems, free radical damage to cells and tissues, and defence mechanisms against free radical damage.
Formerly: Free Radical Research Communications (8755-0199)
Related titles: CD-ROM ed.; Microform ed.; Online - full text ed.: ISSN 1029-2470. GBP 1,767, USD 2,469 to institutions (effective 2006) (from EBSCO Publishing, Gale Group, IngentaConnect, O C L C Online Computer Library Center, Inc., Swets Information Services).
Indexed: ASCA, AbHyg, AgBio, AgrForAb, AnBrAb, BBCI, BIOBASE, BiolAb, CCI, CPA, ChemAb, CurCont, DSA, ExcerpMed, FCA, FS&TA, ForAb, HortAb, IABS, ISR, IndMed, IndVet, Inpharma, MEDLINE, MSB, MaizeAb, NemAb, NutrAb, OrnHort, PBA, PE&ON, PGegResA, PGrRegA, PHN&I, PN&I, PotatoAb, ProtozoAb, RA&MP, RM&VM, RPP, RRTA, Reac, RiceAb, S&F, SCI, SIA, SeedAb, SoyAb, TDB, TriticAb, VITIS, VetBull, WeedAb.
—BLDSC (4033.326495), CISTI, GNLM, IE, Infotrieve, ingenta. **CCC.**
Published by: Taylor & Francis Ltd (Subsidiary of: Taylor & Francis Group), 4 Park Sq, Milton Park, Abingdon, OX14 4RN, United Kingdom. TEL 44-1235-828600, FAX 44-1235-829000, info@tandf.co.uk, http://www.tandf.co.uk/journals/titles/10715762.asp. Eds. Barry Halliwell, Helmut Sies TEL 49-211-811270. **Subscr. in N. America to:** Taylor & Francis

Inc., Customer Services Dept, 325 Chestnut St, 8th Fl, Philadelphia, PA 19106. TEL 215-625-8900, 800-354-1420, FAX 215-625-8914, customerservice@taylorandfrancis.com; **Subscr. to:** Journals Customer Service, Rankine Rd, Basingstoke, Hants RG24 8PR, United Kingdom. TEL 44-1256-813000, FAX 44-1256-330245, enquiry@tandf.co.uk.

572 GBR ISSN 1353-6516
➤ **FRONTIERS IN METABOLISM.** Text in English. 1996. irreg. price varies. **Document type:** *Monographic series, Academic/Scholarly.*
—BLDSC (4042.037500).
Published by: Portland Press Ltd. (Subsidiary of: Biochemical Society), 3rd Fl, Eagle House, 16 Procter St, London, WC1V 6NX, United Kingdom. TEL 44-20-72804110, FAX 44-20-72804169, sales@portland-services.com, http://www.portlandpress.com, http://www.portlandpress.com/books/. Ed. K Snell. R&P Adam Marshall. **Subscr. to:** Commerce Way, Colchester CO2 8HP, United Kingdom. TEL 44-1206-796351, FAX 44-1206-799331.

572.8 GBR
FRONTIERS IN MOLECULAR BIOLOGY. Text in English. irreg., latest 2003. price varies. **Document type:** *Monographic series.*
Indexed: BIOSIS Prev.
Published by: Oxford University Press, Great Clarendon St, Oxford, OX2 6DP, United Kingdom. TEL 44-1865-556767, FAX 44-1865-556646, enquiry@oup.co.uk, http://www.oup.co.uk/academic/science/bioscience/biochem/fms.

▼ **FRONTIERS IN NATURAL PRODUCT CHEMISTRY.** see *CHEMISTRY*

572 USA
➤ **G W U M C. DEPARTMENT OF BIOCHEMISTRY AND MOLECULAR BIOLOGY. ANNUAL SPRING SYMPOSIA SERIES.** Text in English. 1982. irreg., latest 1997. price varies. **Document type:** *Proceedings, Academic/Scholarly.*
Formerly: G W U M C. Department of Biochemistry. Annual Spring Symposia Series
—BLDSC (1531.702000).
Published by: (George Washington University, Medical Center), Springer-Verlag New York, Inc. (Subsidiary of: Springer Science+Business Media), 233 Spring St, New York, NY 10013. TEL 212-460-1500, FAX 212-460-1575, service@springer-ny.com, http://www.springer-ny.com.

572.86 USA ISSN 1080-742X
GENBANK. Text in English. 1992. bi-m. USD 192; USD 240 foreign (effective 1999). **Document type:** *Academic/Scholarly.* **Description:** Provides DNA sequence data in the traditional GenBank flat file format, including annotation and conceptual translations.
Formerly (until 1993): N C B I - GenBank, Genetic Sequence Databank (Flat File) (1080-7411)
Media: Online - full text.
Published by: U.S. National Library of Medicine, U.S. National Center for Biotechnology Information, Bldg 38A, Rm 8N 803, 8600 Rockville Pike, Bethesda, MD 20894. TEL 301-435-5946, FAX 301-480-2233, info@ncbi.nlm.nih.gov, http://www.ncbi.nlm.nih.gov.

GENE EXPRESSION; international journal of molecular and cellular science. see *BIOLOGY—Genetics*

572.7 GBR
CODEN: ISBLEK
GENE FAMILIES AND ISOZYMES BULLETIN. Text in English. 1967. a. adv. bk.rev. **Document type:** *Bulletin.*
Supersedes (in 1998): Isozyme (0197-887X)
Indexed: SFA, WildRev, ZooRec.
—BLDSC (4096.402460), CISTI, IE, ingenta.
Address: c/o W.R. Chegwidden Ed, Hallam University, Sheffield, City Campus, Pond St, Sheffield, S Yorks S1 1WB, United Kingdom. TEL 44-114-253-3042, FAX 44-114-253-2020, w.r.chegwidden@shu.ac.uk. Circ: 150 (paid).

GENOME RESEARCH. see *BIOLOGY—Genetics*

GENOMICS. see *BIOLOGY—Genetics*

572.86 GBR ISSN 1469-3232
GENOMIKA. Text in English. 1999 (Dec.). 22/yr. GBP 325 in Europe; USD 585 in US & Canada; JPY 80,600 in Japan; GBP 360 rest of world (effective 2001). 8 p./no. 3 cols./p.; back issues avail.; reprints avail. **Document type:** *Newsletter.* **Description:** Provides the latest market and business information on the fast-expanding field of DNA, RNA and protein analysis.
Related titles: E-mail ed.; Online - full text ed.: (from Data-Star, The Dialog Corporation).
Published by: P J B Publications Ltd. (Subsidiary of: T & F Informa plc), 5th Fl, Telephone House, 69-77 Paul Street, London, EC2A 4LQ, United Kingdom. TEL 44-20-70176979, FAX 44-20-70176969, genomika@pjbpubs.com, info@pjbpubs.com, http://www.genomika.com/, http://www.pjbpubs.com. Ed. Philip Greenfield. Pub. Dr. Philip Brown. R&P Annette Watts TEL 44-20-83328961. **Subscr. addr. in N America:** Pharmabooks Ltd., 270 Madison Ave., # 4, New York, NY 10016-0601.

GEOMICROBIOLOGY JOURNAL; an international journal of geomicrobiology and microbial biogeochemistry. see *BIOLOGY—Microbiology*

572.566 USA ISSN 0959-6658
QP702.G577 CODEN: GLYCE3
➤ **GLYCOBIOLOGY.** Text in English. 1991. m. GBP 649, USD 1,025, EUR 974 to institutions; GBP 683, USD 1,079, EUR 1,025 combined subscription to institutions print & online eds. (effective 2006). adv. bk.rev. back issues avail.; reprint service avail. from PSC. **Document type:** *Journal, Academic/Scholarly.* **Description:** Provides a forum for the publication of original research papers on any aspect of the structure and functions of glycobiology or any aspect of proteins that specifically interact with saccharides.
Related titles: Online - full text ed.: ISSN 1460-2423. 1998. GBP 615, USD 972, EUR 923 to institutions (effective 2006) (from EBSCO Publishing, Gale Group, HighWire Press, IngentaConnect, O C L C Online Computer Library Center, Inc., Ovid Technologies, Inc., Oxford University Press Online Journals, ProQuest Information & Learning, Swets Information Services).
Indexed: ASCA, AbHyg, AgBio, Agr, AgrForAb, AnBrAb, B&BAb, BBCI, BIOBASE, BIOSIS Prev, BibAg, BiolAb, CIN, CPA, ChemAb, ChemTitl, CurCont, DSA, ExcerpMed, FCA, HelmAb, HerbAb, HortAb, IABS, ISR, IndMed, IndVet, Inpharma, M&PBA, MEDLINE, MSB, MaizeAb, NemAb, NutrAb, OrnHort, PBA, PGegResA, PN&I, PotatoAb, ProtozoAb, RM&VM, Reac, RevApplEntom, S&F, SCI, SIA, SoyAb, TDB, VetBull, WeedAb.
—BLDSC (4196.303000), CASDDS, CISTI, GNLM, IDS, IE, Infotrieve, ingenta, KNAW, Linda Hall. **CCC.**
Published by: Oxford University Press (Subsidiary of: Oxford University Press), 2001 Evans Rd, Cary, NC 27513. TEL 919-677-0977, 800-852-7323, FAX 919-677-1714, jnlorders@oup-usa.org, http://glycob.oxfordjournals.org/, http://www.us.oup.com. Ed. Ronald L. Schnaar. Pub. Janet Fox. R&P Fiona Willis. adv.: B&W page GBP 380, B&W page USD 685; trim 203 x 279. Circ: 1,200.

➤ **GLYCOBIOLOGY RESEARCH.** see *BIOLOGY—Abstracting, Bibliographies, Statistics*

572 USA ISSN 0282-0080
QP752.G56 CODEN: GLJOEW
➤ **GLYCOCONJUGATE JOURNAL.** Text in English. 1984. 9/yr. EUR 1,268, USD 1,295, GBP 795 combined subscription to institutions print & online eds. (effective 2005). adv. back issues avail.; reprint service avail. from PSC. **Document type:** *Journal, Academic/Scholarly.* **Description:** Publishes articles and reviews on all areas concerned with the composition, degradation, function, interactions, structure, and synthesis of glycoconjugates (glycoproteins, glycolipids, oligosaccharides, polysaccharides, Proteoglycans), including those aspects that are related to disease processes (eg, immunological, inflammatory, and arthritic diseases, infections, metabolic disorders, Malignancy, neurological disorders).
Incorporates (1994-1996): Glycosylation and Disease (0969-3653)
Related titles: Online - full text ed.: ISSN 1573-4986 (from EBSCO Publishing, Gale Group, IngentaConnect, Kluwer Online, O C L C Online Computer Library Center, Inc., Ovid Technologies, Inc., Springer LINK, Swets Information Services).
Indexed: ASCA, AgBio, BBCI, BIOBASE, BIOSIS Prev, BibLing, BiolAb, CCI, CIN, CPA, ChemAb, ChemTitl, CurCont, DSA, ExcerpMed, FCA, HelmAb, HortAb, IABS, ISR, IndMed, IndVet, Inpharma, MEDLINE, MaizeAb, NSCI, NemAb, NutrAb, PBA, PE&ON, ProtozoAb, RA&MP, RCI, RM&VM, RPP, Reac, RefZh, RevApplEntom, S&F, SCI, SIA, SeedAb, TDB, VetBull.
—BLDSC (4196.305000), CASDDS, CISTI, GNLM, IDS, IE, Infotrieve, ingenta, KNAW. **CCC.**
Published by: (International Glyconjugate Organization), Plenum US (Subsidiary of: Springer Science+Business Media), 233 Spring St, New York, NY 10013. TEL 212-460-1500, FAX 212-460-1575, service@springer-ny.com, http://springerlink.metapress.com/openurl.asp?genre=journal&issn=0282-0080, http://www.springeronline.com. Ed. J F G Vliegenthart.

572 USA ISSN 1547-562X
QP514
HARPER'S ILLUSTRATED BIOCHEMISTRY. Text in English. 1939. biennial. USD 44.95 per issue (effective 2003). bk.rev. **Document type:** *Monographic series, Academic/Scholarly.* **Description:** Covers latest case studies, discussions of biochemical diseases, and clinical information intented for medical students.
Former titles (until 2003): Harper's Biochemistry (1043-9811); (until 1988): Harper's Review of Biochemistry (0734-9866); (until 1979): Review of Physiological Chemistry (0080-1976)
—BLDSC (4264.885500).
Published by: McGraw-Hill Education, 2 Penn Plaza, 12th Fl, New York, NY 10121-2298. TEL 212-904-6079, FAX 212-904-6030, customer.service@mcgraw-hill.com, http://www.mheducation.com/. **Subscr. to:** PO Box 545, Blacklick, OH 43004-0545. TEL 800-262-4729, FAX 614-755-5645, medical@mcgraw-hill.com.

HIKAKU SEIRI SEIKAGAKU/COMPARATIVE PHYSIOLOGY AND BIOCHEMISTRY. see *BIOLOGY—Physiology*

HISTOCHEMISTRY AND CELL BIOLOGY. see *BIOLOGY—Cytology And Histology*

572.8 USA ISSN 1554-0014
QR185.8.H93 CODEN: HHYYBF
➤ **HYBRIDOMA.** Text in English. 1981. bi-m. USD 1,155 domestic to institutions; USD 1,405 foreign to institutions; USD 1,368 combined subscription domestic to institutions print & online eds.; USD 1,632 combined subscription foreign to institutions print & online eds. (effective 2006). adv. back issues avail.; reprint service avail. from PSC. **Document type:** *Journal, Academic/Scholarly.* **Description:** Publishes research in molecular immunology and experimental and clinical immunotherapy. Includes papers on the application of monoclonal antibodies for diagnostics and therapy, and original articles on various aspects of hybridoma research.
Former titles (until 2005): Hybridoma and Hybridomics (1536-8599); (until 2001): Hybridoma (0272-457X); Which incorporated (1981-1990): Monoclonal Antibodies (1047-871X); Which was formerly (until 1989): Monoclonal Antibody News (0272-4588)
Related titles: Online - full text ed.: ISSN 1557-8348. USD 411 to individuals; USD 947 to institutions (effective 2005) (from EBSCO Publishing, Gale Group, O C L C Online Computer Library Center, Inc., Swets Information Services).
Indexed: AIDS&CR, ASCA, AgBio, AnBrAb, BCI, BIOBASE, BIOSIS Prev, BioEngAb, BiolAb, CBTA, CIN, ChemAb, ChemTitl, CurCont, DBA, DSA, ExcerpMed, HelmAb, IABS, ISR, ImmunAb, IndMed, IndVet, Inpharma, M&PBA, MEDLINE, NutrAb, PE&ON, PoultAb, ProtozoAb, RM&VM, Reac, RefZh, SCI, SIA, TDB, Telegen, VetBull, WeedAb.
—BLDSC (4340.386000), CASDDS, CISTI, GNLM, IDS, IE, Infotrieve, ingenta. **CCC.**
Published by: Mary Ann Liebert, Inc. Publishers, 140 Huguenot St 3rd Fl, New Rochelle, NY 10801-5215. TEL 914-740-2100, FAX 914-740-2101, 800-654-3237, info@liebertpub.com, http://www.liebertpub.com/publication.aspx?pub_id=20. Ed. Dr. Zenon Steplewski. adv.: B&W page USD 1,150; trim 8.5 x 11. Circ: 1,430 (paid).

572 GBR ISSN 1521-6543
QP501 CODEN: IULIF8
➤ **I U B M B LIFE.** Text in English. 1980. m. GBP 818, USD 1,353 combined subscription to institutions print & online eds. (effective 2006). reprint service avail. from PSC. **Document type:** *Journal, Academic/Scholarly.* **Description:** Devoted to the dissemination of original research findings among the scientific communities of the forty nations represented by the International Union of Biochemistry.
Former titles (until 1999): Biochemistry and Molecular Biology International (1039-9712); (until 1993): Biochemistry International (0158-5231)
Related titles: Online - full text ed.: ISSN 1521-6551. GBP 777, USD 1,285 to institutions (effective 2006) (from EBSCO Publishing, Gale Group, IngentaConnect, O C L C Online Computer Library Center, Inc., Swets Information Services).
Indexed: ASCA, ASFA, AbHyg, AgBio, Agr, AgrForAb, AnBrAb, BBCI, BIOBASE, BIOSIS Prev, BibAg, BiolAb, CCI, CIN, CPA, ChemAb, ChemTitl, CurCont, DSA, ExcerpMed, FCA, ForAb, HelmAb, HortAb, IABS, ISR, IndMed, IndVet, Inpharma, MEDLINE, MaizeAb, NSCI, NemAb, NutrAb, PBA, PE&ON, PGegResA, PGrRegA, PHN&I, PN&I, PotatoAb, PoultAb, ProtozoAb, RA&MP, RM&VM, RPP, Reac, RevApplEntom, RiceAb, S&F, SCI, SFA, SIA, SeedAb, SoyAb, TDB, TriticAb, VetBull, WeedAb, WildRev, ZooRec.
—BLDSC (4588.826000), CASDDS, CISTI, GNLM, IDS, IE, Infotrieve, ingenta, Linda Hall. **CCC.**
Published by: (International Union of Biochemistry and Molecular Biology AUS), Taylor & Francis Ltd (Subsidiary of: Taylor & Francis Group), 4 Park Sq, Milton Park, Abingdon, OX14 4RN, United Kingdom. TEL 44-1235-828600, FAX 44-1235-829000, info@tandf.co.uk, http://www.tandf.co.uk/journals/titles/15216543.asp. Eds. Angelo Azzi, William J Whelan. Circ: 1,000. **Subscr. in N. America to:** Taylor & Francis Inc., Customer Services Dept, 325 Chestnut St, 8th Fl, Philadelphia, PA 19106. TEL 215-625-8900, 800-354-1420, FAX 215-625-8914, customerservice@taylorandfrancis.com; **Subscr. to:** Journals Customer Service, Rankine Rd, Basingstoke, Hants RG24 8PR, United Kingdom. TEL 44-1256-813000, FAX 44-1256-330245, enquiry@tandf.co.uk.

➤ **IMMUNOHISTOCHEMISTRY.** see *BIOLOGY—Abstracting, Bibliographies, Statistics*

572 IND ISSN 0970-6399
CODEN: IJBIEG
➤ **INDIAN JOURNAL OF AGRICULTURAL BIOCHEMISTRY.** Text in English. 1988. s-a. INR 100 domestic to individuals; USD 25 foreign to individuals; USD 10,000 domestic to institutions; USD 2,000 foreign to institutions (effective 2003). bk.rev. 50 p./no.; back issues avail. **Document type:** *Journal, Academic/Scholarly.* **Description:** Publishes original papers and reviews on all aspects of agricultural biochemistry.
Related titles: E-mail ed.; Fax ed.; Online - full text ed.
Indexed: AgBio, CIN, CPA, ChemAb, ChemTitl, FCA, FS&TA, HortAb, I&DA, MaizeAb, PBA, PGegResA, PGrRegA, PHN&I, PN&I, RA&MP, RefZh, S&F, SIA, SeedAb, SoyAb, TriticAb.
—CASDDS, Linda Hall.

B

Published by: Indian Society of Agricultural Biochemists, c/o Dept. of Agricultural Biochemistry, C.S. Azad University of Agricultural Technology, Kanpur, Uttar Pradesh 208 002, India. TEL 91-512-2294641, FAX 91-512-2210408, gps_csau@rediffmail.com. Ed. G G Sanwal. Pub. G.P. Srivastava. R&P G P Srivastava. Circ: 500.

572   IND   ISSN 0301-1208
QP501   CODEN: IJBBBQ
➤ **INDIAN JOURNAL OF BIOCHEMISTRY AND BIOPHYSICS.** Text in English. 1963. bi-m. (in 2 vols.). USD 225 to institutions (effective 2006). adv. back issues avail. **Document type:** *Academic/Scholarly.* **Description:** Provides original research in biochemistry and biophysics.
Formerly (until 1971): Indian Journal of Biochemistry (0019-5081)
Indexed: ASCA, ASFA, AbHyg, AgBio, AnBrAb, AnalAb, BBCI, BIOSIS Prev, BiolAb, CIN, CPA, ChemAb, ChemTitl, CurCont, DBA, DSA, DentInd, ESPM, EngInd, FCA, FS&TA, ForAb, HelmAb, HortAb, INIS AtomInd, ISR, IndMed, IndVet, Inpharma, MEDLINE, MaizeAb, NPU, NutrAb, OrnHort, PBA, PE&ON, PGegResA, PGrRegA, PotatoAb, PoultAb, ProtozoAb, RA&MP, RM&VM, RPP, Reac, RefZh, RevApplEntom, RiceAb, SCI, SFA, SSCI, SeedAb, SoyAb, TDB, TriticAb, VetBull, WeedAb.
—BLDSC (4410.420000), CASDDS, CISTI, Ei, GNLM, IDS, IE, Infotrieve, ingenta, Linda Hall.
Published by: (India. Council of Scientific and Industrial Research, India. Publications and Information Directorate), Scientific Publishers, 5-A New Pali Rd., Near Hotel Taj Hari Mahal, PO Box 91, Jodhpur, Rajasthan 342 003, India. TEL 91-291-2433323, FAX 91-291-2512580, info@scientificpub.com, http://www.scientificpub.com/ bookdetails.php?booktransid=312&bookid=308. Ed. B S Janqi. Circ: 1,000. **Co-sponsor:** Society of Biological Chemists.

572   IND   ISSN 0970-1915
       CODEN: IJCBEY
INDIAN JOURNAL OF CLINICAL BIOCHEMISTRY. Text in English. 1986. s-a. INR 500 domestic; USD 25 foreign (effective 2005). **Document type:** *Journal, Academic/Scholarly.* **Description:** Covers the research areas in the field of Clinical Biochemistry , Pathological , Microbiological , Molecular , Cellular , Genetic and Bioinformatic concepts and other advanced techniques. It serves the public interest in health care by providing leadership in clinical laboratory science to national professional societies , the diagnostics industry, government and non-government organization.
Related titles: Online - full text ed.: free (effective 2005).
Indexed: ExcerpMed.
—BLDSC (4410.742000), IE.
Published by: Association of Clinical Biochemists of India, c/o Dr. N.Rao, Professor, Department of Biochemistry, All India Institute of Medical Sciences, Ansari Nagar, New Delhi, 110 029, India. TEL 91-11-26593545, FAX 91-11-26588641, dnrao311@hotmail.com, http://www.acbindia.org. Ed. Dr. D N Rao.

INSECT BIOCHEMISTRY AND MOLECULAR BIOLOGY. see *BIOLOGY—Entomology*

572   FIN   ISSN 0074-3690
INTERNATIONAL CONGRESS OF HISTOCHEMISTRY AND CYTOCHEMISTRY. PROCEEDINGS. (Proceedings published in host country) Text in Finnish. 1960. quadrennial (Helsinki). price varies. adv. **Document type:** *Proceedings.*
—CISTI.
Published by: University of Helsinki, Department of Anatomy, c/o Dr Pertti Panula, Siltavuorenpenger 20 A, Helsinki, 00170, Finland. Circ: 1,000.

572   GBR   ISSN 1357-2725
QP501   CODEN: IJBBFU
➤ **THE INTERNATIONAL JOURNAL OF BIOCHEMISTRY & CELL BIOLOGY.** Text in English. 1970. 12/yr. EUR 3,108 in Europe to institutions; JPY 412,600 in Japan to institutions; USD 3,477 to institutions except Europe and Japan (effective 2006). adv. charts; illus.; stat. index. back issues avail.; reprint service avail. from PQC. **Document type:** *Journal, Academic/Scholarly.* **Description:** Provides comprehensive coverage of new research in growth areas of biochemistry.
Formerly (until 1995): International Journal of Biochemistry (0020-711X)
Related titles: Microfilm ed.: (from PQC); Online - full text ed.: (from EBSCO Publishing, Gale Group, IngentaConnect, ScienceDirect, Swets Information Services).
Indexed: ASCA, AbHyg, AgBio, Agr, AnBrAb, BBCI, BIOBASE, BIOSIS Prev, BioCN&I, BiolAb, CCI, CIN, CPA, ChemAb, ChemTitl, CurCont, DBA, DSA, DentInd, EngInd, ExcerpMed, FCA, ForAb, HelmAb, HortAb, IABS, ISR, IndMed, IndVet, Inpharma, MEDLINE, NSCI, NemAb, NutrAb, OrnHort, PBA, PE&ON, PGegResA, PGrRegA, PN&I, PoultAb, ProtozoAb, RA&MP, RM&VM, RPP, Reac, RefZh, RevApplEntom, S&F, SCI, SFA, SIA, SSCI, SeedAb, TDB, TriticAb, VetBull, WeedAb, WildRev, ZooRec.
—BLDSC (4542.135000), CASDDS, CISTI, Ei, GNLM, IDS, IE, Infotrieve, ingenta, Linda Hall. **CCC.**

Published by: Pergamon (Subsidiary of: Elsevier Science & Technology), The Boulevard, Langford Ln, East Park, Kidlington, Oxford OX5 1GB, United Kingdom. TEL 44-1865-843000, FAX 44-1865-843010, http:// www.elsevier.com/locate/biocel. Ed. Dr. Geoffrey J Laurent. Circ: 1,000. **Subscr. to:** Elsevier BV, PO Box 211, Amsterdam 1000 AE, Netherlands. nlinfo-f@elsevier.nl, http://www.elsevier.nl.

572.8   NLD   ISSN 0141-8130
QP801.P64   CODEN: IJBMDR
➤ **INTERNATIONAL JOURNAL OF BIOLOGICAL MACROMOLECULES.** Text in English. 1979. 10/yr. EUR 1,709 in Europe to institutions; JPY 227,000 in Japan to institutions; USD 1,911 elsewhere to institutions; EUR 187 in Europe to qualified personnel; JPY 24,900 in Japan to qualified personnel; USD 208 elsewhere to qualified personnel (effective 2006). adv. bk.rev. abstr.; illus. index. back issues avail. **Document type:** *Journal, Academic/Scholarly.* **Description:** Reports research into the structure of natural macromolecules: proteins, carbohydrates, nucleic acids, viruses and membranes.
Related titles: Microform ed.: (from PQC); Online - full text ed.: (from EBSCO Publishing, Gale Group, IngentaConnect, ScienceDirect, Swets Information Services).
Indexed: ABIPC, AEA, ASCA, AgBio, AgrForAb, AnBrAb, BBCI, BIOBASE, BIOSIS Prev, BioCN&I, BiolAb, CCI, CIN, CPA, ChemAb, ChemTitl, CurCont, DSA, ExcerpMed, FCA, FPA, FS&TA, ForAb, HelmAb, HerbAb, HortAb, IABS, ISR, IndMed, IndVet, Inpharma, MEDLINE, MSCI, MaizeAb, NutrAb, PBA, PE&ON, PN&I, PotatoAb, ProtozoAb, RA&MP, RPP, Reac, RiceAb, S&F, SCI, SIA, SeedAb, SoyAb, Telegen, TriticAb, VITIS, VetBull, WeedAb.
—BLDSC (4542.151000), CASDDS, CISTI, GNLM, IDS, IE, Infotrieve, ingenta, Linda Hall. **CCC.**
Published by: Elsevier BV (Subsidiary of: Elsevier Science & Technology), Radarweg 29, Amsterdam, 1043 NX, Netherlands. TEL 31-20-4853911, FAX 31-20-4852457, nlinfo-f@elsevier.nl, http://www.elsevier.com/locate/ijbiomac, http://www.elsevier.nl. Eds. A. Dong, J. F. Kennedy.

▼ ➤ **INTERNATIONAL JOURNAL OF BIOLOGICAL SCIENCES.** see *BIOLOGY*

➤ **INTERNATIONAL JOURNAL OF MEDICINAL MUSHROOMS.** see *BIOLOGY—Botany*

➤ **INTERNATIONAL JOURNAL OF MOLECULAR SCIENCES.** see *CHEMISTRY—Organic Chemistry*

➤ **INTERNATIONAL JOURNAL OF MOLECULAR SCIENCES CD-ROM.** see *CHEMISTRY—Organic Chemistry*

➤ **INTERNATIONAL JOURNAL OF NEUROSCIENCE.** see *MEDICAL SCIENCES—Psychiatry And Neurology*

572.65   NLD   ISSN 1573-3149
       CODEN: LPSCEM
➤ **INTERNATIONAL JOURNAL OF PEPTIDE RESEARCH AND THERAPEUTICS.** (Incorporated into Molecular Diversity in 2004) Text in English. 1994. q. EUR 798, USD 998, GBP 638 to institutions print & online eds. (effective 2005). adv. back issues avail.; reprint service avail. from PSC. **Document type:** *Academic/Scholarly.* **Description:** Brings together in a single source the most exciting work in peptide research, including isolation, structural characterization, synthesis, and biological activity of peptides, and thereby aids in the development of unifying concepts from diverse perspectives.
Formerly (until 2005): Letters in Peptide Science (0929-5666)
Related titles: Online - full text ed.: ISSN 1573-3904 (from EBSCO Publishing, Gale Group, IngentaConnect, Kluwer Online, O C L C Online Computer Library Center, Inc., Springer LINK, Swets Information Services).
Indexed: ASCA, BBCI, BIOSIS Prev, BibLing, BiolAb, CIN, ChemAb, ChemTitl, ExcerpMed, MSB, RefZh.
—BLDSC (5185.170180), CASDDS, CISTI, GNLM, IDS, IE, Infotrieve, ingenta. **CCC.**
Published by: Springer-Verlag Dordrecht (Subsidiary of: Springer Science+Business Media), Van Godewijckstraat 30, Dordrecht, 3311 GX, Netherlands. TEL 31-78-6576050, FAX 31-78-6576474, http://springerlink.metapress.com/openurl.asp?genre=journal&issn=1573-3149, http://www.springeronline.com. Eds. Fernando Albericio, Gregg B Fields, John D Wade.

➤ **INTERNATIONAL LABORATORY BUYERS' GUIDE.** see *BIOLOGY—Biotechnology*

572   USA   ISSN 0074-9354
INTERNATIONAL UNION OF BIOCHEMISTRY AND MOLECULAR BIOLOGY. SYMPOSIUM SERIES. Text in English. irreg.
—BLDSC (4588.825000).
Published by: International Union of Biochemistry and Molecular Biology, c/o Dept of Biochemistry, University of Miami, School of Medicine, Miami, FL 33152. http://www.iubmb.org.

572.8   USA   ISSN 1538-6414
       CODEN: IEJMAT
➤ **INTERNET ELECTRONIC JOURNAL OF MOLECULAR DESIGN.** Abbreviated title: I E J M D. Text in English. 2002. m. free (effective 2005). **Document type:** *Journal, Academic/Scholarly.* **Description:** Publishes articles on all aspects of computer-assisted molecular design applications in the chemistry, biochemistry, biology, chemical and pharmaceutical industries.
Media: Online - full content.
Published by: BioChem Press, Sealy Ctr. for Structural Biology, Dept. of Human Biological Chemistry & Genetics, University of Texas Medical Branch, 301 University Blvd., Galveston, TX 77555-1157. TEL 409-747-6806, http:// www.biochempress.com, http://www.hbcg.utmb.edu/. Ed. Ovidiu Ivanciuc.

572   GBR   ISSN 1462-2149
INTERNET JOURNAL OF SCIENCE - BIOLOGICAL CHEMISTRY. Text in English. 1997. irreg. back issues avail. **Document type:** *Journal, Academic/Scholarly.* **Description:** Includes all aspects of chemistry, but with particular emphasis on studies of biologically important molecules.
Media: Online - full text.
Published by: Emedia Science Ltd, P O Box 92, New Ferry, CH63 9WA, United Kingdom. TEL 44-151-647-0008, FAX 44-702-095-9300, sales@emedia-science.co.uk, http://www.netsci-journal.com/, http://www.emedia-science.co.uk. Ed. Dr. Paul Heelis.

IRON METABOLISM. see *BIOLOGY—Abstracting, Bibliographies, Statistics*

572   ITA   ISSN 0021-2938
       CODEN: IJBIAC
➤ **ITALIAN JOURNAL OF BIOCHEMISTRY.** Text in English. 1955-1995 (Dec.); resumed. bi-m. EUR 25 to members; EUR 60 to individuals; EUR 250 to institutions (effective 2003). adv. bk.rev. charts; illus. index. reprint service avail. from ISI. **Document type:** *Academic/Scholarly.*
Indexed: ASCA, ASFA, AnalAb, BIOSIS Prev, BiolAb, CIN, ChemAb, ChemTitl, CurCont, DSA, ExcerpMed, ISR, IndMed, IndVet, MEDLINE, NPU, NSCI, NemAb, NutrAb, PoultAb, SCI.
—BLDSC (4588.340000), CASDDS, CISTI, GNLM, IE, Infotrieve, ingenta, Linda Hall.
Published by: Biomedia srl, Via Carlo Farini 81, Milan, 20159, Italy. TEL 39-02-69001316, FAX 39-02-69001311, bm@biomedia.net. Circ: 600.

572.4   ITA   ISSN 1121-1709
       CODEN: IMEME
➤ **ITALIAN JOURNAL OF MINERAL & ELECTROLYTE METABOLISM.** Text in English. 1987. q. EUR 133 to individuals; EUR 206 to institutions (effective 2005). adv. **Document type:** *Journal, Academic/Scholarly.* **Description:** Deals with mineral and electrolyte metabolism and with calcified tissue.
Formerly (until 1990): Giornale Italiano di Metabolismo Minerale ed Elettrolitico (0394-1566)
Related titles: Online - full text ed.: (from EBSCO Publishing).
Indexed: BBCI, BIOBASE, CIN, ChemAb, ChemTitl, ExcerpMed, IABS.
—BLDSC (4588.340640), CASDDS, GNLM, IDS, ingenta. **CCC.**
Published by: (Italian Society of Mineral and Electrolyte Metabolism), Edizioni Minerva Medica, Corso Bramante 83-85, Turin, 10126, Italy. TEL 39-011-678282, FAX 39-011-674502, journals.dept@minervamedica.it, http://www.minervamedica.it. adv.: B&W page USD 1,200, color page USD 2,000; trim 280 x 215. Circ: 2,000 (paid).

➤ **IYAKU ANZENSEI KENKYUKAI KAIHO/JAPANESE SOCIETY FOR BIOPHARMACEUTICAL STATISTICS. BULLETIN.** see *PHARMACY AND PHARMACOLOGY*

➤ **IYAKU ANZENSEI KENKYUKAI TEIREIKAI SHIRYO/PROCEEDINGS OF REGULAR MEETINGS ON BIOPHARMACEUTICAL STATISTICS.** see *PHARMACY AND PHARMACOLOGY*

572   USA
J B C PAPERS IN PRESS. (Journal of Biological Chemistry) Text in English. irreg.
Media: Online - full text.
Published by: American Society for Biochemistry and Molecular Biology, Inc., 9650 Rockville Pike, Bethesda, MD 20814-3996. TEL 301-530-7145, FAX 301-571-1824, http://www.jbc.org/ pips/pips.0.shtml, http://www.asbmb.org.

572   CHN   ISSN 1007-7146
JIGUANG SHENGWU XUEBAO/ACTA LASER BIOLOGY SINICA. Text in Chinese. 1992. bi-m. CNY 10 per issue (effective 2003). **Document type:** *Journal, Academic/Scholarly.*
Formerly: Jiguang Shengwuxue/Laser Biology (1004-5767)
Related titles: Online - full content ed.; Online - full text ed.: (from East View Information Services).
Indexed: RefZh.
—BLDSC (0628.925000), IE, ingenta.

Published by: Hunan Shifan Daxue, Shengming Kexue Xueyuan/Hunan Normal University, College of Life Sciences, Yuelushan, Changsha, 410081, China. TEL 86-731-8872527, FAX 86-731-8883310, jgswxb@mail.hunnu.edu.cn, http://jgswxb.periodicals.net.cn/default.html, http://www2.hunnu.edu.cn/~biology/. Ed. Neng-Shu Hu.

572.8 BRA ISSN 1517-5693

JORNAL BRASILEIRO DE REPRODUCAO ASSISTIDA. Text in Portuguese. 1997. 3/yr.
Indexed: ExcerpMed.
Published by: Villimpress, Av Cav Paschoal Innechi, 1675, Jardim Independencia, Ribeirao Preto, SP, 14076, Brazil. TEL 16-6285696, FAX 16-6264813, http://www.villimpress.com.br/.

612.015 616.4 AUT ISSN 1023-7763
CODEN: JMINFV

➤ **JOURNAL FUER MINERALSTOFFWECHSEL**; Zeitschrift fuer Physiologie, Pathophysiologie und Klinik des Mineralstoffwechsels. Text in German. 1994. q. EUR 36 (effective 2005). adv. abstr.; bibl. 32 p./no. 3 cols./p.; back issues avail. **Document type:** *Journal, Academic/Scholarly.* **Description:** Presents available scientific information on safety and efficacy issues related to osteoporosis and the intake of calcium and vitamin D.
Related titles: Online - full text ed.: ISSN 1680-9408. 2001. free (effective 2005).
Indexed: ExcerpMed.
—BLDSC (5020.144500), IE, ingenta.
Published by: Krause & Pachernegg GmbH, Mozartgasse 10, Gablitz, 3003, Austria. TEL 43-2231-612580, FAX 43-2231-6125810, k_u_p@eunet.at, http://www.kup.at/journals/mineralstoffwechsel/index.html, http://www.kup.at/verlag.htm. Eds. Dr. Heinrich Resch, Dr. Peter Bernecker. Circ: 6,500 (paid).

➤ **JOURNAL OF BASIC MICROBIOLOGY**; an international journal on biochemistry, physiology, genetics, morphology and ecology of microorganisms. see *BIOLOGY—Microbiology*

572.33 GBR ISSN 0883-9115
CODEN: JBCPEV

➤ **JOURNAL OF BIOACTIVE AND COMPATIBLE POLYMERS.** Text in English. 1986. bi-m. GBP 735, USD 1,139 to institutions; GBP 766, USD 1,186 combined subscription to institutions print & online eds. (effective 2006). back issues avail.; reprints avail. **Document type:** *Journal, Academic/Scholarly.* **Description:** Provides a forum for both biological scientists and polymer chemists to publish refereed research papers and short communications in an area that is of common interest.
Related titles: E-mail ed.; Online - full content ed.; Online - full text ed.: ISSN 1530-8030. GBP 727, USD 1,127 to institutions (effective 2006) (from C S A, EBSCO Publishing, Gale Group, O C L C Online Computer Library Center, Inc., Sage Publications, Inc., Swets Information Services).
Indexed: ASCA, B&BAb, BIOSIS Prev, BioEngAb, BiolAb, BrCerAb, C&ISA, CCI, CIN, CerAb, ChemAb, ChemTitl, CivEngAb, CorrAb, CurCont, E&CAJ, EMA, ESPM, EngInd, ExcerpMed, IAA, ISR, M&TEA, MBF, METADEX, MSCI, RAPRA, RefZh, SCI, SolStAb, TTI, ToxAb, WAA.
—BLDSC (4951.567000), CASDDS, CISTI, Ei, GNLM, IDS, IE, Infotrieve, ingenta, Linda Hall. **CCC.**
Published by: Sage Science Press (UK) (Subsidiary of: Sage Publications, Inc.), 1 Oliver's Yard, 55 City Rd, London, EC1Y 1SP, United Kingdom. TEL 44-20-73248500, FAX 44-20-73248600, info@sagepub.com, http://www.sagepub.co.uk/journal.aspx?pid=105612. Ed. Raphael M Ottenbrite. Circ: 185 (paid). **Subscr. in the Americas to:** Sage Publications, Inc., 2455 Teller Rd, Thousand Oaks, CA 91320. TEL 805-499-0721, FAX 805-499-0871, journals@sagepub.com.

572 NLD ISSN 0165-022X
QP519.7 CODEN: JBBMDG

➤ **JOURNAL OF BIOCHEMICAL AND BIOPHYSICAL METHODS.** Text in Dutch. 1979. 12/yr. EUR 1,481 in Europe to institutions; JPY 196,300 in Japan to institutions; USD 1,652 elsewhere to institutions (effective 2006). adv. bk.rev. back issues avail.; reprint service avail. from ISI. **Document type:** *Academic/Scholarly.* **Description:** Publishes research papers dealing with the development of new methods or the significant modification of existing techniques to solve biological problems.
Related titles: Microform ed.: (from PQC); Online - full text ed.: (from EBSCO Publishing, Gale Group, IngentaConnect, ScienceDirect, Swets Information Services).
Indexed: AEA, ASCA, ASFA, AgBio, AgrForAb, AnBrAb, B&BAb, BBCI, BIOBASE, BIOSIS Prev, BioCN&I, BioEngAb, BiolAb, CCI, CEABA, CIN, CPA, ChemAb, ChemTitl, CurCont, DSA, ESPM, EngInd, ExcerpMed, FCA, FPA, FS&TA, ForAb, HerbAb, HortAb, ISR, IndMed, IndVet, Inpharma, Inspec, M&PBA, MEDLINE, MSB, MaizeAb, NutrAb, OrnHort, PHN&I, PN&I, PotatoAb, PoultAb, RA&MP, RM&VM, RPP, Reac, RefZh, RiceAb, S&F, SCI, SIA, SeedAb, SoyAb, TriticAb, VITIS, VetBull, WeedAb.
—BLDSC (4951.570000), AskIEEE, CASDDS, CISTI, GNLM, IDS, IE, Infotrieve, ingenta, Linda Hall. **CCC.**
Published by: Elsevier BV (Subsidiary of: Elsevier Science & Technology), Radarweg 29, Amsterdam, 1043 NX, Netherlands. TEL 31-20-4853911, FAX 31-20-4852457, nlinfo-f@elsevier.nl, http://www.elsevier.com/locate/jbbm, http://www.elsevier.nl. Eds. F. Kilar, S Hjerten.

572 JPN ISSN 0021-924X
QP501 CODEN: JOBIAO

➤ **JOURNAL OF BIOCHEMISTRY.** Text in English. 1922. m. GBP 205, USD 349, EUR 308 to institutions; GBP 216, USD 367, EUR 324 combined subscription to institutions print & online eds. (effective 2006). adv. abstr.; bibl.; charts; illus.; stat. index. back issues avail.; reprints avail. **Document type:** *Journal, Academic/Scholarly.* **Description:** Publishes original papers in the fields of biochemistry, molecular biology, cell, and biotechnology.
Related titles: Microfilm ed.: (from PMC); Online - full text ed.: GBP 194, USD 330, EUR 291 to institutions (effective 2006) (from EBSCO Publishing, Gale Group, IngentaConnect).
Indexed: ASCA, ASFA, AbHyg, AgBio, Agr, AgrForAb, AnBrAb, ApicAb, B&BAb, BBCI, BIOBASE, BIOSIS Prev, BibAg, BioCN&I, BiolAb, CCI, CIN, CPA, CRFR, ChemAb, ChemTitl, CurCont, DBA, DSA, DentInd, EngInd, ExcerpMed, FCA, FS&TA, ForAb, GenetAb, HGA, HelmAb, HortAb, IABS, INIS AtomInd, ISR, IndMed, IndVet, Inpharma, MBA, MEDLINE, MSB, NPU, NSCI, NemAb, NutrAb, OrnHort, PBA, PE&ON, PGegResA, PHN&I, PN&I, PotatoAb, PoultAb, ProtozoAb, RA&MP, RM&VM, RPP, Reac, RefZh, RevApplEntom, RiceAb, S&F, SCI, SIA, SeedAb, SoyAb, TDB, TriticAb, VetBull, WeedAb.
—BLDSC (4952.000000), CASDDS, CINDOC, CISTI, Ei, GNLM, IDS, IE, Infotrieve, ingenta, KNAW, Linda Hall. **CCC.**
Published by: Nihon Seikagakkai/Japanese Biochemical Society, Ishikawa Bldg., 25-16 Hongo 5-chome, Bunkyo-ku, Tokyo, 113-0033, Japan. TEL 81-3-38151913, FAX 81-3-38151934, jbs-ho@bcasj.or.jp, http://jb.oxfordjournals.org/, http://jb.bcasj.or.jp/. Ed. Tairo Oshima. Circ: 2,650. **Dist. by:** Business Center for Academic Societies Japan, 5-16-19 Honkomagome, Bunkyo-ku, Tokyo 113-0021, Japan. TEL 81-3-58145811.

572 KOR ISSN 1225-8687
QD415.A1 CODEN: JBMBE5

➤ **JOURNAL OF BIOCHEMISTRY AND MOLECULAR BIOLOGY.** Text in English. 1968. bi-m. EUR 408 combined subscription print & online eds.; EUR 81.60 per issue (effective 2004). 100 p./no.; **Document type:** *Journal, Academic/Scholarly.*
Formerly (until 1995): Korean Biochemical Journal (0368-4881)
Related titles: ◆ Online - full text ed.: Journal of Biochemistry and Molecular Biology Online. ISSN 0219-1024.
Indexed: BBCI, BIOSIS Prev, BiolAb, CIN, ChemAb, ChemTitl, FS&TA, SIA, ZooRec.
—BLDSC (4952.110000), CASDDS, GNLM, IDS, IE, Infotrieve, ingenta. **CCC.**
Published by: Biochemical Society of the Republic of Korea, The Korea Science and Technology Center, Rm 801, 635-4, Yeoksam-dong, Kangnam-Seoul, 135-703, Korea, S. TEL 82-2-5087434, FAX 82-2-5087578, bsrk@gly.biochem.or.kr, http://www.jbmb.or.kr, http://www.biochem.or.kr. Ed. Changwon Kang.

572 HKG ISSN 0219-1024

JOURNAL OF BIOCHEMISTRY AND MOLECULAR BIOLOGY ONLINE. Text in English. bi-m. free (effective 2005). **Document type:** *Academic/Scholarly.*
Media: Online - full text (from EBSCO Publishing). **Related titles:** ◆ Print ed.: Journal of Biochemistry and Molecular Biology. ISSN 1225-8687.
Published by: Springer Hong-Kong Ltd. (Subsidiary of: Springer Science+Business Media), Unit 1702, Tower 1, Enterprise Square, 9 Sheung Yuet Rd, Kowloon Bay, Kowloon, Hong Kong. TEL 852-2723-9698, FAX 852-2724-2366, springer@springer.com.hk.

572.43 USA ISSN 0145-479X
QH511.A1 CODEN: JBBID4

➤ **JOURNAL OF BIOENERGETICS AND BIOMEMBRANES.** Text in English. 1970. bi-m. EUR 788, USD 805, GBP 495 combined subscription to institutions print & online eds. (effective 2005). adv. bibl.; charts; illus. back issues avail.; reprint service avail. from PSC. **Document type:** *Journal, Academic/Scholarly.* **Description:** Publishes original research contributions in the areas of bioenergetics, biomembranes and transport, including muscle contraction, electron transport, ATP synthesis, and membrane transport.
Formerly (until 1976): Journal of Bioenergetics (0449-5705)
Related titles: Microfilm ed.: (from PQC); Online - full text ed.: ISSN 1573-6881 (from EBSCO Publishing, Gale Group, IngentaConnect, Kluwer Online, O C L C Online Computer Library Center, Inc., Ovid Technologies, Inc., Springer LINK, Swets Information Services).
Indexed: ABIPC, ASCA, ASFA, AbHyg, AgBio, B&BAb, BBCI, BIOBASE, BIOSIS Prev, BibLing, BioEngAb, BiolAb, CCI, CIN, CPA, ChemAb, ChemTitl, CurCont, ExcerpMed, FCA, HortAb, IABS, ISR, IndMed, IndVet, Inpharma, Inspec, MEDLINE, MaizeAb, NutrAb, OrnHort, PBA, PE&ON, PGrRegA, PotatoAb, ProtozoAb, RA&MP, Reac, RefZh, S&F, SCI, SeedAb, TDB, TriticAb, WeedAb.
—BLDSC (4952.820000), AskIEEE, CASDDS, CISTI, GNLM, IDS, IE, Infotrieve, ingenta, Linda Hall. **CCC.**
Published by: Plenum US (Subsidiary of: Springer Science+Business Media), 233 Spring St, New York, NY 10013. TEL 212-460-1500, FAX 212-460-1575, service@springer-ny.com, http://springerlink.metapress.com/openurl.asp?genre=journal&issn=0145-479X, http://www.springeronline.com. Ed. Peter L Pedersen.

572 USA ISSN 0021-9258
QP501 CODEN: JBCHA3

➤ **JOURNAL OF BIOLOGICAL CHEMISTRY.** Text in English. 1905. w. free to members. adv. illus. index. 1000 p./no.; back issues avail.; reprint service avail. from PQC. **Document type:** *Journal, Academic/Scholarly.*
Related titles: Microform ed.: (from PMC, PQC); Online - full text ed.: ISSN 1083-351X. free (effective 2004) (from EBSCO Publishing, HighWire Press).
Indexed: ABIPC, AIDS Ab, ASCA, ASFA, AbHyg, AgBio, Agr, AgrForAb, AnBrAb, B&AI, BBCI, BIOBASE, BIOSIS Prev, BPRC&P, BibAg, BioCN&I, BiolAb, CCI, CIN, CPA, CRFR, CTA, ChemAb, ChemTitl, ChemoAb, CurCont, DBA, DSA, DentInd, ESPM, EngInd, ExcerpMed, FCA, FPA, FS&TA, ForAb, GenetAb, HGA, HelmAb, HerbAb, HortAb, IABS, INIS AtomInd, ISR, ImmunAb, IndMed, IndVet, Inpharma, MBA, MEDLINE, MSB, MaizeAb, NSA, NSCI, NemAb, NucAcAb, NutrAb, OGFA, OrnHort, PBA, PE&ON, PGegResA, PGrRegA, PHN&I, PN&I, PotatoAb, PoultAb, ProtozoAb, RA&MP, RM&VM, RPP, Reac, RefZh, RevApplEntom, RiceAb, S&F, SCI, SFA, SIA, SeedAb, SoyAb, TDB, Telegen, TriticAb, VITIS, VetBull, WeedAb, WildRev, ZooRec.
—BLDSC (4953.000000), CASDDS, CINDOC, CISTI, GNLM, IDS, IE, Infotrieve, ingenta, Linda Hall. **CCC.**
Published by: American Society for Biochemistry and Molecular Biology, Inc., 9650 Rockville Pike, Bethesda, MD 20814-3996. asbmb@asbmb.faseb.org, http://www.jbc.org, http://www.asbmb.org. Ed. Herbert Tabor. Circ: 6,000.

➤ **JOURNAL OF BIOLOGICAL INORGANIC CHEMISTRY.** see *CHEMISTRY—Inorganic Chemistry*

➤ **JOURNAL OF BIOLOGICAL PHYSICS AND CHEMISTRY.** see *BIOLOGY—Biophysics*

572.4 NLD ISSN 0925-2738
QP519.9.N83 CODEN: JBNME9

➤ **JOURNAL OF BIOMOLECULAR N M R.** (Nuclear Magnetic Resonance) Text in English. 1991. m. EUR 1,698, USD 1,735, GBP 1,058 combined subscription to institutions print & online eds. (effective 2005). adv. reprint service avail. from PSC. **Document type:** *Journal, Academic/Scholarly.* **Description:** Publishes research on technical developments and innovative applications of nuclear magnetic resonance spectroscopy for the study of the structure and dynamic properties of biopolymers in solution, liquid crystals, solids and in mixed environments such as membranes.
Related titles: Online - full text ed.: ISSN 1573-5001 (from EBSCO Publishing, Gale Group, IngentaConnect, Kluwer Online, O C L C Online Computer Library Center, Inc., Ovid Technologies, Inc., Springer LINK, Swets Information Services).
Indexed: ASCA, AbHyg, Agr, B&BAb, BBCI, BIOSIS Prev, BibLing, BioCN&I, BioEngAb, BiolAb, CCI, CIN, ChemAb, ChemTitl, CurCont, DSA, ExcerpMed, ISR, IndMed, IndVet, Inpharma, MEDLINE, NucAcAb, NutrAb, PN&I, ProtozoAb, RM&VM, Reac, RefZh, RevApplEntom, SCI, TDB, VetBull.
—BLDSC (4953.830000), CASDDS, CISTI, GNLM, IDS, IE, Infotrieve, ingenta, Linda Hall. **CCC.**
Published by: Springer-Verlag Dordrecht (Subsidiary of: Springer Science+Business Media), Van Godewijckstraat 30, Dordrecht, 3311 GX, Netherlands. TEL 31-78-6576050, FAX 31-78-6576474, http://springerlink.metapress.com/openurl.asp?genre=journal&issn=0925-2738, http://www.springeronline.com. Ed. Kurt Wuethrich.

572.8 USA ISSN 1087-0571
RS189 CODEN: JBISF3

➤ **JOURNAL OF BIOMOLECULAR SCREENING.** Text in English. 1996. 8/yr. USD 822, GBP 531 to institutions; USD 856, GBP 553 combined subscription to institutions print & online eds. (effective 2006). adv. back issues avail.; reprints avail. **Document type:** *Journal, Academic/Scholarly.* **Description:** Covers chemistry, biology, automation and information management, including all aspects of the discovery process, from basic research through the early stages of product development.
Related titles: Online - full content ed.: (from EBSCO Publishing); Online - full text ed.: ISSN 1552-454X. USD 814, GBP 525 to institutions (effective 2006) (from Gale Group, O C L C Online Computer Library Center, Inc., Sage Publications, Inc., Swets Information Services).
Indexed: AbHyg, BCI, BIOSIS Prev, BiolAb, CIN, ChemAb, ChemTitl, CurCont, ExcerpMed, IndMed, MEDLINE, MSB, ProtozoAb, RA&MP, RM&VM, TDB.
—BLDSC (4953.845000), CASDDS, CISTI, GNLM, IDS, IE, Infotrieve, ingenta. **CCC.**

B

Published by: (Society for Biomolecular Screening), Sage Science Press (US) (Subsidiary of: Sage Publications, Inc.), 2455 Teller Rd, Thousand Oaks, CA 91320. TEL 805-499-0721, FAX 805-499-0871, info@sagepub.com, http://www.sagepub.com/journal.aspx?pid=9162. Ed. Larry Walker. adv.: B&W page USD 1,370; trim 8.375 x 10.875. Circ: 2,550 (paid). **Subscr. outside the Americas to:** Sage Publications Ltd., 1 Oliver's Yard, 55 City Rd, London EC1 1SP, United Kingdom. TEL 44-20-73740645, FAX 44-20-73748741, subscription@sagepub.co.uk.

572.65 USA ISSN 0739-1102
QH506 CODEN: JBSDD6

➤ **JOURNAL OF BIOMOLECULAR STRUCTURE & DYNAMICS.** Text in English. 1983. bi-m. USD 109 to individuals; USD 1,080 to institutions; USD 1,250 to corporations (effective 2000). **Document type:** *Journal, Academic/Scholarly.* **Description:** Covers both experimental and theoretical investigations in the area of nucleic acids, nucleotides, proteins, peptides, membranes, polysacharides and all their components, metal complexes and model systems.
Related titles: Online - full text ed.: (from EBSCO Publishing).
Indexed: ASFA, AgBio, Agr, AnBrAb, B&BAb, BBCI, BIOBASE, BIOSIS Prev, BiolAb, CIN, ChemAb, ChemTitl, CurCont, ExcerpMed, GenetAb, HGA, HelmAb, IABS, INIS AtomInd, ISR, IndMed, IndVet, Inpharma, MEDLINE, NucAcAb, PN&I, PoultAb, ProtozoAb, RM&VM, Reac, RefZh, SCI, VetBull.
—BLDSC (4953.850000), CASDDS, CISTI, GNLM, IDS, IE, Infotrieve, ingenta, Linda Hall. **CCC.**
Published by: Adenine Press, 2066 Central Ave, Schenectady, NY 12304. TEL 518-456-0784, FAX 518-452-4955, stone@adeninepress.com, http://www.adeninepress.com. Ed. Ramaswamy H Sarma.

➤ **JOURNAL OF BRAIN SCIENCE.** see *MEDICAL SCIENCES—Psychiatry And Neurology*

572 USA ISSN 1079-5383
CODEN: JCELF3

➤ **JOURNAL OF CAPILLARY ELECTROPHORESIS.** Text in English. 1994. bi-m. USD 200 domestic to individuals; USD 260 foreign to individuals; USD 425 domestic to institutions; USD 490 foreign to institutions (effective 2005). **Document type:** *Journal, Academic/Scholarly.*
Indexed: AnalAb, ChemAb, MEDLINE, MSB.
—CINDOC, CISTI, IE, Infotrieve.
Published by: International Scientific Communications, Inc., 30 Controls Dr, PO Box 670, Shelton, CT 06484-0870. TEL 203-926-9300, FAX 203-926-9310, brian.howard@iscpubs.com, iscpubs@iscpubs.com, http://www.iscpubs.com/jce/. Ed. Brian Howard.

572 USA ISSN 0730-2312
QH506 CODEN: JCEBD5

➤ **JOURNAL OF CELLULAR BIOCHEMISTRY.** Text in English. 1972. 18/yr. (in 4 vols., 3 nos./vol.). USD 7,150 domestic to institutions; USD 7,366 in Canada & Mexico to institutions; USD 7,492 elsewhere to institutions; USD 7,865 combined subscription domestic to institutions print & online eds.; USD 8,081 combined subscription in Canada & Mexico to institutions print & online eds.; USD 8,207 combined subscription elsewhere to institutions print & online eds. (effective 2006). adv. bk.rev. charts; illus.; stat. back issues avail.; reprint service avail. from ISI. **Document type:** *Journal, Academic/Scholarly.* **Description:** Publishes timely reviews, commentaries, and descriptions of original research in areas where complex cellular, photogenic, clinical, or animal model systems are studied by biochemical, genetic or quantitative ultrastructural approaches.
Former titles (until 1982): Journal of Supramolecular Structure and Cellular Biochemistry (0275-3723); (until 1981): Journal of Supramolecular Structure (0091-7419)
Related titles: Microform ed.: (from PQC); Online - full content ed.: ISSN 1097-4644. 1996. USD 7,150 to institutions (effective 2006); Online - full text ed.: (from EBSCO Publishing, Swets Information Services, Wiley InterScience); ♦ Supplement(s): Journal of Cellular Biochemistry. Supplement. ISSN 0733-1959.
Indexed: ASCA, AbAn, AbHyg, AgBio, AnBrAb, BBCI, BIOSIS Prev, BiolAb, CIN, ChemAb, ChemTitl, CurCont, DBA, DSA, ExcerpMed, GenetAb, HortAb, INIS AtomInd, ISR, IndMed, IndVet, Inpharma, MEDLINE, MSCI, NSCI, NemAb, NutrAb, PoultAb, ProtozoAb, RA&MP, RM&VM, RPP, Reac, RefZh, S&F, SCI, SFA, SSCI, VetBull, WildRev, ZooRec.
—BLDSC (4955.010000), CASDDS, CISTI, GNLM, IDS, IE, Infotrieve, ingenta, Linda Hall. **CCC.**
Published by: John Wiley & Sons, Inc., 111 River St, Hoboken, NJ 07030-5774. TEL 201-748-6000, FAX 201-748-5915, uscs-wis@wiley.com, http://www3.interscience.wiley.com/cgi-bin/jhome/35503, http://www.wiley.com. Eds. C F Fox, Gary S Stein. adv.: B&W page GBP 640, color page GBP 1,515; trim 174 x 254. Circ: 850. **Subscr. outside the Americas to:** John Wiley & Sons Ltd., The Atrium, Southern Gate, Chichester, West Sussex PO19 8SQ, United Kingdom. TEL 44-1243-843335, 0800-243407, FAX 44-1243-843232, cs-journals@wiley.co.uk.

572 USA ISSN 0733-1959
CODEN: JCBSD7

➤ **JOURNAL OF CELLULAR BIOCHEMISTRY. SUPPLEMENT.** Text in English. 1972. irreg., latest 2002. price varies. back issues avail. **Document type:** *Academic/Scholarly.*
Former titles (until 1982): Journal of Supramolecular Structure and Cellular Biochemistry. Supplement (0730-6652); (until 1981): Journal of Supramolecular Structure. Supplement (0161-3294)
Related titles: ♦ Supplement to: Journal of Cellular Biochemistry. ISSN 0730-2312.
Indexed: BIOSIS Prev, BiolAb, ChemAb, IndMed, MEDLINE, SFA, WildRev, ZooRec.
—BLDSC (4955.011000), CISTI, IE, Infotrieve, ingenta, Linda Hall. **CCC.**
Published by: John Wiley & Sons, Inc., 111 River St, Hoboken, NJ 07030-5774. TEL 201-748-6000, 800-825-7550, FAX 201-748-5915, uscs-wis@wiley.com, http://www.wiley.com. **Subscr. outside the Americas to:** John Wiley & Sons Ltd., The Atrium, Southern Gate, Chichester, West Sussex PO19 8SQ, United Kingdom. TEL 44-1243-843335, 0800-243407, FAX 44-1243-843232, cs-journals@wiley.co.uk.

➤ **JOURNAL OF CEREBRAL BLOOD FLOW AND METABOLISM.** see *MEDICAL SCIENCES—Psychiatry And Neurology*

➤ **JOURNAL OF CHEMICAL AND BIOCHEMICAL KINETICS.** see *CHEMISTRY*

➤ **JOURNAL OF CHEMICAL NEUROANATOMY.** see *MEDICAL SCIENCES—Psychiatry And Neurology*

➤ **JOURNAL OF CHROMATOGRAPHY. B, ANALYTICAL TECHNOLOGIES IN THE BIOMEDICAL AND LIFE SCIENCES.** see *CHEMISTRY*

572 613.2 JPN ISSN 0912-0009
CODEN: JCBNER

➤ **JOURNAL OF CLINICAL BIOCHEMICAL AND NUTRITION.** Text in English. 1986. bi-m. free to members. **Document type:** *Journal, Academic/Scholarly.*
Indexed: BBCI, BIOBASE, BIOSIS Prev, BiolAb, DSA, ExcerpMed, HortAb, IABS, ISR, IndVet, Inpharma, NutrAb, PE&ON, ProtozoAb, RA&MP, Reac, SCI, SoyAb, VetBull.
—BLDSC (4958.381850), CISTI, IE, Infotrieve, ingenta.
Published by: Institute of Applied Biochemistry, Gifu International Institute of Biotechnology, Mitake-cho 2193-128, Kani-gun, Gifu 505-0116, Japan. TEL 81-574-675500, FAX 81-298-534605, office@applbio.or.jp, http://www.applbio.or.jp/.

➤ **JOURNAL OF COMPARATIVE PHYSIOLOGY B;** biochemical, systemic, and environmental physiology. see *BIOLOGY—Physiology*

572.7 GBR ISSN 1475-6366
QP601.5 CODEN: JEIMAZ

➤ **JOURNAL OF ENZYME INHIBITION AND MEDICINAL CHEMISTRY.** Text in English. bi-m. GBP 1,144, USD 1,442 combined subscription to institutions print & online eds. (effective 2006). reprint service avail. from PSC. **Document type:** *Journal, Academic/Scholarly.* **Description:** Publishes new knowledge and findings on enzyme inhibitors and inhibitory processes.
Formerly (until 2002): Journal of Enzyme Inhibition (8755-5093)
Related titles: CD-ROM ed.; Microform ed.; Online - full text ed.: ISSN 1475-6374. 2002. GBP 1,087, USD 1,370 to institutions (effective 2006) (from EBSCO Publishing, Gale Group, IngentaConnect, O C L C Online Computer Library Center, Inc., Swets Information Services).
Indexed: ASCA, AbHyg, BBCI, BCI, BIOBASE, BioCN&I, BiolAb, CCI, CPA, ChemAb, CurCont, DBA, ExcerpMed, FCA, FS&TA, HortAb, IABS, ISR, IndMed, Inpharma, MEDLINE, PBA, PE&ON, PotatoAb, ProtozoAb, RM&VM, Reac, SCI, SoyAb, TriticAb.
—BLDSC (4979.465000), CISTI, GNLM, IE, ingenta. **CCC.**
Published by: Taylor & Francis Ltd (Subsidiary of: Taylor & Francis Group), 4 Park Sq, Milton Park, Abingdon, OX14 4RN, United Kingdom. TEL 44-1235-828600, FAX 44-1235-829000, info@tandf.co.uk, http://www.tandf.co.uk/journals/titles/14756366.asp. Ed. H J Smith. **Subscr. to:** Journals Customer Service, Rankine Rd, Basingstoke, Hants RG24 8PR, United Kingdom. TEL 44-1256-813000, FAX 44-1256-330245, enquiry@tandf.co.uk.

572 RUS ISSN 0022-0930
QP1 CODEN: JEBPA9

➤ **JOURNAL OF EVOLUTIONARY BIOCHEMISTRY AND PHYSIOLOGY.** Text in English. 1965. bi-m. EUR 3,208, USD 2,865, GBP 1,998 to institutions (effective 2005). back issues avail. **Document type:** *Journal, Academic/Scholarly.* **Description:** Illuminates the most recent research findings on the evolution of basic forms of metabolism, comparative and developmental physiology, and biochemistry and the biochemical evolution of the animal world.
Related titles: Online - full text ed.: ISSN 1608-3202. EUR 3,208, USD 2,865, GBP 1,998 to institutions (effective 2005) (from EBSCO Publishing, Gale Group, IngentaConnect, Kluwer Online, O C L C Online Computer Library Center, Inc., Ovid Technologies, Inc., Springer LINK, Swets Information Services); ♦ Translation of: Zhurnal Evolyutsionnoi Biokhimii i Fiziologii. ISSN 0044-4529.
Indexed: ASCA, ASFA, BBCI, BibLing, BiolAb, ESPM, ExcerpMed, IABS, IndMed, NSCI.
—BLDSC (0414.450000), CASDDS, CISTI, IDS, IE, Infotrieve, ingenta, Linda Hall. **CCC.**
Published by: (Rossiiskaya Akademiya Nauk/Russian Academy of Sciences), M A I K Nauka - Interperiodica, Profsoyuznaya ul 90, Moscow, 117997, Russian Federation. TEL 7-095-3347420, FAX 7-095-3360666, compmg@maik.ru, http://www.maik.rssi.ru/cgi-bin/journal.pl?name=evolbp&page=main, http://www.maik.ru. **Subscr. to:** Springer-Verlag Dordrecht, Journals Department, PO Box 322, Dordrecht, Netherlands. TEL 31-78-6576392, FAX 31-78-6576474.

➤ **JOURNAL OF HEALTH SCIENCE/EISEI KAGAKU.** see *ENVIRONMENTAL STUDIES—Toxicology And Environmental Safety*

➤ **JOURNAL OF HISTOTECHNOLOGY.** see *BIOLOGY—Cytology And Histology*

572 USA ISSN 0162-0134
QP501 CODEN: JIBIDJ

➤ **JOURNAL OF INORGANIC BIOCHEMISTRY.** Text in English. 1971. 12/yr. EUR 2,156 in Europe to institutions; JPY 286,100 in Japan to institutions; USD 2,412 elsewhere to institutions (effective 2006). adv. bk.rev. charts; illus. Index. **Document type:** *Journal, Academic/Scholarly.* **Description:** Publishes research papers and short communications in all areas of inorganic biochemistry.
Formerly (until vol.10): Bioinorganic Chemistry (0006-3061)
Related titles: Microform ed.: (from PQC); Online - full text ed.: (from EBSCO Publishing, Gale Group, IngentaConnect, ScienceDirect, Swets Information Services).
Indexed: ASCA, AgBio, Agr, ApicAb, BBCI, BIOBASE, BIOSIS Prev, BibAg, BiolAb, BrCerAb, CCI, CEABA, CIN, CPA, Cadscan, CerAb, ChemAb, ChemTitl, CorrAb, CurCont, DSA, EMA, ExcerpMed, FCA, ForAb, HortAb, IABS, INIS AtomInd, ISR, IndMed, IndVet, Inpharma, LeadAb, M&TEA, MBF, MEDLINE, METADEX, MSB, NutrAb, PBA, PE&ON, ProtozoAb, RCI, RM&VM, RPP, Reac, RefZh, S&F, SCI, SeedAb, SoyAb, VetBull, WAA, WeedAb, Zincscan.
—BLDSC (5007.150000), CASDDS, CISTI, GNLM, IDS, IE, Infotrieve, ingenta, Linda Hall. **CCC.**
Published by: Elsevier Inc. (Subsidiary of: Elsevier Science & Technology), 360 Park Ave. S, New York, NY 10010-1710. TEL 212-633-3730, 888-437-4636, usinfo-f@elsevier.com, http://www.elsevier.com/locate/jinorgbio. Ed. Dr. J H Dawson. **Subscr. outside the Americas to:** Elsevier BV, PO Box 211, Amsterdam 1000 AE, Netherlands. TEL 31-20-485-3757, FAX 31-20-485-3432.

572.57 USA ISSN 0022-2275
QP751 CODEN: JLPRAW

➤ **JOURNAL OF LIPID RESEARCH.** Text in English. 1959. m. USD 180 combined subscription domestic to non-members print & online; USD 248 combined subscription in Canada to non-members print & online; USD 235 combined subscription elsewhere to non-members print & online; USD 155 combined subscription domestic to members print & online; USD 221 combined subscription in Canada to members print & online; USD 210 combined subscription elsewhere to members print & online; USD 575 combined subscription domestic to institutions print & online; USD 671 combined subscription in Canada to institutions print & online; USD 630 combined subscription elsewhere to institutions print & online (effective 2005). adv. bibl.; illus. Index. back issues avail. **Document type:** *Journal, Academic/Scholarly.* **Description:** Publishes original articles and invited reviews on subjects involving lipids in any scientific discipline.
Related titles: Microform ed.: (from PQC); Online - full text ed.: J L R Online. ISSN 1539-7262. USD 150 to non-members; USD 125 to members; USD 460 to institutions (effective 2005) (from HighWire Press); J L R Papers in Press. free (effective 2005) (from EBSCO Publishing).
Indexed: ASCA, AbHyg, AgBio, Agr, AnBrAb, AnalAb, BBCI, BIOBASE, BIOSIS Prev, BibAg, BiolAb, BiolDig, CCI, CIN, ChemAb, ChemTitl, CurCR, CurCont, DBA, DSA, DentInd, ExcerpMed, FS&TA, IABS, INIS AtomInd, ISR, IndChem, IndMed, IndVet, Inpharma, MEDLINE, MSB, MaizeAb, NPU, NRN, NemAb, NutrAb, PE&ON, PN&I, PoultAb, ProtozoAb, RCI, RDA, RM&VM, Reac, RefZh, RevApplEntom, SCI, SFA, SIA, SoyAb, TDB, THA, Telegen, VetBull, WAE&RSA, WildRev, ZooRec.
—BLDSC (5010.500000), CASDDS, CINDOC, CISTI, GNLM, IDS, IE, Infotrieve, ingenta, Linda Hall. **CCC.**
Published by: American Society for Biochemistry and Molecular Biology, Inc., 9650 Rockville Pike, Bethesda, MD 20814-3996. TEL 301-530-7106, FAX 301-571-5723, jlr@jlr.faseb.org, asbmb@asbmb.faseb.org, http://www.jlr.org/, http://www.asbmb.org. Ed. Edward A Dennis. adv.: B&W page USD 880, color page USD 1,975; trim 8.5 x 11. Circ: 1,900.

➤ **JOURNAL OF MEMBRANE SCIENCE.** see *CHEMISTRY—Physical Chemistry*

572 GBR ISSN 0022-2836
QH301 CODEN: JMOBAK
➤ **JOURNAL OF MOLECULAR BIOLOGY.** Text in English. 1959. 50/yr. EUR 920 in Europe to individuals; JPY 99,400 in Japan to individuals; USD 853 to individuals except Europe and Japan; EUR 7,002 in Europe to institutions; JPY 756,300 in Japan to institutions; USD 6,226 to institutions except Europe and Japan (effective 2006). adv. bibl.; charts; illus. index,cum.index. reprints avail. **Document type:** *Journal, Academic/Scholarly.* **Description:** Presents original scientific research concerning studies of organisms or their components at the molecular level.
Related titles: Online - full text ed.: J M B Online. ISSN 1089-8638. 199? (from EBSCO Publishing, Gale Group, IngentaConnect, O C L C Online Computer Library Center, Inc., ScienceDirect, Swets Information Services).
Indexed: AIDS Ab, ASCA, ASFA, AbHyg, AgBio, Agr, AgrForAb, AnBrAb, B&AI, BBCI, BCI, BIOBASE, BIOSIS Prev, BibAg, BioCN&I, BiolAb, Biostat, CCI, CMCI, CPA, CTA, ChemAb, ChemTitl, ChemoAb, CurCont, DBA, DSA, ESPM, ExcerpMed, FCA, FPA, FS&TA, ForAb, GenetAb, HGA, HelmAb, HerbAb, HortAb, IABS, ISR, IndMed, IndVet, Inpharma, MBA, MEDLINE, MSB, MaizeAb, NSA, NemAb, NucAcAb, NutrAb, OrnHort, PBA, PGegResA, PGrRegA, PN&I, PotatoAb, PoultAb, ProtozoAb, RA&MP, RM&VM, RPP, Reac, RefZh, RevApplEntom, RiceAb, S&F, SCI, SFA, SIA, SeedAb, SoyAb, TDB, TriticAb, VetBull, WeedAb, WildRev, ZooRec.
—BLDSC (5020.700000), CASDDS, CISTI, GNLM, IDS, IE, Infotrieve, ingenta, Linda Hall. **CCC.**
Published by: Academic Press (Subsidiary of: Elsevier Science & Technology), Harcourt Pl, 32 Jamestown Rd, London, NW1 7BY, United Kingdom. TEL 44-20-7424-4200, FAX 44-20-7483-2293, apsubs@acad.com, http://www.elsevier.com/locate/jmb. Ed. P Wright. R&P Catherine John. Adv. contact Nik Screen.

572.7 NLD ISSN 1381-1177
TP248.65.E59 CODEN: JMCEF8
➤ **JOURNAL OF MOLECULAR CATALYSIS B: ENZYMATIC.** Text in English. 1975; N.S. 1995. 24/yr. EUR 996 in Europe to institutions; JPY 132,300 in Japan to institutions; USD 1,115 elsewhere to institutions (effective 2006). adv. back issues avail. **Document type:** *Journal, Academic/Scholarly.* **Description:** Devoted to research and developments in the applications of whole-cell and cell-free enzymes as catalysts in organic synthesis.
Supersedes in part (in 1995): Journal of Molecular Catalysis (0304-5102)
Related titles: Microform ed.: N.S. (from PQC); Online - full text ed.: N.S. (from EBSCO Publishing, Gale Group, IngentaConnect, ScienceDirect, Swets Information Services).
Indexed: ASCA, BBCI, BIOSIS Prev, BiolAb, C&ISA, CCI, CEABA, ChemAb, ChemTitl, CurCont, E&CAJ, EngInd, ExcerpMed, ISR, RCI, RefZh, SCI, SolStAb, VITIS.
—BLDSC (5020.705060), CASDDS, CISTI, IDS, IE, Infotrieve, ingenta, Linda Hall. **CCC.**
Published by: Elsevier BV (Subsidiary of: Elsevier Science & Technology), Radarweg 29, Amsterdam, 1043 NX, Netherlands. TEL 31-20-4853911, FAX 31-20-4852457, nlinfo-f@elsevier.nl, http://www.elsevier.com/locate/molcatb, http://www.elsevier.nl. Ed. R A Sheldon.

➤ **JOURNAL OF MOLECULAR HISTOLOGY.** see *BIOLOGY—Cytology And Histology*

➤ **JOURNAL OF MYCOPATHOLOGICAL RESEARCH.** see *BIOLOGY—Microbiology*

➤ **JOURNAL OF NATURAL PRODUCTS.** see *PHARMACY AND PHARMACOLOGY*

573.84 GBR ISSN 0022-3042
QP351 CODEN: JONRA9
➤ **JOURNAL OF NEUROCHEMISTRY.** Text in English. 1956. fortn. GBP 480, EUR 720 combined subscription in Europe to individuals print & online eds.; USD 805 combined subscription in the Americas to individuals & Carilbean, print & online eds.; GBP 528 combined subscription elsewhere to individuals print & online eds.; GBP 1,787 combined subscription in Europe to institutions print & online eds.; USD 3,302 combined subscription in the Americas to institutions & Caribbean, print & online eds.; GBP 2,161 combined subscription elsewhere to institutions print & online eds. (effective 2006). adv. bk.rev. bibl.; charts; illus. index. back issues avail.; reprint service avail. from PQC. **Document type:** *Journal, Academic/Scholarly.* **Description:** Provides complete coverage of the biochemical aspects of behavior and brain function.
Related titles: Microform ed.: (from PQC); Online - full text ed.: ISSN 1471-4159. GBP 456 in Europe to individuals; USD 765 in the Americas to individuals & Caribbean; GBP 501 elsewhere to individuals; GBP 1,697 in Europe to institutions; USD 3,137 in the Americas to institutions & Caribbean; GBP 2,054 elsewhere to institutions (effective 2006) (from Blackwell Synergy, EBSCO Publishing, Gale Group, HighWire Press, IngentaConnect, O C L C Online Computer Library Center, Inc., Ovid Technologies, Inc., Swets Information Services).
Indexed: AIDS Ab, ASCA, ASFA, B&BAb, BBCI, BIOBASE, BIOSIS Prev, BiolAb, BiolDig, CCI, CIN, CTA, ChemAb, ChemTitl, ChemoAb, CurCont, DBA, DSA, DentInd, ExcerpMed, IABS, ISR, IndMed, IndVet, Inpharma, MEDLINE, MSB, NSA, NSCI, NutrAb, PE&ON, Reac, RefZh, SCI, SFA, SSCI, TDB, THA, VetBull, e-psyche.
—BLDSC (5021.500000), CASDDS, CISTI, GNLM, IDS, IE, Infotrieve, ingenta, KNAW, Linda Hall. **CCC.**
Published by: (International Society for Neurochemistry USA), Blackwell Publishing Ltd., 9600 Garsington Rd, Oxford, OX4 2ZG, United Kingdom. TEL 44-1865-776868, FAX 44-1865-714591, customerservices@oxon.blackwellpublishing.com, http://www.blackwellpublishing.com/journals/JNC. Eds. Anthony J Turner, Brian Collier. adv.: B&W page USD 915, color page USD 2,070. Circ: 2,189 (paid).

➤ **THE JOURNAL OF NUTRITIONAL BIOCHEMISTRY.** see *NUTRITION AND DIETETICS*

➤ **JOURNAL OF PHARMACOLOGICAL AND TOXICOLOGICAL METHODS.** see *ENVIRONMENTAL STUDIES—Toxicology And Environmental Safety*

572 CHE ISSN 1011-1344
QH515 CODEN: JPPBEG
➤ **JOURNAL OF PHOTOCHEMISTRY AND PHOTOBIOLOGY, B: BIOLOGY.** Text in English. 1987. 12/yr. EUR 70 in Europe to individuals; JPY 9,200 in Japan to individuals; USD 79 elsewhere to individuals; EUR 2,831 in Europe to institutions; JPY 392,100 in Japan to institutions; USD 3,166 elsewhere to institutions (effective 2006). bk.rev. back issues avail. **Document type:** *Journal, Academic/Scholarly.* **Description:** Publishes papers for scientists who seek to understand light and its interactions with the processes of life. Also includes technological developments, forthcoming events, conference reports, and reports on current areas of research.
Related titles: Microform ed.: (from PQC); Online - full text ed.: (from EBSCO Publishing, Gale Group, IngentaConnect, ScienceDirect, Swets Information Services).
Indexed: ASCA, ASFA, AbHyg, AgBio, AgrForAb, B&BAb, BBCI, BIOBASE, BIOSIS Prev, BiolAb, CCI, CIN, CPA, CTA, ChemAb, ChemTitl, CurCont, DSA, EngInd, ExcerpMed, FCA, FPA, ForAb, GenetAb, HerbAb, HortAb, IABS, ISR, IndMed, IndVet, Inpharma, JW-D, M&GPA, MEDLINE, MaizeAb, NutrAb, OrnHort, PBA, PE&ON, PGrRegA, PhotoAb, PhysBer, PotatoAb, ProtozoAb, RA&MP, RM&VM, RPP, Reac, RefZh, RiceAb, S&F, SCI, SeedAb, SoyAb, TDB, TriticAb, VetBull, WeedAb, ZooRec.
—BLDSC (5034.850000), CASDDS, CISTI, GNLM, IDS, IE, Infotrieve, ingenta, Linda Hall. **CCC.**
Published by: (European Society for Photobiology), Elsevier S.A., PO Box 564, Lausanne 1, 1001, Switzerland. TEL 41-21-3207381, FAX 41-21-3235444, http://www.elsevier.com/locate/jphotobiol. Eds. F Bohm, K Winckler, L Matyus. **Subscr. to:** Elsevier BV, PO Box 211, Amsterdam 1000 AE, Netherlands. TEL 31-20-485-3757, FAX 31-20-485-3432, nlinfo-f@elsevier.nl, http://www.elsevier.nl.

➤ **JOURNAL OF PHYSIOLOGY AND BIOCHEMISTRY.** see *MEDICAL SCIENCES*

572 IND ISSN 0971-7811
CODEN: JPBBEE
➤ **JOURNAL OF PLANT BIOCHEMISTRY AND BIOTECHNOLOGY.** Text in English. 1992. s-a. INR 400, USD 100 (effective 2003). reprints avail. **Document type:** *Academic/Scholarly.* **Description:** Publishes research papers in the area of plant biochemistry, plant molecular biology, microbial genetics and plant biotechnology.
Indexed: ASCA, AgBio, AgrForAb, BBCI, BCI, BIOBASE, BIOSIS Prev, BioCN&I, BiolAb, CEABA, CIN, CPA, ChemAb, ChemTitl, CurCont, DBA, DSA, FCA, FS&TA, ForAb, HerbAb, HortAb, IABS, MaizeAb, OrnHort, PBA, PGegResA, PGrRegA, PHN&I, PlantSci, PotatoAb, RA&MP, RPP, RevApplEntom, RiceAb, S&F, SIA, SeedAb, SoyAb, TriticAb, WeedAb.
—BLDSC (5040.509000), CASDDS, CISTI, IDS, IE, ingenta.
Published by: Society for Plant Biochemistry and Biotechnology, Division of Biochemistry, Indian Agricultural Research Institute, New Delhi, 110 012, India. TEL 91-11-25784006, FAX 91-11-25766420, mll_bio@iari.res.in, mll_bio@yahoo.co.in. Ed. M L Lodha. Pub. S L Mehta. Circ: 7,000 (paid).

572.6 USA ISSN 1535-3893
QD431.A1 CODEN: JPROBS
➤ **JOURNAL OF PROTEOME RESEARCH.** Text in English. 2002. bi-m. USD 1,372 in North America to institutions; USD 1,457 elsewhere to institutions; USD 201 in North America to members; USD 286 elsewhere to members; USD 151 in North America to students; USD 236 elsewhere to students (effective 2006). adv. back issues avail. **Document type:** *Journal, Academic/Scholarly.* **Description:** Provides content encompassing all aspects of systems-oriented, global protein analysis and function, emphasizing the synergy between physical and life sciences resulting in a multi-disciplinary appraoch to the understanding of biological processes. It integrates the fields of chemistry, biology, applied physics, and computer science.
Related titles: Online - full text ed.: ISSN 1535-3907. USD 70 (effective 2006) (from EBSCO Publishing, Swets Information Services).
Indexed: AnalAb, BBCI, BIOSIS Prev, BiolAb, ChemAb, CurCont, ExcerpMed, ISR, MSB, SCI.
—BLDSC (5042.960000), CISTI, IE, Linda Hall. **CCC.**
Published by: American Chemical Society, 1155 16th St, N W, Washington, DC 20036. TEL 202-872-4614, 800-227-5558, FAX 202-776-8264, service@acs.org, http://pubs.acs.org/jpr. Ed. William S Hancock. adv.: B&W page USD 3,040; trim 10.1875 x 10.875. Circ: 1,200.

572 GBR ISSN 0960-0760
QP801.S6 CODEN: JSBBEZ
➤ **THE JOURNAL OF STEROID BIOCHEMISTRY AND MOLECULAR BIOLOGY.** Text in English. 1970. 25/yr. EUR 4,614 in Europe to institutions; JPY 612,300 in Japan to institutions; USD 5,161 to institutions except Europe and Japan; EUR 342 in Europe to qualified personnel; JPY 45,500 in Japan to qualified personnel; USD 383 to qualified personnel except Europe and Japan (effective 2006). adv. bk.rev. abstr. back issues avail. **Document type:** *Academic/Scholarly.* **Description:** Covers recent experimental and theoretical developments in disciplines related to steroids.
Formerly (until 1991): Journal of Steroid Biochemistry (0022-4731)
Related titles: Microfilm ed.: (from PQC); Online - full text ed.: (from EBSCO Publishing, Gale Group, IngentaConnect, ScienceDirect, Swets Information Services).
Indexed: ASCA, ASFA, AbHyg, AgBio, AnBrAb, AnalAb, B&BAb, BBCI, BIOBASE, BIOSIS Prev, BiolAb, CCI, CIN, ChemAb, ChemTitl, CurCont, DSA, ExcerpMed, GenetAb, HGA, HelmAb, HortAb, IABS, ISR, IndMed, IndVet, Inpharma, MEDLINE, MSB, NPU, NSCI, NemAb, NucAcAb, NutrAb, PE&ON, PGegResA, PN&I, PoultAb, ProtozoAb, RA&MP, RM&VM, RPP, RRTA, Reac, RefZh, RevApplEntom, SCI, SFA, SSCI, SoyAb, VetBull, WeedAb.
—BLDSC (5066.850010), CASDDS, CISTI, GNLM, IDS, IE, Infotrieve, ingenta, Linda Hall. **CCC.**
Published by: Pergamon (Subsidiary of: Elsevier Science & Technology), The Boulevard, Langford Ln, East Park, Kidlington, Oxford OX5 1GB, United Kingdom. TEL 44-1865-843000, FAX 44-1865-843010, http://www.elsevier.com/locate/jsbmb. Ed. Jorge R Pasqualini. Circ: 1,250. **Subscr. to:** Elsevier BV, PO Box 211, Amsterdam 1000 AE, Netherlands. TEL 31-20-485-3757, FAX 31-20-485-3432, nlinfo-f@elsevier.nl, http://www.elsevier.nl.

572 ITA ISSN 0075-4447
JOURNEES BIOCHIMIQUES LATINES. RAPPORTS✶. Text in French, Italian. irreg. (every 2-3 yrs.), latest 1968, 9th, Monaco. **Document type:** *Proceedings.*
Published by: Prof. A. Bonsignore, University of Genoa, Genoa, GE, Italy.

572 SCG ISSN 0354-3447
CODEN: JMBIFF
➤ **JUGOSLOVENSKA MEDICINSKA BIOHEMIJA.** Text in English, Serbo-Croatian; Summaries in English. 1982. 4/yr. YUN 3,300 domestic; USD 50 foreign (effective 2005). adv. bk.rev. 80 p./no. 2 cols./p.; back issues avail. **Document type:** *Journal, Academic/Scholarly.* **Description:** Publishes scientific papers on clinical chemistry.
Supersedes in part (in 1992): Jugoslavenska Medicinska Biokemija (0352-1311)
Indexed: ASCA, BBCI, BIOBASE, ChemAb, ChemTitl, ExcerpMed, IABS, RefZh.
—BLDSC (5073.848000), CASDDS, GNLM, IDS.
Published by: Drustvo Medicinskih Biohemicara Jugoslavije/Yugoslav Society of Medical Biochemists, Vojvode Stepe 450, Postanski Fah 146, Belgrade, 11000. TEL 381-11-3615631, FAX 381-11-3615631, dmbj@eunet.yu, http://www.dmbj.org.yu. Ed., Adv. contact Nada Majkic-Singh. Circ: 1,000 (paid and controlled).

572 JPN ISSN 0453-073X
QD415.A1 CODEN: KASEAA
KAGAKU TO SEIBUTSU/CHEMISTRY AND BIOLOGY. Text in Japanese. 1962. m. **Document type:** *Journal, Academic/Scholarly.*
Indexed: ChemAb, ChemTitl, IABS, INIS AtomInd, JPI.
—CASDDS.
Published by: (Nippon Nogei Kagakkai/Japan Society for Bioscience, Biotechnology, and Agrochemistry), Gakkai Shuppan Senta/Japan Scientific Societies Press, 6-2-10 Hongo Bunkyoku, Tokyo, 113-0033, Japan. TEL 86-3-38142001, FAX 86-3-38142002, info@jssp.co.jp, http://www.jsbba.or.jp/02/kaseiindex.html, http://www.jssp.co.jp/.

572 JPN ISSN 0911-8691
KANSANKA SHISHITSU KENKYU/LIPID PEROXIDE AND RESEARCH. Text in Japanese. a. JPY 4,000.
Indexed: INIS AtomInd.
Published by: Nihon Kasanka Shishitsu Furi Rajikaru Gakkai/Japanese Society of Lipid Peroxide and Free Radical Research, c/o Mr Kunio Yagi, Oyo Seikgaku Kenkyujo, Kani-gun, Mitakecho, Gifu-ken 505-01, Japan.

572 RUS
KHIMIYA I BIZNES. Text in English, Russian. 1991. bi-m. USD 110 in United States. adv. charts; pat.; stat.; tr.lit. back issues avail. **Document type:** *Consumer.* **Description:** Presents activities of chemical enterprises in Russia and C.I.S. and their relations with world market.
Formerly: Agrokhim Biznes (0869-8481)

Related titles: Diskette ed.
Indexed: CBNB, RefZh.
Published by: Interchim, Ul Dostoevskogo 2, Moscow, 103030, Russian Federation. TEL 7-095-2884187, ahbmag@aha.ru. Ed. Anatoli Pekhov. adv.: B&W page USD 1,200, color page USD 1,700. Circ: 5,000 (paid). US dist. addr.: East View Information Services, 3020 Harbor Ln. N., Minneapolis, MN 55447. TEL 612-550-0961.

KISO ROKA GAKKAI SAKYURA/BIOMEDICAL GERONTOLOGY CIRCULAR. see *GERONTOLOGY AND GERIATRICS*

572 JPN ISSN 0912-8921
KISO ROKA KENKYU/BIOMEDICAL GERONTOLOGY. Text in English, Japanese. 1977. s-a.
Published by: Nihon Kiso Roka Gakkai/Japan Society for Biomedical Gerontology, Tokyoto Rojin Sogo Kenkyujo, 35-2 Sakae-cho, Itabashi-ku, Tokyo, 173-0015, Japan.

572.4 CZE ISSN 1210-7921
CODEN: KBMEF
➤ **KLINICKA BIOCHEMIE A METABOLISMUS.** Text in Czech, Slovak; Summaries in Czech, English. 1972. q. EUR 72, USD 98 foreign (effective 2005). adv. bk.rev. **Document type:** *Journal, Academic/Scholarly.*
Formerly (until 1993): Biochemia Clinica Bohemoslovaca (0139-9608)
Indexed: BIOBASE, ChemAb, ChemTitl, ExcerpMed, IABS.
—BLDSC (5099.284790), CASDDS, GNLM. **CCC.**
Published by: (Ceska Lekarska Spolecnost J.E. Purkyne/Czech Medical Association), Nakladatelske Stredisko C L S J.E. Purkyne, Sokolska 31, Prague, 12026, Czech Republic. nts@cls.cz, http://www.clsjep.cz/nts/casop/biochemie/biochemie.asp. Ed. A Kazda. adv.: B&W page CZK 21,100, color page CZK 31,600; 250 x 170. Circ: 950.

➤ **KLINISK KEMI**; medlemsblad foer S F K K. see *MEDICAL SCIENCES*

➤ **KLINISK KEMI I NORDEN.** see *MEDICAL SCIENCES*

572.8 NLD ISSN 0075-7535
QP519 CODEN: LTBBDT
➤ **LABORATORY TECHNIQUES IN BIOCHEMISTRY AND MOLECULAR BIOLOGY.** Text in English. 1968. irreg., latest vol.29, 2000. price varies. back issues avail. **Document type:** *Monographic series, Academic/Scholarly.* **Description:** Covers all aspects of laboratory work in biochemistry and molecular biology.
Indexed: EngInd.
—BLDSC (5141.915000), CISTI, Ei, IE, Infotrieve, KNAW. **CCC.**
Published by: Elsevier BV (Subsidiary of: Elsevier Science & Technology), Radarweg 29, Amsterdam, 1043 NX, Netherlands. TEL 31-20-4853911, FAX 31-20-4852457, nlinfo-f@elsevier.nl, http://www.elsevier.nl. Eds. P C van der Vliet, S. Pillai.

➤ **LE LAIT.** see *BIOLOGY—Microbiology*

➤ **LECTINS.** see *BIOLOGY—Abstracting, Bibliographies, Statistics*

572 USA ISSN 0740-7394
LINSCOTT'S DIRECTORY OF IMMUNOLOGICAL AND BIOLOGICAL REAGENTS. Text in English. 1983. biennial. **Document type:** *Directory, Trade.* **Description:** More than 100,000 listings for products and services available from more than 500 commercial and governmental sources worldwide.
Related titles: Online - full content ed.: USD 75.
Published by: Linscott's Directory, 6 Grove St., Mill Valley, CA 94941. TEL 415-389-9674, FAX 415-389-6025, linsdir@sbcglobal.net, http://www.linscottsdirectory.com.

572.57 GBR ISSN 0956-666X
CODEN: LITEEI
LIPID TECHNOLOGY. Text in English. 1989. m. GBP 395, USD 755; GBP 445 combined subscription print & email; USD 850 combined subscription print & email (effective 2005). abstr.; pat.; stat. cum.index: 1989-1998. back issues avail. **Document type:** *Newsletter, Trade.* **Description:** Contains commissioned feature articles from leading experts, news stories, and regular sections on nutrition, analysis, patent abstracts, research highlights, and market updates.
Incorporates (1995-2003): Lipid Technology Newsletter (1357-7166)
Related titles: E-mail ed.
Indexed: FS&TA, RefZh.
—BLDSC (5221.797000), IE, ingenta. **CCC.**
Published by: P.J. Barnes & Associates, PO Box 200, Bridgwater, TA7 0YZ, United Kingdom. TEL 44-1823-698973, FAX 44-1823-698971, editor@pjbarnes.co.uk, sales@pjbarnes.co.uk, http://www.pjbarnes.co.uk/lt/lipidtechnology.htm. Ed. Frank D Gunstone. Pub. Peter J Barnes.

572.57 USA ISSN 0024-4201
QP501 CODEN: LPDSAP
➤ **LIPIDS.** Text in English. 1966. m. USD 145 domestic to individuals; USD 170 foreign to individuals; USD 372 domestic to institutions; USD 402 foreign to institutions; USD 426 combined subscription domestic to individuals for print & online eds.; USD 456 combined subscription foreign to individuals for print & online eds (effective 2005). adv. charts; illus. back issues avail.; reprint service avail. from PQC. **Document type:** *Journal, Academic/Scholarly.* **Description:** Contains original research on lipids, biochemistry, and related biomedical subjects.
Related titles: Microfilm ed.: (from PQC); Online - full text ed.: USD 145 to individuals (effective 2003) (from EBSCO Publishing, ProQuest Information & Learning).
Indexed: ASCA, ASFA, AbHyg, AgBio, Agr, AgrForAb, AnBrAb, AnalAb, BBCI, BIOBASE, BIOSIS Prev, BibAg, BioCN&I, BiolAb, CCI, CIN, CPA, ChemAb, ChemTitl, ChromAb, CurCont, DSA, EngInd, ExcerpMed, FCA, FPA, FS&TA, ForAb, HelmAb, HortAb, IABS, ISR, IndMed, IndVet, Inpharma, MEDLINE, MSB, MaizeAb, NPU, NRN, NSCI, NemAb, NutrAb, OrnHort, PBA, PE&ON, PGegResA, PGrRegA, PHN&I, PN&I, PotatoAb, PoultAb, ProtozoAb, RA&MP, RGAb, RM&VM, RPP, Reac, RefZh, RevApplEntom, RiceAb, S&F, SCI, SFA, SIA, SSCI, SeedAb, SoyAb, TDB, THA, TOSA, TriticAb, VITIS, VetBull, WAE&RSA, WeedAb, WildRev, ZooRec.
—BLDSC (5221.850000), CASDDS, CISTI, Ei, GNLM, IDS, IE, Infotrieve, ingenta, Linda Hall. **CCC.**
Published by: (American Oil Chemists' Society), A O C S Press, 2211 W Bradley Ave, Champaign, IL 61821. TEL 217-359-2344, FAX 217-351-8091, publications@aocs.org, http://www.aocs.org/press/lipids.htm. Ed. Howard R Knapp. Pubs. Greg Reed, Mary Lane. R&P Greg Reed. adv.: B&W page USD 725; 8.25 x 11. Circ: 1,500 (paid).

572.7 GBR ISSN 1476-511X
➤ **LIPIDS IN HEALTH AND DISEASE.** Text in English. 2002. irreg. free (effective 2006). **Document type:** *Journal, Academic/Scholarly.* **Description:** Publishes papers in the area of lipids that applies to lipid biochemistry, pharmacology, toxicology, their role in health and disease, synthesis of new lipid compounds and their actions and significance in health and disease.
Media: Online - full content (from EBSCO Publishing, National Library of Medicine).
—CCC.
Published by: BioMed Central Ltd. (Subsidiary of: Current Science Ltd), Middlesex House, 34-42 Cleveland St, London, W1T 4LB, United Kingdom. TEL 44-20-76319131, FAX 44-20-76319923, info@biomedcentral.com, http://www.lipidworld.com, http://www.biomedcentral.com. Ed. Undurti N. Das.

➤ **LUMINESCENCE**; journal of biological and chemical luminescence. see *CHEMISTRY—Physical Chemistry*

572.8 DEU ISSN 1616-5187
QD380 CODEN: MBAIBU
➤ **MACROMOLECULAR BIOSCIENCE.** Text in English. 2001. m. EUR 1,298 in Europe; CHF 1,998 in Switzerland & Liechtenstein; USD 1,698 elsewhere; EUR 1,428 combined subscription in Europe print & online eds.; CHF 2,198 combined subscription print & online eds. in Switzerland & Liechtenstein; USD 1,868 combined subscription elsewhere print & online eds. (effective 2006). bk.rev. **Document type:** *Journal, Academic/Scholarly.* **Description:** Publishes papers and reviews in the field of chemistry, physics, biotechnology, characterization, modification, and biomedical applications of biomaterials including biopolymers (polymers from natural and renewable resources, such as proteins, peptides, carbohydrates, nucleic acids), programmable biosynthesis of new polymers, biomineralization, biomimetics, biocomposites, and membranes.
Related titles: Online - full text ed.: ISSN 1616-5195. EUR 1,298 in Europe; CHF 1,998 in Switzerland & Liechtenstein; USD 1,698 elsewhere (effective 2006) (from EBSCO Publishing, Swets Information Services, Wiley InterScience).
Indexed: BBCI, BIOBASE, CCI, ChemAb, ExcerpMed, MSCI, RefZh, VITIS.
—BLDSC (5330.396400), CISTI, IE, ingenta, Linda Hall. **CCC.**
Published by: Wiley - V C H Verlag GmbH & Co. KGaA (Subsidiary of: John Wiley & Sons, Inc.), Boschstr 12, Weinheim, 69469, Germany. TEL 49-6201-6060, FAX 49-6201-606328, macromol@wiley-vch.de, subservice@wiley-vch.de, info@wiley-vch.de, http://www.wiley-vch.de/vch/journals/2127/index.html. Ed. Ingrid Meisel. R&P Claudia Jerke.

▼ ➤ **MECHANICS & CHEMISTRY OF BIOSYSTEMS.** see *BIOLOGY—Bioengineering*

➤ **MEDICAL ENGINEERING & PHYSICS.** see *MEDICAL SCIENCES*

572 BGR ISSN 0204-9716
➤ **MEDITSINSKI PREGLED. KLINICHNA LABORATORIIA.** Text in Bulgarian. 1970. q. BGL 14 domestic; USD 40 foreign (effective 2005). adv. bk.rev. abstr.; bibl. index. 48 p./no.; back issues avail. **Document type:** *Journal, Academic/Scholarly.* **Description:** Abstracts of foreign publications in the field of medical laboratory, includes methods, techniques and equipment.
Indexed: RefZh.
Published by: Meditsinski Universitet - Sofia, Tsentralna Meditsinska Biblioteka, Tsentur za Informatsiia po Meditsina/Medical University - Sofia, Central Medical Library, Medical Information Center, 1 Sv Georgi Sofiiski ul, Sofia, 1431, Bulgaria. TEL 359-2-9522342, FAX 359-2-9522393, lydia@medun.acad.bg, http://www.medun.acad.bg/cmb_htm/cmb1_home_bg.htm. Ed. Dr. K Tsachev. R&P, Adv. contact Lydia Tacheva. B&W page USD 50, color page USD 150; 12 x 18. Circ: 200.

572.7 USA ISSN 1046-2023
QP519.7 CODEN: MTHDE9
➤ **METHODS.** Key Title: Methods (San Diego). Text in English. 1990. 12/yr. EUR 270 in Europe to individuals; JPY 28,100 in Japan to individuals; USD 202 to individuals except Europe and Japan; EUR 567 in Europe to institutions; JPY 59,300 in Japan to institutions; USD 424 to institutions except Europe and Japan; EUR 134 in Europe to students; JPY 14,000 in Japan to students; USD 116 to students except Europe and Japan (effective 2006). abstr. back issues avail. **Document type:** *Journal, Academic/Scholarly.* **Description:** Contains topic-oriented articles that cover new methods applicable to a number of disciplines.
Incorporates (in 1995): Methods - GenoMethods (1078-1501); (1992-1995): NeuroProtocols (1058-6741); (in 1995): Methods - Immunomethods (1078-151X); Which was formerly (1992-1994): Immunomethods (1058-6687)
Related titles: Online - full text ed.: ISSN 1095-9130. USD 453 (effective 2002) (from EBSCO Publishing, Gale Group, IngentaConnect, O C L C Online Computer Library Center, Inc., ScienceDirect, Swets Information Services).
Indexed: ASCA, BBCI, BIOSIS Prev, BiolAb, CIN, ChemAb, ChemTitl, CurCont, ExcerpMed, ISR, IndMed, MEDLINE, NSCI, RefZh, SCI.
—BLDSC (5746.575000), CASDDS, CINDOC, CISTI, GNLM, IDS, IE, Infotrieve, ingenta, Linda Hall. **CCC.**
Published by: Academic Press (Subsidiary of: Elsevier Science & Technology), 525 B St, Ste 1900, San Diego, CA 92101-4495. TEL 619-231-6616, FAX 619-699-6422, apsubs@acad.com, http://www.elsevier.com/locate/ymeth, http://www.academicpress.com. Eds. Dr. Kenneth W Adolph, P Michael Conn, John N Abelson, Melvin I Simon.

572.7 USA ISSN 0076-6879
QP601 CODEN: MENZAU
➤ **METHODS IN ENZYMOLOGY.** Text in English. 1955. irreg., latest vol.405, 2005, Nov. USD 149, EUR 135, GBP 99 per vol. (effective 2005). reprint service avail. from ISI. **Document type:** *Monographic series, Academic/Scholarly.*
Related titles: Online - full text ed.: ISSN 1557-7988 (from ScienceDirect).
Indexed: ASCA, ASFA, AbHyg, Agr, BBCI, BCI, BIOSIS Prev, BiolAb, CCI, CIN, ChemAb, ChemTitl, DSA, DentInd, ESPM, ExcerpMed, INIS AtomInd, ISR, IndMed, LHB, MBA, MEDLINE, MSB, NutrAb, ProtozoAb, RM&VM, RevApplEntom, SCI, SFA, SIA.
—BLDSC (5748.060000), CASDDS, CISTI, GNLM, IE, Infotrieve, ingenta, KNAW. **CCC.**
Published by: Academic Press (Subsidiary of: Elsevier Science & Technology), 525 B St, Ste 1900, San Diego, CA 92101-4495. usbkinfo@elsevier.com, apsubs@acad.com, http://www.sciencedirect.com/science/bookseries/00766879, http://www.academicpress.com. Eds. John N Abelson, Melvin I Simon.

572 USA ISSN 0076-6941
QD271 CODEN: MBANAA
➤ **METHODS OF BIOCHEMICAL ANALYSIS.** Text in English. 1954. irreg., latest 1993. USD 250 per vol. (effective 2005). **Document type:** *Monographic series, Academic/Scholarly.*
Indexed: ASCA, AbHyg, BBCI, BIOSIS Prev, BiolAb, CIN, ChemAb, ChemTitl, CompR, DBA, ISR, IndMed, MEDLINE, MathR, NutrAb, SCI.
—BLDSC (5747.000000), CASDDS, CISTI, GNLM, IE, Infotrieve, ingenta, Linda Hall. **CCC.**
Published by: John Wiley & Sons, Inc., 111 River St, Hoboken, NJ 07030-5774. TEL 201-748-6000, 800-825-7550, FAX 201-748-5915, uscs-wis@wiley.com, http://www.wiley.com/WileyCDA/WileyTitle/productCd-0471582603.html. Ed. David Glick.

➤ **MICROBIAL PATHOGENESIS.** see *MEDICAL SCIENCES—Communicable Diseases*

➤ **MICROBIOLOGY AND MOLECULAR BIOLOGY REVIEWS.** see *BIOLOGY—Microbiology*

➤ **MITTEILUNGEN AUS LEBENSMITTELUNTERSUCHUNG UND HYGIENE/TRAVAUX DE CHIMIE ALIMENTAIRE ET D'HYGIENE.** see *NUTRITION AND DIETETICS*

572.8 NLD ISSN 0166-6851
QL757 CODEN: MBIPDP
➤ **MOLECULAR AND BIOCHEMICAL PARASITOLOGY.** Text in Dutch. 1980. 12/yr. EUR 3,795 in Europe to institutions; JPY 504,400 in Japan to institutions; USD 4,245 to institutions except Europe and Japan (effective 2006). adv. back issues avail. **Document type:** *Journal, Academic/Scholarly.* **Description:** Provides a medium for the rapid publication of investigations of the molecular biology, molecular immunology and biochemistry of parasitic protozoa and helminths and their interactions with the host.
Related titles: Microform ed.: (from PQC); Online - full text ed.: (from EBSCO Publishing, Gale Group, IngentaConnect, ScienceDirect, Swets Information Services).
Indexed: AIDS&CR, ASCA, ASFA, AbHyg, AgBio, Agr, AgrForAb, AnBrAb, BBCI, BIOBASE, BIOSIS Prev, BibAg, BioCN&I, BiolAb, ChemAb, ChemTitl, CurCont, DBA, DSA, ESPM, ExcerpMed, GenetAb, HGA, HelmAb, HortAb, IABS, ISR, ImmunAb, IndMed, IndVet, Inpharma, MBA, MEDLINE, NemAb, NucAcAb, NutrAb, PBA, PN&I, PotatoAb, PoultAb, ProtozoAb, RA&MP, RM&VM, RPP, Reac, RevApplEntom, SCI, SIA, SoyAb, TDB, VetBull, ZooRec.
—BLDSC (5900.753000), CASDDS, CISTI, GNLM, IDS, IE, Infotrieve, ingenta. **CCC.**
Published by: Elsevier BV (Subsidiary of: Elsevier Science & Technology), Radarweg 29, Amsterdam, 1043 NX, Netherlands. TEL 31-20-4853911, FAX 31-20-4852457, nlinfo-f@elsevier.nl, http://www.elsevier.com/locate/molbiopara, http://www.elsevier.nl. Eds. A P Waters, C E Clayton.

572 USA ISSN 0300-8177
QR151 CODEN: MCBIB8
➤ **MOLECULAR AND CELLULAR BIOCHEMISTRY**; an international journal for chemical biology in health and disease. Text in English. 1973. 26/yr. EUR 5,298, USD 5,375, GBP 3,318 combined subscription to institutions print & online eds. (effective 2005). adv. bk.rev. bibl.; illus. back issues avail.; reprint service avail. from PQC,PSC. **Document type:** *Journal, Academic/Scholarly.* **Description:** Publishes original, full-length research papers and short communications in all areas of the biochemical sciences, the emphasis being on those papers which present novel findings relevant to the biochemical basis of cellular function and disease processes, as well as the mechanics of action of hormones and chemical agents.
Supersedes: Enzymologia (0013-9424)
Related titles: Microform ed.: (from PMC, PQC); Online - full text ed.: ISSN 1573-4919 (from EBSCO Publishing, Gale Group, IngentaConnect, Kluwer Online, O C L C Online Computer Library Center, Inc., Ovid Technologies, Inc., Springer LINK, Swets Information Services).
Indexed: ASCA, ASFA, AbHyg, AgBio, Agr, AgrForAb, AnBrAb, AnalAb, BBCI, BCI, BIOBASE, BIOSIS Prev, BibAg, BibLing, BiolAb, ChemAb, ChemTitl, CurCont, DBA, DSA, DentInd, ExcerpMed, FCA, FPA, FS&TA, ForAb, GenetAb, HGA, HelmAb, HortAb, IABS, ISR, IndMed, IndVet, Inpharma, MEDLINE, MSB, MaizeAb, NSCI, NutrAb, OrnHort, PBA, PE&ON, PGegResA, PN&I, PoultAb, ProtozoAb, RA&MP, RDA, RM&VM, RPP, RRTA, Reac, RefZh, RevApplEntom, S&F, SCI, SIA, SeedAb, SoyAb, TDB, TriticAb, VITIS, VetBull, WeedAb.
—BLDSC (5900.756000), CASDDS, CISTI, GNLM, IDS, IE, Infotrieve, ingenta, Linda Hall. **CCC.**
Published by: Springer-Verlag New York, Inc. (Subsidiary of: Springer Science+Business Media), 233 Spring St, New York, NY 10013. TEL 212-460-1500, FAX 212-460-1575, service@springer-ny.com, http://springerlink.metapress.com/openurl.asp?genre=journal&issn=0300-8177, http://www.springer-ny.com. Ed. Naranjan S Dhalla. Circ: 1,000. **Subscr. to:** Journal Fulfillment, PO Box 2485, Secaucus, NJ 07096-2485. TEL 201-348-4033, FAX 201-348-4505, journals@springer-ny.com.

572.8 USA ISSN 0270-7306
QH506 CODEN: MCEBD4
➤ **MOLECULAR AND CELLULAR BIOLOGY.** Text in English. 1981. fortn. USD 927 domestic to institutions; USD 997 in Canada to institutions; USD 1,109 in Europe to institutions; USD 1,170 in Latin America to institutions; USD 1,179 elsewhere to institutions (effective 2006). adv. illus. Index. back issues avail.; reprint service avail. from PQC. **Document type:** *Journal, Academic/Scholarly.* **Description:** Covers the molecular biology of eukaryotic cells of both microbial and higher organisms. Sections include gene expression, transcriptional regulation, cell growth and development, nucleocytoplasmic communication, cell and organelle structure and assembly, DNA dynamics and chromosome structure, and mammalian genetic models with minimal or complex phenotypes.
Related titles: CD-ROM ed.: ISSN 1067-8824. 1992. USD 500 in North America; USD 524 elsewhere; Microform ed.: (from PQC); Online - full text ed.: ISSN 1098-5549. USD 868 to institutions (effective 2006) (from EBSCO Publishing, National Library of Medicine).
Indexed: AEBA, AIDS Ab, AIDS&CR, ASCA, ASFA, AbHyg, AgBio, AnBrAb, B&AI, B&BAb, BBCI, BCI, BIOBASE, BIOSIS Prev, BiolAb, CIN, CPA, CTA, ChemAb, ChemTitl, ChemoAb, CurCont, DBA, DSA, DentInd, ESPM, ExcerpMed, GenetAb, HGA, HelmAb, HerbAb, HortAb, IABS, INIS AtomInd, ISR, IndMed, IndVet, Inpharma, M&PBA, MBA, MEDLINE, MaizeAb, NSA, NSCI, NemAb, NucAcAb, NutrAb, OGFA, PBA, PE&ON, PGegResA, PotatoAb, PoultAb, ProtozoAb, RM&VM, RPP, Reac, RefZh, RevApplEntom, S&F, SCI, SFA, Telegen, TriticAb, VetBull, WeedAb, ZooRec.
—BLDSC (5900.757000), CASDDS, CISTI, GNLM, IDS, IE, Infotrieve, ingenta, KNAW, Linda Hall. **CCC.**
Published by: American Society for Microbiology, 1752 N St, N W, Washington, DC 20036-2904. FAX 202-942-9347, asmjournals@asm.org, subscriptions@asmusa.org, http://mcb.asm.org/, http://www.asm.org. Ed. Andrew B. Onderdonk. Circ: 10,668 (paid). **Subscr. to:** PO Box 11127, Birmingham, AL 35201-1127. TEL 205-995-1567, 800-633-4931, FAX 205-995-1588.

572.6 USA ISSN 1535-9476
QP551 CODEN: MCPOBS
➤ **MOLECULAR AND CELLULAR PROTEOMICS.** Text in English. 2002. m. USD 635 combined subscription to individuals print & online eds.; USD 985 combined subscription to institutions print & online eds.; USD 30 per issue (effective 2004). adv. **Document type:** *Journal, Academic/Scholarly.* **Description:** Consists of original articles and short reviews that deal with the structural and functional properties of proteins and their expression, particularly with respect to development.
Related titles: Online - full text ed.: ISSN 1535-9484. 2002. USD 275 to individuals; USD 625 to institutions; free to members ASBMB (effective 2004) (from EBSCO Publishing, HighWire Press).
Indexed: AbHyg, AgBio, AnalAb, B&BAb, BBCI, BIOSIS Prev, BioCN&I, BiolAb, CPA, ExcerpMed, GenetAb, HortAb, MSB, PBA, PHN&I, ProtozoAb, TDB, WeedAb.
—BLDSC (5900.761050), CISTI, IE, Infotrieve, ingenta, Linda Hall. **CCC.**
Published by: American Society for Biochemistry and Molecular Biology, Inc., 9650 Rockville Pike, Bethesda, MD 20814-3996. TEL 301-530-7145, FAX 301-571-1824, mcp@asbmb.faseb.org, asbmb@asbmb.faseb.org, http://www.mcponline.org/, http://www.asbmb.org. Ed. Dr. Ralph A. Bradshaw. adv.: B&W page USD 900; trim 8.375 x 10.875. Circ: 2,500.

572 RUS ISSN 0026-8933
QH506 CODEN: MOLBBJ
➤ **MOLECULAR BIOLOGY.** Text in English. 1967. bi-m. EUR 3,655, USD 3,248, GBP 2,278 combined subscription to institutions print & online eds. (effective 2005). back issues avail. **Document type:** *Journal, Academic/Scholarly.* **Description:** Covers advances in the field of chemical and physical bases of principal life phenomena, including studies on the chemistry and physics of the most important biopolymers (proteins and nucleic acids), their structure, and their functions.
Related titles: Microfilm ed.: (from PQC); Online - full text ed.: ISSN 1608-3245 (from EBSCO Publishing, Gale Group, IngentaConnect, Kluwer Online, O C L C Online Computer Library Center, Inc., Ovid Technologies, Inc., Springer LINK, Swets Information Services); ♦ Translation of: Molekulyarnaya Biologiya. ISSN 0026-8984.
Indexed: ASCA, ASFA, AnBrAb, B&AI, BBCI, BCI, BibLing, BiolAb, CCI, ChemAb, ChemTitl, CurCont, ExcerpMed, FCA, IABS, ISR, IndMed, Inpharma, MEDLINE, PE&ON, Reac, SCI.
—BLDSC (0416.235000), CASDDS, CISTI, GNLM, IDS, IE, Infotrieve, ingenta, Linda Hall. **CCC.**
Published by: (Rossiiskaya Akademiya Nauk/Russian Academy of Sciences), M A I K Nauka - Interperiodica, Profsoyuznaya ul 90, Moscow, 117997, Russian Federation. TEL 7-095-3347420, FAX 7-095-3360666, compmg@maik.ru, http://www.maik.rssi.ru/journals/molbio.htm, http://www.maik.ru. Ed. Lev Kiselev. **Subscr. to:** Springer-Verlag Dordrecht, Journals Department, PO Box 322, Dordrecht, Netherlands. TEL 31-78-6576392, FAX 31-78-6576474.

572 NLD ISSN 0301-4851
QH506 CODEN: MLBRBU
➤ **MOLECULAR BIOLOGY REPORTS**; an international journal on molecular and cellular biology. Text in Dutch. 1973. q. EUR 498, USD 508, GBP 315 combined subscription to institutions print & online eds. (effective 2005). adv. bk.rev. reprint service avail. from PSC. **Document type:** *Journal, Academic/Scholarly.* **Description:** Publishes original research papers on molecular and cellular biology, including DNA replication, protein biosynthesis and related subjects.
Related titles: Microform ed.: (from PQC); Online - full text ed.: ISSN 1573-4978 (from EBSCO Publishing, Gale Group, IngentaConnect, Kluwer Online, O C L C Online Computer Library Center, Inc., Ovid Technologies, Inc., Springer LINK, Swets Information Services).
Indexed: ASCA, ASFA, AbHyg, AgBio, Agr, AnBrAb, B&BAb, BBCI, BCI, BIOBASE, BIOSIS Prev, BibLing, BioCN&I, BiolAb, CIN, CPA, ChemAb, ChemTitl, CurCont, DBA, ExcerpMed, FCA, ForAb, GenetAb, HGA, HelmAb, HerbAb, HortAb, IABS, ISR, IndMed, IndVet, Inpharma, MEDLINE, MSB, NucAcAb, NutrAb, OrnHort, PBA, PGegResA, PoultAb, RA&MP, RPP, Reac, RefZh, RiceAb, SCI, SIA, Telegen, VetBull, WeedAb.
—BLDSC (5900.798000), CASDDS, CISTI, GNLM, IDS, IE, Infotrieve, ingenta, Linda Hall. **CCC.**
Published by: Springer-Verlag Dordrecht (Subsidiary of: Springer Science+Business Media), Van Godewijckstraat 30, Dordrecht, 3311 GX, Netherlands. TEL 31-78-6576050, FAX 31-78-6576474, http://springerlink.metapress.com/openurl.asp?genre=journal&issn=0301-4851, http://www.springeronline.com. Eds. Andre J van Wijnen, Gary S Stein.

➤ **MOLECULAR BIOLOGY TECHNIQUES.** see *BIOLOGY—Abstracting, Bibliographies, Statistics*

572.4 576.5 USA ISSN 1096-7192
QP501 CODEN: MGMEFF
➤ **MOLECULAR GENETICS AND METABOLISM.** Text in English. 1969. 12/yr. EUR 513 in Europe to individuals; JPY 53,600 in Japan to individuals; USD 447 to individuals except Europe and Japan; EUR 1,358 in Europe to institutions; JPY 141,800 in Japan to institutions; USD 1,054 to institutions except Europe and Japan; EUR 168 in Europe to students; JPY 17,700 in Japan to students; USD 147 to students except Europe and Japan (effective 2006). adv. index. back issues avail. **Document type:** *Academic/Scholarly.* **Description:** Publishes papers describing original research in biochemistry, physiological chemistry, and metabolic biology. Emphasis is on the determination of the interrelations among reactions, sequences, and formed elements of the cell.
Former titles (until 1998): Biochemical and Molecular Medicine (1077-3150); (until 1995): Biochemical Medicine and Metabolic Biology (0885-4505); (until 1986): Biochemical Medicine (0006-2944)
Related titles: Online - full text ed.: ISSN 1096-7206. USD 1,103 (effective 2002) (from EBSCO Publishing, Gale Group, IngentaConnect, O C L C Online Computer Library Center, Inc., ScienceDirect, Swets Information Services).
Indexed: ASCA, AbHyg, AgBio, Agr, AnBrAb, AnalAb, B&BAb, BBCI, BIOBASE, BIOSIS Prev, BiolAb, CIN, ChemAb, ChemTitl, CurCont, DBA, DSA, DentInd, ExcerpMed, GenetAb, IABS, ISR, IndMed, IndVet, Inpharma, MEDLINE, MSB, NemAb, NucAcAb, NutrAb, PE&ON, PoultAb, ProtozoAb, RDA, RM&VM, Reac, SCI, SSCI, SoyAb, TDB, TOSA, VetBull.
—BLDSC (5900.817540), CASDDS, CISTI, GNLM, IDS, IE, ingenta, Linda Hall. **CCC.**
Published by: Academic Press (Subsidiary of: Elsevier Science & Technology), 525 B St, Ste 1900, San Diego, CA 92101-4495. TEL 619-231-6616, 800-894-3434, FAX 619-699-6422, apsubs@acad.com, http://www.elsevier.com/locate/ymgme, http://www.academicpress.com. Ed. Dr. Edward R B McCabe.

➤ **MOLECULAR GENETICS, MICROBIOLOGY AND VIROLOGY.** see *BIOLOGY—Microbiology*

572 GBR ISSN 0161-5890
QR180 CODEN: MOIMD5
➤ **MOLECULAR IMMUNOLOGY.** Text in English, French, German, Spanish. 1964. 14/yr. EUR 2,807 in Europe to institutions; JPY 372,900 in Japan to institutions; USD 3,141 to institutions except Europe and Japan; EUR 328 in Europe to qualified personnel; JPY 43,500 in Japan to qualified personnel; USD 367 to qualified personnel except Europe and Japan (effective 2006). adv. bk.rev. charts; illus. index. back issues avail. **Document type:** *Journal, Academic/Scholarly.* **Description:** Communicates immunological knowledge which can be delineated at the molecular level.
Formerly: Immunochemistry (0019-2791)
Related titles: Microfilm ed.: (from PQC); Online - full text ed.: (from EBSCO Publishing, Gale Group, IngentaConnect, ScienceDirect, Swets Information Services).
Indexed: AIDS&CR, ASCA, AbHyg, AgBio, AnBrAb, ApicAb, BBCI, BCI, BIOBASE, BIOSIS Prev, BiolAb, CIN, ChemAb, ChemTitl, CurCont, DBA, DSA, DentInd, ExcerpMed, FoMM, ForAb, GenetAb, HGA, HelmAb, HortAb, IABS, ISR, ImmunAb, IndMed, IndVet, Inpharma, MEDLINE, NemAb, NutrAb, PBA, PE&ON, PN&I, ProtozoAb, RM&VM, Reac, RevApplEntom, SCI, SFA, SoyAb, TDB, VetBull, WeedAb.
—BLDSC (5900.817700), CASDDS, CISTI, GNLM, IDS, IE, Infotrieve, ingenta, Linda Hall. **CCC.**
Published by: Pergamon (Subsidiary of: Elsevier Science & Technology), The Boulevard, Langford Ln, East Park, Kidlington, Oxford OX5 1GB, United Kingdom. TEL 44-1865-843000, FAX 44-1865-843010, http://www.elsevier.com/locate/molimm. Eds. C. J.M. Melief, M. R. Daha. Circ: 2,100. **Subscr. to:** Elsevier BV, PO Box 211, Amsterdam 1000 AE, Netherlands. TEL 31-20-485-3757, FAX 31-20-485-3432, nlinfo-f@elsevier.nl, http://www.elsevier.nl.

572.8 GBR ISSN 0968-7688
QH601 CODEN: MMEBE7
➤ **MOLECULAR MEMBRANE BIOLOGY.** Text in English. 1978. bi-m. GBP 598, USD 988 combined subscription to institutions print & online eds. (effective 2006). adv. abstr. index. reprint service avail. from PSC. **Document type:** *Journal, Academic/Scholarly.* **Description:** Provides specialists in physiology, biochemistry, biophysics and medicine, with a forum for research in the study of membranes.
Formerly (until 1994): Membrane Biochemistry (0149-046X)
Related titles: Online - full text ed.: ISSN 1464-5203. GBP 568, USD 939 to institutions (effective 2006) (from EBSCO Publishing, Gale Group, IngentaConnect, O C L C Online Computer Library Center, Inc., Swets Information Services).

B

Indexed: ASFA, AbHyg, AgBio, AnBrAb, BBCI, BIOBASE, BIOSIS Prev, BiolAb, CIN, CPA, ChemAb, ChemTitl, CurCont, DSA, ExcerpMed, HortAb, IABS, ISR, IndMed, IndVet, Inpharma, MEDLINE, NutrAb, OrnHort, PBA, PGegResA, PoultAb, RA&MP, RM&VM, Reac, RefZh, SCI, TDB, TriticAb, VetBull.
—BLDSC (5900.817955), CASDDS, CISTI, GNLM, IDS, IE, Infotrieve, ingenta, KNAW, Linda Hall. **CCC.**
Published by: Taylor & Francis Ltd (Subsidiary of: Taylor & Francis Group), 4 Park Sq, Milton Park, Abingdon, OX14 4RN, United Kingdom. TEL 44-1235-828600, FAX 44-1235-829000, info@tandf.co.uk, http://www.tandf.co.uk/journals/titles/09687688.asp. **Subscr. in N. America to:** Taylor & Francis Inc., Customer Services Dept, 325 Chestnut St, 8th Fl, Philadelphia, PA 19106. TEL 800-354-1420, FAX 215-625-8914; **Subscr. to:** Journals Customer Service, Rankine Rd, Basingstoke, Hants RG24 8PR, United Kingdom. TEL 44-1256-813000, FAX 44-1256-330245, enquiry@tandf.co.uk.

B

573.8 USA ISSN 0893-7648
QP365.2 CODEN: MONBEW
➤ **MOLECULAR NEUROBIOLOGY**; a review journal. Abbreviated title: M N. Text in English. 1987. bi-m. USD 345 to individuals; USD 665 to institutions; USD 355 combined subscription to individuals print & online eds.; USD 695 combined subscription to institutions print & online eds. (effective 2005). adv. bk.rev. abstr.; bibl.; charts; illus. index. 100 p./no.; back issues avail. **Document type:** *Journal, Academic/Scholarly.* **Description:** Publishes review articles for neuroscientists needing to keep abreast of current experimental and clinical brain research at the molecular level.
Related titles: Online - full text ed.: USD 295 to individuals; USD 590 to institutions (effective 2004) (from EBSCO Publishing, Gale Group, IngentaConnect, O C L C Online Computer Library Center, Inc., Ovid Technologies, Inc., Swets Information Services).
Indexed: ASCA, ASFA, AgBio, AnBrAb, B&BAb, BBCI, BIOSIS Prev, BiolAb, CIN, CTA, ChemAb, ChemTitl, ChemoAb, CurCont, ExcerpMed, ISR, IndMed, IndVet, Inpharma, MEDLINE, NSA, NSCI, PE&ON, Reac, RefZh, SCI, e-psyche.
—BLDSC (5900.817980), CASDDS, CISTI, GNLM, IDS, IE, Infotrieve, ingenta, KNAW. **CCC.**
Published by: Humana Press, Inc., 999 Riverview Dr, Ste 208, Totowa, NJ 07512. TEL 973-256-1699, FAX 973-256-8341, humana@humanapr.com, http://humanapress.com/journals.pasp. Eds. Jacques Mallet, Nicolas G Bazan. Pub. Thomas B. Lanigan Jr. R&P Wendy A. Warren. Adv. contacts John Chasse, Thomas B. Lanigan Jr. **Subscr. addr. in Japan:** Maruzen Co., Ltd., 3-10 Nihonbashi, 2-Chome, Chuo-ku, Tokyo 103, Japan. TEL 81-3-3275-8591, FAX 81-3-3275-0657, journal@maruzen.co.jp, http://www.maruzen.co.jp.

572.8 USA ISSN 0894-0282
SB732.6 CODEN: MPMIEL
➤ **MOLECULAR PLANT - MICROBE INTERACTIONS.** Variant title: M P M I(Molecular Plant - Microbe Interactions). Text in English. 1988. m. USD 114 combined subscription domestic to members print & online eds.; USD 130 combined subscription in Canada to members print & online eds.; USD 143 combined subscription elsewhere to members print & online eds. (effective 2005). back issues avail. **Document type:** *Journal, Academic/Scholarly.* **Description:** Devoted to significant research on the molecular genetics and molecular biology of pathological, symbiotic, and associative interactions of microbes with plants or microbes that affect such interactions.
Related titles: CD-ROM ed.; Online - full text ed.: (from EBSCO Publishing, ProQuest Information & Learning).
Indexed: ASCA, ASFA, AgBio, Agr, AgrForAb, BBCI, BCI, BIOSIS Prev, BioCN&I, BiolAb, CIN, CPA, ChemAb, ChemTitl, CurCont, DSA, ESPM, FCA, FS&TA, ForAb, GenetAb, HerbAb, HortAb, IABS, ISR, IndMed, MBA, MEDLINE, MaizeAb, NemAb, OrnHort, PBA, PGegResA, PGrRegA, PHN&I, PN&I, PlantSci, PotatoAb, RA&MP, RM&VM, RPP, RiceAb, S&F, SCI, SIA, SeedAb, SoyAb, TDB, TriticAb, VITIS, WeedAb.
—BLDSC (5900.826000), CASDDS, CISTI, GNLM, IDS, IE, Infotrieve, ingenta, Linda Hall. **CCC.**
Published by: American Phytopathological Society, 3340 Pilot Knob, St. Paul, MN 55121-2097. TEL 651-454-7250, 800-328-7560, FAX 651-454-0766, aps@scisoc.org, http://www.apsnet.org/mpmi. Ed. Herman Spaink. Adv. contact Rhonda Wilke. Circ: 1,492. **Co-sponsor:** International Society for Molecular Plant - Microbe Interactions.

572.8 USA ISSN 1040-452X
QP251 CODEN: MREDEE
➤ **MOLECULAR REPRODUCTION AND DEVELOPMENT.** Text in English. 1988. m. (in 3 vols., 4 nos./vol.). USD 5,350 domestic to institutions; USD 5,494 in Canada & Mexico to institutions; USD 5,578 elsewhere to institutions; USD 5,885 combined subscription domestic to institutions print & online eds.; USD 6,029 combined subscription in Canada & Mexico to institutions print & online eds.; USD 6,113 combined subscription elsewhere to institutions print & online eds. (effective 2006). adv. bk.rev. back issues avail. **Document type:** *Journal, Academic/Scholarly.* **Description:** Covers molecular biology of spermatogenesis, oogenesis, and embryonic and fetal development.
Incorporates (1978-1990): Gamete Research (0148-7280)
Related titles: Microform ed.: (from PQC); Online - full text ed.: ISSN 1098-2795. 1996. USD 5,350 to institutions (effective 2006) (from EBSCO Publishing, Swets Information Services, Wiley InterScience).
Indexed: ASCA, ASFA, AbHyg, AgBio, Agr, AnBrAb, B&BAb, BBCI, BCI, BIOBASE, BIOSIS Prev, BiolAb, CIN, ChemAb, ChemTitl, CurCont, DSA, ExcerpMed, GenetAb, HGA, HelmAb, IABS, ISR, IndMed, IndVet, Inpharma, MEDLINE, NemAb, NucAcAb, NutrAb, PE&ON, PN&I, PoultAb, RA&MP, RPP, Reac, RefZh, RevApplEntom, SCI, SIA, SoyAb, VetBull, ZooRec.
—BLDSC (5900.828000), CASDDS, CISTI, GNLM, IDS, IE, Infotrieve, ingenta, Linda Hall. **CCC.**
Published by: John Wiley & Sons, Inc., 111 River St, Hoboken, NJ 07030-5774. TEL 201-748-6000, FAX 201-748-5915, uscs-wis@wiley.com, http://www3.interscience.wiley.com/cgi-bin/jhome/37692, http://www.wiley.com. Ed. Ralph B Gwatkin. adv.: B&W page GBP 640, color page GBP 1,515; trim 210 x 279. Circ: 800. **Subscr. outside the Americas to:** John Wiley & Sons Ltd., The Atrium, Southern Gate, Chichester, West Sussex PO19 8SQ, United Kingdom. TEL 44-1243-843335, 0800-243407, FAX 44-1243-843232, cs-journals@wiley.co.uk.

➤ **MOLECULAR THERAPY.** see *MEDICAL SCIENCES—Oncology*

572.8 USA ISSN 1090-0535
CODEN: MVEPFB
➤ **MOLECULAR VISION.** Text in English. 1995. irreg. free (effective 2005). abstr. back issues avail. **Document type:** *Journal, Academic/Scholarly.* **Description:** Dedicated to the dissemination of research results in molecular biology, cell biology and the generics of the visual system.
Media: Online - full text.
Indexed: AgBio, AnBrAb, BBCI, BCI, BIOSIS Prev, BiolAb, CurCont, ExcerpMed, ISR, IndMed, IndVet, MEDLINE, RM&VM, SCI, TDB, ZooRec.
Address: Lab B-5500 Emory Eye Center, 1327 Clifton Rd N E, Atlanta, GA 30322. TEL 404-778-2231, 404-778-2231, molvis@emory.edu, http://www.molvis.org/molvis/. Ed. Dr. Stephen M Cristol.

572.8 RUS ISSN 0026-8984
QH506 CODEN: MOBIBO
MOLEKULYARNAYA BIOLOGIYA. Text in Russian. 1967. bi-m. RUR 1,230 for 6 mos. domestic (effective 2004). charts. index. **Document type:** *Journal, Academic/Scholarly.* **Description:** Covers advances in the field of chemical and physical bases of principal life phenomena, including studies on the chemistry and physics of the most important biopolymers (proteins and nucleic acids), their structure, and their functions.
Related titles: Online - full text ed.; ♦ English Translation: Molecular Biology. ISSN 0026-8933.
Indexed: ASFA, BIOSIS Prev, BiolAb, ChemAb, DBA, ExcerpMed, IndMed, MEDLINE, RefZh, ZooRec.
—BLDSC (0115.926000), CASDDS, CISTI, GNLM, Infotrieve, KNAW, Linda Hall. **CCC.**
Published by: (Rossiiskaya Akademiya Nauk/Russian Academy of Sciences), Izdatel'stvo Nauka, Profsoyuznaya ul 90, Moscow, 117864, Russian Federation. TEL 7-095-3347151, FAX 7-095-4202220, secret@naukaran.ru, http://www.maik.rssi.ru/journals/molbio.htm, http://www.naukaran.ru.

572.8 RUS ISSN 1728-2918
▼ **MOLEKULYARNAYA MEDITSINA.** Text in Russian. 2003. q. USD 200 foreign (effective 2005). **Document type:** *Journal, Academic/Scholarly.*
Indexed: RefZh.
—BLDSC (0115.927750).
Published by: Izdatel'stvo Meditsina/Meditsina Publishers, ul B Pirogovskaya, d 2, str 5, Moscow, 119435, Russian Federation. TEL 7-095-2483324, meditsina@mtu-net.ru, http://www.medlit.ru. Ed. Mikhail A Paltsev. **Dist. by:** East View Information Services, 3020 Harbor Ln. N., Minneapolis, MN 55447. TEL 763-550-0961, FAX 763-559-2931, eastview@eastview.com, http://www.eastview.com.

572 POL ISSN 0077-0485
CODEN: MOBCA5
MONOGRAFIE BIOCHEMICZNE. Text in Polish. 1962. irreg., latest vol.45, 2002. price varies. bk.rev. bibl.; charts; illus. 60 p./no. 1 cols./p.; back issues avail. **Document type:** *Monographic series, Academic/Scholarly.*
—CASDDS.
Published by: Polskie Towarzystwo Biochemiczne, Ul Pasteura 3, Warsaw, 02093, Poland. TEL 48-22-6686280, FAX 48-22-6582099, konarska@nencki.gov.pl, ptbioch@nencki.gov.pl, http://www.ptbioch.edu.pl. Ed. Liliana Konarska. **Dist by:** Ars Polona, Krakowskie Przedmiescie 7, Warsaw, Poland.

MUTAGENESIS. see *BIOLOGY—Genetics*

MUTATION RESEARCH; fundamental and molecular mechanisms of mutagenesis. see *BIOLOGY—Genetics*

MUTATION RESEARCH - FUNDAMENTAL AND MOLECULAR MECHANISMS OF MUTAGENESIS. see *BIOLOGY—Genetics*

MUTATION RESEARCH - GENETIC TOXICOLOGY AND ENVIRONMENTAL MUTAGENESIS. see *BIOLOGY—Genetics*

NATURAL PRODUCT RESEARCH. see *CHEMISTRY*

▼ **NATURE CHEMICAL BIOLOGY.** see *CHEMISTRY*

572 GBR ISSN 1479-0734
NATURE LABSCENE. Text in English. 1986. bi-m. free (effective 2006). adv. software rev. tr.lit. back issues avail. **Document type:** *Journal, Trade.*
Former titles (until 2002): Nature Labscene U K (1474-6301); (until 2001): U K Product Review (0968-6797)
—BLDSC (6046.674900).
Published by: Nature Publishing Group (Subsidiary of: Macmillan Publishers Ltd.), The MacMillan Building, 4 Crinan St, London, N1 9XW, United Kingdom. TEL 44-20-78334000, FAX 44-20-78433601, http://www.nature.com. adv.: B&W page GBP 1,170. Circ: 15,000 (controlled). **Subscr. to:** Brunel Rd, Houndmills, Basingstoke, Hamps RG21 6XS, United Kingdom. TEL 44-1256-329242, FAX 44-1256-812358, subscriptions@nature.com.

572.65 GBR ISSN 0143-4179
CODEN: NRPPDD
➤ **NEUROPEPTIDES (EDINBURGH).** Text in English. 1979. 6/yr. EUR 281 in Europe to individuals; JPY 30,400 in Japan to individuals; USD 251 elsewhere to individuals; EUR 1,613 in Europe to institutions; JPY 174,300 in Japan to institutions; USD 1,435 elsewhere to institutions (effective 2006). adv. bk.rev. bibl. back issues avail. **Document type:** *Journal, Academic/Scholarly.* **Description:** Contains articles dealing with the structure, distribution, actions and functions of peptides in the central and peripheral nervous systems.
Related titles: Online - full text ed.: (from EBSCO Publishing, O C L C Online Computer Library Center, Inc., ScienceDirect, Swets Information Services).
Indexed: ASFA, AnBeAb, BBCI, BIOBASE, BIOSIS Prev, BiolAb, CIN, ChemAb, ChemTitl, CurCont, ESPM, ExcerpMed, IABS, ISR, IndMed, Inpharma, MEDLINE, NSA, NSCI, PE&ON, Reac, RefZh, SCI.
—BLDSC (6081.516000), CASDDS, CISTI, GNLM, IDS, IE, Infotrieve, ingenta, KNAW. **CCC.**
Published by: Churchill Livingstone (Subsidiary of: Elsevier Health Sciences), Robert Stevenson House, 1-3, Baxter's Pl, Leith Walk, Edinburgh, Midlothian EH1 3AF, United Kingdom. TEL 44-131-5562424, FAX 44-131-5581278, Neuropeptides@yahoo.com, journals@harcourt.com, http://www.elsevier.com/locate/npep, http://www.harcourt-international.com/. Eds. D R Gehlert, Dr. Jacqueline N Crawley. Pub. Gillian Griffith. R&P Catherine John TEL 212-424-4200. Adv. contact David Dunnachie. Circ: 390.

➤ **NEUROSCIENCES.** see *MEDICAL SCIENCES—Psychiatry And Neurology*

572 CHE ISSN 1424-862X
QP517.C45 CODEN: NEURIQ
➤ **NEUROSIGNALS.** Text in English. 1992. bi-m. CHF 1,097 in Europe to institutions; CHF 1,117.40 elsewhere to institutions; CHF 1,181 combined subscription in Europe to institutions print & online eds.; CHF 1,201.40 combined subscription elsewhere to institutions print & online eds. (effective 2006). adv. back issues avail. **Document type:** *Journal, Academic/Scholarly.* **Description:** Provides a platform for new ideas, novel concepts, and innovative hypotheses which do not always conform to classical theories and teaching. Publishes original articles, reviews and communications in the broad field of production, transmission, processing, recognition, effects, modification and evolution of biological signals.
Former titles (until vol.10, no.6, 2001): Biological Signals and Receptors (1422-4933); (until 1998): Biological Signals (1016-0922)
Related titles: Microform ed.: (from PQC); Online - full text ed.: ISSN 1424-8638. CHF 1,055 to institutions (effective 2006) (from EBSCO Publishing, O C L C Online Computer Library Center, Inc., Swets Information Services).
Indexed: ASCA, BBCI, BIOBASE, BIOSIS Prev, BiolAb, CIN, ChemAb, ChemTitl, ExcerpMed, IABS, IndMed, MEDLINE, MSB, NSCI.
—BLDSC (6081.289700), CASDDS, CISTI, GNLM, IDS, IE, Infotrieve, ingenta, KNAW. **CCC.**
Published by: S. Karger AG, Allschwilerstr 10, Basel, 4009, Switzerland. TEL 41-61-3061111, FAX 41-61-3061234, karger@karger.ch, http://www.karger.com/NSG, http://www.karger.ch. Ed. Nancy Y. Ip. adv.: page CHF 1,630; trim 210 x 280. Circ: 600 (paid and controlled).

572 NLD ISSN 0167-7306
QD415 CODEN: NCBIDL
➤ **NEW COMPREHENSIVE BIOCHEMISTRY.** Text in English. 1979. irreg., latest vol.36, 2002. price varies. back issues avail. **Document type:** *Monographic series, Academic/Scholarly.* **Description:** Informs scientists of developments in the biochemical sciences and provides them with an authoritative reference work.
Supersedes (in 1981): Comprehensive Biochemistry
Related titles: Online - full text ed.: (from ScienceDirect).
Indexed: CIN, ChemAb, ChemTitl.
—BLDSC (6082.890000), CASDDS, CISTI, IE, ingenta. **CCC.**

Published by: Elsevier BV (Subsidiary of: Elsevier Science & Technology), Radarweg 29, Amsterdam, 1043 NX, Netherlands. TEL 31-20-4853911, FAX 31-20-4852457, nlinfo-f@elsevier.nl, http://www.elsevier.nl. Eds. G. Bernardi, L L M van Deenen.

572 JPN ISSN 0913-3348
CODEN: NOKKEL
NIHON OYO KOSO KYOKAISHI/JAPAN FOUNDATION FOR APPLIED ENZYMOLOGY. JOURNAL. Text in Japanese. a.
Indexed: ChemAb.
—BLDSC (6112.915600), CASDDS.
Published by: Nihon Oyo Koso Kyokai/Japan Foundation of Applied Enzymology, 16-89 Kashima 3-chome, Yodogawa-ku, Osaka-shi, 532-0031, Japan.

NIHON SEIKAGAKKAI KINKI SHIBU REIKAI YOSHISHU/JAPANESE BIOCHEMICAL SOCIETY. KINKI BRANCH OFFICE. ABSTRACTS OF MEETING. see *FISH AND FISHERIES—Abstracting, Bibliographies, Statistics*

NIHON SENSHOKUTAI KENSA GAKKAI SHOROKUSHU/ JAPANESE ASSOCIATION FOR CHROMOSOME ANALYSIS. ABSTRACT OF ANNUAL MEETING. see *BIOLOGY—Abstracting, Bibliographies, Statistics*

572.87 JPN ISSN 0917-8155
NIHON SENSHOKUTAI KENSA GAKKAI ZASSHI/JAPANESE ASSOCIATION FOR CHROMOSOME ANALYSIS. OFFICIAL JOURNAL. Text in English, Japanese; Summaries in English. 1983. q.
Published by: Nihon Senshokutai Kensa Gakkai, c/o Kurasuta Koa Kenkyujo Idenshi Kenkyubu, 11-18 Tsubamesawa-Higashi 3-chome, Miyagino-ku, Sendai-shi, Miyagi-ken 983-0000, Japan.

NIHON TANPAKU KOGAKKAI NENKAI PUROGURAMU YOSHISHU/PROTEIN ENGINEERING SOCIETY OF JAPAN. ABSTRACTS OF THE MEETING. see *FISH AND FISHERIES—Abstracting, Bibliographies, Statistics*

NITRIC OXIDE. see *BIOLOGY—Abstracting, Bibliographies, Statistics*

572 571.4 USA ISSN 1089-8603
QP535.N1 CODEN: NIOXF5
➤ **NITRIC OXIDE: BIOLOGY AND CHEMISTRY.** Variant title: Archives of Biochemistry and Biophysics Part B. Text in English. 1997. 8/yr. EUR 272 in Europe to individuals; JPY 28,500 in Japan to individuals; USD 208 to individuals except Europe and Japan; EUR 575 in Europe to institutions; JPY 59,900 in Japan to institutions; USD 439 to institutions except Europe and Japan (effective 2006). **Document type:** *Academic/Scholarly.* **Description:** Provides a forum for the rapid publication of scientific investigation across the broad field of nitric oxide research.
Related titles: Online - full text ed.: ISSN 1089-8611. USD 463 (effective 2002) (from EBSCO Publishing, Gale Group, IngentaConnect, O C L C Online Computer Library Center, Inc., ScienceDirect, Swets Information Services); ♦ Series: Archives of Biochemistry and Biophysics. ISSN 0003-9861.
Indexed: AbHyg, AgBio, AnBrAb, BBCI, BIOBASE, BIOSIS Prev, BioCN&I, BiolAb, CPA, CurCont, DSA, ExcerpMed, FCA, HelmAb, HortAb, IABS, ISR, IndMed, IndVet, MEDLINE, NutrAb, PotatoAb, ProtozoAb, RA&MP, RM&VM, SCI, WeedAb.
—BLDSC (6113.671750), CINDOC, CISTI, IE, Infotrieve, ingenta, Linda Hall. **CCC.**
Published by: (Nitric Oxide Society, Krebs Convention Management Services), Academic Press (Subsidiary of: Elsevier Science & Technology), 525 B St, Ste 1900, San Diego, CA 92101-4495. TEL 619-231-6616, 800-894-3434, FAX 619-699-6422, apsubs@acad.com, http://www.elsevier.com/locate/yniox, http://www.academicpress.com. Ed. Dr. J. R. Lancaster Jr.

572 USA ISSN 1550-7629
▼ ➤ **NUCLEAR RECEPTOR SIGNALING.** Text in English. 2003. irreg. free (effective 2005). **Document type:** *Journal, Academic/Scholarly.* **Description:** Seeks to establish a current, interactive forum for sharing information and opinions of scientists active in the field of nuclear receptor signaling.
Media: Online - full text.
Published by: Nuclear Receptor Signaling Atlas http://www.nursa.org.

➤ **NUCLEIC ACIDS ABSTRACTS (ONLINE EDITION).** see *BIOLOGY—Abstracting, Bibliographies, Statistics*

572.65 USA ISSN 0933-1891
QP620 CODEN: NAMBE8
NUCLEIC ACIDS AND MOLECULAR BIOLOGY. Text in English. 1987. irreg., latest vol.15, 2004. price varies. **Document type:** *Monographic series, Academic/Scholarly.*
Indexed: Agr, BIOSIS Prev, ChemAb, ChemTitl, DBA.
—BLDSC (6183.745000), CASDDS, CISTI, GNLM, IE, ingenta, KNAW. **CCC.**
Published by: Springer-Verlag New York, Inc. (Subsidiary of: Springer Science+Business Media), 233 Spring St, New York, NY 10013. TEL 212-460-1500, 800-777-4643, FAX 212-473-6272, http://www.springer-ny.com.

572.6 GBR ISSN 0305-1048
QP620 CODEN: NARHAD
➤ **NUCLEIC ACIDS RESEARCH.** Abbreviated title: N A R. Text in English. 1974. 22/yr. GBP 1,652, USD 2,855, EUR 2,478 to institutions (effective 2006). adv. illus. index. 248 p./no.; back issues avail.; reprint service avail. from PSC. **Document type:** *Journal, Academic/Scholarly.* **Description:** International rapid-publication journal on nucleic acids, constituents and analogues. Publishing RFLP sequence reprints, sequence data, NMR assignment data and methods.
Related titles: CD-ROM ed.: ISSN 1362-4954. 1995; Online - full text ed.: ISSN 1362-4962. free (effective 2006) (from EBSCO Publishing, Gale Group, HighWire Press, IngentaConnect, National Library of Medicine, O C L C Online Computer Library Center, Inc., Ovid Technologies, Inc., Oxford University Press Online Journals, ProQuest Information & Learning, Swets Information Services).
Indexed: AEA, ASCA, ASFA, AbHyg, AgBio, Agr, AnBrAb, BBCI, BCI, BIOBASE, BIOSIS Prev, BibAg, BioCN&I, BioEngAb, BiolAb, CBTA, CCI, CEABA, CIN, CPA, ChemAb, ChemTitl, CurCont, DBA, DSA, ESPM, EntAb, ExcerpMed, FCA, FS&TA, FaBeAb, ForAb, GenetAb, HGA, HelmAb, HerbAb, HortAb, IABS, INIS AtomInd, ISR, IndMed, IndVet, Inpharma, M&PBA, MBA, MEDLINE, MSB, MaizeAb, NSCI, NemAb, NucAcAb, NutrAb, PBA, PGegResA, PGrRegA, PN&I, PotatoAb, PoultAb, ProtozoAb, RCI, RM&VM, RPP, Reac, RefZh, RevApplEntom, RiceAb, S&F, SCI, SIA, SeedAb, SoyAb, TDB, TriticAb, VITIS, VetBull, WeedAb.
—BLDSC (6183.850000), CASDDS, CISTI, GNLM, IDS, IE, Infotrieve, ingenta, Linda Hall. **CCC.**
Published by: Oxford University Press, Great Clarendon St, Oxford, OX2 6DP, United Kingdom. TEL 44-1865-556767, FAX 44-1865-556646, jnl.orders@oup.co.uk, http://nar.oxfordjournals.org/, http://www.oxfordjournals.org/. Eds. Michael Gait, Richard J Roberts. Pub. David Prosser. R&P Fiona Bennett. adv.: B&W page GBP 480, B&W page USD 860; trim 215 x 280. Circ: 1,730.

572.65 GBR ISSN 0261-3166
CODEN: NACSD8
NUCLEIC ACIDS SYMPOSIUM SERIES. Text in English. 1975. s-a. reprints avail. **Document type:** *Proceedings, Academic/Scholarly.*
Formerly (until 1978): Nucleic Acids Research. Special Publication (0309-1872)
Related titles: Online - full text ed.: (from HighWire Press).
Indexed: ChemAb, ChemTitl, IndMed, MEDLINE, MSB.
—CASDDS, CISTI, GNLM, IE, Infotrieve, Linda Hall. **CCC.**
Published by: Oxford University Press, Great Clarendon St, Oxford, OX2 6DP, United Kingdom. TEL 44-1865-556767, FAX 44-1865-556646, enquiry@oup.co.uk, http://nass.oupjournals.org, http://www.oup.co.uk/. Pub. Julie Hoare. R&P Fiona Bennett.

572.85 USA ISSN 1525-7770
QD320 CODEN: NNNAFY
NUCLEOSIDES, NUCLEOTIDES AND NUCLEIC ACIDS; an international journal for rapid communication. Text in English. 1974. m. GBP 1,401, USD 2,312 combined subscription to institutions print & online eds. (effective 2006). adv. bibl.; charts; illus. reprint service avail. from PSC. **Document type:** *Journal, Academic/Scholarly.* **Description:** Latest research papers emphasize the synthesis, biological activities, new and improved synthetic methods, and significant observations related to new compounds.
Former titles: Nucleosides and Nucleotides (0732-8311); Supersedes in part (in 1982): Journal of Carbohydrates, Nucleosides, Nucleotides
Related titles: Microform ed.: (from RPI); Online - full text ed.: ISSN 1532-2335. GBP 1,331, USD 2,196 to institutions (effective 2006) (from EBSCO Publishing, O C L C Online Computer Library Center, Inc., Swets Information Services).
Indexed: ABIPC, ASCA, BBCI, BIOBASE, BIOSIS Prev, BiolAb, CCI, CIN, ChemAb, ChemInfo, ChemTitl, CurCR, CurCont, ExcerpMed, IABS, ISR, IndChem, IndMed, Inpharma, MEDLINE, MSB, NucAcAb, NutrAb, PE&ON, ProtozoAb, RCI, Reac, RefZh, SCI.
—BLDSC (6184.092000), CASDDS, CISTI, Ei, GNLM, IDS, IE, Infotrieve, ingenta, Linda Hall. **CCC.**
Published by: Taylor & Francis Inc. (Subsidiary of: Taylor & Francis Group), 325 Chestnut St, Ste 800, Philadelphia, PA 19016. TEL 215-625-8900, 800-354-1420, FAX 215-625-8914, info@taylorandfrancis.com, http://www.tandf.co.uk/journals/titles/15257770.asp, http://www.taylorandfrancis.com. Ed. John A Secrist. Adv. contact Sharon Moran. B&W page USD 600. Circ: 450.

▼ **NUTRITION & METABOLISM.** see *MEDICAL SCIENCES*

NUTRITION BYTES; exemplary papers from the human biochemistry & nutrition laboratory. see *NUTRITION AND DIETETICS*

572 NZL ISSN 1172-7101
CODEN: NZBIED
NZ BIOSCIENCE. Text in English. 1993. q. free to qualified personnel (effective 2005). adv. **Document type:** *Journal.*
Indexed: INIS AtomInd.
Published by: Ancat Holdings Ltd., Howick, PO Box 38-546, Auckland, New Zealand. TEL 64-9-5353475, FAX 64-9-5353476, bioscience@ancat.co.nz, ancat@ancat.co.nz, http://www.ancat.co.nz/biosci.htm. Adv. contact Robert B Lyon. B&W page NZD 950. Circ: 1,350 (free).

O M I C S: A JOURNAL OF INTEGRATIVE BIOLOGY. see *BIOLOGY—Genetics*

572.57 GBR
THE OILY PRESS LIPID LIBRARY. Text in English. irreg. **Document type:** *Monographic series, Academic/Scholarly.*
—BLDSC (6252.622500).
Published by: P J Barnes and Associates, PO Box 200, Bridgwater, TA7 0YZ, United Kingdom. TEL 44-1823-698973, FAX 44-1823-698971, sales@pbarnes.demon.co.uk, http://www.pbarnes.demon.co.uk. Ed. Michael I Gurr.

572 DEU
OLD HERBORN UNIVERSITY SEMINAR MONOGRAPHS. Text in English. irreg., latest vol.5, 1994. **Document type:** *Monographic series.*
Indexed: ChemAb, ChemTitl.
—BLDSC (6253.813500), ingenta.
Published by: Institute for Microbiology and Biochemistry, Kornmarkt 34, Herborn, 35745, Germany. TEL 02772-41033, FAX 02772-41039.

OLIGONUCLEOTIDES. see *BIOLOGY—Genetics*

ONCOGENE; including Oncogene Reviews. see *MEDICAL SCIENCES—Oncology*

▼ **ORGANIC & BIOMOLECULAR CHEMISTRY.** see *CHEMISTRY—Organic Chemistry*

572 JPN
OSAKA SHIKA DAIGAKU SEIKAGAKU KYOSHITSU GYOSEKISHU/OSAKA DENTAL UNIVERSITY. DEPARTMENT OF BIOCHEMISTRY. ACHIEVEMENT. Text in English, Japanese. 1961. irreg.
Published by: Osaka Shika Daigaku, Seirigaku Kyoshitsu, 1-47, Kyobashi, Higashi-ku, Osaka-shi, 540, Japan.

572.6 JPN ISSN 0078-6705
QP551
OSAKA UNIVERSITY. INSTITUTE FOR PROTEIN RESEARCH. MEMOIRS/OSAKA DAIGAKU TANPAKUSHITSU KENKYUSHO KIYO. Text in English. 1959. a. per issue exchange basis. **Document type:** *Abstract/Index.*
Indexed: NutrAb, RefZh.
—CISTI, Linda Hall.
Published by: Osaka Daigaku, Tanpakushitsu Kenkyusho/Osaka University, Institute for Protein Research, 3-2 Yamada-Oka, Suita-shi, Osaka-fu 565-0871, Japan. TEL 81-6-877-5111, FAX 81-6-876-2533. Ed. Toshio Takagi. Circ: 300.

OXIDATION COMMUNICATIONS. see *CHEMISTRY—Organic Chemistry*

OXYGEN RADICALS. see *BIOLOGY—Abstracting, Bibliographies, Statistics*

572 PHL ISSN 0115-6403
CODEN: BPBSDA
P B S BULLETIN. Text in English. 1978. a. PHP 50, USD 10. adv. bk.rev.
—CASDDS.
Published by: Philippine Biochemical Society, c/o Dept. of Biochemistry, University of the College of Medicine, PO Box 593, Manila, Philippines. FAX 63-2-50-17-06. Ed. E M T Mendoza. Circ: 200.

572 PAK ISSN 1681-4525
QP501 CODEN: PJBIAL
PAKISTAN JOURNAL OF BIOCHEMISTRY AND MOLECULAR BIOLOGY. Text in English. 1968. s-a. PKR 100, USD 50. adv. **Document type:** *Academic/Scholarly.*
Formerly: Pakistan Journal of Biochemistry (0300-8185)
Related titles: CD-ROM ed.
Indexed: BiolAb, ChemAb, ChemTitl, ExtraMED.
—BLDSC (6340.897500), CASDDS, CISTI, Linda Hall.
Published by: Pakistan Society of Biochemists, Institute of Chemistry, University of Punjab, Lahore, 54590, Pakistan. Ed. Nazrul S Hasnain. Circ: 400.

PAKISTAN JOURNAL OF PHARMACEUTICAL SCIENCES. see *PHARMACY AND PHARMACOLOGY*

PATHOPHYSIOLOGY. see *BIOLOGY—Physiology*

572.65 JPN ISSN 0388-3698
QP552.P4 CODEN: PECHDP
PEPTIDE CHEMISTRY. Text in English. 1962. a.
Indexed: ApicAb, CCI, ChemAb, ChemTitl.
—CASDDS.
Published by: Protein Research Foundation, Peptide Institute/Tanpakushitsu Kenkyu Shoreikai Pepuchido Kenkyujo, 4-1-2 Ina, Mino-shi, Osaka-fu 562-0015, Japan. TEL 81-727-29-4124, query@prf.or.jp, http://www.prf.or.jp/.

▼ new title ➤ refereed ✶ unverified ♦ full entry avail.

PEPTIDE INFORMATION. see *BIOLOGY—Abstracting, Bibliographies, Statistics*

572.65 USA ISSN 0196-9781
QP552.P4 CODEN: PPTDD5
➤ **PEPTIDES.** Text in English. 1980. 12/yr. EUR 253 in Europe to individuals; JPY 33,500 in Japan to individuals; USD 283 to individuals except Europe and Japan; EUR 3,562 in Europe to institutions; JPY 473,100 in Japan to institutions; USD 3,986 to institutions except Europe and Japan (effective 2006). adv. illus. index. back issues avail.; reprint service avail. from PQC,ISI. **Document type:** *Journal, Academic/Scholarly.* **Description:** Contains original contributions on the chemistry, biochemistry, endocrinology, gastroenterology, physiology and pharmacology of peptides and their neurological, psychological and behavioral effects.
Related titles: Microfilm ed.: (from PQC); Online - full text ed.: (from EBSCO Publishing, Gale Group, IngentaConnect, ScienceDirect, Swets Information Services).
Indexed: ASFA, AbHyg, AgBio, AnBeAb, AnBrAb, BBCI, BIOBASE, BIOSIS Prev, BiolAb, CCI, CIN, CPA, ChemAb, ChemTitl, CurCont, DSA, DentInd, ESPM, EntAb, ExcerpMed, FCA, GenetAb, HelmAb, HortAb, IABS, IPsyAb, ISR, IndMed, IndVet, Inpharma, MEDLINE, MSB, NSCI, NemAb, NutrAb, PBA, PE&ON, PGegResA, PHN&I, PN&I, PoultAb, ProtozoAb, PsycInfo, PsycholAb, RA&MP, RM&VM, RPP, Reac, RefZh, SAA, SCI, SIA, SeedAb, SoyAb, TDB, VetBull, WeedAb, e-psyche.
—BLDSC (6422.954000), CASDDS, CISTI, GNLM, IDS, IE, Infotrieve, ingenta, KNAW, Linda Hall. **CCC.**
Published by: Elsevier Inc. (Subsidiary of: Elsevier Science & Technology), 360 Park Ave. S, New York, NY 10010-1710. TEL 212-633-3730, 888-437-4636, FAX 212-633-3140, peptides@tulane.edu, usinfo-f@elsevier.com, http://www.elsevier.com/locate/peptides. Ed. Dr. Abba J Kastin. Adv. contact Majorie Valle. Circ: 448 (paid and free).

➤ **PESTICIDE BIOCHEMISTRY AND PHYSIOLOGY.** see *AGRICULTURE—Crop Production And Soil*

572.43 NLD ISSN 0166-8595
CODEN: PHRSDI
➤ **PHOTOSYNTHESIS RESEARCH**; an international journal. Text in English. 1980. m. EUR 1,688, USD 1,718, GBP 1,108 combined subscription to institutions print & online eds. (effective 2005). adv. bk.rev. back issues avail.; reprint service avail. from PSC. **Document type:** *Journal, Academic/Scholarly.* **Description:** Publishes papers dealing with basic and applied aspects of photosynthesis, including light absorption and emission, primary photochemistry, photorespiration, molecular biology, environmental and ecological aspects, and bacterial and algal photosynthesis.
Related titles: Microform ed.: (from PQC); Online - full text ed.: ISSN 1573-5079 (from EBSCO Publishing, Gale Group, IngentaConnect, Kluwer Online, O C L C Online Computer Library Center, Inc., Ovid Technologies, Inc., Springer LINK, Swets Information Services).
Indexed: AEA, ASCA, ASFA, AgBio, Agr, AgrForAb, BBCI, BIOBASE, BIOSIS Prev, BibLing, BiolAb, CCI, CIN, CPA, ChemAb, ChemTitl, CurCont, EngInd, FCA, ForAb, HerbAb, HortAb, I&DA, IABS, ISR, Inpharma, Inspec, MBA, MaizeAb, OrnHort, PBA, PGegResA, PGrRegA, PlantSci, PotatoAb, RA&MP, RPP, Reac, RefZh, RiceAb, S&F, SCI, SIA, SoyAb, TriticAb, VITIS, WeedAb.
—BLDSC (6474.365000), AskIEEE, CASDDS, CISTI, Ei, IDS, IE, Infotrieve, ingenta, Linda Hall. **CCC.**
Published by: Springer-Verlag Dordrecht (Subsidiary of: Springer Science+Business Media), Van Godewijckstraat 30, Dordrecht, 3311 GX, Netherlands. TEL 31-78-6576050, FAX 31-78-6576474, http://springerlink.metapress.com/openurl.asp?genre=journal&issn=0166-8595, http://www.springeronline.com. Ed. David B Knaff.

➤ **PHYSIOLOGICAL CHEMISTRY AND PHYSICS AND MEDICAL N M R.** (Nuclear Magnetic Resonance) see *BIOLOGY—Biophysics*

572.8 USA ISSN 1094-8341
QH506 CODEN: PHGEFP
➤ **PHYSIOLOGICAL GENOMICS.** Text in English. 1999. m. USD 195 domestic to non-members; USD 210 in Canada & Mexico to non-members; USD 225 elsewhere to non-members; USD 285 domestic to institutions; USD 300 in Canada & Mexico to institutions; USD 315 elsewhere to institutions; USD 200 combined subscription domestic to non-members print & online eds.; USD 215 combined subscription in Canada & Mexico to non-members print & online eds.; USD 230 combined subscription elsewhere to non-members print & online eds.; USD 95 combined subscription domestic to members print & online eds.; USD 110 combined subscription in Canada & Mexico to members print & online eds.; USD 125 combined subscription elsewhere to members print & online eds.; USD 295 combined subscription domestic to institutions print & online eds.; USD 310 combined subscription in Canada & Mexico to institutions print & online eds.; USD 325 combined subscription elsewhere to institutions print & online eds. (effective 2006). bk.rev. **Document type:** *Newsletter, Academic/Scholarly.* **Description:** Publishes the result of a wide variety of studies from human and from informative model systems with techniques linking genes and pathways to physiology from prokaryotes to eukaryotes.
Related titles: Online - full text ed.: ISSN 1531-2267. 1999 (Jul.). USD 165 to non-members; USD 250 to institutions (effective 2006) (from EBSCO Publishing, HighWire Press).
Indexed: B&BAb, BBCI, BCI, BIOSIS Prev, BiolAb, CurCont, ExcerpMed, GenetAb, ISR, IndMed, Inpharma, MEDLINE, NucAcAb, PE&ON, Reac, SCI.
—BLDSC (6484.730000), CISTI, IE, Infotrieve, ingenta. **CCC.**
Published by: American Physiological Society, 9650 Rockville Pike, Bethesda, MD 20814-3991. TEL 301-634-7164, FAX 301-634-7241, info@the-aps.org, http://www.physiolgenomics.org/, http://www.the-aps.org. Ed. Allen W Cowley Jr.

➤ **PHYTOCHEMICAL ANALYSIS.** see *BIOLOGY—Botany*

572 NLD ISSN 0197-8969
CODEN: APPEDR
PHYTOCHEMICAL SOCIETY OF EUROPE. ANNUAL PROCEEDINGS. Text in English. 1968. irreg., latest vol.47, 2002, Dec. price varies. adv. **Document type:** *Proceedings.*
Former titles (until 1978): Phytochemical Society. Annual Proceedings (0309-9393); (until 1972): Phytochemical Society Symposium. Proceedings (8755-9684)
Indexed: BIOSIS Prev, CIN, ChemAb, ChemTitl.
—BLDSC (6787.560000), CISTI, IE, ingenta. **CCC.**
Published by: Springer-Verlag Dordrecht (Subsidiary of: Springer Science+Business Media), Van Godewijckstraat 30, Dordrecht, 3311 GX, Netherlands. TEL 31-78-6576050, FAX 31-78-6576474, http://www.springeronline.com.

PIVARSTVO. see *BEVERAGES*

THE PLANT CELL. see *BIOLOGY—Botany*

576.8 CAN ISSN 0735-9640
QK981 CODEN: PMBRD4
➤ **PLANT MOLECULAR BIOLOGY REPORTER.** Text in Dutch. 1980. q. USD 66 membership; USD 36 to students (effective 2001). adv. back issues avail. **Document type:** *Journal, Academic/Scholarly.* **Description:** Includes news and opinions about progress in the developing area of plant molecular biology.
Formerly (until 1983): Plant Molecular Biology Newsletter (0733-0537)
Related titles: Online - full text ed.: ISSN 1572-9818 (from EBSCO Publishing, Gale Group, IngentaConnect, O C L C Online Computer Library Center, Inc., Swets Information Services).
Indexed: ASCA, AgBio, Agr, AgrForAb, BCI, BibAg, BibLing, BiolAb, CIN, CPA, ChemAb, ChemTitl, CurCont, FCA, FS&TA, ForAb, HortAb, MaizeAb, NemAb, OrnHort, PBA, PGegResA, PGrRegA, PotatoAb, RA&MP, RPP, RefZh, RevApplEntom, RiceAb, SIA, SeedAb, SoyAb, TriticAb, VITIS, WeedAb.
—BLDSC (6520.360000), CASDDS, CISTI, IDS, IE, Infotrieve, ingenta. **CCC.**
Published by: (International Society for Plant Molecular Biology NLD), N R C Research Press, Building M 55, Ottawa, ON K1A 0R6, Canada. TEL 613-993-0362, 800-668-1222, FAX 613-952-7656, pubs@nrc-cnrc.gc.ca, http://www.nrc.ca/cisti/journals/ispmb/reporter.html, http://pubs.nrc-cnrc.gc.ca. Ed. Don Bourque. adv.: page USD 500; 7.5 x 4.25. Circ: 2,500.

➤ **PLANT PHYSIOLOGY AND BIOCHEMISTRY.** see *BIOLOGY—Botany*

572 GBR ISSN 0964-5845
CODEN: PPRMEN
➤ **PORTLAND PRESS RESEARCH MONOGRAPH.** Text in English. 1992. irreg., latest vol.12, 1998. price varies. back issues avail. **Document type:** *Monographic series, Academic/Scholarly.*
Indexed: BIOSIS Prev, CIN, ChemAb, ChemTitl.
—BLDSC (6555.660000), CASDDS, CISTI, ingenta.
Published by: Portland Press Ltd. (Subsidiary of: Biochemical Society), 3rd Fl, Eagle House, 16 Procter St, London, WC1V 6NX, United Kingdom. TEL 44-20-72804110, FAX 44-20-72804169, sales@portland-serices.com, http://www.portlandpress.com, http://www.portlandpress.com/books/. R&P Adam Marshall. **Subscr. to:** Commerce Way, Colchester CO2 8HP, United Kingdom. TEL 44-1206-796351, FAX 44-1206-799331.

572 POL ISSN 0032-5422
QP501 CODEN: PSTBAH
POSTEPY BIOCHEMII. Text in Polish; Summaries in English. 1953. q. USD 80 (effective 2003). bk.rev. charts; illus.; bibl. index. 100 p./no. 2 cols./p.; back issues avail. **Document type:** *Journal, Academic/Scholarly.*
Indexed: AgrAg, AgrLib, AnBrAb, BiolAb, CIN, ChemAb, ChemTitl, DSA, IndMed, MEDLINE.
—CASDDS, CISTI, GNLM, Linda Hall.
Published by: Polskie Towarzystwo Biochemiczne, Ul Pasteura 3, Warsaw, 02093, Poland. TEL 48-22-6686280, FAX 48-22-6582099, postepy@nencki.gov.pl, ptbioch@nencki.gov.pl, http://www.ptbioch.edu.pl. Ed. Grazyna Palamarczyk. Circ: 1,810. **Dist. by:** Ars Polona, Krakowskie Przedmiescie 7, Warsaw, Poland.

572 USA ISSN 1082-6068
QH324 CODEN: PBBIF4
➤ **PREPARATIVE BIOCHEMISTRY AND BIOTECHNOLOGY.** Text in English. 1971. q. USD 1,214, GBP 735 combined subscription to institutions print & online eds. (effective 2006). adv. reprint service avail. from PSC. **Document type:** *Journal, Academic/Scholarly.* **Description:** An international forum of research results dealing with all aspects of preparitive techniques in biotechnology, and other topics.
Formerly: Preparative Biochemistry (0032-7484)
Related titles: Microform ed.: (from RPI); Online - full text ed.: ISSN 1532-2297. USD 1,153, GBP 698 to institutions (effective 2006) (from EBSCO Publishing, O C L C Online Computer Library Center, Inc., Swets Information Services).
Indexed: AEBA, ASCA, ASFA, AgBio, Agr, BBCI, BIOBASE, BIOSIS Prev, BioEngAb, BiolAb, CIN, CPA, ChemAb, ChemTitl, CurCont, DBA, DSA, ESPM, ExcerpMed, FCA, ForAb, HortAb, IAA, IABS, INIS AtomInd, ISR, IndMed, IndVet, Inpharma, M&PBA, MBA, MEDLINE, NutrAb, PBA, PGrRegA, PollutAb, RA&MP, Reac, RefZh, SCI, SoyAb, VetBull, WeedAb.
—BLDSC (6607.841000), CASDDS, CISTI, GNLM, IDS, IE, Infotrieve, ingenta, Linda Hall. **CCC.**
Published by: Taylor & Francis Inc. (Subsidiary of: Taylor & Francis Group), 325 Chestnut St, Ste 800, Philadelphia, PA 19016. TEL 215-625-8900, 800-354-1420, FAX 215-625-2940, info@taylorandfrancis.com, http://www.tandf.co.uk/journals/titles/10826068.asp, http://www.taylorandfrancis.com. Ed. Dr. Jack Cazes. Circ: 300.

572 RUS ISSN 0555-1099
QH345 CODEN: PBMIAK
PRIKLADNAYA BIOKHIMIYA I MIKROBIOLOGIYA. Text in Russian. 1965. bi-m. RUR 1,050 for 6 mos. domestic (effective 2004). **Document type:** *Journal, Academic/Scholarly.*
Related titles: Online - full text ed.; ♦ English Translation: Applied Biochemistry and Microbiology. ISSN 0003-6838.
Indexed: ABIPC, ASFA, BIOSIS Prev, BiolAb, CBTA, CEABA, CIN, CPA, ChemAb, ChemTitl, DBA, FCA, FS&TA, HerbAb, HortAb, IndMed, MBA, MEDLINE, RefZh, SeedAb, VITIS.
—BLDSC (0131.920000), CASDDS, CISTI, East View, GNLM, KNAW, Linda Hall. **CCC.**
Published by: (Rossiiskaya Akademiya Nauk/Russian Academy of Sciences), Izdatel'stvo Nauka, Profsoyuznaya ul 90, Moscow, 117864, Russian Federation. TEL 7-095-3347151, FAX 7-095-4202220, secret@naukaran.ru, http://www.maik.ru/cgi-bin/list.pl?page=prikbio, http://www.naukaran.ru.

PROCESS BIOCHEMISTRY. see *BIOLOGY—Biotechnology*

572 DEU ISSN 0079-6336
QH611 CODEN: PHCCAS
➤ **PROGRESS IN HISTOCHEMISTRY AND CYTOCHEMISTRY.** Text in English. 1970. 4/yr. EUR 342 to institutions; EUR 373 in Europe to institutions; JPY 49,300 in Japan to institutions; USD 408 to institutions except Europe and Japan (effective 2006). adv. **Document type:** *Journal, Academic/Scholarly.* **Description:** Publishes comprehensive and analytical reviews within the entire field of histochemistry and cytochemistry.
Related titles: Online - full text ed.: (from bigchalk, EBSCO Publishing, ProQuest Information & Learning, ScienceDirect).
Indexed: ASCA, BBCI, BIOBASE, BIOSIS Prev, BiolAb, ChemAb, ChemTitl, ExcerpMed, ISR, IndMed, MEDLINE, SCI.
—BLDSC (6868.437000), CASDDS, CISTI, GNLM, IE, Infotrieve, ingenta. **CCC.**
Published by: Elsevier GmbH, Urban & Fischer Verlag (Subsidiary of: Elsevier Science & Technology), Loebdergraben 14a, Jena, 07743, Germany. TEL 49-3641-626430, FAX 49-3641-626432, info@urbanfischer.de, http://www.elsevier.com/locate/proghistcyt, http://www.urbanfischer.de. Eds. D Sasse, U Schumacher, Dr. W Graumann. R&P Martin Huber TEL 49-3641-626430. Adv. contact Sabine Schroeter TEL 49-3641-626445. B&W page EUR 320, color page EUR 1,265; 170 x 240. Circ: 250 (paid and controlled). **Non-German speaking countries subscr. to:** Nature Publishing Group, Brunel Rd, Houndmills, Basingstoke, Hamps RG21 6XS, United Kingdom. TEL 44-1256-302629, FAX 44-1256-476117

➤ **PROGRESS IN MOLECULAR AND SUBCELLULAR BIOLOGY.** see *BIOLOGY—Cytology And Histology*

572.57 NLD ISSN 0168-9614
QP552.L5 CODEN: PPLIEF
PROGRESS IN PROTEIN - LIPID INTERACTIONS. Text in English. 1985. irreg., latest vol.2, 1986. price varies. back issues avail. **Document type:** *Monographic series.*
—CASDDS, CISTI, Linda Hall.
Published by: Elsevier BV (Subsidiary of: Elsevier Science & Technology), Radarweg 29, Amsterdam, 1043 NX, Netherlands. TEL 31-20-4853911, FAX 31-20-4852457, nlinfo-f@elsevier.nl, http://www.elsevier.nl. Eds. A Watts, J J H H M De Pont.

PROSTAGLANDINS - BIOLOGY. see *MEDICAL SCIENCES—Abstracting, Bibliographies, Statistics*

PROSTAGLANDINS, LEUKOTRIENES AND CANCER. see *MEDICAL SCIENCES—Oncology*

572.7 616.3 615.1 USA
PROTEASE INHIBITOR REFERENCE. Text in English. 1997. a. USD 269 (effective 1999). **Document type:** *Trade.*
Published by: Thomson American Health Consultants, Inc. (Subsidiary of: Thomson Corporation, Healthcare Information Group), 3525 Piedmont Rd, N E, Bldg 6, Ste 400, Atlanta, GA 30305. TEL 404-262-5511, FAX 404-262-7837, customerservice@ahcpub.com, http://www.ahcpub.com.

572.65 NLD ISSN 0929-8665
QP551 CODEN: PPELEN
➤ **PROTEIN AND PEPTIDE LETTERS**; international journal for rapid publication of short papers in protein and peptide science. Text in English. 1994. 6/yr. EUR 640, USD 640 to institutions (academic), print or online; EUR 1,020, USD 1,020 to corporations print or electronic; EUR 170, USD 170 combined subscription to individuals print & online; EUR 710, USD 710 combined subscription to institutions (academic), print & online; EUR 1,220, USD 1,220 combined subscription to corporations print & online (effective 2004). adv. **Document type:** *Journal, Academic/Scholarly.* **Description:** Features short reviews, communications and crystallization reports.
Related titles: Online - full text ed.: (from EBSCO Publishing, Gale Group, IngentaConnect, Swets Information Services).
Indexed: ASCA, ASFA, BBCI, BIOBASE, BIOSIS Prev, BiolAb, CIN, ChemAb, ChemTitl, IABS, MSB, SCI.
—BLDSC (6935.935000), CASDDS, CISTI, GNLM, IDS, IE, Infotrieve, ingenta. **CCC.**
Published by: Bentham Science Publishers Ltd., PO Box 1673, Hilversum, BR 1200, Netherlands. TEL 31-35-6923800, FAX 31-35-6980150, M.Bentham@inter.nl.net, http://www.bentham.org/ppl. Eds. John D Wade, R J Leatherbarrow, Ben M Dunn. **Subscr. addr. in the US:** Bentham Science Publishers Ltd., 1400 Pine St, PO Box 640310, San Francisco, CA 94164-0310. FAX 415-775-4503, shidding@worldonline.nl.

572 USA ISSN 1741-0126
TP248.P77 CODEN: PEDSBR
➤ **PROTEIN ENGINEERING DESIGN AND SELECTION.** Short title: P E D S. Text in English. 1986. m. GBP 717, USD 1,219, EUR 1,076 to institutions; GBP 755, USD 1,284, EUR 1,133 combined subscription to institutions print & online eds. (effective 2006). adv. bk.rev. illus. index. 124 p./no.; back issues avail.; reprint service avail. from PSC. **Document type:** *Journal, Academic/Scholarly.* **Description:** International research results advancing the understanding of the structural and biochemical basis of protein function.
Formerly (until 2004): Protein Engineering (0269-2139)
Related titles: Online - full text ed.: ISSN 1741-0134. GBP 680, USD 1,156, EUR 1,020 to institutions (effective 2006) (from EBSCO Publishing, Gale Group, HighWire Press, IngentaConnect, O C L C Online Computer Library Center, Inc., Ovid Technologies, Inc., Oxford University Press Online Journals, ProQuest Information & Learning, Swets Information Services).
Indexed: AEBA, AIDS&CR, ASCA, ASFA, AgBio, AnBrAb, B&BAb, BBCI, BCI, BIOBASE, BIOSIS Prev, BioEngAb, BiolAb, CBTA, CCI, CPA, ChemAb, ChemTitl, CurCont, DBA, DSA, ESPM, EngInd, ExcerpMed, FCA, FS&TA, HortAb, IABS, ISR, IndMed, IndVet, Inpharma, M&PBA, MBA, MEDLINE, NucAcAb, PBA, PGegResA, PN&I, PoultAb, ProtozoAb, RM&VM, RPP, Reac, RefZh, SCI, SIA, SeedAb, SoyAb, Telegen, ToxAb, TriticAb, VetBull, VirolAbstr.
—BLDSC (6936.055000), CASDDS, CISTI, Ei, GNLM, IDS, IE, Infotrieve, ingenta, Linda Hall. **CCC.**
Published by: Oxford University Press (Subsidiary of: Oxford University Press), 2001 Evans Rd, Cary, NC 27513. TEL 919-677-0977, FAX 919-677-1714, wao@oup-usa.org, jnlorders@oup-usa.org, http://peds.oxfordjournals.org/, http://www.us.oup.com. Eds. Alan Fersht, Greg Winter, Valerie Daggett. adv.: page GBP 300, page USD 570. Circ: 900.

572.8 USA ISSN 1046-5928
QP551 CODEN: PEXPEJ
➤ **PROTEIN EXPRESSION AND PURIFICATION.** Text in English. 1990. 12/yr. EUR 405 in Europe to individuals; JPY 42,200 in Japan to individuals; USD 306 to individuals except Europe and Japan; EUR 839 in Europe to institutions; JPY 87,700 in Japan to institutions; USD 636 to institutions except Europe and Japan; EUR 201 in Europe to students; JPY 21,000 in Japan to students; USD 176 to students except Europe and Japan (effective 2006). back issues avail. **Document type:** *Academic/Scholarly.* **Description:** Presents papers on protein isolations based on conventional fractionation techniques as well as those employing the variety of molecular biological procedures used in the expression of proteins.
Related titles: Online - full text ed.: ISSN 1096-0279. USD 617 (effective 2002) (from EBSCO Publishing, Gale Group, IngentaConnect, O C L C Online Computer Library Center, Inc., ScienceDirect, Swets Information Services).
Indexed: ASCA, ASFA, BBCI, BCI, BIOBASE, BIOSIS Prev, BiolAb, CCI, CIN, ChemAb, ChemTitl, CurCont, DSA, FS&TA, IABS, ISR, IndMed, Inpharma, MEDLINE, MSB, NutrAb, Reac, RefZh, SCI.
—BLDSC (6936.060000), CASDDS, CISTI, GNLM, IDS, IE, Infotrieve, ingenta, Linda Hall. **CCC.**
Published by: Academic Press (Subsidiary of: Elsevier Science & Technology), 525 B St, Ste 1900, San Diego, CA 92101-4495. TEL 619-231-6616, 800-894-3434, FAX 619-699-6422, apsubs@acad.com, http://www.elsevier.com/locate/yprep, http://www.academicpress.com. Ed. R. R. Burgess.

572.4 USA ISSN 1572-3887
QP551 CODEN: JPCHD2
➤ **THE PROTEIN JOURNAL.** Text in English. 1982. 8/yr. EUR 998, USD 1,018, GBP 628 combined subscription to institutions print & online eds. (effective 2005). adv. back issues avail.; reprint service avail. from PSC. **Document type:** *Journal, Academic/Scholarly.* **Description:** Publishes original research investigating the molecular basis for protein function. Covers all aspects of protein activity.
Formerly (until 2004): Journal of Protein Chemistry (0277-8033)
Related titles: Microfilm ed.: (from PQC); Online - full text ed.: ISSN 1573-4943 (from EBSCO Publishing, Gale Group, IngentaConnect, Kluwer Online, O C L C Online Computer Library Center, Inc., Ovid Technologies, Inc., Springer LINK, Swets Information Services).
Indexed: ASCA, ASFA, AbHyg, AgBio, AgrForAb, AnBrAb, B&BAb, BBCI, BIOBASE, BIOSIS Prev, BibLing, BiolAb, CCI, CIN, CPA, ChemAb, ChemTitl, CurCont, DSA, ESPM, EngInd, ExcerpMed, FCA, ForAb, GenetAb, HerbAb, HortAb, IABS, ISR, IndMed, IndVet, Inpharma, MEDLINE, MSB, MaizeAb, NutrAb, OrnHort, PBA, PGegResA, PHN&I, RA&MP, RM&VM, RPP, Reac, RefZh, RevApplEntom, RiceAb, S&F, SCI, SIA, SeedAb, SoyAb, TDB, TriticAb, VetBull.
—BLDSC (6936.090000), CASDDS, CISTI, Ei, GNLM, IDS, IE, Infotrieve, ingenta, Linda Hall. **CCC.**
Published by: Plenum US (Subsidiary of: Springer Science+Business Media), 233 Spring St, New York, NY 10013. TEL 212-460-1500, FAX 212-460-1575, service@springer-ny.com, http://springerlink.metapress.com/openurl.asp?genre=journal&issn=1572-3887, http://www.springeronline.com. Ed. M Zouhair Atassi.

572.65 JPN
PROTEIN - PEPTIDE SEQUENCE DATA BASE. Short title: P R F - S E Q D B. Text in Japanese. base vol. plus updates 6/yr. USD 2,500. abstr. **Description:** Consists of amino acid sequences of peptides and proteins, including sequences predicted from genes. Literature in which sequence is presented is searchable.
Media: Magnetic Tape. **Related titles:** CD-ROM ed.; Diskette ed.
Published by: Protein Research Foundation, Peptide Institute/Tanpakushitsu Kenkyu Shoreikai Pepuchido Kenkyujo, 4-1-2 Ina, Mino-shi, Osaka-fu 562-0015, Japan. TEL 81-727-29-4124, query@prj.or.jp, http://www.pfr.or.jp/.

572 USA ISSN 0961-8368
QP551 CODEN: PRCIEI
➤ **PROTEIN SCIENCE.** Text in English. 1992. m. USD 240 domestic to individuals; USD 296 in Canada & Mexico to individuals; USD 320 elsewhere to individuals; USD 1,195 domestic to institutions; USD 1,251 in Canada & Mexico to institutions; USD 1,275 elsewhere to institutions; USD 195 domestic to students; USD 251 in Canada & Mexico to students; USD 275 elsewhere to students (effective 2005). adv. bk.rev. illus. back issues avail. **Document type:** *Journal, Academic/Scholarly.* **Description:** Publishes papers on protein structure, function, and biochemical significance.
Related titles: Online - full text ed.: ISSN 1469-896X. 1999 (from EBSCO Publishing, HighWire Press, O C L C Online Computer Library Center, Inc.); Supplement(s): Protein Science. Diskette Appendix. ISSN 1359-5040. 1991.
Indexed: AEBA, ASCA, B&BAb, BBCI, BIOBASE, BIOSIS Prev, BiolAb, CCI, CIN, ChemAb, ChemTitl, CurCont, DSA, ExcerpMed, FS&TA, IABS, ISR, IndMed, Inpharma, M&PBA, MEDLINE, MSB, NucAcAb, Reac, SCI, SSCI.
—BLDSC (6936.105500), CASDDS, CISTI, GNLM, IDS, IE, Infotrieve, ingenta, KNAW, Linda Hall. **CCC.**
Published by: (Protein Society), Cold Spring Harbor Laboratory Press, Publications Department, 500 Sunnyside Blvd., Woodbury, NY 11797-2924. TEL 516-422-4100, FAX 516-422-4097, cshpress@cshl.edu, http://www.proteinscience.org/, http://www.cshl.org. Ed. Mark Hermodson. Adv. contact Ms. Marcie Siconolfi TEL 516-422-4010.

572 JPN
PROTEIN SCIENCE SOCIETY OF JAPAN. NEWSLETTER. Text in Japanese. 1988. 4/yr. free to members. **Document type:** *Newsletter, Academic/Scholarly.*
Formerly (until 2001): Protein Engineering Society of Japan. Newsletter
Published by: Protein Science Society of Japan, 4-1-2 Ina, Minoh, Osaka, 562-8686, Japan. TEL 81-72-7294124, pssj@peptide.co.jp, http://www.pssj.jp/. Ed. Tairo Oshima.

572.6 CHE ISSN 1424-4721
PROTEIN SPOTLIGHT. Text in English. 2000. m. free. **Document type:** *Academic/Scholarly.* **Description:** Contains articles focused on particular proteins of interest.
Media: Online - full content.
Published by: Institut Suisse de Bioinformatique, Groupe Swiss - Prot, CMU - 1 rue Michel Servet, Geneva 4, 1211 Switzerland. TEL 41-22-7025050, FAX 41-22-7025858, spotlight@isb-sib.ch, http://www.expasy.ch/spotlight/, http://www.expasy.ch/people/swissprot.html.

PROTEINS: POST-TRANSLATIONAL PROCESSING. see *BIOLOGY—Abstracting, Bibliographies, Statistics*

572 USA
QP551 CODEN: PSFGEY
➤ **PROTEINS: STRUCTURE, FUNCTION, AND BIOINFORMATICS.** Text in English. 1987. 16/yr. USD 3,575 domestic to institutions; USD 3,767 in Canada & Mexico to institutions; USD 3,879 elsewhere to institutions; USD 3,933 combined subscription domestic to institutions print & online eds.; USD 4,125 combined subscription in Canada & Mexico to institutions print & online eds.; USD 4,237 combined subscription elsewhere to institutions print & online eds. (effective 2006). adv. bk.rev. abstr. Supplement avail.; back issues avail. **Document type:** *Journal, Academic/Scholarly.* **Description:** Concentrates on advances in all areas of biochemistry: structure, function, genetics, computation, and design.
Formerly: Proteins: Structure, Function, and Genetics (0887-3585)
Related titles: Microform ed.: (from PQC); Online - full text ed.: ISSN 1097-0134. USD 3,575 to institutions (effective 2006) (from EBSCO Publishing, Swets Information Services, Wiley InterScience).
Indexed: ASCA, ASFA, AbHyg, AgBio, AgrForAb, AnBrAb, ApicAb, B&BAb, BBCI, BCI, BIOBASE, BIOSIS Prev, BioEngAb, BiolAb, CCI, CPA, ChemAb, ChemTitl, CurCont, DSA, ESPM, ExcerpMed, FCA, FPA, FS&TA, ForAb, HelmAb, HerbAb, HortAb, IABS, INIS AtomInd, ISR, IndMed, IndVet, Inpharma, MBA, MEDLINE, MSB, NemAb, NutrAb, PBA, ProtozoAb, RA&MP, RM&VM, RPP, Reac, RefZh, RevApplEntom, S&F, SCI, SIA, SeedAb, SoyAb, TDB, VetBull.
—BLDSC (6936.164000), CASDDS, CISTI, GNLM, IDS, IE, Infotrieve, ingenta, Linda Hall. **CCC.**
Published by: John Wiley & Sons, Inc., 111 River St, Hoboken, NJ 07030-5774. TEL 201-748-6000, FAX 201-748-5915, uscs-wis@wiley.com, http://www3.interscience.wiley.com/cgi-bin/jhome/36176, http://www.wiley.com. Ed. E E Lattman. adv.: B&W page GBP 640, color page GBP 1,515; trim 210 x 279. Circ: 1,200. **Subscr. outside the Americas to:** John Wiley & Sons Ltd., The Atrium, Southern Gate, Chichester, West Sussex PO19 8SQ, United Kingdom. TEL 44-1243-843335, 0800-243407, FAX 44-1243-843232, cs-journals@wiley.co.uk.

572.6 GBR ISSN 1477-5956
▼ ➤ **PROTEOME SCIENCE.** Text in English. 2003. irreg. free (effective 2006). **Document type:** *Journal, Academic/Scholarly.* **Description:** Contains original research in the general area of proteomics, including structural biology, mass spectrometry, protein arrays, bioinformatics, HTS assays, protein chemistry, cell biology, signal transduction and physiology.
Related titles: Online - full text ed.: free (effective 2005).
Indexed: ExcerpMed.
—CCC.
Published by: BioMed Central Ltd. (Subsidiary of: Current Science Ltd), Middlesex House, 34-42 Cleveland St, London, W1T 4LB, United Kingdom. TEL 44-20-76319131, FAX 44-20-76319923, info@biomedcentral.com, http://www.proteomesci.com/home/, http://www.biomedcentral.com. Ed. Martin Latterich.

572 DEU ISSN 1615-9853
CODEN: PROTC7
➤ **PROTEOMICS.** Text in English. 2001. 24/yr. EUR 2,224 in Europe; CHF 3,088 Switzerland & Liechtenstein; USD 2,598 elsewhere; EUR 2,447 combined subscription in Europe print & online eds.; CHF 3,397 combined subscription in Switzerland & Liechtenstein for print & online eds.; USD 2,858 combined subscription elsewhere print & online eds. (effective 2006). bk.rev. abstr.; bibl.; charts; illus. back issues avail.; reprints avail. **Document type:** *Journal, Academic/Scholarly.* **Description:** Aims to integrate the various areas of proteomics, including methodological developments in protein separation and characterization, advances in bioinformatics, and novel applications of proteomics in all areas of the life sciences and industry.
Related titles: Online - full text ed.: ISSN 1615-9861. 2001. EUR 2,224 in Europe; CHF 3,088 in Switzerland & Liechtenstein; USD 2,598 elsewhere (effective 2006) (from EBSCO Publishing, Swets Information Services, Wiley InterScience).
Indexed: AbHyg, AgBio, AnBrAb, AnalAb, B&BAb, BBCI, BCI, BIOBASE, BIOSIS Prev, BioCN&I, BioEngAb, BiolAb, CPA, ChemAb, CurCont, DSA, ExcerpMed, FCA, GenetAb, HelmAb, HerbAb, HortAb, ISR, IndVet, M&PBA, MSB, NemAb, NucAcAb, NutrAb, PBA, ProtozoAb, RA&MP, RM&VM, RPP, RiceAb, S&F, SCI, SIA, SeedAb, TriticAb, VetBull.
—BLDSC (6936.178000), CISTI, IE, Infotrieve, ingenta, Linda Hall. **CCC.**
Published by: Wiley - V C H Verlag GmbH & Co. KGaA (Subsidiary of: John Wiley & Sons, Inc.), Boschstr 12, Weinheim, 69469, Germany. TEL 49-6201-6060, FAX 49-6201-606328, subservice@wiley-vch.de, info@wiley-vch.de, http://www.wiley-vch.de/home/proteomics. Ed. Michael J Dunn. R&P Claudia Jerke. Adv. contact Achim Kraus.

572 USA ISSN 1535-2722
PROTEOMICS WEEKLY. Text in English. 1999. w.
Related titles: Online - full text ed.: ISSN 1537-1352 (from ProQuest Information & Learning).
Published by: NewsRx, PO Box 830409, Birmingham, AL 35283-0409. TEL 770-507-7777, FAX 770-507-7788, info@newsrx.com.

R N A. (Ribonucleic Acid) see *BIOLOGY—Genetics*

572   USA   ISSN 1547-6286
QP623
▼ ▶ R N A BIOLOGY. (Ribonucleic Acid) Text in English. 2004. bi-m. USD 80 combined subscription in US & Canada to individuals print & online eds.; USD 130 combined subscription elsewhere to individuals print & online eds.; USD 450 combined subscription in US & Canada to institutions print & online eds.; USD 500 combined subscription elsewhere to institutions print & online eds. (effective 2005). Document type: *Journal, Academic/Scholarly.*
Related titles: Online - full text ed.: ISSN 1555-8584.
Indexed: ExcerpMed.
Published by: Landes Bioscience, 810 S Church St, Georgetown, TX 78626. TEL 512-863-7762, 800-736-9948, FAX 512-863-0081, info@landesbioscience.com, http://www.landesbioscience.com/journals/rnabiology/index.php.

572   IND
RECENT RESEARCH DEVELOPMENT IN COMPARATIVE BIOCHEMISTRY AND PHYSIOLOGY. Text in English. a., latest vol.2, 2001.
Published by: Transworld Research Network, T C 36-248 (1), Trivandrum, Kerala 695 008, India. http://www.transworldresearch.com.

572   IND
RECENT RESEARCH DEVELOPMENTS IN ANALYTICAL BIOCHEMISTRY. Text in English. a., latest vol.1, 2001.
—BLDSC (7305.087230).
Published by: Transworld Research Network, T C 36-248 (1), Trivandrum, Kerala 695 008, India. http://www.transworldresearch.com.

572.43   IND
RECENT RESEARCH DEVELOPMENTS IN BIOENERGETICS. Text in English. a., latest vol.2, 2001.
Published by: Transworld Research Network, T C 36-248 (1), Trivandrum, Kerala 695 008, India. http://www.transworldresearch.com.

RECENT RESEARCH DEVELOPMENTS IN BIOPHYSICAL CHEMISTRY. see *BIOLOGY—Biophysics*

572.57   IND
RECENT RESEARCH DEVELOPMENTS IN LIPIDS. Text in English. a., latest vol.4, 2000.
Published by: Transworld Research Network, T C 36-248 (1), Trivandrum, Kerala 695 008, India. http://www.transworldresearch.com.

572.33   IND
RECENT RESEARCH DEVELOPMENTS IN MACROMOLECULES. Text in English. USD 40 (effective 1999).
Formerly: Recent Research Developments in Macromolecules Research
—BLDSC (7305.087437).
Published by: Transworld Research Network, T C 36-248 (1), Trivandrum, Kerala 695 008, India.

572.8   IND
RECENT RESEARCH DEVELOPMENTS IN MOLECULAR & CELLULAR BIOLOGY. Text in English. a.
—BLDSC (7305.087485).
Published by: Research Signpost, T.C. 37/661 (2), Fort P.O., Trivandrum, Kerala, India.

573.84   IND
RECENT RESEARCH DEVELOPMENTS IN NEUROCHEMISTRY. Text in English. a.
—BLDSC (7305.087495).
Published by: Research Signpost, T.C. 37/661 (2), Fort P.O., Trivandrum, Kerala, India.

572   IND
RECENT RESEARCH DEVELOPMENTS IN SEROID BIOCHEMISTRY & MOLECULAR BIOLOGY. Text in English. a.
Published by: Transworld Research Network, T C 36-248 (1), Trivandrum, Kerala 695 008, India. http://www.transworldresearch.com.

THE RECEPTORS. see *MEDICAL SCIENCES—Psychiatry And Neurology*

▼ REFERATIVNYI ZHURNAL. BIOKHIMIYA. see *BIOLOGY—Abstracting, Bibliographies, Statistics*

REFERATIVNYI ZHURNAL. BIOLOGIYA. FIZIKO-KHIMICHESKAYA BIOLOGIYA. see *BIOLOGY—Abstracting, Bibliographies, Statistics*

REFERATIVNYI ZHURNAL. BIOORGANICHESKAYA KHIMIYA. MAKROMOLEKULY. see *CHEMISTRY—Abstracting, Bibliographies, Statistics*

REFERATIVNYI ZHURNAL. FIZIOLOGIYA I BIOKHIMIYA RASTENII. see *BIOLOGY—Abstracting, Bibliographies, Statistics*

REFERATIVNYI ZHURNAL. MOLEKULYARNAYA BIOLOGIYA. see *BIOLOGY—Abstracting, Bibliographies, Statistics*

572   FRA   ISSN 0336-1640
REGARD SUR LA BIOCHIMIE. Text in French. 1974. q.
Document type: *Newsletter.*
Published by: Societe Francaise de Biochimie et Biologie Moleculaire, Centre Universitaire, 45, rue des Saints-Peres, Paris Cedex 06, 75270, France. TEL 33-1-4286-3377, FAX 33-1-4286-3373, sfbbm@cep.u-psud.fr, http://coli.polytechnique.fr/sfbbm.

572.65   NLD   ISSN 0167-0115
CODEN: REPPDY
▶ REGULATORY PEPTIDES. Text in Dutch. 1980. 21/yr. EUR 2,943 in Europe to institutions; JPY 390,600 in Japan to institutions; USD 3,292 to institutions except Europe and Japan (effective 2006). abstr. reprint service avail. from ISI. Document type: *Academic/Scholarly.* Description: Provides a medium for the rapid publication of interdisciplinary studies on the physiology and pathology of peptides of the gut, endocrine and nervous systems which regulate cell or tissue function.
Related titles: Microform ed.: (from PQC); Online - full text ed.: (from EBSCO Publishing, Gale Group, IngentaConnect, ScienceDirect, Swets Information Services); Supplement(s): ISSN 0169-5134. 1980.
Indexed: ASCA, ASFA, AbHyg, AgBio, AnBrAb, BBCI, BIOBASE, BIOSIS Prev, BiolAb, CIN, ChemAb, ChemTitl, CurCont, DSA, ExcerpMed, IABS, ISR, IndMed, IndVet, Inpharma, MEDLINE, NSCI, NutrAb, PE&ON, PN&I, PoultAb, Reac, RevApplEntom, SCI, SFA, VetBull.
—BLDSC (7350.030000), CASDDS, CISTI, GNLM, IDS, IE, Infotrieve, ingenta, KNAW. CCC.
Published by: Elsevier BV (Subsidiary of: Elsevier Science & Technology), Radarweg 29, Amsterdam, 1043 NX, Netherlands. TEL 31-20-4853911, FAX 31-20-4852457, nlinfo-f@elsevier.nl, http://www.elsevier.com/locate/regpep, http://www.elsevier.nl. Eds. M I Phillips, Wolfgang E Schmidt. Subscr. to: PO Box 211, Amsterdam 1000 AE, Netherlands. TEL 31-20-485-3757, FAX 31-20-485-3432.

▶ RELAZIONI CLINICO SCIENTIFICHE. see *MEDICAL SCIENCES*

▶ REPRODUCTION, NUTRITION, DEVELOPMENT. see *BIOLOGY*

▶ REPRODUCTION. SUPPLEMENT. see *BIOLOGY—Physiology*

▶ REPRODUCTIVE TOXICOLOGY. see *BIOLOGY—Physiology*

572.65   JPN   ISSN 0387-4141
CODEN: HAMKE3
RESEARCH COMMITTEE OF ESSENTIAL AMINO ACIDS. REPORTS/HISSU AMINOSAN KENKYU. Text in Japanese. 1958. bi-m. charts. Description: Contains research reports focusing on nutrition and its physiological effects.
Indexed: CIN, ChemAb, ChemTitl.
—CASDDS.
Published by: Research Committee of Essential Amino Acids/Hissu Aminosan Kenkyu linkai, Kyoritsu Joshi Daigaku Kasei Gakubu Shokumotsu Gakka, 2-1 Hitotsubashi 2-chome, Chiyoda-ku, Tokyo, 101-0003, Japan.

572.8   USA   ISSN 1087-111X
QP501   CODEN: RCBBFC
▶ RESEARCH COMMUNICATIONS IN BIOCHEMISTRY AND CELL & MOLECULAR BIOLOGY. Text in English. 1997. q. USD 200 domestic; USD 235 foreign (effective 2004). illus. back issues avail.; reprints avail. Document type: *Journal, Academic/Scholarly.* Description: Publishes laboratory and clinical research in biochemicistry and cytology, with applications in the medical and biological sciences.
Indexed: BIOSIS Prev, BiolAb, ChemAb, ExcerpMed, ZooRec.
—BLDSC (7736.430000), CISTI, IE, ingenta. CCC.
Published by: P J D Publications Ltd, PO Box 966, Westbury, NY 11590. TEL 516-626-0650, FAX 516-626-4456, sankar@pjdonline.com, http://www.pjdonline.com. Ed. Akira Tsugita.

▶ REVIEWS OF PHYSIOLOGY, BIOCHEMISTRY AND PHARMACOLOGY. see *BIOLOGY—Physiology*

▶ RIBOSOMES AND TRANSLATION. see *BIOLOGY—Abstracting, Bibliographies, Statistics*

572   ROM   ISSN 1582-3318
QP501   CODEN: RRBCAD
ROMANIAN JOURNAL OF BIOCHEMISTRY. Text and summaries in English, French, German, Russian. 1964. 2/yr. charts; illus. index.
Formerly (until 2000): Revue Roumaine de Biochimie (0001-4214)
Related titles: Online - full text ed.
Indexed: AbHyg, AgBio, AnBrAb, AnalAb, BIOSIS Prev, BiolAb, CIN, CPA, ChemAb, ChemTitl, CurCont, DBA, DSA, ExcerpMed, FCA, HelmAb, HortAb, INIS AtomInd, IndVet, NPU, NutrAb, OrnHort, PBA, PN&I, PotatoAb, PoultAb, RA&MP, RM&VM, RPP, S&F, SoyAb, TriticAb, VetBull.
—BLDSC (8019.626000), CASDDS, CISTI, GNLM, IE, ingenta, KNAW, Linda Hall.
Published by: (Academia Romana), Editura Academiei Romane/Publishing House of the Romanian Academy, Calea 13 Septembrie 13, Sector 5, Bucharest, 76117, Romania. TEL 40-21-4119008, FAX 40-21-4103983, edacad@ear.ro, http://www.ear.ro. Ed. Mihai Serban. Circ: 1,000. Dist. by: Rodipet S.A., Piata Presei Libere 1, sector 1, PO Box 33-57, Bucharest 3, Romania. TEL 40-21-2224126, 40-21-2226407, rodipet@rodipet.ro.

RUSSIAN JOURNAL OF BIOORGANIC CHEMISTRY. see *CHEMISTRY—Organic Chemistry*

572 660.6   USA   ISSN 1052-6781
S A A S BULLETIN. BIOCHEMISTRY AND BIOTECHNOLOGY. (Southern Association of Agricultural Scientists) Text in English. 1988. irreg. Document type: *Monographic series, Academic/Scholarly.*
—BLDSC (8062.260000).
Published by: Southern Association of Agricultural Scientists, Biochemistry and Biotechnology Section, LSU AgCenter, PO Box 25203, Baton Rouge, LA 70794-5203. TEL 225-578-4164, FAX 225.578.4143, mlegendre@agcenter.lsu.edu, http://www.saasinc.org.

572   IND
S B C NEWSLETTER. Text in English. 3/yr.
Published by: Society of Biological Chemists, Department of Biochemistry, Indian Institute of Science, Bangalore, Karnataka 560 012, India.

572   JPN   ISSN 0031-9082
QP501   CODEN: SBBKA4
SEIBUTSU BUTSURI KAGAKU/PHYSICO-CHEMICAL BIOLOGY. Text in English, Japanese. 1951. bi-m. JPY 8,000 per issue membership (effective 2004). adv. bk.rev. illus. Index.
Document type: *Journal, Academic/Scholarly.*
Related titles: Online - full text ed.: ISSN 1349-9785 (from J-Stage).
Indexed: BIOSIS Prev, BiolAb, ChemAb, ChemTitl, RefZh.
—CASDDS, CISTI. CCC.
Published by: Denki Eido Gakkai/Society of Electrophoresis, Business Center for Academic Societies Japan, 5-16-9 Hon Komagome, Bunkyo-ku, Tokyo, 113-8622, Japan. TEL 81-3-58145801, Attoda@tmig.or.jp, http://proteome.tmig.or.jp/JES/J_index_body.html. Circ: 1,600.

572   JPN
SEIBUTSU KINO KANKEI SHIRYOSHU/FINDINGS OF BIOFUNCTIONAL CHEMISTRY. Text in Japanese. 1990. a.
Published by: (Norin Suisan Gijutsu Kaigi Jimukyoku), Norin Suisansho/Ministry of Agriculture, Forestry and Fisheries, 2-1 Kasumigaseki 1-chome, Chiyoda-ku, Tokyo, 100-0013, Japan.

572   JPN   ISSN 0037-1017
CODEN: SEIKAQ
SEIKAGAKU/JAPANESE BIOCHEMICAL SOCIETY. JOURNAL. Text in Japanese. 1925. m. JPY 18,000. adv. bk.rev. charts; illus. index.
Indexed: ASCA, BBCI, BiolAb, ChemAb, ChemTitl, CurCont, IndMed, JTA, MEDLINE, RefZh, SCI.
—BLDSC (8219.700000), CASDDS, CISTI, GNLM, IDS, IE, Infotrieve, ingenta, Linda Hall. CCC.
Published by: Nihon Seikagakkai/Japanese Biochemical Society, c/o Ishikawa Bldg 3F, 25-16 Hongo 5-chome, Bunkyo-ku, Tokyo, 113-0033, Japan. FAX 03-3815-1934. Ed. Y Nagai. Circ: 20,709.

SEITAI NO KAGAKU/MEDICAL SCIENCE. see *BIOLOGY*

572 660   JPN   ISSN 1344-6924
QD431.A1   CODEN: TKKDE4
▶ SEITAIBUNSI KAISEKI KENKYU SENTA DAYORI. Text in Japanese. 1980. a., latest vol.21, 2000. back issues avail. Document type: *Academic/Scholarly.* Description: Contains structural biology research reports at the research center.
Former titles (until Mar. 1999): Tanpakushitsu Kogaku Kiso Kenkyu Senta Dayori (0916-1554); (until 1988): Kessho Kaiseki Kenkyu Senta Dayori (0388-6409)
—BLDSC (8228.227500), CASDDS.
Published by: (Fuzoku Seitaibunsi Kaiseki/Research Center for Structural Biology), Osaka Daigaku, Tanpakushitsu Kenkyusho/Osaka University, Institute for Protein Research, 3-2 Yamada-Oka, Suita-shi, Osaka-fu 565-0871, Japan. TEL 81-6-6879-8634, FAX 81-6-6879-8636, kusunoki@protein.osaka-u.ac.jp, http://www.protein.osaka-u.ac.jp/. Ed. Masami Kusunoki.

▶ SENSORS. see *CHEMISTRY—Analytical Chemistry*

572.6   USA
SEQUENCES OF PROTEINS OF IMMUNOLOGICAL INTEREST. Text in English. irreg., latest vol.5, 1994. USD 30 in North America; USD 51 elsewhere. Document type: *Academic/Scholarly.* Description: Discusses N.I.H. research in this area; includes summary distribution tables, variability plots, protein index, antibody specificity index, and general reference index.

Published by: U.S. National Center for Biotechnology Information, National Library of Medicine, Bldg 38A, Rm 8N 803, 8600 Rockville Pike, Bethesda, MD 20894. TEL 301-496-2475, FAX 301-480-9241, info@ncbi.nlm.nih.gov. **Subscr. to:** National Technical Information Service, Government Research Center, 5285 Port Royal Rd, Springfield, VA 22161. TEL 703-605-6060, 800-363-2068, http://www.ntis.gov.

572 DEU
SERVA MAIN CATALOG (YEAR). Text in German. a. **Document type:** *Catalog.*
Published by: Serva Feinbiochemica GmbH und Co. KG, Carl-Benz-Str 7, Heidelberg, 69115, Germany. TEL 06221-502-0, FAX 06221-502113.

572 CHN ISSN 1000-3282
QP501 CODEN: SHYCD4
➤ **SHENGWU HUAXUE YU SHENGWU WULI JINZHAN/PROGRESS IN BIOCHEMISTRY AND BIOPHYSICS.** Text in Chinese. 1973. bi-m. CNY 150 (effective 2004). adv. **Document type:** *Journal, Academic/Scholarly.* **Description:** Covers the latest scientific developments in biochemistry, biophysics, molecular biology, and neuroscience. Includes review articles, research papers, short communications, and lectures on basic theories and applied knowledge.
Related titles: Online - full text ed.: (from East View Information Services, WanFang Data Corp.).
Indexed: ASCA, B&BAb, BBCI, ChemAb, ChemTitl, M&PBA, RefZh.
—BLDSC (6865.968000), CASDDS, IDS, IE, ingenta, Linda Hall.
Published by: (Zhongguo Kexueyuan, Shengwu Wuli Yanjiusuo/Chinese Academy of Sciences, Institute of Biophysics), Kexue Chubanshe/Science Press, 16 Donghuang Cheng Genbei Jie, Beijing, 100717, China. TEL 86-10-64000246, FAX 86-10-64030255, prog@sun5.ibp.ac.cn, http://swhx.periodicals.net.cn/default.html, http://www.sciencep.com/. Circ: 11,000. **Dist. by:** China International Book Trading Corp, 35 Chegongzhuang Xilu, Haidian District, PO Box 399, Beijing 100044, China. TEL 86-10-68412045, FAX 86-10-68412023, cibtc@mail.cibtc.com.cn, http://www.cibtc.com.cn.

572 JPN ISSN 0285-1520
SHISHITSU SEIKAGAKU KENKYU/JAPANESE CONFERENCE ON THE BIOCHEMISTRY OF LIPIDS. PROCEEDINGS. Text in English, Japanese. 1961. a. **Document type:** *Proceedings.*
Published by: Nihon Shishitsu Seikagaku Kenkyukai/Japanese Conference on the Biochemistry of Lipids, c/o Teikyo Daigaku Igakubu Dai 1 Seikagaku Kyoshitsu, 11-1 Kaga 2-chome, Itabashi-ku, Tokyo, 173-0003, Japan.

572 JPN
SHISHITSU SEIKAGAKU KENKYU CIRCULAR/JAPANESE CONFERENCE ON THE BIOCHEMISTRY OF LIPIDS. CIRCULAR. Text in Japanese. 1964. a.
Published by: Nihon Shishitsu Seikagaku Kenkyukai/Japanese Conference on the Biochemistry of Lipids, c/o Teikyo Daigaku Igakubu Dai 1 Seikagaku Kyoshitsu, 11-1 Kaga 2-chome, Itabashi-ku, Tokyo, 173-0003, Japan.

SIGNAL TRANSDUCTION; receptors, mediators and genes. see *BIOLOGY—Cytology And Histology*

SIGNAL TRANSDUCTION & CYCLIC NUCLEOTIDES. see *BIOLOGY—Abstracting, Bibliographies, Statistics*

572 USA
SOCIETY FOR BIOMATERIALS. ANNUAL MEETING PROCEEDINGS. Text in English. a.
—BLDSC (1087.866100).
Published by: Society for Biomaterials, 17000 Commerce Pkwy., Ste. C, Mount Laurel, NJ 08054-2267. director@biomaterials.org, http://www.biomaterials.org.

SOCIETY FOR NEUROSCIENCE. ABSTRACTS. see *MEDICAL SCIENCES—Psychiatry And Neurology*

572 IND ISSN 0300-0486
CODEN: PSBCAW
SOCIETY OF BIOLOGICAL CHEMISTS. PROCEEDINGS. Text in English. a.
Indexed: BiolAb.
—CISTI.
Published by: Society of Biological Chemists, Department of Biochemistry, Indian Institute of Science, Bangalore, Karnataka 560 012, India.

572 GBR ISSN 0038-0717
S590 CODEN: SBIOAH
➤ **SOIL BIOLOGY & BIOCHEMISTRY.** Text in English. 1969. 12/yr. EUR 2,244 in Europe to institutions; JPY 298,000 in Japan to institutions; USD 2,509 to institutions except Europe and Japan; EUR 292 in Europe to qualified personnel; JPY 38,700 in Japan to qualified personnel; USD 327 to qualified personnel except Europe and Japan (effective 2006). adv. bk.rev. charts; stat.; abstr. reprints avail. **Document type:** *Journal, Academic/Scholarly.* **Description:** Provides a forum for research on soil organisms, their biochemical activities, and the influence on the soil environment and plant growth.
Related titles: Microfiche ed.: (from MIM); Microfilm ed.: (from PQC); Online - full text ed.: (from EBSCO Publishing, Gale Group, IngentaConnect, ScienceDirect, Swets Information Services).
Indexed: AEA, ASCA, ASFA, AbHyg, AgBio, Agr, AgrForAb, ApEcolAb, B&AI, B&BAb, BIOBASE, BIOSIS Prev, BibAg, BioCN&I, BiolAb, BiolDig, CBTA, CIN, CPA, ChemAb, ChemTitl, CurCont, DBA, DSA, EIA, EPB, ESPM, EnerInd, EntAb, ExcerpMed, FCA, FPA, ForAb, GEOBASE, HerbAb, HortAb, I&DA, IABS, ISR, M&GPA, M&TEA, MBA, MSB, MaizeAb, NemAb, NutrAb, OrnHort, PBA, PGegResA, PGrRegA, PN&I, PlantSci, PollutAb, PotatoAb, PoultAb, ProtozoAb, RA&MP, RPP, RevApplEntom, RiceAb, S&F, S&MA, SCI, SIA, SWRA, SeedAb, SoyAb, TriticAb, WRCInf, WeedAb, ZooRec.
—BLDSC (8321.820100), CASDDS, CISTI, IDS, IE, Infotrieve, ingenta, Linda Hall. **CCC.**
Published by: (Council of Biological and Medical Abstracts), Pergamon (Subsidiary of: Elsevier Science & Technology), The Boulevard, Langford Ln, East Park, Kidlington, Oxford OX5 1GB, United Kingdom. TEL 44-1865-843000, FAX 44-1865-843010, http://www.elsevier.com/locate/soilbio. Eds. D Coleman, Dr. G Andersson, J S Waid, R Burns. Circ: 1,250 (paid). **Subscr. to:** Elsevier BV, PO Box 211, Amsterdam 1000 AE, Netherlands. TEL 31-20-485-3757, FAX 31-20-485-3432, nlinfo-f@elsevier.nl, http://www.elsevier.nl.

➤ **SOSHIKI BAIYO KENKYU/TISSUE CULTURE RESEARCH COMMUNICATIONS.** see *BIOLOGY—Cytology And Histology*

540 NLD ISSN 0712-4813
CODEN: SPIJDZ
➤ **SPECTROSCOPY**; an international journal. Text in English. 1982. bi-m. EUR 593, USD 712 combined subscription print & online eds. (effective 2006). bk.rev. **Document type:** *Journal, Academic/Scholarly.* **Description:** Covers all aspects of spectroscopy in chemistry.
Incorporates (1980-1983): European Journal of Mass Spectrometry in Biochemistry, Medicine and Environmental Research (0379-8399)
Related titles: Microform ed.: (from PQC); Online - full text ed.: (from Northern Light Technology, Inc.); (from EBSCO Publishing, Gale Group, IngentaConnect, O C L C Online Computer Library Center, Inc., Swets Information Services).
Indexed: ASCA, AnalAb, BiolAb, CCI, CIN, ChemAb, ChemTitl, CurCont, EngInd, ExcerpMed, MSB, MSCI, SCI.
—BLDSC (8411.113800), CASDDS, CISTI, Ei, GNLM, IDS, IE, Infotrieve, ingenta. **CCC.**
Published by: I O S Press, Nieuwe Hemweg 6B, Amsterdam, 1013 BG, Netherlands. TEL 31-20-6883355, FAX 31-20-6203419, order@iospress.nl, http://www.iospress.nl. Ed. Parvez I Haris. R&P Ms. Carry Koolbergen TEL 31-20-6382189. Adv. contact Ms. Jolijn van Eunen. Circ: 300. **Subscr. to:** I O S Press, Inc, 4502 Rachael Manor Dr., Fairfax, VA 22032-3631. iosbooks@iospress.com; Kinokuniya Co. Ltd., Shinjuku 3-chome, Shinjuku-ku, Tokyo 160-0022, Japan. FAX 81-3-3439-1094, journal@kinokuniya.co.jp, http://www.kinokuniya.co.jp; Globe Publication Pvt. Ltd., C-62 Inderpuri, New Delhi 100 012, India. TEL 91-11-579-3211, 91-11-579-3212, FAX 91-11-579-8876, custserve@globepub.com, http://www.globepub.com.

➤ **THE SPECTRUM.** see *CHEMISTRY—Physical Chemistry*

▼ ➤ **SPRINGER SERIES ON CHEMICAL SENSORS AND BIOSENSORS.** see *CHEMISTRY*

➤ **STEROID RECEPTORS.** see *BIOLOGY—Abstracting, Bibliographies, Statistics*

572.579 USA ISSN 0039-128X
QP752.S7 CODEN: STEDAM
➤ **STEROIDS.** Text in English. 1963. 14/yr. EUR 1,308 in Europe to institutions; JPY 173,700 in Japan to institutions; USD 1,463 to institutions except Europe and Japan (effective 2006). adv. bk.rev. abstr.; bibl.; charts. index. back issues avail.; reprints avail. **Document type:** *Journal, Academic/Scholarly.* **Description:** Provides a forum for the communication of articles dealing with all aspects of steroid hormones.
Related titles: Microform ed.: (from PQC); Online - full text ed.: (from EBSCO Publishing, Gale Group, IngentaConnect, ScienceDirect, Swets Information Services).
Indexed: ASCA, AbHyg, AgBio, AnBrAb, AnalAb, BBCI, BIOBASE, BIOSIS Prev, BiolAb, CCI, CIN, CPA, ChemAb, ChemTitl, CurCR, CurCont, DBA, DSA, DentInd, ExcerpMed, HortAb, IABS, ISR, IndChem, IndMed, IndVet, Inpharma, MEDLINE, MSB, NPU, NutrAb, OrnHort, PE&ON, PGrRegA, PN&I, PoultAb, ProtozoAb, RA&MP, RCI, RM&VM, RPP, Reac, RevApplEntom, S&F, SCI, SeedAb, SoyAb, TDB, VetBull, WeedAb.
—BLDSC (8464.600000), CASDDS, CINDOC, CISTI, GNLM, IDS, IE, Infotrieve, ingenta, KNAW, Linda Hall. **CCC.**
Published by: Elsevier Inc. (Subsidiary of: Elsevier Science & Technology), 360 Park Ave. S, New York, NY 10010-1710. TEL 212-633-3730, 888-437-4636, usinfo-f@elsevier.com, http://www.elsevier.com/locate/steroids. Eds. Richard Hochberg, William Rosner. Adv. contact Majorie Valle. Circ: 593 (paid and free).

572 JPN
SYMPOSIUM ON BIO-HYBRID. Text in Japanese. 1986. a. JPY 1,000. **Document type:** *Proceedings.*
Formerly: Tanpakushitsu Haiburiddo Kenkyukai - Symposium on Protein-Hybrid
Published by: Tanpakushitsu Haiburiddo Kenkyukai/Protein-Hybrid Society, Toin Gakuen Yokohama Daigaku, Kogakubu Zairyo Kogakka, 1614 kurogane-cho, Aoba-ku, Yokohama-shi, Kanagawa-ken 225-0025, Japan. TEL 81-45-974-5060, FAX 81-45-972-5972. Ed., R&P Yuji Inada. Circ: 500 (paid).

572 GBR ISSN 1355-7912
SYNTHETIC BIOTRANSFORMATIONS✶. Text in English. 1996. q. GBP 48 to individuals; GBP 154 to institutions. **Document type:** *Academic/Scholarly.*
—**CCC.**
Published by: Carfax Publishing Ltd. (Subsidiary of: Taylor & Francis Group), 4 Park Sq, Milton Park, Abingdon, Oxfordshire OX14 4RN, United Kingdom. TEL 44-1235-828600, FAX 44-1235-829000, enquiry@tandf.co.uk, http://www.tandf.co.uk.

TAIWAN NONGYE HUAXUE YU SHIPIN KEXUE/TAIWANESE JOURNAL OF AGRICULTURAL CHEMISTRY AND FOOD SCIENCE. see *FOOD AND FOOD INDUSTRIES*

572 JPN ISSN 0039-9450
QP501 CODEN: TAKKAJ
TANPAKUSHITSU KAKUSAN KOSO/PROTEIN, NUCLEIC ACID, ENZYME. Text in Japanese. 1956. m. JPY 16,200 (effective 2001). adv. bk.rev. bibl.; charts; illus. s-a. index.
Indexed: CIN, ChemAb, ChemTitl, DentInd, IndMed, JPI, JTA, MEDLINE, RefZh.
—BLDSC (6936.100000), CASDDS, CISTI, GNLM, Linda Hall.
Published by: Kyoritsu Shuppan Co. Ltd., 4-6-19 Kohinata, Bunkyo-ku, Tokyo, 112-0006, Japan. TEL 81-3-3947-2511, FAX 81-3-3947-2539, kaneko@kyoritsu-pub.co.jp, http://kyoritsu-pub.co.jp. Ed. Yumiko Kita. R&P Yasuo Hirayama TEL 81-3-3947-2517. Circ: 6,000.

572 JPN
TETSU TAISHA KENKYUKAI PUROGURAMU SHOROKUSHU/CONFERENCE ON CURRENT TOPICS FOR IRON METABOLISM. PROGRAM AND ABSTRACTS. Text in Japanese. 1977. a.
Published by: Tetsu Taisha Kenkyukai/Iron Metabolism Research, Shigei Igaku Kenkyujo, 2117 Yamada, Okayama-shi, 701-0202, Japan.

THALAMUS AND RELATED SYSTEMS. see *BIOLOGY*

572 DEU ISSN 1437-7993
➤ **TOPICS IN BIOLOGICAL INORGANIC CHEMISTRY.** Text in English. irreg., latest vol.3, 2000. **Document type:** *Monographic series, Academic/Scholarly.* **Description:** Designed to promote the advancement of bioinorganic chemistry by presenting overviews of areas where new insights of interest to a larger scientific audience are emerging.
Indexed: BIOSIS Prev.
—BLDSC (8867.428150), CISTI, ingenta.
Published by: Springer-Verlag Heidelberg (Subsidiary of: Springer Science+Business Media), Tiergartenstr 17, Heidelberg, 69121, Germany. TEL 49-6221-487502, FAX 49-6221-413982, subscriptions@springer.de.

➤ **TOXICOLOGY IN VITRO.** see *ENVIRONMENTAL STUDIES—Toxicology And Environmental Safety*

➤ **TRAFFIC**; the international journal of intracellular transport. see *BIOLOGY—Cytology And Histology*

572 GBR ISSN 0968-0004
QH345 CODEN: TBSCDB
➤ **TRENDS IN BIOCHEMICAL SCIENCES.** Variant title: T i B S. Text in English. 1976. 12/yr. EUR 181 in Europe to individuals; JPY 22,000 in Japan to individuals; USD 198 elsewhere to individuals; EUR 1,232 in Europe to institutions; JPY 170,900 in Japan to institutions; USD 1,378 elsewhere to institutions (effective 2006). adv. bk.rev. illus. index. back issues avail.; reprints avail. **Document type:** *Journal, Academic/Scholarly.* **Description:** Provides students and researchers with information on recent developments in a wide range of biochemically based sciences.
Related titles: Microfilm ed.: (from PQC); Online - full text ed.: ISSN 0167-7640 (from EBSCO Publishing, Gale Group, IngentaConnect, ScienceDirect, Swets Information Services).
Indexed: ASCA, ASFA, AbHyg, AgBio, AnBrAb, BBCI, BIOBASE, BIOSIS Prev, BiolAb, CCI, CPA, CTA, ChemAb, ChemTitl, CurCont, DBA, DSA, ESPM, ExcerpMed, FCA, FPA, FS&TA, GSI, GenetAb, HGA, HelmAb, HortAb, IABS, ISR, IndMed, IndVet, Inpharma, MEDLINE, MaizeAb, NSA, NemAb, NucAcAb, NutrAb, PBA, PE&ON, PGegResA, PGrRegA, ProtozoAb, RM&VM, RPP, Reac, RefZh, S&F, SCI, SFA, SSCI, TDB, VetBull, WeedAb, WildRev.
—BLDSC (9049.546000), CASDDS, CISTI, IDS, IE, Infotrieve, ingenta. **CCC.**

B

Published by: (International Union of Biochemistry and Molecular Biology AUS), Elsevier Ltd., Trends Journals (Subsidiary of: Elsevier Science & Technology), 68 Hills Rd, Cambridge, CB2 1LA, United Kingdom. TEL 44-1-223-311114, FAX 44-1223-464430, TTEC@elsevier.co.uk, http://www.elsevier.com/locate/tibs. Eds. A Romina Emilianus, E K Wilson, F Hutton. Adv. contact Thelma Reid. **Subscr. to:** Elsevier Current Trends Subscriptions, PO Box 331, Haywards Heath, W Sussex RH16 3FG, United Kingdom. TEL 44-1444-475650, FAX 44-1444-445423.

➤ **TRENDS IN BIOTECHNOLOGY.** see *BIOLOGY—Biotechnology*

➤ **TUMOR BIOLOGY**; from basic science to clinical application. see *MEDICAL SCIENCES—Oncology*

➤ **U.S. ENVIRONMENTAL PROTECTION AGENCY. OFFICE OF PESTICIDE PROGRAMS. CBI REVIEW.** see *AGRICULTURE—Crop Production And Soil*

572 UKR
QP501 CODEN: UBZKAA

UKRAINS'KYI BIOKHIMICHNYI ZHURNAL/UKRAINIAN BIOCHEMICAL JOURNAL. Text in Russian; Summaries in English, Russian. 1926. bi-m. USD 148 foreign (effective 2004). adv. bk.rev. abstr.; bibl.; charts; illus. index. **Document type:** *Journal, Academic/Scholarly.*
Former titles: Ukrainskii Biokhimicheskii Zhurnal (0201-8470); (until 1978): Ukrains'kyi Biokhimichnyi Zhurnal (0372-3909)
Indexed: ASCA, ASFA, ApicAb, BIOSIS Prev, BiolAb, CIN, ChemAb, DBA, DSA, Djerelo, ESPM, INIS AtomInd, IndMed, IndVet, MEDLINE, NutrAb, RefZh, VetBull, ZooRec.
—BLDSC (0384.180000), CASDDS, CISTI, East View, GNLM, IDS, IE, Infotrieve, ingenta, KNAW, Linda Hall. **CCC.**
Published by: Natsional'na Akademiya Nauk Ukrainy, Instytut Biokhimii im. A.V. Palladina, vul N Leontovicha 9, Kyiv, Ukraine. TEL 380-44-2241181. Ed. V K Lishko. Circ: 1,496. **US dist. addr.:** East View Information Services, 3020 Harbor Ln. N., Minneapolis, MN 55447. TEL 800-477-1005, FAX 800-800-3839, eastview@eastview.com, http://www.eastview.com.

572.8 BRA ISSN 0485-1854
CODEN: AMMJA3

UNIVERSIDADE FEDERAL DO RIO DE JANEIRO. DEPARTAMENTO DE MICROBIOLOGIA GERAL. ANAIS DE MICROBIOLOGIA. Text in Portuguese. 1951. a.
—CISTI.
Published by: Universidade Federal do Rio de Janeiro, Departamento de Microbiologia Geral, Centro de Ciencias da Saude, Bloco I, Cidade Universitaria, Ilha do Fundao, Rio de Janeiro, 21941-590, Brazil.

WALTER AND ANDREE DE NOTTBECK FOUNDATION SCIENTIFIC REPORTS. see *BIOLOGY—Microbiology*

572 NGA ISSN 0043-2989
CODEN: WAJBAK

WEST AFRICAN JOURNAL OF BIOLOGICAL AND APPLIED CHEMISTRY. Text in English. 1957. q. NGN 40. adv. bk.rev. charts. **Document type:** *Academic/Scholarly.*
Indexed: BiolAb, CIN, ChemAb, ChemTitl, FCA, HerbAb, NutrAb.
—CASDDS, CISTI, Linda Hall.
Address: U.I. Post Office, University of Ibadan, PO Box 4021, Ibadan, Oyo, Nigeria. TEL 234-22-410247. Ed. Olumbe Bassir. Circ: 1,000.

WUHAN LIANGSHI GONGYE XUEYUAN XUEBAO/WUHAN FOOD INDUSTRY COLLEGE. JOURNAL. see *AGRICULTURE—Feed, Flour And Grain*

572 GBR ISSN 0049-8254
QP909 CODEN: XENOBH

➤ **XENOBIOTICA**; the fate of foreign compounds in biological systems. Text in English. 1971. m. GBP 1,519, USD 2,504 combined subscription to institutions print & online eds. (effective 2006). adv. bk.rev. charts; stat. index. reprint service avail. from PSC. **Document type:** *Journal, Academic/Scholarly.* **Description:** Covers three main areas: general xenobiochemistry, molecular toxicology, and clinical pharmacokinetics and metabolism.
Related titles: Online - full text ed.: ISSN 1366-5928. GBP 1,443, USD 2,379 to institutions (effective 2006) (from EBSCO Publishing, Gale Group, IngentaConnect, O C L C Online Computer Library Center, Inc., Swets Information Services).
Indexed: ASCA, ASFA, Agr, AgrForAb, BBCI, BIOBASE, BIOSIS Prev, BibAg, BiolAb, CCI, CIN, ChemAb, CurCont, DBA, DSA, DentInd, EPB, ESPM, ExcerpMed, ForAb, HelmAb, IABS, ISR, IndMed, IndVet, Inpharma, LHB, MBA, MEDLINE, MSB, NutrAb, PE&ON, PN&I, PollutAb, PoultAb, ProtozoAb, RA&MP, RM&VM, Reac, RefZh, RevApplEntom, SAA, SCI, SoyAb, ToxAb, VetBull, WeedAb, ZooRec.
—BLDSC (9367.020000), CASDDS, CISTI, GNLM, IDS, IE, Infotrieve, ingenta, Linda Hall. **CCC.**
Published by: Taylor & Francis Ltd (Subsidiary of: Taylor & Francis Group), 4 Park Sq, Milton Park, Abingdon, OX14 4RN, United Kingdom. TEL 44-1235-828600, FAX 44-1235-829000, info@tandf.co.uk, http://www.tandf.co.uk/journals/titles/00498254.asp. Ed. G G Gibson. **Subscr. in N. America to:** Taylor & Francis Inc., Customer Services Dept, 325 Chestnut St, 8th Fl, Philadelphia, PA 19106. TEL 215-625-8900, 800-354-1420, FAX 215-625-8914; **Subscr. to:** Journals Customer Service, Rankine Rd, Basingstoke, Hants RG24 8PR, United Kingdom. TEL 44-1256-813000, FAX 44-1256-330245, enquiry@tandf.co.uk.

➤ **ZHIWU SHENGLI XUEBAO/ACTA PHYTOPHYSIOLOGICA SINICA.** see *BIOLOGY—Botany*

572 CHN ISSN 1007-7626
QP501 CODEN: SHZAE4

➤ **ZHONGGUO SHENGWU HUAXUE YU FENZI SHENGWU XUEBAO/CHINESE JOURNAL OF BIOCHEMISTRY AND MOLECULAR BIOLOGY.** Text mainly in Chinese; Text occasionally in English. 1985. bi-m. CNY 132; CNY 22 per issue (effective 2004). adv. bk.rev. 160 p./no.; **Document type:** *Journal, Academic/Scholarly.* **Description:** Contains research reports and short communications on biochemistry and molecular biology.
Formerly (until vol.13, no.6, 1997): Shengwu Huaxue Zazhi/Chinese Biochemical Journal (1000-8543)
Related titles: Online - full content ed.: (from WanFang Data Corp.); Online - full text ed.: (from East View Information Services).
Indexed: ChemAb, ChemTitl, RefZh.
—BLDSC (3180.295650), CASDDS, IE, ingenta.
Published by: Zhongguo Shengwu Huaxue yu Fenzi Shengwu Xuehui, Peking Xueyuan Lu, Peking Daxue Yixuebu, Shenghualou 331 Shi, Beijing, 100083, China. shxb@bjmu.edu.cn, http://www.zgswhxyfzswxb.periodicals.net.cn, http://bcmb.bjmu.edu.cn/. Eds. De-fu Liu, Nai-heng Zhang, Tong Lu. R&P Tong Lu. adv.: page CNY 1,000; 210 x 297. Circ: 2,100 (paid and controlled). **Dist. outside of China by:** China International Book Trading Corp, 35 Chegongzhuang Xilu, Haidian District, PO Box 399, Beijing 100044, China. TEL 86-10-68412045, FAX 86-10-68412023, cibtc@mail.cibtc.com.cn, http://www.cibtc.com.cn/.

572 RUS ISSN 0044-4529
QH345.Z5 CODEN: ZEBFAJ

➤ **ZHURNAL EVOLYUTSIONNOI BIOKHIMII I FIZIOLOGII.** Text in Russian; Summaries in English. 1965. bi-m. USD 305 foreign (effective 2005). bk.rev. charts; illus. index. **Document type:** *Journal, Academic/Scholarly.* **Description:** Illuminates the most recent research findings on the evolution of basic forms of metabolism, comparative and developmental physiology, and biochemistry and the biochemical evolution of the animal world.
Related titles: ♦ English Translation: Journal of Evolutionary Biochemistry and Physiology. ISSN 0022-0930.
Indexed: AnBrAb, BIOSIS Prev, BiolAb, CIN, ChemAb, ChemTitl, ExcerpMed, FCA, IAA, IndMed, MEDLINE, RefZh, SeedAb, SoyAb, ZooRec.
—BLDSC (0067.700000), CASDDS, CISTI, GNLM, KNAW, Linda Hall. **CCC.**
Published by: (Rossiiskaya Akademiya Nauk/Russian Academy of Sciences), Izdatel'stvo Nauka, Sankt-Peterburgskoe Otdelenie, Sechenov Institute of Evolutionary Physiology and Biochemistry, pr. Morisa Toreza 44, St Petersburg, 194223, Russian Federation. TEL 7-812-5527901, FAX 7-812-5523012, http://www.maik.rssi.ru/journals/evolbp.htm. Ed. Vladimir L Svidersky. **Dist. by:** East View Information Services, 3020 Harbor Ln. N., Minneapolis, MN 55447. TEL 800-477-1005, FAX 800-800-3839, eastview@eastview.com, http://www.eastview.com.

BIOLOGY—Biophysics

➤ **ACTA AGROPHYSICA.** see *AGRICULTURE*

➤ **ACTA BIOCHIMICA ET BIOPHYSICA SINICA.** see *BIOLOGY—Biochemistry*

➤ **ACTA BIOCHIMICA POLONICA.** see *BIOLOGY—Biochemistry*

571 CHN ISSN 1000-6737

ACTA BIOPHYSICS SINICA. Text in Chinese; Summaries in English. 1985. q. CNY 200 domestic; USD 100 foreign (effective 2000). abstr.; bibl.; charts; illus.; mkt. index. back issues avail. **Document type:** *Academic/Scholarly.* **Description:** Covers molecular biophysics, cell and membrane biophysics, neurobiophysics, bioinformatics, biocybernetics, theoretical biophysics, radiation and environmental biophysics, biomechanics, and biophysical expermental techniques.
Related titles: CD-ROM ed.; Online - full text ed.: (from East View Information Services).
Indexed: ZooRec.
—BLDSC (0603.300000).
Published by: Biophysical Society of China, 15 Datun Rd, Chaoyang District, Beijing, China. TEL 86-10-6488-8458, FAX 86-10-6487-7837, acta@sun5.ibp.ac.cn. Ed. Yang Fuyu. R&P Ke-Ding Lu. Adv. contact Xue-Hong Liang. Circ: 800 (paid); 200 (controlled).

ACTA UNIVERSITATIS LODZIENSIS: FOLIA BIOCHIMICA ET BIOPHYSICA. see *BIOLOGY—Biochemistry*

571.47 USA ISSN 1570-2197

➤ **ADVANCES IN ELECTROMAGNETIC FIELDS IN LIVING SYSTEMS.** Text in English. 1994. irreg., latest vol.4, 2005. price varies. **Document type:** *Monographic series, Academic/Scholarly.* **Description:** Presents research on the theory, interactions and applications of electromagnetic fields in biology and medicine.
—BLDSC (0704.750000), ingenta.
Published by: Springer-Verlag New York, Inc. (Subsidiary of: Springer Science+Business Media), 233 Spring St, New York, NY 10013. TEL 212-460-1500, FAX 212-460-1575, service@springer-ny.com, http://www.springer-ny.com. Ed. J C Lin.

571.4 JPN ISSN 0385-213X

AMIRAZE SHINPOJUMU/PROCEEDINGS OF THE SYMPOSIUM ON AMYLASE. Text in English, Japanese. 1965. a. **Document type:** *Proceedings.*
Published by: Amiraze Kenkyukai/Amylase Research Society, Shiritsu Kogyo Kenkyujo, 6-50 Morinomiya 1-chome, Joto-ku, Osaka-shi, 536-0025, Japan.

571.45 USA ISSN 1056-8700
QH505 CODEN: ABBSE4

➤ **ANNUAL REVIEW OF BIOPHYSICS AND BIOMOLECULAR STRUCTURE.** Text in English. 1972. a., latest vol.33, 2004. USD 196 to institutions print or online ed.; USD 235 combined subscription to institutions print & online eds. (effective 2006). bibl.; charts; abstr. index, cum.index every 5 yrs. back issues avail.; reprint service avail. from PSC. **Document type:** *Academic/Scholarly.* **Description:** Original reviews of critical literature and current developments in biophysics and biomolecular structure.
Former titles (until vol.20, 1991): Annual Review of Biophysics and Biophysical Chemistry (0883-9182); (until vol.14, 1985): Annual Review of Biophysics and Bioengineering (0084-6589)
Related titles: Microfilm ed.: (from PQC); Online - full content ed.: ISSN 1545-4266. USD 194 (effective 2005) (from HighWire Press); Online - full text ed.: (from bigchalk, EBSCO Publishing, ProQuest Information & Learning, Swets Information Services).
Indexed: ASCA, BBCI, BIOBASE, BIOSIS Prev, BioEngAb, BiolAb, CCI, CIN, CIS, CTA, ChemAb, ChemTitl, CurCont, ESPM, ExcerpMed, IABS, ISR, IndMed, Inpharma, Inspec, MEDLINE, NSA, NucAcAb, Reac, SCI.
—BLDSC (1522.060000), CASDDS, CISTI, GNLM, IDS, IE, Infotrieve, ingenta, KNAW, Linda Hall. **CCC.**
Published by: Annual Reviews, 4139 El Camino Way, Palo Alto, CA 94303-0139. TEL 650-493-4400, 800-523-8635, FAX 650-424-0910, service@annualreviews.org, http://arjournals.annualreviews.org/loi/biophys, http://www.annualreviews.org. Ed. Douglas C Rees. R&P Laura Folkner.

➤ **ARCHIVES OF BIOCHEMISTRY AND BIOPHYSICS.** see *BIOLOGY—Biochemistry*

➤ **B B A - GENERAL SUBJECTS.** see *BIOLOGY—Biochemistry*

➤ **B B A - MOLECULAR AND CELL BIOLOGY OF LIPIDS.** (Biochimica and Biophysica Acta) see *BIOLOGY—Biochemistry*

➤ **B B A - PROTEINS AND PROTEOMICS.** see *BIOLOGY—Biochemistry*

571.4 USA ISSN 1056-9138
CODEN: BENUEY

B E N E R DIGEST UPDATE. (Biological Effects of Nonionizing Electromagnetic Radiation) Text in English. 1991. q. USD 440 (effective 2004). Index. back issues avail. **Document type:** *Journal, Abstract/Index.*
Published by: Information Ventures, Incorporated, 42 S. 15th St., Suite 700, Philadelphia, PA 19102-2299. TEL 215-569-2300, FAX 215-569-2575, IVI@infoventures.com, http://infoventures.com/emf/bener, http://www.infoventures.com.

571.43 JPN

BAIOMEKANIZUMU/BIOMECHANISMS. Text in Japanese; Summaries in English. 1972. biennial. JPY 18,000 per issue.
Published by: Baiomekanizumu Gakkai/Society of Biomechanisms Japan, Department of Mechanical Engineering, School of Science and Engineering , Waseda University, #59-327 3-4-1 Okubo, Shinjuku-ku, Tokyo, 169-8555, Japan.

571.43 JPN ISSN 0285-0885
QH513

BAIOMEKANIZUMU GAKKAISHI/SOCIETY OF BIOMECHANISMS. JOURNAL. Text in Japanese; Summaries in English. 1969. q. free to members.
Related titles: Online - full text ed.: (from J-Stage).
—CCC.

Published by: Baiomekanizumu Gakkai/Society of Biomechanisms Japan, Department of Mechanical Engineering, School of Science and Engineering , Waseda University, #59-327 3-4-1 Okubo, Shinjuku-ku, Tokyo, 169-8555, Japan. biomech@paradise.mech.waseda.ac.jp, http://www.jstage.jst.go.jp/browse/sobim/_vols/-char/ja, http://www.sugano.mech.waseda.ac.jp/biomech/index.htm.

571.43 JPN

BAIOMEKANIZUMU GAKUJUTSU KOENKAI YOKOSHU/SOCIETY OF BIOMECHANISMS. PROCEEDINGS OF THE ANNUAL MEETING. Text in English, Japanese. 1980. a. JPY 4,000.

Published by: Baiomekanizumu Gakkai/Society of Biomechanisms Japan, Department of Mechanical Engineering, School of Science and Engineering , Waseda University, #59-327 3-4-1 Okubo, Shinjuku-ku, Tokyo, 169-8555, Japan.

BIOCHEMICAL AND BIOPHYSICAL RESEARCH COMMUNICATIONS. see *BIOLOGY—Biochemistry*

BIOCHEMISTRY AND BIOPHYSICS CITATION INDEX. see *BIOLOGY—Abstracting, Bibliographies, Statistics*

BIOCHIMICA ET BIOPHYSICA ACTA; international journal of biochemistry and biophysics. see *BIOLOGY—Biochemistry*

BIOELECTROCHEMISTRY. see *BIOLOGY—Biochemistry*

571.4 USA ISSN 0197-8462
QP82.2.E43 CODEN: BLCTDO

➤ **BIOELECTROMAGNETICS.** Text in English. 1980. 8/yr. USD 1,199 domestic to institutions; USD 1,295 in Canada & Mexico to institutions; USD 1,351 elsewhere to institutions; USD 1,319 combined subscription domestic to institutions print & online eds.; USD 1,415 combined subscription in Canada & Mexico to institutions print & online eds.; USD 1,471 combined subscription elsewhere to institutions print & online eds. (effective 2006). adv. bk.rev. bibl.; charts; illus. index. back issues avail. **Document type:** *Journal, Academic/Scholarly.* **Description:** Devoted to research on biological systems as they are influenced by natural or manufactured electric and-or magnetic fields at frequencies from D.C. to visible light.

Related titles: Microform ed.: 1998 (from PQC); Online - full content ed.: ISSN 1521-186X. USD 1,199 to institutions (effective 2006); Online - full text ed.: (from EBSCO Publishing, Swets Information Services, Wiley InterScience).

Indexed: ASCA, AgBio, AnBrAb, B&BAb, BBCI, BIOSIS Prev, BioEngAb, BiolAb, CIN, CPA, ChemAb, ChemTitl, CurCont, DentInd, ESPM, ExcerpMed, FCA, HortAb, ISR, IndMed, Inpharma, Inspec, MEDLINE, NSCI, NemAb, NutrAb, Reac, RefZh, SCI, SSCI, SeedAb, VetBull.

—BLDSC (2072.009000), AskIEEE, CASDDS, CISTI, GNLM, IDS, IE, Infotrieve, ingenta, Linda Hall. **CCC.**

Published by: (Bioelectromagnetics Society), John Wiley & Sons, Inc., 111 River St, Hoboken, NJ 07030-5774. TEL 201-748-6000, FAX 201-748-5915, uscs-wis@wiley.com, http://www.interscience.wiley.com/jpages/0197-8462/, http://www.wiley.com. Ed. Ben Greenebaum. adv.: B&W page GBP 640, color page GBP 1,515; trim 210 x 279. Circ: 950. **Subscr. outside the Americas to:** John Wiley & Sons Ltd., The Atrium, Southern Gate, Chichester, West Sussex PO19 8SQ, United Kingdom. TEL 44-1243-843335, 0800-243407, FAX 44-1243-843232, cs-journals@wiley.co.uk.

571.4 USA ISSN 0889-4191

BIOELECTROMAGNETICS SOCIETY NEWSLETTER. Text in English. 1978. 6/yr. USD 65 domestic to non-members; USD 75 foreign to non-members. bk.rev. back issues avail. **Document type:** *Newsletter.*

Published by: Bioelectromagnetics Society, 7519 Ridge Rd, Frederick, MD 21702-3519. TEL 301-663-4252, FAX 301-371-8955. Ed. Mary Ellen O'Connor. Circ: 800.

571.4 RUS ISSN 0006-3029
QH505.A1 CODEN: BIOFAI

➤ **BIOFIZIKA.** Text in Russian; Summaries in English. 1956. bi-m. RUR 1,340 for 6 mos. domestic; USD 342 foreign (effective 2004). index. **Document type:** *Journal, Academic/Scholarly.*

Related titles: ♦ English Translation: Biophysics. ISSN 0006-3509.

Indexed: ASCA, ApicAb, BBCI, BIOSIS Prev, BiolAb, CIN, CPA, ChemAb, ChemTitl, CurCont, DBA, DSA, DentInd, ExcerpMed, IAA, ISR, IndMed, Inpharma, Inspec, MEDLINE, NSCI, NutrAb, PGrRegA, PhysBer, PsycholAb, Reac, RefZh, SCI, SIA, ZooRec.

—BLDSC (0018.030000), AskIEEE, CASDDS, CISTI, East View, GNLM, IDS, IE, Infotrieve, Linda Hall. **CCC.**

Published by: (Rossiiskaya Akademiya Nauk/Russian Academy of Sciences), Izdatel'stvo Nauka, Profsoyuznaya ul 90, Moscow, 117864, Russian Federation. TEL 7-095-3347151, FAX 7-095-4202220, secret@naukaran.ru, http://www.maik.rssi.ru/cgi-bin/list.pl?page=biofiz, http://www.naukaran.ru. **Dist. by:** M K - Periodica, ul Gilyarovskogo 39, Moscow 129110, Russian Federation. TEL 7-095-2845008, FAX 7-095-2813798, info@periodicals.ru, http://www.mkniga.ru.

571.4 RUS ISSN 0301-2425
QH573

➤ **BIOFIZIKA ZHIVOI KLETKI/BIOPHYSICS OF LIVING CELLS.** Text in Russian. 1970. irreg. USD 40. adv. bk.rev. illus. reprint service avail. from IRC. **Document type:** *Academic/Scholarly.* —Linda Hall.

Published by: (Rossiiskaya Akademiya Nauk/Russian Academy of Sciences, Institut Biofiziki Kletki/Institute of Cell Biophysics), Radical Enterprise, A-ya 84 (AB 7-67), Pushchino, Moskovskaya Oblast' 142292, Russian Federation. TEL 7-095-238-7940, vkar@ibfk.nifhi.ac.ru. Ed. V N Kharnaukhov. Adv. contact V.N. Kharnaukhov. Circ: 500.

571.4 RUS ISSN 0233-4755
QH601 CODEN: BIMEE9

➤ **BIOLOGICHESKIE MEMBRANY.** Text in Russian. 1984. bi-m. USD 294 foreign (effective 2005). adv. bk.rev. index. **Document type:** *Journal, Academic/Scholarly.* **Description:** Presents experimental and theoretical work on the physics, chemistry and biology of membranes at the molecular and cellular levels.

Indexed: AEA, AgBio, AnBrAb, BBCI, BIOSIS Prev, BiolAb, CIN, CPA, ChemAb, ChemTitl, CurCont, FCA, HortAb, ISR, NutrAb, PBA, PGegResA, PGrRegA, PotatoAb, RM&VM, RPP, RefZh, SCI, TriticAb, ZooRec.

—BLDSC (0017.845000), CASDDS, CISTI, East View, IDS, Linda Hall. **CCC.**

Published by: (Rossiiskaya Akademiya Nauk/Russian Academy of Sciences), Izdatel'stvo Nauka, Profsoyuznaya ul 90, Moscow, 117864, Russian Federation. TEL 7-095-3347151, FAX 7-095-4202220, biomem@eimb.ru, secret@naukaran.ru, http://www.naukaran.ru. adv.: page USD 100.

571.4 BGR ISSN 0204-7594

BIOMEKHANIKA/BIOMECHANICS. Text in Bulgarian, Russian; Summaries in English, Russian. 1974. irreg. BGL 2 per issue. bibl.; illus. reprint service avail. from IRC.

Indexed: BSLMath, BiolAb.

—GNLM, Linda Hall.

Published by: (Bulgarska Akademiya na Naukite/Bulgarian Academy of Sciences, Tsentralna Laboratoriia po Biomekhanika), Universitetsko Izdatelstvo Sv. Kliment Okhridski/Publishing House of the Sofia University St. Kliment Ohridski, Akad G Bonchev 6, Sofia, 1113, Bulgaria. Ed. G Brankov. Circ: 470. **Dist. by:** Hemus, 6 Rouski Blvd., Sofia 1000, Bulgaria.

571.4 UKR ISSN 0374-6569
CODEN: BNKABJ

BIONIKA; respublikanskii mezhvedomstvennyi sbornik nauchnykh trudov. Text in Russian. 1965. a. USD 199.

Indexed: Inspec.

—AskIEEE, CISTI, Linda Hall. **CCC.**

Published by: (Natsional'na Akademiya Nauk Ukrainy, Instytut Hidromekhaniky), Natsional'na Akademiya Nauk Ukrainy, vul Volodymyrs'ka 54, Kyiv, 01601, Ukraine. TEL 380-44-2352239, FAX 380-44-2343243, vgr@ihm.Kiev.ua, prez@nas.gov.ua, http://www.nas.gov.ua.

571.4 NLD ISSN 0301-4622
QH345 CODEN: BICIAZ

➤ **BIOPHYSICAL CHEMISTRY.** Text in English. 1974. 21/yr. EUR 3,586 in Europe to institutions; JPY 476,000 in Japan to institutions; USD 4,013 elsewhere to institutions; EUR 228 in Europe to qualified personnel; JPY 30,200 in Japan to qualified personnel; USD 254 elsewhere to qualified personnel (effective 2006). adv. bk.rev. Index. back issues avail.; reprint service avail. from ISI. **Document type:** *Journal, Academic/Scholarly.* **Description:** Devoted to the interpretation of biological phenomena in terms of the principles and methods of physics and chemistry.

Related titles: Microform ed.: (from PQC); Online - full text ed.: (from EBSCO Publishing, Gale Group, IngentaConnect, ScienceDirect, Swets Information Services).

Indexed: ASCA, ASFA, AbHyg, ApicAb, BBCI, BIOBASE, BIOSIS Prev, BiolAb, CCI, CIN, CPA, ChemAb, ChemTitl, CurCont, DSA, ExcerpMed, HelmAb, HortAb, IABS, ISR, IndMed, IndVet, Inpharma, MEDLINE, NutrAb, PE&ON, ProtozoAb, RA&MP, RM&VM, RPP, Reac, S&F, SCI, SeedAb, VetBull.

—BLDSC (2089.380000), CASDDS, CISTI, GNLM, IDS, IE, Infotrieve, ingenta, Linda Hall. **CCC.**

Published by: Elsevier BV (Subsidiary of: Elsevier Science & Technology), Radarweg 29, Amsterdam, 1043 NX, Netherlands. TEL 31-20-4853911, FAX 31-20-4852457, nlinfo-f@elsevier.nl, http://www.elsevier.com/locate/biophyschem, http://www.elsevier.nl. Eds. A. Cooper, Dr. Enrico Di Cera. **Subscr. to:** Elsevier, Subscription Customer Service, 6277 Sea Harbor Dr, Orlando, FL 32887-4800. TEL 407-345-4020, 877-839-7126, FAX 407-363-1354.

571.4 USA ISSN 0006-3495
QH505.A1 CODEN: BIOJAU

➤ **BIOPHYSICAL JOURNAL.** Text in English. 1960. m. (in 2 vols., 6 nos./vol.). USD 1,007 combined subscription domestic print & online eds.; USD 1,137 combined subscription in Canada print & online eds.; USD 1,063 combined subscription elsewhere print & online eds. (effective 2005); includes Biophysical Society. Annual Meeting. Abstracts. adv. bibl.; charts; illus.; abstr. index. back issues avail.; reprints avail. **Document type:** *Journal, Academic/Scholarly.* **Description:** Reports on the latest theoretical and experimental developments in biophysical research.

Related titles: Microfiche ed.: (from PQC); Microfilm ed.: (from PQC); Online - full text ed.: ISSN 1542-0086. 1997. USD 760 domestic; USD 813.20 in Canada; USD 760 elsewhere (effective 2002) (from bigchalk, EBSCO Publishing, HighWire Press, Northern Light Technology, Inc., ProQuest Information & Learning); ♦ Supplement(s): Biophysical Society. Annual Meeting. Abstracts. ISSN 0523-6800.

Indexed: ASCA, ASFA, AbHyg, AgBio, Agr, AnBrAb, ApMecR, ApicAb, BBCI, BIOBASE, BIOSIS Prev, BPRC&P, BibAg, BiolAb, CCI, CIN, CPA, CTA, ChemAb, ChemTitl, CurCont, DSA, EngInd, ExcerpMed, FCA, FS&TA, HelmAb, HerbAb, HortAb, IABS, INIS AtomInd, ISR, IndMed, IndVet, Inpharma, Inspec, MEDLINE, MSCI, NSCI, NemAb, NutrAb, PBA, PE&ON, PhysBer, ProtozoAb, RM&VM, Reac, RefZh, RevApplEntom, SCI, SFA, SIA, TDB, TriticAb, VetBull.

—BLDSC (2089.400000), AskIEEE, CASDDS, CISTI, Ei, GNLM, IDS, IE, Infotrieve, ingenta, Linda Hall. **CCC.**

Published by: Biophysical Society, 9650 Rockville Pike, Bethesda, MD 20814. TEL 301-634-7114, FAX 301-634-7133, ckenney@biophysics.org, http://www.biophysj.org, http://www.biophysics.org/. Ed. Robert Callender. Adv. contact Kathleen Glisson TEL 301-634-7264. B&W page USD 1,000, color page USD 1,500.

➤ **BIOPHYSICAL SOCIETY. ANNUAL MEETING. ABSTRACTS.** see *BIOLOGY—Abstracting, Bibliographies, Statistics*

571.4 RUS ISSN 0006-3509
QH505.A1 CODEN: BIOPAE

➤ **BIOPHYSICS.** Text in English. 1957. bi-m. USD 3,575 in North America; USD 3,727 elsewhere (effective 2004). adv. abstr.; charts. index. back issues avail.; reprint service avail. from PQC. **Document type:** *Journal, Academic/Scholarly.* **Description:** Covers a wide scope of problems related to the main physical mechanisms of processes taking place on different organization levels in biosystems.

Related titles: Online - full text ed.; ♦ Translation of: Biofizika. ISSN 0006-3029.

Indexed: ASFA, ApMecR, BiolAb, CTA, ExcerpMed, IndMed, Inspec.

—BLDSC (0406.100000), AskIEEE, CISTI, GNLM, IE, Infotrieve, ingenta, Linda Hall. **CCC.**

Published by: M A I K Nauka - Interperiodica, Profsoyuznaya ul 90, Moscow, 117997, Russian Federation. TEL 7-095-3347420, FAX 7-095-3360666, compmg@maik.ru, http://www.maik.ru/journals/biophys.htm. Ed. Evgenii E Fesenko. Circ: 1,000. **Subscr. to:** Interperiodica, PO Box 1831, Birmingham, AL 35201-1831. TEL 205-995-1567, 800-633-4931, FAX 205-995-1588. **Dist. by:** East View Information Services.

571.4 POL ISSN 0138-0818

BIOPHYSICS OF MEMBRANE TRANSPORT. Text in English. 1975. irreg. **Document type:** *Monographic series, Academic/Scholarly.*

—BLDSC (2089.430000).

Published by: Akademia Rolnicza we Wroclawiu/Agricultural University of Wroclaw, Ul Norwida 25, Wroclaw, 50375, Poland. TEL 48-71-3205101, FAX 48-71-3205404, wyd@ozi.ar.wroc.pl, http://www.ar.wroc.pl.

571.7 NLD ISSN 0006-355X
QH505 CODEN: BRHLAU

➤ **BIORHEOLOGY**; an international journal. Text in English, French, German. 1962. bi-m. EUR 853, USD 1,022 combined subscription print & online eds. (effective 2006). adv. bk.rev. charts; illus. back issues avail. **Document type:** *Journal, Academic/Scholarly.* **Description:** Features articles on deformation and flow-related processes, in vivo and extra vivum, on biological systems under physiological and pathological conditions.

Related titles: Microfilm ed.: (from PQC); Online - full text ed.: (from EBSCO Publishing, Gale Group, IngentaConnect, O C L C Online Computer Library Center, Inc., ScienceDirect, Swets Information Services).

Indexed: AEA, ASCA, AnBrAb, ApMecR, BBCI, BIOSIS Prev, BiolAb, CIN, CPA, ChemAb, ChemTitl, CurCont, DSA, ExcerpMed, FS&TA, HortAb, IABS, IBZ, ISR, IndMed, IndVet, Inpharma, Inspec, MEDLINE, MSCI, NutrAb, PE&ON, Reac, RefZh, SCI, SIA, VetBull.

—BLDSC (2089.500000), AskIEEE, CASDDS, CISTI, GNLM, IDS, IE, Infotrieve, ingenta, Linda Hall. **CCC.**

Published by: (International Society of Biorheology), I O S Press, Nieuwe Hemweg 6B, Amsterdam, 1013 BG, Netherlands. TEL 31-20-6883355, FAX 31-20-6203419, order@iospress.nl, http://www.iospress.nl/html/0006355x.php. Ed. Harry L Goldsmith. R&P Ms. Carry Koolbergen TEL 31-20-6382189. Adv. contact Ms. Jolijn van Eunen. Circ: 350. **Subscr. to:** I O S Press, Inc, 4502 Rachael Manor Dr., Fairfax, VA 22032-3631. iosbooks@iospress.com; Globe Publication Pvt. Ltd., C-62 Inderpuri, New Delhi 100 012, India; Kinokuniya Co. Ltd., Shinjuku 3-chome, Shinjuku-ku, Tokyo 160-0022, Japan.

➤ **BIOSENSORS AND BIOELECTRONICS.** see *BIOLOGY—Biotechnology*

➤ **CANCER BIOCHEMISTRY BIOPHYSICS.** see *MEDICAL SCIENCES—Oncology*

➤ **CELL BIOCHEMISTRY AND BIOPHYSICS.** see *BIOLOGY—Cytology And Histology*

B

571.464 USA ISSN 0011-2240
QH324 CODEN: CRYBAS
➤ **CRYOBIOLOGY.** Text in English. 1964. 6/yr. EUR 719 in Europe to institutions; JPY 75,000 in Japan to institutions; USD 537 to institutions except Europe and Japan; EUR 110 in Europe to students; JPY 11,400 in Japan to students; USD 96 to students except Europe and Japan (effective 2006). adv. index. **Document type:** *Journal, Academic/Scholarly.*
Description: Publishes research articles on all aspects of low temperature biology.
Related titles: Online - full text ed.: ISSN 1090-2392. USD 575 (effective 2002) (from EBSCO Publishing, Gale Group, IngentaConnect, O C L C Online Computer Library Center, Inc., ScienceDirect, Swets Information Services).
Indexed: AEBA, ASCA, ASFA, Agr, AnBrAb, BIOSIS Prev, BioEngAb, BiolAb, CIN, CPA, ChemAb, ChemTitl, CurCont, DSA, ESPM, ExcerpMed, ForAb, HortAb, ISR, IndMed, IndVet, Inpharma, Inspec, M&PBA, MBA, MEDLINE, NutrAb, Reac, SCI, SFA, SIA, VetBull, WildRev, ZooRec.
—BLDSC (3490.135000), CASDDS, CISTI, GNLM, IDS, IE, Infotrieve, ingenta, Linda Hall. **CCC.**
Published by: (Society for Cryobiology), Academic Press (Subsidiary of: Elsevier Science & Technology), 525 B St, Ste 1900, San Diego, CA 92101-4495. TEL 619-231-6616, 800-894-3434, apsubs@acad.com, http://www.elsevier.com/locate/cryo. Ed. David E Pegg. Circ: 500 (paid and controlled).

571.4 USA ISSN 0070-2129
QH511.A1 CODEN: CUTBAO
➤ **CURRENT TOPICS IN BIOENERGETICS.** Text in English. 1966. irreg., latest vol.17, 1994. reprint service avail. from ISI. **Document type:** *Academic/Scholarly.*
Indexed: ASCA, BBCI, BIOSIS Prev, BiolAb, CIN, ChemAb, ChemTitl, ISR, NutrAb, SCI.
—BLDSC (3504.870000), CASDDS, CISTI, Linda Hall. **CCC.**
Published by: Academic Press (Subsidiary of: Elsevier Science & Technology), 525 B St, Ste 1900, San Diego, CA 92101-4495. apsubs@acad.com, http://www.academicpress.com. Ed. C P Lee.

571.4 POL ISSN 1232-9630
CURRENT TOPICS IN BIOPHYSICS. Text in English, Polish. 1971. s-a. USD 20 to individuals; USD 30 to institutions (effective 2005). **Document type:** *Journal, Academic/Scholarly.*
Formerly (until 1992): Zagadnienia Biofizyki Wspolczesnej (0137-9690)
Related titles: Online - full text ed.
Indexed: AgrLib.
Published by: Polskie Towarzystwo Biofizyczne/Polish Biophysical Society, Katedra Biofizyki, Akademia Medyczna, ul Chalubinskiego 10, Wroclaw, 50368, Poland.

DOKLADY BIOCHEMISTRY AND BIOPHYSICS. see *BIOLOGY—Biochemistry*

571.4 EGY ISSN 1110-6565
EGYPTIAN JOURNAL OF BIOPHYSICS. Text in English. 1994. a. **Document type:** *Journal, Academic/Scholarly.*
Published by: Egyptian Biophysical Society, Physics Department, Faculty of Science, Cairo University, Gamiat El-Qahira Str, Cairo, Egypt. TEL 20-2-5675737, 20-2-5727022, fadelali@frcu.eun.eg, http://derp.sti.sci.eg/data/0324.htm. Ed. Dr. Fadhel Muhammad Aly.

571.4 USA ISSN 1536-8378
QP341 CODEN: EBMLCC
➤ **ELECTROMAGNETIC BIOLOGY AND MEDICINE.** Text in English. 1982. q. GBP 960, USD 1,585 combined subscription to institutions print & online eds. (effective 2006). adv. reprint service avail. from PSC. **Document type:** *Journal, Academic/Scholarly.* **Description:** Examines questions concerning the role of intrinsic electromagnetism in the regulation of living systems.
Former titles (until 2001): Electro- and Magnetobiology (1061-9526); (until 1991): Journal of Bioelectricity (0730-823X)
Related titles: Microform ed.: (from RPI); Online - full text ed.: ISSN 1536-8386. GBP 912, USD 1,506 to institutions (effective 2006) (from EBSCO Publishing, O C L C Online Computer Library Center, Inc., Swets Information Services).
Indexed: ASCA, BBCI, BiolAb, CPA, ChemAb, CurCont, ExcerpMed, FCA, ForAb, ISR, Inpharma, Inspec, Reac, RefZh, RiceAb, SCI, SeedAb, TriticAb, WeedAb.
—BLDSC (3699.478500), AskIEEE, CASDDS, CISTI, GNLM, IDS, IE, ingenta. **CCC.**
Published by: (International Society for Bioelectricity), Taylor & Francis Inc. (Subsidiary of: Taylor & Francis Group), 325 Chestnut St, Ste 800, Philadelphia, PA 19016. TEL 215-625-8900, 800-354-1420, FAX 215-625-2940, info@taylorandfrancis.com, http://www.tandf.co.uk/journals/titles/15368378.asp, http://www.taylorandfrancis.com. Eds. Dr. Abraham Liboff, Dr. Joseph R Salvatore. Circ: 250.

➤ **EMERGING BIOCHEMICAL AND BIOPHYSICAL TECHNIQUES.** see *BIOLOGY—Biochemistry*

➤ **EURO COURSES. HEALTH PHYSICS AND RADIATION PROTECTION.** see *ENERGY—Nuclear Energy*

571.4 DEU ISSN 0175-7571
QH505 CODEN: EBJOE8
➤ **EUROPEAN BIOPHYSICS JOURNAL.** Text in English. 8/yr. EUR 998 combined subscription to institutions print & online eds. (effective 2005). adv. reprint service avail. from ISI. **Document type:** *Journal, Academic/Scholarly.* **Description:** Topics covered include molecular and structural interactions, membrane and receptor biophysics, thermodynamics, and energetics of biological processes.
Former titles: European Biophysical Journal; (until 1984): Biophysics of Structure and Mechanism (0340-1057); Supersedes in part (in 1974): Biophysik (0006-3517)
Related titles: Microform ed.: (from PQC); Online - full text ed.: ISSN 1432-1017 (from EBSCO Publishing, Springer LINK, Swets Information Services).
Indexed: ASCA, BBCI, BIOBASE, BIOSIS Prev, BiolAb, CCI, CIN, ChemAb, ChemTitl, CurCont, DSA, EngInd, ExcerpMed, FCA, IABS, ISR, IndMed, Inpharma, Inspec, MEDLINE, NutrAb, PhysBer, ProtozoAb, RPP, Reac, RefZh, RevApplEntom, SCI, SSCI, SeedAb.
—BLDSC (3829.489400), AskIEEE, CASDDS, CISTI, Ei, GNLM, IDS, IE, Infotrieve, ingenta, Linda Hall. **CCC.**
Published by: Springer-Verlag (Subsidiary of: Springer Science+Business Media), Tiergartenstr 17, Heidelberg, 69121, Germany. TEL 49-6221-3450, FAX 49-6221-345229, http://link.springer.de/link/service/journals/00249/index.htm. Adv. contact Stephan Kroeck TEL 49-30-827875739. **Subscr. in the Americas to:** Springer-Verlag New York, Inc., Journal Fulfillment, PO Box 2485, Secaucus, NJ 07096-2485. TEL 800-777-4643, 201-348-4033, FAX 201-348-4505, journals@springer-ny.com, http://www.springer-ny.com; **Subscr. to:** Springer GmbH Auslieferungsgesellschaft, Haberstr 7, Heidelberg 69126, Germany. TEL 49-6221-345-0, FAX 49-6221-345-4229, subscriptions@springer.de.

➤ **EXCERPTA MEDICA. SECTION 27: BIOPHYSICS, BIO-ENGINEERING AND MEDICAL INSTRUMENTATION.** see *BIOLOGY—Abstracting, Bibliographies, Statistics*

➤ **F E B S LETTERS.** see *BIOLOGY—Biochemistry*

➤ **FARMACEVTSKI VESTNIK**; strokovno glasilo slovenske farmacije. see *PHARMACY AND PHARMACOLOGY*

➤ **FIZIKA SOZNANIYA I ZHYZNI, KOSMOLOGIYA I ASTROFIZIKA.** see *PHYSICS*

571.4 664 USA ISSN 1557-1858
▼ **FOOD BIOPHYSICS.** Text in English. forthcoming 2006 (Mar.). q.
Related titles: Online - full text ed.: ISSN 1557-1866. forthcoming 2006 (Mar.).
Published by: Springer Science+Business Media, Inc., 233 Spring St, New York, NY 10013. TEL 212-460-1500, FAX 212-473-6272.

571.4 JPN ISSN 0435-1096
CODEN: GFSYAR
GAMMA FIELD SYMPOSIA. Text in English; Summaries in Japanese. 1962. a. per issue exchange basis. **Document type:** *Proceedings.*
Indexed: AgBio, CPA, ChemAb, FCA, HortAb, INIS AtomInd, MaizeAb, NutrAb, PBA, PGrRegA, RPP, RefZh, RiceAb, SeedAb, SoyAb, TriticAb, WeedAb.
—BLDSC (4069.200000), CASDDS, Linda Hall.
Published by: Institute of Radiation Breeding (NIAR, MAFF), Naka-gun, P.O. Box 3, Ohmiya-machi, Ibaraki-ken 319-22, Japan. TEL 81-2955-2-1138, FAX 81-2955-3-1075.

GENERAL PHYSIOLOGY AND BIOPHYSICS. see *BIOLOGY—Physiology*

571.4 NLD ISSN 1383-8121
CODEN: HBPHFH
HANDBOOK OF BIOLOGICAL PHYSICS. Text in English. 1995. irreg., latest vol.4, 2001. price varies. back issues avail. **Document type:** *Monographic series, Academic/Scholarly.* **Description:** Reports noteworthy research in the subspecialty of biological physics.
Indexed: CIN, ChemAb, ChemTitl.
—BLDSC (4250.345300), CASDDS, CISTI.
Published by: Elsevier BV, North-Holland (Subsidiary of: Elsevier Science & Technology), Sara Burgerhartstraat 25, Amsterdam, 1055 KV, Netherlands. TEL 31-20-485-3911, FAX 31-20-485-2457, nlinfo-f@elsevier.nl, http://www.elsevier.nl. Ed. A Hoff. **Subscr. to:** Elsevier BV, PO Box 211, Amsterdam 1000 AE, Netherlands. TEL 31-20-485-3757, FAX 31-20-485-3432, http://www.elsevier.nl.

571.4 USA ISSN 0073-0475
CODEN: HBBIAD
➤ **HARVARD BOOKS IN BIOPHYSICS.** Text in English. 1965. irreg., latest vol.3, 1983. price varies. adv. **Document type:** *Monographic series, Academic/Scholarly.*
Indexed: BiolAb, ChemAb.
—CASDDS.
Published by: (Harvard University Medical School, Department of Biophysics), Harvard University Press, 79 Garden St, Cambridge, MA 02138. TEL 617-495-2600, FAX 617-495-5898, http://www.hup.harvard.edu. R&P Mindy Koyanis TEL 617-495-2619. Adv. contact Denise Waddington.

571.4 JPN
HOSEIKEN NYUSU/RADIATION BIOLOGY CENTER NEWS. Text in Japanese. 1977. q. membership.
Published by: Kyoto Daigaku, Hoshasen Seibutsu Kenkyu Senta/Kyoto University, Radiation Biology Center, Yoshidakonoe-cho, Sakyo-ku, Kyoto-shi, 606-8315, Japan.

571.4 JPN ISSN 0441-747X
CODEN: HSKEAT
➤ **HOSHASEN SEIBUTSU KENKYU/RADIATION BIOLOGY RESEARCH COMMUNICATION.** Text in Japanese. 1965. q. JPY 3,000; USD 45 foreign. adv. bk.rev. **Document type:** *Academic/Scholarly.*
Indexed: ChemAb, INIS AtomInd.
—BLDSC (7227.945000), CASDDS.
Published by: Hoshasen Seibutsu Kenkyukai/Society of Radiation Biology Research, c/o Research Reactor Institute, Kyoto University, Sennan-gun, Kumatori-cho, Osaka 590-04, Japan. TEL 81-724-51-2628, FAX 81-724-51-2628, akahon@rri.kyoto-u.ac.jp. Ed. Takeo Ohnishi. R&P, Adv. contact Hiroshi Utsumi.

➤ **INDIAN PACING AND ELECTROPHYSIOLOGY JOURNAL.** see *BIOLOGY—Physiology*

➤ **INTERNATIONAL AGROPHYSICS**; a quarterly journal on physics in environmental and food sciences. see *AGRICULTURE—Crop Production And Soil*

➤ **INTERNATIONAL BIOPHYSICS CONGRESS. ABSTRACTS.** see *BIOLOGY—Abstracting, Bibliographies, Statistics*

➤ **INTERNATIONAL JOURNAL OF RADIATION BIOLOGY.** see *MEDICAL SCIENCES—Oncology*

➤ **JOURNAL OF BIOCHEMICAL AND BIOPHYSICAL METHODS.** see *BIOLOGY—Biochemistry*

571.4 NLD ISSN 0092-0606
QH505 CODEN: JBPHBZ
➤ **JOURNAL OF BIOLOGICAL PHYSICS**; an international journal for the formulation and application of physical and mathematical models in the biological sciences. Text in English. 1973. q. EUR 356, USD 356, GBP 223 combined subscription to institutions print & online eds. (effective 2005). adv. bk.rev. reprint service avail. from PSC. **Document type:** *Journal, Academic/Scholarly.* **Description:** Provides a medium for the community of biophysicists to publish its results and discuss its aims and methods. It welcomes papers which use the tools of physics, both experimental and theoretical, in an innovative way to study biological problems, as well as research aimed at providing a better understand of the physical principles underlying biological processes.
Related titles: Microform ed.: (from PQC); Online - full text ed.: ISSN 1573-0689 (from EBSCO Publishing, Gale Group, IngentaConnect, Kluwer Online, O C L C Online Computer Library Center, Inc., Ovid Technologies, Inc., Springer LINK, Swets Information Services).
Indexed: ASCA, Agr, BBCI, BIOSIS Prev, BibLing, BioCN&I, BiolAb, CIN, CPA, ChemAb, ChemTitl, ExcerpMed, FCA, Inspec, NemAb, PBA, ProtozoAb, RefZh, RevApplEntom, SIA, SeedAb.
—BLDSC (4953.150000), AskIEEE, CASDDS, CISTI, IDS, IE, Infotrieve, ingenta, Linda Hall. **CCC.**
Published by: (European Physical Society), Springer-Verlag Dordrecht (Subsidiary of: Springer Science+Business Media), Van Godewijckstraat 30, Dordrecht, 3311 GX, Netherlands. TEL 31-78-6576050, FAX 31-78-6576474, http://springerlink.metapress.com/openurl.asp?genre=journal&issn=0092-0606, http://www.springeronline.com. Eds. Michel Peyrard, Sonya Bahar.

571.4 GEO ISSN 1512-0856
➤ **JOURNAL OF BIOLOGICAL PHYSICS AND CHEMISTRY.** Abbreviated title: J B P C. Text in English. 2001. q. **Document type:** *Journal, Academic/Scholarly.*
Indexed: Inspec.
—BLDSC (4953.153000), IE.
Published by: Association of Modern Scientific Investigation, 1 Mosashvili St, Tbilisi, 380062, Georgia. tata16@gmx.net, http://www.amsi.ge. Ed. Jeremy Ramsden. **Co-publisher:** Collegium Basilea.

➤ **JOURNAL OF BIOMOLECULAR N M R.** (Nuclear Magnetic Resonance) see *BIOLOGY—Biochemistry*

571.4 GBR ISSN 1050-6411
QP321 CODEN: JEKIE3
➤ **JOURNAL OF ELECTROMYOGRAPHY & KINESIOLOGY.** Text in English. 1991. 6/yr. EUR 134 in Europe to individuals; JPY 17,700 in Japan to individuals; USD 150 to individuals except Europe and Japan; EUR 562 in Europe to institutions; JPY 74,500 in Japan to institutions; USD 629 to institutions except Europe and Japan (effective 2006). adv. charts; illus. back issues avail.; reprint service avail. from PQC. **Document type:** *Academic/Scholarly.* **Description:** Presents original articles on the study of muscle interaction and motion, using both mechanical and electrical detection techniques.
Related titles: Microform ed.: (from PQC); Online - full text ed.: (from EBSCO Publishing, Gale Group, IngentaConnect, ScienceDirect, Swets Information Services).

Indexed: AMED, ASCA, B&BAb, BIOBASE, BioEngAb, CurCont, ErgAb, ExcerpMed, FoSS&M, IABS, ISR, IndMed, Inpharma, Inspec, MEDLINE, NSCI, PEI, Reac, SCI, SSCI.
—BLDSC (4974.855000), CISTI, GNLM, IDS, IE, Infotrieve, ingenta. **CCC.**
Published by: Elsevier Ltd. (Subsidiary of: Elsevier Science & Technology), The Boulevard, Langford Ln, Kidlington, Oxford, OX5 1GB, United Kingdom. TEL 44-1865-843000, FAX 44-1865-843010, http://www.elsevier.com/locate/jelekin. Eds. Toshio Moritani, Dr. Moshe Solomonow. Circ: 1,000. **Subscr. to:** Elsevier BV, PO Box 211, Amsterdam 1000 AE, Netherlands. TEL 31-20-485-3757, FAX 31-20-485-3432, nlinfo-f@elsevier.nl, http://www.elsevier.nl.

➤ **JOURNAL OF ENVIRONMENTAL RADIOACTIVITY.** see *ENVIRONMENTAL STUDIES*

➤ **JOURNAL OF LUMINESCENCE.** see *PHYSICS—Optics*

➤ **JOURNAL OF PURE AND APPLIED ULTRASONICS.** see *PHYSICS—Sound*

➤ **JOURNAL OF SUBMICROSCOPIC CYTOLOGY AND PATHOLOGY.** see *BIOLOGY—Cytology And Histology*

571.4 GBR ISSN 0306-4565
QH516 CODEN: JTBIDS
➤ **JOURNAL OF THERMAL BIOLOGY.** Text in English. 1976. 8/yr. EUR 1,183 in Europe to institutions; JPY 157,100 in Japan to institutions; USD 1,324 to institutions except Europe and Japan; EUR 202 in Europe to qualified personnel; JPY 27,000 in Japan to qualified personnel; USD 227 to qualified personnel except Europe and Japan (effective 2006). adv. bk.rev. illus.; stat. index. back issues avail. **Document type:** *Academic/Scholarly.* **Description:** Covers research into the mechanisms by which living organisms respond to temperature change.
Related titles: Microfilm ed.: (from PQC); Online - full text ed.: (from EBSCO Publishing, Gale Group, IngentaConnect, ScienceDirect, Swets Information Services).
Indexed: AEA, ASCA, ASFA, AgBio, Agr, AnBeAb, AnBrAb, ApicAb, BBCI, BIOBASE, BIOSIS Prev, BioCN&I, BiolAb, CIN, CPA, CRFR, CTA, ChemAb, ChemTitl, CurCont, DSA, ESPM, EntAb, ExcerpMed, FCA, FPA, ForAb, HerbAb, HortAb, IABS, ISR, IndVet, Inpharma, Inspec, MEDLINE, MaizeAb, NemAb, NutrAb, OrnHort, PBA, PN&I, PotatoAb, PoultAb, ProtozoAb, RM&VM, RRTA, Reac, RefZh, RevApplEntom, S&F, SCI, SFA, SIA, TDB, TriticAb, VetBull, WeedAb, WildRev, ZooRec.
—BLDSC (5069.095000), AskIEEE, CASDDS, CISTI, IDS, IE, Infotrieve, ingenta, Linda Hall. **CCC.**
Published by: Pergamon (Subsidiary of: Elsevier Science & Technology), The Boulevard, Langford Ln, East Park, Kidlington, Oxford OX5 1GB, United Kingdom. TEL 44-1865-843000, FAX 44-1865-843010, http://www.elsevier.com/locate/jtherbio. Eds. James Heath, K. Bowler. Circ: 1,000. **Subscr. to:** Elsevier BV, PO Box 211, Amsterdam 1000 AE, Netherlands. TEL 31-20-485-3757, FAX 31-20-485-3432, nlinfo-f@elsevier.nl, http://www.elsevier.nl.

➤ **MEDECINE NUCLEAIRE**; imagerie fonctionelle et metabolique. see *MEDICAL SCIENCES—Radiology And Nuclear Medicine*

571.4 RUS ISSN 0134-8485
CODEN: MFBVAX
MOLEKULYARNAYA FIZIKA I BIOFIZIKA VODNYKH SISTEM. Text in Russian. 1973. irreg. illus.
Supersedes: Struktura i Rol' Vody v Zhivom Organizme (0585-4393)
Indexed: ChemAb.
—CASDDS.
Published by: Izdatelstvo Sankt-Peterburgskogo Universiteta, Universitetskaya nab 7-9, St Petersburg, 199034, Russian Federation.

571.4 JPN ISSN 0913-4778
NIHON BAIOREOROJI GAKKAISHI/JAPANESE SOCIETY OF BIORHEOLOGY. JOURNAL. Variant title: B & R. Text in Japanese; Summaries in English. 1987. q. JPY 2,000. **Document type:** *Academic/Scholarly.*
Published by: Nihon Baioreoroji Gakkai/Japanese Society of Biorheology, Gunma Prefectural Cardiovascular Center, Kho 3-12, Kameizumi-Machi, Maebashi-shi, Gunma-ken 371-0004, Japan. Ed. Suguru Ikemoto. Pub. Khoichi Taniguchi.

571.4 JPN ISSN 0915-0374
NIHON SEITAI JIKI GAKKAISHI/JAPAN BIOMAGNETISM AND BIOELECTROMAGNETICS SOCIETY. JOURNAL. Text in English, Japanese. 1988. s-a.
Published by: Nihon Seitai Jiki Gakkai, Daigaku Igakubu, Iyo Denshi Kenkyu Shisetsu, 3-1 Hongo 7-chome, Bunkyo-ku, Tokyo, 113-0033, Japan.

NITRIC OXIDE: BIOLOGY AND CHEMISTRY. see *BIOLOGY—Biochemistry*

571.4 USA ISSN 0748-6642
QP501 CODEN: PCPNER
➤ **PHYSIOLOGICAL CHEMISTRY AND PHYSICS AND MEDICAL N M R.** (Nuclear Magnetic Resonance) Text in English. 1969. s-a., latest vol.35, 2003. USD 100 (effective 2004). bk.rev. index. back issues avail. **Document type:** *Journal, Academic/Scholarly.* **Description:** Reviews of and reports on original research in biophysics, biochemistry, cellular physiology, nuclear magnetic resonance and related areas.
Formerly (until 1983): Physiological Chemistry and Physics (0031-9325)
Indexed: ASCA, ApicAb, BBCI, BIOSIS Prev, BiolAb, CCI, CIN, ChemAb, ChemTitl, CurCont, HelmAb, IndMed, Inpharma, Inspec, MEDLINE, Reac, RefZh, RevApplEntom, SCI, VITIS.
—BLDSC (6484.710000), CASDDS, CISTI, GNLM, IDS, IE, Infotrieve, ingenta, Linda Hall. **CCC.**
Published by: Pacific Press, Inc., PO Box 1452, Melville, NY 11747. TEL 631-694-2929, FAX 631-390-0053, pacificpressny@aol.com. Ed., R&P Gilbert N Ling TEL 631-694-2929 ext. 246. Pub. Raymond V Damadian. Circ: 350 (paid).

571.46 UKR ISSN 0869-2327
CODEN: KRBIEQ
PROBLEMY KRIOBIOLOGII/PROBLEMS OF CRYOBIOLOGY. Text in Russian; Summaries in English. 1985. q. USD 105 in North America. **Description:** Provides basic information to researchers investigating the various phenomena involved in the interaction between low temperatures and living cells or tissue, as well as to clinicians who are undertaking trials of hypothermia.
Formerly: Kriobiologiya (0233-7673)
Indexed: CIN, ChemAb, ChemTitl, RefZh, ZooRec.
—CASDDS, CISTI, East View, GNLM, Linda Hall.
Published by: Natsional'na Akademiya Nauk Ukrainy, Instytut Problem Kriobiolohii i Kriomedytsyny/National Ukrainian Academy of Sciences, Institute of Problems of Cryobiology and Cryomedicine, Ul Pereyaslavskaya 23, Kharkov, 310015, Ukraine. TEL 721039, FAX 720084. Ed. V I Grishchenko. **US dist. addr.:** East View Information Services, 3020 Harbor Ln. N., Minneapolis, MN 55447. TEL 612-550-0961.

571.4 GBR ISSN 0079-6107
QH505.A1 CODEN: PBIMAC
➤ **PROGRESS IN BIOPHYSICS & MOLECULAR BIOLOGY.** Text in English. 1950. 9/yr. EUR 1,964 in Europe to institutions; JPY 261,000 in Japan to institutions; USD 2,198 to institutions except Europe and Japan (effective 2006). abstr. index. **Document type:** *Academic/Scholarly.* **Description:** Integrates developments in the physical and biological sciences.
Formerly (until 1962): Progress in Biophysics and Biophysical Chemistry (0096-4174)
Related titles: Microfilm ed.: (from PQC); Online - full text ed.: (from EBSCO Publishing, Gale Group, IngentaConnect, ScienceDirect, Swets Information Services).
Indexed: ASCA, AgBio, AnBrAb, ApMecR, BBCI, BCI, BIOBASE, BIOSIS Prev, BiolAb, CCI, ChemAb, ChemTitl, CurCont, ExcerpMed, IABS, ISR, IndMed, Inpharma, Inspec, MEDLINE, MSB, NemAb, PBA, Reac, SCI, WeedAb.
—BLDSC (6866.100000), AskIEEE, CASDDS, CISTI, GNLM, IDS, IE, ingenta, Linda Hall. **CCC.**
Published by: Pergamon (Subsidiary of: Elsevier Science & Technology), The Boulevard, Langford Ln, East Park, Kidlington, Oxford OX5 1GB, United Kingdom. TEL 44-1865-843000, FAX 44-1865-843010, http://www.elsevier.com/locate/pbiomolbio. Eds. Denis Noble, Tom L Blundell. **Subscr. to:** Elsevier BV, PO Box 211, Amsterdam 1000 AE, Netherlands. TEL 31-20-485-3757, FAX 31-20-485-3432, nlinfo-f@elsevier.nl, http://www.elsevier.nl.

571.4 GBR ISSN 0033-5835
QH505.A1 CODEN: QURBAW
➤ **QUARTERLY REVIEWS OF BIOPHYSICS**; a review journal of biological function, structure and mechanism. Text in English, French, German. 1968. q. GBP 245 to institutions; USD 420 in North America to institutions; GBP 275 combined subscription to institutions print & online eds.; USD 470 combined subscription in North America to institutions print & online eds. (effective 2006). adv. bibl.; charts; illus. index. back issues avail.; reprint service avail. from PSC. **Document type:** *Journal, Academic/Scholarly.* **Description:** Reviews recent progress and problems in biophysics and molecular biology.
Related titles: Microform ed.: (from PQC); Online - full text ed.: ISSN 1469-8994. GBP 230 to institutions; USD 394 in North America to institutions (effective 2006) (from EBSCO Publishing, O C L C Online Computer Library Center, Inc., Swets Information Services).
Indexed: ASCA, ASFA, AgBio, ApMecR, BBCI, BIOBASE, BIOSIS Prev, BiolAb, CIN, CPA, ChemAb, ChemTitl, CurCont, DSA, ExcerpMed, IABS, ISR, IndMed, Inpharma, MEDLINE, MSB, NutrAb, Reac, RefZh, SCI.
—BLDSC (7206.300000), CASDDS, CISTI, GNLM, IDS, IE, Infotrieve, ingenta, Linda Hall. **CCC.**
Published by: (International Union for Pure and Applied Biophysics), Cambridge University Press, The Edinburgh Bldg, Shaftesbury Rd, Cambridge, CB2 2RU, United Kingdom. TEL 44-1223-312393, FAX 44-1223-315052, journals@cambridge.org, http://www.uk.cambridge.org/journals/qrb/, http://uk.cambridge.org/journals. Eds. Gerhard Wagner, Stephen Goldstein. R&P Linda Nicol TEL 44-1223-325757. Adv. contact Rebecca Curtis TEL 44-1223-325757. **Subscr. to:** Cambridge University Press, 100 Brook Hill Dr, West Nyack, NY 10994. TEL 845-353-7500, FAX 845-353-4141, journals_subscriptions@cup.org

543.0858 USA
R L B L NEWSLETTER. Text in English. 1977. s-a. looseleaf. free. **Document type:** *Newsletter, Trade.* **Description:** Covers ultrafast laser spectroscopy. Audience: biophysicists, chemists, physicists, educators and researchers.
Published by: Regional Laser & Biotechnology Laboratories, Dept. of Chemistry, University of Pennsylvania, Philadelphia, PA 19104-6323. TEL 215-898-3605, FAX 215-898-0590, ttroxler@sas.upenn.edu, http://rlbl.chem.upenn.edu. Ed. Thomas Troxler. Circ: 2,000 (paid and controlled).

571.4 DEU ISSN 0301-634X
QH505.A1 CODEN: REBPAT
➤ **RADIATION AND ENVIRONMENTAL BIOPHYSICS.** Text in English. 1963. q. EUR 1,348 combined subscription to institutions print & online eds. (effective 2005). adv. charts; illus. index. back issues avail.; reprint service avail. from ISI. **Document type:** *Journal, Academic/Scholarly.* **Description:** Covers the biophysics of ionizing and non-ionizing radiation. Examines the biological effects of temperature, pressure, gravitational forces, electricity, and magnetism, and the biophysical aspects of environmental and space influence.
Supersedes in part (in 1974): Biophysik (0006-3517)
Related titles: Microform ed.: (from PQC); Online - full text ed.: ISSN 1432-2099 (from EBSCO Publishing, Springer LINK, Swets Information Services).
Indexed: ASCA, ASFA, AbHyg, AgBio, BBCI, BIOSIS Prev, BiolAb, CIN, CIS, CPA, ChemAb, ChemTitl, CurCont, DSA, ESPM, EnvEAb, ExcerpMed, FCA, ForAb, H&SSA, HortAb, I&DA, ISR, IndMed, IndVet, Inpharma, Inspec, MEDLINE, NutrAb, OrnHort, PBA, PGegResA, PHN&I, PollutAb, Reac, RefZh, S&F, SCI, SeedAb, TriticAb, WeedAb.
—BLDSC (7227.930000), AskIEEE, CASDDS, CISTI, GNLM, IDS, IE, Infotrieve, ingenta, Linda Hall. **CCC.**
Published by: Springer-Verlag (Subsidiary of: Springer Science+Business Media), Tiergartenstr 17, Heidelberg, 69121, Germany. TEL 49-6221-3450, FAX 49-6221-345229, http://link.springer.de/link/service/journals/00411/index.htm. Ed. A Kellerer. Adv. contact Stephan Kroeck TEL 49-30-827875739. **Subscr. in the Americas to:** Springer-Verlag New York, Inc., Journal Fulfillment, PO Box 2485, Secaucus, NJ 07096-2485. TEL 800-777-4643, 201-348-4033, FAX 201-348-4505, journals@springer-ny.com, http://www.springer-ny.com; **Subscr. to:** Springer GmbH Auslieferungsgesellschaft, Haberstr 7, Heidelberg 69126, Germany. TEL 49-6221-345-0, FAX 49-6221-345-4229, subscriptions@springer.de.

➤ **RADIATION RESEARCH**; an international journal. see *PHYSICS—Nuclear Physics*

➤ **RADIATSIONNAYA BIOLOGIYA, RADIOEKOLOGIYA.** see *MEDICAL SCIENCES—Radiology And Nuclear Medicine*

➤ **RECENT RESEARCH DEVELOPMENTS IN BIOENERGETICS.** see *BIOLOGY—Biochemistry*

571.4 IND
RECENT RESEARCH DEVELOPMENTS IN BIOPHYSICAL CHEMISTRY. Text in English. a., latest vol.2, 2001.
Published by: Transworld Research Network, T C 36-248 (1), Trivandrum, Kerala 695 008, India. http://www.transworldresearch.com.

REFERATIVNYI ZHURNAL. BIOFIZIKA. see *BIOLOGY—Abstracting, Bibliographies, Statistics*

REFERATIVNYI ZHURNAL. BIOLOGIYA. FIZIKO-KHIMICHESKAYA BIOLOGIYA. see *BIOLOGY—Abstracting, Bibliographies, Statistics*

REFERATIVNYI ZHURNAL. BIONIKA. BIOKIBERNETIKA. BIOINZHENERIYA. see *BIOLOGY—Abstracting, Bibliographies, Statistics*

REFERATIVNYI ZHURNAL. RADIATSIONNAYA BIOLOGIYA. see *BIOLOGY—Abstracting, Bibliographies, Statistics*

REPRODUCTION, NUTRITION, DEVELOPMENT. see *BIOLOGY*

571.4 ROM ISSN 1220-515X
CODEN: RJBEEZ
ROMANIAN JOURNAL OF BIOPHYSICS. Text in English, French, German; Summaries in English. 1991. q.
Related titles: Online - full text ed.
Indexed: CIN, ChemAb, ChemTitl, INIS AtomInd.
—BLDSC (8019.628000), CASDDS, CISTI, Linda Hall.

▼ new title ➤ refereed ✶ unverified ◆ full entry avail.

Published by: (Societatea Nationala de Biofizica Pura si Aplicata), Editura Academiei Romane/Publishing House of the Romanian Academy, Calea 13 Septembrie 13, Sector 5, Bucharest, 76117, Romania. TEL 40-21-4119008, FAX 40-21-4103983, edacad@ear.ro. Ed. C Dimoftache. **Dist. by:** Rodipet S.A., Piata Presei Libere 1, sector 1, PO Box 33-57, Bucharest 3, Romania. TEL 40-21-2224126, 40-21-2226407, rodipet@rodipet.ro.

571.4 JPN ISSN 0582-4052
CODEN: SEBUAL
➤ **SEIBUTSU BUTSURI/BIOPHYSICS.** Text in English, Japanese. 1961. bi-m. JPY 8,000 membership (effective 2004). adv. **Document type:** *Journal, Academic/Scholarly.* **Description:** Contains review articles covering all fields of biophysics plus business news of the society and various other information.
Related titles: Online - full content ed.: ISSN 1347-4219. free (effective 2005); Online - full text ed.: (from J-Stage).
Indexed: CIN, ChemAb, ChemTitl, INIS AtomInd, JPI.
—BLDSC, CASDDS, Linda Hall. **CCC.**
Published by: Nihon Seibutsu Butsuri Gakkai/Biophysical Society of Japan, Realize Inc., 4-1-4 Hongo, Bunkyo-ku, Tokyo, 113-0033, Japan. TEL 81-3-3815-8511, FAX 81-3-3815-8529, rlz@ppp.bekkoame.or.jp, bpsjp@biophys.jp, http://www.jstage.jst.go.jp/browse/biophys, http://www.biophys.jp/. Ed. Yutaka Kirino. Adv. contact Shinichi Kojima. Circ: 3,500.

➤ **SEIBUTSU BUTSURI KAGAKU/PHYSICO-CHEMICAL BIOLOGY.** see *BIOLOGY—Biochemistry*

➤ **SEITAI NO KAGAKU/MEDICAL SCIENCE.** see *BIOLOGY*

➤ **SHENGWU HUAXUE YU SHENGWU WULI JINZHAN/PROGRESS IN BIOCHEMISTRY AND BIOPHYSICS.** see *BIOLOGY—Biochemistry*

➤ **STEFAN UNIVERSITY PRESS SERIES ON ACHIEVEMENTS IN PHYSICS.** see *PHYSICS*

➤ **VIRTUAL JOURNAL OF ULTRAFAST SCIENCE.** see *PHYSICS*

BIOLOGY—Biotechnology

see also ENGINEERING—Chemical Engineering

➤ **A S F A MARINE BIOTECHNOLOGY ABSTRACTS (ONLINE EDITION).** see *BIOLOGY—Abstracting, Bibliographies, Statistics*

660.6 NLD ISSN 1742-7061
▼ ➤ **ACTA BIOMATERIALIA.** Text in English. 2005. 6/yr. EUR 645 in Europe to institutions; JPY 85,500 in Japan to institutions; USD 721 to institutions except Europe and Japan (effective 2006). **Document type:** *Journal, Academic/Scholarly.* **Description:** Contains original research reports, review papers and communications in the broadly defined field of biomaterials science, with an emphasis on the relationship between biomaterial structure and function at all length scales.
Related titles: Online - full text ed.: (from EBSCO Publishing, ScienceDirect, Swets Information Services).
—IE. **CCC.**
Published by: Elsevier BV (Subsidiary of: Elsevier Science & Technology), Radarweg 29, Amsterdam, 1043 NX, Netherlands. TEL 31-20-4853911, FAX 31-20-4852457, nlinfo-f@elsevier.nl, http://www.elsevier.com/locate/actabiomat, http://www.elsevier.nl. Ed. W Wagner.

660.6 330 USA
▼ **ACUMEN JOURNAL OF SCIENCES.** Text in English. 2003. 8/yr. USD 200; USD 18.95 per issue (effective 2004). **Document type:** *Magazine, Academic/Scholarly.* **Description:** Analyzes discoveries, innovations and challenges in the life sciences and explains their commercial, economic, and policy implications for senior decision makers in business, academia and government.
Published by: Acumen Sciences, Llc, 111 Sutter St., Ste. 500, San Francisco, CA 94104-4519. info@acumenjournal.com, http://acumenjournal.com. Ed. Jason Pontin. Pub. Eric Greenberg. **Subscr. to:** 505 Montgomery St, 11th Fl, San Francisco, CA 94111. subscriptions@acumenjournal.com.

660.6 630 NLD ISSN 0169-0566
➤ **ADVANCES IN AGRICULTURAL BIOTECHNOLOGY.** Text in English. 1983. irreg., latest vol.26, 1989. price varies. back issues avail. **Document type:** *Monographic series, Academic/Scholarly.*
Indexed: Agr.
Published by: Springer-Verlag Dordrecht (Subsidiary of: Springer Science+Business Media), Van Godewijckstraat 30, Dordrecht, 3311 GX, Netherlands. TEL 31-78-6576050, FAX 31-78-6576474, http://www.springeronline.com.

660.63 USA ISSN 0724-6145
TP248.3 CODEN: ABEBDZ
ADVANCES IN BIOCHEMICAL ENGINEERING - BIOTECHNOLOGY. Text in English. 1972. irreg., latest vol.100, 2005. price varies. reprint service avail. from ISI. **Document type:** *Monographic series, Academic/Scholarly.* **Description:** Publishes new research in biochemical engineering and other areas of biotechnology.
Formerly: Advances in Biochemical Engineering (0065-2210)
Related titles: Online - full text ed.: ISSN 1616-8542.
Indexed: Agr, BCI, BIOSIS Prev, BibAg, CBTA, CIN, ChemAb, ChemTitl, DBA, EngInd, FS&TA, IndMed, MEDLINE.
—BLDSC (0699.925500), CASDDS, CISTI, Ei, GNLM, IE, Infotrieve, ingenta, KNAW, Linda Hall. **CCC.**
Published by: Springer-Verlag New York, Inc. (Subsidiary of: Springer Science+Business Media), 233 Spring St, New York, NY 10013. TEL 212-460-1500, FAX 212-473-6272, journals@springer-ny.com, http://www.springer-ny.com. Ed. T Scheper.

660.6 USA ISSN 1061-8945
R857.B54 CODEN: ABIOER
ADVANCES IN BIOSENSORS. Text in English. 1991. irreg., latest vol.5, 2003. price varies. back issues avail. **Document type:** *Monographic series, Academic/Scholarly.* **Description:** Presents a unique compendium of research papers, in which eminent authorities in the field of biosensors provide an up-to-date overview of their laboratories contribution, summarizing the primary research as it has appeared, possibly scattered, in the journal and conference literature, and reflecting on their findings.
Indexed: BIOSIS Prev.
—BLDSC (0700.275000), CASDDS, CISTI. **CCC.**
Published by: J A I Press Inc. (Subsidiary of: Elsevier Science & Technology), 360 Park Ave S, New York, NY 10010-1710. TEL 212-989-5800, FAX 212-633-3990, usinfo-f@elsevier.com, http://www.elsevier.com/wps/find/bookdescription.cws_home/BS_ADVBIO/description#description. Ed. Anthony P Turner.

660.6 572.8 576.5 POL ISSN 1230-025X
➤ **ADVANCES IN CLINICAL AND EXPERIMENTAL MEDICINE.** Text and summaries in English, Polish. 1992. bi-m. PLZ 300 domestic; EUR 300 foreign; PLZ 50 per issue domestic; EUR 50 per issue foreign (effective 2005). adv. abstr.; bibl.; illus.; stat. 120 p./no. 2 cols./p.; back issues avail.; reprints avail. **Document type:** *Journal, Academic/Scholarly.* **Description:** Publishes original and clinical studies, review articles, and case reports on various aspects of medicine.
Formerly (until 1998): Postepy Medycyny Klinicznej i Doswiadczalnej
Related titles: CD-ROM ed.; Diskette ed.; E-mail ed.; Fax ed.
Indexed: ExcerpMed.
—BLDSC (0703.864000), IE, ingenta.
Published by: Akademia Medyczna we Wroclawiu/Wroclaw Medical University, Wybrzeze L Pasteura 2, Wroclaw, 50367, Poland. redakcja@wyd.am.wroc.pl, http://www.am.wroc.pl/advances/advances.html. Ed. Antonina Harlozinska-Szmyrka. Adv. contact Urszula Madrzak. page PLZ 3,000, page EUR 750;. Circ: 400.

660.6 576.5 USA
ADVANCES IN GENE TECHNOLOGY. Text in English. 1990. irreg., latest vol.2, 1991. price varies. **Document type:** *Monographic series, Academic/Scholarly.*
Published by: J A I Press Inc. (Subsidiary of: Elsevier Science & Technology), 360 Park Ave S, New York, NY 10010-1710. TEL 212-989-5800, 800-325-4177, FAX 212-633-3990, usinfo-f@elsevier.com, http://www.elsevier.com.

666.6 CUB ISSN 1027-2860
➤ **ADVANCES IN MODERN BIOTECHNOLOGY/AVANCES EN BIOTECNOLOGIA MODERNA.** Text in English, Spanish. 1992. irreg. USD 12 domestic; USD 15 foreign (effective 2000). back issues avail. **Document type:** *Proceedings, Academic/Scholarly.* **Description:** Presents short papers of oral and poster presentations for scientific congresses.
Published by: (Center for Genetic Engineering and Biotechnology), Elfos Scientiae, Ave 31 entre 158 y 190, Cubanacan, Playa, PO Box 6072, Havana, 10600, Cuba. elfos.scientiae@cigb.edu.cu, http://www.elfosscientiae.com. Ed., R&P Guillermo J Padron. Circ: 2,000. **Subscr. to:** EBSCO Mexico, SA de CV, Ensenada 91, Col. Hipodromo Condesa, Mexico, DF 06170, Mexico. TEL 52-5-2738218, FAX 52-5-2735550.

660.6 USA ISSN 1684-5315
TP248.13
➤ **AFRICAN JOURNAL OF BIOTECHNOLOGY.** Text in English. 2002. m. free (effective 2005). back issues avail. **Document type:** *Academic/Scholarly.* **Description:** Covers all areas of applied biochemistry, industrial microbiology, molecular biology, genomics and proteomics, food and agricultural technologies, and metabolic engineering.
Media: Online - full content (from International Network for the Availability of Scientific Publications, African Journals Online).
Indexed: BiolAb, ExcerpMed.
Published by: Academic Journals, PO Box 5170-00200, Nairobi, Kenya. ajb_acadjourn@yahoo.com, ajb@academicjournals.org, http://www.academicjournals.org/AJB/index.htm. Ed. George Ude TEL 301-860-3347.

363.7 EGY ISSN 1110-5879
CODEN: AJMBFV
➤ **THE AFRICAN JOURNAL OF MYCOLOGY AND BIOTECHNOLOGY.** Text in Arabic. 1993. q. USD 100 to individual members; USD 200 to corporations (effective 2003). adv. back issues avail. **Document type:** *Academic/Scholarly.* **Description:** Devoted to the rapid publication of fundamental advances in basic and applied mycology, environmental mycology, and fungal biotechnology.
Related titles: Diskette ed.
Indexed: AEA, AbHyg, AgBio, AgrForAb, BIOSIS Prev, BioCN&I, BiolAb, CPA, ChemAb, DSA, FCA, FPA, ForAb, HerbAb, HortAb, I&DA, MaizeAb, NutrAb, OrnHort, PBA, PHN&I, RA&MP, RM&VM, RPP, RevApplEntom, RiceAb, S&F, SIA, SeedAb, SoyAb, TDB, TriticAb, WeedAb.
—BLDSC (0732.532000), CASDDS, IE, ingenta.
Published by: Regional Center for Mycology and Biotechnology, Al-Azhar University, Cairo, Egypt. razakaa@soficome.com.eg, http://derp.sti.sci.eg/data/0260.htm. Ed., R&P A.A. Razak. Adv. contact A A Razak. B&W page EGP 500, color page EGP 1,000; trim 11 x 18. Circ: 750. **Subscr. to:** Nasr City, P O Box 8104, Cairo 11371, Egypt.

➤ **AGBIOFORUM.** see *AGRICULTURE—Agricultural Economics*

➤ **AGBIOTECH BULLETIN (ONLINE).** see *AGRICULTURE*

➤ **AGBIOTECH NEWS AND INFORMATION.** see *BIOLOGY—Abstracting, Bibliographies, Statistics*

➤ **AGBIOTECH REPORTER**; agricultural research - business. see *AGRICULTURE*

660.6 GBR ISSN 1466-4909
AGRAFOOD BIOTECH. Text in English. 1999. 24/yr. GBP 544 domestic; GBP 598 in Europe; GBP 648 elsewhere (effective 2005). back issues avail. **Document type:** *Newsletter, Trade.* **Description:** Reports on developments in biotechnology, products, new legislation, regulation and controls, consumer attitudes to releases and commercialization, performances of bioscience companies, intellectual property news including copyright, trade marks and patents, research and development, people and dairy events.
—CISTI.
Published by: Agra Europe (London) Ltd. (Subsidiary of: T & F Informa plc), 80 Calverley Rd, Tunbridge Wells, Kent TN1 2UN, United Kingdom. TEL 44-1892-533813, FAX 44-1892-544895, marketing@agra-net.com, http://www.agra-net.com. Ed. Katherine Williams.

AGRI-INDUSTRY EUROPE. see *AGRICULTURE*

AGRICULTURAL RESEARCH; solving problems for the growing world. see *AGRICULTURE—Crop Production And Soil*

660.6 USA ISSN 0749-3223
CODEN: ABLAEY
AMERICAN BIOTECHNOLOGY LABORATORY. Text in English. 1983. 13/yr. free to qualified personnel (effective 2005). adv. charts; illus.; stat.; tr.lit. **Document type:** *Magazine, Trade.*
Related titles: Special ed(s).: American Biotechnology Laboratory. Buyers' Guide.
Indexed: ASCA, Agr, BIOBASE, BIOSIS Prev, BiolAb, C&ISA, CBTA, CIN, ChemAb, ChemTitl, E&CAJ, EngInd, IAA, IABS, MEDLINE, MSB, Telegen.
—BLDSC (0810.806000), CASDDS, Ei, GNLM, IDS, IE, Infotrieve, ingenta, KNAW.
Published by: International Scientific Communications, Inc., 30 Controls Dr, PO Box 670, Shelton, CT 06484-0870. TEL 203-926-9300, FAX 203-926-9310, iscpubs@iscpubs.com, http://www.iscpubs.com. Eds. Brian Howard, Susan Messinger. adv.: B&W page USD 4,970, color page USD 5,915. Circ: 70,016 (controlled).

▼ **AMERICAN JOURNAL OF BIOCHEMISTRY AND BIOTECHNOLOGY.** see *BIOLOGY—Biochemistry*

AMERICAN JOURNAL OF PHARMACOGENOMICS. see *BIOLOGY—Genetics*

660.6 636 USA ISSN 1049-5398
SF140.B54 CODEN: ANBTEN
➤ **ANIMAL BIOTECHNOLOGY.** Text in English. 1984. s-a. USD 1,092, GBP 661 combined subscription to institutions print & online eds. (effective 2006). adv. reprint service avail. from PSC. **Document type:** *Journal, Academic/Scholarly.* **Description:** Covers the identification and manipulation of genes and their products in domesticated animals.
Related titles: Online - full text ed.: ISSN 1532-2378. USD 1,037, GBP 628 to institutions (effective 2006) (from EBSCO Publishing, O C L C Online Computer Library Center, Inc., Swets Information Services).
Indexed: AEBA, ASCA, ASFA, AbHyg, AgBio, Agr, AnBrAb, B&BAb, BCI, BIOSIS Prev, BioEngAb, BiolAb, CIN, ChemAb, ChemTitl, CurCont, DBA, DSA, EPB, ESPM, EngInd, FS&TA, GenetAb, HGA, ISR, IndMed, IndVet, MEDLINE, MaizeAb, NutrAb, PBA, PGegResA, PN&I, PoultAb, RefZh, SCI, SIA, VetBull, WAE&RSA.
—BLDSC (0902.975000), CASDDS, IDS, IE, Infotrieve, ingenta. **CCC.**

Published by: Taylor & Francis Inc. (Subsidiary of: Taylor & Francis Group), 325 Chestnut St, Ste 800, Philadelphia, PA 19016. TEL 215-625-8900, 800-354-1420, FAX 215-625-2940, info@taylorandfrancis.com, http://www.tandf.co.uk/journals/titles/10495398.asp, http://www.taylorandfrancis.com. Ed. Dr. Lawrence B Schook. R&P Elaine Inverso. Adv. contact Mary Drabot. B&W page USD 550. Circ: 300 (paid).

660.62 NLD ISSN 0003-6072
QR1 CODEN: ALJMAO
➤ **ANTONIE VAN LEEUWENHOEK**; international journal of general and molecular microbiology. Text in English. 1935. 4/yr. EUR 1,555, USD 1,585, GBP 1,025 combined subscription to institutions print & online eds. (effective 2005); Subscription includes Biodegradation.. adv. charts; stat. index. reprint service avail. from PSC. **Document type:** *Academic/Scholarly.* **Description:** Publishes fundamental and applied research connected with microbiology, including food microbiology, medical microbiology and applications of microbiology in biotechnology.
Supersedes (in 1934): Nederlandsch Tijdschrift voor Hygiene, Microbiologie en Serologie (0369-3821)
Related titles: Microform ed.: (from PQC); Online - full text ed.: ISSN 1572-9699 (from EBSCO Publishing, Gale Group, IngentaConnect, Kluwer Online, O C L C Online Computer Library Center, Inc., Ovid Technologies, Inc., Springer LINK, Swets Information Services).
Indexed: ASCA, ASFA, AbHyg, AgBio, AgrForAb, BCI, BIOBASE, BIOSIS Prev, BibLing, BioCN&I, BioDAb, BiolAb, CBTA, CIN, CPA, ChemAb, ChemTitl, CurCont, DBA, DSA, ESPM, ExcerpMed, FCA, FLUIDEX, FPA, FS&TA, ForAb, GEOBASE, HerbAb, HortAb, IABS, ISR, IndMed, IndVet, Inpharma, MBA, MEDLINE, NemAb, NutrAb, OrnHort, PBA, PGegResA, PGrRegA, PHN&I, PN&I, PotatoAb, PoultAb, ProtozoAb, RA&MP, RM&VM, RPP, Reac, RefZh, RevApplEntom, RiceAb, S&F, SAA, SCI, SFA, SIA, SoyAb, TDB, TriticAb, VITIS, VetBull, VirolAbstr, WeedAb.
—BLDSC (1553.000000), CASDDS, CISTI, GNLM, IDS, IE, Infotrieve, ingenta, KNAW, Linda Hall. **CCC.**
Published by: (Stichting Antonie van Leeuwenhoek), Springer-Verlag Dordrecht (Subsidiary of: Springer Science+Business Media), Van Godewijckstraat 30, Dordrecht, 3311 GX, Netherlands. TEL 31-78-6576050, FAX 31-78-6576474, http://springerlink.metapress.com/openurl.asp?genre=journal&issn=0003-6072, http://www.springeronline.com. Ed. Iain Sutcliffe.

➤ **APPLIED AND ENVIRONMENTAL MICROBIOLOGY.** see *BIOLOGY—Microbiology*

660.6 USA ISSN 1063-6358
APPLIED BIOCATALYSIS. Text in English. 1991. irreg.
—**CCC.**
Published by: Marcel Dekker Inc. (Subsidiary of: Taylor & Francis Group), 270 Madison Ave, New York, NY 10016-0602. TEL 212-696-9000, FAX 212-685-4540, custserv@dekker.com, http://www.dekker.com.

APPLIED BIOCHEMISTRY AND BIOTECHNOLOGY. see *BIOLOGY—Biochemistry*

660.6 NZL ISSN 1175-9534
▼ ➤ **APPLIED BIOTECHNOLOGY, FOOD SCIENCE AND POLICY.** Text in English. 2003 (Mar.). q. NZD 495 in Australia & New Zealand to individuals; JPY 32,700 in Japan to individuals; USD 265 in US & Canada to individuals; GBP 175 elsewhere to individuals; NZD 795 in Australia & New Zealand to institutions; JPY 51,000 in Japan to institutions; USD 410 in US & Canada to institutions; GBP 275 elsewhere to institutions (effective 2003). **Document type:** *Journal, Academic/Scholarly.* **Description:** Focuses on practical applications of developments in biotechnology to food research, production, processing, storage, marketing, distribution and regulation.
Related titles: Online - full text ed.: (from EBSCO Publishing, Swets Information Services).
Indexed: ExcerpMed, FS&TA.
—BLDSC (1571.917000), IE.
Published by: Open Mind Journals Ltd., PO Box 300-729, Albany, Auckland, 1311, New Zealand. TEL 64-9-4146471, FAX 64-9-4146491, biotech@openmindjournals.com, info@openmindjournals.com, http://www.openmindjournals.com/biotech.html. Ed. Dr. David Everett. Pub. Tim Hill. R&P Kate Broughton.

660.62 DEU ISSN 0175-7598
QR53 CODEN: AMBIDG
➤ **APPLIED MICROBIOLOGY AND BIOTECHNOLOGY.** Text in English. 1975. 18/yr. EUR 4,188 combined subscription to institutions print & online eds. (effective 2005). back issues avail.; reprint service avail. from ISI. **Document type:** *Journal, Academic/Scholarly.* **Description:** Publishes original papers, short communications and mini-reviews on the following aspects of applied microbiology and biotechnology: biotechnology, biochemical engineering, applied genetics and regulation, applied microbial and cell physiology, food biotechnology, and environmental biotechnology.
Former titles (until 1984): European Journal of Applied Microbiology and Biotechnology (0171-1741); European Journal of Applied Microbiology (0340-2118)
Related titles: Microform ed.: (from PQC); Online - full text ed.: ISSN 1432-0614 (from EBSCO Publishing, Springer LINK, Swets Information Services).
Indexed: AEA, AEBA, AESIS, AS&TI, ASCA, ASFA, AbHyg, AgBio, Agr, AgrForAb, AnBrAb, B&AI, BBCI, BCI, BIOBASE, BIOSIS Prev, BioCN&I, BioDAb, BioEngAb, BiolAb, CBTA, CCI, CEABA, CIN, CPA, ChemAb, ChemTitl, CurCont, DBA, DSA, ESPM, EnvEAb, ExcerpMed, FCA, FLUIDEX, FPA, FS&TA, ForAb, GEOBASE, HelmAb, HerbAb, HortAb, I&DA, IABS, ISR, IndMed, IndVet, Inpharma, M&PBA, MBA, MEDLINE, MSB, MSCI, MaizeAb, NemAb, NutrAb, OceAb, OrnHort, PBA, PE&ON, PGegResA, PGrRegA, PHN&I, PN&I, PollutAb, PotatoAb, PoultAb, ProtozoAb, RA&MP, RM&VM, RPP, Reac, RefZh, RevApplEntom, RiceAb, S&F, SCI, SIA, SWRA, SeedAb, SoyAb, TDB, TriticAb, VITIS, VetBull, WAE&RSA, WRCInf, WeedAb, WildRev.
—BLDSC (1576.100000), CASDDS, CINDOC, CISTI, GNLM, IDS, IE, Infotrieve, ingenta, Linda Hall. **CCC.**
Published by: Springer-Verlag (Subsidiary of: Springer Science+Business Media), Tiergartenstr 17, Heidelberg, 69121, Germany. TEL 49-6221-3450, FAX 49-6221-345229, http://link.springer.de/link/service/journals/00253/index.htm. Ed. Alexander Steinbuechel. Adv. contact Stephan Kroeck TEL 49-30-827875739. **Subscr. in the Americas to:** Springer-Verlag New York, Inc., Journal Fulfillment, PO Box 2485, Secaucus, NJ 07096-2485. TEL 800-777-4643, 201-348-4033, FAX 201-348-4505, journals@springer-ny.com, http://www.springer-ny.com; **Subscr. to:** Springer GmbH Auslieferungsgesellschaft, Haberstr 7, Heidelberg 69126, Germany. TEL 49-6221-345-0, FAX 49-6221-345-4229, subscriptions@springer.de.

▼ ➤ **AQUATIC RESOURCES, CULTURE AND DEVELOPMENT.** see *EARTH SCIENCES—Oceanography*

660.6 EGY ISSN 1110-6875
➤ **ARAB JOURNAL OF BIOTECHNOLOGY.** Text in Arabic. 1998. s-a. (July & December). USD 25 to individuals; USD 100 to institutions (effective 2000). **Document type:** *Journal, Academic/Scholarly.* **Description:** Aims at the advancement and dissemination of knowledge in agriculture, medicine, veterenary medicine, environment and pharmacology.
Related titles: CD-ROM ed.: EGP 50 per issue in Egypt; USD 30 per issue rest of world (effective 2000); Diskette ed.; E-mail ed.; Fax ed.
Published by: Arab Council for Graduate Studies & Scientific Research, Tharwat Street, Cairo Univ, Hostel, Giza, 12613, Egypt. TEL 20-2-3602784, FAX 20-2-3602658, acgssr@intouch.com, http://derp.sti.sci.eg/data/0326.htm. Ed. Dr. Dheyaa El-Qadhi.

➤ **ARTIFICIAL CELLS, BLOOD SUBSTITUTES, AND BIOTECHNOLOGY.** see *MEDICAL SCIENCES—Experimental Medicine, Laboratory Technique*

660.6 SGP
ASIA PACIFIC BIOTECH DIRECTORY (YEAR). Text in English. a., latest 2003. USD 120 (effective 2002). **Document type:** *Directory, Academic/Scholarly.* **Description:** Features top biotechnology companies, biotech research institutes and venture capitalists in this region.
Published by: K H Biotech Services Pte. Ltd. (Subsidiary of: World Scientific Publishing Co. Pte. Ltd.), 5 Toh Tuck Link, Singapore, 596224, Singapore. TEL 65-6467 7667, FAX 65-6466 5775, biotech_edit@wspc.com.sg, http://www.asiabiotech.com.sg/.

660.6 SGP ISSN 0219-0303
➤ **ASIA - PACIFIC BIOTECH NEWS (ENGLISH EDITION)**; an international fortnightly report on biotechnology in the Asia-Pacific. Text in English. 1997. bi-m. USD 206 combined subscription to institutions print & online eds.; USD 94 combined subscription in developing nations to institutions print & online eds. (effective 2006). adv. back issues avail. **Document type:** *Journal, Academic/Scholarly.* **Description:** Offers coverage of news mainly in the fields of food, agriculture, pharmaceuticals and health care. Contains new government policies and regulations, company profiles, corporate deals, industry trends, new product developments and patents, new biotech techniques, technological updates and new drugs.
Related titles: Online - full text ed.: (from EBSCO Publishing).
Published by: K H Biotech Services Pte. Ltd. (Subsidiary of: World Scientific Publishing Co. Pte. Ltd.), 5 Toh Tuck Link, Singapore, 596224, Singapore. TEL 65-6467 7667, FAX 65-6466 5775, biotech_edit@wspc.com.sg, http://www.asiabiotech.com.sg/. Ed. Nam Hai Chua.

660.6 MYS ISSN 0128-7451
➤ **ASIA - PACIFIC JOURNAL OF MOLECULAR BIOLOGY & BIOTECHNOLOGY.** Text in English. s-a. **Document type:** *Academic/Scholarly.*
Indexed: AEBA, BCI, BioEngAb, ESPM, GenetAb, HGA, M&PBA.
Published by: Universiti Putra Malaysia, 4th Fl, Administrative Bldg, 43400 UPM, Serdang, Selangor, Malaysia. TEL 603-8948-6101ext 1087, FAX 603-8943-8955, rschinfo@admin.upm.edu.my, http://www.admin.upm.edu.my/~research.

➤ **ASIAN - AUSTRALASIAN JOURNAL OF ANIMAL SCIENCES.** see *AGRICULTURE—Poultry And Livestock*

660.6 IND ISSN 0972-7566
ASIAN BIOTECHNOLOGY AND DEVELOPMENT REVIEW. Text in English. irreg. **Description:** To generate wider awareness of the issues involved and emerging developments in the area of biotechnologies.
Former titles (until 2001): R I S Biotechnology and Development Review; (until 1995): Biotechnology and Development Review
Published by: Research and Information System for the Non-Aligned and Other Developing Countries, Zone IV-B, Fourth Fl, India Habitat Centre, Lodhi Rd, New Delhi, 110 003t, India. TEL 91-11-24682177, FAX 91-11-24682173, sachin@ris.org.in, http://www.ris.org.in/abdr.html.

ASSOCIATION OF GENETIC TECHNOLOGISTS. JOURNAL. see *BIOLOGY—Genetics*

660.6 AUS ISSN 1036-7128
CODEN: AUBIE5
AUSTRALASIAN BIOTECHNOLOGY. Text in English. 1987. bi-m. AUD 90; AUD 120 foreign (effective 1999). adv. bk.rev. index. back issues avail. **Document type:** *Newsletter.*
Formerly (until 1991): Australian Journal of Biotechnology (0819-3355)
Indexed: AESIS, ASCA, AgBio, AnBrAb, ArtHuCI, BCI, BIOBASE, BioCN&I, CBNB, CBTA, CEABA, CIN, ChemAb, ChemTitl, DBA, DSA, ExcerpMed, FPA, FS&TA, HortAb, IABS, MEDLINE, NutrAb, PBA, ProtozoAb, RPP, RevApplEntom, S&F, SIA, WAE&RSA, WeedAb.
—BLDSC (1793.610000), CASDDS, CISTI, IDS, IE, Infotrieve, ingenta.
Published by: Ausbiotech Ltd., 576 Swan St, Richmond, VIC 3121, Australia. TEL 61-3-9208-4200, FAX 61-3-9208-4201, admin@ausbiotech.org, http://www.ausbiotech.org/. Eds. D Tribe, M Playne. R&P Barbara Arnold. Adv. contact Gary Dolder. Circ: 1,200 (paid).

660.6 AUS
AUSTRALIAN BIOTECHNOLOGY NEWS. Text in English. 2002 (Mar.). w. **Document type:** *Academic/Scholarly.*
Published by: I D G Communications Pty. Ltd., 88 Christie St, St Leonards, NSW 2065, Australia. TEL 61-9-2439-5133, FAX 61-2-94395512, http://www.biotechnews.com.au, http://www.idg.com.au.

660.6 GBR
B B S R C BUSINESS. Text in English. 1967. q. free. charts; illus. **Document type:** *Newsletter.* **Description:** Presents research in biology and biotechnology, agriculture, food, chemicals, and pharmaceuticals.
Supersedes in part (in Apr. 1994): A F R C News (0267-8489)
Indexed: EnvAb.
Published by: Biotechnology and Biological Sciences Research Council, Polaris House, N Star Ave, Swindon, Wilts SN2 1UH, United Kingdom. TEL 44-1793-413200, FAX 44-1793-413201, http://www.bbsrc.ac.uk. Ed. Monica Winstanley.

660.6 USA
B I O'S EDITORS' AND REPORTERS' GUIDE TO BIOTECHNOLOGY. Text in English. a. free. **Description:** Source of facts, figures, and ideas for coverage of biotechnology.
Published by: Biotechnology Industry Organization, 1225 I (Eye) St N W, Ste 400, Washington, DC 20005-5958. TEL 202-857-0244, FAX 202-857-0237, info@bio.org, http://www.bio.org, http://www.bio.org/.

660.6 GBR ISSN 1472-6750
TP248.13 CODEN: BBMIE6
➤ **B M C BIOTECHNOLOGY.** (BioMed Central) Text in English. 2000. m. free (effective 2006). adv. **Document type:** *Journal, Academic/Scholarly.* **Description:** Publishes original research articles in the manipulation of biological macromolecules or organisms for use in experimental procedures or in the pharmaceutical, agrobiological and allied industries.
Media: Online - full content (from EBSCO Publishing, National Library of Medicine).
Indexed: BCI, BIOSIS Prev, BiolAb, ExcerpMed, MEDLINE.
—Infotrieve. **CCC.**
Published by: BioMed Central Ltd. (Subsidiary of: Current Science Ltd), Middlesex House, 34-42 Cleveland St, London, W1T 4LB, United Kingdom. TEL 44-20-76319131, FAX 44-20-76319923, info@biomedcentral.com, http://www.biomedcentral.com/bmcbiotechnol/. Ed. Peter Newmark. Adv. contact Deborah Cockerill.

660.6 USA ISSN 1040-9416
B T CATALYST. (Biotechnology Catalyst) Text in English. 1987. m. free. back issues avail. **Document type:** *Newsletter.* **Description:** Offers a source of information on North Carolina's growing biotechnology community.
Related titles: Online - full text ed.: 2000 (from Factiva, Gale Group).
Published by: North Carolina Biotechnology Center, 15 T W Alexander Dr, Research Triangle Park, NC 27709. TEL 919-541-9366, info@ncbiotech.org, http://www.ncbiotech.org/ncindustry/news/btcat/btcat.cfm. Ed. Leslie Broberg.

BABRAHAM INSTITUTE. CORPORATE PLAN. see *BIOLOGY—Physiology*

BABRAHAM PUBLICATIONS. see *BIOLOGY—Biochemistry*

B

660.6 JPN
BAIOINDASUTORI NENKAN/YEARBOOK OF BIOINDUSTRY. Text in Japanese. 1985. a. JPY 55,000.
Published by: C M C Co. Ltd., 5-4 Uchikanda 1-chome, Chiyoda-ku, Tokyo, 101-0047, Japan.

660.6 JPN
BAIOTEKUNOROJI JOHO/BIOTECHNOLOGY INFORMATION. Text in Japanese. irreg.
Published by: (Norin Suisan Gijutsu Kaigi Jimukyoku), Norin Suisansho/Ministry of Agriculture, Forestry and Fisheries, 2-1 Kasumigaseki 1-chome, Chiyoda-ku, Tokyo, 100-0013, Japan.

660.6 JPN
BAIOTEKUNOROJI REBYU/BIOTECHNOLOGY REVIEW. Text in Japanese. 1988. a. JPY 80,000.
Published by: C M C Co. Ltd., 5-4 Uchikanda 1-chome, Chiyoda-ku, Tokyo, 101-0047, Japan.

BEITRAEGE ZUR TABAKFORSCHUNG INTERNATIONAL; contributions to tobacco research. see *TOBACCO*

BEN-GURION UNIVERSITY OF THE NEGEV. INSTITUTES FOR APPLIED RESEARCH. SCIENTIFIC ACTIVITIES. see *AGRICULTURE*

660.5 USA ISSN 1538-5728
BIO - I T WORLD. Text in English. 2002. m. free to qualified personnel (effective 2003). back issues avail. **Document type:** *Magazine, Trade.*
Related titles: Online - full text ed.: (from EBSCO Publishing).
Published by: Bio - I T World, Inc (Subsidiary of: I D G Communications Inc.), 492 Old Connecticut Path, Framingham, MA 01701-9208. TEL 508-628-4700, FAX 508-628-4766, http://www.bio-itworld.com, http://www.bio-itworld.com/.

660.6 JPN ISSN 0910-6545
CODEN: BIINEG
BIO INDUSTRY/BAIO INDASUTORI. Text in Japanese. 1984. m. JPY 52,500 per issue (effective 2005).
Indexed: ChemAb.
—BLDSC (2066.656900), CASDDS.
Published by: C M C Publishing Co., Ltd., 1-13-1 Uchikanda, Chiyoda-ku, Tokyo, 101-0047, Japan. TEL 81-3-32932061, FAX 81-3-32932069, info@cmcbooks.co.jp, http://www.cmcbooks.co.jp/.

660.6 USA
BIO NEWS; news & events from the biotechnology industry. Text in English. bi-m. free to members (effective 2005). adv. **Document type:** *Newsletter.*
Published by: Biotechnology Industry Organization, 1225 I (Eye) St N W, Ste 400, Washington, DC 20005-5958. TEL 202-962-9200, info@bio.org, http://www.bio.org, http://www.bio.org/. Ed., R&P Megan Matthews. Adv. contact Susan Rathbone. B&W page USD 4,070, color page USD 5,670; trim 11 x 17. Circ: 10,089 (paid).

BIO-SCIENCE LAW REVIEW. see *LAW—Corporate Law*

660.6 BEL
BIO TECH INTERNATIONAL. Abbreviated title: B T I. Text in English. 1989. bi-m. USD 95 in the Americas; EUR 90 elsewhere (effective 2002). adv. illus.; tr.lit. **Document type:** *Magazine, Trade.* **Description:** Provides a mix of technology, research, product & industry news.
Former titles: Biotech Tech International; (until 1999): Biotech Products International
Published by: Reed Business Information - Belgium (Subsidiary of: Reed Business Information International), Rue des Palais 100, Brussels, B-1030, Belgium. TEL 32-2-240-2611, FAX 32-2-240-2778, http://www.biotech-online.com/. Pub., R&P Dr. Bernard Leger. Adv. contact Astrid Wydouw. Circ: 27,003 (controlled).

660.6 USA ISSN 1534-9926
BIOARRAY NEWS; the global weekly of biochips & microarrays. Text in English. w. (50/yr.). USD 845 in North America; GBP 599, EUR 985 elsewhere (effective 2003). adv. reprints avail. **Document type:** *Newsletter.* **Description:** Delivers news and analysis on the technologies, companies and people of the industry.
Related titles: Online - full text ed.
Published by: GenomeWeb, LLC, PO Box 998, Peck Slip Stn., New York, NY 10272-0998. TEL 212-269-4747, FAX 212-269-3686, http://www.bioarraynews.com, http://www.genome.com. Ed. Jennifer Friedlin.

660.6 GBR ISSN 1024-2422
TP248.65.E59 CODEN: BOBOEQ
➤ **BIOCATALYSIS AND BIOTRANSFORMATION.** Text in English. bi-m. GBP 710, USD 927 combined subscription to institutions print & online eds. (effective 2006). adv. bk.rev. back issues avail.; reprint service avail. from PSC. **Document type:** *Journal, Academic/Scholarly.* **Description:** International journal covering the industrial exploitation of biological catalysts for the interconversion of chemical species.
Formerly: Biocatalysis (0886-4454)
Related titles: CD-ROM ed.; Microform ed.; Online - full text ed.: ISSN 1029-2446. GBP 675, USD 881 to institutions (effective 2006) (from EBSCO Publishing, Gale Group, IngentaConnect, O C L C Online Computer Library Center, Inc., Swets Information Services).
Indexed: AEBA, ASCA, ASFA, B&BAb, BBCI, BCI, BIOBASE, BioEngAb, CCI, CEABA, ChemAb, CurCont, DBA, ESPM, EngInd, ExcerpMed, FS&TA, IABS, ISR, Inpharma, MBA, RCI, Reac, SCI.
—BLDSC (2066.809100), CISTI, Ei, IE, Infotrieve, ingenta, Linda Hall. **CCC.**
Published by: Taylor & Francis Ltd (Subsidiary of: Taylor & Francis Group), 4 Park Sq, Milton Park, Abingdon, OX14 4RN, United Kingdom. TEL 44-1235-828600, FAX 44-1235-829000, info@tandf.co.uk, http://www.tandf.co.uk/journals/titles/10242422.html. Ed. David Leak. **Subscr. in N America to:** Taylor & Francis Inc., Customer Services Dept, 325 Chestnut St, 8th Fl, Philadelphia, PA 19106. TEL 215-625-8900, 800-354-1420, FAX 215-625-8914, customerservice@taylorandfrancis.com

➤ **BIOCENTURY EXTRA.** see *BUSINESS AND ECONOMICS*

➤ **BIOCENTURY PART II.** see *BUSINESS AND ECONOMICS*

➤ **BIOCENTURY QUARTERLY STOCK REPORTS.** see *BUSINESS AND ECONOMICS—Investments*

➤ **BIOCENTURY: THE BERNSTEIN REPORT ON BIOBUSINESS.** see *BUSINESS AND ECONOMICS*

➤ **BIOCHIMIE.** see *BIOLOGY—Biochemistry*

660.6 GBR
BIOCOMMERCE DATA'S BUSINESS PROFILE SERIES. VOLUME 1: THE U S BIOTECHNOLOGY DIRECTORY. Text in English. 2000 (Apr.). irreg. price varies with each vol.. **Document type:** *Monographic series, Trade.* **Description:** Provides information such as profile, personnel, addresses & phone numbers, products & services on over 860 companies involved in biotechnology in the US.
Related titles: ♦ Series: BioCommerce Data's Business Profile Series. Volume 4: The U K Biotechnology Directory; ♦ BioCommerce Data's Business Profile Series. Volume 2. The European Biotechnology Directory; ♦ BioCommerce Data's Business Profile Series. Volume 3: The International Biotechnology Directory.
Published by: Scrip Reports (Subsidiary of: P J B Publications Ltd.), 18/20 Hill Rise, Richmond, Surrey TW10 6UA, United Kingdom. TEL 44-20-8332-8964, FAX 44-20-8332-8992, 44-20-8948-6866, custserv@repsinfo.demon.co.uk, http://www.pjbpubs.com/scriprep/index.html.

660.6 GBR
BIOCOMMERCE DATA'S BUSINESS PROFILE SERIES. VOLUME 2. THE EUROPEAN BIOTECHNOLOGY DIRECTORY. Text in English. 2000 (May). irreg. price varies with each vol.. **Document type:** *Monographic series, Trade.* **Description:** Contains over 650 profiles of biotechnology companies in 25 European countries, including 15 review articles and contact details for European venture capitalists, trade associations and universities. All profiles have been extensively revised and updated.
Related titles: ♦ Series: BioCommerce Data's Business Profile Series. Volume 4: The U K Biotechnology Directory; ♦ BioCommerce Data's Business Profile Series. Volume 1: The U S Biotechnology Directory; ♦ BioCommerce Data's Business Profile Series. Volume 3: The International Biotechnology Directory.
Published by: Scrip Reports (Subsidiary of: P J B Publications Ltd.), 18/20 Hill Rise, Richmond, Surrey TW10 6UA, United Kingdom. TEL 44-20-8332-8964, FAX 44-20-8332-8992, 44-20-8948-6866, custserv@repsinfo.demon.co.uk, http://www.pjbpubs.com/scriprep/index.html.

660.6 GBR
BIOCOMMERCE DATA'S BUSINESS PROFILE SERIES. VOLUME 3: THE INTERNATIONAL BIOTECHNOLOGY DIRECTORY. Text in English. 2000 (Jun.). irreg. price varies with each vol.. **Document type:** *Monographic series, Trade.* **Description:** Provides information on 530 worldwide biotechnology companies and trade associations, giving you access to over 1,000 key industry contacts.
Related titles: ♦ Series: BioCommerce Data's Business Profile Series. Volume 4: The U K Biotechnology Directory; ♦ BioCommerce Data's Business Profile Series. Volume 1: The U S Biotechnology Directory; ♦ BioCommerce Data's Business Profile Series. Volume 2. The European Biotechnology Directory.
Published by: Scrip Reports (Subsidiary of: P J B Publications Ltd.), 18/20 Hill Rise, Richmond, Surrey TW10 6UA, United Kingdom. TEL 44-20-8332-8964, FAX 44-20-8332-8992, 44-20-8948-6866, custserv@repsinfo.demon.co.uk, http://www.pjbpubs.com/scriprep/index.html.

660.6 GBR
BIOCOMMERCE DATA'S BUSINESS PROFILE SERIES. VOLUME 4: THE U K BIOTECHNOLOGY DIRECTORY. Text in English. 1988. a., latest 2000, 11th Edition. GBP 195, USD 320, JPY 47,000 per vol. (effective 2000). adv. **Document type:** *Directory.* **Description:** Profiles more than 1000 U.K. organizations involved in biotechnology. Contains review articles.
Formerly: The U K Biotechnology Handbook (Year)
Related titles: Online - full text ed.; ♦ Series: BioCommerce Data's Business Profile Series. Volume 1: The U S Biotechnology Directory; ♦ BioCommerce Data's Business Profile Series. Volume 2. The European Biotechnology Directory; ♦ BioCommerce Data's Business Profile Series. Volume 3: The International Biotechnology Directory.
—BLDSC (9082.651700).
Published by: Scrip Reports (Subsidiary of: P J B Publications Ltd.), 18/20 Hill Rise, Richmond, Surrey TW10 6UA, United Kingdom. TEL 44-20-8332-8964, FAX 44-20-8332-8992, 44-20-8948-6866, custserv@repsinfo.demon.co.uk, http://www.pjbpubs.com/scriprep/index.html.

660.6 USA
BIOCONNECTION. Text in English. 1986. 3/yr. back issues avail. **Document type:** *Academic/Scholarly.*
Published by: Michigan Biotechnology Institute, 3900 Collins Rd, Box 27609, Lansing, MI 48909. TEL 517-337-3181, FAX 517-337-2122. Ed. Gretchen Smith. Circ: 2,500 (controlled).

358.3882 USA
THE BIODEFENCE FUNDING REPORT. Text in English. w. USD 547 (effective 2005). **Description:** Helps to track the unfolding world of biodefense and homeland security.
Media: Online - full text.
Published by: Washington Business Information, Inc., 300 N Washington St, Ste 200, Falls Church, Arlington, VA 22046. TEL 703-538-7600, 888-838-5578, FAX 703-538-7676, customerservice@fdanews.com, http://www.fdanews.com/dailies/biodefense.

BIOENGINEERING ABSTRACTS (ONLINE EDITION). see *BIOLOGY—Abstracting, Bibliographies, Statistics*

660 USA
▼ **BIOEXECUTIVE INTERNATIONAL.** Text in English. 2004. bi-m. adv. **Document type:** *Magazine, Trade.* **Description:** Contains business and marketing news and information aimed at the biotech industry.
Published by: Informa Life Sciences Group (Subsidiary of: T & F Informa plc), 1 Research Dr, Ste 400A, P. O. Box 770, Westborough, MA 01581-0770. TEL 508-616-5550, FAX 508-616-5533, info@bioexecutiveintl.com, http://www.bioexecutiveintl.com.

BIOFORUM EUROPE. see *BIOLOGY*

BIOFORUM FRANCE. see *BIOLOGY*

660.6 BGR ISSN 1310-2699
BIOLOGIA, EKOLOGIA I BIOTEKHBOLOGII. Text in Bulgarian. bi-m. USD 36 foreign (effective 2002). **Document type:** *Journal, Academic/Scholarly.*
Indexed: RefZh.
Published by: Ministerstvo na Obrazovanieto i Naukata na Republika Bulgaria/Ministry of Education and Sciences of the Republic of Bulgaria, 125 Tzarigradsko Shosse Blvd., Bl. 5, PO Box 336, Sofia, 1113, Bulgaria. TEL 359-2-705298, http://www.minedu.government.bg. **Dist. by:** Sofia Books, ul Silivria 16, Sofia 1404, Bulgaria. TEL 359-2-9586257, info@sofiabooks-bg.com, http://www.sofiabooks-bg.com.

BIOMATERIALS. see *MEDICAL SCIENCES*

660.6 NLD ISSN 1389-0344
QH442 CODEN: BIENFV
➤ **BIOMOLECULAR ENGINEERING.** Text in Dutch. 1983. 6/yr. EUR 110 in Europe to individuals; JPY 14,500 in Japan to individuals; USD 123 to individuals except Europe and Japan; EUR 532 in Europe to institutions; JPY 70,500 in Japan to institutions; USD 595 to institutions except Europe and Japan (effective 2006). abstr.; bibl. reprints avail. **Document type:** *Journal, Academic/Scholarly.* **Description:** Publishes papers on new methods, materials and instruments for biomolecular engineering, molecular biology, cell biology, biochemistry, and genetics.
Former titles (until 1999): Genetic Analysis: Biomolecular Engineering - Techniques and Applications (1050-3862); (until 1990): Genetic Analysis Techniques (0735-0651)
Related titles: Microform ed.: (from PQC); Online - full text ed.: (from EBSCO Publishing, Gale Group, IngentaConnect, ScienceDirect, Swets Information Services).
Indexed: ASCA, ASFA, AgBio, Agr, AnBrAb, BBCI, BCI, BIOBASE, BIOSIS Prev, BioEngAb, BiolAb, CIN, ChemAb, ChemTitl, CurCont, DBA, DSA, ESPM, ExcerpMed, FCA, GenetAb, HGA, HelmAb, HerbAb, HortAb, IABS, ISR, IndMed, IndVet, Inpharma, M&PBA, MBA, MEDLINE, MSB, MaizeAb, NemAb, NucAcAb, NutrAb, PBA, PGrRegA, PN&I, ProtozoAb, RA&MP, RM&VM, Reac, RevApplEntom, S&F, SCI, SIA, SoyAb, TDB, Telegen, VetBull, WAE&RSA, WeedAb.
—BLDSC (2089.255000), CASDDS, CISTI, GNLM, IDS, IE, Infotrieve, ingenta, Linda Hall. **CCC.**

Published by: Elsevier BV (Subsidiary of: Elsevier Science & Technology), Radarweg 29, Amsterdam, 1043 NX, Netherlands. TEL 31-20-4853911, FAX 31-20-4852457, nlinfo-f@elsevier.nl, http://www.elsevier.com/locate/geneanabioeng, http://www.elsevier.nl. Ed. Dr. Cassandra L Smith.

660.6 GBR ISSN 1065-612X
HD9999.B443 CODEN: BOPEEW

BIOPEOPLE. Text in English. 1992. q. USD 110 in US & Canada; JPY 12,200 in Japan; GBP 70 rest of world (effective 2003). adv. 3 cols./p.; back issues avail.; reprints avail. **Document type:** *Newsletter, Trade.* **Description:** Features the personalities behind the business and science of biotechnology.
—**CCC.**
Published by: P J B Publications Ltd. (Subsidiary of: T & F Informa plc), 5th Fl, Telephone House, 69-77 Paul Street, London, EC2A 4LQ, United Kingdom. TEL 44-20-70176979, FAX 44-20-70176969, info@pjbpubs.com, http://www.pjbpubs.com. Ed. Sukaina Virji. Pub. Dr. Philip Brown. R&P Annette Watts TEL 44-20-83328961. Adv. contact Peter Coltart TEL 44-20-83328802. B&W page USD 2,640, color page USD 4,334. **Subscr. in N. America:** Pharmabooks Ltd., 270 Madison Ave., # 4, New York, NY 10016-0601.

BIOPHOENIX DATABASE ON CD-ROM. see *MEDICAL SCIENCES*

BIOPHOTONICS INTERNATIONAL; photonic solutions for biotechnology and medicine. see *MEDICAL SCIENCES*

BIOPOLIMERY I KLETKA/BIOPOLYMERS AND CELL. see *BIOLOGY—Genetics*

620 DEU ISSN 1615-7591
TP248.3 CODEN: BBEIBV

➤ **BIOPROCESS AND BIOSYSTEMS ENGINEERING**; bioreactors, upstream and downstream processes, measurement and control. Text in English. 1986. bi-m. EUR 1,188 combined subscription to institutions print & online eds. (effective 2005). adv. back issues avail. **Document type:** *Journal, Academic/Scholarly.* **Description:** Devoted to engineering closely related to biotechnology and all technical and economic aspects of the processes in which natural or derived biological substances are the basic material.
Formerly (until 2000): Bioprocess Engineering (0178-515X)
Related titles: Online - full text ed.: ISSN 1615-7605 (from EBSCO Publishing, Springer LINK, Swets Information Services).
Indexed: AEBA, ASCA, ASFA, AgBio, Agr, BCI, BIOBASE, BIOSIS Prev, BioCN&I, BioDAb, BioEngAb, BiolAb, CBTA, CEABA, CIN, CMCI, ChemAb, ChemTitl, CurCont, DBA, DSA, ESPM, EngInd, ExcerpMed, HortAb, IABS, ISR, M&PBA, MSB, MaizeAb, PotatoAb, ProtozoAb, RA&MP, RPP, RevApplEntom, S&F, SCI, SIA, Telegen, VITIS, WAE&RSA, WeedAb.
—BLDSC (2089.474180), CASDDS, CISTI, Ei, IDS, IE, Infotrieve, ingenta. **CCC.**
Published by: Springer-Verlag (Subsidiary of: Springer Science+Business Media), Tiergartenstr 17, Heidelberg, 69121, Germany. TEL 49-6221-3450, FAX 49-6221-345229, http://link.springer.de/link/service/journals/00449/index.htm. Ed. Matthias Reuss. Adv. contact Stephan Kroeck TEL 49-30-827875739. B&W page EUR 600, color page EUR 1,640. Circ: 300 (paid). **Subscr. in the Americas to:** Springer-Verlag New York, Inc., Journal Fulfillment, PO Box 2485, Secaucus, NJ 07096-2485. TEL 800-777-4643, 201-348-4033, FAX 201-348-4505, journals@springer-ny.com, http://www.springer-ny.com; **Subscr. to:** Springer GmbH Auslieferungsgesellschaft, Haberstr 7, Heidelberg 69126, Germany. TEL 49-6221-345-0, FAX 49-6221-345-4229, subscriptions@springer.de.

660.6 USA ISSN 1538-8786
TP248.3

➤ **BIOPROCESSING**; advances and trends in biological product development. Text in English. 2002 (Mar.). bi-m. free to qualified personnel (effective 2005). adv. back issues avail. **Document type:** *Journal, Academic/Scholarly.* **Description:** Provides valuable information on industry trends, key people, and the technologies and services available from the industry's leading supplier companies.
—BLDSC (2089.474270), CISTI, IE.
Published by: The Williamsburg Bioprocessing Foundation, PO Box 1229, Virginia Beach, VA 23451. TEL 757-423-8823, FAX 757-423-2065, editor@bioprocessingjournal.com, wbf@wilbio.com, advertising@bioprocessingjournal.com, http://www.bioprocessingjournal.com, http://www.wilbio.com. Pub. Keith L. Carson. Adv. contact Manisha Trivedi.

➤ **BIOQUALITY.** see *PHARMACY AND PHARMACOLOGY*

333.8 NLD ISSN 0960-8524
TP360 CODEN: BIRTEB

➤ **BIORESOURCE TECHNOLOGY.** Text in English. 1979. 18/yr. EUR 2,710 in Europe to institutions; JPY 359,600 in Japan to institutions; USD 3,031 elsewhere to institutions; EUR 86 in Europe to qualified personnel; JPY 11,500 in Japan to qualified personnel; USD 97 elsewhere to qualified personnel (effective 2006). adv. bk.rev. charts; illus. back issues avail. **Document type:** *Journal, Academic/Scholarly.* **Description:** Publishes original papers, review articles, case studies and other material for the professional in the fundamentals, applications and management of bioresource technology.
Incorporates (1981-1991): Biomass (0144-4565); Which incorporated (1981-1988): Energy in Agriculture (0167-5826); Former titles (until 1991): Biological Wastes (0269-7483); (until 1987): Agricultural Wastes (0141-4607)
Related titles: Online - full text ed.: (from EBSCO Publishing, Gale Group, IngentaConnect, ScienceDirect, Swets Information Services).
Indexed: ABIPC, AEA, AEBA, AESIS, AIT, ASCA, ASFA, AgBio, Agr, AgrForAb, AnBrAb, B&BAb, BCI, BIOBASE, BIOSIS Prev, BibAg, BioCN&I, BioDAb, BioEngAb, BiolAb, CBTA, CIN, CPA, CTFA, ChemAb, ChemTitl, CurCont, DBA, DSA, EIA, EPB, ESPM, EnerInd, EnerRev, EngInd, EnvAb, EnvEAb, ExcerpMed, FCA, FLUIDEX, FPA, FS&TA, ForAb, GEOBASE, GasAb, HelmAb, HerbAb, HortAb, I&DA, IABS, ISMEC, ISR, IndMed, IndVet, Inspec, MEDLINE, MSCI, MaizeAb, NemAb, NutrAb, OrnHort, PBA, PGrRegA, PHN&I, PN&I, PollutAb, PotatoAb, PoultAb, ProtozoAb, RA&MP, RDA, RM&VM, RPP, RRTA, RevApplEntom, RiceAb, S&F, S&MA, SCI, SFA, SIA, SSCI, SWRA, SeedAb, SoyAb, TDB, TOSA, TriticAb, VITIS, VetBull, WAE&RSA, WRCInf, WTA, WasteInfo, WeedAb, WildRev, ZooRec.
—BLDSC (2089.495000), CASDDS, CINDOC, CISTI, Ei, IDS, IE, Infotrieve, ingenta, Linda Hall. **CCC.**
Published by: Elsevier BV (Subsidiary of: Elsevier Science & Technology), Radarweg 29, Amsterdam, 1043 NX, Netherlands. TEL 31-20-4853911, FAX 31-20-4852457, nlinfo-f@elsevier.nl, http://www.elsevier.com/locate/biortech, http://www.elsevier.nl. Ed. S C Ricke. **Co-sponsors:** Biomass and Biofuels Association, UK; Biomass Energy Research Association, US.

660.6029 USA ISSN 0887-6207
HD9999.B44

BIOSCAN; the worldwide biotech industry reporting service. Text in English. 1986. bi-m. looseleaf. USD 1,597 for print or online or CD-ROM eds.; USD 532 newsstand/cover (effective 2006). **Document type:** *Directory, Academic/Scholarly.* **Description:** Provides information on more than 1,800 biotechnology companies worldwide. Includes company name, address, phone numbers and names of officers, research & development activities, joint ventures, products, information on corporate financial history, investments, and mergers.
Incorporates (1995-1997): Agri - BioScan
Related titles: CD-ROM ed.; Diskette ed.; Online - full text ed.
—CISTI.
Published by: Thomson American Health Consultants, Inc. (Subsidiary of: Thomson Corporation, Healthcare Information Group), 3525 Piedmont Rd, N E, Bldg 6, Ste 400, Atlanta, GA 30305. TEL 404-262-5511, FAX 404-262-7837, customerservice@ahcpub.com, http://www.ahcpub.com. Pub. Phyllis Steckler. R&P Betsy Durkin.

660.6 572 JPN ISSN 0916-8451
QH345 CODEN: BBBIEJ

➤ **BIOSCIENCE, BIOTECHNOLOGY, AND BIOCHEMISTRY.** Text in English. 1924. m. USD 360 to non-members; USD 100 to members (effective 2005). adv. **Document type:** *Journal, Academic/Scholarly.* **Description:** Publishes original papers and reviews in the fields of bioscience, biotechnology and biochemistry.
Formerly (until 1992): Agricultural and Biological Chemistry (0002-1369); (until 1960): Agricultural Chemical Society of Japan. Journal (0375-8397)
Related titles: Online - full text ed.: ISSN 1347-6947. 2001. free (effective 2005) (from J-Stage); ♦ Japanese ed.: Nippon Nogeikagaku Kaishi. ISSN 0002-1407.
Indexed: AEA, AEBA, ASCA, ASFA, AbHyg, AgBio, AgrForAb, AnBrAb, AnalAb, ApicAb, B&AI, B&BAb, BBCI, BCI, BIOBASE, BIOSIS Prev, BioCN&I, BioDAb, BioEngAb, BiolAb, CBTA, CCI, CEABA, CIN, CPA, CTFA, ChemAb, ChemTitl, ChemoAb, CurCont, DBA, DSA, EIA, ESPM, EnerInd, EnvAb, ExcerpMed, FCA, FPA, FS&TA, FaBeAb, ForAb, GenetAb, HGA, HelmAb, HerbAb, HortAb, I&DA, IABS, ISR, IndMed, IndVet, M&PBA, MBA, MEDLINE, MOS, MSB, MaizeAb, NPU, NSCI, NemAb, NutrAb, OrnHort, PBA, PGegResA, PGrRegA, PHN&I, PN&I, PlantSci, PotatoAb, PoultAb, ProtozoAb, RA&MP, RCI, RM&VM, RPP, RRTA, RefZh, RevApplEntom, RiceAb, S&F, S&MA, SCI, SFA, SIA, SSCI, SWRA, SeedAb, SoyAb, TDB, Telegen, TriticAb, VITIS, VetBull, WAE&RSA, WeedAb, WildRev.
—BLDSC (2089.611470), CASDDS, CINDOC, CISTI, GNLM, IDS, IE, Infotrieve, ingenta, KNAW, Linda Hall. **CCC.**
Published by: Japan Society for Bioscience Biotechnology and Agrochemistry/Nippon Nogeikagaku Kai, Gakkai Center Bldg, 2-4-16 Yayoi, Bunkyo-ku, Tokyo, 113-0032, Japan. TEL 81-3-38118789, FAX 81-3-38151920, henshu@jsbba.or.jp, http://www.jstage.jst.go.jp/browse/bbb/-char/en, http://www.jsbba.or.jp/. Ed. Isomaro Yamagushi. Circ: 3,000.
Dist. by: Japan Publications Trading Co., Ltd., Book Export II Dept, PO Box 5030, Tokyo International, Tokyo 101-3191, Japan. TEL 81-3-32923753, FAX 81-3-32920410, infoserials@jptco.co.jp, http://www.jptco.co.jp; Maruzen Co., Ltd., Import & Export Dept, PO Box 5050, Tokyo International, Tokyo 100-3191, Japan. TEL 81-3-32733234, FAX 81-3-32716076.

600 USA ISSN 1538-7135
RC88.9.T47

▼ ➤ **BIOSECURITY AND BIOTERRORISM**; biodefense strategy, practice and science. Text in English. 2003. q. USD 450 domestic to institutions; USD 541 foreign to institutions; USD 494 combined subscription domestic to institutions print & online eds.; USD 618 combined subscription foreign to institutions print & online eds. (effective 2006). adv. **Document type:** *Journal, Academic/Scholarly.* **Description:** Covers bioscience, medical and public health response, infrastructure and institutions, international collaboration, food safety, and citizen response and responsibility. It provides a forum for debate and exploration. It will play a role in establishing educational efforts and interaction on issues of research, policy, prevention, and preparedness.
Related titles: Online - full text ed.: ISSN 1557-850X. 2003. USD 396 to institutions (effective 2006) (from EBSCO Publishing, Gale Group, O C L C Online Computer Library Center, Inc., Swets Information Services).
Indexed: B&BAb, BioEngAb, ChemoAb, CurCont, ESPM, H&SSA, RiskAb, SSCI.
—BLDSC (2089.611880), IE, ingenta. **CCC.**
Published by: Mary Ann Liebert, Inc. Publishers, 140 Huguenot St 3rd Fl, New Rochelle, NY 10801-5215. TEL 914-740-2100, FAX 914-740-2101, info@liebertpub.com, http://www.liebertpub.com/BSP. Eds. Dr. Tara O'Toole, Dr. Thomas V Inglesby. adv.: B&W page USD 1,260; trim 8.5 x 11. Circ: 2,000 (paid).

660.6 GBR ISSN 0956-5663
R857.B54 CODEN: BBIOE4

➤ **BIOSENSORS AND BIOELECTRONICS.** Text in English. 1985. 12/yr. EUR 1,535 in Europe to institutions; JPY 203,800 in Japan to institutions; USD 1,717 to institutions except Europe and Japan (effective 2006). adv. bk.rev. charts; illus. index. back issues avail. **Document type:** *Journal, Academic/Scholarly.* **Description:** Covers research, technology and applications of biosensors and the exploitation of biochemicals in electronic devices.
Formerly (until 1989): Biosensors (0265-928X)
Related titles: Online - full text ed.: (from EBSCO Publishing, Gale Group, IngentaConnect, ScienceDirect, Swets Information Services).
Indexed: AEA, ASCA, ASFA, AbHyg, AgBio, Agr, AnBrAb, AnalAb, B&BAb, BBCI, BCI, BIOBASE, BIOSIS Prev, BioEngAb, BiolAb, C&ISA, CBTA, CCI, CEABA, CIN, CPA, ChemAb, ChemTitl, ChemoAb, CurCont, DBA, DSA, E&CAJ, ESPM, EngInd, EnvAb, ExcerpMed, FCA, HelmAb, HortAb, IABS, ISR, IndMed, IndVet, Inspec, M&PBA, MEDLINE, MSB, NemAb, NutrAb, PBA, PGegResA, PHN&I, PN&I, PotatoAb, PoultAb, ProtozoAb, RA&MP, RM&VM, RPP, RefZh, RevApplEntom, S&F, SCI, SIA, SolStAb, Telegen, VITIS, VetBull, WAE&RSA, WeedAb.
—BLDSC (2089.611910), AskIEEE, CASDDS, CISTI, Ei, GNLM, IDS, IE, Infotrieve, ingenta, Linda Hall. **CCC.**
Published by: Pergamon (Subsidiary of: Elsevier Science & Technology), The Boulevard, Langford Ln, East Park, Kidlington, Oxford OX5 1GB, United Kingdom. TEL 44-1865-843000, FAX 44-1865-843010, http://www.elsevier.com/locate/bios. Ed. A P F Turner. **Subscr. to:** Elsevier BV, PO Box 211, Amsterdam 1000 AE, Netherlands. TEL 31-20-485-3757, FAX 31-20-485-3432, nlinfo-f@elsevier.nl, http://www.elsevier.nl.

660.6 DEU ISSN 0937-2725
CODEN: BWGEE9

➤ **BIOTEC.** Text in German. 1989. bi-m. EUR 38 domestic; EUR 62 foreign; EUR 9 newsstand/cover (effective 2005). adv. **Document type:** *Magazine, Trade.*
—BLDSC (2089.732200), IE, ingenta. **CCC.**
Published by: Vereinigte Fachverlage GmbH, Lise-Meitner-Str 2, Mainz, 55129, Germany. TEL 49-6131-9920, FAX 49-6131-992100, info@vfmz.de, http://www.industrie-service.de. adv.: B&W page EUR 3,350, color page EUR 4,580. Circ: 11,670 (paid and controlled).

620 USA

BIOTECH BRIEF. Text in English. bi-m. USD 97 domestic; USD 106 in US & Canada; USD 116 elsewhere (effective 2003).
Formerly: Biotech Week (1045-1404)
Related titles: Online - full text ed.: (from Gale Group, O C L C Online Computer Library Center, Inc.).
Published by: Life Sciences Documentation, 6114 Lasalle Ave., Ste 408, Oakland, CA 94611-2802. TEL 510-251-9493, wick@netcom.com. Ed., Pub. Potter Wickware.

B

▼ *new title* ➤ *refereed* ✶ *unverified* ♦ *full entry avail.*

660.6 USA ISSN 0899-5702
BIOTECH BUSINESS. Text in English. 1988. m. USD 150 in North America; USD 165 elsewhere (effective 2001). pat.
Document type: *Newsletter, Trade.* **Description:** Focuses on the latest fast-breaking developments in the technology and business of biotechnology. Provides news on patents, international business deals, licensing agreements, and developments in human, animal, and plant genetic engineering.
Related titles: Online - full text ed.: (from bigchalk, Data-Star, EBSCO Publishing, Factiva, Florida Center for Library Automation, Gale Group, LexisNexis, ProQuest Information & Learning, The Dialog Corporation).
Indexed: ABIn.
—CCC.
Published by: Worldwide Videotex, PO Box 3273, Boynton Beach, FL 33424-3273. TEL 561-738-2276, markedit@juno.com, http://www.wvpubs.com. Ed., Pub. Mark Wright.

B

660.6 USA ISSN 1543-687X
▼ **BIOTECH BUSINESS WEEK.** Text in English. 2003. w. USD 2,329 in US & Canada; USD 2,529 elsewhere; USD 2,529 combined subscription in US & Canada for print & online eds.; USD 2,729 combined subscription elsewhere for print & online eds. (effective 2003). **Document type:** *Journal, Trade.*
Description: Contains news and information from pharmaceutical and biotechnology companies with a focus on business trends and analysis.
Related titles: Online - full text ed.: ISSN 1543-6861. USD 1,629 (effective 2003) (from Factiva, LexisNexis, ProQuest Information & Learning).
Published by: NewsRx, PO Box 5528, Atlanta, GA 31107-0528. TEL 800-726-4550, FAX 303-290-9025, info@newsrx.com, http://www.newsrx.net/welcome_680.cgi, http://www.newsrx.com.

660.6 681 USA
BIOTECH EQUIPMENT UPDATE. Text in English. m. USD 150 in North Africa; USD 165 elsewhere (effective 2001). **Document type:** *Newsletter, Trade.* **Description:** Covers news and the latest information about biotechnology laboratory and manufacturing equipment and products.
Related titles: Online - full text ed.
Published by: Worldwide Videotex, PO Box 3273, Boynton Beach, FL 33424-3273. TEL 561-738-2276, markedit@juno.com, http://www.wvpubs.com. Ed., Pub., R&P Mark Wright.

660.6 332 USA
BIOTECH FINANCIAL REPORTS. Text in English. 1992. m. looseleaf. USD 150 in North America; USD 165 elsewhere (effective 2001). pat. back issues avail. **Document type:** *Newsletter, Trade.*
Related titles: E-mail ed.; Online - full text ed.
Published by: Worldwide Videotex, PO Box 3273, Boynton Beach, FL 33424-3273. TEL 561-738-2276, markedit@juno.com, http://www.wvpubs.com. Ed., Pub., R&P Mark Wright.

BIOTECH LAW WEEKLY. see *LAW*

330 660.6 340 USA
BIOTECH MARKET NEWS & LEGAL STRATEGIES. Text in English. 1985. m. USD 322 (effective 1998). **Document type:** *Newsletter.*
Former titles (until 2001): BioTech Market News and Strategies (0740-1221); (until 1983): Biotechnology Marketing Strategies
Published by: Chandler Publishing Ltd., PO Box 11155, Ft. Lauderdale, FL 33339. TEL 954-522-4344, FAX 954-522-7750. Ed. Edward J Chandler. Circ: 15,000.

660 DNK ISSN 1603-9939
▼ ➤ **BIOTECH MEDICAL**; skandinavisk tidsskrift for bioteknologi. Text in Danish. 2005. bi-m. **Document type:** *Journal, Academic/Scholarly.* **Description:** Focus on Danish biotech research.
Published by: Scanpublisher A-S, Emiliekildevej 35, Klampenborg, 2930, Denmark. TEL 45-39-908000, FAX 45-39-908280, info@scanpublisher.dk, http://www.scanpublisher.dk. Ed. Birger Pedersen TEL 45-39-908000.

➤ **BIOTECH NAVIGATOR.** see *BUSINESS AND ECONOMICS—Investments*

660.6 USA ISSN 1535-5470
BIOTECH NEWS INTERNATIONAL. Text in English. bi-m.
Description: Contains the latest news and applications in the various specialties that make up the biotechnology and life sciences research field worldwide.
Formerly: Biotech Lab International (1091-725X)
Published by: Globetech Publishing, 8 Cannon Rd, Wilton, CT 06897. TEL 203-762-3432, FAX 203-762-8640.

660.6 USA ISSN 0898-2813
BIOTECH PATENT NEWS. Text in English. 1987. m. **Description:** Provides updates on the latest events in the world of patented biotechnology.
Related titles: Online - full text ed.: (from Factiva, Gale Group, O C L C Online Computer Library Center, Inc.).
—BLDSC (2089.745000).
Address: PO Box 4482, Metuchen, NJ 08840. biotech@biotechpatent.com, http://www.biotechpatent.com/, http://biotechpatent.com.

660.6 USA ISSN 1532-1320
TP248.175
BIOTECH PATENT REPORT. Text in English. 2000. bi-m.
Description: Provides information about new laws, rules, regulations and guidelines concerning biotechnology patents and the text of CAFC biotechnology patent litigation.
Published by: Biotech Patent News, PO Box 4482, Metuchen, NJ 08840. biotech@biotechpatent.com, http://biotechpatent.com.

BIOTECH-REPORT. see *BUSINESS AND ECONOMICS—Investments*

660.6 330 NZL
BIOTECH UNLIMITED. Text in English. 2002 (Nov.). q. **Document type:** *Magazine, Academic/Scholarly.* **Description:** Focuses on the business of New Zealand biosciences.
Published by: I D G Communications Ltd., Wellesley St., PO Box 6813, Auckland, 1036, New Zealand. TEL 64-9-377-9902, FAX 64-9-377-4604, idg@idg.co.nz, http://www.idg.net.nz. Ed., Pub. Vincent Heeringa. **Co-sponsors:** Bell Gully; SolNet/Sun; Industry New Zealand.

BIOTECH UPDATE (MIAMI BEACH). see *BUSINESS AND ECONOMICS*

660.6 USA ISSN 1535-5284
BIOTECH WATCH. Text in English. d. USD 1,005 in United States (effective 2005 - 2006).
Media: Online - full text (from The Bureau of National Affairs, Inc.).
—CCC.
Published by: The Bureau of National Affairs, Inc., 1231 25th St., NW, Washington, DC 20037. TEL 800-372-1033, http://www.bna.com. **Subscr. to:** 9435 Key West Ave, Rockville, MD 20850.

660.6 USA ISSN 1535-2757
BIOTECH WEEK. Text in English. 1988. w. USD 1,459 (effective 2002). **Description:** Covers news highlights from all CW Henderson newsweeklies and includes cross-reference information for further investigation.
Related titles: Online - full text ed.: (from ProQuest Information & Learning).
Published by: NewsRx, PO Box 5528, Atlanta, GA 31107-0528. TEL 800-726-4550, FAX 303-290-9025, info@newsrx.com, http://www.cwhorders.com, http://www.newsrx.com.

BIOTECHNIC AND HISTOCHEMISTRY; a journal for microtechnic and histochemistry. see *BIOLOGY—Microscopy*

660.6 USA ISSN 0736-6205
QH324 CODEN: BTNQDO
➤ **BIOTECHNIQUES**; the journal of laboratory technology for bioresearch. Text in English. 1983. 12/yr. free to qualified personnel. adv. bk.rev. back issues avail.; reprints avail.
Document type: *Journal, Academic/Scholarly.*
Related titles: Online - full text ed.: (from EBSCO Publishing); Regional ed(s).: BioTechniques (Euro Edition).
Indexed: ASCA, AgBio, Agr, AnBrAb, BBCI, BCI, BIOBASE, BIOSIS Prev, BioCN&I, BiolAb, CCI, CIN, CPA, CTA, ChemAb, ChemTitl, CurCont, DBA, EngInd, ExcerpMed, FS&TA, ForAb, HortAb, IABS, INIS AtomInd, ISR, IndMed, IndVet, Inpharma, MEDLINE, NemAb, PBA, PE&ON, ProtozoAb, RPP, Reac, RefZh, RevApplEntom, S&F, SCI, SFA, SeedAb, Telegen, TriticAb, VetBull, WeedAb.
—BLDSC (2089.820000), CASDDS, CISTI, Ei, GNLM, IDS, IE, Infotrieve, ingenta, Linda Hall. **CCC.**
Published by: Eaton Publishing Co., One Research Dr, Suite 400A, PO Box 1070, Westboro, MA 01581. TEL 508-655-8282, FAX 508-655-9910, bioeditor@biotechniques.com, http://www.biotechniques.com. Ed., R&P James Ellingboe. Pub. Frank Eaton. Adv. contact Esta Campbell. Circ: 60,000 (controlled).

660.6 POL ISSN 0860-7796
BIOTECHNOLOGIA; przeglad informacyjny. Text in Polish. 1988. q. **Document type:** *Journal, Academic/Scholarly.*
Indexed: AgrAg, AgrLib.
Published by: (Polska Akademia Nauk, Instytut Chemii Bioorganicznej), Polska Akademia Nauk, Komitet Biotechnologii, Centrum Badan Molekularnych i Makromolekularnych, ul H Sienkiewicza 112, Lodz, 90363, Poland. TEL 48-42-6819744, FAX 48-42-6815483, okruszek@bio.cbmm.lodz.pl. Ed. Tomasz Twardowski TEL 48-61-8528503.

DAS BIOTECHNOLOGIE JAHR- UND ADRESSBUCH. see *BUSINESS AND ECONOMICS—Trade And Industrial Directories*

660.6 PAK ISSN 1682-296X
➤ **BIOTECHNOLOGY.** Text in English. 2002. q. USD 350 (effective 2005). **Document type:** *Journal, Academic/Scholarly.* **Description:** Subjects covered include: agricultural biotechnology, environmental biotechnology, applied immunology, genomics, molecular engineering, gene therapy and tissue engineering.
Related titles: Online - full text ed.: ISSN 1682-2978. 2004. free (effective 2005).
Indexed: C&ISA, E&CAJ, FCA, IAA.
Published by: Asian Network for Scientific Information, 308-Lasani Town, Sargodha Rd, Faisalabad, 38090, Pakistan. TEL 92-41-2001145, FAX 92-41-731433, http://www.ansinet.org/c4p.php?j_id=biotech.

660.6 610.28 USA ISSN 0734-9750
TP248.2 CODEN: BIADDD
➤ **BIOTECHNOLOGY ADVANCES.** Text in English. 1983. 6/yr. EUR 1,427 in Europe to institutions; JPY 189,300 in Japan to institutions; USD 1,595 elsewhere to institutions (effective 2006). pat.; abstr. back issues avail. **Document type:** *Journal, Academic/Scholarly.* **Description:** Covers all aspects of biotechnology, including relevant developments in the related disciplines of biology, chemistry, and engineering.
Related titles: Microfilm ed.: (from PQC); Online - full text ed.: (from EBSCO Publishing, Gale Group, IngentaConnect, ScienceDirect, Swets Information Services).
Indexed: AEBA, ASCA, ASFA, AbHyg, AgBio, Agr, AgrForAb, BCI, BIOBASE, BIOSIS Prev, BibAg, BioCN&I, BioDAb, BioEngAb, CBTA, CCI, CIN, CPA, CTA, ChemAb, ChemTitl, CurCont, DBA, DSA, ESPM, EngInd, FCA, FPA, ForAb, GEOBASE, HortAb, I&DA, IABS, ISR, IndVet, M&PBA, MBA, NSA, NemAb, NutrAb, OrnHort, P&BA, PBA, PGegResA, PGrRegA, PHN&I, PollutAb, PoultAb, RA&MP, RPP, RefZh, RevApplEntom, RiceAb, S&F, SCI, SIA, SeedAb, SoyAb, TDB, Telegen, TriticAb, WAE&RSA, WeedAb.
—BLDSC (2089.845000), CASDDS, CISTI, Ei, GNLM, IDS, IE, Infotrieve, ingenta, Linda Hall. **CCC.**
Published by: Elsevier Inc. (Subsidiary of: Elsevier Science & Technology), 360 Park Ave. S, New York, NY 10010-1710. TEL 212-633-3730, 888-437-4636, usinfo-f@elsevier.com, http://www.elsevier.com/locate/biotechadv. Ed. M Moo-Young.

660.6 612.015 GBR ISSN 0885-4513
QP501 CODEN: BABIEC
➤ **BIOTECHNOLOGY AND APPLIED BIOCHEMISTRY.** Text in English. 1979. bi-m. GBP 216.06, EUR 350, USD 390 combined subscription print & online (effective 2005). adv. index. back issues avail. **Document type:** *Journal, Academic/Scholarly.* **Description:** Publication of articles concerning expression, purification, characterization and application of biological macromolecules in therapeutics and diagnostics with medical, dental and veterinary applications.
Formerly: Journal of Applied Biochemistry (0161-7354)
Related titles: CD-ROM ed.; Online - full text ed.: ISSN 1470-8744. GBP 209.15, USD 335, EUR 305 to institutions (effective 2005) (from EBSCO Publishing, Swets Information Services).
Indexed: ABIPC, AEBA, AS&TI, ASCA, ASFA, AbHyg, AgBio, Agr, AnBrAb, BBCI, BCI, BIOBASE, BIOSIS Prev, BioCN&I, BioDAb, BioEngAb, BiolAb, CBTA, CCI, CEABA, CIN, CLL, CPA, ChemAb, ChemTitl, CurCont, DBA, DSA, ESPM, EngInd, ExcerpMed, FCA, FPA, FS&TA, ForAb, HortAb, IABS, ISR, IndMed, IndVet, Inpharma, M&PBA, MBA, MEDLINE, MSB, MaizeAb, NutrAb, PBA, PE&ON, PGrRegA, PN&I, PotatoAb, ProtozoAb, RA&MP, RM&VM, RPP, Reac, RevApplEntom, S&F, SCI, SIA, SoyAb, TDB, TTI, VetBull.
—BLDSC (2089.848000), CASDDS, CINDOC, CISTI, Ei, GNLM, IDS, IE, Infotrieve, ingenta, Linda Hall. **CCC.**
Published by: (International Union of Biochemistry and Molecular Biology USA), Portland Press Ltd. (Subsidiary of: Biochemical Society), 3rd Fl, Eagle House, 16 Procter St, London, WC1V 6NX, United Kingdom. TEL 44-20-72804110, FAX 44-20-72804169, sales@portland-services.com, editorial@portlandpress.com, http://www.babonline.org, http://www.portlandpress.com. Ed. P Shamlou. R&P Adam Marshall. Circ: 600. **Subscr. to:** Commerce Way, Colchester CO2 8HP, United Kingdom. TEL 44-1206-796351, FAX 44-1206-799331.

660.6 USA ISSN 0006-3592
QH324 CODEN: BIBIAU
➤ **BIOTECHNOLOGY AND BIOENGINEERING.** Text in English. 1958. 18/yr. USD 5,995 domestic to institutions; USD 6,211 in Canada & Mexico to institutions; USD 6,337 elsewhere to institutions; USD 6,595 combined subscription domestic to institutions print & online eds.; USD 6,811 combined subscription in Canada & Mexico to institutions print & online eds.; USD 6,937 combined subscription elsewhere to institutions print & online eds. (effective 2006). adv. bibl.; charts; illus. index. back issues avail.; reprints avail.
Document type: *Journal, Academic/Scholarly.* **Description:** Presents original research on all aspects of biochemical and microbial technology.
Related titles: CD-ROM ed.: (from The Dialog Corporation); Microform ed.: (from PQC); Online - full content ed.: ISSN 1097-0290. USD 5,995 to institutions (effective 2006); Online - full text ed.: (from EBSCO Publishing, Swets Information Services, Wiley InterScience); ◆ Series: Combinatorial Chemistry. ISSN 1464-3383.
Indexed: ABIPC, AEA, AEBA, AESIS, ASCA, ASFA, AbHyg, AgBio, Agr, AgrForAb, AnBrAb, AnalAb, B&AI, B&BAb, BCI, BIOBASE, BIOSIS Prev, BioCN&I, BioDAb, BioEngAb, BiolAb, C&ISA, CBTA, CCI, CEA, CEABA, CIN, CPA, ChemAb, ChemTitl, CivEngAb, CurCont, DBA, DSA, E&CAJ, EIA, ESPM, EnerInd, EngInd, EnvEAb, ExcerpMed, FCA, FPA, FS&TA, ForAb, GasAb, HelmAb, HerbAb, HortAb, I&DA, IABS, IAOP, ISR, IndMed, IndVet, Inpharma, M&PBA, M&TEA,

MBA, MEDLINE, MSB, MSCI, MaizeAb, NemAb, NutrAb, OrnHort, PBA, PGegResA, PGrRegA, PN&I, PollutAb, PotatoAb, PoultAb, RA&MP, RM&VM, RPP, Reac, RefZh, RevApplEntom, RiceAb, S&F, S&MA, SCI, SIA, SJW, SWRA, SeedAb, SolStAb, SoyAb, TCEA, TDB, TriticAb, VITIS, VetBull, WAE&RSA, WRCInf, WeedAb.
—BLDSC (2089.850000), CASDDS, CISTI, Ei, GNLM, IDS, IE, Infotrieve, ingenta, Linda Hall. **CCC.**
Published by: John Wiley & Sons, Inc., 111 River St, Hoboken, NJ 07030-5774. TEL 800-825-7550, FAX 201-748-5915, uscs-wis@wiley.com, http://www3.interscience.wiley.com/cgi-bin/jhome/71002188, http://www.wiley.com. Ed. Douglas S Clark. adv.: B&W page GBP 640, color page GBP 1,515. Circ: 1,700. **Subscr. addr. outside the Americans:** John Wiley & Sons Ltd., The Atrium, Southern Gate, Chichester, West Sussex PO19 8SQ, United Kingdom. TEL 44-1243-843335, 0800-243407, FAX 44-1243-843232, cs-journals@wiley.co.uk.

➤ **BIOTECHNOLOGY & BIOENGINEERING ABSTRACTS.** see *CHEMISTRY—Abstracting, Bibliographies, Statistics*

660.6 GBR ISSN 1360-4791
TP248.195.G7
BIOTECHNOLOGY AND BIOLOGICAL SCIENCES RESEARCH COUNCIL. ANNUAL REPORT. Text in English. a. **Document type:** *Academic/Scholarly.*
—Linda Hall.
Published by: Biotechnology and Biological Sciences Research Council, Polaris House, N Star Ave, Swindon, Wilts SN2 1UH, United Kingdom. TEL 44-1793-413200, FAX 44-1793-413201, http://www.bbsrc.ac.uk.

660.6 GBR
BIOTECHNOLOGY AND BIOLOGICAL SCIENCES RESEARCH COUNCIL. STRATEGIC PLAN. Text in English. irreg. **Document type:** *Corporate.*
Formerly: Biotechnology and Biological Sciences Research Council. Corporate Plan
—BLDSC (8474.031513).
Published by: Biotechnology and Biological Sciences Research Council, Polaris House, N Star Ave, Swindon, Wilts SN2 1UH, United Kingdom. TEL 44-1793-413200, FAX 44-1793-413201, http://www.bbsrc.ac.uk.

660.6 KOR ISSN 1226-8372
CODEN: BBEIAU
BIOTECHNOLOGY AND BIOPROCESS ENGINEERING. Text in English. 1996. bi-m. USD 60 to individuals; USD 240 to libraries (effective 2003). **Document type:** *Journal, Academic/Scholarly.* **Description:** Contains research articles, notes and reviews that report new and significant findings that advance the understanding of applied biology & biochemistry, molecular biology & biomolecular engineering, biocatalysis & biotransformation, combinatorial chemistry, microbiology & metabolic engineering, pharmaceutics & biomaterials, bioprocess control & system engineering, bioseparation, biosensor & bioelectronics, cell culture engineering, environmental biotechnology, food technology, and nanobiotechnology.
Indexed: BCI, ChemAb, ExcerpMed.
—BLDSC (2089.860302), IE.
Published by: Korean Society for Biotechnology and Bioengineering/Han'gug Saengmul Gonghaghoe, Korea Science and Technology Center #704, Yeogsam-dong, Kangnam-ku, Seoul, 135-703, Korea, S. ksbbhome@unitel.co.kr, http://bbe.or.kr/ksbb_bbe/index.asp. Eds. Nam Chang Ho, Yong Choi Cha.

660.6 572.43 BGR ISSN 1310-2818
➤ **BIOTECHNOLOGY AND BIOTECHNOLOGICAL EQUIPMENT**; international scientific-theoretical and applied publication. Text in English. 1984. 3/yr. EUR 95 foreign to individual members; BGL 185 domestic to institutional members; EUR 210 foreign to institutional members (effective 2004). adv. abstr.; illus. 220 p./no.; back issues avail. **Document type:** *Journal, Academic/Scholarly.* **Description:** Contains reviews, original papers and short communications.
Related titles: CD-ROM ed.; Diskette ed.; E-mail ed.; Fax ed.
Indexed: BCI, RefZh, VITIS.
—BLDSC, ingenta.
Published by: Diagnosis Press Ltd., 5 Malusba Str, Sofia, 1164, Bulgaria. TEL 359-2-9632302, diagnosis@ibn.bg, http://www.diagnosisp.com. Ed. Dr. Atanas Ivanov Atanassov Sr. R&P, Adv. contact Mrs. Snejana Krasteva Pavlova. Circ: 250 (paid); 250 (controlled). **Co-publisher:** Bulgarian Oncological Society.

663.1 NLD ISSN 0924-9877
➤ **BIOTECHNOLOGY AND DEVELOPMENT MONITOR.** Text in English. 1989. q. free. **Document type:** *Journal, Academic/Scholarly.* **Description:** Analyzes worldwide developments in biotechnology, and trade and technology related international regulation, in the context of its socio-economic implications for developing countries.
Related titles: Online - full text ed.: free (effective 2005).
Indexed: AgBio, AnBrAb, BCI, BioCN&I, FCA, ForAb, HortAb, MaizeAb, NutrAb, PBA, PGegResA, PotatoAb, RDA, RPP, RiceAb, S&F, SIA, SeedAb, SoyAb, TriticAb, WAE&RSA, WeedAb.
—BLDSC (2089.860350), IE, ingenta.
Address: Wibautstraat 224, Amsterdam, 1097 DN, Netherlands. TEL 31-20-5618163, FAX 31-20-5618164, monitor@biotech-monitor.nl, http://www.biotech-monitor.nl. Ed. Bert Ernste.

660.6 610 GBR ISSN 0264-8725
TP248.13 CODEN: BGERES
➤ **BIOTECHNOLOGY AND GENETIC ENGINEERING REVIEWS.** Text in English. 1984. a. GBP 110, EUR 187 (effective Jun. 2005). index. back issues avail. **Document type:** *Journal, Academic/Scholarly.* **Description:** Contains original major review articles covering important developments in industrial, agricultural and medical applications of biotechnology, with particular emphasis on the generic manipulation of the organisms concerned.
Indexed: ASCA, AbHyg, AgBio, Agr, B&AI, BCI, BIOBASE, BIOSIS Prev, BiolAb, CBTA, CIN, CPA, ChemAb, ChemTitl, CurCont, DBA, DSA, EngInd, ExcerpMed, FCA, ForAb, HortAb, IABS, ISR, IndMed, IndVet, MEDLINE, MaizeAb, PBA, PlantSci, PotatoAb, RiceAb, SCI, Telegen, TriticAb, VITIS, VetBull, WeedAb.
—BLDSC (2089.860500), CASDDS, CISTI, Ei, GNLM, IE, Infotrieve, ingenta, KNAW, Linda Hall. **CCC.**
Published by: Intercept Ltd, PO Box 716, Andover, Hants SP10 1YG, United Kingdom. TEL 44-1264-334748, FAX 44-1264-334058, intercept@andover.co.uk, http://www.intercept.co.uk/gb/rechrev.html. Ed. Stephen Harding. Circ: 300. **Subscr. to:** Extenza - Turpin, Pegasus Dr, Stratton Business Park, Biggleswade, Beds SG18 8TQ, United Kingdom. TEL 44-4767-604875, FAX 44-1767-601640, custservturpin @turpinltd.com.

660.6 NLD ISSN 1387-2656
TP248.13 CODEN: BAREFD
➤ **BIOTECHNOLOGY ANNUAL REVIEW.** Text in English. 1995. a., latest vol.8, 2002. price varies. illus. **Document type:** *Academic/Scholarly.* **Description:** Reviews developments in biotechnology, including technical advances and applications in medicine, agriculture, marine biology, industry, bioremediation and the environment.
Related titles: Online - full text ed.: (from ScienceDirect).
Indexed: AgBio, AnBrAb, B&BAb, BioCN&I, BioEngAb, CIN, ChemAb, ChemTitl, ExcerpMed, IndMed, IndVet, NutrAb, PBA, RPP, RevApplEntom, WAE&RSA.
—BLDSC (2089.860650), IE, ingenta.
Published by: Elsevier BV (Subsidiary of: Elsevier Science & Technology), Radarweg 29, Amsterdam, 1043 NX, Netherlands. TEL 31-20-4853911, FAX 31-20-4852457, nlinfo-f@elsevier.nl, http://www.elsevier.nl. Ed. M Raafat El-Gewely.

660.6 USA
BIOTECHNOLOGY AT WORK SERIES. Text in English. irreg., latest vol.10, 1992. **Document type:** *Monographic series.* **Description:** Covers the latest developments of biotechnology in the environmental, agricultural and medical fields.
Published by: Biotechnology Industry Organization, 1225 I (Eye) St N W, Ste 400, Washington, DC 20005-5958. TEL 202-857-0244, FAX 202-857-0237, info@bio.org, http://www.bio.org, http://www.bio.org/. R&P Dan Eramian.

BIOTECHNOLOGY CITATION INDEX. see *BIOLOGY—Abstracting, Bibliographies, Statistics*

660.607 GBR ISSN 0955-6621
TP248.13 CODEN: BIEDEY
➤ **BIOTECHNOLOGY EDUCATION.** Text in English. 1990. 4/yr. GBP 75 (effective 1993). back issues avail. **Document type:** *Academic/Scholarly.* **Description:** Resource for teachers and students in the biological sciences.
Related titles: Microfilm ed.: (from PQC).
Indexed: CIN, ChemAb, ChemTitl.
—CASDDS. **CCC.**
Published by: Helix Publishing, 1 Howard Ct, 94-96 Blackheath Hill, Greenwich, London, SE10 8AF, United Kingdom. Ed. Paul Wymer.

570 660.6 USA
BIOTECHNOLOGY GUIDE U.S.A. Text in English. 1989. a. USD 249 (effective 1998). **Document type:** *Academic/Scholarly.* **Description:** Profiles over 1,300 companies active in biotechnology, lists venture capital firms, and analyzes the biotechnology industry.
Published by: Institute for Biotechnology Information, c/o Mark Dibner, Pres., Box 14569, Research Triangle Park, NC 27709-4569. TEL 919-544-5111, FAX 919-544-5401, ibi@mindspring.com, http://www.biotechinfo.com.

660.6 USA ISSN 1052-6153
CODEN: BHANE3
BIOTECHNOLOGY HANDBOOKS. Text in English. 1987. irreg., latest vol.10, 1999. price varies. **Document type:** *Monographic series, Academic/Scholarly.*
Indexed: Agr, BIOSIS Prev, CIN, ChemAb, ChemTitl.
—BLDSC (2089.861590), CASDDS, CISTI, ingenta. **CCC.**
Published by: Springer-Verlag New York, Inc. (Subsidiary of: Springer Science+Business Media), 233 Spring St, New York, NY 10013. TEL 212-460-1500, FAX 212-460-1575, service@springer-ny.com, http://www.springer-ny.com. Eds. Anthony Atkinson, Roger F Sherwood. **Dist. by:** Journal Fulfillment, PO Box 2485, Secaucus, NJ 07096-2485.

353.997280971 USA
▼ **BIOTECHNOLOGY HEALTHCARE.** Text in English. 2004. bi-m. USD 80; USD 12 newsstand/cover (effective 2005). **Document type:** *Magazine, Trade.* **Description:** Provides a guide for decision makers in the rapidly evolving biotechnology products market.
Related titles: Online - full text ed.
Published by: MediMedia USA, Inc. (Subsidiary of: United Business Media plc), 780 Township Line Rd, Yardley, PA 19067. TEL 267-685-2300, 800-969-7237, FAX 267-685-2951, info@medimedia.com, http://www.biotechnologyhealthcare.com, http://www.medimedia.com. Ed. Dr. David Nash.

660.6 630 USA ISSN 0934-943X
CODEN: BAFOEG
BIOTECHNOLOGY IN AGRICULTURE AND FORESTRY. Text in English. 1986. irreg., latest vol.54, 2004. price varies. reprint service avail. from ISI. **Document type:** *Monographic series, Academic/Scholarly.* **Description:** Links basic and applied research, providing literature and the information on plant tissue culture, genetic engineering, molecular biology, plant breeding and horticulture.
Indexed: Agr, BIOSIS Prev, CIN, ChemAb, ChemTitl, VITIS.
—BLDSC (2089.847000), CASDDS, CISTI, IE, ingenta. **CCC.**
Published by: Springer-Verlag New York, Inc. (Subsidiary of: Springer Science+Business Media), 233 Spring St, New York, NY 10013. TEL 212-460-1500, 800-777-4643, FAX 212-473-6272, http://www.springer-ny.com.

660.6 630 GBR ISSN 0960-202X
CODEN: BIAGEN
BIOTECHNOLOGY IN AGRICULTURE SERIES. Text in English. 1990. irreg. price varies. **Document type:** *Monographic series, Academic/Scholarly.*
Indexed: Agr, BIOSIS Prev.
—BLDSC (2089.847300), IE, ingenta. **CCC.**
Published by: Oxford University Press, Great Clarendon St, Oxford, OX2 6DP, United Kingdom. TEL 44-1865-556767, FAX 44-1865-556646, enquiry@oup.co.uk, http://www.us.oup.com/us/catalog/general/series/BiotechnologyinAgricultureSeries/?view=usa, http://www.oup.co.uk/.

660.6 615.1 USA ISSN 1074-6072
HD9666.1
BIOTECHNOLOGY IN THE U.S. PHARMACEUTICAL INDUSTRY. Text in English. 1995. a. USD 279 (effective 1998). **Document type:** *Academic/Scholarly.*
Published by: Institute for Biotechnology Information, c/o Mark Dibner, Pres., Box 14569, Research Triangle Park, NC 27709-4569. TEL 919-544-5111, FAX 919-544-5401, ibi@mindspring.com, http://www.biotechinfo.com.

BIOTECHNOLOGY INDUSTRY GUIDE. see *BIOLOGY*

BIOTECHNOLOGY INFORMATION. see *BIOLOGY—Abstracting, Bibliographies, Statistics*

660.6029 GBR ISSN 1369-4278
BIOTECHNOLOGY INTERNATIONAL YEARBOOK (YEAR)✶. Text in English. a. GBP 185, USD 296. adv. **Description:** Lists top companies in the biotechnology industry. Gives main products, company analysis and financial details.
Published by: Cartermill Publishing (Subsidiary of: Financial Times Professional), Maple House, 149 Tottenham Ct Rd, London, W1P 9LL, United Kingdom. TEL 44-20-7896-2424, lizg@pearson-pro.com, http://www.fthealthcare.com.

BIOTECHNOLOGY INVESTOR'S FORUM. see *BUSINESS AND ECONOMICS—Investments*

660.6 DEU ISSN 1860-6768
▼ **BIOTECHNOLOGY JOURNAL.** Text in English. forthcoming 2006. m. **Document type:** *Journal, Academic/Scholarly.*
Related titles: Online - full text ed.: ISSN 1860-7314. forthcoming.
Published by: Wiley - V C H Verlag GmbH & Co. KGaA (Subsidiary of: John Wiley & Sons, Inc.), Boschstr 12, Weinheim, 69469, Germany. TEL 49-6201-6060, FAX 49-6201-606328, info@wiley-vch.de, http://www.vchgroup.de.

343.0786606 USA ISSN 0730-031X
KF3827.G4 CODEN: BLREEL
➤ **BIOTECHNOLOGY LAW REPORT.** Text in English. 1982. bi-m. USD 1,834 domestic to institutions; USD 2,084 foreign to institutions; USD 2,193 combined subscription domestic to institutions print & online eds.; USD 2,443 combined subscription foreign to institutions print & online eds. (effective 2006). adv. bk.rev. back issues avail.; reprint service avail. from PSC. **Document type:** *Journal, Academic/Scholarly.* **Description:** Includes papers by leading international experts and up-to-date information on legal issues related to biotechnology.
Related titles: Online - full text ed.: ISSN 1557-8704. USD 1,732 to institutions (effective 2006) (from EBSCO Publishing, Gale Group, O C L C Online Computer Library Center, Inc., Swets Information Services).
Indexed: ABC, ASCA, ArtHuCI, BCI, CBTA, SSCI, Telegen.
—IDS, IE, Infotrieve. **CCC.**

Published by: Mary Ann Liebert, Inc. Publishers, 140 Huguenot St 3rd Fl, New Rochelle, NY 10801-5215. TEL 914-740-2100, FAX 914-740-2101, elman@elman.com, info@liebertpub.com, http://www.liebertpub.com/blr. Ed. Gerry J Elman. Pub. Patricia Hogan. Adv. contact Katherine Cane TEL 914-834-3689. B&W page USD 1,000; trim 8.5 x 11. Circ: 1,000 (paid).

660.6 NLD ISSN 0141-5492
QR53 CODEN: BILED3
➤ **BIOTECHNOLOGY LETTERS.** Text in Dutch. 1979. s-m. EUR 2,528, USD 2,568, GBP 1,668 combined subscription to institutions print & online eds. (effective 2005). adv. abstr.; bibl.; charts; illus. reprint service avail. from PSC. **Document type:** *Journal, Academic/Scholarly.* **Description:** Covers topics relating to actual or potential applications of biological reactions effected by microbial, plant, or animal cells and derived bio-catalysts.
Incorporates (1987-2000): Biotechnology Techniques (0951-208X)
Related titles: Online - full text ed.: ISSN 1573-6776. USD 2,568 (effective 2005) (from EBSCO Publishing, Gale Group, IngentaConnect, Kluwer Online, O C L C Online Computer Library Center, Inc., Springer LINK, Swets Information Services).
Indexed: AEA, AEBA, AESIS, ASCA, ASFA, AbHyg, AgBio, Agr, AgrForAb, AnBrAb, BCI, BIOBASE, BIOSIS Prev, BibAg, BibLing, BioCN&I, BioDAb, BioEngAb, BiolAb, CBTA, CCI, CEABA, CIN, CPA, CTFA, ChemAb, ChemTitl, CurCont, DBA, DSA, EIA, ESPM, EnvAb, EnvEAb, ExcerpMed, FCA, FPA, FS&TA, ForAb, HelmAb, HerbAb, HortAb, I&DA, IABS, ISR, IndVet, Inpharma, M&PBA, MBA, MaizeAb, NemAb, NutrAb, OrnHort, PBA, PGegResA, PGrRegA, PHN&I, PN&I, PollutAb, PotatoAb, PoultAb, ProtozoAb, RA&MP, RCI, RM&VM, RPP, Reac, RefZh, RevApplEntom, RiceAb, S&F, SCI, SFA, SIA, SeedAb, SoyAb, TDB, Telegen, TriticAb, VITIS, VetBull, WeedAb.
—BLDSC (2089.863000), CASDDS, CIS, CISTI, GNLM, IDS, IE, Infotrieve, ingenta, Linda Hall. **CCC.**
Published by: Springer-Verlag Dordrecht (Subsidiary of: Springer Science+Business Media), Van Godewijckstraat 30, Dordrecht, 3311 GX, Netherlands. TEL 31-78-6576050, FAX 31-78-6576474, http://springerlink.metapress.com/openurl.asp?genre=journal&issn=0141-5492, http://www.springeronline.com. Ed. Colin Ratledge.

660.6 USA ISSN 0273-3226
CODEN: BINWEY
BIOTECHNOLOGY NEWS. Text in English. 1981. 30/yr. USD 743 in US & Canada; USD 775 elsewhere (effective 2005). bk.rev. tr.lit. index. back issues avail. **Document type:** *Newsletter.* **Description:** Written for executives in the biotechnology industry. Covers company news, regulatory changes, financial trends, technical developments, market analyses and patents.
Related titles: Supplement(s): Bioindustry Directory; Pharma Industry Directory.
Indexed: Agr, CBTA, CEABA, CIN, ChemAb, ChemTitl.
—BLDSC (2089.867000), CASDDS, CISTI. **CCC.**
Published by: C T B International Publishing Inc., PO Box 218, Maplewood, NJ 07040-0218. TEL 973-966-0997, FAX 973-966-0242, info@ctbintl.com, http://www.ctbintl.com. Eds. Beth Kearny, Christopher Brogna. Pub. Oykue Brogna. R&P Christopher Brogna.

660.6 USA
BIOTECHNOLOGY NEWS' BIOINDUSTRY DIRECTORY. Text in English. a. **Document type:** *Directory.*
Published by: C T B International Publishing Inc., PO Box 218, Maplewood, NJ 07040-0218. TEL 973-379-7749, FAX 973-379-1158.

660.6 USA ISSN 8756-7938
TP248.13 CODEN: BIPRET
BIOTECHNOLOGY PROGRESS. Text in English. 1985. bi-m. USD 998 in North America to institutions; USD 1,043 elsewhere to institutions; USD 108 in North America to members; USD 153 elsewhere to members; USD 81 in North America to students; USD 126 elsewhere to students (effective 2006). adv. bibl.; charts; illus. index. back issues avail.; reprint service avail. from PQC. **Document type:** *Magazine, Trade.* **Description:** Reports developments and research results impacting the food, pharmaceutical and bioengineering fields.
Related titles: Microform ed.: (from PQC); Online - full text ed.: ISSN 1520-6033. USD 70 (effective 2006) (from EBSCO Publishing, Swets Information Services).
Indexed: AEA, AEBA, AESIS, AS&TI, ASCA, ASFA, AbHyg, AgBio, Agr, AgrForAb, B&BAb, BCI, BIOBASE, BIOSIS Prev, BioCN&I, BioEngAb, BiolAb, CBTA, CCI, CEABA, CIN, CPA, ChemAb, ChemTitl, CivEngAb, CurCont, DBA, DSA, ESPM, EngInd, EnvAb, EnvEAb, FCA, FPA, FS&TA, ForAb, GenetAb, HelmAb, HortAb, IABS, ISMEC, ISR, IndMed, IndVet, Inpharma, M&PBA, MBA, MEDLINE, MaizeAb, NemAb, NutrAb, OrnHort, PBA, PGegResA, PGrRegA, PHN&I, PN&I, PlantSci, PollutAb, PotatoAb, PoultAb, ProtozoAb, RA&MP, RM&VM, RPP, Reac, RefZh, RevApplEntom, RiceAb, S&F, SCI, SIA, SWRA, SeedAb, SoyAb, TDB, TTI, Telegen, TriticAb, VITIS, VetBull, WeedAb.
—BLDSC (2089.868330), CASDDS, CINDOC, CISTI, Ei, GNLM, IDS, IE, Infotrieve, ingenta, Linda Hall. **CCC.**
Published by: (American Institute of Chemical Engineers), American Chemical Society, 1155 16th St, N W, Washington, DC 20036. TEL 202-872-4614, 800-227-5558, FAX 202-776-8264, steps@alche.org, service@acs.org, http://pubs.acs.org/bp. Ed. Debora A Bittaker. adv.: page USD 1,940. Circ: 2,800. **Subscr. to:** Member & Subscriber Services, PO Box 3337, Columbus, OH 43210. TEL 614-447-3776, 800-333-9511, FAX 614-447-3671.

660.6 GBR
BIOTECHNOLOGY RESEARCH SERIES. Text in English. 1992. irreg. price varies. **Document type:** *Monographic series.*
Formerly: Plant and Microbial Biotechnology Research Series
Indexed: CIN, ChemAb, ChemTitl.
—BLDSC.
Published by: Cambridge University Press, The Edinburgh Bldg, Shaftesbury Rd, Cambridge, CB2 2RU, United Kingdom. TEL 44-1223-312393, FAX 44-1223-315052, information@cambridge.org, http://publishing.cambridge.org/series/pmbr. R&P Linda Nicol TEL 44-1223-325757.

660.6 GBR ISSN 0740-7378
BIOTECHNOLOGY SERIES. Text in English. 1982. irreg.
—CISTI.
Published by: Butterworth - Heinemann (Subsidiary of: Elsevier Ltd., Books Division), Linacre House, Jordan Hill, Oxford, OX2 8DP, United Kingdom. TEL 44-1865-310366, FAX 44-1865-310898, http://www.bh.com.

660.6 USA
BIOTECHNOLOGY STATE OF THE INDUSTRY REPORT. Text in English. 1993. a. USD 429 domestic; USD 459 foreign (effective 2001). **Document type:** *Trade.* **Description:** Covers market trends and technical developments in the biotechnology industry.
Published by: Thomson American Health Consultants, Inc. (Subsidiary of: Thomson Corporation, Healthcare Information Group), 3525 Piedmont Rd, N E, Bldg 6, Ste 400, Atlanta, GA 30305. TEL 404-262-5511, FAX 404-262-7837, customerservice@ahcpub.com, http://www.ahcpub.com.

660.6 CUB ISSN 0864-4551
CODEN: BTAPEP
➤ **BIOTECNOLOGIA APLICADA.** Text in Spanish, English. 1984. q. USD 60 to individuals; USD 75 to institutions (effective 2002). adv. index. back issues avail. **Document type:** *Academic/Scholarly.* **Description:** Offers original papers on all fields of modern biotechnology.
Formerly (until 1990): Interferon y Biotecnologia (0258-9222)
Related titles: CD-ROM ed.; Online - full text ed.: ISSN 1027-2852. 1995. USD 30 to individuals; USD 42 to institutions (effective 2000) (from EBSCO Publishing).
Indexed: AEBA, BIOBASE, BIOSIS Prev, BioEngAb, BiolAb, CBTA, ChemAb, DBA, ESPM, ExcerpMed, IABS, M&PBA, MBA, MSB.
—CINDOC, CISTI, GNLM.
Published by: (Iberian - Latin - American Society of Biotechnology Applied to Health), Elfos Scientiae, Ave 31 entre 158 y 190, Cubanacan, Playa, PO Box 6072, Havana, 10600, Cuba. elfos.scientiae@cigb.edu.cu, http://www.elfosscientiae.com. Ed., R&P Guillermo J Padron. Pub. Manuel Limonta. Adv. contact Guillermo J Padrone. color page USD 1,000; trim 11 x 8.5. Circ: 2,500. **Subscr. to:** EBSCO Mexico, SA de CV, Ensenada 91, Col. Hipodromo Condesa, Mexico, DF 06170, Mexico.

➤ **BIOTECNOLOGIA VEGETAL.** see *BIOLOGY—Botany*

660.6 ITA ISSN 1720-0350
BIOTECNOLOGIE 2000. Text in English. 2001. bi-m. EUR 20 (effective 2005).
Related titles: Online - full text ed.: ISSN 1720-1713.
Published by: Morgan Edizioni Tecniche Srl, Viale Zara 9, Milan, MI 20124, Italy. TEL 39-02-69001227, FAX 39-02-69001229, http://www.biotecnologie2000.com.

660.6 610.28 RUS ISSN 0234-2758
TP248.13 CODEN: BTKNEZ
➤ **BIOTEKHNOLOGIYA.** Text in Russian; Summaries in English. 1984. bi-m. USD 192 foreign (effective 2005). adv. cum.index: 1985-1995. back issues avail. **Document type:** *Journal, Academic/Scholarly.* **Description:** Presents papers and reviews on biotechnology and bioengineering.
Related titles: Diskette ed.
Indexed: AEA, AbHyg, AgBio, AnBrAb, BIOSIS Prev, BioCN&I, BiolAb, CEABA, CIN, CPA, ChemAb, ChemTitl, DSA, FCA, FPA, ForAb, HerbAb, HortAb, IndVet, MaizeAb, NemAb, NutrAb, OrnHort, PBA, PGegResA, PGrRegA, PHN&I, PN&I, PotatoAb, PoultAb, RA&MP, RM&VM, RPP, RefZh, RevApplEntom, RiceAb, S&F, SIA, SeedAb, TDB, TriticAb, VetBull, WeedAb.
—BLDSC (0017.999000), CASDDS. **CCC.**
Published by: (G N I I Genetika, State Scientific Research Institute for Genetics and Selection of Industrial Microorganisms), Izdatel'stvo Nauka, Profsoyuznaya ul 90, Moscow, 117864, Russian Federation. TEL 7-095-3347151, FAX 7-095-4202220, boss@genetika.ru, secret@naukaran.ru, http://www.maik.rssi.ru/cgi-bin/journal.pl?name=biotech&page=main, http://www.naukaran.ru. Ed. V G Debabov. adv.: page RUR 15,000, page USD 500; trim 220 x 160. Circ: 600. **Dist. by:** East View Information Services, 3020 Harbor Ln. N., Minneapolis, MN 55447. TEL 800-477-1005, FAX 800-800-3839, eastview@eastview.com, http://www.eastview.com.

616 JPN ISSN 0914-2223
CODEN: BITPE9
➤ **BIOTHERAPY.** Text in Japanese; Summaries in English. 1987. bi-m. JPY 12,000 (effective 2003). adv. bk.rev. back issues avail. **Document type:** *Journal, Academic/Scholarly.* **Description:** Covers immunology, molecular biology, cytology and gene therapy. Focuses especially on biological response modifiers. Serves as the official journal of the Society.
Related titles: Microfilm ed.
Indexed: BiolAb, ExcerpMed, INIS AtomInd.
—BLDSC (2089.873900), GNLM, IE, ingenta.
Published by: (Biological Response Modifiers Society), Japanese Journal of Cancer and Chemotherapy Publishers Inc., Risshu Bldg. 2/F, 2-2-3 Nihonbashi, Chuo-ku, Tokyo, 103-0027, Japan. TEL 81-3-32780052, FAX 81-3-32810435. Ed., Pub. Tetsuo Taguchi. Adv. contact Katsuko Watanabe. Circ: 2,000 (paid).

660.6 CHE ISSN 1660-8984
▼ ➤ **BIOVALLEY MONOGRAPHS.** Text in English. 2005. irreg., latest vol.2, 2005. price varies. **Document type:** *Monographic series, Academic/Scholarly.* **Description:** Aims to promote cooperation between pharmaceutical companies, research institutions and universities, to support the foundation of start-up companies, and to encourage communication among representatives from science, economics, politics and the general public in relation to life sciences.
Published by: S. Karger AG, Allschwilerstr 10, Basel, 4009, Switzerland. TEL 41-61-3061111, FAX 41-61-3061234, karger@karger.ch, http://www.karger.ch. Ed. P Poindron.

660.6 GBR ISSN 0892-1903
CODEN: BIVIEW
BIOVENTURE VIEW. Text in English. 1986. s-m. EUR 800 in Europe print or online ed.; USD 940 in US & Canada print or online ed.; JPY 117,000 in Japan print or online ed.; GBP 484 elsewhere print or online ed. (effective 2005). adv. 3 cols./p.; back issues avail.; reprints avail. **Document type:** *Newsletter, Trade.* **Description:** Offers analysis of the companies, products, and events that drive the multibillion-dollar biotechnology industry.
Related titles: E-mail ed.: EUR 705 in Europe; USD 755 in US & Canada; JPY 117 in Japan; GBP 484 elsewhere (effective 2005); delivered in PDF format; Online - full text ed.: (from CompuServe Inc., Data-Star, Factiva, Gale Group, Northern Light Technology, Inc.).
Indexed: Agr, RefZh.
—BLDSC (2090.100000). **CCC.**
Published by: P J B Publications Ltd. (Subsidiary of: T & F Informa plc), 5th Fl, Telephone House, 69-77 Paul Street, London, EC2A 4LQ, United Kingdom. TEL 44-20-70176979, FAX 44-20-70176969, info@pjbpubs.com, http://www.pjbpubs.com/bioventure_view/index.htm. Ed. Michelle Grayson TEL 44-20-70176904. Pub. Dr. Philip Brown. Adv. contact Jason Douglas TEL 212-262-8230. B&W page USD 900; trim 11 x 8.5. Circ: 327 (paid). **Subscr. addr. in N America:** Pharmabooks Ltd., 270 Madison Ave., # 4, New York, NY 10016-0601.

660.6 610.28 CRI ISSN 0255-7924
BOLETIN DE BIOTECNOLOGIA. Text in Spanish. 1984. q. free. bk.rev.
Published by: Consejo Nacional para Investigaciones Cientificas y Tecnologicas, Apdo. 10318-1000, Zapote, San Jose, Costa Rica. TEL 506-224-4172, FAX 506-225-7041, info@www.conicit.go.cr, http://www.conicit.go.cr. Circ: 1,500.

570 660.6 BRA ISSN 1516-8913
QH301 CODEN: ABTTAP
➤ **BRAZILIAN ARCHIVES OF BIOLOGY AND TECHNOLOGY;** an international journal. Text mainly in English; Abstracts in Portuguese. 1946. q. BRL 130 domestic; USD 130 elsewhere (effective 2005). adv. abstr.; bibl.; charts; illus.; stat. 120 p./no.; back issues avail. **Document type:** *Magazine, Academic/Scholarly.* **Description:** Presents original research on biological sciences, agriculture and food technology.
Formerly (until 1997): Arquivos de Biologia e Tecnologia (0365-0979)
Related titles: Microform ed.: (from PQC); Online - full text ed.: free (effective 2005) (from SciELO).
Indexed: AEA, ASCA, ASFA, AbHyg, AgBio, AgrForAb, AnBrAb, BIOSIS Prev, BioCN&I, BioDAb, BiolAb, CIN, CPA, ChemAb, ChemTitl, CurCont, DSA, ESPM, ExcerpMed, FCA, FPA, FS&TA, ForAb, HelmAb, HerbAb, HortAb, I&DA, IndMed, IndVet, MaizeAb, NemAb, NutrAb, OrnHort, PBA, PGegResA, PGrRegA, PHN&I, PN&I, PotatoAb, PoultAb, RA&MP, RM&VM, RPP, RefZh, RevApplEntom, RiceAb, S&F, SIA, SWRA, SeedAb, SoyAb, TDB, TriticAb, VetBull, WeedAb, ZooRec.

—BLDSC (2277.287000), CASDDS, CISTI, IDS, IE, ingenta, Linda Hall.
Published by: Instituto de Tecnologia do Parana, Rua Professor Algacyr Munhoz Mader, 3775, C Industrial, Curitiba, PR 81350-010, Brazil. TEL 55-41-3163053, FAX 55-41-2450844, niet@tecpar.br, http://www.tecpar.br. Ed. Carlos R Soccol. Pub., R&P, Adv. contact Ana Cristina Francisco TEL 55-41-3462872. B&W page USD 500; 8 x 13. Circ: 230 (paid); 70 (controlled).

660.6 CAN ISSN 1711-0114
SB494.5.B563
C F I A'S BIOTECHNOLOGY HIGHLIGHTS REPORT. Text in English. 2002. a. **Document type:** *Government.*
Related titles: Online - full content ed.
Published by: Canadian Food Inspection Agency, 59 Camelot Dr, Ottawa, ON K1A 0Y9, Canada. TEL 613-225-2342, 800-442-2342, FAX 613-228-6125, cfiamaster@inspection.gc.ca, http://www.inspection.gc.ca.

C S A AGRICULTURAL & ENVIRONMENTAL BIOTECHNOLOGY ABSTRACTS. see *AGRICULTURE—Abstracting, Bibliographies, Statistics*

660.6 GBR ISSN 0957-0330
CODEN: CSBIED
CAMBRIDGE STUDIES IN BIOTECHNOLOGY. Text in English. 1985. irreg. price varies. **Document type:** *Monographic series.*
Indexed: BIOSIS Prev, FS&TA.
—BLDSC (3015.992500), CISTI.
Published by: Cambridge University Press, The Edinburgh Bldg, Shaftesbury Rd, Cambridge, CB2 2RU, United Kingdom. TEL 44-1223-312393, FAX 44-1223-315052, information@cambridge.org, http://publishing.cambridge.org/series/csb. R&P Linda Nicol TEL 44-1223-325757.

660.6 CAN ISSN 1188-455X
CANADIAN BIOTECH NEWS. Text in English. 1988. 52/yr. CND 500, USD 425 (effective 1999). adv. bk.rev. back issues avail. **Document type:** *Newsletter.* **Description:** Covers economics and finance in biotechnology. Includes information on company developments, patents and technology transfer.
Incorporates (in 1997): Intron - Canadian Molecular Biology; Formerly (until vol.4, no.10): New Biotech Business (0838-5777)
Related titles: E-mail ed.; Microfiche ed.: (from MML).
Indexed: CBCARef, CBPI.
—CISTI.
Published by: Canadian Biotechnology News Service, 20 Stonepark Lane, Nepean, ON K2H 9P4, Canada. TEL 613-726-0115, FAX 613-726-7344, http://www.faxon.ca/publishers/subscripton-rates.html. Ed. Peter Winter. Adv. contact Carole Winter. Circ: 3,000.

660.6 CAN
CANADIAN BIOTECH RESEARCH. Text in English. 1996. m. CND 120, USD 180 (effective 1999). **Document type:** *Trade.* **Description:** Provides articles and news on the application of biotech research to various sections. Principle focus is the health care, but applications of biotechnology to agriculture and the environment are also covered.
Published by: Canadian Biotechnology News Service, 20 Stonepark Lane, Nepean, ON K2H 9P4, Canada. TEL 613-726-0115, FAX 613-726-7344, pwinter@netcom.ca, http://www.faxon.ca/publishers/subscription-rates.html. Ed. Peter Winter. Circ: 3,000 (controlled).

CANADIAN BIOTECHNOLOGY. see *BUSINESS AND ECONOMICS—Trade And Industrial Directories*

660.6 CAN ISSN 1497-8741
TP248.195.C2
CANADIAN BIOTECHNOLOGY ADVISORY COMMITTEE. ANNUAL REPORT. Text in Multiple languages. 2000. a. back issues avail.
Related titles: Online - full text ed.: ISSN 1497-9969. 2000.
Published by: Canadian Biotechnology Advisory Committee, 240 Sparks St 5th Fl, West Tower Ste 561E, Ottawa, ON K1A OH5, Canada. TEL 613-954-7059, FAX 613-946-2847, info@cbac-ccb.ca, http://cbac-cccb.ic.gc.ca/epic/internet/incbac-cccb.nsf/en/h_ah00037e.html, http://www.cbac-ccb.ca/.

CELL TRANSPLANTATION. see *BIOLOGY—Cytology And Histology*

CEREVISIA (EDITION BILINGUE); Belgian journal of brewing and biotechnology. see *BEVERAGES*

CHEMISTRY & INDUSTRY. see *CHEMISTRY*

▼ **CHINESE JOURNAL OF AGRICULTURAL BIOTECHNOLOGY.** see *AGRICULTURE*

620 CHN ISSN 1672-3678
▼ ➤ **CHINESE JOURNAL OF BIOPROCESS ENGINEERING.** Text in English. 2003. q. USD 150 (effective 2003). **Document type:** *Journal, Academic/Scholarly.* **Description:** Features original reports of recent experimental results and descriptions of new technologies in biological engineering.
Indexed: AEBA, B&BAb, BioEngAb, ESPM.
Address: 200 N Zhongshan Rd, PO Box 54, Nanjing University of Technology, Nanjing, 210009, China. TEL 86-25-3239983, FAX 86-25-3412316, shengwu@njut.edu.cn. Ed. Lu Zhixin.

➤ **CLONING AND STEM CELLS.** see *BIOLOGY—Genetics*

➤ **COMLINE: BIOTECHNOLOGY AND MEDICAL INDUSTRY OF JAPAN.** see *MEDICAL SCIENCES*

660.6 BEL ISSN 1379-1176
S5 CODEN: MFLRA3
COMMUNICATIONS IN AGRICULTURAL AND APPLIED BIOLOGICAL SCIENCES. Text and summaries in English. 1933. q. **Document type:** *Bulletin, Academic/Scholarly.*
Former titles (until 2002): Universiteit Gent. Faculteit van de Landbouwkundige en Toegepaste Biologische Wetenschappen. Mededelingen (1373-7503); (until 1970): Rijksuniversiteit Gent. Faculteit Landbouwwetenschappen. Mededelingen (0368-9697); (until 1970): Rijksfaculteit Landbouwwetenschappen te Gent. Mededelingen (0369-1721); (until 1966): Mededelingen van de Landbouwhogeschool en de Opzoekingsstations van de Staat te Gent (0369-0695); Incorporates (1949-1962): Rijkslandbouwhogeschool Gent. Laboratorium voor Houttechnologie. Mededelingen (0369-0660)
Related titles: ♦ Includes: International Symposium on Crop Protection. Proceedings.
Indexed: AEA, AbHyg, AgBio, AgrForAb, Agrind, AnBrAb, BIOSIS Prev, BioCN&I, BiolAb, CIN, CPA, CTFA, ChemAb, ChemTitl, DBA, DSA, ExcerpMed, FCA, FPA, FS&TA, ForAb, HelmAb, HerbAb, HortAb, I&DA, IndMed, IndVet, MaizeAb, NemAb, NutrAb, OrnHort, PBA, PGegResA, PGrRegA, PHN&I, PN&I, PotatoAb, PoultAb, RA&MP, RDA, RM&VM, RPP, RRTA, RevApplEntom, RiceAb, S&F, S&MA, SIA, SeedAb, SoyAb, TDB, TriticAb, VITIS, VetBull, WAE&RSA, WeedAb, ZooRec.
—BLDSC (3359.185000), CASDDS, CISTI, IE, Linda Hall.
Published by: Universiteit Gent, Faculteit van de Landbouwkundige en Toegepaste Biologische Wetenschappen, Coupure Links 653, Gent, 9000, Belgium. TEL 32-9-2645902, FAX 32-9-2646245. Ed. O Van Cleemput. Circ: 300.

660.6 USA ISSN 0738-8551
TP248.13 CODEN: CRBTE5
➤ **CRITICAL REVIEWS IN BIOTECHNOLOGY.** Text in English. 1983. q. USD 744, GBP 450 combined subscription to institutions print & online eds. (effective 2006). reprint service avail. from PSC. **Document type:** *Journal, Academic/Scholarly.* **Description:** Presents state-of-the-art review articles covering the spectrum of technologies involving the use of living organisms and biological processes in a wide range of industrial, agricultural, and medical applications.
Related titles: Online - full text ed.: ISSN 1549-7801. USD 707, GBP 428 to institutions (effective 2006) (from EBSCO Publishing, Gale Group, IngentaConnect, O C L C Online Computer Library Center, Inc., ProQuest Information & Learning, ScienceDirect, Swets Information Services).
Indexed: AEBA, AESIS, ASCA, ASFA, AbHyg, AgBio, Agr, AgrForAb, BCI, BIOBASE, BIOSIS Prev, BioEngAb, BrCerAb, C&ISA, CBTA, CIN, CPA, CerAb, ChemAb, ChemTitl, CorrAb, CurCont, DBA, DSA, E&CAJ, EMA, EPB, ESPM, EngInd, EntAb, ExcerpMed, FCA, FS&TA, ForAb, HortAb, IAA, IABS, INIS AtomInd, ISR, IndMed, M&PBA, M&TEA, MBA, MBF, MEDLINE, METADEX, MaizeAb, NutrAb, PBA, PHN&I, RA&MP, RPP, RefZh, RiceAb, S&F, SCI, SFA, SIA, SoyAb, WAA, WeedAb, WildRev.
—BLDSC (3487.472400), CASDDS, CISTI, GNLM, IDS, IE, Infotrieve, ingenta, Linda Hall. **CCC.**
Published by: Taylor & Francis Inc. (Subsidiary of: Taylor & Francis Group), 325 Chestnut St, Ste 800, Philadelphia, PA 19016. TEL 215-625-8900, 800-354-1420, FAX 215-625-2940, info@taylorandfrancis.com, http://www.tandf.co.uk/journals/titles/07388551.asp, http://www.taylorandfrancis.com. Eds. Graham Stewart, Inge Russell. **Subscr. outside N. America to:** Taylor & Francis Ltd, Journals Customer Service, Rankine Rd, Basingstoke, Hants RG24 8PR, United Kingdom. TEL 44-1256-813000, FAX 44-1256-330245, enquiry@tandf.co.uk.

➤ **CURRENT ADVANCES IN APPLIED MICROBIOLOGY & BIOTECHNOLOGY.** see *BIOLOGY—Abstracting, Bibliographies, Statistics*

➤ **CURRENT BIOTECHNOLOGY.** see *BIOLOGY—Abstracting, Bibliographies, Statistics*

➤ **CURRENT ISSUES IN MOLECULAR BIOLOGY.** see *BIOLOGY—Microbiology*

660.6 GBR ISSN 0958-1669
TP248.13 CODEN: CUOBE3
➤ **CURRENT OPINION IN BIOTECHNOLOGY.** Text in English. 1990. 6/yr. EUR 543 in Europe to individuals; JPY 65,800 in Japan to individuals; USD 589 to individuals except Europe and Japan; EUR 1,624 in Europe to institutions; JPY 225,300 in Japan to institutions; USD 1,816 to institutions except Europe and Japan (effective 2006). adv. bibl.; illus. back issues avail. **Document type:** *Academic/Scholarly.* **Description:** Presents review articles followed by annotated bibliographies for researchers and educators in biotechnology. Includes a "Paper Alert" section, giving brief summaries of relevant papers recently published in other journals.
Related titles: Online - full text ed.: (from EBSCO Publishing, Gale Group, IngentaConnect, O C L C Online Computer Library Center, Inc., ScienceDirect, Swets Information Services).
Indexed: AEA, AEBA, AESIS, ASCA, ASFA, AbHyg, AgBio, AnBrAb, B&BAb, BCI, BIOBASE, BIOSIS Prev, BioCN&I, BioEngAb, BiolAb, CCI, CEABA, CIN, CPA, ChemAb, ChemTitl, CivEngAb, CurCont, DSA, ESPM, EngInd, EnvEAb, ExcerpMed, FCA, FPA, ForAb, HerbAb, HortAb, IABS, IPA, ISR, IndMed, IndVet, Inpharma, M&PBA, MBA, MEDLINE, MSB, MaizeAb, NutrAb, PBA, PE&ON, PGegResA, PGrRegA, PollutAb, PoultAb, RA&MP, RPP, Reac, RevApplEntom, S&F, SCI, SIA, SWRA, SeedAb, SoyAb, TDB, VetBull, WAE&RSA, WeedAb.
—BLDSC (3500.772500), CASDDS, CISTI, Ei, GNLM, IDS, IE, Infotrieve, ingenta. **CCC.**
Published by: Elsevier Ltd., Current Opinion Journals (Subsidiary of: Elsevier Science & Technology), 84 Theobald's Rd., London, WC1X 8RR, United Kingdom. TEL 44-20-7611-4000, FAX 44-20-7611-4001, 44-20-7611-4468, http://www.elsevier.com/locate/copbio, http://www.current-opinion.com. Eds. Kenneth Timmis, Martin Rosenberg. Circ: 1,000.

660.6 338.476 NLD ISSN 1389-2010
CODEN: CPBUBP
➤ **CURRENT PHARMACEUTICAL BIOTECHNOLOGY.** Text in English. 2000 (Jun.). q. EUR 860, USD 860 to institutions (academic), print or online; EUR 1,550, USD 1,550 to corporations print or online; EUR 210, USD 210 combined subscription to individuals print & online; EUR 940, USD 940 combined subscription to institutions (academic), print & online; EUR 1,860, USD 1,860 combined subscription to corporations print & online (effective 2004). adv. **Document type:** *Journal, Academic/Scholarly.* **Description:** Features reviews in pharmaceutical biotechnology and related areas.
Related titles: Online - full text ed.: (from EBSCO Publishing, Gale Group, IngentaConnect, Swets Information Services).
Indexed: B&BAb, BCI, BIOSIS Prev, BioEngAb, CTA, ChemAb, ExcerpMed, M&PBA.
—BLDSC (3501.280450), CISTI, IE, Infotrieve, ingenta. **CCC.**
Published by: Bentham Science Publishers Ltd., PO Box 1673, Hilversum, BR 1200, Netherlands. TEL 31-35-6923800, FAX 31-35-6980150, M.Bentham@inter.nl.net, http://www.bentham.org/cpb. Ed. Alain Rolland. **Subscr. addr. in the US:** Bentham Science Publishers Ltd., 1400 Pine St, PO Box 640310, San Francisco, CA 94164-0310. FAX 415-775-4503, shidding@worldonline.nl.

581.2 NLD ISSN 0924-1949
CODEN: CPBAE2
➤ **CURRENT PLANT SCIENCE AND BIOTECHNOLOGY IN AGRICULTURE.** Text in Dutch. 1985. irreg., latest vol.41, 2005. price varies. back issues avail. **Document type:** *Monographic series, Academic/Scholarly.* **Description:** Scholarly monographs and conference papers reporting state of the art research findings and techniques in plant science and biotechnology, with particular emphasis on agricultural applications.
Indexed: Agr, BIOSIS Prev, CIN, ChemAb, ChemTitl.
—BLDSC (3501.284300), CASDDS, CISTI, IE, ingenta. **CCC.**
Published by: Springer-Verlag Dordrecht (Subsidiary of: Springer Science+Business Media), Van Godewijckstraat 30, Dordrecht, 3311 GX, Netherlands. TEL 31-78-6576050, FAX 31-78-6576474, http://www.springeronline.com. Ed. Peter Craufurd.

➤ **CYTOTECHNOLOGY;** international journal of cell culture and biotechnology. see *BIOLOGY—Cytology And Histology*

660.6 DEU ISSN 0934-3792
D E C H E M A BIOTECHNOLOGY CONFERENCES. Text in English. 1988. irreg. price varies. **Document type:** *Monographic series, Academic/Scholarly.*
—**CCC.**
Published by: D E C H E M A e.V., Theodor-Heuss-Allee 25, Frankfurt Am Main, 60486, Germany. TEL 49-69-7564349, FAX 49-69-7564201, forsyth@dechema.de, http://www.dechema.de.

DERWENT BIOTECHNOLOGY ABSTRACTS. see *BIOLOGY—Abstracting, Bibliographies, Statistics*

DEVELOPMENTS IN BIOLOGICALS. see *METROLOGY AND STANDARDIZATION*

610.285 660.6 NLD ISSN 0925-7640
DEVELOPMENTS IN BIOTHERAPY. Text in Dutch. 1991. irreg., latest vol.1, 1991. price varies. **Document type:** *Monographic series.*
Published by: Springer-Verlag Dordrecht (Subsidiary of: Springer Science+Business Media), Van Godewijckstraat 30, Dordrecht, 3311 GX, Netherlands. TEL 31-78-6576050, FAX 31-78-6576474, http://www.springeronline.com.

660.6 170 FRA ISSN 1257-0907
DICTIONNAIRE PERMANENT: BIOETHIQUE ET BIOTECHNOLOGIES. Text in French. 1995. 2 base vols. plus m. updates. looseleaf. EUR 385 base vol(s). (effective 2004). **Description:** Covers legal and business issues in bioethics and biotechnology.

B

Published by: Editions Legislatives, 80 Avenue de la Marne, Montrouge, Cedex 92546, France. TEL 33-1-40923636, FAX 33-1-40923663, infocom@editions-legislatives.fr, http://www.editions-legislatives.fr. Ed. Daniel Vigneau.

DIRECTORY OF AUSTRALIAN BIOTECHNOLOGY COMPANIES. see *BUSINESS AND ECONOMICS—Trade And Industrial Directories*

660.6025 570   USA
DIRECTORY OF BIOTECHNOLOGY CENTERS. Text in English. 1987. a. USD 79 (effective 1998). **Document type:** *Directory, Academic/Scholarly.* **Description:** Provides information on approximately 100 biotechnology centers in the United States. The directory is arranged alphabetically by state.
Published by: Institute for Biotechnology Information, c/o Mark Dibner, Pres., Box 14569, Research Triangle Park, NC 27709-4569. TEL 919-544-5111, FAX 919-544-5401, ibi@mindspring.com, http://www.biotechinfo.com.

660.6   USA   ISSN 1539-6509
► **DISCOVERY MEDICINE**; discovery class of medicine, research technology, and tools. Text in English. 2001. bi-m. USD 49.95 combined subscription domestic to individuals print & online eds.; USD 99.95 combined subscription foreign to individuals print & online eds.; USD 349 combined subscription domestic to institutions print & online eds.; USD 399 combined subscription elsewhere to institutions print & online eds. (effective 2005). **Document type:** *Journal, Academic/Scholarly.* **Description:** Summarizes significant findings, and the research technology used in the discoveries, from major biomedical journals.
Related titles: Ed. USD 39.95 to individuals; USD 499 to institutions (effective 2005).
Published by: Solariz, Inc., 57 W Timonium Rd, Ste 207, Timonium, MD 21093. TEL 410-252-3631, 800-515-4399, FAX 410-252-3634, service@discoverymedicine.com, http://www.discoverymedicine.com. Ed. Dr. Benjamin Yang. Pub. Dr. Peter H. Rheinstein. Adv. contact Dan Miller.

► **DRUG DISCOVERY TODAY.** see *PHARMACY AND PHARMACOLOGY*

▼ ► **DRUG DISCOVERY TODAY: DISEASE MECHANISMS.** see *PHARMACY AND PHARMACOLOGY*

▼ ► **DRUG DISCOVERY TODAY: DISEASE MODELS.** see *PHARMACY AND PHARMACOLOGY*

▼ ► **DRUG DISCOVERY TODAY: TECHNOLOGIES.** see *PHARMACY AND PHARMACOLOGY*

▼ ► **DRUG DISCOVERY TODAY: THERAPEUTIC STRATEGIES.** see *PHARMACY AND PHARMACOLOGY*

► **ECOLOGICAL ENGINEERING.** see *ENVIRONMENTAL STUDIES*

660.6   EGY   ISSN 1110-6093
EGYPTIAN JOURNAL OF BIOTECHNOLOGY/AL-MAGALLAT AL-MISRIYYAT LIL-TIKNULUGYA AL-HAYAWIYYAT. Text in English. 1997. s-a. **Document type:** *Journal, Academic/Scholarly.*
—BLDSC (3664.295000).
Published by: (Al-Azhar University, Faculty of Pharmacy), The Egyptian Society of Bio-Medical Sciencese, 31 Madinat al-Zubat Bldg, Emtedad-Ramsis Str, Nasr City, Cairo, Egypt. http://derp.sti.sci.eg/data/0210.htm. Ed. Dr. Muhammad Saif-El-Din Muhammad Ashour.

660.6   CHL   ISSN 0717-3458
TP248.13   CODEN: EEBIF6
► **ELECTRONIC JOURNAL OF BIOTECHNOLOGY.** Short title: E J B. Text in English. 1998. q. free (effective 2005). adv. **Document type:** *Journal, Academic/Scholarly.* **Description:** Publishes papers from all areas of biotechnology, including molecular biology and environmental aspects, as well as computer applications in biotechnology.
Incorporates (1995-1999): Biofilm (1360-3655).
Media: Online - full content (from SciELO).
Indexed: AbHyg, AgBio, Agr, AgrForAb, AnBrAb, B&BAb, BCI, BIOSIS Prev, BioCN&I, BiolAb, CPA, ExcerpMed, FCA, FS&TA, HerbAb, HortAb, MaizeAb, NemAb, NutrAb, PAIS, PBA, PGegResA, PGrRegA, PHN&I, PotatoAb, ProtozoAb, RA&MP, RDA, RM&VM, RPP, RiceAb, S&F, SIA, SoyAb, TDB, TriticAb, VITIS, WAE&RSA, WeedAb.
—CASDDS.
Published by: Pontificia Universidad Catolica de Valparaiso, Av. Brasil 2950, Casilla 4059, Valparaiso, Chile. TEL 56-32-273000, FAX 56-32-212746, gmunoz@ucv.cl, http://www.ejbiotechnology.info/, http://www.ejb.ucv.cl. Ed., R&P Graciela Munoz TEL 56-32-273120. Pub. Atillo Bustos. Adv. contact Alejandra Munoz TEL 56-32-273287.
Co-sponsor: Comision Nacional de Investigacion Cientifica y Tecnologica.

660.6   USA   ISSN 1521-4591
ELECTRONICS AND BIOTECHNOLOGY ADVANCED. FORUM SERIES. Text in English. 1995. irreg., latest vol.3, 1999. price varies.
Indexed: CIN, ChemAb, ChemTitl.

—BLDSC (3703.120000).
Published by: (Electronics and Biotechnology Advanced), Springer-Verlag New York, Inc. (Subsidiary of: Springer Science+Business Media), 233 Spring St, New York, NY 10013. TEL 212-460-1500, FAX 212-460-1575, service@springer-ny.com, http://www.springer-ny.com.

591 636.089   USA   ISSN 1083-4699
EMBRYO TRANSFER NEWSLETTER. Text in English. 1978. q. USD 80 membership; USD 40 to students (effective 2000). adv. bk.rev. abstr. **Document type:** *Newsletter.* **Description:** Features articles and announcements related to embryo transfer.
Related titles: Online - full text ed.
—CISTI.
Published by: International Embryo Transfer Society, 1111 N Dunlap Ave, Savoy, IL 61874. TEL 217-356-3182, FAX 217-398-4119, iets@assochq.org, http://www.uets.org. Ed. Matt Wheeler. R&P, Adv. contact Fran Gardner. Circ: 1,100 (paid).

EMERGING TECHNOLOGY SERIES: GENETIC ENGINEERING AND BIOTECHNOLOGY. see *BIOLOGY—Genetics*

660.6 620   DEU   ISSN 1618-0240
TA164
ENGINEERING IN LIFE SCIENCES. Text in English. 2001. bi-m. EUR 698 in Europe; CHF 1,068 in Switzerland & Liechtenstein; USD 918 elsewhere; EUR 768 combined subscription in Europe print & online eds.; CHF 1,175 combined subscription in Switzerland & Liechtenstein for print & online eds.; USD 1,010 combined subscription elsewhere print & online eds. (effective 2006). **Document type:** *Journal, Academic/Scholarly.* **Description:** Provides useful insight into engineering applications with all papers on microbiology, genetics, biochemistry, and chemistry being technologically relevant.
Incorporates (1981-2004): Acta Biotechnologica (0138-4988)
Related titles: Online - full text ed.: ISSN 1618-2863. EUR 698 in Europe; CHF 1,068 in Switzerland & Liechtenstein; USD 918 elsewhere (effective 2006) (from EBSCO Publishing, Swets Information Services, Wiley InterScience).
Indexed: AEBA, B&BAb, BCI, BioEngAb, ExcerpMed, FS&TA.
—BLDSC (3764.680000), CISTI, IE, Linda Hall. **CCC.**
Published by: Wiley - V C H Verlag GmbH & Co. KGaA (Subsidiary of: John Wiley & Sons, Inc.), Boschstr 12, Weinheim, 69469, Germany. TEL 49-6201-6060, FAX 49-6201-606328, info@wiley-vch.de, http://www3.interscience.wiley.com/cgi-bin/jabout/85007410/2129_info.html, http://www.wiley-vch.de. Ed. Babel W Leipzig.

ENVIRONMENTAL MICROBIOLOGY. see *BIOLOGY—Microbiology*

660.62   USA   ISSN 0141-0229
CODEN: EMTED2
► **ENZYME AND MICROBIAL TECHNOLOGY.** Text in English. 1979. 14/yr. EUR 271 in Europe to individuals; JPY 35,900 in Japan to individuals; USD 303 elsewhere to individuals; EUR 2,361 in Europe to institutions; JPY 313,500 in Japan to institutions; USD 2,640 elsewhere to institutions (effective 2006). adv. bk.rev. illus. index. back issues avail. **Document type:** *Journal, Academic/Scholarly.* **Description:** Encompasses basic and applied aspects of the use of enzymes, microbes and cells of mammalian or plant origin. Also covers economic and legal issues bearing on the "new" biotechnology.
Related titles: Microform ed.: (from PQC); Online - full text ed.: (from EBSCO Publishing, Gale Group, IngentaConnect, ScienceDirect, Swets Information Services).
Indexed: AEA, AEBA, AESIS, ASCA, ASFA, AgBio, AgrForAb, AnBrAb, AnalAb, BBCI, BCI, BIOBASE, BIOSIS Prev, BioCN&I, BioDAb, BioEngAb, BiolAb, CBTA, CCI, CEABA, CIN, CPA, CTFA, ChemAb, ChemTitl, CurCont, DBA, DSA, ESPM, EngInd, ExcerpMed, FCA, FPA, FS&TA, ForAb, HelmAb, HerbAb, HortAb, IABS, ISMEC, ISR, Inpharma, M&PBA, MBA, MEDLINE, MSCI, MaizeAb, NemAb, NutrAb, OrnHort, P&BA, PBA, PGegResA, PGrRegA, PN&I, PotatoAb, RA&MP, RM&VM, RPP, Reac, RefZh, RevApplEntom, RiceAb, S&F, SCI, SIA, SoyAb, TDB, Telegen, TriticAb, VITIS, WeedAb.
—BLDSC (3791.933000), CASDDS, CISTI, Ei, GNLM, IDS, IE, Infotrieve, ingenta, Linda Hall. **CCC.**
Published by: Elsevier Inc. (Subsidiary of: Elsevier Science & Technology), 360 Park Ave. S, New York, NY 10010-1710. TEL 212-633-3730, 888-437-4636, usinfo-f@elsevier.com, http://www.elsevier.com/locate/enzmictec. Eds. Dr. Raymond E Spier, Dr. Sheldon W May.

► **EUROPEAN BIOPHARMACEUTICAL REVIEW.** see *PHARMACY AND PHARMACOLOGY*

660.6029   GBR
THE EUROPEAN BIOTECHNOLOGY DIRECTORY (YEAR). Text in English. 1998. a. GBP 215, USD 355 (effective 2000). adv. charts; illus. back issues avail. **Document type:** *Directory.* **Description:** Profiles more than 900 European organizations involved involved in biotechnology.
Related titles: Online - full text ed.

Published by: BioCommerce Data Ltd. (Subsidiary of: P J B Publications Ltd.), 18-20 Hill Rise, Richmond, Surrey TW10 6UA, United Kingdom. TEL 44-20-8332-4660, FAX 44-20-8332-4666, biocom@dial.pipex.com, http://www.pjbpubs.com/bcd. Eds. A Crafts Lighty TEL 44-181-332-8983, R Williams. Adv. contact Tom Jamison TEL 44-181-332-8871.

660.6   DEU   ISSN 1618-8276
EUROPEAN BIOTECHNOLOGY SCIENCE & INDUSTRY NEWS. Text in English. 2002. 10/yr. EUR 60; EUR 30 to students (effective 2004). adv. **Document type:** *Journal, Trade.*
Published by: Biocom AG, Stralsunder Str 58-59, Berlin, 13355, Germany. TEL 49-30-2649210, FAX 49-30-26492111, service@biocom.de, http://www.biocom.de. Eds. Andreas Mietzsch, Thomas Gabrielczyk, Veronika Szentpetery. Adv. contact Oliver Schnell. B&W page EUR 3,000. Circ: 14,800 (paid and controlled).

EUROPEAN MATERIALS RESEARCH SOCIETY, SYMPOSIA PROCEEDINGS. see *ENGINEERING—Engineering Mechanics And Materials*

660.62   JPN   ISSN 1431-0651
QR97.A1   CODEN: EXTRFI
► **EXTREMOPHILES**; life under extreme conditions. Text in English. 1997. bi-m. (in 1 vol., 6 nos./vol.). EUR 432 combined subscription to institutions print & online eds. (effective 2005). adv. **Document type:** *Journal, Academic/Scholarly.* **Description:** International journal for both basic and applied research on microrganisms living under extreme conditions.
Related titles: Online - full text ed.: ISSN 1433-4909 (from EBSCO Publishing, Springer LINK, Swets Information Services).
Indexed: ASCA, ASFA, BBCI, BCI, BIOBASE, BIOSIS Prev, BiolAb, CurCont, ESPM, IABS, ISR, IndMed, MEDLINE, SCI.
—BLDSC (3854.505650), CASDDS, CISTI, IDS, IE, Infotrieve, ingenta, Linda Hall. **CCC.**
Published by: Springer-Verlag Tokyo (Subsidiary of: Springer Science+Business Media), 3-13 Hongo 3-chome, Bunkyo-ku, Tokyo, 113-0033, Japan. TEL 81-3-38120331, FAX 81-3-38187454, orders@svt-ebs.co.jp, http://link.springer-ny.com/link/service/journals/00792/index.htm, http://www.springer-tokyo.co.jp/. Ed. Koki Horikoshi. Adv. contact Stephan Kroeck TEL 49-30-827875739. B&W page JPY 70,000. **Subscr. in the Americas to:** Springer-Verlag New York, Inc., Journal Fulfillment, PO Box 2485, Secaucus, NJ 07096-2485. TEL 800-777-4643, 201-348-4033, FAX 201-348-4505, journals@springer-ny.com, http://www.springer-ny.com.

► **F E M S MICROBIOLOGY.** see *BIOLOGY—Microbiology*

660.6029   GBR
F T BIOTECHNOLOGY & PHARMACEUTICAL COMPANIES DATABASE CD-ROM (YEARS). (Financial Times) Text in English. 1997. a. adv. **Description:** Serves as a guide to the activities, performance and personnel of pharmaceutical and biotechnology companies worldwide.
Media: CD-ROM.
Published by: Financial Times Healthcare, Maple House, 149 Tottenham Ct Rd, London, W1P 9LL, United Kingdom. TEL 44-207-896-2066, FAX 44-20-7896-2213, lizg@pearson-pro.com, http://www.fthealthcare.com. Adv. contact Liz Godden.

660.6 608.7   USA
FEDERAL BIO-TECHNOLOGY TRANSFER DIRECTORY. Text in English. 1994. a. adv. **Document type:** *Directory.* **Description:** Catalogs all federal government inventions and technology transfer in the biomedical and basic biotechnology fields from 1980 to present.
Published by: Biotechnology Information Institute, 1700 Rockville Pike, Ste 400, Rockville, MD 20852. TEL 301-424-0255, FAX 301-424-0257. Ed., R&P, Adv. contact Ronald A Rader.

660.6   USA
FIERCEBIOTECH. Text in English. d. free. **Document type:** *Newsletter, Trade.* **Description:** Contains up-to-date information on biotech companies and the biotech industry.
Media: E-mail.
Published by: FierceMarkets, Inc., 1319 F St, NW, Ste 604, Washington, DC 20004. TEL 202-628-8778, info@fiercemarkets.com, http://www.fiercebiotech.com, http://www.fiercemarkets.com. Ed. John Carroll. Adv. contact Mat Rik.

FISHING INDUSTRY RESEARCH INSTITUTE. ANNUAL REPORT OF THE DIRECTOR/VISNYWERHEID-NAVORSINGSINSTITUUT. JAARVERSLAG VAN DIE DIREKTEUR. see *FOOD AND FOOD INDUSTRIES*

660.6   NLD   ISSN 1569-268X
FOCUS ON BIOTECHNOLOGY. Text in English. 2001. irreg., latest vol.10, 2004. price varies. **Document type:** *Monographic series, Academic/Scholarly.*
—BLDSC (3964.203845).

Published by: Springer-Verlag Dordrecht (Subsidiary of: Springer Science+Business Media), Van Godewijckstraat 30, Dordrecht, 3311 GX, Netherlands. TEL 31-78-6576050, FAX 31-78-6576474, http://www.springeronline.com. Eds. Jozef Anne, Marcel Hofman.

660.6 664 GBR ISSN 0960-3085
TP368 CODEN: FBPREO

➤ **FOOD AND BIOPRODUCTS PROCESSING.** Variant title: Institution of Chemical Engineers. Transactions. Part C, Food and Bioproducts Processing. Text in English. 1991. q. GBP 270 domestic to institutions print or online; GBP 285 foreign to institutions print or online; GBP 322.99 combined subscription domestic to institutions print & online; GBP 341 combined subscription foreign to institutions print & online (effective 2005). adv. **Document type:** *Journal, Academic/Scholarly.*
Description: Presents papers on processing aspects of food - drink and biochemical engineering.
Supersedes in part: Institution of Chemical Engineers. Transactions
Related titles: Online - full text ed.: ISSN 1744-3571 (from EBSCO Publishing, Gale Group, O C L C Online Computer Library Center, Inc., Swets Information Services).
Indexed: ASCA, ASFA, Agr, AgrForAb, BCI, BrTechI, C&ISA, CEABA, CIN, CMCI, ChemAb, ChemTitl, DBA, DSA, E&CAJ, ESPM, EngInd, FCA, FS&TA, H&SSA, HortAb, IMMAb, ISMEC, M&TEA, MaizeAb, OrnHort, PHN&I, PotatoAb, RA&MP, RefZh, S&F, SIA, SeedAb, SolStAb, SoyAb, TriticAb, VITIS.
—BLDSC (3977.026870), CASDDS, CINDOC, CISTI, Ei, IDS, IE, Infotrieve, ingenta, Linda Hall. **CCC.**
Published by: Institution of Chemical Engineers, George E Davis Bldg, 165-189 Railway Terr, Rugby, Warks CV21 3HQ, United Kingdom. TEL 44-1788-578214, FAX 44-1788-560833, http://www.icheme.org/learning/. Adv. contact Jo Cheshire.
Subscr. to: Portland Press Ltd., Commerce Way, Colchester CO2 8HP, United Kingdom. TEL 44-1206-796351, FAX 44-1206-799331, sales@portland-services.com.

660.6 664 USA ISSN 0890-5436
TP248.65.F66 CODEN: FBIOEE

➤ **FOOD BIOTECHNOLOGY.** Text in English. 1987. 3/yr. GBP 661, USD 1,092 combined subscription to institutions print & online eds. (effective 2006). adv. reprint service avail. from PSC. **Document type:** *Journal, Academic/Scholarly.*
Description: Brings together the most current research on biotechnology in the areas of food production and processing.
Related titles: Online - full text ed.: ISSN 1532-4249. GBP 628, USD 1,037 to institutions (effective 2006) (from EBSCO Publishing, O C L C Online Computer Library Center, Inc., Swets Information Services).
Indexed: AEBA, ASCA, ASFA, AgBio, Agr, AgrForAb, BCI, BIOBASE, BIOSIS Prev, BioEngAb, BiolAb, CBTA, CIN, CPA, ChemAb, ChemTitl, ChemoAb, CurCont, DBA, DSA, ESPM, EngInd, EnvAb, FCA, FPA, FS&TA, ForAb, H&SSA, HortAb, IABS, IndVet, MBA, MaizeAb, NutrAb, OrnHort, PBA, PGegResA, PGrRegA, PHN&I, RA&MP, RDA, RPP, RefZh, RiceAb, SIA, SeedAb, SoyAb, TDB, VITIS, VetBull, WAE&RSA.
—BLDSC (3977.071000), CASDDS, CISTI, Ei, IDS, IE, Infotrieve, ingenta, Linda Hall. **CCC.**
Published by: Taylor & Francis Inc. (Subsidiary of: Taylor & Francis Group), 325 Chestnut St, Ste 800, Philadelphia, PA 19016. TEL 215-625-8900, 800-354-1420, FAX 215-625-2940, info@taylorandfrancis.com, http://www.tandf.co.uk/journals/titles/08905436.asp, http://www.taylorandfrancis.com. Ed. Dr. Kalidas Shetty. R&P Elaine Inverso. Adv. contact Mary Drabot. B&W page USD 550. Circ: 300.

664 HRV ISSN 1330-9862
CODEN: FTBRFD

➤ **FOOD TECHNOLOGY AND BIOTECHNOLOGY.** Text and summaries in English. 1963. q. EUR 10 domestic to individuals; EUR 20 foreign to individuals; EUR 40 domestic to institutions; EUR 90 foreign to institutions (effective 2005). adv. bk.rev. index. 80 p./no. 2 cols./p.; back issues avail.; reprints avail. **Document type:** *Journal, Academic/Scholarly.*
Description: Publishes original articles, reviews, preliminary communications, notes and professional papers that deal with all aspects of applied food science and biotechnology. Covers chemistry and biochemistry, and microbiology and sensory evaluation of food science.
Formerly (until vol.34, 1996): Prehrambeno-Tehnoloska i Biotehnoloska Revija (0352-9193)
Related titles: E-mail ed.; Online - full text ed.: ISSN 1334-2606. 2000. free (effective 2005).
Indexed: ASCA, AbHyg, AgBio, AgrForAb, AnBrAb, BCI, BIOSIS Prev, BioCN&I, BiolAb, CIN, CPA, ChemAb, ChemTitl, CurCont, DSA, FCA, FPA, FS&TA, ForAb, HerbAb, HortAb, IndVet, MaizeAb, NutrAb, OrnHort, PBA, PGegResA, PGrRegA, PHN&I, PN&I, PotatoAb, PoultAb, RA&MP, RM&VM, RPP, RefZh, RevApplEntom, RiceAb, S&F, SIA, SeedAb, SoyAb, TriticAb, VITIS, VetBull, WeedAb.
—BLDSC (3984.032000), CASDDS, IDS, IE, ingenta.
Published by: (Slovensko Mikrobiolosko Drustvo/Slovenian Microbiological Society SVN, Hrvatsko Drustvo za Biotehnologiju/Croatian Society for Biotechnology), Sveuciliste u Zagrebu, Prehrambeno-Biotehnoloski Fakultet/University of Zagreb, Faculty of Food Technology and Biotechnology, Kaciceva 23, Zagreb, 10000, Croatia. ftb@mapbf.pbf.hr, imanacan@pbf.hr, http://public.carnet.hr/ftbrfd/, http://www.pbf.hr. Eds. Ines Macan, Pavao Mildner. adv.: B&W page MRK 1,000, color page MRK 1,500. Circ: 600 (paid and controlled).

660.6 DEU

➤ **FORTSCHRITT-BERICHTE V D I. REIHE 17: BIOTECHNIK - MEDIZINTECHNIK.** Text in German. 1966. irreg., latest vol.233, 2003. price varies. **Document type:** *Monographic series, Academic/Scholarly.*
Former titles (until 1996): Fortschritt-Berichte V D I. Reihe 17: Biotechnik (0178-9600); (until 1985): Fortschrittberichte der V D I Zeitschriften. Reihe 17: Biotechnik (0341-1702); (until 1973): Fortschrittberichte der V D I Zeitschriften. Reihe 17: Lebensmitteltechnik (0341-1710)
—CISTI. **CCC.**
Published by: V D I Verlag GmbH, Heinrichstr. 24, Duesseldorf, 40239, Germany. TEL 49-211-61880, FAX 49-211-6188112, info@vdi-nachrichten.com, http://www.vdi-verlag.de.

➤ **FRONTIERS IN BIOMEDICAL POLYMER APPLICATIONS.** see *PHARMACY AND PHARMACOLOGY*

660.65 NLD ISSN 0378-1119
QH442 CODEN: GENED6

➤ **GENE.** Text in English. 1977. 42/yr. EUR 677 in Europe to individuals; JPY 89,300 in Japan to individuals; USD 758 to individuals except Europe and Japan; EUR 8,987 in Europe to institutions; JPY 1,193,100 in Japan to institutions; USD 10,053 to institutions except Europe and Japan (effective 2006). adv. back issues avail.; reprints avail. **Document type:** *Journal, Academic/Scholarly.* **Description:** Explores and analyzes gene structure, function and regulation, recombinant DNA techniques, mapping, sequencing and study of plant, animal, human and microbial genomes, as well as basic and practical applications of genetic engineering and RNA technology.
Related titles: Microform ed.: (from PQC); Online - full text ed.: Gene - C O M B I S (from EBSCO Publishing, Gale Group, IngentaConnect, ScienceDirect, Swets Information Services).
Indexed: ASCA, ASFA, AbAn, AbHyg, AgBio, Agr, AgrForAb, AnBrAb, B&AI, BBCI, BCI, BIOBASE, BIOSIS Prev, BibAg, BioCN&I, BiolAb, CBTA, CEABA, CIN, CPA, ChemAb, ChemTitl, CurCont, DBA, DSA, ESPM, EntAb, ExcerpMed, FCA, FPA, FS&TA, ForAb, GenetAb, HGA, HelmAb, HerbAb, HortAb, IABS, ISR, IndMed, IndVet, MBA, MEDLINE, MaizeAb, NSCI, NemAb, NucAcAb, NutrAb, OrnHort, PBA, PGegResA, PGrRegA, PHN&I, PN&I, PotatoAb, PoultAb, ProtozoAb, RA&MP, RM&VM, RPP, RefZh, RevApplEntom, RiceAb, S&F, S&MA, SAA, SCI, SFA, SIA, SeedAb, SoyAb, TDB, Telegen, TriticAb, VITIS, VetBull, WeedAb, WildRev, ZooRec.
—BLDSC (4096.402000), CASDDS, CISTI, GNLM, IDS, IE, Infotrieve, ingenta, Linda Hall. **CCC.**
Published by: Elsevier BV (Subsidiary of: Elsevier Science & Technology), Radarweg 29, Amsterdam, 1043 NX, Netherlands. TEL 31-20-4853911, FAX 31-20-4852457, nlinfo-f@elsevier.nl, http://www.elsevier.com/locate/gene, http://www.elsevier.nl. Ed. G Bernardi. Pub. Jaap van Harten.

➤ **GENE THERAPY AND REGULATION**; an international interdisciplinary journal. see *BIOLOGY—Genetics*

660.6 576.5 GBR ISSN 1354-1366

GENETHICS NEWS✶ . Text in English. 1994. bi-m. GBP 14.95 (effective 2001). adv. bk.rev. charts; illus. back issues avail.
Document type: *Newsletter, Academic/Scholarly.*
Description: Covers ethical, social and environmental issues related to genetics and biotechnology.
Address: FREEPOST (LON 6013), PO Box 6313, London, N16 0DY, United Kingdom. TEL 44-20-8809-4513, FAX 44-20-7502-7516, genethicsnews@compuserve.com, http://www.ink.uk.com/gen_p.htm, http://ourworld.compuserve.com/homepages/genethicsnews. Ed., Pub. Dr. David King. Circ: 500 (paid).

GENETIC ENGINEERING. see *BIOLOGY—Genetics*

660.65 576 USA ISSN 0196-3716
QH442 CODEN: GENGDC

➤ **GENETIC ENGINEERING**; principles and methods. Text in English. 1979. irreg., latest vol.26, 2004. price varies.
Document type: *Monographic series, Academic/Scholarly.*
Description: Presents state-of-the-art discussions in modern genetics and genetic engineering. It publishes important reviews of the broadest interest to geneticists and their colleagues in affiliated disciplines.
Indexed: Agr, CBTA, CIN, ChemAb, ChemTitl, DBA, IndMed, MEDLINE.
—BLDSC (4111.847000), CASDDS, CISTI, GNLM, IE, Infotrieve, ingenta, KNAW. **CCC.**
Published by: Springer-Verlag New York, Inc. (Subsidiary of: Springer Science+Business Media), 233 Spring St, New York, NY 10013. TEL 212-460-1500, FAX 212-460-1575, service@springer-ny.com, http://www.springer-ny.com. Ed. J K Setlow.

➤ **GENETIC ENGINEERING NEWS**; the information source of the biotechnology industry. see *BIOLOGY—Genetics*

➤ **GENEWATCH.** see *BIOLOGY—Genetics*

660.6 USA ISSN 1530-7107
TP248.6

GENOME TECHNOLOGY. Text in English. 2000. m. USD 89 (effective 2003). back issues avail.
Related titles: Online - full text ed.
Indexed: Inpharma, PE&ON, Reac.
—Linda Hall. **CCC.**
Published by: GenomeWeb, LLC, PO Box 998, Peck Slip Stn., New York, NY 10272-0998. TEL 212-269-4747, FAX 212-269-3686, http://www.genome-technology.com/, http://www.genome.com.

GENOMICS. see *BIOLOGY—Genetics*

660.6 USA ISSN 1536-7495
CODEN: GPERA6

GENOMICS & PROTEOMICS; tools, techniques, and people in the post-genomic world. Text in English. 2001. 8/yr. free to qualified personnel; USD 81.90 domestic; USD 118.90 in Canada; USD 113.90 in Mexico; USD 226.90 elsewhere (effective 2004). adv.
Related titles: Online - full text ed.: (from EBSCO Publishing, H.W. Wilson, O C L C Online Computer Library Center, Inc.).
Indexed: B&AI.
—BLDSC (4116.314200), IE.
Published by: Reed Business Information (Subsidiary of: Reed Business), 100 Enterprise Dr, Ste 600, PO Box 912, Rockaway, NJ 07866-0912. TEL 973-920-7000, 800-222-0289, tkoppal@reedbusiness.com, http://www.genpromag.com, http://www.reedbusiness.com. Ed. Tanuja Koppal. Pub. Joan Boyce TEL 516-541-8566. adv.: B&W page USD 4,560; trim 7.875 x 10.5. Circ: 22,050.

660.6 USA

THE GLOBAL BIOTECHNOLOGY INDUSTRY TO 2010: STATUS AND PROGNOSIS. Text in English. USD 7,500 (effective 2000). **Description:** Offers analysis about a complex and fast-evolving business whose products are transforming the practice of medicine.
Published by: Decision Resources, Inc., Bay Colony Corporate Center, 1100 Winter St, Waltham, MA 02154-1238. TEL 781-487-3737, 781-487-5750, FAX 781-487-3735, carbone@dresources.com, http://www.dresources.com. Ed. Dr. Hermann A M Mucke.

660.62 CHN ISSN 1001-6678
QR53 CODEN: GOWEEK

GONGYE WEISHENGWU/INDUSTRIAL MICROBIOLOGY. Text in Chinese. 1986. q. USD 120 (effective 1999). adv. bk.rev.
Document type: *Academic/Scholarly.* **Description:** Covers the industrial application of biotechnology.
Related titles: Online - full text ed.: (from East View Information Services).
Indexed: CIN, ChemAb, ChemTitl, DBA, SIA.
—BLDSC (4457.895000), CASDDS.
Published by: Shanghai Gongye Weishengwu Yanjiusuo/Shanghai Institute of Industrial Microbiology, 353 Guiping Rd, Shanghai, 200233, China. TEL 86-21-6482-2988. Ed. Hu Jun. Circ: 5,000. **Co-sponsor:** National Information Center of Industrial Microbiology.

660.6 GBR ISSN 1466-1330

HELIX; the magazine for international biotechnology. Text in English. 1999 (May). 10/yr. GBP 200 domestic; GBP 220, USD 352 foreign (effective 2000); GBP 24 newsstand/cover.
Document type: *Academic/Scholarly.* **Description:** Features articles on the end user sector, developments in raw materials and industry services, and features on R&D production and laboratory equipment. Covers key conferences and exhibitions.
Published by: D M G World Media Ltd. (Subsidiary of: Daily Mail and General Trust PLC), Queensway House, 2 Queensway, Redhill, Surrey RH1 1QS, United Kingdom. TEL 44-1737-855527, FAX 44-1737-855470, cbaumforth@dmg.co.uk, http://www.dmg.co.uk/helix/, http://www.dmgworldmedia.com.

660.6 JPN ISSN 0915-3411

HYOGO BAIOTEKUNOROJI KONWAKAI KAIHO/HYOGO BIOTECHNOLOGY ASSOCIATION. ANNUAL REPORT. Text in Japanese. 1987. a. JPY 3,500.
Published by: Hyogo Baiotekunoroji Konwakai/Hyogo Biotechnology Association, Hyogo Kenritsu Sangyo Kaikan, 28-33 Nakayamatedori 7-chome, Chuo-ku, Kobe-shi, Hyogo-ken 650-0004, Japan.

660.6 JPN ISSN 0912-6686

I C BIOTECH. ANNUAL REPORTS. Text in English. 1978. a.
Document type: *Academic/Scholarly.*
Formerly (until 1985): International Center of Cooperative Research and Development in Microbial Engineering. Annual Reports (0387-5377)

▼ new title ➤ refereed ✶ unverified ♦ full entry avail.

Published by: Osaka University, International Center for Biotechnology/Osaka Daigaku Seibutsu Kogaku Kokusai Koryu Senta, 2-1 Yamada-Oka, Suita-shi, Osaka-fu 565-0871, Japan. TEL 81-6-879-7455, FAX 81-6-879-7454, yoshida@icb.osaka-u.ac.jp, http://www.icb.osaka-u.ac.jp/. Ed. Toshiomi Yoshida.

660.6 USA
I E E E BIOMEDICAL ENGINEERING DAYS. Text in English. a. **Document type:** *Proceedings, Trade.*
Published by: Institute of Electrical and Electronics Engineers, Inc., 3 Park Ave, 17th Fl, New York, NY 10016-5997. TEL 212-419-7900, 800-678-4333, FAX 212-752-4929, customer.service@ieee.org, http://www.ieee.org.

610.28 USA ISSN 1089-7771
R858.A1 CODEN: ITIBFX
I E E E TRANSACTIONS ON INFORMATION TECHNOLOGY IN BIOMEDICINE. Text in English. 1997. q. USD 375 (effective 2006). **Document type:** *Journal, Academic/Scholarly.* **Description:** Covers national and international developments in biomedical and health applications using information and computer networking.
Related titles: CD-ROM ed.; Microfiche ed.; Online - full text ed.: (from EBSCO Publishing, Swets Information Services).
Indexed: AS&TI, B&BAb, C&ISA, CurCont, E&CAJ, EngInd, IndMed, Inspec, MEDLINE, RefZh, SolStAb.
—BLDSC (4363.196500), CISTI, IE, Infotrieve, ingenta, Linda Hall. **CCC.**
Published by: Institute of Electrical and Electronics Engineers, Inc., 445 Hoes Ln, Piscataway, NJ 08854-1331. TEL 732-981-0060, 800-701-4333, FAX 732-981-1721, subscription-service@ieee.org, http://www.ieee.org. Ed. Swamy Laxminarayan. **Subscr. to:** Maruzen Co., Ltd., 3-10 Nihonbashi 2-chome, Chuo-ku, Tokyo 103-0027, Japan. FAX 81-3-3275-0657; Universal Subscription Agency, Pvt. Ltd., 877, Udyog Vihar, V, Gurgoan 122001, India. TEL 91-124-347261, FAX 91-124-342496. **Co-sponsor:** Engineering in Medicine and Biology Society.

660.6 GBR ISSN 1478-1581
TP248.13 CODEN: IPNEAY
▼ **I E E PROCEEDINGS - NANOBIOTECHNOLOGY.** Text in English. 2003. bi-m. USD 1,045 in the Americas print or online; GBP 615 elsewhere print or online; USD 1,254 combined subscription in the Americas print & online; GBP 738 combined subscription elsewhere print & online; USD 174 per issue in the Americas; GBP 103 per issue elsewhere (effective 2005). **Document type:** *Proceedings, Academic/Scholarly.* **Description:** Covers all aspects of this emerging science especially relating to the interactions between biomolecules and biomolecular assemblies with electronic structures or materials.
Related titles: Online - full text ed.: ISSN 1740-9748 (from EBSCO Publishing).
Indexed: Inspec, RefZh.
—BLDSC (4362.751940), CISTI, IE, Linda Hall. **CCC.**
Published by: Institution of Electrical Engineers, Michael Faraday House, Six Hills Way, Stevenage, Herts SG1 2AY, United Kingdom. TEL 44-1438-313311, FAX 44-1438-313465, proceedings@iee.org.uk, inspec@iee.org, http://www.iee.org/Publish/Journals/ProfJourn/Proc/NBT/Index.cfm. Eds. John Ryan, Jon Cooper.

610.285 FRA ISSN 1297-9562
➤ **I T B M - R B M.** (Innovation et Technologie en Biologie et Medecine - Revue Europeenne de Biotechnologie Medicale) (In 2 sections: RBM La Revue (4 nos.); RBM News (6 nos.)) Text and summaries in English, French. 2000. 6/yr. EUR 260.66 domestic to institutions; EUR 279 in Europe to institutions; JPY 34,600 in Japan to institutions; USD 336 elsewhere to institutions (effective 2006). **Document type:** *Journal, Academic/Scholarly.* **Description:** Publishes objective, scientific medical and technical information on all aspects of biomedical technology involved in cardiology, radiology, NMR, surgery, intensive care and emergency medicine, resuscitation and clinical chemistry equipment.
Formed by the merger of part of (1979-2000): Revue Europeenne de Biotechnologie Medicale (0222-0776); (1980-2000): Innovation et Technologie en Biologie et Medecine (0243-7228)
Related titles: Online - full text ed.: (from EBSCO Publishing, Gale Group, IngentaConnect, ScienceDirect, Swets Information Services).
Indexed: BIOBASE, ExcerpMed.
—BLDSC (4588.506700), CISTI, GNLM, IE, ingenta.
Published by: Elsevier France, Editions Scientifiques et Medicales (Subsidiary of: Elsevier Science & Technology), 23 Rue Linois, Paris, 75724, France. TEL 33-1-71724600, FAX 33-1-71724650, rbm@elsevier.fr, http://www.elsevier.com/locate/rbmret, http://www.elsevier.fr. Ed. J Rousseau. Circ: 6,000. **Subscr. to:** Elsevier BV, PO Box 211, Amsterdam 1000 AE, Netherlands. nlinfo-f@elsevier.nl, http://www.elsevier.nl.

660.6 FRA ISSN 1297-9570
CODEN: INTECI
I T B M - R B M NEWS. (Innovation et Technologie en Biologie et Medecine - Revue Europeenne de Biotechnologie Medicale) Text in English, French. 1979. 6/yr. EUR 47.39 domestic to institutions; EUR 58 in Europe to institutions; JPY 6,300 in Japan to institutions; USD 69 elsewhere to institutions (effective 2006). **Document type:** *Journal, Academic/Scholarly.* **Description:** Presents news and analysis on biomedical technology management and offers a full description of innovative products.
Supersedes in part (in 2000): Revue Europeenne de Biotechnologie Medicale (0222-0776)
Related titles: Online - full text ed.: (from EBSCO Publishing, Gale Group, IngentaConnect, ScienceDirect, Swets Information Services).
Indexed: ExcerpMed.
—BLDSC (4588.506800), CISTI, IE, ingenta. **CCC.**
Published by: Elsevier France, Editions Scientifiques et Medicales (Subsidiary of: Elsevier Science & Technology), 23 Rue Linois, Paris, 75724, France. TEL 33-1-71724600, FAX 33-1-71724650, http://www.elsevier.com/locate/rbmnew, http://www.elsevier.fr. Ed. Didier Pinaudeau. **Subscr. to:** Elsevier BV, PO Box 211, Amsterdam 1000 AE, Netherlands. TEL 31-20-485-3757, FAX 31-20-485-3432, nlinfo-f@elsevier.nl, http://www.elsevier.nl.

IN VITRO CELLULAR & DEVELOPMENTAL BIOLOGY - PLANT. see *BIOLOGY—Botany*

579.62 IND ISSN 0972-5849
INDIAN JOURNAL OF BIOTECHNOLOGY. Text in English. 2002. q. INR 300, USD 100; INR 100, USD 30 newsstand/cover (effective 2002). **Document type:** *Journal, Academic/Scholarly.* **Description:** Publishes articles and reviews in agricultural, animal, environmental, industrial, medical, and microbial biotechnology, bioinformatics, and the socio-legal and ethical aspects of biotechnology.
Indexed: AEBA, ASFA, AbHyg, AgBio, AgrForAb, AnBrAb, B&BAb, BioCN&I, BioEngAb, BiolAb, CPA, DSA, ESPM, ExcerpMed, FCA, FS&TA, ForAb, HelmAb, HerbAb, HortAb, IndVet, M&PBA, MaizeAb, NemAb, OrnHort, PBA, PGegResA, PGrRegA, PN&I, PotatoAb, ProtozoAb, RA&MP, RM&VM, RPP, S&F, SIA, SeedAb, SoyAb, TDB, TriticAb, VetBull, WeedAb.
—BLDSC (4410.425000), IE.
Published by: National Institute of Science Communication and Information Resources, K.S. Krishnan Marg, New Delhi, 110 012, India. TEL 91-11-5726014, FAX 91-11-5787062, vkg@niscom.res.in, http://www.niscom.res.in/. Ed. R. D. Kak.

660.61 USA ISSN 1550-9087
▼ ➤ **INDUSTRIAL BIOTECHNOLOGY.** Text in English. 2005 (Mar.). q. USD 455 domestic to institutions; USD 515 foreign to institutions; USD 515 combined subscription domestic to institutions print & online eds.; USD 575 combined subscription foreign to institutions print & online eds. (effective 2006). **Description:** Provides a forum for the emerging field of industrial biotechnology. It publishes the latest developments on the new tools and applications of biotechnology for industrial applications including food processing, textiles, alternative energy sources, and improving the environmental sustainability of manufacturing applications.
Related titles: Online - full text ed.: USD 395 to institutions (effective 2006).
Published by: Mary Ann Liebert, Inc. Publishers, 140 Huguenot St 3rd Fl, New Rochelle, NY 10801-5215. TEL 914-740-2100, FAX 914-740-2101, 800-654-3237, info@liebertpub.com, http://www.liebertpub.com/publication.aspx?pub_id=140.

660.6 USA ISSN 1549-9766
▼ **INSIDE BIOASSAYS;** the global weekly for high-throughput discovery. Text in English. 2004. 50/yr. USD 895 (effective 2005). adv.
Media: Online - full content.
Published by: GenomeWeb, LLC, PO Box 998, Peck Slip Stn., New York, NY 10272-0998. TEL 212-269-4747, FAX 212-269-3686, http://www.insidebioassays.com/index.htm, http://www.genome.com. Eds. Ben Butkus, Marian Moser Jones. Adv. contact Judy Block.

660.6 GBR ISSN 0964-8305
QP517.B5 CODEN: IBBIES
➤ **INTERNATIONAL BIODETERIORATION AND BIODEGRADATION.** Text in English. 1965. 8/yr. EUR 1,311 in Europe to institutions; JPY 174,300 in Japan to institutions; USD 1,467 elsewhere to institutions (effective 2006). adv. bk.rev. bibl.; charts; illus. index. back issues avail. **Document type:** *Journal, Academic/Scholarly.* **Description:** Presents original research papers and reviews on the biological causes of deterioration or advantageous biological upgrading of all types of materials.
Formerly (until 1992): International Biodeterioration (0265-3036); Which was formed by the merger of (1965-1983): International Biodeterioration Bulletin (0020-6164); (1974-1983): Waste Materials Biodegradation Research Titles (0305-0262); (1972-1983): Biodeterioration Research Titles; Which was formerly (1967-1971): I B B R I S. International Biodeterioration Bulletin Reference Index Supplement (0018-8573)
Related titles: Online - full text ed.: (from DIMDI, EBSCO Publishing, Gale Group, IngentaConnect, ScienceDirect, Swets Information Services, The Dialog Corporation).
Indexed: ABIPC, AEA, AEBA, ASCA, ASFA, AbHyg, AgBio, Agr, AgrForAb, AnBrAb, BCI, BIOBASE, BIOSIS Prev, BioCN&I, BioEngAb, BiolAb, BrCerAb, C&ISA, CEABA, CIN, CPA, Cadscan, CerAb, ChemAb, ChemTitl, CivEngAb, CorrAb, CurCont, DBA, DSA, E&CAJ, EMA, EPB, ESPM, EngInd, EnvAb, EnvEAb, ExcerpMed, FCA, FLUIDEX, FPA, FS&TA, ForAb, GEOBASE, HelmAb, HerbAb, HortAb, I&DA, IAA, IABS, IndVet, LeadAb, M&GPA, M&TEA, MBA, MBF, METADEX, MaizeAb, NAA, NutrAb, OrnHort, PBA, PHN&I, PN&I, PollutAb, PotatoAb, PoultAb, ProtozoAb, RA&MP, RM&VM, RPP, RRTA, RefZh, RevApplEntom, RiceAb, S&F, SCI, SIA, SWRA, SeedAb, SolStAb, SoyAb, TDB, TriticAb, VITIS, VetBull, WAA, WAE&RSA, WSCA, WTA, WeedAb, WildRev, Zincscan.
—BLDSC (4537.147000), CASDDS, CISTI, Ei, IDS, IE, Infotrieve, ingenta, Linda Hall. **CCC.**
Published by: (Biodeterioration Society), Elsevier Ltd. (Subsidiary of: Elsevier Science & Technology), The Boulevard, Langford Ln, Kidlington, Oxford, OX5 1GB, United Kingdom. TEL 44-1865-843000, FAX 44-1865-843010, http://www.elsevier.com/locate/ibiod. Ed. B. Flannigan. Circ: (controlled). **Subscr. to:** Elsevier BV, PO Box 211, Amsterdam 1000 AE, Netherlands. TEL 31-20-485-3757, FAX 31-20-485-3432, nlinfo-f@elsevier.nl, http://www.elsevier.nl. **Co-sponsor:** Pan-American Biodeterioration Society.

620.1 GBR
QH530.5.I56
INTERNATIONAL BIODETERIORATION SYMPOSIUM. PROCEEDINGS. Variant title: Biodeterioration and Biodegradation. Text in English. biennial (8th 1990, Windsor, Canada). GBP 135. bibl.; illus. **Document type:** *Proceedings, Academic/Scholarly.*
Published by: Pergamon (Subsidiary of: Elsevier Science & Technology), The Boulevard, Langford Ln, East Park, Kidlington, Oxford OX5 1GB, United Kingdom. TEL 44-1865-843000, FAX 44-1865-843010. Ed. H W Rossmore. **Subscr. to:** Elsevier BV, PO Box 211, Amsterdam 1000 AE, Netherlands. TEL 31-20-485-3757, FAX 31-20-485-3432, nlinfo-f@elsevier.nl, http://www.elsevier.nl.

660.6 GBR ISSN 0888-7225
TP248.13
INTERNATIONAL BIOTECHNOLOGY LABORATORY. Text in English. 1983. 6/yr. free to qualified personnel. adv. bk.rev. charts; illus.; stat.; tr.lit. **Document type:** *Journal, Trade.* **Description:** Provides complete coverage of the latest products for the life science marketplace, together with concise articles covering innovations in laboratory practice and applications of new instrumentation, apparatus, and related products. Distributed to subscribers in Europe and the Middle East.
Related titles: Special ed(s).: International Biotechnology Laboratory. Buyers' Guide.
Indexed: CBTA, CEABA, DBA, MSB.
—BLDSC (4537.195100), IE, ingenta. **CCC.**
Published by: International Scientific Communications, Ltd., ISC House, 12 Bridge Ave, Maidenhead, Berkshire GB-SL6 1RR, United Kingdom. TEL 44-1628-789982, FAX 44-1628-789984. adv.: B&W page USD 4,255, color page USD 5,815. Circ: 37,000 (controlled).

INTERNATIONAL JOURNAL OF ANIMAL SCIENCES. see *AGRICULTURE—Poultry And Livestock*

▼ **INTERNATIONAL JOURNAL OF BIOLOGICAL SCIENCES.** see *BIOLOGY*

660.2 GBR ISSN 0963-6048
TP248.13 CODEN: IJBNBS
➤ **INTERNATIONAL JOURNAL OF BIOTECHNOLOGY.** Abbreviated title: I J B T. Text in English. 1999. q. USD 450 to institutions; USD 545 combined subscription to institutions print & online eds. (effective 2005). adv. back issues avail.; reprints avail. **Document type:** *Journal, Academic/Scholarly.* **Description:** Provides an international forum and authoritative source of information in the fields of biotechnology and biotechnics with an emphasis on the management and economics as well as the political and social issues.
Related titles: Online - full text ed.: ISSN 1741-5020. USD 450 to institutions (effective 2005) (from EBSCO Publishing).
Indexed: ABIn, AEBA, ASFA, AgBio, B&BAb, BioEngAb, BrCerAb, C&ISA, CerAb, CivEngAb, CorrAb, DSA, E&CAJ, EMA, EPB, ESPM, EnvEAb, ExcerpMed, GEOBASE, HerbAb, HortAb, IAA, IndVet, M&PBA, M&TEA, MBF, METADEX, MaizeAb, NutrAb, PBA, PGegResA, PollutAb, RDA, RRTA, RefZh, RiceAb, RiskAb, S&F, SeedAb, SolStAb, TDB, VetBull, WAA, WAE&RSA.
—BLDSC (4542.155200), CISTI, IE, ingenta, Linda Hall.
Published by: Inderscience Publishers, IEL Editorial Office, PO Box 735, Olney, Bucks MK46 5WB, United Kingdom. TEL 44-1234-240519, FAX 44-1234-240515, ijbt@inderscience.com, editor@inderscience.com, http://www.inderscience.com/ijbt. Ed. Dr. Mohammed A Dorgham. R&P Jeanette Brooks. Adv. contact Cheryl Busby. **Subscr. to:** World Trade Centre Bldg, 29 route de Pre-Bois, Case Postale 896, Geneva 15 1215, Switzerland. FAX 41-22-7910885, subs@inderscience.com.

660.6 CAN ISSN 1206-7865
INTERNATIONAL JOURNAL OF ENVIRONMENTAL & BIODIVERSITY AWARENESS✶. Text in Arabic, English. 1997. q. CND 400 (effective 2000). adv. bk.rev. **Document type:** *Journal, Academic/Scholarly.* **Description:** Designed for concise, cooperative publication of simple accelerated and creative ideas for awareness of environmental monitoring and control.
Published by: M.I. Ismail, Ed. & Pub., P O Box 98029, Mississauga, ON L5L 3A0, Canada. FAX 516-277-2875.

660.6 USA
INTERNATIONAL LABORATORY BUYERS' GUIDE. Text in English. 1972. a. back issues avail. **Document type:** *Trade.*
Related titles: Microfiche ed.; Online - full text ed.
Published by: International Scientific Communications, Inc., 30 Controls Dr, PO Box 670, Shelton, CT 06484-0870. TEL 203-926-9300, FAX 203-926-9310, iscpubs@iscpubs.com, http://www.iscpubs.com. Ed. Brian Howard. Pub. William Wham. adv.: B&W page USD 7,835, color page USD 10,570. Circ: 90,000. **U.K. subscr. to:** I.S.C. House, Progress Business Centre, 5 Whittle Pkwy., Slough, Berks SL1 6QQ, United Kingdom. TEL 44-1625-669199, 44-1628-668881.

660.6 USA ISSN 1540-2630
QH1
▼ ➤ **THE INTERNET JOURNAL OF GENOMICS AND PROTEOMICS.** Text in English. 2003. s-a. free to individuals; USD 500 to institutions (effective 2005). adv. **Document type:** *Journal, Academic/Scholarly.*
Media: Online - full content.
Published by: Internet Scientific Publications, L.L.C., 23 Rippling Creek Dr, Sugar Land, TX 77479. TEL 832-443-1193, FAX 281-240-1533, wenker@ispub.com, http://www.ispub.com/ostia/index.php?xmlFilePath=journals/ijgp/front.xml.

660.6 CAN
INTRON - CANADIAN MOLECULAR BIOLOGY. Text in English. 1993. bi-m. CND 90 (effective 1999). **Document type:** *Trade.* **Description:** Examines the application of molecular biology to the life sciences.
Published by: Canadian Biotechnology News Service, 20 Stonepark Lane, Nepean, ON K2H 9P4, Canada. TEL 613-726-0115, FAX 613-726-7344. Ed. Peter Winter. R&P Carole Winter. Circ: 6,000 (controlled).

ISRAEL AGRITECHNOLOGY FOCUS. see *AGRICULTURE*

660.6 ITA
JOURNAL OF APPLIED BIOMATERIALS AND BIOMECHANICS. Text in English. 3/yr. EUR 145.50 in Europe to individuals; EUR 163 elsewhere to individuals; EUR 197.50 in Europe to institutions; EUR 215 elsewhere to institutions; EUR 87.50 in Europe residents; EUR 105 elsewhere residents (effective 2004). **Document type:** *Journal, Academic/Scholarly.* **Description:** Publishes reviews, editorials and case reports dealing with clinical and laboratory investigations in the fast growing field of biomaterial sciences.
Published by: Wichtig Editore s.r.l., Via Friuli 72, Milan, MI 20135, Italy. TEL 39-02-55195443, FAX 39-02-55195971, info@wichtig-publisher.com, http://www.jabb.biz, http://www.wichtig-publisher.com. Ed. Alberto Cigada. Pub. Dr. Diego Brancaccio.

660.6 USA ISSN 1556-6560
▼ **JOURNAL OF BIOBASED MATERIALS AND BIOENERGY.** Text in English. forthcoming 2006 (Apr.). 3/yr. USD 380 (effective 2006).
Related titles: Online - full text ed.: ISSN 1556-6579. forthcoming 2006 (Apr.).
Published by: American Scientific Publishers, 25650 N Lewis Way, Stevenson Ranch, CA 91381-1439. TEL 661-254-0807, FAX 661-254-1207, http://www.aspbs.com/jbmbe.

660.6 346.065 USA ISSN 1095-5127
K10 CODEN: JBBUF8
THE JOURNAL OF BIOLAW AND BUSINESS. Text in English. 1997. q. USD 295 (effective 2005). **Description:** Designed for attorneys, biotechnology and pharmaceutical executives, investors and other professionals involved in the biotechnology and life science sectors.
Related titles: Online - full text ed.: (from EBSCO Publishing).
Indexed: ASFA, B&BAb, BIOBASE, BioEngAb, CurCont, ESPM, ExcerpMed, H&SSA, RiskAb.
—BLDSC (4952.950000), IE.
Published by: BioLaw, 292 Prince St, West Newton, MA 02465. TEL 617-244-4762, FAX 617-964-0971, http://www.biolawbusiness.com.

660.284 NLD ISSN 0920-5063
R857.P6 CODEN: JBSEEA
➤ **JOURNAL OF BIOMATERIALS SCIENCE. POLYMER EDITION.** Text in English. 1989. m. USD 1,813 combined subscription in the Americas print & online eds.; EUR 1,450 combined subscription elsewhere print & online eds. (effective 2006). back issues avail.; reprint service avail. from PSC. **Document type:** *Journal, Academic/Scholarly.* **Description:** Explores research on the mechanisms of interactions between biomaterials and living organisms, focusing at the molecular and cellular levels.
Related titles: Online - full content ed.: ISSN 1568-5624. 2000. USD 1,632 in the Americas; EUR 1,305 elsewhere (effective 2006); Online - full text ed.: (from EBSCO Publishing, Gale Group, IngentaConnect, Kluwer Online, O C L C Online Computer Library Center, Inc., Springer LINK, Swets Information Services).
Indexed: ASCA, BIOSIS Prev, BiolAb, BrCerAb, C&ISA, CCI, CIN, CerAb, ChemAb, ChemTitl, CorrAb, CurCont, DBA, E&CAJ, EMA, ExcerpMed, IAA, ISR, IndMed, IndVet, Inpharma, Inspec, M&TEA, MBF, MEDLINE, METADEX, MSCI, RAPRA, RM&VM, Reac, SCI, SSCI, SolStAb, TTI, VetBull, WAA.
—BLDSC (4953.517000), CASDDS, CISTI, GNLM, IE, Infotrieve, ingenta, Linda Hall. **CCC.**
Published by: V S P (Subsidiary of: Brill Academic Publishers), Brill Academic Publishers, PO Box 9000, Leiden, 2300 PA, Netherlands. TEL 31-71-5353500, FAX 31-71-5317532, vsppub@brill.nl, http://www.brill.nl/m_catalogue_sub6_id9739.htm, http://www.vsppub.com. Eds. M Vert, S L Cooper, T Tsuruta. **Dist. by:** Extenza - Turpin, Pegasus Dr, Stratton Business Park, Biggleswade, Beds SG18 8TQ, United Kingdom. TEL 44-1767-604954, FAX 44-1767-601640, marketing@extenza-turpin.com, http://www.extenza-turpin.com.

660.6 610 USA ISSN 1549-3296
R856 CODEN: JBMRBG
▼ ➤ **JOURNAL OF BIOMEDICAL MATERIALS RESEARCH. PART A.** Text in English. 2003. 16/yr. USD 6,750 domestic to institutions; USD 7,038 in Canada & Mexico to institutions; USD 7,206 elsewhere to institutions; USD 7,425 combined subscription domestic to institutions print & online eds.; USD 7,713 combined subscription in Canada & Mexico to institutions print & online eds.; USD 7,881 combined subscription elsewhere to institutions print & online eds. (effective 2006); Incl. Part B - Applied Biomaterials. adv. illus. Supplement avail.; back issues avail.; reprint service avail. from PQC. **Document type:** *Journal, Academic/Scholarly.* **Description:** Covers biomaterial topics including the science and technology of alloys, polymers, ceramics, and reprocessed animal and human tissues in surgery, dentistry, artificial organs, and other medical devices.
Supersedes in part (1966-2002): Journal of Biomedical Materials Research (0021-9304); Incorporated (1990-1995): Journal of Applied Biomaterials (1045-4861)
Related titles: Microform ed.: (from PQC); Online - full text ed.: ISSN 1552-4965. 1996. USD 6,750 to institutions (effective 2006) (from EBSCO Publishing, Swets Information Services, Wiley InterScience).
Indexed: ASCA, ASFA, ApMecR, B&AI, B&BAb, BiolAb, C&ISA, CCI, CIN, ChemAb, ChemTitl, CivEngAb, CurCont, DentInd, E&CAJ, EngInd, ExcerpMed, IAA, ISR, IndMed, Inpharma, MBA, METADEX, MSB, MSCI, RAPRA, Reac, SCI.
—BLDSC (4953.720000), CASDDS, CISTI, Ei, GNLM, IDS, IE, Infotrieve, ingenta, KNAW, Linda Hall.
Published by: (Society for Biomaterials), John Wiley & Sons, Inc., 111 River St, Hoboken, NJ 07030-5774. TEL 800-825-7550, FAX 201-748-5915, uscs-wis@wiley.com, http://www.interscience.wiley.com/jpages/0021-9304/, http://www.wiley.com. Ed. James Anderson. adv.: B&W page GBP 640, color page GBP 1,515; trim 210 x 279. **Subscr. outside the Americas to:** John Wiley & Sons Ltd., The Atrium, Southern Gate, Chichester, West Sussex PO19 8SQ, United Kingdom. TEL 44-1243-779777, FAX 44-1243-775878, cs-journals@wiley.co.uk. **Co-sponsor:** European Society for Biomaterials.

660.6 610 USA ISSN 1552-4973
R857.M3 CODEN: JBMRGL
▼ ➤ **JOURNAL OF BIOMEDICAL MATERIALS RESEARCH. PART B: APPLIED BIOMATERIALS.** Text in English. 2003. bi-m. USD 6,176 domestic to institutions; USD 6,416 in Canada & Mexico to institutions; USD 6,620 elsewhere to institutions; USD 6,794 combined subscription domestic to institutions print & online eds.; USD 7,034 combined subscription in Canada & Mexico to institutions print & online eds.; USD 7,238 combined subscription elsewhere to institutions print & online eds. (effective 2005); Incl. Part A - Journal of Biomedical Materials Research. **Document type:** *Journal, Academic/Scholarly.* **Description:** Covers device development, implant retrieval and analysis, manufacturing, regulation of devices, liability and legal issues, standards, reviews of different device areas, and clinical applications.
Supersedes in part (in 2003): Journal of Biomedical Materials Research (0021-9304); Incorporated (1990-1995): Journal of Applied Biomaterials (1045-4861)
Related titles: Online - full content ed.: ISSN 1552-4981. USD 6,176 to institutions (effective 2005); Incl. Part A - Journal of Biomedical Materials Research; Online - full text ed.: (from EBSCO Publishing, Swets Information Services, Wiley InterScience).
Indexed: BrCerAb, C&ISA, CerAb, CorrAb, CurCont, E&CAJ, EMA, IAA, M&TEA, MBF, METADEX, MSCI, SCI, WAA.
—BLDSC (4953.725000), CISTI, IE, Linda Hall.
Published by: (Society for Biomaterials), John Wiley & Sons, Inc., 111 River St, Hoboken, NJ 07030-5774. TEL 201-748-6000, FAX 201-748-5915, uscs-wis@wiley.com, http://www.interscience.wiley.com/jpages/0021-9304:1/, http://www.wiley.com. Ed. James Anderson.

➤ **JOURNAL OF BIOMEDICINE AND BIOTECHNOLOGY.** see *MEDICAL SCIENCES*

660.6 576.5 USA ISSN 1524-0215
➤ **JOURNAL OF BIOMOLECULAR TECHNIQUES.** Text in English. 1998. q. USD 75 combined subscription to individuals print & online eds.; USD 100 combined subscription to institutions print & online eds. (effective 2005). **Document type:** *Journal, Academic/Scholarly.* **Description:** Aims to promote the central role biotechnology plays in contemporary research activities, to disseminate information among biomolecular resource facilities, and to communicate the biotechnology research conducted by the Association's research groups, association members and interested investigators.
Related titles: Online - full text ed.: (from EBSCO Publishing, HighWire Press).
—BLDSC (4953.870000), IE.
Published by: The Association of Biomolecular Resource Facilities, 2019 Galisteo St, Bldg. I, Santa Fe, NM 87505. TEL 505-983-8102, FAX 505-989-1073, abrf@abrf.org, http://jbt.abrf.org/, http://www.abrf.org. Ed. Clayton W. Naeve TEL 901-495-3861.

▼ ➤ **JOURNAL OF BIOPHARMACEUTICS AND BIOTECHNOLOGY.** see *PHARMACY AND PHARMACOLOGY*

➤ **JOURNAL OF BIOSCIENCE AND BIOENGINEERING.** see *BIOLOGY—Bioengineering*

660.6 NLD ISSN 0168-1656
CODEN: JBITD4
➤ **JOURNAL OF BIOTECHNOLOGY.** Text and summaries in English. 1984. 24/yr. EUR 3,305 in Europe to institutions; JPY 437,500 in Japan to institutions; USD 3,697 to institutions except Europe and Japan (effective 2006); y. adv. bk.rev. abstr. back issues avail.; reprint service avail. from ISI. **Document type:** *Academic/Scholarly.* **Description:** Provides a medium for full-length and short articles on various aspects of biotechnology.
Related titles: Microform ed.: (from PQC); Online - full text ed.: (from EBSCO Publishing, Gale Group, IngentaConnect, ScienceDirect, Swets Information Services).
Indexed: AEA, AEBA, AESIS, ASCA, ASFA, AbHyg, AgBio, Agr, AgrForAb, AnBrAb, B&AI, BCI, BIOBASE, BIOSIS Prev, BibAg, BioCN&I, BioDAb, BioEngAb, BiolAb, CBTA, CCI, CEABA, CIN, CPA, ChemAb, CurCont, CybAb, DBA, DSA, ESPM, EngInd, ExcerpMed, FCA, FPA, FS&TA, ForAb, HerbAb, HortAb, IABS, ISR, IndMed, IndVet, Inpharma, M&PBA, MBA, MEDLINE, MSB, MSCI, MaizeAb, NemAb, NutrAb, OrnHort, PBA, PE&ON, PGegResA, PGrRegA, PHN&I, PN&I, PotatoAb, ProtozoAb, RA&MP, RM&VM, RPP, Reac, RefZh, RevApplEntom, RiceAb, S&F, SCI, SIA, SeedAb, SoyAb, TDB, Telegen, TriticAb, VITIS, VetBull, WAE&RSA, WeedAb.
—BLDSC (4954.120000), CASDDS, CISTI, Ei, GNLM, IDS, IE, Infotrieve, ingenta, Linda Hall. **CCC.**
Published by: Elsevier BV (Subsidiary of: Elsevier Science & Technology), Radarweg 29, Amsterdam, 1043 NX, Netherlands. TEL 31-20-4853911, FAX 31-20-4852457, jbiotech@genetik.uni-bielefeld.de, nlinfo-f@elsevier.nl, http://www.elsevier.com/locate/jbiotec, http://www.elsevier.nl. Ed. A. Puehler.

660.6 GBR ISSN 0268-2575
TP248.13 CODEN: JCTBED
➤ **JOURNAL OF CHEMICAL TECHNOLOGY AND BIOTECHNOLOGY.** Text in English. 1951. m. USD 1,900 to institutions; USD 2,090 combined subscription to institutions print & online eds. (effective 2006). adv. illus. index. back issues avail.; reprint service avail. from ISI. **Document type:** *Journal, Academic/Scholarly.* **Description:** Covers studies related to the conversion of scientific discovery into products and processes in the areas of biotechnology and chemical technology, especially where these two areas interact.
Supersedes (as of 1986): Journal of Chemical Technology and Biotechnology. Part A: Chemical Technology (0264-3413); Journal of Chemical Technology and Biotechnology. Part B: Biotechnology (0264-3421); Which supersedes in part (with vol.33, 1983): Journal of Chemical Technology and Biotechnology (0142-0356); Journal of Applied Chemistry and Biotechnology (0375-9210); Which was formerly: Journal of Applied Chemistry (0021-8871)
Related titles: Microform ed.: (from PMC, PQC); Online - full content ed.: ISSN 1097-4660. 1996. USD 1,900 to institutions (effective 2006); Online - full text ed.: (from EBSCO Publishing, Gale Group, IngentaConnect, Swets Information Services, Wiley InterScience).
Indexed: AEA, AEBA, AESIS, APIAb, APICat, APIH&E, APIOC, APIPR, APIPS, APITS, AS&TI, ASCA, ASFA, AbHyg, AgBio, Agr, AgrForAb, AnalAb, B&BAb, BCI, BIOBASE, BIOSIS Prev, BibAg, BioCN&I, BioEngAb, BiolAb, BrCerAb, BrTechI, CBTA, CCI, CEA, CEABA, CISA, CLL, CPA, CTE, Cadscan, ChemAb, ChemInfo, CurCont, DBA, DSA, EIA, ESPM, EngInd, EnvAb, EnvEAb, ExcerpMed, FCA, FLUIDEX, FPA, FS&TA, ForAb, GEOBASE, GasAb, HortAb, I&DA, IABS, IMMAb, ISR, IndVet, Inspec, LeadAb, M&PBA, MEDLINE, MaizeAb, NutrAb, OrnHort, PBA, PGrRegA, PHN&I, PollutAb, PotatoAb, PoultAb, RAPRA, RCI, RM&VM, RPP, RefZh, RevApplEntom, RiceAb, S&F, SCI, SFA, SIA, SWRA, SoyAb, TCEA, Telegen, VITIS, VetBull, WRCInf, WSCA, WTA, WeedAb, WildRev, Zincscan.
—BLDSC (4957.089000), CASDDS, CINDOC, CISTI, Ei, IDS, IE, Infotrieve, ingenta, Linda Hall. **CCC.**

Published by: (Society of Chemical Industry), John Wiley & Sons Ltd. (Subsidiary of: John Wiley & Sons, Inc.), The Atrium, Southern Gate, Chichester, West Sussex PO19 8SQ, United Kingdom. TEL 44-1243-779777, FAX 44-1243-775878, customer@wiley.co.uk, http://www3.interscience.wiley.com/cgi-bin/jhome/2517, http://www.wiley.co.uk. Ed. J Melling. adv.: B&W page GBP 650, color page GBP 1,550; trim 210 x 297. Circ: 950. **Subscr. in the Americas to:** John Wiley & Sons, Inc., 111 River St, Hoboken, NJ 07030-5774. TEL 201-748-6645, 800-225-5945, subinfo@wiley.com.

660.6 GBR ISSN 1462-8732
CODEN: JCBOAQ

➤ **JOURNAL OF COMMERCIAL BIOTECHNOLOGY.** Text in English. 1994. q. GBP 100 in Europe to individuals based at educational establishments; USD 155 in North America to individuals based at educational establishments; GBP 115 elsewhere to individuals based at educational establishments; GBP 370 in Europe to institutions; USD 560 in North America to institutions; GBP 385 elsewhere to institutions (effective 2005). bk.rev. 96 p./no. 2 cols./p.; back issues avail.; reprint service avail. from PSC. **Document type:** *Journal, Academic/Scholarly.* **Description:** Provides systematic, comprehensive coverage of business and strategic management, regulation and research.

Formerly (until 1998): Journal of Biotechnology in Healthcare (1353-3010)

Related titles: Online - full text ed.: ISSN 1478-565X (from bigchalk, EBSCO Publishing, Gale Group, IngentaConnect, O C L C Online Computer Library Center, Inc., ProQuest Information & Learning, Swets Information Services).

Indexed: ABIn, AgBio, AnBrAb, DBA, ExcerpMed, IndVet, PBA, PN&I, RefZh, WAE&RSA.

—BLDSC (4961.071000), CISTI, IE, ingenta. **CCC.**

Published by: Palgrave Macmillan Ltd. (Subsidiary of: Macmillan Publishers Ltd.), Houndmills, Basingstoke, Hants RG21 6XS, United Kingdom. TEL 44-1256-329242, FAX 44-1256-810526, journal-info@palgrave.com, http://www.palgrave-journals.com/. Circ: 600 (paid).

660.62 DEU ISSN 1367-5435
QR53 CODEN: JIMBFL

➤ **JOURNAL OF INDUSTRIAL MICROBIOLOGY AND BIOTECHNOLOGY.** Text in English. 1986. m. EUR 1,080 combined subscription to institutions print & online eds. (effective 2005). adv. bk.rev. illus.; charts; stat. cum.index. back issues avail.; reprints avail. **Document type:** *Journal, Academic/Scholarly.* **Description:** Publishes original research articles, short communications, critical reviews in the fields of biotechnology, fermentation, environmental microbiology, biodegradation, biodeterioration, quality control, and other areas of applied microbiology.

Formerly: Journal of Industrial Microbiology (0169-4146)

Related titles: Online - full text ed.: ISSN 1476-5535 (from EBSCO Publishing, O C L C Online Computer Library Center, Inc., Springer LINK, Swets Information Services).

Indexed: AEA, AEBA, ASCA, ASFA, AbHyg, AgBio, Agr, AgrForAb, AnBrAb, BCI, BIOBASE, BIOSIS Prev, BioCN&I, BioDAb, BioEngAb, BiolAb, CBTA, CEABA, CIN, ChemAb, ChemTitl, CurCont, DBA, DSA, ESPM, EngInd, ExcerpMed, FCA, FPA, FS&TA, ForAb, HerbAb, HortAb, IABS, ISR, IndVet, Inpharma, M&PBA, MBA, MEDLINE, MaizeAb, NemAb, NutrAb, PBA, PE&ON, PHN&I, PN&I, PotatoAb, PoultAb, ProtozoAb, RA&MP, RM&VM, RPP, Reac, RevApplEntom, S&F, SCI, SIA, SeedAb, SoyAb, TriticAb, VITIS, VetBull, WAE&RSA, WeedAb.

—BLDSC (5006.330500), CASDDS, CISTI, Ei, IDS, IE, Infotrieve, ingenta, Linda Hall. **CCC.**

Published by: (Society for Industrial Microbiology USA), Springer-Verlag (Subsidiary of: Springer Science+Business Media), Tiergartenstr 17, Heidelberg, 69121, Germany. TEL 49-6221-3450, FAX 49-6221-345229. Ed. Dr. Joseph J Cooney. Adv. contact Stephan Kroeck TEL 49-30-827875739. **Subscr. to:** Springer GmbH Auslieferungsgesellschaft, Haberstr 7, Heidelberg 69126, Germany. TEL 49-6221-345-0, FAX 49-6221-345-4229, subscriptions@springer.de; Springer-Verlag New York, Inc., Journal Fulfillment, PO Box 2485, Secaucus, NJ 07096-2485. TEL 800-777-4643, 201-348-4033, FAX 201-348-4505, journals@springer-ny.com, http://www.springer-ny.com.

▼ ➤ **JOURNAL OF INTERNATIONAL BIOTECHNOLOGY LAW.** see *LAW*

660.62 KOR ISSN 1017-7825
CODEN: JOMBES

➤ **JOURNAL OF MICROBIOLOGY AND BIOTECHNOLOGY.** Text in English. 1991. bi-m. KRW 25,000 domestic; USD 50 foreign (effective 2005). 96 p./no.; **Document type:** *Journal, Academic/Scholarly.* **Description:** Devoted to the advancement and dissemination of scientific knowledge concerning microbiology, biotechnology, and related academic disciplines.

Related titles: ◆ Korean ed.: Han'gug Mi'saengmul Saengmyeong Gong Haghoeji. ISSN 1598-642X.

Indexed: ASCA, BCI, BIOBASE, BIOSIS Prev, BiolAb, ChemAb, ChemTitl, ExcerpMed, IABS, ISR, MSB, SCI, VITIS.

—BLDSC (5019.285900), CASDDS, CISTI, IDS, IE, Infotrieve, ingenta. **CCC.**

Published by: Korean Society for Applied Microbiology, The Korea Science and Technology Center 507, 635-4 Yeogsam-dong, Kangnam-Gu, Seoul, 135-703, Korea, S. TEL 82-2-5524733, FAX 82-2-5524732, http://society.kisti.re.kr/~ksam/jmb/index.html, http://society.kisti.re.kr/~ksam/index.html. Ed. Ick-Dong Yoo.

➤ **JOURNAL OF MYCOPATHOLOGICAL RESEARCH.** see *BIOLOGY—Microbiology*

660.6 GBR ISSN 1477-3155
T174.7

➤ **JOURNAL OF NANOBIOTECHNOLOGY.** Text in English. irreg. free (effective 2006). **Document type:** *Journal, Academic/Scholarly.* **Description:** Covers all aspects of scientific and technological advances in the fields of medical, biological and nanoscale sciences.

Media: Online - full content (from EBSCO Publishing, National Library of Medicine).

Indexed: ExcerpMed.

—CCC.

Published by: BioMed Central Ltd. (Subsidiary of: Current Science Ltd), Middlesex House, 34-42 Cleveland St, London, W1T 4LB, United Kingdom. TEL 44-20-73230323, FAX 44-20-76319923, nanobiotechnology@uku.co.uk, info@biomedcentral.com, http://www.jnanobiotechnology.com/home, http://www.biomedcentral.com. Ed. Dr. Mikhail Soloviev.

➤ **JOURNAL OF PLANT BIOCHEMISTRY AND BIOTECHNOLOGY.** see *BIOLOGY—Biochemistry*

660.6 543 SWE ISSN 1651-1778

KEMIVAERLDEN BIOTECH. Text in Swedish. 2002. 9/yr. SEK 363 domestic; SEK 461 foreign (effective 2003). adv.

—BLDSC (5089.358100).

Published by: Mentor Online AB, Tryffelslingan 10, PO Box 72001, Lidingoe, 18172, Sweden. TEL 46-8-6704100, FAX 46-8-6616455. Ed. Sverker Nyman TEL 46-8-6704270. Adv. contact Stephan Martins TEL 46-8-6704185. B&W page SEK 20,960, color page SEK 26,850; 210 x 297. Circ: 12,000.

660.6 658.8 GBR

KEY NOTE MARKET REPORT: BIOTECHNOLOGY. Variant title: Biotechnology. Text in English. irreg., latest vol.4, 1991. **Document type:** *Trade.*

Former titles: Key Note Report: Biotechnology; (until 1988): Key Note Report. Biotechnology Products (0268-4497)

Indexed: BibAg.

—CCC.

Published by: Key Note Ltd., Field House, 72 Oldfield Rd, Hampton, Mddx TW12 2HQ, United Kingdom. TEL 44-20-8481-8750, FAX 44-20-8783-0049, info@keynote.co.uk, http://www.keynote.co.uk.

660.6 JPN

KINKI BIO-INDUSTRY CONFERENCE. BIO INDUSTRY. Text in Japanese. bi-m.

Published by: Kinki Baioindasutori Shinko Kaigi/Kinki Bio-Industry Conference, Kagaku Gijutsu Senta, 8-4 Utsubohon-Machi 1-chome, Nishi-ku, Osaka-shi, 550-0004, Japan.

663 641 DEU ISSN 0341-2067

KLEINBRENNEREI. Text in German. 1949. m. EUR 37.20 domestic; EUR 41 foreign; EUR 3 newsstand/cover (effective 2004). adv. bk.rev. **Document type:** *Magazine, Trade.* **Description:** Covers all aspects of the biotechnology of fruit and grain distillation.

Indexed: FS&TA.

—BLDSC (5099.083000). **CCC.**

Published by: Verlag Eugen Ulmer GmbH, Wollgrasweg 41, Stuttgart, 70599, Germany. TEL 49-711-45070, FAX 49-711-4507120, info@ulmer.de, http://www.ulmer.de. Ed. H J Pieper. Adv. contact Dieter Boger. B&W page EUR 1,976, color page EUR 2,516; trim 185 x 260. Circ: 8,463 (paid and controlled).

660.6 DEU ISSN 1611-0854

LABORWELT. Text in German. 2000. bi-m. free to qualified personnel. adv. **Document type:** *Journal, Trade.*

Published by: Biocom AG, Stralsunder Str 58-59, Berlin, 13355, Germany. TEL 49-30-2649210, FAX 49-30-26492111, service@biocom.de, http://www.biocom.de. Eds. Thomas Gabrielczyk, Veronika Szentpetery. Adv. contact Oliver Schnell. B&W page EUR 4,000. Circ: 20,000 (paid and controlled).

▼ **LIFE SCIENCE LABORATORY.** see *MEDICAL SCIENCES*

660.6 DEU ISSN 1618-3037

M P I SERIES IN BIOLOGICAL CYBERNETICS. (Max-Planck-Institut) Text in German. 2001. irreg., latest vol.4, 2003. price varies. **Document type:** *Monographic series, Academic/Scholarly.*

Published by: (Max-Planck-Institut fuer biologische Kybernetik), Logos Verlag Berlin, Comeniushof, Gubener Str 47, Berlin, 10243, Germany. TEL 49-30-42851090, FAX 49-30-42851092, redaktion@logos-verlag.de, http://www.logos-verlag.de. Ed. Nicos Logothetis.

MACROMOLECULAR BIOSCIENCE. see *BIOLOGY—Biochemistry*

▼ **MACROVIEW.** see *PHARMACY AND PHARMACOLOGY*

660.6 630 CRI ISSN 1016-0469

➤ **MANEJO INTEGRADO DE PLAGAS.** Text in Spanish. 1992. q. **Document type:** *Journal, Academic/Scholarly.* **Description:** It serves as a forum to exchange information on the results of research in the field of agriculture.

Indexed: AgBio, AgrForAb, BioCN&I, FCA, FPA, ForAb, HerbAb, HortAb, MaizeAb, NemAb, OrnHort, PBA, PGegResA, PHN&I, RDA, RM&VM, RPP, S&F, SIA, SeedAb, SoyAb, WAE&RSA, WeedAb, ZooRec.

Published by: Centro Agronomico Tropical de Investigacion y Ensenanza/Tropical Agricultural Research and Training Center, Catie, Turrialba, 7170, Costa Rica. TEL 506-556-6431, FAX 506-556-1533, http://www.catie.ac.cr. Circ: 1,000.

660.62 USA ISSN 1436-2228
TP248.27.M37 CODEN: MABIFW

➤ **MARINE BIOTECHNOLOGY.** Text in English. 1998. bi-m. (in 1 vol., 6 nos./vol.). EUR 578 combined subscription to institutions print & online eds. (effective 2005). adv. illus. back issues avail.; reprints avail. **Document type:** *Journal, Academic/Scholarly.* **Description:** Addresses biotechnology applications of marine life, including the study of the biological processes of oceans and organisms.

Formed by the merger of (1992-1998): Molecular Marine Biology and Biotechnology (1053-6426); (1993-1998): Journal of Marine Biotechnology (0941-2905)

Related titles: Online - full text ed.: ISSN 1436-2236 (from EBSCO Publishing, Springer LINK, Swets Information Services).

Indexed: ASCA, ASFA, AgBio, AnBrAb, B&BAb, BCI, BIOBASE, BIOSIS Prev, BioEngAb, BiolAb, CIN, ChemAb, ChemTitl, CurCont, DBA, DSA, ESPM, ForAb, GEOBASE, HGA, HortAb, IABS, ISR, IndMed, IndVet, MBA, MEDLINE, NutrAb, OceAb, OrnHort, PBA, PN&I, PollutAb, ProtozoAb, RM&VM, RPP, RefZh, S&F, SCI, SFA, SIA, TDB, VetBull, ZooRec.

—BLDSC (5373.730000), CASDDS, CISTI, IDS, IE, Infotrieve, ingenta, Linda Hall. **CCC.**

Published by: (American Society of Molecular Marine Biology & Biotechnology), Springer-Verlag New York, Inc. (Subsidiary of: Springer Science+Business Media), 233 Spring St, New York, NY 10013. TEL 212-460-1500, 800-777-4643, FAX 212-473-6272, journals@springer-ny.com, http://link.springer.de/link/service/journals/10126, http://www.springer-ny.com. Eds. J Grant Burgess, Shigetoh Miyachi TEL 81-3-5684-6211, Thomas T Chen TEL 860-486-5011. **Subscr. outside the Americas to:** Springer GmbH Auslieferungsgesellschaft, Haberstr 7, Heidelberg 69126, Germany. TEL 49-6221-345-0, FAX 49-6221-345-4229, subscriptions@springer.de; **Subscr. to:** Journal Fulfillment, PO Box 2485, Secaucus, NJ 07096-2485. TEL 201-348-4033, FAX 201-348-4505.

➤ **MATERIALS SCIENCE AND ENGINEERING C: BIOMIMETIC MATERIALS, SENSORS AND SYSTEMS.** see *ENGINEERING—Engineering Mechanics And Materials*

➤ **MEDICAL AND BIOMEDICAL ENGINEERING REPORTS.** see *ENGINEERING*

➤ **MEDICAL & PHARMACEUTICAL BIOTECHNOLOGY ABSTRACTS (ONLINE EDITION).** see *MEDICAL SCIENCES—Abstracting, Bibliographies, Statistics*

660.6 USA ISSN 0737-8483

MEMBRANE & SEPARATION TECHNOLOGY NEWS. Text in English. 1982 (Sep.). m. USD 500 domestic; USD 550 foreign; USD 45 newsstand/cover domestic; USD 50 newsstand/cover foreign (effective 2005). **Document type:** *Newsletter, Academic/Scholarly.*

Related titles: Online - full text ed.: (from Data-Star, Factiva, Florida Center for Library Automation, Gale Group, LexisNexis, Northern Light Technology, Inc., The Dialog Corporation).

—CCC.

Published by: Business Communications Co., Inc., 25 Van Zant St, Ste 13, Norwalk, CT 06855-1781. TEL 203-853-4266, FAX 203-853-0348, info@bccresearch.com, http://www.buscom.com/letters/mstnpromo/mstnpromo.html, http://www.bccresearch.com. Ed. Alan Hall. Pub. Louis Naturman. Circ: 375.

660.6 USA ISSN 1054-4984
TP159.M4

MEMBRANE TECHNOLOGY REVIEWS. Text in English. 1986. a., latest 1997. USD 1,850 (effective 2005). **Document type:** *Academic/Scholarly.* **Description:** For academic and industrial scientists and engineers who are participating in new areas of membrane research and development. Covers oil and water separations, downstream processing of biologicals, wastewater treatment and the synthesis of specialties based on new vegetable oils.

Published by: Business Communications Co., Inc., 25 Van Zant St, Ste 13, Norwalk, CT 06855-1781. TEL 203-853-4266, FAX 203-853-0348, info@bccresearch.com, http://www.bccresearch.com.

660.6 USA
➤ **METHODS IN BIOTECHNOLOGY.** Text in English. 1996. irreg., latest vol.16, 2002. price varies. illus. Index. 400 p./no.; back issues avail.; reprints avail. **Document type:** *Monographic series, Academic/Scholarly.* **Description:** Offers the latest step-by-step laboratory methods for biotechnology and enzyme engineering.
Indexed: MSB.
—BLDSC (5747.050000), ingenta.
Published by: Humana Press, Inc., 999 Riverview Dr, Ste 208, Totowa, NJ 07512. TEL 973-256-1699, FAX 973-256-8341, humana@humanapr.com, http://humanapress.com/journals.pasp. Ed. John M Walker. R&P Richard Hruska.

660.6 JPN
MICROBIAL UTILIZATION OF RENEWABLE RESOURCES. Text in English. 1980. a. **Document type:** *Proceedings, Academic/Scholarly.*
Indexed: CIN, ChemAb, ChemTitl.
Published by: Osaka University, International Center for Biotechnology/Osaka Daigaku Seibutsu Kogaku Kokusai Koryu Senta, 2-1 Yamada-Oka, Suita-shi, Osaka-fu 565-0871, Japan. TEL 81-6-879-7455, FAX 81-79-7454, http://www.icb.osaka-u.ac.jp/. Ed. Toshiomi Yoshida.

MICROSPHERES, MICROCAPSULES & LIPOSOMES. see *PHARMACY AND PHARMACOLOGY*

660.6 ITA ISSN 1120-4826
CODEN: MIBIFK
➤ **MINERVA BIOTECNOLOGICA.** Text in English. 1989. q. EUR 133 to individuals; EUR 206 to institutions (effective 2005). adv. **Document type:** *Journal, Academic/Scholarly.* **Description:** Covers biotechnology and molecular biology.
Related titles: Microform ed.: (from PQC); Online - full text ed.: (from bigchalk, Northern Light Technology, Inc., ProQuest Information & Learning).
Indexed: ASCA, BCI, BIOBASE, ExcerpMed, IABS, RefZh, VITIS.
—BLDSC (5794.053000), IDS, IE, ingenta. **CCC.**
Published by: Edizioni Minerva Medica, Corso Bramante 83-85, Turin, 10126, Italy. TEL 39-011-678282, FAX 39-011-674502, journals.dept@minervamedica.it, http://www.minervamedica.it. Pub. Alberto Oliaro. Adv. contact F Filippo. B&W page USD 1,200, color page USD 2,000; trim 280 x 215. Circ: 5,000 (paid).

660.6 610 USA ISSN 1073-6085
TP248.13 CODEN: MLBOEO
➤ **MOLECULAR BIOTECHNOLOGY.** Abbreviated title: M B. (Part B of Applied Biochemistry and Biotechnology (ISSN 0273-2289)) Text in English. 1994. 9/yr. USD 195 to individuals; USD 595 to institutions; USD 205 combined subscription to individuals print & online eds.; USD 645 combined subscription to institutions print & online eds. (effective 2005). adv. bk.rev.; software rev. 120 p./no.; back issues avail.; reprints avail. **Document type:** *Journal, Academic/Scholarly.* **Description:** Provides detailed laboratory protocols and methods for molecular biology techniques, and publishes review articles and critical research results on the application of these techniques in basic and applied research in biotechnology.
Related titles: Online - full text ed.: USD 185 to individuals; USD 585 to institutions (effective 2005) (from EBSCO Publishing, IngentaConnect, O C L C Online Computer Library Center, Inc., Ovid Technologies, Inc., Swets Information Services).
Indexed: AEBA, ASCA, AgBio, Agr, AnBrAb, BCI, BIOBASE, BIOSIS Prev, BibAg, BioEngAb, BiolAb, CEABA, CIN, ChemAb, ChemTitl, CurCont, ESPM, ExcerpMed, FS&TA, IndMed, M&PBA, MBA, MEDLINE, MSB, PBA, RefZh, VITIS.
—BLDSC (5900.798400), CASDDS, CISTI, GNLM, IDS, IE, Infotrieve, ingenta, Linda Hall. **CCC.**
Published by: Humana Press, Inc., 999 Riverview Dr, Ste 208, Totowa, NJ 07512. TEL 973-256-1699, FAX 973-256-8341, humana@humanapr.com, http://humanapress.com/journals.pasp. Ed. John M Walker. Pub. Thomas B. Lanigan Jr. R&P Wendy A. Warren. Adv. contacts John Chasse, Thomas B. Lanigan Jr. Circ: 500. **Subscr. to:** Maruzen Co., Ltd., 3-10 Nihonbashi, 2-Chome, Chuo-ku, Tokyo 103, Japan. TEL 81-3-3275-8591, FAX 81-3-3275-0657, journal@maruzen.co.jp, http://www.maruzen.co.jp.

➤ **MOLECULAR BREEDING**; new strategies in plant improvement. see *BIOLOGY—Botany*

➤ **MOLECULAR IMAGING.** see *BIOLOGY—Cytology And Histology*

660.6 USA
NANOBIOTECH NEWS. Text in English. w. USD 995 (effective 2005). **Document type:** *Newsletter, Trade.* **Description:** Provides intelligence, news and analysis on the emerging nanobiotech market.
Published by: National Health Information, LLC, PO Box 15429, Atlanta, GA 30333. TEL 404-607-9500, FAX 404-607-0095, nhi@nhionline.net, http://www.nhionline.net.

660.6 USA ISSN 1551-1286
▼ ➤ **NANOBIOTECHNOLOGY.** Text in English. 2005. q. USD 195 to individuals; USD 725 to institutions (effective 2005). **Document type:** *Journal, Academic/Scholarly.*
Related titles: Online - full text ed.: ISSN 1551-1294. USD 695 (effective 2004).
—**CCC.**
Published by: Humana Press, Inc., 999 Riverview Dr, Ste 208, Totowa, NJ 07512. TEL 973-256-1699, FAX 973-256-8341, humana@humanapr.com, http://humanapress.com.

660.6029 USA ISSN 1074-9942
HD9999.B443
NATIONAL BIOTECH REGISTER. Text in English. 1992. a. USD 87.50 (effective 2001). adv. pat. 184 p./no. 3 cols./p.; **Document type:** *Directory, Trade.* **Description:** Provides current, comprehensive coverage of material on research and development activity in the biotechnology industry. Outlines the focus of 3500 leading companies and classifies them by research activity.
Published by: Barry Inc., PO Box 551, Wilmington, MA 01887-0551. TEL 978-658-0442, FAX 978-657-8691, info@biotech-register.com, http://www.biotech-register.com. Ed. Joan Carrns. Adv. contact Sharon Baratta TEL 978-658-0442. Circ: 6,000 (controlled).

660.6 USA ISSN 1087-0156
TP248.3 CODEN: NABIF9
➤ **NATURE BIOTECHNOLOGY.** Text in English. 1983. m. EUR 1,744 in Europe to institutions Eurozone; USD 2,025 in the Americas to institutions; GBP 1,125 to institutions in the UK & elsewhere; EUR 153 combined subscription in Europe to individuals Eurozone; print & online; USD 178 combined subscription in the Americas to individuals print & online; GBP 99 combined subscription to individuals in the UK & elsewhere; print & online (effective 2006). bk.rev. charts; illus.; tr.lit. back issues avail. **Document type:** *Journal, Academic/Scholarly.* **Description:** Provides a first source for finding reports on the increasing number of important developments in the international industrial biotechnology industries.
Formerly (until vol.14, no.3, Mar. 1996): Bio-Technology (0733-222X)
Related titles: E-mail ed.; Microfilm ed.: (from PQC); Online - full text ed.: (from EBSCO Publishing, Swets Information Services).
Indexed: ABIPC, AEBA, AIDS&CR, ASCA, ASFA, AbHyg, AgBio, Agr, AnBrAb, B&AI, B&BAb, BCI, BIOBASE, BIOSIS Prev, BioCN&I, BioEngAb, BiolAb, BiolDig, CBTA, CEABA, CIJE, CIN, CPA, CTA, ChemAb, ChemTitl, ChemoAb, CurCont, DBA, DSA, ESPM, EngInd, EntAb, ExcerpMed, FCA, FPA, FS&TA, ForAb, GenetAb, HGA, HelmAb, HerbAb, HortAb, IABS, INIS AtomInd, ISR, IndMed, IndVet, Inpharma, M&PBA, MBA, MEDLINE, MaizeAb, NRN, NSA, NemAb, NucAcAb, NutrAb, OGFA, PBA, PE&ON, PGegResA, PGrRegA, PHN&I, PN&I, PotatoAb, PoultAb, ProtozoAb, RA&MP, RASB, RM&VM, RPP, Reac, RefZh, RevApplEntom, RiceAb, S&F, SCI, SIA, SSCI, SeedAb, SoyAb, TDB, Telegen, TriticAb, VITIS, VetBull, ViroIAbstr, WAE&RSA, WRCInf, WeedAb.
—BLDSC (6046.257000), CASDDS, CISTI, Ei, GNLM, IDS, IE, Infotrieve, ingenta, Linda Hall. **CCC.**
Published by: Nature Publishing Group (Subsidiary of: Macmillan Publishers Ltd.), 345 Park Ave S, 10th Fl, New York, NY 10010. TEL 212-726-9200, FAX 212-696-9635, biotech@natureny.com, http://www.nature.com/nbt. Ed. Andrew Marshall. Pub. Beatrice Renault. Circ: 15,000 (paid). **Subscr. in the Americas to:** PO Box 5161, Brentwood, TN 37024-5161. TEL 615-850-5315, 800-524-0384, FAX 615-377-0525, subscriptions@natureny.com; **Subscr. to:** Nature Publishing Group, Brunel Rd, Houndmills, Basingstoke, Hamps RG21 6XS, United Kingdom. TEL 44-1256-329242, FAX 44-1256-812358, subscriptions@nature.com.

➤ **NATURE BIOTECHNOLOGY DIRECTORY (YEAR).** see *BUSINESS AND ECONOMICS—Trade And Industrial Directories*

660.6 NGA ISSN 0189-1731
NIGERIAN JOURNAL OF BIOTECHNOLOGY. Text in English. 1983. a. **Document type:** *Journal, Academic/Scholarly.*
Indexed: AEBA, B&BAb, ESPM, M&PBA.
Published by: Biotechnology Society of Nigeria, c/o University of Jos, Faculty of Natural Sciences, P MB 2084, Jos, Nigeria. aginaseng@yahoo.com. Ed. Umaru D Ali.

660.6 JPN ISSN 0285-4600
NIKKEI BIOTECHNOLOGY/NIKKEI BAIOTEKU. Text in Japanese. 1981. bi-w. JPY 151,200 (effective 2000). **Document type:** *Newsletter, Trade.* **Description:** Covers biotechnology developments.
Published by: Nikkei Business Publications Inc. (Subsidiary of: Nihon Keizai Shimbun, Inc.), 2-7-6 Hirakawa-cho, Chiyoda-ku, Tokyo, 102-8622, Japan. TEL 81-3-5210-8311, FAX 81-3-5210-8530, info@nikkeibp-america.com, http://www.nikkeibp.com. Ed. Isao Yokoyama. Pub. Hitoshi Sawai. **Dist. in America by:** Nikkei Business Publications America Inc., 575 Fifth Ave, 20th Fl, New York, NY 10017.

660.6 630.24 JPN ISSN 0002-1407
CODEN: NNKKAA
NIPPON NOGEIKAGAKU KAISHI/AGRICULTURAL CHEMICAL SOCIETY OF JAPAN. JOURNAL/JAPAN SOCIETY FOR BIOSCIENCE, BIOTECHNOLOGY, AND AGROCHEMISTRY. JOURNAL. Text in Japanese; Contents page in English. 1924. m. USD 200 to non-members; USD 80 to members. adv. bk.rev. **Document type:** *Academic/Scholarly.* **Description:** Contains original and review papers in the fields of bioscience, biotechnology and biochemistry.
Related titles: ♦ English ed.: Bioscience, Biotechnology, and Biochemistry. ISSN 0916-8451.
Indexed: ASCA, ASFA, AgBio, AgrForAb, AnBrAb, BIOSIS Prev, BioCN&I, BiolAb, CBTA, CEABA, CIN, CPA, ChemAb, ChemTitl, CurCR, CurCont, DSA, FCA, FPA, FS&TA, ForAb, HerbAb, HortAb, INIS AtomInd, IndChem, IndVet, JTA, MOS, MSB, MaizeAb, NPU, NemAb, NutrAb, OrnHort, PBA, PGegResA, PGrRegA, PHN&I, PotatoAb, RA&MP, RCI, RDA, RM&VM, RPP, RefZh, RevApplEntom, RiceAb, S&F, SFA, SIA, SeedAb, SoyAb, TDB, TriticAb, VetBull, WeedAb.
—BLDSC (6113.431500), CASDDS, CISTI, IDS, IE, Linda Hall. **CCC.**
Published by: Nippon Nogeikagaku Kai/Japan Society for Bioscience, Biotechnology and Agrochemistry, c/o Japan Academic Societies Centre Bldg, 2-4-16 Yayoi, Bunkyo-ku, Tokyo, 113-0032, Japan. FAX 81-3-3815-1920, http://www.jsbba.or.jp/e/index_e.html. Ed. Shuichi Kaminogawa. Circ: 13,800.

NONGYE SHENGWU JISHU XUEBAO/JOURNAL OF AGRICULTURAL BIOTECHNOLOGY. see *AGRICULTURE*

660.6 USA
NORTH AMERICAN BIOTECHNOLOGY DIRECTORY. Text in English. a. USD 95 (effective 2002). **Document type:** *Directory, Trade.*
Published by: Atlantic Communications, 1635 W Alabama, Houston, TX 77006. TEL 713-529-1616, FAX 713-520-0936.

660.6 USA
NUTRACEUTICAL SCIENCE AND TECHNOLOGY. Text in English. irreg., latest vol.2, 2004. USD 175 per vol. (effective 2005). **Document type:** *Monographic series, Academic/Scholarly.*
—BLDSC (6187.204500).
Published by: Marcel Dekker Inc. (Subsidiary of: Taylor & Francis Group), 270 Madison Ave, New York, NY 10016-0602. TEL 212-696-9000, FAX 212-685-4540, custserv@dekker.com, http://www.dekker.com. Ed. Fereidoon Shahidi. **Subscr. to:** 6000 Broken Sound Pkwy NW, Ste. 300, Boca Raton, FL 33487-2713. TEL 800-228-1160.

O M I C S: A JOURNAL OF INTEGRATIVE BIOLOGY. see *BIOLOGY—Genetics*

660.6 JPN ISSN 0912-7550
OKAYAMAKEN BAIOTEKUNOROJI KENKYUJO KENKYU NENPO/OKAYAMA PREFECTURAL RESEARCH INSTITUTE OF BIOTECHNOLOGY. ANNUAL REPORT. Text in Japanese. 1986. a.
Published by: Okayamaken Baiotekunoroji Kenkyujo/Okayama Prefectural Research Institute of Biotechnology, 1174-1 Kodaoki, Akaiwa-gun, Sanyo-cho, Okayama-ken 709-0800, Japan. TEL 08695-5-0271, FAX 08695-5-1914. Ed. Nobutomo Takagi.

P T INDUSTRIEEL MANAGEMENT. (Polytechnisch Tijdschrift) see *ENGINEERING*

615.285 USA ISSN 1078-0467
CODEN: PHBIEB
PHARMACEUTICAL BIOTECHNOLOGY. Text in English. 1992. irreg., latest vol.14, 2002. price varies. back issues avail. **Document type:** *Monographic series, Academic/Scholarly.* **Description:** Scholarly monographs on theoretical and practical advances in the pharmaceutical sciences, focusing on biotechnology applications and developments in drug dosage design.
Indexed: CIN, ChemAb, ChemTitl, IndMed, MEDLINE.
—BLDSC (6442.770000), CISTI, IE, Infotrieve, ingenta. **CCC.**
Published by: Springer-Verlag New York, Inc. (Subsidiary of: Springer Science+Business Media), 233 Spring St, New York, NY 10013. TEL 212-460-1500, FAX 212-460-1575, service@springer-ny.com, http://www.springer-ny.com.

PHARMACEUTICAL STRATEGIC ALLIANCES; the drug and biotech alliances reference guide. see *PHARMACY AND PHARMACOLOGY*

660.6 PHL ISSN 0117-0503
PHILIPPINE JOURNAL OF BIOTECHNOLOGY. Text in English. 1990. s-a. PHP 100; USD 40 foreign. 6455.0800000.
Indexed: IPP.
Published by: Philippine Council for Advanced Science and Technology Research and Development, Department of Science and Technology, Taguig Mm, Philippines. TEL 63-49-536-1620, FAX 63-49-536-2721, ecu@biotech.uplb.edu.ph. Ed. Reynaldo E Dela Cruz. **Co-sponsors:** National Institute of Molecular Biology and Biotechnology; University of Philippines Los Banos.

PIRTFERM PAPERS. see *ENVIRONMENTAL STUDIES—Waste Management*

660.6 USA
PLANKETT'S BIOTECH & GENETICS INDUSTRY ALMANAC. Text in English. a. USD 249.99 (effective 2005). **Description:** Complete guide to research, growth companies, proteomics, genomics.

B

▼ new title ➤ refereed ✶ unverified ♦ full entry avail.

Published by: Plunkett Research, Ltd, PO Drawer 541737, Houston, TX 77254-1737. TEL 713-932-0000, FAX 713-932-7080, info@plunkettresearch.com, http://www.plunkettresearch.com.

PLANT BIOTECHNOLOGY. see *BIOLOGY—Abstracting, Bibliographies, Statistics*

PLANT BIOTECHNOLOGY. see *BIOLOGY—Botany*

PLANT BIOTECHNOLOGY. see *BIOLOGY—Botany*

PLANT GENE RESEARCH; basic knowledge and application. see *BIOLOGY—Genetics*

PLANT PROTECTION QUARTERLY. see *AGRICULTURE—Crop Production And Soil*

PLANT TISSUE CULTURE AND BIOTECHNOLOGY. see *BIOLOGY—Botany*

571.2 NLD
PLANT TISSUE CULTURE MANUAL; fundamentals and applications. Text in English. 1991. base vol. plus irreg. updates. looseleaf. price varies. Supplement avail. **Document type:** *Academic/Scholarly.* **Description:** Presents a broad range of techniques for research workers in the fields of cell and molecular biology, physiology, plant breeding and propagation and genetic engineering.
Published by: Springer-Verlag Dordrecht (Subsidiary of: Springer Science+Business Media), Van Godewijckstraat 30, Dordrecht, 3311 GX, Netherlands. TEL 31-78-6576050, FAX 31-78-6576474, http://www.springeronline.com. Ed. Keith Lindsey.

POLITECHNIKA LODZKA. ZESZYTY NAUKOWE. CHEMIA SPOZYWCZA I BIOTECHNOLOGIA. see *CHEMISTRY—Organic Chemistry*

660.6 630 NLD ISSN 0925-5214
SB129 CODEN: PBTEED
➤ **POSTHARVEST BIOLOGY AND TECHNOLOGY.** Text in English. 1991. 12/yr. EUR 1,103 in Europe to institutions; JPY 146,500 in Japan to institutions; USD 1,236 to institutions except Europe and Japan (effective 2006). adv. bk.rev. back issues avail. **Document type:** *Journal, Academic/Scholarly.* **Description:** Contains original papers and review articles on biological and technological research on postharvest handling or treatment, quality evaluation, packaging, transportation, storage and distribution of agronomic (including forage) and horticultural crops.
Related titles: Microform ed.: (from PQC); Online - full text ed.: (from EBSCO Publishing, Gale Group, IngentaConnect, ScienceDirect, Swets Information Services).
Indexed: AEA, ASCA, ASFA, AgBio, Agr, AgrForAb, B&BAb, BIOBASE, BioCN&I, CIN, CPA, ChemAb, ChemTitl, CurCont, DSA, ESPM, EntAb, FCA, FS&TA, ForAb, GardL, HortAb, IABS, ISR, MaizeAb, NutrAb, OrnHort, PBA, PGegResA, PGrRegA, PHN&I, PlantSci, PotatoAb, PoultAb, RA&MP, RPP, RevApplEntom, RiceAb, S&F, SCI, SIA, SeedAb, SoyAb, TriticAb, VITIS, WAE&RSA, WeedAb.
—BLDSC (6563.921500), CASDDS, CISTI, IDS, IE, Infotrieve, ingenta. **CCC.**
Published by: Elsevier BV (Subsidiary of: Elsevier Science & Technology), Radarweg 29, Amsterdam, 1043 NX, Netherlands. TEL 31-20-4853911, FAX 31-20-4852457, nlinfo-f@elsevier.nl, http://www.elsevier.com/locate/postharvbio, http://www.elsevier.nl. Eds. I B Ferguson, R P Cavalieri.

660.6 USA ISSN 1542-9431
RM301.25 CODEN: PRECC8
▼ ➤ **PRECLINICA.** Text in English. 2003 (Mar./Apr.). bi-m. USD 65 to individuals; USD 200 to institutions; free to qualified personnel (effective 2005). **Document type:** *Journal, Academic/Scholarly.* **Description:** Covers all aspects of preclinical research required before clinical trials.
—BLDSC (6604.090000), IE. **CCC.**
Published by: Eaton Publishing Co., One Research Dr, Suite 400A, PO Box 1070, Westboro, MA 01581. TEL 508-614-1414, FAX 508-616-2930, http://www.preclinica.com. Ed. Fintan R. Steele.

➤ **PREPARATIVE BIOCHEMISTRY AND BIOTECHNOLOGY.** see *BIOLOGY—Biochemistry*

660.6 GBR ISSN 1359-5113
TP500 CODEN: PRBCAP
➤ **PROCESS BIOCHEMISTRY.** Text in English. 1966. 12/yr. EUR 1,356 in Europe to institutions; JPY 179,900 in Japan to institutions; USD 1,515 to institutions except Europe and Japan (effective 2006). adv. bk.rev. charts; illus.; tr.lit. index. **Document type:** *Journal, Academic/Scholarly.* **Description:** Reports advances in the science and technology of the application of living organisms to processing and production methods in the food, beverage and pharmaceutical industries, and the energy, waste and water treatment industries.
Formerly (until 1991): Process Biochemistry International (0963-4940); (until 1990): Process Biochemistry (0032-9592)
Related titles: Microform ed.: (from PQC); Online - full text ed.: (from EBSCO Publishing, Gale Group, IngentaConnect, ScienceDirect, Swets Information Services).
Indexed: AEA, AEBA, ASCA, ASFA, AbHyg, AgBio, Agr, AgrForAb, AnBrAb, BBCI, BCI, BIOBASE, BIOSIS Prev, BibAg, BioCN&I, BioEngAb, BiolAb, BrTechI, CBTA, CCI, CEA, CEABA, CIN, CPA, ChemAb, ChemTitl, CurCont, DBA, DSA, EIA, ESPM, EnerInd, EngInd, EnvEAb, ExcerpMed, FCA, FPA, FS&TA, ForAb, HerbAb, HortAb, I&DA, IABS, ISR, IndVet, Inpharma, M&PBA, MBA, MEDLINE, MaizeAb, NutrAb, OrnHort, PBA, PGegResA, PGrRegA, PHN&I, PN&I, PollutAb, PotatoAb, PoultAb, RA&MP, RM&VM, RPP, Reac, RevApplEntom, RiceAb, S&F, SCI, SIA, SeedAb, SoyAb, TCEA, Telegen, TriticAb, VITIS, VetBull, WRCInf.
—BLDSC (6849.983500), CASDDS, CISTI, Ei, GNLM, IDS, IE, ingenta, Linda Hall. **CCC.**
Published by: Elsevier Ltd. (Subsidiary of: Elsevier Science & Technology), The Boulevard, Langford Ln, Kidlington, Oxford, OX5 1GB, United Kingdom. TEL 44-1865-843000, FAX 44-1865-843010, nlinfo-f@elsevier.nl, http://www.elsevier.com/locate/procbio. Eds. B C Saha, J Boudrant, J J Zhong. Circ: 3,750. **Subscr. to:** Elsevier BV, PO Box 211, Amsterdam 1000 AE, Netherlands. TEL 31-20-485-3757, FAX 31-20-485-3432, http://www.elsevier.nl.

➤ **PROGRESS IN BIOMEDICAL RESEARCH.** see *BIOLOGY—Bioengineering*

663.1 NLD ISSN 0921-0423
CODEN: PBITE3
➤ **PROGRESS IN BIOTECHNOLOGY.** Text in English. 1985. irreg., latest vol.22, 2002. price varies. back issues avail. **Document type:** *Monographic series, Academic/Scholarly.* **Description:** Surveys developments in applied and theoretical research in all areas of biotechnology.
Indexed: Agr, BIOSIS Prev, CIN, ChemAb, ChemTitl, DBA.
—BLDSC (6866.160000), CASDDS, CISTI, IE, ingenta, KNAW. **CCC.**
Published by: Elsevier BV (Subsidiary of: Elsevier Science & Technology), Radarweg 29, Amsterdam, 1043 NX, Netherlands. TEL 31-20-4853911, FAX 31-20-4852457, nlinfo-f@elsevier.nl, http://www.elsevier.nl.

660.6 USA ISSN 1537-6079
PROTEOMONITOR; the global newsweekly of proteomics technology. Text in English. 2001 (Oct.). w. (50 times a year). USD 95 in North America (effective 2003). adv. back issues avail.
Related titles: Online - full text ed.
Published by: GenomeWeb, LLC, PO Box 998, Peck Slip Stn., New York, NY 10272-0998. TEL 212-269-4747, FAX 212-269-3686, http://www.proteomonitor.com, http://www.genome.com. Ed. John S. MacNeil.

363.7 NLD ISSN 1569-1705
RE-VIEWS IN ENVIRONMENTAL SCIENCE AND BIO-TECHNOLOGY. Text in English. 2002. q. EUR 275, USD 276, GBP 181 combined subscription to institutions print & online eds. (effective 2005). adv. reprint service avail. from PSC. **Document type:** *Journal, Academic/Scholarly.* **Description:** Aim is twofold: to enable the reader to keep up to date on developments and to present a view of where the developments in environmental science and biotechnology will lead to.
Related titles: Online - full text ed.: ISSN 1572-9826 (from EBSCO Publishing, Gale Group, IngentaConnect, Kluwer Online, O C L C Online Computer Library Center, Inc., Springer LINK, Swets Information Services).
Indexed: B&BAb, BibLing, BioEngAb, ESPM, EnvEAb, PollutAb, WRCInf.
—BLDSC (7790.525300), CISTI, IE, Infotrieve, ingenta. **CCC.**
Published by: Springer-Verlag Dordrecht (Subsidiary of: Springer Science+Business Media), Van Godewijckstraat 30, Dordrecht, 3311 GX, Netherlands. TEL 31-78-6576050, FAX 31-78-6576474, http://springerlink.metapress.com/openurl.asp?genre=journal&issn=1569-1705, http://www.springeronline.com. Ed. Piet Lens.

RECENT RESEARCH DEVELOPMENTS IN PLASMAS. see *CHEMISTRY—Organic Chemistry*

RESOURCE AND ENVIRONMENTAL BIOTECHNOLOGY. see *METALLURGY*

660.6 COL ISSN 0123-3475
REVISTA COLOMBIANA DE BIOTECNOLOGIA. Text in Spanish. 1999. s-a. **Document type:** *Journal, Academic/Scholarly.*
Indexed: AEBA, ASFA, B&BAb, BioEngAb, ESPM, M&PBA.
—BLDSC (7851.400500), IE.
Published by: Universidad Nacional de Colombia, Instituto de Biotecnologia, Edificio Manuel Ancizar 224, Ciudad Universitaria, Bogota, 14490, Colombia. TEL 57-1-3165450, FAX 57-1-3165415, http://www.rcb.unal.edu.co.

660.6 RUS
➤ **RUSSIAN JOURNAL OF BIOMECHANICS.** Text in English. 1997. q. USD 54 foreign (effective 2004). **Document type:** *Journal, Academic/Scholarly.* **Description:** Presents achievements of Russian biomechanical research. Aims to improve the information interchange between specialists on biomechanics from Russia and other countries.
Published by: Rossiiskaya Akademiya Estestvennykh Nauk, Zapadno-Ural'skoe Otdelenie/Russian Academy of Natural Sciences, West-Urals Branch, ul Kuibysheva, d 39, Perm', 614600, Russian Federation. TEL 7-3422-455147, nyashin@theormech.pstu.ac.ru, http://biomech.ac.ru. Ed. Yurii I Nyashin. **Dist. by:** M K - Periodica, ul Gilyarovskogo 39, Moscow 129110, Russian Federation. TEL 7-095-2845008, FAX 7-095-2813798, info@periodicals.ru, http://www.mkniga.ru.

➤ **S A A S BULLETIN. BIOCHEMISTRY AND BIOTECHNOLOGY.** (Southern Association of Agricultural Scientists) see *BIOLOGY—Biochemistry*

660.62 USA ISSN 1043-4976
S I M INDUSTRIAL MICROBIOLOGY NEWS. Text in English. 1989. bi-m. USD 90 membership (effective 2004). adv. **Document type:** *Newsletter, Trade.*
Published by: Society for Industrial Microbiology, 3929 Old Lee Highway, Ste 92A, Fairfax, VA 22030-2421. TEL 703-691-3357, FAX 703-691-7991, info@simhq.org, http://www.simhq.org. adv.: B&W page USD 900, color page USD 1,900; trim 8.5 x 11.

660.6 JPN ISSN 0287-3796
CODEN: SAKOEO
SAIBO KOGAKU/CELL TECHNOLOGY. Text in Japanese. 1982. m. JPY 22,680 (effective 2005). **Document type:** *Journal, Academic/Scholarly.*
Indexed: CIN, ChemAb, ChemTitl.
—CASDDS, CISTI.
Published by: Shujunsha Co. Ltd., 3-5-1 Kanda-Nishikicho, Chiyoda-ku, Tokyo, 101-0054, Japan. http://www.shujunsha.co.jp/journal/saibo/index.html. Ed. Yayoi Tanaka.

660.6 JPN ISSN 0912-3628
SAIBO KOGAKU, BESSATSU/CELL TECHNOLOGY, SPECIAL ISSUE. Text in Japanese. 1986. irreg. JPY 3,700. **Document type:** *Academic/Scholarly.*
Published by: Shujunsha Co. Ltd., 3-5-1 Kanda-Nishikicho, Chiyoda-ku, Tokyo, 101-0054, Japan. Ed. Yayoi Tanaka.

660 581.3 ESP ISSN 1002-5154
SEEDLING. Text in English. 1984. q. **Description:** Each issue contains an editorial, 3-4 articles, book reviews, interviews and more.
Related titles: Online - full content ed.; Online - full text ed.: (from East View Information Services).
Indexed: AgBio, AgrForAb, AnBrAb, BioCN&I, FCA, FPA, ForAb, HortAb, MaizeAb, PBA, PGegResA, PHN&I, PotatoAb, RA&MP, RRTA, S&F, SIA, SeedAb, SoyAb, WAE&RSA, WeedAb.
Published by: Genetic Resources Action International, Girona 25, pral., Barcelona, E-08010, Spain. TEL 34-93-3011381, FAX 34-93-3011627, grain@grain.org, http://www.grain.org/seedling.

▼ **SERIES ON BIOMATERIALS AND BIOENGINEERING.** see *BIOLOGY—Bioengineering*

660.6 CHN ISSN 1003-3505
SHENGWU GONGCHENG JINZHAN/PROGRESS IN BIOTECHNOLOGY. Text in Chinese. 1976. bi-m. USD 30 (effective 2000). adv. **Document type:** *Academic/Scholarly.* **Description:** Reports the new developments in the field of biotechnology all over the world.
Related titles: CD-ROM ed.; Online - full text ed.: (from East View Information Services).
—BLDSC (6866.170000).
Published by: Zhongguo Kexueyuan, Wenxian Qingbao Zhongxin/Chinese Academy of Sciences, Documentation and Information Center, 8 Kexueyuan Nanlu, Zhongguancun, Beijing, 100080, China. TEL 86-1-6256-2548, FAX 86-1-6256-7325. Ed. Zhang Shuyong. R&P Ziyi Chen. adv.: page USD 500. Circ: 5,000.

660.6 CHN ISSN 1000-3061
TP248.13 CODEN: SGXUED
➤ **SHENGWU GONGCHENG XUEBAO/CHINESE JOURNAL OF BIOTECHNOLOGY.** Text in Chinese; Summaries in English. 1985. bi-m. CNY 38 newsstand/cover (effective 2005). adv. abstr. **Document type:** *Journal, Academic/Scholarly.* **Description:** Contains research papers on genetic, fermentation, cell and enzyme engineering. Includes new methods for strain breeding, kinetics, regulation of biosynthesis; biochemical engineering unit operations and processes, resource development and environmental protection.
Related titles: Online - full text ed.: (from East View Information Services, WanFang Data Corp.).
Indexed: CIN, ChemAb, ChemTitl, IndMed, MEDLINE, RefZh.
—BLDSC (3180.297000), CASDDS, IE, Infotrieve, ingenta.

Published by: (Zhongguo Kexueyuan, Weishengwu Yanjiusuo/Chinese Academy of Sciences, Institute of Microbiology), Kexue Chubanshe/Science Press, 16 Donghuang Cheng Genbei Jie, Beijing, 100717, China. TEL 86-10-64000246, FAX 86-10-64030255, cjb@sun.im.ac.cn, http://swgcxb.periodicals.net.cn/default.html, http://www.sciencep.com/. Circ: 6,000. **Dist. by:** China International Book Trading Corp, 35 Chegongzhuang Xilu, Haidian District, PO Box 399, Beijing 100044, China. TEL 86-10-68412045, FAX 86-10-68412023, cibtc@mail.cibtc.com.cn, http://www.cibtc.com.cn.

▼ ➤ **SMALL.** see *ENGINEERING—Engineering Mechanics And Materials*

➤ **SOSHIKI BAIYO KENKYU/TISSUE CULTURE RESEARCH COMMUNICATIONS.** see *BIOLOGY—Cytology And Histology*

660.6 USA ISSN 1057-705X
HD9999.B443
STATE-BY-STATE BIOTECHNOLOGY DIRECTORY; centers, companies, and contacts. Text in English. 1990. a. USD 149. **Document type:** *Directory.* **Description:** Lists the state contacts, biotechnology centers, and biotechnology companies in all 50 states.
—**CCC.**
Published by: Institute for Biotechnology Information, c/o Mark Dibner, Pres., Box 14569, Research Triangle Park, NC 27709-4569. TEL 919-544-5111, ibi@mindspring.com, http://www.bitechinfo.com.

▼ **STEM CELL REVIEWS.** see *BIOLOGY—Genetics*

SYNTHETIC BIOTRANSFORMATIONS. see *BIOLOGY—Biochemistry*

660.6 GBR ISSN 0167-7799
TP248.13 CODEN: TRBIDM
➤ **TRENDS IN BIOTECHNOLOGY.** Text in English. 1983. 12/yr. EUR 181 in Europe to individuals; JPY 22,000 in Japan to individuals; USD 198 elsewhere to individuals; EUR 1,232 in Europe to institutions; JPY 170,900 in Japan to institutions; USD 1,378 elsewhere to institutions (effective 2006). adv. bk.rev. illus. index. back issues avail.; reprints avail. **Document type:** *Academic/Scholarly.* **Description:** Covers all aspects of applied biosciences, including microbiology, molecular biology, immunology, plant and animal cell culture, agriculture, and medicine.
Related titles: Online - full text ed.: (from EBSCO Publishing, Gale Group, IngentaConnect, ScienceDirect, Swets Information Services).
Indexed: AEBA, AS&TI, ASCA, ASFA, AbHyg, AgBio, Agr, AnBrAb, BCI, BIOBASE, BIOSIS Prev, BioCN&I, BioEngAb, BiolAb, CBTA, CCI, CEABA, CIN, CPA, CTA, ChemAb, ChemoAb, CurCont, DSA, ESPM, EngInd, ExcerpMed, FS&TA, ForAb, GEOBASE, HelmAb, HortAb, IABS, IPA, ISR, IndMed, IndVet, Inpharma, M&PBA, MBA, MEDLINE, MaizeAb, NSA, NemAb, NutrAb, OrnHort, PBA, PE&ON, PN&I, RCI, RM&VM, RPP, Reac, RefZh, RevApplEntom, RiceAb, S&F, SCI, SoyAb, Telegen, VITIS, WAE&RSA, WeedAb.
—BLDSC (9049.547000), CASDDS, CISTI, GNLM, IDS, IE, Infotrieve, ingenta, Linda Hall. **CCC.**
Published by: Elsevier Ltd., Trends Journals (Subsidiary of: Elsevier Science & Technology), 68 Hills Rd, Cambridge, CB2 1LA, United Kingdom. TEL 44-1223-315961, FAX 44-1223-464430, http://www.elsevier.com/locate/tibtech. Eds. A Hinde, S Berry. Adv. contact Thelma Reid. **Subscr. to:** Elsevier Current Trends Subscriptions, PO Box 331, Haywards Heath, W Sussex RH16 3FG, United Kingdom. TEL 44-1444-475650, FAX 44-1444-445423.

➤ **TRENDS IN PLANT SCIENCE.** see *BIOLOGY—Botany*

660.6 ROM ISSN 1224-7774
UNIVERSITATEA DE STIINTE AGRONOMICE SI MEDICINA VETERINARA. LUCRARI STIINTIFICE. SERIA F, BIOTEHNOLOGII. Text in Romanian; Summaries in English. a. per issue exchange basis only. **Document type:** *Academic/Scholarly.*
Formerly (until 1995): Universitatea de Stiinte Agronomice. Lucrari Stiintifice. Seria F, Biotehnologii Vegetale, Biotehnologii Industriale, Biotehnologii Animale
Published by: Universitatea de Stiinte Agronomice si Medicina Veterinara, Bd. Marasti 59, Sector 1, Bucharest, 71331, Romania. TEL 40-1-2242576, FAX 40-1-2232693.

620 USA
VALIDATED BIOSYSTEMS. Text in English. irreg. **Document type:** *Newsletter.* **Description:** Contains information about a contract bioprocess engineering firm specializing in downstream processing.
Related titles: Online - full text ed.
Published by: Validated Biosystems, Inc. info@validated.com, http://www.validated.com/.

570 330 USA
VENTUREWIRE LIFESCIENCE. Text in English. d. USD 395 (effective 2002). **Document type:** *Newsletter, Trade.* **Description:** Contains news and information focused on key developments at venture-backed life science companies.
Media: E-mail.
Published by: Dow Jones Newsletters (Subsidiary of: Dow Jones Newswires), 1155 Av of the Americas, New York, NY 10036. TEL 212-597-5716, http://www.venturewire.com/m_lifescience.asp.

660.6092 GBR
WHO'S WHO IN WORLD BIOTECHNOLOGY (YEAR). Text in English. 1997. a. GBP 165 (effective 1998). adv. **Description:** Contains details on senior personnel in the biotechnology industry.
Published by: (Coventry University, Biophoenix Project), Financial Times Healthcare, Maple House, 149 Tottenham Ct Rd, London, W1P 9LL, United Kingdom. TEL 44-207-896-2066, FAX 44-20-7896-2213, lizg@pearson-pro.com, http://www.fthealthcare.com, http://www.fthealthcare .com. Adv. contact Liz Godden.

660.62 NLD ISSN 0959-3993
QR53 CODEN: WJMBEY
➤ **WORLD JOURNAL OF MICROBIOLOGY AND BIOTECHNOLOGY.** Text in English. 1985. 9/yr. EUR 1,878, USD 1,918, GBP 1,238 combined subscription to institutions print & online eds. (effective 2005). adv. bk.rev. back issues avail.; reprint service avail. from PSC. **Document type:** *Journal, Academic/Scholarly.* **Description:** Publishes research papers, short communications, technical communications and review articles on all aspects of applied microbiology and biotechnology, including management of culture collections, foodstuffs and biological control agents.
Formerly (until 1990): Mircen - Journal of Applied Microbiology and Biotechnology (0265-0762)
Related titles: CD-ROM ed.; Online - full text ed.: ISSN 1573-0972 (from EBSCO Publishing, Gale Group, IngentaConnect, Kluwer Online, O C L C Online Computer Library Center, Inc., Ovid Technologies, Inc., Springer LINK, Swets Information Services).
Indexed: AEA, AEBA, AESIS, ASCA, ASFA, AbHyg, AgBio, Agr, AgrForAb, BCI, BIOBASE, BIOSIS Prev, BibLing, BioCN&I, BioEngAb, BiolAb, CBTA, CEABA, CIN, CPA, ChemAb, ChemTitl, CurCont, DBA, DSA, ESPM, EnvEAb, FCA, FPA, FS&TA, ForAb, HelmAb, HerbAb, HortAb, I&DA, IABS, IndVet, JDDR, M&PBA, MBA, MaizeAb, NemAb, NutrAb, OrnHort, PBA, PGegResA, PGrRegA, PHN&I, PN&I, PlantSci, PollutAb, PotatoAb, PoultAb, ProtozoAb, RA&MP, RM&VM, RPP, RefZh, RevApplEntom, RiceAb, S&F, SIA, SeedAb, SoyAb, TDB, TOSA, TriticAb, VITIS, VetBull, VirolAbstr, WAE&RSA, WeedAb.
—BLDSC (9356.073500), CASDDS, CISTI, IDS, IE, Infotrieve, ingenta. **CCC.**
Published by: (International Union of Microbiological Societies), Springer-Verlag Dordrecht (Subsidiary of: Springer Science+Business Media), Van Godewijckstraat 30, Dordrecht, 3311 GX, Netherlands. TEL 31-78-6576050, FAX 31-78-6576474, http://springerlink.metapress.com/openurl.asp?genre=journal&issn=0959-3993, http://www.springeronline.com. Eds. Colin Ratledge, Peter J Large.

660.6 615.19 USA
WORLDWIDE BIOTECH. Text in English. 1989. m. USD 150 in North America; USD 165 elsewhere (effective 2001). bk.rev. back issues avail. **Document type:** *Newsletter, Trade.* **Description:** Provides news and information on biotechnology as an international industry, reporting on the deals between US biotechnology companies and both US and international pharmaceutical corporations. Monitors the emerging EC marketplace and the growing Japanese interest.
Related titles: Online - full text ed.: (from Data-Star, The Dialog Corporation).
Published by: Worldwide Videotex, PO Box 3273, Boynton Beach, FL 33424-3273. TEL 561-738-2276, markedit@juno.com, http://www.wvpubs.com. Ed., Pub. Mark Wright.

BIOLOGY—Botany

see also AGRICULTURE—Crop Production And Soil ; FORESTS AND FORESTRY ; GARDENING AND HORTICULTURE

580 DNK ISSN 0904-6453
CODEN: AAUREL
A A U REPORTS. Variant title: Aarhus University Reports. Text in Danish, English; Summaries in English. 1976. irreg. DKK 98 (effective 2004). illus. **Document type:** *Monographic series, Academic/Scholarly.*
Formerly (until 1988): Aarhus University. Botanical Institute. Reports (0105-4236)
Indexed: BIOSIS Prev.
—BLDSC (0537.695100), CISTI.
Published by: (Aarhus Universitet, Botanical Institute), Aarhus Universitetsforlag/Aarhus University Press, Langelandsgade 177, Aarhus N, 8200, Denmark. TEL 45-89425370, FAX 45-89425380, unipress@au.dk, http://www.unipress.dk. Ed. H Balslev. Circ: 300.

A E T F A T INDEX; releve des travaux de phanerogamie systematique et des taxons nouveaux concernant l'Afrique au sud du Sahara et Madagascar. see *BIOLOGY—Abstracting, Bibliographies, Statistics*

580 USA
A O S A - S C S T SEED TECHNOLOGIST NEWS. Text in English. 1927. 3/yr. USD 35 (effective 2000). abstr. cum.index: 1927-1940; 1941-1970. **Document type:** *Newsletter.*
Formerly (until 1998): Association of Official Seed Analysts. News Letter (0004-5764)
Indexed: FCA, HerbAb, MaizeAb, SeedAb, SoyAb, TOSA.
Published by: Association of Official Seed Analysts / Society of Commercial Seed Technologists, PMB #411, 1763 E University Blvd, Ste A, Las Cruces, NM 88001. TEL 505-522-1437, FAX 402-476-6547. Ed. Diane Mesa. R&P Tami Greer. Circ: 500.

580 632 USA ISSN 1051-1113
A P S MONOGRAPH SERIES. (American Phytopathological Society) Text in English. 1961. irreg., latest 1986. price varies. back issues avail. **Document type:** *Monographic series, Academic/Scholarly.* **Description:** Explores current topics and research in plant diseases.
Formerly (until 198?): American Phytopathological Society. Monographs (0569-6992)
Indexed: BIOSIS Prev, BiolAb, PBA, RPP.
Published by: (American Phytopathological Society), A P S PRESS, 3340 Pilot Knob Rd., St. Paul, MN 55121-2097. TEL 651-454-7250, 800-328-7560, FAX 651-454-0766, aps@scisoc.org, http:/www.shopapspress.org, http://www.apsnet.org.

571.2 USA ISSN 1535-5489
A S P B NEWS; the newsletter of the American Society of Plant Biologists. Text in English. 1974. bi-m. USD 30 to non-members; USD 2 to members (effective 2003). adv. back issues avail. **Document type:** *Newsletter, Academic/Scholarly.* **Description:** Keeps society members informed on items of professional interest.
Former titles: A S P P News (1098-9706); American Society of Plant Physiologists. Newsletter (1098-9803); (until 1990): A S P P Newsletter (0279-9936)
Related titles: Online - full text ed.: ISSN 1544-9149.
Published by: American Society of Plant Biologists, 15501 Monona Dr, Rockville, MD 20855-2768. TEL 301-251-0560, FAX 301-279-2996, nancyw@aspb.org, http://www.aspb.org. Ed., R&P, Adv. contact Nancy Winchester. Pub. John Lisack Jr. page USD 900; trim 8 x 10. Circ: 6,000.

A T C C CATALOGUE OF PLANT VIRUSES AND ANTISERA. see *BIOLOGY—Microbiology*

579.5 USA
QK600.73.U62
A T C C FILAMENTOUS FUNGI. Text in English. 1986. irreg., latest vol.19, 1996. USD 34 in North America; USD 44 elsewhere. **Document type:** *Catalog.*
Formerly: A T C C Catalogue of Filamentous Fungi (1065-0598); Which superseded in part (in 1991): American Type Culture Collection. Catalogue of Fungi - Yeasts (1053-3370); Which superseded in part: American Type Culture Collection. Catalogue of Strains 1: Algae, Bacteria, Bacteriophages, Plasmids, Fungi, Plant Viruses and Antisera and Protozoa
—CISTI.
Published by: American Type Culture Collection, 10801 University Blvd, Manassas, VA 20110. TEL 800-638-6597, FAX 301-816-4361, sales@ATCC.org.

579.562 USA
A T C C YEASTS. Text in English. 1986. irreg., latest vol.19, 1995. USD 35 in North America; USD 47 elsewhere. **Document type:** *Catalog.*
Formerly (until 1995): A T C C Catalogue of Yeasts; Which superseded in part (in 1991): American Type Culture Collection. Catalogue of Fungi - Yeasts (1053-3370); Which superseded in part: American Type Culture Collection. Catalogue of Strains 1
—CISTI.
Published by: American Type Culture Collection, 10801 University Blvd, Manassas, VA 20110. TEL 800-638-6597, FAX 301-816-4361. Eds. M J Edwards, S C Jong.

ABSTRACTS OF MYCOLOGY. see *BIOLOGY—Abstracting, Bibliographies, Statistics*

580 TWN ISSN 0006-8063
QK1 CODEN: BBASA6
➤ **ACADEMIA SINICA. BOTANICAL BULLETIN.** Key Title: Zhongyang Yanjiuyuan Zhiwuxue Huikan. Text in English; Summaries in Chinese. 1960. q. USD 60 per vol. to individuals; USD 100 per vol. to institutions; USD 15 per issue to individuals; USD 25 per issue to institutions (effective 2002). adv. bibl.; charts; illus.; stat. index, cum.index. **Document type:** *Academic/Scholarly.* **Description:** Publishes both original and review papers on all aspects of modern plant science from researchers around the world.
Related titles: CD-ROM ed.; Microfilm ed.
Indexed: ASCA, AgBio, AgrForAb, BIOBASE, BIOSIS Prev, BioCN&I, BiolAb, CIN, CPA, Cadscan, ChemAb, ChemTitl, CurCont, DSA, FCA, FPA, FS&TA, ForAb, HerbAb, HortAb, I&DA, ISR, LeadAb, MaizeAb, NutrAb, OrnHort, PBA, PGegResA, PGrRegA, PHN&I, PlantSci, PotatoAb, RA&MP, RM&VM, RPP, RevApplEntom, RiceAb, S&F, SCI, SIA, SeedAb, SoyAb, TriticAb, VITIS, WeedAb, Zincscan.
—BLDSC (2253.000000), CASDDS, CISTI, IDS, IE, ingenta, KNAW, Linda Hall.

B

Published by: Academia Sinica, Institute of Botany/Chung Yang Yen Chiu Yuan, Chih Wu Hsueh Yen Chiu So, Nankang, Taipei, 11529, Taiwan. TEL 886-2-2789-9590, FAX 886-2-2782-7954, boyhlin@ccvax.sinica.edu.tw, http://ejournal.sinica.edu.tw/bbas/, http://botany.sinica.edu.tw. Ed. Yaw Huei Lin. Pub. Jei Fu Shaw. Circ: 570 (paid and controlled). **Dist. by:** Lily Journal and Book Co. & Ltd., 4F-3, No 125, Roosevelt Rd, Sec3, Taipei, Taiwan. TEL 886-2-2363-3168, FAX 886-2-2362-7448, hcling@ms4.hint.net.

➤ **ACTA AGRICULTURAE SLOVENICA.** see *AGRICULTURE—Crop Production And Soil*

580 POL ISSN 0065-0951
SB13 CODEN: AAGWAU
ACTA AGROBOTANICA. Text in Polish, English; Summaries in English, French, Polish. 1953. irreg., latest vol.41, no.2, 1990. price varies. illus.
Indexed: AgBio, AgrAg, AgrForAb, AgrLib, BIOSIS Prev, BioCN&I, BiolAb, CPA, ChemAb, ExcerpMed, FCA, FPA, ForAb, HerbAb, HortAb, I&DA, MaizeAb, NemAb, NutrAb, OrnHort, PBA, PGegResA, PGrRegA, PHN&I, PotatoAb, RA&MP, RM&VM, RPP, RevApplEntom, S&F, SIA, SeedAb, SoyAb, TriticAb, WAE&RSA, WeedAb.
—BLDSC (0589.500000), CASDDS, CISTI, Linda Hall.
Published by: Polskie Towarzystwo Botaniczne/Polish Botanical Society, Al Ujazdowskie 4, Warsaw, 00478, Poland. Ed. M Saniewski. Circ: 300. **Dist. by:** Ars Polona, Krakowskie Przedmiescie 7, Warsaw, Poland.

986.1 580 COL ISSN 0120-548X
CODEN: ABICEP
➤ **ACTA BIOLOGICA COLOMBIANA.** Text in Spanish. 1982. 2/yr. COP 6,000 (effective 2005). abstr. back issues avail. **Document type:** *Journal, Academic/Scholarly.* **Description:** Describes many aspects of the studies done by the Department of Biology at the National University and includes data on Colombian flora and fauna.
Related titles: Online - full text ed.
Indexed: BIOSIS Prev, BiolAb, VITIS, ZooRec.
Published by: Universidad Nacional de Colombia, Facultad de Biologia, Apartado Aereo 14490, Bogota, Colombia. TEL 57-1-368-4273, FAX 57-1-225-5192, racbiocol_fcbog@unal.edu.co, http://www.virtual.unal.edu.co/revistas/actabiol. Ed. Dr. Marcela Camacho. Circ: 500.

580 POL ISSN 0001-5296
CODEN: ABCBAM
➤ **ACTA BIOLOGICA CRACOVIENSIA. BOTANICA.** Text in English. 1958. a., latest vol.44, 2002. price varies. charts; illus. index. **Document type:** *Academic/Scholarly.* **Description:** Problems of karyology, cytotaxonomy and embryology of Cormophyta; plant-derived active substances; and physiology and morphogenesis of lower plants.
Indexed: AgBio, AgrAg, AgrLib, AnBrAb, BIOSIS Prev, BiolAb, CPA, ChemAb, CurCont, FCA, ForAb, HerbAb, HortAb, IBR, KWIWR, OrnHort, PBA, PGegResA, PGrRegA, RA&MP, RM&VM, RPP, RevApplEntom, S&F, SCI, SIA, SeedAb, TriticAb, WeedAb.
—BLDSC (0602.400000), CASDDS, CISTI, KNAW, Linda Hall.
Published by: (Polska Akademia Nauk, Oddzial w Krakowie, Komisja Biologiczna), Polska Akademia Nauk, Oddzial w Krakowie, ul sw Jana 28, Krakow, 31018, Poland. TEL 48-12-4224853, FAX 48-12-4222791. Circ: 950.

580 570 LVA ISSN 1407-8953
ACTA BIOLOGICA UNIVERSITATIS DAUGAVPILIENSIS. Text in English. 2001. s-a. **Description:** Publishes papers focusing on the questions related to the general problems of biology. Also covers research of flora, vegetation, fauna, distribution, taxonomy, ecology, and conservation of species in the Baltic region.
Indexed: ASFA, AbHyg, AnBrAb, BioCN&I, CPA, DSA, EntAb, FCA, FPA, ForAb, HerbAb, HortAb, OrnHort, PBA, PGegResA, PotatoAb, RA&MP, RM&VM, RPP, S&F, SIA, TriticAb, WeedAb, ZooRec.
Published by: Daugavpils Universitate, Biologijas Katedras Vaditajs, Vienibas 13-229, Daugavpils, 5401, Latvia. TEL 54-26719, FAX 54-26719, beetles@dau.lv, http://www.bio.dpu.lv/zurnali.php?p=actabiologica. Ed. Arvids Barsevskis.

580 ESP ISSN 0210-7597
➤ **ACTA BOTANICA BARCINONENSIA.** Text in Multiple languages; Abstracts in English. 1964. irreg., latest vol.45, 1998. price varies. **Document type:** *Journal, Academic/Scholarly.* **Description:** Covers both articles and monographs mainly on plant taxonomy and phytocenology, vascular plants and cryptogams of the Western Mediterranean area.
Supersedes (since 1978): Acta Geobotanica Barcinonensia (0065-1222)
Indexed: BiolAb, ForAb, HerbAb, HortAb, I&DA, IECT, PBA, PGegResA, RA&MP, RPP, RefZh, RevApplEntom, RiceAb, S&F, SeedAb, TriticAb, WeedAb.
—CINDOC.
Published by: (Universitat de Barcelona, Facultat de Biologia), Universitat de Barcelona, Servei de Publicacions, Gran Via Corts Catalanes 585, Barcelona, 08007, Spain. TEL 34-93-4021100, llimona@bio.ub.es, http://www.publicacions.ub.es. Ed. Josep M Ninot. Circ: 1,000.

580 HRV ISSN 0365-0588
CODEN: ABCRA2
➤ **ACTA BOTANICA CROATICA.** Text and summaries in English. 1925. 2/yr. HRK 300 domestic; USD 80 foreign (effective 2000 - 2001). adv. bk.rev. bibl.; illus. index, cum.index. back issues avail. **Document type:** *Academic/Scholarly.* **Description:** Publishes original scientific papers on various fields of botany.
Indexed: ASFA, AbHyg, AgBio, AgrForAb, BIOBASE, BIOSIS Prev, BiolAb, CIN, CPA, ChemAb, ChemTitl, FCA, ForAb, HerbAb, HortAb, I&DA, MaizeAb, OrnHort, PBA, PGegResA, PGrRegA, PotatoAb, ProtozoAb, RA&MP, RM&VM, RPP, S&F, SIA, SeedAb, SoyAb, TriticAb, WeedAb, ZooRec.
—CASDDS, Linda Hall.
Published by: (Bioloski Odjel), Sveuciliste u Zagrebu, Prirodoslovno-Matematicki Fakultet/University of Zagreb, Faculty of Science, Division of Biology, Rooseveltov trg 6, Zagreb, 10000, Croatia. TEL 385-1-4895561, grozdana@lipa.botanic.hr, http://hirc.botanic.hr/actabot/actahome.htm. Ed. Damir Vilicic. Adv. contact Grozdana Sirotic. B&W page USD 200, color page USD 300. Circ: 400.

580 CUB ISSN 0138-6824
ACTA BOTANICA CUBANA. Text in Spanish, English. 1980. 15/yr. USD 75 (effective 2000); or exchange basis. bibl.; charts; illus. **Document type:** *Academic/Scholarly.*
Formerly: Acta Botanica Cuba
Indexed: BiolAb.
Published by: Academia de Ciencias de Cuba, Instituto de Ecologia y Sistematica, Carretera de Varona Km3 1/2, Capdevila, Havana, Cuba. TEL 53-7-448419, FAX 53-7-338054, ecologia@ceniai.cu. Circ: 2,000.

580 FIN ISSN 0001-5369
QH7 CODEN: ABFEAC
➤ **ACTA BOTANICA FENNICA.** Text in English. 1925. irreg., latest vol.47, 2004. price varies. abstr.; charts; illus. cum.index: nos.1-40, 41-100, 100-125, 125-137, 138-142. 2 cols./p.; back issues avail. **Document type:** *Journal, Academic/Scholarly.* **Description:** Original botanical monographs by Finnish and foreign botanists.
Related titles: Online - full content ed.
Indexed: ASFA, ApEcolAb, BIOBASE, BIOSIS Prev, BiolAb, ChemAb, ESPM, FCA, HortAb, MBA, PBA, PGegResA, PollutAb, RefZh, VITIS.
—CASDDS, CISTI, KNAW, Linda Hall.
Published by: Finnish Zoological and Botanical Publishing Board, P Rautatiekatu 13, University of Helsinki, P O Box 17, Helsinki, 00014, Finland. TEL 358-9-19128805, FAX 358-9-19128806, sekj@.helsinki.fi, sekj@helsinki.fi, http://www.sekj.org/ActaBot.html, http://www.sejk.org. Ed. Krzysztof Raciborski. Circ: 850. **Subscr. to:** Tiedekirja OY - Vetenskapsbokhandeln. **Co-sponsor:** Suomen Tiedeseura/Finnish Society of Sciences and Letters.

580 FRA ISSN 1253-8078
QK1 CODEN: ABGAE9
➤ **ACTA BOTANICA GALLICA.** Text in French. 1854. q. EUR 67 domestic; EUR 99.04 foreign (effective 2005). bk.rev. index. **Document type:** *Bulletin, Academic/Scholarly.* **Description:** Focuses on all aspects of botany.
Formerly: Actualites Botaniques (0181-1789); Supersedes (in 1978): Societe Botanique de France. Colloques
Indexed: AEA, ASCA, ASFA, AgBio, AgrForAb, AnBrAb, ApicAb, BIOSIS Prev, BiolAb, CIN, CPA, ChemAb, ChemTitl, CurCont, ESPM, FCA, FPA, ForAb, HerbAb, HortAb, I&DA, MaizeAb, NutrAb, OrnHort, PBA, PGegResA, PGrRegA, PHN&I, PotatoAb, RA&MP, RM&VM, RPP, RevApplEntom, RiceAb, S&F, SIA, SeedAb, SoyAb, TDB, TriticAb, VITIS, WeedAb.
—BLDSC (0606.200000), CASDDS, CISTI, IDS, IE, Infotrieve, ingenta, Linda Hall. **CCC.**
Published by: Societe Botanique de France, Faculte de Pharmacie, Departement de Botanique, 3 rue du Professeur Laguesse, B.P. 83, Lille, Cedex 59007, France. TEL 33-1-46835520, FAX 33-1-46831303, defouca@phare.univ-lille2.fr, http://www.bium.univ-paris5.fr/sbf/pub_abg.htm. Ed. Bruno de Foucault. Circ: 1,300.

580 HUN ISSN 0236-6495
QK1 CODEN: ABOHE2
ACTA BOTANICA HUNGARICA. Text and summaries in English, Spanish, Russian, German, French. 1954. q. USD 292 (effective 2006). adv. bk.rev. charts; illus.; abstr.; bibl. index. 95 p./no.; back issues avail. **Document type:** *Journal, Academic/Scholarly.* **Description:** Publishes papers by Hungarian botanists. Covers ecology, cytology, phytology, algology, mycology, bryology, taxonomy, paleobotany and more.
Formerly (until 1982): Academiae Scientiarum Hungaricae. Acta Botanica (0001-5350)
Related titles: Online - full text ed.: ISSN 1588-2578 (from EBSCO Publishing, Swets Information Services).
Indexed: ASCA, AgBio, AgrForAb, AnBrAb, BIOSIS Prev, BiolAb, CIN, CPA, ChemAb, ChemTitl, CurCont, ExcerpMed, FCA, FPA, ForAb, HerbAb, HortAb, I&DA, MaizeAb, NutrAb, OrnHort, PBA, PGegResA, PGrRegA, PotatoAb, RA&MP, RM&VM, RPP, RRTA, RefZh, RiceAb, S&F, SIA, SeedAb, TDB, TriticAb, WeedAb.
—CASDDS, CISTI, Linda Hall. **CCC.**
Published by: (Janus Pannonius University, Hungarian Natural History Museum, Magyar Tudomanyos Akademia/Hungarian Academy of Sciences), Akademiai Kiado Rt. (Subsidiary of: Wolters Kluwer N.V.), Prielle Kornelia U. 19, Budapest, 1117, Hungary. TEL 36-1-4648282, FAX 36-1-4648221, journals@akkrt.hu, http://www.akkrt.hu. Ed. Attila Borhidi.

580 IND ISSN 0379-508X
QK1 CODEN: ABOIB2
➤ **ACTA BOTANICA INDICA.** Text in English. 1973. s-a. USD 40 (effective 2006). adv. bk.rev. bibl.; illus. cum.index. reprint service avail. from ISI. **Document type:** *Academic/Scholarly.*
Indexed: AgrForAb, ApicAb, BIOSIS Prev, BiolAb, CPA, CurCont, ExcerpMed, FCA, HerbAb, HortAb, RPP, RiceAb, S&F, TriticAb, WeedAb.
—BLDSC (0606.750000), CISTI, ingenta, Linda Hall.
Published by: Society for the Advancement of Botany, Department of Botany, Meerut College, Meerut, Uttar Pradesh 250 006, India. Ed. Dr. V Singh. Circ: 1,000. **Subscr. to:** I N S I O Scientific Books & Periodicals, P O Box 7234, Indraprastha HPO, New Delhi 110 002, India. info@insio.com, http://www.insio.com.

580 ISL ISSN 0374-5066
QK325.5
ACTA BOTANICA ISLANDICA. Text in English, French, German; Summaries in English. 1972. irreg., latest vol.13, 2000. USD 20 (effective 2003). bk.rev. bibl.; illus. **Document type:** *Academic/Scholarly.* **Description:** Original research in the flora and vegetation of Iceland with emphasis on floristics, plant sociology, taxonomy, ecology.
Supersedes (1963-1968): Flora
Indexed: BIOSIS Prev, BiolAb.
—CISTI, Linda Hall.
Published by: Icelandic Institute of Natural History/Akureyri Division, PO Box 180, Akureyri, 602, Iceland. TEL 354-4600500, FAX 354-4600501, hkris@ni.is, nia@ni.is, http://www.ni.is. Eds. Gudridur Gydae Eyjolfsdottir, Hoerdur Kristinsson. Circ: 190.

580 633 ESP ISSN 0210-9506
CODEN: ABMAE5
➤ **ACTA BOTANICA MALACITANA.** Text in English, French, Italian, Spanish. 1975. a. EUR 18 (effective 2005). adv. bk.rev. bibl.; charts; illus. index. back issues avail. **Document type:** *Journal, Academic/Scholarly.* **Description:** Disseminates results of original works relating to any aspect of botany; including systematic botany, chorology, aerobiology, taxonomy and ecology.
Related titles: E-mail ed.; Online - full text ed.
Indexed: AgrForAb, ApicAb, BIOSIS Prev, BiolAb, CPA, FCA, FPA, ForAb, HerbAb, HortAb, I&DA, IECT, OrnHort, PBA, PGegResA, RA&MP, RefZh, S&F, SIA, SeedAb, WeedAb.
—CINDOC.
Published by: Universidad de Malaga, Facultad de Ciencias, Apartado 59, Malaga, 29080, Spain. TEL 34-5-2133342, FAX 34-52-131944, abm@uma.es, http://www.uma.es/Estudios/Departamentos/BiolVeg/. Ed. Baltasar Cabezudo Artero. Circ: 600.

580 MEX ISSN 0187-7151
ACTA BOTANICA MEXICANA. Text in Spanish. 1988. q. USD 30 (effective 2003). 70 p./no.; back issues avail. **Document type:** *Journal, Academic/Scholarly.*
Indexed: AgBio, AgrForAb, ApicAb, CPA, ForAb, HelmAb, HerbAb, HortAb, MaizeAb, OrnHort, PBA, PGegResA, PotatoAb, RA&MP, RM&VM, RPP, S&F, SeedAb, WeedAb.
Published by: Instituto de Ecologia, Apartado Postal 63, Xalapa, VERACRUZ 91000, Mexico. TEL 228-842-1800, FAX 228-818-7809, libros@ecologia.edu.mx, http://www.ecologia.edu.mx. Ed. Jerzy Rzedowski.

580 SVK
ACTA BOTANICA SLOVACA. Text in Slovak; Summaries in English, German, Russian. irreg. price varies.
Former titles: Acta Botanica; Acta Instituti Botanici
Published by: (Slovenska Akademia Vied/Slovak Academy of Sciences), Vydavatel'stvo Slovenskej Akademie Vied Veda/Veda, Publishing House of the Slovak Academy of Sciences, Dubravska cesta 9, Bratislava, 84234, Slovakia. **Dist. by:** Slovart G.T.G. s.r.o., Krupinska 4, PO Box 152, Bratislava 85299, Slovakia. TEL 421-2-63839472, FAX 421-2-63839485, http://www.slovart-gtg.sk.

580 VEN ISSN 0084-5906
CODEN: ABOVA6
➤ **ACTA BOTANICA VENEZUELICA.** Text and summaries in English, Spanish. 1965. irreg. price varies. charts; illus. **Document type:** *Academic/Scholarly.*
Related titles: Online - full text ed.: free (effective 2005).
Indexed: AgBio, AgrForAb, BIOSIS Prev, BiolAb, FCA, FPA, ForAb, HerbAb, HortAb, OrnHort, PBA, PGegResA, PotatoAb, RA&MP, RevApplEntom, S&F, SeedAb, WeedAb.
—CISTI.
Published by: Fundacion Instituto Botanico de Venezuela, Jardin Botanico de Caracas, Ave. Salvador Allende, Apdo 2156, Caracas, DF 1010-A, Venezuela. TEL 58-2-6053970, FAX 58-2-6053970, llamozas@camelot.rect.ucv.vel, http://www.scielo.org.ve/scielo.php?script=sci_serial&lng=es&pid=0084-5906&nrm=iso, http://wwwucv.ve/fibv.htm. Circ: 1,000.

➤ **ACTA HORTI BOTANICI BUCURESTIENSIS.** see *GARDENING AND HORTICULTURE*

579.5 POL ISSN 0001-625X
QK600 CODEN: ACMYAC
ACTA MYCOLOGICA. Text and summaries in English, French, German, Polish. 1965. irreg., latest vol.25, no.2, 1990. price varies. bk.rev. bibl.; charts; illus. **Description:** Examines research in botany.
Indexed: ASFA, AbHyg, AgrAg, AgrLib, BIOSIS Prev, BioCN&I, BioDAb, BiolAb, CPA, ChemAb, ESPM, FCA, ForAb, HelmAb, HerbAb, HortAb, MBA, MaizeAb, NemAb, PBA, PGegResA, PotatoAb, RM&VM, RPP, RevApplEntom, S&F, SeedAb, SoyAb, TriticAb, VITIS, WeedAb.
—BLDSC (0639.300000), CASDDS, IE, ingenta, Linda Hall.
Published by: Polskie Towarzystwo Botaniczne/Polish Botanical Society, Al Ujazdowskie 4, Warsaw, 00478, Poland. Ed. Alina Skirgiello. Circ: 320.

ACTA PALAEOBOTANICA; international journal of palaeobotany and palynology. see *PALEONTOLOGY*

581 POL ISSN 0137-5881
CODEN: APPLDE
➤ **ACTA PHYSIOLOGIAE PLANTARUM.** Text in English. 1978. q. EUR 120 foreign (effective 2005). adv. bk.rev. illus. **Document type:** *Journal, Academic/Scholarly.* **Description:** Publishes papers, reviews and short communications covering theoretical as well as practical aspects of plant physiology and related sciences.
Indexed: ASCA, AgBio, AgrAg, AgrForAb, AgrLib, BIOBASE, BIOSIS Prev, BiolAb, CIN, CPA, ChemAb, ChemTitl, CurCont, DSA, ExcerpMed, FCA, FPA, ForAb, HerbAb, HortAb, I&DA, IABS, MaizeAb, NutrAb, OrnHort, PBA, PGegResA, PGrRegA, PHN&I, PlantSci, PotatoAb, RA&MP, RM&VM, RPP, RevApplEntom, RiceAb, S&F, SIA, SeedAb, SoyAb, TriticAb, VITIS, WeedAb.
—BLDSC (0650.700000), CASDDS, CISTI, IE, Infotrieve, ingenta, Linda Hall.
Published by: Polska Akademia Nauk, Instytut Fizjologii Roslin/Polish Academy of Sciences, Franciszek Gorski Institute of Plant Physiology, Niezapominajek 21, Krakow, 30239, Poland. ifr@ifr-pan.krakow.pl, http://agrobiol.sggw.waw.pl/katedry/kfr/app/. Circ: 400. **Dist. by:** Ars Polona, Krakowskie Przedmiescie 7, Warsaw, Poland. TEL 48-22-9263914, FAX 48-22-9265334, arspolona@arspolona.com.pl, http://www.arspolona.com.pl.

580.9485 SWE ISSN 0084-5914
CODEN: APGSAL
➤ **ACTA PHYTOGEOGRAPHICA SUECICA.** Text in English. 1929. s-a. EUR 70 per vol. (effective 2005). adv. reprints avail. **Document type:** *Monographic series, Academic/Scholarly.*
Indexed: ASFA, BIOSIS Prev, BiolAb, ESPM, FCA, FPA, ForAb, GEOBASE, HerbAb, PBA, S&F, SeedAb.
—BLDSC (0656.000000), CISTI, IE, ingenta, KNAW, Linda Hall.
Published by: (Svenska Vaextgeografiska Saellskapet/Swedish Phytogeographical Society), Opulus Press, Gamla Vaegen 40, Grangaerde, 77013, Sweden. TEL 46-240-641250, FAX 46-240-640880, info@opuluspress.se, http://www.opuluspress.se. Ed. Erik Sjoegren. Adv. contact Lena Lundgren. Circ: 300.

571.9 HUN ISSN 0238-1249
CODEN: APEHEG
ACTA PHYTOPATHOLOGICA ET ENTOMOLOGICA HUNGARICA. Text in English. 1966. q. USD 296 (effective 2006). adv. bk.rev. bibl.; charts; illus.; maps. 120 p./no.; back issues avail. **Document type:** *Journal, Academic/Scholarly.* **Description:** Publishes papers on the infectious diseases of plants, damages caused by insects and investigates the basic aspects of chemical and biological protection.
Formerly (until 1985): Academiae Scientiarum Hungaricae. Acta Phytopathologica (0001-6780)
Related titles: Online - full text ed.: ISSN 1588-2691 (from EBSCO Publishing, Gale Group, IngentaConnect, Swets Information Services).
Indexed: AEA, ASFA, AgBio, AgrForAb, B&BAb, BIOSIS Prev, BioCN&I, BiolAb, CIN, CPA, ChemAb, CurCont, DSA, ESPM, EntAb, FCA, ForAb, GEOBASE, HerbAb, HortAb, MBA, MaizeAb, NemAb, NutrAb, OrnHort, PBA, PGegResA, PGrRegA, PHN&I, PotatoAb, RA&MP, RPP, RevApplEntom, RiceAb, S&F, SeedAb, SoyAb, TriticAb, VITIS, WeedAb, ZooRec.
—BLDSC (0656.450000), CASDDS, CISTI, IDS, IE, ingenta, KNAW, Linda Hall. **CCC.**
Published by: (Magyar Tudomanyos Akademia/Hungarian Academy of Sciences), Akademiai Kiado Rt. (Subsidiary of: Wolters Kluwer N.V.), Prielle Kornelia U. 19, Budapest, 1117, Hungary. TEL 36-1-4648282, FAX 36-1-4648221, journals@akkrt.hu, http://www.akkrt.hu.

580 JPN ISSN 1346-7565
QK1 CODEN: SHBCAM
ACTA PHYTOTAXONOMICA ET GEOBOTANICA. Text in English, Japanese. 1932. 2/yr. JPY 8,000. bk.rev. index. **Document type:** *Academic/Scholarly.*
Formerly (until 2001): Shokubutsu Bunrui, Chiri (0001-6799)
Related titles: Microform ed.
Indexed: BIOSIS Prev, BiolAb, ChemAb, FCA, HerbAb, JPI, RPP.
—CASDDS, CISTI, Linda Hall. **CCC.**
Published by: The Japanese Society for Plant Taxonomists, c/o Atsuko Takano, Ph.D., Museum of Nature & Human Activities, Hyogo, Yayoigaoka 6, Sanda, 669-1546, Japan. TEL 81-795-59-2012, FAX 81-795-59-2019. Circ: 750. **Dist. by:** Japan Publications Trading Co., Ltd., Book Export II Dept, PO Box 5030, Tokyo International, Tokyo 101-3191, Japan. TEL 81-3-32923753, FAX 81-3-32920410, infoserials@jptco.co.jp, http://www.jptco.co.jp.

580 SWE ISSN 0347-4917
ACTA REGIAE SOCIETATIS SCIENTIARUM ET LITTERARUM GOTHOBURGENSIS. BOTANICA. Text in Swedish. 1972. irreg., latest vol.4, 1995. price varies: also exchange basis. **Document type:** *Monographic series, Academic/Scholarly.*
Supersedes in part: Goeteborgs Kungliga Vetenskaps- och Vitterhets- Samhaelle. Handlingar
—Linda Hall.
Published by: Kungliga Vetenskaps- och Vitterhets-Samhaelle, c/o Goeteborgs Universitetsbibliotek, PO Box 222, Goeteborg, 40530, Sweden. TEL 46-31-7731733, FAX 46-31-163797.

580 POL ISSN 0001-6977
QK1 CODEN: ASBNA2
➤ **ACTA SOCIETATIS BOTANICORUM POLONIAE/POLISH JOURNAL OF BOTANY.** Text in English; Summaries in Polish. 1923. q. EUR 55 foreign (effective 2005). bibl. **Document type:** *Journal, Academic/Scholarly.* **Description:** Publishes original papers, short communications, and critical reviews in all fields of botany.
Indexed: ASCA, AgBio, AgrAg, AgrLib, BIOSIS Prev, BiolAb, CIN, CPA, ChemAb, ChemTitl, CurCont, EIA, EnerInd, FCA, FPA, ForAb, HerbAb, HortAb, I&DA, MaizeAb, NemAb, OrnHort, PBA, PGegResA, PGrRegA, PotatoAb, RA&MP, RM&VM, RPP, S&F, SeedAb, TOSA, TriticAb, WeedAb.
—BLDSC (0583.000000), CASDDS, CISTI, IDS, IE, ingenta.
Published by: Polskie Towarzystwo Botaniczne/Polish Botanical Society, Al Ujazdowskie 4, Warsaw, 00478, Poland. TEL 48-22-6213669, FAX 48-22-6211922, jfab@ozi.ar.wroc.pl, mirek@ib-pan.krakow.pl, http://www.biol.uni.wroc.pl/instbot/flash/asbp/asbp.html, http://bobas.ib-pan.krakow.pl. Ed. Jerzy Fabiszewski. Circ: 660. **Dist. by:** Ars Polona, Krakowskie Przedmiescie 7, Warsaw, Poland. TEL 48-22-9263914, FAX 48-22-9265334, arspolona@arspolona.com.pl, http://www.arspolona.com.pl.

580.7 POL ISSN 0208-6174
QK322
ACTA UNIVERSITATIS LODZIENSIS: FOLIA BOTANICA. Text in Polish; Summaries in Multiple languages. 1955-1974; N.S. 1981. irreg. **Document type:** *Academic/Scholarly.* **Description:** Articles and notices on flora and vegetation of Poland with special attention to the studies on plant cover synanthropization.
Supersedes in part: Uniwersytet Lodzki. Zeszyty Naukowe. Seria 2: Nauki Matematyczno-Przyrodnicze (0076-0366)
Indexed: AgrLib, RefZh.
—CISTI, KNAW, Linda Hall.
Published by: Wydawnictwo Uniwersytetu Lodzkiego/Lodz University Press, ul Jaracza 34, Lodz, 90262, Poland. TEL 331671. **Dist. by:** Ars Polona, Krakowskie Przedmiescie 7, Warsaw, Poland.

580 POL ISSN 0860-3111
ACTA UNIVERSITATIS LODZIENSIS: FOLIA PHYSIOLOGICA CYTOLOGICA ET GENETICA. Text and summaries in English, Polish. 1955-1974; N.S. 1986. irreg. **Document type:** *Academic/Scholarly.* **Description:** Articles on plant sciences, especially plant physiology and biochemistry, plant cytology and cytochemistry, plant cytogenetics, and plant biotechnology including cultures in vitro and micropropagation of plants.
Supersedes in part: Uniwersytet Lodzki. Zeszyty Naukowe. Seria 2: Nauki Matematyczno-Przyrodnicze (0076-0366)
—CISTI, Linda Hall.
Published by: Wydawnictwo Uniwersytetu Lodzkiego/Lodz University Press, ul Jaracza 34, Lodz, 90262, Poland. TEL 331671. **Dist. by:** Ars Polona, Krakowskie Przedmiescie 7, Warsaw, Poland.

580 POL ISSN 0524-451X
QK1
ACTA UNIVERSITATIS WRATISLAVIENSIS. PRACE BOTANICZNE. Text and summaries in English, Polish. 1964. irreg. price varies. charts; illus. **Document type:** *Academic/Scholarly.*
Indexed: AgrAg, AgrLib.
—KNAW, Linda Hall.
Published by: (Uniwersytet Wroclawski), Wydawnictwo Uniwersytetu Wroclawskiego Spolka z o.o., Pl Uniwersytecki 9-13, Wroclaw, 50-137, Poland. TEL 48-71-441006, FAX 48-71-402735. Ed. Jadwiga Aniol Kwiatkowska. Circ: 250.

580.74 AUS ISSN 0313-4083
QK431 CODEN: JABGDP
ADELAIDE BOTANIC GARDEN. JOURNAL. Text in English. 1976. irreg. price varies. bk.rev. back issues avail.
Indexed: AgrForAb, BIOSIS Prev, BiolAb, CPA, ForAb, HortAb, OrnHort, PBA, PGegResA, RefZh, S&F, WeedAb.
—Linda Hall.
Published by: Botanic Gardens of Adelaide, North Terrace, Adelaide, SA 5000, Australia. TEL 61-8-8228-2308, FAX 61-8-8223-1809. Ed. H R Toelken. Circ: 200.

580 IND
ADVANCE IN FRONTIERS OF PLANT SCIENCES. Text in English. irreg., latest vol.31, 2000. USD 10 (effective 2000). **Document type:** *Academic/Scholarly.*
Published by: H P C Publishers Distributors Pvt. Ltd., 4805 Bharat Ram Rd, 24 Darya Ganj, New Delhi, 110 002, India. TEL 91-11-3254401, FAX 91-11-619-3511, hpcpd@nda.vsnl.net.in, hpcpd@hpc.cc, http://www.hpc.cc, http://www.bizdelhi.com/publisher/hpc, http://www.indianindustry.com. **Co-publisher:** Biblia Impex Pvt. Ltd.

580 USA ISSN 0065-2296
QK1 CODEN: ABTRAJ
➤ **ADVANCES IN BOTANICAL RESEARCH.** Text in English. 1963. irreg., latest vol.38, 2002. USD 159.95 per vol. vol.40 (effective 2004). reprint service avail. from ISI. **Document type:** *Academic/Scholarly.* **Description:** Publishes in-depth and up-to-date reviews on a wide range of topics in plant sciences.
Related titles: Online - full text ed.: (from ScienceDirect).
Indexed: ASCA, ASFA, AgBio, Agr, B&AI, BIOSIS Prev, BioCN&I, BiolAb, CIN, CPA, ChemAb, ChemTitl, FCA, FPA, ForAb, HerbAb, HortAb, I&DA, ISR, OrnHort, PBA, PGegResA, RA&MP, S&F, SCI, SeedAb, WeedAb.
—BLDSC (0700.500000), CASDDS, CISTI, IE, ingenta, Linda Hall. **CCC.**
Published by: Academic Press (Subsidiary of: Elsevier Science & Technology), 525 B St, Ste 1900, San Diego, CA 92101-4495. TEL 619-231-6616, 800-894-3434, FAX 619-699-6422, apsubs@acad.com, http://www.academicpress.com. Ed. J Callow.

B

580 DEU ISSN 0253-6226
QK532.4 CODEN: ABRYDX
ADVANCES IN BRYOLOGY. Text in English. 1981. irreg., latest vol.6, 1997. USD 110 per issue (effective 2004 & 2005). **Document type:** *Monographic series, Academic/Scholarly.*
Indexed: BIOSIS Prev.
—BLDSC (0700.700000), CASDDS, Linda Hall.
Published by: J. Cramer in der Gebrueder Borntraeger Verlagsbuchhandlung, Johannesstr 3A, Stuttgart, 70176, Germany. TEL 49-711-3514560, FAX 49-711-35145699, mail@borntraeger-cramer.de, http://www.schweizerbart.de/j/advances-in-bryology. Ed. N Miller.

580.74 USA ISSN 0741-8280
➤ **ADVANCES IN ECONOMIC BOTANY.** Text in English. 1983. irreg., latest vol.15, 2004. price varies. back issues avail. **Document type:** *Monographic series, Academic/Scholarly.* **Description:** Presents original research and symposia dealing with the uses and management of plants.
Indexed: AbAn, ApicAb, BIOSIS Prev.
—BLDSC (0704.550000), IE, ingenta, Linda Hall. **CCC.**
Published by: New York Botanical Garden Press, 200th Street & Kazimiroff Blvd, Bronx, NY 10458-5126. TEL 718-817-8918, FAX 718-817-8842, nybgpress@nybg.org, http://www.nybg.org. Ed. C Peters.

580 USA ISSN 0736-4539
SB599 CODEN: APLPD6
➤ **ADVANCES IN PLANT PATHOLOGY.** Text in English. 1982. irreg., latest vol.11, 1995. USD 182.95 per vol. vol.11 (effective 2004). reprint service avail. from ISI. **Document type:** *Academic/Scholarly.* **Description:** Focuses on issues of plant pathology and sustainability, such as short term economic plans versus long term economic visions in farming and forestry.
Indexed: Agr, ChemAb.
—CASDDS, Linda Hall. **CCC.**
Published by: Academic Press (Subsidiary of: Elsevier Science & Technology), 525 B St, Ste 1900, San Diego, CA 92101-4495. TEL 619-231-6616, 800-894-3434, apsubs@acad.com, http://www.academicpress.com. Eds. D S Ingram, P H Williams.

580 IND ISSN 0970-3586
QK1 CODEN: APTSEM
ADVANCES IN PLANT SCIENCES. Text in English. 1988. s-a. USD 60 (effective 2000). **Document type:** *Academic/Scholarly.*
Indexed: AEA, AbHyg, AgBio, AgrForAb, BIOSIS Prev, BioCN&I, BiolAb, CPA, DSA, FCA, FPA, ForAb, HerbAb, HortAb, I&DA, IndVet, MaizeAb, NemAb, NutrAb, OrnHort, PBA, PGegResA, PGrRegA, PHN&I, PotatoAb, PoultAb, RA&MP, RDA, RM&VM, RPP, RevApplEntom, RiceAb, S&F, SIA, SeedAb, SoyAb, TDB, TriticAb, VITIS, WAE&RSA, WeedAb, ZooRec.
—BLDSC (0710.170000), IE, ingenta, Linda Hall.
Published by: (Academy of Plant Sciences, India), H P C Publishers Distributors Pvt. Ltd., 4805 Bharat Ram Rd, 24 Darya Ganj, New Delhi, 110 002, India. TEL 91-11-3254401, FAX 91-11-619-3511, hpcpd@nda.vsnl.net.in, hpcpd@hpc.cc, http://www.hpc.cc, http://www.indianindustry.com.

580 IND ISSN 0971-6386
QK1
ADVANCES IN PLANT SCIENCES RESEARCH. Text in English. 1991. s-a. USD 240 (effective 2003). **Document type:** *Journal, Academic/Scholarly.*
Published by: Scientific Publishers, 5-A New Pali Rd., Near Hotel Taj Hari Mahal, PO Box 91, Jodhpur, Rajasthan 342 003, India. TEL 91-291-2433323, FAX 91-291-2512580, info@scientificpub.com, http://www.scientificpub.com.

▼ *new title* ➤ *refereed* ✶ *unverified* ♦ *full entry avail.*

580 IND ISSN 0376-480X
QK658 CODEN: APSRDD
ADVANCES IN POLLEN SPORE RESEARCH. Text in English. 1976. a., latest vol.21, 1996. USD 65. **Document type:** *Monographic series.* **Description:** Reports, interprets and evaluates progress in the field of pollen spore research.
Indexed: BiolAb, CurCont.
—CASDDS, CISTI, Linda Hall. **CCC.**
Published by: Today and Tomorrow's Printers & Publishers, 24 B-5 Desh Bandhu Gupta Rd., Karol Bagh, New Delhi, 110 005, India. tp@vsnl.net. Ed. C P Malik. **Dist. in U.S. by:** Scholarly Publications, 2825 Wilcrest Dr, Ste 255, Houston, TX 77042. TEL 713-781-0070, 713-781-2112.

580 NLD ISSN 0168-8022
CODEN: AVSCDA
➤ **ADVANCES IN VEGETATION SCIENCE.** Text in English. 1980. irreg., latest vol.19, 2000. price varies. back issues avail. **Document type:** *Monographic series, Academic/Scholarly.*
Indexed: AgrForAb, BIOSIS Prev, BiolAb, CPA, FCA, ForAb, HerbAb, HortAb, I&DA, PGrRegA, RA&MP, RPP, S&F, SIA, WeedAb.
—BLDSC (0711.750000), CISTI. **CCC.**
Published by: Springer-Verlag Dordrecht (Subsidiary of: Springer Science+Business Media), Van Godewijckstraat 30, Dordrecht, 3311 GX, Netherlands. TEL 31-78-6576050, FAX 31-78-6576474, http://www.springeronline.com.

B

➤ **AFRICAN JOURNAL OF RANGE & FORAGE SCIENCE.** see *AGRICULTURE—Crop Production And Soil*

580 ZAF ISSN 1023-3121
➤ **AFRICAN PLANT PROTECTION.** Text in English. 1995. s-a. ZAR 120 in Southern Africa to individuals; USD 60 elsewhere to individuals; ZAR 175 in Southern Africa to institutions; USD 70 elsewhere to institutions (effective 2004). bk.rev. illus. back issues avail. **Document type:** *Academic/Scholarly.* **Description:** Publishes research articles and short communications relating to the protection of plants and crops.
Related titles: Online - full text ed.: (from International Network for the Availability of Scientific Publications, African Journals Online).
Indexed: AEA, ASFA, AgBio, AgrForAb, BIOSIS Prev, BioCN&I, BiolAb, CPA, ESPM, FCA, ForAb, HerbAb, HortAb, ISAP, MaizeAb, NemAb, OrnHort, PBA, PGegResA, PHN&I, PotatoAb, RDA, RM&VM, RPP, RevApplEntom, RiceAb, S&F, SIA, SeedAb, SoyAb, TriticAb, WAE&RSA, WeedAb, ZooRec.
Address: PO Box 26320, Arcadia, Pretoria 0007, South Africa. TEL 27-12-667-2016, 27-12-329-3269 ext 223, FAX 27-12-667-2494, 27-12-329-3278, rietls@plant2.agric.za, http://www.inasp.info/ajol/journals.html. Ed. F C Wehner. R&P Martie Botha-Greeff TEL 27-14-536-3150. Circ: 250.

➤ **AFRICAN VIOLET MAGAZINE.** see *GARDENING AND HORTICULTURE*

580 USA ISSN 0738-145X
AGRICELL REPORT. Text in English. 1983. m. USD 329 domestic; USD 359 foreign (effective 2005).
—CISTI. **CCC.**
Published by: Agritech Consultants, Inc., 3779 Briarhill St, Mohegan Lake, NY 10547-1003. TEL 914-528-3469, AGRICELL@AOL.COM.

581 JPN
AKASAWA SHOKUBUTSU JIKKENSHITSU SHOKUBUTSU BUNRUI KENKYU HOKOKU/AKASAWA BOTANICAL LABORATORY. PHYTOTAXONOMIC REPORTS. Text in Japanese. 1987. a. JPY 200.
Published by: Akasawa Shokubutsu Hyohonko/Akasawa Botanical Laboratory and Herbarium, 11-13 Kawahara-Nakamura, Itano-gun, Kitajima, Tokushima-ken 771-0200, Japan.

AKITA-KEN KAJU SHIKENJUO KENKYUU HUOKOKU/AKITA FRUIT-TREE EXPERIMENT STATION. BULLETIN. see *AGRICULTURE*

AKITA KENRITSU DAIGAKU TANKI DARGAKUBU KIYO/AKITA PREFECTURAL COLLEGE OF AGRICULTURE. BULLETIN. see *AGRICULTURE*

580 577 BRA ISSN 0103-4944
➤ **ALBERTOA.** Text in Portuguese; Summaries in English. 1986. 3/yr. per issue exchange basis. bibl. index. back issues avail. **Document type:** *Bulletin, Academic/Scholarly.* **Description:** Covers taxonomy and ecology.
Indexed: AEA, ASFA, ForAb, RefZh.
Published by: Museu Nacional, Departamento de Botanica. Herbarium, Caixa Postal 34031, Rio de Janeiro, 22460-970, Brazil. TEL 55-021-22947313. Eds. Cesar Mendes Pereira, J P P Carauta, Rosa Maria Nepomuceno. Circ: 1,000.

➤ **ALEXANDRIA JOURNAL OF AGRICULTURAL RESEARCH.** see *AGRICULTURE*

579.8 KOR ISSN 1226-2617
ALGAE. Text in Korean. 1996. bi-m. **Document type:** *Journal, Academic/Scholarly.*
Formerly (until 1995): Joryu Haghoeji/Korean Journal of Phycology (1016-2607)
Indexed: ASFA, ESPM.
—BLDSC (0786.999800), IE.
Published by: Han'gug Joryu Haghoe/Korean Society of Phycology, Sangmyung University, Department of Biology, Seoul, 110-743, Korea, S. TEL 82-2-22875125, FAX 82-2-3951895, jhlee@sangmyung.ac.kr, http://bric.postech.ac.kr/phycology/.

ALGOLOGICAL STUDIES; Archiv fur Hydrobiologie, Supplementbaende. see *BIOLOGY*

580 UKR ISSN 0868-8540
➤ **AL'GOLOGIYA/ALGOLOGY.** Text in Ukrainian. 1991. q. USD 179 foreign (effective 2005). adv. bk.rev. bibl.; charts; illus. back issues avail. **Document type:** *Journal, Academic/Scholarly.* **Description:** Covers general problems of algology. Includes physiology, biochemistry, biophysics, flora and geograpfy, fossil algae, new and rare taxons, applied algology and history of algology.
Indexed: ASFA, Djerelo, ESPM, RefZh, ZooRec.
Published by: Natsional'na Akademiya Nauk Ukrainy, Instytut Botaniky im. M.G. Kholodnoho, vul Tereshchenkivs'ka 2, Kyiv, 01601, Ukraine. inst@botany.kiev.ua. Ed. S P Wasser. Circ: 500. **US dist. addr.:** East View Information Services, 3020 Harbor Ln. N., Minneapolis, MN 55447. TEL 763-550-0961, FAX 763-559-2931, eastview@eastview.com, http://www.eastview.com.

580 USA ISSN 0065-6275
QK149 CODEN: ALSOA7
➤ **ALISO**; a journal of taxonomic and evolutionary botany. Text in English. 1948. s-a. USD 45 (effective 2005). back issues avail. **Document type:** *Journal, Academic/Scholarly.* **Description:** Publication of research papers on plants or fungi, especially works ertaining to taxonomy and evolution - with special emphasis on plants of the southwestern United States and Mexico - but not restricted to such.
Indexed: AgBio, Agr, BIOSIS Prev, BioCN&I, BiolAb, CPA, FCA, FPA, ForAb, HerbAb, HortAb, MaizeAb, OrnHort, PBA, PGegResA, RA&MP, RM&VM, RefZh, RevApplEntom, S&F, SeedAb, WeedAb, ZooRec.
—CISTI, Linda Hall.
Published by: Rancho Santa Ana Botanic Garden, 1500 N College Ave, Claremont, CA 91711. TEL 909-625-8767, FAX 909-626-3489, ann.joslin@cgu.edu, http://www.rsabg.org/aliso.html. Ed. Vanessa Ashworth. R&P Clement W Hamilton TEL 909-625-8767 ext. 220. Adv. contact Irene Holiman TEL 909-625-8767 ext. 236. Circ: 350 (paid).

580 IND ISSN 0971-4693
➤ **ALLELOPATHY JOURNAL.** Text in English. 1994. m. USD 150 to individuals developed countries; USD 300 to libraries developed countries; USD 100 to individuals developing countries; USD 200 to libraries developing countries; USD 60 to individuals least developed countries; USD 120 to libraries least developed countries; USD 45 to individuals under developed countries; USD 90 to libraries under developed countries (effective 2005). adv. bk.rev. back issues avail.; reprints avail. **Document type:** *Journal, Academic/Scholarly.* **Description:** Contains research papers and reviews on the current developments in allelopathy and recent abstracts on allelopathy. Also includes biographies of eminent scientists.
Indexed: AgBio, AgrForAb, BioCN&I, BiolAb, CPA, ChemAb, CurCont, FCA, FPA, ForAb, HerbAb, HortAb, I&DA, ISA, MaizeAb, NemAb, OrnHort, PBA, PGegResA, PGrRegA, PotatoAb, RA&MP, RM&VM, RPP, RevApplEntom, RiceAb, S&F, SIA, SeedAb, SoyAb, TDB, TriticAb, WeedAb.
—BLDSC (0789.896000), IE, ingenta. **CCC.**
Published by: International Allelopathy Foundation, 8/15, CCS Haryana Agricultural University, Hisar, Haryana 125 004, India. allelopathy1947@yahoo.com, alleopathy@hau.nic.in, http://www.allelopathy-books.com. Ed. S S Narwal. adv.: page USD 200. Circ: 300 (paid).

580 USA ISSN 0735-8032
QK1 CODEN: LLRTD5
➤ **ALLERTONIA**; a series of occasional papers. Text in English. 1975. irreg., latest vol.8, no.6, 2001. price varies. abstr. index. back issues avail. **Document type:** *Monographic series, Academic/Scholarly.* **Description:** Presents results of original botanical or horticultural research.
Indexed: BIOSIS Prev, BiolAb, ChemAb, SPPI.
—CASDDS, Linda Hall.
Published by: National Tropical Botanical Garden, 3530 Papalina Rd, Kalaheo, HI 96741. TEL 808-332-7324, FAX 808-332-9765, http://www.ntbg.org. Ed., Pub., R&P David H Lorence TEL 808-332-7324 ext 223. Circ: 300.

580 ITA ISSN 0065-6429
CODEN: ALLIAM
➤ **ALLIONIA.** Text in English, French, Italian. 1952. a. per issue exchange basis. **Document type:** *Academic/Scholarly.* **Description:** Contains articles on plant sciences, especially mycology, taxonomy of flowering plants, phytogeography, phytosociology and lichenology.
Indexed: BIOSIS Prev, BiolAb, CPA, ChemAb, FCA, FPA, ForAb, HerbAb, HortAb, MycolAb, OrnHort, PBA, PGegResA, RA&MP, RM&VM, RPP, RevApplEntom, S&F, SeedAb, VITIS, WeedAb.
—CASDDS, CISTI.
Published by: Universita degli Studi di Torino, Dipartimento di Biologia Vegetale, Viale Pierandrea Mattioli, 25, Turin, TO 10125, Italy. TEL 39-11-6699884, FAX 39-11-655839. Ed. Arturo Ceruti. Circ: 500.

579.8 ZAF ISSN 0002-6301
➤ **ALOE.** Text in English. 1963. q. ZAR 110, USD 40 (effective 2002). adv. bk.rev. charts; illus. index, cum.index: 1963-1990 (vols.1-33). **Document type:** *Academic/Scholarly.* **Description:** Contains popular accounts of individual species, field trips, detailed growing tips, plant locations, and plant ecology.
Indexed: CPA, FPA, ForAb, HortAb, I&DA, ISAP, OrnHort, PBA, PGegResA, RA&MP, S&F, SeedAb, TDB.
Published by: Succulent Society of South Africa/Vetplantvereniging van Suid-Afrika, PO Box 12580, Hatfield, 0028, South Africa. TEL 27-12-993-3588, FAX 27-12-993-3588, gasteria@mweb.co.za. Ed. F E Steffens. Adv. contact A Costa. Circ: 1,500 (paid and controlled).

582.14 635.955 ZWE ISSN 1016-524X
QK495.C11
ALOE, CACTUS & SUCCULENT SOCIETY OF ZIMBABWE. INGENS BULLETIN. Text in English. 1989. 2/yr. ZAR 80, GBP 12, USD 20 to individuals; ZAR 120, GBP 20, USD 30 to institutions (effective 1999). adv. **Document type:** *Bulletin, Academic/Scholarly.*
Formerly (until 1989): Aloe, Cactus and Succulent Society of Rhodesia. Quarterly Newsletter (0378-0686)
Published by: Aloe Cactus and Succulent Society of Zimbabwe, PO Box CY 300, Causeway, Harare, Zimbabwe. TEL 263-4-481418. Ed. Michael J Kimberley. R&P Doreen Richards. Adv. contact Michael J Kimberly. Circ: 1,000.

580 635 GBR ISSN 1475-0449
ALPINE GARDENER. Text in English. 1930. q. GBP 22 domestic membership including Ireland; GBP 24 foreign membership; GBP 10 to students (effective 2005). adv. bk.rev. illus. index, cum.index vols.1-61. back issues avail.; reprints avail. **Document type:** *Journal.* **Description:** Contains detailed description of plant cultivation as well as journeys to mountain regions in search of plants.
Formerly (until vol.68, 2000): Alpine Garden Society Quarterly Bulletin (0002-6476); Incorporates: Alpine Gardening (0952-8598)
Indexed: GardL, RefZh.
—BLDSC (0802.149200), CISTI, IE, ingenta.
Published by: Alpine Garden Society, A G S Centre, Avon Bank, Pershore, Worcs WR10 3JP, United Kingdom. TEL 44-1386-554790, FAX 44-1386-554801, ags@alpinegardensociety.org, http://www.alpinegardensociety.org/alpinegardener/index.asp. Ed., R&P Dr. C Grey-Wilson. Adv. contact Mr. J Pratt. Circ: 11,500 (paid).

571.2 USA ISSN 0192-7280
AMERICAN ASSOCIATION OF STRATIGRAPHIC PALYNOLOGISTS, INC. MEMBERSHIP DIRECTORY. Text in English. biennial.
Published by: American Association of Stratigraphic Palynologists Foundation, c/o Vaughn M Bryant, Jr, Palynology Laboratory, Texas A & M Univ, College Station, TX 77843-4352. TEL 979-845-5255, FAX 979-845-4070, vbryant@tamu.edu, http://www.palynology.org.

587.3 USA ISSN 0002-8444
QK520 CODEN: AMFJA2
➤ **AMERICAN FERN JOURNAL.** Text in English. 1910. q. USD 35 in North America to libraries; USD 45 elsewhere to libraries; USD 25 in North America membership; USD 32 elsewhere membership (effective 2006); includes Fiddlehead Forum newsletter. bk.rev. illus. index, cum.index: vols.1-25. 32 p./no. 1 cols./p.; back issues avail. **Document type:** *Journal, Academic/Scholarly.* **Description:** Technical reports on all aspects of the biology of ferns. Targets advanced amateur and professional botanists.
Related titles: Microfiche ed.: (from IDC); Microfilm ed.: (from PMC); Online - full text ed.: (from BioOne, C S A, O C L C Online Computer Library Center, Inc.).
Indexed: ASCA, ASFA, AgBio, Agr, BIOBASE, BIOSIS Prev, BioCN&I, BiolAb, CPA, ChemAb, CurCont, ForAb, GardL, HortAb, ISR, OrnHort, PBA, PGegResA, PGrRegA, RefZh, RevApplEntom, S&F, SCI, WeedAb.
—BLDSC (0815.000000), IDS, IE, Infotrieve, ingenta, Linda Hall.
Published by: American Fern Society, Inc., PO Box 299, Saint Louis, MO 63166-0299. hickeyrj@muohien.edu, http://www.amerfernsoc.org. Ed. R James Hickey. Circ: 1,000 (paid).

580 USA ISSN 0002-9122
QK1 CODEN: AJBOAA

➤ **AMERICAN JOURNAL OF BOTANY**; devoted to all branches of plant sciences. Text in English. 1914. m. USD 445 combined subscription domestic print & online eds.; USD 460 combined subscription in Canada & Mexico print & online eds.; USD 485 combined subscription elsewhere print & online eds. (effective 2005); includes Plant Science Bulletin. adv. bibl.; charts; illus. index. back issues avail. **Document type:** *Journal, Academic/Scholarly.* **Description:** Devoted to every aspect of scientific botany. Provides researchers and the public with the current work in all areas of the botanical sciences.

Related titles: Microfiche ed.: (from IDC); Microfilm ed.: (from PMC); Online - full text ed.: ISSN 1537-2197. USD 600; free to members (effective 2002) (from EBSCO Publishing, H.W. Wilson, HighWire Press, JSTOR (Web-based Journal Archive), O C L C Online Computer Library Center, Inc.).

Indexed: AEA, ASCA, ASFA, AgBio, Agr, AgrForAb, ApEcolAb, ApicAb, B&AI, B&BAb, BIOBASE, BIOSIS Prev, BibAg, BioCN&I, BiolAb, BiolDig, CIN, CPA, CTFA, ChemAb, ChemTitl, CurCont, DBA, ESPM, EntAb, ExcerpMed, FCA, FPA, ForAb, GEOBASE, GSI, GenetAb, HGA, HerbAb, HortAb, I&DA, IABS, ISR, MBA, MEDLINE, MaizeAb, NutrAb, OceAb, OrnHort, PBA, PGegResA, PGrRegA, PHN&I, PlantSci, PollutAb, PotatoAb, PoultAb, RA&MP, RPP, RRTA, RefZh, RevApplEntom, RiceAb, S&F, SCI, SIA, SWRA, SeedAb, SoyAb, TriticAb, VITIS, WeedAb, ZooRec.

—BLDSC (0822.000000), CASDDS, CISTI, IDS, IE, ingenta, Linda Hall.

Published by: Botanical Society of America, Inc. (Columbus), Business Office, 2813 Blossom Ave., Columbus, OH 43231-2921. TEL 614-292-3519, FAX 614-247-6444, orders@allenpress.com, http://www.amjbot.org/, http://www.botany.org/bsa/ajb/index.html, http://www.allenpress.com. Ed. Karl V Niklas. R&P Kimberly Hiser. Adv. contact Allen Press. Circ: 5,000. **Subscr.to:** Allen Press Inc., PO Box 1897, Lawrence, KS 66044.

571.2 USA ISSN 1557-4539

▼ **AMERICAN JOURNAL OF PLANT PHYSIOLOGY.** Text in English. forthcoming 2006 (Jan.). q.

Related titles: Online - full text ed.: ISSN 1557-4547. forthcoming 2006 (Jan.).

Published by: Science Publications, Vails Gate Heights Dr, PO Box 879, Vails Gate, NY 12584. scipub@gmail.com, http://www.scipub.org.

AMERICAN SOCIETY FOR HORTICULTURAL SCIENCE. JOURNAL. see *GARDENING AND HORTICULTURE*

580 USA ISSN 1048-7794

AMERICAN SOCIETY OF PLANT TAXONOMISTS NEWSLETTER. Abbreviated title: A S P T Newsletter. Text in English. 1987. s-a. (Jul., Dec.). print ed. incld. with membership. adv. **Document type:** *Newsletter, Academic/Scholarly.*

Related titles: Online - full text ed.: free.

—Linda Hall.

Published by: American Society of Plant Taxonomists, c/o Elizabeth A. Kellogg, Dept/ of Biology, Univ. of Missouri St. Louis, 8001 Natural Bridge Rd, St. Louis, MO 63121. TEL 314-516-6217, FAX 314-516-6233, tkellogg@umsl.edu, http://www.sysbot.org.

580 DEU ISSN 0721-6513

ANDRIAS. Text mainly in German; Summaries in English. 1981. irreg. price varies. back issues avail. **Document type:** *Journal, Academic/Scholarly.* **Description:** Contains taxonomy, systematics, distribution and ecology of animals.

Indexed: BIOSIS Prev, BiolAb, ZooRec.

Published by: Staatliches Museum fuer Naturkunde Karlsruhe, Erbprinzenstr 13, Karlsruhe, 76133, Germany. TEL 49-721-1752111, FAX 49-721-1752110, hhoefer_smnk@compuserve.com, http://www.smnk.de. Ed. Siegfried Rietschel.

582.13 IND

ANGIOSPERM TAXONOMY. Text in English. s-a. USD 150 (effective 2000). **Document type:** *Academic/Scholarly.*

Published by: H P C Publishers Distributors Pvt. Ltd., 4805 Bharat Ram Rd, 24 Darya Ganj, New Delhi, 110 002, India. TEL 91-11-3254401, FAX 91-11-619-3511, hpcpd@nda.vsnl.net.in, hpcpd@hpc.cc, http://www.hpc.cc, http://www.bizdelhi.com/publisher/hpc, http://www.indianindustry.com. **Co-publisher:** Industrial Association Angios Tax, Department of Botony.

580 FIN ISSN 0003-3847
QK1 CODEN: ABOFAQ

➤ **ANNALES BOTANICI FENNICI.** Text in English. 1964. 6/yr. EUR 44 combined subscription to individuals printed and online editions; EUR 34 to individuals online edition; EUR 10 per issue to individuals; EUR 88 combined subscription to institutions printed and online editions; EUR 66 to institutions online edition; EUR 20 per issue to institutions (effective 2005). charts; illus.; maps; stat. index. 2 cols./p.; back issues avail. **Document type:** *Journal, Academic/Scholarly.* **Description:** Short, original botanical papers by Finnish and foreign botanists. Terrestrial and aquatic ecology, phytogeography and palaeoecology of Boreal zone, plant taxonomy, effect of air pollution on plants, and cryptogamic botany.

Supersedes in part (1931-1964): Societas Zoologicae-Botanicae Fennicae Vanamo. Annales Botanici (0365-0960); Supersedes in part (1946-1964): Societas Zoologicae-Botanicae Fennicae Vanamo. Archivum (0365-7280)

Related titles: Online - full text ed.: EUR 51 (effective 2003) (from EBSCO Publishing).

Indexed: ASCA, ASFA, AgBio, AgrForAb, ApEcolAb, ArcBib, BIOBASE, BIOSIS Prev, BiolAb, CIN, CPA, ChemAb, ChemTitl, CurCont, ESPM, ExcerpMed, FCA, FPA, ForAb, HerbAb, HortAb, I&DA, IABS, IBR, ISR, MBA, MaizeAb, OceAb, OrnHort, PBA, PGegResA, PGrRegA, PlantSci, RA&MP, RPP, RRTA, RefZh, S&F, SCI, SeedAb, TriticAb, VITIS, WeedAb.

—BLDSC (0969.210000), CASDDS, CISTI, IDS, IE, Infotrieve, ingenta, Linda Hall.

Published by: Finnish Zoological and Botanical Publishing Board, P Rautatiekatu 13, University of Helsinki, P O Box 17, Helsinki, 00014, Finland. TEL 358-9-19128805, FAX 358-9-19128806, sekj@helsinki.fi, http://www.sekj.org/AnnBot.html, http://www.sejk.org. Ed. Johannes Enroth. Circ: 800. **Dist. by:** Tiedekirja OY - Vetenskapsbokhandeln.

580 ITA ISSN 0365-0812
QK1 CODEN: ABORAS

ANNALI DI BOTANICA. Text in Multiple languages; Summaries in English, Italian. 1885. a. per issue exchange basis only. bk.rev. charts; illus. index. **Document type:** *Bulletin, Academic/Scholarly.* **Description:** Deals with problems of ecology and the European vegetation survey program.

Supersedes (in 1902): Istituto Botanico di Roma. Annuario

Indexed: BiolAb, ChemAb, RM&VM, VITIS.

—CASDDS, CISTI, Linda Hall.

Published by: (Biblioteca), Universita degli Studi di Roma "La Sapienza", Dipartimento di Biologia Vegetale, Piazzale Aldo Moro, 5, Rome, RM 00185, Italy. TEL 39-06-49917130, FAX 39-06-49917130, pignatti@axrma.uniroma1.it. Ed. Alessandro Pignatti. R&P Ubrizsy Savoia. Circ: 500.

580 GBR ISSN 0305-7364
QK1 CODEN: ANBOA4

➤ **ANNALS OF BOTANY.** Text in English. 1887. 13/yr. GBP 532, USD 949, EUR 798 to institutions; GBP 560, USD 999, EUR 840 combined subscription to institutions print & online eds. (effective 2006). adv. bk.rev. bibl.; charts; illus. index, cum.index. vols.1-25 (present series). 128 p./no.; back issues avail.; reprints avail. **Document type:** *Journal, Academic/Scholarly.* **Description:** Emphasizes current research in growth, mathematical models of physiological processes, and plant ultrastructure.

Related titles: Microfiche ed.: (from IDC); Microfilm ed.: (from PMC); Online - full text ed.: ISSN 1095-8290. GBP 504, USD 899, EUR 756 to institutions (effective 2006) (from EBSCO Publishing, Gale Group, HighWire Press, IngentaConnect, O C L C Online Computer Library Center, Inc., Ovid Technologies, Inc., Oxford University Press Online Journals, ProQuest Information & Learning, ScienceDirect, Swets Information Services); Supplement(s): ISSN 0892-323X.

Indexed: AEA, ASCA, ASFA, AgBio, Agr, AgrForAb, ApEcolAb, B&AI, BIOBASE, BIOSIS Prev, BibAg, BioCN&I, BioDAb, BiolAb, CIN, CPA, CTFA, ChemAb, ChemTitl, CurCont, DBA, ESPM, ExcerpMed, FCA, FPA, FS&TA, FaBeAb, ForAb, GEOBASE, HGA, HerbAb, HortAb, I&DA, IABS, ISR, MaizeAb, NemAb, NutrAb, OceAb, OrnHort, PBA, PGegResA, PGrRegA, PHN&I, PlantSci, PotatoAb, PoultAb, RA&MP, RPP, RevApplEntom, RiceAb, S&F, S&MA, SCI, SFA, SIA, SWRA, SeedAb, SoyAb, TOSA, TriticAb, VITIS, WeedAb, WildRev.

—BLDSC (1040.000000), CASDDS, CISTI, IDS, IE, Infotrieve, ingenta, Linda Hall. **CCC.**

Published by: Oxford University Press, Great Clarendon St, Oxford, OX2 6DP, United Kingdom. TEL 44-1865-556767, FAX 44-1865-556646, annals-botany@bristol.ac.uk, jnl.orders@oup.co.uk, enquiry@oup.co.uk, http://aob.oxfordjournals.org/, http://www.oxfordjournals.org/. Ed. Michael Jackson. Pub. Cathy Kennedy. R&P Fiona Bennett. adv.: B&W page GBP 270, B&W page USD 485, color page GBP 520, color page USD 935; trim 210 x 276. Circ: 830. **Co-sponsor:** Annals of Botany Company.

580 IND ISSN 0971-3573

ANNALS OF PLANT PROTECTION SCIENCES. Text in English. 1993. s-a. USD 70 (effective 2000). **Document type:** *Academic/Scholarly.*

Indexed: AgBio, AgrForAb, BioCN&I, CPA, FCA, FPA, ForAb, HerbAb, HortAb, I&DA, MaizeAb, NemAb, NutrAb, OrnHort, PBA, PGegResA, PGrRegA, PHN&I, PotatoAb, PoultAb, RA&MP, RDA, RM&VM, RPP, RevApplEntom, RiceAb, S&F, SIA, SeedAb, SoyAb, TriticAb, WAE&RSA, WeedAb.

—BLDSC (1043.523000).

Published by: (Society of Plant Protection Sciences), H P C Publishers Distributors Pvt. Ltd., 4805 Bharat Ram Rd, 24 Darya Ganj, New Delhi, 110 002, India. TEL 91-11-3254401, FAX 91-11-619-3511, hpcpd@giasdl01.vsnl.net.in, hpcpd@hpc.cc, http://www.hpc.cc, http://www.indianindustry.com.

ANNOTATIONES ZOOLOGICAE ET BOTANICAE. see *BIOLOGY—Zoology*

580 GBR ISSN 1460-1494

ANNUAL PLANT REVIEWS. Text in English. 1998. irreg., latest 2005, May. price varies. **Document type:** *Monographic series, Academic/Scholarly.*

—BLDSC (1089.725100), IE, ingenta. **CCC.**

Published by: Blackwell Publishing Ltd., 9600 Garsington Rd, Oxford, OX4 2ZG, United Kingdom. TEL 44-1865-776868, FAX 44-1865-714591, customerservices@oxon.blackwellpublishing.com, http://www.blackwellpublishing.com. Ed. Jeremy Roberts.

580 USA ISSN 0066-4286
SB599 CODEN: APPYAG

➤ **ANNUAL REVIEW OF PHYTOPATHOLOGY.** Text in English. 1963. a., latest vol.42, 2004. USD 188 to institutions print or online ed.; USD 226 combined subscription to institutions print & online eds. (effective 2006). bibl.; charts; abstr. index, cum.index. back issues avail.; reprint service avail. from PSC. **Document type:** *Academic/Scholarly.* **Description:** Synthesizes and filters primary research to identify the principal contributions in the field of phytopathology.

Related titles: Microfilm ed.: (from PQC); Online - full content ed.: ISSN 1545-2107. USD 183 (effective 2005) (from HighWire Press); Online - full text ed.: (from bigchalk, EBSCO Publishing, H.W. Wilson, O C L C Online Computer Library Center, Inc., ProQuest Information & Learning, Swets Information Services).

Indexed: ASCA, ASFA, AgBio, Agr, B&AI, B&BAb, BIOBASE, BIOSIS Prev, BibAg, BioCN&I, BioDAb, BiolAb, CIN, CPA, ChemAb, ChemTitl, CurCont, DBA, ESPM, EnvAb, EnvInd, ExcerpMed, FCA, FPA, ForAb, GardL, HerbAb, HortAb, IABS, ISR, MBA, MRD, MaizeAb, NemAb, OrnHort, PBA, PGegResA, PHN&I, PlantSci, PotatoAb, RA&MP, RPP, RevApplEntom, RiceAb, S&F, SCI, SeedAb, SoyAb, TriticAb, VITIS, WeedAb.

—BLDSC (1527.200000), CASDDS, CISTI, IDS, IE, Infotrieve, ingenta, Linda Hall. **CCC.**

Published by: Annual Reviews, 4139 El Camino Way, Palo Alto, CA 94303-0139. TEL 650-493-4400, 800-523-8635, FAX 650-424-0910, service@annualreviews.org, http://arjournals.annualreviews.org/loi/phyto, http://www.annualreviews.org. Ed. Neal K Van Alfen. R&P Laura Folkner.

571.2 USA ISSN 1543-5008
CODEN: ARPBDW

➤ **ANNUAL REVIEW OF PLANT BIOLOGY.** Text in English. 1950. a. USD 197 to institutions print or online ed.; USD 236 combined subscription to institutions print & online eds. (effective 2006). bibl.; charts; abstr. index, cum.index. back issues avail.; reprint service avail. from PSC. **Document type:** *Journal, Academic/Scholarly.* **Description:** Synthesizes and filters primary research to identify the principal contributions in the fields of plant physiology and plant molecular biology.

Former titles (until vol. 52, 2001): Annual Review of Plant Physiology and Plant Molecular Biology (1040-2519); (until vol.38, 1987): Annual Review of Plant Physiology (0066-4294)

Related titles: Microfilm ed.: (from PQC); Online - full text ed.: ISSN 1545-2123. USD 165 (effective 2003) (from bigchalk, EBSCO Publishing, H.W. Wilson, HighWire Press, O C L C Online Computer Library Center, Inc., ProQuest Information & Learning, Swets Information Services).

Indexed: ABIPC, ASCA, ASFA, AgBio, Agr, B&AI, B&BAb, BBCI, BIOBASE, BiolAb, CIN, CPA, ChemAb, ChemTitl, CurCont, DBA, FCA, FPA, ForAb, GSI, GardL, GenetAb, HGA, HerbAb, HortAb, IABS, ISR, MEDLINE, MRD, MaizeAb, NucAcAb, OrnHort, PBA, PGegResA, PGrRegA, PHN&I, PlantSci, PsycholAb, RPP, RiceAb, S&F, SCI, SeedAb, TriticAb, VITIS, VetBull, WeedAb.

—BLDSC (1527.600000), CASDDS, CISTI, IDS, IE, ingenta, Linda Hall. **CCC.**

Published by: Annual Reviews, 4139 El Camino Way, Palo Alto, CA 94303-0139. TEL 650-493-4400, 800-523-8635, FAX 650-424-0910, service@annualreviews.org, http://arjournals.annualreviews.org/loi/arplant, http://www.annualreviews.org. Eds. Deborah P Delmer, Samuel Gubins. R&P Laura Folkner.

587.3 USA ISSN 1051-2926

ANNUAL REVIEW OF PTERIDOLOGICAL RESEARCH. Text in English. a., latest vol.13, 1999, issued 2001. USD 15 to non-members; USD 10 to members (effective 2002). **Document type:** *Academic/Scholarly.* **Description:** Contains a complete list of publications on all aspects of pteridology for a calendar year, supplemented by an index to authors and subjects. The review also includes a directory of name, address, telephone number, fax number, e-mail address and a description of fern- related interests for those who answer our annual questionnaire.

—Linda Hall.

B

Published by: International Association of Pteridologists, Box 499, Edgecomb, ME 04556. jmsharpe@juno.com, http://amerfernsoc.org/arpr.html.

APPLIED BOTANY ABSTRACTS. see *BIOLOGY—Abstracting, Bibliographies, Statistics*

580 631.5 ZAF ISSN 0259-5605
CODEN: APLSEG

APPLIED PLANT SCIENCE/TOEGEPASTE PLANTWETENSKAP. Text in English, Dutch. 1987. s-a. **Description:** Publishes information on weed science focused mainly on southern Africa.
Indexed: ASFA, Agr, CPA, ESPM, FCA, HerbAb, HortAb, I&DA, MaizeAb, NutrAb, PBA, PGrRegA, PotatoAb, RPP, S&F, SWRA, SeedAb, SoyAb, TriticAb, WeedAb.
—CISTI, IE.
Published by: Southern African Weed Science Society, Sunnyside, PO Box 27552, Pretoria, 0132, South Africa.
Co-sponsors: Soil Science Society of Southern Africa; Southern African Society of Crop Production.

580 SWE ISSN 1402-2001
QK900 CODEN: AVSCFC

➤ **APPLIED VEGETATION SCIENCE.** Text in English. 1998. 2/yr. EUR 169; EUR 211 combined subscription pritn & online eds. (effective 2005). bk.rev. 150 p./no. 2 cols./p.; **Document type:** *Journal, Academic/Scholarly.* **Description:** Journal is the official organ of the International Association of Vegetation Science (IAVS).
Related titles: Online - full content ed.: EUR 127 (effective 2005); Online - full text ed.: (from BioOne, C S A, EBSCO Publishing, O C L C Online Computer Library Center, Inc., Swets Information Services).
Indexed: AEA, Agr, AgrForAb, AnBrAb, BIOBASE, BIOSIS Prev, BioCN&I, BiolAb, CPA, CurCont, EA, EPB, FCA, ForAb, GardL, HerbAb, HortAb, I&DA, MaizeAb, NemAb, NutrAb, PBA, PGegResA, PN&I, PoultAb, RA&MP, RPP, RRTA, RevApplEntom, RiceAb, S&F, SIA, SeedAb, SoyAb, VetBull, WeedAb.
—BLDSC (1580.113100), CISTI, IE, Infotrieve, ingenta, Linda Hall.
Published by: (International Association for Vegetation Science NLD), Opulus Press, Gamla Vaegen 40, Grangaerde, 77013, Sweden. TEL 46-240-641250, FAX 46-240-640880, info@opuluspress.se, http://www.opuluspress.se. Eds. R Lubke, S. Diaz.

581.76 USA ISSN 0893-7702
AQUAPHYTE. Text in English. 1981. s-a. free. bk.rev. abstr.; bibl. back issues avail. **Document type:** *Newsletter, Academic/Scholarly.* **Description:** Publishes items of interest to managers, researchers, and regulators of aquatic and invasive plants; includes literature reviews and meeting announcements.
Indexed: ASFA, AgBio, HerbAb, HortAb, PBA, PGegResA, RA&MP, S&F, TDB, WeedAb.
Published by: (Center for Aquatic and Invasive Plants), University of Florida, Center for Aquatic Plants, 7922 N W 71st St, Gainesville, FL 32653. TEL 352-392-1799, FAX 352-392-3462, varamey@nervm.nerdc.ufl.edu, http://aquat1.ifas.ufl.edu/. Ed., R&P Victor Ramey. Circ: 5,500.

579.177 NLD ISSN 0304-3770
CODEN: AQBODS

➤ **AQUATIC BOTANY.** Text in English. 1975. 8/yr. EUR 1,218 in Europe to institutions; JPY 161,800 in Japan to institutions; USD 1,362 to institutions except Europe and Japan (effective 2006). adv. bk.rev. bibl.; illus.; abstr. Index. back issues avail.; reprints avail. **Document type:** *Journal, Academic/Scholarly.* **Description:** Concerned with fundamental studies on structure, function, dynamics and classification of plant-dominated aquatic ecosystems.
Related titles: Microform ed.: (from PQC); Online - full text ed.: (from EBSCO Publishing, Gale Group, IngentaConnect, ScienceDirect, Swets Information Services).
Indexed: AEA, APD, ASCA, ASFA, AgBio, AnBrAb, ApEcolAb, BIOBASE, BIOSIS Prev, BioCN&I, BiolAb, CIN, CPA, Cadscan, ChemAb, ChemTitl, CurCont, EPB, ESPM, EnvAb, EnvInd, ExcerpMed, FLUIDEX, ForAb, GEOBASE, HerbAb, HortAb, I&DA, IABS, ISR, IndVet, LeadAb, MBA, MSCT, OceAb, OrnHort, PBA, PGegResA, PGrRegA, PHN&I, PlantSci, PoultAb, RA&MP, RPP, RRTA, S&F, SCI, SFA, SIA, SPPI, SWRA, SeedAb, SoyAb, WeedAb, WildRev, Zincscan, ZooRec.
—BLDSC (1582.370000), CASDDS, CISTI, IDS, IE, Infotrieve, ingenta. **CCC.**
Published by: Elsevier BV (Subsidiary of: Elsevier Science & Technology), Radarweg 29, Amsterdam, 1043 NX, Netherlands. TEL 31-20-4853911, FAX 31-20-4852457, nlinfo-f@elsevier.nl, http://www.elsevier.com/locate/aquabot, http://www.elsevier.nl. Eds. Dr. G Bowes, Jan Vermaat.
Subscr. in the Americas to: Elsevier, Subscription Customer Service, 6277 Sea Harbor Dr, Orlando, FL 32887-4800. TEL 407-345-4020, 877-839-7126, FAX 407-363-1354.

579.177 USA ISSN 1463-4988

➤ **AQUATIC ECOSYSTEM HEALTH & MANAGEMENT.** Text in English. 1998. q. GBP 265, USD 438 combined subscription to institutions print & online eds. (effective 2006). abstr. back issues avail.; reprint service avail. from PSC. **Document type:** *Journal, Academic/Scholarly.* **Description:** Promotes understanding of the structure, function and performance of healthy and damaged aquatic ecosystems from integrated, multi-disciplinary and sustainable perspectives.
Related titles: Microfilm ed.; Online - full text ed.: ISSN 1539-4077. GBP 252, USD 416 to institutions (effective 2006) (from EBSCO Publishing, Gale Group, IngentaConnect, O C L C Online Computer Library Center, Inc., ScienceDirect).
Indexed: ASFA, ApEcolAb, B&BAb, BIOBASE, BiolAb, ESPM, EnvEAb, OceAb, PollutAb, RefZh, SWRA, ToxAb, ZooRec.
—BLDSC (1582.372700), CISTI, IE, Infotrieve, ingenta. **CCC.**
Published by: (Aquatic Ecosystem Health and Management Society NLD), Taylor & Francis Inc. (Subsidiary of: Taylor & Francis Group), 325 Chestnut St, Ste 800, Philadelphia, PA 19016. TEL 215-625-8900, 800-354-1420, FAX 215-625-2940, 215-625-8914, info@taylorandfrancis.com, http://www.tandf.co.uk/journals/titles/14634988.asp, http://www.taylorandfrancis.com. Ed. Dr. M Munawar. **Subscr. outside N. America to:** Taylor & Francis Ltd, Journals Customer Service, Rankine Rd, Basingstoke, Hants RG24 8PR, United Kingdom. TEL 44-1256-813000, FAX 44-1256-330245, enquiry@tandf.co.uk.

➤ **THE AQUATIC GARDENER.** see *GARDENING AND HORTICULTURE*

580 635 USA ISSN 1046-9397
AQUATIC PLANT NEWS. Text in English. 1986. q. USD 70 (effective 2000). **Document type:** *Newsletter, Academic/Scholarly.*
Published by: Aquatic Plant Management Society, Inc., 821265, Vicksburg, MS 39182-1265. TEL 239-694-6959, FAX 239-694-6959. Ed. Dr. John Madsen.

578.77 NLD ISSN 0921-8572

➤ **AQUATIC PLANT STUDIES.** Text in Dutch. 1987. irreg., latest vol.2, 1989. price varies. back issues avail. **Document type:** *Monographic series, Academic/Scholarly.* **Description:** Examines research in aquatic botany.
Published by: Elsevier BV (Subsidiary of: Elsevier Science & Technology), Radarweg 29, Amsterdam, 1043 NX, Netherlands. TEL 31-20-4853911, FAX 31-20-4852457, nlinfo-f@elsevier.nl, http://www.elsevier.nl.

635 USA
AQUILEGIA. Text in English. 1976. 6/yr. membership only. **Document type:** *Newsletter.*
Formerly: Colorado Native Plant Society. Newsletter
Published by: Colorado Native Plant Society, PO Box 200, Ft. Collins, CO 80522. Ed. Tamara Naumann.

580 FIN ISSN 0570-5169
CODEN: ASBOD8

➤ **AQUILO. SERIE BOTANICA.** Text in English, German. 1963. s-a. price varies. back issues avail. **Document type:** *Academic/Scholarly.* **Description:** Covers botany, ecology, pollution and plant physiology.
Indexed: ASFA, AgrForAb, BIOSIS Prev, BiolAb, CPA, ChemAb, ESPM, ForAb, GEOBASE, HortAb, I&DA, PBA, PGrRegA, PHN&I, RA&MP, S&F, SWRA, SeedAb.
—CASDDS.
Published by: Societas Amicorum Naturae Ouluensis, Department of Botany, University of Oulu, Linnanmaa, Oulu, 90570, Finland. TEL 358-8-553-1546, FAX 358-981-553-1500, se@abore. Ed., R&P Pekka Lahdesmaki. Circ: 305 (controlled).

580 LBN ISSN 0255-982X
ARAB JOURNAL OF PLANT PROTECTION. Text in Arabic; Abstracts in English. 1983. s-a.
Indexed: ZooRec.
—BLDSC (1583.239600).
Published by: Arab Society for Plant Protection, PO Box 113, Beirut, 6057, Lebanon.

571.2 USA ISSN 1543-8120

▼ **THE ARABIDOPSIS BOOK.** Text in English. 2003. irreg. free (effective 2003). **Document type:** *Journal, Academic/Scholarly.* **Description:** Contains a compilation of over 100 invited chapters, each reviewing in detail an important and interesting aspect of the plant Arabidopsis thaliana, with reference to what is known in other plants and in other kingdoms.
Media: Online - full text (from BioOne, C S A).
Published by: American Society of Plant Biologists, 15501 Monona Dr, Rockville, MD 20855-2768. TEL 301-251-0560, FAX 301-279-2996, info@aspb.org, http://www.aspb.org.

580 DEU ISSN 1434-1662
ARBEITSGEMEINSCHAFT SAECHSISCHER BOTANIKER. BERICHTE. Text in German. 1959. a. bk.rev. illus. **Document type:** *Journal, Academic/Scholarly.* **Description:** Contains studies in botany, geobotany, and taxonomy.
Indexed: BiolAb.
Published by: Technische Universitaet Dresden, Institut fuer Botanik, Mommsenstr 13, Dresden, 01062, Germany. Circ: 800.

583.56 635.93356 DEU ISSN 0172-875X
ARBEITSKREIS FUER MAMMILLARIENFREUNDE. MITTEILUNGSBLATT. Text in German; Summaries in English. 1977. 4/yr. EUR 33 (effective 2003). adv. bk.rev. 44 p./no.; back issues avail. **Document type:** *Newsletter, Academic/Scholarly.*
Published by: Arbeitskreis fuer Mammillarienfreunde e.V., Niederdonker Str 31, Duesseldorf, 40547, Germany. TEL 49-211-592263, FAX 49-211-592285, AfM-Geschaeftsstelle@t-online.de, http://www.afm-mammillaria.de. Ed. Bernd Hofmann. R&P Othmar Appenzeller. Adv. contact Wolfgang Plein. Circ: 650.

ARBOR AGE. see *FORESTS AND FORESTRY*

ARBORETUM LEAVES. see *GARDENING AND HORTICULTURE*

ARCHIV FUER HYDROBIOLOGIE; Official journal of the International Association of Theoretical and Applied Limnology. see *BIOLOGY*

ARCHIV FUER HYDROBIOLOGIE. SUPPLEMENT-BAND: LARGE RIVERS. see *BIOLOGY*

ARCHIV FUER HYDROBIOLOGIE. SUPPLEMENT-BAND: UNTERSUCHUNGEN DES ELBE-AESTUARS. see *BIOLOGY*

ARCHIV FUER HYDROBIOLOGIE. SUPPLEMENT VOLUMES, MONOGRAPHIC STUDIES. see *BIOLOGY*

580 ITA ISSN 1122-7214
QK101

➤ **ARCHIVIO GEOBOTANICO;** international journal of geobotany, plant ecology and taxonomy. Text in English, French, Italian; Summaries in English, French. 1995. s-a. EUR 52 (effective 2004). bk.rev. charts; illus. index. back issues avail. **Document type:** *Academic/Scholarly.*
Formed by the merger of (1925-1992): Archivio Botanico Italiano (1121-2101); Which was formerly (until 1988): Archivio Botanico e Biogeografico Italiano (0004-0053); (until 1955): Archivio Botanico (1121-225X); (until 1935): Archivio Botanico per la Sistematica, Fitogeografia e Genetica (1120-5482); And (1888-1992): Atti dell'Istituto Botanico e del Laboratorio Crittogamico dell'Universita di Pavia (0373-3947); Which was formerly (until 1981): Atti dell'Istituto Botanico dell'Universita e del Laboratorio Crittogamico di Pavia (0367-6951); (until 1941): Atti dell'Istituto Botanico Giovanni Briosi e del Laboratorio Crittogamico Italiano (1122-8121); (until 1929): Universita di Pavia. Istituto Botanico. Atti (0365-298X)
Indexed: BIOSIS Prev, BiolAb, FCA, HerbAb, RefZh, VITIS.
—CISTI, Linda Hall.
Published by: Universita degli Studi di Pavia, Dipartimento di Ecologia del Territorio, Via S Epifanio 14, Pavia, PV 27100, Italy. TEL 39-0382-504841, FAX 39-0382-34240, grossi@et.unipv.it, secoter@et.unipv.it, http://et.unipv.it. Ed. Augusto Pirola. R&P Graziano Rossi. Circ: 600.

580 ESP ISSN 1131-5199
ARCHIVOS DE FLORA IBERICA. Text in Spanish. 1991. irreg. price varies.
Indexed: IECT.
Published by: Real Jardin Botanico de Madrid, Plaza Murillo, 2, Madrid, 28014, Spain.

580 RUS ISSN 0131-1379
ARCTOA: A JOURNAL OF BRYOLOGY. Text in English; Summaries in Russian. 1992. s-a. USD 15 to members; USD 20 to non-members (effective 2004). **Document type:** *Journal, Academic/Scholarly.*
—CISTI.
Published by: K M K Scientific Press Ltd., c/o Dr K G Mikhailov, Zoologicheskii Muzei MGU, Bol'shaya Nikitskaya 6, Moscow, 125009, Russian Federation. TEL 7-095-2925796, FAX 7-095-2032717, arctoa@eignatova.home.bio.msu.ru, kmk2000@online.ru, http://herba.msu.ru/journals/arctoa, http://www.orc.ru/~kmkweb. Ed. M S Ignatov.

ARNOLDIA. see *GARDENING AND HORTICULTURE*

AROIDEANA. see *GARDENING AND HORTICULTURE*

635.968 550 150 USA
AROMATIC NEWS; news from the Aromatic News Project. Text in English. q. **Document type:** *Newsletter.*
Indexed: CINAHL.
Published by: Aromatic Plant Project, PO Box 225336, San Francisco, CA 94122-5336. TEL 877-966-4227, FAX 415-564-6799, http://www.aromaticplantproject.com/.

580 FRA ISSN 0066-8184
ARVERNIA BIOLOGICA: BOTANIQUE; recueil des travaux des laboratoires botaniques de l'U.F.R. de recherche scientifique et technique. Text in French. 1930. irreg. per issue exchange basis only. **Document type:** *Academic/Scholarly.*
Indexed: VITIS.
Published by: Universite de Clermont-Ferrand II (Blaise Pascal), Laboratoire de Biologie Vegetale, 4 rue Ledru, Clermont-Ferrand, Cedex 1 63038, France.

580 IND ISSN 0971-2402
CODEN: ASCIEU
➤ **ASIAN JOURNAL OF PLANT SCIENCE.** Text in English. 1989. s-a. INR 100, USD 20. bk.rev. back issues avail. **Document type:** *Academic/Scholarly.* **Description:** Contains research papers and review articles covering all fields of plant science.
Related titles: Diskette ed.
Indexed: ApicAb, BiolAb, ISA.
Published by: Ranjana Malvey Pub., 6-4-361 26 A Anjarieya Swamy Colony, Bholakpur, Secunderabad, Andhra Pradesh 500 380, India. Eds. K Vaidyanath, M Prabhakar.

580 PAK ISSN 1682-3974
ASIAN JOURNAL OF PLANT SCIENCES. Text in English. 2002. bi-m. **Document type:** *Journal, Academic/Scholarly.* **Description:** Articles published provide broad coverage of the plant sciences, from molecular biology to ecology, including: development, growth regulation, molecular cell biology and genetics, signal transduction, photosynthesis, pathogen resistance, nutrition, water relations and gas exchange, symbiosis (especially mycorrhizae and rhizobia,) stress physiology, population genetics, ecology and molecular systematics.
Related titles: Online - full text ed.: ISSN 1812-5697. 2004. free (effective 2005).
Indexed: FCA.
Published by: Asian Network for Scientific Information, 308-Lasani Town, Sargodha Rd, Faislabad, 38090, Pakistan. TEL 92-41-2001145, FAX 92-41-731433, http://www.ansinet.org/c4p.php?j_id=ajps.

580 IND ISSN 0971-1678
ASPECT OF PLANT SCIENCES. Text in English. 1976 (vol.14). irreg., latest vol.15, 1996. INR 495, USD 65. **Document type:** *Academic/Scholarly.* **Description:** Contains articles of theoretical and methodological interest, as well as studies based on empirical research in the field of plant sciences.
—CISTI. **CCC.**
Published by: Today and Tomorrow's Printers & Publishers, 24 B-5 Desh Bandhu Gupta Rd., Karol Bagh, New Delhi, 110 005, India. tp@vsnl.net. Eds. C B Gena, T N Bhardwaja. **Dist. in U.S. by:** Scholarly Publications, 2825 Wilcrest Dr, Ste 255, Houston, TX 77042. TEL 713-781-0070.

580 635 GBR ISSN 0265-1491
QH301
ASPECTS OF APPLIED BIOLOGY. Text in English. 1982. irreg. price varies. back issues avail. **Document type:** *Monographic series, Academic/Scholarly.* **Description:** Proceedings of conferences held by the Association.
Indexed: AEA, AbHyg, AgBio, Agr, AgrForAb, AnBrAb, BioCN&I, CPA, DSA, FCA, FPA, FS&TA, ForAb, HelmAb, HerbAb, HortAb, I&DA, MaizeAb, NemAb, NutrAb, OrnHort, PBA, PGegResA, PGrRegA, PHN&I, PN&I, PotatoAb, PoultAb, ProtozoAb, RA&MP, RM&VM, RPP, RRTA, RiceAb, S&F, SIA, SeedAb, SoyAb, TriticAb, WAE&RSA, WeedAb, ZooRec.
—BLDSC (1745.901600), CISTI, IE, ingenta. **CCC.**
Published by: Association of Applied Biologists, Horticultural Research International, c/o Warwick HRI, Wellesbourne, Warwick, CV35 9EF, United Kingdom. TEL 44-1789-470382, FAX 44-1789-470234, michelle.aab@warwick.ac.uk, http://www.aab.org.uk.

571.2 FRA ISSN 0296-3086
ASSOCIATION DES NATURALISTES DE LA VALLEE DU LOING ET DU MASSIF DE FONTAINEBLEAU. BULLETIN. Text in French. q.
Indexed: ZooRec.
Published by: Association des Naturalistes de la Vallee du Loing et du Massif de Fontainebleau, Laboratoire de Biologie Vegetale, Route de la Tour-Denecourt, Fontainebleau, 77300, France.

580 EGY ISSN 1110-7340
ASSUIT UNIVERSITY. FACULTY OF SCIENCE. BULLETIN. SECTION D. BOTANY. Text in English. 1988. s-a. free (effective 2004). **Document type:** *Bulletin, Academic/Scholarly.*
Supersedes in part (in 1988): Assiut University. Faculty of Science. Bulletin. Section C. Biology and Geology (1010-2698); Which was formerly (until 1982): Assiut University. Faculty of Science. Bulletin. Section B. Biological and Geological Studies (0254-6256); Which superseded in part (in 1979): Assiut University. Science and Technology. Bulletin (0379-3389)
Published by: Assiut University, Faculty of Science, c/o Dr. Muhammad Bahey, Assiut, Egypt. TEL 20-88-411376, FAX 20-88-342708, science@aun.edu.eg, sup@aun.eun.eg, http://derp.sti.sci.eg/data/0298.htm, http://www.aun.eun.eg. Ed. Dr. Muhammad Bahey-El-Din Hasan Mazen.

551.5 FIN
ATLAS FLORAE EUROPAEAE. Text in English. 1972. irreg., latest vol.12, 1999. price varies. illus.; maps. back issues avail. **Document type:** *Monographic series, Academic/Scholarly.* **Description:** Maps of distribution of vascular plants in Europe.
Indexed: BibAg, BiolAb, ChemAb, CurCont.
Published by: Societas Biologica Fennica Vanamo, Unioninkatu 44, PO Box 7, Helsinki, 00014, Finland. TEL 358-9-191-24420, FAX 358-9-191-24456, http://www.fmnh.helsinki.fi. Ed. Arto Kurtto TEL 358-9-19124430. **Dist. by:** Akateeminen Kirjakauppa, Keskuskatu 1, Helsinki 00100, Finland. **Co-sponsor:** Committee for Mapping the Flora of Europe.

580 POL ISSN 0067-0294
ATLAS FLORY POLSKIEJ I ZIEM OSCIENNYCH/FLORAE POLONICAE TERRARUNIQUE ADIACENTIUM SCONOGRAPHIA. Text in English, Polish. 1960. irreg. price varies. bk.rev. maps. back issues avail. **Document type:** *Academic/Scholarly.*
Indexed: BiolAb.
Published by: Polska Akademia Nauk, Instytut Botaniki im. W. Szafera/Polish Academy of Sciences, W. Szafer Institute of Botany, ul Lubicz 46, Krakow, 31512, Poland. TEL 48-12-4241737, FAX 48-12-4219790, office@ib-pan.krakow.pl. Ed. Wladyslaw Wojewoda. R&P Mirek Zbigniew.

588.2 POL
ATLAS ROZMIESZCZENIA GEOGRAFICZNEGO MCHOW W POLSCE/ATLAS OF THE GEOGRAPHICAL DISTRIBUTION OF MOSSES IN POLAND. Text in English, Polish. 1962. irreg. price varies. **Document type:** *Academic/Scholarly.* **Description:** Presents distribution maps for all varieties of mosses known to occur in Poland. The text describes the history of the species, its ecology, and reviews in detail its world distribution.
Published by: Akademia Nauk, Instytut Botaniki im. W. Szafera, Ul Lubicz 46, Krakow, 31512, Poland. TEL 48-12-4215144, FAX 48-12-4219790, wysocki@ib-pan.krakow.pl. Ed. Ryszard Ochyra. R&P Leoan Stuchlik. Circ: 500 (paid).

579.7 POL
ATLAS ROZMIESZCZENIA GEOGRAFICZNEGO POROSTOW W POLSCE/ATLAS OF THE GEOGRAPHICAL DISTRIBUTION OF LICHENS IN POLAND. Text in English, Polish. 1993. irreg., latest vol.2, 1999. price varies. bk.rev. maps. 64 p./no. 2 cols./p.; back issues avail. **Document type:** *Academic/Scholarly.* **Description:** Presents lichens distribution maps in Poland. Provides description of each species and full list of localities.
Published by: Polska Akademia Nauk, Instytut Botaniki im. W. Szafera/Polish Academy of Sciences, W. Szafer Institute of Botany, ul Lubicz 46, Krakow, 31512, Poland. TEL 48-12-4241737, FAX 48-12-4210790, office@ib-pan.krakow.pl. Ed. Stanislaw Cieslinski. R&P Mirek Zbigniew. Circ: 300 (paid).

571.2 AUS ISSN 0815-3191
CODEN: AAPPDN
➤ **AUSTRALASIAN PLANT PATHOLOGY.** Text in English. 1972. q. AUD 380 in Australia & New Zealand to institutions; USD 345 elsewhere to institutions (effective 2005); individual subscr. included with membership to Australasian Plant Pathology Society. adv. bk.rev. back issues avail. **Document type:** *Journal, Academic/Scholarly.* **Description:** Publishes research papers, short research notes, general articles, review articles, and disease notes or new records.
Formerly (until 1978): Australian Plant Pathology Society. Newsletter (0156-0972)
Related titles: Online - full text ed.: (from EBSCO Publishing, Gale Group, O C L C Online Computer Library Center, Inc., Swets Information Services).
Indexed: ASCA, AgBio, AgrForAb, BIOSIS Prev, BioCN&I, BiolAb, CPA, CurCont, FCA, FPA, ForAb, HerbAb, HortAb, I&DA, IndVet, MaizeAb, NemAb, OrnHort, PBA, PGegResA, PHN&I, PN&I, PotatoAb, PoultAb, RA&MP, RM&VM, RPP, RevApplEntom, RiceAb, S&F, SIA, SeedAb, SoyAb, TriticAb, VITIS, WAE&RSA, WeedAb, ZooRec.
—BLDSC (1796.095000), CASDDS, CISTI, IDS, IE, Infotrieve, ingenta. **CCC.**
Published by: (Australasian Plant Pathology Society), C S I R O Publishing, 150 Oxford St, PO Box 1139, Collingwood, VIC 3066, Australia. TEL 61-3-96627500, FAX 61-3-96627555, publishing@csiro.au, http://www.publish.csiro.au/nid/39.htm. Ed. E J Cother. Circ: 550.

635.0994 AUS ISSN 1033-3673
AUSTRALIAN GARDEN HISTORY. Text in English. 1989. bi-m. AUD 47 to individuals; AUD 73 to institutions (effective 2002). illus. 24 p./no.; **Document type:** *Journal.*
Indexed: AusPAIS, GardL.
Published by: Australian Garden History Society, Gate Lodge, 100 Birdwood Ave, Melbourne, VIC 3004, Australia. TEL 61-3-96505043, FAX 61-3-96508470, wild@beyond.net.au, info@gardenhistory.org.au, http://www.gardenhistorysociety.org.au/journal.htm. Ed. Nina Crone.

580 AUS ISSN 0067-1924
QK1 CODEN: AJBTAP
➤ **AUSTRALIAN JOURNAL OF BOTANY.** Text in English. 1953. bi-m. AUD 165 combined subscription in Australia & New Zealand to individuals for print & online eds.; USD 165 combined subscription elsewhere to individuals for print & online eds.; AUD 895 combined subscription in Australia & New Zealand to institutions for print & online eds.; USD 795 combined subscription elsewhere to institutions for print & online eds. (effective 2004). adv. Index. 144 p./no.; back issues avail. **Document type:** *Journal, Academic/Scholarly.* **Description:** Publishes original research in plant sciences: ecology and ecophysiology, conservation biology and biodiversity, forest biology and management, cell biology and molecular, palaeobotany, reproductive biology and genetics, mycology and pathology, and structure and development.
Related titles: Microform ed.: (from PQC); Online - full text ed.: AUD 150 in Australia & New Zealand to individuals; USD 130 elsewhere to individuals; AUD 800 in Australia & New Zealand to institutions; USD 715 elsewhere to institutions (effective 2004) (from EBSCO Publishing, O C L C Online Computer Library Center, Inc., Swets Information Services).
Indexed: AEA, AESIS, ASCA, ASFA, AgBio, Agr, AgrForAb, B&AI, B&BAb, BIOBASE, BIOSIS Prev, BioCN&I, BiolAb, CIN, CPA, ChemAb, ChemTitl, CurCont, DSA, EPB, ESPM, FCA, FPA, FS&TA, ForAb, GEOBASE, HerbAb, HortAb, I&DA, IABS, INIS AtomInd, ISR, IndVet, MBA, MaizeAb, NutrAb, OrnHort, PBA, PGegResA, PGrRegA, PHN&I, PlantSci, PotatoAb, RA&MP, RM&VM, RPP, RevApplEntom, RiceAb, S&F, SCI, SIA, SPPI, SeedAb, SoyAb, TriticAb, VITIS, WeedAb.
—BLDSC (1805.000000), CASDDS, CISTI, IDS, IE, Infotrieve, ingenta, Linda Hall. **CCC.**
Published by: (C S I R O Australia), C S I R O Publishing, 150 Oxford St, PO Box 1139, Collingwood, VIC 3066, Australia. TEL 61-3-96627613, FAX 61-3-96627611, simone.farrer@csiro.au, publishing@csiro.au, http://www.publish.csiro.au/journals/ajb. Circ: 800.

580.994 AUS ISSN 0005-0008
CODEN: ANPLAV
AUSTRALIAN PLANTS. Text in English. 1959. q. free to members. adv. bk.rev. charts; illus. index every 2 yrs. reprint service avail. from PQC. **Document type:** *Journal, Academic/Scholarly.* **Description:** Examines the Australian flora for horticultural development and its conservation. Provides a link between the academic scientist and the general public by representing current scientific research in a popular manner.
Related titles: Microfilm ed.: (from PQC); Online - full text ed.: ISSN 1326-7469.
Indexed: AEA, AgBio, AgrForAb, BiolAb, CPA, ForAb, GardL, HortAb, OrnHort, PBA, PGegResA, PGrRegA, PHN&I, Pinpoint, RA&MP, RPP, RRTA, S&F, SeedAb.
Published by: Society for Growing Australian Plants, 860 Henry Lawson Dr, Picnic Point, NSW 2213, Australia. TEL 61-2-773-9866, asgaponline@yahoo.com.au, http://farrer.riv.csu.edu.au/ASGAP/apoline.html, http://www.ozemail.com.au/~sgap/apoline.html. Ed. W H Payne. Circ: 10,000 (paid).

580 AUS ISSN 1030-1887
CODEN: ASBOE9
➤ **AUSTRALIAN SYSTEMATIC BOTANY.** Text in English. 1972. bi-m. AUD 165 combined subscription in Australia & New Zealand to individuals print & online eds.; USD 165 combined subscription elsewhere to individuals print & online eds.; AUD 840 combined subscription in Australia & New Zealand to institutions print & online eds.; USD 725 combined subscription elsewhere to institutions print & online eds. (effective 2004). abstr.; bibl.; charts; illus.; maps. 160 p./no.; back issues avail. **Document type:** *Journal, Academic/Scholarly.* **Description:** Devoted to the taxonomy, biogeography and evolution of all plant groups.
Supersedes (in 1988): Brunonia (0313-4245); Which was formerly: Commonwealth Scientific and Industrial Research Organization. Herbarium Australiense. Brunonia; Commonwealth Scientific and Industrial Research Organization. Herbarium Australiense. Contributions from Herbarium Australiense.
Related titles: Microform ed.: (from PQC); Online - full text ed.: AUD 140 in Australia & New Zealand to individuals; USD 130 elsewhere to individuals; AUD 750 in Australia & New Zealand to institutions; USD 650 elsewhere to institutions (effective 2004) (from EBSCO Publishing, Gale Group, O C L C Online Computer Library Center, Inc., Swets Information Services).
Indexed: ASCA, AgBio, Agr, AgrForAb, BIOBASE, BIOSIS Prev, BioCN&I, BiolAb, CPA, CurCont, FCA, FPA, ForAb, GEOBASE, HerbAb, HortAb, IABS, ISR, OrnHort, PBA, PGegResA, PlantSci, RA&MP, RM&VM, RPP, RevApplEntom, S&F, SCI, SeedAb, SoyAb, WeedAb, ZooRec.
—BLDSC (1822.350000), CISTI, IDS, IE, Infotrieve, ingenta, Linda Hall. **CCC.**
Published by: (C S I R O Australia), C S I R O Publishing, 150 Oxford St, PO Box 1139, Collingwood, VIC 3066, Australia. TEL 61-3-96627500, FAX 61-3-96627611, simone.farrer@csiro.au, publishing@csiro.au, http://www.publish.csiro.au/journals/asb. Circ: 500.

B

▼ new title ➤ refereed ✶ unverified ♦ full entry avail.

580.74 AUS ISSN 0155-4131
CODEN: AUSTDK
AUSTROBAILEYA. Text in English. 1977. a. USD 28.75 to individuals; USD 46 to institutions (effective 2003). back issues avail. **Document type:** *Journal, Academic/Scholarly.*
Description: Focuses on systematic botany and related fields, with emphasis on the flora of Queensland, tropical Australia, and nearby countries.
Formerly (until 1977): Queensland Herbarium. Contributions
Indexed: ASFA, AgrForAb, BIOSIS Prev, BiolAb, ForAb, HerbAb, HortAb, OrnHort, PBA, PGegResA, RPP, S&F, SeedAb, WeedAb.
Published by: Queensland Herbarium, Environmetal Protection Agency, Brisbane Botanic Gardens, Mt Coot-tha Rd, Toowong, QLD 4066, Australia. TEL 61-7-3896-9326, FAX 61-7-3896-9624, queensland.herbarium@epa.qld.gov.au, http://www.env.qld.gov.au/environment/science/herbarium/.

580 NLD ISSN 0005-2728
QD1
➤ **B B A - BIOENERGETICS.** (Biochimica et Biophysica Acta) Text in Dutch. 1963. 12/yr. EUR 2,201 in Europe to institutions; JPY 292,400 in Japan to institutions; USD 2,463 elsewhere to institutions (effective 2006). back issues avail. **Document type:** *Journal, Academic/Scholarly.* **Description:** Covers the area of biological energy transfer and conversion, focusing on the kinetics and thermodynamics of molecular mechanisms involved in photosynthesis, mitochondrial and bacterial respiration, oxidative phosphorylation, motility and transport, as well as the underlying molecular structures.
Formed by the merger of (1965-1966): Biochimica et Biophysica Acta. Biophysics including Photosynthesis (0926-6585); Which was formerly (1963-1964): Biochimica et Biophysica Acta. Specialized Section on Biophysical Subjects (0926-6577); (1965-1966): Biochimica et Biophysica Acta. Enzymology and Biological Oxidations (0926-6593); Which was formerly (1963-1964): Biochimica et Biophysica Acta. Specialized Section on Enzymological Subjects (0926-6569)
Related titles: Microform ed.: (from PQC); Online - full text ed.: (from EBSCO Publishing, Gale Group, IngentaConnect, ScienceDirect, Swets Information Services); ♦ Series of: Biochimica et Biophysica Acta. ISSN 0006-3002.
Indexed: ASCA, AgBio, AnBrAb, BBCI, BIOBASE, CIN, CPA, ChemAb, ChemTitl, CurCont, DBA, DSA, ExcerpMed, FCA, HelmAb, HerbAb, HortAb, IABS, ISR, IndVet, Inpharma, NutrAb, PBA, PGegResA, PN&I, PotatoAb, ProtozoAb, RPP, Reac, RefZh, RevApplEntom, S&F, SCI, SoyAb, TDB, TriticAb, VetBull, WeedAb.
—CISTI, GNLM, IDS, IE. **CCC.**
Published by: Elsevier BV (Subsidiary of: Elsevier Science & Technology), Radarweg 29, Amsterdam, 1043 NX, Netherlands. TEL 31-20-4853911, FAX 31-20-4852457, nlinfo-f@elsevier.nl, http://www.elsevier.com/locate/bbabio, http://www.elsevier.nl.

580 CAN ISSN 1188-603X
B E N. (Botanical Electronic News) Text in English. 1991. bi-m. bk.rev.; software rev. abstr.; bibl. back issues avail. **Document type:** *Newsletter, Academic/Scholarly.* **Description:** Deals with plant ecology predominantly in British Columbia, Canada and the Pacific Northwest and with broader reference to the entire planet.
Media: E-mail.
Published by: (Victoria Free-Net Association), B E N, c/o Adolf Ceska, P O Box 8546, Victoria, BC V8W 3S2, Canada. TEL 250-477-1211, FAX 250-387-2733, majordomo@victoria.tc.ca, http://www.victoria.tc.ca. Ed. Adolf Ceska.

571.2 GBR ISSN 1471-2229
QK728 CODEN: BPBMAN
➤ **B M C PLANT BIOLOGY.** Text in English. 2001. m. free (effective 2006). adv. **Document type:** *Journal, Academic/Scholarly.* **Description:** Publishes original research articles in all aspects of cellular, tissue-level, organismal, functional and developmental aspects of plants.
Media: Online - full content (from EBSCO Publishing, National Library of Medicine).
Indexed: BIOSIS Prev, BiolAb, FCA.
—Infotrieve. **CCC.**
Published by: BioMed Central Ltd. (Subsidiary of: Current Science Ltd), Middlesex House, 34-42 Cleveland St, London, W1T 4LB, United Kingdom. TEL 44-20-76319131, FAX 44-20-76319923, info@biomedcentral.com, http://www.biomedcentral.com/bmcplantbiol/. Ed. Peter Newmark. Adv. contact Deborah Cockerill.

➤ **B S B I ABSTRACTS**; abstracts from literature relating to the vascular plants of the British Isles. see *BIOLOGY—Abstracting, Bibliographies, Statistics*

580 GBR ISSN 0309-930X
B S B I NEWS. Text in English. 1972. 3/yr. GBP 20 in United Kingdom membership; GBP 22 elsewhere membership (effective 2001). **Document type:** *Newsletter.* **Description:** Contains topical information of the society's activities and meetings, as well as other features of interest to persons studying the botany of the British Isles.
—Linda Hall.
Published by: Botanical Society of the British Isles, c/o Department of Botany, The Natural History Museum, Cromwell Rd, London, SW7 5BD, United Kingdom. TEL 44-20-7942-5002, bsbihgs@aol.com. Ed. R G Ellis.

580 POL ISSN 0067-2815
QK322 CODEN: BFNBEI
➤ **BADANIA FIZJOGRAFICZNE NAD POLSKA ZACHODNIA. SERIA B. BOTANIKA.** Text in Polish; Summaries in English, French, German. 1948. a., latest vol.51, 2002. price varies. illus.; charts; abstr.; bibl. **Document type:** *Bulletin, Academic/Scholarly.*
Supersedes in part (in 1974): Badania Fizjograficzne nad Polska Zachodnia. Seria B. Biologia (0373-7497)
Indexed: AgrLib, ZooRec.
Published by: (Poznanskie Towarzystwo Przyjaciol Nauk, Wydzial Matematyczno-Przyrodniczy), Poznanskie Towarzystwo Przyjaciol Nauk/Poznan Society for the Advancement of the Arts and Sciences, ul Sew Mielzynskiego 27-29, Poznan, 61725, Poland. TEL 48-61-8527441, FAX 48-61-8522205, sekretariat@ptpn.poznan.pl, wydawnictwo@ptpn.poznan.pl, http://www.ptpn.poznan.pl. Eds. Andrzej Brzeg, Maria Lisiewska. Circ: 280. **Dist. by:** Ars Polona, Krakowskie Przedmiescie 7, Warsaw, Poland. TEL 48-22-9263914, FAX 48-22-9265334, arspolona@arspolona.com.pl, http://www.arspolona.com.pl.

635.9349 584.9 USA ISSN 1554-8295
BAMBOO; magazine of the American Bamboo Society. Text in English. 1980. bi-m. free to members (effective 2005); includes Journal. back issues avail. **Document type:** *Newsletter.* **Description:** Information on the biology, culture, uses and history of bamboo, and information on activities of the A B S.
Former titles (until 2001): Magazine of the American Bamboo Society; (until 2000): American Bamboo Society Newsletter (1528-6010)
Published by: American Bamboo Society, Inc., 750 Krumkill Rd, Albany, NY 12203-5976. TEL 518-458-7618, FAX 518-458-7625, http://www.halcyon.com/p1rabbit/bamboo/abs.html. Ed. Michael Bartholomew. Circ: 1,000 (paid).

580 635 JPN ISSN 0289-2111
CODEN: BAJOE2
BAMBOO JOURNAL. Text in English, Japanese. 1981. a.
Indexed: CIN, ChemAb, ChemTitl.
—CASDDS.
Published by: Japan Society of Bamboo Development and Protection/Nihon no Take o Mamoru Kai, Dento Sangyo Kaikan, 9-2 Okazakiseishoji-cho, Sakyo-ku, Kyoto-shi, 606-8343, Japan.

584.9 635.9349 USA ISSN 1535-7635
BAMBOO SCIENCE & CULTURE; the journal of the American Bamboo Society. Text in English. 1980. irreg. free to members (effective 2005); includes Newsletter. back issues avail. **Description:** Information on the biology, culture and history of bamboo, including its many uses.
Formerly (until 2000): American Bamboo Society. Journal (0197-3789)
Indexed: GardL.
Published by: American Bamboo Society, Inc., 750 Krumkill Rd, Albany, NY 12203-5976. TEL 518-458-7618, FAX 518-458-7625, http://www.halcyon.com/p1rabbit/bamboo/abs.html. Ed. Kenneth Brennecke. Circ: 1,000 (paid).

580 BGD ISSN 0253-5416
QK358.7 CODEN: BJBTB3
➤ **BANGLADESH JOURNAL OF BOTANY.** Text in English. 1972. 2/yr. BDT 599 per vol. domestic; USD 66 per issue foreign (effective 2002). adv. bk.rev. 100 p./no.; back issues avail. **Document type:** *Journal, Academic/Scholarly.*
Related titles: CD-ROM ed.
Indexed: ASCA, AgBio, AgrForAb, AnBrAb, BIOSIS Prev, BioCN&I, BiolAb, CPA, ChemAb, CurCont, ExtraMED, FCA, FPA, FS&TA, ForAb, HerbAb, HortAb, I&DA, MaizeAb, NemAb, NutrAb, OrnHort, PBA, PGegResA, PGrRegA, PotatoAb, ProtozoAb, RA&MP, RM&VM, RPP, RiceAb, S&F, SIA, SeedAb, SoyAb, TDB, TriticAb, WeedAb, ZooRec.
—BLDSC (1861.670000), CASDDS, CISTI, IDS, ingenta, Linda Hall.
Published by: Bangladesh Botanical Society, c/o Department of Botany, University of Dhaka, Dhaka, 1000, Bangladesh. TEL 880-2-505848 ext 6048, FAX 880-2-865583, botany@du.bangla.net. Ed. M R Khan. adv.: page USD 3,000. Circ: 1,000.

580 USA ISSN 0198-7356
CODEN: AJEVAC
➤ **BARTONIA.** Text in English. 1909. a. USD 20 to members; USD 25 to non-members (effective 2004). bk.rev. **Document type:** *Journal, Academic/Scholarly.*
Indexed: Agr, BIOSIS Prev, BiolAb, CIS.
—BLDSC (1863.830000). **CCC.**
Published by: Philadelphia Botanical Club, c/o Academy of Natural Sciences, 1900 Benjamin Franklin Pkwy, Philadelphia, PA 19103. TEL 215-299-1000, http://www.swarthmore.edu/NatSci/Biology/bio_professors/latham/bartonia.html. Ed. Alfred E Schuyler. Circ: 350.

580 CHE ISSN 0067-4605
QK1 CODEN: BAUHBX
BAUHINIA; Zeitschrift der Basler Botanischen Gesellschaft. Text mainly in German; Text occasionally in English, French, Italian. 1955. irreg., latest vol.15, 2001. EUR 26 per issue (effective 2001). **Document type:** *Journal, Academic/Scholarly.*
Indexed: BIOSIS Prev, BiolAb, PBA.
Published by: (Basler Botanische Gesellschaft), Verlag Wepf und Co., Eisengasse 5, Basel, 4001, Switzerland. TEL 41-61-3119585, FAX 41-61-3119576, wepf@dial.eunet.ch, http://www.wepf.ch. Ed. E Schreier. Circ: 500.

580 DEU ISSN 0341-3624
BAUM-ZEITUNG; fuer Baumfreunde, Natur und Umwelt. Text in German. 1966. 8/yr. EUR 4.30 newsstand/cover (effective 2004). adv. bk.rev. back issues avail. **Document type:** *Magazine, Trade.*
Indexed: AIAP, RefZh.
Published by: Thalacker Medien, Bernhard Thalacker Verlag GmbH und Co. KG, Postfach 8364, Braunschweig, 38133, Germany. TEL 49-531-380040, FAX 49-531-3800425, info@thalackermedien.de, http://www.thalackermedien.de. adv.: B&W page EUR 1,305.60, color page EUR 2,493.60. Circ: 2,000 (paid and controlled).

580 DEU ISSN 0373-7640
QK1
BAYERISCHE BOTANISCHE GESELLSCHAFT. BERICHTE. Text in German; Summaries in English, German. 1890. a. bk.rev. index. back issues avail. **Document type:** *Journal, Academic/Scholarly.*
Indexed: BIOSIS Prev, BiolAb, IBR, RefZh.
—CISTI.
Published by: Bayerische Botanische Gesellschaft, Menzinger Str 67, Munich, 80638, Germany. TEL 49-89-17861264, FAX 49-89-17861193. Ed., R&P Wolfgang Lippert. Circ: 1,200.

BEGONIAN. see *GARDENING AND HORTICULTURE*

579.5 AUT ISSN 1016-0019
BEIHEFTE ZUR SYDOWIA. Text in German. 1957. irreg. price varies. **Document type:** *Monographic series, Academic/Scholarly.*
Related titles: ♦ Supplement to: Sydowia: Annales Mycologici. ISSN 0082-0598.
—Linda Hall.
Published by: Verlag Ferdinand Berger und Soehne GmbH, Wienerstr 80, Horn, N 3580, Austria. TEL 43-2982-4161332, FAX 43-2982-4161382, office@berger.at, http://www.berger.at.

580 DEU ISSN 0005-8041
QK1 CODEN: BEPFAT
BEITRAEGE ZUR BIOLOGIE DER PFLANZEN. Text in English, German. 1870. irreg. price varies. adv. charts; illus. index. **Document type:** *Monographic series, Academic/Scholarly.*
Indexed: ASFA, AgrForAb, BIOSIS Prev, BiolAb, CPA, ChemAb, ESPM, ExcerpMed, FCA, FPA, ForAb, HerbAb, HortAb, OrnHort, PBA, PGegResA, RPP, S&F, SeedAb, VITIS, WeedAb.
—BLDSC (1878.800000), CISTI, IE, Infotrieve, ingenta, Linda Hall. **CCC.**
Published by: Duncker und Humblot GmbH, Carl-Heinrich-Becker-Weg 9, Berlin, 12165, Germany. TEL 49-30-7900060, FAX 49-30-79000631, info@duncker-humblot.de, http://www.duncker-humblot.de. adv.: page EUR 260; trim 115 x 185.

571.2 DEU ISSN 0948-5538
BEITRAEGE ZUR ZUECHTUNGSFORSCHUNG. Text in German, English. 1995. irreg. price varies. **Document type:** *Monographic series, Academic/Scholarly.*
Indexed: AgBio, BioCN&I, CPA, FCA, ForAb, HerbAb, HortAb, MaizeAb, NemAb, NutrAb, OrnHort, PBA, PGegResA, PGrRegA, PHN&I, PotatoAb, RA&MP, RPP, RefZh, S&F, SIA, SeedAb, TriticAb, WeedAb.
—BLDSC (1887.637250), IE, ingenta.
Published by: Bundesanstalt fuer Zuechtungsforschung an Kulturpflanzen, Neuer Weg 22-23, Quedlinburg, 06484, Germany. TEL 49-3946-47244, FAX 49-3946-47202, bafz-al@bafz.de, http://www.bafz.de. Ed. K Peter. Circ: 300 (controlled).

580 ESP ISSN 1132-2179
➤ **BELARRA.** Text in Spanish, English, Basque. 1987. a., latest vol.16. back issues avail. **Document type:** *Journal, Academic/Scholarly.*
Indexed: IECT, PGegResA, RPP.
—CINDOC.
Published by: Sociedad Micologica Barakaldo, Apdo. 182, Barakaldo, (Bizkaia) 48900, Spain. smbarakaldo@hotmail.com, http://www.micologica-barakaldo.org/. Pub. Alberto Agirre.

580 BEL ISSN 0778-4031
QK1 CODEN: BJBOEP
➤ **BELGIAN JOURNAL OF BOTANY.** Text in English, French; Text occasionally in Flemish, German. 1862. 2/yr. EUR 20 domestic to individuals; EUR 25 foreign to individuals; EUR 50 to libraries; EUR 10 to students (effective 2003). adv. bk.rev. bibl.; charts; illus. cum.index: vols. 1-25, 26-49, 51-75, 76-100. 100 p./no.; back issues avail. **Document type:** *Journal, Academic/Scholarly.* **Description:** International journal open to all fields of plant science.
Formerly (until 1990): Societe Royale de Botanique de Belgique. Bulletin (0037-9557)
Related titles: Microfiche ed.: (from IDC); Microform ed.: (from PMC); Online - full text ed.: (from IngentaConnect).

Indexed: ASCA, AgBio, BIOSIS Prev, BiolAb, CPA, CurCont, ExcerpMed, FCA, FPA, ForAb, HerbAb, HortAb, I&DA, PBA, PGegResA, RPP, RRTA, RefZh, S&F, SFA, SIA, SeedAb, SoyAb, TriticAb, WAE&RSA, WeedAb, ZooRec.
—BLDSC (1888.023240), CASDDS, CISTI, IE, ingenta, Linda Hall.
Published by: Societe Royale de Botanique de Belgique, National Botanic Garden of Belgium, Domaine de Bouchout, Meise, 1860, Belgium. TEL 32-2-2600937, FAX 32-2-2600945. R&P. Adv. contact Olivier Raspe. color page EUR 200; 16 x 25. Circ: 600. **Subscr. to:** National Botanic Garden of Belgium.

580   NLD   ISSN 0169-4375
QK1
BELMONTIA. Text in Dutch. 1974. irreg., latest vol.21, 1989. per issue exchange basis. **Description:** Covers various research in botany.
Published by: Agricultural University, Department of Plant Taxonomy, Generaal Foulkesweg 37, PO Box 8010, Wageningen, 6700 ED, Netherlands.

BIBLIOGRAFIE BOTANICZNE/BOTANICAL BIBLIOGRAPHIES. see *BIOLOGY—Abstracting, Bibliographies, Statistics*

BIBLIOGRAPHIA PHYTOSOCIOLOGICA SYNTAXONOMICA. see *BIOLOGY—Abstracting, Bibliographies, Statistics*

BIBLIOGRAPHY OF SYSTEMATIC MYCOLOGY. see *BIOLOGY—Abstracting, Bibliographies, Statistics*

580.74   DEU   ISSN 0067-7892
BIBLIOTHECA BOTANICA; Originalabhandlungen aus dem Gesamtgebiet der Botanik. Text in German, English. 1886. irreg. EUR 93 per issue domestic; EUR 97.10 per issue foreign (effective 2005). **Document type:** *Monographic series, Academic/Scholarly.*
—CISTI, Linda Hall. **CCC.**
Published by: E. Schweizerbart'sche Verlagsbuchhandlung, Johannesstr 3A, Stuttgart, 70176, Germany. TEL 49-711-3514560, FAX 49-711-35145699, mail@schweizerbart.de, http://www.schweizerbart.de/j/bibliotheca-botanica.

580   DEU   ISSN 1436-7270
BIBLIOTHECA DIATOMOLOGICA. Text in English, German. 1983. irreg., latest vol.51, 2005. price varies. **Document type:** *Monographic series, Academic/Scholarly.*
Indexed: BIOSIS Prev.
Published by: J. Cramer in der Gebrueder Borntraeger Verlagsbuchhandlung, Johannesstr 3A, Stuttgart, 70176, Germany. TEL 49-711-3514560, FAX 49-711-35145699, mail@borntraeger-cramer.de, http://www.schweizerbart.de/j/bibliotheca-diatomologica. Ed. H Lange Bertalot.

579.7   DEU   ISSN 1436-1698
QK580.7   CODEN: BLICD3
BIBLIOTHECA LICHENOLOGICA. Text in English, French, German. 1973. irreg., latest vol.90, 2004. price varies. **Document type:** *Monographic series, Academic/Scholarly.*
Indexed: BIOSIS Prev, CIN, CPA, ChemAb, ChemTitl, ForAb, I&DA, PGrRegA, RA&MP, RPP, S&F.
—BLDSC (2019.128600), CASDDS, IE, ingenta.
Published by: J. Cramer in der Gebrueder Borntraeger Verlagsbuchhandlung, Johannesstr 3A, Stuttgart, 70176, Germany. TEL 49-711-3514560, FAX 49-711-35145699, mail@borntraeger-cramer.de, http://www.schweizerbart.de/j/bibliotheca-lichenologica. Ed. V Wirth.

579.5   DEU   ISSN 0067-8066
QK600   CODEN: BIMYDY
BIBLIOTHECA MYCOLOGICA. Text in German. 1967. irreg., latest vol.199, 2004. price varies. **Document type:** *Monographic series, Academic/Scholarly.*
Indexed: AgBio, BIOSIS Prev, BiolAb, ForAb, HortAb, NutrAb, PBA, PGegResA, PGrRegA, RM&VM, RPP, S&F.
—CISTI.
Published by: J. Cramer in der Gebrueder Borntraeger Verlagsbuchhandlung, Johannesstr 3A, Stuttgart, 70176, Germany. TEL 49-711-3514560, FAX 49-711-35145699, mail@borntraeger-cramer.de, http://www.schweizerbart.de/j/bibliotheca-mycologica.

580   DEU   ISSN 0067-8112
BIBLIOTHECA PHYCOLOGICA. Text in German, English, Spanish. 1967. irreg., latest vol.111, 2003. USD 96 per issue (effective 2005). **Document type:** *Monographic series, Academic/Scholarly.*
Indexed: BIOSIS Prev, BiolAb, ZooRec.
—BLDSC (2019.330000), IE, ingenta.
Published by: J. Cramer in der Gebrueder Borntraeger Verlagsbuchhandlung, Johannesstr 3A, Stuttgart, 70176, Germany. TEL 49-711-3514560, FAX 49-711-35145699, mail@borntraeger-cramer.de, http://www.schweizerbart.de/j/bibliotheca-phycologica. Eds. L Kies, R Schnetter.

571.2   SCG   ISSN 0354-6160
BILJNI LEKAR. Text in Serbo-Croatian. 1995. bi-m.
Indexed: RefZh.

Published by: Univerzitet u Novom Sadu, Poljoprivridni Fakultet, Institut za Zastitu Bilja i Zivotne Sredine "Dr. Pavle Vukasovic"/University in Novi Sad, Faculty of Agriculture, Institute for Plant Protection and Environment "Dr. Pavle Vukasovic", Trg. D. Odradovica 8, Novi Sad, 21000. TEL 381-21-450355, FAX 381-21-59761.

581.3   SCG   ISSN 0351-9430
BILTEN ZA HMELJ, SIRAK I LEKOVITO BILJE/HOPS, SORGHUMS AND MEDICINAL HERBS BULLETIN. Text in Serbo-Croatian; Summaries in English. 1969. q. exchange basis. adv. bk.rev. back issues avail. **Document type:** *Magazine, Trade.*
Indexed: BiolAb, HortAb.
Published by: Institut za Ratarstvo i Povrtarstvo/Institute of Field and Vegetable Crops, Maksima Gorkog 30, Novi Sad, Vojvodina 21000. sabo@ifvcns.ns.ac.yu, http://www.ifvcns.co.yu. Ed. Jan Kisgeci. Circ: 600.

BIOCOSME MESOGEEN. see *HISTORY—History Of Europe*

580   NLD   ISSN 0006-3134
QK1   CODEN: BPABAJ
➤ **BIOLOGIA PLANTARUM;** journal for experimental botany. Text in English, French, German; Summaries in Czech, English. 1952. 4/yr. EUR 1,287, USD 1,288, GBP 847 combined subscription to institutions print & online eds. (effective 2005). adv. bk.rev. abstr.; bibl.; charts; illus. index. **Document type:** *Journal, Academic/Scholarly.* **Description:** Publishes original papers and brief communications in the fields of plant physiology, experimental ecology, experimental morphology, genetics, cytology, biochemistry and pathology.
Supersedes in part (in 1959): Ceskoslovenska Biologie (0411-6038)
Related titles: Microform ed.: (from PQC); Online - full text ed.: ISSN 1573-8264 (from EBSCO Publishing, Gale Group, IngentaConnect, Kluwer Online, O C L C Online Computer Library Center, Inc., Ovid Technologies, Inc., Springer LINK, Swets Information Services).
Indexed: AEA, ASCA, ASFA, AgBio, AgrForAb, AnBrAb, B&BAb, BBCI, BIOBASE, BIOSIS Prev, BibLing, BioCN&I, BiolAb, CPA, ChemAb, CurCont, DSA, ESPM, ExcerpMed, FCA, FPA, FS&TA, FaBeAb, ForAb, GenetAb, HGA, HerbAb, HortAb, I&DA, IABS, ISR, MaizeAb, NucAcAb, OrnHort, PBA, PGegResA, PGrRegA, PHN&I, PlantSci, PotatoAb, RA&MP, RM&VM, RPP, RefZh, RiceAb, S&F, S&MA, SCI, SIA, SSCI, SWRA, SeedAb, SoyAb, TOSA, TriticAb, VITIS, WeedAb, ZooRec.
—BLDSC (2072.850000), CASDDS, CISTI, IDS, IE, Infotrieve, ingenta, Linda Hall. **CCC.**
Published by: (Akademie Ved Ceske Republiky CZE, Ustav Experimentalni Botaniky), Springer-Verlag Dordrecht (Subsidiary of: Springer Science+Business Media), Van Godewijckstraat 30, Dordrecht, 3311 GX, Netherlands. TEL 31-78-6576050, FAX 31-78-6576474, http://springerlink.metapress.com/openurl.asp?genre=journal&issn=0006-3134, http://www.springeronline.com. Ed. J Catsky.

580   SVK   ISSN 1335-6372
      CODEN: BLOAAO
BIOLOGIA. SECTION BOTANY. Text in English. 1946. s-a. USD 138 foreign for 3 sections (effective 2005). adv. bk.rev. charts; illus. index. 120 p./no. 2 cols./p.; reprints avail. **Document type:** *Journal, Academic/Scholarly.* **Description:** Brings original experimental and descriptive works in basic biological research from taxonomy, phytocenology, physiology and cytology.
Formerly (until 1994): Biologia. A: Botanika (0862-1128); **Supersedes in part** (in 1969): Biologia (0006-3088)
Related titles: ◆ Series: Biologia. Section Zoology. ISSN 1335-6380; ◆ Biologia. Section: Cellular and Molecular Biology. ISSN 1335-6399.
Indexed: ASFA, AbHyg, AgrForAb, BioDAb, BiolAb, CPA, ChemAb, CurCont, ESPM, ExcerpMed, FPA, ForAb, HerbAb, I&DA, IndMed, MaizeAb, NutrAb, PBA, PGrRegA, PHN&I, RM&VM, RefZh, RevApplEntom, SFA, SIA, SeedAb, SoyAb, TriticAb, WeedAb, WildRev, ZooRec.
—BLDSC (2072.700000), CASDDS, CISTI, GNLM, IDS, IE, ingenta, KNAW, Linda Hall.
Published by: (Slovenska Akademia Vied, Botanicky Ustav/Slovak Academy of Sciences, Institute of Botany), Slovak Academic Press Ltd., Nam Slobody 6, PO Box 57, Bratislava, 81005, Slovakia. Ed. Frantisek Hindak.

571.2   USA   ISSN 0887-2236
SB732.6
BIOLOGICAL AND CULTURAL TESTS FOR CONTROL OF PLANT DISEASES. Short title: B & C Tests. Text in English. 1986. a. USD 38 (effective 2005). back issues avail. **Document type:** *Monographic series, Academic/Scholarly.* **Description:** Reviews current experiments in disease control. Also includes short guidelines on how to prepare reports and how to convert US units of measurement to the metric system.
Related titles: Online - full content ed.; Online - full text ed.: (from EBSCO Publishing).
Indexed: AEA, AgBio, BioCN&I, FCA, HerbAb, HortAb, NemAb, OrnHort, PBA, PotatoAb, S&F, SoyAb, TriticAb.
—CISTI, Linda Hall.

Published by: (American Phytopathological Society), A P S PRESS, 3340 Pilot Knob Rd., St. Paul, MN 55121-2097. TEL 651-454-7250, 800-328-7560, FAX 651-454-0766, aps@scisoc.org, http://www.apsnet.org/online/BCtests/. Ed. Steven C Bost. Circ: 1,453.

BIOLOGICAL SOCIETY OF WASHINGTON. PROCEEDINGS. see *BIOLOGY*

581.652   CAN
THE BIOLOGY OF CANADIAN WEEDS. Text in English. irreg., latest vol.4. **Document type:** *Monographic series, Academic/Scholarly.*
Published by: Agricultural Institute of Canada, 141 Laurier Ave W, Ste 1112, Ottawa, ON K1P 5J3, Canada. TEL 613-232-9459, FAX 613-594-5190, pcavers@julian.uwo.ca, journals@aic.ca, http://pubs.nrc-cnrc.gc.ca/aic-journals/weeds.html, http://www.aic.ca. Ed. P B Cavers.

BIOSCIENCE AND MICROFLORA. see *BIOLOGY*

571.2   CUB   ISSN 1609-1841
➤ **BIOTECNOLOGIA VEGETAL.** Text in Spanish. 2000. 3/yr. USD 50; USD 20 per issue (effective 2003). **Document type:** *Journal, Academic/Scholarly.* **Description:** Publishes scientific articles, short communications and reports on cell tissue and culture, mass propagation, in vitro selection and mutagenesis, conservation of in vitro germplasm and genetic engineering.
Indexed: AgBio, CPA, FCA, ForAb, HortAb, OrnHort, PBA, PGegResA, PGrRegA, PHN&I, PotatoAb, RPP, S&F, SIA, SeedAb.
Published by: Instituto de Biotecnologia de las Plantas, Carretera a Camajuani km 5.5, Santa Clara, Villa Clara, Cuba. TEL 53-42-281257, FAX 53-42-281329, ogregorio@uclv.edu.cu, yalvarado@ibp.uclv.edu.cu, http://www.cuba.cu/ciencia/ibp/revista.html. Ed. Daniel Agramonte Penalver. Adv. contact Yelenys Alvarado Capo. Circ: 500 (paid and controlled).

580   USA   ISSN 0893-3138
BISHOP MUSEUM BULLETINS IN BOTANY. Text in English. 1922. irreg., latest vol.3, 1993. price varies. reprint service avail. from PQC. **Description:** Covers botany of Hawaii and the Pacific Basin.
Supersedes in part (in 1987): Bernice P. Bishop Museum Bulletin (0005-9439)
—CISTI, Linda Hall.
Published by: (Bernice Pauahi Bishop Museum), Bishop Museum Press, 1525 Bernice St, Box 19000 A, Honolulu, HI 96817. TEL 808-847-3511, FAX 808-841-8968. Circ: 300.

580   ESP   ISSN 0212-8314
QK329
BLANCOANA. Text in Spanish. 1983. a. EUR 3 (effective 2005). **Document type:** *Journal, Academic/Scholarly.* **Description:** Presents information on vascular plants.
Indexed: IECT.
—CINDOC.
Published by: Universidad de Jaen, Facultad de Ciencias Experimentales, Herbario Jaen, Jaen, 23071, Spain. TEL 34-953-012159, FAX 34-953-012141, agricola@mundiprensa.es. Ed. Carlos Fernandez Lopez. **Dist. by:** Libreria Agricola, Fernando VI, 2, Madrid 28004, Spain. TEL 34-91-4190940.

580   USA
THE BLAZING STAR. Text in English. 1972. bi-m. free to members (effective 2005). **Document type:** *Newsletter, Consumer.* **Description:** Covers issues regarding California native flora in its native habitat, including politics, preservation, and history.
Related titles: Online - full text ed.
Published by: California Native Plant Society, Santa Clara Valley Chapter, 2707 K St, Ste 1, Sacramento, CA 95816-5113. TEL 916-447-2677, FAX 916-447-2727, cnps@cnps.org, http://www.stanford.edu/~rawlings/blazcon.htm, http://www.cnps.org. Ed. Cynthia Gilbert.

580   NLD   ISSN 0006-5196
QK1   CODEN: BLMAAE
➤ **BLUMEA;** a journal of plant-taxonomy and plant-geography. Text in Dutch. 1936. s-a. EUR 90 (effective 2002). charts; illus. index. back issues avail. **Document type:** *Journal, Academic/Scholarly.* **Description:** International journal on descriptive botany of Phanerogams, as well as Cryptogams, excluding fungi, with emphasis on the Malesian area. Coverage includes taxonomy, plant geography, morphology and anatomy.
Related titles: Microfiche ed.: (from IDC); ◆ Supplement(s): Blumea. Supplement. ISSN 0373-4293.
Indexed: ASCA, ASFA, AgBio, AgrForAb, BIOBASE, BIOSIS Prev, BiolAb, CurCont, ESPM, FCA, FPA, ForAb, HerbAb, HortAb, IABS, OrnHort, PBA, PGegResA, PlantSci, RA&MP, S&F, SPPI, SeedAb, WeedAb.
—CISTI, IE, Infotrieve, Linda Hall.
Published by: National Herbarium Nederland/Leiden Branch, PO Box 9514, Leiden, 2300 RA, Netherlands. TEL 31-71-5273570, FAX 31-71-5273522, adema@rulrhb.leidenuniv.nl, zoelen@rhbcml.leidenuniv.nl, http://www.nhncml.leidenuniv.nl. Eds. F Adema, H P Nooteboom, R W J M van der Ham. Circ: 600.

B

580 NLD ISSN 0373-4293
CODEN: BLSUE6
➤ **BLUMEA. SUPPLEMENT.** Text in Dutch. 1975. irreg., latest vol.11, 1998. price varies. illus. back issues avail. **Document type:** *Monographic series, Academic/Scholarly.* **Description:** Taxonomic monographs and extensive studies in comparative botany.
Supersedes in part (in 1992): Leiden Botanical Series (0169-8508)
Related titles: ♦ Supplement to: Blumea. ISSN 0006-5196.
Indexed: BIOSIS Prev, BiolAb, ZooRec.
—CISTI, Linda Hall.
Published by: National Herbarium Nederland/Leiden Branch, PO Box 9514, Leiden, 2300 RA, Netherlands. TEL 31-71-5273570, FAX 31-71-5273522, ardema@rulrhb.leidenuniv.nl, zoelen@rhbcml.leidenuniv.nl, http://www.nhncml.leidenuniv.nl. Eds. F Adema, H P Nooteboom, R W J M van der Ham.

580 NOR ISSN 0006-5269
QK1 CODEN: BLYTAT
BLYTTIA. Text in Norwegian; Summaries in English. 1943. q. NOK 374 in Scandinavia to individuals; NOK 478 elsewhere to individuals; NOK 540 in Scandinavia to institutions; NOK 688 elsewhere to institutions; effective 1997. adv. bk.rev. bibl.; charts; illus. index. back issues avail.; reprint service avail. from ISI. **Document type:** *Academic/Scholarly.* **Description:** Covers all aspects of botany with emphasis on investigation of the Norwegian flora.
Indexed: ASFA, AgrForAb, BIOSIS Prev, BibAg, BiolAb, ESPM, FCA, FPA, ForAb, GEOBASE, HerbAb, HortAb, OrnHort, PBA, PGegResA, PGrRegA, PoultAb, ProtozoAb, RA&MP, RPP, S&F, SeedAb, SoyAb, TriticAb, WeedAb.
—BLDSC (2116.000000), IE, ingenta. **CCC.**
Published by: Norsk Botanisk Forening/Norwegian Botanical Association, c/o Botanisk Museum, PO Box 1172, Blindern, Oslo, 0318, Norway. TEL 47-22-85-17-01, FAX 47-22-85-18-35, blyttia@nbf.uio.no, http://toyen.uio.no/botanisk/nbf/blyttia/index.htm. Ed. Jan Wesenberg. adv.: B&W page NOK 2,850, color page NOK 6,400.

580.74 AUS
BOARD OF THE BOTANIC GARDENS AND STATE HERBARIUM. ANNUAL REPORT. Text in English. 1857. a., latest 1999-2000. free. bibl.; charts; stat. back issues avail. **Document type:** *Corporate.*
Formerly: Adelaide Botanic Garden Board. Annual Report (0728-7704)
Published by: Botanic Gardens of Adelaide, North Terrace, Adelaide, SA 5000, Australia. TEL 61-8-8228-2320, 61-8-8222-9311, FAX 61-8-8223-3635, 61-8-8222-9399, clift.dorothy@savgov.sa.gov.au, gardens.botanic@savgov.sa.gov.au, http://www.botanicgardens.sa.gov.au. Circ: 300 (controlled).

BOCAGIANA. see *BIOLOGY—Zoology*

580.74 CHE ISSN 0373-2975
QK1 CODEN: BOISB2
BOISSIERA. Text in French. 1936. irreg., latest vol.57. **Document type:** *Monographic series, Academic/Scholarly.*
Indexed: BIOSIS Prev, BiolAb, ForAb, HerbAb, PBA, PGegResA, RefZh, S&F, SeedAb.
—Linda Hall.
Published by: Conservatoire et Jardin Botaniques de la Ville de Geneve, Universite de Geneve, 1 Chemin de l'Imperatrice, Chambesy, CH-1292, Switzerland. TEL 41-22-4185100, FAX 41-22-4185101, http://wwwcjb.unige.ch/editions/boissiera.html.

580 COL
BOLETIN BOTANICO LATINOAMERICANO. Text in Spanish. 1978. s-a. USD 10 (effective 2000). bk.rev. bibl. **Document type:** *Bulletin.* **Description:** Devoted to bibliographies in some issues, directories in others, but in most cases to miscellaneous botany news.
Published by: Asociacion Latinoamericana de Botanica, Instituto de Ciencias Nacionales, Universidad Nacional, PO Box 7495, Bogota, CUND, Colombia. TEL 57-1-3165000 ext 11535, FAX 57-1-3165365, eforero@ciencias.ciencias.unal.edu.co. Ed. Enrique Forero. Circ: 1,000.

579.5 CHL ISSN 0716-114X
QK600
BOLETIN MICOLOGICO. Text in English, Spanish. 1982. a., latest vol.15. USD 20. **Description:** Publishes research papers, notes, commentaries, reviews and conference proceedings on general mycology.
Indexed: AgrForAb, BioCN&I, CPA, DSA, FCA, FPA, ForAb, HerbAb, HortAb, IndVet, MaizeAb, NutrAb, PBA, PGegResA, PHN&I, PoultAb, RM&VM, RPP, RevApplEntom, S&F, SIA, SeedAb, SoyAb, TDB, TriticAb, VetBull, WeedAb.
—GNLM.
Published by: Universidad de Valparaiso, Facultad de Medicina, Casilla 92-V, Valparaiso, Chile. TEL 56-32-507370, FAX 56-32-212011, eduardo.piontelli@uv.cl. Ed., R&P Eduardo Piontelli TEL 56-32-212011.

BOLETIN VETIVER. see *AGRICULTURE—Crop Production And Soil*

580 ARG ISSN 0524-0476
BONPLANDIA. Text in Spanish. 1960. irreg. looseleaf. per issue exchange basis. back issues avail. **Document type:** *Academic/Scholarly.*
Indexed: ForAb, HortAb, OrnHort, PBA, VITIS.
—CISTI.
Published by: Instituto de Botanica del Nordeste, Sargento Cabral, 2131, Casilla de Correos 209, Corrientes, 3400, Argentina. TEL 0783-27309, FAX 0783-27131. Ed. Carmen L Cristobal. Circ: 700.

580 USA
BOREALIS. Text in English. 1982. 8/yr. USD 12 domestic; USD 30 foreign (effective 2000). adv. bk.rev. **Document type:** *Newsletter.*
Formerly: Alaska Native Plant Society. Newsletter
Published by: Alaska Native Plant Society, PO Box 141613, Anchorage, AK 99514-1613. TEL 907-333-8212. Ed. Ginny Moore. R&P, Adv. contact Verna Pratt. B&W page USD 25. Circ: 180.

580 GBR ISSN 0962-7448
BOTANIC GARDENS MICROPROPAGATION NEWS. Text in English. 1990. s-a. GBP 30 per 3 issues (voluntary) (effective 2001). 1 cols./p.; back issues avail. **Document type:** *Journal, Academic/Scholarly.* **Description:** Includes short papers describing micropropagation protocols for threatened plants and native plant species.
Related titles: Online - full text ed.
—BLDSC (2251.877000), ingenta.
Published by: Royal Botanic Gardens, Kew, Richmond, Surrey TW9 3AB, United Kingdom. TEL 44-20-83325000, FAX 44-20-83325197, microprop@rbgkew.or.uk, info@kew.org, http://www.rbgkew.org.uk/science/micropropagation/bgmnews.html, http://www.rbgkew.org.uk/index.html. Ed., R&P, Adv. contact Margaret M Ramsay. Circ: 1,000.

580 IND ISSN 0045-2629
QH301 CODEN: BTNCAD
THE BOTANICA. Text in English. 1950. a. INR 60, USD 10 to individual members; INR 100, USD 15 to non-members (effective 2000). adv. bk.rev. bibl. index. **Document type:** *Academic/Scholarly.*
Indexed: BiolAb, EnvAb, FCA, HerbAb.
—CASDDS, CISTI.
Published by: Delhi University Botanical Society, Department of Botany, University of Delhi, New Delhi, 110 007, India. TEL 91-11-7257725, FAX 91-11-7257829. Ed., R&P A K Bhatnagar. Pub., Adv. contact V P Singh. Circ: 1,000 (controlled).

580 ESP ISSN 0214-4565
QK329 CODEN: BCOOA3
➤ **BOTANICA COMPLUTENSIS.** Text in Spanish. 1968. a., latest vol.25, 2001. EUR 18 in the European Union; EUR 30 elsewhere (effective 2005). adv. bk.rev. bibl.; illus.; maps. 350 p./no.; **Document type:** *Journal, Academic/Scholarly.* **Description:** Covers all aspects of basic investigations and applications in the field of Botany.
Former titles (until 1986): Universidad Complutense. Departamento de Botanica. Trabajos (0212-4890); (until 1982): Universidad Complutense. Departamento de Botanica y Fisiologia Vegetal. Trabajos (0210-5179); (until 1975): Universidad Complutense. Departamento de Botanica. Trabajos (0377-8371); (until 1974): Universidad de Madrid. Departamento de Botanica y Fisiologia Vegetal. Trabajos (0580-468X)
Related titles: CD-ROM ed.: EUR 56 to individuals; EUR 74 to institutions (effective 2003).
Indexed: BIOBASE, BioDAb, IECT.
—CASDDS, CINDOC, CISTI.
Published by: (Universidad Complutense de Madrid, Facultad de Ciencias Biologicas), Universidad Complutense de Madrid, Servicio de Publicaciones, C Isaac Peral s/n, Ciudad Universitaria, Madrid, 28040, Spain. TEL 34-91-3946934, FAX 34-91-3946978, botanicacomplutensis@bio.ucm.es, servicio@publicaciones.ucm.es, http://www.ucm.es/publicaciones. Ed. Santiago Pajaron. Circ: 400.

580 SWE ISSN 0068-0370
BOTANICA GOTHOBURGENSIA. Text in English, German, Norwegian, Swedish. 1963. irreg., latest vol.7, 1978. price varies. **Document type:** *Monographic series, Academic/Scholarly.*
Related titles: ♦ Series of: Acta Universitatis Gothoburgensis. ISSN 0346-7740.
Published by: Acta Universitatis Gothoburgensis, Renstroemsgatan 4, P O Box 222, Goeteborg, 40530, Sweden. TEL 46-31-773-17-33, FAX 46-31-163-797. Eds. Christer Sundquist, Lennart Andersson.

580 CHE ISSN 0253-1453
QK1 CODEN: BOHEDP
➤ **BOTANICA HELVETICA.** Text in English, French, German, Italian. 1891. s-a. EUR 378 to institutions (effective 2005). charts; illus. index. back issues avail. **Document type:** *Journal, Academic/Scholarly.*
Formerly (until 1981): Schweizerische Botanische Gesellschaft. Berichte (0080-7281)
Related titles: Online - full text ed.: ISSN 1420-9063 (from Springer LINK).
Indexed: ASCA, AbHyg, AgBio, AgrForAb, BIOBASE, BIOSIS Prev, BiolAb, CPA, CurCont, FCA, ForAb, GEOBASE, HerbAb, HortAb, IABS, IndVet, OrnHort, PBA, PGegResA, PN&I, PlantSci, RPP, RRTA, RefZh, S&F, SeedAb, VITIS, WeedAb.
—BLDSC (2252.008000), CISTI, IDS, IE, Infotrieve, ingenta, KNAW, Linda Hall. **CCC.**
Published by: (Schweizerische Botanische Gesellschaft), Birkhaeuser Verlag AG (Subsidiary of: Springer Science+Business Media), Viaduktstr 42, Postfach 133, Basel, 4051, Switzerland. TEL 41-61-2050707, FAX 41-61-2050799, info@birkhauser.ch, http://www.birkhauser.ch/journals/3500/3500_tit.htm. Circ: 1,100. **Subscr. in the Americas to:** Springer-Verlag New York, Inc., Journal Fulfillment, PO Box 2485, Secaucus, NJ 07096-2485. TEL 800-777-4643, 201-348-4033, FAX 201-348-4505, journals@birkhauser.com; **Subscr. to:** Springer GmbH Auslieferungsgesellschaft, Haberstr 7, Heidelberg 69126, Germany. TEL 49-6221-345-0, FAX 49-6221-345-4229, birkhauser@springer.de.

580 LTU
BOTANICA LITHUANICA. Text in Lithuanian. 1995. q. Supplement avail. **Document type:** *Journal, Academic/Scholarly.*
Published by: Botanikos Institutas, Zaliuju Ezeru g. 49, Vilnius, LT-08406, Lithuania. TEL 370-5-2711618, FAX 370-5-2729950, botanica.lithuanica@botanika.lt, botanika@botanika.lt, http://botanika.lt/lituanica/index.html, http://www.botanika.lt/.

580 ESP ISSN 0211-7150
QK422
➤ **BOTANICA MACARONESICA.** Text in Spanish. 1976. s-a. per issue exchange basis. **Document type:** *Academic/Scholarly.* **Description:** Provides articles on botany, conservation and nature in the Macaronesian floristic area.
Indexed: ForAb, IECT, RefZh, S&F.
—CINDOC.
Published by: Jardin Botanico Canario Viera y Clavijo, Apartado de Correo 14, Plaza De Tafira Alta, S/N, L Palmas De Gran Canaria, Canary Islands 35017, Spain. TEL 34-28-353604, FAX 34-28-352250, jadcan@ext.step.es. Circ: 300.

579.177 DEU ISSN 0006-8055
QK564 CODEN: BOTNA7
➤ **BOTANICA MARINA.** Text in English. 1957. bi-m. EUR 1,070 to institutions; EUR 1,158 combined subscription to institutions print & online eds.; EUR 196 newsstand/cover (effective 2006). adv. charts; illus.; abstr. index index. back issues avail.; reprint service avail. from PSC. **Document type:** *Journal, Academic/Scholarly.* **Description:** Publishes results of basic research in marine botany, microbiology and mycology for scientists and universities.
Related titles: Online - full text ed.: ISSN 1437-4323. 1999. EUR 1,070 to institutions (effective 2006) (from EBSCO Publishing, O C L C Online Computer Library Center, Inc., Swets Information Services).
Indexed: ASCA, ASFA, AgBio, B&BAb, BIOBASE, BIOSIS Prev, BiolAb, CIN, CPA, CTO, ChemAb, ChemTitl, CurCont, DBA, ESPM, FCA, FLUIDEX, ForAb, GEOBASE, HortAb, IABS, ISR, MBA, NutrAb, OceAb, PBA, PGrRegA, PlantSci, RM&VM, RPP, RefZh, S&F, SCI, SFA, SIA, SPPI, SWRA, WAE&RSA, WeedAb, ZooRec.
—BLDSC (2252.100000), CASDDS, CISTI, IDS, IE, Infotrieve, ingenta, Linda Hall. **CCC.**
Published by: Walter de Gruyter GmbH & Co. KG, Genthiner Str. 13, Berlin, 10785, Germany. TEL 49-30-260050, FAX 49-30-26005251, bot.mar.editorial@degruyter.de, http://www.degruyter.de/journals/bm, http://www.degruyter.com/journals/bm. Ed. A R O Chapman. Adv. contact Dietlind Makswitat TEL 49-30-260050. B&W page EUR 500; trim 170 x 260. Circ: 450 (paid).

580 GBR ISSN 1364-4335
BOTANICAL CORNWALL. Text in English. 1987. irreg., latest vol.10. GBP 5 per vol. (effective 2003). back issues avail. **Document type:** *Monographic series, Academic/Scholarly.*
Formerly (until 1992): Botanical Cornwall Newsletter (0963-4045)
—BLDSC (2253.500000).
Published by: Botanical Cornwall Group, c/o Ian Bennallick, Director, Lower Polmorla, St.Wenn, Bodmin, Cornwall PL30 5PE, United Kingdom. ian@bennallick.fsnet.co.uk, http://www.floracam.co.uk/bcg/bot_corn.php.

BOTANICAL DESCRIPTIONS OF CEREAL VARIETIES. see *AGRICULTURE—Feed, Flour And Grain*

580.9438 POL
➤ **BOTANICAL GUIDEBOOKS.** Text in English, Polish; Summaries in English. 1990. irreg. price varies. bibl.; illus.; maps. back issues avail. **Document type:** *Monographic series, Academic/Scholarly.* **Description:** Guides to Polish botanical institutions, collections and collectors, botanical literature and directories as well as botanical field-guides and basic information regarding various branches of botany.
Formerly (until 2001): Polish Botanical Studies. Guidebook Series (0867-0749)
Indexed: AgrAg, AgrLib, HortAb, NutrAb, PBA, PGegResA, S&F, SeedAb, TriticAb, WeedAb.
—CISTI.

Published by: Polska Akademia Nauk, Instytut Botaniki im. W. Szafera/Polish Academy of Sciences, W. Szafer Institute of Botany, ul Lubicz 46, Krakow, 31512, Poland. TEL 48-12-4241711, FAX 48-12-4219790, office@ib-pan.krakow.pl. Ed. Zbigniew Mirek. Pub. Jacek W Wieser. R&Ps Leon Stuchlik, Mirek Zbigniew. Circ: 1,000 (paid).

580 GBR ISSN 1359-4869
QK1 CODEN: BJSCE6
BOTANICAL JOURNAL OF SCOTLAND. Text in English. 1836. s-a. GBP 82 in Europe; USD 157 in North America; GBP 87 elsewhere (effective 2005). adv. bk.rev. bibl.; charts; illus. **Document type:** *Academic/Scholarly.* **Description:** Reading for everyone concerned with botanical issues, not only within Scotland but the world over.
Former titles (until 1991): Botanical Society of Edinburgh Transactions (0374-6607); (until 1970): Botanical Society of Edinburgh. Transactions and Proceedings (0372-0578)
Related titles: Online - full text ed.: (from EBSCO Publishing).
Indexed: Agr, AgrForAb, BIOSIS Prev, BiolAb, CPA, ForAb, HerbAb, HortAb, I&DA, NutrAb, OrnHort, PBA, PGegResA, PGrRegA, RPP, RefZh, RevApplEntom, S&F, SeedAb, WAE&RSA, WeedAb, ZooRec.
—BLDSC (2254.600000), CISTI, IE, ingenta, Linda Hall. **CCC.**
Published by: (Botanical Society of Scotland), Edinburgh University Press, 22 George Sq, Edinburgh, Midlothian EH8 9LF, United Kingdom. TEL 44-131-650-6207, FAX 44-131-662-0053, journals@eup.ed.ac.uk, http://www.eup.ed.ac.uk/newweb/journals/Botanical/. Pub. Vivian C Bone. Adv. contact Douglas McNaughton TEL 44-131-6504420. Circ: 650.

580 USA ISSN 0006-8101
QK1 CODEN: BOREA4
➤ **THE BOTANICAL REVIEW**; interpreting botanical progress. Text in English. 1935. q. USD 126 domestic to institutions; USD 139 foreign to institutions (effective 2005). adv. bibl.; illus. index. back issues avail.; reprints avail. **Document type:** *Journal, Academic/Scholarly.* **Description:** Review and synthesis of articles in all fields of plant science. Includes list of books received.
Related titles: Microfiche ed.: (from IDC); Microform ed.: (from PMC, PQC); Online - full text ed.: (from BioOne, C S A, Florida Center for Library Automation, Gale Group, H.W. Wilson, Northern Light Technology, Inc., O C L C Online Computer Library Center, Inc.).
Indexed: AESIS, ASCA, ASFA, AgBio, Agr, AgrForAb, B&AI, BIOBASE, BIOSIS Prev, BibAg, BiolAb, CPA, ChemAb, CurCont, EPB, ESPM, EnvAb, EnvInd, FCA, FPA, ForAb, GSI, HerbAb, HortAb, I&DA, ISR, OrnHort, PBA, PGegResA, PGrRegA, PoultAb, RA&MP, RPP, RefZh, RiceAb, S&F, SCI, SSCI, SeedAb, SoyAb, TDB, VITIS, WeedAb.
—BLDSC (2256.000000), CASDDS, CIS, CISTI, IDS, IE, Infotrieve, ingenta, Linda Hall. **CCC.**
Published by: New York Botanical Garden Press, 200th Street & Kazimiroff Blvd, Bronx, NY 10458-5126. TEL 718-817-8918, FAX 718-817-8842, nybgpress@nybg.org, http://sciweb.nybg.org/science2/BotanicalReview.asp, http://www.nybg.org. Ed. Dennis W Stevenson. R&P Carole J Young. Circ: 2,000.

580 IND ISSN 0006-8128
QK358 CODEN: BBSUAY
BOTANICAL SURVEY OF INDIA. BULLETIN. Text in English. 1959. q. price varies. bk.rev. charts; illus. index. back issues avail.
Indexed: BiolAb, FCA, FPA, ForAb, HerbAb, ISA.
—CISTI, Linda Hall.
Published by: Botanical Survey of India, c/o Ministry of the Environment and Forests, Paryavaran Bhavan, C G O Complex Phase II Lodi Rd., New Delhi, 110 002, India. TEL 436-3951. Ed. A R K Sastry. Circ: 250 (controlled).

580 IND
BOTANICAL SURVEY OF INDIA. OCCASIONAL PUBLICATIONS. Text in English. irreg. price varies.
Published by: Botanical Survey of India, c/o Ministry of the Environment and Forests, Paryavaran Bhavan, C G O Complex Phase II Lodi Rd., New Delhi, 110 002, India. TEL 436-3951.

580 RUS ISSN 0006-8136
QK1 CODEN: BOTZA9
➤ **BOTANICHESKII ZHURNAL.** Text in Russian; Summaries in English. 1916. m. USD 441 foreign (effective 2005). adv. bk.rev. index. **Document type:** *Journal, Academic/Scholarly.*
Indexed: ASFA, AgBio, AgrForAb, BIOSIS Prev, BiolAb, CIN, CPA, ChemAb, ChemTitl, ExcerpMed, FCA, FPA, ForAb, HerbAb, HortAb, I&DA, IAA, MaizeAb, NutrAb, OrnHort, PBA, PGegResA, PGrRegA, PotatoAb, RA&MP, RPP, RRTA, RefZh, RiceAb, S&F, SIA, SeedAb, SoyAb, TriticAb, WeedAb.
—CASDDS, CISTI, East View, KNAW, Linda Hall. **CCC.**
Published by: (Rossiiskaya Akademiya Nauk/Russian Academy of Sciences, Rossiiskaya Akademiya Nauk, Sankt-Peterburgskoe Otdelenie), Izdatel'stvo Nauka, Sankt-Peterburgskoe Otdelenie, Mendeleevskaya liniya 1, St Petersburg, 199034, Russian Federation. TEL 7-812-3286291. Ed. A L Takhtadzhan. **US dist. addr.:** East View Information Services, 3020 Harbor Ln. N., Minneapolis, MN 55447. TEL 800-477-1005, FAX 800-800-3839, eastview@eastview.com, http://www.eastview.com.

580 GBR ISSN 0956-3237
THE BOTANICS. Text in English. q. **Document type:** *Newsletter.*
Indexed: RefZh.
Published by: Royal Botanic Garden Edinburgh, Inverleith Row, Edinburgh, EH3 5LR, United Kingdom. TEL 44-131-552-7171, FAX 44-131-552-0382. Ed. Norma Gregory.

580 DEU ISSN 0938-1759
BOTANICUS BRIEF; info for plant lovers around the world. Text in German. 1977. m. bk.rev. index. back issues avail. **Document type:** *Newsletter.*
Address: Gartenweg 9 a, Landau, 76829, Germany. TEL 49-6341-98777-0, FAX 49-6341-987774, botanicus.frank@t-online.de. Ed. Dieter Frank. Circ: 1,000.

580 HUN ISSN 0006-8144
CODEN: BOKOAX
BOTANIKAI KOZLEMENYEK/BOTANICAL PROCEEDINGS. Text in Hungarian; Summaries in English, German. 1901. q. USD 26.50. adv. bk.rev. charts; illus. index.
Formerly (until 1908): Novenytani Kozlemenyek (0200-299X)
Indexed: ASFA, BiolAb, CPA, ChemAb, CurCont, ESPM, FCA, HerbAb, OrnHort, PGrRegA, RPP, SeedAb, WeedAb.
—CASDDS, CISTI, Linda Hall.
Published by: Magyar Biologiai Tarsasag/Hungarian Biological Society, Fo utca 68, Budapest, 1027, Hungary.

580 FRA ISSN 0981-3519
BOTANIQUE LORRAINE. Text in French. 1985. a.
Published by: Association des Amis des Conservatoire et Jardins Botaniques de Nancy, 100, rue du Jardin Botanique, Villers-les-Nancy, 54 000, France. TEL 33-3-8341-4747, FAX 33-3-8327-8659, http://www.cjbn.uhp-nancy.fr/ajabona.html.

580 DEU ISSN 0006-8152
CODEN: BJPPAQ
➤ **BOTANISCHE JAHRBUECHER FUER SYSTEMATIK, PFLANZENGESCHICHTE UND PFLANZENGEOGRAPHIE.** Text in English, French, German. 1880. 4/yr. EUR 86 per issue domestic; EUR 89.70 per issue foreign (effective 2005). adv. bk.rev. bibl.; charts; illus. **Document type:** *Journal, Academic/Scholarly.*
Related titles: Online - full text ed.: (from EBSCO Publishing, Gale Group, IngentaConnect, Swets Information Services).
Indexed: BIOSIS Prev, BiolAb, FCA, HerbAb, IBR, PBA, TriticAb.
—CISTI, IE, Infotrieve, Linda Hall. **CCC.**
Published by: E. Schweizerbart'sche Verlagsbuchhandlung, Johannesstr 3A, Stuttgart, 70176, Germany. TEL 49-711-3514560, FAX 49-711-35145699, mail@schweizerbart.de, http://www.schweizerbart.de/j/botanische-jahrbucher.

580.74 570 DEU ISSN 0945-4292
BOTANISCHER VEREIN VON BERLIN UND BRANDENBURG. VERHANDLUNGEN. Text in German. 1859. a. EUR 15 (effective 2005). bk.rev. **Document type:** *Proceedings, Academic/Scholarly.*
Former titles (until 1991): Berliner Botanischer Verein. Verhandlung (0724-3111); (until 1982): Botanischer Verein der Provinz Brandenburg. Verhandlungen (0724-312X)
Indexed: BIOSIS Prev, BiolAb, RefZh.
—Linda Hall.
Published by: Botanischer Verein von Berlin und Brandenburg e.V., Koenigin-Luise-Str 6-8, Berlin, 14195, Germany. starfinger@gp.tu-berlin.de, http://www.botanischer-verein-brandenburg.de. Ed. Gunther Klemm.

BOTANISK CENTRALBIBLIOTEK. FORTEGNELSE OVER LOEBENDE PERIODICA VED BOTANISK CENTRALBIBLITEK. see *BIOLOGY—Abstracting, Bibliographies, Statistics*

580 JPN ISSN 0287-9794
BOTANY. Text in Japanese. 1951. a.
Published by: Kumamoto Kinen Shokubutsu Saishukai/ Kumamoto Herbalists Association, Kumamoto Hakubutsukan, 3-2 Furukyo-machi, Kumamoto-shi, Kumamoto-ken 860-0007, Japan.

580 ZAF ISSN 0006-8241
QK1 CODEN: BTHLAA
➤ **BOTHALIA.** Text in English. 1921. s-a. ZAR 200 domestic; USD 50 foreign (effective 2005). illus. index. reprint service avail. from ISI. **Document type:** *Journal, Academic/Scholarly.* **Description:** Main fields covered include taxonomy, ecology, anatomy, and cytology.
Indexed: AEA, ASCA, AgBio, Agr, AgrForAb, BIOBASE, BIOSIS Prev, BioDAb, BiolAb, CPA, CurCont, FCA, FPA, ForAb, HerbAb, HortAb, IABS, ISAP, OrnHort, PBA, PGegResA, PlantSci, RA&MP, RPP, S&F, SFA, WeedAb.
—BLDSC (2261.000000), CISTI, IDS, IE, Infotrieve, ingenta.
Published by: National Botanical Institute, NBI Bookshop, Private Bag X101, Pretoria, Cape Province 0001, South Africa. TEL 27-21-8043200, FAX 27-21-8043211, bookshop@nbipre.nbi.ac.za, http://www.nbi.ac.za/products/publications/bothalia.htm. Ed. G Germishuizen. R&P B A Momberg. Circ: 400.

580 USA
BOYCE THOMPSON INSTITUTE FOR PLANT RESEARCH. ANNUAL REPORT. Text in English. 1924. a. free. charts; illus. **Document type:** *Corporate.*
Related titles: Online - full text ed.
Indexed: IBZ, RPP, RevApplEntom.
—BLDSC (1118.295000).
Published by: Boyce Thompson Institute for Plant Research, Inc., Tower Rd, Cornell University, Ithaca, NY 14853. TEL 607-254-1234, FAX 607-254-1242, http://bti.cornell.edu. Ed. J L Frank. Circ: 2,000 (paid).

580 BRA ISSN 0084-800X
QK1 CODEN: BRADD8
BRADEA; boletin do herbarium bradeanum. Text in Portuguese; Summaries in English. 1969. irreg. BRL 35 domestic; BRL 40 foreign. abstr.; bibl.; charts; illus. index. **Document type:** *Bulletin.* **Description:** Presents original papers in botany, with emphasis on the flora of Brazil.
Indexed: AGBP, AIAP, BIOSIS Prev, BiolAb.
Published by: Herbarium Bradeanum, Centro, Caixa Postal 15005, Rio De Janeiro, RJ 20155-970, Brazil. Ed. Margarth Emmerich. R&P Miriam Cristina Alvarez Pereira. Circ: 400 (controlled).

580 635.933 GBR ISSN 0265-086X
➤ **BRADLEYA.** Text in English. 1983. a. GBP 14 domestic; GBP 17, USD 32 foreign (effective 2004). bk.rev. illus. index. back issues avail. **Document type:** *Academic/Scholarly.* **Description:** Presents current research and papers on cacti and other succulent plants. Serves as yearbook of the society.
Formerly: Cactus and Succulent Journal of Great Britain (0007-9375)
Indexed: OrnHort, PBA.
Published by: British Cactus & Succulent Society, 71 Lakes Ln, Newport Pagnell, Bucks MK16 8HT, United Kingdom. TEL 44-1908-611650, treasurer@bcss.org.uk. Ed. Dr. Colin Walker. Circ: 1,300. **Subscr. to:** Mr. D.V. Slade, Mr. DV Slade, 15 Brentwood Crescent, Hull Rd, York Y01 5HU, United Kingdom. TEL 44-1904-410512.

➤ **BRAUNSCHWEIGER NATURKUNDLICHE SCHRIFTEN.** see *BIOLOGY—Zoology*

571.2 BRA ISSN 1677-0420
CODEN: RBFVEG
➤ **BRAZILIAN JOURNAL OF PLANT PHYSIOLOGY.** Text and summaries in English, Portuguese. 1989. s-a. adv. bk.rev. abstr.; bibl.; charts; stat. back issues avail. **Document type:** *Journal, Academic/Scholarly.* **Description:** Publishes original articles and scientific reviews in plant physiology and related areas.
Formerly (until 2001): Revista Brasileira de Fisiologia Vegetal (0103-3131)
Related titles: Microform ed.: 1989 (from PQC); Online - full text ed.: free (effective 2005).
Indexed: AEA, ATA, AgBio, AgrForAb, Agrind, BIOBASE, BiolAb, CIN, CPA, ChemAb, ChemTitl, DBA, DSA, FCA, ForAb, HerbAb, HortAb, I&DA, MaizeAb, NemAb, OrnHort, PBA, PGegResA, PGrRegA, PHN&I, RA&MP, RPP, RiceAb, S&F, SIA, SeedAb, SoyAb, TriticAb, VITIS, WeedAb.
—CASDDS, CISTI. **CCC.**
Published by: Sociedade Brasileira de Fisiologia Vegetal, Instituto de Biologia, Depto Fisiologia Vegetal - IB, CP 6109 Unicamp, Campinas, 13083-970, Brazil. TEL 55-19-37886213, pmazza@unicamp.br, http://www.scielo.br/rbfv. Ed. Paulo Gimenez Mazzafera. adv.: page USD 1,000. Circ: 1,000.

583.51 GBR ISSN 0264-3405
BRITISH CACTUS & SUCCULENT JOURNAL. Text in English. 1945. q. GBP 15 domestic; GBP 20, USD 38 foreign (effective 2004). adv. bk.rev. illus. index. back issues avail. **Document type:** *Journal, Academic/Scholarly.* **Description:** Contains scholarly and popular discussions of classification, history of succulents, geographic and travel articles, and descriptions of collections.
Formerly (until 1982): National Cactus and Succulent Journal (0027-8858)
Indexed: BiolAb, HortAb, OrnHort.
Published by: British Cactus & Succulent Society, 71 Lakes Ln, Newport Pagnell, Bucks MK16 8HT, United Kingdom. TEL 44-1908-611650, treasurer@bcss.org.uk. Ed. Mr. D I Nevelle. Circ: 5,600 (controlled).

BRITISH JOURNAL OF PHYTOTHERAPY. see *ALTERNATIVE MEDICINE*

579.7 GBR ISSN 0300-4562
BRITISH LICHEN SOCIETY BULLETIN. Text in English. 1958. 2/yr. GBP 15, USD 30 to individuals; GBP 18.50, USD 37 to institutions (effective 1999). adv. bk.rev. bibl.; charts; illus.; stat. cum.index. **Document type:** *Bulletin.* **Description:** Contains topical items, historical material, and recent reviews about lichens.
Media: Duplicated (not offset).
Published by: British Lichen Society, Department of Life Science, c/o The Natural History Museum, Cromwell Rd, London, SW7 5BD, United Kingdom. TEL 44-115-9513211, FAX 44-115-9513251, jmgray@argonet.co.uk, http://www.argonet.co.uk/users/jmgray/. Ed. P W Lambley. Circ: 600. **Subscr. to:** J.M. Gray, Penmore, Perranuthnoe, Penzance, Cornwall TR20 9NF, United Kingdom.

B

579.5 GBR ISSN 0275-0287
BRITISH MYCOLOGICAL SOCIETY. SYMPOSIUM SERIES. Text in English. 1977. irreg., latest no.23, 2001. price varies.
Document type: *Proceedings, Academic/Scholarly.*
Indexed: Agr, BIOSIS Prev.
Published by: (British Mycological Society), Cambridge University Press, The Edinburgh Bldg, Shaftesbury Rd, Cambridge, CB2 2RU, United Kingdom. TEL 44-1223-312393, information@cambridge.org, https://booktrade.cambridge.org/series.asp?series=BMS, http://www.cup.cam.ac.uk/.

580 GBR ISSN 0301-9195
QK520 CODEN: BPSBA7
BRITISH PTERIDOLOGICAL SOCIETY. BULLETIN. Abbreviated title: B P S Bulletin. Text in English. 1973. a. GBP 33 (effective 2002); includes Fern Gazette and Pteridologist. illus. 48 p./no. 1 cols./p.; back issues avail. **Document type:** *Bulletin, Corporate.* **Description:** Reports on activities and meetings of the society.
Supersedes: British Pteridological Society. Newsletter (0068-2403)
Indexed: BiolAb, RefZh.
—BLDSC (2423.650000), Linda Hall.
Published by: British Pteridological Society, c/o Botany Department, Natural History Museum, Cromwell Rd, London, SW7 5BD, United Kingdom. TEL 44-20-79425756, bulletin@ebps.org.uk, http://www.ebps.org.uk. Ed. A M Paul. Circ: 800.

B

BRITISH SOCIETY FOR PLANT GROWTH REGULATION. MONOGRAPHS. see *AGRICULTURE—Crop Production And Soil*

580 USA ISSN 0007-196X
QK1 CODEN: BRTAAN
➤ **BRITTONIA.** Text in English. 1931. q. USD 115 domestic to institutions; USD 123 foreign to institutions (effective 2005). adv. bk.rev. abstr.; bibl.; illus. index. back issues avail.
Document type: *Journal, Academic/Scholarly.* **Description:** Original research articles on subjects encompassing the field of systematic botany.
Related titles: Online - full text ed.: (from BioOne, C S A, JSTOR (Web-based Journal Archive), O C L C Online Computer Library Center, Inc.).
Indexed: ASCA, ASFA, AgBio, Agr, AgrForAb, BIOBASE, BIOSIS Prev, BiolAb, CPA, ChemAb, CurCont, FCA, FPA, ForAb, HerbAb, HortAb, IABS, ISR, OrnHort, PBA, PGegResA, PlantSci, RA&MP, RPP, RefZh, S&F, SCI, SIA, SPPI, SeedAb, TriticAb, VITIS, WeedAb.
—BLDSC (2348.250000), CASDDS, CISTI, IDS, IE, ingenta, Linda Hall. **CCC.**
Published by: New York Botanical Garden Press, 200th Street & Kazimiroff Blvd, Bronx, NY 10458-5126. TEL 718-817-8918, FAX 718-817-8842, nybgpress@nybg.org, http://sciweb.nybg.org/science2/Brittonia.asp, http://www.nybg.org. Ed. Thomas Zanoni. R&P Carole J Young. Circ: 700.

584.85 USA ISSN 0090-8738
QK495.B76
➤ **BROMELIAD SOCIETY. JOURNAL.** Key Title: Journal of the Bromeliad Society. Text in English. 1951. bi-m. USD 30 (effective 2001). adv. bk.rev. illus. index. **Document type:** *Academic/Scholarly.* **Description:** Promotes and maintains general and scientific interest in research and preservation of the bromeliad plant family.
Formerly: Bromeliad Society Bulletin (0007-2184)
Indexed: Agr, GardL.
Published by: Bromeliad Society, Inc., 720 Millertown Rd, Auburn, CA 95603. TEL 530-885-0201, bsi@nerbm.nerdc.ufl.edu, http://bsi.org. Eds. Bruce Holst, Susan Murphy. adv.: color page USD 950, B&W page USD 625. Circ: 1,700 (paid). **Subscr. to:** Carolyn Schoenau, PO Box 12981, Gainesville, FL 32604-0981. TEL 352-372-6589, FAX 352-372-8823.

580 DEU ISSN 0724-0155
DIE BROMELIE. Text in German. 1980. 3/yr. EUR 29 to members (effective 2004). adv. bk.rev. back issues avail. **Document type:** *Journal, Academic/Scholarly.*
Published by: Deutsche Bromelien-Gesellschaft e.V., Burgstaller Str 21, Kirchberg, 71737, Germany. TEL 49-7144-36639, dbg-geschaeftsstelle@dbg-web.de, http://www.dbg-web.de. Ed. Wolfgang Tittelbach. Circ: 400.

588.2 FIN ISSN 1235-3949
BRYOBROTHERA. Text in English, Finnish; Summaries in English. 1992. irreg., latest vol.7, 2001. prices vary.
—BLDSC (2353.983000).
Published by: Finnish Bryological Society, Mailantic 109, P O Box 47, Kirkniemi, FIN-08800, Finland. TEL 358-9-3431380, FAX 358-9-349441, http://www.fmnh.helsinki.fi/sammalseura/english.html. Ed. Timo Koponen.

580 DEU ISSN 0723-2470
CODEN: TOENEW
BRYOLOGISCHE BEITRAEGE. Text in English, German. 1982. a. back issues avail. **Document type:** *Journal, Academic/Scholarly.*
Published by: I D H - Verlag, Funkenstr 13, Bad Muenstereifel, 53902, Germany. Ed. Ruprecht Duell.

579.7 USA ISSN 0007-2745
QK534 CODEN: BRYOAM
➤ **BRYOLOGIST.** Text in English, French, German, Spanish; Summaries in English. 1898. q. USD 55 domestic to individuals; USD 60 foreign to individuals; USD 70 domestic to institutions; USD 75 foreign to institutions; USD 45 to students (effective 2005). bk.rev. abstr.; bibl.; charts; illus.; stat. cum.index: 1898-1957, 1958-1972. back issues avail.; reprint service avail. from PQC. **Document type:** *Journal, Academic/Scholarly.* **Description:** Devoted to the study of bryophytes and lichens.
Related titles: Microfiche ed.: (from IDC); Microform ed.: (from PQC); Online - full text ed.: (from BioOne, C S A, O C L C Online Computer Library Center, Inc.).
Indexed: ASCA, ASFA, Agr, BIOBASE, BIOSIS Prev, BiolAb, CIN, CPA, ChemAb, ChemTitl, CurCont, EnvAb, EnvInd, FPA, ForAb, HerbAb, HortAb, IABS, ISR, NemAb, OrnHort, PBA, PGegResA, PlantSci, RA&MP, RPP, RRTA, RefZh, S&F, SCI, SPPI, WeedAb.
—BLDSC (2354.000000), CASDDS, CISTI, IDS, IE, Infotrieve, ingenta, Linda Hall.
Published by: American Bryological & Lichenological Society, Lloyd Stark, Department of Biological Sciences, University of Nevada, 4505 Maryland Parkway, P. O. Box 454004, Las Vegas, NV 89154-4004. TEL 402-554-2491, FAX 402-554-3532, lrs@unlv.edu, http://www.unomaha.edu/~abls/bryologist.html, http://www.abls.org. Ed., R&P, Adv. contact Dale H Vitt TEL 403-492-3390. Pub. Lloyd Stark. Circ: 1,000 (paid). **Dist. by:** Allen Press Inc.

579.7 CZE ISSN 0862-8904
➤ **BRYONORA.** Text in Czech. 1988. s-a. **Document type:** *Bulletin, Academic/Scholarly.* **Description:** Publishes short original and compilatory contributions from the fields of bryology and lichenology, complete listing of Czech and Slovak bryological and lichenological literature, selected titles from the abroad bryological and lichenological literature.
—BLDSC (2354.010000).
Published by: (Akademie Ved Ceske Republiky, Botanicky Ustav/Academy of Sciences of the Czech Republic, Institute of Botany), Ceska Botanicka Spolecnost/Czech Botanical Society, Benatska 2, Prague, 12801, Czech Republic. kucera@bf.jcu.cz, botspol@natur.cuni.cz, http://www.natur.cuni.cz/cbs. Ed. Jan Kucera TEL 420-387-772383.

580 DEU ISSN 0258-3348
QK532.4 CODEN: BRBIDS
BRYOPHYTORUM BIBLIOTHECA. Text in English, German. 1973. irreg., latest vol.61, 2004. price varies. **Document type:** *Monographic series, Academic/Scholarly.*
Indexed: BIOSIS Prev.
—BLDSC (2354.020000), CASDDS. **CCC.**
Published by: J. Cramer in der Gebrueder Borntraeger Verlagsbuchhandlung, Johannesstr 3A, Stuttgart, 70176, Germany. TEL 49-711-3514560, FAX 49-711-35145699, mail@borntraeger.cramer.de, http://www.schweizerbart.de/j/bryophytorum-bibliotheca. Eds. J P Frahm, S R Gradstein.

580 NLD ISSN 1010-6251
BULLETIN EUCARPIA. Text in Dutch. 1966. a. free to members. adv. bibl. back issues avail. **Document type:** *Bulletin, Trade.* **Description:** Publishes brief items of news and information relating to plant breeding, including reports of section activities and schedules of conferences and symposia.
Supersedes: Eucarpia - Bulletin d'Information (0071-2221)
Indexed: PBA.
Published by: European Association for Research on Plant Breeding, c/o MJ de Jeu, Sec-Gen, PO Box 315, Wageningen, 6700 AH, Netherlands. marjo.dejeu@users.pv.wau.nl, http://www.eucarpia.org/. Ed., Adv. contact Mrs. M.J. de Jeu. R&P Mrs. M J de Jeu. Circ: 1,250.

BULLETIN OF MEDICO-ETHNO-BOTANICAL RESEARCH. see *ALTERNATIVE MEDICINE*

580 IND ISSN 0970-4612
QK1 CODEN: BPBPE2
➤ **BULLETIN OF PURE & APPLIED SCIENCES. SECTION B: BOTANY.** Text in English. 1982. s-a. INR 300, USD 50 (effective 2005). adv. bk.rev. 90 p./no.; back issues avail. **Document type:** *Journal, Academic/Scholarly.* **Description:** Research papers related with Botanical Science and Plant Science.
Supersedes in part (in 1983): Bulletin of Pure & Applied Sciences (0970-4604)
—CISTI, Linda Hall. **CCC.**
Published by: A.K. Sharma, Ed. & Pub., 19-A, D D A Flats, Mansarover Park, Shahdara, New Delhi, 110 032, India. TEL 91-11-2117408, bulletin@mantraonline.com, ajaykumarsharma1955@yahoo.com. Ed., Pub., R&P, Adv. contact A K Sharma. B&W page INR 1,000, B&W page USD 50, color page INR 2,000, color page USD 100. Circ: 600.

380 JPN
BUNRUI. Text in English. 2001. q.
Published by: The Japanese Society for Plant Taxonomists, c/o Atsuko Takano, Ph.D., Museum of Nature & Human Activities, Hyogo, Yayoigaoka 6, Sanda, 669-1546, Japan. TEL 81-795-59-2012, FAX 81-795-59-2019.

580 NLD ISSN 0169-6289
C B S NEWSLETTER. Text in Dutch. 1983. s-a. free. **Document type:** *Newsletter.*
—KNAW.
Published by: Centraalbureau voor Schimmelcultures/Fungal Biodiversity Center, Uppsalalaan 8, Utrecht, 3584 CT, Netherlands. TEL 31-30-2122600, FAX 31-30-2512097, info@cbs.knaw.nl, http://www.cbs.knaw.nl. Ed., R&P R A Samson.

580 USA
C N P S INVENTORY OF RARE AND ENDANGERED VASCULAR PLANTS OF CALIFORNIA. Text in English. irreg., latest vol.5, 1993. USD 22.95 (effective 1999).
Description: Presents information on distribution, rarity, endangerment, legal status, habitat, plant growth form, blooming time, and literature sources for over 1,700 species, subspecies and varieties of California's endangered flora.
Published by: California Native Plant Society, 2707 K St., # 1, Sacramento, CA 95816-5113. Eds. Bruce M Pavlik, Mark W Skinner.

580 MEX ISSN 0526-717X
➤ **CACTACEAS Y SUCULENTAS MEXICANAS.** Text in Spanish; Abstracts in English, Spanish. 1955. q. MXP 250 domestic to individuals; USD 25 foreign to individuals (effective 2003). bk.rev. abstr.; bibl.; charts; illus.; maps. cum.index every 4 yrs. back issues avail.; reprints avail. **Document type:** *Journal, Academic/Scholarly.* **Description:** Covers systematic and floristic botany, succulent plants phytogeography, physiology and ecology. For both scientists and amateurs.
Indexed: AgBio, AgrForAb, BioCN&I, CPA, ForAb, HerbAb, HortAb, OrnHort, PBA, PGegResA, PGrRegA, RA&MP, S&F, SeedAb, WAE&RSA, WeedAb.
Published by: Sociedad Mexicana de Cactologia A.C., Apdo Postal 60-487, San Pedro de los Pinos, DF 03801, Mexico. TEL 52-55-6229003, cactus@miranda.ecologia.unam.mx, http://www.ecologia.unam.mx/laboratorios/dinamica_de_poblaciones/cacsucmex/cacsucmex_main.html. Eds. Jeronimo Reyes, Dr. Jordan K Golubov, Dr. Maria C Mandujano. Circ: 800.

583.56 USA ISSN 0007-9367
CACTUS AND SUCCULENT JOURNAL. Text in English. 1929. bi-m. USD 35 domestic membership individual; USD 40 foreign membership individuals; USD 45 domestic membership institutions (effective 2005). adv. bk.rev. illus. index. back issues avail.; reprint service avail. from PQC.
Document type: *Journal, Academic/Scholarly.* **Description:** Contains scholarly articles on new species, descriptions of plants, and discussions on horticultural practices, plus popular articles covering geographic localities and collections, and cultivation issues.
Related titles: Microform ed.: (from PQC).
Indexed: AgBio, Agr, AgrForAb, BiolAb, CPA, FPA, ForAb, GardL, HerbAb, HortAb, I&DA, OrnHort, PBA, PGegResA, RA&MP, RDA, RPP, RevApplEntom, S&F, SeedAb, WAE&RSA.
—CISTI, Linda Hall.
Published by: Cactus & Succulent Society of America, Inc., 2391 E Cactus St, PO Box 2615, Pahrump, NV 89048. TEL 310-556-1923, FAX 310-286-9629, U4BIA@aol.com, http://www.cssainc.org. Pub., R&P, Adv. contact Jerry Barad. Circ: 5,000.

580 BEL ISSN 0774-4706
CACTUSSEN EN VETPLANTEN. Text in Dutch. 1984. m. back issues avail. **Document type:** *Bulletin, Consumer.*
Description: Information about cacti and other succulents for plant enthusiasts.
Published by: Belgische Vereniging voor Liefhebbers van Cactussen en Andere Vetplanten, Kasteellei 111, Wijnegem, 2110, Belgium. TEL 32-3-3537258, FAX 32-3-3537258, cactusvetplant@online.be, http://user.online.be/cactusvetplant. Ed. Edvard van Hoofstadt.

635 USA
CALIFORNIA NATIVE PLANT SOCIETY. BULLETIN. Text in English. 1979. 4/yr. membership only. **Document type:** *Bulletin.*
Former titles: California Native Plant Society. Journal; (until 1992): California Native Plant Society. Bulletin (1046-1442)
Indexed: GardL.
Published by: California Native Plant Society, 2707 K St., # 1, Sacramento, CA 95816-5113. TEL 916-447-2677.

580 USA ISSN 0190-8723
CALIFORNIA NATIVE PLANT SOCIETY. SPECIAL PUBLICATION. Text in English. 1974. m.
Published by: California Native Plant Society, 2707 K St., # 1, Sacramento, CA 95816-5113. TEL 916-447-2677.

580.6071 CAN ISSN 0008-3046
CANADIAN BOTANICAL ASSOCIATION. BULLETIN. Text in English, French. 1967. q. CND 45 membership (effective 2005). adv. bk.rev. **Document type:** *Newsletter.*
—CISTI. **CCC.**
Published by: Canadian Botanical Association, c/o Martin Dube, Campus d'Edmundston, Universite de Moncton, Edmundston, NB E3V 2S8, Canada. TEL 506-737-5154, FAX 506-737-5373, martin@umce.ca, http://www.uoguelph.ca/botany/cba. Ed. Martin Dube. Circ: 300 (paid).

580 CAN ISSN 0008-4026
QK1 CODEN: CJBOAW
➤ **CANADIAN JOURNAL OF BOTANY/JOURNAL CANADIEN DE BOTANIQUE.** Text mainly in English; Text occasionally in French. 1929. m. CND 207 domestic to individuals; USD 207 foreign to individuals; CND 627 domestic to institutions; USD 627 foreign to institutions (effective 1999). adv. bibl.; charts; illus. Index. back issues avail.; reprint service avail. from PQC. **Document type:** *Journal, Academic/Scholarly.*
Formerly (until 1950): Canadian Journal of Research. Section C: Botanical Sciences (0366-7405); Which superseded in part (in 1935): Canadian Journal of Research (0366-6581)
Related titles: Microfiche ed.: (from MML); Microform ed.: (from MML, PMC, PQC); Online - full text ed.: ISSN 1480-3305 (from bigchalk, EBSCO Publishing, Gale Group, IngentaConnect, Micromedia ProQuest, O C L C Online Computer Library Center, Inc., ProQuest Information & Learning, Swets Information Services).
Indexed: ABIPC, ABS&EES, AEA, APD, ASCA, ASFA, AbHyg, AgBio, Agr, AgrForAb, ApEcolAb, ApicAb, B&AI, BIOBASE, BIOSIS Prev, BibAg, BioCN&I, BioDAb, BiolAb, CBCARef, CIN, CPA, CTFA, ChemAb, ChemTitl, CurCont, DBA, EPB, ESPM, EngInd, EntAb, EnvAb, EnvInd, ExcerpMed, FCA, FPA, FS&TA, FaBeAb, ForAb, GEOBASE, GenetAb, HGA, HelmAb, HerbAb, HortAb, I&DA, IABS, ISR, IndVet, M&GPA, MBA, MaizeAb, NemAb, NutrAb, OrnHort, PBA, PGegResA, PGrRegA, PHN&I, PN&I, PlantSci, PollutAb, PotatoAb, ProtozoAb, RA&MP, RM&VM, RPP, RRTA, RefZh, RevApplEntom, RiceAb, S&F, S&MA, SCI, SIA, SWRA, SeedAb, SoyAb, TOSA, TriticAb, VITIS, WAE&RSA, WTA, WeedAb, ZooRec.
—BLDSC (3030.000000), CASDDS, CIS, CISTI, IDS, IE, Infotrieve, ingenta, Linda Hall. **CCC.**
Published by: N R C Research Press, Building M 55, Ottawa, ON K1A 0R6, Canada. TEL 613-993-0362, 800-668-1222, FAX 613-952-7656, research.journals@nrc.ca, pubs@nrc-cnrc.gc.ca, http://pubs.nrc-cnrc.gc.ca/cgi-bin/rp/rp2_desc_e?cjb. Ed. Bruce P Dancik. Adv. contact Judy Heyman. B&W page CND 675; trim 11 x 8.5. Circ: 1,506.

➤ **CANADIAN JOURNAL OF HERBALISM.** see *ALTERNATIVE MEDICINE*

632 CAN ISSN 0706-0661
CODEN: CJPPD6
➤ **CANADIAN JOURNAL OF PLANT PATHOLOGY.** Text in English, French. 1979. q. CND 75 domestic; USD 85 foreign. back issues avail. **Document type:** *Academic/Scholarly.*
Description: Publication of original research in plant pathology including technology aspects of plant disease control.
Related titles: Online - full text ed.: (from EBSCO Publishing).
Indexed: AEA, ASCA, AgBio, Agr, AgrForAb, B&AI, BIOBASE, BIOSIS Prev, BioCN&I, BioDAb, BiolAb, CIN, CPA, CTFA, ChemAb, ChemTitl, CurCont, DBA, EnvAb, FCA, FPA, FaBeAb, ForAb, HerbAb, HortAb, I&DA, IABS, MaizeAb, NemAb, NutrAb, OrnHort, PBA, PGegResA, PGrRegA, PHN&I, PN&I, PlantSci, PotatoAb, PoultAb, RA&MP, RDA, RM&VM, RPP, RRTA, RefZh, RevApplEntom, RiceAb, S&F, SIA, SeedAb, SoyAb, TOSA, TriticAb, WAE&RSA, WeedAb.
—BLDSC (3034.400000), CASDDS, CISTI, IDS, IE, Infotrieve, ingenta, Linda Hall. **CCC.**
Published by: Canadian Phytopathological Society, Dept of Environmental Biology, University of Guelph, Guelph, ON N1G 2W1, Canada. TEL 519-824-4120, FAX 519-837-0442, http://www.cps-scp.ca/cjppeng.htm. Ed. Dr. Zamir K Punja TEL 604-291-4471. Circ: 900.

580 CAN ISSN 0008-4220
CODEN: CPLSAY
➤ **CANADIAN JOURNAL OF PLANT SCIENCE.** Text in English, French. 1921. q. CND 80 domestic to individuals; CND 91 domestic to individuals print & online eds.; CND 85 foreign to individuals; CND 99 foreign to individuals print & online eds.; CND 125 domestic to institutions; CND 142 domestic to institutions print & online eds.; CND 155 foreign to institutions; CND 177 foreign to institutions print & online eds. (effective 2004). bibl.; charts; illus.; stat. index. reprint service avail. from PQC. **Document type:** *Journal, Academic/Scholarly.*
Description: Research on agronomy and horticulture.
Supersedes in part (in 1956): Canadian Journal of Agricultural Science (0366-6557); Which was formerly (until 1952): Scientific Agriculture (0370-887X)
Related titles: Microform ed.: (from PMC, PQC); Online - full text ed.: (from EBSCO Publishing, O C L C Online Computer Library Center, Inc., Swets Information Services).
Indexed: AEA, ASCA, ASFA, AgBio, Agr, AgrForAb, B&AI, BIOBASE, BIOSIS Prev, BibAg, BioCN&I, BiolAb, CIN, CPA, ChemAb, ChemTitl, CurCont, DBA, DSA, EPB, ESPM, EntAb, EnvAb, EnvEAb, ExcerpMed, FCA, FPA, FS&TA, ForAb, GEOBASE, HGA, HerbAb, HortAb, I&DA, IABS, ISR, IndVet, MaizeAb, NemAb, NutrAb, OrnHort, PBA, PGegResA, PGrRegA, PHN&I, PN&I, PlantSci, PollutAb, PotatoAb, PoultAb, RA&MP, RM&VM, RPP, RefZh, RevApplEntom, RiceAb, S&F, S&MA, SCI, SIA, SWRA, SeedAb, SoyAb, Telegen, TriticAb, VITIS, VetBull, WAE&RSA, WeedAb.
—BLDSC (3034.500000), CASDDS, CIS, CISTI, IDS, IE, Infotrieve, ingenta, Linda Hall. **CCC.**
Published by: (Canadian Society of Agronomy), Agricultural Institute of Canada, 141 Laurier Ave W, Ste 1112, Ottawa, ON K1P 5J3, Canada. TEL 613-232-9459, FAX 613-594-5190, journals@aic.ca, http://pubs.nrc-cnrc.gc.ca/aic-journals/cjps.html, http://www.aic.ca. Ed. Dr. Yousef A Papadopoulos TEL 902-896-0400. R&P T Fenton. Circ: 1,200.

➤ **CANADIAN PLANT DISEASE SURVEY.** see *AGRICULTURE*

571.2 CAN ISSN 1183-9597
CANADIAN SOCIETY OF PLANT PHYSIOLOGISTS. BULLETIN/SOCIETE CANADIENNE DE PHYSIOLOGIE VEGETALE. BULLETIN. Text in English, French. 1957. q. CND 45 to members. adv. bk.rev. back issues avail. **Document type:** *Bulletin.*
Published by: Canadian Society of Plant Physiologists/Societe Canadienne de Physiologie Vegetale, Agriculture, Research Station, Harrow, ON N0R 1G0, Canada. TEL 519-738-2251, FAX 519-738-2929, cspp@uoguelph.ca, http://www.uoguelph.ca/~cspp. Ed. Dr. Lorna Woodrow. Circ: 550.

580.74 CHE ISSN 0373-2967
QK1 CODEN: CNDLAR
CANDOLLEA. Text in French. 1924. s-a. **Document type:** *Journal, Academic/Scholarly.*
Indexed: AgrForAb, BIOSIS Prev, BiolAb, CPA, CurCont, FPA, ForAb, HerbAb, HortAb, OrnHort, PBA, PGegResA, RA&MP, RPP, RRTA, RefZh, S&F, VITIS, WeedAb.
—BLDSC (3046.760000), IE, Infotrieve, ingenta, Linda Hall.
Published by: Conservatoire et Jardin Botaniques de la Ville de Geneve, Universite de Geneve, 1 Chemin de l'Imperatrice, Chambesy, CH-1292, Switzerland. TEL 41-22-4185100, FAX 41-22-4185101, http://wwwcjb.unige.ch/editions/candollea.html.

580 NZL ISSN 0110-5892
CANTERBURY BOTANICAL SOCIETY. JOURNAL. Text in English. 1968. a., latest vol.36, 2002. NZD 20 domestic to non-members; NZD 40 foreign to non-members (effective 2003). adv. 112 p./no.; back issues avail. **Document type:** *Journal, Academic/Scholarly.* **Description:** Contains short general-interest articles and papers with particular emphasis on the botany of the indigenous plants of New Zealand species lists and distributions.
Indexed: INZP.
—CCC.
Published by: Canterbury Botanical Society (NZ) Inc., Riccarton, PO Box 8212, Christchurch, New Zealand. TEL 64-3-3527922, marg.bert@xtra.co.nz. Ed. Colin Burrows. R&P W Harris. Adv. contact M R Geerkens. Circ: 250.

633.202 CHN ISSN 1004-5759
CAOYE XUEBAO/ACTA PRATACULTURAE SINICA. Text in Chinese. 1990. q. CNY 32 per issue; CNY 8 newsstand/cover (effective 2004). **Document type:** *Journal, Academic/Scholarly.*
Related titles: Online - full text ed.: (from East View Information Services).
Indexed: AEA, AgBio, AgrForAb, AnBrAb, CPA, DSA, FCA, FPA, ForAb, HerbAb, HortAb, I&DA, IndVet, MaizeAb, NutrAb, OrnHort, PBA, PGegResA, PGrRegA, PHN&I, PN&I, PotatoAb, RA&MP, RDA, RPP, RRTA, RiceAb, S&F, SIA, SeedAb, SoyAb, TDB, TriticAb, VetBull, WAE&RSA, WeedAb.
—BLDSC (0661.335000), IE, ingenta.
Published by: Zhongguo Caoxuehui/Chinese Grassland Society, Haidian-qu, 2, Yuanminyuna Xi Lu, Beijing, 100094, China. csgrass@public.bta.net.cn, http://www.cau.edu.cn/grass/xuehui.htm. **Dist. by:** China International Book Trading Corp, 35 Chegongzhuang Xilu, Haidian District, PO Box 399, Beijing 100044, China. TEL 86-10-68412045, FAX 86-10-68412023, cibtc@mail.cibtc.com.cn, http://www.cibtc.com.cn.

333.74 CHN ISSN 1009-5500
CAOYUAN YU CAOPING/GRASSLAND AND TURF. Text in Chinese. 1981. q. **Document type:** *Journal, Academic/Scholarly.*
Related titles: Online - full text ed.: (from WanFang Data Corp.).
Published by: Gansu Nongye Daxue, Andian-qu Yingmen-cu 1-hao, Lanzhou-shi, 730070, China. TEL 86-931-7631144, FAX 86-931-7632044, runqin@public.lz.gs.cn, http://cyycp.periodicals.com.cn/default.html.

580 USA
CAREERS IN BOTANY. Text in English. 1965. irreg., latest 1995. USD 1 (effective 1999). **Document type:** *Academic/Scholarly.*
Former titles: Botany as a Profession (0068-0397); Botanical Society of America. Miscellaneous Publications
Published by: Botanical Society of America, Inc. (Columbus), Business Office, 2813 Blossom Ave., Columbus, OH 43231-2921. TEL 614-292-3519. Ed. Marshall D Sundberg. R&P Kimberly Hiser.

583.75 USA ISSN 0190-9215
QK917
CARNIVOROUS PLANT NEWSLETTER. Text in English. 1971. q. USD 25 membership (effective 2005). adv. bk.rev.; film rev. bibl.; illus. back issues avail. **Document type:** *Newsletter, Consumer.* **Description:** Covers anything pertaining to carnivorous plants, natural history, and culture.
Indexed: GardL.
Published by: International Carnivorous Plant Society, Inc., PMB 321, 1564-A Fitzgerald Dr, Pinole, CA 94564-2229. barryrice@carnivorousplants.org, http://www.carnivorousplants.org/cpn/cpnmain.html. Eds. Barry Rice, Jan Schlower. Circ: 1,000 (paid and controlled).

CAROLINEA; Beitraege zur Naturkundlichen Forschung in Suedwestdeutschland. see *BIOLOGY—Zoology*

580.975 577 USA ISSN 0008-7475
QK1 CODEN: CSTNAC
➤ **CASTANEA.** Text in English. 1936. q. USD 40 (effective 2005). adv. bk.rev. bibl. index, cum.index. back issues avail. **Document type:** *Journal, Academic/Scholarly.* **Description:** Considers, reviews, and educates about the botany of Eastern North America.
Related titles: Online - full text ed.: (from BioOne, C S A, ProQuest Information & Learning).
Indexed: ASFA, AgBio, Agr, AgrForAb, ApEcolAb, BIOSIS Prev, BibAg, BioCN&I, BiolAb, CPA, CurCont, ESPM, FPA, ForAb, GEOBASE, HerbAb, HortAb, I&DA, NutrAb, OrnHort, PBA, PGegResA, PN&I, PoultAb, RA&MP, RPP, RRTA, RefZh, RevApplEntom, RiceAb, S&F, SeedAb, WeedAb.
—BLDSC (3064.000000), CASDDS, CISTI, IE, ingenta, Linda Hall.
Published by: Southern Appalachian Botanical Society, c/o Charles N Horn, Treasurer, Biology Dept, Newberry College, 2100 College St, Newberry, SC 29108. TEL 803-321-5257, FAX 803-321-5636, chorn@newberry.edu, http://newberrynet.com/sabs. Ed., Adv. contact Audrey Mellichamp TEL 704-687-4065. R&P Charles Horn. Circ: 1,100.

580 USA
▼ **CASTANEA: OCCASIONAL PAPERS IN EASTERN BOTANY.** Text in English. 2003. irreg., latest vol.1, 2003. USD 20 per vol. (effective 2003). **Document type:** *Monographic series, Academic/Scholarly.* **Description:** Features long manuscripts not appropriate for a regular issue of Castanea, collections of shorter manuscripts that treat topics not usually published in Castanea, and proceedings arising from symposia and conferences.
Indexed: BiolAb.
Published by: Southern Appalachian Botanical Society, c/o Charles N Horn, Treasurer, Biology Dept, Newberry College, 2100 College St, Newberry, SC 29108. TEL 803-321-5257, FAX 803-321-5636, chorn@newberry.edu, http://www.newberrynet.com/sabs/Castanea/OccPap.htm, http://newberrynet.com/sabs.

635 USA
CASTILLEJA. Text in English. 1981. 4/yr. USD 7.50 to members. bk.rev. **Document type:** *Newsletter.* **Description:** Provides general interest plant information.
Formerly: W N P S Newsletter
Published by: Wyoming Native Plant Society, PO Box 3452, Laramie, WY 82071. Ed. Walter Fertig. Circ: 200.

580 AUT
CATALOGUS FLORAE AUSTRIA. Text in German. irreg. price varies. 418 p./no.; back issues avail. **Document type:** *Monographic series, Academic/Scholarly.*
Published by: Verlag der Oesterreichischen Akademie der Wissenschaften, Postgasse 7/4, Vienna, W 1011, Austria. TEL 43-1-515813402, FAX 43-1-515813400, verlag@oeaw.ac.at, http://verlag.oeaw.ac.at.

580 GBR ISSN 0268-2907
CECIDOLOGY. Text in English. 1986. s-a.
Indexed: BioCN&I, ForAb, HortAb, NemAb, RPP, WeedAb, ZooRec.
—BLDSC (3096.930090), IE.
Published by: British Plant Gall Society, 2 The Dene, Nettleham, Lincolnshire, LN2 2LS, United Kingdom. TEL 01522-875939, http://www.btinternet.com/~bpgs/Society.html. Ed. Mr. M Chinery.

CENTRAL PLANTATION CROPS RESEARCH INSTITUTE. ANNUAL REPORT. see *AGRICULTURE*

CENTRAL PLANTATION CROPS RESEARCH INSTITUTE. RESEARCH HIGHLIGHTS. see *AGRICULTURE*

580 ITA
CENTRO MICOLOGICO FRIULANO. BOLLETTINO. Text in Italian. 1976. a.
Published by: Centro Micologico Friulano, Via Beato Odorico da Pordenone, 3, Udine, UD 33100, Italy.

CEREAL RUST BULLETIN. see *AGRICULTURE—Crop Production And Soil*

580 COL ISSN 0121-0866
➤ **CESPEDESIA.** Text in Spanish; Summaries in English, Spanish. 1972. irreg. COP 30,000 domestic; COP 70,000 foreign (effective 2004). illus. back issues avail. **Document type:** *Journal, Academic/Scholarly.*
Indexed: ApicAb, ZooRec.
Published by: Museo de Ciencias Naturales, Calle 6 No 24-80 Avenida Roosevelt, Cali, Colombia. TEL 57-2-5146844, FAX 57-2-5583466, inciva@telesat.com.co. Ed., Pub. German Parra Valencia. R&P Jose Marin Riascos. Circ: 500 (paid).

▼ new title ➤ refereed ✶ unverified ♦ full entry avail.

579.5 JPN
CHIBA UNIVERSITY. RESEARCH CENTER FOR PATHOGENIC FUNGI AND MICROBIAL TOXICOSES. PROCEEDINGS OF THE INTERNATIONAL SYMPOSIUM. Text in English. irreg. **Document type:** *Proceedings.*
Published by: Chiba University, Research Center for Pathogenic Fungi and Microbial Toxicoses/Chiba Daigaku Shinkaku Biseibutsu Kenkyu Senta, 8-1 Inohana 1-chome, Chuo-ku, Chiba-shi, 260-0856, Japan.

380 CHL ISSN 0717-4632
CHLORIS CHILENSIS; revista chilena de flora y vegetacion. Text in Spanish. 1998. s-a. free (effective 2005). back issues avail.
Media: Online - full text.
Published by: Sebastian Teillier steillier@chlorischile.cl, http://www.chlorischile.cl/.

580 JPN ISSN 1343-0882
CHONAI SAIKINGAKU ZASSHI/JOURNAL OF INTESTINAL MICROBIOLOGY. Text in Japanese. 1987. s-a. JPY 2,500 newsstand/cover (effective 2004). back issues avail. **Document type:** *Journal, Academic/Scholarly.*
Formerly (until 1997): Bifizusu (0914-2509); Which was formed by the merger of (1981-1987): Bifidus: Bibliography of Bifidobacteria and Microflora (0285-7006); (1985-1987): Bifidus, Fructus et Semina (0911-7636); (1984-1987): Nihon Bifizusukin Senta Nyusu (0914-3262)
Related titles: Online - full text ed.: ISSN 1349-8363 (from J-Stage).
Indexed: AbHyg, AgBio, DSA, IndVet, NutrAb, PN&I, SIA, VetBull.
—BLDSC (5007.697500), CISTI, IE, ingenta.
Published by: Nihon Bifizusukin Senta/Japan Bifidus Foundation, 1-24-11 Sugamo,Toshima-ku, Tokyo, 170-0002, Japan. 003@ipec-pub.co.jp, http://bifidus.bcasj.or.jp/journal_of_intestinal_microbiolo.htm, http://www.ipec-pub.co.jp/jbf/.

B

580 ESP ISSN 1132-7685
CIENCIAS DE LA TIERRA. (In 5 series: Botania, Geografia, Geologia, Paleontologia, Zoologia) Text in Spanish. 1984. irreg., latest vol.20, 1997. price varies.
Indexed: IECT.
Published by: Instituto de Estudios Riojanos, C. Muro de la Mata, 8 principal, Logrono, 26071, Spain. TEL 34-941-262064, FAX 34-941-246667.

580.74 333.72 GBR
CITES NEWS - PLANTS; a newsletter for the European region of the CITES plants. (Issue 4 available in German.) Text in English. 1994. irreg. **Document type:** *Newsletter.*
Related titles: French ed.: Cites News - Plantes; Spanish ed.: Noticias Cites - Plantas.
Published by: Royal Botanic Gardens, Kew, Richmond, Surrey TW9 3AB, United Kingdom. TEL 44-20-83325000, FAX 44-20-83325197, info@rbgkew.org.uk, http://www.rbgkew.org.uk/herbarium/caps/cites/index.html, http://www.rbgkew.org.uk/index.html. Ed. Jacqui Roberts.

580 ESP ISSN 0010-0730
CODEN: COBOAX
COLLECTANEA BOTANICA. Text in Multiple languages. 1945. a. USD 15; or exchange basis. bk.rev. bibl.; charts; illus. back issues avail. **Document type:** *Bulletin.*
Indexed: BIOSIS Prev, BiolAb, FCA, HerbAb, IECT, RefZh, ZooRec.
—BLDSC (3299.000000), CINDOC, CISTI, Linda Hall.
Published by: Institut Botanic de Barcelona, Parc de Montjuic, Avinguda dels Montanyans, Barcelona, 08038, Spain. TEL 34-93-325-8050, jmmontserrat@ibb.csic.es. Circ: 1,050.

580 DEU ISSN 1430-0540
COLLOQUES PHYTOSOCIOLOGIQUES. Text in English, French, German. 1975. irreg., latest vol.28, 2004. price varies. charts; illus. back issues avail. **Document type:** *Monographic series, Academic/Scholarly.*
Indexed: BIOSIS Prev, BiolAb.
—BLDSC (3315.006000).
Published by: J. Cramer in der Gebrueder Borntraeger Verlagsbuchhandlung, Johannesstr 3A, Stuttgart, 70176, Germany. TEL 49-711-3514560, FAX 49-711-35145699, mail@borntraeger-cramer.de, http://www.schweizerbart.de. Ed. J M Gehu.

580 590 HUN ISSN 1585-8553
QK900 CODEN: CEOCAQ
➤ **COMMUNITY ECOLOGY**; an interdisciplinary journal reporting progress in community and population studies. Text and summaries in English. 2000. s-a. USD 192 (effective 2006). adv. bk.rev. abstr.; charts; bibl. 120 p./no.; back issues avail. **Document type:** *Journal, Academic/Scholarly.* **Description:** Aims to create a common global forum for community ecologists dealing with plant, animal and/or microbial communities from terrestrial, marine or freshwater systems.
Formed by the merger of (1971-2000): Abstracta Botanica (0133-6215); Coenoses (0393-9154)
Related titles: Online - full text ed.: ISSN 1588-2756 (from EBSCO Publishing, Gale Group, IngentaConnect, Swets Information Services).
Indexed: BIOSIS Prev, BiolAb, GEOBASE, ZooRec.
—BLDSC (3363.623450), CISTI.
Published by: Akademiai Kiado Rt. (Subsidiary of: Wolters Kluwer N.V.), Prielle Kornelia U. 19, Budapest, 1117, Hungary. TEL 36-1-4648282, FAX 36-1-4648221, journals@akkrt.hu, http://www.terraalapitvany.hu/comecol/, http://www.akkrt.hu. Eds. J Podani, N C Kenkel. Pub. Piroska Polyanszky TEL 36-1-46482333.

580 BRA ISSN 0102-3306
QK263
CONGRESSO NACIONAL DE BOTANICA. ANAIS. Text in Portuguese; Summaries in English, Portuguese, Spanish. 1950. a. charts; illus. **Document type:** *Proceedings.*
Related titles: Online - full text ed.: free (effective 2005).
Indexed: AEA, AgBio, AgrForAb, CPA, FCA, FPA, ForAb, HerbAb, HortAb, I&DA, OrnHort, PBA, PGegResA, PoultAb, RA&MP, RDA, RPP, RiceAb, S&F, SeedAb, WAE&RSA, WeedAb.
Published by: Sociedade Botanica do Brasil, c/o Museu Paraense Emilio Goeldi, Caixa Postal 399, Belem, PARA 60000, Brazil. FAX 091-229-1412.

580 ISR
➤ **CONSPECTUS FLORAE ORIENTALIS.** Text in English. 1980. irreg., latest vol.9, 1997. USD 15 per issue (effective 1999). adv. **Document type:** *Monographic series, Academic/Scholarly.* **Description:** Annotated catalog of the flora of the Middle East.
Published by: Israel Academy of Sciences and Humanities, 43 Jabotinski St, P O Box 4040, Jerusalem, 91040, Israel. TEL 972-2-5676233, FAX 972-2-5666059, tami@academy.ac.il, http://www.academy.ac.il. Ed. Zofia Lasman. Adv. contact Tami Korman.

580 USA
CONSTANCEA. Text in English. irreg. free (effective 2005).
Formerly (until 2002): University of California Publications in Botany
Media: Online - full text. **Related titles:** Microfilm ed.: (from BHP).
Published by: (University of California at Berkeley, University and Jepson Herbaria), University of California Press, Book Series, 2120 Berkeley Way, Berkeley, CA 94720. TEL 510-642-4247, FAX 510-643-7127, askucp@ucpress.edu, http://ucjeps.berkeley.edu/constancea, http://www.ucpress.edu/books/series.html. Ed. Richard L Moe. **Subscr. to:** California - Princeton Fulfillment Services, 1445 Lower Ferry Rd, Ewing, NJ 08618. TEL 800-777-4726, FAX 800-999-1958, orders@cpfs.pupress.princeton.edu.

580 ROM ISSN 0069-9616
CODEN: CBGBBV
CONTRIBUTII BOTANICE. Text in Romanian. 1958. a. per issue exchange basis only. **Document type:** *Bulletin.*
Indexed: ChemAb, RPP.
—CASDDS, CISTI.
Published by: Universitatea Gradina Botanica, Str. Gheorghe Bilascu 42, Cluj-Napoca, 3400, Romania. TEL 40-64192152, grbot@bioge.ubbcluj.ro.

580.74 USA ISSN 0736-0509
CODEN: CNYGEJ
➤ **CONTRIBUTIONS FROM THE NEW YORK BOTANICAL GARDEN.** Text in English. 1898-1931; resumed 1984. irreg., latest vol.20, 1993. price varies. back issues avail. **Document type:** *Monographic series, Academic/Scholarly.* **Description:** Reprint classic works, translations and annotated bibliographies on botanical subjects.
Indexed: BIOSIS Prev.
—CCC.
Published by: New York Botanical Garden Press, 200th Street & Kazimiroff Blvd, Bronx, NY 10458-5126. TEL 718-817-8721, FAX 718-817-8842. Ed. W Buck.

580 USA ISSN 0097-1618
CONTRIBUTIONS FROM THE UNITED STATES NATIONAL HERBARIUM. Text in English. 1890. irreg. price varies. **Document type:** *Monographic series.*
Indexed: FCA, ForAb, HerbAb, HortAb, PBA, PGegResA, RefZh.
—CISTI.
Published by: Smithsonian Institution, National Museum of Natural History, M R C 0166, P O Box 37012, Washington, DC 20013-7012. TEL 202-357-2534, FAX 202-786-2563, http://www.nmnh.si.edu. Ed. Robert J. Soreng.

579.5 NLD ISSN 0929-7839
COOLIA. Text in Dutch. 1954. q. EUR 20 membership (effective 2003). **Document type:** *Journal, Academic/Scholarly.*
Indexed: CPA, FPA, ForAb, HortAb, PBA, PGegResA, S&F.
Published by: Nederlandse Mycologische Vereniging, Hooischelf 13, Malden, 6581 SL, Netherlands. TEL 31-24-3582421, m.dam@paog-fmw.kun.nl, http://www-mlf.sci.kun.nl/nmv/c_index.htm, http://www-mlf.sci.kun.nl/nmv/nmv_e.htm.

578.7789 GUM ISSN 0278-324X
QH95.8 CODEN: CRENDZ
CORAL REEF NEWSLETTER. Text in English. 1972. s-a. bk.rev. abstr.; bibl.; illus. **Document type:** *Newsletter.*
Media: Online - full text.
Published by: University of Guam, Marine Laboratory, UOG Station, Mangilao, 96923, Guam. TEL 671-735-2184, FAX 671-734-6767, http://www.bishop.hawaii.org/bishop/psa/, http://www.uog.edu/marinelab/. Ed. Lucius G Eldredge. Circ: 1,300.

CORNELL PLANTATIONS MAGAZINE. see *COLLEGE AND ALUMNI*

580 ITA ISSN 0010-9258
CORRIERE FITOPATOLOGICO. Text in Italian. 1963. s-a. free. illus.
Published by: Bayer Italia SpA, Viale Certosa, 126, Milan, MI 20149, Italy. Ed. Loredano P Lazzarini. Circ: 60,000.

COUNCIL ON BOTANICAL AND HORTICULTURAL LIBRARIES. NEWSLETTER. see *GARDENING AND HORTICULTURE*

CREX. see *BIOLOGY—Ornithology*

635 USA ISSN 0891-9100
➤ **CROSSOSOMA**; journal of the Southern California botanists. Text in English. 1975. s-a. USD 15 domestic to individuals; USD 25 domestic to institutions; USD 35 foreign to institutions (effective 2002). bk.rev. back issues avail. **Document type:** *Academic/Scholarly.* **Description:** Covers the study, preservation, and conservation of native plants of California.
Published by: Southern California Botanists, c/o Alan Romspert, Department of Biology, California State University, Fullerton, CA 92834. TEL 714-278-7034, FAX 714-278-4289, aromspert@fullerton.edu. Ed. Carl Wishner. Pub., R&P Alan Romspert. Circ: 300 (paid).

635 USA
CROSSWORDS. Text in English. 3/yr. membership only.
Published by: Gesneriad Hybridizers Association, 4115 Pillar Dr, Rt 1, Whitmore Lake, MI 48189.

580 CHE ISSN 0257-9421
CODEN: CRHEEO
CRYPTOGAMICA HELVETICA. Text in French, German, Italian. 1898. irreg., latest vol.15, 1977. price varies. bibl.; charts; illus. index. back issues avail. **Document type:** *Newsletter.*
Formerly: Beitraege zur Kryptogamenflora der Schweiz
Indexed: BIOSIS Prev, BiolAb.
Published by: (Bern. Schweizerische Naturforschende Gesellschaft), F. Flueck-Wirth, Krypto, PO Box, Teufen Ar, 9053, Switzerland. FAX 41-71-3331664.

579.8 FRA ISSN 0181-1568
CODEN: CRALD9
➤ **CRYPTOGAMIE ALGOLOGIE.** Text and summaries in English, French. 1924. q. EUR 153.97 in Europe to institutions; USD 172 in the Americas to institutions; EUR 316 combined subscription in Europe to institutions with Bryologie and Mycologie; USD 350 combined subscription in the Americas to institutions with Bryologie and Mycologie (effective 2001). bk.rev. abstr.; bibl.; charts; illus. index. back issues avail. **Document type:** *Academic/Scholarly.* **Description:** Publishes papers concerning all aspects of research on marine and freshwater algae.
Supersedes (in 1980): Revue Algologique (0035-0702); Incorporates (in 1978): Societe Phycologique de France. Bulletin (0081-122X)
Related titles: Online - full text ed.: (from EBSCO Publishing, Gale Group, IngentaConnect, ScienceDirect, Swets Information Services).
Indexed: ASCA, ASFA, BIOBASE, BIOSIS Prev, BiolAb, ChemAb, CurCont, ESPM, GEOBASE, MSCT, RefZh, SPPI, ZooRec.
—CASDDS, CISTI, IDS, IE, Infotrieve, ingenta, Linda Hall.
Published by: Museum National d'Histoire Naturelle, 57 Rue Cuvier, Paris, 75231 Cedex 05, France. TEL 33-1-40793777, http://www.mnhn.fr. Circ: 500.

579.7 FRA ISSN 1290-0796
QK532.4 CODEN: CRBRFY
➤ **CRYPTOGAMIE BRYOLOGIE.** Text and summaries in English, French, Spanish. 1874. q. EUR 146.05 in Europe to institutions; USD 172 in the Americas to institutions; EUR 316 combined subscription in Europe to institutions with Algologie & Mycologie; USD 350 combined subscription in the Americas to institutions with Algologie & Mycologie (effective 2001). bk.rev. abstr.; bibl.; illus. index. back issues avail. **Document type:** *Academic/Scholarly.* **Description:** Publishes research results from all fields of bryology and lichenology.
Formerly (until 1998): Cryptogamie: Bryologie et Lichenologie (0181-1576); Which superseded (in 1980): Revue Bryologique et Lichenologique (0399-0575)
Related titles: Microfiche ed.: (from IDC); Online - full text ed.: (from EBSCO Publishing, Gale Group, IngentaConnect, ScienceDirect, Swets Information Services).
Indexed: ASCA, ASFA, BIOBASE, BIOSIS Prev, BiolAb, ChemAb, CurCont, ExcerpMed, ForAb, GEOBASE, HortAb, I&DA, MBA, OrnHort, PBA, PGegResA, RPP, RRTA, RefZh, S&F, WeedAb.
—BLDSC (3490.155370), CASDDS, CISTI, IDS, IE, Infotrieve, ingenta, Linda Hall. **CCC.**
Published by: Museum National d'Histoire Naturelle, 57 Rue Cuvier, Paris, 75231 Cedex 05, France. TEL 33-1-40793777, http://www.mnhn.fr. Circ: 450.

579.5 FRA ISSN 0181-1584
QK600 CODEN: CRMYD6
➤ **CRYPTOGAMIE MYCOLOGIE.** Text and summaries in English, French, Spanish. 1934. q. EUR 146.05 in Europe to institutions; USD 172 in the Americas to institutions; EUR 316 combined subscription in Europe to institutions with Algologie & Bryologie; USD 350 combined subscription in the Americas to institutions with Algologie & Bryologie (effective 2001). bk.rev. bibl. index. back issues avail. **Document type:** *Academic/Scholarly.* **Description:** Publishes results and synthesis papers concerning the biology of fungi.
Supersedes (in 1980): Revue de Mycologie (0484-8578)
Related titles: Online - full text ed.: (from EBSCO Publishing, Gale Group, IngentaConnect, ScienceDirect, Swets Information Services).
Indexed: ASCA, ASFA, BIOBASE, BIOSIS Prev, BioCN&I, BiolAb, CurCont, FPA, ForAb, HerbAb, HortAb, IndVet, MBA, MaizeAb, MycolAb, PBA, PGegResA, PHN&I, RA&MP, RM&VM, RPP, RefZh, S&F, SeedAb, TOSA.
—BLDSC (3490.155450), CASDDS, CISTI, IDS, IE, Infotrieve, ingenta, Linda Hall. **CCC.**
Published by: Museum National d'Histoire Naturelle, 57 Rue Cuvier, Paris, 75231 Cedex 05, France. TEL 33-1-40793777, http://www.mnhn.fr. Circ: 450.

571.92 ESP ISSN 0213-4128
CUADERNOS DE FITOPATOLOGIA; revista de fitopatologia terapeutica. Text in Spanish. 1984. q. EUR 33.28 domestic; EUR 57 foreign (effective 2005). **Description:** Publishes articles dedicated to the study of the diseases of agricultural crops.
Indexed: DBA, IECT.
—CINDOC.
Published by: Ediciones y Promociones L.A.V., C/Jose Maria de Haro 51, Valencia, 46022, Spain. TEL 34-96-3720261, FAX 34-96-3710516, http://www.edicioneslav.es/fitopatologia/200584/index.htm. Ed. Francisco Salvador Planes Planes.

579.5 ESP ISSN 1132-0605
CUADERNOS DE TRABAJO DE FLORA MICOLOGICA IBERICA. Text in Spanish. 1990. irreg. price varies.
Indexed: ForAb, IECT, RPP, S&F.
—CINDOC.
Published by: Real Jardin Botanico de Madrid, Plaza Murillo, 2, Madrid, 28014, Spain. **Co-sponsor:** Consejo Superior de Investigaciones Cientificas.

580 615 CUB ISSN 0138-8037
CUBA. CENTRO DE INFORMACION Y DOCUMENTACION AGROPECUARIO. BOLETIN DE RESENAS. SERIE: PLANTAS MEDICINALES. Abstracts in English. 1983. irreg. CUP 1; or exchange basis. charts; stat.
Formerly: Cuba. Centro de Informacion y Divulgacion Agropecuario. Boletin de Resenas. Serie: Plantas Medicinales
Indexed: Agrind.
—CISTI.
Published by: Centro de Informacion y Documentacion Agropecuario, Gaveta Postal 4149, Havana, 4, Cuba. TEL 301672, TELEX 051-1007. **Dist. by:** Ediciones Cubanas, Obispo No. 461, Apdo. 605, Havana, Cuba.

580 AUS ISSN 0727-9620
QK445 CODEN: CUNNEY
CUNNINGHAMIA. Text in English. 1981. 2/yr. AUD 70 to individuals; AUD 100 to institutions; AUD 105 foreign (effective 2000). **Document type:** *Academic/Scholarly.* **Description:** Provides papers on plant ecological research in eastern Australia including vegetation maps highlighting management and conservation issues.
Indexed: BIOSIS Prev, BiolAb.
Published by: National Herbarium of New South Wales, Royal Botanic Gardens Sydney, Mrs Macquaries Rd, Sydney, NSW 2000, Australia. TEL 61-2-92318100, FAX 61-2-92412797, doug_benson@rbgsyd.gov.au, http://www.rbgsyd.gov.au. Ed. Doug Benson. R&P Lynne Munnich. Circ: 1,000.

CURRENT ADVANCES IN PLANT SCIENCE. see *BIOLOGY—Abstracting, Bibliographies, Statistics*

571.2 GBR ISSN 1369-5266
QK1 CODEN: COPBFZ
➤ **CURRENT OPINION IN PLANT BIOLOGY.** Text in English. 1998. 6/yr. EUR 270 in Europe to individuals; JPY 32,800 in Japan to individuals; USD 293 elsewhere to individuals; EUR 1,232 in Europe to institutions; JPY 170,900 in Japan to institutions; USD 1,378 elsewhere to institutions (effective 2006). adv. **Document type:** *Academic/Scholarly.* **Description:** Covers the latest research in the field of plant biology.
Related titles: Online - full text ed.: USD 227 in North America to individuals; USD 247 in North America to individuals with print ed; GBP 137 elsewhere to individuals; GBP 150 elsewhere to individuals with print ed; USD 822 in North America to institutions includes print ed; USD 500 elsewhere to institutions includes print ed (effective 1999 & 2000) (from EBSCO Publishing, Gale Group, IngentaConnect, ScienceDirect, Swets Information Services).
Indexed: AEBA, AIDS&CR, ASFA, AgBio, Agr, ApEcolAb, B&BAb, BIOBASE, BIOSIS Prev, BioCN&I, CPA, CurCont, ESPM, FCA, FPA, FS&TA, ForAb, GardL, GenetAb, HGA, HerbAb, HortAb, ISR, IndMed, MBA, MEDLINE, MaizeAb, NemAb, NucAcAb, OrnHort, PBA, PGegResA, PGrRegA, PHN&I, PotatoAb, ProtozoAb, RA&MP, RPP, RevApplEntom, RiceAb, S&F, SCI, SIA, SeedAb, SoyAb, TriticAb, WeedAb.
—BLDSC (3500.776950), CASDDS, CISTI, IDS, IE, Infotrieve, ingenta. **CCC.**
Published by: Elsevier Ltd., Current Opinion Journals (Subsidiary of: Elsevier Science & Technology), 84 Theobald's Rd., London, WC1X 8RR, United Kingdom. TEL 44-20-7611-4000, FAX 44-20-7611-4001, 44-20-7611-4468, http://www.elsevier.com/locate/pbi, http://www.current-opinion.com. Eds. D. Weigel, J. Dangl, Sharon Whitehead TEL 44-20-7611-4147.

571.2 IND ISSN 0972-4796
CURRENT TOPICS IN PHYTOCHEMISTRY. Text in English. 1997. a.
Indexed: AEBA, B&BAb, ESPM.
—BLDSC (3504.898200).
Published by: Research Trends, T.C. 17/250(3), Chadiyara Rd, Poojapura, Trivandrum, Kerala 695 012, India.

580 333.78 GBR ISSN 1355-4905
QK1
➤ **CURTIS'S BOTANICAL MAGAZINE.** Text in English. 1787. q. GBP 49, EUR 74 combined subscription in Europe to individuals print & online eds.; USD 91 combined subscription in the Americas to individuals & Caribbean (print & online eds.); GBP 54 combined subscription elsewhere to individuals print & online eds.; GBP 266 combined subscription in Europe to institutions print & online eds.; USD 492 combined subscription in the Americas to institutions & Caribbean (print & online eds.); GBP 293 combined subscription elsewhere to institutions print & online eds. (effective 2006). adv. bk.rev. illus. back issues avail. **Document type:** *Magazine, Academic/Scholarly.* **Description:** 24 botanically precise plant portraits with such topics as history, conservation and economic uses of a world-wide range of plants.
Former titles: Kew Magazine (0265-3842); (until 1984): Curtis's Botanical Magazine (0011-4073); (until 1800): Botanical Magazine (0951-2446)
Related titles: Microfiche ed.: (from IDC); Microform ed.; Online - full text ed.: ISSN 1467-8748. GBP 253 in Europe to institutions; USD 467 in the Americas to institutions & Caribbean; GBP 278 elsewhere to institutions (effective 2006) (from Blackwell Synergy, EBSCO Publishing, Gale Group, IngentaConnect, O C L C Online Computer Library Center, Inc., Swets Information Services).
Indexed: Agr, AgrForAb, BIOSIS Prev, BiolAb, CPA, FPA, ForAb, GardL, HerbAb, HortAb, OrnHort, PBA, PGegResA, ProtozoAb, RA&MP, RPP, S&F, TDB, WeedAb.
—BLDSC (3506.000000), CISTI, IE, Infotrieve, Linda Hall. **CCC.**
Published by: (Royal Botanic Gardens, Kew), Blackwell Publishing Ltd., 9600 Garsington Rd, Oxford, OX4 2ZG, United Kingdom. TEL 44-1865-776868, FAX 44-1865-714591, customerservices@oxon.blackwellpublishing.com, http://www.blackwellpublishing.com/journals/CURT. Ed. Martyn Rix. Circ: 1,400. **Co-sponsor:** Bentham-Moxon Trust.

580 635 USA
CYCAD SOCIETY NEWSLETTER. Text in English. 1976. q. USD 20 (effective 2001). back issues avail.
Published by: Cycad Society, University of Louisiana at Lafayette, Lafayette, LA 70504. TEL 337-482-5705. Ed. Garrie P Landry. Circ: 450.

580 GBR ISSN 0775-1400
CYPERACEAE NEWSLETTER. Text in English. 1987. a.
Published by: Royal Botanic Gardens, Kew, Richmond, Surrey TW9 3AB, United Kingdom. TEL 44-20-83325000, FAX 44-20-83325197, info@rbgkew.org.uk, http://www.rbgkew.org.uk/index.html. Eds. D A Simpson, P Goetghebeur.

CZECH JOURNAL OF GENETICS AND PLANT BREEDING. see *BIOLOGY—Genetics*

579.5 CZE ISSN 1211-0981
QK600
➤ **CZECH MYCOLOGY.** Text in English. 1947. q. EUR 83, USD 86 (effective 2005). bk.rev. abstr.; charts; illus. index. **Document type:** *Journal, Academic/Scholarly.* **Description:** Devoted to all aspects of mycology, especially to taxonomy (systematics); physiology, the genetics of fungi, mycological toxicology, phytopathology, etc.
Formerly (until 1994): Ceska Mykologie (0009-0476)
Indexed: BIOSIS Prev, BioCN&I, BiolAb, CPA, ChemAb, ExcerpMed, FCA, FPA, FS&TA, ForAb, HortAb, IndVet, MaizeAb, NemAb, NutrAb, PBA, PGegResA, PHN&I, RM&VM, RPP, S&F, SeedAb, TriticAb, VetBull.
—BLDSC (3507.371600), CISTI, IE, ingenta.
Published by: Ceska Vedecka Spolecnost pro Mykologii, PO Box 106, Prague, 11121, Czech Republic. TEL 420-2-24497259, jan.holec@nm.cz, http://www.natur.cuni.cz/cvsm/czmycang.htm. Ed. Zdenek Pouzar. Circ: 850.

580 DNK ISSN 0416-6906
DANSK DENDROLOGISK AARSSKRIFT. Text in Danish, Norwegian, Swedish; Summaries in English, French, German. 1949. a. price varies. bk.rev.
Indexed: AgrForAb, BiolAb, FPA, ForAb, HortAb, OrnHort, PBA, PGegResA, RPP.
Published by: Dansk Dendrologisk Forening, c/o Arboretet, Kirkegaardsvej 3 A, Hoersholm, 2970, Denmark.

DANTHONIA. see *CONSERVATION*

580 SWE ISSN 1101-5527
➤ **DAPHNE**; tidskrift foer botanik i Soedermanland och Uppland. Text in Swedish. 1990. s-a. SEK 90 to members (effective 2001). **Document type:** *Journal, Academic/Scholarly.* **Description:** Publishes local botanical reports for botanists in the Stockholm area.
Indexed: WeedAb.
Published by: Stockholms Universitet, Botaniska Institutionen, Stockholm, 10691, Sweden. http://www.botan.su.se. Ed. Mora Aronsson. Circ: 500.

580 ARG ISSN 0011-6793
QK1 CODEN: DARWAG
➤ **DARWINIANA.** Text in English, Spanish; Summaries in English. 1922. s-a. USD 80 (effective 2003). bk.rev. bibl.; illus.; charts; maps. 290 p./no.; back issues avail. **Document type:** *Journal, Academic/Scholarly.* **Description:** Botanical research on systematics, anatomy, cytogenetics, embryology, evolution, palynology, ecology, plant geography and floristics.
Indexed: ASFA, BIOSIS Prev, BiolAb, ChemAb, ESPM, ExcerpMed, FCA, FPA, ForAb, GEOBASE, HerbAb, PBA, RPP, RefZh, VITIS.
—CISTI, KNAW, Linda Hall.
Published by: (Academia Nacional de Ciencias Exactas, Fisicas y Naturales), Instituto de Botanica Darwinion, Labarden 200, Casilla de Correo 22, San Isidro, Buenos Aires BHYD1642, Argentina. TEL 54-11-47428534, FAX 54-11-47474748, fzuloaga@darwin.edu.ar, postmaster@darwin.edu.ar, http://www.darwin.edu.ar/Darwiniana/indice.htm. Ed., R&P Fernando Zuloaga. Circ: 600. **Co-sponsor:** Consejo Nacional de Investigaciones Cientificas y Tecnicas.

582 634.9 POL ISSN 1641-1307
QK1 CODEN: DENDC3
➤ **DENDROBIOLOGY.** Text in English. 1955. s-a. PLZ 30 per issue domestic; USD 30 per issue foreign (effective 2003). adv. bibl.; charts; illus.; abstr. reprints avail. **Document type:** *Journal, Academic/Scholarly.*
Former titles (until 2000): Arboretum Kornickie (0066-5878); Kornik, Poland. Instytut Dendrologii i Pomologii. Prace
Related titles: Online - full text ed.: free (effective 2005).
Indexed: AgBio, AgrAg, AgrLib, BioCN&I, BiolAb, CIN, CPA, ChemAb, ChemTitl, FPA, ForAb, HortAb, NemAb, OrnHort, PBA, PGegResA, PGrRegA, PoultAb, RPP, RefZh, S&F, SeedAb.
—CASDDS, CISTI.
Published by: Polska Akademia Nauk, Instytut Dendrologii/Polish Academy of Sciences, Institute of Dendrology, Ul Parkowa 5, Kornik, 62035, Poland. TEL 48-61-8170033, FAX 48-61-8170166, idkornik@rose.man.poznan.pl, http://www.idpan.poznan.pl/dendrobiology. Ed., Adv. contact Piotr Karolewski. Circ: 540. **Co-sponsor:** Arboretum Kornickie.

634.9 DEU ISSN 1125-7865
➤ **DENDROCHRONOLOGIA.** Text in English. 1983. 4/yr. EUR 116 in Europe to individuals; JPY 14,500 in Japan to individuals; USD 113 elsewhere to individuals; EUR 163 in Europe to institutions; JPY 23,300 in Japan to institutions; USD 198 elsewhere to institutions (effective 2006). adv. **Document type:** *Journal, Academic/Scholarly.* **Description:** Contains research and information dealing with the growth rings of trees and the application of tree-ring studies to problems in a wide variety of fields including, but not limited to, archaeology, geology, ecology, hydrology, climatology, forestry, and botany.
Related titles: Online - full text ed.: (from EBSCO Publishing, Gale Group, IngentaConnect, O C L C Online Computer Library Center, Inc., ScienceDirect, Swets Information Services).
Indexed: Agr, BiolAb, CPA, FPA, ForAb, HerbAb, HortAb, I&DA, M&GPA, OrnHort, PBA, PGegResA, S&F, WAE&RSA.
Published by: (Istituto Italiano di Dendrocronologia ITA), Elsevier GmbH, Urban & Fischer Verlag (Subsidiary of: Elsevier Science & Technology), Loebdergraben 14a, Jena, 07743, Germany. TEL 49-3641-626462, FAX 49-3641-626432, journals@urbanfischer.de, http://www.elsevier.com/locate/dendro, http://www.urbanfischer.de. Ed. Paolo Cherubini. adv.: B&W page EUR 400, color page EUR 1,345; trim 210 x 280. Circ: 400 (paid and controlled). **Non-German speaking countries subscr. to:** Nature Publishing Group.

B

631.5709489 DNK
DENMARK. MINISTERIET FOR FOEDEVARER, LANDBRUG OG FISKERI. DANMARKS JORDBRUGSFORSKNING. MEDDELELSER FRA SORTSAFPROEVNINGEN/DANISH GAZETTE FOR PLANT VARIETIES; information om plantenyhedsbeskyttelse og sortslisteoptagelse. Text in Danish, English, French, German. 1982. 5/yr. free. adv. **Document type:** *Bulletin, Government.* **Description:** Information on variety listing and plant breeders' rights, pertinent legislation and news of the EEC and the International Union for Protection of Plant Varieties.
Formerly: Bekendtgoerelser fra Plantenyhedsnaevnet
Published by: Ministeriet for Foedevarer, Landbrug og Fiskeri, Danmarks Jordbrugsforskning, Afdeling for Sortsafproevning/Ministry of Food, Agriculture, and Fisheries. Danish Institute of Agricultural Sciences. Department of Variety Testing, Tystofte, Teglvaerksvej 10, PO Box 7, Skaelskor, 4230, Denmark. TEL 45 58 16 06 00, FAX 45-58-16-06-06. Ed., R&P Gerhard Deneken. Adv. contact Randi Jensen. Circ: 260.

DEP. PLANTENGENETICA EN-VEREDELING. ACTIVITEITENVERSLAG/BELGIUM. AGRICULTURE RESEARCH CENTER. DEPARTMENT OF PLANT GENETICS AND BREEDING. REPORT. see *GARDENING AND HORTICULTURE*

580 DEU
➤ **DESCRIPTIONS OF ECTOMYCORRHIZAE.** Text in English. irreg. looseleaf. **Document type:** *Journal, Academic/Scholarly.*
Indexed: BIOSIS Prev, BiolAb.
Published by: Einhorn Verlag GmbH, Sebaldstr 9-11, Schwaebisch Gmuend, 73525, Germany. TEL 49-7171-927800, FAX 49-7171-37122, einhorn-verlag@t-online.de. Ed. Reinhard Agerer.

580 635 USA ISSN 0734-3434
QK938.D4
➤ **DESERT PLANTS.** Text in English. 1979. s-a. USD 20 domestic to individuals; USD 25 foreign to individuals; USD 50 to institutions (effective 2005). bk.rev. illus. available on request. 32 p./no. 2 cols./p.; back issues avail.; reprints avail. **Document type:** *Journal, Academic/Scholarly.* **Description:** Discusses information on the subject of plants indigenous or adapted to arid and sub-arid regions.
Indexed: AbAn, Agr, AgrForAb, ForAb, GardL, HortAb, SFA, SeedAb, TriticAb, WildRev.
—BLDSC (3559.650000), CISTI, IE, ingenta, Linda Hall.
Address: 2120 E Allen Rd, Tucson, AZ 85719. TEL 520-318-7046, FAX 520-318-7272, mnorem@ag.arizona.edu. Ed., R&P, Adv. contact Margaret Norem. Circ: 800 (paid).

➤ **DEVELOPMENTS IN PLANT AND SOIL SCIENCES.** see *AGRICULTURE—Crop Production And Soil*

581.3 NLD ISSN 0168-7972
CODEN: DPGBD6
➤ **DEVELOPMENTS IN PLANT GENETICS AND BREEDING.** Text in English. 1983. irreg., latest vol.6, 2000. price varies. back issues avail. **Document type:** *Monographic series, Academic/Scholarly.* **Description:** Reviews new research in botanical genetics and plant breeding.
Indexed: BIOSIS Prev.
—BLDSC (3579.086130), CASDDS, CISTI.
Published by: Elsevier BV (Subsidiary of: Elsevier Science & Technology), Radarweg 29, Amsterdam, 1043 NX, Netherlands. TEL 31-20-4853911, FAX 31-20-4852457, nlinfo-f@elsevier.nl, http://www.elsevier.nl.

571.92 NLD ISSN 0929-1318
DEVELOPMENTS IN PLANT PATHOLOGY. Text in English. 1993. irreg., latest vol.16, 2004. price varies. **Document type:** *Monographic series, Academic/Scholarly.*
Indexed: BIOSIS Prev, CIN, ChemAb, ChemTitl, ZooRec.
—BLDSC (3579.086150), IE, ingenta.
Published by: (British Society for Plant Pathology GBR), Springer-Verlag Dordrecht (Subsidiary of: Springer Science+Business Media), Van Godewijckstraat 30, Dordrecht, 3311 GX, Netherlands. TEL 31-78-6576050, FAX 31-78-6576474, http://www.springeronline.com.

580 JPN ISSN 0911-9310
DIATOM. Text in English, Japanese. 1985. a.
Published by: Nihon Keiso Gakkai/Japanese Society of Diatomology, 8-9-813 Hon-cho 3-chome, Koganei-shi, Tokyo-to 184-0004, Japan.

579.85 GBR ISSN 0269-249X
QK569.D54 CODEN: DIRSEU
➤ **DIATOM RESEARCH.** Text in English; Text occasionally in French, German. 2/yr. USD 225.10 domestic; USD 233.20 foreign (effective 2005). **Document type:** *Journal, Academic/Scholarly.*
Formerly (until 1984): Bacillaria (0170-0189)
Indexed: BIOSIS Prev, BiolAb, CurCont, GEOBASE.
—BLDSC (3580.235300), IE, ingenta, Linda Hall. **CCC.**
Published by: Biopress Ltd., 17 Wimbledon Rd, Bristol, BS6 7YA, United Kingdom. Biopress@blueyonder.co.uk. Eds. Dr. Jeffrey R Johansen, Dr. Karen K Serieyssol.

580.96881 NAM ISSN 0012-3013
QK413
DINTERIA; contributions to the flora and vegetation of Namibia. Text and summaries in Afrikaans, English, German. 1968. irreg., latest vol.25, 1997. price varies. illus. index. back issues avail. **Document type:** *Academic/Scholarly.*
Indexed: AgrForAb, CPA, FPA, ForAb, HerbAb, HortAb, I&DA, ISAP, PGegResA, RDA, S&F, WAE&RSA, WeedAb.
—BLDSC (3588.550000).
Published by: Namibia Scientific Society, PO Box 67, Windhoek, Namibia. TEL 264-61-225372. Ed. Ben Strohbach. Circ: 1,000.

580 DEU ISSN 0070-6728
QK1 CODEN: DIBOD5
DISSERTATIONES BOTANICAE. Text in German, English. 1967. irreg., latest vol.393, 2004. price varies. **Document type:** *Monographic series, Academic/Scholarly.*
Indexed: BIOSIS Prev, BiolAb, HerbAb, VITIS.
—CISTI.
Published by: J. Cramer in der Gebrueder Borntraeger Verlagsbuchhandlung, Johannesstr 3A, Stuttgart, 70176, Germany. TEL 49-711-3514560, FAX 49-711-35145699, mail@borntraeger-cramer.de, http://www.schweizerbart.de/j/dissertationes-botanicae.

571.92 GBR ISSN 0012-396X
DISTRIBUTION MAPS OF PLANT DISEASES. Text in English. 1942. s-a. looseleaf. USD 875 combined subscription in the Americas to institutions except Canada; print & online eds.; GBP 500 combined subscription elsewhere to institutions print & online eds. (effective 2006). charts; maps. reprints avail. **Document type:** *Academic/Scholarly.* **Description:** Comprises a series of maps giving the world distribution of a plant pathogen, incorporating information from the literature and records of the International Mycological Institute Biosystematic Reference Collection.
Related titles: Online - full text ed.: 2006.
Indexed: FPA, ForAb, PotatoAb, ProtozoAb, RPP, RevApplEntom, SIA, TriticAb.
—BLDSC (3604.000000), CISTI.
Published by: CABI Publishing (Subsidiary of: CAB International), CAB International, Wallingford, Oxfordshire OX10 8DE, United Kingdom. TEL 44-1491-832111, FAX 44-1491-833508, cabi@cabi.org, http://www.cabi-publishing.org/. **Subscr. addr. in N America:** CABI Publishing North America, 875 Massachusetts Ave, 7th Fl, Cambridge, MA 02139. TEL 617-395-4056, 800-528-4841, FAX 617-354-6875, cabi-nao@cabi.org.

580 BEL ISSN 0779-1100
DISTRIBUTIONES PLANTARUM AFRICANARUM. Text in French. 1969. irreg., latest 1999. looseleaf. price varies. maps. 30 p./no.; back issues avail. **Document type:** *Monographic series, Academic/Scholarly.*
—Linda Hall.
Published by: Jardin Botanique National de Belgique/Nationale Plantentuin van Belgie, Domaine de Bouchout, Nieuwelaan 38, Meise, 1860, Belgium. TEL 32-2-2693905, http://www.br.fgov.be. Ed. P Bamps. Adv. contact Katrien Clarysse.

580 DOM
DOMINICAN REPUBLIC. CENTRO NACIONAL DE INVESTIGACIONES AGROPECUARIAS. LABORATORIO DE SANIDAD VEGETAL. SANIDAD VEGETAL✶. Text in Spanish. irreg. (5-6/yr.). free.
Media: Duplicated (not offset).
Published by: Centro Nacional de Investigaciones Agropecuarias, Laboratorio de Sanidad Vegetal, San Cristobal, Dominican Republic. Circ: (controlled).

580 USA ISSN 1064-4032
QK1
DOUGLASIA. Text in English. 1976. q. USD 50 membership (effective 2001). bk.rev. **Document type:** *Newsletter, Academic/Scholarly.*
Published by: Washington Native Plant Society, 6310 NE 74th St., Ste. 215E, Seattle, WA 98115-8171. TEL 206-760-8022. Ed. Richard Robohm. R&P Catherine Hovanic TEL 206-527-3210. Adv. contact Richard Easterly.

580 IND ISSN 0970-2695
DR. H.S. GOUR VISHWAVIDYALAYA, SAGAR BOTANICAL SOCIETY. BULLETIN. Text in English. 1948. s-a. INR 30 to individuals; INR 60 to institutions. adv. bk.rev. **Document type:** *Bulletin.*
Formerly (until 1983): University of Sagar. Botanical Society. Bulletin (0376-1908)
Indexed: BiolAb.
—CISTI.
Published by: Dr. H.S. Gour Vishwavidyalaya Sagar Botanical Society, Department of Botany, Gour Nagar, Sagar, Madhya Pradesh 470 003, India. TEL 91-7582-25452, FAX 91-7582-23236. Ed. Dr. T R Sahu. Circ: 300.

577 BIH ISSN 0352-0781
DRUSTVO EKOLOGA BOSNE I HERCEGOVINE. BILTEN. SERIJA A - EKOLOSKE MONOGRAFIJE✶. Text in Serbo-Croatian; Summaries in English, German, Russian. 1982. biennial.
Published by: (Drustvo Ekologa Bosne i Hercegovine), Oslobodjenje, Dzemala Bijedica 185, Sarajevo, 71000, Bosnia Herzegovina. TEL 071 659-377. Ed. Radomir Lakusic. **Subscr. to:** Drustvo Ekologa BiH, Vojvode R Putnika 43-a, Sarajevo 71000, Bosnia Herzegovina.

577 BIH ISSN 0352-0811
DRUSTVO EKOLOGA BOSNE I HERCEGOVINE. BILTEN. SERIJA B - NAUCNI SKUPOVI I SAVJETOVANJA✶. Text in Serbo-Croatian; Summaries in English, German, Russian. 1982. biennial. BAD 12,000, USD 20.
Published by: (Drustvo Ekologa Bosne i Hercegovine), Oslobodjenje, Dzemala Bijedica 185, Sarajevo, 71000, Bosnia Herzegovina. TEL 071 659-377. Ed. Radomir Lakusic. Circ: 500. **Subscr. to:** Drustvo Ekologa BiH, Vojvode R Putnika 43-a, Sarajevo 71000, Bosnia Herzegovina.

580 BEL ISSN 0251-1134
➤ **DUMORTIERA.** Text in French, Dutch. 1975. 3/yr. EUR 10 domestic; EUR 11 foreign (effective 2003). charts; illus.; maps. 60 p./no.; back issues avail. **Document type:** *Bulletin, Academic/Scholarly.*
Indexed: RefZh.
Published by: Jardin Botanique National de Belgique/Nationale Plantentuin van Belgie, Domaine de Bouchout, Nieuwelaan 38, Meise, 1860, Belgium. TEL 32-2-2693905, http://www.br.fgov.be. Adv. contact Katrien Clarysse.

580 USA ISSN 0013-0001
SB1 CODEN: ECBOA5
➤ **ECONOMIC BOTANY**; devoted to applied botany and plant utilization. Text in English. 1947. q. USD 106 domestic to individuals; USD 118 foreign to individuals; USD 122 domestic to institutions; USD 134 foreign to institutions (effective 2005). adv. bk.rev. abstr.; bibl.; illus. Index. back issues avail.; reprints avail. **Document type:** *Journal, Academic/Scholarly.* **Description:** Presents original research on the uses of plants by people.
Related titles: Microform ed.: (from PMC, PQC); Online - full text ed.: (from BioOne, C S A, H.W. Wilson, O C L C Online Computer Library Center, Inc.).
Indexed: A&ATA, AEA, ASCA, ASFA, AbHyg, AgBio, Agr, AgrForAb, AnBrAb, ArtHuCI, B&AI, BAS, BIOBASE, BIOSIS Prev, BibAg, BioDAb, BiolAb, BiolDig, CIN, CPA, ChemAb, ChemTitl, CurCont, DBA, DSA, EIA, EPB, ESPM, EnvAb, ExcerpMed, FCA, FPA, FS&TA, ForAb, GardL, HerbAb, HortAb, IABS, ISR, IndVet, MaizeAb, NutrAb, OrnHort, PBA, PGegResA, PHN&I, PlantSci, PollutAb, PotatoAb, ProtozoAb, RA&MP, RDA, RPP, RRTA, RefZh, RiceAb, S&F, SCI, SIA, SPPI, SSCI, SWRA, SeedAb, SoyAb, TDB, TriticAb, VITIS, VetBull, WAE&RSA, WeedAb.
—BLDSC (3651.700000), CASDDS, CISTI, IDS, IE, Infotrieve, ingenta, Linda Hall. **CCC.**
Published by: (Society for Economic Botany), New York Botanical Garden Press, 200th Street & Kazimiroff Blvd, Bronx, NY 10458-5126. TEL 718-817-8918, FAX 718-817-8842, nybgpress@nybg.org, http://sciweb.nybg.org/science2/EconomicBotany.asp, http://www.nybg.org. Ed. Donald Ugent. R&P Carole J Young. Circ: 2,000.

580 577.27 DEU ISSN 0949-3026
➤ **ECOTROPICA.** Text in English. 1995. s-a. EUR 60 membership; EUR 30 to students; EUR 80 to institutional members (effective 2003). **Document type:** *Journal, Academic/Scholarly.* **Description:** Contributes to a broadening of the knowledge of tropical ecosystems by analyzing their structures and processes at every ecologically relevant level of organization.
Indexed: AgrForAb, BIOSIS Prev, BioCN&I, BiolAb, CPA, FPA, ForAb, HerbAb, HortAb, I&DA, IndVet, NutrAb, OrnHort, PBA, PGegResA, PoultAb, RA&MP, RDA, RRTA, S&F, SeedAb, WAE&RSA, WeedAb, ZooRec.
—BLDSC (3659.555400), CISTI.
Published by: Society for Tropical Ecology/Gesellschaft fuer Tropenoekologie, c/o Thomas Zuchner, Auf der Weckenbitze, Hennef, 53773, Germany. TEL 49-2248-446966, kl.schuchmann.zfmk@uni-bonn.de, http://www.gtoe.de. Ed. Karl-L. Schuchmann.

580 DEU
➤ **ECOTROPICAL MONOGRAPHS.** Text in English. irreg. EUR 55 per issue. **Document type:** *Monographic series, Academic/Scholarly.* **Description:** Contains original research in the field of tropical ecology.
Indexed: BIOSIS Prev, BiolAb, ZooRec.
Published by: Society for Tropical Ecology/Gesellschaft fuer Tropenoekologie, c/o Thomas Zuchner, Auf der Weckenbitze, Hennef, 53773, Germany. TEL 49-2248-446966, kl.schuchmann.zfmk@uni-bonn.de, http://www.gtoe.de. Ed. Karl-L. Schuchmann.

580 GBR ISSN 0960-4286
QK1 CODEN: NRYBAD
EDINBURGH JOURNAL OF BOTANY; an international journal of plant systematics and biodiversity. Text in English. 1900. 3/yr. USD 245 in North America to institutions; GBP 148 elsewhere to institutions; USD 264 combined subscription in North America to institutions print & online eds.; GBP 162 combined subscription elsewhere to institutions print & online eds. (effective 2006). adv. bk.rev. illus. reprint service avail. from PQC. **Document type:** *Journal, Academic/Scholarly.* **Description:** Covers plant systematics and related areas of biodiversity, conservation, and phytogeography in southwest Asia and the Himalayas, as well as elsewhere throughout the world.
Formerly (until 1990): Royal Botanic Garden, Edinburgh. Notes (0080-4274)
Related titles: Online - full text ed.: ISSN 1474-0036. USD 230 in North America to institutions; GBP 140 elsewhere to institutions (effective 2006) (from EBSCO Publishing, O C L C Online Computer Library Center, Inc., Swets Information Services).
Indexed: AgBio, Agr, BIOBASE, BIOSIS Prev, BiolAb, FCA, ForAb, HerbAb, HortAb, OrnHort, PBA, PGegResA, RefZh, S&F, TriticAb.
—BLDSC (3660.973000), CISTI, IE, Infotrieve, ingenta. **CCC.**
Published by: Cambridge University Press, The Edinburgh Bldg, Shaftesbury Rd, Cambridge, CB2 2RU, United Kingdom. TEL 44-1223-312393, FAX 44-1223-315052, journals@cambridge.org, http://uk.cambridge.org/journals/EJB/. Ed. Crinan Alexander. R&P Linda Nicol TEL 44-1223-325757. Adv. contact Rebecca Curtis TEL 44-1223-325757. Circ: 550. **Subscr. addr. in N America:** Cambridge University Press, 100 Brook Hill Dr, West Nyack, NY 10994. TEL 845-353-7500, FAX 845-353-4141, journals_subscriptions@cup.org

580 EGY ISSN 0375-9237
QK1 CODEN: EGJBAY
➤ **EGYPTIAN JOURNAL OF BOTANY/AL-MAGALLAT AL-MISRIYYAT LI-ILM AL-NABAT.** Text in English; Summaries in English, Arabic. 1958. s-a. USD 77 (effective 2002). charts; illus. reprint service avail. from IRC. **Document type:** *Journal, Academic/Scholarly.*
Former titles (until 1971): Journal of Botany of the United Arab Republic (0021-9363); (until 1959): Egyptian Journal of Botany
Indexed: AgBio, AgrForAb, BIOSIS Prev, BiolAb, CIN, CPA, ChemAb, ChemTitl, FCA, FaBeAb, ForAb, HerbAb, HortAb, I&DA, NutrAb, OrnHort, PBA, PGegResA, PGrRegA, PotatoAb, RA&MP, RM&VM, RPP, RRTA, RiceAb, S&F, SIA, SeedAb, SoyAb, TDB, TriticAb, WeedAb.
—BLDSC (3664.300000), CASDDS, CISTI, ingenta, Linda Hall.
Published by: (Botanical Society of Egypt, Research Department), National Information and Documentation Centre (NIDOC), Tahrir St., Dokki, Awqaf P.O., Giza, Egypt. TEL 20-2-3371696, FAX 20-2-3371746, http://derp.sti.sci.eg/data/0208.htm. Ed. Dr. Kamal-El-Din Hasan El-Batanouni. Circ: 1,000.

580 EGY ISSN 1110-0230
EGYPTIAN JOURNAL OF PHYTOPATHOLOGY/AL-MAGALLAT AL-MIRIYYAT LI-AMRADH AL-NABAT. Text in English; Summaries in Arabic, English. 1969. s-a. USD 57 (effective 2003). reprint service avail. from IRC. **Document type:** *Journal, Academic/Scholarly.*
Formerly (until 1971): Journal of Phytopathology of the United Arab Republic (0374-8669)
Indexed: BioCN&I, BioDAb, BiolAb, ChemAb, FCA, FS&TA, FaBeAb, HerbAb, HortAb, I&DA, PotatoAb, RPP, SeedAb.
—Linda Hall.
Published by: (Egyptian Phytopathological Society, Research Department), National Information and Documentation Centre (NIDOC), Tahrir St., Dokki, Awqaf P.O., Giza, Egypt. TEL 20-2-3371696, FAX 20-2-3371746, http://derp.sti.sci.eg/data/0130.htm. Ed. Dr. Maher Ragab. Circ: 1,000.

EKOLOGIA/ECOLOGY. see *BIOLOGY*

580 DEU ISSN 0170-4818
➤ **ENGLERA.** Text and summaries in English, German. 1979. irreg. price varies. back issues avail. **Document type:** *Monographic series, Academic/Scholarly.* **Description:** Original papers in the fields of taxonomic and floristic botany.
Indexed: AgBio, CPA, ForAb, GEOBASE, HerbAb, HortAb, PBA, PGegResA, RefZh, SeedAb, WeedAb.
—Linda Hall.
Published by: Botanischer Garten und Botanisches Museum Berlin-Dahlem, Koenigin Luise Str 6-8, Berlin, 14191, Germany. TEL 49-30-83850194, FAX 49-30-83850253, n.kilian@bgbm.org, library@bgbm.org, http://www.bgbm.fu-berlin.de/bgbm/library/publikat/englera.htm. Ed. H W Lack. Circ: 800.

580 NLD ISSN 0098-8472
QK757 CODEN: EEBODM
➤ **ENVIRONMENTAL AND EXPERIMENTAL BOTANY.** Text in English. 1961. 9/yr. EUR 882 in Europe to institutions; JPY 116,800 in Japan to institutions; USD 986 elsewhere to institutions (effective 2006). adv. bk.rev. charts; illus. index. back issues avail. **Document type:** *Journal, Academic/Scholarly.* **Description:** Publishes research papers on the physical and biological mechanisms that relate to the working of plant systems and their interaction with the environment, including radiation botany, cytogenetics, chemical mutagenesis, pollution effects, phytopathology, and topics in the soil sciences pertaining to plant growth.
Formerly (until 1976): Radiation Botany (0033-7560)
Related titles: Microfilm ed.: (from PQC); Online - full text ed.: (from EBSCO Publishing, Gale Group, IngentaConnect, ScienceDirect, Swets Information Services).
Indexed: AEA, ASCA, ASFA, AbHyg, AgBio, Agr, AgrForAb, B&AI, BIOBASE, BIOSIS Prev, BibAg, BioCN&I, BiolAb, CIN, CPA, CTFA, ChemAb, ChemTitl, CurCont, EPB, ESPM, EnvAb, ExcerpMed, FCA, FPA, FS&TA, ForAb, GEOBASE, HerbAb, HortAb, I&DA, IABS, ISR, Inspec, MBA, MEDLINE, MaizeAb, NemAb, NutrAb, OrnHort, PBA, PGegResA, PGrRegA, PHN&I, PlantSci, PollutAb, PotatoAb, ProtozoAb, RA&MP, RPP, RefZh, RevApplEntom, RiceAb, S&F, SCI, SIA, SWRA, SeedAb, SoyAb, TriticAb, WeedAb.
—BLDSC (3791.383000), CASDDS, CISTI, IDS, IE, Infotrieve, ingenta, Linda Hall. **CCC.**
Published by: Elsevier BV (Subsidiary of: Elsevier Science & Technology), Radarweg 29, Amsterdam, 1043 NX, Netherlands. TEL 31-20-4853911, FAX 31-20-4852457, nlinfo-f@elsevier.nl, http://www.elsevier.com/locate/envexpbot, http://www.elsevier.nl. Ed. J C Kader. Circ: 1,200.

580 USA
EPIPHYLLUM BULLETIN. Variant title: E S A Bulletin. Text in English. 1945. q. USD 15 domestic; USD 20 in Canada & Mexico; USD 25 elsewhere (effective 1999). adv. **Document type:** *Newsletter.* **Description:** Contains Epi Society news plus articles of interest to epicacti enthusiasts.
Indexed: TelAb.
Published by: Epiphyllum Society of America, PO Box 92633, Long Beach, CA 90809-2633. TEL 562-438-4554, esa-editor@juno.com, http://www.epiphyllum.org. Ed., Adv. contact Raymond Eden. Circ: 500.

ERLANGER BAUSTEINE ZUR FRAENKISCHEN HEIMATFORSCHUNG. see *HISTORY*

580 VEN ISSN 0252-8274
CODEN: ERNSDF
ERNSTIA. Text mainly in Spanish; Text occasionally in French, Portuguese; Summaries in English, Spanish. 1981. irreg. (approx. 7/yr.). per issue exchange basis. back issues avail.
Indexed: AgrForAb, BIOSIS Prev, BioCN&I, BiolAb, CPA, FCA, FPA, ForAb, HerbAb, HortAb, OrnHort, PBA, PGegResA, PotatoAb, S&F, SeedAb, WeedAb.
Published by: (Instituto de Botanica Agricola, Herbario), Universidad Central de Venezuela, Facultad de Agronomia, Apdo. 4579, Maracay, Aragua 2101, Venezuela. Ed. Baltasar Trujillo. Circ: 200.

ESTACION EXPERIMENTAL DE AULA DEI. ANALES. see *AGRICULTURE—Crop Production And Soil*

580 615 IND ISSN 0971-1252
➤ **ETHNOBOTANY.** Text in English. 1989. a. USD 40 to institutions (effective 2006). adv. bk.rev. back issues avail. **Document type:** *Journal, Academic/Scholarly.* **Description:** Carries original research papers, review articles, short communications on ethnobotany, ethno-medicine, ethno-chemistry, ethno-pharmacology, ethno-taxonomy, ethno-pharmacognosy.
Indexed: AgrForAb, FPA, ForAb, HortAb, OrnHort, PBA, PGegResA, RA&MP, RDA, S&F, TDB, TriticAb, WeedAb.
Published by: (Society of Ethnobotanists), Deep Publications, B-1 / 118, 2nd Fl, Paschim Vihar, New Delhi, Bihar 110 063, India. TEL 91-11-25259514, FAX 91-11-51698399, deep_pub@hotmail.com, http://www.scientificpub.com/bookdetails.php?booktransid=475&bookid=471. Ed. Roma Mitra. Pub., Adv. contact Vipul Jain. R&P Vikas Jain. page INR 1,800, page USD 100; trim 15 x 20. Circ: 600 (paid and controlled).

580 USA ISSN 1547-3465
DU624.65
▼ ➤ **ETHNOBOTANY RESEARCH AND APPLICATIONS**; a journal of plants, people and applied research. Text in English. 2003 (Dec.). q. free (effective 2005). **Document type:** *Journal, Academic/Scholarly.* **Description:** Multi-disciplinary journal devoted to the rapid dissemination of current research.
Media: Online - full content.
Published by: University of Hawaii, Ethnobotany Program, 3190 Maile Way Rm. 101, Honolulu, HI 96822. TEL 808-956-8369, FAX 808-956-3923, botany@hawaii.edu, http://www.ethnobotanyjournal.org, http://www.botany.hawaii.edu/ethnobotany. Ed. Will McClatchey.

579.8 GBR ISSN 0967-0262
QK564 CODEN: EJPHE5
➤ **EUROPEAN JOURNAL OF PHYCOLOGY.** Text in English. 1953. q. (plus one supplement). GBP 299, USD 491 combined subscription to institutions print & online eds. (effective 2006). adv. bk.rev. illus. index. Supplement avail.; back issues avail.; reprint service avail. from PSC. **Document type:** *Journal, Academic/Scholarly.* **Description:** Contains scientific research articles on the study of algae.
Supersedes (in 1993): British Phycological Journal (0007-1617); Which was formerly: British Phycological Bulletin
Related titles: Online - full text ed.: ISSN 1469-4433. GBP 284, USD 466 to institutions (effective 2006) (from EBSCO Publishing, Gale Group, IngentaConnect, O C L C Online Computer Library Center, Inc., Swets Information Services).
Indexed: ASCA, ASFA, B&BAb, BIOBASE, BIOSIS Prev, BiolAb, CurCont, ESPM, FLUIDEX, GEOBASE, IABS, ISR, MBA, OceAb, PBA, RefZh, SCI, ZooRec.
—BLDSC (3829.734500), CISTI, IDS, IE, Infotrieve, ingenta, Linda Hall. **CCC.**
Published by: (British Phycological Society), Taylor & Francis Ltd (Subsidiary of: Taylor & Francis Group), 4 Park Sq, Milton Park, Abingdon, OX14 4RN, United Kingdom. TEL 44-1235-828600, FAX 44-1235-829000, ejp@qub.ac.uk, info@tandf.co.uk, http://www.tandf.co.uk/journals/titles/09670262.asp. Eds. Eileen Cox, Matt Dring. **Subscr. in N. America to:** Taylor & Francis Inc., Customer Services Dept, 325 Chestnut St, 8th Fl, Philadelphia, PA 19106. TEL 215-625-8900, 800-354-1420, FAX 215-625-8914, customerservice@taylorandfrancis.com; **Subscr. to:** Journals Customer Service, Rankine Rd, Basingstoke, Hants RG24 8PR, United Kingdom. TEL 44-1256-813000, FAX 44-1256-330245, enquiry@tandf.co.uk.

B

571.92 NLD ISSN 0929-1873
SB599 CODEN: EPLPEH
➤ **EUROPEAN JOURNAL OF PLANT PATHOLOGY.** Text in English. 1895. m. EUR 1,298, USD 1,348, GBP 855 combined subscription to institutions print & online eds. (effective 2005). adv. bk.rev. abstr.; bibl.; charts; illus. index, cum.index every 25 yrs. reprint service avail. from PSC. **Document type:** *Journal, Academic/Scholarly.* **Description:** Covers the entire field of plant diseases and pests, including mycological and virological topics, entomological, nematological, weed and plant protection problems.
Former titles: Netherlands Journal of Plant Pathology (0028-2944); (until 1962): Tijdschrift over Planteziekte (0926-3454)
Related titles: Microform ed.: (from SWZ); Online - full text ed.: ISSN 1573-8469 (from EBSCO Publishing, Gale Group, IngentaConnect, Kluwer Online, O C L C Online Computer Library Center, Inc., Ovid Technologies, Inc., Springer LINK, Swets Information Services).
Indexed: AIDS&CR, ASCA, ASFA, AbHyg, AgBio, Agr, AgrForAb, B&BAb, BIOBASE, BIOSIS Prev, BibLing, BioCN&I, BiolAb, CIN, CPA, ChemAb, ChemTitl, CurCont, DBA, DSA, ESPM, FCA, FPA, FS&TA, FaBeAb, ForAb, GEOBASE, HerbAb, HortAb, IABS, ISR, IndVet, MBA, MaizeAb, NemAb, NutrAb, OrnHort, PBA, PGegResA, PGrRegA, PHN&I, PN&I, PlantSci, PotatoAb, PoultAb, RA&MP, RM&VM, RPP, RefZh, RevApplEntom, RiceAb, S&F, SCI, SIA, SSCI, SeedAb, SoyAb, TOSA, TriticAb, VITIS, VetBull, VirolAbstr, WeedAb.
—BLDSC (3829.736200), CASDDS, CISTI, IDS, IE, Infotrieve, ingenta, Linda Hall. **CCC.**
Published by: (European Foundation for Plant Pathology), Springer-Verlag Dordrecht (Subsidiary of: Springer Science+Business Media), Van Godewijckstraat 30, Dordrecht, 3311 GX, Netherlands. TEL 31-78-6576050, FAX 31-78-6576474, http://springerlink.metapress.com/openurl.asp?genre=journal&issn=0929-1873, http://www.springeronline.com. Ed. Mike Cooke. Circ: 1,300.

582.14 635.955 ZWE ISSN 0301-441X
QK495.L72
EXCELSA. Text in English. 1971. biennial. USD 20 to individuals; USD 30 to institutions (effective 2000). adv. bk.rev. bibl.; charts; illus. index, cum.index: 1971-1986. back issues avail. **Document type:** *Journal, Academic/Scholarly.* **Description:** Publishes articles on the succulent flora of Zimbabwe, Africa, and the rest of the world.
Published by: Aloe Cactus and Succulent Society of Zimbabwe, PO Box CY 300, Causeway, Harare, Zimbabwe. TEL 263-4-481418, dorichards@zol.co.zw. Ed. Michael J Kimberley. Pub., Adv. contact Michael J Kimberly. R&P Doreen Richards. Circ: 1,000.

582.14 ZWE ISSN 1022-5919
EXCELSA TAXONOMIC SERIES. Text in English. 1978. irreg., latest vol.4. adv. bibl.; charts; illus. index. **Document type:** *Monographic series.*
Published by: Aloe Cactus and Succulent Society of Zimbabwe, PO Box CY 300, Causeway, Harare, Zimbabwe. TEL 263-4-481418, dorichards@zol.co.zw. Ed. Michael J Kimberley. R&P Doreen Richards. Adv. contact Michael J Kimberly. Circ: 1,000.

580 USA ISSN 0071-3392
CODEN: EXBOAG
EXPERIMENTAL BOTANY; AN INTERNATIONAL SERIES OF MONOGRAPHS. Text in English. 1964. irreg., latest vol.19, 1984. reprint service avail. from ISI. **Document type:** *Monographic series.*
Indexed: BiolAb.

—CASDDS, CISTI. **CCC.**
Published by: Academic Press (Subsidiary of: Elsevier Science & Technology), 525 B St, Ste 1900, San Diego, CA 92101-4495. apsubs@acad.com, http://www.academicpress.com. Eds. J Cronshaw, J F Sutcliffe.

580 ITA ISSN 0254-9727
SB599 CODEN: FAOPA2
F A O PLANT PROTECTION BULLETIN (MULTILINGUAL EDITION); a publication of the world reporting service on plant diseases, pests, and their control. (Food and Agriculture Organization of the United Nations) Text in English, French, Spanish. 1952. q. bibl.; charts; illus. index. reprint service avail. from PQC. **Document type:** *Bulletin.* **Description:** Reports on the incidence and spread of plant diseases and pests, quarantine measures and major operations for prevention and control.
Formerly (until 1981): F A O Plant Protection Bulletin (0014-5637)
Related titles: Microfilm ed.: (from PQC).
Indexed: ASFA, B&AI, BioCN&I, BioDAb, BiolAb, ChemAb, CurCont, ExcerpMed, FCA, FPA, ForAb, HerbAb, HortAb, INIS AtomInd, MaizeAb, OrnHort, PBA, PotatoAb, RASB, RPP, RevApplEntom, RiceAb, S&MA, SPPI, SeedAb, SoyAb, TOSA, TriticAb, WeedAb.
—CISTI, Linda Hall.
Published by: Food and Agriculture Organization of the United Nations, Sales and Marketing Group, Viale delle Terme di Caracalla, Rome, 00100, Italy. TEL 39-06-57054350, FAX 39-06-57053360, fi-publications@fao.org, http://www.fao.org. Ed. K Zammarano. Circ: 6,000.

B

FASLNAMAH-I GIYAHAN-I DARUYI/JOURNAL OF MEDICINAL PLANTS. see *ALTERNATIVE MEDICINE*

FAUNE ET FLORE TROPICALES. see *BIOLOGY—Zoology*

580 DEU ISSN 0014-8962
QK45 CODEN: FRZBAW
➤ **FEDDES REPERTORIUM**; Zeitschrift fuer botanische Taxonomie und Geobotanik. Text in English, German. 1905. 4/yr. EUR 858 in Europe; CHF 1,368 in Switzerland & Liechtenstein; USD 1,068 elsewhere; EUR 944 combined subscription in Europe print & online eds.; CHF 1,505 combined subscription in Switzerland & Liechtenstein for print & online eds.; USD 1,175 combined subscription elsewhere print & online eds. (effective 2006). bibl.; charts; illus. index. **Document type:** *Journal, Academic/Scholarly.* **Description:** Covers all groups of the plant world including extant and fossil.
Former titles (until 1965): Feddes Repertorium Specierum Novarum Regni Vegetabilis (0375-121X); (until 1943): Repertorium Specierum Novarum Regni Vegetabilis (0233-1772); (until 1910): Repertorium Novarum Specierum Regni Vegetabilis (0233-1829)
Related titles: Online - full text ed.: ISSN 1522-239X. 2002. EUR 858 in Europe to institutions; CHF 1,368 to institutions in Switzerland & Liechtenstein; USD 1,068 elsewhere to institutions (effective 2006) (from EBSCO Publishing, Swets Information Services, Wiley InterScience).
Indexed: AgBio, AgrForAb, BIOBASE, BIOSIS Prev, BiolAb, CPA, FCA, FPA, ForAb, HerbAb, HortAb, IABS, OrnHort, PBA, PGegResA, PlantSci, PotatoAb, RA&MP, RPP, RRTA, RiceAb, S&F, SIA, SeedAb, TriticAb, WeedAb.
—BLDSC (3901.700000), CISTI, IE, ingenta, Linda Hall. **CCC.**
Published by: Wiley - V C H Verlag GmbH & Co. KGaA (Subsidiary of: John Wiley & Sons, Inc.), Boschstr 12, Weinheim, 69469, Germany. TEL 49-6201-6060, FAX 49-6201-606328, adsales@wiley-vch.de, subservice@wiley-vch.de, http://www3.interscience.wiley.com/cgi-bin/jhome/60500205, http://www.wiley-vch.de. Ed. Guenther Natho. R&P Claudia Rutz. Adv. contact Aenne Anders TEL 49-6201-606552. **Subscr. in the Americas to:** John Wiley & Sons, Inc.. TEL 201-748-6645, FAX 201-748-6088, subinfo@wiley.com; **Subscr. outside of Germany, Austria & Switzerland to:** John Wiley & Sons Ltd., The Atrium, Southern Gate, Chichester, West Sussex PO19 8SQ, United Kingdom. TEL 44-1243-779777, FAX 44-1243-775878.

580 GBR ISSN 0308-0838
QK520 CODEN: FEGADG
➤ **FERN GAZETTE.** Text in English. 1909. s-a. GBP 33 (effective 2002); includes Bulletin and Pteridologist. abstr.; bibl.; charts; illus.; maps. index. 48 p./no. 1 cols./p.; back issues avail. **Document type:** *Journal, Academic/Scholarly.* **Description:** Focuses on the taxonomy, cytology, ecology, chemistry and morphology of pteridophytes.
Formerly: British Fern Gazette (0524-5826)
Related titles: Microfiche ed.: (from IDC).
Indexed: BIOBASE, BIOSIS Prev, BiolAb, PBA, PGegResA, RefZh, WeedAb.
—BLDSC (3907.300000), IE, ingenta, Linda Hall.
Published by: British Pteridological Society, c/o Botany Department, Natural History Museum, Cromwell Rd, London, SW7 5BD, United Kingdom. TEL 44-20-79425756, ferngazette@ebps.org.uk, http://www.ebps.org.uk. Ed. J M Camus. Circ: 650.

➤ **FIDDLEHEAD FORUM.** see *GARDENING AND HORTICULTURE*

579.5 GBR ISSN 1468-1641
QK600
FIELD MYCOLOGY. Text in English. 199?. q. USD 58 in North America to institutions; GBP 36 elsewhere to institutions (effective 2005). **Document type:** *Journal, Academic/Scholarly.* **Description:** Devoted to the identification and study of wild fungi in Britain and Europe.
—**CCC.**
Published by: (British Mycological Society), Elsevier Ltd. (Subsidiary of: Elsevier Science & Technology), The Boulevard, Langford Ln, Kidlington, Oxford, OX5 1GB, United Kingdom. TEL 44-1865-843000, 44-1865-843672, nlinfo-f@elsevier.nl, http://www.elsevier.com. Ed. Geoffrey Kibby.

580 USA ISSN 0015-0746
QK1 CODEN: FLDBAG
➤ **FIELDIANA: BOTANY.** Text in English. 1895. irreg. price varies. bibl.; charts; illus. index. back issues avail.; reprint service avail. from PQC. **Document type:** *Monographic series, Academic/Scholarly.* **Description:** Focuses on systematics, geographic distribution studies and flora, chiefly of Central and South America.
Indexed: ASFA, BIOSIS Prev, BiolAb, ChemAb, FPA, ForAb, HortAb, MBA, OrnHort, PBA, PGegResA, RefZh.
—CISTI, Linda Hall.
Published by: Field Museum, Roosevelt Rd at Lake Shore Dr, Chicago, IL 60605-2496. TEL 312-922-9410, FAX 312-427-7269. Circ: 550.

580 590 FIN ISSN 0356-4509
FINLANDS NATUR. Text in Finnish. 1942. bi-m.
Indexed: RefZh.
Published by: Natur och Miljo r.f., Nylandsgatan 24 A, Helsingfors, 00120, Finland. TEL 358-9-6122290, FAX 358-9-61222910, fn@naturochmiljo.fi, http://www.naturochmiljo.fi/NOM/finnatur.html. Ed. Magnus Ostman. Circ: 5,100.

579.8 615 ARG ISSN 1514-0792
➤ **FITOCIENCIA REVISTA.** Text in Spanish. 1997. q. USD 45. adv. bk.rev. illus. back issues avail. **Document type:** *Monographic series, Academic/Scholarly.* **Description:** Publishes results of research on phytotherapy, phytopharmacology and phytotoxicology obtained with Latin American plant extracts.
Published by: Isis Ediciones s.r.l., Machado 637, Capital Federal, Buenos Aires 1405, Argentina. TEL 54-1-982-0980, FAX 54-1-982-0980. Ed. Angelica Prieto. Circ: 5,000.

571.2 PER ISSN 0430-6155
➤ **FITOPATOLOGIA.** Text in English, Portuguese, Spanish; Summaries in English, Spanish. 1966. q. USD 60 (effective 1999 & 2000). adv. bk.rev. **Document type:** *Academic/Scholarly.* **Description:** Covers plant pathology, with an emphasis on Latin America. Includes research papers, methodology, reviews and notes.
Indexed: ASFA, AgBio, AgrForAb, BIOSIS Prev, BioCN&I, BioDAb, BiolAb, CPA, CTFA, ChemAb, FCA, FPA, ForAb, HerbAb, HortAb, MaizeAb, NemAb, OrnHort, PBA, PGegResA, PHN&I, PotatoAb, RA&MP, RPP, RevApplEntom, RiceAb, S&F, SeedAb, SoyAb, TriticAb, VITIS, WAE&RSA, WeedAb.
—BLDSC (3948.235000), CISTI, IE, ingenta, Linda Hall.
Published by: Asociacion Latinoamericana de Fitopatologia, Apdo Postal 1558, La Molina, Lima 12, Peru. FAX 51-1-3495638, TELEX 25672 PE, e.french@cgiar.org. Ed. Teresa Icochea. R&P, Adv. contact Edward French TEL 650-833-6635. Circ: 700.

571.92 BRA ISSN 0100-4158
CODEN: FIBRD2
➤ **FITOPATOLOGIA BRASILEIRA.** Text in Portuguese; Text occasionally in English, Spanish; Summaries in English, Portuguese. 1976. q. BRL 200, USD 150 to non-members (effective 1999). adv. bk.rev. index. back issues avail. **Document type:** *Academic/Scholarly.* **Description:** Presents original research that contributes to the development of plant pathology.
Related titles: Online - full text ed.: free (effective 2005).
Indexed: AEA, AgBio, AgrForAb, BIOSIS Prev, BioCN&I, BioDAb, BiolAb, CIN, CPA, ChemAb, ChemTitl, ExcerpMed, FCA, ForAb, HerbAb, HortAb, MaizeAb, NemAb, NutrAb, OrnHort, PBA, PGegResA, PGrRegA, PHN&I, PN&I, PotatoAb, RA&MP, RDA, RPP, RevApplEntom, RiceAb, S&F, S&MA, SIA, SeedAb, SoyAb, TOSA, TriticAb, VITIS, WAE&RSA, WeedAb.
—BLDSC (3948.235500), CASDDS, CISTI, IE, ingenta, Linda Hall.
Published by: Sociedade Brasileira Fitopatologia, St Complementares (P Piloto), Caixa Postal 04482, Brasilia, DF 70919-970, Brazil. TEL 55-61-3217454, FAX 55-61-3217454, sbfito@solar.com.br, http://www.scielo.br/fb, http://www.solar.com.br/~fitobras/. Ed. Claudio Costa. Adv. contact Renato Resende. Circ: 1,300.

580 630 VEN ISSN 0798-0035
CODEN: FIVEEU
FITOPATOLOGIA VENEZOLANA; revista de la Sociedad Venezolana de Fitopatologia. Text in English, French, Portuguese, Spanish. 1988. s-a.
Indexed: ASFA, AgrForAb, BIOSIS Prev, BioCN&I, BiolAb, FCA, ForAb, HortAb, MaizeAb, NemAb, OrnHort, PBA, PHN&I, PotatoAb, RA&MP, RDA, RPP, RiceAb, S&F, SeedAb, WAE&RSA, ZooRec.
Published by: Sociedad Venezolana de Fitopatologia, Apdo Postal 2105, Maracay, 2101, Venezuela. rencro@telcel.net.ve, http://www.repav-fpolar.info.ve/fitopato/main.html, http://www.redpav-fpolar.info.ve/. Ed. Claudio Mazzarri.

580 ITA ISSN 1125-9078
➤ **FITOSOCIOLOGIA.** Text in English, French, Italian, Spanish; Summaries in English, French. 1964. bi-m. exchange basis. adv. bk.rev. illus. back issues avail. **Document type:** *Academic/Scholarly.* **Description:** Contains original articles in the field of phytosociology, proceedings of scientific meetings.
Formerly (until 1989): Societa Italiana di Fitosociologia. Notiziario (1120-4605)
Indexed: BiolAb.
Published by: Societa Italiana di Fitosociologia/Italian Society for Phytosociology, c/o Gabriella Buffa, Dept. of Biology, Via Ugo Bassi, 58 b, Padua, PD 35131, Italy. FAX 39-49-8276230, http://www.bio.unipd.it/fitosociologia/. Ed. Doardo Biondi. Adv. contact Gabriella Buffa. Circ: 350.

580 BRA ISSN 0100-4204
CODEN: FTSSDV
➤ **FITOSSANIDADE.** Text in Portuguese. 1974. irreg. free. adv. bibl.; charts; illus. **Document type:** *Academic/Scholarly.*
Indexed: RevApplEntom.
—CASDDS, CISTI.
Published by: Fitossanitaristas do Ceara, Rua Livreiro Edesio, 612-401, D Torres, Fortaleza, CE 60135-620, Brazil. TEL 55-85-2571242, FAX 55-82-4721396, fmsales@ufc.br. Ed. Fernando Montenegro de Sales. Circ: 1,000.

580 HUN ISSN 1219-2155
FITOTERAPIA. Text in Hungarian; Contents page in English, Hungarian. 1995. irreg. HUF 250.
Indexed: NutrAb, ProtozoAb.
Published by: Magyar Fitoterapias Tarsasag, Zrinyi utca 3, Budapest, 1051, Hungary. TEL 1171488. Ed. Zoltan Hanko.

581.634 NLD ISSN 0367-326X
RS164 CODEN: FTRPAE
➤ **FITOTERAPIA.** Text in English, French, Italian; Summaries in English. 1934. 8/yr. EUR 261 in Europe to institutions; JPY 34,500 in Japan to institutions; USD 292 to institutions except Europe and Japan (effective 2006). adv. bk.rev. back issues avail. **Document type:** *Journal, Academic/Scholarly.* **Description:** Publishes articles concerning chemistry, pharmacology and the use of medicinal plants and their derivatives.
Related titles: Microform ed.: (from PQC); Online - full text ed.: (from EBSCO Publishing, Gale Group, IngentaConnect, ScienceDirect, Swets Information Services).
Indexed: AIDS&CR, ASFA, AbHyg, AgBio, AgrForAb, ApicAb, B&BAb, BBCI, BIOBASE, BIOSIS Prev, BioCN&I, BiolAb, CIN, CINAHL, CPA, ChemAb, ChemTitl, DBA, DSA, ESPM, ExcerpMed, FCA, FPA, ForAb, HelmAb, HerbAb, HortAb, I&DA, IDIS, IPA, IndMed, IndVet, MBA, MEDLINE, MSB, MaizeAb, NPU, NemAb, NutrAb, OrnHort, PBA, PGegResA, PGrRegA, PHN&I, PN&I, PotatoAb, ProtozoAb, RA&MP, RDA, RM&VM, RPP, RiceAb, S&F, SIA, SeedAb, TDB, VITIS, VetBull, VirolAbstr, WAE&RSA, WeedAb.
—BLDSC (3948.250000), CASDDS, CISTI, GNLM, IDS, IE, Infotrieve, ingenta, KNAW, Linda Hall. **CCC.**
Published by: (Idena SpA ITA), Elsevier BV (Subsidiary of: Elsevier Science & Technology), Radarweg 29, Amsterdam, 1043 NX, Netherlands. TEL 31-20-4853911, FAX 31-20-4852457, nlinfo-f@elsevier.nl, http://www.elsevier.com/locate/fitote, http://www.elsevier.nl. Ed. F. Pelizzoni. Circ: 4,000 (controlled).

580 RUS ISSN 0015-3303
QK710 CODEN: FZRSAV
FIZIOLOGIYA RASTENII. Text in Russian. 1957. bi-m. USD 314 foreign (effective 2005). bk.rev. charts; illus. index. **Document type:** *Journal, Academic/Scholarly.* **Description:** Covers the full spectrum of plant physiology, bringing together the related aspects of biophysics, biochemistry, cytology, anatomy and genetics.
Related titles: Online - full text ed.; ♦ English Translation: Russian Journal of Plant Physiology. ISSN 1021-4437.
Indexed: AEA, BIOSIS Prev, BiolAb, CPA, ChemAb, FCA, FaBeAb, ForAb, HerbAb, HortAb, I&DA, MaizeAb, OrnHort, PGrRegA, PotatoAb, RefZh, RiceAb, S&MA, SIA, SeedAb, SoyAb, TriticAb, VITIS, WeedAb, ZooRec.
—CASDDS, CISTI, East View, Linda Hall. **CCC.**
Published by: (Rossiiskaya Akademiya Nauk/Russian Academy of Sciences), Izdatel'stvo Nauka, Profsoyuznaya ul 90, Moscow, 117864, Russian Federation. TEL 7-095-3347151, FAX 7-095-4202220, Pavel@ippras.ru, secret@naukaran.ru, http://www.maik.rssi.ru/cgi-bin/list.pl?page=fizrast, http://www.naukaran.ru. Circ: 2,800. **Dist. by:** East View Information Services, 3020 Harbor Ln. N., Minneapolis, MN 55447. TEL 800-477-1005, FAX 800-800-3839, eastview@eastview.com, http://www.eastview.com.

580 DEU ISSN 0367-2530
CODEN: FLRABG

➤ **FLORA.** Text in English. 1818. 6/yr. EUR 203 in Europe to individuals; JPY 27,000 in Japan to individuals; USD 228 to individuals except Europe and Japan; EUR 564 to institutions; EUR 670 in Europe to institutions; JPY 88,900 in Japan to institutions; USD 704 to institutions except Europe and Japan (effective 2006). adv. bk.rev. bibl.; charts; illus. index. cum.index. back issues avail.; reprint service avail. from ISI. **Document type:** *Journal, Academic/Scholarly.* **Description:** Contains research papers dealing with plant structure (morphology and anatomy), plant distribution (chorology) and plant functional ecology (ecophysiology, population ecology, and ecosystem ecology).
Formerly (until 1970): Flora oder Allgemeine Botanische Zeitung. Abt. B, Morphologie und Geobotanik (0367-1801)
Related titles: Online - full text ed.: (from bigchalk, EBSCO Publishing, Gale Group, IngentaConnect, O C L C Online Computer Library Center, Inc., ProQuest Information & Learning, ScienceDirect, Swets Information Services).
Indexed: ASFA, AgBio, Agr, AgrForAb, BIOBASE, BIOSIS Prev, BibAg, BibInd, BiolAb, CPA, ChemAb, CurCont, ExcerpMed, FCA, FPA, ForAb, GEOBASE, GardL, HerbAb, HortAb, I&DA, IBR, ISR, OrnHort, PBA, PGegResA, PGrRegA, PHN&I, PN&I, PlantSci, PoultAb, RA&MP, RPP, S&F, SCI, SIA, SeedAb, TriticAb, WeedAb.
—BLDSC (3953.500000), CASDDS, CISTI, IDS, IE, Infotrieve, ingenta, Linda Hall. **CCC.**
Published by: Elsevier GmbH, Urban & Fischer Verlag (Subsidiary of: Elsevier Science & Technology), Loebdergraben 14a, Jena, 07743, Germany. TEL 49-3641-6263, FAX 49-3641-626443, info@urbanfischer.de, http://www.elsevier.com/locate/flora, http://www.urbanfischer.de/journals. Eds. Eckehart J. Jaeger, Otto L. Lange, Rainer Loesch TEL 49-211-8114878. R&P Frances Rothwell. Adv. contact Cora Grotzke. B&W page EUR 400, color page EUR 1,345; trim 210 x 280. Circ: 350 (paid and controlled).

580 ECU ISSN 0015-380X
FLORA. Text in English, Spanish. 1937. irreg. per issue exchange basis. bk.rev. abstr.; bibl.; charts; illus.
Indexed: BiolAb, CurCont, ISR.
Published by: Instituto Ecuatoriano de Ciencias Naturales/Ecuadorian Institute of Natural Sciences, Center, Apdo 408, Quito, Pichincha, Ecuador. Ed. M Acosta Solis. Circ: 2,000.

580 RUS
FLORA. Text in Russian. bi-m. USD 109 in United States.
Indexed: RefZh.
Published by: Izdatel'skii Dom Ova Press, Ul Krasnokazarmennaya 12, A-ya 8, Moscow, 111250, Russian Federation. TEL 7-095-9181397, FAX 7-095-9181449. Ed. A D Vorob'ev. **US dist. addr.:** East View Information Services, 3020 Harbor Ln. N., Minneapolis, MN 55447. TEL 612-550-0961.

580 NLD
FLORA AGARICINA NEERLANDICA. Text in English. 1988. irreg., latest vol.3, 1995. effective 1999. back issues avail. **Document type:** *Monographic series.* **Description:** Publishes studies on families of agarics and boleti as occurring in the Netherlands and adjacent regions.
Published by: (Rijksherbarium - Hortus Botanicus), A A Balkema (Subsidiary of: Taylor & Francis The Netherlands), PO Box 1675, Rotterdam, 3000 BR, Netherlands. TEL 31-10-413-5947, sales@balkema.nl, http://www.balkema.nl. **Dist. in U.S by:** Ashgate Publishing Co, Old Post Rd, Brookfield, VT 05036. TEL 800-535-9544.

580 COL ISSN 0120-4351
CODEN: FLCOEK
FLORA DE COLOMBIA. Text in Spanish. 1983. irreg. per issue exchange basis. **Document type:** *Monographic series.*
Indexed: BIOSIS Prev, BiolAb.
—CISTI.
Published by: Universidad Nacional de Colombia, Instituto de Ciencias, PO Box 7495, Bogota, CUND, Colombia. TEL 57-1-3165305, FAX 57-1-3165365, mgandrad@ciencias.ciencias.unal.edu.co, dicn@ciencias.ciencias.unal.edu.co, http://www.matematicas.unal.edu.co/ICN/, http://www.icn.unal.edu.co. Ed. Gloria Galeano. R&P Jaime Uribe M. Circ: 2,000.

580 VEN ISSN 0798-8613
FLORA DE VENEZUELA. Text in Spanish. 1964. irreg. price varies. charts; illus.
Published by: Fundacion Instituto Botanico de Venezuela, Jardin Botanico de Caracas, Ave. Salvador Allende, Apdo 2156, Caracas, DF 1010-A, Venezuela. TEL 58-2-6053970, FAX 58-2-6053970, llamozas@camelot.rect.ucv.vel, http://wwwucv.ve/fibv.htm. Ed. Silvia Llamozas.

580.74 CHE ISSN 0254-8453
FLORA DEL PARAGUAY. Text in Spanish. 1983. irreg., latest vol.36, 2001. **Document type:** *Monographic series, Academic/Scholarly.*
Indexed: BIOSIS Prev.
Published by: Conservatoire et Jardin Botaniques de la Ville de Geneve, Universite de Geneve, 1 Chemin de l'Imperatrice, Chambesy, CH-1292, Switzerland. TEL 41-22-4185100, FAX 41-22-4185101, http://wwwcjb.unige.ch/editions/fdp.html. Eds. R. Ramella, R. Spichiger.

580 DEU ISSN 0071-576X
FLORA ET VEGETATIO MUNDI. Text in English, French, German. 1960. irreg., latest vol.10, 1992. price varies. **Document type:** *Monographic series, Academic/Scholarly.*
Indexed: BIOSIS Prev, BiolAb.
Published by: J. Cramer in der Gebrueder Borntraeger Verlagsbuchhandlung, Johannesstr 3A, Stuttgart, 70176, Germany. TEL 49-711-3514560, FAX 49-711-35145699, mail@borntraeger-cramer.de, http://www.schweizerbart.de/j/flora-et-vegetatio-mundi.

580 NLD ISSN 0071-5778
➤ **FLORA MALESIANA BULLETIN.** Text in Dutch. 1947. a. EUR 18 per issue (effective 2002); free to qualified personnel. bk.rev. abstr.; bibl.; charts; illus. cum.index every 4 yrs. Supplement avail.; back issues avail. **Document type:** *Newsletter, Academic/Scholarly.* **Description:** Covers progress in Malesian botany, including expeditions, fieldwork, herbaria, and recent publications of interest to botanists with an interest in the botany of the Pacific and Australasian regions.
Indexed: AgrForAb, ForAb, HerbAb, HortAb, OrnHort, PBA, PGegResA, RA&MP, RDA, RRTA, S&F, WeedAb.
Published by: National Herbarium Nederland/Leiden Branch, PO Box 9514, Leiden, 2300 RA, Netherlands. TEL 31-71-5273570, FAX 31-71-5273522, veldkamp@rulrhb.leidenuniv.nl, zoelen@rhbcml.leidenuniv.nl, http://www.nhncml.leidenuniv.nl. Eds. J F Veldkamp, M A Rifai, M C Roos.

580 NLD ISSN 0374-7778
CODEN: FMSPA4
➤ **FLORA MALESIANA. SERIES 1: SPERMATOPHYTA (SEED PLANTS).** (Vols. 2 & 3 not published) Text in English. 1950. irreg., latest vol.15, 2000. price varies. bibl.; illus. index. back issues avail. **Document type:** *Monographic series, Academic/Scholarly.* **Description:** Offers a systematic account of the seed plants occurring in Malesia.
Indexed: BIOSIS Prev.
—Linda Hall.
Published by: (Foundation Flora Malesiana), National Herbarium Nederland/Leiden Branch, PO Box 9514, Leiden, 2300 RA, Netherlands. TEL 31-71-5273570, FAX 31-71-5273522, zoelen@rulhub.leidenuniv.nl, zoelen@rhbcml.leidenuniv.nl, http://www.nhncml.leidenuniv.nl. Eds. C Kalkman, W J J O de Wilde.

580 NLD ISSN 0071-5786
➤ **FLORA MALESIANA. SERIES 2: PTERIDOPHYTA (FERNS & FERN ALLIES).** Text in English. 1959. irreg., latest vol.3, 1998. price varies. charts; illus. index. back issues avail. **Document type:** *Monographic series, Academic/Scholarly.* **Description:** Offers a systematic account of ferns and fern allies occurring in Malesia.
Indexed: BiolAb, ForAb.
—Linda Hall.
Published by: (Foundation Flora Malesiana), National Herbarium Nederland/Leiden Branch, PO Box 9514, Leiden, 2300 RA, Netherlands. TEL 31-71-5273570, FAX 31-71-5273522, zoelen@rulrhb.leidenuniv.nl, zoelen@rhbcml.leidenuniv.nl, http://www.nhncml.leidenuniv.nl. Eds. C Kalkman, H P Nooteboom. Circ: 1,300.

580 USA ISSN 0071-5794
QK205 CODEN: FLNMAV
FLORA NEOTROPICA. Text in English. 1968. irreg. price varies. back issues avail. **Document type:** *Monographic series.* **Description:** Taxonomic treatments of all plants native to the new world tropics.
Indexed: BIOSIS Prev.
—KNAW. **CCC.**
Published by: (Organization for Flora Neotropica), New York Botanical Garden Press, 200th Street & Kazimiroff Blvd, Bronx, NY 10458-5126. TEL 718-817-8721, FAX 718-817-8842. Eds. James L Luteyn, Scott A Mori.

580 AUS ISSN 0726-3449
FLORA OF AUSTRALIA. Text in English. 1981. irreg., latest vol.58, 2001. **Document type:** *Monographic series.* **Description:** Describes the flowering plants, pines, ferns, mosses, liverworts and lichens to the species level.
Indexed: BIOSIS Prev.
—**CCC.**
Published by: Australian Biological Resources Study, GPO Box 787, Canberra, ACT 2601, Australia. TEL 61-2-62509506, FAX 61-2-62509555, abrs@ea.gov.au, http://www.deh.gov.au/biodiversity/abrs/publications/flora-of-australia/index.html.

580 DNK ISSN 0347-8742
CODEN: FLECDR
FLORA OF ECUADOR. Text in English. 1973. irreg. price varies.
Formerly: Opera Botanica. Series B. Flora of Ecuador
Indexed: BIOSIS Prev, BiolAb.
Published by: Nordic Publications in Botany, Gothersgade 130, Copenhagen K, 1123, Denmark. Eds. Gunnar Harling, Lennart Andersson. Circ: 500.

580 ZAF
FLORA OF SOUTHERN AFRICA. Text in English, Afrikaans. 1963. irreg., latest 1999. price varies. illus. index. back issues avail. **Document type:** *Monographic series, Academic/Scholarly.* **Description:** Taxonomic treatises on the flora of Southern Africa (ie, south of Angola, Zambia, Zimbabwe, Mozambique).
Published by: National Botanical Institute, NBI Bookshop, Private Bag X101, Pretoria, Cape Province 0001, South Africa. TEL 27-21-8043200, FAX 27-21-8043211, bookshop@nbipre.nbi.ac.za, http://www.nbi.ac.za. Ed. G Germishuizen. R&P E Du Plessis. Circ: 300.

580 ISR
FLORA OF THE U.S.S.R. Text in English. irreg.
Published by: Israel Program for Scientific Translations, P O Box 7145, Jerusalem, Israel.

580.09569403 ISR
FLORA PALAESTINA. Text in English. 1966. irreg., latest 1995. price varies. adv. Supplement avail. **Document type:** *Monographic series.* **Description:** Illustrated compendium of the flora of the region.
Published by: Israel Academy of Sciences and Humanities, 43 Jabotinski St, P O Box 4040, Jerusalem, 91040, Israel. TEL 972-2-5676233, FAX 972-2-5666059, tami@academy.ac.il, http://www.academy.ac.il. Ed. Zofia Lasman. Adv. contact Tami Korman.

B

580 POL
➤ **FLORA POLSKI: GRZYBY/FLORA OF POLAND: FUNGI.** Text in English, Polish. 1957. irreg., latest vol.27, 1998. price varies. back issues avail. **Document type:** *Monographic series, Academic/Scholarly.*
Formerly: Flora Polska: Rosliny Zarodnikowe Polski i Ziem Osciennych (0071-5824)
Indexed: BIOSIS Prev, PBA, RPP.
Published by: Polska Akademia Nauk, Instytut Botaniki im. W. Szafera/Polish Academy of Sciences, W. Szafer Institute of Botany, ul Lubicz 46, Krakow, 31512, Poland. TEL 48-12-4241737, FAX 48-12-4219790, office@ib-pan.krakow.pl. Ed. Alina Skirgiello. Pub. Jacek W Wieser. R&P Mirek Zbigniew. Circ: 500 (paid).

580 POL
FLORA POLSKI: ROSLINY NACZYNIOWE/FLORA OF POLAND: VASCULAR PLANTS. Text in Polish. 1919. irreg., latest vol.15. price varies. illus. back issues avail. **Document type:** *Academic/Scholarly.*
Formerly: Flora Polska: Rosliny Naczyniowe Polski i Ziem Osciennych (0071-5816)
Indexed: BiolAb.
Published by: Polska Akademia Nauk, Instytut Botaniki im. W. Szafera/Polish Academy of Sciences, W. Szafer Institute of Botany, ul Lubicz 46, Krakow, 31512, Poland. TEL 48-12-4241737, FAX 48-12-4210790, office@ib-pan.krakow.pl. Ed. Zbigniew Mirek. Pub. Jacek W Wieser. R&P Mirek Zbigniew. Circ: 800.

580 POL ISSN 0071-5840
➤ **FLORA SLODKOWODNA POLSKI/FRESHWATER FLORA OF POLAND.** Text in Polish. 1963. irreg. price varies. bibl. back issues avail. **Document type:** *Monographic series, Academic/Scholarly.*
Published by: Polska Akademia Nauk, Instytut Botaniki im. W. Szafera/Polish Academy of Sciences, W. Szafer Institute of Botany, ul Lubicz 46, Krakow, 31512, Poland. TEL 48-12-4241737, FAX 48-12-4219790, office@ib-pan.krakow.pl. Ed. Jadwiga Sieminska. Pub. Jacek W Wieser. R&P Mirek Zbigniew. Circ: 870.

580 BEL ISSN 0779-116X
FLORE D'AFRIQUE CENTRALE (ZAIRE - RWANDA - BURUNDI). Text in French. 1953. irreg., latest 2000. price varies. illus. back issues avail. **Document type:** *Monographic series, Academic/Scholarly.*
Formerly: Flore du Congo, du Rwanda et du Burundi
Indexed: FPA, ForAb.
Published by: Jardin Botanique National de Belgique/Nationale Plantentuin van Belgie, Domaine de Bouchout, Nieuwelaan 38, Meise, 1860, Belgium. TEL 32-2-2693905, http://www.br.fgov.be. Ed. P Bamps. Adv. contact Katrien Clarysse.

580 FRA ISSN 0430-666X
FLORE DE LA NOUVELLE CALEDONIE ET DEPENDANCES. Text in French. 1967. irreg., latest vol.23, 1999. **Document type:** *Monographic series.*
Published by: (Museum National d'Histoire Naturelle, Laboratoire de Phanerogamie), Museum National d'Histoire Naturelle, 57 Rue Cuvier, Paris, 75231 Cedex 05, France. TEL 33-1-40793777, morat@mnhn.fr, http://www.mnhn.fr. Ed. P Morat. **Co-sponsor:** Association de Botanique Tropicale.

580 FRA
FLORE DE MADAGASCAR ET DES COMORES. Text in French. 1936. irreg., latest vol.175, 1998. **Document type:** *Monographic series.*

Published by: (Museum National d'Histoire Naturelle, Laboratoire de Phanerogamie), Museum National d'Histoire Naturelle, 57 Rue Cuvier, Paris, 75231 Cedex 05, France. TEL 33-1-40793777, morat@mnhn.fr, http://www.mnhn.fr. Ed. P Morat. **Co-sponsor:** Association de Botanique Tropicale.

580 FRA ISSN 0071-5867
FLORE DU CAMBODGE, DU LAOS ET DU VIETNAM. Text in French. 1960. irreg., latest vol.30, 2001. **Document type:** *Monographic series.*
Published by: (Museum National d'Histoire Naturelle, Laboratoire de Phanerogamie), Museum National d'Histoire Naturelle, 57 Rue Cuvier, Paris, 75231 Cedex 05, France. TEL 33-1-40793777, morat@mnhn.fr, http://www.mnhn.fr. Ed. P Morat. **Co-sponsor:** Association de Botanique Tropicale.

B

580 CMR ISSN 0071-5875
FLORE DU CAMEROUN. Text in French. 1963. irreg., latest 1992. price varies. adv. bk.rev. back issues avail. **Document type:** *Academic/Scholarly.* **Description:** Teaches about 7,500 types of plants and flowers from Cameroon.
Related titles: Microfiche ed.
Indexed: ForAb, PBA, PGegResA.
Published by: Ministere de la Recherche Scientifique et Technique, Herbier National, BP 1601, Yaounde, Cameroon. TEL 237-314416, FAX 237-201854. Ed., Pub. Benoit Satabie. Circ: 550.

580 FRA ISSN 0071-5883
FLORE DU GABON. Text in French. 1961. irreg., latest vol.35, 1999. **Document type:** *Monographic series.*
Related titles: Supplement(s): Gramineae. FRF 170.
Published by: (Museum National d'Histoire Naturelle, Laboratoire de Phanerogamie), Museum National d'Histoire Naturelle, 57 Rue Cuvier, Paris, 75231 Cedex 05, France. TEL 33-1-40793777, morat@mnhn.fr, http://www.mnhn.fr. Ed. P Morat. **Co-sponsor:** Association de Botanique Tropicale.

579.5 BEL ISSN 0379-1890
CODEN: FICALL
FLORE ILLUSTREE DES CHAMPIGNONS D'AFRIQUE CENTRALE. Text in French. 1935; N.S. 1970. irreg., latest vol.17, 1997. price varies. illus. back issues avail. **Document type:** *Monographic series, Academic/Scholarly.*
Formerly (until no.17, 1970): Flore Iconographique des Champignons du Congo (0374-7700)
—KNAW.
Published by: Jardin Botanique National de Belgique/Nationale Plantentuin van Belgie, Domaine de Bouchout, Nieuwelaan 38, Meise, 1860, Belgium. TEL 32-2-2693905, http://www.br.fgov.be. Adv. contact Katrien Clarysse.

579.8 BEL ISSN 0779-1089
FLORE PRATIQUE DES ALGUES D'EAU DOUCE DE BELGIQUE. Text in French. 1986. irreg., latest vol.5, 2001. price varies. back issues avail. **Document type:** *Monographic series, Academic/Scholarly.*
Published by: Jardin Botanique National de Belgique/Nationale Plantentuin van Belgie, Domaine de Bouchout, Nieuwelaan 38, Meise, 1860, Belgium. TEL 32-2-2693905, http://www.br.fgov.be. Ed. P Compere. Adv. contact Katrien Clarysse.

580 USA
FLORIDA. DEPARTMENT OF AGRICULTURE AND CONSUMER SERVICES. BOTANY CIRCULAR. Text in English. 1976. bi-m. looseleaf. free. **Document type:** *Government.*
Indexed: WeedAb.
Published by: Department of Agriculture and Consumer Services, Division of Plant Industry, 1911 S W 34th St, Box 147100, Gainesville, FL 32614-7100. TEL 904-372-3505, FAX 904-955-2301. R&P Denise Feiber.

580 USA ISSN 0428-6294
SB21 CODEN: BFACDN
FLORIDA. DEPARTMENT OF AGRICULTURE AND CONSUMER SERVICES. DIVISION OF PLANT INDUSTRY. BULLETIN SERIES. Text in English. irreg., latest vol.15, 1993. price varies. **Document type:** *Bulletin, Government.*
Formerly: Plant Pathology Bulletins
Indexed: BioCN&I, FCA, ForAb, HerbAb, HortAb, OrnHort, PBA, RA&MP, RPP, RiceAb, S&F, SIA, WeedAb.
—BLDSC (6521.100000), CISTI, Linda Hall.
Published by: Department of Agriculture and Consumer Services, Division of Plant Industry, 1911 S W 34th St, Box 147100, Gainesville, FL 32614-7100. TEL 904-372-3505, FAX 904-955-2301.

571.9 USA ISSN 0032-0870
CODEN: FPPCB6
FLORIDA. DEPARTMENT OF AGRICULTURE AND CONSUMER SERVICES. PLANT PATHOLOGY CIRCULAR. Text in English. 1962. bi-m. looseleaf. free. **Document type:** *Government.*
Indexed: BiolAb, CurCont, ForAb, HortAb, MaizeAb, OrnHort, RPP, WeedAb.
Published by: Department of Agriculture and Consumer Services, Division of Plant Industry, 1911 S W 34th St, Box 147100, Gainesville, FL 32614-7100. TEL 904-372-3505, FAX 904-955-2301.

FLORIDA. DIVISION OF PLANT INDUSTRY. BIENNIAL REPORT. see *AGRICULTURE*

FLORIDA TURF DIGEST. see *AGRICULTURE—Crop Production And Soil*

580 DEU ISSN 0934-456X
CODEN: FLRUEB
FLORISTISCHE RUNDBRIEFE; Zeitschrift fuer floristische Geobotanik, Populationsoekologie. Text in German, English. 1967. irreg. EUR 11 (effective 2003). bk.rev. 120 p./no. 2 cols./p.; back issues avail. **Document type:** *Magazine, Academic/Scholarly.*
Formerly (until 1987): Goettinger Floristische Rundbriefe (0340-4145)
Indexed: BIOSIS Prev, BiolAb, RefZh.
Published by: (Ruhr-Universitaet Bochum, Spezielle Botanik), Bochumer Universitaetsverlag GmbH, Querenburger Hoehe 281, Bochum, 44801, Germany. TEL 49-234-9719780, FAX 49-234-9719786, bou@bou.de, http://bou.de. Ed. Henning Haeupler. Circ: 1,400.

580 BEL ISSN 1375-176X
FLOWERING NEWSLETTER. Text in English. 1987. s-a.
—BLDSC (3958.495000), IE, ingenta.
Published by: Universite de Liege, SartTilman, Liege, 4000, Belgium. http://www.ulg.ac.be.

580.96 ZAF ISSN 0015-4504
QK396
FLOWERING PLANTS OF AFRICA. Text in English. 1921. irreg. ZAR 120 in Southern Africa; USD 40 elsewhere (effective 2000). illus. index. back issues avail. **Document type:** *Monographic series, Academic/Scholarly.* **Description:** Presents color plates of African plants with accompanying text.
Formerly: Flowering Plants of South Africa
Indexed: BIOSIS Prev, BiolAb.
—IE.
Published by: National Botanical Institute, NBI Bookshop, Private Bag X101, Pretoria, Cape Province 0001, South Africa. TEL 27-21-8043200, FAX 27-21-8043211, bookshop@nbipre.nbi.ac.za, http://www.nbi.ac.za. Ed. G Germishuizen. R&P E Du Plessis. Circ: 500.

580 ESP ISSN 0210-6574
FOLIA BOTANICA MISCELLANEA. Text in Spanish. 1979. irreg. price varies. **Document type:** *Journal, Academic/Scholarly.*
Indexed: IECT.
Published by: (Universitat de Barcelona, Facultat de Biologia), Universitat de Barcelona, Servei de Publicacions, Gran Via Corts Catalanes 585, Barcelona, 08007, Spain. TEL 34-93-4021100, http://www.publicacions.ub.es.

580 EST
FOLIA CRYPTOGAMICA ESTONICA. Abbreviated title: F C E. Text in Estonian. a. per issue exchange basis. **Description:** Publishes papers on mycology, lichenology, bryology and phycology.
Indexed: RPP.
Published by: Estonian Naturalists' Society, Struve st 2, Tartu, 2400, Estonia. Ed. Urmas Koljalg. **Co-sponsor:** Tartu Ulikooli, Institute of Zoology and Botany/University of Tartu.

580 CZE ISSN 1211-9520
QK1 CODEN: FGPBA7
➤ **FOLIA GEOBOTANICA.** Text in English. 1966. q. EUR 193; EUR 241 combined subscription print & online eds. (effective 2005). bk.rev. charts; illus. index. **Document type:** *Journal, Academic/Scholarly.* **Description:** Devoted to geobotany (plant sociology, synecology and autecology, paleoecology, plant geography), plant taxonomy (algae, fungi, bryophytes, higher plants), nomenclature, and cytotaxonomy.
Formerly (until 1998): Folia Geobotanica et Phytotaxonomica (0015-5551)
Related titles: Online - full text ed.: EUR 145 (effective 2005) (from EBSCO Publishing, Swets Information Services).
Indexed: ASCA, ASFA, AgBio, AgrForAb, BIOSIS Prev, BioCN&I, BiolAb, CPA, CurCont, FCA, ForAb, GEOBASE, HerbAb, HortAb, I&DA, ISR, MaizeAb, OrnHort, PBA, PGegResA, PotatoAb, RA&MP, RPP, RefZh, S&F, SCI, SeedAb, TriticAb, WeedAb.
—BLDSC (3969.970000), CISTI, IDS, IE, Infotrieve, ingenta. **CCC.**
Published by: Akademie Ved Ceske Republiky, Botanicky Ustav/Academy of Sciences of the Czech Republic, Institute of Botany, Pruhonice, 25243, Czech Republic. TEL 420-2-67750065, FAX 420-2-67750031, fialova@ibot.cas.cz, http://www.ibot.cas.cz/folia. Eds. K Marhold, T Herben. **Dist. by:** Opulus Press, Gamla Vaegen 40, Grangaerde 77013, Sweden. TEL 46-240-641250, FAX 46-240-640880, http://www.opuluspress.se.

580 CZE ISSN 0139-9667
FOLIA MUSEI RERUM NATURALIUM BOHEMIAE OCCIDENTALIS. BOTANICA. Text in Czech. 1972. s-a. back issues avail. **Document type:** *Monographic series, Academic/Scholarly.*
Indexed: HerbAb.
Published by: Zapadoceske Muzeum, Kopeckeho sady 2, Plzen, 30135, Czech Republic. TEL 42-19-7236541, FAX 42-19-7236541, zpcm@pm.cesnet.cz. Ed. Jaroslav Kraft.

571.2 561 NLD
➤ **FOSSILIUM CATALOGUS: PLANTAE.** Text in English. 1913. irreg., latest vol.105, 2002. price varies. illus. back issues avail. **Document type:** *Monographic series, Academic/Scholarly.* **Description:** Describes complete records of palaeontological botanical finds.
Published by: Backhuys Publishers BV, Postbus 321, Leiden, 2300 AH, Netherlands. TEL 31-71-517-0208, FAX 31-71-517-1856, backhuys@backhuys.com, http://www.backhuys.com. Ed. H W J van Amerom. Circ: 300 (paid).

635 USA ISSN 0532-3215
FOUR SEASONS (BERKELEY). Text in English. 1964. a., latest vol.11. USD 16 for 4 nos. (effective 2002). bk.rev. **Description:** Covers all aspects of California native plants. Includes both technical and semi-popular articles.
—CISTI.
Published by: East Bay Regional Park District, Tilden Regional Park, Botanic Garden, Berkeley, CA 94708-2396. TEL 510-841-8732, FAX 510-848-6025, BGarden@ebparks.org. Ed., R&P Stephen W Edwards. Circ: 400.

580 POL ISSN 1640-629X
QK322
➤ **FRAGMENTA FLORISTICA ET GEOBOTANICA POLONICA.** Text in Polish; Summaries in English. 1994. a., latest vol.7, 2001. USD 32 (effective 1998). bk.rev. back issues avail. **Document type:** *Journal, Academic/Scholarly.* **Description:** Publishes original papers relevant mainly to the Polish territory, covering all aspects of botany, especially vegetation monographs and articles on plant taxonomy and ecology, phytogeography, cryptogamic botany, plant anatomy, cytology and embryology as well as biosystematics, evolutionary botany and experimental embryology.
Formerly (until 2000): Fragmenta Floristica et Geobotanica. Series Polonica (1233-0132)
Indexed: AgrLib, BIOSIS Prev, BiolAb, FCA, ForAb, GEOBASE, HerbAb, HortAb, MaizeAb, OrnHort, PBA, PGegResA, RPP, RefZh, S&F, SeedAb, WeedAb.
—BLDSC (4032.101000).
Published by: Polska Akademia Nauk, Instytut Botaniki im. W. Szafera/Polish Academy of Sciences, W. Szafer Institute of Botany, ul Lubicz 46, Krakow, 31512, Poland. TEL 48-12-4241737, FAX 48-12-4219790, office@ib-pan.krakow.pl. Ed. Ludwik Frey. Pub. Jacek W Wieser. R&P Mirek Zbigniew. Adv. contact Jacek Wieser. Circ: 500 (paid).

➤ **FRAGMENTA PHYTOMEDICA ET HERBOLOGICA.** see *AGRICULTURE*

580 USA ISSN 0092-1793
QK149
FREMONTIA. Text in English. 1972. q. USD 35 domestic; USD 45 foreign (effective 2004). adv. bk.rev. index. back issues avail. **Description:** Provides articles of general interest about California's native plants.
Related titles: Online - full text ed.
Indexed: AGBP, GardL.
—BLDSC (4033.830000).
Published by: California Native Plant Society, 2707 K St., # 1, Sacramento, CA 95816-5113. publications@cnps.org, http://www.cnps.org/publications/publications.htm#fremontia. Ed. Phyllis Faber. Circ: 9,000.

FRUITROP (FRENCH EDITION). see *GARDENING AND HORTICULTURE*

FRUITS; fruit and horticultural productions in tropical and Mediterranean regions. see *GARDENING AND HORTICULTURE*

580 635 JPN ISSN 0287-3494
FUJI TAKERUI SHOKUBUTSUEN HOKOKU/FUJI BAMBOO GARDEN. REPORTS. Text in Japanese; Summaries in English, Japanese. 1956. a.
Published by: Nihon Take Sasa no Kai/Japan Bamboo Society, c/o Fuji Takerui Shokubutsuen, 885 Minami-Ishiki, Sunto-gun, Nagaizumi-cho, Shizuoka-ken 411-0932, Japan.

580 JPN ISSN 0913-2546
FUKUOKA NO SHOKUBUTSU/BOTANY OF FUKUOKA. Text in Japanese. 1974. a.
Published by: Fukuoka Shokubutsu Kenkyukai/Botanical Society of Fukuokai, c/o Mr Hijiri Masumura, 76 Yamanoi, Chikugo-shi, Fukuoka-ken 833-0031, Japan.

571.2 AUS ISSN 1445-4408
QK710 CODEN: FPBUCP
➤ **FUNCTIONAL PLANT BIOLOGY;** an international journal of plant function. Text in English. 1974. m. AUD 200 combined subscription in Australia & New Zealand to individuals print & online eds.; USD 200 combined subscription elsewhere to individuals print & online eds.; AUD 1,270 combined subscription in Australia & New Zealand to institutions print & online eds.; USD 1,135 combined subscription elsewhere to institutions print & online eds. (effective 2004). adv. index. 100 p./no.; back issues avail. **Document type:** *Journal, Academic/Scholarly.* **Description:** Covers all aspects of plant physiology, including biochemistry and biophysics, cell biology, genetics, plant-environment interactions, plant-microbe interactions and molecular biology.

Formerly (until Jan.2002): Australian Journal of Plant Physiology (0310-7841)
Related titles: Microform ed.: (from PQC); Online - full text ed.: AUD 180 in Australia & New Zealand to individuals; USD 160 elsewhere to individuals; AUD 1,140 in Australia & New Zealand to institutions; USD 1,020 elsewhere to institutions (effective 2004) (from EBSCO Publishing, Gale Group, O C L C Online Computer Library Center, Inc., Swets Information Services).
Indexed: ABIPC, ASCA, ASFA, AgBio, Agr, AgrForAb, B&BAb, BBCI, BIOBASE, BIOSIS Prev, BioCN&I, BiolAb, CIN, CPA, CTFA, ChemAb, ChemTitl, CurCont, DBA, ESPM, EngInd, ExcerpMed, FCA, FPA, FS&TA, ForAb, GEOBASE, GenetAb, HGA, HerbAb, HortAb, I&DA, IABS, INIS AtomInd, ISR, MaizeAb, OrnHort, PBA, PGegResA, PGrRegA, PHN&I, PlantSci, PotatoAb, RA&MP, RPP, RevApplEntom, RiceAb, S&F, SCI, SIA, SWRA, SeedAb, SoyAb, TOSA, TriticAb, VITIS, WeedAb.
—BLDSC (4055.653250), CASDDS, CISTI, IDS, IE, Infotrieve, ingenta, Linda Hall. **CCC.**
Published by: (C S I R O Australia), C S I R O Publishing, 150 Oxford St, PO Box 1139, Collingwood, VIC 3066, Australia. TEL 61-3-96627625, FAX 61-3-96627611, fpb@publish.csiro.au, publishing@csiro.au, http://www.publish.csiro.au/journals/fpb. Ed. Barry Osmond. Circ: 800.

580 ARG ISSN 0074-025X
FUNDACION MIGUEL LILLO. MISCELANEA. Text in Spanish; Summaries in English, French, German. 1937. irreg., latest vol.117, 2001. bk.rev. charts; illus.; abstr. back issues avail. **Document type:** *Monographic series, Academic/Scholarly.*
Indexed: ASFA, BiolAb, EntAb, HortAb, PBA, PGegResA, RA&MP, RefZh, TDB, ZooRec.
—BLDSC (5811.728000), CISTI.
Published by: Fundacion Miguel Lillo, Miguel Lillo, 251, San Miguel de Tucuman, Tucuman 4000, Argentina. TEL 54-0381-4239960, FAX 54-0381-4330868, fmlinfonoa@tucbbs.com.ar, http://www.lillo.org.ar. Ed. Jose A Haedo Rossi. Circ: 500.

579.5 HKG ISSN 1560-2745
QK600
FUNGAL DIVERSITY. Text in English. 1998. triennial. USD 60 to individuals; USD 120 to institutions; USD 30 to students (effective 2004). **Document type:** *Journal, Academic/Scholarly.*
Indexed: BIOSIS Prev, BiolAb, CurCont.
—BLDSC (4056.627500).
Published by: Fungal Diversity Press, University of Hong Kong, Research Centre of Fungal Diversity, Pokfulam Rd, Hong Kong, Hong Kong. kdhyde@hkucc.hku.hk, http://www.hku.hk/ecology/mycology/FD/index.htm. Ed. Dr. Kevin D Hyde TEL 852-22990611.

579.5 HKG ISSN 1608-6791
FUNGAL DIVERSITY RESEARCH SERIES. Text in English. 2000. irreg., latest vol.12, 2003. price varies. **Document type:** *Monographic series, Academic/Scholarly.*
Indexed: BIOSIS Prev.
Published by: Fungal Diversity Press, University of Hong Kong, Research Centre of Fungal Diversity, Pokfulam Rd, Hong Kong, Hong Kong. http://www.hku.hk/ecology/mycology/FDRS/index.htm. Ed. Dr. Kevin D Hyde TEL 852-22990611.

579.5 USA ISSN 1087-1845
QK600 CODEN: EXMYD2
➤ **FUNGAL GENETICS AND BIOLOGY.** Text in English. 1977. 12/yr. EUR 331 in Europe to individuals; JPY 34,500 in Japan to individuals; USD 256 elsewhere to individuals; EUR 744 in Europe to institutions; JPY 77,900 in Japan to institutions; USD 577 elsewhere to institutions; EUR 111 in Europe to students; JPY 11,500 in Japan to students; USD 97 elsewhere to students (effective 2006). adv. bk.rev. index. back issues avail. **Document type:** *Journal, Academic/Scholarly.* **Description:** Publishes experimental investigations that relate structure and function to growth, reproduction, morphogenesis, and differentiation of fungi and their traditional allies.
Formerly (until vol.20, no.1, 1996): Experimental Mycology (0147-5975)
Related titles: Online - full text ed.: ISSN 1096-0937. USD 565 (effective 2002) (from EBSCO Publishing, Gale Group, IngentaConnect, O C L C Online Computer Library Center, Inc., ScienceDirect, Swets Information Services).
Indexed: ASCA, AbHyg, AgBio, Agr, AgrForAb, B&BAb, BIOBASE, BIOSIS Prev, BibAg, BioCN&I, BioDAb, BiolAb, CBTA, CIN, CPA, ChemAb, ChemTitl, CurCont, DBA, ExcerpMed, FCA, FPA, ForAb, GenetAb, HGA, HelmAb, HerbAb, HortAb, IABS, ISR, IndMed, IndVet, Inpharma, MBA, MEDLINE, MaizeAb, NemAb, NutrAb, PBA, PE&ON, PGegResA, PGrRegA, PHN&I, PotatoAb, ProtozoAb, RM&VM, RPP, Reac, RevApplEntom, RiceAb, S&F, SCI, SIA, SoyAb, TDB, TriticAb, VITIS, VetBull, WeedAb.
—BLDSC (4056.630000), CASDDS, CISTI, GNLM, IDS, IE, Infotrieve, ingenta, Linda Hall. **CCC.**
Published by: Academic Press (Subsidiary of: Elsevier Science & Technology), 525 B St, Ste 1900, San Diego, CA 92101-4495. TEL 619-231-6616, 800-894-3434, apsubs@acad.com, http://www.elsevier.com/locate/yfgbi, http://www.academicpress.com. Ed. N Gow.

580 USA
THE GAILLARDIA. Text in English. 1986. q. free. **Document type:** *Newsletter, Consumer.*
Published by: Oklahoma Native Plant Society, 2435 S Peoria Ave, Tulsa, OK 74114. http://dir.gardenweb.com/directory/onps. Ed. Chad Cox. Circ: 400 (paid and controlled).

580 PRT ISSN 0379-9506
QK1 CODEN: GOBTAO
GARCIA DE ORTA: SERIE DE BOTANICA. Text in Portuguese. 1953. irreg., latest vol.14, 1999. price varies. back issues avail. **Document type:** *Academic/Scholarly.*
Supersedes in part (in 1973): Garcia de Orta (0016-4569)
Indexed: AgrForAb, BIOSIS Prev, BioCN&I, BiolAb, FPA, ForAb, HerbAb, HortAb, PBA, PGegResA, RA&MP, S&F, SIA, SeedAb, WeedAb.
Published by: Instituto de Investigacao Cientifica Tropical, Rua da Junqueira, 30, Lisbon, 1349-007, Portugal. TEL 351-21-3622621, FAX 351-21-3631460, iict@iict.pt. Circ: 1,000. **Subscr. to:** Centro de Documentacao e Informacao, Rua de Jau, 47, Lisbon 1300, Portugal. TEL 351-21-3644846, FAX 351-21-3628218.

580 SGP ISSN 0374-7859
CODEN: GABUAV
➤ **GARDENS' BULLETIN, SINGAPORE.** Text in English. 1891. s-a. SGD 100 (effective 2000). adv. bk.rev. index. back issues avail. **Document type:** *Academic/Scholarly.* **Description:** Consists of scientific research in the fields of plant taxonomy, horticulture, phytogeography, morphology, anatomy, with an emphasis on West Malesian areas.
Indexed: AgBio, Agr, BIOSIS Prev, BiolAb, FCA, FPA, ForAb, HerbAb, HortAb, OrnHort, PBA, PGegResA, PGrRegA, RPP, RefZh, RevApplEntom, SPPI, SeedAb, WeedAb.
—BLDSC (4072.000000).
Published by: National Parks Board, Singapore Botanic Gardens, Cluny Rd, Singapore, 259569, Singapore. TEL 65-4741165. Ed. Dr. Ruth Kiew. Circ: 400. **Dist. by:** The Library, Botanic Gardens, 1 Cluny Rd, Singapore 259569, Singapore. TEL 65-4719921, FAX 65-4754295.

➤ **GARDENSTYLE.** see *LIFESTYLE*

➤ **GAYANA: BOTANICA.** see *BIOLOGY—Abstracting, Bibliographies, Statistics*

➤ **GENETICS AND BREEDING/GENETICS AND BREEDING.** see *BIOLOGY—Genetics*

582.13 POL ISSN 0867-1710
CODEN: GENUEL
GENUS; international journal of invertebrate taxonomy. Text in English. 1990. q. EUR 65 foreign (effective 2005). **Document type:** *Journal, Academic/Scholarly.*
Indexed: ASFA, AgrAg, EntAb, GenetAb, HGA, RefZh, ZooRec.
Published by: Polish Taxonomical Society, Univeristy of Wroclaw, Institute of Zoology, Wroclaw, Poland. cassidae@biol.uni.wroc.pl, http://www.biol.uni.wroc.pl/cassidae/pttaxtitle.html. Ed. Lech Borowiec. **Dist. by:** Ars Polona, Krakowskie Przedmiescie 7, Warsaw, Poland. TEL 48-22-9263914, FAX 48-22-9265334, arspolona@arspolona.com.pl, http://www.arspolona.com.pl.

580 CHE ISSN 1420-6803
QK1 CODEN: BGBIAG
GEOBOTANICAL INSTITUTE E T H. BULLETIN. Text in English, German. 1928. a. CHF 40 (effective 2000). adv. back issues avail. **Document type:** *Academic/Scholarly.* **Description:** Progress reports and technical articles by the Institute.
Formerly (until 1996): Geobotanisches Institut E T H, Stiftung Ruebel, Zurich. Berichte (0373-7896)
Indexed: ASFA, Agr, BIOBASE, BIOSIS Prev, BiolAb, CurCont, ESPM, ForAb, HerbAb, HortAb, I&DA, IBR, NutrAb, PBA, PGegResA, PHN&I, RA&MP, RPP, RefZh, S&F, SWRA, SeedAb, WRCInf, WeedAb.
—CISTI.
Published by: (Stiftung Ruebel), Eidgenoessische Technische Hochschule Zuerich, Geobotanisches Institut, Zurichbergstr 38, Zuerich, 8044, Switzerland. TEL 41-1-6322756, FAX 41-1-6321215, langenauer@geobot.umnw.ethz.ch, http://www.geobot.umnw.ethz.ch/publications/periodicals/period.html. Ed. Peter Edwards. Adv. contact Sabine Guesewell. Circ: 1,400.

580 CHE ISSN 0254-9433
CODEN: VGRZAR
GEOBOTANISCHES INSTITUT E T H, STIFTUNG RUEBEL, ZURICH. VEROEFFENTLICHUNGEN. Text and summaries in German, English. 1923. irreg., latest vol.129, 1998. CHF 75. adv. charts; illus.; stat. back issues avail. **Document type:** *Monographic series, Academic/Scholarly.*
Indexed: BIOBASE, BiolAb, CurCont, ExcerpMed, FCA, ForAb, HerbAb, HortAb, IBR, PGrRegA, RRTA, S&F, SeedAb, WeedAb.
—Linda Hall.
Published by: (Stiftung Ruebel), Eidgenoessische Technische Hochschule Zuerich, Geobotanisches Institut, Zurichbergstr 38, Zuerich, 8044, Switzerland. TEL 41-1-6322756, FAX 41-1-6321215, http://www.geobof.umnw.ethz.ch/publications/periodicals/period.html. Adv. contact Sabine Guesewell. Circ: 550.

GEOBOTANY. see *EARTH SCIENCES—Geology*

580 JPN ISSN 0911-422X
➤ **GIFUKEN SHOKUBUTSU KENKYUKAISHI/GIFU BOTANICAL SOCIETY. BULLETIN.** Text in Japanese. 1984. a. JPY 3,000. **Document type:** *Bulletin, Academic/Scholarly.*
Published by: Gifuken Shokubutsu Kenkyukai/Gifu Botanical Society, Gifu Daigaku Kyoikugakubu, Seibutsugaku Kyoshitsu Shokubutsu, Bunrui Kenkyushitsu, Yanagi-To, Gifu-shi, 501-1112, Japan. TEL 058-293-2258, FAX 058-293-2207, takahash@cc.gifu-u.ac.jp. Ed. Hiroshi Takahashi. Circ: 300.

580 IRL ISSN 0332-0235
CODEN: RSEND3
➤ **GLASRA.** Text in English. 1976-1987; N.S. 1990. a. per issue exchange basis. bk.rev. **Document type:** *Journal, Academic/Scholarly.*
Formerly: National Botanic Gardens Glasnevin. Contributions
Indexed: Agr.
—BLDSC (4189.600000), CISTI.
Published by: National Botanic Gardens, Glasnevin, Dublin, 9, Ireland. TEL 353-1-8374388, FAX 353-1-8360080, nbg@indigo.ie. Ed., R&P Matthew Jebb. Circ: 400.

583.95 USA ISSN 0017-1352
THE GLOXINIAN; the journal for gesneriad growers. Text in English. 1951. q. USD 20; USD 25 foreign (effective 1999). adv. bk.rev. abstr.; bibl.; charts; illus.; maps; stat. 56 p./no.; back issues avail. **Document type:** *Magazine, Consumer.* **Description:** A publication and organization to afford a convenient and beneficial association of persons interested in gesneriads.
Indexed: BiolAb.
Published by: American Gloxinia and Gesneriad Society, Inc., c/o Michael A Riley, Business Manager, 101 W 104th St, New York, NY 10025. TEL 212-666-2395, FAX 212-666-5114, Riley2362@aol.com, http://www.aggs.org. Ed., R&P Jeanne Katzenstein TEL 973-627-2755. Adv. contact Tom Bruning. B&W page USD 165, color page USD 500; trim 7.25 x 4.25. Circ: 3,200 (paid).

571.2 NLD ISSN 0017-2294
QK320
GORTERIA; tijdschrift voor de floristiek. Text in Dutch; Summaries in English. 1961. bi-m. EUR 20.50 (effective 2002). bk.rev. charts; illus. index. back issues avail. **Document type:** *Journal, Academic/Scholarly.* **Description:** Papers on the flora of the Netherlands and adjoining countries.
Related titles: ♦ Supplement(s): Gorteria. Supplement. ISSN 0928-8228.
Indexed: AgBio, BiolAb, FCA, ForAb, GEOBASE, HerbAb, HortAb, I&DA, MaizeAb, OrnHort, PBA, PGegResA, RRTA, S&F, TriticAb, WeedAb.
—IE, Infotrieve.
Published by: National Herbarium Nederland/Leiden Branch, PO Box 9514, Leiden, 2300 RA, Netherlands. TEL 31-71-5273570, FAX 31-71-5273522, meijden@rulrhb.leidenuniv.nl, http://www.nhncml.leidenuniv.nl. Ed. R van der Meijden. Circ: 1,400.

580 NLD ISSN 0928-8228
➤ **GORTERIA. SUPPLEMENT.** Text in English. 1975. irreg., latest vol.5, 2000. price varies. illus. back issues avail. **Document type:** *Monographic series, Academic/Scholarly.* **Description:** Publishes in-depth scholarly studies of topics relating to the flora of the Netherlands.
Supersedes in part (in 1992): Leiden Botanical Series (0169-8508)
Related titles: ♦ Supplement to: Gorteria. ISSN 0017-2294.
—CISTI.
Published by: National Herbarium Nederland/Leiden Branch, PO Box 9514, Leiden, 2300 RA, Netherlands. TEL 31-71-5273570, FAX 31-71-5273522, publications@nhn.leidenuniv.nl, http://www.nationaalherbarium.nl.

580 NOR ISSN 0017-3134
QK658 CODEN: GRNABF
➤ **GRANA**; international journal of palynology and aerobiology. Text in English. 1954. q. GBP 255, USD 420 combined subscription to institutions print & online eds. (effective 2006). adv. bibl.; illus. reprint service avail. from PSC. **Document type:** *Journal, Academic/Scholarly.* **Description:** Presents original articles, mainly on theoretical palynology.
Formerly (until 1970): Grana Palynologica (0374-793X)
Related titles: Online - full text ed.: ISSN 1651-2049. GBP 242, USD 399 to institutions (effective 2006) (from EBSCO Publishing, Gale Group, IngentaConnect, O C L C Online Computer Library Center, Inc., Swets Information Services); ♦ Supplement(s): Grana. Supplement. ISSN 1104-0963.
Indexed: AEA, ASCA, AbHyg, AgrForAb, ApicAb, BIOBASE, BIOSIS Prev, BiolAb, BrGeoL, CPA, CurCont, EnvAb, EnvInd, FCA, FPA, ForAb, GEOBASE, HerbAb, HortAb, I&DA, IABS, IndVet, MaizeAb, OrnHort, PBA, PGegResA, PN&I, PlantSci, ProtozoAb, RA&MP, RM&VM, RPP, RevApplEntom, S&F, SIA, SeedAb, TDB, TriticAb, VetBull, WeedAb.
—BLDSC (4209.600000), CISTI, IDS, IE, Infotrieve, ingenta, Linda Hall. **CCC.**

Published by: (Taylor & Francis A B SWE), Taylor & Francis A S (Subsidiary of: Taylor & Francis Group), Biskop Gunnerusgate 14A, PO Box 12 Posthuset, Oslo, 0051, Norway. TEL 47-23-103460, FAX 47-23-103461, journals@tandf.no, http://www.tandf.co.uk/journals/titles/00173134.asp. Ed. Else Marie Friis. Circ: 700. **Subscr. to:** Taylor & Francis Ltd, Journals Customer Service, Rankine Rd, Basingstoke, Hants RG24 8PR, United Kingdom. TEL 44-1256-813000, FAX 44-1256-330245, enquiry@tandf.co.uk.

580 NOR ISSN 1104-0963
GRANA. SUPPLEMENT. Text in English. 1993. irreg. **Document type:** *Monographic series, Academic/Scholarly.*
Related titles: ◆ Supplement to: Grana. ISSN 0017-3134.
—Infotrieve. **CCC.**
Published by: Taylor & Francis A S (Subsidiary of: Taylor & Francis Group), Biskop Gunnerusgate 14A, PO Box 12 Posthuset, Oslo, 0051, Norway. TEL 47-23-103460, FAX 47-23-103461.

580 NLD ISSN 0167-2932
GRASDUINEN. Text in Dutch. 1979. m. EUR 40.05 (effective 2003). adv. illus. **Document type:** *Magazine, Consumer.*
Published by: Sanoma Magazines Belgium, Telecomlaan 5-7, Diegem, 1831, Belgium. TEL 32-2-7762211, FAX 32-2-776-2317, http://www.vnu.nl/vnu/organisatie, http://www.sanoma-magazines.be/HomePage.aspx?flash=1&Language=nl. Circ: 55,000.

580 635 USA
GROWING NATIVE. Text in English. 1990. bi-m. USD 35 (effective 2001). bk.rev.; Website rev. bibl.; illus. back issues avail.; reprints avail. **Document type:** *Newsletter.* **Description:** Describes California native flora and supplies information on propagating and growing plants; interviews gardeners, often funny.
Indexed: GardL.
Published by: (Growing Native Research Institute), Louise Lacey, Ed. & Pub., PO Box 489, Berkeley, CA 94701. TEL 510-232-9865, ladylfab@earthlink.net, http://www.growingnative.net. R&P Louise Lacey.

580 CHN ISSN 1000-3142
QK355 CODEN: GUZHEI
➤ **GUANGXI ZHIWU/GUIHAIA.** Text in Chinese, English. 1981. q. USD 24 per vol.; CNY 6 newsstand/cover domestic; USD 6 newsstand/cover foreign (effective 2000). **Document type:** *Academic/Scholarly.* **Description:** Contains papers and reports studying plants, including systematic botany, plant ecology, structure botany, physiology, molecular botany, and plant genetic. Also includes reviews for new methods, new technology, new advances in botany research.
Related titles: ◆ CD-ROM ed.: Chinese Academic Journals Full-Text Database. Science & Engineering, Series A. ISSN 1007-8010; Online - full content ed.: (from WanFang Data Corp.); Online - full text ed.: (from East View Information Services).
—BLDSC (4223.859270).
Published by: Guangxi Zhiwu Yanjiusuo/Guangxi Institute of Botany, Yanshan, Guilin, Guangxi 541006, China. TEL 86-773-3550103, 86-773-3550067, FAX 86-773-3550074, guihaia@elong.com, zwszzg@public.glptt.gx.cn. Ed. Feng Li.

580.71025 USA ISSN 0072-8500
QK1
GUIDE TO GRADUATE STUDY IN BOTANY FOR THE UNITED STATES AND CANADA. Text in English. 1966. irreg., latest 1995. adv. **Document type:** *Directory.* **Description:** Provides data on degree programs and faculty of plant science departments in the United States and Canada.
Published by: Botanical Society of America, Inc. (Columbus), Business Office, 2813 Blossom Ave., Columbus, OH 43231-2921. TEL 614-292-3519, FAX 614-247-6444. Eds. Bijan Dehgan, William Stern. R&P Kimberly Hiser. Adv. contact Allen Press.

580 ESP ISSN 1135-7924
GUINEANA; revista de botanica. Text in Spanish. 1995. a., latest vol.8. EUR 25 per issue (effective 2005). illus. 400 p./no.; back issues avail. **Document type:** *Monographic series, Academic/Scholarly.* **Description:** Journal's scope comprises the systematic, taxonomy, floristic and ecology of all plant groups: algae, fungi, bryophites and vascular plants.
Related titles: Online - full text ed.
Indexed: IECT.
—CINDOC.
Published by: (Universidad del Pais Vasco, Facultad de Ciencias, Departamento de Botanica), Universidad del Pais Vasco, Servicio Editorial, Apartado 1397, Bilbao, 48080, Spain. TEL 34-94-6015126, FAX 34-94-4801314, luxedito@lg.ehu.es, http://www.ehu.es/servicios/se_az/pags/p31.htm. Ed., Pub. Mr. Javier Loidi. R&P, Adv. contact Mr. Juan J Rodriguez.

GUNNERIA. see *BIOLOGY*

GUOWAI YIYAO (ZHIWUYAO FENCE)/FOREIGN MEDICINES (PLANT MEDICINE). see *PHARMACY AND PHARMACOLOGY*

H S I BULLETIN. see *GARDENING AND HORTICULTURE*

578.012 590 SVN ISSN 1581-4661
HACQUETIA. Text in Slovenian, English. s-a. EUR 18.30 per vol. domestic to individuals; EUR 24.70 per vol. domestic to institutions (effective 2005). **Document type:** *Journal, Academic/Scholarly.*
Indexed: RefZh.
Published by: Zalozba Z R C/Scientific Research Centre Publishing, Novi trg 2, P.O. Box 306, Ljubljana, 1001, Slovenia. TEL 386-1-4706474, FAX 386-1-4257719, hacquetia@zrc-sazu.si, zalozba@zrc-sazu.si, http://bijh.zrc-sazu.si/bio/SI/Hacquetia/index.asp, http://www.zrc-sazu.si/zalozba. Ed., R&P Andraz Carni. Pub. Vojislav Likar TEL 386-1-4706477. Adv. contact Tinka Selic.

580 JPN ISSN 0388-2845
HANA NO WA/HIROSHIMA CITY PARK ASSOCIATION. NEWS. Text in Japanese. 1980. q. **Document type:** *Newsletter.*
Published by: Hiroshimashi Koen Kyokai/Hiroshima City Park Association, 3-495 Kura-Shige, Saeki-ku, Hiroshima-shi, 731-5156, Japan.

580 NLD ISSN 0302-3141
QK911 CODEN: HVSCEK
HANDBOOK OF VEGETATION SCIENCE. Text in English. irreg., latest vol.19, no.2, 1996. price varies. **Document type:** *Monographic series.*
Indexed: BIOSIS Prev.
—**CCC.**
Published by: Springer-Verlag Dordrecht (Subsidiary of: Springer Science+Business Media), Van Godewijckstraat 30, Dordrecht, 3311 GX, Netherlands. TEL 31-78-6576050, FAX 31-78-6576474, http://www.springeronline.com. Ed. Richard Pott.

580 USA ISSN 1043-4534
QK1
➤ **HARVARD PAPERS IN BOTANY.** Text in English. 1989. irreg. price varies. illus. **Document type:** *Monographic series, Academic/Scholarly.* **Description:** Discusses botanical papers.
Formed by the merger of (1932-1989): Botanical Museum Leaflets (0006-8098); (1969-1989): Farlow Herbarium of Cryptogamic Botany. Occasional Papers (0090-8754); (1891-1989): Harvard University. Gray Herbarium. Contributions (0195-6094)
Indexed: Agr, BIOSIS Prev, BiolAb, ChemAb, FCA, HerbAb, PBA.
—BLDSC (4268.375000), CISTI, IE, ingenta, Linda Hall.
Published by: Harvard University Herbaria, 22 Divinity Ave, Cambridge, MA 02138. TEL 617-495-2360, FAX 617-495-9484, gromero@oeb.harvard.edu. Ed. Gustavo Romero.

583.56 USA ISSN 1070-0048
SB438
➤ **HASELTONIA.** Text in English. 1993. a. USD 30 domestic; USD 32 foreign (effective 2001). **Document type:** *Journal, Academic/Scholarly.* **Description:** Haseltonia is named in honor of Scott E. Haselton, first editor of the Journal. This is the yearbook of the CSSA and has articles of interest to the botanist and amateur.
Indexed: CurCont, GardL.
Published by: Cactus & Succulent Society of America, Inc., 2391 E Cactus St, PO Box 2615, Pahrump, NV 89048. TEL 310-556-1923, FAX 310-286-9629, http://www.cssainc.org.

580 JPN ISSN 0073-0912
QK533 CODEN: JHBLAI
HATTORI SHOKUBUTSU KENKYUJO HOKOKU/HATTORI BOTANICAL LABORATORY. JOURNAL; devoted to bryology and lichenology. Text in Multiple languages. 1947. 2/yr. membership. cum.index: no.1-50. back issues avail. **Document type:** *Journal, Academic/Scholarly.*
Indexed: Agr, BIOSIS Prev, BiolAb, ChemAb, CurCont, ISR, PBA, RPP, SCI.
—BLDSC (4757.900000), CASDDS, CISTI, IE, Infotrieve, ingenta, Linda Hall.
Published by: Hattori Botanical Laboratory/Hattori Shokubutsu Kenkyujo, 2-112-2, Funatsuka, Miyazaki, 880-0031, Japan. FAX 81-985-290905, hattorib@pastel.ocn.ne.jp, http://www7.ocn.ne.jp/~hattorib/journal-j.html, http://www7.ocn.ne.jp/~hattorib/index-j.html. Ed. Sinske Hattori. Circ: 500.

HEATHER SOCIETY. YEARBOOK. see *GARDENING AND HORTICULTURE*

580.9438 POL ISSN 0018-0599
CODEN: HPBIA9
➤ **HERBA POLONICA.** Text in English, German, Polish; Summaries in English. 1955. q. USD 40 foreign (effective 2005). adv. bk.rev. bibl.; charts; illus. index. **Document type:** *Journal, Academic/Scholarly.*
Formerly: Instytut Roslin Leczniczy. Biuletyn
Related titles: Online - full text ed.
Indexed: AbHyg, AgBio, AgrAg, AgrForAb, AgrLib, AnalAb, B&AI, BibAg, BiolAb, CIN, CPA, ChemAb, ChemTitl, CurCont, DBA, ExcerpMed, FCA, FPA, ForAb, HelmAb, HortAb, IPA, MSB, MaizeAb, NutrAb, OrnHort, PBA, PGegResA, PGrRegA, PHN&I, PoultAb, RA&MP, RM&VM, RPP, RevApplEntom, S&F, SIA, SeedAb, SoyAb, TDB, TriticAb, WAE&RSA, WeedAb.
—CASDDS, GNLM.
Published by: Instytut Roslin i Przetworow Zielarskich/Research Institute of Medicinal Plants, ul Libelta 27, Poznan, 61707, Poland. TEL 48-61-8524003, FAX 48-61-8527463, ak_iripz@man.poznan.pl, akp@iripz.pl, http://www.iripz.pl/index2.php/1/0/show/76/. Ed. Przemyslaw M Mrozikiewicz. Adv. contact Anna Krajewska Patan. Circ: 1,000. **Co-sponsor:** State Committe for Scientific Research.

581.63 615.321 USA ISSN 0899-5648
RS164
HERBALGRAM; the journal of the American Botanical Council & the Herb Research Foundation. Text in English. 1983. q. USD 50 to individual members; USD 100 to institutional members; USD 250 to corporations (effective 2005). adv. bk.rev.; software rev.; video rev. stat.; tr.lit.; charts; illus.; mkt. Index. back issues avail. **Document type:** *Magazine, Consumer.* **Description:** Covers many of the facets of the Herb movement, both within the US and abroad. Covers herbs and medicinal plants, history of their use, legal and regulatory developments regarding sales and marketing.
Related titles: Online - full text ed.: (from EBSCO Publishing).
Indexed: AbHyg, Agr, CPA, ForAb, GardL, HortAb, NutrAb, OrnHort, PBA, PGegResA, PHN&I, RA&MP, RefZh, S&F, TDB, WAE&RSA.
—GNLM.
Published by: American Botanical Council, 6200 Manor Rd, Austin, TX 78723. FAX 512-926-2345, abc@herbalgram.org, http://www.herbalgram.org/herbalgram/index.html. Ed., Pub. Mark Blumenthal. R&P Barbara Johnston TEL 512-451-4820. Adv. contact Debbie Jones. B&W page USD 1,892, color page USD 2,882; trim 8.625 x 11.125. Circ: 50,000 (paid).

581.634 FRA ISSN 1250-6273
HERBALIA. Text in French. 1994. q. bk.rev. **Document type:** *Newsletter.*
Published by: Institut Interprofessionnel des Plantes a Parfum Medicinales et Aromatiques, ZI des Trois Routes, Chemille, 49120, France. TEL 33-2-41303079, FAX 33-2-41305948. Ed. Gilles Verniau. Circ: 400.

580.74 USA
HERBARIUM PACIFICUM NEWS. Text in English. 3/yr. **Document type:** *Newsletter.*
Published by: Bishop Museum Herbarium Pacificum, 1525 Bernice St, Honolulu, HI 96817. TEL 808-847-3511, FAX 808-841-8968, library@bishopmuseum.org, http://www.bishopmuseum.org/research/natsci/botany.

580 DEU ISSN 0439-0687
QK314 CODEN: HFBRAY
HESSISCHE FLORISTISCHE BRIEFE. Text in German. 1952. q. EUR 15 (effective 2003). adv. bk.rev. **Document type:** *Journal, Academic/Scholarly.*
Indexed: BIOSIS Prev, BiolAb, RefZh.
Published by: Naturwissenschaftlicher Verein Darmstadt e.V., Bessungerstr 125-C, Darmstadt, 64295, Germany. TEL 49-6151-133288. Ed. Michael Hoellwarth. Circ: 800.

580.952 JPN ISSN 0046-7413
QK369 CODEN: HKBAAI
➤ **HIKOBIA.** Text and summaries in English, Japanese. 1950. a., latest vol.13, no.1, 1999. JPY 4,000, USD 4,000 (effective 2000 & 2001). bk.rev. illus.; stat. back issues avail. **Document type:** *Academic/Scholarly.* **Description:** Covers the flora, taxonomy and vegetation of Japan.
Indexed: BIOSIS Prev, BiolAb, FCA, ForAb, HerbAb.
—BLDSC (4312.800000), CISTI.
Published by: Hikobia Botanical Society/Hikobiakai, c/o Laboratory of Plant Taxonomy & Ecology, Dept of Biological Science, Faculty of Science, Hiroshima University, 3-1, Kagamiyama 1-chome, Higashi-hiroshima-shi, 739-8526, Japan. TEL 81-824-24-7451, FAX 81-824-24-0734, hdeguch@ipc.hiroshima-u.ac.jp. Ed., Adv. contact Hironori Deguchi. Circ: 400.

➤ **HIMALAYAN JOURNAL OF ENVIRONMENT AND ZOOLOGY.** see *BIOLOGY—Zoology*

580 JPN
HIROSHIMA UNIVERSITY. FACULTY OF SCIENCE. BOTANICAL INSTITUTE. RESEARCH REPORT. Text in English. a.
Published by: Hiroshima University, Faculty of Science/Hiroshima Daigaku Rigakubu Chikyu Wakuseisisutemugaku, 1-3 Kagamiyama, Higashihiroshima-shi, Hiroshima-ken 739-0046, Japan.

580 635 JPN ISSN 0386-5304
HIROSHIMASHI SHOKUBUTSU KOEN KIYO/HIROSHIMA BOTANICAL GARDEN. BULLETIN. Text in English, Japanese. 1977. a. **Document type:** *Bulletin.*
Published by: Hiroshimashi Shokubutsu Koen/Hiroshima Botanical Garden, 3-495 Kura-Shige, Saeki-ku, Hiroshima-shi, Hiroshima-ken 731-5156, Japan.

580 635 JPN ISSN 0387-8597
HIROSHIMASHI SHOKUBUTSU KOEN SAIBAI KIROKU/HIROSHIMA BOTANICAL GARDEN. INVESTIGATION. Text in Japanese. 1979. a.
Published by: Hiroshimashi Shokubutsu Koen/Hiroshima Botanical Garden, 3-495 Kura-Shige, Saeki-ku, Hiroshima-shi, Hiroshima-ken 731-5156, Japan.

580 579   BRA   ISSN 0073-2877
QK263   CODEN: HOEHAE
➤ HOEHNEA. Text and summaries in English, Portuguese. 1971.
3/yr. price varies. abstr.; bibl.; charts; illus.; maps; stat. 90
p./no.; back issues avail. **Document type:** *Bulletin,
Academic/Scholarly.* **Description:** Hoehnea publishes original
research articles in all areas of Botany, like Plant Morphology
and anatomy, Taxonomy of all plant groups, Plant Physiology
and Ecology.
Supersedes in part: Arquivos de Botanica do Estado de Sao
Paulo (0374-5031); Incorporates (1962-1987, vol.14): Rickia
(0080-3014); Which also supersedes in part: Arquivos de
Botanica do Estado de Sao Paulo
Indexed: BIOSIS Prev, BiolAb, RefZh.
—CASDDS, CISTI.
Published by: Instituto de Botanica, Caixa Postal 4005, Sao
Paulo, SP 0106-970, Brazil. TEL 55-11-50736300, FAX
55-11-50733678, hoehneaibt@yahoo.com,
http://www.ibot.sp.gov.br. Ed., R&P, Adv. contact Marina
Capelari. Pub. Luis Mauro Barbosa. Circ: 1,000; 1,000
(controlled).

580   JPN
HOKKAIDO DAIGAKU NOGAKUBU FUZOKU SHOKUBUTSUEN
NENPO/HOKKAIDO UNIVERSITY. FACULTY OF
AGRICULTURE. BOTANIC GARDEN. ANNUAL REPORT.
Text in Japanese. a. **Document type:** *Academic/Scholarly.*
Published by: Hokkaido Daigaku, Nogakubu Fuzoku
Shokubutsuen/Hokkaido University, Faculty of Agriculture,
Botanic Garden, Nishi 8-chome, Kita 3-jo, Chuo-ku,
Sapporo-shi, Hokkaido 060-0003, Japan. Ed. Hideki
Takahashi.

HOKKAIDO UNIVERSITY. INSTITUTE OF ALGOLOGICAL
RESEARCH. SCIENTIFIC PAPERS/HOKKAIDO DAIGAKU
RIGAKUBU KAISO KENKYUJO OBUN HOKOKU. see
EARTH SCIENCES—Oceanography

HOME - GROWN CEREALS AUTHORITY. CEREALS R & D
CONFERENCE. PROCEEDINGS. see *AGRICULTURE—Crop
Production And Soil*

HOME - GROWN CEREALS AUTHORITY. PROJECT REPORT.
see *AGRICULTURE—Crop Production And Soil*

HOME - GROWN CEREALS AUTHORITY. RESEARCH REVIEW.
see *AGRICULTURE—Crop Production And Soil*

580   DEU   ISSN 0340-4196
QK314
HOPPEA. Text in German; Summaries in English, German. 1815.
a. price varies. bk.rev. bibl. index. back issues avail.
Document type: *Journal, Academic/Scholarly.* **Description:**
Studies flora and vegetation of Bavaria.
—Linda Hall.
Published by: Regensburgische Botanische Gesellschaft, Institut
fuer Botanik, Universitaet Regensburg, Universitaetsstr 31,
Regensburg, 93040, Germany. TEL 49-941-943-3124, FAX
49-941-943-3106, http://www.biologie.uni-regensburg.de/
botanik/schoenfelder/vbg/hoppea.html. Ed. Peter Schoenfelder.

571.2   NLD   ISSN 1389-4749
HORTUS BOTANICUS CATALOGUE SERIES. Text in English.
1998. EUR 23 (effective 2002). **Description:** It is a new
series of catalogues on plants grown in the Leiden Hortus
Botanicus. This catalogue lists about 6200 accessions
covering over 1500 species in cultivation in the greenhouses
of the Botanical Garden of Leiden University since 1954.
Published by: National Herbarium Nederland/Leiden Branch, PO
Box 9514, Leiden, 2300 RA, Netherlands. TEL
31-71-5273570, FAX 31-71-5273522, http://
www.nhncml.leidenuniv.nl. Ed. J. de Koning.

HOSTASCIENCE. see *GARDENING AND HORTICULTURE*

580 740   USA   ISSN 0192-3641
HUNT INSTITUTE FOR BOTANICAL DOCUMENTATION.
BULLETIN. Text in English. 1979. s-a. USD 4 per vol.
domestic; USD 5 per vol. foreign (effective 2004). **Document
type:** *Newsletter, Academic/Scholarly.*
—Linda Hall. **CCC.**
Published by: Hunt Institute for Botanical Documentation,
Carnegie Mellon University, 5000 Forbes Ave, Pittsburgh, PA
15213-3890. TEL 412-268-2434, FAX 412-268-5677,
huntinst@andrew.cmu.edu, http://huntbot.andrew.cmu.edu/
HIBD/Publications/HI-Pubs/Pub-Bulletin.shtml. Ed., R&P
Scarlett Townsend. Circ: 700.

580   USA   ISSN 0073-4071
QK1
➤ HUNTIA; a journal of botanical history. Text in English. 1963.
irreg., latest vol.11, no.1. USD 60 per vol. (effective 2005).
bk.rev. back issues avail. **Document type:** *Journal,
Academic/Scholarly.* **Description:** Publishes articles on all
aspects of the history of botany and is published irregularly in
one or more numbers per volume or approximately 200 pages
by the Hunt Institute for Botanical Documentation.
Indexed: Agr, RefZh.
—Linda Hall. **CCC.**

Published by: Hunt Institute for Botanical Documentation,
Carnegie Mellon University, 5000 Forbes Ave, Pittsburgh, PA
15213-3890. TEL 412-268-2434, FAX 412-268-5677,
huntinst@andrew.cmu.edu, http://huntbot.andrew.cmu.edu/
HIBD/Publications/HI-Pubs/Pub-Huntia.shtml. Ed., R&P
Scarlett Townsend. Circ: 350.

580 674   NLD   ISSN 0928-1541
QK647   CODEN: IAJOEB
➤ I A W A JOURNAL. Text in English. 1931; N.S. 1980. q. free
to members (effective 2002). bk.rev. index. back issues avail.
Document type: *Journal, Academic/Scholarly.* **Description:**
Published at the Nationaal Herbarium Nederland, Leiden
University branch, The Netherlands. Devoted to research on
the microstructure of wood and bark and related plant
products such as bamboo, rattan and palms. Also covers
fundamental, systematic and evolutionary botanical aspects
and applied forestry.
Former titles (until 1993): I A W A Bulletin (0254-3915); I A W A
Publications
Indexed: A&ATA, ABIPC, ASCA, AgrForAb, BIOBASE, BIOSIS
Prev, BiolAb, CPA, CurCont, FPA, ForAb, HortAb, I&DA, IABS,
NAA, NemAb, OrnHort, P&BA, PBA, PGegResA, PGrRegA,
PlantSci, RA&MP, RDA, RPP, RefZh, RiceAb, S&F, VITIS,
WeedAb.
—BLDSC (4359.675100), CISTI, IDS, IE, Infotrieve, ingenta,
Linda Hall. **CCC.**
Published by: International Association of Wood Anatomists, PO
Box 80102, Utrecht, 3508 TC, Netherlands. FAX
31-30-251-8061, eevn@euronet.nl, http://www.kuleuven.ac.be/
bio/sys/iawa, http://courses.ncsu.edu/classes/wps202001/
IAWA/iawa.htm. Eds. E A Wheeler, P Baas. R&P Regis Miller.
Circ: 800. **Co-publisher:** National Herbarium
Nederland/Leiden Branch.

579.5   GBR
I S M S NEWSLETTER. Text in English. q. **Document type:**
Newsletter.
Indexed: HortAb, WAE&RSA.
Published by: International Society for Mushroom Science, c/o
Kerry Burton, Executive Secretary ISMS, 196 Rugby Rd,
Leamington Spa, Warcs CV32 6DU, United Kingdom.
http://www.hri.ac.uk/isms/.

579.5   BEL   ISSN 0779-1070
ICONES MYCOLOGICAE. Text in French. 1982. irreg., latest
1986. price varies. illus. back issues avail. **Document type:**
Monographic series, Academic/Scholarly.
Published by: Jardin Botanique National de Belgique/Nationale
Plantentuin van Belgie, Domaine de Bouchout, Nieuwelaan
38, Meise, 1860, Belgium. TEL 32-2-2693905,
http://www.br.fgov.be. Ed. J Rammeloo. Adv. contact Katrien
Clarysse.

653.934   MEX   ISSN 0188-4018
                                        CODEN: EUQIEM
ICONES ORCHIDACEARUM. Text in English, Spanish. 1990.
irreg. MXP 450; USD 45 per vol. (effective 2003). illus. index.
200 p./no.; back issues avail. **Document type:** *Monographic
series.* **Description:** Contains botanical illustrations dedicated
to orchids with descriptions and data on distribution, habitat
and conservation.
Published by: Herbarium Amo, Lago Tanganica 18, Granada,
Mexico City, DF 11520, Mexico. TEL 52-55-52623193, FAX
52-55-55314349. Eds. Eric Hagsater, Miguel Angel
Soto-Arenas. R&P Nora A Esponda. Circ: 600. **Subscr. to:**
Apdo Postal 53-123, Mexico City, D.F. 11320 , Mexico.

580   SEN   ISSN 0073-4403
ICONES PLANTARUM AFRICANARUM. Text in French. 1953.
irreg.
Published by: Institut Fondamental d'Afrique Noire/Cheikh Anta
Diop, BP 206, Dakar, Senegal.

580   DEU
ICONOGRAPHIA DIATOMOLOGICA. Text in English. irreg., latest
vol.11, 2002. price varies. **Document type:** *Monographic
series.*
Indexed: BIOSIS Prev.
Published by: Koeltz Scientific Books, PO Box 1360,
Koenigstein, 61453, Germany. TEL 49-6174-93720, FAX
49-6174-937240, koeltz@t-online.de, http://www.koeltz.com.

580   BRA   ISSN 0073-4705
QK1   CODEN: IHBOAG
➤ IHERINGIA. SERIE BOTANICA. Text in Portuguese;
Summaries in English, Spanish. 1958. s-a. exchange
agreements with other institutions. abstr.; bibl.; illus. back
issues avail. **Document type:** *Journal, Academic/Scholarly.*
Description: Published by the Museum of Natural Sciences of
the Zoobotanic Foundation, Rio Grande do Sul, this journal
publishes articles and scientific commentaries on all subjects
related to botany.
Indexed: ASFA, AgrForAb, BIOSIS Prev, BiolAb, CPA, ChemAb,
ESPM, FCA, ForAb, HerbAb, HortAb, I&DA, IndVet, OrnHort,
PBA, PGegResA, PGrRegA, RA&MP, RPP, RefZh, S&F,
SWRA, SeedAb, WeedAb, ZooRec.
—BLDSC (4363.520000), CISTI. **CCC.**

Published by: (Museu de Ciencias Naturais), Fundacao
Zoobotanica do Rio Grande do Sul, Caixa Postal 1188, Porto
Alegre, RS 90690-000, Brazil. TEL 55-51-33202000, FAX
55-51-33363281, iheringia-bot@fzb.rs.gov.br,
biblioteca@fzb.rs.gov.br, http://www.fzb.rs.gov.br. Ed. Lezilda
Carvalho Torgan. Circ: 600.

➤ IMMERGRUENE BLAETTER. see *GARDENING AND
HORTICULTURE*

381   AUS
IN FLOWER THIS WEEK. Text in English. 1997. w. **Document
type:** *Newsletter.* **Description:** Includes news articles about
plants flowering in Australia.
Media: Online - full text.
Published by: Australian National Botanical Gardens, GPO Box
1777, Canberra, ACT 2601, Australia. TEL 61-2-6250-9450,
FAX 61-2-6250-9528, murray.fagg@ea.gov.au,
http://www.anbg.gov.au/iftw. Ed. Fagg Murray.

581.3   GBR   ISSN 1054-5476
QK725   CODEN: IVCPEO
➤ IN VITRO CELLULAR & DEVELOPMENTAL BIOLOGY -
PLANT. Text in English. 1965. 6/yr. GBP 215 domestic to
institutions; USD 230 in North America to institutions; USD
380 elsewhere to institutions; GBP 230 combined subscription
domestic to institutions print & online eds.; USD 340
combined subscription in North America to institutions print &
online eds.; USD 400 combined subscription elsewhere to
institutions print & online eds. (effective 2006). adv. bk.rev.
index. back issues avail. **Document type:** *Journal,
Academic/Scholarly.* **Description:** Publishes original papers in
plant cellular and developmental biology with emphasis on the
developmental, molecular and cellular biology of cells, tissues,
and organs.
Supersedes in part (in 1991): In Vitro Cellular and
Developmental Biology (0883-8364); Which was formerly: In
Vitro (0073-5655)
Related titles: Microform ed.: (from PQC); Online - full text ed.:
ISSN 1475-2689. GBP 210 domestic to institutions; USD 305
in North America to institutions; USD 370 elsewhere to
institutions (effective 2006) (from bigchalk, BioOne, C S A,
EBSCO Publishing, Gale Group, IngentaConnect, Ovid
Technologies, Inc., ProQuest Information & Learning, Swets
Information Services).
Indexed: AEA, AEBA, ASCA, AgBio, Agr, AgrForAb, B&BAb,
BBCI, BCI, BIOBASE, BIOSIS Prev, BioEngAb, BiolAb, CIN,
CPA, ChemAb, ChemTitl, CurCont, DBA, DSA, ESPM, FCA,
FPA, ForAb, HerbAb, HortAb, IABS, ISR, IndMed, MBA,
MaizeAb, NemAb, NutrAb, OrnHort, PBA, PGegResA,
PGrRegA, PHN&I, PlantSci, PotatoAb, RA&MP, RDA, RPP,
RefZh, RevApplEntom, RiceAb, S&F, SCI, SIA, SeedAb,
SoyAb, TDB, TriticAb, VITIS, WAE&RSA, WeedAb.
—BLDSC (4372.500800), CASDDS, CISTI, GNLM, IDS, IE,
Infotrieve, ingenta, Linda Hall. **CCC.**
Published by: (International Association for Plant Tissue Culture
ISR, Society for In Vitro Biology USA), CABI Publishing
(Subsidiary of: CAB International), CAB International,
Wallingford, Oxfordshire OX10 8DE, United Kingdom. TEL
44-1491-832111, FAX 44-1491-833508, http://www.cabi-
publishing.org/. Ed. Eng-Chong Pua. Pub. David Smith TEL
44-1491-829325. adv.: B&W page USD 275; trim 8.25 x 11.
Circ: 3,600 (paid).

➤ INDEX OF FUNGI. see *BIOLOGY—Abstracting, Bibliographies,
Statistics*

580   ISR
INDEX SEMINUM; wild and cultivated plants. Text in English. a.
free.
Published by: Tel Aviv University, Department of Botany, Ramat
Aviv, Tel Aviv, 69978, Israel. TEL 03-420151. Ed. Yeduha
Tankus.

580.968   ZAF
INDEX SEMINUM; list of plant genetic resources available in
South Africa. Text in English. 1994. a. **Document type:**
Abstract/Index.
Published by: (Tripura. Department of Agriculture), Directorate of
Plant and Quality Control, National Genebank, Private Bag
X258, Pretoria, 0001, South Africa.

580   CZE
INDEX SEMINUM ET PLANTARUM. Text in Czech. a. **Document
type:** *Academic/Scholarly.* **Description:** Serves as a forum of
exchange for seeds of wild and cultivated plants.
Published by: Akademie Ved Ceske Republiky, Botanicky
Ustav/Academy of Sciences of the Czech Republic, Institute of
Botany, Pruhonice, 25243, Czech Republic. TEL
420-2-67750065, FAX 420-2-67750031, bartova@ibot.cas.cz,
http://www.lib.cas.cz/knav/journals/eng/Index_Seminum.htm.
Ed. Evzenie Bartova.

INDEX TO PLANT CHROMOSOME NUMBERS. see
BIOLOGY—Abstracting, Bibliographies, Statistics

580   IND   ISSN 0254-4091
QK358   CODEN: IBREDR
INDIAN BOTANICAL REPORTER. Text in English. s-a. INR 40,
USD 10 to individuals; INR 75, USD 20 to institutions.
Indexed: ASFA, BiolAb, CIN, ChemAb, ChemTitl, ESPM, FCA,
HerbAb, RPP, SWRA.

▼ *new title*   ➤ *refereed*   ∗ *unverified*   ◆ *full entry avail.*

—CASDDS.
Published by: Marathwada University, Department of Botany, Executive Editor, Aurangabad, 431 004, India.

587.31 IND ISSN 0970-2741
QK529.I4 CODEN: IFJOEC
➤ **INDIAN FERN JOURNAL**; an international journal of pteridology. Text in English. 1984. a. USD 50 (effective 2005). adv. bk.rev. 150 p./no. 1 cols./p.; back issues avail. **Document type:** *Academic/Scholarly.* **Description:** Promotes the cause of botany in general and research on the ferns and fern allies in particular. Fosters public interest in the conservation of ferns and fern allies.
Indexed: BIOSIS Prev, BiolAb.
—CISTI, Linda Hall.
Published by: Indian Fern Society, Punjabi University, Department of Botany, Patiala, Punjab 147 002, India. TEL 91-175-2286652, ssbu28@rediffmail.com. Ed. S.S. Bir. R&P S S Bir TEL 91-175-282652. adv.: B&W page USD 50; trim 150 x 200. Circ: 200.

580 IND ISSN 0073-6376
INDIAN FOREST RECORDS (NEW SERIES) BOTANY. Text in English. 1937. irreg., latest vol.6, no.1, 1980. price varies.
Indexed: BiolAb, FPA, ForAb, ISA, RevApplEntom.
—CISTI, Linda Hall.
Published by: Forest Research Institute & Colleges, P.O. New Forest, Dehra Dun, Uttar Pradesh, India. Circ: 500.

580 IND ISSN 0250-829X
QK358 CODEN: IJBODX
INDIAN JOURNAL OF BOTANY. Text in English. 1978. s-a. INR 100, USD 25. adv. bk.rev. Supplement avail. **Document type:** *Academic/Scholarly.* **Description:** Presents original research in plant science.
Indexed: ASFA, BiolAb, CIN, ChemAb, ChemTitl, ESPM, ExcerpMed, FCA, HerbAb, HortAb, IndVet, Inspec, MaizeAb, RM&VM, S&MA, SeedAb, TOSA, TriticAb, WeedAb.
—CASDDS, CISTI, Linda Hall.
Published by: S. Krishnamurthy, 6-1-127-2 Khairatabad, Hyderabad, Andhra Pradesh 500 004, India. Ed. A Satyanarayana. Circ: 500.

581.35 IND ISSN 0019-5200
SB123 CODEN: IJGBAG
INDIAN JOURNAL OF GENETICS AND PLANT BREEDING. Text in English. 1960. q. USD 300 to institutions (effective 2006). adv. bk.rev. charts; illus. index, cum.index: vols.1-20, vols.21-30. **Document type:** *Academic/Scholarly.* **Description:** Covers electrical and electronics, metallurgy, mechanical, chemical, software engineering and computer science, mining, steel, environmental technology, power and energy.
Indexed: AgBio, AgrForAb, AnBrAb, BIOSIS Prev, BiolAb, CIN, CPA, CTFA, ChemAb, ChemTitl, CurCont, DSA, FCA, FaBeAb, ForAb, GenetAb, HGA, HerbAb, HortAb, I&DA, MaizeAb, OrnHort, PBA, PGegResA, PGrRegA, PHN&I, PotatoAb, RA&MP, RPP, RevApplEntom, RiceAb, S&F, SIA, SeedAb, SoyAb, TOSA, TriticAb, WeedAb.
—CASDDS, CISTI, IE, Infotrieve, Linda Hall.
Published by: (Indian Society of Genetics and Plant Breeding, Division of Genetics), Scientific Publishers, 5-A New Pali Rd., Near Hotel Taj Hari Mahal, PO Box 91, Jodhpur, Rajasthan 342 003, India. TEL 91-291-2433323, FAX 91-291-2512580, info@scientificpub.com, http://www.scientificpub.com/bookdetails.php?booktransid=321&bookid=317. Ed. Mihir Sen. adv.: B&W page USD 422, color page USD 845. Circ: 9,000.

579.5 IND
CODEN: IJMPAK
➤ **INDIAN JOURNAL OF MYCOLOGY AND PLANT PATHOLOGY.** Text in English. 1971. q. USD 250 to institutions (effective 2006). adv. bk.rev. bibl.; charts; illus. back issues avail. **Document type:** *Journal, Academic/Scholarly.*
Former titles (until 1997): Journal of Mycology and Plant Pathology (0971-9393); (until 1996): Indian Journal of Mycology and Plant Pathology (0303-4097)
Indexed: AEA, ASFA, AgBio, AgrForAb, B&BAb, BIOSIS Prev, BibAg, BioCN&I, BiolAb, CIN, CPA, CTFA, ChemAb, ESPM, FCA, FPA, FaBeAb, ForAb, HerbAb, HortAb, ISA, MBA, MaizeAb, NemAb, NutrAb, OrnHort, PBA, PGegResA, PGrRegA, PHN&I, PotatoAb, PoultAb, RA&MP, RDA, RM&VM, RPP, RevApplEntom, RiceAb, S&F, S&MA, SIA, SeedAb, SoyAb, TOSA, TriticAb, VITIS, WAE&RSA, WeedAb.
—CASDDS, CISTI, Linda Hall.
Published by: (Indian Society of Mycology and Plant Pathology), Scientific Publishers, 5-A New Pali Rd., Near Hotel Taj Hari Mahal, PO Box 91, Jodhpur, Rajasthan 342 003, India. TEL 91-291-2433323, FAX 91-291-2512580, info@scientificpub.com, http://www.scientificpub.com/bookdetails.php?booktransid=339&bookid=335. Circ: 500. **Dist. overseas by:** H P C Publishers Distributors Pvt. Ltd.

581.3 IND
INDIAN JOURNAL OF PLANT GENETIC RESOURCES. Text in English. 1988. s-a. INR 100 domestic to individuals; USD 50 foreign to individuals; INR 500 domestic to institutions; USD 250 foreign to institutions. adv. **Document type:** *Academic/Scholarly.* **Description:** For botanists, geneticists, plant breeders, and those concerned with plant genetic resources.
Published by: Indian Society of Plant Genetic Resources, NBPGR Campus, Pusa, New Delhi, 110 012, India. TEL 91-11-5789208, FAX 91-11-5786414, bbsingh@nbpgr.delhi.nic.in. Ed. B.B. Singh. R&P B B Singh. Circ: 500.

571.2 IND ISSN 0019-5502
QK710 CODEN: IPPYA2
➤ **INDIAN JOURNAL OF PLANT PHYSIOLOGY.** Text in English. 1958; N.S. 1996. q. USD 120 to institutions (effective 2006). bk.rev. back issues avail. **Document type:** *Academic/Scholarly.*
Indexed: AgBio, AgrForAb, BIOSIS Prev, BiolAb, CIN, CPA, CTFA, ChemAb, ChemTitl, CurCont, DSA, FCA, FPA, FS&TA, ForAb, HerbAb, HortAb, I&DA, INIS AtomInd, MaizeAb, NutrAb, OrnHort, PBA, PGegResA, PGrRegA, PHN&I, PotatoAb, PoultAb, RA&MP, RPP, RevApplEntom, RiceAb, S&F, S&MA, SIA, SeedAb, SoyAb, TOSA, TriticAb, VITIS, WeedAb.
—BLDSC (4420.150000), CASDDS, CISTI, IE, ingenta, Linda Hall.
Published by: Indian Society for Plant Physiology, Division of Plant Physiology, Indian Agricultural Research Institute, New Delhi, 110 012, India. http://www.scientificpub.com/bookdetails.php?booktransid=328&bookid=324. Ed. M C Ghildyel. Circ: 1,000 (paid and controlled). **Dist. by:** Scientific Publishers, 5-A New Pali Rd., Near Hotel Taj Hari Mahal, PO Box 91, Jodhpur, Rajasthan 342 003, India. TEL 91-291-2433323, FAX 91-291-2512580, info@scientificpub.com, http://www.scientificpub.com.

571.92 IND ISSN 0537-2410
INDIAN PHYTOPATHOLOGICAL SOCIETY. BULLETIN. Text in English. 1963. irreg.
Indexed: BiolAb, RPP.
—Linda Hall.
Published by: Indian Phytological Society, c/o Indian Agricultural Research Institute, Division of Mycology, New Delhi, 110 012, India.

580 IND ISSN 0367-973X
SB599 CODEN: IPHYAU
INDIAN PHYTOPATHOLOGY. Text in English. 1948. q. USD 150 to institutions (effective 2006). adv. bk.rev. **Document type:** *Journal, Academic/Scholarly.* **Description:** Covers news and information about the researches in phytopathology in India.
Media: Duplicated (not offset).
Indexed: AgBio, AgrForAb, BioCN&I, BiolAb, CIN, CPA, CTFA, ChemAb, ChemTitl, DBA, DSA, ExcerpMed, FCA, FPA, FaBeAb, ForAb, HerbAb, HortAb, I&DA, MaizeAb, NemAb, OrnHort, PBA, PGegResA, PGrRegA, PHN&I, PotatoAb, PoultAb, RA&MP, RDA, RM&VM, RPP, RevApplEntom, RiceAb, S&F, S&MA, SIA, SeedAb, SoyAb, TDB, TOSA, TriticAb, WAE&RSA, WeedAb, ZooRec.
—BLDSC (4427.000000), CASDDS, CISTI, IE, Infotrieve, ingenta, Linda Hall.
Published by: (Indian Agricultural Research Institute, Nematological Society of India, Indian Phytopathological Society), Scientific Publishers, 5-A New Pali Rd., Near Hotel Taj Hari Mahal, PO Box 91, Jodhpur, Rajasthan 342 003, India. TEL 91-291-2433323, FAX 91-291-2512580, info@scientificpub.com, http://www.scientificpub.com/bookdetails.php?booktransid=331&bookid=327. Circ: 2,000. **Dist. overseas by:** H P C Publishers Distributors Pvt. Ltd.

580 CUB
INFORMACION EXPRESS. SERIE: PLANTAS MEDICINALES Y FLORES. Text in Spanish. 1985. a. CUP 30 domestic; USD 3 in North America; USD 6 in Europe; USD 5 elsewhere. stat.
Indexed: Agrind.
Published by: Centro de Informacion y Documentacion Agropecuario, Gaveta Postal 4149, Havana, 4, Cuba. TEL 301672. **Dist. by:** Ediciones Cubanas, Obispo No. 527, Apdo. 605, Havana, Cuba.

581.3 FRA ISSN 0073-7917
INFORMATIONS ANNUELLES DE CARYOSYSTEMATIQUE ET CYTOGENETIQUE✶. Text in French. 1967. a. price varies.
Published by: Institut Botanique Strasbourg, 8 rue Goethe, Strasbourg, 67000, France.

580 ITA ISSN 0020-0697
QK1 CODEN: IBOIBM
➤ **INFORMATORE BOTANICO ITALIANO**; bollettino della Societa Botanica Italiana. Text in Italian; Summaries in English, Italian. 1969. 2/yr. EUR 110 (effective 2003). bk.rev. abstr.; illus.; bibl.; charts. index. 350 p./no.; back issues avail. **Document type:** *Journal, Academic/Scholarly.*
Indexed: BIOSIS Prev, BiolAb.
—Linda Hall.
Published by: Societa Botanica Italiana, Via Giorgio La Pira, 4, Florence, FI 50121, Italy. TEL 39-055-2757379, FAX 39-055-2757467, sbi@unifi.it, http://www.unifi.it/unifi/bioveg/sb/ibi.htm. Ed. Carlo Blasi. Circ: 1,300.

571.92 ITA ISSN 0020-0735
CODEN: INFTAP
INFORMATORE FITOPATOLOGICO. Short title: I F. Text in Italian. 1951. m. (11/yr.). EUR 62 domestic; EUR 110 foreign (effective 2005). adv. bk.rev. illus.; tr.lit. index. 80 p./no.; **Document type:** *Magazine, Trade.* **Description:** Examines all aspects and problems of phytopathology.
Related titles: Online - full text ed.
Indexed: AEA, AbHyg, AgBio, AgrForAb, BioCN&I, BiolAb, CBNB, CPA, ChemAb, DSA, FCA, FPA, ForAb, HortAb, I&DA, MaizeAb, NemAb, NutrAb, OrnHort, PBA, PGegResA, PHN&I, PN&I, PotatoAb, ProtozoAb, RA&MP, RDA, RM&VM, RPP, RRTA, RevApplEntom, RiceAb, S&F, SIA, SeedAb, SoyAb, TriticAb, VITIS, WAE&RSA, WeedAb.
—BLDSC (4496.800000), CASDDS, CISTI, IE, ingenta.
Published by: Il Sole 24 Ore Edagricole, Via Goito 13, Bologna, BO 40126, Italy. TEL 39-051-62267, FAX 39-051-490200, http://www.edagricole.it. Ed. Giorgio Setti. Circ: 5,300.

580 USA ISSN 1067-909X
QK600
INOCULUM. Text in English. 1948. bi-m. USD 60 to members (effective 2002). **Document type:** *Newsletter.*
Formerly (until 1992): Mycological Society of America Newsletter (0541-4938)
Related titles: Online - full text ed.; ◆ Supplement to: Mycologia. ISSN 0027-5514.
Indexed: RM&VM.
Published by: Mycological Society of America, c/o Lorelei Norvell, Ed, Pacific Northwest Mycology Service, 6720 N W Skyline Blvd, Portland, OR 97229-1309. TEL 503-297-3296, FAX 503-296-6745, lorelei@teleport.com, http://www.erin.utoronto.ca/~w3msa, http://msafungi.org. Circ: 1,500.

580 ESP ISSN 0211-707X
QH7
INSTITUCIO CATALANA D'HISTORIA NATURAL. TREBALLS. Text in Spanish. 1915. irreg.
Indexed: IECT, ZooRec.
Published by: Institucion Catalana de Historia Natural, Carme, 47, Barcelona, 08001, Spain.

580 DEU ISSN 0344-5615
QK1 CODEN: MIAHDA
➤ **INSTITUT FUER ALLGEMEINE BOTANIK UND BOTANISCHER GARTEN. MITTEILUNGEN.** Text in English, German; Summaries in English. 1914. irreg., latest vol.29, 2000. per issue exchange basis. bk.rev. illus. **Document type:** *Bulletin, Academic/Scholarly.*
Indexed: AgBio, BIOSIS Prev, BiolAb, ChemAb, ForAb, HortAb, MaizeAb, PBA, PGegResA, RPP, S&F, WeedAb.
—BLDSC (5848.600000), CASDDS, CISTI. **CCC.**
Published by: Universitaet Hamburg, Institut fuer Allgemeine Botanik und Botanischer Garten, Ohnhorststr 18, Hamburg, 22609, Germany. FAX 49-40-42816256, bibliothek@botanik.uni-hamburg.de. Ed. M Engels. Circ: 550 (controlled).

580 FRA ISSN 0762-1167
INSTITUT NATIONAL DE LA RECHERCHE AGRONOMIQUE. STATION D'AMELIORATION DES PLANTES MARAICHERES D'AVIGNON - MONTFAVET. RAPPORT D'ACTIVITE. Text in French. 196?. a.
Published by: Institut National de la Recherche Agronomique (INRA), Service des Publications, Route de Saint Cyr, Versailles, Cedex 78026, France. TEL 33-1-30833406, FAX 33-1-30833449, inra-editions@versailles.inra.fr, http://www.inra.fr/index.html.

580 BRA ISSN 0074-0055
QK263
INSTITUTO DE BOTANICA. BOLETIM. Text in Portuguese. 1963. irreg.
Indexed: BIOSIS Prev, BiolAb.
Published by: Instituto de Botanica, Caixa Postal 4005, Sao Paulo, SP 0106-970, Brazil. TEL 55-11-50736300, FAX 55-11-50733678, http://www.ibot.sp.gov.br.

571.2 ROM ISSN 0365-575X
CODEN: APSVBN
INSTITUTUL DE CERCETARI PENTRU PROTECTIA PLANTELOR. ANALELE/RESEARCH INSTITUTE FOR PLANT PROTECTION. ANNALS. Text in Romanian; Summaries in English, Russian. 1965. a. ROL 150. back issues avail.
Indexed: AgBio, BioCN&I, BiolAb, CIN, CPA, ChemAb, ChemTitl, FCA, FaBeAb, HerbAb, HortAb, MaizeAb, OrnHort, PBA, PGegResA, PGrRegA, PHN&I, PotatoAb, PoultAb, RA&MP, RM&VM, RPP, RevApplEntom, S&F, SIA, SeedAb, TriticAb, WAE&RSA, WeedAb.
—CASDDS, CISTI.
Published by: (Academy of Agricultural and Forestry Sciences), Centrul de Material Didactic si Propag. Agricola, Cal. Serban Voda 34, Bucharest, Romania. Circ: 500. **Subscr. to:** Research Institute for Plant Protection, Bd. Ion Ionescu de la Brad 8, Bucharest 71592, Romania.

580 USA
INTERMOUNTAIN FLORA. Text in English. 1972. irreg., latest vol.34, 1998. price varies. illus. back issues avail. **Document type:** *Monographic series, Academic/Scholarly.* **Description:** Provides keys, descriptions, and illustrations of the vascular plants of the intermountain region of the western United States, an ecologically rich region with comparatively little coverage.
—BLDSC (4534.590000).
Published by: New York Botanical Garden Press, 200th Street & Kazimiroff Blvd, Bronx, NY 10458-5126. TEL 718-817-8721, FAX 718-817-8842, http://www.nybg.org. Pub. Carole J Young.

580 JPN
➤ **THE INTERNATIONAL JOURNAL FOR WHEAT GENETICS AND BREEDING.** Text in English. 1954. 2/yr. JPY 2,000, USD 25 (effective 2001). adv. bk.rev. 50 p./no.; back issues avail. **Document type:** *Journal, Academic/Scholarly.* **Description:** Covers the genetics and breeding of wheat (Triticum).
Formerly: Kihara Institute for Biological Research. Wheat Information Service (0510-3517)
Indexed: AgBio, BiolAb, CPA, FCA, HerbAb, I&DA, MaizeAb, NemAb, PBA, PGegResA, PGrRegA, PHN&I, RPP, RefZh, RiceAb, SeedAb, TriticAb, WeedAb.
—CISTI.
Published by: Kihara Memorial Yokohama Foundation for the Advancement of Life Sciences, 641-12 Maioka-cho, Totsuka-ku, Yokohama-shi, Kanagawa-ken 244-0813, Japan. TEL 81-45-825-3487, FAX 81-45-825-3307, yamabosi@yokohama-cu.ac.jp. Ed. Kozo Nishikawa. R&P, Adv. contact Hisashi Tsujimoto. Circ: 750.

580 PAK ISSN 1811-9700
▼ ➤ **INTERNATIONAL JOURNAL OF BOTANY.** Text in English. 2004. q. **Document type:** *Journal, Academic/Scholarly.* **Description:** Publishes research papers on all aspects of plant science, including cell and molecular biology, ecology, mycology and plant pathology, phycology, physiology and biochemistry, structure and development, systematics, phytogeography, and paleobotany.
Related titles: Online - full text ed.: ISSN 1811-9719. free (effective 2005).
Published by: Asian Network for Scientific Information, 308-Lasani Town, Sargodha Rd, Faislabad, 38090, Pakistan. TEL 92-41-2001145, FAX 92-41-731433, http://www.ansinet.org/c4p.php?j_id=ijb, http://www.ansinet.net.

579.7 USA ISSN 1521-9437
CODEN: IMMUFR
➤ **INTERNATIONAL JOURNAL OF MEDICINAL MUSHROOMS.** Text in English. 1999. q. USD 108 to individuals; USD 428 to institutions (effective 2005). **Document type:** *Journal, Academic/Scholarly.* **Description:** Contains original research articles and critical reviews on a broad range of subjects pertaining to medicinal mushrooms, including systematics, nomenclature, taxonomy, morphology, medicinal value, biotechnology, and more.
Related titles: Online - full text ed.: (from EBSCO Publishing).
Indexed: AMED, AbHyg, AgBio, BIOBASE, BIOSIS Prev, BiolAb, CPA, ExcerpMed, FPA, HortAb, IndVet, NemAb, NutrAb, OrnHort, PBA, PGegResA, PGrRegA, PHN&I, RA&MP, RDA, RM&VM, RPP, S&F, SIA, TDB, TriticAb, VetBull, WAE&RSA, WeedAb.
—BLDSC (4542.349500). **CCC.**
Published by: Begell House Inc., 145 Madison Ave, New York, NY 10016-6717. TEL 212-725-1999, FAX 212-213-8368, orders@begellhouse.com, http://www.begellhouse.com/ijmm/ijmm.html. Ed. Solomon P. Wasser.

580 USA ISSN 1058-5893
QK1 CODEN: IPLSE2
➤ **INTERNATIONAL JOURNAL OF PLANT SCIENCES.** Text in English. 1875. bi-m. USD 55 combined subscription to individuals print & online eds.; USD 670 combined subscription domestic to institutions print & online eds.; USD 16 per issue to individuals; USD 119 per issue to institutions (effective 2006). adv. bk.rev. bibl.; charts; illus. Index. 190 p./no.; reprint service avail. from PQC,ISI. **Document type:** *Journal, Academic/Scholarly.* **Description:** Presents the results of original investigations in all areas of plant biology, including development, physiology, reproductive biology, evolution, cell biology, genetics, ecology, systematics, and paleobotany.
Former titles (until Mar. 1992): Botanical Gazette (0006-8071); (until 1876): Botanical Bulletin (1529-4560)
Related titles: Microfiche ed.: (from IDC); Online - full text ed.: ISSN 1537-5315. USD 603 to institutions (effective 2006) (from bigchalk, EBSCO Publishing, Florida Center for Library Automation, Gale Group, JSTOR (Web-based Journal Archive), O C L C Online Computer Library Center, Inc., ProQuest Information & Learning).
Indexed: ABIPC, ASCA, AgBio, Agr, AgrForAb, ApEcolAb, B&AI, B&BAb, BIOBASE, BIOSIS Prev, BioCN&I, BiolAb, BiolDig, CIN, CPA, ChemAb, ChemTitl, CurCont, DBA, EPB, ESPM, EntAb, ExcerpMed, FCA, FPA, FS&TA, ForAb, GEOBASE, GSI, GenetAb, HerbAb, HortAb, I&DA, IABS, ISR, MEDLINE, MaizeAb, NemAb, NutrAb, OrnHort, PBA, PGegResA, PGrRegA, PHN&I, PlantSci, RA&MP, RM&VM, RPP, RefZh, RevApplEntom, RiceAb, S&F, SCI, SIA, SWRA, SeedAb, SoyAb, TOSA, TriticAb, VITIS, WeedAb.
—BLDSC (4542.468700), CASDDS, CISTI, IDS, IE, Infotrieve, ingenta, Linda Hall. **CCC.**
Published by: University of Chicago Press, Journals Division, 1111 E. 60th St, Chicago, IL 60637. http://www.journals.uchicago.edu/IJPS. Eds. Larry Hufford, Manfred Ruddat, Peter R Crane, William E Friedman. Adv. contact Cheryl Jones. page USD 475; trim 8.5 x 11. Circ: 1,000.

580 IND ISSN 0254-0126
SB724 CODEN: IJTSEY
INTERNATIONAL JOURNAL OF TROPICAL PLANT DISEASES. Text in English. 1983. s-a. INR 900, USD 85 (effective 2001). bk.rev. back issues avail. **Document type:** *Academic/Scholarly.* **Description:** Publishes research findings, new ideas and selected reviews on all aspects of plant pathological problems.
Indexed: AgBio, AgrForAb, BioCN&I, BiolAb, CPA, CurCont, FCA, FPA, FS&TA, ForAb, HortAb, NemAb, OrnHort, PBA, PGegResA, PHN&I, PotatoAb, RA&MP, RM&VM, RPP, RevApplEntom, RiceAb, S&F, S&MA, SeedAb, SoyAb, TOSA, TriticAb, VITIS, WeedAb.
—BLDSC (4542.696160), CISTI, IE, Infotrieve, ingenta, Linda Hall. **CCC.**
Published by: Scientific Publishers, 5-A New Pali Rd., Near Hotel Taj Hari Mahal, PO Box 91, Jodhpur, Rajasthan 342 003, India. TEL 91-291-2433323, FAX 91-291-2512580, info@scientificpub.com, http://www.scientificpub.com. **Dist. in U.S. by:** Scholarly Publications, 2825 Wilcrest Dr, Ste 255, Houston, TX 77042.

579.8 USA ISSN 1521-9429
QK564
➤ **INTERNATIONAL JOURNAL ON ALGAE.** Text in English. 1999. q. USD 585 (effective 2002). **Document type:** *Journal, Academic/Scholarly.* **Description:** Contains original studies on the relationship of the study of algae with science, the theoretical and methodological problems of the study of algae, and the history and development of the study of algae.
Related titles: Online - full text ed.: (from EBSCO Publishing).
Indexed: BIOSIS Prev, BiolAb.
—CISTI.
Published by: Begell House Inc., 145 Madison Ave, New York, NY 10016-6717. TEL 212-725-1999, FAX 212-213-8368, orders@begellhouse.com, http://www.begellhouse.com/ija/ija.html. Ed. Solomon P. Wasser.

580 USA ISSN 0254-8844
INTERNATIONAL ORGANIZATION OF PLANT BIOSYSTEMATISTS. NEWSLETTER. Text in English. 1983. s-a. USD 14. bk.rev. back issues avail. **Document type:** *Newsletter.* **Description:** Exchanges personal and scientific developments between students of plant evolutionary processes, mainly on the species level.
Published by: International Organization of Plant Biosystematists, c/o Peter C. Hoch, Missouri Botanical Garden, P.O. Box 299, St. Louis, MO 63166-0299. TEL 314-577-5175, FAX 314-577-9596, hoch@mobot.org. Ed. K M Urbanska. Circ: 500. **Co-sponsor:** Swiss Federal Institute of Technology (ETH).

622.331 553.21 FIN ISSN 0782-7784
CODEN: IPEJE8
➤ **INTERNATIONAL PEAT JOURNAL.** Text in English. 1986. irreg., latest vol.12, 2004. EUR 19 (effective 2005). bk.rev. back issues avail. **Document type:** *Academic/Scholarly.*
—CASDDS.
Published by: International Peat Society, Vapaudenkatu 12, Jyvaskyla, 40100, Finland. TEL 358-14-3385440, FAX 358-14-3385410, ips@peatsociety.fi, http://www.peatsociety.fi/publica/journal.htm. Ed. Jack Rieley.

579.88 NOR ISSN 0074-7874
QK564
➤ **INTERNATIONAL SEAWEED SYMPOSIUM. PROCEEDINGS.** (Published by host country) Text in English. 1952. triennial, latest vol.18, 2004. price varies. adv. **Document type:** *Proceedings, Academic/Scholarly.* **Description:** Technical papers on seaweed (algae) utilization: biology, ecology, chemistry, processing and commerce. For academics and industry.
Indexed: BiolAb.
—CISTI, Linda Hall. **CCC.**
Published by: International Seaweed Association, c/o Tor Bokn, Norwegian Institute of Water Research, PO Box 173, Kjelsaas, Oslo, 0411, Norway. tor.bokn@niva.no, http://www.intseaweedassoc.org. Circ: 400.

579.5 GBR
INTERNATIONAL SOCIETY FOR MUSHROOM SCIENCE. SYMPOSIA PROCEEDINGS. Text in English. irreg., latest 1990, 4th, Sydney. **Document type:** *Proceedings.*
Published by: International Society for Mushroom Science, c/o Kerry Burton, Executive Secretary ISMS, 196 Rugby Rd, Leamington Spa, Warcs CV32 6DU, United Kingdom. http://www.hri.ac.uk/isms/.

580 IND ISSN 0539-0346
INTERNATIONAL SOCIETY OF PLANT MORPHOLOGISTS. YEARBOOK. Text in English. 1951. a. USD 55. bk.rev.
Published by: International Society of Plant Morphologists, University of Delhi, Department of Botany, New Delhi, 110 007, India. Circ: 1,200.

580 UKR ISSN 0257-9936
CODEN: IAKRBM
INTRODUKTSIYA I AKKLIMATYZATSIYA RASTENII; respublikanskii mezhvedomstvennyi sbornik nauchnykh trudov. Text in Ukrainian. 1965. s-a.
Formerly (until 1984): Introduktsiya ta Akklimatyzatsiya Rozlyn na Ukrayini (0579-4005)
Indexed: ForAb, HortAb, SeedAb.
—CASDDS, CISTI, Linda Hall.
Published by: (Tsentral'nyi Botanicheskii Sad), Natsional'na Akademiya Nauk Ukrainy, vul Volodymyrs'ka 54, Kyiv, 01601, Ukraine. http://www.nas.gov.ua. **Dist. by:** M K - Periodica, ul Gilyarovskogo 39, Moscow 129110, Russian Federation. **Co-sponsor:** Donetskii Botanicheskii Sad.

571.92 IRN ISSN 0006-2774
IRANIAN JOURNAL OF PLANT PATHOLOGY/BIMARIHAYE GUIAHI. Text in English, Persian, Modern; Summaries in English, Persian, Modern. 1963. a. free. bibl.; charts; illus. **Document type:** *Journal, Academic/Scholarly.* **Description:** Publishes original research papers and short reports in the area of plant pathology as the journal of the Iranian Phytopathological Society.
Indexed: AgBio, AgrForAb, BIOSIS Prev, BioCN&I, BiolAb, ChemAb, DSA, FCA, FPA, FS&TA, ForAb, HerbAb, HortAb, MaizeAb, NemAb, OrnHort, PBA, PGegResA, PHN&I, PotatoAb, RA&MP, RDA, RPP, RevApplEntom, RiceAb, S&F, SIA, SeedAb, SoyAb, TriticAb, VITIS, WAE&RSA, WeedAb.
—BLDSC (4567.529000), Linda Hall.
Published by: (Iranian Phytopathological Society), Plant Pests and Diseases Research Institute/Mu'assasah Tahqiqat Afat va Bimarihay Giyahi, P O Box 1454, Tehran, 19395, Iran. TEL 98-21-2403012, FAX 98-21-2403691, http://www.magiran.com/rostaniha. Ed. K. Izadpanah. Circ: 2,000.

IRELAND. DEPARTMENT OF AGRICULTURE AND FOOD. CEREAL VARIETIES RECOMMENDED LIST (YEAR). see *AGRICULTURE—Crop Production And Soil*

IRELAND. DEPARTMENT OF AGRICULTURE AND FOOD. HERBAGE VARIETIES RECOMMENDED LIST (YEAR). see *AGRICULTURE—Crop Production And Soil*

IRELAND. DEPARTMENT OF AGRICULTURE AND FOOD. POTATO VARIETY EVALUATION RESULTS; and recommended list. see *AGRICULTURE—Crop Production And Soil*

IRELAND. DEPARTMENT OF AGRICULTURE AND FOOD. ROOT FODDER CROP, PULSE AND OILSEED VARIETIES RECOMMENDED LIST (YEAR). see *AGRICULTURE—Crop Production And Soil*

580 USA
➤ **ISELYA**; botanical journal. Text in English. 1979. q. USD 8 to individuals; USD 10 to institutions. back issues avail. **Document type:** *Academic/Scholarly.*
Published by: X Club, Department of Biological Science, Nicholls State University, Thibodaux, LA 70310. Circ: 200.

580 ISR ISSN 0792-9978
QK1 CODEN: IJUPEU
➤ **ISRAEL JOURNAL OF PLANT SCIENCES.** Text in English. 1951. q. USD 180 to individuals; USD 360 to institutions (effective 2005). adv. bk.rev. charts; illus. index. 80 p./no.; **Document type:** *Academic/Scholarly.* **Description:** Publishes original research covering all aspects of basic and applied plant sciences, including systematics and evolution, plant physiology, geobotany, phytochemistry, and molecular plant biology.
Formerly (until vol.42, 1994): Israel Journal of Botany (0021-213X); Supersedes: Research Council of Israel. Bulletin (Section D) (0375-9148); Palestine Journal of Botany
Related titles: Online - full text ed.: (from EBSCO Publishing).
Indexed: AEA, ASCA, ASFA, AgBio, AgrForAb, ApEcolAb, BIOBASE, BIOSIS Prev, BioCN&I, BiolAb, CIN, CPA, CTFA, ChemAb, ChemTitl, CurCont, ESPM, FCA, FPA, FS&TA, ForAb, GEOBASE, HerbAb, HortAb, I&DA, IABS, ISR, MBA, MaizeAb, NemAb, NutrAb, OrnHort, PBA, PGegResA, PGrRegA, PlantSci, PotatoAb, RA&MP, RPP, RRTA, RevApplEntom, RiceAb, S&F, S&MA, SCI, SIA, SeedAb, TDB, TriticAb, WeedAb, ZooRec.
—BLDSC (4583.812800), CASDDS, CISTI, IDS, IE, Infotrieve, ingenta, Linda Hall. **CCC.**
Published by: Laser Pages Publishing Ltd., P O Box 35409, Jerusalem, 91352, Israel. laserpages@netmedia.net.il, http://www.sciencefromisrael.com. Ed. A M Mayer. R&P Rachel Lichtensztajn. Adv. contact Elcya Weiss. Circ: 500.

580 ESP ISSN 0213-8530
➤ **ITINERA GEOBOTANICA.** Text in Spanish. 1987. a. price varies. bk.rev. **Document type:** *Bulletin, Academic/Scholarly.*
Indexed: ForAb, HerbAb, IECT, RRTA, S&F.
—CINDOC.
Published by: Universidad de Leon, Secretariado de Publicaciones, Campus de Verganza, s-n, Leon, 24007, Spain. TEL 34-987-291558, FAX 34-987-291558, dbvlhc@unileon.es. Ed. Angel Penas Merino. Circ: 1,000 (controlled).

571.2 JPN ISSN 0912-2214
J S P P NEWSLETTER. Text in English. 1979. a. membership. **Document type:** *Newsletter.*
Published by: Japanese Society of Plant Physiologists/Nihon Shokubutsu Seiri Gakkai, Shimodachuri-Dori, Ogawa Higashi, Kamigyo-ku, Kyoto-shi, 602-8084, Japan. FAX 81-75-415-3662, jspp@nacos.com, http://www.nacos.com/jspp. Ed. Tatsuo Sugiyama.

579.8 JPN
CODEN: NSOGAJ
➤ **JAPANESE JOURNAL OF PHYCOLOGY (JAPANESE EDITION).** Text in Japanese. 1953. 3/yr. adv. bk.rev. cum.index: vols.1-10; vols.11-20. **Document type:** *Academic/Scholarly.* **Description:** Contains original research articles, research notes, reviews and Society information and activities.

B

Supersedes in part (in 1995): Japanese Journal of Phycology (Bilingual Edition); Which was formerly: Sorui - Japanese Society of Phycology. Bulletin (0038-1578)
Indexed: ASFA, BiolAb, ChemAb, CurCont, JPI, RefZh, SSCI, ZooRec.
—BLDSC (4657.200000), CASDDS, CISTI.
Published by: Japanese Society of Phycology/Nihon Sorui Gakkai, c/o Division of Biological Sciences, Graduate School of Science, Hokkaido University, Sapporo, 060, Japan. TEL 81-11-706-2745, FAX 81-11-746-1512, horig@bio.hokudai.ac.jp. Ed. Isao Inouye. Circ: 3,000.

571.2 JPN
JAPANESE SOCIETY OF PLANT PHYSIOLOGISTS. NEWS/NIHON SHOKUBUTSU SEIRI GAKKAI TSUSHIN. Text in Japanese. 1968. 3/yr. **Document type:** *Newsletter.*
Published by: Japanese Society of Plant Physiologists/Nihon Shokubutsu Seiri Gakkai, Shimodachuri-Dori, Ogawa Higashi, Kamigyo-ku, Kyoto-shi, 602-8084, Japan. FAX 81-75-415-3662, jspp@nacos.com, http://www.nacos.com/jspp. Ed. Tatsuo Sugiyama.

B

580.74 BRA ISSN 0103-2550
QK1
JARDIM BOTANICO DO RIO DE JANEIRO. ARQUIVOS. Text in Portuguese. 1915; N.S. 1947. a. bk.rev. abstr.; bibl. **Document type:** *Journal, Academic/Scholarly.* **Description:** Presents results of research conducted by the botanical garden.
Related titles: Microfiche ed.: (from IDC).
Indexed: BIOSIS Prev, BiolAb.
—CISTI, Linda Hall.
Published by: (Biblioteca Barbosa Rodrigues), Jardim Botanico do Rio de Janeiro, Rua Pacheco Leao 915, Rio de Janeiro, RJ 22460-030, Brazil. TEL 55-21-2748246, FAX 55-21-2744897. Circ: 1,000.

580.74 ESP ISSN 1135-366X
JARDIN BOTANICO DE CORDOBA. MONOGRAFIAS. Text in Spanish. 1994. s-a. EUR 18 domestic; EUR 24 foreign (effective 2005). **Document type:** *Monographic series, Academic/Scholarly.*
Published by: (Universidad de Cordoba, Departamento de Biologia Vegetal y Ecologia), Universidad de Cordoba, Servicio de Publicaciones, Ave. Menendez Pidal, s-n, Cordoba, 14071, Spain. TEL 34-957-218125, FAX 34-957-218196, publicaciones@uco.es, http://www.uco.es/. Ed. E Dominguez Vilches.

579.5 ESP ISSN 0365-0790
JARDIN BOTANICO DE MADRID. ANALES. Text in Spanish. a.
—BLDSC (0880.350000), CISTI, IE, ingenta.
Published by: Real Jardin Botanico de Madrid, Plaza Murillo, 2, Madrid, 28014, Spain. TEL 34-1-4203017, FAX 34-1-4200157.

580 ESP ISSN 0211-1322
QK1 CODEN: AJBMD7
➤ **JARDIN BOTANICO DE MADRID. ANALES.** Text in English, French, German, Italian, Latin, Portuguese, Spanish; Summaries in English. 1940. s-a. EUR 23.75 (effective 2005). bk.rev. bibl.; charts; illus. index. back issues avail. **Document type:** *Journal, Academic/Scholarly.* **Description:** Covers systematic botany and related subjects, particularly plant ecology.
Formerly (1950-1978): Instituto Botanico A.J. Cavanilles. Anales
Related titles: CD-ROM ed.
Indexed: AgBio, AgrForAb, Agrind, BIOSIS Prev, BioCN&I, BiolAb, CPA, FCA, FPA, ForAb, HerbAb, HortAb, I&DA, IECT, OrnHort, PBA, PGegResA, PotatoAb, RA&MP, RPP, RRTA, RefZh, RevApplEntom, RiceAb, S&F, SeedAb, TriticAb, WeedAb.
—BLDSC (0880.350000), CINDOC, CISTI.
Published by: Consejo Superior de Investigaciones Cientificas, Departamento de Publicaciones, Vitruvio 8, Madrid, 28006, Spain. TEL 34-91-561-2833, FAX 34-91-562-9634, TELEX 42182-CSIC-E, publ@orgc.csic.es, http://www.csic.es/publica. Ed. Carlos Lado. Circ: 850.

580 DOM ISSN 0254-6434
JARDIN BOTANICO NACIONAL "DR. RAFAEL M. MOSCOSO." BOLETIN. Text in English, Spanish. 1977. a., latest 1983. per issue exchange basis. illus.; charts; bibl. 200 p./no.; back issues avail. **Document type:** *Bulletin.*
Published by: Jardin Botanico Nacional "Dr. Rafael M. Moscoso", Apdo Postal 21-9, Santo Domingo, Dominican Republic. TEL 809-3852611, FAX 809-3850446, j.botanico@codetel.net.do, http://www.jbn-sdq.org. Ed. Milciades Mejia Pimental.

580 CUB ISSN 0253-5696
QK227 CODEN: RJBNDR
JARDIN BOTANICO NACIONAL. REVISTA. Text in Spanish; Summaries in English, Spanish. 1980. 3/yr. CUP 4.50 domestic; USD 24 in North America; USD 25 in South America; USD 26 in Europe. back issues avail.
Indexed: AgBio, AgrForAb, BioCN&I, CPA, FCA, FPA, ForAb, HerbAb, HortAb, NemAb, OrnHort, PBA, PGegResA, PGrRegA, RA&MP, RDA, RPP, RRTA, RefZh, RiceAb, S&F, SeedAb, SoyAb.
—CISTI, KNAW.
Published by: (Universidad de La Habana, Direccion de Informacion Cientifica y Tecnica), Ediciones Cubanas, Obispo No. 527, Apdo. 605, Havana, Cuba.

580.74 BEL
LES JARDINS D'EDEN/TUINEN VAN EDEN. Text in Dutch, French. 1993. q. EUR 22 domestic; EUR 25 in Netherlands; EUR 33 in Europe (effective 2005). illus. back issues avail. **Document type:** *Consumer.* **Description:** Includes everything related to the garden: art, architecture, traveling, gastronomy, and particular plants and trees.
Published by: Back to Basics, Taxanderlei 43, Schoten, 2900, Belgium. TEL 32-3-658-0968, FAX 32-3-658-3708, info@edenmagazine.be, http://www.edenmagazine.be/index.html. Ed., Pub. Jinge Lim. Adv. contact Alain Mathieu. Circ: 60,000.

580 AUT
JOANNEA BOTANIK. Text in German; Summaries in English. 1972. irreg. price varies. bk.rev. bibl.; illus. **Document type:** *Academic/Scholarly.* **Description:** Results of research on the flora and vegetation of the province of Styria.
Former titles (until 1999): Landesmuseum Joanneum. Referat Botanik. Mitteilungen; Landesmuseum Joanneum. Abteilung fuer Botanik. Mitteilungen
Published by: Landesmuseum Joanneum, Referat Botanik, Raubergasse 10, Graz, St 8010, Austria. TEL 43-316-80179750, FAX 43-316-80179800, post@lmj-bot.stmk.gv.at. Ed., R&P Detlef Ernet. Circ: 600.
Co-sponsor: Steiermaerkische Landesregierung.

580 FRA ISSN 1280-8202
LE JOURNAL DE BOTANIQUE. Text in French. 1997. q.
Published by: Societe Botanique de France, Faculte de Pharmacie, Departement de Botanique, 3 rue du Professeur Laguesse, B.P. 83, Lille, Cedex 59007, France. TEL 33-1-46835520, FAX 33-1-46831303.

580 DEU ISSN 1613-9216
QK1 CODEN: JABOFH
➤ **JOURNAL OF APPLIED BOTANY AND FOOD QUALITY.** Text in English, German. 1904. 3/yr. EUR 388 in North America & Europe to institutions; EUR 397 elsewhere to institutions (effective 2004). bk.rev. back issues avail. **Document type:** *Journal, Academic/Scholarly.*
Former titles (until 2004): Journal of Applied Botany (0949-5460); (until 1995): Angewandte Botanik (0066-1759); (until 1919): Jahresbericht der Vereinigung fuer Angewandte Botanik (0344-6220); (until 1907): Jahresbericht der Vertreter der Angewandten Botanik (0344-6212)
Related titles: Microform ed.: (from SWZ); Online - full text ed.: ISSN 1439-040X.
Indexed: AEA, ASCA, ASFA, AgBio, AgrForAb, ApicAb, BIOBASE, BIOSIS Prev, BiolAb, CIN, CPA, ChemAb, ChemTitl, CurCont, DBA, ESPM, ExcerpMed, FCA, FPA, FS&TA, FaBeAb, ForAb, GEOBASE, HerbAb, HortAb, I&DA, IABS, ISR, MaizeAb, NutrAb, OrnHort, PBA, PGegResA, PGrRegA, PHN&I, PlantSci, PollutAb, PotatoAb, RA&MP, RPP, RefZh, RevApplEntom, RiceAb, S&F, SCI, SIA, SeedAb, SoyAb, TriticAb, VITIS, WeedAb.
—BLDSC (4940.658000), CASDDS, CISTI, IDS, IE, ingenta, Linda Hall. **CCC.**
Published by: Blackwell Verlag GmbH (Subsidiary of: Blackwell Publishing Ltd.), Kurfuerstendamm 57, Berlin, 10707, Germany. TEL 49-30-32790634, FAX 49-30-32790610, verlag@blackwell.de, http://www.blackwell.de. Ed. H J Jaeger.

581.3 POL ISSN 1234-1983
SB123 CODEN: JAGEFC
➤ **JOURNAL OF APPLIED GENETICS**; an international journal of genetics and breeding. Text and summaries in English. 1960. q. PLZ 80 domestic; USD 120 foreign (effective 2005). adv. bk.rev. abstr.; bibl.; charts; illus. index. back issues avail. **Document type:** *Journal, Academic/Scholarly.* **Description:** Publishes original scientific papers on plant and animal genetics and breeding, on microorganisms and human genetics.
Formerly (until 1995): Genetica Polonica (0016-6715)
Related titles: Online - full text ed.: free (effective 2005).
Indexed: ASFA, AbHyg, AgBio, AgrAg, AgrLib, AnBrAb, B&BAb, BIOSIS Prev, BiolAb, CPA, ChemAb, CurCont, DSA, ExcerpMed, FCA, FS&TA, ForAb, GenetAb, HGA, HerbAb, HortAb, I&DA, INIS AtomInd, ISR, IndVet, MaizeAb, NemAb, NutrAb, PBA, PGegResA, PGrRegA, PHN&I, PN&I, PotatoAb, PoultAb, RA&MP, RPP, RefZh, RevApplEntom, RiceAb, S&F, SCI, SIA, SeedAb, SoyAb, TriticAb, VetBull, WeedAb.
—BLDSC (4942.612000), CASDDS, CISTI, IE, Infotrieve, ingenta. **CCC.**
Published by: Polska Akademia Nauk, Instytut Genetyki Roslin/Polish Academy of Sciences, Institute of Plant Genetics, ul Strzeszynska 34, Poznan, 60479, Poland. TEL 48-61-6550200, FAX 48-61-8233671, office@igr.poznan.pl, http://jay.au.poznan.pl/JAG/, http://www.igr.poznan.pl. Eds. Maciej Szydlowski, Maria Surma, Michal Witt, Marek Switonski. R&P Eleonora Dybizbanska. Adv. contact Bogumila Szymanska. Circ: 350. **Subscr. to:** Ars Polona, Krakowskie Przedmiescie 7, Warsaw, Poland. TEL 48-22-9263914, FAX 48-22-9265334, arspolona@arspolona.com.pl, http://www.arspolona.com.pl.

579.8 NLD ISSN 0921-8971
SH388.7 CODEN: JAPPEL
➤ **JOURNAL OF APPLIED PHYCOLOGY.** Text in English. 1989. bi-m. EUR 758, USD 768, GBP 498 combined subscription to institutions print & online eds. (effective 2005). back issues avail.; reprint service avail. from PSC. **Document type:** *Journal, Academic/Scholarly.* **Description:** Publishes work on the commercial use of algae, including fundamental research, techniques and practical applications in biotechnology, genetic engineering, pollution control and monitoring, and other areas.
Related titles: Microform ed.: (from PQC); Online - full text ed.: ISSN 1573-5176 (from EBSCO Publishing, Gale Group, IngentaConnect, Kluwer Online, O C L C Online Computer Library Center, Inc., Springer LINK, Swets Information Services); ♦ Supplement to: Hydrobiologia. ISSN 0018-8158.
Indexed: AEA, ASCA, ASFA, AbHyg, AgBio, AgrForAb, AnBrAb, B&BAb, BCI, BIOBASE, BIOSIS Prev, BibLing, BioCN&I, BiolAb, CIN, CPA, ChemAb, ChemTitl, CurCont, DSA, ESPM, FCA, FLUIDEX, FPA, FamI, ForAb, GEOBASE, HerbAb, HortAb, I&DA, IABS, ISR, IndVet, MBA, MSCT, NemAb, NutrAb, OceAb, OrnHort, PBA, PGegResA, PGrRegA, PHN&I, PN&I, PlantSci, PollutAb, PoultAb, ProtozoAb, RA&MP, RM&VM, RPP, RefZh, RevApplEntom, S&F, SCI, SFA, SIA, SSI, SWRA, SoyAb, TDB, TriticAb, VetBull, WAE&RSA, WRCInf, WeedAb, WildRev, ZooRec.
—BLDSC (4943.880000), CASDDS, CISTI, Ei, IDS, IE, Infotrieve, ingenta, Linda Hall. **CCC.**
Published by: Springer-Verlag Dordrecht (Subsidiary of: Springer Science+Business Media), Van Godewijckstraat 30, Dordrecht, 3311 GX, Netherlands. TEL 31-78-6576050, FAX 31-78-6576474, http://springerlink.metapress.com/openurl.asp?genre=journal&issn=0921-8971, http://www.springeronline.com. Ed. Michael A Borowitzka.

580 635 USA ISSN 0146-6623
SB614 CODEN: JAPMDB
➤ **JOURNAL OF AQUATIC PLANT MANAGEMENT.** Text in English. 1961. s-a. USD 70 (effective 2000). back issues avail. **Document type:** *Academic/Scholarly.* **Description:** Encourages scientific research and promotes the control and management of aquatic plants through scientifically sound procedures.
Formerly (until 1976): Hyacinth Control Journal (0146-9533)
Indexed: AEA, ASCA, ASFA, AgBio, B&BAb, BIOSIS Prev, BioCN&I, BiolAb, CPA, ChemAb, CivEngAb, CurCont, ESPM, ForAb, HerbAb, HortAb, I&DA, ISR, MBA, OceAb, OrnHort, PBA, PGrRegA, PoultAb, RPP, RRTA, RefZh, RevApplEntom, RiceAb, S&F, SCI, SFA, SIA, SWRA, SeedAb, WAE&RSA, WeedAb, ZooRec.
—BLDSC (4947.160000), CASDDS, CISTI, IDS, IE, ingenta, Linda Hall.
Published by: Aquatic Plant Management Society, Inc., P O Box 821265, Vicksburg, MS 39182. TEL 203-761-3202, FAX 203-761-3327, http://www.apms.org/japm.htm. Ed. Michael D Netherland. Circ: 600.

584.9 584.5 NLD ISSN 1569-1586
➤ **JOURNAL OF BAMBOO AND RATTAN.** Text in English. 2001 (Oct.). q. EUR 76, USD 95 combined subscription to individuals print & online eds.; EUR 210, USD 262 combined subscription to institutions print & online eds. (effective 2005). reprint service avail. from PSC. **Document type:** *Journal, Academic/Scholarly.* **Description:** Provides a forum for scientific articles and reviews on all aspects of fast growing, multi-purpose pliable species.
Related titles: Online - full content ed.; Online - full text ed.: ISSN 1569-1594. EUR 68, USD 86 to individuals; EUR 189, USD 236 to institutions (effective 2005) (from EBSCO Publishing, Gale Group, IngentaConnect, Kluwer Online, O C L C Online Computer Library Center, Inc., Springer LINK, Swets Information Services).
Indexed: AEA, AgrForAb, CPA, EPB, FCA, FPA, ForAb, HortAb, OrnHort, PBA, PGegResA, RA&MP, RDA, S&F, SoyAb, WAE&RSA.
—IE. **CCC.**
Published by: V S P (Subsidiary of: Brill Academic Publishers), Brill Academic Publishers, PO Box 9000, Leiden, 2300 PA, Netherlands. TEL 31-71-5353500, FAX 31-71-5317532, vsppub@brill.nl, http://www.vsppub.com/journals/jn-JouBamRat.html. Ed. Jules J A Janssen TEL 31-40-247-2948.
Dist. by: Extenza - Turpin, Pegasus Dr, Stratton Business Park, Biggleswade, Beds SG18 8TQ, United Kingdom. TEL 44-1767-604954, FAX 44-1767-601640, marketing@extenza-turpin.com, http://www.extenza-turpin.com.

588.2 GBR ISSN 0373-6687
QK534 CODEN: JBRYAR
➤ **JOURNAL OF BRYOLOGY.** Text in English. 1972 (vol.7). q. USD 164 in North America to individuals; GBP 89 elsewhere to individuals; USD 440 in North America to institutions; GBP 259 elsewhere to institutions (effective 2005); includes online access. adv. bk.rev. abstr. back issues avail.; reprint service avail. from ISI. **Document type:** *Journal, Academic/Scholarly.* **Description:** Promotes the study of mosses and liverworts.
Formerly: British Bryological Society. Transactions (0068-1385)
Related titles: Online - full text ed.: ISSN 1743-2820 (from EBSCO Publishing, Gale Group, IngentaConnect, Swets Information Services).
Indexed: ASCA, Agr, BIOBASE, BiolAb, CurCont, EPB, ISR, SCI.
—BLDSC (4954.570000), IDS, IE, Infotrieve, ingenta, Linda Hall. **CCC.**

Published by: (British Bryological Society), Maney Publishing, Hudson Rd, Leeds, W Yorks LS9 7DL, United Kingdom. TEL 44-113-2497481, FAX 44-113-2486983, maney@maney.co.uk, http://www.maney.co.uk/bryology.html. Ed. J W Bates. Adv. contact Mary Starkey TEL 44-113-2846124. Circ: 760. **US Subscr. addr.:** Maney Publishing North America, 875 Massachusetts Ave, 7th Fl., Cambridge, MA 02139. TEL 866-297-5154, FAX 617-354-6875, maney@maneyusa.com.

580 643.9 ZAF ISSN 0259-1901
JOURNAL OF DENDROLOGY. Text and summaries in Afrikaans, English. 1981. irreg. ZAR 12. bk.rev. back issues avail. **Document type:** *Academic/Scholarly.*
Indexed: ForAb, ISAP.
Published by: Dendrological Society/Dendrologiese Vereniging, PO Box 15277, Sinoville, 0129, South Africa. TEL 27-12-5674009, FAX 27-12-5671029. Ed. F Von Breitenbach. Circ: 2,500.

581.6 578.012 IND ISSN 0250-9768
CODEN: JETBDQ
JOURNAL OF ECONOMIC AND TAXONOMIC BOTANY. Text in English. 1976. 3/yr. USD 240 to institutions (effective 2006). **Document type:** *Journal, Academic/Scholarly.*
Related titles: Series: Journal of Economic and Taxonomic Botany Additional Series. ISSN 0970-3306. 1986.
Indexed: AgBio, AgrForAb, BIOSIS Prev, BioCN&I, BiolAb, CPA, DSA, FCA, FPA, ForAb, HerbAb, HortAb, I&DA, IndVet, MaizeAb, NutrAb, OrnHort, PBA, PGegResA, PGrRegA, PHN&I, PotatoAb, ProtozoAb, RA&MP, RDA, RM&VM, RPP, RRTA, RevApplEntom, RiceAb, S&F, SIA, SeedAb, SoyAb, TDB, VITIS, WAE&RSA, WeedAb, ZooRec.
—BLDSC (4972.620000), IE, ingenta, Linda Hall.
Published by: Scientific Publishers, 5-A New Pali Rd., Near Hotel Taj Hari Mahal, PO Box 91, Jodhpur, Rajasthan 342 003, India. TEL 91-291-2433323, FAX 91-291-2512580, info@scientificpub.com, http://www.scientificpub.com/bookdetails.php?booktransid=335&bookid=331. Ed. J K Maheshwari.

JOURNAL OF ETHNOBIOLOGY. see *ANTHROPOLOGY*

JOURNAL OF EVOLUTIONARY BIOLOGY. see *BIOLOGY—Genetics*

580 GBR ISSN 0022-0957
QK1 CODEN: JEBOA6
➤ **JOURNAL OF EXPERIMENTAL BOTANY.** Text in English. 1950. 15/yr. GBP 763, USD 1,373, EUR 1,145 to institutions; GBP 803, USD 1,445, EUR 1,205 combined subscription to institutions print & online eds. (effective 2006). adv. bk.rev. illus. index. back issues avail.; reprint service avail. from PSC. **Document type:** *Journal, Academic/Scholarly.* **Description:** Presents papers in the fields of plant physiology, biochemistry, biophysics, molecular biology, and related topics.
Related titles: Microform ed.: (from PQC); Online - full text ed.: ISSN 1460-2431. 1997. GBP 723, USD 1,301, EUR 1,085 to institutions (effective 2006) (from EBSCO Publishing, Gale Group, HighWire Press, IngentaConnect, O C L C Online Computer Library Center, Inc., Ovid Technologies, Inc., Oxford University Press Online Journals, ProQuest Information & Learning, Swets Information Services).
Indexed: ABIPC, AEA, ASCA, ASFA, AgBio, Agr, AgrForAb, AnBrAb, B&AI, B&BAb, BBCI, BIOBASE, BIOSIS Prev, BibAg, BioCN&I, BiolAb, CCI, CIN, CPA, CTA, CTFA, Cadscan, ChemAb, ChemTitl, CurCont, DBA, DSA, ESPM, EngInd, ExcerpMed, FCA, FPA, FS&TA, FaBeAb, ForAb, GenetAb, HGA, HerbAb, HortAb, I&DA, IABS, ISR, IndMed, Inpharma, LeadAb, MEDLINE, MSB, MaizeAb, OrnHort, PBA, PGegResA, PGrRegA, PHN&I, PlantSci, PollutAb, PotatoAb, RA&MP, RPP, RRTA, Reac, RevApplEntom, RiceAb, S&F, SCI, SIA, SWRA, SeedAb, SoyAb, TOSA, TriticAb, VITIS, WeedAb, Zincscan.
—BLDSC (4981.000000), CASDDS, CISTI, IDS, IE, Infotrieve, ingenta, Linda Hall. **CCC.**
Published by: (Society for Experimental Biology), Oxford University Press, Great Clarendon St, Oxford, OX2 6DP, United Kingdom. TEL 44-1865-556767, FAX 44-1865-556646, j.exp.bot@lancaster.ac.uk, jnl.orders@oup.co.uk, http://jxb.oxfordjournals.org/, http://www.oxfordjournals.org/. Ed. W J Davies. Pub. David Prosser. R&P Fiona Bennett. adv.: B&W page GBP 290, B&W page USD 520; trim 216 x 279. Circ: 1,100.

➤ **JOURNAL OF FRUIT AND ORNAMENTAL PLANT RESEARCH.** see *GARDENING AND HORTICULTURE*

571.92 JPN ISSN 1345-2630
SB599 CODEN: JGPPBQ
➤ **JOURNAL OF GENERAL PLANT PATHOLOGY.** Text in English. 2000. bi-m. EUR 288 combined subscription to institutions print & online eds. (effective 2005). **Document type:** *Journal, Academic/Scholarly.* **Description:** Encompasses a broad range of plant pathology subdisciplines from diagnosis and control of plant disease in agricultural fields to molecular analysis of pathogens, hosts and their interactions.
Related titles: Online - full text ed.: ISSN 1610-739X (from EBSCO Publishing, ProQuest Information & Learning, Springer LINK, Swets Information Services).
Indexed: AgBio, AgrForAb, BIOSIS Prev, BioCN&I, BiolAb, CPA, FCA, ForAb, HerbAb, HortAb, MaizeAb, OrnHort, PBA, PotatoAb, RA&MP, RPP, RefZh, RiceAb, S&F, SIA, SeedAb, SoyAb, TriticAb, VITIS, WeedAb.
—BLDSC (4989.070000), CISTI, IE, Infotrieve, ingenta. **CCC.**
Published by: (Phytopathological Society of Japan/Nihon Shokubutsu Byori Gakkai), Springer-Verlag Tokyo (Subsidiary of: Springer Science+Business Media), 3-13 Hongo 3-chome, Bunkyo-ku, Tokyo, 113-0033, Japan. TEL 81-3-38120331, FAX 81-3-38187454, http://www.springer-tokyo.co.jp/. Ed. Ichiro Uyeda. Adv. contact Stephan Kroeck TEL 49-30-827875739. **Subscr. in the Americas to:** Springer-Verlag New York, Inc., Journal Fulfillment, PO Box 2485, Secaucus, NJ 07096-2485. TEL 800-777-4643, 201-348-4033, FAX 201-348-4505, journals@springer-ny.com, http://www.springer-ny.com; **Subscr. to:** Springer GmbH Auslieferungsgesellschaft, Haberstr 7, Heidelberg 69126, Germany. TEL 49-6221-345-0, FAX 49-6221-345-4229, subscriptions@springer.de.

➤ **JOURNAL OF HERBS, SPICES & MEDICINAL PLANTS.** see *GARDENING AND HORTICULTURE*

580 GBR ISSN 1672-9072
QK1 CODEN: CJBOE2
➤ **JOURNAL OF INTEGRATIVE PLANT BIOLOGY.** Text in English. 1989. m. USD 189 combined subscription in the Americas to individuals print & online eds.; EUR 168 combined subscription in Europe to individuals print & online eds.; GBP 112 combined subscription elsewhere to individuals print & online eds.; USD 600 combined subscription in the Americas to institutions print & online eds.; GBP 356 combined subscription elsewhere to institutions print & online eds. (effective 2006). adv. bk.rev. 96 p./no.; **Document type:** *Journal, Academic/Scholarly.* **Description:** Publishes original articles on all aspects of plant sciences with emphasis on basic research. Includes reviews, notes, short communications, and institution briefs.
Former titles (until 2004): Acta Botanica Sinica (1672-6650); Chinese Journal of Botany (1001-0718)
Related titles: Online - full text ed.: ISSN 1744-7909. USD 570 in the Americas to institutions; GBP 338 elsewhere to institutions (effective 2006) (from Blackwell Synergy, EBSCO Publishing, Gale Group, IngentaConnect, O C L C Online Computer Library Center, Inc., Swets Information Services); ♦ Chinese ed.: Zhiwu Xuebao. ISSN 0577-7496.
Indexed: FCA.
—BLDSC (5007.538427). **CCC.**
Published by: (Chinese Academy of Sciences, Institute of Botany CHN), Blackwell Publishing Ltd., 9600 Garsington Rd, Oxford, OX4 2ZG, United Kingdom. TEL 44-1865-776868, FAX 44-1865-714591, customerservices@oxon.blackwellpublishing.com, http://www.blackwellpublishing.com/journals/JIPB. Eds. Hong Ma, Xing-Guo Han. Circ: 5,000. **Subscr. in China to:** Chinese Academy of Sciences, Institute of Botany, 20 Nanxincun, Xiangshan, Beijing 100093, China.

580.952 JPN ISSN 0022-2062
JOURNAL OF JAPANESE BOTANY/SHOKUBUTSU KENKYU ZASSHI. Text in Japanese. 1916. bi-m. JPY 8,500. adv. bk.rev. **Document type:** *Bulletin.*
Indexed: AEA, ASFA, AgBio, BIOBASE, BIOSIS Prev, BiolAb, CPA, ESPM, FCA, FPA, ForAb, HerbAb, HortAb, OrnHort, PBA, PGegResA, RA&MP, RPP, RevApplEntom, S&F, SeedAb, SoyAb, TDB, WeedAb.
—BLDSC (5008.900000), IE, ingenta, Linda Hall.
Published by: Tsumura & Co., Tsumura Laboratory, 3586 Yoshiwara, Inashiki-gun, Ami-machi, Ibaraki-ken 300-1155, Japan. FAX 81-298-89-2158, info@jjbot.com, http://jjbot.com. Ed. Shoji Shibata. Pub., R&P, Adv. contact Minoru Okada TEL 81-298-89-3832. Circ: 1,200.

580 IND
JOURNAL OF MEDICINAL AND AROMATIC PLANT SCIENCES. Text in English. 1979. q. USD 150 (effective 2006). adv. bk.rev. **Document type:** *Journal, Academic/Scholarly.* **Description:** Publishes papers contributing to the knowledge, understanding and progress of various scientific disciplines, including agriculture, biochemistry, biotechnology, botony, chemistry, genetics, molecular biology, physiology, pathology, pharmacognosy, plant breeding, pharmacology, material processing, technology and other as related to medicunal plants and other natural product plants.
Former titles: Current Research on Medicinal and Aromatic Plants (0253-7125); (until 1979): Central Indian Medicinal Plants Organisation. Newsletter
Indexed: AEA, ASFA, AgBio, AgrForAb, BIOSIS Prev, BioCN&I, BiolAb, CPA, ChemAb, DSA, FCA, FPA, FS&TA, ForAb, HelmAb, HortAb, I&DA, MaizeAb, NemAb, NutrAb, OrnHort, PBA, PGegResA, PGrRegA, PHN&I, PotatoAb, ProtozoAb, RA&MP, RDA, RM&VM, RPP, RRTA, RevApplEntom, RiceAb, S&F, SIA, SeedAb, SoyAb, TDB, TriticAb, WAE&RSA, WeedAb.
—CASDDS, CISTI, GNLM.
Published by: Central Institute of Medicinal and Aromatic Plants, Council of Scientific & Industrial Research, P.O. CIMAP, P O Box 1, Lucknow, Uttar Pradesh 226 015, India. TEL 91-522-359623, FAX 91-522-342666, TELEX 0535-298 CIMAP IN, root@cimap.sirnetd.ernet.in, http://www.scientificpub.com/bookdetails.php?booktransid=457&bookid=453. Ed. Sushil Kumar. Adv. contact Ashok Sharma. Circ: 250. **Dist. by:** H P C Publishers Distributors Pvt. Ltd., 4805 Bharat Ram Rd, 24 Darya Ganj, New Delhi 110 002, India. TEL 91-11-325-4401, FAX 91-11-619-3511.

JOURNAL OF NEW SEEDS; innovations in production, biotechnology, quality and marketing. see *AGRICULTURE—Crop Production And Soil*

571.845 IND ISSN 0022-3379
QE993 CODEN: JPLYAR
JOURNAL OF PALYNOLOGY. Text in English. 1966. s-a. INR 700, USD 60. adv. bk.rev. illus. cum.index. back issues avail.; reprints avail. **Document type:** *Academic/Scholarly.* **Description:** Covers all aspects of pollen spore studies, from algae to angiosperms, from the present day plants to fossil plants.
Formerly (until 1972): Palynological Bulletin (0031-0492)
Indexed: AgrForAb, BiolAb, CPA, ChemAb, CurCont, FCA, ForAb, HortAb, MaizeAb, OrnHort, PBA, PGegResA, PGrRegA, RA&MP, RM&VM, RPP, RiceAb, S&F, SIA, SeedAb, WeedAb.
—CASDDS, CISTI, Linda Hall. **CCC.**
Published by: (Palynological Society of India), Today and Tomorrow's Printers & Publishers, 24 B-5 Desh Bandhu Gupta Rd., Karol Bagh, New Delhi, 110 005, India. TEL 9111-572-1928, FAX 9111-721-0073, tp@vsnl.net. Ed. A R Kulkarnj Bir Bahadur. R&P R K Jain. Circ: 400. **Dist. in U.S. by:** Scholarly Publications, 2825 Wilcrest Dr, Ste 255, Houston, TX 77042. TEL 713-781-0070.

579.8 USA ISSN 0022-3646
QK564 CODEN: JPYLAJ
➤ **JOURNAL OF PHYCOLOGY.** Text in English. 1965. bi-m. USD 554 combined subscription in the Americas to institutions & Caribbean (print & online eds.); USD 564 combined subscription in Canada & Mexico to institutions print & online eds.; GBP 407 combined subscription elsewhere to institutions print & online eds. (effective 2006). adv. abstr.; bibl.; charts; illus. Index. back issues avail.; reprints avail. **Document type:** *Journal, Academic/Scholarly.* **Description:** Publishes international research to provide a common medium for the ecologist, physiologist, cell biologist, molecular biologist and biochemist.
Related titles: Online - full text ed.: ISSN 1529-8817. 2000. USD 526 in the Americas to institutions & Caribbean; USD 536 in Canada & Mexico to institutions; GBP 387 elsewhere to institutions (effective 2006) (from Blackwell Synergy, EBSCO Publishing, Gale Group, HighWire Press, IngentaConnect, O C L C Online Computer Library Center, Inc., Swets Information Services).
Indexed: ABIPC, ASCA, ASFA, AbHyg, AgBio, B&BAb, BIOBASE, BIOSIS Prev, BiolAb, CCI, CIN, CPA, ChemAb, ChemTitl, CurCont, ESPM, ForAb, GEOBASE, HortAb, I&DA, IABS, ISR, IndVet, MBA, NutrAb, OceAb, PBA, PGegResA, PlantSci, ProtozoAb, RPP, S&F, SCI, SFA, SIA, VetBull, WeedAb, ZooRec.
—BLDSC (5035.500000), CASDDS, CINDOC, CISTI, IDS, IE, Infotrieve, ingenta, Linda Hall. **CCC.**
Published by: (Phycological Society of America CAN), Blackwell Publishing, Inc. (Subsidiary of: Blackwell Publishing Ltd.), Commerce Place, 350 Main St, Malden, MA 02148. TEL 781-388-8206, FAX 781-388-8232, subscrip@blackwellpub.com, http://www.blackwellpublishing.com/journals/JPY. Ed. Patricia A Wheeler TEL 541-737-9176. Circ: 2,000. **Co-sponsor:** American Association for the Advancement of Science.

571.9 DEU ISSN 0931-1785
CODEN: JPHYEB
➤ **JOURNAL OF PHYTOPATHOLOGY/PHYTOPATHOLOGISCHE ZEITSCHRIFT.** Text in English, German; Summaries in English, German. m. EUR 270 combined subscription in Europe to individuals print & online eds.; USD 291 combined subscription in the Americas to individuals & Caribbean, print & online eds.; GBP 180 combined subscription elsewhere to individuals print & online eds.; GBP 872 combined subscription in Europe to institutions print & online eds.; USD 1,464 combined subscription in the Americas to institutions & Caribbean, print & online eds.; GBP 959 combined subscription elsewhere to institutions print & online eds. (effective 2006). bk.rev. illus.; stat. index. back issues avail. **Document type:** *Journal, Academic/Scholarly.* **Description:** Publishes original scientific articles and short communications on all aspects of phytopathology, and on relevant related subjects.
Former titles (until 1986): Phytopathologische Zeitschrift (0031-9481); (until 1929): Forschungen auf dem Gebiet der Pflanzenkrankheiten und der Immunitat im Pflanzenreich
Related titles: Microform ed.: (from PMC); Online - full text ed.: ISSN 1439-0434. GBP 828 in Europe to institutions; USD 1,391 in the Americas to institutions & Caribbean; GBP 911 elsewhere to institutions (effective 2006) (from Blackwell Synergy, EBSCO Publishing, Gale Group, IngentaConnect, O C L C Online Computer Library Center, Inc., Swets Information Services).

▼ new title ➤ refereed ✶ unverified ♦ full entry avail.

Indexed: ASCA, ASFA, AgBio, Agr, AgrForAb, B&BAb, BIOBASE, BIOSIS Prev, BioCN&I, BiolAb, CIN, CPA, CTFA, ChemAb, ChemTitl, CurCont, DBA, EPB, ESPM, ExcerpMed, FCA, FPA, FS&TA, FaBeAb, ForAb, GEOBASE, HerbAb, HortAb, ISR, MBA, MaizeAb, NemAb, OrnHort, PBA, PGegResA, PGrRegA, PHN&I, PotatoAb, RA&MP, RDA, RM&VM, RPP, RefZh, RevApplEntom, RiceAb, S&F, SCI, SIA, SeedAb, SoyAb, TriticAb, VITIS, WAE&RSA, WeedAb.
—BLDSC (5040.250000), CASDDS, CISTI, IDS, IE, Infotrieve, ingenta, Linda Hall. **CCC.**
Published by: Blackwell Verlag GmbH (Subsidiary of: Blackwell Publishing Ltd.), Kurfuerstendamm 57, Berlin, 10707, Germany. TEL 49-30-32790634, FAX 49-30-32790610, verlag@blackwell.de, http://www.blackwellpublishing.com/journals/JPH, http://www.blackwell.de. Eds. Alan Brunt, John Laurence. Circ: 700 (paid and controlled).

580 KOR ISSN 1226-9239
QK370
JOURNAL OF PLANT BIOLOGY. Text in English, Korean; Abstracts in English. 1958. q. looseleaf. KRW 24,000, USD 30 to individuals; USD 60 to institutions. adv. abstr.; bibl.; illus.; pat.; stat. back issues avail. **Document type:** *Academic/Scholarly.* **Description:** Publishes original research and review articles on all aspects of plant science, including information on autotrophic microorganisms.
Formerly (until 1994): Korean Journal of Botany - Singmul Hakhoe Chi (0583-421X)
Related titles: CD-ROM ed.; E-mail ed.; Fax ed.
Indexed: BIOSIS Prev, BiolAb, CPA, ChemTitl, CurCont, PGegResA, PGrRegA, VITIS, WeedAb.
—BLDSC (5040.509500), CASDDS, CISTI, IE, ingenta, Linda Hall.
Published by: Botanical Society of Korea, 968-3 Pongchon-Dong Kwanak-Gu, 402 Keumsong Bldg, Seoul, 151051, Korea, S. TEL 82-2-884-0384, FAX 82-2-884-0385, hcb@plaza.snu.ac.kr. Ed. Gyn Heung An. Pub. Kwang Woong Lee. adv.: B&W page KRW 400,000, color page KRW 600,000; 200 x 260. Circ: 750. **Co-sponsor:** Ministry of Education.

580 IND
QK861 CODEN: PBJODQ
JOURNAL OF PLANT BIOLOGY. Text in English. 1974. s-a. INR 250, USD 40 to non-members; INR 50, USD 10 to members; USD 125 to students; USD 800 to libraries (effective 2000). adv. bibl.; charts. **Description:** An international, inter-disciplinary periodical devoted to plant biology research. Aims to provide a focal point for the publication of standard research articles in applied and basic plant biology, to provide a valuable source of reference for research laboratories and libraries.
Former titles: Plant Physiology & Biochemistry (0254-3591); (until 1982): Plant Biochemical Journal (0379-5578)
Related titles: Microfiche ed.: (from NTI).
Indexed: ABIPC, AgBio, AgrForAb, BiolAb, CPA, ChemAb, CurCont, DSA, FCA, FPA, ForAb, HerbAb, HortAb, I&DA, MaizeAb, NemAb, NutrAb, OrnHort, PBA, PGegResA, PGrRegA, PHN&I, RA&MP, RPP, RiceAb, S&F, SIA, SeedAb, SoyAb, TriticAb, WeedAb.
—BLDSC (5040.509400), CASDDS, CISTI, IE, ingenta, Linda Hall.
Published by: Society for Plant Physiology and Biochemistry, c/o Y.P. Abrol, Water Technology Centre, Agricultural Research Institute, New Delhi, 110 012, India. Ed. S Mahadevan. adv.: B&W page INR 10,000, color page INR 15,000.

580 USA ISSN 0721-7595
QK745 CODEN: JPGRDI
➤ **JOURNAL OF PLANT GROWTH REGULATION.** Text in English. 1981. q. EUR 548 combined subscription to institutions print & online eds. (effective 2005). adv. back issues avail.; reprint service avail. from PSC,ISI. **Document type:** *Journal, Academic/Scholarly.* **Description:** Focuses on natural and synthetic plant growth substances and on their effects on plant growth and development.
Related titles: Microform ed.: (from PQC); Online - full text ed.: ISSN 1435-8107 (from EBSCO Publishing, Springer LINK, Swets Information Services).
Indexed: ABIPC, AEBA, ASCA, ASFA, AgBio, Agr, AgrForAb, AnBrAb, B&BAb, BIOBASE, BIOSIS Prev, BibAg, BiolAb, CIN, CPA, CTFA, ChemAb, ChemTitl, CurCont, DBA, ESPM, EngInd, FCA, FPA, FaBeAb, ForAb, HerbAb, HortAb, I&DA, IABS, ISR, MEDLINE, MaizeAb, NemAb, OrnHort, PBA, PGegResA, PGrRegA, PHN&I, PlantSci, PotatoAb, RA&MP, RPP, RRTA, RiceAb, S&F, SCI, SeedAb, SoyAb, TriticAb, VITIS, WeedAb.
—BLDSC (5040.514300), CASDDS, CISTI, IDS, IE, Infotrieve, ingenta, Linda Hall. **CCC.**
Published by: Springer-Verlag New York, Inc. (Subsidiary of: Springer Science+Business Media), 233 Spring St, New York, NY 10013. TEL 212-460-1500, 800-777-4643, FAX 212-473-6272, journals@springer-ny.com, http://link.springer.de/link/service/journals/00344/, http://www.springer-ny.com. Ed. Jutta Ludwig-Mueller. R&P Ian Gross. Adv. contact Brian Skepton. **Subscr. outside the Americas to:** Springer GmbH Auslieferungsgesellschaft, Haberstr 7, Heidelberg 69126, Germany. TEL 49-6221-345-0, FAX 49-6221-345-4229, subscriptions@springer.de; **Subscr. to:** Journal Fulfillment, PO Box 2485, Secaucus, NJ 07096-2485. TEL 201-348-4033, FAX 201-348-4505. **Co-sponsors:** International Plant Growth Substances Association; Plant Growth Regulation Society of America.

571.2 GBR ISSN 1742-9145
▼ ➤ **JOURNAL OF PLANT INTERACTIONS.** Text in English. 2005. q. GBP 209, USD 345 combined subscription to institutions print & online eds. (effective 2006). **Document type:** *Journal, Academic/Scholarly.* **Description:** Presents original research and reviews in the fields of the many aspects of interaction between plants and their surrounding environment.
Related titles: Online - full content ed.: ISSN 1742-9153. forthcoming 2005. GBP 199, USD 328 (effective 2006).
Published by: Taylor & Francis Ltd (Subsidiary of: Taylor & Francis Group), 4 Park Sq, Milton Park, Abingdon, OX14 4RN, United Kingdom. TEL 44-1235-828600, FAX 44-1235-829000, info@tandf.co.uk, http://www.tandf.co.uk/journals/titles/17429145.asp. Ed. Dr. Massimo Maffei. **Subscr. in N America to:** Taylor & Francis Inc., Customer Services Dept, 325 Chestnut St, 8th Fl, Philadelphia, PA 19106. TEL 215-625-8900, 800-354-1420, FAX 215-625-8914, customerservice@taylorandfrancis.com; **Subscr. outside N America to:** Journals Customer Service, Rankine Rd, Basingstoke, Hants RG24 8PR, United Kingdom. TEL 44-1256-813000, FAX 44-1256-330245, enquiry@tandf.co.uk.

580 USA ISSN 0190-4167
QK867 CODEN: JPNUDS
➤ **JOURNAL OF PLANT NUTRITION.** Text in English. 1978. m. GBP 1,423, USD 2,231 combined subscription to institutions print & online eds. (effective 2006). adv. reprint service avail. from PSC. **Document type:** *Journal, Academic/Scholarly.* **Description:** Published papers exploring the influence of the mineral elements on plant physiology and growth.
Related titles: Microform ed.: (from RPI); Online - full text ed.: ISSN 1532-4087. GBP 1,352, USD 2,348 (effective 2006) (from EBSCO Publishing, O C L C Online Computer Library Center, Inc., Swets Information Services).
Indexed: AEA, ASCA, ASFA, AgBio, Agr, AgrForAb, B&AI, BIOBASE, BIOSIS Prev, BibAg, BiolAb, CIN, CPA, CTFA, Cadscan, ChemAb, ChemTitl, CurCont, DSA, EPB, ESPM, EnvAb, EnvInd, FCA, ForAb, GardL, HerbAb, HortAb, I&DA, IABS, ISR, LeadAb, MaizeAb, NemAb, NutrAb, OrnHort, PBA, PGegResA, PGrRegA, PHN&I, PN&I, PlantSci, PollutAb, PotatoAb, PoultAb, RA&MP, RDA, RPP, RefZh, RiceAb, S&F, S&MA, SCI, SIA, SWRA, SeedAb, SoyAb, TOSA, TriticAb, VITIS, WAE&RSA, WeedAb, Zincscan.
—BLDSC (5040.515000), CASDDS, CISTI, IDS, IE, Infotrieve, ingenta. **CCC.**
Published by: Taylor & Francis Inc. (Subsidiary of: Taylor & Francis Group), 325 Chestnut St, Ste 800, Philadelphia, PA 19106. TEL 215-625-8900, 800-354-1420, FAX 215-625-8914, info@taylorandfrancis.com, http://www.tandf.co.uk/journals/titles/01904167.asp, http://www.taylorandfrancis.com. Ed. Dr. Harry A Mills. R&P Elaine Inverso. Adv. contact Mary Drabot. page USD 600. Circ: 500 (paid).

➤ **JOURNAL OF PLANT NUTRITION AND SOIL SCIENCE/ZEITSCHRIFT FUER PFLANZENERNAEHRUNG UND BODENKUNDE.** see *BIOLOGY—Abstracting, Bibliographies, Statistics*

571.92 ITA ISSN 1125-4653
CODEN: RPVGA9
➤ **JOURNAL OF PLANT PATHOLOGY.** Text in Multiple languages. 1892. q. EUR 78 domestic; USD 100 foreign (effective 2004). adv. bk.rev. bibl.; charts; illus. index. 100 p./no.; reprints avail. **Document type:** *Journal, Academic/Scholarly.* **Description:** Publishes original research papers and short notes on fundamental and applied aspects of plant pathology.
Formerly (until 1997): Rivista di Patologia Vegetale (0035-6441)
Indexed: AEA, ASFA, AgBio, AgrForAb, B&BAb, BIOSIS Prev, BioCN&I, BiolAb, CPA, ChemAb, CurCont, ESPM, FCA, FPA, ForAb, HerbAb, HortAb, MBA, MaizeAb, MycolAb, NemAb, OrnHort, PBA, PGegResA, PGrRegA, PHN&I, PotatoAb, RA&MP, RPP, RefZh, RevApplEntom, S&F, SIA, SeedAb, SoyAb, TriticAb, VITIS, WAE&RSA, WeedAb.
—CASDDS, CISTI, Linda Hall.
Published by: (Societa Italiana di Patologia Vegetale), Edizioni E T S, Piazza Carrara 16-19, Pisa, Italy. TEL 39-050-29544, FAX 39-050-20158, info@edizioniets.it, http://www.agr.unipi.it/sipav/jpp, http://www.edizioniets.it. Eds. Giovanni P Martelli, Antonino Catara. Adv. contact G Vannacci. Circ: 400.

571.2 DEU ISSN 0176-1617
QK1 CODEN: JPPHEY
➤ **JOURNAL OF PLANT PHYSIOLOGY.** Text in English. 1909. 12/yr. EUR 293 in Europe to individuals; JPY 36,400 in Japan to individuals; USD 285 elsewhere to individuals; EUR 1,247 to institutions in Germany, Austria, Switzerland; EUR 1,616 in Europe to institutions; JPY 214,300 in Japan to institutions; USD 1,705 elsewhere to institutions (effective 2006). adv. bk.rev. abstr.; charts; illus. Index. **Document type:** *Journal, Academic/Scholarly.* **Description:** Covers the whole spectrum of scientific research from phytochemistry to plant cell biology, molecular biology, whole plant physiology, and developmental biology.
Incorporates: Biochemie und Physiologie der Pflanzen (B P P) (0015-3796); Formerly (until 1984): Zeitschrift fuer Pflanzenphysiologie (0044-328X)
Related titles: Online - full text ed.: (from bigchalk, EBSCO Publishing, Gale Group, IngentaConnect, O C L C Online Computer Library Center, Inc., ProQuest Information & Learning, ScienceDirect, Swets Information Services).
Indexed: ABIPC, AEA, AEBA, ASCA, ASFA, AgBio, Agr, AgrForAb, BBCI, BIOBASE, BIOSIS Prev, BioEngAb, BiolAb, CIN, CPA, ChemAb, ChemTitl, CurCont, DBA, DSA, ESPM, EngInd, FCA, FPA, FS&TA, ForAb, HerbAb, HortAb, I&DA, IABS, ISR, MBA, MaizeAb, NutrAb, OrnHort, PBA, PGegResA, PGrRegA, PHN&I, PlantSci, PollutAb, PotatoAb, ProtozoAb, RA&MP, RPP, RRTA, RevApplEntom, RiceAb, S&F, SCI, SIA, SeedAb, SoyAb, TriticAb, VITIS, WAE&RSA, WeedAb.
—BLDSC (5040.518500), CASDDS, CISTI, IDS, IE, Infotrieve, ingenta, Linda Hall. **CCC.**
Published by: (Spanish Society of Plant Physiology ESP, Portuguese Society of Plant Physiology PRT), Elsevier GmbH, Urban & Fischer Verlag (Subsidiary of: Elsevier Science & Technology), Loebdergraben 14a, Jena, 07743, Germany. TEL 49-3641-626430, FAX 49-3641-626432, info@urbanfischer.de, http://www.elsevier.com/locate/jpp, http://www.urbanfischer.de/journals. Ed. Christian Wilhelm. adv.: B&W page EUR 485, color page EUR 1,430; 210 x 280. Circ: 775 (paid and controlled). **Non-German speaking countries subscr. to:** Nature Publishing Group, Brunel Rd, Houndmills, Basingstoke, Hamps RG21 6XS, United Kingdom. TEL 44-1256-302629, FAX 44-1256-476117

580 595.7 POL ISSN 1427-4345
SB599 CODEN: JPPRFV
JOURNAL OF PLANT PROTECTION RESEARCH. Text in English; Summaries in Polish. 1960. q. EUR 82 foreign (effective 2005). bk.rev. abstr. **Document type:** *Journal, Academic/Scholarly.*
Formerly (until vol.37, 1997): Instytut Ochrony Roslin. Prace Naukowe (0554-8004)
Indexed: AEA, AbHyg, AgrAg, AgrForAb, AgrLib, BIOSIS Prev, BioCN&I, BiolAb, CIN, CPA, ChemAb, ChemTitl, DBA, FCA, FPA, ForAb, HerbAb, HortAb, I&DA, MaizeAb, NemAb, OrnHort, PBA, PGegResA, PGrRegA, PHN&I, PotatoAb, RA&MP, RM&VM, RPP, RefZh, RevApplEntom, RiceAb, S&F, SIA, SeedAb, SoyAb, TriticAb, WAE&RSA, WeedAb, ZooRec.
—BLDSC (5040.520300), CASDDS, CISTI.
Published by: Instytut Ochrony Roslin/Institute of Plant Protection, ul Miczurina 20, Poznan, 60318, Poland. TEL 48-61-8649173, FAX 48-61-8676301, d.wolna@ior.poznan.pl, http://www.ior.poznan.pl. Ed. Jerzy J Lipa. **Dist. by:** Ars Polona, Krakowskie Przedmiescie 7, Warsaw, Poland. TEL 48-22-9263914, FAX 48-22-9265334, arspolona@arspolona.com.pl, http://www.arspolona.com.pl. **Co-sponsor:** Polska Akademia Nauk, Komitet Ochrony Roslin/Polish Academy of Sciences, Committee of Plant Protection.

580 JPN ISSN 0918-9440
QK1 CODEN: JPLREA
➤ **JOURNAL OF PLANT RESEARCH.** Text in English. 1887. bi-m. EUR 255 combined subscription to institutions print & online eds. (effective 2005). adv. **Document type:** *Journal, Academic/Scholarly.* **Description:** Publishes original papers and review articles on all aspects of plant science.
Formerly: Botanical Magazine, Tokyo (0006-808X)
Related titles: Microfiche ed.: (from IDC); Online - full text ed.: ISSN 1618-0860 (from EBSCO Publishing, Springer LINK, Swets Information Services).
Indexed: AEBA, ASCA, ASFA, AgBio, Agr, AgrForAb, ApEcolAb, B&BAb, BIOSIS Prev, BioCN&I, BioEngAb, BiolAb, CIN, CPA, ChemAb, ChemTitl, CurCont, ESPM, FCA, FPA, FaBeAb, ForAb, GenetAb, HGA, HerbAb, HortAb, I&DA, ISR, MaizeAb, OrnHort, PBA, PGegResA, PGrRegA, PHN&I, PollutAb, RA&MP, RM&VM, RPP, RiceAb, S&F, SCI, SIA, SPPI, SeedAb, SoyAb, TriticAb, WeedAb, ZooRec.
—BLDSC (5040.522000), CASDDS, CISTI, IDS, IE, Infotrieve, ingenta, Linda Hall. **CCC.**
Published by: (Botanical Society of Japan), Springer-Verlag Tokyo (Subsidiary of: Springer Science+Business Media), 3-13 Hongo 3-chome, Bunkyo-ku, Tokyo, 113-0033, Japan. TEL 81-3-38120331, FAX 81-3-38187454, http://www.springeronline.com/sgw/cda/frontpage/0,11855,5-0-70-1169736-0,00.html?referer=www.springeronline.com/east/journal/10265, http://www.springer-tokyo.co.jp/. Ed. Hiroshi Tobe. Adv. contact Stephan Kroeck TEL 49-30-827875739. Circ: 2,600 (paid). **Subscr. in the Americas to:** Springer-Verlag New York, Inc., Journal Fulfillment, PO Box 2485, Secaucus, NJ 07096-2485. TEL 800-777-4643, 201-348-4033, FAX 201-348-4505, journals@springer-ny.com, http://www.springer-ny.com; **Subscr. to:** Springer GmbH Auslieferungsgesellschaft, Haberstr 7, Heidelberg 69126, Germany. TEL 49-6221-345-0, FAX 49-6221-345-4229, subscriptions@springer.de.

580 EGY ISSN 1110-5380
JOURNAL OF UNION OF ARAB BIOLOGISTS CAIRO. B. BOTANY. Text in English. a. **Document type:** *Journal, Academic/Scholarly.*
—BLDSC (4910.568500).
Published by: Union of Arab Biologists, Faculty of Science, Cairo University, Cairo University Campus, Cairo, Egypt. info@egsz.org, http://derp.sti.sci.eg/data/0223.htm, http://www.egsz.org.

580 SWE ISSN 1100-9233
CODEN: JVESEK

➤ **JOURNAL OF VEGETATION SCIENCE.** Text in English. 1990. bi-m. EUR 434; EUR 543 combined subscription print & online eds. (effective 2005). adv. bk.rev. 150 p./no. 2 cols./p.; back issues avail. **Document type:** *Journal, Academic/Scholarly.* **Description:** Publishes original articles, short notes and review articles in the field of vegetation science, both methodological and theoretical studies, and descriptive and experimental studies of plant communities and plant populations.

Related titles: Online - full text ed.: (from BioOne, C S A, EBSCO Publishing, O C L C Online Computer Library Center, Inc., Swets Information Services); Supplement(s): Special Features in Vegetarion Science. ISSN 1104-7402.

Indexed: ASCA, AgBio, Agr, AgrForAb, BIOBASE, BIOSIS Prev, BibAg, BiolAb, CPA, CurCont, EA, EPB, EZ&PSA, FCA, FPA, ForAb, GEOBASE, HerbAb, HortAb, I&DA, IABS, INIS AtomInd, ISR, NutrAb, OrnHort, PBA, PGegResA, PlantSci, RA&MP, RDA, RPP, RRTA, RevApplEntom, S&F, SCI, SeedAb, SoyAb, TriticAb, VITIS, VetBull, WAE&RSA, WeedAb.

—BLDSC (5072.277000), CISTI, IE, Infotrieve, ingenta, Linda Hall.

Published by: (International Association for Vegetation Science NLD), Opulus Press, Gamla Vaegen 40, Grangaerde, 77013, Sweden. TEL 46-240-641250, FAX 46-240-640880, info@opuluspress.se, http://www.opuluspress.se. Eds. J P Bakker, S. Diaz. Circ: 1,500.

580 DEU ISSN 0022-7846

KAKTEEN UND ANDERE SUKKULENTEN. Text in German. 1892. m. EUR 32 domestic; EUR 35 foreign (effective 2001). adv. bibl.; charts; illus. back issues avail. **Document type:** *Magazine, Academic/Scholarly.* **Description:** International in scope, containing original descriptions of new species, plus popular or scholarly articles covering field trips, botanical gardens, horticulture, and geographic sites.

Indexed: BiolAb.

Published by: Deutsche Kakteen Gesellschaft e.V., Oos-Str 18, Pforzheim, 75179, Germany. TEL 49-7231-281550, FAX 49-7231-281551, geschaeftsstelle@deutschekakteengesellschaft.de, http://www.deutschekakteengesellschaft.de. Ed. Gerhard Lauchs. Adv. contact M Thumser. Circ: 9,000.

580 JPN

KAN'AOI KENKYU/KANAOI RESEARCH. Text in Japanese. 1985. a.

Published by: Yasuo Koshimizu Pub., 1190 Shimo-Ozuki, Hadano-shi, Kanagawa-ken 257-0004, Japan.

580 FIN ISSN 0453-3402
QK600 CODEN: KRSTA4

➤ **KARSTENIA**; the mycological journal. Text in English. 1950. s-a. EUR 20 in Nordic countries; EUR 33 elsewhere. bk.rev. index. **Document type:** *Academic/Scholarly.*

Indexed: BIOSIS Prev, BiolAb, ChemAb, FPA, ForAb, RPP, RefZh.

—CASDDS, CISTI.

Published by: Societas Mycologica Fennica/Finnish Mycological Society, University of Helsinki, PL 7, Helsinki, 00014, Finland. TEL 358-9-708-4784, FAX 358-9-708-4830, orvo.vitikainen@helsinki.fi. Ed. Orvo Vitikainen. Circ: 800.

580 635 GBR ISSN 0961-4141

KEW. Text in English. 1991. q. GBP 14 domestic; GBP 26 foreign (effective 2001). bk.rev. **Document type:** *Magazine, Consumer.*

Published by: Friends of the Royal Botanic Gardens, Kew, Kew Gardens, Richmond, Surrey TW9 3AB, United Kingdom. TEL 44-20-83325906, FAX 44-20-83325901. Ed. Spence Gunn. Pub. Michael Godfrey. Circ: 28,264.

580 GBR ISSN 0075-5974
QK1 CODEN: KEWBAF

➤ **KEW BULLETIN.** Text in English. 1946. q. GBP 170; GBP 55 per issue (effective 2005). bk.rev. illus. reprints avail. **Document type:** *Journal, Government.* **Description:** Contains original articles of interest mainly to vascular plant and mycological systematists.

Related titles: Microfilm ed.: (from BHP); Microform ed.: (from PQC); Online - full text ed.: (from ProQuest Information & Learning).

Indexed: AgBio, Agr, AgrForAb, ApicAb, BIOBASE, BIOSIS Prev, BiolAb, FCA, FPA, ForAb, HerbAb, HortAb, IABS, OrnHort, PBA, PGegResA, PlantSci, RA&MP, RPP, RevApplEntom, S&F, SeedAb, WeedAb, ZooRec.

—BLDSC (5091.000000), CISTI, IE, Infotrieve, ingenta, Linda Hall. **CCC.**

Published by: Royal Botanic Gardens, Kew, Richmond, Surrey TW9 3AB, United Kingdom. TEL 44-20-83325000, FAX 44-20-83325197, info@kew.org, http://www.rbgkew.org.uk/publications/kewbulletin.html, http://www.rbgkew.org.uk/index.html. Circ: 550. **Subscr. to:** Stationery Office (Norwich), St Crispins House, Duke St, PO Box 29, Norwich NR3 1PD, United Kingdom. TEL 44-870-600-5522, FAX 44-870-600-5533, customer.services@theso.co.uk.

580 GBR

KEW RECORD OF TAXONOMIC LITERATURE (YEAR). Text in English. a. GBP 40 (effective 2000).

Published by: H.S.M.O., Royal Botanical Gardens, Kew, PO Box 276, London, SW8 5DT, United Kingdom. TEL 44-20-7873-9090, FAX 44-20-7870-0011, http://www.itsofficial.co.uk. Circ: 200.

KEW RECORD OF TAXONOMIC LITERATURE RELATING TO VASCULAR PLANTS. see *BIOLOGY—Abstracting, Bibliographies, Statistics*

580.74 GBR ISSN 0967-8018

KEW SCIENTIST; news from the living collection, the herbarium and the laboratories at Kew and Wakehurst Place. Text in English. 1992. s-a. **Description:** Allows those with a general interest in botany to keep in touch with work in progress. It also provides contact points for those interested in collaboration or in obtaining further information.

Formed by the merger of (1988-1992): Jodrell Newsletter (0955-6206); E C O S Newsletter

Related titles: Online - full content ed.

Published by: Royal Botanic Gardens, Kew, Richmond, Surrey TW9 3AB, United Kingdom. TEL 44-20-83325000, FAX 44-20-83325197, info@rbgkew.org.uk, http://www.rbgkew.org.uk/kewscientist/, http://www.rbgkew.org.uk/index.html.

579.5 JPN ISSN 0388-8266
CODEN: KJKKAH

KINJIN KENKYUJO HOKOKU/TOTTORI MYCOLOGICAL INSTITUTE. REPORTS. Text in English, Japanese. 1961. a. JPY 4,000. **Description:** Covers fungal taxonomy, edology, physiology and genetics, and mushroom cultivation.

Indexed: AgBio, Agrind, BIOSIS Prev, BioCN&I, BiolAb, CPA, FPA, ForAb, HortAb, JPI, PBA, PGegResA, RPP, RefZh.

—BLDSC (7619.600000).

Published by: Nihon Kinoko Senta, Kinjin Kenkyujo/Japan Kinoko Research Centre, Tottori Mycological Institute, 211 Hirohata, Kokoge, Tottori-shi, Tottori-ken 689-11, Japan. TEL 81-857-51-8111, FAX 81-857-53-1986. Circ: 700.

580 JPN ISSN 0914-3823

KINKI SHOKUBUTSU DOKOKAI KAIHO/KINKI BOTANICAL SOCIETY. NEWS. Text in Japanese. 1951. 3/yr.

Published by: Kinki Shokubutsu Dokokai/Kinki Botanical Society, c/o Mr Kozi Hirano, 36-15, Sayamadai 3-chome, Sakai-shi, Osaka 581, Japan.

580 JPN

KINKI SHOKUBUTSU DOKOKAI KAISHI/KINKI BOTANICAL SOCIETY. BULLETIN. Text in Japanese. 1950. biennial. membership. adv. back issues avail.

Published by: Kinki Shokubutsu Dokokai/Kinki Botanical Society, c/o Mr Kozi Hirano, 36-15, Sayamadai 3-chome, Sakai-shi, Osaka 581, Japan.

580 ZWE ISSN 0451-9930
QK381

KIRKIA; the Zimbabwe journal of botany. Text in English. 1960. s-a. ZWD 30, USD 10. bk.rev. back issues avail. **Document type:** *Academic/Scholarly.*

Indexed: AgrForAb, BIOSIS Prev, BiolAb, FCA, FPA, ForAb, HerbAb, HortAb, I&DA, OrnHort, PBA, PGegResA, RPP, S&F.

—BLDSC (5097.560000), CISTI, ingenta, Linda Hall.

Published by: (Zimbabwe. Ministry of Lands and Agriculture, Zimbabwe. Department of Research and Specialist Services), R & S S Information Services, Causeway, PO Box CY 594, Harare, Zimbabwe. TEL 263-4-725313, FAX 263-4-728317. Eds. J R Timberlake, S Kativu. Circ: 600.

580 JPN ISSN 0387-7361

KITAKYUSHU SHOKUBUTSU TOMO NO KAI KAIHO/KITAKYUSHU BOTANICAL ASSOCIATION. JOURNAL. Text in Japanese. 1979. a.

Published by: Kitakyushu Shokubutsu Tomo no Kai/Kitakyushu Botanical Association, c/o Mr Shigeru Kobayashi, 13-3 Ihori 3-chome, Kokurakita-ku, Kitakyushu-shi, Fukuoka-ken 803-0000, Japan.

579.55 KOR ISSN 0253-651X
QK600 CODEN: HKCHDD

KOREAN JOURNAL OF MYCOLOGY. Text in English, Korean. 1972. q. KRW 30,000, USD 40 to members. bk.rev. back issues avail. **Document type:** *Academic/Scholarly.*

Indexed: BiolAb, ChemAb, ForAb, RM&VM, RPP, S&F.

—BLDSC (5113.567000), CASDDS, CISTI.

Published by: Korean Society of Mycology, Department of Agrobiology, College of Agriculture, Dongguk University, Seoul, 100-715, Korea, S. Ed. Kwon Sang Yoon. Circ: 1,000.

579.5 KOR

KOREAN SOCIETY OF MYCOLOGY. NEWSLETTER. Text in English, Korean. s-a. KRW 15,000, USD 40 to members. **Document type:** *Bulletin.*

Published by: Korean Society of Mycology, Department of Agrobiology, College of Agriculture, Dongguk University, Seoul, 100-715, Korea, S. TEL 82-269-6980, FAX 82-269-6980. Ed. Kwon Sang Yoon.

580 ARG ISSN 0075-7314
QK1 CODEN: KURTAK

➤ **KURTZIANA.** Text in English, Spanish, Portuguese; Summaries in English. 1961. biennial. USD 30 (effective 2000). bk.rev. abstr.; bibl.; illus.; maps. back issues avail. **Document type:** *Journal, Academic/Scholarly.* **Description:** Illustrated articles on different branches of botany, with emphasis on embryology, morphology and taxonomy.

Indexed: BIOSIS Prev, BiolAb, RefZh.

—CISTI.

Published by: Universidad Nacional de Cordoba, Museo Botanico, Casilla de Correos 495, Cordoba, 5000, Argentina. kurtzian@imbiv.unc.edu.ar. Ed. Ana M Anton. Circ: 400.

580 JPN

KYOTO SHOKUBUTSU/KYOTO BOTANY. Text in Japanese. bi-m.

Published by: Kyoto Shokubutsu Dokokai/Kyoto Botanical Association, c/o Mr Shin'ichi Nishizawa, Omiya Nishi Iru, Motosenganji, Kamigyo-ku, Kyoto-shi, 602, Japan.

580 JPN

KYOTO UNIVERSITY. FACULTY OF AGRICULTURE. PLANT GERM-PLASM INSTITUTE. REPORT. Text in English. 1974. irreg.

Published by: (Plant Germ-Plasm Institute), Kyoto University, Faculty of Agriculture/Kyoto Daigaku Nogakubu Fuzoku Shokubutsu Seishokushitsu Kenkyu Shisetsu, Kyoku, 1 Nakajo-Mozumecho, Muko-shi, Kyoto-Fu 617-0000, Japan.

580 ESP ISSN 1132-2365

LACTARIUS. Text in Spanish. 1992. a. EUR 2 (effective 2003). **Document type:** *Newspaper, Academic/Scholarly.*

Indexed: BioCN&I, FPA, ForAb, IECT, RPP, S&F.

—CINDOC.

Published by: Universidad de Jaen, Facultad de Ciencias Experimentales, Herbario Jaen, Jaen, 23071, Spain. TEL 34-953-012159, FAX 34-953-012141, agricola@mundiprensa.es. **Dist. by:** Libreria Agricola, Fernando VI, 2, Madrid 28004, Spain. TEL 34-91-4190940. **Co-sponsor:** Asociacion Micologica Lactarius.

580 ESP ISSN 0210-7708
QK329 CODEN: LAGAEL

LAGASCALIA. Text in Spanish. 1971. a. EUR 15 per issue (effective 2005). illus. **Document type:** *Journal, Academic/Scholarly.*

Indexed: BIOSIS Prev, BiolAb, IECT, OrnHort, PCI, SeedAb.

—CINDOC. **CCC.**

Published by: (Universidad de Sevilla, Facultad de Biologia), Universidad de Sevilla, Secretariado de Publicaciones, Porvenir 27, Sevilla, 41013, Spain. TEL 34-95-4487444, FAX 34-95-4487443, secpub10@us.es, http://www.us.es/publius/inicio.html. Ed. Enrigue Valdivieso Gonzalez. Circ: 300.

580 630 AUS

LATHYRUS LATHYRISM NEWSLETTERS. Text in English. 2000. irreg. free (effective 2005). **Document type:** *Journal, Academic/Scholarly.* **Description:** The Department of Agriculture of Western Australia, The University of Western Australia, CSIRO and Murdoch University collaborate to produce leading edge legume research.

Media: Online - full text.

Published by: University of Western Australia, Centre for Legumes in Mediterranean Agriculture, 35 Stirling Hwy, Mail Bag MO80, Crawley, W.A. 6009, Australia. TEL 61-8-64882505, FAX 61-8-64881140, clima@cyllene.uwa.edu.au, http://www.clima.uwa.edu.au/news/lathyrus.

580 ESP ISSN 0210-9778
QK329 CODEN: LAZAEE

LAZAROA. Text in Spanish. 1979. a., latest vol.22, 2001. EUR 21 in the European Union; EUR 35 elsewhere (effective 2005). back issues avail. **Document type:** *Journal, Academic/Scholarly.* **Description:** Covers taxonomy, flora, plant-sociology, geobotany.

Related titles: CD-ROM ed.: EUR 48 to individuals; EUR 66 to institutions (effective 2003).

Indexed: BioCN&I, FCA, ForAb, GEOBASE, HerbAb, HortAb, IECT, OrnHort, PBA, PGegResA, RA&MP, RefZh, S&F, SIA, SeedAb, WeedAb.

—CINDOC.

Published by: (Universidad Complutense de Madrid, Facultad de Farmacia), Universidad Complutense de Madrid, Servicio de Publicaciones, C Isaac Peral s/n, Ciudad Universitaria, Madrid, 28040, Spain. TEL 34-91-3946934, FAX 34-91-3946978, lazaroa@farm.ucm.es, servicio@publicaciones.ucm.es, http://www.ucm.es/publicaciones. Ed. Salvador Rivas Martinez.

580 DEU

LEAF VENATION PATTERNS. Text in English. 1986. irreg., latest vol.9, 2003. price varies. **Document type:** *Monographic series, Academic/Scholarly.*

Indexed: BIOSIS Prev.

Published by: Gebrueder Borntraeger Verlagsbuchhandlung, Johannesstr. 3A, Stuttgart, 70176, Germany. TEL 49-711-3514560, FAX 49-711-35145699, mail@schweizerbart.de, http://www.schweizerbart.de/pubs/series/leaf-venation-patterns500.html.

580 USA
LEAFLETS; newsletter of the Southern California Botanists. Text in English. 1992. 6/yr. Included with Crossoma with membership. **Description:** Covers field trips and events of interest to members.
Published by: Southern California Botanists, c/o Alan Romspert, Department of Biology, California State University, Fullerton, CA 92834. TEL 714-278-7034, FAX 714-278-4289, aromspert@fullerton.edu. Ed. Steve Boyd. Pub., R&P Alan Romspert.

LECTINS. see *BIOLOGY—Abstracting, Bibliographies, Statistics*

580 BEL ISSN 0457-4184
➤ **LEJEUNIA**; revue de botanique. Text in English, French; Summaries in English, French. N.S. 1961. irreg., latest vol.166, 2000. price varies. back issues avail. **Document type:** *Bulletin, Academic/Scholarly.* **Description:** Publishes studies on topics in botany, with particular emphasis on the flora and vegetation of Belgium, France, and Africa.
Indexed: AgrForAb, B&AI, BIOSIS Prev, BiolAb, FCA, ForAb, HerbAb, I&DA, PGegResA, RPP, RefZh, RiceAb, S&F, WeedAb.
Published by: Botanical Society in Liege, Universite de Liege, Departement de Botanique, Sart Tilman, Liege, 4000, Belgium. TEL 32-4-3663850, FAX 32-4-3663910. Ed. J. Lambinon. R&P J Lambinon.

B

588.2 GBR ISSN 0024-2829
QK580.7 CODEN: LCHNB8
➤ **THE LICHENOLOGIST**; an international journal. Text in English. 1968. bi-m. GBP 396 to institutions; USD 606 in North America to institutions; GBP 440 combined subscription to institutions print & online eds.; USD 676 combined subscription in North America to institutions print & online eds. (effective 2006). bk.rev. charts; illus. cum.index. reprints avail. **Document type:** *Journal, Academic/Scholarly.* **Description:** Devoted to the study of lichen-forming fungi and reports of lichenology worldwide.
Related titles: Online - full text ed.: ISSN 1096-1135. GBP 370 to institutions; USD 565 in North America to institutions (effective 2006) (from EBSCO Publishing, Gale Group, IngentaConnect, O C L C Online Computer Library Center, Inc., ScienceDirect, Swets Information Services).
Indexed: ASCA, BIOBASE, BIOSIS Prev, BiolAb, ChemAb, CurCont, EIA, EnerInd, ExcerpMed, IABS, ISR, PlantSci, RPP, S&F, SCI.
—BLDSC (5207.850000), CASDDS, CISTI, IDS, IE, Infotrieve, ingenta, Linda Hall.
Published by: (British Lichen Society), Cambridge University Press, The Edinburgh Bldg, Shaftesbury Rd, Cambridge, CB2 2RU, United Kingdom. TEL 44-1223-312393, FAX 44-1223-315052, journals@cambridge.org, http://uk.cambridge.org/journals/journal_catalogue.asp?historylinks=ALPHA&mnemonic=LIC, http://www.cup.cam.ac.uk/. Eds. A F Braithwaite, Peter D Crittenden. Circ: 900. **Subscr. to:** Cambridge University Press, 100 Brook Hill Dr, West Nyack, NY 10994. TEL 845-353-7500, FAX 845-353-4141, journals_subscriptions@cup.org

579.7 VEN ISSN 1316-4899
➤ **LICHENS.** Text in English; Summaries in Multiple languages. 1997. s-a. adv. bk.rev. bibl.; illus. reprints avail. **Document type:** *Academic/Scholarly.*
Indexed: BIOBASE.
Published by: Centro de Investigacion y Reproduccion de Especies Silvestres, Apartado Postal 397, Merida, 5101, Venezuela. cires@ciens.ula.ve, http://www.ciens.ula.ve/~cires. Ed., Pub. Hector Fernando Aguilar. Adv. contact Lieselotte Hoeger de Aguilar. Circ: 2,500.

580 ARG ISSN 0075-9481
QK1 CODEN: LLOAAW
LILLOA; revista de botanica. Text in Latin, Spanish; Summaries in English, French, German, Italian. 1937. irreg., latest vol.40, no.2, 2001. per issue exchange basis only. bk.rev. charts; illus.; bibl.; abstr. back issues avail. **Document type:** *Monographic series, Academic/Scholarly.*
Indexed: ASFA, BIOSIS Prev, BiolAb, ESPM, FCA, FPA, ForAb, HerbAb, HortAb, PBA, RPP, RefZh, S&F, WeedAb, ZooRec.
—BLDSC (5218.000000), CISTI.
Published by: Fundacion Miguel Lillo, Centro de Informacion Geo-Biologico del NOA, Miguel Lillo, 251, San Miguel De Tucuman, Tucuman 4000, Argentina. TEL 54-0381-4239960, FAX 54-0381-4330868, fmlinfonoa@tucbbs.com.ar, http://www.lillo.org.ar. Ed. Jose A Haedo Rossi.

588.2 NLD ISSN 0105-0761
QK533 CODEN: LNBGAX
LINDBERGIA. Text in English. 1971. 3/yr., latest vol.1, no.3. SEK 770 (effective 2002 - 2003).
Indexed: Agr, BIOBASE, BIOSIS Prev, BiolAb, RefZh.
—BLDSC (5220.750000), CISTI, IE, ingenta.
Published by: (Dutch Bryological and Lichenological Society, Nordic Bryological Society NOR), Lindbergia, c/o Heinjo During, Dept of Plant Ecology & Evolutionary Biology, P.O. Box 800.84, Utrecht, 3508 TB, Netherlands. FAX 31-30-2518366, h.j.during@bio.uu.nl, oikostech@ekol.lu.se. Ed. Heinjo During.

580 GBR ISSN 0024-4074
QH1 CODEN: BJLSAF
➤ **LINNEAN SOCIETY. BOTANICAL JOURNAL.** Text in English. 1855. m. (in 3 vols., 4 nos./vol.). GBP 1,218 combined subscription in Europe to institutions print & online eds.; USD 2,251 combined subscription in the Americas to institutions & Caribbean (print & online eds.); GBP 1,340 combined subscription elsewhere to institutions print & online eds. (effective 2006). adv. bibl.; illus. index. reprints avail. **Document type:** *Journal, Academic/Scholarly.* **Description:** Vehicle of the Society for the publication of original research papers in the plant sciences.
Formerly: Linnean Society of London. Journal
Related titles: Microform ed.: (from BHP); Online - full text ed.: ISSN 1095-8339. GBP 1,157 in Europe to institutions; USD 2,139 in the Americas to institutions & Caribbean; GBP 1,273 elsewhere to institutions (effective 2006) (from Blackwell Synergy, EBSCO Publishing, Gale Group, IngentaConnect, O C L C Online Computer Library Center, Inc., ScienceDirect, Swets Information Services).
Indexed: ASCA, ASFA, AgBio, Agr, AgrForAb, ApEcolAb, B&BAb, BIOBASE, BIOSIS Prev, BibAg, BiolAb, BrGeoL, CPA, ChemAb, CurCont, ESPM, EntAb, FCA, FPA, ForAb, GEOBASE, GenetAb, HGA, HerbAb, HortAb, I&DA, IABS, ISR, MBA, MaizeAb, NemAb, NutrAb, OceAb, OrnHort, PBA, PGegResA, PlantSci, PotatoAb, RA&MP, RDA, RPP, RefZh, RevApplEntom, S&F, SCI, SFA, SPPI, SWRA, SeedAb, TriticAb, VITIS, WeedAb, WildRev, ZooRec.
—BLDSC (2254.300000), CASDDS, CISTI, IDS, IE, Infotrieve, ingenta, Linda Hall. **CCC.**
Published by: (Linnean Society of London), Blackwell Publishing Ltd., 9600 Garsington Rd, Oxford, OX4 2ZG, United Kingdom. TEL 44-1865-776868, FAX 44-1865-714591, customerservices@oxon.blackwellpublishing.com, http://www.blackwellpublishing.com/journals/BOJ. Ed. Dianne Edwards. R&P Sophie Savage. Adv. contact Jenny Applin.

➤ **LINNEAN SOCIETY OF NEW SOUTH WALES. PROCEEDINGS.** see *BIOLOGY—Zoology*

635 580 USA ISSN 1057-3224
LONGWOOD GRADUATE PROGRAM SEMINARS. Text in English. 1969. a. free. **Description:** Articles on issues in public horticulture management, with information on course offerings for the University of Delaware's master's program in public horticulture administration.
Formerly (until 1985): Longwood Program Seminars (0886-6384)
Published by: (Longwood Graduate Program in Public Horticulture Administration), University of Delaware, College of Agricultural Sciences, 153 Townsend Hall, Newark, DE 19717-1303. TEL 302-451-2517, FAX 302-292-3651. Eds. James E Swasey, Lynn Hershey Chesson. Circ: 800 (controlled).

580 ARG ISSN 0076-0897
QK261 CODEN: LRTZA4
LORENTZIA. Text in Spanish. 1970. irreg., latest vol.8, 1995. USD 10 (effective 2001). bk.rev. abstr.; bibl.; illus. **Document type:** *Directory, Academic/Scholarly.* **Description:** Original illustrated articles on different branches of botany, mostly morphology and taxonomy.
Indexed: BIOSIS Prev, BiolAb.
—CISTI.
Published by: Universidad Nacional de Cordoba, Museo Botanico, Casilla de Correos 495, Cordoba, 5000, Argentina. kurtzian@imbiv.edu.ar, kurtzian@imbiv.unc.edu.ar. Ed. Ana M Anton. Circ: 400.

580 USA ISSN 1097-993X
QK1 CODEN: WRGHA6
LUNDELLIA; a botanical journal. Text in English. 1945. a. USD 30 per issue (effective 2005). **Document type:** *Journal, Academic/Scholarly.*
Formerly (until 1998): Wrightia (0084-2648)
Indexed: BiolAb.
—BLDSC (5306.805700), CISTI, Linda Hall.
Published by: University of Texas, Plant Resources Center, c/o Tom Wendt, 1 University Station F0404, Austin, TX 78712-0471. lundell@uts.cc.utexas.edu, http://www.biosci.utexas.edu/prc/lundel.html. Ed. Beryl B. Simpson.

580 577 171.7 USA ISSN 0024-9637
QK1 CODEN: MADRAU
➤ **MADRONO**; a West American journal of botany. Text in English. 1916. q. USD 27 to individuals; USD 60 to institutions; USD 17 to students (effective 2004). bk.rev. bibl.; charts; illus. index. back issues avail. **Document type:** *Journal, Academic/Scholarly.* **Description:** Covers biology including ecology, evolution, geography, conservation for western Americas.
Indexed: ASFA, AgBio, Agr, AgrForAb, BIOSIS Prev, BiolAb, CPA, ChemAb, ESPM, FCA, FPA, ForAb, HerbAb, HortAb, I&DA, IAA, MaizeAb, OrnHort, PBA, PGegResA, RDA, RPP, RefZh, S&F, SFA, SIA, SWRA, SeedAb, WAE&RSA, WeedAb, WildRev, ZooRec.
—CISTI, IE, Infotrieve, Linda Hall.
Published by: Allen Press Inc., c/o Sue Bainridge, Jepson Herbarium, University of California, 1001 Valley Life Sciences Bldg, No. 2465, Berkeley, CA 94720. TEL 510-643-5008, FAX 510-643-5093, suebain@sscl.berkeley.edu, http://www.calbotsoc.org/madrono.html. Ed. John Callaway. R&P Susan Bainbridge TEL 510-643-7008. Circ: 946 (paid). **Subscr. to:** Subscription Fulfillment & Business Services, 810 E 10th St, Lawrence, KS 66044. TEL 785-843-1235, FAX 785-843-1274, orders@allenpress.com.

580 HUN ISSN 0076-2482
QR1 CODEN: MAKUB7
MAGYARORSZAG KULTURFLORAJA. Text in Latin, Hungarian. 1956. irreg., latest vol.71, 2001. price varies. back issues avail. **Document type:** *Academic/Scholarly.*
Indexed: BiolAb, SeedAb.
Published by: Magyar Termeszettudomanyi Muzeum, Baross utca 13, Budapest, 1088, Hungary. TEL 36-1-2101330, FAX 36-1-371669, http://www.nhmus.hu.

MAINE AGRICULTURAL AND FOREST EXPERIMENT STATION. MISCELLANEOUS REPORT. see *AGRICULTURE*

MAINE AGRICULTURAL AND FOREST EXPERIMENT STATION. TECHNICAL BULLETIN. see *AGRICULTURE*

MALAYSIAN OIL PALM STATISTICS (YEAR). see *ENERGY—Abstracting, Bibliographies, Statistics*

MALAYSIAN PALM OIL UPDATE. see *ENERGY*

MARSCHENRAT ZUR FOERDERUNG DER FORSCHUNG IM KUESTENGEBIET DER NORDSEE. NACHRICHTEN. see *SCIENCES: COMPREHENSIVE WORKS*

579.5 USA ISSN 0099-8400
CODEN: MCLVAS
➤ **MCILVAINEA**; journal of amateur mycology. Text in English. 1972. a. membership. back issues avail. **Document type:** *Journal, Academic/Scholarly.* **Description:** Publishes research articles on mushrooms.
Formerly: Journal McIlvanea
Indexed: AbHyg, BiolAb, ForAb, HortAb, IndVet, NutrAb, OrnHort, PGegResA, RA&MP, RM&VM, RPP, S&F, WeedAb.
Published by: North American Mycological Association, 6615 Tudor Ct., Gladstone, OR 97027-1032. TEL 503-657-7358, judyr@hevanet.com, ExecSec@namyco.org, http://www.namyco.org. Ed. Betty Guttman. Circ: 2,200.

➤ **MEDICAL MYCOLOGY.** see *MEDICAL SCIENCES—Communicable Diseases*

➤ **MEDICINAL AND AROMATIC PLANTS.** see *ALTERNATIVE MEDICINE*

571.2 DEU ISSN 1430-953X
MEDICINAL PLANT CONSERVATION. Text in English. 1995. irreg., latest vol.10, 2004. **Document type:** *Newsletter, Academic/Scholarly.*
Indexed: AgBio, FPA, ForAb, HortAb, OrnHort, PGegResA, PGrRegA, PHN&I, RA&MP, S&F, TDB, WAE&RSA.
—BLDSC (5533.986500).
Published by: (I U C N Species Survival Commission, Medicinal Plant Specialist Group CAN), Bundesamt fuer Naturschutz, Konstantinstr 110, Bonn, 53179, Germany. TEL 49-228-84910, FAX 49-228-8491200, pbox-bfn@bfn.de, http://www.bfn.de.

MEDICINAL PLANT REPORT; proizvodnja i plasman lekovitog, zacinskog i aromaticnog bilja. see *AGRICULTURE—Crop Production And Soil*

580 367 GBR ISSN 0955-8276
MESEMB STUDY BULLETIN. Text in English, Latin. 1986. q. GBP 6 domestic; GBP 10 foreign (effective 2000). adv. bk.rev. illus. index every 2 yrs. back issues avail. **Document type:** *Bulletin.* **Description:** Contains information about Mesembryanthemaceae plants.
Published by: Mesemb Study Group, Brenfield, Bolney Rd, Ansty, Haywards Heath, W Sussex RH17 5AW, United Kingdom. TEL 44-1444-441193, FAX 44-1444-454061, msg@cactus-mall.com, http://www.cactus-mall.com/msg/index.html. Ed., R&P, Adv. contact Suzanne Mace TEL 44-1444-459151. Circ: 550.

580 USA ISSN 0026-203X
QK1 CODEN: MBOTAU
➤ **MICHIGAN BOTANIST.** Text in English. 1962. q. USD 16 to institutions (effective 2005). adv. bk.rev. bibl. cum.index every 3 yrs. **Document type:** *Academic/Scholarly.* **Description:** Papers of scientific interest on various areas of botany for the Great Lakes region.
Indexed: Agr, BiolAb, CurCont, MMI, RPP, RefZh.
—CISTI.
Published by: Michigan Botanical Club, Inc., University of Michigan Herbarium, 2001 N University Bldg, 1205 N University Ave, Ann Arbor, MI 48109-1057. TEL 313-764-2407. Ed. Dr. Neil A Harriman. Adv. contact Thomas Clough. Circ: 800.

579.5   USA   ISSN 1534-2581
➤ **MICOLOGIA APLICADA INTERNATIONAL.** Text in English.
2001. s-a. USD 50 (effective 2005). adv. bk.rev. abstr.; bibl.;
illus. Index. back issues avail.; reprints avail. **Document type:**
Magazine, Academic/Scholarly. **Description:** Publishes
original review papers on all aspects of applied and economic
mycology.
Formed by the merger of (1988-2000): Micologia Neotropical
Aplicada (0187-8921); (1995-2000): International Journal of
Mushroom Sciences (1083-8139)
Related titles: CD-ROM ed.; Diskette ed.; Fax ed.; Microfilm ed.
Indexed: AgBio, Agr, AgrForAb, BIOSIS Prev, BiolAb, CPA, FPA,
FS&TA, ForAb, HortAb, MaizeAb, NutrAb, OrnHort, PBA,
PGegResA, PHN&I, RA&MP, RDA, RPP, RiceAb, S&F,
TriticAb, WAE&RSA.
—BLDSC (5756.720000).
Address: 445 Vassar Ave, Berkeley, CA 94708. TEL
510-526-2492, FAX 510-898-2120, http://www.ird.org.mx. Eds.,
R&Ps D Martinez Carrera, R H Kurtzman. Circ: 500.
Co-sponsors: Institut de Recherche pour le Developpement (
I R D); Instituto de Micologia Neotropical Aplicada; Colegio
de Posgraduados.

579.5   ITA   ISSN 0394-2597
MICOLOGIA E VEGETAZIONE MEDITERRANEA. Text in English,
Italian. 1986. s-a. free to members. bibl.; illus. **Document
type:** *Journal, Academic/Scholarly.*
Published by: Gruppo Edologista Micologico Abruzzese, Casella
Postale 307, Avezzano, AQ 67051, Italy. TEL 39-863-23223.
Circ: 1,200.

579.5   ITA   ISSN 0390-0460
QK600   CODEN: MIITDI
MICOLOGIA ITALIANA. Text in Italian. 1972. 3/yr. EUR 35
domestic; EUR 40 foreign (effective 2005). bk.rev. index.
Document type: *Journal, Academic/Scholarly.* **Description:**
Covers ecology, toxicology, physiology, biochemistry and the
production of macro-fungi.
Indexed: ASFA, ApicAb, BIOSIS Prev, BiolAb, ForAb, MBA,
RM&VM, RPP, S&F, VITIS.
—BLDSC (5756.700000), IE, ingenta, Linda Hall.
Published by: (Unione Micologica Italiana), Patron Editore, Via
Badini 12, Quarto Inferiore, BO 40050, Italy. TEL
39-051-767003, FAX 39-051-768252, info@patroneditore.com,
http://www.patroneditore.com. Circ: 1,600.

579.5   RUS   ISSN 0026-3648
                                         CODEN: MIFIB2
➤ **MIKOLOGIYA I FITOPATOLOGIYA.** Text in Russian. 1967.
bi-m. USD 131. **Document type:** *Academic/Scholarly.*
Indexed: ASCA, ASFA, AgBio, BIOSIS Prev, BioCN&I, BiolAb,
CIN, CPA, CTFA, ChemAb, ChemTitl, CurCont, DBA, DSA,
ESPM, FCA, FPA, ForAb, HerbAb, HortAb, ISR, MBA,
MaizeAb, NemAb, NutrAb, OrnHort, PBA, PGegResA,
PGrRegA, PHN&I, PotatoAb, RA&MP, RM&VM, RPP, RRTA,
RefZh, RevApplEntom, RiceAb, S&F, SCI, SIA, SeedAb,
SoyAb, TriticAb, VITIS, WeedAb, ZooRec.
—BLDSC (0114.750000), CASDDS, CISTI, IDS, IE, ingenta,
Linda Hall. CCC.
Published by: (Rossiiskaya Akademiya Nauk/Russian Academy
of Sciences), Izdatel'stvo Nauka, Sankt-Peterburgskoe
Otdelenie, Mendeleevskaya liniya 1, St Petersburg, 199034,
Russian Federation. **US dist. addr.:** East View Information
Services, 3020 Harbor Ln. N., Minneapolis, MN 55447. TEL
800-477-1005, FAX 800-800-3839, eastview@eastview.com,
http://www.eastview.com.

➤ **MISSISSIPPI NATIVE PLANTS.** see *GARDENING AND
HORTICULTURE*

580   USA   ISSN 0026-6493
QK1   CODEN: AMBGA7
➤ **MISSOURI BOTANICAL GARDEN. ANNALS.** Text in English,
Spanish; Notes in Latin. 1914. q. USD 150 domestic; USD
160 in Canada & Mexico; USD 185 elsewhere (effective
2004); includes Novon. bk.rev. illus.; abstr.; maps. index. 200
p./no.; back issues avail.; reprint service avail. from PQC.
Document type: *Journal, Academic/Scholarly.* **Description:**
Publishes papers primarily in systematic botany and related
fields.
Supersedes in part (1890-1912): Missouri Botanical Garden.
Annual Report (0893-3243)
Related titles: Microfiche ed.: (from IDC); Microfilm ed.: (from
PQC); Online - full text ed.: (from JSTOR (Web-based Journal
Archive)).
Indexed: ASCA, ASFA, AgBio, Agr, AgrForAb, B&AI, BIOBASE,
BIOSIS Prev, BioCN&I, BiolAb, BiolDig, CPA, ChemAb,
CurCont, FCA, FPA, ForAb, HerbAb, HortAb, IABS, ISR,
OrnHort, PBA, PGegResA, PN&I, PlantSci, RA&MP, RM&VM,
RPP, RefZh, RevApplEntom, S&F, SCI, SFA, SIA, SPPI,
SeedAb, WeedAb, ZooRec.
—BLDSC (1029.000000), CISTI, IE, Infotrieve, ingenta, Linda
Hall.
Published by: Missouri Botanical Garden, PO Box 299, St. Louis,
MO 63166-0299. TEL 314-577-5112, FAX 314-577-9594,
http://www.mbgpress.org/allenpress2004prices.pdf?
PHPSESSID=bc431419c3ae108babfaeef0afcb5875. Ed.
Victoria C Hollowell. Circ: 850. **Dist. by:** Allen Press Inc., PO
Box 1897, Lawrence, KS 66044. TEL 785-843-1235, FAX
785-843-1274, orders@allenpress.com, http://
www.allenpress.com.

580.73   USA   ISSN 1060-7854
QK1
MISSOURI BOTANICAL GARDEN. ANNUAL REPORT. Text in
English. 1913. a. illus. **Document type:** *Bulletin.* **Description:**
Publishes announcements and materials concerning the
Missouri Botanical Garden.
Supersedes in part (in 1987): Missouri Botanical Garden. Bulletin
(0026-6507); Which superseded in part (in 1912): Missouri
Botanical Garden. Annual Report (0893-3243)
Related titles: Online - full text ed.: (from JSTOR (Web-based
Journal Archive)).
Indexed: FPA.
—CISTI, Linda Hall.
Published by: Missouri Botanical Garden, PO Box 299, St. Louis,
MO 63166-0299. Ed. Susan Caine. Circ: 30,000.

580   USA   ISSN 0161-1542
                                         CODEN: MSBOE5
**MISSOURI BOTANICAL GARDEN. MONOGRAPHS IN
SYSTEMATIC BOTANY.** Key Title: Monographs in Systematic
Botany from the Missouri Botanical Garden. Text in English,
Spanish. 1978. irreg. illus. back issues avail. **Document type:**
Monographic series, Academic/Scholarly.
Indexed: ApicAb, BIOSIS Prev.
—BLDSC (5917.740000), CISTI, IE, ingenta.
Published by: Missouri Botanical Garden, PO Box 299, St. Louis,
MO 63166-0299. TEL 314-577-9547, FAX 314-577-9594,
http://www.mbgpress.org. Ed. Victoria C Hollowell.

580.74   JPN   ISSN 0917-043X
MIYABEA/ILLUSTRATED FLORA OF HOKKAIDO. Text in
English. 1991. irreg. **Document type:** *Academic/Scholarly.*
Published by: Hokkaido Daigaku, Nogakubu Fuzoku
Shokubutsuen/Hokkaido University, Faculty of Agriculture,
Botanic Garden, Nishi 8-chome, Kita 3-jo, Chuo-ku,
Sapporo-shi, Hokkaido 060-0003, Japan. Ed. Hideki
Takahashi.

579.8   JPN   ISSN 0288-139X
**MIZUKUSA KENKYUKAI KAIHO/WATER PLANT SOCIETY.
BULLETIN.** Text in Japanese; Summaries in English,
Japanese. 1980. 3/yr. JPY 1,000 per issue (effective 2000).
Document type: *Bulletin.*
—CCC.
Published by: Mizukusa Kenkyukai/Water Plant Society, Kobe
Daigaku Kokusaibunkagakubu Seibutsugaku, 2-1
Tsurukabu-To 1-chome, Nada-ku, Kobe-shi, Hyogo-ken
657-8501, Japan. kadono@kobe-u.ac.jp. Ed., R&P Yasuro
Kadono.

580   IND   ISSN 0971-7269
MODERN TRENDS IN PLANT SCIENCES. Text in English. 1995.
s-a. USD 120 (effective 2005). **Document type:** *Journal,
Academic/Scholarly.* **Description:** Focuses on biotechnology,
cytogenetics, morphology, vegetative propagation, physiology,
taxonomy, anatomy, growth and yield survey, conservation,
pharmacology, ethnobotany, introduction and trials etc.
Published by: International Book Distributors, 9/3, Rajpur Rd.,
First Fl, Dehra Dun, Uttar Pradesh 248 001, India.
ibdbooks@sancharnet.in. Pub. R.P. Singh.

572.8   NLD   ISSN 1380-3743
QK981.4   CODEN: MOBRFL
➤ **MOLECULAR BREEDING**; new strategies in plant
improvement. Text in English. 1995. 8/yr. EUR 768, USD 788,
GBP 508 combined subscription to institutions print & online
eds. (effective 2005). adv. back issues avail.; reprint service
avail. from PSC. **Document type:** *Journal,
Academic/Scholarly.* **Description:** Publishes papers on all
aspects of applied plant molecular biology.
Related titles: Online - full text ed.: ISSN 1572-9788 (from
EBSCO Publishing, Gale Group, IngentaConnect, Kluwer
Online, O C L C Online Computer Library Center, Inc., Ovid
Technologies, Inc., Springer LINK, Swets Information
Services).
Indexed: AEBA, ASCA, AgBio, Agr, AgrForAb, AnBrAb, BCI,
BIOBASE, BIOSIS Prev, BibAg, BibLing, BioCN&I, BiolAb,
CIN, CPA, ChemAb, ChemTitl, CurCont, DSA, ESPM, FCA,
FS&TA, ForAb, GenetAb, HGA, HerbAb, HortAb, IABS, ISR,
MaizeAb, NemAb, NutrAb, OrnHort, PBA, PGegResA,
PGrRegA, PHN&I, PN&I, PlantSci, PotatoAb, RA&MP, RDA,
RPP, RefZh, RevApplEntom, RiceAb, SCI, SIA, SeedAb,
SoyAb, TriticAb, VITIS, WAE&RSA, WeedAb.
—BLDSC (5900.799500), CASDDS, CISTI, IDS, IE, Infotrieve,
ingenta. CCC.
Published by: Springer-Verlag Dordrecht (Subsidiary of: Springer
Science+Business Media), Van Godewijckstraat 30, Dordrecht,
3311 GX, Netherlands. TEL 31-78-6576050, FAX
31-78-6576474, http://springerlink.metapress.com/openurl.asp?
genre=journal&issn=1380-3743, http://www.springeronline.com.
Ed. Paul Christou.

580   USA   ISSN 1619-5221
QK865   CODEN: MMPSEB
MOLECULAR METHODS OF PLANT ANALYSIS. Text in English.
1956. irreg., latest vol.23, 2003. price varies. **Document type:**
Monographic series, Academic/Scholarly. **Description:**
Describes molecular methods alongside the more traditional
methods of analysis with hints as to their limitations.
Formerly (until 2002): Modern Methods of Plant Analysis
(0937-8340); Supersedes (in 1985): Moderne Methoden der
Pflanzenanalyse (0077-0183)

Indexed: Agr, BibAg, ChemAb, ChemTitl.
—BLDSC (5900.817958), CASDDS, CISTI, IE. CCC.
Published by: Springer-Verlag New York, Inc. (Subsidiary of:
Springer Science+Business Media), 233 Spring St, New York,
NY 10013. TEL 212-460-1500, 800-777-4643, FAX
212-473-6272, http://www.springer-ny.com. Eds. H F Linskens,
J J Jackson, R B Inman.

MOLECULAR PLANT - MICROBE INTERACTIONS. see
BIOLOGY—Biochemistry

571 616.07   GBR   ISSN 1464-6722
SB732.65   CODEN: MPPAFD
MOLECULAR PLANT PATHOLOGY. Text in English. 2000. bi-m.
GBP 80, EUR 120 combined subscription in Europe to
individuals print & online eds.; USD 148 combined
subscription in the Americas to individuals & Caribbean, print
& online eds.; GBP 88 combined subscription elsewhere to
individuals print & online eds.; GBP 482 combined
subscription in Europe to institutions print & online eds.; USD
890 combined subscription in the Americas to institutions &
Caribbean, print & online eds.; GBP 530 combined
subscription elsewhere to institutions print & online eds.
(effective 2006). adv. reprint service avail. from PSC.
Document type: *Journal.* **Description:** Features submissions
from all areas of molecular plant pathology including research
on diseases caused by fungi, oomycetes, viruses, nematodes,
bacteria, insects, parasitic plants and other organisms.
Related titles: Online - full text ed.: ISSN 1364-3703. GBP 458 in
Europe to institutions; USD 847 in the Americas to institutions
& Caribbean; GBP 504 elsewhere to institutions (effective
2006) (from Blackwell Synergy, EBSCO Publishing, Gale
Group, IngentaConnect, O C L C Online Computer Library
Center, Inc., Swets Information Services).
Indexed: AEBA, AgBio, Agr, AgrForAb, B&BAb, BBCI, BCI,
BIOBASE, BIOSIS Prev, BioCN&I, BioEngAb, BiolAb, CPA,
CurCont, ESPM, FCA, HerbAb, HortAb, MaizeAb, NemAb,
OrnHort, PBA, PGegResA, PGrRegA, PHN&I, PN&I,
PotatoAb, RA&MP, RM&VM, RPP, RefZh, RiceAb, SIA,
SeedAb, SoyAb, TriticAb, VITIS, WeedAb.
—BLDSC (5900.826100), IE, Infotrieve, ingenta, Linda Hall.
CCC.
Published by: (British Society for Plant Pathology), Blackwell
Publishing Ltd., 9600 Garsington Rd, Oxford, OX4 2ZG,
United Kingdom. TEL 44-1865-776868, FAX 44-1865-714591,
customerservices@oxon.blackwellpublishing.com,
http://www.blackwellpublishing.com/journals/MPP. Ed. G D
Foster. Pub. Sue Hewitt. R&P Sophie Savage. Adv. contact
Jenny Applin. B&W page GBP 400.

580   ESP   ISSN 0213-6201
MONOGRAFIAS DE FLORA Y VEGETACION BETICAS. Text in
Spanish. 1986. a. **Document type:** *Monographic series.*
Indexed: IECT.
—CINDOC.
Published by: Universidad de Granada, Facultad de Ciencias,
Dep. de Algebra y Fundamentos, Fuentenueva, S/N, Granada,
18001, Spain.

580   POL   ISSN 0077-0655
QK1
MONOGRAPHIAE BOTANICAE. Text in English, Polish;
Summaries in English, German. 1953. irreg., latest vol.64,
1983. price varies. bibl. **Document type:** *Monographic series.*
Indexed: AgrLib, BIOSIS Prev, BiolAb, FCA, HerbAb, PBA, RPP.
—CISTI.
Published by: Polskie Towarzystwo Botaniczne/Polish Botanical
Society, Al Ujazdowskie 4, Warsaw, 00478, Poland. Ed. M
Kostyniuk. **Dist. by:** Ars Polona, Krakowskie Przedmiescie 7,
Warsaw, Poland.

580   DOM   ISSN 0254-6442
QK227.7
MOSCOSOA. Text in Spanish. 1976. a. DOP 150 domestic; USD
15 foreign (effective 2001). **Document type:** *Bulletin.*
Indexed: BIOSIS Prev, BiolAb.
Published by: (Compugraf C. por A.), Jardin Botanico Nacional
"Dr. Rafael M. Moscoso", Apdo Postal 21-9, Santo Domingo,
Dominican Republic. TEL 809-3852611, FAX 809-3850446,
j.botanico@codetel.net.do, http://www.jbn-sdq.org. Ed.
Milciades Mejia Pimental.

580   AUS   ISSN 0077-1813
QK431   CODEN: MAJBAC
➤ **MUELLERIA.** Text in English. 1955. a. AUD 30 domestic; AUD
35 foreign (effective 2002). adv. bk.rev. illus. index; vol.11
(1998). back issues avail. **Document type:** *Journal,
Academic/Scholarly.* **Description:** publishes original research
or review articles concerning the systematics, biogeography or
conservation of plants, algue and fungi.
Indexed: BIOSIS Prev, BiolAb, FCA, GEOBASE, HerbAb, PBA.
Published by: Royal Botanic Gardens (Melbourne), Private Bag
2000, South Yarra, VIC 3141, Australia. TEL 61-3-9252-2300,
FAX 61-3-9252-2350, muelleria@rbg.vic.gov.au,
http://www.rbg.vic.gov.au/muell. Ed. Teresa Lebel TEL
61-3-9252-2361. Circ: 400.

➤ **MUSEE ROYAL DE L'AFRIQUE CENTRALE. ANNALES -
SCIENCES ECONOMIQUES. SERIE IN 8/KONINKLIJK
MUSEUM VOOR MIDDEN-AFRIKA. ANNALEN -
ECONOMISCHE WETENSCHAPPEN. REEKS IN 8.** see
AGRICULTURE—Agricultural Economics

▼ *new title*   ➤ *refereed*   * *unverified*   ◆ *full entry avail.*

➤ **MUSEO CIVICO DI STORIA NATURALE DI FERRARA. ANNALI.** see *EARTH SCIENCES—Geology*

551 300 ITA ISSN 1590-8399
QH7 CODEN: BMCVD3
MUSEO CIVICO DI STORIA NATURALE DI VERONA. BOLLETTINO. BOTANICA ZOOLOGIA. Text in Multiple languages. 2000. a., latest vol.23, 1999. back issues avail. **Document type:** *Bulletin.*
Supersedes in part (in 2000): Museo Civico di Storia Naturale di Verona. Bollettino (0392-0062)
Indexed: AICP, BIOSIS Prev, BiolAb, RefZh, ZooRec.
—Linda Hall.
Published by: Museo Civico di Storia Naturale di Verona, Lungadige Porta Vittoria 9, Verona, VR 37129, Italy. TEL 39-045-8079400, FAX 39-045-8035639, mcsnat@comune.verona.it, http://www.museostorianaturaleverona.it. Circ: 600.

580 ARG ISSN 0372-4611
MUSEO DE LA PLATA. REVISTA. SECCION BOTANICA. Text in Spanish. 1890. irreg.
Supersedes in part (in 1936): Museo de La Plata. Revista (0375-1147)
Indexed: RefZh.
—CISTI.
Published by: Universidad Nacional de La Plata, Facultad de Ciencias Naturales y Museo, Avenidas 60 y 122, La Plata, Buenos Aires, Argentina. TEL 54-221-4258252, facultad@museo.fcnym.unlp.edu.ar.

581 BRA ISSN 0100-008X
QK263 CODEN: BMBMB3
MUSEU BOTANICO MUNICIPAL. BOLETIM. Text in English, German, Portuguese; Summaries in English, German. 1971. irreg. back issues avail. **Document type:** *Bulletin.*
Indexed: BiolAb.
Published by: Museu Botanico Municipal, Centro, Caixa Postal 1142, Curitiba, PR 80001-970, Brazil. Circ: 1,000.

580 BRA ISSN 0080-3197
QK1 CODEN: BMJBA9
MUSEU NACIONAL. BOLETIM. BOTANICA. Text in Portuguese. 1944. irreg., latest vol.121, 2002. per issue exchange basis. illus.
Supersedes in part (1923-1941): Museu Nacional. Boletim (0100-1507)
Indexed: BIOSIS Prev, BiolAb.
—CISTI, Linda Hall.
Published by: Museu Nacional, Quinta da Boa Vista, Sao Cristovao, Rio de Janeiro, RJ 20940-040, Brazil. TEL 55-21-25688262, FAX 55-21-25681352, museu@mn.ufrj.br, http://www.acd.ufjr.br/~museuhp/homep.htm.

580 BRA
QK263
MUSEU PARAENSE EMILIO GOELDI. BOLETIM. NOVA SERIE BOTANICA. Text in Portuguese. 1958; N.S. 1984. s-a. BRL 12, USD 15 per issue (effective 2000). bk.rev. bibl.; charts; illus.; maps. **Description:** Original papers in botanical research.
Formerly (until 1984, no.59): Museu Paraense Emilio Goeldi. Boletim. Nova Serie: Botanica (0077-2216)
Indexed: ASFA, AgrForAb, BIOSIS Prev, BiolAb, CPA, FPA, ForAb, HerbAb, HortAb, I&DA, NutrAb, OrnHort, PBA, PGegResA, RA&MP, RDA, RPP, RefZh, S&F, SIA, SeedAb, TDB.
—BLDSC (2143.410000).
Published by: Conselho Nacional de Desenvolvimento Cientifico e Tecnologico, Museu Paraense Emilio Goeldi, Comercio, Caixa Postal 399, Belem, PA 66017-970, Brazil. TEL 091-274-2195, FAX 091-274-1811, mgdoc@musu-goeldi.br. Circ: 1,000.

580 590 DEU ISSN 0947-1057
MUSEUM HEINEANUM. ABHANDLUNGEN UND BERICHTE. Variant title: Abhandlungen und Berichte aus dem Museum Heineanum. Text in German; Summaries in English. 1990. biennial. EUR 7.50 (effective 2003). adv. bk.rev. back issues avail. **Document type:** *Journal, Academic/Scholarly.*
Indexed: ZooRec.
Published by: Museum Heineanum, Domplatz 37, Halberstadt, 38820, Germany. TEL 49-3941-551460, FAX 49-3941-551469, heineanum-hbs@t-online.de, http://www.heineanum.de. Ed., Pub. Bernd Nicolai. adv.: page EUR 200; trim 120 x 175. Circ: 500 (paid); 300 (controlled).

580.74 571.2 FRA ISSN 1280-8571
QK1 CODEN: BMNBDW
➤ **MUSEUM NATIONAL D'HISTOIRE NATURELLE. ADANSONIA.** Text and summaries in English, French. 1906. s-a. EUR 39.56 to individuals; EUR 79.13 to institutions (effective 2004). adv. bk.rev. charts; illus. index. 250 p./no.; back issues avail. **Document type:** *Journal, Academic/Scholarly.* **Description:** Examines the inventory and analyzes and interprets the biodiversity of vascular plants. It publishes original botanical research, particularly in systematics and related areas, including plant morphology, anatomy, biology, ecology, phylogeny, and biogeography.
Formerly (until 1997): Museum National d'Histoire Naturelle. Bulletin - Section B - Adansonia (Botanique, Phytochimie) (0240-8937); Which was formed by the 1981 merger of: Adansonia (0001-804X); Which superseded (1909-1960): Notulae Systematicae (0374-9223); And: Museum National d'Histoire Naturelle. Bulletin - Botanique, Biologie, et Ecologie Vegetales, Phytochimie (0181-0634); Which was formed by the 1978 merger of: Museum National d'Histoire Naturelle. Bulletin - Botanique (0376-4443); Museum National d'Histoire Naturelle. Bulletin - Ecologie Generale (0376-4427); Museum National d'Histoire Naturelle. Bulletin - Sciences Physico-chimiques (0376-4478); Each of which superseded (in 1972): Museum National d'Histoire Naturelle. Bulletin (1148-8425); Which was formerly (until 1907): Museum d'Histoire Naturelle. Bulletin (0027-4070)
Related titles: Online - full text ed.: 2000. free (effective 2005).
Indexed: AgBio, AgrForAb, BIOSIS Prev, BiolAb, CPA, CurCont, FCA, FPA, ForAb, HerbAb, HortAb, OrnHort, PBA, PGegResA, RefZh, S&F, SFA, SPPI, SeedAb, WeedAb.
—BLDSC (0678.300100), CASDDS, CISTI, Linda Hall.
Published by: (Museum National d'Histoire Naturelle, Laboratoire de Phanerogamie), Museum National d'Histoire Naturelle, 57 Rue Cuvier, Paris, 75231 Cedex 05, France. TEL 33-1-40793777, adanson@mnhn.fr, http://www.mnhn.fr/publication/adanson/aadanson.html. Circ: 700.

579.5 USA
THE MUSHROOM CULTURE; the journal of mushroom cultivation. Text in English. q. USD 20 domestic; USD 30 foreign (effective 2002). illus. **Document type:** *Newsletter, Consumer.*
Published by: F M R C, PO Box 18105, Pensacola, FL 32523-8105. TEL 850-327-4378, FloridaMycology@cs.com, http://www.mushroomsfmrc.com/cgi-bin/webc/home.html.

579.5 GBR ISSN 0144-0551
CODEN: MUSJDK
MUSHROOM JOURNAL. Text in English. 1945. m. GBP 161.24 overseas Associate membership; GBP 384.97 overseas Trade Membership (effective 2000). adv. bk.rev. charts; illus.; mkt.; stat. index. **Document type:** *Trade.* **Description:** News and information on all aspects of the industry in the UK and worldwide.
Formerly: M G A Bulletin (0024-8150)
Indexed: AEA, Agr, BioCN&I, CTFA, ESPM, FS&TA, HortAb, MBA, NemAb, NutrAb, RRTA, RevApplEntom, TriticAb, WAE&RSA.
—BLDSC (5990.150000), CASDDS, CISTI.
Published by: Mushroom Growers' Association, 2 St Pauls St, Stamford, Lincs PE9 2BE, United Kingdom. TEL 44-1780-766888. Ed. Trudy Johnston. R&P, Adv. contact Melissa Nairn. B&W page GBP 348, color page GBP 496; trim 210 x 297. Circ: 1,000 (controlled).

579.6 635.8 IND ISSN 0972-4885
➤ **MUSHROOM RESEARCH.** Text in English. 1992. biennial. INR 225, USD 60 to individual members; INR 525, USD 110 to libraries (effective 2003). bk.rev. 60 p./no.; back issues avail. **Document type:** *Journal, Academic/Scholarly.* **Description:** Mushrooms, Fleshy fungi, Edible fungi.
Formerly (until Jun.2001): International Journal of Mushroom Research and Development
—BLDSC (5990.168000).
Published by: Mushroom Society of India, National Centre for Mushroom Research and Training, Chambaghat, Solan, Himachal Pradesh 173 213, India. TEL 91-1792-230767, FAX 91-1792-231207, tewari_rp@rediffmail.com. Eds. Dr. S K Singh, R D Rai. Adv. contact Dr. R C Upadhyay.

579.5 GBR ISSN 0077-2364
CODEN: MUSCAU
MUSHROOM SCIENCE. Variant title: International Congress on Mushroom Science. Proceedings. Text and summaries in English, French, German. 1950. quadrennial. free membership (effective 2005). **Document type:** *Proceedings.* **Description:** Focuses on mycological research.
Indexed: BIOSIS Prev, BiolAb, CIN, ChemAb, ChemTitl, FS&TA, RPP.
—BLDSC (5990.170000), CASDDS, CISTI.
Published by: International Society for Mushroom Science, c/o Kerry Burton, Executive Secretary ISMS, 196 Rugby Rd, Leamington Spa, Warcs CV32 6DU, United Kingdom. http://www.hri.ac.uk/isms/.

580 COL ISSN 0027-5123
QK1 CODEN: MUTSAF
MUTISIA; acta botanica colombiana. Text in English, French, German, Spanish. 1952. q. USD 10; or exchange basis. adv. bibl.; illus. **Document type:** *Monographic series.*
Indexed: BiolAb.
—CISTI.
Published by: Universidad Nacional de Colombia, Instituto de Ciencias, PO Box 7495, Bogota, CUND, Colombia. TEL 57-1-3165305, FAX 57-1-3165365, dicn@ciencias.ciencias.unal.edu.co, http://www.icn.unal.edu.co. R&P Jaime Uribe M. Adv. contact Jaime Uribe M. Circ: 1,000.

579.52 VEN ISSN 1316-4880
➤ **MYCETEAE.** Text in English; Summaries in Multiple languages. 1997. s-a. adv. bk.rev. reprints avail. **Document type:** *Academic/Scholarly.*
Published by: Centro de Investigacion y Reproduccion de Especies Silvestres, Apartado Postal 397, Merida, 5101, Venezuela. cires@ciens.ula.ve, http://www.ciens.ula.ve/~cires. Ed. Hector Fernando Aguilar. Adv. contact Lieselotte Hoeger de Aguilar. Circ: 2,500.

579.5 USA ISSN 0027-5514
QK600 CODEN: MYCOAE
➤ **MYCOLOGIA.** Text in English. 1909. bi-m. free to members; USD 203 combined subscription in US & Canada to institutions print & online eds; USD 219 combined subscription elsewhere to institutions print & online eds (effective 2005). adv. bk.rev. bibl.; charts; illus. index. back issues avail.; reprints avail. **Document type:** *Journal, Academic/Scholarly.* **Description:** Presents original research and review articles on fungi including lichens.
Formed by the merger of: Mycological Bulletin; Journal of Mycology
Related titles: Microform ed.: (from PMC, PQC); Online - full content ed.: ISSN 1557-2536. 2000. USD 180 to institutions (effective 2005); Online - full text ed.: (from EBSCO Publishing); ♦ Supplement(s): Inoculum. ISSN 1067-909X.
Indexed: ASCA, ASFA, AbHyg, AgBio, Agr, AgrForAb, B&AI, BIOBASE, BIOSIS Prev, BibAg, BioCN&I, BiolAb, CBTA, CIN, CPA, ChemAb, ChemTitl, CurCont, DBA, DSA, EntAb, EnvAb, FCA, FPA, FS&TA, ForAb, GEOBASE, HerbAb, HortAb, IABS, ISR, IndVet, MBA, MEDLINE, MaizeAb, NemAb, NutrAb, OrnHort, PBA, PGegResA, PGrRegA, PHN&I, PlantSci, PotatoAb, ProtozoAb, RA&MP, RM&VM, RPP, RefZh, RevApplEntom, RiceAb, S&F, SCI, SIA, SPPI, SeedAb, SoyAb, TDB, TriticAb, VITIS, VetBull, WeedAb, ZooRec.
—BLDSC (5993.000000), CASDDS, CIS, CISTI, GNLM, IDS, IE, Infotrieve, ingenta, KNAW, Linda Hall. **CCC.**
Published by: Mycological Society of America, c/o Karen Snetselaar, Treasurer, Biology Department, St Joseph's University, 5600 City Ave, Philadelphia, PA 19131. TEL 610-660-1826, FAX 610-660-1832, msa@allenpress.com, http://www.msafungi.org, http://msafungi.org. Ed. Dr. Don Natvig TEL 505-277-5977. Adv. contact L Hardwick TEL 800-627-0629. Circ: 2,000. **Dist. by:** Allen Press Inc., PO Box 1897, Lawrence, KS 66044.

579.5 GBR ISSN 0027-5522
CODEN: CMIMAE
MYCOLOGICAL PAPERS. Text in English. 1925. irreg., latest no.176, 2000. price varies. **Document type:** *Monographic series, Academic/Scholarly.* **Description:** Provides authoritative monographic accounts of taxonomy and systematics of fungi.
Indexed: BIOSIS Prev, BiolAb, HerbAb, RPP.
—BLDSC (5994.060000), CISTI, Linda Hall. **CCC.**
Published by: CABI Publishing (Subsidiary of: CAB International), CAB International, Wallingford, Oxfordshire OX10 8DE, United Kingdom. TEL 44-1491-832111, FAX 44-1491-833508, cabi@cabi.org, http://www.cabi-publishing.org/AllOtherProducts.asp?SubjectArea=&PID=516. **Subscr. addr. in N America:** CABI Publishing North America, 875 Massachusetts Ave, 7th Fl, Cambridge, MA 02139. TEL 617-395-4056, 800-528-4841, FAX 617-354-6875, cabi-nao@cabi.org.

579.5 DEU ISSN 1617-416X
➤ **MYCOLOGICAL PROGRESS**; international journal of fungal sciences. Text in English. 2002. q. EUR 78 to individuals; EUR 98 to institutions; EUR 58 to members (effective 2003). **Document type:** *Journal, Academic/Scholarly.* **Description:** Publishes papers on all aspects of fungi, including lichens.
Indexed: BiolAb.
—BLDSC (5994.080000), CISTI, IE, ingenta.
Published by: (Deutsche Gesellschaft fuer Mykologie), I H W - Verlag, Edith-Stein-Str. 2, Eching, 85378, Germany. FAX 49-89-3192257, http://www.mycological-progress.com, http://www.ihw-verlag.de. Ed. Franz Oberwinkler.

579.5 GBR ISSN 0953-7562
QK600 CODEN: MYCRER
➤ **MYCOLOGICAL RESEARCH.** Text in English. 1896. m. GBP 720 domestic to institutions; USD 1,160 foreign to institutions; GBP 790 combined subscription domestic to institutions print & online eds.; USD 1,276 combined subscription foreign to institutions print & online eds. (effective 2005). adv. bk.rev. bibl.; charts; illus. index. back issues avail.; reprints avail. **Document type:** *Journal, Academic/Scholarly.* **Description:** Covers all aspects of fungi (including lichens, slime moulds and yeasts): molecular biology, physiology, plant pathology, systematics, ultrastructure, biochemistry, biodeterioration, biotechnology, and genetics.
Formerly (until 1989): British Mycological Society. Transactions (0007-1536)
Related titles: Microform ed.: (from PQC); Online - full text ed.: ISSN 1469-8102. GBP 686 domestic to institutions; USD 1,100 foreign to institutions (effective 2005) (from EBSCO Publishing, O C L C Online Computer Library Center, Inc., ScienceDirect, Swets Information Services).
Indexed: ASCA, ASFA, AgBio, Agr, AgrForAb, B&AI, BIOBASE, BIOSIS Prev, BibAg, BioCN&I, BiolAb, CIN, CPA, ChemAb, ChemTitl, CurCont, DBA, FCA, FPA, ForAb, GEOBASE, HelmAb, HerbAb, HortAb, I&DA, IABS, ISR, IndVet, MBA, MaizeAb, NemAb, NutrAb, OrnHort, PBA, PGegResA, PHN&I, PlantSci, PotatoAb, PoultAb, ProtozoAb, RA&MP, RDA, RM&VM, RPP, RefZh, RevApplEntom, RiceAb, S&F, SCI, SIA, SPPI, SeedAb, SoyAb, TOSA, TriticAb, VITIS, VetBull, WAE&RSA, WTA, WeedAb, ZooRec.

—BLDSC (5994.100000), CASDDS, CISTI, IDS, IE, Infotrieve, ingenta, Linda Hall. **CCC.**
Published by: (British Mycological Society), Elsevier Ltd. (Subsidiary of: Elsevier Science & Technology), The Boulevard, Langford Ln, Kidlington, Oxford, OX5 1GB, United Kingdom. TEL 44-1865-843000, 44-1865-843672, nlinfo-f@elsevier.nl, http://www.elsevier.com. Ed. David Hawksworth.

579.5 GBR ISSN 0269-915X
QK600 CODEN: MYCOEI
MYCOLOGIST. Text in English. 1967. q. USD 90 in North America to institutions; GBP 55 elsewhere to institutions; USD 98 combined subscription in North America to institutions print & online eds.; GBP 60 combined subscription elsewhere to institutions print & online eds. (effective 2005). adv. bk.rev. abstr. back issues avail. **Document type:** *Journal, Academic/Scholarly.* **Description:** Aims to advance the study of mycology at all levels; to educate mycologists at all stages of knowledge; and to forge links between all mycological societies.
Formerly (until 1987): British Mycological Society. Bulletin (0007-1528)
Related titles: Microform ed.: (from PQC); Online - full text ed.: ISSN 1474-0605. USD 82 in North America to institutions; GBP 50 elsewhere to institutions (effective 2005) (from EBSCO Publishing, O C L C Online Computer Library Center, Inc., ScienceDirect, Swets Information Services).
Indexed: ASFA, AbHyg, AgrForAb, BIOBASE, BIOSIS Prev, BioCN&I, BiolAb, CPA, DBA, FPA, FS&TA, ForAb, HerbAb, HortAb, IndVet, MBA, MaizeAb, NemAb, NutrAb, OrnHort, PBA, PGegResA, PHN&I, PotatoAb, PoultAb, RA&MP, RM&VM, RPP, RefZh, RevApplEntom, S&F, SIA, TDB, TriticAb, VITIS, VetBull, WeedAb.
—BLDSC (5995.705000), CISTI, IE, Infotrieve, ingenta, Linda Hall. **CCC.**
Published by: (British Mycological Society), Elsevier Ltd. (Subsidiary of: Elsevier Science & Technology), The Boulevard, Langford Ln, Kidlington, Oxford, OX5 1GB, United Kingdom. TEL 44-1865-843000, 44-1865-843672, nlinfo-f@elsevier.nl, http://www.elsevier.com. Ed. Nicholas Clipson.

579.5 GBR
MYCOLOGISTNEWS. Text in English. q. **Document type:** *Newsletter, Academic/Scholarly.* **Description:** Contains information on Society meetings and forthcoming events, awards, publications, local groups, forays, keys for identification, and field mycology.
Published by: British Mycological Society, Joseph Banks Bldg, Royal Botanic Gardens, Kew, Richmond, Surrey TW9 3AB, United Kingdom. info@britmycolsoc.org.uk, http://www.britmycolsoc.org.uk.

579.5 USA ISSN 0730-9597
CODEN: MYSEDX
➤ **MYCOLOGY SERIES.** Text in English. 1979. irreg., latest vol.21, 2004. USD 195 per vol. vol.21 (effective 2004). adv. **Document type:** *Monographic series, Academic/Scholarly.*
Indexed: Agr, BIOSIS Prev, CIN, ChemAb, ChemTitl.
—BLDSC (5995.710000), CASDDS, CISTI, IE, ingenta. **CCC.**
Published by: Marcel Dekker Inc. (Subsidiary of: Taylor & Francis Group), 270 Madison Ave, New York, NY 10016-0602. TEL 212-696-9000, FAX 212-685-4540, journals@dekker.com, http://www.dekker.com. Pub. Russell Dekker. R&P Julia Mulligan. Adv. contact Eridania Perez. **Subscr. to:** 6000 Broken Sound Pkwy NW, Ste. 300, Boca Raton, FL 33487-2713. TEL 800-228-1160.

579.5 NLD ISSN 0301-486X
QK600 CODEN: MYCPAH
➤ **MYCOPATHOLOGIA.** Text in English. 1938. 8/yr. EUR 1,148, USD 1,168, GBP 725 combined subscription to institutions print & online eds. (effective 2005). bk.rev. illus. reprint service avail. from PSC. **Document type:** *Journal, Academic/Scholarly.* **Description:** Covers the study of the role of fungi in disease and biodeterioration. As such, the journal covers a range of topics that is unique in breadth and depth, including original articles and critical reviews in the fields of medical and veterinary mycology, plant mycology (crop protection), mycotoxicosis, mycetism, entomopathogenic fungi, environmental aeromycology, and applied industrial mycology.
Formerly: Mycopathologia et Mycologia - Applicata (0027-5530)
Related titles: Microform ed.: (from PQC); Online - full text ed.: ISSN 1573-0832 (from EBSCO Publishing, Gale Group, IngentaConnect, Kluwer Online, O C L C Online Computer Library Center, Inc., ProQuest Information & Learning, Springer LINK, Swets Information Services).
Indexed: ASCA, ASFA, AbHyg, AgBio, Agr, AgrForAb, AnBrAb, ApicAb, B&BAb, BIOBASE, BIOSIS Prev, BibLing, BioCN&I, BiolAb, CIN, CPA, ChemAb, ChemTitl, CurCont, DBA, DSA, ESPM, ExcerpMed, FCA, FPA, FS&TA, ForAb, HelmAb, HerbAb, HortAb, I&DA, IABS, ISR, IndMed, IndVet, Inpharma, MBA, MEDLINE, MaizeAb, NRN, NemAb, NutrAb, OrnHort, PBA, PGegResA, PGrRegA, PHN&I, PN&I, PlantSci, PoultAb, ProtozoAb, RA&MP, RM&VM, RPP, Reac, RefZh, RevApplEntom, RiceAb, S&F, SAA, SCI, SFA, SIA, SeedAb, SoyAb, TDB, TriticAb, VetBull, WeedAb.
—BLDSC (5995.740000), CASDDS, CISTI, GNLM, IDS, IE, Infotrieve, ingenta, KNAW, Linda Hall. **CCC.**
Published by: (C A B International Mycological Institute GBR), Springer-Verlag Dordrecht (Subsidiary of: Springer Science+Business Media), Van Godewijckstraat 30, Dordrecht, 3311 GX, Netherlands. TEL 31-78-6576050, FAX 31-78-6576474, http://springerlink.metapress.com/openurl.asp?genre=journal&issn=0301-486X, http://www.springeronline.com. Ed. Vishnu Chaturvedi.

579.5 USA ISSN 0027-5549
MYCOPHILE. Text in English. 1960. 6/yr. membership. bk.rev. **Document type:** *Newsletter.*
Media: Duplicated (not offset).
Published by: North American Mycological Association, 6615 Tudor Ct., Gladstone, OR 97027-1032. TEL 503-657-7358, brightcloud@mciworld.com, judyr@hevanet.com. Ed. Judy Roger. Circ: 2,000 (controlled).

579.5 DEU ISSN 0940-6360
QK604.2.M92 CODEN: MCOREZ
➤ **MYCORRHIZA.** Text in English. 1991. 8/yr. EUR 1,288 combined subscription to institutions print & online eds. (effective 2005). adv. back issues avail. **Document type:** *Journal, Academic/Scholarly.* **Description:** Devoted to all aspects of research into the symbiosis between higher plants and certain fungi or mushrooms, covering original papers and reviews on all types of mycorrhizae.
Related titles: Online - full text ed.: ISSN 1432-1890. 199? (from EBSCO Publishing, Springer LINK, Swets Information Services).
Indexed: ASCA, AgBio, Agr, AgrForAb, B&BAb, BIOBASE, BIOSIS Prev, BioCN&I, BiolAb, CIN, CPA, ChemAb, ChemTitl, CurCont, ESPM, FCA, ForAb, GEOBASE, HerbAb, HortAb, I&DA, IABS, ISR, MaizeAb, NemAb, OrnHort, PBA, PGrRegA, PHN&I, PlantSci, PotatoAb, RA&MP, RPP, RefZh, RevApplEntom, RiceAb, S&F, SCI, SIA, SeedAb, SoyAb, TriticAb, WeedAb.
—BLDSC (5995.752000), CASDDS, CISTI, IDS, IE, Infotrieve, ingenta. **CCC.**
Published by: Springer-Verlag (Subsidiary of: Springer Science+Business Media), Tiergartenstr 17, Heidelberg, 69121, Germany. TEL 49-6221-3450, FAX 49-6221-345229, http://link.springer.de/link/service/journals/00572/index.htm. Adv. contact Stephan Kroeck TEL 49-30-827875739. **Subscr. in the Americas to:** Springer-Verlag New York, Inc., Journal Fulfillment, PO Box 2485, Secaucus, NJ 07096-2485. TEL 800-777-4643, 201-348-4033, FAX 201-348-4505, journals@springer-ny.com, http://www.springer-ny.com; **Subscr. to:** Springer GmbH Auslieferungsgesellschaft, Haberstr 7, Heidelberg 69126, Germany. TEL 49-6221-345-0, FAX 49-6221-345-4229, subscriptions@springer.de.

580 IND ISSN 0970-695X
MYCORRHIZA NEWS. Text in English. 1989. q. INR 100, USD 40; USD 30 in developing nations (effective 2001). **Document type:** *Newsletter.* **Description:** Official newsletter of the Mycorrhiza Network Asia, providing a forum for views and findings on mycorrhiza.
Indexed: AgrForAb, FCA, ForAb, HortAb, OrnHort, RPP, RiceAb, S&F, WeedAb.
—BLDSC (5995.752500).
Published by: Tata Energy Research Institute, Darbari Seth Block, Habitat Place, Lodhi Road, New Delhi, 110 003, India. TEL 91-11-4682100, FAX 91-11-4682144, outreach@teri.res.in. Circ: 1,200.

579.5 JPN ISSN 1340-3540
QK600 CODEN: MNCEED
➤ **MYCOSCIENCE.** Text in English. 1956. bi-m. EUR 188 combined subscription to institutions print & online eds. (effective 2005). adv. bk.rev. abstr.; charts; illus. **Document type:** *Journal, Academic/Scholarly.*
Formerly (until 1994): Mycological Society of Japan. Transactions (0029-0289)
Related titles: Online - full text ed.: ISSN 1618-2545 (from EBSCO Publishing, Springer LINK, Swets Information Services).
Indexed: AEA, ASFA, AbHyg, AgBio, AgrForAb, Agrind, B&BAb, BIOBASE, BIOSIS Prev, BioCN&I, BiolAb, CIN, CPA, ChemAb, ChemTitl, CurCont, DSA, ESPM, FCA, FPA, ForAb, HelmAb, HerbAb, HortAb, IndVet, JPI, MaizeAb, NemAb, NutrAb, OrnHort, PBA, PGegResA, PHN&I, PlantSci, PoultAb, ProtozoAb, RA&MP, RM&VM, RPP, RRTA, RefZh, RevApplEntom, RiceAb, S&F, SIA, SeedAb, SoyAb, TDB, TriticAb, VITIS, VetBull, WeedAb, ZooRec.
—BLDSC (5995.752800), CASDDS, IE, ingenta. **CCC.**
Published by: (Mycological Society of Japan), Springer-Verlag Tokyo (Subsidiary of: Springer Science+Business Media), 3-13 Hongo 3-chome, Bunkyo-ku, Tokyo, 113-0033, Japan. TEL 81-3-38120331, FAX 81-3-38187454, orders@svt-ebs.co.jp, http://link.springer.de/link/service/journals/10267/, http://www.springer-tokyo.co.jp/. Ed. Makoto Kakishima. Adv. contact Stephan Kroeck TEL 49-30-827875739. Circ: 1,500. **Subscr. in the Americas to:** Springer-Verlag New York, Inc., Journal Fulfillment, PO Box 2485, Secaucus, NJ 07096-2485. TEL 800-777-4643, 201-348-4033, FAX 201-348-4505, journals@springer-ny.com, http://www.springer-ny.com; **Subscr. to:** Springer GmbH Auslieferungsgesellschaft, Haberstr 7, Heidelberg 69126, Germany. TEL 49-6221-345-0, FAX 49-6221-345-4229, subscriptions@springer.de.

579.5 USA ISSN 0093-4666
QK603.2 CODEN: MYXNAE
➤ **MYCOTAXON.** Text in English, French. 1974. q. USD 150 domestic to individuals; USD 190 foreign to individuals; USD 330 domestic to institutions; USD 370 foreign to institutions (effective 2005). bk.rev. illus. back issues avail.; reprints avail. **Document type:** *Journal, Academic/Scholarly.* **Description:** Covers taxonomy and nomenclature of fungi, including lichens.
Related titles: Microform ed.: (from PQC).
Indexed: ASCA, AbHyg, AgBio, Agr, AgrForAb, BIOSIS Prev, BibAg, BioCN&I, BiolAb, CurCont, FCA, FPA, ForAb, HerbAb, HortAb, ISR, IndVet, NemAb, OrnHort, PBA, PGegResA, RA&MP, RM&VM, RPP, RefZh, RevApplEntom, RiceAb, S&F, SCI, SeedAb, TDB, TriticAb, VITIS, VetBull, WeedAb, ZooRec.
—BLDSC (5995.760000), CISTI, IDS, IE, Infotrieve, ingenta, Linda Hall. **CCC.**
Published by: Mycotaxon Ltd., PO Box 264, Ithaca, NY 14851-0264. TEL 607-273-0508, 727-322-0112, FAX 607-273-4357, 727-321-1460, info@mycotaxon.com, http://www.mycotaxon.com. Ed. Lorelei L Norvell. R&P Richard P Korf. Circ: 650 (controlled).

579.5 ESP ISSN 1575-068X
MYKES. Text in Gallegan. 1998. a. EUR 6 (effective 2002).
Indexed: AgrForAb, FPA, ForAb, HortAb, IECT, RPP, S&F, WeedAb.
—CINDOC.
Published by: Grupo Micoloxico Galego Luis Freire, Apartado1649, Vigo, 36200, Spain. TEL 34-986-436961, FAX 34-986-220387.

579.5 USA
N A T S CURRENT NEWS. Text in English. 1983. bi-m. USD 10 domestic; USD 15 foreign (effective 2001). bk.rev. **Document type:** *Newsletter.* **Description:** Fosters knowledge of truffles and truffle-like fungi.
Published by: North American Truffling Society, Inc., PO Box 296, Corvallis, OR 97339. TEL 541-752-2243. Ed. Pat Rawlinson. Circ: 250 (paid).

584.4 USA ISSN 0099-8745
SB409.5.U6 CODEN: OKHAAN
NA OKIKA O HAWAII/HAWAII ORCHID JOURNAL. Text in English. 1972. q. USD 20 (effective 2000). adv. bk.rev. abstr.; illus. back issues avail. **Document type:** *Bulletin.* **Description:** Devoted to orchid culture, classification and breeding. Has information on orchid shows and events in Hawaii. Reviews orchid books and journals.
Formed by the merger of: Pacific Orchid Society of Hawaii. Bulletin (0030-8838); Na Pua Okika o Hawaii Nei - Orchids of Hawaii (0027-7304)
Indexed: BiolAb, HortAb.
Published by: Honolulu Orchid Society, 3335 Huelani Dr, Honolulu, HI 98822-1276. TEL 808-988-7229, FAX 808-988-4569. Ed. Yoneo Sagawa. Circ: 750. **Co-sponsor:** Pacific Orchid Society.

580 JPN ISSN 0385-9916
NAGANOKEN SHOKUBUTSU KENKYUKAISHI/BOTANICAL SOCIETY OF NAGANO. BULLETIN. Text in Japanese. 1967. a. JPY 2,400.
Published by: Naganoken Shokubutsu Kenkyukai/Botanical Society of Nagano, Shinshu Daigaku Kyoyobu, 1-1 Asahi 3-chome, Matsumoto-shi, Nagano-ken 390-0802, Japan.

580 JPN ISSN 0386-7080
NARA SHOKUBUTSU KENKYU/NARA BOTANY. Text in Japanese. 1978. a. JPY 1,000.
Published by: Nara Shokubutsu Kenkyukai/Botanical Society of Nara, c/o Mr Suganuma, 239-41 Tsutsui-cho, Yamatokoriyama-shi, Nara-ken 639-1123, Japan.

580 SVK ISSN 0323-2646
NASE LIECIVE RASTLINY. Text in Slovak. bi-m. USD 27.
Indexed: HortAb, SeedAb, WeedAb.
Published by: Herba, Svabinsheho 4-a, Bratislava, 85101, Slovakia.

580.74 IRL ISSN 0790-0422
➤ **NATIONAL BOTANIC GARDENS. OCCASIONAL PAPERS.** Text in English. 1981. irreg., latest vol.12, 1999. per issue exchange basis. **Document type:** *Academic/Scholarly.*
—BLDSC (6218.200000).
Published by: National Botanic Gardens, Glasnevin, Dublin, 9, Ireland. TEL 353-1-8374388, FAX 353-1-8360080, nbg@indigo.ie. Ed. Matthew Jebb. Circ: 400.

580 IND
➤ **NATIONAL BOTANIC RESEARCH INSTITUTE, LUCKNOW. PROGRESS REPORT.** Text in English. 1966. a. free. **Document type:** *Academic/Scholarly.* **Description:** Covers all branches of botany includng crytogamic botany, angiosperms, plant taxonomy, ethnobotany, biodiversity, seed biology, palynology, pharmacognosy, plant breeding and genetics, tissue culture, microbiology, floriculture, biochemistry and more.
Former titles: National Botanic Gardens, Lucknow. Progress Report; National Botanic Gardens, Lucknow. Annual Report (0076-1400)
Indexed: BiolAb, ChemAb.

B

▼ new title ➤ refereed ✶ unverified ♦ full entry avail.

Published by: National Botanical Research Institute Lucknow, Lucknow, Uttar Pradesh 226 001, India. TEL 91-522-271031, FAX 91-522-282849, TELEX 0535-315, manager@nbri.sirnetd.ernet.in. Eds. Anil K Gauniyal, M R Ahamad. Circ: 500 (controlled). **Affiliate:** Council of Scientific and Industrial Research.

580   ZAF   ISSN 1021-7460
QK73.S65
NATIONAL BOTANICAL INSTITUTE. ANNUAL REVIEW. Text in English. 1913. a., latest 1997-1998. free. **Document type:** *Government.* **Description:** Garden and horticultural services, environmental education services, research and scientific services.
Former titles: National Botanic Gardens. Report; National Botanic Gardens of South Africa. Report
Published by: National Botanical Institute, NBI Bookshop, Private Bag X101, Pretoria, Cape Province 0001, South Africa. TEL 27-21-8043200, FAX 27-21-8043211, bookshop@nbipre.nbi.ac.za, http://www.nbi.ac.za. Circ: 2,000 (controlled).

580.74   IND   ISSN 0971-2976
QK1   CODEN: BUBPAX
NATIONAL BOTANICAL SOCIETY. JOURNAL. Text in English. 1947. s-a. INR 150, USD 40 (effective 2000). adv. bk.rev. charts; illus. reprints avail. **Document type:** *Academic/Scholarly.*
Formerly (until vol.44, 1990): Botanical Society of Bengal. Bulletin (0006-811X)
Indexed: BiolAb, ChemAb, FCA, HerbAb, S&F.
—CASDDS, CISTI, Linda Hall.
Published by: National Botanical Society, 35 Ballygunge Circular Rd., Kolkata, West Bengal 700 019, India. TEL 91-33-475-3681. Ed. R Mallick. Adv. contact N Paria. Circ: 250. **Dist. by:** H P C Publishers Distributors Pvt. Ltd., 4805 Bharat Ram Rd, 24 Darya Ganj, New Delhi 110 002, India. TEL 91-11-325-4401, FAX 91-11-619-3511.

580   JPN   ISSN 0385-2431
QK1   CODEN: BMBBD6
NATIONAL SCIENCE MUSEUM. BULLETIN. SERIES B: BOTANY/KOKURITSU KAGAKU HAKUBUTSUKAN KENKYU HOKOKU. B RUI: SHOKUBUTSUGAKU. Text in English. 1939. q. per issue exchange basis. charts; illus.
Supersedes in part (in 1975): National Science Museum. Bulletin (0028-0119)
Indexed: ASFA, AgBio, Agr, BIOSIS Prev, BiolAb, ChemAb, ESPM, ForAb, HerbAb, HortAb, OrnHort, PBA, PGegResA, RPP, SeedAb, WeedAb, ZooRec.
—CISTI.
Published by: Monbusho, Kokuritsu Kagaku Hakubutsukan/Ministry of Education, Science and Culture, National Science Museum, 7-20 Ueno-Koen, Taito-ku, Tokyo, 110-0007, Japan. Ed. Shigeru Fukuda. Circ: 1,000.

580   USA
NATIVE PLANT SOCIETY OF NEW MEXICO. NEWSLETTER. Text in English. 1976. bi-m. USD 12 membership (effective 1999). adv. bk.rev. **Document type:** *Newsletter.* **Description:** Provides information on activities of chapters throughout New Mexico, and includes articles on topics relating to native plants, landscaping, plant descriptions, conservation, ethnobotany.
Published by: Native Plant Society of New Mexico, PO Box 5917, Santa Fe, NM 87502. Ed. Tim McKimmie. Circ: 550.

580   USA   ISSN 1525-7215
NATIVE PLANTS. Text in English. 1984. q. free to members (effective 2005). **Document type:** *Magazine, Consumer.* **Description:** Promotes preservation and reestablishment of native North American plants in natural and planned landscapes.
Formerly (until 1999): Wildflower (Austin, 1984) (0898-8803)
Indexed: BiolDig, GardL.
Published by: Lady Bird Johnson Wildflower Center, 4801 La Crosse Ave, Austin, TX 78739. TEL 512-292-4200, FAX 512-292-4627, wildflower@wildflower.org, http://www.wildflower.org. Ed. Chris Kosta. Circ: 21,500 (controlled and free).

580   USA   ISSN 1522-8339
SB439
➤ **NATIVE PLANTS JOURNAL.** Text in English. 2000. 3/yr. USD 42.50 domestic to individuals; USD 53 foreign to individuals; USD 82.50 domestic to libraries; USD 94 foreign to libraries (effective 2006). bk.rev. abstr.; charts; illus.; maps; stat. back issues avail. **Document type:** *Journal, Academic/Scholarly.* **Description:** Provides technical and practical information on the growing and planting of North American native plants for restoration, conservation, reforestation, landscaping, and roadsides.
Related titles: Online - full text ed.: ISSN 1548-4785 (from H.W. Wilson, O C L C Online Computer Library Center, Inc., Project MUSE, ProQuest Information & Learning, Swets Information Services).
Indexed: AEA, Agr, AgrForAb, CPA, FCA, ForAb, GardL, HerbAb, HortAb, I&DA, OrnHort, PBA, PGegResA, PGrRegA, PHN&I, RA&MP, RiceAb, S&F, SeedAb, WAE&RSA, WeedAb.
—CISTI, IE, Linda Hall. **CCC.**

Published by: Indiana University Press, 601 N Morton St, Bloomington, IN 47404. http://iupjournals.org/npj/. Ed. R Kasten Dumroese.

580 590   DEU   ISSN 0941-0627
QH149   CODEN: BNGOEA
➤ **NATURFORSCHENDE GESELLSCHAFT DER OBERLAUSITZ. BERICHTE.** Text in German; Summaries in English. 1991. a. EUR 15 (effective 2003). bk.rev. abstr.; bibl.; illus.; maps. **Document type:** *Monographic series, Academic/Scholarly.* **Description:** Provides information on all natural aspects of the Oberlausitz region of Germany.
Indexed: ForAb, I&DA, RevApplEntom, S&F, WeedAb, ZooRec.
—Linda Hall.
Published by: Naturforschende Gesellschaft der Oberlausitz, Postfach 300154, Goerlitz, 02806, Germany. TEL 49-3581-4760800, FAX 49-3581-4760101, dunger-ebersbach@t-online.de. Ed., Pub. Wolfram Dunger. Circ: 700 (paid and controlled).

➤ **NATURHISTORISCHES MUSEUM IN WIEN. ANNALEN. SERIE B: BOTANIK UND ZOOLOGIE.** see *BIOLOGY—Zoology*

580   DEU   ISSN 0373-7586
QH5   CODEN: ABNGAO
NATURKUNDEMUSEUMS GOERLITZ. ABHANDLUNGEN UND BERICHTE. Text in English. 1827. irreg.
Formerly (until 1942): Naturforschenden Gesellschaft zu Goerlitz. Abhandlungen (0232-136X)
Indexed: BioCN&I, FCA, ForAb, HelmAb, HortAb, I&DA, IndVet, NemAb, PGegResA, RRTA, S&F, WeedAb, ZooRec.
—CISTI, Linda Hall.
Published by: Staatliches Museum fuer Naturkunde Goerlitz, Am Museum 1, Goerlitz, 02826, Germany. TEL 03581, FAX 406542, museum@naturkundemuseum-bw.de, http://www.naturkundemuseum-bw.de.

580   DEU   ISSN 0547-9789
NATURWISSENSCHAFTLICHER VEREIN WUPPERTAL. JAHRESBERICHTE; Heft 52. Text in German; Summaries in English. 1851. a. bk.rev. illus. index. back issues avail. **Document type:** *Journal, Academic/Scholarly.* **Description:** Publishes articles on the botany and zoology of the Bergisches Land for scientists and the educated lay person.
Indexed: ZooRec.
—Linda Hall.
Published by: Naturwissenschaftlicher Verein Wuppertal, Eibenweg 44, Wuppertal, 42111, Germany. TEL 49-202-77486, FAX 49-202-5638026. Eds. Uwe Luensmann, Wolfgang Kolbe. Circ: 1,000.

NEMATOLOGIA MEDITERRANEA. see *AGRICULTURE—Crop Production And Soil*

580 615.19   NPL
NEPAL. DEPARTMENT OF MEDICINAL PLANTS. ANNUAL REPORT. Text in English. 1969. a. free.
Published by: Ministry of Forests, Department of Medicinal Plants, Thapathali, Katmandu, Nepal. Circ: 500.

580   JPN
NETTAI DOSHOKUBUTSU TOMO NO KAI KAIHO/NEWS OF THE TROPICAL PLANTS AND ANIMALS. Text in Japanese. 1972. 4/yr. JPY 3,000 (effective 2001). adv. 24 p./no.; **Document type:** *Newsletter.*
Published by: Nettai Doshokubutsu Tomo no Kai/Society of Tropical Plants and Animals, Atagawa Banana Wanien Kenkyushitsu, Atagawa Onsen, Kamo-gun, Higashiizumachi, Shizuoka-ken 413-0302, Japan. TEL 81-557-23-1105, 81-557-23-1108, FAX 81-557-23-0866, 81-557-23-1109, wanien@i-younet.ne.jp, http://www4.i-younet.ne.jp/~wanien. Ed. Hideo Shimizu. Adv. contact Satoshi Kimura.

580   JPN
NETTAI SHOKUBUTSU CHOSA KENKYU NENPO/ANNUAL BULLETIN OF TROPICAL ARBORETUM. Text in Japanese. 1977. a.
Published by: Kaiyo Hakurankai Kinen Koen Kanri Zaidan/Management Foundation of National Ocean Expo Memorial Park, 424 Ishikawa, kunigami-gun, Motobu-cho, Okinawa-ken 905-0206, Japan.

580   IND   ISSN 0377-1741
QK1
NEW BOTANIST; an international quarterly journal of plant science research. Text in English. 1974. q. INR 700, USD 60. adv. cum.index. back issues avail. **Document type:** *Academic/Scholarly.* **Description:** Deals with the higher reaches of knowledge in plant sciences.
Indexed: BiolAb, CurCont, ForAb, ZooRec.
—BLDSC (6082.370000), CISTI, IE, ingenta, Linda Hall. **CCC.**
Published by: Today and Tomorrow's Printers & Publishers, 24 B-5 Desh Bandhu Gupta Rd., Karol Bagh, New Delhi, 110 005, India. tp@vsnl.net. Ed. J N Govil. Circ: 437. **Dist. in U.S. by:** Scholarly Publications, 2825 Wilcrest Dr, Ste 255, Houston, TX 77042. TEL 713-781-2212, 713-781-0070.

580   GBR
➤ **NEW DISEASE REPORTS.** Text in English. 2000. irreg. free (effective 2005). **Document type:** *Journal, Academic/Scholarly.* **Description:** Online global reporting service for new and significant plant disease situations.
Media: Online - full text.
Published by: British Society for Plant Pathology membership@bspp.org.uk, http://www.bspp.org.uk/ndr/. Ed. Rick Mumford.

580   USA
NEW ENGLAND WILD FLOWER CONSERVATION NOTES. Text in English. 1966. a. (every 12-18 mos.). free to members (effective 2005). adv. cum.index: 1982-1987. back issues avail. **Document type:** *Academic/Scholarly.* **Description:** Articles on botanical and horticultural subjects concerning native plants and their habitats.
Former titles: Wild Flower Notes; (until 1984): Wild Flower Notes and News; (until 1981): Wild Flower Notes and News; (until 1980): New England Wild Flower Notes
Indexed: GardL.
Published by: New England Wild Flower Society, Inc., Garden in the Woods, 180 Hemenway Rd, Framingham, MA 01701. TEL 508-877-7630, FAX 508-877-6553, newfs@newfs.org, http://www.newfs.org/. Circ: 4,500.

580   IND
NEW GLIMPSES IN PLANT RESEARCH. Text in English. 1986. a. price varies. **Document type:** *Monographic series.*
Formerly (until 1991): Glimpses in Plant Research (0971-1686)
Published by: Today and Tomorrow's Printers & Publishers, 24 B-5 Desh Bandhu Gupta Rd., Karol Bagh, New Delhi, 110 005, India. tp@vsnl.net. Ed. J N Govil. **Dist. in US by:** Scholarly Publications, 2825 Wilcrest Dr, Ste 255, Houston, TX 77042. TEL 713-781-0070.

580   GBR   ISSN 0028-646X
QK1   CODEN: NEPHAV
➤ **NEW PHYTOLOGIST.** Text in English. 1902. m. GBP 131, EUR 197 combined subscription in Europe to individuals print & online eds.; USD 242 combined subscription in the Americas to individuals & Caribbean, print & online eds.; GBP 144 combined subscription elsewhere to individuals print & online eds.; GBP 1,188 combined subscription in Europe to institutions print & online eds.; USD 2,196 combined subscription in the Americas to institutions & Caribbean, print & online eds.; GBP 1,307 combined subscription elsewhere to institutions print & online eds. (effective 2006). adv. bk.rev. illus. index. back issues avail.; reprint service avail. from PSC. **Document type:** *Journal, Academic/Scholarly.* **Description:** Presents research papers, review articles on all aspects of the plant sciences.
Related titles: Microfilm ed.: (from BHP); Microform ed.: (from BHP, PQC); Online - full text ed.: New Phytologist Online. ISSN 1469-8137. 1998. GBP 125, EUR 188 in Europe to individuals; USD 232 in the Americas to individuals & Caribbean; GBP 138 elsewhere to individuals; GBP 1,129 in Europe to institutions; USD 2,087 in the Americas to institutions & Caribbean; GBP 1,242 elsewhere to institutions (effective 2006) (from Blackwell Synergy, EBSCO Publishing, Gale Group, IngentaConnect, JSTOR (Web-based Journal Archive), O C L C Online Computer Library Center, Inc., Swets Information Services).
Indexed: AEA, ASCA, ASFA, AgBio, Agr, AgrForAb, ApEcolAb, B&BAb, BBCI, BIOBASE, BIOSIS Prev, BioCN&I, BiolAb, BrArAb, BrGeoL, CIN, CMCI, CPA, ChemAb, ChemTitl, CurCont, DBA, EIA, EPB, ESPM, EnerInd, EnvAb, EnvInd, FCA, FPA, FS&TA, FaBeAb, ForAb, GEOBASE, GenetAb, HGA, HerbAb, HortAb, I&DA, IABS, ISR, M&GPA, MBA, MaizeAb, NemAb, NumL, NutrAb, OrnHort, PBA, PGegResA, PGrRegA, PHN&I, PlantSci, PollutAb, PotatoAb, ProtozoAb, RA&MP, RPP, RevApplEntom, RiceAb, S&F, S&MA, SCI, SIA, SWRA, SeedAb, SoyAb, TOSA, TriticAb, VITIS, WAE&RSA, WeedAb.
—BLDSC (6085.000000), CASDDS, CISTI, IDS, IE, Infotrieve, ingenta, Linda Hall. **CCC.**
Published by: (New Phytologist Trust), Blackwell Publishing Ltd., 9600 Garsington Rd, Oxford, OX4 2ZG, United Kingdom. TEL 44-1865-776868, FAX 44-1865-714591, customerservices@oxon.blackwellpublishing.com, http://www.blackwellpublishing.com/journals/NPH. Ed. F Ian Woodward TEL 44-114-2224374. R&P Sophie Savage. Adv. contact Jenny Applin.

580   USA   ISSN 0077-8931
QK1   CODEN: MYBGAJ
➤ **NEW YORK BOTANICAL GARDEN. MEMOIRS.** Key Title: Memoirs of the New York Botanical Garden. Text in English. 1900. irreg., latest vol.84, 1999. price varies. index. back issues avail. **Document type:** *Monographic series, Academic/Scholarly.* **Description:** Publishes full-length manuscripts and original research on plant systematics.
Indexed: AgrForAb, BIOSIS Prev, BiolAb, ForAb, RPP, WeedAb.
—BLDSC (5628.600000), CISTI, IE, ingenta, Linda Hall. **CCC.**
Published by: New York Botanical Garden Press, 200th Street & Kazimiroff Blvd, Bronx, NY 10458-5126. TEL 718-817-8721, FAX 718-817-8842. Ed. William Buck. R&P Carole J Young.

➤ **NEW ZEALAND GROWING TODAY.** see *AGRICULTURE—Crop Production And Soil*

580 NZL ISSN 0028-825X
QK1 CODEN: NZJBAS

➤ **NEW ZEALAND JOURNAL OF BOTANY.** Text in English. 1963. q. NZD 210, USD 140 combined subscription to individuals print & online eds.; NZD 445, USD 320 combined subscription to institutions print & online eds. (effective 2006). adv. abstr.; bibl.; charts; illus. index. back issues avail. **Document type:** *Academic/Scholarly.* **Description:** Publishes papers on all fields of botany focusing on the South Pacific region.

Related titles: Online - full text ed.: NZD 180, USD 120 to individuals; NZD 380, USD 275 to institutions (effective 2006) (from EBSCO Publishing).

Indexed: ASCA, ASFA, AgBio, AgrForAb, ApEcolAb, BIOBASE, BIOSIS Prev, BioCN&I, BiolAb, CPA, ChemAb, CurCont, ESPM, EnvAb, FCA, FPA, ForAb, GEOBASE, GenetAb, HGA, HerbAb, HortAb, I&DA, IABS, INIS AtomInd, ISR, OceAb, OrnHort, PBA, PGegResA, PGrRegA, PHN&I, PlantSci, RA&MP, RPP, RevApplEntom, S&F, SCI, SIA, SPPI, SWRA, SeedAb, TriticAb, WAE&RSA, WeedAb.

—BLDSC (6093.200000), CASDDS, CISTI, IDS, IE, Infotrieve, ingenta, Linda Hall. **CCC.**

Published by: R S N Z Publishing, PO Box 598, Wellington, New Zealand. TEL 64-4-4727421, FAX 64-4-4731841, sales@rsnz.org, http://www.rsnz.govt.nz/publish/nzjb/. Ed. F M Kell. Circ: 450. **Subscr. to:** R S N Z Publishing, PO Box 7075, Lawrence, KS 66044-7075. TEL 785-843-1235, FAX 785-843-1274, sir@allenpress.com.

581 JPN ISSN 0915-4914

NEWSLETTER OF HIMALAYAN BOTANY. Text in English. 1986. s-a. JPY 3,000 (effective 2003). adv. bk.rev. **Document type:** *Newsletter, Academic/Scholarly.*

Published by: Society of Himalayan Botany/Himalaya Shokubutsu Kenkyukai, University Museum, University of Tokyo, 3-1 Hongo 7-chome, Bunkyo-ku, Tokyo, 113-0033, Japan. FAX 81-3-5841-8456, akiyama@kahaku.go.jp. Ed. Shuichi Noshiro. R&P Hideaki Ohba. Adv. contact Shinobu Akiyama.

580 NGA ISSN 0795-8692
SB299.P3

➤ **NIGERIAN JOURNAL OF PALMS AND OIL SEEDS.** Text in English. 1953. irreg. USD 50 (effective 1999). adv. bk.rev. illus. index. back issues avail. **Document type:** *Journal, Academic/Scholarly.* **Description:** Deals with production and breeding of oil palm, coconut, raphia and date palms and other oil bearing seeds. Aims at researches and producers of these crops.

Formerly: Nigerian Institute for Oil Palm Research. Journal (0078-0715)

Indexed: BiolAb, CTFA, HortAb, PBA, RPP, S&F.

Published by: Nigerian Institute for Oil Palm Research, PMB 1030, Benin City, Edo, Nigeria. TEL 234-52-440130, 234-52-602485, FAX 234-52-602486, nifor@infoweb.abs.net. Ed. D A Okiy. Circ: 1,000 (paid).

380 JPN

NIHON SHOKUBUTSU BUNRUI GAKKAI. Text in Japanese. 2001. q. **Document type:** *Newsletter, Academic/Scholarly.*

Published by: The Japanese Society for Plant Taxonomists, c/o Atsuko Takano, Ph.D., Museum of Nature & Human Activities, Hyogo, Yayoigaoka 6, Sanda, 669-1546, Japan. TEL 81-795-59-2012, FAX 81-795-59-2019.

580 JPN

NIHON SHOKUBUTSU BUNRUI GAKKAI KAIHO. Text and summaries in Japanese. 1952. s-a. JPY 3,000. **Document type:** *Proceedings, Academic/Scholarly.*

Formerly (until 2001): Japan Society of Plant Taxonomists. Proceedings (0911-6052)

—CCC.

Published by: The Japanese Society for Plant Taxonomists, c/o Atsuko Takano, Ph.D., Museum of Nature & Human Activities, Hyogo, Yayoigaoka 6, Sanda, 669-1546, Japan. TEL 81-795-59-2012, FAX 81-795-59-2019. Circ: 350.

580 JPN

NIHON SHOKUBUTSU BUNRUI GAKKAI TAIKAI HAPPYO YOSHISHU/JAPAN SOCIETY OF PLANT TAXONOMISTS. PROCEEDING OF THE ANNUAL MEETING. Text in English, Japanese. a.

Published by: Nihon Shokubutsu Bunrui Gakkai/Japan Society of Plant Taxonomists, Tokyo Toritsu Daigaku Rigakubu, Makino Hyohonkan, 1-1 Minami-Osawa, Hachioji-shi, Tokyo-to 192-0364, Japan.

571.92 JPN

NIHON SHOKUBUTSU BYORI GAKKAI SHOKUBUTSU KANSEN SEIRI DANWAKAI/SYMPOSIUM ON PHYSIOLOGICAL PLANT PATHOLOGY IN JAPAN. PROCEEDINGS. Text in Japanese; Summaries in English. a. **Document type:** *Proceedings.*

Published by: Nihon Shokubutsu Byori Gakkai, Shokubutsu Kansen Seiri Danwakai/Phytopathological Society of Japan, Symposium on Physiological Plant Pathology, Iwate Daigaku Nogakubu, Shokubutsu Byorigaku Koza, 18-8 Ueda 3-chome, Morioka-shi, Iwate-ken 020-0066, Japan.

580 JPN

NIHON SHOKUBUTSU GAKKAI TAIKAI KENKYU HAPPYO KIROKU/BOTANICAL SOCIETY OF JAPAN. PROCEEDINGS OF THE ANNUAL MEETING. Text in Japanese. 1878. a. JPY 4,000 (effective 2000). adv. bk.rev. **Document type:** *Proceedings.*

Address: Toshin Bldg, 2-27-2 Hongo, Bunkyo-ku, Tokyo, 113-0033, Japan. TEL 81-3-3814-5675, FAX 81-3-3814-5352. Adv. contact T Morigaki.

580 JPN

NIHON SHOKUBUTSU SAIBOU BUNSHISEIBUTU GAKKAI KOROKIAMU/JAPANESE SOCIETY FOR PLANT CELL AND MOLECULAR BIOLOGY. CULTURE COLLOQUIUM. Text in English, Japanese. 1988. biennial.

Formerly: Nihon Shokubutsu Soshiki Baiyo Gakkai Shokubutsu Soshiki Baiyo Korokiamu - Japanese Association for Plant Tissue Culture. Plant Tissue Culture Colloquium

Published by: Nihon Shokubutsu Saibou Bunshiseibutu Gakkai/Japanese Society for Plant Cell and Molecular Biology, 30-15 Hongo 5-chome, Bunkyo-ku, Tokyo, 113-0033, Japan.

571.2 JPN

NIHON SHOKUBUTSU SEIRI GAKKAI NENKAI OYOBI SHINPOJUMU KOEU YOSHISHU/JAPANESE SOCIETY OF PLANT PHYSIOLOGISTS. PROCEEDINGS OF THE ANNUAL MEETING AND SYMPOSIUM. Text in Japanese. 1960. a. JPY 4,000 (effective 2001). back issues avail. **Document type:** *Proceedings.*

Published by: Japanese Society of Plant Physiologists/Nihon Shokubutsu Seiri Gakkai, Shimodachuri-Dori, Ogawa Higashi, Kamigyo-ku, Kyoto-shi, 602-8084, Japan. FAX 81-75-415-3662, jspp@nacos.com, http://www.nacos.com/jspp.

580 JPN ISSN 0389-5246

NIHON SHOKUBUTSUEN KYOKAISHI/JAPAN ASSOCIATION OF BOTANICAL GARDENS. BULLETIN. Text in Japanese; Summaries in English, Japanese. 1966. a. JPY 3,000 to non-members; JPY 2,000 to members.

Published by: Nihon Shokubutsuen Kyokai/Japan Association of Botanical Gardens, Daigaku Rigakubu Fuzuoku Shokubutsuen, 7-1 Hakusan 3-chome, Bunkyo-ku, Tokyo, 112-0000, Japan. TEL 81-424-83-2300, FAX 81-424-88-5832. Ed. Yasuyuki Ueda.

579.5 JPN ISSN 0913-7955

NIPPON KIN GAKKAI NYUSU/MYCOLOGICAL SOCIETY OF JAPAN. NEWS. Text in Japanese. 1968. s-a.

Indexed: EngInd.

Published by: Nippon Kin Gakkai/Mycological Society of Japan, Nihon Gakkai Jimu Senta, 16-9 Honkomagome 5-chome, Bunkyo-ku, Tokyo, 113-0021, Japan.

580 JPN ISSN 0287-3257

NIPPON SHIDA NO KAI KAIHO/NIPPON FERNIST CLUB. JOURNAL. Text in Japanese. 1952. 3/yr.

Published by: Nippon Shida no Kai/Nippon Fernist Club, Tokyo Nogyo Daigaku Seibutsugaku Kenkyushitsu, 1-1 Sakuragaoka 1-chome, Setagaya-ku, Tokyo, 157, Japan.

580 DNK ISSN 0107-055X
QK1 CODEN: NJBODK

➤ **NORDIC JOURNAL OF BOTANY.** Text in English. 1981. bi-m. DKK 3,000 to individuals (effective 2004). bk.rev. abstr.; bibl.; illus. 128 p./no. 2 cols./p.; Supplement avail.; back issues avail.; reprint service avail. from PQC. **Document type:** *Journal, Academic/Scholarly.*

Formed by the merger of (1866-1981): Botanisk Tidsskrift (0006-8187); (1839-1981): Botaniska Notiser (0006-8195); (1932-1981): Friesia (0016-1403); (1952-1981): Norwegian Journal of Botany (0300-1156)

Related titles: Microfiche ed.: (from IDC); (from BHP); Microform ed.: (from PQC); ♦ Supplement(s): Opera Botanica. ISSN 0078-5237.

Indexed: ASCA, ASFA, AgBio, AgrForAb, ApEcolAb, ApicAb, BIOBASE, BIOSIS Prev, BioCN&I, BiolAb, CIN, CPA, ChemAb, ChemTitl, ESPM, EntAb, ExcerpMed, FCA, FPA, ForAb, GEOBASE, HerbAb, HortAb, IABS, ISR, MBA, NemAb, OrnHort, PBA, PGegResA, PGrRegA, PlantSci, RA&MP, RPP, RefZh, S&F, SCI, SWRA, SeedAb, TriticAb, VITIS, WeedAb, ZooRec.

—BLDSC (6117.926000), CASDDS, CISTI, IDS, IE, Infotrieve, ingenta, Linda Hall. **CCC.**

Published by: Council for Nordic Publication in Botany, c/o Botanical Museum, Gothersgade 130, Copenhagen K, 1123, Denmark. TEL 45-33-144906, FAX 45-33-144960, office@nordic-botany.dk, http://www.nordic-botany.dk. Eds. Dorte F. Boesen, Ivan Nielsen. Circ: 700.

580.73 USA ISSN 0029-1641

NORFOLK BOTANICAL GARDEN SOCIETY BULLETIN✶. Text in English. 1940. m. membership. adv. bk.rev. charts; illus.

Published by: Norfolk Botanical Garden Society, 37 Watermill Ct., The Woodlands, TX 77380-4307. TEL 804-425-5344. Ed. William Genz. Circ: 500.

580 NOR ISSN 0802-2992

NORGES TEKNISK-NATURVITENSKAPELIGE UNIVERSITET. VITENSKAPSMUSEET. RAPPORT. BOTANISK SERIE. Text in English, Norwegian; Summaries in English. 1974. irreg. exchange basis. **Document type:** *Monographic series, Academic/Scholarly.* **Description:** Contains reports and other material connected to the botanical activity and the geographical area for which the museum is responsible.

(until 1987): Kongelige Norske Videnskabers Selskab, Museet. Rapport. Botanisk Serie (0332-8090)

Indexed: BiolAb, RefZh.

—BLDSC (7287.649550).

Published by: Norges Teknisk-Naturvitenskapelige Universitet, Vitenskapmuseet/Norwegian University of Science and Technology, Museum of Natural History and Archaeology, Trondheim, 7491, Norway. TEL 47-73-59-21-45, FAX 47-73-59-22-23, inger.growen@vm.ntnu.no, http://www.ntnu.no/vmuseet/botavd/botserie.html. Circ: 275 (controlled).

580 USA ISSN 0078-1312
QK110 CODEN: NAFLBY

➤ **NORTH AMERICAN FLORA.** Text in English. 1905-1952; N.S. 1956. irreg. price varies. back issues avail. **Document type:** *Monographic series, Academic/Scholarly.* **Description:** Takes a taxonomic treatment of plants native to North America and its geologically related areas.

Indexed: BiolAb.

—CISTI, Linda Hall. **CCC.**

Published by: New York Botanical Garden Press, 200th Street & Kazimiroff Blvd, Bronx, NY 10458-5126. TEL 718-817-8918, FAX 718-817-8842, http://www.nybg.org. Ed. W Buck.

580 635 USA

NORTH CAROLINA BOTANICAL GARDEN NEWSLETTER. Text in English. 1971. bi-m. membership. bk.rev. illus. back issues avail. **Document type:** *Newsletter.* **Description:** Reports on North Carolina Botanical Garden activities and events. Updates readers on progress of the Master plan. Features articles on native plant propagation, cultivation, and conservation. Also includes columns on current conservation issues; a seed exchange list; nature trails; herbs; a calendar of events which includes field trips, courses, lectures, and workshops; as well as volunteer activities.

Published by: North Carolina Botanical Garden, University of North Carolina, CB 3375 Totten Center, Chapel Hill, NC 27599-3375. TEL 919-962-0522, FAX 919-962-3531, bksmthrs@email.unc.edu, http://www.unc.edu/depts/ncbg. Ed. Sandra Brooks Mathers. Circ: 4,300.

NORTH CAROLINA TURFGRASS. see *AGRICULTURE—Crop Production And Soil*

580 577 508 USA ISSN 1092-6194
QH105.M2

➤ **NORTHEASTERN NATURALIST.** Text in English. 1993. q. USD 40 domestic to individuals; USD 45 in Canada & Mexico to individuals; USD 49 elsewhere to individuals; USD 60 domestic to institutions; USD 65 in Canada & Mexico to institutions; USD 69 elsewhere to institutions (effective 2005). bk.rev. None published. 128 p./no. 1 cols./p.; back issues avail. **Document type:** *Journal, Academic/Scholarly.* **Description:** Features research articles on terrestrial, fresh-water, and marine organisms and their environments; with a regional focus on northeastern North America.

Formerly (until 1995): Maine Naturalist (1063-3626)

Related titles: Online - full text ed.: (from BioOne, C S A, EBSCO Publishing, Northern Light Technology, Inc., O C L C Online Computer Library Center, Inc., ProQuest Information & Learning).

Indexed: ASFA, AnBrAb, BIOBASE, BIOSIS Prev, BioCN&I, BiolAb, BiolDig, CPA, CurCont, EPB, ESPM, EntAb, ForAb, HerbAb, HortAb, IndVet, OrnHort, PGegResA, PoultAb, RefZh, S&F, SWRA, SeedAb, WAE&RSA, WeedAb, WildRev, ZooRec.

—BLDSC (6150.315000), IE, Infotrieve, Linda Hall.

Published by: Humboldt Field Research Institute, 59 Eagle Hill Rd, PO Box 9, Steuben, ME 04680-0009. TEL 207-546-2821, FAX 207-546-3042, office@eaglehill.us, http://www.eaglehill.us/jngeninf.html. Ed. Glen H Mittelhauser. Pub., R&P, Adv. contact Joerg-Henner Lotze TEL 207-546-2821. Circ: 1,000 (paid).

580 USA ISSN 0078-1703
CODEN: PNWSBF

NORTHEASTERN WEED SCIENCE SOCIETY. PROCEEDINGS. Text in English. 1946. a. price varies. index. back issues avail. **Document type:** *Proceedings.*

Formerly (until 1971): Northeastern Weed Control Conference. Proceedings (0096-7068)

Indexed: Agr, BiolAb, ChemAb, DBA, FCA, HortAb, OrnHort, WeedAb.

—BLDSC (6841.865000), CASDDS, CISTI, IE, ingenta, Linda Hall.

Published by: Northeastern Weed Science Society, c/o Hilary A Sandler, PhD, UMass Cranberry Station, 1 State Bog Rd, PO Box 569, East Wareham, MA 02538. TEL 508-295-2212 ext 21, FAX 508-295-6387, hsandler@umext.umass.edu, http://www.newss.org. Ed. Mark J Van Gessel. Circ: 700.

B

580.09436 AUT
NOTIZEN ZUR FLORA DER STEIERMARK. Text in German. 1974. irreg. price varies. **Document type:** *Academic/Scholarly.* **Description:** Results of research on the flora of the province of Styria.
Published by: Landesmuseum Joanneum, Referat Botanik, Raubergasse 10, Graz, St 8010, Austria. TEL 43-316-80179750, FAX 43-316-80179800, post@lmj-bot.stmk.gv.at. Eds. Arnold Zimmermann, Detlef Ernet. Circ: 400. **Co-sponsor:** Steiermaerkische Landesregierung.

NOTIZIARIO SULLA PROTEZIONE DELLE PIANTE. see *AGRICULTURE—Crop Production And Soil*

580 DEU ISSN 0078-2238
QK504 CODEN: NOHBA9
NOVA HEDWIGA, BEIHEFTE. Text in English, French, German. 1962. irreg., latest vol.126, 2003. price varies. **Document type:** *Monographic series, Academic/Scholarly.*
Indexed: BioDAb, BiolAb, RPP, ZooRec.
—BLDSC (6179.070000), CISTI, IE, ingenta, Linda Hall.
Published by: J. Cramer in der Gebrueder Borntraeger Verlagsbuchhandlung, Johannesstr 3A, Stuttgart, 70176, Germany. TEL 49-711-3514560, FAX 49-711-35145699, mail@borntraeger-cramer.de, http://www.schweizerbart.de/j/nova-hedwiga-beihefte.

580 DEU ISSN 0029-5035
QK504 CODEN: NOHEAI
➤ **NOVA HEDWIGIA**; journal of cryptogamic science. Text in English, French, German. 1852. q. USD 344 foreign for print & online eds. (effective 2005). adv. bk.rev. charts; illus. index every 20 vols. **Document type:** *Journal, Academic/Scholarly.*
Formerly (until 1959): Hedwigia (0367-5734)
Related titles: Online - full text ed.: (from EBSCO Publishing, Gale Group, IngentaConnect, Swets Information Services); Supplement(s): ISSN 1438-9134.
Indexed: ASCA, ASFA, AgBio, AgrForAb, BIOBASE, BIOSIS Prev, BioCN&I, BiolAb, CurCont, ESPM, FCA, FPA, ForAb, HerbAb, HortAb, IABS, ISR, IndVet, NemAb, OrnHort, PBA, PGegResA, PlantSci, RA&MP, RM&VM, RPP, RevApplEntom, S&F, SCI, SPPI, SeedAb, SoyAb, TriticAb, WeedAb, ZooRec.
—BLDSC (6179.050000), CISTI, IDS, IE, Infotrieve, ingenta, Linda Hall. **CCC.**
Published by: J. Cramer in der Gebrueder Borntraeger Verlagsbuchhandlung, Johannesstr 3A, Stuttgart, 70176, Germany. TEL 49-711-3514560, FAX 49-711-35145699, mail@borntraeger-cramer.de, http://www.schweizerbart.de/j/nova-hedwigia.

580 USA ISSN 1055-3177
QK96 CODEN: NOVOEK
➤ **NOVON**; a journal for botanical nomenclature. Text in English, Spanish. 1991. q. USD 140 domestic; USD 150 in Canada & Mexico; USD 175 elsewhere (effective 2002); includes Annals. illus. index. back issues avail. **Document type:** *Journal, Academic/Scholarly.* **Description:** Contains papers discussing the establishment of new nomenclature in vascular plants and bryophytes.
Indexed: AgBio, AgrForAb, BIOBASE, BIOSIS Prev, BiolAb, CurCont, DSA, FCA, ForAb, HerbAb, HortAb, IABS, MaizeAb, OrnHort, PBA, PGegResA, PlantSci, RA&MP, RPP, S&F, SeedAb, TriticAb, VITIS, WeedAb.
—BLDSC (6180.429700), CISTI, IE, Infotrieve, ingenta, Linda Hall.
Published by: (Scientific Publications), Missouri Botanical Garden, PO Box 299, St. Louis, MO 63166-0299. TEL 314-577-9547, FAX 314-577-9594, novon@mobot.org, http://www.mbgpress.org, http://www.mobot.org. R&P Amy McPherson TEL 314-577-5112. Circ: 850.

580 AUS ISSN 0085-4417
QK1 CODEN: NUYTDN
NUYTSIA. Text in English. 1970. irreg., latest vol.12, no.2. AUD 20 per issue (effective 2003).
Indexed: BIOSIS Prev, BiolAb, CALL, ForAb, PBA, WeedAb.
Published by: Department of Conservation and Land Management, Locked Bag 104, Bentley Delivery Centre, W.A. 6893, Australia. TEL 61-89334-0324, FAX 61-89334-0498. Circ: 600.

580 ESP ISSN 0376-5016
O P T I M A NEWSLETTER/INFORMATEUR O P T I M A. Text in English, French. 1975. a., latest vol.35, 2000. CHF 30 membership (effective 2001). adv. bk.rev.; Website rev. **Document type:** *Newsletter, Academic/Scholarly.* **Description:** Includes news about botanical research, reports and announcements of meetings and congresses, news of institutions or societies, list of publications and extensive book and journal reviews.
Published by: Organization for the Phyto-Taxonomic Investigation of the Mediterranean Area, Departamento Biologia Vegetal, Universidad Politecnica de Madrid, Ciudad Universitaria, Madrid, 28040, Spain. TEL 34-91-3365462, FAX 34-91-3365656, iriondo@ccupm.upm.es, http://www.bgbm.fu-berlin.de/optima/. Ed., Adv. contact J M Iriondo. R&P J.M. Iriondo. page USD 500. Circ: 1,000 (controlled).

OIL PALM INDUSTRY ECONOMIC JOURNAL. see *ENERGY*

580 USA ISSN 1536-7738
QK181
OKLAHOMA NATIVE PLANT RECORD. Text in English. 2001. a.
Published by: Oklahoma Native Plant Society, 2435 S Peoria Ave, Tulsa, OK 74114. http://dir.gardenweb.com/directory/onps.

ON THE FRINGE. see *GARDENING AND HORTICULTURE*

580.74 CAN ISSN 0072-9655
ONTARIO ROYAL BOTANICAL GARDENS. TECHNICAL BULLETIN. Text in English. 1957. irreg. price varies. back issues avail. **Document type:** *Bulletin, Academic/Scholarly.*
Published by: Royal Botanical Gardens, P O Box 399, Hamilton, ON L8N 3H8, Canada. TEL 905-527-1158, FAX 905-577-0375. Ed. J Lord. Circ: 1,000 (controlled).

580 DNK ISSN 0078-5237
QK1 CODEN: OPBOA2
➤ **OPERA BOTANICA.** Text in English. 1947. irreg. (.), latest 2001. price varies. adv. bk.rev. index. back issues avail. **Document type:** *Monographic series, Academic/Scholarly.*
Formerly (until 1953): Botaniska Notiser. Supplement (0366-2055); Incorporates (1913-1981): Dansk Botanisk Arkiv (0011-6211)
Related titles: Microfiche ed.: (from IDC); Microform ed.: (from PQC); ♦ Supplement to: Nordic Journal of Botany. ISSN 0107-055X.
Indexed: ApEcolAb, BIOBASE, BIOSIS Prev, BiolAb, CurCont, ESPM, FCA, ForAb, HerbAb, IABS, PBA, PlantSci, PollutAb, RefZh, S&F, SCI, WeedAb.
—BLDSC (6266.700000), CISTI, IE, ingenta, Linda Hall. **CCC.**
Published by: Council for Nordic Publication in Botany, c/o Botanical Museum, Gothersgade 130, Copenhagen K, 1123, Denmark. TEL 45-33-144906, FAX 45-33-144960, office@nordic-botany.dk, http://www.nordic-botany.dk/ob_startpage.html. Ed. Dorte F. Boesen. Circ: 500.

580.74 BEL ISSN 0775-9592
➤ **OPERA BOTANICA BELGICA.** Text in English, French. 1988. irreg., latest 2000. price varies. illus. back issues avail. **Document type:** *Monographic series, Academic/Scholarly.*
Indexed: BIOSIS Prev, RefZh.
—BLDSC (6266.703000), Linda Hall.
Published by: Jardin Botanique National de Belgique/Nationale Plantentuin van Belgie, Domaine de Bouchout, Nieuwelaan 38, Meise, 1860, Belgium. TEL 32-2-2693905, http://www.br.fgov.be. Ed. Elmar Robbrecht. Adv. contact Katrien Clarysse.

580 ARG ISSN 0078-5245
Q33 CODEN: OPLLA9
OPERA LILLOANA. Text in Spanish; Summaries in English, French, German, Italian. 1957. irreg., latest vol.44, 1999. bk.rev. bibl.; illus. back issues avail. **Document type:** *Monographic series, Academic/Scholarly.*
Indexed: ASFA, BIOSIS Prev, BiolAb, ESPM, RefZh, ZooRec.
—CISTI.
Published by: Fundacion Miguel Lillo, Centro de Informacion Geo-Biologico del NOA, Miguel Lillo, 251, San Miguel De Tucuman, Tucuman 4000, Argentina. TEL 54-0381-4239960, FAX 54-0381-4330868, fmlinfonoa@tucbbs.com.ar, http://www.lillo.org.ar. Ed. Jose A Haedo Rossi.

580.74 635.9 GBR ISSN 1359-5199
ORCHID RESEARCH NEWSLETTER. Text in English. 1983. s-a. **Document type:** *Newsletter.*
Related titles: Online - full text ed.
Published by: Royal Botanic Gardens, Kew, Richmond, Surrey TW9 3AB, United Kingdom. TEL 44-20-83325000, FAX 44-20-83325197, info@rbgkew.org.uk, http://www.rbgkew.org.uk/herbarium/orchid/, http://www.rbgkew.org.uk/index.html.

584.4 IND ISSN 0971-5371
ORCHID SOCIETY OF INDIA. JOURNAL. Text in English. 1987. s-a. USD 35 (effective 2000). illus. **Document type:** *Academic/Scholarly.*
Indexed: HortAb, OrnHort, PBA, PGegResA, PGrRegA, RPP, S&F, SIA, SeedAb.
—BLDSC (4837.410000).
Published by: (Orchid Society of India), H P C Publishers Distributors Pvt. Ltd., 4805 Bharat Ram Rd, 24 Darya Ganj, New Delhi, 110 002, India. TEL 91-11-3254401, FAX 91-11-619-3511, hpcpd@nda.vsnl.net.in, hpcpd@hpc.cc, http://www.hpc.cc, http://www.bizdelhi.com/publisher/hpc, http://www.indianindustry.com. **Co-publisher:** T O S I.

584.4 NLD ISSN 0030-4484
ORCHIDEEEN. Text in Dutch. 1934. bi-m. adv. bk.rev. bibl.; illus. **Document type:** *Bulletin, Academic/Scholarly.* **Description:** Covers biological research in ecology, seeding, cultivation, hybridization, and germination. Includes society news, information, reports as well as lists of events and exhibitions.
Incorporates (1972-1978): Orchiteek (0921-7223)
Indexed: HortAb.
Published by: Nederlandse Orchideeen Vereniging, c/o A N J de Ridder, Piet vd Veldenstraat 22, Roelofarendsveen, 2371 TC, Netherlands. TEL 31-71-3312862, hoofdredactie.tijdschrift@nov-orchidee.nl, http://www.nov-orchidee.nl/html/tijdschrift.html, http://www.nov-orchidee..nl. Ed. Yebo Feikema. Circ: 2,200. **Subscr. to:** c/o L. Kristelijn, Apollostraat 4, Aalsmeer 1431 WR, Netherlands.

THE ORGANIC WAY. see *GARDENING AND HORTICULTURE*

ORNITHOLOGISCHER VEREIN ZU HILDESHEIM. NATURKUNDLICHE MITTEILUNGEN. see *BIOLOGY—Ornithology*

584.4 MEX ISSN 0300-3701
SB409.A1
ORQUIDEA (MEX). Text in English, Spanish. 1971. irreg., latest vol.15, 1997. MXP 370 domestic; USD 37 foreign (effective 2003). adv. bk.rev. illus. index. 300 p./no.; back issues avail. **Document type:** *Journal, Academic/Scholarly.* **Description:** Examines the orchids of the neotropics, their taxonomy and ecology.
Indexed: AGBP, BiolAb.
Published by: Herbarium Amo, Lago Tanganica 18, Granada, Mexico City, DF 11520, Mexico. TEL 52-55-52623193, FAX 52-55-55314349. Eds. Eric Hagsater, Miguel Angel Soto-Arenas. R&P Eric Hagsater. Circ: 1,000. **Subscr. to:** Apdo Postal 53-123, Mexico City, D.F. 11320 , Mexico.

OSAKA-SHIRITSU SHIZENSHI HAKUBUTSUKAN SHUZO SHIRYO MOKUROKU/OSAKA MUSEUM OF NATURAL HISTORY. SPECIAL PUBLICATIONS. see *BIOLOGY*

680 USA ISSN 1042-3524
CODEN: PGQUED
➤ **P G R S A QUARTERLY.** Text in English. 1973. q. USD 40 in North America membership; USD 55 elsewhere membership; USD 15 membership (effective 2003). bk.rev. back issues avail. **Document type:** *Journal, Academic/Scholarly.* **Description:** Publishes research papers and technical reviews on applied and basic aspects of plant growth regulation.
Formerly (until 1988): Plant Growth Regulator Society of America. Bulletin (0163-6367)
Related titles: Online - full text ed.: 2003.
Indexed: Agr, CPA, ChemAb, ChemTitl, FCA, HortAb, OrnHort, PBA, PGrRegA, PHN&I, PoultAb, RPP, RevApplEntom, SeedAb, SoyAb.
—CASDDS, CISTI, Linda Hall.
Published by: Plant Growth Regulation Society of America, PO Box 2945, LaGrange, GA 30241. TEL 706-845-9085, FAX 706-883-8215, cbeyl@aamu.edu, assocgroup@mindspring.com, http://www.griffin.peachnet.edu/pgrsa/quarterly_index.htm, http://www.griffin.peachnet.edu/pgrsa/homepage.shtml. Ed. Caula A. Beyl. Circ: 800.

580 PAK ISSN 0556-3321
QK1 CODEN: PJBOB6
➤ **PAKISTAN JOURNAL OF BOTANY.** Text in English. 1969. q. PKR 300, USD 60 per vol. (effective 2003). adv. bk.rev. back issues avail.; reprint service avail. from PQC,ISI. **Document type:** *Journal, Academic/Scholarly.*
Indexed: ASCA, AgBio, AgrForAb, BIOSIS Prev, BioCN&I, BiolAb, CIN, CPA, ChemAb, ChemTitl, CurCont, ExcerpMed, FCA, FPA, FS&TA, ForAb, HerbAb, HortAb, I&DA, MaizeAb, NutrAb, OrnHort, PBA, PGegResA, PGrRegA, PHN&I, PotatoAb, RA&MP, RM&VM, RPP, RiceAb, S&F, SIA, SeedAb, SoyAb, TDB, TriticAb, VITIS, WAE&RSA, WeedAb.
—BLDSC (6340.950000), CASDDS, CISTI, IDS, IE, ingenta, Linda Hall. **CCC.**
Published by: Pakistan Botanical Society, Dept. of Botany, University of Karachi, Karachi, 75270, Pakistan. TEL 92-21-4387867, FAX 92-21-4963373, shaji@super.net.pk, http://www.pjbot.org. Ed., R&P Dr. Abdul Ghaffar. Circ: 1,000 (controlled).

580 PAK ISSN 1019-763X
SB605.P3 CODEN: ISNYAD
PAKISTAN JOURNAL OF PHYTOPATHOLOGY. Text in English. s-a.
Indexed: AgBio, AgrForAb, BioCN&I, CPA, FCA, FPA, ForAb, HelmAb, HerbAb, HortAb, MaizeAb, NemAb, PBA, PGegResA, PHN&I, PotatoAb, PoultAb, RA&MP, RDA, RPP, RiceAb, S&F, SIA, SeedAb, SoyAb, TriticAb, WAE&RSA, WeedAb.
Published by: Pakistan Phytopathological Society, Department of Plant Pathology, University of Agriculture, Faisalabad, 38040, Pakistan. TEL 92-41-30281 ext 208, FAX 92-41-647846, mushroomking041@yahoo.com.

580 PAK ISSN 1016-0035
➤ **PAKPHYTON.** Text in English. 1989. a. PKR 150 domestic; USD 50 foreign (effective 2003). **Document type:** *Academic/Scholarly.*
Published by: Agriculturalists Breeders and Botanists' Club of Pakistan, Department of Botany, University of the Punjab, Quaid-e-Azam Campus, Lahore, 54590, Pakistan. TEL 92-42-9231152, FAX 92-42-9230481. Eds. Dr. K A Siddiqui, Shahida Hasnain. Circ: 150.

580 IND ISSN 0031-0174
QE901 CODEN: PLBOAJ
➤ **PALAEOBOTANIST.** Text in English, French, German, Hindi. 1952. 3/yr. USD 150 (effective 2001). bk.rev. bibl.; charts; illus. back issues avail. **Document type:** *Journal, Academic/Scholarly.* **Description:** Original research papers and review papers on palaeobotany and allied disciplines in botany and earth sciences.
Indexed: AESIS, ASFA, AbAn, BiolAb, ESPM, GenetAb, HGA, IBR, ISA, PollutAb, ZooRec.
—BLDSC (6343.400000), CISTI, Linda Hall.

Published by: (Birbal Sahni Institute of Palaeobotany), Scientific Publishers, 5-A New Pali Rd., Near Hotel Taj Hari Mahal, PO Box 91, Jodhpur, Rajasthan 342 003, India. TEL 91-291-2433323, FAX 91-291-2512580, info@scientificpub.com, http://www.scientificpub.com. Ed. B S Venkatachala. Pub. Anshu K Sinha. Circ: 400.

➤ **PALM OIL TECHNICAL BULLETIN.** see *ENERGY*

580 USA ISSN 1523-4495
SB299.P3 CODEN: PRNCAH
PALMS. Text in English. 1956. q. free to members. adv. bk.rev. illus. back issues avail.; reprint service avail. from PQC. **Document type:** *Journal, Academic/Scholarly.* **Description:** Contains scientific and popular articles on taxonomy and horticulture of the Palmae.
Formerly (until 1998): Principes (0032-8480)
Related titles: Microfilm ed.: (from PQC).
Indexed: AEA, AgBio, AgrForAb, ApicAb, BIOSIS Prev, BibAg, BiolAb, CPA, ChemAb, FPA, FS&TA, ForAb, GardL, HerbAb, HortAb, OrnHort, PBA, PGegResA, PGrRegA, PHN&I, RA&MP, RDA, RPP, RRTA, RefZh, RevApplEntom, S&F, SeedAb, WAE&RSA, WeedAb, ZooRec.
—BLDSC (6345.563980), IE, ingenta.
Published by: International Palm Society, Inc., PO Box 1897, Lawrence, KS 66044-8897. TEL 785-843-1235, FAX 785-843-1274, palms@allenpress.com, http://www.palms.org. Ed., Adv. contact Natalie Uhl. Circ: 3,000.

580 USA ISSN 1548-3061
SB413.P3
PASSIFLORA; the journal and newsletter of Passiflora Society International. Text in English. s-a. free to members (effective 2004).
Published by: Passiflora Society International, c/o Butterfly World at Tradewinds Park, 3600 W. Sample Rd., Coconut Creek, FL 33073. info@passiflora.org, http://www.passiflora.org. Ed. Phil Schappert.

579.5 NLD ISSN 0031-5850
QK600
➤ **PERSOONIA;** a mycological journal. Text in English, French, German. 1959. s-a. price varies. illus. index. back issues avail. **Document type:** *Journal, Academic/Scholarly.* **Description:** Devoted to the taxonomy of fungi.
Indexed: ASCA, ASFA, AgBio, BIOBASE, BIOSIS Prev, BiolAb, CurCont, ForAb, HortAb, NutrAb, PBA, PGegResA, RM&VM, RPP, RefZh, S&F.
—BLDSC (6428.104000), IE, ingenta, Linda Hall.
Published by: National Herbarium Nederland/Leiden Branch, PO Box 9514, Leiden, 2300 RA, Netherlands. TEL 31-71-5273570, FAX 31-71-5273522, noordeloos@rulrhb.leidenuniv.nl, zoelen@rhbcml.leidenuniv.nl, http://www.nhncml.leidenuniv.nl. Eds. M E Noordeloos, M M Nauta. Circ: 300.

581.7 DEU ISSN 1433-8319
QK900
➤ **PERSPECTIVES IN PLANT ECOLOGY, EVOLUTION AND SYSTEMATICS.** Text in English. 1998. 4/yr. EUR 53 in Europe to individuals; JPY 6,600 in Japan to individuals; USD 52 to individuals except Europe and Japan; EUR 111 to institutions; EUR 126 in Europe to institutions; JPY 17,000 in Japan to institutions; USD 137 to institutions except Europe and Japan (effective 2006). adv. **Document type:** *Journal, Academic/Scholarly.* **Description:** Provides a platform for reviews and monographs in the fields of ecology, evolution and systematics of plants.
Related titles: Online - full text ed.: (from EBSCO Publishing, Gale Group, IngentaConnect, O C L C Online Computer Library Center, Inc., ScienceDirect, Swets Information Services).
Indexed: ASFA, AgBio, ApEcolAb, B&BAb, BIOBASE, BIOSIS Prev, BioCN&I, BiolAb, CPA, CurCont, ESPM, FPA, ForAb, GEOBASE, GenetAb, HGA, HerbAb, HortAb, I&DA, MaizeAb, OrnHort, PBA, PGegResA, PGrRegA, RA&MP, RDA, RPP, RefZh, RevApplEntom, S&F, SWRA, SeedAb, WAE&RSA, WeedAb, ZooRec.
—BLDSC (6428.149200), CISTI, IE, Infotrieve, ingenta. **CCC.**
Published by: (Geobotanisches Institut E T H, Stiftung Ruebel), Elsevier GmbH, Urban & Fischer Verlag (Subsidiary of: Elsevier Science & Technology), Loebdergraben 14a, Jena, 07743, Germany. TEL 49-3641-626430, FAX 49-3641-626432, info@urbanfischer.de, http://www.elsevier.com/locate/ppees, http://www.urbanfischer.de. Eds. Hansjoerg Dietz, Johannes Kollmann, Peter J. Edwards. R&P Martin Huber TEL 49-3641-626430. Adv. contact Sabine Schroeter TEL 49-3641-626445. B&W page EUR 400, color page EUR 1,345; 210 x 280. Circ: 350 (paid and controlled).
Non-German speaking countries subscr. to: Nature Publishing Group, Brunel Rd, Houndmills, Basingstoke, Hamps RG21 6XS, United Kingdom. TEL 44-1256-302629, FAX 44-1256-476117

580 BRA ISSN 0373-840X
QK263
PESQUISAS: PUBLICACOES DE BOTANICA. Key Title: Pesquisas. Botanica. Text in Portuguese. 1957. irreg. per issue exchange basis. **Document type:** *Academic/Scholarly.*
Supersedes in part (in 1960): Instituto Anchietano de Pesquisas. Pesquisas (0480-1873)
Indexed: BIOSIS Prev, BiolAb.
—CISTI.
Published by: (Universidade do Vale do Rio dos Sinos, Instituto Anchietano de Pesquisas), Unisinos, Av Unisinos, 950, Sao Leopoldo, RS 93022-000, Brazil. TEL 55-51-5908239, FAX 55-51-5908238.

PEST MANAGEMENT RECOMMENDATIONS FOR COMMERCIAL TREE-FRUIT PRODUCTION. see *AGRICULTURE—Crop Production And Soil*

571.9 ITA ISSN 1120-7698
PETRIA; giornale di patologia delle piante. Text in Italian; Summaries in Italian, English. 1991. q.
Indexed: AgBio, AgrForAb, BioCN&I, CPA, FCA, FPA, ForAb, HortAb, NemAb, OrnHort, PBA, PGegResA, PGrRegA, PHN&I, PotatoAb, RA&MP, RPP, RefZh, RevApplEntom, SeedAb, SoyAb, TriticAb, VITIS, WeedAb.
—BLDSC (6430.355500).
Published by: Istituto Sperimentale per la Patologia Vegetale, Via Giuseppe Carlo Bertero 22, Rome, 00156, Italy. TEL 39-06-820701, FAX 39-06-86802296, ispave@ispave.it, http://www.ispave.it.

580 AUT ISSN 0031-6733
CODEN: PFLZAQ
DER PFLANZENARZT; Fachzeitschrift fuer Pflanzenschutz, Vorratsschutz, Pflanzenernaehrung. Text in German. 1948. 8/yr. EUR 47.50 domestic; EUR 60 foreign (effective 2004). adv. bk.rev. charts; illus. index. **Document type:** *Magazine, Trade.*
Indexed: BiolAb, ChemAb, DBA, FCA, HerbAb, HortAb, PotatoAb, RPP, RRTA, RevApplEntom, TriticAb, VITIS, WAE&RSA.
—CASDDS, CISTI. **CCC.**
Published by: Oesterreichischer Agrarverlag GmbH, Achauer Str 49a, Leopoldsdorf, N 2333, Austria. TEL 43-2235-4040, FAX 43-2235-404929, office@agrarverlag.at, http://www.agrarverlag.at. Ed. Gabriele Luttenberger. Adv. contact Romana Hummer. B&W page EUR 3,042, color page EUR 3,666; trim 175 x 260. Circ: 4,800 (paid and controlled).

580 DEU ISSN 0079-1342
CODEN: PFZNAQ
PFLANZENSCHUTZ-NACHRICHTEN. Text in English, German; Summaries in French, Spanish. 1948. 3/yr. free. **Document type:** *Journal, Academic/Scholarly.*
Related titles: ♦ German ed.: Pflanzenschutz-Nachrichten Bayer. ISSN 0340-1723; English ed.: ISSN 0170-0405.
Indexed: BiolAb, ChemAb.
—CASDDS, Linda Hall.
Published by: Bayer AG, Geschaeftsbereich Pflanzenschutz, Kaiser-Wilhelm-Allee, Leverkusen, 51368, Germany. TEL 49-2173-384114, FAX 49-2173-383454, http://www.bayer-agro.de. Circ: 8,750.

580 AUT ISSN 0031-675X
SB605.A84
➤ **PFLANZENSCHUTZBERICHTE.** Text in German; Summaries in English. 1947. 2/yr. EUR 35.61 (effective 2004). adv. bk.rev. charts; illus. index. **Document type:** *Bulletin, Government.* **Description:** Original articles about plant protection and welfare.
Indexed: AgBio, BioCN&I, BiolAb, CPA, DBA, ExcerpMed, FCA, ForAb, HerbAb, HortAb, MaizeAb, NemAb, OrnHort, PBA, PGegResA, PHN&I, RA&MP, RPP, RefZh, RevApplEntom, S&F, SIA, SeedAb, SoyAb, TriticAb, VITIS, WAE&RSA, WeedAb, ZooRec.
—BLDSC (6439.050000), CISTI, IE, ingenta, Linda Hall.
Published by: Bundesamt und Forschungszentrum fuer Landwirtschaft, Institut fuer Phytomedizin, Spargelfeldstrasse 191, Vienna, W 1226, Austria. TEL 43-1-732165501, FAX 43-1-732165194, gbedlan@bfl.ac.at. Eds. Bruno Zwatz, Gerhard Bedlan. R&P Bruno Zwatz. Circ: 100 (paid); 500 (controlled).

580 DEU ISSN 0079-1369
PHANEROGAMARUM MONOGRAPHIAE. Text in German. 1969. irreg., latest vol.23, 2000. price varies. **Document type:** *Monographic series, Academic/Scholarly.*
Indexed: BiolAb.
Published by: J. Cramer in der Gebrueder Borntraeger Verlagsbuchhandlung, Johannesstr 3A, Stuttgart, 70176, Germany. TEL 49-711-3514560, FAX 49-711-35145699, mail@borntraeger-cramer.de, http://www.schweizerbart.de/j/phanerogamarum-monographiae.

PHARMACOGNOSY, PHYTOCHEMISTRY, MEDICINAL PLANTS. see *PHARMACY AND PHARMACOLOGY*

571.92 PHL ISSN 0115-0804
CODEN: PHPHD9
➤ **PHILIPPINE PHYTOPATHOLOGY.** Text in English. 1965. s-a. USD 30 domestic; USD 300 foreign (effective 2003). adv. 30 p./no.; back issues avail. **Document type:** *Journal, Academic/Scholarly.* **Description:** Contains research results on basic, applied, and molecular plant pathology.
Formerly (until 2001): Journal of Tropical Plant Pathology
—CASDDS.
Published by: Philippine Phytopathological Society, c/o Department of Plant Pathology, University of at Los Banos, College, Laguna, 4031, Philippines. TEL 64-41-5362512, FAX 64-49-5363438, tod@ipb.uplb.edu.ph. Ed., R&P Teodora Dizon. Adv. contact Ceferino Baniqued TEL 63-2-5244451. Circ: 450.

580 CZE ISSN 0300-3604
QK882 CODEN: PHSYB5
➤ **PHOTOSYNTHETICA;** international journal for photosynthesis research. Text in English. 1967. q. EUR 827, USD 868, GBP 548 combined subscription to institutions print & online eds. (effective 2005). adv. bk.rev. bibl.; illus. index. 160 p./no. 2 cols./p.; back issues avail. **Document type:** *Journal, Academic/Scholarly.* **Description:** Covers photosynthesis research, publishing original papers as well as reviews on special topics, bibliography of reviews and methodological papers, reports on conferences.
Related titles: Microform ed.: (from PQC); Online - full text ed.: ISSN 1573-9058 (from EBSCO Publishing, Gale Group, IngentaConnect, Kluwer Online, O C L C Online Computer Library Center, Inc., Ovid Technologies, Inc., Springer LINK, Swets Information Services).
Indexed: AEA, ASCA, ASFA, AgBio, AgrForAb, BBCI, BIOBASE, BIOSIS Prev, BibLing, BiolAb, CPA, CTFA, ChemAb, ChemTitl, CurCont, ESPM, ExcerpMed, FCA, FPA, ForAb, HerbAb, HortAb, I&DA, IABS, ISR, MaizeAb, OrnHort, PBA, PGegResA, PGrRegA, PHN&I, PlantSci, PollutAb, PotatoAb, RA&MP, RPP, RefZh, RiceAb, S&F, S&MA, SCI, SIA, SeedAb, SoyAb, TriticAb, VITIS, WAE&RSA, WeedAb.
—BLDSC (6474.370000), CASDDS, CISTI, IDS, IE, Infotrieve, ingenta, Linda Hall. **CCC.**
Published by: Akademie Ved Ceske Republiky, Ustav Experimentalni Botaniky/Academy of Sciences of the Czech Republic, Institute of Experimental Botany, Na Karlovce 1A, Prague 6, 160 00, Czech Republic. TEL 420-2-33331032, FAX 420-2-24310113, photosynthetica@ueb.cas.cz, http://www.ueb.cas.cz/ps/ps.htm. Ed., Adv. contact Zdenek Sestak. page USD 250; 170 x 250. Circ: 350 (paid); 50 (controlled). **Co-publisher:** Springer-Verlag Dordrecht.

579.8 USA ISSN 0031-8884
QK564 CODEN: PYCOAD
➤ **PHYCOLOGIA.** Text in English, French. 1961. 6/yr. free to members. adv. bk.rev. bibl.; charts; illus. Index. back issues avail.; reprint service avail. from ISI. **Document type:** *Journal, Academic/Scholarly.* **Description:** Covers all aspects of algal biology: original research articles, major topical reviews, research notes, commentaries, book reviews, announcements of meetings and field courses and memorials of prominent phycologists.
Related titles: Microform ed.: (from PQC, SWZ); Online - full text ed.: (from bigchalk, Micromedia ProQuest, Northern Light Technology, Inc., O C L C Online Computer Library Center, Inc., ProQuest Information & Learning).
Indexed: ASCA, ASFA, BIOBASE, BIOSIS Prev, BiolAb, ChemAb, CurCont, ESPM, IAA, IABS, ISR, M&TEA, MBA, OceAb, PBA, PlantSci, S&F, SCI, SPPI, ZooRec.
—BLDSC (6474.650000), CASDDS, CISTI, IDS, IE, Infotrieve, ingenta, Linda Hall.
Published by: International Phycological Society, 810 East 10th St, PO Box 1897, Lawrence, KS 66044-8897. TEL 913-843-1235, 800-627-0629, FAX 913-843-1274, http://www.intphycsoc.org/IPSPhycologia.lasso, http://www.intphycsoc.org/default.lasso. Ed. Hiroshi Kawai. Circ: 1,250.

579.8 CAN ISSN 0045-3072
PHYCOLOGICAL NEWSLETTER✶. Text in English. 1965. 3/yr. membership. bk.rev. **Document type:** *Newsletter.* **Description:** News of scientific interest to biologists who study algae; including conference news, research, travel and employment opportunities.
Published by: Phycological Society of America, c/o Dr John P van der Meer, Inst for Marine Biosciences, 1411 Oxford St, Halifax, NS B3H 3Z1, Canada. TEL 902-426-4927, FAX 902-426-9413. Ed. Richard McCourt. Circ: 1,200.

579.8 AUS ISSN 1322-0829
QK564 CODEN: PHREFC
➤ **PHYCOLOGICAL RESEARCH.** Text in English. 1953. q. USD 186 combined subscription in the Americas to individuals & Caribbean, print & online eds.; EUR 171 combined subscription in Europe to individuals print & online eds.; GBP 114 combined subscription elsewhere to individuals print & online eds.; USD 516 combined subscription in the Americas to institutions & Caribbean, print & online eds.; GBP 318 combined subscription elsewhere to institutions print & online eds. (effective 2006). bk.rev. cum.index: vols.1-10; vols.11-20. **Document type:** *Journal, Academic/Scholarly.* **Description:** Contains original research articles, research notes, and reviews on all aspects of phycology.
Supersedes in part (in 1995): Japanese Journal of Phycology (Bilingual Edition); Which was formerly: Sorui - Japanese Society of Phycology. Bulletin (0038-1578)
Related titles: Online - full text ed.: ISSN 1440-1835. USD 490 in the Americas to institutions & Caribbean; GBP 302 elsewhere to institutions (effective 2006) (from Blackwell Synergy, EBSCO Publishing, Gale Group, IngentaConnect, O C L C Online Computer Library Center, Inc., Swets Information Services).

▼ new title ➤ refereed ✶ unverified ♦ full entry avail.

Indexed: ASFA, BIOBASE, BIOSIS Prev, BiolAb, CIN, ChemAb, ChemTitl, CurCont, ESPM, ExcerpMed, GEOBASE, IABS, MBA, OceAb, PlantSci, PollutAb, RefZh, ZooRec.
—BLDSC (6474.755000), CASDDS, CISTI, IE, Infotrieve, ingenta. **CCC.**
Published by: (Japanese Society of Phycology/Nihon Sorui Gakkai JPN), Blackwell Publishing Asia (Subsidiary of: Blackwell Publishing Ltd.), 550 Swanston St, Carlton South, VIC 3053, Australia. TEL 61-383591011, FAX 61-383591120, subs@blackwellpublishingasia.com, http://www.blackwellpublishing.com/journals/PRE. Ed. Kazuo Okuda. Circ: 1,000. **Subscr. to:** PO Box 378, Carlton South, VIC 3053, Australia.

580 IND ISSN 0554-1182
QK564 CODEN: PHKSBF
PHYKOS. Text in English. 1962. s-a. USD 40. abstr. **Document type:** *Academic/Scholarly.*
Indexed: ASFA, BiolAb, ChemAb, ChemTitl, CurCont, ESPM, MBA, ZooRec.
—CISTI, Linda Hall.
Published by: (Phycological Society of India), Today and Tomorrow's Printers & Publishers, 24 B-5 Desh Bandhu Gupta Rd., Karol Bagh, New Delhi, 110 005, India. tp@vsnl.net. Ed. G S Venkataraman. **Dist. in U.S. by:** Scholarly Publications, 7310 Elcresta Dr, Houston, TX 77083.

571.2 DNK ISSN 0031-9317
QK1 CODEN: PHPLAI
➤ **PHYSIOLOGIA PLANTARUM.** Text in English, French, German. 1948. m. USD 991 combined subscription in the Americas to institutions & Caribbean (print & online eds.); GBP 590 combined subscription elsewhere to institutions print & online eds. (effective 2006). adv. charts; illus. reprint service avail. from ISI. **Document type:** *Journal, Academic/Scholarly.*
Related titles: Microform ed.: (from PMC, SWZ); Online - full text ed.: ISSN 1399-3054. USD 941 in the Americas to institutions & Caribbean; GBP 561 elsewhere to institutions (effective 2006) (from Blackwell Synergy, EBSCO Publishing, Gale Group, IngentaConnect, O C L C Online Computer Library Center, Inc., Swets Information Services).
Indexed: ABIPC, AEA, ASCA, ASFA, AgBio, AgrForAb, B&AI, B&BAb, BBCI, BIOBASE, BIOSIS Prev, BiolAb, CIN, CPA, CTFA, Cadscan, ChemAb, ChemTitl, CurCont, DSA, ESPM, EngInd, ExcerpMed, FCA, FPA, FS&TA, FaBeAb, ForAb, GenetAb, HGA, HerbAb, HortAb, I&DA, IABS, INIS AtomInd, ISR, LeadAb, MEDLINE, MaizeAb, NutrAb, OrnHort, PBA, PGegResA, PGrRegA, PHN&I, PlantSci, PollutAb, PotatoAb, RA&MP, RPP, RevApplEntom, RiceAb, S&F, SCI, SIA, SeedAb, SoyAb, TriticAb, VITIS, WeedAb, Zincscan.
—BLDSC (6484.000000), CASDDS, CISTI, IDS, IE, Infotrieve, ingenta, Linda Hall. **CCC.**
Published by: (Scandinavian Society for Plant Physiology), Blackwell Munksgaard (Subsidiary of: Blackwell Publishing Ltd.), Rosenoerns Alle 1, PO Box 227, Copenhagen V, 1502, Denmark. TEL 45-77-333333, FAX 45-77-333377, info@mks.blackwellpublishing.com, http://www.blackwellpublishing.com/journals/PPL, http://www.munksgaard.dk/. Ed. Per Gardestroem. Circ: 2,000.
Co-sponsor: European Societies of Plant Physiology.

571.92 GBR ISSN 0885-5765
SB599 CODEN: PMPPEZ
➤ **PHYSIOLOGICAL AND MOLECULAR PLANT PATHOLOGY.** Text in English. 1971. 12/yr. EUR 979 in Europe to institutions; JPY 105,700 in Japan to institutions; USD 868 to institutions except Europe and Japan (effective 2006). adv. bk.rev. charts; illus. index. reprints avail. **Document type:** *Academic/Scholarly.* **Description:** Deals with all aspects of the physiology and biochemistry of the plant host-parasite relationship at all levels of complexity, from the molecular to the whole organism.
Formerly: Physiological Plant Pathology (0048-4059)
Related titles: Online - full text ed.: ISSN 1096-1178. USD 965 (effective 2002) (from EBSCO Publishing, Gale Group, IngentaConnect, O C L C Online Computer Library Center, Inc., ScienceDirect, Swets Information Services).
Indexed: ASCA, ASFA, AgBio, Agr, AgrForAb, B&BAb, BBCI, BIOBASE, BIOSIS Prev, BibAg, BioCN&I, BiolAb, CPA, CTFA, ChemAb, ChemTitl, CurCont, DBA, ESPM, FCA, FPA, FS&TA, ForAb, GenetAb, HGA, HerbAb, HortAb, IABS, ISR, Inpharma, MBA, MEDLINE, MaizeAb, NPU, NemAb, OrnHort, PBA, PGegResA, PGrRegA, PHN&I, PlantSci, PotatoAb, RA&MP, RPP, Reac, RefZh, RevApplEntom, RiceAb, S&F, SCI, SIA, SPPI, SeedAb, SoyAb, TriticAb, VITIS, WeedAb.
—BLDSC (6484.533000), CASDDS, CISTI, IDS, IE, Infotrieve, ingenta, Linda Hall. **CCC.**
Published by: Academic Press (Subsidiary of: Elsevier Science & Technology), Harcourt Pl, 32 Jamestown Rd, London, NW1 7BY, United Kingdom. TEL 44-20-7424-4200, FAX 44-20-7483-2293, apsubs@acad.com, http://www.elsevier.com/locate/pmpp. Ed. R. Hammerschmidt. R&P Catherine John. Adv. contact Nik Screen.

571.2 IND ISSN 0971-5894
PHYSIOLOGY AND MOLECULAR BIOLOGY OF PLANTS; an international journal of plant research. Text in English. biennial. INR 200 domestic to individuals; USD 40 foreign to individuals; INR 500 domestic to libraries; USD 60 foreign to libraries; INR 250 newsstand/cover.
Indexed: AEBA, ASFA, AgBio, AgrForAb, BIOBASE, BIOSIS Prev, BiolAb, CPA, ESPM, FCA, FPA, ForAb, GenetAb, HerbAb, HortAb, I&DA, MaizeAb, OrnHort, PBA, PGegResA, PGrRegA, PotatoAb, RA&MP, RDA, RPP, RiceAb, S&F, SIA, SeedAb, SoyAb, TriticAb, VITIS, WeedAb.
—BLDSC (6488.240000), IE, ingenta.
Published by: The Society of Green World, Bareilly, Department of Plant Science, Rohilkhand University, Bareilly, Uttar Pradesh 243 006, India. Ed. H S Srivastava.

PHYSIS. see *BIOLOGY—Zoology*

580 GBR ISSN 0958-0344
QK865 CODEN: PHANEL
➤ **PHYTOCHEMICAL ANALYSIS.** Text in English. 1990. bi-m. USD 1,525 to institutions; USD 1,678 combined subscription to institutions print & online eds. (effective 2006). adv. back issues avail.; reprints avail. **Document type:** *Journal, Academic/Scholarly.* **Description:** Publishes original articles on the application of analytical methodology in the plant sciences.
Related titles: Microform ed.: (from PQC); Online - full text ed.: ISSN 1099-1565. USD 1,525 to institutions (effective 2006) (from EBSCO Publishing, Swets Information Services, Wiley InterScience).
Indexed: ASCA, ASFA, AgBio, Agr, AgrForAb, AnalAb, BBCI, BIOBASE, BIOSIS Prev, BioCN&I, BiolAb, CCI, CPA, ChemAb, ChemTitl, ChromAb, CurCont, DSA, ESPM, ExcerpMed, FCA, FPA, ForAb, HelmAb, HerbAb, HortAb, IABS, ISR, IndVet, MSB, MaizeAb, NemAb, NutrAb, OrnHort, PBA, PGegResA, PGrRegA, PHN&I, PotatoAb, ProtozoAb, RA&MP, RDA, RM&VM, RPP, RevApplEntom, RiceAb, S&F, SCI, SIA, SWRA, SeedAb, SoyAb, TDB, TriticAb, VITIS, WeedAb.
—BLDSC (6489.695000), CASDDS, CISTI, GNLM, IDS, IE, Infotrieve, ingenta, Linda Hall. **CCC.**
Published by: John Wiley & Sons Ltd. (Subsidiary of: John Wiley & Sons, Inc.), The Atrium, Southern Gate, Chichester, West Sussex PO19 8SQ, United Kingdom. TEL 44-1243-779777, FAX 44-1243-775878, customer@wiley.co.uk, http://www3.interscience.wiley.com/cgi-bin/jhome/5152, http://www.wiley.co.uk. Ed. Barry Charlwood. adv.: B&W page GBP 650, color page GBP 1,550; trim 210 x 297. Circ: 350. **Subscr. to:** John Wiley & Sons, Inc., 111 River St, Hoboken, NJ 07030-5774. TEL 201-748-6645, 800-225-5945, subinfo@wiley.com.

580 USA
PHYTOCHEMICAL SOCIETY. PROCEEDINGS. Text in English. 1965. irreg., latest vol.22, 1984. reprint service avail. from ISI. **Document type:** *Proceedings.*
Formerly: Phytochemical Society Symposia Series. Proceedings
Indexed: BiolAb.
Published by: (Phytochemical Society), Academic Press (Subsidiary of: Elsevier Science & Technology), 525 B St, Ste 1900, San Diego, CA 92101-4495. apsubs@acad.com, http://www.academicpress.com.

580 GBR ISSN 0031-9422
QK861 CODEN: PYTCAS
➤ **PHYTOCHEMISTRY.** Text in English, French, German. 1962. 24/yr. EUR 4,131 in Europe to institutions; JPY 548,200 in Japan to institutions; USD 4,622 to institutions except Europe and Japan; EUR 630 in Europe to qualified personnel; JPY 83,700 in Japan to qualified personnel; USD 706 to qualified personnel except Europe and Japan (effective 2006). adv. bk.rev. charts; illus. index. reprints avail. **Document type:** *Academic/Scholarly.* **Description:** Covers research on all aspects of pure and applied plant biochemistry.
Related titles: Microfiche ed.: (from MIM); Microfilm ed.: (from PQC); Online - full text ed.: (from EBSCO Publishing, Gale Group, IngentaConnect, ScienceDirect, Swets Information Services).
Indexed: ABIPC, AEBA, AESIS, ASCA, ASFA, AbHyg, AgBio, Agr, AgrForAb, AnalAb, ApicAb, B&AI, B&BAb, BBCI, BIOBASE, BIOSIS Prev, BibAg, BioCN&I, BiolAb, CCI, CIN, CPA, CTFA, ChemAb, ChemInfo, ChemTitl, CurCR, CurCont, DBA, DSA, ESPM, EnvAb, ExcerpMed, FCA, FPA, FS&TA, FaBeAb, ForAb, HelmAb, HerbAb, HortAb, I&DA, IABS, ISR, IndChem, IndMed, IndVet, MBA, MEDLINE, MSB, MaizeAb, NPU, NemAb, NutrAb, OrnHort, PBA, PGegResA, PGrRegA, PHN&I, PlantSci, PotatoAb, ProtozoAb, RA&MP, RCI, RM&VM, RPP, RefZh, RevApplEntom, RiceAb, S&F, S&MA, SCI, SIA, SPPI, SeedAb, SoyAb, TDB, TOSA, TriticAb, VITIS, VetBull, WAE&RSA, WeedAb.
—BLDSC (6489.800000), CASDDS, CINDOC, CISTI, IDS, IE, Infotrieve, ingenta, Linda Hall. **CCC.**
Published by: (Phytochemical Society of Europe), Pergamon (Subsidiary of: Elsevier Science & Technology), The Boulevard, Langford Ln, East Park, Kidlington, Oxford OX5 1GB, United Kingdom. TEL 44-1865-843000, FAX 44-1865-843010, http://www.elsevier.com/locate/phytochem. Eds. D Strack, G. P. Bolwell, N G Lewis. Circ: 2,500. **Subscr. to:** Elsevier BV, PO Box 211, Amsterdam 1000 AE, Netherlands. TEL 31-20-485-3757, FAX 31-20-485-3432, nlinfo-f@elsevier.nl, http://www.elsevier.nl. **Co-sponsor:** Phytochemical Society of North America.

580 NLD ISSN 1568-7767
CODEN: PRHEBS
➤ **PHYTOCHEMISTRY REVIEWS.** Text in English. 2002. 3/yr. EUR 315, USD 315, GBP 207 combined subscription to institutions print & online eds. (effective 2005). adv. reprint service avail. from PSC. **Document type:** *Journal, Academic/Scholarly.* **Description:** Publishes papers in three topical issues covering results from meetings, issues dealing with the advancement of knowledge of the plants in respect of their chemistry, function, biosynthesis, effects on plants and animal physiology and pathology, and the application of such knowledge in agriculture and industry.
Related titles: Online - full text ed.: ISSN 1572-980X (from EBSCO Publishing, Gale Group, IngentaConnect, Kluwer Online, O C L C Online Computer Library Center, Inc., Springer LINK, Swets Information Services).
Indexed: AEBA, B&BAb, BibLing, ChemAb, ESPM, ExcerpMed.
—BLDSC (6489.850000), CISTI, IE, Infotrieve, ingenta. **CCC.**
Published by: Springer-Verlag Dordrecht (Subsidiary of: Springer Science+Business Media), Van Godewijckstraat 30, Dordrecht, 3311 GX, Netherlands. TEL 31-78-6576050, FAX 31-78-6576474, http://springerlink.metapress.com/openurl.asp?genre=journal&issn=1568-7767, http://www.springeronline.com. Ed. Robert Verpoorte.

580 DEU ISSN 0340-269X
QK911 CODEN: PYCEBI
➤ **PHYTOCOENOLOGIA**; journal of the International Association for Vegetation Science. Text in English, French, German, Spanish. 1974. q. EUR 130 per issue foreign (effective 2005); includes online access. index. **Document type:** *Journal, Academic/Scholarly.*
Related titles: Online - full text ed.: (from EBSCO Publishing, Gale Group, IngentaConnect, Swets Information Services).
Indexed: ASFA, AgrForAb, BIOSIS Prev, BiolAb, CPA, CurCont, FPA, ForAb, GEOBASE, HerbAb, HortAb, I&DA, ISR, NutrAb, OrnHort, PGegResA, PN&I, RA&MP, RefZh, S&F, SCI, SeedAb, VITIS, WeedAb.
—BLDSC (6489.900000), IDS, IE, Infotrieve, ingenta. **CCC.**
Published by: (International Society for Vegetation Science), Gebrueder Borntraeger Verlagsbuchhandlung, Johannesstr. 3A, Stuttgart, 70176, Germany. TEL 49-711-3514560, FAX 49-711-35145699, mail@schweizerbart.de, http://www.schweizerbart.de/j/phytocoenologia.

580 BGR ISSN 1310-7771
QK333
PHYTOLOGIA BALCANICA. Text in English. 1950. 3/yr. plus a. updates. USD 105 foreign (effective 2002). adv. back issues avail.; reprint service avail. from IRC. **Document type:** *Journal, Academic/Scholarly.* **Description:** Publishes articles in the following scientific fields: taxonomy, biosystem of higher plants, paleobotanics, etc.
Former titles (until 1995): Fitologija (English Edition) (1310-5043); (until 1993): Fitologija (Bulgarsko Izdanie) (0324-0975); (until 1975): Bulgarska Akademiia na Naukite. Botanicheskii Institut. Izvestiia (0068-3655)
Indexed: AMED, BIOSIS Prev, BSLBiol, BiolAb, RefZh.
—CISTI, Linda Hall.
Published by: (Bulgarska Akademiya na Naukite, Botanicheskii Institut/Bulgarian Academy of Sciences, Institute of Botany), Akademichno Izdatelstvo Prof. Marin Drinov/Prof. Marin Drinov Academic Publishing House, Akad G Bonchev 6, Sofia, 1113, Bulgaria. http://www.bio.bas.bg/~phytbalc/. Ed. Emanuel Palamarev. Circ: 480. **Dist. by:** Pensoft Publishers, Akad G Bonchev 6, Sofia 1113, Bulgaria. TEL 359-2-716451, FAX 359-2-704508, pensoft@mbox.infotel.bg, http://www.pensoft.net; **Dist. by:** Sofia Books, ul Silivria 16, Sofia 1404, Bulgaria. TEL 359-2-9586257, info@sofiabooks-bg.com, http://www.sofiabooks-bg.com. **Co-publisher:** Pensoft Publishers.

571.3 IND ISSN 0031-9449
QK1 CODEN: PHYMAW
PHYTOMORPHOLOGY; an international journal of plant morphology. Text in English, German, French. 1951. q. USD 120 to institutions (effective 2006). adv. bk.rev. bibl.; charts; illus.; stat. index. back issues avail. **Document type:** *Journal, Academic/Scholarly.* **Description:** Contains original research articles in taxonomy, reproductive biology (SEM, TEM, Cytochemical), experimental biology, cytology and other botanical sciences employing interdisciplinary approaches.
Indexed: ABIPC, AgBio, AgrForAb, B&AI, BIOSIS Prev, BiolAb, CPA, ChemAb, DSA, EngInd, FCA, FPA, ForAb, HerbAb, HortAb, I&DA, INIS AtomInd, MaizeAb, OrnHort, PBA, PGegResA, PGrRegA, PHN&I, PotatoAb, RA&MP, RDA, RM&VM, RPP, RevApplEntom, RiceAb, S&F, S&MA, SIA, SeedAb, SoyAb, TDB, TriticAb, WAE&RSA, WeedAb.
—CISTI, IE, Infotrieve, Linda Hall.
Published by: (International Society of Plant Morphologists), Scientific Publishers, 5-A New Pali Rd., Near Hotel Taj Hari Mahal, PO Box 91, Jodhpur, Rajasthan 342 003, India. TEL 91-291-2433323, FAX 91-291-2512580, info@scientificpub.com, http://www.scientificpub.com/bookdetails.php?booktransid=344&bookid=340. Ed. N N Bhandari. Circ: 1,200.

580 ARG ISSN 0031-9457
QK1 CODEN: PHYBAX
➤ **PHYTON**; international journal of experimental botany. Text in English, French, German, Italian, Portuguese, Spanish. 1951. 2/yr. USD 44.50 (effective 1999). adv. bk.rev. index. reprint service avail. from PQC. **Document type:** *Academic/Scholarly.* **Description:** Devoted to experimental botanical sciences (physiology and biochemistry) but occasionally includes research articles on ecology, morphology and taxonomy, phytochemistry, soils and pharmacology and botanical medicine.
Related titles: Microform ed.: (from PQC).
Indexed: ABIPC, ASCA, ASFA, AgBio, Agr, AgrForAb, BIOSIS Prev, BibAg, BioCN&I, BiolAb, CIN, CPA, ChemAb, ChemTitl, CurCont, ESPM, EngInd, FCA, FPA, ForAb, HerbAb, HortAb, I&DA, MaizeAb, NutrAb, OrnHort, PBA, PGegResA, PGrRegA, PotatoAb, RA&MP, RPP, RevApplEntom, RiceAb, S&F, SCI, SIA, SeedAb, SoyAb, TriticAb, VITIS, WeedAb.
—BLDSC (6494.100000), CASDDS, CISTI, IDS, IE, Infotrieve, Linda Hall.
Published by: Fundacion Romulo Raggio, Gaspar Campos, 861, Vicente Lopez, Buenos Aires 1638, Argentina. TEL 54-114-7961456, FAX 54-114-7910868. Ed. Miguel Raggio. R&P Linda Artaza. Circ: 500 (controlled). **Co-sponsor:** Sociedad Latinoamericana de Fisiologia Vegetal.

580 AUT ISSN 0079-2047
QK1 CODEN: PHYNAZ
➤ **PHYTON. ANNALES REI BOTANICAE.** Text in German. 1949. a. (plus 2 updates/yr.). EUR 42.90 per upd. (effective 2003). **Document type:** *Journal, Academic/Scholarly.*
Indexed: ASCA, Agr, BIOBASE, BIOSIS Prev, BiolAb, ChemAb, ChemTitl, CurCont, ForAb, HerbAb, HortAb, MaizeAb, OrnHort, PGegResA, PGrRegA, RPP, S&F, SeedAb, SoyAb, TriticAb, VITIS, WeedAb.
—BLDSC (6494.000000), CASDDS, CISTI, IDS, IE, Infotrieve, ingenta, Linda Hall.
Published by: Verlag Ferdinand Berger und Soehne GmbH, Wienerstr 80, Horn, N 3580, Austria. TEL 43-2982-4161332, FAX 43-2982-4161382, office@berger.at, http://www.berger.at. Eds. D Grill, H Teppner.

571.92 ITA ISSN 0031-9465
CODEN: PYMDAU
PHYTOPATHOLOGIA MEDITERRANEA. Text in English. 1960. q. EUR 77 to individuals print & online eds.; EUR 110 to institutions print & online eds. (effective 2003). bk.rev. charts; illus. index. **Document type:** *Journal, Academic/Scholarly.* **Description:** Deals with the main areas of plant pathology as epidemiology, control, biochemical and physiological aspects.
Related titles: Online - full text ed.: ISSN 1593-2095. 2001.
Indexed: ASFA, AgBio, AgrForAb, BIOSIS Prev, BioCN&I, BiolAb, CPA, ChemAb, ChemTitl, DBA, FCA, ForAb, HerbAb, HortAb, I&DA, MaizeAb, NemAb, OrnHort, PBA, PGegResA, PGrRegA, PHN&I, PotatoAb, RA&MP, RM&VM, RPP, RevApplEntom, RiceAb, S&F, SIA, SeedAb, SoyAb, TriticAb, VITIS, WAE&RSA, WeedAb.
—BLDSC (6494.600000), CASDDS, CISTI, IE, Infotrieve, ingenta.
Published by: (Mediterranean Phytopathological Union), Firenze University Press, Borgo Albizi 28, Florence, 50122, Italy. TEL 39-055-2347658, FAX 39-055-242944, phymed@unifi.it, e-press@unifi.it, http://www.unifi.it/istituzioni/mpu/phymed.htm, http://epress.unifi.periodici.it. Ed. G Surico. Circ: 3,000.

580.876 POL ISSN 1230-0462
➤ **PHYTOPATHOLOGIA POLONICA.** Text in English. 1974. s-a. EUR 52 foreign (effective 2005). bk.rev.; Website rev. 200 p./no.; back issues avail.; reprints avail. **Document type:** *Journal, Academic/Scholarly.* **Description:** Presents research works on diseases caused by fungi, bacteria and viruses on agricultural, horticultural and forest plants.
Formerly (until 1990): Polska Akademia Nauk. Wydzial Nauk Rolniczych i Lesnych. Zeszyty Problemowe Postepow Nauk Rolniczych. Phytopathologia Polonica (1230-0810)
Indexed: AEA, AgBio, AgrAg, AgrForAb, AgrLib, BioCN&I, CPA, FCA, FPA, ForAb, HerbAb, HortAb, MaizeAb, NemAb, OrnHort, PBA, PGegResA, PGrRegA, PHN&I, PotatoAb, RA&MP, RM&VM, RPP, S&F, SIA, SeedAb, TriticAb, WeedAb.
—BLDSC (6494.800000).
Published by: Polskie Towarzystwo Fitopatologiczne/Polish Phytopathological Society, ul Wojska Polskiego 71c, Poznan, 60625, Poland. TEL 48-61-8487711, mmanka@owl.au.poznan.pl, http://www.au.poznan.pl/ptfit. Ed., R&P Malgorzata Manka. Circ: 300. **Dist. by:** Ars Polona, Krakowskie Przedmiescie 7, Warsaw, Poland. TEL 48-22-9263914, FAX 48-22-9265334, arspolona@arspolona.com.pl, http://www.arspolona.com.pl. **Co-sponsor:** Komitet Badan Naukowych/Committee of Scientific Research.

580 GBR ISSN 0069-7141
SB599 CODEN: CMPYAH
PHYTOPATHOLOGICAL PAPERS. Text in English. 1956. irreg. price varies. **Document type:** *Monographic series, Academic/Scholarly.* **Description:** Explores plantopathological topics; includes country lists of plant diseases and crop diseases.
Indexed: BiolAb, HortAb, RPP.
—CISTI, Linda Hall.
Published by: CABI Publishing (Subsidiary of: CAB International), CAB International, Wallingford, Oxfordshire OX10 8DE, United Kingdom. TEL 44-1491-832111, FAX 44-1491-833508, cabi@cabi.org, http://www.cabi-publishing.org/. **Subscr. addr. in N America:** CABI Publishing North America, 875 Massachusetts Ave, 7th Fl, Cambridge, MA 02139. TEL 617-395-4056, 800-528-4841, FAX 617-354-6875, cabi-nao@cabi.org.

571.92 JPN
CODEN: NSBGAM
PHYTOPATHOLOGICAL SOCIETY OF JAPAN. ANNALS/NIHON SHOKUBUTSU BYORI GAKKAIHO. Text in English, Japanese. 1918. 6/yr. USD 50 to individuals; USD 115 to institutions.
Formerly: Japanese Journal of Phytopathology (0031-9473)
Indexed: ASFA, BIOSIS Prev, BioCN&I, BioDAb, BiolAb, CPA, ChemAb, ESPM, FCA, FPA, FS&TA, FaBeAb, ForAb, HerbAb, HortAb, I&DA, INIS AtomInd, MBA, MaizeAb, OrnHort, PBA, PHN&I, PotatoAb, RPP, RefZh, RevApplEntom, RiceAb, S&F, SWRA, SeedAb, SoyAb, TriticAb, VITIS, WeedAb.
—BLDSC (4658.050000), CASDDS, CISTI, IE, ingenta. **CCC.**
Published by: Phytopathological Society of Japan/Nihon Shokubutsu Byori Gakkai, Shokubo Bldg, 1-43-11 Komagome, Toshima-ku, Tokyo, 170-0003, Japan. FAX 81-3-3943-6021. Ed. H Kunoh. Circ: 2,600.

571.9 USA ISSN 0031-949X
CODEN: PHYTAJ
➤ **PHYTOPATHOLOGY**; international journal of the American Phytopathological Society. Text in English. 1911. m. USD 80 domestic to individuals; USD 97 in Canada to individuals; USD 105 elsewhere to individuals; USD 506 domestic to institutions; USD 578 foreign to institutions (effective 2005). bk.rev. abstr.; bibl.; charts; illus. index. back issues avail. **Document type:** *Journal, Academic/Scholarly.* **Description:** Contains original research in the field of plant pathology.
Related titles: Microform ed.: USD 550 domestic; USD 611 foreign (effective 2001) (from PMC, PQC); Online - full content ed.; Online - full text ed.: (from EBSCO Publishing, ProQuest Information & Learning).
Indexed: AEA, AEBA, ASCA, ASFA, AbHyg, AgBio, Agr, AgrForAb, ApicAb, B&AI, BIOSIS Prev, BibAg, BioCN&I, BiolAb, BiolDig, CBTA, CEABA, CIN, CIS, CPA, CTFA, ChemAb, ChemTitl, CurCont, DBA, ESPM, EnvAb, EnvInd, ExcerpMed, FCA, FPA, FS&TA, FaBeAb, ForAb, HerbAb, HortAb, I&DA, IABS, ISR, MBA, MEDLINE, MaizeAb, NemAb, NutrAb, OrnHort, PBA, PGegResA, PGrRegA, PHN&I, PN&I, PlantSci, PotatoAb, PoultAb, ProtozoAb, RA&MP, RM&VM, RPP, RevApplEntom, RiceAb, S&F, S&MA, SCI, SIA, SeedAb, SoyAb, TOSA, Telegen, TriticAb, VITIS, WAE&RSA, WeedAb, ZooRec.
—BLDSC (6497.000000), CASDDS, CIS, CISTI, GNLM, IDS, IE, Infotrieve, ingenta, Linda Hall. **CCC.**
Published by: American Phytopathological Society, 3340 Pilot Knob, St. Paul, MN 55121-2097. TEL 651-454-7250, 800-328-7560, FAX 651-454-0766, aps@scisoc.org, http://www.aspnet.org/phyto, http://www.apsnet.org. Ed. Christopher Mundt. Adv. contact Rhonda Wilke. Circ: 2,032 (paid).

571.9 USA ISSN 0278-0267
PHYTOPATHOLOGY NEWS. Text in English. 1967. m. USD 20 (effective 2003). bk.rev. illus. **Document type:** *Academic/Scholarly.* **Description:** Conveys news to friends and members of the society.
Related titles: Online - full text ed.: (from ProQuest Information & Learning).
Published by: (American Phytopathological Society), A P S PRESS, 3340 Pilot Knob Rd., St. Paul, MN 55121-2097. TEL 651-454-7250, 800-328-7560, FAX 651-454-0766, aps@scisoc.org, http://www.apsnet.org. Pub. Steven C Nelson. Circ: 4,634.

579.5 CAN ISSN 0031-9511
CODEN: PYTPAX
➤ **PHYTOPROTECTION.** Text and summaries in English, French. 1963. 3/yr. CND 45 domestic to individuals; CND 50 in United States to individuals; CND 60 foreign to individuals; CND 75 domestic to institutions; CND 80 in United States to institutions; CND 90 foreign to institutions (effective 2005). adv. charts; illus. index, cum.index. back issues avail. **Document type:** *Journal, Academic/Scholarly.* **Description:** Presents original scientific research papers or notes dealing with all aspects of plant protection; includes abstracts of papers presented at the annual meeting of the Society.
Indexed: ASCA, ASFA, AgBio, Agr, AgrForAb, BIOSIS Prev, BibAg, BioCN&I, BiolAb, CBCARef, CPA, ChemAb, ChemTitl, CurCont, EPB, ESPM, EntAb, EnvAb, FCA, FPA, ForAb, HerbAb, HortAb, ISR, MBA, MaizeAb, NemAb, OrnHort, PBA, PGegResA, PGrRegA, PHN&I, PlantSci, PotatoAb, RPP, RefZh, RevApplEntom, S&F, SCI, SeedAb, SoyAb, TriticAb, VITIS, WeedAb, ZooRec.
—BLDSC (6497.050000), CASDDS, CIS, CISTI, IDS, IE, ingenta, Linda Hall. **CCC.**
Published by: Societe de Protection des Plantes du Quebec/Quebec Society for the Protection of Plants, c/o Gilles Emond, Editor, 3488, chemin Sainte-Foy, Sainte-Foy, PQ G1X 1S8, Canada. TEL 418-653-2631, FAX 418-653-3029, phytoprotection@videotron.ca, http://www.phytoprotection.ca, http://www.sppq.qc.ca/qspp.htm. Ed. Emond Gilles. Adv. contact Jean Charles Cote. Circ: 400.

580 IND ISSN 0972-4206
➤ **PHYTOTAXONOMY.** Text in English. 2001. a. INR 400 domestic; USD 60 foreign (effective 2005). adv. bk.rev. **Document type:** *Journal, Academic/Scholarly.* **Description:** Covers elements of plant diversity, flowering plants, ferns, algae etc.
Published by: Deep Publications, B-1 / 118, 2nd Fl, Paschim Vihar, New Delhi, Bihar 110 063, India. TEL 91-11-25259514, FAX 91-11-51698399, deep_pub@hotmail.com. Ed. D K Upreti. adv.: page INR 1,800, page USD 100; trim 15 x 20. Circ: 300 (paid and controlled).

615.53 GBR ISSN 0951-418X
RS164 CODEN: PHYREH
➤ **PHYTOTHERAPY RESEARCH**; an international journal devoted to medical and scientific research on plants and plant products. Text in English. 1987. m. USD 2,180 to institutions; USD 2,398 combined subscription to institutions print & online eds. (effective 2006). adv. back issues avail.; reprints avail. **Document type:** *Journal, Academic/Scholarly.* **Description:** Publishes original medical plant research, including biochemistry and molecular pharmacology, toxicology, pathology, and the clinical application of herbs and natural products to both human and animal medicine.
Related titles: Microform ed.: (from PQC); Online - full text ed.: ISSN 1099-1573. USD 2,180 to institutions (effective 2006) (from EBSCO Publishing, Swets Information Services, Wiley InterScience).
Indexed: AMED, ASCA, ASFA, AbHyg, AgBio, Agr, AgrForAb, AnBrAb, BIOBASE, BibAg, BioCN&I, CCI, CIN, CPA, ChemAb, ChemTitl, CurCont, DSA, ExcerpMed, FPA, ForAb, HelmAb, HortAb, IABS, ISR, IndMed, IndVet, Inpharma, MEDLINE, NPU, NemAb, NutrAb, OrnHort, PBA, PE&ON, PGegResA, PGrRegA, PHN&I, PN&I, PotatoAb, PoultAb, ProtozoAb, RA&MP, RDA, RM&VM, RPP, Reac, RevApplEntom, RiceAb, SCI, SIA, SSCI, SeedAb, SoyAb, TDB, TriticAb, WeedAb.
—BLDSC (6497.060000), CASDDS, GNLM, IDS, IE, Infotrieve, ingenta, KNAW. **CCC.**
Published by: John Wiley & Sons Ltd. (Subsidiary of: John Wiley & Sons, Inc.), The Atrium, Southern Gate, Chichester, West Sussex PO19 8SQ, United Kingdom. TEL 44-1243-779777, FAX 44-1243-775878, customer@wiley.co.uk, http://www3.interscience.wiley.com/cgi-bin/jhome/12567, http://www.wiley.co.uk. Ed. Elizabeth M Williamson. adv.: B&W page GBP 650, color page GBP 1,550; trim 210 x 297. Circ: 450. **Subscr. in the Americas to:** John Wiley & Sons, Inc., 111 River St, Hoboken, NJ 07030-5774. TEL 201-748-6645, 800-225-5945, subinfo@wiley.com.

➤ **PLANT ANALYSIS PROCEDURES.** see *AGRICULTURE—Crop Production And Soil*

➤ **PLANT AND CELL PHYSIOLOGY.** see *BIOLOGY—Cytology And Histology*

571.92 NLD ISSN 0032-079X
SB13 CODEN: PLSOA2
➤ **PLANT AND SOIL**; international journal on plant-soil relationships. Text in English, French, German. 1949. 22/yr. EUR 4,248, USD 4,285, GBP 2,778 combined subscription to institutions print & online eds. (effective 2005). adv. bibl.; charts; illus. index. reprint service avail. from PSC. **Document type:** *Journal, Academic/Scholarly.* **Description:** Publishes original research articles dealing with fundamental and applied aspects of plant nutrition, soil fertility, plant-microbe associations, soil microbiology, soil-borne diseases, soil and plant ecology, agrochemistry and agrophysics.
Related titles: Microform ed.: (from PMC, PQC); Online - full text ed.: ISSN 1573-5036 (from EBSCO Publishing, Gale Group, IngentaConnect, Kluwer Online, O C L C Online Computer Library Center, Inc., Ovid Technologies, Inc., Springer LINK, Swets Information Services).
Indexed: AEA, AEBA, AESIS, ASCA, ASFA, AgBio, Agr, AgrForAb, AnBrAb, B&AI, BIOBASE, BIOSIS Prev, BibLing, BioCN&I, BiolAb, CPA, CTFA, Cadscan, ChemAb, ChemTitl, CurCont, DBA, DSA, EIA, EPB, ESPM, EnerInd, EnvAb, EnvInd, ExcerpMed, FCA, FPA, FS&TA, FaBeAb, ForAb, GEOBASE, GenetAb, HGA, HelmAb, HerbAb, HortAb, I&DA, IABS, ISR, LeadAb, MBA, MaizeAb, NemAb, NutrAb, OrnHort, PBA, PGegResA, PGrRegA, PN&I, PlantSci, PollutAb, PotatoAb, PoultAb, RA&MP, RPP, RRTA, RefZh, RevApplEntom, RiceAb, S&F, S&MA, SCI, SIA, SWRA, SeedAb, SoyAb, TDB, TOSA, TriticAb, VITIS, WAE&RSA, WeedAb, Zincscan.
—BLDSC (6513.000000), CASDDS, CISTI, IDS, IE, Infotrieve, ingenta, Linda Hall. **CCC.**
Published by: (Koninklijk Genootschap voor Landbouwwetenschap), Springer-Verlag Dordrecht (Subsidiary of: Springer Science+Business Media), Van Godewijckstraat 30, Dordrecht, 3311 GX, Netherlands. TEL 31-78-6576050, FAX 31-78-6576474, http://springerlink.metapress.com/openurl.asp?genre=journal&issn=0032-079X, http://www.springeronline.com. Ed. Hans Lambers.

580 DEU ISSN 1435-8603
QK1 CODEN: PBIOFN

➤ **PLANT BIOLOGY.** Text in English. 1999. bi-m. EUR 495.90 domestic to institutions; EUR 508.80 in Europe to institutions; EUR 532.80 elsewhere to institutions; EUR 98 newsstand/cover (effective 2006). adv. bibl.; charts; illus. index. back issues avail.; reprints avail. **Document type:** *Journal, Academic/Scholarly.* **Description:** Publishes original problem oriented research papers, rapid communications, and review articles in all major areas of plant science.

Formed by the merger of (1882-1999): Botanica Acta (0932-8629); Which was formerly (until 1987): Deutsche Botanische Gesellschaft. Berichte (0365-9631); (1952-1999): Acta Botanica Neerlandica (0044-5983); Which incorporated (1846-1952): Nederlandsch Kruidkundig Archief; (1904-1952): Recueil des Travaux Botaniques Neerlandais

Related titles: Microfiche ed.: (from IDC); Online - full text ed.: ISSN 1438-8677 (from EBSCO Publishing, O C L C Online Computer Library Center, Inc., Swets Information Services).

Indexed: AEA, ASCA, ASFA, AgBio, ApicAb, BIOBASE, BIOSIS Prev, BioCN&I, BiolAb, CIN, CPA, ChemAb, ChemTitl, CurCont, ESPM, ExcerpMed, FCA, FPA, ForAb, GEOBASE, HerbAb, HortAb, I&DA, IABS, ISR, IndIslam, MaizeAb, OrnHort, PBA, PGegResA, PGrRegA, PHN&I, PlantSci, PotatoAb, ProtozoAb, RA&MP, RPP, RefZh, RevApplEntom, RiceAb, S&F, SCI, SIA, SeedAb, SoyAb, TriticAb, WeedAb, ZooRec.

—BLDSC (6513.730000), CASDDS, CISTI, IDS, IE, Infotrieve, ingenta, Linda Hall. **CCC.**

Published by: (Deutsche Botanische Gesellschaft), Georg Thieme Verlag, Ruedigerstr 14, Stuttgart, 70469, Germany. TEL 49-711-8931421, FAX 49-711-8931410, plantbiol@thieme.de, leser.service@thieme.de, http://www.thieme.de/plantbiology. Eds. H Rennenberg, Dr. J T M Elzenga. R&P Peter Eich. Adv. contact Andreas Schweiger TEL 49-711-8931245. B&W page EUR 1,120, color page EUR 2,200; 175 x 250. Circ: 2,500 (paid and controlled). **Subscr. to:** Thieme Medical Publishers, 333 Seventh Ave, New York, NY 10001. custserv@thieme.com, http://www.thieme.com/journals.

580 GBR ISSN 1126-3504
QK1 CODEN: GBOIAX

➤ **PLANT BIOSYSTEMS**; giornale botanico italiano. Text in English. 1844. 3/yr. GBP 222, USD 353 combined subscription to institutions print & online eds. (effective 2006). charts; illus. 150 p./no.; back issues avail.; reprint service avail. from PSC. **Document type:** *Journal, Academic/Scholarly.*

Formerly (until 1997): Giornale Botanico Italiano (0017-0070)

Related titles: Online - full text ed.: ISSN 1724-5575. GBP 211, USD 335 to institutions (effective 2006) (from EBSCO Publishing, Gale Group, IngentaConnect, O C L C Online Computer Library Center, Inc., Swets Information Services).

Indexed: ASFA, AgBio, AgrForAb, BIOBASE, BIOSIS Prev, BiolAb, CPA, ChemAb, CurCont, ESPM, FCA, FPA, ForAb, GardL, HerbAb, HortAb, I&DA, MaizeAb, OrnHort, PBA, PGegResA, PGrRegA, PotatoAb, RA&MP, RDA, RM&VM, RPP, RRTA, RefZh, RiceAb, S&F, SIA, SeedAb, TOSA, TriticAb, WAE&RSA, WeedAb.

—CASDDS, CISTI, Linda Hall.

Published by: (Societa Botanica Italiana ITA), Taylor & Francis Ltd (Subsidiary of: Taylor & Francis Group), 4 Park Sq, Milton Park, Abingdon, OX14 4RN, United Kingdom. TEL 44-1235-828600, FAX 44-1235-829000, info@tandf.co.uk, http://www.tandf.co.uk/journals/titles/11263504.asp. Ed. Giovanni Cristofolini. Circ: 650.

➤ **PLANT BIOTECHNOLOGY.** see *BIOLOGY—Abstracting, Bibliographies, Statistics*

580 660.6 JPN ISSN 1342-4580
CODEN: SSBAET

PLANT BIOTECHNOLOGY. Text in English, Japanese. 1984. q. (3/yr until 1996). JPY 7,500 to individuals; JPY 11,500 to institutions (effective 2003). **Document type:** *Journal, Academic/Scholarly.*

Formerly (until 1996): Shokubutsu Soshiki Baiyo/Plant Tissue Culture Letters (0289-5773)

Related titles: Online - full content ed.: ISSN 1347-6114; Online - full text ed.: (from J-Stage).

Indexed: AEBA, B&BAb, BioEngAb, ChemAb, ESPM, FS&TA, JPI.

—BLDSC (6513.770000), IE, ingenta. **CCC.**

Published by: Japanese Society for Plant Cell and Molecular Biology, c/o Yokendo, Member service, JSPCMB, 5-30-15 Hongo Bunkyo-ku, Tokyo, 113, Japan. FAX 81-3-3812-2615, http://plantbiotechnology.jstage.jst.go.jp/, http://www.kazusa.or.jp/ja/plant/jspcmb/. **Dist. by:** Business Center for Academic Societies Japan, Koshin Bldg, 6-16-3 Hongo, Bunkyo-ku, Tokyo 113-0033, Japan; **Dist. in U.S. by:** International Specialized Book Services Inc., 5804 N E Hassalo St, Portland, OR 97213-3644.

580 660.6 GBR ISSN 1467-7644
SB106.B56 CODEN: PBJLAE

PLANT BIOTECHNOLOGY. Text in English. 2000; N.S.. bi-m., latest vol.1, no.2, 2002. GBP 86, EUR 129 combined subscription in Europe to individuals print & online eds.; USD 160 combined subscription in the Americas to individuals & Caribbean, print & online eds.; GBP 95 combined subscription elsewhere to individuals print & online eds.; GBP 472 combined subscription in Europe to institutions print & online eds.; USD 872 combined subscription in the Americas to institutions & Caribbean, print & online eds.; GBP 519 combined subscription elsewhere to institutions print & online eds. (effective 2006). **Document type:** *Journal.*

Related titles: Online - full text ed.: ISSN 1467-7652. GBP 448 in Europe to institutions; USD 828 in the Americas to institutions & Caribbean; GBP 493 elsewhere to institutions (effective 2006) (from Blackwell Synergy, EBSCO Publishing, Gale Group, IngentaConnect, O C L C Online Computer Library Center, Inc., Swets Information Services).

Indexed: AEBA, B&BAb, BCI, BioEngAb, CurCont, ESPM, FCA, TTI.

—BLDSC (6513.780000), CISTI, IE. **CCC.**

Published by: Blackwell Publishing Ltd., 9600 Garsington Rd, Oxford, OX4 2ZG, United Kingdom. TEL 44-1865-776868, FAX 44-1865-714591, customerservices@oxon.blackwellpublishing.com, http://www.blackwellpublishing.com/journals/PBI. Ed. Keith J Edwards TEL 44-117-3317079. Pub. Amanda McLean Inglis. R&P Sophie Savage. Adv. contact Jenny Applin.

571.2 DEU ISSN 0179-9541
SB123 CODEN: PLABED

➤ **PLANT BREEDING/ZEITSCHRIFT FUER PFLANZENZUECHTUNG.** Text in English, German. 1913. 6/yr. EUR 138 combined subscription in Europe to individuals print & online eds.; USD 150 combined subscription in the Americas to individuals & Caribbean, print & online eds.; GBP 92 combined subscription elsewhere to individuals print & online eds.; GBP 883 combined subscription in Europe to institutions print & online eds.; USD 1,484 combined subscription in the Americas to institutions & Caribbean, print & online eds.; GBP 971 combined subscription elsewhere to institutions print & online eds. (effective 2006). bk.rev. abstr.; bibl.; illus.; stat. index. back issues avail.; reprint service avail. from PSC. **Document type:** *Journal, Academic/Scholarly.* **Description:** Covers all areas of plant breeding, including plant genetics, plant physiology, plant pathology, and plant growth and development.

Former titles (until 1986): Zeitschrift fuer Pflanzenzuechtung (0044-3298); (until 1939): Zeitschrift fuer Zuechtung. Reihe A: Pflanzenzuechtung (0369-9315); (until 1930): Zeitschrift fuer Pflanzenzuechtung (0179-9525)

Related titles: ◆ Online - full text ed.: Plant Breeding Online. ISSN 1439-0523; ◆ Supplement(s): Advances in Plant Breeding. ISSN 0301-2727.

Indexed: AEBA, AgBio, Agr, AgrForAb, B&BAb, BCI, BIOBASE, BIOSIS Prev, BibAg, BioEngAb, BiolAb, CPA, ChemAb, ChemTitl, CurCont, DBA, DSA, ESPM, FCA, FS&TA, FaBeAb, ForAb, HerbAb, HortAb, I&DA, IABS, ISR, Inspec, MaizeAb, NemAb, NutrAb, OrnHort, PBA, PGegResA, PGrRegA, PHN&I, PlantSci, PotatoAb, RA&MP, RM&VM, RPP, RefZh, RevApplEntom, RiceAb, S&F, S&MA, SCI, SIA, SeedAb, SoyAb, TriticAb, VITIS, WeedAb.

—BLDSC (6513.980000), CASDDS, CISTI, IDS, IE, Infotrieve, ingenta. **CCC.**

Published by: Blackwell Verlag GmbH (Subsidiary of: Blackwell Publishing Ltd.), Kurfuerstendamm 57, Berlin, 10707, Germany. TEL 49-30-32790634, FAX 49-30-32790610, verlag@blackwell.de, http://www.blackwellpublishing.com/journals/PBR, http://www.blackwell.de. Eds. C Jung, W E Weber. Circ: 600.

571.2 DEU ISSN 1439-0523

PLANT BREEDING ONLINE. Text in English. 6/yr. GBP 839 in Europe to institutions; USD 1,410 in the Americas to institutions & Caribbean; GBP 922 elsewhere to institutions (effective 2006). **Document type:** *Academic/Scholarly.*

Media: Online - full text (from Blackwell Synergy, EBSCO Publishing, Gale Group, IngentaConnect, O C L C Online Computer Library Center, Inc., Swets Information Services). **Related titles:** ◆ Print ed.: Plant Breeding. ISSN 0179-9541.

Published by: Blackwell Verlag GmbH (Subsidiary of: Blackwell Publishing Ltd.), Kurfuerstendamm 57, Berlin, 10707, Germany. TEL 49-30-32790634, FAX 49-30-32790610, abo@blackwis.de, http://www.blackwell-science.com/~cgilib/jnlpage.bin?Journal=XPLBR&File=XPLBR&Page=aims, http://www.blackwell.de.

PLANT BREEDING SERIES. see *AGRICULTURE—Crop Production And Soil*

571.2 572.8 USA ISSN 1040-4651
QK725 CODEN: PLCEEW

➤ **THE PLANT CELL.** Text in English. 1989. m. USD 300 combined subscription to non-members print & online eds.; USD 150 combined subscription to individual members print & online eds.; USD 2,160 combined subscription to institutional members print & online eds.; USD 145 combined subscription to students print & online eds. (effective 2005). adv. illus. Index. 250 p./no.; back issues avail.; reprints avail. **Document type:** *Journal, Academic/Scholarly.* **Description:** Presents original research articles in the areas of plant cell development and molecular biology.

Related titles: Microfiche ed.; Microfilm ed.; Online - full text ed.: ISSN 1532-298X. 1989. free to members; USD 1,500 to institutions Plant Physiology & The Plant Cell incl. (effective 2003) (from bigchalk, EBSCO Publishing, HighWire Press, National Library of Medicine, ProQuest Information & Learning).

Indexed: ABIPC, AEBA, ASCA, AgBio, Agr, AgrForAb, AnBrAb, B&AI, B&BAb, BBCI, BCI, BIOBASE, BIOSIS Prev, BioCN&I, BioEngAb, BiolAb, CPA, ChemAb, ChemTitl, CurCont, DBA, ESPM, EngInd, FCA, FPA, FS&TA, ForAb, GenetAb, HGA, HerbAb, HortAb, IABS, ISR, IndMed, MEDLINE, MaizeAb, NemAb, NucAcAb, OrnHort, PBA, PGegResA, PGrRegA, PHN&I, PlantSci, PotatoAb, RA&MP, RPP, RefZh, RevApplEntom, RiceAb, S&F, SCI, SIA, SeedAb, SoyAb, TriticAb, VITIS, WeedAb.

—BLDSC (6514.180000), CASDDS, CISTI, IDS, IE, Infotrieve, ingenta, Linda Hall. **CCC.**

Published by: American Society of Plant Biologists, 15501 Monona Dr, Rockville, MD 20855-2768. TEL 301-251-0560, FAX 301-279-2996, jlong@aspb.org, beths@aspp.org, http://www.plantcell.org, http://www.aspb.org. Ed. Richard Jorgensen. R&P Nancy Winchester. Adv. contact Nicole Roach. Circ: 3,100 (paid).

571.2 DEU ISSN 0721-7714
QK725 CODEN: PCRPD8

➤ **PLANT CELL REPORTS.** Text in English. 1981. m. EUR 1,418 combined subscription to institutions print & online eds. (effective 2005). adv. back issues avail.; reprint service avail. from ISI. **Document type:** *Journal, Academic/Scholarly.* **Description:** Devoted to all aspects of plant cell and plant cell culture research including physiology, cytology, biochemistry, molecular biology, plant genetics, and phytopathology.

Related titles: Microform ed.: (from PQC); Online - full text ed.: ISSN 1432-203X (from EBSCO Publishing, Springer LINK, Swets Information Services).

Indexed: ABIPC, AEBA, ASCA, AgBio, Agr, AgrForAb, BIOBASE, BIOSIS Prev, BibAg, BioEngAb, BiolAb, CPA, CTFA, ChemAb, ChemTitl, CurCont, DBA, DSA, ESPM, EngInd, FCA, FPA, FS&TA, FaBeAb, ForAb, GenetAb, HGA, HerbAb, HortAb, IABS, ISR, Inpharma, MaizeAb, NemAb, NutrAb, OrnHort, PBA, PGegResA, PGrRegA, PHN&I, PN&I, PlantSci, PotatoAb, RA&MP, RPP, RRTA, Reac, RefZh, RevApplEntom, RiceAb, SCI, SIA, SeedAb, SoyAb, TriticAb, VITIS, WeedAb.

—BLDSC (6514.250000), CASDDS, CISTI, IDS, IE, Infotrieve, ingenta, Linda Hall. **CCC.**

Published by: Springer-Verlag (Subsidiary of: Springer Science+Business Media), Tiergartenstr 17, Heidelberg, 69121, Germany. TEL 49-6221-3450, FAX 49-6221-345229, subscriptions@springer.de, http://link.springer.de/link/service/journals/00299/index.htm, http://www.springer.de. Adv. contact Stephan Kroeck TEL 49-30-827875739. **Subscr. in N. America to:** Springer-Verlag New York, Inc., Journal Fulfillment, PO Box 2485, Secaucus, NJ 07096-2485. TEL 201-348-4033, FAX 201-348-4505, journals@springer-ny.com; **Subscr. to:** Springer GmbH Auslieferungsgesellschaft. subscriptions@springer.de.

580 IND ISSN 0970-4914

➤ **PLANT DISEASE RESEARCH.** Text in English. 1984. s-a. INR 1,000 (effective 2001). bk.rev. 125 p./no. 2 cols./p.; back issues avail.; reprints avail. **Document type:** *Journal, Academic/Scholarly.*

Indexed: AEA, AgBio, AgrForAb, BioCN&I, CPA, DSA, FCA, FPA, ForAb, HerbAb, HortAb, I&DA, MaizeAb, NemAb, OrnHort, PBA, PGegResA, PHN&I, PotatoAb, PoultAb, RA&MP, RDA, RM&VM, RPP, RiceAb, S&F, SIA, SeedAb, SoyAb, TriticAb, WAE&RSA, WeedAb, ZooRec.

—BLDSC (6515.020000), IE, ingenta.

Published by: Indian Society of Plant Pathologists, Agricultural University, Ludhiana, Punjab 141 004, India. TEL 91-161-401960, FAX 91-161-400945, secretary_insopp@yahoo.com. Ed. R K Goel.

581.7 NLD ISSN 1385-0237
QK901 CODEN: PLECF3

➤ **PLANT ECOLOGY.** Text in English. 1949. m. EUR 3,148, USD 3,265, GBP 2,075 combined subscription to institutions print & online eds. (effective 2005). adv. bk.rev. reprint service avail. from PSC. **Document type:** *Journal, Academic/Scholarly.* **Description:** Publishes original scientific papers dealing with the ecology of vascular plants and bryophytes in terrestrial, aquatic and wetland ecosystems.

Formerly: Vegetatio (0042-3106)

Related titles: Microform ed.: (from PQC); Online - full text ed.: ISSN 1573-5052 (from EBSCO Publishing, Gale Group, IngentaConnect, Kluwer Online, O C L C Online Computer Library Center, Inc., Ovid Technologies, Inc., Springer LINK, Swets Information Services).

Indexed: ASCA, ASFA, AgBio, Agr, AgrForAb, ApEcolAb, BIOBASE, BIOSIS Prev, BibAg, BibLing, BiolAb, BrArAb, CPA, CivEngAb, CurCont, EIA, ESPM, EnerInd, FCA, FPA, ForAb, GEOBASE, GenetAb, HGA, HerbAb, HortAb, I&DA, IABS, IBR, ISR, MaizeAb, NutrAb, OrnHort, PBA, PGegResA, PGrRegA, PHN&I, PlantSci, PoultAb, RA&MP, RPP, RefZh, RevApplEntom, S&F, SCI, SWRA, SeedAb, SoyAb, TriticAb, WeedAb.

—BLDSC (6515.400000), CISTI, IDS, IE, Infotrieve, ingenta, Linda Hall. **CCC.**

Published by: Springer-Verlag Dordrecht (Subsidiary of: Springer Science+Business Media), Van Godewijckstraat 30, Dordrecht, 3311 GX, Netherlands. TEL 31-78-6576050, FAX 31-78-6576474, http://springerlink.metapress.com/openurl.asp?genre=journal&issn=1385-0237, http://www.springeronline.com. Ed. Arnold G van der Valk.

580 ZAF
PLANT FOR LIFE; the biomass initiative newsletter. Text in English. 1993. irreg. illus. **Document type:** *Newsletter.*
Published by: Progreen, PO Box 2035, Gallo Manor, Johannesburg 2052, South Africa.

PLANT GENE RESEARCH; basic knowledge and application. see *BIOLOGY—Genetics*

PLANT GENETIC RESOURCES ABSTRACTS. see *BIOLOGY—Abstracting, Bibliographies, Statistics*

581.35 ITA ISSN 0048-4334
SD123.3
➤ **PLANT GENETIC RESOURCES NEWSLETTER.** Text in English, French, Spanish. 1957. q. free. bk.rev.; Website rev. abstr.; bibl.; charts; illus.; maps. **Document type:** *Journal, Academic/Scholarly.* **Description:** Publishes research articles, short articles, and reports on all aspects of plant genetic resources work, including news and conference reports.
Formerly: Plant Introduction Newsletter
Related titles: Online - full text ed.
Indexed: AgBio, AgrForAb, BiolDig, CPA, CTFA, EnvAb, FCA, FS&TA, ForAb, HerbAb, HortAb, MaizeAb, NutrAb, PBA, PGegResA, PGrRegA, RA&MP, RPP, RevApplEntom, RiceAb, S&MA, SeedAb, SoyAb, TOSA, Telegen, TriticAb, VITIS.
—BLDSC (6517.800000), ingenta.
Published by: International Plant Genetic Resources Institute, Via dei Tre Denari 472/a, Maccarese (Fiumicino), Rome, 00057, Italy. TEL 39-06-6118233, FAX 39-06-61979661, p.neate@cgiar.org, http://www.ipgri.cgiar.org. Ed. Paul Neate. Circ: 5,000 (controlled).

580 NLD ISSN 0167-6903
SB128 CODEN: PGRED3
➤ **PLANT GROWTH REGULATION**; an international journal on plant growth and development. Text in English. 1981. 9/yr. EUR 888, USD 908, GBP 588 combined subscription to institutions print & online eds. (effective 2005). adv. back issues avail.; reprint service avail. from PSC. **Document type:** *Journal, Academic/Scholarly.* **Description:** Publishes original papers linking fundamental and applied research on the natural hormonal regulation of plant processes and the effects of growth regulating substances on plant growth and development.
Related titles: Microform ed.: (from PQC); Online - full text ed.: ISSN 1573-5087 (from EBSCO Publishing, Gale Group, IngentaConnect, Kluwer Online, O C L C Online Computer Library Center, Inc., Ovid Technologies, Inc., Springer LINK, Swets Information Services).
Indexed: ABIPC, AEA, ASCA, AgBio, Agr, AgrForAb, BIOBASE, BIOSIS Prev, BibAg, BibLing, BiolAb, CPA, ChemAb, ChemTitl, CurCont, DBA, DSA, EngInd, FCA, FS&TA, ForAb, HerbAb, HortAb, I&DA, IABS, ISR, MSB, MaizeAb, NemAb, OrnHort, PBA, PGegResA, PGrRegA, PHN&I, PlantSci, PotatoAb, RA&MP, RPP, RefZh, RiceAb, S&F, SCI, SIA, SeedAb, SoyAb, TriticAb, VITIS, WeedAb.
—BLDSC (6517.845000), CASDDS, CISTI, IDS, IE, Infotrieve, ingenta, Linda Hall. **CCC.**
Published by: Springer-Verlag Dordrecht (Subsidiary of: Springer Science+Business Media), Van Godewijckstraat 30, Dordrecht, 3311 GX, Netherlands. TEL 31-78-6576050, FAX 31-78-6576474, http://springerlink.metapress.com/openurl.asp?genre=journal&issn=0167-6903, http://www.springeronline.com. Ed. Chris J Atkinson.

580 595.7 USA ISSN 1535-1025
SB950.A1
➤ **PLANT HEALTH PROGRESS.** Text in English. irreg. USD 750 to institutions (effective 2004); Subscr. includes Crop Management & Forage and Grazinglands. adv. **Document type:** *Journal, Academic/Scholarly.* **Description:** Covers all aspects of applied plant pathology. entomology, nematology and related areas.
Media: Online - full content.
Indexed: AbHyg, AgBio, BioCN&I, CPA, FCA, ForAb, HerbAb, HortAb, MaizeAb, NemAb, NutrAb, OrnHort, PBA, PGegResA, PGrRegA, PotatoAb, PoultAb, RA&MP, RPP, S&F, SeedAb, SoyAb, TriticAb, WAE&RSA, WeedAb.
Published by: Plant Management Network, 3340 Pilot Knob Rd, St Paul, MN 55121-2097. TEL 651-454-7250, 800-328-7590, FAX 651-454-0766, editorialoffice@plantmanagementnetwork.org, http://www.plantmanagementnetwork.org/php/. Ed. Timothy Murray TEL 509-335-7515. Pub., R&P, Adv. contact Miles Wimer.

580 GBR ISSN 0960-7412
QK728 CODEN: PLJUED
➤ **THE PLANT JOURNAL.** Text in English. 1991. fortn. GBP 217, EUR 324 combined subscription in Europe to individuals print & online eds.; USD 402 combined subscription in the Americas to individuals & Caribbean, print & online eds.; GBP 239 combined subscription elsewhere to individuals print & online eds.; GBP 1,888 combined subscription in Europe to institutions print & online eds.; USD 3,489 combined subscription in the Americas to institutions & Caribbean, print & online eds.; GBP 2,077 combined subscription elsewhere to institutions print & online eds. (effective 2006). adv. bk.rev. illus. index. **Document type:** *Journal, Academic/Scholarly.* **Description:** Presents papers on advances in the enabling technologies of molecular biology, cell biology, biochemistry, and genetics, as related to plant cell organization, gene regulation, and protein function in plants.
Related titles: Microform ed.: (from PQC); Online - full text ed.: The Plant Journal Online. ISSN 1365-313X. 1998. GBP 207, EUR 311 in Europe to individuals; USD 383 in the Americas to individuals & Caribbean; GBP 228 elsewhere to individuals; GBP 1,794 in Europe to institutions; USD 3,315 in the Americas to institutions & Caribbean; GBP 1,973 elsewhere to institutions (effective 2006) (from Blackwell Synergy, EBSCO Publishing, Gale Group, IngentaConnect, O C L C Online Computer Library Center, Inc., Ovid Technologies, Inc., Swets Information Services).
Indexed: AEA, AEBA, AIDS&CR, ASCA, ASFA, AgBio, Agr, AgrForAb, B&BAb, BBCI, BCI, BIOBASE, BIOSIS Prev, BioCN&I, BioEngAb, BiolAb, CIN, CPA, ChemAb, ChemTitl, CurCont, DSA, ESPM, EngInd, FCA, FPA, FS&TA, ForAb, GenetAb, HGA, HerbAb, HortAb, IABS, ISR, IndMed, MBA, MEDLINE, MaizeAb, NemAb, NucAcAb, NutrAb, OrnHort, PBA, PGegResA, PGrRegA, PHN&I, PlantSci, PotatoAb, ProtozoAb, RA&MP, RDA, RM&VM, RPP, RefZh, RevApplEntom, RiceAb, S&F, SCI, SIA, SeedAb, SoyAb, TriticAb, VITIS, WAE&RSA, WeedAb.
—BLDSC (6519.200000), CASDDS, CISTI, IDS, IE, Infotrieve, ingenta. **CCC.**
Published by: (Society for Experimental Biology), Blackwell Publishing Ltd., 9600 Garsington Rd, Oxford, OX4 2ZG, United Kingdom. TEL 44-1865-776868, FAX 44-1865-714591, customerservices@oxon.blackwellpublishing.com, http://www.blackwellpublishing.com/journals/TPJ. Ed. Harry Klee TEL 352-392-8249. Pub. Amanda McLean Inglis. R&P Sophie Savage. Adv. contact Jenny Applin. Circ: 1,220.

580 GBR ISSN 1746-4811
▼ **PLANT METHODS.** Text in English. 2005. irreg. **Document type:** *Journal, Academic/Scholarly.* **Description:** Covers all aspects of plant biology examined from a technological viewpoint.
Media: Online - full text.
Published by: BioMed Central Ltd. (Subsidiary of: Current Science Ltd), Middlesex House, 34-42 Cleveland St, London, W1T 4LB, United Kingdom. TEL 44-20-76319131, FAX 44-20-76319923, info@biomedcentral.com, http://www.plantmethods.com, http://www.biomedcentral.com. Ed. Brian G Forde.

571.92 GBR ISSN 0032-0862
SB599 CODEN: PLPAAD
➤ **PLANT PATHOLOGY**; a record of current work on plant diseases and pests. Text in English. 1952. bi-m. GBP 596 combined subscription in Europe to institutions print & online eds.; USD 1,102 combined subscription in the Americas to institutions & Caribbean (print & online eds.); GBP 656 combined subscription elsewhere to institutions print & online eds. (effective 2006). adv. bk.rev. bibl.; charts; illus. index. reprint service avail. from PQC. **Document type:** *Journal, Academic/Scholarly.* **Description:** Covers all aspects of plant pathology.
Related titles: Microform ed.: (from PQC); Online - full text ed.: Plant Pathology Online. ISSN 1365-3059. 1998. GBP 566 in Europe to institutions; USD 1,047 in the Americas to institutions & Caribbean; GBP 623 elsewhere to institutions (effective 2006) (from Blackwell Synergy, EBSCO Publishing, Gale Group, IngentaConnect, O C L C Online Computer Library Center, Inc., Ovid Technologies, Inc., Swets Information Services).
Indexed: ASCA, ASFA, AgBio, Agr, AgrForAb, B&AI, B&BAb, BIOBASE, BIOSIS Prev, BioCN&I, BiolAb, CBTA, CEABA, CPA, CTFA, ChemAb, ChemTitl, CurCont, DBA, DSA, EPB, ESPM, FCA, FPA, FS&TA, ForAb, GEOBASE, GenetAb, HGA, HelmAb, HerbAb, HortAb, IABS, ISR, MBA, MaizeAb, NemAb, OrnHort, PBA, PGegResA, PGrRegA, PHN&I, PlantSci, PotatoAb, ProtozoAb, RA&MP, RM&VM, RPP, RefZh, RevApplEntom, RiceAb, S&F, SCI, SIA, SeedAb, SoyAb, TOSA, TriticAb, VITIS, WeedAb, ZooRec.
—BLDSC (6521.000000), CASDDS, CISTI, IDS, IE, Infotrieve, ingenta, Linda Hall. **CCC.**
Published by: (British Society for Plant Pathology), Blackwell Publishing Ltd., 9600 Garsington Rd, Oxford, OX4 2ZG, United Kingdom. TEL 44-1865-776868, FAX 44-1865-714591, customerservices@oxon.blackwellpublishing.com, http://www.blackwellpublishing.com/journals/PPA. Ed. Richard Shattock. Pub. Sue Hewitt. R&P Sophie Savage. Adv. contact Jenny Applin. Circ: 1,460.

580 PAK ISSN 1812-5387
▼ ➤ **PLANT PATHOLOGY JOURNAL.** Text in English. 2004. q. USD 350 (effective 2005). **Document type:** *Journal, Academic/Scholarly.* **Description:** Subjects covered include: mycology, bacteriology, virology, physiological plant pathology, plant-parasite interactions, post-harvest diseases, non infectious diseases, plant protection.
Related titles: Online - full text ed.: ISSN 1812-5425. free (effective 2005).
Indexed: C&ISA, E&CAJ, IAA.
Published by: Asian Network for Scientific Information, 308-Lasani Town, Sargodha Rd, Faislabad, 38090, Pakistan. TEL 92-41-2001145, FAX 92-41-731433, http://www.ansinet.org/c4p.php?j_id=ppj, http://www.ansinet.net.

580 KOR
THE PLANT PATHOLOGY JOURNAL. Text in English. 1985. bi-m. USD 100 worldwide (effective 2000). **Document type:** *Journal, Academic/Scholarly.* **Description:** Covers fundamental and applied investigations on all aspects of plant pathology and their traditional allies.
Formerly (until vol.14, 1999): Han'gug Sigmul Byeongri Haghoeji / Korean Journal of Plant Pathology (0256-8608)
Indexed: AgBio, AgrForAb, BioCN&I, CPA, FCA, FS&TA, ForAb, HerbAb, HortAb, MaizeAb, NemAb, OrnHort, PBA, PGrRegA, PHN&I, PotatoAb, RA&MP, RM&VM, RPP, RRTA, RevApplEntom, RiceAb, S&F, SIA, SeedAb, SoyAb, TriticAb, WeedAb.
—BLDSC (6521.610000), CISTI, ingenta.
Published by: (Han-gug Sigmul Byeongri Hag-hoe/Korean Society of Plant Pathology), Han Rim Won Publishing Company, 206-3 Ohjang-Dong, Choong Gu, Seoul, 100-310, Korea, S. TEL 82-2-2273-4201, FAX 82-2-2266-9083, hanrim@chollian.dacom.co.kr. Ed. Yin-Won Lee.

571.9 USA ISSN 0032-0889
QK1 CODEN: PLPHAY
➤ **PLANT PHYSIOLOGY.** Text in English. 1926. m. USD 235 to individual members; USD 1,375 combined subscription to institutions print & online eds. Plant Physiology & The Plant Cell incl. (effective 2005). adv. illus. q. index. back issues avail.; reprint service avail. from PQC. **Document type:** *Journal, Academic/Scholarly.* **Description:** International journal devoted to the physiology, biochemistry, cellular and molecular biology, biophysics, and environmental biology of plants.
Related titles: Microfiche ed.; Microfilm ed.: (from MIM, PMC, PQC); Online - full text ed.: ISSN 1532-2548. 1998. free to members; USD 1,500 to institutions Plant Physiology & The Plant Cell incl. (effective 2002) (from bigchalk, EBSCO Publishing, HighWire Press, National Library of Medicine, ProQuest Information & Learning).
Indexed: ABIPC, AEBA, ASCA, ASFA, AgBio, Agr, AgrForAb, AnBrAb, B&AI, BBCI, BIOBASE, BIOSIS Prev, BibAg, BioCN&I, BioEngAb, BiolAb, CIN, CPA, CTFA, ChemAb, ChemTitl, CurCont, DBA, DSA, EngInd, EnvAb, EnvInd, ExcerpMed, FCA, FPA, FS&TA, FaBeAb, ForAb, GenetAb, HGA, HerbAb, HortAb, I&DA, IABS, INIS AtomInd, ISR, IndMed, MEDLINE, MaizeAb, NemAb, NucAcAb, NutrAb, OrnHort, PBA, PGegResA, PGrRegA, PHN&I, PlantSci, PotatoAb, PoultAb, RA&MP, RDA, RM&VM, RPP, RefZh, RevApplEntom, RiceAb, S&F, S&MA, SCI, SIA, SeedAb, SoyAb, TOSA, TriticAb, VITIS, WAE&RSA, WeedAb.
—BLDSC (6521.800000), CASDDS, CISTI, IDS, IE, Infotrieve, ingenta, Linda Hall. **CCC.**
Published by: American Society of Plant Biologists, 15501 Monona Dr, Rockville, MD 20855-2768. TEL 301-251-0560, FAX 301-309-9196, 301-279-2996, mjunior@aspb.org, http://www.plantphysiol.org, http://www.aspb.org. Ed. Natasha V Raikhel. Pub. John Lisack Jr. R&P Nancy Winchester. Adv. contact Greg Kerr TEL 215-675-9133. Circ: 3,700 (paid).

571.9 FRA ISSN 0981-9428
QK710 CODEN: PPBIEX
➤ **PLANT PHYSIOLOGY AND BIOCHEMISTRY.** Text in English. 1963. 12/yr. EUR 695 in Europe to institutions; JPY 92,300 in Japan to institutions; USD 779 to institutions except Europe and Japan (effective 2006). adv. bk.rev. charts; illus. back issues avail.; reprints avail. **Document type:** *Journal, Academic/Scholarly.* **Description:** Embraces physiology, biochemistry, biophysics, structure and genetics at various levels from the molecular to the whole plant and environment.
Formerly (until 1987): Physiologie Vegetale. (0031-9368); Incorporates (1965-1969): Societe Francaise de Physiologie Vegetale. Bulletin (0375-961X); (1959-1969): Annales de Physiologie Vegetale (0570-1643)
Related titles: Microform ed.: (from MIM, PQC); Online - full text ed.: (from EBSCO Publishing, Gale Group, IngentaConnect, ScienceDirect, Swets Information Services).
Indexed: AEBA, ASCA, ASFA, AgBio, AgrForAb, B&BAb, BBCI, BIOBASE, BIOSIS Prev, BioCN&I, BiolAb, CPA, CTFA, ChemAb, ChemTitl, CurCont, ESPM, ExcerpMed, FCA, FPA, FS&TA, ForAb, HerbAb, HortAb, I&DA, IABS, ISR, MEDLINE, MaizeAb, OrnHort, PBA, PGegResA, PGrRegA, PHN&I, PN&I, PlantSci, PotatoAb, RA&MP, RM&VM, RPP, RevApplEntom, RiceAb, S&F, SCI, SIA, SeedAb, SoyAb, TriticAb, VITIS, WeedAb.
—BLDSC (6522.090000), CASDDS, CISTI, IDS, IE, Infotrieve, ingenta, Linda Hall. **CCC.**

B

Published by: (Societe Francaise de Physiologie Vegetale), Elsevier France, Editions Scientifiques et Medicales (Subsidiary of: Elsevier Science & Technology), 23 Rue Linois, Paris, 75724, France. TEL 33-1-71724600, FAX 33-1-71724650, academic@elsevier-fr.com, http://www.elsevier.com/locate/plaphy, http://www.elsevier.fr. Ed. Jean-Claude Kader. Circ: 1,000. **Subscr. to:** Elsevier BV, PO Box 211, Amsterdam 1000 AE, Netherlands.

➤ **PLANT PRESS.** see *GARDENING AND HORTICULTURE*

580 JPN ISSN 1343-943X
CODEN: PPTSFI

➤ **PLANT PRODUCTION SCIENCE.** Text in English. 1998. q. JPY 6,000 to individuals; JPY 15,000 to institutions; JPY 4,000 to students (effective 2001). 120 p./no.; reprints avail. **Document type:** *Journal, Academic/Scholarly.* **Description:** Publishes articles reporting original research findings on field crops and resource plants, their production, and related subjects.
Related titles: Online - full text ed.: ISSN 1349-1008. free (effective 2005) (from J-Stage).
Indexed: AEA, AgBio, Agr, AgrForAb, BIOBASE, BIOSIS Prev, BiolAb, CPA, CurCont, DSA, FCA, FS&TA, ForAb, HerbAb, HortAb, I&DA, MaizeAb, OrnHort, PBA, PGegResA, PGrRegA, PHN&I, PN&I, PotatoAb, RA&MP, RPP, RiceAb, S&F, SIA, SeedAb, SoyAb, TriticAb, WAE&RSA, WeedAb.
—BLDSC (6522.750000), CISTI, IE, Infotrieve, ingenta, Linda Hall.
Published by: Crop Science Society of Japan, c/o Graduate School of Agriculture, Tohoku University, 1-1 Tsutsumidori Amemiya-cho, Aoba, Sendai 981-8555, Japan. TEL 81-22-717-8638, FAX 81-22-717-8637, http://www.jstage.jst.go.jp/browse/pps, http://wwwsoc.nii.ac.jp/cssj/index-e.html. Ed. Makie Kokubun. Pub. Shigemi Akita. R&P Y Gotoh. Circ: 1,500. **Subscr. to:** Kyoritsu Publishing Co. Ltd., 2-22-4 Shinkawa, Chuo-ku, Tokyo 104-0033, Japan. TEL 81-3-3551-9891, FAX 81-3-3553-2047, cssj-jim@ab.inbox.ne.jp.

➤ **PLANT PROTECTION QUARTERLY.** see *AGRICULTURE—Crop Production And Soil*

580 NLD

➤ **PLANT RESOURCES OF SOUTH-EAST ASIA.** Short title: P R O S E A. Text in English. 1989. irreg., latest vol.15, 2003. price varies. illus.; charts; bibl.; abstr. back issues avail. **Document type:** *Monographic series, Academic/Scholarly.*
Indexed: ForAb, HortAb, RA&MP.
Published by: Backhuys Publishers BV, Postbus 321, Leiden, 2300 AH, Netherlands. TEL 31-71-517-0208, FAX 31-71-517-1856, backhuys@backhuys.com, http://www.backhuys.com.

580 IRL ISSN 0168-9452
QK1 CODEN: PLSCE4

➤ **PLANT SCIENCE.** Text in English. 1973. 12/yr. EUR 3,757 in Europe to institutions; JPY 498,900 in Japan to institutions; USD 4,204 to institutions except Europe and Japan (effective 2006). adv. bk.rev. illus. index. back issues avail. **Document type:** *Journal, Academic/Scholarly.* **Description:** Publishes papers in all areas of experimental plant biology under the four major section headings of physiology and biochemistry, genetics and molecular biology, cell and tissue studies in vitro, and general research.
Formerly (until vol.37, 1984): Plant Science Letters (0304-4211)
Related titles: Microform ed.: (from PQC); Online - full text ed.: (from EBSCO Publishing, Gale Group, IngentaConnect, ScienceDirect, Swets Information Services).
Indexed: ABIPC, AEBA, AIA, ASCA, ASFA, AgBio, Agr, AgrForAb, B&BAb, BBCI, BIOBASE, BIOSIS Prev, BioCN&I, BioEngAb, BiolAb, BiolDig, CPA, ChemAb, ChemTitl, CurCont, DBA, DSA, ESPM, ExcerpMed, FCA, FPA, FS&TA, FaBeAb, ForAb, GenetAb, HGA, HerbAb, HortAb, I&DA, IABS, ISR, MEDLINE, MSB, MaizeAb, NemAb, NutrAb, OrnHort, PBA, PGegResA, PGrRegA, PHN&I, PotatoAb, ProtozoAb, RA&MP, RDA, RM&VM, RPP, RefZh, RevApplEntom, RiceAb, S&F, S&MA, SCI, SIA, SeedAb, SoyAb, TDB, Telegen, TriticAb, VITIS, WAE&RSA, WeedAb.
—BLDSC (6523.390000), CASDDS, CISTI, IDS, IE, Infotrieve, ingenta, Linda Hall. **CCC.**
Published by: Elsevier Ireland Ltd (Subsidiary of: Elsevier Science & Technology), Elsevier House, Brookvale Plaza, E. Park, Shannon, Co. Clare, Ireland. TEL 353-61-709600, FAX 353-61-709100, plantsci@wsu.edu, nlinfo@elsevier.nl, http://www.elsevier.com/locate/plantsci, http://www.elsevier.nl. Eds. G. Spangenberg, M Delseny, T W Okita. R&P Annette Moloney. Circ: 700. **Subscr. to:** Elsevier BV, PO Box 211, Amsterdam 1000 AE, Netherlands. TEL 31-20-485-3757, FAX 31-20-485-3432, http://www.elsevier.nl.

580 USA ISSN 0032-0919
QK1 CODEN: PSBLAP

➤ **PLANT SCIENCE BULLETIN✱.** Text in English. 1955. q. USD 15 to members (effective 2004). adv. bk.rev. illus. Index. reprint service avail. from PQC. **Document type:** *Newsletter, Academic/Scholarly.*
Related titles: Microform ed.: 1955 (from PQC); Online - full text ed.: ISSN 1537-9752.
Indexed: BiolAb, RefZh, VITIS.
—BLDSC (6523.450000), CISTI, IE, Infotrieve, ingenta, Linda Hall.
Published by: Botanical Society of America, Inc., c/o Department of Genetics, Ohio State University, 1735 Neil Ave, Columbus, OH 43210. psb@botany.org, leverich@sluvca.slu.edu, http://www.botany.org/bsa/psb. Ed., R&P Joe Leverich. Circ: 3,100.

580 AUS ISSN 0913-557X
CODEN: PSBIEK

➤ **PLANT SPECIES BIOLOGY.** Text in English. 1986. 3/yr., latest vol.17, no.3, 2002. USD 168 combined subscription in the Americas to individuals & Caribbean, print & online eds.; EUR 155 combined subscription in Europe to individuals print & online eds.; GBP 103 combined subscription elsewhere to individuals print & online eds.; USD 348 combined subscription in the Americas to institutions & Caribbean, print & online eds.; GBP 214 combined subscription elsewhere to institutions print & online eds. (effective 2006). back issues avail. **Document type:** *Academic/Scholarly.* **Description:** Aims to communicate and exchange knowledge and ideas on plant species and their biological aspects including life histories, population dynamics, molecular biosystematics, co-evolutionary networks among plants and other organisms, and mechanisms of speciation.
Related titles: Online - full text ed.: ISSN 1442-1984. USD 331 in the Americas to institutions; GBP 203 elsewhere to institutions (effective 2006) (from Blackwell Synergy, EBSCO Publishing, Gale Group, IngentaConnect, O C L C Online Computer Library Center, Inc., Swets Information Services).
Indexed: AgBio, Agr, ApEcolAb, ApicAb, BIOBASE, BIOSIS Prev, BiolAb, CPA, ESPM, FCA, ForAb, HerbAb, HortAb, I&DA, IABS, MaizeAb, OrnHort, PBA, PGegResA, PGrRegA, PlantSci, RevApplEntom, S&F, SIA, SeedAb, SoyAb, TriticAb, WeedAb, ZooRec.
—BLDSC (6523.615000), IE, Infotrieve, ingenta. **CCC.**
Published by: (Society for the Study of Species Biology/Shu Seibutsu Gakkai JPN), Blackwell Publishing Asia (Subsidiary of: Blackwell Publishing Ltd.), 550 Swanston St, Carlton South, VIC 3053, Australia. TEL 61-383591011, FAX 61-383591120, subs@blackwellpublishingasia.com, http://www.blackwellpublishing.com/journals/PSB. Ed. Shoichi Kawano. R&P Chris Hum. **Subscr. to:** PO Box 378, Carlton South, VIC 3053, Australia.

580 AUT ISSN 0378-2697
QK1 CODEN: ESPFBP

➤ **PLANT SYSTEMATICS AND EVOLUTION;** Entwicklungsgeschichte und Systematik der Pflanzen. Text in English. 1851. s-m. (in 6 vols., 4 nos./vol.). EUR 2,564 combined subscription to institutions print & online eds. (effective 2005). adv. bk.rev. bibl.; charts; illus.; stat.; abstr. back issues avail.; reprint service avail. from ISI. **Document type:** *Journal, Academic/Scholarly.* **Description:** Publishes original papers and reviews on plant systematics in the broadest sense, encompassing evolutionary, phytogenetic and biogeographical studies at the populational, specific and higher taxonomic levels.
Former titles (until 1974): Oesterreichische Botanische Zeitschrift (0029-8948); (until 1858): Oesterreichisches Botanisches Wochenblatt (1029-0729)
Related titles: Microfiche ed.: (from BHP); Microform ed.: (from BHP, PQC); Online - full text ed.: ISSN 1615-6110 (from EBSCO Publishing, Springer LINK, Swets Information Services); ♦ Supplement(s): Plant Systematics and Evolution. Supplement.
Indexed: ASCA, ASFA, AgBio, Agr, AgrForAb, ApicAb, BIOBASE, BIOSIS Prev, BiolAb, CIN, CPA, ChemAb, ChemTitl, CurCont, FCA, ForAb, GenetAb, HGA, HerbAb, HortAb, IABS, ISR, IndVet, MaizeAb, OrnHort, PBA, PGegResA, PlantSci, PotatoAb, RA&MP, RPP, RevApplEntom, RiceAb, S&F, SCI, SIA, SeedAb, SoyAb, TOSA, TriticAb, WeedAb, ZooRec.
—BLDSC (6523.640000), CASDDS, CISTI, IDS, IE, Infotrieve, ingenta, Linda Hall. **CCC.**
Published by: Springer-Verlag Wien (Subsidiary of: Springer Science+Business Media) journals@springer.at, http://www.springer.at/pse. Ed. F H Hellwig. R&P Angela Foessl TEL 43-1-3302415517. Adv. contact Michael Katzenberger TEL 43-1-3302415220. B&W page EUR 1,000; 170 x 250. **Subscr. in the Americas to:** Springer-Verlag New York, Inc., Journal Fulfillment, PO Box 2485, Secaucus, NJ 07096-2485. TEL 800-777-4643, 201-348-4033, FAX 201-348-4505, journals@springer-ny.com, http://www.springer-ny.com; **Subscr. to:** Springer GmbH Auslieferungsgesellschaft, Haberstr 7, Heidelberg 69126, Germany. TEL 49-6221-345-0, FAX 49-6221-345-4229, subscriptions@springer.de.

580 AUT
CODEN: PSESEV

➤ **PLANT SYSTEMATICS AND EVOLUTION. SUPPLEMENT.** Text in English. 1977. irreg., latest 2000. price varies. adv. bibl.; charts; illus.; stat. back issues avail.; reprint service avail. from ISI. **Document type:** *Monographic series, Academic/Scholarly.* **Description:** Publishes selected papers on the morphology and systematics of plants.
Formerly: Plant Systematics and Evolution. Supplementum (0172-6668)
Related titles: ♦ Supplement to: Plant Systematics and Evolution. ISSN 0378-2697.
Indexed: BIOSIS Prev.
—BLDSC (6523.640200), CASDDS, CISTI, IE, ingenta.
Published by: Springer-Verlag Wien (Subsidiary of: Springer Science+Business Media) TEL 43-1-3302415-0, FAX 43-1-330242665, journals@springer.at, http://www.springer.at. Ed. F H Hellwig. R&P Angela Foessl TEL 43-1-3302415517. Adv. contact Michael Katzenberger TEL 43-1-3302415220. B&W page EUR 1,000; 170 x 230. **Subscr. in N. America to:** Springer-Verlag New York, Inc., 233 Spring St, New York, NY 10013. TEL 800-777-4643, FAX 201-348-4505, orders@springer-ny.com.

333.95416 GBR ISSN 1358-4103

PLANT TALK; news and views on plant conservation worldwide. Text in English. 1995. q. GBP 17, USD 28 to individuals; GBP 40, USD 68 to institutions (effective 2000). adv. bk.rev. illus. **Document type:** *Academic/Scholarly.* **Description:** Includes regular features such as a notice board, reports on new flora, plant checklists and reviews of Red Data Books, the books listing endangered plants. Articles cover conservation techniques, examples of plant conservation in action, and news.
Indexed: ForAb, GardL, PBA, RefZh, SeedAb, WAE&RSA.
—Linda Hall.
Published by: Botanical Information Company Ltd., PO Box 500, Kingston Upon Thames, Surrey KT2 5XB, United Kingdom. FAX 44-20-8974-5127, plant-talk@dial.pipex.com, hhttp://www.plant-talk.org. Circ: 1,800 (paid). **Subscr. to:** PO Box 354841, Palm Coast, FL 32135-4841.

580 BGD ISSN 1018-8029

➤ **PLANT TISSUE CULTURE.** Text in English. 1991. s-a. BDT 600 domestic; USD 80 in Asia; USD 86 elsewhere (effective 2003). adv. bk.rev. abstr. 120 p./no.; reprints avail. **Document type:** *Journal, Academic/Scholarly.* **Description:** Publishes original papers on tissue culture related topics including plant transformation and genetic engineering of plant sciences.
—BLDSC (6523.650000), CISTI.
Published by: Bangladesh Association for Plant Tissue Culture, University of Dhaka, Department of Botany, Dhaka, 1000, Bangladesh. FAX 880-2-865583, TELEX 632458 MEGNA BJ, baptc@drik.bgd.drik.net, baptc@bd.drik.net, http://www.baptc.org. Ed. A.S. Islam. R&P A S Islam TEL 880-2-508614. Circ: 500.

571.2 660.6 ISR ISSN 1025-6717

PLANT TISSUE CULTURE AND BIOTECHNOLOGY. Text in English. 1971; N.S. 1995. q. USD 130 to institutions (effective 2001). adv. bk.rev. bibl. **Document type:** *Newsletter.* **Description:** Publishes reports on novel research activities, protocols, feature articles, research reports, and news in the fields of plant tissue culture and biotechnology.
Formerly (until 1995): International Association for Plant Tissue and Culture. Newsletter (0740-0209)
Indexed: VITIS.
—CISTI.
Published by: International Association for Plant Tissue Culture, Department of Ornamental Horticulture, ARO, The Volcani Center, P.O. Box 6, Bet Dagan, 50205, Israel. TEL 972-3-9683500, FAX 972-3-9660589, vcwatad@volcani.agri.gov.il, http://indycc1.agri.huji.ac.il/~tzvika/iaptc/ip-home.htm. Ed. Meira Ziv. Circ: 4,000.

PLANT TISSUE CULTURE MANUAL; fundamentals and applications. see *BIOLOGY—Biotechnology*

PLANT VARIETY PROTECTION; gazette and newsletter of UPOV. see *AGRICULTURE—Crop Production And Soil*

580 DEU ISSN 0032-0935
QK1 CODEN: PLANAB

➤ **PLANTA;** an international journal of plant biology. Text in English. 1925. 18/yr. EUR 3,878 combined subscription to institutions print & online eds. (effective 2005). adv. charts; illus. Index. back issues avail.; reprint service avail. from ISI. **Document type:** *Journal, Academic/Scholarly.* **Description:** Presents original articles on structural and functional botany, covering all aspects of plant biology, from biochemistry, biotechnology, and molecular and cell biology, to studies with tissues, organs, whole plants, and populations (crop physiology and physiological ecology).
Related titles: Microform ed.: (from PMC, PQC); Online - full text ed.: ISSN 1432-2048 (from EBSCO Publishing, Springer LINK, Swets Information Services).
Indexed: ABIPC, AEA, ASFA, AgBio, Agr, AgrForAb, AnBrAb, B&AI, B&BAb, BBCI, BIOBASE, BIOSIS Prev, BibAg, BioCN&I, BiolAb, CCI, CPA, CTFA, ChemAb, ChemTitl, CurCont, DBA, DSA, EngInd, FCA, FPA, FS&TA, FaBeAb, ForAb, GenetAb, HGA, HerbAb, HortAb, I&DA, IAA, IABS, ISR, IndMed, MBA, MEDLINE, MSB, MaizeAb, NemAb, OrnHort, PBA, PGegResA, PGrRegA, PHN&I, PlantSci, PotatoAb, PoultAb, ProtozoAb, RA&MP, RM&VM, RPP, RefZh, RevApplEntom, RiceAb, S&F, S&MA, SCI, SIA, SeedAb, SoyAb, TOSA, TriticAb, VITIS, WeedAb.
—BLDSC (6524.000000), CASDDS, CISTI, IDS, IE, Infotrieve, ingenta, Linda Hall. **CCC.**
Published by: Springer-Verlag (Subsidiary of: Springer Science+Business Media), Tiergartenstr 17, Heidelberg, 69121, Germany. TEL 49-6221-3450, FAX 49-6221-345229, http://link.springer.de/link/service/journals/00425. Eds. Anastasios Melis, Dorothea Bartels. Adv. contact Stephan Kroeck TEL 49-30-827875739. **Subscr. in the Americas to:** Springer-Verlag New York, Inc., Journal Fulfillment, PO Box

B

2485, Secaucus, NJ 07096-2485. TEL 800-777-4643, 201-348-4033, FAX 201-348-4505, journals@springer-ny.com, http://www.springer-ny.com; **Subscr. to:** Springer GmbH Auslieferungsgesellschaft, Haberstr 7, Heidelberg 69126, Germany. TEL 49-6221-345-0, FAX 49-6221-345-4229, subscriptions@springer.de.

580 BRA ISSN 0100-8358
CODEN: PLDADO
PLANTA DANINHA. Text in Portuguese, Spanish, English. 1978. 3/yr. free to members; BRL 110 domestic; USD 100 foreign (effective 2004). **Document type:** *Journal, Academic/Scholarly.* **Description:** Publishes technical-scientific articles, notes and review articles of a critical nature in the field of biology, physiology, pharmaceutical control and plant-decontaminating values, herbicides, growth regulators, defoliants, desiccants, application technology and similar issues.
Related titles: Online - full text ed.: 2003. free (effective 2005).
Indexed: AgBio, AgrForAb, BioCN&I, CPA, FCA, ForAb, HerbAb, HortAb, I&DA, MaizeAb, OrnHort, PBA, PGegResA, PGrRegA, PHN&I, PN&I, RA&MP, S&F, SIA, SeedAb, SoyAb, TriticAb, WAE&RSA, WeedAb.
—CISTI.
Published by: Sociedade Brasileira da Ciencia das Plantas Daninhas/Brazilian Society of Herb Science, Departamento de Fitotecnica - UFV, Vicosa, MG 36570-000, Brazil. http://www.scielo.br/scielo.php?script=sci_serial&pid=0100-8358&nrm=iso&lng=en.

580 VEN ISSN 1316-1547
PLANTULA. Text in Spanish. 1996. q. **Document type:** *Journal.*
Indexed: ASFA, AgrForAb, BIOSIS Prev, BiolAb, ForAb, HerbAb, HortAb, PBA, PGegResA, S&F, SeedAb, WeedAb.
Published by: Universidad de Los Andes, Facultad de Ciencias, Centro Jardin Botanico, La Hechicera, Apartado 52, Merida, 5212, Venezuela. plantula@ciens.ula.ve, http://www.venezuelainnovadora.gov.ve/publicacion_88.html. Ed. Javier Sanchez.

580 ESP ISSN 1135-8408
➤ **POLEN.** Text in Spanish, English, French; Summaries in Spanish, English, French. 1984. a., latest vol.10, 1999. EUR 18 domestic; EUR 21 foreign (effective 2005). bk.rev. back issues avail. **Document type:** *Journal, Academic/Scholarly.* **Description:** Includes original papers about Palinology and Aerobiology.
Formerly: Asociacion de Palinologos de Lengua Espanola. Anales (0213-1811)
Indexed: IECT.
—CINDOC.
Published by: (Universidad de Cordoba, Departamento de Biologia Vegetal y Ecologia), Universidad de Cordoba, Servicio de Publicaciones, Ave. Menendez Pidal, s-n, Cordoba, 14071, Spain. TEL 34-957-218125, FAX 34-957-218196, publicaciones@uco.es, http://www.uco.es/. Ed. E Dominguez Vilches. Circ: 500.

580 POL ISSN 1641-8190
CODEN: PBJOAN
➤ **POLISH BOTANICAL JOURNAL.** Text in English. 1954. s-a. EUR 39 per vol. (effective 2005). bk.rev. bibl.; charts; illus. 200 p./no. 2 cols./p.; **Document type:** *Journal, Academic/Scholarly.* **Description:** Publishes original papers covering all aspects of botany, especially vegetation monographs and articles on plant taxonomy and ecology, phytogeography, cryptogamic botany, plant anatomy, cytology and embryology as well as biosystematics, evolutionary botany and experimental embryology.
Formerly (until 2001): Fragmenta Floristica et Geobotanica (0015-931X)
Indexed: AgrAg, AgrForAb, AgrLib, BIOSIS Prev, BiolAb, FCA, FPA, ForAb, GEOBASE, HerbAb, HortAb, IBR, OrnHort, PBA, PGegResA, RPP, RefZh, RiceAb, S&F, SeedAb, TriticAb, WeedAb.
—BLDSC (6543.575400), CISTI.
Published by: Polska Akademia Nauk, Instytut Botaniki im. W. Szafera/Polish Academy of Sciences, W. Szafer Institute of Botany, ul Lubicz 46, Krakow, 31512, Poland. TEL 48-12-4215144, FAX 48-12-4219790, wojcicki@ib-pan.krakow.pl, office@ib-pan.krakow.pl, http://www.ib-pan.krakow.pl. Ed. Jan Wojcicki. Pub. Jacek W Wieser. R&P Leon Stuchlik. Circ: 600 (paid).

580.9438 POL ISSN 0867-0730
QK322
➤ **POLISH BOTANICAL STUDIES.** Text and summaries in English. 1990. irreg. (1-3/yr.). price varies. bk.rev. **Document type:** *Monographic series, Academic/Scholarly.* **Description:** Covers taxonomy, ecology, evolution, morphology, anatomy and cytology of all plant groups as well as palaeobotany.
Indexed: AgrAg, AgrLib, BIOSIS Prev, BiolAb, FCA, ForAb, HortAb, PBA, PGegResA, RefZh, SeedAb.
—BLDSC (6543.575500), CISTI.
Published by: Polska Akademia Nauk, Instytut Botaniki im. W. Szafera/Polish Academy of Sciences, W. Szafer Institute of Botany, ul Lubicz 46, Krakow, 31512, Poland. TEL 48-12-4241737, FAX 48-12-4219790, office@ib-pan.krakow.pl, http://www.ib-pan.krakow.pl. Ed. Zbigniew Mirek. Pub. Jacek W Wieser. R&P Mirek Zbigniew. Adv. contact Jacek Wieser. Circ: 500.

580 POL ISSN 0080-357X
QK322 CODEN: RSDPAZ
POLSKIE TOWARZYSTWO BOTANICZNE. SEKCJA DENDROLOGICZNA. ROCZNIK. Text in English, Polish; Summaries in English, German, Polish, Russian. 1926. irreg. price varies. illus.
Indexed: BiolAb.
Published by: Polskie Towarzystwo Botaniczne/Polish Botanical Society, Al Ujazdowskie 4, Warsaw, 00478, Poland. Ed. Tadeusz Gorczynski. **Dist. by:** Ars Polona, Krakowskie Przedmiescie 7, Warsaw, Poland.

580 BRA ISSN 0102-6976
QK263
PONTIFICIA UNIVERSIDADE CATOLICA DO RIO GRANDE DO SUL. MUSEU DE CIENCIAS E TECNOLOGIA. COMUNICACOES. SERIE BOTANICA. Variant title: Museu de Ciencias da P U C R G S. Comunicacoes. Serie Botanica. Text in Portuguese. 1971. irreg.
Supersedes in part (in 1985): Museu de Ciencias da P U C R S. Comunicacoes (0100-4573)
Indexed: ASFA, ESPM.
—CISTI.
Published by: Pontificia Universidade Catolica do Rio Grande do Sul. Museu de Ciencias e Tecnologia, Av Ipiranga 6681, Predio 40, Porto Alegre, RS 90619-900, Brazil. TEL 55-512-3203597, http://www.mct.pucrs.br/. **Subscr. to:** Av Ipiranga 6681, Predio 33, Caixa Postal 1429, Porto Alegre, RS 90619-900, Brazil. edipucrs@pucrs.br, http://www.pucrs.br/edipucrs.

580 CZE ISSN 0032-7786
QK1 CODEN: PRESAK
➤ **PRESLIA.** Text in English, German, Czech; Summaries in English, German. 1914. q. CZK 360, EUR 82 per vol. (effective 2003). bk.rev.; rec.rev. charts; illus. index, cum.index. 100 p./no.; back issues avail. **Document type:** *Bulletin, Academic/Scholarly.*
Indexed: AgBio, BIOSIS Prev, BiolAb, ChemAb, CurCont, FCA, FPA, ForAb, GEOBASE, HerbAb, HortAb, OrnHort, PBA, PGegResA, RA&MP, RDA, RPP, S&F, SeedAb, TriticAb, WAE&RSA, WeedAb.
—BLDSC (6611.000000), CISTI, IE, ingenta, KNAW, Linda Hall.
Published by: Ceska Botanicka Spolecnost/Czech Botanical Society, Benatska 2, Prague, 12801, Czech Republic. botspol@natur.cuni.cz, http://www.ibot.cas.cz/preslia/, http://www.natur.cuni.cz/cbs. Ed. Petr Pysek. Circ: 1,200 (paid). **Dist. in Western countries by:** Kubon & Sagner Buchexport - Import GmbH, Postfach 24, Munich 34 8000, Germany.

580 USA ISSN 0340-4773
QK1 CODEN: PRBODU
PROGRESS IN BOTANY. Text in English. 1949. irreg., latest vol.57, 1996. price varies. reprint service avail. from ISI. **Document type:** *Monographic series.*
Formerly: Fortschritte der Botanik (0071-7878)
Indexed: ASFA, BIOSIS Prev, BiolAb, ChemAb, ChemTitl, ESPM, FCA, HerbAb, PBA, RPP, S&F, VITIS, WeedAb, ZooRec.
—BLDSC (6866.330000), CASDDS, CISTI, IE, ingenta, Linda Hall. **CCC.**
Published by: Springer-Verlag New York, Inc. (Subsidiary of: Springer Science+Business Media), 233 Spring St, New York, NY 10013. TEL 212-460-1500, FAX 212-473-6272.

579.8 GBR ISSN 0167-8574
QK564 CODEN: PPREEX
➤ **PROGRESS IN PHYCOLOGICAL RESEARCH.** Text in Dutch. 1982. irreg., latest vol.11. price varies. **Document type:** *Monographic series, Academic/Scholarly.*
Indexed: ChemAb, ChemTitl, ZooRec.
—CASDDS, CISTI, IE, Linda Hall.
Published by: Biopress Ltd., 17 Wimbledon Rd, Bristol, BS6 7YA, United Kingdom. Biopress@blueyonder.co.uk. Eds. D. J. Chapman, F. E. Round.

580 USA ISSN 0749-7741
CODEN: PTRID4
➤ **PTERIDOLOGIA.** Text in English. 1979. irreg. price varies. back issues avail. **Document type:** *Monographic series, Academic/Scholarly.* **Description:** Technical monographs on ferns and fern-allies.
Indexed: BiolAb.
Published by: American Fern Society, Inc., PO Box 299, Saint Louis, MO 63166-0299. http://www.amerfernsoc.org. Circ: 200 (paid).

580 635 GBR ISSN 0266-1640
QK520 CODEN: PTEREZ
PTERIDOLOGIST. Text in English. 1984. a. GBP 25 (effective 2002); includes Bulletin and Fern Gazette. bk.rev. illus. 48 p./no. 1 cols./p.; back issues avail. **Document type:** *Academic/Scholarly.* **Description:** Contains articles about growing ferns, fern varieties and fern history, plus other items of interest concerning ferns and allied plants.
Indexed: RefZh.
—Linda Hall.
Published by: British Pteridological Society, c/o Botany Department, Natural History Museum, Cromwell Rd, London, SW7 5BD, United Kingdom. TEL 44-20-79425756, pteridologist@ebps.org.uk, http://www.ebps.org.uk. Ed. B A Thomas. Circ: 800.

580 JPN ISSN 0915-2059
PURANTA/PLANTA. Text in Japanese. 1989. bi-m. JPY 520 per issue.
Published by: Kenseisha Inc., 6-4 Kakigaracho-Nihonbashi 1-chome, Chuo-ku, Tokyo, 103-0000, Japan.

581.636 KEN ISSN 0048-6043
SB952.P9 CODEN: PYRPAN
➤ **PYRETHRUM POST.** Text in English. 1948. s-a. USD 40 (effective 1999). bk.rev. abstr.; charts; stat. biennial index. 44 p./no. 2 cols./p.; back issues avail.; reprints avail. **Document type:** *Journal, Academic/Scholarly.* **Description:** Provides a vehicle to disseminate scientific research findings about pyrethrum and related products.
Related titles: CD-ROM ed.
Indexed: AgBio, Agr, AnalAb, BIOSIS Prev, BiolAb, CIN, ChemAb, ChemTitl, DBA, ExcerpMed, HortAb, IndVet, NemAb, PBA, PHN&I, RA&MP, RevApplEntom, SAA, TDB, VetBull.
—BLDSC (7162.000000), CASDDS, CISTI, Linda Hall.
Published by: (Pyrethrum Bureau), Ketona Publishers, Pyrethrum Board of Kenya, PO Box 420, Nakuru, Kenya. TEL 254-37-211567, 43-6245-833810, FAX 254-37-45274, 43-6245-82356, TELEX 33080 PYBOARD KE. Ed. James N Kuria.

583.56 PER ISSN 1022-5897
➤ **QUEPO.** Text in Spanish. 1987. a. PEN 15 domestic; USD 15 foreign (effective 2000). adv. bk.rev. illus. 112 p./no.; **Document type:** *Academic/Scholarly.* **Description:** Deals with cacti conservancy, knowledge of native genera and species and growing methods.
Published by: Sociedad Peruana de Cactus y Suculentas, Apdo. 3215, Lima, 100, Peru. TEL 51-11-4792360, FAX 51-11-47923630, carlosto@ec-red.com, http://www.cactus-mall.com/specs/index.html. Ed., Adv. contact Carlos Ostolaza. Circ: 3,000.

580 JPN ISSN 0285-0850
RAIKEN/LICHEN. Text in Japanese. 1972. 2/yr. JPY 2,000 (effective 1999). adv. bk.rev. **Document type:** *Academic/Scholarly.*
Published by: Chiirui Kenkyukai/Lichenological Society of Japan, c/o H Harada, Natural History Museum & Institute, Chiba, 955-2 Aoba-cho, Chuo-ku, Chiba-shi, 260-0852, Japan. FAX 81-43-266-2481. Ed. N Hamada. R&P H. Harada. Adv. contact H Harada. Circ: 250.

580 USA ISSN 1094-1398
RANCHO SANTA ANA BOTANIC GARDEN OCCASIONAL PUBLICATIONS. Text in English. 1997. irreg. price varies. illus. back issues avail. **Document type:** *Academic/Scholarly.* **Description:** Publishes the results of original botanic research by the Garden staff. Occasionally includes proceedings of symposia sponsored by the Garden.
Published by: Rancho Santa Ana Botanic Garden, 1500 N College Ave, Claremont, CA 91711. TEL 909-625-8767, FAX 909-626-3489, ann.joslin@cgu.edu. Ed. Richard K Benjamin. R&P Clement W Hamilton TEL 909-625-8767 ext. 220. Circ: 300 (paid).

580 RUS ISSN 0033-9946
SB108.R9 CODEN: RRESA8
➤ **RASTITEL'NYE RESURSY/VEGETATIVE RESOURCES.** Text in Russian. 1965. q. USD 185 foreign (effective 2005). index. **Document type:** *Journal, Academic/Scholarly.* **Description:** Publishes scholarly papers in following fields: plant resources of various countries, groups of useful plants, biology, morphology, ontogenesis, anatomy, ecology, structure of useful plants populations, ethnobotany, etc.
Indexed: AEA, AbHyg, AgBio, AgrForAb, BIOSIS Prev, BioCN&I, BiolAb, CIN, CPA, ChemAb, ChemTitl, DSA, FCA, FPA, ForAb, HelmAb, HerbAb, HortAb, I&DA, IndVet, MaizeAb, NemAb, NutrAb, OrnHort, PBA, PGegResA, PGrRegA, PHN&I, PotatoAb, ProtozoAb, RA&MP, RM&VM, RPP, RefZh, RevApplEntom, RiceAb, S&F, SIA, SeedAb, SoyAb, TDB, TriticAb, WAE&RSA, WeedAb.
—CASDDS, CISTI, East View, KNAW, Linda Hall. **CCC.**
Published by: (Rossiiskaya Akademiya Nauk/Russian Academy of Sciences), Izdatel'stvo Nauka, Sankt-Peterburgskoe Otdelenie, Mendeleevskaya liniya 1, St Petersburg, 199034, Russian Federation. TEL 7-812-3286291. Circ: 875. **US dist. addr.:** East View Information Services, 3020 Harbor Ln. N., Minneapolis, MN 55447. TEL 800-477-1005, FAX 800-800-3839, eastview@eastview.com, http://www.eastview.com.

580 590 GBR
➤ **RAY SOCIETY PUBLICATIONS.** Text in English. 1844. irreg., latest vol.165, 2001. price varies. **Document type:** *Monographic series, Academic/Scholarly.* **Description:** Specialist scientific monographs in zoological and biological topics; facsimilies of historical works in natural sciences; translations and updates of existing works.
Related titles: Microfiche ed.
Indexed: ZooRec.
—BLDSC (7296.590000).
Published by: Ray Society, c/o The Dept. of Zoology, The Natural History Museum, S Kensington, London, SW7 5BD, United Kingdom. TEL 44-20-942-5276, FAX 44-20-942-5054, nje@nhm.ac.uk. R&P Dr. N J Evans TEL 0207-942-5532. Circ: 750.

B

580 ESP ISSN 0210-363X
REAL ACADEMIA DE CIENCIAS EXACTAS, FISICAS Y NATURALES. MEMORIA. SERIE CIENCIAS NATURALES. Text in Spanish. 1931. irreg. price varies.
Indexed: IECT.
—BLDSC (5668.320000).
Published by: Real Academia de Ciencias Exactas Fisicas y Naturales, Valverde, 22, Madrid, 28004, Spain.

571.2 USA ISSN 0079-9920
QK861 CODEN: RAPHBE
RECENT ADVANCES IN PHYTOCHEMISTRY. Text in English. 1968. a., latest vol.38, 2004. price varies. back issues avail. **Document type:** *Monographic series, Academic/Scholarly.*
Indexed: Agr, BIOSIS Prev, CIN, ChemAb, ChemTitl.
—BLDSC (7303.900000), CASDDS, CISTI, IE, Infotrieve, ingenta, Linda Hall. **CCC.**
Published by: Elsevier Inc. (Subsidiary of: Elsevier Science & Technology), 360 Park Ave. S, New York, NY 10010-1710. http://www.elsevier.com. Eds. B F Matthews, J A Saunders, J T Romeo.

580 IND
RECENT RESEARCH DEVELOPMENTS IN PLANT BIOLOGY. Text in English. a. **Document type:** *Journal, Academic/Scholarly.*
—BLDSC (7305.087610).
Published by: Research Signpost, T.C. 37/661 (2), Fort P.O., Trivandrum, Kerala, India.

580 CHN ISSN 1005-3395
REDAI YAREDAI ZHIWU XUEBAO/JOURNAL OF TROPICAL AND SUBTROPICAL BOTANY. Text in English. 1993. q. **Document type:** *Journal, Academic/Scholarly.*
Related titles: Online - full content ed.: (from WanFang Data Corp.); Online - full text ed.: (from East View Information Services).
Indexed: AgBio, AgrForAb, BioCN&I, CPA, FCA, FPA, ForAb, HerbAb, HortAb, I&DA, MaizeAb, OrnHort, PBA, PGegResA, PGrRegA, PHN&I, RA&MP, RM&VM, RPP, S&F, SIA, SeedAb, SoyAb, TDB, TriticAb, VITIS, WeedAb.
—BLDSC (5070.668000).
Published by: Zhongguo Kexueyuan, Huanan Zhiwuyuan/Chinese Academy of Sciences, South China Institute of Botany, Leyeju, Huanan Zhiwuyuan, Guangzhou, 510650, China. TEL 86-20-85232414, FAX 86-20-85231711, jtsb@scib.ac.cn, http://rdyrdzwxb.wanfangdata.com.cn/default.html, http://www.scib.ac.cn/. **Dist. by:** China International Book Trading Corp, 35 Chegongzhuang Xilu, Haidian District, PO Box 399, Beijing 100044, China. TEL 86-10-68412045, FAX 86-10-68412023, cibtc@mail.cibtc.com.cn, http://www.cibtc.com.cn.

571.2 CHN ISSN 1000-2561
SB111 CODEN: RZXUEX
➤ **REDAI ZUOWU XUEBAO/CHINESE JOURNAL OF TROPICAL CROPS.** Text in Chinese; Abstracts in Chinese, English. 1980. q. CNY 8, USD 4 (effective 2001). 80 p./no.; back issues avail. **Document type:** *Journal, Academic/Scholarly.* **Description:** Contains papers on agronomical, pathological, physiological, genetic, entomological and ecological aspects of various tropical crops.
Related titles: Online - full text ed.: (from East View Information Services).
Indexed: ZooRec.
—BLDSC (3180.681000).
Published by: Zhongguo Redai Nongye Kexueyuan/Chinese Academy of Tropical Agricultural Sciences, Baodao Xincun, Danxian, Hainan 571737, China. TEL 86-898-23300136, FAX 86-898-23300157. Ed. Rangshui Yu. **Co-sponsor:** Huanan Redai Nangye Daxue/South China University of Tropical Agriculture.

➤ **REFERATIVNYI ZHURNAL. BOTANIKA.** see *BIOLOGY—Abstracting, Bibliographies, Statistics*

➤ **REFERATIVNYI ZHURNAL. BOTANIKA. VODOROSLI, GRIBY, LISHAINIKI.** see *BIOLOGY—Abstracting, Bibliographies, Statistics*

➤ **REFERATIVNYI ZHURNAL. BOTANIKA. VYSSHIE RASTENIYA.** see *BIOLOGY—Abstracting, Bibliographies, Statistics*

➤ **REFERATIVNYI ZHURNAL. FITOPATOLOGIYA.** see *BIOLOGY—Abstracting, Bibliographies, Statistics*

➤ **REFERATIVNYI ZHURNAL. LEKARTSVENNYE RASTENIYA.** see *BIOLOGY—Abstracting, Bibliographies, Statistics*

➤ **REFERATIVNYI ZHURNAL. RASTENIEVODSTVO (BIOLOGICHESKIE OSNOVY).** see *BIOLOGY—Abstracting, Bibliographies, Statistics*

580 NLD ISSN 0080-0694
QK96
REGNUM VEGETABILE; a series of publications for the use of plant taxonomists and plant geographers. Text in Dutch. irreg. price varies. **Document type:** *Monographic series.*
Related titles: ◆ Series: Index to Plant Chromosome Numbers. ISSN 0073-6007.
Indexed: BIOSIS Prev, BibAg, BiolAb.
—BLDSC (7345.000000), CISTI, IE, ingenta.
Published by: (International Association for Plant Taxonomy), Bohn Stafleu van Loghum B.V. (Subsidiary of: Wolters Kluwer N.V.), Postbus 246, Houten, 3990 GA, Netherlands. boekhandels@bsl.nl, http://www.bsl.nl. Ed. F A Stafleu. Circ: 1,500.

580 IDN ISSN 0034-365X
QK1 CODEN: RNWDAP
REINWARDTIA; a journal on taxonomic botany, plant sociology, physiology and ecology. Text in English. 1950. irreg. price varies. bk.rev. index. **Document type:** *Journal, Academic/Scholarly.*
Indexed: Agr, BIOSIS Prev, BiolAb, ZooRec.
Published by: Indonesian Institute of Sciences, R & D Centre for Biology, Jalan Juanda 18, Bogor, Indonesia. TEL 62-251-321038, FAX 62-251-325854. Circ: 400.

583.56 CHE ISSN 0486-4271
QK96
REPERTORIUM PLANTARUM SUCCULENTARUM. Text in English. 1951. a. USD 6.50 (effective 2003). 50 p./no. 2 cols./p.; back issues avail. **Document type:** *Bulletin, Academic/Scholarly.* **Description:** Listing of new names of and new literature on succulent plants, including cacti.
—Linda Hall.
Published by: International Organization for Succulent Plant Study, c/o Sukkulenten-Sammlung, Mythenquai 88, Zuerich, 8002, Switzerland. TEL 41-43-3443480, FAX 41-43-3443488, sukkulenten@gsz.stzh.ch. Ed. U. Eggli. Circ: 600 (paid).

580 550 ISL
RESEARCH INSTITUTE NEDRI-AS. BULLETIN. Text in English, German, Icelandic; Summaries in English. 1969. irreg.
Indexed: BiolAb.
Published by: Rannsoknarstofnunin Nedri-As/Research Institute Nedri-As, Hveragerdi, Iceland.

580 GBR ISSN 0951-6654
RESEARCH STUDIES IN BOTANY AND RELATED APPLIED FIELDS. Text in English. 1982. irreg., latest vol.15, 2001. price varies. **Document type:** *Monographic series.*
Related titles: CD-ROM ed.
—BLDSC (7773.217000), ingenta.
Published by: Research Studies Press Ltd., 16 Coach House Cloisters, 10 Hitchin St, Baldock, Hertfordshire SG7 6AE, United Kingdom. TEL 44-1462-895060, FAX 44-1462-892546, http://www.research-studies-press.co.uk. Ed. P S Nutman.

571.2 GBR
RESEARCH STUDIES IN PLANT SCIENCE. Text in English. irreg., latest vol.1, 2003. price varies.
Published by: Research Studies Press Ltd., 16 Coach House Cloisters, 10 Hitchin St, Baldock, Hertfordshire SG7 6AE, United Kingdom. TEL 44-1462-895060, FAX 44-1462-892546, info@research-studies-press.co.uk, http://www.research-studies-press.co.uk. Ed. D Murray.

REVIEW OF AROMATIC AND MEDICINAL PLANTS. see *BIOLOGY—Abstracting, Bibliographies, Statistics*

REVIEW OF MEDICAL AND VETERINARY MYCOLOGY. see *BIOLOGY—Abstracting, Bibliographies, Statistics*

REVIEW OF PLANT PATHOLOGY; consisting of abstracts and reviews of current literature on plant pathology. see *BIOLOGY—Abstracting, Bibliographies, Statistics*

REVIEW OF THE MALAYSIAN OIL PALM INDUSTRY (YEAR). see *ENERGY*

580 IND ISSN 0254-1300
REVIEW OF TROPICAL PLANT PATHOLOGY. Text in English. 1984. irreg. price varies. Supplement avail. **Document type:** *Monographic series.*
Indexed: BiolAb, CurCont.
—CISTI. **CCC.**
Published by: Today and Tomorrow's Printers & Publishers, 24 B-5 Desh Bandhu Gupta Rd., Karol Bagh, New Delhi, 110 005, India. tp@vsnl.net. Eds. J P Varma, S P Raychaudhuri. **Dist. in U.S. by:** Scholarly Publications, 2825 Wilcrest Dr, Ste 255, Houston, TX 77042. TEL 713-781-0070.

616.969 580 ARG ISSN 0325-4755
REVISTA ARGENTINA DE MICOLOGIA. Text in Spanish. 1978. 3/yr.
Published by: Asociacion Argentina de Micologia, Paraguay 2155, Buenos Aires, 1121, Argentina. TEL 54-11-4962 7274, FAX 54-11-4962 5404, micomuniz@connmed.com.ar.

580 BRA ISSN 0100-8404
QK263 CODEN: RRBODI
➤ **REVISTA BRASILEIRA DE BOTANICA/BRAZILIAN JOURNAL OF BOTANY.** Text in English, Portuguese, Spanish; Summaries in English, Portuguese. 1978. 4/yr. BRL 100 domestic; USD 100 foreign (effective 2002). abstr.; illus.; maps. 120 p./no.; back issues avail.; reprints avail. **Document type:** *Journal, Academic/Scholarly.* **Description:** Presents results of original research in botanical science.
Related titles: Online - full text ed.: free (effective 2005) (from SciELO).
Indexed: AgrForAb, BIOSIS Prev, BiolAb, CIN, CPA, ChemAb, ChemTitl, FCA, FPA, ForAb, HerbAb, HortAb, MaizeAb, OrnHort, PBA, PGegResA, PGrRegA, PHN&I, RA&MP, RefZh, RevApplEntom, S&F, SIA, SeedAb, WeedAb, ZooRec.
—CASDDS, CISTI.
Published by: Sociedade Botanica de Sao Paulo, Indianopolis, Caixa Postal 57088, Sao Paulo, SP 04093-970, Brazil. TEL 55-11-50736300, FAX 55-11-50733678, sbsp@botanicasp.org.br, http://www.scielo.br/rbb, http://www.botanicasp.org.br. Ed. Jefferson Prado. Circ: 500.

615.53 615.32 BRA ISSN 1516-0572
REVISTA BRASILEIRA DE PLANTAS MEDICINAIS/BRAZILIAN JOURNAL OF MEDICINAL PLANTS. Text in Portuguese; Summaries in English, Portuguese. 1998. 3/yr. BRL 20, USD 35 (effective 2000).
Indexed: AgBio, AgrForAb, BIOSIS Prev, BiolAb, CPA, DSA, ExcerpMed, FPA, FS&TA, ForAb, HelmAb, HortAb, I&DA, NutrAb, OrnHort, PBA, PGegResA, PGrRegA, PHN&I, PoultAb, ProtozoAb, RA&MP, RDA, RM&VM, RPP, S&F, SeedAb, TDB.
—BLDSC (7845.495000), IE.
Published by: Fundacao do Instituto de Biociencias (F U N D I B I O), U N E S P Campus de Botucatu, Distrito de Rubiao Jr., Botucatu, SP 18618 000, Brazil. TEL 55-14-8206255, FAX 55-14-8213744, broetto@ibb.unesp.br. Ed. Fernando Broetto.

571.92 BRA ISSN 0301-0406
REVISTA DE PATOLOGIA TROPICAL. Text in Portuguese. 1972. s-a. BRL 25 domestic; USD 35 foreign (effective 2002). **Document type:** *Academic/Scholarly.*
Indexed: AbHyg, BIOSIS Prev, BioCN&I, BiolAb, DSA, HelmAb, HortAb, IndVet, MaizeAb, NutrAb, PHN&I, PN&I, PoultAb, ProtozoAb, RA&MP, RDA, RM&VM, RPP, RRTA, RefZh, RevApplEntom, S&F, TDB, VetBull.
Published by: Universidade Federal de Goias, Instituto de Patologia Tropical e Saude Publica, Caixa Postal 131, Goiania, GO 74001-970, Brazil. TEL 55-62-2616797, FAX 55-62-202-3066, revista@iptsp.ufg.br, http://www.iptsp.ufg.br.

579.5 MEX ISSN 0187-3180
CODEN: RMMIEL
➤ **REVISTA MEXICANA DE MICOLOGIA.** Text in Spanish; Summaries in English, Spanish. 1968. a. adv. bk.rev. bibl.; charts; illus. index. cum.index. reprint service avail. from PQC. **Document type:** *Academic/Scholarly.*
Former titles (until 1985): Sociedad Mexicana de Micologia. Boletin (0085-6223); Sociedad Mexicana de Micologia. Boletin Informativo
Media: Duplicated (not offset). **Related titles:** Microform ed.: (from PQC).
Indexed: BiolAb, ForAb, HortAb, IndVet, PotatoAb, RM&VM, RPP, SIA, SeedAb, TriticAb, VetBull.
Published by: Sociedad Mexicana de Micologia, Calle INSURGENTES SUR 3700, Col Insurgentes Cuicuilco, Apartado Postal 101 63, Mexico City, DF 04530, Mexico. Ed. Joachim Cifuentes. Circ: 1,000.

➤ **REVUE DES SCIENCES NATURELLES D'AUVERGNE.** see *BIOLOGY*

580 ROM ISSN 0250-5517
QK1 CODEN: RRBVD5
REVUE ROUMAINE DE BIOLOGIE. SERIE BIOLOGIE VEGETALE. Text in English, French, German, Russian, Spanish. 1956. s-a. bk.rev. charts; illus. **Document type:** *Academic/Scholarly.*
Supersedes in part (in 1976): Revue Roumaine de Biologie (0250-6572); Which was formed by the 1974 merger of: Revue Roumaine de Biologie. Serie Botanique (0035-3914); Revue Roumaine de Biologie. Serie Zoologie (0035-3922); Both of which supersede (in 1964): Revue de Biologie (0484-8462)
Related titles: Online - full text ed.
Indexed: BioCN&I, BiolAb, CIN, ChemAb, ChemTitl, ExcerpMed, FCA, ForAb, HerbAb, HortAb, PBA, RPP, SeedAb, TriticAb, VITIS, WeedAb.
—CASDDS, CISTI, GNLM, KNAW, Linda Hall.
Published by: (Academia Romana, Institutul de Stiinte Biologice), Editura Academiei Romane/Publishing House of the Romanian Academy, Calea 13 Septembrie 13, Sector 5, Bucharest, 76117, Romania. TEL 40-21-4119008, FAX 40-21-4103983, edacad@ear.ro, http://www.ear.ro. Ed. Micolae Boscaiu. **Dist. by:** Rodipet S.A., Piata Presei Libere 1, sector 1, PO Box 33-57, Bucharest 3, Romania. TEL 40-21-2224126, 40-21-2226407, rodipet@rodipet.ro.

580 IND ISSN 0971-2313
QK358 CODEN: RHEEE2
➤ **RHEEDEA.** Text in English. 1991. s-a. INR 300 domestic to individuals; USD 150 foreign to individuals; INR 400 domestic to institutions; USD 200 foreign to institutions (effective 2001). bk.rev. **Document type:** *Academic/Scholarly.* **Description:** Contains original research papers on all aspects of flowering plant taxonomy.
Indexed: BIOSIS Prev, BiolAb.
—BLDSC (7960.100990), IE, ingenta.

Published by: Indian Association for Angiosperm Taxonomy, c/o University of Calicut, Department of Botany, Calicut, Kerala, India. TEL 91-0494-401144 x407, FAX 91-0494-400-269, akpradeep1@rediffmail.com, http://members.rediff.com/iaat. Ed. M. Sivadasan. Circ: 300.

580 USA ISSN 0035-4902
QK1 CODEN: RHODAB
➤ **RHODORA.** Text in English. 1899. q. USD 40 to individuals; USD 80 to institutions (effective 2005). bk.rev. charts; illus. index. back issues avail.; reprint service avail. from PQC. **Document type:** *Journal, Academic/Scholarly.* **Description:** Devoted primarily to the flora of North America.
Indexed: ASCA, ASFA, AgBio, Agr, AgrForAb, ApicAb, BIOSIS Prev, BibAg, BiolAb, CPA, ChemAb, CurCont, ESPM, FCA, FPA, ForAb, HerbAb, HortAb, I&DA, OrnHort, PBA, PGegResA, RPP, RefZh, S&F, SeedAb, WeedAb.
—BLDSC (7963.200000), CISTI, IE, Infotrieve, ingenta, Linda Hall.
Published by: New England Botanical Club, Inc., 22 Divinity Ave, Cambridge, MA 02138. TEL 617-308-3656, janets@hypatia.unh.edu, http://www.huh.harvard.edu/nebc/Rhodora.html. Ed., R&P Janet R Sullivan. Circ: 850 (paid).

579.5 ITA ISSN 0394-9486
RIVISTA DI MICOLOGIA. Text in Italian; Summaries in English, Italian. 1957. q. EUR 21 domestic; EUR 31 foreign (effective 2005). adv. bk.rev. bibl.; charts; illus. index. 96 p./no.; **Document type:** *Journal, Academic/Scholarly.* **Description:** Covers articles and research papers in the field of mycology.
Formerly (until 1986): Gruppo Micologico "G. Bresadola". Bollettino (0392-4874)
Indexed: ForAb, HerbAb, HortAb, OrnHort, PBA, PGegResA, RPP, S&F.
Published by: Associazione Micologica Bresadola, Via A Volta, 46, Trento, TN 38100, Italy. TEL 39-0461-913960, FAX 39-0461-913960, amb@ambbresadola.it, http://www.ambbresadola.it. Circ: 13,500.

580 BRA ISSN 0370-6583
QH301 CODEN: RODRAD
RODRIGUESIA; revista do Jardim Botanico do Rio de Janeiro. Text in Portuguese, Spanish, English. 1935; N.S. 1939 (Sep.). s-a., latest vol.51. bk.rev. abstr.; bibl. **Document type:** *Magazine, Consumer.*
Indexed: BiolAb, FPA, ForAb, RPP, RefZh.
—CISTI, Linda Hall.
Published by: (Biblioteca Barbosa Rodrigues), Jardim Botanico do Rio de Janeiro, Rua Pacheco Leao 915, Rio de Janeiro, RJ 22460-030, Brazil. TEL 55-21-2748246, FAX 55-21-2744897, bibiiot@jbrj.gov.br.

ROSE HYBRIDIZERS ASSOCIATION NEWSLETTER. see *GARDENING AND HORTICULTURE*

580 IRN ISSN 1608-4306
ROSTANIHA/BOTANICAL JOURNAL OF IRAN; botanical journal of Iran. Text in Persian, Modern; Summaries in English. 2000. a. (4 nos./vol.). free. charts; illus.; stat. **Document type:** *Journal, Academic/Scholarly.*
Indexed: BIOSIS Prev, BiolAb, CPA, FCA, FPA, ForAb, HerbAb, HortAb, PBA, PGegResA, PGrRegA, PotatoAb, RPP, S&F, SeedAb, TriticAb, WeedAb.
—Linda Hall.
Published by: Plant Pests and Diseases Research Institute/Mu'assasah Tahqiqat Afat va Bimarihay Giyahi, P O Box 1454, Tehran, 19395, Iran. TEL 98-21-2403012, FAX 98-21-2403691, http://www.magiran.com/rostaniha. Ed. M. Iranshahr.

580.095694 ISR ISSN 0333-9904
QK378
ROTEM. Text in Hebrew; Summaries in English. q. ILS 40. **Description:** Articles on the plants of Israel.
Indexed: IHP.
Published by: (Israel Plant Information Center), Society for the Protection of Nature in Israel, 4 Hashefela St, Tel Aviv, 66183, Israel. TEL 972-3-375063. Ed. G Pollack A Shmida.

ROTENBURGER SCHRIFTEN. see *HISTORY—History Of Europe*

580 ESP ISSN 0212-9108
RUIZIA; monografias del real jardin botanico. Text mainly in Spanish; Text occasionally in English, German. 1984. irreg. price varies or on exchange basis. bibl.; illus. index. back issues avail. **Document type:** *Monographic series.*
Indexed: HerbAb, IECT, PBA, PGegResA, RefZh.
—CINDOC, CISTI.
Published by: Real Jardin Botanico de Madrid, Plaza Murillo, 2, Madrid, 28014, Spain. TEL 34-1-4203017, FAX 34-1-4200157, TELEX 42182 CSIC E. Ed. Maria Teresa Telleria. Circ: 1,000. **Subscr. to:** Servicio de Publicaciones del C.S.I.C., Vitruvio, 8, Madrid 28006, Spain.

571.2 RUS ISSN 1021-4437
QK1 CODEN: RJPPE2
➤ **RUSSIAN JOURNAL OF PLANT PHYSIOLOGY.** Text in English. 1957. bi-m. EUR 3,348, USD 3,028, GBP 2,088 combined subscription to institutions print & online eds. (effective 2005). back issues avail. **Document type:** *Journal, Academic/Scholarly.* **Description:** Covers the full spectrum of plant physiology, bringing together the related aspects of biophysics, biochemistry, cytology, anatomy and genetics.
Incorporates: Russian Plant Physiology (1070-3292); Which was formerly (until 1994): Soviet Plant Physiology (0038-5719)
Related titles: Microfilm ed.: (from PQC); Online - full text ed.: ISSN 1608-3407 (from EBSCO Publishing, Gale Group, IngentaConnect, Kluwer Online, O C L C Online Computer Library Center, Inc., Ovid Technologies, Inc., Springer LINK, Swets Information Services); ♦ Translation of: Fiziologiya Rastenii. ISSN 0015-3303.
Indexed: AEA, ASCA, AgBio, AgrForAb, BibLing, BioCN&I, BiolAb, CPA, CTFA, ChemAb, ChemTitl, CurCont, DSA, FCA, FaBeAb, ForAb, HerbAb, HortAb, I&DA, IABS, ISR, MaizeAb, NemAb, OrnHort, PBA, PGegResA, PGrRegA, PHN&I, PotatoAb, RA&MP, RPP, RevApplEntom, RiceAb, S&F, SCI, SIA, SeedAb, SoyAb, TriticAb, VITIS, WeedAb.
—BLDSC (0420.763200), CASDDS, CISTI, IDS, IE, Infotrieve, ingenta, Linda Hall. **CCC.**
Published by: (Rossiiskaya Akademiya Nauk/Russian Academy of Sciences), M A I K Nauka - Interperiodica, Profsoyuznaya ul 90, Moscow, 117997, Russian Federation. TEL 7-095-3347420, FAX 7-095-3360666, compmg@maik.ru, http://www.maik.rssi.ru/journals/plntphys.htm, http://www.maik.ru. Ed. Vladimir V Kuznetsov. **Subscr. to:** Springer-Verlag Dordrecht, Journals Department, PO Box 322, Dordrecht, Netherlands. TEL 31-78-6576392, FAX 31-78-6576474.

580 RUS ISSN 1682-3540
PG3801
➤ **RUSSIAN JOURNAL OF THERIOLOGY.** Text in English. 2002. s-a. USD 40 foreign to individuals; USD 60 foreign to institutions (effective 2003). **Document type:** *Journal, Academic/Scholarly.* **Description:** Intended for general and special papers from all areas of theriology (taxonomy, phylogeny, morphology, palaeontology, ecology, zoogeography, faunistics).
Published by: K M K Scientific Press Ltd., c/o Dr K G Mikhailov, Zoologicheskii Muzei MGU, Bol'shaya Nikitskaya 6, Moscow, 125009, Russian Federation. TEL 7-095-2925796, FAX 7-095-2032717, kmk2000@online.ru, http://www.orc.ru/~kmkweb/rjt.htm. Pub. K Mikhailov.

580 JPN ISSN 0917-2157
SAGA NO SHOKUBUTSU/BOTANY OF SAGA. Text in Japanese. 1966. a.
Published by: Saga Shokubutsu Tomo no Kai/Botanical Society of Saga, c/o Mr Inoue, 4-6 Kono-Higashi 3-chome, Saga-shi, 840-0804, Japan.

580 USA
SAGE NOTES. Text in English. 1981. 4/yr. USD 10 to members (effective 1998). adv. bk.rev. **Document type:** *Newsletter.*
Published by: Idaho Native Plant Society, PO Box 9451, Boise, ID 83707. Ed. Sarah Walker. Circ: 400.

580 JPN ISSN 0917-6470
SAGO KOMYUNIKESHON/SAGO COMMUNICATION. Text in English, Japanese. 1990. 3/yr. free. bk.rev. **Document type:** *Academic/Scholarly.* **Description:** Covers sago palm research, industrialization, utilization and other sago palm related subjects.
Published by: Tsukuba Sago Kikin/Tsukuba Sago Fund, c/o Tsukuba Sago Fund, Institute of Applied Biochemistry, 791-27 Inaoka, Tsukuba-shi, Ibaraki-ken 305-0071, Japan. TEL 81-298-53-6631, FAX 81-298-53-4605, hisajima@sakura.cc.tsukuba.ac.jp. Ed. Shigeru Hisajima. Circ: 650.

580 JPN ISSN 0910-6863
SAITAMA-KEN HANA UEKI SENTA SHIKEN SEISEKISHO/SAITAMA PREFECTURE GARDEN PLANTS CENTER. TEST RESULTS. Text in Japanese. a.
Published by: Saitamaken Hana Ueki Senta/Saitama Prefecture Garden Plants Center, 124 Kushibiki, Fukaya-shi, Saitama-ken 366-0815, Japan.

580 CHE ISSN 0373-2525
QK1 CODEN: SAUSDH
➤ **SAUSSUREA**; journal de la Societe Botanique de Geneve. Text in French. 1970. a. CHF 49 to libraries (effective 2003). adv. illus.; abstr. **Document type:** *Journal, Academic/Scholarly.* **Description:** Disseminates scientific information in all fields of botany.
Supersedes: Societe Botanique de Geneve. Travaux (0583-8177)
Related titles: English ed.; German ed.; Italian ed.; Latin ed.; Spanish ed.
Indexed: BIOSIS Prev, BiolAb.
—CASDDS, CISTI, Linda Hall.
Published by: Societe Botanique de Geneve, Case Postale 60, Chambesy-Geneva, 1292, Switzerland. TEL 41-22-4185128, FAX 41-22-4185101, http://www.socbotge.ch. Ed., R&P Philippe Clerc. Adv. contact Andreas Fink TEL 41-22-8230223. page CHF 1,000. Circ: 400.

580 DEU ISSN 0085-5960
QK1 CODEN: SVGKAX
SCHRIFTENREIHE FUER VEGETATIONSKUNDE. Text in German. 1966. irreg., latest vol.34, 2000. price varies. charts; illus.; stat. **Document type:** *Monographic series, Government.*
Indexed: BiolAb.
Published by: (Germany. Bundesforschungsanstalt fuer Naturschutz und Landschaftsoekologie), Landwirtschaftsverlag GmbH, Huelsebrockstr 2, Muenster, 48165, Germany. TEL 49-2501-801-0, FAX 49-2501-801204, zentrale@lv-h.de, http://www.agrarshop.de.

579.7 CHE ISSN 0373-2959
CODEN: SZPLA7
SCHWEIZERISCHE ZEITSCHRIFT FUER PILZKUNDE/BOLLETTINO SVIZZERO DI MICOLOGIA/BULLETIN SUISSE DE MYCOLOGIE. Text in French, German, Italian. 1922. 10/yr. CHF 35. adv. bk.rev. illus. back issues avail. **Document type:** *Academic/Scholarly.* **Description:** Contains comprehensive information on all types of fungi, including special features on mushrooms and a fungus of the month.
Indexed: RPP.
Published by: Association Swiss Societies of Mycology, Registr 23, Obfelden, 8912, Switzerland. Ed., Adv. contact Ivan Cucchi. Circ: 5,200.

B

580.74 BEL ISSN 0779-2387
CODEN: SBBCBF
➤ **SCRIPTA BOTANICA BELGICA.** Text in English. 1992. irreg., latest vol.22, 2002. price varies. back issues avail. **Document type:** *Monographic series, Academic/Scholarly.*
Indexed: BIOSIS Prev, RefZh, ZooRec.
—BLDSC (8212.320000), IE, ingenta.
Published by: Jardin Botanique National de Belgique/Nationale Plantentuin van Belgie, Domaine de Bouchout, Nieuwelaan 38, Meise, 1860, Belgium. TEL 32-2-2693905, http://www.br.fgov.be. Ed. Elmar Robbrecht. Adv. contact Katrien Clarysse.

580 DEU ISSN 0341-3772
CODEN: SCGEDL
SCRIPTA GEOBOTANICA. Text in German. 1970. irreg. price varies. **Document type:** *Monographic series, Academic/Scholarly.*
—CASDDS, Linda Hall.
Published by: (Universitaet Goettingen, Lehrstuhl fuer Geobotanik), Verlag Erich Goltze GmbH und Co. KG, Hans-Boeckler-Str 7, Goettingen, 37079, Germany. TEL 49-551-506760, FAX 49-551-5067622. Ed. Hans Heller.

580 GBR
SEDUM SOCIETY NEWSLETTER. Text in English. 1987. q. GBP 7.50 domestic; GBP 12.50 in Europe; GBP 15 elsewhere. bk.rev. **Document type:** *Newsletter.*
Published by: Sedum Society, c/o Ron Mills, 173 Colchester Rd, W. Bergholt, Colchester, Essex CO6 3JY, United Kingdom. Ed. Ray Stephenson.

SEED ABSTRACTS. see *BIOLOGY—Abstracting, Bibliographies, Statistics*

580 CHE ISSN 0251-0952
SB114.A1 CODEN: SSTCBK
➤ **SEED SCIENCE AND TECHNOLOGY.** Abbreviated title: S S T. Text and summaries in English, French, German. 1973. 3/yr. CHF 300 (effective 2003). back issues avail. **Document type:** *Journal, Academic/Scholarly.*
Supersedes (1925-1972): International Seed Testing Association. Proceedings (0020-8663)
Related titles: Microfilm ed.: (from PQC).
Indexed: AEA, ASCA, AgBio, AgrForAb, BIOBASE, BIOSIS Prev, BioCN&I, BiolAb, CPA, ChemAb, CurCont, DBA, DSA, FCA, FPA, ForAb, HerbAb, HortAb, I&DA, IABS, MaizeAb, OrnHort, PBA, PGegResA, PGrRegA, PHN&I, PlantSci, RA&MP, RDA, RM&VM, RPP, RefZh, RevApplEntom, RiceAb, S&F, SIA, SeedAb, SoyAb, TriticAb, WAE&RSA, WeedAb.
—BLDSC (8218.140000), CASDDS, CISTI, IDS, IE, Infotrieve, ingenta, Linda Hall.
Published by: International Seed Testing Association, Zuerichstr 50, PO Box 308, Bassersdorf, 8303, Switzerland. TEL 41-1-8386000, FAX 41-1-8386001, ista.office@ista.ch, http://www.seedtest.org. Ed. A Buelow Olsen. Circ: 1,200.

581 GBR ISSN 1365-9863
THE SEED SEARCH. Text in English. 1996. a., latest 4th Ed. **Document type:** *Directory, Trade.* **Description:** Includes over 40 thousand seeds and where to buy them worldwide.
Published by: Karen Platt, Ed & Pub., 35 Longfield Rd, Crookes, Sheffield, S10 1QW, United Kingdom. k@seedsearch.demon.co.uk, mdove1@aol.com, http://www.seedsearch.demon.co.uk.

580 USA ISSN 0361-185X
QK1 CODEN: SELBDH
➤ **SELBYANA**; the journal of Marie Selby Botanical Gardens. Text in English; Abstracts occasionally in Spanish. 1975. a. USD 50 to individuals; USD 80 to institutions (effective 2004). bibl.; charts; illus.; maps. back issues avail. **Document type:** *Journal, Academic/Scholarly.* **Description:** Publishes original, biological research on tropical plants, especially epiphytes and their forest canopy habitats, including rain forests.

▼ new title ➤ refereed ✶ unverified ♦ full entry avail.

Indexed: AEA, AgBio, Agr, AgrForAb, BIOSIS Prev, BioCN&I, BiolAb, CPA, FPA, ForAb, HortAb, I&DA, OrnHort, PBA, PGegResA, PoultAb, RA&MP, RDA, RRTA, RefZh, S&F, SeedAb, TDB, WAE&RSA, WeedAb, ZooRec.
—Linda Hall.
Published by: Selby Botanical Gardens Press, 811 S Palm Ave, Sarasota, FL 34236-7726. TEL 941-366-5730 ext 264, FAX 941-951-1474, sbgpress@selby.org, http://www.selby.org/index.php?submenu=ResearchResources&src=gendocs&link=sbg_press&category=Research, http://www.selby.org/research/pubs.htm. Ed. Bruce Holst. R&P Barry Walden Walsh TEL 941-951-1474. Circ: 250.

580 631.5 UKR
SELEKTSIYA I NASINNYTSTVO; mizhvidomchyi tematychnyi naukovyi zbirnyk. Text in Ukrainian. 1964. irreg.
Formerly (until 1991): Selektsiya i Semenovodstvo (0582-5075)
—CISTI.
Published by: (Ukraine. Ministerstvo Sil'skoho Hospodarstva Ukrainy/Ministry of Agriculture of Ukraine), Vydavnytstvo Urozhai, Yaroslaviv val 10, Kyiv, 242034, Ukraine. TEL 0044-220-1626. Ed. D P Korzh.

B

580 BRA ISSN 0375-1651
➤ **SELLOWIA**; anais botanicos. Text and summaries in English, Portuguese. 1949. a., latest vol.49, 2000. USD 10 (effective 2002). adv. **Document type:** *Monographic series, Academic/Scholarly.*
Indexed: AgBio, CPA, ForAb, HortAb, PBA, PGegResA, S&F, SeedAb, WAE&RSA.
Published by: Herbario "Barbosa Rodrigues", Av Coronel Marcos Konder, 800, Centro, Itajai, SC 88301-122, Brazil. TEL 55-47-3488725, FAX 55-47-3488725, hbr@cttmar.univali.br. Ed., Pub. Ademir Reis. R&P, Adv. contact Zilda Helena Deschamps Bernardes. Circ: 1,000.

580 DEU ISSN 0944-0178
QK95 CODEN: SNDTER
SENDTNERA. Text in English, French, German, Spanish; Summaries in English. 1950. irreg. (1-2/yr.). per issue exchange basis. charts; illus. index. **Document type:** *Bulletin.*
Formerly (until 1991): Botanische Staatssammlung Muenchen. Mitteilungen (0006-8179)
Media: Duplicated (not offset).
Indexed: BIOSIS Prev, BiolAb, ForAb, HerbAb, HortAb, OrnHort, PBA, PGegResA, RPP, RefZh.
Published by: Botanische Staatssammlung Muenchen, Menzinger Str 67, Munich, 80638, Germany. TEL 49-89-17861254, FAX 49-89-17861240. Eds. F Schuhwerk, J Grau. Circ: 500 (controlled). **Co-sponsor:** Institut fuer Systematische Botanik.

580 JPN ISSN 0385-3985
SENNKE/TOHUKU PLANT ASSOCIATION. NEWS. Text in Japanese. 1973. a. JPY 1,000.
Published by: Tohoku Shokubutsu Aikokai, c/o Miyakonojo Shiritsu Kyodokan, 7-22 Himegi-cho, Miyakonojo-shi, Miyazaki-ken 885-0073, Japan. Ed. Itsuo Ogura. Circ: 150.

588.2 JPN ISSN 1343-0254
➤ **SENTAIRUI KENKYU/BRYOLOGICAL RESEARCH.** Text in Japanese, English; Summaries in English. 1972. 3/yr. JPY 3,000 (effective 2002). bk.rev. 44 p./no.; back issues avail. **Document type:** *Proceedings, Academic/Scholarly.* **Description:** Covers the scientific study of bryophyte.
Formerly (until 1997): Nihon Sentairui Gakkai Kaiho (0285-0869)
—BLDSC (2353.984000), IE.
Published by: Nihon Sentairui Gakkai/Bryological Society of Japan, Department of Biological Science, Graduate School of Science, Hiroshima University, 1-3-1 Kagamiyama, Higashi-hiroshima-shi, Hiroshima-ken 739-8526, Japan. TEL 81-824-24-7451, FAX 81-824-24-0734, hasegawa@nankyudai.ac.jp, http://sc1.cc.kochi-u.ac.jp/~bryosoc/. Ed. Jiro Hasegawa. Adv. contact Hironori Deguchi. Circ: 350 (controlled).

580 CZE ISSN 0231-9705
SEVEROCESKOU PRIRODOU. Text in Czech. 1969. irreg., latest vol.30, 1997. CZK 30 (effective 1999). **Document type:** *Bulletin.*
Published by: Okresni Vlastivedne Muzeum, Mirove nam 171, Litomerice, 41201, Czech Republic. TEL 420-416-731339, kubatk@pf.ujep.cz. R&P Karel Kubat.

575.6 DEU ISSN 0934-0882
QK827 CODEN: SPLRE7
➤ **SEXUAL PLANT REPRODUCTION.** Text in English. 1988. q. EUR 788 combined subscription to institutions print & online eds. (effective 2005). adv. back issues avail. **Document type:** *Journal, Academic/Scholarly.* **Description:** Focuses on experimental approaches to the dynamics and mechanisms of sexual processes in all plant forms.
Related titles: Microform ed.: (from PQC); Online - full text ed.: ISSN 1432-2145 (from EBSCO Publishing, Springer LINK, Swets Information Services).
Indexed: ASCA, AgBio, Agr, AgrForAb, BBCI, BIOBASE, BIOSIS Prev, BibAg, BiolAb, CPA, ChemAb, ChemTitl, CurCont, FCA, ForAb, HerbAb, HortAb, IABS, ISR, MaizeAb, OrnHort, PBA, PGegResA, PGrRegA, PlantSci, PotatoAb, RA&MP, RPP, RiceAb, SCI, SIA, SeedAb, SoyAb, TriticAb, VITIS, WeedAb.
—BLDSC (8254.484700), CASDDS, CISTI, IDS, IE, Infotrieve, ingenta, Linda Hall. **CCC.**
Published by: Springer-Verlag (Subsidiary of: Springer Science+Business Media), Tiergartenstr 17, Heidelberg, 69121, Germany. TEL 49-6221-3450, FAX 49-6221-345229, http://link.springer.de/link/service/journals/00497/index.htm. Adv. contact Stephan Kroeck TEL 49-30-827875739. **Subscr. in the Americas to:** Springer-Verlag New York, Inc., Journal Fulfillment, PO Box 2485, Secaucus, NJ 07096-2485. TEL 800-777-4643, 201-348-4033, FAX 201-348-4505, journals@springer-ny.com, http://www.springer-ny.com; **Subscr. to:** Springer GmbH Auslieferungsgesellschaft, Haberstr 7, Heidelberg 69126, Germany. TEL 49-6221-345-0, FAX 49-6221-345-4229, subscriptions@springer.de.

➤ **SHIDA SHOKUBUTSU BUNKEN MOKUROKU/ BIBLIOGRAPHY OF PTERIDOPHYTES BY JAPANESE FERNISTS.** see *BIOLOGY—Abstracting, Bibliographies, Statistics*

635.8 CHN ISSN 1005-9873
SHIYONGJUN XUEBAO/ACTA EDULIS FUNGI. Text in Chinese. 1994. q. **Document type:** *Journal, Academic/Scholarly.*
Related titles: Online - full text ed.: (from East View Information Services).
—BLDSC (0612.485000).
Published by: Shanghai Academy of Agricultural Sciences, Edible Fungi Research Institute, Shanghai, 201106, China. **Dist. by:** China International Book Trading Corp, 35 Chegongzhuang Xilu, Haidian District, PO Box 399, Beijing 100044, China. TEL 86-10-68412045, FAX 86-10-68412023, cibtc@mail.cibtc.com.cn, http://www.cibtc.com.cn.

580 JPN ISSN 0917-9798
SHIZUOKA SHOKUBUTSU KENKYU KAISHI/BOTANICAL SOCIETY OF SHIZUOKA. BULLETIN. Text in Japanese. 1987. every 4 yrs.
Published by: Shizuoka Shokubutsu Kenkyukai/Botanical Society of Shizuoka, c/o Mr Takehiko Suzaki, 7-3 Nakanodai 2-chome, Ihara-gun, Fujikawa-cho, Shizuoka-ken 421-3302, Japan.

580 JPN ISSN 0388-6212
SHOKUBUTSU CHIRI BUNRUI KENKYU/JOURNAL OF PHYTOGEOGRAPHY AND TAXONOMY. Text in English, Japanese. 1952. s-a. membership.
Published by: Shokubutsu Chiri Bunrui Gakkai/Society for the Study of Phytogeography and Taxonomy, c/o Mr Tatemi Shimizu, Kanazawa Daigaku Rigakubu, 1-1 Marunochi, Kanazawa-shi, Ishikawa-ken 920-0937, Japan.

580 JPN
SHOKUBUTSU KAGAKU CHOSETSU GAKKAI TAIKAI KENKYU HAPPYO KIROKUSHU/SOCIETY FOR CHEMICAL REGULATION OF PLANTS. PROCEEDINGS OF ANNUAL MEETING. Text in Japanese. 1965. a. **Document type:** *Proceedings.*
Published by: Shokubutsu Kagaku Chousetsu Gakkai/Japanese Society for Chemical Regulation of Plants, c/o Shokucho Bldg., Taito 1-26-6, Taito-ku, Tokyo, 110-0016, Japan.

580 JPN
SHOKUBUTSU KAGAKU SHINPOJUMU/SYMPOSIUM ON PHYTOCHEMISTRY. Text in Japanese; Summaries in English. a.
Published by: Shokubutsu Kagaku Kenkyukai/Phytochemical Society of Japan, Daigaku Yakugakubu, Syoyakugaku Shokubutsu Kagaku Kyoshitsu, 3-1 Hongo 7-chome, Bunkyo-ku, Tokyo, 113-0033, Japan.

580 JPN ISSN 1346-5406
CODEN: SKACD7
SHOKUBUTSU NO SEICHOU CHOUSETSU/REGULATION OF PLANT GROWTH & DEVELOPMENT. Text in Japanese. 1966. s-a. JPY 1,800.
Formerly (until 2000): Shokubutsu no Kagaku Chosetsu (0388-9130)
Indexed: AEA, AgBio, Agrind, CPA, ChemAb, ChemTitl, FCA, ForAb, HerbAb, HortAb, MaizeAb, OrnHort, PBA, PGegResA, PGrRegA, PHN&I, PotatoAb, RA&MP, RPP, RiceAb, S&F, SeedAb, SoyAb, TriticAb, WAE&RSA, WeedAb.
—BLDSC (7345.730000), CASDDS, IE, ingenta. **CCC.**
Published by: Shokubutsu Kagaku Chousetsu Gakkai/Japanese Society for Chemical Regulation of Plants, c/o Shokucho Bldg., Taito 1-26-6, Taito-ku, Tokyo, 110-0016, Japan. http://wwwsoc.nii.ac.jp/jscrp.

580 JPN
SHOKUBUTSU NO TOMO/BOTANICAL SOCIETY. JOURNAL. Text in Japanese. 1953. m. JPY 200 per issue.
Published by: Nihon Shokubutsu Tomo no Kai/Botanical Society, 20-12 Higashi-cho 5-chome, Koganei-shi, Tokyo-to 184-0011, Japan.

SHOKUBUTSU SOSHIKI SAIBOU BUNSHISEIBUTSU GAKKAI TAIKAI SHINPOJUMU KOEN YOSHISHU/JAPANESE SOCIETY FOR PLANT CELL AND MOLECULAR BIOLOGY. ABSTRACTS OF THE MEETING AND SYMPOSIUM. see *BIOLOGY—Abstracting, Bibliographies, Statistics*

580 JPN ISSN 0289-8233
SHOKUCHO/PHYTO-REGULATORS RESEARCH. Text in Japanese. 1967. m. JPY 400 per issue.
Published by: Nihon Shokubutsu Chosetsuzai Kenkyu Kyokai/Japan Association for Advancement of Phyto-Regulators, 26-6 Taito 1-chome, Taito-ku, Tokyo, 110-0016, Japan.

580 JPN ISSN 0286-6102
SHOKUCHU SHOKUBUTSU KENKYUKAI KAISHI/ INSECTIVOROUS PLANT SOCIETY. JOURNAL. Text in Japanese; Summaries in English. 1950. q. JPY 4,500, USD 40 (effective 2003). bk.rev. 30 p./no.; back issues avail. **Document type:** *Bulletin, Academic/Scholarly.*
Indexed: RefZh.
Published by: Shokuchu Shokubutsu Kenkyukai/Insectivorous Plant Society, c/o Department of Biology, Nippon Dental University, 9-20 Fujimi 1-chome, Chiyoda-ku, Tokyo, 102-0071, Japan. TEL 81-3-3261-8311, FAX 81-3-3264-8399, zvbo1357@nifty.ne.jp, http://www2.odn.ne.jp/~chr79360/. Ed. Shigeo Kurata. Circ: 600.

580 JPN ISSN 0915-003X
SHOKUSEISHI KENKYU/JAPANESE JOURNAL OF HISTORICAL BOTANY. Text in Japanese; Summaries in English. 1986. 2/yr. JPY 2,000.
—BLDSC (4655.175000).
Published by: Shokuseishi Kenkyukai/Japanese Association of Historical Botany, c/o Osaka Shiritsu Daigaku Rigakubu Seibutsugakka, 3-138 Sugimo-io 3-chome, Sumiyoshi-ku, Osaka-shi, 558-0022, Japan.

580 635 GBR ISSN 1352-4623
SHOWS (YEAR). Text in English. 1993. a. GBP 16.50 domestic membership; USD 34 in United States membership; GBP 18 elsewhere membership (effective 2000). **Document type:** *Bulletin.*
Published by: Alpine Garden Society, A G S Centre, Avon Bank, Pershore, Worcs WR10 3JP, United Kingdom. TEL 44-1386-554790, FAX 44-1386-554801, ags@alpinegardensociety.org, http://www.alpinegardensociety.org.

580 JPN ISSN 0913-5561
SHU SEIBUTSUGAKU KENKYU/STUDY OF SPECIES BIOLOGY. Text in Japanese. 1977. a.
Published by: Shu Seibutsu Gakkai/Society for the Study of Species Biology, c/o Kyoto Daigaku Rigakubu Shokubutsugaku Kyoshitsu, Oiwakecho, Kitashirakawa, Sakyo-ku, Kyoto-shi, 606, Japan.

580 JPN ISSN 0389-8865
SHUMI NO SAN'YASO/WILD FLOWERS AND ALPINE PLANTS. Text in Japanese. 1979. m. JPY 1,000 per issue.
Published by: Gekkan Satsuki Kenkyusha/Monthly Magazine of Satsuki Publishing Co., 2005-2 Onaribashi-cho 1-chome, Kanuma-shi, Tochigi-ken 322-0005, Japan.

580 JPN ISSN 0288-741X
SHUSHI SEITAI/SEED ECOLOGY. Text in English, Japanese; Summaries in English. 1969. a.
Published by: Shushi Seitai Danwakai/Research Group of Seed Ecology, Tohoku Daigaku Rigakubu Fuzoku Shokubutsuen, Kawauchi, Aoba-ku, Sendai-shi, Miyagi-ken 980-0862, Japan.

580 USA ISSN 0883-1475
➤ **SIDA: BOTANICAL MISCELLANY.** Text in English. 1987. irreg., latest vol.21, 2001. price varies. Website rev. **Document type:** *Monographic series, Academic/Scholarly.*
—CISTI, Linda Hall.
Published by: Botanical Research Institute of Texas, Inc., 509 Pecan St, Fort Worth, TX 76102-4060. TEL 817-332-4441, FAX 817-332-4112, sida@brit.org, info@brit.org, http://www.brit.org. Ed. Barney L Lipscomb TEL 817-332-7432. R&P Yonie Hudson. Circ: 850.

580 USA ISSN 0036-1488
QK1 CODEN: SCBTA4
➤ **SIDA: CONTRIBUTIONS TO BOTANY.** Text in English. 1962. s-a. USD 27 to individuals; USD 50 domestic to libraries; USD 60 foreign to libraries (effective 2000). bk.rev.; Website rev. index. reprints avail. **Document type:** *Academic/Scholarly.*
Indexed: AGBP, Agr, BIOBASE, BIOSIS Prev, BiolAb, IABS, PlantSci, RefZh, VITIS.
—CISTI, Linda Hall.
Published by: Botanical Research Institute of Texas, Inc., 509 Pecan St, Fort Worth, TX 76102-4060. TEL 817-332-4441, FAX 817-332-4112, sida@brit.org, info@brit.org, http://www.brit.org/sida/SidaContBot.htm, http: www.brit.org. Ed. Barney L Lipscomb TEL 817-332-7432. R&P Yonie Hudson. Circ: 850.

580 KOR ISSN 1225-8318
SIGMUL BUNRYU HAG-HOEJI/KOREAN JOURNAL OF PLANT TAXONOMY. Text in Korean. 1969. q. **Document type:** *Journal, Academic/Scholarly.*
—BLDSC (5113.574100).
Published by: Han-gug Sigmul Bunryu Hag-hoe/Plant Taxonomic Society of Korea, Soonchunhyang University, Department of Biology, Chungnam, 336-745, Korea, S. TEL 82-41-5301254, FAX 82-41-5301256, shinhy@sch.ac.kr, http://www.kaobs.or.kr/plant/.

581.2 JPN ISSN 1226-1203
SIGMUL BYEONG GWA NONG-EOB/RESEARCH IN PLANT DISEASE. Text in Korean. 1995. s-a. **Document type:** *Journal, Academic/Scholarly.*
Indexed: AEA, AgBio, BioCN&I, FCA, ForAb, HortAb, MaizeAb, NemAb, OrnHort, PBA, PHN&I, PotatoAb, RA&MP, RPP, RiceAb, S&F, SeedAb, SoyAb.
—BLDSC (7755.075730), CISTI.
Published by: Han-gug Sigmul Byeongri Hag-hoe/Korean Society of Plant Pathology, School of Agricultural Biotechnology, Seoul National University, Seoul, 441-744, Korea, S. kspp@shinbiro.com, http://society.kordic.re.kr/~kspp/. Ed. Young Ho Kim.

581.3 DEU ISSN 0037-5349
CODEN: SIGEAQ
➤ **SILVAE GENETICA**; Zeitschrift fuer Forstgenetik und Forstpflanzenzuechtung. Text in English, French, German. 1951. 6/yr. EUR 256.15 domestic; EUR 259.70 foreign (effective 2004). adv. bk.rev. abstr.; charts; illus. index. **Document type:** *Journal, Academic/Scholarly.* **Description:** Includes announcements and reports on meetings and congresses on forest tree breeding and genetics as well as other related fields.
Formerly (until 1957): Zeitschrift fuer Forstgenetik und Forstpflanzenzuechtung (0342-5878)
Indexed: ABIPC, ASCA, ASFA, AgBio, Agr, AgrForAb, B&BAb, BIOBASE, BIOSIS Prev, BiolAb, CIS, CPA, ChemAb, CurCont, Englnd, FPA, ForAb, GenetAb, HGA, HortAb, IABS, ISR, NemAb, OrnHort, PBA, PGegResA, PGrRegA, PlantSci, RA&MP, RPP, RefZh, RevApplEntom, S&F, SCI, SeedAb, VITIS.
—BLDSC (8281.500000), CASDDS, CISTI, IDS, IE, Infotrieve, ingenta, Linda Hall. **CCC.**
Published by: J.D. Sauerlaender's Verlag, Finkenhofstr 21, Frankfurt Am Main, 60322, Germany. TEL 49-69-555217, FAX 49-69-5964344, muhs@holz.uni-hamburg.de, aulbach@sauerlaender-verlag.com, http://www.bfafh.de/inst2/silvaege.htm, http://www.sauerlaender-verlag.de. Ed. H J Muhs.

580 SGP ISSN 0129-3729
Q80.S5 CODEN: JSNABL
SINGAPORE NATIONAL ACADEMY OF SCIENCE. JOURNAL. Text in English. 1977. a. SGD 32, USD 20.
Indexed: BAS, BiolAb, CIN, ChemAb, ChemTitl, Inspec, SFA, ZentMath.
—AskIEEE, CISTI, Linda Hall.
Published by: National University of Singapore, Department of Botany, Lower Kent Ridge Rd, Singapore, 0511, Singapore. Ed. A N Rao. Circ: 1,500.

580 BRA
SISTEMATICA DE PLANTAS INVASORAS. Text in Portuguese. 1988. biennial. USD 36.30.
Published by: Instituto Campineiro de Ensino Agricola, Rua Antonio Lapa, 78, Cambui, Caixa Postal 1148, Campinas, SP 13025-240, Brazil. TEL 32-4999, FAX 0192-470443. Circ: 3,000. **Subscr. to:** Rua Romualdo Andreazzi, 425, Jd Trevo, Campinas, SP 13036-100, Brazil.

582.16 CZE ISSN 0323-0724
SLEZSKE ZEMSKE MUZEUM. CASOPIS. SERIE C. DENDROLOGIE. Text in Czech. 1952. s-a.
Published by: Slezske Zemske Muzeum, Masarykova tr 35, Opava, 74646, Czech Republic.

580 USA ISSN 0081-024X
QK1 CODEN: SCBYAJ
SMITHSONIAN CONTRIBUTIONS TO BOTANY. Text in English. 1969. irreg., latest vol.90, 1999. free. reprint service avail. from PQC. **Document type:** *Monographic series.*
Indexed: ASFA, BIOSIS Prev, BiolAb, FPA, ForAb, HerbAb, HortAb, OceAb, OrnHort, PBA, PGegResA, RefZh, SFA, SeedAb.
—BLDSC (8311.530000), CISTI, Linda Hall. **CCC.**
Published by: Smithsonian Institution Press, 750 Ninth St., N. W., Suite 4300, Washington, DC 20560-0950. TEL 202-275-2233, FAX 202-275-2274. Ed. Diane Tyler. Circ: 1,400.

580 ARG ISSN 0373-580X
CODEN: BABOAQ
SOCIEDAD ARGENTINA DE BOTANICA. BOLETIN. Text in Spanish; Text occasionally in English; Summaries in English. 1945. q. USD 50. bk.rev. back issues avail.
Indexed: BiolAb.
—Linda Hall.
Published by: Sociedad Argentina de Botanica, Casilla de Correos 22, San Isidro, Buenos Aires 1642, Argentina. Ed. Nilda M Bacigalupo. Circ: 800. **Dist by:** Fernando Garcia Cambeiro, Skyway USA Ste 100, 7225 NW 25th St, P O Box 014, Miami, FL 33122.

581.634 ARG
➤ **SOCIEDAD ARGENTINA PARA LA INVESTIGACION DE PRODUCTOS AROMATICOS. ANALES.** Text in Spanish; Summaries in English, Spanish. 1977. irreg. (1-2/yr.). USD 35. **Document type:** *Proceedings, Academic/Scholarly.*
Description: Devoted to aromatic and medicinal plant research and marketing: agricultural, chemical, analytical, industrial, economic, statistical, ethno-botanical.
Formerly: Sociedad Argentina para la Investigacion de Productos Aromaticos. Boletin
Published by: Sociedad Argentina para la Investigacion de Productos Aromaticos, Libertad, 1079 Piso 2, Capital Federal, Buenos Aires 1012, Argentina. TEL 54-1-383-2360, postmaster@saipa.org.ar. Ed. Arnaldo L Bandoni. adv.: page USD 150. Circ: 600.

580 MEX ISSN 0366-2128
➤ **SOCIEDAD BOTANICA DE MEXICO. BOLETIN.** Text in English, Spanish. 1944. s-a. USD 30. bk.rev. charts; illus. cum.index: 1944-1990. **Document type:** *Bulletin, Academic/Scholarly.* **Description:** Presents papers on botanical research.
Indexed: BIOSIS Prev, BiolAb, FPA, ForAb, HortAb, OrnHort.
Published by: Sociedad Botanica de Mexico, A.C., Apdo. Postal 70-385, Del. Coyoacan; Ciudad Universitaria, Mexico City, DF 04510, Mexico. oyama@servidor.unam.mx. Ed. Ken Oyana. Circ: 1,000.

588.3 ESP ISSN 1132-8029
SOCIEDAD ESPANOLA DE BRIOLOGIA. BOLETIN. Text in Spanish. 1992. s-a.
Indexed: IECT.
—CINDOC.
Published by: Sociedad Espanola de Briologia, c/o Dept. of Medio Ambiente, Universida Europea de Madrid, Villaviciosa de Odon, Madrid, 28670, Spain.

579.5 ESP ISSN 0214-140X
QK608.S7
➤ **SOCIEDAD MICOLOGICA DE MADRID. BOLETIN.** Text in Spanish. 1976. s-a. bk.rev. **Document type:** *Bulletin, Academic/Scholarly.*
Formerly (until 1985): Sociedad Micologica Castellana (0210-7937)
Indexed: IECT.
—CINDOC.
Published by: Sociedad Micologica de Madrid, c/o Real Jardin Botanico, Claudio Moyano, 1, Madrid, 28014, Spain. FAX 34-1-4200157. Ed. Francisco D Calonge. Circ: 600.

580 PRT ISSN 0373-4641
SOCIEDADE BROTERIANA. ANUARIO. Text in Multiple languages; Summaries in English, French, Portuguese. 1935. a. **Document type:** *Corporate.* **Description:** Covers research on botanical science and history.
Indexed: BIOSIS Prev, BiolAb.
—CISTI, KNAW.
Published by: Sociedade Broteriana, Calcada Martim de Freitas, Coimbra, 3000-393, Portugal. TEL 351-239-855210, FAX 351-239-855211, socbrot@ci.uc.pt, http://www.fct.uc.pt. Eds. J F Mesquita, M T Leitao. Circ: 750. **Co-sponsor:** Universidade de Coimbra, Departamento de Botanica.

580 PRT ISSN 0081-0657
QK1 CODEN: BBRTAQ
SOCIEDADE BROTERIANA. BOLETIM. Text in Multiple languages; Summaries in English, French, Portuguese. 1880. a. **Document type:** *Bulletin.* **Description:** Covers research on taxonomic botany, cytotaxonomy, plant physiology, cytology, and electron microscopy.
Indexed: BIOSIS Prev, BiolAb, CPA, FCA, HerbAb, HortAb, PGrRegA, WeedAb.
—CISTI, KNAW, Linda Hall.
Published by: Sociedade Broteriana, Calcada Martim de Freitas, Coimbra, 3000-393, Portugal. TEL 351-239-855210, FAX 351-239-855211, socbrot@ci.uc.pt, http://www.fct.uc.pt. Eds. J F Mesquita, M T Leitao. Circ: 1,100. **Co-sponsor:** Universidade de Coimbra, Departamento de Botanica.

580.6 FRA ISSN 0037-9034
SOCIETE DE BOTANIQUE DU NORD DE LA FRANCE. BULLETIN. Text in French. 1947. a. bk.rev. **Document type:** *Bulletin.* **Description:** Studies the flora and vegetation of northern France.
Indexed: BiolAb.
Published by: Societe de Botanique du Nord de la France, Tresorerie, 14 les Hirsons, Lievin, 62800, France. Circ: 500. **Subscr. to:** S B N F, CCP Lille No. 284658 F, Centre de Cheque Postaux de Lille, Lille 59000, France.

SOCIETE DES SCIENCES NATURELLES DE L'OUEST DE LA FRANCE. BULLETIN. see *BIOLOGY—Zoology*

SOCIETE D'ETUDE DES SCIENCES NATURELLES DE NIMES ET DU GARD. BULLETIN. see *SCIENCES: COMPREHENSIVE WORKS*

SOCIETE D'ETUDE DES SCIENCES NATURELLES DE VAUCLUSE. BULLETIN. see *SCIENCES: COMPREHENSIVE WORKS*

SOCIETE D'ETUDES SCIENTIFIQUES DE L'ANJOU. BULLETIN. see *SCIENCES: COMPREHENSIVE WORKS*

580 590 FRA ISSN 0374-0706
CODEN: BSHCDD
SOCIETE D'HISTOIRE NATURELLE DE COLMAR. BULLETIN. Text in French. 1860. a., latest vol.63, 1995-97. bibl.; illus.; maps. back issues avail. **Document type:** *Bulletin.* **Description:** contains articles about the natural history of Alsace. Includes topics in zoology, botany, and geology.
Indexed: ZooRec.
—CISTI.
Published by: Societe d'Histoire Naturelle de Colmar, 11 rue de Turenne, Colmar, 68000, France. TEL 33-3-89238415, FAX 33-3-89412962.

571.2 FRA ISSN 0755-2491
SOCIETE D'HISTOIRE NATURELLE DU PAYS DE MONTBELIARD. BULLETIN. Text in French. 1958. a. **Document type:** *Journal, Academic/Scholarly.*
Indexed: ZooRec.
Published by: Societe d'Histoire Naturelle du Pays de Montbeliard, 138 Rue du General Leclerc, Seloncourt, 25230, France. philippe.vergon@wanadoo.fr.

579.5 FRA ISSN 0395-7527
SOCIETE MYCOLOGIQUE DE FRANCE. BULLETIN TRIMESTRIEL. Text in French. 1885. q. **Document type:** *Bulletin, Academic/Scholarly.*
Indexed: AgrForAb, FPA, ForAb, HortAb, NutrAb, PBA, PGegResA, RM&VM, S&F.
—CISTI, IE, Infotrieve, Linda Hall.
Published by: Societe Mycologique de France, 20 rue Rottembourg, Paris, 75012, France. TEL 33-1-44679690, FAX 33-1-44679690, smf@mycofrance.org, http://www.mycofrance.org.

580.74 NOR ISSN 0800-6865
➤ **SOMMERFELTIA.** Text in English. 1985. irreg. (approx. 2/yr.), latest vol.29, 2001. price varies. back issues avail. **Document type:** *Monographic series, Academic/Scholarly.*
Related titles: ♦ Supplement(s): Sommerfeltia. Supplement. ISSN 0802-8478.
Indexed: BiolAb.
—BLDSC (8327.839000), IE, ingenta, Linda Hall. **CCC.**
Published by: University of Oslo, Botanical Museum, Blindern, PO Box 1172, Oslo N, 0318, Norway. TEL 47-22-85-16-29, FAX 47-22-85-18-35, r.h.okland@nhm.uio.no. Ed., R&P Rune Halvorsen Oekland. Circ: 200.

580.74 NOR ISSN 0802-8478
SOMMERFELTIA. SUPPLEMENT. Text in English. 1990. irreg. price varies. back issues avail. **Document type:** *Monographic series, Academic/Scholarly.*
Related titles: ♦ Supplement to: Sommerfeltia. ISSN 0800-6865.
—Linda Hall.
Published by: University of Oslo, Botanical Museum, Blindern, PO Box 1172, Oslo N, 0318, Norway. TEL 47-22-85-16-29, FAX 47-22-85-18-35, r.h.okland@nhm.uio.no, http://www.toyen.uio.no/botanisk/sommerf/sm_intro.htm. Ed., R&P Rune Halvorsen Oekland.

580 635 USA ISSN 1075-1386
SONORAN QUARTERLY. Text in English. 1947. q. USD 40 to members. bk.rev. illus. **Document type:** *Bulletin.* **Description:** Covers desert gardening, horticulture and desert conservation and restoration.
Formerly: Saguaroland Bulletin (0275-6919)
Media: Duplicated (not offset).
Published by: Desert Botanical Garden, 1201 N Galvin Pkwy, Phoenix, AZ 85008. TEL 602-941-1225, http://www.dbg.org. Ed., R&P Jessica Roe. Circ: 6,000.

580 634.9 FIN ISSN 0359-3568
SORBIFOLIA. Text in Finnish, Swedish; Summaries in English. 1970. q. EUR 20. back issues avail. **Document type:** *Journal, Academic/Scholarly.*
Formerly (until 1982): Dendrologian Seuran Tiedotuksia (0355-0613)
Published by: Dendrologian Seura/Finnish Dendrological Society, c/o Botanical Museum, University of Helsinki, PO Box 7, Helsinki, 10014, Finland. FAX 358-9-19124456, http://www.dendrologianseura.fi/. Ed. Henry Vaere TEL 358-9-19124433.

580 ZAF ISSN 0254-6299
QK396 CODEN: SAJBDD
➤ **SOUTH AFRICAN JOURNAL OF BOTANY.** Text in English. 1975. q. ZAR 342 domestic to individuals; ZAR 380 in Africa to individuals; USD 145 elsewhere to individuals; ZAR 495 domestic to institutions; ZAR 495 in Africa to institutions; USD 220 elsewhere to institutions (effective 2004). adv. bk.rev. illus.; bibl.; maps; abstr. index. Supplement avail.; back issues avail. **Document type:** *Journal, Academic/Scholarly.*
Description: Brings an original contribution to any field of botany and offers a reference source for those who are interested in the extensive southern African flora and vegetation.
Incorporates (in 1985): Journal of South African Botany (0022-4618)
Related titles: Online - full text ed.: ISSN 1727-9321 (from EBSCO Publishing, Gale Group, IngentaConnect, International Network for the Availability of Scientific Publications, African Journals Online).

Indexed: ASCA, ASFA, AgBio, Agr, AgrForAb, ApEcolAb, ApicAb, B&BAb, BIOBASE, BIOSIS Prev, BioCN&I, BiolAb, CIN, CPA, ChemAb, ChemTitl, CurCont, ESPM, FCA, FPA, ForAb, GEOBASE, GenetAb, HGA, HelmAb, HerbAb, HortAb, I&DA, IABS, IBR, INIS AtomInd, ISAP, IndVet, MBA, MaizeAb, NutrAb, OrnHort, PBA, PGegResA, PGrRegA, PHN&I, PlantSci, ProtozoAb, RA&MP, RDA, RM&VM, RPP, RRTA, RevApplEntom, S&F, SIA, SWRA, SeedAb, SoyAb, TDB, TriticAb, VITIS, VetBull, WAE&RSA, WeedAb.
—BLDSC (8338.730000), CASDDS, CISTI, IDS, IE, ingenta, Linda Hall.
Published by: (South African Association of Botanists), National Inquiry Services Centre (Pty) Ltd (Subsidiary of: N I S C USA), PO Box 377, Grahamstown, 6140, South Africa. TEL 27-46-622-9698, FAX 27-46-622-9550, info@nisc.co.za, subs@nisc.co.za, http://www.inasp.info/ajol/journals/sajb/about.html, http://www.nisc.co.za. Ed. Johannes van Staden. Pub., Adv. contact Georgina Jones. R&P Margaret Crampton. B&W page USD 300; trim 175 x 245. Circ: 750. **Co-sponsor:** National Botanic Gardens of South Africa, Kirstenbosch Botanic Garden.

➤ **SOUTH AFRICAN JOURNAL OF PLANT AND SOIL.** see *AGRICULTURE—Crop Production And Soil*

577 595.7 USA ISSN 1528-7092
QH1 CODEN: SNOAAL
➤ **SOUTHEASTERN NATURALIST.** Text in English. 2002 (Mar.). q. USD 45 domestic to individuals; USD 50 in Canada & Mexico to individuals; USD 54 elsewhere to individuals; USD 75 domestic to institutions; USD 80 in Canada & Mexico to institutions; USD 84 elsewhere to institutions (effective 2005). **Document type:** *Journal, Academic/Scholarly.* **Description:** Features research articles and notes on terrestrial, freshwater, and marine organisms and their habitats in the southeastern United States.
Related titles: Online - full text ed.: 2002 (from BioOne, C S A, EBSCO Publishing, O C L C Online Computer Library Center, Inc.).
Indexed: ASFA, AgBio, AnBrAb, BIOSIS Prev, BiolAb, CurCont, ESPM, EntAb, FPA, ForAb, GardL, HerbAb, HortAb, IndVet, OrnHort, PBA, PGegResA, PN&I, PoultAb, RPP, RefZh, S&F, SWRA, SeedAb, WAE&RSA, WeedAb, ZooRec.
—BLDSC (8352.467000), IE, Linda Hall.
Published by: Humboldt Field Research Institute, 59 Eagle Hill Rd, PO Box 9, Steuben, ME 04680-0009. TEL 207-546-2821, FAX 207-546-3042, office@eaglehill.us, http://www.eaglehill.us/jsgeninf.html. Ed. Glen H Mittelhauser. Pub., R&P, Adv. contact Joerg-Henner Lotze TEL 207-546-2821.

571.9 ZAF
SOUTHERN AFRICAN PLANT PATHOLOGY. Text in Afrikaans, English. 1981. s-a. illus. **Document type:** *Newsletter.*
Formerly (until vol.14): S.A. Plant Pathologist (1018-4309)
Published by: Southern African Society for Plant Pathology, Private Bag X5013, Stellenbosch, 7599, South Africa.

SOYBEAN ABSTRACTS (ONLINE EDITION). see *BIOLOGY—Abstracting, Bibliographies, Statistics*

SPAIN. MINISTERIO DE AGRICULTURA, PESCA Y ALIMENTACION. BOLETIN DE SANIDAD VEGETAL: PLAGAS. see *AGRICULTURE—Crop Production And Soil*

580 ZAF ISSN 1025-322X
STRELITZIA. Text in English. 1994. irreg., latest vol.8, 1998. price varies. back issues avail. **Document type:** *Monographic series, Academic/Scholarly.* **Description:** Publishes proceedings and treatises on ecology, taxonomy and economic botany.
Formed by the 1989 merger of: Kirstenbosh Botanic Gardens. Annals (0258-3305); Which was formerly (until 1986): Journal of South African Botany. Supplementary Volume (0258-5626); And: Botanical Society of South Africa. Memoirs (0252-9432); Which was formerly (until 1977): South Africa. Department of Agricultural Technical Services. Botanical Survey Memoir (0375-1546); Botanical Survey of South Africa Memoir (0374-2083)
Indexed: BIOSIS Prev, BiolAb, FPA, ForAb, S&F.
—Linda Hall.
Published by: National Botanical Institute, NBI Bookshop, Private Bag X101, Pretoria, Cape Province 0001, South Africa. TEL 27-21-8043200, FAX 27-21-8043211, bookshop@nbipre.nbi.ac.za, http://www.nbi.ac.za. R&Ps B A Momberg, E Du Plessis.

580 ESP ISSN 0211-9714
CODEN: STBOEA
STUDIA BOTANICA. Text in Spanish. 1982. a., latest vol.18, 1999. **Document type:** *Academic/Scholarly.*
Indexed: BIOSIS Prev, BiolAb, HerbAb, HortAb, IECT, TriticAb, WeedAb.
—CINDOC.
Published by: (Universidad Pontificia de Salamanca, Departamento de Biologia Vegetal, Botanica), Ediciones Universidad de Salamanca, Apartado 325, Salamanca, 37080, Spain. TEL 34-923-294598, FAX 34-923-262579, http://www3.usal.es/~eus/indexsp.htm. Ed. Miguel Ladero Alvarez. Circ: 500.

580 HUN ISSN 0301-7001
QK311 CODEN: SBHUBV
STUDIA BOTANICA HUNGARICA. Text in English. 1961-1969; resumed 1973. a. USD 24 (effective 2001). illus. back issues avail. **Document type:** *Journal, Academic/Scholarly.*
Description: Contains papers written by museum staff members or based on material deposited there.
Incorporates (1961-1969): Fragmenta Botanica (0532-3347)
Indexed: BIOSIS Prev, BiolAb.
Published by: Magyar Termeszettudomanyi Muzeum, Baross utca 13, Budapest, 1088, Hungary. TEL 36-1-2101330, FAX 36-1-3171669, perego@zoo.zoo.nhmus.hu, http://www.nhmus.hu. Eds. Bea Papp, I Matskasi TEL 36-1-2677100. R&P, Adv. contact I Matskasi TEL 36-1-2677100. Circ: 350.

580 POL ISSN 0082-5557
QK1.T7
STUDIA SOCIETATIS SCIENTIARUM TORUNENSIS. SECTIO D. BOTANICA. Text in Polish; Summaries in English, German. 1951. irreg., latest vol.12, no.2, 1990. price varies. **Document type:** *Monographic series.*
Indexed: BiolAb.
Published by: Towarzystwo Naukowe w Toruniu, Ul-Wysoka 16, Torun, 81100, Poland. TEL 48-56-23941. Ed. Klemens Kepczynski.

579.5 NLD ISSN 0166-0616
QK600 CODEN: SMYCA2
➤ **STUDIES IN MYCOLOGY.** Text in English. 1972. irreg., latest vol.46, 2001. price varies. back issues avail. **Document type:** *Academic/Scholarly.* **Description:** Publishes studies relating to mycological taxonomy.
Indexed: ASCA, AbHyg, AgBio, BIOSIS Prev, BioCN&I, BiolAb, ChemAb, CurCont, ISR, IndVet, RM&VM, RPP, S&F, SCI.
—BLDSC (8491.145000), CASDDS, CISTI, IDS, IE, ingenta, KNAW.
Published by: Centraalbureau voor Schimmelcultures/Fungal Biodiversity Center, Uppsalalaan 8, Utrecht, 3584 CT, Netherlands. TEL 31-30-2122600, FAX 31-30-2512097, info@cbs.knaw.nl, http://www.cbs.knaw.nl. Ed. R.A. Samson. R&P R A Samson.

580 NLD ISSN 0928-3420
CODEN: SPLCEU
➤ **STUDIES IN PLANT SCIENCE.** Text in English. 1991. irreg., latest vol.8, 2001. price varies. back issues avail. **Document type:** *Monographic series, Academic/Scholarly.* **Description:** Disseminates research in all areas of botany.
Indexed: Agr, CIN, ChemAb, ChemTitl, MSB.
—BLDSC (8491.223520), CASDDS, CISTI. **CCC.**
Published by: Elsevier BV (Subsidiary of: Elsevier Science & Technology), Radarweg 29, Amsterdam, 1043 NX, Netherlands. TEL 31-20-4853911, FAX 31-20-4852457, nlinfo-f@elsevier.nl, http://www.elsevier.nl.

580 ROM ISSN 1220-5001
STUDII SI CERCETARI DE BIOLOGIE. SERIA BIOLOGIE VEGETALA. Text in Romanian. 1948. 2/yr.
Supersedes in part (in 1975): Studii si Cercetari de Biologie (1015-2237); Which was formed by the merger of (1958-1973): Studii si Cercetari de Biologie. Serie Botanica (0370-8934); Which was formerly (until 1963): Studii si Cercetari de Biologie. Seria Biologie Vegetala (0365-5997); And (1958-1973): Studii si Cercetari de Biologie. Serie Zoologie (0370-8950); Which was formerly (until 1963): Studii si Cercetari de Biologie. Seria Biologie Animala (0365-5962)
Indexed: BiolAb, CIN, ChemAb, ChemTitl, FCA, HerbAb, PBA, RPP, RefZh, TriticAb.
—BLDSC (8492.800000), CISTI, Linda Hall.
Published by: (Academia Romana), Editura Academiei Romane/Publishing House of the Romanian Academy, Calea 13 Septembrie 13, Sector 5, Bucharest, 76117, Romania. Ed. Nicolae Boscaiu. **Dist. by:** Rodipet S.A., Piata Presei Libere 1, sector 1, PO Box 33-57, Bucharest 3, Romania. TEL 40-21-2224126, 40-21-2226407, rodipet@rodipet.ro.

580 JPN ISSN 0917-1347
SUGE NO KAI KAIHO/JAPANESE CYPERACEAE NEWSLETTER. Text in Japanese. 1990. 2/yr. **Document type:** *Newsletter.*
Published by: Suge no Kai/Japanese Cyperaceae Association, Okayama Rika Daigaku Rigakubu Seibutsugaku Kyoshitsu, 1-1 Ridai-cho, Okayama-shi, 700-0005, Japan.

580 BRA ISSN 0100-5405
CODEN: SUPHDV
➤ **SUMMA PHYTOPATHOLOGICA.** Text mainly in Portuguese; Text occasionally in English, Spanish. 1975. q. BRL 50, USD 40 to non-members (effective 2003). adv. bk.rev. abstr.; bibl.; charts. back issues avail. **Document type:** *Academic/Scholarly.* **Description:** Covers plant diseases and plant pathogens.
Indexed: AEA, AgBio, AgrForAb, BIOSIS Prev, BioCN&I, BiolAb, CIN, CPA, ChemAb, ChemTitl, FCA, FPA, FS&TA, ForAb, HerbAb, HortAb, I&DA, MaizeAb, NemAb, NutrAb, OrnHort, PBA, PGegResA, PGrRegA, PHN&I, PotatoAb, PoultAb, RA&MP, RPP, RefZh, RevApplEntom, RiceAb, S&F, SIA, SeedAb, SoyAb, TOSA, TriticAb, VITIS, WAE&RSA, WeedAb.
—CASDDS.
Published by: Grupo Paulista de Fitopatologia, Fazenda Experimental Lageado, Botucatu, SP 18603-970, Brazil. TEL 55-14-6802-7262, FAX 55-14-68027206, summa@fca.unesp.br, http://www.summanet.com.br. Ed. Nilton Luiz de Souza. Circ: 1,000.

579.5 DNK ISSN 0106-7451
SVAMPE. Text in Danish; Summaries in English. 1980. 2/yr. DKK 120 (effective 2003). bk.rev. charts; illus. **Document type:** *Bulletin.*
Indexed: ForAb, S&F.
Published by: Foreningen til Svampekundskabens Fremme/Danish Mycological Society, Soendermarken 75, Espergaerde, 3060, Denmark. TEL 45-24-460223, svampe@e-box.dk, http://www.mycosoc.dk/svampe/svampe.htm. Ed. Jan Vesterholt. Circ: 2,400.

580 SWE ISSN 0039-646X
QK1 CODEN: SBOTAS
SVENSK BOTANISK TIDSKRIFT. Text in English, French, German, Latin, Swedish. 1907. bi-m. SEK 295 domestic; SEK 435 in Europe; SEK 535 elsewhere (effective 2004). adv. bk.rev. bibl.; charts; illus. index, cum.index every 20 yrs. back issues avail. **Document type:** *Academic/Scholarly.*
Related titles: Microfiche ed.: (from BHP, IDC).
Indexed: ASFA, AgrForAb, BIOSIS Prev, BiolAb, ChemAb, FCA, FPA, ForAb, GEOBASE, HerbAb, HortAb, OrnHort, PBA, PGegResA, PoultAb, RA&MP, RPP, RRTA, S&F, SeedAb, WeedAb.
—BLDSC (8556.000000), CISTI, IE, ingenta, Linda Hall. **CCC.**
Published by: Svenska Botaniska Foereningen, Avd. foer Vaextekologi, Uppsala Universitet, Villavaegen 14, Uppsala, 75236, Sweden. TEL 46-18-4712891, FAX 46-18-553419, linda.svensson@sbf.c.se, sbt@sbf.c.se, http://www.sbf.c.se/sbt.htm. Ed. Bengt Carlsson. Adv. contact Linda Svensson. Circ: 2,800.

579.6 SWE ISSN 1653-0357
SVENSK MYKOLOGISK TIDSKRIFT. Text in Swedish. 1980. biennial. SEK 200 domestic; SEK 250 foreign (effective 2005). **Document type:** *Journal, Academic/Scholarly.*
Former titles (until 2005): Jordstjaernan (0280-5057); (until 1982): Sveriges Mykologiska Foerening. Medlemsblad (0280-1825); Incorporates (1983-2004): Windahlia (0282-082X)
Published by: Sveriges Mykologiska Foerening/Swedish Mychological Society, c/o Hjalmar Croneborg, PO Box 7007, Uppsala, 75007, Sweden. info@svampar.se, http://www.svampar.se. Eds. Jan Nilsson, Mikael Jeppson.

580 SWE ISSN 0375-2038
QH44 CODEN: SLARAM
➤ **SVENSKA LINNE-SALLSKAPET AARSSKRIFT/SWEDISH LINNEUS SOCIETY. YEARBOOK.** Text in English, Swedish; Summaries in English. 1918. a. SEK 100, USD 20 (effective 1999). bk.rev. **Document type:** *Academic/Scholarly.*
Indexed: MLA-IB, ZooRec.
Published by: Linne-Sallskapet, Department of Culture Sciences, Biskopsgatan 7, Lund, 22362, Sweden. TEL 46-46-222-75-89, FAX 46-46-222-46-06, gunnar.broberg@kult.lu.se. Ed. Gunnar Broberg. Circ: 800.

580 IND ISSN 0256-9493
➤ **SWAMY BOTANICAL CLUB. JOURNAL;** a journal of plant sciences. Text in English. 1984. q. USD 40 to individuals; USD 80 to institutions. adv. bk.rev. back issues avail. **Document type:** *Academic/Scholarly.* **Description:** Contains research papers on all aspects of plant sciences.
Published by: Swamy Botanical Club, Dept. of Plant Sciences, c/o Dr. K.V. Krishnamurthy, Bharathidasan University, Tiruchirappalli, Tamil Nadu 620 024, India. TEL 91-431-660351, FAX 91-431-660245, TELEX 0455-253 BARD IN, kvk@bdu.ernet.in. R&P K V Krishnamurthy. adv.: B&W page INR 3,500. Circ: 250.

579.5 AUT ISSN 0082-0598
QK600 CODEN: SYAMAU
SYDOWIA: ANNALES MYCOLOGICI; editii in notitiam scientiae mycologicae universalis. Text in English, German, Latin. 1947. a. EUR 79.95 (effective 2003). **Document type:** *Journal, Academic/Scholarly.*
Related titles: Microfiche ed.: (from BHP); ♦ Supplement(s): Beihefte Zur Sydowia. ISSN 1016-0019.
Indexed: AgBio, AgrForAb, BIOSIS Prev, BioCN&I, BiolAb, CurCont, FCA, FPA, FS&TA, ForAb, HelmAb, HerbAb, HortAb, ISR, NemAb, PBA, PGegResA, PHN&I, RA&MP, RM&VM, RPP, RevApplEntom, S&F, SCI, SeedAb, VITIS, WeedAb.
—BLDSC (8578.900000), IDS, IE, ingenta, Linda Hall.
Published by: Verlag Ferdinand Berger und Soehne GmbH, Wienerstr 80, Horn, N 3580, Austria. TEL 43-2982-4161332, FAX 43-2982-4161382, office@berger.at, http://www.berger.at. Ed. O Petrini.

580 SWE ISSN 0082-0644
SYMBOLAE BOTANICAE UPSALIENSES. Text and summaries in English, French, German. 1932. irreg., latest vol.33, no.1, 2000. price varies. back issues avail. **Document type:** *Monographic series, Academic/Scholarly.*
Related titles: ♦ Series of: Acta Universitatis Upsaliensis. ISSN 0346-5462.
Indexed: AgBio, AgrForAb, BIOSIS Prev, BiolAb, FCA, ForAb, HerbAb, HortAb, PBA, PGegResA, RPP, SeedAb, WeedAb.
—CISTI, KNAW, Linda Hall.

Published by: (Uppsala Universitet, Botaniske Institutionerna, Uppsala), Uppsala Universitet, Acta Universitatis Upsaliensis/University Publications from Uppsala, PO Box 256, Uppsala, 75105, Sweden. TEL 46-18-4713922, http://www.ub.uu.se/upu/auu. Ed. Bengt Landgren. **Dist. by:** Almqvist & Wiksell International.

580 USA ISSN 0363-6445
QK95
➤ **SYSTEMATIC BOTANY.** Text in English. 1976. q. USD 145 combined subscription to institutions print & online eds. (effective 2006). adv. bk.rev. illus. back issues avail. **Document type:** *Journal, Academic/Scholarly.* **Description:** This society is organized to foster, encourage and promote education and research in the field of plant taxonomy, to include those areas and fields of study that contribute to and bear upon the theory and practice of plant systematics.
Related titles: Online - full content ed.: ISSN 1548-2324 (from BioOne); Online - full text ed.: (from BioOne, C S A, EBSCO Publishing, Gale Group, IngentaConnect, JSTOR (Web-based Journal Archive), O C L C Online Computer Library Center, Inc.).
Indexed: ASCA, ASFA, AgBio, Agr, AgrForAb, B&AI, B&BAb, BIOBASE, BIOSIS Prev, BibAg, BiolAb, CPA, CurCont, ESPM, FCA, FPA, ForAb, GenetAb, HerbAb, HortAb, IABS, ISR, MaizeAb, OrnHort, PBA, PGegResA, PlantSci, PotatoAb, RA&MP, RefZh, S&F, SCI, SeedAb, SoyAb, TOSA, TriticAb, VITIS, WeedAb.
—BLDSC (8589.181500), CISTI, IDS, IE, Infotrieve, ingenta, Linda Hall. **CCC.**
Published by: American Society of Plant Taxonomists, University of Wyoming, Dept. of Botany 3165, 1000 E University Ave., Laramie, WY 82071-3165. FAX 307-766-2851, aspt@uwyo.edu, http://www.sysbot.org/, http://www.aspt.net/. Ed. Patrick S Herendeen. Circ: 1,700 (paid).

578.012 USA ISSN 0737-8211
QK95
➤ **SYSTEMATIC BOTANY MONOGRAPHS.** Text in English. 1980. irreg. (4-6/yr.), latest vol.64. price varies. bibl.; charts; illus.; maps; abstr. back issues avail. **Document type:** *Monographic series, Academic/Scholarly.* **Description:** Monographs in taxonomic botany for professional botanists and ecologists.
Indexed: AgrForAb, ApicAb, ForAb, PBA, PGegResA, PotatoAb. **—CCC.**
Published by: American Society of Plant Taxonomists, University of Wyoming, Dept. of Botany 3165, 1000 E University Ave., Laramie, WY 82071-3165. chra@umich.edu. Circ: 500 (paid).

580.74 BEL ISSN 1374-7886
QK1 CODEN: STGPF5
➤ **SYSTEMATICS AND GEOGRAPHY OF PLANTS/NATIONALE PLANTENTUIN VAN BELGIE. BULLETIN.** Text in French, English. 1902. s-a. EUR 95 (effective 2003). bk.rev. illus.; charts; maps. cum.index: vols.26-50. back issues avail. **Document type:** *Journal, Academic/Scholarly.* **Description:** International journal devoted to the systematics of all plant groups and fungi, including related fields such as phytogeography, evolution, comparative morphology, pollen and spores, and vegetation studies. It publishes original research papers (especially those with regional emphasis on Western Europe and tropical Africa,) articles and book reviews.
Former titles (until 1999): Jardin Botanique National de Belgique. Bulletin (0303-9153); (until 1967): Jardin Botanique de l'État a Bruxelles. Bulletin (0374-6313)
Indexed: AGBP, AgBio, AgrForAb, B&AI, BIOBASE, BIOSIS Prev, BiolAb, CPA, FCA, FPA, ForAb, HerbAb, HortAb, I&DA, NutrAb, OrnHort, PBA, PGegResA, ProtozoAb, RA&MP, RDA, RPP, RefZh, S&F, SIA, SeedAb, SoyAb, TDB, WeedAb.
—BLDSC (8589.235000), CISTI, Linda Hall.
Published by: Jardin Botanique National de Belgique/Nationale Plantentuin van Belgie, Domaine de Bouchout, Nieuwelaan 38, Meise, 1860, Belgium. TEL 32-2-2693905, http://www.br.fgov.be. Ed. Elmar Robbrecht. Adv. contact Katrien Clarysse.

580 630 POL ISSN 0860-3294
SZCZECINSKIE ROCZNIKI NAUKOWE. NAUKI PRZYRODNICZE I ROLNICZE. Variant title: Annales Scientiarum Stetinenses, Nauki Przyrodnicze i Rolnicze. Text in Polish. 1986. a. price varies. **Document type:** *Academic/Scholarly.*
Indexed: AgrLib.
Published by: Szczecinskie Towarzystwo Naukowe, ul Wojska Polskiego 96, Szczecin, 71481, Poland. TEL 48-91-4231862, wtarc@univ.szczecin.pl, http://www.stn.szc.pl.

579.5 USA
T E O N A N A C A T L; the international journal of psychoactive mushrooms. Text in English. 2002 (Aug.). q. USD 20 domestic; USD 30 foreign (effective 2002).
Related titles: E-mail ed.
Published by: F M R C, PO Box 18105, Pensacola, FL 32523-8105. TEL 850-327-4378, FloridaMycology@cs.com, http://www.mushroomsfmrc.com/cgi-bin/webc/home.html.

TAIWAN AGRICULTURAL RESEARCH INSTITUTE. RESEARCH SUMMARY. see *AGRICULTURE*

TAIWAN LINYE KEXUE/TAIWAN JOURNAL OF FOREST SCIENCE. see *FORESTS AND FORESTRY*

579.8 JPN ISSN 0385-3373
TANSUI SORUI KENKYU/STUDIES OF FRESHWATER ALGAE. Text in Japanese. 1975. every 5 yrs.
Published by: Tansui Sorui Kenkyukai/Society of Freshwater Algology, c/o Mr Ichiro Ito, 1148-7 Ino-Machi, Takasaki-shi, Gunma-ken 370-0004, Japan.

580 NLD ISSN 0167-9406
CODEN: TUSCD8
➤ **TASKS FOR VEGETATION SCIENCE.** Text in English. 1981. irreg., latest vol.39, 2003. price varies. **Document type:** *Monographic series, Academic/Scholarly.*
Indexed: Agr, BIOSIS Prev, ZooRec.
—BLDSC (8606.667400), CASDDS, CISTI. **CCC.**
Published by: Springer-Verlag Dordrecht (Subsidiary of: Springer Science+Business Media), Van Godewijckstraat 30, Dordrecht, 3311 GX, Netherlands. TEL 31-78-6576050, FAX 31-78-6576474, http://www.springeronline.com. Eds. Anselm Kratochwil, Helmut Lieth.

580 AUT ISSN 0040-0262
QK1 CODEN: TAXNAP
➤ **TAXON**; international journal of plant taxonomy, phylogeny and evolution. Text in English. 1951. q. USD 295 (effective 2006). adv. bk.rev. bibl.; charts; illus.; maps. index. cum.index: vols.1-30. 250 p./no. 2 cols./p.; back issues avail.; reprints avail. **Document type:** *Journal, Academic/Scholarly.* **Description:** Covers systematic and evolutionary biology with emphasis on botany.
Related titles: Online - full text ed.: (from EBSCO Publishing, Gale Group, IngentaConnect, JSTOR (Web-based Journal Archive)).
Indexed: ASCA, ASFA, AgBio, Agr, AgrForAb, B&AI, BIOBASE, BIOSIS Prev, BiolAb, CPA, ChemAb, CurCont, DSA, FCA, FPA, ForAb, GEOBASE, GardL, HerbAb, HortAb, IABS, ISR, OrnHort, PBA, PGegResA, PlantSci, PotatoAb, RA&MP, RPP, RevApplEntom, S&F, SCI, SeedAb, TriticAb, VITIS, WeedAb, ZooRec.
—BLDSC (8611.820000), CASDDS, CISTI, IDS, IE, Infotrieve, ingenta, Linda Hall.
Published by: International Association for Plant Taxonomy, Institute of Botany, University of Vienna, Rennweg 14, Vienna, 1030, Austria. TEL 43-1-427754098, FAX 43-1-427754099, editors@iapt-taxon.org, http://www.botanik.univie.ac.at/iapt/taxon/, http://www.iapt-taxon.org. Eds. Dr. Elvira Hoerandl, Dr. Veronika Mayer, Dr. Tod Stuessy. R&P Dr. Alessandra Ricciuti Lamonea. Circ: 2,500.

➤ **TELMA.** see *EARTH SCIENCES*

580 AUS ISSN 0312-9764
CODEN: TELODX
TELOPEA. Text in English. 1975. s-a. AUD 55 to individuals; AUD 90 to institutions; AUD 95 foreign (effective 2000). illus. **Document type:** *Academic/Scholarly.* **Description:** Articles on plant systematics with information on plant anatomy, cytology, botanical history and bibliography.
Supersedes: New South Wales National Herbarium. Contributions (0077-8753)
Indexed: AgBio, AgrForAb, BIOSIS Prev, BiolAb, CPA, FCA, ForAb, HerbAb, HortAb, IndVet, OrnHort, PBA, PGegResA, RA&MP, S&F, SeedAb, VITIS, WAE&RSA, WeedAb.
—CISTI.
Published by: National Herbarium of New South Wales, Royal Botanic Gardens Sydney, Mrs Macquaries Rd, Sydney, NSW 2000, Australia. TEL 61-2-92318100, FAX 61-2-92412797, http://www.rbgsyd.gov.au. Ed. Peter Wilson. R&P Lynne Munnich. Circ: 1,000.

580 USA
TENNESSEE NATIVE PLANT SOCIETY. NEWSLETTER. Text in English. 1978. bi-m. USD 15 to individuals; USD 20 to institutions; USD 10 to students. adv. bk.rev. **Document type:** *Newsletter.* **Description:** Botanical news on the native flora of Tennessee.
Published by: Tennessee Native Plant Society, University of Tennessee at Knoxville, Department of Botany, Knoxville, TN 37996-1100. TEL 615-598-5532. Ed. Candy Swan. Circ: 250.

580 SVK ISSN 1210-0420
➤ **THAISZIA/JOURNAL OF BOTANY.** Text mainly in English; Abstracts in Slovak. 1991. s-a. SKK 100, USD 30. bk.rev. abstr.; bibl.; charts; illus.; maps. index. back issues avail. **Document type:** *Academic/Scholarly.* **Description:** Publishes scientific papers in all fields of botany but primarily in the sub-specialties of biosystemics, taxonomy, floristics, phytogeography, phytocoenology, ecology, ecophysiology, paleobotany, and karyology.
Indexed: BIOSIS Prev, BiolAb, CPA, FCA, FPA, ForAb, HerbAb, HortAb, IABS, NutrAb, OrnHort, PBA, PGegResA, RA&MP, RPP, S&F, SeedAb, TriticAb, WeedAb.
—BLDSC (8814.138000), IE, ingenta.
Published by: University of P.J. Safarik, Botanical Garden, Manesova 23, Kosice, 04352, Slovakia. TEL 42-95-6331555, FAX 42-95-6337353, thaiszia@kosice.upjs.sk. adv.: page USD 330.

580 ITA ISSN 0563-3745
CODEN: THSAA
THALASSIA SALENTINA. Text in Italian; Summaries in English, French. 1966. a. per issue exchange basis. back issues avail.
Indexed: ASFA, BiolAb, ESPM, RefZh, ZooRec.
Published by: Universita degli Studi di Lecce, Stazione di Biologia Marina di Porto Cesareo, C.P. 193, Lecce, LE 73100, Italy. TEL 099 29854. Circ: 400.

580 USA ISSN 1090-1876
TIPULARIA; a botanical magazine. Text in English. 1986. a. USD 25 membership (effective 2003). bk.rev. **Document type:** *Magazine, Academic/Scholarly.* **Description:** Documents the interesting plants, locations and people in Georgia botany.
Published by: Georgia Botanical Society, c/o Carol Nourse, Treasurer, 320 Ashton Dr, Athens, GA 30606-1622. TEL 706-353-8222, members@gabotsoc.org, http://www.gabotsoc.org/tipularia.htm. Eds. Eric Van de Genachte, Shan Cammack. R&P David Emory. Circ: 450.

579.8 JPN ISSN 0911-1271
TOCHU KASO/CORDYCEPS. Text in Japanese. 1981. a.
Published by: Nihon Tochu Kaso no Kai/Japan Cordyceps Club, c/o Mr Nobuo Yahagi, 374-1 Kamabuchi, Mogami-gun, Mamurogawa-machi, Yamagata-ken 999-5604, Japan.

581.35 USA
TOMATO GENETICS COOPERATIVE REPORT. Text in English. 1950. a. USD 15. **Document type:** *Newsletter.*
Published by: Tomato Genetics Cooperative, Cornell University, Department of Plant Breeding, 252 Emerson Hall, Ithaca, NY 14853-1901. TEL 607-255-4573, FAX 607-255-6683, tf12@cornell.edu, http://genome.cornell.edu/tgc/. Ed. Theresa M Fulton. Circ: 400.

580.74 USA ISSN 1095-5674
QK1 CODEN: BTBCAL
➤ **TORREY BOTANICAL SOCIETY. JOURNAL.** Text in English. 1870. q. USD 55 domestic; USD 60 foreign (effective 2004). adv. bk.rev. bibl.; charts; illus. index, cum.index: vols.1-75. back issues avail.; reprint service avail. from PQC,ISI. **Document type:** *Journal, Academic/Scholarly.* **Description:** Provides original research in all aspects of botany, except horticulture.
Formerly (until 1997): Torrey Botanical Club. Bulletin (0040-9618); Which incorporated (1901-1945): Torreya (0096-3844)
Related titles: Microform ed.: (from PQC); Online - full text ed.: (from bigchalk, JSTOR (Web-based Journal Archive), ProQuest Information & Learning).
Indexed: ASFA, AgBio, Agr, AgrForAb, ApEcolAb, BIOBASE, BIOSIS Prev, BiolAb, CPA, ChemAb, CurCont, EIA, ESPM, EnerInd, EnvAb, EnvInd, ExcerpMed, FCA, FPA, ForAb, GEOBASE, HerbAb, HortAb, I&DA, IABS, ISR, MaizeAb, OrnHort, PBA, PGegResA, PN&I, PlantSci, RA&MP, RPP, RRTA, RefZh, RevApplEntom, S&F, SCI, SWRA, SeedAb, TDB, WeedAb.
—BLDSC (4909.600000), CASDDS, CISTI, IDS, IE, ingenta, Linda Hall. **CCC.**
Published by: Torrey Botanical Society, Box 1897, Lawrence, KS 66044-8897. TEL 785-843-1235, FAX 785-843-1274, torrey@allenpress.com, orders@allenpress.com, http://www.torreybotanical.org/journal.html. Adv. contact John Gillen TEL 718-518-4130. page USD 350. Circ: 1,304.
Subscr. to: Allen Press Inc.

580.74 USA
TORREY BOTANICAL SOCIETY. MEMOIRS. Text in English. 1889. irreg.
Formerly: Torrey Botanical Club. Memoirs (0097-3807)
Indexed: BIOSIS Prev, BiolAb.
—CISTI, Linda Hall.
Published by: Torrey Botanical Society, Box 1897, Lawrence, KS 66044-8897. TEL 785-843-1235, FAX 785-843-1274, orders@allenpress.com, torrey@allenpress.com, http://www.torreybotanical.org.

571.2 MAR
TRAVAUX DE L'INSTITUT SCIENTIFIQUE. SERIE BOTANIQUE. Text in French. irreg.
Published by: Universite Mohammed V, Institut Scientifique, Ave Ibn Batouta, BP 703, Rabat-Agdal, Rabat, 10106, Morocco. TEL 212-37-774548, FAX 212-37-774540.

581.3 DEU ISSN 1614-2942
▼ ➤ **TREE GENETICS & GENOMES.** Text in English. 2005. 4/yr. EUR 378 (effective 2005). **Document type:** *Journal, Academic/Scholarly.* **Description:** Covers all aspects theoretical and applied tree genetics.
Related titles: Online - full text ed.: ISSN 1614-2950 (from Springer LINK).
—BLDSC (9047.298500). **CCC.**
Published by: Springer-Verlag (Subsidiary of: Springer Science+Business Media), Tiergartenstr 17, Heidelberg, 69121, Germany. TEL 49-6221-3450, FAX 49-6221-345229, subscriptions@springer.de, http://www.springer.de. Ed. D B Neale. Adv. contact Stephan Kroeck TEL 49-30-827875739.

582.16 CAN ISSN 0829-318X
QK475 CODEN: TRPHEM
➤ **TREE PHYSIOLOGY**; an international botanical journal. Text in English. 1986. m. CND 1,292 domestic to institutions print & online eds.; USD 1,360 foreign to institutions print & online eds. (effective 2006). adv. bk.rev. illus. index. 1536 p./no.; reprints avail. **Document type:** *Journal, Academic/Scholarly.* **Description:** International journal devoted to research reports and technical reviews on all aspects of the physiology of trees.
Related titles: Online - full text ed.: CND 180 domestic; USD 130 foreign (effective 2003) (from EBSCO Publishing, The Dialog Corporation).
Indexed: AEA, ASCA, AgBio, Agr, AgrForAb, ApEcolAb, BIOBASE, BIOSIS Prev, BibAg, BioCN&I, BiolAb, CIN, CPA, ChemAb, CurCont, ESPM, EnvAb, FCA, FPA, ForAb, GEOBASE, HerbAb, HortAb, I&DA, IABS, ISR, MEDLINE, OrnHort, PBA, PGegResA, PGrRegA, PlantSci, PollutAb, RA&MP, RPP, RefZh, RevApplEntom, S&F, SCI, SIA, SWRA, SeedAb, SoyAb, WeedAb.
—BLDSC (9047.625000), CASDDS, CISTI, IE, Infotrieve, ingenta, Linda Hall.
Published by: Heron Publishing, 202-3994 Shelbourne St, Victoria, BC V8N 3E2, Canada. TEL 250-721-9921, FAX 250-721-9924, treephysiology@heronpublishing.com, publisher@heronpublishing.com, http://heronpublishing.com/tphome.html. Pub., R&P Alfred Burdett.

580 USA ISSN 1536-1098
QK477 CODEN: TRBUAL
TREE-RING RESEARCH. Text in English. 1935. a. USD 15 (effective 1999). charts; illus.; maps. cum.index. **Document type:** *Bulletin, Academic/Scholarly.*
Formerly (until 2000): Tree - Ring Bulletin (0041-2198)
Indexed: Agr, AnthLit, BiolAb, BrArAb, FPA, ForAb, NumL, SeedAb.
—CISTI, Linda Hall.
Published by: Tree - Ring Society, University of Arizona, Tree Ring Laboratory, Tucson, AZ 85721. TEL 520-621-1608, FAX 520-621-8229. Ed., R&P Jeffrey S Dean TEL 520-621-2320. Circ: 375.

582.16 634.9 DEU ISSN 0931-1890
CODEN: TRESEY
➤ **TREES**; structure and function. Text in English. 1987. bi-m. EUR 1,098 combined subscription to institutions print & online eds. (effective 2005). adv. illus. Index. back issues avail.; reprints avail. **Document type:** *Journal, Academic/Scholarly.* **Description:** Features articles treating physiology, biochemistry, functional anatomy, structure and ecology of trees and other woody plants.
Related titles: Online - full text ed.: ISSN 1432-2285 (from EBSCO Publishing, Springer LINK, Swets Information Services).
Indexed: AgBio, Agr, AgrForAb, BIOBASE, BIOSIS Prev, BiolAb, CPA, CurCont, FPA, ForAb, HerbAb, HortAb, I&DA, IABS, ISR, OrnHort, PBA, PGegResA, PGrRegA, PlantSci, RA&MP, RDA, RPP, RRTA, RefZh, RevApplEntom, S&F, SCI, SIA, SeedAb, WAE&RSA, WeedAb.
—BLDSC (9047.910500), CASDDS, CISTI, IDS, IE, Infotrieve, ingenta, Linda Hall. **CCC.**
Published by: Springer-Verlag (Subsidiary of: Springer Science+Business Media), Tiergartenstr 17, Heidelberg, 69121, Germany. TEL 49-6221-3450, FAX 49-6221-345229, http://link.springer-ny.com. Adv. contact Stephan Kroeck TEL 49-30-827875739. **Subscr. in the Americas to:** Springer-Verlag New York, Inc., Journal Fulfillment, PO Box 2485, Secaucus, NJ 07096-2485. TEL 800-777-4643, 201-348-4033, FAX 201-348-4505, journals@springer-ny.com, http://www.springer-ny.com; **Subscr. to:** Springer GmbH Auslieferungsgesellschaft, Haberstr 7, Heidelberg 69126, Germany. TEL 49-6221-345-0, FAX 49-6221-345-4229, subscriptions@springer.de.

➤ **TREEWORKER.** see *FORESTS AND FORESTRY*

580 GBR ISSN 1360-1385
QK1 CODEN: TPSCF9
➤ **TRENDS IN PLANT SCIENCE.** Text in English. 1996. 12/yr. EUR 181 in Europe to individuals; JPY 22,000 in Japan to individuals; USD 198 elsewhere to individuals; EUR 1,232 in Europe to institutions; JPY 170,900 in Japan to institutions; USD 1,378 elsewhere to institutions (effective 2006). adv. software rev. illus. back issues avail.; reprints avail. **Document type:** *Academic/Scholarly.* **Description:** Informs researchers on important trends and developments in all areas of specialty in botany and related disciplines.
Related titles: Online - full text ed.: (from EBSCO Publishing, Gale Group, IngentaConnect, ScienceDirect, Swets Information Services).
Indexed: AEBA, ASFA, AbHyg, AgBio, Agr, AnBrAb, ApEcolAb, BIOBASE, BIOSIS Prev, BioCN&I, BioEngAb, BiolAb, CPA, ChemAb, CurCont, ESPM, FCA, FPA, FS&TA, ForAb, GSI, GardL, GenetAb, HGA, HerbAb, HortAb, I&DA, IABS, ISR, IndMed, MEDLINE, MaizeAb, NemAb, NutrAb, OrnHort, PBA, PGegResA, PGrRegA, PHN&I, PN&I, PlantSci, PotatoAb, ProtozoAb, RA&MP, RPP, RefZh, RevApplEntom, RiceAb, S&F, SCI, SIA, SeedAb, SoyAb, TriticAb, VITIS, WAE&RSA, WeedAb.
—BLDSC (9049.675450), CISTI, IDS, IE, Infotrieve, ingenta. **CCC.**
Published by: Elsevier Ltd., Trends Journals (Subsidiary of: Elsevier Science & Technology), 68 Hills Rd, Cambridge, CB2 1LA, United Kingdom. TEL 44-1223-315961, FAX 44-1223-464430, plants@elsevier.co.uk, http://www.elsevier.com/locate/tplants. Eds. C Woods, Susanne Brink. Adv. contact Thelma Reid. **Subscr. to:** Elsevier Current Trends Subscriptions, PO Box 331, Haywards Heath, W Sussex RH16 3FG, United Kingdom. TEL 44-1444-475650, FAX 44-1444-445423.

580 NPL ISSN 0259-0964
➤ **TRIBHUVAN UNIVERSITY. NATURAL HISTORY MUSEUM. JOURNAL.** Variant title: Journal of Natural History Museum. Text in English. 1977. irreg. (in 20 vols.). NPR 200 domestic; USD 10 foreign (effective 2003). bk.rev. **Document type:** *Journal, Academic/Scholarly.*
Published by: Tribhuvan University, Natural History Museum, Swoyambhu, Kathmandu, Nepal. TEL 977-1-4271899, FAX 977-1-4264106, nhm@htp.com.np. Ed. Karan Shah. R&P Dr. Keshab Shrestha. Circ: 500.

580 IND ISSN 0564-3295
QH540 CODEN: ISTEBI
➤ **TROPICAL ECOLOGY.** Text in English, French, Spanish, Portuguese. 1960. s-a. USD 100 to institutions (effective 2006). adv. bk.rev. back issues avail. **Document type:** *Directory, Academic/Scholarly.* **Description:** Publishes original research papers, reviews on topical themes, scientific correspondence, exhaustive book reviews. Covers all areas of ecology relating to tropics and subtropics.
Indexed: ASFA, AgrForAb, AnBrAb, ApEcolAb, B&BAb, BAS, BIOBASE, BIOSIS Prev, BioCN&I, BiolAb, CPA, CTFA, ChemAb, CurCont, EPB, ESPM, EntAb, ExcerpMed, FCA, FPA, ForAb, GEOBASE, GenetAb, HGA, HelmAb, HerbAb, HortAb, I&DA, IABS, IndVet, NemAb, NutrAb, OrnHort, PBA, PGegResA, PN&I, PlantSci, PoultAb, ProtozoAb, RA&MP, RDA, RM&VM, RPP, RRTA, RefZh, RevApplEntom, RiceAb, S&F, SFA, SIA, SWRA, SeedAb, TDB, TriticAb, VetBull, WAE&RSA, WeedAb, WildRev, ZooRec.
—BLDSC (9056.070000), CASDDS, CISTI, IE, Infotrieve, ingenta, Linda Hall. **CCC.**
Published by: (International Society for Tropical Ecology), Scientific Publishers, 5-A New Pali Rd., Near Hotel Taj Hari Mahal, PO Box 91, Jodhpur, Rajasthan 342 003, India. TEL 91-291-2433323, FAX 91-291-2512580, info@scientificpub.com, http://www.scientificpub.com/bookdetails.php?booktransid=351&bookid=347. Ed. K P Singh. R&P, Adv. contact K.P. Singh. Circ: 700 (paid). **Dist. by:** H P C Publishers Distributors Pvt. Ltd., 4805 Bharat Ram Rd, 24 Darya Ganj, New Delhi 110 002, India.

580 DEU ISSN 0302-9417
QK474.5
TROPISCHE UND SUBTROPISCHE PFLANZENWELT. Text in German. 1973. irreg., latest vol.101, 2002. price varies. **Document type:** *Monographic series, Academic/Scholarly.*
—CISTI.
Published by: (Akademie der Wissenschaften und der Literatur, Mainz), Franz Steiner Verlag Stuttgart GmbH, Birkenwaldstr 44, Stuttgart, 70191, Germany. TEL 49-711-25820, FAX 49-711-2582390, franz.steiner.verlag@t-online.de, http://www.steiner-verlag.de. Ed. Werner Rauh. R&P Sabine Koerner.

580 JPN ISSN 0289-3568
QK1
TSUKUBA JIKKEN SHOKUBUTSUEN KENKYU HOKOKU/TSUKUBA BOTANICAL GARDEN. ANNUALS. Text in English, Japanese. 1983. irreg.
Indexed: JPI.
Published by: (Tsukuba Jikken Shokubutsuen), Monbusho, Kokuritsu Kagaku Hakubutsukan/Ministry of Education, Science and Culture, National Science Museum, 1-1 Amakubo 4-chome, Tsukuba-shi, Ibaraki-ken 305-0005, Japan.

TULANE STUDIES IN ZOOLOGY AND BOTANY. see *BIOLOGY—Zoology*

580 TUR ISSN 1300-008X
CODEN: DTBDEG
➤ **TURKISH JOURNAL OF BOTANY/TURK BOTANIK DERGISI.** Text and summaries in English; Abstracts occasionally in Turkish. 1976. 6/yr. USD 150 (effective 2005). **Document type:** *Journal, Academic/Scholarly.*
Formerly (until 1994): Doga Turkish Journal of Botany - Doga Turk Botanik Dergisi (1011-0887)
Related titles: Online - full text ed.: ISSN 1303-6106. free (effective 2005) (from EBSCO Publishing).
Indexed: AgBio, AgrForAb, BIOSIS Prev, BioDAb, BiolAb, CPA, FCA, FPA, ForAb, GEOBASE, HerbAb, HortAb, I&DA, IndVet, MaizeAb, NutrAb, OrnHort, PBA, PGegResA, PGrRegA, PHN&I, RA&MP, RM&VM, RPP, RRTA, RevApplEntom, RiceAb, S&F, SIA, SeedAb, SoyAb, TDB, TriticAb, VITIS, WeedAb, ZooRec.
—BLDSC (9072.467300), CASDDS, CISTI, Linda Hall.
Published by: Scientific and Technical Research Council of Turkey - TUBITAK/Turkiye Bilimsel ve Teknik Arastirma Kurumu, Ataturk Bulvari No. 221, Kavaklidere, Ankara, 06100, Turkey. TEL 90-312-468-5300, FAX 90-312-426-8073, bdym@tubitak.gov.tr, http://journals.tubitak.gov.tr/botany/index.php, http://www.tubitak.gov.tr. Ed. Dr. Adil Guner.

580 796.352 USA ISSN 1541-0277
U S G A TURFGRASS AND ENVIRONMENTAL RESEARCH ONLINE; using science to benefit golf. (United States Golf Association) Text in English. 2002 (Mar.). irreg.
Media: Online - full content.
Published by: United States Golf Association, P. O. Box 746, Far Hills, NJ 07931. TEL 908-234-2300, FAX 908-234-9687, http://usgatero.msu.edu, http://www.usga.org. Ed. Jeff Nus.

580 UKR ISSN 0372-4123
QK1 CODEN: UKBZAW
➤ **UKRAIN'SKYI BOTANICHNYI ZHURNAL/UKRAINIAN BOTANICAL JOURNAL**; nauchnyi zhurnal. Text in Ukrainian; Summaries in English, Russian. 1921. bi-m. USD 289 foreign (effective 2005). bk.rev. illus. index. **Document type:** *Journal, Academic/Scholarly.* **Description:** Covers general questions of botany, floristics, resource management, morphology, systematics of higher and lower plants, geobotany, soil science, evolution, history of plants, geography of plants, history of flora and vegetation, algology, micrology, cytology, embriology, physiology and biochemistry of plants.
Indexed: ASFA, AgrForAb, AnBrAb, BIOSIS Prev, BioCN&I, BiolAb, ChemAb, Djerelo, ESPM, FCA, FPA, ForAb, HerbAb, HortAb, I&DA, IAA, INIS AtomInd, IndVet, MaizeAb, NutrAb, OrnHort, PBA, PGegResA, PN&I, PotatoAb, RA&MP, RPP, RefZh, S&F, SIA, SWRA, SeedAb, SoyAb, TOSA, TriticAb, VITIS, WAE&RSA, WeedAb, ZooRec.
—BLDSC (0384.195000), CASDDS, CISTI, East View, KNAW. **CCC.**
Published by: Natsional'na Akademiya Nauk Ukrainy, Instytut Botaniky im. M.G. Kholodnoho, vul Tereshchenkivs'ka 2, Kyiv, 01601, Ukraine. inst@botany.kiev.ua. Ed. Konstyantyn M Sitnik. **US dist. addr.:** East View Information Services, 3020 Harbor Ln. N., Minneapolis, MN 55447. TEL 763-550-0961, FAX 763-559-2931, eastview@eastview.com, http://www.eastview.com.

➤ **UNIVERSAL'S POPULAR PLANTS AND FLOWERS SERIES. TREES, SHRUBS AND GROUND COVERS.** see *GARDENING AND HORTICULTURE*

580 MEX ISSN 0187-7054
UNIVERSIDAD DE GUADALAJARA. INSTITUTO DE BOTANICA. BOLETIN. Text and summaries in English, Spanish. 1974-1978; resumed 1991. s-a. MXP 135, USD 25 per issue (effective 2004). bk.rev. bibl.; illus. **Document type:** *Bulletin.* **Description:** Text in English or Spanish; summaries in English and Spanish.
Supersedes (in 1978): Universidad de Guadalajara. Instituto de Botanica. Boletin Informativo
Indexed: AgBio, AgrForAb, BioCN&I, ForAb, HerbAb, HortAb, OrnHort, PBA, PGegResA, S&F, WeedAb.
Published by: (Centro Universitario de Ciencias Biologicas y Agropecuarias), Universidad de Guadalajara, Instituto de Botanica, Apdo. Postal 1-139, Zapopan, JALISCO 45110, Mexico. mharker@maiz.cucba.udg.mx. Ed. Roberto Gonzalez Tamayo. Circ: 300.

579.5 ESP
UNIVERSIDAD DE JAEN. FACULTAD DE CIENCIAS EXPERIMENTALES. MONOGRAFIAS. Text in Spanish. 1990. irreg. price varies. **Document type:** *Monographic series, Academic/Scholarly.* **Description:** Covers mycology.
Published by: Universidad de Jaen, Facultad de Ciencias Experimentales, Herbario Jaen, Jaen, 23071, Spain. TEL 34-953-012159, FAX 34-953-012141, agricola@mundiprensa.es. Ed. Carlos Fernandez Lopez. **Dist. by:** Libreria Agricola, Fernando VI, 2, Madrid 28004, Spain. TEL 34-91-4190940.

580 MEX ISSN 0185-254X
QK1 CODEN: AMXSAH
UNIVERSIDAD NACIONAL AUTONOMA DE MEXICO. INSTITUTO DE BIOLOGIA. ANALES: SERIE BOTANICA. Text in English, French, Spanish; Summaries in English, French, Spanish. 1967. s-a. MXP 100, USD 30 per issue (effective 2000). adv. abstr.; charts; illus.; stat. back issues avail. **Document type:** *Monographic series, Academic/Scholarly.* **Description:** Covers anatomy, cytology, taxonomy, phytochemistry and other biological areas, with emphasis on Mexican study.
Supersedes in part: Universidad Nacional Autonoma de Mexico. Instituto de Biologia. Anales (0076-7174)
Indexed: ASFA, BIOSIS Prev, BioDAb, BiolAb, ForAb, PBA, PGegResA, RM&VM, SeedAb, TriticAb, WeedAb.
—CISTI, Linda Hall.
Published by: Universidad Nacional Autonoma de Mexico, Instituto de Biologia, Ciudad Universitaria, Apdo Postal 70-233, Mexico City, DF 04510, Mexico. TEL 52-5-622-5690, FAX 52-5-622-5687, javierd@mail.ibiologia.unam.mx, http://www.ibiologia.unam.mx. Ed. Alfonso N Garcia Aldrete. Adv. contact Javier Dominguez Galicia. Circ: 1,000.

580 PRT ISSN 0066-8079
UNIVERSIDADE DE LISBOA. INSTITUTO BOTANICO. ARTIGO DE DIVULGACAO. Text in Portuguese. 1945. irreg. price varies. adv. **Document type:** *Academic/Scholarly.*
Published by: Universidade de Lisboa, Instituto Botanico, Museu, Laboratorio e Jardim Botanico, Rua da Escola Politecnica 58, Lisbon Codex, 1294, Portugal. TEL 351-21-3921801, FAX 351-21-3970882, jbbiblio@fc.ul.pt, http://www.jb.ul.pt/. Ed. F M Catarino. Adv. contact Manuel Dos Santos Lopes.

580 BRA ISSN 0302-2439
QK263
UNIVERSIDADE DE SAO PAULO. BOLETIM DE BOTANICA. Text in English, Portuguese. 1973. a., latest vol.20, 2002. free. illus.; abstr.; bibl. back issues avail.; reprints avail. **Document type:** *Bulletin, Academic/Scholarly.* **Description:** Publishes original scientific research on botany.
Supersedes (1937-1969): Universidade de Sao Paulo. Faculdade de Filosofia, Ciencias y Letras. Botanica
Indexed: BIOSIS Prev, BiolAb, CurCont, ForAb, HerbAb, HortAb, OrnHort, PBA, PGegResA, RefZh, WeedAb.
—CISTI.
Published by: Universidade de Sao Paulo, Departamento de Botanica, Pinheiros, Caixa Postal 11461, Sao Paulo, SP 05422-970, Brazil. TEL 55-11-30917595, FAX 55-11-30917547, jrpirani@ib.usp.br, http://www.ib.usp.br/. Ed. Jose Rubens Pirani. Circ: 800. **Co-sponsor:** Instituto de Biociencias.

580 ITA ISSN 0373-5931
UNIVERSITA DI FERRARA. ANNALI. SEZIONE 4: BOTANICA. Text in Italian. 1951. a. price varies.
Published by: (Universita degli Studi di Ferrara), Casa Editrice Leo S. Olschki, Viuzzo del Pozzetto 8, Florence, 50126, Italy. TEL 39-055-6530684, FAX 39-055-6530214, celso@olschki.it, http://www.olschki.it.

580.74 EGY ISSN 0068-5313
CODEN: CJHPBW
UNIVERSITY OF CAIRO. HERBARIUM. PUBLICATIONS. Text in English. 1968. a. free to botanical institutions and interested botanists.
—CASDDS.
Published by: University of Cairo, Botany Department, Herbarium, Giza, 12613, Egypt. Ed. Vivi Taerkholm. Circ: 1,500.

580 TZA
UNIVERSITY OF DAR ES SALAAM. BOTANY DEPARTMENT. DEPARTMENTAL HERBARIUM PUBLICATIONS. Text in English. 1971. irreg. USD 5.
Published by: University of Dar es Salaam, Botany Department, PO Box 35060, Dar Es Salaam, Tanzania. Ed. Bob Wingfield Clive. Circ: 40.

580 USA ISSN 0091-1860
QK1 CODEN: CUMHDA
➤ **UNIVERSITY OF MICHIGAN. HERBARIUM. CONTRIBUTIONS.** Text in English, Spanish; Summaries in English. 1939. irreg., latest vol.21, 1997. price varies. cum.index: 1939-1942; 1966-1972. **Document type:** *Academic/Scholarly.*
Indexed: Agr, AgrForAb, BIOSIS Prev, BiolAb, ForAb, HerbAb, HortAb, OrnHort, PBA, PGegResA, S&F.
—CISTI, Linda Hall.
Published by: University of Michigan, Herbarium, North University Building, Ann Arbor, MI 48109-1057. TEL 313-764-2407, FAX 313-647-5719. Circ: 250.

➤ **UNIVERSITY OF WAIKATO. ANTARCTIC RESEARCH UNIT. REPORT.** see *EARTH SCIENCES—Geology*

580 SCG ISSN 0351-1588
UNIVERZITET U BEOGRADU. INSTITUT ZA BOTANIKU I BOTANICKE BASTE. GLASNIK✶. Text in English, Serbian. 1928. a. adv. bk.rev. **Document type:** *Academic/Scholarly.*
Indexed: CPA, FCA, HerbAb, PGrRegA, WeedAb.
Published by: Univerzitet u Beogradu, Institut za Botaniku i Botanicke Baste, Takovska 43, Belgrade. TEL 381-11-768857, vstev@eunet.yu. Ed. Milorad M Jankovic.

580 POL ISSN 1509-9156
QK322 CODEN: ZJPBDD
UNIWERSYTET JAGIELLONSKI. INSTYTUT BOTANIKI. PRACE BOTANICZNE/JAGELLONIAN UNIVERSITY. INSTITUTE OF BOTANY. BOTANICAL PAPERS. Text and summaries in English, Polish. 1973. irreg., latest vol.36, 2001. price varies. **Document type:** *Monographic series, Academic/Scholarly.*
Formerly (until 1998): Uniwersytet Jagiellonski. Zeszyty Naukowe. Prace Botaniczne (0302-8585)
Indexed: AgrLib, BiolAb, ChemAb.
—CASDDS, CISTI, Linda Hall.
Published by: (Uniwersytet Jagiellonski, Instytut Botaniki/Jagiellonian University, Institute of Botany), Wydawnictwo Uniwersytetu Jagiellonskiego/Jagiellonian University Press, ul Grodzka 26, Krakow, 31044, Poland. TEL 48-12-4312364, FAX 48-12-4301995, wydaw@if.uj.edu.pl, http://www.wuj.pl. Ed. Anna Stengl.

580 561 DEU ISSN 0939-6314
QK900 CODEN: VHAREV
➤ **VEGETATION HISTORY AND ARCHAEOBOTANY.** Text in English. 1992. q. EUR 378 combined subscription to institutions print & online eds. (effective 2005). adv. back issues avail. **Document type:** *Journal, Academic/Scholarly.* **Description:** Encompasses the entire field of vegetation history, mainly flora and vegetation development during the Holocene period.
Related titles: Online - full text ed.: ISSN 1617-6278 (from EBSCO Publishing, Springer LINK, Swets Information Services).
Indexed: AEA, ASCA, AgrForAb, AnBrAb, BIOSIS Prev, BiolAb, BrArAb, CPA, CurCont, FCA, FPA, ForAb, HerbAb, HortAb, ISR, NumL, NutrAb, OrnHort, PBA, PGegResA, RA&MP, RefZh, S&F, SCI, SeedAb, TriticAb, VITIS, WeedAb.
—BLDSC (9153.130000), IDS, IE, Infotrieve, ingenta. **CCC.**
Published by: Springer-Verlag (Subsidiary of: Springer Science+Business Media), Tiergartenstr 17, Heidelberg, 69121, Germany. TEL 49-6221-3450, FAX 49-6221-345229, http://link.springer.de/link/service/journals/00334/index.htm. Ed. Felix Bittmann. Adv. contact Stephan Kroeck TEL 49-30-827875739. **Subscr. in the Americas to:** Springer-Verlag New York, Inc., Journal Fulfillment, PO Box 2485, Secaucus, NJ 07096-2485. TEL 800-777-4643, 201-348-4033, FAX 201-348-4505, journals@springer-ny.com, http://www.springer-ny.com; **Subscr. to:** Springer GmbH Auslieferungsgesellschaft, Haberstr 7, Heidelberg 69126, Germany. TEL 49-6221-345-0, FAX 49-6221-345-4229, subscriptions@springer.de.

580 ZAF ISSN 0042-3203
QK1
VELD & FLORA. Variant title: Veld. Text in English, Afrikaans. 1915. q. ZAR 130 to libraries (effective 2001). bk.rev. illus. index. **Document type:** *Journal, Academic/Scholarly.*
Formerly: Botanical Society of South Africa. Journal (0068-0419)
Indexed: BiolAb, GardL, ISAP, PBA, RefZh.
—BLDSC (9154.240000), IE, ingenta, Linda Hall.
Published by: Botanical Society of South Africa, Private Bag X10, Claremont, Cape Province 7735, South Africa. TEL 27-21-797-2090, FAX 27-21-797-2376, info@botanicalsociety.org.za, http://www.botanicalsociety.org.za. Ed. Caroline Voget. R&P Dave McDonald. Circ: 18,000.

580 USA ISSN 1545-049X
▼ **VERDANT REFLECTIONS.** Text in English. 2003 (Win.). q. USD 23 (effective 2003).
Related titles: Online - full text ed.: ISSN 1548-467X.
Published by: Southern Oregon Coast Botanical Academy, PO Box 122, Bandon, OR 97411. TEL 541-347-1114, SOCBotanical@cfaith.com. Ed. Douglas Scofield.

581 USA ISSN 1085-9632
VIRGINIA NATIVE PLANT SOCIETY. BULLETIN. Text in English. 1982. 5/yr. USD 30 to individuals; USD 40 to institutions; USD 15 newsstand/cover (effective 2005). bk.rev. illus. back issues avail.; reprints avail. **Document type:** *Newsletter.* **Description:** Promotes the conservation of native flora and plant habitats throughout the state of Virginia. Includes material on botany, conservation, gardening, and environmental legislation.
Formerly: Virginia Wildflower Preservation Society. Bulletin
Published by: Virginia Native Plant Society, 400 Blandy Farm Lane, Unit 2, Boyce, VA 22620. TEL 540-837-1600, FAX 540-377-6495, vnpsofc@shentel.net, http://www.vnps.org, http://www.unps.org. Ed., R&P Nancy Sorrells. Circ: 1,600 (paid).

VIRGINIA TURFGRASS JOURNAL. see *AGRICULTURE—Crop Production And Soil*

580 635.9 GBR ISSN 1470-0123
VITEX. Text in English. 1992. a. **Document type:** *Newsletter, Academic/Scholarly.*
Formerly (until 2000): Lamiales Newsletter (1358-2305)
Indexed: HortAb.
Published by: Royal Botanic Gardens, Kew, Richmond, Surrey TW9 3AB, United Kingdom. TEL 44-20-83325000, FAX 44-20-83325197, info@rbgkew.org.uk, http://www.rbgkew.org.uk/index.html. Eds. Alan Paton, Ray Harley, Tivvy Harvey.

580 DEU ISSN 0723-7812
VORTRAEGE FUER PFLANZENZUECHTUNG. Text in German. irreg., latest vol.65, 2004. price varies. **Document type:** *Monographic series, Academic/Scholarly.*
Indexed: AgBio, PBA, RPP, TriticAb, VITIS.
—**CCC.**
Published by: Gesellschaft fuer Pflanzenzuechtung e.V., Von Sieboldstr 8, Goettingen, 37075, Germany. TEL 49-551-394361, FAX 49-551-394601, sekretaer@gpz-online.de, http://www.gpz-online.de.

580 USA ISSN 1540-3599
VULPIA: CONTRIBUTIONS FROM THE NORTH CAROLINA STATE HERBARIUM. Text in English. 2002 (Oct.). irreg.
Media: Online - full content.
Published by: North Carolina State University, Herbarium, Dept. of Botany, Campus Box 7612, Raleigh, NC 27695-7612. TEL 919-515-2700, FAX 919-515-3436, http://www.cals.ncsu.edu/botany/ncsc/vulpia. Ed. Alexander Krings.

635 USA ISSN 1097-2714
➤ **WASHINGTON NATIVE PLANT SOCIETY. OCCASIONAL PAPERS.** Text in English. irreg. membership only. **Document type:** *Academic/Scholarly.*
Published by: Washington Native Plant Society, 6310 NE 74th St., Ste. 215E, Seattle, WA 98115-8171. TEL 206-760-8022. Ed. Richard Robohm. R&P Catherine Hovanic TEL 206-527-3210.

333.91 USA ISSN 0161-3561
WATER, WOODS & WILDLIFE. Text in English. 1971. bi-m. USD 10. adv. bk.rev. back issues avail. **Document type:** *Consumer.*
Published by: Wildwood Publishing, Inc., PO Box 16074, St. Paul, MN 55116-0074. TEL 612-698-9358. Ed. Dan Hinton. Circ: 4,300.

580 GBR ISSN 0043-1532
QK1
➤ **WATSONIA.** Text in English. 1949. s-a. GBP 20 domestic membership; EUR 33 in Europe membership; GBP 22, EUR 37 elsewhere membership (effective 2004). bk.rev. charts; illus.; stat. cum.index. **Document type:** *Journal, Academic/Scholarly.* **Description:** Contains scientific papers and short notes on the taxonomy, biosystematics, ecology, distribution, conservation and history of British and Irish plants. It also publishes plant records, and obituaries.
Indexed: ASFA, AgBio, Agr, BIOSIS Prev, BiolAb, CPA, FCA, FPA, ForAb, HerbAb, HortAb, NutrAb, OrnHort, PBA, PGegResA, RPP, RefZh, S&F, SeedAb, WeedAb.
—BLDSC (9280.000000), CISTI, IE, Infotrieve, ingenta, Linda Hall.
Published by: Botanical Society of the British Isles, c/o Department of Botany, The Natural History Museum, Cromwell Rd, London, SW7 5BD, United Kingdom. TEL 44-20-7942-5002, bsbihgs@aol.com, http://www.bsbi.org.uk/html/watsonia.html. Ed. Martin N Sanford. Circ: 3,000.

580 ITA ISSN 0083-7792
CODEN: WBIAAJ
➤ **WEBBIA;** raccolta di studi botanici. Text in Multiple languages. 1905. 2/yr. adv. bk.rev. **Document type:** *Academic/Scholarly.*
Related titles: Microfiche ed.: (from IDC).
Indexed: AgrForAb, BIOSIS Prev, BiolAb, FCA, ForAb, HerbAb, HortAb, OrnHort, PBA, PGegResA, RA&MP, RefZh, S&F, SeedAb, TriticAb, WeedAb.
—BLDSC (9284.000000), CISTI, IE, Infotrieve, ingenta.
Published by: Universita degli Studi di Firenze, Museo di Storia Naturale - Botanica, Via La Pira 4, Florence, 50121, Italy. TEL 39-055-275762, FAX 39-055-289006, musbot@unifi.it, http://www.unifi.it/msn/botan/bofr_ita.htm. Circ: 250 (paid).

581.652 JPN ISSN 0372-798X
CODEN: ZASKAN
WEED RESEARCH. Text in English, Japanese. 1962. q. JPY 5,000. back issues avail.
Indexed: AgrForAb, BioCN&I, BiolAb, CPA, CurCont, DBA, FCA, ForAb, HerbAb, HortAb, I&DA, IndVet, MaizeAb, OrnHort, PBA, PGegResA, PGrRegA, PoultAb, RA&MP, RPP, RevApplEntom, RiceAb, S&F, SeedAb, SoyAb, TOSA, TriticAb, WeedAb.
—CASDDS, CISTI, IE.
Published by: Weed Science Society of Japan, Shokucho Bldg 26-6 Taito, Taito 1-chome, Taito-ku, Tokyo, 110-0016, Japan. Ed. Kozo Ishizuka. Circ: 2,000.

580 GBR
WEEDS WORLD. Text in English. 1994. 3/yr.
Published by: Nottingham Arabidopsis Stock Centre, Department of Life Sciences, Nottingham, NG7 2RD, United Kingdom. http://www.nasc.nott.ac.uk. Ed. Mary Anderson.

580 KOR ISSN 1226-8763
WEON'YE GWAHAG GI'SULJI/KOREAN JOURNAL OF HORTICULTURAL SCIENCE AND TECHNOLOGY. Text in Korean. 1998. bi-m. **Document type:** *Journal, Academic/Scholarly.* **Description:** Provides technology and news which can be used in both industry and horticultural science.
Indexed: AgrForAb, AnBrAb, CPA, FCA, ForAb, HerbAb, HortAb, I&DA, MaizeAb, OrnHort, PBA, PGegResA, PGrRegA, PotatoAb, RA&MP, SIA, SeedAb, TriticAb, WeedAb.
—BLDSC (9295.237700), IE.
Published by: Han'gug Weon'ye Haghoe/Korean Society for Horticultural Science, Naitonal Horticultural Research Institute, Imok-dong 475 Jangan-gu, Suwon, Gyeonggi-do 440-706, Korea, S. TEL 82-31-2416885, FAX 82-31-2429280, http://www.horticulture.or.kr.

WESTERN NORTH AMERICAN NATURALIST. MONOGRAPHS. see *BIOLOGY—Zoology*

580 USA ISSN 0091-4487
SB610 CODEN: WSWPAF
WESTERN SOCIETY OF WEED SCIENCE. PROCEEDINGS. Text in English. 1938. a. **Document type:** *Proceedings, Academic/Scholarly.*
Indexed: Agr, BioCN&I, ChemAb, ChemTitl, DBA, FCA, ForAb, HerbAb, HortAb, MaizeAb, OrnHort, PBA, PotatoAb, RPP, S&F, SeedAb, SoyAb, TriticAb, WAE&RSA, WeedAb.
—BLDSC (6834.300000), CASDDS, CISTI, IE, ingenta, Linda Hall.
Published by: Western Society of Weed Science, c/o Wanda Graves, Bus Mgr, Box 963, Newark, CA 94560. TEL 510-790-1252, FAX 510-790-1252.

580 USA ISSN 0090-8142
WESTERN SOCIETY OF WEED SCIENCE. RESEARCH PROGRESS REPORT. Text in English. 1952. a. USD 25 (effective 2005). **Document type:** *Academic/Scholarly.*

B

▼ new title ➤ refereed ✶ unverified ♦ full entry avail.

Indexed: Agr, DBA, FCA, HerbAb, HortAb, PBA, RA&MP, S&F, SeedAb, WeedAb.
—CISTI, Linda Hall.
Published by: Western Society of Weed Science, c/o Wanda Graves, Bus Mgr, Box 963, Newark, CA 94560. TEL 510-790-1252, FAX 510-790-1252.

580.74   USA
WHAT'S UP AT CHEEKWOOD. Text in English. 1961. bi-m. membership. adv. **Document type:** *Newsletter.* **Description:** Informs members of happenings and exhibits at Cheekwood.
Former titles: Cheekwood - Tennessee Botanical Gardens and Museum of Art; Cheekwood - Tennessee Botanical Gardens and Fine Arts Center (Calendar); Cheekwood Mirror
Published by: Tennessee Botanical Gardens & Museum of Art, 1200 Forrest Park Dr, Nashville, TN 37205. TEL 615-353-2163, FAX 615-353-2168. Ed. Lisa Hanley. Adv. contact Sherry Brown. Circ: 7,400.

580   POL   ISSN 0043-5090
    CODEN: WIBOA7
➤ **WIADOMOSCI BOTANICZNE.** Text in Polish; Summaries in English. 1957. q. USD 38 (effective 1998). bk.rev. bibl. **Document type:** *Journal, Academic/Scholarly.* **Description:** Offers a wide spectrum of publications summarizing and reviewing problems from different branches of botany as well as current news in Polish and world botany; also provides information on botanical collections, scientific expeditions, symposia and congresses.
Indexed: AgBio, AgrForAb, AgrLib, BIOSIS Prev, BiolAb, CPA, ChemAb, FCA, ForAb, HerbAb, HortAb, I&DA, IndVet, MaizeAb, OrnHort, PBA, PGegResA, PGrRegA, RA&MP, RM&VM, RPP, RefZh, S&F, SeedAb, VetBull, WeedAb.
—CASDDS, CISTI.
Published by: Polska Akademia Nauk, Instytut Botaniki im. W. Szafera/Polish Academy of Sciences, W. Szafer Institute of Botany, ul Lubicz 46, Krakow, 31512, Poland. TEL 48-12-4241737, FAX 48-12-4219790, office@ib-pan.krakow.pl. Ed. Stefania Laster. Pub. Jacek W Wieser. R&P Mirek Zbigniew. Circ: 600 (paid). **Dist. by:** Ars Polona, Krakowskie Przedmiescie 7, Warsaw, Poland. **Co-sponsor:** Polskie Towarzystwo Botaniczne/Polish Botanical Society.

580   USA   ISSN 1083-7299
THE WILD FOODS FORUM. Text in English. 1990. bi-m. USD 15 domestic; USD 16.50 foreign; USD 2 newsstand/cover (effective 2000). bk.rev.; video rev. illus. index. back issues avail. **Document type:** *Newsletter.* **Description:** Features stories on wild edible foods and their health benefits, rare or poisonous plants, trip reports, upcoming events and survival skills.
Published by: Eco Images, PO Box 61413, Virginia Beach, VA 23466-1413. TEL 757-421-3929, wildfood@infi.net, http://www.pilot.infi.net/~wildfood. Ed. Vickie Shufer. R&P Vicki Shufer. adv.: page USD 85; trim 10.5 x 8. Circ: 600 (paid).

581   CAN   ISSN 0842-5132
WILDFLOWER; North America's magazine of wild flora. Text in English. 1985. q. CND 35 domestic; USD 35 foreign; CND 9 newsstand/cover (effective 1999 - 2000). adv. bk.rev. illus.; maps. cum.index: 1984-1994. back issues avail.; reprints avail. **Document type:** *Consumer.* **Description:** Offers articles and information to readers across the continent for all levels of botanical knowledge and interest.
Indexed: BiolDig, GardL.
—CISTI.
Address: P O Box 335, Sta F, Toronto, ON M4Y 2L7, Canada. TEL 416-466-6428, FAX 416-466-6428, jheditor@wildflower.com, http://www.wildflowermag.com. Ed. James L Hodgins. R&P, Adv. contact Zile Zichmanis. B&W page USD 1,076; trim 10 x 7.5. Circ: 2,500.

580   DEU   ISSN 0511-9618
QK1
➤ **WILLDENOWIA.** Text in English. 1953. s-a. EUR 120 (effective 2003). bk.rev. index. back issues avail. **Document type:** *Journal, Academic/Scholarly.* **Description:** Original papers in the fields of taxonomic and floristic botany.
Indexed: ASFA, AgrForAb, B&BAb, BiolAb, FCA, FPA, ForAb, HerbAb, HortAb, I&DA, IBR, OrnHort, PBA, PGegResA, RA&MP, RPP, RRTA, RefZh, S&F, SeedAb, TriticAb, WeedAb.
—BLDSC (9318.900000), IE, ingenta, Linda Hall.
Published by: Botanischer Garten und Botanisches Museum Berlin-Dahlem, Koenigin Luise Str 6-8, Berlin, 14191, Germany. TEL 49-30-83850194, FAX 49-30-83850253, n.kilian@bgbm.org, library@bgbm.org, http://www.bgbm.fu-berlin.de/bgbm/library/publikat/willdenowia.htm. Ed. N Kilian. Circ: 1,000.

579.5   JPN
WORLD DIRECTORY OF COLLECTIONS OF CULTURES OF MICROORGANISMS. Text in English. 1989. irreg., latest vol.4, 1993. JPY 15,450. **Description:** Lists of scientific names of 334,312 strains of bacteria and 351,263 strains of fungi and yeasts.
Formerly: Guide to World Data Center on Microorganism (0915-6682)

Published by: W F C C World Data Centre on Microorganisms/Baiyo Seibutsu Sekai Deta Senta, Center for Information Biology, National Institute of Genetics, 1111 Yata, Mishima-shi, Shizuoka-ken 411-0801, Japan. Ed. Hideaki Sugawara. **Dist. by:** Japan Publications Trading Co., Ltd., Book Export II Dept, PO Box 5030, Tokyo International, Tokyo 101-3191, Japan. FAX 81-3-32920410.

580   CHN   ISSN 1000-470X
QK1   CODEN: WZYAFY
WUHAN ZHIWUXUE YANJIU/JOURNAL OF WUHAN BOTANICAL RESEARCH. Text in Chinese. 1983. q. CNY 48 (effective 2004). illus. 96 p./no.; **Document type:** *Journal, Academic/Scholarly.* **Description:** Covers the latest scientific research and reports on new theories, technologies, achievements and trends in all branches of botanical science.
Related titles: Online - full text ed.: (from East View Information Services, WanFang Data Corp.).
—BLDSC (5072.700000).
Published by: (Zhongguo Kexueyuan, Wuhan Zhiwuyuan/Chinese Academy of Sciences, Wuhan Botanical Garden), Kexue Chubanshe/Science Press, 16 Donghuang Cheng Genbei Jie, Beijing, 100717, China. TEL 86-10-64000246, FAX 86-10-64030255, editor@rose.whiob.ac.cn, http://whzwxyj.periodicals.net.cn/default.html, http://www.sciencep.com/. Ed. Zheng Zhong. **Dist. overseas by:** China International Book Trading Corp, 35 Chegongzhuang Xilu, Haidian District, PO Box 399, Beijing 100044, China. TEL 86-10-68412045, FAX 86-10-68412023, cibtc@mail.cibtc.com.cn, http://www.cibtc.com.cn.

581   CHN   ISSN 1000-4025
XIBEI ZHIWU XUEBAO/ACTA BOTANICA BOREALI-OCCIDENTALLA SINICA. Text in Chinese. 1980. bi-m. CNY 8, USD 3.38 (effective 2002). **Document type:** *Journal, Academic/Scholarly.*
Related titles: Online - full content ed.: (from WanFang Data Corp.); Online - full text ed.: (from East View Information Services).
Indexed: AEBA, AgBio, AgrForAb, B&BAb, BIOSIS Prev, BiolAb, CPA, ESPM, FCA, FPA, ForAb, GenetAb, HerbAb, HortAb, I&DA, MaizeAb, OrnHort, PBA, PGegResA, PGrRegA, PHN&I, RA&MP, RefZh, S&F, SIA, SeedAb, SoyAb, TriticAb, VITIS, WeedAb.
—BLDSC (0605.810000), IE, ingenta.
Published by: Shanxi-sheng Kexueyuan, Xiaozhai Dong Lu 3-Hao, Xi'an, 712100, China. TEL 86-29-7012025, FAX 86-29-5244651, http://xbzwxb.periodicals.com.cn/default.html. **Dist. by:** China International Book Trading Corp, 35 Chegongzhuang Xilu, Haidian District, PO Box 399, Beijing 100044, China. TEL 86-10-68412045, FAX 86-10-68412023, cibtc@mail.cibtc.com.cn, http://www.cibtc.com.cn.

580   JPN
YAKKOSO TSUCHITORIMOCHI NO TOMO/PARASITIC PLANTS MAGAZINE. Text in Japanese. 1976. q. JPY 6,000, USD 35.
Published by: Yakkoso Tsuchitorimochi o Hogo Suru Kai/Preserving Society of Mitrastemon and Balanophora, c/o Mr Eitaro Akusawa, 19-4 Mejirodai 3-chome, Bunkyo-ku, Tokyo, 112-0015, Japan. Ed. Eitaro Akuzawa. Circ: 1,500.

580   JPN   ISSN 0914-5036
YAMANASHI SHOKUBUTSU KENKYU/BOTANICAL SOCIETY OF YAMANASHI. BULLETIN. Text in Japanese. 1987. a.
Published by: Yamanashi Shokubutsu Kenkyukai/Botanical Society of Yamanashi, c/o Mr Eiji Okubo, 2800-109 Yamamiya-cho, Kofu-shi, Yamanashi-ken 400-0075, Japan.

580   CHN   ISSN 1001-9782
YAREDAI ZHIWU TONGXUN/SUBTROPICAL PLANT RESEARCH COMMUNICATIONS. Text in Chinese. 1972. s-a. CNY 3. **Document type:** *Bulletin.*
Published by: Fujian Institute of Subtropical Botany/Fujian Yaredai Zhiwu Yanjiusuo, Dianqian, Xiamen, Fujian 361006, China. TEL 621047. Ed. Huang Weinan. **Dist. overseas by:** China National Publishing Industry Trading Corporation, PO Box 782, Beijing 100011, China.

580   JPN   ISSN 0912-2451
YASO/WILD PLANTS. Text in Japanese. 1935. bi-m. JPY 3,500. adv. 16 p./no.; **Document type:** *Bulletin.*
Published by: Yagai Shokubutsu Kenkyukai/Wild Plants Lover's Club, c/o Mr Nobushige Kato, 1-18 Wakaba, Shinjuku-ku, Tokyo, 160-0011, Japan. TEL 81-3-3357-9090. Eds. Akira Yamamoto, Nobushige Kato. Adv. contact Bansei Makino. Circ: 500.

580   JPN
YASO NO TOMO/ICHIHARA BOTANICAL ASSOCIATION. JOURNAL. Text in Japanese. a.
Published by: Ichihara Shokubutsu Kenkyukai/Ichihara Botanical Association, c/o Mr Yuji Nemoto, 219 Yama-Guchi, Ichihara-shi, Chiba-ken 290-0558, Japan.

580   JPN
YASO TOMO NO KAI/SOCIETY OF THE WILD GRASS. NEWS. Text in Japanese. a.
Address: c/o Mr Yoshitaka Takahashi, 9-7 Saiku-Machi, Shinjuku-ku, Tokyo, 162-0838, Japan.

579.562   GBR   ISSN 0749-503X
    CODEN: YESTE3
➤ **YEAST;** a forum for yeast researchers. Text in English. 1985. 16/yr. USD 2,525 to institutions; USD 2,778 combined subscription to institutions print & online eds. (effective 2006). adv. back issues avail.; reprints avail. **Document type:** *Journal, Academic/Scholarly.* **Description:** Contains original research articles along with major and minor reviews and short communications on all aspects of saccharomyces and other yeast genera.
Related titles: Microform ed.: (from PQC); Online - full text ed.: ISSN 1097-0061. USD 2,525 to institutions (effective 2006) (from EBSCO Publishing, Swets Information Services, Wiley InterScience).
Indexed: AbHyg, AgBio, B&BAb, BBCI, BCI, BIOBASE, BIOSIS Prev, BioCN&I, BiolAb, CIN, ChemAb, CurCont, DBA, DSA, ExcerpMed, FS&TA, GenetAb, HGA, IABS, ISR, IndMed, Inpharma, MBA, MEDLINE, MSB, NucAcAb, NutrAb, PGegResA, ProtozoAb, RM&VM, RPP, Reac, SCI, SIA, TDB, Telegen, VITIS.
—BLDSC (9417.976000), CASDDS, CISTI, GNLM, IDS, IE, ingenta, Linda Hall. CCC.
Published by: John Wiley & Sons Ltd. (Subsidiary of: John Wiley & Sons, Inc.), The Atrium, Southern Gate, Chichester, West Sussex PO19 8SQ, United Kingdom. TEL 44-1243-779777, FAX 44-1243-775878, customer@wiley.co.uk, http://www3.interscience.wiley.com/cgi-bin/jhome/3895, http://www.wiley.co.uk. Ed. S G Oliver. adv.: B&W page GBP 650, color page GBP 1,550; trim 200 x 260. **Subscr. in the Americas to:** John Wiley & Sons, Inc., 111 River St, Hoboken, NJ 07030-5774. TEL 201-748-6645, 800-225-5945, subinfo@wiley.com

580   CHN   ISSN 0253-2700
QK1   CODEN: YCWCDP
➤ **YUNNAN ZHIWU YANJIU/ACTA BOTANICA YUNNANICA.** Text in Chinese; Abstracts in English. 1979. bi-m. CNY 90 (effective 2004). adv. bk.rev. abstr. 126 p./no.; **Document type:** *Journal, Academic/Scholarly.* **Description:** Publishes original papers and notes on various fields of botany, including phytotaxonomy, phytogeography, phytochemistry, plant physiology, morphology, ecology and geobotany, domestication of introduced species, utilization of plant resources, and new techniques and achievements in China and abroad.
Related titles: CD-ROM ed.; Online - full text ed.: (from East View Information Services).
Indexed: AgBio, AgrForAb, BIOSIS Prev, BiolAb, CIN, CPA, ChemAb, ChemTitl, FCA, FPA, FS&TA, ForAb, HerbAb, HortAb, MaizeAb, OrnHort, PBA, PGegResA, PGrRegA, PHN&I, PotatoAb, RA&MP, RDA, RPP, RefZh, RevApplEntom, RiceAb, S&F, SIA, SeedAb, SoyAb, TriticAb, VITIS, WAE&RSA, WeedAb.
—BLDSC (0608.120000), CASDDS, IE, ingenta, Linda Hall.
Published by: (Zhongguo Kexueyuan, Kunming Zhiwu Yanjiusuo/Chinese Academy of Sciences, Kunming Institute of Botany), Kexue Chubanshe/Science Press, 16 Donghuang Cheng Genbei Jie, Beijing, 100717, China. TEL 86-10-64000246, FAX 86-10-64030255. Ed. Zhengyi Wu. Adv. contact Aiqin Liu. Circ: 1,300 (paid and controlled).

579.5   DEU   ISSN 0170-110X
QK600   CODEN: ZEMYDW
ZEITSCHRIFT FUER MYKOLOGIE. Text in German. s-a.
Indexed: FPA, ForAb, RPP, S&F.
—BLDSC (9473.770000), IE, Linda Hall.
Published by: Deutsche Gesellschaft fuer Mykologie, Postfach 700447, Munchen, 81304, Germany. TEL 49-89-7605353, FAX 49-89-76977474.

580   DEU   ISSN 0340-8159
    CODEN: ZPFPAA
➤ **ZEITSCHRIFT FUER PFLANZENKRANKHEITEN UND PFLANZENSCHUTZ.** Text and summaries in English, German. 1891. bi-m. EUR 496 domestic; EUR 497.30 foreign; EUR 85 per issue (effective 2004). adv. bk.rev. abstr.; bibl.; charts; illus. index. **Document type:** *Journal, Academic/Scholarly.* **Description:** Contains scientific articles and research in horticulture.
Former titles (until 1970): Zeitschrift fuer Pflanzenkrankheiten, Pflanzenpathologie und Pflanzenschutz (0044-3271); (until 1929): Zeitschrift fuer Pflanzenkrankheiten und Pflanzenschutz (0372-9729); (until 1926): Zeitschrift fuer Pflanzenkrankheiten und Gallenkunde (0372-8528); (until 1922): Zeitschrift fuer Pflanzenkrankheiten (0938-9350)
Indexed: AEA, ASCA, ASFA, AgBio, AgrForAb, BIOBASE, BIOSIS Prev, BioCN&I, BiolAb, CIN, CPA, ChemAb, ChemTitl, CurCont, DBA, FCA, FPA, FS&TA, FaBeAb, ForAb, GEOBASE, HerbAb, HortAb, I&DA, IABS, IBR, ISR, MaizeAb, NemAb, NutrAb, OrnHort, PBA, PGegResA, PGrRegA, PHN&I, PlantSci, PotatoAb, PoultAb, RA&MP, RM&VM, RPP, RefZh, RevApplEntom, RiceAb, S&F, SCI, SIA, SeedAb, SoyAb, TOSA, TriticAb, VITIS, VetBull, WAE&RSA, WeedAb.
—BLDSC (5040.510000), CISTI, IE, Infotrieve, ingenta, Linda Hall. CCC.
Published by: (Deutsche Phytomedizinische Gesellschaft eV), Verlag Eugen Ulmer GmbH, Wollgrasweg 41, Stuttgart, 70599, Germany. TEL 49-711-45070, FAX 49-711-4507120, info@ulmer.de, http://www.ulmer.de. Ed. H Buchenauer. R&P Gerd Friedrich. adv.: B&W page EUR 467; trim 130 x 210. Circ: 350 (paid and controlled).

➤ **ZEITSCHRIFT FUER PHYTOTHERAPIE.** see *MEDICAL SCIENCES*

580 635 CHN ISSN 0529-1542
SB750
ZHIWU BAOHU/PLANT PROTECTION. Text in Chinese. 1963. bi-m. USD 3 per issue. adv. 56 p./no.;
Related titles: Online - full text ed.: (from East View Information Services, WanFang Data Corp.).
Indexed: AEA, AgBio, AgrForAb, BioCN&I, CPA, FCA, FPA, ForAb, HerbAb, HortAb, MaizeAb, NemAb, NutrAb, OrnHort, PBA, PGegResA, PGrRegA, PHN&I, PN&I, PotatoAb, ProtozoAb, RA&MP, RDA, RM&VM, RPP, RiceAb, S&F, SIA, SeedAb, SoyAb, TDB, TriticAb, WAE&RSA, WeedAb.
—BLDSC (6522.850000), IE, ingenta.
Published by: Zhongguo Zhiwu Baohu Xuehui/China Society of Plant Protection, Zhongguo Nongke Yuan Zhibao Suo, 2, Yuanmingyuan Xilu, Beijing, 100094, China. zwbh68@263.net, http://zwbh.wanfangdata.com.cn/default.html. Ed. Li Guangbo. R&P Yunlu Xie. Adv. contact Hongrong Gao. **Dist. by:** China International Book Trading Corp, 35 Chegongzhuang Xilu, Haidian District, PO Box 399, Beijing 100044, China. TEL 86-10-68412045, FAX 86-10-68412023, cibtc@mail.cibtc.com.cn, http://www.cibtc.com.cn/.

580 CHN ISSN 0577-7518
CODEN: CWPHA2
ZHIWU BAOHU XUEBAO/ACTA PHYTOPHYLACICA SINICA. Text in Chinese; Abstracts in English. 1963. q. CNY 80, USD 28.80 (effective 2005). **Document type:** *Journal, Academic/Scholarly.* **Description:** Contains research reports in this field of botany.
Related titles: Online - full text ed.: (from WanFang Data Corp.).
Indexed: AEA, AgBio, AgrForAb, BioCN&I, BiolAb, CPA, CTFA, FCA, FPA, ForAb, HelmAb, HerbAb, HortAb, I&DA, MaizeAb, NemAb, OrnHort, PBA, PGegResA, PGrRegA, PHN&I, PN&I, PotatoAb, PoultAb, ProtozoAb, RA&MP, RM&VM, RPP, RevApplEntom, RiceAb, S&F, SIA, SeedAb, SoyAb, TDB, TriticAb, WAE&RSA, WeedAb, ZooRec.
—BLDSC (0656.700000), CISTI, Linda Hall.
Published by: Zhongguo Zhiwu Baohu Xuehui/China Society of Plant Protection, Department of Plant Protection, China Agricultural University, Beijing, 100094, China. TEL 86-10-62892528, zbxb@cau.edu.cn, http://zwbhxb.periodicals.net.cn/default.html. Ed. Kexun Huang. **Dist. outside of China by:** China International Book Trading Corp, 35 Chegongzhuang Xilu, Haidian District, PO Box 399, Beijing 100044, China. TEL 86-10-68412045, FAX 86-10-68412023, cibtc@mail.cibtc.com.cn, http://www.cibtc.com.cn/.

580 CHN ISSN 0412-0914
SB599 CODEN: CWSPDA
➤ **ZHIWU BINGLI XUEBAO/ACTA PHYTOPATHOLOGICA SINICA.** Text in Chinese. q. USD 1.80 per issue. 96 p./no.; **Document type:** *Academic/Scholarly.*
Related titles: Online - full text ed.: (from East View Information Services).
Indexed: AgBio, AgrForAb, BioCN&I, CPA, CTFA, FCA, FPA, FS&TA, ForAb, HerbAb, HortAb, MaizeAb, NemAb, OrnHort, PBA, PGegResA, PGrRegA, PHN&I, PotatoAb, RA&MP, RM&VM, RPP, RevApplEntom, RiceAb, S&F, SIA, SeedAb, SoyAb, TriticAb, WeedAb, ZooRec.
—BLDSC (0656.500000), Linda Hall.
Published by: Zhongguo Zhiwu Bingli Xuehui/China Phytopathological Society, Department of Plant Protection, Beijing University of Agriculture, Beijing, 100094, China. TEL 86-10-62892364, FAX 86-10-62891025. Ed. Zeng Shimai.

580 CHN ISSN 0529-1526
QK355
➤ **ZHIWU FENLEI XUEBAO/ACTA PHYTOTAXONOMICA SINICA.** Text in Chinese; Summaries in English. 1951. bi-m. CNY 150 (effective 2004). adv. **Document type:** *Journal, Academic/Scholarly.* **Description:** Contains original papers on phytotaxonomy, phytogeography, phytosystematics, and biosystematics. Also includes discussions from various schools and activities both in China and abroad.
Related titles: Online - full text ed.: (from East View Information Services).
Indexed: BiolAb, CurCont, ForAb, HortAb, OrnHort, PBA, PGegResA, RA&MP, RevApplEntom, SeedAb, TriticAb, VITIS, ZooRec.
—BLDSC (0657.500000), CISTI, Linda Hall.
Published by: (Zhongguo Kexueyuan, Zhiwu Yanjiusuo/Chinese Academy of Sciences, Botanical Institute), Kexue Chubanshe/Science Press, 16 Donghuang Cheng Genbei Jie, Beijing, 100717, China. TEL 86-10-64000246, FAX 86-10-64030255, aps@caf.forestry.ac.cn, http://www.plantsystematics.com/, http://www.sciencep.com/. Circ: 6,000. **Dist. by:** China International Book Trading Corp, 35 Chegongzhuang Xilu, Haidian District, PO Box 399, Beijing 100044, China. TEL 86-10-68412045, FAX 86-10-68412023, cibtc@mail.cibtc.com.cn, http://www.cibtc.com.cn.

571.2 CHN ISSN 0257-4829
QK710 CODEN: CWSPDA
➤ **ZHIWU SHENGLI XUEBAO/ACTA PHYTOPHYSIOLOGICA SINICA.** Text in Chinese; Summaries in English. 1964. q. CNY 12.80 newsstand/cover (effective 2002). adv. **Document type:** *Academic/Scholarly.* **Description:** Contains original papers on plant physiology, including plant cell physiology, whole plant physiology, crop physiology, ecological physiology, plant biochemistry and biophysics.
Related titles: Online - full content ed.: (from WanFang Data Corp.); Online - full text ed.: (from East View Information Services).
Indexed: AgBio, AgrForAb, BIOSIS Prev, BiolAb, CIN, CPA, CTFA, ChemAb, ChemTitl, ExcerpMed, FCA, FS&TA, ForAb, HerbAb, HortAb, I&DA, MaizeAb, OrnHort, PBA, PGrRegA, PHN&I, RA&MP, RPP, RiceAb, S&F, S&MA, SeedAb, SoyAb, TriticAb, VITIS, WeedAb.
—BLDSC (0656.750000), CASDDS, CISTI, Infotrieve, Linda Hall.
Published by: (Chinese Society of Plant Physiology), Kexue Chubanshe, Shanghai Banshechu, Fenglin Lu 270-hao, Shanghai, 200032, China. TEL 86-21-64042111, spshb@online.sh.cn, http://www.sciencepress.com.cn/gb/content/2001-12/13/content_80.htm. Circ: 7,000. **Dist. by:** China International Book Trading Corp, 35 Chegongzhuang Xilu, Haidian District, PO Box 399, Beijing 100044, China. TEL 86-10-68412045, FAX 86-10-68412023, cibtc@mail.cibtc.com.cn, http://www.cibtc.com.cn.

571.2 CHN ISSN 0412-0922
CODEN: CHWSAX
ZHIWU SHENGLIXUE TONGXUN/PLANT PHYSIOLOGY COMMUNICATIONS. Text in Chinese. 1951. bi-m. CNY 72 (effective 2004). adv. bk.rev. **Document type:** *Journal, Academic/Scholarly.* **Description:** Contains original papers, communications, and review articles on plant physiology, biochemistry, and biophysics, from the molecular level to the community level. Also contains columns on techniques and methods, teaching, and news.
Related titles: Online - full text ed.: (from East View Information Services, WanFang Data Corp.).
Indexed: AgBio, AgrForAb, CIN, CPA, ChemAb, ChemTitl, FCA, FPA, ForAb, HerbAb, HortAb, I&DA, MaizeAb, OrnHort, PBA, PGegResA, PGrRegA, PHN&I, PotatoAb, RA&MP, RPP, RiceAb, S&F, SIA, SeedAb, SoyAb, TriticAb, WeedAb.
—BLDSC (6522.100000), CASDDS, CISTI, IE, ingenta.
Published by: (Chinese Society of Plant Physiology), Kexue Chubanshe/Science Press, 16 Donghuang Cheng Genbei Jie, Beijing, 100717, China. TEL 86-10-64000246, FAX 86-10-64030255, zkzhou@iris.sipp.ac.cn, http://zwslxtx.periodicals.net.cn/default.html, http://www.sciencep.com/. **Dist. by:** China International Book Trading Corp, 35 Chegongzhuang Xilu, Haidian District, PO Box 399, Beijing 100044, China. TEL 86-10-68412045, FAX 86-10-68412023, cibtc@mail.cibtc.com.cn, http://www.cibtc.com.cn.

580 CHN ISSN 1005-264X
QK355
➤ **ZHIWU SHENGTAI XUEBAO/ACTA PHYTOECOLOGICA SINICA.** Text in Chinese, English. 1955. bi-m. CNY 228 (effective 2004). adv. bk.rev. **Document type:** *Academic/Scholarly.* **Description:** Contains original research papers on plant ecology, including plant ecophysiology, population ecology, community ecology, vegetation science, landscape ecology, ecosystem ecology, and conservation.
Formerly (until 1994): Zhiwu Shengtaixue yu Diziwuxue Xuebao - Acta Phytoecologica et Geobotanica Sinica (1000-0011)
Related titles: Online - full text ed.: (from East View Information Services).
Indexed: BiolAb, FCA, RefZh.
—BLDSC (0655.950000), CISTI, Linda Hall.
Published by: (Zhongguo Kexueyuan, Zhiwu Yanjiusuo/Chinese Academy of Sciences, Botanical Institute), Kexue Chubanshe/Science Press, 16 Donghuang Cheng Genbei Jie, Beijing, 100717, China. TEL 86-10-64000246, FAX 86-10-64030255, apes@95777.com; apes@ns.ibcas.ac.cn, http://www.plant-ecology.com/dybf.asp, http://www.sciencep.com/. Eds. Yihui Hu, Yonghong Li. R&P Yihui Hu. Adv. contact Yonghong Li. Circ: 1,300. **Dist. by:** China International Book Trading Corp, 35 Chegongzhuang Xilu, Haidian District, PO Box 399, Beijing 100044, China. TEL 86-10-68412045, FAX 86-10-68412023, cibtc@mail.cibtc.com.cn, http://www.cibtc.com.cn.

580 CHN ISSN 0577-7496
QK1 CODEN: CHWHAY
➤ **ZHIWU XUEBAO/ACTA BOTANICA SINICA.** Text in Chinese; Summaries in English. 1951. m. USD 540 (effective 2004). adv. bibl.; charts; illus. index. back issues avail. **Document type:** *Academic/Scholarly.* **Description:** Original papers on the applications and theory of plant morphology, cytology, chemistry, physiology, biochemistry, ecology, geobotany, and paleobotany. Also covers the domestication of spices and plant genetics.
Related titles: Online - full text ed.: (from East View Information Services); ♦ English ed.: Journal of Integrative Plant Biology. ISSN 1672-9072.
Indexed: AEA, AgBio, AgrForAb, BBCI, BIOSIS Prev, BioCN&I, BioDAb, BiolAb, CIN, CPA, ChemAb, ChemTitl, FCA, FPA, FS&TA, ForAb, GEOBASE, HerbAb, HortAb, I&DA, MaizeAb, OrnHort, PBA, PGegResA, PGrRegA, PHN&I, PotatoAb, ProtozoAb, RA&MP, RPP, RRTA, RevApplEntom, RiceAb, S&F, S&MA, SeedAb, SoyAb, TOSA, TriticAb, VITIS, WeedAb, ZooRec.
—CASDDS, CISTI, IDS, IE, ingenta, Linda Hall.
Published by: (Chinese Academy of Sciences/Zhongguo Kexueyuan), Kexue Chubanshe/Science Press, 16 Donghuang Cheng Genbei Jie, Beijing, 100717, China. TEL 86-10-64000246, FAX 86-10-64030255, http://www.chineseplantscience.com/Eindex.asp. Ed. Cheng Tsui. Circ: 12,000. **Dist. by:** China International Book Trading Corp, 35 Chegongzhuang Xilu, Haidian District, PO Box 399, Beijing 100044, China. TEL 86-10-68412045, FAX 86-10-68412023, cibtc@mail.cibtc.com.cn, http://www.cibtc.com.cn. **Co-sponsor:** Chinese Botanical Society.

580 CHN ISSN 1000-0631
QK355
ZHIWU ZAZHI/PLANTS JOURNAL. Variant title: Journal of Botany. Text in Chinese. 1973. bi-m. CNY 30 (effective 2004). **Document type:** *Journal, Academic/Scholarly.* **Description:** Closely incorporates the production practices of agriculture, forestry, horticulture, and medicinal herbs, and introduces a basic knowledge of botany and of China's rich botanical resources. Helpful for middle school instruction and for amateurs interested in botany.
Related titles: Online - full text ed.: (from East View Information Services).
—Linda Hall.
Published by: (Zhongguo Zhiwu Xuehui), Kexue Chubanshe/Science Press, 16 Donghuang Cheng Genbei Jie, Beijing, 100717, China. TEL 86-10-64000246, FAX 86-10-64030255, http://zhiwzz.periodicals.net.cn/default.html, http://www.sciencep.com/. **Dist. by:** China International Book Trading Corp, 35 Chegongzhuang Xilu, Haidian District, PO Box 399, Beijing 100044, China. TEL 86-10-68412045, FAX 86-10-68412023, cibtc@mail.cibtc.com.cn, http://www.cibtc.com.cn.

580 CHN ISSN 1004-0978
QK900 CODEN: ZZYHEJ
➤ **ZHIWU ZIYUAN YU HUANJING/JOURNAL OF PLANT RESOURCES AND ENVIRONMENT.** Text in Chinese. 1992. q. CNY 6 newsstand/cover (effective 2005). adv. bk.rev. **Document type:** *Journal, Academic/Scholarly.* **Description:** Publishes original articles, research notes and reviews dealing with basic and applied studies in plant resources and environment.
Related titles: Online - full text ed.: (from WanFang Data Corp.).
Indexed: AgBio, AgrForAb, BIOSIS Prev, BiolAb, CIN, CPA, ChemAb, ChemTitl, FCA, FPA, FS&TA, ForAb, HerbAb, HortAb, I&DA, MaizeAb, NutrAb, OrnHort, PBA, PGegResA, PGrRegA, PHN&I, RA&MP, RDA, RM&VM, RPP, RRTA, RevApplEntom, RiceAb, S&F, SIA, SeedAb, SoyAb, TriticAb, WAE&RSA, WeedAb.
—BLDSC (5040.523000), CASDDS, IE, ingenta.
Published by: (Jiangsu Institute of Botany), Zhongguo Kexueyuan, Jiangsu-sheng Zhiwu Yanjiusuo/Chinese Academy of Sciences, Jiangsu Province Institute of Botany, 1 Qian Hu Hou Cun, Outside Zhongshan Gate, Nanjing, 210014, China. TEL 86-25-84347016, FAX 86-25-84432074, nbgxx@jlonline.com, ibgadsch@jsnet1.js.sti.ac.cn, http://zwzyyhjxb.periodicals.net.cn/, http://www.sti.js.cn/jssti/enterprise/garden/. **Co-sponsor:** Jiangsu Society of Botany.

580 CHN
ZHIWUXUE TONGBAO/BOTANICAL BULLETIN. Text in Chinese. q.
Indexed: IABS.
Published by: Zhongguo Kexueyuan, Zhiwu Yanjiusuo/Chinese Academy of Sciences, Botanical Institute, 20 Nanxincun, Xiangshan, Beijing, 100093, China. TEL 893831. Ed. Zhu Zhiqing.

579.5 CHN ISSN 1003-8310
ZHONGGUO SHIYONGJUN/EDIBLE FUNGI OF CHINA. Text in Chinese. 1985. bi-m. CNY 4, USD 1.90 per issue (effective 2003). **Document type:** *Journal, Academic/Scholarly.*
Related titles: Online - full text ed.: (from East View Information Services).
Indexed: AgBio, CPA, DSA, FPA, FS&TA, ForAb, HortAb, IndVet, MaizeAb, OrnHort, PBA, PGegResA, PGrRegA, PotatoAb, RA&MP, S&F, SIA, SoyAb, TDB, TriticAb, WAE&RSA.
—BLDSC (3660.620000), IE, ingenta.
Published by: Zhongguo Shiyongjun Xiehui, 14, Zhongjiao Road, Kunmingshi, Yunnan 650223, China. http://zgsyj.periodicals.com.cn/default.html. **Dist. by:** China International Book Trading Corp, 35 Chegongzhuang Xilu, Haidian District, PO Box 399, Beijing 100044, China. TEL 86-10-68412045, FAX 86-10-68412023, cibtc@mail.cibtc.com.cn, http://www.cibtc.com.cn.

704.9434 CHN ISSN 1000-6567
ZHUZI YANJIU HUIKAN/JOURNAL OF BAMBOO RESEARCH. Text in Chinese. 1982. q. **Document type:** *Journal, Academic/Scholarly.*
Related titles: Online - full text ed.: (from East View Information Services, WanFang Data Corp.).
Indexed: AgBio, AgrForAb, BioCN&I, CPA, DSA, FPA, ForAb, HortAb, I&DA, NemAb, OrnHort, PBA, PGegResA, PGrRegA, PotatoAb, RRTA, S&F, WAE&RSA.
Published by: Zhuzi Yanjiu Kaifa Zhongxin, 138, Wenyi Lu, Hangzhou, 310012, China. TEL 86-571-88869210, FAX 86-571-88856871, bamboowulr@yahoo.com.cn, http://zzyjhk.periodicals.net.cn/.

ZIVA/LIVE; casopis pro biologickou praci. see *BIOLOGY*

B

ZOOLOGISCH - BOTANISCHE GESELLSCHAFT, VIENNA. ABHANDLUNGEN. see *BIOLOGY—Zoology*

BIOLOGY—Computer Applications

570.285 SGP
▼ **ADVANCES IN BIOINFORMATICS AND COMPUTATIONAL BIOLOGY.** Text in English. 2005. irreg., latest vol.2, 2005, Jun. price varies. **Document type:** *Monographic series, Academic/Scholarly.* **Description:** Covers the frontier between computing and biology, beyond the bioinformatics community and include researchers extending from the quantitative science domain to that of experimental biology.
Published by: World Scientific Publishing Co. Pte. Ltd., 5 Toh Tuck Link, Singapore, 596224, Singapore. TEL 65-466-5775, FAX 65-467-7667, series@wspc.com.sg, http://www.wspc.com/books/series/abcb_series.shtml, http://www.worldscientific.com. Eds. Limsoon Wong, Ying Xu. **Subscr. to:** Farrer Rd, PO Box 128, Singapore 912805, Singapore. TEL 65-382-5663, FAX 65-382-5919. **Dist. in Europe by:** World Scientific Publishing Ltd., 57 Shelton St, London WC2H 9HE, United Kingdom. TEL 44-20-78360888, FAX 44-20-78362020, sales@wspc.co.uk.; **Dist. in the US by:** World Scientific Publishing Co., Inc., 1060 Main St, River Edge, NJ 07661. TEL 201-487-9655, 800-227-7562, FAX 201-487-9656, 888-977-2665, wspc@wspc.com.

570.285 NZL ISSN 1175-5636
QH324.2 CODEN: ABPIC8
➤ **APPLIED BIOINFORMATICS.** Text in English. 2002. q. USD 250 combined subscription to individuals print & online eds.; USD 525 combined subscription to institutions print & online eds. (effective 2005). **Document type:** *Journal, Academic/Scholarly.* **Description:** Features articles that provide the practising bioinformaticist with information relating to global and regional bioinformatics resources, and a future view of this developing field.
Related titles: Online - full content ed.: USD 215 to individuals; USD 395 to institutions (effective 2005); Online - full text ed.: (from EBSCO Publishing, Gale Group, IngentaConnect, Ovid Technologies, Inc., Swets Information Services).
Indexed: ExcerpMed.
—BLDSC (1571.901000), IE, ingenta. **CCC.**
Published by: Adis International Ltd. (Subsidiary of: Wolters Kluwer BV), 41 Centorian Dr, Mairangi Bay, Private Bag 65901, Auckland, 1311, New Zealand. TEL 64-9-4770700, FAX 64-9-4770766, JournalABI@adis.co.nz, etoc@adisonline.info, http://adisonline.info/abi/default.asp, http://www.adis.com.

570.285 GBR ISSN 1471-2105
QH506 CODEN: BBMIC4
➤ **B M C BIOINFORMATICS.** (BioMed Central) Text in English. 2000. m. free (effective 2006). adv. back issues avail. **Document type:** *Journal, Academic/Scholarly.* **Description:** Publishes original research articles in all aspects of computational methods used in the analysis and annotation of sequences and structures, as well as all other areas of computational biology.
Media: Online - full content (from EBSCO Publishing, National Library of Medicine).
Indexed: BCI, BIOSIS Prev, BiolAb, ExcerpMed, MEDLINE.
—Infotrieve. **CCC.**
Published by: BioMed Central Ltd. (Subsidiary of: Current Science Ltd), Middlesex House, 34-42 Cleveland St, London, W1T 4LB, United Kingdom. TEL 44-20-76319131, FAX 44-20-76319923, info@biomedcentral.com, http://www.biomedcentral.com/bmcbioinformatics/. Ed. Peter Newmark. Adv. contact Deborah Cockerill.

570.285 JPN
▼ **BIO-IT WORLD JAPAN.** Text in English. 2003. q. **Document type:** *Magazine, Trade.*
Published by: I D G Japan, Inc., Hongo 3-4-5, Bunkyo-ku, Tokyo, 1130033, Japan. TEL 81-3-5800-3111, FAX 81-3-5800-3590, http://www.idg.co.jp/bioit/index.html. Ed. Naoyuki Sakai.

570.285 SGP
➤ **BIOCOMPUTING (YEAR).** Variant title: Pacific Symposium on Biocomputing. Proceedings. Text in English. a. price varies. **Document type:** *Proceedings, Academic/Scholarly.*
—BLDSC (6331.530000).
Published by: World Scientific Publishing Co. Pte. Ltd., 5 Toh Tuck Link, Singapore, 596224, Singapore. http://psb.stanford.edu/psb-online/, http://www.worldscientific.com. Ed. Dr. Russ B Altman. **Subscr. in N. Amerca to:** Farrer Rd, PO Box 128, Singapore 912805, Singapore.

570.285 GBR ISSN 1367-4803
QH324.2 CODEN: BOINFP
➤ **BIOINFORMATICS.** Text in English. 1985. 24/yr. GBP 1,116, USD 2,009, EUR 1,674 to institutions; GBP 1,175, USD 2,115, EUR 1,763 combined subscription to institutions print & online eds. (effective 2006). adv. illus.; tr.lit. index. 100 p./no.; back issues avail.; reprint service avail. from PSC. **Document type:** *Journal, Academic/Scholarly.* **Description:** International applications-orientated journal publishing full papers, program reviews, new applications and developments for newcomers and computer-literate bioscientists.
Formerly (until 1998): Computer Applications in the Biosciences (Print) (0266-7061)
Related titles: Online - full text ed.: ISSN 1367-4811. 199?. GBP 1,008, USD 1,714, EUR 1,512 (effective 2006) (from EBSCO Publishing, Gale Group, HighWire Press, IngentaConnect, O C L C Online Computer Library Center, Inc., Ovid Technologies, Inc., Oxford University Press Online Journals, ProQuest Information & Learning, Swets Information Services).
Indexed: AIA, ASCA, ASFA, Agr, B&BAb, BCI, BIOSIS Prev, BibAg, BioEngAb, BiolAb, CADCAM, CBTA, CEABA, CIN, CMCI, ChemAb, ChemTitl, CompAb, CompLI, CurCont, ExcerpMed, FCA, IAOP, ISR, IndMed, Inpharma, M&PBA, MEDLINE, NucAcAb, OceAb, Reac, RefZh, SCI, Telegen.
—BLDSC (2072.348000), CASDDS, CISTI, Ei, GNLM, IDS, IE, Infotrieve, ingenta, Linda Hall. **CCC.**
Published by: Oxford University Press, Great Clarendon St, Oxford, OX2 6DP, United Kingdom. TEL 44-1865-556767, FAX 44-1865-556646, jnlorders@oup-usa.com, jnl.orders@oup.co.uk, http://bioinformatics.oxfordjournals.org/, http://www.oxfordjournals.org/. Pub. David Prosser. R&P Fiona Bennett. Adv. contact Helen Pearson. B&W page GBP 275, B&W page USD 495, color page GBP 500, color page USD 900; 178 x 255. Circ: 1,200.

570.285 GBR ISSN 1462-1355
THE BIOINFORMER. Text in English. 1997. q. free. **Document type:** *Newsletter.* **Description:** Focuses on bioinformatics research, services and developments at the Institute, including a list of the most worthwhile symposia and conferences on the field.
Related titles: Online - full text ed.: ISSN 1462-1363.
—CISTI.
Published by: European Bioinformatics Institute, Welcome Trust Genome Campus, Hinxton, Cambs CB10 1SD, United Kingdom. TEL 44-1223-494635, FAX 44-1223-494468, pow@ebi.ac.uk, http://bioinformer.ebi.ac.uk/. Ed. Jean Jack M Riethoven. R&P Jean Jack M Reithoven. Circ: 3,000.

570.285 DEU ISSN 0340-1200
Q350 CODEN: BICYAF
➤ **BIOLOGICAL CYBERNETICS**; communication and control in organisms and automata. Text in English. 1961. m. EUR 3,168 combined subscription to institutions print & online eds. (effective 2005). adv. bk.rev. charts; illus. index. back issues avail.; reprint service avail. from ISI. **Document type:** *Journal, Academic/Scholarly.* **Description:** Provides experimental and theoretical information in the fields of quantitative analysis of behavior, quantitative physiological studies of information processing in receptors, neural systems and effectors, and computational studies of perceptual motor information processing tasks.
Supersedes: Kybernetik (0023-5946)
Related titles: Microform ed.: (from PQC); Online - full text ed.: ISSN 1432-0770 (from EBSCO Publishing, Springer LINK, Swets Information Services).
Indexed: ASCA, ASFA, B&BAb, BIOSIS Prev, BioEngAb, BiolAb, CIS, CMCI, CompAb, CompR, CurCont, DentInd, EngInd, ExcerpMed, ISR, IndMed, Inpharma, Inspec, MEDLINE, MathR, NSA, NSCI, PotatoAb, Reac, RefZh, RevApplEntom, SCI, SIA, SSCI, ZentMath, ZooRec.
—BLDSC (2075.170000), AskIEEE, CISTI, Ei, GNLM, IDS, IE, Infotrieve, ingenta, Linda Hall. **CCC.**
Published by: Springer-Verlag (Subsidiary of: Springer Science+Business Media), Tiergartenstr 17, Heidelberg, 69121, Germany. TEL 49-6221-3450, FAX 49-6221-345229, http://link.springer.de/link/service/journals/00422/index.htm. Eds. G Hauske TEL 49-89-2892-3476, J L van Hemmen TEL 49-89-289-12362. Adv. contact Stephan Kroeck TEL 49-30-827875739. **Subscr. in the Americas to:** Springer-Verlag New York, Inc., Journal Fulfillment, PO Box 2485, Secaucus, NJ 07096-2485. TEL 800-777-4643, 201-348-4033, FAX 201-348-4505, journals@springer-ny.com, http://www.springer-ny.com; **Subscr. to:** Springer GmbH Auslieferungsgesellschaft, Haberstr 7, Heidelberg 69126, Germany. TEL 49-6221-345-0, FAX 49-6221-345-4229, subscriptions@springer.de.

570.285 JPN
BIOMEDICAL FUZZY SYSTEMS ASSOCIATION. JOURNAL. Text in Japanese. 1999. a., latest vol.5, no.1, 2003. **Document type:** *Journal, Academic/Scholarly.*
Media: Online - full content.
Published by: Baiomedikaru Faji Shisutemu Kenkyukai/ Biomedical Fuzzy Systems Association, Watada Laboratory, Graduate School of IPS, Waseda University, 2-7 Hibikino, Wakamatsu, Kitakyushu, Fukuoka 808-0135, Japan. junzow@osb.att.ne.jp, http://www.f.waseda.jp/watada/BMFSA/. Ed. Masahiro Nakano TEL 81-93-6917159.

570.285 JPN ISSN 1345-1529
➤ **BIOMEDICAL SOFT COMPUTING AND HUMAN SCIENCES.** Text in English. 1998. a., latest vol.9, no.1, 2003. **Document type:** *Journal, Academic/Scholarly.* **Description:** Publishes original research and review articles concerned with the application of fuzzy, neuro, chaos, genetic algorithms and other novel engineering methodologies to the biomedical field including analysis and modeling for human sciences.
Related titles: Online - full content ed.
—BLDSC (2087.880500).
Published by: Baiomedikaru Faji Shisutemu Kenkyukai/ Biomedical Fuzzy Systems Association, Watada Laboratory, Graduate School of IPS, Waseda University, 2-7 Hibikino, Wakamatsu, Kitakyushu, Fukuoka 808-0135, Japan. junzow@osb.att.ne.jp, http://www.f.waseda.jp/watada/BMFSA/. Ed. Akikazu Tamaki TEL 81-832-575039.

570.285 GBR ISSN 1467-5463
QH441.2 CODEN: BBIMFX
➤ **BRIEFINGS IN BIOINFORMATICS.** Text in English. 2000. q. GBP 100 in Europe to individuals based at universities or other educational establishments; USD 155 in North America to individuals based at universities or other educational establishments; GBP 115 elsewhere to individuals based at universities or other educational establishments; GBP 200 in Europe to institutions; USD 310 in North America to institutions; GBP 215 elsewhere to institutions (effective 2004). bk.rev.; software rev.; Website rev. 96 p./no. 2 cols./p.; back issues avail.; reprint service avail. from PSC. **Document type:** *Journal, Academic/Scholarly.* **Description:** A review journal for the users of database and analytical tools of genetic and molecular biology.
Related titles: Online - full content ed.: ISSN 1477-4054; Online - full text ed.: (from bigchalk, EBSCO Publishing, Gale Group, IngentaConnect, O C L C Online Computer Library Center, Inc., ProQuest Information & Learning, Swets Information Services).
Indexed: AgBio, AnBrAb, BCI, CurCont, ExcerpMed, MaizeAb, NemAb, PBA, ProtozoAb, RPP, RefZh, RiceAb, VetBull, WeedAb.
—BLDSC (2283.958363), IE, ingenta.
Published by: Henry Stewart Publications, Russell House, 28-30 Little Russell St, London, WC1A 2HN, United Kingdom. TEL 44-20-74043040, FAX 44-20-74042081, enquiries@hspublications.co.uk, qweny@henrystewart.co.uk, http://www.henrystewart.com/journals/bib/. Pub. Julie Kerry. R&P, Adv. contact Daryn Moody. Circ: 1,000 (paid and free). **Subscr. addr. in N America:** Henry Stewart Publications, Subscriptions Office, PO Box 10812, Birmingham, AL 35202-1588. TEL 800-633-4931, FAX 205-955-1588, hsp@ebsco.com; **Subscr. addr. outside N America:** Museum House, 25 Museum St, London WC1A 1JT, United Kingdom. TEL 44-20-73232916, FAX 44-20-73232918, subscriptions@hspublications.co.uk.

570.285 NLD ISSN 1568-2684
COMPUTATIONAL BIOLOGY. Text in English. 2000 (Sept.). irreg., latest vol.5, 2004, Nov. price varies. **Document type:** *Monographic series, Academic/Scholarly.* **Description:** Aims at publishing recent work devoted to specific issues in computer-assisted analysis of biological data with a particular emphasis on molecular biology.
—BLDSC (3390.576500).
Published by: Springer-Verlag Dordrecht (Subsidiary of: Springer Science+Business Media), Van Godewijckstraat 30, Dordrecht, 3311 GX, Netherlands. TEL 31-78-6576050, FAX 31-78-6576474, http://www.springeronline.com. Eds. G Myers, P A Pevzner, R Giegerich, W Fitch.

570.285 GBR ISSN 1025-5842
QH513 CODEN: CMBEFS
COMPUTER METHODS IN BIOMECHANICS AND BIOMEDICAL ENGINEERING. Text in English. 1997. bi-m. GBP 399, USD 597 combined subscription to institutions print & online eds. (effective 2006). reprint service avail. from PSC. **Document type:** *Journal, Academic/Scholarly.* **Description:** Focuses on the importance of integrating the disciplines of engineering with medical technology and clinical expertise.
Related titles: Online - full text ed.: ISSN 1476-8259. GBP 379, USD 567 to institutions (effective 2006) (from EBSCO Publishing, Gale Group, IngentaConnect, O C L C Online Computer Library Center, Inc., Swets Information Services).
Indexed: B&BAb, BioEngAb, BiolAb, MEDLINE.
—BLDSC (3394.100250), CISTI, IE, Infotrieve. **CCC.**
Published by: Taylor & Francis Ltd (Subsidiary of: Taylor & Francis Group), 4 Park Sq, Milton Park, Abingdon, OX14 4RN, United Kingdom. TEL 44-1235-828600, FAX 44-1235-829000, info@tandf.co.uk, http://www.tandf.co.uk/journals/titles/10255842.asp. Ed. John Middleton. **Subscr. to:** Journals Customer Service, Rankine Rd, Basingstoke, Hants RG24 8PR, United Kingdom. TEL 44-1256-813000, FAX 44-1256-330245, enquiry@tandf.co.uk.

570.285 GBR ISSN 0010-4825
R858.A1 CODEN: CBMDAW
➤ **COMPUTERS IN BIOLOGY AND MEDICINE.** Text in English. 1971. 12/yr. EUR 324 in Europe to individuals; JPY 43,100 in Japan to individuals; USD 363 to individuals except Europe and Japan; EUR 1,953 in Europe to institutions; JPY 259,100 in Japan to institutions; USD 2,184 to institutions except Europe and Japan (effective 2006). adv. bk.rev. back issues avail. **Document type:** *Academic/Scholarly.* **Description:** Provides an international medium for the exchange of research, ideas and information on all aspects of the growing use of computers in the fields of bioscience and medicine.
Related titles: Microfilm ed.: (from PQC); Online - full text ed.: (from EBSCO Publishing, Gale Group, IngentaConnect, ScienceDirect, Swets Information Services).

Indexed: ASCA, ASFA, AnBrAb, ApMecR, B&BAb, BIOBASE, BIOSIS Prev, BioEngAb, BiolAb, Biostat, CIN, CIS, CMCI, ChemAb, ChemTitl, CompAb, CompC, CompD, CompLI, CurCont, EngInd, ExcerpMed, IABS, INI, ISR, IndMed, Inpharma, Inspec, LISA, MEDLINE, PE&ON, Reac, SCI, Telegen.
—BLDSC (3394.880000), AskIEEE, CASDDS, CISTI, Ei, GNLM, IDS, IE, Infotrieve, ingenta, Linda Hall. **CCC.**
Published by: Pergamon (Subsidiary of: Elsevier Science & Technology), The Boulevard, Langford Ln, East Park, Kidlington, Oxford OX5 1GB, United Kingdom. TEL 44-1865-843000, FAX 44-1865-843010, http://www.elsevier.com/locate/compbiomed. Ed. Dr. Robert S Ledley. Circ: 1,200. **Subscr. to:** Elsevier BV, PO Box 211, Amsterdam 1000 AE, Netherlands. TEL 31-20-485-3757, FAX 31-20-485-3432, nlinfo-f@elsevier.nl, http://www.elsevier.nl.

570.285 USA
CURRENT PROTOCOLS IN BIOINFORMATICS. Text in English. base vol. plus q. updates. looseleaf. USD 535 combined subscription to institutions base volume & updates; USD 275 renewals to institutions (effective 2006). **Document type:** *Academic/Scholarly.* **Description:** Delivers practical advice which allows scientists of all computational abilities to quickly master bioinformatics methods and apply them to their own research.
Related titles: Online - full content ed.
Published by: John Wiley & Sons, Inc., 111 River St, Hoboken, NJ 07030-5774. TEL 201-748-6000, 800-825-7550, FAX 201-748-5915, protocol@wiley.com, http://www.does.org/cp/bioinfo.html, http://www.wiley.com. Ed. Andreas D Baxevanis. **Subscr. to:** PO Box 5597, Somerset, NJ 08875. TEL 732-650-4630, FAX 732-650-4623; John Wiley & Sons Ltd., The Atrium, Southern Gate, Chichester, West Sussex PO19 8SQ, United Kingdom. TEL 44-1243-779777, FAX 44-1243-775878, cs-journals@wiley.co.uk.

FOUNDATIONS OF GENETIC ALGORITHMS. see *COMPUTERS—Artificial Intelligence*

570.285 USA ISSN 1545-5963
QH324.2
▼ **I E E E - A C M TRANSACTIONS ON COMPUTATIONAL BIOLOGY AND BIOINFORMATICS.** (Institute of Electrical and Electronics Engineers - Association for Computing Machinery) Text in English. 2004 (Jan.). q. USD 345 domestic to non-members; USD 384 foreign to non-members; USD 36 domestic to members; USD 75 foreign to members; USD 18 domestic to students; USD 57 foreign to students; USD 414 combined subscription domestic to non-members print & online eds.; USD 453 combined subscription foreign to non-members print & online eds.; USD 43 combined subscription domestic to members print & online eds.; USD 82 combined subscription foreign to members print & online eds.; USD 22 combined subscription domestic to students print & online eds.; USD 61 combined subscription foreign to students print & online eds. (effective 2006). **Document type:** *Journal, Academic/Scholarly.*
Related titles: Online - full text ed.: ISSN 1557-9964. USD 276 to non-members; USD 29 to members; USD 14 to students (effective 2006) (from Association for Computing Machinery, Inc., EBSCO Publishing, I E E E).
Indexed: Inspec, RefZh.
—BLDSC (4362.787530), IE, Linda Hall.
Published by: (Association for Computing Machinery, Inc.), Institute of Electrical and Electronics Engineers, Inc., 3 Park Ave, 17th Fl, New York, NY 10016-5997. TEL 212-419-7900, FAX 212-752-4929, subscription-service@ieee.org, http://www.ieee.org.

I F M B E NEWS. (International Federation for Medical & Biological Engineering) see *BIOLOGY—Bioengineering*

570.285 NLD ISSN 1386-6338
CODEN: ISBIFC
➤ **IN SILICO BIOLOGY**; an international journal on computational molecular biology. Text in English. 1998. q. EUR 413, USD 497 combined subscription print & online eds. (effective 2006). back issues avail. **Document type:** *Journal, Academic/Scholarly.* **Description:** Promotes the development of a more integrated view of living systems.
Related titles: Online - full text ed.: ISSN 1434-3207. USD 440 in North America; EUR 365 elsewhere (effective 2006) (from EBSCO Publishing, Gale Group, IngentaConnect, O C L C Online Computer Library Center, Inc., Swets Information Services).
Indexed: BIOBASE, BIOSIS Prev, BiolAb, ExcerpMed, Inspec.
—BLDSC (4372.459600), CISTI, IE, Infotrieve, ingenta. **CCC.**
Published by: I O S Press, Nieuwe Hemweg 6B, Amsterdam, 1013 BG, Netherlands. TEL 31-20-6883355, FAX 31-20-6203419, info@iospress.nl, order@iospress.nl, http://www.bioinfo.de/isb/, http://www.iospress.nl. Ed. Edgar Wingender TEL 49-531-6181-427. R&P Ms. Carry Koolbergen TEL 31-20-6382189. Adv. contact Ms. Jolijn van Eunen. Circ: 300. **Subscr. to:** I O S Press, Inc, 4502 Rachael Manor Dr., Fairfax, VA 22032-3631. iosbooks@iospress.com; Globe Publication Pvt. Ltd., C-62 Inderpuri, New Delhi 100 012, India. TEL 91-11-579-3211, 91-11-579-3212, custserve@globepub.com, http://www.globepub.com; Kinokuniya Co. Ltd., Shinjuku 3-chome, Shinjuku-ku, Tokyo 160-0022, Japan. FAX 81-3-3439-1094, journal@kinokuniya.co.jp, http://www.kinokuniya.co.jp.

570.285 USA ISSN 1081-2911
➤ **INFORMATION TECHNOLOGY REPORT.** Text in English. 1995. irreg. price varies. bibl. **Document type:** *Government.* **Description:** Publishes conference proceedings, synthesis, annotated bibliographies, and other scholarly reports.
Related titles: Microform ed.: 1995 (from NTI); Online - full text ed.: (from Factiva).
Indexed: ASFA, ESPM, PollutAb, ZooRec.
—Linda Hall.
Published by: U.S. Department of the Interior, National Biological Service, C St between 18th & 19th Sts N W, Washington, DC 20240. **Orders to:** U.S. Fish and Wildlife Service, Publications Unit, MS 130, Webb Bldg, 4401 N Fairfax Dr, Arlington, VA 22203.

570.285 USA ISSN 1553-0833
QH506
INTERNATIONAL CONFERENCE ON INTELLIGENT SYSTEMS FOR MOLECULAR BIOLOGY. PROCEEDINGS✶. Text in English. a. illus. **Document type:** *Proceedings.*
Indexed: IndMed.
—BLDSC (4538.827090).
Published by: (American Association for Artificial Intelligence), A A A I Press, 445 Burgess Dr, Menlo Park, CA 94025-3442. TEL 650-328-3123, FAX 650-321-4457, info@aaai.org, http://www.aaai.org.

570.285 GBR ISSN 1744-5485
▼ ➤ **INTERNATIONAL JOURNAL OF BIOINFORMATICS RESEARCH AND APPLICATIONS.** Text in English. 2005. 4/yr. USD 450; USD 545 combined subscription print & online eds. (effective 2005). **Document type:** *Journal, Academic/Scholarly.* **Description:** Aims to develop, promote and coordinate the development and practice of bioinformatics and computational biology.
Related titles: Online - full text ed.: ISSN 1744-5493. USD 450 (effective 2005).
Indexed: C&ISA, E&CAJ, IAA.
—BLDSC (4542.150750).
Published by: Inderscience Publishers, IEL Editorial Office, PO Box 735, Olney, Bucks MK46 5WB, United Kingdom. TEL 44-1234-240519, FAX 44-1234-240515, ijbra@inderscience.com, info@inderscience.com, http://www.inderscience.com/ijbra. Ed. Yi Pan.

➤ **INTERNATIONAL JOURNAL OF EVOLUTIONARY OPTIMIZATION.** see *BIOLOGY—Genetics*

➤ **INTERNATIONAL JOURNAL OF MEDICAL INFORMATICS.** see *MEDICAL SCIENCES—Computer Applications*

➤ **JOURNAL OF MOLECULAR GRAPHICS AND MODELLING.** see *CHEMISTRY—Computer Applications*

570.285 GBR ISSN 0140-0118
R895.A1 CODEN: MBECDY
➤ **MEDICAL & BIOLOGICAL ENGINEERING & COMPUTING.** Text in English. 1962. bi-m. USD 925 in the Americas to non-members print or online; GBP 545 elsewhere to non-members print or online; USD 1,110 combined subscription in the Americas to non-members print & online; GBP 654 combined subscription elsewhere to non-members print & online; USD 142 per issue in the Americas to non-members; GBP 83 per issue elsewhere to non-members (effective 2005). adv. bk.rev. abstr.; bibl.; charts; illus. index. **Document type:** *Journal, Academic/Scholarly.* **Description:** Contains technical papers on subjects such as medical electronics, biomechanics, medical computing, patient monitoring, nuclear medicine, imaging, rehabilitation and biosensors.
Incorporates (in 1998): Cellular Engineering (1357-5481); Which superseded: Journal of Cellular Engineering (1364-4068); Former titles: Medical and Biological Engineering (0025-696X); Biological Engineering; Medical Electronics
Related titles: Microform ed.: (from PQC); Online - full text ed.: (from EBSCO Publishing); ♦ Supplement(s): I F M B E News. ISSN 1359-0944.
Indexed: AMED, ASCA, ApMecR, B&BAb, BIOSIS Prev, BiolAb, C&ISA, CCI, CIS, CMCI, ChemAb, CompC, CompD, CompLI, CurCont, CybAb, E&CAJ, EngInd, ErgAb, ExcerpMed, ISR, IndMed, IndVet, Inpharma, Inspec, MEDLINE, MSB, NSCI, RPP, Reac, RevApplEntom, SCI, SSCI, SolStAb, VITIS, VetBull.
—BLDSC (5525.770000), AskIEEE, CASDDS, CISTI, Ei, GNLM, IDS, IE, Infotrieve, ingenta, Linda Hall. **CCC.**
Published by: Institution of Electrical Engineers, Michael Faraday House, Six Hills Way, Stevenage, Herts SG1 2AY, United Kingdom. TEL 44-1438-313311, FAX 44-1438-313465, inspec@iee.org, http://www.iee.org/Publish/Journals/ProfJourn/MBEC/. Ed. Alan Murray. Circ: 1,300. **Subscr. to:** INSPEC, I E E, Publication Sales Dept., PO Box 96, Stevenage, Herts SG1 2SD, United Kingdom.

570.285 AUS ISSN 1443-2250
➤ **ONLINE JOURNAL OF BIOINFORMATICS.** Text in English. 1999. a. USD 180 to individuals; USD 360 to institutions (effective 2004). adv. abstr.; tr.mk. back issues avail. **Document type:** *Journal, Academic/Scholarly.* **Description:** Focuses on original research work either as full-text reports on short communications. Intended to meet the demand of rapid growth in the use of computer science in biology.
Media: Online - full content.
Published by: Pestsearch International Pty. Ltd., 173 Chatswood Rd, Daisy Hill, QLD 4127, Australia. TEL 61-7-33882588, onlinejournals@comcen.com.au, http://www.cpb.ouhsc.edu/ojvr/bioinfo.htm. Ed. V H Guerrini.

570.285 USA ISSN 1553-734X
▼ ➤ **P L O S COMPUTATIONAL BIOLOGY.** (Public Library of Science) Text in English. 2005 (Jun). m. free (effective 2005). **Document type:** *Journal, Academic/Scholarly.* **Description:** Publishes research articles on all aspects of computational biology applied to different and integrated biological scales, from molecules and cells to patient populations and ecosystems.
Related titles: Online - full text ed.: ISSN 1553-7358. free (effective 2005).
Indexed: B&BAb, BioEngAb.
Published by: Public Library of Science, 185 Berry St, Ste 1300, San Francisco, CA 94107. TEL 415-624-1200, plos@plos.org, http://www.ploscompbiol.org/, http://www.publiclibraryofscience.org. Ed. Philip E Bourne.

570.285 GBR ISSN 1741-2471
QH631
▼ ➤ **SYSTEMS BIOLOGY.** Text in English. 2004. 4/yr. GBP 395; GBP 474 combined subscription print & online eds. (effective 2005). **Document type:** *Journal, Academic/Scholarly.* **Description:** Contains research and papers that use computational and mathematical models to analyze, model and simulate cellular networks, interactions and pathways.
Related titles: Online - full text ed.: ISSN 1741-248X. GBP 395 (effective 2005) (from EBSCO Publishing).
Indexed: ExcerpMed, Inspec.
—BLDSC (8589.323750), IE.
Published by: Institution of Electrical Engineers, Michael Faraday House, Six Hills Way, Stevenage, Herts SG1 2AY, United Kingdom. TEL 44-1438-313311, FAX 44-1438-313465, inspec@iee.org, http://www.iee.org/Publish/Journals/ProfJourn/Sb/index.cfm.

BIOLOGY—Cytology And Histology

B

➤ **THE A G T CYTOGENETICS LABORATORY TECHNICAL MANUAL.** (Association of Genetic Technologists) see *BIOLOGY—Genetics*

➤ **THE A G T INTERNATIONAL MEMBERSHIP DIRECTORY.** see *MEDICAL SCIENCES—Experimental Medicine, Laboratory Technique*

571.6 USA ISSN 1060-8982
A S C B NEWSLETTER. Text in English. 1979. m. free to members (effective 2005). adv. illus. **Document type:** *Newsletter, Trade.* **Description:** Updates members on grant and award opportunities, public policy briefings, meeting announcements, news of interest to basic scientists, placement announcements, members in the news, and more.
Published by: American Society for Cell Biology, 8120 Woodmont Ave, Ste 750, Bethesda, MD 20814-2762. TEL 301-347-9300, FAX 301-347-9310, ascbinfo@ascb.org, http://www.ascb.org. Ed. Elizabeth Marincola. adv.: page USD 950; bleed 9 x 11.5. Circ: 10,000.

571.6 USA
A T C C CELL LINES AND HYBRIDOMAS. Text in English. irreg., latest vol.8, 1994. USD 22 in North America; USD 32 elsewhere. **Document type:** *Catalog.*
Former titles: A T C C Catalogue of Cell Lines and Hybridomas; Supersedes in part: American Type Culture Collection. Catalogue of Strains 2: Animal Cell Lines, Animal Viruses, Bacterial Viruses, Mycoviruses, Plant Viruses, Rickettsiae, Chlamydiae; Which was formerly titled: American Type Culture Collection. Catalogue of Strains 2: Animal Cell Lines, Animal Viruses, Bacterial Viruses, Mycoviruses, Rickettsiae, Chlamydiae; American Type Culture Collection. Catalogue of Strains: 2. Animal Viruses, Rickettsiae, Chlamydiae; American Type Culture Collection. Catalogue of Viruses, Rickettsiae, Chlamydiae
Published by: American Type Culture Collection, 10801 University Blvd, Manassas, VA 20110. TEL 800-638-6597, FAX 301-816-4361, sales@ATCC.org. Ed. R Hay.

571.6 USA
A T C C QUALITY CONTROL METHODS FOR CELL LINES. Text in English. 1992. irreg. USD 40; USD 45 foreign.
Published by: American Type Culture Collection, 10801 University Blvd, Manassas, VA 20110. TEL 800-638-6597, FAX 301-816-4361, Sales@ATCC.org.

571.6 USA ISSN 0001-5547
RG1 CODEN: ACYTAN
➤ **ACTA CYTOLOGICA**; the journal of clinical cytology and cytopathology. Text in English. 1957. bi-m. USD 260 domestic to individuals; USD 340 foreign to individuals; USD 360 domestic to institutions; USD 440 foreign to institutions (effective 2004). adv. bk.rev. abstr.; bibl.; illus.; stat. index. back issues avail. **Document type:** *Academic/Scholarly.*
Related titles: Microfilm ed.: (from WWS); Microform ed.: (from PMC).

Indexed: AESIS, AIDS Ab, ASCA, AbHyg, BBCI, BIOBASE, BIOSIS Prev, BiolAb, ChemAb, CurCont, DSA, DentInd, ExcerpMed, ForAb, HelmAb, IABS, INI, ISR, IndMed, IndVet, Inpharma, MEDLINE, NSCI, NutrAb, PE&ON, ProtozoAb, RDA, RM&VM, RPP, Reac, RefZh, SCI, TDB, VetBull.
—BLDSC (0612.100000), CASDDS, CISTI, GNLM, IDS, IE, Infotrieve, ingenta, KNAW. **CCC.**
Published by: (International Academy of Cytology), Science Printers and Publishers, Inc., 8342 Olive Blvd., St. Louis, MO 63132. TEL 314-991-4440, FAX 314-991-4654, editor@acta-cytol.com, http://www.acta-cytol.com. Ed. Dr. Marluce Bibbo. Pub., R&P, Adv. contact Donna Kessel. Circ: 6,080.

571.6 JPN ISSN 0044-5991
QM551 CODEN: ACHCBO
➤ **ACTA HISTOCHEMICA ET CYTOCHEMICA/NIHON SOSHIKI SAIBO KAGAKKAI GAKKAISHI.** Text in English. 1960. bi-m. JPY 2,000 per issue (effective 2004). adv. bk.rev. abstr.; bibl.; charts; illus. Index. reprint service avail. from PQC. **Document type:** *Journal, Academic/Scholarly.* **Description:** Features original articles in all fields of histochemistry and cytochemistry. Contains proceedings of the annual meeting of the society.
Related titles: Microform ed.: (from PQC); Online - full text ed.: ISSN 1347-5800. 2000. free (effective 2005) (from J-Stage).
Indexed: ASCA, AnBrAb, BBCI, BIOBASE, BIOSIS Prev, BiolAb, CIN, CTA, ChemAb, ChemTitl, CurCont, DSA, ExcerpMed, IABS, INIS AtomInd, ISR, IndVet, Inpharma, NutrAb, PE&ON, Reac, RefZh, SCI, VetBull, WeedAb.
—BLDSC (0624.040000), CASDDS, CISTI, GNLM, IDS, IE, Infotrieve, ingenta, KNAW, Linda Hall. **CCC.**
Published by: Nihon Soshiki Saibo Kagakukai/Japan Society of Histochemistry and Cytochemistry, c/o Nakanishi Printing Co, Shimotachiuri-Ogawa, Kamikyo-ku, Kyoto-shi, 602, Japan. TEL 81-75-4153661, FAX 81-75-4153662, HBE02610@niftyserve.or.jp, jshc@nacos.com, http://www.jstage.jst.go.jp/browse/ahc/_vols/-char/en, http://www.nacos.com/jshc/. Circ: 1,800. **Dist. overseas by:** Japan Publications Trading Co., Ltd., Book Export II Dept, PO Box 5030, Tokyo International, Tokyo 101-3191, Japan. TEL 81-3-32923753, FAX 81-3-32920410, infoserials@jptco.co.jp, http://www.jptco.co.jp.

➤ **ADVANCES IN ANATOMY, EMBRYOLOGY AND CELL BIOLOGY.** see *BIOLOGY*

571.6 NLD ISSN 1381-1932
➤ **ADVANCES IN CELLULAR AND MOLECULAR BIOLOGY OF PLANTS.** Text in English. 1994. irreg., latest vol.6, 2001. price varies. back issues avail. **Document type:** *Monographic series, Academic/Scholarly.* **Description:** Chronicles the most important advances in the cellular and molecular biology of plants and stimulates further interest and research in the plant sciences.
Indexed: Agr.
—BLDSC (0703.308000), CASDDS, CISTI, ingenta. **CCC.**
Published by: Springer-Verlag Dordrecht (Subsidiary of: Springer Science+Business Media), Van Godewijckstraat 30, Dordrecht, 3311 GX, Netherlands. TEL 31-78-6576050, FAX 31-78-6576474, http://www.springeronline.com. Ed. Indra K Vasil.

571.6 NLD
ADVANCES IN MOLECULAR AND CELL BIOLOGY. Text in English. 1987. a., latest vol.30, 2000. price varies. **Document type:** *Monographic series, Academic/Scholarly.*
Formerly (until 1990): Advances in Cell Biology (0898-8455)
Indexed: Agr, BIOSIS Prev.
—BLDSC (0709.439050), GNLM, ingenta.
Published by: Elsevier BV (Subsidiary of: Elsevier Science & Technology), PO Box 1527, Amsterdam, 1000, Netherlands. TEL 31-20-4853852, FAX 31-20-4853342, nlinfo-f@elsevier.nl, http://www.elsevier.com/inca/tree/?key=B1AMCB, http://www.elsevier.nl. Ed. E E Bittar TEL 608-262-0784. Pub. Hendrik van Leusen TEL 31-20-4853852.

ADVANCES IN TISSUE BANKING. see *MEDICAL SCIENCES*

571.6 GBR ISSN 1474-9718
QH608 CODEN: ACGECQ
AGING CELL. Text in English. 3/yr. GBP 95, EUR 142 combined subscription in Europe to individuals print & online eds.; USD 174 combined subscription in the Americas to individuals & the Caribbean (print & onlin eds.); GBP 104 combined subscription elsewhere to individuals print & online eds.; GBP 546 combined subscription in Europe to institutions print & online eds.; USD 1,008 combined subscription in the Americas to institutions & the Caribbean (print & online eds.); GBP 600 combined subscription elsewhere to institutions print & online eds. (effective 2006); GBP 38 combined subscription elsewhere to members print & online eds. (effective 2005). **Description:** Covers genes and functional genomics, cell proliferation, senescence and death, signaling and gene expression, cell stress and damage, integrative physiology, biodemography and comparative studies, and new theories of aging and longevity.
Related titles: Online - full text ed.: ISSN 1474-9726. GBP 90, EUR 135 in Europe to individuals; USD 166 in the Americas to individuals & Caribbean; GBP 100 elsewhere to individuals; GBP 519 in Europe to institutions; USD 958 in the Americas to institutions & Caribbean; GBP 570 elsewhere to institutions (effective 2006) (from Blackwell Synergy, EBSCO Publishing, Gale Group, IngentaConnect, O C L C Online Computer Library Center, Inc., Ovid Technologies, Inc., Swets Information Services).
Indexed: ChemAb, ExcerpMed.
—BLDSC (0736.360500), IE.
Published by: (Anatomical Society of Great Britain and Ireland), Blackwell Publishing Ltd., 9600 Garsington Rd, Oxford, OX4 2ZG, United Kingdom. TEL 44-1865-776868, FAX 44-1865-714591, customerservices@oxon.blackwellpublishing.com, http://www.blackwellpublishing.com/journals/ACE. Eds. Marc Tatar, Tim Cowan.

AMERICAN JOURNAL OF KIDNEY DISEASES. see *MEDICAL SCIENCES—Urology And Nephrology*

AMERICAN JOURNAL OF PHYSIOLOGY: CELL PHYSIOLOGY. see *BIOLOGY—Physiology*

AMERICAN JOURNAL OF PHYSIOLOGY: LUNG CELLULAR AND MOLECULAR PHYSIOLOGY. see *BIOLOGY—Physiology*

ANATOMICAL SCIENCE INTERNATIONAL. see *BIOLOGY*

571.6 NLD
ANIMAL CELL TECHNOLOGY; basic and applied aspects. Text in Dutch. irreg., latest vol.13, 2004. price varies. **Document type:** *Proceedings, Academic/Scholarly.*
Indexed: BIOSIS Prev.
—BLDSC (0903.160000), ingenta.
Published by: Springer-Verlag Dordrecht (Subsidiary of: Springer Science+Business Media), Van Godewijckstraat 30, Dordrecht, 3311 GX, Netherlands. TEL 31-78-6576050, FAX 31-78-6576474, http://www.springeronline.com.

571.6 USA ISSN 1081-0706
QH573 CODEN: ARDBF8
➤ **ANNUAL REVIEW OF CELL AND DEVELOPMENTAL BIOLOGY.** Text in English. 1985. a. USD 200 to institutions print or online ed.; USD 240 combined subscription to institutions print & online eds. (effective 2006). illus.; abstr. index, cum.index. back issues avail.; reprint service avail. from PSC. **Document type:** *Academic/Scholarly.* **Description:** Synthesizes and filters primary research to identify the principal contributions in the fields of developmental and cell biology.
Formerly (until vol.10, 1994): Annual Review of Cell Biology (0743-4634)
Related titles: Microfilm ed.: (from PQC); Online - full content ed.: ISSN 1530-8995. USD 193 (effective 2005) (from HighWire Press); Online - full text ed.: (from bigchalk, EBSCO Publishing, H.W. Wilson, O C L C Online Computer Library Center, Inc., ProQuest Information & Learning, Swets Information Services).
Indexed: ASCA, ASFA, B&AI, BBCI, BIOBASE, BIOSIS Prev, BiolDig, CIN, CTA, ChemAb, ChemTitl, CurCont, ESPM, ExcerpMed, GenetAb, HGA, IABS, ISR, IndMed, Inpharma, MEDLINE, NSA, PE&ON, Reac, SCI.
—BLDSC (1522.108500), CASDDS, CISTI, GNLM, IDS, IE, Infotrieve, ingenta, KNAW, Linda Hall. **CCC.**
Published by: Annual Reviews, 4139 El Camino Way, Palo Alto, CA 94303-0139. TEL 650-493-4400, 800-523-8635, FAX 650-424-0910, service@annualreviews.org, http://arjournals.annualreviews.org/loi/cellbio, http://www.annualreviews.org. Ed. Randy Schekman. R&P Laura Folkner.

571.6 JPN
ANNUAL REVIEW SAIBO SEIBUTSUGAKU/ANNUAL REVIEW OF CELL BIOLOGY. Text in Japanese. a. JPY 7,980 (effective 1998). adv. **Document type:** *Academic/Scholarly.*
Published by: Chugai Igakusha, 62 Yarai-cho, Shinjuku-ku, Tokyo, 162-0805, Japan. R&P M Takahashi. Adv. contact M. Takahashi.

571.6 USA ISSN 1360-8185
QH671 CODEN: APOPFN
➤ **APOPTOSIS;** an international journal on programmed cell death. Text in English. 1996. bi-m. EUR 694, USD 694, GBP 434 combined subscription to institutions print & online eds. (effective 2005). adv. reprint service avail. from PSC. **Document type:** *Directory, Academic/Scholarly.* **Description:** Provides the rapid publication of innovative basic and clinically oriented investigations into apoptosis and programmed cell-death.
Related titles: Online - full text ed.: ISSN 1573-675X (from EBSCO Publishing, Gale Group, IngentaConnect, Kluwer Online, O C L C Online Computer Library Center, Inc., Ovid Technologies, Inc., Springer LINK, Swets Information Services).
Indexed: AbHyg, AgBio, BCI, BIOBASE, BIOSIS Prev, BibLing, BiolAb, ChemAb, CurCont, ExcerpMed, ISR, IndMed, Inpharma, MEDLINE, PE&ON, ProtozoAb, RA&MP, Reac, RefZh, SCI.
—BLDSC (1568.884400), CASDDS, CISTI, IDS, IE, Infotrieve, ingenta. **CCC.**
Published by: Springer-Verlag New York, Inc. (Subsidiary of: Springer Science+Business Media), 233 Spring St, New York, NY 10013. TEL 212-460-1500, FAX 212-460-1575, service@springer-ny.com, http://springerlink.metapress.com/openurl.asp?genre=journal&issn=1360-8185, http://www.springer-ny.com. Ed. Mels Sluyser. **Subscr. to:** Journal Fulfillment, PO Box 2485, Secaucus, NJ 07096-2485. TEL 201-348-4033, FAX 201-348-4505, journals@springer-ny.com.

571.5 JPN ISSN 0914-9465
CODEN: AHCYEZ
➤ **ARCHIVES OF HISTOLOGY AND CYTOLOGY/SOSHIKI SAIBOGAKU KIROKU.** Text in English. 1950. 5/yr. JPY 33,000 to institutions; JPY 16,000 to individuals (effective 2005). adv. bk.rev. charts; illus. Index. 100 p./no.; back issues avail. **Document type:** *Journal, Academic/Scholarly.* **Description:** Publishes original works on the histology and histochemistry of man and animals.
Formerly (until 1988): Archivum Histologicum Japonicum (0004-0681)
Related titles: Online - full text ed.: ISSN 1349-1717. free (effective 2005) (from J-Stage).
Indexed: ASCA, ASFA, AbAn, B&BAb, BIOSIS Prev, BioEngAb, BiolAb, CIN, ChemAb, ChemTitl, CurCont, DSA, DentInd, ExcerpMed, ISR, IndMed, Inpharma, MEDLINE, NSCI, NutrAb, PE&ON, Reac, SCI, ZooRec.
—BLDSC (1634.413000), CASDDS, CISTI, GNLM, IDS, IE, Infotrieve, ingenta, KNAW.
Published by: International Society of Histology and Cytology/Kokusai Soshiki Saibou Gakkai, c/o Division of Microscopic Anatomy & Bio-imaging, Department of Cellular Function, Niigata University Grad. School of Medical & Dental Sciences, 1 Asahimachi-dori, Niigata, 951-8510, Japan. TEL 81-25-2272062, FAX 81-25-2241767, t-ushiki@med.niigata-u.ac.jp, http://www.ishc.net. Eds. Tatsuo Ushiki, Yasuo Uchiyama TEL 81-6-68793120. Circ: 700 (controlled).

➤ **ASSOCIATION OF GENETIC TECHNOLOGISTS. JOURNAL.** see *BIOLOGY—Genetics*

571.6 NLD ISSN 0005-2736
QD1
➤ **B B A - BIOMEMBRANES.** (Biochimica et Biophysica Acta) Text in Dutch. 1947. 12/yr. EUR 4,269 in Europe to institutions; JPY 566,900 in Japan to institutions; USD 4,776 elsewhere to institutions (effective 2006). **Document type:** *Journal, Academic/Scholarly.* **Description:** Focuses on research in membrane structure and organization, membrane fluidity and lipid composition, model membranes, and membrane-protein interactions.
Incorporates (1972-2002): B B A - Reviews on Biomembranes (0304-4157)
Related titles: Microform ed.: (from PQC); Online - full text ed.: (from EBSCO Publishing, Gale Group, IngentaConnect, ScienceDirect, Swets Information Services); ◆ Series of: Biochimica et Biophysica Acta. ISSN 0006-3002.
Indexed: ASCA, AbHyg, AgBio, AnBrAb, BBCI, BIOBASE, BioCN&I, CPA, CurCont, DBA, DSA, EngInd, ExcerpMed, FCA, HelmAb, HortAb, IABS, ISR, IndVet, Inpharma, MaizeAb, NemAb, NutrAb, OrnHort, PBA, PE&ON, PGegResA, PGrRegA, PHN&I, PN&I, PoultAb, ProtozoAb, RA&MP, RM&VM, RPP, Reac, RefZh, RevApplEntom, RiceAb, S&F, SCI, SIA, SeedAb, SoyAb, TDB, TriticAb, VetBull, WeedAb.
—CISTI, Ei, IDS, IE. **CCC.**
Published by: Elsevier BV (Subsidiary of: Elsevier Science & Technology), Radarweg 29, Amsterdam, 1043 NX, Netherlands. TEL 31-20-4853911, FAX 31-20-4852457, nlinfo-f@elsevier.nl, http://www.elsevier.com/locate/bbamem, http://www.elsevier.nl.

571.6 NLD ISSN 0167-4889
➤ **B B A - MOLECULAR CELL RESEARCH.** Text in Dutch. 1982. 12/yr. EUR 2,201 in Europe to institutions; JPY 292,400 in Japan to institutions; USD 2,463 elsewhere to institutions (effective 2006). back issues avail. **Document type:** *Journal, Academic/Scholarly.* **Description:** Focuses on intact cellular studies at the molecular level. Includes hormone and neurotransmitter action, molecular endocrinology, cell regulation, as well as whole-cell and whole-tissue spectroscopy.
Related titles: Microform ed.: (from PQC); Online - full text ed.: (from EBSCO Publishing, Gale Group, IngentaConnect, ScienceDirect, Swets Information Services); ◆ Series of: Biochimica et Biophysica Acta. ISSN 0006-3002.
Indexed: ASCA, AgBio, AnBrAb, BBCI, BIOBASE, BiolAb, CPA, ChemAb, CurCont, DBA, DSA, ExcerpMed, FCA, HelmAb, HortAb, IABS, ISR, IndChem, IndMed, IndVet, Inpharma, NutrAb, PBA, PN&I, PoultAb, RA&MP, RM&VM, RPP, Reac, RefZh, RevApplEntom, RiceAb, SCI, VetBull, WeedAb.
—CISTI, IDS, IE. **CCC.**
Published by: Elsevier BV (Subsidiary of: Elsevier Science & Technology), Radarweg 29, Amsterdam, 1043 NX, Netherlands. TEL 31-20-4853911, FAX 31-20-4852457, nlinfo-f@elsevier.nl, http://www.elsevier.com/locate/bbamcr, http://www.elsevier.nl.

571.6 GBR ISSN 1471-2121
QH573 CODEN: BCBMAY
➤ **B M C CELL BIOLOGY.** (BioMed Central) Text in English. 2000. m. free (effective 2006). adv. **Document type:** *Journal, Academic/Scholarly.* **Description:** Publishes original research articles in all aspects of cell biology including cellular compartments, traffic, signalling, motility, adhesion and division.
Media: Online - full content (from EBSCO Publishing, National Library of Medicine).
Indexed: BIOSIS Prev, BiolAb, ExcerpMed, MEDLINE.
—Infotrieve. **CCC.**
Published by: BioMed Central Ltd. (Subsidiary of: Current Science Ltd), Middlesex House, 34-42 Cleveland St, London, W1T 4LB, United Kingdom. TEL 44-20-76319131, FAX 44-20-76319923, info@biomedcentral.com, http://www.biomedcentral.com/bmccellbiol/. Ed. Peter Newmark. Adv. contact Deborah Cockerill.

571.5 USA ISSN 0891-2106
QL807
BASIC HISTOLOGY. Text in English. 1975. triennial. USD 54.95 per vol. (effective 2005). **Document type:** *Monographic series.* **Description:** Contains detailed descriptions of the function and specialization of the four tissue groups with chapters devoted to each organ and organ system.
—CISTI.
Published by: McGraw-Hill Education, 2 Penn Plaza, 12th Fl, New York, NY 10121-2298. TEL 212-904-6079, FAX 212-904-6030, customer.service@mcgraw-hill.com, http://www.mheducation.com/. **Subscr. to:** PO Box 545, Blacklick, OH 43004-0545. TEL 800-262-4729, FAX 614-755-5645, medical@mcgraw-hill.com.

571.6 616.01 BGR ISSN 1310-392X
BIO-MEDICAL REVIEWS. Text in English. 1992. a. **Document type:** *Journal, Academic/Scholarly.* **Description:** Includes review articles focused on updated knowledge in disease-oriented molecular cell biology.
Indexed: ExcerpMed, IndVet.
—BLDSC (2087.876000).
Published by: Bulgarian-American Center, c/o George N Chaldakov, Medical University of Varna, Varna, 9002, Bulgaria. TEL 359-52-454394, FAX 359-52-222584, chaldakov@yahoo.com, http://www.chaldakov.com/bmr. Ed. George N Chaldakov.

571.6 ARG ISSN 0327-9545
CODEN: BOCEEZ
➤ **BIOCELL.** Text in English. 1972. 3/yr. (in 1 vol., 3 nos./vol.). USD 80 to individuals; USD 100 to institutions. adv. charts; illus. index. reprint service avail. from ISI. **Document type:** *Academic/Scholarly.* **Description:** Covers all aspects of biological electron microscopy and cell biology, from the molecular level to cell and tissue organization.
Former titles (until 1993): Microscopia Electronica y Biologia Celular - Electronic Microscopy and Cellular Biology (0326-3142); (until 1983): Revista de Microscopia Electronica
Indexed: ASCA, AgBio, AgrForAb, AnBrAb, BIOBASE, BIOSIS Prev, BiolAb, CIN, CPA, ChemAb, ChemTitl, CurCont, DSA, ExcerpMed, FCA, FPA, ForAb, HortAb, IABS, ISR, IndMed, Inpharma, MEDLINE, NutrAb, OrnHort, PBA, PGegResA, PGrRegA, PHN&I, PotatoAb, ProtozoAb, RA&MP, RM&VM, RPP, Reac, SCI, SIA, SeedAb, TDB, TriticAb, VITIS, VetBull, WeedAb, ZooRec.
—BLDSC (2066.809400), CASDDS, CISTI, GNLM, IDS, IE, Infotrieve, ingenta.
Published by: (Instituto de Histologia y Embriologia, Universidad Nacional de Cuyo), Centro Regional de Investigaciones Cientificas y Tecnologicas, Casilla de Correos 131, Mendoza, 5500, Argentina. TEL 54-61-205020 ext. 2670, FAX 54-61-380232, biocell@fmed2.uncu.edu.ar. Eds. Mario H Burgos, Ramon S Piezzi. Adv. contact Gabriel Puebla. B&W page USD 200, color page USD 300. Circ: 300 (controlled).
Co-sponsors: Latin American Electron Microscopy Society; Sociedad Iberoamericana de Biologia Celular.

➤ **BIOCHEMISTRY AND CELL BIOLOGY/BIOCHIMIE ET BIOLOGIE CELLULAIRE.** see *BIOLOGY—Biochemistry*

571.6 DEU
BIOFORUM ZELLBIOLOGIE. Text in German. 2002. s-a. EUR 10 in Europe to institutions; USD 14 elsewhere to institutions (effective 2006). adv. **Document type:** *Magazine, Trade.*
Published by: G I T Verlag GmbH (Subsidiary of: Wiley - V C H Verlag GmbH & Co. KGaA), Roesslerstr 90, Darmstadt, 64293, Germany. TEL 49-6151-80900, info@gitverlag.com, service@wiley-vch.de, http://en.media.gitverlag.com/html/bio_zell_2003, http://www.gitverlag.com. adv.: B&W page EUR 2,750, color page EUR 4,230. Circ: 7,000 (controlled).

BIOLOGICHESKIE MEMBRANY. see *BIOLOGY—Biophysics*

571.6 USA ISSN 0887-3224
QP88.23 CODEN: ICOTAR
BIOLOGY OF EXTRACELLULAR MATRIX. Text in English. 1963. irreg. index. **Document type:** *Monographic series.*
Formerly (until 1986): International Review of Connective Tissue Research (0074-767X)
Indexed: BiolAb, DentInd, ExcerpMed, ISR, IndMed, MEDLINE, NutrAb, SCI.
—CASDDS, CISTI, GNLM, KNAW, Linda Hall. **CCC.**
Published by: Academic Press (Subsidiary of: Elsevier Science & Technology), 525 B St, Ste 1900, San Diego, CA 92101-4495. apsubs@acad.com, http://www.academicpress.com.

571.6 GBR ISSN 0248-4900
QH212.E4 CODEN: BCELDF
➤ **BIOLOGY OF THE CELL.** Text in English. 1962. m. GBP 520.83, USD 915, EUR 759 combined subscription to institutions print & online (effective 2005). adv. charts; illus. index. **Document type:** *Journal, Academic/Scholarly.* **Description:** Presents reports, review articles and rapid communications concerning the structure and function of cells in the context of developmental biology, genetics, immunology and physiology.
Former titles (until 1981): Biologie Cellulaire (0399-0311); (until 1977): Journal de Microscopie et Biologie Cellulaire (0395-9260); (until 1975): Journal de Microscopie (0021-7921)
Related titles: Microform ed.: (from PQC); Online - full text ed.: ISSN 1768-322X. GBP 527, USD 822, EUR 683 to institutions (effective 2005) (from EBSCO Publishing, Gale Group, IngentaConnect, ScienceDirect, Swets Information Services).
Indexed: ASCA, ASFA, AgBio, AnBrAb, BBCI, BIOBASE, BIOSIS Prev, BiolAb, CIN, CPA, ChemAb, ChemTitl, CurCont, DSA, DentInd, ExcerpMed, FCA, ForAb, HerbAb, HortAb, IABS, ISR, IndMed, IndVet, Inpharma, MEDLINE, MaizeAb, NemAb, NucAcAb, NutrAb, OrnHort, PBA, PGrRegA, ProtozoAb, RA&MP, RM&VM, RPP, Reac, RevApplEntom, SCI, SFA, SIA, TriticAb, VetBull, WeedAb, ZooRec.
—BLDSC (2087.045000), CASDDS, CISTI, GNLM, IDS, IE, Infotrieve, ingenta, Linda Hall. **CCC.**
Published by: (Universite Paris, Institute Jacques-Monod FRA, European Cell Biology Organization DEU), Portland Press Ltd. (Subsidiary of: Biochemical Society), 3rd Fl, Eagle House, 16 Procter St, London, WC1V 6NX, United Kingdom. TEL 44-20-72804110, FAX 44-20-72804169, editorial@portlandpress.com, http://www.biolcell.org/, http://www.portlandpress.com. Ed. H Beverly Osborne. Circ: 3,000. **Subscr. to:** Commerce Way, Colchester CO2 8HP, United Kingdom. TEL 44-1206-796351, FAX 44-1206-799331, sales@portland-services.com. **Co-sponsors:** Societe Francaise de Microscopie Electronique; Societe de Biologie Cellulaire de France.

571.6 USA ISSN 0144-8463
QH506 CODEN: BRPTDT
➤ **BIOSCIENCE REPORTS;** molecular and cellular biology of the cell surface. Text in English. 1981. bi-m. EUR 868, USD 888, GBP 545 combined subscription to institutions print & online eds. (effective 2005). adv. back issues avail.; reprint service avail. from PSC. **Document type:** *Monographic series, Academic/Scholarly.* **Description:** Publishes research papers in all areas of cell surface function, including biochemical genetics, development, pharmacology, endocrinology, and immunology.
Related titles: Microfilm ed.: (from PQC); Online - full text ed.: ISSN 1573-4935 (from EBSCO Publishing, Gale Group, IngentaConnect, Kluwer Online, O C L C Online Computer Library Center, Inc., Ovid Technologies, Inc., Springer LINK, Swets Information Services).
Indexed: ASCA, AbHyg, AgBio, Agr, AnBrAb, BBCI, BIOBASE, BIOSIS Prev, BibLing, BiolAb, CBTA, CEABA, CIN, CPA, ChemAb, ChemTitl, CurCont, DBA, DSA, ExcerpMed, FCA, HelmAb, HortAb, IABS, ISR, IndMed, IndVet, Inpharma, MEDLINE, MaizeAb, NemAb, NutrAb, PBA, PE&ON, PGegResA, PHN&I, PotatoAb, PoultAb, ProtozoAb, RA&MP, RPP, Reac, RefZh, RevApplEntom, S&F, SCI, SIA, SeedAb, SoyAb, TDB, VetBull, WeedAb.
—BLDSC (2089.611600), CASDDS, CISTI, GNLM, IDS, IE, Infotrieve, ingenta, Linda Hall. **CCC.**
Published by: (Biochemical Society GBR), Plenum US (Subsidiary of: Springer Science+Business Media), 233 Spring St, New York, NY 10013. TEL 212-460-1500, FAX 212-460-1575, service@springer-ny.com, http://springerlink.metapress.com/openurl.asp?genre=journal&issn=0144-8463, http://www.springeronline.com.

➤ **BIOTECHNIC AND HISTOCHEMISTRY;** a journal for microtechnic and histochemistry. see *BIOLOGY—Microscopy*

➤ **BLOOD.** see *MEDICAL SCIENCES—Hematology*

571.6 GBR
BRITISH SOCIETY FOR CELL BIOLOGY. SYMPOSIA. Text in English. 1976. irreg. price varies. **Document type:** *Proceedings.*
Indexed: BiolAb.
Published by: Cambridge University Press, The Edinburgh Bldg, Shaftesbury Rd, Cambridge, CB2 2RU, United Kingdom. TEL 44-1223-312393, FAX 44-1223-315052, information@cambridge.org, http://www.cup.cam.ac.uk/. R&P Linda Nicol TEL 44-1223-325757.

571.5 571.6 GBR
BRITISH SOCIETY FOR DEVELOPMENTAL BIOLOGY. SYMPOSIA. Text in English. 1973. irreg. price varies. **Document type:** *Proceedings.*
Indexed: BiolAb.
Published by: Cambridge University Press, The Edinburgh Bldg, Shaftesbury Rd, Cambridge, CB2 2RU, United Kingdom. TEL 44-1223-312393, FAX 44-1223-315052, information@cambridge.org, http://www.cup.cam.ac.uk/. R&P Linda Nicol TEL 44-1223-325757.

CALCIUM AND CALCIFIED TISSUE ABSTRACTS (ONLINE EDITION). see *BIOLOGY—Abstracting, Bibliographies, Statistics*

CANADIAN JOURNAL OF PLANT PATHOLOGY. see *BIOLOGY—Botany*

CANCER CELL INTERNATIONAL. see *MEDICAL SCIENCES—Oncology*

571.3 ITA ISSN 0008-7114
QH1 CODEN: CARYAB
➤ **CARYOLOGIA;** international journal of cytology, cytosystematics and cytogenetics. Text and summaries in English. 1948. 4/yr. EUR 200; EUR 220 print & online eds. (effective 2003). bibl.; charts; illus. **Document type:** *Journal, Academic/Scholarly.*
Indexed: ASCA, ASFA, AgBio, AgrForAb, AnBrAb, BIOSIS Prev, BiolAb, CPA, ChemAb, CurCont, ESPM, ExcerpMed, FCA, ForAb, HelmAb, HerbAb, HortAb, ISR, MaizeAb, OrnHort, PBA, PGegResA, PN&I, ProtozoAb, RA&MP, RPP, RefZh, RevApplEntom, S&F, SCI, SFA, SIA, SeedAb, SoyAb, TriticAb, WeedAb, ZooRec.
—BLDSC (3057.960000), CASDDS, CISTI, IE, Infotrieve, ingenta, Linda Hall. **CCC.**
Published by: Universita degli Studi di Firenze, Dipartimento di Biologia Vegetale, Via La Pira 4, Florence, FI 50121, Italy. TEL 39-055-2756215, FAX 39-055-2757373, caryo@unifi.it, http://www.unifi.it/bioveg. Ed. Fernando Fabbri.

B

571.6 USA ISSN 0092-8674
QH573 CODEN: CELLB5
➤ **CELL.** Text in English. 1974. 26/yr. EUR 296 in Europe to individuals; JPY 32,400 in Japan to individuals; USD 172 in Canada to individuals; USD 172 in United States to individuals; USD 259 to individuals except Europe and Japan; EUR 1,359 in Europe to institutions; JPY 141,800 in Japan to institutions; USD 1,049 in United States to institutions; USD 1,049 in Canada to institutions; USD 1,181 to institutions except Europe and Japan (effective 2006). adv. bk.rev. charts; illus. Index. back issues avail.; reprint service avail. from PQC,ISI. **Document type:** *Journal, Academic/Scholarly.* **Description:** Publishes research and reports on developments in molecular biology.
Related titles: Online - full text ed.: ISSN 1097-4172. USD 99 to individuals (effective 2001) (from EBSCO Publishing, Gale Group, IngentaConnect, ScienceDirect, Swets Information Services).
Indexed: ABIPC, AEBA, AIDS Ab, AIDS&CR, ASCA, ASFA, AbHyg, AgBio, AnBrAb, B&AI, BBCI, BIOBASE, BIOSIS Prev, BiolAb, BiolDig, CPA, CTA, ChemAb, ChemoAb, CurCont, DBA, DSA, DentInd, ESPM, EngInd, ExcerpMed, FCA, FS&TA, GSI, GenetAb, HGA, HelmAb, HortAb, IABS, INIS AtomInd, ISR, ImmunAb, IndMed, IndVet, Inpharma, JW-P, M&PBA, MBA, MEDLINE, MS&D, MaizeAb, NSA, NSCI, NemAb, NucAcAb, NutrAb, OGFA, OrnHort, PBA, PE&ON, PGegResA, PGrRegA, PotatoAb, PoultAb, ProtozoAb, RM&VM, RPP, Reac, RefZh, RevApplEntom, S&F, S&MA, SCI, SSCI, SeedAb, TDB, Telegen, TriticAb, VetBull, WeedAb, ZooRec.
—BLDSC (3097.600000), CASDDS, CISTI, GNLM, IE, Infotrieve, ingenta, Linda Hall. **CCC.**
Published by: Cell Press (Subsidiary of: Elsevier Science & Technology), 1100 Massachusetts Ave, Cambridge, MA 02138. TEL 617-661-7057, FAX 617-661-7061, editor@cell.com, http://www.elsevier.com/locate/cell, http://www.cellpress.com/. Ed. Emilie Marcus. Adv. contact Sande Giaccone TEL 212-633-3914. B&W page USD 3,020, color page USD 4,375. Circ: 9,252 (paid). **Subscr. to:** 6277 Sea Harbor Dr, Orlando, FL 32887. TEL 407-345-3000, 866-314-2355, FAX 407-363-9661, subs@cell.com.

571.6 GBR ISSN 1475-9268
QH605
➤ **CELL & CHROMOSOME.** Text in English. 2002. m. free (effective 2006). **Document type:** *Journal, Academic/Scholarly.* **Description:** Publishes original articles in the rapidly proliferating field of cell and chromosome biology.
Media: Online - full content (from EBSCO Publishing, National Library of Medicine).
Indexed: ExcerpMed.
—**CCC.**
Published by: BioMed Central Ltd. (Subsidiary of: Current Science Ltd), Middlesex House, 34-42 Cleveland St, London, W1T 4LB, United Kingdom. TEL 44-20-76319131, FAX 44-20-76319923, info@biomedcentral.com, http://www.cellandchromosome.com/home/, http://www.biomedcentral.com. Ed. Baldev K. Vig.

571.6 IND ISSN 0254-2935
CODEN: CCREE3
➤ **CELL AND CHROMOSOME RESEARCH JOURNAL.** Text in English. 1978. 2/yr. INR 150, USD 20. bk.rev. back issues avail. **Document type:** *Academic/Scholarly.*
Formerly (until 1981): Cell and Chromosome Research Association. Newsletter
Indexed: BIOSIS Prev, BiolAb, CIN, ChemAb, ChemTitl.
—CASDDS, CISTI.
Published by: (Association for Cell and Chromosome Research), University of Calcutta, Centre of Advanced Studies in Botany, 35 Ballygunge Circular Rd., Kolkata, West Bengal 700 019, India. FAX 91-33-4754772. Ed. Sibdas Ghosh. Circ: 200.

571.5 NLD ISSN 1389-9333
➤ **CELL AND TISSUE BANKING.** Text in English. 2000. q. EUR 191, USD 191, GBP 126 combined subscription to institutions print & online eds. (effective 2005). adv. reprint service avail. from PSC. **Document type:** *Journal, Academic/Scholarly.* **Description:** Provides information to scientists and clinicians involved in the banking and transplantation of cells and tissues.
Related titles: Online - full text ed.: ISSN 1573-6814 (from EBSCO Publishing, Gale Group, IngentaConnect, Kluwer Online, O C L C Online Computer Library Center, Inc., Ovid Technologies, Inc., ProQuest Information & Learning, Springer LINK, Swets Information Services).
Indexed: AbHyg, AgBio, B&BAb, BIOBASE, BibLing, BioEngAb, BiolAb, CTA, ExcerpMed, M&PBA, RefZh, TDB.
—BLDSC (3097.678000), CISTI, IE, Infotrieve, ingenta. **CCC.**
Published by: Springer-Verlag Dordrecht (Subsidiary of: Springer Science+Business Media), Van Godewijckstraat 30, Dordrecht, 3311 GX, Netherlands. TEL 31-78-6576050, FAX 31-78-6576474, http://springerlink.metapress.com/openurl.asp?genre=journal&issn=1389-9333, http://www.springeronline.com. Ed. Rudiger von Versen.

571.6 DEU ISSN 0302-766X
QH301 CODEN: CTSRCS
➤ **CELL AND TISSUE RESEARCH.** Text in English. m. EUR 5,168 combined subscription to institutions print & online eds. (effective 2005). adv. reprint service avail. from ISI. **Document type:** *Journal, Academic/Scholarly.* **Description:** Presents significant advances encompassing the broad field of cell biology and microscopical anatomy, ranging from invertebrates to mammals, including humans.
Former titles (until 1974): Zeitschrift fuer Zellforschung und Mikroskopische Anatomie (0340-0336); (until 1945): Zeitschrift fuer Zellforschung und Mikroskopische Anatomie. Abteilung A (0340-0387); Which superseded in part (in 1939): Zeitschrift fuer Zellforschung und Mikroskopische Anatomie (0044-3794); Which was formerly (until 1924): Archiv fuer Zellforschung (0365-8503)
Related titles: Microform ed.: (from PQC); Online - full text ed.: ISSN 1432-0878 (from EBSCO Publishing, ProQuest Information & Learning, Springer LINK, Swets Information Services).
Indexed: ASCA, ASFA, AgBio, AnBrAb, ApicAb, B&BAb, BBCI, BIOBASE, BIOSIS Prev, BioCN&I, BiolAb, CIN, ChemAb, ChemTitl, CurCont, DSA, DentInd, ESPM, EntAb, ExcerpMed, GenetAb, HelmAb, IABS, ISR, IndMed, IndVet, Inpharma, MEDLINE, NSCI, NemAb, NutrAb, PE&ON, PN&I, PoultAb, RM&VM, Reac, RefZh, RevApplEntom, S&F, SCI, SFA, TDB, VetBull, WildRev, ZooRec.
—BLDSC (3097.700000), CASDDS, CISTI, GNLM, IDS, IE, Infotrieve, ingenta, KNAW, Linda Hall. **CCC.**
Published by: Springer-Verlag (Subsidiary of: Springer Science+Business Media), Tiergartenstr 17, Heidelberg, 69121, Germany. TEL 49-6221-3450, FAX 49-6221-345229, http://link.springer.de/link/service/journals/00441/index.htm. Ed. K Unsicker. Adv. contact Stephan Kroeck TEL 49-30-827875739. B&W page EUR 680, color page EUR 1,720. Circ: 650 (paid and controlled). **Subscr. in the Americas to:** Springer-Verlag New York, Inc., Journal Fulfillment, PO Box 2485, Secaucus, NJ 07096-2485. TEL 800-777-4643, 201-348-4033, FAX 201-348-4505, journals@springer-ny.com, http://www.springer-ny.com; **Subscr. to:** Springer GmbH Auslieferungsgesellschaft, Haberstr 7, Heidelberg 69126, Germany. FAX 49-6221-345-4229, subscriptions@springer.de.

571.6 USA ISSN 1085-9195
QH573 CODEN: CBBIFV
➤ **CELL BIOCHEMISTRY AND BIOPHYSICS.** Abbreviated title: C B B. Text in English. 1979. 6/yr. USD 335 to individuals; USD 605 to institutions; USD 350 combined subscription to individuals print & online eds.; USD 645 combined subscription to institutions print & online eds. (effective 2005). adv. bk.rev. bibl.; charts; illus. 100 p./no.; back issues avail.; reprints avail. **Document type:** *Journal, Academic/Scholarly.* **Description:** Publishes original papers covering experimental, methodological and theoretical investigations on cells, tissues, organelles and subfragments with emphasis on the mechanisms of cell behavior.
Formerly (until 1996): Cell Biophysics (0163-4992)
Related titles: Online - full text ed.: USD 320 to individuals; USD 575 to institutions (effective 2005) (from EBSCO Publishing, Gale Group, IngentaConnect, O C L C Online Computer Library Center, Inc., Ovid Technologies, Inc., Swets Information Services).
Indexed: ASCA, BBCI, BIOBASE, BIOSIS Prev, BiolAb, CIN, ChemAb, ChemTitl, CurCont, DBA, ExcerpMed, ISR, IndMed, MEDLINE, SCI.
—BLDSC (3097.701000), CASDDS, CISTI, GNLM, IDS, IE, Infotrieve, ingenta, Linda Hall. **CCC.**
Published by: Humana Press, Inc., 999 Riverview Dr, Ste 208, Totowa, NJ 07512. TEL 973-256-1699, FAX 973-256-8341, humana@humanapr.com, http://humanapress.com/journals.pasp. Ed. Edward Massaro. Pub. Thomas B. Lanigan Jr. R&P Wendy A. Warren. Adv. contacts John Chasse, Thomas B. Lanigan Jr. **Subscr. to:** Maruzen Co., Ltd., 3-10 Nihonbashi, 2-Chome, Chuo-ku, Tokyo 103, Japan. TEL 81-3-3275-8591, FAX 81-3-3275-0657, journal@maruzen.co.jp, http://www.maruzen.co.jp.

➤ **CELL BIOCHEMISTRY AND FUNCTION.** see *BIOLOGY—Biochemistry*

➤ **CELL BIOLOGY AND TOXICOLOGY;** an international journal devoted to research at the cellular level. see *ENVIRONMENTAL STUDIES—Toxicology And Environmental Safety*

571.6 USA ISSN 1536-7509
QH583
➤ **CELL BIOLOGY EDUCATION.** Text in English. 2002. q. free (effective 2005). **Document type:** *Journal, Academic/Scholarly.* **Description:** The aim of this journal is to provide an opportunity for scientists and others to publish high-quality, peer-reviewed, educational scholarship, to provide a forum for discussion of educational issues and to promote recognition and reward for educational scholarship.
Media: Online - full content (from National Library of Medicine).
Indexed: BiolDig, ExcerpMed.
Published by: American Society for Cell Biology, 8120 Woodmont Ave, Ste 750, Bethesda, MD 20814-2762. TEL 301-347-9300, cbe@ascb.org, http://www.cellbioed.org, http://www.ascb.org.

571.6 GBR ISSN 1065-6995
QH573 CODEN: CBIIEV
➤ **CELL BIOLOGY INTERNATIONAL.** Text in English. 1977. 12/yr. EUR 819 in Europe to institutions; JPY 88,500 in Japan to institutions; USD 727 to institutions except Europe and Japan (effective 2006). adv. bk.rev. reprints avail. **Document type:** *Journal, Academic/Scholarly.* **Description:** Offers plant and animal scientists the opportunity to inform their peers of new data within a few weeks whether as full papers, or as short reports. Promotes the aims of most cell biologists with papers relating to structure and function, as well as new techniques.
Formerly (until 1993): Cell Biology International Reports (0309-1651)
Related titles: Online - full text ed.: ISSN 1095-8355. USD 769 (effective 2002) (from EBSCO Publishing, Gale Group, IngentaConnect, O C L C Online Computer Library Center, Inc., ScienceDirect, Swets Information Services).
Indexed: ASCA, ASFA, AgBio, AnBrAb, BBCI, BIOBASE, BIOSIS Prev, BioCN&I, BiolAb, CIN, CPA, ChemAb, ChemTitl, CurCont, DSA, DentInd, ExcerpMed, FCA, ForAb, HelmAb, HerbAb, HortAb, IABS, ISR, IndMed, IndVet, Inpharma, MEDLINE, MaizeAb, NutrAb, OrnHort, PBA, PGegResA, PGrRegA, PN&I, PotatoAb, PoultAb, ProtozoAb, RA&MP, RM&VM, RPP, Reac, RevApplEntom, RiceAb, S&F, SCI, SFA, SIA, SeedAb, TDB, THA, TriticAb, VetBull, WeedAb.
—BLDSC (3097.707000), CASDDS, CISTI, GNLM, IDS, IE, Infotrieve, ingenta, Linda Hall. **CCC.**
Published by: (International Federation for Cell Biology), Academic Press (Subsidiary of: Elsevier Science & Technology), 24-28 Oval Rd, London, NW1 7DX, United Kingdom. TEL 44-20-72674466, FAX 44-20-74822293, apsubs@acad.com, http://www.elsevier.com/locate/cellbi. Ed. D. Wheatley. R&P Catherine John. Adv. contact Nik Screen. **Subscr. to:** Harcourt Publishers Ltd., Foots Cray High St, Sidcup, Kent DA14 5HP, United Kingdom. TEL 44-20-8300-3322, FAX 44-20-8309-0807.

571.6 GBR ISSN 0143-4160
CODEN: CECADV
➤ **CELL CALCIUM.** Text in English. 1980. 12/yr. EUR 1,478 in Europe to institutions; JPY 159,700 in Japan to institutions; USD 1,312 elsewhere to institutions (effective 2006). adv. bibl. **Document type:** *Journal, Academic/Scholarly.* **Description:** Covers all fields of calcium metabolism and signalling in living systems, including all aspects of calcium in biological systems from inorganic chemistry to physiology, molecular biology and pathology.
Related titles: Microform ed.: (from PQC); Online - full text ed.: (from EBSCO Publishing, O C L C Online Computer Library Center, Inc., ScienceDirect, Swets Information Services).
Indexed: ASFA, AgBio, AnBrAb, B&BAb, BBCI, BIOBASE, BIOSIS Prev, BiolAb, CIN, CTA, ChemAb, ChemTitl, CurCont, DSA, DentInd, ExcerpMed, GenetAb, HelmAb, HortAb, IABS, ISR, IndMed, Inpharma, MEDLINE, NutrAb, PBA, PE&ON, PGegResA, PN&I, ProtozoAb, RA&MP, Reac, RefZh, SCI, VetBull, WeedAb, ZooRec.
—BLDSC (3097.724000), CASDDS, CISTI, GNLM, IDS, IE, Infotrieve, ingenta, KNAW. **CCC.**
Published by: Churchill Livingstone (Subsidiary of: Elsevier Health Sciences), Robert Stevenson House, 1-3, Baxter's Pl, Leith Walk, Edinburgh, Midlothian EH1 3AF, United Kingdom. TEL 44-131-5562424, FAX 44-131-5581278, journals@harcourt.com, http://www.elsevier.com/locate/ceca, http://www.harcourt-international.com/. Ed. Dr. Alex Verkhratsky TEL 44-161-2755414. Pub. Gillian Griffith. R&P Catherine John TEL 212-424-4200. Adv. contact Kathy Crawford. Circ: 495. **Subscr. to:** Harcourt Publishers Ltd., Foots Cray High St, Sidcup, Kent DA14 5HP, United Kingdom. TEL 44-20-83085700, FAX 44-20-8309-0807.

571.6 USA ISSN 1538-4101
CODEN: CCEYAS
➤ **CELL CYCLE.** Text in English. 2002 (Jan.). bi-m. USD 80 combined subscription in US & Canada print & online; USD 123 combined subscription elsewhere print & online (effective 2003). adv. **Document type:** *Journal, Academic/Scholarly.* **Description:** Covers all aspects of cell cycle research from yeast to man, including the basic cell cycle and its application to cancer, development, stem cells, cell death and cell senescence.
Related titles: Online - full content ed.: ISSN 1551-4005; Online - full text ed.: (from EBSCO Publishing).
Indexed: CurCont, ExcerpMed.
—BLDSC (3097.746500), IE.
Published by: Landes Bioscience, 810 S Church St, Georgetown, TX 78626. TEL 512-863-7762, 800-736-9948, FAX 512-863-0081, orders@landesbioscience.com, http://www.landesbioscience.com/journals/cc/. Ed. Mikhail V Blagosklonny. R&P, Adv. contact Kimberly A Mitchell TEL 512-863-7762.

571.6 GBR ISSN 1350-9047
QH671 CODEN: CDDIEK
➤ **CELL DEATH AND DIFFERENTIATION.** Text in English. 1994. m. EUR 1,000 in Europe to institutions; USD 1,165 in the Americas to institutions; GBP 646 to institutions in the UK & elsewhere; EUR 300 combined subscription in Europe to individuals print & online eds.; USD 325 combined subscription in the Americas to individuals print & online eds.; GBP 194 combined subscription to individuals in the UK & elsewhere; print & online eds. (effective 2006). adv. bk.rev. charts; illus.; stat. back issues avail. **Document type:** *Journal, Academic/Scholarly.* **Description:** Aims to provide a forum for high-quality papers on cell death, proliferation, differentiation, and development in various eukaryotic models.
Related titles: Online - full text ed.: (from EBSCO Publishing, O C L C Online Computer Library Center, Inc., Swets Information Services).
Indexed: AIDS&CR, ASCA, AbHyg, AgBio, AnBrAb, BBCI, BIOBASE, BIOSIS Prev, BioCN&I, BiolAb, CIN, CPA, ChemAb, ChemTitl, CurCont, DSA, ESPM, ExcerpMed, FCA, ForAb, GenetAb, HelmAb, IABS, ISR, IndMed, IndVet, Inpharma, MEDLINE, NemAb, NucAcAb, NutrAb, OGFA, PE&ON, PGrRegA, ProtozoAb, RA&MP, RM&VM, Reac, RefZh, S&F, SCI, SeedAb, VetBull.
—BLDSC (3097.748600), CASDDS, CISTI, GNLM, IDS, IE, Infotrieve, ingenta, KNAW. **CCC.**
Published by: Nature Publishing Group (Subsidiary of: Macmillan Publishers Ltd.), The MacMillan Building, 4 Crinan St, London, N1 9XW, United Kingdom. TEL 44-20-78334000, FAX 44-20-78433601, cell.death.differ@uniroma2.it, http://www.nature.com/cdd. Ed. Gerry Melino TEL 39-06-20427299. adv.: B&W page GBP 595, color page GBP 1,090; trim 210 x 280. Circ: 600. **Subscr. to:** Brunel Rd, Houndmills, Basingstoke, Hamps RG21 6XS, United Kingdom. TEL 44-1256-329242, FAX 44-1256-812358, subscriptions@nature.com.

➤ **CELL DIFFERENTIATION.** see *BIOLOGY—Abstracting, Bibliographies, Statistics*

➤ **CELL MEMBRANES.** see *BIOLOGY—Abstracting, Bibliographies, Statistics*

571.6 USA ISSN 1550-4131
▼ ➤ **CELL METABOLISM.** Text in English. 2005 (Jan.). 12/yr. USD 135 in US & Canada to individuals; JPY 23,800 in Japan to individuals; EUR 234 in Europe to individuals; USD 198 elsewhere to individuals; USD 841 in US & Canada to institutions; JPY 111,000 in Japan to institutions; EUR 1,051 in Europe to institutions; USD 946 elsewhere to institutions (effective 2006). **Document type:** *Journal, Academic/Scholarly.* **Description:** Provides a forum for the exchange of ideas and concepts across the entire metabolic research community, cultivating new areas and fostering cross-disciplinary collaborations in basic research and clinical investigation.
Related titles: Online - full text ed.: (from EBSCO Publishing, ScienceDirect).
Published by: Cell Press (Subsidiary of: Elsevier Science & Technology), 1100 Massachusetts Ave, Cambridge, MA 02138. TEL 617-661-7057, FAX 617-397-2850, metabolism@cell.com, cell@cell.com, http://www.elsevier.com/locate/cellmet, http://www.cellpress.com/. Ed. Charlotte Wang. Adv. contact Sande Giaccone TEL 212-633-3914.

571.6 USA ISSN 0886-1544
QH647 CODEN: CMCYEO
➤ **CELL MOTILITY AND THE CYTOSKELETON.** Text in English. 1980. m. USD 4,295 domestic to institutions; USD 4,439 in Canada & Mexico to institutions; USD 4,523 elsewhere to institutions; USD 4,725 combined subscription domestic to institutions print & online eds.; USD 4,869 combined subscription in Canada & Mexico to institutions print & online eds.; USD 4,953 combined subscription elsewhere to institutions print & online eds. (effective 2006). adv. bibl.; charts; illus. index. back issues avail. **Document type:** *Journal, Academic/Scholarly.* **Description:** Specializes in the rapid publication of articles concerning all phenomena related to cell motility, including structural, biochemical, biophysical and theoretical approaches.
Formerly (until 1986): Cell Motility (0271-6585)
Related titles: Microform ed.: (from PQC); Online - full content ed.: ISSN 1097-0169. 1998. USD 4,295 to institutions (effective 2006); Online - full text ed.: (from EBSCO Publishing, Swets Information Services, Wiley InterScience).
Indexed: ASCA, AbHyg, AgBio, AnBrAb, BBCI, BIOBASE, BIOSIS Prev, BiolAb, CIN, CPA, ChemAb, ChemTitl, CurCont, ESPM, EngInd, ExcerpMed, FCA, GenetAb, HelmAb, IABS, ISR, IndMed, IndVet, Inpharma, MEDLINE, MaizeAb, NSCI, NemAb, PBA, PE&ON, ProtozoAb, RA&MP, Reac, SCI, VetBull, WeedAb, ZooRec.

B

—BLDSC (3097.826000), CASDDS, CISTI, Ei, GNLM, IDS, IE, Infotrieve, ingenta, Linda Hall. **CCC.**

Published by: John Wiley & Sons, Inc., 111 River St, Hoboken, NJ 07030-5774. TEL 201-748-6000, FAX 201-748-5915, uscs-wis@wiley.com, http://www.interscience.wiley.com/jpages/0886-1544/, http://www.wiley.com. Ed. B R Brinkley. adv.: B&W page GBP 640, color page GBP 1,515; trim 210 x 279. Circ: 700. **Subscr. outside the Americas to:** John Wiley & Sons Ltd., The Atrium, Southern Gate, Chichester, West Sussex PO19 8SQ, United Kingdom. TEL 44-1243-843335, 0800-243407, FAX 44-1243-843232, cs-journals@wiley.co.uk.

571.6 USA ISSN 1538-344X
TP248.27.A53 CODEN: CPTECY

➤ **CELL PRESERVATION TECHNOLOGY.** Text in English. 2002. q. USD 382 domestic to institutions; USD 419 foreign to institutions; USD 450 combined subscription domestic to institutions print & online eds.; USD 488 combined subscription foreign to institutions print & online eds. (effective 2006). adv. back issues avail.; reprints avail. **Document type:** *Journal, Academic/Scholarly.* **Description:** Provides information on the diverse spectrum of preservation technologies including cryopreservation, dry-state (anhydrobiosis), glassy-state and hypothermic maintenance, cellular and molecular mechanisms, preservation engineering-bioprocessing, optimization protocols-biopackaging, natural systems models, and ethical/legal/regulatory considerations.

Related titles: Online - full text ed.: USD 337 to institutions (effective 2006) (from EBSCO Publishing, Gale Group, O C L C Online Computer Library Center, Inc., Swets Information Services).

Indexed: B&BAb, BioEngAb, ExcerpMed, M&PBA.

—BLDSC (3097.852000), CISTI, IE, ingenta. **CCC.**

Published by: Mary Ann Liebert, Inc. Publishers, 140 Huguenot St 3rd Fl, New Rochelle, NY 10801-5215. TEL 914-740-2100, FAX 914-740-2101, 800-654-3237, info@liebertpub.com, http://www.liebertpub.com/cpt/. Ed. John G. Baust. Adv. contact Harriet Matysko.

571.6 GBR ISSN 0960-7722
QH631 CODEN: CPROEM

➤ **CELL PROLIFERATION.** Text in English. 1968. bi-m. GBP 146, EUR 219 combined subscription in Europe to individuals print & online eds.; USD 277 combined subscription in the Americas to individuals & Caribbean, print & online eds.; GBP 165 combined subscription elsewhere to individuals print & online eds.; GBP 676 combined subscription in Europe to institutions print & online eds.; USD 1,248 combined subscription in the Americas to institutions & Caribbean, print & online eds.; GBP 743 combined subscription elsewhere to institutions print & online eds. (effective 2006). adv. bk.rev. charts; illus. index. back issues avail.; reprint service avail. from ISI,PSC. **Document type:** *Journal, Academic/Scholarly.* **Description:** Devoted to studies into all aspects of cell proliferation and differentiation in normal and abnormal states.

Formerly (until 1991): Cell and Tissue Kinetics (0008-8730)

Related titles: Microform ed.: (from PQC); Online - full text ed.: ISSN 1365-2184. 1997. GBP 642 in Europe to institutions; USD 1,186 in the Americas to institutions & Caribbean; GBP 706 elsewhere to institutions (effective 2006) (from Blackwell Synergy, EBSCO Publishing, Gale Group, IngentaConnect, O C L C Online Computer Library Center, Inc., Swets Information Services); Supplement(s): ISSN 1477-8408.

Indexed: ASCA, AbHyg, AnBrAb, BIOBASE, BIOSIS Prev, BiolAb, CIN, CIS, CPA, ChemAb, ChemTitl, CurCont, DSA, DentInd, ExcerpMed, ForAb, IABS, ISR, IndMed, IndVet, Inpharma, MEDLINE, PBA, PE&ON, ProtozoAb, Reac, RefZh, SCI, VetBull.

—BLDSC (3097.854000), CASDDS, CISTI, GNLM, IDS, IE, Infotrieve, ingenta, Linda Hall. **CCC.**

Published by: (Cell Kinetics Society), Blackwell Publishing Ltd., 9600 Garsington Rd, Oxford, OX4 2ZG, United Kingdom. TEL 44-1865-776868, FAX 44-1865-714591, customerservices@oxon.blackwellpublishing.com, http://www.blackwellpublishing.com/journals/CPR. Eds. C Sarraf TEL 44-20-79115000 ext 3549, Dr Sasaki TEL 81-836-222221, Z Darzynkiewicz TEL 914-347-2801. Pub. Elizabeth Whelan. R&P Sophie Savage. Adv. contact Jenny Applin. Circ: 465. **Co-sponsors:** European Study Group for Cell Proliferation; International Cell Cycle Society.

571.6 GBR

▼ **CELL RESEARCH.** Text in English. forthcoming 2006. m. EUR 620 in Europe to institutions eurozone; USD 720 in the Americas to institutions; GBP 400 to institutions in the UK & elsewhere (effective 2006). **Document type:** *Journal, Academic/Scholarly.*

Related titles: Online - full text ed.: forthcoming.

Published by: Nature Publishing Group (Subsidiary of: Macmillan Publishers Ltd.), The MacMillan Building, 4 Crinan St, London, N1 9XW, United Kingdom. TEL 44-20-78334000, FAX 44-20-78433601, http://www.nature.com.

571.6 JPN ISSN 0386-7196
QH573 CODEN: CSFUDY

➤ **CELL STRUCTURE AND FUNCTION.** Text in English. 1975. bi-m. USD 136 (effective 2004). bk.rev. back issues avail. **Document type:** *Journal, Academic/Scholarly.* **Description:** Covers cell biology and molecular biology of eucaryotes and procaryotes.

Related titles: Online - full text ed.: ISSN 1347-3700. free (effective 2005) (from J-Stage).

Indexed: ASCA, AgBio, AnBrAb, BBCI, BIOBASE, BIOSIS Prev, BiolAb, CIN, ChemAb, ChemTitl, CurCont, ExcerpMed, HortAb, IABS, INIS AtomInd, ISR, IndMed, IndVet, Inpharma, Inspec, MEDLINE, NemAb, NutrAb, PBA, PE&ON, ProtozoAb, RA&MP, Reac, SCI, SoyAb, VetBull, WeedAb, ZooRec.

—BLDSC (3097.870000), CASDDS, CISTI, GNLM, IDS, IE, Infotrieve, ingenta, KNAW, Linda Hall. **CCC.**

Published by: Japan Society for Cell Biology/Nihon Saibo Seibutsu Gakkai, Shimodachuri Ogawa Higashi, Kamigyo-ku, Kyoto-shi, 602-8048, Japan. TEL 81-75-4153661, FAX 81-75-4153662, csf@nacos.com, jscb@nacos.com, http://csf.jstage.jst.go.jp/, http://www.nacos.com/jscb/. Circ: 1,600.

571.6 USA ISSN 0963-6897
QP89 CODEN: CTRAE8

➤ **CELL TRANSPLANTATION.** Text in English. 1992. 8/yr. USD 1,075 combined subscription domestic print & online eds.; USD 1,125 combined subscription foreign print & online eds. (effective 2005). index. back issues avail. **Document type:** *Journal, Academic/Scholarly.* **Description:** Deals with a wide range of topics including physiological, medical, preclinical, tissue engineering, and device-oriented aspects of transplantation of nervous system, endocrine, growth factor-secreting, bone marrow, epithelial, endothelial, and genetically engineered cells.

Related titles: Microfilm ed.: (from PQC); Online - full text ed.: ISSN 1555-3892 (from EBSCO Publishing, Gale Group, IngentaConnect, ScienceDirect, Swets Information Services).

Indexed: ASCA, BIOBASE, BIOSIS Prev, BiolAb, CurCont, ExcerpMed, IABS, ISR, IndMed, Inpharma, MEDLINE, NSCI, PE&ON, Reac, RefZh, SCI.

—BLDSC (3097.877000), CISTI, GNLM, IDS, IE, Infotrieve, ingenta, KNAW. **CCC.**

Published by: Cognizant Communication Corporation, 3 Hartsdale Rd, Elmsford, NY 10523-3701. TEL 914-592-7720, FAX 914-592-8981, cogcomm@aol.com, http://www.cognizantcommunication.com. Ed. Dr. Paul Sanberg.

➤ **CELLS, TISSUES, ORGANS**; in vivo, in vitro. see *MEDICAL SCIENCES*

➤ **CELLULAR IMMUNOLOGY.** see *MEDICAL SCIENCES—Allergology And Immunology*

579 GBR ISSN 1462-5814
QR1 CODEN: CEMIF5

CELLULAR MICROBIOLOGY. Text in English. 1999. m. GBP 121, EUR 200 combined subscription in Europe to individuals print & online eds.; USD 223 combined subscription in the Americas to individuals & Caribbean, print & online eds.; GBP 133 combined subscription elsewhere to individuals print & online eds.; GBP 773 combined subscription in Europe to institutions print & online eds.; USD 1,428 combined subscription in the Americas to institutions & Caribbean, print & online eds.; GBP 850 combined subscription elsewhere to institutions print & online eds. (effective 2006). adv. reprint service avail. from PSC. **Document type:** *Journal, Academic/Scholarly.* **Description:** Articles on the intersection of microbial and host-cell biology focusing on host cell responses elicited by the interaction with micro-organisms. Equal emphasis is placed on responses to prokaryotic, viral and eukaryotic micro-organisms in mammalian systems and other hosts such as plants and insects.

Related titles: ♦ Online - full text ed.: Cellular Microbiology Online. ISSN 1462-5822.

Indexed: AbHyg, AgBio, BCI, BIOBASE, BIOSIS Prev, BioCN&I, BiolAb, ChemAb, CurCont, DSA, ESPM, ExcerpMed, HelmAb, HortAb, IndMed, IndVet, Inpharma, MEDLINE, NemAb, NutrAb, PE&ON, ProtozoAb, RM&VM, RPP, Reac, RefZh, S&F, SIA, SoyAb, TDB, VetBull, VirolAbstr, ZooRec.

—BLDSC (3097.933400), CISTI, IE, Infotrieve, ingenta. **CCC.**

Published by: Blackwell Publishing Ltd., 9600 Garsington Rd, Oxford, OX4 2ZG, United Kingdom. TEL 44-1865-776868, FAX 44-1865-714591, customerservices@oxon.blackwellpublishing.com, http://www.blackwellpublishing.com/journals/CMI. Eds. Philippe Sansonetti TEL 33-1-40613095, Dr. Richard S Stephens TEL 510-643-1008. Pub. Allen Stevens. R&P Sophie Savage. Adv. contact Jenny Applin. Circ: 200.

579 GBR ISSN 1462-5822

➤ **CELLULAR MICROBIOLOGY ONLINE.** Text in English. m. GBP 111, EUR 183 in Europe to individuals; USD 205 in the Americas to individuals & Caribbean; GBP 122 elsewhere to individuals; GBP 734 in Europe to institutions; USD 1,357 in the Americas to institutions & Caribbean; GBP 808 elsewhere to institutions (effective 2006). **Document type:** *Academic/Scholarly.*

Media: Online - full text (from Blackwell Synergy, EBSCO Publishing, Gale Group, IngentaConnect, O C L C Online Computer Library Center, Inc., Swets Information Services).

Related titles: ♦ Print ed.: Cellular Microbiology. ISSN 1462-5814.

Published by: Blackwell Publishing Ltd., 9600 Garsington Rd, Oxford, OX4 2ZG, United Kingdom. TEL 44-1865-776868, FAX 44-1865-714591, customerservices@oxon.blackwellpublishing.com, http://www.blackwellpublishing.com/journal.asp?ref=1462-5814&site=1.

571.6 USA ISSN 0892-0346
CODEN: ADCND7

➤ **CELLULAR NEUROBIOLOGY.** Text in English. 1980. irreg. back issues avail.; reprint service avail. from ISI. **Document type:** *Academic/Scholarly.*

Formerly (until 1984): Advances in Cellular Neurobiology (0270-0794)

Indexed: BiolAb, ChemAb, e-psyche.

—CASDDS, CISTI, GNLM. **CCC.**

Published by: Academic Press (Subsidiary of: Elsevier Science & Technology), 525 B St, Ste 1900, San Diego, CA 92101-4495. apsubs@acad.com, http://www.academicpress.com. Ed. Sergey Federoff.

571.6 NLD ISSN 1570-5870
CODEN: ACPAER

➤ **CELLULAR ONCOLOGY.** Text in English. 1989. 8/yr. (in 2 vols). EUR 663, USD 797 combined subscription print & online eds. (effective 2006). adv. bibl.; illus. index. back issues avail. **Document type:** *Journal, Academic/Scholarly.* **Description:** Addresses all aspects of analytical and quantitative approaches to cytology and histology with emphasis on applications to pathology.

Formerly (until 2004): Analytical Cellular Pathology (0921-8912); Which incorporated (1985-2003): Analytical and Quantitative Cytology and Histology (0884-6812)

Related titles: Online - full text ed.: (from EBSCO Publishing, Gale Group, IngentaConnect, O C L C Online Computer Library Center, Inc., Swets Information Services).

Indexed: ASCA, AbHyg, BBCI, BIOBASE, BIOSIS Prev, BiolAb, CIN, ChemAb, ChemTitl, CurCont, ExcerpMed, IABS, ISR, IndMed, Inpharma, MEDLINE, NutrAb, Reac, SCI, TDB.

—BLDSC (3097.933450), CASDDS, CISTI, GNLM, IDS, IE, Infotrieve, ingenta. **CCC.**

Published by: (European Society for Analytical Cellular Pathology), I O S Press, Nieuwe Hemweg 6B, Amsterdam, 1013 BG, Netherlands. TEL 31-20-688-3355, FAX 31-20-620-3419, info@iospress.nl, http://www.iospress.nl/html/15705870.php. Ed. Gerrit Meijer. R&P Ms. Carry Koolbergen TEL 31-20-6382189. Adv. contact Ms. Jolijn van Eunen. Circ: 400. **Subscr. to:** I O S Press, Inc., 4502 Rachael Manor Dr., Fairfax, VA 22032-3631. iosbooks@iospress.com; Globe Publication Pvt. Ltd., C-62 Inderpuri, New Delhi 100 012, India. TEL 91-11-579-3211, 91-11-579-3212, custserve@globepub.com, http://www.globepub.com; Kinokuniya Co. Ltd., Shinjuku 3-chome, Shinjuku-ku, Tokyo 160-0022, Japan. FAX 81-3-3439-1094, journal@kinokuniya.co.jp, http://www.kinokuniya.co.jp.

571.6 CHE ISSN 1015-8987
QH573 CODEN: CEPBEW

➤ **CELLULAR PHYSIOLOGY AND BIOCHEMISTRY**; international journal of experimental cellular physiology, biochemistry and pharmacology. Text in English. 1991-1999; resumed 2000. m. CHF 1,842 in Europe to institutions; CHF 1,882.80 elsewhere to institutions; CHF 1,982 combined subscription in Europe to institutions print & online eds.; CHF 2,022.80 combined subscription elsewhere to institutions print & online eds. (effective 2006). adv. back issues avail. **Document type:** *Journal, Academic/Scholarly.* **Description:** Covers mechanisms of intracellular transmission; cellular pharmacology; maintenance, regulation, and disturbance of cell volume; regulation of cell growth and differentiation; control of cellular metabolism; and molecular biology and function of ion carriers.

Related titles: Online - full text ed.: ISSN 1421-9778. CHF 1,758 to institutions (effective 2006) (from EBSCO Publishing, O C L C Online Computer Library Center, Inc., Swets Information Services).

Indexed: ASCA, BBCI, BIOBASE, BIOSIS Prev, BiolAb, CIN, ChemAb, ChemTitl, CurCont, ExcerpMed, IABS, ISR, IndMed, Inpharma, MEDLINE, Reac, SCI.

—BLDSC (3097.934000), CASDDS, CISTI, GNLM, IDS, IE, Infotrieve, ingenta, KNAW, Linda Hall. **CCC.**

Published by: (Cellular Physiology and Biochemistry DEU), S. Karger AG, Allschwilerstr 10, Basel, 4009, Switzerland. TEL 41-61-3061111, FAX 41-61-3061234, karger@karger.ch, http://www.karger.com/CPB, http://www.karger.ch. Eds. F Lang, S Grinstein, W Guggino. adv.: page USD 1,195.

571.6 USA ISSN 0898-6568
QH604.2 CODEN: CESIEY

➤ **CELLULAR SIGNALLING.** Text in English. 1989. 12/yr. EUR 249 in Europe to individuals; JPY 33,200 in Japan to individuals; USD 279 to individuals except Europe and Japan; EUR 1,708 in Europe to institutions; JPY 226,800 in Japan to institutions; USD 1,911 to institutions except Europe and Japan (effective 2006). back issues avail. **Document type:** *Journal, Academic/Scholarly.* **Description:** Publishes original papers on all aspects of the mechanisms, actions and structural components of cellular signalling systems, with emphasis on the production, regulation and action of second messengers, receptors, regulatory proteins, effector systems, and the effect of cellular signalling events.

Related titles: Microfilm ed.: (from PQC); Online - full text ed.: (from EBSCO Publishing, Gale Group, IngentaConnect, ScienceDirect, Swets Information Services).

Indexed: ASCA, ASFA, AbHyg, AnBrAb, BBCI, BIOBASE, BIOSIS Prev, BiolAb, CIN, CTA, ChemAb, ChemTitl, CurCont, ExcerpMed, HortAb, IABS, ISR, IndMed, IndVet, Inpharma, MEDLINE, NSCI, NemAb, PoultAb, ProtozoAb, RA&MP, RM&VM, Reac, SCI.

B

—BLDSC (3097.942000), CASDDS, CISTI, GNLM, IDS, IE, Infotrieve, ingenta, KNAW, Linda Hall. **CCC.**

Published by: Elsevier Inc. (Subsidiary of: Elsevier Science & Technology), 360 Park Ave. S, New York, NY 10010-1710. TEL 212-633-3730, 888-437-4636, jmanley@elsevier.com, usinfo-f@elsevier.com, http://www.elsevier.com/locate/cellsig. Ed. Dr. Miles D Houslay. Adv. contact John Maney. Circ: 273 (paid).

➤ **CHLOROPLASTS.** see *BIOLOGY—Abstracting, Bibliographies, Statistics*

571.6 JPN ISSN 1344-1051
QH600 CODEN: CHSCF4

➤ **CHROMOSOME SCIENCE.** Text in English. 1997. q. JPY 8,500 to individuals; JPY 12,000 to institutions (effective 2001). adv. charts; stat. back issues avail.; reprints avail. **Document type:** *Journal, Academic/Scholarly.* **Description:** Covers chromosone morphology of wild fauna and flora, chromosome abbreviations by RI and chemical mutagenesis as it pertains to cancer and other diseases. Also includes analysis of chromosome structure and genome sizes of certain fauna and flora.

Formed by the merger of (1960-1997): Chromosome Information Service (0574-9549); (1976-1997): Sensyokutai - Kromosomo (0385-4655); Which was formerly (1946-1976): Senshokutai (0371-1641)

Indexed: ASFA, B&BAb, BIOSIS Prev, BiolAb, GenetAb, HGA, MBA, RefZh, ZooRec.

—BLDSC (3184.270000), CASDDS, CISTI, GNLM, ingenta, Linda Hall. **CCC.**

Published by: Senshokutai/Society of Chromosome Research, c/o Laboratory of Plant Chromosome and Gene Stock, Graduate School of Science, Hiroshima University, 1-4-3 Kagamiyama, Higashi-hiroshima City, 739-8526, Japan. TEL 81-824-24-7490, FAX 81-824-24-0738, kkondo@ue.ipc.hiroshima-u.ac.jp. Eds. Katsuhiko Kondo, Michihiro Yoshida. R&P, Adv. contact Katsuhiko Kondo. Circ: 400 (paid).

➤ **CIENCIA BIOLOGICA: BIOLOGIA MOLECULAR E CELULAR.** see *BIOLOGY—Biochemistry*

➤ **CLINICAL CYTOGENETICS.** see *BIOLOGY—Abstracting, Bibliographies, Statistics*

571.5 USA ISSN 0300-8207
QP88.23 CODEN: CVTRBC

➤ **CONNECTIVE TISSUE RESEARCH.** Text in English. 1972. 5/yr. GBP 1,503, USD 2,255 combined subscription to institutions print & online eds. (effective 2006). adv. bk.rev. charts; illus. index. reprint service avail. from PSC. **Document type:** *Journal, Academic/Scholarly.* **Description:** Aims to present original and significant research in all basic areas of connective tissue and matrix biology.

Related titles: CD-ROM ed.: ISSN 1026-7433. 1995; Online - full text ed.: ISSN 1607-8438. 2000. GBP 1,428, USD 2,142 to institutions (effective 2006) (from EBSCO Publishing, Gale Group, IngentaConnect, O C L C Online Computer Library Center, Inc., Swets Information Services).

Indexed: ASCA, ASFA, AnBrAb, BBCI, BIOBASE, BiolAb, CTA, ChemAb, CurCont, DentInd, ExcerpMed, IABS, ISR, IndMed, Inpharma, MEDLINE, MS&D, NutrAb, PE&ON, Reac, SCI.

—BLDSC (3417.665000), CISTI, GNLM, IE, Infotrieve, ingenta. **CCC.**

Published by: Taylor & Francis Inc. (Subsidiary of: Taylor & Francis Group), 325 Chestnut St, Ste 800, Philadelphia, PA 19016. TEL 215-625-8900, 800-354-1420, FAX 215-625-8914, info@taylorandfrancis.com, http://www.tandf.co.uk/journals/titles/03008207.asp, http://www.taylorandfrancis.com. Ed. Arthur Veis TEL 312-503-1355. **Subscr. to:** Taylor & Francis Ltd, Journals Customer Service, Rankine Rd, Basingstoke, Hants RG24 8PR, United Kingdom. TEL 44-1256-813000, FAX 44-1256-330245, enquiry@tandf.co.uk.

➤ **CURRENT ADVANCES IN CELL & DEVELOPMENTAL BIOLOGY.** see *BIOLOGY—Abstracting, Bibliographies, Statistics*

➤ **CURRENT COMMUNICATIONS IN CELL AND MOLECULAR BIOLOGY SERIES.** see *BIOLOGY—Biochemistry*

571.6 GBR ISSN 0955-0674
QH573 CODEN: COCBE3

➤ **CURRENT OPINION IN CELL BIOLOGY.** Text in English. 1989. 6/yr. EUR 270 in Europe to individuals; JPY 32,800 in Japan to individuals; USD 293 elsewhere to individuals; EUR 1,232 in Europe to institutions; JPY 170,900 in Japan to institutions; USD 1,378 elsewhere to institutions (effective 2006). adv. bibl.; illus. back issues avail. **Document type:** *Academic/Scholarly.* **Description:** Directed toward researchers, educators and students in cell biology. Presents review articles, followed by annotated bibliographies of references consulted. Includes a "Paper Alert" section, giving brief summaries of relevant papers recently published in other journals.

Related titles: CD-ROM ed.; Online - full text ed.: USD 227 in North America to individuals; USD 247 in North America to individuals with print ed; GBP 137 elsewhere to individuals; GBP 150 elsewhere to individuals with print ed; USD 822 in North America to institutions includes print ed; GBP 500 elsewhere to institutions includes print ed (effective 1999 & 2000) (from EBSCO Publishing, Gale Group, IngentaConnect, O C L C Online Computer Library Center, Inc., ScienceDirect, Swets Information Services).

Indexed: ASCA, ASFA, BIOBASE, BIOSIS Prev, CIN, CTA, ChemAb, ChemTitl, CurCont, ESPM, ExcerpMed, GenetAb, HGA, IABS, ISR, IndMed, Inpharma, MEDLINE, NSA, NucAcAb, PE&ON, Reac, RefZh, SCI.

—BLDSC (3500.773500), CASDDS, CISTI, GNLM, IDS, IE, Infotrieve, ingenta. **CCC.**

Published by: Elsevier Ltd., Current Opinion Journals (Subsidiary of: Elsevier Science & Technology), 84 Theobald's Rd., London, WC1X 8RR, United Kingdom. TEL 44-20-7611-4000, FAX 44-20-7611-4001, 44-20-7611-4468, http://www.elsevier.com/locate/ceb, http://www.current-opinion.com. Eds. Ari Helenius, Don Cleveland. Circ: 3,200.

571.6 USA

CURRENT PROTOCOLS IN CELL BIOLOGY. Text in English. base vol. plus q. updates. looseleaf. USD 635 combined subscription to institutions base vol. & updates; USD 355 renewals to institutions (effective 2006). **Document type:** *Academic/Scholarly.*

Related titles: CD-ROM ed.: USD 620 combined subscription to institutions for base vol. & updates; USD 350 renewals to institutions (effective 2006); Online - full text ed.

Published by: John Wiley & Sons, Inc., 111 River St, Hoboken, NJ 07030-5774. TEL 201-748-6000, 800-825-7550, FAX 201-748-5915, protocol@wiley.com, http://lib.harvard.edu/e-resources/details/c/cuprcebi.html, http://www.wiley.com. **Subscr. outside the Americas:** John Wiley & Sons Ltd., The Atrium, Southern Gate, Chichester, West Sussex PO19 8SQ, United Kingdom. TEL 44-1243-779777, FAX 44-1243-775878, cs-journals@wiley.co.uk; **Subscr. to:** PO Box 5597, Somerset, NJ 08875. TEL 732-650-4630, FAX 732-650-4623.

571.6 USA

CURRENT PROTOCOLS IN CYTOMETRY. Text in English. 1997. base vol. plus q. updates. looseleaf. USD 635 combined subscription to institutions base vol. & updates; USD 330 renewals to institutions (effective 2006). **Document type:** *Academic/Scholarly.*

Related titles: CD-ROM ed.: USD 620 combined subscription to institutions base vol. & updates; USD 325 renewals to institutions (effective 2006); Online - full text ed.

—BLDSC (3501.532000).

Published by: (International Society for Analytical Cytology), John Wiley & Sons, Inc., 111 River St, Hoboken, NJ 07030-5774. TEL 201-748-6000, 800-825-7550, FAX 201-748-5915, protocol@wiley.com, http://www3.interscience.wiley.com/c_p/index.htm, http://www.wiley.com. Ed. Paul Robinson. **Dist. in UK by:** John Wiley & Sons Ltd., The Atrium, Southern Gate, Chichester, West Sussex PO19 8SQ, United Kingdom. TEL 44-1243-779777, FAX 44-1243-775878, cs-journals@wiley.co.uk; **Subscr. to:** PO Box 5597, Somerset, NJ 08875. TEL 732-650-4630, FAX 732-650-4623.

571.64 USA ISSN 1063-5823
QH601 CODEN: CTMTA2

➤ **CURRENT TOPICS IN MEMBRANES.** Text in English. 1970. irreg., latest vol.54, 2003. USD 159.95 vol.54 (effective 2004). reprints avail. **Document type:** *Academic/Scholarly.* **Description:** Covers the history and overall impact of extracellular ATP signaling, methods to detect ATP release and signaling, the molecular and cell biology of purinergic receptors, the pharmacology of purinergic receptors, the ion channel biophysics and biochemistry of P2X purinergic receptor channels, and the physiology and pathophysiology of purinergic receptors.

Formerly (until 1991): Current Topics in Membranes and Transport (0070-2161)

Related titles: Online - full text ed.: (from ScienceDirect).

Indexed: BBCI, BIOSIS Prev, BiolAb, ChemAb, ISR, NutrAb, SCI.

—BLDSC (3504.884980), CASDDS, CISTI, GNLM, IE, ingenta, Linda Hall. **CCC.**

Published by: Academic Press (Subsidiary of: Elsevier Science & Technology), 525 B St, Ste 1900, San Diego, CA 92101-4495. TEL 619-231-6616, 800-894-3434, apsubs@acad.com, http://www.academicpress.com. Eds. Arnest Kleinzeller, Felix Bronner.

➤ **CYTOGENETIC AND GENOME RESEARCH.** see *BIOLOGY—Genetics*

571.6 GBR ISSN 1742-6413

▼ ➤ **CYTOJOURNAL.** Text in English. 2004. irreg. free (effective 2006). **Document type:** *Journal, Academic/Scholarly.* **Description:** Publishes research in the field of cytopathology and related areas.

Media: Online - full text (from National Library of Medicine).

Indexed: ExcerpMed.

Published by: BioMed Central Ltd. (Subsidiary of: Current Science Ltd), Middlesex House, 34-42 Cleveland St, London, W1T 4LB, United Kingdom. TEL 44-20-76319131, FAX 44-20-76319923, info@biomedcentral.com, http://www.cytojournal.com, http://www.biomedcentral.com.

571.6 JPN ISSN 0011-4545
QH301 CODEN: CYTOAN

➤ **CYTOLOGIA/KITOROGIA;** international journal of cytogenetics and cell biology. Text in English. 1929. q. JPY 25,000; JPY 6,500 newsstand/cover (effective 2004). adv. **Document type:** *Journal, Academic/Scholarly.* **Description:** Contains original contributions in the field of cytology of plants and animals, covering cyto-morphology, cyto-physiology, physical chemistry of the cell and cell constituents, genetical study on a cytological basis, research on the cell and cell constituents in living and fixed conditions, serology, vital staining biochemistry and biophysics of cells and tissues, electron microscopy, microdissection, tissue culture, molecular cell biology, and microtechnique and all other research methods.

Related titles: Microfilm ed.: (from PMC); Online - full text ed.: (from J-Stage).

Indexed: ASFA, AgBio, Agr, AgrForAb, AnBrAb, BIOBASE, BIOSIS Prev, BioCN&I, BiolAb, CIN, CPA, CTFA, ChemAb, ChemTitl, CurCont, ExcerpMed, FCA, FaBeAb, ForAb, GenetAb, HGA, HelmAb, HerbAb, HortAb, IABS, INIS AtomInd, ISR, IndVet, MEDLINE, MaizeAb, NemAb, NutrAb, OrnHort, PBA, PGegResA, PGrRegA, PHN&I, PN&I, PotatoAb, PoultAb, RA&MP, RM&VM, RPP, RefZh, RevApplEntom, RiceAb, S&F, S&MA, SCI, SIA, SeedAb, SoyAb, TDB, TOSA, TriticAb, VetBull, WeedAb, ZooRec.

—BLDSC (3506.800000), CASDDS, CISTI, GNLM, IE, Infotrieve, ingenta, Linda Hall. **CCC.**

Published by: Nihon Mendel Kyokai/Japan Mendel Society, Toshin Bldg., Hongo 2-27-2, Bunkyo-ku, Tokyo, 113-0033, Japan. TEL 81-3-38145675, FAX 81-3-38145352, jmendel-soc@umin.ac.jp, http://www.jstage.jst.go.jp/browse/cytologia/_vols/-char/ja. Ed. Tsuneyoshi Kuroiwa. Pub., R&P Hideo Hirokawa. Circ: 1,000.

➤ **CYTOLOGY AND GENETICS.** see *BIOLOGY—Genetics*

571.6 USA ISSN 1552-4922
QH573 CODEN: CYTODQ

➤ **CYTOMETRY. PART A.** Text in English. 1983. 18/yr. USD 1,270 domestic to institutions; USD 1,486 in Canada & Mexico to institutions; USD 1,612 elsewhere to institutions; USD 1,397 combined subscription domestic to institutions print & online eds.; USD 1,613 combined subscription in Canada & Mexico to institutions print & online eds.; USD 1,739 combined subscription elsewhere to institutions print & online eds. (effective 2006); subscr. includes part B. adv. bk.rev. bibl.; charts; illus. index. back issues avail.; reprint service avail. from ISI. **Document type:** *Journal, Academic/Scholarly.* **Description:** Covers all aspects of cytology, including image and flow cytometry, flow sorting, and applications of quantitative analytical cytology to basic research and clinical medicine.

Supersedes in part (in 2003): Cytometry (0196-4763); Incorporates (1993-1999): Bioimaging (0966-9051)

Related titles: Microfilm ed.: (from WWS); Microform ed.: (from PQC); Online - full content ed.: ISSN 1552-4930. USD 1,270 to institutions (effective 2006); Online - full text ed.: (from EBSCO Publishing, Swets Information Services, Wiley InterScience); Supplement(s): Cytometry. Supplement. ISSN 1046-7386. 1987.

Indexed: ASCA, BBCI, BiolAb, CIN, ChemAb, ChemTitl, CurCont, ExcerpMed, IABS, ISR, IndMed, Inpharma, PE&ON, ProtozoAb, Reac, RevApplEntom, SCI.

—BLDSC (3506.855100), CASDDS, CISTI, GNLM, IDS, IE, Infotrieve, ingenta, KNAW, Linda Hall.

Published by: (International Society for Analytical Cytology), John Wiley & Sons, Inc., 111 River St, Hoboken, NJ 07030-5774. TEL 201-748-6000, FAX 201-748-5915, cytometry@nwu.edu, uscs-wis@wiley.com, http://www.interscience.wiley.com/jpages/0196-4763/, http://www.wiley.com. Ed. Charles L Goolsby, Ph.D. adv.: B&W page GBP 640, color page GBP 1,515; trim 210 x 279. Circ: 3,300. **Subscr. outside the Americas to:** John Wiley & Sons Ltd., The Atrium, Southern Gate, Chichester, West Sussex PO19 8SQ, United Kingdom. TEL 44-1243-779777, FAX 44-1243-775878, cs-journals@wiley.co.uk.

571.6 USA ISSN 1552-4949

▼ **CYTOMETRY. PART B: CLINICAL CYTOMETRY.** Text in English. 2003. 6/yr. USD 1,185 domestic to institutions; USD 1,365 in Canada & Mexico to institutions; USD 1,518 elsewhere to institutions; USD 1,304 combined subscription domestic to institutions print & online eds.; USD 1,484 combined subscription in Canada & Mexico to institutions print & online eds.; USD 1,637 combined subscription elsewhere to institutions print & online eds. (effective 2005); subscr. includes Parts A. **Document type:** *Journal, Academic/Scholarly.* **Description:** Focuses on the development and application of analytical cytology and cytomics related to the current and future practice of clinical cytometry.

Supersedes in part (in 2003): Cytometry (0196-4763); Incorporates (1993-1999): Bioimaging (0966-9051)

Related titles: Online - full text ed.: ISSN 1552-4957 (from EBSCO Publishing, Wiley InterScience).

Indexed: CurCont, SCI.

—BLDSC (3506.855200), CISTI, IE, Linda Hall.

Published by: (Clinical Cytometry Society), John Wiley & Sons, Inc., 111 River St, Hoboken, NJ 07030-5774. TEL 201-748-6000, FAX 201-748-5915, cytometry@nwu.edu, uscs-wis@wiley.com, http://www.interscience.wiley.com/jpages/0196-4763:1/, http://www.wiley.com. Ed. Charles L Goolsby, Ph.D.

B

571.6 JPN ISSN 0916-6920
CODEN: CYRSET

CYTOMETRY RESEARCH. Text in Japanese. 1991. s-a. free to members. **Document type:** *Journal, Academic/Scholarly.*
Formed by the merger of (1984-1990): Furo Saitometori/Flow Cytometry (0915-1958); (1989-1990): F C M - Cell Biology (0915-3276)
Related titles: Online - full content ed.
Indexed: INIS AtomInd.
Published by: Nihon Saitometori Gakkai/Japan Cytometry Society, Kanda-Surugadai 1-8, Chiyoda-Ku, Tokyo, 101-0062, Japan. TEL 81-3-32922051 ext 2928, FAX 81-3-32921470, cytometry-society@umin.ac.jp, http://cytometry.umin.jp/kaisi.htm.

571.6 GBR ISSN 0956-5507
RB43 CODEN: CYTPEU

➤ **CYTOPATHOLOGY.** Text in English. 1990. bi-m. GBP 414 combined subscription in Europe to institutions print & online eds.; USD 766 combined subscription in the Americas to institutions & Caribbean (print & online eds.); GBP 456 combined subscription elsewhere to institutions print & online eds. (effective 2006). adv. bk.rev. bibl.; charts; illus. back issues avail.; reprint service avail. from PSC. **Document type:** *Journal, Academic/Scholarly.* **Description:** Contains original articles and critical reviews on all aspects of clinical cytology.
Related titles: Microform ed.: (from PQC); Online - full text ed.: ISSN 1365-2303. 1997. GBP 393 in Europe to institutions; USD 727 in the Americas to institutions & Caribbean; GBP 433 elsewhere to institutions (effective 2006) (from Blackwell Synergy, EBSCO Publishing, Gale Group, IngentaConnect, O C L C Online Computer Library Center, Inc., Ovid Technologies, Inc., Swets Information Services); Supplement(s): Cytopathology. Supplement. ISSN 1350-4037.
Indexed: ASCA, AbHyg, BIOBASE, CurCont, ExcerpMed, HelmAb, IABS, ISR, IndMed, Inpharma, MEDLINE, PE&ON, PN&I, ProtozoAb, RM&VM, Reac, SCI, TDB.
—BLDSC (3506.856000), CISTI, GNLM, IDS, IE, Infotrieve, ingenta, KNAW. **CCC.**
Published by: (British Society for Clinical Cytology), Blackwell Publishing Ltd., 9600 Garsington Rd, Oxford, OX4 2ZG, United Kingdom. TEL 44-1865-776868, FAX 44-1865-714591, customerservices@oxon.blackwellpublishing.com, http://www.blackwellpublishing.com/journals/CYT. Ed. Dr. Gabrijela Kocjan. Pub. Elizabeth Whelan. R&P Sophie Savage. Adv. contact Jenny Applin. Circ: 980.

➤ **CYTOSKELETON.** see *BIOLOGY—Abstracting, Bibliographies, Statistics*

571.6 NLD ISSN 0920-9069
CODEN: CYTOER

➤ **CYTOTECHNOLOGY**; international journal of cell culture and biotechnology. Text in English. 1988. 9/yr. EUR 1,378, USD 1,408, GBP 908 combined subscription to institutions print & online eds. (effective 2005). adv. back issues avail.; reprint service avail. from PSC. **Document type:** *Journal, Academic/Scholarly.* **Description:** Represents a central repository for information on both the infrastructure of cell technology and the applied use of cell cultures, thus providing a panoramic perspective of the many facets and disciplines needed to develop successful cell cultures.
Incorporates (1975-2003): Methods in Cell Science (1381-5741); Which was formerly (until 1995): Journal of Tissue Culture Methods (0271-8057); (until 1978): T C A Manual (Tissue Culture Association) (0361-0268)
Related titles: Microform ed.: (from PQC); Online - full text ed.: ISSN 1573-0778 (from EBSCO Publishing, Gale Group, IngentaConnect, Kluwer Online, O C L C Online Computer Library Center, Inc., Ovid Technologies, Inc., Springer LINK, Swets Information Services).
Indexed: AEA, AEBA, ASCA, ASFA, AgBio, AnBrAb, BCI, BIOBASE, BIOSIS Prev, BibLing, BioCN&I, BioEngAb, BiolAb, CurCont, DBA, DSA, ESPM, ExcerpMed, HortAb, IABS, IndVet, M&PBA, MBA, MEDLINE, MSCI, NSCI, NutrAb, PBA, PN&I, PoultAb, RA&MP, RM&VM, RefZh, RevApplEntom, RiceAb, VetBull.
—BLDSC (3506.882000), CASDDS, CISTI, GNLM, IDS, IE, Infotrieve, ingenta, Linda Hall. **CCC.**
Published by: Springer-Verlag Dordrecht (Subsidiary of: Springer Science+Business Media), Van Godewijckstraat 30, Dordrecht, 3311 GX, Netherlands. TEL 31-78-6576050, FAX 31-78-6576474, http://springerlink.metapress.com/openurl.asp?genre=journal&issn=0920-9069, http://www.springeronline.com.

571.6 GBR ISSN 0951-0818
CODEN: DVCBAP

DEVELOPMENTAL AND CELL BIOLOGY SERIES. Text in English. irreg. price varies. illus. **Document type:** *Monographic series.*
Formerly: Developmental and Cell Biology Monographs
Indexed: BIOSIS Prev, ZooRec.
—BLDSC (3579.050100).
Published by: Cambridge University Press, The Edinburgh Bldg, Shaftesbury Rd, Cambridge, CB2 2RU, United Kingdom. TEL 44-1223-312393, FAX 44-1223-315052, information@cambridge.org, http://www.cup.cam.ac.uk/. R&P Linda Nicol TEL 44-1223-325757.

571.6 USA ISSN 1534-5807
QH 573 CODEN: DCEEBE

DEVELOPMENTAL CELL. Text in English. 2001. 12/yr. EUR 234 in Europe to individuals; JPY 23,800 in Japan to individuals; USD 135 in Canada to individuals; USD 135 in United States to individuals; USD 198 to individuals except Europe and Japan; EUR 1,024 in Europe to institutions; JPY 105,600 in Japan to institutions; USD 786 in United States to institutions; USD 786 in Canada to institutions; USD 887 to institutions except Europe and Japan (effective 2006). adv. back issues avail. **Document type:** *Journal, Academic/Scholarly.* **Description:** Covers the field of cell and developmental biology.
Related titles: Online - full text ed.: USD 125 to individuals (effective 2004) (from EBSCO Publishing, Gale Group, IngentaConnect, ScienceDirect).
Indexed: B&BAb, BIOBASE, BIOSIS Prev, BiolAb, CTA, ChemAb, CurCont, ESPM, EntAb, ExcerpMed, GenetAb, ISR, NSA, NucAcAb, SCI.
—BLDSC (3579.054230), CISTI, IE, Linda Hall. **CCC.**
Published by: Cell Press (Subsidiary of: Elsevier Science & Technology), 1100 Massachusetts Ave, Cambridge, MA 02138. TEL 617-661-7057, FAX 617-661-7061, devcelleditor@cell.com, http://www.elsevier.com/locate/devcel, http://www.cellpress.com/. Ed. Deborah Sweet. Pub. Lynne Herndon. Adv. contact Sande Giaccone TEL 212-633-3914. B&W page USD 1,050, color page USD 2,405; trim 8.5 x 11. Circ: 1,065 (paid). **Subscr. to:** 6277 Sea Harbor Dr, Orlando, FL 32887. TEL 407-345-3000, 866-314-2355, FAX 407-363-9661, subs@cell.com.

DEVELOPMENTS IN MOLECULAR AND CELLULAR BIOCHEMISTRY. see *BIOLOGY—Biochemistry*

571.6 USA ISSN 8755-1039
CODEN: DICYE7

➤ **DIAGNOSTIC CYTOPATHOLOGY.** Text in English. 1985. m. USD 1,810 domestic to institutions; USD 1,954 in Canada & Mexico to institutions; USD 2,038 elsewhere to institutions; USD 1,991 combined subscription domestic to institutions print & online eds.; USD 2,135 combined subscription in Canada & Mexico to institutions print & online eds.; USD 2,219 combined subscription elsewhere to institutions print & online eds. (effective 2006). adv. bk.rev. abstr.; illus. back issues avail. **Document type:** *Journal, Academic/Scholarly.* **Description:** International forum for original research and review articles on clinical aspects of cytology, encompassing such areas as flow cytometry, electron microscopy, image analysis, and immunocytochemistry.
Related titles: Microform ed.: (from PQC); Online - full content ed.: ISSN 1097-0339. USD 1,810 to institutions (effective 2006); Online - full text ed.: (from EBSCO Publishing, Swets Information Services, Wiley InterScience).
Indexed: ASCA, AbHyg, BIOSIS Prev, BiolAb, CurCont, ExcerpMed, HelmAb, IndMed, Inpharma, MEDLINE, PE&ON, ProtozoAb, RM&VM, Reac, RefZh, TDB.
—BLDSC (3579.656500), CISTI, GNLM, IDS, IE, Infotrieve, ingenta, KNAW. **CCC.**
Published by: John Wiley & Sons, Inc., 111 River St, Hoboken, NJ 07030-5774. TEL 201-748-6000, FAX 201-748-5915, uscs-wis@wiley.com, http://www3.interscience.wiley.com/cgi-bin/jhome/39095, http://www.wiley.com. Ed. Carlos W M Bedrossian. adv.: B&W page GBP 640, color page GBP 1,515; trim 210 x 279. Circ: 1,750. **Subscr. outside the Americas to:** John Wiley & Sons Ltd., The Atrium, Southern Gate, Chichester, West Sussex PO19 8SQ, United Kingdom. TEL 44-1243-843335, 0800-243407, FAX 44-1243-843232, cs-journals@wiley.co.uk.

➤ **THE E M B O JOURNAL.** see *BIOLOGY—Biochemistry*

➤ **EGYPTIAN JOURNAL OF GENETICS AND CYTOLOGY.** see *BIOLOGY—Genetics*

571.5 EGY ISSN 1110-0559

THE EGYPTIAN JOURNAL OF HISTOLOGY/AL-MAGALLAT AL-MISRIYYAT LI-'LM AL-ANSIGAT. Text in English. 1978. s-a. EGP 15 domestic; USD 15 foreign. **Document type:** *Journal, Academic/Scholarly.*
Published by: The Egyptian Society of Histology and Cytology, Faculty of Medicine, Al-Azhar University, Madinet Nasr, Cairo, Egypt. http://derp.sti.sci.eg/data/0119.htm. Ed. Dr. Abdel-Wahed Ahmad Bussaila.

571.6 DEU ISSN 0256-1514

➤ **ENDOCYTOBIOSIS AND CELL RESEARCH.** Text in English. 1984. 3/yr. adv. bk.rev. index. back issues avail. **Document type:** *Journal, Academic/Scholarly.* **Description:** Aims to promote the flow of information and to stimulate the cooperation between symbiosis researchers and cell biologists.
Indexed: ASCA, CurCont, ISR, SCI, ZooRec.
—BLDSC (3743.095000), CISTI, GNLM, IDS, IE, ingenta. **CCC.**
Published by: International Society on Endocytobiology, c/o Rainer M. Maier, Menzinger Str 67, Munich, 80638, Germany. TEL 49-89-17861288, FAX 49-89-1782274, raimaier@botanik.biologie.uni-muenchen.de, http://www.endocytobiology.org. Eds. D C Smith, H E A Schenk, K W Jeon.

571.6 DEU ISSN 0171-9335
QH573 CODEN: EJCBDN

➤ **EUROPEAN JOURNAL OF CELL BIOLOGY.** Text in English. 1969. 12/yr. EUR 339 in Europe to individuals; JPY 43,700 in Japan to individuals; USD 334 elsewhere to individuals; EUR 1,247 to institutions; EUR 1,437 in Europe to institutions; JPY 190,100 in Japan to institutions; USD 1,540 elsewhere to institutions (effective 2006). adv. back issues avail. **Document type:** *Journal, Academic/Scholarly.* **Description:** Publishes reviews, original articles and short communications on the structure, function and macromolecular organization of cells and cell components.
Formerly: Cytobiologie (0070-2463)
Related titles: Online - full text ed.: (from bigchalk, EBSCO Publishing, Gale Group, IngentaConnect, O C L C Online Computer Library Center, Inc., ProQuest Information & Learning, ScienceDirect, Swets Information Services); Supplement(s): European Journal of Cell Biology. Supplement. ISSN 0724-5130. 1983.
Indexed: ASCA, ASFA, AbHyg, AgBio, AnBrAb, BBCI, BIOBASE, BIOSIS Prev, BiolAb, CIN, CPA, ChemAb, ChemTitl, CurCont, DBA, DSA, DentInd, ExcerpMed, FCA, GenetAb, HortAb, IABS, ISR, IndMed, IndVet, Inpharma, MEDLINE, NutrAb, PBA, PE&ON, PGrRegA, PoultAb, ProtozoAb, RM&VM, RPP, Reac, RefZh, RevApplEntom, RiceAb, SCI, SoyAb, TriticAb, VetBull.
—BLDSC (3829.725700), CASDDS, CISTI, GNLM, IE, Infotrieve, ingenta, Linda Hall. **CCC.**
Published by: (Deutsche Gesellschaft fuer Zellbiologie e.V., Deutsche Gesellschaft fuer Elektronenmikroskopie e.V.), Elsevier GmbH, Urban & Fischer Verlag (Subsidiary of: Elsevier Science & Technology), Loebdergraben 14a, Jena, 07743, Germany. TEL 49-3641-626462, FAX 49-3641-626432, journals@urbanfischer.de, http://www.elsevier.com/locate/ejcb, http://www.urbanfischer.de/journals. Eds. Hans Bloemendal TEL 31-24-3616755, Manfred Schliwa, Reinhard Jahn TEL 49-551-2011635, Sabine Werner TEL 41-1-6333941. R&P Frances Rothwell. Adv. contact Cora Grotzke. B&W page EUR 485, color page EUR 1,430; trim 210 x 280. Circ: 720 (paid and controlled). **Subscr. in non-German speaking countries to:** Nature Publishing Group, Brunel Rd, Houndmills, Basingstoke, Hamps RG21 6XS, United Kingdom. TEL 44-1256-302629, FAX 44-1256-476117, subscriptions@nature.com.

➤ **EUROPEAN JOURNAL OF HISTOCHEMISTRY.** see *BIOLOGY—Biochemistry*

571.6 USA ISSN 0014-4827
QH581 CODEN: ECREAL

➤ **EXPERIMENTAL CELL RESEARCH.** Text in English. 1950. 20/yr. EUR 655 in Europe to individuals; JPY 68,400 in Japan to individuals; USD 570 to individuals except Europe and Japan; EUR 5,727 in Europe to institutions; JPY 598,200 in Japan to institutions; USD 4,985 to institutions except Europe and Japan (effective 2006). adv. bibl.; charts; illus. index. back issues avail.; reprints avail. **Document type:** *Journal, Academic/Scholarly.* **Description:** Promotes the understanding of cell biology by publishing experimental studies on the general organization and activity of cells.
Related titles: Online - full text ed.: ISSN 1090-2422. USD 4,913 (effective 2002) (from EBSCO Publishing, Gale Group, IngentaConnect, O C L C Online Computer Library Center, Inc., ScienceDirect, Swets Information Services).
Indexed: ASCA, ASFA, AbHyg, AgBio, Agr, AnBrAb, B&AI, B&BAb, BBCI, BIOBASE, BIOSIS Prev, BibAg, BiolAb, CIN, ChemAb, ChemTitl, CurCont, DBA, DSA, DentInd, ExcerpMed, GenetAb, HGA, IABS, INIS AtomInd, ISR, IndMed, IndVet, Inpharma, MEDLINE, NSCI, NutrAb, PN&I, ProtozoAb, RM&VM, Reac, RefZh, SCI, TDB, VetBull.
—BLDSC (3838.980000), CASDDS, CISTI, GNLM, IDS, IE, Infotrieve, ingenta, Linda Hall. **CCC.**
Published by: (International Society for Cell Biology), Academic Press (Subsidiary of: Elsevier Science & Technology), 525 B St, Ste 1900, San Diego, CA 92101-4495. TEL 619-231-6616, 800-894-3434, apsubs@acad.com, http://www.elsevier.com/locate/yexcr, http://www.academicpress.com. Ed. U. Lendahl.

571.6 POL ISSN 0239-8508
CODEN: FHCYEM

➤ **FOLIA HISTOCHEMICA ET CYTOBIOLOGICA.** Text and summaries in English. 1963. q. EUR 40 in Europe to individuals; EUR 50 elsewhere to individuals; EUR 50 in Europe to institutions; EUR 65 elsewhere to institutions (effective 2005). bk.rev. charts; illus.; abstr.; bibl. index. back issues avail. **Document type:** *Journal, Academic/Scholarly.* **Description:** Publishes review articles, original articles, letters to the editor, proceedings of scientific congresses/symposia. Covers development and applications of modern histochemical techniques, cell biology and pathology, cell-microenvironment interaction, tissue organization and pathology.
Formerly (until 1984): Folia Histochemica et Cytochemica (0015-5586)
Indexed: ASCA, AgrAg, AgrLib, AnBrAb, BBCI, BIOSIS Prev, BiolAb, CIN, ChemAb, ChemTitl, CurCont, ExcerpMed, IABS, INIS AtomInd, ISR, IndMed, MEDLINE, NutrAb, SCI.
—BLDSC (3970.295000), CASDDS, CISTI, GNLM, IDS, IE, Infotrieve, ingenta, Linda Hall. **CCC.**
Published by: Polskie Towarzystwo Histochemikow i Cytochemikow/Polish Histochemical and Cytochemical Society, PO Box 843, Krakow, 30960, Poland. mmlitwin@cyf-kr.edu.pl, http://ampat.amu.edu.pl/czasopis/fhec.htm. Ed. Jan A Litwin. Circ: 500.

B

▼ new title ➤ refereed ✶ unverified ♦ full entry avail.

➤ **FOLIA MICROBIOLOGICA.** see *BIOLOGY—Biochemistry*

571.6 JPN ISSN 0386-4766
CODEN: SAIBD8

GEKKAN SAIBO/CELL. Text in Japanese. 1969. m. JPY 1,600 per issue (effective 1998). **Document type:** *Academic/Scholarly.*
Indexed: ChemAb.
—CASDDS, CISTI.
Published by: Nyu Saiensusha/New Science Co., 3-8-14 Takanawa, Minato-ku, Tokyo, 108-0074, Japan. hk-ns@mk1.macnet.or.jp, http://www.macnet.or.jp/co/hk-ns. Ed. Hisako Fukuda.

GENES TO CELLS. see *BIOLOGY—Genetics*

GENETIC RESOURCES AND CROP EVOLUTION; an international journal. see *BIOLOGY—Genetics*

GENOME. see *BIOLOGY—Genetics*

HEREDITAS. see *BIOLOGY—Genetics*

B

571.6 DEU ISSN 0948-6143
QH611 CODEN: HCBIFP

➤ **HISTOCHEMISTRY AND CELL BIOLOGY.** Text in English. 1958. m. (in 2 vols., 6 nos./vol.). EUR 3,088 combined subscription to institutions print & online eds. (effective 2005). adv. charts; illus. back issues avail.; reprint service avail. from ISI. **Document type:** *Journal, Academic/Scholarly.*
Description: Contains original papers on all areas of cyto- and histochemistry, especially morphology and cell biology. Focus is on theory and methodology (including fractionation, homogenization techniques, autoradiography, polarization optics, and fluorescence microscopy).
Former titles: Histochemistry (0301-5564); Histochemie - Histochemistry - Histochimie (0018-2222)
Related titles: Microform ed.: (from PQC); Online - full text ed.: ISSN 1432-119X (from EBSCO Publishing, ProQuest Information & Learning, Springer LINK, Swets Information Services).
Indexed: ASCA, AbHyg, AgBio, AnBrAb, BBCI, BIOBASE, BIOSIS Prev, BiolAb, CIN, CPA, ChemAb, ChemTitl, CurCont, DSA, DentInd, ExcerpMed, HelmAb, HortAb, IABS, ISR, IndMed, IndVet, Inpharma, Kidney, MEDLINE, NSCI, NemAb, NutrAb, OrnHort, PN&I, ProtozoAb, Reac, RefZh, SCI, SIA, TDB, VetBull, ZooRec.
—BLDSC (4316.003100), CASDDS, CISTI, GNLM, IDS, IE, Infotrieve, ingenta, Linda Hall. **CCC.**
Published by: (Society for Histochemistry), Springer-Verlag (Subsidiary of: Springer Science+Business Media), Tiergartenstr 17, Heidelberg, 69121, Germany. TEL 49-6221-3450, FAX 49-6221-345229, subscriptions@springer.de, http://link.springer.de/link/service/journals/00418/index.htm, http://www.springer.de. Eds. Dr. D Drenckhahn, Dr. J Roth. Adv. contact Stephan Kroeck TEL 49-30-827875739. **Subscr. in the Americas to:** Springer-Verlag New York, Inc., Journal Fulfillment, PO Box 2485, Secaucus, NJ 07096-2485. TEL 800-777-4643, 201-348-4033, FAX 201-348-4505; **Subscr. to:** Springer GmbH Auslieferungsgesellschaft, Haberstr 7, Heidelberg 69126, Germany. TEL 49-6221-345-0, FAX 49-6221-345-4229, subscriptions@springer.de.

571.5 616.07 ESP ISSN 0213-3911
CODEN: HIHIES

➤ **HISTOLOGY AND HISTOPATHOLOGY**; cellular and molecular biology. Text in English. 1986. q., latest vol.16. EUR 440 (effective 2005). adv. 330 p./no.; back issues avail. **Document type:** *Journal, Academic/Scholarly.* **Description:** Publishes original works in anatomy, histology, histopathology and cell biology.
Related titles: Online - full text ed.: (from EBSCO Publishing).
Indexed: ASCA, AbHyg, AnBrAb, BBCI, BIOBASE, BIOSIS Prev, BiolAb, CIN, ChemAb, ChemTitl, CurCont, ExcerpMed, IABS, ISR, IndMed, IndVet, Inpharma, MEDLINE, MaizeAb, NSCI, NutrAb, PN&I, PoultAb, RA&MP, RM&VM, Reac, S&F, SCI, TDB, VetBull, ZooRec.
—BLDSC (4316.023100), CASDDS, CISTI, GNLM, IDS, IE, Infotrieve, ingenta, KNAW. **CCC.**
Address: Plaza Fuensanta, 2-7o C, Murcia, 30008, Spain. FAX 34-968-364150, jfmadrid@um.es, http://www.hh.um.es, http://www.ehu.es/histol-histopathol/. Eds., R&Ps Dr. Francisco Hernandez, Dr. Juan F Madrid. Pub. Dr. Francisco Hernandez. Adv. contact Dr. Juan F Madrid.

571.6 AUT ISSN 1609-5537

➤ **HOFBAUER CELLS.** Text in English. 2000. q. USD 75 domestic; USD 115 foreign; USD 35 newsstand/cover (effective 2001). adv. back issues avail.; reprints avail. **Document type:** *Journal, Academic/Scholarly.* **Description:** Publishes articles, case reports, reviews, and letters that aim to improve communications in understanding the multidisciplinary fields of modern Hofbauer cell research and placenta research.
Related titles: Online - full text ed.: ISSN 1609-5545.
Published by: V I C E R Publishing, PO Box 14, Vienna, A-1097, Austria. TEL 43-676-9568085, FAX 43-676-9568086, vicer@vicer.org, http://www.vicer.org. Ed., R&P Roland Hofbauer. adv.: B&W page USD 1,700, color page USD 2,200. Circ: 1,000 (paid and controlled).

➤ **HONYU DOBUTSU SHIKEN BUNKAKAI KAIHO/MAMMALIAN MUTAGENICITY STUDY GROUP COMMUNICATIONS.** see *BIOLOGY—Genetics*

➤ **IMMUNOHISTOCHEMISTRY.** see *BIOLOGY—Abstracting, Bibliographies, Statistics*

➤ **INSTITUTE FOR FERMENTATION, OSAKA. RESEARCH COMMUNICATIONS/HAKKO KENKYUJO HOKOKU.** see *BIOLOGY—Microbiology*

571.6 GBR ISSN 0957-0799
CODEN: IINCEH

INTERCELLULAR AND INTRACELLULAR COMMUNICATIONS. Text in English. 1986. irreg. price varies. **Document type:** *Monographic series.*
Indexed: BIOSIS Prev, CIN, ChemAb, ChemTitl.
—CASDDS, CISTI.
Published by: Cambridge University Press, The Edinburgh Bldg, Shaftesbury Rd, Cambridge, CB2 2RU, United Kingdom. TEL 44-1223-312393, FAX 44-1223-315052, information@cambridge.org, http://www.cup.cam.ac.uk/.

INTERNATIONAL CONGRESS OF HISTOCHEMISTRY AND CYTOCHEMISTRY. PROCEEDINGS. see *BIOLOGY—Biochemistry*

THE INTERNATIONAL JOURNAL OF BIOCHEMISTRY & CELL BIOLOGY. see *BIOLOGY—Biochemistry*

INTERNATIONAL ORGANIZATION OF PLANT BIOSYSTEMATISTS. NEWSLETTER. see *BIOLOGY—Botany*

571.6 USA ISSN 0074-7696
QH573 CODEN: IRCYAJ

➤ **INTERNATIONAL REVIEW OF CYTOLOGY.** Text in English. 1952. irreg., latest vol.225, 2003. USD 149.95 per vol. vol.235 (effective 2004). index; cum.index: 1952-1960, vols.1-9 in vol.10. reprint service avail. from ISI. **Document type:** *Academic/Scholarly.*
Related titles: Online - full text ed.: (from ScienceDirect).
Indexed: ASFA, AbHyg, AgBio, Agr, AnBrAb, BBCI, BIOBASE, BIOSIS Prev, BibAg, BiolAb, CIN, CPA, ChemAb, ChemTitl, ExcerpMed, FCA, GenetAb, HGA, IABS, ISR, IndMed, MEDLINE, MaizeAb, NSCI, PBA, RM&VM, RevApplEntom, SCI, SFA, TDB, TriticAb, WildRev, ZooRec.
—BLDSC (4547.050000), CASDDS, CISTI, GNLM, IE, Infotrieve, ingenta, KNAW, Linda Hall. **CCC.**
Published by: Academic Press (Subsidiary of: Elsevier Science & Technology), 525 B St, Ste 1900, San Diego, CA 92101-4495. TEL 619-231-6616, 800-894-3434, apsubs@acad.com, http://www.academicpress.com. Eds. G H Bourne, J F Danielli.

571.6 USA ISSN 0021-9525
QH301 CODEN: JCLBA3

➤ **THE JOURNAL OF CELL BIOLOGY.** Text in English. 1955. bi-w. USD 360 in US & Canada to individuals print ed.; USD 600 elsewhere to individuals print ed.; USD 1,350 in US & Canada to institutions print ed.; USD 1,590 elsewhere to institutions print ed. (effective 2005). adv. charts; illus.; abstr.; bibl. Index. 242 p./no. 2 cols./p.; back issues avail.; reprint service avail. from PQC,ISI. **Document type:** *Journal, Academic/Scholarly.* **Description:** Provides a forum for articles in all branches of contemporary cell biological research from the international community.
Formerly (until 1961): Journal of Biophysical and Biochemical Cytology (0095-9901)
Related titles: Microform ed.: (from PQC); Online - full text ed.: (from EBSCO Publishing, HighWire Press).
Indexed: ABIPC, ASCA, ASFA, AbHyg, AgBio, Agr, AnBrAb, B&AI, BBCI, BIOBASE, BIOSIS Prev, BibAg, BiolAb, CIN, CPA, CTA, ChemAb, ChemTitl, ChemoAb, CurCont, DBA, DSA, DentInd, ESPM, ExcerpMed, FCA, ForAb, GSI, GenetAb, HGA, HelmAb, HerbAb, HortAb, IABS, INIS AtomInd, ISR, IndMed, IndVet, Inpharma, MBA, MEDLINE, MaizeAb, NSA, NSCI, NemAb, NucAcAb, NutrAb, OrnHort, PBA, PGegResA, PN&I, PoultAb, ProtozoAb, RM&VM, RPP, Reac, RefZh, RevApplEntom, S&F, SCI, SeedAb, TDB, TriticAb, VetBull, WeedAb, ZooRec.
—BLDSC (4954.920000), CASDDS, CISTI, GNLM, IDS, IE, Infotrieve, ingenta, Linda Hall. **CCC.**
Published by: Rockefeller University Press, 1114 First Ave, New York, NY 10021-8325. TEL 212-327-8572, FAX 212-327-7944, rcellbio@rockefeller.edu, rupcd@rockefeller.edu, http://www.jcb.org, http://www.rupress.org, http://www.rockefeller.edu/rupress. Ed. Ira Mellman. Pub. Michael Rossner. R&P Laura Smith TEL 212-327-8025. Adv. contact Lorna Peterson TEL 212-327-8880. color page USD 2,165, B&W page USD 765; 7.75 x 10.25. Circ: 3,931.

571.6 GBR ISSN 0021-9533
QH573 CODEN: JNCSAI

➤ **JOURNAL OF CELL SCIENCE.** Text in English. 1852. s-m. USD 475 in North America to individuals; EUR 426 in Europe to individuals eurozone; GBP 280 to individuals in the UK & elsewhere; USD 2,295 in North America to institutions; EUR 2,072 in Europe to institutions eurozone; GBP 1,360 to institutions in the UK & elsewhere; USD 570 combined subscription in North America to individuals print & online; EUR 509 combined subscription in Europe to individuals eurozone; print & online; GBP 340 combined subscription to individuals in the UK & elsewhere; print & online; USD 2,650 combined subscription in North America to institutions print & online; EUR 2,392 combined subscription in Europe to institutions eurozone; print & online; GBP 1,570 combined subscription to institutions in the UK & elsewhere; print & online (effective 2005). adv. charts; illus. index, cum.index. reprints avail. **Document type:** *Journal, Academic/Scholarly.*
Description: Covers all aspects of cell biology. Of interest to cell biologists, molecular biologists, geneticists, and particularly those working in the cell cycle and cell signaling fields.
Formerly (until 1966): Quarterly Journal of Microscopical Science (0370-2952)
Related titles: Microfilm ed.: (from BHP); Online - full text ed.: ISSN 1477-9137. USD 112 in North America to individuals; EUR 101 in Europe to individuals eurozone; GBP 67 to individuals in the UK & elsewhere; USD 1,995 in North America to institutions; EUR 1,808 in Europe to institutions eurozone; GBP 1,190 to institutions in the UK & elsewhere (effective 2005) (from EBSCO Publishing, HighWire Press); Supplement(s): Journal of Cell Science. Supplement. ISSN 0269-3518. 1984.
Indexed: AIDS&CR, ASCA, ASFA, AbHyg, AgBio, Agr, AnBrAb, B&AI, B&BAb, BBCI, BIOBASE, BIOSIS Prev, BibAg, BiolAb, CBTA, CIN, CPA, CTA, ChemAb, ChemTitl, ChemoAb, CurCont, DSA, DentInd, ESPM, ExcerpMed, FCA, ForAb, GenetAb, HelmAb, HortAb, IABS, ISR, IndMed, IndVet, Inpharma, MBA, MEDLINE, MaizeAb, NSA, NSCI, NemAb, NucAcAb, NutrAb, OGFA, OrnHort, PBA, PE&ON, PGegResA, PGrRegA, PN&I, PotatoAb, PoultAb, ProtozoAb, RM&VM, RPP, Reac, RefZh, RevApplEntom, RiceAb, S&F, SCI, SFA, SoyAb, TDB, TriticAb, VetBull, WeedAb, ZooRec.
—BLDSC (4954.960000), CASDDS, CISTI, GNLM, IE, Infotrieve, ingenta, Linda Hall. **CCC.**
Published by: The Company of Biologists Ltd., Bidder Building, 140 Cowley Rd, Cambridge, CB4 4DL, United Kingdom. TEL 44-1223-426164, FAX 44-1223-423353, sales@thecob.demon.co.uk, http://jcs.biologists.org, http://www.biologists.com. Ed. Dr. Fiona M Watt. R&P Dr. Richard Sever. Adv. contact Miss Amanda Sheppardson. Circ: 1,550.

➤ **JOURNAL OF CELLULAR BIOCHEMISTRY.** see *BIOLOGY—Biochemistry*

➤ **JOURNAL OF CELLULAR BIOCHEMISTRY. SUPPLEMENT.** see *BIOLOGY—Biochemistry*

571.6 GBR ISSN 1359-7388
RB25

➤ **JOURNAL OF CELLULAR PATHOLOGY.** Text in English. 1996. q. GBP 48 to individuals; GBP 121 to institutions (effective 2003). back issues avail. **Document type:** *Academic/Scholarly.* **Description:** Contains articles on current and new techniques appropriate to cellular pathology in its broadest sense and relevant to hospitals and to industrial and research laboratories.
Indexed: ExcerpMed.
—BLDSC (4955.015000), ingenta. **CCC.**
Published by: Greenwich Medical Media, 137 Euston Rd, London, NW1 2AA, United Kingdom. TEL 44-20-7388-5444, FAX 44-20-7383-5445, gm@greenwich-medical.co.uk, http://www.greenwich-medical.co.uk. Ed. John Bancroft. R&P Joolz Longley. **Subscr. to:** Royal Society of Medicine Press Ltd., PO Box 9002, London W1A 0ZA, United Kingdom. TEL 44-20-7290-2927, 44-20-7290-2928, rsmjournals@rsm.ac.uk.

➤ **JOURNAL OF CELLULAR PHYSIOLOGY.** see *BIOLOGY—Physiology*

➤ **JOURNAL OF CLINICAL ONCOLOGY.** see *MEDICAL SCIENCES—Oncology*

571.6 IND ISSN 0970-9371

JOURNAL OF CYTOLOGY. Text in English. 1984. q. INR 75 domestic to individuals; USD 25 foreign to individuals; INR 150 domestic to institutions; USD 50 foreign to institutions (effective 2005). **Description:** Disseminate the scientific work carried out in the field of cytology.
—BLDSC (4965.980000).
Published by: Indian Academy of Cytologists, Department of Pathology, Armed Forces Medical College, Pune, Maharastra 411 040, India. TEL 91-20-26306014, jcytology@rediffmail.com, editor@cytoindia.com, http://www.cytologyindia.com. Ed. Col. S Satyanarayana.

THE JOURNAL OF CYTOLOGY AND GENETICS. see *BIOLOGY—Genetics*

571.5 USA ISSN 0022-1554
QP501 CODEN: JHCYAS
➤ **JOURNAL OF HISTOCHEMISTRY AND CYTOCHEMISTRY.** Text in English. 1953. m. USD 700 combined subscription print & online eds. (effective 2005). adv. bk.rev. bibl.; charts; illus. index. back issues avail. **Document type:** *Journal, Academic/Scholarly.* **Description:** Publishes papers that report the development of new histochemical and cytochemical methods, significant modifications of existing techniques, or original research in which histochemical and cytochemical methods make a significant contribution.
Related titles: Online - full text ed.: ISSN 1551-5044. 1953. USD 110 to individuals; USD 650 to institutions (effective 2004) (from EBSCO Publishing, HighWire Press).
Indexed: ASCA, AgBio, AnBrAb, BBCI, BIOBASE, BIOSIS Prev, BiolAb, CIN, ChemAb, ChemTitl, CurCont, DSA, DentInd, ExcerpMed, IABS, ISR, IndMed, IndVet, Inpharma, MEDLINE, MSB, NSCI, NutrAb, PN&I, PoultAb, Reac, RefZh, SAA, SCI, TDB, VetBull.
—BLDSC (5000.000000), CASDDS, CISTI, GNLM, IDS, IE, Infotrieve, ingenta, KNAW, Linda Hall. **CCC.**
Published by: Histochemical Society, 1914 N. 34th St., Ste 400, Seattle, WA 98103-9090. TEL 206-616-5894, FAX 206-616-5842, mail@histochemicalsociety.org, http://intl.jhc.org, http://www.histochemicalsociety.org. Eds. Dr. Denis G Baskin, Denis G. Baskin. Adv. contact Meg McGough. B&W page USD 475, color page USD 1,225. Circ: 2,200.

571.5 USA ISSN 0147-8885
RB43 CODEN: JOHIDN
➤ **JOURNAL OF HISTOTECHNOLOGY.** Text in English. 1977. q. USD 70 domestic to individuals; USD 100 foreign to individuals; USD 80 domestic to institutions; USD 110 foreign to institutions (effective 2004). adv. bk.rev. charts; illus.; tr.lit. index. 89 p./no. 2 cols./p.; back issues avail. **Document type:** *Journal, Academic/Scholarly.* **Description:** Publishes original articles, brief reports, notes on techniques, case studies dealing with anatomy, histochemistry, pathology, microscopy, and immunohistochemistry. Includes articles on applications and evaluations of commercially prepared kits, continuing education, and medical news.
Indexed: ASCA, AbHyg, BBCI, BIOSIS Prev, BiolAb, CIN, ChemAb, ChemTitl, CurCont, ExcerpMed, ISR, IndVet, Inpharma, PoultAb, ProtozoAb, RM&VM, Reac, RefZh, RevApplEntom, SCI.
—BLDSC (5002.400000), CASDDS, CISTI, GNLM, IDS, IE, Infotrieve, ingenta, KNAW. **CCC.**
Published by: National Society for Histotechnology, 4201 Northview Dr, Ste 502, Bowie, MD 20716-2604. TEL 301-262-6221, FAX 301-262-9188, histo@nsh.org, http://www.nsh.org/pubs/TofC.html. Ed. James Hendricks. R&P Roberta Mosedale. Circ: 5,000 (paid).

571.6 USA ISSN 0022-2631
QH601 CODEN: JMBBBO
➤ **JOURNAL OF MEMBRANE BIOLOGY**; an international journal for studies on the structure, function and genesis of biomembranes. Text in English. 1969. 18/yr. (in 6 vols., 3 nos./vol.). EUR 2,298 combined subscription to institutions print & online eds. (effective 2005). adv. back issues avail.; reprint service avail. from ISI. **Document type:** *Journal, Academic/Scholarly.* **Description:** Contains articles examining the nature, structure, function, and genesis of biological membranes, and the physics and chemistry of artificial membranes as relevant to biomembranes.
Related titles: Microform ed.: (from PQC); Online - full text ed.: ISSN 1432-1424 (from EBSCO Publishing, ProQuest Information & Learning, Springer LINK, Swets Information Services).
Indexed: ASCA, ASFA, AbHyg, Agr, AnBrAb, B&BAb, BBCI, BIOBASE, BIOSIS Prev, BioCN&I, BioEngAb, BiolAb, CIN, CPA, ChemAb, ChemTitl, CurCont, DSA, ExcerpMed, FCA, GenetAb, HortAb, IABS, ISR, IndMed, Inpharma, MEDLINE, NSCI, NemAb, NutrAb, PoultAb, ProtozoAb, RM&VM, RPP, Reac, RefZh, RevApplEntom, SCI, SIA, TDB, VetBull.
—BLDSC (5017.600000), CASDDS, CISTI, GNLM, IDS, IE, Infotrieve, ingenta, Linda Hall. **CCC.**
Published by: Springer-Verlag New York, Inc. (Subsidiary of: Springer Science+Business Media), 233 Spring St, New York, NY 10013. TEL 212-460-1500, FAX 212-473-6272, journals@springer-ny.com, http://link.springer.de/link/service/journals/00232/, http://www.springer-ny.com. Ed. W R Loewenstein. R&P Ian Gross. Adv. contact Brian Skepton. **Subscr. outside the Americas to:** Springer GmbH Auslieferungsgesellschaft, Haberstr 7, Heidelberg 69126, Germany. TEL 49-6221-345-0, FAX 49-6221-345-4229, subscriptions@springer.de; **Subscr. to:** Journal Fulfillment, PO Box 2485, Secaucus, NJ 07096-2485. TEL 800-777-4643, 201-348-4033, FAX 201-348-4505.

571.5 NLD ISSN 1567-2379
QH611 CODEN: HISJAE
➤ **JOURNAL OF MOLECULAR HISTOLOGY.** Text in English. 1969. 9/yr. EUR 1,628, USD 1,665, GBP 1,098 combined subscription to institutions print & online eds. (effective 2005). adv. bk.rev. charts; illus. index. reprint service avail. from PQC,PSC,ISI. **Document type:** *Journal, Academic/Scholarly.* **Description:** Publishes original research papers in those areas of biochemistry, biophysics and cell biology concerned with the chemical composition and activities of tissues, cells and cellular components.
Formerly (until 2004): The Histochemical Journal (0018-2214)
Related titles: Online - full text ed.: ISSN 1573-6865 (from EBSCO Publishing, Gale Group, IngentaConnect, Kluwer Online, O C L C Online Computer Library Center, Inc., Ovid Technologies, Inc., Springer LINK, Swets Information Services).
Indexed: AEA, ASCA, AbHyg, AgBio, AnBrAb, BBCI, BIOBASE, BIOSIS Prev, BibLing, BiolAb, CIN, ChemAb, ChemTitl, CurCont, DSA, DentInd, ExcerpMed, HelmAb, HortAb, IABS, ISR, IndMed, IndVet, Inpharma, MEDLINE, NSCI, NemAb, NutrAb, PHN&I, PN&I, PoultAb, ProtozoAb, RM&VM, RPP, Reac, SCI, TDB, VetBull.
—BLDSC (5020.713500), CASDDS, CISTI, GNLM, IDS, IE, Infotrieve, ingenta, Linda Hall. **CCC.**
Published by: (Royal Microscopical Society GBR), Springer-Verlag Dordrecht (Subsidiary of: Springer Science+Business Media), Van Godewijckstraat 30, Dordrecht, 3311 GX, Netherlands. TEL 31-78-6576050, FAX 31-78-6576474, http://springerlink.metapress.com/openurl.asp?genre=journal&issn=1567-2379, http://www.springeronline.com. Eds. Brian Key, Ismo Virtanen.

➤ **JOURNAL OF MUSCLE RESEARCH AND CELL MOTILITY.** see *MEDICAL SCIENCES—Orthopedics And Traumatology*

571.6 USA ISSN 0300-4864
QP351 CODEN: JNCYA2
➤ **JOURNAL OF NEUROCYTOLOGY**; a journal of cellular neurobiology. Text in English. 1972. 6/yr. EUR 948, USD 958, GBP 365 combined subscription to institutions print & online eds. (effective 2005). adv. bk.rev. bibl.; illus. index. reprint service avail. from PQC,PSC,ISI. **Document type:** *Journal, Academic/Scholarly.* **Description:** Publishes research papers (and occasionally reviews and letters) dealing the structure and function of nervous tissue. The scope of the Journal is wide: it embraces the organization and fine structure, and the associated molecular biology, biochemistry, cytochemistry, biophysics, physiology and pharmacology of neurons, receptor and glial cells, synapses and other intercellular specializations, in vertebrates and invertebrates under normal, experimental and pathological condititions.
Related titles: Online - full text ed.: ISSN 1573-7381 (from EBSCO Publishing, Gale Group, IngentaConnect, Kluwer Online, O C L C Online Computer Library Center, Inc., Ovid Technologies, Inc., ProQuest Information & Learning, Springer LINK, Swets Information Services).
Indexed: ASCA, ASFA, BBCI, BIOBASE, BIOSIS Prev, BibLing, BiolAb, ChemAb, ChemTitl, CurCont, DentInd, ExcerpMed, IABS, ISR, IndMed, Inpharma, MEDLINE, NSA, NSCI, Reac, SCI.
—BLDSC (5021.540000), CASDDS, CISTI, GNLM, IDS, IE, Infotrieve, ingenta, Linda Hall. **CCC.**
Published by: Springer-Verlag New York, Inc. (Subsidiary of: Springer Science+Business Media), 233 Spring St, New York, NY 10013. TEL 212-460-1500, FAX 212-460-1575, service@springer-ny.com, http://springerlink.metapress.com/openurl.asp?genre=journal&issn=0300-4864, http://www.springer-ny.com. Ed. A R Lieberman. **Subscr. to:** Journal Fulfillment, PO Box 2485, Secaucus, NJ 07096-2485. TEL 201-348-4033, FAX 201-348-4505, journals@springer-ny.com.

571.6 ITA ISSN 1122-9497
CODEN: JSCPEE
➤ **JOURNAL OF SUBMICROSCOPIC CYTOLOGY AND PATHOLOGY.** Text in English. 1969. q. **Document type:** *Journal, Academic/Scholarly.* **Description:** Presents papers dealing with applications of electronmicroscopy, biology, physiology and experimental and diagnostic pathology.
Formerly (until 1988): Journal of Submicroscopic Cytology (0022-4782)
Indexed: ASCA, BIOSIS Prev, BiolAb, CIN, ChemAb, ChemTitl, CurCont, ExcerpMed, ISR, IndMed, Inpharma, MEDLINE, Reac, SCI, SFA, ZooRec.
—BLDSC (5066.930500), CASDDS, CISTI, GNLM, IDS, IE, Infotrieve, ingenta, KNAW, Linda Hall.
Published by: N I E Nuova Immagine Editrice, Strada di Montechiaro 56, Siena, 53100, Italy. TEL 39-0577-42625, FAX 39-0577-44633. Circ: 500.

571.6 EGY ISSN 1110-7456
JOURNAL OF UNION OF ARAB BIOLOGISTS. CYTOGENETICS, ECOLOGY AND TOXONOMY. Text in English. 1999. a. **Document type:** *Journal, Academic/Scholarly.*
—BLDSC (4910.568500).
Published by: Union of Arab Biologists, Faculty of Science, Cairo University, Cairo University Campus, Cairo, Egypt. info@egsz.org, http://derp.sti.sci.eg/data/0347.htm, http://www.egsz.org. Ed. Dr. Yousef Wali.

KLINICHNA I TRANSFUZIONNA HEMATOLOGIIA/CLINICAL AND TRANSFUSION HAEMATOLOGY. see *MEDICAL SCIENCES—Hematology*

LEUCOCYTES. see *MEDICAL SCIENCES—Abstracting, Bibliographies, Statistics*

LIPPINCOTT-RAVEN PRESS SERIES ON MOLECULAR AND CELLULAR BIOLOGY. see *BIOLOGY*

LYSOSOMES AND ENDOCYTOSIS. see *BIOLOGY—Abstracting, Bibliographies, Statistics*

MACROPHAGES. see *MEDICAL SCIENCES—Abstracting, Bibliographies, Statistics*

571.64 JPN ISSN 0385-1036
CODEN: MAKUD9
➤ **MAKU/MEMBRANE.** Text in Japanese; Summaries in English. 1976. bi-m. JPY 2,884 (effective 2005). adv. bk.rev. 90 p./no.; back issues avail. **Document type:** *Journal, Academic/Scholarly.*
Indexed: BIOSIS Prev, BiolAb, ChemAb, ChemTitl, ExcerpMed.
—BLDSC (5548.025000), CASDDS, CISTI. **CCC.**
Published by: Nihon Maku Gakkai/Membrane Society of Japan, Hongo 5-26-5-702, Bunkyo-ku, Tokyo, 113-0033, Japan. membrane@muu.biglobe.ne.jp, http://wwwsoc.nacsis.ac.jp/membrane/index.html. Ed. Yoshinori Nozuwa. Circ: 850.

571.6 AUT ISSN 1609-5510
➤ **MAST CELLS.** Text in English. 2000. q. USD 75 domestic; USD 115 foreign; USD 35 newsstand/cover (effective 2001). adv. back issues avail. **Document type:** *Journal, Academic/Scholarly.* **Description:** Publishes articles, case reports, reviews, and letters that aim to improve communications in understanding the multidisciplinary field of modern mast cell research.
Related titles: Online - full text ed.: ISSN 1609-5529.
Published by: V I C E R Publishing, PO Box 14, Vienna, A-1097, Austria. TEL 43-676-9568085, FAX 43-676-9568086, vicer@vicer.org, http://www.vicer.org. Ed., R&P Roland Hofbauer. adv.: B&W page USD 1,700, color page USD 2,200. Circ: 1,000 (paid and controlled).

B

571.6 IRL ISSN 0925-4773
QH607 CODEN: MEDVE6
➤ **MECHANISMS OF DEVELOPMENT.** Text in English. 1972. 12/yr. EUR 206 in Europe to individuals; JMD 27,700 in Japan to individuals; USD 232 elsewhere to individuals; EUR 3,449 in Europe to institutions; JPY 457,700 in Japan to institutions; USD 3,857 elsewhere to institutions (effective 2006); with Gene Expression Patterns. charts; illus. back issues avail.; reprints avail. **Document type:** *Journal, Academic/Scholarly.* **Description:** Disseminates research in developmental biology, with emphasis on the characterization of molecular mechanisms underlying the development processes in plants and vertebrate and non-vertebrate animals.
Former titles (until 1990): Cell Differentiation and Development (0922-3371); (until 1988): Cell Differentiation (0045-6039)
Related titles: Microform ed.: (from PQC); Online - full text ed.: (from EBSCO Publishing, Gale Group, IngentaConnect, ScienceDirect, Swets Information Services).
Indexed: ASCA, AgBio, AnBrAb, BBCI, BIOBASE, BIOSIS Prev, BiolAb, CIN, ChemAb, ChemTitl, CurCont, DSA, ExcerpMed, IABS, ISR, IndMed, IndVet, Inpharma, MEDLINE, NSCI, NemAb, PBA, PHN&I, PN&I, PoultAb, Reac, RevApplEntom, RiceAb, S&F, SCI, VetBull, ZooRec.
—BLDSC (5424.571280), CASDDS, CISTI, GNLM, IDS, IE, Infotrieve, ingenta, Linda Hall. **CCC.**
Published by: Elsevier Ireland Ltd (Subsidiary of: Elsevier Science & Technology), Elsevier House, Brookvale Plaza, E. Park, Shannon, Co. Clare, Ireland. TEL 353-61-709600, FAX 353-61-709100, http://www.elsevier.com/locate/modo. **Subscr. to:** Elsevier BV, PO Box 211, Amsterdam 1000 AE, Netherlands. TEL 31-20-485-3757, FAX 31-20-485-3432, nlinfo-f@elsevier.nl, http://www.elsevier.nl.

571.64 NLD ISSN 0927-5193
CODEN: MSSREV
➤ **MEMBRANE SCIENCE AND TECHNOLOGY SERIES.** Text in English. 1991. irreg., latest vol.7, 2003. price varies. **Document type:** *Monographic series, Academic/Scholarly.* **Description:** Discusses advances in membrane science and technology.
Indexed: BIOSIS Prev, CCI, CIN, ChemAb, ChemTitl.
—BLDSC (5548.026350), CASDDS, CISTI. **CCC.**
Published by: Elsevier BV (Subsidiary of: Elsevier Science & Technology), Radarweg 29, Amsterdam, 1043 NX, Netherlands. TEL 31-20-4853911, FAX 31-20-4852457, nlinfo-f@elsevier.nl, http://www.elsevier.nl.

➤ **METABOLIC ENGINEERING.** see *BIOLOGY—Bioengineering*

571.6 USA ISSN 0091-679X
QH585 CODEN: MCBLAG
➤ **METHODS IN CELL BIOLOGY.** Text in English. 1964. irreg., latest vol.71, 2003. USD 139.95 per vol. (effective 2003). illus. reprint service avail. from ISI. **Document type:** *Academic/Scholarly.*
Formerly: Methods in Cell Physiology (0091-6579)
Indexed: ASCA, BBCI, BIOSIS Prev, BiolAb, CIN, ChemAb, ChemTitl, ExcerpMed, ISR, IndMed, MEDLINE, NutrAb, RPP, SCI, ZooRec.
—BLDSC (5747.250000), CASDDS, CISTI, GNLM, IE, Infotrieve, ingenta, KNAW. **CCC.**
Published by: Academic Press (Subsidiary of: Elsevier Science & Technology), 525 B St, Ste 1900, San Diego, CA 92101-4495. apsubs@acad.com, http://www.academicpress.com. Ed. Leslie Wilson.

571.6   GBR   ISSN 1475-2859
TP248.27.M53

➤ **MICROBIAL CELL FACTORIES.** Text in English. 2002. irreg. free (effective 2006). **Document type:** *Journal, Academic/Scholarly.* **Description:** Focuses on the development, use and investigation of microbial cells such as bacteria, yeast and filamentous fungi, as producers of recombinant proteins and natural products or as catalyzers of biological transformations of industrial interest.
Media: Online - full content (from EBSCO Publishing, National Library of Medicine).
Indexed: ExcerpMed.
—CCC.
Published by: BioMed Central Ltd. (Subsidiary of: Current Science Ltd), Middlesex House, 34-42 Cleveland St, London, W1T 4LB, United Kingdom. TEL 44-20-76319131, FAX 44-20-76319923, info@biomedcentral.com, http://www.microbialcellfactories.com, http://www.biomedcentral.com. Ed. Antonio Villaverde.

➤ **MICROBIAL PATHOGENESIS.** see *MEDICAL SCIENCES—Communicable Diseases*

➤ **MITOCHONDRIA.** see *BIOLOGY—Abstracting, Bibliographies, Statistics*

➤ **MITOCHONDRION.** see *BIOLOGY—Microbiology*

571.657   USA   ISSN 1542-5355
MITOMATTERS. Text in English. 2002 (Winter). q.
Related titles: Online - full text ed.: ISSN 1542-5436.
Published by: Mitochondria Research Society, P. O. Box 306, Riderwood, MD 21139. TEL 410-502-7303, FAX 410-502-7244, http://www.mitoresearch.org.

571.6   GBR   ISSN 1470-0573
MOLECULAR AND CELL BIOLOGY OF HUMAN DISEASES. Text in English. 1992. a., latest vol.5, 1995. **Document type:** *Monographic series, Academic/Scholarly.*
Indexed: CIN, ChemAb, ChemTitl, IndMed, RevApplEntom.
—BLDSC (5900.755000).
Published by: Chapman & Hall Ltd. (Subsidiary of: International Thomson Publishing Group), Journals Department, 2-6 Boundary Row, London, SE1 8HN, United Kingdom. TEL 44-20-7865-0066, FAX 44-20-7522-9623.

MOLECULAR AND CELLULAR BIOCHEMISTRY; an international journal for chemical biology in health and disease. see *BIOLOGY—Biochemistry*

MOLECULAR AND CELLULAR BIOLOGY. see *BIOLOGY—Biochemistry*

MOLECULAR AND CELLULAR PROTEOMICS. see *BIOLOGY—Biochemistry*

MOLECULAR BIOLOGY. see *BIOLOGY—Biochemistry*

571.6   USA   ISSN 1059-1524
QH604   CODEN: MBCEEV
➤ **MOLECULAR BIOLOGY OF THE CELL.** Text in English. 1990. m. USD 125 membership (effective 2005). adv. abstr.; bibl.; charts; illus. index. back issues avail. **Document type:** *Journal, Academic/Scholarly.* **Description:** Interdisciplinary approach to molecular aspects of cell biology; publishes complete, scholarly papers.
Formerly: Cell Regulation (1044-2030)
Related titles: Online - full text ed.: (from EBSCO Publishing, HighWire Press, National Library of Medicine).
Indexed: ASCA, AbHyg, AgBio, AnBrAb, BBCI, BIOBASE, BIOSIS Prev, BiolAb, CIN, CPA, ChemAb, ChemTitl, CurCont, DSA, ExcerpMed, FCA, HortAb, IABS, ISR, IndMed, IndVet, Inpharma, MEDLINE, NemAb, PBA, PGegResA, PGrRegA, PoultAb, ProtozoAb, RA&MP, RM&VM, RPP, Reac, RevApplEntom, S&F, SCI, SIA, SSCI, TDB, TriticAb, VetBull, WeedAb, ZooRec.
—BLDSC (5900.788000), CASDDS, CISTI, GNLM, IDS, IE, Infotrieve, ingenta, Linda Hall.
Published by: American Society for Cell Biology, 9650 Rockville Pike, Bethesda, MD 20814-3992. TEL 301-530-7153, FAX 301-571-7139, mbc@ascb.org, http://www.molbiolcell.org/. Ed. David Botstein. R&P H Joseph. Adv. contact R Sommer. Circ: 10,000 (paid).

➤ **MOLECULAR BIOLOGY REPORTS**; an international journal on molecular and cellular biology. see *BIOLOGY—Biochemistry*

571.6   USA   ISSN 1097-2765
QH506   CODEN: MOCEFL
➤ **MOLECULAR CELL.** Text in English. 1997. 24/yr. EUR 296 in Europe to individuals; JPY 32,400 in Japan to individuals; USD 172 in Canada to individuals; USD 172 in United States to individuals; USD 259 to individuals except Europe and Japan; EUR 1,359 in Europe to institutions; JPY 141,800 in Japan to institutions; USD 1,049 in United States to institutions; USD 1,049 in Canada to institutions; USD 1,181 to institutions except Europe and Japan (effective 2006). adv. back issues avail. **Document type:** *Journal, Academic/Scholarly.* **Description:** Extends coverage from structure to human diseases, concentrating on molecular analyses.
Related titles: Online - full text ed.: ISSN 1097-4164. USD 159 to individuals (effective 2004) (from EBSCO Publishing, Gale Group, IngentaConnect, ScienceDirect).
Indexed: ABIPC, AIDS Ab, AIDS&CR, ASFA, AbHyg, AgBio, AnBrAb, B&BAb, BBCI, BIOSIS Prev, BiolAb, CPA, ChemAb, CurCont, EngInd, ExcerpMed, GenetAb, HGA, INIS AtomInd, ISR, ImmunAb, IndMed, IndVet, M&PBA, MBA, MEDLINE, MaizeAb, NSA, NemAb, NucAcAb, OGFA, PBA, PGegResA, PGrRegA, ProtozoAb, RPP, RevApplEntom, SCI, TDB, VetBull, VirolAbstr, WeedAb, ZooRec.
—BLDSC (5900.802750), CISTI, IE, Infotrieve, ingenta, Linda Hall. **CCC.**
Published by: Cell Press (Subsidiary of: Elsevier Science & Technology), 1100 Massachusetts Ave, Cambridge, MA 02138. TEL 617-397-2826, FAX 617-661-7061, molecule@cell.org, editor@cell.com, http://www.elsevier.com/locate/molcel, http://www.cellpress.com/. Ed. Dorit Zuk. Pub. Lynne Herndon. Adv. contact Sande Giaccone TEL 212-633-3914. B&W page USD 1,335, color page USD 2,695. Circ: 2,301 (paid).
Subscr. to: 6277 Sea Harbor Dr, Orlando, FL 32887. TEL 407-345-3000, 866-314-2355, FAX 407-363-9661, subs@cell.com.

571.6   CAN   ISSN 1535-3508
RC78.7.D53   CODEN: MIOMBP
➤ **MOLECULAR IMAGING.** Text in English. 2002. q. CND 156.25 domestic to individuals; USD 125 elsewhere to individuals; CND 397.50 domestic to institutions; USD 318 elsewhere to institutions; CND 187 combined subscription domestic to individuals print & online eds.; USD 150 combined subscription elsewhere to individuals print & online eds.; CND 477 combined subscription domestic to institutions print & online eds.; USD 381 combined subscription elsewhere to institutions print & online eds. (effective 2006). adv. back issues avail. **Document type:** *Journal, Academic/Scholarly.* **Description:** Contains studies which combine advances in non-invasive molecular imaging modalities with molecular and cellular biology.
Related titles: Online - full text ed.: ISSN 1536-0121. CND 171.85 domestic to individuals; USD 137 elsewhere to individuals; CND 437.25 domestic to institutions; USD 349 elsewhere to institutions (effective 2006) (from EBSCO Publishing, Gale Group, IngentaConnect, O C L C Online Computer Library Center, Inc., Swets Information Services).
Indexed: Inspec, RefZh.
—BLDSC (5900.817660), CISTI, IE. **CCC.**
Published by: (Society for Molecular Imaging USA), B.C. Decker Inc., 20 Hughson St S, LCD 1, PO Box 620, Hamilton, ON L8N 3K7, Canada. TEL 905-522-7017, 800-568-7281, FAX 905-522-7839, 888-311-4987, manette@molecularimaging.org, info@bcdecker.com, http://www.bcdecker.com. adv.: page USD 650; trim 8.5 x 11.

➤ **MOLECULAR MEMBRANE BIOLOGY.** see *BIOLOGY—Biochemistry*

➤ **MOLECULAR VISION.** see *BIOLOGY—Biochemistry*

➤ **MONALDI ARCHIVES FOR CHEST DISEASE.** see *MEDICAL SCIENCES—Respiratory Diseases*

➤ **MONOGRAPHS IN CLINICAL CYTOLOGY.** see *MEDICAL SCIENCES*

571.6   NLD   ISSN 1010-8793
    CODEN: NASBE4
➤ **N A T O ADVANCED SCIENCE INSTITUTES SERIES H: CELL BIOLOGY.** (North Atlantic Treaty Organization) Text in Dutch. 1986. irreg., latest vol.106, 1998. price varies. reprint service avail. from ISI. **Document type:** *Monographic series, Academic/Scholarly.*
Formerly: N A T O Advanced Study Institute. Series H: Cell Biology
Related titles: Online - full text ed.
Indexed: Agr, CIN, ChemAb, ChemTitl, ZooRec.
—BLDSC (6033.648830), CASDDS, CISTI, ingenta, KNAW. **CCC.**
Published by: (North Atlantic Treaty Organization, Scientific Affairs Division BEL), Springer-Verlag Dordrecht (Subsidiary of: Springer Science+Business Media), Van Godewijckstraat 30, Dordrecht, 3311 GX, Netherlands. TEL 31-78-6576050, FAX 31-78-6576474, http://www.springeronline.com.

571.6   GBR   ISSN 1465-7392
QH573   CODEN: NCBIFN
➤ **NATURE CELL BIOLOGY.** Text in English. 1999 (May). m. EUR 1,240 in Europe to institutions; USD 1,440 in the Americas to institutions; GBP 800 to institutions in the UK & elsewhere; EUR 271 combined subscription in Europe to individuals print & online eds.; USD 199 combined subscription in the Americas to individuals print & online eds.; GBP 175 combined subscription to individuals in the UK & elsewhere; print & online eds. (effective 2006). adv. illus. back issues avail.; reprints avail. **Document type:** *Journal, Academic/Scholarly.* **Description:** Publishes applied and theoretical research in cell biology.
Related titles: Online - full text ed.: (from EBSCO Publishing, Swets Information Services).
Indexed: AbHyg, AgBio, AnBrAb, BBCI, BIOBASE, BIOSIS Prev, BiolAb, CPA, ChemAb, CurCont, ExcerpMed, FCA, ISR, IndMed, IndVet, MBA, MEDLINE, MaizeAb, NemAb, NutrAb, PBA, PGegResA, ProtozoAb, RPP, RevApplEntom, SCI, SeedAb, SoyAb, VetBull, WeedAb, ZooRec.
—BLDSC (6046.280100), CISTI, IE, Infotrieve, ingenta, Linda Hall. **CCC.**
Published by: Nature Publishing Group (Subsidiary of: Macmillan Publishers Ltd.), The MacMillan Building, 4 Crinan St, London, N1 9XW, United Kingdom. TEL 44-20-78334000, FAX 44-20-78433601, subscriptions@nature.com, http://www.nature.com/naturecellbiology. Ed. Bernd Pulverer.
Subscr. in Asia to: Nature Japan KK, MG Ichigaya Bldg. 5F, 19-1 Haraikatamachi, Shinjuku-ku, Tokyo 162-0841, Japan. TEL 81-3-3267-8751, FAX 81-3 3267-8746, subscriptions@naturejpn.com; **Subscr. in the US to:** Nature Publishing Group, PO Box 5161, Brentwood, TN 37024-5161. TEL 615-850-5315, 800-524-0384, FAX 615-377-0525, subscriptions@natureny.com; **Subscr. to:** Brunel Rd, Houndmills, Basingstoke, Hamps RG21 6XS, United Kingdom. TEL 44-1256-329242, FAX 44-1256-812358, subscriptions@nature.com.

➤ **NERVE CELL BIOLOGY.** see *BIOLOGY—Abstracting, Bibliographies, Statistics*

➤ **NIHON SAIBO SEIBUTSU GAKKAI TAIKAI KOEN YOSHISHU/JAPAN SOCIETY FOR CELL BIOLOGY. ABSTRACTS OF THE MEETING.** see *BIOLOGY—Abstracting, Bibliographies, Statistics*

571.6   JPN
NIHON SOSHIKI BAIYO GAKKAI KAIIN TSUSHIN/JAPANESE TISSUE CULTURE ASSOCIATION. NEWS. Text in Japanese. 4/yr. **Document type:** *Academic/Scholarly.*
Published by: Nihon Soshiki Baiyo Gakkai/Japanese Tissue Culture Association, Hiroshima University School of Medicine, 1-2-3 Kasumi, Minami-ku, Hiroshima, 990-0823, Japan. jtca-office@umin.ac.jp, http://jtca.umin.jp/. Ed. Hiroyoshi Hoshi.

571.6   ITA
NOTIZIARIO DI CITOLOGIA. Text in Italian. 1980. 3/yr. **Document type:** *Bulletin, Academic/Scholarly.*
Published by: Pacini Editore SpA, Via A. Gherardesca 1, Ospedaletto, PI 56121, Italy. TEL 39-050-313011, FAX 39-050-3130300, pacini.editore@pacinieditore.it, http://www.pacinionline.it. Ed. G Giacomini.

571.6   IND   ISSN 0029-568X
QH573   CODEN: NULSAK
➤ **NUCLEUS**; international journal of cytology and allied topics. Text in English. 1958. 3/yr. INR 600, USD 60 (effective 2003). adv. bk.rev. charts; illus. index. Supplement avail.; back issues avail. **Document type:** *Academic/Scholarly.*
Indexed: AnBrAb, BiolAb, CIN, ChemAb, ChemTitl, ExcerpMed, HortAb, MBA, OrnHort, PBA, RevApplEntom, ZooRec.
—BLDSC (6184.202000), CASDDS, CISTI, IE, Infotrieve, ingenta, Linda Hall.
Published by: University of Calcutta, Department of Botany, Centre for Advanced Study in Cell and Chromosome Research, 35 Ballygunj Circular Rd., Kolkata, West Bengal 700 019, India. TEL 91-33-440-5802, FAX 91-33-478-7603. Ed., Adv. contact Archana Sharma. Pub. Arun Kumar Sharma. Circ: 500.

➤ **PATHOBIOLOGY**; journal of immunopathology, molecular, and cellular biology. see *MEDICAL SCIENCES—Allergology And Immunology*

➤ **PERSPECTIVES IN CYTOLOGY & GENETICS**; proceedings of the all India Congress of cytology and genetics. see *BIOLOGY—Genetics*

571.6   DNK   ISSN 0893-5785
QL767   CODEN: PCREEA
➤ **PIGMENT CELL RESEARCH.** Text in English. 1987. bi-m. USD 626 combined subscription in the Americas to institutions & Caribbean (print & online eds.); GBP 373 combined subscription elsewhere to institutions print & online eds. (effective 2006). adv. charts; illus. reprint service avail. from PSC. **Document type:** *Journal, Academic/Scholarly.*

B

Related titles: Online - full text ed.: ISSN 1600-0749. USD 595 in the Americas to institutions & Caribbean; GBP 354 elsewhere to institutions (effective 2006) (from Blackwell Synergy, EBSCO Publishing, Gale Group, IngentaConnect, O C L C Online Computer Library Center, Inc., Ovid Technologies, Inc., Swets Information Services); Supplement(s): Pigment Cell Research. Supplement. ISSN 0906-9305. 1988.
Indexed: ASCA, AgBio, AnBrAb, BBCI, BIOBASE, BIOSIS Prev, BiolAb, ChemAb, ChemTitl, CurCont, ExcerpMed, HortAb, ISR, IndMed, Inpharma, MEDLINE, MS&D, PE&ON, PoultAb, Reac, SCI, TDB, VetBull, ZooRec.
—BLDSC (6500.148000), CASDDS, CISTI, GNLM, IDS, IE, Infotrieve, ingenta, KNAW. **CCC.**
Published by: (International Federation of Pigment Cell Societies), Blackwell Munksgaard (Subsidiary of: Blackwell Publishing Ltd.), Rosenoerns Alle 1, PO Box 227, Copenhagen V, 1502, Denmark. TEL 45-77-333333, FAX 45-77-333377, info@mks.blackwellpublishing.com, http://www.blackwellpublishing.com/journals/PCR, http://www.munksgaard.dk/. Ed. Vincent Hearing. Adv. contact Louise McCrae. Circ: 600.

571.6 GBR ISSN 0032-0781
QK710 CODEN: PCPHA5
➤ **PLANT AND CELL PHYSIOLOGY.** Text in English. 1960. m. GBP 406, USD 690, EUR 609 to institutions; GBP 256, USD 435, EUR 384 in developing nations to institutions; GBP 427, USD 726, EUR 641 combined subscription to institutions print & online eds. (effective 2006). adv. index. 144 p./no.; back issues avail.; reprint service avail. from PSC. **Document type:** *Journal, Academic/Scholarly.* **Description:** Covers broad areas of plant sciences, including physiology, biochemistry, biophysics, chemistry, molecular and cell biology, as well as gene engineering of plants and microorganisms.
Related titles: Microform ed.: (from PMC); Online - full text ed.: ISSN 1471-9053. GBP 384, USD 653, EUR 576 to institutions (effective 2006) (from EBSCO Publishing, Gale Group, HighWire Press, IngentaConnect, O C L C Online Computer Library Center, Inc., Ovid Technologies, Inc., ProQuest Information & Learning, Swets Information Services).
Indexed: ABIPC, AEA, AEBA, ASCA, ASFA, AgBio, Agr, AgrForAb, B&AI, BBCI, BIOBASE, BIOSIS Prev, BibAg, BiolAb, CPA, CTA, ChemAb, ChemTitl, CurCont, DBA, DSA, ESPM, FCA, FPA, FS&TA, FaBeAb, ForAb, GenetAb, HGA, HerbAb, HortAb, I&DA, IABS, INIS AtomInd, ISR, IndMed, MBA, MEDLINE, MaizeAb, OrnHort, PBA, PGegResA, PGrRegA, PHN&I, PlantSci, PotatoAb, ProtozoAb, RA&MP, RPP, RefZh, RevApplEntom, RiceAb, S&F, SCI, SIA, SeedAb, SoyAb, TriticAb, VITIS, WeedAb.
—BLDSC (6512.250000), CASDDS, CISTI, IE, Infotrieve, ingenta, Linda Hall. **CCC.**
Published by: (Japanese Society of Plant Physiologists/Nihon Shokubutsu Seiri Gakkai JPN), Oxford University Press, Great Clarendon St, Oxford, OX2 6DP, United Kingdom. TEL 44-1865-556767, FAX 44-1865-556646, jspp@nacos.com, jnl.orders@oup.co.uk, enquiry@oup.co.uk, http://pcp.oxfordjournals.org/, http://www.oxfordjournals.org/. Ed. Hiroo Fukuda. Pub. Janet Boulin. R&P Fiona Bennett. Circ: 3,400.

571.5 NLD ISSN 0167-6857
TP248.27.P55 CODEN: PTCEDJ
➤ **PLANT CELL, TISSUE AND ORGAN CULTURE**; an international journal on in vitro culture of higher plants. Text in English. 1981. m. EUR 2,098, USD 2,135, GBP 1,398 combined subscription to institutions print & online eds. (effective 2005). adv. bk.rev. back issues avail.; reprint service avail. from PSC. **Document type:** *Journal, Academic/Scholarly.* **Description:** Publishes original results of fundamental research on plant cells, tissues and organs, including plant genetics and biotechnology.
Related titles: Microform ed.: (from PQC); Online - full text ed.: ISSN 1573-5044 (from EBSCO Publishing, Gale Group, IngentaConnect, Kluwer Online, O C L C Online Computer Library Center, Inc., Ovid Technologies, Inc., Springer LINK, Swets Information Services).
Indexed: ABIPC, AEA, AEBA, ASCA, AgBio, Agr, AgrForAb, B&BAb, BCI, BIOBASE, BIOSIS Prev, BibAg, BibLing, BioCN&I, BioEngAb, BiolAb, CBTA, CEABA, CIN, CPA, CTFA, ChemAb, ChemTitl, CurCont, DBA, DSA, EngInd, EnvAb, FCA, FPA, FS&TA, ForAb, HerbAb, HortAb, IABS, ISR, MaizeAb, NemAb, OrnHort, PBA, PGegResA, PGrRegA, PHN&I, PlantSci, PotatoAb, RA&MP, RPP, RefZh, RevApplEntom, RiceAb, S&F, SCI, SIA, SeedAb, SoyAb, TDB, Telegen, TriticAb, VITIS, WeedAb.
—BLDSC (6514.300000), CASDDS, CISTI, Ei, IDS, IE, Infotrieve, ingenta, Linda Hall. **CCC.**
Published by: Springer-Verlag Dordrecht (Subsidiary of: Springer Science+Business Media), Van Godewijckstraat 30, Dordrecht, 3311 GX, Netherlands. TEL 31-78-6576050, FAX 31-78-6576474, http://springerlink.metapress.com/openurl.asp?genre=journal&issn=0167-6857, http://www.springeronline.com.

571.6 POL ISSN 0324-833X
QH573 CODEN: PBKODV
➤ **POSTEPY BIOLOGII KOMORKI/ADVANCES IN CELL BIOLOGY.** Text in Polish; Summaries in English. 1974. q. PLZ 150 domestic; EUR 21 in Europe; USD 25 elsewhere (effective 2005). bk.rev. bibl.; illus. 180 p./no. 1 cols./p.; **Document type:** *Journal, Academic/Scholarly.*
Related titles: Online - full content ed.
Indexed: AgrAg, AgrLib, BIOSIS Prev, BiolAb, CIN, ChemAb, ChemTitl, INIS AtomInd, RefZh.
—CASDDS.
Published by: (Polskie Towarzystwo Anatomiczne/Polish Anatomical Society), Fundacja Biologii Komorki i Biologii Molekularnej/Foundation for Cell Biology and Molecular Biology, Centrum Medyczne Ksztalcenia Podyplomowego, Ul Marymoncka 99, Warsaw, 01813, Poland. TEL 48-22-8340344, FAX 48-22-8340470, jkawiak@cmkp.edu.pl, http://www.pbkom.pl/pbkom/. Ed., R&P Jerzy Kawiak. Circ: 640. **Co-sponsor:** Polskie Towarzystwo Biologii Komorki/Polish Society for Cell Biology.

571.6 USA ISSN 1087-2957
QH605 CODEN: PCCRF9
PROGRESS IN CELL CYCLE RESEARCH. Text in English. 1995. irreg., latest vol.5, 2003. price varies.
Indexed: CIN, ChemAb, ChemTitl, IndMed, MEDLINE.
—BLDSC (6866.750000), CASDDS, CISTI, IE, Infotrieve, ingenta. **CCC.**
Published by: Springer-Verlag New York, Inc. (Subsidiary of: Springer Science+Business Media), 233 Spring St, New York, NY 10013. TEL 212-460-1500, FAX 212-460-1575, service@springer-ny.com, http://www.springer-ny.com.

571.6 NLD ISSN 0924-8315
CODEN: PRCREB
➤ **PROGRESS IN CELL RESEARCH.** Text in English. 1990. irreg., latest vol.4, 1994. price varies. **Document type:** *Monographic series, Academic/Scholarly.* **Description:** Covers the field of cell biology, bringing together quality research work in this rapidly changing area.
Indexed: ChemAb, ChemTitl.
—BLDSC (6866.760000), CASDDS, CISTI, ingenta. **CCC.**
Published by: Elsevier BV (Subsidiary of: Elsevier Science & Technology), Radarweg 29, Amsterdam, 1043 NX, Netherlands. TEL 31-20-4853911, FAX 31-20-4852457, nlinfo-f@elsevier.nl, http://www.elsevier.nl.

➤ **PROGRESS IN HISTOCHEMISTRY AND CYTOCHEMISTRY.** see *BIOLOGY—Biochemistry*

571.6 USA ISSN 0079-6484
QH506 CODEN: PMSBA4
➤ **PROGRESS IN MOLECULAR AND SUBCELLULAR BIOLOGY.** Text in English. 1969. irreg., latest vol.33, 2003. price varies. reprint service avail. from ISI. **Document type:** *Monographic series, Academic/Scholarly.* **Description:** Provides comprehensive information on all aspects of contemporary molecular biology, including applications in biotechnology and molecular medicine.
Indexed: Agr, BIOSIS Prev, BiolAb, ChemAb, ChemTitl, IndMed, MEDLINE, ZooRec.
—CASDDS, CISTI, GNLM, Infotrieve, KNAW, Linda Hall. **CCC.**
Published by: Springer-Verlag New York, Inc. (Subsidiary of: Springer Science+Business Media), 233 Spring St, New York, NY 10013. TEL 212-460-1500, 800-777-4643, FAX 212-473-6272, http://www.springer-ny.com. Ed. F E Hahn.

571.6 AUT ISSN 0033-183X
QH573 CODEN: PROTA5
➤ **PROTOPLASMA**; an international journal of cell biology. Text in English. 1926. 16/yr. EUR 1,462 combined subscription to institutions print & online eds. (effective 2005). adv. charts; illus.; abstr. index. back issues avail.; reprint service avail. from ISI. **Document type:** *Journal, Academic/Scholarly.* **Description:** Aims to specialize in the area between structural and molecular analysis of biological systems from gene expression to the subcellular and supracellular levels.
Related titles: Microform ed.: (from PQC); Online - full text ed.: ISSN 1615-6102 (from EBSCO Publishing, Springer LINK, Swets Information Services).
Indexed: ABIPC, ASCA, AgBio, Agr, AgrForAb, AnBrAb, BBCI, BIOBASE, BIOSIS Prev, BibAg, BiolAb, CIN, CPA, ChemAb, ChemTitl, CurCont, DBA, ExcerpMed, FCA, FPA, ForAb, HerbAb, HortAb, IABS, INIS AtomInd, ISR, IndMed, IndVet, Inpharma, MEDLINE, MaizeAb, NemAb, OrnHort, PBA, PGegResA, PGrRegA, PHN&I, PlantSci, PotatoAb, ProtozoAb, RA&MP, RM&VM, RPP, Reac, RevApplEntom, RiceAb, S&F, SCI, SIA, SeedAb, SoyAb, TriticAb, VITIS, VetBull, WeedAb, ZooRec.
—BLDSC (6937.000000), CASDDS, CISTI, GNLM, IDS, IE, Infotrieve, ingenta, Linda Hall. **CCC.**
Published by: Springer-Verlag Wien (Subsidiary of: Springer Science+Business Media) journals@springer.at, http://www.springer.at/protoplasma. Ed. P Nick. R&P Angela Foessl TEL 43-1-3302415517. Adv. contact Michael Katzenberger TEL 43-1-3302415220. B&W page EUR 1,000; 170 x 240. **Subscr. in the Americas to:** Springer-Verlag New York, Inc., Journal Fulfillment, PO Box 2485, Secaucus, NJ 07096-2485. TEL 800-777-4643, 201-348-4033, FAX 201-348-4505, journals@springer-ny.com, http://www.springer-ny.com; **Subscr. to:** Springer GmbH Auslieferungsgesellschaft. subscriptions@springer.de.

➤ **RECENT RESEARCH DEVELOPMENTS IN MOLECULAR & CELLULAR BIOLOGY.** see *BIOLOGY—Biochemistry*

➤ **REFERATIVNYI ZHURNAL. TSITOLOGIYA.** see *BIOLOGY—Abstracting, Bibliographies, Statistics*

➤ **RESEARCH COMMUNICATIONS IN BIOCHEMISTRY AND CELL & MOLECULAR BIOLOGY.** see *BIOLOGY—Biochemistry*

571.6 USA ISSN 0080-1844
QH607 CODEN: RCLDAT
RESULTS AND PROBLEMS IN CELL DIFFERENTIATION. Text in English. 1968. irreg., latest vol.40, 2002. price varies. reprint service avail. from ISI. **Document type:** *Monographic series, Academic/Scholarly.* **Description:** Presents and explores selected questions of cell and developmental biology. Provides concise information on the most recent advances.
Indexed: BIOSIS Prev, BiolAb, CIN, ChemAb, ChemTitl, IndMed, MEDLINE, ZooRec.
—BLDSC (7780.220000), CASDDS, CISTI, GNLM, IE, Infotrieve, ingenta, KNAW. **CCC.**
Published by: Springer-Verlag New York, Inc. (Subsidiary of: Springer Science+Business Media), 233 Spring St, New York, NY 10013. TEL 212-460-1500, 800-777-4643, FAX 212-473-6272, http://www.springer-ny.com.

571.6 FRA ISSN 0181-7582
CODEN: RCBBDA
REVUE DE CYTOLOGIE ET DE BIOLOGIE VEGETALES - LE BOTANISTE. Text in French. 1934. a. (in 4 parts). bk.rev. charts; illus. index. **Document type:** *Academic/Scholarly.*
Formed by the merger of: Botaniste (0045-2637); Revue de Cytologie et de Biologie Vegetales (0035-1067)
Related titles: Microform ed.: (from PMC).
Indexed: BiolAb, ChemAb, FCA, HerbAb, PBA, S&MA.
—CASDDS, Linda Hall.
Published by: Laboratoire de Biologie Vegetale Appliquee, 61 rue de Buffon, Paris, 75005, France. TEL 33-1-40793561, FAX 33-1-40793562, coudere@mnhn.fr. Eds. Jean Claude Laberche, Robert Gorenflot. Pub. Henri Couderc. Circ: 11,350.

B

RIBOSOMES AND TRANSLATION. see *BIOLOGY—Abstracting, Bibliographies, Statistics*

SAIBO KOGAKU/CELL TECHNOLOGY. see *BIOLOGY—Biotechnology*

SAIBO KOGAKU, BESSATSU/CELL TECHNOLOGY, SPECIAL ISSUE. see *BIOLOGY—Biotechnology*

571.6 JPN
SAIBO SEIBUTSU/CELL BIOLOGY. Text in Japanese. 1990. bi-m. **Document type:** *Newsletter.*
Published by: Nihon Saibo Seibutsu Gakkai/Japan Society for Cell Biology, Ogawa Higashi Iru, Shimodachuri Dori, Kamigyi-ku, Kyoto-shi, 602, Japan. FAX 81-75-415-3662. Ed. Akihiko Nakano.

571.6 GBR ISSN 1084-9521
QH573 CODEN: SCDBFX
➤ **SEMINARS IN CELL AND DEVELOPMENTAL BIOLOGY.** Text in English. 1996. 6/yr. EUR 188 in Europe to individuals; JPY 20,200 in Japan to individuals; USD 179 elsewhere to individuals; EUR 625 in Europe to institutions; JPY 67,500 in Japan to institutions; USD 556 elsewhere to institutions (effective 2006). adv. reprints avail. **Document type:** *Academic/Scholarly.* **Description:** Covers the latest advances in molecular cell biology and developmental biology.
Formed by the merger of (1990-1996): Seminars in Cell Biology (1043-4682); (1990-1996): Seminars in Developmental Biology (1044-5781)
Related titles: Online - full text ed.: ISSN 1096-3634. USD 587 (effective 2002) (from EBSCO Publishing, Gale Group, IngentaConnect, O C L C Online Computer Library Center, Inc., ScienceDirect, Swets Information Services).
Indexed: ASCA, ASFA, AgBio, AnBrAb, B&BAb, BIOBASE, BIOSIS Prev, CIN, CPA, CTA, ChemAb, ChemTitl, ChemoAb, CurCont, ExcerpMed, FCA, GenetAb, HGA, ISR, IndMed, Inpharma, MEDLINE, NSA, NemAb, NucAcAb, PBA, PGegResA, PN&I, Reac, SCI, VetBull, WeedAb, ZooRec.
—BLDSC (8239.448346), CASDDS, CISTI, GNLM, IDS, IE, Infotrieve, ingenta, KNAW, Linda Hall. **CCC.**
Published by: Academic Press (Subsidiary of: Elsevier Science & Technology), Harcourt Pl, 32 Jamestown Rd, London, NW1 7BY, United Kingdom. TEL 44-20-72674466, FAX 44-20-74822293, apsubs@acad.com, http://www.elsevier.com/locate/semcdb. Ed. John Davey. R&P Catherine John. Adv. contact Nik Screen. **Subscr. to:** Journal Subscription Fulfilment Department, Foots Cray High St, Sidcup, Kent DA14 5HP, United Kingdom.

➤ **SEMINARS IN HEMATOLOGY.** see *MEDICAL SCIENCES—Hematology*

➤ **SEMINARS IN RESPIRATORY INFECTIONS.** see *MEDICAL SCIENCES—Respiratory Diseases*

571.6 SGP
SERIES ON CELL AND MOLECULAR BIOLOGY. Text in English. 1999. irreg., latest vol.2. price varies. **Document type:** *Monographic series, Academic/Scholarly.*
Published by: World Scientific Publishing Co. Pte. Ltd., 5 Toh Tuck Link, Singapore, 596224, Singapore. TEL 65-466-5775, FAX 65-467-7667, wspc@wspc.com.sg, series@wspc.com.sg, http://www.wspc.com/books/series/scmb_series.shtml, http://www.worldscientific.com. Ed. Ch A Paternak. **Dist. by:** World Scientific Publishing Co., Inc., 1060 Main St, River Edge, NJ 07661. TEL 201-487-9655, 800-227-7562, FAX 201-487-9656, 888-977-2665; World Scientific Publishing Ltd., 57 Shelton St, London WC2H 9HE, United Kingdom. TEL 44-20-78360888, FAX 44-20-78362020.

571.6 JPN ISSN 0915-3896
SHINKEI SOSHIKI NO SEICHO SAISEI ISHOKU/NEURAL GROWTH, REGENERATION AND TRANSPLANTATION. Text in Japanese. 1989. a. **Document type:** *Academic/Scholarly.*
Published by: (Shinkei Soshiki no Seicho Saisei Ishoku Kenkyukai/Japanese Society for Neural Growth, Regeneration and Transplantation), Nyuronsha, 21-19-305 Higashi-Gotanda 5-chome, Shinagawa-ku, Tokyo, 141-0022, Japan.

571.6 CHN ISSN 0001-5334
QH301 CODEN: SYSWAE
➤ **SHIYAN SHENGWU XUEBAO/ACTA BIOLOGIAE EXPERIMENTALIS SINICA.** Variant title: Shih Yen Sheng Wu Hsueh Pao. Text in Chinese; Summaries in English. 1936. q. CNY 12 domestic; USD 33.20 foreign (effective 1999). adv. charts; illus. back issues avail. **Document type:** *Academic/Scholarly.* **Description:** Covers cell biology and publishes papers of experimental biology mainly in the fields of cell biology, developmental biology, reproductive biology, cancer biology, and immunobiology.
Indexed: BiolAb, CIN, ChemAb, ChemTitl, IndMed, IndVet, MEDLINE, PN&I, ZooRec.
—BLDSC (0601.700000), CASDDS, CISTI, GNLM, IE, Infotrieve, ingenta, Linda Hall.
Published by: (Shanghai Xibao Shengwu Yanjiusuo/Shanghai Institute of Cell Biology), Shanghai Kexue Jishu Chubanshe/Shanghai Scientific & Technical Publishers, Ruijin Er Rd, Shanghai, 200020, China. TEL 86-21-64736055, FAX 86-21-64730679, edto@sunm.shcnc.ac.cn. Ed. Wang Yahui. Adv. contact Ping Luo. **Subscr. to:** China International Book Trading Corp, 35 Chegongzhuang Xilu, Haidian District, PO Box 399, Beijing 100044, China. TEL 86-10-68412045, FAX 86-10-68412023, cibtc@mail.cibtc.com.cn, http://www.cibtc.com.cn/.

B

571.6 DEU ISSN 1615-4053
CODEN: STIRCI
➤ **SIGNAL TRANSDUCTION**; receptors, mediators and genes. Text in English. 2001. bi-m. EUR 464 in Europe; CHF 868 in Switzerland & Liechtenstein; USD 564 elsewhere; EUR 511 combined subscription in Europe print & online eds.; CHF 955 combined subscription in Switzerland & Liechtenstein for print & online eds.; USD 621 combined subscription elsewhere print & online eds. (effective 2006). abstr. reprints avail. **Document type:** *Journal, Academic/Scholarly.* **Description:** Covers all stages of signal transfer between cell surface and nucleus as well as the control of general cell physiology in normal and transformed cells.
Related titles: Online - full content ed.: ISSN 1615-4061. 2000. EUR 464 in Europe; CHF 868 in Switzerland & Liechtenstein; USD 564 elsewhere (effective 2006); Online - full text ed.: (from EBSCO Publishing, Swets Information Services, Wiley InterScience).
Indexed: BIOBASE, ChemAb, ExcerpMed.
—BLDSC (8275.989100), CISTI, IE. **CCC.**
Published by: Wiley - V C H Verlag GmbH & Co. KGaA (Subsidiary of: John Wiley & Sons, Inc.), Boschstr 12, Weinheim, 69469, Germany. TEL 49-6201-6060, FAX 49-6201-606328, signaltrans@wiley-vch.de, adsales@wiley-vch.de, subservice@wiley-vch.de, info@wiley-vch.de, http://www.signaltrans.de, http://www.wiley-vch.de. R&P Claudia Rutz. Adv. contact Aenne Anders TEL 49-6201-606552.

➤ **SOMATIC CELL AND MOLECULAR GENETICS.** see *BIOLOGY—Genetics*

571.6 JPN ISSN 0912-3636
➤ **SOSHIKI BAIYO KENKYU/TISSUE CULTURE RESEARCH COMMUNICATIONS.** Text mainly in English; Text occasionally in Japanese. 1982. 4/yr. JPY 6,000 membership (effective 2005). **Document type:** *Journal, Academic/Scholarly.* **Description:** Covers cytology and histology, biological chemistry, biotechnology, genetics, physiology, cell biology and molecular biology.
—**CCC.**
Published by: Nihon Soshiki Baiyo Gakkai/Japanese Tissue Culture Association, Hiroshima University School of Medicine, 1-2-3 Kasumi, Minami-ku, Hiroshima, 990-0823, Japan. TEL 81-82-2575665, FAX 81-82-2575669, jtca-office@umin.ac.jp, http://jtca.umin.jp/. Ed. Hiroyoshi Hoshi. Circ: 1,200.

571.6 JPN
SOSHIKI SAIBO KAGAKU KOSHUKAI/COURSE TEXT OF HISTOCHEMISTRY AND CYTOCHEMISTRY. Text in Japanese. 1976. a. JPY 6,000.
Indexed: CIN, ChemAb, ChemTitl.
Published by: (Nihon Soshiki Saibo Kagakkai/Japan Society of Histochemistry and Cytochemistry), Gakusai Kikaku K.K., 5-24 Mejiro 2-chome, Toshima-ku, Tokyo, 171-0031, Japan.

STEM CELL WEEK. see *MEDICAL SCIENCES*

571.6 GBR ISSN 0040-8166
QH573 CODEN: TICEBI
➤ **TISSUE AND CELL.** Text in English. 1969. 6/yr. EUR 1,035 in Europe to institutions; JPY 111,800 in Japan to institutions; USD 920 to institutions except Europe and Japan (effective 2006). adv. abstr.; charts; illus. index. **Document type:** *Journal, Academic/Scholarly.* **Description:** Presents research papers on the organization of cells, their components and extracellular products.
Related titles: Microform ed.: (from PQC); Online - full text ed.: (from EBSCO Publishing, O C L C Online Computer Library Center, Inc., ScienceDirect, Swets Information Services).
Indexed: ASCA, ASFA, AbHyg, AgBio, AgrForAb, AnBrAb, ApicAb, BBCI, BIOBASE, BIOSIS Prev, BiolAb, BiolDig, CIN, ChemAb, ChemTitl, CurCont, DSA, EntAb, ExcerpMed, ForAb, HelmAb, IABS, ISR, IndMed, IndVet, Inpharma, MEDLINE, NemAb, NutrAb, PBA, PGrRegA, PN&I, PoultAb, ProtozoAb, RM&VM, RPP, Reac, RefZh, RevApplEntom, S&F, SCI, SFA, TDB, VetBull, ZooRec.
—BLDSC (8858.680000), CASDDS, CISTI, GNLM, IDS, IE, Infotrieve, ingenta, KNAW, Linda Hall. **CCC.**
Published by: Churchill Livingstone (Subsidiary of: Elsevier Health Sciences), Robert Stevenson House, 1-3, Baxter's Pl, Leith Walk, Edinburgh, Midlothian EH1 3AF, United Kingdom. TEL 44-131-5562424, FAX 44-131-5581278, cservice@harcourt.com, journals@harcourt.com, http://www.elsevier.com/locate/tice, http://www.harcourt-international.com/. Ed. R Dallai. Pub. Gillian Griffith. R&P Catherine John TEL 212-424-4200. Adv. contact David Dunnachie. Circ: 660. **Subscr. to:** Harcourt Publishers Ltd., Foots Cray High St, Sidcup, Kent DA14 5HP, United Kingdom. TEL 44-20-83085700, FAX 44-20-8309-0807.

➤ **TISSUE CULTURE.** see *BIOLOGY—Abstracting, Bibliographies, Statistics*

571.5 USA ISSN 1076-3279
R857.T55 CODEN: TIENFP
➤ **TISSUE ENGINEERING.** Text in English. 1993. m. USD 775 domestic to institutions; USD 926 foreign to institutions; USD 920 combined subscription domestic to institutions print & online eds.; USD 1,073 combined subscription foreign to institutions print & online eds. (effective 2006). adv. back issues avail.; reprint service avail. from PSC. **Document type:** *Journal, Academic/Scholarly.* **Description:** Provides information on an interdisciplinary field dedicated to engineering new tissue that applies the principles and methods of engineering and the life sciences toward the fundamental understanding of structure-function relationships in normal and pathologic tissue and the development of biological substitutes.
Related titles: Online - full text ed.: ISSN 1557-8690. USD 735 worldwide to institutions (effective 2006) (from EBSCO Publishing, Gale Group, O C L C Online Computer Library Center, Inc., ProQuest Information & Learning, Swets Information Services).
Indexed: B&BAb, BCI, BIOSIS Prev, BioEngAb, BiolAb, CIN, CTA, ChemAb, ChemTitl, CurCont, ExcerpMed, ISR, IndMed, Inpharma, M&PBA, MEDLINE, PE&ON, Reac, SCI.
—CASDDS, CISTI, IDS, IE, Infotrieve, Linda Hall. **CCC.**
Published by: (Tissue Engineering Society International), Mary Ann Liebert, Inc. Publishers, 140 Huguenot St 3rd Fl, New Rochelle, NY 10801-5215. TEL 914-740-2100, FAX 914-740-2101, 800-654-3237, info@liebertpub.com, http://www.liebertpub.com/ten. Eds. Dr. Anthonios G. Mikos, Dr. Peter C Johnson TEL 919-425-2921. adv.: B&W page USD 1,285; trim 8.5 x 11. Circ: 1,400 (paid).

571.6 CHE ISSN 0250-0868
CODEN: IJTEDP
➤ **TISSUE REACTIONS.** Text in English. q. CHF 400 (effective 2003). Index. **Document type:** *Journal, Academic/Scholarly.* **Description:** Contains the results of research on problems related to alterations of physiological origin, either experimentally induced or of a pathogenic nature, which occur at cellular or tissue levels.
Indexed: ASFA, BIOBASE, BIOSIS Prev, BiolAb, CurCont, DBA, DSA, ExcerpMed, HortAb, ISR, IndMed, Inpharma, MEDLINE, NutrAb, PE&ON, RA&MP, Reac, RefZh, SCI, VITIS.
—BLDSC (4542.695600), CASDDS, CISTI, GNLM, IDS, IE, Infotrieve, ingenta, KNAW. **CCC.**
Published by: Bioscience Ediprint Inc., Rue Alexandre Gavard 16, Carouge, 1227, Switzerland. TEL 41-22-3003383, FAX 41-22-3002489, bioscience.smey@gkb.com. Ed. A Bertelli.

571.6 DNK ISSN 1398-9219
QH509 CODEN: TRAFFA
➤ **TRAFFIC**; the international journal of intracellular transport. Text in English. 2000. m. EUR 218 combined subscription in Europe to individuals print & online eds.; USD 244 combined subscription in the Americas to individuals & Caribbean, print & online eds.; GBP 145 combined subscription elsewhere to individuals print & online eds.; USD 869 combined subscription in the Americas to institutions & Caribbean, print & online eds.; GBP 517 combined subscription elsewhere to institutions print & online eds. (effective 2006). adv. bk.rev. index. back issues avail.; reprint service avail. from PSC. **Document type:** *Journal, Academic/Scholarly.* **Description:** Publishes research and review articles dealing with structural biology, cell biology, protein biochemistry, molecular biology, morphology, intracellular signalling and genetic and infectious diseases in for mammalian and non-mammalian systems.
Related titles: Online - full text ed.: ISSN 1600-0854. 2000. EUR 207 in Europe to individuals; USD 231 in the Americas to individuals & Caribbean; GBP 138 elsewhere to individuals; USD 826 in the Americas to institutions & Caribbean; GBP 491 elsewhere to institutions (effective 2006) (from Blackwell Synergy, EBSCO Publishing, Gale Group, IngentaConnect, O C L C Online Computer Library Center, Inc., Ovid Technologies, Inc., Swets Information Services).
Indexed: BIOBASE, ChemAb, CurCont, ExcerpMed, IndMed, MEDLINE.
—BLDSC (8881.575000), CISTI, IE, Infotrieve, ingenta. **CCC.**
Published by: Blackwell Munksgaard (Subsidiary of: Blackwell Publishing Ltd.), Rosenoerns Alle 1, PO Box 227, Copenhagen V, 1502, Denmark. TEL 45-77-333333, FAX 45-77-333377, info@mks.blackwellpublishing.com, http://www.blackwellpublishing.com/journals/TRA, http://www.munksgaard.dk/. Ed. Lisa Hannan. Adv. contact Louise McCrae.

➤ **TRANSPLANTATION PROCEEDINGS.** see *MEDICAL SCIENCES—Surgery*

571.6 GBR ISSN 0962-8924
QH573 CODEN: TCBIEK
➤ **TRENDS IN CELL BIOLOGY.** Text in English. 1991. 12/yr. EUR 181 in Europe to individuals; JPY 22,000 in Japan to individuals; USD 198 to individuals except Europe and Japan; EUR 1,232 in Europe to institutions; JPY 170,900 in Japan to institutions; USD 1,378 to institutions except Europe and Japan (effective 2006). adv. bk.rev.; software rev. illus. index. back issues avail.; reprints avail. **Document type:** *Academic/Scholarly.* **Description:** Provides comprehensive coverage of new research developments, methodologies, and theories in all specializations of cell biology.
Related titles: Online - full text ed.: (from EBSCO Publishing, Gale Group, IngentaConnect, ScienceDirect, Swets Information Services).
Indexed: AIDS Ab, AIDS&CR, ASCA, ASFA, BBCI, BIOBASE, BIOSIS Prev, BiolAb, CIN, CTA, ChemAb, CurCont, ESPM, ExcerpMed, GenetAb, HGA, IABS, ISR, ImmunAb, IndMed, Inpharma, MEDLINE, NSA, NucAcAb, PE&ON, Reac, RefZh, SCI.
—BLDSC (9049.552000), CASDDS, CISTI, GNLM, IDS, IE, Infotrieve, ingenta. **CCC.**
Published by: Elsevier Ltd., Trends Journals (Subsidiary of: Elsevier Science & Technology), 68 Hills Rd, Cambridge, CB2 1LA, United Kingdom. TEL 44-1223-315961, FAX 44-1223-464430, TCB@elsevier.co.uk, http://www.elsevier.com/locate/tcb. Eds. D Hatton, Deborah Sweet, P Carmeliet. Adv. contact Thelma Reid. **Subscr. to:** Elsevier Current Trends Subscriptions, PO Box 331, Haywards Heath, W Sussex RH16 3FG, United Kingdom. TEL 44-1444-475650, FAX 44-1444-445423.

➤ **TRENDS IN MICROBIOLOGY.** see *BIOLOGY—Microbiology*

➤ **TSITOLOGIYA I GENETIKA**; mezhdunarodnyi nauchnyi zhurnal. see *BIOLOGY—Genetics*

571.6 CHN ISSN 0253-9977
QH573 CODEN: XISZD3
XIBAO SHENGWUXUE ZAZHI. Text in Chinese. 1979. q. (English ed. s-a.). USD 4 (effective 1997). **Document type:** *Academic/Scholarly.*
Related titles: Chinese ed.: Journal of Cytology.
Indexed: CIN, ChemAb, ChemTitl.
—CASDDS.
Published by: Zhongguo Kexueyuan, Shanghai Xibao Shengwu Yanjiusuo/Chinese Academy of Sciences, Shanghai Institute of Cytology, 320 Yueyang Lu, Shanghai, 200031, China. TEL 315030. Ed. Jiake Tso.

ZHONGGUO XIUFU CHONGJIAN WAIKE ZAZHI/CHINESE JOURNAL OF REPARATIVE AND RECONSTRUCTIVE SURGERY. see *MEDICAL SCIENCES—Surgery*

BIOLOGY—Entomology

see also AGRICULTURE—Crop Production And Soil ; ENGINEERING—Chemical Engineering

A E S BUG CLUB NEWS. see *CHILDREN AND YOUTH—For*

363.78 USA
A M C A NEWSLETTER. Text in English. 1976. bi-m. looseleaf. membership. adv. charts; illus.; maps. back issues avail.; reprints avail. **Document type:** *Newsletter, Academic/Scholarly.* **Description:** Helps members keep informed about association-related activities.
Former titles: A M C A Vector Review; A M C A Newsletter (0195-4180)
Related titles: Online - full text ed.
—CISTI.
Published by: American Mosquito Control Association, 681 Us Highway 1., N Brunswick, NJ 08902-3390. TEL 732-344-4645, FAX 732-542-3267, amca@mosquito.org, http://www.mosquito.org. Ed. Clark Wood. Pub. Matthew Piscitelli. R&P M S Chromsky. Circ: 1,600.

ABSTRACTS OF ENTOMOLOGY. see *BIOLOGY—Abstracting, Bibliographies, Statistics*

595.7 RUS ISSN 0132-8077
QL458
ACARINA; Russian journal of acarology. Text in English, Russian. 1993. s-a. USD 20 to individuals; USD 30 to institutions (effective 2003). illus. back issues avail. **Document type:** *Journal, Academic/Scholarly.* **Description:** Covers the morphology, taxonomy, zoogeography, evolution and development of ticks and mites.

Indexed: AbHyg, AgBio, AgrForAb, BIOSIS Prev, BioCN&I, BiolAb, ForAb, HelmAb, HerbAb, IndVet, MaizeAb, PBA, PoultAb, ProtozoAb, RM&VM, RevApplEntom, S&F, TDB, VetBull, ZooRec.
Published by: K M K Scientific Press Ltd., c/o Dr K G Mikhailov, Zoologicheskii Muzei MGU, Bol'shaya Nikitskaya 6, Moscow, 125009, Russian Federation. TEL 7-095-2925796, FAX 7-095-2032717, kmk2000@online.ru, http://www.orc.ru/ ~kmkweb/acarina.htm. Ed. Olga V Voltzit. Pub., Adv. contact K Mikhailov.

595.42   GBR   ISSN 1361-8091
QL458.A2
ACAROLOGY BULLETIN. Text in English. 1996. q. USD 10 membership (effective 2001). back issues avail. Document type: Bulletin, Abstract/Index. Description: Aims at providing members with information about mites and ticks and enhancing the communication among members.
Related titles: Online - full text ed.
Published by: Systematic and Applied Acarology Society, c/o Dr. Anne S. Baker, Dep. of Entomology, Natural History Museum, London, SW7 5BD, United Kingdom. http://www.nhm.ac.uk/ hosted_sites/acarlogy/saas/ab.html. Eds. Renjie Hu, Zhi-Qiang Zhang.

595.7   ITA   ISSN 0065-0757
ACCADEMIA NAZIONALE ITALIANA DI ENTOMOLOGIA. RENDICONTI. Text in Italian. 1952. irreg., latest vol.45, 1997. price varies.
Indexed: ZooRec.
Published by: Accademia Nazionale Italiana di Entomologia, Via Lanciola, 12-A, Cascine del Riccio, Florence, FI 50125, Italy. TEL 39-55-209182, FAX 39-55-209177.

505.7   CZE   ISSN 0374-1036
QL461   CODEN: AEMPBY
ACTA ENTOMOLOGICA. Text in English. 1923. irreg. price varies. Document type: Academic/Scholarly.
Related titles: ♦ Supplement(s): Acta Entomologica. Supplementum. ISSN 0231-8571.
Indexed: ZooRec.
—CISTI, Linda Hall.
Published by: (Prirodovedecke Muzeum), Narodni Muzeum, Vaclavske nam 68, Prague, 11579, Czech Republic. TEL 420-2-24497350, FAX 420-2-22246047. Ed. Josef Jelinek.

595.7   CHL   ISSN 0716-5072
            CODEN: AECHEV
➤ ACTA ENTOMOLOGICA CHILENA. Text in English, Spanish; Summaries in English. 1986. a. USD 37 (effective 2002). bk.rev. illus. back issues avail. Document type: Bulletin, Academic/Scholarly. Description: Covers research in taxonomy, biology, ecology, insects and mites.
Supersedes (1960-1974): Centro de Estudios Entomologicos. Publicaciones (0376-2106)
Indexed: ASFA, ApicAb, BIOSIS Prev, BioCN&I, BiolAb, ESPM, EntAb, HortAb, IndVet, ProtozoAb, RevApplEntom, S&F, SoyAb, TDB, TriticAb, VetBull, WeedAb, ZooRec.
Published by: Universidad Metropolitana de Ciencias de la Educacion, Instituto de Entomologia, J P Alessandri, 774, Santiago, Chile. TEL 56-2-2412457, FAX 56-2-2412723, http://www.umcc.cl. Ed. Jaime Solervicens. Circ: 650.

595.7   POL   ISSN 1230-7777
➤ ACTA ENTOMOLOGICA SILESIANA. Text in English, German, Polish; Summaries in English. 1993. s-a. PLZ 8; USD 10 foreign (effective 1999). abstr.; bibl.; illus.; maps. Document type: Academic/Scholarly.
Indexed: AgrAg, AgrLib, EntAb, ZooRec.
Published by: Slaskie Towarzystwo Entomologiczne, Pl Jana III Sobieskiego 2, Bytom, 41902, Poland. TEL 48-32-2813401, FAX 48-32-2813401, dobosz@us.edu.pl.

595.7   SVN   ISSN 1318-1998
ACTA ENTOMOLOGICA SLOVENICA. Text in Slovenian. 1993. s-a.
Indexed: EntAb, HGA, ZooRec.
—BLDSC (0615.503000), IE, ingenta.
Published by: (Prirodoslovni Muzej Slovenije/Slovenian Museum of Natural History, Slovenska Akademija Znanosti in Umetnosti, Znanstvenoraziskovalni Center, Bioloski Institut J Hadzija, Slovensko Entomolosko Drustvo Stefana Michielija/Slovenian Entomological Society), Zalozba Z R C/Scientific Research Centre Publishing, Novi trg 2, P.O. Box 306, Ljubljana, 1001, Slovenia. TEL 386-1-4706474, FAX 386-1-4257794, zalozba@zrc-sazu.si, http://www2.pms-lj.si/ biblioteka/acta_entomologica.html, http://www.zrc-sazu.si/ zalozba. Ed. Andrej Gogala.

505.7   CZE   ISSN 0231-8571
ACTA ENTOMOLOGICA. SUPPLEMENTUM. Text in English. 1967. irreg.
Related titles: ♦ Supplement to: Acta Entomologica. ISSN 0374-1036.
Indexed: ASFA, ESPM, ZooRec.
—Linda Hall.
Published by: Narodni Muzeum, Vaclavske nam 68, Prague, 11579, Czech Republic. TEL 420-2-24497350, FAX 420-22246047.

595.7   CZE   ISSN 0554-9264
            CODEN: AFAEBG
ACTA FAUNISTICA ENTOMOLOGICA. Text in English, German, Russian. 1956. irreg. price varies. Document type: Academic/Scholarly.
Related titles: ♦ Supplement(s): Acta Faunistica Entomologica. Supplementum. ISSN 0551-7931.
Indexed: BiolAb, RevApplEntom, ZooRec.
—Linda Hall.
Published by: (Prirodovedecke Muzeum), Narodni Muzeum, Vaclavske nam 68, Prague, 11579, Czech Republic. TEL 420-2-24497350, FAX 420-2-22246047. Ed. Josef Jelinek.

595.7   CZE   ISSN 0551-7931
ACTA FAUNISTICA ENTOMOLOGICA. SUPPLEMENTUM. Text in English, German, Russian. 1959. irreg.
Related titles: ♦ Supplement to: Acta Faunistica Entomologica. ISSN 0554-9264.
Published by: Narodni Muzeum, Vaclavske nam 68, Prague, 11579, Czech Republic. TEL 420-2-24497350, FAX 420-2-22246047.

595.7   FRA   ISSN 0257-0076
QL496
➤ ACTES DES COLLOQUES INSECTES SOCIAUX. Text in French. 1983. a. back issues avail. Document type: Proceedings, Academic/Scholarly. Description: Features the annual meetings of the French section of the International Union for the Study of Social Insects.
Related titles: E-mail ed.; Fax ed.
Indexed: ZooRec.
—BLDSC (0675.113670).
Published by: International Union for the Study of Social Insects, French Section, L E P A - Universite Paul Sabatier, Bat.4, R 3, 118 Route de Narbonne, Toulouse, Cedex 4 31062, France. TEL 33-5-61558871, FAX 33-5-61556154, fourcass@cict.fr. Eds. J P Lachaud, V Fourcassie.

595.7   USA   ISSN 0065-2806
QL495   CODEN: AIPYAZ
➤ ADVANCES IN INSECT PHYSIOLOGY. Text in English. 1963. irreg., latest vol.29, 2002. USD 139.95 per vol. vol.30 (effective 2004). reprint service avail. from ISI. Document type: Academic/Scholarly. Description: Publishing eclectic volumes containing comprehensive and in-depth reviews on all aspects of insect physiology.
Related titles: Online - full text ed.: (from ScienceDirect).
Indexed: ASCA, ASFA, AbHyg, Agr, AnBeAb, B&AI, BIOSIS Prev, BioCN&I, BiolAb, CIN, ChemAb, ChemTitl, EntAb, ISR, RevApplEntom, SCI, TDB, ZooRec.
—BLDSC (0709.230000), CASDDS, CISTI, Linda Hall. CCC.
Published by: Academic Press (Subsidiary of: Elsevier Science & Technology), 525 B St, Ste 1900, San Diego, CA 92101-4495. TEL 619-231-6616, 800-894-3434, apsubs@acad.com, http://www.academicpress.com.

595.7   ZAF   ISSN 1021-3589
QL461   CODEN: AFREE2
➤ AFRICAN ENTOMOLOGY; journal of the Entomological Society of Southern Africa. Text and summaries in English, Afrikaans. 1937; N.S. 1993. s-a. ZAR 175 domestic to members; ZAR 195 in Southern Africa to members; USD 70 elsewhere to members; ZAR 225 domestic to institutions; ZAR 245 in Southern Africa to institutions; USD 150 elsewhere to institutions; ZAR 98 domestic to students; ZAR 118 in Southern Africa to students; USD 40 elsewhere to students; ZAR 275 combined subscription domestic to institutions print & online eds.; ZAR 295 combined subscription in Southern Africa to institutions print & online eds.; USD 155 combined subscription elsewhere to institutions print & online eds. (effective 2005); subscrip. includes supplement Rostrum. adv. bk.rev. abstr.; bibl.; charts; illus.; maps; stat. index. 150 p./no.; back issues avail. Document type: Journal, Academic/Scholarly. Description: Publishes articles on African entomology and arachnology.
Formerly (until 1993): Entomological Society of Southern Africa. Journal (0013-8789)
Related titles: CD-ROM ed.; ♦ Supplement(s): Rostrum. ISSN 1026-4914.
Indexed: AEA, ASCA, ASFA, AgBio, Agr, AgrForAb, AnBrAb, ApicAb, B&BAb, BIOBASE, BIOSIS Prev, BioCN&I, BiolAb, ChemoAb, CurCont, EntAb, FCA, ForAb, HGA, HerbAb, HortAb, IABS, IBR, ISAP, IndVet, MaizeAb, NemAb, OrnHort, PBA, PGegResA, PHN&I, PlantSci, PoultAb, ProtozoAb, RA&MP, RM&VM, RPP, RevApplEntom, S&F, SeedAb, TDB, TriticAb, VITIS, WeedAb, ZooRec.
—BLDSC (0732.438700), CISTI, IDS, IE, Infotrieve, ingenta, Linda Hall.
Published by: Entomological Society of Southern Africa/Entomologiese Vereniging van Suidelike Afrika, PO Box 13162, Hatfield, Pretoria 0028, South Africa. FAX 27-12-3293278, avzyl@iafrica.com, http:// journals.sabinet.co.za/essa. Ed., Adv. contact S A Hanrahan. B&W page ZAR 2,500. Circ: 600.

632.7   GBR   ISSN 1461-9555
SB599   CODEN: AFEGB8
➤ AGRICULTURAL AND FOREST ENTOMOLOGY. Text in English. 1998. q. GBP 86, EUR 129 combined subscription in Europe to individuals print & online eds.; USD 156 combined subscription in the Americas to individuals & the Caribbean (print & onlin eds.); GBP 93 combined subscription elsewhere to individuals print & online eds.; GBP 397 combined subscription in Europe to institutions print & online eds.; USD 734 combined subscription in the Americas to institutions & the Caribbean (print & online eds.); GBP 437 combined subscription elsewhere to institutions print & online eds. (effective 2006). adv. reprint service avail. from PSC. Document type: Journal, Academic/Scholarly. Description: Publishes primary research papers, reviews and short communications on entomological research relevant to the control of insect and other arthropod pests.
Related titles: Online - full text ed.: ISSN 1461-9563. GBP 377 in Europe to institutions; USD 697 in the Americas to institutions & Caribbean; GBP 415 elsewhere to institutions (effective 2006) (from Blackwell Synergy, EBSCO Publishing, Gale Group, IngentaConnect, O C L C Online Computer Library Center, Inc., Swets Information Services).
Indexed: AEA, AgBio, Agr, AgrForAb, BIOBASE, BioCN&I, CPA, CurCont, EntAb, FCA, FPA, ForAb, HerbAb, HortAb, IndVet, MaizeAb, NemAb, NutrAb, OrnHort, PBA, PGegResA, PHN&I, PotatoAb, RA&MP, RPP, RefZh, RevApplEntom, RiceAb, S&F, SIA, SeedAb, SoyAb, TriticAb, VITIS, VetBull, WeedAb, ZooRec.
—BLDSC (0742.880000), IE, Infotrieve, ingenta. CCC.
Published by: Blackwell Publishing Ltd., 9600 Garsington Rd, Oxford, OX4 2ZG, United Kingdom. TEL 44-1865-776868, FAX 44-1865-714591, customerservices@oxon.blackwellpublishing.com, http://www.blackwellpublishing.com/journals/AFE. Eds. Allan D Watt, Keith F A Walters. R&P Sophie Savage. Adv. contact Jenny Applin.

595.7   JPN   ISSN 0389-2751
AKITU/KYOTO ENTOMOLOGICAL SOCIETY. JOURNAL. Text in English. 1937-1965; resumed 1974. a. membership. Document type: Academic/Scholarly.
Formerly: Akutu (0389-231X)
Published by: Kyoto Konchu Gakkai/Kyoto Entomological Society, Furitsu Daigaku Konchugaku Kenkyushitsu, 1-5 Shimo-Gamohangi-cho, Sakyo-ku, Kyoto-shi, 606-0823, Japan.

595.7   USA   ISSN 0065-6143
ALDRICH ENTOMOLOGY CLUB. NEWSLETTER. Text in English. 1962. irreg., latest vol.17, 1997. free. Document type: Newsletter. Description: Reports current research activities of the faculty, staff, students & alumni of the club.
Published by: (Aldrich Entomology Club), University of Idaho, Department of Entomology, 675 Perimeter Dr, Moscow, ID 83844. TEL 208-885-6276, FAX 208-885-7760. Ed. James Johnson. Circ: 250.

595.78   FRA   ISSN 0002-5208
            CODEN: ALEXBX
ALEXANOR; revue francaise de lepidopterologie. Text in French. 1959. q. adv. bk.rev. abstr.; charts; illus. index every 2 yrs.
Indexed: ASFA, BIOSIS Prev, BiolAb, EntAb, RefZh, ZooRec.
Address: 45 rue de Buffon, Paris, 75005, France. TEL 33-1-40793412. Ed. G C Luquet. Circ: 1,000.

595.7   ESP   ISSN 1133-5319
DP302.C32
ALMORAIMA. Text in Spanish. 1988. s-a.
Indexed: ZooRec.
Published by: Mancomunidad de Municipios de la Comarca del Campo de Gibraltar, Avda Virgen del Carmen 15-1, Algeciras, 11201, Spain. TEL 956-655-811, FAX 956-655-960, camara@camaracampodegibraltar.com.

595.7   GBR   ISSN 0266-8351
THE AMATEUR ENTOMOLOGIST. Text in English. 1939. irreg., latest vol.23. price varies. back issues avail. Document type: Monographic series. Description: Publishes handbooks and papers of interest to nonprofessional entomologists.
Indexed: ZooRec.
—BLDSC (0807.000000).
Published by: Amateur Entomologists' Society, Amateur Entomologists Society, PO Box 8774, London, SW7 5ZG, United Kingdom. wayj@nhm.ac.uk, http://www.theaes.org. Subscr. to: A.E.S. Publications, The Hawthorns, Frating Rd, Great Bromley, Colchester, Essex CO7 7JN, United Kingdom.

595.7   GBR   ISSN 0266-836X
AMATEUR ENTOMOLOGISTS' SOCIETY. BULLETIN. Text in English. 1935. bi-m. GBP 12.50 membership; GBP 15 foreign membership (effective 1999). adv. bk.rev. index. back issues avail. Document type: Bulletin. Description: Contains articles and notes on entomology and covers society activities and announcements.
Indexed: ZooRec.

B

▼ new title   ➤ refereed   ✳ unverified   ♦ full entry avail.

Published by: Amateur Entomologists' Society, Amateur Entomologists Society, PO Box 8774, London, SW7 5ZG, United Kingdom. wayj@nhm.ac.uk, http://www.theaes.org. Ed., R&P Wayne Jarvis. Adv. contact Rob Dyke. Circ: 2,000. **Subscr to:** A.E.S. Registrar, PO Box 0776, London SW7 5ZG, United Kingdom; A.E.S. Publications, The Hawthorns, Frating Rd, Great Bromley, Colchester, Essex CO7 7JN, United Kingdom.

595.7 GBR
AMATEUR ENTOMOLOGISTS' SOCIETY. LEAFLET. Text in English. irreg., latest vol.37. price varies. back issues avail. **Document type:** *Monographic series.* **Description:** Informs persons interested in studying and collecting insects.
Published by: Amateur Entomologists' Society, Amateur Entomologists Society, PO Box 8774, London, SW7 5ZG, United Kingdom. wayj@nhm.ac.uk, http://www.theaes.org. **Subscr. to:** A.E.S. Publications, The Hawthorns, Frating Rd, Great Bromley, Colchester, Essex CO7 7JN, United Kingdom.

595.7 GBR ISSN 1363-3198
AMATEUR ENTOMOLOGISTS' SOCIETY. PAMPHLET. Text in English. irreg., latest vol.14, 1993. price varies. back issues avail. **Document type:** *Monographic series.* **Description:** Contains information of interest to persons who like to study insects.
Indexed: ZooRec.
Published by: Amateur Entomologists' Society, Amateur Entomologists Society, PO Box 8774, London, SW7 5ZG, United Kingdom. wayj@nhm.ac.uk, http://www.theaes.org. **Subscr. to:** A.E.S. Publications, The Hawthorns, Frating Rd, Great Bromley, Colchester, Essex CO7 7JN, United Kingdom.

AMEMBOA; news and results on Thai heteroptera. see *BIOLOGY*

595.7 USA ISSN 1087-450X
AMERICAN BUTTERFLIES. Text in English. q. 48 p./no.; back issues avail. **Document type:** *Magazine, Consumer.*
Indexed: ZooRec.
Published by: North American Butterfly Association, 4 Delaware Rd, Morristown, NJ 07960. http://www.naba.org/pubs/abm.html. Ed. Jeffrey Glassberg.

595.7 USA ISSN 0569-4450
QL461
➤ **AMERICAN ENTOMOLOGICAL INSTITUTE. CONTRIBUTIONS.** Text in English. 1964. irreg., latest vol.33, 2003. price varies. back issues avail. **Document type:** *Academic/Scholarly.* **Description:** Publishes papers on systematic entomology.
Indexed: ASFA, Agr, B&BAb, BIOSIS Prev, BiolAb, HGA, RevApplEntom, ZooRec.
—Linda Hall.
Published by: American Entomological Institute, 3005 S W 56th Ave, Gainesville, FL 32608-5047. dr_x@msn.com, http://www.amentinst.org. Ed., R&P David B Wahl. Circ: 200.

595.7 USA ISSN 0065-8162
➤ **AMERICAN ENTOMOLOGICAL INSTITUTE. MEMOIRS.** Text in English. 1961. irreg., latest vol.71, 2003. price varies. index. back issues avail. **Document type:** *Monographic series, Academic/Scholarly.* **Description:** Monographs and catalogues dealing with systematic entomology.
Related titles: CD-ROM ed.
Indexed: ASFA, BIOSIS Prev, BiolAb, CurCont, ZooRec.
—CISTI.
Published by: American Entomological Institute, 3005 S W 56th Ave, Gainesville, FL 32608-5047. dr_x@msn.com, http://www.amentinst.org. Ed., R&P David B Wahl. Circ: 200.

595.7 USA ISSN 0065-8170
QL461 CODEN: AESMAK
AMERICAN ENTOMOLOGICAL SOCIETY. MEMOIRS. Text in English. 1916. irreg., latest vol.42, 1994. price varies. index. back issues avail. **Document type:** *Academic/Scholarly.*
Indexed: ASFA, BIOSIS Prev, BiolAb, EntAb, HGA, ZooRec.
—Linda Hall.
Published by: American Entomological Society, Academy of Natural Sciences, 1900 Benjamin Franklin Pkwy, Philadelphia, PA 19103-1195. TEL 215-561-3978, FAX 215-299-1028, aes@say.acnatsci.org, http://www.acnatsci.org/hosted/aes/.

595.7 USA ISSN 0002-8320
QL461
➤ **AMERICAN ENTOMOLOGICAL SOCIETY. TRANSACTIONS.** Text in English. 1867. q. USD 30 domestic; USD 34 foreign (effective 2005). bibl.; illus. index. **Document type:** *Journal, Academic/Scholarly.*
Former titles (until 1879): American Entomological Society. Entomological Section of the Academy of Natural Sciences. Transactions and Proceedings; (until 1877): American Entomological Society. Transactions (0886-1145)
Indexed: ASCA, ASFA, Agr, AgrForAb, B&BAb, BIOSIS Prev, BioCN&I, BiolAb, BiolDig, CurCont, EntAb, FCA, ForAb, GenetAb, HGA, HerbAb, HortAb, IndVet, PBA, RM&VM, RefZh, RevApplEntom, RiceAb, S&F, TDB, VITIS, VetBull, WeedAb, ZooRec.
—BLDSC (8886.600000), CISTI, IDS, IE, Infotrieve, ingenta, Linda Hall.
Published by: American Entomological Society, Academy of Natural Sciences, 1900 Benjamin Franklin Pkwy, Philadelphia, PA 19103-1195. TEL 215-561-3978, FAX 215-299-1028, aes@say.acnatsci.org, http://www.acnatsci.org/hosted/aes/. Ed. D Otte. R&P Daniel Otte.

595.7 USA ISSN 1046-2821
QL461 CODEN: AENUEN
➤ **AMERICAN ENTOMOLOGIST**; entomological articles of general interest. Text in English. 1955. q. USD 44 domestic to individuals; USD 59 in Canada & Mexico to individuals; USD 62 elsewhere to individuals; USD 84 domestic to institutions; USD 99 in Canada & Mexico to institutions; USD 102 elsewhere to institutions (effective 2005). adv. bk.rev. Index. back issues avail. **Document type:** *Journal, Academic/Scholarly.* **Description:** Entomological articles of general interest.
Formerly (until 1990): Entomological Society of America. Bulletin (0013-8754)
Related titles: Microform ed.: (from PQC).
Indexed: ASFA, Agr, BIOSIS Prev, BioCN&I, BiolAb, CIS, ChemAb, ChemoAb, EntAb, FCA, FPA, ForAb, HGA, HortAb, MaizeAb, NutrAb, OrnHort, PBA, PHN&I, PotatoAb, ProtozoAb, RA&MP, RM&VM, RPP, RRTA, RevApplEntom, TDB, TriticAb, WAE&RSA, WeedAb, ZooRec.
—BLDSC (0813.940100), CISTI, IE, ingenta, Linda Hall. **CCC.**
Published by: Entomological Society of America, 10001 Derekwood Ln, Ste 100, Lanham, MD 20706-4876. TEL 301-731-4535, FAX 301-731-4538, pubs@entsoc.org, esa@entsoc.org, http://www.entsoc.org. Ed. Gene Kristky. Circ: 6,000.

363.78 USA ISSN 8756-971X
RA640 CODEN: JAMAET
➤ **AMERICAN MOSQUITO CONTROL ASSOCIATION. JOURNAL.** Text in English. 1940. q. USD 125 (effective 2005). adv. bk.rev. abstr.; bibl.; charts; illus. index. **Document type:** *Journal, Academic/Scholarly.* **Description:** Provides information on the biology and control of mosquitoes and other vectors which affect the health of man and animals; the prevention of vector-borne disease and protection of human and animal health, with concern toward protection of the environment.
Incorporates (1969-1995): Mosquito Systematics (0091-3669); Supersedes (in 1985): Mosquito News (0027-142X)
Related titles: Microform ed.: 1940 (from PMC); Supplement(s): American Mosquito Control Association. Journal. Supplement. ISSN 1046-3607. 1988.
Indexed: AEA, AIDS&CR, ASCA, ASFA, AbHyg, AgBio, Agr, AgrForAb, AnBrAb, B&BAb, BIOBASE, BIOSIS Prev, BioCN&I, BiolAb, CIN, ChemAb, ChemTitl, CurCont, DBA, ESPM, EntAb, FPA, ForAb, HelmAb, HerbAb, HortAb, ISR, IndMed, IndVet, M&GPA, MBA, MEDLINE, NemAb, NutrAb, PN&I, PoultAb, ProtozoAb, RA&MP, RDA, RM&VM, RRTA, RevApplEntom, RiceAb, SCI, SFA, SPPI, SWRA, SeedAb, SoyAb, TDB, VetBull, WAE&RSA, WeedAb, WildRev, ZooRec.
—BLDSC (4689.125000), CASDDS, CISTI, GNLM, IDS, IE, Infotrieve, ingenta, Linda Hall. **CCC.**
Published by: American Mosquito Control Association, 681 Us Highway 1., N Brunswick, NJ 08902-3390. TEL 732-344-4645, FAX 732-542-3267, amca@mosquito.org, http://www.mosquito.org. Ed. Dr. Ronald A Ward. Circ: 1,600.

595.7 JPN ISSN 0288-4402
AMICA. Text in Japanese. 1953. irreg. membership.
Indexed: ZooRec.
Published by: Toyamaken Konchu Dokokai/Entomological Society of Toyama Prefecture, c/o Mr Toru Mizuno, Akada, Shimoniikawa-gun, Unazukimachi, Toyama-ken 938-02, Japan.

595.7 DEU ISSN 1437-0867
ANGEWANDTE CARABIDOLOGIE. Text in German. 1998. irreg. price varies. **Document type:** *Monographic series, Academic/Scholarly.*
Related titles: Supplement(s): Angewandte Carabidologie. Supplement. ISSN 1612-3867. 1999.
Indexed: ZooRec.
Published by: Gesellschaft fuer Angewandte Carabidologie e.V., Johann-Strauss-Str 22, Filderstadt, 70794, Germany. TEL 49-7158-2164, FAX 49-7158-65313, gb_atp@t-online.de, http://www.angewandte-carabidologie.de.

595.7 IND ISSN 0970-3721
ANNALS OF ENTOMOLOGY. Text in English. 1983. 2/yr. INR 1,000 domestic; USD 500 foreign (effective 2003). adv. bk.rev. back issues avail.; reprints avail. **Document type:** *Journal, Academic/Scholarly.*
Indexed: AgrForAb, BioCN&I, CPA, ForAb, HortAb, PBA, PHN&I, RefZh, S&F, SIA, SeedAb, TDB, WAE&RSA, WeedAb, ZooRec.
Published by: Surya International Publications, 4-B, Nashville Rd, Dehra Dun, Uttaranchal 248 001, India. TEL 91-135-2711936, FAX 91-135-2654173, surya_pub@rediffmail.com, http://www.suryapublication.com. Ed. S K Kulshreshtha. adv.: B&W page USD 100, color page USD 500; trim 9.5 x 7. Circ: 300 (paid).

THE ANNALS OF MEDICAL ENTOMOLOGY. see *MEDICAL SCIENCES*

THE ANNALS OF MEDICAL ENTOMOLOGY NEWSLETTER. see *MEDICAL SCIENCES*

595.7 USA ISSN 0066-4170
QL461 CODEN: ARENAA
➤ **ANNUAL REVIEW OF ENTOMOLOGY.** Text in English. 1956. a., latest vol.49, 2004. USD 185 to institutions print or online ed.; USD 222 combined subscription to institutions print & online eds. (effective 2006). bibl.; abstr. index; cum.index every 5 yrs. back issues avail.; reprint service avail. from PSC. **Document type:** *Academic/Scholarly.* **Description:** Synthesizes and filters the vast amount of primary research to identify the principal contributions in entomology.
Related titles: Microfilm ed.: (from PQC); Online - full content ed.: ISSN 1545-4487. USD 179 (effective 2005) (from HighWire Press); Online - full text ed.: (from bigchalk, EBSCO Publishing, H.W. Wilson, O C L C Online Computer Library Center, Inc., ProQuest Information & Learning, Swets Information Services).
Indexed: ASCA, ASFA, AbHyg, AgBio, Agr, AgrForAb, AnBeAb, ApEcolAb, ApicAb, B&AI, B&BAb, BIOBASE, BIOSIS Prev, BibAg, BioCN&I, BiolAb, CIN, CPA, ChemAb, ChemTitl, ChemoAb, CurCont, DBA, ESPM, EntAb, EnvAb, ExcerpMed, FCA, ForAb, GEOBASE, GenetAb, HGA, HelmAb, HortAb, IABS, ISR, IndMed, IndVet, MEDLINE, MRD, MaizeAb, NemAb, NutrAb, OrnHort, PBA, PGegResA, PHN&I, PotatoAb, ProtozoAb, RM&VM, RPP, RRTA, RevApplEntom, RiceAb, S&F, SCI, SIA, SoyAb, TDB, TriticAb, VITIS, VetBull, WeedAb, ZooRec.
—BLDSC (1522.500000), CASDDS, CISTI, GNLM, IDS, IE, Infotrieve, ingenta, Linda Hall. **CCC.**
Published by: Annual Reviews, 4139 El Camino Way, Palo Alto, CA 94303-0139. TEL 650-493-4400, 800-523-8635, FAX 650-424-0910, service@annualreviews.org, http://arjournals.annualreviews.org/loi/ento, http://www.annualreviews.org. Ed. May R Berenbaum. R&P Laura Folkner.

595.7 GBR ISSN 0140-1890
QL461
ANTENNA. Text in English. 1976. q. GBP 24.50 in Europe; GBP 25 elsewhere. **Document type:** *Proceedings.*
Supersedes: Royal Entomological Society of London. Proceedings (0080-4355)
Indexed: AEA, AgBio, AgrForAb, BioCN&I, CPA, FCA, FPA, ForAb, HerbAb, HortAb, IndVet, NemAb, NutrAb, PBA, PHN&I, ProtozoAb, RM&VM, RPP, RRTA, RevApplEntom, RiceAb, S&F, TDB, TriticAb, VetBull, WAE&RSA, WeedAb, ZooRec.
—BLDSC (1542.200000), IE, ingenta, Linda Hall.
Published by: Royal Entomological Society, 41 Queens Gate, London, SW7 5HR, United Kingdom. TEL 44-171-584-8361, FAX 44-171-581-8505, royenson@demon.co.uk, reg@royensoc.co.uk, http://www.demon.co.uk/royensoc, http://www.royensoc.co.uk.

595.72 FRA ISSN 0044-8435
CODEN: APDGB5
➤ **APIDOLOGIE.** Text in English; Summaries in English, French, German. 1970. q. EUR 321 combined subscription domestic print & online eds.; EUR 361 combined subscription in the European Union print & online eds.; EUR 393 combined subscription elsewhere print & online eds. (effective 2005). bk.rev. abstr. reprint service avail. from ISI. **Document type:** *Journal, Academic/Scholarly.* **Description:** Studies bee behavior, bee-plant interactions, pollination, bee genetics, and pathology.
Formed by the merger of (1958-1970): Annales de l'Abeille (0570-1597); (1950-1970): Zeitschrift fuer Bienenforschung (0044-2399)
Related titles: Online - full content ed.: Apidologie Online. ISSN 1297-9678; Online - full text ed.: (from EBSCO Publishing, Swets Information Services).
Indexed: ASCA, AgBio, AgrForAb, ApicAb, BIOBASE, BIOSIS Prev, BibAg, BioCN&I, BiolAb, CIN, CPA, ChemAb, ChemTitl, CurCont, EntAb, ExcerpMed, FPA, FS&TA, ForAb, GEOBASE, HortAb, IABS, ISR, IndVet, MaizeAb, NSCI, NemAb, NutrAb, PBA, PHN&I, ProtozoAb, RA&MP, RM&VM, RPP, RevApplEntom, S&F, SCI, SIA, SeedAb, SoyAb, VetBull, WeedAb, ZooRec.
—BLDSC (1568.563000), CASDDS, CISTI, IDS, IE, Infotrieve, ingenta, Linda Hall. **CCC.**
Published by: (France. Institut National de la Recherche Agronomique (INRA)), E D P Sciences, 17 Ave du Hoggar, Parc d'Activites de Courtaboeuf, BP 112, Cedex A, Les Ulis, F-91944, France. TEL 33-1-69187575, FAX 33-1-69860678, subscribers@edpsciences.org, http://www.edpsciences.org/docinfos/INRA-APIDO/OnlineINRA-APIDO.html. Circ: 2,000. **Co-sponsor:** Du Deutscher Imkerbund e.V., GW.

595.7 IRN ISSN 1026-5007
➤ **APPLIED ENTOMOLOGY AND PHYTOPATHOLOGY/AFAT VA BIMARIHAY GIYAHI.** Text in Persian, Modern; Summaries in English. 1946. q. free (effective 2003). charts; illus.; stat. **Document type:** *Journal, Academic/Scholarly.* **Description:** Publishes original research reports and short communications on insect pests, pesticides, and related topics.
Formerly (until 1990): Entomologie et Phytopathologie Appliquees (0013-8800)
Indexed: AgrForAb, BioCN&I, BiolAb, ChemAb, FCA, ForAb, HerbAb, HortAb, MaizeAb, NemAb, OrnHort, PBA, PGegResA, PHN&I, PotatoAb, RPP, RefZh, RevApplEntom, RiceAb, S&F, SIA, SeedAb, TriticAb, WeedAb, ZooRec.
—BLDSC (1572.380000), CISTI, Linda Hall.

B

Published by: Plant Pests and Diseases Research Institute/Mu'assasah Tahqiqat Afat va Bimarihay Giyahi, P O Box 1454, Tehran, 19395, Iran. TEL 98-21-2403012, FAX 98-21-2403691, http://www.magiran.com/rostaniha. Ed. Dr. Ebrahim Behdad. Circ: 2,000.

595.7 JPN ISSN 0003-6862
QL461 CODEN: APEZAW

➤ **APPLIED ENTOMOLOGY AND ZOOLOGY.** Text in English. 1966. q. USD 50 (effective 2002). adv. bibl.; charts; illus. **Document type:** *Journal, Academic/Scholarly.* **Description:** Publishes articles concerned with applied zoology, applied entomology, agricultural chemicals and pest control in English.
Related titles: Online - full text ed.: ISSN 1347-605X. 2000. free (effective 2005) (from J-Stage).
Indexed: AEA, ASCA, ASFA, AgBio, AgrForAb, BIOSIS Prev, BioCN&I, BioDAb, BiolAb, CIN, CPA, CTFA, ChemAb, ChemTitl, CurCont, DBA, DSA, EntAb, FCA, FPA, FS&TA, ForAb, HelmAb, HerbAb, HortAb, INIS AtomInd, ISR, IndVet, MaizeAb, NemAb, NutrAb, OrnHort, PBA, PGegResA, PHN&I, PotatoAb, PoultAb, ProtozoAb, RA&MP, RM&VM, RPP, RevApplEntom, RiceAb, S&F, S&MA, SCI, SIA, SeedAb, SoyAb, TDB, TriticAb, VITIS, VetBull, WeedAb, ZooRec.
—BLDSC (1572.400000), CASDDS, CISTI, IDS, IE, Infotrieve, ingenta, Linda Hall.
Published by: Japanese Society of Applied Entomology and Zoology/Nihon Oyo Dobutsu Konchu Gakkai, c/o Japan Plant Protection Association, 1-43-11 Komagome, Toshima-ku, Tokyo, 170-0003, Japan. TEL 81-3-3943-6021, FAX 81-3-3943-6021, http://www.jstage.jst.go.jp/browse/aez. Ed., R&P Masakazu Shiga. Adv. contact Yoshiaki Kono. Circ: 1,900. **Dist. by:** Japan Publications Trading Co., Ltd., Book Export II Dept, PO Box 5030, Tokyo International, Tokyo 101-3191, Japan. TEL 81-3-32923753, FAX 81-3-32920410, infoserials@jptco.co.jp, http://www.jptco.co.jp.

595.7 NLD ISSN 0165-0424
CODEN: AQINDQ

➤ **AQUATIC INSECTS**; international journal of freshwater entomology. Text in English. 1979. q. GBP 341, USD 611 combined subscription to institutions print & online eds. (effective 2006). adv. reprint service avail. from PSC. **Document type:** *Journal, Academic/Scholarly.* **Description:** Discusses the taxonomy, ecology, and the shared habitats unifying various groups of these. Explores ways in which aquatic insects act as bioindicators.
Related titles: Online - full text ed.: GBP 324, USD 580 to institutions (effective 2006) (from EBSCO Publishing, Gale Group, IngentaConnect, O C L C Online Computer Library Center, Inc., Swets Information Services).
Indexed: ABIPC, ASCA, ASFA, AgBio, AnBeAb, BIOBASE, BIOSIS Prev, BiolAb, CurCont, ESPM, EntAb, IABS, ISR, IndVet, PoultAb, RM&VM, RefZh, RevApplEntom, SCI, SPPI, TDB, VetBull, ZooRec.
—BLDSC (1582.386000), CISTI, IDS, IE, Infotrieve, ingenta, Linda Hall. **CCC.**
Published by: Taylor & Francis The Netherlands (Subsidiary of: Taylor & Francis Group), Schipolweg 107 C, PO Box 447, Leiden, 2316 XC, Netherlands. TEL 31-715-243080, FAX 31-715-234571, infoho@swets.nl, http://www.tandf.co.uk/journals/titles/01650424.asp, http://www.tandf.co.uk/swets.asp. Ed. P Zwick. R&P J van der Valk. adv.: page EUR 300; trim 120 x 195.

595.7 CHE ISSN 1018-4171
ARACHNOLOGISCHE MITTEILUNGEN. Text in English, German. 1991. s-a. EUR 10 membership (effective 2005). **Document type:** *Journal, Academic/Scholarly.* **Description:** Articles cover faunistics, taxonomy, systematics, ecology, and behavior of European arachnids.
Related titles: ♦ Supplement(s): Arachnologische Mitteilungen. Sonderband. ISSN 1420-1445.
Indexed: ASFA, BiolAb, ZooRec.
Published by: Arachnologische Gesellschaft eV, c/o Naturhistorisches Museum, Augustinergasse 2, Basel, 4001, Switzerland. ambros.haeggi@bs.ch, http://arages.frank-lepper.de/publikationen.html, http://www.arages.de. Eds. Helmut Stumpf, Ulrich Simon.

595.7 CHE ISSN 1420-1445
ARACHNOLOGISCHE MITTEILUNGEN. SONDERBAND. Text in English, German. 1995. irreg.
Related titles: ♦ Supplement to: Arachnologische Mitteilungen. ISSN 1018-4171.
Indexed: ZooRec.
Published by: Arachnologische Gesellschaft eV, c/o Naturhistorisches Museum, Augustinergasse 2, Basel, 4001, Switzerland. ambros.haeggi@bs.ch, http://www.arages.de. Eds. Helmut Stumpf, Ulrich Simon.

595.7 TUR
ARASTIRMA ESERLERI SERISI ✶. Text in Turkish; Summaries in English, French, German. 1952. irreg. free. index. back issues avail.
Indexed: BiolAb.
Published by: Ministry of Agriculture, Forest and Rural Affairs, Regional Plant Protection Research Institute, Fatih Caddesi 37, Kalaba, Ankara, Turkey. Circ: 600.

595.7 MLT
ARCHIPELAGO. Text in English. q.
Published by: Nature Trust, P.O. Box 9, Valletta, CMR 01, Malta. info@naturetrustmalta.org, http://www.naturetrustmalta.org/.

595.7 USA ISSN 0739-4462
QL495 CODEN: AIBPEA

➤ **ARCHIVES OF INSECT BIOCHEMISTRY AND PHYSIOLOGY.** Text in English. 1983. m. USD 2,599 domestic to institutions; USD 2,719 in Canada & Mexico to institutions; USD 2,821 elsewhere to institutions; USD 2,859 combined subscription domestic to institutions print & online eds.; USD 2,979 combined subscription in Canada & Mexico to institutions print & online eds.; USD 3,081 combined subscription elsewhere to institutions print & online eds. (effective 2006). adv. back issues avail. **Document type:** *Journal, Academic/Scholarly.* **Description:** Provides an international forum for scientists interested in the field of insect biochemistry and physiology.
Related titles: Microform ed.: (from PQC); Online - full content ed.: ISSN 1520-6327. 1997. USD 2,599 to institutions (effective 2006); Online - full text ed.: (from EBSCO Publishing, Swets Information Services, Wiley InterScience).
Indexed: ASCA, ASFA, AgBio, Agr, AgrForAb, B&BAb, BBCI, BIOSIS Prev, BibAg, BioCN&I, BiolAb, CCI, CIN, CPA, ChemAb, ChemTitl, CurCont, DSA, EntAb, ForAb, GenetAb, HGA, HerbAb, HortAb, ISR, IndMed, IndVet, Inpharma, MEDLINE, MaizeAb, NSCI, NutrAb, OrnHort, PBA, PGrRegA, PHN&I, PotatoAb, ProtozoAb, RM&VM, RPP, Reac, RefZh, RevApplEntom, SCI, SIA, SoyAb, TDB, VetBull, WeedAb, ZooRec.
—BLDSC (1634.650000), CASDDS, CISTI, GNLM, IDS, IE, Infotrieve, ingenta, Linda Hall. **CCC.**
Published by: (Entomological Society of America), John Wiley & Sons, Inc., 111 River St, Hoboken, NJ 07030-5774. TEL 201-748-6000, FAX 201-748-5915, uscs-wis@wiley.com, http://www.interscience.wiley.com/jpages/0739-4462/, http://www.wiley.com. Ed. David Stanley. adv.: B&W page GBP 640, color page GBP 1,515; trim 174 x 254. **Subscr. outside the Americas to:** John Wiley & Sons Ltd., The Atrium, Southern Gate, Chichester, West Sussex PO19 8SQ, United Kingdom. TEL 44-1243-843335, 0800-243407, FAX 44-1243-843232, cs-journals@wiley.co.uk.

595.7 JPN
ARI/MYRMECOLOGICAL SOCIETY OF JAPAN. JOURNAL. Text in Japanese; Summaries in English. 1965. a. JPY 1,000 to members (effective 1998). **Document type:** *Proceedings.*
Indexed: ZooRec.
Published by: Nihon Arirui Kenkyukai/Myrmecological Society of Japan, c/o Shiraume Gakuen Tanki Daigaku, 1-830 Ogawa-cho, Kodaira-shi, Tokyo-to 187-0032, Japan. TEL 81-423-42-2311. Ed. Fuminori Ito. Pub. Masao Kubota. R&P Masaki Kondoh. Circ: 180 (controlled).

595.7 GBR ISSN 1467-8039
QL494 CODEN: ASDRCQ

➤ **ARTHROPOD STRUCTURE & DEVELOPMENT.** Text in English. 1972. 4/yr. EUR 1,087 in Europe to institutions; JPY 144,200 in Japan to institutions; USD 1,217 to institutions except Europe and Japan (effective 2006). adv. bk.rev. reprint service avail. from PQC. **Document type:** *Journal, Academic/Scholarly.* **Description:** Covers topics including gross morphology, paleomorphology, macro- and micro-anatomy, ultrastructure, and embryonic and post-embryonic development.
Formerly (until 1999): International Journal of Insect Morphology and Embryology (0020-7322)
Related titles: Microfilm ed.: (from PQC); Online - full text ed.: (from EBSCO Publishing, Gale Group, IngentaConnect, ScienceDirect, Swets Information Services).
Indexed: ASCA, ASFA, AgBio, Agr, AgrForAb, BIOBASE, BIOSIS Prev, BioCN&I, BiolAb, ChemAb, CurCont, EntAb, ExcerpMed, ForAb, HortAb, IABS, ISR, MEDLINE, NemAb, PHN&I, PN&I, RM&VM, RefZh, RevApplEntom, SCI, ZooRec.
—BLDSC (1733.894000), CISTI, IDS, IE, Infotrieve, ingenta, Linda Hall. **CCC.**
Published by: Pergamon (Subsidiary of: Elsevier Science & Technology), The Boulevard, Langford Ln, East Park, Kidlington, Oxford OX5 1GB, United Kingdom. TEL 44-1865-843000, FAX 44-1865-843010, arthropod@neurobio.arizona.edu, http://www.elsevier.com/locate/asd. Eds. N J Strausfeld, R A Steinbrecht. Circ: 1,000. **Subscr. to:** Elsevier BV, PO Box 211, Amsterdam 1000 AE, Netherlands. TEL 31-20-485-3757, FAX 31-20-485-3432, nlinfo-f@elsevier.nl, http://www.elsevier.nl.

595.7 RUS ISSN 0136-006X

➤ **ARTHROPODA SELECTA**; Russian journal of arthropoda research. Text mainly in English, Russian. 1992. q. USD 56 to individuals; USD 70 to institutions (effective 2005). adv. bk.rev. illus. back issues avail. **Document type:** *Journal, Academic/Scholarly.* **Description:** Focuses on the morphology, taxonomy, zoogeography, evolution and development of insects, both recent and fossil, as well as faunistics and phylogeny.
Indexed: BIOSIS Prev, BiolAb, ZooRec.
—BLDSC (1733.897000), CISTI. **CCC.**
Published by: K M K Scientific Press Ltd., c/o Dr K G Mikhailov, Zoologicheskii Muzei MGU, Bol'shaya Nikitskaya 6, Moscow, 125009, Russian Federation. TEL 7-095-2925796, FAX 7-095-2032717, kmk2000@online.ru, http://www.orc.ru/~kmkweb/arthropoda_selecta.htm. Ed. Kirill G Mikhailov.

595.7 CAN
ARTHROPODS OF CANADIAN GRASSLANDS. Text in English. 1983. a.
Published by: Biological Survey of Canada, Canadian Museum of Nature, Box 3443, Station Dg, Ottawa, ON K1P 6P4, Canada. bsc@mus-nature.ca.

595.7 USA ISSN 0066-8036
QL434 CODEN: AFNLAX
ARTHROPODS OF FLORIDA AND NEIGHBORING LAND AREAS. Text in English. 1965. irreg., latest vol.16, 1998. price varies. back issues avail. **Document type:** *Catalog, Government.*
Indexed: BIOSIS Prev, BibAg, BiolAb, ZooRec.
—CISTI.
Published by: Department of Agriculture and Consumer Services, Division of Plant Industry, 1911 S W 34th St, Box 147100, Gainesville, FL 32614-7100. TEL 904-372-3505, FAX 904-955-2301. Ed. J B Heppner. R&P Denise Feiber.

595.7 JPN ISSN 0910-5123
ARUBO/ALBO. Text in Japanese. s-a. membership.
Published by: Kagoshima Konchu Dokokai/Kagoshima Entomological Society, Sameshima Hifuka, 8-8 Komatsubara 1-chome, Kagoshima-shi, 891-0114, Japan.

595.7 ESP ISSN 0210-8984
QL482.S8 CODEN: BAEEDE

➤ **ASOCIACION ESPANOLA DE ENTOMOLOGIA. BOLETIN.** Text in Spanish; Abstracts in English, Spanish. 1978. s-a. adv. bk.rev. bibl.; charts; illus. back issues avail. **Document type:** *Bulletin, Academic/Scholarly.*
Indexed: ASFA, BIOSIS Prev, BiolAb, EntAb, FCA, HGA, IBR, IECT, RefZh, ZooRec.
—CINDOC.
Published by: Asociacion Espanola de Entomologia, Facultad de Ciencias Biologicas, Universidad de Valencia, Burjassot, Valencia 46100, Spain. TEL 34-6-3864680, FAX 34-6-3864651, baixeras@uu.es. Ed. Maria Jesua Verdu. R&P, Adv. contact Joaquin Baixeras.

595.7 592 FRA ISSN 1262-3350

➤ **ASSOCIATION POUR LA PROMOTION DE LA PROTECTION DES INVERTEBRES. CAHIERS.** Cover title: Cahiers de l'A P P I. Text in French. 1997. q. bk.rev.; software rev. bibl.; charts; illus.; maps. cum.index: 1997-1999. back issues avail. **Document type:** *Monographic series, Academic/Scholarly.* **Description:** Covers insect and invertebrate conservation issues.
Published by: Association pour la Promotion de la Protection des Invertebres, 15 rue Mouton Duvernet, Paris, 75014, France. TEL 33-1-45413925, appi@multimania.org, http://www.multimania.org/appi. Pub., R&P Valerie Chansigaud. Circ: 500.

595.7 ITA ISSN 0004-6000
CODEN: BRETA5

➤ **ASSOCIAZIONE ROMANA DI ENTOMOLOGIA. BOLLETTINO.** Text in Italian. 1946. a. free to members. bk.rev. bibl.; charts; illus. index. **Document type:** *Bulletin, Academic/Scholarly.* **Description:** Presents entomological papers, mainly about central and southern Italy.
Indexed: ASFA, BIOSIS Prev, BioCN&I, BiolAb, EntAb, ForAb, HerbAb, RM&VM, RefZh, RevApplEntom, S&F, ZooRec.
Published by: Associazione Romana di Entomologia, c/o Museo Civico di Zoologia, Via Ulisse Aldrovandi, 18, Rome, RM 00197, Italy. tenebrio@hotmail.com, http://www.entoroma.it/bollettino.htm. Ed. Augusto Vigna Taglianti. R&P Simone Fattorini. Circ: 800.

595.7 DEU ISSN 0171-0079
CODEN: ATLNDS
ATALANTA. Text in English, German. 1964. s-a. EUR 33 membership; EUR 11 newsstand/cover (effective 2003). adv. bk.rev. index. back issues avail. **Document type:** *Journal, Academic/Scholarly.*
Indexed: BIOSIS Prev, BiolAb, IBR, RefZh, ZooRec.
—Linda Hall.
Published by: Deutsche Forschungszentrale fuer Schmetterlingswanderungen, Humboldtstr 13 A, Marktleuthen, 95168, Germany. TEL 49-9285-480, FAX 49-9285-8238. Ed. Ulf Eitschberger. Circ: 1,200.

595.7 AUS ISSN 0374-5147
AUSTRALIAN ENTOMOLOGICAL SOCIETY. MISCELLANEOUS PUBLICATIONS. Text in English. irreg. price varies.
Indexed: ASFA, ApicAb, BIOSIS Prev, BiolAb, ZooRec.
Published by: Australian Entomological Society, c/o Dr Laurence Mound, CSIRO Entomology, Dr Laurence Mound, GPO Box 1700, Canberra, ACT 2601, Australia.

595.7 AUS ISSN 1320-6133
CODEN: AUENEZ

➤ **AUSTRALIAN ENTOMOLOGIST.** Text in English. 1972. q. AUD 25 domestic to individuals; AUD 30 in Asia to individuals; AUD 35 elsewhere to individuals; AUD 30 domestic to institutions; AUD 40 foreign to institutions (effective 2002). adv. bk.rev. back issues avail. **Document type:** *Academic/Scholarly.* **Description:** Devoted to the natural history and systematics of the native insect and related arthropod fauna of the Australian region, including the islands of the South West Pacific.

B

▼ *new title* ➤ *refereed* ✶ *unverified* ♦ *full entry avail.*

Formerly: Australian Entomological Magazine (0311-1881)
Indexed: ASFA, Agr, AgrForAb, B&BAb, BIOSIS Prev, BioCN&I, BiolAb, CurCont, EntAb, ForAb, GenetAb, HGA, HerbAb, HortAb, OrnHort, PoultAb, RA&MP, RPP, RRTA, RevApplEntom, RiceAb, SeedAb, TDB, WeedAb, ZooRec.
—Linda Hall.
Published by: Entomological Society of Queensland, PO Box 537, Indooroopilly, QLD 4068, Australia. TEL 61-7-3365-2271, FAX 61-7-3846-1226, susanandjeff@hotkey.net.au. Ed. David Hancock. Adv. contact Susan Wright TEL 61-7-3840-7704. Circ: 500 (controlled).

595.7 AUS ISSN 1326-6756
QL487
➤ **AUSTRALIAN JOURNAL OF ENTOMOLOGY.** Text in English. 1962. q. GBP 166 combined subscription in Australia & New Zealand to institutions print & online eds.; USD 376 combined subscription in the Americas to institutions print & online eds.; GBP 231 combined subscription elsewhere to institutions print & online eds. (effective 2006). adv. bk.rev. charts; illus. Index. **Document type:** *Journal, Academic/Scholarly.* **Description:** Publishes research in the biology, taxonomy, ecology, and control of insects and arachnids in Australia.
Formerly (until 1996): Australian Entomological Society. Journal (0004-9050)
Related titles: Online - full text ed.: ISSN 1440-6055. GBP 157 in Australia & New Zealand to institutions; USD 357 in the Americas to institutions & Caribbean; GBP 219 elsewhere to institutions (effective 2006) (from Blackwell Synergy, EBSCO Publishing, Gale Group, IngentaConnect, O C L C Online Computer Library Center, Inc., Swets Information Services).
Indexed: ASCA, ASFA, AbHyg, AgBio, Agr, AgrForAb, AnBeAb, ApEcolAb, BIOBASE, BIOSIS Prev, BioCN&I, BiolAb, CPA, ChemAb, CurCont, DBA, ESPM, EntAb, FCA, FPA, ForAb, HGA, HerbAb, HortAb, ISR, IndVet, MaizeAb, NemAb, NutrAb, OceAb, OrnHort, PBA, PGegResA, PHN&I, PotatoAb, PoultAb, ProtozoAb, RA&MP, RM&VM, RefZh, RevApplEntom, RiceAb, S&F, SCI, SIA, SPPI, SeedAb, SoyAb, TDB, TriticAb, VITIS, VetBull, WeedAb, ZooRec.
—BLDSC (1807.640000), CASDDS, CISTI, IDS, IE, Infotrieve, ingenta, Linda Hall. **CCC.**
Published by: (Australian Entomological Society, Bureau of Sugar Experiment Stations), Blackwell Publishing Asia (Subsidiary of: Blackwell Publishing Ltd.), 550 Swanston St, Carlton South, VIC 3053, Australia. TEL 61-383591011, FAX 61-383591120, subs@blackwellpublishingasia.com, http://www.blackwellpublishing.com/journals/AEN. Ed. John Matthiessen. **Subscr. to:** PO Box 378, Carlton South, VIC 3053, Australia. subscriptions@blacksci-asia.com.au.

595.7 LVA ISSN 1407-8619
BALTIC JOURNAL OF COLEOPTEROLOGY. Text in English. 2001. s-a. **Document type:** *Journal, Academic/Scholarly.*
Related titles: Supplement(s): Notiophilus.
Indexed: AgrForAb, BioCN&I, EntAb, FCA, ForAb, GEOBASE, HortAb, OrnHort, PHN&I, PotatoAb, S&F, SeedAb, TriticAb, ZooRec.
Published by: Baltijas Koleopterologijas Instituts/Baltic Institute of Coleopterology, Biologijas Katedra, Daugavpils Universitate, Vienibas iela 13-229, Daugavpils, 5401, Latvia. TEL 371-54-26719, beetles@dau.lv, http://www.bio.dpu.lv. Ed. Arvid Barshevskis.

595.7 BGD ISSN 1021-1004
BANGLADESH JOURNAL OF ENTOMOLOGY. Text in English. 1991. s-a.
Indexed: ASFA, AgrForAb, B&BAb, BioCN&I, CPA, EntAb, FCA, FPA, ForAb, HerbAb, HortAb, IndVet, PBA, PHN&I, RA&MP, S&F, SIA, SeedAb, SoyAb, TriticAb, WAE&RSA, ZooRec.
—BLDSC (1861.670740).
Published by: Bangladesh Entomological Society, c/o Dr. K A M Shahadat Hossain Mondal, University of Rajshahi, Rajshahi, 6205, Bangladesh.

595.7 FIN ISSN 0355-4791
BAPTRIA. Text in Finnish; Summaries in English, Swedish. 1976. q. **Document type:** *Journal, Academic/Scholarly.*
Published by: Suomen Perhostutkijain Seura ry/Lepidopterological Society of Finland, Laemmittaejaenkatu 2 A, Helsinki, 00810, Finland. TEL 358-9-4772310, FAX 358-9-4772311, toimisto@perhostutkijainseura.fi, http://www.perhostutkijainseura.fi.

595.773 JPN
BATTARIGISU/JAPANESE SOCIETY OF ORTHOPTERA. BULLETIN. Text in Japanese. 1978. irreg. JPY 600 per issue.
Published by: Nihon Chokushirui Kenkyukai/Japanese Society of Orthoptera, c/o Mr Yasutsugu Kano, 1-31 Kikyogaoka 5-chome, Nabari-shi, Mie-ken 518-0400, Japan.

595.78 GBR ISSN 0265-8690
BEEKEEPER'S ANNUAL. Text in English. 1982. a. **Document type:** *Consumer.*
Published by: Northern Bee Books, Scout Bottom Farm, Mytholmroyd, Hebden Bridge, W Yorks HX7 5JS, United Kingdom. TEL 44-1422-882751, FAX 44-1422-886157. Ed. John Phipps. Adv. contact Julie Dower.

595.78 GBR ISSN 0268-4780
THE BEEKEEPER'S QUARTERLY. Text in English. 1984. q. GBP 16 (effective 2000). adv. bk.rev. back issues avail. **Document type:** *Newsletter, Consumer.*
Published by: Northern Bee Books, Scout Bottom Farm, Mytholmroyd, Hebden Bridge, W Yorks HX7 5JS, United Kingdom. TEL 44-1422-882751, FAX 44-1422-886157. Ed. John Phipps. Adv. contact Julie Dower. page GBP 175; trim 195 x 283. Circ: 2,600 (paid).

595.7 DEU ISSN 0005-805X
QL461 CODEN: BEIEAP
BEITRAEGE ZUR ENTOMOLOGIE/CONTRIBUTIONS TO ENTOMOLOGY. Text in English, German. 1951. s-a. EUR 120 (effective 2004). adv. bk.rev. charts; illus. index. **Document type:** *Journal, Academic/Scholarly.* **Description:** Contains original contributions concerning insect systematics, phylogeny, zoogeography, faunistics, ecology, applied entomology, entomological bibliography, and the history of entomology.
Related titles: Online - full text ed.
Indexed: ASFA, BioCN&I, BiolAb, ChemAb, EntAb, HGA, HortAb, RM&VM, RefZh, RevApplEntom, S&F, SeedAb, WeedAb, ZooRec.
—BLDSC (1879.000000), CISTI, IE, ingenta. **CCC.**
Published by: (Deutsches Entomologisches Institut), Verlag Goecke und Evers, Sportplatzweg 5, Keltern-Weiler, 75210, Germany. TEL 49-7236-7174, FAX 49-7236-7325, books@goeckeevers.de, http://www.goeckeevers.de. Ed. Holger Dathe. adv.: B&W page EUR 400.

595.7 BEL ISSN 1374-5514
QL461 CODEN: BASEBE
➤ **BELGIAN JOURNAL OF ENTOMOLOGY.** Text in English, French. 1855. q. bk.rev. index. **Document type:** *Academic/Scholarly.*
Former titles (until 1999): Societe Royale Belge d'Entomologie. Bulletin et Annales (0374-6038); (until 1972): Societe Royale d'Entomologie de Belgique. Bulletin et Annales (0049-1128); (until 1955): Societe Entomologique de Belgique. Bulletin et Annales (0774-5923); (until 1925): Societe Entomologique de Belgique. Annales (0774-5915); Societe Entomologique Belge. Annales (0774-5893)
Indexed: AgrForAb, BIOSIS Prev, BioCN&I, BiolAb, EntAb, ForAb, GenetAb, HGA, PBA, PGegResA, PHN&I, PoultAb, RM&VM, RefZh, RevApplEntom, S&F, ZooRec.
—CISTI, Linda Hall.
Published by: Societe Royal Belge d'Entomologie, rue Vautierstraat 29, Brussels, 1000, Belgium. TEL 32-2-627-4296, FAX 32-2-627-4132, gcoulon@kbinirsmb.be, srbe@sciencesnaturelles.be. Ed. Georges Coulon. **Dist. by:** Backhuys Publishers BV, Postbus 321, Leiden 2300 AH, Netherlands. TEL 31-71-517-0208, FAX 31-71-517-1856.

595.7 NLD ISSN 1386-6141
CODEN: BOCOFW
➤ **BIOCONTROL;** journal of the International Organisation for Biological Control. Text in English, French, German, Italian, Spanish. 1956. bi-m. EUR 498, USD 518, GBP 328 combined subscription to institutions print & online eds. (effective 2005). adv. bk.rev. charts; illus. reprint service avail. from PSC. **Document type:** *Academic/Scholarly.* **Description:** Covers the biological control of invertebrate, vertebrate, weed pests, and plant diseases; subject range in biology and ecology of organisms.
Formerly (until 1997): Entomophaga (0013-8959)
Related titles: Online - full text ed.: ISSN 1573-8248 (from EBSCO Publishing, Gale Group, IngentaConnect, Kluwer Online, O C L C Online Computer Library Center, Inc., Ovid Technologies, Inc., Springer LINK, Swets Information Services).
Indexed: ASCA, AgBio, AgrForAb, ApEcolAb, BIOBASE, BIOSIS Prev, BibLing, BioCN&I, BiolAb, CIN, CPA, CTFA, ChemAb, ChemTitl, CurCont, ESPM, EntAb, FCA, ForAb, GEOBASE, HelmAb, HerbAb, HortAb, I&DA, ISR, IndVet, MBA, MaizeAb, NemAb, NutrAb, OrnHort, PBA, PGegResA, PHN&I, PN&I, PotatoAb, ProtozoAb, RA&MP, RM&VM, RPP, RefZh, RevApplEntom, RiceAb, S&F, SCI, SIA, SeedAb, SoyAb, TDB, TriticAb, VITIS, VetBull, WAE&RSA, WeedAb, ZooRec.
—BLDSC (2071.086000), CASDDS, CISTI, IDS, IE, Infotrieve, ingenta, Linda Hall. **CCC.**
Published by: (International Organization for Biological Control FRA), Springer-Verlag Dordrecht (Subsidiary of: Springer Science+Business Media), Van Godewijckstraat 30, Dordrecht, 3311 GX, Netherlands. TEL 31-78-6576050, FAX 31-78-6576474, http://springerlink.metapress.com/openurl.asp?genre=journal&issn=1386-6141, http://www.springeronline.com. Ed. Heikki M T Hokkanen. Circ: 1,000.

➤ **BIOCONTROL SCIENCE AND TECHNOLOGY.** see *AGRICULTURE—Crop Production And Soil*

595.7 CAN ISSN 0833-6326
BIOLOGICAL SURVEY OF CANADA. MONOGRAPH SERIES. Text in English. 1987. irreg. **Document type:** *Monographic series.*
Indexed: ZooRec.
—CISTI.
Published by: Biological Survey of Canada, Canadian Museum of Nature, Box 3443, Station Dg, Ottawa, ON K1P 6P4, Canada. bsc@mus-nature.ca.

595.7 CAN
BIOLOGICAL SURVEY OF CANADA. NEWSLETTER. Text in English. 1997. s-a.
Published by: Biological Survey of Canada, Canadian Museum of Nature, Box 3443, Station Dg, Ottawa, ON K1P 6P4, Canada. bsc@mus-nature.ca.

595.7 CAN ISSN 1200-2852
BIOLOGICAL SURVEY OF CANADA. TAXONOMIC SERIES. Text in English. 1989. irreg.
Indexed: ZooRec.
Published by: Biological Survey of Canada, Canadian Museum of Nature, Box 3443, Station Dg, Ottawa, ON K1P 6P4, Canada. bsc@mus-nature.ca.

595.7 DEU ISSN 0179-5295
CODEN: BIZEE6
BIOLOGISCHE ZEITSCHRIFT. Text in German. 1986. irreg. price varies. adv. bk.rev.
Indexed: ArtHuCI, ZooRec.
Published by: Research and Consulting Institute, Lister Weg 40, Hamburg, 22117, Germany. Ed. R Sergel.

595.7 USA ISSN 0893-3146
QL489.A1
BISHOP MUSEUM BULLETINS IN ENTOMOLOGY. Text in English. 1922. irreg., latest vol.7, 1997. price varies. reprint service avail. from PQC. **Description:** Covers insects and other arthropods of Hawaii and the Pacific Basin.
Supersedes in part (in 1987): Bernice P. Bishop Museum Bulletin (0005-9439)
Indexed: Agr, BIOSIS Prev, RefZh, RevApplEntom, ZooRec.
—CISTI, Linda Hall.
Published by: (Bernice Pauahi Bishop Museum), Bishop Museum Press, 1525 Bernice St, Box 19000 A, Honolulu, HI 96817. TEL 808-847-3511, FAX 808-841-8968. Circ: 300.

595.7 DEU ISSN 0724-4223
BOMBUS; faunistische Mitteilungen aus Nordwestdeutschland. Text in German. 1937. irreg. back issues avail. **Document type:** *Academic/Scholarly.*
Indexed: BiolAb, ZooRec.
Published by: Verein fuer Naturwissenschaftliche Heimatforschung zu Hamburg e.V., Zoologisches Institut und Museum, Martin-Luther-King-Platz 3, Hamburg, 20146, Germany. Ed. Thomas Tischler. Circ: 300 (controlled).

595.7 NLD ISSN 1386-3460
BRACHYTRON. Text in Dutch; Summaries in English. 1997. s-a. **Description:** Covers the distribution, ecology, behavior, and identification of the Dutch dragonfly fauna.
Indexed: ASFA, ZooRec.
Published by: Nederlandse Vereniging voor Libellenstudie/Dutch Dragonfly Association, c/o Marcel Wasscher, Minstraat 15 bis, Utrecht, 3582, Netherlands. http://www.libellen.org. Ed. Klaas-Douwe Dijkstra.

595.7 GBR ISSN 0952-7583
BRITISH JOURNAL OF ENTOMOLOGY AND NATURAL HISTORY. Text in English. q.
Formerly (until 1987): British Entomological and Natural History Society. Proceedings and Transactions (0525-5252)
Indexed: AEA, ASFA, Agr, AgrForAb, BioCN&I, FPA, ForAb, HGA, HerbAb, HortAb, OrnHort, PBA, RA&MP, S&F, WeedAb, ZooRec.
—BLDSC (2307.780000), IE, ingenta.
Published by: The British Entomological and Natural History Society, The Pelham-Clinton Bldg, Dinton Pastures Country Park, Davis Street, Hurst, Reading, Berkshire, RG10 0TH, United Kingdom.

595.7 USA ISSN 1061-3781
QL520.2.A1
➤ **BULLETIN OF AMERICAN ODONATOLOGY.** Text in English, Spanish. 1992. irreg. USD 15 per vol. (effective 2000). bk.rev. back issues avail. **Document type:** *Journal, Academic/Scholarly.* **Description:** Contains studies of New World odonata, including regional faunal surveys, descriptions of immature (larval) stages, systematics, and taxonomy.
Indexed: ZooRec.
Published by: Dragonfly Society of the Americas, 2091 Partridge Ln, Binghamton, NY 13903. TEL 607-722-4939. Ed. Thomas W Donnelly. Circ: 250 (paid).

595.7 GBR ISSN 0007-4853
QL461 CODEN: BEREA2
➤ **BULLETIN OF ENTOMOLOGICAL RESEARCH;** containing original and review articles on economic entomology. Text in English. 1910. bi-m. USD 945 in the Americas to institutions except Canada; GBP 540 elsewhere to institutions; USD 1,015 combined subscription in the Americas to institutions except Canada; print & online eds.; GBP 280 combined subscription elsewhere to institutions print & online eds. (effective 2006). adv. bibl.; charts; illus. index. back issues avail.; reprints avail. **Document type:** *Journal, Academic/Scholarly.* **Description:** Contains original research papers on insects, mites, and ticks of economic importance in the agricultural, medical and veterinary medical fields in all parts of the world.

B

Related titles: Microfiche ed.: (from BHP); Online - full text ed.: ISSN 1475-2670. USD 805 in the Americas to institutions except Canada; GBP 460 elsewhere to institutions (effective 2006) (from DIMDI, EBSCO Publishing, Gale Group, H.W. Wilson, IngentaConnect, O C L C Online Computer Library Center, Inc., Ovid Technologies, Inc., Swets Information Services, The Dialog Corporation).
Indexed: ASCA, ASFA, AbHyg, AgBio, Agr, AgrForAb, AnBeAb, ApEcolAb, B&AI, B&BAb, BIOBASE, BIOSIS Prev, BibAg, BioCN&I, BioDAb, BiolAb, CIN, CPA, CTFA, ChemAb, ChemTitl, CurCont, DBA, DSA, ESPM, EntAb, FCA, FPA, ForAb, GEOBASE, GenetAb, HGA, HelmAb, HerbAb, HortAb, IABS, ISR, IndMed, IndVet, MEDLINE, MaizeAb, NemAb, NutrAb, OrnHort, PBA, PGegResA, PHN&I, PlantSci, PotatoAb, PoultAb, ProtozoAb, RA&MP, RM&VM, RPP, RefZh, RevApplEntom, RiceAb, S&F, S&MA, SCI, SIA, SPPI, SeedAb, SoyAb, TDB, TOSA, TriticAb, VITIS, VetBull, WeedAb, ZooRec.
—BLDSC (2853.000000), CASDDS, CISTI, GNLM, IDS, IE, Infotrieve, ingenta, Linda Hall. **CCC.**
Published by: CABI Publishing (Subsidiary of: CAB International), CAB International, Wallingford, Oxfordshire OX10 8DE, United Kingdom. TEL 44-1491-832111, FAX 44-1491-833508, orders@cabi.org, http://www.cabi-publishing.org/. Ed. Dr. B Symondson. adv.: B&W page GBP 225, B&W page USD 360; 170 x 225. Circ: 286. **N. America office:** CABI Publishing North America, 875 Massachusetts Ave, 7th Fl, Cambridge, MA 02139. TEL 617-395-4056, 800-528-4841, FAX 617-354-6875, cabi-nao@cabi.org.

595.7 ITA ISSN 1721-8861
QL461
BULLETIN OF INSECTOLOGY. Text in English; Summaries in Italian. 1928. a. **Document type:** *Bulletin, Academic/Scholarly.*
Formerly (until 2002): Universita degli Studi di Bologna. Istituto di Entomologia Guido Grandi. Bollettino (1120-0979)
Indexed: AEA, ASFA, AgrForAb, BIOSIS Prev, BioCN&I, BiolAb, CPA, ESPM, EntAb, FCA, ForAb, HerbAb, HortAb, MaizeAb, OrnHort, PBA, PHN&I, PotatoAb, PoultAb, RA&MP, RPP, RefZh, RiceAb, S&F, SIA, SeedAb, TriticAb, WeedAb.
—BLDSC (2864.491000), CISTI, IE, ingenta.
Published by: Universita degli Studi di Bologna, Istituto di Entomologia Guido Grandi, Via Filippo Re 6, Bologna, 40126, Italy. TEL 39-51-2091550, FAX 39-51-251052, http://www.entom.agrsci.unibo.it/Bol%20Ist%20Entom.htm.

595.7 CHE ISSN 0256-3991
➤ **BULLETIN ROMAND D'ENTOMOLOGIE.** Text in French; Summaries in English, French. 1981. s-a. CHF 20 (effective 2000). bk.rev. back issues avail. **Document type:** *Journal, Academic/Scholarly.*
Indexed: RefZh, ZooRec.
Published by: Societe Entomologique de Geneve, Museum d'Histoire Naturelle, Case Postale 6434, Geneva 6, 1211, Switzerland. TEL 41-22-4186300, FAX 41-22-4186301. Ed. Jean Wuest. Circ: 450 (paid).

595.789 639.975 GBR
➤ **BUTTERFLY.** Text in English. 3/yr. GBP 24 domestic; GBP 26 foreign (effective 2003). adv. bk.rev.; software rev. charts; illus.; stat. 36 p./no.; back issues avail. **Document type:** *Magazine, Academic/Scholarly.* **Description:** Magazine for the members of Butterfly Conservation.
Former titles: Butterfly Conservation News (1362-2323); (until 19??): British Butterfly Conservation Society. News (0962-4392)
Published by: Butterfly Conservation, Manor Yard, East Lulworth, Wareham, Dorset BH20 5QP, United Kingdom. TEL 44-870-7744309, FAX 44-1929-400210, info@butterfly-conservation.org, http://www.butterfly-conservation.org. Ed. Malcolm Tait. Pub. Ian McAuliffe. Adv. contact Caroline McLoughlin TEL 44-20-89623020. B&W page GBP 300, color page GBP 450; trim 210 x 297. Circ: 12,000.

595.7 USA ISSN 1541-9746
BUTTERFLY GARDENER. Text in English. q.
Indexed: GardL.
Published by: North American Butterfly Association, 4 Delaware Rd, Morristown, NJ 07960. http://www.naba.org.

BUZZ WORDS. see *PUBLIC HEALTH AND SAFETY*

595.7 AUS ISSN 1443-8577
SB921
C S I R O ENTOMOLOGY. REPORT OF RESEARCH. (Commonwealth Scientific and Industrial Research Organisation) Text in English. 1960. biennial. AUD 15 (effective 2001); exchange basis. back issues avail. **Document type:** *Corporate.* **Description:** Technical description of work in progress at the largest entomological research institution in Australia.
Former titles: Commonwealth Scientific and Industrial Research Organisation. Division of Entomology. Report of Research; (until 1987): Commonwealth Scientific and Industrial Research Organisation. Division of Entomology. Report (1037-3500); (until 1983): Commonwealth Scientific and Industrial Research Organisation. Division of Entomology. Annual Report (0728-5825)
Related titles: Online - full content ed.
Indexed: BioCN&I, RevApplEntom, WeedAb.
—CISTI.
Published by: Commonwealth Scientific and Industrial Research Organisation, Division of Entomology, GPO Box 1700, Canberra, ACT 2601, Australia. TEL 61-2-62464001, FAX 61-2-62464000, info@ento.csiro.au, http://www.csiro.au. Ed. Malcolm Robertson. R&P Norm White TEL 61-2-62464009. Circ: 1,500.

595.7 USA ISSN 0068-5631
QL475.C3 CODEN: BCINA4
➤ **CALIFORNIA INSECT SURVEY. BULLETIN.** Text in English. 1950. irreg., latest vol.27, 1986. price varies. **Document type:** *Monographic series, Academic/Scholarly.*
Indexed: AbHyg, BiolAb, RevApplEntom, TDB.
—CISTI, Linda Hall.
Published by: (California Insect Survey), University of California Press, Book Series, 2120 Berkeley Way, Berkeley, CA 94720. TEL 510-642-4247, FAX 510-643-7127, askucp@ucpress.edu, http://www.ucpress.edu/books/BCIS.ser.html, http://www.ucpress.edu/books/series.html. **Orders to:** California - Princeton Fulfillment Services, 1445 Lower Ferry Rd, Ewing, NJ 08618. TEL 800-777-4726, FAX 800-999-1958, orders@cpfs.pupress.princeton.edu.

595.7 CAN ISSN 0008-347X
CODEN: CAENAF
➤ **CANADIAN ENTOMOLOGIST.** Text mainly in English; Text occasionally in French. 1868. bi-m. CND 300 domestic print & online eds.; USD 300 foreign print & online eds. (effective 2005). bk.rev. bibl.; charts; illus.; stat. index. back issues avail.; reprint service avail. from PQC. **Document type:** *Journal, Academic/Scholarly.* **Description:** It publishes results of original observations and research on all aspects of entomology.
Related titles: Microfiche ed.: (from IDC); Microform ed.: (from PMC, PQC); Online - full text ed.: (from EBSCO Publishing, Micromedia ProQuest, ProQuest Information & Learning).
Indexed: ASCA, ASFA, AgBio, Agr, AgrForAb, AnBeAb, ApEcolAb, B&AI, B&BAb, BIOBASE, BIOSIS Prev, BibAg, BioCN&I, BiolAb, CIS, CPA, ChemAb, CurCont, DBA, EIA, ESPM, EnerInd, EntAb, ExcerpMed, FCA, FPA, ForAb, GEOBASE, GenetAb, HGA, HerbAb, HortAb, IABS, IBR, ISR, MaizeAb, NemAb, NutrAb, OrnHort, PBA, PGegResA, PHN&I, PlantSci, PotatoAb, PoultAb, ProtozoAb, RA&MP, RM&VM, RPP, RevApplEntom, RiceAb, S&F, SCI, SIA, SeedAb, TOSA, TriticAb, VITIS, WAE&RSA, WeedAb, ZooRec.
—BLDSC (3022.000000), CASDDS, CISTI, IDS, IE, Infotrieve, ingenta, Linda Hall. **CCC.**
Published by: (Entomological Society of Canada), N R C Research Press, Building M 55, Ottawa, ON K1A 0R6, Canada. TEL 613-993-0362, pubs@nrc-cnrc.gc.ca, http://www.esc-sec.org/canent1.htm, http://pubs.nrc-cnrc.gc.ca. Ed. Richard A Ring. Pub. Jose Mari Perez TEL 613-993-9094. Circ: 1,200.

595.7 NLD
➤ **CATALOGUE OF PALAEARCTIC DIPTERA.** Text in Dutch. 1984. irreg., latest vol.13, 1993. price varies. illus. **Document type:** *Monographic series, Academic/Scholarly.* **Description:** Catalogs the main taxonomic nomenclatural and distribution data of some 25,000 fly species from the arctic regions.
Published by: Elsevier BV (Subsidiary of: Elsevier Science & Technology), Radarweg 29, Amsterdam, 1043 NX, Netherlands. TEL 31-20-4853911, FAX 31-20-4852457, nlinfo-f@elsevier.nl, http://www.elsevier.nl. Eds. A Soos, L Papp.

595.7 ESP ISSN 1134-6108
CATALOGUS DE LA ENTOMOFAUNA ARAGONESA. Text in Spanish. 1994. irreg.
Related titles: ♦ Supplement to: Sociedad Entomologica Aragonesa. Boletin. ISSN 1134-6094.
Indexed: ZooRec.
Published by: Sociedad Entomologica Aragonesa, Ave. Radio Juventud, 37, Zaragoza, 50012, Spain. TEL 34-976-324415, FAX 34-976-535697, amelic@retemail.es, http://entomologia.rediris.es/sea/index.htm.

595.772 IND ISSN 0008-8676
SB767 CODEN: CECIAI
CECIDOLOGIA INTERNATIONALE. Text in English. 1966. 3/yr. USD 125. adv. bk.rev. bibl.; charts; illus. **Description:** Examines phylogenetic studies on cecimyiid and other cecidozoa; their eco-biology, cecidogenesis, biochemistry, regular and pathological morphogenesis. Includes plant- and cecidozoa-pathogen relationships as well as karyological studies.
Formed by the merger of: Cecidologia Indica; Marcellia
Related titles: Microfilm ed.
Indexed: BioCN&I, BiolAb, FPA, ForAb, HortAb.
Published by: Cecidological Society of India, 14 Park Rd., Allahabad, Uttar Pradesh 211 002, India. TEL 51958. Ed. Prabha Grover. Circ: 250.

595.7 JPN ISSN 0388-6492
CELASTRINA. Text in Japanese. 1978. s-a. JPY 1,400 per issue.
Published by: Tsugaru Konchu Dokokai/Tsugaru Insect Lover's Society, c/o Mr Tadashi Kudo, 323-1 Doi, Kitatsugaru-gun, Itayanagimachi, Aomori-ken 038-36, Japan.

595.7 USA
CENTER FOR ENTOMOLOGICAL STUDIES. MEMOIRS. Text in English. a.
Indexed: ZooRec.
Published by: Center for Systematic Entomology, PO Box 147100, Gainesville, FL 32614-7100. hamona@doacs.state.fl.us.

595.7 MLT ISSN 1560-8417
THE CENTRAL MEDITERRANEAN NATURALIST. Text in English. 1996. a.
Indexed: ZooRec.
Published by: Nature Trust, P.O. Box 9, Valletta, CMR 01, Malta. info@naturetrustmalta.org, http://www.naturetrustmalta.org/.

595.7 TUR
CENTRE FOR ENTOMOLOGICAL STUDIES. MEMOIRS. Text in English, French, German. 1991. irreg.
Indexed: ZooRec.
Published by: Centre for Entomological Studies, Yuzuncu Yil Universitesi, Fen-Edebiyat Fakultesi, Biyoloji Bolumu, Zeve - Kampus Van, Ankara, Turkey. a_kocak@mailcity.com.

595.7 TUR ISSN 1015-8235
CODEN: MCESEM
CENTRE FOR ENTOMOLOGICAL STUDIES. MISCELLANEOUS PAPERS. Text in English, French, German. 1989. irreg.
Indexed: ZooRec.
—BLDSC (5813.890000).
Published by: Centre for Entomological Studies, Yuzuncu Yil Universitesi, Fen-Edebiyat Fakultesi, Biyoloji Bolumu, Zeve - Kampus Van, Ankara, Turkey. a_kocak@mailcity.com.

595.7 BEL ISSN 0778-4686
CERCLE DES LEPIDOPTERISTES DE BELGIQUE. BULLETIN. Text in French. 1972. bi-m.
Indexed: ZooRec.
Published by: Cercle des Lepidopteristes de Belgique, Rue Vautier 29 B, Bruxelles, 1000, Belgium.

595.7 BEL
CETONIIDARUM GENERUM LEXICON. Text in French, English. 2000. q.
Indexed: ZooRec.
Published by: Cetoniimania, 5 rue Georges Willame, Nivelles, 1400, Belgium. robert.alexis@yucom.be.

595.7 BEL ISSN 1376-7402
CETONIIDARUM SPECIERUM LEXICON. Text in French, English. 2000. q.
Related titles: Supplement(s): Cetoniimania. ISSN 1376-5035.
Indexed: ZooRec.
Published by: Cetoniimania, 5 rue Georges Willame, Nivelles, 1400, Belgium. robert.alexis@yucom.be.

595.7 TWN ISSN 0258-462X
QL461 CODEN: CKUCEY
CHINESE JOURNAL OF ENTOMOLOGY/ZHONGHUA KUNCHONG. Text in English. 1981. s-a.
Related titles: Supplement(s): Chinese Journal of Entomology. Special Publication. ISSN 1017-7981. 1987.
Indexed: AEA, ASFA, AgBio, AgrForAb, AnBeAb, BioCN&I, EntAb, HortAb, MaizeAb, NemAb, NutrAb, OrnHort, PBA, PHN&I, ProtozoAb, RA&MP, RiceAb, SIA, WeedAb, ZooRec.
—CISTI.
Published by: Entomological Society of China, 27, Lane 113, Roosevelt Rd, Sec 4, Taipei, Taiwan 10765, Taiwan.

CHOJU KANKEI TOKEI/ANNUAL STATISTICS OF BIRDS AND ANIMALS. see *BIOLOGY—Abstracting, Bibliographies, Statistics*

595.7 JPN ISSN 0913-8323
CHOKEN FIELD/STUDY OF BUTTERFLY. Text in Japanese. 1986. m. JPY 1,480, USD 76 per issue.
Published by: Choken Shuppan, 13-27 Sojiji 1-chome, Ibaraki-shi, Osaka-fu 567-0801, Japan. TEL 81-726-27-9828, FAX 81-726-27-4464, chouken@po.aianet.or.jp. Ed. Yoshiaki Shouji.

595.762 USA ISSN 0590-6334
QL596.C56
➤ **CICINDELA**✶ ; a quarterly journal devoted to cicindelidae. Text in English. 1969. q. USD 10 (effective 2003). bk.rev. bibl.; charts; illus.; stat. 1 cols./p.; back issues avail. **Document type:** *Journal, Academic/Scholarly.* **Description:** Covers and specializes in one family of beetles.
Indexed: Agr, BIOSIS Prev, BiolAb, RefZh, ZooRec.
Address: 2521 Jones Pl W, Bloomington, MN 55431-2837. Ed. Ronald L Huber. Circ: 160.

595.7 GBR ISSN 0965-5794
➤ **THE COLEOPTERIST.** Text in English. 1980. 3/yr. GBP 7 in the European Union to individuals; GBP 10 elsewhere to individuals; GBP 10 to institutions (effective 2002). adv. bk.rev. illus. back issues avail. **Document type:** *Magazine, Academic/Scholarly.* **Description:** Publishes material about the coleoptera and strepsiptera from, or likely to occur in, The British Isles.
Formerly (until 1992): Coleopterist's Newsletter (0959-9711)
Indexed: ZooRec.
—BLDSC (3296.995000).

B

Published by: The Coleopterist, c/o P J Hodge, 8 Harvard Rd, Ringmer, Lewes, E Sussex BN8 5HK, United Kingdom. peter.j.hodge@tesco.net, http://www.coleopterist.org.uk. Ed. Mr. A J W Allen. adv.: B&W page GBP 25. Circ: 300.

595.76 USA ISSN 0010-065X
QL571 CODEN: COBLAO
➤ **THE COLEOPTERISTS BULLETIN.** Text mainly in English. 1947. q. USD 30 to individuals; USD 50 to institutions (effective 2002). bk.rev. abstr.; bibl.; illus.; maps. 55 year author index on CD-Rom with vols 1-55 (1947-2001). 150 p./no.; back issues avail. **Document type:** *Journal, Academic/Scholarly.* **Description:** Contains papers on all aspects of the study of beetles - living and fossil, including systematics, phylogeny, biogeography, behavior, ecology, and techniques for study.
Incorporating: Coleopterists Newsletter (0045-7337)
Related titles: Online - full text ed.: (from BioOne, C S A, O C L C Online Computer Library Center, Inc.).
Indexed: ASCA, Agr, AgrForAb, BIOSIS Prev, BibAg, BioCN&I, BioDAb, BiolAb, CurCont, EntAb, FCA, FS&TA, ForAb, GEOBASE, HelmAb, HerbAb, HortAb, IndVet, MaizeAb, NutrAb, OrnHort, PBA, PHN&I, PotatoAb, RA&MP, RM&VM, RefZh, RevApplEntom, S&F, SeedAb, TriticAb, WeedAb, ZooRec.
—BLDSC (3297.000000), IDS, IE, Infotrieve, ingenta, Linda Hall.
Published by: The Coleopterists Society, 3294 Meadowview Rd, Sacramento, CA 95832-1448. TEL 916-262-1160, FAX 916-262-1190, treasurer@coleopsoc.org, http://www.coleopsoc.org/, http://www. coleopsoc.org. Ed. Dr. Chris Carlton TEL 225-578-1838. Circ: 800.

595.7 USA
▼ **THE COLEOPTERISTS SOCIETY MONOGRAPHS. PATRICIA VAURIE SERIES.** Text in English. 2003. irreg.
Indexed: ZooRec.
Published by: The Coleopterists Society, 3294 Meadowview Rd, Sacramento, CA 95832-1448. TEL 916-262-1160, FAX 916-262-1190, http://www. coleopsoc.org.

595.7 USA
▼ **THE COLEOPTERISTS SOCIETY. SPECIAL PUBLICATIONS.** Text in English. 2003. irreg.
Published by: The Coleopterists Society, 3294 Meadowview Rd, Sacramento, CA 95832-1448. TEL 916-262-1160, FAX 916-262-1190, http://www. coleopsoc.org.

595.76 ESP ISSN 1130-7609
CODEN: CMONEH
COLEOPTEROLOGICAL MONOGRAPHS. Text in English, French, Spanish; Summaries in English. 1990. irreg. **Document type:** *Monographic series.*
Indexed: RevApplEntom, ZooRec.
—CINDOC.
Published by: Asociacion Europea de Coleopterologia/European Association of Coleopterology, Dept. de Biologia Animal - Artropodes, Universitat de Barcelona, Avinguda Diagonal, 645, Barcelona, 08028, Spain. TEL 34-93-402-1443, FAX 34-93-411-0887. Circ: 600.

595.7 ITA
CONGRESSO NAZIONALE DI ENTOMOLOGIA. ATTI. Text in Italian. 1957. irreg., latest 1998, 18th, Maratea. price varies.
Indexed: ZooRec.
Published by: Accademia Nazionale Italiana di Entomologia, Via Lanciola, 12-A, Cascine del Riccio, Florence, FI 50125, Italy. TEL 39-55-209182, FAX 39-55-209177.

595.7 592 FRA ISSN 1287-3683
➤ **CONNAISSANCE DES INVERTEBRES.** Text in French. 1997. q. bk.rev.; software rev. bibl.; charts; illus.; maps. index,cum.index: 1997-1999. back issues avail. **Document type:** *Monographic series, Academic/Scholarly.*
Published by: Association pour la Promotion de la Protection des Invertebres, 15 rue Mouton Duvernet, Paris, 75014, France. TEL 33-1-45413925, appi@multimania.com, http://www.multimania.com/appi. Pub. Valerie Chansigaud. Circ: 500.

595.7 USA ISSN 0097-0905
CONNECTICUT. AGRICULTURAL EXPERIMENT STATION, NEW HAVEN. BULLETIN. Text in English. 1877. irreg., latest vol.941, 1997. free (effective 2004). back issues avail. **Document type:** *Journal, Academic/Scholarly.*
Indexed: Agr, BioCN&I, BiolAb, CPA, ChemAb, EIA, EnerInd, EnvAb, FCA, FPA, ForAb, HerbAb, HortAb, I&DA, IndVet, MaizeAb, NutrAb, OrnHort, PBA, PGrRegA, PHN&I, PN&I, PoultAb, RA&MP, RPP, S&F, SIA, SeedAb, TDB, WAE&RSA.
—BLDSC (2458.500000), CISTI, Linda Hall.
Published by: Agricultural Experiment Station, 123 Huntington St, P O Box 1106, New Haven, CT 06504-1106. TEL 203-974-8446, paul.gough@po.state.ct.us, vickie.bomba@po.state.ct.us, http://www.state.ct.us/caes. Ed. Paul Gough. Circ: 2,000.

595.7 GBR ISSN 1369-1090
CONOPID RECORDING SCHEME NEWSLETTER. Text in English. irreg. free to members issued with Dipterists Bulletin (effective 2003). back issues avail. **Document type:** *Newsletter, Academic/Scholarly.*
Related titles: ◆ Supplement to: Dipterists Forum. Bulletin.. ISSN 1358-5029.
Published by: Dipterists Forum, c/o Membership Secretary,, Ger Y Parc, Marianglas, Tynygongl, Benllech, Gwynedd LL74 8NS, United Kingdom. TEL 44-1248-853775, e.howe@ccw.gov.uk, http://www.sel.barc.usda.gov/diptera/society.htm#dipforum. Ed. Mr. D. Clements.

595.7 USA
CONTEMPORARY TOPICS IN ENTOMOLOGY. Text in English. irreg., latest vol.2, 1994. price varies. **Document type:** *Monographic series.*
Published by: Springer-Verlag New York, Inc. (Subsidiary of: Springer Science+Business Media), 233 Spring St, New York, NY 10013. TEL 212-460-1500, FAX 212-460-1575, service@springer-ny.com, http://www.springer-ny.com. Eds. Helmut S van Ernden, Thomas A Miller.

595.7 USA ISSN 1084-0745
QL461
➤ **CONTRIBUTIONS ON ENTOMOLOGY, INTERNATIONAL.** Text in English. 1995. irreg., latest vol.5, 2002-2003. USD 75 per vol. (effective 2003). abstr.; bibl.; illus.; maps. 400 p./no. 1 cols./p.; **Document type:** *Journal, Academic/Scholarly.* **Description:** Publishes articles on entomology.
Indexed: BIOSIS Prev, BiolAb, HortAb, RevApplEntom, ZooRec.
—BLDSC (3458.407000), Linda Hall.
Published by: Associated Publishers, 358102, Gainesville, FL 32635-8102. assopubl@yahoo.com, http://www.mapress.com/AP/. Ed., Pub., R&P Virendra K Gupta. Circ: 100 (paid).

595.7 USA ISSN 1082-5932
GN476.78
CULTURAL ENTOMOLOGY DIGEST. Text in English. 1993. a. USD 12; USD 18 foreign (effective 1999). **Document type:** *Newsletter.* **Description:** Documents the reasons, beliefs, and symbolism behind the inclusion of insects within all factes of the humanities.
Related titles: Online - full text ed.
Published by: IO Vision, PO Box 796, Kalaheo, HI 96741-0796. TEL 808-332-6630, dexter@iovision.com, info@iovision.com, http://www.insects.org/ced/index.html. Ed. Dexter Sear. Circ: 400 (paid).

595.7 DEU ISSN 0931-4873
QL461
D G A A E NACHRICHTEN. Text in German. 1987. irreg. (3-4/yr.). membership. bk.rev.; video rev. back issues avail. **Document type:** *Newsletter, Academic/Scholarly.*
Indexed: AbHyg, AgBio, BioCN&I, CPA, FCA, ForAb, HortAb, MaizeAb, NemAb, OrnHort, PBA, PHN&I, RRTA, TriticAb, ZooRec.
Published by: Deutsche Gesellschaft fuer Allgemeine und Angewandte Entomologie, Schicklerstr 5, Eberswalde, 16225, Germany. TEL 49-3334-589818, FAX 49-3334-212379, blank@dei-eberswalde.de, http://www.dgaae.de. Ed., R&P H. Bathon. Circ: 850 (controlled).

595.7 DNK ISSN 0109-7164
DANMARKS DYRELIV/ANIMAL LIFE OF DENMARK. Text in Danish; Summaries in English. 1984. irreg., latest vol.9, 2000. price varies. illus. back issues avail. **Document type:** *Monographic series, Academic/Scholarly.* **Description:** Covers the insect fauna of Denmark and Fennoscandia or the whole of Northern Europe.
Indexed: ZooRec.
Published by: Apollo Books, Kirkeby Sand 19, Stenstrup, 5771, Denmark. TEL 45-62-26-37-37, FAX 45-62-26-37-80, apollobooks@vip.cybercity.dk, http://www.apollobooks.com. Ed. L. Lyneborg.

595.7 DNK ISSN 0108-1551
DANSK FAUNISTISK BIBLIOTEK. Text in Danish; Summaries in English. 1981. irreg., latest 1999. price varies. back issues avail. **Document type:** *Monographic series, Academic/Scholarly.* **Description:** Provides identification and distribution of North European insect families.
Published by: Apollo Books, Kirkeby Sand 19, Stenstrup, 5771, Denmark. TEL 45-62-26-37-37, FAX 45-62-26-37-80, apollobooks@vip.cybercity.dk, http://www.apollobooks.com. Ed. L. Lyneborg.

595.7 GBR
DERBYSHIRE & NOTTINGHAMSHIRE ENTOMOLOGICAL SOCIETY. JOURNAL. Text in English. q.
Indexed: ZooRec.
Published by: Derbyshire & Nottinghamshire Entomological Society, Derby Museum & Art Gallery, The Strand, Derby, DE1 1BS, United Kingdom. TEL 0-1332-716655, dbud01@aol.com, http://www.dbrc.freeserve.co.uk/html/insects.html.

595.7 DEU ISSN 0344-9084
QL461
DEUTSCHE GESELLSCHAFT FUER ALLGEMEINE UND ANGEWANDTE ENTOMOLOGIE. MITTEILUNGEN. Text in English, German. 1978. irreg., latest vol.14, 2004. price varies. back issues avail. **Document type:** *Bulletin, Academic/Scholarly.*
Indexed: AEA, AbHyg, AgBio, AgrForAb, BioCN&I, CPA, DSA, FCA, FPA, FaBeAb, ForAb, HerbAb, HortAb, IndVet, MaizeAb, NemAb, NutrAb, OrnHort, PBA, PGegResA, PHN&I, PotatoAb, PoultAb, ProtozoAb, RA&MP, RPP, RRTA, RefZh, RevApplEntom, RiceAb, S&F, SIA, SeedAb, TDB, TriticAb, VetBull, WeedAb, ZooRec.
—BLDSC (5839.380000). **CCC.**
Published by: Deutsche Gesellschaft fuer Allgemeine und Angewandte Entomologie, Schicklerstr 5, Eberswalde, 16225, Germany. TEL 49-3334-589818, FAX 49-3334-212379, blank@dei-eberswalde.de, http://www.dgaae.de. Ed. D. Mossakowski.

595.1 GBR ISSN 0953-7260
➤ **DIPTERISTS DIGEST.** Text in English. 1988. s-a. GBP 7 domestic; GBP 8 foreign (effective 2003). bk.rev. back issues avail. **Document type:** *Journal, Academic/Scholarly.* **Description:** Covers all aspects of diptera stidy.
Published by: Dipterists Forum, c/o Membership Secretary,, Ger Y Parc, Marianglas, Tynygongl, Benllech, Gwynedd LL74 8NS, United Kingdom. TEL 44-1248-853775, e.howe@ccw.gov.uk, http://www.sel.barc.usda.gov/diptera/tdipdig.htm, http://www.sel.barc.usda.gov/diptera/society.htm#dipforum. Ed. Peter Chandler.

595.7 333.72 GBR ISSN 1358-5029
DIPTERISTS FORUM. BULLETIN. Variant title: Bulletin of the Dipterists Forum. Text in English. s-a. looseleaf. GBP 5 domestic; GBP 6 foreign (effective 2003). bk.rev. bibl.; charts; illus.; maps. back issues avail. **Document type:** *Bulletin.* **Description:** Reports on latest findings of studies on Diptera; news from recording schemes, new identification keys, includes copies of recording scheme newsletters.
Formerly (until 1995): Diptera Recording Schemes Bulletin (0963-2182)
Related titles: ◆ Supplement(s): Conopid Recording Scheme Newsletter. ISSN 1369-1090.
Published by: Dipterists Forum, c/o Membership Secretary,, Ger Y Parc, Marianglas, Tynygongl, Benllech, Gwynedd LL74 8NS, United Kingdom. TEL 44-1248-853775, e.howe@ccw.gov.uk, http://www.sel.barc.usda.gov/diptera/society.htm#dipforum. Ed. Darwyn Sumner. Circ: 270.

DISTRIBUTION MAPS OF PLANT PESTS. see *AGRICULTURE*

595.7 JPN ISSN 0913-7335
DONACIIST. Text in Japanese. 1987. a.
Published by: Nekuihamushi Kenkyukai/Donaciists' Society, Yokohama, Kanagawa Kenritsu Hakubutsukan, 5-60 Minaminaka-Dori, Naka-ku, Yokohama-shi, Kanagawa-ken 231-0006, Japan.

595 MEX ISSN 1028-3420
DUGESIANA. Text in Spanish. s-a.
Indexed: ZooRec.
Published by: Universidad de Guadalajara, Centro de Estudios de Zoologica, Zapopan, Jalisco 45100, Mexico. snavarre@maiz.cucba.udg.mx.

595.7 USA ISSN 0273-7353
E S A NEWSLETTER. Text in English. 1978. m. USD 20 to individuals; USD 38 to institutions (effective 2004). adv. 8 p./no.; back issues avail. **Document type:** *Newsletter, Academic/Scholarly.* **Description:** Contains feature articles, meeting announcements, listing of employment opportunities, notices of grants and awards, member profiles, and branch and section news.
Published by: Entomological Society of America, 10001 Derekwood Ln, Ste 100, Lanham, MD 20706-4876. TEL 301-731-4535, FAX 301-731-4538, esa@entsoc.org, http://www.entsoc.org. adv.: page USD 385. Circ: 6,000 (paid).

595.7 GBR ISSN 0307-6946
QL461 CODEN: EENTDT
➤ **ECOLOGICAL ENTOMOLOGY.** Text in English. 1834. bi-m. EUR 188, GBP 125 combined subscription in Europe to individuals print & online eds.; USD 230 combined subscription in the Americas to individuals & Caribbean (print & online eds.); GBP 137 combined subscription elsewhere to individuals print & online eds.; GBP 545 combined subscription in Europe to institutions print & online eds.; USD 1,006 combined subscription in the Americas to institutions & Caribbean (print & online eds.); GBP 599 combined subscription elsewhere to institutions print & online eds. (effective 2006). adv. bk.rev. charts; illus. back issues avail.; reprints avail. **Document type:** *Journal, Academic/Scholarly.* **Description:** Publishes original research papers on the ecology of insects.
Formerly (until 1976): Royal Entomological Society of London. Transactions (0035-8894)
Related titles: Microfiche ed.: (from BHP); ◆ Online - full text ed.: Ecological Entomology Online. ISSN 1365-2311.
Indexed: ASCA, ASFA, AbHyg, AgBio, Agr, AgrForAb, AnBeAb, AnBrAb, ApEcolAb, ApicAb, B&AI, B&BAb, BIOBASE, BIOSIS Prev, BioCN&I, BiolAb, CPA, CurCont, DBA, ESPM, EntAb, FCA, FPA, FS&TA, ForAb, GEOBASE, GenetAb, HGA, HelmAb, HerbAb, HortAb, IABS, ISR, IndVet, MaizeAb, NutrAb, OrnHort, PBA, PGegResA, PHN&I, PlantSci, ProtozoAb, RM&VM, RPP, RefZh, RevApplEntom, RiceAb, S&F, SCI, SIA, SeedAb, SoyAb, TDB, THA, TriticAb, VITIS, VetBull, WeedAb, ZooRec.

—BLDSC (3648.870000), CISTI, IDS, IE, Infotrieve, ingenta, Linda Hall. **CCC.**
Published by: (Royal Entomological Society), Blackwell Publishing Ltd., 9600 Garsington Rd, Oxford, OX4 2ZG, United Kingdom. TEL 44-1865-776868, FAX 44-1865-714591, customerservices@oxon.blackwellpublishing.com, http://www.blackwellpublishing.com/journals/EEN. Ed. Mark D E Fellowes TEL 44-118-9875123. Pub. Sue Hewitt. R&P Sophie Savage. Adv. contact Jenny Applin. Circ: 1,045.

595.7 GBR ISSN 1365-2311
➤ **ECOLOGICAL ENTOMOLOGY ONLINE.** Text in English. bi-m. GBP 518 in Europe to institutions; USD 956 in the Americas to institutions & Caribbean; GBP 569 elsewhere to institutions (effective 2006). **Document type:** *Academic/Scholarly.*
Media: Online - full text (from Blackwell Synergy, EBSCO Publishing, Gale Group, IngentaConnect, O C L C Online Computer Library Center, Inc., Swets Information Services).
Related titles: Microfiche ed.: (from BHP); ♦ Print ed.: Ecological Entomology. ISSN 0307-6946.
Published by: Blackwell Publishing Ltd., 9600 Garsington Rd, Oxford, OX4 2ZG, United Kingdom. TEL 44-1865-776868, FAX 44-1865-714591, customerservices@oxon.blackwellpublishing.com, http://www.blackwellpublishing.com.

595.7 EST ISSN 1406-3433
EESTI PUTUKATE LEVIKUATLAS/DISTRIBUTION MAPS OF ESTONIAN INSECTS. Text in Estonian. 1998. irreg., latest 2000. **Document type:** *Monographic series, Academic/Scholarly.*
Indexed: BIOSIS Prev.
Published by: (Eesti Looduseuurijate Selts, Entomoloogiasektsioon/Estonian Naturalists' Society, Section of Entomology), Eesti Loodusfoto, Lennuki 26, Tallinnas, Estonia. TEL 372-6-414534.

595.7 JPN ISSN 0387-5733
ELYTRA. Text in English, Japanese. 1973. s-a.
Indexed: ZooRec.
Published by: Nihon Shoshi Gakkai/Japanese Society of Coleopterology, Kokuritsu Kagaku Hakubutsukan Dobutsu Kenkyubu, 23-1 Hiyakunin-cho 3-chome, Shinjuku-ku, Tokyo, 169-0073, Japan.

595.76 ESP ISSN 0214-1353
CODEN: ELTREZ
ELYTRON. Text in Spanish. 1987. a.
Formerly (until 1987): Asociacion Europea de Coleopterologia. Boletin (0214-1361)
Indexed: ASFA, BIOSIS Prev, BiolAb, EntAb, ForAb, HerbAb, HortAb, IECT, PotatoAb, RevApplEntom, S&F, ZooRec.
—BLDSC (3732.563000), CINDOC. **CCC.**
Published by: Asociacion Europea de Coleopterologia/European Association of Coleopterology, Dept. de Biologia Animal - Artropodes, Universitat de Barcelona, Avinguda Diagonal, 645, Barcelona, 08028, Spain. TEL 3-4021443, FAX 3-4110887. Ed. Jose Carlos Otero.

597.7 BRA
EMBRAPA SOJA. CONGRESSO BRASILEIRO DE ENTOMOLOGIA. RESUMOS. Key Title: Congresso Brasileiro de Entomologia. Resumos. Text in Portuguese. irreg., latest 1997, 16th, Bahia.
Indexed: ZooRec.
—BLDSC (3733.096800).
Published by: Empresa Brasileira de Pesquisa Agropecuaria, Embrapa Soja (Subsidiary of: Empresa Brasileira de Pesquisa Agropecuaria), Rodovia Carlos Joao Strass (Londrina/Warta), Acesso Orlando Amaral, Caixa Postal 231, Londrina, PR 86001-970, Brazil. TEL 55-43-371-6000, FAX 55-43-371-6100, sac@cnpso.emprapa.br, http://www.cnpso.emprapa.br, http://www.embrapa.br. **Co-sponsor:** Sociedade Entomologica do Brasil.

595.7 USA ISSN 0734-9874
CODEN: ENTMEY
ENTOMOGRAPHY. Text in English. 1982. a. USD 50.
Description: Annual review for biosystematics.
Indexed: BiolAb.
—Linda Hall.
Published by: Entomography Publications, 7451 Albezzia Ln, Sacramento, CA 95828. TEL 916-682-9752. Eds. Charles S Papp, Thomas D Eichlin. Circ: 750.

595.7 BEL ISSN 1371-7057
ENTOMOLOGIA AFRICANA. Text in English, French. 1996. a.
Published by: Societe d'Entomologie Africaine, 57 rue Genot, Chenee, 4032, Belgium. socentaf@yahoo.com, http://www.entomoafricana.org/.

595.7 BEL
ENTOMOLOGIA AFRICANA. COLLECTION HORS SERIE. Text in French, English. irreg.
Published by: Societe d'Entomologie Africaine, 57 rue Genot, Chenee, 4032, Belgium. socentaf@yahoo.com, http://www.entomoafricana.org/.

595.7 HRV ISSN 1330-6200
QL482.C87 CODEN: ECROEL
ENTOMOLOGIA CROATICA. Text in Croatian, English. 1971. a.
Supersedes in part (in 1995): Acta Entomologica Jugoslavica (0350-5510)
Indexed: AgBio, AgrForAb, BioCN&I, FCA, ForAb, HortAb, MaizeAb, PHN&I, RefZh, S&F, SoyAb, TriticAb, WeedAb, ZooRec.
—Linda Hall.
Published by: Hrvatsko Entomolosko Drustvo/Croatian Entomological Society, c/o Zavod za Poljoprivredni Zoologiju, Agronomski fakultet, Svetosimunska 25, Zagreb, 10000, Croatia. maceljski@agr.hr, http://www.agr.hr/hed/hrv/ec/contents.htm. Ed. Milan Maceljski.

595.7 GBR ISSN 0013-8703
QL461 CODEN: ETEAAT
➤ **ENTOMOLOGIA EXPERIMENTALIS ET APPLICATA.** Text in English, French, German. 1958. q. GBP 1,038 combined subscription in Europe to institutions print or online ed.; USD 1,919 combined subscription in the Americas to institutions & Caribbean (print & online eds.); GBP 1,142 combined subscription elsewhere to institutions print & online eds. (effective 2006). index. reprints avail. **Document type:** *Journal, Academic/Scholarly.* **Description:** Publishes scientific studies and applications of the experimental biology and ecology of insects and other land arthropods.
Related titles: Microform ed.: (from PQC); Online - full text ed.: ISSN 1570-7458. GBP 987 in Europe to institutions; USD 1,823 in the Americas to institutions & Caribbean; GBP 1,085 elsewhere to institutions (effective 2006) (from Blackwell Synergy, EBSCO Publishing, Gale Group, IngentaConnect, O C L C Online Computer Library Center, Inc., Springer LINK, Swets Information Services).
Indexed: AEA, ASCA, ASFA, AgBio, Agr, AgrForAb, AnBeAb, B&BAb, BIOBASE, BIOSIS Prev, BioCN&I, BioDAb, BiolAb, CIN, CPA, CTFA, ChemAb, ChemTitl, CurCont, DBA, EntAb, FCA, FPA, ForAb, GEOBASE, GenetAb, HGA, HelmAb, HerbAb, HortAb, I&DA, IABS, ISR, IndVet, MaizeAb, NemAb, NutrAb, OrnHort, PBA, PGegResA, PGrRegA, PHN&I, PlantSci, PotatoAb, PoultAb, ProtozoAb, RA&MP, RM&VM, RPP, RRTA, RefZh, RevApplEntom, RiceAb, S&F, SCI, SIA, SeedAb, SoyAb, TDB, TriticAb, VITIS, VetBull, WAE&RSA, WeedAb, ZooRec.
—BLDSC (3776.750000), CASDDS, CISTI, IDS, IE, Infotrieve, ingenta, Linda Hall. **CCC.**
Published by: (Nederlandse Entomologische Vereniging NLD), Blackwell Publishing Ltd., 9600 Garsington Rd, Oxford, OX4 2ZG, United Kingdom. TEL 44-1865-776868, FAX 44-1865-714591, customerservices@oxon.blackwellpublishing.com, http://www.blackwellpublishing.com/journals/EEA. Eds. Dr. J J A van Loon, Dr. S B J Menken.

595.7 DEU ISSN 0171-8177
QL461 CODEN: ENGND5
➤ **ENTOMOLOGIA GENERALIS**; Zeitschrift fuer allgemeine und angewandte Entomologie/journal of general and applied entomology. Text in German; Summaries in English. 1974. 4/yr. EUR 248 domestic; EUR 259.50 foreign (effective 2005). **Document type:** *Journal, Academic/Scholarly.*
Formerly (until 1978): Entomologica Germanica (0340-2266)
Indexed: ASCA, ASFA, Agr, AnBrAb, ApicAb, BIOBASE, BIOSIS Prev, BioCN&I, BiolAb, CurCont, EntAb, FCA, ForAb, HGA, HerbAb, HortAb, I&DA, IBR, MaizeAb, NemAb, OrnHort, ProtozoAb, RM&VM, RPP, RRTA, RevApplEntom, S&F, SIA, TDB, TriticAb, VITIS, WeedAb, ZooRec.
—BLDSC (3776.820000), CISTI, IDS, IE, Infotrieve, ingenta, Linda Hall. **CCC.**
Published by: E. Schweizerbart'sche Verlagsbuchhandlung, Johannesstr 3A, Stuttgart, 70176, Germany. TEL 49-711-3514560, FAX 49-711-35145699, mail@schweizerbart.de, http://www.schweizerbart.de/j/entomologia-generalis. Ed. A W Steffan.

595.7 GRC ISSN 0254-5381
ENTOMOLOGIA HELLENICA. Text in English. 1983. s-a.
Indexed: Agr, BIOSIS Prev, BiolAb.
Published by: Entomologike Etaireia Ellados/Hellenic Entomological Society, Kifisia, P.O. Box 51214, Athens, 14510, Greece. lioan@otenet.gr, http://www.entomon-hellas.gr.

595.7 CHE ISSN 0253-2484
ENTOMOLOGICA BASILIENSIA. Text in German. 1975. a.
Indexed: ASFA, AgBio, BioCN&I, ESPM, EntAb, ForAb, GenetAb, HerbAb, HortAb, PHN&I, PollutAb, RefZh, S&F, ZooRec.
Published by: Naturhistorisches Museum Basel, Augustinergasse 2, Basel, 4001, Switzerland. TEL 41-61-2665500, FAX 41-61-2665546.

595.7 FIN ISSN 0785-8760
QL482.F5 CODEN: ENFEE8
➤ **ENTOMOLOGICA FENNICA.** Text in English. 1990. q. EUR 32 in Europe; EUR 44 elsewhere (effective 2005). bk.rev. back issues avail. **Document type:** *Journal, Academic/Scholarly.* **Description:** Contains original research reports and reviews on ecology, faunistics, behavior, and systematics of insects and other terrestrial arthropods. Mainly a forum for Finnish and Nordic entomologists, but articles from other countries related to Finnish research or to the boreal region are included.
Formed by the merger of (1947-1990): Acta Entomologica Fennica (0001-561X); (1935-1990): Annales Entomologici Fennici (0003-4428); (1921-1990): Notulae Entomologicae (0029-4594)
Indexed: ASCA, ASFA, Agr, AgrForAb, BIOSIS Prev, BioCN&I, BiolAb, CurCont, ESPM, EntAb, FPA, ForAb, HGA, HerbAb, HortAb, IBR, OrnHort, RM&VM, RPP, RefZh, RevApplEntom, S&F, ZooRec.
—BLDSC (3777.130000), CASDDS, CISTI, IDS, IE, ingenta, Linda Hall. **CCC.**
Address: c/o Kai Ruohamaeki, Department of Biology, University of Turku, Turku, 20014, Finland. TEL 358-2-3335766, FAX 358-9-635017, 358-2-3336550, http://www.entomologicafennica.org/. Ed. Kai Ruohamaeki TEL 358-2-3335766. Circ: 700. **Distr. by:** Bookstore Tiedekirja, Kirkkokatu 14, Helsinki 00170, Finland. FAX 358-9-635017. **Co-publishers:** Helsingin Hyoenteistieteellinen Yhdistys/Entomological Society of Helsinki; Suomen Perhostutkijain Seura ry/Lepidopterological Society of Finland.

595.7 ROM ISSN 1224-2594
ENTOMOLOGICA ROMANICA. Text in Romany. 1996. a.
Indexed: ASFA, EntAb, ZooRec.
Published by: Societatea Lepidopterologica Romana/Romanian Lepidopterological Society, Republicii 48, Cluj, 3400, Romania. TEL 40-64-191238, icb@mail.dntcj.ro.

595.7 USA ISSN 0013-872X
QL461 CODEN: ETMNA6
➤ **ENTOMOLOGICAL NEWS.** Text in English. 1890. 5/yr. USD 30 domestic to institutions; USD 34 foreign to institutions (effective 2005). bk.rev. charts; illus. index. reprint service avail. from PQC. **Document type:** *Academic/Scholarly.*
Related titles: Microform ed.: (from PQC).
Indexed: AEA, ASCA, ASFA, Agr, AgrForAb, BIOBASE, BIOSIS Prev, BioCN&I, BiolAb, BiolDig, ChemAb, CurCont, EntAb, FCA, FaBeAb, ForAb, HerbAb, HortAb, IABS, IndVet, MEDLINE, NemAb, NutrAb, OrnHort, PBA, PHN&I, PoultAb, ProtozoAb, RA&MP, RM&VM, RefZh, RevApplEntom, RiceAb, S&F, SFA, SeedAb, SoyAb, TDB, TriticAb, VITIS, WeedAb, WildRev, ZooRec.
—BLDSC (3778.500000), CISTI, GNLM, IDS, IE, Infotrieve, ingenta, Linda Hall.
Published by: American Entomological Society, Academy of Natural Sciences, 1900 Benjamin Franklin Pkwy, Philadelphia, PA 19103-1195. TEL 215-561-3978, FAX 215-299-1028, aes@say.acnatsci.org, http://www.geocities.com/entomologicalnews, http://www.acnatsci.org/hosted/aes/. Ed. Jorge A Santiago-Blay. Circ: 750.

595.7 SVK ISSN 1335-5899
ENTOMOLOGICAL PROBLEMS. Text in English. 1961. s-a.
Supersedes (in 1993): Entomologicke Problemy (0071-0792)
Related titles: Supplement(s): Entomological Problems. Supplement.
Indexed: ZooRec.
—BLDSC (3778.600000), IE.
Published by: Slovak Academic Press Ltd., Nam Slobody 6, PO Box 57, Bratislava, 81005, Slovakia. sap@sappress.sk, http://www.sappress.sk. **Dist. by:** Slovart G.T.G. s.r.o., Krupinska 4, PO Box 152, Bratislava 85299, Slovakia. TEL 421-2-63839472, FAX 421-2-63839485, http://www.slovart-gtg.sk.

595.7 TUR ISSN 1302-0250
ENTOMOLOGICAL RESEARCH SOCIETY. JOURNAL. Text in English. 1999 (Feb.). 3/yr. free (effective 2004). **Document type:** *Journal, Academic/Scholarly.*
Indexed: ASFA, AgrForAb, BIOSIS Prev, BioCN&I, BiolAb, ESPM, EntAb, FCA, ForAb, HerbAb, HortAb, RA&MP, S&F, TDB, WeedAb, ZooRec.
—BLDSC (4741.270000).
Published by: Gazi Entomological Research Society, 110 Bahcelievler P Isl. Mud, PO Box 110, Ankara, 06502, Turkey. TEL 90-3122151630, entomol@gazi.edu.tr, http://www.entomol.gazi.edu.tr/info.htm. Ed. Dr. Metin Aktas.

595.7 RUS ISSN 0013-8738
QL461 CODEN: ENREBV
➤ **ENTOMOLOGICAL REVIEW.** Text in English. 1959. 9/yr. USD 3,668 in North America; USD 4,171 elsewhere (effective 2004). adv. bk.rev. bibl.; charts; illus. index. **Document type:** *Journal, Academic/Scholarly.* **Description:** Covers all aspects of entomology: systematics, faunistics, ecology, morphology, physiology and biochemistry of insects, as well as biological and chemical control of insect pests.
Incorporates (1916-2000): Russian Journal of Zoology (1560-0912)
Related titles: Microform ed.: (from PQC); ♦ Partial translation of: Zoologicheskii Zhurnal. ISSN 0044-5134; ♦ Partial translation of: Entomologicheskoe Obozrenie. ISSN 0367-1445.
Indexed: ASFA, ApicAb, BiolAb, EntAb.
—BLDSC (0411.740000), CISTI, IE, Infotrieve, ingenta, Linda Hall. **CCC.**
Published by: (Russkoye Entomologicheskoye Obshchestvo/Russian Entomological Society, Rossiiskaya Akademiya Nauk, Zoologicheskii Institut/Russian Academy of Sciences, Zoological Institute), M A I K Nauka - Interperiodica, Profsoyuznaya ul 90, Moscow, 117997, Russian Federation. TEL 7-095-3347420, FAX 7-095-3360666, compmg@maik.ru, http://www.maik.ru/journals/enteng.htm. Ed. Gleb Medvedev. Circ: 425. **Dist. by:** Interperiodica, PO Box 1831, Birmingham, AL 35201-1831. TEL 205-995-1567, 800-633-4931, FAX 205-995-1588. **Co-publisher:** Entomological Society of America.

595.7 AUS ISSN 1343-8786
QL461
ENTOMOLOGICAL SCIENCE. Text in English. 1998. q. USD 164 combined subscription in the Americas to individuals & Caribbean, print & online eds.; EUR 153 combined subscription in Europe to individuals print & online eds.; GBP 102 combined subscription elsewhere to individuals print & online eds.; USD 451 combined subscription in the Americas to institutions & Caribbean, print & online eds.; GBP 279 combined subscription elsewhere to institutions print & online eds. (effective 2006). **Document type:** *Journal, Academic/Scholarly.* **Description:** Publishes original research papers and reviews from any entomological discipline or from directly allied fields in ecology, behavioral biology, physiology, biochemistry, development, genetics, systematics, morphology, evolution and general entomology.
Supersedes in part (in 1998): Japanese Journal of Entomology - Konchu (0915-5805); Which was formerly (until 1989): Konchu (0013-8770)
Related titles: Online - full text ed.: ISSN 1479-8298. GBP 238 in Japan to institutions (effective 2004); USD 428 in the Americas to institutions; GBP 265 elsewhere to institutions (effective 2006) (from Blackwell Synergy, EBSCO Publishing, Gale Group, IngentaConnect, O C L C Online Computer Library Center, Inc.).
Indexed: ASFA, AgBio, AgrForAb, AnBeAb, BIOSIS Prev, BioCN&I, BiolAb, CPA, CurCont, EntAb, FCA, FS&TA, ForAb, HGA, HerbAb, HortAb, NutrAb, OrnHort, PBA, PHN&I, PoultAb, RM&VM, RevApplEntom, RiceAb, S&F, SeedAb, VITIS, WeedAb, ZooRec.
—BLDSC (3778.675000), CISTI, IE, ingenta, Linda Hall. **CCC.**
Published by: (Entomological Society of Japan/Nihon Konchu Gakkai JPN), Blackwell Publishing Asia (Subsidiary of: Blackwell Publishing Ltd.), 550 Swanston St, Carlton South, VIC 3053, Australia. TEL 61-383591011, FAX 61-383591120, subs@blackwellpublishingasia.com, http://www.blackwellpublishing.com/journals/ENS. Ed. Jun-ichi Kojima.

595.7 CAN ISSN 0071-0709
ENTOMOLOGICAL SOCIETY OF ALBERTA. PROCEEDINGS. Text in English. 1953. a. CND 10. cum.index every 10 yrs. **Document type:** *Proceedings.*
—CISTI.
Published by: Entomological Society of Alberta, c/o Dept Biological Sciences, University of Alberta, Edmonton, AB T6G 2E9, Canada. TEL 403-492-3308, FAX 403-492-9234, michelew@gpu.srv.ualberta.ca. Ed. M L Williamson. Circ: 150.

595.7 USA ISSN 0013-8746
QL461 CODEN: AESAAI
➤ **ENTOMOLOGICAL SOCIETY OF AMERICA. ANNALS;** devoted to the interest of classical entomology. Text in English. 1908. bi-m. USD 103 domestic to individuals; USD 123 in Canada & Mexico to individuals; USD 129 elsewhere to individuals; USD 210 domestic to institutions; USD 230 in Canada & Mexico to institutions; USD 236 elsewhere to institutions; USD 315 combined subscription domestic to individuals print & online eds.; USD 335 combined subscription in Canada & Mexico to individuals print & online eds.; USD 341 combined subscription elsewhere to individuals print & online eds.; USD 154.50 combined subscription domestic to institutions print & online eds.; USD 174.50 combined subscription in Canada & Mexico to institutions print & online eds.; USD 180.50 combined subscription elsewhere to institutions print & online eds. (effective 2004). adv. bk.rev. abstr.; bibl.; charts; illus. index. reprints avail. **Document type:** *Journal, Academic/Scholarly.* **Description:** Focuses on the basic aspects of the biology of arthropods. Articles are divided into the following sections: systematics, ecology and population biology, arthropod biology, physiology, biochemistry, and toxicology, morphology, histology, and fine structure, genetics, behavior.
Related titles: Microform ed.: (from MIM, PMC, PQC); Online - full text ed.: (from BioOne, C S A, EBSCO Publishing, Gale Group, IngentaConnect, O C L C Online Computer Library Center, Inc.).
Indexed: AEA, ASCA, ASFA, AbHyg, AgBio, Agr, AgrForAb, AnBeAb, ApEcolAb, B&AI, B&BAb, BIOSIS Prev, BibAg, BioCN&I, BioDAb, BiolAb, CIN, CIS, CPA, CTFA, ChemAb, ChemTitl, ChemoAb, CurCont, DBA, EPB, ESPM, EntAb, ExcerpMed, FCA, FPA, ForAb, GEOBASE, GenetAb, HGA, HelmAb, HerbAb, HortAb, ISR, IndVet, MEDLINE, MaizeAb, NutrAb, OrnHort, PBA, PGegResA, PHN&I, PotatoAb, PoultAb, ProtozoAb, RA&MP, RM&VM, RPP, RevApplEntom, RiceAb, S&F, SCI, SFA, SIA, SeedAb, SoyAb, TDB, TriticAb, VITIS, VetBull, WeedAb, WildRev, ZooRec.
—BLDSC (1025.000000), CASDDS, CISTI, GNLM, IDS, IE, Infotrieve, ingenta, Linda Hall. **CCC.**
Published by: Entomological Society of America, 10001 Derekwood Ln, Ste 100, Lanham, MD 20706-4876. TEL 301-731-4535, FAX 301-731-4538, esa@entsoc.org, http://www.entsoc.org/pubs. Eds. Leo Lachance, Todd Shelley. Circ: 2,800.

595.7 CAN ISSN 0071-0733
QL461 CODEN: JEBCA4
➤ **ENTOMOLOGICAL SOCIETY OF BRITISH COLUMBIA. JOURNAL.** Text in English. 1906. a. CND 20 domestic; CND 24 foreign (effective 2005). adv. bk.rev. **Document type:** *Academic/Scholarly.*
Related titles: Microform ed.: (from PQC); Online - full text ed.: (from ProQuest Information & Learning).
Indexed: ASFA, Agr, AgrForAb, ApicAb, BIOSIS Prev, BioCN&I, BiolAb, EntAb, FCA, FPA, ForAb, HGA, HerbAb, HortAb, IndVet, MaizeAb, OrnHort, PotatoAb, ProtozoAb, RM&VM, RPP, RefZh, RevApplEntom, S&F, VetBull, WeedAb, ZooRec.
—CISTI, Linda Hall. **CCC.**
Published by: Entomological Society of British Columbia, BC Ministry of Forests, Kalamalka Forestry Center, 3401 Reservoir Road, Vernon, BC V1B 2C7, Canada. TEL 250-549-5696, FAX 250-542-2230, Robb.Bennett@gems6.gov.bc.ca, ward.strong@gems7.gov.bc.ca, http://www.harbour.com/commorgs/ESBC/index.html. Ed. Dr. Ward Strong. R&P R G Bennett. Circ: 250 (paid).

595.7 CAN ISSN 0071-0741
QL461
ENTOMOLOGICAL SOCIETY OF CANADA. BULLETIN. Text in English. 1969. q. included with subscription to Canadian Entomologist. **Document type:** *Bulletin.*
Indexed: ApicAb, BioCN&I, HortAb, RevApplEntom, WeedAb, ZooRec.
—BLDSC (2505.150000), CISTI, IE, Infotrieve, Linda Hall. **CCC.**
Published by: Entomological Society of Canada, 393 Winston Ave, Ottawa, ON K2A 1Y8, Canada. TEL 613-725-2619, FAX 613-725-9349, http://esc-sec.org/bulletin1.htm. Ed. H Barclay.

595.7 EGY ISSN 1110-7162
ENTOMOLOGICAL SOCIETY OF EGYPT. BULLETIN. Text in English. irreg. EGP 10 domestic; USD 20 foreign (effective 2003). **Document type:** *Bulletin, Academic/Scholarly.*
Supersedes in part (in 1995): Societe Entomologique d'Egypte. Bulletin (1110-080X)
Related titles: ♦ Arabic ed.: Societe Entomologique d'Egypte. Bulletin. ISSN 0081-0983.
Published by: Entomological Society of Egypt/Societe Entomologique d'Egypte, 14 Ramses St, P O Box 430, Cairo, Egypt. TEL 20-2-5750979, http://derp.sti.sci.eg/data/0072.htm.

595.7 EGY ISSN 1110-0885
SB950.3.E3 CODEN: BEGEBG
ENTOMOLOGICAL SOCIETY OF EGYPT. BULLETIN. ECONOMIC SERIES. Text in Arabic. 1966. irreg., latest vol.9, 1975. EGP 3, USD 5. **Document type:** *Bulletin, Academic/Scholarly.*
Indexed: ASFA, BioCN&I, BioDAb, BiolAb, EntAb, MaizeAb.
—CASDDS.
Published by: Entomological Society of Egypt/Societe Entomologique d'Egypte, 14 Ramses St, P O Box 430, Cairo, Egypt. TEL 20-2-5750979, http://derp.sti.sci.eg/data/0083.htm.

595.7 IND ISSN 0013-8762
CODEN: BENTAR
ENTOMOLOGICAL SOCIETY OF INDIA. BULLETIN OF ENTOMOLOGY. Text in English. 1970 (vol.11). s-a. INR 16, USD 3.50. bibl.; charts; illus.
Indexed: AgrForAb, BioCN&I, FCA, ForAb, HortAb, IndVet, PBA, PGegResA, PHN&I, PotatoAb, RiceAb, S&F, SeedAb, TriticAb, VetBull.
—CISTI, Linda Hall.
Published by: Entomological Society of India, c/o Division of Entomology, Indian Agricultural Research Institute, New Delhi, 110012, India. Ed. Dr. S K Prasad.

595.7 CAN ISSN 0315-2146
QL461
➤ **ENTOMOLOGICAL SOCIETY OF MANITOBA. PROCEEDINGS.** Text in English. 1945. a. CND 10 (effective 2000). **Document type:** *Proceedings, Academic/Scholarly.* **Description:** Includes annual meeting details, abstracts of scientific papers from the meeting and original scientific papers of particular interest to prairie and forest entomologists.
Indexed: BioCN&I, BiolAb, FCA, ForAb, PHN&I, PoultAb, RefZh, RevApplEntom, TriticAb, WildRev, ZooRec.
—CISTI, Linda Hall. **CCC.**
Published by: Entomological Society of Manitoba, Inc., 195 Dafoe Rd, Winnipeg, MB R3T 2M9, Canada. TEL 204-786-9033, vanderwl@uwinnipeg.ca. R&P Desiree Vanderwel. Circ: 300 (paid).

595.7 NZL ISSN 0110-4527
CODEN: BESZD5
ENTOMOLOGICAL SOCIETY OF NEW ZEALAND. BULLETIN. Text in English. 1972. irreg., latest vol.13, 2000. price varies. back issues avail. **Document type:** *Monographic series.* **Description:** Monographs with original research and directories on New Zealand entomology.
Indexed: AnBrAb, BIOSIS Prev, BiolAb, ZooRec.
—BLDSC (2505.160000), CISTI, Linda Hall.
Published by: Entomological Society of New Zealand, Mt Albert Research Centre, Private Bag 92169, Auckland, New Zealand. FAX 64-9-8497093, mplmjb@dslak.co.nz.

595.7 CAN ISSN 0071-0768
QL461 CODEN: PESOAL
➤ **ENTOMOLOGICAL SOCIETY OF ONTARIO. PROCEEDINGS;** annual publication of entomological research. Text in English, French; Abstracts in English. 1871. a. CND 35. adv. bk.rev. index. **Document type:** *Proceedings, Academic/Scholarly.* **Description:** Covers basic and applied entomology.
Former titles (until 1958): Entomological Society of Ontario. Annual Report (0317-1914); (until 1872): Annual Report on the Noxious Insects of the Province of Ontario (0821-7793)
Related titles: Microfilm ed.: (from PQC).
Indexed: ASFA, AgrForAb, ApicAb, BIOSIS Prev, BioCN&I, BiolAb, ChemAb, CurCont, EntAb, FCA, FPA, ForAb, HGA, HortAb, PBA, PHN&I, ProtozoAb, RefZh, RevApplEntom, S&F, SCI, SeedAb, VITIS, WeedAb, ZooRec.
—CASDDS, CISTI, Linda Hall. **CCC.**
Published by: Entomological Society of Ontario, Queen s University, Dept of Biology, Kingston, ON K7L 3N6, Canada. TEL 613-545-6136, FAX 613-545-6617, harmsenr@biology.queensu.ca, http://www.utoronto.ca/forest/eso/eso.htm. Ed. Dr. R Harmsen. Circ: 375 (paid). **Subscr. to:** Dr. D.B. Lyons, Natural Resources Canada, Canadian Forest Service, P O Box 490, Sault Ste Marie, ON P6A 5M7, Canada.

595.7 USA ISSN 0071-0776
ENTOMOLOGICAL SOCIETY OF PENNSYLVANIA. NEWSLETTER. Text in English. 1965. 4/yr. membership. **Document type:** *Newsletter.*
Published by: Entomological Society of Pennsylvania, Dept of Entomology, PennState University, 501 AFI Bldg, University Park, PA 16802. TEL 814-863-4640. Circ: 90.

595.7 ZAF ISSN 0373-4242
CODEN: MESAAE
➤ **ENTOMOLOGICAL SOCIETY OF SOUTHERN AFRICA. MEMOIRS.** Text in English. 1947. irreg., latest 1991, Memoirs of African Entomology. ZAR 50, USD 20 per issue (effective 2003). bk.rev. back issues avail. **Document type:** *Monographic series, Academic/Scholarly.* **Description:** Scientific monographs on southern African entomology and arachnology.
Related titles: CD-ROM ed.; Online - full text ed.
Indexed: BiolAb, CurCont, HerbAb, ISAP, RevApplEntom, S&F, WeedAb, ZooRec.
—Linda Hall.
Published by: Entomological Society of Southern Africa/Entomologiese Vereniging van Suidelike Afrika, PO Box 13162, Hatfield, Pretoria 0028, South Africa. avzyl@iafrica.com, http://journals.sabinet.co.za/essa. Ed., Adv. contact S A Hanrahan. Circ: 600.

595.7 ZAF ISSN 1010-2566
ENTOMOLOGICAL SOCIETY OF SOUTHERN AFRICA. PROCEEDINGS OF THE CONGRESS. Text in English. 1974. biennial. USD 20 (effective 2003). bk.rev. abstr. back issues avail. **Document type:** *Proceedings, Academic/Scholarly.*
Indexed: BiolAb, CurCont, ISAP, RevApplEntom, ZooRec.
—BLDSC (6843.720300).
Published by: Entomological Society of Southern Africa/Entomologiese Vereniging van Suidelike Afrika, PO Box 13162, Hatfield, Pretoria 0028, South Africa. avzyl@iafrica.com, http://journals.sabinet.co.za/essa. R&P S A Hanrahan.

595.7 USA ISSN 0096-5839
QL461 CODEN: MESWAC
➤ **ENTOMOLOGICAL SOCIETY OF WASHINGTON. MEMOIRS.** Text in English. 1939. irreg., latest vol.21, 1998. price varies. back issues avail. **Document type:** *Monographic series, Academic/Scholarly.*
Indexed: ASFA, BIOSIS Prev, BioCN&I, EntAb, HGA, RRTA, RevApplEntom, WeedAb, ZooRec.
—CISTI.
Published by: Entomological Society of Washington, c/o Dept of Entomology, Smithsonian Institution MRC 168, Washington, DC 20560. Ed. David R Smith. R&P Dr. Michael G Pogue.

595.7 USA ISSN 0013-8797
QL461 CODEN: PESWAB
ENTOMOLOGICAL SOCIETY OF WASHINGTON. PROCEEDINGS. Text in English. 1884. q. USD 60 domestic to non-members; USD 70 foreign to non-members (effective 2005). bk.rev. charts; illus.; stat. index. back issues avail. **Document type:** *Journal, Academic/Scholarly.* **Description:** Publishes original scientific research articles on insects, especially on general biology and taxonomy.
Indexed: ASCA, ASFA, AbHyg, AgBio, Agr, AgrForAb, BIOBASE, BIOSIS Prev, BibAg, BioCN&I, BiolAb, CPA, ChemAb, CurCont, EntAb, FCA, FPA, ForAb, HGA, HerbAb, HortAb, IABS, IndVet, NutrAb, OrnHort, PBA, PGegResA, PHN&I, PoultAb, RM&VM, RPP, RevApplEntom, RiceAb, S&F, SFA, SIA, SeedAb, SoyAb, TriticAb, VetBull, WeedAb, WildRev, ZooRec.
—BLDSC (6698.000000), CISTI, IDS, IE, Infotrieve, ingenta, Linda Hall.
Published by: Entomological Society of Washington, c/o Dept of Entomology, Smithsonian Institution MRC 168, Washington, DC 20560. TEL 202-382-1786, FAX 202-786-9422. Ed. David R Smith. Circ: 840 (paid).

595.7 RUS ISSN 0367-1445
CODEN: ETOBAE
ENTOMOLOGICHESKOE OBOZRENIE. Text in Russian. 1901. q. USD 284 foreign (effective 2005). **Document type:** *Journal, Academic/Scholarly.* **Description:** Covers all aspects of entomology: systematics, faunistics, ecology, morphology, physiology and biochemistry of insects, as well as biological and chemical control of insect pests.

Related titles: ♦ Partial English translation(s): Entomological Review. ISSN 0013-8738.
Indexed: ASFA, AgBio, AgrForAb, BIOSIS Prev, BioCN&I, BiolAb, DBA, FCA, ForAb, HerbAb, HortAb, IndVet, MaizeAb, OrnHort, PBA, PHN&I, PotatoAb, RA&MP, RDA, RM&VM, RPP, RRTA, RefZh, RevApplEntom, RiceAb, S&F, TDB, TriticAb, VITIS, VetBull, WAE&RSA, ZooRec.
—CISTI, East View, Linda Hall. **CCC.**
Published by: (Russkoye Entomologicheskoye Obshchestvo/Russian Entomological Society), Rossiiskaya Akademiya Nauk, Zoologicheskii Institut/Russian Academy of Sciences, Zoological Institute, Universitetskaya nab 1, St Petersburg, 199034, Russian Federation. TEL 7-812-3280011, FAX 7-812-3282941, admin@zin.ru, http://www.zin.ru/journals/entrev/index.html. Ed. G S Medvedev.

595.7 CHE ISSN 1013-7041
ENTOMOLOGISCHE BERICHTE LUZERN. Text in German. 1979. s-a. **Document type:** *Journal, Academic/Scholarly.*
Indexed: ASFA, ESPM, EntAb, RefZh, ZooRec.
Published by: Natur-Museum Luzern, c/o Dr. L. Reser (Rezbanyai), Kasernenplatz 6, Luzern, 6003, Switzerland. ladislaus.reser@lu.ch, http://www.naturmuseum.ch.

595.7 NLD ISSN 0013-8827
QL461 CODEN: ETBRAV
ENTOMOLOGISCHE BERICHTEN. Text in Dutch, English. 1901. bi-m. free membership (effective 2005). bk.rev. charts; illus. index. **Document type:** *Academic/Scholarly.*
Indexed: ASFA, AbHyg, AgrForAb, ApicAb, BIOSIS Prev, BioCN&I, BiolAb, EntAb, FCA, ForAb, HerbAb, HortAb, IndVet, NemAb, OrnHort, ProtozoAb, RM&VM, RPP, RevApplEntom, S&F, SIA, SeedAb, TDB, WeedAb, ZooRec.
—BLDSC (3781.000000), CISTI, IE, ingenta, Linda Hall.
Published by: Nederlandse Entomologische Vereniging, Plantage Middenlaan 64, Amsterdam, 1018 DH, Netherlands. http://www.nev.nl/eb/index.html. Ed. Herman de Jong. Circ: 1,000.

595.7 DEU ISSN 0013-8835
CODEN: EBBSAA
ENTOMOLOGISCHE BLAETTER FUER BIOLOGIE UND SYSTEMATIK DER KAEFER. Text in German, English. 1905. 3/yr. EUR 50 (effective 2005). adv. bk.rev. charts; illus.; maps. index. back issues avail. **Document type:** *Journal, Academic/Scholarly.*
Formerly (until 1945): Entomologische Blaetter (0342-412X)
Indexed: BIOSIS Prev, BiolAb, EntAb, RevApplEntom, ZooRec.
—CISTI, IE, Infotrieve. **CCC.**
Published by: (Naturhistorischer Verein der Rheinlande und Westfalens), Verlag Goecke und Evers, Sportplatzweg 5, Keltern-Weiler, 75210, Germany. TEL 49-7236-7174, FAX 49-7236-7325, books@goeckeevers.de, http://www.goeckeevers.de. Circ: 500 (paid and controlled).

595.7 DEU ISSN 0232-5535
CODEN: ENBEDL
ENTOMOLOGISCHE NACHRICHTEN UND BERICHTE. Text in German. 1982. irreg. **Document type:** *Monographic series, Academic/Scholarly.*
Formed by the merger of (1957-1982): Entomologische Berichte (0425-1075); (1957-1982): Entomologische Nachrichten (0425-1083); Which was formerly (until 1961): Nachrichtenblatt der Oberlausitzer Insektenfreunde (0323-7990)
Indexed: BIOSIS Prev, BioCN&I, BiolAb, ForAb, HerbAb, HortAb, IndVet, OrnHort, RPP, S&F, ZooRec.
—BLDSC (3782.250000), CISTI, IE, ingenta.
Published by: Entomofaunistische Gesellschaft e.V., Postfach 202731, Dresden, 01193, Germany. klausnitzer.col@t-online.de, http://www.entomologie.de/efg/. Ed., Pub. Bernhard Klausnitzer.

595.7 DEU ISSN 0013-8843
QL461
ENTOMOLOGISCHE ZEITSCHRIFT. Text in German. 1890. m. EUR 39 domestic; EUR 42.60 foreign; EUR 4 newsstand/cover (effective 2004). adv. bk.rev. **Document type:** *Magazine, Academic/Scholarly.* **Description:** Contains original contributions on entomology as well as articles for hobby entomologists and collectors.
Incorporating: Insektenboerse (0020-1839)
Indexed: ASFA, AgrForAb, BioCN&I, BiolAb, ChemAb, EntAb, ForAb, HGA, HerbAb, HortAb, OrnHort, RA&MP, RefZh, S&F, WeedAb, ZooRec.
—Linda Hall. **CCC.**
Published by: (Internationales Entomologisches Verein), Verlag Eugen Ulmer GmbH, Wollgrasweg 41, Stuttgart, 70599, Germany. TEL 49-711-45070, FAX 49-711-4507120, info@ulmer.de, http://www.ulmer.de. Ed. Clas Naumann. Pub. Roland Ulmer. R&P Gerd Friedrich. adv.: B&W page EUR 416; 185 x 260. Circ: 2,320 (paid and controlled).

595.7 SWE ISSN 0013-886X
CODEN: ETTIAQ
➤ **ENTOMOLOGISK TIDSKRIFT.** Text in English, Swedish. 1880. 4/yr. SEK 220 domestic; SEK 320 in Scandinavia to individuals; SEK 340 in Scandinavia to institutions; SEK 420 elsewhere (effective 2002). adv. bk.rev. charts; illus. index, cum.index: 1880-1959. back issues avail. **Document type:** *Academic/Scholarly.* **Description:** Covers entomology: faunistics, ecology, conservation biology, taxonomy and reviews.
Indexed: ASFA, ApicAb, BIOSIS Prev, BioCN&I, BiolAb, EntAb, FPA, ForAb, HerbAb, HortAb, NemAb, OrnHort, PBA, RM&VM, RRTA, RevApplEntom, S&F, SeedAb, ZooRec.
—CISTI, Linda Hall.
Published by: Sveriges Entomologiska Foerening/Entomological Society of Sweden, Lunds Universitet, Zoologiska Institutionen, Helgonavagen 3, Lund, 22362, Sweden. TEL 46-046-222 93 34, FAX 46-046-222 45 41, ola.atlegrim@szooek.slu.se, http://www.sef.nu/et.htm. Ed. Ragnar Hall. Adv. contact Ola Atlegrim. Circ: 1,000. **Subscr. to:** c/o Ole Atlegrim, Soedra Slevgraend 121, Umea 90627, Sweden. TEL 46-90-165858.

595.7 DNK ISSN 0013-8851
QL482.D4 CODEN: ETMDAA
ENTOMOLOGISKE MEDDELELSER. Text in Danish, English; Summaries in English. 1887. 2/yr. DKK 300 (effective 2002). adv. bk.rev. charts; illus. **Document type:** *Academic/Scholarly.*
Indexed: ASFA, AgrForAb, BIOSIS Prev, BioCN&I, BiolAb, EntAb, FCA, ForAb, HGA, HerbAb, HortAb, OrnHort, PBA, PotatoAb, PoultAb, RM&VM, RPP, RefZh, RevApplEntom, S&F, WeedAb, ZooRec.
—BLDSC (3785.000000), CISTI, IE, ingenta, Linda Hall.
Published by: Entomologisk Forening/Entomological Society of Copenhagen, c/o Zoologisk Museum, Universitetsparken 15, Copenhagen O, 2100, Denmark. TEL 45-35-32-10-00, FAX 45-35-32-10-10. Circ: 700.

595.7 FRA ISSN 0013-8886
CODEN: ETMGAJ
L'ENTOMOLOGISTE; revue d'amateurs. Text in French. 1944. bi-m. EUR 41 in the European Union; EUR 48 elsewhere (effective 2003). adv. bk.rev. charts; illus.
Indexed: ASFA, BIOSIS Prev, BiolAb, MaizeAb, RefZh, RevApplEntom, ZooRec.
Published by: (Museum National d'Histoire Naturelle, Laboratoire d'Entomologie), Museum National d'Histoire Naturelle, 57 Rue Cuvier, Paris, 75231 Cedex 05, France. TEL 33-1-40793777, http://www.mnhn.fr. Ed. R M Quentin.

595.7 GBR ISSN 0013-8894
CODEN: ETGAA5
➤ **ENTOMOLOGIST'S GAZETTE.** Text in English. 1950. q. GBP 32, USD 66.50 domestic; GBP 34, USD 71 in Europe; GBP 36, USD 75 elsewhere (effective 2003). adv. bk.rev. charts; illus. 72 p./no. 1 cols./p.; back issues avail. **Document type:** *Journal, Academic/Scholarly.* **Description:** Devoted to Palaearctic entomology. Contains articles and notes on the biology, ecology, distribution, taxonomy and systematics of all orders of insect, with a bias towards lepidoptera.
Indexed: ASFA, BIOBASE, BIOSIS Prev, BioCN&I, BiolAb, EntAb, FCA, ForAb, HerbAb, HortAb, IABS, IndVet, OrnHort, PGegResA, PHN&I, RM&VM, RPP, RefZh, RevApplEntom, S&F, SFA, VetBull, WeedAb, WildRev, ZooRec.
—BLDSC (3787.000000), CISTI, IE, ingenta, Linda Hall.
Published by: Gem Publishing Co., Brightwood, Bell Ln, Brightwell-cum-Sotwell, Wallingford, Oxon OX10 0QD, United Kingdom. TEL 44-1491-833882, FAX 44-1491-825161, info@gempublishing.co.uk, http://www.gem.publishing.co.uk. Ed. W G Tremewan. Adv. contact F C Morton. page GBP 40; trim 110 x 176. Circ: 400 (paid).

595.7 GBR ISSN 0013-8908
QL461 CODEN: ENMMAT
➤ **ENTOMOLOGIST'S MONTHLY MAGAZINE.** Text in English. 1864. q. GBP 36, USD 75 domestic; GBP 37.50, USD 78 in Europe; GBP 39, USD 81 elsewhere (effective 2003). adv. bk.rev. illus. index. 86 p./no. 1 cols./p.; back issues avail. **Document type:** *Journal, Academic/Scholarly.* **Description:** Contains articles on all orders of insects and terrestrial arthropods, specializing in the British fauna and groups other than lepidoptera.
Related titles: Microfiche ed.: (from IDC); Microfilm ed.: (from BHP).
Indexed: ASFA, AbHyg, AgrForAb, AnBrAb, BIOSIS Prev, BioCN&I, BiolAb, EntAb, FCA, FPA, FS&TA, ForAb, HelmAb, HerbAb, HortAb, NemAb, NutrAb, OrnHort, PBA, PHN&I, PoultAb, RA&MP, RM&VM, RPP, RefZh, RevApplEntom, RiceAb, S&F, SIA, TDB, WeedAb, ZooRec.
—BLDSC (3788.000000), CISTI, IE, Infotrieve, ingenta, Linda Hall.
Published by: Gem Publishing Co., Brightwood, Bell Ln, Brightwell-cum-Sotwell, Wallingford, Oxon OX10 0QD, United Kingdom. TEL 44-1491-833882, FAX 44-1491-825161, info@gempublishing.co.uk, http://www.gem.publishing.co.uk. Ed. K G V Smith. Pub., R&P G Morton. Adv. contact F C Morton. page GBP 40; trim 110 x 176. Circ: 475 (paid).

595.7 GBR ISSN 0013-8916
CODEN: ERJVAZ
ENTOMOLOGIST'S RECORD AND JOURNAL OF VARIATION. Text in English. 1890. bi-m. GBP 28, USD 50 (effective 2003). adv. bk.rev. index. 48 p./no.; back issues avail. **Document type:** *Journal, Academic/Scholarly.*
Related titles: Microfiche ed.: (from IDC).
Indexed: ASFA, BIOSIS Prev, BiolAb, RefZh, ZooRec.
—BLDSC (3789.000000), IE, ingenta, Linda Hall.
Published by: Entomologist's Record, 109 Waveney Dr, Chelsford, Essex CM1 7QA, United Kingdom. Ed. C W Plant. Circ: 700.

595.7 COL ISSN 0122-5480
ENTOMOLOGO; boletin de la Sociedad Colombiana de Entomologia "Socolen". Text in Spanish. 1973. s-a.
Indexed: BioCN&I, ForAb, HortAb, OrnHort, PGegResA, PHN&I, TDB, ZooRec.
Published by: Sociedad Colombiana de Entomologia, Apdo Aereo 11366, Bogota, Colombia. TEL 57-1-2218706, FAX 57-1-2219263, secretario@socolen.org.co, http://www.socolen.com.co, http://www.socolen.org.co. Ed. Paulina Munoz.

ENTOMOLOGY ABSTRACTS. see *BIOLOGY—Abstracting, Bibliographies, Statistics*

595.7 BRA ISSN 0103-975X
ENTOMOLOGY NEWSLETTER. Text in Portuguese. 1974. irreg. free.
Indexed: BioCN&I, BiolAb, HortAb, RevApplEntom, WeedAb.
Published by: International Society of Sugar Cane Technologists, c/o IAA-Planalsucar, Caixa Postal 153 158, Araras, SP 13600-000, Brazil. TELEX 019-1872. Ed. P S M Botelho. Circ: 150.

595.7 IND ISSN 0377-9335
QL461 CODEN: ENTOD5
➤ **ENTOMON.** Text in English. 1976. q. INR 300 domestic to individuals; USD 100 foreign to individuals; INR 1,500 domestic to institutions; USD 200 foreign to institutions (effective 2003). adv. bk.rev. **Document type:** *Academic/Scholarly.*
Indexed: ASFA, AgBio, AgrForAb, BIOSIS Prev, BioCN&I, BioDAb, BiolAb, CIN, ChemAb, ChemTitl, CurCont, DSA, EntAb, FCA, FPA, ForAb, HerbAb, HortAb, ISR, IndVet, MaizeAb, NemAb, NutrAb, OrnHort, PBA, PHN&I, ProtozoAb, RA&MP, RM&VM, RPP, RevApplEntom, RiceAb, S&F, SCI, SIA, SeedAb, SoyAb, TDB, TOSA, TriticAb, VITIS, VetBull, WeedAb, ZooRec.
—BLDSC (3790.300000), CASDDS, CISTI, IE, ingenta, Linda Hall.
Published by: Association for Advancement of Entomology, c/o Department of Zoology, University of Kariavattom, Trivandrum, Kerala 695 581, India. TEL 91-471-447712, FAX 91-471-447158, dmur@md3.vsnl.net.in, http://www.river-valley.com.entomon. Ed., R&P Dr. D Muraleedharan. Circ: 400.

595.7 DNK ISSN 0106-2808
➤ **ENTOMONOGRAPH.** Text in Dutch. 1978. irreg., latest vol.13, 2001. price varies. back issues avail. **Document type:** *Monographic series, Academic/Scholarly.* **Description:** Scholarly studies of individual species and families of insects from different regions of the world.
Indexed: BIOSIS Prev, ZooRec.
Published by: Apollo Books, Kirkeby Sand 19, Stenstrup, 5771, Denmark. TEL 45-62-26-37-37, FAX 45-62-26-37-80, apollobooks@vip.cybercity.dk, http://www.apollobooks.com. Ed. L. Lyneborg.

595.7 VEN ISSN 1317-5262
QL481.V4
ENTOMOTROPICA. Text in Spanish, English, Portuguese. 1941. s-a. **Description:** Publishes original papers on tropical and Iberian entomological fauna dealing with all its different, inlcluding parainsecta, collembola, arachnids and myriapods.
Formerly (until 2001): Boletin de Entomologia Venezolana (1316-2284)
Related titles: Online - full text ed.: free (effective 2005).
Indexed: ASFA, AgrForAb, BioCN&I, EntAb, FCA, HGA, HortAb, IndVet, MaizeAb, OrnHort, PBA, PotatoAb, ProtozoAb, RPP, RiceAb, SoyAb, TDB, VetBull, WeedAb, ZooRec.
Published by: Sociedad Venezolana de Entomologia, Instituto de Zoologia Agricola, Facultad de Agronomia, Universidad Central de Venezuela, Apdo 4579, Maracay, 2101, Venezuela. http://www.entomotropica.org/.

595.7 USA ISSN 0046-225X
CODEN: EVETBX
➤ **ENVIRONMENTAL ENTOMOLOGY.** Text in English. 1972. bi-m. USD 111 domestic to individuals; USD 131 in Canada & Mexico to individuals; USD 137 elsewhere to individuals; USD 225 foreign to institutions; USD 245 in Canada & Mexico to institutions; USD 251 elsewhere to institutions; USD 166.50 combined subscription domestic to individuals print & online eds.; USD 186.50 combined subscription in Canada & Mexico to individuals print & online eds.; USD 192.50 combined subscription elsewhere to individuals print & online eds.; USD 337.50 combined subscription domestic to institutions print & online eds.; USD 357.50 combined subscription in Canada & Mexico to institutions print & online eds.; USD 363.50 combined subscription elsewhere to institutions print & online eds. (effective 2005). adv. abstr.; bibl.; charts; illus.; stat. index. reprint service avail. from PQC. **Document type:** *Journal, Academic/Scholarly.* **Description:** Reports of research on the interaction of insects with the biological, chemical, and physical aspects of their environment.
Related titles: Microform ed.: (from MIM, PQC); Online - full text ed.: (from BioOne, C S A, EBSCO Publishing, Gale Group, IngentaConnect, O C L C Online Computer Library Center, Inc.).

B

Indexed: AEA, AEBA, ASCA, ASFA, AbHyg, AgBio, Agr, AgrForAb, AnBeAb, ApEcolAb, ApicAb, B&AI, BIOBASE, BIOSIS Prev, BibAg, BioCN&I, BiolAb, CIN, CIS, CPA, CTFA, ChemAb, ChemTitl, CurCont, DSA, EIA, EPB, ESPM, EntAb, EnvAb, ExcerpMed, FCA, FPA, FaBeAb, ForAb, GEOBASE, GenetAb, HGA, HelmAb, HerbAb, HortAb, I&DA, IABS, ISR, IndVet, MBA, MaizeAb, NemAb, NutrAb, OrnHort, PBA, PGegResA, PGrRegA, PHN&I, PN&I, PlantSci, PotatoAb, PoultAb, ProtozoAb, RA&MP, RM&VM, RPP, RRTA, RevApplEntom, RiceAb, S&F, S&MA, SCI, SFA, SIA, SeedAb, SoyAb, TriticAb, VITIS, VetBull, WAE&RSA, WeedAb, WildRev, ZooRec.
—BLDSC (3791.464000), CASDDS, CISTI, IDS, IE, Infotrieve, ingenta, Linda Hall. **CCC.**
Published by: Entomological Society of America, 10001 Derekwood Ln, Ste 100, Lanham, MD 20706-4876. TEL 301-731-4535, FAX 301-731-4538, pubs@entsoc.org, esa@entsoc.org, http://www.entsoc.org. Ed. Dr. E Alan Cameron. Circ: 3,100.

595.7 JPN ISSN 0071-1268
QL483.J3
ESAKIA. Text in English, French, German. 1960. irreg. membership. bk.rev. charts; illus.
Indexed: ASFA, AgrForAb, BIOSIS Prev, BiolAb, EntAb, FCA, ForAb, HerbAb, HortAb, OrnHort, RefZh, RevApplEntom, S&F, SoyAb, ZooRec.
—IE.
Published by: (Hikosan Biological Laboratory), Kyushu University, Faculty of Agriculture/Kyushu Daigaku Nogakubu, Hikosan, Tagawa-gun, Soeda-machi, Fukuoka-ken 824-0721, Japan. Ed. Katsura Morimoto.

595.7 CZE ISSN 1210-5759
QL461 CODEN: EJENE2
➤ **EUROPEAN JOURNAL OF ENTOMOLOGY.** Text and summaries in English. 1904. q. USD 80 in Europe to individuals; USD 105 elsewhere to individuals; USD 200 in Europe to institutions; USD 225 elsewhere to institutions (effective 2005). adv. bk.rev. bibl.; charts; illus. 128 p./no. 2 cols./p.; back issues avail. **Document type:** *Journal, Academic/Scholarly.* **Description:** Includes articles on all aspects of entomology (taxonomy, morphology, genetics, physiology, ecology, zoogeography), Myriapoda, Chelicerata and terrestrial Crustacea.
Formerly (until vol.90, 1993): Acta Entomologica Bohemoslovaca (0001-5601)
Related titles: Online - full text ed.: (from ProQuest Information & Learning).
Indexed: ASCA, ASFA, AgBio, AgrForAb, AnBrAb, ApEcolAb, ApicAb, B&BAb, BIOSIS Prev, BioCN&I, BiolAb, CIN, CPA, ChemAb, ChemTitl, CurCont, ESPM, EntAb, FCA, ForAb, GEOBASE, GenetAb, HGA, HerbAb, HortAb, IBR, ISR, MBA, NemAb, NutrAb, OrnHort, PBA, PGegResA, PHN&I, PotatoAb, RM&VM, RefZh, RevApplEntom, S&F, SCI, SoyAb, TriticAb, VITIS, WeedAb, ZooRec.
—BLDSC (3829.728850), CASDDS, CISTI, IDS, IE, ingenta, Linda Hall.
Published by: Akademie Ved Ceske Republiky, Entomologicky Ustav/Czech Academy of Sciences, Institute of Entomology, Branisovska 31, Ceske Budejovice, 37005, Czech Republic. TEL 420-38-7775213, FAX 420-38-5310354, eje@entu.cas.cz, http://www.eje.cz. Eds. Ivo Hodek, Petr Svacha TEL 420-38-7775258. R&P Petr Svacha TEL 420-38-7775258. adv.: page USD 100; 170 x 247. Circ: 224.

595.7 RUS ISSN 1684-4866
EVRAZIATSKII ENTOMOLOGICHESKII ZHURNAL/EUROASIAN ENTOMOLOGICAL JOURNAL. Text in Russian, English. 2002. biennial. USD 247 foreign (effective 2005). **Document type:** *Journal, Academic/Scholarly.*
Indexed: RefZh, ZooRec.
—BLDSC (0056.353700).
Published by: Siberian Zoological Museum, Institute of Animal Systematics and Ecology, Frunze St 11, Novosibirsk 91, 630091, Russian Federation. sch-sch@mail.ru. Ed. Sergei E Tshernyshev. **Dist. by:** East View Information Services, 3020 Harbor Ln. N., Minneapolis, MN 55447. TEL 763-550-0961, 800-477-1005, FAX 763-559-2931, 800-800-3839, eastview@eastview.com, http://www.eastview.com.

595.7 CAN ISSN 0318-6725
FABRERIES. Text in French. 1975. s-a. CND 25, USD 30; USD 40 to institutions. bk.rev. bibl. back issues avail. **Document type:** *Monographic series.*
Indexed: ASFA, AgrForAb, BioCN&I, CPA, EntAb, ForAb, HerbAb, HortAb, OrnHort, PBA, RevApplEntom, S&F, WeedAb, ZooRec.
—CISTI.
Published by: Association Des Entonmologistes Amateur Quebec Inc., 302 Gabrielle-Roy, Varennes, PQ J3X 1L8, Canada. TEL 450-652-6087, info@aeaq.qc.ca, http://www.aeaq.qc.ca, http://wwwaeaq.qc.ca. Circ: 200.

595.7 RUS ISSN 1026-051X
FAR EASTERN ENTOMOLOGIST. Text in English, Russian. 1994. m.
Indexed: ZooRec.
Published by: Russkoe Entomologicheskoye Obshchestvo/ Russian Entomological Society, Universitetskaya nab, 1, Sankt Peterburg, 1990934, Russian Federation. TEL 812-3281212, res@zin.ru, http://www.zin.ru/societies/res/.

595.70948 NLD ISSN 0106-8377
CODEN: FESCDE
➤ **FAUNA ENTOMOLOGICA SCANDINAVICA.** Text in English. 1973. a. price varies. illus. back issues avail. **Document type:** *Monographic series, Academic/Scholarly.* **Description:** Scholarly studies aiding in the identification and study of specific insect classes indigenous to Fennoscandia and Denmark.
Indexed: ASFA, BIOSIS Prev, BiolAb, EntAb, HGA, ZooRec.
—BLDSC (3897.945000), IE, ingenta. **CCC.**
Published by: (Societas Entomologica Scandinavica), Brill Academic Publishers, PO Box 9000, Leiden, 2300 PA, Netherlands. TEL 31-71-53-53-500, FAX 31-71-53-17-532, cs@brill.nl, http://www.brill.nl. Ed. N P Kristensen. R&P Elizabeth Venekamp. **Subscr. in N. America to:** PO Box 605, Herndon, VA 20172. TEL 703-661-1585, 800-337-9255, FAX 703-661-1501, cs@brillusa.com. **Distr. outside N. America by:** c/o Turpin Distribution, Stratton Business Park, Pegasus Drive, Biggleswade, BEDFORDSHIRE SG 18 8TQ, United Kingdom. TEL 44-1767-604-954, FAX 44-1767-601-640, brill@turpin-distribution.com.

595.7 CHE ISSN 1422-6367
FAUNA HELVETICA. Text in German, French, English. 1998. irreg. **Document type:** *Monographic series, Academic/Scholarly.* **Description:** Comprises identification books and catalogues of the Swiss entomological fauna.
Formed by the merger of (1959-1998): Insecta Helvetica. Fauna (0537-7390); (1966-1998): Documenta Faunistica Helvetiae (1421-5624); Which was formerly (until 1987): Insecta Helvetica. Catalogus (1420-6900)
Indexed: BIOSIS Prev, ZooRec.
Published by: (Centre Suisse de Cartographie de la Faune), Schweizerische Entomologische Gesellschaft/Societe Entomologique Suisse, c/o Dr. Yves Gonseth, CSCF Terreaux 14, Neuchatel, 2000, Switzerland. TEL 41-32-7257257, FAX 41-32-7177969, yves.gonseth@cscf.unine.ch, http://www.ephemeroptera.de/Eph_deu/Buch/fauna_helvetica_d.html, http://www.seg.unibe.ch.

595.7 NLD ISSN 1388-3895
FAUNA MALESIANA HANDBOOK. Text in English. 1998. irreg. price varies. **Document type:** *Academic/Scholarly.*
Indexed: ZooRec.
Published by: Brill Academic Publishers, PO Box 9000, Leiden, 2300 PA, Netherlands. TEL 31-71-53-53-500, FAX 31-71-53-17-532, cs@brill.nl, http://www.brill.nl. **Subscr. in N. America to:** PO Box 605, Herndon, VA 20172. TEL 703-661-1585, 800-337-9255, FAX 703-661-1501, cs@brillusa.com. **Distr. outside N. America by:** c/o Turpin Distribution, Stratton Business Park, Pegasus Drive, Biggleswade, BEDFORDSHIRE SG 18 8TQ, United Kingdom. TEL 44-1767-604-954, FAX 44-1767-601-640, brill@turpin-distribution.com.

595.7 JPN ISSN 0917-9046
FAUNAUKITAMU/FAUNA IN OITAMA DISTRICT. Text in Japanese. 1990. m. **Document type:** *Academic/Scholarly.* **Description:** Lists of insects in Yamagata Prefecture.
Published by: Yonezawa Shiritsu Uesugi Hakubutsukan/ Yonezawa Municipal Uesugi Museum, 1-4 Marunochi, Yonezawa-shi, Yamagata-ken 992-0052, Japan. TEL 81-238-23-7302, FAX 81-238-22-7302. Ed. Koichi Kusakari.

595.7 USA
FLEA NEWS. Text in English. 1980. s-a. free to qualified personnel. bk.rev. **Document type:** *Newsletter.* **Description:** Devoted to matters involving insects belonging to the order Siphonaptera (fleas) and related subjects.
Related titles: Online - full text ed.
Address: 3906 Stone Brooke Cir, Ames, IA 50010-4174. TEL 515-232-7714, FAX 515-233-1851, relewis@iastate.edu, http://www.public.iastate.edu/~entomology/FleaNews/AboutFleaNews.html. Ed., R&P Robert Lewis. Circ: 175.

595.7 DEU
FLIES OF THE NEARCTIC REGION. Text in English, German. 1980. irreg., latest vol.8, no.14, 2003. price varies. **Document type:** *Monographic series, Academic/Scholarly.*
Indexed: ZooRec.
Published by: E. Schweizerbart'sche Verlagsbuchhandlung, Johannesstr 3A, Stuttgart, 70176, Germany. TEL 49-711-3514560, FAX 49-711-35145699, mail@schweizerbart.de, http://www.schweizerbart.de. Ed. Graham C D Griffiths.

595.7 USA ISSN 0013-8932
CODEN: FPECAI
FLORIDA. DEPARTMENT OF AGRICULTURE AND CONSUMER SERVICES. ENTOMOLOGY CIRCULAR. Text in English. 1962. bi-m. looseleaf. free (effective 2005). **Document type:** *Government.*
Indexed: BioCN&I, BiolAb, HortAb, IndVet, PHN&I, RPP, RevApplEntom, ZooRec.
—BLDSC (3789.660000).
Published by: Department of Agriculture and Consumer Services, Division of Plant Industry, 1911 S W 34th St, Box 147100, Gainesville, FL 32614-7100. TEL 904-372-3505, FAX 904-955-2301. R&P Denise Feiber.

595.7 USA ISSN 0015-4040
QL461 CODEN: FETMAC
➤ **FLORIDA ENTOMOLOGIST;** an international journal for the Americas. Text in English. 1917. q. bk.rev. bibl.; charts; illus. index. **Document type:** *Journal, Academic/Scholarly.*
Related titles: Online - full text ed.: free (effective 2005) (from BioOne, C S A, EBSCO Publishing, O C L C Online Computer Library Center, Inc., ProQuest Information & Learning).
Indexed: AEA, ASCA, ASFA, AbHyg, AgBio, Agr, AgrForAb, AnBeAb, AnBrAb, ApEcolAb, BIOBASE, BIOSIS Prev, BibAg, BioCN&I, BioDAb, BiolAb, CIN, CPA, ChemAb, ChemTitl, CurCont, DBA, ESPM, EntAb, FCA, FPA, ForAb, GEOBASE, HelmAb, HerbAb, HortAb, IABS, ISR, IndVet, MaizeAb, NemAb, OrnHort, PBA, PGegResA, PHN&I, PotatoAb, ProtozoAb, RA&MP, RM&VM, RPP, RRTA, RevApplEntom, RiceAb, S&F, SCI, SFA, SIA, SSCI, SeedAb, SoyAb, TriticAb, WAE&RSA, WeedAb, WildRev, ZooRec.
—BLDSC (3956.000000), CASDDS, CISTI, IDS, IE, Infotrieve, ingenta, Linda Hall.
Published by: Florida Entomological Society, c/o R M Baranowski, Ed, 18905 S W 280 St, Homestead, FL 33031. TEL 813-324-5502, FAX 904-374-5852. Circ: 800.

595.7 USA ISSN 0885-5943
QL434.A1 CODEN: OPFADH
FLORIDA STATE COLLECTION OF ARTHROPODS. OCCASIONAL PAPERS. Text in English. 1981. irreg., latest vol.10, 1999. price varies. back issues avail. **Document type:** *Government.*
Indexed: BIOSIS Prev, BiolAb, ZooRec.
—Linda Hall.
Published by: Department of Agriculture and Consumer Services, Division of Plant Industry, 1911 S W 34th St, Box 147100, Gainesville, FL 32614-7100. TEL 904-372-3505, FAX 904-336-2300. Ed. J B Heppner. R&P Denise Feiber.

595.7 HUN ISSN 0373-9465
CODEN: ROKOA5
FOLIA ENTOMOLOGICA HUNGARICA/ROVARTANI KOZLEMENYEK. Text in English, German, French. 1923. a. USD 48 (effective 2001). illus. back issues avail. **Document type:** *Journal, Academic/Scholarly.* **Description:** Contains papers written by museum staff members or based on materials deposited there.
Indexed: ASFA, AnBrAb, BIOSIS Prev, BioCN&I, BiolAb, EntAb, FCA, ForAb, HerbAb, HortAb, OrnHort, PBA, PotatoAb, RPP, RevApplEntom, S&F, SIA, TriticAb, ZooRec.
—CISTI.
Published by: Magyar Termeszettudomanyi Muzeum, Baross utca 13, Budapest, 1088, Hungary. TEL 36-1-2677100, FAX 36-1-3171669, perego@zoo.zoo.nhmus.hu, http://www.nhmus.hu. Ed. S Mahunka. R&P, Adv. contact I Matskasi TEL 36-1-2677100. Circ: 350.

595.7 MEX ISSN 0430-8603
QL477 CODEN: FEMXAA
➤ **FOLIA ENTOMOLOGICA MEXICANA.** Text and summaries in English, Spanish. 1961. 3/yr. MXP 250 domestic; USD 35 foreign (effective 2001). adv. bk.rev. abstr.; bibl.; charts; illus. index, cum.index: 1961-1971. **Document type:** *Journal, Academic/Scholarly.* **Description:** Presents papers on physiology, morphology, systematics, ecology, and all experimental and applied branches of entomology, arachnology and acarology.
Indexed: ASFA, AgrForAb, ApicAb, BIOSIS Prev, BioCN&I, BiolAb, EntAb, FCA, ForAb, GenetAb, HGA, HelmAb, HortAb, MaizeAb, NemAb, OrnHort, PHN&I, PoultAb, RA&MP, RM&VM, RPP, RefZh, RevApplEntom, S&F, SIA, SoyAb, TDB, ZooRec.
—Linda Hall.
Published by: Sociedad Mexicana de Entomologia, A.C., Consejo Editorial Folia Entomologica Mexicana, Apdo. Postal 63, Xalapa, VERACRUZ 91000, Mexico. TEL 52-28-421800, FAX 52-28-187809, folia@ecologia.edu.mx, http://www.ecologia.edu.mx/folentmex. Ed., R&P Sergio Ibanez-Bernal. Adv. contact Arturo Bonet Ceballos. Circ: 800.

595.7 USA ISSN 1210-4108
FOLIA HEYROVSKYANA. Text in English, Multiple languages. 1993. irreg. price varies. bibl. **Document type:** *Academic/Scholarly.* **Description:** Disseminates research in multiple areas of entomology.
Related titles: Supplement(s): Folia Heyrovskyana. Supplementum.
Indexed: ASFA, BIOSIS Prev, BioCN&I, BiolAb, EntAb, ForAb, HortAb, PGegResA, RM&VM, RevApplEntom, ZooRec.
—Linda Hall.
Published by: International Scholars Publications, 7831 Woodmont Ave, Ste 345, Bethesda, MD 20814. TEL 301-654-7414, 800-557-8254, FAX 301-654-7336, austinsp1@aol.com, pensoft@main.infotel.bg.

595.7 USA
THE FOOD INSECTS NEWSLETTER. Text in English. 1988. 3/yr. USD 9 (effective 2000). adv. bk.rev. **Document type:** *Newsletter, Academic/Scholarly.* **Description:** Covers all aspects pertaining to the global use of insects as food: production, harvest, nutritional value, economics, and environmental implications.

Published by: Florence V. Dunkel, Ed. & Pub., c/o Florence V Dunkel, Ed, Department of Entomology, Montana State University, 324 Leon Johnson Hall, Bozeman, MT 59717-0302. TEL 406-994-5065, FAX 406-585-5608, ueyfd@msu.oscs.montana.edu, http://www.hollowtop.com/finl_html/finl.html. Pub., Adv. contact Robert E Diggs. R&P Florence V Dunkel. Circ: 900.

595.76 JPN ISSN 0429-2871
FRAGMENTA COLEOPTEROLOGICA. Text in English. 1961. irreg. (approx. a.).
Indexed: BiolAb.
Address: Wako-Hatagaya B-406, Honmachi 1-26-10, Shibuya-ku, Tokyo, Japan. Circ: 100.

595.7 ITA ISSN 0429-288X
QL461
FRAGMENTA ENTOMOLOGICA. Text in English, French, German, Italian, Spanish; Summaries in Italian, English. 1951. s-a. per issue exchange basis only. bk.rev.
Indexed: ASFA, AgrForAb, BIOSIS Prev, BioCN&I, BiolAb, EntAb, ForAb, GenetAb, HGA, HortAb, RefZh, RevApplEntom, S&F, VITIS, ZooRec.
—CISTI.
Published by: Universita degli Studi di Roma "La Sapienza", 5 Piazzale Aldo Moro, Rome, 00185, Italy. TEL 39-06-49911, http://www.uniroma1.it. Circ: 400.

595.7 ITA ISSN 0532-7679
FRUSTULA ENTOMOLOGICA. Text in Italian. 1958. irreg.
Indexed: AEA, ASFA, AbHyg, B&BAb, BioCN&I, EntAb, FCA, ForAb, GenetAb, HortAb, PGegResA, PHN&I, PotatoAb, ProtozoAb, RPP, S&F, SIA, SoyAb, TDB, ZooRec.
Published by: Istituto di Entomologia Agraria, Universita degli studi di Pisa, Pisa, Italy.

595.7 JPN ISSN 0915-0323
FUKUI CHUHO/ENTOMOLOGICAL JOURNAL OF FUKUI. Text in Japanese; Summaries in English, Japanese. 1987. s-a.
Indexed: ZooRec.
Published by: Fukui Konchu Kenkyukai/Fukui Entomological Society, c/o Mr Masaru Osada, Fukui Shiritsu Kyodo Shizen Kagaku Hakubutsukan, 147 Asuwa-Kami-cho, Fukui-shi, 918-8006, Japan.

595.7 JPN
FUKUISHIMA NO MUSHI/INSECTS OF FUKUISHIMA. Text in Japanese. 1980. a.
Published by: Fukushima Mushi no Kai/Fukuishima Insect Lovers' Association, c/o Mr Tadao Saito, 18-5 Sakuradai-Tazawa, Fukushima-shi, 960-0000, Japan.

595.7 JPN ISSN 0916-1112
FUTAO/INSECTS JOURNAL. Text in English, Japanese. 1989. irreg. (2-4/yr.). JPY 5,000 (effective 2000 & 2001). **Document type:** *Bulletin.*
Indexed: ZooRec.
Published by: Futao-kai/Entomologists Association, c/o Hiroto Hanafusa, 688-2 Tashima, Tottori-shi, 680-0804, Japan. tashima@orange.ocn.ne.jp. Ed. Hiroto Hanafusa.

595.7 AUS ISSN 0158-0760
QL487 CODEN: GAENDS
➤ **GENERAL AND APPLIED ENTOMOLOGY.** Text in English. 1964. a., latest vol.32, 2003. AUD 20 (effective 2003). adv. bk.rev. illus.; maps. back issues avail.; reprints avail. **Document type:** *Journal, Academic/Scholarly.* **Description:** Stimulates interest in all branches of entomology and related subjects, for example, medical, veterinary, industrial, forest and agriculture entomology.
Formerly (until vol. 10, 1978): Entomological Society of Australia (N.S.W.). Journal (0071-0725)
Indexed: AEA, ASI, AbHyg, AgrForAb, BioCN&I, BiolAb, ChemAb, FCA, ForAb, HerbAb, HortAb, IndVet, NutrAb, PBA, PGegResA, PGrRegA, PHN&I, RM&VM, RPP, RRTA, RevApplEntom, S&F, TriticAb, VetBull, WAE&RSA, WeedAb, ZooRec.
—CASDDS, CISTI, Linda Hall.
Published by: Entomological Society of New South Wales Inc., Entomology Department, c/o Australian Museum - Entomology Department, 6 College St, Sydney, NSW 2000, Australia. TEL 61-2-46406376, garry.levot@agric.nsw.gov.au, http://www.entsocnsw.netfirms.com/journal.htm. Ed. Dr. Garry Levot. Circ: 250.

595.7 JPN ISSN 0433-3950
GENSEI/ENTOMOLOGICAL SOCIETY OF KOCHI. JOURNAL. Text in Japanese. 1952. 2/yr.
Indexed: ZooRec.
Published by: Kochi Konchu Kenkyukai/Entomological Society of Kochi, Kochi Daigaku Nogakubu, Otsu 200, Monobe, Nankoku-shi, Kochi-ken 783-0093, Japan.

595.7 ITA ISSN 0392-7296
QL482.I8 CODEN: GIENDG
➤ **GIORNALE ITALIANO DI ENTOMOLOGIA.** Text in English, French, Italian, Portuguese, Spanish. 1982. a. EUR 35 domestic; EUR 59 foreign (effective 2004). adv. illus. index. back issues avail. **Document type:** *Journal, Academic/Scholarly.*
Indexed: ASFA, AgrForAb, BIOSIS Prev, BioCN&I, BiolAb, ESPM, EntAb, ForAb, GenetAb, HGA, HortAb, OrnHort, PollutAb, RM&VM, RefZh, RevApplEntom, WeedAb, ZooRec.
—Linda Hall.
Published by: Marco Berra Ed. & Pub., Casella Postale 188, Cremona, CR 26100, Italy. gide@dinet.it. R&P, Adv. contact Marco Berra. Circ: 250 (paid).

595.7 USA ISSN 0090-0222
QL461 CODEN: GRLEAG
➤ **THE GREAT LAKES ENTOMOLOGIST.** Text in English. 1966. s-a. USD 30 per vol. (effective 2001). bk.rev. bibl.; charts; illus. cum.index. back issues avail.; reprint service avail. from PQC. **Document type:** *Academic/Scholarly.*
Formerly (until 1971): Michigan Entomologist (0026-2145)
Related titles: Microfilm ed.: (from PQC).
Indexed: ASCA, ASFA, Agr, BIOBASE, BIOSIS Prev, BibAg, BioCN&I, BiolAb, CPA, CurCont, EntAb, FCA, ForAb, HerbAb, HortAb, IABS, ISR, MMI, MaizeAb, NutrAb, OrnHort, PBA, PGegResA, PlantSci, PotatoAb, PoultAb, ProtozoAb, RM&VM, RPP, RefZh, RevApplEntom, S&F, SCI, SFA, SeedAb, SoyAb, TriticAb, WAE&RSA, WeedAb, WildRev, ZooRec.
—BLDSC (4214.530000), CISTI, IDS, IE, ingenta, Linda Hall. **CCC.**
Published by: Michigan Entomological Society, c/o Dept of Entomology, Michigan State Univ, East Lansing, MI 48824. TEL 517-321-2192. Ed. Randy F Cooper. Circ: 650.

595.7 USA
GRESSITT CENTER NEWS. Text in English. 1989. s-a. free. back issues avail. **Document type:** *Newsletter.* **Description:** Covers Pacific entomology and activities of Gressitt Center for research.
Published by: Bishop Museum, Department of Entomology, PO Box 19000 A, Honolulu, HI 96817. TEL 808-848-4196, FAX 808-841-8968. Ed. Gordon M Nishida. Circ: 800.

595.7 ESP ISSN 0213-3873
GRUPO ENTOMOLOGICO DE MADRID. BOLETIN. Text in Spanish. 1985. a. free.
Indexed: IECT.
Published by: Grupo Entomologico de Madrid, c/o Fac. de Ciencias, Univ. Autonoma de Madrid, Cantoblanco, (Madrid) 28693, Spain.

595.7 GBR ISSN 0962-5852
HANDBOOKS FOR THE IDENTIFICATION OF BRITISH INSECTS. Text in English. irreg.
Indexed: ZooRec.
—BLDSC (4250.530000).
Published by: Royal Entomological Society, 41 Queens Gate, London, SW7 5HR, United Kingdom. TEL 44-20-75848361, FAX 44-20-75818505, reg@royensoc.co.uk, http://www.royensoc.co.uk.

595.7 KOR ISSN 1011-9493
QL461 CODEN: KJETAE
HAN'GUK KONCHUNG HAKHOE CHI/KOREAN JOURNAL OF ENTOMOLOGY. Text in English, Korean; Summaries in English. 1971. q. USD 10. back issues avail.
Indexed: ASFA, AgBio, AgrForAb, ApicAb, BIOSIS Prev, BioCN&I, BiolAb, EntAb, ForAb, HGA, HelmAb, HerbAb, HortAb, IndVet, NutrAb, PotatoAb, ProtozoAb, RA&MP, RDA, RM&VM, RPP, RevApplEntom, RiceAb, S&F, SIA, SoyAb, TDB, WeedAb, ZooRec.
—BLDSC (5113.545000).
Published by: Han'guk Konchung Hachoe/Entomological Society of Korea, Korean Entomological Institute, Department of Biology, Korea University, Seoul, 136-701, Korea, S. Ed. Yoo Hang Shin.

595.7 USA ISSN 0073-134X
QL461 CODEN: PHESAI
➤ **HAWAIIAN ENTOMOLOGICAL SOCIETY. PROCEEDINGS.** Text in English. 1906. irreg. price varies. reprint service avail. from PQC. **Document type:** *Journal, Academic/Scholarly.* **Description:** Technical items on systematics, biology and control of insects and related organisms. Emphasis is on Hawaii and the Pacific area.
Indexed: ASFA, Agr, ApicAb, BIOSIS Prev, BioCN&I, BiolAb, EntAb, HGA, RefZh, WeedAb, ZooRec.
—BLDSC (6707.000000), CISTI, Linda Hall.
Published by: Hawaiian Entomological Society, c/o Entomology Dept, Bishop Museum, 1525 Bernice St, Honolulu, HI 96817. TEL 808-956-7076, FAX 808-956-2428. Ed., R&P Neal L Evenhuis. Circ: 600.

➤ **HESSISCHE FAUNISTISCHE BRIEFE.** see *BIOLOGY—Zoology*

595.7 DEU ISSN 0724-1348
➤ **HETEROCERA SUMATRANA.** Text in English, German. 1982. irreg., latest vol.12, no.3, 2002. EUR 20 per issue (effective 2004). bibl.; illus. back issues avail. **Document type:** *Monographic series, Academic/Scholarly.* **Description:** Discusses entomological research of moths and butterflies.
Indexed: BIOSIS Prev, BiolAb, EntAb, ZooRec.
Published by: Heterocera Sumatrana Society e.V., Kreuzburger Str 6, Goettingen, 37085, Germany. TEL 49-551-76786, FAX 49-551-7709198, lwr.kobes@t-online.de. Ed. Lutz W.R. Kobes. R&P Lutz W R Kobes.

595.7 JPN ISSN 0389-827X
HIROSHIMA MUSHI NO KAI KAIHO/ENTOMOLOGICAL SOCIETY OF HIROSHIMA. JOURNAL. Text in Japanese. 1962. a.
Published by: Hiroshima Mushi no Kai/Entomological Society of Hiroshima, c/o Mr Murkami, 6963-2 Numatachotomo, Asaminami-ku, Hiroshima-shi, 731-3161, Japan.

595.78 USA ISSN 1070-4140
QL541
➤ **HOLARCTIC LEPIDOPTERA.** Text in English. 1994. s-a. USD 45 (effective 2005). bibl.; illus.; tr.lit. index, cum.index. back issues avail. **Document type:** *Journal, Academic/Scholarly.* **Description:** General taxonomy and conservation of north temperate species of moths and butterflies from North America and Eurasia.
Indexed: AgrForAb, BIOSIS Prev, BioCN&I, BiolAb, EntAb, ForAb, HortAb, RefZh, RevApplEntom, ZooRec.
—BLDSC (4322.290100), IE, ingenta, Linda Hall.
Published by: Association for Tropical Lepidoptera, PO Box 141210, Gainesville, FL 32614-1210. TEL 352-392-5894, FAX 352-373-3249, jbhatl@aol.com, http://www.troplep.org/hl.htm, http://www.troplep.org/atl.htm. Ed. J B Heppner. Circ: 1,250.

595.7 JPN ISSN 0917-3560
HOTARU JOHO KOKAN/STUDY GROUP ON FIREFLY. REPORT. Text in Japanese. irreg.
Published by: Zenkoku Hotaru Kenkyukai/Study Group on Firefly, c/o Mr Murakami, 15-19 Hama-Saka 2-chome, Tottori-shi, 680-0001, Japan.

595.7 JPN
HOTARU KENKYU TAIKAI/REPORT OF MEETING ON FIREFLY. Text in Japanese. a.
Published by: Zenkoku Hotaru Kenkyukai/Study Group on Firefly, c/o Mr Murakami, 15-19 Hama-Saka 2-chome, Tottori-shi, 680-0001, Japan.

I B R A CONFERENCE ON TROPICAL BEES. see *AGRICULTURE*

595.7 IND ISSN 0073-6392
QL483.I4 CODEN: IFREAI
INDIAN FOREST RECORDS (NEW SERIES) ENTOMOLOGY. Text in English. 1935. irreg., latest vol.14, no.2, 1981. price varies.
Indexed: BiolAb, ForAb, ISA, RevApplEntom.
—CISTI, Linda Hall.
Published by: Forest Research Institute & Colleges, P.O. New Forest, Dehra Dun, Uttar Pradesh, India. Circ: 500.

595.7 IND ISSN 0367-8288
INDIAN JOURNAL OF ENTOMOLOGY. Text in English. 1939. q.
Indexed: AEA, ASFA, AgBio, AgrForAb, BioCN&I, CPA, FCA, FPA, ForAb, HGA, HortAb, IndVet, MaizeAb, NemAb, NutrAb, OrnHort, PBA, PGegResA, PGrRegA, PHN&I, PotatoAb, PoultAb, RA&MP, RDA, RPP, RiceAb, S&F, SIA, SeedAb, SoyAb, TriticAb, VetBull, WAE&RSA, WeedAb, ZooRec.
—BLDSC (4412.000000), CISTI, IE, ingenta, Linda Hall.
Published by: Entomological Society of India, c/o Division of Entomology, Indian Agricultural Research Institute, New Delhi, 110012, India.

595.733 IND ISSN 0970-969X
➤ **INDIAN ODONATOLOGY.** Text in English. 1988. irreg. price varies. **Document type:** *Academic/Scholarly.* **Description:** Highlights the various characteristics of the dragonfly fauna from the Oriental region.
Published by: International Odonatological Society, D-f Saraswati Nagar, Jodhpur, Rajasthan 342 005, India. TEL 91-291-40766. Ed. B K Tyagi. Circ: 200.

595.7 GBR ISSN 0965-1748
QL495 CODEN: IBMBES
➤ **INSECT BIOCHEMISTRY AND MOLECULAR BIOLOGY.** Text in English. 1971. 12/yr. EUR 2,026 in Europe to institutions; JPY 268,900 in Japan to institutions; USD 2,265 to institutions except Europe and Japan; EUR 172 in Europe to qualified personnel; JPY 22,800 in Japan to qualified personnel; USD 192 to qualified personnel except Europe and Japan (effective 2006). adv. abstr. back issues avail.; reprint service avail. from PQC. **Document type:** *Journal, Academic/Scholarly.* **Description:** Covers neurochemistry, hormone and pheromone biochemistry, enzymes and metabolism, hormone action and gene regulation, gene characterization and structure, pharmacology, immunology and cell and tissue culture.
Formerly (until 1992): Insect Biochemistry (0020-1790)
Related titles: Microfilm ed.: (from PQC); Online - full text ed.: (from EBSCO Publishing, Gale Group, IngentaConnect, ScienceDirect, Swets Information Services).
Indexed: ASCA, ASFA, AbHyg, AgBio, Agr, AgrForAb, AnBrAb, ApicAb, B&BAb, BBCI, BIOBASE, BIOSIS Prev, BioCN&I, BiolAb, CIN, CPA, ChemAb, ChemTitl, CurCont, DBA, DSA, EntAb, FCA, FPA, ForAb, GenetAb, HGA, HelmAb, HerbAb, HortAb, IABS, ISR, IndMed, IndVet, MEDLINE, MaizeAb, NPU, NemAb, NucAcAb, NutrAb, PBA, PGegResA, PGrRegA, PHN&I, PN&I, PotatoAb, ProtozoAb, RA&MP, RM&VM, RPP, RefZh, RevApplEntom, RiceAb, S&F, SCI, SIA, SeedAb, SoyAb, TDB, TriticAb, VetBull, WeedAb, ZooRec.
—BLDSC (4516.852000), CASDDS, CISTI, IDS, IE, Infotrieve, ingenta, Linda Hall. **CCC.**

B

Published by: Pergamon (Subsidiary of: Elsevier Science & Technology), The Boulevard, Langford Ln, East Park, Kidlington, Oxford OX5 1GB, United Kingdom. TEL 44-1865-843000, FAX 44-1865-843010, http://www.elsevier.com/locate/ibmb. Eds. A. S. Raikhel, R. Feyereisen. Circ: 1,015. Subscr. to: Elsevier BV, PO Box 211, Amsterdam 1000 AE, Netherlands. TEL 31-20-485-3757, FAX 31-20-485-3432, nlinfo-f@elsevier.nl, http://www.elsevier.nl.

595.7   GBR   ISSN 0962-1075
QL493.5   CODEN: IMBIE3
➤ INSECT MOLECULAR BIOLOGY. Text in English. bi-m. GBP 174, EUR 261 combined subscription in Europe to individuals print & online eds.; USD 323 combined subscription in the Americas to individuals & Caribbean, print & online eds.; GBP 192 combined subscription elsewhere to individuals print & online eds.; GBP 632 combined subscription in Europe to institutions print & online eds.; USD 1,171 combined subscription in the Americas to institutions & Caribbean, print & online eds.; GBP 697 combined subscription elsewhere to institutions print & online eds. (effective 2006). adv. back issues avail.; reprint service avail. from PSC. Document type: Journal, Academic/Scholarly. Description: Publishes only high-quality original research articles on the structure, function, mapping, organization, expression and evolution of insect genes/genomes. It serves both the fundamental and applied aspects of insect molecular biology, and papers relating to the medical and agricultural sectors are welcome, as are those on the interaction of micro-organisms with their insect hosts.
Related titles: Microform ed.: (from PQC); Online - full text ed.: ISSN 1365-2583. GBP 600 in Europe to institutions; USD 1,109 in the Americas to institutions & Caribbean; GBP 660 elsewhere to institutions (effective 2006) (from Blackwell Synergy, EBSCO Publishing, Gale Group, IngentaConnect, O C L C Online Computer Library Center, Inc., Swets Information Services).
Indexed: ASCA, ASFA, AbHyg, AgBio, Agr, AgrForAb, AnBrAb, B&BAb, BCI, BIOBASE, BIOSIS Prev, BibAg, BioCN&I, BiolAb, CIN, ChemAb, ChemTitl, CurCont, DSA, EntAb, FCA, ForAb, GenetAb, HGA, HelmAb, HortAb, IABS, ISR, IndMed, IndVet, Inpharma, MEDLINE, MaizeAb, NemAb, NucAcAb, PHN&I, PotatoAb, ProtozoAb, RM&VM, RPP, Reac, RefZh, RevApplEntom, RiceAb, SCI, SIA, SoyAb, TDB, VetBull, ZooRec.
—BLDSC (4516.885000), CASDDS, CISTI, GNLM, IDS, IE, Infotrieve, ingenta, Linda Hall. CCC.
Published by: (Royal Entomological Society), Blackwell Publishing Ltd., 9600 Garsington Rd, Oxford, OX4 2ZG, United Kingdom. TEL 44-1865-776868, FAX 44-1865-714591, customerservices@oxon.blackwellpublishing.com, http://www.blackwellpublishing.com/journals/IMB. Eds. A A James, L Field. Pub. Sue Hewitt. R&P Sophie Savage. Adv. contact Jenny Applin. Circ: 310.

595.7   GBR   ISSN 1672-9609
INSECT SCIENCE. Text in English. 1994. q. EUR 107 combined subscription in Europe to individuals; USD 179 combined subscription in the Americas to individuals & Caribbean; GBP 107 combined subscription elsewhere to individuals; USD 392 combined subscription in the Americas to institutions & Caribbean; GBP 233 combined subscription elsewhere to institutions (effective 2006). bk.rev. Document type: Journal, Academic/Scholarly. Description: Publishes papers in all fields of research in insects and other terrestrial arthropods.
Formerly (until 2004): Entomologia Sinica (1005-295X)
Related titles: Online - full text ed.: ISSN 1744-7917. USD 342 in the Americas to institutions & Caribbean; GBP 137 elsewhere to institutions (effective 2005) (from Blackwell Synergy, East View Information Services, EBSCO Publishing, O C L C Online Computer Library Center, Inc., Swets Information Services).
Indexed: ASFA, AgBio, AgrForAb, AnBeAb, ApEcolAb, B&BAb, BioCN&I, CPA, EntAb, FCA, ForAb, GenetAb, HGA, HerbAb, HortAb, IndVet, NemAb, OrnHort, PBA, PHN&I, PotatoAb, ProtozoAb, RM&VM, RPP, RefZh, RevApplEntom, RiceAb, S&F, SoyAb, TDB, TriticAb, WAE&RSA, WeedAb, ZooRec.
—BLDSC (4516.918500), CISTI, IE, ingenta. CCC.
Published by: (Zhongguo Kexueyuan, Dongwu Yanjiusuo/Chinese Academy of Sciences, Institute of Zoology CHN, Entomological Society of China TWN), Blackwell Publishing Ltd., 9600 Garsington Rd, Oxford, OX4 2ZG, United Kingdom. TEL 44-1865-776868, FAX 44-1865-714591, customerservices@oxon.blackwellpublishing.com, http://www.blackwellpublishing.com/journals/INS. Dist. by: China International Book Trading Corp.

595.7   DNK   ISSN 1399-560X
QL461   CODEN: ENTSBF
➤ INSECT SYSTEMATICS AND EVOLUTION; an international journal of systematic entomology. Text in English. 1936. 4/yr. DKK 1,490 (effective 2004). bibl.; charts; illus. 120 p./no. 2 cols./p.; back issues avail. Document type: Journal, Academic/Scholarly. Description: Presents research and articles from all areas of systematic entomological research throughout the world.
Former titles (until 2000): Entomologica Scandinavica (0013-8711); (until 1970): Opuscula Entomologica (0375-0205)
Indexed: ASCA, ASFA, AgBio, AgrForAb, B&BAb, BIOSIS Prev, BioCN&I, BioDAb, BiolAb, CurCont, EntAb, FPA, ForAb, GenetAb, HGA, HortAb, IndVet, PBA, RM&VM, RevApplEntom, S&F, TDB, VetBull, WeedAb, ZooRec.

—BLDSC (4516.919000), CISTI, IE, Infotrieve, ingenta, Linda Hall. CCC.
Published by: (Societas Entomologica Scandinavica NLD), Apollo Books, Kirkeby Sand 19, Stenstrup, 5771, Denmark. TEL 45-62-263737, FAX 45-62-263780, apollobooks@vip.cybercity.dk, http://www.zmuc.dk/entoweb/insysevol/, http://www.apollobooks.com. Eds. Nils Moeller Andersen, Verner Michelsen. Circ: 500 (paid).

595.7   USA   ISSN 1043-6057
INSECT WORLD∗. Text in English. 1989. bi-m. USD 35 (effective 2000). bk.rev. illus. Document type: Newsletter. Description: Contains information for children and adults with an interest in insects.
Published by: Young Entomologists' Society, Inc., 6907 W Grand River Ave, Lansing, MI 48906-9131. TEL 517-887-0499, YESbug@aol.com. Ed. Gary Dunn.

595.7   KOR   ISSN 1225-0104
QL483.K8
INSECTA KOREANA. Text in English. 1982. a., latest vol.16. USD 30 (effective 2002).
Related titles: Online - full text ed.
Indexed: ASFA, BioCN&I, EntAb, ForAb, HortAb, OrnHort, PBA, RA&MP, WeedAb, ZooRec.
—Linda Hall.
Published by: Center for Insect Systematics, c/o College of Agriculture & Life Science, Kangwon National University, Chuncheon, Kangwon, 200-701, Korea, S. TEL 82-361-2507258, FAX 82-361-2562085, cispa@cc.kangwon.ac.kr, http://www.kangwon.ac.kr/~cisweb/pub.html.

595.7   JPN
QL461   CODEN: IMATAR
➤ INSECTA MATSUMURANA. NEW SERIES. Text and summaries in English. 1926; N.S. 1973. irreg. per issue exchange basis. charts; illus. Document type: Academic/Scholarly.
Formerly: Insecta Matsumurana - Hokkaido University. Faculty of Agriculture. Journal. Series of Entomology (0020-1804)
Indexed: ASFA, AgrForAb, BIOSIS Prev, BioCN&I, BiolAb, ForAb, HortAb, PBA, RM&VM, RefZh, RevApplEntom, ZooRec.
—IE, Linda Hall.
Published by: (Laboratory of Systematic Entomology), Hokkaido University, Faculty of Agriculture/Hokkaido Dagaiku Nogakubu, Nishi-9-chome, Kita 9-jo, Kita-ku, Sapporo, 060-8589, Japan. TEL 81-11-706-2486, FAX 81-11-706-4939, ohara@res.agr.hokudai.ac.jp. Ed. Masaaki Suwa.

595.7   USA   ISSN 0749-6737
                                          CODEN: INMUEX
➤ INSECTA MUNDI. Text in English. 1985. q. USD 35 domestic; USD 41 foreign (effective 2005). adv. bk.rev. bibl.; charts; illus. back issues avail. Document type: Academic/Scholarly.
Indexed: Agr, AgrForAb, BioCN&I, BiolAb, FCA, FPA, ForAb, HortAb, RM&VM, RefZh, RevApplEntom, WeedAb, ZooRec.
—BLDSC (4517.200000), IE, ingenta.
Published by: Center for Systematic Entomology, PO Box 147100, Gainesville, FL 32614-7100. hamona@doacs.state.fl.us, http://centerforsystematicentomology.org/insecta_mundi.htm. Ed. Dr. M C Thomas.

595.7   CHE   ISSN 0020-1812
QL496   CODEN: INSOA7
➤ INSECTES SOCIAUX. Text in English, French, German. 1952. q. EUR 598 combined subscription to institutions print & online eds. (effective 2005). bibl.; charts; illus. back issues avail.; reprint service avail. from ISI. Document type: Journal, Academic/Scholarly. Description: Covers the various aspects of the biology and evolution of social insects and other presocial arthropods.
Incorporates (1952-1953): Union Internationale pour l'Etude des Insectes Sociaux. Section Francaise. Bulletin (1149-8121)
Related titles: Microform ed.: (from PQC); Online - full text ed.: ISSN 1420-9098 (from EBSCO Publishing, Springer LINK, Swets Information Services).
Indexed: ASCA, ASFA, AgBio, AgrForAb, AnBeAb, ApEcolAb, ApicAb, BIOBASE, BIOSIS Prev, BioCN&I, BiolAb, CPA, ChemAb, ChemoAb, CurCont, ESPM, EntAb, FPA, ForAb, GEOBASE, HerbAb, HortAb, IABS, IBR, ISR, NutrAb, OrnHort, ProtozoAb, RA&MP, RM&VM, RPP, RefZh, RevApplEntom, S&F, SCI, SIA, SeedAb, SoyAb, WAE&RSA, WeedAb, ZooRec.
—BLDSC (4518.000000), CISTI, IDS, IE, Infotrieve, ingenta, Linda Hall. CCC.
Published by: (International Union for the Study of Social Insects), Birkhaeuser Verlag AG (Subsidiary of: Springer Science+Business Media), Viaduktstr 42, Postfach 133, Basel, 4051, Switzerland. TEL 41-61-2050707, FAX 41-61-2050799, insects@birkhauser.ch, info@birkhauser.ch, http://link.springer.de/link/service/journals/00040/index.htm, http://www.birkhauser.ch/journals. Ed. Johan Billen TEL 32-16-323975. Circ: 700. Subscr. in the Americas to: Springer-Verlag New York, Inc., Journal Fulfillment, PO Box 2485, Secaucus, NJ 07096-2485. TEL 800-777-4643, 201-348-4033, FAX 201-348-4505; Subscr. to: Springer GmbH Auslieferungsgesellschaft, Haberstr 7, Heidelberg 69126, Germany. TEL 49-6221-345-0, FAX 49-6221-345-4229, subscriptions@springer.de.

595.7   USA
INSECTIMES∗. Text in English. q.
Published by: Nor-Am Chemical Company, PO Box 12014, Research Triangle Park, NC 27709-2014. TEL 302-477-3014, FAX 302-477-3013. Circ: 19,000.

595.7   KOR
INSECTS OF KOREA. Text in English. irreg. Document type: Monographic series.
Published by: Center for Insect Systematics, c/o College of Agriculture & Life Science, Kangwon National University, Chuncheon, Kangwon, 200-701, Korea, S. TEL 82-361-2507258, FAX 82-361-2562085, cispa@cc.kangwon.ac.kr, http://www.kangwon.ac.kr/~cisweb/pub.html.

595.7   USA   ISSN 0073-8115
QL489.M5   CODEN: IMICAG
INSECTS OF MICRONESIA. Text in English; Text occasionally in French, German. 1954. irreg. price varies. reprint service avail. from PQC. Description: Systematics of terrestrial arthropods of Micronesia.
Indexed: BiolAb.
Published by: Bishop Museum Press, 1525 Bernice St, Box 19000 A, Honolulu, HI 96817. TEL 808-947-3511.

595.7   USA   ISSN 0098-1222
QL475.V5
➤ INSECTS OF VIRGINIA. Text in English. 1969. irreg. per issue exchange basis. bibl.; charts; illus.; maps. back issues avail. Document type: Monographic series, Academic/Scholarly. Description: Contains manual for identification of insects in-state, useful at college or professional level.
—CISTI.
Address: Virginia Museum of Natural History, 1001 Douglas Ave., Martinsville, VA 24112. TEL 540-666-8629, rhoffman@vmnh.org. Ed. Richard Hoffman. Circ: 1,000.

595.7   NOR
INSEKT-NYTT. Text in Norwegian; Summaries in English. q.
Published by: Norsk Entomologisk Forening, c/o Egil Michaelsen, Kurlandveien 35, Sarpsborg, 1727, Norway.

595.7   BEL   ISSN 0374-6232
                                          CODEN: BIETBB
➤ INSTITUT ROYAL DES SCIENCES NATURELLES DE BELGIQUE. BULLETIN. SERIE ENTOMOLOGIE. Text in English. 1930. a., latest vol.72, 2002. EUR 33.47 (effective 2003). bibl.; charts; illus. cum.index. back issues avail. Document type: Bulletin, Academic/Scholarly.
Indexed: BIOSIS Prev, BioCN&I, BiolAb, EntAb, ForAb, HerbAb, HortAb, IndVet, PGegResA, PoultAb, RA&MP, RDA, RRTA, RefZh, RevApplEntom, S&F, SFA, VetBull, WeedAb, WildRev, ZooRec.
—Linda Hall.
Published by: Koninklijk Belgisch Instituut voor Natuurwetenschappen/Institut Royal des Sciences Naturelles de Belgique, Vautierstraat 29, Brussels, 1000, Belgium. TEL 32-2-6274211, FAX 32-2-6274113, leon.baert@naturalsciences.be, bib@naturalsciences.be, http://www.naturalsciences.be. Ed. Leon Baert. Circ: 1,500.

595.7   BRA   ISSN 0020-3629
INSTITUTO AGRONOMICO DO SUL. ESCOLA DE AGRONOMIA ELISEU MACIEL. ARQUIVOS DE ENTOMOLOGIA. SERIE A & SERIE B∗. Text in Portuguese. 1959. s-a. USD 1.50. bk.rev. bibl.; charts; illus.
Published by: Universidade Federal de Pelotas, Faculdade de Agronomie "Eliseu Maciel", Centro, Caixa Postal 15, Pelotas, RGS 96001-970, Brazil. Ed. Ceslao Mario De Biezanko. Circ: 1,500.

595.7   MEX   ISSN 1405-356X
INSTITUTO NACIONAL DE INVESTIGACIONES FORESTALES, AGRICOLAS Y PECUARIAS. BOLETIN DIVULGATIVO. Text in Spanish; Summaries in English, Spanish. 1961. irreg. latest vol.80, 1994. price varies. back issues avail.
Formerly (until 1985): Instituto Nacional de Investigaciones Forestales. Boletin Divulgativo (0185-2361)
Indexed: BiolAb, FPA, ForAb.
Published by: Instituto Nacional de Investigaciones Forestales Agricolas y Pecuarias, Biblioteca Nacional Forestal Ing. Roberto Villasenor Angeles, Ave. PROGRESO 5, Col Vivero de Coyoacan, Delegacion Coyoacan, Mexico City, DF 04110, Mexico. TEL 52-5-6584333, FAX 52-5-5548849, comef@inifap2.inifap.conacyt.mx.

595.7   MEX   ISSN 1405-3551
SD147
INSTITUTO NACIONAL DE INVESTIGACIONES FORESTALES, AGRICOLAS Y PECUARIAS. BOLETIN TECNICO. Text in Spanish; Summaries in English, Spanish. 1961. irreg., latest vol.142. price varies. back issues avail.
Formerly (until 1985): Instituto Nacional de Investigaciones Forestales. Boletin Tecnico (0185-2310)
Indexed: AEA, BiolAb, FPA, ForAb, S&F.
Published by: Instituto Nacional de Investigaciones Forestales Agricolas y Pecuarias, Biblioteca Nacional Forestal Ing. Roberto Villasenor Angeles, Ave. PROGRESO 5, Col Vivero de Coyoacan, Delegacion Coyoacan, Mexico City, DF 04110, Mexico. TEL 52-5-6584333, FAX 52-5-5548849, comef@inifap2.inifap.conacyt.mx.

595.7 MEX ISSN 1405-3578
INSTITUTO NACIONAL DE INVESTIGACIONES FORESTALES, AGRICOLAS Y PECUARIAS. PUBLICACION ESPECIAL. Text in Spanish; Summaries in English, Spanish. 1961. irreg., latest vol.63, 1995. price varies. back issues avail.
Formerly (until 1985): Instituto Nacional de Investigaciones Forestales. Publicacion Especial (0185-2566)
Indexed: BiolAb, FPA, ForAb.
Published by: Instituto Nacional de Investigaciones Forestales Agricolas y Pecuarias, Biblioteca Nacional Forestal Ing. Roberto Villasenor Angeles, Ave. PROGRESO 5, Col Vivero de Coyoacan, Delegacion Coyoacan, Mexico City, DF 04110, Mexico. TEL 52-5-6584333, FAX 52-5-5548849, comef@inifap2.inifap.conacyt.mx.

595.7 KEN
INTERNATIONAL CENTRE OF INSECT PHYSIOLOGY AND ECOLOGY. ANNUAL REPORT. Text in English. 1973. a. illus. **Document type:** *Corporate.*
—BLDSC (1309.941000).
Published by: (International Centre of Insect Physiology and Ecology), I C I P E Science Press, PO Box 72913, Nairobi, Kenya. TEL 802573-9, TELEX 25066-DUDU. Ed. A N Mengech TEL 254-2-861680. Circ: 1,500.

595.7 AUS ISSN 0074-364X
INTERNATIONAL CONGRESS OF ENTOMOLOGY. Text in English. 1910. quadrennial (Vancouver, Canada; 19th, Beijing, China; 20th , Florence, Italy). price varies. **Document type:** *Proceedings.*
Indexed: BiolAb, IndVet, ZooRec.
Published by: Council for International Congresses of Entomology, c/o Dr. Whitten, CSIRO Div. of Entomology, GPO Box 1700, Canberra, ACT 2601, Australia.

595.7 USA
INTERNATIONAL ENTOMOLOGY RESOURCE GUIDE: THE INSECT STUDY SOURCEBOOK✶ . Text in English. 1986. biennial. USD 10; (Canada & Mexico $13; other $14). **Document type:** *Directory.* **Description:** Cross-referenced resource guide to entomological equipment, services, livestock, specimens, books and organizations.
Formerly: Y E S International Entomology Resource Guide
Published by: Young Entomologists' Society, Inc., 6907 W. Grand River Ave., Lasing, MI 48906-9131. TEL 517-887-0499, YESbug@aol.com. Ed. Gary A Dunn. Circ: 1,000.

595.42 USA ISSN 0164-7954
CODEN: IJOADM
➤ **INTERNATIONAL JOURNAL OF ACAROLOGY.** Text in English. 1975. q. USD 150 to individuals; USD 1,100 to institutions (effective 2004). adv. bk.rev. abstr. 80 p./no. 2 cols./p.; back issues avail. **Document type:** *Journal, Academic/Scholarly.* **Description:** Publishes original research work on a wide variety of acarological subjects including mite and tick behavior, biochemistry, biology, control, ecology, evolution, morphology, physiology, systematics and taxonomy.
Indexed: AEA, ASFA, AbHyg, AgrForAb, AnBrAb, BIOSIS Prev, BioCN&I, BiolAb, CurCont, EntAb, FCA, ForAb, HerbAb, HortAb, IndVet, MaizeAb, NutrAb, OrnHort, PBA, PHN&I, PoultAb, RM&VM, RPP, RefZh, RevApplEntom, S&F, SFA, SIA, TriticAb, VITIS, VetBull, WeedAb, WildRev, ZooRec.
—CISTI, IE, Infotrieve.
Published by: Indira Publishing House, PO Box 250456, West Bloomfield, MI 48325-0456. TEL 248-661-2529, FAX 248-661-4066, v.prasad@ix.netcom.com, http://pw2.netcom.com/~v.prasad/IJA_Web_Pages/, http://www.indirapublishinghouse.com. Ed. Jim Amrine Jr.

595.7 NLD ISSN 1388-7890
➤ **INTERNATIONAL JOURNAL OF ODONATOLOGY.** Cover title: Pantala. Text in English. 1998. s-a. EUR 75 (effective 2002). back issues avail. **Document type:** *Journal, Academic/Scholarly.* **Description:** Addresses ecology, ethology, physiology, genetics, taxonomy, phylogeny and geographic distribution of odonata.
Formerly (until 2001): Pantala - International Journal of Odonatology
Indexed: ZooRec.
—BLDSC (4542.417000).
Published by: (Worldwide Dragonfly Association), Backhuys Publishers BV, Postbus 321, Leiden, 2300 AH, Netherlands. TEL 31-71-517-0208, FAX 31-71-517-1856, backhuys@backhuys.com, http://www.backhuys.com. Ed. H J Dumont. Pub. Wil Peters. Circ: 250 (paid); 150 (controlled).

595.7 GBR ISSN 1742-7584
SB818 CODEN: ISIADL
➤ **INTERNATIONAL JOURNAL OF TROPICAL INSECT SCIENCE.** Text in English, French; Abstracts in English, French. 1980. q. USD 370 in the Americas to institutions except Canada; GBP 210 elsewhere to institutions; USD 385 combined subscription in the Americas to institutions except Canada; print & online eds.; GBP 220 combined subscription elsewhere to institutions print & online eds. (effective 2006). adv. bk.rev. index. back issues avail.; reprint service avail. from PQC. **Document type:** *Journal, Academic/Scholarly.* **Description:** Publishes original research articles, short communications, and review articles dealing with basic and applied tropical insect sciences. Advocates an ecologically sensitive approach to pest control, focusing on integrated pest management.
Formerly (until 2004): Insect Science and Its Application (0191-9040)
Related titles: Microform ed.: (from MIM, PQC); Online - full text ed.: ISSN 1742-7592. USD 315 in the Americas to institutions except Canada; GBP 180 elsewhere to institutions (effective 2006) (from EBSCO Publishing, Gale Group, IngentaConnect, International Network for the Availability of Scientific Publications, African Journals Online, Ovid Technologies, Inc., Swets Information Services).
Indexed: AEA, ASCA, ASFA, ATA, AbHyg, AgBio, Agr, AgrForAb, BIOSIS Prev, BioCN&I, BiolAb, CIN, CPA, CTFA, ChemAb, ChemTitl, CurCont, DBA, DSA, EIA, EnerInd, EntAb, FCA, FPA, FS&TA, ForAb, HelmAb, HerbAb, HortAb, IndVet, MaizeAb, NemAb, NutrAb, OrnHort, PBA, PGegResA, PGrRegA, PHN&I, PotatoAb, PoultAb, ProtozoAb, RA&MP, RDA, RM&VM, RPP, RevApplEntom, RiceAb, S&F, S&MA, SIA, SeedAb, SoyAb, TDB, TobAb, TriticAb, VetBull, WAE&RSA, WeedAb, ZooRec.
—BLDSC (4516.918000), CASDDS, CISTI, IDS, IE, Infotrieve, ingenta, Linda Hall. **CCC.**
Published by: (International Centre of Insect Physiology and Ecology KEN), CABI Publishing (Subsidiary of: CAB International), CAB International, Wallingford, Oxfordshire OX10 8DE, United Kingdom. TEL 44-1491-832111, FAX 44-1491-833508, publishing@cabi.org, http://www.cabi-publishing.org/. Ed. H R Herren. adv.: B&W page USD 520. Circ: 300. **Co-sponsor:** African Association of Insect Scientists.

632.7 GBR ISSN 0020-8256
SB950 CODEN: IPCLBZ
INTERNATIONAL PEST CONTROL; crop protection, public health, wood preservation. Text in English. 1959. bi-m. GBP 140, USD 308 (effective 2005). adv. bk.rev. charts; illus.; tr.lit. index. **Document type:** *Journal, Academic/Scholarly.* **Description:** Deals with all aspects of pest eradication and prevention.
Indexed: AEA, AbHyg, AgBio, AgrForAb, B&AI, BIOSIS Prev, BioCN&I, BiolAb, CBNB, CIN, CPA, ChemAb, ChemTitl, DBA, EPB, ExcerpMed, FCA, FPA, ForAb, GEOBASE, HelmAb, HerbAb, HortAb, IndVet, MaizeAb, NemAb, OrnHort, PBA, PHN&I, PROMT, PotatoAb, PoultAb, ProtozoAb, RA&MP, RM&VM, RPP, RevApplEntom, RiceAb, S&F, SAA, SFA, SeedAb, SoyAb, TDB, TriticAb, VetBull, WAE&RSA, WeedAb, WildRev, ZooRec.
—BLDSC (4544.910000), CASDDS, CISTI, IE, Infotrieve, ingenta, Linda Hall. **CCC.**
Published by: Research Information Ltd., Grenville Court, Britwell Rd, Burnham, Bucks SL1 8DF, United Kingdom. TEL 44-1628-600499, FAX 44-1628-600488, info@researchinformation.co.uk, http://www.researchinformation.co.uk/ipco.html. Ed. David Macdonald. Pub. Kumar Patel TEL 44-20-8328-2470. Adv. contact Ras Patel. B&W page GBP 576. Circ: 4,800.

595.7 DEU ISSN 1019-2808
QL461
INTERNATIONALER ENTOMOLOGISCHER VEREIN. MITTEILUNGEN. Text in English, German. 1969. 4/yr. EUR 20 membership (effective 2005). bk.rev. index. back issues avail. **Document type:** *Journal, Academic/Scholarly.*
Indexed: ASFA, BiolAb, RefZh, ZooRec.
Published by: Internationaler Entomologischer Verein e.V., c/o Dr. Michael Geisthardt, Auringer Str 22, Wiesbaden, 65207, Germany. TEL 49-6127-991497, geisthardt@entomology-iev.de, http://www.entomology-iev.de.

595.7 ISR ISSN 0075-1243
QL461 CODEN: IJENB9
➤ **ISRAEL JOURNAL OF ENTOMOLOGY.** Text in English. 1966. a. USD 40 (effective 1997). adv. bk.rev. **Document type:** *Academic/Scholarly.* **Description:** Publishes original contributions in all areas of entomology.
Indexed: ASFA, AgBio, BIOSIS Prev, BioCN&I, BiolAb, ChemAb, EntAb, ForAb, GEOBASE, HGA, HortAb, PHN&I, RPP, RevApplEntom, S&F, SIA, SeedAb, WeedAb, ZooRec.
—BLDSC (4583.803500), CASDDS, CISTI, Linda Hall.
Published by: Entomological Society of Israel, P O Box 6, Bet Dagan, 50200, Israel. TEL 972-3-9683520, FAX 972-3-9604180, TELEX 381476-AROVC-IL. Ed. A Friedberg. Circ: 200.

595.7 JPN ISSN 0448-8628
JAPAN ENTOMOLOGICAL ACADEMY. BULLETIN. Text in English; Summaries in Japanese. 1964. irreg.
Published by: Japan Entomological Academy/Konchu Akademi, Nanzan Daigaku Seibutsugaku Kenkyushitsu, 18 Yamazato-cho, Showa-ku, Nagoya-shi, Aichi-ken 466-0824, Japan.

595.7 JPN ISSN 0916-1058
JAPAN HYMENOPTERISTS ASSOCIATION. SPECIAL PUBLICATIONS. Text in English. 1976. irreg. JPY 6,000 per issue.
Published by: Japan Hymenopterists Association/Nihon Hachirui Kenkyukai, c/o Dr. Tsuneki, 4-15 Asahigaoka, Mishima-shi, Shizuoka-ken 411-0000, Japan.

616.968 590 JPN
JAPAN SOCIETY OF MEDICAL ENTOMOLOGY AND ZOOLOGY. Text in English. q. USD 45 to non-members (effective 2003); membership incl. subscr.. **Document type:** *Journal, Academic/Scholarly.* **Description:** Publishes original articles and research notes concerning entomology and zoology in medical and related fields.
Address: Department of Infectious Disease Control, Oita Medical University, 1-1 Idaigaoka, Hasama-machi, Oita, 879-5593, Japan. TEL 81-97-5865702, http://wwwmez.med.uoeh-u.ac.jp/~mez/eng/ejournal.html, http://wwwmez.med.uoeh-u.ac.jp/~mez/index.html. Ed. Hiroyuki Takaoka TEL 81-97-5865701.

595.7 JPN ISSN 1343-8794
JAPANESE JOURNAL OF ENTOMOLOGY. NEW SERIES/KONCHU. NYU SHIRIZU. Text in English, French, German, Japanese. 1926; N.S. 1998. q. JPY 10,000 to non-members; JPY 8,000 to members. adv. bk.rev. index. cum.index. **Document type:** *Bulletin.*
Supersedes in part (in 1998): Japanese Journal of Entomology - Konchu (0915-5805); Which was formerly (until 1989): Konchu (0013-8770); Former titles: Insect; Entomology
Indexed: ASFA, AgBio, B&BAb, BIOSIS Prev, BioCN&I, BiolAb, EntAb, ForAb, GenetAb, HGA, HortAb, IndVet, OrnHort, PHN&I, PoultAb, RPP, RevApplEntom, RiceAb, SPPI, WeedAb, ZooRec.
—BLDSC (4651.810010), CISTI, IE, ingenta, Linda Hall.
Published by: Entomological Society of Japan/Nihon Konchu Gakkai, c/o Dept of Zoology, National Science Museum (Natl Hist), 3-23-1 Hiyakunin-cho, Shinjuku-ku, Tokyo, 169-0073, Japan. TEL 81-3-3364-7129, FAX 81-3-3364-7104. Ed. Hiroshi Shima. Adv. contact Hiroshi Kajita. Circ: 1,550. **Dist. by:** Business Center for Academic Societies Japan, 5-16-19 Honkomagome, Bunkyo-ku, Tokyo 113-0021, Japan. TEL 81-3-58145811.

595.7 JPN ISSN 1341-1160
QL468 CODEN: TSHEAA
JAPANESE JOURNAL OF SYSTEMATIC ENTOMOLOGY/ SHIKOKU KONCHU GAKKAI KAIHO. Text in English. 1950. 2/yr. JPY 3,000. bibl.; charts; illus.
Formerly (until 1995): Shikoku Entomological Society. Transactions (0037-3680)
Indexed: ASFA, BIOSIS Prev, BioCN&I, BiolAb, EntAb, ForAb, HGA, HortAb, RevApplEntom, SPPI, TDB, ZooRec.
Published by: Shikoku Entomological Society/Shikoku Konchu Gakkai, Ehime Daigaku Nogakubu Konchugaku Kyoshitsu, 5-7 Tarumi 3-chome, Matsuyama-shi, Ehime-ken 790-0905, Japan. Circ: 450.

595.7 CHN ISSN 1005-0507
JISHENGCHONG YU YIXUE KUNCHONG XUEBAO/ACTA PARASITOLOGICA ET MEDICA ENTOMOLOGICA SINICA. Variant title: Parasitosis and Medical Entomology. Text in Chinese. 1993. q. CNY 32 domestic; USD 13.60 foreign (effective 2005). **Document type:** *Journal, Academic/Scholarly.*
Related titles: Online - full content ed.: (from WanFang Data Corp.); Online - full text ed.: (from East View Information Services).
Indexed: AbHyg, AgBio, AgrForAb, BioCN&I, ForAb, HelmAb, HerbAb, HortAb, IndVet, NemAb, NutrAb, PN&I, PoultAb, ProtozoAb, RA&MP, RDA, RefZh, RiceAb, S&F, TDB, VetBull.
—BLDSC (0643.350000), IE, ingenta.
Address: 20 Fengtaidong Dajie, Beijing, 100071, China. TEL 86-10-66948579, Entomolparasitol@sohu.com, http://jscyyxkcxb.periodicals.net.cn/. **Dist. by:** China International Book Trading Corp, 35 Chegongzhuang Xilu, Haidian District, PO Box 399, Beijing 100044, China. TEL 86-10-68412045, FAX 86-10-68412023, cibtc@mail.cibtc.com.cn, http://www.cibtc.com.cn.

595.7 IND
➤ **JOURNAL OF ACAROLOGY.** Text in English. 1976. s-a. INR 100, USD 30. bk.rev. back issues avail. **Document type:** *Academic/Scholarly.*
Formerly: Indian Journal of Acarology (0970-1400)
Indexed: BiolAb, RevApplEntom, ZooRec.
Published by: Acarological Society of India, University of Agricultural Sciences, Entomology Division, G.K.V.K., Bangalore, Karnataka 560 065, India. TEL 91-80-330153, TELEX 845-8393 OASK IN. Ed. G P Channabasavanna. Circ: 250.

595.7 USA ISSN 1523-5475
SB599 CODEN: JAENES
➤ **JOURNAL OF AGRICULTURAL AND URBAN ENTOMOLOGY.** Text in English. 1984. q. USD 50 domestic; USD 60 in Canada & Mexico; USD 75 elsewhere (effective 2002). adv. bk.rev. index. back issues avail. **Document type:** *Academic/Scholarly.* **Description:** Publishes results of original research on insects and other arthropods of agricultural and urban importance (humans, livestock, poultry, and wildlife included).
Formerly: Journal of Agricultural Entomology (0735-939X)
Indexed: AEA, AEBA, ASCA, ASFA, AgBio, Agr, AgrForAb, BIOSIS Prev, BioCN&I, BiolAb, CIN, ChemAb, ChemTitl, CurCont, ESPM, EntAb, FCA, FPA, HGA, HerbAb, HortAb, ISR, IndMed, IndVet, MBA, MaizeAb, OrnHort, PBA, PHN&I, PotatoAb, PoultAb, ProtozoAb, RA&MP, RM&VM, RPP, RefZh, RevApplEntom, RiceAb, S&F, SCI, SIA, SeedAb, SoyAb, TriticAb, VITIS, VetBull, WeedAb, ZooRec.
—BLDSC (4920.190000), CASDDS, CISTI, IDS, Linda Hall.

B

Published by: South Carolina Entomological Society, Inc., PO Box 582, Clemson, SC 29633. TEL 864-944-8401, FAX 864-656-5065, rmcwhrt@clemson.edu, http://entweb.clemson.edu/scesweb. Ed. David K Weaver. R&P, Adv. contact Randy C McWhorter Jr. B&W page USD 45; trim 9 x 6. Circ: 375 (paid).

➤ **JOURNAL OF AGRICULTURAL SCIENCE.** see *AGRICULTURE*

595.752 IND ISSN 0970-3810
➤ **JOURNAL OF APHIDOLOGY.** Text in English. 1987. s-a. INR 250, USD 40 (effective 2000). adv. bk.rev. **Document type:** *Academic/Scholarly.* **Description:** Contains original research and reviews in the fields of aphid research, including evolution, biosystematics, cytogenetics, bioecology, population dynamics of aphids and their predators and parasitoids, trophic interactions and aphid control.
Indexed: ZooRec.
—Linda Hall.
Published by: Aphidological Society India, Aphid Biocontrol Laboratory, Department of Zoology, Gorakhpur University, Gorakhpur, Uttar Pradesh 273 009, India. TEL 91-551-314292, FAX 91-551-336797. Ed., R&P, Adv. contact Rajendra Singh. page INR 500, page USD 75. Circ: 500.

B

595.7 DEU ISSN 0931-2048
SB599 CODEN: JOAEEB
➤ **JOURNAL OF APPLIED ENTOMOLOGY/ZEITSCHRIFT FUER ANGEWANDTE ENTOMOLOGIE.** Text in English, French, German; Abstracts in English. 1913. 10/yr. EUR 156, GBP 104 combined subscription in Europe to individuals print & online eds.; USD 159 combined subscription in the Americas to individuals & Caribbean (print & online eds.); GBP 114 combined subscription elsewhere to individuals print & online eds.; GBP 1,064 combined subscription in Europe to institutions print & online eds.; USD 1,788 combined subscription in the Americas to institutions & Caribbean (print & online eds.); GBP 1,170 combined subscription elsewhere to institutions print & online eds. (effective 2006). bk.rev. illus.; stat. back issues avail.; reprint service avail. from ISI. **Document type:** *Journal, Academic/Scholarly.* **Description:** Presents current research in entomology applied to agriculture, forestry, biomedical areas, food, and feed storage.
Formerly (until 1986): Zeitschrift fuer Angewandte Entomologie (0044-2240); Which incorporated (1913-1958): Deutsche Gesellschaft fuer Angewandte Entomologie. Verhandlungen (0372-5413)
Related titles: ♦ Online - full text ed.: Journal of Applied Entomology Online. ISSN 1439-0418.
Indexed: AEA, ASCA, ASFA, AgBio, Agr, AgrForAb, AnBeAb, AnBrAb, ApEcolAb, ApicAb, B&BAb, BIOBASE, BIOSIS Prev, BioCN&I, BiolAb, CPA, CTFA, ChemAb, ChemoAb, CurCont, DBA, DSA, EPB, ESPM, EntAb, ExcerpMed, FCA, FPA, ForAb, GEOBASE, HGA, HelmAb, HerbAb, HortAb, IABS, ISR, IndVet, MBA, MaizeAb, NemAb, NutrAb, OrnHort, PBA, PGegResA, PGrRegA, PHN&I, PotatoAb, ProtozoAb, RA&MP, RM&VM, RPP, RefZh, RevApplEntom, RiceAb, S&F, SCI, SIA, SeedAb, SoyAb, TDB, TriticAb, VITIS, VetBull, WeedAb, WildRev, ZooRec.
—BLDSC (4942.605000), CASDDS, CISTI, IDS, IE, Infotrieve, ingenta, Linda Hall. **CCC.**
Published by: Blackwell Verlag GmbH (Subsidiary of: Blackwell Publishing Ltd.), Kurfuerstendamm 57, Berlin, 10707, Germany. TEL 49-30-32790634, FAX 49-30-32790610, verlag@blackwell.de, http://www.blackwellpublishing.com/journals/JEN, http://www.blackwell.de. Ed. Reinhard Schopf. Circ: 550.

595.7 DEU ISSN 1439-0418
JOURNAL OF APPLIED ENTOMOLOGY ONLINE. Text in English, French, German. 10/yr. GBP 1,011 in Europe to institutions; USD 1,699 in the Americas to institutions & Caribbean; GBP 1,112 elsewhere to institutions (effective 2006). **Document type:** *Academic/Scholarly.*
Media: Online - full text (from Blackwell Synergy, EBSCO Publishing, Gale Group, IngentaConnect, O C L C Online Computer Library Center, Inc., Swets Information Services). **Related titles:** ♦ Print ed.: Journal of Applied Entomology. ISSN 0931-2048.
Indexed: CurCont, ISR, SCI.
Published by: Blackwell Verlag GmbH (Subsidiary of: Blackwell Publishing Ltd.), Kurfuerstendamm 57, Berlin, 10707, Germany. TEL 49-30-32790679, FAX 49-30-32790610, abo@blackwis.de, http://www.blackwell-science.com/~cgilib/jnlpage.bin?Journal=XJAE&File=XJAE&Page=aims, http://www.blackwell.de.

632 595.7 KOR ISSN 1226-8615
JOURNAL OF ASIA PACIFIC ENTOMOLOGY. Text in English. 1998. s-a. **Document type:** *Journal, Academic/Scholarly.*
Indexed: ASFA, AgBio, AnBrAb, BioCN&I, EntAb, FCA, ForAb, HortAb, IndVet, MaizeAb, NemAb, OrnHort, PBA, PGegResA, PHN&I, PotatoAb, ProtozoAb, RA&MP, RPP, RiceAb, S&F, SIA, WAE&RSA, WeedAb, ZooRec.
—BLDSC (4947.219550), CISTI, IE, Linda Hall.
Published by: Korean Society of Applied Entomology, c/o Dept. of Entomology, Agricultural Sciences Institute, Rural Development Administration, Suwon, 441707, Korea, S. TEL 0331-291-3681, FAX 0331-291-5830.

595.7 USA ISSN 0022-0493
SB599 CODEN: JEENAI
➤ **JOURNAL OF ECONOMIC ENTOMOLOGY.** Text in English. 1908. bi-m. USD 114 domestic to individuals; USD 137 in Canada & Mexico to individuals; USD 154 elsewhere to individuals; USD 265 domestic to institutions; USD 288 in Canada & Mexico to institutions; USD 295 elsewhere to institutions; USD 186 combined subscription domestic to individuals print & online eds.; USD 209 combined subscription in Canada & Mexico to individuals print & online eds.; USD 216 combined subscription elsewhere to individuals print & online eds.; USD 398 combined subscription domestic to institutions print & online eds.; USD 421 combined subscription in Canada & Mexico to institutions print & online eds.; USD 421 combined subscription elsewhere to institutions print & online eds. (effective 2005). adv. bk.rev. bibl.; charts; illus. index. back issues avail.; reprints avail. **Document type:** *Journal, Academic/Scholarly.* **Description:** Reports on the economic significance of insects.
Related titles: Microform ed.: (from PMC, PQC); Online - full text ed.: (from BioOne, C S A, EBSCO Publishing, Gale Group, IngentaConnect, O C L C Online Computer Library Center, Inc.).
Indexed: AEA, AEBA, ASCA, ASFA, AbHyg, AgBio, Agr, AgrForAb, AnBeAb, AnBrAb, ApicAb, B&AI, BIOSIS Prev, BibAg, BioCN&I, BiolAb, BiolDig, CIN, CIS, CPA, CTFA, ChemAb, ChemTitl, CurCont, DBA, DSA, EPB, ESPM, EntAb, ExcerpMed, FCA, FPA, FS&TA, ForAb, GenetAb, HGA, HerbAb, HortAb, I&DA, IABS, ISR, IndMed, IndVet, MBA, MEDLINE, MaizeAb, NemAb, NutrAb, OrnHort, PBA, PGegResA, PGrRegA, PHN&I, PN&I, PlantSci, PotatoAb, PoultAb, ProtozoAb, PsycholAb, RA&MP, RM&VM, RPP, RRTA, RefZh, RevApplEntom, RiceAb, S&F, S&MA, SAA, SCI, SFA, SIA, SSCI, SeedAb, SoyAb, TDB, THA, TOSA, TriticAb, VITIS, VetBull, WAE&RSA, WeedAb, WildRev, ZooRec.
—BLDSC (4973.000000), CASDDS, CISTI, GNLM, IDS, IE, Infotrieve, ingenta, Linda Hall. **CCC.**
Published by: Entomological Society of America, 10001 Derekwood Ln, Ste 100, Lanham, MD 20706-4876. TEL 301-731-4535, FAX 301-731-4538, esa@entsoc.org, http://www.entsoc.org/Pubs/Periodicals/EE/index.htm. Ed. John T Trumble. Circ: 4,300.

595.7 IND ISSN 0378-9519
CODEN: JEREDP
JOURNAL OF ENTOMOLOGICAL RESEARCH. Text in English. 1977. q. INR 1,500 domestic; USD 90 foreign (effective 2004). adv. bk.rev. back issues avail. **Document type:** *Academic/Scholarly.* **Description:** Encompasses all the varied aspects of entomological research. Felt-need in scientific research due to emphasis on intra-, inter- and multi disciplinary approach. It also covers recent research on non-insect pests comprising mites, rats, birds, snails, etc.
Indexed: AEA, ASFA, AgrForAb, ApicAb, BIOSIS Prev, BioCN&I, BiolAb, CIN, CPA, CTFA, ChemAb, ChemTitl, EntAb, FCA, FPA, ForAb, GenetAb, HGA, HerbAb, HortAb, IndVet, MaizeAb, NemAb, NutrAb, OrnHort, PBA, PGegResA, PHN&I, PotatoAb, PoultAb, ProtozoAb, RA&MP, RDA, RM&VM, RPP, RevApplEntom, RiceAb, S&F, S&MA, SIA, SeedAb, SoyAb, TDB, TOSA, TriticAb, VetBull, WAE&RSA, WeedAb, ZooRec.
—BLDSC (4979.293000), CASDDS, CISTI, IE, ingenta, Linda Hall.
Published by: Malhotra Publishing House (M P H), B-6 DSIDC Packaging Complex, Kirti Nagar, New Delhi, 110 015, India. TEL 91-11-25157006, FAX 91-11-25934597, mph@vsnl.com, http://www.mph-india.com. Ed. Prakash Sarup. Circ: 400.

595.7 USA ISSN 0749-8004
SB818 CODEN: JESCEP
➤ **JOURNAL OF ENTOMOLOGICAL SCIENCE.** Text in English. 1966. q. USD 20 to individuals; USD 50 to institutions; USD 5 to students (effective 2004). bk.rev. charts; illus. **Document type:** *Journal, Academic/Scholarly.*
Formerly (until Jan. 1985): Georgia Entomological Society. Journal (0016-8238)
Indexed: AEA, ASCA, ASFA, AgBio, Agr, AgrForAb, AnBrAb, BIOBASE, BIOSIS Prev, BioCN&I, BiolAb, CIN, CPA, CTFA, ChemAb, ChemTitl, CurCont, EntAb, FCA, FPA, FS&TA, ForAb, HGA, HelmAb, HerbAb, HortAb, IABS, ISR, IndVet, MaizeAb, NemAb, NutrAb, OrnHort, PBA, PGrRegA, PHN&I, PotatoAb, PoultAb, ProtozoAb, RA&MP, RM&VM, RPP, RevApplEntom, RiceAb, S&F, S&MA, SCI, SIA, SeedAb, SoyAb, TOSA, TriticAb, VITIS, VetBull, WAE&RSA, WeedAb, WildRev, ZooRec.
—BLDSC (4979.293500), CASDDS, CISTI, IDS, IE, Infotrieve, ingenta, Linda Hall.
Published by: Georgia Entomological Society, Inc., c/o Wayne A. Gardner, Department of Entomology, Georgia Experiment Sta, 1109 Experiment St, Griffin, GA 30223-1797. TEL 770-228-7288, FAX 770-228-7287, http://www.cpes.peachnet.edu/ga-ent-soc/journal.htm. Ed. Dr. Wayne A Gardner. Circ: 786.

595.7 CAN ISSN 1070-9428
QL563 CODEN: JHYREJ
JOURNAL OF HYMENOPTERA RESEARCH. Text in English. 1992. a. USD 40 membership (effective 2005). **Document type:** *Journal, Academic/Scholarly.*
Indexed: AgBio, AgrForAb, BioCN&I, EntAb, ForAb, HerbAb, HortAb, OrnHort, RiceAb, S&F, SIA, SeedAb, WeedAb, ZooRec.
—BLDSC (5004.504000).
Published by: International Society of Hymenopterists, c/o John Huber, Eastern Cereal & Oilseed Research Centre, K.W. Neatby Bldg., Ottawa, ON K1A 0C6, Canada. huberj@ncccot.agr.ca.

595.7 USA ISSN 0892-7553
QL496 CODEN: JIBEE8
➤ **JOURNAL OF INSECT BEHAVIOR.** Text in English. 1988. bi-m. EUR 708, USD 728, GBP 448 combined subscription to institutions print & online eds. (effective 2005). adv. bk.rev. bibl.; charts; illus. index. back issues avail.; reprint service avail. from PSC. **Document type:** *Journal, Academic/Scholarly.* **Description:** Covers the ethology, ecology, neurophysiology, genetics, pharmacology and behavior of insects and terrestrial arthropods.
Related titles: Microfilm ed.: (from PQC); Online - full text ed.: ISSN 1572-8889 (from EBSCO Publishing, Gale Group, IngentaConnect, Kluwer Online, O C L C Online Computer Library Center, Inc., Ovid Technologies, Inc., Springer LINK, Swets Information Services).
Indexed: ASCA, ASFA, AbHyg, AgBio, Agr, AgrForAb, AnBeAb, ApEcolAb, ApicAb, B&BAb, BIOBASE, BIOSIS Prev, BibAg, BibLing, BioCN&I, BiolAb, CPA, ChemoAb, CurCont, DSA, ESPM, EntAb, FCA, FPA, ForAb, HelmAb, HortAb, IABS, IndVet, MaizeAb, NutrAb, OrnHort, PBA, PGegResA, PHN&I, PN&I, PsycInfo, PsycholAb, RM&VM, RefZh, RevApplEntom, RiceAb, SIA, SeedAb, SoyAb, TriticAb, VITIS, VetBull, WeedAb, ZooRec, e-psyche.
—BLDSC (5007.450000), CISTI, IDS, IE, Infotrieve, ingenta, Linda Hall. **CCC.**
Published by: Plenum US (Subsidiary of: Springer Science+Business Media), 233 Spring St, New York, NY 10013. TEL 212-460-1500, FAX 212-460-1575, service@springer-ny.com, http://springerlink.metapress.com/openurl.asp?genre=journal&issn=0892-7553, http://www.springeronline.com. Eds. Thomas L Payne, Timothy D Paine.

595.7 NLD ISSN 1366-638X
QL461 CODEN: JICOFA
➤ **JOURNAL OF INSECT CONSERVATION**; an international journal devoted to the conservation of inects and related invertebrates. Text in English. 1997. q. EUR 574, USD 575, GBP 378 combined subscription to institutions print & online eds. (effective 2005). adv. bk.rev. back issues avail.; reprint service avail. from PSC. **Document type:** *Journal, Academic/Scholarly.* **Description:** Publishes papers on all aspects of conservation and biodiversity related to the insects and closely related groups such as Arachnids and Myriapods, including ecological work which has conservation implications. Research papers may address the subject at the community, population or species level, may cover aspects of behaviour, taxonomy or genetics, be theoretical or practical, and be local or global in nature.
Related titles: Online - full text ed.: ISSN 1572-9753 (from EBSCO Publishing, Gale Group, IngentaConnect, Kluwer Online, O C L C Online Computer Library Center, Inc., Springer LINK, Swets Information Services).
Indexed: ASFA, AgBio, AgrForAb, ApEcolAb, BIOSIS Prev, BibLing, BioCN&I, BiolAb, EPB, ESPM, EntAb, FPA, ForAb, GEOBASE, HerbAb, HortAb, IndVet, NutrAb, OrnHort, PBA, PGegResA, RDA, RM&VM, RRTA, RefZh, RevApplEntom, S&F, TDB, WAE&RSA, ZooRec.
—BLDSC (5007.460000), IE, Infotrieve, ingenta. **CCC.**
Published by: Springer-Verlag Dordrecht (Subsidiary of: Springer Science+Business Media), Van Godewijckstraat 30, Dordrecht, 3311 GX, Netherlands. TEL 31-78-6576050, FAX 31-78-6576474, http://springerlink.metapress.com/openurl.asp?genre=journal&issn=1366-638X, http://www.springeronline.com. Ed. Tim R New.

595.7 GBR ISSN 0022-1910
QL461 CODEN: JIPHAF
➤ **JOURNAL OF INSECT PHYSIOLOGY.** Text in English, French, German. 1957. 12/yr. EUR 2,220 in Europe to institutions; JPY 294,800 in Japan to institutions; USD 2,485 to institutions except Europe and Japan; EUR 202 in Europe to qualified personnel; JPY 27,000 in Japan to qualified personnel; USD 227 to qualified personnel except Europe and Japan (effective 2006). adv. bk.rev. bibl.; charts; illus. index. back issues avail.; reprint service avail. from PQC. **Document type:** *Journal, Academic/Scholarly.* **Description:** Publishes contributions from the fields of endocrinology, pheromones, neurobiology, physiological pharmacology, behavior, nutrition, homeostasis, and reproductive processes of insects.
Related titles: Microfiche ed.: (from MIM); Microfilm ed.: (from PQC); Online - full text ed.: (from EBSCO Publishing, Gale Group, IngentaConnect, ScienceDirect, Swets Information Services).
Indexed: ASCA, ASFA, AbHyg, AgBio, Agr, AgrForAb, AnBeAb, ApicAb, B&AI, BIOBASE, BIOSIS Prev, BibAg, BioCN&I, BiolAb, CIN, CPA, ChemAb, ChemTitl, CurCont, DBA, DSA, EntAb, FCA, ForAb, GEOBASE, HelmAb, HortAb, IABS, ISR, IndVet, Inpharma, MEDLINE, MSB, MaizeAb, NSCI, NemAb, NutrAb, PBA, PHN&I, PotatoAb, PoultAb, ProtozoAb, RA&MP, RM&VM, RPP, Reac, RefZh, RevApplEntom, RiceAb, S&F, SCI, SIA, SeedAb, SoyAb, TDB, TriticAb, VITIS, VetBull, WeedAb, ZooRec.
—BLDSC (5007.500000), CASDDS, CISTI, IDS, IE, Infotrieve, ingenta, Linda Hall. **CCC.**

Published by: Pergamon (Subsidiary of: Elsevier Science & Technology), The Boulevard, Langford Ln, East Park, Kidlington, Oxford OX5 1GB, United Kingdom. TEL 44-1865-843000, FAX 44-1865-843010, jiphysiol@osu.edu, http://www.elsevier.com/locate/jinsphys. Eds. D L Denlinger TEL 614-292-6425, S E Reynolds. Circ: 1,800. **Subscr. to:** Elsevier BV, PO Box 211, Amsterdam 1000 AE, Netherlands. TEL 31-20-485-3757, FAX 31-20-485-3432, nlinfo-f@elsevier.nl, http://www.elsevier.nl.

595.7 IND ISSN 0970-3837
QL461 CODEN: JINSE8
JOURNAL OF INSECT SCIENCE. Text in English. 1988. s-a. **Document type:** *Journal, Academic/Scholarly.*
Related titles: Online - full text ed.: (from EBSCO Publishing).
Indexed: ASFA, AgrForAb, AnBeAb, BIOSIS Prev, BioCN&I, BiolAb, EntAb, FCA, FPA, ForAb, HortAb, MaizeAb, PBA, PGegResA, PHN&I, PotatoAb, SoyAb, WAE&RSA, ZooRec.
—BLDSC (5007.502000), CISTI, IE, ingenta, Linda Hall.
Published by: Punjab Agricultural University, Department of Entomology, Ludhiana, Punjab 141 004, India.

595.7 USA ISSN 1536-2442
QL461 CODEN: JISTCY
➤ **JOURNAL OF INSECT SCIENCE.** Text in English. irreg. free (effective 2005). stat.; illus. back issues avail. **Document type:** *Journal, Academic/Scholarly.* **Description:** Covers biology of insects and their agricultural and medical impact.
Media: Online - full content (from BioOne, National Library of Medicine). **Related titles:** Online - full text ed.: (from BioOne, C S A).
Indexed: AnBeAb, ApEcolAb, BIOSIS Prev, BiolAb, CurCont, ESPM, EntAb, ZooRec.
—Linda Hall.
Published by: Library of the University of Arizona, c/o Henry Hagedorn, Ed., University of Arizona, Dept of Entomology, 410 Forbes Ave, Tucson, AZ 85721. TEL 520-621-5358, FAX 520-621-1150, jis@insectscience.org, http://www.insectscience.org/.

595.7 616.968 USA ISSN 0022-2585
RA639.5 CODEN: JMENA6
➤ **JOURNAL OF MEDICAL ENTOMOLOGY.** Text in English. 1964. bi-m. USD 103 domestic to individuals; USD 123 in Canada & Mexico to individuals; USD 129 elsewhere to individuals; USD 210 domestic to institutions; USD 230 in Canada & Mexico to institutions; USD 236 elsewhere to institutions; USD 154.50 combined subscription domestic to individuals; USD 174.50 combined subscription in Canada & Mexico to individuals; USD 180.50 combined subscription elsewhere to individuals; USD 315 combined subscription domestic to institutions print & online eds.; USD 335 combined subscription in Canada & Mexico to institutions print & online eds.; USD 341 combined subscription elsewhere to institutions print & online eds. (effective 2004). adv. bk.rev. bibl.; charts; illus.; maps. index. back issues avail.; reprint service avail. from PQC. **Document type:** *Journal, Academic/Scholarly.* **Description:** Covers all phases of medical entomology.
Related titles: Microform ed.: (from PQC); Online - full text ed.: (from BioOne, C S A, EBSCO Publishing, Gale Group, IngentaConnect, O C L C Online Computer Library Center, Inc.).
Indexed: AEA, ASCA, ASFA, AbHyg, AgBio, Agr, AgrForAb, AnBeAb, AnBrAb, BIOSIS Prev, BibAg, BioCN&I, BiolAb, BiolDig, ChemAb, ChemTitl, CurCont, DBA, DentInd, EPB, ESPM, EntAb, ExcerpMed, FPA, FoVS&M, ForAb, GenetAb, HGA, HelmAb, HortAb, ISR, IndMed, IndVet, MEDLINE, MaizeAb, NemAb, NutrAb, PHN&I, PN&I, PoultAb, ProtozoAb, RA&MP, RM&VM, RPP, RRTA, RefZh, RevApplEntom, RiceAb, S&F, SAA, SCI, SFA, SIA, SPPI, SoyAb, TDB, TriticAb, VetBull, WAE&RSA, WeedAb, WildRev, ZooRec.
—BLDSC (5017.060000), CASDDS, CISTI, GNLM, IDS, IE, Infotrieve, ingenta, Linda Hall. **CCC.**
Published by: Entomological Society of America, 10001 Derekwood Ln, Ste 100, Lanham, MD 20706-4876. TEL 301-731-4535, FAX 301-731-4538, esa@entsoc.org, http://www.entsoc.org/pubs. Eds. William K Reisen, John Edman. Circ: 1,600.

595.7 616.968 USA
➤ **JOURNAL OF MEDICAL ENTOMOLOGY ONLINE.** Text in English. bi-m. USD 124 to individuals; USD 242 to institutions (effective 2000). **Document type:** *Academic/Scholarly.*
Media: Online - full content.
Published by: Entomological Society of America, 10001 Derekwood Ln, Ste 100, Lanham, MD 20706-4876. TEL 301-731-4535, FAX 301-731-4538, esa@entsoc.org, http://www.entsoc.org/pubs.

595.7 USA ISSN 1082-6467
QL506 CODEN: DLMAF7
➤ **JOURNAL OF ORTHOPTERA RESEARCH.** Text in English. 1992. s-a. USD 20 membership; USD 10 to students (effective 2005). bk.rev. bibl.; charts; illus. back issues avail. **Document type:** *Journal, Academic/Scholarly.* **Description:** Covers all aspects of original research on orthoptera, senus latu, and blattodea, mantodea, phasmatodea, grylloblattodea, and dermaptera.
Related titles: Online - full text ed.: (from BioOne, C S A, O C L C Online Computer Library Center, Inc.).
Indexed: BIOSIS Prev, BiolAb, EntAb, ZooRec.
—Linda Hall.
Published by: The Orthopterists' Society, c/o Jeffrey Lockwood, Dept of Renewable Resources, University of Wyoming, Laramie, WY 82071. TEL 307-766-4260, FAX 307-766-5549, lockwood@uwyo.edu, http://www.orthoptera.org/. Ed. G K Morris. Circ: 300 (controlled).

595.7 DEU ISSN 1612-4758
CODEN: ASCHFS
➤ **JOURNAL OF PEST SCIENCE.** Text in German; Summaries in English, German. 1925. q. EUR 370 combined subscription print & online eds.; EUR 111 per issue (effective 2004). adv. bk.rev. abstr.; illus.; stat. index. back issues avail. **Document type:** *Journal, Academic/Scholarly.* **Description:** Contains original research papers on all aspects of damage inflicted by viruses, bacteria, insects and higher animals on plants.
Former titles (until 2004): Anzeiger fuer Schaedlingskunde (1436-5693); (until 1999): Anzeiger fuer Schaedlingskunde, Pflanzenschutz, Umweltschutz (0340-7330); (until 1975): Anzeiger fuer Schaedlingskunde, Pflanzen- und Umweltschutz (0340-7322); (until 1973): Anzeiger fuer Schaedlingskunde und Pflanzenschutz (0003-6307); (until 1968): Anzeiger fuer Schaedlingskunde (0365-6608); Which incorporated (1949-1953): Schaedlingsbekaempfung (0370-9019)
Related titles: Online - full text ed.: ISSN 1612-4766. EUR 311 (effective 2003) (from Blackwell Synergy, EBSCO Publishing, Gale Group, IngentaConnect, O C L C Online Computer Library Center, Inc., Springer LINK, Swets Information Services).
Indexed: ASCA, AgBio, AgrForAb, ApicAb, B&BAb, BIOSIS Prev, BioCN&I, BioDAb, BiolAb, ChemAb, CurCont, DBA, ESPM, EntAb, ExcerpMed, FCA, FPA, FS&TA, ForAb, GEOBASE, HelmAb, HerbAb, HortAb, IndVet, KWIWR, MaizeAb, NemAb, NutrAb, OrnHort, PBA, PHN&I, PotatoAb, PoultAb, ProtozoAb, RA&MP, RPP, RefZh, RevApplEntom, RiceAb, S&F, S&MA, SIA, SeedAb, SoyAb, TriticAb, VITIS, VetBull, WeedAb, ZooRec.
—BLDSC (1567.650000), CASDDS, CISTI, IDS, IE, Infotrieve, ingenta, Linda Hall. **CCC.**
Published by: Springer-Verlag (Subsidiary of: Springer Science+Business Media), Tiergartenstr 17, Heidelberg, 69121, Germany. TEL 49-6221-3450, FAX 49-6221-345229, orders@springer.de, http://www.springer.de. Ed. Dr. W Schwenke. Adv. contact Stephan Kroeck TEL 49-30-827875739. **Subscr. to:** Springer GmbH Auslieferungsgesellschaft. subscriptions@springer.de; Springer-Verlag New York, Inc.. TEL 800-777-4643, journals@springer-ny.com.

➤ **JOURNAL OF PLANT PROTECTION RESEARCH.** see *BIOLOGY—Botany*

595.78 USA ISSN 0022-4324
QL541 CODEN: JRLPAE
JOURNAL OF RESEARCH ON THE LEPIDOPTERA. Text in English. 1962. q. free to members. adv. bk.rev. charts; illus. cum.index covering 27 yrs. back issues avail. **Document type:** *Journal, Academic/Scholarly.* **Description:** Directed to professionals and serious amateurs in the study of lepidoptera. Particular emphasis is placed on all aspects of butterfly biology including genetics, ecology and conservation biology.
Indexed: ASFA, AgBio, Agr, BIOSIS Prev, BioCN&I, BiolAb, ChemAb, EntAb, FCA, ForAb, HerbAb, HortAb, RevApplEntom, S&F, ZooRec.
—CISTI, Linda Hall.
Published by: Lepidoptera Research Foundation, Inc., 9620 Heather Rd, Beverly Hills, CA 90210. TEL 310-274-1052, FAX 310-275-3290, mattoni@ucla.edu. Eds. Rudolf H T Mattoni, Scott E Miller. R&P Leona Mattoni. Circ: 550.

595.7 GBR ISSN 0022-474X
TX599 CODEN: JSTPAR
➤ **JOURNAL OF STORED PRODUCTS RESEARCH.** Text in English. 1965. 4/yr. EUR 1,021 in Europe to institutions; JPY 135,700 in Japan to institutions; USD 1,143 to institutions except Europe and Japan (effective 2006). adv. bk.rev. charts; illus.; stat.; abstr. back issues avail. **Document type:** *Academic/Scholarly.* **Description:** Covers research dealing with the biology, ecology, physiology, behavior, taxonomy, genetics or control of the insects and organisms associated with stored products.
Related titles: Microfilm ed.: (from PQC); Online - full text ed.: (from EBSCO Publishing, Gale Group, IngentaConnect, ScienceDirect, Swets Information Services).
Indexed: AEA, ASCA, ASFA, AgBio, Agr, AgrForAb, BIOBASE, BIOSIS Prev, BibAg, BioCN&I, BiolAb, CIN, CPA, ChemAb, ChemTitl, CurCont, DBA, DSA, ESPM, EngInd, EntAb, ExcerpMed, FCA, FPA, FS&TA, HerbAb, HortAb, IABS, ISR, MBA, MEDLINE, MaizeAb, NutrAb, OrnHort, PBA, PGegResA, PHN&I, PlantSci, RA&MP, RM&VM, RPP, RevApplEntom, RiceAb, S&MA, SCI, SeedAb, SoyAb, TDB, TriticAb, WAE&RSA, WeedAb, ZooRec.
—BLDSC (5066.871000), CASDDS, CISTI, Ei, IDS, IE, Infotrieve, ingenta, Linda Hall. **CCC.**
Published by: Pergamon (Subsidiary of: Elsevier Science & Technology), The Boulevard, Langford Ln, East Park, Kidlington, Oxford OX5 1GB, United Kingdom. TEL 44-1865-843000, FAX 44-1865-843010, http://www.elsevier.com/locate/jspr. Ed. P F Credland. Circ: 1,000. **Subscr. to:** Elsevier BV, PO Box 211, Amsterdam 1000 AE, Netherlands. TEL 31-20-485-3757, FAX 31-20-485-3432, nlinfo-f@elsevier.nl, http://www.elsevier.nl.

595.7 JPN ISSN 0287-6477
KAKOCHO/NAGOYA ENTOMOLOGICAL SOCIETY. JOURNAL. Text in Japanese. 1949. 4/yr. membership.
Published by: Nagoya Konchu Dokokai/Nagoya Entomological Society, c/o Mr Ando, 5-24 Otowa 1-chome, Ichinomiya-shi, Aichi-ken 491-0045, Japan.

595.7 JPN ISSN 0288-3821
KANAGAWA CHUHO/KANAGAWA ENTOMOLOGIST'S ASSOCIATION. JOURNAL. Text in Japanese. 1954. 2/yr.
Published by: Kanagawa Konchu Danwakai/Kanagawa Entomologist's Association, Kanagawa Kenritsu Hakubutsukan, 5-10 Minaminaka-Dori, Naka-ku, Yokohama-shi, Kanagawa-ken 231-0006, Japan.

595.7 JPN ISSN 0915-4698
KANDOKON/JAPANESE JOURNAL OF ENVIRONMENT, ENTOMOLOGY AND ZOOLOGY. Text in English, Japanese. 1989. 4/yr. membership.
—CCC.
Published by: Nihon Kankyu Dobutsu Konchu Gakkai/Japanese Society of Environmental Entomology and Zoology, 12-19 Nishi-Hon-Machi 1-chome, Nishi-ku, Osaka-shi, 550-0005, Japan.

595.7 USA ISSN 0022-8567
QL461 CODEN: JKESA7
➤ **KANSAS ENTOMOLOGICAL SOCIETY. JOURNAL.** Text in English. 1928. q. USD 85 to institutions; USD 88 in Canada & Mexico to institutions; USD 100 elsewhere to institutions (effective 1999). bk.rev. abstr.; bibl.; charts; illus. index. back issues avail.; reprint service avail. from PQC. **Document type:** *Academic/Scholarly.* **Description:** Covers research on all aspects of the science of entomology.
Related titles: Microform ed.: (from PQC).
Indexed: AEA, ASCA, ASFA, AbHyg, AgBio, Agr, AgrForAb, AnBrAb, BIOSIS Prev, BioCN&I, BiolAb, CPA, ChemAb, CurCont, EntAb, FCA, FPA, ForAb, GEOBASE, HerbAb, HortAb, ISR, IndVet, MaizeAb, NutrAb, OrnHort, PBA, PGegResA, PHN&I, PoultAb, ProtozoAb, RM&VM, RPP, RefZh, RevApplEntom, S&F, S&MA, SCI, SFA, SeedAb, SoyAb, TriticAb, VITIS, VetBull, WeedAb, WildRev, ZooRec.
—BLDSC (4810.400000), CISTI, IE, ingenta, Linda Hall. **CCC.**
Published by: Kansas Entomological Society, PO Box 1897, Lawrence, KS 66044-8897. TEL 785-843-1235, FAX 785-843-1274, orders@allenpress.com, http://www.allenpress.com. Ed. Leonard Ferrington. Circ: 800. **Subscr. to:** Allen Press Inc., PO Box 1897, Lawrence, KS 66044. **Co-sponsor:** Central States Entomological Society.

595.7 JPN ISSN 0913-9613
KEICHITSU. Text in Japanese. 1983. 2/yr. JPY 3,000.
Published by: Gifuken Konchu Bunpu Kenkyukai/Entomological Distribution Society of Gifu Prefecture, Figu Daigaku Kyoiku Gakubu, 1-1 Yanagi-To, Gifu-shi, 501-1112, Japan.

595.7 JPN ISSN 0913-5421
KINOKUNI/WAKAYAMA INSECT SOCIETY. BULLETIN. Text in Japanese. 1971. s-a.
Published by: Wakayama Konchu Kenkyukai/Wakayama Insect Society, c/o Mr Isao Matoba, 1410 Yuasa, Arida-gun, Yuasa-cho, Wakayama-ken 643-0004, Japan.

595.7 JPN ISSN 0915-9754
KISHIDAIA/TOKYO SPIDER STUDY GROUP. BULLETIN. Variant title: Tokyo Kumo Danwakai Kaishi. Text in Japanese. 1969. s-a. JPY 3,800; JPY 2,000 to students (effective 2000). **Document type:** *Newsletter.*
Published by: Tokyo Kumo Danwakai, c/o Dr. Hirotsugu Ono, National Science Museum, 23-1 Hiyakunin-cho 3-chome, Shinjuku-ku, Tokyo, 169-0073, Japan. Ed. Tomoyuki Kimura. Circ: 250.

595.7 CZE ISSN 1210-6100
KLAPALEKIANA. Text in Czech, English, German; Summaries in English. 1965. s-a. CZK 400; USD 30 foreign. bk.rev. abstr.; bibl.; illus.; maps. index. back issues avail. **Document type:** *Bulletin.* **Description:** Covers taxonomy, biology, and ecology, focusing mainly on the Paleoarctic Region.
Indexed: ASFA, ESPM, EntAb, ZooRec.
Published by: Ceska Spolecnost Entomologicka/Czech Entomological Society, Vinicna 7, Prague, 12800, Czech Republic. Ed. Jan Vitner.

595.7 POL ISSN 0075-6350
KLUCZE DO OZNACZANIA OWADOW POLSKI. Text in Polish. 1954. irreg., latest vol.157, 1998. price varies. bibl. back issues avail. **Document type:** *Monographic series, Academic/Scholarly.* **Description:** Serves as a handbook and tool for identification of Polish insects.
Indexed: BioCN&I, BiolAb, RevApplEntom, ZooRec.
—CISTI.
Published by: Polskie Towarzystwo Entomologiczne/Polish Entomological Society, ul Sienkiewicza 21, Wroclaw, 50-335, Poland. TEL 48-71-3225041, buszko@biol.uni.torun.pl, http://www.au.poznan.pl/wydzialy/ogrodniczy/pte/index.html. R&P Jaroslaw Buszko. Circ: 800. **Subscr. to:** Biblioteka, ul Przybyszewskiego 63/77, Wroclaw 51-148, Poland. TEL 48-71-3247237.

B

▼ new title ➤ refereed ∗ unverified ◆ full entry avail.

595.76   JPN   ISSN 0910-8785
QL592.J3
KOCHU NYUSU/COLEOPTERISTS' NEWS. Text in Japanese.
1968. q. JPY 1,500.
Indexed: ZooRec.
Published by: Nihon Shoshi Gakkai/Japanese Society of
Coleopterology, Kokuritsu Kagaku Hakubutsukan Dobutsu
Kenkyubu, 23-1 Hiyakunin-cho 3-chome, Shinjuku-ku, Tokyo,
169-0073, Japan.

595.7   JPN   ISSN 0023-3218
KONCHU TO SHIZEN/NATURE AND INSECTS. Text in
Japanese. 1966. m. JPY 1,300 per issue (effective 1998).
Document type: *Academic/Scholarly.*
Indexed: ZooRec.
Published by: Nyu Saiensusha/New Science Co., 3-8-14
Takanawa, Minato-ku, Tokyo, 108-0074, Japan.
hk-ns@mk1.macnet.or.jp, http://www.macnet.or.jp/co/hk-ns.

632 595.7   KOR   ISSN 1225-0171
KOREAN JOURNAL OF APPLIED ENTOMOLOGY. Text in
Korean; Summaries in English. 1962. q. KRW 15,000, USD
30 (effective 1991). index. back issues avail. **Document type:**
Journal, Academic/Scholarly.
Formerly (until 1988): Korean Journal of Plant Protection
Indexed: AgBio, AgrForAb, AnBrAb, BIOSIS Prev, BioCN&I,
BiolAb, CPA, FCA, FPA, FS&TA, ForAb, HelmAb, HerbAb,
HortAb, MaizeAb, NemAb, OrnHort, PBA, PGegResA, PHN&I,
PotatoAb, RA&MP, RM&VM, RPP, RevApplEntom, RiceAb,
S&F, SoyAb, TDB, TriticAb, WAE&RSA, ZooRec.
—BLDSC (5113.513500), IE, ingenta.
Published by: Korean Society of Applied Entomology, c/o Dept.
of Entomology, Agricultural Sciences Institute, Rural
Development Administration, Suwon, 441707, Korea, S. TEL
0331-291-3681, FAX 0331-291-5830. Ed. Seung Chan Lee.
Circ: 600.

595.7   JPN   ISSN 0912-5957
**KUMAMOTO KONCHU DOKOKAIHO/KUMAMOTO
ENTOMOLOGICAL ASSOCIATION. NEWS.** Text in Japanese.
1955. irreg. membership.
Published by: Kumamoto Konchu Dokokai/Kumamoto
Entomological Association, c/o Mr Isao Otsuka, 2169
Kengun-Machi, Kumamoto-shi, 862-0919, Japan.

595.7   JPN   ISSN 0917-7906
KUMO/CHUBU SPIDER STUDY GROUP. REPORT. Text in
Japanese. a.
Published by: Chubu Kumo Kondankai/Chubu Spider Study
Group, c/o Mr Ogata, 10-6 Yamayashiki-Higashiyama,
Chiriyu-shi, Aichi-ken 472-0000, Japan.

595.7   CHN   ISSN 1000-7482
KUNCHONG FENLEI XUEBAO/ENTOMOTAXONOMIA. Text in
Chinese. 1979. q. CNY 5 newsstand/cover. **Document type:**
Journal, Academic/Scholarly.
Related titles: Online - full text ed.: (from East View Information
Services, WanFang Data Corp.).
Indexed: ASFA, AgBio, AgrForAb, BIOSIS Prev, BioCN&I, BiolAb,
EntAb, FPA, ForAb, HerbAb, HortAb, IndVet, RiceAb, S&F,
SeedAb, TDB, TriticAb, VetBull, ZooRec.
—BLDSC (5123.470000).
Published by: Xibei Nonglin Keji Daxue, Yangling, Shanxi,
712100, China. TEL 86-29-7092524, FAX 86-29-7092190,
yalinzh@Public.xa.sn.cn, http://kcflxb.periodicals.net.cn/
default.html. **Dist. by:** China International Book Trading Corp,
35 Chegongzhuang Xilu, Haidian District, PO Box 399, Beijing
100044, China. TEL 86-10-68412045, FAX 86-10-68412023,
cibtc@mail.cibtc.com.cn, http://www.cibtc.com.cn.

595.7   CHN   ISSN 0454-6296
QL461   CODEN: KCHPA2
➤ **KUNCHONG XUEBAO/ACTA ENTOMOLOGICA SINICA.** Text
in Chinese; Summaries in English. 1950. bi-m. CNY 132
(effective 2004). adv. index. **Document type:**
Academic/Scholarly. **Description:** Contains theses dealing
with insect faunistics, systematics, morphology, physiology,
ecology, insecticide toxicology, and pathology, especially
concerning injurious and beneficial insects in agriculture,
forestry, animal husbandry, and medicine.
Related titles: Online - full content ed.: (from WanFang Data
Corp.); Online - full text ed.: (from East View Information
Services).
Indexed: ASCA, ASFA, AbHyg, AgBio, AgrForAb, ApicAb, BIOSIS
Prev, BioCN&I, BiolAb, CIN, CPA, CTFA, ChemAb, ChemTitl,
DSA, EntAb, FCA, FPA, FaBeAb, ForAb, HelmAb, HerbAb,
HortAb, IndVet, MaizeAb, NemAb, NutrAb, OrnHort, PBA,
PGrRegA, PHN&I, PN&I, PotatoAb, ProtozoAb, RA&MP,
RM&VM, RPP, RefZh, RevApplEntom, RiceAb, S&F, SCI,
SeedAb, SoyAb, TDB, TOSA, TriticAb, VetBull, WeedAb,
ZooRec.
—BLDSC (0615.500000), CASDDS, CISTI, IE, ingenta, Linda
Hall.

Published by: (Zhongguo Kexueyuan, Dongwu Yanjiusuo/Chinese
Academy of Sciences, Institute of Zoology, Zhongguo
Kunchong Xuehui), Kexue Chubanshe/Science Press, 16
Donghuang Cheng Genbei Jie, Beijing, 100717, China. TEL
86-10-64000246, FAX 86-10-64030255,
huanglq@panda.ioz.ac.cn, http://kcxb.periodicals.com.cn/
default.html, http://www.sciencep.com/. Ed. Qin Junde. Circ:
11,000. **Dist. by:** China International Book Trading Corp, 35
Chegongzhuang Xilu, Haidian District, PO Box 399, Beijing
100044, China. TEL 86-10-68412045, FAX 86-10-68412023,
cibtc@mail.cibtc.com.cn, http://www.cibtc.com.cn.

595.7   CHN   ISSN 0452-8255
QL461   CODEN: KCCSAK
KUNCHONG ZHISHI/ENTOMOLOGICAL KNOWLEDGE. Text in
Chinese. 1955. bi-m. CNY 90 (effective 2004). adv. **Document
type:** *Journal, Academic/Scholarly.* **Description:** Introduces
basic knowledge of entomology. Contains entomological
research reports, information on experiment techniques,
academic discussions, and articles on specific topics.
Related titles: Online - full text ed.: (from East View Information
Services).
Indexed: AEA, AgBio, AgrForAb, BioCN&I, CIN, CPA, ChemAb,
ChemTitl, EntAb, FCA, FPA, ForAb, HerbAb, HortAb, IndVet,
MaizeAb, NemAb, OrnHort, PBA, PGegResA, PHN&I,
PotatoAb, ProtozoAb, RDA, RPP, RefZh, RiceAb, S&F, SIA,
SeedAb, SoyAb, TDB, TriticAb, VetBull, WAE&RSA, WeedAb,
ZooRec.
—CASDDS.
Published by: (Chinese Academy of Sciences/Zhongguo
Kexueyuan), Kexue Chubanshe/Science Press, 16 Donghuang
Cheng Genbei Jie, Beijing, 100717, China. TEL
86-10-64000246, FAX 86-10-64030255, http://
www.sciencep.com/. Ed. Liu Youjiao. **Dist. by:** China
International Book Trading Corp, 35 Chegongzhuang Xilu,
Haidian District, PO Box 399, Beijing 100044, China. TEL
86-10-68412045, FAX 86-10-68412023,
cibtc@mail.cibtc.com.cn, http://www.cibtc.com.cn.

595.7   CHN   ISSN 1002-0926
CODEN: KYJIED
**KUNCHONGXUE YANJIU JIKAN/CONTRIBUTIONS FROM
SHANGHAI INSTITUTE OF ENTOMOLOGY.** Text in Chinese;
Contents page in English. irreg., latest vol.7, 1987. CNY 4.50
per issue.
Indexed: CIN, ChemAb, ChemTitl.
—CASDDS.
Published by: (Chinese Academy of Sciences/Zhongguo
Kexueyuan), Shanghai Kexue Jishu Chubanshe/Shanghai
Scientific and Technical Publishers, 450 Ruijin Er Rd,
Shanghai, 200020, China.

595.78   DNK   ISSN 0075-8787
QL541   CODEN: LEPDAV
LEPIDOPTERA. Text in Danish; Summaries in English.
1946-1951; N.S. 1965. s-a. DKK 300 (effective 2001).
cum.index: 1965-70.
Indexed: BiolAb, ZooRec.
Published by: Lepidopterologisk Forening, c/o Flemming
Vilhelmsen, Soendervigvej 29, Vanlose, 2720, Denmark. Ed.
Per Stadel Nielsen. Circ: 600.

595.78   USA   ISSN 1062-6581
CODEN: TLNEET
LEPIDOPTERA NEWS. Text in English. q. USD 25 (effective
2005). **Document type:** *Newsletter, Academic/Scholarly.*
Description: Provides up-to-date information about ATL news
and activities, and other information of interest to members.
Regular subjects include new books, events, activites,
members in the news, etc.
Indexed: ApEcolAb, BioCN&I, ESPM, RRTA, RefZh, WeedAb.
Published by: Association for Tropical Lepidoptera, PO Box
141210, Gainesville, FL 32614-1210. TEL 352-392-5894, FAX
352-373-3249, jbhatl@aol.com, http://www.troplep.org/tl-
news.htm, http://www.troplep.org/atl.htm. Ed. J B Heppner.

595.78   USA   ISSN 0024-0966
QL541   CODEN: JLPSAZ
➤ **LEPIDOPTERISTS' SOCIETY. JOURNAL.** Text in English.
1947. a. USD 60 (effective 2002). bk.rev. bibl.; charts; illus.
index. 45 p./no.; back issues avail. **Document type:** *Journal,
Academic/Scholarly.* **Description:** Contains taxonomic
descriptions and research findings on all aspects of butterflies
and moths (lepidoptera).
Supersedes in part (in 1959): Lepidopterists' News (0457-5628)
Indexed: AEA, ASFA, AgBio, Agr, AgrForAb, BIOSIS Prev,
BioCN&I, BiolAb, EntAb, ForAb, GEOBASE, HerbAb, HortAb,
MaizeAb, NutrAb, PBA, PoultAb, RefZh, RevApplEntom, S&F,
VITIS, WeedAb, ZooRec.
—BLDSC (4814.200000), CISTI, IE, ingenta, Linda Hall.
Published by: (Lepidopterists' Society), Allen Press Inc., PO Box
1897, Lawrence, KS 66044. Ed. Carla M Penz. Circ: 1,500
(paid).

595.78   USA   ISSN 0075-8795
LEPIDOPTERISTS' SOCIETY. MEMOIRS. Text in English. 1964.
irreg., latest 1991. **Document type:** *Monographic series.*
Published by: Lepidopterists' Society, c/o Ron Leuschner, Publ
Coord, 1900 John St, Manhattan Beach, CA 90266-2608. Ed.
William E Miller.

595.7   USA   ISSN 0091-1348
QL541
LEPIDOPTERISTS'S SOCIETY. NEWS. Text in English. 1947. q.
USD 45 domestic to individuals; USD 50 foreign to individuals;
USD 60 to institutions (effective 2005). **Document type:**
Academic/Scholarly. **Description:** Provides information on the
study and scientific research of butterflies and moths, their
habits and distribution.
Supersedes in part (in 1959): Lepidopterists's News (0457-5628)
Indexed: BioCN&I, ForAb, HortAb, NutrAb, OrnHort, RefZh,
RevApplEntom, WeedAb.
—Linda Hall.
Published by: (University of Texas at Austin, Department of
Zoology, Lepidopterist's Society), Allen Press Inc., PO Box
1897, Lawrence, KS 66044. philjs@mail.utexas.edu,
http://alpha.furman.edu/~snyder/snyder/lep/pu.htm,
http://www.esb.utexas.edu/philjs/news/news.html. Ed. Phil
Schappert. Circ: 1,700.

595.7 333.95   DEU   ISSN 0723-6514
➤ **LIBELLULA.** Text in English, German. 1981. s-a. EUR 25 in
Europe (effective 2005). adv. Supplement avail.; back issues
avail. **Document type:** *Journal, Academic/Scholarly.*
Description: Presents original papers on the biology and
conservation of dragonflies (Odonata), with a special
emphasis on European species.
Indexed: BIOSIS Prev, BiolAb, EntAb, ZooRec.
Published by: Gesellschaft Deutschsprachiger Odonatologen
e.V., Hamfelderedder 7A, Boernsen, 21039, Germany. TEL
49-8442-956510, http://www.libellula.org. Ed. Dr. Florian
Weihrauch. R&P, Adv. contact Mrs. Gabi Peitzner. Circ: 610
(paid).

595.7   BEL   ISSN 0024-4090
CODEN: LBRBAE
➤ **LINNEANA BELGICA/EUROPEAN ENTOMOLOGY
JOURNAL.** Text in English, French; Summaries in Dutch,
English, German. 1958. q. EUR 70 (effective 2004). bk.rev.
bibl.; charts; illus.; stat. index. back issues avail. **Document
type:** *Bulletin, Academic/Scholarly.*
Indexed: ASFA, BIOSIS Prev, BiolAb, EntAb, RefZh, ZooRec.
Address: c/o R Leestmans, Ed, Krabbosstraat 179, Beersel
Dworp, 1653, Belgium. FAX 32-2-3803979,
http://users.skynet.be/jdelacre/linneana.htm. Ed. R Leestmans.

➤ **MEDICAL & VETERINARY ENTOMOLOGY.** see *MEDICAL
SCIENCES*

➤ **MEDICAL & VETERINARY ENTOMOLOGY ONLINE.** see
MEDICAL SCIENCES

595.7   USA   ISSN 1083-6284
➤ **MEMOIRS ON ENTOMOLOGY, INTERNATIONAL.** Text in
English. 1995. irreg., latest vol.15, 2001. price varies. abstr.;
bibl.; illus.; maps. 1 cols./p.; back issues avail. **Document
type:** *Monographic series, Academic/Scholarly.* **Description:**
Channel for monographic works on insects in all areas and
disciplines.
Indexed: BIOSIS Prev, BioCN&I, RPP, RevApplEntom, WeedAb,
ZooRec.
—BLDSC (5642.129000), CISTI.
Published by: Associated Publishers, 358102, Gainesville, FL
32635-8102. assopubl@yahoo.com, http://www.mapress.com/
AP/. Ed., Pub., R&P Virendra K Gupta. Circ: 100 (paid).

595.7   USA
METALEPTEA. Text in English. irreg. (2-4/yr.). free membership.
Document type: *Newsletter, Academic/Scholarly.*
Description: Contains news about the society's meetings and
publications, information about members, book reviews, and
short articles about members' research projects and other
orthoptera-related matters.
Published by: The Orthopterists' Society, c/o Jeffrey Lockwood,
Dept of Renewable Resources, University of Wyoming,
Laramie, WY 82071. TEL 307-766-4260, FAX 307-766-5549,
lockwood@uwyo.edu, http://viceroy.eeb.uconn.edu/OrthSoc/
metaleptea.htm, http://www.orthoptera.org/.

595.78   ZAF   ISSN 1018-6409
➤ **METAMORPHOSIS.** Text in English. 1983. q. ZAR 80, USD 45
(effective 1999). back issues avail. **Document type:**
Academic/Scholarly. **Description:** Promotes the study,
conservation and discussion of all aspects of lepodoptara (i.e.,
butterflies).
Indexed: BioCN&I, ForAb, HortAb, OrnHort, RM&VM,
RevApplEntom, S&F, WeedAb, ZooRec.
Published by: Lepidopterists Society of Africa, 183 Van der
Merwe St, Rietondale, 0084, South Africa. TEL
27-11-953-1168, FAX 27-11-953-4812,
staude@caseynet.co.za. Ed., Pub. Hermann Staude. Circ:
500.

595.7   USA   ISSN 1554-2092
MICHIGAN ENTOMOLOGICAL SOCIETY. NEWSLETTER. Text in
English. 1956. irreg. (3-4/yr.). USD 5 to non-members
(effective 2000). back issues avail. **Document type:**
Academic/Scholarly.
Published by: Michigan Entomological Society, c/o Dept of
Entomology, Michigan State Univ, East Lansing, MI 48824.
TEL 517-321-2192. Ed. Robert Haack.

595.78 DNK ISSN 1395-9506
MICROLEPIDOPTERA OF EUROPE. Text in English. 1996. irreg., latest vol.5, 2003. price varies. bibl.; illus.; maps. back issues avail. **Document type:** *Monographic series, Academic/Scholarly.* **Description:** Provides brief, concise identification guides to all European Microlepidoptera.
Indexed: ZooRec.
Published by: Apollo Books, Kirkeby Sand 19, Stenstrup, 5771, Denmark. TEL 45-62-26-37-37, FAX 45-62-26-37-80, apollobooks@vip.cybercity.dk. Eds. L. Lyneborg, O. Kursholt, P. Huemer.

595.7 USA ISSN 1051-3108
QL461
MISSISSIPPI ENTOMOLOGICAL MUSEUM SERIES. Text in English. 1989. irreg.
—CISTI, Linda Hall.
Published by: Mississippi State University, Department of Entomology and Plant Pathology, Mississippi Entomological Museum, Box 9575, Mississippi State, MS 39762-9775. TEL 662-325-2990, FAX 662-325-8837, http://www.msstate.edu/org/mississippientmuseum/.

638.1 JPN ISSN 0388-2217
CODEN: MIKAE6
MITSUBACHI KAGAKU/HONEYBEE SCIENCE. Text in Japanese; Summaries in English. 1980. q. JPY 10,000 (effective 2005). 48 p./no.; **Document type:** *Journal, Academic/Scholarly.*
Indexed: AbHyg, AgBio, AgrForAb, BioCN&I, CPA, FPA, ForAb, HortAb, IndVet, NutrAb, PBA, PGegResA, PHN&I, RA&MP, RDA, RM&VM, RPP, SIA, SeedAb, SoyAb, TDB, VetBull, WAE&RSA, ZooRec.
—BLDSC (4326.347100), IE, ingenta. **CCC.**
Published by: Tamagawa University, Honeybee Science Research Center, Honeybee Science Research Center, 6-1-1, Tamagawa-gakuen, Machida, Tokyo, 194-8610, Japan. HSRC@agr.tamagawa.ac.jp, http://www.tamagawa.ac.jp/sisetu/gakujutu/honey/2005/contents/hs.htm. **Dist. outside of Japan by:** Japan Publications Trading Co., Ltd., Book Export II Dept, PO Box 5030, Tokyo International, Tokyo 101-3191, Japan. FAX 81-3-32920410, infoserials@jptco.co.jp, http://www.jptco.co.jp.

595.7 DEU ISSN 1435-1951
QL461 CODEN: DENZAX
➤ **MITTEILUNGEN AUS DEM MUSEUM FUER NATURKUNDE IN BERLIN - DEUTSCHE ENTOMOLOGISCHE ZEITSCHRIFT**; an international journal of systematic entomology. Text in English, German. 1857. s-a. EUR 358 in Europe; CHF 618 in Switzerland & Liechtenstein; USD 458 elsewhere; EUR 394 combined subscription in Europe print & online eds.; CHF 680 combined subscription in Switzerland & Liechtenstein for print & online eds.; USD 504 combined subscription elsewhere print & online eds. (effective 2006). abstr.; bibl.; charts; illus. index. **Document type:** *Journal, Academic/Scholarly.* **Description:** Publishes original papers on both scientific and applied entomology, as well as arachnology and aracology.
Former titles (until 1999): Deutsche Entomologische Zeitschrift (0012-0073); (until 1875): Berliner Entomologische Zeitung (0323-6145)
Related titles: Microfiche ed.: (from BHP, IDC); Online - full text ed.: ISSN 1522-2403. EUR 358 in Europe; CHF 618 in Switzerland & Liechtenstein; USD 458 elsewhere (effective 2006) (from EBSCO Publishing, Wiley InterScience).
Indexed: ASCA, ASFA, BiolAb, CurCont, ESPM, EntAb, FaBeAb, HGA, HortAb, MBA, RefZh, RevApplEntom, RiceAb, S&F, ZooRec.
—CISTI, IDS, Linda Hall. **CCC.**
Published by: Wiley - V C H Verlag GmbH & Co. KGaA (Subsidiary of: John Wiley & Sons, Inc.), Boschstr 12, Weinheim, 69469, Germany. TEL 49-6201-6060, FAX 49-6201-606328, adsales@wiley-vch.de, subservice@wiley-vch.de, info@wiley-vch.de, http://www.wiley-vch.de. Ed. H Hoch. R&P Claudia Rutz. Adv. contact Aenne Anders TEL 49-6201-606552. **Subscr. in the Americas to:** John Wiley & Sons, Inc.. TEL 201-748-6645, FAX 201-748-6088, subinfo@wiley.com; **Subscr. outside Germany, Austria & Switzerland to:** John Wiley & Sons Ltd., The Atrium, Southern Gate, Chichester, West Sussex PO19 8SQ, United Kingdom. TEL 44-1243-779777, FAX 44-1243-775878.

595.7 DEU ISSN 0340-4943
QL461
MUENCHENER ENTOMOLOGISCHE GESELLSCHAFT. MITTEILUNGEN. Text in English, German. 1910. a. bk.rev. back issues avail. **Document type:** *Proceedings.* **Description:** Articles on insect taxonomy, systematics, phylogeny, evolution and biogeography.
Indexed: BiolAb, ZooRec.
Published by: (Muenchener Entomologische Gesellschaft), Verlag Dr. Friedrich Pfeil, Wolfratshauser Str 27, Munich, 81379, Germany. info@pfeil-verlag.de, http://www.pfeil-verlag.de. Circ: 1,200.

595.7 590 ITA ISSN 0394-5782
➤ **MUSEO CIVICO DI STORIA NATURALE DI FERRARA. STAZIONE DI ECOLOGIA. QUADERNI.** Text in English, Italian; Summaries in English. 1987. a., latest vol.13. 130 p./no.; back issues avail. **Document type:** *Journal, Academic/Scholarly.* **Description:** Contains information on animal populations and communities.
Indexed: ZooRec.
Published by: Museo Civico di Storia Naturale di Ferrara, Via Filippo de Pisis, 24, Ferrara, FE 44100, Italy. TEL 39-0532-203381, FAX 39-0532-210508, museo.storianaturale@comune.fe.it, http://www.comune.fe.it/storianaturale. Ed. Carla Corazza. Pub. Fausto Pesarini. Circ: 350.

595.7 JPN ISSN 0388-418X
MUSHI/MONTHLY JOURNAL OF ENTOMOLOGY. Text in English, Japanese. 1971. m. JPY 980 per issue.
Indexed: ZooRec.
Published by: Mushisha, Nakano Yubinkyo-ku, P.O. Box 10, Tokyo, 164, Japan.

595.7 POL ISSN 0867-1966
QL461 CODEN: AUSEEA
➤ **MUZEUM GORNOSLASKIE W BYTOMIU. ROCZNIK. SERIA ENTOMOLOGIA/UPPER SILESIAN MUSEUM IN BUTOM. ANNALS. SERIES ENTOMOLGY.** Text in English; Summaries in Polish. 1990. a. USD 25. **Document type:** *Proceedings, Academic/Scholarly.*
Indexed: ASFA, AgrLib, EntAb, ZooRec.
Published by: Muzeum Gornoslaskie w Bytomiu/The Museum of Upper Silesia, Pl Jana III Sobieskiego 2, Bytom, 41902, Poland. TEL 48-32-28182941, dobosz@us.edu.pl, mgbytom@us.edu.pl. Ed. Roland Dobosz.

595.7 AUS
MYRMECIA. Text in English. 1965. q. AUD 110 membership (effective 2004). **Document type:** *Bulletin.* **Description:** Reports on noteworthy news and activities at the Australian Entomological Society.
Formerly (until 1988): Australian Entomological Society. News Bulletin
Published by: Australian Entomological Society, c/o Dr Laurence Mound, CSIRO Entomology, Dr Laurence Mound, GPO Box 1700, Canberra, ACT 2601, Australia. http://www.agric.nsw.gov.au/Hort/ascu/myrmecia/myrmecia.htm.

595.7 DEU ISSN 0027-7452
NACHRICHTENBLATT DER BAYERISCHEN ENTOMOLOGEN. Text in English, German. 1952. q. included in subscr. to its Mitteilungen. back issues avail. **Document type:** *Bulletin.* **Description:** Articles on systematics, faunistics, behaviour and morphology of insects.
Indexed: ApicAb, BIOSIS Prev, BiolAb, ZooRec.
—CISTI. **CCC.**
Published by: (Muenchener Entomologische Gesellschaft), Verlag Dr. Friedrich Pfeil, Wolfratshauser Str 27, Munich, 81379, Germany. info@pfeil-verlag.de, http://www.pfeil-verlag.de. Ed. E G Burmeister.

595.7 JPN
NAGOYA KONCHU DOKOKAI RENRAKU GEPPO/N A P I NEWS. Text in Japanese. 1953. bi-m.
Published by: Nagoya Konchu Dokokai/Nagoya Entomological Society, c/o Mr Ando, 5-24 Otowa 1-chome, Ichinomiya-shi, Aichi-ken 491-0045, Japan.

595.7 IRN ISSN 0259-9996
➤ **NAMAH-YI ANJUMAN-I HASHARAHSHINASAN-I IRAN/JOURNAL OF ENTOMOLOGICAL SOCIETY OF IRAN.** Text in Persian, Modern; Summaries in English. 1973. a., latest vol.19, 2000. free to qualified personnel (effective 2005). abstr.; bibl.; charts; illus.; maps; pat.; stat. back issues avail. **Document type:** *Bulletin, Academic/Scholarly.* **Description:** All branches of entomology like as: Systematics, Taxonomy, Phsiology, Plant Protection etc.
Related titles: Supplement(s): Namah-yi Anjuman-i Hasharahshinasan-i Iran. Shumarah Fawq al-Adah. ISSN 1010-0008.
Indexed: BIOSIS Prev, BiolAb, FCA, ZooRec.
Published by: (Entomological Society of Iran), Plant Pests and Diseases Research Institute/Mu'assasah Tahqiqat Afat va Bimarihay Giyahi, P O Box 1454, Tehran, 19395, Iran. TEL 98-21-2403012, FAX 98-21-2403691, http://www.magiran.com/rostaniha. Ed. Dr. E Sadeghi.

595.7 BEL ISSN 0028-0666
CODEN: NAMOA9
NATURA MOSANA. Text in French. 1948. q. bk.rev. bibl. index. **Document type:** *Bulletin, Academic/Scholarly.*
Indexed: BiolAb, ChemAb, RefZh, ZooRec.
Published by: (Societe des Naturalistes Namur-Luxembourg, Societe Botanique de Liege asbl), Natura Mosana, Rue de Bruxelles 61, Namur, 5000, Belgium. Ed. J Margot.

NATURAL HISTORY OF THE NATIONAL PARKS OF HUNGARY. see *CONSERVATION*

595.7 NLD ISSN 0548-1163
NEDERLANDSE ENTOMOLOGISCHE VERENIGING. MONOGRAPHS. Text in Dutch, English. 1964. irreg., latest vol.10, 1983. price varies. illus. **Document type:** *Monographic series.*
Indexed: ASFA, BiolAb.
Published by: Nederlandse Entomologische Vereniging, Plantage Middenlaan 64, Amsterdam, 1018 DH, Netherlands.

595.7 BRA ISSN 1519-566X
SB935.B7 CODEN: ASENBI
➤ **NEOTROPICAL ENTOMOLOGY.** Text in English, Portuguese, Spanish; Summaries in English. 1972. 6/yr. USD 60 (effective 2004). 150 p./no.; **Document type:** *Journal, Academic/Scholarly.* **Description:** Publishes scientific articles and short communications in entomology.
Formerly: Sociedade Entomologica do Brasil. Anais (0301-8059)
Related titles: Online - full text ed.: free (effective 2005).
Indexed: ASFA, Agr, ApicAb, BioCN&I, BioDAb, BiolAb, CIN, CTFA, ChemAb, ChemTitl, CurCont, EntAb, FCA, FS&TA, ForAb, HGA, HortAb, IndVet, MaizeAb, PBA, PGegResA, PHN&I, PotatoAb, PoultAb, ProtozoAb, RM&VM, RPP, RevApplEntom, RiceAb, S&MA, SeedAb, SoyAb, TriticAb, VITIS, VetBull, WeedAb, ZooRec.
—BLDSC (6075.660200), CASDDS, IE, ingenta, Linda Hall.
Published by: Sociedade Entomologica do Brasil, Instituto Agronomico de Parana, Centro, Caixa Postal 481, Londrina, PR 86001-970, Brazil. TEL 55-43-33762000, FAX 55-43-3376210, http://www.seb.org.br. Ed. Sueli Souza Martinez. R&P Daniel Ricardo Sosa Gomes. Circ: 1,200.

595.7 NLD
NETHERLANDS ENTOMOLOGICAL SOCIETY. EXPERIMENTAL AND APPLIED ENTOMOLOGY SECTION. PROCEEDINGS. Text in English. 1990. a. **Document type:** *Proceedings.*
Indexed: ASFA, ApicAb, BioCN&I, ChemAb, ChemTitl, ForAb, HortAb, OrnHort, PHN&I, ProtozoAb, RPP, RevApplEntom, S&F, WeedAb, ZooRec.
—ingenta.
Published by: Nederlandse Entomologische Vereniging, Plantage Middenlaan 64, Amsterdam, 1018 DH, Netherlands.

595.7 DEU ISSN 0722-3773
QL461 CODEN: NENAD3
NEUE ENTOMOLOGISCHE NACHRICHTEN; Beitraege zur Oekologie, Faunistik und Systematik von Lepidopteren. Text in German, English. 1982. irreg. price varies. back issues avail. **Document type:** *Monographic series, Academic/Scholarly.*
Indexed: BIOSIS Prev, BiolAb, ZooRec.
—**CCC.**
Published by: Entomologisches Museum, Humboldtstr 13 A, Marktleuthen, 95168, Germany. TEL 49-9285-480, FAX 49-9285-8238. Ed., Pub. Ulf Eitschberger.

595.7 JPN ISSN 0028-4955
CODEN: NENTAN
NEW ENTOMOLOGIST/NYU ENTOMOROJISUTO. Text in English, Japanese. 1951. s-a. JPY 3,000, USD 14. charts; illus. index.
Indexed: BiolAb, ZooRec.
Published by: Entomological Society of Shinshu/Shinshu Konchu Gakkai, Shinshu Daigaku Nogakubu Oyo Konchugaku Kyoshitsu, 8304, Kamiina-gun, Minamiminowa-mura, Nagano-ken 399-4511, Japan. Ed. Nagao Koyama.

595.7 USA ISSN 0028-7199
QL461 CODEN: JNYEAI
➤ **NEW YORK ENTOMOLOGICAL SOCIETY. JOURNAL**; devoted to entomology in general. Text in English. 1893. q. USD 23 to individuals; USD 65 domestic to institutions; USD 75 foreign to institutions; USD 15 to students (effective 2005). bk.rev. bibl.; charts; illus. index. back issues avail. **Document type:** *Academic/Scholarly.* **Description:** Presents original contributions to insect biology, including systematics, biogeography and natural history.
Related titles: Online - full text ed.: (from BioOne, C S A, O C L C Online Computer Library Center, Inc.).
Indexed: ASCA, ASFA, AgBio, Agr, AgrForAb, ApicAb, BIOSIS Prev, BioCN&I, BiolAb, CurCont, EntAb, ForAb, HerbAb, HortAb, PBA, RA&MP, RM&VM, RevApplEntom, S&F, SFA, WeedAb, WildRev, ZooRec.
—BLDSC (4832.900000), CISTI, IE, Infotrieve, ingenta, Linda Hall.
Published by: New York Entomological Society, c/o American Museum of Natural History, Central Park West at 79th St, New York, NY 10024-5192. TEL 212-769-5613, FAX 212-769-5277, nyes@amnh.org. Ed. Dan Polhemus. Circ: 600.

595.7 636.0832 NZL ISSN 0110-6325
NEW ZEALAND BEEKEEPER. Short title: N.Z. Beekeeper. Text in English. q. NZD 38; USD 38 foreign. adv. bk.rev. **Document type:** *Newsletter, Academic/Scholarly.*
Indexed: INZP, RevApplEntom, SIA.
—CISTI.
Published by: National Beekeepers Association of New Zealand (Inc.), P.O. Box 3079, Napier, New Zealand. TEL 64-6-8433446, FAX 64-6-8434845, natbeeknz@xtra.co.nz. Ed., Pub., R&P, Adv. contact Harry Brown. Circ: 1,250.

595.7 NZL ISSN 0077-9962
QL487.5 CODEN: NEZEA4
➤ **NEW ZEALAND ENTOMOLOGIST.** Text in English. 1951. a. NZD 38 domestic; USD 40 foreign (effective 2001). bk.rev. index in vols.1-4. back issues avail. **Document type:** *Academic/Scholarly.* **Description:** Original research in New Zealand and South Pacific entomology.
Indexed: ASFA, AbHyg, AgrForAb, BIOSIS Prev, BioCN&I, BiolAb, EntAb, ForAb, GenetAb, HGA, HerbAb, HortAb, ISR, IndVet, NemAb, OrnHort, PGegResA, RefZh, RevApplEntom, S&F, SPPI, SeedAb, SoyAb, TriticAb, VetBull, WeedAb, ZooRec.

B

▼ new title ➤ refereed ✶ unverified ♦ full entry avail.

—CISTI, Linda Hall.
Published by: Entomological Society of New Zealand, Mt Albert Research Centre, Private Bag 92169, Auckland, New Zealand. FAX 64-9-8497093, mplmjb@dslak.co.nz. Ed. J Early. Circ: 700.

595.7   NGA   ISSN 0331-0094
QL461   CODEN: NJENDW
NIGERIAN JOURNAL OF ENTOMOLOGY. Text in English. 1974. s-a. NGN 20. illus. **Document type:** *Academic/Scholarly.*
Supersedes: Entomological Society of Nigeria. Bulletin (0425-1067)
Indexed: AgBio, AgrForAb, BioCN&I, BiolAb, ChemAb, FCA, FPA, ForAb, HerbAb, HortAb, IndVet, MaizeAb, OrnHort, PBA, PHN&I, PotatoAb, RA&MP, RPP, RevApplEntom, RiceAb, S&F, SeedAb, SoyAb, TDB, VetBull, WAE&RSA, WeedAb.
—CASDDS.
Published by: Entomological Society of Nigeria, c/o Anthony Youdeowei, Department of Agricultural Biology, University of Ibadan, Ibadan, Oyo, Nigeria. Ed. Olupomi Ajayi. Circ: 500.

595.7   JPN   ISSN 0918-1067
QL458
NIHON DANI GAKKAISHI/ACAROLOGICAL SOCIETY OF JAPAN. JOURNAL. Text in English, Japanese; Summaries in English. 1974. s-a. JPY 5,000 to members. adv. bk.rev.
Document type: *Academic/Scholarly.*
Formerly (until 1992): Danirui Kenkyukai Kaiho - Japanese Association for Acarology. Proceedings (0285-4856)
Related titles: Online - full text ed.: ISSN 1880-2273 (from J-Stage).
Indexed: ZooRec.
—CCC.
Published by: Nihon Dani Gakkai/Acarological Society of Japan, c/o Dr. N. Takada, Ed., Fukui Medical University, P.O. Box No. 1910-1191, Matsuoka, Japan. TEL 81-776-61-3111, FAX 81-776-23-0663, yhyano@fmsrsa.fukui-med.ac.jp, fujisaki@obihiro.ac.jp, http://www.affrc.go.jp:8001/acari/index.html. R&P N Takada. Adv. contact K Fujisaki. Circ: 350.

NIHON KONCHU GAKKAI TAIKAI KOEN YOSHI/ ENTOMOLOGICAL SOCIETY OF JAPAN. ABSTRACTS OF ANNUAL MEETING. see *BIOLOGY—Abstracting, Bibliographies, Statistics*

595.7   JPN   ISSN 0387-9003
➤ **NIHON OYO DOBUTSU KONCHU GAKKAI CHUGOKU SHIBU KAIHO/JAPANESE SOCIETY OF APPLIED ENTOMOLOGY AND ZOOLOGY. CHUGOKU BRANCH. JOURNAL.** Text in Japanese; Summaries in English, Japanese. 1959. a. price varies. **Document type:** *Academic/Scholarly.*
Published by: Nihon Oyo Dobutsu Konchu Gakkai, Chugoku Shibu/Japanese Society of Applied Entomology and Zoology, Chugoku Branch, Chugoku Nogyo Shikenjo, 12-1 Nishi-Fukatsu-cho 6-chome, Fukuyama-shi, Hiroshima-ken 721-0975, Japan. TEL 81-0849-23-4100, FAX 81-0849-24-7893. Ed. Kazuki Miura. Pub. Nasahiro Kobayashi. Circ: 250.

595.7   JPN   ISSN 0021-4914
QL461   CODEN: NIPTAR
➤ **NIHON OYO DOBUTSU KONCHU GAKKAISHI/JAPANESE JOURNAL OF APPLIED ENTOMOLOGY AND ZOOLOGY.** Text in Japanese; Summaries in English. 1957. q. JPY 8,000 domestic membership; USD 50 foreign membership (effective 2004). adv. bk.rev. abstr. Index. **Document type:** *Journal, Academic/Scholarly.*
Formed by the merger of (1929-1957): Oyo Dobutsugaku Zasshi / Japanese Journal of Applied Zoology (0369-8017); (1938-1957): Oyo Konchu (0369-8025)
Related titles: Online - full text ed.: ISSN 1347-6068. free (effective 2005) (from J-Stage).
Indexed: AEA, ASCA, ASFA, AgBio, AgrForAb, BIOSIS Prev, BioCN&I, BiolAb, ChemAb, CurCont, DBA, DSA, ExcerpMed, FCA, FPA, FS&TA, ForAb, HGA, HerbAb, HortAb, INIS AtomInd, ISR, MaizeAb, NemAb, NutrAb, OrnHort, PBA, PGegResA, PHN&I, PotatoAb, ProtozoAb, RA&MP, RPP, RevApplEntom, RiceAb, S&F, SCI, SFA, SIA, SoyAb, TriticAb, VITIS, VetBull, WeedAb, WildRev, ZooRec.
—BLDSC (4650.850000), CASDDS, CISTI, IDS, IE, ingenta, Linda Hall. **CCC.**
Published by: Japanese Society of Applied Entomology and Zoology/Nihon Oyo Dobutsu Konchu Gakkai, c/o Japan Plant Protection Association, 1-43-11 Komagome, Toshima-ku, Tokyo, 170-0003, Japan. TEL 81-3-3943-6021, FAX 81-3-3943-6021. Ed. Masakazu Shiga. Adv. contact Yoshiaki Kono. Circ: 2,600. **Dist. by:** Japan Publications Trading Co., Ltd., Book Export II Dept, PO Box 5030, Tokyo International, Tokyo 101-3191, Japan. TEL 81-3-32923753, FAX 81-3-32920410, infoserials@jptco.co.jp, http://www.jptco.co.jp.

595.7   JPN   ISSN 0915-2067
NIHON SEMI NO KAI KAIHO/CICADA. Text in Japanese. 1978. 3/yr. membership.
Published by: Nihon Semi no Kai/Japan Cicada Club, c/o Mr Hashimoto, 43-11 Eifuku 2-chome, Suginami-ku, Tokyo, 168-0064, Japan.

NIHON SHOKUBUTSU BYORI GAKKAI DOJO DENSENBYO DANWAKAI KOEN YOSHISHU/PHYTOPATHOLOGICAL SOCIETY OF JAPAN. ABSTRACTS OF THE MEETING OF SOIL BORNE DISEASE. see *BIOLOGY—Abstracting, Bibliographies, Statistics*

NIHON SHOKUBUTSU BYORI GAKKAI SHOKUBUTSU KANSEN SEIRI DANWAKAI/SYMPOSIUM ON PHYSIOLOGICAL PLANT PATHOLOGY IN JAPAN. PROCEEDINGS. see *BIOLOGY—Botany*

595.76   JPN
NIHON SHOSHIMOKU GAKKAI TOKUBETSU HOKOKU/JAPANESE SOCIETY OF COLEOPTEROLOGY. SPECIAL BULLETIN. Text in English, Japanese. irreg.
Published by: Nihon Shoshi Gakkai/Japanese Society of Coleopterology, Kokuritsu Kagaku Hakubutsukan Dobutsu Kenkyubu, 23-1 Hiyakunin-cho 3-chome, Shinjuku-ku, Tokyo, 169-0073, Japan.

595.78   DNK
NOCTUIDAE EUROPAEAE. Text in English, French. 1990. irreg., latest vol.7, 1997. price varies. illus. back issues avail.
Document type: *Monographic series, Academic/Scholarly.*
Description: Provides a revision of the European species of the lepidoptera family Noctuidae.
Published by: Apollo Books, Kirkeby Sand 19, Stenstrup, 5771, Denmark. TEL 45-62-26-37-37, FAX 45-62-26-37-80, apollobooks@vip.cybercity.dk, http://www.apollobooks.com. Ed. M. Fibiger.

595.7   NOR
NORSKE INSEKTTABELLER. Text in English. irreg.
Published by: Norsk Entomologisk Forening, c/o Egil Michaelsen, Kurlandveien 35, Sarpsborg, 1727, Norway.

595.7   NOR   ISSN 1501-8415
QL461   CODEN: FNSBD6
NORWEGIAN JOURNAL OF ENTOMOLOGY. Text in English; Summaries in Norwegian. 1920. s-a. NOK 200 to non-members (effective 2000). adv. cum.index every 3 yrs. back issues avail. **Document type:** *Journal, Academic/Scholarly.* **Description:** Publishes original new information generally relevant to Norwegian entomology, with emphasis on papers which are mainly faunal or zoogeographical in scope or content.
Former titles (until 1999): Fauna Norvegica Series B. Norwegian Journal of Entomology (0332-7698); (until 1978): Norwegian Journal of Entomology (0332-575X); (until 1974): Norsk Entomologisk Tidsskrift (0029-1897)
Indexed: ASFA, AgBio, AgrForAb, AnBrAb, BIOSIS Prev, BioCN&I, BiolAb, EntAb, FCA, ForAb, HelmAb, HerbAb, HortAb, IBR, KWIWR, MBA, NemAb, PBA, PotatoAb, PoultAb, RRTA, RevApplEntom, S&F, SIA, TriticAb, WeedAb, ZooRec.
—BLDSC (6152.285000), CISTI, IE, ingenta, Linda Hall. **CCC.**
Published by: Norsk Entomologisk Forening, c/o Egil Michaelsen, Kurlandveien 35, Sarpsborg, 1727, Norway. jana.stenlokk@rl.telia.no, Ed. Lars Ove Hansen. Circ: 900.

595.78   DNK   ISSN 0342-7536
➤ **NOTA LEPIDOPTEROLOGICA.** Text in English, French, German. 1977. q. EUR 35 to individual members; EUR 45 to institutional members (effective 2005). back issues avail.
Document type: *Journal, Academic/Scholarly.* **Description:** Publishes contributions on systematic and faunistic lepidopterology.
Indexed: BIOBASE, BIOSIS Prev, BiolAb, EntAb, IABS, RefZh, ZooRec.
—BLDSC (6152.826000), IE, ingenta. **CCC.**
Published by: Societas Europaea Lepidopterologica, c/o Niels Peder Kristensen, Zoologisk Museum, Universitetsparken 15, Copenhagen, 2100, Denmark. http://www.soceurlep.org/contents.htm. Ed. Matthias Nuss. Circ: 700 (paid); 20 (controlled). **Dist. by:** Apollo Books, Kirkeby Sand 19, Stenstrup 5771, Denmark. TEL 45-62-263737, FAX 45-62-263780, apollobooks@vip.cybercity.dk, http://www.apollobooks.com.

595.7   FRA   ISSN 0374-9797
                            CODEN: NRETAZ
NOUVELLE REVUE D'ENTOMOLOGIE; revue internationale de taxonomie et de biogeographie entomologiques. Text in French. 1971. q. EUR 50 to individuals; EUR 67 to institutions (effective 2005). **Document type:** *Journal, Academic/Scholarly.*
Indexed: ASFA, AgrForAb, BIOSIS Prev, BioCN&I, BiolAb, EntAb, FCA, ForAb, HortAb, WeedAb, ZooRec.
—Linda Hall. **CCC.**
Address: BP 96, Fontenay-sous-Bois, 94123, France. editeur@nouvelle.revue.entomo.org, http://www.nouvelle-revue-entomo.org. Eds. Patrice Bordat, Armand Matocq.

595.7   DEU   ISSN 0948-6038
NOVA SUPPLEMENTA ENTOMOLOGICA. Text in German. 1985. a. EUR 62 (effective 2005). **Document type:** *Journal, Academic/Scholarly.* **Description:** Contains catalogs which provide a systematic look at the collection, archive and library contents of the German Entomological Institute.
Related titles: Online - full text ed.
Indexed: BIOSIS Prev, BiolAb, RevApplEntom, ZooRec.
—CCC.

Published by: (Deutsches Entomologisches Institut), Verlag Goecke und Evers, Sportplatzweg 5, Keltern-Weiler, 75210, Germany. TEL 49-7236-7174, FAX 49-7236-7325, books@goeckeevers.de, http://www.goeckeevers.de. Ed. Holger Dathe.

595.7   USA   ISSN 0362-2622
QL461
➤ **OCCASIONAL PAPERS IN ENTOMOLOGY.** Text in English. 1959. irreg. per issue exchange basis. illus. **Document type:** *Academic/Scholarly.*
Continues: California. Bureau of Entomology. Occasional Papers
Indexed: BiolAb, ZooRec.
—CISTI, Linda Hall.
Published by: (California. Analysis & Identification), Department of Food and Agriculture, Division of Plant Industry, 1220 N St, Sacramento, CA 95814. TEL 916-445-5421. Ed. Fred G Andrews. Circ: 200 (controlled).

595.7   JPN   ISSN 0912-6155
OKERA/IBARAKI INSECT SOCIETY. NEWS. Text in Japanese. biennial.
Published by: Ibaraki Konchu Dokokai, c/o Mr Katsuyoshi Ichige, 493 Senba-cho, Mito-shi, Ibaraki-ken 310-0851, Japan.

OPUSCULA ZOOLOGICA FLUMINENSIA. see *BIOLOGY—Zoology*

595.7   USA   ISSN 0030-5316
QL461   CODEN: ORINAE
➤ **ORIENTAL INSECTS;** an international journal of systematic entomology of the old world tropics. Text in English. 1967. a., latest vol.37, 2003. USD 71 domestic; USD 75 foreign (effective 2003). adv. bk.rev. abstr.; bibl.; charts; illus. index. 400 p./no. 1 cols./p.; back issues avail.; reprint service avail. from PQC. **Document type:** *Journal, Academic/Scholarly.*
Description: Provides an outlet to the works of systematic entomologists working on Oriental and old world fauna.
Indexed: ASCA, ASFA, AgrForAb, BIOSIS Prev, BibAg, BioCN&I, BiolAb, CurCont, EntAb, ForAb, HortAb, ISA, PHN&I, PotatoAb, ProtozoAb, RA&MP, RM&VM, RevApplEntom, RiceAb, S&F, SPPI, SeedAb, WeedAb, ZooRec.
—IE, Infotrieve, Linda Hall.
Published by: (Oriental Insects), Associated Publishers, 358102, Gainesville, FL 32635-8102. assopubl@yahoo.com, http://www.mapress.com/AP/. Ed., Pub., R&P Virendra K Gupta. Circ: 200.

➤ **OSAKA-SHIRITSU SHIZENSHI HAKUBUTSUKAN SHUZO SHIRYO MOKUROKU/OSAKA MUSEUM OF NATURAL HISTORY. SPECIAL PUBLICATIONS.** see *BIOLOGY*

595.7   PAK   ISSN 1018-1180
➤ **PAKISTAN JOURNAL OF ENTOMOLOGY.** Text in English; Summaries in English. 1986. s-a. PKR 200 domestic; USD 30 newsstand/cover foreign (effective 2000). back issues avail.
Document type: *Journal, Academic/Scholarly.*
Published by: Entomological Society of Karachi, Entomological Society of Karachi, Karachi University, Department of Zoology, Karachi, Pakistan. TEL 92-21-6979471, azhar@inet.com.pk. Pub. Azhar A Khan. R&P S. N. H. Naqvi. Circ: 1,000.

595.7   USA   ISSN 0031-0603
QL461   CODEN: PPETA9
➤ **PAN-PACIFIC ENTOMOLOGIST.** Text in English. 1924. q., latest vol.78, 2002. USD 40 (effective 2003). bk.rev. bibl.; illus. index. 80 p./no.; back issues avail. **Document type:** *Journal, Academic/Scholarly.*
Indexed: ASCA, ASFA, Agr, AgrForAb, AnBeAb, ApEcolAb, ApicAb, BIOSIS Prev, BibAg, BioCN&I, BiolAb, ChemAb, CurCont, ESPM, EntAb, FCA, FPA, ForAb, GenetAb, HGA, HerbAb, HortAb, IndVet, NutrAb, OrnHort, PBA, PotatoAb, RM&VM, RRTA, RevApplEntom, RiceAb, S&F, SFA, SeedAb, VetBull, WeedAb, WildRev, ZooRec.
—BLDSC (6357.427000), CISTI, IDS, IE, Infotrieve, ingenta, Linda Hall. **CCC.**
Published by: Pacific Coast Entomological Society, c/o California Academy of Sciences, Golden Gate Park, San Francisco, CA 94118-4599. TEL 415-750-7227, FAX 415-750-7228, vlee@calacademy.org. Ed. Ronald E Somerby. R&P Vincent F Lee TEL 415-750-7230. Circ: 750.

595.7   JPN
PANORPODES. Text in Japanese. 1976. a.
Published by: Choshimoku Danwakai/Study Group of Mecopterologist in Japan, c/o Mr Nobuo Suzuki, Nihon Joshi Taiiku Tanki Daigaku Kyoyo Dai 2 Kenkyushitsu, 19-1 Kitaka-Rasuyama 8-chome, Setagaya-ku, Tokyo, 157-0061, Japan.

PARASITICA. see *BIOLOGY*

632.7   BEL   ISSN 0771-5277
➤ **PHEGEA;** driemaandelijks tijdschrift van de Vlaamse vereniging voor entomologie. Text in Dutch, English, French. 1973. q. EUR 25 domestic; EUR 30 foreign (effective 2002). bk.rev. bibl.; maps; illus. 40 p./no.; back issues avail.
Document type: *Journal, Academic/Scholarly.* **Description:** Includes original papers on Palaearctic entomology.
Indexed: RefZh, ZooRec.

Published by: Vlaamse Vereniging voor Entomologie, Nieuwe Donk 50, Antwerp, 2100, Belgium. TEL 32-3-322-0235, willy.deprins@antwerpen.be. Ed. W de Prins.

595.7 PHL ISSN 0048-3753
➤ **THE PHILIPPINE ENTOMOLOGIST.** Text in English. 1968. s-a. PHP 700 domestic; USD 55 foreign (effective 2003). adv. bk.rev. charts; illus.; abstr.; bibl. 100 p./no.; back issues avail. **Document type:** *Academic/Scholarly.* **Description:** Contains scientific articles, notes, reviews and opinions in entomology and related sciences.
Indexed: AgrForAb, BioCN&I, ChemAb, FCA, FS&TA, ForAb, HelmAb, HortAb, MaizeAb, OrnHort, PBA, PGegResA, PHN&I, PotatoAb, RA&MP, RDA, RPP, RevApplEntom, RiceAb, S&MA, SeedAb, TOSA, TriticAb, WAE&RSA, WeedAb, ZooRec.
Published by: Philippine Association of Entomologists, c/o Department of Entomology, University of the Philippines at Los Banos, Laguna, 4031, Philippines. TEL 63-49-5361315, FAX 63-49-5363527, http://www.laguna.net/pae. Ed., Adv. contact Mr. Ireneo Lit Jr. Circ: 1,000.

595.7 GBR ISSN 0307-6962
QL495 CODEN: PENTDE
➤ **PHYSIOLOGICAL ENTOMOLOGY.** Text in English. 1976. 5/yr. GBP 80, EUR 120 combined subscription in Europe to individuals print & online eds.; USD 146 combined subscription in the Americas to individuals & Caribbean, print & online eds.; GBP 87 combined subscription elsewhere to individuals print & online eds.; GBP 377 combined subscription in Europe to institutions print & online eds.; USD 694 combined subscription in the Americas to institutions & Caribbean, print & online eds.); GBP 413 combined subscription elsewhere to institutions print & online eds. (effective 2006). adv. bk.rev. bibl.; illus. index. back issues avail.; reprint service avail. from ISI. **Document type:** *Journal, Academic/Scholarly.* **Description:** Designed primarily to serve the interests of experimentalists who work on the behavior of insects and other arthropods.
Formerly: Journal of Entomology (A) (0047-2409)
Related titles: Microform ed.: (from PQC); ♦ Online - full text ed.: Physiological Entomology Online. ISSN 1365-3032.
Indexed: ASCA, ASFA, AbHyg, AgBio, Agr, AgrForAb, AnBeAb, ApicAb, B&BAb, BIOBASE, BIOSIS Prev, BibAg, BioCN&I, BiolAb, CPA, ChemAb, ChemTitl, ChemoAb, CurCont, EntAb, ForAb, GEOBASE, GenetAb, HGA, HortAb, I&DA, IABS, ISR, IndVet, MSB, MaizeAb, NutrAb, OrnHort, PBA, PGegResA, PHN&I, PotatoAb, ProtozoAb, RM&VM, RPP, RefZh, RevApplEntom, S&F, SCI, SIA, SeedAb, TDB, TriticAb, VITIS, VetBull, WeedAb, ZooRec.
—BLDSC (6484.720000), CASDDS, CISTI, IDS, IE, Infotrieve, ingenta, Linda Hall. **CCC.**
Published by: (Royal Entomological Society), Blackwell Publishing Ltd., 9600 Garsington Rd, Oxford, OX4 2ZG, United Kingdom. TEL 44-1865-776868, FAX 44-1865-714591, customerservices@oxon.blackwellpublishing.com, http://www.blackwellpublishing.com/journals/PEN. Eds. G J Goldsworthy, Jim Hardie, W M Blaney. Pub. Sue Hewitt. R&P Sophie Savage. Adv. contact Jenny Applin. Circ: 660.

595.7 GBR ISSN 1365-3032
➤ **PHYSIOLOGICAL ENTOMOLOGY ONLINE.** Text in English. q. GBP 357 in Europe to institutions; USD 660 in the Americas to institutions & Caribbean; GBP 393 elsewhere to institutions (effective 2006). **Document type:** *Academic/Scholarly.*
Media: Online - full text (from Blackwell Synergy, EBSCO Publishing, Gale Group, IngentaConnect, O C L C Online Computer Library Center, Inc., Swets Information Services).
Related titles: Microform ed.: (from PQC); ♦ Print ed.: Physiological Entomology. ISSN 0307-6962.
Published by: Blackwell Publishing Ltd., 9600 Garsington Rd, Oxford, OX4 2ZG, United Kingdom. TEL 44-1865-776868, FAX 44-1865-714591, customerservices@oxon.blackwellpublishing.com, http://www.blackwellpublishing.com.

595.7 IND
PHYTOPHAGA. Text in English. s-a. INR 100 domestic to individuals; USD 25 foreign to individuals; INR 250 domestic to institutions; USD 40 foreign to institutions. **Document type:** *Academic/Scholarly.* **Description:** Publishes original research articles and reviews on topics of entomological interest, principally relating to insect-plant interactions, and biology of plant feeding insects.
—BLDSC (6497.015000).
Published by: S. Viswanathan (Printers & Publishers) Pvt. Ltd., 38 McNichols Rd., Chetput, Chennai, Tamil Nadu 600 031, India. Ed. T N Ananthakrishnan.

PLANT HEALTH PROGRESS. see *BIOLOGY—Botany*

PLANT PROTECTION RESEARCH INSTITUTE. ANNUAL REPORT. see *AGRICULTURE—Crop Production And Soil*

595.7 POL ISSN 0032-3780
QL461 CODEN: PEBEA8
➤ **POLSKIE PISMO ENTOMOLOGICZNE/POLISH JOURNAL OF ENTOMOLOGY.** Text and summaries in English. 1922. q. USD 54. bk.rev. bibl.; charts; illus. index. **Document type:** *Academic/Scholarly.*
Indexed: ASFA, AgrAg, AgrForAb, AgrLib, BIOSIS Prev, BioCN&I, BiolAb, ChemAb, EntAb, FCA, ForAb, HerbAb, HortAb, MaizeAb, NemAb, OrnHort, PBA, PGegResA, PHN&I, RA&MP, RM&VM, RevApplEntom, S&F, TriticAb, WeedAb, ZooRec.
—BLDSC (6547.000000), CASDDS, CISTI.
Published by: Polskie Towarzystwo Entomologiczne/Polish Entomological Society, ul Sienkiewicza 21, Wroclaw, 50-335, Poland. TEL 48-71-3225041, http://www.au.poznan.pl/wydzialy/ogrodniczy/pte/index.html. Ed. Ryszard Szadziewski. Circ: 500. **Subscr. to:** Biblioteka, ul Przybyszewskiego 63/77, Wroclaw 51-148, Poland. TEL 48-71-3247237.

595.7 TUR ISSN 1015-8243
PRIAMUS. Text in English, French, German. 1981. irreg.
Published by: Centre for Entomological Studies, Yuzuncu Yil Universitesi, Fen-Edebiyat Fakultesi, Biyoloji Bolumu, Zeve - Kampus Van, Ankara, Turkey. a_kocak@mailcity.com.

595.7 USA ISSN 0033-2615
QL461 CODEN: PYCHAQ
➤ **PSYCHE (CAMBRIDGE, 1874)**; journal of entomology. Text in English. 1874. irreg. USD 35 per vol. to individuals; USD 45 per vol. to institutions (effective 2004). illus. index. **Document type:** *Journal, Academic/Scholarly.*
Indexed: BiolAb, ChemAb, RILM, RevApplEntom, S&F.
—BLDSC (6946.110000), CISTI, IE, Infotrieve, Linda Hall.
Published by: Cambridge Entomological Club, 26 Oxford St, Cambridge, MA 02138. TEL 617-496-1034, psyche@oeb.harvard.edu, http://psyche.entclub.org/, http://entclub.org/. Ed. K M Horton. R&P K.M. Horton. Circ: 700.

570 595.7 AUT ISSN 1028-6764
➤ **QUADRIFINA**; Bulletin zur Erforschung der Lepidopteren. Text and summaries in English, German. 1998. irreg. price varies. adv. bk.rev. index. **Document type:** *Bulletin, Academic/Scholarly.* **Description:** Publishes research on lepidoptera: butterflies, moths, and skippers.
Indexed: ZooRec.
Published by: Naturhistorisches Museum in Wien, Burgring 7, Postfach 417, Vienna, W 1014, Austria. TEL 43-1-52177-497, FAX 43-1-52177-229, http://www.nhm-wien.ac.at. Ed., Pub., Adv. contact Martin Loedl. Circ: 150 (paid); 50 (controlled).

➤ **REFERATIVNYI ZHURNAL. ENTOMOLOGIYA.** see *BIOLOGY—Abstracting, Bibliographies, Statistics*

595.7 DEU ISSN 0070-7279
QL461 CODEN: RCHBA3
REICHENBACHIA; Zeitschrift fuer taxonomische Entomologie. Text in English, French, German. 1875. a. price varies. bk.rev. back issues avail. **Document type:** *Journal, Academic/Scholarly.* **Description:** Explores taxonomy and systematics of insecta and arachnida.
Supersedes in part (in 1960): Abhandlungen und Berichte aus dem Staatlichen Museum fuer Tierkunde Dresden (0138-4147); Which was formerly (until 1939): Abhandlungen und Berichte der Museen fuer Tierkunde und Voelkerkunde zu Dresden (0138-5909); (until 1923): Abhandlungen und Berichte des Zoologischen und Anthropologisch-Ethnographischen Museums zu Dresden (0233-125X); (until 1886): Koenigliches Zoologisches Museum zu Dresden. Mitteilungen (0233-1306)
Indexed: BIOSIS Prev, BiolAb, ZooRec.
—BLDSC (7350.350000), IE, ingenta, Linda Hall. **CCC.**
Published by: Staatliche Naturhistorische Sammlungen Dresden, Museum fuer Tierkunde, Augustusstr 2, Dresden, 01067, Germany. tk@snsd.de, http://www.snsd.de/mtd_info.htm. Ed. Rainer Emmrich. Circ: 350.

REVIEW OF MEDICAL AND VETERINARY ENTOMOLOGY. see *MEDICAL SCIENCES—Abstracting, Bibliographies, Statistics*

595.7 BRA ISSN 0085-5626
CODEN: RBREAL
➤ **REVISTA BRASILEIRA DE ENTOMOLOGIA.** Text in English, Portuguese, Spanish; Summaries in English. 1954. q. USD 80 (effective 1999). bk.rev. **Document type:** *Academic/Scholarly.* **Description:** Publishes original papers in entomology, including groups of arthropoda.
Related titles: Online - full text ed.: free (effective 2005).
Indexed: ASFA, AgrForAb, BIOSIS Prev, BioCN&I, BiolAb, CPA, EntAb, FCA, ForAb, GenetAb, HGA, HerbAb, HortAb, IndVet, MaizeAb, NemAb, NutrAb, OrnHort, PBA, PHN&I, PotatoAb, PoultAb, ProtozoAb, RA&MP, RM&VM, RPP, RevApplEntom, RiceAb, S&F, SoyAb, TDB, VetBull, WeedAb, ZooRec.
—Linda Hall.
Published by: Sociedade Brasileira de Entomologia, Ipiranga, Caixa Postal 42672, Sao Paulo, SP 04299-970, Brazil. TEL 55-11-274-3455 ext. 260, FAX 55-11-2743690, sbe@ib.usp.br, http://www.ib.usp.br/sbe/. Ed. Carlos Ribeiro Vilela. Circ: 600.

595.7 CHL ISSN 0034-740X
QL461
➤ **REVISTA CHILENA DE ENTOMOLOGIA.** Text in English, Spanish. 1951. a. price varies. adv. bk.rev. bibl.; charts; illus. **Document type:** *Academic/Scholarly.*
Indexed: ASFA, AgrForAb, BIOSIS Prev, BioCN&I, BiolAb, CPA, EntAb, FCA, ForAb, GenetAb, HGA, HerbAb, HortAb, NemAb, OrnHort, PHN&I, PotatoAb, RA&MP, RevApplEntom, S&F, SeedAb, TOSA, TriticAb, VITIS, WeedAb, ZooRec.
—BLDSC (7848.600000), IE, ingenta.
Published by: Sociedad Chilena de Entomologia, Casilla 21132, Santiago, 21, Chile. dlanfran@uach.cl, http://www.udec.cl/~insectos. Ed. Dolly Lanfranco. R&P Jaime Solervicens. Circ: 500.

595.7 COL ISSN 0120-0488
REVISTA COLOMBIANA DE ENTOMOLOGIA. Text in Spanish; Abstracts in English; Summaries in English. 1975. q. COP 120,000 domestic; USD 60 foreign (effective 2005). abstr.; bibl.; illus. back issues avail. **Document type:** *Magazine, Academic/Scholarly.* **Description:** For professional entomologists in all disciplines related to the field; with principal emphasis on neotropical regions.
Indexed: AbHyg, AgBio, AgrForAb, BioCN&I, FCA, FPA, FS&TA, ForAb, HerbAb, HortAb, IndVet, MaizeAb, NemAb, NutrAb, OrnHort, PBA, PGegResA, PHN&I, PotatoAb, ProtozoAb, RA&MP, RPP, RevApplEntom, RiceAb, S&F, SIA, SoyAb, TDB, TriticAb, VetBull, WeedAb, ZooRec.
Published by: Sociedad Colombiana de Entomologia, Apdo Aereo 11366, Bogota, Colombia. TEL 57-1-2218706, FAX 57-1-2219263, secretario@socolen.org.co, http://www.socolen.com.co, http://www.socolen.org.co. Ed. Paulina Munoz. Circ: 500.

595.7 NIC ISSN 1021-0296
QL481.N5 CODEN: RNIEEU
REVISTA NICARAGUENSE DE ENTOMOLOGIA. Text in Spanish. 1987. q.
Indexed: BioCN&I, EntAb, GenetAb, HGA, NemAb, ProtozoAb, TDB, ZooRec.
Published by: Asociacion Nicaraguense de Entomologia, Museo Entomologico, Servicio Entomologico Autonomo, Box 527, Leon, Nicaragua.

595.7 PER ISSN 0080-2425
REVISTA PERUANA DE ENTOMOLOGIA. Text in English, Spanish; Summaries in English. 1958. a. PEN 50,000, USD 8. adv. bk.rev.
Indexed: BiolAb, RevApplEntom, ZooRec.
Published by: Sociedad Entomologica del Peru, Apdo. 4796, Lima, 100, Peru. Ed. Pedro G Aguilar. Circ: 1,000.

595.7 JPN ISSN 0910-6839
ROSTRIA/HEMIPTEROLOGICAL SOCIETY OF JAPAN. TRANSACTIONS. Text in English, Japanese. 1962. a. JPY 2,000 (effective 2003). adv. 60 p./no.; back issues avail. **Document type:** *Journal, Academic/Scholarly.*
Indexed: ZooRec.
Published by: Nihon Hanshirui Gakkai/Hemipterological Society of Japan, Kokuritsu Kagaku Hakubutsukan Dobutsu Kenkyubu, 23-1 Hiyakunin-cho 3-chome, Shinjuku-ku, Tokyo, 169-0073, Japan. Ed. Masaaki Tomokuni. Circ: 220.

595.7 ZAF ISSN 1026-4914
ROSTRUM. Text and summaries in English, Afrikaans. s-a. included in subscrip. to African Entomology. adv. back issues avail. **Document type:** *Newsletter.*
Related titles: ♦ Supplement to: African Entomology. ISSN 1021-3589.
Indexed: ISAP.
Published by: Entomological Society of Southern Africa/Entomologiese Vereniging van Suidelike Afrika, PO Box 13162, Hatfield, Pretoria 0028, South Africa. http://journals.sabinet.co.za/essa. Adv. contact E Allsop.

595.7 GBR ISSN 0080-4363
CODEN: RESSBM
ROYAL ENTOMOLOGICAL SOCIETY OF LONDON. SYMPOSIA. Text in English. 1961. biennial, latest vol.20. **Document type:** *Monographic series.*
Related titles: Microfiche ed.: (from BHP).
Indexed: Agr, BiolAb, RevApplEntom, ZooRec.
—BLDSC (8584.600000), CASDDS, CISTI, ingenta, Linda Hall.
Published by: (Royal Entomological Society), CABI Publishing (Subsidiary of: CAB International), CAB International, Wallingford, Oxfordshire OX10 8DE, United Kingdom. TEL 44-1491-832111, FAX 44-1491-833508, cabi@cabi.org, http://www.cabi-publishing.org/. Circ: 2,000.

595.7 RUS ISSN 0132-8069
➤ **RUSSIAN ENTOMOLOGICAL JOURNAL.** Text in English; Abstracts in Russian. 1992. q. USD 48 to individuals; USD 58 to institutions (effective 2005). adv. bk.rev. back issues avail. **Document type:** *Journal, Academic/Scholarly.* **Description:** Covers morphology, taxonomy, faunistics, phylogeny, evolution and insects.
Indexed: BIOSIS Prev, BioCN&I, BiolAb, ForAb, HerbAb, HortAb, PHN&I, RM&VM, RefZh, RevApplEntom, S&F, TDB, ZooRec.
—BLDSC (8052.702000), CISTI. **CCC.**
Published by: (Moskovskii Gosudarstvennyi Universitet im. M.V. Lomonosova, Zoologicheskii Muzei), K M K Scientific Press Ltd., c/o Dr K G Mikhailov, Zoologicheskii Muzei MGU, Bol'shaya Nikitskaya 6, Moscow, 125009, Russian Federation. TEL 7-095-2925796, FAX 7-095-2032717, kmk2000@online.ru, http://www.orc.ru/~kmkweb/rej.htm. Ed. Lev N Medvedev. adv.: B&W page USD 50, color page USD 100.

595.7 RUS
RUSSKOE ENTOMOLOGICHESKOE OBSHCHESTVO. TRUDY. Text in Russian. 1861. irreg., latest vol.74, 2003. **Document type:** *Academic/Scholarly.*
Published by: Russkoe Entomologicheskoye Obshchestvo/ Russian Entomological Society, Universitetskaya nab, 1, Sankt Peterburg, 1990934, Russian Federation. TEL 812-3281212, res@zin.ru, http://www.zin.ru/societies/res/horae.htm. Ed. Vladimir I Tobias.

595.7 JPN ISSN 0910-9889
RYUKYU NO KONCHU/INSECTS OF LOOCHOOS. Text in Japanese. 1977. irreg. JPY 3,500 per issue.
Published by: Okinawa Konchu Dokokai/Okinawa Entomological Society, c/o Mr Kunio Nagamine, 13-67 Takara 2-chome, Naha-shi, Okinawa-ken 901-0145, Japan.

595.78 ESP ISSN 0300-5267
QL541 CODEN: SRLPEF
➤ **S H I L A P**; revista de lepidopterologia. Key Title: Shilap: Sociedad Hispano-Luso-Americana de Lepidopterologia. Text in Spanish, English, French, German, Italian, Portuguese; Summaries in English, Spanish. 1973. q. EUR 60.10 (effective 2002). adv. bk.rev. index. back issues avail. **Document type:** *Bulletin, Academic/Scholarly.* **Description:** Aims future collaboration among lepidopterist worldwide to support scientific work and nature-conservation in the field of lepidopterology, to produce its own publications and hold every two years a congress of lepidopterology.
Related titles: E-mail ed.; Fax ed.
Indexed: BiolAb, EntAb, ForAb, HortAb, IECT, PBA, RefZh, RevApplEntom, S&F, SeedAb, WeedAb, ZooRec.
—CINDOC.
Published by: Sociedad Hispano-Luso-Americana de Lepidopterologia, Apdo. de Correos 331, Madrid, 28080, Spain. FAX 34-91-4475609, avives@eresmas.net. Ed. Antonio Vives. Circ: 2,000.

595.7 JPN ISSN 1346-0951
SAIKAKU TSUSHIN. Text in Japanese. 2000. s-a.
Indexed: ZooRec.
Published by: Koganemushi-Kenkyukai/Japanese Society of Scarabaeoideans, c/o Shinya Kawai, 4-16-3, Simouma, Setagaya-ku, Tokyo, 154-0002, Japan. kogane@kawamo.co.jp, http://www.kawamo.co.jp/kogane.

595.7 JPN ISSN 0915-2652
SF542.75.J3 CODEN: SKNHEK
SANSHI KONCHU NOGYO GIJUTSU KENKYUSHO HOKOKU/NATIONAL INSTITUTE OF SERICULTURAL AND ENTOMOLOGICAL SCIENCE. BULLETIN. Text in Japanese. 1990. irreg. (1-2/yr).
Indexed: BIOSIS Prev, BiolAb, RefZh, ZooRec.
—BLDSC (2640.532000).
Published by: National Institute of Sericultural and Entomological Science, 1-2 Owashi, Tsukuba-shi, Ibaraki-ken 305-0851, Japan.

595.7 JPN ISSN 0915-2679
SF542.75.J3
SANSHI. KONCHU NOGYO GIJUTSU KENKYUSHO SHIRYO/NATIONAL INSTITUTE OF SERICULTURAL AND ENTOMOLOGICAL SCIENCE. MISCELLANEOUS PUBLICATION. Text in Japanese. 1989. irreg.
Indexed: RevApplEntom, ZooRec.
Published by: National Institute of Sericultural and Entomological Science, 1-2 Owashi, Tsukuba-shi, Ibaraki-ken 305-0851, Japan.

595.7 JPN ISSN 0910-5131
SATSUMA/KAGOSHIMA ENTOMOLOGICAL SOCIETY. RESEARCH REPORT. Text in Japanese. 1952. s-a. membership.
Published by: Kagoshima Konchu Dokokai/Kagoshima Entomological Society, Sameshima Hifuka, 8-8 Komatsubara 1-chome, Kagoshima-shi, 891-0114, Japan.

595.7 FRA ISSN 0250-3980
SERICOLOGIA. Text in French. 1949. irreg.
Formerly (until 1977): Revue du Ver a Soie (0250-3999)
Published by: Commission Sericole Internationale, 25, quai Jean-Jacques-Rousseau, La Mulatiere, 69350, France. TEL 33-4-7850-4198, FAX 33-4-7886-0957.

595.7 NLD ISSN 0924-4611
CODEN: SEENAF
➤ **SERIES ENTOMOLOGICA.** Text in Dutch. 1966. irreg., latest vol.57, 2003. price varies. **Document type:** *Monographic series, Academic/Scholarly.*
Indexed: BiolAb, ChemAb, ChemTitl, ZooRec.
—BLDSC (8250.158000), ingenta. **CCC.**
Published by: Springer-Verlag Dordrecht (Subsidiary of: Springer Science+Business Media), Van Godewijckstraat 30, Dordrecht, 3311 GX, Netherlands. TEL 31-78-6576050, FAX 31-78-6576474, http://www.springeronline.com.

595.4 EGY ISSN 1110-502X
➤ **SERKET**: the arachnological bulletin of the Middle East and North Africa. Text in English. 1987. s-a. USD 25 for 2 yrs. to individuals; USD 35 for 2 yrs. to institutions (effective 2002 - 2003). back issues avail. **Document type:** *Journal, Academic/Scholarly.*
Indexed: EntAb, ZooRec.
Address: 41, El-Manteqa El-Rabia St, Heliopolis, Cairo, 11341, Egypt. TEL 202-6371164, el_hennawy@hotmail.com, http://groups.msn.com/serket. Ed., Pub. Col. Hisham K. El-Hennawy.

595.7 ESP ISSN 1134-7783
➤ **SESSIO CONJUNTA D'ENTOMOLOGIA.** Text in Spanish, Catalan; Summaries in Spanish, Catalan, English. 1980. biennial, latest vol.11, 1999. EUR 36 membership (effective 2002). back issues avail. **Document type:** *Bulletin, Academic/Scholarly.*
Indexed: ZooRec.
Published by: Societat Catalana de Lepidopterologia, Apartat de Correus 35049, Barcelona, 08080, Spain. eolivell@pic.xtec.es, http://www.iec.es/ichn. Circ: 500. **Co-sponsor:** Institucio Catalana d"Historia Natural.

595.7 JPN ISSN 0388-9491
SHIROARI/TERMITE. Text in Japanese. 1962. q.
Published by: Nihon Shiroari Taisaku Kyokai/Japan Termite Control Association, 2-9 Shinjuku 1-chome, Shinjuku-ku, Tokyo, 160-0022, Japan.

595.7 CZE ISSN 1211-7420
SILVA GABRETA; scientific studies from the Bohemian Forest. Text in Czech, English, German; Abstracts in English. 1997. a. EUR 20 in Europe; EUR 25 elsewhere (effective 2003).
Indexed: ASFA, ESPM, EntAb, SWRA.
Address: Susicka 399, Kasperske Hory, 34192, Czech Republic. TEL 420-376528731, FAX 420-376582493, silva.gabreta@npsumava.cz, vrba@hbu.cas.cz, http://www.npsumava.cz/stranky.php?idc=470. Eds. Jiri Manek, Libor Dvorak, Jaroslav Vrba TEL 420-387775872.

595.7 ESP ISSN 1578-1666
SOCIEDAD ANDALUZA DE ENTOMOLOGIA. BOLETIN. Text in Spanish. 2001. q.
Indexed: ZooRec.
Published by: Sociedad Andaluza de Entomologia, Avd del Corregidor 4, Cordoba, 14004, Spain. TEL 957-293086.

595.7 ESP ISSN 1134-6094
SOCIEDAD ENTOMOLOGICA ARAGONESA. BOLETIN. Key Title: Boletin de la S E A. Text in Spanish. 1993. q.
Related titles: Online - full text ed.: Aracnet. 1990; ◆ Supplement(s): Catalogus de la Entomofauna Aragonesa. ISSN 1134-6108.
Indexed: BioCN&I, ForAb, HortAb, IECT, IndVet, PN&I, RA&MP, S&F, VetBull, ZooRec.
—CINDOC.
Published by: Sociedad Entomologica Aragonesa, Ave. Radio Juventud, 37, Zaragoza, 50012, Spain. TEL 34-976-324415, FAX 34-976-535697, amelic@retemail.es, http://entomologia.rediris.es/sea/index.htm.

595.7 ARG ISSN 1515-1557
SOCIEDAD ENTOMOLOGICA ARGENTINA. BOLETIN INFORMATIVO. Cover title: S E A. Text in Spanish. 1987. s-a. USD 35 membership professionals; USD 15 membership students (effective 2002).
Indexed: ASFA, EntAb.
Published by: Sociedad Entomologica Argentina, Superior Institute of Entomologia, Miguel Lillo 205, S.M of Tucuman, 4000, Argentina. TEL 54-381-4230056, FAX 54-381-4248025.

595.7 ARG ISSN 0373-5680
QL481.A74
SOCIEDAD ENTOMOLOGICA ARGENTINA. REVISTA. Text in Spanish. 1926. s-a.
Indexed: ASFA, AgBio, BIOSIS Prev, BioCN&I, BiolAb, EntAb, ForAb, HGA, HortAb, IndVet, MaizeAb, NemAb, PoultAb, ProtozoAb, RPP, SeedAb, SoyAb, VetBull, WeedAb, ZooRec.
—Linda Hall.
Published by: Sociedad Entomologica Argentina, Superior Institute of Entomologia, Miguel Lillo 205, S.M of Tucuman, 4000, Argentina.

595.7 PRT ISSN 0870-7227
CODEN: BTIPEV
SOCIEDADE PORTUGUESA DE ENTOMOLOGIA. BOLETIM. Text in English, Portuguese. 1979. irreg.
Related titles: ◆ Supplement(s): Sociedade Portuguesa de Entomologia. Boletim. Suplemento. ISSN 0871-0554.
Indexed: ASFA, AgBio, B&BAb, BIOSIS Prev, BioCN&I, BiolAb, ESPM, EntAb, FCA, ForAb, GenetAb, HerbAb, HortAb, IndVet, PHN&I, ZooRec.
Published by: Sociedade Portuguesa de Entomologia, Apdo 8221, Lisbon, 1800, Portugal.

595.7 PRT ISSN 0871-0554
SOCIEDADE PORTUGUESA DE ENTOMOLOGIA. BOLETIM. SUPLEMENTO. Text in English, Portuguese. 1985. irreg. **Document type:** *Monographic series.*
Related titles: ◆ Supplement to: Sociedade Portuguesa de Entomologia. Boletim. ISSN 0870-7227.
Indexed: ASFA, BIOSIS Prev, BiolAb, EntAb, ZooRec.
Published by: Sociedade Portuguesa de Entomologia, Apdo 8221, Lisbon, 1800, Portugal.

595.7 ITA ISSN 0373-3491
QL461 CODEN: BENIAS
SOCIETA ENTOMOLOGICA ITALIANA. BOLLETTINO. Text in English, French, German, Italian; Summaries in English. 1869. 3/yr. price varies. bk.rev. **Document type:** *Bulletin, Academic/Scholarly.*
Formerly (until 1922): Societa Entomologica Italiana. Bullettino (1126-277X)
Indexed: ASFA, AgrForAb, BIOSIS Prev, BioCN&I, BiolAb, EntAb, FPA, ForAb, HGA, HerbAb, HortAb, PHN&I, RevApplEntom, WeedAb, ZooRec.
—Linda Hall.
Published by: Societa Entomologica Italiana, Via Brigata Liguria, 9, Genoa, GE 16121, Italy. http://www.socentomit.it.

595.7 ITA ISSN 0037-8747
SOCIETA ENTOMOLOGICA ITALIANA. MEMORIE. Text in Italian. 1922. a. price varies. **Document type:** *Monographic series, Academic/Scholarly.*
Indexed: ASFA, BIOSIS Prev, BiolAb, EntAb, HGA, PoultAb, RevApplEntom, S&F, ZooRec.
—CISTI, Linda Hall.
Published by: Societa Entomologica Italiana, Via Brigata Liguria, 9, Genoa, GE 16121, Italy. http://www.socentomit.it.

595.78 ESP ISSN 1132-7669
➤ **SOCIETAT CATALANA DE LEPIDOPTEROLOGIA. BULLETI.** Text in Catalan, Spanish; Summaries in English, Catalan, Spanish. 1977. s-a. EUR 36 membership (effective 2002). bk.rev. bibl. back issues avail. **Document type:** *Bulletin, Academic/Scholarly.* **Description:** Devoted to the study of biology, faunistics, distribution, taxonomy, and systematics of Catalonian lepidoptera.
Formerly (until 1979): Comissio de Lepidopterologia. Comunicacions (1132-7650)
Indexed: ZooRec.
Published by: Societat Catalana de Lepidopterologia, Apartat de Correus 35049, Barcelona, 08080, Spain. eolivell@pic.xtec.es, http://www.iec.es/ichn. Ed. Jordi Dantart. Circ: 150 (paid); 100 (controlled).

595.78 ESP ISSN 0210-6159
➤ **SOCIETAT CATALANA DE LEPIDOPTEROLOGIA. TREBALLS.** Text in Spanish, Catalan. 1978. irreg., latest vol.15, 2000. EUR 36 membership (effective 2002). back issues avail. **Document type:** *Bulletin, Academic/Scholarly.*
Indexed: ZooRec.
Published by: Societat Catalana de Lepidopterologia, Apartat de Correus 35049, Barcelona, 08080, Spain. eolivell@pic.xtec.es, http://www.iec.es/ichn. Circ: 250.

595.7 ROM ISSN 1221-5244
SOCIETATEA LEPIDOPTEROLOGICA ROMANA. BULETIN DE INFORMARE/ROMANIAN LEPIDOPTEROLOGICAL SOCIETY. INFORMATION BULLETIN. Text in Romany. 1990. q.
Published by: Societatea Lepidopterologica Romana/Romanian Lepidopterological Society, Republicii 48, Cluj, 3400, Romania. TEL 40-64-191238.

595.7 FRA ISSN 0037-9271
QL461 CODEN: ASEQAQ
➤ **SOCIETE ENTOMOLOGIQUE DE FRANCE. ANNALES.** Text and summaries in English, French, Italian, Spanish. 1832. q. adv. bk.rev. illus. index. **Document type:** *Academic/Scholarly.*
Related titles: Microfiche ed.: (from IDC).
Indexed: AEA, ASCA, AgBio, AgrForAb, ApicAb, BIOSIS Prev, BioCN&I, BiolAb, CurCont, ExcerpMed, FCA, FaBeAb, ForAb, HelmAb, HortAb, IBR, MaizeAb, NemAb, OrnHort, PBA, PHN&I, PotatoAb, ProtozoAb, RM&VM, RPP, RRTA, RevApplEntom, S&F, SCI, SeedAb, TDB, TriticAb, VITIS, ZooRec.
—BLDSC (0947.000000), CISTI, IE, Infotrieve, ingenta, Linda Hall. **CCC.**
Published by: Societe Entomologique, C.C.P. 4424-45 Z Paris, 45 rue Buffon, Paris, 75005, France. TEL 33-1-40794300, FAX 33-1-40493699. Ed. Jacques Bitsch. Adv. contact Helene Perrin. Circ: 800.

595.7 FRA ISSN 0037-928X
CODEN: SOROEL
➤ **SOCIETE ENTOMOLOGIQUE DE FRANCE. BULLETIN.** Text and summaries in English, French, German, Spanish. 1846. 5/yr. bk.rev. charts; illus.; bibl. **Document type:** *Bulletin, Academic/Scholarly.* **Description:** Covers issues and explorations in the fields of entomology, ecology and biology.
Related titles: Microfiche ed.: (from BHP).
Indexed: ASFA, AbHyg, AgrForAb, BIOSIS Prev, BioCN&I, BiolAb, FCA, FaBeAb, ForAb, HGA, HerbAb, HortAb, IndVet, NutrAb, OrnHort, PBA, PotatoAb, RM&VM, RefZh, RevApplEntom, RiceAb, S&F, SPPI, TDB, ZooRec.
—CISTI. **CCC.**
Published by: Societe Entomologique, C.C.P. 4424-45 Z Paris, 45 rue Buffon, Paris, 75005, France. TEL 33-1-40793384, FAX 33-1-40793699, jpierre@mnhn.fr. Pub. Jacques Pierre. Circ: 950.

595.7 FRA ISSN 0373-4544
SOCIETE ENTOMOLOGIQUE DE MULHOUSE. BULLETIN. Text in French. 1894. q. EUR 33 (effective 2002). bk.rev. **Document type:** *Bulletin.* **Description:** Biology, systematics, new descriptions of all orders of insects.

Indexed: ZooRec.
Published by: Societe Entomologique de Mulhouse, 35 place de la Reunion, Mulhouse, 68100, France.

595.7 CAN ISSN 0071-0784
CODEN: SEQMA4
SOCIETE ENTOMOLOGIQUE DU QUEBEC. MEMOIRES. Text in French; Summaries in English. 1968. irreg. illus.
Indexed: BiolAb.
—CISTI, Linda Hall.
Published by: Societe Entomologique du Quebec, c/o Claude Bouchard, Treas, Scientific Complex D 1 300, 2700 rue Einstein, Ste Foy, Quebec, PQ G1P 3W8, Canada. TEL 418-656-2131.

595.7 BEL ISSN 1374-8297
SOCIETE ROYALE BELGE D'ENTOMOLOGIE. BULLETIN. Text in French, Dutch, English. a. **Document type:** *Bulletin.*
Indexed: AbHyg, BIOSIS Prev, BioCN&I, BiolAb, EntAb, FCA, ForAb, GenetAb, HerbAb, HortAb, MaizeAb, PoultAb, RefZh, S&F, TriticAb, ZooRec.
—CISTI.
Published by: Societe Royale Belge d'Entomologie/Royal Belgian Entomological Society, Vautierstraat 29, Brussels, 1000, Belgium. TEL 32-2-6274132, srbe@naturalsciences.be. Ed. Isabelle Coppee.

595.7 BEL ISSN 0376-2025
SOCIETE ROYALE BELGE D'ENTOMOLOGIE. MEMOIRES. Text in French. 1806. irreg., latest vol.40, 2002. price varies.
Description: Contains revisionary works on world invertebrates and studies dealing with entomological problems.
Indexed: BIOSIS Prev, BiolAb, RevApplEntom, ZooRec.
—CISTI.
Published by: Societe Royal Belge d'Entomologie, rue Vautierstraat 29, Brussels, 1000, Belgium. srbe@sciencesnaturelles.be, http://www.kbinirsnb.be/srbe/societe3.htm.

595.7 ZAF ISSN 0255-0180
CODEN: RAAEAV
SOUTH AFRICA. DEPARTMENT OF AGRICULTURE. ENTOMOLOGY MEMOIR. Text in English. 1923. irreg. (approx. 4/yr.). price varies. charts; illus.; stat. **Document type:** *Government.*
Former titles: South Africa. Department of Agriculture and Fisheries. Entomology Memoirs (0370-3096); (until 1980): South Africa. Department of Agricultural Technical Services. Entomology Memoirs (0013-8940)
Indexed: BioCN&I, BiolAb, FPA, ForAb, RevApplEntom.
—Linda Hall.
Published by: Department of Agriculture, Private Bag X144, Pretoria, 0001, South Africa. TEL 27-12-3197141, FAX 27-12-3232516. Ed. Ronelle Hechter. Circ: 700.

595.7 USA ISSN 0147-1724
QL475.S68 CODEN: SENTDD
➤ **SOUTHWESTERN ENTOMOLOGIST.** Text in English. 1976. q. free to members. bibl.; charts; illus.; stat. index. back issues avail. **Document type:** *Journal, Academic/Scholarly.*
Description: Contains scientific research.
Related titles: ♦ Supplement(s): Southwestern Entomologist. Supplement. ISSN 1055-8799.
Indexed: AEA, ASCA, ASFA, AgBio, Agr, AgrForAb, AnBeAb, BIOBASE, BIOSIS Prev, BioCN&I, BiolAb, CIN, CPA, CTFA, ChemAb, ChemTitl, CurCont, DBA, EntAb, FCA, FPA, ForAb, HGA, HerbAb, HortAb, IABS, ISR, IndVet, MaizeAb, OrnHort, PBA, PGegResA, PHN&I, PlantSci, PoultAb, ProtozoAb, RA&MP, RM&VM, RPP, RefZh, RevApplEntom, RiceAb, S&F, S&MA, SCI, SIA, SeedAb, SoyAb, TDB, TOSA, TriticAb, VITIS, VetBull, WAE&RSA, WeedAb, ZooRec.
—BLDSC (8357.160000), CASDDS, IDS, IE, Infotrieve, ingenta, Linda Hall.
Published by: Society of Southwestern Entomologists, 17360 Coit Rd, Dallas, TX 75252. TEL 972-952-9222, FAX 972-952-9632, http://sswe.tamu.edu. Ed. D Bay. Circ: 471.

595.7 USA ISSN 1055-8799
QL475.S68 CODEN: SSOED3
➤ **SOUTHWESTERN ENTOMOLOGIST. SUPPLEMENT.** Text in English. irreg. free to members. **Document type:** *Academic/Scholarly.* **Description:** Contains scientific research.
Formerly (until 1989): Supplement to the Southwestern Entomologist (0277-7878)
Related titles: ♦ Supplement to: Southwestern Entomologist. ISSN 0147-1724.
Indexed: Agr, BIOSIS Prev, BiolAb, CIS, ZooRec.
—BLDSC (8357.160100), CASDDS, Linda Hall.
Published by: Society of Southwestern Entomologists, 17360 Coit Rd, Dallas, TX 75252. TEL 972-952-9222, FAX 972-952-9632, http://sswe.tamu.edu. Ed. D Bay.

595.7 DEU ISSN 0373-8981
QL461 CODEN: SMTEBI
STAATLICHES MUSEUM FUER TIERKUNDE DRESDEN. ENTOMOLOGISCHE ABHANDLUNGEN. Text in English, French, German. 1961. a. price varies. bk.rev. index. back issues avail. **Document type:** *Academic/Scholarly.*
Description: Explores taxonomy, systematics, morphology, bionomics, ecology and zoogeography of Insecta and Arachnida.
Indexed: BIOSIS Prev, BiolAb, IBR, RefZh, ZooRec.
—CISTI, Linda Hall. **CCC.**
Published by: Staatliche Naturhistorische Sammlungen Dresden, Museum fuer Tierkunde, Augustusstr 2, Dresden, 01067, Germany. tk@snsd.de, http://www.snsd.de/mtd_info.htm. Ed. Rainer Emmrich. Circ: 550.

595.7 DEU ISSN 0945-3954
➤ **STUDIA DIPTEROLOGICA.** Text in German. 1994. 2/yr. EUR 55 domestic; EUR 60 foreign (effective 2005). bk.rev.
Document type: *Journal, Academic/Scholarly.* **Description:** Publishes original papers on dipterologica.
Related titles: ♦ Supplement(s): Studia Dipterologica. Supplement. ISSN 1433-4968.
Indexed: AgBio, AgrForAb, BioCN&I, ForAb, HerbAb, HortAb, IndVet, OrnHort, PN&I, PoultAb, RM&VM, RPP, RefZh, RevApplEntom, S&F, TDB, VetBull, WeedAb, ZooRec.
—BLDSC (8482.385400).
Published by: Ampyx Verlag, Seebener Str 190, Halle, 06114, Germany. TEL 49-345-5226726, FAX 49-345-5226726, stark@ampyx-verlag.de, http://www.studia-dipt.de. Eds. Andreas Stark, Frank Menzel.

595.7 DEU ISSN 1433-4968
STUDIA DIPTEROLOGICA. SUPPLEMENT. Text in German; Summaries in English. 1997. irreg., latest vol.3, 1998.
Document type: *Monographic series, Academic/Scholarly.*
Description: Aims to publish longer monographic contributions on dipterologica.
Related titles: ♦ Supplement to: Studia Dipterologica. ISSN 0945-3954.
Indexed: RM&VM, RevApplEntom, ZooRec.
Published by: Ampyx Verlag, Seebener Str 190, Halle, 06114, Germany. TEL 49-345-5226726, FAX 49-345-5226726, stark@ampyx-verlag.de. Eds. Andreas Stark, Frank Menzel.

595.7 JPN ISSN 0915-7883
SURUGA NO KONCHU/INSECTS IN SURUGA. Text in Japanese. 1953. q. JPY 2,600 domestic; JPY 3,000 foreign; JPY 650 per issue domestic; JPY 750 per issue foreign (effective 2000).
Document type: *Bulletin.*
Published by: Shizuoka Konchu Dokokai/Shizuoka Entomological Society, c/o Mr Takahashi, 13-11 Kita-Ando 5-chome, Shizuoka-shi, 420-0881, Japan. TEL 81-54-245-6901. Ed. Mayumi Takahashi.

595.42 GBR ISSN 1362-1971
➤ **SYSTEMATIC AND APPLIED ACAROLOGY.** Text in English. 1996. a. USD 35 to individuals; USD 78 to institutions (effective 2004). **Document type:** *Journal, Academic/Scholarly.* **Description:** Publishes research papers from around the world on all aspects of mites and ticks.
Indexed: AgBio, AgrForAb, BioCN&I, DSA, FCA, ForAb, HortAb, IndVet, MaizeAb, NutrAb, OrnHort, PBA, PHN&I, PotatoAb, RA&MP, RDA, RPP, RiceAb, S&F, TDB, TriticAb, VetBull, WAE&RSA, WeedAb, ZooRec.
—BLDSC (8589.175900), IE, ingenta.
Published by: Systematic and Applied Acarology Society, c/o Dr. Anne S. Baker, Dep. of Entomology, Natural History Museum, London, SW7 5BD, United Kingdom. saas@acarology.org, http://www.nhm.ac.uk/hosted_sites/acarology/saas/saa.html. Ed. Zhi-Qiang Zhang.

595.42 GBR ISSN 1461-0183
➤ **SYSTEMATIC AND APPLIED ACAROLOGY SPECIAL PUBLICATIONS.** Text in English. 1997. irreg. **Document type:** *Monographic series, Academic/Scholarly.*
Indexed: BIOSIS Prev, BioCN&I, BiolAb, ForAb, HerbAb, HortAb, IndVet, PGegResA, RA&MP, S&F, TDB, VetBull, ZooRec.
Published by: Systematic and Applied Acarology Society, c/o Dr. Anne S. Baker, Dep. of Entomology, Natural History Museum, London, SW7 5BD, United Kingdom. http://www.nhm.ac.uk/hosted_sites/acarology/saas/saasp.html. Ed. Zhi-Qiang Zhang.

595.7 GBR ISSN 0307-6970
QL461 CODEN: SYENDM
➤ **SYSTEMATIC ENTOMOLOGY.** Text in English. 1976. q. GBP 158, EUR 216 combined subscription in Europe to individuals print & online eds.; USD 292 combined subscription in the Americas to individuals & Carribean, print & online eds.; GBP 174 combined subscription elsewhere to individuals print & online eds.; GBP 680 combined subscription in Europe to institutions print & online eds.; USD 1,257 combined subscription in the Americas to institutions & Carribean, print & online eds.; GBP 748 combined subscription elsewhere to institutions print & online eds. (effective 2006). adv. bk.rev. illus. Index. back issues avail.; reprint service avail. from ISI.
Document type: *Journal, Academic/Scholarly.* **Description:** Publishes original contributions to insect taxonomy and systematics.
Formerly: Journal of Entomology (B) (0047-2417)
Related titles: Microform ed.: (from PQC); ♦ Online - full text ed.: Systematic Entomology Online. ISSN 1365-3113.
Indexed: ASCA, ASFA, AbHyg, AgBio, Agr, AgrForAb, ApicAb, B&BAb, BIOBASE, BIOSIS Prev, BioCN&I, BiolAb, CurCont, ESPM, EntAb, ForAb, GEOBASE, GenetAb, HGA, HerbAb, ISR, IndVet, PBA, PGegResA, PoultAb, ProtozoAb, RM&VM, RevApplEntom, RiceAb, S&F, SCI, SIA, TDB, VetBull, WildRev, ZooRec.
—BLDSC (8589.184000), CISTI, IDS, IE, Infotrieve, ingenta, Linda Hall. **CCC.**
Published by: (Royal Entomological Society), Blackwell Publishing Ltd., 9600 Garsington Rd, Oxford, OX4 2ZG, United Kingdom. TEL 44-1865-776868, FAX 44-1865-714591, customerservices@oxon.blackwellpublishing.com, http://www.blackwellpublishing.com/journals/SEN. Eds. Frank-Thorsten Krell, Peter S Cranston. Pub. Sue Hewitt. R&P Sophie Savage. Adv. contact Jenny Applin. Circ: 635.

595.7 GBR ISSN 1365-3113
➤ **SYSTEMATIC ENTOMOLOGY ONLINE.** Text in English. 1998. q. GBP 646 in Europe to institutions; USD 1,193 in the Americas to institutions & Caribbean; GBP 710 elsewhere to institutions (effective 2006). **Document type:** *Academic/Scholarly.*
Media: Online - full text (from Blackwell Synergy, EBSCO Publishing, Gale Group, IngentaConnect, O C L C Online Computer Library Center, Inc., Swets Information Services).
Related titles: Microform ed.: (from PQC); ♦ Print ed.: Systematic Entomology. ISSN 0307-6970.
Published by: Blackwell Publishing Ltd., 9600 Garsington Rd, Oxford, OX4 2ZG, United Kingdom. TEL 44-1865-776868, FAX 44-1865-714591, customerservices@oxon.blackwellpublishing.com, http://www.blackwellpublishing.com.

595.7 TWN ISSN 1680-7650
TAIWAN KUNCHONG/FORMOSAN ENTOMOLOGIST. Text in Chinese. 1981. q. **Document type:** *Journal, Academic/Scholarly.*
Indexed: AbHyg, AgBio, AgrForAb, BioCN&I, CPA, FCA, ForAb, HelmAb, HortAb, PBA, PGegResA, PHN&I, PotatoAb, ProtozoAb, S&F, SeedAb.
Published by: Taiwan Kunchong Xuehui/Taiwan Entomological Society, 113-27, Roosevelt Rd, Section 4, Tapei, Taiwan.

595.7 JPN ISSN 0917-3102
TATEHAMODOKI/MIYAZAKI ENTOMOLOGICAL SOCIETY. JOURNAL. Text in Japanese. a.
Indexed: ZooRec.
Published by: Miyazaki Konchu Dokokai/Miyazaki Entomological Society, Miyazakiken Sogo Hakubutsukan, 4-4 Jingu 2-chome, Miyazaki-shi, 880-0053, Japan.

595.7 NLD ISSN 0040-7496
CODEN: TCMUD8
TIJDSCHRIFT VOOR ENTOMOLOGIE. Text in Dutch, English, French, German. 1858. s-a. EUR 36.50 domestic to members; EUR 46.50 foreign to members (effective 2005). charts; illus.
Document type: *Academic/Scholarly.*
Indexed: ASFA, AgBio, BIOSIS Prev, BioCN&I, BiolAb, EntAb, ForAb, PBA, RM&VM, RevApplEntom, TriticAb, ZooRec.
—BLDSC (8841.000000), CISTI, IE, Infotrieve, ingenta, Linda Hall. **CCC.**
Published by: Nederlandse Entomologische Vereniging, Plantage Middenlaan 64, Amsterdam, 1018 DH, Netherlands. tev@nev.nl, http://www.nev.nl/tve/index.html. Ed. E J van Nieukerken.

595.7 JPN ISSN 0493-3168
TINEA. Text in English; Summaries in Japanese. 1953. irreg.
Indexed: ZooRec.
Published by: Japan Heterocerists' Society/Nihon Garui Gakkai, Kokuritsu Kagaku Hakubutsukan Bunkan, Hiyakunin-cho 3-chome, Shinjuku-ku, Tokyo, 169-0073, Japan.

595.7 JPN
TOBU/HYAKUMANGOKU BUTTERFLY STUDY GROUP. NEWS. Text in Japanese. bi-m.
Published by: Hyakumangoku Chodankai/Hyakumangoku Butterfly Study Group, c/o Mr Matsui, 871-15 Obamachi Higashi, Kanazawa-shi, Ishikawa-ken 920-01, Japan.

595.7 JPN ISSN 0913-5847
TOHOKU KONCHU/JOURNAL OF ENTOMOLOGY IN TOHOKU DISTRICT. Text in Japanese. 1964. a.
Published by: Nihon Konchu Gakkai, Tohoku Shibu/Entomological Society of Japan, Tohoku Branch, Tohoku Gakui Daigaku Kyoyogakubu, Seibutsugaku Kenkyushitsu, 9-1 Tenjinzawa-Ichinazaka, Izumi-ku, Sendai-shi, Miyagi-ken 981-3100, Japan.

595.7333 JPN ISSN 0495-8314
TOMBO/ACTA ODONATOLOGICA. Text in English, Japanese. 1958. a. membership.
Indexed: ZooRec.
Published by: Nihon Tonbo Gakkai/Society of Odonatology, Tokyo, c/o Mr Shojiro Asahina, 4-24 Takadanobaba 4-chome, Shinjuku-ku, Tokyo, 160-0000, Japan.

595.7 JPN ISSN 1342-1263
TOYOSATO MUSEUM OF ENTOMOLOGY. BULLETIN. Text in English. 1992. a. free. illus. back issues avail. **Document type:** *Bulletin, Academic/Scholarly.* **Description:** Publishes research in all areas of entomology.
Indexed: ZooRec.
Published by: Toyosato Museum of Entomology/Tsukuba-shi Yukari-no-mori Konchukan, 676 To-Higashi, Tsukuba-shi, Ibaraki-ken 300-2633, Japan. TEL 81-29-847-5061, FAX 81-29-847-0044. Ed. Yoshinobu Uemura.

B

595.76 USA ISSN 0082-6391
QL596.T2
TRIBOLIUM INFORMATION BULLETIN. Text in English. 1958. a. USD 29 to individuals; USD 31 to institutions (effective 2000). **Document type:** *Newsletter.* **Description:** Contains research, teaching, and technical notes on beetles; covers wild type and mutant stocks in laboratories throughout the world. Includes personal and geographical directories and current bibliography on all aspects of research on Tribolium and other Coleoptera.
Related titles: Microfilm ed.
Indexed: ZooRec.
Published by: California State University, San Bernardino, School of Natural Sciences, 5500 Universtiy Parkway, San Bernardino, CA 92407. TEL 909-880-5305, FAX 909-880-5407. Ed. A Sokoloff. Circ: 85.

595.78 USA ISSN 1048-8138
QL560.6 CODEN: TRLEER
➤ **TROPICAL LEPIDOPTERA.** Text in English, French, German, Portuguese, Spanish. 1990. s-a. USD 45 (effective 2005); . adv. bibl.; illus.; tr.lit. index, cum.index. Supplement avail.; back issues avail. **Document type:** *Journal, Academic/Scholarly.* **Description:** General taxonomy and conservation of tropical and subtropical moths and butterflies.
Indexed: ASFA, BIOSIS Prev, BioCN&I, BiolAb, EntAb, ForAb, MaizeAb, RefZh, RevApplEntom, ZooRec.
—BLDSC (9056.320000), IE, ingenta, Linda Hall.
Published by: Association for Tropical Lepidoptera, PO Box 141210, Gainesville, FL 32614-1210. TEL 352-392-5894, FAX 352-373-3249, jbhatl@aol.com, http://www.troplep.org/tl.htm, http://www.troplep.org/atl.htm. Ed. J B Heppner. Circ: 1,250.

B

595.78 JPN
TSUISO/WEEKLY BUTTERFLY'S TSUISO. Text in Japanese. 1975. 3/m. JPY 300 per issue.
Published by: Mokuyosha, 53-15-402 Eifuku 3-chome, Suginami-ku, Tokyo, 168-0064, Japan. TEL 81-3-3324-1153. Ed. Yasusuke Nishiyama.

595.7 COL ISSN 0121-733X
UNIVERSIDAD DEL VALLE. MUSEO DE ENTOMOLOGIA. BOLETIN. Text in Spanish. 1993. a.
Indexed: ZooRec.
Published by: Universidad del Valle, Museo de Entomologia, Ciudad Universitaria-Melendez, Edificio 320, espacio 3061, Cali, Colombia. TEL 57-2-3212100, http://entomologia.univalle.edu.co/.

UNIVERSITATEA DE STIINTE AGRONOMICE SI MEDICINA VETERINARA. LUCRARI STIINTIFICE. SERIA A, AGRONOMIE. see *AGRICULTURE—Crop Production And Soil*

595.7 USA ISSN 0068-6417
QL461 CODEN: UCPEAH
➤ **UNIVERSITY OF CALIFORNIA PUBLICATIONS IN ENTOMOLOGY.** Text in English. 1906. irreg., latest vol.124, 2005. price varies. back issues avail. **Document type:** *Monographic series, Academic/Scholarly.* **Description:** Researches the biology of various insect species from all parts of the world.
Indexed: AbHyg, BIOSIS Prev, BiolAb, RM&VM, RevApplEntom, TDB, ZooRec.
—CISTI, Linda Hall. **CCC.**
Published by: University of California Press, Book Series, 2120 Berkeley Way, Berkeley, CA 94720. TEL 510-642-4247, FAX 510-643-7127, askucp@ucpress.edu, http://www.ucpress.edu/books/UCENT.ser.html, http://www.ucpress.edu/books/series.html. **Orders to:** California - Princeton Fulfillment Services, 1445 Lower Ferry Rd, Ewing, NJ 08618. TEL 800-777-4726, FAX 800-999-1958, orders@cpfs.pupress.princeton.edu.

595.78 NLD ISSN 0923-1846
VLINDERS. Text in Dutch; Summaries in English. 1986. q. adv. bk.rev. bibl.; charts; illus.; stat. back issues avail. **Description:** Provides information on butterflies in the Netherlands and Flanders, Belgium. Covers occurance, ecology, management information on conservation, and research and policy issues.
Indexed: ZooRec.
Published by: De Vlinderstichting, PO Box 506, Wageningen, 6700 AM, Netherlands. TEL 31-317-467346, FAX 31-317-420296, info@vlinderstichting.nl, http://www.vlinderstichting.nl.

595.774 DEU ISSN 0947-9538
VOLUCELLA. Text in English, German. 1995. a. EUR 20 (effective 2005). **Document type:** *Journal, Academic/Scholarly.* **Description:** Covers all aspects concerning Syrphidae (hoverflies), especially from the fields of taxonomy, systematics, morphology, ecology, ethology, biogeography, faunistics, and conservation.
Indexed: ASFA, ESPM, ZooRec.
Published by: Dieter Doczkal, Ed. & Pub., Koenigsberger Str 4, Malsch, 76316, Germany. ulrich.schmid.SMNS@naturkundemuseum-bw.de, http://www.naturkundemuseum-bw.de/stuttgart/volucella/. **Co-publisher:** Ulrich Schmid, Ed. & Pub.

595.7 NZL ISSN 0111-7696
THE WETA; news bulletin. Text in English. 1977. s-a. NZD 10 domestic; USD 10 foreign (effective 2001). back issues avail. **Document type:** *Bulletin.*
Indexed: BioCN&I, ForAb, HortAb, OrnHort, RevApplEntom, S&F, WeedAb, ZooRec.
Published by: Entomological Society of New Zealand, Mt Albert Research Centre, Private Bag 92169, Auckland, New Zealand. FAX 64-9-8497093, mplmjb@dslak.co.nz.

595.7 POL ISSN 0138-0737
WIADOMOSCI ENTOMOLOGICZNE/ENTOMOLOGICAL NEWS. Text in Polish. q.
Indexed: ASFA, AgrAg, AgrLib, BioCN&I, EntAb, ForAb, HerbAb, HortAb, OrnHort, RPP, RRTA, S&F, SeedAb, ZooRec.
Published by: Polskie Towarzystwo Entomologiczne/Polish Entomological Society, ul Sienkiewicza 21, Wroclaw, 50-335, Poland. TEL 48-71-3225041, http://www.au.poznan.pl/wydzialy/ogrodniczy/pte/index.html. **Subscr. to:** Biblioteka, ul Przybyszewskiego 63/77, Wroclaw 51-148, Poland. TEL 48-71-3247237.

WILDLIFE AUSTRALIA. see *CONSERVATION*

363.78 USA ISSN 1053-0738
WING BEATS OF THE AMERICAN MOSQUITO CONTROL ASSOCIATION. Text in English. 1990. q. USD 125 to non-members; USD 100 membership (effective 2003). **Document type:** *Journal, Academic/Scholarly.*
—Linda Hall.
Published by: American Mosquito Control Association, 681 Us Highway 1., N Brunswick, NJ 08902-3390. TEL 732-344-4645, FAX 732-542-3267, amca@mosquito.org, http://www.mosquito.org.

595.7 DNK ISSN 1398-8700
QL468
➤ **WORLD CATALOGUE OF INSECTS.** Text in English. 1998. irreg., latest vol.5, 2003. price varies. bibl.; illus. back issues avail. **Document type:** *Catalog, Academic/Scholarly.* **Description:** Features Worldscale, authoritative catalogues of monophyletic insect taxa containing standard nomenclatural information on all names pertaining to the taxon treated, including type locality and distribution to the extent this is relevant.
Indexed: BIOSIS Prev, ZooRec.
Published by: Apollo Books, Kirkeby Sand 19, Stenstrup, 5771, Denmark. TEL 45-62-26-37-37, FAX 45-62-26-37-80, apollobooks@vip.cybercity.dk, http://www.apollobooks.com. Ed. M Hansen.

➤ **WORLD CROP PESTS.** see *AGRICULTURE—Crop Production And Soil*

➤ **WORLDWIDE DIRECTORY OF AGROBIOLOGICALS ON CD-ROM.** see *AGRICULTURE*

595.7 JPN ISSN 0917-5695
YOSEGAKI/SAITAMA ENTOMOLOGIST'S ASSOCIATION. JOURNAL. Text in Japanese. 1963. q. JPY 3,000. **Document type:** *Proceedings.*
Published by: Saitama Konchu Danwakai/Saitama Entomologist's Association, c/o Mr Makibayashi, 2-864 Amanuma-cho, Omiya-shi, Saitama-ken 330-0834, Japan. TEL 81-48-642-4023. Ed. T Usui. Circ: 400.

595.7 JPN ISSN 0387-5695
YUGATO/JOURNAL OF RESEARCH ON MOTHS. Text in Japanese; Summaries in English. 1959. q. JPY 6,000 to members (effective 2000). bk.rev. **Document type:** *Bulletin.*
Indexed: ZooRec.
Published by: Yugakai/Yugato Society, c/o Dr. Rikio Sato, 2-27-29 Shindori-Nishi, Niigata-shi, 950-2036, Japan. TEL 81-25-262-5176, FAX 81-25-261-2936. Ed. Rikio Sato. Circ: 300.

595.7 ESP ISSN 1131-933X
QL461
ZAPATERI. Text in Spanish. 1991. a.
Indexed: ZooRec.
—CINDOC.
Published by: Sociedad Entomologica Aragonesa, Ave. Radio Juventud, 37, Zaragoza, 50012, Spain. TEL 34-976-324415, FAX 34-976-535697, amelic@retemail.es, http://entomologia.rediris.es/sea/zapateri/index.htm, http://entomologia.rediris.es/sea/index.htm.

ZEITSCHRIFT FUER PFLANZENKRANKHEITEN UND PFLANZENSCHUTZ. see *BIOLOGY—Botany*

595.7 DEU
QL461 CODEN: EMZMAJ
➤ **ZOOLOGISCHES INSTITUT UND ZOOLOGISCHES MUSEUM HAMBURG. ENTOMOLOGISCHE MITTEILUNGEN.** Text in English, German; Summaries in English. 1952. s-a. looseleaf. exchange basis. bk.rev. cum.index. back issues avail. **Document type:** *Academic/Scholarly.*
Formerly: Zoologisches Museum Hamburg. Entomologische Mitteilungen (0044-5223)
Indexed: ASFA, BIOSIS Prev, BioDAb, BiolAb, ESPM, ForAb, HortAb, IBR, IndVet, RM&VM, RPP, RefZh, RevApplEntom, TDB, VITIS, VetBull, ZooRec.
—BLDSC (3781.900000). **CCC.**
Published by: Zoologisches Institut und Zoologisches Museum Hamburg, Martin-Luther-King-Platz 3, Hamburg, 20146, Germany. FAX 49-40-428383937. Ed. H Struempel. Circ: 400. **Co-sponsor:** Universitaet Hamburg, Zoologisches Institut.

BIOLOGY—Genetics

571.6 576.5 USA
THE A G T CYTOGENETICS LABORATORY TECHNICAL MANUAL. (Association of Genetic Technologists) Text in English. irreg., latest vol.3, 1997. USD 159 per issue (effective 2004). **Description:** Provides an exhaustive survey of techniques for visualization and analysis of human chromosome patterns in diagnosis and research. Contains chapters on peripheral blood culture, continuous cell lines, prenatal diagnosis and culture, solid tumors, fragile sites, molecular cytogenetics etc.
Published by: (Association of Genetic Technologists), Lippincott Williams & Wilkins (Subsidiary of: Wolters Kluwer N.V.), 530 Walnut St, Philadelphia, PA 19106-3621. custserv@lww.com, http://www.lww.com.

576.5 SCG ISSN 0534-0012
QH431.A1 CODEN: GNTKDF
ACTA BIOLOGICA IUGOSLAVICA. SERIJA F: GENETIKA. Key Title: Genetika. Text in Serbo-Croatian. 1969. 3/yr. **Document type:** *Journal, Academic/Scholarly.*
Indexed: ChemAb, CurCont.
—CASDDS, CISTI, Linda Hall.
Published by: Drustvo Geneticara Srbije/Serbian Genetics Society, Nemanjina 6, PO Box 44, Belgrade.

576.5 URY ISSN 0797-6852
ACTA GENETICA ET TERATOLOGICA. Text in Spanish; Summaries in English. 1991. a. USD 20. illus. index. back issues avail. **Document type:** *Academic/Scholarly.*
Published by: Fernando Mane-Garzon, Ed. & Pub., Casilla de Correo 157, Montevideo, Uruguay. Circ: 500.

599.9 ITA ISSN 0001-5660
CODEN: AGMGAK
ACTA GENETICAE MEDICAE ET GEMELLOLOGIAE: TWIN RESEARCH. Text in Italian. 1952. q. adv. bk.rev. abstr.; bibl.; charts; illus. index. reprint service avail. from ISI. **Document type:** *Journal, Academic/Scholarly.*
Formerly (until 1979): Acta Geneticae Medicae et Gemellologiae (1120-9623)
Related titles: Microfilm ed.
Indexed: AICP, ASCA, AbAn, BIOSIS Prev, BiolAb, CurCont, DSA, DentInd, ExcerpMed, ISR, IndMed, MEDLINE, PsycInfo, PsycholAb, SCI, SSCI, e-psyche.
—BLDSC (0618.000000), CISTI, GNLM, IE, Infotrieve, KNAW.
Published by: Associazione Istituto di Genetica Medica e Gemellologia Gregorio Mendel, Piazza Galeno, 5, Rome, RM 00161, Italy. TEL 39-6-8554658, FAX 39-6-44291069, mendel@mclink.it, http://www.mendel.it. Ed. Luigi Gedda.

576.5 CZE ISSN 0085-0748
CODEN: FMDLAJ
ACTA MUSEI MORAVIAE. SUPPLEMENTUM: FOLIA MENDELIANA. Text in English, French, German; Summaries in English. 1966. a. USD 18 (effective 2000). **Document type:** *Academic/Scholarly.*
Related titles: ♦ Supplement to: Acta Musei Moraviae. Scientiae Biologicae. ISSN 1211-8788.
Indexed: AICP, BiolAb.
—KNAW, Linda Hall.
Published by: Moravske Zemske Muzeum, Zelny trh 6, Brno, 65937, Czech Republic. TEL 420-5-42321205, FAX 420-5-42212792, mzm@mzm.cz, http://www.mzm.cz. Ed. Anna Matalova.

ADVANCES IN CLINICAL AND EXPERIMENTAL MEDICINE. see *BIOLOGY—Biotechnology*

ADVANCES IN GENE TECHNOLOGY. see *BIOLOGY—Biotechnology*

576.5 USA ISSN 0065-2660
QH431.A1 CODEN: ADGEAV
➤ **ADVANCES IN GENETICS.** Text in English. 1947. irreg., latest vol.48, 2003. USD 139.95 vol.49 (effective 2004). reprint service avail. from ISI. **Document type:** *Monographic series, Academic/Scholarly.* **Description:** Publishes important reviews of the broadest interest to geneticists and their colleagues in affiliated disciplines.
Incorporates (1991-1995): Molecular Genetic Medicine (1057-2805)
Related titles: Online - full text ed.: (from ScienceDirect); ♦ Supplement(s): Advances in Genetics. Supplement. ISSN 0065-2679.
Indexed: ASCA, ASFA, AbHyg, Agr, AnBrAb, B&AI, B&BAb, BCI, BIOSIS Prev, BiolAb, CIN, CTFA, ChemAb, ChemTitl, DBA, GenetAb, HGA, ISR, IndMed, MEDLINE, PBA, PoultAb, RevApplEntom, SCI, SFA, TDB, Telegen.
—BLDSC (0708.000000), CASDDS, CISTI, GNLM, IE, ingenta, Linda Hall. **CCC.**

Published by: Academic Press (Subsidiary of: Elsevier Science & Technology), 525 B St, Ste 1900, San Diego, CA 92101-4495. TEL 619-231-6616, 800-894-3434, FAX 619-699-6422, apsubs@acad.com, http://www.academicpress.com. Ed. M Demerec.

576.5 USA ISSN 0065-2679
ADVANCES IN GENETICS. SUPPLEMENT. Text in English. 1966. irreg. price varies. **Document type:** *Monographic series.*
Related titles: ♦ Supplement to: Advances in Genetics. ISSN 0065-2660.
—CISTI, Linda Hall. **CCC.**
Published by: Academic Press (Subsidiary of: Elsevier Science & Technology), 525 B St, Ste 1900, San Diego, CA 92101-4495. TEL 619-231-6616, 800-894-3434, FAX 619-699-6422, apsubs@acad.com, http://www.academicpress.com.

599.9 USA ISSN 0065-275X
QH431.A1 CODEN: ADHGA8
➤ **ADVANCES IN HUMAN GENETICS.** Text in English. 1970. irreg., latest vol.22, 1994. price varies. **Document type:** *Monographic series, Academic/Scholarly.*
Indexed: ASCA, B&AI, BCI, BIOSIS Prev, BiolAb, CIN, ChemAb, ExcerpMed, IABS, ISR, IndMed, MEDLINE, SCI.
—CASDDS, CISTI, GNLM, IDS, Infotrieve, KNAW, Linda Hall. **CCC.**
Published by: Springer-Verlag New York, Inc. (Subsidiary of: Springer Science+Business Media), 233 Spring St, New York, NY 10013. TEL 212-460-1500, FAX 212-460-1575, service@springer-ny.com, http://www.springer-ny.com.

576.5 NGA ISSN 0795-6762
➤ **AFRICAN JOURNAL OF GENETICS.** Text in English. 1988. q. USD 10 (effective 2003). bk.rev. **Document type:** *Journal, Academic/Scholarly.*
Related titles: French ed.: Journal Africain de Genetique.
Published by: Global Press, Ugbowo, PO Box 10123, Benin City, Nigeria. TEL 234-52-200250, TELEX 41365. Ed. O S A Aromose.

➤ **ALISO;** a journal of taxonomic and evolutionary botany. see *BIOLOGY—Botany*

171.7 174.957 573.6 USA ISSN 1526-5161
R725.5
➤ **AMERICAN JOURNAL OF BIOETHICS.** Text in English. 2001. bi-m. GBP 244, USD 403 combined subscription to institutions print & online eds. (effective 2006). bk.rev. illus. back issues avail.; reprint service avail. from PSC. **Document type:** *Journal, Academic/Scholarly.* **Description:** Provides a collection of scholarship about emerging issues in bioethics.
Related titles: Online - full text ed.: ISSN 1536-0075. GBP 220, USD 264 to institutions (effective 2006) (from EBSCO Publishing, Gale Group, IngentaConnect, O C L C Online Computer Library Center, Inc., Project MUSE, Swets Information Services).
Indexed: BIOSIS Prev, BiolAb, CINAHL, CurCont, PAIS, PhilInd, SSCI.
—BLDSC (0821.950000), IE, Infotrieve. **CCC.**
Published by: Routledge (Subsidiary of: Taylor & Francis Ltd), 325 Chestnut St., Suite 800, Philadelphia, PA 19106. TEL 215-625-8900, 800-354-1420, FAX 215-625-8914, journals@routledge.com, http://www.tandf.co.uk/journals/titles/15265161.asp, http://www.routledge.com. Ed. Glenn McGee.

599.9 USA ISSN 0002-9297
QH431.A1 CODEN: AJHGAG
➤ **AMERICAN JOURNAL OF HUMAN GENETICS.** Text in English. 1948. m. (in 2 vols., 6 nos./vol.). USD 1,025 combined subscription print & online eds.; USD 91 per issue (effective 2006). adv. bk.rev. charts; illus.; stat. Index. reprint service avail. from PSC. **Document type:** *Journal, Academic/Scholarly.* **Description:** Examines research into and the application of genetic principles in medicine, psychology, anthropology, and social services, as well as in related areas of molecular and cell biology.
Related titles: Microform ed.: (from MIM, PQC); Online - full text ed.: ISSN 1537-6605 (from EBSCO Publishing, Florida Center for Library Automation, Gale Group, National Library of Medicine, O C L C Online Computer Library Center, Inc., ProQuest Information & Learning).
Indexed: AICP, ASCA, AbAn, AbHyg, AnBrAb, B&AI, B&BAb, BAS, BCI, BDM&CN, BIOBASE, BIOSIS Prev, BiolAb, Biostat, CIN, CINAHL, CIS, CTA, ChPerI, ChemAb, ChemTitl, CurCont, DSA, DSHAb, ExcerpMed, FamI, FoMM, GSI, GenetAb, HGA, IABS, ISR, IndMed, Inpharma, MEDLINE, MS&D, NSA, NSCI, PE&ON, Reac, SCI, SFA, SPPI, THA, Telegen.
—BLDSC (0825.000000), CASDDS, CISTI, GNLM, IDS, IE, Infotrieve, ingenta, KNAW, Linda Hall. **CCC.**
Published by: (American Society of Human Genetics), University of Chicago Press, Journals Division, Journals Division, PO Box 37005, Chicago, IL 60637. TEL 773-753-3347, 773-702-7600, 877-705-1878, FAX 773-753-0811, 877-705-1879, subscriptions@press.uchicago.edu, http://www.journals.uchicago.edu/AJHG. Ed. Stephen T. Warren. Adv. contact Cheryl Jones. page USD 475; trim 8.25 x 10.88. Circ: 3,000 (paid).

576.5 USA ISSN 1552-4825
RB155 CODEN: AJMGDA
➤ **AMERICAN JOURNAL OF MEDICAL GENETICS. PART A.** Text in English. 1977. 28/yr. USD 10,750 domestic to institutions; USD 11,182 in Canada & Mexico to institutions; USD 11,434 elsewhere to institutions; USD 11,825 combined subscription domestic to institutions print & online eds.; USD 12,257 combined subscription in Canada & Mexico to institutions print & online eds.; USD 12,509 combined subscription elsewhere to institutions print & online eds. (effective 2006); subscr. includes Part B & C. adv. bk.rev. charts; illus. index. back issues avail.; reprint service avail. from ISI. **Document type:** *Journal, Academic/Scholarly.* **Description:** Covers all biological and medical aspects of genetic disorders and birth defects, as well as in-depth documentation of phenotype analysis within the current context of genotype/phenotype correlations.
Supersedes in part (in 2003): American Journal of Medical Genetics (0148-7299)
Related titles: Microform ed.: (from PQC); Online - full content ed.: ISSN 1552-4833. USD 10,750 to institutions (effective 2006); includes parts A, B, C; Online - full text ed.: (from EBSCO Publishing, Swets Information Services, Wiley InterScience).
Indexed: ASCA, B&BAb, BCI, BDM&CN, BiolAb, CurCont, DentInd, ExcerpMed, FamI, HGA, ISR, IndMed, Inpharma, Kidney, MS&D, NSCI, NutrAb, PE&ON, Reac, RefZh, SCI, SSCI, THA.
—BLDSC (0827.900000), CISTI, GNLM, IDS, IE, Infotrieve, ingenta, KNAW.
Published by: John Wiley & Sons, Inc., 111 River St, Hoboken, NJ 07030-5774. TEL 201-748-6000, FAX 201-748-5915, uscs-wis@wiley.com, http://www3.interscience.wiley.com/cgi-bin/jabout/33129/ProductInformation.html, http://www.wiley.com. Eds. John C Carey, John M Opitz. adv.: B&W page USD 1,080, color page USD 1,420; trim 8.25 x 11. Circ: 150 (paid and controlled). **Subscr. outside the Americas to:** John Wiley & Sons Ltd., The Atrium, Southern Gate, Chichester, West Sussex PO19 8SQ, United Kingdom. TEL 44-1243-779777, FAX 44-1243-775878, cs-journals@wiley.co.uk.

576.5 USA ISSN 1552-4841
AMERICAN JOURNAL OF MEDICAL GENETICS. PART B: NEUROPSYCHIATRIC GENETICS. Text in English. 1977. 8/yr. USD 9,995 domestic to institutions; USD 10,395 in Canada & Mexico to institutions; USD 10,735 elsewhere to institutions; USD 10,995 combined subscription domestic to institutions print & online eds.; USD 11,395 combined subscription in Canada & Mexico to institutions print & online eds.; USD 11,735 combined subscription elsewhere to institutions print & online eds. (effective 2005); includes part A & C. adv. **Document type:** *Journal, Academic/Scholarly.* **Description:** Provides a forum for experimental and clinical investigations of the genetic mechanisms underlying neurologic and psychiatric disorders.
Supersedes in part (in 2003): American Journal of Medical Genetics (0148-7299)
Related titles: Online - full text ed.: ISSN 1552-4876 (from EBSCO Publishing, Swets Information Services, Wiley InterScience); ♦ Print ed.: American Journal of Medical Genetics. Part C: Seminars in Medical Genetics. ISSN 1552-4868.
Indexed: BCI, CurCont, NSCI, SCI.
—BLDSC (0827.930000), CISTI, IE.
Published by: John Wiley & Sons, Inc., 111 River St, Hoboken, NJ 07030-5774. TEL 201-748-6000, FAX 201-748-5915, uscs-wis@wiley.com, http://www.interscience.wiley.com/jpages/0148-7299:1/, http://www.wiley.com. Eds. John C Carey, Ming T Tsuang, Stephen V Faraone.

576.5 USA ISSN 1552-4868
AMERICAN JOURNAL OF MEDICAL GENETICS. PART C: SEMINARS IN MEDICAL GENETICS. Text in English. 1977. 4/yr. USD 9,995 domestic to institutions; USD 10,395 in Canada & Mexico to institutions; USD 10,735 elsewhere to institutions; USD 10,995 combined subscription domestic to institutions print & online eds.; USD 11,395 combined subscription in Canada & Mexico to institutions print & online eds.; USD 11,735 combined subscription elsewhere to institutions print & online eds. (effective 2005); subscr. includes Part A & B. adv. **Document type:** *Journal, Academic/Scholarly.* **Description:** Serves as both an educational resource and review forum, providing critical, in-depth retrospectives for students, practitioners, and associated professionals working in fields of human and medical genetics.
Supersedes in part (in 2003): American Journal of Medical Genetics (0148-7299)
Related titles: Online - full text ed.: ISSN 1552-4876 (from EBSCO Publishing, Swets Information Services, Wiley InterScience); ♦ Print ed.: American Journal of Medical Genetics. Part B: Neuropsychiatric Genetics. ISSN 1552-4841.
Indexed: BCI, CurCont, SCI.
—BLDSC (0827.940000), CISTI, IE.
Published by: John Wiley & Sons, Inc., 111 River St, Hoboken, NJ 07030-5774. TEL 201-748-6000, FAX 201-748-5915, uscs-wis@wiley.com, http://www.interscience.wiley.com/jpages/0148-7299:2/, http://www.wiley.com. Eds. John C Carey, Ming T Tsuang, Stephen V Faraone.

599.9 NZL ISSN 1175-2203
CODEN: AJPMC8
AMERICAN JOURNAL OF PHARMACOGENOMICS. Text in English. 2001. q. USD 240 combined subscription to individuals print & online eds.; USD 1,105 combined subscription to institutions print & online eds. (effective 2004). abstr. **Document type:** *Journal, Academic/Scholarly.* **Description:** Includes articles on cutting edge developments and clinical implications of genomic research and technology.
Related titles: Online - full text ed.: USD 235 to individuals; USD 1,090 to institutions (effective 2004) (from EBSCO Publishing, Gale Group, IngentaConnect, O C L C Online Computer Library Center, Inc., Ovid Technologies, Inc., Swets Information Services).
Indexed: BIOBASE, ExcerpMed, Inpharma, PE&ON, Reac.
—BLDSC (0830.500000), CISTI, IE, Infotrieve. **CCC.**
Published by: Adis International Ltd. (Subsidiary of: Wolters Kluwer BV), 41 Centorian Dr, Mairangi Bay, Private Bag 65901, Auckland, 1311, New Zealand. TEL 64-9-477-0700, FAX 64-9-477-0766, pharmacogenomics@adis.co.nz, http://www.adis.com/page.asp?ObjectID=50. Ed. Anne Bardsley-Elliot.

591.35 FRA ISSN 1014-2339
ANIMAL GENETIC RESOURCES INFORMATION/BOLETIN DE INFORMACION SOBRE RECURSOS GENETICOS ANIMALES/BULLETIN D'INFORMATION SUR LES RESOURCES GENETIQUES ANIMALES. Text in Multiple languages. 1983. q.
Indexed: AgBio, AnBrAb, DSA, FS&TA, HelmAb, IndVet, PN&I, PoultAb, ProtozoAb, VetBull, WAE&RSA.
—BLDSC (0903.570000), CISTI, IE, ingenta.
Published by: United Nations Environment Programme/ Programme des Nations Unies pour l'Environnement, Tour Mirabeau, 39-43 quai Andre Citroen, Paris, Cedex 15 75739, France. TEL 33-1-44371450, FAX 33-1-44371474, http://www.unepie.org/home.html.

575.1 GBR ISSN 0268-9146
CODEN: ANGEE3
➤ **ANIMAL GENETICS.** Text in English. 1970. bi-m. GBP 531 combined subscription in Europe to institutions print & online eds.; USD 983 combined subscription in the Americas to institutions & the Caribbean (print & online eds.); GBP 585 combined subscription elsewhere to institutions print & online eds. (effective 2006). adv. bk.rev. illus. index. back issues avail.; reprint service avail. from PSC. **Document type:** *Journal, Academic/Scholarly.* **Description:** Reports frontline research on immunogenetics, molecular genetics and functional genomics of economically important and domesticated animals.
Formerly (until 1986): Animal Blood Groups and Biochemical Genetics (0003-3480)
Related titles: Microform ed.: (from PQC); Online - full text ed.: ISSN 1365-2052. GBP 504 in Europe to institutions; USD 934 in the Americas to institutions & Caribbean; GBP 556 elsewhere to institutions (effective 2006) (from Blackwell Synergy, EBSCO Publishing, Gale Group, IngentaConnect, O C L C Online Computer Library Center, Inc., Ovid Technologies, Inc., Swets Information Services).
Indexed: ASCA, ASFA, AgBio, Agr, AnBrAb, B&BAb, BCI, BIOBASE, BIOSIS Prev, BioEngAb, BiolAb, CIN, ChemAb, ChemTitl, CurCont, DSA, ExcerpMed, FoVS&M, GenetAb, HGA, HelmAb, IABS, ISR, IndMed, IndVet, Inpharma, MEDLINE, PBA, PN&I, PoultAb, ProtozoAb, Reac, RefZh, SCI, SFA, VetBull, WildRev, ZooRec.
—BLDSC (0903.572000), CASDDS, CISTI, GNLM, IDS, IE, Infotrieve, ingenta, Linda Hall. **CCC.**
Published by: (International Society for Animal Genetics), Blackwell Publishing Ltd., 9600 Garsington Rd, Oxford, OX4 2ZG, United Kingdom. TEL 44-1865-776868, FAX 44-1865-714591, customerservices@oxon.blackwellpublishing.com, http://www.blackwellpublishing.com/journals/AGE. Ed. Noelle E Cockett TEL 435-797-3903. Pub. Amanda McLean Inglis. R&P Sophie Savage. Adv. contact Jenny Applin. Circ: 515.

599.9 GBR ISSN 0003-4800
HQ750.A1 CODEN: ANHGAA
➤ **ANNALS OF HUMAN GENETICS.** Text in English. 1925. bi-m. GBP 138, EUR 207 combined subscription in Europe to individuals print & online eds.; USD 252 combined subscription in the Americas to individuals & the Caribbean (print & online eds.); GBP 150 combined subscription elsewhere to individuals print & online eds.; GBP 337 combined subscription in Europe to institutions print & online eds.; USD 623 combined subscription in the Americas to institutions & the Caribbean (print & online eds.); GBP 371 combined subscription elsewhere to institutions print & online eds. (effective 2006). adv. bk.rev. charts; illus. index. back issues avail.; reprint service avail. from PSC. **Document type:** *Journal, Academic/Scholarly.* **Description:** Concerned with the application of scientific techniques to the study of human inheritance, such as gene mapping, cytogenetics, clinical genetics or mathematical models.
Formerly: Annals of Eugenics
Related titles: Microform ed.: (from PQC); Online - full text ed.: ISSN 1469-1809. GBP 320 in Europe to institutions; USD 593 in the Americas to institutions & the Caribbean; GBP 353 elsewhere to institutions (effective 2006) (from Blackwell Synergy, EBSCO Publishing, Gale Group, IngentaConnect, O C L C Online Computer Library Center, Inc., Swets Information Services).

B

▼ new title ➤ refereed ✶ unverified ♦ full entry avail.

Indexed: AICP, ASCA, AbAn, AbHyg, AgBio, AnBrAb, AnthLit, BCI, BDM&CN, BIOBASE, BIOSIS Prev, BibInd, BiolAb, CIS, ChemAb, CurCont, DSA, ExcerpMed, FamI, IABS, ISR, IndMed, IndVet, Inpharma, MEDLINE, MathR, NutrAb, PBA, PsycholAb, RDA, Reac, RefZh, RevApplEntom, SCI, SSCI, ST&MA, TDB, THA, VetBull.
—BLDSC (1041.000000), CASDDS, CISTI, GNLM, IDS, IE, Infotrieve, ingenta, Linda Hall. **CCC.**
Published by: Blackwell Publishing Ltd., 9600 Garsington Rd, Oxford, OX4 2ZG, United Kingdom. TEL 44-1865-776868, FAX 44-1865-714591, customerservices@oxon.blackwellpublishing.com, http://www.blackwellpublishing.com/journals/AHG. Ed. Sue Povey.

576.5 USA ISSN 0066-4197
QH431.A1 CODEN: ARVGB7
➤ **ANNUAL REVIEW OF GENETICS.** Text in English. 1967. a., latest vol.39, 2004. USD 188 to institutions print or online ed.; USD 226 combined subscription to institutions print & online eds. (effective 2006). bibl.; charts; abstr. index, cum.index. back issues avail.; reprint service avail. from PSC. **Document type:** *Academic/Scholarly.* **Description:** Reviews synthesize and filter primary research in order to identify the principal contributions in the field of genetics.
Related titles: Microfilm ed.: (from PQC); Online - full content ed.: ISSN 1545-2948. USD 183 (effective 2005) (from Florida Center for Library Automation, HighWire Press, Northern Light Technology, Inc.); Online - full text ed.: (from bigchalk, EBSCO Publishing, Gale Group, H.W. Wilson, O C L C Online Computer Library Center, Inc., ProQuest Information & Learning, Swets Information Services).
Indexed: ASCA, ASFA, AbAn, AbHyg, AgBio, Agr, AnBeAb, AnBrAb, ApEcolAb, B&AI, BCI, BIOBASE, BIOSIS Prev, BibAg, BioCN&I, BiolAb, BiolDig, CIN, CTA, ChemAb, ChemTitl, ChemoAb, CurCont, DBA, ESPM, EntAb, ExcerpMed, FPA, ForAb, GSI, GenetAb, HGA, HortAb, IABS, ISR, IndMed, IndVet, Inpharma, JDDR, MBA, MEDLINE, MRD, NSA, NemAb, NutrAb, PBA, PGegResA, ProtozoAb, RM&VM, RPP, Reac, RevApplEntom, S&F, SCI, SeedAb, TDB, THA, WeedAb, ZooRec.
—BLDSC (1522.565000), CASDDS, CISTI, GNLM, IDS, IE, Infotrieve, ingenta, KNAW, Linda Hall. **CCC.**
Published by: Annual Reviews, 4139 El Camino Way, Palo Alto, CA 94303-0139. TEL 650-493-4400, 800-523-8635, FAX 650-424-0910, service@annualreviews.org, http://arjournals.annualreviews.org/loi/genet, http://www.annualreviews.org. Ed. Allan Campbell. R&P Laura Folkner.

599.9 USA ISSN 1527-8204
QH447 CODEN: ARGHC4
ANNUAL REVIEW OF GENOMICS AND HUMAN GENETICS. Text in English. 2000. a., latest vol.5, 2004. USD 191 to institutions print or online ed.; USD 229 combined subscription to institutions print & online eds. (effective 2006). abstr.; charts; bibl. back issues avail.; reprint service avail. from PSC. **Document type:** *Journal, Academic/Scholarly.*
Related titles: Online - full content ed.: ISSN 1545-293X. USD 187 (effective 2005); Online - full text ed.: (from EBSCO Publishing, Swets Information Services).
Indexed: ASFA, AbHyg, AgBio, AnBrAb, B&BAb, BBCI, BCI, BIOBASE, BIOSIS Prev, ChemAb, CurCont, ESPM, ExcerpMed, GenetAb, ISR, Inpharma, NemAb, NutrAb, PE&ON, Reac, SCI.
—BLDSC (1522.565100), CISTI, IE, Infotrieve, Linda Hall. **CCC.**
Published by: Annual Reviews, 4139 El Camino Way, Palo Alto, CA 94303-0139. TEL 650-493-4400, 800-523-8635, FAX 650-424-0910, service@annualreviews.org, http://arjournals.annualreviews.org/loi/genom, http://www.annualreviews.org. Ed. Eric Lander. R&P Laura Folkner.

APPLIED MICROBIOLOGY AND BIOTECHNOLOGY. see *BIOLOGY—Biotechnology*

591.15 ESP ISSN 1138-4212
EL ARCA. Text in Spanish. 1997. s-a. EUR 12 domestic; EUR 15 foreign (effective 2005). **Document type:** *Journal, Academic/Scholarly.*
Published by: (Sociedad Espanola para los Recursos Geneticos y Animales), Universidad de Cordoba, Servicio de Publicaciones, Ave. Menendez Pidal, s-n, Cordoba, 14071, Spain. TEL 34-957-218125, FAX 34-957-218196, publicaciones@uco.es, http://www.uco.es/. Ed. Evangelina Rodero Serrano.

ARCHIVES OF MICROBIOLOGY. see *BIOLOGY—Microbiology*

572.8 USA ISSN 1523-7834
RB155.6
ASSOCIATION OF GENETIC TECHNOLOGISTS. JOURNAL. Text in English. 1975. q. USD 105 domestic; USD 130 foreign; free to members (effective 2005). adv. bk.rev. back issues avail. **Document type:** *Journal, Academic/Scholarly.* **Description:** Covers clinical cytogenetics and molecular cytogenetics for laboratory and medical personnel.
Former titles (until 1998): Applied Cytogenetics (1056-5191); (until 1990): Karyogram (0732-8745)
Indexed: BiolAb.
—BLDSC (4704.176000), KNAW.
Published by: Association of Genetic Technologists, AGT Executive Office, PO Box 15945-288, Lenexa, KS 66285-5945. TEL 913-541-0497, FAX 913-599-5340, marterry@juno.com, agt-info@goAMP.com, http://www.agt-info.org. Ed. Mark J Terry TEL 313-916-7029. Circ: 1,700.

576.5 ITA ISSN 0066-9830
CODEN: AAGNA3
ASSOCIAZIONE GENETICA ITALIANA. ATTI. Text and summaries in English, Italian. 1955. a.
Indexed: AnBrAb, BiolAb, CurCont.
—CISTI, Linda Hall.
Published by: Associazione Genetica Italiana, c/o Istituto di Biologia Animale, Via Leonardo Loredan, 10, Padua, PD 35131, Italy. Ed. G A Danieli. Circ: 300.

591.35 CAN
ATLANTIC SALMON FEDERATION. SALMON GENETICS RESEARCH PROGRAM. ANNUAL REPORT. Text in English. a.
Published by: Atlantic Salmon Federation, Salmon Genetics Research Program, PO Box 429, St Andrews, NB E0G 2X0, Canada.

ATLANTIC SALMON FEDERATION. SALMON GENETICS RESEARCH PROGRAM. REPORT SERIES. see *BIOLOGY*

AUSTRALIAN AND NEW ZEALAND DIRECTORY OF GENETICS SUPPORT GROUPS, SERVICES AND INFORMATION. see *BIOLOGY—Abstracting, Bibliographies, Statistics*

576.5 ARG ISSN 1666-0390
➤ **B A G. JOURNAL OF BASIC AND APPLIED GENETICS.** (Basic and Applied Genetics) Text in Spanish; Summaries in English. 1976. s-a. bk.rev. back issues avail. **Document type:** *Journal, Academic/Scholarly.* **Description:** Covers all areas of genetics.
Formerly (until 2001): Mendeliana (0325-223X)
Indexed: B&BAb, BIOBASE, BIOSIS Prev, BiolAb, EntAb, ExcerpMed, GenetAb.
—KNAW.
Published by: Sociedad Argentina de Genetica, Rodriguez Pena 36, 6 to. Piso, Depto. A, Buenos Aires, Buenos Aires 1020, Argentina. sag@sag.org.ar, http://www.sag.org.ar. Ed. Sol L Rabasa. Circ: 650.

576.5 NLD ISSN 0167-4781
➤ **B B A - GENE STRUCTURE AND EXPRESSION.** Text in Dutch. 1962. 12/yr. EUR 2,888 in Europe to institutions; JPY 383,500 in Japan to institutions; USD 3,231 elsewhere to institutions (effective 2006). back issues avail. **Document type:** *Journal, Academic/Scholarly.* **Description:** Examines DNA and RNA structures. Includes sequence data, nucleic acid and protein interaction, DNA modifying enzymes and replication. Explores transcription mechanisms and factors as well as control of gene expression.
Related titles: Microform ed.: (from PQC); Online - full text ed.: (from EBSCO Publishing, Gale Group, IngentaConnect, ScienceDirect, Swets Information Services); ◆ Series of: Biochimica et Biophysica Acta. ISSN 0006-3002.
Indexed: AEA, ASCA, AbHyg, AgBio, AgrForAb, AnBrAb, BBCI, BCI, BIOBASE, BioDAb, BiolAb, CPA, ChemAb, CurCont, DBA, DSA, ExcerpMed, FCA, FPA, ForAb, HelmAb, HerbAb, HortAb, IABS, ISR, IndChem, IndMed, IndVet, Inpharma, MaizeAb, NemAb, NucAcAb, NutrAb, PBA, PGegResA, PGrRegA, PHN&I, PN&I, PotatoAb, PoultAb, ProtozoAb, RA&MP, RM&VM, RPP, Reac, RefZh, RevApplEntom, RiceAb, S&F, SCI, SIA, SeedAb, SoyAb, TDB, TriticAb, VetBull, WeedAb.
—CISTI, IDS, IE. **CCC.**
Published by: Elsevier BV (Subsidiary of: Elsevier Science & Technology), Radarweg 29, Amsterdam, 1043 NX, Netherlands. TEL 31-20-4853911, FAX 31-20-4852457, nlinfo-f@elsevier.nl, http://www.elsevier.com/locate/bbaexp, http://www.elsevier.nl.

599.9 NLD ISSN 0925-4439
CODEN: BBADEX
➤ **B B A - MOLECULAR BASIS OF DISEASE.** Text in Dutch. 12/yr. EUR 1,322 in Europe to institutions; JPY 175,500 in Japan to institutions; USD 1,478 elsewhere to institutions (effective 2006). **Document type:** *Journal, Academic/Scholarly.* **Description:** Focuses on a fundamental biochemical and genetic approach to understanding dysfunction in human disease states and their models.
Related titles: Microfilm ed.: (from PQC); Online - full text ed.: (from EBSCO Publishing, Gale Group, IngentaConnect, ScienceDirect, Swets Information Services); ◆ Series of: Biochimica et Biophysica Acta. ISSN 0006-3002.
Indexed: ASCA, AbHyg, AgBio, BBCI, BIOBASE, BioCN&I, CurCont, DBA, DSA, ExcerpMed, FoMM, HelmAb, IABS, ISR, IndVet, Inpharma, NutrAb, PN&I, ProtozoAb, RA&MP, RM&VM, Reac, RefZh, S&F, SCI, TDB, VetBull.
—CISTI, IDS, IE. **CCC.**
Published by: Elsevier BV (Subsidiary of: Elsevier Science & Technology), Radarweg 29, Amsterdam, 1043 NX, Netherlands. TEL 31-20-4853911, FAX 31-20-4852457, nlinfo-f@elsevier.nl, http://www.elsevier.com/locate/bbadis, http://www.elsevier.nl.

576.8 GBR ISSN 1471-2148
QH359 CODEN: BEBMCG
➤ **B M C EVOLUTIONARY BIOLOGY.** (BioMed Central) Text in English. 2000. m. free (effective 2006). adv. **Document type:** *Journal, Academic/Scholarly.* **Description:** Publishes original research articles in all aspects of molecular and non-molecular evolution of all organisms, as well as phylogenetics and palaeontology.
Media: Online - full content (from EBSCO Publishing, National Library of Medicine).
Indexed: BIOSIS Prev, BiolAb, CurCont, FCA, MEDLINE, ZooRec.
—Infotrieve. **CCC.**
Published by: BioMed Central Ltd. (Subsidiary of: Current Science Ltd), Middlesex House, 34-42 Cleveland St, London, W1T 4LB, United Kingdom. TEL 44-20-76319131, FAX 44-20-76319923, info@biomedcentral.com, http://www.biomedcentral.com/bmcevolbiol/. Ed. Peter Newmark. Adv. contact Deborah Cockerill.

599.9 GBR ISSN 1471-2156
QH426 CODEN: BGMEDS
➤ **B M C GENETICS.** (BioMed Central) Text in English. 2000. m. free (effective 2006). adv. **Document type:** *Journal, Academic/Scholarly.* **Description:** Publishes original research articles in all aspects of inheritance and variation in individuals and among populations.
Media: Online - full content (from EBSCO Publishing, National Library of Medicine).
Indexed: BCI, BIOSIS Prev, BiolAb, ExcerpMed, MEDLINE, ZooRec.
—Infotrieve. **CCC.**
Published by: BioMed Central Ltd. (Subsidiary of: Current Science Ltd), Middlesex House, 34-42 Cleveland St, London, W1T 4LB, United Kingdom. TEL 44-20-76319131, FAX 44-20-76319923, info@biomedcentral.com, http://www.biomedcentral.com/bmcgenet/. Ed. Peter Newmark. Adv. contact Deborah Cockerill.

576.8 GBR ISSN 1471-2164
QH447 CODEN: BGMEET
➤ **B M C GENOMICS.** (BioMed Central) Text in English. 2000. m. free (effective 2006). adv. **Document type:** *Journal, Academic/Scholarly.* **Description:** Publishes original research articles in all aspects of gene mapping, sequencing and analysis, functional genomics, and proteomics.
Media: Online - full content (from EBSCO Publishing, National Library of Medicine).
Indexed: BCI, BIOSIS Prev, BiolAb, ExcerpMed, MEDLINE.
—Infotrieve. **CCC.**
Published by: BioMed Central Ltd. (Subsidiary of: Current Science Ltd), Middlesex House, 34-42 Cleveland St, London, W1T 4LB, United Kingdom. TEL 44-20-76319131, FAX 44-20-76319923, info@biomedcentral.com, http://www.biomedcentral.com/bmcgenomics/. Ed. Peter Newmark. Adv. contact Deborah Cockerill.

599 GBR ISSN 1471-2350
CODEN: BMGMAR
➤ **B M C MEDICAL GENETICS.** (BioMed Central) Text in English. 2000 (Nov.). irreg. free (effective 2006). **Document type:** *Journal, Academic/Scholarly.* **Description:** Publishes original research articles in all aspects of medical genetics.
Media: Online - full content (from EBSCO Publishing, National Library of Medicine).
Indexed: ExcerpMed, MEDLINE.
—Infotrieve. **CCC.**
Published by: BioMed Central Ltd. (Subsidiary of: Current Science Ltd), Middlesex House, 34-42 Cleveland St, London, W1T 4LB, United Kingdom. TEL 44-20-76319131, FAX 44-20-76319923, info@biomedcentral.com, http://www.biomedcentral.com/bmcmedgenet/. Ed. Fiona Godlee.

591.35 FRA ISSN 0153-6281
B T I A; la revue francaise de la genetique et de la reproduction. (Bulletin Technique de l'Insemination Artificielle) Text in French. 1976. q. adv. bk.rev. **Document type:** *Bulletin.* **Description:** For specialists in the reproduction and insemination of cattle, including veterinarians and owners of livestock.
Published by: (Association pour l'Information en Insemination Artificielle), Societe de Diffusion de la Presse Agricole, BP 47, Lempdes, 63370, France. TEL 33-4-73421717, FAX 33-4-73913560, TELEX 397-467. Ed. Maurice Lacroix. Adv. contact Jeanne Fischer.

BABRAHAM INSTITUTE. CORPORATE PLAN. see *BIOLOGY—Physiology*

BABRAHAM INSTITUTE. REPORT. see *BIOLOGY—Physiology*

BABRAHAM PUBLICATIONS. see *BIOLOGY—Biochemistry*

576.5 BGR ISSN 1311-0160
CODEN: BJMGFN
BALKAN JOURNAL OF MEDICAL GENETICS. Text in English. 1998. q. USD 120 foreign (effective 2005). **Document type:** *Journal, Academic/Scholarly.*
Indexed: BIOBASE, ExcerpMed.
—CISTI.

Published by: Meditsinski Universitet - Sofia, Tsentralna Meditsinska Biblioteka, Tsentur za Informatsiia po Meditsina/Medical University - Sofia, Central Medical Library, Medical Information Center, 1 Sv Georgi Sofiiski ul, Sofia, 1431, Bulgaria. TEL 359-2-9522342, FAX 359-2-9522393, pslavova@medun.acad.bg, http://www.medun.acad.bg/cmb_htm/cmb1_home_bg.htm. **Dist. by:** Sofia Books, ul Silivria 16, Sofia 1404, Bulgaria. TEL 359-2-9586257, info@sofiabooks-bg.com, http://www.sofiabooks-bg.com.

576.5 610 USA ISSN 0001-8244 CODEN: BHGNAT

➤ **BEHAVIOR GENETICS**; an international journal devoted to research in the inheritance of behavior in animals and man. Text in English. 1970. bi-m. EUR 938, USD 958, GBP 588 combined subscription to institutions print & online eds. (effective 2005). adv. bk.rev. bibl.; charts; illus.; stat. index. back issues avail.; reprint service avail. from PSC. **Document type:** *Journal, Academic/Scholarly.* **Description:** Explores the genetic analysis of complex traits.
Related titles: Microfilm ed.: (from PQC); Online - full text ed.: ISSN 1573-3297 (from EBSCO Publishing, Gale Group, IngentaConnect, Kluwer Online, O C L C Online Computer Library Center, Inc., Ovid Technologies, Inc., Springer LINK, Swets Information Services).
Indexed: ASCA, AbAn, AddicA, AgBio, AnBeAb, AnBrAb, ApicAb, B&BAb, BIOBASE, BIOSIS Prev, BibLing, BioCN&I, BioEngAb, BiolAb, CDA, CIS, CurCont, DSA, EntAb, ExcerpMed, FamI, GenetAb, HGA, HortAb, IABS, ISR, IndMed, IndVet, Inpharma, MEDLINE, NSCI, NutrAb, PBA, PoultAb, PsycInfo, PsycholAb, RASB, RM&VM, Reac, RefZh, RevApplEntom, SCI, SFA, SSCI, VetBull, WildRev, ZooRec, e-psyche.
—BLDSC (1876.691000), CISTI, GNLM, IDS, IE, Infotrieve, ingenta, KNAW. **CCC.**
Published by: (Behavior Genetics Association), Plenum US (Subsidiary of: Springer Science+Business Media), 233 Spring St, New York, NY 10013. TEL 212-460-1500, FAX 212-460-1575, service@springer-ny.com, http://springerlink.metapress.com/openurl.asp?genre=journal&issn=0001-8244, http://www.springeronline.com.

➤ **BILTEN ZA HMELJ, SIRAK I LEKOVITO BILJE/HOPS, SORGHUMS AND MEDICINAL HERBS BULLETIN.** see *BIOLOGY—Botany*

➤ **BILTEN ZA TRANSFUZIOLOGIJU.** see *MEDICAL SCIENCES—Hematology*

576.5 340 DEU ISSN 1437-1634

BIO- UND GENTECHNIK. Text in German. 1991. irreg. looseleaf. price varies. **Document type:** *Monographic series, Trade.*
Formerly: Gentechnikgesetz (0939-2211)
Published by: Erich Schmidt Verlag GmbH & Co. (Berlin), Genthiner Str 30G, Berlin, 10785, Germany. TEL 49-30-250085-0, FAX 49-30-25008521, vertrieb@esvmedien.de, http://www.erich-schmidt-verlag.de.

576.5 USA ISSN 0006-2928
QH431 CODEN: BIGEBA

➤ **BIOCHEMICAL GENETICS.** Text in English. 1967. m. EUR 1,098, USD 1,118, GBP 688 combined subscription to institutions print & online eds. (effective 2005). adv. back issues avail. **Document type:** *Journal, Academic/Scholarly.* **Description:** Publishes original research results in biochemical genetics.
Related titles: Microfilm ed.: (from PQC); Online - full text ed.: ISSN 1573-4927 (from EBSCO Publishing, Gale Group, IngentaConnect, Kluwer Online, O C L C Online Computer Library Center, Inc., Ovid Technologies, Inc., Springer LINK, Swets Information Services).
Indexed: ASCA, ASFA, AbAn, AgBio, Agr, AnBrAb, B&AI, B&BAb, BBCI, BCI, BIOBASE, BIOSIS Prev, BibAg, BibLing, BiolAb, CIN, CPA, ChemAb, ChemTitl, CurCont, DBA, DSA, DentInd, EntAb, ExcerpMed, FCA, ForAb, GenetAb, HGA, HelmAb, HortAb, IABS, ISR, IndMed, IndVet, Inpharma, MEDLINE, MaizeAb, NemAb, OrnHort, PBA, PGegResA, PGrRegA, PN&I, PoultAb, PsycholAb, RM&VM, RPP, Reac, RefZh, RevApplEntom, RiceAb, S&MA, SCI, SFA, SeedAb, SoyAb, TDB, TriticAb, VetBull, WildRev, ZooRec.
—BLDSC (2066.980000), CASDDS, CISTI, GNLM, IDS, IE, Infotrieve, ingenta, Linda Hall. **CCC.**
Published by: Plenum US (Subsidiary of: Springer Science+Business Media), 233 Spring St, New York, NY 10013. TEL 212-460-1500, FAX 212-460-1575, service@springer-ny.com, http://springerlink.metapress.com/openurl.asp?genre=journal&issn=0006-2928, http://www.springeronline.com. Eds. Hugh S Forrest, Nigel S Atkinson.

➤ **BIOMOLECULAR ENGINEERING.** see *BIOLOGY—Biotechnology*

599.9 GBR

BIONEWS. Text in English. 1999. w. free (effective 2001).
Media: Online - full text. **Related titles:** E-mail ed.
Published by: Progress Educational Trust, 140 Gray's Inn Rd, London, WC1X 8AX , United Kingdom. admin@progress.org.uk, http://www.progress.org.uk. Ed. Kirsty Horsey. **Co-sponsor:** AstraZeneca.

576.5 579.2 660.6 UKR ISSN 0233-7657
QP801.B69 CODEN: BIKLEK

➤ **BIOPOLIMERY I KLETKA/BIOPOLYMERS AND CELL.** Text and summaries in English, Russian, Ukrainian. 1985. bi-m. USD 180 foreign (effective 2004). 80 p./no. 2 cols./p.; **Document type:** *Journal, Academic/Scholarly.* **Description:** Devoted to advancement and dissimination of fundamental and practical knowledge concerning the molecular and cellular biology: structure and function of biopolymers, genetic engineering and biotechnology, genome regulation and molecular mechanisms of differentiation in eukaryotic cells.
Indexed: BIOSIS Prev, BiolAb, CIN, ChemAb, ChemTitl, Djerelo, RefZh, TriticAb.
—BLDSC (0017.994000), CASDDS, CISTI, GNLM, IE, ingenta, Linda Hall. **CCC.**
Published by: Natsional'na Akademiya Nauk Ukrainy, Instytut Molekulyarnoi Biolohii i Henetyky, Vul Akad Zabolotnogo 150, Kiev, 03143, Ukraine. TEL 380-44-2660789, FAX 380-44-2660759. Eds. Anna El'skaya, Gennady K Matsuka. Adv. contacts Gennady K Matsuka, Oleksandr Kornelyuk. Circ: 200 (paid). **Dist. by:** Derzhavne Pidpryemstvo z Rozpovsyudzhennya Periodychnykh Vydan' Presa, 2a, Petrozavodska, Kyiv 03999, Ukraine. info@presa.ua, http://www.presa.ua.

576.5 USA

BIOWORLD GENOMICS REVIEW: THE RACE FOR DRUGS. Text in English. a. USD 419 (effective 2005).
Published by: Thomson American Health Consultants, Inc. (Subsidiary of: Thomson Corporation, Healthcare Information Group), 3525 Piedmont Rd, N E, Bldg 6, Ste 400, Atlanta, GA 30305. TEL 404-262-5511, FAX 404-262-7837, customerservice@ahcpub.com, http://www.bioworld.com/servlet/com.accumedia.web.Dispatcher?next=bioWorldGenomics, http://www.ahcpub.com.

576.5 ARG ISSN 0067-9720
QH442

BOLETIN GENETICO. Text and summaries in English, Spanish. 1965. irreg., latest vol.15, 1989. USD 15; or exchange.
Indexed: BiolAb.
Published by: (Argentina. Departamento de Genetica), Instituto Nacional de Tecnologia Agropecuaria, Centro de Investigaciones en Ciencias Agronomicas, Casilla de Correos 25, Castelar, Buenos Aires 1712, Argentina.

576.5 GBR ISSN 1473-9550
QH447

BRIEFINGS IN FUNCTIONAL GENOMICS AND PROTEOMICS. Text in English. 2002. q. GBP 70 in Europe to individuals based at educational establishments; USD 105 in North America to individuals based at educational establishments; GBP 85 elsewhere to individuals based at educational establishments; GBP 170 in Europe to institutions; USD 260 in North America to institutions; GBP 185 elsewhere to institutions (effective 2004). **Document type:** *Journal, Academic/Scholarly.* **Description:** Reviews the techniques, protocols and approaches in genome and proteome research; as well as providing background information on state-of-the-art technologies, the journal will provide valuable insight and relevant practical advice.
Related titles: Online - full content ed.: ISSN 1477-4062; Online - full text ed.: (from EBSCO Publishing, Gale Group, IngentaConnect, O C L C Online Computer Library Center, Inc., ProQuest Information & Learning, Swets Information Services).
Indexed: AgBio, AnBrAb, ExcerpMed, PBA, PN&I, PoultAb, RefZh, RiceAb, WeedAb.
—BLDSC (2283.958368), CISTI, IE, ingenta.
Published by: Henry Stewart Publications, Russell House, 28-30 Little Russell St, London, WC1A 2HN, United Kingdom. TEL 44-20-74043040, FAX 44-20-74042081, enquiries@hspublications.co.uk, qweny@henrystewart.co.uk, http://www.henrystewart.com/journals/fgp/index.html. **Subscr. addr. in N America:** Henry Stewart Publications, Subscriptions Office, PO Box 10812, Birmingham, AL 35202-1588. TEL 800-633-4931, FAX 205-955-1588, hsp@ebsco.com; **Subscr. addr. outside N America:** Museum House, 25 Museum St, London WC1A 1JT, United Kingdom. TEL 44-20-73232916, FAX 44-20-73232918, subscriptions@hspublications.co.uk.

576.5 PRT ISSN 0870-7235 CODEN: BRGED7

BROTERIA GENETICA. Text in English, French, German, Italian, Portuguese, Spanish. 1902. q. EUR 13 domestic; USD 24 foreign (effective 2005). bk.rev. bibl.; charts; illus. index, cum.index: 1902-1917; 1918-1959. **Document type:** *Academic/Scholarly.*
Supersedes (in 1980): Broteria: Ciencias Naturais (0007-2427)
Related titles: Microfiche ed.: (from IDC).
Indexed: BiolAb, ChemAb, MLA, PN&I, SFA, WildRev, ZooRec.
—BLDSC (2351.020000), CISTI, ingenta, Linda Hall.
Published by: (Sociedade Portuguesa de Genetica), Edicoes Broteria, Rua Maestro Antonio Taborda, 14, Lisbon, 1249-094, Portugal. TEL 351-21-3961660, FAX 351-21-3956629. Ed. Luis Archer. Circ: 1,000.

CANCER GENE THERAPY. see *MEDICAL SCIENCES—Oncology*

CANCER GENETICS AND CYTOGENETICS. see *MEDICAL SCIENCES—Oncology*

CELL PRESERVATION TECHNOLOGY. see *BIOLOGY—Cytology And Histology*

576.5 DEU ISSN 0009-5915
QH301 CODEN: CHROAU

➤ **CHROMOSOMA**; biology of the nucleus. Text in English. 1939. 8/yr. EUR 1,398 combined subscription to institutions print & online eds. (effective 2005). adv. bibl.; charts; illus. index. back issues avail.; reprint service avail. from ISI. **Document type:** *Journal, Academic/Scholarly.* **Description:** Publishes original papers and current review articles relating the molecular structure and function of chromosomes to that of the nucleus.
Related titles: Microform ed.: (from PQC); Online - full text ed.: ISSN 1432-0886 (from EBSCO Publishing, Springer LINK, Swets Information Services).
Indexed: ASCA, ASFA, AbAn, AgBio, Agr, AnBrAb, B&BAb, BCI, BIOBASE, BIOSIS Prev, BibAg, BioCN&I, BiolAb, CIN, ChemAb, ChemTitl, CurCont, DentInd, ExcerpMed, GenetAb, HGA, HortAb, IABS, ISR, IndMed, IndVet, Inpharma, MBA, MEDLINE, MaizeAb, NemAb, OrnHort, PBA, PGegResA, ProtozoAb, Reac, RefZh, RevApplEntom, SCI, SFA, TriticAb, VetBull, WildRev, ZooRec.
—BLDSC (3184.000000), CASDDS, CISTI, IDS, IE, Infotrieve, ingenta, Linda Hall. **CCC.**
Published by: Springer-Verlag (Subsidiary of: Springer Science+Business Media), Tiergartenstr 17, Heidelberg, 69121, Germany. TEL 49-6221-3450, FAX 49-6221-345229, http://www.springeronline.com/sgw/cda/frontpage/0,10735,5-40109-70-1066702-0,00.html. Ed. Erich Nigg. Adv. contact Stephan Kroeck TEL 49-30-827875739. **Subscr. in the Americas to:** Springer-Verlag New York, Inc., Journal Fulfillment, PO Box 2485, Secaucus, NJ 07096-2485. TEL 800-777-4643, 201-348-4033, FAX 201-348-4505, journals@springer-ny.com, http://www.springer-ny.com; **Subscr. to:** Springer GmbH Auslieferungsgesellschaft, Haberstr 7, Heidelberg 69126, Germany. TEL 49-6221-345-0, FAX 49-6221-345-4229, subscriptions@springer.de.

B

➤ **CLINICAL CYTOGENETICS.** see *BIOLOGY—Abstracting, Bibliographies, Statistics*

576.5 DNK ISSN 0009-9163
RB155 CODEN: CLGNAY

➤ **CLINICAL GENETICS**; an international journal of genetics and molecular medicine. Text in English. 1970. m. EUR 348 combined subscription in Europe to individuals print & online eds.; USD 390 combined subscription in the Americas to individuals & Caribbean, print & online eds.; GBP 232 combined subscription elsewhere to individuals print & online eds.; USD 1,057 combined subscription in the Americas to institutions & Caribbean, print & online eds.; GBP 629 combined subscription elsewhere to institutions print & online eds. (effective 2006). adv. bibl.; charts; illus. reprint service avail. from PSC,ISI. **Document type:** *Journal, Academic/Scholarly.* **Description:** Publishes research related to molecular approaches to genetic disease and the application of these advances for the practicing geneticist. The journal focuses on understanding how changes in specific genes may result in an altered phenotype, and how knowledge of these changes may result in new therapy.
Related titles: Online - full text ed.: ISSN 1399-0004. EUR 330 in Europe to individuals; USD 370 in the Americas to individuals & Caribbean; GBP 220 elsewhere to individuals; USD 1,005 in the Americas to institutions & Caribbean; GBP 598 elsewhere to institutions (effective 2006) (from Blackwell Synergy, EBSCO Publishing, Gale Group, IngentaConnect, O C L C Online Computer Library Center, Inc., Ovid Technologies, Inc., Swets Information Services).
Indexed: ASCA, AbAn, B&BAb, BCI, BDM&CN, BIOBASE, BIOSIS Prev, BioEngAb, BiolAb, CTD, ChemAb, CurCont, DSA, DentInd, DokArb, ExcerpMed, GenetAb, HGA, IABS, ISR, IndMed, Inpharma, MEDLINE, MS&D, NSCI, NutrAb, PE&ON, Reac, SCI, SSCI.
—BLDSC (3286.287000), CASDDS, CISTI, GNLM, IDS, IE, Infotrieve, ingenta, KNAW. **CCC.**
Published by: Blackwell Munksgaard (Subsidiary of: Blackwell Publishing Ltd.), Rosenoerns Alle 1, PO Box 227, Copenhagen V, 1502, Denmark. TEL 45-77-333333, FAX 45-77-333377, clingen@interchg.ubc.ca, customerservice@munksgaard.dk, http://www.blackwellpublishing.com/journals/CGE, http://www.munksgaard.dk/. Ed. Dr. Michael R Hayden TEL 604-822-8037. Adv. contacts Eric Rozario TEL 45-77-333301, Sandra Read. Circ: 1,100.

660.65 USA ISSN 1536-2302
QH442.2 CODEN: CSCLBO

➤ **CLONING AND STEM CELLS.** Text in English. 1999. q. USD 639 domestic to institutions; USD 757 foreign to institutions; USD 759 combined subscription domestic to institutions print & online eds.; USD 881 combined subscription foreign to institutions print & online eds. (effective 2006). adv. back issues avail.; reprint service avail. from PSC. **Document type:** *Journal, Academic/Scholarly.* **Description:** Covers all aspects of cloning research and applications.
Formerly (until Aug. 2001): Cloning (1520-4553)

Related titles: Online - full text ed.: ISSN 1557-7457. USD 581 to institutions (effective 2006) (from EBSCO Publishing, Gale Group, O C L C Online Computer Library Center, Inc., Swets Information Services).
Indexed: AEBA, ASFA, AgBio, Agr, AnBrAb, B&BAb, BCI, BIOBASE, BIOSIS Prev, BioEngAb, BiolAb, ChemAb, ESPM, ExcerpMed, GenetAb, M&PBA, SoyAb.
—BLDSC (3286.692300), CISTI, IE, Infotrieve, ingenta. **CCC.**
Published by: Mary Ann Liebert, Inc. Publishers, 140 Huguenot St 3rd Fl, New Rochelle, NY 10801-5215. TEL 914-740-2100, FAX 914-740-2101, 800-654-3237, info@liebertpub.com, http://www.liebertpub.com/clo. Ed. Ian Wilmut. adv.: B&W page USD 1,335; trim 8.5 x 11. Circ: 1,000 (paid).

599.9 CHE ISSN 1422-2795
CODEN: COGEFX

COMMUNITY GENETICS. Text in English. 1998. q. CHF 844 in Europe to institutions; CHF 857.60 elsewhere to institutions; CHF 909 combined subscription in Europe to institutions print & online eds.; CHF 922.60 combined subscription elsewhere to institutions print & online eds. (effective 2006). adv. back issues avail. **Document type:** *Journal, Academic/Scholarly.* **Description:** International forum for research in the expanding field of community genetics, an area of medical care responding to the explosion of developments in human genetics which impact both the individual and society.
Related titles: Online - full text ed.: ISSN 1422-2833. CHF 816 to institutions (effective 2006) (from EBSCO Publishing, O C L C Online Computer Library Center, Inc., ProQuest Information & Learning, Swets Information Services).
Indexed: ExcerpMed.
—BLDSC (3363.627500), CISTI, GNLM, IE, Infotrieve, ingenta, KNAW. **CCC.**
Published by: S. Karger AG, Allschwilerstr 10, Basel, 4009, Switzerland. TEL 41-61-3061111, FAX 41-61-3061234, karger@karger.ch, http://www.karger.com/CMG, http://www.karger.ch. Ed. L P ten Kate. adv.: page USD 1,185.

576.8 333.95 NLD ISSN 1566-0621
QH75.A1 CODEN: CGOEAC

➤ **CONSERVATION GENETICS.** Text in English. 2000. bi-m. EUR 292, USD 293, GBP 192 combined subscription to institutions print & online eds. (effective 2005). adv. reprint service avail. from PSC. **Document type:** *Journal, Academic/Scholarly.* **Description:** Focuses on the conservation of genetic diversity and in general, the application of genetic methods towards resolving problems in conservation.
Related titles: Online - full text ed.: ISSN 1572-9737 (from EBSCO Publishing, Gale Group, IngentaConnect, Kluwer Online, O C L C Online Computer Library Center, Inc., Ovid Technologies, Inc., Springer LINK, Swets Information Services).
Indexed: ASFA, ApEcolAb, B&BAb, BIOBASE, BibLing, BiolAb, CurCont, EPB, ESPM, EntAb, GEOBASE, GenetAb, PollutAb, RefZh, ZooRec.
—BLDSC (3418.058000), CISTI, IE, Infotrieve, ingenta, Linda Hall. **CCC.**
Published by: Springer-Verlag Dordrecht (Subsidiary of: Springer Science+Business Media), Van Godewijckstraat 30, Dordrecht, 3311 GX, Netherlands. TEL 31-78-6576050, FAX 31-78-6576474, http://springerlink.metapress.com/openurl.asp?genre=journal&issn=1566-0621, http://www.springeronline.com. Ed. A Rus Hoelzel.

576.5 NLD ISSN 0929-712X

➤ **CONTEMPORARY ISSUES IN GENETICS AND EVOLUTION.** Text in English. 1993. irreg., latest vol.11, 2004. price varies. **Document type:** *Monographic series, Academic/Scholarly.*
Indexed: BIOSIS Prev.
—BLDSC (3425.184215), IE, ingenta, KNAW. **CCC.**
Published by: Springer-Verlag Dordrecht (Subsidiary of: Springer Science+Business Media), Van Godewijckstraat 30, Dordrecht, 3311 GX, Netherlands. TEL 31-78-6576050, FAX 31-78-6576474, http://www.springeronline.com.

576.5 USA ISSN 0162-7279

CRANIOFACIAL GROWTH SERIES. Text in English. 1972. irreg. price varies.
—BLDSC (3487.048000), CISTI, IE, ingenta.
Published by: University of Michigan, Center for Human Growth and Development, 300 N Ingalls, 10th Fl, Ann Arbor, MI 48109-0406. TEL 734-764-2443, FAX 734-936-9288, http://www.umich.edu/~chgdwww/.

576.5 USA ISSN 1045-4403
QH450 CODEN: CRGEEJ

➤ **CRITICAL REVIEWS IN EUKARYOTIC GENE EXPRESSION.** Text in English. 1990. q. USD 117 to individuals; USD 563 to institutions (effective 2005). adv. **Document type:** *Journal, Academic/Scholarly.* **Description:** Assimilates and presents timely concepts and experimental approaches that contribute to the advances in understanding gene regulation, organization and structure.
Related titles: Online - full text ed.: (from EBSCO Publishing).
Indexed: ASCA, Agr, B&BAb, BCI, BIOBASE, BIOSIS Prev, CIN, ChemAb, ChemTitl, ExcerpMed, GenetAb, HGA, IABS, IndMed, MBA, MEDLINE, NucAcAb.
—BLDSC (3487.475300), CASDDS, CISTI, GNLM, IDS, IE, Infotrieve, ingenta, KNAW, Linda Hall. **CCC.**
Published by: Begell House Inc., 145 Madison Ave, New York, NY 10016-6717. TEL 212-725-1999, FAX 212-213-8368, orders@begellhouse.com, http://www.begellhouse.com/crege/crege.html. Ed. Gary S Stein. Pub. Dr. William Begell. R&P, Adv. contact Jung K Ra.

➤ **CURRENT ADVANCES IN GENETICS & MOLECULAR BIOLOGY.** see *BIOLOGY—Abstracting, Bibliographies, Statistics*

➤ **CURRENT DIRECTIONS IN AUTOIMMUNITY.** see *MEDICAL SCIENCES—Allergology And Immunology*

576.5 NLD ISSN 1566-5232
CODEN: CGTUAH

➤ **CURRENT GENE THERAPY;** the international journal for in-depth reviews on gene therapy. Text in English. 2001. q. EUR 580, USD 580 to institutions (academic), print or online; EUR 1,040, USD 1,040 to corporations print or online; EUR 140, USD 140 combined subscription to individuals print & online; EUR 640, USD 640 combined subscription to institutions (academic), print & online; EUR 1,250, USD 1,250 combined subscription to corporations print & online (effective 2004). adv. **Document type:** *Journal, Academic/Scholarly.* **Description:** Focused on providing the readership with current and comprehensive reviews on all aspects of gene therapy.
Related titles: Online - full text ed.: (from EBSCO Publishing, Gale Group, IngentaConnect, Swets Information Services).
Indexed: B&BAb, BCI, BIOSIS Prev, BioEngAb, CurCont, ESPM, ExcerpMed, GenetAb, H&SSA, M&PBA.
—BLDSC (3496.950000), CISTI, IE, Infotrieve, ingenta. **CCC.**
Published by: Bentham Science Publishers Ltd., PO Box 1673, Hilversum, BR 1200, Netherlands. TEL 31-35-6923800, FAX 31-35-6980150, M.Bentham@inter.nl.net, http://www.bentham.org/cgt. Ed. Ignacio Anegon. **Subscr. addr. in the US:** Bentham Science Publishers Ltd., 1400 Pine St, PO Box 640310, San Francisco, CA 94164-0310. FAX 415-775-4503, shidding@worldonline.nl.

576.5 DEU ISSN 0172-8083
QH426 CODEN: CUGED5

➤ **CURRENT GENETICS;** lower eukaryotes and organelles. Text in English. 1980. m. EUR 1,928 combined subscription to institutions print & online eds. (effective 2005). adv. reprint service avail. from ISI. **Document type:** *Journal, Academic/Scholarly.* **Description:** Covers the genetics of eukaryotes, with an emphasis on yeasts, other fungi, protists, and cell organelles.
Related titles: Microform ed.: (from PQC); Online - full text ed.: ISSN 1432-0983 (from EBSCO Publishing, Springer LINK, Swets Information Services).
Indexed: ASCA, ASFA, AbHyg, AgBio, Agr, AgrForAb, AnBrAb, BCI, BIOBASE, BIOSIS Prev, BibAg, BioCN&I, BiolAb, CBTA, CIN, CPA, ChemAb, ChemTitl, CurCont, DBA, DSA, ESPM, EntAb, ExcerpMed, FCA, FPA, FS&TA, FaBeAb, ForAb, GenetAb, HGA, HerbAb, HortAb, IABS, ISR, IndMed, IndVet, Inpharma, MBA, MEDLINE, MaizeAb, NucAcAb, NutrAb, OrnHort, PBA, PGegResA, PGrRegA, PHN&I, PotatoAb, ProtozoAb, RM&VM, RPP, Reac, RefZh, RevApplEntom, RiceAb, S&F, S&MA, SCI, SIA, SeedAb, SoyAb, TDB, TriticAb, VITIS, VetBull, WeedAb, ZooRec.
—BLDSC (3496.960000), CASDDS, CISTI, GNLM, IDS, IE, Infotrieve, ingenta, Linda Hall. **CCC.**
Published by: Springer-Verlag (Subsidiary of: Springer Science+Business Media), Tiergartenstr 17, Heidelberg, 69121, Germany. TEL 49-6221-3450, FAX 49-6221-345229, current.genetics@gmm.gu.se. Ed. Stefan Hohmann TEL 46-31-7732595. Adv. contact Stephan Kroeck TEL 49-30-827875739. **Subscr. in the Americas to:** Springer-Verlag New York, Inc., Journal Fulfillment, PO Box 2485, Secaucus, NJ 07096-2485. TEL 800-777-4643, 201-348-4033, FAX 201-348-4505, journals@springer-ny.com, http://www.springer-ny.com; **Subscr. to:** Springer GmbH Auslieferungsgesellschaft, Haberstr 7, Heidelberg 69126, Germany. TEL 49-6221-345-0, FAX 49-6221-345-4229, subscriptions@springer.de.

576.5 NLD ISSN 1389-2029
CODEN: CGUEA8

➤ **CURRENT GENOMICS.** Text in English. 2000 (Jun.). 6/yr. EUR 1,180, USD 1,180 to institutions (academic), print or online; EUR 2,090, USD 2,090 to corporations print or online; EUR 280, USD 280 combined subscription to individuals print & online; EUR 1,295, USD 1,295 combined subscription to institutions (academic), print & online; EUR 2,500, USD 2,500 combined subscription to corporations print & online (effective 2004). adv. **Document type:** *Journal, Academic/Scholarly.* **Description:** Features reviews in genomics, functional genomics and related areas.
Related titles: Online - full text ed.: (from EBSCO Publishing, Gale Group, IngentaConnect, Swets Information Services).
Indexed: BIOBASE, BIOSIS Prev, ChemAb, EntAb, ExcerpMed, GenetAb, M&PBA, NucAcAb.
—BLDSC (3496.980000), CISTI, IE, Infotrieve. **CCC.**
Published by: Bentham Science Publishers Ltd., PO Box 1673, Hilversum, BR 1200, Netherlands. TEL 31-35-6923800, FAX 31-35-6980150, M.Bentham@inter.nl.net, http://www.bentham.org/cg. Ed. Christian Neri. **Subscr. addr. in the US:** Bentham Science Publishers Ltd., 1400 Pine St, PO Box 640310, San Francisco, CA 94164-0310. FAX 415-775-4503, shidding@worldonline.nl.

➤ **CURRENT ISSUES IN MOLECULAR BIOLOGY.** see *BIOLOGY—Microbiology*

576.5 GBR ISSN 0959-437X
QH426 CODEN: COGDET

➤ **CURRENT OPINION IN GENETICS & DEVELOPMENT.** Text in English. 1991. 6/yr. EUR 270 in Europe to individuals; JPY 32,800 in Japan to individuals; USD 293 elsewhere to individuals; EUR 1,232 in Europe to institutions; JPY 170,900 in Japan to institutions; USD 1,378 elsewhere to institutions (effective 2006). adv. bibl.; illus. back issues avail. **Document type:** *Academic/Scholarly.* **Description:** Directed toward researchers, educators and students of genetics and development. Presents review articles, followed by annotated bibliographies of references consulted. Includes a "Paper Alert" section, giving brief summaries of relevant papers recently published in other journals.
Related titles: CD-ROM ed.; Online - full text ed.: USD 227 in North America to individuals; USD 247 in North America to individuals with print ed; GBP 137 elsewhere to individuals; GBP 150 elsewhere to individuals with print ed; USD 822 in North America to institutional members includes print ed; GBP 500 elsewhere to institutional members includes print ed (effective 1999 & 2000) (from EBSCO Publishing, Gale Group, IngentaConnect, O C L C Online Computer Library Center, Inc., ScienceDirect, Swets Information Services).
Indexed: ASCA, ASFA, AbHyg, AgBio, AnBrAb, B&BAb, BCI, BIOBASE, BIOSIS Prev, BioEngAb, CIN, CPA, CTA, ChemAb, ChemTitl, CurCont, ExcerpMed, GenetAb, HGA, HelmAb, HortAb, IABS, ISR, IndMed, IndVet, Inpharma, MEDLINE, MaizeAb, NSA, NemAb, NucAcAb, NutrAb, PBA, PE&ON, PGegResA, PGrRegA, PN&I, ProtozoAb, Reac, SCI, SeedAb, TDB, VetBull, WeedAb, ZooRec.
—BLDSC (3500.775100), CASDDS, CISTI, GNLM, IDS, IE, Infotrieve, ingenta. **CCC.**
Published by: Elsevier Ltd., Current Opinion Journals (Subsidiary of: Elsevier Science & Technology), 84 Theobald's Rd., London, WC1X 8RR, United Kingdom. TEL 44-20-7611-4000, FAX 44-20-7611-4001, 44-20-7611-4468, cbiol@cursci.co.uk, http://www.elsevier.com/locate/gde, http://www.current-opinion.com. Eds. D. C. Page, Matthew P. Scott. Circ: 20,000.

▼ ➤ **CURRENT PHARMACOGENOMICS.** see *PHARMACY AND PHARMACOLOGY*

599.9 USA

CURRENT PROTOCOLS IN HUMAN GENETICS. Text in English. 2 base vols. plus q. updates. looseleaf. USD 710 combined subscription to institutions base vols. & updates; USD 430 renewals to institutions (effective 2006). **Document type:** *Academic/Scholarly.*
Related titles: CD-ROM ed.: USD 695 combined subscription to institutions base vol. & updates; USD 425 renewals to institutions (effective 2006); Online - full text ed.
Published by: John Wiley & Sons, Inc., 111 River St, Hoboken, NJ 07030-5774. TEL 201-748-6000, 800-825-7550, FAX 201-748-5915, protocol@wiley.com, http://www.does.org/masterli/cphg.html, http://www.wiley.com. **Subscr. to:** John Wiley & Sons Ltd., The Atrium, Southern Gate, Chichester, West Sussex PO19 8SQ, United Kingdom. TEL 44-1243-779777, FAX 44-1243-775878, cs-journals@wiley.co.uk; PO Box 5597, Somerset, NJ 08875. TEL 732-650-4630, FAX 732-650-4623.

576.5 CHE ISSN 1424-8581
QH431 CODEN: CGRYAJ

➤ **CYTOGENETIC AND GENOME RESEARCH.** Text in English, French, German. 1962. 16/yr. (in 4 vols.). CHF 4,420 in Europe to institutions; CHF 4,474.40 elsewhere to institutions; CHF 4,764 combined subscription in Europe to institutions print & online eds.; CHF 4,818.40 combined subscription elsewhere to institutions print & online eds. (effective 2006). adv. charts; illus. index. reprints avail. **Document type:** *Journal, Academic/Scholarly.*
Former titles (until 2002): Cytogenetics and Cell Genetics (0301-0171); (until 1973): Cytogenetics (0011-4537)
Related titles: Microform ed.; Online - full text ed.: ISSN 1424-859X. CHF 4,308 to institutions (effective 2006) (from bigchalk, EBSCO Publishing, O C L C Online Computer Library Center, Inc., ProQuest Information & Learning, Swets Information Services).
Indexed: ASCA, ASFA, AbAn, AbHyg, AgBio, AnBrAb, B&BAb, BBCI, BCI, BIOBASE, BIOSIS Prev, BiolAb, CIN, ChemAb, ChemTitl, CurCont, DSA, ExcerpMed, FCA, GenetAb, HGA, HortAb, IABS, ISR, IndMed, IndVet, Inpharma, MBA, MEDLINE, MaizeAb, NSCI, NemAb, NucAcAb, PBA, PE&ON, PGegResA, PN&I, PoultAb, Reac, SCI, SFA, SoyAb, TDB, TriticAb, VetBull, WeedAb, ZooRec.
—BLDSC (3506.757000), CASDDS, CISTI, GNLM, IDS, IE, Infotrieve, ingenta, KNAW, Linda Hall. **CCC.**
Published by: S. Karger AG, Allschwilerstr 10, Basel, 4009, Switzerland. TEL 41-61-3061111, FAX 41-61-3061234, karger@karger.ch, http://www.karger.com/CGR, http://www.karger.ch. Ed. M Schmid. adv.: page CHF 1,710. Circ: 1,500 (paid and controlled).

572.8 GBR ISSN 1043-4666
QR185.8.C95 CODEN: CYTIE9
➤ **CYTOKINE.** Text in English. 1989. 24/yr. EUR 620 in Europe to individuals; JPY 67,000 in Japan to individuals; USD 628 to individuals except Europe and Japan; EUR 1,435 in Europe to institutions; JPY 154,800 in Japan to institutions; USD 1,274 to institutions except Europe and Japan (effective 2006). adv. reprints avail. **Document type:** *Academic/Scholarly.*
Description: Publishes original work on all cytokines including interleukins, cytotoxins, hematopoietic factors, transforming growth factors, interferons, and other known or new cytokines.
Related titles: Online - full text ed.: ISSN 1096-0023. USD 1,344 (effective 2002) (from EBSCO Publishing, Gale Group, IngentaConnect, O C L C Online Computer Library Center, Inc., ScienceDirect, Swets Information Services).
Indexed: ASCA, ASFA, AbHyg, AgBio, AnBrAb, BBCI, BIOSIS Prev, BiolAb, CIN, ChemAb, ChemTitl, CurCont, DSA, ExcerpMed, HelmAb, ISR, ImmunAb, IndMed, IndVet, Inpharma, MEDLINE, NutrAb, PBA, PE&ON, PN&I, PoultAb, ProtozoAb, RA&MP, RM&VM, RPP, Reac, RevApplEntom, SCI, SIA, SoyAb, TDB, TriticAb, VetBull.
—BLDSC (3506.778000), CASDDS, CISTI, GNLM, IDS, IE, Infotrieve, ingenta, KNAW. **CCC.**
Published by: (International Cytokine Society), Academic Press (Subsidiary of: Elsevier Science & Technology), Harcourt Pl, 32 Jamestown Rd, London, NW1 7BY, United Kingdom. TEL 44-20-7424-4200, FAX 44-20-7483-2293, apsubs@acad.com, http://www.elsevier.com/locate/cytokine. Eds. Gordon W Duff, Scott K Durum. R&P Catherine John. Adv. contact Nik Screen. **Subscr. to:** Harcourt Publishers Ltd., Foots Cray High St, Sidcup, Kent DA14 5HP, United Kingdom. TEL 44-208-3085700, FAX 44-20-83090807.

576.5 USA ISSN 0095-4527
QH426 CODEN: CYGEDX
➤ **CYTOLOGY AND GENETICS.** Text in English. 1974. bi-m. USD 2,210 per vol. in US & Canada; USD 2,510 per vol. elsewhere (effective 2006). bibl.; charts; illus.; abstr. index. back issues avail. **Document type:** *Journal, Academic/Scholarly.* **Description:** Covers genetic structure of populations, genotoxic effects in plants, animals and humans, heredity, breeding, and genetic diagnostics.
Related titles: ♦ Translation of: Tsitologiya i Genetika. ISSN 0564-3783.
Indexed: BiolAb, ExcerpMed, SFA, WildRev, ZooRec.
—BLDSC (0411.088000), CISTI, GNLM, IE, Infotrieve, ingenta. **CCC.**
Published by: (Natsional'na Akademiya Nauk Ukrainy UKR), Allerton Press, Inc., 18 W 27th St, New York, NY 10001. TEL 646-424-9686, FAX 646-424-9695, journals@allertonpress.com, http://www.allertonpress.com/journals/cyt.htm. Ed. Yuri Y. Gleba.

581.3 CZE ISSN 1212-1975
CODEN: SUSLDO
➤ **CZECH JOURNAL OF GENETICS AND PLANT BREEDING.** Text and summaries in English; Summaries in Czech, Slovak. 1965. q. USD 64 (effective 2003). bk.rev. back issues avail. **Document type:** *Academic/Scholarly.* **Description:** Publishes original scientific studies concerning genetics, plant selection, seed growing, biology of plants, and phytopathology.
Former titles (until 1998): Genetika a Slechteni (0862-8629); (until 1989): U V T I Z Sbornik - Genetika a Slechteni (0036-5378)
Indexed: AgBio, BibAg, BiolAb, CPA, ChemAb, FCA, HerbAb, HortAb, MaizeAb, NemAb, OrnHort, PBA, PGegResA, PGrRegA, PHN&I, PotatoAb, RA&MP, RPP, RefZh, RevApplEntom, RiceAb, S&F, SeedAb, SoyAb, TriticAb, VITIS, WeedAb.
—BLDSC (3507.371470), CASDDS, CISTI, IE, ingenta.
Published by: Ceska Akademie Zemedelskych Ved, Ustav Zemedelskych a Potravinarskych Informaci/Czech Academy of Agricultural Sciences, Institute of Agricultural and Food Information, Slezska 7, Prague 2, 120 56, Czech Republic. TEL 420-2-227010203, FAX 420-2-227010116, braun@uzpi.cz, http://www.cazv.cz. Ed. Mrs. Marcela Braunova. R&P Mr. Jan Rydlo. Circ: 300. **Co-sponsor:** Ceska Akademie Zemedelskych Ved/Czech Academy of Agricultural Sciences.

➤ **D N A PROBES.** (Deoxyribonucleic Acid) see *BIOLOGY—Abstracting, Bibliographies, Statistics*

➤ **DEVELOPMENTAL & COMPARATIVE IMMUNOLOGY.** see *MEDICAL SCIENCES—Allergology And Immunology*

➤ **DEVELOPMENTS IN PLANT GENETICS AND BREEDING.** see *BIOLOGY—Botany*

576.8 GBR ISSN 1476-0681
➤ **DIRECTED & APPLIED EVOLUTION.** Text in English. 2002. irreg. free (effective 2004). **Document type:** *Journal, Academic/Scholarly.* **Description:** Publishes research and commentary on evolutionary processes and the evolutionary manipulation of nucleic acids, genes, proteins, metabolism, and organisms.
Media: Online - full content.
Published by: BioMed Central Ltd. (Subsidiary of: Current Science Ltd), Middlesex House, 34-42 Cleveland St, London, W1T 4LB, United Kingdom. TEL 44-20-76319131, FAX 44-20-76319923, daevo@ellingtonlab.org, info@biomedcentral.com, http://www.daevo.com, http://www.biomedcentral.com. Eds. Andrew Ellington, Jim Bull.

576.5 USA ISSN 0070-7333
QL537.M6
DROSOPHILA INFORMATION SERVICE. Text in English. 1934. a. USD 15 domestic; USD 18 foreign (effective 2005). **Document type:** *Academic/Scholarly.* **Description:** Publishes research articles, descriptions of new mutations, stock lists, directory information, as well as general interest topics for Drosophila researchers.
Indexed: ZooRec.
Address: Department of Zoology, 730 Van Vleet Oval, University of Oklahoma, Norman, OK 73019. TEL 405-325-4821, FAX 405-325-7560, jthompson@ou.edu, http://www.ou.edu/journals/dis/. Ed. James N Thompson Jr. Circ: 1,200.

576.5 GBR ISSN 1469-221X
QH506 CODEN: ERMEAX
➤ **E M B O REPORTS.** (European Molecular Biology Organization) Text in English. 2000 (Jul). m. EUR 129 combined subscription in Europe to individuals print & online eds.; USD 136 combined subscription in the Americas to individuals print & online eds.; GBP 83 combined subscription to individuals in the UK & elsewhere; print & onlie eds. (effective 2006). adv. bk.rev. back issues avail. **Document type:** *Journal, Academic/Scholarly.* **Description:** Intended for rapid publications of short, high quality papers in all areas of molecular biology.
Related titles: Online - full text ed.: E M B O Reports Online. ISSN 1469-3178. 2000 (from EBSCO Publishing, Gale Group, HighWire Press, O C L C Online Computer Library Center, Inc., Swets Information Services).
Indexed: AbHyg, AgBio, AnBrAb, BBCI, BCI, BIOBASE, BIOSIS Prev, BiolAb, CPA, ChemAb, CurCont, DSA, ExcerpMed, FCA, ForAb, HelmAb, HortAb, ISR, IndVet, Inpharma, MEDLINE, MaizeAb, NemAb, NutrAb, PBA, PE&ON, PGegResA, PN&I, PoultAb, ProtozoAb, RDA, RM&VM, RPP, Reac, RefZh, S&F, SCI, SoyAb, TDB, VetBull, WAE&RSA, WeedAb, ZooRec.
—BLDSC (3733.086000), CISTI, IE, Infotrieve, ingenta, Linda Hall. **CCC.**
Published by: (European Molecular Biology Organization), Nature Publishing Group (Subsidiary of: Macmillan Publishers Ltd.), The MacMillan Building, 4 Crinan St, London, N1 9XW, United Kingdom. TEL 44-20-78334000, FAX 44-20-78433601, subscriptions@nature.com, NatureReviews@nature.com, http://www.emboreports.org, http://www.nature.com. Ed. Frank Gannon. adv.: page GBP 260, page USD 470. Circ: 1,000.

576.5 EGY ISSN 0046-161X
QH426 CODEN: EJGCA9
EGYPTIAN JOURNAL OF GENETICS AND CYTOLOGY. Text in Arabic. 1972. s-a. USD 50 to individuals; USD 150 to institutions (effective 2001). adv. abstr. reprint service avail. from PQC. **Document type:** *Journal, Academic/Scholarly.*
Indexed: AnBrAb, BiolAb, CTFA, CurCont, DSA, ExcerpMed, FaBeAb, MaizeAb, SeedAb, SoyAb, TriticAb, WeedAb, ZooRec.
—CISTI.
Published by: Egyptian Society of Genetics and Cytology, University of Cairo, Faculty of Agriculture, Department of Genetics, Giza, Egypt. http://derp.sti.sci.eg/data/0116.htm. Eds. A R Selim, Dr. S. H. Hassanien. R&P Dr. S. H. Hassanien. Adv. contact Dr. Fatthy M. Abdel-Tawab. Circ: 500.

576.5 AUT ISSN 1020-5209
EMERGING TECHNOLOGY SERIES: GENETIC ENGINEERING AND BIOTECHNOLOGY. Text in German. 1982. q. USD 40; free in developing nations.
Formerly (until 1996): Genetic Engineering and Biotechnology: Monitor (1012-537X)
Indexed: WAE&RSA.
—CISTI.
Published by: (Statistical and Networking), United Nations Industrial Development Organization, Postfach 300, Vienna, W 1400, Austria. TEL 43-1-26026-3736, FAX 43-1-2606-6843, drhind@unido.org, http://www.unido.org. Ed. V Campbell. Circ: 1,800.

ENDOCYTOBIOSIS AND CELL RESEARCH. see *BIOLOGY—Cytology And Histology*

ENTREZ DOCUMENT RETRIEVAL SYSTEM. see *BIOLOGY—Abstracting, Bibliographies, Statistics*

576.549 USA ISSN 0893-6692
QH465.C5 CODEN: EMMUEG
➤ **ENVIRONMENTAL AND MOLECULAR MUTAGENESIS.** Text in English. 1979. 9/yr. USD 855 domestic to institutions; USD 963 in Canada & Mexico to institutions; USD 1,026 elsewhere to institutions; USD 941 combined subscription domestic to institutions print & online eds.; USD 1,049 combined subscription in Canada & Mexico to institutions print & online eds.; USD 1,112 combined subscription elsewhere to institutions print & online eds. (effective 2006). adv. bk.rev. bibl.; illus. **Document type:** *Journal, Academic/Scholarly.*
Description: Provides an international forum for research on basic mechanisms of mutation, the detection of mutagens, and the implications of environmental mutagens for human health.
Formerly: Environmental Mutagenesis (0192-2521)
Related titles: Online - full content ed.: ISSN 1098-2280. USD 855 to institutions (effective 2006); Online - full text ed.: (from EBSCO Publishing, Swets Information Services, Wiley InterScience); ♦ Supplement(s): Environmental and Molecular Mutagenesis. Supplement. ISSN 0898-3003.
Indexed: ASCA, ASFA, AbHyg, AgBio, AgrForAb, AnBrAb, B&BAb, BIOBASE, BIOSIS Prev, BiolAb, CIN, CSNB, ChemAb, ChemTitl, CurCont, DSA, DokArb, ESPM, ExcerpMed, FS&TA, GenetAb, HGA, HortAb, IABS, ISR, IndMed, IndVet, Inpharma, LHB, MEDLINE, NRN, NemAb, NucAcAb, NutrAb, PBA, PE&ON, PGrRegA, PollutAb, ProtozoAb, RM&VM, Reac, RefZh, RevApplEntom, SCI, SFA, SWRA, TDB, ToxAb, VetBull, WeedAb, WildRev.
—BLDSC (3791.383100), CASDDS, CISTI, GNLM, IDS, IE, Infotrieve, ingenta, Linda Hall. **CCC.**
Published by: (Environmental Mutagen Society), John Wiley & Sons, Inc., 111 River St, Hoboken, NJ 07030-5774. TEL 201-748-6000, 800-825-7550, FAX 201-748-5915, uscs-wis@wiley.com, http://www3.interscience.wiley.com/cgi-bin/jhome/10009058, http://www.wiley.com. Ed. Robert H Heflich. adv.: B&W page GBP 640, color page GBP 1,515; trim 174 x 254. Circ: 1,500. **Subscr. outside the Americas to:** John Wiley & Sons Ltd., The Atrium, Southern Gate, Chichester, West Sussex PO19 8SQ, United Kingdom. TEL 44-1243-843335, 0800-243407, FAX 44-1243-843232, cs-journals@wiley.co.uk.

576.549 USA ISSN 0898-3003
ENVIRONMENTAL AND MOLECULAR MUTAGENESIS. SUPPLEMENT. Text in English. 1987. irreg., latest vol.33, 2002. price varies. back issues avail. **Document type:** *Academic/Scholarly.*
Related titles: ♦ Supplement to: Environmental and Molecular Mutagenesis. ISSN 0893-6692.
Indexed: BiolAb, ExcerpMed, IndMed.
—BLDSC (3791.383110), IE, ingenta. **CCC.**
Published by: (Environmental Mutagen Society), John Wiley & Sons, Inc., 111 River St, Hoboken, NJ 07030-5774. TEL 201-748-6000, FAX 201-748-5915, uscs-wis@wiley.com, http://www.wiley.com.

613.94 USA
EUGENICS SPECIAL INTEREST GROUP BULLETIN. Text in English. 1970. irreg. USD 6. **Document type:** *Bulletin.*
Published by: Eugenics Special Interest Group, PO Box 138, East Schodack, NY 12163. TEL 518-732-2390, willardh2@juno.com. Ed. Willard Hoyt.

572.8 FRA ISSN 1148-5493
CODEN: ECYNEJ
➤ **EUROPEAN CYTOKINE NETWORK.** Text in English. 1990. 4/yr. EUR 213 combined subscription domestic to individuals print & online eds.; EUR 224 combined subscription in the European Union to individuals print & online eds.; EUR 234 combined subscription elsewhere to individuals print & online eds.; EUR 374 combined subscription domestic to institutions print & online eds.; EUR 385 combined subscription in the European Union to institutions print & online eds.; EUR 395 combined subscription elsewhere to institutions print & online eds. (effective 2006). **Document type:** *Journal, Academic/Scholarly.* **Description:** Serves as a link between immunological, biological, molecular, hematological and oncological researchers and clinicians.
Related titles: Online - full text ed.: (from EBSCO Publishing).
Indexed: ASCA, AbHyg, AgBio, AnBrAb, BBCI, BIOBASE, BIOSIS Prev, BiolAb, CIN, ChemAb, ChemTitl, CurCont, DSA, ExcerpMed, ForAb, HelmAb, IABS, ISR, IndMed, Inpharma, MEDLINE, NutrAb, PE&ON, ProtozoAb, RA&MP, RM&VM, Reac, RevApplEntom, SCI, TDB.
—BLDSC (3829.688820), CASDDS, CISTI, GNLM, IDS, IE, Infotrieve, ingenta, KNAW. **CCC.**
Published by: John Libbey Eurotext, 127 Avenue de la Republique, Montrouge, 92120, France. TEL 33-1-46730660, FAX 33-1-40840999, contact@jle.com, http://www.john-libbey-eurotext.fr. Eds. Didier Fradelizi, Jacques Bertoglio. **Subscr. to:** A T E I, 3 av. Pierre Kerautret, Romainville 92230, France. TEL 33-1-48408686, FAX 33-1-48400731, atei@club-internet.fr.

B

▼ new title ➤ refereed ✶ unverified ♦ full entry avail.

599.9 GBR ISSN 1018-4813
RB155 CODEN: EJHGEU
➤ **EUROPEAN JOURNAL OF HUMAN GENETICS.** Text in English. 1993. 12/yr. EUR 1,300 in Europe to institutions; USD 1,404 in the Americas to institutions; GBP 838 to institutions in the UK & elsewhere; EUR 600 combined subscription in Europe to individuals print & online eds.; USD 660 combined subscription in the Americas to individuals print & online eds.; GBP 387 combined subscription to individuals in the UK & elsewhere; print & online eds. (effective 2006). adv. charts; illus.; stat. back issues avail. **Document type:** *Journal, Academic/Scholarly.* **Description:** Contains information on the development of research, education and medical application in the field of human genetics.
Related titles: Microform ed.: (from PQC); Online - full text ed.: (from EBSCO Publishing, O C L C Online Computer Library Center, Inc., Swets Information Services).
Indexed: ASCA, AbHyg, AgBio, AnBrAb, B&BAb, BCI, BIOSIS Prev, BiolAb, CIN, ChemAb, ChemTitl, CurCont, ExcerpMed, Faml, GenetAb, ISR, IndMed, Inpharma, MEDLINE, PE&ON, PGegResA, RM&VM, Reac, SCI, TDB.
—BLDSC (3829.730020), CASDDS, CISTI, GNLM, IDS, IE, Infotrieve, ingenta, KNAW. **CCC.**
Published by: (European Society of Human Genetics), Nature Publishing Group (Subsidiary of: Macmillan Publishers Ltd.), The MacMillan Building, 4 Crinan St, London, N1 9XW, United Kingdom. TEL 44-20-78334000, FAX 44-20-78433601, subscriptions@nature.com, http://www.nature.com/ejhg. Ed. Gert-Jan B van Ommen TEL 31-71-5276315. **Subscr. to:** Brunel Rd, Houndmills, Basingstoke, Hamps RG21 6XS, United Kingdom. TEL 44-1256-329242, FAX 44-1256-812358, subscriptions@nature.com.

B

576.5 FRA ISSN 1769-7212
CODEN: AGTQAH
➤ **EUROPEAN JOURNAL OF MEDICAL GENETICS.** Text and summaries in English. 1957. 6/yr. EUR 433 in Europe to institutions; JPY 57,400 in Japan to institutions; USD 483 to institutions except Europe and Japan (effective 2006). bk.rev. charts; illus. **Document type:** *Journal, Academic/Scholarly.* **Description:** Covers all aspects of human and medical genetics and of the genetics of experimental models. Also includes reports on rare genetic variants, DNA variants, gene mapping, and linkage studies.
Formerly (until 2004): Annales de Genetique (0003-3995)
Related titles: Online - full text ed.: (from EBSCO Publishing, Gale Group, IngentaConnect, ScienceDirect, Swets Information Services).
Indexed: ASCA, AbAn, AnBrAb, BCI, BDM&CN, BIOBASE, BIOSIS Prev, BiolAb, ChemAb, CurCont, DSA, DentInd, ExcerpMed, IABS, ISR, IndMed, Inpharma, MEDLINE, Reac, RefZh, SCI, SFA, SSCI, WildRev, ZooRec.
—BLDSC (0975.300000), CASDDS, CISTI, GNLM, IDS, IE, Infotrieve, ingenta. **CCC.**
Published by: (Semaine des Hopitaux), Elsevier France, Editions Scientifiques et Medicales (Subsidiary of: Elsevier Science & Technology), 23 Rue Linois, Paris, 75724, France. TEL 33-1-71724600, FAX 33-1-71724650, academic@elsevier-fr.com, http://www.elsevier.com/locate/ejmg. Ed. K Devriendt. Circ: 1,000. **Subscr. to:** Elsevier BV, PO Box 211, Amsterdam 1000 AE, Netherlands. TEL 31-20-485-3757, FAX 31-20-485-3432, nlinfo-f@elsevier.nl, http://www.elsevier.nl.

576.8 USA ISSN 0014-3820
QH301 CODEN: EVOLAO
➤ **EVOLUTION**; international journal of organic evolution. Text in English. 1947. m. USD 300 domestic print & online eds.; USD 320 foreign print & online eds. (effective 2004). adv. bk.rev. bibl.; charts; illus.; stat. index. back issues avail.; reprints avail. **Document type:** *Journal, Academic/Scholarly.* **Description:** Reports observations and perspectives in evolutionary biology.
Related titles: Microform ed.: (from PQC); Online - full text ed.: (from BioOne, C S A, EBSCO Publishing, Gale Group, H.W. Wilson, JSTOR (Web-based Journal Archive), Northern Light Technology, Inc., O C L C Online Computer Library Center, Inc.).
Indexed: ASCA, ASFA, AbAn, AbHyg, AgBio, Agr, AgrForAb, AnBeAb, AnBrAb, ApEcolAb, ApicAb, B&AI, BIOBASE, BIOSIS Prev, BibAg, BioCN&I, BiolAb, BiolDig, CIN, CIS, CPA, ChemAb, ChemTitl, CurCont, DSA, ESPM, EntAb, ExcerpMed, FCA, FPA, FS&TA, ForAb, GEOBASE, GSI, GenetAb, HGA, HelmAb, HerbAb, HortAb, IAA, IABS, ISR, IndMed, IndVet, Inpharma, KWIWR, MBA, MEDLINE, MaizeAb, NemAb, NutrAb, OceAb, OrnHort, PBA, PE&ON, PGegResA, PHN&I, PhilInd, PlantSci, PoultAb, ProtozoAb, RA&MP, RM&VM, RPP, Reac, RefZh, RevApplEntom, S&F, S&VD, SCI, SFA, SPPI, SSCI, SeedAb, SoyAb, TDB, TriticAb, VITIS, VetBull, WeedAb, WildRev, ZooRec.
—BLDSC (3834.000000), CASDDS, CISTI, IE, Infotrieve, ingenta, Linda Hall.
Published by: Society for the Study of Evolution, c/o Allen Press, Inc, Box 1897, Lawrence, KS 66044-8897. TEL 785-843-1235, 800-627-0629, FAX 785-843-1274, ssoe@allenpress.com, http://lsvl.la.asu.edu/evolution/, http://www.lsvl.la.asu.edu/evolution. Ed. Donald M Waller. Circ: 4,500.

576.8 USA ISSN 0071-3260
QH366.A1 CODEN: EVBIAI
➤ **EVOLUTIONARY BIOLOGY.** Text in English. 1967. irreg., latest vol.33, 2003. price varies. **Document type:** *Monographic series, Academic/Scholarly.*
Indexed: ASCA, AbAn, Agr, BIOSIS Prev, BiolAb, BiolDig, CIN, ChemAb, ChemTitl, ISR, SCI, SFA, SSCI, WildRev, ZooRec.
—BLDSC (3834.400000), CASDDS, CISTI, IDS, IE, ingenta, KNAW, Linda Hall. **CCC.**
Published by: Springer-Verlag New York, Inc. (Subsidiary of: Springer Science+Business Media), 233 Spring St, New York, NY 10013. TEL 212-460-1500, FAX 212-460-1575, service@springer-ny.com, http://www.springer-ny.com.

➤ **EVOLUTIONARY FOUNDATIONS OF HUMAN BEHAVIOR.** see *PSYCHOLOGY*

➤ **EXCERPTA MEDICA. SECTION 22: HUMAN GENETICS.** see *BIOLOGY—Abstracting, Bibliographies, Statistics*

➤ **F E M S YEAST RESEARCH.** see *BIOLOGY—Microbiology*

➤ **FAMILIAL CANCER.** see *MEDICAL SCIENCES—Oncology*

576.5 USA ISSN 1541-4728
▼ **FRONTIERS IN GENOMIC MEDICINE.** Text in English. forthcoming 2006 (Jun). q. **Document type:** *Journal, Academic/Scholarly.*
Published by: Stefan University Press, PO Box 2946, La Jolla, CA 92038-2946. FAX 858-395-6768, press@stefan-university.edu, http://www.stefan-university.edu/press.htm. Ed., Pub. Vladislav Stefan.

576.5 DEU ISSN 1438-793X
QH447 CODEN: FIGUBY
➤ **FUNCTIONAL & INTEGRATIVE GENOMICS.** Text in English. 2000. q. EUR 113.30 combined subscription to institutions print & online eds. (effective 2005). adv. reprint service avail. from PSC. **Document type:** *Journal, Academic/Scholarly.* **Description:** Devoted to large-scale studies of genomes and their functions, including systems analysis of biological processes..
Related titles: Microform ed.; Online - full text ed.: ISSN 1438-7948 (from EBSCO Publishing, ProQuest Information & Learning, Springer LINK, Swets Information Services).
Indexed: Agr, BIOBASE, BIOSIS Prev, BiolAb, ChemAb, ExcerpMed, ZooRec.
—BLDSC (4055.595000), CISTI, IE, Infotrieve. **CCC.**
Published by: Springer-Verlag (Subsidiary of: Springer Science+Business Media), Tiergartenstr 17, Heidelberg, 69121, Germany. TEL 49-6221-3450, FAX 49-6221-345229, http://link.springer.de/link/service/journals/10142/index.htm. Ed. Rudi Appels. Adv. contact Stephan Kroeck TEL 49-30-827875739. **Subscr. in the Americas to:** Springer-Verlag New York, Inc., Journal Fulfillment, PO Box 2485, Secaucus, NJ 07096-2485. TEL 800-777-4643, 201-348-4033, FAX 201-348-4505, journals@springer-ny.com, http://www.springer-ny.com; **Subscr. to:** Springer GmbH Auslieferungsgesellschaft, Haberstr 7, Heidelberg 69126, Germany. TEL 49-6221-345-0, FAX 49-6221-345-4229, subscriptions@springer.de.

➤ **GATHERED VIEW.** see *MEDICAL SCIENCES*

➤ **GENBANK.** see *BIOLOGY—Biochemistry*

➤ **GENE.** see *BIOLOGY—Biotechnology*

576.5 572.8 USA ISSN 1052-2166
QH450 CODEN: GEEXEJ
➤ **GENE EXPRESSION**; international journal of molecular and cellular science. Text in English. 1991. bi-m. USD 95 combined subscription domestic to individuals print & online eds.; USD 135 combined subscription foreign to individuals print & online eds.; USD 700 combined subscription domestic to institutions print & online eds.; USD 725 combined subscription foreign to institutions print & online eds. (effective 2005). adv. back issues avail. **Document type:** *Journal, Academic/Scholarly.* **Description:** Publishes papers on all aspects of gene including its structure, function and regulation in prokaryotes, eukaryotes and viruses. Topics on DNA replication, DNA repair, gene transcription, transcriptional control, RNA processing, posttranscriptional control, oncogenes, molecular mechanisms of action of hormones, molecular mechanisms of cellular differentiation, growth and development, protein syntheses, and posttranslational control.
Related titles: Online - full text ed.: ISSN 1555-3884 (from EBSCO Publishing, Gale Group, IngentaConnect).
Indexed: ASFA, Agr, BCI, BIOBASE, BIOSIS Prev, BiolAb, ESPM, EntAb, ExcerpMed, GenetAb, IABS, IndMed, MBA, MEDLINE, NucAcAb.
—BLDSC (4096.402395), CASDDS, CISTI, GNLM, IDS, IE, Infotrieve, ingenta, KNAW. **CCC.**
Published by: Cognizant Communication Corporation, 3 Hartsdale Rd, Elmsford, NY 10523-3701. TEL 914-592-7720, FAX 914-592-8981, cogcomm@aol.com, http://www.cognizantcommunication.com. Ed. Samson Jacob. Pub., R&P Robert N Miranda. Adv. contact Lori Miranda.

576.5 NLD ISSN 1567-133X
QH450 CODEN: GEPEAD
GENE EXPRESSION PATTERNS. Abbreviated title: G E P. Text in English. 2001. 8/yr. with Mechanisms of Development. **Document type:** *Journal, Academic/Scholarly.* **Description:** Devoted to the publication of "cloning and expression" papers, papers reporting patterns of expression of interesting or important genes during development, or the results of molecular or gene expression screens analysing interesting developmental events or stages.
Related titles: Online - full text ed.: (from EBSCO Publishing, Gale Group, IngentaConnect, ScienceDirect, Swets Information Services); ♦ Series of: Brain Research. ISSN 0006-8993; ♦ Supplement to: Brain Research. ISSN 0006-8993.
Indexed: B&BAb, BBCI, BIOSIS Prev, BiolAb, ChemAb, ExcerpMed, GenetAb, NucAcAb, RefZh.
—BLDSC (4096.402453), CISTI, IE, ingenta. **CCC.**
Published by: Elsevier BV (Subsidiary of: Elsevier Science & Technology), Radarweg 29, Amsterdam, 1043 NX, Netherlands. TEL 31-20-4853911, FAX 31-20-4852457, nlinfo-f@elsevier.nl, http://www.elsevier.com/locate/modgep, http://www.elsevier.nl.

576.5 USA
THE GENE LETTER. Text in English. 1996. bi-m. **Document type:** *Newsletter.* **Description:** Covers the scientific, ethical, legal and social aspects of genetics.
Media: Online - full text.
Published by: (Shriver Center, Inc.), Shriver Center, 200 Trapelo Rd, Waltham, MA 02452. TEL 781-642-0292, FAX 781-642-0292, dwertz@shriver.org, webmaster@shriver.org, http://www.geneletter.org. Eds. Dorothy C Wertz, Philip R Reilly. R&P Dorothy C Wertz. Circ: 25,500.

GENE THERAPY (SHEFFIELD). see *BIOLOGY—Abstracting, Bibliographies, Statistics*

576.5 660.6 NLD ISSN 1388-9532
CODEN: GTREBR
➤ **GENE THERAPY AND REGULATION**; an international interdisciplinary journal. Text in English. 1999. q. EUR 225, USD 281 combined subscription print & online eds. (effective 2005). back issues avail.; reprint service avail. from PSC. **Document type:** *Journal, Academic/Scholarly.* **Description:** Explores all aspects of research on gene therapy and ancillary basic cell- and molecular biology approaches, including molecular cloning, sequencing, and gene regulation.
Related titles: Online - full content ed.: 2000; Online - full text ed.: ISSN 1568-5586. EUR 203, USD 253 (effective 2005) (from EBSCO Publishing, Gale Group, IngentaConnect, Kluwer Online, O C L C Online Computer Library Center, Inc., Ovid Technologies, Inc., Springer LINK, Swets Information Services).
Indexed: B&BAb, BIOBASE, BioEngAb, ChemAb, ExcerpMed, GenetAb, M&PBA.
—BLDSC (4096.402728), CISTI, IE. **CCC.**
Published by: V S P (Subsidiary of: Brill Academic Publishers), Brill Academic Publishers, PO Box 9000, Leiden, 2300 PA, Netherlands. TEL 31-71-5353500, FAX 31-71-5317532, vsppub@brill.nl, http://www.vsppub.com/journals/jn-GenTheReg.html. Ed. Roger Bertolotti TEL 33-4-93817381. **Dist. by:** Extenza - Turpin, Pegasus Dr, Stratton Business Park, Biggleswade, Beds SG18 8TQ, United Kingdom. TEL 44-1767-604954, FAX 44-1767-601640, marketing@extenza-turpin.com, http://www.extenza-turpin.com.

576.5 USA
▼ **GENE THERAPY BUSINESS NEWS.** Text in English. 2003. bi-w. USD 295 to corporations (effective 2003). **Document type:** *Academic/Scholarly.* **Description:** Covers news of the more than 160 global public and private companies involved in gene therapy research.
Media: Online - full content.
Published by: DataTrends Publications, Inc., PO Box 4460, Leesburg, VA 20177-8541. TEL 703-779-0574, FAX 703-779-2267, info@datatrendspublications.com, http://www.datatrendspublications.com/GTBN.htm, http://www.datatrendspublications.com/default.htm.

576.5 GBR ISSN 1462-6438
GENES. Text in English. 1983. irreg. price varies.
—BLDSC (4111.759600).
Published by: Oxford University Press, Great Clarendon St, Oxford, OX2 6DP, United Kingdom. TEL 44-1865-556767, FAX 44-1865-556646, enquiry@oup.co.uk, http://www.oup.co.uk/.

576.5 USA ISSN 0890-9369
QH426 CODEN: GEDEEP
➤ **GENES & DEVELOPMENT.** Text in English. 1987. s-m. USD 140 domestic to individuals; USD 224 in Canada & Mexico to individuals; USD 260 elsewhere to individuals; USD 1,058 domestic to institutions; USD 1,142 in Canada & Mexico to institutions; USD 1,178 elsewhere to institutions; USD 196 domestic to students; USD 232 foreign to students (effective 2005). adv. illus. Index. back issues avail.; reprint service avail. from PSC. **Document type:** *Journal, Academic/Scholarly.* **Description:** Publishes research papers of general interest and biological significance in molecular biology, molecular genetics, and related areas.

Related titles: Online - full text ed.: ISSN 1549-5477. 1997 (from EBSCO Publishing, HighWire Press, National Library of Medicine).

Indexed: ASCA, ASFA, AbAn, AbHyg, AgBio, AgrForAb, AnBrAb, B&AI, BCI, BIOBASE, BIOSIS Prev, BioCN&I, BiolAb, BiolDig, CIN, CPA, CTA, ChemAb, ChemTitl, CurCont, DSA, ESPM, EntAb, ExcerpMed, FCA, GSI, GenetAb, HGA, HelmAb, HortAb, IABS, ISR, IndMed, IndVet, Inpharma, MBA, MEDLINE, MaizeAb, NSA, NemAb, NucAcAb, NutrAb, OrnHort, PBA, PE&ON, PGegResA, PGrRegA, PN&I, PoultAb, ProtozoAb, RM&VM, RPP, Reac, RefZh, RevApplEntom, RiceAb, S&F, SCI, SSCI, SeedAb, Telegen, TriticAb, VetBull, WeedAb, WildRev, e-psyche.

—BLDSC (4111.759700), CASDDS, CISTI, GNLM, IDS, IE, Infotrieve, ingenta, Linda Hall. **CCC.**

Published by: (Genetics Society), Cold Spring Harbor Laboratory Press, Publications Department, 500 Sunnyside Blvd., Woodbury, NY 11797-2924. TEL 516-422-4100, 800-843-4388, FAX 516-422-4097, cshpress@cshl.edu, http://www.genesdev.org/, http://www.cshl.org. Ed. T Grodzicker. Adv. contact Ms. Marcie Siconolfi TEL 516-422-4010.

576.5 JPN ISSN 1341-7568
QH426 CODEN: GGSYF5

➤ **GENES & GENETIC SYSTEMS.** Text in English. 1921. bi-m. USD 130. adv. bk.rev. back issues avail. **Document type:** *Journal, Academic/Scholarly.* **Description:** Covers a wide range in the field of genetics: general genetics, molecular genetics, cytogenetics, population genetics and evolution, and genome research.

Formerly (until vol.70, no.6, 1996): Idengaku Zasshi/Japanese Journal of Genetics (0021-504X)

Related titles: Online - full text ed.: free (effective 2005) (from EBSCO Publishing, J-Stage).

Indexed: ASFA, AgBio, Agrind, AnBrAb, BCI, BIOSIS Prev, BioCN&I, BiolAb, CIN, CPA, ChemAb, ChemTitl, CurCont, ESPM, EntAb, ExcerpMed, FCA, FaBeAb, ForAb, GenetAb, HGA, HerbAb, HortAb, INIS AtomInd, ISR, IndMed, IndVet, Inpharma, JPI, JTA, MEDLINE, MaizeAb, OrnHort, PBA, PGegResA, PGrRegA, PN&I, PotatoAb, PoultAb, RPP, Reac, RevApplEntom, RiceAb, SCI, SFA, SIA, SeedAb, SoyAb, TriticAb, VetBull, WeedAb, WildRev, ZooRec.

—BLDSC (4111.762100), CASDDS, CISTI, GNLM, IDS, IE, Infotrieve, ingenta, Linda Hall. **CCC.**

Published by: Genetics Society of Japan/Nihon Iden Gakkai, Yata 1111, National Institute of Genetics, Mishima, Shizuoka 411-8540, Japan. shinagaw@biken.osaka-u.ac.jp, japgenet@lab.nig.ac.jp, http://www.jstage.jst.go.jp/browse/ggs/_vols/-char/en, http://wwwsoc.nii.ac.jp/gsj3/index.html. Ed., R&P Hideo Shinagawa. Circ: 2,000. **Dist. by:** Business Center for Academic Societies Japan, 5-16-19 Honkomagome, Bunkyo-ku, Tokyo 113-0021, Japan. TEL 81-3-58145811.

576.5 GBR ISSN 1466-4879
QR184 CODEN: GEIMA2

➤ **GENES AND IMMUNITY**; genetics, genomics and function. Text in English. 1999. 8/yr. EUR 720 in Europe to institutions Eurozone; USD 840 in the Americas to institutions; GBP 466 to institutions in the UK & elsewhere; EUR 160 combined subscription in Europe to individuals Eurozone; print & online; USD 180 combined subscription in the Americas to individuals print & online; GBP 104 combined subscription to individuals in the UK & elsewhere; print & online (effective 2006). **Document type:** *Journal, Academic/Scholarly.* **Description:** Provides a forum for research in immunobiology, bringing together studies which focus on the role of genetic, genomic and functional diversity in determining normal and abnormal immunological function.

Related titles: Online - full text ed.: ISSN 1476-5470 (from EBSCO Publishing, O C L C Online Computer Library Center, Inc., Ovid Technologies, Inc., Swets Information Services).

Indexed: AIDS&CR, B&BAb, BCI, BIOBASE, BIOSIS Prev, BiolAb, ExcerpMed, GenetAb, ImmunAb, IndMed, MEDLINE.

—BLDSC (4111.762200), CISTI, IE, Infotrieve, ingenta. **CCC.**

Published by: Nature Publishing Group (Subsidiary of: Macmillan Publishers Ltd.), The MacMillan Building, 4 Crinan St, London, N1 9XW, United Kingdom. TEL 44-20-78334000, FAX 44-20-78433601, subscriptions@nature.com, http://www.nature.com/gene. Eds. Grant Gallagher, Michael F Seldin. **Subscr. to:** Brunel Rd, Houndmills, Basingstoke, Hamps RG21 6XS, United Kingdom. TEL 44-1256-329242, FAX 44-1256-812358, subscriptions@nature.com.

599.9 613.2 USA ISSN 1555-8932

▼ ➤ **GENES & NUTRITION.** Text in English. forthcoming 2006 (Feb.). q. USD 200 to individuals; USD 400 to institutions (effective 2006). **Document type:** *Journal, Academic/Scholarly.*

Published by: New Century Health Publishers, LLC, PO Box 50702, New Orleans, LA 70150-0702. FAX 504-242-7690, info@nutraceuticalresearch.org, http://www.nutraceuticalresearch.org.

576.5 DNK ISSN 1601-1848
QP356.22 CODEN: GBBEAO

➤ **GENES, BRAIN AND BEHAVIOR.** Text in English. 2002. 8/yr. GBP 335 combined subscription in Europe to institutions print & online eds.; USD 620 combined subscription in the Americas to institutions & Caribbean (print & online eds.); GBP 369 combined subscription elsewhere to institutions print & online eds. (effective 2006). adv. **Document type:** *Journal, Academic/Scholarly.* **Description:** Covers the analysis of the behavioral and neural phenotypes with the unifying theme being the genetic approach as a tool to increase our understanding of these phenotypes.

Related titles: Online - full text ed.: ISSN 1601-183X. GBP 319 in Europe to institutions; USD 590 in the Americas to institutions & Caribbean; GBP 351 elsewhere to institutions (effective 2006) (from Blackwell Synergy, EBSCO Publishing, Gale Group, IngentaConnect, O C L C Online Computer Library Center, Inc., Ovid Technologies, Inc., Swets Information Services).

Indexed: AnBeAb, B&BAb, BiolAb, ExcerpMed, GenetAb, NSA, NSCI.

—BLDSC (4111.762300), CISTI, IE, ingenta. **CCC.**

Published by: (International Behavioural and Neural Genetics Society GBR), Blackwell Munksgaard (Subsidiary of: Blackwell Publishing Ltd.), Rosenoerns Alle 1, PO Box 227, Copenhagen V, 1502, Denmark. TEL 45-77-333333, FAX 45-77-333377, info@mks.blackwellpublishing.com, http://www.blackwellpublishing.com/journals/G2B, http://www.munksgaard.dk/. Ed. Wim E Crusio. Adv. contact Louise McCrae. B&W page USD 775, color page USD 1,936; trim 210 x 280.

572.8 USA ISSN 1045-2257
RC268.4 CODEN: GCCAES

➤ **GENES, CHROMOSOMES & CANCER.** Text in English. 1989. m. USD 1,825 domestic to institutions; USD 1,969 in Canada & Mexico to institutions; USD 2,053 elsewhere to institutions; USD 2,008 combined subscription domestic to institutions print & online eds.; USD 2,152 combined subscription in Canada & Mexico to institutions print & online eds.; USD 2,236 combined subscription elsewhere to institutions print & online eds. (effective 2006). adv. back issues avail. **Document type:** *Journal, Academic/Scholarly.* **Description:** Covers all aspects of genomic abnormalities related to neoplasia. Particular emphasis is placed on work combining molecular and cytogenetic analysis of the acquired genetic alterations of cancer cells.

Related titles: Microform ed.: (from PQC); Online - full content ed.: ISSN 1098-2264. USD 1,825 to institutions (effective 2006); Online - full text ed.: (from EBSCO Publishing, Swets Information Services, Wiley InterScience).

Indexed: AIDS&CR, ASCA, B&BAb, BCI, BIOBASE, BIOSIS Prev, BiolAb, CIN, ChemAb, ChemTitl, CurCont, ExcerpMed, GenetAb, HGA, IABS, ISR, IndMed, Inpharma, MEDLINE, NucAcAb, OGFA, PE&ON, Reac, RefZh, SCI.

—BLDSC (4111.763000), CASDDS, CISTI, GNLM, IDS, IE, Infotrieve, ingenta, KNAW. **CCC.**

Published by: John Wiley & Sons, Inc., 111 River St, Hoboken, NJ 07030-5774. TEL 201-748-6000, FAX 201-748-5915, uscs-wis@wiley.com, http://www3.interscience.wiley.com/cgi-bin/jhome/38250, http://www.wiley.com. Eds. Felix Mitelman, Janet D Rowley. adv.: B&W page GBP 640, color page GBP 1,515; trim 210 x 279. Circ: 800. **Subscr. outside the Americas to:** John Wiley & Sons Ltd., The Atrium, Southern Gate, Chichester, West Sussex PO19 8SQ, United Kingdom. TEL 44-1243-843335, 0800-243407, FAX 44-1243-843232, cs-journals@wiley.co.uk.

576.5 GBR ISSN 1356-9597
QH441.5 CODEN: GECEFL

➤ **GENES TO CELLS.** Text in English. 1996. m. GBP 123, EUR 186 combined subscription in Europe to individuals print & online eds.; USD 219 combined subscription in the Americas to individuals & Caribbean, print & online eds.; GBP 135 combined subscription elsewhere to individuals print & online eds.; GBP 1,020 combined subscription in Europe to institutions print & online eds.; USD 1,819 combined subscription in the Americas to institutions & Caribbean, print & online eds.; GBP 1,122 combined subscription elsewhere to institutions print & online eds. (effective 2006). **Document type:** *Journal, Academic/Scholarly.* **Description:** Provides an international forum for papers relating to physiological, biophysical, and evolutionary ecology.

Related titles: Online - full text ed.: ISSN 1365-2443. GBP 968 in Europe to institutions; USD 1,727 in the Americas to institutions & Caribbean; GBP 1,067 elsewhere to institutions (effective 2006) (from Blackwell Synergy, EBSCO Publishing, Gale Group, HighWire Press, IngentaConnect, O C L C Online Computer Library Center, Inc., Ovid Technologies, Inc., Swets Information Services).

Indexed: ASFA, AgBio, AnBrAb, B&BAb, BCI, BIOSIS Prev, BiolAb, CIN, CPA, ChemAb, ChemTitl, CurCont, DSA, ExcerpMed, GenetAb, HGA, HortAb, ISR, IndMed, MBA, MEDLINE, MaizeAb, NemAb, NucAcAb, NutrAb, PBA, PGegResA, PoultAb, RPP, SCI, VetBull, WeedAb.

—BLDSC (4111.762500), CASDDS, CISTI, GNLM, IDS, IE, Infotrieve, ingenta, KNAW, Linda Hall. **CCC.**

Published by: (Nihon Bunshi Seibutsu Gakkai/Biology Molecular Society of Japan JPN), Blackwell Publishing Ltd., 9600 Garsington Rd, Oxford, OX4 2ZG, United Kingdom. TEL 44-1865-776868, FAX 44-1865-714591, customerservices@oxon.blackwellpublishing.com, http://www.blackwellpublishing.com/journals/GTC. Ed. Dr. Jun-ichi Tomizawa. Pub. Sue Hewitt. R&P Sophie Savage. Adv. contact Martine Cariou Keen. Circ: 695.

576.5 USA ISSN 1526-954X
QH453 CODEN: GNESFY

➤ **GENESIS: THE JOURNAL OF GENETICS AND DEVELOPMENT.** Text in English. 1979. m. USD 2,135 domestic to institutions; USD 2,279 in Canada & Mexico to institutions; USD 2,363 elsewhere to institutions; USD 2,349 combined subscription domestic to institutions print & online eds.; USD 2,493 combined subscription in Canada & Mexico to institutions print & online eds.; USD 2,577 combined subscription elsewhere to institutions print & online eds. (effective 2006). adv. bk.rev. bibl.; illus. back issues avail. **Document type:** *Journal, Academic/Scholarly.* **Description:** Covers molecular and developmental genetics and provides a forum for research on all organisms, including prokaryotes, plants, insects, worms, and mammals.

Formerly (until 2000): Developmental Genetics (0192-253X)

Related titles: Microform ed.: (from PQC); Online - full content ed.: ISSN 1526-968X. USD 2,135 to institutions (effective 2006); Online - full text ed.: (from EBSCO Publishing, Swets Information Services, Wiley InterScience).

Indexed: ASCA, ASFA, AbHyg, AgBio, Agr, AnBrAb, BCI, BIOBASE, BIOSIS Prev, BibAg, BiolAb, CIN, CPA, ChemAb, ChemTitl, CurCont, DSA, ExcerpMed, FCA, ForAb, GenetAb, HGA, IABS, ISR, IndMed, IndVet, Inpharma, MBA, MEDLINE, MaizeAb, NemAb, NucAcAb, NutrAb, PBA, PE&ON, PGegResA, PGrRegA, PHN&I, PN&I, PoultAb, ProtozoAb, RA&MP, Reac, RefZh, RevApplEntom, RiceAb, SCI, SeedAb, TDB, VetBull, WeedAb, ZooRec.

—BLDSC (4111.807500), CASDDS, CISTI, GNLM, IDS, IE, Infotrieve, ingenta. **CCC.**

Published by: John Wiley & Sons, Inc., 111 River St, Hoboken, NJ 07030-5774. TEL 201-748-6000, FAX 201-748-5915, uscs-wis@wiley.com, http://www3.interscience.wiley.com/cgi-bin/jhome/68503812, http://www.wiley.com. Eds. Richard Behringer, Terry Magnuson. adv.: B&W page GBP 640, color page GBP 1,515; trim 210 x 279. Circ: 550. **Subscr. outside the Americas to:** John Wiley & Sons Ltd., The Atrium, Southern Gate, Chichester, West Sussex PO19 8SQ, United Kingdom. TEL 44-1243-843335, 0800-243407, FAX 44-1243-843232, cs-journals@wiley.co.uk.

576.5 USA

GENETALK. Text in English. q. free to members (effective 2004). **Document type:** *Newsletter.* **Description:** Includes important announcements from the association as well as relevant updates within the industry and regions.

Published by: Association of Genetic Technologists, AGT Executive Office, PO Box 15945-288, Lenexa, KS 66285-5945. TEL 913-541-0497, FAX 913-599-5340, agt-info@goAMP.com, http://www.agt-info.org.

GENETHICS NEWS. see *BIOLOGY—Biotechnology*

576.50151 USA ISSN 1568-2587

GENETIC ALGORITHMS AND EVOLUTIONARY COMPUTATION. Cover title: G E N A. Text in English. 2000. irreg., latest vol.11, 2004. price varies. **Document type:** *Monographic series, Academic/Scholarly.* **Description:** Publishes research monographs, edited collections, and graduate-level texts in this rapidly growing field. These genetic algorithms and techniques of evolutionary computation are solving problems and inventing new hardware and software that rival human designs.

—BLDSC (4096.391000), CISTI, IE. **CCC.**

Published by: Springer-Verlag New York, Inc. (Subsidiary of: Springer Science+Business Media), 233 Spring St, New York, NY 10013. TEL 212-460-1500, FAX 212-460-1575, service@springer-ny.com, http://www.springer-ny.com. Ed. David E Goldberg.

576.5 CHE ISSN 1015-8146
RB155.7 CODEN: GECOEG

➤ **GENETIC COUNSELING.** Summaries in English, French, German. 1952. 4/yr. CHF 235 to individuals; CHF 330 to institutions (effective 2004). adv. bk.rev. abstr.; charts; illus.; stat. index, cum.index. Supplement avail.; reprint service avail. from IRC. **Document type:** *Journal, Academic/Scholarly.*

Formerly (until 1990): Journal de Genetique Humaine (0021-7743)

Indexed: ASCA, AnthLit, BCI, BDM&CN, BIOSIS Prev, BiolAb, ChemAb, CurCont, DIP, DentInd, ExcerpMed, FamI, IBR, IBZ, INI, ISR, IndMed, Inpharma, MEDLINE, PE&ON, PsycInfo, PsycholAb, Reac, SCI, SSCI.

—BLDSC (4111.845000), CISTI, GNLM, IDS, IE, Infotrieve, ingenta, KNAW, Linda Hall. **CCC.**

Published by: Editions Medecine et Hygiene, 78 avenue de la Rosarale, Case Postale 456, Geneva 4, 1211, Switzerland. TEL 41-22-7029311, FAX 41-22-7029355, abonnements@medhyg.ch, http://www.medecinehygiene.ch/new_site/revuesgrp/geneticcoun.php, http://www.medhyg.ch. Ed. J P Fryns. Circ: 800.

576.5 USA
GENETIC DRIFT. Text in English. q.
Media: Online - full text.
Published by: Mountain States Genetic Network, 8129 W Fremont Ave, Littleton, CO 80128. TEL 303-978-0125, http://www.mostgene.org/gd/gdlist.htm, http://www.mostgene.org/index.htm. Ed. Caral Clericuzia.

576.5 JPN
GENETIC ENGINEERING. Text in English. 1985. irreg.
Published by: Associazione Biologica Italo-Giapponese/Nichii Seibutsugaku Kyokai, Nagoya Daigaku Rigakubu Rinkai Jikkenjo, Furo-cho, Chikusa-ku, Nagoya-shi, Aichi-ken 464-0814, Japan.

GENETIC ENGINEERING; principles and methods. see *BIOLOGY—Biotechnology*

576.5 USA ISSN 0270-6377
TP248.6 CODEN: GENNDX
GENETIC ENGINEERING NEWS; the information source of the biotechnology industry. Text in English. 1981. 21/yr., latest vol.21, 2001. adv. bk.rev. pat.; stat.; tr.lit. **Document type:** *Magazine, Trade.* **Description:** Covers the biotechnology-bioprocess industry. Examines significant issues, regulatory and scale-up guidelines, R&D, financial news including public offerings, mergers, and venture capital, corporate profiles, reports, and news.
Indexed: ASCA, AgBio, Agr, AnBrAb, B&I, BCI, BibAg, CIN, ChemAb, ChemTitl, IndVet, SSCI, Telegen.
—CASDDS, GNLM, IDS, IE, Infotrieve, Linda Hall. **CCC.**
Published by: Mary Ann Liebert, Inc. Publishers, 140 Huguenot St 3rd Fl, New Rochelle, NY 10801-5215. TEL 914-740-2100, FAX 914-740-2101, 800-654-3237, info@liebertpub.com, http://www.genengnews.com/, http://www.liebertpub.com. Ed. John Sterling. Adv. contact Harriet Matysko.

576.5 USA ISSN 0741-0395
➤ **GENETIC EPIDEMIOLOGY.** Text in English. 8/yr. USD 2,550 domestic to institutions; USD 2,646 in Canada & Mexico to institutions; USD 2,702 elsewhere to institutions; USD 2,805 combined subscription domestic to institutions print & online eds.; USD 2,901 combined subscription in Canada & Mexico to institutions print & online eds.; USD 2,957 combined subscription elsewhere to institutions print & online eds. (effective 2006). adv. bk.rev. back issues avail. **Document type:** *Journal, Academic/Scholarly.* **Description:** Provides a forum for research concerned with the etiology, distribution, and control of disease in groups of relatives and with the inherited predisposition to, or causes of, diseases in populations.
Related titles: Microform ed.: (from PQC); Online - full content ed.: ISSN 1098-2272. USD 2,550 to institutions (effective 2006); Online - full text ed.: (from EBSCO Publishing, Swets Information Services, Wiley InterScience).
Indexed: ASCA, AnBrAb, B&BAb, BCI, BIOSIS Prev, BiolAb, ChemAb, CurCont, ExcerpMed, FamI, GenetAb, HGA, ISR, IndMed, Inpharma, MEDLINE, PE&ON, Reac, RefZh, SCI, SSCI, THA.
—BLDSC (4111.848000), CISTI, GNLM, IDS, IE, Infotrieve, ingenta, KNAW. **CCC.**
Published by: John Wiley & Sons, Inc., 111 River St, Hoboken, NJ 07030-5774. TEL 201-748-6000, FAX 201-748-5915, uscs-wis@wiley.com, http://www3.interscience.wiley.com/cgi-bin/jhome/35841, http://www.wiley.com. Ed. Daniel J Schaid. adv.: B&W page GBP 640, color page GBP 1,515; trim 174 x 254. Circ: 850. **Subscr. outside the Americas to:** John Wiley & Sons Ltd., The Atrium, Southern Gate, Chichester, West Sussex PO19 8SQ, United Kingdom. TEL 44-1243-843335, 0800-243407, FAX 44-1243-843232, cs-journals@wiley.co.uk.

➤ **GENETIC EPISTEMOLOGIST.** see *PSYCHOLOGY*

576.5 USA
GENETIC RESOURCE. Text in English. 1983. s-a. USD 15. bk.rev. **Document type:** *Newsletter.* **Description:** Covers clinical genetics and related public health policy issues for lay and professional readers.
Published by: New England Regional Genetics Group, PO Box 670, Mount Desert, ME 04660-0670. TEL 207-839-5324, FAX 207-839-8637. Ed. Robin J R Blatt. R&P Joseph Robinson TEL 207-288-2704. Circ: 7,000.

576.5 NLD ISSN 0925-9864
SB123.3 CODEN: GRCEE9
➤ **GENETIC RESOURCES AND CROP EVOLUTION**; an international journal. Short title: G R A C E. Text in English. 1953. 8/yr. EUR 908, USD 928, GBP 598 combined subscription to institutions print & online eds. (effective 2005). adv. back issues avail.; reprint service avail. from PSC. **Document type:** *Journal, Academic/Scholarly.* **Description:** Publishes original articles on taxonomical, morphological, cytological, ethnobotanical and biochemical research of genetic resources, including contributions on broader issues in gene-bank management, such as collection, storage, maintenance and documentation.
Formerly (until 1992): Kulturpflanze (0075-7209)
Related titles: Microform ed.: (from PQC); Online - full text ed.: ISSN 1573-5109 (from EBSCO Publishing, Gale Group, IngentaConnect, Kluwer Online, O C L C Online Computer Library Center, Inc., Ovid Technologies, Inc., Springer LINK, Swets Information Services).
Indexed: AEBA, ASCA, AgBio, Agr, AgrForAb, ApicAb, BIOBASE, BIOSIS Prev, BibLing, BiolAb, CMCI, CPA, ChemAb, CurCont, ESPM, FCA, ForAb, GEOBASE, GenetAb, HGA, HerbAb, HortAb, IABS, MBA, MaizeAb, NemAb, OrnHort, PBA, PGegResA, PGrRegA, PHN&I, PN&I, PlantSci, PotatoAb, RA&MP, RPP, RefZh, RevApplEntom, RiceAb, S&F, SIA, SeedAb, SoyAb, TDB, TriticAb, VITIS, WeedAb.
—BLDSC (4111.907000), CASDDS, CISTI, IDS, IE, Infotrieve, ingenta. **CCC.**
Published by: Springer-Verlag Dordrecht (Subsidiary of: Springer Science+Business Media), Van Godewijckstraat 30, Dordrecht, 3311 GX, Netherlands. TEL 31-78-6576050, FAX 31-78-6576474, http://springerlink.metapress.com/openurl.asp?genre=journal&issn=0925-9864, http://www.springeronline.com. Ed. Karl Hammer.

576.5 USA ISSN 0272-9032
CODEN: GTNEEA
GENETIC TECHNOLOGY NEWS. Text in English. 1981. w. (51/yr). USD 1,152 (effective 2005). abstr.; bibl.; charts; pat.; stat.; tr.lit. back issues avail. **Document type:** *Newsletter, Trade.* **Description:** Explores genetic engineering and its uses in the chemical, pharmaceutical, food processing and energy industries, as well as in agriculture, animal breeding and medicine.
Related titles: Online - full text ed.: (from Factiva); Supplement(s): Patent Update; Strategic Partners Report; Market Forecast.
Indexed: Agr, CBTA, CIN, ChemAb, ChemTitl.
—BLDSC (4111.923000), CASDDS.
Published by: Frost & Sullivan, 7550 W Interstate 10, Ste 9, San Antonio, TX 78229. TEL 210-348-1000, FAX 210-348-1003, http://www.frost.com. Ed. Manoj Kenkare.

576.5 USA ISSN 1090-6576
CODEN: GETEF4
➤ **GENETIC TESTING.** Text in English. 1997. q. USD 654 domestic to institutions; USD 804 foreign to institutions; USD 775 combined subscription domestic to institutions print & online eds.; USD 925 combined subscription foreign to institutions print & online eds. (effective 2006). adv. back issues avail.; reprint service avail. from PSC. **Document type:** *Journal, Academic/Scholarly.* **Description:** Focuses on all aspects of genetic testing, including prenatal diagnosis, risk assessment, methodologies, ethical and legal uses.
Related titles: Online - full text ed.: ISSN 1557-7473. USD 218 to individuals; USD 522 to institutions (effective 2005) (from EBSCO Publishing, Gale Group, O C L C Online Computer Library Center, Inc., Swets Information Services).
Indexed: BIOSIS Prev, BiolAb, CurCont, ExcerpMed, FoMM, INI, IndMed, MEDLINE.
—BLDSC (4111.926000), CASDDS, CISTI, IDS, IE, Infotrieve, ingenta. **CCC.**
Published by: Mary Ann Liebert, Inc. Publishers, 140 Huguenot St 3rd Fl, New Rochelle, NY 10801-5215. TEL 914-740-2100, FAX 914-740-2101, 800-654-3237, info@liebertpub.com, http://www.liebertpub.com/gte. Ed. Dr. Peter R Rowley. adv.: B&W page USD 1,095; trim 8.5 x 11. Circ: 1,000 (paid).

576.5 GBR ISSN 1479-0556
QR189.5.D53
▼ ➤ **GENETIC VACCINES AND THERAPY.** Text in English. 2003. irreg. free (effective 2006). **Document type:** *Journal, Academic/Scholarly.* **Description:** Publishes papers on all aspects of gene-based therapies for the prevention and control of disease.
Media: Online - full text (from EBSCO Publishing, National Library of Medicine).
Indexed: ExcerpMed.
Published by: BioMed Central Ltd. (Subsidiary of: Current Science Ltd), Middlesex House, 34-42 Cleveland St, London, W1T 4LB, United Kingdom. TEL 44-20-76319131, FAX 44-20-76319923, info@biomedcentral.com, http://www.gvt-journal.com/home/, http://www.biomedcentral.com. Ed. Shyam S Mohapatra.

576.5 NLD ISSN 0016-6707
QH301 CODEN: GENEA3
➤ **GENETICA**; the international journal on genetics. Text in English. 1919. 9/yr. EUR 1,898, USD 1,938, GBP 1,255 combined subscription to institutions print & online eds. (effective 2005). adv. illus. back issues avail.; reprint service avail. from PSC. **Document type:** *Journal, Academic/Scholarly.*
Related titles: Microform ed.: (from PQC); Online - full text ed.: ISSN 1573-6857 (from EBSCO Publishing, Gale Group, IngentaConnect, Kluwer Online, O C L C Online Computer Library Center, Inc., Ovid Technologies, Inc., Springer LINK, Swets Information Services).
Indexed: AEA, ASCA, ASFA, AbHyg, AgBio, AgrForAb, AnBrAb, BCI, BIOBASE, BIOSIS Prev, BibLing, BioCN&I, BiolAb, CIN, CPA, ChemAb, ChemTitl, CurCont, EntAb, ExcerpMed, FCA, FS&TA, ForAb, GenetAb, HGA, HelmAb, HerbAb, HortAb, IABS, ISR, IndMed, IndVet, Inpharma, MEDLINE, MaizeAb, NemAb, OrnHort, PBA, PGegResA, PHN&I, PN&I, PotatoAb, PoultAb, ProtozoAb, RA&MP, RM&VM, RPP, Reac, RefZh, RevApplEntom, RiceAb, S&F, SAA, SCI, SFA, SIA, SSCI, SeedAb, SoyAb, TDB, TriticAb, VITIS, VetBull, WeedAb, WildRev, ZooRec.
—BLDSC (4112.000000), CASDDS, CISTI, GNLM, IDS, IE, Infotrieve, ingenta, Linda Hall. **CCC.**
Published by: Springer-Verlag Dordrecht (Subsidiary of: Springer Science+Business Media), Van Godewijckstraat 30, Dordrecht, 3311 GX, Netherlands. TEL 31-78-6576050, FAX 31-78-6576474, http://springerlink.metapress.com/openurl.asp?genre=journal&issn=0016-6707, http://www.springeronline.com. Eds. Pierre Capy, Ronny C Woodruff.

576.5 GBR ISSN 0016-6723
QH431.A1 CODEN: GENRA8
➤ **GENETICAL RESEARCH.** Text in English. 1960. bi-m. GBP 366 to institutions; USD 630 in North America to institutions; GBP 396 combined subscription to institutions print & online eds.; USD 678 combined subscription in North America to institutions print & online eds. (effective 2006). adv. bk.rev. charts; illus. index. back issues avail.; reprint service avail. from PQC,PSC. **Document type:** *Journal, Academic/Scholarly.* **Description:** Covers current research in all branches of genetics: for geneticists, molecular and developmental biologists, and plant and animal breeders.
Related titles: Microform ed.: (from PQC); Online - full text ed.: ISSN 1469-5073. GBP 340 to institutions; USD 580 in North America to institutions (effective 2006) (from EBSCO Publishing, O C L C Online Computer Library Center, Inc., Ovid Technologies, Inc., Swets Information Services).
Indexed: ASCA, ASFA, AbAn, AbHyg, AgBio, Agr, AnBrAb, B&AI, BCI, BIOBASE, BIOSIS Prev, BibAg, BioCN&I, BiolAb, Biostat, CBTA, CIN, CIS, CPA, ChemAb, ChemTitl, CurCont, DBA, DSA, DentInd, ESPM, EntAb, ExcerpMed, ForAb, GenetAb, HGA, HelmAb, HerbAb, HortAb, IABS, ISR, IndMed, IndVet, Inpharma, MBA, MEDLINE, MaizeAb, MathR, NemAb, NutrAb, PBA, PGegResA, PHN&I, PN&I, ProtozoAb, RM&VM, RPP, Reac, RefZh, RevApplEntom, RiceAb, S&F, SCI, SFA, SeedAb, SoyAb, TDB, Telegen, TriticAb, VITIS, VetBull, WeedAb, WildRev, ZooRec.
—BLDSC (4114.250000), CASDDS, CISTI, GNLM, IDS, IE, Infotrieve, ingenta, Linda Hall. **CCC.**
Published by: Cambridge University Press, The Edinburgh Bldg, Shaftesbury Rd, Cambridge, CB2 2RU, United Kingdom. TEL 44-1223-312393, FAX 44-1223-315052, genet.res@ed.ca.uk, journals@cambridge.org, http://uk.cambridge.org/journals/grh. Eds. D J Finnegan, Trudy F.C. Mackay, W G Hill. R&P Linda Nicol TEL 44-1223-325757. Adv. contact Rebecca Curtis TEL 44-1223-325757. **Subscr. to:** Cambridge University Press, 100 Brook Hill Dr, West Nyack, NY 10994. TEL 845-353-7500, FAX 845-353-4141, journals_subscriptions@cup.org

576.5 USA ISSN 0016-6731
QH431 CODEN: GENTAE
➤ **GENETICS**; a periodical record of investigations bearing on heredity and variation. Text in English. 1916. m. USD 850 combined subscription domestic to institutions print & online eds.; USD 870 combined subscription in Canada & Mexico to institutions print & online eds.; USD 940 combined subscription elsewhere to institutions print & online eds. (effective 2006). adv. abstr.; bibl.; charts; illus. index. back issues avail.; reprint service avail. from PQC. **Document type:** *Journal, Academic/Scholarly.* **Description:** Aims to facilitate communication among scientists and professors who are involved in research and education relative to the study of special organisms.
Related titles: Microform ed.: (from MIM, PMC, PQC); Online - full text ed.: USD 630 (effective 2006) (from EBSCO Publishing, HighWire Press, ProQuest Information & Learning).
Indexed: ASCA, ASFA, AbAn, AbHyg, AgBio, Agr, AgrForAb, AnBrAb, ApicAb, B&AI, B&BAb, BCI, BIOBASE, BIOSIS Prev, BioCN&I, BiolAb, BiolDig, CIN, CMCI, CPA, CRFR, CTA, CTFA, ChemAb, ChemTitl, CurCont, DBA, DSA, ESPM, EntAb, ExcerpMed, FCA, FPA, FS&TA, FaBeAb, ForAb, GSI, GenetAb, HGA, HelmAb, HerbAb, HortAb, IABS, ISR, IndMed, IndVet, MBA, MEDLINE, MaizeAb, NemAb, NucAcAb, NutrAb, OceAb, OrnHort, PBA, PGegResA, PGrRegA, PHN&I, PN&I, PotatoAb, PoultAb, ProtozoAb, RA&MP, RM&VM, RPP, RefZh, RevApplEntom, RiceAb, S&F, S&MA, SCI, SFA, SIA, SeedAb, SoyAb, TDB, TriticAb, VITIS, VetBull, WeedAb, WildRev, ZooRec.
—BLDSC (4115.000000), CASDDS, CISTI, GNLM, IDS, IE, Infotrieve, ingenta, Linda Hall. **CCC.**
Published by: Genetics Society of America, 9650 Rockville Pike, Bethesda, MD 20814. TEL 301-530 7029, FAX 301-571 5728, staff@dues.faseb.org, http://www.genetics.org/contents-by-date.0.shtml. Ed. Elizabeth W Jones. Circ: 5,000. **Subscr. to:** FASEB, Subscriptions, Rm L-2310, 9650 Rockville Pike, Bethesda, MD 20814-3998. FAX 301-634-7099.

➤ **GENETICS ABSTRACTS.** see *BIOLOGY—Abstracting, Bibliographies, Statistics*

581.3 BGR
CODEN: GESKAC
GENETICS AND BREEDING/GENETICS AND BREEDING. Text in Bulgarian; Summaries in English, Russian. 1968. bi-m. USD 80 foreign (effective 2005). bk.rev. bibl.; charts; illus. back issues avail.; reprint service avail. from IRC. **Document type:** *Journal, Academic/Scholarly.* **Description:** Designed for science-related audience, it covers plant, animal, misrobial genetics and breeding.
Formerly (until 1996): Genetika i Selektsiia (0016-6766)
Indexed: ASFA, AnBrAb, BSLBiol, BiolAb, ChemAb, DSA, GenetAb, HGA, HortAb, IndVet, MaizeAb, PGrRegA, PN&I, PoultAb, SeedAb, WeedAb.
—CASDDS, CISTI, Linda Hall.

Published by: Bulgarska Akademiya na Naukite, Institut po Genetika/Bulgarian Academy of Sciences, Institute of Genetics, c/o Dr Boyan Dimitrov, Sofia, 1113, Bulgaria. TEL 359-2-9746228, FAX 359-2-9785516, genetika@bas.bg, http://ig.bas.bg/Periodics.htm. Ed. Kostadin Gecheff. Circ: 1,010. **Dist. by:** Sofia Books, ul Silivria 16, Sofia 1404, Bulgaria. TEL 359-2-9586257, info@sofiabooks-bg.com, http://www.sofiabooks-bg.com.

GENETICS & ENVIRONMENTAL BUSINESS WEEK. see *BUSINESS AND ECONOMICS*

576.5 363.7 USA ISSN 1552-2547
GENETICS & ENVIRONMENTAL HEALTH WEEK. Text in English. w. USD 2,595 in US & Canada; USD 2,795 elsewhere; USD 2,825 in US & Canada; USD 3,055 elsewhere (effective 2005). **Document type:** *Newsletter, Academic/Scholarly.* **Description:** Covers the latest clinical developments in identifying genetic and environmental risk factors, including stem cell research, genomic discoveries and impact studies on air, water and soil pollutants, which may have an effect on human health.
Related titles: Online - full content ed.: ISSN 1552-2555; Online - full text ed.: (from ProQuest Information & Learning).
Published by: NewsRx, PO Box 5528, Atlanta, GA 31107-0528. TEL 800-726-4550, FAX 303-290-9025, info@newsrx.com, http://www.newsrx.com/product_descriptions/GENETICS_AND_ENVIRONMENTAL_HEALTH_WEEK.HTM.

576.5 BRA ISSN 1415-4757
QH426 CODEN: GMBIFG
➤ **GENETICS AND MOLECULAR BIOLOGY.** Text in English; Summaries in English, Portuguese. 1978. q. BRL 60 domestic to individuals; USD 50 foreign to individuals; BRL 70 domestic to institutions; USD 90 foreign to institutions (effective 1999). adv. bk.rev. abstr. index. back issues avail. **Document type:** *Academic/Scholarly.* **Description:** Publishes the results of original research in evolution, genetics, molecular biology and their application to the improvement of plants, animals and human well-being.
Formerly (until 1998): Brazilian Journal of Genetics (0100-8455)
Related titles: Online - full text ed.: free (effective 2005) (from SciELO).
Indexed: AbHyg, AgBio, AgrForAb, AnBrAb, BCI, BIOBASE, BIOSIS Prev, BioCN&I, BiolAb, CIN, CPA, ChemAb, ChemTitl, CurCont, DBA, DSA, ESPM, EntAb, ExcerpMed, FCA, ForAb, GenetAb, HelmAb, HerbAb, HortAb, IABS, INIS AtomInd, IndVet, Inpharma, MaizeAb, NemAb, NutrAb, OrnHort, PBA, PE&ON, PGegResA, PGrRegA, PN&I, PoultAb, ProtozoAb, RA&MP, RDA, RM&VM, RPP, Reac, RefZh, RevApplEntom, RiceAb, S&F, S&MA, SCI, SFA, SIA, SeedAb, SoyAb, TDB, TriticAb, VetBull, WeedAb, ZooRec.
—BLDSC (4115.091500), CASDDS, CISTI, GNLM, IDS, IE, ingenta, KNAW, Linda Hall.
Published by: Sociedade Brasileira de Genetica, Rua Capitao Adelmio Norberto da Silva 736, At B Vista, Ribeirao Preto, SP 14025-670, Brazil. TEL 55-16-6218540, FAX 55-16-6201253, rbg@genbov.fmrp.usp.br, http://www.scielo.br/. Ed. Francisco A. Moura Duarte. R&P Francisco A Moura Duarte. Circ: 2,000.

576.5 BRA ISSN 1676-5680
QH442 CODEN: GGMRBI
➤ **GENETICS AND MOLECULAR RESEARCH.** Variant title: G M R Genetics and Molecular Research. Text in English. 2002. q. free (effective 2005). **Document type:** *Journal, Academic/Scholarly.*
Media: Online - full text (from SciELO).
Indexed: B&BAb, BiolAb, EntAb, ExcerpMed, GenetAb.
Published by: Fundacao de Pesquisas Cientificas de Ribeirao Preto, Rua Hudson 655, Jardim Canada, Ribeirao Preto, 14024-000, Brazil. funpecrp@uol.com.br, http://www.funpecrp.com.br/gmr.

576.5 USA ISSN 1098-3600
RB155 CODEN: GEMEF3
➤ **GENETICS IN MEDICINE.** Text in English. 1998. 9/yr. USD 437 to individuals; USD 837 to institutions (effective 2006). adv. **Document type:** *Journal, Academic/Scholarly.* **Description:** Offers an unprecedented forum for the presentation of innovative, practice-focused papers in contemporary genetics medicine, including such areas as clinical genetics, biochemical genetics, cytogenetics, molecular genetics, public health genetics, genetic epidemiology, common disease genetics, genetic counseling, and genetic education.
Related titles: Online - full text ed.: ISSN 1530-0366. USD 647.40 domestic academic site license; USD 683.40 foreign academic site license; USD 722.10 domestic corporate site license; USD 758.10 foreign corporate site license (effective 2002) (from EBSCO Publishing, Ovid Technologies, Inc., Swets Information Services).
Indexed: AbHyg, B&BAb, BCI, BIOBASE, BIOSIS Prev, BiolAb, CurCont, ExcerpMed, GenetAb, MEDLINE, TDB.
—BLDSC (4115.151000), CISTI, IE, Infotrieve, ingenta. **CCC.**
Published by: (American College of Medical Genetics), Lippincott Williams & Wilkins (Subsidiary of: Wolters Kluwer N.V.), 530 Walnut St, Philadelphia, PA 19106-3621. TEL 215-521-8300, FAX 215-521-8902, custserv@lww.com, http://www.geneticsinmedicine.org/, http://www.lww.com. Ed. Richard A King TEL 612-626-4224. Pub. Kerry O'Rourke TEL 410-528-8517. adv.: B&W page USD 710, color page USD 1,535. Circ: 1,565 (paid). **Subscr. to:** PO Box 1620, Hagerstown, MD 21741. TEL 301-223-2300, 800-638-3030, FAX 301-223-2365.

599.9 GBR ISSN 1471-3624
GENETICS LAW MONITOR. Text in English. bi-m. GBP 187 to individuals; GBP 140 academic rate (effective 2001). **Description:** Presents papers about the legal, ethical and social implications of human genetics.
—BLDSC (4115.145000).
Published by: Monitor Press Ltd. (Subsidiary of: T & F Informa plc), Suffolk House, Church Field Rd, Sudbury, Suffolk CO10 2YA, United Kingdom. TEL 44-1787-378607, FAX 44-1787-880201, media.enquiries@informa.com, http://www.geneticslawmonitor.com/, http://www.monitorpress.co.uk. Ed. Iain Goldrein. R&P Zoe Turner.

576.5 ZAF ISSN 0259-0301
GENETICS NEWSLETTER/GENETIKA NUUSBRIEF. Text in Afrikaans, English. 1968. q. membership. bk.rev.
Media: Duplicated (not offset).
Published by: South African Genetic Society, c/o Department of Genetics, University of Stellenbosch, Stellenbosch, South Africa. Ed. Dr. A E Retief. Circ: (controlled).

591.35 636.081 FRA ISSN 0999-193X
SF105 CODEN: GSEVE9
➤ **GENETICS, SELECTION, EVOLUTION.** Text in English; Summaries in English, French. 1969. bi-m. EUR 331 combined subscription domestic print & online eds.; EUR 387 combined subscription in the European Union print & online eds.; EUR 394 combined subscription elsewhere print & online eds. (effective 2005). bk.rev. charts; illus. index. reprint service avail. from ISI. **Document type:** *Journal, Academic/Scholarly.* **Description:** International journal open to original research papers in the field of animal genetics and evolution. Areas of interest include all aspects related to cytogenetics: cellular, biotechnical, factorial, mathematical, quantitative and population genetics.
Former titles (until 1989): Genetique, Selection, Evolution (0754-0264); (until 1983): Annales de Genetique et de Selection Animale (0003-4002)
Related titles: Online - full text ed.: Genetics, Selection, Evolution Online. ISSN 1297-9686 (from EBSCO Publishing, Swets Information Services).
Indexed: ASCA, ASFA, AbHyg, AgBio, AnBrAb, BIOBASE, BIOSIS Prev, BiolAb, CIN, CPA, ChemAb, ChemTitl, CurCont, DSA, ESPM, EntAb, FCA, FS&TA, ForAb, GEOBASE, GenetAb, HGA, HelmAb, HerbAb, HortAb, IABS, ISR, IndVet, MBA, MEDLINE, NemAb, NutrAb, OrnHort, PBA, PGegResA, PGrRegA, PHN&I, PN&I, PoultAb, ProtozoAb, RA&MP, RM&VM, RPP, RRTA, RevApplEntom, RiceAb, S&F, SCI, SFA, SeedAb, TDB, TriticAb, VITIS, VetBull, WAE&RSA, WeedAb, WildRev, ZooRec.
—BLDSC (4115.158000), CASDDS, CISTI, IDS, IE, Infotrieve, ingenta, Linda Hall. **CCC.**
Published by: (France. Institut National de la Recherche Agronomique (INRA)), E D P Sciences, 17 Ave du Hoggar, Parc d'Activites de Courtaboeuf, BP 112, Cedex A, Les Ulis, F-91944, France. TEL 33-1-69187575, FAX 33-1-69860678, subscribers@edpsciences.org, http://www.edpsciences.org. Eds. B Bibe, J R David. Circ: 2,000.

576.5 GBR
GENETICS SOCIETY. NEWSLETTER. Text in English. 2/yr. GBP 25 membership (effective 2000 & 2001). Website rev. illus. back issues avail. **Document type:** *Newsletter, Academic/Scholarly.* **Description:** Updates members of the Genetical Society of Great Britain to important and noteworthy news and events.
Formerly: Genetical Society. Newsletter
Published by: Genetics Society, Roslin Biocentre, Roslin Institute, Roslin, EH25 9PS, United Kingdom. john.armour@nottingham.ac.uk, mail@genetics.org.uk, http://www.genetics.org.uk/newsletter/welcome.htm. Ed. John Armour. Adv. contact Jayne Richards TEL 44-131-5274472.

576.5 CAN ISSN 0316-4357
QH426
GENETICS SOCIETY OF CANADA BULLETIN. Text in English. 1959. q. CND 25; CND 30 foreign (effective 1999). adv. bk.rev. **Document type:** *Bulletin.*
—CISTI, Linda Hall.
Published by: Genetics Society of Canada, 141 Laurier Av W, Ste 1112, Ottawa, ON K1P 5J3, Canada. TEL 613-232-9459, FAX 613-594-5190. Ed., Pub., R&P, Adv. contact Michael Bentley TEL 403-220-6794. Circ: 450.

GENETICS SOCIETY OF JAPAN. ABSTRACTS OF THE ANNUAL MEETING/NIHON IDEN GAKKAI TAIKAI PUROGURAMU YOKOSHU. see *BIOLOGY—Abstracting, Bibliographies, Statistics*

576.5 RUS ISSN 0016-6758
CODEN: GNKAA5
GENETIKA. Text in Russian. 1965. m. RUR 990 for 6 mos. domestic (effective 2004). bk.rev. index. **Document type:** *Journal, Academic/Scholarly.* **Description:** Investigates genetic processes at the molecular, cellular, organismic, and population levels, with articles on the impact of modern genetics and environmental concerns.
Related titles: Online - full text ed.; ♦ English Translation: Russian Journal of Genetics. ISSN 1022-7954.
Indexed: AbHyg, AgBio, AnBrAb, BDM&CN, BIOSIS Prev, BioCN&I, BiolAb, CIN, CPA, CTFA, ChemAb, ChemTitl, CurCont, DBA, DSA, DentInd, ExcerpMed, FCA, ForAb, HelmAb, HerbAb, HortAb, ISR, IndMed, IndVet, Inpharma, MEDLINE, MaizeAb, NemAb, NutrAb, OrnHort, PBA, PGegResA, PGrRegA, PHN&I, PN&I, PotatoAb, PoultAb, ProtozoAb, RA&MP, RM&VM, RPP, Reac, RefZh, RevApplEntom, S&F, SCI, SFA, SIA, SSCI, SeedAb, SoyAb, TriticAb, VITIS, VetBull, WeedAb, WildRev, ZooRec.
—BLDSC (0047.080000), CASDDS, CISTI, East View, GNLM, IDS, IE, Infotrieve, ingenta, KNAW, Linda Hall. **CCC.**
Published by: (Rossiiskaya Akademiya Nauk/Russian Academy of Sciences), Izdatel'stvo Nauka, Profsoyuznaya ul 90, Moscow, 117864, Russian Federation. TEL 7-095-3347151, FAX 7-095-4202220, secret@naukaran.ru, http://www.maik.rssi.ru/cgi-bin/list.pl?page=genrus, http://www.naukaran.ru.

576.5 USA ISSN 0740-9737
CODEN: GEWAE6
➤ **GENEWATCH.** Text in English. 1982. bi-m. USD 35 domestic to individuals; USD 40 in Canada & Mexico to individuals; USD 43 elsewhere to individuals; USD 50 domestic to non-profit organizations; USD 55 in Canada & Mexico to non-profit organizations; USD 58 elsewhere to non-profit organizations; USD 100 domestic to corporations; USD 105 in Canada & Mexico to corporations; USD 108 elsewhere to corporations (effective 2005). bk.rev.; video rev. charts; bibl.; illus.; maps. 20 p./no. 3 cols./p.; back issues avail. **Document type:** *Magazine, Academic/Scholarly.* **Description:** Contains articles, commentary, international news, and legislative updates on social issues pertaining to genetic engineering and biotechnology.
Indexed: Agr, AltPI, Telegen.
—IDS.
Published by: Council for Responsible Genetics (CRG), 5 Upland Rd, Ste 3, Cambridge, MA 02140-2717. TEL 617-868-0870, FAX 617-491-5344, suzanne@gene-watch.org, crg@gene-watch.org, http://www.gene-watch.org/pages/genewatch.html. Ed. Martin Teitel. R&P Kimberly Wilson. Circ: 2,000 (paid).

576.8 CAN ISSN 0831-2796
QH431.A1 CODEN: GENOE3
➤ **GENOME.** Text mainly in English; Text occasionally in French. 1957. bi-m. CND 142 domestic to individuals; USD 142 foreign to individuals; CND 377 domestic to institutions; USD 377 foreign to institutions (effective 1999). adv. charts; illus.; stat. index. back issues avail. **Document type:** *Academic/Scholarly.* **Description:** Publishes papers in applied and basic genetics and cytology.
Formerly: Canadian Journal of Genetics and Cytology - Journal Canadien de Genetique et de Cytologie (0008-4093)
Related titles: Microfiche ed.: (from MML); Microfilm ed.: (from PMC); Microform ed.: (from MML); Online - full text ed.: ISSN 1480-3321 (from bigchalk, EBSCO Publishing, Gale Group, IngentaConnect, Micromedia ProQuest, O C L C Online Computer Library Center, Inc., ProQuest Information & Learning, Swets Information Services).
Indexed: ASCA, ASFA, AbAn, AgBio, Agr, AgrForAb, AnBrAb, B&AI, B&BAb, BCI, BIOBASE, BIOSIS Prev, BioCN&I, BiolAb, CBCARef, CBTA, CIN, CPA, CTFA, ChemAb, ChemTitl, CurCont, DBA, DSA, EntAb, ExcerpMed, FCA, ForAb, GSI, GenetAb, HGA, HerbAb, HortAb, IABS, ISR, IndMed, IndVet, Inpharma, MEDLINE, MaizeAb, NemAb, OrnHort, PBA, PGegResA, PGrRegA, PHN&I, PN&I, PlantSci, PotatoAb, PoultAb, ProtozoAb, RA&MP, RDA, RM&VM, RPP, RRTA, Reac, RefZh, RevApplEntom, RiceAb, S&F, S&MA, SCI, SFA, SIA, SeedAb, SoyAb, TriticAb, VITIS, VetBull, WAE&RSA, WeedAb, WildRev, ZooRec.
—BLDSC (4116.312000), CASDDS, CISTI, GNLM, IDS, IE, Infotrieve, ingenta, KNAW, Linda Hall. **CCC.**
Published by: (Genetics Society of Canada), N R C Research Press, Building M 55, Ottawa, ON K1A 0R6, Canada. TEL 613-993-0362, 800-668-1222, FAX 613-952-7656, pubs@nrc-cnrc.gc.ca, http://pubs.nrc-cnrc.gc.ca/cgi-bin/rp/rp2_desc_e?gen. Ed. Bruce P Dancik. Adv. contact Judy Heyman. B&W page CND 675; trim 11 x 8.5. Circ: 1,138.

572.86 CHE ISSN 1660-9263
▼ **GENOME DYNAMICS.** Text in English. forthcoming 2006. irreg. price varies. **Document type:** *Monographic series, Academic/Scholarly.*
Published by: S. Karger AG, Allschwilerstr 10, Basel, 4009, Switzerland. TEL 41-61-3061111, FAX 41-61-3061234, karger@karger.ch, http://www.karger.com/gendy, http://www.karger.ch.

572.86 JPN ISSN 0919-9454
GENOME INFORMATICS WORKSHOP. PROCEEDINGS. Text in English. a. **Document type:** *Proceedings, Academic/Scholarly.*
Formerly (until 1993): Genome Informatics Workshop

B

▼ *new title* ➤ *refereed* ✶ *unverified* ♦ *full entry avail.*

Published by: Universal Academy Press, Inc., BR-Hongo-5 Bldg, 6-16-2, Hongo, Bunkyo-ku, Tokyo, 113-0033, Japan. TEL 81-3-38137232, FAX 81-3-38135932, general@uap.co.jp, http://www.uap.co.jp/uap/Publication/SERIES/GIS/.

572.86 USA ISSN 1088-9051
QP606.D46 CODEN: GEREFS

➤ **GENOME RESEARCH.** Text in English. 1991. m. USD 123 domestic to individuals; USD 179 in Canada & Mexico to individuals; USD 203 elsewhere to individuals; USD 1,010 domestic to institutions; USD 1,066 in US & Canada to institutions; USD 1,090 elsewhere to institutions; USD 98 domestic to students; USD 154 foreign to students (effective 2005). adv. illus. back issues avail.; reprint service avail. from PSC. **Document type:** *Journal, Academic/Scholarly.*
Description: Focuses on genome studies in all species, including genetic and physical mapping, DNA sequencing, gene discovery, informatics, statistical and mathematical methods and genome structure as well as technological innovations and applications.
Formerly (until Aug 1995): P C R Methods and Applications (Polymerase Chain Reaction) (1054-9803)
Related titles: Online - full text ed.: ISSN 1549-5469. 1997 (from EBSCO Publishing, HighWire Press, National Library of Medicine).
Indexed: AEA, ASCA, AbHyg, AgBio, AnBrAb, BCI, BIOBASE, BIOSIS Prev, BiolAb, CIN, CPA, ChemAb, ChemTitl, CurCont, DSA, ExcerpMed, FCA, FS&TA, GSI, GenetAb, HGA, HelmAb, HerbAb, HortAb, IABS, ISR, IndMed, IndVet, Inpharma, MEDLINE, MaizeAb, NemAb, NucAcAb, NutrAb, PBA, PE&ON, PGegResA, PGrRegA, PN&I, PotatoAb, PoultAb, ProtozoAb, RM&VM, RPP, Reac, RevApplEntom, RiceAb, S&F, SCI, SIA, SoyAb, TDB, TriticAb, VetBull, WeedAb.
—BLDSC (4116.313800), CASDDS, CISTI, GNLM, IDS, IE, Infotrieve, ingenta, KNAW, Linda Hall. **CCC.**
Published by: Cold Spring Harbor Laboratory Press, Publications Department, 500 Sunnyside Blvd., Woodbury, NY 11797-2924. TEL 516-422-4100, 800-843-4388, FAX 516-422-4097, cshpress@cshl.edu, http://www.genome.org/, http://www.cshl.org. Ed. L Goodman. Adv. contact Ms. Marcie Siconolfi TEL 516-422-4010.

599.9 USA ISSN 0888-7543
QH445.2 CODEN: GNMCEP

➤ **GENOMICS.** Text in English. 1987. 12/yr. EUR 622 in Europe to individuals; JPY 65,000 in Japan to individuals; USD 476 to individuals except Europe and Japan; EUR 3,352 in Europe to institutions; JPY 350,100 in Japan to institutions; USD 2,535 to institutions except Europe and Japan; EUR 70 in Europe to students; JPY 7,300 in Japan to students; USD 60 to students except Europe and Japan (effective 2006). back issues avail. **Document type:** *Journal, Academic/Scholarly.* **Description:** Emphasizes the integration of basic and applied research in human and comparative gene mapping, molecular cloning, large-scale restriction mapping, and DNA sequencing and computational analysis.
Related titles: Online - full text ed.: ISSN 1089-8646. USD 2,688 (effective 2002) (from EBSCO Publishing, Gale Group, IngentaConnect, O C L C Online Computer Library Center, Inc., ScienceDirect, Swets Information Services).
Indexed: ASCA, AbAn, AbHyg, AgBio, Agr, AnBrAb, B&BAb, BBCI, BCI, BIOBASE, BIOSIS Prev, BibAg, BiolAb, CIN, CIS, ChemAb, ChemTitl, CurCont, DBA, DSA, ExcerpMed, GenetAb, HGA, HelmAb, IABS, INIS AtomInd, ISR, IndMed, IndVet, Inpharma, MEDLINE, NSCI, NemAb, NucAcAb, NutrAb, PBA, PE&ON, PN&I, PoultAb, ProtozoAb, Reac, RefZh, S&F, SCI, SSCI, SoyAb, Telegen, TriticAb, VetBull, WeedAb.
—BLDSC (4116.314000), CASDDS, CISTI, GNLM, IDS, IE, Infotrieve, ingenta, Linda Hall. **CCC.**
Published by: Academic Press (Subsidiary of: Elsevier Science & Technology), 525 B St, Ste 1900, San Diego, CA 92101-4495. TEL 619-231-6616, 800-894-3434, apsubs@acad.com, http://www.elsevier.com/locate/ygeno, http://www.academicpress.com. Eds. Dr. N A Jenkins, Dr. R S Kucherlapati, Dr. V A McKusick.

599.935 USA ISSN 1531-6467

GENOMICS & GENETICS WEEKLY. Text in English. 1999. w. USD 1,247 in US & Canada print only; USD 1,368 elsewhere print only; USD 1,367 in US & Canada print & online eds.; USD 1,487 elsewhere print & online eds. (effective 2002). **Description:** Provides a complete overview of genetics, genes, and gene protein products in human health and disease.
Related titles: Online - full text ed.: ISSN 1532-4591. USD 875 (effective 2002) (from Gale Group, O C L C Online Computer Library Center, Inc., ProQuest Information & Learning).
Published by: NewsRx, PO Box 5528, Atlanta, GA 31107-0528. TEL 800-726-4550, FAX 303-290-9025, info@newsrx.com, http://www.cwhorders.com, http://www.newsrx.com. Pub. Susan Hasty.

576.5 CHN ISSN 1672-0229

GENOMICS PROTEOMICS & BIOINFORMATICS. Text in English. q. CNY 45, USD 36 (effective 2005). **Document type:** *Journal, Academic/Scholarly.*
Related titles: Online - full text ed.: (from WanFang Data Corp.).
Indexed: ExcerpMed.
—BLDSC (4116.314300).
Published by: (Chinese Academy of Sciences, Beijing Genomics Institute), Kexue Chubanshe/Science Press, 16 Donghuang Cheng Genbei Jie, Beijing, 100717, China. TEL 86-10-64000246, FAX 86-10-64030255, editor@genomics.org.cn, http://www.gpbjournal.org/index.jsp, http://www.sciencep.com/. Eds. Huanming Yang, Jun Yu.
Co-sponsor: Chinese Academy of Sciences, Institute of Genetics and Developmental Biology.

576.5 GBR ISSN 1746-5354

▼ ➤ **GENOMICS, SOCIETY AND POLICY.** Text in English. 2005. 3/yr. free (effective 2005). **Document type:** *Journal, Academic/Scholarly.* **Description:** Covers interdisciplinary research on the social, ethical and legal aspects of genomics and related emergent technologies such as nanotechnology and stem cell research.
Media: Online - full text.
Published by: Lancaster University, Furness College, c/o Ms Sue Burrows, Man Editor, CESAGen, Lancaster, LA1 4YG, United Kingdom. TEL 44-1524-594874, FAX 44-1524-592503, http://www.gspjournal.com. Eds. Hub Zwart, Ruth Chadwick.

572.86 USA

GENOMICS SOURCE BOOK. Text in English. 1997. a. USD 349; USD 379 foreign (effective 1999). **Document type:** *Trade.*
Published by: Thomson American Health Consultants, Inc. (Subsidiary of: Thomson Corporation, Healthcare Information Group), 3525 Piedmont Rd, N E, Bldg 6, Ste 400, Atlanta, GA 30305. TEL 404-262-5511, FAX 404-262-7837, customerservice@ahcpub.com, http://www.ahcpub.com.

GENOMU IGAKU/GENOME MEDICINE. see *MEDICAL SCIENCES*

GUIDE TO STEM CELL COMPANIES. see *BUSINESS AND ECONOMICS—Trade And Industrial Directories*

576.5 CHN ISSN 1001-1048

GUOWAI YIXUE (YICHUANXUE FENCE)/FOREIGN MEDICAL SCIENCES (GENETICS). Text in Chinese. 1978. bi-m. CNY 36 domestic; USD 20.40 foreign (effective 2005). **Document type:** *Journal, Academic/Scholarly.*
Related titles: Online - full text ed.: (from East View Information Services, WanFang Data Corp.).
Published by: Ha'erbin Yike Daxue, 157, Baojian Lu, Ha'erbin, 150086, China. TEL 86-451-86669596, FAX 86-451-86662947, genetics@ems.hrbmu.edu.cn, http://gwyx-yc.periodicals.net.cn/. **Dist. by:** China International Book Trading Corp, 35 Chegongzhuang Xilu, Haidian District, PO Box 399, Beijing 100044, China. TEL 86-10-68412045, FAX 86-10-68412023, cibtc@mail.cibtc.com.cn, http://www.cibtc.com.cn.

599.9 616.9792 USA ISSN 1063-0627
CODEN: HAIRE4

➤ **HARVARD AIDS INSTITUTE SERIES ON GENE REGULATION OF HUMAN RETROVIRUSES*.** Text in English. 1991. irreg. price varies. reprint service avail. from PQC. **Document type:** *Proceedings, Academic/Scholarly.*
Indexed: BIOSIS Prev, CIN, ChemAb, ChemTitl, e-psyche.
—CASDDS, CISTI.
Published by: (Harvard AIDS Institute), Lippincott Williams & Wilkins (Subsidiary of: Wolters Kluwer N.V.), 530 Walnut St, Philadelphia, PA 19106-3621. TEL 301-223-2300, 800-638-3030, FAX 301-223-2400.

576.5 USA ISSN 0018-0661
QH431.A1 CODEN: HEREAY

➤ **HEREDITAS.** Text in English. 1920. bi-m. USD 240 combined subscription to individuals print & online eds. (effective 2005). adv. abstr.; bibl.; illus. index, cum.index: vols.1-40. back issues avail.; reprint service avail. from PSC. **Document type:** *Journal, Academic/Scholarly.* **Description:** Devoted to the publication of original research in all aspects of genetics and cytology.
Formerly: Hereditas-Genetiskt Arkiv
Related titles: Microfilm ed.: (from PQC); Online - full text ed.: ISSN 1601-5223. free (effective 2005) (from Blackwell Synergy, EBSCO Publishing, Gale Group, IngentaConnect, O C L C Online Computer Library Center, Inc., Swets Information Services).
Indexed: ASFA, AbAn, AgBio, AgrForAb, AnBrAb, ApEcolAb, B&BAb, BCI, BIOBASE, BIOSIS Prev, BioCN&I, BiolAb, CIN, CPA, ChemAb, ChemTitl, CurCont, DentInd, ESPM, EntAb, ExcerpMed, FCA, FaBeAb, ForAb, GenetAb, HGA, HelmAb, HerbAb, HortAb, IABS, ISR, IndMed, IndVet, Inpharma, MEDLINE, MaizeAb, PBA, PGegResA, PGrRegA, PN&I, PoultAb, ProtozoAb, RA&MP, RM&VM, RPP, Reac, RefZh, RevApplEntom, RiceAb, S&F, SCI, SFA, SeedAb, SoyAb, TDB, Telegen, TriticAb, VetBull, WeedAb, WildRev, ZooRec.
—BLDSC (4299.000000), CASDDS, CISTI, GNLM, IE, Infotrieve, ingenta, Linda Hall. **CCC.**
Published by: (Mendelian Society of Lund SWE, Scandinavian Association of Geneticists SWE), Blackwell Publishing, Inc. (Subsidiary of: Blackwell Publishing Ltd.), Commerce Place, 350 Main St, Malden, MA 02148. TEL 781-388-8206, FAX 781-388-8232, subscrip@blackwellpub.com, http://www.blackwellpublishing.com/submit.asp?ref=0018-0661. Ed. Anssi Saura.

576.5 GBR ISSN 0018-067X
QH431 CODEN: HDTYAT

➤ **HEREDITY.** Text in English. 1947. m. EUR 700 in Europe to institutions; USD 815 in the Americas to institutions; GBP 453 to institutions in the UK & elsewhere; EUR 240 combined subscription in Europe to individuals print & online eds.; USD 265 combined subscription in the Americas to individuals print & online eds.; GBP 156 combined subscription to individuals in the UK & elsewhere; print & online eds. (effective 2006). adv. bk.rev. bibl.; charts; illus. index. back issues avail.; reprints avail. **Document type:** *Journal, Academic/Scholarly.*
Description: Publishes articles in all areas of genetics, focusing on the genetics of eukaryotes.
Related titles: Microform ed.: (from PQC); Online - full text ed.: ISSN 1365-2540 (from Blackwell Synergy, EBSCO Publishing, IngentaConnect, O C L C Online Computer Library Center, Inc., Swets Information Services).
Indexed: ASCA, ASFA, AbAn, AbHyg, AgBio, Agr, AgrForAb, AnBrAb, ApEcolAb, ApicAb, B&AI, BCI, BIOBASE, BIOSIS Prev, BioCN&I, BiolAb, CIN, CIS, CPA, CRFR, ChemAb, ChemTitl, CurCont, ESPM, EntAb, ExcerpMed, FCA, FPA, FS&TA, ForAb, GEOBASE, GSI, GenetAb, HGA, HelmAb, HerbAb, HortAb, IABS, ISR, IndMed, IndVet, Inpharma, MEDLINE, MaizeAb, NemAb, OrnHort, PBA, PGegResA, PHN&I, PN&I, PotatoAb, PoultAb, ProtozoAb, RA&MP, RM&VM, RPP, Reac, RefZh, RevApplEntom, RiceAb, S&F, SCI, SFA, SeedAb, SoyAb, TDB, THA, TriticAb, VITIS, VetBull, WeedAb, WildRev, ZooRec.
—BLDSC (4300.000000), CASDDS, CISTI, GNLM, IDS, IE, Infotrieve, ingenta, Linda Hall. **CCC.**
Published by: Nature Publishing Group (Subsidiary of: Macmillan Publishers Ltd.), The MacMillan Building, 4 Crinan St, London, N1 9XW, United Kingdom. TEL 44-20-78334000, FAX 44-20-78433601, subscriptions@nature.com, NatureReviews@nature.com, http://www.nature.com/hdy/. Circ: 1,075. **Subscr. addr.:** Brunel Rd, Houndmills, Basingstoke, Hamps RG21 6XS, United Kingdom. TEL 44-1256-329242, FAX 44-1256-812358.

591.35 636.234 NLD ISSN 1380-5622

HIGHLIGHTS. Text in English. 1994. q. **Document type:** *Journal, Trade.*
Indexed: RefZh.
Published by: Holland Genetics, P. O. Box 5073, Arnhem, 6802 EB, Netherlands. TEL 31-26-3898500, FAX 31-26-3898555, HG@cr-delta.nl, http://www.hg.nl.

576.549 JPN ISSN 0918-5976
CODEN: MMGCEK

➤ **HONYU DOBUTSU SHIKEN BUNKAKAI KAIHO/ MAMMALIAN MUTAGENICITY STUDY GROUP COMMUNICATIONS.** Text in English, Japanese. 1988. a. JPY 2,000. adv. bk.rev. **Document type:** *Academic/Scholarly.*
Description: Contains papers reporting results (including negative data) of original research concerning mutagenesis, chromosome breakage, and related subjects in mammalian cells and mammals.
Indexed: CIN, ChemAb, ChemTitl.
—CASDDS.
Published by: Nihon Kankyo Hen'igen Gakkai, Honyu Dobutsu Shiken Bunkakai/Environmental Mutagen Society of Japan, Mammalian Mutagenicity Study Group, Shokuhin Yakuhin Anzen Senta Hadano Kenkyujo. 729-5 Ochiai, Hadano-shi, Kanagawa-ken 257-0025, Japan. Ed. Makoto Hayashi.

576.5 USA ISSN 0018-7143
GN1 CODEN: HUBIAA

➤ **HUMAN BIOLOGY (DETROIT)**; the international journal of population biology and genetics. Text in English. 1929. bi-m. USD 66 to individuals; USD 190 to institutions; USD 35 to students & seniors (effective 2005). adv. bk.rev. charts; illus. index. back issues avail.; reprint service avail. from PQC. **Document type:** *Journal, Academic/Scholarly.* **Description:** Focuses on genetics areas, including population genetics, evolutionary and genetic demography, quantitative genetics, genetic epidemiology, behavioral genetics, molecular genetics; also growth and physiological parameters of genetic and environmental interactions.
Related titles: Microform ed.: (from PQC); Online - full text ed.: ISSN 1534-6617. 2001 (from bigchalk, Chadwyck-Healey Inc., EBSCO Publishing, Florida Center for Library Automation, Gale Group, H.W. Wilson, O C L C Online Computer Library Center, Inc., Project MUSE, ProQuest Information & Learning, Swets Information Services).
Indexed: A&ATA, ABS&EES, AICP, AbAn, AgeL, AnthLit, B&AI, BAS, BDM&CN, BIOBASE, BIOSIS Prev, BMAb, BiolAb, BiolDig, CIS, ChemAb, CurCont, DSA, DokArb, ExcerpMed, FamI, GSI, IABS, ISR, IndIslam, IndMed, Inpharma, MEA&I, MEDLINE, NutrAb, PCI, PE&ON, PopulInd, PsycholAb, RASB, Reac, SCI, SENA, SOPODA, SPPI, SSA, SSCI, SociolAb, TDB.
—BLDSC (4336.000000), CASDDS, CISTI, GNLM, IDS, IE, Infotrieve, ingenta, KNAW, Linda Hall. **CCC.**
Published by: Wayne State University Press, The Leonard N Simons Bldg, 4809 Woodward Ave, Detroit, MI 48201-1309. TEL 313-577-6120, FAX 313-577-6131, humbial@anthro.utah.edu, http://wsupress.wayne.edu/journals/humanbio.htm. Ed. Sarah Williams-Blangers. Circ: 1,654.

576.5 JPN ISSN 0914-7470

HUMAN CELL. Text in English, Japanese. 1988. q. JPY 12,600 (effective 2005). **Document type:** *Journal, Academic/Scholarly.*

Indexed: INIS AtomInd, MEDLINE.
—BLDSC (4336.033000), IE.
Published by: Japan Human Cell Society, Department of Anatomy 2, Jikei University School of Medicine, 3-25-8, Nishi-shinbashi, Minato-ku, Tokyo, 105-8461, Japan. TEL 81-3-34379094, FAX 81-3-34332065, info@human-cell.com, http://www.flyingfish.net/shop/jhcs/.

599.935 USA ISSN 1063-2158
HUMAN EVOLUTION, BEHAVIOR, AND INTELLIGENCE. Text in English. 1992. irreg. price varies. **Document type:** *Monographic series.*
Indexed: e-psyche.
Published by: Praeger Publishers (Subsidiary of: Greenwood Publishing Group Inc.), 88 Post Rd W, Box 5007, Westport, CT 06881-5007. TEL 203-226-3571, FAX 203-222-1502.

599.9 USA ISSN 1043-0342
RB155.8 CODEN: HGTHE3
➤ **HUMAN GENE THERAPY.** Text in English. 1990. m. USD 2,631 domestic to institutions; USD 2,971 foreign to institutions; USD 3,148 combined subscription domestic to institutions print & online eds.; USD 3,496 combined subscription foreign to institutions print & online eds. (effective 2006). adv. back issues avail.; reprint service avail. from PSC. **Document type:** *Journal, Academic/Scholarly.* **Description:** Publishes papers on the transfer of genes in mammals, including humans. Covers improvements in vector development, delivery systems and animal models, as well as ethical, legal, and regulatory issues.
Related titles: Online - full text ed.: ISSN 1557-7422. USD 2,512 to institutions (effective 2006) (from EBSCO Publishing, Gale Group, O C L C Online Computer Library Center, Inc., Swets Information Services).
Indexed: ASCA, AbHyg, AgBio, AnBrAb, B&BAb, BCI, BIOBASE, BIOSIS Prev, BioEngAb, BiolAb, CIN, CTA, ChemAb, ChemTitl, CurCont, DBA, ExcerpMed, FoMM, GenetAb, HGA, IABS, IPA, ISR, IndMed, IndVet, Inpharma, M&PBA, MEDLINE, NSA, NutrAb, PE&ON, ProtozoAb, Reac, SCI, TDB, VetBull.
—BLDSC (4336.092000), CASDDS, CISTI, GNLM, IDS, IE, Infotrieve, ingenta, KNAW. **CCC.**
Published by: Mary Ann Liebert, Inc. Publishers, 140 Huguenot St 3rd Fl, New Rochelle, NY 10801-5215. TEL 914-740-2100, FAX 914-740-2101, 800-654-3237, info@liebertpub.com, http://www.liebertpub.com/publication.aspx?pub_id=19&crit=Human%20Gene%20Therapy. Ed. James M Wilson TEL 215-898-0819. adv.: B&W page USD 1,150; trim 8.5 x 11. Circ: 24,450.

599.9 DEU ISSN 0340-6717
QH31 CODEN: HUGEDQ
➤ **HUMAN GENETICS.** Text in English. 1913. m. (in 2 vols., 6 nos./vol.). EUR 3,698 combined subscription to institutions print & online eds. (effective 2005). adv. charts; illus. back issues avail.; reprint service avail. from ISI,PSC. **Document type:** *Journal, Academic/Scholarly.* **Description:** Covers human genetics, cytogenetics, biochemical genetics, population genetics, immunogenetics, pharmacogenetics, genetic diagnosis and counseling.
Former titles (until 1975): Humangenetik (0018-7348); (until 1964): Zeitschrift fuer Menschliche Vererbungs-und Konstitutionslehre (0375-5320); (until 1934): Zeitschrift fuer Konstitutionslehre (0177-347X); (until 1921): Zeitschrift fuer Angewandte Anatomie und Konstitutionslehre (0177-3488)
Related titles: Microform ed.: (from PQC); Online - full text ed.: ISSN 1432-1203 (from EBSCO Publishing, Springer LINK, Swets Information Services).
Indexed: ASCA, AnBrAb, B&BAb, BAS, BCI, BDM&CN, BIOBASE, BIOSIS Prev, BiolAb, CIN, ChemAb, ChemTitl, CurCont, ExcerpMed, FamI, FoMM, GenetAb, HGA, IABS, ISR, IndMed, Inpharma, MEDLINE, MS&D, PE&ON, Reac, RefZh, RevApplEntom, SCI, SSCI.
—BLDSC (4336.095000), CASDDS, CISTI, GNLM, IDS, IE, Infotrieve, ingenta, KNAW, Linda Hall. **CCC.**
Published by: Springer-Verlag (Subsidiary of: Springer Science+Business Media), Tiergartenstr 17, Heidelberg, 69121, Germany. TEL 49-6221-3450, FAX 49-6221-345229, http://link.springer.de/link/service/journals/00439/index.htm. Eds. Dr. David N Cooper TEL 44-2920-744042, Dr. Thomas J Hudson. Adv. contact Stephan Kroeck TEL 49-30-827875739. **Subscr. in the Americas to:** Springer-Verlag New York, Inc., Journal Fulfillment, PO Box 2485, Secaucus, NJ 07096-2485. TEL 800-777-4643, 201-348-4033, FAX 201-348-4505, journals@springer-ny.com, http://www.springer-ny.com; **Subscr. to:** Springer GmbH Auslieferungsgesellschaft, Haberstr 7, Heidelberg 69126, Germany. TEL 49-6221-345-0, FAX 49-6221-345-4229, subscriptions@springer.de.

599.9 USA ISSN 0172-7699
HUMAN GENETICS. SUPPLEMENT. Text in English. 1978. irreg. price varies. reprint service avail. from ISI. **Document type:** *Academic/Scholarly.*
Related titles: Microform ed.: (from PQC).
Indexed: IndMed, MEDLINE.
—CISTI. **CCC.**
Published by: Springer-Verlag New York, Inc. (Subsidiary of: Springer Science+Business Media), 233 Spring St, New York, NY 10013. TEL 212-460-1500, FAX 212-473-6272.

611.01816 USA
HUMAN GENOME PROGRAM REPORT. Text in English. 1990. biennial. free. **Document type:** *Government.*
Related titles: Online - full text ed.
Published by: U.S. Department of Energy, Human Genome Program, Office of Health and Environmental Research, ER 72 GTN, Washington, DC 20585. TEL 301-903-6488, FAX 301-903-5051, adamsonae@ornl.gov, http://www.ornl.gov/hgmis. Eds. Anne E Adamson, Daniel W Drell. R&P Betty Mansfield TEL 423-576-6669. Circ: 12,300; 12,300 (controlled). **Subscr. to:** National Technical Information Service, Government Research Center, 5285 Port Royal Rd, Springfield, VA 22161. TEL 703-605-6060, 800-363-2068, http://www.ntis.gov. **Co-sponsor:** Oak Ridge National Laboratory. Human Genome Management Information System.

576.5 615 GBR ISSN 1473-9542
▼ **HUMAN GENOMICS.** Text in English. 2003 (Nov.). bi-m. GBP 100 in Europe to individuals based at educational establishments; USD 160 in North America to individuals based at educational establishments; GBP 115 elsewhere to individuals based at educational establishments; GBP 200 in Europe to institutions; USD 320 in North America to institutions; USD 215 elsewhere to institutions (effective 2004). adv. bk.rev. **Document type:** *Journal, Academic/Scholarly.* **Description:** Provides a forum for the publication of primary research and reviews relating to the application of genomic research in drug discovery and medicine.
Related titles: Online - full content ed.: ISSN 1479-7364; Online - full text ed.: (from EBSCO Publishing, Gale Group, IngentaConnect, ProQuest Information & Learning).
Indexed: ExcerpMed, RefZh.
—BLDSC (4336.098800), IE.
Published by: Henry Stewart Publications, Russell House, 28-30 Little Russell St, London, WC1A 2HN, United Kingdom. TEL 44-20-74043040, FAX 44-20-74042081, qweny@henrystewart.co.uk, http://www.henrystewart.com/journals/hg/index.html. adv.: B&W page GBP 885, color page GBP 1,195; bleed 221 x 285. **Subscr. in N America to:** Henry Stewart Publications, Subscriptions Office, PO Box 10812, Birmingham, AL 35202-1588. TEL 800-633-4931, FAX 205-955-1588, hsp@ebsco.com.

599.935 CHE ISSN 0001-5652
RB155 CODEN: HUHEAS
➤ **HUMAN HEREDITY**; international journal of human and medical genetics. Text in English. 1948. 8/yr. CHF 1,748 in Europe to institutions; CHF 1,775.20 elsewhere to institutions; CHF 1,884 combined subscription in Europe to institutions print & online eds.; CHF 1,911.20 combined subscription elsewhere to institutions print & online eds. (effective 2006). adv. bibl.; charts; illus.; stat. index. back issues avail. **Document type:** *Journal, Academic/Scholarly.* **Description:** Devoted to methodological and applied research on the genetics of human populations, linkage analysis, and the genetic mechanisms of disease.
Formerly (Until 1968): Acta Genetica et Statistica Medica (0365-2785)
Related titles: Microform ed.; Online - full text ed.: ISSN 1423-0062. CHF 1,692 to institutions (effective 2006) (from EBSCO Publishing, O C L C Online Computer Library Center, Inc., ProQuest Information & Learning, Swets Information Services).
Indexed: AICP, ASCA, AbAn, AbHyg, AnBrAb, AnthLit, BCI, BDM&CN, BIOSIS Prev, BiolAb, CIN, CIS, ChemAb, ChemTitl, CurCont, DokArb, ExcerpMed, FamI, ISR, IndMed, Inpharma, MEDLINE, NutrAb, PE&ON, RRTA, Reac, SCI, THA, WAE&RSA.
—BLDSC (4336.150000), CASDDS, CISTI, GNLM, IDS, IE, Infotrieve, ingenta, KNAW, Linda Hall. **CCC.**
Published by: S. Karger AG, Allschwilerstr 10, Basel, 4009, Switzerland. TEL 41-61-3061111, FAX 41-61-3061234, karger@karger.ch, http://www.karger.com/HHE, http://www.karger.ch. Ed. J Ott. adv.: page USD 1,195. Circ: 1,000.

599.9 GBR ISSN 0964-6906
RB155.5 CODEN: HMGEE5
➤ **HUMAN MOLECULAR GENETICS.** Text in English. 1992. 26/yr. GBP 1,147, USD 2,065, EUR 1,721 to institutions; GBP 1,207, USD 2,173, EUR 1,811 combined subscription to institutions print & online eds. (effective 2006). adv. back issues avail.; reprint service avail. from PSC. **Document type:** *Journal, Academic/Scholarly.* **Description:** Concentrates on full-length research papers covering a wide range of topics in all aspects of human molecular genetics.
Related titles: Online - full text ed.: ISSN 1460-2083. 1999. GBP 1,086, USD 1,955, EUR 1,629 to institutions (effective 2006) (from EBSCO Publishing, Gale Group, HighWire Press, IngentaConnect, O C L C Online Computer Library Center, Inc., Ovid Technologies, Inc., Oxford University Press Online Journals, ProQuest Information & Learning, Swets Information Services).
Indexed: ASCA, B&BAb, BCI, BIOBASE, BIOSIS Prev, BioEngAb, BiolAb, CIN, CTA, ChemAb, ChemTitl, CurCont, DBA, ExcerpMed, FoMM, GenetAb, HGA, IABS, ISR, IndMed, Inpharma, MEDLINE, NSA, NSCI, PE&ON, Reac, SCI.
—BLDSC (4336.198000), CASDDS, CISTI, GNLM, IDS, IE, Infotrieve, ingenta, Linda Hall. **CCC.**
Published by: Oxford University Press, Great Clarendon St, Oxford, OX2 6DP, United Kingdom. TEL 44-1865-556767, FAX 44-1865-556646, jnl.orders@oup.co.uk, http://hmg.oxfordjournals.org/, http://www.oxfordjournals.org/. Pub. David Prosser. R&P Fiona Bennett. adv.: B&W page GBP 445, B&W page USD 800, color page GBP 705, color page USD 1,265; trim 215 x 280. Circ: 1,160.

576.549 USA ISSN 1059-7794
RB155.5 CODEN: HUMUE3
➤ **HUMAN MUTATION.** Text in English. 1992. m. (in 2 vols., 6 nos./vol.). USD 1,185 domestic to institutions; USD 1,329 in Canada & Mexico to institutions; USD 1,413 elsewhere to institutions; USD 1,304 combined subscription domestic to institutions print & online eds.; USD 1,448 combined subscription in Canada & Mexico to institutions print & online eds.; USD 1,532 combined subscription elsewhere to institutions print & online eds. (effective 2006). adv. bk.rev. back issues avail. **Document type:** *Journal, Academic/Scholarly.* **Description:** Publishes original research articles, mutation updates, briefs on new mutations and reviews on broad aspects of mutation research as related to understanding the human genome and medical aspects of genetic disorders. For molecular, human and medical geneticists in academic, industrial and clinical research settings.
Related titles: Microform ed.: (from PQC); Online - full content ed.: ISSN 1098-1004. 1996. USD 1,185 to institutions (effective 2006); Online - full text ed.: (from EBSCO Publishing, ProQuest Information & Learning, Swets Information Services, Wiley InterScience).
Indexed: ASCA, B&BAb, BCI, BIOBASE, BIOSIS Prev, BiolAb, CIN, ChemAb, ChemTitl, CurCont, ExcerpMed, FoMM, GenetAb, HGA, IABS, ISR, IndMed, Inpharma, MEDLINE, PE&ON, Reac, RefZh, SCI.
—BLDSC (4336.217000), CASDDS, CISTI, GNLM, IDS, IE, Infotrieve, ingenta, KNAW. **CCC.**
Published by: John Wiley & Sons, Inc., 111 River St, Hoboken, NJ 07030-5774. TEL 201-748-6000, FAX 201-748-5915, uscs-wis@wiley.com, http://www3.interscience.wiley.com/cgi-bin/jhome/38515, http://www.wiley.com. Eds. Haig H Kazazian Jr., Richard G Cotton. adv.: B&W page GBP 640, color page GBP 1,515; trim 210 x 279. Circ: 750. **Subscr. outside the Americas to:** John Wiley & Sons Ltd., The Atrium, Southern Gate, Chichester, West Sussex PO19 8SQ, United Kingdom. TEL 44-1243-843335, 0800-243407, FAX 44-1243-843232, cs-journals@wiley.co.uk.

➤ **ICHTHYOSIS FOCUS.** see *MEDICAL SCIENCES—Dermatology And Venereology*

599.935 JPN ISSN 0387-0022
CODEN: IDENBZ
IDEN/HEREDITY. Text in Japanese. 1947. m. JPY 900 per issue. Supplement avail.
Indexed: CIN, ChemAb, ChemTitl.
—BLDSC (4362.424000), CASDDS, CISTI.
Published by: (Idengaku Fukyukai/Association for Propagation of the Knowledge of Genetics), Shokabo Publisher Co. Ltd., 8-1 Yonban-cho, Chiyoda-ku, Tokyo, 102-0081, Japan.

599.9 610 JPN ISSN 1343-0971
IDENSHI IGAKU/GENE & MEDICINE. Text in Japanese. 1997. q. **Document type:** *Journal, Academic/Scholarly.*
—BLDSC (4096.402360).
Published by: Medical Do, 1-3-18 Nishihommachi Nishi-ku, Osaka, 550-0005, Japan. TEL 81-6-6531-7800, FAX 81-6-6531-7785, home@medicaldo.co.jp, http://www.medicaldo.co.jp/.

576.5 DEU ISSN 0093-7711
QR184 CODEN: IMNGBK
➤ **IMMUNOGENETICS.** Text in English. 1974. m. EUR 1,798 combined subscription to institutions print & online eds. (effective 2005). adv. reprint service avail. from ISI. **Document type:** *Journal, Academic/Scholarly.* **Description:** Covers the areas of immunogenetics of cell interaction and tissue differentiation and development, phylogeny of alloantigens, and genetic control of immune response and disease susceptibility.
Related titles: Microform ed.: (from PQC); Online - full text ed.: ISSN 1432-1211 (from EBSCO Publishing, Springer LINK, Swets Information Services).
Indexed: AIDS&CR, ASCA, AbHyg, AgBio, AnBrAb, BCI, BIOBASE, BIOSIS Prev, BioCN&I, BiolAb, CIN, ChemAb, ChemTitl, CurCont, DBA, DentInd, ExcerpMed, GenetAb, HGA, HelmAb, IABS, ISR, ImmunAb, IndMed, IndVet, Inpharma, MEDLINE, PN&I, PoultAb, ProtozoAb, RA&MP, RM&VM, Reac, RefZh, RevApplEntom, SAA, SCI, SFA, TDB, VetBull, WildRev, ZooRec.
—BLDSC (4369.665000), CASDDS, CISTI, GNLM, IDS, IE, Infotrieve, ingenta, KNAW. **CCC.**
Published by: Springer-Verlag (Subsidiary of: Springer Science+Business Media), Tiergartenstr 17, Heidelberg, 69121, Germany. TEL 49-6221-3450, FAX 49-6221-345229, http://link.springer.de/link/service/journals/00251/index.htm. Ed. Dr. Ronald E Bontrop. Adv. contact Stephan Kroeck TEL 49-30-827875739. **Subscr. in the Americas to:** Springer-Verlag New York, Inc., Journal Fulfillment, PO Box

B

2485, Secaucus, NJ 07096-2485. TEL 800-777-4643, 201-348-4033, FAX 201-348-4505, journals@springer-ny.com, http://www.springer-ny.com; **Subscr. to:** Springer GmbH Auslieferungsgesellschaft, Haberstr 7, Heidelberg 69126, Germany. TEL 49-6221-345-0, FAX 49-6221-345-4229, subscriptions@springer.de.

➤ **IN VITRO CELLULAR & DEVELOPMENTAL BIOLOGY - PLANT.** see *BIOLOGY—Botany*

➤ **INDIAN JOURNAL OF GENETICS AND PLANT BREEDING.** see *BIOLOGY—Botany*

599.935 IND ISSN 0374-826X CODEN: INJHA9

➤ **INDIAN JOURNAL OF HEREDITY.** Text in English. 1969. q. INR 600, USD 38. adv. bk.rev. back issues avail. **Document type:** *Academic/Scholarly.* **Description:** Covers basic and applied genetics of plants and animals (including humans). Covers reproduction, anthropology, biometrics, environment, silviculture, sericulture, apiculture, animal production, hereditary disorders, genetic engineering, gene juggling and sex ratios and studies.
Related titles: Online - full text ed.: (from Ovid Technologies, Inc.).
Indexed: AnBrAb, BiolAb, ChemAb, ExcerpMed, PBA.
—CASDDS, CISTI, Linda Hall.
Published by: Genetic Association of India, P.O. Ganguwala Jatan, Dist. Sri Ganganagar, 335 026, India. TEL 482315. Ed., R&P N.S. Sidhu. Pub. N S Sidhu. Circ: 300.

B

599.9 IND ISSN 0971-6866

➤ **INDIAN JOURNAL OF HUMAN GENETICS.** Text in English. 1995. s-a. INR 500 domestic; USD 50 foreign (effective 2005). **Document type:** *Journal, Academic/Scholarly.* **Description:** Devoted to the growth and dissemination of knowledge of human genetics and related fields in India.
Related titles: Online - full text ed.: free (effective 2005) (from EBSCO Publishing, Gale Group).
Indexed: ExcerpMed.
—BLDSC (4415.230000).
Published by: (The Indian Society of Human Genetics), Medknow Publications Pvt Ltd., A-108/109, Kanara Business Center, Off Link Rd, Ghatkopar (E), Mumbai, Maharastra 400 075, India. TEL 91-22-55031818, FAX 91-22-55031817, ijs@medknow.com, http://www.bioline.org.br/hg, http://www.medknow.com. Ed. Dr. Dipika Mohanty. Circ: 800 (paid and controlled).

599.9 IND ISSN 0378-8156
GN49 CODEN: IJPGDB

➤ **INDIAN JOURNAL OF PHYSICAL ANTHROPOLOGY AND HUMAN GENETICS.** Text in English. 1975-1994; N.S. 1997. m. USD 150 to institutions (effective 2006). adv. bk.rev. bibl.; charts. cum.index every 10 yrs. **Document type:** *Academic/Scholarly.* **Description:** Serves as a medium for scholarly studies devoted to biological aspects of human populations including genetics, evolution, ecology, dermography, growth, physiology, biochemistry, pharmacology, disease patterns and behaviour of individuals comprising them.
Indexed: AICP, AnthLit, BAS, BiolAb.
—GNLM, Linda Hall.
Published by: Ethnographic & Folk Culture Society, L-II-31 Sector B, Aliganj Housing Scheme, P O Box 209, Lucknow, Uttar Pradesh 226 024, India. TEL 91-522-372362, http://www.scientificpub.com/bookdetails.php?booktransid=327&bookid=323. Ed. B R K Shukla. R&P Nadeem Hasnain. Adv. contact Kamal Kishore. page INR 1,000; 195 x 145. Circ: 350.

➤ **INDIAN JOURNAL OF PLANT GENETIC RESOURCES.** see *BIOLOGY—Botany*

➤ **INFECTION, GENETICS AND EVOLUTION.** see *MEDICAL SCIENCES*

576.5 CUB ISSN 0138-6832

INFORMACION EXPRESS. SERIE: GENETICA Y REPRODUCCION. Text in Spanish. 1977. 3/yr. USD 6; in N. America; S. America $9; Europe $10; others $14; or exchange basis.
Indexed: Agrind.
—CISTI.
Published by: Centro de Informacion y Documentacion Agropecuario, Gaveta Postal 4149, Havana, 4, Cuba. **Dist. by:** Ediciones Cubanas, Obispo No. 527, Apdo. 605, Havana, Cuba.

576.5 USA ISSN 1546-6426
QH426

▼ **INFORMATION PLUS REFERENCE SERIES. GENETICS AND GENETIC ENGINEERING.** Text in English. 2003. biennial. USD 40 per vol. (effective 2005). **Document type:** *Monographic series, Academic/Scholarly.*
Related titles: Online - full content ed.; ♦ Series of: Information Plus Reference Series.
Published by: Gale Group (Subsidiary of: Thomson Corporation), 27500 Drake Rd, Farmington Hills, MI 48331-3535. TEL 248-699-4253, 800-877-4253, FAX 248-699-8035, http://www.galegroup.com.

INFORMATIONS ANNUELLES DE CARYOSYSTEMATIQUE ET CYTOGENETIQUE. see *BIOLOGY—Botany*

576.5 USA

INSIDE THE JACKSON LABORATORY. Text in English. 1952. q. free. charts; illus.
Former titles: Jax (0021-5570); Jackson Laboratory News
Published by: Jackson Laboratory, 600 Main St, Bar Harbor, ME 04609. TEL 207-288-6051. Ed. Luther Young. Circ: 14,000.

576.5 USA

THE INSTITUTE FOR GENOMIC RESEARCH. INTERNATIONAL GENOME SEQUENCING AND ANALYSIS CONFERENCE. Text in English. a., latest vol.15, 2003. **Document type:** *Proceedings, Academic/Scholarly.*
Indexed: BIOSIS Prev.
Published by: The Institute For Genomic Research, 9712 Medical Center Dr, Rockville, MD 20850. TEL 301-838-0200, FAX 301-838-0208.

INSTITUTE OF PRIMATE RESEARCH. ANNUAL REPORT. see *BIOLOGY—Zoology*

599.90285 JPN

INTERNATIONAL JOURNAL OF EVOLUTIONARY OPTIMIZATION. Text in Japanese. irreg. **Description:** Aims to collect and disseminate the progressive body of knowledge on evolutionary optimization and other areas of machine learning, via a single organized medium. Includes genetic algorithms, genetic programming, evolutionary programming and evolution strategies.
Related titles: Online - full text ed.
Published by: (Bionic Design Laboratory), Kanazawa University, Department of Human and Mechanical Systems Engineering, Kanazawa, 920, Japan. TEL 81-762-34-4758, FAX 81-762-34-4668, sourav@kenroku.ipc.kanazawa-u.ac.jp, http://genetic.hm.t.kanazawa-u.ac.jp/evopt/. Ed. Sourav Kundu.

599.9 IND ISSN 0972-3757

➤ **INTERNATIONAL JOURNAL OF HUMAN GENETICS.** Text in English. 2001. q. INR 1,500 domestic to individuals; USD 60 foreign to individuals; INR 2,000 domestic to institutions; USD 100 foreign to institutions (effective 2004). bk.rev. 80 p./no. 2 cols./p.; back issues avail.; reprints avail. **Document type:** *Journal, Academic/Scholarly.* **Description:** Publishes articles on all aspects of Human Genetics and also covers ethical issues and genetic counseling. It aims to serve as a forum of life scientists and health professionals especially those who share a common interest in understanding human beings.
Indexed: BiolAb.
—BLDSC (4542.288350), IE.
Published by: Kamla-Raj Enterprises, Chawri Bazar, 2273 Gali Bari Paharwali, New Delhi, 110 006, India. TEL 91-124-5360430, FAX 91-124-2218073, kre@touchtelindia.net, http://www.krepublishers.com. Ed. M K Bhasin. Pub. Ramesh Kumar. Circ: 200 (paid and controlled).

576.5 GBR ISSN 1744-3121
QR184 CODEN: EJOIE3

➤ **INTERNATIONAL JOURNAL OF IMMUNOGENETICS.** Text in English. 1974. bi-m. GBP 698 combined subscription in Europe to institutions print & online eds.; USD 1,290 combined subscription in the Americas to institutions & Caribbean (print & online eds.); GBP 768 combined subscription elsewhere to institutions print & online eds. (effective 2006). adv. bk.rev. abstr.; bibl.; illus. index. back issues avail.; reprint service avail. from ISI,PSC. **Document type:** *Journal, Academic/Scholarly.* **Description:** Publishes original contributions on the genetic control of components of the immune system and their interactions in both humans and experimental animals.
Former titles (until 2004): European Journal of Immunogenetics (0960-7420); Journal of Immunogenetics (0305-1811)
Related titles: Microform ed.: (from PQC); Online - full text ed.: ISSN 1744-313X. GBP 663 in Europe to institutions; USD 1,226 in the Americas to institutions & Caribbean; GBP 730 elsewhere to institutions (effective 2006) (from Blackwell Synergy, EBSCO Publishing, Gale Group, IngentaConnect, O C L C Online Computer Library Center, Inc., Ovid Technologies, Inc., Swets Information Services); Supplement(s): European Journal of Immunogenetics. Supplement. ISSN 1367-3661. 1997.
Indexed: AIDS&CR, AbHyg, AnBrAb, B&BAb, BCI, BIOBASE, BIOSIS Prev, BiolAb, CBTA, CIN, ChemAb, ChemTitl, CurCont, DSA, ExcerpMed, GenetAb, HGA, IABS, ISR, ImmunAb, IndMed, IndVet, Inpharma, MEDLINE, PE&ON, Reac, RefZh, SCI, TDB, VetBull.
—BLDSC (4542.300300), CASDDS, CISTI, GNLM, IDS, IE, Infotrieve, ingenta, KNAW. **CCC.**
Published by: (British Society for Histocompatibility and Immunogenetics), Blackwell Publishing Ltd., 9600 Garsington Rd, Oxford, OX4 2ZG, United Kingdom. TEL 44-1865-776868, FAX 44-1865-714591, customerservices@oxon.blackwellpublishing.com, http://www.blackwellpublishing.com/journal.asp?ref=1744-3121&site=1. Ed. Paul J Travers. Pub. Allen Stevens. R&P Sophie Savage. Adv. contact Jenny Applin. Circ: 435.

576.549 JPN

J E M S NEWS. (Japan - Environmental Mutagen Society) Text in Japanese. 1972. s-a. adv. **Document type:** *Newsletter.*
Published by: Nihon Kankyo Hen'igen Gakkai/Japanese Environmental Mutagen Society, 9-6-41 Akasaka, Minato-ku, Tokyo, 107-0052, Japan. Ed. Shizuyo Sutoh. R&P Ken Ichiro Tanabe TEL 81-3-3947-8891. Adv. contact Ken-ichiro Tanabe.

599.9 USA ISSN 0447-3353 CODEN: JALEBX

JAMES ARTHUR LECTURE ON THE EVOLUTION OF THE HUMAN BRAIN. Text in English. 1956. irreg., latest vol.68, 1998. price varies. **Document type:** *Monographic series.*
Indexed: BiolAb, e-psyche.
—BLDSC (4645.500000), CISTI.
Published by: American Museum of Natural History, Central Park West at 79th St, New York, NY 10024-5192. TEL 212-769-5656, FAX 212-769-5653, scipubs@amnh.org, http://www.amnh.org. Ed. Brenda Jones. Circ: 1,000.

JOURNAL OF APPLIED GENETICS; an international journal of genetics and breeding. see *BIOLOGY—Botany*

576.5 GBR ISSN 1740-2557

▼ ➤ **JOURNAL OF AUTOIMMUNE DISEASES.** Text in English. 2004. irreg. free (effective 2006). **Document type:** *Journal, Academic/Scholarly.* **Description:** Covers topics on clinical and experimental research in autoimmunity.
Media: Online - full text (from National Library of Medicine).
Indexed: ExcerpMed.
Published by: BioMed Central Ltd. (Subsidiary of: Current Science Ltd), Middlesex House, 34-42 Cleveland St, London, W1T 4LB, United Kingdom. TEL 44-20-76319131, FAX 44-20-76319923, info@biomedcentral.com, http://www.jautoimdis.com/home/, http://www.biomedcentral.com. Ed. David D'Cruz.

➤ **JOURNAL OF BASIC MICROBIOLOGY;** an international journal on biochemistry, physiology, genetics, morphology and ecology of microorganisms. see *BIOLOGY—Microbiology*

➤ **JOURNAL OF BIOMOLECULAR TECHNIQUES.** see *BIOLOGY—Biotechnology*

➤ **JOURNAL OF BIOSOCIAL SCIENCE.** see *SOCIOLOGY*

576.5 IND ISSN 0253-7605 CODEN: JCGEDO

➤ **THE JOURNAL OF CYTOLOGY AND GENETICS.** Text in English. 1966. s-a. (in 1 vol.). INR 200 domestic to individuals; USD 50 foreign to individuals; INR 500 domestic to institutions (effective 2003). bk.rev. 100 p./no. 1 cols./p.; back issues avail.; reprints avail. **Document type:** *Journal, Academic/Scholarly.*
Indexed: ChemAb, CurCont, PBA, ZooRec.
—CASDDS, CISTI, Linda Hall.
Published by: Society of Cytologists and Geneticists, 261 7th Main Vijayanagar II Stage, Bangalore, 560040, India. TEL 91-80-3387421, edcytolgenet@hotmail.com. Ed., Pub., R&P, Adv. contact B H M Nijalingappa. Circ: 350 (controlled). **Dist. by:** H P C Publishers Distributors Pvt. Ltd., 4805 Bharat Ram Rd, 24 Darya Ganj, New Delhi 110 002, India. FAX 91-11-6192511.

➤ **JOURNAL OF ENDOCRINE GENETICS.** see *MEDICAL SCIENCES—Endocrinology*

576.8 GBR ISSN 1010-061X
QH359 CODEN: JEBIEQ

➤ **JOURNAL OF EVOLUTIONARY BIOLOGY.** Text in English. 1988. bi-m. GBP 1,006 combined subscription in Europe to institutions print & online eds.; USD 1,858 combined subscription in the Americas to institutions & Caribbean (print & online eds.); GBP 1,106 combined subscription elsewhere to institutions print & online eds. (effective 2006). adv. index. back issues avail.; reprint service avail. from PSC. **Document type:** *Journal, Academic/Scholarly.* **Description:** Covers both micro- and macro-evolution of all types of organisms, integrating perspective across molecular and microbial evolution, behavior, genetics, ecology, life histories, development, paeolntology, systematics and morphology.
Related titles: Online - full text ed.: ISSN 1420-9101. GBP 955 in Europe to institutions; USD 1,766 in the Americas to institutions & Caribbean; GBP 1,051 elsewhere to institutions (effective 2006) (from Blackwell Synergy, EBSCO Publishing, Gale Group, IngentaConnect, O C L C Online Computer Library Center, Inc., Ovid Technologies, Inc., Swets Information Services).
Indexed: ASCA, ASFA, AgBio, AgrForAb, AnBeAb, AnBrAb, ApEcolAb, B&BAb, BIOBASE, BIOSIS Prev, BioCN&I, BiolAb, CIN, CPA, ChemAb, ChemTitl, CurCont, ESPM, EntAb, FCA, ForAb, GEOBASE, GenetAb, HGA, HelmAb, HortAb, IABS, ISR, IndVet, MBA, NemAb, NutrAb, OrnHort, PBA, PGegResA, PGrRegA, PHN&I, PoultAb, ProtozoAb, RA&MP, RM&VM, RPP, RevApplEntom, S&F, SCI, SFA, SeedAb, TDB, TriticAb, VetBull, WeedAb, ZooRec.
—BLDSC (4979.642100), CASDDS, CISTI, IDS, IE, Infotrieve, ingenta. **CCC.**

Published by: (European Society for Evolutionary Biology), Blackwell Publishing Ltd., 9600 Garsington Rd, Oxford, OX4 2ZG, United Kingdom. TEL 44-1865-776868, FAX 44-1865-714591, customerservices@oxon.blackwellpublishing.com, http://www.blackwellpublishing.com/journals/JEB. Eds. D J Fairbairn TEL 909-787-4791, Juha Merila TEL 358-40-8374165. Pub. Amanda McLean Inglis. R&P Tracey Davies. Adv. contact Jenny Applin. Circ: 630.

576.5 USA ISSN 1099-498X
QH448.4 CODEN: JGMEFG

➤ **JOURNAL OF GENE MEDICINE.** Text in English. 1999. m. USD 820 to institutions; USD 902 combined subscription to institutions print & online eds. (effective 2006). bk.rev. reprint service avail. from PSC. **Document type:** *Journal, Academic/Scholarly.* **Description:** Presents articles on all aspects of gene therapy, including design and production of vectors, research into mechanisms and underlying gene transfer, precilinical studies and clinical trials.

Related titles: Online - full text ed.: ISSN 1521-2254. USD 820 to institutions (effective 2006) (from EBSCO Publishing, ProQuest Information & Learning, Swets Information Services, Wiley InterScience).

Indexed: B&BAb, BCI, BioEngAb, CurCont, ExcerpMed, GenetAb, IndMed, Inpharma, M&PBA, MEDLINE, NucAcAb, PE&ON, Reac.

—BLDSC (4987.668000), CISTI, IE, Infotrieve, ingenta. **CCC.**

Published by: (European Society of Gene Therapy), John Wiley & Sons, Inc., 111 River St, Hoboken, NJ 07030-5774. TEL 201-748-6000, 800-825-7550, FAX 201-748-5915, uscs-wis@wiley.com, http://www.interscience.wiley.com/jpages/1099-498X, http://www.wiley.com. Eds. Kay E Davies, Olivier Danos, Richard Mulligan. **Subscr. in the Americas to:** John Wiley & Sons Ltd., The Atrium, Southern Gate, Chichester, West Sussex PO19 8SQ, United Kingdom. TEL 44-1243-843335, 0800-243407, FAX 44-1243-843232, cs-journals@wiley.co.uk.

576.5 USA ISSN 0022-1325
L11 CODEN: JGPYAI

➤ **THE JOURNAL OF GENETIC PSYCHOLOGY.** Text in English. 1891. q. USD 171 domestic to individuals; USD 185 foreign to individuals; USD 192 domestic to institutions; USD 206 foreign to institutions; USD 48 per issue (effective academic year 2005 - 2006). adv. bibl.; charts. index. back issues avail.; reprint service avail. from PSC. **Document type:** *Journal, Academic/Scholarly.* **Description:** Devoted to research and theory in developmental, clinical and educational psychology.

Former titles (until 1954): The Pedagogical Seminary and Journal of Genetic Psychology (0885-6559); (until 1924): The Pedagogical Seminary (0891-9402)

Related titles: CD-ROM ed.: (from ProQuest Information & Learning); Microfilm ed.: (from PMC); Online - full text ed.: (from bigchalk, Chadwyck-Healey Inc., EBSCO Publishing, Florida Center for Library Automation, Gale Group, H.W. Wilson, Northern Light Technology, Inc., O C L C Online Computer Library Center, Inc., ProQuest Information & Learning).

Indexed: AMHA, ASCA, AgeL, BDM&CN, BiolAb, CDA, CIJE, CJA, CurCont, DIP, DSHAb, ECER, ERA, ETA, ExcerpMed, FamI, IBR, IBZ, INI, IPsyAb, IndMed, L&LBA, MEA, MEA&I, MEDLINE, PCI, PhilInd, PsySCDP, PsycInfo, PsycholAb, RASB, RHEA, RefZh, SEA, SENA, SOMA, SOPODA, SSCI, SSI, SWA, SWR&A, TEA, e-psyche.

—BLDSC (4989.900000), CISTI, GNLM, IDS, IE, Infotrieve, ingenta. **CCC.**

Published by: (Helen Dwight Reid Educational Foundation), Heldref Publications, 1319 18th St, NW, Washington, DC 20036-1802. TEL 202-296-6267, 800-365-9753, FAX 202-293-6130, gnt@heldref.org, subscribe@heldref.org, http://www.heldref.org/jgeneticp.php. Adv. contact Chante Douglas. B&W page USD 260; trim 5 x 7.5. Circ: 608 (paid).

576.5 IND ISSN 0022-1333
QH301 CODEN: JOGNAU

➤ **JOURNAL OF GENETICS.** Text in English. 1910. 3/yr. INR 175 domestic to individuals; USD 30 foreign to individuals; INR 250 domestic to institutions; USD 100 foreign to institutions (effective 2005). bk.rev.; software rev. charts; illus.; abstr. 60 p./no. 2 cols./p.; back issues avail.; reprint service avail. from IRC. **Document type:** *Journal, Academic/Scholarly.* **Description:** Includes topics on genetics and evolutionary biology.

Related titles: Online - full text ed.: free (effective 2005).

Indexed: ASCA, AbHyg, AgBio, AgrForAb, AnBrAb, ApicAb, B&AI, BCI, BIOSIS Prev, BioCN&I, BiolAb, CIN, CMCI, CPA, ChemAb, ChemTitl, CurCont, DSA, ExcerpMed, ForAb, HortAb, INIS AtomInd, ISR, IndVet, Inpharma, NutrAb, PBA, PGegResA, PGrRegA, PN&I, PotatoAb, ProtozoAb, RM&VM, RPP, Reac, RevApplEntom, RiceAb, S&F, SCI, SFA, SeedAb, VetBull, WeedAb.

—BLDSC (4990.000000), CASDDS, CISTI, GNLM, IDS, IE, Infotrieve, ingenta, Linda Hall.

Published by: Indian Academy of Sciences, C.V. Raman Ave., Sadashivanagar, P O Box 8005, Bangalore, Karnataka 560 080, India. TEL 91-80-23612546, FAX 91-80-23616094, jgenet@ias.ernet.in, http://www.ias.ac.in/jgenet/index.html. Ed. K VijayRaghavan. R&P G Madhavan. Circ: 1,100.

591.35 ITA ISSN 0394-9257
SB123 CODEN: JGBREX

➤ **JOURNAL OF GENETICS & BREEDING;** a journal devoted to agricultural genetics. Text in English. 1946. q. EUR 129.11 (effective 2005). adv. bk.rev. charts; illus. index. **Document type:** *Magazine, Trade.* **Description:** Focuses on biochemical and molecular genetics, genetic fundamentals of breeding, breeding methodology and genetic aspects of "in vitro" culture.

Formerly: Genetica Agraria (0016-6685)

Indexed: AgBio, AgrForAb, AnBrAb, BIOBASE, BIOSIS Prev, BiolAb, CIN, CPA, CTFA, ChemAb, ChemTitl, DSA, FCA, FS&TA, FaBeAb, ForAb, HerbAb, HortAb, I&DA, IABS, MaizeAb, NemAb, NutrAb, OrnHort, PBA, PGegResA, PGrRegA, PHN&I, PlantSci, PotatoAb, RA&MP, RPP, RefZh, RevApplEntom, RiceAb, S&MA, SeedAb, SoyAb, TriticAb, VetBull.

—BLDSC (4990.200000), CASDDS, CISTI, IE, Infotrieve, ingenta.

Published by: Istituto Sperimentale per la Cerealicoltura, Via Cassia 176, Rome, RM 00191, Italy. TEL 39-06-3295705, FAX 39-06-36306022, http://www.cerealicoltura.it. Eds. A Bianchi, A J Pryor. Circ: 300 (controlled).

576.5 USA ISSN 1551-7551
QH447 CODEN: GLEEA7

➤ **JOURNAL OF GENOME SCIENCE AND TECHNOLOGY.** Text in English. 2002. q. USD 159 domestic to individuals; USD 174 foreign to individuals; USD 485 domestic to institutions; USD 510 foreign to institutions (effective 2004). abstr. back issues avail. **Document type:** *Journal, Academic/Scholarly.* **Description:** Aims to consolidate research activities on the analysis of whole genomes relevant to human, animals, plants and micro-organisms.

Formerly (until 2004): Genome Letters (1537-3053)

Related titles: Online - full text ed.: ISSN 1551-756X (from EBSCO Publishing, Gale Group, IngentaConnect).

Indexed: ChemAb, ExcerpMed.

—BLDSC (4116.313460), CISTI. **CCC.**

Published by: American Scientific Publishers, 25650 N Lewis Way, Stevenson Ranch, CA 91381-1439. TEL 661-254-0807, FAX 661-254-1207, editor@aspbs.com, http://www.aspbs.com/genomelett/index.htm.

599.935 GBR ISSN 0022-1503
S494.A2 CODEN: JOHEA8

➤ **JOURNAL OF HEREDITY.** Text in English. 1910. bi-m. GBP 191, USD 323, EUR 287 to institutions; GBP 201, USD 340, EUR 302 combined subscription to institutions print & online eds. (effective 2006). adv. bk.rev. bibl.; charts; illus. Index. back issues avail.; reprint service avail. from PQC,PSC. **Document type:** *Journal, Academic/Scholarly.* **Description:** Publishes original research, reviews and historical articles in organismic genetics.

Related titles: Microfiche ed.: (from IDC); Microform ed.: (from PMC, PQC); Online - full text ed.: ISSN 1465-7333. GBP 181, USD 306, EUR 272 to institutions (effective 2006) (from EBSCO Publishing, Gale Group, HighWire Press, IngentaConnect, O C L C Online Computer Library Center, Inc., Oxford University Press Online Journals, Swets Information Services).

Indexed: AEA, ASCA, ASFA, AbAn, AgBio, Agr, AgrForAb, AnBrAb, ApicAb, B&AI, B&BAb, BCI, BIOBASE, BIOSIS Prev, BibAg, BioCN&I, BiolAb, CIN, CIS, CPA, CRFR, CTFA, ChemAb, ChemTitl, CurCont, DBA, DSA, EntAb, ExcerpMed, FCA, FPA, FS&TA, ForAb, GSI, GenetAb, HGA, HelmAb, HerbAb, HortAb, IABS, ISR, IndMed, IndVet, Inpharma, MEDLINE, MaizeAb, NemAb, NutrAb, OrnHort, PBA, PGegResA, PHN&I, PN&I, PoultAb, ProtozoAb, PsycholAb, RA&MP, RM&VM, RPP, Reac, RefZh, RevApplEntom, RiceAb, S&F, S&MA, SAA, SCI, SFA, SIA, SeedAb, SoyAb, TDB, THA, Telegen, TriticAb, VetBull, WeedAb, WildRev, ZooRec.

—BLDSC (4998.000000), CASDDS, CISTI, GNLM, IDS, IE, Infotrieve, ingenta, Linda Hall. **CCC.**

Published by: (American Genetic Association USA), Oxford University Press, Great Clarendon St, Oxford, OX2 6DP, United Kingdom. TEL 44-1865-556767, FAX 44-1865-556646, jnl.orders@oup.co.uk, http://jhered.oxfordjournals.org/, http://www.oxfordjournals.org/. Ed. Stephen O'Brien. Pub. Janet Fox. adv.: B&W page GBP 400, B&W page USD 640; trim 190 x 255. Circ: 1,600.

➤ **JOURNAL OF HUMAN ECOLOGY;** international, interdisciplinary journal of man-environment relationship. see *ENVIRONMENTAL STUDIES*

599.9 GBR ISSN 0047-2484
GN281 CODEN: JHEVAT

➤ **JOURNAL OF HUMAN EVOLUTION.** Text in English. 1972. 12/yr. EUR 513 in Europe to individuals; JPY 55,300 in Japan to individuals; USD 511 elsewhere to individuals; EUR 1,394 in Europe to institutions; JPY 150,400 in Japan to institutions; USD 1,238 elsewhere to institutions (effective 2006). adv. bk.rev. charts; illus. index. reprints avail. **Document type:** *Academic/Scholarly.* **Description:** Concentrates on papers covering all aspects of human evolution.

Related titles: Online - full text ed.: ISSN 1095-8606. USD 1,307 (effective 2002) (from EBSCO Publishing, Gale Group, IngentaConnect, O C L C Online Computer Library Center, Inc., ScienceDirect, Swets Information Services).

Indexed: AICP, ASCA, AbAn, AnthLit, ArtHuCI, BIOSIS Prev, BiolAb, Biostat, BrArAb, CTA, CurCont, ExcerpMed, GEOBASE, GSI, IBSS, ISR, IndMed, MEA&I, MEDLINE, NAA, SCI, SSCI, WildRev, ZooRec.

—BLDSC (5003.415000), GNLM, IDS, IE, Infotrieve, ingenta, Linda Hall. **CCC.**

Published by: Academic Press (Subsidiary of: Elsevier Science & Technology), Harcourt Pl, 32 Jamestown Rd, London, NW1 7BY, United Kingdom. TEL 44-20-7424-4200, FAX 44-20-7483-2293, apsubs@acad.com, http://www.elsevier.com/locate/jhevol. Eds. F. Spoor, Susan Anton, William H. Kimbel.

599.9 JPN ISSN 1434-5161
QH431 CODEN: JHGEFR

➤ **JOURNAL OF HUMAN GENETICS.** Text in English. 1956. m. (in 1 vol., 12 nos./vol.). EUR 385 combined subscription to institutions print & online eds. (effective 2005). adv. bk.rev. **Document type:** *Journal, Academic/Scholarly.* **Description:** Covers all aspects of human genetics, including gene cloning and mapping, linkage analysis, mutational analysis, evolution, cancer genetics, and gene therapy, as well as genetic and functional analysis of animal models of disease or behavior.

Former titles (until Oct. 1997): Japanese Journal of Human Genetics (0916-8478); (until 1992): Jinrui Idengaku Zasshi (0021-5074)

Related titles: Online - full text ed.: ISSN 1435-232X (from EBSCO Publishing, Springer LINK, Swets Information Services).

Indexed: ASCA, AbAn, B&BAb, BCI, BIOBASE, BIOSIS Prev, BiolAb, CIN, ChemAb, ChemTitl, CurCont, ExcerpMed, GenetAb, HGA, IABS, ISR, IndMed, Inpharma, Inspec, JPI, MEDLINE, PE&ON, Reac, SCI, THA.

—BLDSC (5003.415500), CASDDS, CISTI, GNLM, IDS, IE, Infotrieve, ingenta, KNAW, Linda Hall. **CCC.**

Published by: (Japan Society of Human Genetics), Springer-Verlag Tokyo (Subsidiary of: Springer Science+Business Media), 3-13 Hongo 3-chome, Bunkyo-ku, Tokyo, 113-0033, Japan. TEL 81-3-38120331, FAX 81-3-38187454, http://link.springer.de/link/service/journals/10038/index.htm, http://www.springer-tokyo.co.jp/. Ed. Yusuke Nakamura. Adv. contact Stephan Kroeck TEL 49-30-827875739. Circ: 23,000. **Subscr. in the Americas to:** Springer-Verlag New York, Inc., Journal Fulfillment, PO Box 2485, Secaucus, NJ 07096-2485. TEL 800-777-4643, 201-348-4033, FAX 201-348-4505, journals@springer-ny.com, http://www.springer-ny.com; **Subscr. to:** Springer GmbH Auslieferungsgesellschaft, Haberstr 7, Heidelberg 69126, Germany. TEL 49-6221-345-0, FAX 49-6221-345-4229, subscriptions@springer.de.

599.9 GBR ISSN 0022-2593
QH431 CODEN: JMDGAE

➤ **JOURNAL OF MEDICAL GENETICS.** Text in English. 1964. m. GBP 391, USD 716, EUR 579 to institutions print or online; GBP 167, USD 306, EUR 247 combined subscription to individuals print & online eds.; GBP 438, USD 802, EUR 648 combined subscription to institutions print & online eds. (effective 2006). adv. bk.rev. charts; illus. index. reprint service avail. from PQC. **Document type:** *Journal, Academic/Scholarly.* **Description:** Devoted to all areas of medical genetics, including clinical applications of molecular genetics, dysmorphology (the delineation and genetic basis of new syndromes), ethical and social aspects of medical genetics, and the development of medical genetic services.

Related titles: CD-ROM ed.: (from Ovid Technologies, Inc.); Microform ed.: (from PQC); Online - full text ed.: J M G Online. ISSN 1468-6244. GBP 75, USD 137, EUR 111 to individuals (effective 2006) (from bigchalk, EBSCO Publishing, Gale Group, HighWire Press, Northern Light Technology, Inc., O C L C Online Computer Library Center, Inc., Ovid Technologies, Inc., ProQuest Information & Learning).

Indexed: ASCA, AbAn, AbHyg, AnBrAb, ArtHuCI, B&BAb, BCI, BDM&CN, BIOBASE, BIOSIS Prev, BioEngAb, BiolAb, CIN, ChemAb, ChemTitl, CurCont, DentInd, ExcerpMed, FamI, GenetAb, HGA, IABS, ISR, IndMed, IndVet, Inpharma, MEDLINE, MS&D, NSCI, NutrAb, PE&ON, Reac, SCI, SPPI, SSCI, TDB, VetBull.

—BLDSC (5017.070000), CASDDS, CISTI, GNLM, IDS, IE, Infotrieve, ingenta, KNAW. **CCC.**

Published by: B M J Publishing Group, B M A House, Tavistock Sq, London, WC1H 9JR, United Kingdom. TEL 44-20-73874499, FAX 44-20-73836400, jmg@bmjgroup.com, info.norththames@bma.org.uk, http://jmg.bmjjournals.com/, http://www.bmjjournals.com/, http://www.bmjpg.com/. Eds. Chris Eng, Eamonn R Maher. Pub. Alex Williamson. R&P Carol Torselli TEL 44-20-73836169. Adv. contact Euan Currer TEL 44-20-73836181.

576.8 USA ISSN 0022-2844
QH366.A1 CODEN: JMEVAU

➤ **JOURNAL OF MOLECULAR EVOLUTION.** Text in English. 1971. m. (in 2 vols., 6 nos./vol.). EUR 1,798 combined subscription to institutions print & online eds. (effective 2005). adv. reprint service avail. from ISI. **Document type:** *Journal, Academic/Scholarly.* **Description:** Covers molecular evolution and molecular biology. Includes a new focus on the evolutionary aspects of molecular population genetics.

Related titles: Microform ed.: (from PQC); Online - full text ed.: ISSN 1432-1432 (from EBSCO Publishing, Springer LINK, Swets Information Services).

B

▼ *new title* ➤ *refereed* ✶ *unverified* ♦ *full entry avail.*

Indexed: ASCA, ASFA, AbHyg, AgBio, Agr, AnBrAb, B&AI, BBCI, BCI, BIOBASE, BIOSIS Prev, BibAg, BioCN&I, BiolAb, CCI, CIS, CPA, ChemAb, ChemTitl, CurCont, DSA, EngInd, ExcerpMed, FPA, FS&TA, ForAb, GenetAb, HGA, HelmAb, HerbAb, HortAb, IAA, IABS, ISR, IndMed, IndVet, Inpharma, MEDLINE, MaizeAb, NemAb, OrnHort, PBA, PGegResA, PHN&I, PN&I, PoultAb, ProtozoAb, RA&MP, RM&VM, RPP, Reac, RefZh, RevApplEntom, RiceAb, S&F, SCI, SFA, SIA, SeedAb, SoyAb, TDB, TriticAb, VITIS, VetBull, WeedAb, WildRev, ZooRec.
—BLDSC (5020.710000), CASDDS, CISTI, Ei, GNLM, IDS, IE, Infotrieve, ingenta, Linda Hall. **CCC.**
Published by: (The International Society of Molecular Evolution), Springer-Verlag New York, Inc. (Subsidiary of: Springer Science+Business Media), 233 Spring St, New York, NY 10013. TEL 212-460-1500, 800-777-4643, FAX 212-473-6272, journals@springer-ny.com, http://link.springer.de/link/service/journals/00239, http://www.springer-ny.com. Ed. Martin Kreitman TEL 773-702-1222. R&P Ian Gross. Adv. contact Brian Skepton. **Subscr. outside the Americas to:** Springer GmbH Auslieferungsgesellschaft, Haberstr 7, Heidelberg 69126, Germany. TEL 49-6221-345-0, FAX 49-6221-345-4229, subscriptions@springer.de; **Subscr. to:** Journal Fulfillment, PO Box 2485, Secaucus, NJ 07096-2485. TEL 201-348-4033, FAX 201-348-4505.

B

➤ **JOURNAL OF MOLECULAR MICROBIOLOGY AND BIOTECHNOLOGY.** see *BIOLOGY—Microbiology*

576.5 NLD ISSN 1345-711X
CODEN: JSFGAW

➤ **JOURNAL OF STRUCTURAL AND FUNCTIONAL GENOMICS.** Text in English. 2000. q., latest vol.4, 2003. EUR 406, USD 409, GBP 254 combined subscription to institutions print & online eds. (effective 2005). adv. reprint service avail. from PSC. **Document type:** *Journal, Academic/Scholarly.* **Description:** Provides a forum for the exchange and discussion of new data in structural and functional genomics.
Related titles: Online - full text ed.: ISSN 1570-0267 (from EBSCO Publishing, Gale Group, IngentaConnect, Kluwer Online, O C L C Online Computer Library Center, Inc., Springer LINK, Swets Information Services).
Indexed: BIOBASE, BibLing, BiolAb, ChemAb, ExcerpMed, RefZh.
—BLDSC (5066.874200), CISTI, IE, Infotrieve, ingenta. **CCC.**
Published by: Springer-Verlag Dordrecht (Subsidiary of: Springer Science+Business Media), Van Godewijckstraat 30, Dordrecht, 3311 GX, Netherlands. TEL 31-78-6576050, FAX 31-78-6576474, http://springerlink.metapress.com/openurl.asp?genre=journal&issn=1345-711X, http://www.springeronline.com. Ed. Yoji Arata.

576.549 JPN ISSN 0910-0865
CODEN: KHKEEN

KANKYO HEN'IGEN KENKYU/ENVIRONMENTAL MUTAGEN RESEARCH. Text in English, Japanese. 1978. 3/yr. membership. **Document type:** *Journal, Academic/Scholarly.*
Indexed: CIN, ChemAb, ChemTitl.
—BLDSC (5085.475000), CASDDS. **CCC.**
Published by: Nihon Kankyo Hen'igen Gakkai/Japanese Environmental Mutagen Society, 9-6-41 Akasaka, Minato-ku, Tokyo, 107-0052, Japan. TEL 81-3-34755618, FAX 81-3-34755619, http://www.j-ems.org/journal/index.html.

599.9 CHE ISSN 1422-6251
QH431 CODEN: MOHGAD

➤ **KEY ISSUES IN HUMAN GENETICS.** Text in English. 1966. irreg., latest vol.14, 1992. price varies; price varies. reprint service avail. from ISI. **Document type:** *Monographic series, Academic/Scholarly.* **Description:** Publishes sophisticated genetic studies transformed into clear interpretations of their medical importance.
Formerly: Monographs in Human Genetics (0077-0876)
Indexed: BIOSIS Prev, BiolAb, CIN, ChemAb, ChemTitl, CurCont, IndMed, MEDLINE.
—CASDDS, CISTI, GNLM, Infotrieve, KNAW. **CCC.**
Published by: S. Karger AG, Allschwilerstr 10, Basel, 4009, Switzerland. TEL 41-61-3061111, FAX 41-61-3061234, karger@karger.ch, http://www.karger.com/bookseries/KIHUG/kihug.htm, http://www.karger.ch. Ed. S Ayme.

576.5 JPN ISSN 0080-8539
CODEN: SEZIA3

KIHARA SEIBUTSUGAKU KENKYUJO. SEIKEN JIHO/KIHARA INSTITUTE FOR BIOLOGICAL RESEARCH. REPORT. Text in Japanese. 1941. a. JPY 1,000, USD 8 to members. **Document type:** *Bulletin.*
Indexed: Agrind, BIOSIS Prev, BiolAb, JPI, VITIS.
—CISTI.
Published by: Yokohama City University, Kihara Institute for Biological Research/Yokohama Shiritsu Daigaku Kihara Seibutsugaku Kenkyujo, 22-2 Seto Kanazawa-ku, Minami-ku, Yokohama, Kanagawa-ken 232-0000, Japan.

576.5 JPN
KIKAN KEISEI KENKYUKAI KAISHI/JAPANESE SOCIETY FOR BASIC AND APPLIED ORGAN RESEARCH. BULLETIN. Text in Japanese. a.
Published by: Kikan Keisei Kenkyukai, Nagoya Daigaku Igakubu, Koku Gekagaku Kyoshitsu, 65 Tsurumai-cho, Showa-ku, Nagoya-shi, Aichi-ken 466-0065, Japan.

KIKAN KEISEI KENKYUKAI KOEN YOSHISHU/JAPANESE SOCIETY FOR BASIC AND APPLIED ORGAN RESEARCH. ABSTRACTS OF THE MEETING. see *BIOLOGY—Abstracting, Bibliographies, Statistics*

576.5 JPN
KIKAN KEISEI NYUSU/JAPANESE SOCIETY FOR BASIC AND APPLIED ORGAN RESEARCH. NEWS. Text in Japanese. 1989. irreg.
Indexed: RASB.
Published by: Kikan Keisei Kenkyukai, Nagoya Daigaku Igakubu, Koku Gekagaku Kyoshitsu, 65 Tsurumai-cho, Showa-ku, Nagoya-shi, Aichi-ken 466-0065, Japan.

576.5 JPN
KOKURITSU IDENGAKU KENKYUJO NENPO. Text in Japanese. 1949. a.
Related titles: ♦ English ed.: National Institute of Genetics. Annual Report (English Edition). ISSN 0077-4995.
Published by: Ministry of Education, National Institute of Genetics/Monbusho Kokuritsu Idengaku Kenkyujo, 1111 Yata, Mishima-shi, Shizuoka-ken 411-0801, Japan.

576.5 KOR ISSN 0254-5934
QH426 CODEN: KJGEDG

➤ **KOREAN JOURNAL OF GENETICS/HAN'GUG YUJEON HAGHOEJI.** Text in Korean. 1979. q. KRW 70,000 domestic; USD 100 foreign. adv. bk.rev. **Document type:** *Proceedings, Academic/Scholarly.* **Description:** Publishes original reports on any field of genetics.
Indexed: ASCA, BCI, BIOSIS Prev, BiolAb, CIN, ChemAb, ChemTitl, SFA, ZooRec.
—BLDSC (5113.551000), CASDDS, CISTI, IE, ingenta.
Published by: Genetics Society of Korea/Han'gug Yujeon Haghoe, Seoul National University, Dept. of Biology, College of Natural Science, Sinlimdong Sab 56-1, Kwanakguseoul, 151-742, Korea, S. TEL 82-53-950-6353, FAX 82-53-943-2762, yselee@kyungpook.ac.kr, http://www.bric.postech.ac.kr/gsk/. Circ: 500.

576.5021 USA
LINKAGE NEWSLETTER. Text in English. 1987. irreg. (2-3/yr.). free. adv. bk.rev. **Document type:** *Newsletter.* **Description:** Focuses on human linkage analysis with particular emphasis on statistical problems and computer programs.
Published by: Rockefeller University, Laboratory of Statistical Genetics, 1230 York Ave, PO Box 192, New York, NY 10021-6399. TEL 212-960-2507, FAX 212-327-7996, ott@rockvax.rockefeller.edu, http://linkage.rockefeller.edu. Ed., Pub., Adv. contact Jurg Ott.

599.935 USA ISSN 0938-8990
QL738.5 CODEN: MAMGEC

➤ **MAMMALIAN GENOME.** Text in English. 1991. m. (in 1 vol., 12 nos./vol.). EUR 1,115 combined subscription to institutions print & online eds. (effective 2005). adv. back issues avail.; reprint service avail. from ISI. **Document type:** *Journal, Academic/Scholarly.* **Description:** Presents articles on experimental, theoretical, and technical aspects of genome organization, the evolution of mice, humans, and other mammalian species.
Incorporates (1949-1997): Mouse Genome (0959-0587)
Related titles: Microform ed.: (from PQC); Online - full text ed.: ISSN 1432-1777 (from EBSCO Publishing, Springer LINK, Swets Information Services).
Indexed: ASCA, ASFA, AbHyg, AgBio, AnBrAb, B&BAb, BCI, BIOBASE, BIOSIS Prev, BiolAb, ChemAb, ChemTitl, CurCont, DSA, ExcerpMed, FoVS&M, GenetAb, HGA, HelmAb, IABS, ISR, IndMed, IndVet, Inpharma, MEDLINE, NSA, NemAb, NutrAb, PBA, PN&I, PoultAb, ProtozoAb, RPP, Reac, RefZh, SCI, SIA, SoyAb, VetBull, WildRev.
—BLDSC (5357.450000), CASDDS, CISTI, GNLM, IDS, IE, Infotrieve, ingenta, KNAW, Linda Hall. **CCC.**
Published by: (International Mammalian Genome Society), Springer-Verlag New York, Inc. (Subsidiary of: Springer Science+Business Media), 233 Spring St, New York, NY 10013. TEL 212-460-1500, 800-777-4643, FAX 212-473-6272, journals@springer-ny.com, http://link.springer.de/link/service/journals/00335/, http://www.springer-ny.com. Eds. Dr. Joseph H Nadeau, Dr. Steve D M Brown. R&P Ian Gross. Adv. contact Brian Skepton. **Subscr. outside the Americas to:** Springer GmbH Auslieferungsgesellschaft, Haberstr 7, Heidelberg 69126, Germany. TEL 49-6221-345-0, FAX 49-6221-345-4229, subscriptions@springer.de; **Subscr. to:** Journal Fulfillment, PO Box 2485, Secaucus, NJ 07096-2485. TEL 201-348-4033, FAX 201-348-4505.

➤ **MANKIND QUARTERLY**; an international quarterly journal dealing with both physical and cultural anthropology including related subjects such as psychology, demography, genetics, linguistics and mythology. see *ANTHROPOLOGY*

576.5 DEU ISSN 0936-5931
CODEN: MGENEZ

➤ **MEDIZINISCHE GENETIK.** Text in German. 1989. 4/yr. EUR 80 to individuals; EUR 113 to institutions (effective 2005). adv. bk.rev. bibl. **Document type:** *Journal, Academic/Scholarly.* **Description:** Contains case reports on genetic counseling, ethics, diagnoses, patenting, and other questions.
Indexed: ExcerpMed, RefZh.
—BLDSC (5535.076700), GNLM, IE, ingenta. **CCC.**
Published by: Berufsverband Deutscher Humangenetiker e.V., Goethestr 29, Munich, 80336, Germany. TEL 49-89-55027855, FAX 49-89-55027856, verlag@medgenetik.de, http://www.medgenetik.de/medgenetik/. Ed., R&P Christine Scholz. Pub. Jan Murken. Adv. contact Wolfgang Kroner. color page EUR 1,400; trim 210 x 297. Circ: 1,850. **Co-sponsor:** Gesellschaft fuer Humangenetik e.V.

576.5 IND ISSN 0970-9649

➤ **MENDEL**; multidisciplinary international journal of science. Text in English. 1984. q. INR 200, USD 100 to individuals; INR 500, USD 200 to institutions (effective 2001). adv. bk.rev. 100 p./no.; back issues avail.; reprints avail. **Document type:** *Yearbook, Academic/Scholarly.* **Description:** Publishes papers and general articles of common interest in all fields of science and medicine.
Published by: Mendelian Society of India, 194-B S K Puri, Patna, Bihar 800 001, India. TEL 91-612-233741. Ed. R N Trivedi. Circ: 750 (controlled).

576.5 USA ISSN 1067-2389
QH442 CODEN: MEMGE6

METHODS IN MOLECULAR GENETICS. Text in English. 1993. irreg., latest vol.8, 1996. **Document type:** *Monographic series.*
Indexed: Agr, BIOSIS Prev, ChemAb, ChemTitl.
—BLDSC (5748.202200), CASDDS, CISTI, ingenta. **CCC.**
Published by: Academic Press (Subsidiary of: Elsevier Science & Technology), 525 B St, Ste 1900, San Diego, CA 92101-4495. TEL 619-231-6616, 800-894-3434, FAX 619-699-6422, apsubs@acad.com, http://www.academicpress.com.

576.5 DEU ISSN 1617-4615
QH431 CODEN: MGGOAA

➤ **MOLECULAR GENETICS AND GENOMICS**; an international journal. Short title: M G G. Text in English. 1908. m. EUR 3,188 combined subscription to institutions print & online eds. (effective 2005). adv. charts; illus. Index. back issues avail.; reprint service avail. from ISI. **Document type:** *Journal, Academic/Scholarly.* **Description:** For biotechnicians, microbiologists, virologists, and biochemists. Covers the genetics of prokaryotes, including plastids, mitochondria, plasmids, "jumping genes," and transposable elements. Provides background research on the molecular genetics of eukaryotes, and its practical applications in genetic engineering.
Former titles (until 2001): Molecular and General Genetics (0026-8925); (until 1966): Zeitschrift fuer Vererbungslehre (0372-8609); (until 1957): Zeitschrift fuer Induktive Abstammungs- und Vererbungslehre (0372-901X)
Related titles: Microform ed.: (from PQC); Online - full text ed.: ISSN 1617-4623 (from EBSCO Publishing, Springer LINK, Swets Information Services).
Indexed: ASCA, ASFA, AbHyg, AgBio, Agr, AgrForAb, AnBrAb, B&AI, B&BAb, BBCI, BCI, BIOBASE, BIOSIS Prev, BibAg, BioCN&I, BiolAb, CBTA, CEABA, CIN, CPA, CTFA, ChemAb, ChemTitl, CurCont, DBA, DSA, EntAb, ExcerpMed, FCA, FPA, FS&TA, ForAb, GenetAb, HGA, HerbAb, HortAb, IABS, ISR, IndMed, IndVet, MBA, MEDLINE, MaizeAb, NemAb, NucAcAb, NutrAb, OrnHort, PBA, PGegResA, PGrRegA, PHN&I, PotatoAb, PoultAb, ProtozoAb, RA&MP, RM&VM, RPP, RefZh, RevApplEntom, RiceAb, S&F, SCI, SIA, SeedAb, SoyAb, TDB, TriticAb, VITIS, VetBull, WeedAb, WildRev, ZooRec.
—BLDSC (5900.817535), CASDDS, CISTI, GNLM, IDS, IE, Infotrieve, ingenta, Linda Hall. **CCC.**
Published by: Springer-Verlag (Subsidiary of: Springer Science+Business Media), Tiergartenstr 17, Heidelberg, 69121, Germany. TEL 49-6221-3450, FAX 49-6221-345229, http://link.springer.de/link/service/journals/00438/index.htm. Ed. Dr. Cornelis P Hollenberg TEL 49-211-811-5370. Adv. contact Stephan Kroeck TEL 49-30-827875739. **Subscr. in the Americas to:** Springer-Verlag New York, Inc., Journal Fulfillment, PO Box 2485, Secaucus, NJ 07096-2485. TEL 800-777-4643, 201-348-4033, FAX 201-348-4505, journals@springer-ny.com, http://www.springer-ny.com; **Subscr. to:** Springer GmbH Auslieferungsgesellschaft, Haberstr 7, Heidelberg 69126, Germany. TEL 49-6221-345-0, FAX 49-6221-345-4229, subscriptions@springer.de.

➤ **MOLECULAR GENETICS AND METABOLISM.** see *BIOLOGY—Biochemistry*

➤ **MOLECULAR GENETICS, MICROBIOLOGY AND VIROLOGY.** see *BIOLOGY—Microbiology*

➤ **MOLECULAR NEUROBIOLOGY**; a review journal. see *BIOLOGY—Biochemistry*

576.5 USA ISSN 1055-7903
QH367.5 CODEN: MPEVEK
➤ **MOLECULAR PHYLOGENETICS AND EVOLUTION.** Text in English. 1992. 12/yr. EUR 407 in Europe to individuals; JPY 42,500 in Japan to individuals; USD 309 to individuals except Europe and Japan; EUR 884 in Europe to institutions; JPY 92,400 in Japan to institutions; USD 671 to institutions except Europe and Japan; EUR 205 in Europe to students; JPY 21,300 in Japan to students; USD 178 to students except Europe and Japan (effective 2006). adv. back issues avail. **Document type:** *Academic/Scholarly.* **Description:** Provides a forum for molecular studies that advance our understanding of phylogeny and evolution. Encourages collaboration of molecular biologists and computer scientists with systematic and evolutionary biologists.
Related titles: Online - full text ed.: ISSN 1095-9513. USD 622 (effective 2002) (from EBSCO Publishing, Gale Group, IngentaConnect, O C L C Online Computer Library Center, Inc., ScienceDirect, Swets Information Services).
Indexed: ASCA, ASFA, AgBio, AgrForAb, AnBrAb, B&BAb, BBCI, BIOBASE, BIOSIS Prev, BioCN&I, BiolAb, CIN, CPA, ChemAb, ChemTitl, CurCont, EntAb, FCA, FPA, ForAb, GenetAb, HelmAb, HerbAb, HortAb, ISR, IndMed, IndVet, MEDLINE, MaizeAb, NutrAb, OrnHort, PBA, PGegResA, PHN&I, PN&I, PotatoAb, PoultAb, ProtozoAb, RA&MP, RM&VM, RPP, RevApplEntom, S&F, SCI, SFA, SIA, SeedAb, SoyAb, TDB, TriticAb, VetBull, WeedAb, ZooRec.
—BLDSC (5900.819800), CASDDS, CISTI, GNLM, IDS, IE, Infotrieve, ingenta, Linda Hall. **CCC.**
Published by: Academic Press (Subsidiary of: Elsevier Science & Technology), 525 B St, Ste 1900, San Diego, CA 92101-4495. TEL 619-231-6616, 800-894-3434, FAX 619-699-6422, apsubs@acad.com, http://www.elsevier.com/locate/ympev, http://www.academicpress.com. Ed. Dr. Morris Goodman.

➤ **MOLEKULYARNAYA GENETIKA, MIKROBIOLOGIYA I VIRUSOLOGIYA/MOLECULAR GENETICS, MICROBIOLOGY AND VIROLOGY.** see *BIOLOGY—Microbiology*

576.549 GBR ISSN 0267-8357
QH465.A1 CODEN: MUTAEX
➤ **MUTAGENESIS.** Text in English. 1986. bi-m. GBP 441, USD 794, EUR 662 to institutions; GBP 464, USD 835, EUR 696 combined subscription to institutions print & online eds. (effective 2006). adv. bk.rev. illus. index. 128 p./no.; back issues avail.; reprint service avail. from PSC. **Document type:** *Journal, Academic/Scholarly.* **Description:** International, multi-disciplinary journal for genetic toxicology research. Includes genetic mutation studies, mutagenicity testing guidelines, test program results, letters, and reviews.
Related titles: Online - full text ed.: ISSN 1464-3804. GBP 418, USD 752, EUR 627 to institutions (effective 2006) (from EBSCO Publishing, Gale Group, HighWire Press, IngentaConnect, O C L C Online Computer Library Center, Inc., Ovid Technologies, Inc., Oxford University Press Online Journals, Swets Information Services).
Indexed: ASCA, ASFA, AbHyg, AgBio, AnBrAb, B&BAb, BIOBASE, BIOSIS Prev, BiolAb, CIN, CPA, ChemAb, ChemTitl, CurCont, DSA, ESPM, EnvEAb, ExcerpMed, GenetAb, HGA, HelmAb, HortAb, IABS, ISR, IndMed, IndVet, Inpharma, MEDLINE, MaizeAb, NucAcAb, NutrAb, OrnHort, PBA, PGrRegA, PHN&I, PN&I, PoultAb, ProtozoAb, RA&MP, RM&VM, Reac, RevApplEntom, S&F, SCI, SoyAb, TDB, ToxAb, TriticAb, VITIS, VetBull, WRCInf, WeedAb.
—BLDSC (5991.895500), CASDDS, CISTI, GNLM, IDS, IE, Infotrieve, ingenta, KNAW, Linda Hall. **CCC.**
Published by: (U.K. Environmental Mutagen Society), Oxford University Press, Great Clarendon St, Oxford, OX2 6DP, United Kingdom. TEL 44-1865-556767, FAX 44-1865-556646, jnl.orders@oup.co.uk, http://mutage.oxfordjournals.org/, http://www.oxfordjournals.org/. Eds. Dr. J L Schwartz, M Hayashi, David Phillips. Pub. David Prosser. R&P Fiona Bennett. adv.: B&W page GBP 220, B&W page USD 420; trim 178 x 255. Circ: 406. **Subscr. in U.S. to:** Oxford University Press, 2001 Evans Rd, Cary, NC 27513. jnlorders@oup-usa.org.

576.549 NLD ISSN 0027-5107
➤ **MUTATION RESEARCH**; fundamental and molecular mechanisms of mutagenesis. Text in English, French, German. 1964. 24/yr. adv. charts; illus. **Document type:** *Journal, Academic/Scholarly.* **Description:** The scope of Mutation Research: Molecular and Fundamental Mechanisms broadly encompasses all aspects of research that address the detection of mutations, the mechanisms by which mutations in genes and chromosomes arise, and the modulation of mutagenesis by mutation avoidance pathways such as DNA repair, cell cycle control and apoptosis. It includes the role of genetic variation in the genesis and manifestation of mutations, ranging from the variable manner in which xenobiotics are metabolized to variations in the capacity of cells to replicate and repair damaged DNA. It also includes the contributions of these mechanisms, when perturbed, to animal disease models and to human disease, with particular emphasis on carcinogenic mechanisms.
Related titles: Microform ed.: (from PQC); Online - full text ed.: (from EBSCO Publishing, Gale Group, IngentaConnect, ScienceDirect, Swets Information Services); ♦ Series: D N A Repair. ISSN 1568-7864; ♦ Mutation Research - Genetic Toxicology and Environmental Mutagenesis. ISSN 1383-5718; ♦ Mutation Research - Mutation Research Letters. ISSN 0165-7992; ♦ Mutation Research - Fundamental and Molecular Mechanisms of Mutagenesis. ISSN 1386-1964; ♦ Mutation Research - Reviews. ISSN 1383-5742.
Indexed: ASFA, AbAn, AbHyg, AgBio, AgrForAb, AnBrAb, B&BAb, BBCI, BCI, BIOBASE, BIOSIS Prev, BiolAb, CCI, CIN, CISA, CPA, ChemAb, ChemTitl, CurCont, DSA, DentInd, DokArb, ESPM, ExcerpMed, FCA, FS&TA, FaBeAb, ForAb, GenetAb, HelmAb, HortAb, I&DA, INI, ISR, IndMed, IndVet, Inpharma, LHB, MBA, MEDLINE, MaizeAb, NemAb, NucAcAb, NutrAb, OrnHort, PBA, PE&ON, PGegResA, PGrRegA, PHN&I, PN&I, PoultAb, ProtozoAb, RA&MP, RM&VM, RPP, RRTA, Reac, RevApplEntom, S&F, SCI, SFA, SSCI, SeedAb, SoyAb, TDB, TriticAb, VetBull, WeedAb, WildRev, ZooRec.
—BLDSC (5991.900000), CISTI, IDS, IE, Infotrieve, ingenta, Linda Hall. **CCC.**
Published by: Elsevier BV (Subsidiary of: Elsevier Science & Technology), Radarweg 29, Amsterdam, 1043 NX, Netherlands. TEL 31-20-4853911, FAX 31-20-4852457, nlinfo-f@elsevier.nl, http://www.elsevier.com/locate/mut, http://www.elsevier.nl. Eds. L. H.F. Mullenders, L. R. Ferguson, Dr. P. J. Stambrook.

576.549 NLD ISSN 1386-1964
QH431 CODEN: MUREAV
➤ **MUTATION RESEARCH - FUNDAMENTAL AND MOLECULAR MECHANISMS OF MUTAGENESIS.** Text in English, French, German. 1964. 16/yr. price varies, available only as part of full set. adv. charts; illus. index. back issues avail. **Document type:** *Journal, Academic/Scholarly.* **Description:** Publishes complete research papers in the are of mutation research which focus on fundamental mechanism, underlying phenotypic and genotypic expression of genetic damage.
Incorporates (in 1995): Mutation Research. Mutation Research Letters (0165-7992); Which superseded in part (in 1981): Mutation Research (0027-5107)
Related titles: Microform ed.: (from PQC); Online - full text ed.; ♦ Series of: Mutation Research. ISSN 0027-5107.
Indexed: ASCA, ASFA, AgBio, AnBrAb, B&BAb, BBCI, BCI, BiolAb, ChemAb, CurCont, DSA, ExcerpMed, FS&TA, HGA, IABS, ISR, IndMed, IndVet, Inpharma, MBA, NutrAb, PE&ON, RM&VM, RPP, Reac, RefZh, RevApplEntom, SCI, WeedAb.
—BLDSC (5991.900000), CASDDS, IDS, Linda Hall.
Published by: Elsevier BV (Subsidiary of: Elsevier Science & Technology), Radarweg 29, Amsterdam, 1043 NX, Netherlands. TEL 31-20-4853911, FAX 31-20-4852457, nlinfo-f@elsevier.nl, http://www.mutationresearch.com/, http://www.elsevier.nl. Eds. L. H.F. Mullenders, L. R. Ferguson, Dr. P. J. Stambrook.

576.549 NLD ISSN 1383-5718
CODEN: MRGTE
➤ **MUTATION RESEARCH - GENETIC TOXICOLOGY AND ENVIRONMENTAL MUTAGENESIS.** Text in Dutch. 1997. 18/yr. EUR 4,272 in Europe to institutions; JPY 567,300 in Japan to institutions; USD 4,778 to institutions except Europe and Japan (effective 2006); price varies, available only as part of a set. back issues avail. **Document type:** *Journal, Academic/Scholarly.*
Formed by the 1997 merger of: Mutation Research - Section on Environmental Mutagenesis and Related Subjects (0165-1161); Which was formerly (1969-1972): Environmental Mutagen Society. Newsletter (0013-9319); (1976-1997): Mutation Research - Genetic Toxicology Testing (0165-1218); Which superseded in part: Mutation Research (0027-5107)
Related titles: Microform ed.: (from PQC); Online - full text ed.: (from EBSCO Publishing, Gale Group, IngentaConnect, ScienceDirect, Swets Information Services); ♦ Series of: Mutation Research. ISSN 0027-5107.
Indexed: ASCA, ASFA, AbHyg, AgBio, AgrForAb, AnBrAb, B&BAb, BBCI, BIOBASE, BioCN&I, CPA, CurCont, DSA, ESPM, ExcerpMed, FCA, FPA, FS&TA, ForAb, GenetAb, HGA, HelmAb, HortAb, I&DA, IABS, ISR, IndMed, IndVet, Inpharma, MBA, MaizeAb, NemAb, NucAcAb, NutrAb, OrnHort, PBA, PE&ON, PGrRegA, PHN&I, ProtozoAb, RA&MP, RM&VM, RPP, Reac, RefZh, RevApplEntom, RiceAb, S&F, SCI, SIA, SeedAb, SoyAb, TDB, ToxAb, TriticAb, VetBull, WeedAb.
—CISTI, IDS, IE. **CCC.**
Published by: Elsevier BV (Subsidiary of: Elsevier Science & Technology), Radarweg 29, Amsterdam, 1043 NX, Netherlands. TEL 31-20-4853911, FAX 31-20-4852457, nlinfo-f@elsevier.nl, http://www.elsevier.com/locate/gentox, http://www.elsevier.nl. Eds. H. Hayatsu, M. D. Shelby, R. A. Baan.

576.549 NLD ISSN 1383-5742
➤ **MUTATION RESEARCH - REVIEWS.** Text in English. 1975. 6/yr. EUR 921 in Europe to institutions; JPY 122,200 in Japan to institutions; USD 1,030 to institutions except Europe and Japan (effective 2006). back issues avail. **Document type:** *Academic/Scholarly.* **Description:** Encompasses the entire spectrum of the science of mutation research and its applications.
Formerly (until 1997): Mutation Research - Reviews in Genetic Toxicology (0165-1110); Which superseded in part (in 1975): Mutation Research (0027-5107)
Related titles: Online - full text ed.: (from EBSCO Publishing, Gale Group, IngentaConnect, ScienceDirect, Swets Information Services); ♦ Series of: Mutation Research. ISSN 0027-5107.
Indexed: ASFA, AbHyg, AgBio, AnBrAb, B&BAb, BBCI, BIOBASE, CurCont, DSA, ESPM, ExcerpMed, FPA, GenetAb, HGA, HelmAb, HortAb, IABS, ISR, IndVet, Inpharma, MBA, NutrAb, OrnHort, PBA, PGegResA, PollutAb, RA&MP, RM&VM, Reac, RefZh, S&F, SCI, TDB, ToxAb.
—CISTI, IDS, IE. **CCC.**
Published by: Elsevier BV (Subsidiary of: Elsevier Science & Technology), Radarweg 29, Amsterdam, 1043 NX, Netherlands. TEL 31-20-4853911, FAX 31-20-4852457, nlinfo-f@elsevier.nl, http://www.elsevier.com/locate/mutrev, http://www.elsevier.nl. Eds. David M. DeMarini, M. D. Waters.

576.5 USA ISSN 1060-8788
N C B I NEWS. Text in English. 1991. 4/yr. free. **Document type:** *Newsletter, Government.* **Description:** Informs the biomedical community about N.C.B.I. research activities and the availability of molecular biology database and software services.
Related titles: Online - full text ed.
Published by: U.S. National Center for Biotechnology Information, National Library of Medicine, Bldg 38A, Rm 8N 803, 8600 Rockville Pike, Bethesda, MD 20894. TEL 301-496-2475, FAX 301-480-9241, info@ncbi.nlm.nih.gov, http://www.ncbi.nlm.nih.gov/Web/Newsltr/. Circ: 25,000.

576.5 IND ISSN 0970-6135
NATIONAL BUREAU OF FISH GENETIC RESOURCES. ANNUAL REPORT. Text in English. 1985. a.
Indexed: ESPM.
Published by: National Bureau of Fish Genetic Resources, 351-28 Radha Swami Bhawan, Duriyapur PO, Rajendranagar, Lucknow, Uttar Pradesh 226002, India. FAX 91-522-442403, nbfgr@lwl.vsnl.net.in.

576.5 JPN ISSN 0077-4995
QH431.A1
NATIONAL INSTITUTE OF GENETICS. ANNUAL REPORT (ENGLISH EDITION). Text in English. 1949. a. free.
Related titles: ♦ Japanese ed.: Kokuritsu Idengaku Kenkyujo Nenpo.
Indexed: ASFA, AnBrAb, B&BAb, ESPM, GenetAb, HGA, RefZh, RevApplEntom.
—BLDSC (1364.700000), CISTI, Linda Hall.
Published by: Ministry of Education, National Institute of Genetics/Monbusho Kokuritsu Idengaku Kenkyujo, 1111 Yata, Mishima-shi, Shizuoka-ken 411-0801, Japan. Circ: 600.

576.5 USA ISSN 1061-4036
QH431 CODEN: NGENEC
➤ **NATURE GENETICS.** Text in English. 1992. m. USD 1,710 in the Americas to institutions; GBP 950 elsewhere to institutions; EUR 271 combined subscription in Europe to individuals Eurozone; print & online; USD 199 combined subscription in the Americas to individuals print & online; GBP 175 combined subscription to individuals in the Uk & elseweher; print & online (effective 2006). adv. illus. Index. back issues avail.; reprints avail. **Document type:** *Journal, Academic/Scholarly.* **Description:** Comprehensive coverage of new developments and issues in all branches of genetics, with particular emphasis on the human genome project and genetic aspects of disease.
Related titles: Online - full text ed.: (from EBSCO Publishing, Swets Information Services); ♦ Supplement to: Nature. ISSN 0028-0836.
Indexed: ASCA, ASFA, AbHyg, AgBio, Agr, AnBrAb, ArtHuCI, B&AI, BCI, BIOBASE, BIOSIS Prev, BibAg, BiolAb, BiolDig, CIN, CTA, ChemAb, ChemTitl, ChemoAb, CurCont, DBA, DSA, DiabCont, ESPM, EntAb, ExcerpMed, GenetAb, HGA, HelmAb, HortAb, IABS, ISR, IndMed, IndVet, Inpharma, JW-D, JW-N, MEDLINE, MSB, MaizeAb, NSA, NemAb, NutrAb, PBA, PE&ON, PGegResA, PGrRegA, PN&I, PoultAb, ProtozoAb, RPP, Reac, RefZh, RiceAb, S&F, SCI, SSCI, SeedAb, SoyAb, TDB, TriticAb, VITIS, VetBull, WeedAb, WildRev.
—BLDSC (6046.625000), CASDDS, CISTI, GNLM, IDS, IE, Infotrieve, ingenta. **CCC.**
Published by: Nature Publishing Group (Subsidiary of: Macmillan Publishers Ltd.), 345 Park Ave S, 10th Fl, New York, NY 10010. TEL 212-726-9200, FAX 212-696-9635, http://www.genetics.nature.com. Ed. Myles Axton. Pub. Nigel Fletcher-Jones. Circ: 3,000. **Subscr. in Asia to:** Nature Japan KK, MG Ichigaya Bldg. 5F, 19-1 Haraikatamachi, Shinjuku-ku, Tokyo 162-0841, Japan. TEL 81-3-3267-8751, FAX 81-3 3267-8746, subscriptions@naturejpn.com; **Subscr. in the Americas to:** PO Box 5161, Brentwood, TN 37024-5161. TEL 615-850-5315, 800-524-0384, FAX 615-377-0525, subscriptions@natureny.com; **Subscr. to:** Nature Publishing Group, Brunel Rd, Houndmills, Basingstoke, Hamps RG21 6XS, United Kingdom. TEL 44-1256-329242, FAX 44-1256-812358, subscriptions@nature.com, http://www.nature.com.

B

576.5 GBR ISSN 1471-0056
QH426 CODEN: NRGAAM

➤ **NATURE REVIEWS. GENETICS.** Text in English. 2000 (Oct.). m. EUR 1,395 in Europe to institutions Eurozone; USD 1,620 in the Americas to institutions; GBP 900 to institutions in the UK & elsewhere; EUR 210 combined subscription in Europe to individuals Eurozone; print & online; USD 225 combined subscription in the Americas to individuals print & online; GBP 136 combined subscription to individuals in the UK & elsewhere; print & online (effective 2006). adv. back issues avail.; reprints avail. **Document type:** *Journal, Academic/Scholarly.* **Description:** Covers wide-ranging subjects in modern genetics, including genomics, functional genomics, evolutionary genetics, technology, multifactorial genetics, disease, chromosome biology, epigenetics, developmental biology, gene expression.

Related titles: Online - full content ed.: ISSN 1471-0064; Online - full text ed.: (from EBSCO Publishing, Swets Information Services).

Indexed: ASFA, AgBio, AnBeAb, AnBrAb, B&BAb, BCI, BIOBASE, BIOSIS Prev, CTA, ChemAb, CurCont, EntAb, ExcerpMed, GenetAb, ISR, Inpharma, MEDLINE, MaizeAb, NSA, NemAb, NutrAb, PBA, PE&ON, PGegResA, Reac, S&F, SCI, WeedAb, ZooRec.

—BLDSC (6047.225000), CISTI, IE, Infotrieve, ingenta. **CCC.**

Published by: Nature Publishing Group (Subsidiary of: Macmillan Publishers Ltd.), The MacMillan Building, 4 Crinan St, London, N1 9XW, United Kingdom. TEL 44-20-78334000, FAX 44-20-78433601, NatureReviews@nature.com, http://www.nature.com/reviews/genetics. Ed. Magdalena Skipper. **Subscr. in N & S America to:** Nature Publishing Group, PO Box 5161, Brentwood, TN 37024-5161. TEL 615-850-5315, 800-524-0384, FAX 615-377-0525; **Subscr. to:** Brunel Rd, Houndmills, Basingstoke, Hamps RG21 6XS, United Kingdom. TEL 44-1256-329242, FAX 44-1256-812358.

599.9 DEU ISSN 1364-6745
CODEN: NEROFX

➤ **NEUROGENETICS.** Text in English. 1997. q. EUR 450 combined subscription to institutions print & online eds. (effective 2005). adv. back issues avail. **Document type:** *Journal, Academic/Scholarly.* **Description:** Publishes findings that contribute to a better understanding of the genetic basis of normal and abnormal function of the nervous system.

Related titles: Online - full text ed.: ISSN 1364-6753 (from EBSCO Publishing, Springer LINK, Swets Information Services).

Indexed: BCI, BiolAb, ExcerpMed, FoMM, IndMed, MEDLINE, NSCI, RefZh, e-psyche.

—BLDSC (6081.371550), CASDDS, CISTI, IDS, IE, Infotrieve, ingenta. **CCC.**

Published by: Springer-Verlag (Subsidiary of: Springer Science+Business Media), Tiergartenstr 17, Heidelberg, 69121, Germany. TEL 49-6221-3450, FAX 49-6221-345229, http://link.springer.de/link/service/journals/10048/index.htm. Eds. Dr. James R Lupski TEL 713-798-5073, Dr. Manuel B Graeber TEL 44-208-846-7794, Dr. Ulrich Mueller TEL 49-641-9941609. Adv. contact Stephan Kroeck TEL 49-30-827875739. **Subscr. in the Americas to:** Springer-Verlag New York, Inc., Journal Fulfillment, PO Box 2485, Secaucus, NJ 07096-2485. TEL 800-777-4643, 201-348-4033, FAX 201-348-4505, journals@springer-ny.com, http://www.springer-ny.com; **Subscr. to:** Springer GmbH Auslieferungsgesellschaft, Haberstr 7, Heidelberg 69126, Germany. TEL 49-6221-345-0, FAX 49-6221-345-4229, subscriptions@springer.de.

599.9 GBR ISSN 1463-6778
CODEN: NGSOFI

➤ **NEW GENETICS AND SOCIETY.** Text in English. 1981. 3/yr. GBP 420, USD 728 combined subscription to institutions print & online eds. (effective 2006). adv. bk.rev. reprint service avail. from PSC. **Document type:** *Journal, Academic/Scholarly.* **Description:** Provides an international platform for discussion of key issues raised by the exploitation of the new genetics. Publishes social science research alongside theoretical and methodological contributions.

Former titles: Genetic Engineer and Biotechnologist (0959-020X); (until 1990): International Industrial Biotechnology (0269-7815); (until 1986): Industrial Biotechnology (0268-3024); (until 1985): Industrial Biotechnology Wales (0266-9854)

Related titles: Online - full text ed.: ISSN 1469-9915. GBP 399, USD 692 to institutions (effective 2006) (from EBSCO Publishing, Gale Group, IngentaConnect, O C L C Online Computer Library Center, Inc., ProQuest Information & Learning, Swets Information Services); Supplement(s): European Bio Patent Watch.

Indexed: AEA, AEBA, ASCA, ASFA, AbHyg, AgBio, AnBrAb, B&BAb, BCI, CBTA, CEABA, DBA, ESPM, EngInd, ExcerpMed, FS&TA, GenetAb, HGA, IBSS, M&PBA, MBA, NutrAb, PBA, RDA, RefZh, RiskAb, S&F, SSA, SSCI, SociolAb, Telegen, WAE&RSA.

—BLDSC (6084.211700), CASDDS, CISTI, Ei, GNLM, IDS, IE, Infotrieve, ingenta. **CCC.**

Published by: (G B Biotechnology Ltd.), Routledge (Subsidiary of: Taylor & Francis Group), 4 Park Sq, Milton Park, Abingdon, Oxon OX14 4RN, United Kingdom. TEL 44-1235-828600, FAX 44-1235-829000, info@routledge.co.uk, http://www.tandf.co.uk/journals/titles/14636778.asp, http://www.routledge.co.uk. Eds. Harry Rothman, Peter Glasner. **Subscr. to:** Taylor & Francis Ltd, Journals Customer Service, Rankine Rd, Basingstoke, Hants RG24 8PR, United Kingdom. TEL 44-1256-813000, FAX 44-1256-330245.

576.5 NGA ISSN 0189-9686

NIGERIAN JOURNAL OF GENETICS. Text in English. 19??. irreg.

Indexed: B&BAb, GenetAb.

Published by: Obafemi Awolowo University, Ile Ife, Osun State, Nigeria.

NIHON JINRUI IDEN GAKKAI TAIKAI SHOROKUSHU/JAPAN SOCIETY OF HUMAN GENETICS. ABSTRACTS OF THE ANNUAL MEETING. see *BIOLOGY—Abstracting, Bibliographies, Statistics*

576.3 DNK ISSN 1603-3914

NORDISKE GENRESSURSER; husdyr, kulturplanter, skogtraer. Text in Danish, Norwegian, Swedish. 2002. a., latest 2004. **Document type:** *Yearbook.*

Media: Online - full content. **Related titles:** English ed.: Nordic GENEresources. ISSN 1603-3922; Finnish ed.: Pohjolan GEENIvarat. ISSN 1603-3930.

Published by: Nordisk Ministerraad/Nordic Council of Ministers, Store Strandstraede 18, Copenhagen K, 1255, Denmark. TEL 45-33-960200, FAX 45-33-960202, es@nmr.dk, http://www.nordgen.net/publikasjoner/nordiskegenressurser.htm, http://www.norden.dk. Ed. Liv Loenne Dille. Circ: 14,500.

576.5 GBR

NORWICH RESEARCH PARK NEWSLETTER. Text in English. 1987. s-a. USD 10. back issues avail. **Document type:** *Newsletter.*

Formerly: Biological Research in Norwich

Published by: University of East Anglia, School of Biological Sciences, Norwich, Norfolk NR4 7TJ, United Kingdom. TEL 0603-592197, FAX 0603-259492. Ed. Richard James. Circ: 600.

NUCLEUS; international journal of cytology and allied topics. see *BIOLOGY—Cytology And Histology*

572.86 611.01816 USA ISSN 1536-2310
QH442 CODEN: OMICAE

➤ **O M I C S: A JOURNAL OF INTEGRATIVE BIOLOGY.** Text in English. 1994. q. USD 730 domestic to institutions; USD 907 foreign to institutions; USD 866 combined subscription domestic to institutions print & online eds.; USD 1,047 combined subscription foreign to institutions print & online eds. (effective 2006). adv. back issues avail.; reprint service avail. from PSC. **Document type:** *Journal, Academic/Scholarly.* **Description:** Offers a unique repository for genome and DNA sequencing; mapping, informatics, biological interpretations, human disease, ethical, legal, and social issues, new technology, and computational approaches.

Former titles (until 2001): Microbial & Comparative Genomics (1090-6592); (until 1996): Genome Science and Technology (1070-2830)

Related titles: Online - full text ed.: USD 674 to institutions (effective 2006) (from EBSCO Publishing, Gale Group, O C L C Online Computer Library Center, Inc., Swets Information Services).

Indexed: ASFA, AbHyg, AgBio, Agr, AgrForAb, AnBrAb, B&BAb, BIOSIS Prev, BioCN&I, BiolAb, CIN, CPA, ChemAb, ChemTitl, ESPM, ExcerpMed, GenetAb, HGA, HortAb, I&DA, IndMed, IndVet, MBA, MEDLINE, NemAb, NucAcAb, PBA, PGegResA, RA&MP, RPP, RefZh, S&F, SeedAb, SoyAb, TriticAb, VetBull, WeedAb.

—BLDSC (6256.428650), CASDDS, CISTI, IE, Infotrieve, ingenta. **CCC.**

Published by: Mary Ann Liebert, Inc. Publishers, 140 Huguenot St 3rd Fl, New Rochelle, NY 10801-5215. TEL 914-740-2100, FAX 914-740-2101, 800-654-3237, info@liebertpub.com, http://www.liebertpub.com/publication.aspx?pub_id=43. adv.: B&W page USD 1,975; trim 8.5 x 11. Circ: 1,154 (paid).

576.5 USA ISSN 1545-4576
QP625.O47 CODEN: OLIGAJ

➤ **OLIGONUCLEOTIDES.** Text in English. 1991. q. USD 563 domestic to institutions; USD 700 foreign to institutions; USD 669 combined subscription domestic to institutions print and online eds.; USD 805 combined subscription foreign to institutions print and online eds. (effective 2006). adv. back issues avail.; reprint service avail. from PSC. **Document type:** *Journal, Academic/Scholarly.* **Description:** Deals with man-made substances and their effects on gene expression at the RNA and DNA levels both in vitro and in vivo.

Former titles (until Aug.2003): Antisense and Nucleic Acid Drug Development (1087-2906); (until 1997): Antisense Research and Development (1050-5261)

Related titles: Online - full text ed.: USD 526 worldwide to institutions (effective 2006) (from EBSCO Publishing, Gale Group, O C L C Online Computer Library Center, Inc., ProQuest Information & Learning, Swets Information Services).

Indexed: ASCA, AgBio, AnBrAb, B&BAb, BCI, BIOSIS Prev, BioEngAb, BiolAb, CIN, ChemAb, ChemTitl, CurCont, DBA, ExcerpMed, ISR, IndMed, IndVet, Inpharma, M&PBA, MEDLINE, NucAcAb, PBA, PE&ON, PN&I, PoultAb, RM&VM, Reac, SCI, VetBull.

—BLDSC (6255.470000), CASDDS, CISTI, GNLM, IDS, IE, Infotrieve, ingenta, KNAW. **CCC.**

Published by: Mary Ann Liebert, Inc. Publishers, 140 Huguenot St 3rd Fl, New Rochelle, NY 10801-5215. TEL 914-740-2100, FAX 914-740-2101, 800-654-3237, info@liebertpub.com, http://www.liebertpub.com/ard. Eds. Arthur M Krieg, C A Stein, C. Frank Bennett. adv.: B&W page USD 1,150; trim 8.5 x 11. Circ: 1,245 (paid).

➤ **ONCOGENE**; including Oncogene Reviews. see *MEDICAL SCIENCES—Oncology*

572.8 GBR

➤ **OXFORD MONOGRAPHS ON MOLECULAR GENETICS.** Text in English. 1966. irreg., latest vol.34, 1997. price varies. **Document type:** *Monographic series, Academic/Scholarly.*

Formerly (until 1997): Oxford Monographs on Medical Genetics (1352-240X)

Indexed: BIOSIS Prev.

—BLDSC (6321.007500), IE, ingenta.

Published by: Oxford University Press, Great Clarendon St, Oxford, OX2 6DP, United Kingdom. TEL 44-1865-556767, FAX 44-1865-556646, enquiry@oup.co.uk, http://www.oup.co.uk/.

576.8 GBR ISSN 0265-072X
QH359 CODEN: OSEBE3

OXFORD SURVEYS IN EVOLUTIONARY BIOLOGY. Text in English. 1984. a., latest vol.8, 1992. price varies. bk.rev. **Document type:** *Academic/Scholarly.*

Indexed: AnBrAb, BIOSIS Prev, SFA, WildRev, ZooRec.

—CISTI. **CCC.**

Published by: Oxford University Press, Great Clarendon St, Oxford, OX2 6DP, United Kingdom. TEL 44-1865-556767, FAX 44-1865-556646, enquiry@oup.co.uk, http://www.oup-usa.org/catalogs/general/series/, http://www.oup.co.uk/. **Subscr. in N. America to:** Oxford University Press, 2001 Evans Rd, Cary, NC 27513. jnlorders@oup-usa.org.

576.5 USA ISSN 1553-7390

▼ ➤ **P L O S GENETICS.** (Public Library of Science) Text in English. 2005 (July). m. free (effective 2006). **Document type:** *Journal, Academic/Scholarly.* **Description:** Publishes human studies, as well as research on model organisms from mice and flies, to plants and bacteria.

Related titles: Online - full text ed.: ISSN 1553-7404. free (effective 2005).

Indexed: B&BAb, GenetAb.

Published by: Public Library of Science, 185 Berry St, Ste 1300, San Francisco, CA 94107. TEL 415-624-1200, plos@plos.org, http://www.plosgenetics.org/, http://www.publiclibraryofscience.org.

576.5 IND

➤ **PERSPECTIVES IN CYTOLOGY & GENETICS**; proceedings of the all India Congress of cytology and genetics. Text in English. 1971. triennial. INR 600 domestic; USD 200 foreign (effective 2002). 800 p./no.; back issues avail. **Document type:** *Academic/Scholarly.* **Description:** Contains proceedings of the all India Congress of cytology and genetics.

Indexed: ZooRec.

—BLDSC (6428.140000).

Published by: (Calcutta University, Department of Botany), All India Congress of Cytology & Genetics, c/o G.K. Manna & S.C. Roy, B10 - 250 Kalyani, Kalyani, West Bengal 41235, India. TEL 91-33-4182214, 91-33-4753681. Eds. G K Manna, S C Roy. Pub. S C Roy. Circ: 300 (paid).

576.5 USA ISSN 1744-6872
CODEN: PHMCEE

➤ **PHARMACOGENETICS AND GENOMICS.** Text in English. 1991. m., latest vol.11. USD 326 to individuals; USD 1,179 to institutions (effective 2006). adv. Index. back issues avail.; reprints avail. **Document type:** *Journal, Academic/Scholarly.* **Description:** Devoted to the rapid publication of research papers, brief review articles, and short communications on genetic variation in response to drugs and other chemicals.

Formerly (until 2005): Pharmacogenetics (0960-314X)

Related titles: Online - full text ed.: ISSN 1744-6880 (from EBSCO Publishing, O C L C Online Computer Library Center, Inc., Ovid Technologies, Inc., Swets Information Services).

Indexed: ASCA, BBCI, BCI, BIOBASE, BIOSIS Prev, BiolAb, ChemAb, ChemTitl, CivEngAb, CurCont, DBA, ExcerpMed, IABS, IDIS, IPA, ISR, IndMed, Inpharma, MEDLINE, PE&ON, Reac, RefZh, SCI, SSCI.

—BLDSC (6446.249100), CASDDS, CISTI, GNLM, IDS, IE, Infotrieve, ingenta, KNAW, Linda Hall. **CCC.**

Published by: Lippincott Williams & Wilkins (Subsidiary of: Wolters Kluwer N.V.), 530 Walnut St, Philadelphia, PA 19106-3621. TEL 215-521-8300, FAX 215-521-8902, http://www.jpharmacogenetics.com, http://www.lww.com. Eds. M Eichelbaum, W E Evans. Pub. Phil Daly. Circ: 180. **Subscr. to:** PO Box 1620, Hagerstown, MD 21741. TEL 800-777-2295, FAX 301-824-7390.

581.3 AUT ISSN 0175-2073
PLANT GENE RESEARCH; basic knowledge and application. Text in English. 1984. irreg., latest 1999. price varies.
Document type: *Monographic series, Academic/Scholarly.*
Indexed: BIOSIS Prev.
—CCC.
Published by: Springer-Verlag Wien (Subsidiary of: Springer Science+Business Media) TEL 43-1-3302415-0, FAX 43-1-330242665, books@springer.at, http://www.springer.at. Ed. T Hohn. R&P Angela Foessl TEL 43-1-3302415517. **Subscr. to:** Springer-Verlag New York, Inc., 233 Spring St, New York, NY 10013. TEL 800-777-4643, FAX 201-348-4505, orders@springer-ny.com.

590 POL ISSN 0137-1649
CODEN: PMZTAP
➤ **POLSKA AKADEMIA NAUK. INSTYTUT GENETYKI I HODOWLI ZWIERZAT. PRACE I MATERIALY ZOOTECHNICZNE.** Text in Polish. 1963. irreg. **Document type:** *Academic/Scholarly.*
Former titles (until 1973): Polska Akademia Nauk. Instytut Genetyki i Hodowli Zwierzat. Biuletyn (0137-2157); (until 1970): Polska Akademia Nauk. Zaklad Hodowli Doswiadczalnej Zwierzat. Biuletyn (0554-5943)
Indexed: AgBio, AgrLib, AnBrAb, B&BAb, BIOSIS Prev, BiolAb, DSA, FS&TA, GenetAb, IndVet, MaizeAb, NutrAb, PN&I, PoultAb, RefZh, SIA, SoyAb, VetBull.
—CASDDS.
Published by: Polska Akademia Nauk, Instytut Genetyki i Hodowli Zwierzat, Mrokow, Jastrzebiec, 05-551, Poland. TEL 48-22-7561711, FAX 48-22-7561699, TELEX 814749 GHPAN PL.

590 POL ISSN 1231-8388
➤ **POLSKA AKADEMIA NAUK. INSTYTUT GENETYKI I HODOWLI ZWIERZAT. PRACE I MATERIALY ZOOTECHNICZNE. ZESZYT SPECIALNY.** Text in Polish. 1992. irreg. **Document type:** *Academic/Scholarly.*
Indexed: AgBio, AgrLib, AnBrAb, DSA, IndVet, NutrAb, PN&I, PoultAb, VetBull, WAE&RSA.
Published by: Polska Akademia Nauk, Instytut Genetyki i Hodowli Zwierzat, Mrokow, Jastrzebiec, 05-551, Poland. TEL 48-22-7561711, FAX 48-22-7561699.

576.5 USA ISSN 0955-8829
CODEN: PSGEEX
➤ **PSYCHIATRIC GENETICS.** Text in English. 1990. q. USD 289 to individuals; USD 687 to institutions (effective 2006). adv. bk.rev. index. **Document type:** *Journal, Academic/Scholarly.*
Description: Forum for novel approaches using new technologies to better understand the normal and abnormal brain.
Related titles: CD-ROM ed.; Online - full text ed.: USD 685.10 domestic academic site license; USD 685.10 foreign academic site license; USD 764.15 domestic corporate site license; USD 764.15 foreign corporate site license (effective 2002) (from EBSCO Publishing, O C L C Online Computer Library Center, Inc., Ovid Technologies, Inc., Swets Information Services).
Indexed: ASCA, BCI, BIOBASE, BIOSIS Prev, BiolAb, ExcerpMed, IABS, IndMed, Inpharma, MEDLINE, NSCI, PE&ON, PsycInfo, PsycholAb, Reac, RefZh, SSCI, e-psyche.
—BLDSC (6946.214050), CISTI, GNLM, IDS, IE, Infotrieve, ingenta, KNAW. **CCC.**
Published by: Lippincott Williams & Wilkins (Subsidiary of: Wolters Kluwer N.V.), 530 Walnut St, Philadelphia, PA 19106-3621. TEL 215-521-8300, FAX 215-521-8902, http://www.psychgenetics.com, http://www.lww.com. Ed. Dr. John L. Nurnberger. Adv. contact Ray Thibodeau. Circ: 800. **Subscr. to:** PO Box 1620, Hagerstown, MD 21741. TEL 800-777-2295, FAX 301-824-7390.

➤ **PSYCHOLOGIA, ETOLOGIA, GENETYKA.** see *PSYCHOLOGY*

512.8 USA ISSN 1355-8382
QP623 CODEN: RNARFU
➤ **R N A.** (Ribonucleic Acid) Text in English. 1995. m. USD 260 domestic to individuals; USD 316 in Canada & Mexico to individuals; USD 340 elsewhere to individuals; USD 760 domestic to institutions; USD 816 in Canada & Mexico to institutions; USD 840 elsewhere to institutions (effective 2004). adv. bk.rev. **Document type:** *Journal, Academic/Scholarly.*
Description: Surveys original research in all areas of RNA structure and function in eukaryotic, prokaryotic, and viral systems.
Related titles: Online - full text ed.: ISSN 1469-9001. 2003 (Jan. vol.9, issue 1). USD 210 to individuals; USD 660 to institutions; USD 208 to students (effective 2004) (from EBSCO Publishing, HighWire Press, O C L C Online Computer Library Center, Inc., Swets Information Services).
Indexed: ASCA, ASFA, B&BAb, BBCI, CurCont, ExcerpMed, FCA, GenetAb, HGA, IABS, IndMed, Inpharma, ProtozoAb, Reac, SCI.
—BLDSC (7993.990800), CASDDS, CISTI, GNLM, IDS, IE, Infotrieve, ingenta, Linda Hall. **CCC.**
Published by: (R N A Society GBR), Cold Spring Harbor Laboratory Press, Publications Department, 500 Sunnyside Blvd., Woodbury, NY 11797-2924. TEL 516-422-4100, 800-843-4388, FAX 516-422-4097, cshpress@cshl.edu, http://www.rnajournal.org, http://www.cshl.org. Ed. Dr. Timothy W Nilsen. Adv. contact Ms. Marcie Siconolfi TEL 516-422-4010.

➤ **REFERATIVNYI ZHURNAL. BIOLOGIYA. GENETIKA: TSITOLOGIYA.** see *BIOLOGY—Abstracting, Bibliographies, Statistics*

➤ **REFERATIVNYI ZHURNAL. GENETIKA CHELOVEKA.** see *BIOLOGY—Abstracting, Bibliographies, Statistics*

➤ **REFERATIVNYI ZHURNAL. GENETIKA I SELEKTSIYA MIKROORGANIZMOV.** see *BIOLOGY—Abstracting, Bibliographies, Statistics*

➤ **REFERATIVNYI ZHURNAL. GENETIKA I SELEKTSIYA SEL'SKOKHOZYAISTVENNYKH ZHIVOTNYKH.** see *BIOLOGY—Abstracting, Bibliographies, Statistics*

➤ **REFERATIVNYI ZHURNAL. GENETIKA I SELEKTSIYA VOZDELYVAEMYKH RASTENII.** see *BIOLOGY—Abstracting, Bibliographies, Statistics*

➤ **REFERATIVNYI ZHURNAL. OBSHCHAYA GENETIKA.** see *BIOLOGY—Abstracting, Bibliographies, Statistics*

576.5 USA ISSN 1534-830X
➤ **REPBASE REPORTS.** Text in English. 2001 (Sept.). m. back issues avail. **Document type:** *Academic/Scholarly.*
Description: Contains short reports on Transposable Elements and other repetitive DNA not reported anywhere else.
Media: Online - full content.
Published by: Genetic Information Research Institute, 1925 Landings Dr., Mountain View, CA 94043-0808. webmaster@grinst.org, http://www.girinst.org/ Repbase_Reports.html. Ed. Jerzy Jurka.

576.5 CUB ISSN 1682-6760
REVISTA CUBANA DE GENETICA MEDICA. Text in Spanish. 1999. 3/yr. back issues avail.
Media: Online - full text.
Published by: Centro Provincial de Genetica Medica, Frank Pais No. 323, Esq. Bartolome Maso y Brigadier Reeves, Sancti Spiritus, Cuba. http://www.sld.cu/instituciones/geness/esp/ revista/rcgh.htm.

REVISTA DE DERECHO Y GENOMA HUMANO. see *LAW*

599.9 170 COL
REVISTA TEMAS DE BIOETICA. Text in Spanish. 2001. irreg. COP 20,000 domestic; USD 20 in Latin America; USD 40 elsewhere (effective 2003).
Published by: (Universidad de Antioquia, Instituto de Filosofia), Universidad de Antioquia, Calle 67, 53-108, Apartado Aereo 1226, Medellin, Colombia. TEL 57-4-2630011, FAX 57-4-2638282, comunicaciones@udea.edu.co, http://www.udea.edu.co.

576.5 RUS ISSN 1022-7954
QH431 CODEN: RJGEEQ
➤ **RUSSIAN JOURNAL OF GENETICS.** Text in English. 1965. m. EUR 3,345, USD 3,048, GBP 2,088 combined subscription to institutions print & online eds. (effective 2005). back issues avail. **Document type:** *Journal, Academic/Scholarly.*
Description: Investigates genetic processes at the molecular, cellular, organismic, and population levels, with articles on the impact of modern genetics and environmental concerns.
Formerly (until 1994): Soviet Genetics (0038-5409)
Related titles: Microfilm ed.: (from PQC); Online - full text ed.: ISSN 1608-3369 (from EBSCO Publishing, Gale Group, IngentaConnect, Kluwer Online, O C L C Online Computer Library Center, Inc., Ovid Technologies, Inc., Springer LINK, Swets Information Services); ♦ Translation of: Genetika. ISSN 0016-6758.
Indexed: BCI, BibLing, BiolAb, CIN, ChemAb, ChemTitl, CurCont, ExcerpMed, GenetAb, IABS, ISR, IndMed, MEDLINE, SCI, SFA, WildRev.
—BLDSC (0420.760960), CASDDS, CISTI, GNLM, IE, Infotrieve, ingenta. **CCC.**
Published by: (Rossiiskaya Akademiya Nauk/Russian Academy of Sciences), M A I K Nauka - Interperiodica, Profsoyuznaya ul 90, Moscow, 117997, Russian Federation. TEL 7-095-3347420, FAX 7-095-3360666, compmg@maik.ru, http://www.maik.rssi.ru/journals/geneng.htm, http://www.maik.ru. Ed. Georgii Georgiev. **Subscr. to:** Springer-Verlag Dordrecht, Journals Department, PO Box 322, Dordrecht, Netherlands. TEL 31-78-6576392, FAX 31-78-6576474.

➤ **SEEDLING.** see *BIOLOGY—Biotechnology*

576.8 JPN ISSN 0911-0445
SHINKA SEIBUTSUGAKU KENKYUJO KENKYU HOKOKU/RESEARCH INSTITUTE OF EVOLUTIONARY BIOLOGY. SCIENCE REPORT. Text in English, Japanese. 1982. irreg.
Indexed: ZooRec.
Published by: Shinka Seibutsugaku Kenkyujo, 4-28 Kami-Yoga 2-chome, Setagaya-ku, Tokyo, 158-0098, Japan.

SILVAE GENETICA; Zeitschrift fuer Forstgenetik und Forstpflanzenzuechtung. see *BIOLOGY—Botany*

613.94 USA ISSN 0037-766X
HQ750.A1 CODEN: SOBIAL
➤ **SOCIAL BIOLOGY.** Text in English. 1954. 2/yr. USD 105 (effective 2001). bk.rev. abstr.; charts; illus. index. back issues avail.; reprint service avail. from PQC. **Document type:** *Academic/Scholarly.* **Description:** Furthers knowledge of the biological and cultural forces affecting human populations and their evolution.
Former titles (until 1968): Eugenics Quarterly (0097-2762); (until 1953): Eugenical News (0361-7769)
Related titles: Microform ed.: (from PQC); Online - full text ed.: (from O C L C Online Computer Library Center, Inc., ProQuest Information & Learning).
Indexed: ASCA, AbAn, AbHyg, AgeL, AnthLit, ArtHuCI, B&AI, BIOSIS Prev, BiolAb, BiolDig, CLFP, ChemAb, CurCont, DSA, ESPM, ExcerpMed, FamI, IBR, IBSS, IPsyAb, IndMed, JDDR, MEDLINE, NutrAb, PAIS, PopulInd, PsycInfo, PsycholAb, RiskAb, SOPODA, SSA, SSCI, SSI, SociolAb, TDB, WAE&RSA, e-psyche.
—BLDSC (8318.055000), CISTI, GNLM, IDS, IE, Infotrieve, ingenta.
Published by: Society for the Study of Social Biology, 1129 E 8th St, Box 2349, Port Angeles, WA 98362. TEL 360-457-6530, FAX 360-457-6530, osb-rb@olympus.net, http:// www.allenpress.com. Ed. Richard H Osborne. Circ: 1,650. **Subscr. to:** Allen Press Inc., PO Box 1897, Lawrence, KS 66044.

576.5 USA ISSN 0740-7750
QH426 CODEN: SCMGDN
➤ **SOMATIC CELL AND MOLECULAR GENETICS.** Text in English. 1975. 4/yr. EUR 913, USD 914, GBP 585 combined subscription to institutions print & online eds. (effective 2005). adv. reprint service avail. from PSC. **Document type:** *Journal, Academic/Scholarly.* **Description:** Publishes original research conducted in the fields of cellular and molecular genetics of higher eukaryotic systems.
Formerly (until 1984): Somatic Cell Genetics (0098-0366)
Related titles: Microfilm ed.: (from PQC); Online - full text ed.: ISSN 1572-9931 (from EBSCO Publishing, Gale Group, IngentaConnect, Kluwer Online, O C L C Online Computer Library Center, Inc., Springer LINK, Swets Information Services).
Indexed: ASCA, ASFA, AbHyg, AgBio, AnBrAb, B&BAb, BCI, BIOBASE, BIOSIS Prev, BibLing, BiolAb, CIN, ChemAb, ChemTitl, CurCont, DBA, ExcerpMed, GenetAb, HGA, IABS, ISR, IndMed, Inpharma, MBA, MEDLINE, NemAb, Reac, RefZh, SCI, Telegen.
—BLDSC (8327.808800), CASDDS, CISTI, GNLM, IDS, IE, Infotrieve, ingenta, Linda Hall. **CCC.**
Published by: Plenum US (Subsidiary of: Springer Science+Business Media), 233 Spring St, New York, NY 10013. TEL 212-460-1500, FAX 212-460-1575, service@springer-ny.com, http://springerlink.metapress.com/ openurl.asp?genre=journal&issn=0740-7750, http://www.springeronline.com.

➤ **SOUTH ASIAN ANTHROPOLOGIST.** see *ANTHROPOLOGY*

581.3 USA
SOYBEAN GENETICS NEWSLETTER (ONLINE EDITION). Text in English. 1974. a. **Document type:** *Newsletter, Trade.*
Description: Provides a forum for the exchange of ideas among soybean scientists.
Formerly: Soybean Genetics Newsletter (Print Edition) (1054-2116)
Media: Online - full text.
Indexed: Agr.
—CISTI.
Published by: Soybean Genetics Newsletter sgn@osu.edu, http://www.soygenetics.org/.

576.5 USA ISSN 1568-1009
QH431.A1 CODEN: SGSYBV
➤ **STADLER GENETICS SYMPOSIUM. SERIES.** Text in English. 1971. irreg., latest 2000, 22nd Symposium. price varies.
Document type: *Proceedings, Academic/Scholarly.*
Formerly (until 1984): Stadler Genetics Symposium. Proceedings (0081-4148)
Indexed: Agr, AnBrAb, BiolAb, ChemAb, RiceAb.
—CASDDS, CISTI, KNAW, Linda Hall. **CCC.**
Published by: Springer-Verlag New York, Inc. (Subsidiary of: Springer Science+Business Media), 233 Spring St, New York, NY 10013. TEL 212-460-1500, FAX 212-460-1575, service@springer-ny.com, http://www.springer-ny.com.

576.5021 USA ISSN 1544-6115
STATISTICAL APPLICATIONS IN GENETICS AND MOLECULAR BIOLOGY. Text in English. 2002. s-a. USD 35 to individuals; USD 365 to institutions (effective 2006).
Media: Online - full content (from O C L C Online Computer Library Center, Inc.).
Indexed: ExcerpMed, MathR, MathSciNet.
Published by: Berkeley Electronic Press, 2809 Telegraph Ave., Ste 202, Berkeley, CA 94705. TEL 510-665-1200, FAX 510-665-1201, info@bepress.com, http://www.bepress.com/ sagmb. Eds. Elizabeth Thompson, Gary Churchill, Nicholas P Jewell.

B

576.5 USA ISSN 1528-4883
➤ **THE STEFAN UNIVERSITY JOURNAL OF GENOMIC MEDICINE.** Text in English. 1999. irreg. **Document type:** *Journal, Academic/Scholarly.*
Published by: Stefan University Press, PO Box 2946, La Jolla, CA 92038-2946. TEL 858-245-6674, FAX 858-395-6768, press@stefan-university.edu, http://www.stefan-university.edu/press.htm. Ed. Vladislav Stefan. Adv. contact M. Bloom.

576.5 USA
STEM CELL BUSINESS NEWS. Text in English. 2002. bi-w. USD 295 to corporations print or online ed.; USD 219 to non-profit organizations print or online ed. (effective 2003). **Document type:** *Journal, Academic/Scholarly.* **Description:** Covers news of public and private companies involved in stem cell research, including research findings, legislation and regulation, experimental therapies, finance and funding, earnings, people, patents, strategic alliances, and much more. Whether you're a competitor, supplier, investor, analyst, etc.
Related titles: Online - full content ed.
Published by: DataTrends Publications, Inc., PO Box 4460, Leesburg, VA 20177-8541. TEL 703-779-0574, FAX 703-779-2267, info@datatrendspublications.com, http://www.datatrendspublications.com/SCBN.htm, http://www.datatrendspublications.com/default.htm.

576.5 USA ISSN 1538-327X
STEM CELL RESEARCH NEWS. Text in English. 1999. bi-w. USD 295 to corporations print or online ed.; USD 219 to non-profit organizations print or online ed. (effective 2005). **Document type:** *Newsletter, Academic/Scholarly.* **Description:** Covers the legislative and regulatory activities affecting stem cell research, plus all the latest findings involving the central nervous system, the circulatory system, the pancreas, the heart, etc.
Related titles: Online - full content ed.
Published by: DataTrends Publications, Inc., PO Box 4460, Leesburg, VA 20177-8541. dtrends@1x.netcom.com, info@datatrendspublications.com, http://www.datatrendspublications.com/SCRN.htm, http://www.datatrendspublications.com/default.htm. Ed. Paul G Ochs. Pub. Paul G. Ochs.

599.9 660.6 USA ISSN 1550-8943
▼ **STEM CELL REVIEWS.** Text in English. 2005. q.
—CCC.
Published by: Humana Press, Inc., 999 Riverview Dr, Ste 208, Totowa, NJ 07512. TEL 973-256-1699, FAX 973-256-8341, humana@humanapr.com, http://humanapress.com.

THALAMUS AND RELATED SYSTEMS. see *BIOLOGY*

576.5 DEU ISSN 0040-5752
SB123 CODEN: THAGA6
➤ **THEORETICAL AND APPLIED GENETICS;** international journal of plant breeding research. Short title: T A G. Text in English. 1929. 16/yr. (in 2 vols., 8 nos./vol.). EUR 4,698 combined subscription to institutions print & online eds. (effective 2005). adv. back issues avail.; reprint service avail. from ISI. **Document type:** *Journal, Academic/Scholarly.* **Description:** Reflects the continuing progress of plant and animal breeding genetics, including fundamental and applied aspects.
Supersedes: Zuechter
Related titles: Microform ed.: (from PQC); Online - full text ed.: ISSN 1432-2242 (from EBSCO Publishing, Springer LINK, Swets Information Services).
Indexed: ABIPC, AEA, AEBA, ASCA, ASFA, AgBio, Agr, AgrForAb, AnBrAb, ApicAb, BCI, BIOBASE, BIOSIS Prev, BibAg, BioCN&I, BioEngAb, BiolAb, CBTA, CEABA, CIN, CIS, CPA, CTFA, ChemAb, ChemTitl, CurCont, DBA, DSA, ESPM, EngInd, EntAb, ExcerpMed, FCA, FPA, FS&TA, FaBeAb, ForAb, GenetAb, HGA, HerbAb, HortAb, I&DA, IABS, ISR, Inpharma, MaizeAb, NemAb, NutrAb, OrnHort, PBA, PGegResA, PGrRegA, PHN&I, PlantSci, PotatoAb, PoultAb, RA&MP, RM&VM, RPP, RRTA, Reac, RefZh, RevApplEntom, RiceAb, S&F, S&MA, SCI, SFA, SIA, SeedAb, SoyAb, TOSA, TriticAb, VITIS, WAE&RSA, WeedAb, WildRev, ZooRec.
—BLDSC (8814.552000), CASDDS, CISTI, GNLM, IDS, IE, Infotrieve, ingenta, Linda Hall. **CCC.**
Published by: Springer-Verlag (Subsidiary of: Springer Science+Business Media), Tiergartenstr 17, Heidelberg, 69121, Germany. TEL 49-6221-3450, FAX 49-6221-345229, http://link.springer.de/link/service/journals/00122/index.htm. Ed. H C Becker. Adv. contact Stephan Kroeck TEL 49-30-827875739. **Subscr. in the Americas to:** Springer-Verlag New York, Inc., Journal Fulfillment, PO Box 2485, Secaucus, NJ 07096-2485. TEL 800-777-4643, 201-348-4033, FAX 201-348-4505, journals@springer-ny.com, http://www.springer-ny.com; **Subscr. to:** Springer GmbH Auslieferungsgesellschaft, Haberstr 7, Heidelberg 69126, Germany. TEL 49-6221-345-0, FAX 49-6221-345-4229, subscriptions@springer.de.

➤ **TOMATO GENETICS COOPERATIVE REPORT.** see *BIOLOGY—Botany*

576.5 DEU ISSN 1610-2096
▼ ➤ **TOPICS IN CURRENT GENETICS.** Text in English. 2003. irreg., latest vol.14, 2005. price varies. **Document type:** *Monographic series, Academic/Scholarly.* **Description:** Provides up-to date reviews in cell and molecular biology.
Related titles: Online - full text ed.: ISSN 1610-6970.
—BLDSC (8867.436000), IE.
Published by: Springer-Verlag (Subsidiary of: Springer Science+Business Media), Tiergartenstr 17, Heidelberg, 69121, Germany. TEL 49-6221-3450, FAX 49-6221-345229, hohmann@gmm.gu.se, subscriptions@springer.de, http://www.current-genetics.org/topics.htm, http://www.springer.de. Ed. Stefan Hohmann TEL 46-31-7732595.

576.6 NLD ISSN 0962-8819
QH442.6 CODEN: TRSEES
➤ **TRANSGENIC RESEARCH.** Text in Dutch. 1991. bi-m. EUR 1,228, USD 1,255, GBP 808 combined subscription to institutions print & online eds. (effective 2005). adv. bk.rev. reprint service avail. from PSC. **Document type:** *Journal, Academic/Scholarly.* **Description:** Provides the rapid publication of research in transgenic higher organisms, including their production and properties resulting from the transgenic state, use as experimental tools, exploitation and application, and environmental impact.
Related titles: Online - full text ed.: ISSN 1573-9368 (from EBSCO Publishing, Gale Group, IngentaConnect, Kluwer Online, O C L C Online Computer Library Center, Inc., Ovid Technologies, Inc., Springer LINK, Swets Information Services).
Indexed: AEBA, ASCA, AbHyg, AgBio, Agr, AgrForAb, AnBrAb, B&BAb, BBCI, BCI, BIOBASE, BIOSIS Prev, BibAg, BibLing, BioCN&I, BioEngAb, BiolAb, CIN, CPA, ChemAb, CurCont, DBA, DSA, ESPM, FCA, FPA, ForAb, GenetAb, HGA, HerbAb, HortAb, IABS, ISR, IndMed, IndVet, Inpharma, M&PBA, MEDLINE, MaizeAb, NemAb, NucAcAb, NutrAb, OrnHort, PBA, PGegResA, PGrRegA, PHN&I, PN&I, PlantSci, PotatoAb, PoultAb, RA&MP, RPP, Reac, RefZh, RevApplEntom, RiceAb, S&F, SCI, SIA, SeedAb, SoyAb, TDB, TriticAb, VITIS, VetBull, WeedAb.
—BLDSC (9020.713000), CASDDS, CISTI, GNLM, IDS, IE, Infotrieve, ingenta. **CCC.**
Published by: Springer-Verlag Dordrecht (Subsidiary of: Springer Science+Business Media), Van Godewijckstraat 30, Dordrecht, 3311 GX, Netherlands. TEL 31-78-6576050, FAX 31-78-6576474, http://springerlink.metapress.com/openurl.asp?genre=journal&issn=0962-8819, http://www.springeronline.com. Eds. Bruce Whitelaw, Paul Christou.

576.5 USA ISSN 1023-6171
QH442.6 CODEN: TADTEF
➤ **TRANSGENICS;** biological analysis through dna transfer. Key Title: Transgenics (Basel). Text in English. 1993. q. EUR 95 in Europe to individuals; JPY 15,932 in Japan to individuals; USD 90 elsewhere to individuals; EUR 555 combined subscription in Europe to institutions print & online; JPY 62,300 combined subscription in Japan to institutions print & online; USD 531 combined subscription elsewhere to institutions print & online (effective 2005). 80 p./no.; back issues avail. **Document type:** *Journal, Academic/Scholarly.* **Description:** Presents original reports of biological analysis through DNA transfer in vivo and in vitro.
Formerly (until 1994): Transgene (1068-3283)
Related titles: CD-ROM ed.: ISSN 1026-8162; Online - full text ed.: Transgenics (Lausanne. Online). ISSN 1607-8586. 2000 (from EBSCO Publishing).
Indexed: ExcerpMed, IABS.
—BLDSC (9020.713500), CISTI, GNLM, IE, KNAW. **CCC.**
Published by: Old City Publishing, Inc., 628 N 2nd St, Philadelphia, PA 19123. TEL 215-925-4390, FAX 215-925-4371, info@oldcitypublishing.com, http://www.oldcitypublishing.com/Transgenics/Transgenics.html. Ed. Julius M Cruse.

▼ ➤ **TREE GENETICS & GENOMES.** see *BIOLOGY—Botany*

576.5 GBR ISSN 0168-9525
QH426 CODEN: TRGEE2
➤ **TRENDS IN GENETICS.** Text in English. 1985. 12/yr. EUR 181 in Europe to individuals; JPY 22,000 in Japan to individuals; USD 198 elsewhere to individuals; EUR 1,232 in Europe to institutions; JPY 170,900 in Japan to institutions; USD 1,378 elsewhere to institutions (effective 2006). adv. bk.rev. index. back issues avail.; reprints avail. **Document type:** *Academic/Scholarly.* **Description:** Covers all aspects of genetics, including molecular genetics, differentiation, development, clinical genetics, and recombinant DNA.
Related titles: Online - full text ed.: (from EBSCO Publishing, Gale Group, IngentaConnect, ScienceDirect, Swets Information Services).
Indexed: ASCA, ASFA, AgBio, Agr, AnBrAb, BCI, BIOBASE, BIOSIS Prev, BibAg, BioCN&I, BiolAb, CPA, CTA, ChemAb, CurCont, DBA, EntAb, ExcerpMed, FCA, FS&TA, GenetAb, HGA, HerbAb, HortAb, IABS, ISR, IndMed, IndVet, Inpharma, MEDLINE, MaizeAb, NSA, NemAb, NucAcAb, NutrAb, PBA, PE&ON, PGegResA, PGrRegA, PotatoAb, PoultAb, ProtozoAb, RM&VM, RPP, Reac, RefZh, RevApplEntom, RiceAb, S&F, SCI, SeedAb, TriticAb, VetBull, WeedAb, WildRev, ZooRec.
—BLDSC (9049.598000), CASDDS, CISTI, GNLM, IDS, IE, Infotrieve, ingenta. **CCC.**
Published by: Elsevier Ltd., Trends Journals (Subsidiary of: Elsevier Science & Technology), 68 Hills Rd, Cambridge, CB2 1LA, United Kingdom. TEL 44-1223-315961, FAX 44-1223-464460, TIG@elsevier.co.uk, http://www.elsevier.com/locate/tig. Eds. M Thorne, R Shields. Pub. Peter Desmond. Adv. contact Thelma Reid. **Subscr. to:** Elsevier Current Trends Subscriptions, PO Box 331, Haywards Heath, W Sussex RH16 3FG, United Kingdom. TEL 44-1444-475650, FAX 44-1444-445423.

➤ **TRENDS IN MICROBIOLOGY.** see *BIOLOGY—Microbiology*

576.5 UKR ISSN 0564-3783
CODEN: TGANAK
➤ **TSITOLOGIYA I GENETIKA;** mezhdunarodnyi nauchnyi zhurnal. Text in Ukrainian. 1965. bi-m. USD 40.38 foreign (effective 2005). **Document type:** *Journal, Academic/Scholarly.*
Related titles: ◆ English Translation: Cytology and Genetics. ISSN 0095-4527.
Indexed: ASFA, AbHyg, AgBio, AgrForAb, AnBrAb, BioCN&I, BiolAb, CIN, CPA, CTFA, ChemAb, ChemTitl, DSA, DentInd, ESPM, ExcerpMed, FCA, FPA, ForAb, HerbAb, HortAb, IAA, IndMed, IndVet, MEDLINE, MaizeAb, OrnHort, PBA, PGegResA, PGrRegA, PHN&I, PN&I, PotatoAb, PoultAb, RA&MP, RM&VM, RPP, RefZh, RiceAb, S&F, S&MA, SIA, SeedAb, SoyAb, TDB, TriticAb, VITIS, VetBull, WeedAb, ZooRec.
—BLDSC (0397.030000), CASDDS, CISTI, East View, GNLM, Linda Hall. **CCC.**
Published by: Natsional'na Akademiya Nauk Ukrainy, Instytut Klitynnoi Biolohii ta Henetychnoi Inzhynerii/National Academy of Sciences of Ukraine, Institute of Cell Biology and Genetic Engineering, vul Akad Zabolotnogo 148, Kiev, 252143, Ukraine. cytogen@iicb.kiev.ua, http://www.cytgen.com, http://ln.ua/~iicb. Ed. Yu. Yu. Gleba. **Co-sponsor:** Ukrainska Akademiya Ahrarnykh Nauk, Instytut Ahroekolohii i Biotechnolohii/Ukrainian Academy of Agrarian Sciences, Institute of Agroecology and Biotechnology.

599.9 AUS ISSN 1832-4274
CODEN: TWREFP
➤ **TWIN RESEARCH AND HUMAN GENETICS.** Text in English. 1998. bi-m. AUD 392 domestic; AUD 490 foreign (effective 2005). abstr.; stat. 70 p./no.; back issues avail.; reprints avail. **Document type:** *Journal, Academic/Scholarly.* **Description:** Covers the results of original multiple birth research; also provides timely state-of-the-art reviews on all aspects of twin studies. Topics covered in the journal include: behavioral genetics, complex diseases, endocrinology, foetal pathology, medical, genetics, obstetrics, paediatrics, psychiatric genetics.
Formerly (until 2005): Twin Research (1369-0523)
Related titles: Online - full text ed.: (from EBSCO Publishing, Gale Group, IngentaConnect, O C L C Online Computer Library Center, Inc., Swets Information Services).
Indexed: CurCont, ExcerpMed, IndMed, MEDLINE, PsycInfo, PsycholAb, e-psyche.
—BLDSC (9076.957150), CISTI, IE, Infotrieve, ingenta. **CCC.**
Published by: (International Society for Twin Studies), Australian Academic Press Pty. Ltd., 32 Jeays St, Bowen Hills, QLD 4006, Australia. TEL 61-7-32571176, FAX 61-7-32525908, info@australianacademicpress.com.au, http://www.australianacademicpress.com.au/Publications/Journals/Twin_R/TResearch.htm. Eds. Katherine M Kirk, Nicholas G Martin TEL 61-7-3362-0278.

576.5 571 UKR ISSN 1814-9758
▼ ➤ **UKRAINICA BIOORGANICA ACTA/BIOORGANIC CHEMISTRY JOURNAL/ZHURNAL BIOORHANICHNOI KHIMII.** Text in English, Ukrainian. 2004. s-a. **Document type:** *Journal, Academic/Scholarly.* **Description:** Publishes scientific investigations from all branches of bioorganic chemistry.
Related titles: Online - full text ed.: ISSN 1814-9766. free (effective 2005).
Published by: Natsional'na Akademiya Nauk Ukrainy, Instytut Molekulyarnoi Biolohii i Henetyky, Vul Akad Zabolotnogo 150, Kiev, 03143, Ukraine. http://www.bioorganica.org.ua. Ed. Valery P Kukhar.

576.5 SVK
UNIVERZITA KOMENSKEHO. PEDAGOGICKA FAKULTA V TRNAVE. PRIRODNE VEDY: BIOLOGIA-GENETIKA. Text in Slovak. irreg. (approx. a.). price varies.
Published by: Univerzita Komenskeho, Pedagogicka Fakulta v Trnave, c/o Study and Information Center, Safarikova nam 6, Bratislava, 81806, Slovakia.

VIRUS GENES. see *BIOLOGY—Microbiology*

VITIS; journal of grapevine research. see *AGRICULTURE—Crop Production And Soil*

VITIS - VITICULTURE AND OENOLOGY ABSTRACTS (ONLINE EDITION). see *AGRICULTURE—Crop Production And Soil*

WHO'S WHO IN STEM CELL RESEARCH. see *BUSINESS AND ECONOMICS—Trade And Industrial Directories*

599.935 CHN ISSN 0253-9772
QH426 CODEN: ICHUDW
YICHUAN/HEREDITAS. Text in Chinese. 1979. bi-m. CNY 150 (effective 2005). adv. bk.rev. **Document type:** *Journal, Academic/Scholarly.* **Description:** Contains research reports, breeding work based on genetic theories, information on study results in stages, exchange of teaching instructions, and stories and news tidbits on personalities.
Related titles: Online - full text ed.: (from East View Information Services, WanFang Data Corp.).
Indexed: AEA, AgBio, AnBrAb, BIOSIS Prev, BioCN&I, BiolAb, CIN, CPA, ChemAb, ChemTitl, DSA, FCA, ForAb, HelmAb, HerbAb, HortAb, IndVet, MaizeAb, NemAb, NutrAb, PBA, PGegResA, PGrRegA, PN&I, PoultAb, ProtozoAb, RA&MP, RM&VM, RPP, RefZh, RevApplEntom, RiceAb, S&F, SeedAb, SoyAb, TriticAb, VetBull, WeedAb, ZooRec.
—BLDSC (4298.900000), CASDDS, Linda Hall.
Published by: (Zhongguo Kexueyuan, Yichuan yu Fayu Shengwu Yangjiusuo/Chinese Academy of Sciences, Institute of Genetics and Developmental Biology), Kexue Chubanshe/Science Press, 16 Donghuang Cheng Genbei Jie, Beijing, 100717, China. TEL 86-10-64000246, FAX 86-10-64030255, swli@genetics.ac.cn, http://yc.periodicals.net.cn/default.html, http://www.sciencep.com/. Ed. Yong-Biao Xue. Circ: 31,000. **Dist. by:** China International Book Trading Corp, 35 Chegongzhuang Xilu, Haidian District, PO Box 399, Beijing 100044, China. TEL 86-10-68412045, FAX 86-10-68412023, cibtc@mail.cibtc.com.cn, http://www.cibtc.com.cn.

576.5 CHN ISSN 0379-4172
QH431 CODEN: ICHPCG
➤ **YICHUAN XUEBAO/ACTA GENETICA SINICA.** Text in Chinese; Summaries in English. 1974. m. CNY 300 per issue (effective 2004). adv. back issues avail. **Document type:** *Journal, Academic/Scholarly.* **Description:** Covers genetics research in mainland China, including molecular genetics, genetic engineering, medical genetics, and genetics of plants, animals and microorganisms.
Related titles: Online - full text ed.: (from East View Information Services, WanFang Data Corp.).
Indexed: AnBrAb, BIOBASE, BIOSIS Prev, BiolAb, CIN, CTFA, ChemAb, ExcerpMed, FCA, FaBeAb, IndMed, MEDLINE, MaizeAb, OrnHort, PBA, PGrRegA, PN&I, PoultAb, RefZh, RiceAb, S&MA, SFA, SeedAb, SoyAb, TriticAb, VITIS, ZooRec.
—BLDSC (0617.500000), CASDDS, CISTI, GNLM, Linda Hall.
Published by: (Zhongguo Kexueyuan, Yichuan yu Fayu Shengwu Yangjiusuo/Chinese Academy of Sciences, Institute of Genetics and Developmental Biology), Kexue Chubanshe/Science Press, 16 Donghuang Cheng Genbei Jie, Beijing, 100717, China. TEL 86-10-64000246, FAX 86-10-64030255, zhangyan@genetics.ac.cn, http://ycxb.periodicals.net.cn/default.html. Circ: 16,000.

▼ ➤ **ZEBRAFISH.** see *BIOLOGY—Zoology*

➤ **ZHONGGUO SHENGYU JIANKANG ZAZHI/CHINESE JOURNAL FOR HEALTH OF WOMEN IN CHILDBIRTH.** see *BIRTH CONTROL*

616.042 CHN ISSN 1003-9406
CODEN: ZYXZER
ZHONGHUA YIXUE YICHUANXUE ZAZHI/CHINESE JOURNAL OF MEDICAL GENETICS. Text in Chinese. 1984. bi-m. USD 37.80; USD 6.30 newsstand/cover (effective 2001). **Document type:** *Academic/Scholarly.*
Formerly (until 1991): Yichuan yu Jibing / Heredity and Disease (1002-0756)
Related titles: Online - full text ed.: (from East View Information Services).
Indexed: EngInd, ExcerpMed, IndMed, MEDLINE, RefZh.
—BLDSC (3180.425800), IE, Infotrieve, ingenta.
Published by: Huaxi Yike Daxue/West China University of Medical Sciences, 14, Renmin Nanlu, 3-duan, Chengdu, Sichuan 610041, China. TEL 581130. Ed. Liu Zudong. **Dist. by:** China International Book Trading Corp, 35 Chegongzhuang Xilu, Haidian District, PO Box 399, Beijing 100044, China. TEL 86-10-68412045, FAX 86-10-68412023, cibtc@mail.cibtc.com.cn, http://www.cibtc.com.cn.

ZUOWU PINZHONG ZIYUAN/CROP GENETIC RESOURCES. see *AGRICULTURE—Crop Production And Soil*

576.5 GBR ISSN 0967-1994
QH491 CODEN: ZYGOEB
➤ **ZYGOTE;** the biology of gametes and early embryos. Text in English. 1993. q. GBP 208 to institutions; USD 352 in North America to institutions; GBP 228 combined subscription to institutions print & online eds.; USD 392 combined subscription in North America to institutions print & online eds. (effective 2006). adv. bk.rev. back issues avail.; reprint service avail. from PSC. **Document type:** *Journal, Academic/Scholarly.* **Description:** Provides a multidisciplinary forum for reports on all aspects of early developmental biology. Concentrates on the programming of developmental information during gametogenesis, through its modification at fertilization to the integration of the maternal and embryonic genomes.
Related titles: Online - full text ed.: ISSN 1469-8730. GBP 200 to institutions; USD 338 in North America to institutions (effective 2006) (from EBSCO Publishing, O C L C Online Computer Library Center, Inc., Ovid Technologies, Inc., Swets Information Services).
Indexed: ASCA, AgBio, Agr, AnBrAb, BIOSIS Prev, BiolAb, CurCont, DSA, HortAb, IndMed, IndVet, Inpharma, MEDLINE, OrnHort, PBA, PN&I, PoultAb, Reac, RefZh, SoyAb, VetBull, ZooRec.
—BLDSC (9538.885000), CASDDS, CISTI, GNLM, IDS, IE, Infotrieve, ingenta, KNAW. **CCC.**
Published by: Cambridge University Press, The Edinburgh Bldg, Shaftesbury Rd, Cambridge, CB2 2RU, United Kingdom. TEL 44-1223-312393, FAX 44-1223-315052, journals@cambridge.org, http://uk.cambridge.org/journals/zyg. Eds. Brian Dale, Jacques Cohen, Nori Satoh. R&P Linda Nicol TEL 44-1223-325757. Adv. contact Rebecca Curtis TEL 44-1223-325757. **Subscr. to:** Cambridge University Press, 100 Brook Hill Dr, West Nyack, NY 10994. TEL 845-353-7500, FAX 845-353-4141, journals_subscriptions@cup.org

BIOLOGY—Microbiology

579.2 USA
QR383
A T C C ANIMAL VIRUSES AND ANTISERA, CHLAMYDIAE, AND RICKETTSIAE. Text in English. 1975. irreg., latest vol.7, 1996. USD 36 in North America; USD 48 elsewhere. **Document type:** *Catalog.*
Formerly: A T C C Catalogue of Animal Viruses and Antisera, Chlamydiae, and Rickettsiae (1057-6495); Which supersedes in part (in 1990): American Type Culture Collection. Catalogue of Animal and Plant Viruses, Chlamydiae, Rickettsiae and Virus Antisera (0898-4182); Which supersedes in part (in 1986): American Type Culture Collection. Catalogue of Strains 2: Animal Cell Lines, Animal Viruses, Bacterial Viruses, Mycoviruses, Plant Viruses, Rickettsiae, Chlamydiae (0363-2989)
—CISTI. **CCC.**
Published by: American Type Culture Collection, 10801 University Blvd, Manassas, VA 20110. TEL 800-638-6597, FAX 301-816-4361, sales@atcc.org. Eds. C Buck, G Paulino.

579.3 USA
A T C C BACTERIA & BACTERIOPHAGES. Text in English. 1985. irreg., latest vol.19, 1996. USD 45 in North America; USD 55 elsewhere. **Document type:** *Catalog.*
Formerly: A T C C Catalogue of Bacteria and Bacteriophages (1050-8120); Which supersedes in part: American Type Culture Collection. Catalogue of Strains 1
—CCC.
Published by: American Type Culture Collection, 10801 University Blvd, Manassas, VA 20110. TEL 800-638-6597, FAX 301-816-4361, sales@atcc.org.

579.2 USA
A T C C CATALOGUE OF PLANT VIRUSES AND ANTISERA. Text in English. 1975. irreg., latest vol.7, 1993. USD 5. **Document type:** *Catalog.*
Supersedes in part (in 1990): American Type Culture Collection. Catalogue of Animal and Plant Viruses, Chlamydiae, Rickettsiae and Virus Antisera (0898-4182); Which supersedes in part (in 1986): American Type Culture Collection. Catalogue of Strains 2: Animal Cell Lines, Animal Viruses, Bacterial Viruses, Mycoviruses, Plant Viruses, Rickettsiae, Chlamydiae (0363-2989)
—CISTI.
Published by: American Type Culture Collection, 10801 University Blvd, Manassas, VA 20110. TEL 800-638-6597, FAX 301-816-4361, Sales@ATCC.org.

579.2 USA
A T C C CATALOGUE OF PROTISTS. ALGAE - PROTOZOA. Text in English. 1985. irreg., latest vol.18, 1993. USD 5. **Document type:** *Catalog.*
Published by: American Type Culture Collection, 10801 University Blvd, Manassas, VA 20110. TEL 800-638-6597, FAX 301-816-4361, Sales@ATCC.org. Ed. T A Nerad.

579.2 USA ISSN 1088-2103
A T C C CONNECTION. Text in English. 1981. q. free (effective 2005). **Document type:** *Newsletter.* **Description:** Characterization, preservation, and use of biological cultures.
Former titles (until 1995): A T C C Quarterly Newsletter (0894-9026); (until 1985): American Type Culture Collection. Quarterly Newsletter (0743-4758)
Indexed: Agr, Telegen.
—CCC.
Published by: American Type Culture Collection, 10801 University Blvd, Manassas, VA 20110. news@atcc.org. Ed. E M Brown. Circ: 18,500.

A T C C FILAMENTOUS FUNGI. see *BIOLOGY—Botany*

A T C C YEASTS. see *BIOLOGY—Botany*

579 HUN ISSN 1217-8950
QR1 CODEN: AMIHEF
ACTA MICROBIOLOGICA ET IMMUNOLOGICA HUNGARICA. Text in English. 1954. q. USD 308 (effective 2006). adv. bk.rev. bibl.; charts; illus.; abstr. index. 120 p./no.; back issues avail. **Document type:** *Journal, Academic/Scholarly.* **Description:** Publishes research on medical and veterinary bacteriology, bacterial genetics, virology, mycology, parasitology. Includes immunology and epidemiology, agricultural and industrial microbiology.
Former titles (until 1994): Acta Microbiologica Hungarica (0231-4622); (until 1982): Academiae Scientiarum Hungaricae. Acta Microbiologica (0001-6187)
Related titles: Online - full text ed.: ISSN 1588-2640 (from EBSCO Publishing, Swets Information Services).
Indexed: ASCA, ASFA, AbHyg, AgBio, AgrForAb, BIOSIS Prev, BioCN&I, BiolAb, CBTA, CEABA, CIN, CPA, ChemAb, ChemTitl, CurCont, DBA, DSA, DentInd, ESPM, ExcerpMed, FCA, ForAb, HelmAb, HerbAb, HortAb, I&DA, ISR, IndMed, IndVet, MEDLINE, NPU, NemAb, NutrAb, OrnHort, PBA, PGegResA, PGrRegA, PHN&I, PN&I, PotatoAb, PoultAb, ProtozoAb, RA&MP, RM&VM, RPP, RefZh, RevApplEntom, S&F, SCI, SIA, SoyAb, TDB, TriticAb, VetBull, WAE&RSA, WeedAb.
—BLDSC (0637.978000), CASDDS, CISTI, GNLM, IE, Infotrieve, ingenta, KNAW, Linda Hall. **CCC.**
Published by: (Semmelweis University, Institute of Medical Microbiology, Magyar Tudomanyos Akademia/Hungarian Academy of Sciences), Akademiai Kiado Rt. (Subsidiary of: Wolters Kluwer N.V.), Prielle Kornelia U. 19, Budapest, 1117, Hungary. TEL 36-1-4648282, FAX 36-1-4648221, journals@akkrt.hu, http://www.akkrt.hu.

578.65 616.96 POL ISSN 1230-2821
QL757 CODEN: ACTPEO
➤ **ACTA PARASITOLOGICA.** Text and summaries in English. 1953. q. USD 100 foreign to individuals; USD 180 foreign to institutions (effective 2005). adv. bk.rev. bibl.; illus. index. 80 p./no. 2 cols./p.; **Document type:** *Journal, Academic/Scholarly.* **Description:** Presents full length articles, short research, review articles and book reviews of high scientific quality on all aspects of pure and applied parasitology.
Formerly (until vol.37, 1992): Acta Parasitologica Polonica (0065-1478)
Indexed: AbHyg, AgBio, AgrAg, AgrForAb, AgrLib, AnBrAb, BIOBASE, BIOSIS Prev, BioCN&I, BiolAb, CIN, ChemAb, ChemTitl, CurCont, DSA, ExcerpMed, ForAb, HelmAb, HerbAb, IABS, IndVet, KWIWR, NemAb, NutrAb, PN&I, PoultAb, ProtozoAb, RM&VM, RPP, RefZh, RevApplEntom, S&F, SFA, TDB, VetBull, ZooRec.
—BLDSC (0643.300000), CASDDS, CISTI, GNLM, IDS, IE, ingenta, KNAW.
Published by: Polska Akademia Nauk, Instytut Parazytologii im. Witolda Stefanskiego/Polish Academy of Sciences, Witold Stefanski Institute of Parasitology, Ul Twarda 51-55, Warsaw, 00818, Poland. TEL 48-22-6206226, FAX 48-22-6206227, actapar@twarda.pan.pl, http://www.ipar.pan.pl/acta. Ed. Zdzislaw Swiderski. R&P Katarzyna Niewiadomska TEL 48-22-6979995. Adv. contact Anna Pucilowska. Circ: 350 (paid and controlled). **Dist. by:** Ars Polona, Krakowskie Przedmiescie 7, Warsaw, Poland. TEL 48-22-9263914, FAX 48-22-9265334, arspolona@arspolona.com.pl, http://www.arspolona.com.pl.

578.65 616.96 PRT ISSN 0872-5292
ACTA PARASITOLOGICA PORTUGUESA. Text in Portuguese. 1993. s-a.
Indexed: ASFA, AbHyg, BioCN&I, EntAb, HelmAb, HortAb, IndVet, OrnHort, PN&I, PoultAb, ProtozoAb, RA&MP, RM&VM, RRTA, S&F, TDB, VetBull.
Published by: Sociedade Portuguesa de Parasitologia, Lisbon, Portugal.

579.4 POL ISSN 0065-1583
QL366 CODEN: ACPZAU
➤ **ACTA PROTOZOOLOGICA.** Text in English. 1963. q. USD 200 foreign to institutions (effective 2005). Website rev. illus. back issues avail.; reprint service avail. from ISI. **Document type:** *Journal, Academic/Scholarly.* **Description:** Publishes original papers presenting the results of experimental or theoretical research in all fields of protistology with the exception of faunistic notices of a local character and purely clinical reports.
Related titles: Online - full text ed.: ISSN 1689-0027. free (effective 2005).
Indexed: ASCA, ASFA, AbHyg, AgrAg, AgrLib, BIOBASE, BIOSIS Prev, BioCN&I, BiolAb, CIN, ChemAb, ChemTitl, CurCont, ESPM, EntAb, ExcerpMed, ForAb, HelmAb, HortAb, IABS, ISR, IndVet, MBA, NutrAb, OrnHort, PHN&I, PoultAb, ProtozoAb, RM&VM, RPP, RefZh, RevApplEntom, S&F, SCI, SIA, TDB, VetBull, ZooRec.
—BLDSC (0661.370000), CASDDS, CISTI, IDS, IE, Infotrieve, ingenta, Linda Hall.

▼ new title ➤ refereed ✶ unverified ♦ full entry avail.

Published by: Polska Akademia Nauk, Instytut Biologii Doswiadczalnej im. M. Nenckiego/Polish Academy of Sciences, M. Nencki Institute of Experimental Biology, Ul Pasteura 3, Warsaw, 02093, Poland. TEL 48-22-6598571, FAX 48-22-8225342, dyrekcja@nencki.gov.pl, http://www.nencki.gov.pl/ap.htm, http://www.nencki.gov.pl/default.htm. Ed., R&P Jerzy Sikora. Circ: 460. **Dist. by:** Ars Polona, Krakowskie Przedmiescie 7, Warsaw, Poland. TEL 48-22-9263914, FAX 48-22-9265334, arspolona@arspolona.com.pl, http://www.arspolona.com.pl.

579.2 SVK ISSN 0001-723X
CODEN: AVIRA2

➤ **ACTA VIROLOGICA**; international journal. Text and summaries in English. 1957. bi-m. USD 198 foreign (effective 2005). bk.rev. charts; illus. index. **Document type:** *Journal, Academic/Scholarly.* **Description:** Devoted to original experimental papers in all fields of general virology and molecular biology of viruses, as well as of human and veterinary virology and rickettsiology.

Indexed: AIDS&CR, ASCA, ASFA, AbHyg, AgBio, Agr, AgrForAb, AnBrAb, BIOBASE, BIOSIS Prev, BioCN&I, BiolAb, CIN, CPA, ChemAb, ChemTitl, CurCont, DBA, DSA, DentInd, ESPM, ExcerpMed, FCA, HortAb, IABS, INIS AtomInd, ISR, IndMed, IndVet, Inpharma, MBA, MEDLINE, MaizeAb, PBA, PE&ON, PGegResA, PN&I, PotatoAb, PoultAb, ProtozoAb, RA&MP, RDA, RM&VM, RPP, RRTA, Reac, RevApplEntom, RiceAb, SCI, SFA, SeedAb, SoyAb, TDB, Telegen, TriticAb, VetBull, VirolAbstr, WeedAb, WildRev, ZooRec.

—BLDSC (0671.500000), CASDDS, CISTI, GNLM, IDS, IE, Infotrieve, ingenta, KNAW. **CCC.**

Published by: (Slovenska Akademia Vied, Virologicky Ustav/Slovak Academy of Sciences, Institute of Virology), Slovak Academic Press Ltd., Nam Slobody 6, PO Box 57, Bratislava, 81005, Slovakia. viruacta@savba.sk, sap@sappress.sk, http://www.sappress.sk. Circ: 1,200.

579.37 ITA
QR82.A35 CODEN: ACTID2

ACTINOMYCETES (ONLINE EDITION). Text in Italian. 1965. 3/yr. USD 20 to individuals; USD 60 to institutions (effective 1997). adv. bk.rev. illus. back issues avail. **Document type:** *Newspaper.*

Former titles (until 1999): Actinomycetes (Print Edition) (0732-0574); Biology of the Actinomycetes and Related Organisms; Nocardial Biology

Media: Online - full content.

Indexed: BIOSIS Prev, BioCN&I, BiolAb, ChemAb, RM&VM, RPP.

—CASDDS, CISTI.

Published by: Centro per l'Ecologia Teorica e Applicata, Via Vittorio Veneto, 19, Gorizia, GO 34170, Italy. TEL 39-481-536466, FAX 39-432-536470, bio@biostrat.demon.co.uk, http://bioline.bdt.org.br/ac. Ed. Romano Locci. Adv. contact Fulvio Bisani. Circ: 250. **Subscr. to:** Prof. R. Locci, c/o Chair of Mycology, University of Udine, Aera Rizzi, Via Delle Scienze, 208, Udine, UD 33100, Italy.

579 USA ISSN 0065-2164
QR1 CODEN: ADAMAP

➤ **ADVANCES IN APPLIED MICROBIOLOGY.** Text in English. 1959. irreg., latest vol.51, 2002. USD 119.95 per vol. vol.53 (effective 2004). index. reprint service avail. from ISI. **Document type:** *Academic/Scholarly.* **Description:** Offers intensive reviews of the latest techniques and discoveries in this rapidly moving field.

Related titles: Online - full text ed.: (from ScienceDirect).

Indexed: ASCA, ASFA, Agr, B&AI, BCI, BIOBASE, BIOSIS Prev, BiolAb, CBTA, CEABA, CIN, ChemAb, ChemTitl, DBA, DSA, EngInd, ExcerpMed, FS&TA, IABS, ISR, IndMed, IndVet, MEDLINE, PBA, RevApplEntom, SCI, Telegen, VetBull, WAE&RSA, WeedAb.

—BLDSC (0699.100000), CASDDS, CISTI, Ei, GNLM, IE, Infotrieve, ingenta, Linda Hall. **CCC.**

Published by: Academic Press (Subsidiary of: Elsevier Science & Technology), 525 B St, Ste 1900, San Diego, CA 92101-4495. apsubs@acad.com, http://www.academicpress.com. Ed. Allen Laskin.

579.17 USA ISSN 0147-4863
QR100 CODEN: AMIED5

➤ **ADVANCES IN MICROBIAL ECOLOGY.** Text in English. 1977. irreg., latest vol.16, 2000. price varies. **Document type:** *Monographic series, Academic/Scholarly.*

Indexed: ASCA, ASFA, Agr, ApEcolAb, BIOSIS Prev, CIN, ChemAb, ChemTitl, ESPM, HGA, ISR, MBA, NutrAb, RPP, S&F, SCI, VetBull.

—BLDSC (0709.415000), CASDDS, CISTI, Infotrieve, ingenta, KNAW, Linda Hall. **CCC.**

Published by: Springer-Verlag New York, Inc. (Subsidiary of: Springer Science+Business Media), 233 Spring St, New York, NY 10013. TEL 212-460-1500, FAX 212-460-1575, service@springer-ny.com, http://www.springer-ny.com.

578.65 USA ISSN 0065-2911
QR84 CODEN: AMIPB2

➤ **ADVANCES IN MICROBIAL PHYSIOLOGY.** Text in English. 1967. irreg., latest vol.46, 2002. USD 149.95 per vol. vol.48 (effective 2004). reprint service avail. from ISI. **Document type:** *Monographic series, Academic/Scholarly.* **Description:** Publishes topical and important reviews, interpreting physiology in its broadest context, to include all material that contributes to our understanding of how microorganisms and their component parts work.

Related titles: Online - full text ed.: (from ScienceDirect).

Indexed: ASCA, ASFA, AbHyg, Agr, B&AI, BBCI, BIOBASE, BIOSIS Prev, BiolAb, CIN, ChemAb, ChemTitl, ESPM, ExcerpMed, IABS, ISR, IndMed, MBA, MEDLINE, RM&VM, SCI, TDB.

—BLDSC (0709.420000), CASDDS, CISTI, GNLM, IE, Infotrieve, ingenta, KNAW, Linda Hall. **CCC.**

Published by: Academic Press (Subsidiary of: Elsevier Science & Technology), 525 B St, Ste 1900, San Diego, CA 92101-4495. TEL 619-231-6616, 800-894-3434, apsubs@acad.com, http://www.academicpress.com. Eds. A H Rose, J F Wilkinson.

579.65 USA ISSN 0065-308X
QH547 CODEN: ADPRAD

➤ **ADVANCES IN PARASITOLOGY.** Text in English. 1963. irreg., latest vol.52, 2002. USD 159.95 vol.55 (effective 2004). index. reprint service avail. from ISI. **Document type:** *Monographic series, Academic/Scholarly.* **Description:** Contains comprehensive reviews in all areas of interest in contemporary parasitology.

Related titles: Online - full text ed.: (from ScienceDirect).

Indexed: ASCA, ASFA, AbHyg, AgBio, Agr, B&AI, BIOBASE, BIOSIS Prev, BiolAb, ESPM, ExcerpMed, FoVS&M, HGA, HelmAb, IABS, ISR, IndMed, IndVet, JDDR, MEDLINE, NutrAb, PN&I, ProtozoAb, RA&MP, RM&VM, RPP, RevApplEntom, SCI, TDB, VetBull, ZooRec.

—BLDSC (0709.580000), CASDDS, CISTI, GNLM, IE, ingenta, KNAW, Linda Hall. **CCC.**

Published by: Academic Press (Subsidiary of: Elsevier Science & Technology), 525 B St, Ste 1900, San Diego, CA 92101-4495. TEL 619-231-6616, 800-894-3434, apsubs@acad.com, http://www.academicpress.com. Ed. Ben Dawes.

579.2 USA ISSN 0065-3527
QR360 CODEN: AVREA8

➤ **ADVANCES IN VIRUS RESEARCH.** Text in English. 1953. irreg., latest vol.58, 2002. USD 139.95 per vol. vol.62 (effective 2004). index. reprint service avail. from ISI. **Document type:** *Academic/Scholarly.* **Description:** Covers a diverse range of in-depth reviews providing a valuable overview of the current field of virology.

Formerly (until 1968): Advances in Veterinary Science (0096-7653)

Related titles: Online - full text ed.: ISSN 1557-8399 (from ScienceDirect).

Indexed: AIDS&CR, ASCA, AbHyg, Agr, B&BAb, BIOSIS Prev, BioCN&I, BiolAb, CIN, ChemAb, ChemTitl, ESPM, ExcerpMed, ForAb, GenetAb, HortAb, ISR, IndMed, IndVet, MBA, MEDLINE, PBA, PN&I, PollutAb, RPP, RevApplEntom, SCI, TDB, VetBull, VirolAbstr.

—BLDSC (0712.000000), CASDDS, CISTI, GNLM, IE, ingenta, Linda Hall. **CCC.**

Published by: Academic Press (Subsidiary of: Elsevier Science & Technology), 525 B St, Ste 1900, San Diego, CA 92101-4495. TEL 619-231-6616, 800-894-3434, apsubs@acad.com, http://www.sciencedirect.com/science/journal/00653527, http://www.academicpress.com.

➤ **ADVISORY COMMITTEE ON THE MICROBIOLOGICAL SAFETY OF FOOD. ANNUAL REPORT.** see *FOOD AND FOOD INDUSTRIES*

579 NGA ISSN 1595-689X

AFRICAN JOURNAL OF CLINICAL AND EXPERIMENTAL MICROBIOLOGY. Text in English. 2000. s-a. NGN 1,800 domestic; GBP 30 in Europe; USD 50 in US & Canada; USD 40 in Africa; USD 50 rest of world (effective 2004). back issues avail. **Document type:** *Academic/Scholarly.* **Description:** Includes original research papers covering all aspects of medical microbiology, bacteriology, virology, rickettsiology, chiaydiology, mycology, mycobacteriology, and actinomyceles, parasitology, epidemiology of infectious diseases, immunology in clinical practice, general clinical microbiology, and clinical veterinary microbiology.

Related titles: Online - full text ed.: (from International Network for the Availability of Scientific Publications, African Journals Online).

Address: PO Box 5395, Llorin, Kwara State, 24001, Nigeria. TEL 234-31-222076, ajcem2002@yahoo.com, http://www.inasp.info/ajol/journals/ajcem/index.html. Ed. B.A. Onile.

579 ITA ISSN 1121-9750
CODEN: AAMJEP

➤ **ALPE ADRIA MICROBIOLOGY JOURNAL.** Abbreviated title: A A M J. Text in Italian. 1992. q. adv. abstr. **Document type:** *Academic/Scholarly.* **Description:** Publishes review articles, original papers, correspondence, and congress proceedings in the field of pathogenesis of infections, diagnostic microbiology, epidemiology of infectious diseases, and mechanisms of action of antimicrobial agents.

Indexed: AbHyg, CIN, ChemAb, ChemTitl, DSA, ESPM, ExcerpMed, HelmAb, IABS, IndVet, MBA, NutrAb, ProtozoAb, RM&VM, RevApplEntom, VetBull, ZooRec.

—BLDSC (0801.953000), CASDDS, GNLM.

Published by: Associazione Microbiologici Clinici Italiani, Via Carlo Farini 81, Milan, 20169, Italy. TEL 39-02-69001316, FAX 39-02-69001311, giuseppe.botta@drmm.uniud.it. Circ: 2,500.

➤ **AMERICAN SOCIETY FOR MICROBIOLOGY. ABSTRACTS OF THE GENERAL MEETING.** see *BIOLOGY—Abstracting, Bibliographies, Statistics*

579.3149 GBR ISSN 1075-9964
QH518.5 CODEN: ANAEF8

➤ **ANAEROBE.** Text in English. 1995. 6/yr. EUR 260 in Europe to individuals; JPY 28,000 in Japan to individuals; USD 255 to individuals except Europe and Japan; EUR 493 in Europe to institutions; JPY 53,300 in Japan to institutions; USD 439 to institutions except Europe and Japan (effective 2006). reprints avail. **Document type:** *Journal, Academic/Scholarly.* **Description:** Focuses on studies pertaining to obligate and facultative anaerobes. Seeks to foster communication among a variety of disciplines.

Related titles: Online - full text ed.: ISSN 1095-8274. USD 463 (effective 2002) (from EBSCO Publishing, Gale Group, IngentaConnect, O C L C Online Computer Library Center, Inc., ScienceDirect, Swets Information Services).

Indexed: ASCA, AbHyg, AgBio, AgrForAb, BIOBASE, BIOSIS Prev, BiolAb, CIN, ChemAb, ChemTitl, CurCont, DSA, ExcerpMed, IABS, ISR, IndVet, Inpharma, MaizeAb, NutrAb, PE&ON, PN&I, PoultAb, ProtozoAb, RA&MP, RM&VM, Reac, RefZh, S&F, SCI, SIA, TDB, VITIS, VetBull.

—BLDSC (0859.882000), CASDDS, CISTI, GNLM, IDS, IE, Infotrieve, ingenta, Linda Hall. **CCC.**

Published by: Academic Press (Subsidiary of: Elsevier Science & Technology), 24-28 Oval Rd, London, NW1 7DX, United Kingdom. TEL 44-20-72674466, FAX 44-20-74822293, apsubs@acad.com, http://www.elsevier.com/locate/anaerobe. Ed. Dr. S.M. Finegold. **Subscr. to:** Harcourt Publishers Ltd., Foots Cray High St, Sidcup, Kent DA14 5HP, United Kingdom. TEL 44-20-8300-3322, FAX 44-20-8309-0807.

616.9201 GBR ISSN 1476-0711

➤ **ANNALS OF CLINICAL MICROBIOLOGY AND ANTIMICROBIALS.** Text in English. 2002. irreg. free (effective 2006). adv. **Document type:** *Journal, Academic/Scholarly.* **Description:** Serves as an international forum for the exchange of ideas and information about issues and research concerning clinical microbiology, infectious diseases and antimicrobials.

Media: Online - full content (from EBSCO Publishing, National Library of Medicine).

Indexed: ExcerpMed.

—**CCC.**

Published by: BioMed Central Ltd. (Subsidiary of: Current Science Ltd), Middlesex House, 34-42 Cleveland St, London, W1T 4LB, United Kingdom. TEL 44-20-76319131, FAX 44-20-76319923, info@biomedcentral.com, http://www.ann-clinmicrob.com/home/, http://www.biomedcentral.com. Ed. Hakan Leblebicioglu.

579 JPN

ANNUAL REVIEW MEN'EKI/ANNUAL REVIEW. IMMUNITY. Text in Japanese. 1988. a. JPY 8,925 (effective 1998). adv. **Document type:** *Academic/Scholarly.*

Published by: Chugai Igakusha, 62 Yarai-cho, Shinjuku-ku, Tokyo, 162-0805, Japan. R&P M Takahashi. Adv. contact M. Takahashi.

579 USA ISSN 0066-4227
QR1 CODEN: ARMIAZ

➤ **ANNUAL REVIEW OF MICROBIOLOGY.** Text in English. 1947. a., latest vol.58, 2004. USD 185 to institutions print or online ed.; USD 222 combined subscription to institutions print & online eds. (effective 2006). bibl.; charts; abstr. index, cum.index. back issues avail.; reprint service avail. from PSC. **Document type:** *Academic/Scholarly.* **Description:** Reviews filter and synthesize primary research to identify the principal contributions in microbiology.

Related titles: Microfilm ed.: (from PQC); Online - full content ed.: ISSN 1545-3251. USD 179 (effective 2005) (from Florida Center for Library Automation, HighWire Press, Northern Light Technology, Inc.); Online - full text ed.: (from bigchalk, EBSCO Publishing, Gale Group, H.W. Wilson, O C L C Online Computer Library Center, Inc., ProQuest Information & Learning, Swets Information Services).

Indexed: ABIPC, ABS&EES, AESIS, ASCA, ASFA, AbHyg, AgBio, Agr, B&AI, BIOBASE, BIOSIS Prev, BioDAb, BiolAb, BiolDig, CBTA, CEABA, CIN, CPA, ChemAb, ChemTitl, CurCont, DBA, DSA, ESPM, ExcerpMed, FCA, FPA, FS&TA, ForAb, GSI, IABS, ISR, IndMed, IndVet, Inpharma, JDDR, MBA, MEDLINE, MRD, NemAb, NutrAb, PBA, ProtozoAb, RM&VM, RPP, Reac, RevApplEntom, RiceAb, S&F, SCI, SIA, TDB, THA, VITIS, VetBull, VirolAbstr, ZooRec.

—BLDSC (1523.000000), CASDDS, CINDOC, CISTI, GNLM, IDS, IE, Infotrieve, ingenta, KNAW, Linda Hall. **CCC.**

Published by: Annual Reviews, 4139 El Camino Way, Palo Alto, CA 94303-0139. TEL 650-493-4400, 800-523-8635, FAX 650-424-0910, service@annualreviews.org, http://arjournals.annualreviews.org/loi/micro, http://www.annualreviews.org. Ed. L Nicholas Ornston. R&P Laura Folkner.

579 USA ISSN 0066-4804
RM265 CODEN: AMACCQ
➤ **ANTIMICROBIAL AGENTS AND CHEMOTHERAPY.** Text in English. 1953. m. USD 491 domestic to non-members; USD 515 in Canada to non-members; USD 550 in Europe to non-members; USD 570 in Latin America to non-members; USD 573 elsewhere to non-members (effective 2006). adv. Index. back issues avail.; reprint service avail. from PQC. **Document type:** *Journal, Academic/Scholarly.* **Description:** Forum for new work relating to antimicrobial, antiviral, antiparasitic, and anticancer agents and chemotherapy.
Former titles (until 1961): Antimicrobial Agents Annual (0570-3301); (until 1960): Antibiotics Annual (0570-3131)
Related titles: Online - full text ed.: ISSN 1098-6596. USD 460 to non-members (effective 2006) (from EBSCO Publishing, HighWire Press, National Library of Medicine).
Indexed: AIDS Ab, AIDS&CR, AIIM, ASCA, AbHyg, AgBio, AnBrAb, BIOSIS Prev, BioCN&I, BioEngAb, BiolAb, CCI, CIN, ChemAb, ChemTitl, CurCont, DBA, DSA, DentInd, ESPM, ExcerpMed, HGA, HelmAb, HortAb, IDIS, IPA, ISR, IndMed, IndVet, Inpharma, JDDR, JW-ID, Kidney, M&PBA, MBA, MEDLINE, MS&D, NSCI, NutrAb, PBA, PE&ON, PN&I, PoultAb, ProtozoAb, RA&MP, RM&VM, RPP, Reac, RefZh, RevApplEntom, SAA, SCI, SIA, SoyAb, TDB, Telegen, VetBull, VirolAbstr, WeedAb.
—BLDSC (1549.151000), CASDDS, CISTI, GNLM, IDS, IE, Infotrieve, ingenta, KNAW, Linda Hall. **CCC.**
Published by: American Society for Microbiology, 1752 N St, N W, Washington, DC 20036-2904. TEL 202-942-9319, 202-737-3600, FAX 202-942-9355, asmjournals@asm.org, subscriptions@asmusa.org, http://aac.asm.org/, http://www.asm.org. Ed. George M Eliopoulos. Circ: 11,480 (paid). **Subscr. to:** PO Box 11127, Birmingham, AL 35201-1127. TEL 205-995-1567, 800-633-4931, FAX 205-995-1588.

579.2 NLD ISSN 0166-3542
CODEN: ARSRDR
➤ **ANTIVIRAL RESEARCH.** Text in English. 1981. 12/yr. EUR 2,017 in Europe to institutions; JPY 267,900 in Japan to institutions; USD 2,256 to institutions except Europe and Japan (effective 2006). adv. bk.rev. illus.; abstr. index. back issues avail.; reprints avail. **Document type:** *Journal, Academic/Scholarly.* **Description:** Publishes full-length original articles, short definitive papers and review articles pertaining to the effective control of virus infections in animals and humans, as well as in plants or lower organisms.
Formerly: Journal of Antiviral Research
Related titles: Microform ed.: (from PQC); Online - full text ed.: (from EBSCO Publishing, Gale Group, IngentaConnect, ScienceDirect, Swets Information Services).
Indexed: AIDS Ab, AIDS&CR, ASCA, AbHyg, AgBio, AgrForAb, BIOBASE, BIOSIS Prev, BiolAb, CIN, ChemAb, ChemTitl, CurCont, DBA, DSA, ESPM, ExcerpMed, FPA, ForAb, HortAb, IABS, ISR, IndMed, IndVet, Inpharma, M&PBA, MBA, MEDLINE, NutrAb, PBA, PE&ON, PN&I, PotatoAb, PoultAb, RA&MP, RM&VM, RPP, Reac, RefZh, RevApplEntom, SAA, SCI, SIA, TDB, VetBull, VirolAbstr, WAE&RSA.
—BLDSC (1552.830000), CASDDS, CISTI, GNLM, IDS, IE, Infotrieve, ingenta, Linda Hall. **CCC.**
Published by: (International Society for Antiviral Research), Elsevier BV (Subsidiary of: Elsevier Science & Technology), Radarweg 29, Amsterdam, 1043 NX, Netherlands. TEL 31-20-4853911, FAX 31-20-4852457, nlinfo-f@elsevier.nl, http://www.elsevier.com/locate/antiviral, http://www.elsevier.nl. Eds. Earl R. Kern, Erik de Clerq, Richard J Whitley. **Subscr. to:** PO Box 211, Amsterdam 1000 AE, Netherlands. TEL 31-20-485-3757, FAX 31-20-485-3432.

➤ **ANTIVIRAL THERAPY.** see *MEDICAL SCIENCES—Communicable Diseases*

➤ **ANTONIE VAN LEEUWENHOEK**; international journal of general and molecular microbiology. see *BIOLOGY—Biotechnology*

579 USA ISSN 0099-2240
QR1 CODEN: AEMIDF
➤ **APPLIED AND ENVIRONMENTAL MICROBIOLOGY.** Text in English. 1953. m. USD 643 domestic to non-members; USD 678 in Canada to non-members; USD 735 in Europe to non-members; USD 766 in Latin America to non-members; USD 770 elsewhere to non-members (effective 2006). adv. bibl.; charts; illus. Index. back issues avail.; reprint service avail. from PQC. **Document type:** *Journal, Academic/Scholarly.* **Description:** Addresses all aspects of applied and environmental microbiology, including biotechnology, food microbiology, industrial microbiology, and microbial ecology.
Formerly (until 1976): Applied Microbiology (0003-6919)
Related titles: Online - full text ed.: ISSN 1098-5336. USD 602 to institutions (effective 2006) (from EBSCO Publishing, HighWire Press, National Library of Medicine).
Indexed: ABIPC, AEA, AEBA, AESIS, ASCA, ASFA, AbHyg, AgBio, Agr, AgrForAb, AnBrAb, ApEcolAb, B&AI, BCI, BIOBASE, BIOSIS Prev, BibAg, BioCN&I, BioDAb, BioEngAb, BiolAb, CBTA, CCI, CEABA, CIN, CISA, CPA, ChemAb, ChemTitl, CivEngAb, CurCont, CurPA, DBA, DSA, DentInd, E&PHSE, EIA, EPB, ESPM, EngInd, EntAb, EnvAb, EnvEAb, ExcerpMed, FCA, FLUIDEX, FPA, FS&TA, ForAb, GEOBASE, GP&P, GSI, GenetAb, HGA, HelmAb, HerbAb, HortAb, I&DA, IABS, IBR, INIS AtomInd, IPA, ISR, IndMed, IndVet, Inpharma, JDDR, M&TEA, MBA, MEDLINE, MSB, MSCI, MaizeAb, NemAb, NutrAb, OceAb, OffTech, OrnHort, P&BA, PBA, PE&ON, PGegResA, PGrRegA, PHN&I, PN&I, PetrolAb, PollutAb, PotatoAb, PoultAb, ProtozoAb, RA&MP, RM&VM, RPP, RRTA, Reac, RefZh, Repind, RevApplEntom, RiceAb, S&F, SCI, SFA, SIA, SWRA, SeedAb, SoyAb, TDB, Telegen, TriticAb, VITIS, VetBull, WRCInf, WTA, WasteInfo, WeedAb, WildRev, ZooRec.
—BLDSC (1571.440000), CASDDS, CINDOC, CISTI, Ei, GNLM, IDS, IE, Infotrieve, ingenta, Linda Hall, PADDS. **CCC.**
Published by: American Society for Microbiology, 1752 N St, N W, Washington, DC 20036-2904. TEL 202-942-9319, 202-737-3600, FAX 202-942-9355, djordan@asmusa.org, asmjournals@asm.org, subscriptions@asmusa.org, http://aem.asm.org/, http://www.asm.org. Ed. L. Nicholson Ornston. Circ: 12,658 (paid). **Subscr. to:** PO Box 11127, Birmingham, AL 35201-1127. TEL 205-995-1567, 800-633-4931, FAX 205-995-1588.

➤ **APPLIED BIOCHEMISTRY AND MICROBIOLOGY.** see *BIOLOGY—Biochemistry*

➤ **APPLIED MICROBIOLOGY AND BIOTECHNOLOGY.** see *BIOLOGY—Biotechnology*

579.2 USA ISSN 1041-245X
CODEN: AVREEC
➤ **APPLIED VIROLOGY RESEARCH.** Text in English. 1988. irreg., latest vol.3, 1994. USD 214 per vol. vol.3 (effective 2005). back issues avail. **Document type:** *Monographic series, Academic/Scholarly.*
Indexed: BIOSIS Prev.
—BLDSC (1580.113200), CISTI, KNAW. **CCC.**
Published by: Springer-Verlag New York, Inc. (Subsidiary of: Springer Science+Business Media), 233 Spring St, New York, NY 10013. TEL 212-460-1500, FAX 212-460-1575, service@springer-ny.com, http://www.springer-ny.com. Eds. E Kurstak, R G Marusyk. **Dist. by:** Journal Fulfillment, PO Box 2485, Secaucus, NJ 07096-2485.

579 DEU ISSN 0948-3055
QR106 CODEN: MMFWE7
➤ **AQUATIC MICROBIAL ECOLOGY.** Text in English. 1985. 12/yr. (in 4 vols., 3 nos./vol.). EUR 760 combined subscription domestic for print & online eds.; EUR 770 combined subscription foreign for print & online eds. (effective 2006). bk.rev. back issues avail. **Document type:** *Journal, Academic/Scholarly.* **Description:** Presents original papers, short notes and reviews on basic and applied research devoted to aquatic microbial ecology.
Formerly (until 1995): Marine Microbial Food Webs (0297-8148)
Related titles: ♦ Online - full text ed.: Aquatic Microbial Ecology Online. ISSN 1616-1564.
Indexed: ASCA, ASFA, AnBrAb, ApEcolAb, BIOBASE, BIOSIS Prev, BioCN&I, BiolAb, CurCont, ESPM, ForAb, HGA, HerbAb, I&DA, ISR, IndVet, MBA, NemAb, OceAb, ProtozoAb, S&F, SCI, VetBull, WeedAb, ZooRec.
—BLDSC (1582.395000), CASDDS, CISTI, IE, ingenta, Linda Hall. **CCC.**
Published by: Inter-Research, Nordbuente 23, Oldendorf, 21385, Germany. TEL 49-4132-7127, FAX 49-4132-8883, ir@int-res.com, http://www.int-res.com/journals/ame/index.html. Ed. Fereidoun Rassoulzadegan.

579 DEU ISSN 1616-1564
➤ **AQUATIC MICROBIAL ECOLOGY ONLINE.** Text in English. 9/yr. EUR 600 (effective 2006). **Document type:** *Academic/Scholarly.*
Media: Online - full text (from EBSCO Publishing). **Related titles:** ♦ Print ed.: Aquatic Microbial Ecology. ISSN 0948-3055.
Published by: Inter-Research, Nordbuente 23, Oldendorf, 21385, Germany. TEL 49-4132-7127, FAX 49-4132-8883, webmaster@int-res.com, ir@int-res.com, http://www.int-res.com/journals/ame/index.html.

579 CAN ISSN 1472-3646
QR82.A69 CODEN: ARCHCI
➤ **ARCHAEA**; an international microbiological journal. Text in English. 2002. 6/yr. CND 434 domestic; USD 358 foreign (effective 2006); includes online access. bk.rev. 72 p./no.; back issues avail.; reprints avail. **Document type:** *Journal, Academic/Scholarly.* **Description:** Provides publication of articles dealing with any aspect of research on the Archaea, including biotechnology, environmental adaptation, enzymology, genetics, metabolism, molecular biology, phylogeny, and ultrastructure.
Related titles: Online - full content ed.: ISSN 1472-3654; Online - full text ed.: (from EBSCO Publishing).
Indexed: BIOSIS Prev, BiolAb, ChemAb.
—BLDSC (1594.517000), IE, ingenta.
Published by: Heron Publishing, 202-3994 Shelbourne St, Victoria, BC V8N 3E2, Canada. TEL 250-721-9921, FAX 250-721-9924, publisher@heronpublishing.com, http://archaea.ws, http://heronpublishing.com. Ed. Carl R Woese. Adv. contact Alfred Burdett.

579 DEU ISSN 0302-8933
QR1 CODEN: AMICCW
➤ **ARCHIVES OF MICROBIOLOGY.** Text in English. 1939. m. EUR 2,898 combined subscription to institutions print & online eds. (effective 2005). adv. bibl.; charts; illus. index. back issues avail.; reprint service avail. from ISI. **Document type:** *Journal, Academic/Scholarly.* **Description:** Publishes papers on all areas of basic research in microbiology using biochemical, genetic, microbiological, molecular biological, physiological or physical methods, or combinations thereof.
Formerly: Archiv fuer Mikrobiologie (0003-9276)
Related titles: Microform ed.: (from PQC); Online - full text ed.: ISSN 1432-072X (from EBSCO Publishing, Springer LINK, Swets Information Services).
Indexed: AEA, ASCA, ASFA, AbHyg, AgBio, Agr, AgrForAb, BCI, BIOBASE, BIOSIS Prev, BibAg, BioCN&I, BioDAb, BiolAb, CBTA, CEABA, CIN, ChemAb, ChemTitl, CurCont, DBA, DSA, DentInd, ESPM, ExcerpMed, FCA, FPA, FS&TA, ForAb, GenetAb, HortAb, I&DA, IABS, ISR, IndMed, IndVet, Inpharma, MBA, MEDLINE, MS&D, MaizeAb, NemAb, NutrAb, PBA, PE&ON, PGrRegA, PN&I, PoultAb, ProtozoAb, RA&MP, RM&VM, RPP, Reac, RefZh, S&F, SCI, SFA, SIA, SWRA, SoyAb, TDB, TriticAb, VITIS, VetBull, VirolAbstr, WeedAb.
—BLDSC (1637.940000), CASDDS, CISTI, GNLM, IDS, IE, Infotrieve, ingenta, Linda Hall. **CCC.**
Published by: Springer-Verlag (Subsidiary of: Springer Science+Business Media), Tiergartenstr 17, Heidelberg, 69121, Germany. TEL 49-6221-3450, FAX 49-6221-345229, http://link.springer.de/link/service/journals/00203/index.htm. Eds. Bernhard Schink, Erhard Bremer, Michael T Madigan, Robert K Poole. Adv. contact Stephan Kroeck TEL 49-30-827875739. **Subscr. in the Americas to:** Springer-Verlag New York, Inc., Journal Fulfillment, PO Box 2485, Secaucus, NJ 07096-2485. TEL 800-777-4643, 201-348-4033, FAX 201-348-4505, journals@springer-ny.com, http://www.springer-ny.com; **Subscr. to:** Springer GmbH Auslieferungsgesellschaft, Haberstr 7, Heidelberg 69126, Germany. TEL 49-6221-345-0, FAX 49-6221-345-4229, subscriptions@springer.de.

579.2 AUT ISSN 0304-8608
QR360 CODEN: ARVIDF
➤ **ARCHIVES OF VIROLOGY.** Text in English. 1939. m. EUR 2,498 combined subscription to institutions print & online eds. (effective 2005). adv. charts; illus. index. reprint service avail. from ISI. **Document type:** *Journal, Academic/Scholarly.* **Description:** Publishes original contributions from all branches of research on viruses, virus-like agents, and virus infections of humans, animals, plants, insects, and bacteria.
Formerly: Archiv fuer die Gesamte Virusforschung (0003-9012)
Related titles: Microform ed.: (from PQC); Online - full text ed.: ISSN 1432-8798 (from EBSCO Publishing, ProQuest Information & Learning, Springer LINK, Swets Information Services); ♦ Supplement(s): Archives of Virology. Supplementum. ISSN 0939-1983.
Indexed: AIDS Ab, AIDS&CR, ASCA, ASFA, AbHyg, AgBio, Agr, AgrForAb, AnBrAb, B&BAb, BIOBASE, BIOSIS Prev, BibAg, BioCN&I, BiolAb, CIN, CPA, ChemAb, ChemTitl, CurCont, DBA, DSA, DentInd, ExcerpMed, FCA, FS&TA, ForAb, GenetAb, HGA, HelmAb, HerbAb, HortAb, IABS, INIS AtomInd, ISR, IndMed, IndVet, Inpharma, MEDLINE, MS&D, MaizeAb, NSCI, NucAcAb, NutrAb, OrnHort, PBA, PE&ON, PGegResA, PN&I, PotatoAb, PoultAb, ProtozoAb, RA&MP, RDA, RM&VM, RPP, Reac, RefZh, RevApplEntom, RiceAb, SAA, SCI, SFA, SIA, SoyAb, TDB, TriticAb, VITIS, VetBull, VirolAbstr, WeedAb, WildRev, ZooRec.
—BLDSC (1643.600000), CASDDS, CISTI, GNLM, IDS, IE, Infotrieve, ingenta. **CCC.**
Published by: Springer-Verlag Wien (Subsidiary of: Springer Science+Business Media) journals@springer.at, http://www.springer.at/archvirol. Ed. M H V Van Regenmortel. R&P Angela Foessl TEL 43-1-3302415517. Adv. contact Michael Katzenberger TEL 43-1-3302415220. B&W page EUR 1,000; 170 x 250. **Subscr. in the Americas to:** Springer-Verlag New York, Inc., Journal Fulfillment, PO Box 2485, Secaucus, NJ 07096-2485. TEL 800-777-4643, 201-348-4033, FAX 201-348-4505, journals@springer-ny.com, http://www.springer-ny.com.

579.2 AUT ISSN 0939-1983
CODEN: AVISE9
➤ **ARCHIVES OF VIROLOGY. SUPPLEMENTUM.** Text in English. 1991. irreg., latest vol.17, 2001. price varies. adv. abstr. reprints avail. **Document type:** *Monographic series, Academic/Scholarly.* **Description:** Publishes original papers from all branches of research on viruses, virus-like agents, and virus infections of humans, animals, plants, insects and bacteria.
Related titles: ♦ Supplement to: Archives of Virology. ISSN 0304-8608.
Indexed: Agr, BIOSIS Prev, BiolAb, IndMed, IndVet, MEDLINE, NutrAb, PN&I, PoultAb, VetBull.
—BLDSC (1643.610000), CASDDS, CISTI, IE, Infotrieve, ingenta. **CCC.**
Published by: Springer-Verlag Wien (Subsidiary of: Springer Science+Business Media) TEL 43-1-3302415-0, FAX 43-1-330242665, books@springer.at, http://www.springer.at/archvirol. R&P Angela Foessl TEL 43-1-3302415517. Adv. contact Michael Katzenberger TEL 43-1-3302415220. B&W page EUR 1,000; 170 x 250. **Subscr. in N. America to:** Springer-Verlag New York, Inc., Journal Fulfillment, PO Box 2485, Secaucus, NJ 07096-2485. TEL 800-777-4643, 201-348-4033, FAX 201-348-4505, orders@springer-ny.com.

B

➤ **ARCHIVUM IMMUNOLOGIAE ET THERAPIAE EXPERIMENTALIS.** see *MEDICAL SCIENCES—Allergology And Immunology*

579 614.7 IND ISSN 0972-3005
ASIAN JOURNAL OF MICROBIOLOGY, BIOTECHNOLOGY AND ENVIRONMENTAL SCIENCE. Text in English. q. USD 60 to individuals; USD 170 to institutions (effective 2006).
Indexed: AEBA, ASFA, BIOBASE, ESPM, ExcerpMed, M&PBA, SWRA, ToxAb, WRCInf.
—BLDSC (1742.502000), IE.
Published by: Scientific Publishers, 5-A New Pali Rd., Near Hotel Taj Hari Mahal, PO Box 91, Jodhpur, Rajasthan 342 003, India. TEL 91-291-2433323, FAX 91-291-2512580, info@scientificpub.com, http://www.scientificpub.com.

AUSTRALIAN MYCOTOXIN NEWSLETTER. see *AGRICULTURE—Dairying And Dairy Products*

579 EGY ISSN 1110-1601
AL AZHAR JOURNAL OF MICROBIOLOGY. Text in English. 1987. q. **Document type:** *Journal, Academic/Scholarly.*
—BLDSC (0786.276780).
Published by: Al-Azhar University, Faculty of Pharmacy, Department of Microbiology, Boys, Nasr City, Cairo, Egypt. TEL 20-2-2633050, http://derp.sti.sci.eg/data/0244.htm. Ed. Dr. Muhammad Saif-El-Din Ashour.

B B A - MOLECULAR CELL RESEARCH. see *BIOLOGY—Cytology And Histology*

B M C CLINICAL PATHOLOGY. (BioMed Central) see *MEDICAL SCIENCES—Hematology*

579 GBR ISSN 1471-2180
QR1 CODEN: BMMIBC
➤ **B M C MICROBIOLOGY.** (BioMed Central) Text in English. 2001. m. free (effective 2006). adv. **Document type:** *Journal, Academic/Scholarly.* **Description:** Publishes original research articles in analytical and functional studies of prokaryotic and eukaryotic microorganisms, viruses and small parasites, as well as host and therapeutic responses to them.
Media: Online - full content (from EBSCO Publishing, National Library of Medicine).
Indexed: BIOSIS Prev, BiolAb, ExcerpMed, MEDLINE.
—Infotrieve. **CCC.**
Published by: BioMed Central Ltd. (Subsidiary of: Current Science Ltd), Middlesex House, 34-42 Cleveland St, London, W1T 4LB, United Kingdom. TEL 44-20-76319131, FAX 44-20-76319923, info@biomedcentral.com, http://www.biomedcentral.com/bmcmicrobiol/. Ed. Peter Newmark. Adv. contact Deborah Cockerill.

579.3 ROM ISSN 1220-3696
CODEN: PDNEEV
➤ **BACTERIOLOGIA, VIRUSOLOGIA, PARAZITOLOGIA, EPIDEMIOLOGIA.** Text in Romanian; Summaries in English, French. 1956. 4/yr., latest vol.46, 2001. ROL 600,000 domestic; USD 80 foreign; USD 20 per issue (effective 2001). adv. bk.rev. abstr.; bibl.; charts; illus. Index. back issues avail. **Document type:** *Journal, Academic/Scholarly.*
Former titles (until 1990): Revista de Igiena, Bacteriologie, Virusologie, Parazitologie, Epidemiologie, Pneumoftiziologie: Bacteriologia, Virusologia, Parazitologia, Epidemiologia (0376-4494); (until 1974): Bacteriologie, Virusologie, Parazitologie, Epidemiologie (0301-7338); (until 1973): Microbiologie, Parazitologie, Epidemiologie (0026-2609); (until 1957): Revista de Microbiologie, Parazitologie, Epidemiologie (1220-0956)
Indexed: BiolAb, ChemAb, ExcerpMed, IndMed, IndVet, MEDLINE, NutrAb, PN&I, PoultAb, ProtozoAb, TDB, VetBull.
—BLDSC (1854.950000), CASDDS, CISTI, GNLM, IE, Infotrieve, ingenta.
Published by: Romanian Medical Association, Str. Ionel Perlea Nr.10, Bucharest, 70754, Romania. TEL 401-3141062, FAX 401-4115672. Pub., R&P Marian Negut. Circ: 200 (paid and controlled). **Subscr. to:** ILEXIM, Str. 13 Decembrie 3, PO Box 136-137, Bucharest 70116, Romania.

579.3 USA
➤ **BERGEY'S MANUAL OF DETERMINATIVE BACTERIOLOGY.** Text in English. a. USD 85 (effective 2004). **Document type:** *Monographic series, Academic/Scholarly.*
Published by: Lippincott Williams & Wilkins (Subsidiary of: Wolters Kluwer N.V.), 530 Walnut St, Philadelphia, PA 19106-3621. TEL 215-521-8300, FAX 215-521-8902, http://www.lww.com.

578.65 PER ISSN 1026-2911
➤ **BIOCONTROL.** Text in English, Spanish. 1995. s-a. USD 30 to individuals; USD 130 to institutions. adv. **Document type:** *Monographic series, Academic/Scholarly.*
Related titles: Online - full text ed.
Indexed: AEBA, ASFA, ESPM.
Published by: Centro Internacional para el Control Biologico de Plagas y Patogenos/International Center for the Biological Control of Pests and Pathogens, Apdo Postal 18 1057, Miraflores, Lima 18, Peru. TEL 51-14-792291, FAX 51-14-792291, bioc@amauta.rcp.net.pe. Ed. Hernan Rincon. R&P, Adv. contact Parviz Jatala. Circ: 500 (paid).

➤ **BIOFORUM**; Forschung & Entwicklung. see *BIOLOGY*

➤ **BIOLOGICAL CHEMISTRY**; official scientific journal of the GBM. see *BIOLOGY—Biochemistry*

▼ ➤ **BIOMAGNETIC RESEARCH AND TECHNOLOGY.** see *BIOLOGY—Biochemistry*

➤ **BIOPOLIMERY I KLETKA/BIOPOLYMERS AND CELL.** see *BIOLOGY—Genetics*

579 572 USA ISSN 1064-251X
BIOPROBES. Text in English. 1985. 3/yr.
Related titles: Online - full content ed.
—BLDSC (2089.474160), IE, ingenta.
Published by: Molecular Probes, Inc., 29851 Willow Creek Rd, P.O. Box 22010, Eugene, OR 97402-0469. TEL 541-465-8300, FAX 541-344-6504, bioprobes@probes.com, http://www.molecularprobes.com/lit/bioprobes.html.

579 JPN ISSN 0915-2733
BISEIBUTSU IDEN SHIGEN HAIFU MOKUROKU/CATALOGUE OF MICROORGANISMS. Text in Japanese. 1989. a. **Document type:** *Catalog.*
Published by: Norin Suisansho, Nogyo Seibutsu Shigen Kenkyujo/Ministry of Agriculture, Forestry and Fisheries, National Institute of Agrobiological Resources, 2-1-2 Kannondai, Tsukuba-shi, Ibaraki-ken 305-0856, Japan.

579 JPN ISSN 0915-2830
BISEIBUTSU IDEN SHIGEN TANSAKU SHUSHU CHOSA HOKOKUSHO/REPORTS ON COLLECTION OF MICROBIAL GENETIC RESOURCES. Text in Japanese. 1987. a.
Published by: Norin Suisansho, Nogyo Seibutsu Shigen Kenkyujo/Ministry of Agriculture, Forestry and Fisheries, National Institute of Agrobiological Resources, 2-1-2 Kannondai, Tsukuba-shi, Ibaraki-ken 305-0856, Japan.

BISEIBUTSU KAGAKU BUNRUI KENKYUKAI KOEN YOSHISHU/ABSTRACTS OF ANNUAL MEETING ON MICROBIAL CHEMOTAXONOMY. see *BIOLOGY—Abstracting, Bibliographies, Statistics*

579 JPN
BISEIBUTSU NO SEITAI/MICROBIAL ECOLOGY. Text in Japanese. 1974. a. JPY 4,000 per issue.
Published by: (Nihon Biseibutsu Seitai Gakkai/Japanese Society of Microbial Ecology), Gakkai Shuppan Senta/Japan Scientific Societies Press, 6-2-10 Hongo Bunkyoku, Tokyo, 113-0033, Japan.

579.3 JPN ISSN 0385-5201
RM409 CODEN: BOBODP
BOKIN BOBAI/JOURNAL OF ANTIBACTERIAL AND ANTIFUNGAL AGENTS. Text in Japanese; Summaries in English. 1973. m. subscr. incld. with membership. adv. **Document type:** *Journal, Academic/Scholarly.*
Indexed: CIN, ChemAb, ChemTitl, ExcerpMed, FCA, FS&TA, INIS AtomInd.
—CASDDS, GNLM, IE, ingenta. **CCC.**
Published by: Nihon Bokin Bobai Gakkai/Society for Antibacterial and Antifungal Agents, Japan, 9th Fl, Shin-Kousan Bldg, 1-13-38, Nishimotocho, Nishi-ku, Osaka-shi, 550-0005, Japan. TEL 81-6-65382166, FAX 81-6-65382169, yama28@nifty.com, boukin@nifty.com, http://wwwsoc.nii.ac.jp/saaaj/.

579 ITA ISSN 0394-9877
CODEN: BMILE4
BOLLETTINO DI MICROBIOLOGIA ED INDAGINI DI LABORATORIO. Text in Italian. 1981. q. adv. bk.rev. index.
Published by: Sirse Srl, Via Confu 51, Brescia, BS 25124, Italy. TEL 39-03-0221522, info@sirse.com. Ed. Dr. A Turano. Circ: 2,000.

579 BRA ISSN 1517-8382
QR6 CODEN: BJMRAH
➤ **BRAZILIAN JOURNAL OF MICROBIOLOGY.** Text in Multiple languages. 1970. q. free to members; BRL 55 per issue to non-members (effective 2005). adv. bk.rev. index. back issues avail.; reprint service avail. from ISI. **Document type:** *Academic/Scholarly.* **Description:** Publishes original research papers, research notes, and reviews, covering all aspects of microbiology.
Formerly (until 2000): Revista de Microbiologia (0001-3714)
Related titles: Online - full text ed.: ISSN 1678-4405. free (effective 2005) (from SciELO).
Indexed: ASCA, ASFA, AbHyg, AgBio, BIOBASE, BIOSIS Prev, BioCN&I, BiolAb, ChemAb, ChemTitl, CurCont, DSA, ESPM, ExcerpMed, FCA, FPA, FS&TA, ForAb, HortAb, I&DA, IABS, IndMed, IndVet, MBA, MaizeAb, NutrAb, PBA, PGegResA, PHN&I, PN&I, PoultAb, RM&VM, RPP, RefZh, RevApplEntom, S&F, SIA, TDB, VetBull, VirolAbstr, ZooRec.
—BLDSC (2277.419520), CASDDS, CISTI, GNLM, IDS, IE, ingenta, KNAW.
Published by: Sociedade Brasileira de Microbiologia/Brazilian Society for Microbiology, Instituto de Microbiologia - UFRJ, CCS - Bloco I - Ilha do Fundao, Rio de Janeiro, RJ 21590-900, Brazil. revmicro@icb.usp.br, imadsbm@microbio.ufrj.br, http://www.doaj.org/goto/www.scielo.br/bjm, http://www.biologia.ufrj.br/sociedades/sbm. Eds. Benedito Correa, Bernadette D G M Franco. Pub., Adv. contact Bernadette Franco. Circ: 1,500.

579.65 GBR ISSN 0068-2497
BRITISH SOCIETY FOR PARASITOLOGY. SYMPOSIA. Text in English. 1963. a. Included as a supplement to Parasitology, with the subscription.
—CISTI.
Published by: Cambridge University Press, The Edinburgh Bldg, Shaftesbury Rd, Cambridge, CB2 2RU, United Kingdom. TEL 44-1223-312393, FAX 44-1223-315052, http://uk.cambridge.org/journals/journal_catalogue.asp?historylinks=ALPHA&mnemonic=PAR.

C A SELECTS. ANTIFUNGAL & ANTIMYCOTIC AGENTS. see *BIOLOGY—Abstracting, Bibliographies, Statistics*

579 610 GBR ISSN 1464-2506
C P D BULLETIN. CELLULAR PATHOLOGY. (Continuing Professional Development) Text in English. 1998. 3/yr. GBP 45 domestic to individuals; GBP 60 foreign to individuals; GBP 60 domestic to institutions; GBP 90 foreign to institutions (effective 2004). **Document type:** *Bulletin, Academic/Scholarly.*
Indexed: ExcerpMed.
—**CCC.**
Published by: Rila Publications Ltd., 73 Newman St, London, W1A 4PG, United Kingdom. TEL 44-20-76311299, FAX 44-20-75807166, http://www.rila.co.uk.

C S A VIROLOGY AND AIDS ABSTRACTS. (Cambridge Scientific Abstracts) see *BIOLOGY—Abstracting, Bibliographies, Statistics*

579 CAN ISSN 0008-4166
QR1 CODEN: CJMIAZ
➤ **CANADIAN JOURNAL OF MICROBIOLOGY/JOURNAL CANADIEN DE MICROBIOLOGIE.** Text mainly in English; Text occasionally in French. 1954. m. CND 151 domestic to individuals; USD 151 foreign to individuals; CND 422 domestic to institutions; USD 422 foreign to institutions (effective 1999). adv. bibl.; illus. index. back issues avail.; reprint service avail. from PQC. **Document type:** *Academic/Scholarly.*
Related titles: Microfiche ed.: (from MML); Microform ed.: (from MML, PMC, PQC); Online - full text ed.: ISSN 1480-3275 (from bigchalk, EBSCO Publishing, Gale Group, IngentaConnect, Micromedia ProQuest, O C L C Online Computer Library Center, Inc., ProQuest Information & Learning, Swets Information Services).
Indexed: ABIPC, ASCA, ASFA, AbHyg, AgBio, Agr, AgrForAb, B&AI, BIOBASE, BIOSIS Prev, BibAg, BioCN&I, BioDAb, BiolAb, CBCARef, CBTA, CEABA, CIN, CPA, ChemAb, ChemTitl, CurCont, DBA, DSA, DentInd, ESPM, EngInd, EnvAb, EnvEAb, ExcerpMed, FCA, FPA, FS&TA, ForAb, GEOBASE, GenetAb, HerbAb, HortAb, I&DA, IAA, IABS, ISR, IndMed, IndVet, Inpharma, JDDR, MBA, MEDLINE, MaizeAb, NPU, NemAb, NutrAb, OrnHort, PBA, PE&ON, PGegResA, PGrRegA, PHN&I, PN&I, PollutAb, PotatoAb, PoultAb, ProtozoAb, RA&MP, RM&VM, RPP, Reac, RefZh, RevApplEntom, RiceAb, S&F, SAA, SCI, SFA, SIA, SWRA, SeedAb, SoyAb, TDB, TOSA, Telegen, TriticAb, VITIS, VetBull, VirolAbstr, WTA, WeedAb.
—BLDSC (3033.000000), CASDDS, CISTI, GNLM, IDS, IE, Infotrieve, ingenta, Linda Hall. **CCC.**
Published by: N R C Research Press, Building M 55, Ottawa, ON K1A 0R6, Canada. TEL 613-993-0362, 800-668-1222, FAX 613-952-7656, pubs@nrc-cnrc.gc.ca, http://pubs.nrc-cnrc.gc.ca/cgi-bin/rp/rp2_desc_e?cjm. Ed. Bruce P Dancik. Adv. contact Judy Heyman. B&W page CND 675; trim 11 x 8.5. Circ: 1,341.

➤ **CELLULAR MICROBIOLOGY.** see *BIOLOGY—Cytology And Histology*

➤ **CELLULAR MICROBIOLOGY ONLINE.** see *BIOLOGY—Cytology And Histology*

579 CZE ISSN 0009-0646
CESKOSLOVENSKA SPOLECNOST MIKROBIOLOGICKA. BULLETIN. Text in Czech. 1960. q. membership. bk.rev. bibl.; charts; stat. **Document type:** *Bulletin.*
Published by: Ceskoslovenska Spolecnost Mikrobiologicka, Videnska 1083, Prague, 14220, Czech Republic. TEL 42-2-4752494, FAX 42-2-4713221. Ed. C John. adv.: page CZK 10,000. Circ: 1,150.

579 JPN ISSN 0914-8221
QR245
CHIBA DAIGAKU SHINKAKU BISEIBUTSU KENKYU SENTA HOKOKU/CHIBA UNIVERSITY. RESEARCH CENTER FOR PATHOGENIC FUNGI AND MICROBIAL TOXICOSES. ANNUAL REPORT. Text in Japanese. 1987. a.
—BLDSC (1407.630000).
Published by: Chiba Daigaku, Shinkaku Biseibutsu Kenkyu Senta/Chiba University. Research Center for Pathogenic Fungi and Microbial Toxicoses, 8-1 Inohana 1-chome, Chuo-ku, Chiba-shi, 260-0856, Japan.

CHIBA UNIVERSITY. RESEARCH CENTER FOR PATHOGENIC FUNGI AND MICROBIAL TOXICOSES. PROCEEDINGS OF THE INTERNATIONAL SYMPOSIUM. see *BIOLOGY—Botany*

CLINICAL AND VACCINE IMMUNOLOGY. see *MEDICAL SCIENCES—Allergology And Immunology*

B

CLINICAL MICROBIOLOGY AND INFECTION. see *MEDICAL SCIENCES*

579   USA   ISSN 0196-4399
                              CODEN: CMNEEJ
CLINICAL MICROBIOLOGY NEWSLETTER. Text in English. 1983. 24/yr. USD 75 to individuals; USD 68 in United States to individuals; USD 449 to institutions; USD 449 in United States to institutions (effective 2006). adv. back issues avail. **Document type:** *Newsletter, Academic/Scholarly.* **Description:** For clinical microbiologists, clinical pathologists, laboratory technologists and technicians.
Related titles: Microform ed.: (from PQC); Online - full text ed.: (from EBSCO Publishing, Gale Group, IngentaConnect, ScienceDirect, Swets Information Services).
Indexed: AbHyg, AgBio, BIOSIS Prev, ESPM, ExcerpMed, H&SSA, HelmAb, IndVet, JDDR, MBA, NutrAb, PN&I, PoultAb, ProtozoAb, RA&MP, RM&VM, RevApplEntom, TDB, VetBull, VirolAbstr.
—BLDSC (3286.305600), GNLM, IE, Infotrieve, KNAW. **CCC.**
Published by: Elsevier Inc. (Subsidiary of: Elsevier Science & Technology), 360 Park Ave. S, New York, NY 10010-1710. TEL 212-633-3730, 888-437-4636, FAX 212-633-3820, jmanley@elsevier.com, usinfo-f@elsevier.com, http://www.elsevier.com/locate/clinmicnews. Eds. Betty Forbes, Dr. Mary Jane Ferraro, Dr. Paul A. Granato. adv.: B&W page USD 985, color page USD 1,175.

579   USA   ISSN 0893-8512
QR67   CODEN: CMIREX
➤ **CLINICAL MICROBIOLOGY REVIEWS.** Text in English. 1988. q. USD 410 domestic to institutions; USD 414 in Canada to institutions; USD 419 in Europe to institutions; USD 422 in Latin America to institutions; USD 423 elsewhere to institutions (effective 2006). adv. illus. index. back issues avail.; reprint service avail. from PQC. **Document type:** *Academic/Scholarly.* **Description:** Addresses reviews on all aspects of clinical and medical microbiology, including immunology.
Related titles: CD-ROM ed.; Microform ed.: (from PQC); Online - full text ed.: ISSN 1098-6618. USD 407 to institutions (effective 2006) (from EBSCO Publishing, HighWire Press, National Library of Medicine).
Indexed: ASCA, AbHyg, AgBio, BIOBASE, BIOSIS Prev, BioDAb, BiolAb, CIN, ChemAb, ChemTitl, CurCont, DSA, ESPM, ExcerpMed, FS&TA, GenetAb, H&SSA, HelmAb, HortAb, IABS, ISR, IndMed, IndVet, Inpharma, JDDR, MBA, MEDLINE, NutrAb, PE&ON, PN&I, PoultAb, ProtozoAb, RM&VM, RRTA, Reac, RevApplEntom, SCI, TDB, VetBull, VirolAbstr.
—BLDSC (3286.305650), CASDDS, CISTI, GNLM, IDS, IE, ingenta, KNAW. **CCC.**
Published by: American Society for Microbiology, 1752 N St, N W, Washington, DC 20036-2904. TEL 202-942-9319, FAX 202-942-9347, asmjournals@asm.org, subscriptions@asmusa.org, http://cmr.asm.org/, http://www.asm.org. Ed. Betty A Forbes. Circ: 9,200. **Subscr. to:** PO Box 11127, Birmingham, AL 35201-1127. TEL 205-995-1567, 800-633-4931, FAX 205-995-1588.

579   GBR   ISSN 1462-1843
RA643
➤ **COMMUNICABLE DISEASE AND PUBLIC HEALTH.** Text in English. 1998. q. GBP 102 domestic; GBP 128 foreign (effective 2003). bk.rev. 2 cols./p.; back issues avail. **Document type:** *Journal, Academic/Scholarly.* **Description:** Aims to meet the needs of a wide range of readers who share concern in the management, prevention, and control of communicable diseases.
Formed by the merger of (1983-1998): P H L S Microbiology Digest (0265-3400); (1967-1998): Communicable Disease Report Review (1350-9349); Which superseded in part (in 1991): Communicable Disease Report. Weekly Edition (0144-3186)
Indexed: AEA, AbHyg, DSA, FS&TA, INI, IndMed, IndVet, MEDLINE, NutrAb, PBA, PHN&I, PN&I, PoultAb, ProtozoAb, RA&MP, RDA, RRTA, RiceAb, SAA, SIA, SoyAb, TDB, VetBull, WAE&RSA.
—BLDSC (3341.341900), CISTI, GNLM, IE, ingenta. **CCC.**
Published by: Health Protection Agency, 61 Colindale Ave, London, NW9 5EQ, United Kingdom. TEL 44-20-82006868, FAX 44-20-82007868, lynn.bacon@hpa.org.uk, http://www.phls.co.uk/publications/cdph/index.html. Adv. contact Lynn Bacon. Circ: 2,000.

579   GBR   ISSN 0147-9571
R5   CODEN: CIMIDV
➤ **COMPARATIVE IMMUNOLOGY, MICROBIOLOGY & INFECTIOUS DISEASES.** Text in English. 1978. 6/yr. EUR 843 in Europe to institutions; JPY 111,800 in Japan to institutions; USD 944 elsewhere to institutions (effective 2006). adv. index. **Document type:** *Academic/Scholarly.* **Description:** Provides a forum for physicians and veterinarians specializing in immunology, immunopathology, microbiology and infectious diseases in both humans and animals.
Related titles: Microfilm ed.: (from PQC); Online - full text ed.: (from EBSCO Publishing, Gale Group, IngentaConnect, ScienceDirect, Swets Information Services).

Indexed: AIDS&CR, ASCA, ASFA, AbHyg, AgBio, Agr, AnBrAb, BIOBASE, BIOSIS Prev, BiolAb, CurCont, DBA, DSA, ESPM, ExcerpMed, FoVS&M, HelmAb, IABS, ISR, ImmunAb, IndMed, IndVet, MBA, MEDLINE, NutrAb, PN&I, PoultAb, ProtozoAb, RA&MP, RM&VM, RefZh, RevApplEntom, SCI, TDB, VetBull, VirolAbstr, WAE&RSA, WildRev, ZooRec.
—BLDSC (3363.782600), CISTI, GNLM, IDS, IE, Infotrieve, ingenta, KNAW. **CCC.**
Published by: Pergamon (Subsidiary of: Elsevier Science & Technology), The Boulevard, Langford Ln, East Park, Kidlington, Oxford OX5 1GB, United Kingdom. TEL 44-1865-843000, FAX 44-1865-843010, http://www.elsevier.com/locate/cimid. Eds. B. I. Osburn, Charles Pilet, K. Yamanouchi. Circ: 1,000. **Subscr. to:** Elsevier BV, PO Box 211, Amsterdam 1000 AE, Netherlands. TEL 31-20-485-3757, FAX 31-20-485-3432, nlinfo-f@elsevier.nl, http://www.elsevier.nl.

579   CHE   ISSN 1420-9519
QR1   CODEN: CMICFN
➤ **CONTRIBUTIONS TO MICROBIOLOGY.** Text in English. 1998. irreg., latest vol.12, 2005. price varies. reprint service avail. from ISI. **Document type:** *Monographic series, Academic/Scholarly.* **Description:** Provides a comprehensive, up-to-date review of prions and prion-associated diseases.
Formed by the merger of (1985-1998): Concepts in Immunopathology (0255-7983); (1973-1998): Contributions to Microbiology and Immunology (0301-3081); Which was formerly (1960-1973): Bibliotheca Microbiologia (0067-8058)
Indexed: Agr, BIOSIS Prev, BiolAb, CIN, ChemAb, ChemTitl, CurCont, IndMed, IndVet, MEDLINE, ProtozoAb, VetBull.
—BLDSC (3458.830000), CASDDS, CISTI, GNLM, IE, Infotrieve, ingenta, Linda Hall. **CCC.**
Published by: S. Karger AG, Allschwilerstr 10, Basel, 4009, Switzerland. TEL 41-61-3061111, FAX 41-61-3061234, karger@karger.ch, http://www.karger.com/COMII, http://www.karger.ch. Ed. Axel Schmidt.

579   USA   ISSN 1040-841X
QR1   CODEN: CRVMAC
➤ **CRITICAL REVIEWS IN MICROBIOLOGY.** Text in English. 1971. q. USD 777, GBP 471 combined subscription to institutions print & online eds. (effective 2006). bibl.; charts; illus. back issues avail.; reprint service avail. from PSC. **Document type:** *Journal, Academic/Scholarly.* **Description:** Reviews the many diverse fields of microbiology: viruses, rickettsiae, mycoplasmas, bacteria, fungi, algae, and protozoa.
Formerly: C R C Critical Reviews in Microbiology (0045-6454)
Related titles: Online - full text ed.: ISSN 1549-7828. USD 738, GBP 447 to institutions (effective 2006) (from EBSCO Publishing, Gale Group, IngentaConnect, O C L C Online Computer Library Center, Inc., ProQuest Information & Learning, ScienceDirect, Swets Information Services).
Indexed: ASCA, ASFA, AbHyg, AgBio, Agr, BIOBASE, BIOSIS Prev, BiolAb, BrCerAb, C&ISA, CBTA, CIN, CerAb, ChemAb, ChemTitl, CorrAb, CurCont, DBA, E&CAJ, EMA, EPB, ESPM, ExcerpMed, FS&TA, GenetAb, HelmAb, IAA, IABS, ISR, IndMed, IndVet, Inpharma, M&TEA, MBA, MBF, MEDLINE, METADEX, NRN, NutrAb, PE&ON, ProtozoAb, RM&VM, RPP, Reac, RevApplEntom, S&F, SCI, Telegen, VITIS, VetBull, VirolAbstr, WAA, WeedAb, ZooRec.
—BLDSC (3487.478000), CASDDS, CISTI, GNLM, IDS, IE, Infotrieve, ingenta, Linda Hall. **CCC.**
Published by: Taylor & Francis Inc. (Subsidiary of: Taylor & Francis Group), 325 Chestnut St, Ste 800, Philadelphia, PA 19016. TEL 215-625-8900, 800-354-1420, FAX 215-625-2940, info@taylorandfrancis.com, http://www.tandf.co.uk/journals/titles/1040841x.asp, http://www.taylorandfrancis.com. Ed. Ronald M Atlas. Circ: 620. **Subscr. outside N. America to:** Taylor & Francis Ltd, Journals Customer Service, Rankine Rd, Basingstoke, Hants RG24 8PR, United Kingdom. TEL 44-1256-813000, FAX 44-1256-330245, enquiry@tandf.co.uk.

579   GBR   ISSN 0965-0989
CULTURE (BASINGSTOKE). Text in English. 1978. s-a. free (effective 2004). **Document type:** *Journal.* **Description:** Provides and international publishing forum for papers on microbiology.
Media: Online - full content.
Published by: (Oxoid Limited), Euromed Communications Ltd., The Old Surgery, Liphook Rd, Haslemere, Surrey GU27 1NL, United Kingdom. TEL 44-1428-656665, FAX 44-1428-656643, info@euromed.uk.com, http://www.euromed.uk.com/culturehome.htm.

CURRENT ADVANCES IN APPLIED MICROBIOLOGY & BIOTECHNOLOGY. see *BIOLOGY—Abstracting, Bibliographies, Statistics*

579 616.01   GBR   ISSN 1466-531X
                              CODEN: CIIMFP
➤ **CURRENT ISSUES IN INTESTINAL MICROBIOLOGY.** Text in English. 2000 (Mar.). s-a. GBP 240, USD 480 to institutions (effective 2004). **Document type:** *Journal, Academic/Scholarly.* **Description:** Publishes high-quality review papers in all areas of intestinal microbiology pertaining to human and other animal systems including, microbial ecology, pathogenic organisms, probiotics and prebiotics.
Related titles: Online - full text ed.: Current Issues in Intestinal Microbiology Online. ISSN 1466-5328. 2000. GBP 40, USD 80 to individuals; GBP 80, USD 160 to institutions (effective 2002).

Indexed: AbHyg, AgBio, B&BAb, DSA, ESPM, ExcerpMed, IndVet, NutrAb, PoultAb, SIA, TDB.
—BLDSC (3499.072600), CISTI, IE, Infotrieve, ingenta. **CCC.**
Published by: Horizon Scientific Press, 32 Hewitts Ln, PO Box 1, Wymondham, Norfolk NR18 0EA, United Kingdom. TEL 44-1953-601106, FAX 44-1953-603068, mail@horizonpress.com, orders@horizonpress.com, http://www.ciim.net, http://www.horizonpress.com/. Ed. Gerald W Tannock.

572.8   GBR   ISSN 1467-3037
QH506   CODEN: CMBIF6
➤ **CURRENT ISSUES IN MOLECULAR BIOLOGY.** Text in English. 1998. s-a. USD 480 to institutions (effective 2004). back issues avail. **Document type:** *Journal, Academic/Scholarly.* **Description:** Publishes critical review papers in all areas of molecular microbiology.
Related titles: Online - full content ed.: ISSN 1467-3045. 2002. GBP 40, USD 80 to individuals; GBP 80, USD 160 to institutions (effective 2002).
Indexed: AEBA, AIDS&CR, ASFA, AgBio, AnBrAb, B&BAb, BIOBASE, BIOSIS Prev, DSA, ESPM, ExcerpMed, GenetAb, HortAb, IndVet, M&PBA, NucAcAb, NutrAb, PBA, ProtozoAb, RPP, S&F, VetBull, VirolAbstr, WeedAb.
—BLDSC (3499.075250), CISTI, IE, Infotrieve, ingenta. **CCC.**
Published by: Horizon Scientific Press, 32 Hewitts Ln, PO Box 1, Wymondham, Norfolk NR18 0EA, United Kingdom. TEL 44-1953-601106, FAX 44-1953-603068, mail@horizonpress.com, http://www.horizonpress.com/cimb/.

579   USA   ISSN 0343-8651
QR1   CODEN: CUMIDD
➤ **CURRENT MICROBIOLOGY;** an international journal. Text in English. 1978. m. (in 2 vols., 6 nos./vol.). EUR 928 combined subscription to institutions print & online eds. (effective 2005). adv. illus. back issues avail.; reprint service avail. from ISI. **Document type:** *Journal, Academic/Scholarly.* **Description:** Keeps readers up-to-date in all areas of microbiology, both medical and nonmedical.
Related titles: Microform ed.: (from PQC); Online - full text ed.: ISSN 1432-0991 (from EBSCO Publishing, Springer LINK, Swets Information Services).
Indexed: AEA, ASCA, ASFA, AbHyg, AgBio, Agr, AgrForAb, AnBrAb, BIOBASE, BIOSIS Prev, BioCN&I, BiolAb, CBTA, CEABA, CIN, CPA, ChemAb, ChemTitl, CurCont, DBA, DSA, ESPM, ExcerpMed, FCA, FPA, FS&TA, ForAb, GenetAb, HGA, HelmAb, HerbAb, HortAb, I&DA, ISR, IndMed, IndVet, Inpharma, JDDR, MBA, MEDLINE, MaizeAb, NemAb, NucAcAb, NutrAb, OrnHort, PBA, PE&ON, PGrRegA, PHN&I, PN&I, PotatoAb, PoultAb, ProtozoAb, RA&MP, RM&VM, RPP, Reac, RefZh, RevApplEntom, RiceAb, S&F, SAA, SCI, SFA, SIA, SeedAb, SoyAb, TDB, TriticAb, VITIS, VetBull, VirolAbstr, WeedAb.
—BLDSC (3500.420000), CASDDS, CISTI, GNLM, IDS, IE, Infotrieve, ingenta, Linda Hall. **CCC.**
Published by: Springer-Verlag New York, Inc. (Subsidiary of: Springer Science+Business Media), 233 Spring St, New York, NY 10013. TEL 212-460-1500, 800-777-4643, FAX 212-473-6272, journals@springer-ny.com, http://link.springer.de/link/service/journals/00284/, http://www.springer-ny.com. Ed. Erko Stackebrandt. R&P Ian Gross. Adv. contact Brian Skepton. Circ: 1,000. **Subscr. outside the Americas to:** Springer GmbH Auslieferungsgesellschaft, Haberstr 7, Heidelberg 69126, Germany. TEL 49-6221-345-0, FAX 49-6221-345-4229, subscriptions@springer.de; **Subscr. to:** Journal Fulfillment, PO Box 2485, Secaucus, NJ 07096-2485. TEL 201-348-4033, FAX 201-348-4505.

572.8   NLD   ISSN 1566-5240
                              CODEN: CMMUBP
➤ **CURRENT MOLECULAR MEDICINE.** Text in English. 2001. 8/yr. EUR 1,180, USD 1,180 to institutions (academic), print or online; EUR 2,090, USD 2,090 to corporations print or online; EUR 280, USD 280 combined subscription to individuals print & online; EUR 1,295, USD 1,295 combined subscription to institutions (academic), print & online; EUR 2,500, USD 2,500 combined subscription to corporations print & online (effective 2004). adv. bk.rev. back issues avail. **Document type:** *Journal, Academic/Scholarly.* **Description:** Provides the readership with current and comprehensive reviews on fundamental molecular mechanisms of disease pathogenesis, the development of molecular diagnosis and novel approaches to rational treatment.
Related titles: Online - full text ed.: (from EBSCO Publishing, Gale Group, IngentaConnect, Swets Information Services).
Indexed: B&BAb, BCI, BIOSIS Prev, BioEngAb, CTA, ChemAb, CurCont, ExcerpMed, GenetAb, M&PBA.
—BLDSC (3500.457000), CISTI, IE, Infotrieve, ingenta. **CCC.**
Published by: Bentham Science Publishers Ltd., PO Box 1673, Hilversum, BR 1200, Netherlands. TEL 31-35-6923800, FAX 31-35-6980150, M.Bentham@inter.nl.net, http://www.bentham.org/cmm. Ed. Anil Mukherjee TEL 301-496-7213. **Subscr. addr. in the US:** Bentham Science Publishers Ltd., 1400 Pine St, PO Box 640310, San Francisco, CA 94164-0310. FAX 415-775-4503, shidding@worldonline.nl.

▼ *new title*   ➤ *refereed*   ✳ *unverified*   ◆ *full entry avail.*

B

579 GBR ISSN 1369-5274
QR1 CODEN: COMIF7
➤ **CURRENT OPINION IN MICROBIOLOGY.** Text in English. 1998. 6/yr. EUR 270 in Europe to individuals; JPY 32,800 in Japan to individuals; USD 293 elsewhere to individuals; EUR 1,232 in Europe to institutions; JPY 170,900 in Japan to institutions; USD 1,378 elsewhere to institutions (effective 2006). illus. **Document type:** *Academic/Scholarly.*
Description: Covers developments in the biology of microbes, pathogenic yeast fungi and other micro-organisms. Includes 90 reviews and a guide to significant microbiology papers published within the past year.
Related titles: Online - full text ed.: USD 227 in North America to individuals; USD 247 in North America to individuals with print ed; GBP 137 elsewhere to individuals; GBP 150 elsewhere to individuals with print ed; USD 822 in North America to institutions includes print ed; GBP 500 elsewhere to institutions includes print ed (effective 1999 & 2000) (from EBSCO Publishing, Gale Group, IngentaConnect, ScienceDirect, Swets Information Services).
Indexed: AEA, AIDS&CR, ASFA, AbHyg, AgBio, BIOSIS Prev, BioCN&I, CPA, CurCont, DSA, ESPM, ExcerpMed, FCA, GenetAb, H&SSA, HGA, HelmAb, HerbAb, HortAb, ISR, ImmunAb, IndMed, IndVet, Inpharma, MBA, MEDLINE, MaizeAb, NemAb, NucAcAb, NutrAb, PBA, PE&ON, PN&I, ProtozoAb, RM&VM, RPP, Reac, S&F, SCI, SIA, TDB, VetBull, VirolAbstr, WeedAb.
—BLDSC (3500.775810), CISTI, IDS, IE, Infotrieve, ingenta. **CCC.**
Published by: Elsevier Ltd., Current Opinion Journals (Subsidiary of: Elsevier Science & Technology), 84 Theobald's Rd., London, WC1X 8RR, United Kingdom. TEL 44-20-7611-4000, FAX 44-20-7611-4001, 44-20-7611-4468, http://www.elsevier.com/locate/mib, http://www.current-opinion.com. Eds. Julian Davies, Pascale Cossart.

➤ **CURRENT PROTOCOLS IN IMMUNOLOGY.** see *MEDICAL SCIENCES—Allergology And Immunology*

579 USA
▼ **CURRENT PROTOCOLS IN MICROBIOLOGY.** Text in English. 2005. base vol. plus updates 3/yr. **Document type:** *Academic/Scholarly.* **Description:** Provides detailed, step-by-step instructions for analyzing bacteria, animal and plant viruses, fungi, protozoans and other microbes.
Related titles: CD-ROM ed.: USD 405; USD 225 renewals (effective 2006).
Published by: John Wiley & Sons, Inc., 111 River St, Hoboken, NJ 07030-5774. TEL 201-748-6000, FAX 201-748-5915, protocol@wiley.com, http://www.wiley.com.

579 USA ISSN 0070-217X
QR1 CODEN: CTMIA3
➤ **CURRENT TOPICS IN MICROBIOLOGY AND IMMUNOLOGY.** Text in English. 1906. irreg., latest vol.286, 2004. price varies. reprint service avail. from ISI. **Document type:** *Monographic series, Academic/Scholarly.* **Description:** Provides a synthesis of the latest research findings in the areas of molecular immunology, bacteriology and virology.
Former titles (until 1966): Ergebnisse der Mikrobiologie, Immunitaetsforschung und Experimentellen Therapie (0367-1003); (until 1955): Ergebnisse der Hygiene, Bakteriologie, Immunitatsforschung und Experimentellen Therapie (0367-0503); (until 1913): Jahresbericht ueber die Ergebnisse der Immunitatsforschung und deren Grenzwissenschaften, der Chemotherapie, Zoonosologie, Hygiene u.s.f. (0174-6049)
Indexed: AIDS Ab, AIDS&CR, ASCA, AbHyg, AnBrAb, BIOBASE, BIOSIS Prev, BiolAb, CIN, ChemAb, ChemTitl, ESPM, ExcerpMed, GenetAb, HGA, IABS, ISR, ImmunAb, IndMed, IndVet, MBA, MEDLINE, NucAcAb, PN&I, PoultAb, ProtozoAb, SCI, TDB, VetBull, VirolAbstr, WAE&RSA.
—BLDSC (3504.890000), CASDDS, CISTI, GNLM, IDS, IE, Infotrieve, ingenta, KNAW, Linda Hall. **CCC.**
Published by: Springer-Verlag New York, Inc. (Subsidiary of: Springer Science+Business Media), 233 Spring St, New York, NY 10013. TEL 212-460-1500, 800-777-4643, FAX 212-473-6272, http://www.springer-ny.com.

579.2 IND ISSN 0972-4591
CURRENT TRENDS IN VIROLOGY. Text in English. 1999. a.
—BLDSC (3504.936220).
Published by: Research Trends, T.C. 17/250(3), Chadiyara Rd, Poojapura, Trivandrum, Kerala 695 012, India.

CURRENTS IN HEMATOIMMUNOLOGY. see *MEDICAL SCIENCES—Allergology And Immunology*

DEVELOPMENTAL & COMPARATIVE IMMUNOLOGY. see *MEDICAL SCIENCES—Allergology And Immunology*

579.2 NLD ISSN 0167-8256
CODEN: DMVIDD
➤ **DEVELOPMENTS IN MOLECULAR VIROLOGY.** Text in English. 1981. irreg., latest vol.10, 1989. price varies. **Document type:** *Monographic series, Academic/Scholarly.*
Indexed: CIN, ChemAb, ChemTitl.
—CASDDS, CISTI, KNAW.
Published by: Springer-Verlag Dordrecht (Subsidiary of: Springer Science+Business Media), Van Godewijckstraat 30, Dordrecht, 3311 GX, Netherlands. TEL 31-78-6576050, FAX 31-78-6576474, http://www.springeronline.com.

579 USA ISSN 0732-8893
RB37.A1 CODEN: DMIDDZ
➤ **DIAGNOSTIC MICROBIOLOGY AND INFECTIOUS DISEASE.** Text in English. 1983. 12/yr. USD 519 domestic to individuals; USD 564 foreign to individuals; USD 1,420 domestic to institutions; USD 1,502 foreign to institutions (effective 2006). adv. bk.rev. abstr. index. back issues avail. **Document type:** *Academic/Scholarly.* **Description:** Provides information on the latest developments in clinical microbiology and the diagnosis and treatment of infectious diseases.
Related titles: Microform ed.: (from PQC); Online - full text ed.: (from EBSCO Publishing, Gale Group, IngentaConnect, ScienceDirect, Swets Information Services).
Indexed: AIDS Ab, ASFA, BIOBASE, BIOSIS Prev, BiolAb, CIN, ChemAb, ChemTitl, CurCont, ESPM, ExcerpMed, IABS, INI, ISR, IndMed, Inpharma, Inspec, JDDR, JW-ID, MEDLINE, MS&D, PE&ON, ProtozoAb, Reac, SCI.
—BLDSC (3579.662000), CASDDS, CISTI, GNLM, IDS, IE, Infotrieve, ingenta, KNAW. **CCC.**
Published by: Elsevier Inc. (Subsidiary of: Elsevier Science & Technology), 360 Park Ave. S, New York, NY 10010-1710. TEL 212-633-3730, 888-437-4636, usinfo-f@elsevier.com, http://www.elsevier.com/locate/diagmicrobio. Ed. Dr. Ronald N Jones.

579.17 DEU ISSN 0177-5103
CODEN: DAOREO
➤ **DISEASES OF AQUATIC ORGANISMS.** Text in English. 1985. 18/yr. (in 6 vols., 3 nos./vol.). EUR 1,330 combined subscription domestic for print & online eds.; EUR 1,348 combined subscription foreign for print & online eds. (effective 2006). **Document type:** *Journal, Academic/Scholarly.*
Description: Presents original papers, short notes and reviews on disease phenomena in aquatic organisms.
Related titles: ◆ Online - full text ed.: Diseases of Aquatic Organisms Online. ISSN 1616-1580.
Indexed: ASCA, ASFA, AgBio, AnBrAb, BIOBASE, BIOSIS Prev, BioCN&I, BiolAb, CIN, CRFR, ChemAb, ChemTitl, CurCont, DBA, DSA, ESPM, FoVS&M, GEOBASE, GenetAb, HGA, HelmAb, HortAb, IABS, ISR, IndMed, IndVet, MBA, MEDLINE, NutrAb, OceAb, OrnHort, PBA, PGegResA, PN&I, ProtozoAb, RM&VM, RPP, RevApplEntom, S&F, SCI, SFA, SIA, SWRA, SoyAb, ToxAb, TriticAb, VetBull, WeedAb, WildRev, ZooRec.
—BLDSC (3598.125000), CASDDS, CINDOC, CISTI, IE, ingenta, Linda Hall.
Published by: Inter-Research, Nordbuente 23, Oldendorf, 21385, Germany. TEL 49-4132-7127, FAX 49-4132-8883, ir@int-res.com, http://www.int-res.com/journals/dao/index.html. Ed. Otto Kinne.

579.17 DEU ISSN 1616-1580
➤ **DISEASES OF AQUATIC ORGANISMS ONLINE.** Text in English. 12/yr. EUR 1,050 (effective 2006). **Document type:** *Academic/Scholarly.*
Media: Online - full text (from EBSCO Publishing). **Related titles:** ◆ Print ed.: Diseases of Aquatic Organisms. ISSN 0177-5103.
Published by: Inter-Research, Nordbuente 23, Oldendorf, 21385, Germany. TEL 49-4132-7127, FAX 49-4132-8883, webmaster@int-res.com, ir@int-res.com, http://www.int-res.com/journals/dao/index.html.

➤ **DRUG RESISTANCE UPDATES.** see *MEDICAL SCIENCES*

579 USA ISSN 0141-2620
ECONOMIC MICROBIOLOGY. Text in English. 1977. irreg., latest vol.8, 1983. reprint service avail. from ISI.
Indexed: ChemAb, FS&TA.
—CISTI. **CCC.**
Published by: Academic Press (Subsidiary of: Elsevier Science & Technology), 525 B St, Ste 1900, San Diego, CA 92101-4495. TEL 619-231-6616, 800-894-3434, apsubs@acad.com, http://www.academicpress.com. Ed. A H Rose.

579 EGY ISSN 0022-2704
QR1 CODEN: EJMBA2
➤ **EGYPTIAN JOURNAL OF MICROBIOLOGY/MAGALLAH AL-MISRIYAH LIL-MIKRUBIYULUGIYA.** Text in English; Summaries in Arabic, English. 1966. 3/yr. USD 147 (effective 2003). charts; illus. reprint service avail. from IRC. **Document type:** *Journal, Academic/Scholarly.*
Former titles (until 1971): United Arab Republic Journal of Microbiology (0303-1438); (until 1969): Journal of Microbiology of the United Arab Republic (0301-8172)
Indexed: AbHyg, AgBio, AgrForAb, AnBrAb, BIOSIS Prev, BioCN&I, BiolAb, CBTA, CIN, CPA, ChemAb, ChemTitl, DSA, FCA, FPA, FS&TA, ForAb, HelmAb, HerbAb, HortAb, IndVet, JDDR, MaizeAb, NutrAb, OrnHort, PBA, PGrRegA, PHN&I, PotatoAb, ProtozoAb, RA&MP, RM&VM, RPP, RevApplEntom, RiceAb, S&F, SIA, SeedAb, SoyAb, TDB, TriticAb, VITIS, VetBull, WeedAb.
—BLDSC (3664.405000), CASDDS, CISTI, IE, ingenta, Linda Hall.
Published by: (Society of Applied Microbiology, Research Department), National Information and Documentation Centre (NIDOC), Tahrir St., Dokki, Awqaf P.O., Giza, Egypt. TEL 20-2-3371696, FAX 20-2-3371746, http://derp.sti.sci.eg/data/0123.htm. Ed. Dr. Abdel-Wahhab Muhammad Abdel-Hafezh. Circ: 1,000.

➤ **ENFERMEDADES INFECCIOSAS Y MICROBIOLOGIA.** see *MEDICAL SCIENCES—Communicable Diseases*

579 GBR ISSN 1462-2912
QR100 CODEN: ENMIFM
➤ **ENVIRONMENTAL MICROBIOLOGY.** Text in English. 1999. m. GBP 275, EUR 413 combined subscription in Europe to individuals print & online eds.; USD 509 combined subscription in the Americas to individuals print & online eds.; GBP 303 combined subscription elsewhere to individuals print & online eds.; GBP 1,399 combined subscription in Europe to institutions print & online eds.; USD 2,586 combined subscription in the Americas to institutions & Caribbean (print & online eds.); GBP 1,539 combined subscription elsewhere to institutions print & online eds. (effective 2006). adv. **Document type:** *Journal, Academic/Scholarly.* **Description:** Devoted to the study of microbial processes in the environment, microbial communities and microbial interactions.
Related titles: Online - full text ed.: ISSN 1462-2920. GBP 1,329 in Europe to institutions; USD 2,456 in the Americas to institutions & Caribbean; GBP 1,462 elsewhere to institutions (effective 2006) (from Blackwell Synergy, EBSCO Publishing, Gale Group, IngentaConnect, O C L C Online Computer Library Center, Inc., Ovid Technologies, Inc., Swets Information Services).
Indexed: AEA, AbHyg, AgBio, AgrForAb, AnBrAb, BCI, BIOBASE, BioCN&I, CPA, CurCont, DSA, ESPM, EnvEAb, FCA, FPA, ForAb, HerbAb, HortAb, I&DA, IndMed, IndVet, MEDLINE, MaizeAb, NutrAb, PBA, PGegResA, PGrRegA, PN&I, PollutAb, PotatoAb, PoultAb, ProtozoAb, RPP, RefZh, RevApplEntom, RiceAb, S&F, SIA, SWRA, SeedAb, SoyAb, TDB, TriticAb, VetBull, WeedAb, ZooRec.
—BLDSC (3791.522600), CASDDS, CISTI, IE, Infotrieve, ingenta. **CCC.**
Published by: (Society for Applied Microbiology), Blackwell Publishing Ltd., 9600 Garsington Rd, Oxford, OX4 2ZG, United Kingdom. TEL 44-1865-776868, FAX 44-1865-714591, customerservices@oxon.blackwellpublishing.com, http://www.blackwellpublishing.com/journals/EMI. Eds. David A Stahl, Kenneth N Timmis. Pub. Amanda McLean Inglis. R&P Sophie Savage. Adv. contact Jenny Applin. Circ: 900.

➤ **ENZYME AND MICROBIAL TECHNOLOGY.** see *BIOLOGY—Biotechnology*

579 CZE ISSN 1210-7913
QR1 CODEN: EMIME6
EPIDEMIOLOGIE, MIKROBIOLOGIE, IMUNOLOGIE. Text in Czech, Slovak; Summaries in Czech, English. 1952. q. EUR 92, USD 126 foreign (effective 2005). adv. bk.rev. abstr.; bibl.; charts; illus.; stat. index. **Document type:** *Journal, Academic/Scholarly.*
Formerly (until 1994): Ceskoslovenska Epidemiologie, Mikrobiologie, Imunologie (0009-0522)
Indexed: AbHyg, BIOSIS Prev, BiolAb, CISA, ChemAb, DSA, DokArb, ExcerpMed, ForAb, HelmAb, IndMed, IndVet, MEDLINE, NutrAb, PHN&I, PN&I, PoultAb, ProtozoAb, RM&VM, RPP, RRTA, RevApplEntom, TDB, VetBull.
—BLDSC (3793.573000), CASDDS, CISTI, GNLM, IE, ingenta. **CCC.**
Published by: (Ceska Lekarska Spolecnost J.E. Purkyne/Czech Medical Association), Nakladatelske Stredisko C L S J.E. Purkyne, Sokolska 31, Prague, 12026, Czech Republic. nts@cls.cz, http://www.clsjep.cz/nts/casop/epidemiologie/epidemiologie.asp. Ed. Dr. Pavla Krizova. adv.: B&W page CZK 25,100, color page CZK 35,200; 250 x 170. Circ: 750.
Subscr. to: Myris Trade, V Stihlach 1311, PO Box 2, Prague 4 14201, Czech Republic. TEL 420-2-34035200, FAX 420-2-34035207, myris@myris.cz, http://www.myris.cz.

578.65 GBR ISSN 0950-2688
RA421 CODEN: EPINEU
➤ **EPIDEMIOLOGY AND INFECTION.** Text in English. 1901. bi-m. GBP 396, USD 669 to institutions; GBP 438, USD 744 combined subscription to institutions print & online eds. (effective 2006). adv. bk.rev. charts; illus. index. back issues avail.; reprint service avail. from PQC,PSC. **Document type:** *Journal, Academic/Scholarly.* **Description:** Contains original findings in the fields of microbiology and infectious disease. Emphasis is on epidemiology, prevention and control.
Formerly (until 1987): Journal of Hygiene (0022-1724)
Related titles: Microform ed.: (from PMC, PQC); Online - full text ed.: ISSN 1469-4409. GBP 370 to institutions; USD 630 in North America to institutions (effective 2006) (from EBSCO Publishing, O C L C Online Computer Library Center, Inc., Ovid Technologies, Inc., Swets Information Services).
Indexed: AHCMS, AIDS Ab, ASCA, ASFA, AbHyg, AddicA, AgBio, AnBrAb, BIOBASE, BIOSIS Prev, BioCN&I, BioDAb, BiolAb, Biostat, BrNI, CIN, CIS, ChemAb, ChemTitl, CurCont, DSA, ESPM, EnvEAb, ExcerpMed, FS&TA, H&SSA, H&TI, HelmAb, IABS, INI, ISR, IndMed, IndVet, Inpharma, JDDR, LHB, MBA, MEDLINE, NRN, NutrAb, PBA, PE&ON, PN&I, PollutAb, PoultAb, ProtozoAb, RA&MP, RDA, RM&VM, RPP, RRTA, Reac, RefZh, RevApplEntom, RiceAb, RiskAb, S&F, SAA, SCI, SFA, TDB, THA, VetBull, VirolAbstr, WRCInf, WildRev, ZooRec.
—BLDSC (3793.600000), CASDDS, CISTI, GNLM, IDS, IE, Infotrieve, ingenta, KNAW, Linda Hall. **CCC.**

B

Published by: Cambridge University Press, The Edinburgh Bldg, Shaftesbury Rd, Cambridge, CB2 2RU, United Kingdom. TEL 44-1223-312393, FAX 44-1223-315052, journals@cambridge.org, http://uk.cambridge.org/journals/hyg. Ed. Norman Noah. R&P Linda Nicol TEL 44-1223-325757. Adv. contact Rebecca Curtis TEL 44-1223-325757. **Subscr. to:** Cambridge University Press, 100 Brook Hill Dr, West Nyack, NY 10994. TEL 845-353-7500, FAX 845-353-4141, journals_subscriptions@cup.org

579 USA ISSN 1535-9778
QR74.5 CODEN: ECUEA2

EUKARYOTIC CELL. Text in English. 2002 (Feb.). m. USD 405 domestic to institutions; USD 421 in Canada to institutions; USD 443 in Europe to institutions; USD 457 in Latin America to institutions; USD 458 elsewhere to institutions (effective 2006). adv. **Document type:** *Journal, Academic/Scholarly.* **Description:** Focuses on the study of single eukaryotic microorganisms such as yeast, fungi, algae, protozoa, and social amoebae.

Related titles: Online - full text ed.: ISSN 1535-9786. USD 380 to institutions (effective 2006) (from EBSCO Publishing, HighWire Press, National Library of Medicine).

Indexed: ASFA, AbHyg, AgBio, B&BAb, BIOSIS Prev, BioCN&I, BiolAb, ChemAb, CurCont, ESPM, FCA, GenetAb, HortAb, IndVet, MaizeAb, PotatoAb, ProtozoAb, RA&MP, RM&VM, RPP, RefZh, SIA, SWRA, SoyAb, TDB, VetBull.

—BLDSC (3827.515000), CISTI, IE, ingenta. **CCC.**

Published by: American Society for Microbiology, 1752 N St, N W, Washington, DC 20036-2904. TEL 202-942-9319, FAX 202-942-9347, asmjournals@asm.org, subscriptions@asmusa.org, http://ec.asm.org/, http://www.asm.org. Ed. C. C. Wang. Adv. contact David Baker TEL 410-638-6831. Circ: 2,000 (paid and controlled). **Subscr. to:** PO Box 11127, Birmingham, AL 35201-1127. TEL 205-995-1567, 800-633-4931, FAX 205-995-1588.

579 DEU ISSN 0934-9723
CODEN: EJCDEU

➤ **EUROPEAN JOURNAL OF CLINICAL MICROBIOLOGY & INFECTIOUS DISEASES**; an international journal on pathogenesis, diagnosis, epidemiology, therapy, and prevention of infectious diseases. Text in English. 1982. m. EUR 628 combined subscription to institutions print & online eds. (effective 2005). adv. **Document type:** *Journal, Academic/Scholarly.* **Description:** Presents information and opinions in the fields of clinical microbiology and infectious diseases.

Formerly (until 1987): European Journal of Clinical Microbiology (0722-2211)

Related titles: Online - full text ed.: ISSN 1435-4373 (from EBSCO Publishing, Springer LINK, Swets Information Services).

Indexed: AIDS Ab, AIIM, ASCA, AbHyg, BIOBASE, BiolAb, CIN, ChemAb, ChemTitl, CurCont, DSA, DentInd, ESPM, ExcerpMed, FPA, ForAb, HelmAb, IABS, INI, ISR, IndMed, IndVet, Inpharma, JDDR, JW-ID, MBA, MEDLINE, MS&D, NRN, NutrAb, PE&ON, PN&I, ProtozoAb, RA&MP, RDA, RM&VM, RRTA, Reac, RevApplEntom, SCI, SIA, TDB, VetBull, VirolAbstr.

—BLDSC (3829.727700), CASDDS, CISTI, GNLM, IDS, IE, Infotrieve, ingenta, KNAW. **CCC.**

Published by: Springer-Verlag (Subsidiary of: Springer Science+Business Media), Tiergartenstr 17, Heidelberg, 69121, Germany. TEL 49-6221-3450, FAX 49-6221-345229, EJCMID@compuserve.com, http://link.springer.de/link/service/journals/10096/index.htm. Ed. Dr. I Braveny. Adv. contact Stephan Kroeck TEL 49-30-827875739. Circ: 3,000. **Subscr. in the Americas to:** Springer-Verlag New York, Inc., Journal Fulfillment, PO Box 2485, Secaucus, NJ 07096-2485. TEL 800-777-4643, 201-348-4033, FAX 201-348-4505, journals@springer-ny.com; http://www.springer-ny.com; **Subscr. to:** Springer GmbH Auslieferungsgesellschaft, Haberstr 7, Heidelberg 69126, Germany. TEL 49-6221-345-0, FAX 49-6221-345-4229, subscriptions@springer.de.

➤ **EUROPEAN JOURNAL OF PROTISTOLOGY.** see *PALEONTOLOGY*

➤ **EXCERPTA MEDICA. ABSTRACT JOURNALS.** see *BIOLOGY—Abstracting, Bibliographies, Statistics*

➤ **EXCERPTA MEDICA. SECTION 4: MICROBIOLOGY: BACTERIOLOGY, MYCOLOGY, PARASITOLOGY AND VIROLOGY.** see *BIOLOGY—Abstracting, Bibliographies, Statistics*

578.65 BGR ISSN 1311-6851
RB125

EXPERIMENTAL PATHOLOGY AND PARASITOLOGY. Text in English. irreg.

Related titles: Online - full text ed.

Indexed: BiolAb, RefZh.

Published by: (Bulgarian Academy of Sciences, Institute of Experimental Pathology and Parasitology), Universitetsko Izdatelstvo Sv. Kliment Okhridski/Publishing House of the Sofia University St. Kliment Ohridski, 15 Tsar Osvoboditel Blvd., Sofia, 1504, Bulgaria. TEL 359-2-9792914, http://www.iepp.bas.bg/journal.htm. Ed. Ilarion Yanchev.

579.2 USA

➤ **EXPERIMENTAL VIROLOGY.** Text in English. 1978. irreg., latest vol.4, 1983. reprint service avail. from ISI. **Document type:** *Journal, Academic/Scholarly.*

Published by: Academic Press (Subsidiary of: Elsevier Science & Technology), 525 B St, Ste 1900, San Diego, CA 92101-4495. apsubs@acad.com, http://www.academicpress.com. Eds. F Brown, T W Tinsley.

➤ **EXTREMOPHILES**; life under extreme conditions. see *BIOLOGY—Biotechnology*

616.01 NLD ISSN 0928-8244
QR46 CODEN: FIMIEV

➤ **F E M S IMMUNOLOGY AND MEDICAL MICROBIOLOGY.** Text in English. 1988. 9/m. EUR 924 in Europe to institutions; JPY 122,800 in Japan to institutions; USD 1,034 to institutions except Europe and Japan (effective 2005). back issues avail. **Document type:** *Journal, Academic/Scholarly.* **Description:** Focuses on works describing the mechanisms of immunity and how these can be exploited in the diagnosis and treatment of disease.

Formerly (until 1993): F E M S Microbiology Immunology (0920-8534)

Related titles: Microform ed.: (from PQC); Online - full text ed.: (from EBSCO Publishing, Gale Group, IngentaConnect, ScienceDirect, Swets Information Services); ♦ Series of: F E M S Microbiology. ISSN 0921-8254.

Indexed: AIDS&CR, ASCA, AbHyg, AgBio, Agr, AnBrAb, BIOBASE, BIOSIS Prev, BibAg, BioCN&I, BioEngAb, BiolAb, CIN, ChemAb, ChemTitl, CurCont, DSA, ESPM, ExcerpMed, HelmAb, HortAb, IABS, ISR, ImmunAb, IndMed, IndVet, Inpharma, MBA, MEDLINE, NutrAb, PE&ON, PGegResA, PHN&I, PN&I, PoultAb, ProtozoAb, RA&MP, RM&VM, RPP, Reac, RevApplEntom, S&F, SCI, SIA, SoyAb, TDB, Telegen, VetBull, VirolAbstr.

—BLDSC (3905.291000), CASDDS, CISTI, GNLM, IDS, IE, Infotrieve, ingenta, KNAW, Linda Hall. **CCC.**

Published by: (Federation of European Microbiological Societies GBR), Elsevier BV (Subsidiary of: Elsevier Science & Technology), Radarweg 29, Amsterdam, 1043 NX, Netherlands. TEL 31-20-4853911, FAX 31-20-4852457, nlinfo-f@elsevier.nl, http://www.elsevier.com/inca/publications/store/5/0/6/0/1/9/index.htt, http://www.elsevier.nl. Eds. A. J.W. van Alphen, A. van Belkum.

579.072 NLD ISSN 0921-8254

➤ **F E M S MICROBIOLOGY.** Text in English. 1977. 62/yr. EUR 6,100 in Europe to institutions for full set of FEMS Microbiology series; JPY 810,100 in Japan to institutions for full set of FEMS Microbiology series; USD 6,822 elsewhere to institutions for full set of FEMS Microbiology series (effective 2005); Set includes: FEMS Immunology and Medical Microbiology (ISSN 0928-8244); FEMS Microbiology Ecology (ISSN 0168-6469); FEMS Microbiology Letters (0378-1097); FEMS Microbiology Reviews (ISSN 0168-6445). cum.index. back issues avail. **Document type:** *Journal, Academic/Scholarly.* **Description:** Publishes reports on microbiological research.

Related titles: Microform ed.: (from PQC); ♦ Series: F E M S Microbiology Letters. ISSN 0378-1097; ♦ F E M S Microbiology Ecology. ISSN 0168-6496; ♦ F E M S Immunology and Medical Microbiology. ISSN 0928-8244; ♦ F E M S Microbiology Reviews. ISSN 0168-6445.

Indexed: ApicAb, BiolAb, ChemAb, CurCont, ExcerpMed.

Published by: (Federation of European Microbiological Societies GBR), Elsevier BV (Subsidiary of: Elsevier Science & Technology), Radarweg 29, Amsterdam, 1043 NX, Netherlands. TEL 31-20-4853911, FAX 31-20-4852457, nlinfo-f@elsevier.nl, http://www.elsevier.com/inca/publications/store/5/0/6/0/5/7/index.htt, http://www.elsevier.nl.

579.17 NLD ISSN 0168-6496
CODEN: FMECEZ

➤ **F E M S MICROBIOLOGY ECOLOGY.** Text in English. 1985. m. EUR 1,181 in Europe to institutions; JPY 157,000 in Japan to institutions; USD 1,321 to institutions except Europe and Japan (effective 2005). back issues avail. **Document type:** *Journal, Academic/Scholarly.* **Description:** Details fundamental aspects of the ecology of micro-organisms in a variety of environments and situations.

Related titles: Microform ed.: (from PQC); Online - full text ed.: (from EBSCO Publishing, Gale Group, IngentaConnect, ScienceDirect, Swets Information Services); ♦ Series of: F E M S Microbiology. ISSN 0921-8254.

Indexed: ASCA, ASFA, AbHyg, AgBio, Agr, AgrForAb, AnBrAb, ApEcolAb, BIOBASE, BIOSIS Prev, BibAg, BioCN&I, BioDAb, BiolAb, CIN, CPA, ChemAb, ChemTitl, CurCont, DSA, ESPM, EnvAb, EnvEAb, ExcerpMed, FCA, FPA, ForAb, GEOBASE, GenetAb, HerbAb, HortAb, I&DA, IABS, ISR, IndVet, Inpharma, MBA, MEDLINE, MaizeAb, NemAb, NutrAb, OceAb, PBA, PE&ON, PGegResA, PGrRegA, PHN&I, PN&I, PollutAb, PotatoAb, PoultAb, ProtozoAb, RA&MP, RASB, RM&VM, RPP, Reac, RevApplEntom, RiceAb, S&F, SCI, SIA, SWRA, SeedAb, SoyAb, TDB, Telegen, TriticAb, VITIS, VetBull, WeedAb, ZooRec.

—BLDSC (3905.296000), CASDDS, CISTI, GNLM, IDS, IE, Infotrieve, ingenta, Linda Hall. **CCC.**

Published by: (Federation of European Microbiological Societies GBR), Elsevier BV (Subsidiary of: Elsevier Science & Technology), Radarweg 29, Amsterdam, 1043 NX, Netherlands. TEL 31-20-4853911, FAX 31-20-4852457, nlinfo-f@elsevier.nl, http://www.elsevier.com/locate/femsecol. Ed. R Conrad.

579 NLD ISSN 0378-1097
QR1 CODEN: FMLED7

➤ **F E M S MICROBIOLOGY LETTERS.** Text in English. 1977. 24/yr. EUR 4,101 in Europe to institutions; JPY 544,300 in Japan to institutions; USD 4,586 elsewhere to institutions (effective 2005). adv. back issues avail.; reprint service avail. from ISI. **Document type:** *Journal, Academic/Scholarly.* **Description:** Covers all aspects of microbiology and microbial chemistry.

Related titles: Microform ed.: (from PQC); Online - full text ed.: (from EBSCO Publishing, Gale Group, IngentaConnect, ScienceDirect, Swets Information Services); ♦ Series of: F E M S Microbiology. ISSN 0921-8254.

Indexed: AEA, AEBA, ASCA, ASFA, AbHyg, AgBio, Agr, AgrForAb, AnBrAb, BBCI, BCI, BIOBASE, BIOSIS Prev, BibAg, BioCN&I, BioDAb, BiolAb, CBTA, CEABA, CIN, CPA, ChemAb, ChemTitl, CurCont, DBA, DSA, ESPM, EnvAb, ExcerpMed, FCA, FPA, FS&TA, ForAb, GenetAb, HGA, HelmAb, HerbAb, HortAb, I&DA, IABS, ISR, IndMed, IndVet, Inpharma, MBA, MEDLINE, MSB, MaizeAb, NemAb, NucAcAb, NutrAb, OrnHort, PBA, PGegResA, PGrRegA, PHN&I, PN&I, PotatoAb, PoultAb, ProtozoAb, RA&MP, RM&VM, RPP, Reac, RefZh, RevApplEntom, RiceAb, S&F, SCI, SFA, SIA, SoyAb, TDB, Telegen, TriticAb, VITIS, VetBull, VirolAbstr, WeedAb, WildRev, ZooRec.

—BLDSC (3905.300000), CASDDS, CISTI, GNLM, IDS, IE, Infotrieve, ingenta, Linda Hall. **CCC.**

Published by: (Federation of European Microbiological Societies GBR), Elsevier BV (Subsidiary of: Elsevier Science & Technology), Radarweg 29, Amsterdam, 1043 NX, Netherlands. TEL 31-20-4853911, FAX 31-20-4852457, nlinfo-f@elsevier.nl, http://www.elsevier.com/locate/femslett, http://www.elsevier.nl. Ed. J Cole. **Subscr. to:** Elsevier, Subscription Customer Service, 6277 Sea Harbor Dr, Orlando, FL 32887-4800. TEL 407-345-4020, 877-839-7126, FAX 407-363-1354.

579 NLD ISSN 0168-6445
QR1 CODEN: FMREE4

➤ **F E M S MICROBIOLOGY REVIEWS.** Text in English. 1977. 5/yr. EUR 457 in Europe to institutions; JPY 60,800 in Japan to institutions; USD 512 to institutions except Europe and Japan (effective 2005). back issues avail. **Document type:** *Journal, Academic/Scholarly.* **Description:** Covers the entire field of microbiology with an emphasis on topicality and readability.

Related titles: Microform ed.: (from PQC); Online - full text ed.: (from EBSCO Publishing, Gale Group, IngentaConnect, ScienceDirect, Swets Information Services); ♦ Series of: F E M S Microbiology. ISSN 0921-8254.

Indexed: AEBA, AESIS, ASCA, ASFA, AbHyg, AgBio, Agr, BBCI, BCI, BIOBASE, BIOSIS Prev, BioCN&I, BioDAb, BiolAb, CCI, CEABA, ChemAb, CurCont, DBA, DSA, ESPM, EnvAb, ExcerpMed, FCA, FS&TA, ForAb, GenetAb, I&DA, IABS, ISR, IndMed, IndVet, Inpharma, MBA, MEDLINE, MSCI, NutrAb, PBA, PGrRegA, ProtozoAb, RM&VM, RPP, Reac, RefZh, RiceAb, S&F, SCI, SIA, TDB, VetBull, VirolAbstr, ZooRec.

—BLDSC (3905.305000), CASDDS, CISTI, GNLM, IDS, IE, Infotrieve, ingenta, Linda Hall. **CCC.**

Published by: (Federation of European Microbiological Societies GBR), Elsevier BV (Subsidiary of: Elsevier Science & Technology), Radarweg 29, Amsterdam, 1043 NX, Netherlands. TEL 31-20-4853911, FAX 31-20-4852457, nlinfo-f@elsevier.nl, http://www.elsevier.com/locate/femsrev, http://www.elsevier.nl. Ed. N L Brown.

579 USA ISSN 0163-9188
CODEN: FEMSDW

F E M S SYMPOSIUM. Text in English. irreg., latest vol.75, 1995. price varies. back issues avail. **Document type:** *Proceedings.*

Indexed: Agr, CIN, ChemAb, ChemTitl.

—CASDDS, CISTI, KNAW. **CCC.**

Published by: (Federation of European Microbiological Societies GBR), Springer-Verlag New York, Inc. (Subsidiary of: Springer Science+Business Media), 233 Spring St, New York, NY 10013. TEL 212-460-1500, FAX 212-460-1575, service@springer-ny.com, http://www.springer-ny.com.

579 571 576.5 NLD ISSN 1567-1356
QR151 CODEN: FYREAG

F E M S YEAST RESEARCH. Text in English. 2001. 8/yr. EUR 564 in Europe to institutions; JPY 75,100 in Japan to institutions; USD 634 to institutions except Europe and Japan (effective 2005). back issues avail. **Document type:** *Journal, Academic/Scholarly.* **Description:** Publishes original research papers and mini-reviews that cover both yeast and yeast-like organisms.

Related titles: Online - full text ed.: Federation of European Microbiological Societies Yeast Research Online. ISSN 1567-1364. EUR 129.78 in Europe to institutions; JPY 18,000 in Japan to institutions; USD 146 elsewhere to institutions (effective 2001) (from EBSCO Publishing, Gale Group, IngentaConnect, ScienceDirect, Swets Information Services).

Indexed: Agr, B&BAb, BCI, BIOBASE, BIOSIS Prev, BioEngAb, BiolAb, ChemAb, CurCont, EntAb, ExcerpMed, GenetAb, RefZh, VITIS.

B

▼ *new title* ➤ *refereed* ✶ *unverified* ♦ *full entry avail.*

—BLDSC (3905.325000), CISTI, IE, ingenta, Linda Hall. **CCC.**
Published by: (Federation of European Microbiological Societies GBR), Elsevier BV (Subsidiary of: Elsevier Science & Technology), Radarweg 29, Amsterdam, 1043 NX, Netherlands. TEL 31-20-4853911, FAX 31-20-4852457, femsyr@fems-microbiology.org, nlinfo-f@elsevier.nl, http://www.elsevier.com/locate/femsyr, http://www.elsevier.nl. Ed. Lex Scheffers.

579 USA ISSN 1542-9210
QR46
FOCUS ON MICROBIOLOGY EDUCATION. Text in English. 1995. 3/yr.
Media: Online - full content.
Published by: American Society for Microbiology, 1752 N St, N W, Washington, DC 20036-2904. TEL 202-942-9319, FAX 202-942-9347, http://www.MicrobeLibrary.org/Newsletter/issues.htm, http://www.asm.org. Ed. Marjorie Kelly Cowan.

579 GBR ISSN 0740-0020
QR115 CODEN: FOMIE5
➤ **FOOD MICROBIOLOGY.** Text in English. 1984. 8/yr. EUR 330 in Europe to individuals; JPY 35,600 in Japan to individuals; USD 340 to individuals except Europe and Japan; EUR 840 in Europe to institutions; JPY 90,700 in Japan to institutions; USD 746 to institutions except Europe and Japan (effective 2006). adv. bk.rev. reprints avail. **Document type:** *Journal, Academic/Scholarly.* **Description:** Publishes primary research papers, short research communications, reviews, reports of meetings, and news items dealing with all aspects of the microbiology of foods.
Related titles: Online - full text ed.: ISSN 1095-9998. USD 788 (effective 2002) (from EBSCO Publishing, Gale Group, IngentaConnect, O C L C Online Computer Library Center, Inc., ScienceDirect, Swets Information Services).
Indexed: AEBA, ASCA, ASFA, AbHyg, AgBio, Agr, AnBrAb, BCI, BIOBASE, BIOSIS Prev, BibAg, BioDAb, BiolAb, CIN, CPA, ChemAb, ChemTitl, CurCont, DSA, ESPM, ExcerpMed, FPA, FS&TA, ForAb, H&SSA, HortAb, IABS, ISR, IndVet, MBA, NutrAb, OrnHort, PHN&I, PN&I, PotatoAb, PoultAb, ProtozoAb, RA&MP, RM&VM, RPP, RefZh, RiceAb, SCI, SIA, SeedAb, SoyAb, TDB, TriticAb, VITIS, VetBull.
—BLDSC (3981.300000), CASDDS, CISTI, GNLM, IDS, IE, Infotrieve, ingenta, Linda Hall. **CCC.**
Published by: Academic Press (Subsidiary of: Elsevier Science & Technology), Harcourt Pl, 32 Jamestown Rd, London, NW1 7BY, United Kingdom. TEL 44-20-7424-4200, FAX 44-20-7483-2293, apsubs@acad.com, http://www.elsevier.com/locate/fm. Ed. M. L. Tortorello. R&P Catherine John. Adv. contact Nik Screen.

579.2 DEU ISSN 1431-357X
FRONTIERS OF VIROLOGY. Text in English. 1992. irreg., latest vol.4, 1995. price varies. **Document type:** *Monographic series, Academic/Scholarly.*
Published by: Springer-Verlag (Subsidiary of: Springer Science+Business Media), Haber Str 7, Heidelberg, 69126, Germany. TEL 49-6221-3450, FAX 49-6221-229, orders@springer.de, http://www.springer.de. Eds. Dr. Gholamreza Darai, Dr. Yechiel Becker.

579 USA ISSN 0149-0451
QR103 CODEN: GEJODG
➤ **GEOMICROBIOLOGY JOURNAL**; an international journal of geomicrobiology and microbial biogeochemistry. Text in English. 1978. 8/yr. USD 1,113, GBP 674 combined subscription to institutions print & online eds. (effective 2006). adv. bk.rev. abstr. index. reprint service avail. from PSC. **Document type:** *Journal, Academic/Scholarly.* **Description:** Explores the geologic impact of microbial transformations of materials that make up the Earth's crust, oceans, sea lakes, bottom sediments, soils, mineral deposits, and rocks.
Related titles: Online - full text ed.: ISSN 1521-0529. USD 1,057, GBP 640 to institutions (effective 2006) (from EBSCO Publishing, Gale Group, IngentaConnect, O C L C Online Computer Library Center, Inc., Swets Information Services).
Indexed: AESIS, ASCA, ASFA, AgrForAb, B&BAb, BIOSIS Prev, BiolAb, CBTA, CIN, ChemAb, ChemTitl, CurCont, E&PHSE, ESPM, FCA, ForAb, GEOBASE, GP&P, HerbAb, HortAb, I&DA, INIS AtomInd, ISR, MBA, OffTech, OrnHort, PetrolAb, PollutAb, RPP, RefZh, S&F, SCI, SSCI.
—BLDSC (4147.590000), CASDDS, CISTI, IDS, IE, Infotrieve, ingenta, Linda Hall, PADDS. **CCC.**
Published by: Taylor & Francis Inc. (Subsidiary of: Taylor & Francis Group), 325 Chestnut St, Ste 800, Philadelphia, PA 19016. TEL 215-625-8900, 800-354-1420, FAX 215-625-2940, info@taylorandfrancis.com, http://www.tandf.co.uk/journals/titles/01490451.asp, http://www.taylorandfrancis.com. Eds. Henry Ehrlich, William C Ghiorse. **Subscr. outside N. America to:** Taylor & Francis Ltd, Journals Customer Service, Rankine Rd, Basingstoke, Hants RG24 8PR, United Kingdom. TEL 44-1256-813000, FAX 44-1256-330245, enquiry@tandf.co.uk.

579 ITA ISSN 0390-5462
CODEN: GBVID3
GIORNALE DI BATTERIOLOGIA, VIROLOGIA ED IMMUNOLOGIA. Text in Italian. 1926. s-a. abstr.
Supersedes: Giornale di Batteriologia, Virologia ed Immunologia ed Annali dell'Ospedale Maria Vittoria di Torino. Parte 1. Microbiologia (0301-1453); Which superseded in part: Giornale di Batteriologia, Virologia ed Immunologia ed Annali dell'Ospedale Maria Vittoria di Torino (0017-0267)
Indexed: BiolAb, CIN, ChemAb, ChemTitl, IndMed, IndVet, MEDLINE, RM&VM, TDB, VetBull.
—CASDDS, CISTI, GNLM.
Published by: Ospedale Maria Vittoria, Via Luigi Cibrario, 72, Turin, TO 10144, Italy. TEL 74 92 345.

579 ITA ISSN 0017-0380
GIORNALE DI MICROBIOLOGIA. Text in English, French, German, Italian, Spanish. 1955. q. index.
Indexed: BiolAb, ChemAb, ExcerpMed.
—CISTI, GNLM, Linda Hall.
Published by: Istituto Microbiologia, Via Luigi Mangiagalli, 31, Milan, MI 20133, Italy. Ed. Romolo Deotto. Circ: 650.

GLYCOCONJUGATE JOURNAL. see *BIOLOGY—Biochemistry*

GONGYE WEISHENGWU/INDUSTRIAL MICROBIOLOGY. see *BIOLOGY—Biotechnology*

579.3 CHN ISSN 1001-1072
GUOWAI YIXUE (JISHENGBING FENCE)/FOREIGN MEDICAL SCIENCES (PARASITOSIS). Text in Chinese. 1973. bi-m. CNY 21 domestic; USD 17.40 foreign (effective 2005). **Document type:** *Journal, Academic/Scholarly.*
Related titles: Online - full text ed.: (from East View Information Services, WanFang Data Corp.).
Published by: Zhongguo Yufang Yixue Kexueyuan, Jishengchongbing Yanjiusuo/Chinese Academy of Preventive Medicine, Institute of Parasitic Diseases, 207 Ruijin Erlu, Shanghai, 200025, China. TEL 81-21-64451195, jscbfc2002@yahoo.com.cn, http://gwyx-js.periodicals.net.cn/. **Dist. by:** China International Book Trading Corp, 35 Chegongzhuang Xilu, Haidian District, PO Box 399, Beijing 100044, China. TEL 86-10-68412045, FAX 86-10-68412023, cibtc@mail.cibtc.com.cn, http://www.cibtc.com.cn.

579 CHN ISSN 1001-1129
GUOWAI YIXUE (WEISHENGWUXUE FENCE)/FOREIGN MEDICAL SCIENCES (MICROBIOLOGY). Text in Chinese. 1978. bi-m. CNY 42 domestic; USD 20.40 foreign (effective 2005). **Document type:** *Journal, Academic/Scholarly.*
Related titles: Online - full text ed.: (from WanFang Data Corp.).
Published by: Shanghai Yike Daxue Chubanshe/Shanghai University Press, 138 Yixueyuan Lu, Shanghai, 200032, China. TEL 86-21-64041900 ext 2314, 86-21-54237633, gwyxwfc@163.com, http://gwyx-ww.periodicals.net.cn/. **Dist. by:** China International Book Trading Corp, 35 Chegongzhuang Xilu, Haidian District, PO Box 399, Beijing 100044, China. TEL 86-10-68412045, FAX 86-10-68412023, cibtc@mail.cibtc.com.cn, http://www.cibtc.com.cn.

579 PRK ISSN 1598-642X
HAN'GUG MI'SAENGMUL SAENGMYEONG GONG HAGHOEJI/KOREAN JOURNAL OF MICROBIOLOGY AND BIOTECHNOLOGY. Text in Korean, English. 1973. bi-m. KRW 2,500 domestic; USD 50 foreign (effective 2005). **Document type:** *Journal, Academic/Scholarly.*
Formerly (until 2001): San'eob Misaengmul Haghoeji/Korean Journal of Applied Microbiology and Biotechnology (0257-2389)
Related titles: ♦ English ed.: Journal of Microbiology and Biotechnology. ISSN 1017-7825.
Indexed: BIOBASE, BiolAb, ExcerpMed, FS&TA.
—CISTI, IE.
Published by: Korean Society for Applied Microbiology, The Korea Science and Technology Center 507, 635-4 Yeogsam-dong, Kangnam-Gu, Seoul, 135-703, Korea, S. TEL 82-2-5524733, FAX 82-2-5524732, ksanmi@chollian.dacom.co.kr, http://society.kisti.re.kr/~ksam/kjamb/index.html, http://society.kisti.re.kr/~ksam/index.html.

579 NLD ISSN 1568-9883
QK568.T67
HARMFUL ALGAE. Text in English. 2002. 6/yr. EUR 74 in Europe to individuals; JPY 9,900 in Japan to individuals; USD 84 to individuals except Europe and Japan; EUR 315 in Europe to institutions; JPY 41,800 in Japan to institutions; USD 353 to institutions except Europe and Japan; EUR 74 in Europe to students; JPY 9,900 in Japan to students; USD 84 to students except Europe and Japan (effective 2006). **Document type:** *Journal, Academic/Scholarly.* **Description:** Publishes original research and review papers on microalgae, including cyanobacteria, as well as monitoring, management and control of these organisms.
Related titles: Online - full text ed.: (from EBSCO Publishing, Gale Group, IngentaConnect, ScienceDirect, Swets Information Services).
Indexed: ASFA, AbHyg, AgBio, BioCN&I, BiolAb, CurCont, ESPM, FS&TA, GEOBASE, HerbAb, HortAb, I&DA, IndVet, OceAb, PBA, ProtozoAb, RA&MP, S&F, SeedAb, TDB, WeedAb, ZooRec.
—BLDSC (4264.216500), CISTI, IE, ingenta. **CCC.**
Published by: Elsevier BV (Subsidiary of: Elsevier Science & Technology), Radarweg 29, Amsterdam, 1043 NX, Netherlands. TEL 31-20-4853911, FAX 31-20-4852457, nlinfo-f@elsevier.nl, http://www.elsevier.com/locate/hal, http://www.elsevier.nl. Eds. Dr. Sandra E. Shumway, Theodore Smayda.

579 616.3 616.99 GBR ISSN 1083-4389
QR82.S6
➤ **HELICOBACTER (OXFORD).** Text in English. 1996. bi-m. GBP 125, EUR 188 combined subscription in Europe to individuals print & online eds.; USD 232 combined subscription in the Americas to individuals print & online eds.; GBP 138 combined subscription elsewhere to individuals print & online eds.; GBP 544 combined subscription in Europe to institutions print & online eds.; USD 1,006 combined subscription in the Americas to institutions & Caribbean (print & online eds.); GBP 599 combined subscription elsewhere to institutions print & online eds. (effective 2006). adv. reprint service avail. from PSC. **Document type:** *Journal, Academic/Scholarly.* **Description:** Investigates the critical role Helicobacter plays in peptic ulcers, gastric adenocarcinoma, and primary gastric lymphoma.
Related titles: Online - full text ed.: ISSN 1523-5378. GBP 517 in Europe to institutions; USD 956 in the Americas to institutions & Caribbean; GBP 569 elsewhere to institutions (effective 2006) (from Blackwell Synergy, EBSCO Publishing, Gale Group, IngentaConnect, O C L C Online Computer Library Center, Inc., Ovid Technologies, Inc., Swets Information Services).
Indexed: AbHyg, BIOSIS Prev, BiolAb, CurCont, ESPM, ExcerpMed, HelmAb, HortAb, INI, ISR, IndMed, IndVet, Inpharma, MEDLINE, NutrAb, PE&ON, RA&MP, Reac, RefZh, SCI, SIA, TDB, VetBull.
—BLDSC (4285.102500), CISTI, GNLM, IDS, IE, Infotrieve, ingenta. **CCC.**
Published by: Blackwell Publishing Ltd., 9600 Garsington Rd, Oxford, OX4 2ZG, United Kingdom. TEL 44-1865-776868, FAX 44-1865-714591, customerservices@oxon.blackwellpublishing.com, http://www.blackwellpublishing.com/journals/HEL. Ed. David Y Graham TEL 713-795-0232. Pub. Allen Stevens. R&P Sophie Savage. Adv. contact Jenny Applin. Circ: 1,000.

➤ **HOEHNEA.** see *BIOLOGY—Botany*

529 DEU ISSN 1433-3988
HYGIENE UND MIKROBIOLOGIE. Text in German. 1996. q. EUR 40 in Europe to institutions; JPY 5,500 in Japan to institutions; USD 51 to institutions except Europe and Japan (effective 2005). adv. **Document type:** *Journal, Academic/Scholarly.*
—**CCC.**
Published by: Deutsche Gesellschaft fuer Hygiene und Mikrobiologie, c/o Institut fuer Hygiene und Mikrobiologie, Universitaet Wuerzburg, Josef-Schneider-Str 2, Wuerzburg, 97080, Germany. TEL 49-931-20146165, FAX 49-931-20146445, gkleinwaechter@hygiene.uni-wuerzburg.de, http://www.dghm.org. Ed. Matthias Frosch. adv.: B&W page EUR 1,130, color page EUR 2,105; trim 210 x 280. Circ: 2,950 (paid and controlled).

IMMUNOHISTOCHEMISTRY. see *BIOLOGY—Abstracting, Bibliographies, Statistics*

579 IND ISSN 0970-9320
INDIAN JOURNAL OF COMPARATIVE MICROBIOLOGY, IMMUNOLOGY AND INFECTIOUS DISEASES. Text in English. s-a. USD 400 (effective 2006).
Indexed: AbHyg, AgBio, AnBrAb, DSA, HelmAb, HortAb, IndVet, NutrAb, PBA, PHN&I, PN&I, PoultAb, ProtozoAb, RDA, RM&VM, RPP, SIA, SoyAb, TDB, VetBull, WAE&RSA.
—BLDSC (4410.865000), IE, ingenta.
Published by: Scientific Publishers, 5-A New Pali Rd., Near Hotel Taj Hari Mahal, PO Box 91, Jodhpur, Rajasthan 342 003, India. TEL 91-291-2433323, FAX 91-291-2512580, info@scientificpub.com, http://www.scientificpub.com/bookdetails.php?booktransid=444&bookid=440.

579 IND ISSN 0046-8991
QR1 CODEN: IJMBAC
INDIAN JOURNAL OF MICROBIOLOGY. Text in English. 1961. q. USD 100 to institutions (effective 2006). adv. bk.rev. **Document type:** *Academic/Scholarly.*
Indexed: ASFA, AbHyg, AgBio, AgrForAb, AnBrAb, BioCN&I, BiolAb, CPA, ChemAb, DBA, DSA, ESPM, ExcerpMed, FCA, FPA, FS&TA, ForAb, HerbAb, HortAb, IndMed, IndVet, JDDR, MaizeAb, NutrAb, OrnHort, PBA, PGegResA, PGrRegA, PHN&I, PotatoAb, PoultAb, ProtozoAb, RA&MP, RM&VM, RPP, RevApplEntom, RiceAb, S&F, SIA, SeedAb, SoyAb, TDB, TriticAb, VetBull, WeedAb.
—BLDSC (4417.300000), CASDDS, CISTI, GNLM, IE, ingenta, Linda Hall. **CCC.**
Published by: (Association of Microbiologists of India), Scientific Publishers, 5-A New Pali Rd., Near Hotel Taj Hari Mahal, PO Box 91, Jodhpur, Rajasthan 342 003, India. TEL 91-291-2433323, FAX 91-291-2512580, info@scientificpub.com, http://www.scientificpub.com/bookdetails.php?booktransid=445&bookid=441. Ed. Dr. K S Gopalkrishnan. Circ: 2,000. **Dist. by:** H P C Publishers Distributors Pvt. Ltd.

579   IND   ISSN 0377-4929
CODEN: IJPMDT

➤ **INDIAN JOURNAL OF PATHOLOGY & MICROBIOLOGY.** Text in English. 1949. q. INR 300 to individuals; INR 5,000 to institutions (effective 2004). adv. bk.rev. abstr.; bibl.; charts; illus. index. back issues avail.; reprint service avail. from IRC. **Document type:** *Academic/Scholarly.*
Formerly: Indian Journal of Pathology and Bacteriology (0019-5448)
Related titles: CD-ROM ed.; Diskette ed.
Indexed: BiolAb, ChemAb, DentInd, ExcerpMed, ExtraMED, FS&TA, IndMed, IndVet, JDDR, MEDLINE, NutrAb, RM&VM, RPP, VetBull.
—BLDSC (4417.950000), CISTI, GNLM, IE, Infotrieve, ingenta, KNAW.
Published by: Indian Association of Pathologists and Microbiologists, C/o Harsh Mohan, Dept. of Pathology., Government Medical College, Sector 32-A, Chandigarh, Bihar 160 030, India. TEL 91-172-664136, drharshmohan@yahoo.com, http://www.iapm.net/journal.htm. Ed. Dr. Harsh Mohan. adv.: page INR 7,000. Circ: 4,500.

➤ **INFECTOLOGIA Y MICROBIOLOGIA CLINICA.** see *MEDICAL SCIENCES—Communicable Diseases*

579   GBR   ISSN 0952-1127
INNOVATION IN MICROBIOLOGY SERIES. Text in English. 1983. irreg., latest vol.5, 1993. GBP 55 (effective 2001). **Document type:** *Monographic series.*
—CISTI.
Published by: Research Studies Press Ltd., 16 Coach House Cloisters, 10 Hitchin St, Baldock, Hertfordshire SG7 6AE, United Kingdom. TEL 44-1462-895060, FAX 44-1462-892546, http://www.research-studies-press.co.uk. Ed. A N Sharpe.

579.2   DZA   ISSN 0020-2460
INSTITUT PASTEUR D'ALGERIE. ARCHIVES. Text in English, French. 1921. a. DZD 30, USD 6. bibl.; charts; illus.; stat. index.
Related titles: Microfilm ed.
Indexed: BioCN&I, BiolAb, DSA, ExcerpMed, IndMed, IndVet, MEDLINE, ProtozoAb, RevApplEntom, TDB, VetBull, ZooRec.
—CISTI, GNLM, Linda Hall.
Published by: Institut Pasteur d'Algerie, Rue du Docteur Laveran, Algiers, Algeria. TEL 67-25-02, TELEX 65337. Circ: 1,000.

579.2   SEN   ISSN 0377-3418
QR64.S382
INSTITUT PASTEUR DE DAKAR. RAPPORT SUR LE FONCTIONNEMENT TECHNIQUE. Text in French. 1938. a. free. **Document type:** *Yearbook, Corporate.* **Description:** Reports on medical research activities in virology, immunology and vaccinology, epidemiology and entomology, bacteriology.
Indexed: BiolAb.
Published by: Institut Pasteur Dakar, 36 av Pasteur, PO Box 220, Dakar, Senegal. TEL 221-839-9201, FAX 221-839-9210. Ed., Pub., R&P, Adv. contact Christian Mathiot. Circ: 600.

578.65   GRC   ISSN 0004-6620
CODEN: FIPCAO
INSTITUT PASTEUR HELLENIQUE. ARCHIVES. Text in French; Summaries in English, Greek. 1923. a. free. adv.
Indexed: AbHyg, BiolAb, IndVet, TDB, VetBull.
—CASDDS, GNLM.
Published by: Institut Pasteur Hellenique, 127 Reine Sophie Ave, Athens, 618, Greece. Ed. Charles Serie. Circ: 1,500.

579   JPN   ISSN 0073-8751
QR1
INSTITUTE FOR FERMENTATION, OSAKA. RESEARCH COMMUNICATIONS/HAKKO KENKYUJO HOKOKU. Text and summaries in English. 1963. biennial. JPY 1,300 per issue. cum.index. back issues avail. **Document type:** *Bulletin.* **Description:** Provides information on the institute's taxonomical research studies of microorganisms, basic studies on animal cells, and on the culture collection of the institute.
Formerly (until no.4, 1969): Institute for Fermentation, Osaka. Annual Report
Indexed: BIOSIS Prev, BiolAb, CBTA, MEDLINE, RM&VM, RPP, RefZh, RevApplEntom.
—BLDSC (7736.200000), CISTI.
Published by: Institute for Fermentation Osaka/Hakko Kenkyujo, 17-85 Juso-Hon-Machi 2-chome, Yodogawa-ku, Osaka-shi, 532-0024, Japan. FAX 81-6-6300-6814, yo@mb.infoweb.ne.jp, http://www.soc.nacsis.ac.jp/yo/index.html. Ed. Masao Takeuchi. Circ: 1,300.

579   BRA   ISSN 0073-9855
R25   CODEN: RIALA6
➤ **INSTITUTO ADOLFO LUTZ. REVISTA.** Text in English, Portuguese; Summaries in English, Portuguese. 1941. s-a. exchange basis. bibl.; charts; illus. index. **Document type:** *Journal, Academic/Scholarly.* **Description:** Original papers in experimental and laboratory medicine or public health laboratory with emphasis on microbiology, epidemiology, chemistry and food chemistry.

Indexed: ASFA, AbHyg, AgrForAb, Agrind, AnBrAb, AnalAb, BIOSIS Prev, BiolAb, ChemAb, ChemTitl, DSA, ESPM, ExcerpMed, FCA, FS&TA, HelmAb, HortAb, I&DA, IndMed, IndVet, MBA, MaizeAb, NutrAb, PHN&I, PN&I, PollutAb, PoultAb, ProtozoAb, RA&MP, RM&VM, RPP, RefZh, RevApplEntom, RiceAb, S&F, SIA, SeedAb, SoyAb, TDB, TriticAb, VetBull, VirolAbstr, WAE&RSA, ZooRec.
—BLDSC (7816.000000), CASDDS, Linda Hall.
Published by: (Diretoria Geral), Instituto Adolfo Lutz, Ave. Dr Arnaldo, 355, Centro, Caixa Postal 7027, Sao Paulo, SP 01064-970, Brazil. TEL 55-11-8510111, FAX 55-11-8533505. Ed. Luiz Carlos Meneguetti. Circ: 1,200.

616.9201 579.3   PRT   ISSN 0365-2998
INSTITUTO BACTERIOLOGICO DE CAMARA PESTANA. ARQUIVOS. Text in Multiple languages. 1906. irreg.
Indexed: AbHyg, HelmAb, IndVet, ProtozoAb, RM&VM, TDB.
—BLDSC (1686.900000), CISTI.
Published by: Universidade de Lisboa, Instituto Bacteriologico de Camara Pestana, Rua do Instituto Bacteriologico, Lisbon, 1169-110, Portugal. TEL 351-21-8823290, FAX 351-21-8851437, http://www.ul.pt/ibac.html.

579   USA   ISSN 0276-1076
QR187.5   CODEN: INRFDC
INTERFERON. Text in English. 1979. irreg., latest vol.9, 1987. USD 267.95 per vol. vol.119 (effective 2004). reprint service avail. from ISI.
Indexed: MEDLINE.
—CASDDS, CISTI, GNLM. **CCC.**
Published by: Academic Press (Subsidiary of: Elsevier Science & Technology), 525 B St, Ste 1900, San Diego, CA 92101-4495. TEL 619-231-6616, 800-894-3434, apsubs@acad.com, http://www.academicpress.com. Ed. I Gresser.

INTERNATIONAL CONFERENCE ON INTELLIGENT SYSTEMS FOR MOLECULAR BIOLOGY. PROCEEDINGS. see *BIOLOGY—Computer Applications*

INTERNATIONAL JOURNAL FOR PARASITOLOGY. see *MEDICAL SCIENCES—Communicable Diseases*

579   NLD   ISSN 0924-8579
CODEN: IAAGEA
➤ **INTERNATIONAL JOURNAL OF ANTIMICROBIAL AGENTS.** Text in English. 1991. 12/yr. EUR 1,325 in Europe to institutions; JPY 176,000 in Japan to institutions; USD 1,481 elsewhere to institutions (effective 2006). adv. back issues avail. **Document type:** *Journal, Academic/Scholarly.* **Description:** Provides information on the physical, chemical, pharmacological, in vitro and clinical properties of individual antimicrobial agents and immunotherapy.
Related titles: Microform ed.: (from PQC); Online - full text ed.: (from EBSCO Publishing, Gale Group, IngentaConnect, ScienceDirect, Swets Information Services).
Indexed: AEBA, AIDS Ab, ASCA, AbHyg, AgBio, AgrForAb, AnBrAb, BIOBASE, BIOSIS Prev, BioCN&I, BioEngAb, BiolAb, CIN, ChemAb, ChemTitl, CurCont, DBA, DSA, ESPM, ExcerpMed, HelmAb, HortAb, IABS, INI, ISR, IndMed, IndVet, Inpharma, M&PBA, MBA, MEDLINE, NutrAb, OrnHort, PE&ON, PN&I, PoultAb, ProtozoAb, RA&MP, RDA, RM&VM, RPP, RRTA, Reac, RevApplEntom, SCI, SIA, TDB, VetBull.
—BLDSC (4542.084000), CASDDS, CISTI, GNLM, IDS, IE, Infotrieve, ingenta, KNAW. **CCC.**
Published by: (International Society of Chemotherapy GBR), Elsevier BV (Subsidiary of: Elsevier Science & Technology), Radarweg 29, Amsterdam, 1043 NX, Netherlands. TEL 31-20-4853911, FAX 31-20-4852457, nlinfo-f@elsevier.nl, http://www.elsevier.com/locate/ijantimicag, http://www.elsevier.nl. Ed. Dr. A. M. Geddes.

579   NLD   ISSN 0168-1605
CODEN: IJFMDD
➤ **INTERNATIONAL JOURNAL OF FOOD MICROBIOLOGY.** Text and summaries in English. 1984. 24/yr. EUR 3,251 in Europe to institutions; JPY 431,600 in Japan to institutions; USD 3,635 to institutions except Europe and Japan; EUR 177 in Europe to qualified personnel; JPY 23,100 in Japan to qualified personnel; USD 198 to qualified personnel except Europe and Japan (effective 2006). adv. bk.rev. abstr.; bibl.; charts; illus. back issues avail. **Document type:** *Journal, Academic/Scholarly.* **Description:** Covers all aspects of microbiological safety, quality and acceptability of foods.
Related titles: Microform ed.: (from PQC); Online - full text ed.: (from EBSCO Publishing, Gale Group, IngentaConnect, ScienceDirect, Swets Information Services).
Indexed: AEA, AEBA, ASCA, ASFA, AbHyg, AgBio, Agr, AgrForAb, AnBrAb, ApicAb, B&BAb, BCI, BIOBASE, BIOSIS Prev, BibAg, BioCN&I, BioEngAb, BiolAb, CPA, CurCont, DSA, ESPM, EngInd, ExcerpMed, FCA, FPA, FS&TA, ForAb, H&SSA, HelmAb, HerbAb, HortAb, I&DA, IABS, INI, ISR, IndMed, IndVet, MBA, MEDLINE, MaizeAb, NutrAb, OceAb, OrnHort, PGrRegA, PHN&I, PN&I, PotatoAb, PoultAb, ProtozoAb, RA&MP, RM&VM, RPP, RRTA, RiceAb, S&F, SCI, SIA, SSCI, SeedAb, SoyAb, TDB, TriticAb, VITIS, VetBull, WAE&RSA.
—BLDSC (4542.253000), CASDDS, CISTI, Ei, GNLM, IDS, IE, Infotrieve, ingenta, Linda Hall. **CCC.**

Published by: (International Union of Microbiological Societies), Elsevier BV (Subsidiary of: Elsevier Science & Technology), Radarweg 29, Amsterdam, 1043 NX, Netherlands. TEL 31-20-4853911, FAX 31-20-4852457, nlinfo-f@elsevier.nl, http://www.elsevier.com/locate/ijfoodmicro, http://www.elsevier.nl. Ed. M Jakobsen. Circ: 700. **Co-sponsor:** International Committee on Food Microbiology and Hygiene.

➤ **INTERNATIONAL JOURNAL OF MEDICAL MICROBIOLOGY.** see *MEDICAL SCIENCES—Communicable Diseases*

579.3   GBR   ISSN 1466-5026
QR1   CODEN: ISEMF5
➤ **INTERNATIONAL JOURNAL OF SYSTEMATIC AND EVOLUTIONARY MICROBIOLOGY.** Text in English. 1951. bi-m. GBP 485 combined subscription domestic to institutions print & online; USD 815 combined subscription in North America to institutions print & online; GBP 495 combined subscription elsewhere to institutions print & online (effective 2005). adv. bk.rev. bibl.; charts; illus. index. back issues avail.; reprint service avail. from PQC. **Document type:** *Journal, Academic/Scholarly.* **Description:** Publishes papers concerned with the systematics of bacteria, yeasts and other eukaryotic micro organisms, including taxonomy, nomenclature, identification, characterization, and culture preservation.
Former titles (until 1999): International Journal of Systematic Bacteriology (0020-7713); (until 1966): International Bulletin of Bacteriological Nomenclature and Taxonomy
Related titles: CD-ROM ed.: ISSN 1070-6259. 1992; Microform ed.: (from PQC); Online - full text ed.: ISSN 1466-5034. GBP 440 domestic; USD 735 in North America; USD 445 elsewhere (effective 2005) (from EBSCO Publishing, HighWire Press).
Indexed: ABIPC, AEA, ASCA, ASFA, AbHyg, AgBio, Agr, AgrForAb, AnBrAb, BIOBASE, BIOSIS Prev, BioCN&I, BiolAb, BiolDig, CIN, ChemAb, ChemTitl, CurCont, DSA, ESPM, ExcerpMed, FCA, FPA, FS&TA, ForAb, GenetAb, HerbAb, HortAb, I&DA, IABS, ISR, IndMed, IndVet, Inpharma, MBA, MEDLINE, MaizeAb, NemAb, NutrAb, OrnHort, PBA, PGegResA, PGrRegA, PHN&I, PN&I, PotatoAb, PoultAb, ProtozoAb, RM&VM, RPP, Reac, RefZh, RevApplEntom, RiceAb, S&F, SAA, SCI, SFA, SIA, SoyAb, TDB, TriticAb, VITIS, VetBull, WeedAb, ZooRec.
—BLDSC (4542.688000), CASDDS, CISTI, GNLM, IDS, IE, Infotrieve, ingenta, Linda Hall. **CCC.**
Published by: (International Union of Microbiological Societies NLD, International Committee on Systematic Bacteriology), Society for General Microbiology, Marlborough House, Basingstoke Rd, Spencers Wood, Reading, Berks RG7 1AG, United Kingdom. TEL 44-118-9881800, FAX 44-118-9885656, ijsb@sgm.org.uk, http://ijs.sgmjournals.org, http://www.sgm.ac.uk. Ed. Dr. Peter Kaempfer. R&P Kendra Waite. Adv. contact Dr. Robin Dunford. B&W page USD 656, color page USD 1,312. Circ: 1,100.

579   ESP   ISSN 1139-6709
QR1
➤ **INTERNATIONAL MICROBIOLOGY.** Text in English. 1985. q., latest vol.6. EUR 258 domestic; EUR 267.90 foreign (effective 2005). adv. **Document type:** *Journal, Academic/Scholarly.* **Description:** Publishes original research papers, short communications, critical reviews and opinion letters dealing with all fields of microbiology and addressed to the international scientific community.
Formerly (until 1998): Microbiologia (0213-4101)
Related titles: Online - full text ed.: ISSN 1618-1905. 2001. free (effective 2005) (from EBSCO Publishing, Springer LINK, Swets Information Services).
Indexed: AbHyg, AgBio, AnBrAb, BIOSIS Prev, BiolAb, CurCont, ESPM, FCA, FS&TA, HortAb, IECT, IndMed, IndVet, MEDLINE, NutrAb, PBA, ProtozoAb, RM&VM, RPP, RevApplEntom, S&F, SIA, SoyAb, TDB, VITIS, VetBull, VirolAbstr, WeedAb.
—BLDSC (4544.178500), CINDOC, CISTI, IE, Infotrieve, ingenta. **CCC.**
Published by: Sociedad Espanola de Microbiologia, Vitruvio, 8, Madrid, 28006, Spain. TEL 34-915-613381, FAX 34-915-613299, semicro@wanadoo.es, http://www.im.microbios.org/, http://www.semicro.es. Ed. Ricardo Guerrero. Circ: 2,100.

579   USA
▼ ➤ **THE INTERNET JOURNAL OF MICROBIOLOGY.** Text in English. 2004. irreg. free to individuals; USD 500 to institutions (effective 2005). **Document type:** *Journal, Academic/Scholarly.*
Media: Online - full content.
Published by: Internet Scientific Publications, L.L.C., 23 Rippling Creek Dr, Sugar Land, TX 77479. TEL 832-443-1193, FAX 281-240-1533, wenker@ispub.com, http://www.ispub.com/ostia/index.php?xmlFilePath=journals/ijmb/front.xml.

579   USA   ISSN 1532-0227
CODEN: POCHES
➤ **INTERSCIENCE CONFERENCE ON ANTIMICROBIAL AGENTS AND CHEMOTHERAPY. ABSTRACTS.** Abbreviated title: I C A A C Program and Abstracts. Text in English. 1961. a. price varies. back issues avail. **Document type:** *Proceedings, Academic/Scholarly.*

Former titles (1993): Interscience Conference on Antimicrobial Agents and Chemotherapy. Program and Abstracts (0733-6373); (until 1971): Interscience Conference on Antimicrobial Agents and Chemotherapy. Abstracts of Papers (0535-4544)
Indexed: BIOSIS Prev.
—BLDSC (0564.529000), IDS, Linda Hall.
Published by: American Society for Microbiology, 1752 N St, N W, Washington, DC 20036-2904. TEL 202-737-3600, asmjournals@asm.org, subscriptions@asmusa.org, http://www.asm.org.

579.2 CHE ISSN 0300-5526
QR355 CODEN: IVRYAK
➤ **INTERVIROLOGY**; international journal of basic and medical virology. Text in English. 1973. bi-m. CHF 1,403 in Europe to institutions; CHF 1,423.40 elsewhere to institutions; CHF 1,512 combined subscription in Europe to institutions print & online eds.; CHF 1,532.40 combined subscription elsewhere to institutions print & online eds. (effective 2006). adv. bk.rev. bibl.; charts; illus. back issues avail. **Document type:** *Journal, Academic/Scholarly.* **Description:** Covers progress in both basic and clinical virus research, and aims to provide a forum of exchange among the various disciplines with virology.
Related titles: Microform ed.; Online - full text ed.: ISSN 1423-0100. CHF 1,361 to institutions (effective 2006) (from bigchalk, EBSCO Publishing, Northern Light Technology, Inc., O C L C Online Computer Library Center, Inc., ProQuest Information & Learning, Swets Information Services).
Indexed: AIDS Ab, AIDS&CR, AbHyg, AgBio, B&BAb, BIOSIS Prev, BiolAb, CIN, ChemAb, ChemTitl, CurCont, DSA, ExcerpMed, ForAb, GenetAb, HortAb, ISR, ISRS, IndMed, IndVet, Inpharma, MEDLINE, PBA, PE&ON, PN&I, PotatoAb, PoultAb, ProtozoAb, RM&VM, RPP, Reac, RevApplEntom, SCI, TDB, VetBull, ViroIAbstr.
—BLDSC (4557.472000), CASDDS, CISTI, GNLM, IDS, IE, Infotrieve, ingenta, KNAW, Linda Hall. **CCC.**
Published by: S. Karger AG, Allschwilerstr 10, Basel, 4009, Switzerland. TEL 41-61-3061111, FAX 41-61-3061234, karger@karger.ch, http://www.karger.com/INT, http://www.karger.ch. Ed. U G Liebert. adv.: page USD 1,185. Circ: 1,200.

579 ITA ISSN 0021-2547
CODEN: BISMAP
ISTITUTO SIEROTERAPICO MILANESE. BOLLETTINO. Text and summaries in Multiple languages. 1922. bi-m. adv. bk.rev. charts; illus.; stat.
Indexed: BiolAb, CurCont, DSA, ExcerpMed, IndMed, IndVet, MEDLINE, NutrAb, ProtozoAb, SCI, TDB, VetBull.
—CASDDS, CISTI, GNLM.
Published by: Istituto Sieroterapico Milanese, Via Darwin 22, Milan, 20100, Italy. Ed. Augusto De Barbieri. Circ: 2,000.

616.01 USA ISSN 1054-2744
QR46
➤ **JAWETZ, MELNICK & ADELBERG'S MEDICAL MICROBIOLOGY.** Text in English. 1954. biennial, latest vol.23, 2004. USD 49.95 per issue (effective 2005). 700 p./no.; **Document type:** *Academic/Scholarly.* **Description:** Descriptions of basic microbiology and virology; covers developments in the fields of biochemistry, genetics, pharmacology and immunology.
Former titles (until 1989): Medical Microbiology (1042-8089); (until 1987): Review of Medical Microbiology (0486-6118)
—CISTI. **CCC.**
Published by: McGraw-Hill Companies, Inc., 2 Penn Plaza, New York, NY 10121. TEL 212-512-2000, FAX 212-904-4209, customer.service@mcgraw-hill.com, http://www.mcgraw-hill.com.

➤ **JORNAL BRASILEIRO DE REPRODUCAO ASSISTIDA.** see *BIOLOGY—Biochemistry*

579.3 GBR ISSN 1364-5072
QR1 CODEN: JAMIFK
➤ **JOURNAL OF APPLIED MICROBIOLOGY.** Text in English. 1938. m. GBP 1,628 combined subscription in Europe to institutions print & online eds.; USD 3,009 combined subscription in the Americas to institutions & Caribbean (print & online eds.); GBP 1,791 combined subscription elsewhere to institutions print & online eds. (effective 2006); subscr. includes Letters in Applied Microbiology and supplement. adv. bk.rev. abstr.; bibl. index. back issues avail.; reprint service avail. from PSC. **Document type:** *Journal, Academic/Scholarly.* **Description:** Publishes papers on all aspects of applied microbiology, including environmental, food, agricultural, medical, pharmaceutical, veterinary, taxonomy, soil, water and biodeterioration.
Former titles (until 1997): Journal of Applied Bacteriology (0021-8847); (until 1954): Society for Applied Bacteriology. Proceedings (0370-1778); (until 1945): Society of Agricultural Bacteriologists. Proceedings (0370-1786)
Related titles: Microform ed.: (from PQC); Online - full text ed.: ISSN 1365-2672. GBP 1,547 in Europe to institutions; USD 2,858 in the Americas to institutions & Caribbean; GBP 1,701 elsewhere to institutions (effective 2006) (from Blackwell Synergy, EBSCO Publishing, Gale Group, IngentaConnect, O C L C Online Computer Library Center, Inc., Ovid Technologies, Inc., Swets Information Services); ♦ Supplement(s): Society for Applied Microbiology. Symposium Series. ISSN 1467-4734; ♦ Letters in Applied Microbiology. ISSN 0266-8254; ♦ Journal of Applied Microbiology. Supplement.
Indexed: AEA, AEBA, ASCA, ASFA, AbHyg, AgBio, Agr, AgrForAb, AnBrAb, B&AI, BCI, BIOBASE, BIOSIS Prev, BioCN&I, BioEngAb, BiolAb, CBTA, CEABA, CLL, CPA, ChemAb, CurCont, DBA, DSA, DentInd, ESPM, EngInd, EnvEAb, ExcerpMed, FCA, FLUIDEX, FPA, FS&TA, ForAb, GEOBASE, GenetAb, H&SSA, HGA, HerbAb, HortAb, I&DA, IABS, ISR, IndMed, IndVet, Inpharma, MBA, MEDLINE, MSB, MaizeAb, NemAb, NutrAb, OrnHort, PBA, PE&ON, PGegResA, PGrRegA, PHN&I, PN&I, PST, PollutAb, PotatoAb, PoultAb, ProtozoAb, RA&MP, RM&VM, RPP, RRTA, Reac, RefZh, RevApplEntom, RiceAb, S&F, SCI, SFA, SIA, SWRA, SeedAb, SoyAb, TDB, Telegen, TriticAb, VITIS, VetBull, WRCInf, WeedAb, ZooRec.
—BLDSC (4943.070000), CASDDS, CISTI, Ei, GNLM, IDS, IE, Infotrieve, ingenta, Linda Hall. **CCC.**
Published by: (Society for Applied Bacteriology), Blackwell Publishing Ltd., 9600 Garsington Rd, Oxford, OX4 2ZG, United Kingdom. TEL 44-1865-776868, FAX 44-1865-714591, customerservices@oxon.blackwellpublishing.com, http://www.blackwellpublishing.com/journals/JAM. Ed. A F Godfree. Pub. Amanda McLean Inglis. R&P Sophie Savage. Adv. contact Jenny Applin. Circ: 2,770.

579 GBR
CODEN: SMSSFP
JOURNAL OF APPLIED MICROBIOLOGY. SUPPLEMENT. Text in English. irreg. GBP 1,327 in Europe to institutions; USD 2,365 in the Americas to institutions; GBP 1,460 elsewhere to institutions (effective 2004); included with subscr. to Journal of Applied Microbiology. adv. **Document type:** *Academic/Scholarly.*
Formerly: Journal of Applied Bacteriology. Symposium Supplement (0267-4440)
Related titles: Online - full text ed.; ♦ Supplement to: Journal of Applied Microbiology. ISSN 1364-5072.
Indexed: AEA, AbHyg, BIOBASE, DSA, ESPM, ExcerpMed, FS&TA, IABS, IndVet, NutrAb, PoultAb, ProtozoAb, RRTA, TDB, VetBull.
—BLDSC (8585.784000), CASDDS. **CCC.**
Published by: Blackwell Publishing Ltd., 9600 Garsington Rd, Oxford, OX4 2ZG, United Kingdom. TEL 44-1865-776868, FAX 44-1865-714591, customerservices@oxon.blackwellpublishing.com, http://www.blackwellpublishing.com. Pub. Amanda McLean Inglis. R&P Sophie Savage. Adv. contact Jenny Applin.

JOURNAL OF APPLIED PHYCOLOGY. see *BIOLOGY—Botany*

579.3 USA ISSN 0021-9193
QR1 CODEN: JOBAAY
➤ **JOURNAL OF BACTERIOLOGY.** Text in English. 1916. fortn. USD 883 domestic to institutions; USD 924 in Canada to institutions; USD 980 in Europe to institutions; USD 1,013 in Latin America to institutions; USD 1,018 elsewhere to institutions (effective 2006). abstr.; bibl.; illus. index. back issues avail.; reprint service avail. from PQC. **Document type:** *Journal, Academic/Scholarly.* **Description:** Devoted to the advancement of fundamental knowledge concerning bacteria and other microorganisms, including fungi and other unicellular, eucaryotic organisms.
Related titles: CD-ROM ed.: ISSN 1067-8832. 1992. USD 500 in North America; USD 524 elsewhere (effective 1999); Microform ed.: (from PQC); Online - full text ed.: ISSN 1098-5530. USD 827 to institutions (effective 2006) (from EBSCO Publishing, HighWire Press, National Library of Medicine).
Indexed: ABIPC, AEBA, ASCA, ASFA, AbHyg, AgBio, Agr, AgrForAb, AnBrAb, B&AI, B&BAb, BBCI, BCI, BIOBASE, BIOSIS Prev, BibAg, BioCN&I, BiolAb, BiolDig, CBTA, CCI, CIN, CPA, ChemAb, ChemTitl, CurCont, DBA, DSA, DentInd, ESPM, ExcerpMed, FCA, FPA, FS&TA, GSI, GenetAb, HGA, HelmAb, HerbAb, HortAb, I&DA, IAA, IABS, INIS AtomInd, ISR, IndMed, IndVet, Inpharma, JDDR, MBA, MEDLINE, MS&D, MaizeAb, NemAb, NucAcAb, NutrAb, PBA, PE&ON, PGrRegA, PHN&I, PN&I, PotatoAb, PoultAb, ProtozoAb, RA&MP, RM&VM, RPP, Reac, RefZh, RevApplEntom, RiceAb, S&F, SCI, SFA, SIA, SeedAb, SoyAb, TDB, Telegen, TriticAb, VITIS, VetBull, WRCInf, WeedAb.
—BLDSC (4951.000000), CASDDS, CISTI, GNLM, IDS, IE, Infotrieve, ingenta, Linda Hall. **CCC.**
Published by: American Society for Microbiology, 1752 N St, N W, Washington, DC 20036-2904. TEL 202-942-9319, 202-737-3600, FAX 202-942-9347, asmjournals@asm.org, subscriptions@asmusa.org, http://jb.asm.org/, http://www.asm.org. Eds. Graham C Walker, Philip Matsumura. Circ: 10,839 (paid). **Subscr. to:** PO Box 11127, Birmingham, AL 35201-1127. TEL 205-995-1567, 800-633-4931, FAX 205-995-1588.

616.9201 616.9101 KOR ISSN 1598-2467
CODEN: TMHCDX
JOURNAL OF BACTERIOLOGY AND VIROLOGY/KOREAN SOCIETY FOR MICROBIOLOGY. JOURNAL. Text in Korean; Abstracts and contents page in English. 1957. q. adv. bibl.; charts. **Document type:** *Journal, Academic/Scholarly.* **Description:** Devoted to the dissemination of new knowledge describing bacteria, viruses, fungi, and other micro-organisms and their interactions with host and other related fields.
Formed by the 2001 merger of: Daehan Misaengmul Hakhoe Chi (0253-3162); Daehan Baireoseu Haghoeji (1225-2344)
Indexed: BIOBASE, CIN, ChemAb, ChemTitl, ExcerpMed, IndVet, ProtozoAb, RevApplEntom, VetBull.
—BLDSC (4951.005000), CASDDS, GNLM, IE.
Published by: (Korean Society for Virology/Daehan Virus Hag-Hoe), Korean Society for Microbiology/Taehan Misaengmul Hakhoe, c/o Dept. of Microbiology, Chonnan National University Medical School, 5-1 Hak-dong Dong-ku, Kwangju, 501-190, Korea, S. TEL 82-62-2204132, FAX 82-62-2287294, http://ksmkorea.org/molecules%20&%20cells_3.htm. Ed. Sun Sik Chung. Circ: 400.

579 DEU ISSN 0233-111X
QR1 CODEN: JBMIEQ
➤ **JOURNAL OF BASIC MICROBIOLOGY**; an international journal on biochemistry, physiology, genetics, morphology and ecology of microorganisms. Text in English. 1960. bi-m. EUR 778 in Europe; CHF 1,248 in Switzerland & Liechtenstein; USD 998 elsewhere; EUR 856 combined subscription in Europe print & online eds.; CHF 1,373 combined subscription in Switzerland & Liechtenstein for print & online eds.; USD 1,098 combined subscription elsewhere print & online eds. (effective 2006). adv. bk.rev. abstr.; charts; illus. index. **Document type:** *Journal, Academic/Scholarly.* **Description:** Publishes results of fundamental research on procariotic and eucariotic microorganisms.
Formerly (until 1985): Zeitschrift fuer Allgemeine Mikrobiologie (0044-2208)
Related titles: Online - full text ed.: ISSN 1521-4028. EUR 778 in Europe; CHF 1,248 in Switzerland & Liechtenstein; USD 998 elsewhere (effective 2006) (from EBSCO Publishing, Swets Information Services, Wiley InterScience).
Indexed: ASCA, AbHyg, AgBio, BIOBASE, BIOSIS Prev, BioCN&I, BiolAb, CBTA, CIN, ChemAb, ChemTitl, CurCont, DBA, DSA, ExcerpMed, FCA, FPA, FS&TA, ForAb, HelmAb, HerbAb, HortAb, I&DA, IABS, ISR, IndMed, IndVet, Inpharma, MEDLINE, MaizeAb, NutrAb, PBA, PGegResA, PGrRegA, PHN&I, PoultAb, ProtozoAb, RA&MP, RM&VM, RPP, Reac, RefZh, RevApplEntom, RiceAb, S&F, SCI, SIA, SSCI, SeedAb, SoyAb, TDB, TriticAb, VITIS, VetBull, WeedAb.
—BLDSC (4951.125000), CASDDS, CISTI, GNLM, IDS, IE, Infotrieve, ingenta, Linda Hall. **CCC.**
Published by: Wiley - V C H Verlag GmbH & Co. KGaA (Subsidiary of: John Wiley & Sons, Inc.), Boschstr 12, Weinheim, 69469, Germany. FAX 49-6201-606-117, adsales@wiley-vch.de, subservice@wiley-vch.de, http://www3.interscience.wiley.com/cgi-bin/home. Eds. Erika Kothe, Horst Malke. R&P Claudia Rutz. Adv. contact Aenne Anders TEL 49-6201-606552. **Subscr. in the Americas to:** John Wiley & Sons, Inc., 111 River St, Hoboken, NJ 07030-5774. TEL 201-748-6645, FAX 201-748-6088, subinfo@wiley.com; **Subscr. outside Germany, Austria & Switzerland to:** John Wiley & Sons Ltd., The Atrium, Southern Gate, Chichester, West Sussex PO19 8SQ, United Kingdom. TEL 44-1243-779777, FAX 44-1243-775878.

➤ **JOURNAL OF CLINICAL MICROBIOLOGY.** see *MEDICAL SCIENCES*

579 BGR ISSN 1310-8360
JOURNAL OF CULTURE COLLECTIONS. Text in English; Summaries in English, Bulgarian. 1995. irreg. free (effective 2005). **Description:** Publishes research papers with original results in the field of collection and preservation of microbial and cell cultures and viruses.
Media: Online - full content.
Published by: National Bank for Industrial Microorganisms and Cell Cultures, 125, Tsarigradsko Shausse Blvd., bl. 2, Sofia, 1113, Bulgaria. TEL 359-2-725-865, nbimcc@cablebg.net, http://www.bioline.org.br/cc. Ed. Dr. Angela Yordanova.

579 USA ISSN 1066-5234
QL366 CODEN: JEMIED
➤ **THE JOURNAL OF EUKARYOTIC MICROBIOLOGY.** Text in English. 1954. bi-m. USD 294 combined subscription in the Americas to institutions & Caribbean (print & online eds.); GBP 180 combined subscription elsewhere to institutions print & online eds. (effective 2006). adv. bk.rev. bibl.; charts; illus. Index. back issues avail.; reprint service avail. from PSC. **Document type:** *Journal, Academic/Scholarly.* **Description:** It covers all aspects of these organisms, including their behavior, biochemistry, cellbiology, chemotherapy, development, ecology, evolution, genetics, molecular biology, morphogenetics, parasitology, physiology, systematics, and ultrastructure.
Formerly (until 1993): Journal of Protozoology (0022-3921)
Related titles: Online - full text ed.: ISSN 1550-7408. USD 279 in the Americas to institutions & Caribbean; GBP 171 elsewhere to institutions (effective 2006) (from BioOne, Blackwell Synergy, C S A, EBSCO Publishing, O C L C Online Computer Library Center, Inc., Swets Information Services).

Indexed: ASCA, ASFA, AbHyg, AgBio, Agr, AgrForAb, AnBrAb, B&AI, B&BAb, BIOBASE, BIOSIS Prev, BibAg, BioCN&I, BiolAb, BiolDig, CIN, CRFR, ChemAb, ChemTitl, CurCont, DBA, DSA, DentInd, ExcerpMed, ForAb, GEOBASE, GenetAb, HGA, HelmAb, HortAb, I&DA, IABS, ISR, IndMed, IndVet, Inpharma, MBA, MEDLINE, NutrAb, PN&I, PoultAb, ProtozoAb, RA&MP, RM&VM, RPP, Reac, RevApplEntom, RiceAb, S&F, SCI, SFA, SIA, SoyAb, TDB, VetBull, WeedAb, WildRev, ZooRec.

—BLDSC (4979.602740), CASDDS, CISTI, GNLM, IDS, IE, Infotrieve, ingenta, KNAW, Linda Hall. **CCC.**

Published by: (Society of Protozoologists), Blackwell Publishing, Inc. (Subsidiary of: Blackwell Publishing Ltd.), Commerce Place, 350 Main St, Malden, MA 02148. TEL 781-388-8206, FAX 781-388-8232, http://www.blackwellpublishing.com/journal.asp?ref=1066-5234&site=1. Ed. Denis H Lynn. Circ: 1,800.

➤ **JOURNAL OF FOOD SAFETY.** see *FOOD AND FOOD INDUSTRIES*

579 JPN ISSN 0022-1260
QR1 CODEN: JGAMA9

➤ **THE JOURNAL OF GENERAL AND APPLIED MICROBIOLOGY.** Text in English. 1955. bi-m. JPY 8,000 domestic (effective 2004). charts; illus. reprint service avail. from PQC. **Document type:** *Journal, Academic/Scholarly.*

Description: Devoted to the publication of original papers pertaining to general and applied microbiology.

Related titles: Microform ed.: (from PQC); Online - full text ed.: ISSN 1349-8037 (from J-Stage).

Indexed: AEBA, AESIS, ASCA, ASFA, AgBio, Agr, BCI, BIOBASE, BIOSIS Prev, BioCN&I, BiolAb, CBTA, CEABA, CIN, ChemAb, ChemTitl, CurCont, DBA, DSA, ESPM, EngInd, ExcerpMed, FCA, FS&TA, ForAb, GenetAb, HerbAb, HortAb, IABS, INIS AtomInd, ISR, IndVet, Inpharma, JTA, MBA, NutrAb, PBA, PE&ON, PN&I, RM&VM, RPP, Reac, RefZh, S&F, SCI, SFA, SIA, SoyAb, VITIS, VetBull.

—BLDSC (4987.700000), CASDDS, CISTI, Ei, GNLM, IDS, IE, Infotrieve, ingenta, Linda Hall. **CCC.**

Published by: Microbiology Research Foundation/Oyo Biseibutsugaku Kenkyu Shoreikai, c/o Center for Academic Publications Japan, 4-16, Yayoi 2-chome, Bunkyo-ku, Tokyo, 113-0032, Japan. shoreikai@q00.itscom.net, http://www.iam.u-tokyo.ac.jp/JGAM/general.htm, http://www.iam.u-tokyo.ac.jp/shoureikai/h16/index.html. Circ: 680. **Dist. by:** Maruzen Co., Ltd., Export Dept., PO Box 5050, Tokyo International 100-3191, Japan. FAX 81-3-3278-9256, journal@maruzen.co.jp, http://www.maruzen.co.jp. **Dist. by:** Japan Publications Trading Co., Ltd., Book Export II Dept, PO Box 5030, Tokyo International, Tokyo 101-3191, Japan. TEL 81-3-32923753, FAX 81-3-32920410, infoserials@jptco.co.jp, http://www.jptco.co.jp. **Co-sponsor:** University of Tokyo, Institute of Molecular and Cellular Biosciences.

579.2 GBR ISSN 0022-1317
QR360 CODEN: JGVIAY

➤ **JOURNAL OF GENERAL VIROLOGY.** Text in English. 1967. m. GBP 785 combined subscription domestic to institutions print & online; USD 1,375 combined subscription in North America to institutions print & online; GBP 805 combined subscription elsewhere to institutions print & online (effective 2005). adv. bibl.; charts; illus. index. 3000 p./no. 2 cols./p.; back issues avail.; reprints avail. **Document type:** *Journal, Academic/Scholarly.* **Description:** Contains topical research on all aspects of viruses & prions.

Related titles: Online - full text ed.: ISSN 1465-2099. GBP 710 domestic; GBP 1,240 in North America; GBP 725 elsewhere (effective 2005) (from EBSCO Publishing, HighWire Press).

Indexed: AIDS Ab, AIDS&CR, ASCA, ASFA, AbHyg, AgBio, Agr, AgrForAb, AnBrAb, B&BAb, BCI, BIOBASE, BIOSIS Prev, BibAg, BioCN&I, BiolAb, CBTA, CEABA, CIN, CPA, ChemAb, ChemTitl, CurCont, DBA, DSA, DentInd, ExcerpMed, FCA, FS&TA, ForAb, GenetAb, HGA, HortAb, IABS, ISR, ImmunAb, IndMed, IndVet, Inpharma, JDDR, MEDLINE, MaizeAb, NSCI, NemAb, NucAcAb, NutrAb, OrnHort, PBA, PE&ON, PGegResA, PN&I, PotatoAb, PoultAb, ProtozoAb, RA&MP, RM&VM, RPP, Reac, RefZh, RevApplEntom, RiceAb, S&F, SAA, SCI, SFA, SIA, SoyAb, TDB, TOSA, TriticAb, VITIS, VetBull, VirolAbstr, WeedAb, WildRev, ZooRec.

—BLDSC (4989.300000), CASDDS, CISTI, GNLM, IDS, IE, Infotrieve, ingenta, Linda Hall. **CCC.**

Published by: Society for General Microbiology, Marlborough House, Basingstoke Rd, Spencers Wood, Reading, Berks RG7 1AG, United Kingdom. TEL 44-118-9881800, FAX 44-118-9885656, jgv@sgm.ac.uk, http://vir.sgmjournals.org, http://www.sgm.ac.uk. Ed. Dr. G L Smith. R&P Mrs. Marianne Asbury TEL 44-188-988-1825. Adv. contact Dr. John Brimelow TEL 44-188-988-1808. Circ: 1,550.

➤ **JOURNAL OF INDUSTRIAL MICROBIOLOGY AND BIOTECHNOLOGY.** see *BIOLOGY—Biotechnology*

616.0194 616.014 GBR ISSN 0022-2615
QR46 CODEN: JMMIAV

➤ **THE JOURNAL OF MEDICAL MICROBIOLOGY.** Text in English. 1968. m. GBP 625 combined subscription domestic to institutions print & online; USD 1,095 combined subscription in North America to institutions print & online; GBP 635 combined subscription elsewhere to institutions print & online (effective 2005). adv. bk.rev. bibl.; charts; illus. back issues avail. **Document type:** *Journal, Academic/Scholarly.*

Description: Publishes original articles covering medical, dental, veterinary and food microbiology, including bacteriology, virology, mycology and parasitology.

Supersedes in part (in 1968): Journal of Pathology and Bacteriology (0368-3494)

Related titles: Microform ed.: (from PQC); Online - full text ed.: ISSN 1473-5644. GBP 565 domestic; USD 985 in North America; GBP 570 elsewhere (effective 2005) (from EBSCO Publishing, HighWire Press, O C L C Online Computer Library Center, Inc., Ovid Technologies, Inc.).

Indexed: ASCA, ASFA, AbHyg, AgBio, BIOBASE, BIOSIS Prev, BioCN&I, BiolAb, ChemAb, ChemTitl, CurCont, DBA, DSA, ESPM, ExcerpMed, FS&TA, H&SSA, HelmAb, HortAb, IABS, ISR, IndMed, IndVet, Inpharma, JDDR, MBA, MEDLINE, NutrAb, PE&ON, PN&I, PoultAb, ProtozoAb, RA&MP, RM&VM, RPP, Reac, RevApplEntom, S&F, SCI, SIA, SoyAb, TDB, VetBull, VirolAbstr.

—BLDSC (5017.079000), CASDDS, CISTI, GNLM, IDS, IE, Infotrieve, ingenta, KNAW. **CCC.**

Published by: Society for General Microbiology, Marlborough House, Basingstoke Rd, Spencers Wood, Reading, Berks RG7 1AG, United Kingdom. TEL 44-118-9881800, FAX 44-118-9885656, jsales@sgm.ac.uk, http://jmm.sgmjournals.org, http://www.sgm.ac.uk. Ed. Dr. Ian R Poxton. Pub. Dr. Ron S S Fraser. R&P Mrs. Sarah Ferris. Adv. contact Dr. Robin Dunford. Circ: 1,500.

579 NLD ISSN 0167-7012
QR65 CODEN: JMIMDQ

➤ **JOURNAL OF MICROBIOLOGICAL METHODS.** Text in English. 1983. 12/yr. EUR 2,129 in Europe to institutions; JPY 282,700 in Japan to institutions; USD 2,383 elsewhere to institutions (effective 2006). abstr. back issues avail. **Document type:** *Academic/Scholarly.* **Description:** Publishes original papers and short reviews covering methods on all aspects of microbiology, excluding virology.

Related titles: Microform ed.: (from PQC); Online - full text ed.: (from EBSCO Publishing, Gale Group, IngentaConnect, ScienceDirect, Swets Information Services).

Indexed: ABIPC, AEA, AEBA, ASCA, ASFA, AbHyg, AgBio, Agr, AgrForAb, BCI, BIOBASE, BIOSIS Prev, BioCN&I, BioDAb, BioEngAb, BiolAb, CBTA, CEABA, CIN, ChemAb, ChemTitl, CurCont, DBA, DSA, ESPM, ExcerpMed, FCA, FPA, FS&TA, ForAb, HelmAb, HerbAb, HortAb, I&DA, IABS, ISR, IndMed, IndVet, Inpharma, MBA, MEDLINE, MSB, MaizeAb, NemAb, NutrAb, PBA, PE&ON, PGegResA, PGrRegA, PHN&I, PN&I, PotatoAb, PoultAb, ProtozoAb, RA&MP, RM&VM, RPP, Reac, RevApplEntom, RiceAb, S&F, SCI, SIA, SoyAb, TDB, VITIS, VetBull, VirolAbstr.

—BLDSC (5019.260000), CASDDS, CISTI, GNLM, IDS, IE, Infotrieve, ingenta, Linda Hall. **CCC.**

Published by: Elsevier BV (Subsidiary of: Elsevier Science & Technology), Radarweg 29, Amsterdam, 1043 NX, Netherlands. TEL 31-20-4853911, FAX 31-20-4852457, nlinfo-f@elsevier.nl, http://www.elsevier.com/locate/jmicmeth, http://www.elsevier.nl. Ed. A. Fox.

579 KOR ISSN 1225-8873

➤ **THE JOURNAL OF MICROBIOLOGY.** Text in English. 1995. q. USD 70 includes membership (effective 2003). **Document type:** *Academic/Scholarly.* **Description:** Publishes descriptions of basic research on microorganisms, including fungi and other unicellular eukaryotic organisms. Topics include structure and function, biochemistry, enzymology, metabolism and its regulation, molecular biology, genetics, plasmids and transposons, general microbiology, applied microbiology, genetic engineering, virology, immunology, clinical microbiology, microbial ecology, environmental microbiology, food microbiology, molecular systematics, chemical or physical haracterization of microbial structures or products, and basic biological properties of organisms.

Indexed: AgBio, BCI, BioCN&I, FS&TA, IndVet, PN&I, S&F, SoyAb, VetBull.

—BLDSC (5019.285700), CISTI, IE, ingenta.

Published by: Han-Gug Misaengmul Hag-hoe/The Mircobiological Society of Korea, R803, KSTC New B/D, 635-4, Yeogsam-dong, Kangnam-ku, Seoul, 136-703, Korea, S. TEL 82-2-34533321, FAX 82-2-34533322, msk@msk.or.kr, http://www.msk.or.kr/jm/jmhome.htm. Ed. Doo-Hyun Nam.

➤ **JOURNAL OF MICROBIOLOGY AND BIOTECHNOLOGY.** see *BIOLOGY—Biotechnology*

579 HKG ISSN 1684-1182
QR1 CODEN: CKWCD9

➤ **JOURNAL OF MICROBIOLOGY, IMMUNOLOGY AND INFECTION/WEIMIAN YU GANRAN ZAZHI.** Text in English. 1968. q. USD 90 (effective 2003). adv. abstr. index. 100 p./no.; **Document type:** *Academic/Scholarly.*

Former titles (until 1998): Chinese Journal of Microbiology and Immunology (0253-2662); (until 1980): Chinese Journal of Microbiology (0009-4587)

Related titles: CD-ROM ed.

Indexed: AIDS&CR, ASFA, AbHyg, BIOSIS Prev, BioDAb, BiolAb, CTA, ChemAb, DSA, ESPM, ExcerpMed, ExtraMED, FS&TA, H&SSA, HelmAb, IndMed, IndVet, MEDLINE, NutrAb, PBA, PN&I, PoultAb, ProtozoAb, RA&MP, RM&VM, RevApplEntom, S&F, SoyAb, TDB, VetBull, VirolAbstr, WeedAb.

—BLDSC (5019.320000), CASDDS, CISTI, GNLM, ingenta.

Published by: (Chinese Society of Microbiology TWN), Lippincott Williams & Wilkins Asia, Ste 907-910, New T&T Centre, Harbour City, 7 Canton Rd, Tsimshatsui, Kowtoon, Hong Kong. TEL 852-2610-2339, FAX 852-2421-1123. Ed. Yu Tien Liu. Pub. Czau Sium Yang. Circ: 4,000. **Co-sponsor:** Chinese Society of Immunology, Infectious Diseases Society of Republic of China.

549 CHE ISSN 1464-1801
CODEN: JMMBFF

➤ **JOURNAL OF MOLECULAR MICROBIOLOGY AND BIOTECHNOLOGY.** Text in English. 1999. 6/yr. CHF 1,319 in Europe to institutions; CHF 1,339.40 elsewhere to institutions; CHF 1,421 combined subscription in Europe to institutions pirnt & online eds.; CHF 1,441.40 combined subscription elsewhere to institutions pirnt & online eds. (effective 2006). back issues avail. **Document type:** *Journal, Academic/Scholarly.* **Description:** Publishes high-quality primary research papers, along with reviews and written symposia, in the fields of molecular microbiology and biotechnology.

Related titles: Online - full text ed.: ISSN 1475-3774. CHF 1,277 to institutions (effective 2006) (from EBSCO Publishing, O C L C Online Computer Library Center, Inc., Swets Information Services).

Indexed: AEBA, AIDS&CR, ASFA, AbHyg, AgBio, AgrForAb, B&BAb, BCI, BIOBASE, BIOSIS Prev, BioEngAb, BiolAb, CPA, ChemAb, DSA, ESPM, ExcerpMed, FCA, GenetAb, HortAb, IndMed, IndVet, M&PBA, MBA, MEDLINE, MaizeAb, NutrAb, PBA, PGrRegA, ProtozoAb, RPP, S&F, SIA, TDB, ToxAb, VetBull, VirolAbstr, ZooRec.

—BLDSC (5020.716250), CISTI, IE, Infotrieve, ingenta. **CCC.**

Published by: S. Karger AG, Allschwilerstr 10, Basel, 4009, Switzerland. TEL 41-61-3061111, FAX 41-61-3061234, karger@karger.ch, http://www.karger.com/MMB, http://www.karger.ch. Ed. M H Saier Jr.

579 IND ISSN 0971-3719

➤ **JOURNAL OF MYCOPATHOLOGICAL RESEARCH.** Text in English. 1955. s-a. USD 40 per issue (effective 1999). adv. bk.rev. **Document type:** *Academic/Scholarly.* **Description:** Covers taxonomy, physiology and biochemistry of microorganisms, molecular basis of host-parasite interactions, industrial microbiology and microbial biotechnology.

Formerly: Indian Journal of Mycological Research (0537-2054)

Indexed: AbHyg, AgBio, AgrForAb, BioCN&I, BiolAb, CPA, DSA, FCA, FPA, FS&TA, ForAb, HerbAb, HortAb, ISA, MaizeAb, NemAb, NutrAb, OrnHort, PBA, PGegResA, PGrRegA, PHN&I, PotatoAb, RA&MP, RM&VM, RPP, RevApplEntom, RiceAb, S&F, SIA, SeedAb, SoyAb, TDB, TriticAb, WAE&RSA, WeedAb.

—BLDSC (5021.172000), CISTI, IE, ingenta, Linda Hall.

Published by: Indian Mycological Society, Department of Botany, University of Calcutta, 35 B C Rd., Kolkata, West Bengal 700 019, India. TEL 91-33-5514189, FAX 91-33-4753681. Ed. Nirmalendu Samajpati. Pub. A K Manna. R&P, Adv. contact Anil Kumar Manna. page USD 200. Circ: 500.

➤ **JOURNAL OF PARASITOLOGY.** see *MEDICAL SCIENCES—Communicable Diseases*

579 USA ISSN 1060-3999
QR69.A88 CODEN: JRMMEE

➤ **JOURNAL OF RAPID METHODS AND AUTOMATION IN MICROBIOLOGY.** Text in English. 1992. q. USD 65 combined subscription in the Americas to individuals print & online eds.; EUR 95 combined subscription in Europe to individuals print & online eds.; GBP 63 combined subscription elsewhere to individuals print & online eds.; USD 205 combined subscription in the Americas to institutions print & online eds.; GBP 151 combined subscription elsewhere to institutions print & online eds. (effective 2006). bk.rev. abstr.; bibl.; charts; illus.; stat. back issues avail.; reprint service avail. from PSC. **Document type:** *Journal, Academic/Scholarly.* **Description:** Publishes information on methods developed by scientists for the rapid isolation, detection, enumeration, and identification of microorganisms.

Related titles: Online - full text ed.: ISSN 1745-4581. USD 195 in the Americas to institutions; GBP 143 elsewhere to institutions (effective 2006) (from Blackwell Synergy, EBSCO Publishing, O C L C Online Computer Library Center, Inc., Swets Information Services).

Indexed: AEBA, AbHyg, Agr, B&BAb, BioEngAb, CIN, ChemAb, ChemTitl, CurCont, DSA, ESPM, FS&TA, IndVet, NutrAb, PN&I, PoultAb, ProtozoAb, RM&VM, S&F, SoyAb, VetBull.

—BLDSC (5046.200000), CASDDS, CISTI, IDS, IE, ingenta. **CCC.**

Published by: Blackwell Publishing, Inc. (Subsidiary of: Blackwell Publishing Ltd.), Commerce Place, 350 Main St, Malden, MA 02148. TEL 781-388-8206, FAX 781-388-8232, subscrip@blackwellpub.com, http://www.blackwellpublishing.com. Ed. Daniel Y C Fung.

▼ new title ➤ refereed ✶ unverified ♦ full entry avail.

579 EGY
JOURNAL OF UNION OF ARAB BIOLOGISTS CAIRO. B. MICROBIOLOGY & VIRUSES. Text in English. 1999. a.
Document type: *Journal, Academic/Scholarly.*
—BLDSC (4910.568900).
Published by: Union of Arab Biologists, Faculty of Science, Cairo University, Cairo University Campus, Cairo, Egypt. info@egsz.org, http://derp.sti.sci.eg/data/0348.htm, http://www.egsz.org.

616.9101 EGY ISSN 1110-743X
JOURNAL OF UNION OF ARAB BIOLOGISTS. MICROBIOLOGY AND VIRUSES. Text in English. 1999. a.
Document type: *Journal, Academic/Scholarly.*
—BLDSC (4910.568900).
Published by: Union of Arab Biologists, Faculty of Science, Cairo University, Cairo University Campus, Cairo, Egypt. info@egsz.org, http://derp.sti.sci.eg/data/0348.htm, http://www.egsz.org. Ed. Dr. Yousef Wali.

JOURNAL OF VETERINARY PARASITOLOGY. see *VETERINARY SCIENCE*

B

579.2 NLD ISSN 0166-0934
CODEN: JVMEDH
➤ **JOURNAL OF VIROLOGICAL METHODS.** Text in English. 1980. 16/yr. EUR 3,579 in Europe to institutions; JPY 474,900 in Japan to institutions; USD 4,005 to institutions except Europe and Japan (effective 2006). adv. back issues avail.; reprint service avail. from ISI. **Document type:** *Journal, Academic/Scholarly.* **Description:** Publishes original papers covering techniques on all aspects of virology.
Related titles: Microform ed.: (from PMC, PQC); Online - full text ed.: (from EBSCO Publishing, Gale Group, IngentaConnect, ScienceDirect, Swets Information Services).
Indexed: AEA, AIDS Ab, AIDS&CR, ASCA, ASFA, AbHyg, AgBio, Agr, AnBrAb, B&BAb, BCI, BIOBASE, BIOSIS Prev, BioCN&I, BiolAb, CIN, CPA, ChemAb, ChemTitl, CurCont, DSA, ESPM, ExcerpMed, FCA, ForAb, HortAb, IABS, ISR, IndMed, IndVet, Inpharma, M&PBA, MBA, MEDLINE, MaizeAb, NutrAb, OrnHort, PBA, PE&ON, PN&I, PotatoAb, PoultAb, RA&MP, RM&VM, RPP, Reac, RefZh, RevApplEntom, RiceAb, S&F, SAA, SCI, SFA, SIA, SeedAb, SoyAb, TDB, TriticAb, VITIS, VetBull, VirolAbstr, WeedAb.
—BLDSC (5072.486000), CASDDS, CISTI, GNLM, IDS, IE, Infotrieve, ingenta. **CCC.**
Published by: Elsevier BV (Subsidiary of: Elsevier Science & Technology), Radarweg 29, Amsterdam, 1043 NX, Netherlands. TEL 31-20-4853911, FAX 31-20-4852457, nlinfo-f@elsevier.nl, http://www.elsevier.com/locate/jviromet, http://www.elsevier.nl. Ed. Dr. A J Zuckerman.

579.2 USA ISSN 0022-538X
QR360 CODEN: JOVIAM
➤ **JOURNAL OF VIROLOGY.** Text in English. 1967. fortn. USD 990 domestic to institutions; USD 1,050 in Canada to institutions; USD 1,142 in Europe to institutions; USD 1,193 in Latin America to institutions; USD 1,199 elsewhere to institutions (effective 2006). adv. charts; illus. s-a. index. back issues avail.; reprint service avail. from PQC. **Document type:** *Journal, Academic/Scholarly.* **Description:** Covers viruses obtained in studies using cross-disciplinary approaches of biochemistry, biophysics, cell biology, genetics, immunology, molecular biology, morphology, physiology, pathogenesis, and immunity.
Related titles: CD-ROM ed.: ISSN 1070-6321. 1992. USD 500 in North America; USD 524 elsewhere; Microform ed.: (from PQC); Online - full text ed.: ISSN 1098-5514. USD 927 to institutions (effective 2006) (from EBSCO Publishing, HighWire Press, National Library of Medicine).
Indexed: AIDS Ab, AIDS&CR, ASCA, ASFA, AbHyg, AgBio, Agr, AgrForAb, AnBrAb, B&AI, B&BAb, BBCI, BIOBASE, BIOSIS Prev, BibAg, BioCN&I, BiolAb, CBTA, CPA, ChemAb, ChemTitl, CurCont, DBA, DSA, DentInd, ExcerpMed, FCA, FS&TA, ForAb, GenetAb, HGA, HelmAb, HerbAb, HortAb, IABS, ISR, ImmunAb, IndMed, IndVet, Inpharma, JDDR, JW-ID, M&PBA, MEDLINE, NSA, NSCI, NucAcAb, NutrAb, OGFA, OrnHort, PBA, PE&ON, PGegResA, PN&I, PotatoAb, PoultAb, ProtozoAb, RA&MP, RDA, RM&VM, RPP, Reac, RefZh, RevApplEntom, RiceAb, SAA, SCI, SFA, SIA, SeedAb, SoyAb, TDB, Telegen, TriticAb, VITIS, VetBull, VirolAbstr, WeedAb, WildRev.
—BLDSC (5072.490000), CASDDS, CISTI, GNLM, IDS, IE, Infotrieve, ingenta, Linda Hall. **CCC.**
Published by: American Society for Microbiology, 1752 N St, N W, Washington, DC 20036-2904. TEL 202-737-3600, FAX 202-942-9347, tbarrey@molbio.princeton.edu, asmjournals@asm.org, subscriptions@asmusa.org, http://jvi.asm.org/, http://www.asm.org. Eds. Judith Nedrow, Lynn W Enquist. Circ: 10,225 (paid). **Subscr. to:** PO Box 11127, Birmingham, AL 35201-1127. TEL 205-995-1567, 800-633-4931, FAX 205-995-1588.

576 CHN ISSN 1007-3515
QK609.C5 CODEN: JUXIFB
➤ **JUNWU XITONG/MYCOSYSTEMA.** Text in Chinese. 1982. q. CNY 160 (effective 2004). **Document type:** *Academic/Scholarly.*
Formerly (until 1997): Acta Mycologica Sinica/Zhenjun Xuebao (0256-1883)
Related titles: Online - full text ed.: (from East View Information Services).
Indexed: AEA, AgBio, AgrForAb, BioCN&I, CPA, DSA, FCA, FPA, ForAb, HelmAb, HerbAb, HortAb, I&DA, MaizeAb, NemAb, NutrAb, OrnHort, PBA, PGegResA, PGrRegA, PotatoAb, RA&MP, RM&VM, RPP, RevApplEntom, RiceAb, S&F, SIA, SeedAb, SoyAb, TDB, TriticAb, WeedAb.
—BLDSC (5995.759000), CASDDS, CISTI.
Published by: Kexue Chubanshe/Science Press, 16 Donghuang Cheng Genbei Jie, Beijing, 100717, China. TEL 86-10-64000246, FAX 86-10-64030255, lxjuan@163.net, http://www.sciencep.com/. **Dist. by:** China International Book Trading Corp, 35 Chegongzhuang Xilu, Haidian District, PO Box 399, Beijing 100044, China. TEL 86-10-68412045, FAX 86-10-68412023, cibtc@mail.cibtc.com.cn, http://www.cibtc.com.cn.

579 GBR ISSN 1475-9292
QL368.K5
➤ **KINETOPLASTID BIOLOGY AND DISEASE.** Text in English. 2002 (May). irreg. free (effective 2006). **Document type:** *Journal, Academic/Scholarly.* **Description:** Publishes papers on all aspects of the Order Kinetoplastida, the diseases they cause and the vectors which transmit them.
Media: Online - full content (from EBSCO Publishing, National Library of Medicine).
Indexed: ExcerpMed.
—CCC.
Published by: BioMed Central Ltd. (Subsidiary of: Current Science Ltd), Middlesex House, 34-42 Cleveland St, London, W1T 4LB, United Kingdom. TEL 44-20-76319131, FAX 44-20-76319923, info@biomedcentral.com, http://www.kinetoplastids.com, http://www.biomedcentral.com. Ed. Alberto Davila.

➤ **KISEICHU BUNRUI KEITAI DANWAKAI KAIHO/JAPANESE SOCIETY FOR SYSTEMATIC PARASITOLOGY. CIRCULAR.** see *MEDICAL SCIENCES—Communicable Diseases*

579 CZE ISSN 1211-264X
KLINICKA MIKROBIOLOGIE A INFEKCNI LEKARSTVI. Text in Czech. 1995. bi-m.
Indexed: ExcerpMed.
Published by: Trios s.r.o., Radimova 36, Praha 6, 16900, Czech Republic. TEL 42-2-20517423, FAX 42-2-20517424.

579 JPN
KOEN BISEIBUTSU KENKYUKAI KOEN YOSHISHU/ CONFERENCE ON THE BIOLOGY OF HALOPHILIC MICROORGANISMS. PROCEEDINGS. Text in Japanese. a.
Published by: Koen Biseibutsu Kenkyukai, Shiritsu Kankyo Kagaku Kenkyujo, 8-34 Toji-Yo-cho, Tennoji-ku, Osaka-shi, 543-0026, Japan.

579.2 JPN ISSN 0075-7357
QR360 CODEN: ARIVAK
KYOTO UNIVERSITY. INSTITUTE FOR VIRUS RESEARCH. ANNUAL REPORT✶ /KYOTO DAIGAKU UIRUSU KENKYUJO NENKAN KIYO. Text in English. 1958. a.
Indexed: BiolAb, ChemAb.
—BLDSC (1306.800000), CASDDS.
Published by: (Kyoto University, Institute for Virus Research), Kyoto University Press, Yoshidahon-Machi, Sakyo-ku, Kyoto-shi, 606-8317, Japan. Ed. Seiich Matsumoto. Circ: (controlled).

579.3 GBR
➤ **LACTIC ACID BACTERIA.** Text in English. 1992. irreg. price varies. bibl. **Document type:** *Monographic series, Academic/Scholarly.* **Description:** Scholarly monographs pertaining to the bacteriology and microbiology of lactic acid bacteria in dairy products and related substances, incorporating relevant aspects of toxicological studies.
Published by: Pergamon (Subsidiary of: Elsevier Science & Technology), The Boulevard, Langford Ln, East Park, Kidlington, Oxford OX5 1GB, United Kingdom. TEL 44-1865-843000, FAX 44-1865-843010. **Subscr. to:** Elsevier BV, PO Box 211, Amsterdam 1000 AE, Netherlands. TEL 31-20-485-3757, FAX 31-20-485-3432, nlinfo-f@elsevier.nl, http://www.elsevier.nl.

579 FRA ISSN 0023-7302
CODEN: LAITAG
➤ **LE LAIT.** Text in French; Text and summaries in English, French. 1921. bi-m. EUR 315 combined subscription domestic print & online eds.; EUR 389 combined subscription in the European Union print & online eds.; EUR 406 combined subscription elsewhere print & online eds. (effective 2005). adv. **Document type:** *Academic/Scholarly.* **Description:** Includes scientific articles on the microbiology, biochemistry and physiochemistry of milk and its derivatives, or on transformation procedures.
Related titles: Microform ed.: (from PMC); Online - full text ed.: ISSN 1297-9694 (from EBSCO Publishing, Swets Information Services).
Indexed: AEA, ASCA, AbHyg, AgBio, AgrForAb, B&BAb, BiolAb, CIN, ChemAb, ChemTitl, CurCont, DSA, ExcerpMed, FS&TA, ForAb, HerbAb, ISR, IndVet, NutrAb, PN&I, RA&MP, RM&VM, RPP, S&F, SCI, SIA, SoyAb, VITIS, VetBull.
—BLDSC (5143.800000), CASDDS, CINDOC, CISTI, IDS, IE, Infotrieve, ingenta, Linda Hall. **CCC.**
Published by: (France. Institut National de la Recherche Agronomique (INRA)), E D P Sciences, 17 Ave du Hoggar, Parc d'Activites de Courtaboeuf, BP 112, Cedex A, Les Ulis, F-91944, France. TEL 33-1-69187575, FAX 33-1-69860678, subscribers@edpsciences.org, http://www.edpsciences.org. Ed. J L Maubois. Circ: 2,500.

579 GBR ISSN 0266-8254
QR1 CODEN: LAMIE7
➤ **LETTERS IN APPLIED MICROBIOLOGY.** Text in English. 1985. m. GBP 1,480 combined subscription in Europe to institutions print & online eds.; USD 2,735 combined subscription in the Americas to institutions & the Caribbean (print & online eds.); GBP 1,628 combined subscription elsewhere to institutions print & online eds. (effective 2005); included with subscr. to Journal of Applied Microbiology. adv. reprint service avail. from PSC. **Document type:** *Journal, Academic/Scholarly.* **Description:** Reflects developments in biotechnology in such fields as applied microbial genetics, immunodiagnosis, cell culture and fermentation science.
Related titles: Online - full text ed.: ISSN 1472-765X. GBP 1,406 in Europe to institutions; USD 2,599 in the Americas to institutions & the Caribbean; GBP 1,547 elsewhere to institutions (effective 2005) (from Blackwell Synergy, EBSCO Publishing, Gale Group, IngentaConnect, O C L C Online Computer Library Center, Inc., Ovid Technologies, Inc., Swets Information Services); ♦ Supplement to: Journal of Applied Microbiology. ISSN 1364-5072.
Indexed: AEA, AEBA, ASCA, ASFA, AbHyg, AgBio, Agr, AgrForAb, AnBrAb, BCI, BIOBASE, BIOSIS Prev, BibAg, BioCN&I, BioEngAb, BiolAb, CEABA, CIN, CPA, ChemAb, ChemTitl, CurCont, DBA, DSA, ESPM, ExcerpMed, FCA, FLUIDEX, FPA, FS&TA, ForAb, GEOBASE, H&SSA, HerbAb, HortAb, IABS, ISR, IndMed, IndVet, Inpharma, MBA, MEDLINE, MaizeAb, NemAb, NutrAb, OrnHort, PBA, PGegResA, PGrRegA, PHN&I, PN&I, PollutAb, PotatoAb, PoultAb, ProtozoAb, RA&MP, RM&VM, RPP, Reac, RefZh, RevApplEntom, RiceAb, S&F, SCI, SFA, SIA, SWRA, SeedAb, SoyAb, TDB, TriticAb, VITIS, VetBull, WRCInf, WTA, WeedAb.
—BLDSC (5185.126700), CASDDS, CISTI, GNLM, IDS, IE, ingenta, Linda Hall. **CCC.**
Published by: (Society for Applied Bacteriology), Blackwell Publishing Ltd., 9600 Garsington Rd, Oxford, OX4 2ZG, United Kingdom. TEL 44-1865-776868, FAX 44-1865-714591, customerservices@oxon.blackwellpublishing.com, http://www.blackwellpublishing.com/journals/LAM. Ed. Colin R Harwood TEL 44-191-2227708. Pub. Amanda McLean Inglis. R&P Sophie Savage. Adv. contact Jenny Applin.

➤ **LA LETTRE DE L'INFECTIOLOGUE;** de la microbiologie a la clinique. see *MEDICAL SCIENCES—Communicable Diseases*

➤ **MARINE BIOTECHNOLOGY.** see *BIOLOGY—Biotechnology*

579 POL ISSN 0025-8601
R91 CODEN: MDMIAZ
MEDYCYNA DOSWIADCZALNA I MIKROBIOLOGIA. Text in Multiple languages. 1949. q. EUR 125 foreign (effective 2005).
Document type: *Journal, Academic/Scholarly.*
Indexed: AbHyg, AgBio, AgrLib, BIOSIS Prev, BiolAb, ChemAb, ChemTitl, DSA, DentInd, ExcerpMed, HelmAb, IPA, IndMed, IndVet, MEDLINE, MSB, NutrAb, PN&I, PoultAb, ProtozoAb, RM&VM, RPP, RevApplEntom, SIA, SoyAb, TDB, VetBull.
—BLDSC (5536.000000), CASDDS, CISTI, GNLM, IE, Infotrieve, ingenta.
Published by: Panstwowy Zaklad Higieny/National Institute of Hygiene, Ul Chocimska 24, Warsaw, 00791, Poland. TEL 48-22-5421327, biblioteka@pzh.gov.pl, http://www.pzh.gov.pl. Ed. Stanislaw Kaluzewski. R&P Jolanta Szych. **Dist. by:** Ars Polona, Krakowskie Przedmiescie 7, Warsaw, Poland. TEL 48-22-9263914, FAX 48-22-9265334, arspolona@arspolona.com.pl, http://www.arspolona.com.pl.
Co-sponsor: Polskie Towarzystwo Mikrobiologow/Polish Society of Microbiologists.

579 USA ISSN 0580-9517
QR65 CODEN: MMICEU
➤ **METHODS IN MICROBIOLOGY.** Text in English. 1969. irreg., latest vol.33, 2003. USD 119.95 (effective 2003). **Document type:** *Monographic series, Academic/Scholarly.*
Related titles: Online - full text ed.: (from ScienceDirect).
Indexed: BIOSIS Prev, CIN, ChemAb, ChemTitl, ISR, SCI.
—BLDSC (5748.201000), CASDDS, CISTI, GNLM, IE, ingenta. **CCC.**
Published by: Academic Press (Subsidiary of: Elsevier Science & Technology), 525 B St, Ste 1900, San Diego, CA 92101-4495. TEL 619-231-6616, 800-894-3434, FAX 619-699-6422, apsubs@acad.com, http://www.apnet.com, http://www.academicpress.com.

➤ **MICOLOGIA APLICADA INTERNATIONAL.** see *BIOLOGY—Botany*

579 USA
QR1.A47 CODEN: ASMNBO
➤ **MICROBE.** Text in English. 1935. m. USD 55 in US & Canada to non-members; USD 65 in Europe to non-members; USD 69 in Latin America to non-members; USD 70 elsewhere to non-members (effective 2006). adv. bk.rev. stat. index. back issues avail.; reprint service avail. from PQC. **Document type:** *Newsletter, Academic/Scholarly.* **Description:** Provides information on a broad range of scientific and policy issues to microbiologists; letters; opinion pieces; meetings calendar; reports of legislative activity; and classified employment listings.
Formerly (until 2005): A S M News (Washington) (0044-7897)
Related titles: Microform ed.: (from PQC).
Indexed: BCI, BioDAb, BiolAb, CADCAM, EnvAb, IndMed, IndVet, MBA, PoultAb, RM&VM, RefZh, SSCI, Telegen.
—BLDSC (1745.171000), CISTI, IDS, IE, Infotrieve, ingenta. **CCC.**
Published by: American Society for Microbiology, 1752 N St, N W, Washington, DC 20036-2904. TEL 202-737-3600, FAX 202-942-9355, Asmnews@asmusa.org, asmjournals@asm.org, subscriptions@asmusa.org, http://www.asm.org. Ed. Michael I Goldberg. Circ: 42,000. **Subscr. to:** PO Box 11127, Birmingham, AL 35201-1127. TEL 205-995-1567, 800-633-4931, FAX 205-995-1588.

579 JPN ISSN 1342-6311
MICROBES AND ENVIRONMENTS/JAPANESE SOCIETY OF MICROBIAL ECOLOGY. BULLETIN. Text in English, Japanese; Summaries in English. 1986. s-a. JPY 8,000 domestic membership; JPY 9,000 foreign membership (effective 2004); subscr. c/w membership.
Formerly (until 1995): Nihon Biseibutsu Seitai Gakkaiho (0911-7830)
Related titles: Online - full content ed.: ISSN 1347-4405. 2000; Online - full text ed.: (from J-Stage).
Indexed: ASFA, ESPM, RefZh, ZooRec.
—BLDSC (5756.908000), IE, ingenta. **CCC.**
Published by: Nihon Biseibutsu Seitai Gakkai/Japanese Society of Microbial Ecology, c/o Prof. Kiwamu Minamizawa, Graduate School of Life Science, Tohoku University, Katahira, Aoba-ku, Sendai, Miyagi, 980-8577, Japan. FAX 81-22-217-5684, http://www.jstage.jst.go.jp/browse/jsme2/_vols/-char/en, http://wwwsoc.nii.ac.jp/jsme2/. Ed. Kenji Kato.

579.3 FRA ISSN 1286-4579
CODEN: MCINFS
➤ **MICROBES AND INFECTION**; a journal on infectious agents and host defenses. Text in English. 1999. 15/yr. EUR 1,001 in Europe to institutions; JPY 132,800 in Japan to institutions; USD 1,120 elsewhere to institutions (effective 2006). adv. bk.rev. index. back issues avail.; reprint service avail. from ISI. **Document type:** *Bulletin, Academic/Scholarly.* **Description:** Presents reviews on all aspects of microbiology, immunology and infectious diseases, and aims at providing researchers and teaching staff in these fields.
Formed by the merger of (1903-1999): Institut Pasteur. Bulletin (0020-2452); (1989-1999): Research in Virology (0923-2516); Which was formerly (until 1988): Institut Pasteur. Annales. Virologie (0769-2617); (1980-1985): Annales de Virologie (0242-5017); (1989-1999): Research in Immunology (0923-2494); Which was formerly (until 1988): Institut Pasteur. Annales. Immunologie (0769-2625); (until 1985): Annales d'Immunologie (0300-4910); Which superseded in part (1887-1972): Institut Pasteur. Annales (0020-2444)
Related titles: Microform ed.: (from PMC, PQC); Online - full text ed.: (from EBSCO Publishing, Gale Group, IngentaConnect, ScienceDirect, Swets Information Services).
Indexed: AEBA, AIDS Ab, AIDS&CR, ASCA, ASFA, AbHyg, AgBio, AgrForAb, AnBrAb, BIOBASE, BIOSIS Prev, BiolAb, CIN, CPA, ChemAb, ChemTitl, CurCont, DBA, DSA, ESPM, ExcerpMed, FCA, HelmAb, HortAb, IABS, ISR, ImmunAb, IndMed, IndVet, Inpharma, MBA, MEDLINE, NutrAb, PBA, PN&I, PotatoAb, PoultAb, ProtozoAb, RA&MP, RDA, RM&VM, RPP, RRTA, Reac, RevApplEntom, RiceAb, RiskAb, S&F, SCI, SIA, TDB, ToxAb, VetBull, VirolAbstr, WAE&RSA.
—BLDSC (5756.909000), CASDDS, CISTI, GNLM, IDS, IE, Infotrieve, ingenta, Linda Hall. **CCC.**
Published by: (Institut Pasteur), Elsevier France, Editions Scientifiques et Medicales (Subsidiary of: Elsevier Science & Technology), 23 Rue Linois, Paris, 75724, France. TEL 33-1-71724600, FAX 33-1-71724650, a.dore@elsevier.fr, http://www.elsevier.com/locate/micinf, http://www.pasteur.fr, http://www.elsevier.fr. Ed. Stefan H E Kaufmann. Circ: 1,300. **Subscr. to:** Elsevier BV, PO Box 211, Amsterdam 1000 AE, Netherlands. TEL 31-20-485-3757, FAX 31-20-485-3432.

579 GBR ISSN 0966-6796
MICROBIAL CLEAN-UP. Text in English. 1992. 10/yr. GBP 250, USD 295. back issues avail. **Description:** Covers developments in the use of microbes to eliminate pollutants, effluents, and waste.
Address: 2-3 Cornwall Terr, Regent's Park, London, NW1 4QP, United Kingdom. TEL 0171-935-2382, FAX 0171-486-7083.

MICROBIAL DRUG RESISTANCE; mechanism, epidemiology, and disease. see *MEDICAL SCIENCES*

579 USA ISSN 0095-3628
QR100 CODEN: MCBEBU
➤ **MICROBIAL ECOLOGY**; an international journal. Text in English. 8/yr. (in 2 vols., 4 nos./vol.). EUR 1,038 combined subscription to institutions print & online eds. (effective 2005). adv. back issues avail.; reprint service avail. from PSC,ISI. **Document type:** *Journal, Academic/Scholarly.* **Description:** Publishes original articles in all areas of ecology involving microorganisms.
Related titles: Microform ed.: (from PQC); Online - full text ed.: ISSN 1432-184X (from EBSCO Publishing, Springer LINK, Swets Information Services).
Indexed: AEA, ASCA, ASFA, AbHyg, AgBio, Agr, AgrForAb, ApEcolAb, B&AI, BIOBASE, BIOSIS Prev, BioCN&I, BiolAb, CIN, CPA, ChemAb, ChemTitl, CurCont, DSA, ESPM, ExcerpMed, FCA, FPA, ForAb, GEOBASE, GenetAb, HGA, HerbAb, HortAb, I&DA, IABS, IBR, ISR, IndVet, MBA, MEDLINE, MaizeAb, NemAb, NutrAb, OceAb, PBA, PGegResA, PGrRegA, PHN&I, PN&I, PollutAb, PotatoAb, PoultAb, ProtozoAb, RA&MP, RPP, RevApplEntom, RiceAb, S&F, SCI, SFA, SIA, SWRA, SeedAb, SoyAb, TDB, TriticAb, VITIS, VetBull, VirolAbstr, WeedAb.
—BLDSC (5756.920000), CASDDS, CISTI, IDS, IE, Infotrieve, ingenta, Linda Hall. **CCC.**
Published by: Springer-Verlag New York, Inc. (Subsidiary of: Springer Science+Business Media), 233 Spring St, New York, NY 10013. TEL 212-460-1500, 800-777-4643, FAX 212-473-6272, journals@springer-ny.com, http://link.springer.de/link/service/journals/00248/index.htm, http://www.springer-ny.com. Ed. James K Fredrickson. R&P Ian Gross. Adv. contact Brian Skepton. **Subscr. outside the Americas to:** Springer GmbH Auslieferungsgesellschaft, Haberstr 7, Heidelberg 69126, Germany. TEL 49-6221-345-0, FAX 49-6221-345-4229, subscriptions@springer.de; **Subscr. to:** Journal Fulfillment, PO Box 2485, Secaucus, NJ 07096-2485. TEL 201-348-4033, FAX 201-348-4505.

➤ **MICROBIAL ECOLOGY IN HEALTH & DISEASE.** see *MEDICAL SCIENCES—Communicable Diseases*

➤ **MICROBIOLOGIA MEDICA.** see *MEDICAL SCIENCES*

579.072 DEU ISSN 0944-5013
QR51 CODEN: MCRSEJ
➤ **MICROBIOLOGICAL RESEARCH.** Text in English. 1895. 4/yr. EUR 177 in Europe to individuals; JPY 21,800 in Japan to individuals; USD 173 to individuals except Europe and Japan; EUR 376 to institutions; EUR 438 in Europe to institutions; JPY 58,300 in Japan to institutions; USD 468 to institutions except Europe and Japan (effective 2006). adv. bk.rev. bibl.; charts; illus. index. reprint service avail. from ISI. **Document type:** *Journal, Academic/Scholarly.* **Description:** Publishes original research papers and short communications on prokaryotic and eukaryotic micro-organisms.
Former titles (until 1993): Zentralblatt fuer Mikrobiologie (0232-4393); Zentralblatt fuer Bakteriologie, Parasitenkunde, Infektionskrankheiten und Hygiene: Zweite Abteilung - Naturwissenschaft
Related titles: Online - full text ed.: (from bigchalk, EBSCO Publishing, Gale Group, IngentaConnect, O C L C Online Computer Library Center, Inc., ProQuest Information & Learning, ScienceDirect, Swets Information Services).
Indexed: ASCA, ASFA, AbHyg, AgBio, Agr, AgrForAb, AnBrAb, BIOBASE, BIOSIS Prev, BioCN&I, BiolAb, CEABA, CPA, ChemAb, ChemTitl, CurCont, DBA, DSA, ESPM, FCA, FLUIDEX, FPA, FS&TA, ForAb, GEOBASE, HerbAb, HortAb, I&DA, IABS, IndMed, IndVet, MBA, MEDLINE, MaizeAb, NemAb, NutrAb, OrnHort, PBA, PGegResA, PGrRegA, PHN&I, PN&I, PotatoAb, PoultAb, ProtozoAb, RA&MP, RM&VM, RPP, RevApplEntom, RiceAb, S&F, SIA, SeedAb, SoyAb, TDB, TOSA, TriticAb, VITIS, VetBull, VirolAbstr, WeedAb.
—BLDSC (5757.590000), CASDDS, CISTI, GNLM, IDS, IE, Infotrieve, ingenta, Linda Hall. **CCC.**
Published by: Elsevier GmbH, Urban & Fischer Verlag (Subsidiary of: Elsevier Science & Technology), Loebdergraben 14a, Jena, 07743, Germany. TEL 49-3641-626430, FAX 49-3641-626432, info@urbanfischer.de, http://www.elsevier.com/locate/microbiolres, http://www.urbanfischer.de. Eds. Dr. Gabriele Diekert, Johannes Woestemeyer TEL 49-3641-949311. R&P Martin Huber TEL 49-3641-626430. Adv. contact Sabine Schroeter TEL 49-3641-626445. B&W page EUR 400, color page EUR 1,345; trim 210 x 280. Circ: 280 (paid and controlled). **Non-German speaking countries subscr. to:** Nature Publishing Group, Brunel Rd, Houndmills, Basingstoke, Hamps RG21 6XS, United Kingdom. TEL 44-1256-302629, FAX 44-1256-476117

579 USA ISSN 0889-3381
➤ **THE MICROBIOLOGICAL UPDATE.** Text in English. 1982. m. USD 260 domestic; USD 280 foreign (effective 2004). bk.rev. back issues avail. **Document type:** *Newsletter, Academic/Scholarly.* **Description:** Keeps readers abreast of the latest literature and discussions of microbiological control, along with issues relevant to the pharmaceutical, cosmetics, and medical-device industries.
—BLDSC (5757.630000).
Published by: Microbiological Applications, Inc., 132 San Remo Dr, Islamorada, FL 33036. TEL 305-664-8513, FAX 305-664-8597, http://www.microbioupdate.com/pages/855343/index.htm, http://www.microbioupdate.com/pages/855341/index.htm. Ed. Dr. Murray Sam Cooper. R&P, Adv. contact Claire Sandberg.

579 362 TUN ISSN 0330-8030
MICROBIOLOGIE HYGIENE ALIMENTAIRE. Key Title: M H A. Text in Multiple languages. 1989. 3/yr. **Document type:** *Journal, Academic/Scholarly.*
—BLDSC (5752.862100).
Published by: Association Africaine de Microbiologie et d'Hygiene Alimentaire, c/o Departement de Biochimie, Faculte de Medicine Ibn El Jazzar, Sousse, 4000, Tunisia. TEL 216-3-22600.

B

579 GBR ISSN 1350-0872
QR1 CODEN: MROBEO
➤ **MICROBIOLOGY.** Text in English. 1947. m. GBP 785 combined subscription domestic to institutions print & online; USD 1,375 combined subscription in North America to institutions print & online; GBP 805 combined subscription elsewhere to institutions print & online (effective 2005). adv. bibl.; charts; illus. index. back issues avail.; reprints avail. **Document type:** *Journal, Academic/Scholarly.* **Description:** Contains original work on microorganisms in the laboratory and in the field; emphasis on fundamental studies.
Formerly (until 1993): Journal of General Microbiology (0022-1287)
Related titles: Microfilm ed.: (from PMC); Online - full text ed.: ISSN 1465-2080. GBP 710 domestic; USD 1,240 in North America; GBP 725 elsewhere (effective 2005) (from EBSCO Publishing, HighWire Press).
Indexed: AEBA, ASCA, ASFA, AbHyg, AgBio, Agr, AgrForAb, AnBrAb, B&AI, BBCI, BCI, BIOBASE, BIOSIS Prev, BioCN&I, BiolAb, BiolDig, CBTA, CCI, CEABA, CPA, ChemAb, ChemTitl, CurCont, DBA, DSA, DentInd, ESPM, ExcerpMed, FCA, FPA, FS&TA, ForAb, GSI, GenetAb, HelmAb, HerbAb, HortAb, ISR, IndMed, IndVet, Inpharma, MBA, MEDLINE, MS&D, MSB, MaizeAb, NemAb, NutrAb, OrnHort, PBA, PGegResA, PGrRegA, PN&I, PotatoAb, PoultAb, ProtozoAb, RA&MP, RM&VM, RPP, Reac, RefZh, RevApplEntom, RiceAb, S&F, SAA, SCI, SFA, SIA, SeedAb, SoyAb, TDB, TriticAb, VITIS, VetBull, VirolAbstr, WeedAb.
—BLDSC (5757.750500), CASDDS, CISTI, GNLM, IDS, IE, Infotrieve, ingenta, Linda Hall. **CCC.**
Published by: Society for General Microbiology, Marlborough House, Basingstoke Rd, Spencers Wood, Reading, Berks RG7 1AG, United Kingdom. TEL 44-118-9881800, FAX 44-118-9885656, micro@sgm.ac.uk, http://mic.sgmjournals.org, http://www.sgm.ac.uk. Ed. C M Thomas. R&P Kendra Waite. Adv. contact C Sinclair. Circ: 2,440.

579 RUS ISSN 0026-2617
QR1 CODEN: MIBLAO
➤ **MICROBIOLOGY.** Text in Russian. 1932. bi-m. EUR 3,435, USD 3,098, GBP 2,145 combined subscription to institutions print & online eds. (effective 2005). charts; illus. index. back issues avail. **Document type:** *Journal, Academic/Scholarly.* **Description:** Investigates a wide range of problems in the areas of fundamental and applied microbiology.
Related titles: Microfilm ed.: (from PQC); Online - full text ed.: (from EBSCO Publishing, Gale Group, IngentaConnect, Kluwer Online, O C L C Online Computer Library Center, Inc., Ovid Technologies, Inc., Springer LINK, Swets Information Services); ♦ Translation of: Mikrobiologiya. ISSN 0026-3656.
Indexed: ASCA, AgBio, BCI, BibLing, BioCN&I, BiolAb, CBTA, CPA, ChemAb, ChemTitl, CurCont, DSA, ESPM, FCA, FS&TA, ForAb, HerbAb, HortAb, I&DA, IABS, ISR, IndMed, MaizeAb, NemAb, NutrAb, PBA, PGrRegA, PotatoAb, RA&MP, RM&VM, RPP, RiceAb, S&F, SCI, SIA, SeedAb, SoyAb, TriticAb, WeedAb.
—BLDSC (0416.200000), CASDDS, CISTI, GNLM, IDS, IE, Infotrieve, ingenta, Linda Hall. **CCC.**
Published by: (Rossiiskaya Akademiya Nauk/Russian Academy of Sciences), M A I K Nauka - Interperiodica, Profsoyuznaya ul 90, Moscow, 117997, Russian Federation. TEL 7-095-3347420, FAX 7-095-3360666, compmg@maik.ru, http://www.maik.rssi.ru/journals/micbio.htm, http://www.maik.ru. Ed. M V Ivanov. **Subscr. to:** Springer-Verlag Dordrecht, Journals Department, PO Box 322, Dordrecht, Netherlands. TEL 31-78-6576392, FAX 31-78-6576474.

➤ **MICROBIOLOGY**; Royal Australasian College of Dental Surgeons. Lecture notes in microbiology. see *MEDICAL SCIENCES—Dentistry*

➤ **MICROBIOLOGY ABSTRACTS: SECTION A. INDUSTRIAL & APPLIED MICROBIOLOGY.** see *BIOLOGY—Abstracting, Bibliographies, Statistics*

➤ **MICROBIOLOGY ABSTRACTS: SECTION B. BACTERIOLOGY.** see *BIOLOGY—Abstracting, Bibliographies, Statistics*

➤ **MICROBIOLOGY ABSTRACTS: SECTION C. ALGOLOGY, MYCOLOGY AND PROTOZOOLOGY.** see *BIOLOGY—Abstracting, Bibliographies, Statistics*

▼ **new title** ➤ **refereed** ✶ **unverified** ♦ **full entry avail.**

579 JPN ISSN 0385-5600
QR1 CODEN: MIIMDV
➤ **MICROBIOLOGY AND IMMUNOLOGY.** Text in English. 1957. m. USD 130 to individuals; USD 255 to institutions (effective 2005). adv. charts; illus. **Document type:** *Academic/Scholarly.* **Description:** Devoted to the world-wide dissemination of advanced knowledge in bacteriology, virology, immunology, and related fields.
Formerly (until vol. 21, 1977): Japanese Journal of Microbiology (0021-5139)
Related titles: Microform ed.: (from PMC); Online - full text ed.: ISSN 1348-0421. free (effective 2005) (from EBSCO Publishing, J-Stage).
Indexed: AIDS&CR, ASCA, AbHyg, AgBio, AgrForAb, AnBrAb, BIOBASE, BIOSIS Prev, BiolAb, CBTA, CIN, ChemAb, ChemTitl, CurCont, DBA, DSA, DentInd, ESPM, ExcerpMed, FCA, FPA, ForAb, HelmAb, HortAb, IABS, INIS AtomInd, ISR, ImmunAb, IndMed, IndVet, Inpharma, JDDR, MBA, MEDLINE, NutrAb, PBA, PE&ON, PN&I, PoultAb, ProtozoAb, RA&MP, RM&VM, RPP, RRTA, Reac, RefZh, RevApplEntom, S&F, SCI, SFA, TDB, Telegen, VetBull, VirolAbstr, WeedAb.
—BLDSC (5757.791000), CASDDS, CISTI, GNLM, IDS, IE, Infotrieve, ingenta, Linda Hall. **CCC.**
Published by: (Nihon Saikin Gakkai/Japanese Society for Bacteriology), Center for Academic Publications Japan, 2-4-16 Yayoi, Bunkyo-ku, Tokyo, 113-0032, Japan. TEL 81-3-3817-5821, FAX 81-3-3817-5820, capj@crisscross.com, http://www.sanbi.co.jp/capj/index.html. Circ: 1,500. **Dist. by:** Business Center for Academic Societies Japan, 5-16-19 Honkomagome, Bunkyo-ku, Tokyo 113-0021, Japan. TEL 81-3-58145811, FAX 81-3-58145822. **Co-sponsors:** Japanese Society for Immunology; Nihon Uirusu Gakkai/Japanese Society for Virology.

579 USA ISSN 1092-2172
QR1 CODEN: MMBRF7
➤ **MICROBIOLOGY AND MOLECULAR BIOLOGY REVIEWS.** Text in English. 1937. q. USD 410 domestic to institutions; USD 414 in Canada to institutions; USD 419 in Europe to institutions; USD 422 in Latin America to institutions; USD 423 elsewhere to institutions (effective 2006). adv. bibl.; illus. index. back issues avail.; reprint service avail. from PQC. **Document type:** *Journal, Academic/Scholarly.* **Description:** Presents broad-based reviews on the expanding disciplines of microbiolgy, immunology, and molecular and cellular biology.
Former titles (until 1997): Microbiological Reviews (0146-0749); (until 1978): Bacteriological Reviews (0005-3678)
Related titles: CD-ROM ed.: ISSN 1070-6275. 1992. USD 300 in North America; USD 324 elsewhere (effective 1999); Microform ed.: (from PQC); Online - full text ed.: ISSN 1098-5557. USD 383 to institutions (effective 2006) (from EBSCO Publishing, HighWire Press, National Library of Medicine).
Indexed: ABIPC, ASCA, ASFA, AbHyg, AgBio, Agr, B&AI, BIOBASE, BIOSIS Prev, BioCN&I, BiolAb, BiolDig, CBTA, CEABA, CIN, CPA, ChemAb, ChemTitl, CurCont, DBA, DSA, ESPM, ExcerpMed, FCA, FS&TA, GSI, GenetAb, HGA, HortAb, IABS, ISR, IndMed, IndVet, Inpharma, JDDR, MBA, MEDLINE, NemAb, NucAcAb, NutrAb, PBA, PGegResA, PN&I, PotatoAb, PoultAb, ProtozoAb, RA&MP, RM&VM, RPP, Reac, RefZh, RevApplEntom, S&F, SCI, SeedAb, TDB, Telegen, VetBull, VirolAbstr, WRCInf, ZooRec.
—BLDSC (5757.791300), CASDDS, CISTI, GNLM, IDS, IE, Infotrieve, ingenta, Linda Hall. **CCC.**
Published by: American Society for Microbiology, 1752 N St, N W, Washington, DC 20036-2904. TEL 202-737-3600, FAX 202-942-9355, keene001@mc.duke.edu, asmjournals@asm.org, subscriptions@asmusa.org, http://mmbr.asm.org/, http://www.asm.org. Ed. Jack D. Keene. Circ: 11,694 (paid).

579.072 AUS ISSN 1324-4272
QR1
➤ **MICROBIOLOGY AUSTRALIA.** Text in English. 4/yr. AUD 155 to members (effective 2004). **Document type:** *Journal, Academic/Scholarly.* **Description:** Contains reviews and research papers on a range of topics in microbiology for working scientists in academic research institutes, food, clinical and industrial laboratories.
Formerly (until 1995): Australian Microbiologist (0158-619X)
—BLDSC (5757.791500).
Published by: Australian Society for Microbiology, Unit 23, Commercial Rd, Melbourne, VIC 3004, Australia. TEL 61-3-98678699, FAX 61-3-98678722, http://www.cambridgemedia.com.au, http://www.theasm.com.au/. Circ: 3,300.

579 USA ISSN 1542-8818
QR61
MICROBIOLOGY EDUCATION. Text in English. 2000 (May). a.
Related titles: Online - full text ed.
Published by: American Society for Microbiology, 1752 N St, N W, Washington, DC 20036-2904. TEL 202-942-9319, FAX 202-942-9347, http://www.asm.org/Publications/index.asp?bid=1364.

579 GBR ISSN 1360-4511
MICROBIOLOGY NEWSLETTER. Text in English. m. EUR 375 (effective 2003). **Document type:** *Trade.* **Description:** Focuses on current food safety and related issues, providing carefully researched news, information and comment.
Published by: Leatherhead Food International Ltd., Randalls Rd, Leatherhead, Surrey KT22 7RY, United Kingdom. TEL 44-1372-376761, FAX 44-1372-386228, hbennett@lfra.co.uk. Ed. Richard Lawley.

579 GBR ISSN 1464-0570
QR1
MICROBIOLOGY TODAY. Text in English. 1974. q. GBP 54 combined subscription domestic to institutions print & online; USD 93 combined subscription in North America to institutions print & online; GBP 59 combined subscription elsewhere to institutions print & online (effective 2005). adv. bk.rev. 64 p./no.; back issues avail. **Document type:** *Magazine, Academic/Scholarly.* **Description:** Publishes articles on microbiology; also includes information on society activities.
Former titles (until 1999): Society for General Microbiology. Quarterly (0142-7547); Society for General Microbiology Proceedings (0306-2708)
Related titles: Online - full text ed.: GBP 15 domestic; USD 25 in North America; GBP 16 elsewhere (effective 2004) (from EBSCO Publishing).
Indexed: ASFA, AbHyg, AgBio, DSA, ESPM, HortAb, IndVet, MBA, NutrAb, PBA, PotatoAb, RHEA, RM&VM, RPP, RefZh, VetBull.
—BLDSC (5757.798550), CISTI, IE, ingenta, Linda Hall. **CCC.**
Published by: Society for General Microbiology, Marlborough House, Basingstoke Rd, Spencers Wood, Reading, Berks RG7 1AG, United Kingdom. TEL 44-118-9881800, FAX 44-118-9885656, mtoday@sgm.ac.uk, http://www.socgenmicrobiol.org.uk/pubs/micro_today/, http://www.sgm.ac.uk. Ed. M. Jones. R&P Janice Meekings. Adv. contact Julie Lander TEL 44-1252-357000. Circ: 5,500 (paid).

MICROCIRCULATION. see *MEDICAL SCIENCES*

616.01 579 DNK
MIKROBIOLOGI-NYT. Text in Danish. 1983. q. looseleaf. USD 10. adv. bk.rev. **Document type:** *Newsletter.*
Formerly: Hurtigmetode-nyt (0109-0763)
Published by: Mikrobiologisk Gruppe-Levnedsmiddelselskabet, Ingenioerhuset, Vester Farimagsgade 29, Copenhagen V, 1780, Denmark. TEL 45-53-15-65-65, FAX 45-33-15-37-37. Ed. Poul Sigsgaard. R&P Kalvebad Brygge.

579 RUS ISSN 0026-3656
QR1 CODEN: MIKBA5
➤ **MIKROBIOLOGIYA.** Text in Russian. 1932. bi-m. RUR 1,190 for 6 mos. domestic (effective 2004). charts; illus. index. back issues avail. **Document type:** *Journal, Academic/Scholarly.*
Related titles: Microfilm ed.: (from PQC); Online - full text ed.: ISSN 1608-3237; ♦ Russian Translation: Microbiology. ISSN 0026-2617.
Indexed: BIOSIS Prev, BiolAb, CEABA, DBA, ESPM, FS&TA, IndMed, MEDLINE, RefZh, VITIS, VirolAbstr.
—CASDDS, CISTI, GNLM, KNAW, Linda Hall. **CCC.**
Published by: (Rossiiskaya Akademiya Nauk/Russian Academy of Sciences), Izdatel'stvo Nauka, Profsoyuznaya ul 90, Moscow, 117864, Russian Federation. TEL 7-095-3347151, FAX 7-095-4202220, secret@naukaran.ru, http://www.maik.rssi.ru/cgi-bin/list.pl?page=mikbio, http://www.naukaran.ru.

579 616.9 UKR ISSN 1028-0987
QR1 CODEN: MZHUDX
➤ **MIKROBIOLOHICHNYI ZHURNAL.** Text and summaries in English, Russian, Ukrainian. 1934. bi-m. USD 150 foreign (effective 2005). bk.rev. bibl.; abstr.; illus. index. 75 p./no.; reprints avail. **Document type:** *Journal, Academic/Scholarly.* **Description:** Presents the original materials on problems of general microbiology, soil microbiology, medical microbiology, the genetics of microorganisms, biochemistry of microorganisms, immune chemistry, radiation microbiology, experimental mycology, etc.
Former titles (until 1994): Mikrobiologicheskii Zhurnal (0201-8462); (until 1978): Mikrobiolohichnyi Zhurnal (0026-3664)
Related titles: Diskette ed.; Online - full content ed.
Indexed: ASFA, AbHyg, AgBio, BioCN&I, BiolAb, CPA, ChemAb, DBA, DSA, Djerelo, ESPM, ExcerpMed, FCA, ForAb, HerbAb, HortAb, INIS AtomInd, IndMed, IndVet, MBA, MEDLINE, MaizeAb, NutrAb, PBA, PGrRegA, PHN&I, PN&I, PotatoAb, ProtozoAb, RA&MP, RM&VM, RPP, RefZh, RevApplEntom, RiceAb, S&F, SIA, SeedAb, SoyAb, TriticAb, VetBull, WeedAb.
—CASDDS, CISTI, East View, GNLM, KNAW, Linda Hall. **CCC.**
Published by: Natsional'na Akademiya Nauk Ukrainy, Instytut Mikrobiolohii i Virusolohii im. D.K. Zabolotnoho/National Ukrainian Academy of Sciences, D. K. Zabolotny Institute of Microbiology and Virology, vul Akad Zabolotnogo 154, Kyiv, 03143, Ukraine. smirnov@imv.kiev.ua, http://www.imv.kiev.ua/Microbiolj.htm. Ed. V V Smirnov.

579 TUR ISSN 0374-9096
QR1 CODEN: MIBUBI
➤ **MIKROBIYOLOJI BULTENI/BULLETIN OF MICROBIOLOGY.** Text in Turkish; Summaries in English. 1965. q. USD 100 foreign (effective 2003). adv. abstr. **Document type:** *Journal, Academic/Scholarly.* **Description:** Covers microbiology, medical microbiology, infectious diseases and chemotherapy. Includes case reports and discussions of practical medical microbiology.
Indexed: ApicAb, BIOSIS Prev, BiolAb, ChemAb, ChemTitl, ExcerpMed, IndMed, MEDLINE.
—BLDSC (5761.665000), CASDDS, CISTI, GNLM, IE, Infotrieve, ingenta.
Published by: Ankara Microbiology Society, Hacettepe University Faculty of Medicine, Dept. of Clinical Microbiology, Ankara, 06100, Turkey. TEL 0090-312-3051560, FAX 0090-312-3115250, hutfm-e@servis2.net.tr, http://www.ankaramikrobiyologi.org. Ed. Dr. Ayfer Gunalp. Pub. Durdal Us. R&P, Adv. contact Burcin Sener. Circ: 350 (paid).

579 DEU ISSN 0026-3680
QH201 CODEN: MKKSA2
➤ **MIKROKOSMOS**; Zeitschrift fuer Mikroskopie. Text in German. 1907. 6/yr. EUR 72 in Europe to institutions; JPY 9,900 in Japan to institutions; USD 91 elsewhere to institutions; EUR 45 in Europe to students; JPY 5,900 in Japan to students; USD 44 elsewhere to students (effective 2006). adv. bk.rev. bibl.; charts; illus. index. **Document type:** *Journal, Academic/Scholarly.* **Description:** Covers applied microscopy, microbiology, microchemistry, and microscopical technology.
Indexed: BiolAb, ChemAb, ExcerpMed, ZooRec.
—CASDDS, CISTI, IE, Infotrieve, Linda Hall. **CCC.**
Published by: Elsevier GmbH, Urban & Fischer Verlag (Subsidiary of: Elsevier Science & Technology), Loebdergraben 14a, Jena, 07743, Germany. TEL 49-3641-626430, FAX 49-3641-626432, info@urbanfischer.de, http://www.elsevier.com/locate/mikrokosmos, http://www.urbanfischer.de. Ed. Dr. Klaus Hausmann. R&P Martin Huber TEL 49-3641-626430. Adv. contact Sabine Schroeter TEL 49-3641-626445. B&W page EUR 9,850, color page EUR 1,930; 170 x 240. Circ: 2,450 (paid and controlled). **Non-German speaking countries subscr. to:** Nature Publishing Group, Brunel Rd, Houndmills, Basingstoke, Hamps RG21 6XS, United Kingdom. TEL 44-1256-302629, FAX 44-1256-476117

579 571.6 NLD ISSN 1567-7249
QH603.M5 CODEN: MITOCN
➤ **MITOCHONDRION.** Text in English. 2001. 6/yr. EUR 381 in Europe to institutions; JPY 50,600 in Japan to institutions; USD 426 to institutions except Europe and Japan (effective 2006). **Document type:** *Journal, Academic/Scholarly.* **Description:** Reports on basics of mitochondria from all organisms, ranging from research to pathology and clinical aspects of their diseases.
Related titles: Online - full text ed.: (from EBSCO Publishing, Gale Group, IngentaConnect, ScienceDirect, Swets Information Services).
Indexed: B&BAb, BIOBASE, BIOSIS Prev, BiolAb, ChemAb, CurCont, ExcerpMed, GenetAb, NucAcAb.
—BLDSC (5829.771000), CISTI, IE, ingenta, Linda Hall. **CCC.**
Published by: (Mitochondria Research Society USA), Elsevier BV (Subsidiary of: Elsevier Science & Technology), Radarweg 29, Amsterdam, 1043 NX, Netherlands. TEL 31-20-4853911, FAX 31-20-4852457, nlinfo-f@elsevier.nl, http://www.elsevier.com/locate/mito, http://www.elsevier.nl. Ed. K K Singh.

579 JPN ISSN 0026-8054
MODERN MEDIA/MODAN MEDIA. Text in Japanese. 1955. m. bk.rev. charts; illus.
Indexed: ChemAb, ChemTitl, RefZh.
—BLDSC (5889.700000).
Published by: Eiken Chemical Co. Ltd./Eiken Kagaku K. K., 5-26-20 O-Ji, Kita-ku, Tokyo, 114-0002, Japan. TEL 81-3-3913-6231, FAX 81-3-3914-7027. Ed. Hiromitsu Enomoto. Circ: (controlled).

MOLECULAR AND BIOCHEMICAL PARASITOLOGY. see *BIOLOGY—Biochemistry*

MOLECULAR CARCINOGENESIS. see *MEDICAL SCIENCES—Oncology*

579.17 GBR ISSN 0962-1083
QH541.15.M63 CODEN: MOECEO
➤ **MOLECULAR ECOLOGY.** Text in English. 1992. m. GBP 146, EUR 219 combined subscription in Europe to individuals print & online eds.; USD 257 combined subscription in the Americas to individuals & Caribbean, print & online eds.; GBP 158 combined subscription elsewhere to individuals print & online eds.; GBP 3,326 combined subscription in Europe to institutions print & online eds.; USD 6,145 combined subscription in the Americas to institutions & Caribbean, print & online eds.; GBP 3,658 combined subscription elsewhere to institutions print & online eds.; USD 153 combined subscription in the Americas to students & Caribbean, print & online eds.; EUR 128 combined subscription in Europe to students print & online eds.; GBP 85 combined subscription elsewhere to students print & online eds. (effective 2006); includes Molecular Ecology Notes. adv. bk.rev. bibl.; illus. index. back issues avail.; reprint service avail. from PSC. **Document type:** *Journal, Academic/Scholarly.* **Description:** Directed at the interface of molecular biology with ecology, evolution, and population biology, including population structure and phylogeography.

Related titles: Microform ed.: (from PQC); Online - full text ed.: ISSN 1365-294X. 199?. GBP 3,159 in Europe to institutions; USD 5,838 in the Americas to institutions & Caribbean; GBP 3,475 elsewhere to institutions (effective 2006) (from Blackwell Synergy, EBSCO Publishing, Gale Group, IngentaConnect, O C L C Online Computer Library Center, Inc., Swets Information Services).

Indexed: ASCA, ASFA, AgBio, Agr, AgrForAb, AnBrAb, ApEcolAb, B&BAb, BCI, BIOBASE, BIOSIS Prev, BibAg, BioCN&I, BiolAb, CIN, CPA, ChemAb, ChemTitl, CurCont, EPB, ESPM, EntAb, FCA, FPA, ForAb, GenetAb, HGA, HelmAb, HerbAb, HortAb, IABS, ISR, IndMed, IndVet, Inpharma, MBA, MEDLINE, MaizeAb, NemAb, NutrAb, OrnHort, PBA, PGegResA, PGrRegA, PHN&I, PN&I, PotatoAb, PoultAb, ProtozoAb, RA&MP, RM&VM, RPP, RRTA, Reac, RefZh, RevApplEntom, RiceAb, S&F, SCI, SFA, SIA, SeedAb, SoyAb, TDB, TriticAb, VITIS, VetBull, WeedAb, WildRev, ZooRec.

—BLDSC (5900.817360), CASDDS, CISTI, IDS, IE, Infotrieve, ingenta, Linda Hall. **CCC.**

Published by: Blackwell Publishing Ltd., 9600 Garsington Rd, Oxford, OX4 2ZG, United Kingdom. TEL 44-1865-776868, FAX 44-1865-714591, customerservices@oxon.blackwellpublishing.com, http://www.blackwellpublishing.com/journals/MEC. Ed. Loren Rieseberg TEL 812-855-7614. Pub. Sue Hewitt. R&P Sophie Savage. Adv. contact Jenny Applin. Circ: 740.

579.17 GBR ISSN 1471-8278
QH541.15.M63 CODEN: MENOCX

➤ **MOLECULAR ECOLOGY NOTES.** Text in English. 2001. q. GBP 2,960 in Europe to institutions print & online eds.; USD 5,470 in the Americas to institutions & the Caribbean (print & online eds.); GBP 3,256 elsewhere to institutions print & online eds. (effective 2005); included with subscr. to Molecular Ecology. reprint service avail. from PSC. **Document type:** *Journal, Academic/Scholarly.* **Description:** Provides a vehicle for the rapid dissemination of technical advances in molecular ecology, such as new computer programs, methodological innovations, and molecular marker development.

Related titles: Online - full text ed.: ISSN 1471-8286. GBP 2,812 in Europe to institutions; USD 5,197 in the Americas to institutions & the Caribbean; GBP 3,256 elsewhere to institutions (effective 2005); included with subscr. to Molecular Ecology (from Blackwell Synergy, Gale Group, IngentaConnect, O C L C Online Computer Library Center, Inc., Swets Information Services).

Indexed: ASFA, AgBio, Agr, AgrForAb, AnBrAb, ApEcolAb, B&BAb, BIOBASE, BIOSIS Prev, BioCN&I, BiolAb, CPA, CurCont, ESPM, EntAb, FCA, FPA, ForAb, GenetAb, HelmAb, HerbAb, HortAb, IndVet, MaizeAb, NemAb, OrnHort, PBA, PGegResA, PHN&I, PotatoAb, PoultAb, ProtozoAb, RPP, RefZh, RiceAb, S&F, SeedAb, SoyAb, TDB, TriticAb, VITIS, VetBull, WeedAb, ZooRec.

—BLDSC (5900.817365), CISTI, IE, Infotrieve, ingenta, Linda Hall. **CCC.**

Published by: Blackwell Publishing Ltd., 9600 Garsington Rd, Oxford, OX4 2ZG, United Kingdom. TEL 44-1865-776868, FAX 44-1865-714591, customerservices@oxon.blackwellpublishing.com, http://www.blackwellpublishing.com/journals/MEN. Ed. Kevin Livingstone TEL 210-999-7236.

579 USA ISSN 0891-4168
QH506

➤ **MOLECULAR GENETICS, MICROBIOLOGY AND VIROLOGY.** Text in English. 1986. bi-m. USD 1,555 per vol. in US & Canada; USD 1,855 per vol. elsewhere (effective 2006). abstr.; charts; illus. back issues avail. **Document type:** *Journal, Academic/Scholarly.* **Description:** Covers microbiology, virology, genetic engineering, immunology, DNA, and the methodology of molecular genetics.

Related titles: ♦ Translation of: Molekulyarnaya Genetika, Mikrobiologiya i Virusologiya. ISSN 0208-0613.

—BLDSC (0416.235500), CISTI, GNLM, IE, ingenta. **CCC.**

Published by: (Biotechnologicheskya Akademiya RUS), Allerton Press, Inc., 18 W 27th St, New York, NY 10001. TEL 646-424-9686, FAX 646-424-9695, journals@allertonpress.com, http://www.allertonpress.com/journals/mgv.htm. Ed. Evgeny D Sverdlov.

579 NLD

MOLECULAR MICROBIAL ECOLOGY MANUAL. Text in Dutch. base vol. plus irreg. updates. looseleaf. price varies.

Published by: Springer-Verlag Dordrecht (Subsidiary of: Springer Science+Business Media), Van Godewijckstraat 30, Dordrecht, 3311 GX, Netherlands. TEL 31-78-6576050, FAX 31-78-6576474, http://www.springeronline.com.

579 GBR ISSN 0950-382X
QR74 CODEN: MOMIEE

➤ **MOLECULAR MICROBIOLOGY.** Text in English. s-m. GBP 254, EUR 390 combined subscription in Europe to individuals print & online eds.; USD 469 combined subscription in the Americas to individuals & Caribbean, print & online eds.; GBP 279 combined subscription elsewhere to individuals print & online eds.; GBP 2,565 combined subscription in Europe to institutions print & online eds.; USD 4,741 combined subscription in the Americas to institutions & Caribbean, print & online eds.; GBP 2,822 combined subscription elsewhere to institutions print & online eds. (effective 2006). adv. bibl.; illus. index. back issues avail.; reprint service avail. from PSC. **Document type:** *Journal, Academic/Scholarly.* **Description:** Publishes original research and review articles reporting new developments in the genetics, molecular biology and biochemistry of prokaryotic and eukaryotic microorganisms, and covers the most important advances in bacterial pathogenicity.

Incorporates: Microbiological Sciences (0265-1351)

Related titles: Microform ed.: USD 2,456 in North America to institutions; USD 284 in North America to individuals; GBP 1,449 elsewhere to institutions; GBP 167 elsewhere to individuals (effective 2001); Online - full text ed.: ISSN 1365-2958. 1998. EUR 371, GBP 242 in Europe to individuals; USD 447 in the Americas to individuals & Caribbean; GBP 266 elsewhere to individuals; GBP 2,437 in Europe to institutions; USD 4,504 in the Americas to institutions & Caribbean; GBP 2,681 elsewhere to institutions (effective 2006) (from Blackwell Synergy, EBSCO Publishing, Gale Group, IngentaConnect, O C L C Online Computer Library Center, Inc., Ovid Technologies, Inc., Swets Information Services).

Indexed: ASCA, ASFA, AbHyg, AgBio, Agr, AnBrAb, BBCI, BCI, BIOBASE, BIOSIS Prev, BibAg, BioCN&I, BiolAb, CIN, CPA, ChemAb, ChemTitl, CurCont, DBA, DSA, ESPM, ExcerpMed, FCA, FS&TA, GenetAb, HGA, HelmAb, HerbAb, HortAb, IABS, ISR, IndMed, IndVet, Inpharma, MBA, MEDLINE, MaizeAb, NemAb, NucAcAb, NutrAb, PBA, PE&ON, PGegResA, PGrRegA, PHN&I, PN&I, PotatoAb, PoultAb, ProtozoAb, RA&MP, RM&VM, RPP, Reac, RefZh, RevApplEntom, RiceAb, S&F, SCI, SIA, SoyAb, TDB, Telegen, TriticAb, VITIS, VetBull, VirolAbstr, WeedAb.

—BLDSC (5900.817960), CASDDS, CISTI, GNLM, IDS, IE, Infotrieve, ingenta, Linda Hall. **CCC.**

Published by: Blackwell Publishing Ltd., 9600 Garsington Rd, Oxford, OX4 2ZG, United Kingdom. TEL 44-1865-776868, FAX 44-1865-714591, customerservices@oxon.blackwellpublishing.com, http://www.blackwellpublishing.com/journals/MMI. Ed. Tony Pugsley TEL 33-1-45688494. Pub. Amanda McLean Inglis. R&P Sophie Savage. Adv. contact Jenny Applin. Circ: 1,600.

➤ **MOLECULAR PLANT - MICROBE INTERACTIONS.** see *BIOLOGY—Biochemistry*

➤ **MOLECULAR REPRODUCTION AND DEVELOPMENT.** see *BIOLOGY—Biochemistry*

579 RUS ISSN 0208-0613
QR74 CODEN: MGMVDU

MOLEKULYARNAYA GENETIKA, MIKROBIOLOGIYA I VIRUSOLOGIYA/MOLECULAR GENETICS, MICROBIOLOGY AND VIRUSOLOGY. Text in Russian; Summaries in English. 1983. q. USD 152 foreign (effective 2005). adv. Website rev. abstr. reprints avail. **Document type:** *Journal, Academic/Scholarly.* **Description:** Deals with fundamental and applied problems of molecular genetics, molecular microbiology and molecular virology.

Related titles: ♦ English Translation: Molecular Genetics, Microbiology and Virology. ISSN 0891-4168.

Indexed: BIOSIS Prev, BiolAb, ChemAb, ChemTitl, CurCont, IndMed, MEDLINE, RefZh.

—CASDDS, CISTI, East View, GNLM, Linda Hall. **CCC.**

Published by: Izdatel'stvo Meditsina/Meditsina Publishers, ul B Pirogovskaya, d 2, str 5, Moscow, 119435, Russian Federation. TEL 7-095-2483324, meditsina@mtu-net.ru, http://www.medlit.ru. Ed. Yevgenii D Sverdlov. Pub. A M Stochik. R&P I Izmailova. Adv. contact O A Fadeeva TEL 7-095-923-51-40. Circ: 500. **Dist. by:** M K - Periodica, ul Gilyarovskogo 39, Moscow 129110, Russian Federation. TEL 7-095-2845008, FAX 7-095-2813798, info@periodicals.ru, http://www.mkniga.ru.

578.65 POL ISSN 0540-6722

MONOGRAFIE PARAZYTOLOGICZNE. Text in Polish. 1959. irreg., latest vol.14, 1988. price varies. bibl.; illus. back issues avail. **Document type:** *Monographic series.*

Indexed: BiolAb, ZooRec.

Published by: Polskie Towarzystwo Parazytologiczne/Polish Parasitological Society, Ul Grochowska 272, Warsaw, 03849, Poland. niewiadk@twarda.pan.pl. Ed. Katarzyna Niewiadomska. Circ: 400. **Dist. by:** Ars Polona, Krakowskie Przedmiescie 7, Warsaw, Poland.

579.2 CHE ISSN 0077-0965
CODEN: MONVAK

➤ **MONOGRAPHS IN VIROLOGY.** Text in English. 1967. irreg., latest vol.25, 2005. price varies. reprint service avail. from ISI. **Document type:** *Monographic series, Academic/Scholarly.* **Description:** Reference tools for virologists and non-virologists alike.

Indexed: BIOSIS Prev, BiolAb, ChemAb, CurCont, IndMed, MEDLINE.

—BLDSC (5917.780000), CISTI, GNLM, IE, Infotrieve, ingenta, KNAW. **CCC.**

Published by: S. Karger AG, Allschwilerstr 10, Basel, 4009, Switzerland. TEL 41-61-3061111, FAX 41-61-3061234, karger@karger.ch, http://www.karger.com/MOVIR, http://www.karger.ch. Ed. H W Doerr.

➤ **MYCOBACTERIA.** see *BIOLOGY—Abstracting, Bibliographies, Statistics*

➤ **MYCOPATHOLOGIA.** see *BIOLOGY—Botany*

579 GBR ISSN 1740-1526
QR1 CODEN: NRMACK

▼ **NATURE REVIEWS. MICROBIOLOGY.** Text in English. 2003. m. EUR 1,395 in Europe to institutions Eurozone; USD 1,620 in the Americas to institutions; GBP 900 to institutions in the UK & elsewhere; EUR 210 combined subscription in Europe to individuals Eurozone; print & online; USD 225 combined subscription in the Americas to individuals print & online; GBP 136 combined subscription to individuals in the UK & elsewhere; print & online (effective 2006). **Document type:** *Journal, Academic/Scholarly.*

Related titles: Online - full content ed.; Online - full text ed.: (from EBSCO Publishing, Swets Information Services).

Indexed: CurCont, ExcerpMed, ISR, SCI.

—BLDSC (6047.228000), CISTI, IE. **CCC.**

Published by: Nature Publishing Group (Subsidiary of: Macmillan Publishers Ltd.), The MacMillan Building, 4 Crinan St, London, N1 9XW, United Kingdom. TEL 44-20-78434624, FAX 44-20-78434596, NatureReviews@nature.com, http://www.nature.com/nrmicro/, http://www.nature.com/reviews. Ed. David O'Connell. **Subscr. to:** Brunel Rd, Houndmills, Basingstoke, Hamps RG21 6XS, United Kingdom.

572.8 GBR ISSN 1471-0072
CODEN: NRMCBP

➤ **NATURE REVIEWS. MOLECULAR CELL BIOLOGY.** Text in English. 2000 (Oct.). m. EUR 1,395 in Europe to institutions Eurozone; USD 1,620 in the Americas to institutions; GBP 900 to institutions in the UK & elsewhere; EUR 210 combined subscription in Europe to individuals Eurozone; print & online; USD 225 combined subscription in the Americas to individuals print & online; GBP 136 combined subscription to individuals in the UK & elsewhere; print & online (effective 2006). adv. back issues avail.; reprints avail. **Document type:** *Journal, Academic/Scholarly.* **Description:** Features reviews and perspectives articles on a broad range of topics, and highlight important primary papers and technological progress. Subjects include chromosome biology, nucleic-acid metabolism, gene expression, nuclear transport, protein structure and metabolism, membrane dynamics, bioenergetics, cell signalling, cell growth and division, cytoskeletal dynamics, cell adhesion, developmental cell biology, cell death, cellular microbiology.

Related titles: Online - full text ed.: ISSN 1471-0080 (from EBSCO Publishing, Swets Information Services).

Indexed: ASFA, B&BAb, BBCI, BIOBASE, BIOSIS Prev, CTA, ChemAb, CurCont, ESPM, ExcerpMed, GenetAb, ISR, Inpharma, MEDLINE, NSA, NucAcAb, PE&ON, Reac, SCI.

—BLDSC (6047.230000), CISTI, IE, Infotrieve, ingenta. **CCC.**

Published by: Nature Publishing Group (Subsidiary of: Macmillan Publishers Ltd.), The MacMillan Building, 4 Crinan St, London, N1 9XW, United Kingdom. TEL 44-20-78334000, FAX 44-20-78433601, NatureReviews@nature.com, http://www.nature.com/molcellbio. Ed. Arianne Heinrichs. **Subscr. elsewhere to:** Brunel Rd, Houndmills, Basingstoke, Hamps RG21 6XS, United Kingdom. TEL 44-1256-329242, FAX 44-1256-812358; **Subscr. in N. & S. America to:** Nature Publishing Group, PO Box 5161, Brentwood, TN 37024-5161. TEL 615-850-5315, 800-524-0384, FAX 615-377-0525, subscriptions@natureny.com.

➤ **NEDERLANDS TIJDSCHRIFT VOOR MEDISCHE MICROBIOLOGIE.** see *MEDICAL SCIENCES*

579 ITA ISSN 1121-7138
CODEN: MIBLDR

➤ **THE NEW MICROBIOLOGICA**; quarterly journal of microbiological sciences. Text and summaries in English. 1978. q. EUR 160 domestic; EUR 200 foreign (effective 2005). adv. bk.rev. **Document type:** *Journal, Academic/Scholarly.*

Formerly (until 1992): Microbiologica (0391-5352)

Indexed: ASFA, AbHyg, BIOSIS Prev, BioCN&I, BiolAb, CurCont, DSA, ESPM, ExcerpMed, FS&TA, IndMed, IndVet, Inpharma, MBA, MEDLINE, NutrAb, PBA, PE&ON, PN&I, PotatoAb, PoultAb, ProtozoAb, RA&MP, RM&VM, RPP, RRTA, Reac, RevApplEntom, S&F, SCI, SIA, SoyAb, TDB, Telegen, VetBull.

—BLDSC (5757.400000), CASDDS, CISTI, GNLM, IDS, IE, Infotrieve, ingenta, KNAW.

Published by: (Universita degli Studi di Bologna), Edizioni Medico Scientifiche, Via Riviera 39, Pavia, 27100, Italy. TEL 39-0382-526253, FAX 39-0382-423120, edint@edimes@tin.it, http://www.microbiologica.net. Circ: 500.

B

▼ new title ➤ refereed ✶ unverified ♦ full entry avail.

579.3 JPN
NIHON ARCHAEBACTERIA KENKYUKAI KOENKAI YOSHISHU/JAPAN SOCIETY FOR ARCHAEBACTERIOLOGY. ABSTRACTS OF ANNUAL MEETING. Text in Japanese. 1988. a. **Document type:** *Abstract/Index.*
Published by: Nihon Archaebacteria Kenkyukai/Japan Society for Archaebacteriology, Noda Sangyo Kagaku Kenkyujo, 399 Noda, Noda-shi, Chiba-ken 278-0037, Japan.

NIHON BOKIN BOBAI GAKKAI. NENJI TAIKAI YOSHISHU/SOCIETY FOR ANTIBACTERIAL AND ANTIFUNGAL AGENTS, JAPAN. ABSTRACTS OF THE MEETING. see *BIOLOGY—Abstracting, Bibliographies, Statistics*

NIHON DOJO BISEIBUTSU GAKKAI KOEN YOSHISHU/SOIL MICROBIOLOGICAL SOCIETY OF JAPAN. ABSTRACTS OF THE ANNUAL MEETING. see *BIOLOGY—Abstracting, Bibliographies, Statistics*

579 JPN ISSN 0914-5818
CODEN: ACTIF4
NIHON HOSENKIN GAKKAISHI/ACTINOMYCETOLOGICA. Text in English, Japanese; Summaries in English. 1962. s-a. JPY 7,000 (effective 1999). **Document type:** *Academic/Scholarly.*
Indexed: CIN, ChemAb, ChemTitl.
—BLDSC (0675.405500), CASDDS, IE, ingenta.
Published by: Nihon Hosenkin Gakkai/Society for Actinomycetes, Japan, Biseibutsu Kagaku Kenkyujo, 14-23 Kami-Osaki 3-chome, Shinagawa-ku, Tokyo, 141-0021, Japan. Ed. Sueharu Horinouchi. R&P Nihon Hosenkin Gakkai.

579 664 JPN ISSN 1340-8267
NIHON SHOKUHIN BISEIBUTSU GAKKAI ZASSHI/JAPANESE JOURNAL OF FOOD MICROBIOLOGY. Text in Japanese. 1984. q. **Document type:** *Journal, Academic/Scholarly.*
Formerly (until 1994): Shokuhin to Biseibutsu/Japanese Journal of Food Microbiology (0910-8637)
Indexed: FS&TA.
—BLDSC (4651.950000).
Published by: Nihon Shokuhin Biseibutsu Gakkai/Japanese Society of Food Microbiology, Kounan 4-5-7, Minato-ku, Tokyo University of Fisheries, Department of Food Science & Technology, Tokyo, 108-8477, Japan. http://www.jsfm.jp/.

579.2 JPN
NIHON UIRUSU GAKKAI HOKKAIDO SHIBU KAIHO/SOCIETY OF JAPANESE VIROLOGISTS. HOKKAIDO BRANCH. NEWS. Text in Japanese. a.
Published by: Nihon Uirusu Gakkai, Hokkaido Shibu/Society of Japanese Virologists, Hokkaido Branch, Hokkaido Daigaku Juigakubu Jui Koshu Eiseigaku Koza, Nishi 9-chome, Kita 18-jo, Kita-ku, Sapporo-shi, Hokkaido 060, Japan.

579.2 JPN
NIHON UIRUSU GAKKAI KAIHO/SOCIETY OF JAPANESE VIROLOGISTS. BULLETIN. Text in Japanese. s-a.
Published by: Nihon Uirusu Gakkai, Nihon Gakkai Jimu Senta, 16-9 Honkomagome 5-chome, Bunkyo-ku, Tokyo, 113-0021, Japan.

579.2 JPN
NIHON UIRUSU GAKKAI SOKAI ENZETSU SHOROKU/SOCIETY OF JAPANESE VIROLOGISTS. PROCEEDINGS OF THE ANNUAL MEETING. Text in Japanese. 1953. a. **Document type:** *Proceedings.*
Published by: Nihon Uirusu Gakkai, Nihon Gakkai Jimu Senta, 16-9 Honkomagome 5-chome, Bunkyo-ku, Tokyo, 113-0021, Japan.

616.015 JPN ISSN 0916-4804
CODEN: NIGZE4
NIPPON ISHINKIN GAKKAI ZASSHI/JAPANESE JOURNAL OF MEDICAL MYCOLOGY. Key Title: Nihon Ishinkin Gakkai Zasshi. Text in English. 1960. q. JPY 10,300. adv. bk.rev. Index. back issues avail. **Document type:** *Journal, Academic/Scholarly.*
Formerly (until 1990): Shinkin to Shinkinsho (0583-0516)
Related titles: Online - full text ed.: free (effective 2005).
Indexed: AbHyg, DSA, ExcerpMed, HortAb, IndMed, IndVet, MEDLINE, RA&MP, RM&VM, S&F, SAA, SoyAb, TDB, VetBull, WeedAb.
—CASDDS, CISTI, GNLM. **CCC.**
Published by: Nihon Ishinkin Gakkai/Japanese Society for Medical Mycology, Business Center for Academic Societies, 16-9,Honkomagome 5-chome, Bunkyo-ku, Tokyo, 113-8622, Japan. TEL 81-3-58145801, http://www.jsmm.org/magazine/magazine.html. Circ: 1,000.

579 DNK ISSN 1397-4858
➤ **NYT OM MIKROBIOLOGI.** Text in Danish. 1986. irreg. **Document type:** *Journal, Academic/Scholarly.*
Related titles: Online - full text ed.
Published by: (Dansk Selskab for Klinisk Mikrobiologi), Statens Serum Institut, Artillerivej 5, Copenhagen S, 2300, Denmark. TEL 45-32-683268, FAX 45-32-683868, nyt-om-mikro@ssi.dk, serum@ssi.dk, http://www.ssi.dk/sw3217.asp. Ed. Niels Frimodt-Moeller.

➤ **O M I C S: A JOURNAL OF INTEGRATIVE BIOLOGY.** see *BIOLOGY—Genetics*

➤ **OLD HERBORN UNIVERSITY SEMINAR MONOGRAPH.** see *MEDICAL SCIENCES—Gastroenterology*

579 GBR ISSN 1362-6809
OPINION: SPECIALIST REVIEWS OF KEY PAPERS IN MICROBIOLOGY. Abbreviated title: Opinion: Micro. Text in English. 1996. 3/yr. **Document type:** *Academic/Scholarly.*
Published by: Hayward Medical Communications Ltd. (Subsidiary of: Hayward Group plc), Rosalind Franklin House, The Oaks Business Park, Fordham Rd, Newmarket, CB8 7XN, United Kingdom. TEL 44-20-72404493, FAX 44-20-72404479, admin@hayward.co.uk, http://www.hayward.co.uk. Ed. Tom Rogers. Circ: 1,800. **Subscr. to:** Rosemary House, Lanwades Park, Kentford, Near, Newmarket, Suffolk CB8 7PW, United Kingdom. TEL 44-1638-751515, FAX 44-1638-751517.

579 DNK ISSN 0902-0055
CODEN: OMIMEE
➤ **ORAL MICROBIOLOGY AND IMMUNOLOGY.** Text in English. 1987. bi-m. EUR 254 combined subscription in Europe to individuals print & online eds.; USD 284 combined subscription in the Americas to individuals & Caribbean, print & online eds.; GBP 169 combined subscription elsewhere to individuals print & online eds.; USD 603 combined subscription in the Americas to institutions & Caribbean, print & online eds.; GBP 359 combined subscription elsewhere to institutions print & online eds. (effective 2006). adv. illus. reprint service avail. from PSC. **Document type:** *Journal, Academic/Scholarly.*
Related titles: Online - full text ed.: ISSN 1399-302X. USD 573 in the Americas to institutions & Caribbean; GBP 341 elsewhere to institutions (effective 2006) (from Blackwell Synergy, EBSCO Publishing, Gale Group, IngentaConnect, O C L C Online Computer Library Center, Inc., Ovid Technologies, Inc., Swets Information Services).
Indexed: AIDS&CR, ASCA, AbHyg, BIOBASE, BIOSIS Prev, BiolAb, CIN, CTD, ChemAb, ChemTitl, CurCont, DSA, ESPM, ExcerpMed, IABS, ISR, ImmunAb, Inpharma, MBA, MEDLINE, NutrAb, PE&ON, ProtozoAb, RA&MP, RDA, RM&VM, Reac, SCI, SIA, SoyAb, TDB, VirolAbstr.
—BLDSC (6277.590000), CASDDS, CISTI, GNLM, IDS, IE, Infotrieve, ingenta, KNAW. **CCC.**
Published by: Blackwell Munksgaard (Subsidiary of: Blackwell Publishing Ltd.), Rosenoerns Alle 1, PO Box 227, Copenhagen V, 1502, Denmark. TEL 45-77-333333, FAX 45-77-333377, info@mks.blackwellpublishing.com, http://www.blackwellpublishing.com/journals/OMI, http://www.munksgaard.dk/. Ed. Joergen Slots. Adv. contact Martin Steiniche Nielsen. Circ: 625.

579 ITA ISSN 0390-5454
OSPEDALE MARIA VITTORIA DI TORINO. ANNALI. Text in Italian. s-a.
Supersedes: Giornale di Batteriologia, Virologia ed Immunologia ed Annali dell'Ospedale Maria Vittoria di Torino. Parte 2. Sezione Clinica (0301-1445); Which superseded in part: Giornale di Batteriologia, Virologia ed Immunologia ed Annali dell'Ospedale Maria Vittoria di Torino (0017-0267)
Indexed: BiolAb, DentInd, MEDLINE, TDB.
—CISTI, GNLM.
Published by: Ospedale Maria Vittoria, Via Luigi Cibrario, 72, Turin, TO 10144, Italy. TEL 74 92 345.

664.001579 GBR ISSN 0968-1280
P H L S FOOD AND ENVIRONMENT BULLETIN. Text in English. 1991. m. GBP 58 in United Kingdom; GBP 74 in Europe; GBP 94 elsewhere (effective 2002). **Document type:** *Bibliography.* **Description:** Covers food, water, environmental microbiology related to prevention of infection.
Formerly (until 1992): P H L S Food and Environmental Microbiology Bulletin
Related titles: E-mail ed.
Published by: Health Protection Agency, 61 Colindale Ave, London, NW9 5EQ, United Kingdom. TEL 44-20-82006868, FAX 44-20-82007868, http://www.phls.co.uk/. Ed. Margaret Clennett.

578.65 FRA ISSN 1252-607X
CODEN: PASIED
➤ **PARASITE.** Text and summaries in English, French. 1923. q. EUR 185 in Europe to individuals; EUR 250 elsewhere to individuals; EUR 225 in Europe to institutions; EUR 300 elsewhere to institutions; EUR 145 in Europe to students; EUR 55 newsstand/cover (effective 2003). bk.rev. illus. index. back issues avail.; reprint service avail. from ISI. **Document type:** *Journal, Academic/Scholarly.* **Description:** Contains original work in parasitology research: protozoology, helminthology, entomology, therapeutics, immunology, molecular biology, genetics, epidemiology.
Formerly (until 1994): Annales de Parasitologie Humaine et Comparee (0003-4150)
Related titles: Microform ed.: (from PQC).
Indexed: ABIn, ASCA, ASFA, AbHyg, AgBio, AnBrAb, B&BAb, BIOSIS Prev, BioCN&I, BiolAb, CIN, ChemAb, ChemTitl, CurCont, DSA, ESPM, EntAb, ExcerpMed, ForAb, GenetAb, HelmAb, HerbAb, HortAb, ISR, IndMed, IndVet, MBA, MEDLINE, NemAb, NutrAb, PN&I, PoultAb, ProtozoAb, RA&MP, RDA, RM&VM, RPP, RevApplEntom, SCI, SIA, SoyAb, TDB, TriticAb, VetBull, ZooRec.
—BLDSC (6404.939000), CISTI, GNLM, IDS, IE, Infotrieve, ingenta, Linda Hall. **CCC.**
Published by: (Societe Francaise de Parasitologie), Princeps Editions, 64 av. du General de Gaulle, Issy-les-Moulineaux, 92130, France. TEL 33-1-46382414, FAX 33-1-40957215, princeps.gdumas@wanadoo.fr. Ed. Dr. J M Dumas. Circ: 600.

578.65 CHL ISSN 0717-7704
PARASITOLOGIA LATINOAMERICANA. Text in Spanish. 2002. s-a. USD 40 (effective 2004). **Document type:** *Journal, Academic/Scholarly.*
Formed by the merger of (1977-2002): Parasitologia al Dia (0716-0720); (1946-2002): Boletin Chileno de Parasitologia (0365-9402)
Related titles: Online - full text ed.: ISSN 0717-7712. free (effective 2005).
Indexed: AgBio, AnBrAb, BioCN&I, ForAb, HelmAb, IndVet, PN&I, PoultAb, ProtozoAb, RA&MP, S&F, TDB.
—Linda Hall.
Published by: Sociedad Chilena de Parasitologia, Casilla 9183, Santiago, 1, Chile. FAX 56-2-5416840.

PARASITOLOGY (SHEFFIELD). see *BIOLOGY—Abstracting, Bibliographies, Statistics*

578.65 DEU ISSN 0932-0113
QL757 CODEN: PARREZ
➤ **PARASITOLOGY RESEARCH.** Text in English, French, German; Summaries in English. 1928. 18/yr. EUR 3,588 combined subscription to institutions print & online eds. (effective 2005). adv. charts; illus. back issues avail.; reprint service avail. from ISI. **Document type:** *Journal, Academic/Scholarly.* **Description:** Presents information on the latest developments in parasitology research, with special emphasis on practical aspects such as immunodiagnosis, chemotherapy, and epidemiology. Includes review articles that provide an overview of current advances.
Formerly: Zeitschrift fuer Parasitenkunde (0044-3255)
Related titles: Microform ed.: (from PQC); Online - full text ed.: ISSN 1432-1955 (from EBSCO Publishing, Springer LINK, Swets Information Services).
Indexed: ASCA, ASFA, AbHyg, AgBio, AgrForAb, AnBrAb, BIOSIS Prev, BioCN&I, BiolAb, ChemAb, CurCont, DBA, DSA, ESPM, ExcerpMed, FCA, FoVS&M, ForAb, HelmAb, HortAb, ISR, IndMed, IndVet, Inpharma, MEDLINE, MaizeAb, NemAb, NutrAb, PBA, PE&ON, PGegResA, PN&I, PoultAb, ProtozoAb, RA&MP, RM&VM, RPP, Reac, RefZh, RevApplEntom, S&F, SCI, SFA, SIA, SSCI, SoyAb, TDB, TriticAb, VetBull, WAE&RSA, WeedAb, WildRev, ZooRec.
—BLDSC (6406.120000), CASDDS, CISTI, GNLM, IDS, IE, Infotrieve, ingenta, Linda Hall. **CCC.**
Published by: (Deutschen Gesellschaft fuer Parasitologie), Springer-Verlag (Subsidiary of: Springer Science+Business Media), Tiergartenstr 17, Heidelberg, 69121, Germany. TEL 49-6221-3450, FAX 49-6221-345229, http://link.springer.de/link/service/journals/00436/index.htm. Eds. Dr. B Chobotar, Dr. H Mehlhorn. Adv. contact Stephan Kroeck TEL 49-30-827875739. **Subscr. in the Americas to:** Springer-Verlag New York, Inc., Journal Fulfillment, PO Box 2485, Secaucus, NJ 07096-2485. TEL 800-777-4643, 201-348-4033, FAX 201-348-4505, journals@springer-ny.com, http://www.springer-ny.com; **Subscr. to:** Springer GmbH Auslieferungsgesellschaft, Haberstr 7, Heidelberg 69126, Germany. TEL 49-6221-345-0, FAX 49-6221-345-4229, subscriptions@springer.de.

➤ **PARAZITOLOGIYA/PARASITOLOGY.** see *MEDICAL SCIENCES—Communicable Diseases*

➤ **PATHOBIOLOGY**; journal of immunopathology, molecular, and cellular biology. see *MEDICAL SCIENCES—Allergology And Immunology*

➤ **PENDIK VETERINER MIKROBIYOLOJI DERGISI/JOURNAL OF PENDIK VETERINARY MICROBIOLOGY.** see *VETERINARY SCIENCE*

579 POL ISSN 1733-1331
QR1 CODEN: AMPOAX
➤ **POLISH JOURNAL OF MICROBIOLOGY.** Text and summaries in English. 1952. q. EUR 158 foreign (effective 2005). charts; illus. index. 100 p./no. 1 cols./p.; reprints avail. **Document type:** *Journal, Academic/Scholarly.*
Formerly (until 2004): Acta Microbiologica Polonica (0137-1320); Which was formed by merger of (1969-1975): Acta Microbiologica Polonica. Series A: Microbiologica Generalis (0567-7815); (1969-1975): Acta Microbiologica Polonica. Series B: Microbiologica Applicata (0567-7823); Both of which superseded in part (in 1969): Acta Microbiologica Polonica (0001-6195)
Related titles: Online - full text ed.
Indexed: ASCA, ASFA, AbHyg, AgBio, AgrAg, AgrLib, BIOSIS Prev, BioCN&I, BioDAb, BiolAb, CBTA, CEABA, CIN, CPA, ChemAb, ChemTitl, CurCont, DBA, DSA, ESPM, EnvEAb, ExcerpMed, FCA, FPA, FS&TA, ForAb, HerbAb, HortAb, ISR, IndMed, IndVet, MBA, MEDLINE, MaizeAb, NutrAb, OrnHort, PBA, PGrRegA, PN&I, PollutAb, PoultAb, RA&MP, RM&VM, RPP, RRTA, RefZh, RevApplEntom, S&F, SCI, SIA, SeedAb, SoyAb, TDB, TriticAb, VetBull, VirolAbstr, WAE&RSA, WeedAb.
—BLDSC (6543.671100), CASDDS, CISTI, GNLM, IDS, IE, Infotrieve, ingenta, KNAW, Linda Hall.

Published by: Polskie Towarzystwo Mikrobiologow/Polish Society of Microbiologists, ul Chelmska 30/34, Warsaw, 00725, Poland. TEL 48-22-8413367, FAX 48-22-8412949, izabelaw@biol.uw.edu.pl, http://www.pjm.microbiology.pl. Ed., Adv. contact Krystyna I Wolska. Circ: 600. **Dist. by:** Ars Polona, Krakowskie Przedmiescie 7, Warsaw, Poland. TEL 48-22-9263914, FAX 48-22-9265334, arspolona@arspolona.com.pl, http://www.arspolona.com.pl.

579 POL ISSN 0079-4252
QR1 CODEN: PMKMAV
➤ **POSTEPY MIKROBIOLOGII.** Text in Polish; Summaries in English, Polish. 1962. q. EUR 81 foreign (effective 2005). adv. **Document type:** *Journal, Academic/Scholarly.*
Indexed: AbHyg, AgrLib, CEABA, CIN, ChemAb, ChemTitl, DSA, ExcerpMed, IndVet, RM&VM, RPP, RevApplEntom, S&F.
—CASDDS.
Published by: Polskie Towarzystwo Mikrobiologow/Polish Society of Microbiologists, ul Chelmska 30/34, Warsaw, 00725, Poland. TEL 48-22-8413367, FAX 48-22-8412949, izabelaw@biol.uw.edu.pl. Ed. Jerzy Hrebenda. Circ: 1,150. **Dist. by:** Ars Polona, Krakowskie Przedmiescie 7, Warsaw, Poland. TEL 48-22-9263914, FAX 48-22-9265334, arspolona@arspolona.com.pl, http://www.arspolona.com.pl.

➤ **PRIKLADNAYA BIOKHIMIYA I MIKROBIOLOGIYA.** see *BIOLOGY—Biochemistry*

578.65 616.96 PAK ISSN 1018-2500
➤ **PROCEEDINGS OF PARASITOLOGY.** Text in English. 1985. s-a. PKR 1,000 domestic to individuals; USD 160 foreign to individuals; PKR 2,000 domestic to institutions; USD 200 foreign to institutions (effective Jun. 2003). adv. bk.rev. abstr.; bibl.; illus.; maps. 1 cols./p.; back issues avail.; reprints avail. **Document type:** *Journal, Academic/Scholarly.* **Description:** Studies the prevalence and histopathology of diseases in Pakistan. Publishes information about paraistic diseases in other countries.
Indexed: IndVet, ProtozoAb, RevApplEntom, ZooRec.
—BLDSC (6848.730600), IE, ingenta.
Published by: Baqai Medical University, Department of Parisitology, c/o Prof. Dr. Bilgees Fim, Chairperson, Karachi, 74600, Pakistan. TEL 92-21-6637951, 92-21-4988514, FAX 92-21-02075317, baqaiuniv@hotmail.com, http://www.baqai.edu.pk. Ed., Pub. Dr. Fatima Mujib Bilqees. Adv. contact K A Haseeb TEL 92-21-6637951. B&W page USD 200, color page USD 400. Circ: 1,200. **Dist. by:** Al-Haseeb, A-314, Block D, N. Nazimabad, Karachi 74700, Pakistan. TEL 92-21-6637951, 92-21-4988514, sattar_noor@yahoo.com. **Co-publisher:** Al-Haseeb.

579 NLD ISSN 0079-6352
QR53 CODEN: PIMRAS
➤ **PROGRESS IN INDUSTRIAL MICROBIOLOGY.** Text in Dutch. 1959. irreg., latest vol.36, 2002. price varies. **Document type:** *Monographic series, Academic/Scholarly.* **Description:** Examines in depth several culture media used in food science laboratories.
Indexed: AESIS, Agr, BIOSIS Prev, BiolAb, CBTA, CEABA, CIN, ChemAb, ChemTitl, DBA, FS&TA, MEDLINE.
—BLDSC (6868.500000), CASDDS, CISTI, GNLM, IE, Infotrieve, ingenta, Linda Hall. **CCC.**
Published by: Elsevier BV (Subsidiary of: Elsevier Science & Technology), Radarweg 29, Amsterdam, 1043 NX, Netherlands. TEL 31-20-4853911, FAX 31-20-4852457, nlinfo-f@elsevier.nl, http://www.elsevier.nl. Ed. M E Bushell.

579.4 USA
PROGRESS IN PROTOZOOLOGY. (Published in host country) Text in English. 1961. quadrennial. **Document type:** *Proceedings, Academic/Scholarly.*
Formerly: International Conference on Protozoology. Proceedings (0074-3267)
Published by: International Congress on Protozoology, c/o Lea Bleyman, Dept of Natural Sciences, Baruch College CUNY, 17 Lexington Ave, Box A0505, New York, NY 10010. TEL 212-387-1240, FAX 212-387-1258.

579.4 USA
PROTOCOLS IN PROTOZOOLOGY. Text in English. irreg. looseleaf. USD 50. **Document type:** *Academic/Scholarly.* **Description:** Aims to advance the science by training students and educating others in the understanding and use of protozoa.
Published by: Society of Protozoologists, c/o Allen Press, Inc, Box 1897, Lawrence, KS 66044. TEL 785-843-1235, FAX 785-843-1274. Eds. A T Soldo, J J Lee.

579.2 IND
RECENT RESEARCH DEVELOPMENTS IN ANTIVIRAL RESEARCH. Text in English. a., latest vol.1, 2001.
Published by: Transworld Research Network, T C 36-248 (1), Trivandrum, Kerala 695 008, India. http://www.transworldresearch.com.

579.072 IND
RECENT RESEARCH DEVELOPMENTS IN MICROBIOLOGY. Text in English. USD 90 (effective 1999).
Indexed: BioCN&I, DSA, IndVet, NutrAb, PGrRegA, PHN&I, PotatoAb, PoultAb, ProtozoAb, RM&VM, RevApplEntom, S&F, WeedAb.
—BLDSC (7305.087600).
Published by: Transworld Research Network, T C 36-248 (1), Trivandrum, Kerala 695 008, India.

579.2 IND
RECENT RESEARCH DEVELOPMENTS IN VIROLOGY. Text in English. a., latest vol.3, 2001. USD 85 newsstand/cover per vol. (effective 2002).
—BLDSC (7305.087735).
Published by: Transworld Research Network, T C 36-248 (1), Trivandrum, Kerala 695 008, India. http://www.transworldresearch.com.

REFERATIVNYI ZHURNAL. MIKROBIOLOGIYA OBSHCHAYA. see *BIOLOGY—Abstracting, Bibliographies, Statistics*

REFERATIVNYI ZHURNAL. MIKROBIOLOGIYA PRIKLADNAYA. see *BIOLOGY—Abstracting, Bibliographies, Statistics*

REFERATIVNYI ZHURNAL. MIKROBIOLOGIYA SANITARNAYA I MEDITSINSKAYA. see *BIOLOGY—Abstracting, Bibliographies, Statistics*

REFERATIVNYI ZHURNAL. VIRUSOLOGIYA. see *BIOLOGY—Abstracting, Bibliographies, Statistics*

REFERATIVNYI ZHURNAL. VIRUSOLOGIYA. MIKROBIOLOGIYA. see *BIOLOGY—Abstracting, Bibliographies, Statistics*

RESEARCH COMMUNICATIONS IN BIOCHEMISTRY AND CELL & MOLECULAR BIOLOGY. see *BIOLOGY—Biochemistry*

579.072 FRA ISSN 0923-2508
QR1 CODEN: ANMBCM
➤ **RESEARCH IN MICROBIOLOGY.** Text in English; Abstracts in English, French. 1887. 10/yr. EUR 726 in Europe to institutions; JPY 104,500 in Japan to institutions; USD 838 to institutions except Europe and Japan (effective 2006). adv. bk.rev. abstr.; illus. index. back issues avail.; reprint service avail. from ISI. **Document type:** *Journal, Academic/Scholarly.* **Description:** Publishes original reports, brief notes and position papers on general and molecular microbiology, physiology and microbial genetics, environmental and applied microbiology, industrial microbiology, mycology and medical microbiology.
Former titles (until 1989): Institut Pasteur. Annales. Microbiologie (0769-2609); (until 1985): Annales de Microbiologie (0300-5410); Which superseded in part (in 1972): Institut Pasteur. Annales (0020-2444)
Related titles: Microform ed.: (from PMC, RPI); Online - full text ed.: (from EBSCO Publishing, Gale Group, IngentaConnect, ScienceDirect, Swets Information Services).
Indexed: ASCA, ASFA, AbHyg, BIOBASE, BIOSIS Prev, BioCN&I, BiolAb, CIN, ChemAb, ChemTitl, CurCont, DBA, DSA, ESPM, ExcerpMed, FCA, FS&TA, ForAb, GSI, HerbAb, ISR, IndMed, IndVet, Inpharma, MBA, MEDLINE, NutrAb, PE&ON, PN&I, PoultAb, RM&VM, Reac, RevApplEntom, S&F, SCI, TDB, VITIS, VetBull, VirolAbstr, WeedAb.
—BLDSC (7742.720000), CASDDS, CISTI, GNLM, IDS, IE, Infotrieve, ingenta, Linda Hall. **CCC.**
Published by: (Institut Pasteur), Elsevier France, Editions Scientifiques et Medicales (Subsidiary of: Elsevier Science & Technology), 23 Rue Linois, Paris, 75724, France. TEL 33-1-71724600, FAX 33-1-71724650, http://www.elsevier.com/locate/resmic, http://www.pasteur.fr, http://www.elsevier.fr. Ed. A. Toussaint. Circ: 2,100. **Subscr. to:** Elsevier BV, PO Box 211, Amsterdam 1000 AE, Netherlands. TEL 31-20-485-3757, FAX 31-20-485-3432, http://www.elsevier.nl.

▼ ➤ **RETROVIROLOGY.** see *MEDICAL SCIENCES—Communicable Diseases*

➤ **REVIEWS IN MEDICAL MICROBIOLOGY.** see *MEDICAL SCIENCES*

579.2 GBR ISSN 1052-9276
QR355 CODEN: RMVIEW
➤ **REVIEWS IN MEDICAL VIROLOGY.** Text in English. 1991. bi-m. USD 965 to institutions; USD 1,062 combined subscription to institutions print & online eds. (effective 2006). adv. back issues avail.; reprints avail. **Document type:** *Journal, Academic/Scholarly.* **Description:** Reviews current research and new information on all viruses of medical importance.
Related titles: Microform ed.: (from PQC); Online - full text ed.: ISSN 1099-1654. 1996. USD 965 to institutions (effective 2006) (from EBSCO Publishing, Gale Group, IngentaConnect, ProQuest Information & Learning, Swets Information Services, Wiley InterScience).
Indexed: AIDS&CR, ASCA, AbHyg, AgBio, BIOBASE, BIOSIS Prev, CIN, ChemAb, ChemTitl, CurCont, ExcerpMed, IABS, ISR, IndMed, IndVet, Inpharma, MBA, MEDLINE, PE&ON, PN&I, PotatoAb, PoultAb, RM&VM, RPP, Reac, RefZh, SCI, TDB, VetBull, VirolAbstr, WAE&RSA.
—BLDSC (7792.500000), CASDDS, GNLM, IDS, IE, Infotrieve, ingenta, KNAW. **CCC.**
Published by: John Wiley & Sons Ltd. (Subsidiary of: John Wiley & Sons, Inc.), The Atrium, Southern Gate, Chichester, West Sussex PO19 8SQ, United Kingdom. TEL 44-1243-779777, FAX 44-1243-775878, customer@wiley.co.uk, http://www3.interscience.wiley.com/cgi-bin/jhome/5616, http://www.wiley.co.uk. Ed. Paul Griffiths. Pub. Richard Baggaley. R&P Diane Southern TEL 44-1243-770347. adv.: B&W page GBP 650, color page GBP 1,550; trim 210 x 297. Circ: 400. **Subscr. in the Americas to:** John Wiley & Sons, Inc., 111 River St, Hoboken, NJ 07030-5774. TEL 201-748-6645, 800-225-5945, subinfo@wiley.com.

579 ARG ISSN 0325-7541
QR1 CODEN: RAMID4
➤ **REVISTA ARGENTINA DE MICROBIOLOGIA.** Text in English, Spanish. 1969. q. USD 45 domestic; USD 50 foreign (effective 2005). adv. 64 p./no.; **Document type:** *Journal, Academic/Scholarly.*
Formerly (until 1979): Asociacion Argentina de Microbologia. Revista (0325-1713)
Indexed: AbHyg, AgBio, AgrForAb, BIOSIS Prev, BioCN&I, BiolAb, CIN, CPA, ChemAb, ChemTitl, DSA, ExcerpMed, FCA, FS&TA, ForAb, HerbAb, HortAb, I&DA, INIS AtomInd, IndMed, IndVet, MEDLINE, MaizeAb, NutrAb, PHN&I, PN&I, PoultAb, ProtozoAb, RA&MP, RM&VM, RPP, RefZh, RevApplEntom, S&F, SIA, SoyAb, TDB, VetBull, WeedAb.
—BLDSC (7841.400000), CASDDS, CISTI, GNLM, IE, Infotrieve, ingenta.
Published by: Asociacion Argentina de Microbiologia, Bulnes, 44 P.B. B, Buenos Aires, 1176, Argentina. TEL 54-11-49828557, FAX 54-11-49584888, info@aam.org.ar, http://www.aam.org.ar/. Ed. Dr. Elsa Damonte. Circ: 1,500.

579.3 COL ISSN 1657-4680
REVISTA BIOANALISIS. Text in Spanish. 2002. s-a.
Published by: Universidad de Antioquia, Calle 67, 53-108, Apartado Aereo 1226, Medellin, Colombia. TEL 57-4-2630011, FAX 57-4-2638282, comunicaciones@udea.edu.co, http://www.udea.edu.co.

REVISTA IBEROAMERICANA DE MICOLOGIA. see *MEDICAL SCIENCES*

579 MEX ISSN 0187-4640
QR1 CODEN: RLMIAA
REVISTA LATINOAMERICANA DE MICROBIOLOGIA. Text in Spanish. 1958. q. USD 40. bk.rev. **Document type:** *Academic/Scholarly.* **Description:** Original papers in medical bacteriology, virology, immunology, genetics and molecular biology, parasitology, and industrial and agricultural microbiology.
Former titles (until 1970): Revista Latinoamericana de Microbiologia y Parasitologia (0370-5986); (until 1966): Revista Latinoamericana de Microbiologia (0034-9771)
Indexed: ASFA, AbHyg, AgBio, AgrForAb, B&BAb, BIOBASE, BioCN&I, BiolAb, CPA, ChemAb, ChemTitl, DSA, ESPM, ExcerpMed, FCA, FS&TA, ForAb, HelmAb, HortAb, I&DA, IABS, IndMed, IndVet, MBA, MEDLINE, MaizeAb, NemAb, NutrAb, PBA, PGrRegA, PN&I, PotatoAb, PoultAb, ProtozoAb, RA&MP, RDA, RM&VM, RPP, RefZh, RevApplEntom, RiceAb, S&F, SIA, SoyAb, TDB, TriticAb, VetBull, ZooRec.
—BLDSC (7863.500000), CASDDS, CISTI, GNLM, IE, Infotrieve, ingenta, KNAW, Linda Hall.
Published by: (Asociacion Mexicana de Microbiologia), Asociacion Latinoamericana de Microbiologia, Apdo. Postal 4-862, Mexico City, DF 06400, Mexico. TEL 525-3414795, FAX 525-3963503. Ed. Dr. Jorge Ortigoza Ferado. Circ: 2,500.

REVISTA MEXICANA DE MICOLOGIA. see *BIOLOGY—Botany*

579 PRY ISSN 0556-6908
QR22.P37
REVISTA PARAGUAYA DE MICROBIOLOGIA. Text in Spanish; Summaries in English. 1966. a. USD 10. illus.
Indexed: ExcerpMed, IndVet, RevApplEntom, TDB, VetBull.
Published by: (Catedra de Bacteriologia y Parasitologia), Universidad Nacional de Asuncion, Facultad de Ciencias Medicas, Casilla de Correos 1102, Asuncion, Paraguay. Ed. Dr. Arquimedes Canese.

616.01 JPN ISSN 0915-1753
RINSHO BISEIBUTSU JINSOKU SHINDAN KENKYUKAISHI/ ASSOCIATION FOR RAPID METHOD AND AUTOMATION IN MICROBIOLOGY. JOURNAL. Abbreviated title: J A R M A M. Text in English, Japanese. 1988. s-a. **Document type:** *Journal, Academic/Scholarly.*
Indexed: MEDLINE.
—BLDSC (4705.221700).
Published by: Rinsho Biseibutsu Jinsoku Shindan Kenkyukai/Association for Rapid Method and Automation in Microbiology, Life Sciences Research Center, Gifu University School of Medicine, 40 Tsukasa-machi Gifu-shi, Gifu-shi, 500-8076, Japan. TEL 81-58-2672342, FAX 81-582-659001, http://www.jarmam.gr.jp/jarmam/flame.html.

578.65 ITA ISSN 0035-6387
QL757 CODEN: RPSTAX
RIVISTA DI PARASSITOLOGIA. Text in English, French, German, Italian, Spanish. 1937. 3/yr. USD 60. adv. bk.rev. charts; illus. index.

B

Indexed: ASFA, AbHyg, BiolAb, ChemAb, ESPM, ExcerpMed, IndVet, MBA, MEDLINE, RM&VM, RevApplEntom, TDB, VetBull, ZooRec.
—BLDSC (7992.200000), CASDDS, CISTI, GNLM, IE, Infotrieve, ingenta.
Published by: Istituto di Parassitologia, Universita di Messina, Via Cesare Battisti, 48, Messina, ME 98168, Italy. TEL 090-673136. Circ: 600.

579 ROM ISSN 1222-3891 CODEN: RAMIE5
ROMANIAN ARCHIVES OF MICROBIOLOGY AND IMMUNOLOGY. Text in English; Summaries in English, French. 1928. q. bk.rev. charts; illus.; abstr. index. 96 p./no.; back issues avail.; reprints avail. **Document type:** *Journal, Academic/Scholarly.*
Formerly (until 1991): Archives Roumaines de Pathologie Experimentale et de Microbiologie (0004-0037)
Indexed: ASFA, AbHyg, BiolAb, ChemAb, ExcerpMed, HelmAb, HortAb, IndMed, IndVet, MEDLINE, NutrAb, ProtozoAb, RM&VM, RefZh, RevApplEntom, TDB, VetBull.
—BLDSC (8019.585000), CASDDS, CISTI, GNLM, IE, Infotrieve, ingenta.
Published by: Institutul Cantacuzino, Spl. Independentei 103, Sector 5, Bucharest, 70100, Romania. TEL 40-01-4113800, FAX 40-01-4115672, office@cantacuzino.ro, http://www.cantacuzino.ro. Circ: 1,000.

RUSSIAN ACADEMY OF SCIENCES. ZOOLOGICAL INSTITUTE. CONTRIBUTIONS. see *MEDICAL SCIENCES—Communicable Diseases*

616.96 RUS ISSN 0869-6918
RUSSIAN JOURNAL OF NEMATOLOGY/ROSSIISKII NEMATOLOGICHESKII ZHURNAL. Text in English. 1993. s-a. USD 50 members of nematological societies; USD 30 nematologists from Eastern Europe, China, Vietnam & Cuba; USD 64 to institutions (effective 2004). **Document type:** *Journal, Academic/Scholarly.* **Description:** Covers all aspects of activities in the area of nematology. Generalizes experience in investigation of parasites, in developments of methods for fighting against parasites, treatments of patients, and particularities in disease progress.
Indexed: AgBio, BioCN&I, CPA, CurCont, FCA, ForAb, HelmAb, HerbAb, HortAb, ISR, IndVet, NemAb, OrnHort, PBA, PN&I, PotatoAb, RA&MP, S&F, SCI, SIA, TDB, TriticAb, WeedAb, ZooRec.
—BLDSC (8052.713500), IE, ingenta.
Published by: Rossiiskaya Akademiya Nauk, Institut Parasitologii, Leninsky Pr 33, Moscow, 117071, Russian Federation. TEL 7-095-9521501, FAX 7-095-2365217, s.subbotin@clo.fgov.be, http://www.russjnematology.com. **Dist. by:** East View Information Services, 3020 Harbor Ln. N., Minneapolis, MN 55447. TEL 763-550-0961, 800-477-1005, FAX 763-559-2931, 612-559-2931, 800-800-3839, eastview@eastview.com.

579.3 JPN
SAIKINGAKU GIJUTSU SOSHO/TECHNICAL JOURNAL OF BACTERIOLOGY. Text in Japanese. a. JPY 4,000.
Published by: Nihon Saikin Gakkai, Kyoiku Iinkai/Japanese Society for Bacteriology, Board of Education, Nihon Gakkai Jimu Senta, 16-9 Honkomagome 5-chome, Bunkyo-ku, Tokyo, 113-0021, Japan.

579 GBR ISSN 1746-1448
▼ ➤ **SALINE SYSTEMS.** Text in English. 2005. irreg. free (effective 2006). **Document type:** *Journal, Academic/Scholarly.* **Description:** Publishes on all aspects of basic and applied research on halophilic organisms and saline environments.
Media: Online - full text.
Published by: BioMed Central Ltd. (Subsidiary of: Current Science Ltd), Middlesex House, 34-42 Cleveland St, London, W1T 4LB, United Kingdom. TEL 44-20-76319131, FAX 44-20-76319923, info@biomedcentral.com, http://www.salinesystems.org, http://www.biomedcentral.com. Ed. Shiladitya DasSarma.

➤ **SCHWEIZERISCHE ZEITSCHRIFT FUER PILZKUNDE/ BOLLETTINO SVIZZERO DI MICOLOGIA/BULLETIN SUISSE DE MYCOLOGIE.** see *BIOLOGY—Botany*

579 JPN ISSN 0919-3758
TP500 CODEN: SEKAEA
SEIBUTSU KOGAKU KAISHI. Text in Japanese; Summaries in English. 1977. m. JPY 9,800 domestic membership; JPY 12,000 foreign membership (effective 2004). adv. abstr. **Document type:** *Journal, Academic/Scholarly.* **Description:** features original papers, general remarks, and various other articles on new research in biotechnology and related fields.
Formerly (until 1993): Hakkokogaku Kaishi (0385-6151); Which superseded in part (in 1977): Hakkokogaku Zasshi (0367-5963); Which was formerly (1923-1944): Jozogaku Zasshi (0368-153X)
Indexed: ASCA, AbHyg, AgBio, AnBrAb, BCI, BIOBASE, BIOSIS Prev, BiolAb, CIN, CPA, ChemAb, ChemTitl, CurCont, DBA, DSA, ExcerpMed, FCA, FS&TA, ForAb, HortAb, I&DA, IABS, INIS AtomInd, IndVet, NutrAb, OrnHort, PBA, PGrRegA, RiceAb, S&F, SeedAb, SoyAb, TriticAb.
—BLDSC (8219.044000), CASDDS, CISTI, IDS, Linda Hall. **CCC.**
Published by: Society for Biotechnology, Japan/Seibutsu Kogakkai, c/o Faculty of Engineering, Osaka University, 2-1 Yamadaoka, Suita, Osaka 565-0871, Japan. TEL 81-6-68762731, FAX 81-6-68792034, sbbj@bio.eng.osaka-u.ac.jp, http://wwwsoc.nacsis.ac.jp/sfbj. Ed. Sakayu Shimizu. Pub. Tohru Kobayashi. Adv. contact Takekuma Kuroki.

579 VEN ISSN 1315-2556
SOCIEDAD VENEZOLANA DE MICROBIOLOGIA. BOLETIN. Text in Spanish. 1980. q. back issues avail.
Related titles: Online - full text ed.: free (effective 2005).
Published by: Sociedad Venezolana de Microbiologia, Apdo. Postal 76635, El Marques, Caracas, Venezuela. boletinsvm@yahoo.com, http://www.svm.org.ve/. Ed. Oswaldo Carmona.

579 FRA ISSN 0081-1068
SOCIETE FRANCAISE DE MICROBIOLOGIE. ANNUAIRE. Text in French. 1961. triennial. membership.
Published by: (Societe Francaise de Microbiologie), Institut Pasteur, 25-28 Rue du Docteur Roux, Paris, Cedex 15 75724, France.

578.65 FRA ISSN 1626-0384
SOCIETE FRANCAISE DE PARASITOLOGIE. BULLETIN. Text in French. 2000. a.
Media: Online - full text.
Indexed: ZooRec.
Published by: (Societe Francaise de Parasitologie), Princeps Editions, 64 av. du General de Gaulle, Issy-les-Moulineaux, 92130, France. TEL 33-1-46382414, FAX 33-1-40957215, princeps.gdumas@wanadoo.fr, http://www.tours.inra.fr/sfpar/bulletin/bulletin.htm.

579.3 USA
➤ **SOCIETY FOR APPLIED BACTERIOLOGY. TECHNICAL SERIES.** Text in English. irreg., latest vol.21, 1985. reprint service avail. from ISI. **Document type:** *Monographic series, Academic/Scholarly.*
Indexed: BiolAb, CIN, ChemAb, ChemTitl, FS&TA.
Published by: Academic Press (Subsidiary of: Elsevier Science & Technology), 525 B St, Ste 1900, San Diego, CA 92101-4495. apsubs@acad.com, http://www.academicpress.com.

579.3 GBR ISSN 1467-4734
➤ **SOCIETY FOR APPLIED MICROBIOLOGY. SYMPOSIUM SERIES.** Text in English. 1971. a. includes with subscr. to Journal of Applied Microbiology. reprint service avail. from ISI. **Document type:** *Monographic series, Academic/Scholarly.*
Formerly (until 1998): Society for Applied Bacteriology. Symposium Series (0300-9610)
Related titles: ♦ Supplement to: Journal of Applied Microbiology. ISSN 1364-5072.
Indexed: BIOSIS Prev, BiolAb, CIN, ChemAb, ChemTitl, FS&TA, IndMed, IndVet, MEDLINE, RPP, RevApplEntom, S&F, VetBull.
—BLDSC (8319.193420), CISTI, IE, ingenta. **CCC.**
Published by: (Society for Applied Microbiology), Blackwell Publishing Ltd., 9600 Garsington Rd, Oxford, OX4 2ZG, United Kingdom. TEL 44-1865-776868, FAX 44-1865-714591, customerservices@oxon.blackwellpublishing.com, http://www.blackwellpublishing.com.

579 GBR ISSN 0081-1394
QR1 CODEN: SSGMAI
SOCIETY FOR GENERAL MICROBIOLOGY. SYMPOSIUM. Text in English. 1961. a. price varies. index. back issues avail. **Document type:** *Proceedings, Academic/Scholarly.*
Indexed: BIOSIS Prev, BiolAb, CBTA, CIN, ChemAb, ChemTitl, RPP.
—BLDSC (8585.010000), CASDDS, IE, ingenta, KNAW. **CCC.**
Published by: (Society for General Microbiology USA), Cambridge University Press, The Edinburgh Bldg, Shaftesbury Rd, Cambridge, CB2 2RU, United Kingdom. TEL 44-1223-312393, FAX 44-1223-315052, information@cambridge.org, http://www.socgenmicrobiol.org.uk/pubs/symposia.cfm, http://www.cup.cam.ac.uk/. R&P Linda Nicol TEL 44-1223-325757.

579.3 DEU ISSN 1613-3382
▼ **SOIL BIOLOGY.** Text in English. 2004. irreg., latest vol.4, 2005. price varies. **Document type:** *Monographic series, Academic/Scholarly.* **Description:** Publishes topical volumes in the fields of microbiology, environmental sciences, plant sciences, biotechnology, biochemistry, microbial ecology, mycology and agricultural sciences.
—BLDSC (8321.820050).
Published by: Springer-Verlag (Subsidiary of: Springer Science+Business Media), Tiergartenstr 17, Heidelberg, 69121, Germany. TEL 49-6221-3450, FAX 49-6221-345229, subscriptions@springer.de, http://www.springer.de. Ed. Ajit Varma.

SURGICAL INFECTIONS. see *MEDICAL SCIENCES—Surgery*

579 DEU ISSN 0723-2020
QR1 CODEN: SAMIDF
➤ **SYSTEMATIC AND APPLIED MICROBIOLOGY.** Text in English. 1980. 8/yr. EUR 431 in Europe to individuals; JPY 53,600 in Japan to individuals; USD 420 elsewhere to individuals; EUR 725 to institutions; EUR 829 in Europe to institutions; JPY 118,400 in Japan to institutions; USD 887 elsewhere to institutions (effective 2006). adv. back issues avail. **Document type:** *Journal, Academic/Scholarly.* **Description:** Covers aspects of the systematics of microorganisms and agricultural, food, industrial and ecological microbiology.
Formerly: Zentralblatt fuer Bakteriologie, Mikrobiologie und Hygiene (0172-5564)
Related titles: Online - full text ed.: (from bigchalk, EBSCO Publishing, Gale Group, IngentaConnect, O C L C Online Computer Library Center, Inc., ProQuest Information & Learning, ScienceDirect, Swets Information Services).
Indexed: AEBA, AESIS, ASCA, ASFA, AbHyg, AgBio, Agr, AgrForAb, AnBrAb, B&BAb, BCI, BIOBASE, BIOSIS Prev, BioCN&I, BiolAb, CIN, ChemAb, ChemTitl, CurCont, DBA, DSA, ESPM, ExcerpMed, FCA, FPA, FS&TA, ForAb, HerbAb, HortAb, IABS, ISR, IndMed, IndVet, Inpharma, MBA, MEDLINE, MaizeAb, NutrAb, PBA, PGegResA, PGrRegA, PHN&I, PN&I, PotatoAb, PoultAb, ProtozoAb, RM&VM, RPP, Reac, RefZh, RevApplEntom, RiceAb, S&F, SCI, SIA, SoyAb, TDB, VITIS, VetBull, VirolAbstr, WeedAb.
—BLDSC (8589.176000), CASDDS, CISTI, GNLM, IDS, IE, Infotrieve, ingenta, Linda Hall. **CCC.**
Published by: Elsevier GmbH, Urban & Fischer Verlag (Subsidiary of: Elsevier Science & Technology), Loebdergraben 14a, Jena, 07743, Germany. TEL 49-3641-626430, FAX 49-3641-626432, info@urbanfischer.de, http://www.elsevier.com/locate/sam, http://www.urbanfischer.de/journals. R&P Martin Huber TEL 49-3641-626430. Adv. contact Sabine Schroeter TEL 49-3641-626445. B&W page EUR 400, color page EUR 1,345; 210 x 280. Circ: 350 (paid and controlled). **Non-German speaking countries subscr. to:** Nature Publishing Group, Brunel Rd, Houndmills, Basingstoke, Hamps RG21 6XS, United Kingdom. TEL 44-1256-302629, FAX 44-1256-476117

579 GBR ISSN 0966-842X
QR1 CODEN: TRMIEA
➤ **TRENDS IN MICROBIOLOGY.** Text in English. 1993. 12/yr. EUR 181 in Europe to individuals; JPY 22,000 in Japan to individuals; USD 198 elsewhere to individuals; EUR 1,232 in Europe to institutions; JPY 170,900 in Japan to institutions; USD 1,378 elsewhere to institutions (effective 2006). adv. bk.rev. abstr.; bibl. index. back issues avail.; reprints avail. **Document type:** *Academic/Scholarly.* **Description:** Provides a forum for the discussion of all aspects of infection, covering dynamics, cell biology, immunology, genetics and evolution of infectious organisms, including fungi, and bacteria and viruses, as well as their plant and animal hosts.
Related titles: Microform ed.: (from PQC); Online - full text ed.: (from EBSCO Publishing, Gale Group, IngentaConnect, ScienceDirect, Swets Information Services).
Indexed: AEBA, AIDS Ab, ASCA, ASFA, AbHyg, AgBio, BBCI, BIOBASE, BIOSIS Prev, BioCN&I, BiolAb, ChemAb, DBA, DSA, ESPM, ExcerpMed, FS&TA, HelmAb, HerbAb, HortAb, IABS, ISR, IndMed, IndVet, MBA, MEDLINE, MaizeAb, NemAb, PBA, PN&I, PoultAb, ProtozoAb, RM&VM, RPP, RefZh, RevApplEntom, S&F, SCI, SeedAb, SoyAb, TDB, VirolAbstr, WeedAb.
—BLDSC (9049.664000), CISTI, GNLM, IDS, IE, Infotrieve, ingenta. **CCC.**
Published by: Elsevier Ltd., Trends Journals (Subsidiary of: Elsevier Science & Technology), 68 Hills Rd, Cambridge, CB2 1LA, United Kingdom. TEL 44-1223-315961, FAX 44-1223-464430, TIM@elsevier.co.uk, http://www.elsevier.com/locate/tim. Eds. E Rappocciolo, M Doherty. Adv. contact Thelma Reid. **Subscr. to:** Elsevier Current Trends Subscriptions, PO Box 331, Haywards Heath, W Sussex RH16 3FG, United Kingdom. TEL 44-1444-475650, FAX 44-1444-445423.

616.96 GBR ISSN 1471-4922
QR251 CODEN: TPRACT
➤ **TRENDS IN PARASITOLOGY.** Text in English. 1985. 12/yr. EUR 181 in Europe to individuals; JPY 22,000 in Japan to individuals; USD 198 to individuals except Europe and Japan; EUR 1,232 in Europe to institutions; JPY 170,900 in Japan to institutions; USD 1,378 to institutions except Europe and Japan (effective 2006). bk.rev. illus.; abstr. index. back issues avail.; reprints avail. **Document type:** *Journal, Academic/Scholarly.* **Description:** Provides an interdisciplinary forum for communications in all aspects of current field and laboratory research in parasitology from molecular biology to ecology.
Formerly: Parasitology Today (0169-4758)
Related titles: Online - full text ed.: (from EBSCO Publishing, Gale Group, IngentaConnect, ScienceDirect, Swets Information Services).
Indexed: AIDS&CR, ASCA, ASFA, AbHyg, AgBio, AnBrAb, BIOBASE, BIOSIS Prev, BioCN&I, BiolAb, CINAHL, ChemAb, ChemTitl, CurCont, DBA, DSA, ESPM, EntAb, ExcerpMed, HelmAb, ISR, ImmunAb, IndMed, IndVet, Inpharma, JDDR, MBA, MEDLINE, NemAb, NutrAb, PBA, PE&ON, PN&I, PoultAb, ProtozoAb, RA&MP, RDA, RM&VM, RRTA, Reac, RevApplEntom, SCI, SFA, SIA, TDB, VetBull, WAE&RSA, WeedAb, WildRev, ZooRec.

—BLDSC (9049.669500), CASDDS, CISTI, GNLM, IDS, IE, Infotrieve, ingenta. **CCC.**

Published by: Elsevier Ltd., Trends Journals (Subsidiary of: Elsevier Science & Technology), 68 Hills Rd, Cambridge, CB2 1LA, United Kingdom. TEL 44-1223-315961, FAX 44-1223-464430, parasites@current-trends.com, PT@elsevier.co.uk, http://www.elsevier.com/locate/pt. Eds. Linsey Stapley, Sally Hirst. Circ: 4,600. **Subscr. to:** Elsevier Current Trends Subscriptions, PO Box 331, Haywards Heath, W Sussex RH16 3FG, United Kingdom. TEL 44-1444-475650, FAX 44-1444-445423.

579 JPN ISSN 0912-2184

➤ **TSUCHI TO BISEIBUTSU/SOIL MICROORGANISMS.** Text in English, Japanese. 1954. 2/yr. JPY 3,500 domestic; JPY 4,500 foreign (effective 2000). **Document type:** *Academic/Scholarly.*

Indexed: AEA, AgBio, AgrForAb, BioCN&I, CPA, FCA, ForAb, HerbAb, HortAb, I&DA, MaizeAb, NemAb, NutrAb, OrnHort, PBA, PGegResA, PN&I, PotatoAb, RA&MP, RPP, RevApplEntom, RiceAb, S&F, SIA, SeedAb, SoyAb, TriticAb, WeedAb.

—BLDSC (8322.666500), IE, ingenta. **CCC.**

Published by: Nihon Dojo Biseibutsu Gakkai/Japanese Society of Soil Microbiology, 648 Matsundo, Matsudo City, 271-8510, Japan. TEL 81-47-308-8823, FAX 81-47-308-8824, nowmat@niaes.affrc.go.jp, jssm@midori.h.chiba-u.ac.jp. Ed. Masanori Saito.

➤ **TUNISIA. INSTITUT NATIONAL DES SCIENCES ET TECHNOLOGIES DE LA MER. BULLETIN.** see *EARTH SCIENCES—Oceanography*

579.2 JPN ISSN 0042-6857
CODEN: UIRUAF

UIRUSU/VIRUS. Text in Japanese; Summaries in English. 1951. s-a. JPY 6,000 membership (effective 2005). adv. bk.rev. abstr.; charts; illus. Index. back issues avail. **Document type:** *Journal, Academic/Scholarly.*

Related titles: Online - full text ed.: (from J-Stage).

Indexed: ASFA, BIOSIS Prev, BiolAb, ChemAb, ChemTitl, ESPM, ExcerpMed, IndMed, IndVet, JPI, MEDLINE, RPP, RefZh, VetBull.

—BLDSC (9240.850000), CASDDS, CISTI, GNLM, IE, Infotrieve, ingenta. **CCC.**

Published by: Nihon Uirusu Gakkai/Japanese Society for Virology, Nihon Gakkai Jimu Senta, 5-16-9 Honkomagome, Bunkyo-ku, Tokyo, 113-8622, Japan. TEL 81-3-58145810, FAX 81-3-58145825, http://www.jstage.jst.go.jp/browse/jsv/_vols/-char/ja, http://www0.nih.go.jp/virus/. Circ: 1,200. **Dist. overseas by:** Japan Publications Trading Co., Ltd., Book Export II Dept, PO Box 5030, Tokyo International, Tokyo 101-3191, Japan. TEL 81-3-32923753, FAX 81-3-32920410, infoserials@jptco.co.jp, http://www.jptco.co.jp.

UNIVERSITY OF TOKYO. INSTITUTE OF APPLIED MICROBIOLOGY. REPORTS. see *BIOLOGY—Abstracting, Bibliographies, Statistics*

UNIVERSITY OF WAIKATO. ANTARCTIC RESEARCH UNIT. REPORT. see *EARTH SCIENCES—Geology*

579 NLD ISSN 0378-1135
SF601 CODEN: VMICDQ

➤ **VETERINARY MICROBIOLOGY.** Text in English. 1976. 28/yr. EUR 1,998 in Europe to institutions; JPY 265,400 in Japan to institutions; USD 2,229 elsewhere to institutions (effective 2006). adv. bk.rev. bibl.; illus. index. **Document type:** *Academic/Scholarly.* **Description:** Concerned with microbiological diseases of all animals that are useful to man. Publishes information on pathogenesis, host responses, immunology, epidemiology, disease prevention, treatment, control and comparative studies of diseases affecting man and animals, as well as laboratory studies of the causal agents of diseases of animals.

Related titles: Microform ed.: (from PQC); Online - full text ed.: (from EBSCO Publishing, Gale Group, IngentaConnect, ScienceDirect, Swets Information Services).

Indexed: AEA, AEBA, AESIS, ASCA, ASFA, AbHyg, AgBio, Agr, AnBrAb, BIOBASE, BIOSIS Prev, BioCN&I, BiolAb, CIN, ChemAb, CurCont, DBA, DSA, DentInd, ESPM, ExcerpMed, FS&TA, FoVS&M, HelmAb, IABS, ISR, IndMed, IndVet, Inpharma, MBA, MEDLINE, NutrAb, PBA, PE&ON, PN&I, PoultAb, ProtozoAb, RM&VM, Reac, RefZh, RevApplEntom, SAA, SCI, SFA, SIA, SoyAb, TDB, VetBull, VirolAbstr, WAE&RSA, WildRev, ZooRec.

—BLDSC (9229.120000), CASDDS, CISTI, GNLM, IDS, IE, Infotrieve, ingenta, Linda Hall. **CCC.**

Published by: Elsevier BV (Subsidiary of: Elsevier Science & Technology), Radarweg 29, Amsterdam, 1043 NX, Netherlands. TEL 31-20-4853911, FAX 31-20-4852457, nlinfo-f@elsevier.nl, http://www.elsevier.com/locate/vetmic, http://www.elsevier.nl. Eds. M C Horzinek, Dr. M C Horzinek. **Subscr. to:** PO Box 211, Amsterdam 1000 AE, Netherlands. TEL 31-20-485-3757, FAX 31-20-485-3432.

579.2 FRA ISSN 1267-8694

VIROLOGIE. Text in French. 1997. bi-m. EUR 120 domestic to students print & online eds.; EUR 140 in the European Union to students print & online eds.; EUR 151 elsewhere to students print & online eds. (effective 2005); EUR 229 domestic to institutions print & online eds.; EUR 250 in the European Union to institutions print & online eds.; EUR 260 elsewhere to institutions print & online eds.; EUR 78 domestic to students print & online eds.; EUR 99 in the European Union to students print & online eds.; EUR 109 elsewhere to students print & online eds. (effective 2006). **Document type:** *Journal, Academic/Scholarly.* **Description:** Publishes review articles of the latest research done in basic medical, animal and plant virology.

Related titles: CD-ROM ed.: FRF 590 domestic; FRF 620 foreign (effective 2001); Online - full text ed.: FRF 670 in Europe to individuals; FRF 690 elsewhere to individuals; FRF 1,120 to institutions; FRF 470 to students (effective 2001) (from EBSCO Publishing).

Indexed: BIOSIS Prev, BiolAb, ExcerpMed.

—BLDSC (9240.405000), CISTI, IE, ingenta. **CCC.**

Published by: John Libbey Eurotext, 127 Avenue de la Republique, Montrouge, 92120, France. TEL 33-1-46730660, FAX 33-1-40840999, contact@jle.com, http://www.john-libbey-eurotext.fr. **Subscr. to:** A T E I, 3 av. Pierre Kerautret, Romainville 92230, France. TEL 33-1-48408686, FAX 33-1-48400731, atei@club-internet.fr.

579.2 USA ISSN 0042-6822
QR360 CODEN: VIRLAX

➤ **VIROLOGY.** Text in English. 1955. 26/yr. EUR 866 in Europe to individuals; JPY 90,400 in Japan to individuals; USD 640 to individuals except Europe and Japan; EUR 6,518 in Europe to institutions; JPY 680,800 in Japan to institutions; USD 5,269 to institutions except Europe and Japan; EUR 145 in Europe to students; JPY 15,200 in Japan to students; USD 128 to students except Europe and Japan (effective 2006). adv. bibl.; charts; illus. index. back issues avail.; reprints avail. **Document type:** *Journal, Academic/Scholarly.* **Description:** Publishes the results of basic research in all branches of virology, including the viruses of vertebrates and invertebrates, plants, bacteria, and yeast and fungi.

Related titles: CD-ROM ed.: ISSN 1089-862X; Online - full text ed.: ISSN 1096-0341. USD 5,393 (effective 2002) (from EBSCO Publishing, Gale Group, IngentaConnect, O C L C Online Computer Library Center, Inc., ScienceDirect, Swets Information Services).

Indexed: AIDS Ab, AIDS&CR, ASCA, ASFA, AbHyg, AgBio, Agr, AnBrAb, B&AI, B&BAb, BBCI, BIOBASE, BIOSIS Prev, BibAg, BioCN&I, BiolAb, CIN, CPA, ChemAb, ChemTitl, CurCont, DBA, DSA, DentInd, ExcerpMed, FCA, FS&TA, GSI, GenetAb, HGA, HortAb, IABS, INIS AtomInd, ISR, ImmunAb, IndMed, IndVet, Inpharma, MEDLINE, MaizeAb, NSA, NSCI, NucAcAb, NutrAb, PBA, PE&ON, PN&I, PotatoAb, PoultAb, ProtozoAb, RM&VM, RPP, Reac, RefZh, RevApplEntom, RiceAb, SAA, SCI, SFA, SIA, SPPI, TDB, TriticAb, VITIS, VetBull, VirolAbstr, WildRev.

—BLDSC (9240.500000), CASDDS, CISTI, GNLM, IDS, IE, Infotrieve, ingenta, Linda Hall. **CCC.**

Published by: Academic Press (Subsidiary of: Elsevier Science & Technology), 525 B St, Ste 1900, San Diego, CA 92101-4495. TEL 619-231-6616, 800-894-3434, FAX 619-699-6422, http://www.elsevier.com/locate/yviro, http://www.academicpress.com. Ed. Robert Lamb. **Subscr. to:** Elsevier Inc., 6277 Sea Harbor Dr., Orlando, FL 32887-4800. TEL 407-345-4000, 800-654-2452, FAX 407-363-9661, elspcs@elsevier.com, http://www.elsevier.com/homepage/about/us/regional_sites.htt.

▼ ➤ **VIROLOGY JOURNAL.** see *MEDICAL SCIENCES*

579.2 USA ISSN 0920-8569
CODEN: VIGEET

➤ **VIRUS GENES.** Text in English. 1987. bi-m. EUR 728, USD 748, GBP 455 combined subscription to institutions print & online eds. (effective 2005). adv. bk.rev. back issues avail.; reprint service avail. from PQC,PSC. **Document type:** *Journal, Academic/Scholarly.* **Description:** Publishes the results of studies on the structure and function of virus genes (animal, insect, plant and bacterial).

Related titles: Microform ed.: (from PQC); Online - full text ed.: ISSN 1572-994X (from EBSCO Publishing, Gale Group, IngentaConnect, Kluwer Online, O C L C Online Computer Library Center, Inc., Ovid Technologies, Inc., ProQuest Information & Learning, Springer LINK, Swets Information Services).

Indexed: AIDS&CR, ASCA, ASFA, AbHyg, AgBio, Agr, AnBrAb, B&BAb, BCI, BIOBASE, BIOSIS Prev, BibLing, BioCN&I, BiolAb, CIN, CPA, ChemAb, CurCont, DSA, ExcerpMed, FCA, GenetAb, HGA, HerbAb, HortAb, IABS, ISR, IndMed, IndVet, Inpharma, MEDLINE, MaizeAb, NucAcAb, PBA, PE&ON, PN&I, PotatoAb, PoultAb, RA&MP, RM&VM, RPP, Reac, RefZh, RevApplEntom, RiceAb, SCI, SIA, TDB, TriticAb, VITIS, VetBull, VirolAbstr, WeedAb.

—BLDSC (9240.850500), CASDDS, CISTI, GNLM, IDS, IE, Infotrieve, ingenta. **CCC.**

Published by: Springer-Verlag New York, Inc. (Subsidiary of: Springer Science+Business Media), 233 Spring St, New York, NY 10013. TEL 212-460-1500, FAX 212-460-1575, service@springer-ny.com, http://springerlink.metapress.com/openurl.asp?genre=journal&issn=0920-8569, http://www.springer-ny.com. Ed. Yechiel Becker. **Subscr. to:** Journal Fulfillment, PO Box 2485, Secaucus, NJ 07096-2485. TEL 201-348-4033, FAX 201-348-4505, journals@springer-ny.com.

579.2 NLD ISSN 0168-1702
CODEN: VIREDF

➤ **VIRUS RESEARCH.** Text in English. 1984. 16/yr. EUR 3,213 in Europe to institutions; JPY 427,100 in Japan to institutions; USD 3,594 elsewhere to institutions (effective 2006). adv. bk.rev. bibl.; charts; illus. index. back issues avail.; reprint service avail. from ISI. **Document type:** *Journal, Academic/Scholarly.* **Description:** Publishes original papers on fundamental research concerning virus structure, replication, and pathogenesis.

Related titles: Microform ed.: (from PQC); Online - full text ed.: (from EBSCO Publishing, Gale Group, IngentaConnect, ScienceDirect, Swets Information Services); Supplement(s): Virus Research. Supplement. ISSN 0921-2590. 1985.

Indexed: AIDS Ab, AIDS&CR, ASCA, ASFA, AbHyg, AgBio, AgrForAb, BIOBASE, BIOSIS Prev, BioCN&I, BiolAb, CIN, ChemAb, ChemTitl, CurCont, DSA, ExcerpMed, FCA, ForAb, HerbAb, HortAb, IABS, ISR, IndMed, IndVet, Inpharma, MEDLINE, MSB, MaizeAb, NemAb, NutrAb, OrnHort, PBA, PE&ON, PGegResA, PN&I, PotatoAb, PoultAb, RDA, RM&VM, RPP, Reac, RefZh, RevApplEntom, SCI, SIA, SeedAb, SoyAb, TDB, VITIS, VetBull, VirolAbstr, WAE&RSA, WildRev.

—BLDSC (9240.852000), CASDDS, CISTI, GNLM, IDS, IE, Infotrieve, ingenta, Linda Hall. **CCC.**

Published by: Elsevier BV (Subsidiary of: Elsevier Science & Technology), Radarweg 29, Amsterdam, 1043 NX, Netherlands. TEL 31-20-4853911, FAX 31-20-4852457, nlinfo-f@elsevier.nl, http://www.elsevier.com/locate/virusres, http://www.elsevier.nl. Ed. Brian W J Mahy. Circ: 1,000. **Subscr. to:** PO Box 211, Amsterdam 1000 AE, Netherlands. TEL 31-20-485-3757, FAX 31-20-485-3432.

579.2 RUS ISSN 0507-4088
CODEN: VVIRAT

VOPROSY VIRUSOLOGII/PROBLEMS OF VIROLOGY. Text in Russian; Summaries in English. 1956. bi-m. USD 218 foreign (effective 2005). adv. bk.rev. **Document type:** *Journal, Academic/Scholarly.* **Description:** Deals with advances achieved in virology in Russia and abroad. Publishes papers about viral diseases of man, animals and plants.

Indexed: AIDS&CR, ASCA, ASFA, AbHyg, AgBio, BIOSIS Prev, BioCN&I, BiolAb, CIN, ChemAb, ChemTitl, CurCont, DBA, DSA, DentInd, ExcerpMed, HortAb, IndMed, IndVet, Inpharma, MEDLINE, NutrAb, PBA, PE&ON, PN&I, PoultAb, RM&VM, Reac, RefZh, RevApplEntom, SAA, SCI, TDB, VetBull, VirolAbstr, ZooRec.

—BLDSC (0041.900000), CASDDS, CISTI, GNLM, IDS, IE, Infotrieve, KNAW. **CCC.**

Published by: Izdatel'stvo Meditsina/Meditsina Publishers, ul B Pirogovskaya, d 2, str 5, Moscow, 119435, Russian Federation. TEL 7-095-2483324, meditsina@mtu-net.ru, http://www.medlit.ru. Ed. Dmitrii K Lvov. Pub. A M Stochik. R&P T Kurushina. Adv. contact O A Fadeeva TEL 7-095-923-51-40. Circ: 850. **Dist. by:** M K - Periodica, ul Gilyarovskogo 39, Moscow 129110, Russian Federation. TEL 7-095-2845008, FAX 7-095-2813798, info@periodicals.ru, http://www.mkniga.ru.

579 FIN ISSN 0358-6758

➤ **WALTER AND ANDREE DE NOTTBECK FOUNDATION SCIENTIFIC REPORTS.** Text and summaries in English. 1976. irreg. free. back issues avail. **Document type:** *Academic/Scholarly.* **Description:** Deals with the algae, bacteria, zooplankton and other biota of marine areas, especially the Baltic Sea.

Published by: Walter and Andree de Nottbeck Foundation, c/o Department of Ecology and Systematics, University of Helsinki, Unionsgatan 44, PL 70, Helsinki, 00014, Finland. TEL 358-9-191-86-01, FAX 358-0-191-86-56, carl-adam.haeggstrom@helsinki.fi. Ed. Carl Adam Haeggstrom. Circ: 500. **Dist. by:** Tvarminne Zoological Station, Hangoe 10900, Finland.

579 CHN ISSN 0001-6209
QR1 CODEN: WSHPA8

➤ **WEISHENGWU XUEBAO/ACTA MICROBIOLOGICA SINICA.** Text in Chinese; Summaries in English. 1953. bi-m. CNY 168 (effective 2004). adv. charts; illus. **Document type:** *Journal, Academic/Scholarly.* **Description:** Contains theses on the theory and application of microbiology in industrial, agricultural, medical, and veterinary sciences, as well as virology (including taxomorphology, physio-biochemistry, genetics, and serology.).

Related titles: Online - full text ed.: (from WanFang Data Corp.).

Indexed: ASFA, AgBio, AgrForAb, BIOSIS Prev, BioCN&I, BioDAb, BiolAb, CIN, ChemAb, DSA, ESPM, FCA, HortAb, IndMed, IndVet, MBA, MEDLINE, MaizeAb, PBA, PN&I, PoultAb, ProtozoAb, RM&VM, RPP, RevApplEntom, RiceAb, S&F, SoyAb, TriticAb, VetBull.

—BLDSC (0638.500000), CASDDS, CISTI, GNLM, IE, ingenta, KNAW, Linda Hall.

B

Published by: (Zhongguo Kexueyuan, Weishengwu Yanjiusuo/Chinese Academy of Sciences, Institute of Microbiology, Zhongguo Weishengwu Xuehui/Chinese Microbiology Society), Kexue Chubanshe/Science Press, 16 Donghuang Cheng Genbei Jie, Beijing, 100717, China. TEL 86-10-64000246, FAX 86-10-64030255, actamicro@sun.im.ac.cn, http://wswxb.periodicals.net.cn/default.html. Circ: 11,000. **Dist. by:** China International Book Trading Corp, 35 Chegongzhuang Xilu, Haidian District, PO Box 399, Beijing 100044, China. TEL 86-10-68412045, FAX 86-10-68412023, cibtc@mail.cibtc.com.cn, http://www.cibtc.com.cn.

579 CHN ISSN 0253-2654
QR1 CODEN: WSWPDI
WEISHENGWUXUE TONGBAO/MICROBIOLOGY. Text in Chinese. 1973. bi-m. CNY 114 (effective 2004). adv. **Document type:** *Journal, Academic/Scholarly.* **Description:** Aims to expand the reader's knowledge of microbiology. Carries information on new results, techniques, and methods from the spheres of industry, agriculture, medicine, and veterinary medicine.
Related titles: Online - full text ed.: (from East View Information Services, WanFang Data Corp.).
Indexed: CIN, CTFA, ChemAb, ChemTitl.
—BLDSC (5757.730000), CASDDS, IE.
Published by: (Zhongguo Kexueyuan, Weishengwu Yanjiusuo/Chinese Academy of Sciences, Institute of Microbiology), Kexue Chubanshe/Science Press, 16 Donghuang Cheng Genbei Jie, Beijing, 100717, China. TEL 86-10-64000246, FAX 86-10-64030255, xuj@sun.im.ac.cn, http://wswxtb.periodicals.net.cn/default.html, http://www.sciencep.com/. Circ: 16,000. **Dist. by:** China International Book Trading Corp, 35 Chegongzhuang Xilu, Haidian District, PO Box 399, Beijing 100044, China. TEL 86-10-68412045, FAX 86-10-68412023, cibtc@mail.cibtc.com.cn, http://www.cibtc.com.cn.

579 CHN ISSN 1005-7021
WEISHENGWUXUE ZAZHI (CHAOYANG, 1978)/JOURNAL OF MICROBIOLOGY. Text in Chinese. 1978. bi-m. **Document type:** *Journal, Academic/Scholarly.*
Related titles: Online - full text ed.: (from East View Information Services, WanFang Data Corp.).
Indexed: SIA.
—BLDSC (5019.285600).
Published by: Liaoning Sheng Weishengwu Yanjiusuo, 2-duan, 22, Wenhua Lu, Chaoyang, 122000, China. TEL 86-421-2914613, FAX 86-421-2913910, lnwsuxh@mail.cyptt.ln.cn, http://wswxzz.periodicals.net.cn/.

579 CHN ISSN 1002-056X
WEISHENGWUXUE ZAZHI (CHAOYANG, 1979)/JOURNAL OF MICROBIOLOGY. Text in Chinese. 1979. q. USD 20.
—BLDSC (5019.285600).
Published by: Liaoning Weishengwu Yanjiusuo/Liaoning Institute of Microbiology, No22, Wenhua Lu 2 Duan, Chaoyang, Liaoning 122000, China. TEL 86-421-2814613. Ed. Ding Jian.

579 CHN ISSN 1000-0674
QE719 CODEN: WEXUE9
➤ **WEITI GUSHENGWU XUEBAO/ACTA MICROPALAEONTOLOGICA SINICA.** Text in Chinese; Summaries in English. 1984. q. CNY 72 (effective 2004). adv. bk.rev. **Document type:** *Journal, Academic/Scholarly.* **Description:** Publishes the latest results of studies in morphology, taxonomy, systematics, evolution, stratigraphy, paleobiogeography, and paleoecology. Covers various groups of microfossils, and provides news about academic activities, both in China and abroad.
Related titles: Online - full text ed.: (from East View Information Services, WanFang Data Corp.).
Indexed: BIOSIS Prev, BiolAb, RefZh, ZooRec.
—CISTI.
Published by: (Zhongguo Kexueyuan, Nanjing Dizhi Gushengwu Yanjiusuo/Chinese Academy of Sciences, Nanjing Institute of Geology and Palaeontology), Kexue Chubanshe/Science Press, 16 Donghuang Cheng Genbei Jie, Beijing, 100717, China. TEL 86-10-64000246, FAX 86-10-64030255, chlin@nigpas.ac.cn, http://wtgswxb.periodicals.net.cn/default.html. Circ: 6,000. **Dist. by:** China International Book Trading Corp, 35 Chegongzhuang Xilu, Haidian District, PO Box 399, Beijing 100044, China. TEL 86-10-68412045, FAX 86-10-68412023, cibtc@mail.cibtc.com.cn, http://www.cibtc.com.cn.

➤ **WORLD DIRECTORY OF COLLECTIONS OF CULTURES OF MICROORGANISMS.** see *BIOLOGY—Botany*

➤ **WORLD JOURNAL OF MICROBIOLOGY AND BIOTECHNOLOGY.** see *BIOLOGY—Biotechnology*

579 USA ISSN 1054-772X
QR46
YEAR BOOK OF CLINICAL MICROBIOLOGY. Text in English. 1991. a.
—GNLM.
Published by: C R C Press, LLC (Subsidiary of: Taylor & Francis Group), 2000 N W Corporate Blvd, Boca Raton, FL 33431. TEL 800-272-7737, journals@crcpress.com, http://www.crcpress.com/.

YEAST; a forum for yeast researchers. see *BIOLOGY—Botany*

579.2 CHN ISSN 1003-5125
CODEN: BIZAES
➤ **ZHONGGUO BINGDUXUE/VIROLOGICA SINICA.** Text in Chinese. 1986. q. CNY 40 per issue (effective 2004). adv. **Document type:** *Journal, Academic/Scholarly.* **Description:** Aims to present mainland China's main achievements in virology to the specialized reader. Contains research papers, communications, and notes, as well as reviews and discussions.
Formerly: Bingduxue Zazhi (1000-3223)
Related titles: Online - full text ed.: (from East View Information Services, WanFang Data Corp.).
Indexed: AIDS&CR, BIOSIS Prev, BioCN&I, BiolAb, CIN, ChemAb, ChemTitl, DBA, PBA, RPP, RiceAb, TDB, VITIS, VirolAbstr, ZooRec.
—BLDSC (9240.350000), CASDDS, IE, ingenta.
Published by: (Zhongguo Kexueyuan, Wuhan Bingdu Yanjiusuo/Chinese Academy of Sciences, Institute of Virology), Kexue Chubanshe/Science Press, 16 Donghuang Cheng Genbei Jie, Beijing, 100717, China. TEL 86-10-64000246, FAX 86-10-64030255, bjb@pentium.whiov.ac.cn, http://www.whiov.ac.cn/publish.htm, http://www.sciencep.com/. Circ: 6,000. **Dist. by:** China International Book Trading Corp, 35 Chegongzhuang Xilu, Haidian District, PO Box 399, Beijing 100044, China. TEL 86-10-68412045, FAX 86-10-68412023, cibtc@mail.cibtc.com.cn, http://www.cibtc.com.cn.

579.3 CHN ISSN 1000-7423
CODEN: ZJYZET
ZHONGGUO JISHENGCHONGXUE YU JISHENGCHONGBING ZAZHI/CHINESE JOURNAL OF PARASITOLOGY AND PARASITIC DISEASES. Text in Chinese. bi-m. adv. **Document type:** *Academic/Scholarly.*
Related titles: Online - full text ed.: (from East View Information Services).
Indexed: AbHyg, AgBio, AnBrAb, BioCN&I, DSA, ForAb, HelmAb, HortAb, IndMed, IndVet, MEDLINE, NutrAb, PN&I, PoultAb, ProtozoAb, RA&MP, RDA, RM&VM, RevApplEntom, RiceAb, S&F, SIA, SoyAb, TDB, VetBull, ZooRec.
—BLDSC (3180.465000), GNLM.
Published by: Zhongguo Yufang Yixue Kexueyuan, Jishengchongbing Yanjiusuo/Chinese Academy of Preventive Medicine, Institute of Parasitic Diseases, 207 Ruijin Erlu, Shanghai, 200025, China. TEL 86-21-6437-7008. Ed., R&P Feng Zheng. Adv. contact Minyi Yao.

572.3 CHN ISSN 1002-2694
CODEN: ZRGZAP
➤ **ZHONGGUO RENSHOU GONGHUANBING ZAZHI/CHINESE JOURNAL OF ZOONOSES.** Text in Chinese; Summaries in English. 1985. m. CNY 96; USD 3 newsstand/cover (effective 2003). adv. bk.rev. **Document type:** *Academic/Scholarly.* **Description:** Discusses and examines bacteria and diseases common both to human beings and animals.
Related titles: Online - full content ed.: (from WanFang Data Corp.); Online - full text ed.: (from East View Information Services).
Indexed: AIDS&CR, ASFA, AbHyg, AgBio, AgrForAb, AnBrAb, BioCN&I, DSA, ESPM, HelmAb, HerbAb, HortAb, IndVet, NemAb, NutrAb, PBA, PN&I, PoultAb, ProtozoAb, RA&MP, RDA, RM&VM, RPP, RefZh, RevApplEntom, S&F, TDB, VetBull, VirolAbstr, ZooRec.
—BLDSC (3180.710000), IE, ingenta.
Published by: Fujian-sheng Weisheng Fangyi Zhan/Fujian Center for Disease Control & Prevention, 76, Jintai Lu, Fuzhou, Fujian 350001, China. TEL 86-591-7552018, FAX 86-591-7563582, rsghb@pub2.fz.fj.cn, http://zgrsghbzz.periodicals.net.cn, http://www.fjcdc.com.cn/. Eds. Enshu Yu TEL 86-591-7563582, Longsan Xu. R&P Enshu Yu TEL 86-591-7563582. Adv. contact Huang Feng. **Dist. overseas by:** China International Book Trading Corp, 35 Chegongzhuang Xilu, Haidian District, PO Box 399, Beijing 100044, China. TEL 86-10-68412045, FAX 86-10-68412023, cibtc@mail.cibtc.com.cn, http://www.cibtc.com.cn. **Co-sponsor:** Zhongguo Weishengwu Xuehui/Chinese Microbiology Society.

579 RUS ISSN 0372-9311
QR1 CODEN: ZMEIAV
ZHURNAL MIKROBIOLOGII, EPIDEMIOLOGII I IMMUNOBIOLOGII/JOURNAL OF MICROBIOLOGY, EPIDEMIOLOGY AND IMMUNOBIOLOGY. Text in Russian; Summaries in English. 1924. bi-m. USD 78 foreign (effective 2004). bk.rev. illus. **Document type:** *Journal.* **Description:** Presents original scientific studies and surveys on etiology, laboratory diagnosis and pathogenesis of infectious diseases, theoretical and applied immunology, epidemiology of infectious diseases and methods of their control.
Related titles: Online - full text ed.: (from East View Information Services).
Indexed: AbHyg, BIOSIS Prev, BiolAb, CIN, ChemAb, ChemTitl, CurCont, DSA, DentInd, IndMed, IndVet, MEDLINE, PN&I, ProtozoAb, RM&VM, RPP, RefZh, RevApplEntom, SCI, TDB, VetBull, ZooRec.
—BLDSC (0060.900000), CASDDS, CISTI, East View, GNLM, IDS, IE, Infotrieve, ingenta, Linda Hall. **CCC.**
Published by: (Rossiiskaya Akademiya Meditsinskikh Nauk, Institut Vaktsin i Syvorotok im. I.I. Mechnikova/Russian Academy of Medical Sciences, Mechnikova Institute for Vaccines & Sera), Izdatel'stvo S-Info, A-ya 42, Moscow, 125284, Russian Federation. TEL 7-095-7969294, FAX 7-095-2520920, s-info@si.ru, http://www.s-info.ru. Ed. B F Semenov. Circ: 1,200 (paid). **Dist. by:** M K - Periodica, ul Gilyarovskogo 39, Moscow 129110, Russian Federation. TEL 7-095-2845008, FAX 7-095-2813798, info@periodicals.ru, http://www.mkniga.ru.

BIOLOGY—Microscopy

502.82 USA
ADVANCES IN ACOUSTIC MICROSCOPY. Text in English. 1995. irreg., latest vol.2, 1997. price varies. **Document type:** *Monographic series.*
Published by: Springer-Verlag New York, Inc. (Subsidiary of: Springer Science+Business Media), 233 Spring St, New York, NY 10013. TEL 212-460-1500, FAX 212-460-1575, service@springer-ny.com, http://www.springer-ny.com.

570.282 GBR ISSN 1052-0295
QH613 CODEN: BIHIEU
➤ **BIOTECHNIC AND HISTOCHEMISTRY**; a journal for microtechnic and histochemistry. Variant title: Biotech & Histochem. Text in English. 1926. bi-m. GBP 219, USD 298 combined subscription to institutions print & online eds. (effective 2006). adv. bk.rev. bibl.; charts; illus.; stat. index. reprint service avail. from PSC. **Document type:** *Journal, Academic/Scholarly.* **Description:** Covers new materials, apparatus, and methods involved in the preparation of biological specimens.
Formerly: Stain Technology (0038-9153)
Related titles: Microfilm ed.; Online - full text ed.: ISSN 1473-7760. GBP 208, USD 283 to institutions (effective 2006) (from EBSCO Publishing, Gale Group, IngentaConnect, O C L C Online Computer Library Center, Inc., Swets Information Services).
Indexed: ABIPC, ASCA, AbHyg, Agr, AnBrAb, BBCI, BIOBASE, BIOSIS Prev, BiolAb, CIN, ChemAb, ChemTitl, CurCont, DentInd, ExcerpMed, FCA, ForAb, HortAb, IAA, IABS, ISR, IndMed, IndVet, Inpharma, MEDLINE, MaizeAb, NutrAb, PBA, PGrRegA, PotatoAb, PoultAb, ProtozoAb, RM&VM, RPP, Reac, RevApplEntom, S&F, SCI, SSCI, SeedAb, SoyAb, TDB, VITIS, VetBull.
—BLDSC (2089.777000), CASDDS, CISTI, GNLM, IDS, IE, Infotrieve, ingenta, Linda Hall. **CCC.**
Published by: (Biological Stain Commission USA), Taylor & Francis Ltd (Subsidiary of: Taylor & Francis Group), 4 Park Sq, Milton Park, Abingdon, OX14 4RN, United Kingdom. TEL 44-1235-828600, FAX 44-1235-829000, info@tandf.co.uk, http://www.tandf.co.uk/journals/titles/10520295.asp. Ed. Dr. G S Nettleton. adv.: B&W page USD 565. Circ: 1,362; 1,318 (paid). **Subscr. to:** Journals Customer Service, Rankine Rd, Basingstoke, Hants RG24 8PR, United Kingdom. TEL 44-1256-813000, FAX 44-1256-330245.

502.82 DEU ISSN 0936-6911
➤ **ELEKTRONENMIKROSKOPIE.** Text in German. 1989. irreg. (2-3/yr.). EUR 39; EUR 23 newsstand/cover (effective 2006). **Document type:** *Journal, Academic/Scholarly.*
Indexed: RefZh.
Published by: (Deutsche Gesellschaft fuer Elektronenmikroskopie e.V.), Wissenschaftliche Verlagsgesellschaft mbH, Postfach 101061, Stuttgart, 70009, Germany. TEL 49-711-25820, FAX 49-711-2582290, service@wissenschaftliche-verlagsgesellschaft.de, http://www.wissenschaftliche-verlagsgesellschaft.de.

502.82 ISR ISSN 0071-2647
EUROPEAN CONGRESS ON ELECTRON MICROSCOPY. Text in English. quadrennial, latest 1976, 6th, Jerusalem. **Document type:** *Proceedings.*
Published by: (Israel Society of Electron Microscopy), Tal International, Inquire: Prof. D. Danon, Weizmann Institute of Science, Rehovot, Israel.

570.282 MKD ISSN 0015-9298
CODEN: FRBAAB
FRAGMENTA BALCANICA MUSEI MACEDONICI SCIENTIARUM NATURALIUM. Text in Macedonian. 1954. irreg. (5-9/yr.).
Indexed: BiolAb, RevApplEntom, ZooRec.
Published by: Prirodonaucen Muzej na Makedonija, Bulevar Ilinden 86, Skopje, 91000, Macedonia.

570.282 DEU ISSN 1439-4243
IMAGING & MICROSCOPY. Text in German. 1999. q. EUR 20 in Europe to institutions; USD 24 elsewhere to institutions (effective 2006). **Document type:** *Magazine, Trade.*
—BLDSC (4179.650250).
Published by: G I T Verlag GmbH (Subsidiary of: Wiley - V C H Verlag GmbH & Co. KGaA), Roesslerstr 90, Darmstadt, 64293, Germany. TEL 49-6151-80900, FAX 49-6151-8090146, info@gitverlag.com, http://www.gitverlag.com. Ed. Dr. Martin Friedrich.

INNOVATION; the magazine from Carl Zeiss. see *PHYSICS—Optics*

570.282 JPN ISSN 0022-0744
QC373.E4 CODEN: JELJA7

➤ **JOURNAL OF ELECTRON MICROSCOPY.** Text in English. 1953. bi-m. GBP 280, USD 476, EUR 420 to institutions; GBP 295, USD 502, EUR 443 combined subscription to institutions print & online eds. (effective 2006). adv. bk.rev. abstr.; charts; illus.; stat. back issues avail.; reprint service avail. from PSC. **Document type:** *Journal, Academic/Scholarly.*

Related titles: Microform ed.: (from PQC); Online - full text ed.: ISSN 1477-9986. GBP 266, USD 452, EUR 399 to institutions (effective 2006) (from EBSCO Publishing, HighWire Press, IngentaConnect, O C L C Online Computer Library Center, Inc., Oxford University Press Online Journals, ProQuest Information & Learning, Swets Information Services).

Indexed: ABIPC, ASCA, ASFA, AgBio, AnBrAb, B&BAb, BIOBASE, BIOSIS Prev, BioEngAb, BiolAb, BrCerAb, C&ISA, CCI, CIN, CPA, CerAb, ChemAb, ChemTitl, CivEngAb, CorrAb, CurCont, DSA, DentInd, E&CAJ, EMA, ESPM, EngInd, ExcerpMed, HelmAb, HortAb, IAA, IABS, INIS AtomInd, ISR, IndMed, IndVet, Inpharma, Inspec, JTA, M&TEA, MBF, MEDLINE, METADEX, MSCI, PBA, PE&ON, ProtozoAb, RM&VM, RPP, Reac, RefZh, RevApplEntom, SCI, SolStAb, TriticAb, VetBull, WAA, ZooRec.

—BLDSC (4974.880000), AskIEEE, CASDDS, CISTI, Ei, GNLM, IDS, IE, Infotrieve, ingenta, Linda Hall. **CCC.**

Published by: (Nihon Kenbikyo Gakkai/Japanese Society of Microscopy), Oxford University Press, Oxford Journals, 1-1-17-5 Mukogaoka, Bunkyo-ku, Tokyo, 113-0023, Japan. TEL 81-3-38131461, FAX 81-3-38181522, onjioup@po.iijnet.or.jp, http://jmicro.oxfordjournals.org/, http://www.oup.co.uk. Ed. Hideki Ichinose. Circ: 3,900.

570.282 GBR ISSN 0022-2720
CODEN: JMICAR

➤ **JOURNAL OF MICROSCOPY.** Text in English. 1878. m. GBP 891 combined subscription in Europe to institutions print & online eds.; USD 1,648 combined subscription in the Americas to institutions & Caribbean (print & online eds.); GBP 981 combined subscription elsewhere to institutions print & online eds. (effective 2006). adv. bk.rev. abstr.; bibl.; charts; illus. index. back issues avail.; reprint service avail. from ISI. **Document type:** *Journal, Academic/Scholarly.* **Description:** Publishes review articles, original research papers, short technical notes, short communications, rapid publications and letters to the Editors covering all aspects of microscopy and all aspects of microscopy and analysis.

Formerly (until 1969): Royal Microscopical Society. Journal (0368-3974)

Related titles: Microform ed.: (from PQC); Online - full text ed.: ISSN 1365-2818. GBP 846 in Europe to institutions; USD 1,566 in the Americas to institutions & Caribbean; GBP 932 elsewhere to institutions (effective 2006) (from Blackwell Synergy, EBSCO Publishing, Gale Group, IngentaConnect, O C L C Online Computer Library Center, Inc., Ovid Technologies, Inc., Swets Information Services).

Indexed: ABIPC, ASCA, ASFA, AgBio, Agr, AnBrAb, B&BAb, BIOBASE, BIOSIS Prev, BioCN&I, BiolAb, BrCerAb, C&ISA, CCI, CIS, CISA, CMCI, CPA, CerAb, ChemAb, ChemTitl, CivEngAb, CorrAb, CurCont, DentInd, E&CAJ, EMA, ESPM, ExcerpMed, FCA, ForAb, GenetAb, HelmAb, HerbAb, HortAb, I&DA, IAA, IABS, ISR, IndMed, IndVet, Inpharma, Inspec, M&TEA, MBF, MEDLINE, METADEX, MSCI, MaizeAb, MathR, MathSciNet, NemAb, OrnHort, PBA, PGegResA, PGrRegA, PhotoAb, PhysBer, PollutAb, PotatoAb, ProtozoAb, RM&VM, RPP, Reac, RefZh, RevApplEntom, S&F, SCI, SeedAb, SolStAb, SoyAb, TriticAb, VITIS, WAA, WeedAb.

—BLDSC (5019.695000), AskIEEE, CASDDS, CISTI, GNLM, IDS, IE, Infotrieve, ingenta, Linda Hall. **CCC.**

Published by: (Royal Microscopical Society), Blackwell Publishing Ltd., 9600 Garsington Rd, Oxford, OX4 2ZG, United Kingdom. TEL 44-1865-776868, FAX 44-1865-714591, customerservices@oxon.blackwellpublishing.com, http://www.blackwellpublishing.com/journals/JMI. Ed. Tony Wilson. Pub. Sue Hewitt. R&P Sophie Savage. Adv. contact Jenny Applin. Circ: 1,255.

570.282 JPN ISSN 1860-1480
CODEN: MELMEJ

➤ **MEDICAL MOLECULAR MORPHOLOGY.** Text in English. 1993. q. (in 1 vol., 4 nos./vol.). JPY 20,000; EUR 208 combined subscription to institutions print & online eds. (effective 2005). **Document type:** *Journal, Academic/Scholarly.* **Description:** Investigates the electron microsopic examination of structures, molecules, organelles, cells, tissues, and organs.

Formerly (until 2005): Medical Electron Microscopy (0918-4287); Which superseded the English part of: Nihon Rinsho Denshi Kenbikyo Gakkaishi (0021-4981)

Related titles: Online - full text ed.: ISSN 1860-1499 (from EBSCO Publishing, ProQuest Information & Learning, Springer LINK, Swets Information Services).

Indexed: BIOSIS Prev, BiolAb, CIN, ChemAb, ChemTitl, ExcerpMed.

—BLDSC (5529.997000), CASDDS, CISTI, GNLM, IE, Infotrieve. **CCC.**

Published by: (Clinical Electron Microscopy Society of Japan/Nippon Rinsho Denshi Kenbikyo Gakkai), Springer-Verlag Tokyo (Subsidiary of: Springer Science+Business Media), 3-13 Hongo 3-chome, Bunkyo-ku, Tokyo, 113-0033, Japan. TEL 81-3-38120331, FAX 81-3-38187454, orders@svt-ebs.co.jp, http://link.springer.de/link/service/journals/00795/index.htm, http://www.springer-tokyo.co.jp/. Ed. Michio Mori. Adv. contact Stephan Kroeck TEL 49-30-827875739. **Subscr. in the Americas to:** Springer-Verlag New York, Inc., Journal Fulfillment, PO Box 2485, Secaucus, NJ 07096-2485. TEL 800-777-4643, 201-348-4033, FAX 201-348-4505, journals@springer-ny.com, http://www.springer-ny.com; **Subscr. to:** Springer GmbH Auslieferungsgesellschaft, Haberstr 7, Heidelberg 69126, Germany. TEL 49-6221-345-0, FAX 49-6221-345-4229, subscriptions@springer.de.

➤ **MEDITSINSKI PREGLED. KLINICHNA LABORATORIIA.** see *BIOLOGY—Biochemistry*

570.282 DEU ISSN 0076-6771

METHODENSAMMLUNG DER ELEKTRONENMIKROSKOPIE/ METHODS OF ELECTRON MICROSCOPY. Text in German. 1970. irreg., latest vol.11, 1984. looseleaf. price varies. **Document type:** *Monographic series, Academic/Scholarly.*

Published by: (Deutsche Gesellschaft fuer Elektronenmikroskopie e.V.), Wissenschaftliche Verlagsgesellschaft mbH, Postfach 101061, Stuttgart, 70009, Germany. TEL 49-711-2582-0, FAX 49-711-2582-290, service@wissenschaftliche-verlagsgesellschaft.de, http://www.wissenschaftliche-verlagsgesellschaft.de. Eds. G Schimmel, W Vogell.

502.82 USA ISSN 0026-265X
QD71.M4 CODEN: MICJAN

➤ **MICROCHEMICAL JOURNAL.** Text in English. 1957. 6/yr. EUR 1,003 in Europe to institutions; JPY 133,100 in Japan to institutions; USD 1,121 to institutions except Europe and Japan (effective 2006). adv. bk.rev. abstr.; bibl.; illus. index. back issues avail.; reprints avail. **Document type:** *Academic/Scholarly.* **Description:** Focuses on microscale chemical analysis including clinical methods and procedures.

Related titles: Online - full text ed.: ISSN 1095-9149 (from EBSCO Publishing, Gale Group, IngentaConnect, O C L C Online Computer Library Center, Inc., ScienceDirect, Swets Information Services).

Indexed: A&ATA, ABIPC, ASCA, AnalAb, BIOSIS Prev, BiolAb, CCI, CIN, Cadscan, ChemAb, ChemTitl, CurCont, DSA, EngInd, ExcerpMed, FS&TA, ISR, IndVet, LeadAb, MEDLINE, MSB, NutrAb, RCI, RefZh, RevApplEntom, SCI, VITIS, VetBull, Zincscan.

—BLDSC (5758.400000), CASDDS, CINDOC, CISTI, Ei, IDS, IE, Infotrieve, ingenta, Linda Hall. **CCC.**

Published by: Elsevier Inc. (Subsidiary of: Elsevier Science & Technology), 360 Park Ave. S, New York, NY 10010-1710. TEL 212-633-3730, 888-437-4636, usinfo-f@elsevier.com, http://www.elsevier.com/locate/microc. Ed. Joseph Sneddon. **Subscr. out of Americas to:** Elsevier BV, PO Box 211, Amsterdam 1000 AE, Netherlands. TEL 31-20-485-3757, FAX 31-20-485-3432.

502.82 GBR ISSN 0968-4328
QH201 CODEN: MCONEN

➤ **MICRON.** Text in English. 1993. 8/yr. EUR 1,336 in Europe to institutions; JPY 177,300 in Japan to institutions; USD 1,493 to institutions except Europe and Japan (effective 2006). back issues avail. **Document type:** *Academic/Scholarly.* **Description:** Publishes original research and reviews covering the design, application, practice or theory of microscopy and microanalysis; also covers optical and electron beam systems linked to computer image processing and other image analytical methods.

Formed by the merger of (1987-1993): Electron Microscopy Reviews (0892-0354); (1983-1993): Micron and Microscopica Acta (0739-6260); Which was formed by the merger of (1969-1983): Micron (0047-7206); (1971-1983): Microscopica Acta (0044-376X); Which was formerly (1884-1971): Zeitschrift fuer Wissenschaftliche Mikroskopie und Mikroskopische Technik (0373-031X)

Related titles: Microfilm ed.: (from PQC); Online - full text ed.: (from EBSCO Publishing, Gale Group, IngentaConnect, ScienceDirect, Swets Information Services).

Indexed: ABIPC, ASCA, AgBio, BIOBASE, BIOSIS Prev, BiolAb, BrCerAb, CPA, ChemAb, ChemTitl, CurCont, FCA, HelmAb, HortAb, IABS, ISR, IndMed, IndVet, Inpharma, Inspec, MEDLINE, MaizeAb, NemAb, OrnHort, PBA, ProtozoAb, RPP, Reac, RefZh, RevApplEntom, S&F, SCI, TriticAb, VetBull, WeedAb, ZooRec.

—BLDSC (5759.300000), CASDDS, CISTI, GNLM, IDS, IE, Infotrieve, ingenta, Linda Hall. **CCC.**

Published by: Pergamon (Subsidiary of: Elsevier Science & Technology), The Boulevard, Langford Ln, East Park, Kidlington, Oxford OX5 1GB, United Kingdom. TEL 44-1865-843000, FAX 44-1865-843010, http://www.elsevier.com/locate/micron. Eds. B. K. Jap, D J Cockayne, J. R. Harris, R. F. Egerton. **Subscr. to:** Elsevier BV, PO Box 211, Amsterdam 1000 AE, Netherlands. TEL 31-20-485-3757, FAX 31-20-485-3432, nlinfo-f@elsevier.nl, http://www.elsevier.nl.

➤ **MICROSCOPE.** see *CHEMISTRY—Analytical Chemistry*

570.282 USA ISSN 1051-404X

MICROSCOPE BOOK. Text in English. 1990. s-a. **Document type:** *Catalog.* **Description:** For users of microscopes for analytical procedures.

Published by: Cambrex Group, 112 Washington St, Ste 2, Marblehead, MA 01945-3554. TEL 617-742-8290, FAX 617-742-4942.

570.282 USA ISSN 1041-0716

MICROSCOPE TECHNOLOGY & NEWS*★*. Text in English. 1990. m. USD 197. **Document type:** *Newsletter.*

—**CCC.**

Published by: Cambrex Group, 112 Washington St, Ste 2, Marblehead, MA 01945-3554. TEL 617-742-8290, FAX 617-742-4942.

570.282 CAN ISSN 0383-1825
CODEN: BMSCDQ

➤ **MICROSCOPICAL SOCIETY OF CANADA. BULLETIN.** Text in English. 1973. q. CND 40, USD 42 (effective 2005). adv. bk.rev. bibl.; charts; illus.; tr.lit. back issues avail. **Document type:** *Bulletin, Academic/Scholarly.* **Description:** Presents new developments in microscopy-instrumentation, applications, and biological and materials sciences.

—CISTI. **CCC.**

Published by: Microscopical Society of Canada/Societe de Microscopie du Canada, c/o F Leggett, 2918 13th Ave S, Lethbridge, AB T1K 0T2, Canada. TEL 403-327-4342, FAX 403-382-3156, leggett@em.agr.ca. Ed. Dr. Michael Robertson. Adv. contact Dianne Moyles. page CND 399; trim 9 x 6. Circ: 500 (paid).

570.282 CAN ISSN 0381-1751
CODEN: PMSCDA

MICROSCOPICAL SOCIETY OF CANADA. PROCEEDINGS. Text in English. 1974. a. CND 25 domestic; USD 25 foreign. adv. **Document type:** *Proceedings.*

Indexed: BiolAb.

—CASDDS, Linda Hall.

Published by: Microscopical Society of Canada/Societe de Microscopie du Canada, c/o F Leggett, 2918 13th Ave S, Lethbridge, AB T1K 0T2, Canada. TEL 403-327-4342, FAX 403-382-3156, leggett@em.agr.ca. Circ: 650.

570.282 GBR ISSN 0958-1952

MICROSCOPY AND ANALYSIS (U K EDIITION). Text in English. 1987. bi-m. USD 105 domestic; USD 185 in Europe; USD 265 elsewhere (effective 2006). adv. bk.rev. 60 p./no.; back issues avail.; reprints avail. **Document type:** *Journal, Academic/Scholarly.* **Description:** For users of all types of microscopes in all areas of work.

Related titles: Regional ed(s).: Microscopy and Analysis (Asia / Pacific Ediition); Microscopy and Analysis (The Americas Ediition); Microscopy and Analysis (European Ediition).

Indexed: DSA, FPA, HortAb, IndVet, ProtozoAb, RefZh, WSCA.

—BLDSC (5760.600100), IE, Infotrieve, ingenta, Linda Hall. **CCC.**

Published by: John Wiley & Sons Ltd. (Subsidiary of: John Wiley & Sons, Inc.), The Atrium, Southern Gate, Chichester, West Sussex PO19 8SQ, United Kingdom. TEL 44-1243-779777, FAX 44-1243-775878, microscopy-analysis@wiley.co.uk, cs-journals@wiley.co.uk, http://www.microscopy-analysis.com/, http://www.wiley.co.uk. Ed. Dr. Julian P Heath. Pub. Dr. Ray J Boucher. Adv. contact Jim Tate. B&W page USD 1,390, color page USD 2,170; trim. Circ: 53,000.

502.82 GBR ISSN 1431-9276
QH201 CODEN: MIMIF7

➤ **MICROSCOPY AND MICROANALYSIS.** Text in English. 1971. bi-m. (plus 2 supplementary issues) (in 1 vol., 6 nos./vol.). GBP 385 to institutions; USD 590 in North America to institutions; GBP 425 combined subscription to institutions print & online eds.; USD 655 combined subscription in North America to institutions print & online eds. (effective 2006). adv. Supplement avail.; back issues avail. **Document type:** *Journal, Academic/Scholarly.* **Description:** Provides a forum for microscopy, imaging and compositional anaylsis, including NMR microscopy, near field optical microscopy, scanned probe microscopy, and novel approaches.

Former titles (until 1997): Microscopy Society of America. Journal (1079-8501); (until 1995): Microscopy Society of America. Bullletin (1062-9785); (until 1993): E M S A Bulletin (Electron Microscopy Society of America) (0146-6119)

Related titles: Microform ed.: (from PQC); Online - full text ed.: ISSN 1435-8115. GBP 359 to institutions; USD 550 in North America to institutions (effective 2006) (from EBSCO Publishing, O C L C Online Computer Library Center, Inc., Swets Information Services).

Indexed: BIOSIS Prev, BiolAb, ChemAb, CurCont, Inpharma, Inspec, MEDLINE, Reac, RefZh.

—BLDSC (5760.600150), CASDDS, CISTI, IDS, IE, Infotrieve, ingenta, Linda Hall. **CCC.**

Published by: (Microscopy Society of America USA), Cambridge University Press, The Edinburgh Bldg, Shaftesbury Rd, Cambridge, CB2 2RU, United Kingdom. TEL 44-1223-312393, FAX 44-1223-315052, journals@cambridge.org, http://uk.cambridge.org/journals/journal_catalogue.asp?historylinks=ALPHA&mnemonic=MAM. Ed. Charles E Lyman. Adv. contact Rebecca Curtis TEL 44-1223-325757. **N. American subscr. to:** Springer-Verlag New York, Inc., Journal Fulfillment, PO Box 2485, Secaucus, NJ 07096-2485. TEL 800-777-4643, 201-348-4033, FAX 201-348-4505, http://www.springer-ny.com; **Subscr. to:** Cambridge University Press, 100 Brook Hill Dr, West Nyack, NY 10994. TEL 845-353-7500, FAX 845-353-4141, journals_subscriptions@cup.org **Co-sponsor:** Microbeam Analysis Society.

▼ new title ➤ refereed ★ unverified ♦ full entry avail.

502.82 USA ISSN 1059-910X
CODEN: MRTEEO

➤ **MICROSCOPY RESEARCH AND TECHNIQUE.** Text in English. 1984. 12/yr. USD 6,295 domestic to institutions; USD 6,439 in Canada & Mexico to institutions; USD 6,523 elsewhere to institutions; USD 6,925 combined subscription domestic to institutions print & online eds.; USD 7,069 combined subscription in Canada & Mexico to institutions print & online eds.; USD 7,153 combined subscription elsewhere to institutions print & online eds. (effective 2006). adv. bk.rev. bibl.; illus. back issues avail. **Document type:** *Journal, Academic/Scholarly.* **Description:** Encompasses all aspects of advanced microscopy, focusing on equipment, methodology, and applications in the biological, materials, and medical sciences.
Formerly (until 1992): Journal of Electron Microscopy Technique (0741-0581)
Related titles: Microform ed.: (from PQC); Online - full text ed.: ISSN 1097-0029. 1996. USD 6,295 to institutions (effective 2006) (from EBSCO Publishing, Swets Information Services, Wiley InterScience).
Indexed: ABIPC, AEBA, ASFA, B&BAb, BIOBASE, BioEngAb, BrCerAb, C&ISA, CIN, CTA, CerAb, ChemAb, ChemTitl, CivEngAb, CorrAb, CurCont, E&CAJ, EMA, ESPM, EntAb, ExcerpMed, GenetAb, HGA, IAA, ISR, IndMed, IndVet, M&PBA, M&TEA, MBF, MEDLINE, METADEX, ProtozoAb, RM&VM, RefZh, RevApplEntom, SCI, SolStAb, WAA.
—BLDSC (5760.600850), CASDDS, CISTI, GNLM, IDS, IE, Infotrieve, ingenta, Linda Hall. **CCC.**
Published by: John Wiley & Sons, Inc., 111 River St, Hoboken, NJ 07030-5774. TEL 201-748-6000, FAX 201-748-5915, uscs-wis@wiley.com, http://www.interscience.wiley.com/jpages/1059-910X/, http://www.wiley.com. Ed. George Ruben. adv.: B&W page GBP 640, color page GBP 1,515; trim 210 x 279. Circ: 700. **Subscr. outside the Americas to:** John Wiley & Sons Ltd., The Atrium, Southern Gate, Chichester, West Sussex PO19 8SQ, United Kingdom. TEL 44-1243-843335, 0800-243407, FAX 44-1243-843232, cs-journals@wiley.co.uk.

B

502.82 ZAF
CODEN: VESADE

MICROSCOPY SOCIETY OF SOUTHERN AFRICA. PROCEEDINGS/MIKROSKOPIEVERENIGING VAN SUIDELIKE AFRIKA. VERRIGTINGS. Text in English; Text occasionally in Afrikaans. 1971. a., latest vol.31. ZAR 500 (effective 2003). back issues avail. **Document type:** *Proceedings, Abstract/Index.* **Description:** Publishes abstracts accepted for presentation at the annual conference.
Former titles: Electron Microscopy Society of Southern Africa. Proceedings (0250-0418); Southern African Electron Microscopy Society. Conference Proceedings
Indexed: BiolAb, CIN, ChemAb, ChemTitl, ExcerpMed, Inspec, SFA, ZooRec.
—BLDSC (6757.660000), CASDDS, KNAW.
Published by: Microscopy Society of Southern Africa, Unit for Electron Microscopy, Lab. for Microscopy &Microanalysis, University of Pretoria, Pretoria, 0002, South Africa. TEL 27-12-4202075, FAX 27-12-3625150, hall@scientia.up.ac.za, ahall@postino.up.ac.za. Ed. R H M Cross. Circ: 200.

502.82 USA ISSN 1551-9295

➤ **MICROSCOPY TODAY.** Text in English. bi-m. free domestic; USD 35 foreign (effective 2005).
Published by: Microscopy Society of America, 230 E Ohio St, Ste 400, Chicago, IL 60611. TEL 312-644-1527, FAX 312-644-8557, microscopytoday@tampabay.rr.com, BusinessOffice@microscopy.org, http://www.microscopy-today.com, http://www.microscopy.com. Ed. Ron Anderson.

502.82 NLD ISSN 0165-201X
CODEN: PMEMD4

➤ **PRACTICAL METHODS IN ELECTRON MICROSCOPY.** Text in Dutch. 1973. irreg., latest 1990. price varies. back issues avail. **Document type:** *Monographic series, Academic/Scholarly.* **Description:** Discusses new methods for using electron microscopes in life sciences research.
Indexed: BIOSIS Prev, CIN, ChemAb, ChemTitl.
—BLDSC (6595.080000), CASDDS.
Published by: Elsevier BV, North-Holland (Subsidiary of: Elsevier Science & Technology), Sara Burgerhartstraat 25, Amsterdam, 1055 KV, Netherlands. TEL 31-20-485-3911, FAX 31-20-485-2457, nlinfo-f@elsevier.nl, http://www.elsevier.nl. **Subscr. to:** Elsevier BV, PO Box 211, Amsterdam 1000 AE, Netherlands. TEL 31-20-485-3757, FAX 31-20-485-3432, http://www.elsevier.nl.

570.282 616 GBR ISSN 0969-3823
QH201 CODEN: QJMIEN

➤ **QUEKETT JOURNAL OF MICROSCOPY.** Text in English. 1868. s-a. GBP 35 in Europe to non-members; GBP 45, USD 72 elsewhere to non-members (effective 2005). adv. bk.rev. illus. back issues avail. **Document type:** *Academic/Scholarly.* **Description:** Covers all aspects of light microscopy, it's history, practical application in all branches of science, the instrument, design and usage including photo and video microscopy.
Formerly (until 1993): Microscopy (0026-2838)
Related titles: CD-ROM ed.
Indexed: BIOSIS Prev, BibAg, BiolAb, ChemAb, ExcerpMed, HortAb, RefZh, ZooRec.
—CISTI, Linda Hall.
Published by: Quekett Microscopical Club, 90 The Fairway, South Ruislip, Mddx HA4 0SQ, United Kingdom. TEL 44-1367-710223, FAX 44-1367-718963, qmc@thomashope.freeserve.co.uk. Ed. Dr. B Bracegirdle. Circ: 650.

570.282 GBR

ROYAL MICROSCOPICAL SOCIETY. ANNUAL IMMUNOCYTOCHEMISTRY MEETING. Text in English. a. **Document type:** *Proceedings.*
—BLDSC (1086.249000).
Published by: Royal Microscopical Society, 37-38 St Clements St, Oxford, Berks OX4 1AJ, United Kingdom. TEL 44-1865-248768, FAX 44-1865-791237.

570.282 GBR ISSN 0035-9017
QH201

ROYAL MICROSCOPICAL SOCIETY. PROCEEDINGS. Variant title: Proceedings of the Royal Microscopical Society. Text in English. 1966. q. GBP 257 in Europe to institutions; USD 447 in the Americas to institutions & Caribbean; GBP 284 elsewhere to institutions (effective 2006). adv. abstr.; illus. index. back issues avail.; reprint service avail. from ISI. **Document type:** *Proceedings, Academic/Scholarly.* **Description:** Contain a lively mix of articles, news, views and reports of society business.
Related titles: Online - full text ed.: ISSN 1365-3067 (from EBSCO Publishing).
Indexed: BrCerAb, C&ISA, CerAb, CivEngAb, CorrAb, E&CAJ, EMA, ExcerpMed, F&EA, IAA, M&TEA, MBF, METADEX, SolStAb, WAA.
—BLDSC (6799.500000), CISTI, IE, Infotrieve, Linda Hall. **CCC.**
Published by: Blackwell Publishing Ltd., 9600 Garsington Rd, Oxford, OX4 2ZG, United Kingdom. TEL 44-1865-776868, FAX 44-1865-714591, customerservices@oxon.blackwellpublishing.com, http://www.blackwellpublishing.com/journals/PMS. Eds. Adrian Burden, Timothy F Watson. Pub. Sue Hewitt. R&P Sophie Savage. Adv. contact Jenny Applin. Circ: 2,000.

570.282 GBR

ROYAL MICROSCOPICAL SOCIETY. U K ANNUAL SCANNED PROBE MICROSCOPY MEETING. Text in English. a. **Document type:** *Proceedings.*
Published by: Royal Microscopical Society, 37-38 St Clements St, Oxford, Berks OX4 1AJ, United Kingdom. TEL 44-1865-248768, FAX 44-1865-791237.

570.282 USA ISSN 0161-0457
QH212.S3 CODEN: SCNNDF

➤ **SCANNING;** journal of scanning microscopies. Text in English. 1978. 6/yr., latest vol.23, 2001. USD 215 domestic to individuals; USD 225 foreign to individuals; USD 395 domestic to institutions; USD 435 foreign to institutions (effective 2003). adv. bk.rev. index. 80 p./no.; back issues avail.; reprints avail. **Document type:** *Journal, Academic/Scholarly.*
Related titles: Online - full text ed.: (from EBSCO Publishing).
Indexed: ASCA, AbHyg, BIOSIS Prev, BiolAb, CEABA, CIN, ChemAb, ChemTitl, CurCont, DSA, EngInd, ExcerpMed, FCA, FS&TA, HortAb, ISR, IndMed, Inpharma, Inspec, MEDLINE, MSB, MSCI, MaizeAb, NutrAb, PBA, PHN&I, PhotoAb, ProtozoAb, RA&MP, RM&VM, RPP, Reac, RefZh, RevApplEntom, SCI, SeedAb, TriticAb.
—BLDSC (8087.704000), AskIEEE, CASDDS, CISTI, Ei, GNLM, IDS, IE, Infotrieve, ingenta, Linda Hall. **CCC.**
Published by: (Foundation for Advances in Medicine & Science, Inc.), Foundation for Advances in Medicine and Science, Inc., PO Box 832, Mahwah, NJ 07430-0832. TEL 201-818-1010, FAX 201-818-0086, scanning@fams.org, http://www.scanning-fams.org, http://www.scanning.org. Ed. David C Joy. Pub. Tony Bourgholtzer. R&P Phaedra McGuinness. Adv. contact Judi Cupit. Circ: 6,984.

➤ **SCHWEIZERISCHE ZEITSCHRIFT FUER PILZKUNDE/ BOLLETTINO SVIZZERO DI MICOLOGIA/BULLETIN SUISSE DE MYCOLOGIE.** see *BIOLOGY—Botany*

570.282 NLD ISSN 0304-3991
CODEN: ULTRD6

➤ **ULTRAMICROSCOPY.** Text in Dutch. 1975. 12/yr. EUR 2,172 in Europe to institutions; JPY 288,200 in Japan to institutions; USD 2,429 to institutions except Europe and Japan (effective 2006). back issues avail.; reprints avail. **Document type:** *Academic/Scholarly.* **Description:** Covers all fundamental and technical aspects pertaining to ultramicroscopic elucidation of structure, ranging from particle optics to radiation interaction.
Related titles: Microform ed.: (from PQC); Online - full text ed.: (from EBSCO Publishing, Gale Group, IngentaConnect, ScienceDirect, Swets Information Services).
Indexed: ASCA, B&BAb, BIOSIS Prev, BiolAb, BrCerAb, C&ISA, CCI, CMCI, CerAb, ChemAb, CivEngAb, CorrAb, CurCont, DSA, E&CAJ, EMA, EngInd, ExcerpMed, IAA, ISR, IndMed, Inpharma, Inspec, M&TEA, MBF, MEDLINE, METADEX, MSCI, PhotoAb, PhysBer, Reac, RefZh, SCI, SolStAb, WAA.
—BLDSC (9082.783000), AskIEEE, CASDDS, CISTI, Ei, IDS, IE, Infotrieve, ingenta, Linda Hall. **CCC.**
Published by: Elsevier BV, North-Holland (Subsidiary of: Elsevier Science & Technology), Sara Burgerhartstraat 25, Amsterdam, 1055 KV, Netherlands. TEL 31-20-485-3911, FAX 31-20-485-2457, ultram@msm.ca.ac.uk, nlinfo-f@elsevier.nl, http://www.elsevier.com/locate/ultramic, http://www.elsevier.nl/homepage/about/us/regional_sites.htt, http://www.elsevier.nl. Ed. P. Midgley. **Subscr. to:** Elsevier BV, PO Box 211, Amsterdam 1000 AE, Netherlands. TEL 31-20-485-3757, FAX 31-20-485-3432.

BIOLOGY—Ornithology

see also AGRICULTURE—Poultry And Livestock ; PETS

598 USA ISSN 0199-543X
CODEN: AFAWE5

THE A F A WATCHBIRD; the official publication of the American Federation of Aviculture. Text in English. 1974. q. USD 40 domestic to members; USD 58 foreign to members (effective 2004). adv. bk.rev. illus. reprints avail. **Document type:** *Academic/Scholarly.* **Description:** Contains articles by aviculturists and avian veterinarians on husbandry, care and management of exotic bird species and on nutrition, diseases and disease control.
Indexed: SFA, WildRev.
Published by: American Federation of Aviculture, PO Box 7312, Kansas City, MO 64116-0012. TEL 816-421-2473, FAX 816-421-3214, afaoffice@aol.com, http://www.afabirds.org/. Ed. Sheldon Dingle. R&P Robert Berry TEL 713-434-8076. Adv. contact Sharon Rosenblat. Circ: 4,000.

598 DEU ISSN 0343-7647

A Z - NACHRICHTEN. Text in German. 1954. m. adv. bk.rev. illus.; tr.lit. index. back issues avail. **Document type:** *Newsletter.*
Published by: Vereinigung fuer Artenschutz, Vogelhaltung und Vogelzucht (AZ) e.V., Postfach 1169, Backnang, 71522, Germany. TEL 49-7191-82439, FAX 49-7191-85957. Ed. Theo Pagel. Adv. contact Helmut Uebele. Circ: 27,000.

598 SVN ISSN 0351-2851

ACROCEPHALUS. Text in Slovenian. 1980. bi-m.
Indexed: RefZh, ZooRec.
Published by: Drustvo za Opazovanje in Proucevanje Ptic Slovenije/Bird Watching and Bird Study Association of Slovenia, Langusova 10, Ljubljana, 61000, Slovenia. TEL 386-61-1339516, borut.mozetic@uni-lj.si.

598 DEU ISSN 0233-2914

➤ **ACTA ORNITHOECOLOGICA.** Text in German. 1985. a. **Document type:** *Journal, Academic/Scholarly.*
Indexed: ZooRec.
Address: Thymianweg 25, Jena, 07745, Germany. Eds. E Bezzel, M Goerner.

598 POL ISSN 0001-6454
QL1 CODEN: AORNBL

➤ **ACTA ORNITHOLOGICA.** Text in English; Summaries in Polish. 1933. s-a. EUR 40 to individuals; EUR 80 to institutions (effective 2005). bk.rev. abstr. back issues avail.; reprints avail. **Document type:** *Journal, Academic/Scholarly.* **Description:** Contains original reports, reviews, and short notes involving all fields of ornithology.
Formerly (until 1954): Acta Ornithologica Musei Zoologici Polonici (0866-9775)
Related titles: Online - full text ed.: (from IngentaConnect).
Indexed: ASFA, AgrAg, AgrForAb, AgrLib, AnBrAb, BIOSIS Prev, BioCN&I, BiolAb, CurCont, ForAb, GEOBASE, HortAb, IBR, KWIWR, NemAb, OrnHort, PBA, PGegResA, ProtozoAb, RefZh, S&F, SFA, TDB, WildRev, ZooRec.
—BLDSC (0642.010000), CISTI, IE, ingenta, Linda Hall.
Published by: Polska Akademia Nauk, Muzeum i Instytut Zoologii/Polish Academy of Sciences, Museum & Institute of Zoology, ul Wilcza 64, Warsaw, 00679, Poland. TEL 48-22-6293221, FAX 48-22-6296302, actaorn@miiz.waw.pl, libr@miiz.waw.pl, http://armagedon.pan.pl/miiz/journals/a_ornith/a_ornith.htm, http://www.miiz.waw.pl. Ed. Maciej Luniak. Circ: 500.

598 ZAF ISSN 1025-8264
QL692.A1

AFRICA BIRDS & BIRDING; a magazine for birdwatchers. Text in English. 1949. bi-m. USD 83.50 to individuals; USD 95.50 to institutions. adv. bk.rev. charts; illus. back issues avail. **Document type:** *Consumer.*
Former titles (until 1996): Birding in Southern Africa (1017-1533); (until 1989): Bokmakierie (0006-5838)
Indexed: BiolAb, ISAP, KWIWR, SFA, WildRev, ZooRec.
—Linda Hall.
Published by: (Birdlife South Africa), Black Eagle Publishing, 14 College Rd, Rondebosch, Cape Town, 7700, South Africa. TEL 27-21-6869001, FAX 27-21-6864500, wildmags@blackeaglemedia.co.za. Circ: 6,000.

598 GBR ISSN 1352-481X

AFRICAN BIRD CLUB. BULLETIN. Text in English. 1994. s-a.
Indexed: ZooRec.
Published by: BirdLife International, Wellbrook Ct, Girton Rd, Cambridge, CB3 ONA, United Kingdom. TEL 44-1223-277318, FAX 44-1223-277200, http://www.africanbirdclub.org/.

598 FRA ISSN 0002-4619
CODEN: ALUDAI
ALAUDA; revue internationale d'ornithologie. Text in French; Summaries in English. 1929. q. adv. bk.rev. bibl.; illus.; stat. cum.index: 1929-1972, 1973-1989. Supplement avail.; back issues avail. **Document type:** *Academic/Scholarly.*
Indexed: ASFA, BIOSIS Prev, BiolAb, GEOBASE, IBR, KWIWR, RefZh, SFA, WildRev, ZooRec.
—Linda Hall.
Published by: (Museum National d'Histoire Naturelle, Laboratoire d'Ecologie Generale), Museum National d'Histoire Naturelle, 57 Rue Cuvier, Paris, 75231 Cedex 05, France. TEL 33-1-40793777, xquetzal@aol.com, http://www.mnhn.fr. Ed. J F Dejonghe. Circ: 1,150.

598 GIB ISSN 1352-8734
CODEN: ALCTEE
➤ **ALECTORIS**; occasional papers on the natural history of Gibraltar and its surrounding area. Text in English. 1978. s-a. 1 cols./p.; back issues avail. **Document type:** *Monographic series, Academic/Scholarly.* **Description:** Contains papers and reports of the Strait of Gibraltar Bird Observation with records of birds seen in the study area.
Indexed: SFA, WildRev, ZooRec.
Published by: Gibraltar Ornithological & Natural History Society, Gibraltar Natural History Field Centre, Jew's Gate, Upper Rock Nature Reserve, P O Box 843, Gibraltar, Gibraltar. TEL 350-72639, FAX 350-74022, publish@gonhs.org, http://www.gonhs.org. Ed., R&P Dr. Terence Ocana.

598.9 USA ISSN 0748-8319
QL696.F3
AMERICAN HAWKWATCHER; a journal devoted to raptors & raptor migration. Text in English. 1982. a. USD 35 domestic membership; USD 45 foreign membership (effective 2003). adv. bk.rev. stat. back issues avail. **Document type:** *Journal, Academic/Scholarly.* **Description:** Reports original raptor research results, especially regarding hawk migrations in North America.
Indexed: WLR.
Published by: Wildlife Information Center, Inc., PO Box 198, Slatington, PA 18080-0198. wildlife@fast.net, http://www.wildlife.info.org, http://www.wildlifeinfo.org. Ed., Adv. contact Dan R Kunkle. Circ: 250.

598.41 USA ISSN 0892-6387
AMERICAN PHEASANT AND WATERFOWL SOCIETY MAGAZINE. Text in English. 1975. 10/yr. USD 25 domestic; USD 35 foreign (effective 2000). adv. bk.rev. **Document type:** *Newsletter.*
Published by: American Pheasant and Waterfowl Society, W 2270 US Hwy 10, Granton, WI 54436. TEL 715-238-7291. Ed., R&P Lloyd Ure. Circ: 1,800 (paid).

598 SWE ISSN 0347-9595
CODEN: ANSEET
ANSER. Text in Swedish. 1974. q.
Related titles: ♦ Supplement(s): Anser. Supplement. ISSN 0347-9609.
Indexed: SFA, WildRev, ZooRec.
Published by: Skaanes Ornitologiska Foerening, Ekologihuset, Lund, 22362, Sweden.

598 SWE ISSN 0347-9609
CODEN: ANSUE9
ANSER. SUPPLEMENT. Text in Swedish. 1976. irreg.
Related titles: ♦ Supplement to: Anser. ISSN 0347-9595.
Indexed: ZooRec.
Published by: Skaanes Ornitologiska Foerening, Ekologihuset, Lund, 22362, Sweden.

598 ESP ISSN 1137-831X
QL671
ANUARI ORNITOLOGIC DE LES BALEARS. Text in Catalan. 1987. a.
Formerly (until 1988): Anuari Ornitologic (1137-8301)
Indexed: IECT, ZooRec.
—CINDOC.
Published by: Grup Balear d'Ornitologia i Defensa de la Naturalesa, Veri, 1 3r., Palma de Mallorca, 07001, Spain. TEL 34-971-721105, FAX 34-971-711375, linneo@quercus.es, http://www.gobmallorca.com/.

AQUILO. SERIE ZOOLOGICA. see *BIOLOGY—Zoology*

598 BRA ISSN 0103-5657
CODEN: ARAJEG
ARARAJUBA; revista brasileira de ornitologia. Text in English, Spanish, Portuguese; Abstracts in English. 1985. s-a. USD 50. **Description:** Publishes papers regarding all aspects of avian biology, with emphasis on neotropical birds. Papers published so far included descriptions of new species and subspecies, studies on geographic variation, biogeography, ecology, migration and history of ornithology.
Indexed: BIOBASE, GEOBASE, ZooRec.
Published by: (Brazil. Sociedade Brasileira de Ornitologia), Museu Paraense Milio Goeldi, Comercio, Caixa Postal 399, Belem, PA 66017-970, Brazil. TEL 55-1-2469777, FAX 55-1-2261616, sbo@museu-goeldi.br. Ed. Regina Macedo. Circ: 1,000.

598.176 GBR
ARCTIC BIRDS INTERNATIONAL BREEDING CONDITIONS NEWSLETTER. Text in English. 1998. a.
Indexed: ZooRec.
Published by: International Wader Study Group, National Centre for Ornithology, The Nunnery, Thetford, Norfolk JP24 2PU, United Kingdom.

598 NLD ISSN 0373-2266
QL671 CODEN: ADEAA9
➤ **ARDEA.** Text in English. 1912. s-a. EUR 30 domestic to individuals; EUR 34 in Europe to individuals; EUR 39 elsewhere to individuals; EUR 43 domestic to institutions; EUR 55 in Europe to institutions; EUR 60 elsewhere to institutions (effective 2005). bk.rev. illus. index. back issues avail. **Document type:** *Academic/Scholarly.* **Description:** Publishes papers reporting significant new findings in ornithology, with emphasis on ecology, ethology, taxonomy and zoogeography.
Indexed: ASCA, ASFA, AnBeAb, AnBrAb, ApEcolAb, BIOBASE, BIOSIS Prev, BioCN&I, BiolAb, CurCont, ESPM, ForAb, GEOBASE, HerbAb, IABS, ISR, IndVet, KWIWR, NutrAb, PoultAb, ProtozoAb, RM&VM, RevApplEntom, S&F, SCI, SFA, SPPI, SeedAb, VetBull, WildRev, ZooRec.
—BLDSC (1663.390000), CISTI, IDS, IE, Infotrieve, ingenta, Linda Hall.
Published by: Nederlandse Ornithologische Unie/Netherlands Ornithological Union, c/o Kees Camphuysen, Ankerstraat 20, Oosterend, 1794 BJ, Netherlands. TEL 31-222-318744, jacobird@introweb.nl, http://home.planet.nl/~boude112/ardea/ardea.htm, http://www.nou.nu. Ed. Rob G Bijlsma. Circ: 1,400.

598 ESP ISSN 0570-7358
CODEN: ARDEDF
➤ **ARDEOLA**; revista espanola de ornitologia. Text in Spanish. 1954. s-a. USD 95 in United States (effective 2000). bk.rev. bibl. 350 p./no.; back issues avail.; reprints avail. **Document type:** *Journal, Academic/Scholarly.*
Indexed: CurCont, IECT, KWIWR, RefZh, SFA, WildRev, ZooRec.
—CINDOC.
Published by: Sociedad Espanola de Ornitologia, C/ Melquiades Biencinto 34, Madrid, 28053, Spain. TEL 34-91-4340910, FAX 34-91-4340911, http://www.seo.org/ardeola. Ed., R&P, Adv. contact Mario Diaz.

598.176 GBR ISSN 1388-2511
QL671 CODEN: SEABEV
➤ **ATLANTIC SEABIRD.** Text in English. 1969. q. GBP 10 to individuals; GBP 15 to libraries (effective 2000). bk.rev. illus. **Document type:** *Academic/Scholarly.* **Description:** Presents papers on all aspects of sea bird ecology, behavior, taxonomy and conservation.
Former titles (until 1998): Seabird (0267-9310); (until 1984): Seabird Report (0080-8415); Seabird Bulletin
Indexed: ASFA, SFA, WildRev, ZooRec.
—IE.
Published by: Seabird Group, c/o British Trust for Ornithology, The Nunnery, Nunnery Pl., Thetford, Norfolk, IP24 2PU, United Kingdom. seabird@bto.org. Eds. J Reid, K Camphuysen. Circ: 500.

598 USA ISSN 0004-8038
QL671 CODEN: AUKJAF
➤ **THE AUK**; a quarterly journal of ornithology. Text in English. 1884. q. USD 80 to institutions (effective 2005). adv. bk.rev. bibl.; charts; illus. index, cum.index every 10 yrs. back issues avail.; reprints avail. **Document type:** *Journal, Academic/Scholarly.* **Description:** It reports the results of recent research on the ecology, systematics, physiology, behaviour, and anatomy of birds and includes a worldwide review of current ornithological literature.
Supersedes (1876-1883): Nuttall Ornithological Club. Bulletin
Related titles: Microfiche ed.: (from IDC); Microform ed.: (from PQC); Online - full text ed.: (from BioOne, C S A, EBSCO Publishing, Northern Light Technology, Inc., O C L C Online Computer Library Center, Inc., ProQuest Information & Learning).
Indexed: ASCA, ASFA, AbHyg, AgrForAb, AnBeAb, AnBrAb, ApEcolAb, B&AI, B&BAb, BIOBASE, BIOSIS Prev, BioCN&I, BiolAb, CPA, ChemAb, CurCont, EPB, ESPM, ForAb, GEOBASE, GSI, GenetAb, HGA, HelmAb, HerbAb, HortAb, IABS, IBR, ISR, IndVet, KWIWR, MEDLINE, NutrAb, OceAb, OrnA, OrnHort, OrnithAb, PGegResA, PoultAb, ProtozoAb, PsycInfo, PsycholAb, RM&VM, RefSour, RefZh, RevApplEntom, S&F, SCI, SFA, VetBull, WeedAb, WildRev, ZooRec, e-psyche.
—BLDSC (1792.000000), CISTI, IDS, IE, Infotrieve, ingenta, Linda Hall. **CCC.**
Published by: American Ornithologists' Union, c/o Frederick Sheldon, Museum of Natural History, Louisiana State University, 119 Foster Hall., Baton Rouge, LA 70803. TEL 504-388-2855, auk@uark.edu, order@allenpress.com, http://www.aou.org/auk/index.php3, http://www.aou.org/aou/auk.html. Ed. Spencer Sealy. Circ: 4,500. **Subscr. to:** Allen Press Inc., PO Box 1897, Lawrence, KS 66044.

598 AUS
AUSTRALASIAN SEABIRD BULLETIN. Text in English. 1973. s-a. AUD 22 in Australia & New Zealand to individuals; AUD 29.50 elsewhere to individuals; AUD 27.50 to institutions (effective 2003). bk.rev. back issues avail. **Document type:** *Bulletin, Academic/Scholarly.* **Description:** Presents information on biology and conservation of seabirds with a principal focus on Australasia and the Pacific, Southern and Indian Oceans.
Formerly: Australasian Seabird Group Newsletter
Indexed: ZooRec.
Published by: Australasian Seabird Group, 415 Riverside Rd, Hawthorn East, VIC 3123, Australia. TEL 61-3-9882-2622, FAX 61-3-9882-2677, http://www.birdsaustralia.com.au. Ed. Ashley Bunce.

598 636.6 AUS ISSN 1030-8954
AUSTRALIAN BIRDKEEPER MAGAZINE. Text in English. 1987. bi-m. AUD 56.10 domestic; AUD 68 in New Zealand; AUD 74 elsewhere (effective 2004). adv. 62 p./no.; back issues avail. **Document type:** *Magazine, Consumer.* **Description:** Contains regular full color features and articles on all popular cage and aviary birds. Articles include veterinarian reports, tips on breeding, housing, nutrition and management.
Published by: A B K Publications, PO Box 6288, Tweed Heads South, NSW 2486, Australia. TEL 61-7-55907777, FAX 61-7-55907130, birdkeeper@birdkeeper.com.au, http://www.birdkeeper.com.au/v2/index.html. Ed., R&P Nigel Steele Boyce. Adv. contact Sheryll Steele-Boyce. Circ: 11,000 (paid).

598 AUS ISSN 0311-8150
AUSTRALIAN BIRDS. Text in English. 1966. q. AUD 25, USD 23. bk.rev. **Document type:** *Academic/Scholarly.* **Description:** Covers biology, distribution and status of birds in New South Wales.
Formerly (until Sep. 1974): Birds
Indexed: SFA, WildRev, ZooRec.
Published by: New South Wales Field Ornithologists Club Inc., PO Box Q277, QVB PO, Sydney, NSW 1230, Australia. Ed. Peter Roberts. Circ: 700.

598 AUS ISSN 1448-0107
➤ **AUSTRALIAN FIELD ORNITHOLOGY.** Text in English. 1959. q. AUD 32 domestic; AUD 40 foreign (effective 2005). bk.rev. cum.index every 2 yrs. **Document type:** *Journal, Academic/Scholarly.*
Formerly (until Dec. 2002): Australian Bird Watcher (0045-0316)
Indexed: ASI, BiolAb, RefZh, SFA, WildRev, ZooRec.
—Linda Hall.
Published by: Bird Observers Club of Australia, 183-185 Springvale Rd, Nunawading, VIC 3131, Australia. TEL 61-3-98775342, FAX 61-3-98944048, boca@ozemail.com.au, http://www.birdobservers.org.au/Publications_AFO.asp. Ed. Stephen Debus. R&P Zoe Wilson. Circ: 1,500 (paid).

➤ **AVIAN DISEASES.** see *VETERINARY SCIENCE*

598 CHE ISSN 1424-8743
QL671
➤ **AVIAN SCIENCE.** Text in English. 2001. 4/yr. EUR 100 to libraries (effective 2003). back issues avail.; reprints avail. **Document type:** *Journal, Academic/Scholarly.* **Description:** Publishes original papers and occasional review articles of international interest covering all aspects of ornithology.
Indexed: ZooRec.
—BLDSC (1837.891600), IE, ingenta.
Published by: European Ornithologists' Union, c/o Swiss Ornithological Institute, Sempach, 6204, Switzerland. FAX 41-41-4629710, eou@bluewin.ch, http://www.eou.at. Ed. Peter Jones. Circ: 1,000 (controlled).

598 CAN ISSN 0317-5650
➤ **AVICULTURAL JOURNAL.** Text in English. 1977. bi-m. CND 30 domestic; USD 30 in United States; CND 45 elsewhere (effective 2002). adv. bk.rev. 40 p./no. 2 cols./p.; back issues avail. **Document type:** *Journal, Academic/Scholarly.* **Description:** Aticles dealing with the keeping, breeding and showing of non-indigenous birds in Canada and the conservation and protection of all endangered birds.
Published by: Avicultural Advancement Council of Canada, PO Box 5126, Sta B, Victoria, BC V8R 6N4, Canada. TEL 250-477-9982, FAX 250-477-9935, mark@chemainusmarketing.com, aacc@shaw.ca, http://www.aacc.ca. Ed., R&P, Adv. contact Mark Curtis. page CND 110. Circ: 300 (paid).

598 GBR ISSN 0005-2256
QL671
AVICULTURAL MAGAZINE. Text in English. 1894. q. GBP 18 domestic; GBP 21 foreign (effective 2000). adv. bk.rev. illus. index. back issues avail.; reprint service avail. from PQC. **Document type:** *Academic/Scholarly.* **Description:** Contains articles on a wide range of the world's birds, both common and rare.
Related titles: Microform ed.: (from PQC).
Indexed: BiolAb, SFA, WildRev, ZooRec.
—BLDSC (1839.000000), IE, ingenta.
Published by: Avicultural Society, c/o Bristol Zoological Gardens, Clifton, Bristol, B58 3HA, United Kingdom. TEL 44-1179-70-6176, FAX 44-1179-73-6814. Ed., R&P, Adv. contact Malcolm Ellis. B&W page GBP 100. Circ: 500 (paid).

B

▼ new title ➤ refereed ✶ unverified ♦ full entry avail.

598 DEU ISSN 1430-8819
➤ **AVIFAUNISTISCHER INFORMATIONSDIENST BAYERN.** Text in German. 1994. 2/yr. EUR 35; EUR 4 newsstand/cover (effective 2003); includes Ornithologischer Anzeiger. 30 p./no. 1 cols./p.; back issues avail. **Document type:** *Newsletter, Academic/Scholarly.* **Description:** Presents ornithological discoveries, discussions about birds and bird habitat.
Published by: Ornithologische Gesellschaft in Bayern e.V., Muenchhausenstr 21, Munich, 81247, Germany. TEL 49-89-8107161, FAX 49-89-8107300, k.rachl@pbs-schaller.de, http://www.og-bayern.de. Circ: 1,150 (controlled).

598 ITA ISSN 0404-4266 CODEN: AVOCEP
➤ **AVOCETTA.** Text in English, French, Italian; Summaries in English. 1955. s-a. free to members; EUR 31 domestic to institutions; EUR 35 foreign to institutions (effective 2005). adv. bk.rev. abstr.; charts; illus. back issues avail. **Document type:** *Journal, Academic/Scholarly.* **Description:** Stimulates and organizes ornithological research in Italy.
Indexed: ASFA, OceAb, SFA, WildRev, ZooRec.
—BLDSC (1839.217000), IE, ingenta.
Published by: Centro Italiano Studi Ornitologici, c/o Francesco Mezzavilla, Secy, Via Malviste 4, Silea, TV 31057, Italy. http://www.ciso-coi.org. Eds. A Rolando, B Massa, G Malacarne, P Passerin d'Entreves. Adv. contact N E Baldaccini. **Subscr. to:** CISO.

598 GBR ISSN 0956-5744
AVON BIRD REPORT. Text in English. 1993. a.
Published by: Bristol Ornithological Club, 12 Birbeck Rd, Bristol, BS9 1BD, United Kingdom. h.e.rose@bris.ac.uk.

598 GBR
B O C NEWS. (Bristol Ornithological Club) Text in English. m.
Published by: Bristol Ornithological Club, 12 Birbeck Rd, Bristol, BS9 1BD, United Kingdom. h.e.rose@bris.ac.uk.

598 GBR ISSN 0962-0877 CODEN: BCLIE8
B O U CHECKLIST. Text in English. 1976. a. **Document type:** *Monographic series.*
Indexed: BiolAb, ZooRec.
—BLDSC (2264.150000).
Published by: British Ornithologists' Union, University of Oxford, Department of Zoology, South Parks Rd, Oxford, OX1 3PS, United Kingdom. TEL 44-1442-890080, FAX 44-20-7942-6150. Ed. J Kear.

598.07234 GBR ISSN 0005-3392
QL690.G7 CODEN: BTNWA5
B T O NEWS; a bulletin for bird watchers. Text in English. 1964. 6/yr. free to members (effective 2002). adv. illus. **Document type:** *Bulletin.* **Description:** Keeps members informed about the latest results from surveys and topical issues concerning birds and the environment.
Indexed: RefZh, ZooRec.
—Linda Hall.
Published by: British Trust for Ornithology, The Nunnery, Nunnery Pl, Thetford, Norfolk IP24 2PU, United Kingdom. TEL 44-1842-750050, FAX 44-1842-750030, btostaff@bto.org, general@bto.org, http://www.bto.org/membership/btonews.htm. Ed., R&P Derek Toomer. Circ: 11,000.

598 GBR ISSN 1363-0601
QL679
➤ **B W P UPDATE.** (Birds of the Western Palearctic) Text in English. 1997. 3/yr. GBP 110, USD 190 to institutions; GBP 116, USD 200 combined subscription to institutions print & online (effective 2004). 88 p./no.; back issues avail. **Document type:** *Journal, Academic/Scholarly.*
Related titles: Online - full text ed.: ISSN 1479-9014. GBP 104, USD 180 to institutions (effective 2004) (from EBSCO Publishing, Gale Group, IngentaConnect, O C L C Online Computer Library Center, Inc., Oxford University Press Online Journals, ProQuest Information & Learning, Swets Information Services).
Indexed: BIOSIS Prev, BiolAb, GEOBASE, ZooRec.
—BLDSC (2937.430000), IE, Infotrieve. **CCC.**
Published by: Oxford University Press, Great Clarendon St, Oxford, OX2 6DP, United Kingdom. TEL 44-1865-556767, FAX 44-1865-556646, jnl.orders@oup.co.uk, http://www3.oup.co.uk/bwpjnl/, http://www.oxfordjournals.org/. Ed. Dr. David T. Parkin. Pub. Martin Green. R&P Fiona Bennett. Circ: 1,350.

598 BWA ISSN 1012-2974
➤ **BABBLER.** Text in English. 1981. s-a. BWP 65 domestic; BWP 75 foreign (effective 2000). adv. bk.rev. illus. back issues avail. **Document type:** *Bulletin, Academic/Scholarly.* **Description:** Includes notes, records and papers on birds of Botswana.
Indexed: ZooRec.
Published by: Botswana Bird Club, PO Box 71, Gaborone, Botswana. Ed. Stephanie J Tyler. adv.: B&W page BWP 200. Circ: 350.

598 USA
BACKYARD BIRD NEWS. Text in English. 6/yr. USD 15 domestic; USD 18 in Canada; USD 21 elsewhere (effective 2001). **Description:** Covers news, features and tips on bird watching and feeding.
Published by: Pardson, Inc., 149 Acme St, PO Box 110, Marietta, OH 45750. TEL 800-879-2473, FAX 740-373-8443, http://www.birdersdigest.com/bbn/bbn_index.html. Pubs. Elsa Thompson, W.H. Thompson III. Adv. contact Linda Brejwo.

BARDSEY OBSERVATORY REPORT. see *BIOLOGY*

598 DEU ISSN 0174-1039
BEITRAEGE ZUR AVIFAUNA DES RHEINLANDES. Text in German. 1972. a. **Document type:** *Monographic series.*
Published by: Nordrhein-Westfaelische Ornithologengesellschaft, Freybergweg 9, Wesel, 46483, Germany. johan.mooij@bskw.de. Ed. Hans Eckart Joachim. Circ: 1,000.

598 FRA ISSN 0223-7741 CODEN: BIEVDJ
LA BIEVRE. Text in French. 1979. s-a.
Indexed: BIOSIS Prev, BiolAb, ZooRec.
Published by: Centre Ornithologique Rhone-Alpes (C O R A), Maison Rhodanienne de l'Environnement, 32 Rue Sainte Helene, Lyon, 69002, France. TEL 33-4-72771984, FAX 33-4-72771983, cora@worldnet.fr.

598 152 USA ISSN 0156-1383
QL698.3 CODEN: BBEHDU
BIRD BEHAVIOR; an international and interdisciplinary multimedia journal. Text in English. 1977. s-a. USD 120 combined subscription domestic print & online eds.; USD 145 combined subscription foreign print & online eds. (effective 2005). adv. bk.rev. illus.; stat. index. back issues avail.; reprint service avail. from PQC. **Document type:** *Journal, Academic/Scholarly.* **Description:** Research on descriptive and quantitative analyses of behavior, behavior ecology, experimental psychology and behavioral physiology of birds.
Formerly: Babbler (0314-5921)
Related titles: Microform ed.; Online - full text ed.: (from EBSCO Publishing, Gale Group, IngentaConnect).
Indexed: ASFA, ASI, AnBeAb, BIOSIS Prev, BiolAb, CurCont, EPB, ISR, PsycInfo, PsycholAb, RefZh, SCI, SFA, VetBull, WildRev, ZooRec, e-psyche.
—Linda Hall. **CCC.**
Published by: Cognizant Communication Corporation, 3 Hartsdale Rd, Elmsford, NY 10523-3701. TEL 914-592-7720, FAX 914-592-8981, cogcomm@aol.com, http://www.cognizantcommunication.com. Ed. Dr. David B Miller. Pub., R&P Robert N Miranda. Adv. contact Lori Miranda. Circ: 300.

598 GBR ISSN 0959-2709
QL676.5 CODEN: BCOIEN
➤ **BIRD CONSERVATION INTERNATIONAL.** Text in English. 1991. q. USD 236 in North America to institutions; GBP 145 elsewhere to institutions; USD 256 combined subscription in North America to institutions print & online eds.; GBP 156 combined subscription elsewhere to institutions print & online eds. (effective 2006). adv. bk.rev. back issues avail. **Document type:** *Journal, Academic/Scholarly.* **Description:** Focuses on conservation issues affecting birds, especially globally threatened species, and their habitats.
Related titles: Online - full text ed.: ISSN 1474-0001. USD 225 in North America to institutions; GBP 136 elsewhere to institutions (effective 2006) (from EBSCO Publishing, O C L C Online Computer Library Center, Inc., Swets Information Services).
Indexed: BIOSIS Prev, BiolAb, CurCont, EPB, EnvAb, ForAb, GEOBASE, HerbAb, IndVet, KWIWR, PoultAb, RefZh, S&F, TDB, VetBull, ZooRec.
—BLDSC (2090.625000), IDS, IE, Infotrieve, ingenta, Linda Hall. **CCC.**
Published by: (BirdLife International), Cambridge University Press, The Edinburgh Bldg, Shaftesbury Rd, Cambridge, CB2 2RU, United Kingdom. TEL 44-1223-312393, FAX 44-1223-315052, journals@cambridge.org, http://uk.cambridge.org/journals/journal_catalogue.asp?historylinks=ALPHA&mnemonic=BCI. Eds. Martin Jones, Stuart J Marsden. R&P Linda Nicol TEL 44-1223-325757. Adv. contact Rebecca Curtis TEL 44-1223-325757. **Subscr. to:** Cambridge University Press, 100 Brook Hill Dr, West Nyack, NY 10994. TEL 845-353-7500, FAX 845-353-4141, journals_subscriptions@cup.org.

598 AUS ISSN 0045-2076
BIRD KEEPING IN AUSTRALIA. Text in English. 1958. m. AUD 35. adv. bk.rev. back issues avail.; reprint service avail. from PQC. **Document type:** *Academic/Scholarly.*
Related titles: Microform ed.: (from PQC).
Indexed: Pinpoint.
Published by: Avicultural Society of South Australia, Rundle Mall, PO Box 3234, Adelaide, SA 5000, Australia. TEL 61-8-82643295. Ed., R&P, Adv. contact Neroli Price. Circ: 1,500.

598 GBR ISSN 0006-3649
➤ **BIRD LIFE.** Text in English. 1965. bi-m. GBP 10 to members (effective 1999). adv. bk.rev. illus. **Document type:** *Bulletin, Academic/Scholarly.*
Published by: Young Ornithologist's Club, Royal Society for the Protection of Birds, The Lodge, Potton Rd, Sandy, Beds SG19 2DL, United Kingdom. TEL 44-1767-680551, FAX 44-1767-692365. Ed. Derek Niemann. Adv. contact Lynda Whytock. Circ: 150,000.

598 JAM
BIRD LIFE JAMAICA BROADSHEET. Text in English. 1963. s-w. looseleaf. USD 20 to individuals; USD 40 to institutions (effective 1999). adv. bk.rev. cum.index every 10 nos. back issues avail. **Description:** Covers the study and conservation of Jamaican birds.
Formerly: Gosse Bird Club Broadsheet (1017-348X)
Indexed: SFA, WildRev, ZooRec.
Published by: Bird Life Jamaica, 2 Starlight Ave, Kingston, 6, Jamaica. TEL 876-927-1864, 876-827-8444, FAX 876-978-3243, birdlifeja@yahoo.com. Ed., R&P Catherine Levy TEL 876-927-8444. Circ: 250.

598 ZAF ISSN 1024-5979
BIRD NUMBERS; newsletter of the Avian Demography Unit, University of Cape Town. Text in English. 1993. s-a. ZAR 30 to non-members. illus.; maps. 50 p./no.; back issues avail. **Document type:** *Newsletter, Academic/Scholarly.*
Supersedes (in 1993): S A B A P News
Indexed: ZooRec.
Published by: Avian Demography Unit, c/o Dept of Statistical Sciences, University of Cape Town, Rondebosch, Cape Town 7701, South Africa. batlas@maths.uct.ac.za. Ed. James A Harrison TEL 27-21-6502423.

598 AUS ISSN 0313-5888 CODEN: BOBSE4
BIRD OBSERVER. Text in English. m. free to members. adv. **Document type:** *Newsletter.*
Indexed: SFA, WildRev, ZooRec.
Published by: Bird Observers Club of Australia, 183-185 Springvale Rd, Nunawading, VIC 3131, Australia. TEL 61-3-98775342, FAX 61-3-98944048, boca@ozemail.com.au, http://www.birdobservers.org.au/bird_observer.htm. Ed., R&P, Adv. contact Zoe Wilson.

598 USA ISSN 0893-4630
BIRD OBSERVER. Text in English. 1971. bi-m. USD 21 domestic (effective 2003). adv. back issues avail. **Document type:** *Consumer.* **Description:** Identifies distribution, behavior, identification and occurence of New England Birds.
Indexed: ZooRec.
Published by: Bird Observer of Eastern Massachusetts, PO Box 236, Arlington, MA 02476-0003. cmarsh@jocama.com, http://www.massbird.org/birdobserver/. Ed. Matthew Pelikan. Pub. Brooke Stevens. adv.: B&W page USD 100. Circ: 850 (paid); 50 (controlled).

598 USA ISSN 1074-1755
QL677.4 CODEN: BPOPEX
BIRD POPULATIONS; a journal of global avian biogeography. Text in English. a. USD 35 membership (effective 2004). abstr.; illus. **Document type:** *Journal, Academic/Scholarly.* **Description:** Fosters a global approach to avian research in the area of bird populations.
Indexed: BIOSIS Prev, BiolAb, ZooRec.
—BLDSC (2091.120000), IE, ingenta.
Published by: Institute for Bird Populations, PO Box 1346, Point Reyes Station, CA 94956-1346. TEL 415-663-1436, FAX 415-663-9482, http://www.birdpop.org/birdpop.htm. Ed. David G Ainley.

598 GBR ISSN 0006-3657
QL671 CODEN: BISTAC
➤ **BIRD STUDY**; the science of pure and applied orinthology. Text in English. 1954. 3/yr. GBP 85 in Europe; USD 155 in US & Canada; GBP 95 elsewhere (effective 2005). adv. bk.rev. abstr.; bibl.; charts; illus.; maps; stat. index. 96 p./no. 2 cols./p.; back issues avail.; reprints avail. **Document type:** *Journal, Academic/Scholarly.* **Description:** Serves as journal of the BTO. Contains original papers on all aspects of field ornithology, especially distribution, status censusing, migration, population, habitat and breeding ecology. For professionals and serious amateurs.
Related titles: Microform ed.: (from PQC); Online - full text ed.: (from EBSCO Publishing, Gale Group, IngentaConnect, ProQuest Information & Learning, Swets Information Services).
Indexed: ASCA, ASFA, AgrForAb, AnBeAb, ApEcolAb, BIOBASE, BIOSIS Prev, BiolAb, CurCont, EPB, ESPM, EnvAb, FCA, FPA, ForAb, GEOBASE, HerbAb, IABS, ISR, IndVet, KWIWR, PoultAb, RefZh, RevApplEntom, S&F, SCI, SFA, SeedAb, TriticAb, VetBull, WeedAb, WildRev, ZooRec.
—BLDSC (2092.000000), IDS, IE, Infotrieve, ingenta, Linda Hall. **CCC.**
Published by: British Trust for Ornithology, The Nunnery, Nunnery Pl, Thetford, Norfolk IP24 2PU, United Kingdom. TEL 44-1842-750050, FAX 44-1842-750030, btostaff@bto.org, general@bto.org, http://www.bto.org/membership/birdstudy.htm. Ed. GrahamJohn Martin. R&P, Adv. contact Nick Carter. Circ: 2,400.

598 USA ISSN 0891-771X
SF461.A1
BIRD TALK; dedicated to better care of pet birds. Text in English. 1982. m. USD 13.99 domestic; USD 31.99 foreign; USD 3.99 newsstand/cover domestic; USD 5.99 newsstand/cover foreign (effective 2005). adv. bk.rev. illus. Index. back issues avail.; reprints avail. **Document type:** *Magazine, Consumer.* **Description:** Informs bird owners about all aspects of caring for and enjoying their pets. Describes unusual birds being kept as pets.

Formerly (until 198?): International Bird Talk (0742-8359);
Incorporates (1978-1995): Bird World (0199-5979);
(1928-1950): American Canary Magazine
Indexed: SFA, WildRev.
Published by: Fancy Publications Inc. (Subsidiary of: Bowtie, Inc.), 3 Burroughs, Irvine, CA 92618. TEL 949-855-8822, FAX 949-855-3045, birdtalk@fancypubs.com, http://www.birdtalkmagazine.com. Ed. Melissa Kauffman. Pub. Norman Ridker. adv.: B&W page USD 3,130, color page USD 4,700; 8 x 10.88. Circ: 104,000 (paid). **Dist. in the UK by:** Comag, Tavistock Works, Tavistock Rd, W Drayton, Middx UB7 7QX, United Kingdom. TEL 44-1895-433800, FAX 44-1895-433602.

598   CAN   ISSN 1185-5967
QL685
BIRD TRENDS. Text in English. 1991. a.
Published by: Canadian Wildlife Service/Service Canadien de la Faune, Environment Canada, Ottawa, ON K1A 0H3, Canada. TEL 613-997-1095, FAX 819-953-6283.

598   USA   ISSN 0164-3037
QL677.5
BIRD WATCHER'S DIGEST. Text in English. 1978. bi-m. USD 18.95 domestic; USD 23.95 in Canada & Mexico; USD 28.95 elsewhere (effective 2001). adv. bk.rev. illus. cum.index. back issues avail.; reprints avail. **Document type:** Consumer. **Description:** Discusses birds in the backyard and beyond, and the people who watch them.
Related titles: Microform ed.: (from PQC); Online - full text ed.
Indexed: BiolDig, WLR, WildRev.
Published by: Pardson, Inc., 149 Acme St, PO Box 110, Marietta, OH 45750. TEL 800-879-2473, FAX 740-373-8443, bwd@birdwatchersdigest.com, customerservice@birdwatchersdigest.com, editor@birdwatchersdigest.com, http://www.birdwatchersdigest.com. Ed. W.H. Thompson III. Pubs. Elsa Thompson, W.H. Thompson III. Adv. contact Linda Brejwo. B&W page USD 1,570, color page USD 2,470; bleed 5.5 x 8.25. Circ: 90,000.

598.07234   GBR   ISSN 0269-1434
BIRD WATCHING. Text in English. 1986. m. GBP 30 domestic; GBP 36 foreign; GBP 2.50 newsstand/cover. adv. bk.rev.; video rev. back issues avail. **Document type:** Consumer. **Description:** For every bird watcher. Covers the latest UK sightings, advice and reports.
Published by: Emap Active Ltd. (Apex House) (Subsidiary of: Emap Consumer Media), Apex House, Oundle Rd, Peterborough, PE2 9NP, United Kingdom. TEL 44-1733-898100, FAX 44-1733-341-895, subs@ecm.emap.com, http://www.emap.com. Ed. David Cromack. Pub. Andy Benham. Adv. contact Julie Goodwin. Circ: 21,020 (paid). **Subscr. to:** Tower Publishing Services Ltd., Tower House, Sovereign Park, Market Harborough, Leics LE16 9EF, United Kingdom. TEL 44-1858-468811, FAX 44-1858-432164.

598   USA   ISSN 0895-495X
QL671
BIRDER'S WORLD; exploring birds in the field and backyard. Text in English. 1987. bi-m. USD 24.95 domestic; USD 31.50 foreign; USD 4.95 newsstand/cover (effective 2005). adv. **Document type:** Magazine, Consumer.
Related titles: Online - full text ed.: (from EBSCO Publishing, Gale Group).
Indexed: BiolDig, MagInd, SFA, WildRev.
—Linda Hall.
Published by: Kalmbach Publishing Co., 21027 Crossroads Circle, PO Box 1612, Waukesha, WI 53187-1612. TEL 262-796-8776, FAX 262-796-1615, mail@birdersworld.com, customerservice@kalmbach.com, http://www.birdersworld.com, http://www.kalmbach.com. Ed. Chuck Hagner. Pub. Kevin Keefe. Adv. contact Dina Johnston. B&W page USD 2,405, color page USD 3,367. Circ: 60,689 (paid). **Dist. by:** Hearst Distribution Group Inc., 250 W 55th St, Ste 1115, New York, NY 10019. TEL 212-649-4447, FAX 212-262-1239; **Dist. in UK by:** Comag, Tavistock Works, Tavistock Rd, W Drayton, Middx UB7 7QX, United Kingdom. TEL 44-1895-433600, FAX 44-189-543-3606.

598   USA   ISSN 0161-1836
QL677.5   CODEN: BIRDEV
➤ **BIRDING.** Text in English. 1969. bi-m. USD 45 to non-members; free to members (effective 2005). adv. bk.rev. illus. cum.index every 2 yrs. back issues avail.; reprints avail. **Document type:** Academic/Scholarly. **Description:** Presents articles of relevance to the birder (birdwatcher). Includes primarily bird-finding, bird identification, bird-conservation information.
Indexed: SFA, WildRev, ZooRec.
Published by: American Birding Association, PO Box 6599, Colorado Springs, CO 80934. TEL 719-578-9703, 800-850-2473, FAX 719-578-1480, http://www.americanbirding.org. Ed. Ted Floyd. Circ: 19,000.

598   GBR   ISSN 0969-6024
➤ **BIRDING WORLD.** Text in English. 1987. m. GBP 43 in British Isles; GBP 50 in Europe; GBP 54 elsewhere (effective 2003). adv. bk.rev.; video rev. bibl.; illus.; maps. back issues avail. **Document type:** Academic/Scholarly. **Description:** Focuses on birds and birdwatching, with an emphasis on British and Western Palearctic birds.
Indexed: ZooRec.
Published by: Bird Information Service, Stonerunner, Coast Rd, Cley, Holt, Norfolk NR25 7RZ, United Kingdom. TEL 44-1263-741139, FAX 44-1263-741173, sales@birdingworld.co.uk, http://www.birdingworld.co.uk. Ed. Steve Gantlett. Adv. contact Sue Clarke TEL 44-1263-740913. B&W page GBP 249, color page GBP 450; trim 145 x 225. Circ: 6,000.

598   GBR
BIRDLIFE CONSERVATION SERIES. Text in English. 1980. irreg. price varies. back issues avail. **Document type:** Monographic series. **Description:** Covers a wide range of bird conservation issues on a global scale aimed at the international scientific community.
Former titles (until 1994): I C B P Technical Publications; I C B P Parrot Working Group Meeting. Proceedings (0277-1330)
Indexed: SFA, WildRev, ZooRec.
—BLDSC (2092.232000), CISTI. **CCC.**
Published by: BirdLife International, Wellbrook Ct, Girton Rd, Cambridge, CB3 ONA, United Kingdom. TEL 44-1223-277318, FAX 44-1223-277200, birdlife@gn.apc.org. Ed. Duncan Brooks.

598   GBR   ISSN 1029-6832
BIRDLIFE INTERNATIONAL. ANNUAL REVIEW. Text in English. a.
—BLDSC (1519.925700).
Published by: BirdLife International, Wellbrook Ct, Girton Rd, Cambridge, CB3 ONA, United Kingdom. TEL 44-1223-277318, FAX 44-1223-227200, birdlife@birdlife.org.uk, http://www.birdlife.net.

598   GBR
BIRDLIFE INTERNATIONAL. STUDY REPORT. Text in English. irreg., latest vol.55, 1995. **Document type:** Monographic series.
Formerly: International Council for Bird Preservation. Study Report
Published by: BirdLife International, Wellbrook Ct, Girton Rd, Cambridge, CB3 ONA, United Kingdom. TEL 44-1223-277318, FAX 44-1223-277200. **Dist. in Americas by:** Smithsonian Institution Press, PO Box 960, Herndon, VA 22070-0960. TEL 703-435-7064.

598   GBR   ISSN 1357-6860
          CODEN: BIRDAR
BIRDS. Text in English. 1903. q. free membership (effective 2005). adv. bk.rev. illus. **Document type:** Magazine, Consumer.
Former titles (until 1994): Birds Magazine; (until 1987): Birds (0006-3665); (until 1966): Bird Notes; Incorporates: R S P B Annual Report and Accounts (0080-4509)
Indexed: BiolAb, ChLitAb, KWIWR, RefZh, SFA, WildRev, ZooRec.
Published by: Royal Society for the Protection of Birds, The Lodge, Sandy, Beds SG19 2DL, United Kingdom. TEL 44-1767-680551, FAX 44-1767-683262, membership@rspb.org.uk, http://www.rspb.org.uk/. Ed. Rob Hume. adv.: color page GBP 27,830; bleed 230 x 300. Circ: 582,990.

598   GBR   ISSN 1363-5700
BIRDS AND WILDLIFE IN CUMBRIA. Text in English. 1996. a.
Indexed: ZooRec.
Published by: Cumbria Bird Club, Derwentwater Youth Hostel, Keswick, Borrowdale CA12 5UR, United Kingdom. TEL 017687-77246. Ed. Dave Piercy.

598   AUS
BIRDS AUSTRALIA MONOGRAPH. Text in English. irreg.
Indexed: ZooRec.
Published by: Birds Australia, 415 Riversdale Rd, Hawthorn East, VIC 3123, Australia. TEL 61-3-98822622, FAX 61-3-98822677, mail@birdsaustralia.com.au, http://www.birdsaustralia.com.au.

598   AUS   ISSN 1329-7945
BIRDS AUSTRALIA REPORT. Text in English. 1980. irreg. adv. **Document type:** Bulletin.
Formerly (unil 1997): R A O U Report (0812-8014)
—CCC.
Published by: Birds Australia, 415 Riversdale Rd, Hawthorn East, VIC 3123, Australia. TEL 61-3-98822622, FAX 61-3-98822677. R&P Merrilyn Julian. Adv. contact Lee O'Mahoney.

598   USA
A BIRD'S-EYE VIEW. Text in English. 1992. bi-m. USD 6 (effective 1998). bk.rev. illus.; maps; stat. back issues avail. **Document type:** Newsletter. **Description:** Contains articles written by teenage students for students and others interested in the study of birds.
Published by: American Birding Association, PO Box 6599, Colorado Springs, CO 80934. TEL 719-578-9703, FAX 719-578-1480, winging@aba.org, http://www.americanbirding.org. Ed. Matthew L Pelikan. Circ: 1,200.

598   USA   ISSN 1061-5466
QL681   CODEN: BNOAE8
BIRDS OF NORTH AMERICA. Text in English. 1992. 80/yr. (in 2 vols., 40 nos./vol.). USD 215 per vol.; USD 3,295 per vol. for the 18-vol. set (effective 2000). illus. **Document type:** Monographic series. **Description:** Provides comprehensive descriptive information on all species of birds in North America.
Indexed: ASFA, AnBeAb, ApEcolAb, BIOSIS Prev, BiolAb, ESPM, OceAb, WildRev, ZooRec.
—CCC.
Published by: Academy of Natural Sciences of Philadelphia, Birds of North America, Inc., 1900 Benjamin Franklin Pkwy, Philadelphia, PA 19103-1195. TEL 212-567-1195, 800-627-0629, FAX 215—299-1182, abonds@allenpress.com, http://www.birdsofna.org. Eds. Alan Poole, Frank Gill. Adv. contact Pat Warner. **Co-sponsor:** American Ornithologists' Union.

598   GBR   ISSN 1367-272X
➤ **BIRDS OF OXFORDSHIRE.** Text in English. 1921. a., latest 1999. GBP 6.50 to non-members (effective 2001). illus.; maps; stat.; charts. 100 p./no. 1 cols./p.; back issues avail. **Document type:** Academic/Scholarly. **Description:** Reports on sightings of birds in the county, with notes on distribution and population and other articles relating to the subject.
Formerly (until 1996): Oxford Ornithological Society on the Birds of Oxfordshire. Report. (0957-4123)
Indexed: ZooRec.
Published by: Oxford Ornithological Society, Edward Grey Institute, South Parks Rd, Oxford, OX1 3PS, United Kingdom. http://www.oos.org.uk/. Ed. Ian Lewington. Circ: 350 (paid). **Subscr. to:** Mr. R. Overall, 30 Hunsdon Rd, Iffley, Oxford OX4 4JE, United Kingdom. TEL 44-1865-775632.

598   USA   ISSN 1041-6676
BIRDSCOPE; news and views from Sapsucker woods. Text in English. 1987. q. free to members (effective 2005). **Document type:** Newsletter. **Description:** Explains research programs of the laboratory in lay terms.
Formerly: Cornell University. Cooperative Research Newsletter
Indexed: WildRev, ZooRec.
—Linda Hall.
Published by: Cornell University, Laboratory of Ornithology, Attn: Communications, Cornell Lab of Ornithology, 159 Sapsucker Woods Rd, Ithaca, NY 14850. TEL 607-254-2473, 800-843-2473, FAX 607-254-2415, cornellbirds@cornell.edu, http://www.birds.cornell.edu/publications/birdscope/. Ed. Tim Gallagher. Circ: 14,000 (paid and controlled).

598   USA
BIRDSOURCE; birding with a purpose. Text in English. free. **Document type:** Journal, Consumer.
Media: Online - full content.
Published by: National Audubon Society, 700 Broadway, New York, NY 10003. TEL 212-979-3000, FAX 212-979-3188, editor@audubon.org, http://www.birdsource.org, http://www.audubon.org. **Co-publisher:** Cornell Laboratory of Ornithology.

598.07234   GBR
BIRDWATCH. Text in English. 1992. m. GBP 34.50; GBP 2.95 newsstand/cover (effective 2001). adv. bk.rev.; software rev.; rec.rev.; video rev.; Website rev. back issues avail. **Document type:** Magazine, Consumer.
Former titles: Birdwatch Monthly; (until 1992): Birdwatch Magazine (0967-1870)
Published by: Solo Publishing Ltd., 3D-F Leroy House, 436 Essex Rd, Islington, London, N1 3QP, United Kingdom. TEL 44-20-7704-9495, FAX 44-20-7704-2767, editorial@birdwatch.co.uk, solopublishing@msn.com, http://www.birdwatch.co.uk. Ed., Pub. Dominic Mitchell. Adv. contact Ian Lycett. B&W page GBP 990, color page GBP 1,600; trim 297 x 210. Circ: 15,000 (paid). **Dist. by:** M M C Ltd., Octagon House, White Hart Meadows, Ripley, Woking, Surrey GU23 6HR, United Kingdom. TEL 44-1483-211222, FAX 44-1483-224541.

598.0723471   CAN
BIRDWATCH CANADA. Text in English. 1996. 3/yr. CND 25 to members (effective 2000). bk.rev. **Document type:** Newsletter. **Description:** Focuses on bird-banding and monitoring techniques.
Indexed: WildRev.
Published by: (Long Point Bird Observatory), Bird Studies Canada, P O Box 160, Port Rowan, ON N0E 1M0, Canada. TEL 519-586-3531, FAX 519-586-3532, generalinfo@bsc-eoc.org, http://www.bsc-eoc.org. Ed., R&P Jon D McCracken. Circ: 5,000.

598.07234   GBR
BIRDWATCHER'S YEARBOOK AND DIARY. Text in English. 1981. a. GBP 14 (effective 2001); USD 30. bk.rev. bibl.; charts; illus. 320 p./no.; **Document type:** Directory. **Description:** Lists bird recorders,bird count organisers.bird reports,bird clubs,bird ringing (banding) groups, wildlife trusts, nationaland international organizations, and bird reserves and observatories. Also contains feature articles and references (including tide tables and protected species) and personal bird recording system.
Formerly: Birdwatcher's Yearbook (0144-364X)
Indexed: ZooRec.

Published by: Buckingham Press, 55 Thorpe Park Road, Peterborough, Cambridgeshire PE3 6LJ, United Kingdom. TEL 44-1733-561739, buck.press@btinternet.com. Ed. Hilary Cromack. Circ: 3,000.

598 DNK ISSN 0906-0146
BLAAVAND FUGLESTATION; en oversigt over fugleobservationer. Text in Danish. 1985. irreg.
Formerly (until 1988): Blaavand (0901-0637)
Published by: (Dansk Ornitologisk Forening/Danish Ornithological Society), Blaavand Fuglestation, Fyrvej 81, Blaavand, 6857, Denmark. TEL 45-75-27-86-01.

598 DNK ISSN 0109-257X
BLADSMUTTEN. Text in Danish. 1983. q. DKK 40. adv. bk.rev.
Former titles: Buteo (0109-0755); Vaagen
Indexed: ZooRec.
Published by: Danske Ornithologisk Forening i Vestsjaellands Amt, Drosselvej 12, Ringsted, 4100, Denmark. Ed. Arne H Larsen.

598 ISL ISSN 0256-4181
QL690.I2 CODEN: BLIKES
➤ **BLIKI**; timarit um fugla. Text in Icelandic; Summaries in English. 1983. irreg. (1-2/yr.). ISK 1,150 (effective 2000). bk.rev. bibl.; charts; illus.; stat. back issues avail. **Document type:** *Academic/Scholarly.*
Indexed: SFA, WLR, WildRev, ZooRec.
Published by: Natturufraedistofnun Islands/Icelandic Institute of Natural History, Hlemmur 3, PO Box 5320, Reykjavik, 125, Iceland. TEL 354-590-0500, FAX 354-590-0595, bliki@ni.is, ni@ni.is. Circ: 1,200. **Co-sponsor:** Icelandic Society for the Protection of Birds.

598 CAN ISSN 0382-5655
BLUE BILL. Text in English. 1954. q. membership. bk.rev. **Document type:** *Bulletin.*
Published by: Kingston Field Naturalists, P O Box 831, Kingston, ON K7L 4X6, Canada. TEL 613-545-6139, FAX 613-545-6617. Ed. A A Crowder. Circ: 350.

598 CHL ISSN 0717-1897
BOLETIN CHILENO DE ORNITOLOGIA. Text in Spanish. 1994. a.
Indexed: ZooRec.
Published by: Museo Nacional de Historia Natural, Casilla 787, Santiago, Chile. TEL 56-2-6814095, FAX 56-2-6817182. Ed. Juan Carlos Torres-Mura.

598.07 ITA ISSN 1121-3701
BOLLETTINO DELL'ATTIVITA DI INANELLAMENTO/BULLETIN OF BIRD RINGING ACTIVITY. Text in Italian. 1981. irreg. per issue exchange basis. stat. back issues avail. **Document type:** *Bulletin.*
Related titles: ◆ Supplement(s): Bollettino dell'Attivita di Inanellamento. Supplemento. ISSN 1121-3779.
Published by: Istituto Nazionale per la Fauna Selvatica, Via Ca Fornacetta, 9, Ozzano Dell'emilia, BO 40064, Italy. TEL 39-51-6512111, FAX 39-51-796628. Ed. Mario Spagnesi. Circ: 400.

598.07 ITA ISSN 1121-3779
BOLLETTINO DELL'ATTIVITA DI INANELLAMENTO. SUPPLEMENTO. Text in Italian. 1981. irreg.
Related titles: ◆ Supplement to: Bollettino dell'Attivita di Inanellamento. ISSN 1121-3701.
Published by: Istituto Nazionale per la Fauna Selvatica, Via Ca Fornacetta, 9, Ozzano Dell'emilia, BO 40064, Italy. TEL 39-51-6512111, FAX 39-51-796628, infsammi@iperbole.bologna.it.

598 AUS ISSN 1442-4622
BOOBOOK. Text in English. 1980. s-a. AUD 30 domestic to individuals; AUD 35 foreign to individuals; AUD 35 to families; AUD 45 to institutions (effective 2000). bk.rev. back issues avail. **Document type:** *Bulletin, Academic/Scholarly.* **Description:** Covers the biology and conservation of birds of prey and owls with a principal focus on the Australian region.
Formerly: A R A News
Published by: Australasian Raptor Association, c/o Birds Australia, 415 Riversdale Rd, Hawthorn East, VIC 3123, Australia. TEL 61-3-98822622, FAX 61-3-98822677, membership@birdsaustralia.com.au, http://www.ausraptor.org.au/. Ed. Lyle Smith. Circ: 200.

598 GBR ISSN 0950-2750
BRISTOL ORNITHOLOGY. Text in English. a.
Indexed: ZooRec.
Published by: Bristol Ornithological Club, 12 Birbeck Rd, Bristol, BS9 1BD, United Kingdom. h.e.rose@bris.ac.uk.

598.07234 GBR ISSN 0007-0335
CODEN: BRBIAP
➤ **BRITISH BIRDS.** Text in English. 1907. m. GBP 45 domestic to individuals; GBP 51 foreign to individuals; GBP 83 to institutions (effective 2004). adv. bk.rev. illus. index. back issues avail.; reprint service avail. from PQC. **Document type:** *Journal, Academic/Scholarly.* **Description:** Independent magazine run by and for the benefit of birdwatchers; covers bird identification, behavior, distribution, ecology, and conservation.
Related titles: Microfiche ed.: (from IDC); Microform ed.: (from PQC).
Indexed: ASFA, BIOSIS Prev, BiolAb, CurCont, GEOBASE, IBR, ISR, KWIWR, RefZh, SCI, SFA, WildRev, ZooRec.
—BLDSC (2291.000000), IE, Infotrieve, ingenta, Linda Hall. **CCC.**
Address: The Banks, Mountfield, Roberts Bridge, E Sussex TN32 5JY, United Kingdom. TEL 44-1580-882039, FAX 44-1580-882038, subscriptions@britishbirds.co.uk, http://www.britishbirds.co.uk. Ed. Dr. R Riddington. Adv. contact Ian Lycett. Circ: 9,000.

598.65 GBR ISSN 0965-2264
BRITISH HOMING WORLD'S PIGEON RACING GAZETTE. Variant title: Pigeon Racing Gazette. Text in English. 1946. m. GBP 14.40; GBP 1.20 newsstand/cover (effective 1999). adv. bk.rev. **Document type:** *Newspaper, Consumer.*
Former titles (until 1992): Pigeon Racing Gazette (0963-0031); Pigeon Racing News and Gazette (0048-4164)
Published by: Royal Pigeon Racing Association, The Reddings, Near Cheltenham, Glos GL51 6RN, United Kingdom. TEL 44-1452-713529, FAX 44-1452-857119. Ed. David Glover. Circ: 5,500. **Dist. by:** British Homing World, Severn Rd, Severn Farm Industrial Estate, Welshpool SY21 7DF, United Kingdom. TEL 44-1938-552360, FAX 44-1938-553969.

598 GBR ISSN 0007-1595
QL671 CODEN: BBOCAS
BRITISH ORNITHOLOGISTS' CLUB. BULLETIN. Text in English. 1892. q. GBP 22, USD 45 to non-members; GBP 12, USD 26 to members. bk.rev. bibl.; charts; illus. index, cum.index: 1950-59. back issues avail. **Document type:** *Academic/Scholarly.* **Description:** Emphasizes taxonomy, descriptions of new forms, distribution information, and field studies.
Related titles: Microfiche ed.: (from IDC).
Indexed: BIOSIS Prev, BiolAb, KWIWR, RefZh, SFA, SPPI, WildRev, ZooRec.
—BLDSC (2423.000000), IE, ingenta, Linda Hall. **CCC.**
Published by: British Ornithologists' Club, c/o BOU, British Museum, Tring, Herts HP23 6AP, United Kingdom. Ed. J Feare C. Circ: 800 (paid).

598 GBR ISSN 1363-2965
BRITISH ORNITHOLOGISTS' CLUB. OCCASIONAL PUBLICATIONS. Text in English. irreg.
Indexed: ZooRec.
Published by: British Ornithologists' Club, c/o BOU, British Museum, Tring, Herts HP23 6AP, United Kingdom.

598 GBR ISSN 0068-2675
BRITISH TRUST FOR ORNITHOLOGY. ANNUAL REPORT. Text in English. 1935. a. membership. **Document type:** *Corporate.*
Published by: British Trust for Ornithology, The Nunnery, Nunnery Pl, Thetford, Norfolk IP24 2PU, United Kingdom. TEL 44-1842-750050, FAX 44-1842-750030, btostaff@bto.org, general@bto.org, http://www.bto.org/. Ed. Andy Elvin. Circ: 10,000.

598 GBR
THE BUDGERIGAR. Text in English. 1925. bi-m. GBP 17.50 (effective 2000). adv. bk.rev. back issues avail. **Description:** Reports on the World Budgerigar Organization, the British Budgerigar Society, British area societies, and show reports. Includes articles on feeding, exhibiting, and breeding budgerigars, and interviews with top UK breeders.
Formerly (until 1985): Budgerigar Bulletin (0045-3323)
Published by: Budgerigar Society, c/o Alistair Cameron, Ed, 41 Pegasus Gardens, Quedgeley, Glos GL2 4NP, United Kingdom. TEL 44-1452-725265, FAX 44-1452-530364. Ed., R&P Alistair Cameron. Adv. contact Ellaine Cameron. Circ: 5,000. **Subscr. to:** The Budgerigar Society, 49-53 Hazelwood Rd, Northampton, Northants NN1 1LG, United Kingdom.

598 CAN ISSN 0007-5256
BULLETIN ORNITHOLOGIQUE. Text in English. 1956. q. CND 20 to individuals; CND 28 to institutions. bk.rev. charts. **Document type:** *Bulletin.*
Media: Duplicated (not offset).
Published by: Club des Ornithologues de Quebec, Inc., 2000 bd Montmorency, Quebec, PQ G1J 5E7, Canada. TEL 418-667-6373. Circ: 500.

598 GBR ISSN 0007-9561
CAGE & AVIARY BIRDS. Text in English. 1902. w. GBP 51.38 domestic; USD 106.07 in United States (effective 2004). adv. bk.rev. charts; illus.; tr.lit. **Document type:** *Consumer.* **Description:** Covers all aspects of keeping and breeding birds for the serious enthusiasts.
Published by: I P C Country & Leisure Media Ltd. (Subsidiary of: I P C Media Ltd.), King's Reach Tower, Stamford St, London, SE1 9LS, United Kingdom. TEL 44-870-4445000, http://www.ipcmedia.com. Ed. Donald Taylor TEL 44-20-72616128. adv.: color page GBP 1,854. Circ: 28,245. **Subscr. to:** I P C Media Ltd., Perrymount Rd, Haywards Heath RH16 3DA, United Kingdom. TEL 44-1444-475675, FAX 44-1444-445599.

598 GBR ISSN 0962-4325
THE CALF OF MAN BIRD OBSERVATORY ANNUAL REPORT; annual report for (year). Text in English. 1964. a. GBP 3.50 per issue in British Isles; GBP 4.50 per issue foreign (effective 2002). illus.; maps; stat. back issues avail. **Document type:** *Academic/Scholarly.* **Description:** Contains reports, monthly summaries, ringing report, non avarian report, map, list of contributors.
Published by: Manx National Heritage, Manx Museum, Douglas, Isle of Man, British Isles IM1 3LY, United Kingdom. TEL 44-1624-648000, FAX 44-1624-648001, enquiries@mnh.gov.im, http://www.gov.im/mnh. Circ: 200 (paid).

598 SWE ISSN 0346-9395
CALIDRIS. Text in Swedish. 1972. q. SEK 100 (effective 1990).
Related titles: Supplement(s): Calidris Supplement. ISSN 0282-7344.
Indexed: KWIWR, ZooRec.
Published by: Oelands Ornitologiska Foerening, Fack 15, Faerjestaden, 38600, Sweden.

598 GBR
CAMBRIDGESHIRE BIRD CLUB. ANNUAL REPORT. Text in English. a.
Published by: Cambridgeshire Bird Club, 178 Nuns Way, Cambridge, CB4 2NS, United Kingdom. TEL 44-1223-700656, bruce.s.martin@ntlworld.com, http://www.cambridgebirdclub.org.uk/.

598 GBR
CAMBRIDGESHIRE BIRD CLUB. BULLETIN. Text in English. bi-m. free to members (effective 2004). **Document type:** *Bulletin.* **Description:** Contains a summary of recent reports, topical short articles and items of club news.
Published by: Cambridgeshire Bird Club, 178 Nuns Way, Cambridge, CB4 2NS, United Kingdom. TEL 44-1223-700656, bruce.s.martin@ntlworld.com, http://www.cambridgebirdclub.org.uk/.

598 GBR ISSN 0962-4309
CAMBRIDGESHIRE BIRD REPORT. Text in English. bi-m. GBP 9.50 per issue; free to members (effective 2004).
Indexed: ZooRec.
Published by: Cambridgeshire Bird Club, 178 Nuns Way, Cambridge, CB4 2NS, United Kingdom. TEL 44-1223-700656, bruce.s.martin@ntlworld.com, http://www.cambridgebirdclub.org.uk/.

598 USA ISSN 0162-8186
CARDINAL. Text in English. 1970. bi-m. USD 20 membership; USD 17 to libraries & foreign individuals (effective 2002); Membership includes subscr. to Indiana Audubon Quarterly and Cardinal. illus. 4 p./no. 2 cols./p.; **Document type:** *Newspaper.* **Description:** Features activities of the society, state and federal environmental and conservation issues, and more.
Published by: Indiana Audubon Society, Inc., 3499 S Bird Sanctuary Rd, Connersville, IN 47331 . TEL 765-825-9788, membership@indianaaudubon.org, http://www.indianaaudubon.org. Ed., R&P Scott Arvin TEL 812-877-9593. Circ: 600 (paid). **Subscr. to:** 20451 Brick Road, South Bend, IN 46637-1418.

598 USA ISSN 0095-862X
QL671
CASSINIA. Text in English. 1890. irreg. free to members (effective 2005). **Document type:** *Journal.*
Formerly (until 1901): Delaware Valley Ornithological Club of Philadelphia. Abstract of Proceedings
Published by: Delaware Valley Ornithological Club, c/o Academy of Natural Sciences, 1900 Benjamin Franklin Pkwy, Philadelphia, PA 19103. http://www.acnatsci.org/hosted/dvoc/Publications/Cassina/Cassinia.htm, http://www.dvoc.org. Ed. Art McMorris.

598 GBR ISSN 0956-2230
CEREDIGION BIRD REPORT. Text in English. 1982. a. GBP 3. bibl.; illus.; maps; stat. back issues avail. **Document type:** *Proceedings.* **Description:** Annual report of birds seen in county of Ceredigion supported by short papers.
Published by: Wildlife Trust West Wales, 7 Market St., Haverford West, Pembs SA61 1NF, United Kingdom. TEL 44-1437-765462, FAX 44-1437-767163, wildlife@wildlife-wales.org.uk. Ed. Hywel Roderick. Circ: 350.

598 LKA ISSN 1019-8121
CEYLON BIRD CLUB NOTES. Text in English. 1943. m.
Published by: Ceylon Bird Club, P.O. Box 11, Colombo 1, Sri Lanka. Ed. D P Wijesinghe.

598 LKA
CEYLON BIRD CLUB NOTES. SPECIAL PUBLICATIONS SERIES. Text in English. irreg.
Indexed: ZooRec.
Published by: Ceylon Bird Club, P.O. Box 11, Colombo 1, Sri Lanka. Ed. D P Wijesinghe.

598 DEU ISSN 0174-1004
CHARADRIUS; Zeitschrift fuer Vogelkunde, Vogelschutz und Naturschutz im Rheinland und in Westfalen. Text in German; Summaries in English, German. 1965. q. bk.rev. index. **Document type:** *Journal, Academic/Scholarly.*
Indexed: KWIWR, SFA, WildRev, ZooRec.
Published by: Nordrhein-Westfaelische Ornithologengesellschaft, Freybergweg 9, Wesel, 46483, Germany. TEL 49-281-962520, FAX 49-281-9625222, charadrius@nw-ornithologen.de, johan.mooij@bskw.de, http://www.nw-ornithologen.de. Ed. Stefan Sudmann. Circ: 1,450. **Co-sponsor:** Westfaelische Ornithologen Gesellschaft e.V.

598 GBR ISSN 0959-9096
CHESHIRE AND WIRRAL BIRD REPORT. Text in English. 1968. a. GBP 6.80 per issue (effective 2003). adv. illus.; charts. back issues avail. **Document type:** *Corporate.*
Former titles (until 1989): Cheshire Ornithological Association. Bird Report (0262-7655); (until 1978): Cheshire Bird Report
Published by: Cheshire - Wirral Ornithological Society, 113 Nantwich Rd, Middlewich, Ches CW10 9HD, United Kingdom. TEL 44-1606-832517, info@cawos.org, http://www.cawos.org. Ed. Richard Gabb. R&P D Cogger. Circ: 600.

598 JPN
CHORUI HYOSHIKI CHOSA HOKOKUSHO/BIRD MIGRATION RESEARCH CENTER. REPORT. Text in Japanese. a.
Published by: (Yamashina Chorui Kenkyujo/Yamashina Institute for Ornithology), Kankyocho/Environment Agency, 2-2 Kasumigaseki 1-chome, Chiyoda-ku, Tokyo, 100-0013, Japan.

598 DEU ISSN 0342-8923
CINCLUS. Text in German. 1973. 2/yr. EUR 15 (effective 2004). 52 p./no.; back issues avail. **Document type:** *Journal, Academic/Scholarly.* **Description:** Contains articles of interest to ornithologists and those involved in bird watching and conservation.
Indexed: ZooRec.
Published by: Bund fuer Vogelschutz und Vogelkunde e.V., Buchenstr 12, Herdecke, 58313, Germany. TEL 49-2330-13693, FAX 49-2331-840545, bfvherdeckehagen@yahoo.de, http://home.t-online.de/home/tim.ba/BfVHome.htm. Ed. Walter Klisch. Adv. contact Heinz Grimm TEL 49-2335-2765.

598 USA
QL684.C6 CODEN: CFOJDN
➤ **COLORADO BIRDS.** Text in English. 1965. q. USD 20 to individuals; USD 30 to institutions; USD 16 to students (effective 2003). bk.rev. abstr.; bibl.; illus.; maps; stat. back issues avail. **Document type:** *Bulletin, Academic/Scholarly.* **Description:** Covers identification, distribution, behavior and ecology of Colorado's avifauna.
Former titles (until Oct.2002): Journal of the Colorado Field Ornithologists (1094-0030); (until 1997): C.F.O. Journal (1092-7247); (until 1994): Colorado Field Ornithologists' Journal (1066-7342); (until 1991): C.F.O. Journal (0362-9902); (until 1975): Colorado Field Ornithologists (0010-1591)
Related titles: Microform ed.: (from PQC).
Indexed: BiolAb, SFA, WLR, WildRev, ZooRec.
Published by: Colorado Field Ornithologists, 6035 Parfet St, Arvada, CO 80004. TEL 303-823-5332, editor@cfo-link.org, http://www.cfo-link.org. Ed., R&P Doug Faulkner. Circ: 600.

598 USA ISSN 0010-5422
QL671 CODEN: CNDRAB
➤ **CONDOR**; an international journal of avian biology. Text in English. 1899. q. USD 50 membership (effective 2005). adv. bk.rev. charts; illus.; maps. index, cum.index: 1899-1958. back issues avail.; reprints avail. **Document type:** *Journal, Academic/Scholarly.* **Description:** Devoted to the biology of wild species of birds.
Formerly (until 1900): Cooper Ornithological Club. Bulletin (1553-1031)
Related titles: Microfiche ed.: (from PQC); Online - full text ed.: (from BioOne, C S A, JSTOR (Web-based Journal Archive), O C L C Online Computer Library Center, Inc., ProQuest Information & Learning).
Indexed: ASFA, AgBio, AgrForAb, AnBeAb, AnBrAb, ApEcolAb, B&AI, B&BAb, BIOBASE, BIOSIS Prev, BiolAb, ChemAb, CurCont, EPB, ESPM, ForAb, GenetAb, HGA, HelmAb, HerbAb, ISR, IndVet, NutrAb, OceAb, OrnA, OrnithAb, PGegResA, PoultAb, ProtozoAb, RM&VM, RefZh, RevApplEntom, S&F, SCI, SFA, VetBull, WildRev, ZooRec.
—BLDSC (3406.000000), IDS, IE, Infotrieve, ingenta, Linda Hall.
Published by: Cooper Ornithological Society, Inc., c/o David S. Dobkin, High Desert Ecological Research Institute, 15 SW Colorado Ste 300, Bend, OR 97702. TEL 541-382-1117, condor@hderi.org, http://www.cooper.org/. Circ: 3,300. **Subscr. to:** Ornithological Societies of North America, Business Office, Box 1897, Lawrence, KS 66044-7099.

598 USA ISSN 1077-0283
CODEN: CWARET
➤ **CONNECTICUT WARBLER**; a journal of Connecticut ornithology. Text in English. 1981. q. USD 12 to members (effective 1999). bk.rev. back issues avail. **Document type:** *Academic/Scholarly.*
Indexed: RefZh, SFA, WildRev, ZooRec.
Published by: Connecticut Ornithological Association, Inc., 314 Unquowa Rd, Fairfield, CT 06430-5018. TEL 203-259-2623. Ed. Betty Kleiner. R&P Carl Trichka. Circ: 550 (paid).

598 GBR
CONNOISSEURS BIRD JOURNAL. Text in English. 1981. bi-m. GBP 6.
Published by: Flight Publishing Ltd., 41 Sugden Rd, Thames Ditton, Surrey KT7 0AD, United Kingdom. Ed. M Desnaux. Circ: 20,000.

598 GBR ISSN 0962-0524
COPELAND BIRD OBSERVATORY REPORT. Text in English. a.
Indexed: ZooRec.
Published by: Copeland Bird Observatory, 43 Clare Heights, Ballyclare, Co. Antrim, BT39 9HA, United Kingdom. http://www.cbo.org.uk/.

598 DEU ISSN 0589-686X
➤ **CORAX**; Veroeffentlichungen der ornithologischen Arbeitsgemeinschaft fuer Schleswig-Holstein und Hamburg e.V. Text in German; Summaries in English. 1965. irreg. EUR 30 (effective 2004). bk.rev. 100 p./no. 2 cols./p.; back issues avail. **Document type:** *Journal, Academic/Scholarly.*
Indexed: BiolAb, IBR, KWIWR, RefZh, SFA, WildRev, ZooRec.
Address: Zum Brook 16, Bauersdorf, 24238, Germany. TEL 49-4384-1537, FAX 49-4384-1537, ziesemer@ornithologie-schleswig-holstein.de, http://www.ornithologie-schleswig-holstein.de. Ed., Pub. Dr. Fridtjof Ziesemer. Circ: 850. **Subscr. to:** Karl-Heinz Reiser, Ruhwinkel 8, Medelby 24994, Germany.

598 AUS ISSN 0155-0438
CODEN: CRRLDQ
➤ **CORELLA.** Text in English. 1962. q. free to members. adv. bk.rev. abstr.; charts; illus. Index. **Document type:** *Journal, Academic/Scholarly.* **Description:** Contains original articles on ornithology.
Formerly (until Jan. 1977): Australian Bird Bander (0004-8747)
Indexed: BIOSIS Prev, BiolAb, RefZh, SFA, WildRev, ZooRec.
—BLDSC (3470.803000), IE, ingenta.
Published by: Australian Bird Study Association, PO Box A 313, Sydney South, NSW 1235, Australia. TEL 61-2-95806621, FAX 61-2-47591715, cgcam@anprod.csiro.au, http://www.absa.asn.au/corella.html. Ed., R&P Annette E Cam. Adv. contact S Boddington. Circ: 600 (paid).

598 FRA ISSN 0751-7963
CODEN: CRMNE8
➤ **LE CORMORAN.** Text in French. 1969. 2/yr. **Document type:** *Academic/Scholarly.*
Indexed: SFA, WildRev, ZooRec.
Published by: Groupe Ornithologique Normand, Universite de Caen, Caen, Cedex 14032, France. TEL 31-43-52-56, FAX 31-93-27-07, gonm@wanadoo.fr. Ed. Bruno Lang.

598 GBR ISSN 1353-985X
QL671
COTINGA. Text in English. 1994. s-a.
Indexed: ZooRec.
Published by: Neotropical Bird Club, c/o The Lodge, Sandy, Bedfordshire SG19 2DL, United Kingdom. http://www.neotropicalbirdclub.org/.

598 FRA ISSN 1268-7685
CREX. Text in French. 1996. a. charts; illus.; maps. back issues avail. **Document type:** *Bulletin.* **Description:** Presents articles on ornithology in Maine-et-Loire, ornithological reports, rare bird reports, ornithological syntheses about various species or groups of species and botanical reports.
Related titles: E-mail ed.; Fax ed.; Online - full text ed.
Indexed: ZooRec.
Published by: LPO Anjou, 84 rue Blaise-Pascal, Angers, 49000, France. TEL 33-241-444422, FAX 33-241-682348, anjou@lpo-birdlife.asso.fr, http://www.lpo-anjou.org. Ed. Jean Claude Beaudoin. Pub. Philippe Pouplard.

598 363.7 AUS
CUMBERLAND BIRD OBSERVERS CLUB NEWSLETTER. Text in English. 1979. bi-m. AUD 22 (effective 2000). **Document type:** *Newsletter.*
Published by: Cumberland Bird Observers Club Inc., P.O. Box 550, Baulkham Hills, NSW 1755, Australia. Ed. Jane Miller. Circ: 500.

598 GBR
CUMBRIA BIRD CLUB NEWS. Text in English. q.
Published by: Cumbria Bird Club, Derwentwater Youth Hostel, Keswick, Borrowdale CA12 5UR, United Kingdom. TEL 017687-77246.

598 CAN ISSN 0011-3093
CURLEW. Text in English. 1954. 8/yr. CND 18 to individuals; CND 20 to libraries. bk.rev. **Document type:** *Newsletter.*
Published by: Willow Beach Field Naturalists, P O Box 421, Port Hope, ON L1A 3W4, Canada. TEL 905-372-1028. Ed. Norma Wallace. R&P T Stopps. Circ: 175. **Subscr. to:** c/o Editor, 64 Young St, Port Hope, ON L1A 1M6, Canada.

598 USA ISSN 0742-390X
QL671 CODEN: CUROEN
➤ **CURRENT ORNITHOLOGY.** Text in English. 1983. irreg., latest vol.16, 2001. price varies. charts; illus.; stat. back issues avail. **Document type:** *Monographic series, Academic/Scholarly.* **Description:** Publishes contributions from international ornithologists on a broad spectrum of topics relating to the ecology, biology, and behavior of birds.
Indexed: BIOSIS Prev, BiolDig, SFA, WildRev, ZooRec.
—BLDSC (3500.790000), CISTI, Linda Hall.
Published by: Springer-Verlag New York, Inc. (Subsidiary of: Springer Science+Business Media), 233 Spring St, New York, NY 10013. TEL 212-460-1500, FAX 212-460-1575, service@springer-ny.com, http://www.springer-ny.com. Eds. Charles Thompson, Val Nolan. **Dist. by:** Journal Fulfillment, PO Box 2485, Secaucus, NJ 07096-2485.

598.072344489 DNK ISSN 0011-6394
QL671 CODEN: DOFTAB
➤ **DANSK ORNITOLOGISK FORENINGS TIDSSKRIFT.** Text and summaries in Danish, English. 1906. q. DKK 325 membership includes subscription to Fugle og Natur (effective 2003). bk.rev. bibl.; illus.; stat. 48 p./no. 2 cols./p.; back issues avail. **Document type:** *Journal, Academic/Scholarly.*
Indexed: BIOSIS Prev, BiolAb, KWIWR, RefZh, SFA, WLR, WildRev, ZooRec.
—BLDSC (3526.800000). **CCC.**
Published by: Dansk Ornitologisk Forening/Danish Ornithological Society, Vesterbrogade 138-140, Copenhagen V, 1620, Denmark. TEL 45-33-314404, FAX 45-33-312435, dof@dof.dk, http://www.dof.dk. Ed. Kaj Kampp. Circ: 5,000.

598 NLD ISSN 0167-2878
CODEN: DUBID3
➤ **DUTCH BIRDING.** Text in Dutch. 1979. bi-m. EUR 30 domestic; EUR 33 in Europe; EUR 36 elsewhere (effective 2003). adv. bk.rev. back issues avail. **Document type:** *Journal, Academic/Scholarly.* **Description:** Covers birds in the western Palearctic region.
Indexed: BiolAb, SFA, WildRev, ZooRec.
Published by: Dutch Birding Association, Postbus 75611, Amsterdam, 1070 AP, Netherlands. TEL 31-23-537-8024, FAX 31-23-537-6749, editors@dutchbirding.nl, Arnoud.vandenBerg@inter.nl.net, http://www.dutchbirding.nl. Ed. Arnoud B van den Berg. Circ: 2,500.

598 AUS ISSN 1327-550X
ECLECTUS. Text in English. 1996. s-a. AUD 25 (effective 2000). bk.rev. back issues avail. **Document type:** *Academic/Scholarly.*
Published by: Birds Australia Parrot Association, Birds Australia, 415 Riversdale Rd, Hawthorn East, VIC 3123, Australia. TEL 61-3-9882-2677, FAX 61-3-9882-2677, mail@birdsaustralia.com.au, http://www.birdsaustralia.com.au. Ed. Peter Brown. Circ: 200.

598 AUT ISSN 0013-2373
QL690.A9
EGRETTA; Vogelkundliche Nachrichten aus Oesterreich. Text in German. 1958. s-a. EUR 40 domestic; EUR 44 foreign (effective 2005). bk.rev. bibl.; charts; illus. cum.index every 4 yrs. **Document type:** *Journal, Academic/Scholarly.* **Description:** Publishes articles on ornithological topics with special regard to Austria.
Indexed: BIOSIS Prev, BiolAb, IBR, KWIWR, RefZh, SFA, WildRev, ZooRec.
—BLDSC (3664.215700), IE, ingenta.
Published by: BirdLife Austria, Museumsplatz 1-10-8, Vienna, W 1070, Austria. TEL 43-1-5234651, FAX 43-1-523465150, http://www.birdlife.at. Ed. Gerhard Loupal. Circ: 2,000.

598 USA ISSN 0013-6069
QH76.5.H3 CODEN: ELPABT
➤ **ELEPAIO.** Text in English. 1939. 9/yr., latest vol.61. USD 10, CND 17, EUR 28 (effective 2001). bk.rev. charts. 12 p./no. 3 cols./p.; **Document type:** *Newsletter, Academic/Scholarly.*
Media: Duplicated (not offset).
Indexed: BiolAb, RefZh, SFA, WildRev, ZooRec.
Published by: Hawaii Audubon Society, 850 Richards St, Ste 505, Honolulu, HI 96813-4709. TEL 808-528-1432, FAX 808-537-5294, hiaudsoc@pixi.com. Ed., R&P Linda Shapin. Circ: 2,400.

598 AUS ISSN 0158-4197
QL671 CODEN: EMUUAI
➤ **EMU**; Austral Ornithology. Text in English. 1901. q. AUD 300 combined subscription in Australia & New Zealand to institutions print & online eds.; USD 350 combined subscription elsewhere to institutions print & online eds. (effective 2004). adv. bk.rev. illus. Index. 90 p./no.; back issues avail.; reprint service avail. from PQC. **Document type:** *Journal, Academic/Scholarly.*
Related titles: Microfiche ed.: (from IDC); Microfilm ed.: (from PQC); Online - full text ed.: AUD 270 in Australia & New Zealand to institutions; AUD 225 elsewhere to institutions (effective 2004) (from EBSCO Publishing, Gale Group, O C L C Online Computer Library Center, Inc., Swets Information Services).

B

Indexed: ASCA, ASFA, ASI, AgBio, AgrForAb, AnBeAb, AnBrAb, ApEcolAb, BIOBASE, BIOSIS Prev, BiolAb, CurCont, ESPM, ForAb, GEOBASE, HerbAb, IABS, IBR, ISR, KWIWR, NutrAb, PGegResA, PoultAb, ProtozoAb, S&F, SCI, SFA, SPPI, SeedAb, WeedAb, WildRev, ZooRec.
—BLDSC (3738.000000), IDS, IE, Infotrieve, ingenta, Linda Hall. **CCC.**
Published by: (Birds Australia), C S I R O Publishing, 150 Oxford St, PO Box 1139, Collingwood, VIC 3066, Australia. TEL 61-3-96627622, FAX 61-3-96627611, publishing.emu@csiro.au, publishing@csiro.au, http://www.publish.csiro.au/journals/emu. Circ: 1,500.

598 CAN ISSN 0707-7165
ENVOL/FLIGHT. Text in English, French. 1978. irreg. membership.
Published by: Club d'Amateurs d'Oiseaux de Montreal, 228 de la Salle, Mont St Hilaire, St Hilaire, PQ J3H 3C2, Canada.

B

598 GBR ISSN 0963-2085
ESSEX BIRD REPORT. Text in English. 1961. a.
Indexed: ZooRec.
Published by: Essex Birdwatching Society, 4 Helston Rd, Essex, Chelmsford CM1 6JE, United Kingdom. http://www.essexbirdwatchsoc.co.uk/.

598 GBR
ESSEX BIRDING. Text in English. s-a.
Published by: Essex Birdwatching Society, 4 Helston Rd, Essex, Chelmsford CM1 6JE, United Kingdom. http://www.essexbirdwatchsoc.co.uk/.

598 SWE ISSN 0281-790X
FAAGLAR I BLEKINGE. Variant title: Nya Faaglar i Blekinge. Text in Swedish. 1984. q. SEK 100 to members (effective 1997). adv. bk.rev.
Formed by merger of: Faaglar i Blekinge. Aktuellt; Faaglar i Blekinge. Aarsskrift; Meddelanden fraan Torhamns Faagelstation
Published by: Blekinge Ornitologiska Foerening, Stenhagsvaegen 14, Karlshamn, 37433, Sweden. Ed. Thomas Nilsson. Circ: 450.

598 SWE ISSN 0281-4374
FAAGLAR I DALARNA. Text in Swedish. 1968. q. SEK 75 to members (effective 1991). **Document type:** *Newsletter.*
Formerly (until 1980): Dalarnas Ornitologiska Foerening. Meddelanden
Published by: Dalarnas Ornitologiska Foerening (DOF), c/o Thorhild Jonsson, Traedgaardsgatan 2, Ludvika, 77150, Sweden. Ed. Bertil Rahm.

598 SWE ISSN 0282-4760
FAAGLAR I JAEMTLAND - HAERJEDALEN. Text in Swedish; Abstracts occasionally in English. 1981. q. SEK 90 to members (effective 1990). **Description:** Focuses on ornithology of the Jaemtland region of Sweden. Includes an annual report from the Aansjoen Bird Observatory with English summaries.
Published by: Jaemtlands Laens Ornitologiska Foerening (JORF), c/o Thomas Holmberg, Ed, Roedoen 1824, Krokom, 83591, Sweden. TEL 46-63-34240, FAX 46—63-34240. Circ: 400.

598 SWE ISSN 0283-2852
FAAGLAR I KVISMAREN. Text in Swedish. 1962. a. back issues avail. **Description:** Features the birds and the environmental work in a CW-listed wetland area in the middle of Sweden.
Formerly (until 1986): Verksamheten vid Kvismare Faagelstation
Related titles: ◆ Series of: Meddelande fraan Kvismare Faagelstation. ISSN 0454-7217.
Indexed: RefZh.
Published by: Kvismare Faagelstation, Oerebro, 70595, Sweden. TEL 46-019-23 80 31. Ed. Thomas Eriksson. Circ: 500.

598 SWE ISSN 0282-5554
FAAGLAR I MEDELPAD. Text in Swedish. 1978. s-a. SEK 50 (effective 1991).
Published by: Medelpads Ornitologiska Foerening, c/o N Lundmark, Skarpskyttevagen 6, Sundsvall, 85462, Sweden.

598 SWE ISSN 0349-3970
FAAGLAR I NAERKE. Text in Swedish. 1978. q. SEK 160 to members (effective 2004).
Published by: Naerkes Ornitologiska Foerening (NOF), c/o Christer Nyten, Faagelbaersgatan 24, Orebro, 70360, Sweden. TEL 46-19-256789, http://nof.orebro.se/. Ed. Annike Lorin.

598 SWE ISSN 0281-4153
FAAGLAR I NORDVAESTSKAANE. Text in Swedish. 1970-1984; resumed 1985-1993; resumed 1995. a. SEK 100 to members (effective 2004).
Formerly (until 1990): Rapport fraan Kullabygdens Ornitologiska Foerening (0280-0071); Incorporates (1993-1996): Faagelrapporten (1401-2960)
Related titles: ◆ Supplement to: Faaglar i NV-Skaane. ISSN 1104-3695.
Published by: Kullabygdens Ornitologiska Foerening (KOF), c/o Henrik Ehrenberg, Sckerbruksgatan 13 C, Aengelholm, 26263, Sweden. TEL 46-431-19405, FAX 46-70-5735376, henrik.ehrenberg@kof.se, http://www.kof.nu.

598 SWE ISSN 0281-6903
FAAGLAR I NORRBOTTEN. Text in Swedish. 1982. q. SEK 150; SEK 230 foreign (effective 2005). adv. bk.rev. bibl.; charts; illus. back issues avail. **Document type:** *Magazine, Consumer.* **Description:** Contains articles on birdlife in Norrbotten, the northernmost province of Sweden, and news of events held by Norbottens Ornitologiska Foerening.
Related titles: ◆ Supplement(s): Faglar i Norrbotten. Supplement. ISSN 0283-2348.
Published by: Norrbottens Ornitologiska Foerening, c/o Andreas livbom, Spraenggatan 35, Lulea, 97432, Sweden. TEL 46-920-14342. Ed. Andreas Livbom. Circ: 500 (paid).

598 SWE ISSN 1100-0813
FAAGLAR I NORRKOEPINGSTRAKTEN. Text in Swedish. 1980. q. SEK 100 (effective 1999). adv. **Document type:** *Newsletter.* **Description:** Focuses on the study of bird life within the community boundaries of Norrkoeping and the neighbouring communities of Soederkoeping and Valdemarsvik.
Published by: Faagelfoereningen i Norrkoeping (FiNk), c/o Juhani Vuorinen, Ed, Bergslagsgatan 37, Norrkoping, 60218, Sweden. juhani.vuorinen@facere.se, http://www.torget.se/users/c/cinclus/finkinfo.htm. Ed. Juhani Vuorinen. Circ: 350 (controlled).

598 SWE ISSN 1104-3695
FAAGLAR I NV-SKAANE. Text in Swedish. 1970. q.
Supersedes in part (in 1991): Rapport fraan Kullabygdens Ornitologiska Foerening (0280-0071)
Related titles: ◆ Supplement(s): Faaglar i Nordvaestskaane. ISSN 0281-4153.
Published by: Kullabygdens Ornitologiska Foerening (KOF), c/o Henrik Ehrenberg, Sckerbruksgatan 13 C, Aengelholm, 26263, Sweden. TEL 46-431-19405, FAX 46-70-5735376, henrik.ehrenberg@kof.se, http://www.kof.nu.

598 SWE ISSN 1100-9748
FAAGLAR I OESTRA SMAALAND. Text in Swedish. 1989. q. SEK 100 (effective 2000). **Document type:** *Journal, Academic/Scholarly.*
Published by: Oestra Smaalands Ornitologiska Foerening, c/o A Nilsson, Stenaldersv 26, Oskarshamn, 57240, Sweden.

598 SWE ISSN 0345-3820
FAAGLAR I SOERMLAND. Text in Swedish. 1968. s-a. SEK 70 (effective 1990).
Related titles: ◆ Supplement(s): Faglar i Sormland. Supplement. ISSN 0281-1413.
Published by: Foereningen Soedermanlands Ornitologer (FSO), c/o Swenzen, Skanegatan 5, Katrineholm, 64136, Sweden.

598 SWE ISSN 0349-3911
FAAGLAR I UPPLAND. Text in Swedish. 1974. q. SEK 150 membership (effective 2002).
Related titles: Supplement(s): ISSN 1400-7452. 1989.
Published by: Upplands Ornitologiska Foerening (UOF), c/o Jocce Ekstroem, Dirigentvaegen 19, Uppsala, 75654, Sweden.

598 SWE ISSN 0280-2430
FAAGLAR I VAESTMANLAND. Text in Swedish. 1970. q. SEK 85 to members (effective 1997). bk.rev.
Formerly (until 1980): Meddelanden fraan Vaestmanlands Ornitologiska Foerening
Published by: Vaestmanlands Ornitologiska Foerening, c/o Daniel Green, Knutsgatan 5 b, Vaesteraas, 72214, Sweden. daniel.gren@vlt.se. Ed. Daniel Green. Circ: 500.

598 SWE ISSN 0346-9662
FAAGLAR I X-LAEN. Text in Swedish. 1970. q. SEK 100 (effective 2000). **Document type:** *Bulletin, Academic/Scholarly.* **Description:** Presents papers on regional bird research projects, conservation issues, and actual bird counts.
Former titles (until 1975): Faaglar i Gstr och Hls; (until 1972): Fraan V F's Rapportkommittee Foer Gaestrikland och Haelsingland
Published by: Gaevleborgs Laens Ornitologiska Foerening (GLOF), c/o Per-Owe Loock, Svangatan 4 D, Gavle, 80646, Sweden. pag@hig.se. Ed., Pub. Mats Axbrink. Adv. contact Per-Owe Loock.

598 SWE ISSN 0348-1530
FAAGLAR PAA VAESTKUSTEN. Text in Swedish. 1965. q. SEK 100 to members (effective 1998). **Document type:** *Bulletin.*
Formed by the 1972 merger of: Faaglar paa Vaestkusten; Meddelanden fraan Goeteborgs Ornitologiska Foerening
Related titles: ◆ Supplement(s): Falknytt. ISSN 0280-9710.
Published by: Goeteborgs Ornitologiska Foerening (GOF), Fack 166, Vastra Frolunda, 42122, Sweden. http://www.tripnet.se/GOF. Ed. Goeran Jansson.

598 SWE ISSN 0345-3812
FAAGLEHOBBY; medlemsblad foer Sveriges samarbetand burfaagelfoereningar. Text in Swedish. 1971. 10/yr. SEK 140 (effective 1990).
Published by: Faagelhobby, c/o U Magnusson, Fylkingag 49, Malmo, 21229, Sweden.

598 SWE ISSN 0283-2348
FAGLAR I NORRBOTTEN. SUPPLEMENT. Text in Swedish. 1986. irreg.
Related titles: ◆ Supplement to: Faaglar i Norrbotten. ISSN 0281-6903.
Published by: Norrbottens Ornitologiska Foerening, c/o Andreas livbom, Spraenggatan 35, Lulea, 97432, Sweden. TEL 46-920-267481, tord.gustafsson@lulea.mail.telia.com.

598 SWE ISSN 0281-1413
FAGLAR I SORMLAND. SUPPLEMENT. Text in Swedish. 1981. irreg.
Related titles: ◆ Supplement to: Faaglar i Soermland. ISSN 0345-3820.
Published by: Foereningen Soedermanlands Ornitologer (FSO), c/o Swenzen, Skanegatan 5, Katrineholm, 64136, Sweden.

598 GBR ISSN 0427-9190
CODEN: RFBOD2
FAIR ISLE BIRD OBSERVATORY. REPORT. Text in English. 1949. a. GBP 6 per issue (effective 2001). back issues avail. **Document type:** *Consumer.* **Description:** Find out all about the bird sightings, Observatory news and island events.
Indexed: SFA, WildRev, ZooRec.
Published by: Fair Isle Bird Observatory Trust, Fair Isle Bird Observatory, The Lodge, Fair Isle, Shetland, Shetland ZE2 9JU, United Kingdom. TEL 44-1595-760-258, FAX 44-1595-760-258, fairisle.birdobs@zetnet.co.uk, http://www.fairislebirdobs.co.uk. Ed. Deryk Shaw. R&P, Adv. contact Hollie Craib. Circ: 650.

598 363.7 GBR ISSN 1608-1544
FALCO. Text in English. 1994. s-a.
Indexed: ZooRec.
Published by: Middle East Falcon Research Group, P.O. Box 19, Carmarthen, SA33 5YL, United Kingdom. office@falcons.co.uk.

598.9 GBR
THE FALCONERS AND RAPTOR CONSERVATION MAGAZINE. Text in English. 1989. q. GBP 16.50 domestic; GBP 20 in Europe; GBP 28 elsewhere; GBP 5.50 newsstand/cover. adv. bk.rev.; video rev. illus.; tr.lit. back issues avail. **Document type:** *Consumer.* **Description:** Publishes informational and nostalgic articles on raptor conservation.
Published by: Falconers and Raptor Conservation Magazine, 20 Bridle Rd, Burton Latimer, Kettering, Northants NN15 5QP, United Kingdom. TEL 44-1536-722794, FAX 44-1536-722794. Ed. David Wilson. Adv. contact Lyn Wilson. Circ: 5,000.

598 DEU ISSN 0323-357X
CODEN: FALKA6
DER FALKE; Journal fuer Vogelbeobachter. Text in German. m. EUR 47; EUR 36 to students; EUR 4.60 newsstand/cover (effective 2005). adv. illus. **Document type:** *Magazine, Consumer.* **Description:** Information and news about ornithology and bird protection.
Indexed: BiolAb, IBR, KWIWR, SFA, WildRev, ZooRec.
Published by: Aula Verlag GmbH, Industriepark 3, Wiebelsheim, 56291, Germany. TEL 49-6766-903141, FAX 49-6766-903320, falke@aula-Verlag.de, vertrieb@aula-verlag.de, http://www.falke-journal.de, http://www.birdnet.de/aula. Ed. E Bezzel. R&P Georg Grothe TEL 49-6766-903-252. Adv. contact Petra Bross TEL 49-6766-903251. B&W page EUR 570; trim 190 x 275.

598 DEU
DER FALKE-TASCHENKALENDER FUER VOGELBEOBACHTER. Text in German. 1987. a. **Document type:** *Magazine, Consumer.*
Formerly: Ornithologenkalender (0942-5012)
Indexed: ZooRec.
Published by: Aula Verlag GmbH, Industriepark 3, Wiebelsheim, 56291, Germany. TEL 49-6766-903141, FAX 49-6766-903320, vertrieb@aula-verlag.de, http://www.birdnet.de/aula. Ed. Einhard Bezzel.

598 SWE ISSN 0280-9710
FALKNYTT. Text in Swedish. 1982.
Related titles: ◆ Supplement to: Faaglar paa Vaestkusten. ISSN 0348-1530.
Published by: Goeteborgs Ornitologiska Foerening (GOF), Fack 166, Vastra Frolunda, 42122, Sweden. http://www.tripnet.se/GOF.

598 USA
FIELD NOTES OF RHODE ISLAND BIRDS. Text in English. m. USD 10 (effective 2000). back issues avail. **Document type:** *Bulletin.* **Description:** Birds seen in Rhode Island during the previous month.
Published by: Audubon Society of Rhode Island, 12 Sanderson Rd, Smithfield, RI 02917-2606. TEL 401-949-5454, FAX 401-949-5788. Ed. Christopher Raithel. R&P Eugenia Marks. Circ: 300. **Co-sponsor:** Rhode Island Ornithological Club.

598 USA ISSN 0738-999X
QL684.F6 CODEN: FFNADO
➤ **FLORIDA FIELD NATURALIST.** Text in English. 1972. q. USD 20 domestic membership; USD 25 foreign membership; USD 15 membership student (effective 2005). adv. bk.rev. cum.index every 5 yrs. **Document type:** *Journal, Academic/Scholarly.*
Indexed: BIOSIS Prev, BiolAb, KWIWR, RefZh, SFA, WLR, WildRev, ZooRec.

Published by: Florida Ornithological Society, c/o Dean K. Jue, 3455 Dorchester Ct., Tallahassee, FL 32312-1300. TEL 352-376-6481, engstrom@bio.fsu.edu, http://www.fosbirds.org/FFN/FFNGuidelines.htm, http://fosbirds.org/index.html. Ed. R Todd Engstrom. Circ: 575.

➤ **FOREST & BIRD.** see *CONSERVATION*

598 GBR ISSN 0950-1746
➤ **FORKTAIL.** Text in English. 1986. a. GBP 8 (effective 2003).
Indexed: ZooRec.
—BLDSC (4008.278000), IE, ingenta.
Published by: (Oriental Bird Club), Piscespublications, 36 Kingfisher Ct, Hambridge Rd, Newbury, Berkshire RG14 5SJ, United Kingdom. TEL 44-1635-550380, FAX 44-1635-550230, pisces@naturebureau.co.uk, http://www.orientalbirdclub.org/publications/forktail/guidelines.html, http://www.naturebureau.co.uk.

598.0948 DNK ISSN 0903-1731
FUGLE OG DYR I NORDJYLLAND; rapport fra Nordjysk ornitologisk kartotek. Text in Danish. 1981 (no.18). a. DKK 130 (effective 2004). illus.
Former titles (until 1987): Fugle i Nordjylland (0108-7282); (until 1982): Nordjysk Ornithologisk Kartotek. Rapport
Published by: Foreningen Fugle og Dyr i Nordjylland, Spergelvej 23, Klarup, 9270, Denmark. tsc.vib@mail.tele.dk, http://www.nordfugl.dk. Ed. Tscherning Clausen.

598 DNK ISSN 1395-8860
FUGLE OG NATUR/BIRDS. Text in Danish. 1995. 4/yr. DKK 325 membership includes subscription to Dansk Ornitologisk Forenings Tidsskrift (effective 2003). adv. illus. **Document type:** *Academic/Scholarly.*
Supersedes in part (in 1995): Fugle (0107-3729); Which was formed by the merger of (1959-1980): Feltornitologen (0046-3647); (1969-1980): Fuglevaern (0107-4091); Incorporates (1989): D O F-Nyt (0904-6674)
Indexed: ZooRec.
Published by: Dansk Ornitologisk Forening/Danish Ornithological Society, Vesterbrogade 138-140, Copenhagen V, 1620, Denmark. TEL 45-33-314404, FAX 45-33-312435, fugleognatur@dof.dk, dof@dof.dk, http://www.dof.dk. Ed. Helge Roejlee Christensen. Circ: 12,000.

598.9 ZAF CODEN: GGBREY
G A B A R. (Growth and Biology of African Raptors) Text in English. s-a. ZAR 50, USD 35.
Indexed: SFA, WildRev, ZooRec.
Published by: Raptor Conservation Group, PO Box 72155, Parkview, Johannesburg 2122, South Africa. Ed. Andrew Jenkins.

598.6 GBR CODEN: GCANAJ
GAME CONSERVANCY REVIEW. Text in English. 1968. a. GBP 45 membership (effective 2000); includes Game Conservancy Magazine. adv. illus.; stat. index. back issues avail. **Document type:** *Corporate.* **Description:** Discusses the organization's efforts to promote the conservation of game bird habitats.
Indexed: BiolAb, PoultAb, S&F, SFA, WAE&RSA, WildRev, ZooRec.
Published by: Game Conservancy Trust, The Game Conservancy Trust, Burgate Manor, Fordingbridge, Hants SP6 1EF, United Kingdom. TEL 44-1425-652381, FAX 44-1425-651026, http://www.game-conservancy.org.UK/. Ed. Sophia Miles. Circ: 28,000.

598.6 GBR
GAMEWISE. Text in English. s-a. GBP 45 membership (effective 2000); includes Game Conservancy Review. **Document type:** *Consumer.* **Description:** Promotes the conservation of game bird habitat.
Former titles: Game Conservancy Magazine; Game Conservancy Newsletter
Published by: Game Conservancy Trust, The Game Conservancy Trust, Burgate Manor, Fordingbridge, Hants SP6 1EF, United Kingdom. TEL 44-1425-652381, FAX 44-1425-651026, http://www.game-conservancy.org.uk. R&P Sophia Miles. Circ: 28,000.

598 ESP ISSN 0212-923X CODEN: GARCER
LA GARCILLA; boletin - circular de la sociedad. Text in Spanish. 1954. 3/yr. **Document type:** *Magazine, Consumer.*
Indexed: IECT, RefZh, SFA, WildRev, ZooRec.
—CINDOC.
Published by: Sociedad Espanola de Ornitologia, C/ Melquiades Biencinto 34, Madrid, 28053, Spain. TEL 34-91-4340910, FAX 34-91-4340911, http://www.seo.org/ardeola. Ed. Nereida Cuenca.

598 AUS ISSN 1323-2681
GEELONG BIRD REPORT. Text in English. 1993. a.
Indexed: ZooRec.
Published by: Geelong Field Naturalists Club Inc., Box 1047, Geelong, VIC 3220, Australia. gfnc@vicnet.net.au, http://home.vicnet.net.au/~gfnc/.

598 DEU ISSN 0016-5816 CODEN: GEWEBF
GEFIEDERTE WELT; Fachzeitschrift fuer Vogelpfleger und Vogelzuechter. Text in German. 1874. m. EUR 67.80 domestic; EUR 74 foreign; EUR 6.40 newsstand/cover (effective 2004). adv. bk.rev. abstr.; bibl.; illus. index, cum.index. **Document type:** *Magazine, Consumer.* **Description:** Contains articles and features for bird lovers, keepers and breeders, and all people who are concerned about the protection of species and ethology.
Incorporates (1964-1969): Vogel-Kosmos (0507-2255)
Indexed: BiolAb, RILM, RefZh, SFA, WildRev, ZooRec.
—Linda Hall. **CCC.**
Published by: Verlag Eugen Ulmer GmbH, Wollgrasweg 41, Stuttgart, 70599, Germany. TEL 49-711-45070, FAX 49-711-4507120, info@ulmer.de, http://www.ulmer.de/cms/artikel.dll/gfw. Ed. Dr. Joachim Steinbacher. Adv. contact Annelie Purwing. B&W page EUR 992, color page EUR 2,042; trim 185 x 260. Circ: 7,648 (paid and controlled).

598 USA ISSN 0164-971X
QL671
THE GULL. Text in English. 1917. m. (10/yr.). USD 10 (effective 2005). bk.rev. 10 p./no. 3 cols./p.; back issues avail. **Document type:** *Newsletter, Consumer.* **Description:** Readership are members of the Golden Gate Audubon Society and are dedicated toprotecting and enhancing birds.
Related titles: Online - full content ed.
Published by: Golden Gate Audubon Society, 2530 San Pablo Ave, Ste G, Berkeley, CA 94702. TEL 510-843-2222, FAX 510-843-5351, ggas@goldengateaudubon.org, http://www.goldengateaudubon.org. Ed. Eva Guralnick. R&P Arthur Feinstein. Circ: 5,000 (paid and controlled).

598 GBR ISSN 0438-4903
HAMPSHIRE BIRD REPORT. Text in English. 195?. a.
Indexed: ZooRec.
—BLDSC (4241.525000).
Published by: Hampshire Ornithological Society, c/o Peter Dudley, Honorary Secretary, 3 Copsewood Rd, Hythe, Southampton, SO45 5DX, United Kingdom. TEL 44-2380-847149, http://www.hants.gov.uk/hos/.

598.944 USA CODEN: HMSTE8
HAWK MIGRATION STUDIES. Text in English. 1977. s-a. membership. bk.rev. back issues avail.
Formerly: Hawk Migration Association of North America. Newsletter
Indexed: SFA, WildRev, ZooRec.
Published by: Hawk Migration Association of North America (HMANA), c/o Jeffery Dodge, Ed, 432 Manitou Beach Rd, Hilton, NY 14468. TEL 716-392-5685.

598.07 USA ISSN 1534-9292
HAWK MOUNTAIN NEWS. Text in English. 1939. s-a. free to members (effective 2003). bk.rev. charts. **Description:** Reports on events at the Sanctuary, including studies on and conservation of birds of prey.
Formerly (until 1978): Newsletter. Hawk Mountain Sanctuary Association
Indexed: SFA, WildRev.
Published by: Hawk Mountain Sanctuary Association, 1700 Hawk Mountain Rd, Kempton, PA 19529. TEL 610-756-6961, FAX 610-756-4468, http://www.hawkmountain.org, http://www.hawkmountain.org. Ed. Nancy J Keeler. R&P Nancy Keeler. Circ: 10,000.

598 NLD ISSN 0042-7985 CODEN: VOGLEO
HET/VOGELJAAR. Text in Dutch; Abstracts occasionally in English, German. 1953. 6/yr. EUR 13.50 domestic; EUR 22.75 foreign (effective 2005). adv. bk.rev.; Website rev. abstr.; bibl.; charts; illus. cum.index. **Document type:** *Magazine.*
Related titles: Online - full content ed.
Indexed: ExcerpMed, RefZh, SFA, WildRev, ZooRec.
Published by: Stichting het Vogeljaar, c/o W A Werkman, Boterbloemstraat 20, 5321 RR, Netherlands. TEL 31-73-5991967, http://www.vogelgaar.nl/. Circ: 5,000.

598.65 POL ISSN 0239-9709
HODOWCA GOLEBI POCZTOWYCH. Text in Polish. 1927. m. EUR 37 foreign (effective 2005).
Published by: Polski Zwiazek Hodowcow Golebi Pocztowych, Zarzad Glowny w Chorzowie, Skr. pocztowa 62, Chorzow, 41501, Poland. TEL 48-32-2415984, zg@pzhgp.pl, http://www.pzhgp.pl. **Dist. by:** Ars Polona, Krakowskie Przedmiescie 7, Warsaw, Poland. TEL 48-22-9263914, FAX 48-22-9265334, arspolona@arspolona.com.pl, http://www.arspolona.com.pl.

598 BEL ISSN 0770-1365
L'HOMME ET L'OISEAU. Text in French. 1962. q.
Formerly (until 1975): Comite de Coordination pour la Protection des Oiseaux. Feuille de Contact Trimestrielle (0774-1162)
Related titles: Dutch ed.: Mens en Vogel. ISSN 0770-1314.
Indexed: RefZh, ZooRec.
Published by: Ligue Royale Belge pour la Protection des Oiseaux, 43-45 Rue de Veeweyde, Bruxelles, 1070, Belgium. TEL 32-2-5212850, FAX 32-2-5270989, info@protectiondesoiseaux.be, http://www.protectiondesoiseaux.be.

598 ZWE ISSN 0018-456X
HONEYGUIDE. Text in English. 1954. biennial. ZWD 300 to individuals worldwide; ZWD 300 domestic to institutions; USD 25 foreign to individuals; USD 30 foreign to institutional members (effective 2000). adv. bk.rev. abstr.; charts; illus. cum.index. **Document type:** *Academic/Scholarly.* **Description:** Covers all aspects of ornithology in Zimbabwe.
Indexed: WLR, ZooRec.
Published by: BirdLife Zimbabwe, PO Box CY 161, Causeway, Harare, Zimbabwe. TEL 263-4-882206, birds@zol.co.zw. Ed. M P S Irwin. Circ: 1,000.

598 HKG ISSN 1017-1118 CODEN: HKBRE5
HONG KONG BIRD REPORT. Text in Chinese. 1959. a. HKD 240.
Indexed: SFA, WildRev, ZooRec.
Published by: Hong Kong Bird Watching Society, GPO Box 12460, Hong Kong, Hong Kong. Ed. G J Carey. Circ: 1,000.

598 ARG ISSN 0073-3407
QL685.7 CODEN: HRNOAX
➤ **EL HORNERO**; Revista de Ornitologia Neotropical. Text in English, Spanish; Abstracts in Spanish, English. 1917. biennial, latest vol.16. USD 25 (effective 2005). adv. bk.rev. index. **Document type:** *Journal, Academic/Scholarly.* **Description:** Publishes original results of research on the biology of birds. Articles may be theoretical or empirical, with field or laboratory data, methodological developments, information or ideas about any ornithological area. The journal is oriented to, but not restricted by, neotropical birds. .
Indexed: BIOSIS Prev, BiolAb, SFA, WildRev, ZooRec.
Published by: Asociacion Ornitologica del Plata, 25 De Mayo, 749 2o 6, Capital Federal, Buenos Aires 1002, Argentina. TEL 54-114-31288958, FAX 54-114-3128958, hornero@bg.fcen.uba.ar, info@avesargentinas.org.ar, http://www.avesargentinas.org.ar. Ed., Adv. contact Javier Lopez de Casenave. Circ: 1,000.

598 GBR ISSN 1012-6201 CODEN: ICMOE6
I C B P MONOGRAPHS. (International Council for Bird Preservation) Text in English. 1988. irreg., latest 1989. back issues avail. **Document type:** *Monographic series.* **Description:** Provides information on biological diversity and conservation issues on a regional basis with particular relevance to birds.
Indexed: ZooRec.
Published by: BirdLife International, Wellbrook Ct, Girton Rd, Cambridge, CB3 ONA, United Kingdom. TEL 44-1223-277318, FAX 44-1223-277200, TELEX 818794 ICBP G.

598 USA
I C F BUGLE. Text in English. 1974. q. USD 25; USD 30 foreign (effective 1999). bk.rev. back issues avail. **Document type:** *Newsletter, Academic/Scholarly.* **Description:** Promotes the study and preservation of cranes through news of the foundation and current research and conservation programs.
Formerly: Brogla Bugle
Published by: International Crane Foundation, P O Box 447, Baraboo, WI 53913-0447. TEL 608-356-9462, FAX 608-356-9465, TELEX 297778 ICF UR. Ed., R&P Kate Fitzwilliams. Circ: 7,500.

598 GBR ISSN 0019-1019 CODEN: IBISAL
➤ **IBIS**; the international journal of avian science. Text in English. 1859. q. GBP 278 combined subscription in Europe to institutions print & online eds.; USD 514 combined subscription in the Americas to institutions & Caribbean (print & online eds.); GBP 306 combined subscription elsewhere to institutions print & online eds. (effective 2006). adv. bk.rev.; rec.rev. abstr.; bibl.; charts; illus. index. back issues avail.; reprints avail. **Document type:** *Journal, Academic/Scholarly.* **Description:** It is published by the British Ornithologists' Union, the senior ornithological learned society worldwide, provides original research reports on the systematics, ecology, physiology, behavior, and anatomy of birds.
Related titles: Online - full text ed.: ISSN 1474-919X. GBP 264 in Europe to institutions; USD 489 in the Americas to institutions & Caribbean; GBP 291 elsewhere to institutions (effective 2006) (from Blackwell Synergy, EBSCO Publishing, Gale Group, IngentaConnect, O C L C Online Computer Library Center, Inc., Swets Information Services).
Indexed: ASFA, AnBeAb, AnBrAb, ApEcolAb, B&AI, BIOBASE, BIOSIS Prev, BiolAb, CurCont, EPB, ESPM, EnvAb, ForAb, GEOBASE, HelmAb, HerbAb, I-WA, IABS, ISR, IndVet, KWIWR, OceAb, PoultAb, ProtozoAb, RevApplEntom, S&F, SCI, SFA, VetBull, WildRev, ZooRec.
—BLDSC (4360.000000), CISTI, IDS, IE, Infotrieve, ingenta, Linda Hall. **CCC.**
Published by: (British Ornithologists' Union), Blackwell Publishing Ltd., 9600 Garsington Rd, Oxford, OX4 2ZG, United Kingdom. TEL 44-1865-776868, FAX 44-1865-714591, customerservices@oxon.blackwellpublishing.com, http://www.blackwellpublishing.com/journals/IBI. Ed. Andrew G Gosler. Circ: 2,650.

598 JPN
IGURETTA/EGRETTA. Text in Japanese. 1986. s-a. free. **Document type:** *Newsletter.* **Description:** Covers natural conservation for insects and others.

B

▼ *new title* ➤ *refereed* ✶ *unverified* ♦ *full entry avail.*

Published by: Shirasagi Kinen Hakubutsukan/Shirasagi Memorial Museum, 172 Daiyama, Urawa-shi, Saitama-ken 337-0975, Japan. TEL 81-48-878-0500, FAX 81-48-878-3335. Ed. T Sunose. Circ: 800.

598 USA ISSN 0019-6525
QL671
INDIANA AUDUBON QUARTERLY. Text in English. 1950. q. USD 20 membership; USD 17 to libraries & foreign individuals (effective 2002); membership includes subscr. to Indiana Audubon Quarterly and Cardinal. bk.rev.; software rev. illus. index. 170 p./no. 1 cols./p.; **Document type:** *Bulletin, Academic/Scholarly.* **Description:** Features state Christmas count data, state May Day count data, winter feeder count data, official list of Indiana birds, seasonal field data for birds in the state, essays, etc.
Indexed: BiolAb, SFA, WildRev, ZooRec.
Published by: Indiana Audubon Society, Inc., 3499 S Bird Sanctuary Rd, Connersville, IN 47331 . TEL 765-825-9788, membership@indianaaudubon.org, http://www.indianaaudubon.org. Ed. Charles E Keller. Circ: 600. **Subscr. to:** 20451 Brick Road, South Bend, IN 46637-1418.

598 GBR
INTERBIRDNET ONLINE. Text in English. 1997. m.
Media: Online - full content.
Address: P O Box 1, Studley, Warks B80 7JG, United Kingdom. interbirdnet@dial.pipex.com, http://www.birder.co.uk, http://www.birder.co.uk/indexmain.htm.

598 USA ISSN 0074-7211
INTERNATIONAL ORNITHOLOGICAL CONGRESS. PROCEEDINGS. Text in German. quadrennial, latest vol.23, 2002. **Document type:** *Proceedings, Academic/Scholarly.*
Indexed: BiolAb, ChemAb, KWIWR, SFA, WildRev.
Published by: International Ornithological Congress/Congres Ornithologique International, c/o Prof Dominique Homberger, Louisiana State University, 202 Life Sciences Bldg, Baton Rouge, LA, W 70803-1715. TEL 225-578-1747, FAX 225-578-2597, info@i-o-c.org, http://www.i-o-c.org.

598.176 GBR ISSN 1354-9944
➤ **INTERNATIONAL WADER STUDIES.** Text in English. 1986. irreg., latest vol.9, 1997. GBP 15. **Document type:** *Monographic series, Academic/Scholarly.* **Description:** Publishes proceedings based on conferences, symposia and workshops, and major analyses of single topics in wader biology.
Indexed: ZooRec.
—BLDSC (4551.701500).
Published by: National Centre for Ornithology, Wader Study Group, The Nunnery, Thetford, Norfolk IP24 2PU, United Kingdom. Ed. David Stroud.

598 USA ISSN 0021-0455
CODEN: IOBLAM
IOWA BIRD LIFE. Text in English. 1931. q. USD 20 (effective 1999). bk.rev. charts; illus. cum.index every 5 yrs. **Document type:** *Academic/Scholarly.*
Indexed: BiolAb, SFA, WLR, WildRev, ZooRec.
Published by: Iowa Ornithologists' Union, 4024 Arkansas Dr, Ames, IA 50014. TEL 515-292-3152, oldcoot@iastate.edu. Ed. James J Dinsmore. Circ: 575 (paid).

598 JPN
IPPITSU KEIJO/WILD BIRD SOCIETY OF JAPAN. WAKAYAMA PREFECTURE BRANCH. SURVEY REPORT. Text in Japanese. 1980. q.
Published by: Nihon Yacho no Kai, Wakayamaken Shibu/Wild Bird Society of Japan, Wakayama Prefecture Branch, Kenritsu Hidaka Koko, 45 Shima, Gobo-shi, Wakayama-ken 644-0003, Japan.

598 IRL ISSN 0332-0111
QL690.I7 CODEN: IBIRDL
➤ **IRISH BIRDS.** Text in English. 1977. a., latest vol.7, no.2, 2003. price varies. adv. bk.rev. illus. back issues avail. **Document type:** *Academic/Scholarly.* **Description:** Covers all aspects of birds in Ireland.
Incorporates: Irish Bird Report (0444-5449)
Indexed: ASFA, BiolAb, ZooRec.
—BLDSC (4570.610000), IE, ingenta.
Published by: Birdwatch Ireland, Rockingham House, Newcastle, Co. Wicklow, Ireland. TEL 353-1-2819878, FAX 353-1-2819763, bird@indigo.ie, http://www.birdwatchireland.ie. Circ: 1,000.

➤ **THE ISLAND NATURALIST.** see *CONSERVATION*

➤ **J N C C REPORTS.** see *CONSERVATION*

598 USA ISSN 0021-3845
QL671 CODEN: JPWBAD
JACK-PINE WARBLER. Text in English. 1922. bi-m. USD 15 domestic; USD 20 foreign. adv. bk.rev. charts; illus. reprint service avail. from PQC. **Document type:** *Newsletter.* **Description:** Covers the ornithology and natural history of the Great Lakes region. Includes society news and activities and scientific bird surveys and articles.
Incorporates: Michigan Audubon (0731-9126); Which was formerly: Michigan Audubon Newsletter
Related titles: Microfilm ed.: (from PQC).
Indexed: BiolAb, MMI, SFA, WildRev, ZooRec.
—Linda Hall.
Published by: Michigan Audubon Society, 6011 W. St Joe Hwy., Ste. 403, Lansing, MI 48917-4853. MAS@MichiganAudubon.org, http://www.michiganaudubon.org/jpw/index.html, http://www.michiganaudubon.org/index.html. Ed. Bob Guiliani. Circ: 8,500.

598 JPN ISSN 0913-400X
QL691.J4 CODEN: JJOREH
JAPANESE JOURNAL OF ORNITHOLOGY. Text in English, Japanese. 1915. q. JPY 5,000 to members; JPY 6,000 to non-members (effective 1999). adv. bk.rev. charts; illus. **Document type:** *Academic/Scholarly.*
Formerly: Tori
Indexed: AnBrAb, BIOSIS Prev, BiolAb, FPA, ForAb, HelmAb, HerbAb, IndVet, JPI, PoultAb, S&F, SFA, SeedAb, WildRev, ZooRec.
Published by: Ornithological Society of Japan/Nihon Cho Gakkai, c/o Department of Zoology, National Science Museum, 3-23-1 Hiyakunin-cho, Shinjuku-ku, Tokyo, 169-0073, Japan. TEL 81-3-3364-2311. Ed. Dr. Hiroyuki Morioka. Circ: 900.

598 DNK ISSN 0908-8857
QL671 CODEN: JAVBE9
➤ **JOURNAL OF AVIAN BIOLOGY.** Text in English. 1970. bi-m. EUR 84 combined subscription in Europe to individuals print & online eds.; USD 93 combined subscription in the Americas to individuals print & online eds.; GBP 56 combined subscription elsewhere to individuals print & online eds.; USD 264 combined subscription in the Americas to institutions & Caribbean (print & online eds.); GBP 157 combined subscription elsewhere to institutions print & online eds. (effective 2006). bk.rev. bibl.; charts. index. back issues avail.; reprint service avail. from ISI. **Document type:** *Journal, Academic/Scholarly.*
Formerly (until 1994): Ornis Scandinavica (0030-5693)
Related titles: Online - full text ed.: ISSN 1600-048X. EUR 80 in Europe to individuals; USD 88 in the Americas to individuals & Caribbean; GBP 53 elsewhere to individuals; USD 251 in the Americas to institutions & Caribbean; GBP 149 elsewhere to institutions (effective 2006) (from Blackwell Synergy, EBSCO Publishing, Gale Group, IngentaConnect, O C L C Online Computer Library Center, Inc., Swets Information Services).
Indexed: ASCA, ASFA, AgBio, AgrForAb, AnBrAb, BIOBASE, BIOSIS Prev, BiolAb, BiolDig, CurCont, ForAb, GEOBASE, HelmAb, IABS, IBR, ISR, IndVet, KWIWR, PGegResA, PoultAb, ProtozoAb, RefZh, RevApplEntom, SCI, SFA, VetBull, WildRev, ZooRec.
—BLDSC (4949.950000), IDS, IE, Infotrieve, ingenta, Linda Hall. **CCC.**
Published by: (Scandinavian Ornithologists' Union), Blackwell Munksgaard (Subsidiary of: Blackwell Publishing Ltd.), Rosenoerns Alle 1, PO Box 227, Copenhagen V, 1502, Denmark. TEL 45-77-333333, FAX 45-77-333377, info@mks.blackwellpublishing.com, http://www.blackwellpublishing.com/journals/JAV, http://www.munksgaard.dk/. Ed. Thomas Alerstam. Circ: 750.

598 USA ISSN 1544-4953
QL673
THE JOURNAL OF CARIBBEAN ORNITHOLOGY. Text mainly in English; Text occasionally in Spanish, French. 1988. 3/yr. free to members (effective 2004).
Formerly (until 2004): Pitirre (1527-7151)
Published by: Society for the Conservation and Study of Caribbean Birds, P O Box 863208, Ridgewood, NY 11386. http://www.nmnh.si.edu/BIRDNET/SCSCB/index.html. Ed. Jerome A. Jackson.

598.07 USA ISSN 0273-8570
CODEN: JFORDM
➤ **JOURNAL OF FIELD ORNITHOLOGY.** Text in English. 1930. q. USD 45 in North America; USD 51 elsewhere (effective 2001). bk.rev. bibl.; illus. cum.index: 1951-1960. back issues avail.; reprint service avail. from PQC. **Document type:** *Academic/Scholarly.* **Description:** Publishes original and methodological papers dealing with the ecology, behavior, taxonomy, life history, and zoogeography of birds in their natural habitats.
Formerly: Bird-Banding (0006-3630)
Related titles: Microform ed.: (from PQC); Online - full text ed.: (from BioOne, C S A, O C L C Online Computer Library Center, Inc.).
Indexed: AEA, ASCA, ASFA, AgrForAb, AnBeAb, ApEcolAb, BIOSIS Prev, BiolAb, CurCont, ESPM, ForAb, HerbAb, HortAb, ISR, IndVet, KWIWR, OrnA, OrnithAb, PGegResA, PoultAb, RM&VM, RevApplEntom, S&F, SCI, SFA, SeedAb, VetBull, WeedAb, WildRev, ZooRec.
—BLDSC (4984.110000), IDS, IE, Infotrieve, ingenta, Linda Hall. **CCC.**
Published by: Association of Field Ornithologists, Inc., Dept of Biology, Georgia Southern University, Statesboro, GA 30460. TEL 608-363-2314, FAX 608-363-2052, orders@allenpress.com, osna@allenpress.com, http://www.afonet.org/english/journal.html. Ed. Charles R Brown. R&P Elissa Landre. Circ: 2,200. **Subscr. to:** Allen Press Inc., PO Box 1897, Lawrence, KS 66044.

598 DEU
QL671 CODEN: JORNAH
➤ **JOURNAL OF ORNITHOLOGY.** Text in German, English. 1853. q. EUR 328 combined subscription to institutions print & online eds. (effective 2005). bk.rev. charts; illus. index. **Document type:** *Journal, Academic/Scholarly.*
Formerly (until 2004): Journal fuer Ornithologie (0021-8375); Which incorporated (1851-1858): Naumannia (1435-3164)
Related titles: Microfiche ed.: (from IDC); Online - full text ed.: Journal of Ornithology (Online Edition) (from Blackwell Synergy, EBSCO Publishing, Gale Group, IngentaConnect, O C L C Online Computer Library Center, Inc., Springer LINK, Swets Information Services).
Indexed: ASCA, BIOSIS Prev, BiolAb, ChemAb, CurCont, DIP, FPA, ForAb, GEOBASE, IBR, ISR, IndVet, PGegResA, PoultAb, RefZh, RevApplEntom, S&F, SCI, SFA, TDB, VetBull, WildRev, ZooRec.
—BLDSC (5027.510000), CISTI, IE, Infotrieve, ingenta, Linda Hall. **CCC.**
Published by: (Deutsche Ornithologen-Gesellschaft e.V.), Springer-Verlag (Subsidiary of: Springer Science+Business Media), Tiergartenstr 17, Heidelberg, 69121, Germany. TEL 49-6221-3450, FAX 49-6221-345229, orders@springer.de, http://www.springer.de. Ed. Franz Bairlein. Adv. contact Stephan Kroeck TEL 49-30-827875739. Circ: 3,000. **Subscr. to:** Springer GmbH Auslieferungsgesellschaft, Haberstr 7, Heidelberg 69126, Germany. TEL 49-6221-345-0, FAX 49-6221-345-4229, subscriptions@springer.de; Springer-Verlag New York, Inc., Journal Fulfillment, PO Box 2485, Secaucus, NJ 07096-2485. TEL 800-777-4643, 201-348-4033, FAX 201-348-4505, journals@springer-ny.com.

598.9 USA ISSN 0892-1016
CODEN: JRREEF
➤ **JOURNAL OF RAPTOR RESEARCH.** Text in English. 1967. q. USD 50 domestic to institutions; USD 53 foreign to institutions; USD 33 domestic to individuals; USD 36 foreign to individuals (effective 2004). adv. bk.rev. illus. Index. back issues avail.; reprints avail. **Document type:** *Journal, Academic/Scholarly.* **Description:** It stimulates the dissemination of information concerning raptorial birds among interested persons worldwide and to promote a better public understanding and appreciation of the value of birds of prey.
Formerly (until vol.20, 1987): Raptor Research (0099-9059)
Indexed: ASCA, BIOSIS Prev, BiolAb, CurCont, EnvAb, ForAb, GEOBASE, HelmAb, HerbAb, ISR, IndVet, KWIWR, NutrAb, OrnA, PoultAb, ProtozoAb, RefZh, RevApplEntom, S&F, SCI, SFA, TDB, VetBull, WAE&RSA, WildRev, ZooRec.
—BLDSC (5046.500000), IDS, IE, ingenta. **CCC.**
Published by: Raptor Research Foundation, Inc., Allen Press Box 1897, 810 E 10th St, Lawrence, KS 66044-8897. TEL 785-843-1235, FAX 785-843-1274, osna@allenpress.com, http://www.biology.boisestate.edu/raptor/. Ed. James C Bednarz. Circ: 1,200 (paid).

598 USA ISSN 0022-8729
CODEN: KOSBBW
KANSAS ORNITHOLOGICAL SOCIETY. BULLETIN. Text in English. 1950. q. USD 15 (effective 2000). bk.rev.; rec.rev. charts; illus.; stat. **Document type:** *Bulletin.*
Indexed: BiolAb, SFA, WLR, WildRev, ZooRec.
—Linda Hall.
Published by: Kansas Ornithological Society, c/o Max C Thompson, Ed, Department of Biology, Southwestern College, 100 College St, Winfield, KS 67156-2499. TEL 316-221-8304, FAX 316-221-8382, maxt@jinx.sckans.edu. Ed. Max Thompson. Circ: 450.

598 USA ISSN 0160-5070
CODEN: KEWAA
KENTUCKY WARBLER. Text in English. 1925. q.
Indexed: SFA, WildRev, ZooRec.
Published by: Kentucky Ornithological Society, c/o Brainard Palmer Ball, Jr, 8207 Old, Westport, KY 40222-3913.

598 KEN ISSN 1023-3679
KENYA BIRDS. Text in English. 1992. s-a. USD 12 (effective 2001). **Document type:** *Journal, Academic/Scholarly.* **Description:** Includes news, articles, and reports on all aspects of birding in Kenya, including identification, records, and conservation.
Indexed: ZooRec.
Published by: East Africa Natural History Society, PO Box 44486, Nairobi, 00100, Kenya. TEL 254-2-749957, FAX 254-2-741049, eanhs@africaonline.co.ke, http://www.naturekenya.org. Ed. Leon Bennun TEL 254-2-749986. Circ: 300.

598 USA ISSN 0023-1606
QL671 CODEN: KNGBAW
KINGBIRD. Text in English. 1950. q. USD 25 domestic; USD 33 foreign (effective 2005). charts; illus. back issues avail. **Document type:** *Academic/Scholarly.* **Description:** Covers ornithology of New York State.
Indexed: BiolAb, SFA, WildRev, ZooRec.
Published by: Federation of New York State Bird Clubs, Inc., c/o Brenda Best, PO Box 95, Durhamville, NY 13054. TEL 315-363-2906, subscriptions@fnysbc.org, http://www.nybirds.org/Publications/kingbird.htm, http://www.fnysbc.org. Ed. Shaibal S Mitra. Circ: 1,000 (paid).

598 IDN
➤ **KUKILA**; bulletin of the Indonesian Ornithological Society. Text in English. 1985. a. IDR 20,000 domestic; USD 15 foreign (effective 2005). **Document type:** *Journal, Academic/Scholarly.*
Published by: P I L I - N G O Movement, c/o Adam A. Supriatna, P O Box 146, Bogor, 16001, Indonesia. kukila@pili.or.id, http://www.pili.or.id/kukila/notice.htm, http://www.pili.or.id/kukila/index.htm.

598 NAM ISSN 1023-8484
QL671 CODEN: LANIEC
LANIOTURDUS. Text in English, German. 1965. q. ZAR 50; USD 20 foreign (effective 1999 - 2000). adv. charts; illus.; maps. back issues avail. **Document type:** *Newsletter.* **Description:** Publishes broad-interest articles on bird watching in Namibia and birds in general. Reports scientific reserach to the general public.
Formerly (until 1984): Ornithologische Arbeitsgruppe Mitteilungen (0030-5731)
Indexed: SFA, WildRev, ZooRec.
Published by: Namibia Bird Club, PO Box 67, Windhoek, Namibia. TEL 264-61-225372, ch@aea.met.gov.na. Ed., Adv. contact Christopher Hines. B&W page NAD 200.

598 HRV ISSN 0350-5189
QL671 CODEN: LARSAO
➤ **LARUS.** Text in Croatian, English; Summaries in English. 1947. a. USD 10 (effective 1999 & 2000). bk.rev. **Document type:** *Bulletin, Academic/Scholarly.* **Description:** Publishes original scientific papers, review articles and short notes on all aspects of ornithology.
Indexed: BIOSIS Prev, BiolAb, SFA, WildRev, ZooRec.
Published by: Hrvatska Akademija Znanosti i Umjetnosti, Zavod za Ornitologiju/Croatian Academy of Arts and Sciences, Institute of Ornithology, Ilirski trg 9-2, Zagreb, 10000, Croatia. TEL 385-1-422190, FAX 385-1-422190. Ed. Zvonimir Devide.

598 DEU ISSN 0932-9153
CODEN: LIMIET
LIMICOLA; Zeitschrift fuer Feldornithologie. Text in German; Summaries in English. 1987. bi-m. adv. bk.rev. illus. index. back issues avail. **Document type:** *Academic/Scholarly.*
Indexed: KWIWR, RefZh, SFA, WildRev, ZooRec.
—Linda Hall.
Published by: Limicola Verlag, Ueber dem Salzgraben 11, Einbeck, 37574, Germany. TEL 05561-82224, FAX 05561-82289. Ed. Peter Barthel. Adv. contact Christine Barthel. Circ: 3,000.

598 NLD ISSN 0024-3620
CODEN: LIMOA9
➤ **LIMOSA.** Text in Dutch; Summaries in English. 1928. q. EUR 15.50 domestic to individuals; EUR 26 in Europe to individuals; EUR 29 elsewhere to individuals; EUR 31 domestic to institutions; EUR 44 in Europe to institutions; EUR 48 elsewhere to institutions (effective 2005). adv. bk.rev. charts; illus. index. back issues avail. **Document type:** *Academic/Scholarly.* **Description:** Publishes papers on field ornithology in the Netherlands.
Formerly: Club van Nederlandsche Vogelkundigen. Jaarbericht; Incorporates (1976-1981): Watervogels (0166-0357)
Indexed: BIOSIS Prev, BiolAb, GEOBASE, RefZh, SFA, WildRev, ZooRec.
—BLDSC (5220.000000), IE, Infotrieve, ingenta, Linda Hall.
Published by: Nederlandse Ornithologische Unie/Netherlands Ornithological Union, Burg Suijsstraat 65, Tilburg, 5037 MC, Netherlands. TEL 31-6-53548276, zwablo@tref.nl, http://home.plant.nl/~boude112/limosa/limosa.htm. Ed. Hans Schekkerman. Circ: 2,200. **Subscr. to:** Compagnonsweg 45-47, Ravenswoud 8427 RH, Netherlands.

598 USA ISSN 1059-521X
QL671 CODEN: LIBIE8
LIVING BIRD. Text in English. 1962. q. USD 35 to members (effective 2004). adv. bk.rev. illus. index. reprints avail. **Document type:** *Academic/Scholarly.* **Description:** Covers bird biology, behavior, conservation, art, travel, and reviews of bird equipment.
Former titles (until 1991): Living Bird Quarterly (0732-9210); (until 1982): Living Bird (0459-6137)
Related titles: Microform ed.: (from PQC).
Indexed: BiolAb, BiolDig, RefZh, SFA, WildRev, ZooRec.
—Linda Hall.
Published by: Cornell University, Laboratory of Ornithology, Attn: Communications, Cornell Lab of Ornithology, 159 Sapsucker Woods Rd, Ithaca, NY 14850. TEL 607-254-2473, 800-843-2473, livingbird@cornell.edu, http://birds.cornell.edu/Publications/livingbird/, http://www.birds.cornell.edu/. Ed. Tim Gallagher. Adv. contact Barbara Guttridge. B&W page USD 750, color page USD 1,000; 11 x 8.5. Circ: 22,000.

598 GBR ISSN 0141-4348
CODEN: LOBIBD
LONDON BIRD REPORT. Text in English. 1936. a. GBP 6 (effective 2001). back issues avail. **Document type:** *Bulletin.*
Indexed: SFA, WildRev, ZooRec.
Published by: London Natural History Society, 4 Falkland Ave, London, N3 1QR, United Kingdom. TEL 44-20-8346-4359, http://www.users.globalnet.co.uk/~lnhsweb. Eds. Andrew Self, Patricia Brown. Circ: 1,200.

598.07 CAN ISSN 0317-9575
LONG POINT BIRD OBSERVATORY NEWSLETTER. Text in English. 1969. 3/yr. CND 25 to members (effective 2000). bk.rev. **Document type:** *Newsletter.* **Description:** Focuses on bird-banding and monitoring techniques.
Indexed: SFA, WildRev.
Published by: (Long Point Bird Observatory), Bird Studies Canada, P O Box 160, Port Rowan, ON N0E 1M0, Canada. TEL 519-586-3531, FAX 519-586-3532, generalinfo@bsc-eoc.org, http://www.bsc-eoc.org. Ed., R&P Jon D McCracken. Circ: 1,500.

598 USA ISSN 0024-645X
CODEN: LOONAO
THE LOON. Text in English. 1929. q. USD 25 to individual members (effective 2005); USD 35 to libraries; USD 15 to students (effective 2001). bk.rev. charts; illus.; stat. index. back issues avail.; reprint service avail. from PQC,ISI. **Document type:** *Journal, Academic/Scholarly.* **Description:** Information on birds, with emphasis on birds in Minnesota.
Formerly (until 1964): Flicker (0199-9672)
Indexed: BiolAb, RefZh, SFA, WildRev, ZooRec.
—Linda Hall.
Published by: Minnesota Ornithologists' Union, James Ford Bell Museum of Natural History, University of Minnesota, 10 Church St, S E, Minneapolis, MN 55455-0104. TEL 612-459-4150, FAX 612-459-6621, mou@biosci.cbs.umn.edu, moumembers@juno.com, http://moumn.org. Ed. Anthony Hertzel TEL 763-780-7149. R&Ps Anthony Hertzel TEL 763-780-7149, R B Janssen. Circ: 1,400.

598 DEU ISSN 0024-7391
CODEN: LUSCAJ
LUSCINIA; vogelkundliche Zeitschrift fuer Hessen. Text in German. 1927. a. EUR 10 (effective 2005). adv. bk.rev. charts; illus.; maps; stat. cum.index. **Document type:** *Journal, Academic/Scholarly.*
Indexed: ApicAb, BiolAb, CPerI, KWIWR, SFA, WildRev, ZooRec.
Published by: Vogelkundliche Beobachtungsstation Untermain e.V., Postfach 640163, Frankfurt Am Main, 60355, Germany. TEL 49-69-724637, stwehr@vogelkunde-untermain.de, http://www.vogelkunde-untermain.de. Ed. Ulrich Eidam. Circ: 1,000.

598 USA
MAIL BAG. Text in English. 1943. q. membership. bk.rev. **Description:** News of club events, environmental matters, news of club members, correspondence, poetry, and news and items of general interest to members.
Formerly: B B C Mail Bag
Published by: Brooks Bird Club, Inc., PO Box 4077, Wheeling, WV 26003. TEL 740-635-9246. Ed. William Murray. Circ: 600.

598.176 ZAF ISSN 1018-3337
QL671 CODEN: MAOREL
➤ **MARINE ORNITHOLOGY.** Text in English. 1976. s-a. USD 60 (effective 1999). adv. bk.rev. bibl.; illus. back issues avail. **Document type:** *Academic/Scholarly.* **Description:** Presents contributions concerning international seabird science and conservation.
Formerly (until 1990): Cormorant (0250-0213)
Related titles: Online - full text ed.: free (effective 2005).
Indexed: ASFA, ApEcolAb, BIOSIS Prev, BiolAb, ESPM, GEOBASE, ISAP, OceAb, SFA, WLR, WildRev, ZooRec.
—Linda Hall.
Published by: African Seabird Group, PO Box 34113, Rhodes Gift, 7707, South Africa. TEL 27-21-650-3426, FAX 27-21-650-3434, jcooper@botzoo.uct.ac.za, http://www.marineornithology.org/. Ed. John Cooper. Circ: 400 (paid).

598 USA ISSN 0147-9725
CODEN: MBIREW
➤ **MARYLAND BIRDLIFE.** Text in English. 1945. q. USD 10 (effective 2000). bk.rev. charts; illus. cum.index every 5 yrs. **Document type:** *Academic/Scholarly.*
Indexed: SFA, WildRev, ZooRec.
Published by: Maryland Ornithological Society, Inc., Patuxent Wildlife Research, Laurel, MD 20708-4015. TEL 301-497-5641, FAX 301-497-5624, chan_robbins@usgs.gov. Ed., R&P Chandler S Robbins. Circ: 2,000 (controlled).

598 USA ISSN 1065-2043
QL684.I3
➤ **MEADOWLARK**; a journal of Illinois birds. Text in English. 1992. q. USD 20, CND 25 domestic; CND 30 foreign (effective 2000). adv. **Document type:** *Academic/Scholarly.* **Description:** Serves professional and amateur ornithologists interested in the avian fauna of Illinois.
Published by: Illinois Ornithological Society, PO Box 931, Lake Forest, IL 60045-0931. TEL 847-566-4846, http://www.chias.org.ios. Ed., R&P Sheryl Devore. Adv. contact Michael Hogg. Circ: 700 (paid).

598 SWE ISSN 0454-7217
MEDDELANDE FRAAN KVISMARE FAAGELSTATION. Text mainly in Swedish. 1963. a. price varies. back issues avail. **Document type:** *Monographic series.*
Related titles: ♦ Series: Faaglar i Kvismaren. ISSN 0283-2852.
Published by: Kvismare Faagelstation, Oerebro, 70595, Sweden. TEL 46-019-23 80 31.

598 MLT ISSN 1013-3933
CODEN: ILMEE5
➤ **IL-MERILL.** Text in English. 1970. irreg. MTL 3 (effective 2000). adv. **Document type:** *Academic/Scholarly.*
Indexed: SFA, WildRev, ZooRec.
Published by: BirdLife Malta, Marina Ct 57, Flat 28, Abate Rigord St, Ta' Xbiex, MSD 12, Malta. TEL 356-347646, FAX 356-343239, blm@orbit.net.mt, http://www.waldonet.net.mt/birdlife. Ed. Mark A Falzon. Adv. contact Joe Sultana. Circ: 500 (controlled).

598 USA ISSN 0026-3575
CODEN: MGNTAQ
MIGRANT; a quarterly journal devoted to Tennessee birds. Text in English. 1930. q. USD 15. bk.rev. charts; illus. index. back issues avail. **Document type:** *Academic/Scholarly.* **Description:** Includes articles on Tennessee birds intended for the members of the Tennessee Ornithological Society, covering habitat requirements, behavior, breeding biology, migration, records of rare sightings, count reports, and organizational news.
Indexed: BiolAb, SFA, WildRev, ZooRec.
Published by: Tennessee Ornithological Society, c/o Chris Sloan, 512 Old Hickory Blvd, Apt 1203, Nashville, TN 37209. TEL 615-353-0811, jdjoslin@esper.com. Ed. J Devereux Joslin Jr. R&P J D Joslin. Circ: 950 (paid); 50 (controlled). **Subscr. to:** c/o David J. Trently, 1029 Morrow Rd, Knoxville, TN 37923-1725. TEL 423-531-1473.

598 ITA
MIGRAZIONE E CACCIA. Text in Italian. 1959. bi-m. EUR 13 (effective 2005). adv. bk.rev. bibl. **Document type:** *Magazine, Consumer.*
Former titles (until 1979): Uccellagione e Piccola Caccia; (until 1963): Bollettino dell'Uccellatore
Published by: Associazione Nazionale Uccellatori e Uccellinai (ANUU), Associazione dei Migratoristi Italiani per la Conservazione dell'Ambiente Naturale, Via Evaristo Baschenis, 11 C, Bergamo, BG 24122, Italy. TEL 39-035-243825, FAX 39-035-236925, anuu@galactica.it, http://www.edolimpia.it/lev_1/caccia/migrazione/migrazione.htm. Ed. Pier Luigi Chierici. Circ: 65,000.

598 USA
MINNESOTA BIRDING. Text in English. bi-m. USD 20 (effective 2000). index. **Document type:** *Newsletter.*
Indexed: WildRev.
Published by: Minnesota Ornithologists' Union, James Ford Bell Museum of Natural History, University of Minnesota, 10 Church St, S E, Minneapolis, MN 55455-0104. TEL 612-459-4150, FAX 651-459-6621, mou@biosci.cbs.umn.edu, moumembers@juno.com, http://moumn.org. Ed. Jim Williams.

598 USA ISSN 0737-0393
➤ **MISSISSIPPI KITE.** Text in English. 1965. irreg. USD 15 (effective 2000). bk.rev. **Document type:** *Academic/Scholarly.* **Description:** Presents articles and other information about wild birds in Mississippi.
Indexed: SFA, WildRev.
Published by: Mississippi Ornithological Society, c/o Mississippi Museum of Natural Science, 2148 Riverside Dr, Jackson, MS 39302. TEL 601-354-7303, picus@ra.msstate.edu. Ed. Dr. Mark S Woodrey. Circ: 200. **Subscr. to:** Jan Dubuisson, 22410 Glad Acres, Pass Christian, MS 39571.

598 AUT ISSN 1018-6190
CODEN: MONTEI
MONTICOLA. Text in German. 1966. 2/yr. EUR 15 (effective 2005). **Document type:** *Journal, Academic/Scholarly.*
Indexed: SFA, WildRev, ZooRec.
Published by: Internationale Arbeitsgemeinschaft fuer Alpenornithologie, c/o Dr. Franz Niederwolfsgruber, Pontlatzer Strasse 49, Innsbruck, 6020, Austria. TEL 43-512-262363, FAX 43-512-262376.

598 DEU ISSN 0947-1065
MUSEUM HEINEANUM. ORNITHOLOGISCHE JAHRESBERICHTE. Text in German; Summaries in English. 1976. a. EUR 7.50 (effective 2003). adv. bk.rev. 140 p./no. 1 cols./p.; back issues avail. **Document type:** *Journal, Academic/Scholarly.*
Indexed: ZooRec.
Published by: Museum Heineanum, Domplatz 37, Halberstadt, 38820, Germany. TEL 49-3941-551460, FAX 49-3941-551469, heineanum-hbs@t-online.de, http://www.heineanum.de. Ed., Pub. Bernd Nicolai. adv.: page EUR 200; trim 110 x 150. Circ: 420 (paid); 180 (controlled).

598 BEL ISSN 1780-3756
CODEN: AVESAJ
▼ **NATAGORA.** Text in French; Summaries in Dutch, English, German. 2004. bi-m. EUR 20 (effective 2005). bk.rev. abstr.; charts; illus. index. back issues avail. **Document type:** *Bulletin, Academic/Scholarly.* **Description:** Publishes scientific articles in the field of ornithology, including population evolution, breeding, feeding, behavior, and migration.

B

Formed by the merger of (1979-2004): Reserves Naturelles (0772-9472); Which was formerly (1974-1979): Reserves Naturelles et Ornithologiques de Belgique. Feuille de Contact (0773-0225); (1996-2004): Aves Contact (1371-631X); Which was formerly (until 1996): Societe d'Etudes Ornithologiques "Aves". Feuille de Contact (0772-9561); (1963- 1973): La Societe d'Etudes Ornithologiques "Aves". Feuille de Contact (0772-957X)
Indexed: BIOSIS Prev, BiolAb, KWIWR, RefZh, SFA, WildRev, ZooRec.
Published by: (Reserves Naturelles et Ornithologiques de Belgique, Societe d'Etudes Ornithologiques Aves), Natagora, Rue du Wisconsin 3, Namur, B-5000, Belgium. TEL 32-81-830570, FAX 32-81-830571, info@natagora.be, http://www.natagora.be/index.php?option=com_content&task=view&id=28. Circ: 2,800 (paid).

598 SWE ISSN 0282-390X
NATURHISTORISKA RIKSMUSEET. RINGMAERKNINGSCENTRALEN. REPORT OF SWEDISH BIRD RINGING. Text in English. 1964. a. SEK 80.
Formerly (until 1984): Swedish Museum of Natural History. Report of the Bird Ringing Office (0280-2457)
Indexed: ZooRec.
Published by: Naturhistoriska Riksmuseet/Swedish Museum of Natural History, PO Box 50007, Stockholm, 10405, Sweden. TEL 46-8—51954000, FAX 46-8-51954085, myndigheten @nrm.se, http://www.nrm.se.

598 DEU ISSN 0949-9512
NAUMANN - MUSEUM. BEITRAEGE ZUR GEFIEDERKUNDE UND MORPHOLOGIE DER VOEGEL. Text in German; Summaries in Russian, English. 1993. a. bk.rev. bibl.; illus.; maps. back issues avail. **Document type:** *Bulletin.*
Description: Provides information on the morphology, taxonomy, feather determination, moulting behavior.
Published by: Naumann - Museum, Schlossplatz 4, Koethen, 06366, Germany. TEL 49-3496-212074, FAX 49-3496-212074. Ed. Wolf Dieter Busching.

598 DEU ISSN 0233-0415
NAUMANN - MUSEUM. BLAETTER. Text in German; Summaries in Russian, English. 1980. a. bk.rev. bibl.; illus.; maps. back issues avail. **Document type:** *Bulletin, Academic/Scholarly.*
Description: Includes biographies, histories of ornithology, listings of museum collections and reviews.
Related titles: Diskette ed.; Online - full text ed.
Published by: Naumann - Museum, Schlossplatz 4, Koethen, 06366, Germany. TEL 49-3496-212074, FAX 49-3496-212074.

598 USA ISSN 0028-1816
CODEN: NBBRA4
THE NEBRASKA BIRD REVIEW; a magazine of the ornithology of the Nebraska region. Text in English. 1932. q. USD 12.50; USD 15 in Canada & Mexico; USD 17.50 elsewhere (effective 2000). bk.rev. charts; illus.; stat. **Document type:** *Academic/Scholarly.*
Indexed: BiolAb, SFA, WildRev, ZooRec.
—Linda Hall.
Published by: Nebraska Ornithologists' Union, Inc., Peru State College, Dept of English, Peru, NE 68421. TEL 402-872-2233, clemente@bobcat.peru.edu. Ed., R&P Bill Clemente. Circ: 294 (paid).

NEMOURIA; occasional Papers of the Delaware Museum of Natural History. see *BIOLOGY—Zoology*

NEW HAMPSHIRE AUDUBON. see *CONSERVATION*

598 USA
NEW HAMPSHIRE BIRD RECORDS. Text in English. 1982. q. USD 15 to non-members; USD 10 to members (effective 2000). **Document type:** *Bulletin.* **Description:** Describes bird sightings in New Hampshire.
Published by: Audubon Society of New Hampshire, 3 Silk Farm Rd, Box 528 B, Concord, NH 03301. TEL 603-224-9909, FAX 603-226-0902, http://www.nhaudubon.org. Ed. Becky Suomala. Circ: 300.

598 IND ISSN 0028-9426
NEWSLETTER FOR BIRDWATCHERS. Text in English. 1960. bi-m. INR 60 domestic to individual members; USD 25 foreign to individual members; USD 30 to corporations; USD 10 to students (effective 2000). adv. bk.rev. index. **Document type:** *Newsletter.*
Media: Duplicated (not offset).
Indexed: ZooRec.
Published by: (Birdwatchers Field Club of India), Navbharath Enterprises, No.10 Sirur Park "B" St., Sheshadripuram, Bangalore, Karnataka 560 020, India. TEL 91-80-364142, navbaratblr@vsnl.net.in. Ed. Zafar Futehally. Pub. S Sridhar. Circ: 800.

598 JPN ISSN 0914-4307
NIHON CHORUI HYOSHIKI KYOKAISHI/JAPANESE BIRD BANDING ASSOCIATION. BULLETIN. Text in Japanese; Summaries in English. 1986. 3/yr.
Published by: Nihon Chorui Hyoshiki Kyokai/Japanese Bird Banding Association, Yamashina chorui Kenkyujo, Kono-Yama, Abiko-shi, Chiba-ken 270-1145, Japan.

598.07 USA ISSN 0363-8979
QL677.5 CODEN: NABBDK
NORTH AMERICAN BIRD BANDER. Text in English. 1976. q. USD 15 membership (effective 2003). adv. bk.rev. charts; illus.; abstr.; maps; stat. Index. 52 p./no. 2 cols./p.; back issues avail.; reprints avail. **Document type:** *Journal, Academic/Scholarly.* **Description:** Presents research results which involve banding as a tool.
Incorporates (in 1986): Inland Bird Banding Newsletter; Formed by the 1976 merger of: Western Bird Bander; (until vol.39); E B B A News (0012-7485)
Related titles: Microform ed.: (from PQC).
Indexed: BiolAb, RefZh, SFA, WildRev, ZooRec.
—Linda Hall.
Address: 35 Logan Hill Rd, Candor, NY 13743. TEL 607-659-7366, FAX 607-659-7112, bpbird@pronetisp.net, rjpl@cornell.edu. Ed., R&P Robert Pantle. Adv. contact Roy Slack TEL 315-598-4326. Circ: 2,000. **Co-publishers:** Inland Bird Banding Association; Eastern Bird Banding Association; Western Bird Banding Association.

598 USA ISSN 1525-3708
QL671
NORTH AMERICAN BIRDS; a quarterly journal of ornithological record. Text in English. 1947. q. USD 32 domestic to non-members; USD 37 foreign to non-members; USD 30 domestic to members; USD 35 foreign to members; USD 60 domestic to libraries; USD 70 foreign to libraries (effective 2005). adv. bk.rev. illus.; maps. index. back issues avail.; reprints avail. **Document type:** *Journal, Consumer.*
Description: Provides a complete overview of the changing panorama of North America's birdlife, including outstanding records, range extensions and contractions, population dynamics, and changes in migration patterns or seasonal occurrence.
Former titles (until 1999): National Audubon Society Field Notes (1078-5477); (until 1994): American Birds (0004-7686); (until 1971): Audubon Field Notes (0097-7144)
Related titles: Microform ed.: (from PQC); Online - full text ed.: (from ProQuest Information & Learning).
Indexed: B&AI, BiolAb, BiolDig, KWIWR, SFA, WildRev, ZooRec.
—CISTI, Linda Hall.
Published by: American Birding Association, PO Box 6599, Colorado Springs, CO 80934. TEL 719-578-9703, 800-850-2473, FAX 719-578-1480, http://www.americanbirding.org/pubs/nab/index.html. Ed. Edward S Brinkley. Circ: 6,000. **Co-sponsor:** National Audubon Societ.

598.418 USA ISSN 1094-6144
NORTH AMERICAN SWANS; bulletin of the Trumpeter Swan Society. Text in English. 1969. s-a. membership. back issues avail. **Document type:** *Newsletter.*
Formerly (until June 1997): Trumpeter Swan Society Newsletter (0742-2792)
Indexed: SFA, WildRev.
Published by: Trumpeter Swan Society, 3800 County Rd 24, Maple Plain, MN 55359. TEL 763-476-4663, FAX 763-476-1514, ttss@hennepinparks.org, http://www.taiga.net/swans/index.html. Ed. Madeleine Linck. Circ: 500.

598 GBR ISSN 1363-4844
➤ **NORTHAMPTONSHIRE BIRD REPORT.** Text in English. 1970. a. GBP 5; GBP 5.50 newsstand/cover. charts; illus.; maps; stat. back issues avail. **Document type:** *Journal, Academic/Scholarly.* **Description:** Reports on birds recorded within the County of Northamptonshire each year including ringed (banded) birds, in a systematic and summative list.
Indexed: ZooRec.
Published by: Private Northamptonshire Bird Report Committee, 81 Cavendish Dr, Northampton, Northants NN3 3HL, United Kingdom. TEL 44-01604-627262. Ed. Robert Bullock.

598 CHE ISSN 0029-3725
CODEN: NOOIAV
➤ **NOS OISEAUX.** Text in French; Summaries in English. 1913. a. CHF 40 domestic; CHF 45 foreign (effective 2000). adv. bk.rev. abstr.; charts; illus. index. back issues avail. **Document type:** *Academic/Scholarly.*
Indexed: BiolAb, KWIWR, RefZh, SFA, WildRev, ZooRec.
Published by: Societe Romande pour l'Etude et la Protection des Oiseaux, c/o Musee d'histoire naturelle, La Chaux-de-Fonds, 2300, Switzerland. TEL 41-32-9133976, FAX 41-32-9133976, b.posse@vtx.ch, mhnc@ne.ch. Ed., R&P Bertrand Posse TEL 41-27-7231722. Circ: 2,700. **Subscr. to:** C.C.P. 20-117-8, Neuchatel, Switzerland.

598 POL ISSN 0550-0842
CODEN: NOORAO
➤ **NOTATKI ORNITOLOGICZNE/ORNITHOLOGICAL PAPERS.** Text in Polish; Summaries in English. 1960. q. price on request. adv. bk.rev. **Document type:** *Journal, Academic/Scholarly.* **Description:** Publishes scientific papers, original research reports from all fields of ornithology.
Indexed: AgrLib, BiolAb, RefZh, SFA, WildRev, ZooRec.
Published by: Polskie Towarzystwo Zoologiczne, ul Sienkiewicza 21, Wroclaw, 50335, Poland. TEL 48-71-3225041. Ed. Tadeusz Stawarczyk. R&P Jaroslaw Bogucki. Circ: 15,000.
Dist. by: Ars Polona, Krakowskie Przedmiescie 7, Warsaw, Poland. TEL 48-22-9263914, FAX 48-22-9265334, arspolona@arspolona.com.pl, http://www.arspolona.com.pl.

598 NZL ISSN 0029-4470
QL671 CODEN: NTNSAN
➤ **NOTORNIS.** Text in English. 1939. q. NZD 50 domestic to members; NZD 95, USD 45 foreign to members; NZD 100 domestic to institutions; NZD 180, USD 85 foreign to institutions (effective 2002). bk.rev. index. 64 p./no.; **Document type:** *Journal, Academic/Scholarly.* **Description:** Publishes scientific articles and short notes on birds, with emphasis on New Zealand, the Pacific and the subantarctic areas.
Formerly (until Jul. 1950): New Zealand Bird Notes
Related titles: ♦ Supplement(s): O S N Z News. ISSN 0111-2686.
Indexed: BIOSIS Prev, BiolAb, GEOBASE, SFA, SPPI, WildRev, ZooRec.
—BLDSC (6174.900000), IE, ingenta. **CCC.**
Published by: Ornithological Society of New Zealand Inc., PO Box 12-397, Wellington, New Zealand. TEL 64-6-3546540, FAX 64-3-3493455, piopio@paradise.net.nz, http://www.osnz.org.nz. Ed. G L Lovei. Circ: 1,300.

598 FRA ISSN 1279-6158
NOUV'AILES; journal des adherents au Centre Ornithologique Rhone-Alpes - section Isere. Text in French. 1990. m. bk.rev. bibl. back issues avail. **Document type:** *Bulletin.* **Description:** Features local bird news, news about local bird associations, as well as French and world news.
Indexed: ZooRec.
Published by: Centre Ornithologique Rhone-Alpes (C O R A), Maison Rhodanienne de l'Environnement, 32 Rue Sainte Helene, Lyon, 69002, France. TEL 33-4-72771984, FAX 33-4-72771983, cora@worldnet.fr. Pub. Zaira Harizi.

598 CAN
NOVA SCOTIA BIRDS. Text in English. 1959. 3/yr. CND 15 to individuals; CND 25 to institutions. bk.rev. illus. **Document type:** *Academic/Scholarly.*
Formerly: Nova Scotia Bird Society. Newsletter (0383-9567)
Indexed: SFA, WildRev, ZooRec.
Published by: Nova Scotia Bird Society, c/o Nova Scotia Museum, 1747 Summer St, Halifax, NS B3H 3A6, Canada. TEL 902-429-4610, FAX 902-477-6036. Ed. J Shirley Cohrs. Circ: 750.

598 USA
NUTTALL ORNITHOLOGICAL CLUB. MEMOIRS. Text in English. 1886. irreg., latest vol.12, 1995. price varies. **Document type:** *Monographic series.*
Indexed: ZooRec.
Published by: Nuttall Ornithological Club, c/o Museum of Comparative Zoology, Harvard University, Cambridge, MA 02138. TEL 617-495-2471. Adv. contact William E Davis Jr.

598 USA ISSN 0550-4082
CODEN: NUOPAQ
➤ **NUTTALL ORNITHOLOGICAL CLUB. PUBLICATIONS.** Text in English. 1957. irreg., latest vol.27, 1998. price varies. adv. bibl.; charts; illus.; stat. back issues avail. **Document type:** *Monographic series, Academic/Scholarly.* **Description:** Contains scholarly monographs on ornithological topics from all areas of the world.
Indexed: ZooRec.
—BLDSC (7099.400000).
Published by: Nuttall Ornithological Club, c/o Museum of Comparative Zoology, Harvard University, Cambridge, MA 02138. TEL 617-495-2471. Ed., R&P, Adv. contact Raymond A Paynter Jr. Circ: 1,000.

598 NZL ISSN 0111-2686
O S N Z NEWS. (Ornithological Society of New Zealand) Text in English. 1977. q. adv. bk.rev.; rec.rev.; software rev. **Document type:** *Newsletter.*
Related titles: ♦ Supplement to: Notornis. ISSN 0029-4470.
Indexed: SFA, WildRev.
—BLDSC (6301.435000).
Published by: Ornithological Society of New Zealand Inc., PO Box 12-397, Wellington, New Zealand. TEL 64-6-3546540, FAX 64-3-3493455, piopio@paradise.net.nz, http://www.osnz.org.nz. Ed. Tony Crocker. adv.: page NZD 150.

598 USA ISSN 0474-0750
CODEN: OOSBA7
OKLAHOMA ORNITHOLOGICAL SOCIETY. BULLETIN. Text in English. 1968. q. USD 10 membership; USD 5 to students (effective 2005). illus. **Document type:** *Journal, Academic/Scholarly.*
Indexed: BiolAb, SFA, WLR, WildRev, ZooRec.
Published by: Oklahoma Ornithological Society, PO Box 2931, Claremore, OK 74017. info@okbirds.org, http://www.okbirds.org. Eds. Bryan Coppedge, David Leslie, Jeff Kelly. Circ: 500.

598.07234713 CAN ISSN 0822-3890
CODEN: ONBIE8
➤ **ONTARIO BIRDS.** Text in English. 1983. 3/yr. CND 25 domestic membership; USD 25 in United States membership; USD 35 elsewhere to members (effective 2005). adv. bk.rev. 2 cols./p.; back issues avail. **Document type:** *Journal, Academic/Scholarly.* **Description:** Includes documentation of the status, distribution, identification and behavior of bird's of Ontario.

Indexed: BIOSIS Prev, BiolAb, RefZh, ZooRec.
Published by: Ontario Field Ornithologists, PO Box 455, Sta R, Toronto, ON M4G 4E1, Canada. TEL 416-445-9297, ofo@ofo.ca, http://www.ofo.ca. Eds. Mr. Bill Crins, Mr. Ron Pittaway, Mr. Ron Tozer. R&P Mr. Ron Tozer. Adv. contact Mr. Chester Gryski TEL 416-652-0362. Circ: 1,000.

598 NLD ISSN 0030-3224
SF461.A1
ONZE VOGELS. Text in Dutch. 1939. m. EUR 24 domestic; EUR 26 in Belgium; EUR 58.50 in Europe (effective 2005). adv. bk.rev. charts; illus. index. **Document type:** *Bulletin.*
Description: Information for birdlovers - keeping and breeding with birds.
Published by: Nederlandse Bond van Vogelliefhebbers, Postbus 74, Bergen op Zoom, 2600 AB, Netherlands. TEL 31-164-235007, FAX 31-164-239020, onzevogels@hetnet.nl, info@nbvv.nl, http://www.nbvv.nl. Ed. Gea Stoop. Adv. contact Piet E Deley. Circ: 39,000 (controlled).

ORIEL STRINGER; books for the field ornithologist. see *PUBLISHING AND BOOK TRADE*

598 GBR ISSN 0268-9634
ORIENTAL BIRD CLUB. BULLETIN. Text in English. 1985. s-a.
Indexed: ZooRec.
Published by: Oriental Bird Club, PO Box 324, Bedford, MK42 0WG, United Kingdom. http://www.orientalbirdclub.org.

598.874 USA ISSN 0030-5553
QL671 CODEN: OROLA4
THE ORIOLE. Text in English. 1936. q. USD 12 to libraries; USD 16 foreign to libraries (effective 1999). bk.rev. charts; illus. cum.index every 5 yrs.
Indexed: BIOSIS Prev, BiolAb, SFA, WildRev, ZooRec.
Published by: Georgia Ornithological Society, 181, High Shoals, GA 30645-0181. TEL 912-681-5487, http://www.gos.org. Eds. John Parrish, Ray Chandler. R&P Ray Chandler John Parrish. Circ: 450.

598 CHE ISSN 1018-0370
ORNIS. Text in German. 1931. bi-m. CHF 40 domestic; CHF 50 foreign; CHF 9 newsstand/cover (effective 2004). adv. bk.rev. abstr.; charts; illus.; stat. index. **Document type:** *Magazine, Academic/Scholarly.*
Formerly: Voegel der Heimat (0042-7950)
Indexed: BiolAb, KWIWR, RefZh, ZooRec.
Published by: (Schweizer Vogelschutz SVS - BirdLife Schweiz), Zollikofer AG, Fuerstenlandstr 122, Postfach 2362, St. Gallen, 9001, Switzerland. TEL 41-71-2727370, FAX 41-71-2727586, leserservice@zollikofer.ch, http://www.birdlife.ch, http://www.zollikofer.ch. Circ: 4,500.

598 FIN ISSN 0030-5685
QL671 CODEN: ORFEA6
➤ **ORNIS FENNICA.** Text in English; Summaries in Finnish, Swedish. 1924. q. EUR 25 domestic; EUR 26 in Nordic countries; EUR 44 elsewhere (effective 2005). adv. bk.rev. abstr.; bibl.; charts; illus. index. back issues avail. **Document type:** *Journal, Academic/Scholarly.* **Description:** Publishes descriptive, analytical and experimental papers on the ecology, behavior, and biogeography of birds, with geographical emphasis on Fennoscandia.
Indexed: ASCA, ASFA, AnBeAb, ApEcolAb, BIOSIS Prev, BiolAb, ChemAb, CurCont, ESPM, ForAb, GEOBASE, IBR, ISR, IndVet, KWIWR, PoultAb, ProtozoAb, RA&MP, RefZh, S&F, SCI, SFA, WLR, WildRev, ZooRec.
—BLDSC (6292.000000), IDS, IE, ingenta.
Published by: BirdLife Suomi, Kaeyntiosoite Annankatu 29 A, PO Box 1285, Helsinki, 00101, Finland. TEL 358-9-41353300, FAX 358-9-41353322, http://www.birdlife.fi/julkaisut/of/of-english.shtml. Ed. Jon Brommer.

598 HUN ISSN 1215-1610
QL671
➤ **ORNIS HUNGARICA.** Text in Hungarian. 1991. s-a. HUF 500 (effective 1999). adv. bk.rev. **Document type:** *Academic/Scholarly.* **Description:** Publishes research reports and short articles on the ecology, behaviour and biogeography of birds.
Indexed: ZooRec.
Published by: Birdlife Hungary, Kolto utca 21, Budapest, 1121, Hungary. moskat@zoo.zoo.nhmus.hu. Ed. Csaba Moskat.

➤ **ORNIS JUNIOR.** see *CHILDREN AND YOUTH—For*

598.2 NOR ISSN 1502-0878
QL690.N8 CODEN: FNSCD9
ORNIS NORVEGICA. Text in English. 1978. s-a. NOK 150 to non-members; NOK 160 to members (effective 2002). adv. bk.rev. cum.index. back issues avail. **Document type:** *Academic/Scholarly.* **Description:** Publishes original research dealing with the Norwegian fauna.
Former titles (until 1999): Fauna Norvegica Series C. Norwegian Journal of Ornithology (0332-7701); (until 1978): Cinclus (0332-6012)
Indexed: ASFA, AnBeAb, ApEcolAb, BIOSIS Prev, BiolAb, ESPM, GEOBASE, IBR, SFA, WildRev, ZooRec.
—BLDSC (6292.150000), CISTI, IE, ingenta. **CCC.**
Published by: Norsk Ornitologisk Forening, Sandgata 30 B, Trondheim, 7012, Norway. TEL 47-73-526040, FAX 47-73-524090, kjetil.bevanger@nina.nina.no, http://folk.uio.no/csteel/nof, nof@birdlife.no. Circ: 700.

598.2 SWE ISSN 1102-6812
➤ **ORNIS SVECICA.** Text in Multiple languages. 1991. q. SEK 240 domestic; SEK 290 foreign (effective 2003). bk.rev. back issues avail. **Document type:** *Journal, Academic/Scholarly.*
Indexed: ASFA, ApEcolAb, BIOSIS Prev, BiolAb, ESPM, GEOBASE, RefZh, ZooRec.
—BLDSC (6292.500000).
Published by: Sveriges Ornitologiska Foerening/Swedish Ornithological Society, Ekhagsvaegen 3, Stockholm, 10405, Sweden. TEL 46-8-6122530, FAX 46-8-6122536, info@sofnet.org, http://www.sofnet.org. Ed. Soeren Svensson TEL 46-46-2223821. Circ: 1,400.

598 USA ISSN 0078-6594
QL671 CODEN: ORMNBZ
ORNITHOLOGICAL MONOGRAPHS. Text in English. 1964. irreg. **Document type:** *Monographic series, Academic/Scholarly.*
Indexed: OrnA, OrnithAb, SFA, WildRev, ZooRec.
—**CCC.**
Published by: (Smithsonian Institution, National Museum of Natural History), American Ornithologists' Union, c/o Frederick Sheldon, Museum of Natural History, Louisiana State University, 119 Foster Hall,, Baton Rouge, LA 70803. TEL 504-388-2855. Ed. John Hagen. Circ: 500.

598 USA ISSN 0274-564X
ORNITHOLOGICAL NEWSLETTER. Text in English. 1976. bi-m. free domestic to members. bk.rev. **Document type:** *Newsletter, Consumer.* **Description:** Publishes society news and activities, reports of governmental actions concerning birds, announcements and other items of interest to members.
Related titles: Online - full text ed.
Published by: Ornithological Societies of North America, 3889 E Valleyview, Berrien Springs, MI 49103. TEL 269-471-7886, http://www.birds.cornell.edu/osna/ornnewsl.htm. Ed. Dr. Cheryl Trine. Circ: 4,600 (paid and controlled).

598 CHE ISSN 0030-5707
CODEN: ORBEAK
➤ **DER ORNITHOLOGISCHE BEOBACHTER.** Text in German; Summaries in English. 1902. 4/yr. CHF 60 domestic to members; CHF 65 foreign to members; CHF 65 domestic to non-members; CHF 70 foreign to non-members (effective 2003). adv. bk.rev. bibl.; charts; illus. index. 2 cols./p.; back issues avail. **Document type:** *Journal, Academic/Scholarly.*
Indexed: BiolAb, GEOBASE, IBR, KWIWR, SFA, WildRev, ZooRec.
—BLDSC (6293.170000), IE, ingenta.
Published by: Ala - Schweizerische Gesellschaft fuer Vogelkunde und Vogelschutz, Sempach Stadt, 6204, Switzerland. TEL 41-41-4629700, FAX 41-41-4629710, info@vogelwarte.ch, http://www.vogelwarte.ch. Eds. Dr. Christian Marti, Peter Knaus. Adv. contact Dr. Christian Marti. page CHF 580; 131 x 187. Circ: 1,500.

598 CHE ISSN 1420-5599
➤ **DER ORNITHOLOGISCHE BEOBACHTER. BEIHEFT.** Text in German; Summaries in English. 1970. irreg., latest vol.10, 1999. bibl.; illus. back issues avail. **Document type:** *Monographic series, Academic/Scholarly.*
Indexed: ZooRec.
Published by: Ala - Schweizerische Gesellschaft fuer Vogelkunde und Vogelschutz, Sempach Stadt, 6204, Switzerland. TEL 41-41-4629700, FAX 41-41-4629710, info@vogelwarte.ch, http://www.vogelwarte.ch. Ed. Dr. Christian Marti. Circ: 4,000 (controlled).

598 DEU ISSN 0030-5723
QL671 CODEN: ORMIAJ
➤ **ORNITHOLOGISCHE MITTEILUNGEN**; Monatsschrift fuer Vogelbeobachtung und Feldornithologie. Text in German. 1948. m. EUR 40.20 domestic; EUR 56 foreign (effective 2003). adv. bk.rev. bibl.; charts; illus. index. 32 p./no.; back issues avail. **Document type:** *Journal, Academic/Scholarly.*
Indexed: BiolAb, RefZh, ZooRec.
—Linda Hall.
Address: An der Ronne 184, Cologne, 50859, Germany. TEL 49-2234-70584, FAX 49-2234-79154. Ed., Pub., R&P, Adv. contact Walther Thiede. B&W page EUR 358. Circ: 1,200.

598 DEU ISSN 1438-3748
➤ **ORNITHOLOGISCHER JAHRESBERICHT HELGOLAND.** Text in German. 1991. a. EUR 10 (effective 2005). bk.rev. bibl.; illus. back issues avail. **Document type:** *Journal, Academic/Scholarly.* **Description:** Contains reports and studies on birds in the Helgoland region.
Published by: Ornithologischer Arbeitsgemeinschaft Helgoland, Postfach 869, Helgoland, 27490, Germany. TEL 49-4725-1338, FAX 49-4725-1338, oag@oag-helgoland.de, http://www.oag-helgoland.de. Circ: 1,500 (paid).

598 DEU ISSN 0949-7412
ORNITHOLOGISCHER VEREIN ZU HILDESHEIM. NATURKUNDLICHE MITTEILUNGEN. Text in German. 1977. s-a. bk.rev. **Document type:** *Newsletter, Consumer.*
Formerly (until 1995): Ornithologischer Verein zu Hildesheim. Mitteilungen (0179-5813)
Indexed: ZooRec.
Published by: Ornithologischer Verein zu Hildesheim e.V., Willi-Plappert-Str 5, Alfeld, 31061, Germany. TEL 49-5181-3218. Ed. Heinrich Hofmeister. Circ: 400.

598 FRA ISSN 1254-2962
ORNITHOS; revue d'ornithologie de terrain. Text in French. 1994. bi-m. **Document type:** *Magazine, Consumer.*
Published by: Ligue pour la Protection des Oiseaux, La Corderie Royale, BP 263, Rochefort, 17305 Cedex, France. TEL 33-5-46821234, FAX 33-5-46839586, http://www.lpo.fr.

598 USA ISSN 1075-4377
QL680
ORNITOLOGIA NEOTROPICAL. Text in Multiple languages. 1990. s-a. USD 42 elsewhere; USD 30 in Latin America; USD 75 to libraries; USD 18 to students (effective 2005).
Indexed: BIOSIS Prev, BiolAb, CurCont, ZooRec.
—BLDSC (6293.270000).
Published by: Neotropical Ornithological Society, c/o Bette A. Loiselle, International Center for Tropical Ecology, University of Missouri - St. Louis, St. Louis, MO 63121. http://www.neotropicalornithology.org. Ed. Raymond McNeil.

598.524 ZAF ISSN 0030-6525
QL671 CODEN: OSTHAO
➤ **OSTRICH**; journal of african ornithology. Text in English; Abstracts occasionally in Afrikaans. 1930. q. ZAR 342 domestic to individuals Includes Africa Birds & Birding; ZAR 380 in Africa to individuals Includes Africa Birds & Birding; USD 145 elsewhere to individuals Includes Africa Birds & Birding; ZAR 625 domestic to institutions Includes Africa Birds & Birding; ZAR 520 in Africa to institutions Includes Africa Birds & Birding; USD 325 elsewhere to institutions Includes Africa Birds & Birding (effective 2004). bk.rev. abstr. index. back issues avail. **Document type:** *Journal, Academic/Scholarly.* **Description:** Publishes papers in the general field of ornithology in sub-Saharan Africa and its islands.
Related titles: Online - full text ed.: ISSN 1727-947X. 2003 (from EBSCO Publishing, Gale Group, IngentaConnect, International Network for the Availability of Scientific Publications, African Journals Online).
Indexed: AnBeAb, BiolAb, CurCont, ForAb, HerbAb, ISAP, KWIWR, PGegResA, PoultAb, ProtozoAb, S&F, SFA, WBA, WLR, WMB, WildRev, ZooRec.
—IDS, Linda Hall.
Published by: (Birdlife South Africa), National Inquiry Services Centre (Pty) Ltd (Subsidiary of: N I S C USA), PO Box 377, Grahamstown, 6140, South Africa. TEL 27-46-622-9698, FAX 27-46-622-9550, info@nisc.co.za, http://www.nisc.co.za/journals?id=6. Ed. Richard Dean. Circ: 1,500.

598.524 598.2 USA ISSN 1067-7712
OSTRICH NEWS. Text in English. 1987. m. USD 48. **Document type:** *Trade.*
Published by: Ostrich News, Inc., PO Box 213, Cache, OK 73527-0213. http://www.ostrichnews.com. Ed. Melodye Crawford.

598.524 USA ISSN 1068-5774
SF511
OSTRICH NEWS RATITE DIRECTORY. Text in English. 1987. a. adv. illus.
Former titles (until 1992): National Ostrich - Ratite Directory (1050-981X); National Ostrich - Exotics Directory (1050-9801)
Published by: Ostrich News, Inc., PO Box 213, Cache, OK 73527-0213.

598 GBR ISSN 1363-3201
OXFORD ORNITHOLOGY SERIES. Text in English. 1991. irreg., latest vol.13, 2002. price varies. illus. **Document type:** *Monographic series, Academic/Scholarly.*
Indexed: BIOSIS Prev, ZooRec.
—BLDSC (6321.008650), IE, ingenta.
Published by: Oxford University Press, Great Clarendon St, Oxford, OX2 6DP, United Kingdom. TEL 44-1865-556767, FAX 44-1865-556646, enquiry@oup.co.uk, http://www.oup-usa.org/catalogs/general/series/Oxford_Ornithology_Series.html, http://www.oup.co.uk/. Ed. C M Perrins.

598.6 GBR
➤ **P Q F NEWS.** (Partridge, Quail and Francolin Specialist Group) Text in English. 1993. s-a. GBP 5, USD 8 (effective 2000). bk.rev. illus.; maps; stat. back issues avail. **Document type:** *Bulletin, Academic/Scholarly.* **Description:** Research and conservation of quail, partridges, francolins, snowcocks, and guineafowl.
Related titles: Online - full text ed.
Published by: International Union for Conservation of Nature and Natural Resources, Partridge, Quail and Francolin Specialist Group, Lower Basildon, World Pheasant Association,, PO Box 5, Redding, Berks RG8 9PF, United Kingdom. TEL 44-118-984-5140, FAX 44-118-984-3369, wpa@gn.apc.org. Ed. P. North. R&P Nicola Chalmers-Watson. Circ: 200.

B

▼ new title ➤ refereed ✶ unverified ♦ full entry avail.

598.177 USA ISSN 1089-6317
QL683.P37
PACIFIC SEABIRDS; a publication of the Pacific Seabird Group . Text in English. 1974. 2/yr. USD 25 domestic to individuals; USD 30 foreign to individuals (effective 2005). adv. bk.rev. illus. reprints avail. **Document type:** *Bulletin.* **Description:** Covers issues pertaining to seabird management.
Formerly: Pacific Seabird Group Bulletin (0740-3771)
Indexed: SFA, WildRev, ZooRec.
—Linda Hall.
Published by: Pacific Seabird Group, 4505 University Way, N E, Box 179, Seattle, WA 98105. sspeich@azstarnet.com, http://www.pacificseabirdgroup.org/pubs.html. Ed., R&P Steven Speich. Circ: 400. **Subscr. to:** P S G, 4505 University Way, N.E., Treas., Oregon Institute of Marine Biology, Charleston, OR 94970. TEL 541-888-2581, FAX 541-888-3250.

PAPAGEIEN. see *PETS*

598.65 USA ISSN 0031-2703
QL671 CODEN: PPGNAZ
PASSENGER PIGEON; a magazine of Wisconsin bird study. Text in English. 1939. q. USD 30 (effective 2005). adv. bk.rev.; rec.rev. charts; illus. cum.index. back issues avail. **Document type:** *Journal, Academic/Scholarly.*
Indexed: BiolAb, KWIWR, RefZh, SFA, WildRev, ZooRec.
Published by: Wisconsin Society for Ornithology, 2022 Sherryl Ln, Waukesha, WI 53188-3142. TEL 262-547-6128, dcreel@execpc.com, http://www.uwgb.edu/birds/wso. Ed., Adv. contact Tod Highsmith TEL 608-242-1168. Pub. Christine Reel. R&Ps Christine Reel, Tod Highsmith TEL 608-242-1168. Circ: 1,380 (paid).

598 IND ISSN 0031-3297
QL671 CODEN: PAVOA8
PAVO; the Indian journal of ornithology. Text in English. 1963. s-a. INR 95; USD 25 foreign. adv. bk.rev. charts; illus. index. **Document type:** *Academic/Scholarly.*
Indexed: ASFA, BIOSIS Prev, BiolAb, ChemAb, IBR, NutrAb, ZooRec.
—CASDDS.
Published by: Society of Animal Morphologists & Physiologists, c/o Maharaja Sayajirao University of Baroda, Dept. of Zoology, Faculty of Science, Baroda, Gujarat 390 002, India. Ed. Bonny Pilo. Circ: 200.

598.47 USA
CODEN: SPNWEW
PENGUIN CONSERVATION. Text in English. 1988. 3/yr. USD 15. adv. bk.rev.; software rev. charts; illus.; maps; stat. back issues avail. **Document type:** *Academic/Scholarly.* **Description:** Publishes material dealing with the management, conservation, behavior and biology of penguins in captivity and in the wild.
Formerly: Spheniscus Penguin Newsletter (1045-0076)
Indexed: SFA, WildRev, ZooRec.
—BLDSC (6419.755250).
Published by: Conservation Publications, Inc., 8060 Upper Applegate Rd, Jacksonville, OR 97530-9314. TEL 541-899-1114, FAX 541-899-1131, editor@faunapub.org, http://www.faunapub.org. Ed., R&P, Adv. contact Cynthia Cheney. Circ: 600.

PHOENIX (SOMERSHAM). see *BIOLOGY*

598 FRA ISSN 0999-4637
➤ **LE PISTRAC**; bulletin de l' A R O M P. Text in French. 1979. a. EUR 12 domestic; EUR 15 foreign (effective 2003). back issues avail. **Document type:** *Magazine, Academic/Scholarly.* **Description:** Features birds of Southwestern France.
Indexed: ZooRec.
Published by: Association Regionale Ornithologique du Midi et des Pyrenees, Museum d'Histoire Naturelle, 35, allees Jules-Guesde, Toulouse, 31000, France.

598.65 GBR
RACING PIGEON PICTORIAL INTERNATIONAL. Text in English. 1970. m. GBP 22; GBP 27 foreign. adv. bk.rev. **Document type:** *Bulletin.*
Formerly: Racing Pigeon Pictorial (0033-7404)
Published by: Racing Pigeon Publishing Co. Ltd., 13 Guilford St, London, WC1N 1DX, United Kingdom. TEL 44-171-831-4050, FAX 44-171-831-3766. Ed., Adv. contact Rick Osman. R&P Rick Osmun. Circ: 9,800.

598 JPN
RAICHO CHOSA HOKOKUSHO/RESEARCH REPORT ON PTARMIGAN. Text in Japanese. a.
Published by: Toyama Raicho Kenkyukai/Toyama Ptarmigan Association, Toyama Prefectural Government, 1-7 Shinsokawa, Toyama-shi, 930-0006, Japan.

598.9 USA ISSN 1048-8030
THE RAPTOR REPORT. Text in English. 1973-1990; resumed 1993. a. bk.rev. illus.; stat. **Document type:** *Newsletter.*
Supersedes: California Condor
Published by: Society for the Preservation of Birds of Prey, c/o J Richard Hilton, Ed, Box 66070, Mar Vista Station, Los Angeles, CA 90066. TEL 310-840-2322. Circ: 800.

598 USA ISSN 0034-0146
CODEN: RAVNAR
THE RAVEN (LYNCHBURG). Text in English. 1930. s-a. USD 15 (effective 2000). bk.rev. bibl.; charts; stat. index. **Document type:** *Academic/Scholarly.* **Description:** Features articles about Virginia birdlife.
Indexed: ZooRec.
Published by: Virginia Society of Ornithology, Inc, c/o Thelma Dalmas, 1230 Viewmont Dr, Evington, VA 24550-2006. Ed. C Michael Stinson. Circ: 700.

598 USA
RECORDS OF NEW JERSEY BIRDS. Text in English. q. included with New Jersey Audubon. **Document type:** *Magazine, Consumer.* **Description:** Lists bird sightings in New Jersey, plus reports on wildlife research.
Formerly (until 1978): N J Audubon. Supplement
Related titles: ♦ Supplement to: N J Audubon. ISSN 0886-6619.
Indexed: SFA, WildRev, ZooRec.
Published by: New Jersey Audubon Society, 9 Hardscrabble Rd, PO Box 126, Bernardsville, NJ 07924-0126. hq@njaudubon.org. Ed. Richard Kane.

598 ESP ISSN 1697-4697
➤ **REVISTA CATALANA D'ORNITOLOGIA.** Text in Catalan, English, Spanish; Summaries in English. 1981. a. free to members. back issues avail. **Document type:** *Bulletin, Academic/Scholarly.* **Description:** Publishes original research articles on any subject of ornithology including matters related to bird management or conservation.
Formerly (until 2004): Grup Catala d'Anellament. Butlleti (1130-2070)
Indexed: ZooRec.
—CINDOC.
Published by: Institut Catala d'Ornitologia, Museu de Zoologia, Passeig Picasso s/n, Barcelona, 08003, Spain. TEL 34-93-3194279, FAX 34-93-3104999, ico@ornitologia.org, http://www.ornitologia.org. Ed. Joan Carles Senar.

598 POL ISSN 0035-5429
QL671 CODEN: RINGBN
➤ **THE RING**; ringing - migration - monitoring. Text in English. 1954. s-a. USD 20 foreign (effective 2003). adv. bk.rev. charts; illus. 200 p./no. 1 cols./p.; back issues avail. **Document type:** *Journal, Academic/Scholarly.* **Description:** Deals with bird migration, bird ringing and monitoring bird numbers.
Indexed: AgrAg, KWIWR, SFA, WildRev, ZooRec.
—BLDSC (7971.490000), Linda Hall.
Published by: Polish Zoological Society, Przebendowo, Choczewo, 84210, Poland. TEL 48-58-5722396, FAX 48-58-6763265, ring@univ.gda.pl, http://www.univ.gda.pl. Ed., R&P, Adv. contact Przemyslaw Busse. Circ: 500 (paid and controlled).

598 GBR ISSN 0307-8698
QL671 CODEN: RIMIDQ
➤ **RINGING AND MIGRATION.** Text in English. 1975. s-a. GBP 13.50 to individuals; GBP 27 to institutions; GBP 9 to members (effective 2005). bk.rev. **Document type:** *Newsletter, Academic/Scholarly.* **Description:** Serves as the journal of the Trust's Ringing Scheme and incorporates the Trusts's annual report on bird ringing in Britain and Ireland. Welcomes papers on all aspects of bird ringing and migration studies. Main purpose is to encourage amateur ringers to analyse and write up the results of their work.
Indexed: ASFA, AnBeAb, BIOSIS Prev, BiolAb, GEOBASE, SFA, WildRev, ZooRec.
—BLDSC (7971.492000), IE, ingenta, Linda Hall.
Published by: British Trust for Ornithology, The Nunnery, Nunnery Pl, Thetford, Norfolk IP24 2PU, United Kingdom. TEL 44-1842-750050, FAX 44-1842-750030, btostaff@bto.org, general@bto.org, http://www.bto.org/ringing/ringinfo/ringing-journal.htm. Ed. Ian Hartley. Circ: 2,000; 2,000 (paid).

598.07 NOR ISSN 0803-3927
RINGMERKAREN. Text in Multiple languages. 1989. a. NOK 150 (effective 2002).
Published by: Norsk Ornitologisk Forening, Sandgata 30 B, Trondheim, 7012, Norway. TEL 47-73-526040, FAX 47-73-524090, http://folk.uio.no/csteel/nof, nof@birdlife.no. Eds. A Folvik, Morten Stokke.

598 ITA ISSN 0035-6875
QL690.I8 CODEN: RIORAQ
RIVISTA ITALIANA DI ORNITOLOGIA. Text in Italian. 1909. s-a. adv. bk.rev. illus. index. back issues avail. **Document type:** *Journal, Academic/Scholarly.*
Indexed: BiolAb, IBR, RefZh, SFA, WildRev, ZooRec.
—BLDSC (7987.450000), IE, ingenta.
Published by: Societa Italiana di Scienze Naturali, Corso Venezia 55, Milan, MI 20121, Italy. TEL 39-02-795965, FAX 39-02-795965, http://www.scienzenaturali.org. Ed., Adv. contact Cesare Conci. Circ: 1,000.

598.65 BEL ISSN 0778-2152
ROYALE FEDERATION COLOMBOPHILE BELGE. BULLETIN NATIONAL. Text in French. 1956. bi-m. **Document type:** *Bulletin.*
Formerly: Royale Federation Colombophile Belge. Bulletin Federal (0035-9319)
Related titles: Dutch ed.: Koninklijke Belgische Duivenliefhebbersbond. Bondsblad. ISSN 0778-2144. 1956.
Published by: Royale Federation Colombophile Belge/Koninklijke Belgische Duivenliefhebbersbond, Rue de Livourne 39, Brussels, 1050, Belgium. FAX 32-2-538-5721, nationale@rfcb.be, http://www.kbdb.be. Ed. Marcel Van Den Driessche.

598 DNK ISSN 0108-9315
SANDEVIFTEN. Text in Danish. 1983. q. membership. adv. bk.rev. illus.
Formerly: Fugleiagttagelser i Ringkoebing Amt
Published by: Dansk Ornithologisk Forening i Ringkoebing Amt, Vesterbrogade 140, Copenhagen V, 1620, Denmark. Circ: 300.

598 GBR ISSN 0260-4736
QL676.57.M628 CODEN: SANDE6
➤ **SANDGROUSE.** Text in English. 1980. s-a. GBP 15 domestic to individuals; GBP 20 elsewhere to individuals; GBP 30 to institutions & libraries (effective 2003). adv. bk.rev. abstr.; illus. 80 p./no.; back issues avail. **Document type:** *Journal, Academic/Scholarly.* **Description:** Covers all aspects of ornithology in the Middle East and surrounding areas.
Formerly: Turkish Bird Report
Indexed: RefZh, SFA, WLR, WildRev, ZooRec.
—BLDSC (8072.955500), IE, ingenta.
Published by: Ornithological Society of the Middle East, c/o The Lodge, Sandy, Beds SG19 2DL, United Kingdom. TEL 44-1636-703512, http://www.osme.org. Ed. Guy Kirwan. Adv. contact Andrew Grieve TEL 44-1493-377549. B&W page GBP 100, color page GBP 200. Circ: 1,000.

598 USA
SANDPIPER. Text in English. 1968. 8/yr. USD 15. 4 p./no. 3 cols./p.; **Document type:** *Newsletter.* **Description:** Describes current programs and conservation issues of relevance to the Redwood Region Audubon Society, Eureka CA.
Related titles: Microfilm ed.: (from LIB); ♦ Supplement to: Econews. ISSN 0885-7237.
Published by: Redwood Region Audubon Society, PO Box 1054, Eureka, CA 95501. TEL 707-443-7147, http://www.northcoast.com/rras. Eds. Hal Genger, Ron Le Valley. R&P Hal Genger. Circ: 3,000.

CAN ISSN 0080-6552
SASKATCHEWAN NATURAL HISTORY SOCIETY. SPECIAL PUBLICATIONS. Text in English. 1958. irreg. price varies. bibl.; charts; illus.; maps. back issues avail. **Document type:** *Magazine, Academic/Scholarly.*
Indexed: WLR, ZooRec.
Published by: Nature Saskatchewan, 1860 Lorne St, Rm 206, Regina, SK S4P 2L7, Canada. TEL 306-780-9273, FAX 306-780-9263, bookshop@naturesask.com. Ed. Mary Gilliland.

598 USA ISSN 0582-2637
CODEN: SCSSEM
SCISSORTAIL. Text in English. 1951. q. USD 15 (effective 2003). **Document type:** *Newsletter.*
Indexed: SFA, WildRev, ZooRec.
Published by: Oklahoma Ornithological Society, PO Box 2931, Claremore, OK 74017. oosscissortail@aol.com, info@okbirds.org, http://www.okbirds.org. Ed. Richard A Stuart. Circ: 500.

598 KEN ISSN 0250-4162
QL692.E16
➤ **SCOPUS.** Text in English. 1977. 3/yr. KES 10, USD 16. bk.rev. **Document type:** *Journal, Academic/Scholarly.* **Description:** Publishes original contributions on all aspects of the ornithology of Eastern Africa, from the Sudan to Mozambique.
Indexed: PLESA, ZooRec.
Published by: East Africa Natural History Society, PO Box 44486, Nairobi, 00100, Kenya. TEL 254-2-749957, FAX 254-2-741049, eanhs@africaonline.co.ke, office@naturekenya.org. Ed. Leon Bennun TEL 254-2-749986. R&P Catherine Ngarachu. Circ: 265 (paid).

598 GBR ISSN 0268-3199
SCOTTISH BIRD NEWS. Text in English. 1986. q. adv. **Document type:** *Newsletter.*
Indexed: ZooRec.
—BLDSC (8206.340000).
Published by: Scottish Ornithologists Club, 21 Regent Terr, Edinburgh, EH7 5BT, United Kingdom. TEL 44-131-556-6042, FAX 44-131-558-9947. Ed. Stan Da Prato. Adv. contact Sylvia Laing.

598 GBR ISSN 0036-9144
QL690.S4 CODEN: SCTBB7
➤ **SCOTTISH BIRDS.** Text in English. 1958. s-a. GBP 36. adv. bk.rev. charts; illus. cum.index every 2 yrs. **Document type:** *Academic/Scholarly.*
Indexed: BIOSIS Prev, BiolAb, KWIWR, RefZh, SFA, WLR, WildRev, ZooRec.
—BLDSC (8206.400000), IE, ingenta.
Published by: Scottish Ornithologists Club, 21 Regent Terr, Edinburgh, EH7 5BT, United Kingdom. TEL 44-131-556-6042, FAX 44-131-558-9947. Ed. Stan Da Prato. Adv. contact Sylvia Lang. Circ: 3,000.

598 DEU ISSN 0722-2947
QL671
SEEVOEGEL. Text in English, German. 1980. q. adv. bk.rev.
Document type: *Journal, Academic/Scholarly.*
Indexed: ASFA, ESPM, KWIWR, RefZh, ZooRec.
Published by: Verein Jorsand zum Schutze der Seevoegel und der Natur e.V., c/o Uwe Schneider, Haus der Natur Wulfsdorf, Ahrensburg, 22926, Germany. TEL 49-4102-32656, FAX 49-4102-31983, info@jorsand.de, http://www.jorsand.de. Ed. Nicolaus Peters. Adv. contact Uwe Schneider. Circ: 6,000.

598 ESP
SOCIEDAD ESPANOLA DE ORNITOLOGIA. MONOGRAFIAS. Text in Spanish. 1988. irreg. price varies. **Document type:** *Monographic series, Academic/Scholarly.*
Indexed: SFA, WildRev.
Published by: Sociedad Espanola de Ornitologia, C/ Melquiades Biencinto 34, Madrid, 28053, Spain. TEL 34-91-4340910, FAX 34-91-4340911, http://www.seo.org/ardeola. Ed. Juan Varela.

598 551.46 FRA ISSN 0373-9929
Q46 CODEN: ASNCAT
➤ **SOCIETE DES SCIENCES NATURELLES DE LA CHARENTE-MARITIME.** Text in French; Summaries in English. 1852. a. back issues avail. **Document type:** *Bulletin, Academic/Scholarly.* **Description:** Explores mainly the fauna and flora of Western France, including those from the coast of the Gulf of Gascony.
Indexed: ESPM, ZooRec.
Address: Museum d'Histoire Naturelle, 28, rue Albert 1er, La Rochelle, 17000, France. TEL 33-5-46411825, FAX 33-5-46506365. Pub. R Duguy.

598 GBR ISSN 0081-2048
SOMERSET BIRDS. Text in English. 1924. a. GBP 3.
Published by: Somerset Ornithological Society, Barnfield, Tower Hill Rd, Crewkerne, Somers, United Kingdom. Ed. D K Ballance. Circ: 500.

598.8 JPN
SONGU POSUTO/SONG POST. Text in Japanese. 1983. bi-m. JPY 3,500 to members (effective 2000). **Document type:** *Bulletin.* **Description:** Contains bird walk schedules, bird watching spot guide, research reports and other bird related information.
Published by: Nihon Yacho no Kai, Kyoto Shibu/Wild Bird Society of Japan, Kyoto Chapter, 21-4 Tokiwaoikechou, Ukyo-ku, Kyoto, 616-8211, Japan. Ed. Tetsuo Sawashima. Circ: 1,500.

598 USA ISSN 0038-3252
CODEN: SDBNAR
SOUTH DAKOTA BIRD NOTES. Text in English. 1949. q. USD 12 to non-members (effective 2000). adv. bk.rev. charts; illus. cum.index every 5 yrs. **Document type:** *Academic/Scholarly.*
Indexed: BiolAb, SFA, WLR, WildRev, ZooRec.
Published by: South Dakota Ornithologists' Union, Northern State University, Mathematics and Sciences, 1200 S Jay St, Aberdeen, SD 57401-7198. TEL 605-626-2456, FAX 605-626-3022, tallmand@wolf.northern.edu. Ed. Dan Tallman. Circ: 400.

598 NZL
SOUTHERN BIRD. Text in English. 2000. q. NZD 50 domestic to individual members; USD 45 foreign to individual members; NZD 80 domestic to institutional members; USD 80 foreign to institutional members (effective 2002). bk.rev. **Document type:** *Magazine, Academic/Scholarly.* **Description:** Provides a forum for members to report back on trips, society schemes, interesting bird sightings and to advertise coming trips, meetings and events.
Published by: Ornithological Society of New Zealand Inc., PO Box 12-397, Wellington, New Zealand. TEL 64-6-3546540, FAX 64-3-3493455, piopio@paradise.net.nz, http://www.osnz.org.nz. Ed. Tony Crocker. Circ: 980.

598 ZAF ISSN 1018-7634
CODEN: SOBIDO
SOUTHERN BIRDS. Text in English. 1975. irreg. price varies. adv. bk.rev. abstr.; bibl. back issues avail.
Indexed: BiolAb, ISAP, SFA, WildRev, ZooRec.
Published by: Witwatersrand Bird Club, 239 Barkston Dr, Blairgowrie, Blairgowrie, Randburg 2122, South Africa. FAX 27-11-7877694, http://www.birdlife.org.za. Ed. Carl J Vernon. Circ: 600.

598.9 DNK ISSN 0109-274X
STIGSNAES; rapport. Text in Danish. 1981. a. DKK 30. illus.
Published by: Dansk Ornithologisk Forening i Vestsjaellands, Stigsnaes Fuglestation/Stignaes Bird Observatory, Lille Valmosevej 1, Herlufmagle, 4160, Denmark. Ed. Bent Moeller Soerensen.

598 AUS ISSN 0726-1888
THE STILT; the bulletin of the East Asian - Australasian flyway. Text in English. 1981. s-a. AUD 25; AUD 30 foreign (effective 1999). bk.rev. charts; illus.; maps; stat. cum.index every 2 yrs. back issues avail. **Document type:** *Bulletin, Academic/Scholarly.* **Description:** Deals with the biology and conservation of shorebirds with a principal focus on the East Asian - Australasian flyway.
Indexed: ZooRec.
Published by: Australasian Wader Studies Group, Birds Australia, 415 Riversdale Rd, Hawthorn East, VIC 3123, Australia. TEL 61-3-9882-2622, FAX 61-3-9882-2677, http://www.tasweb.com.au/awsg/stilt/stilt-00.htm. Ed. Dr. David Milton. Circ: 500.

598 JPN ISSN 0910-6901
➤ **STRIX/NIHON YACHO NO KAI KENKYU HOKOKU;** a journal of field ornithology. Text in Japanese; Summaries in English, Japanese. 1982. a. **Document type:** *Journal, Academic/Scholarly.*
Indexed: ZooRec.
—BLDSC (8474.167000).
Published by: Nihon Yacho no Kai/Wild Bird Society of Japan, 1-47-1 Hatsudai, Shibuya-ku, Tokyo, 151-0061, Japan. TEL 81-3-5358-3510, 81-3-5358-3513, FAX 81-3-5358-3608, hensyu@wbsj.org. Ed. M Veta.

598 USA ISSN 0197-9922
UNC
➤ **STUDIES IN AVIAN BIOLOGY.** Text in English. 1900. irreg., latest vol.24. price varies. abstr.; bibl.; charts; illus.; maps. 100 p./no. 2 cols./p.; back issues avail. **Document type:** *Monographic series, Academic/Scholarly.* **Description:** Monographic studies in various aspects of avian biology.
Supersedes (1900-1974): Pacific Coast Avifauna (0161-2913)
Indexed: BIOBASE, EPB, OrnA, OrnithAb, RefZh, SFA, WildRev, ZooRec.
—BLDSC (8489.580000), IE, ingenta, Linda Hall.
Published by: Cooper Ornithological Society, Inc. (Riverside), c/o John Fisher, Western Foundation of Vertebrate Zoology, 439 Calle San Pablo, Camarillo, CA 93012-8506. TEL 805-388-9944, FAX 805-388-8663, http://www.cooper.org. Ed., R&P John T Rotenberry. Circ: 1,000 (controlled).

598 AUS ISSN 1037-258X
CODEN: SUNBE4
➤ **THE SUNBIRD.** Text in English. 1970. irreg. (2-3/yr). free to members; AUD 6.60 to non-members (effective 2003). adv. bk.rev. charts; illus. index. **Document type:** *Journal, Academic/Scholarly.*
Indexed: SFA, WildRev, ZooRec.
—BLDSC (8533.530000), IE, ingenta.
Published by: Queensland Ornithological Society, PO Box 2273, Milton, QLD 4064, Australia. TEL 61-7-32293554, http://www.birdsqueensland.org.au. Ed. David Rounsevell. Circ: 500.

598 CAN ISSN 0834-7050
TCHEBEC. Text in English. 1970-1985; resumed 1992. a. CND 25 to members. illus.; stat. back issues avail. **Document type:** *Newsletter.* **Description:** Reports on bird sightings in the Montreal area and activities of Bird Protection Quebec (Province of Quebec Society for the Protection of Birds).
Indexed: ZooRec.
Published by: Quebec Society for the Protection of Birds, P O Box 43, Sta B, Montreal, PQ H3B 3J5, Canada. TEL 514-247-2185. Ed. David Smith. Circ: 750.

598 USA
TENNESSEE WARBLER. Text in English. 1979. q. back issues avail. **Document type:** *Newsletter.* **Description:** Provides information on upcoming and past events related to the Tennessee Ornithological Society and bird watching activities in Tennessee. Also contains popular articles on bird natural history in Tennessee.
Published by: Tennessee Ornithological Society, c/o Chris Sloan, 512 Old Hickory Blvd, Apt 1203, Nashville, TN 37209. TEL 615-353-0811, 2graham@bellsouth.net. Ed. Theresa Grahman. Circ: 900 (paid). **Subscr. to:** c/o David J. Trently, 1029 Morrow Rd, Knoxville, TN 37923-1725. TEL 423-531-1473.

598 USA ISSN 0040-4543
CODEN: TOSBAS
TEXAS ORNITHOLOGICAL SOCIETY. BULLETIN. Text in English. 1967. a. USD 10 to members. bk.rev. abstr.; illus.
Indexed: BiolAb, RefZh, ZooRec.
Published by: Texas Ornithological Society, 218 Conway Dr, San Angelo, TX 78209. Ed. Jack Clinton Eitniear. Circ: 800.

598 USA ISSN 0009-1987
QL671
THE/CHAT. Text in English. 1937. q. USD 20 to individuals; USD 20 to institutions; USD 15 to students (effective 2004). bk.rev. illus. index. **Document type:** *Bulletin.* **Description:** The ornithological journal of the Carolinas.
Indexed: BiolAb, SFA, WildRev, ZooRec.
Published by: Carolina Bird Club, Inc., PO Box 29555, Raleigh, NC 27626-0555. thechat@carolinabirdclub.org, http://www.carolinabirdclub.org/. Ed. Kent Fiala. Circ: 1,100.

598 GBR
THREATENED BIRDS OF AFRICA AND RELATED ISLANDS; the ICBP-IUCN Red Data Book. Text in English. 1985. irreg. GBP 27.30 domestic; USD 52.25 foreign (effective 1999). illus. **Description:** Describes threatened species of African birds with diagnoses of local threats and specific conservation recommendations.
Published by: BirdLife International, Wellbrook Ct, Girton Rd, Cambridge, CB3 ONA, United Kingdom. TEL 44-1223-277318, FAX 44-1223-277200. **Subscr. in the Americas to:** Smithsonian Institution Press, PO Box 960, Herndon, VA 22070-0960; **Subscr. to:** University Press Marketing, The Old Mill, Mill St, Wantage, Oxon OX12 9AB, United Kingdom. TEL 44-1235-766662, FAX 44-1235-766545. **Co-sponsor:** United Nations, International Union for Conservation of Nature and Natural Resources.

598 GBR
THREATENED BIRDS OF THE AMERICAS; the ICBP-IUCN Red Data Book. Text in English. 1992. irreg. GBP 32.30; USD 77.25 foreign. illus. **Document type:** *Academic/Scholarly.* **Description:** Describes threatened species of North, South, and Central American birds, with diagnoses of local threats and specific conservation recommendations.
Published by: BirdLife International, Wellbrook Ct, Girton Rd, Cambridge, CB3 ONA, United Kingdom. TEL 44-1223-277318, FAX 44-1223-227200. **Subscr. in the Americas to:** Smithsonian Institution Press, PO Box 960, Herndon, VA 22070-0960; **Subscr. to:** University Press Marketing, The Old Mill, Mill St, Wantage, Oxon OX12 9AB, United Kingdom. TEL 44-1235-766662, FAX 44-1235-766545. **Co-sponsor:** United Nations, International Union for Conservation of Nature and Natural Resources.

598 636.596 CHE
TIERWELT. Text in German. w. CHF 69 domestic; CHF 118 foreign (effective 2000). **Document type:** *Magazine, Consumer.*
Published by: (Schweizerische Gesellschaft fuer Ornithologie, Gefluegel-, Kaninchen-, und Taubenzucht), Tierwelt Verlag, Henzmannstr 18, Zofingen, 4800, Switzerland. TEL 41-62-7459494, FAX 41-62-7459444, redaktion@tierwelt.ch, http://www.tierwelt.ch. Ed. Hans-Peter Blaettler. Pub. Bruno Imfeld. Adv. contact Kurt Lipp.

598 JPN
TOKUSHU CHORUI CHOSA. Text in Japanese. a.
Published by: (Nihon Yacho no Kai/Wild Bird Society of Japan), Kankyocho/Environment Agency, 2-2 Kasumigaseki 1-chome, Chiyoda-ku, Tokyo, 100-0013, Japan.

598 ISR ISSN 0333-7383
QL696.F3 CODEN: TORGE8
TORGOS. Text in Hebrew; Summaries in English. s-a. ILS 26.
Description: Features articles about birds found in Israel.
Incorporates: Tzufit (0334-1240)
Indexed: IHP, SFA, WildRev, ZooRec.
Published by: Society for the Protection of Nature in Israel, 4 Hashefela St, Tel Aviv, 66183, Israel. TEL 972-3-375063.

598 JPN
TOSHICHO KENKYUKAI KAISHI/URBAN BIRDS. Text in Japanese. 4/yr.
Published by: Toshicho Kenkyukai/Urban Bird Society of Japan, 31-16-901 Hon-cho, Wako-shi, Saitama-ken 351-0114, Japan.

598.645 USA ISSN 1064-6094
SK325.T8
TURKEY CALL. Text in English. 1973. bi-m. USD 25. adv. illus.; stat. **Document type:** *Consumer.* **Description:** Dedicated to the education, enlightenment, and entertainment of wild turkey enthusiasts everywhere - people who hunt, study, and actively support the restoration and conservation of the American wild turkey.
Published by: National Wild Turkey Federation, Inc., 770 Augusta Rd, PO Box 530, Edgefield, SC 29824-0530. TEL 803-637-3106, FAX 803-637-0034, kroop@nwtf.net, http://www.nwtf.net. Ed., R&P Jay Langston. Adv. contact Danny Young. Circ: 120,000.

598 ITA ISSN 0393-1218
GLI UCCELLI D'ITALIA; e pagine del museo. Text in Italian; Summaries in English. 1976. a. adv. bk.rev. bibl.; charts; illus.; stat. index. back issues avail.
Indexed: KWIWR, ZooRec.
Published by: Societa Ornitologica Italiana, c/o Museo Ornitologico e di Scienze Naturali, Loggettta Lombardesca, Ravenna, RA 48100, Italy. TEL 39-544-482874, FAX 39-544-213641.

598.6 USA
UNIVERSITY OF CALIFORNIA AT DAVIS. GAME BIRD WORKSHOP. PROCEEDINGS. Text in English. 1971. biennial. price varies. **Document type:** *Proceedings.*
Published by: University of California at Davis, Department of Avian Sciences, One Shields Ave, Davis, CA 95616. TEL 916-752-3513, FAX 916-752-8960, raernst@ucdavis.edu. Ed. Dr. R A Ernst. Circ: 100.

598 USA ISSN 1081-0218
V S O NEWSLETTER. (Virginia Society of Ornithology) Text in English. 1956. q.
Published by: Virginia Society of Ornithology, Inc, c/o Thelma Dalmas, 1230 Viewmont Dr, Evington, VA 24550-2006. http://www.ecoventures-travel.com/vso/newsletter.htm. Eds. Alan Schreck, Linda Fields.

▼ new title ➤ refereed ✶ unverified ♦ full entry avail.

598 SWE ISSN 0042-2649
QL671 CODEN: VARFAR
VAAR FAAGELVAERLD. Text in Swedish; Summaries in English. 1942. 8/yr. SEK 430; SEK 520 foreign. adv. bk.rev. abstr.; bibl.; charts; illus.; maps; stat. index. back issues avail.
Related titles: ◆ Supplement(s): Var Fagelvard. Supplement. ISSN 0504-9520.
Indexed: BiolAb, RefZh, SFA, WildRev, ZooRec.
Published by: Sveriges Ornitologiska Foerening/Swedish Ornithological Society, Ekhagsvaegen 3, Stockholm, 10405, Sweden. TEL 46-8-6122530, FAX 46-8-6122536, info@sofnet.org, http://www.sofnet.org. Ed., Adv. contact Anders Wirdheim TEL 46-35-37453. Circ: 10,000.

598.2 NOR ISSN 0332-5601
VAER FUGLEFAUNA. Text in Multiple languages. q.
Indexed: ZooRec.
Published by: Norsk Ornitologisk Forening, Sandgata 30 B, Trondheim, 7012, Norway. TEL 47-73-526040, FAX 47-73-524090, http://folk.uio.no/csteel/nof, nof@birdlife.no. Ed. Magne Myklebust.

598 SWE ISSN 0348-1360
➤ **VAERMLANDSORNITOLOGEN.** Text in Swedish. 1973. s-a. SEK 95 (effective 2002). **Document type:** *Bulletin, Academic/Scholarly.*
Published by: Wermlands Ornitologiska Foerening, Aelvsborgvaegen 6, Kristinehamn, 68143, Sweden. TEL 46-05-50-19023, http://www.xpress.se/~alo1224/vo.html. Circ: 500.

598 CAN ISSN 0316-8239
VANCOUVER ISLAND CAGE BIRD SOCIETY BULLETIN. Text in English. 1954. m. CND 16. adv. bk.rev. charts; illus. back issues avail. **Description:** Promotes captive breeding.
Published by: Vancouver Island Cage Bird Society, 1064 Marigold Rd, Victoria, BC V8Z 4S2, Canada. TEL 604-479-1338. Ed. Wayne Green. Circ: 2,200.

598 SWE ISSN 0504-9520
VAR FAGELVARD. SUPPLEMENT. Text in Swedish. 1950. irreg.
Related titles: ◆ Supplement to: Vaar Faagelvaerld. ISSN 0042-2649.
Indexed: ZooRec.
Published by: Sveriges Ornitologiska Foerening/Swedish Ornithological Society, Ekhagsvaegen 3, Stockholm, 10405, Sweden. TEL 46-8-612-25-30, FAX 46-8-612-25-36.

598 USA
THE VIRTUAL BIRDER; the internet magazine for birders. Text in English. 1996. m.
Media: Online - full content.
Published by: Great Blue Publications TVB@greatblue.com, http://www.virtualbirder.com/vbirder. Ed. Don Crockett.

598 FRA ISSN 1248-2056
VIVRE AVEC LES OISEAUX. Text in French. 1947. bi-m. EUR 25 (effective 2004). illus.
Former titles (until 1993): Journal des Oiseaux (0181-8910); Journal des Oiseaux du Monde; Journal des Oiseaux (0075-4080)
Published by: Info Presse S.A., 33 Rue Traversiere, Boulogne, 92660, France. TEL 33-1-821234323, FAX 33-1-46210070, service-clientele@info-presse.fr, http://www.info-presse.fr. Ed. Francoise De Korte. Pub. Gilles Barissat. Adv. contact Dominique Balen.

598 DEU ISSN 0173-0266
VOGEL UND UMWELT; Zeitschrift fuer Vogelkunde und Naturschutz in Hessen. Text in German. 1980. 3/yr. bk.rev. 240 p./no. 2 cols./p.; back issues avail. **Document type:** *Journal, Government.*
Indexed: KWIWR.
Published by: Hessisches Ministerium fuer Umwelt, Landwirtschaft und Forsten, Hoelderlinstr 1-3, Wiesbaden, 65187, Germany. TEL 49-611-817-0, FAX 49-611-8172181, info@vsw-ffm.hlf-net.de. Circ: 2,000.

598 DEU
DER VOGELFREUND. Text in German. 1947. m. EUR 48 domestic; EUR 60 foreign (effective 2005). adv. bk.rev. **Document type:** *Magazine, Consumer.*
Formerly: Kanarienfreund
Published by: Hanke Verlag GmbH, Amrichshaeuser Str 88, Kuenzelsau, 74653, Germany. TEL 49-7940-544454, FAX 49-7940-544440, info@hanke-verlag.de, http://www.hanke-verlag.de. Pub. Hans Kalis. adv.: B&W page EUR 1,344, color page EUR 1,884; 185 x 265. Circ: 10,000 (controlled).

598 DEU ISSN 0340-403X
VOGELKUNDLICHE BERICHTE AUS NIEDERSACHSEN. Text in German; Summaries in English. 1969. s-a. EUR 20 to individual members; EUR 10 to students (effective 2004). bk.rev. bibl.; charts; illus. index. back issues avail. **Document type:** *Journal, Academic/Scholarly.*
Indexed: BiolAb, RefZh, ZooRec.
Published by: Niedersaechsische Ornithologische Vereinigung, Muehlenstr 9, Hechthausen, 21755, Germany. TEL 49-4753-708, FAX 49-4131-1526132442, info@ornithologie-niedersachsen.de, http://www.ornithologie-niedersachsen.de. Eds. Axel Degen, Juergen Ludwig. Circ: 1,000.

598 DEU
VOGELKUNDLICHE HEFTE EDERTAL FUER DEN KREIS WALDECK-FRANKENBERG. Text in German. 1975. a. EUR 6 (effective 2003). bk.rev. 216 p./no.; back issues avail. **Document type:** *Bulletin, Academic/Scholarly.*
Former titles: Vogelkundliche Hefte Edertal fuer den Landkreis Waldeck-Frankenberg (1431-6722); (until 1988): Vogelkundliche Hefte Edertal fuer den Kreis Waldeck-Frankenberg und den Raum Fritzlar-Homberg (0178-0239); (until 1981): Vogelkundliche Hefte (0178-0220)
Indexed: BIOSIS Prev, BiolAb, IBR, RefZh, ZooRec.
Published by: Hessische Gesellschaft fuer Ornithologie und Naturschutz, Arbeitskreis Waldeck-Frankenberg, Rathausweg 1, Edertal, 34549, Germany. TEL 49-5623-1255, FAX 49-5623-931094. Ed. Wolfgang Luebcke. Circ: 700.

598 AUT ISSN 1025-3270
VOGELKUNDLICHE NACHRICHTEN AUS OBEROESTERREICH; Naturschutz aktuell. Text in German; Summaries in English. 1993. 2/yr. back issues avail. **Document type:** *Journal, Academic/Scholarly.* **Description:** Contains scientific contributions on ornithology and nature conservation in upper Austria.
Indexed: ZooRec.
Published by: Oberoesterreichisches Landesmuseum, Arbeitsgemeinschaft Ornithologie, J.-W.-Klein-Str 73, Linz, 4040, Austria. TEL 43-732-75973357, FAX 43-732-75973399, g.aubrecht@landesmuseum-linz.ac.at, http://www.biologiezentrum.at. Ed. Dr. Gerhard Aubrecht. Circ: 500 (controlled).

598 NLD ISSN 0167-8280
VOGELS. Text in Dutch. 1968. 6/yr. adv. **Document type:** *Bulletin.*
Formerly (until 1981): Lepelaar (0166-8056)
—IE, Infotrieve.
Published by: Vogelbescherming Nederlands, Driebergseweg 16C, Zeist, 3708 JB, Netherlands. TEL 31-30-6937700, FAX 31-30-6918844. Ed. Frans Buissink. R&P H Peeters. Adv. contact Th Hesen.

598 DEU ISSN 0049-6650
CODEN: VOGLAK
VOGELWARTE. Text in German. 1930. 2/yr. bk.rev. **Document type:** *Academic/Scholarly.*
Indexed: ASFA, BIOSIS Prev, BiolAb, GEOBASE, IBR, KWIWR, RefZh, SFA, WildRev, ZooRec.
—BLDSC (9251.380000), IE, ingenta.
Published by: (Vogelwarte Helgoland and Vogelwarte Radolfzell), Verlagsdruckerei Schmidt GmbH, Nuernbergerstr 27-31, Neustadt, 91413, Germany. TEL 49-9161-8860-0, FAX 49-9161-1378. Eds. G Thielcke, W Winkel. Circ: 3,000.

598 DEU ISSN 0042-7993
CODEN: VGLWAM
DIE VOGELWELT; Beitraege zur Vogelkunde. Text in German. 1880. bi-m. EUR 51; EUR 11 newsstand/cover (effective 2005). adv. bk.rev. abstr.; charts; illus. index. **Document type:** *Magazine, Academic/Scholarly.* **Description:** Publishes original papers, review articles and short notes on all aspects of ornithology.
Incorporates (1949-1993): Beitraege zur Vogelkunde (0005-8211)
Indexed: BIOSIS Prev, BiolAb, IBR, KWIWR, RefZh, SFA, WildRev, ZooRec.
—BLDSC (9251.400000), IE, ingenta, Linda Hall. **CCC.**
Published by: (Dachverband Deutscher Avifaunisten), Aula Verlag GmbH, Industriepark 3, Wiebelsheim, 56291, Germany. TEL 49-6766-903141, FAX 49-6766-903320, vertrieb@aula-verlag.de, http://www.birdnet.de/aula. Eds. A J Helbig, M Flade. R&P Irmgard Meissl. Adv. contact Petra Muen. B&W page EUR 480, color page EUR 1,080; trim 155 x 228.

598 DEU ISSN 0344-9270
DIE VOLIERE. Text in German; Summaries in Dutch, English. 1978. 12/yr. EUR 58; EUR 5 newsstand/cover (effective 2003). adv. bk.rev. illus. **Document type:** *Magazine, Academic/Scholarly.*
Indexed: RefZh, VetBull.
—**CCC.**
Published by: Verlag M. und H. Schaper GmbH, Borsigstr 5, Alfeld, 31061, Germany. TEL 49-5181-8009-0, FAX 49-5181-8009-33, info@schaper-verlag.de, http://www.schaper-verlag.de. Ed. B Hachfeld. adv.: B&W page EUR 1,065, color page EUR 1,782. Circ: 6,200 (paid).

598 ZAF ISSN 1606-7479
VULTURE NEWS; the journal of the vulture study group. Text in English. 1979. s-a. ZAR 60 domestic to members; USD 20, GBP 15 foreign to members (effective 2003). adv. bk.rev. abstr.; bibl.; charts; illus.; stat. 62 p./no.; back issues avail. **Document type:** *Journal, Academic/Scholarly.*
Indexed: KWIWR, WildRev, ZooRec.
Published by: Vulture Study Group/Aasvoelstudiegroep, PO Box 72334, Parkview, 2122, South Africa. TEL 27-11-6468617, FAX 27-11-6464631, vsg@ewt.org.za, http://www.ewt.org.za/vulture/index.html. Ed. Mark D Anderson. Circ: 1,000.

598 ZAF ISSN 0250-1481
CODEN: WBCNEW
W B C NEWS. Text in English. 1952. q.
Indexed: SFA, WildRev, ZooRec.
Published by: Witwatersrand Bird Club, 239 Barkston Dr, Blairgowrie, Blairgowrie, Randburg 2122, South Africa. FAX 27-11-7877694, http://www.birdlife.org.za.

598 GBR ISSN 1359-7450
CODEN: WPAJE6
W P A ANNUAL REVIEW. Text in English. a. USD 50. **Document type:** *Bulletin.*
Formerly: W P A Journal (0963-326X)
Indexed: ForAb, SFA, WildRev, ZooRec.
Published by: World Pheasant Association, PO Box 5, World Pheasant Association, Lower Basildon, Reading, RG8 9PF, United Kingdom. TEL 44-1189-845140, FAX 44-1189-843369. Ed. Ed Jenkins. Adv. contact Ted Norris. **U.S. subscr. to:** World Pheasant Association, 5330 W Teal Rd, Petersburg, MI 49270-9305. TEL 734-279-5198.

598.6 GBR ISSN 0963-3278
CODEN: WPANEI
W P A NEWS. Text in English. 1975. q. USD 50. adv. back issues avail. **Document type:** *Bulletin.* **Description:** Contains news, reports and articles concerning conservation and aviculture of the Galliformes (game birds).
Indexed: ForAb, PoultAb, SFA, WildRev, ZooRec.
Published by: World Pheasant Association, PO Box 5, World Pheasant Association, Lower Basildon, Reading, RG8 9PF, United Kingdom. TEL 44-1189-845140, FAX 44-1189-843369, brownear@cass.net, wpa@gn.apc.org. Ed. Derek Bingham. R&P Ted Norris. Adv. contact Keith Howman. Circ: 2,000 (controlled). **U.S. subscr. to:** World Pheasant Association, 5330 W Teal Rd, Petersburg, MI 49270-9305. TEL 734-279-5198.

598.176 GBR
➤ **W S G BULLETIN.** Text in English. 3/yr. **Document type:** *Bulletin, Academic/Scholarly.* **Description:** Publishes scientific papers, reports, notes, news, views and comments on all aspects of wader biology and its application to conservation.
Published by: National Centre for Ornithology, Wader Study Group, The Nunnery, Thetford, Norfolk IP24 2PU, United Kingdom.

598.176 GBR ISSN 0260-3799
WADER STUDY GROUP. BULLETIN. Text in English. 1970. 3/yr. **Document type:** *Bulletin, Academic/Scholarly.* **Description:** Provides a forum for news, notices, ringing recoveries, recent publications, new study methods, articles from all parts of the world about Charadrii (waders or shorebirds)
Indexed: ZooRec.
—BLDSC (2808.850000), IE, ingenta.
Published by: International Wader Study Group, National Centre for Ornithology, The Nunnery, Thetford, Norfolk JP24 2PU, United Kingdom. hsitters@aol.com, http://www.uct.ac.za/depts/stats/adu/wsg.

598.176 USA ISSN 1524-4695
QL671 CODEN: COWAEW
➤ **WATERBIRDS**; the international journal of waterbird biology. Text in English. 1977. 3/yr. USD 90 to members per page; USD 100 to non-members per page (effective 2004). bk.rev. back issues avail. **Document type:** *Academic/Scholarly.* **Description:** Publishes scholarly articles, notes, critical commentary, and reviews on the biology, status, techniques of study, management, and conservation of aquatic birds throughout the world.
Former titles (until 1998): Colonial Waterbirds (0738-6028); (until 1980): Colonial Waterbird Group Conference. Proceedings (1556-5785)
Related titles: Online - full text ed.: (from BioOne, C S A).
Indexed: ASCA, ASFA, AgrForAb, AnBeAb, AnBrAb, ApEcolAb, BioCN&I, BiolAb, CurCont, ESPM, ForAb, GEOBASE, HerbAb, IndVet, KWIWR, OceAb, PoultAb, ProtozoAb, RM&VM, RefZh, RiceAb, S&F, SFA, VetBull, WildRev, ZooRec.
—BLDSC (9279.412500), IDS, IE, ingenta, Linda Hall. **CCC.**
Published by: Waterbird Society, Pacific Cooperative Studies Unit, Department of Botany, University of Hawaii, Honolulu, HI 96822-2279. TEL 808-956-8218, editor@waterbirds.org, membership@osnabirds.org, http://www.waterbirds.org/journal.htm, http://www.nmnh.si.edu. Ed. David Duffy. Circ: 900. **Subscr. to:** Allen Press Inc., PO Box 1897, Lawrence, KS 66044.

598.41 GBR
WATERFOWL. Text in English. 1971. s-a. GBP 20 membership; GBP 28 in Europe membership; GBP 35 elsewhere membership. adv. bk.rev. bibl. **Document type:** *Newsletter.*
Media: Duplicated (not offset).
Published by: British Waterfowl Association, PO Box 23, Leyburn, Yorks DL8 4YW, United Kingdom. TEL 44-1969-663693. Ed. M Thompson. Circ: 1,600.

598 DEU ISSN 0178-7373
WELLENSITTICH MAGAZIN; internationale Fachzeitschrift fuer Zuechter, Halter und Aussteller. Text in German. 1986. 12/yr. EUR 54.50; EUR 4.80 newsstand/cover (effective 2003). adv. **Document type:** *Magazine, Trade.*
—CCC.

Published by: Verlag M. und H. Schaper GmbH, Borsigstr 5, Alfeld, 31061, Germany. TEL 49-5181-8009-0, FAX 49-5181-8009-33, info@schaper-verlag.de, http://www.schaper-verlag.de. adv.: B&W page EUR 943, color page EUR 1,660. Circ: 3,010 (paid).

598 USA ISSN 0160-1121
QL684.C2 CODEN: WSBDAA
➤ **WESTERN BIRDS**; quarterly journal of Western Field Ornithologists . Text in English. 1973. q. USD 25 domestic; USD 35 foreign (effective 2003). adv. bk.rev. illus. index. back issues avail.; reprints avail. **Document type:** *Journal, Academic/Scholarly.* **Description:** Dedicated to the scientific values of ornithology and to its promotion in the western U.S., Canada, and Mexico. Sponsors field trips in California.
Formerly (until 1973): California Birds (0045-3897)
Indexed: BIOSIS Prev, BiolAb, RefZh, SFA, WildRev, ZooRec.
—Linda Hall.
Published by: Western Field Ornithologists, c/o Robbie Fischer, Treasurer, 1359 Solano Dr, Pacifica, CA 94044-4258. TEL 650-359-2068, robbie22@pacbell.net, http://www.wfo-cbrc.org/. Ed., R&P, Adv. contact Philip Unitt TEL 619-232-3821. Circ: 1,000 (paid).

598.163 GBR ISSN 1353-7792
QL690.G7
WETLAND BIRD SURVEY (YEAR): WILDFOWL AND WADER COUNTS. Text in English. a. GBP 30 to non-members (effective 2000). **Document type:** *Bulletin.* **Description:** Summary results of comprehensive waterfowl monitoring scheme in the UK.
Formerly: Wildfowl and Wader Counts (0965-3708)
—BLDSC (9317.245500).
Published by: Wildfowl and Wetlands Trust, Slimbridge, Glos GL2 7BT, United Kingdom. TEL 44-1453-891900, FAX 44-1453-890827, enquiries@wwt.org.uk, publications@wwt.org.uk, http://www.wwt.org.uk. Circ: 4,000. **Co-sponsors:** Joint Nature Conservation Committee; Royal Society for the Protection of Birds; British Trust for Ornithology.

WHO'S WHO IN ORNITHOLOGY. see *BIOGRAPHY*

598 BEL ISSN 0043-5260
DE WIELEWAAL. Text in Dutch. 1933. m. adv. bk.rev. illus.
Indexed: RefZh, ZooRec.
Published by: (Vereniging voor Vogel en Natuurstudie de Wielewaal), De Wielewaal V.Z.W., Graatakker 11, Turnhout, 2300, Belgium. TEL 32-14-472950, FAX 32-14-472951. Ed. G Luyts. Circ: 6,200.

598.07 USA ISSN 0892-5534
QL677.5
WILDBIRD. Text in English. 1987. bi-m. USD 12.99 domestic; USD 21.99 elsewhere (effective 2005). adv. illus. Index. reprints avail. **Document type:** *Consumer.* **Description:** Contains a variety of birding and ornithology features, including tips on bird-watching, species profiles, birding "hotspots," product directories, field testing of the latest equipment, attracting, bird feeding, and bird identification advice.
Indexed: BRI, SFA, WildRev.
—Linda Hall.
Published by: Bowtie, Inc., PO Box 57900, Los Angeles, CA 90057. TEL 213-385-2222, FAX 213-385-8565, j.cain@fancypubs.com, http://www.wildbirdmagazine.com/wb, http://www.animalnetwork.com. Ed. Mary Lou Zarbozk. Pub. Norman Ridker. Adv. contact Don Kremers. B&W page USD 5,670, color page USD 8,300; trim 10.88 x 8. Circ: 114,000 (paid). **Subscr. to:** PO Box 52864, Boulder, CO 80322-2864. TEL 800-542-1600.

598 GBR ISSN 0954-6324
SK351 CODEN: WLDFAB
WILDFOWL. Text in English. 1948. a. GBP 15 to members; GBP 25 to non-members (effective 2000). bk.rev. **Document type:** *Journal.*
Indexed: BIOBASE, BIOSIS Prev, BiolAb, GEOBASE, I-WA, IABS, IBR, IndVet, KWIWR, NutrAb, ProtozoAb, RefZh, SFA, VetBull, WLR, WildRev, ZooRec.
—BLDSC (9317.245000), IE, ingenta, Linda Hall.
Published by: Wildfowl and Wetlands Trust, Slimbridge, Glos GL2 7BT, United Kingdom. TEL 44-1453-891900, FAX 44-1453-890827, enquiries@wwt.org.uk, publications@wwt.org.uk, http://www.wwt.org.uk. Ed. Mark O'Connell. Circ: 2,500.

598 GBR ISSN 0960-4421
WILDFOWL AND WETLANDS. Text in English. 1950. q. GBP 2 (effective 1999). adv. bk.rev. back issues avail. **Document type:** *Magazine.*
Indexed: SFA.
—BLDSC (9317.245800).
Published by: Wildfowl and Wetlands Trust, Slimbridge, Glos GL2 7BT, United Kingdom. TEL 44-1453-891900, FAX 44-1453-890827, enquiries@wwt.org.uk, publications@wwt.org.uk, http://www.wwt.org.uk. Ed. Nikki Straughan. Circ: 75,000.

598 USA ISSN 0043-5643
QL671 CODEN: WILBAI
➤ **WILSON BULLETIN**; a quarterly journal of ornithology. Text in English. 1889. q. USD 40 in North America; USD 45 elsewhere (effective 2004). bk.rev. bibl.; charts; illus. index. back issues avail.; reprints avail. **Document type:** *Journal, Academic/Scholarly.* **Description:** Publishes original studies of birds and short communications describing observations of particular interest.
Related titles: Microform ed.: (from PQC); Online - full text ed.: (from BioOne, C S A, Florida Center for Library Automation, Gale Group, Northern Light Technology, Inc., O C L C Online Computer Library Center, Inc., ProQuest Information & Learning).
Indexed: ASCA, ASFA, AgrForAb, AnBeAb, ApEcolAb, BIOBASE, BIOSIS Prev, BiolAb, CurCont, ESPM, FPA, ForAb, GEOBASE, GSI, GenetAb, HGA, HerbAb, IABS, ISR, IndVet, NutrAb, OceAb, OrnA, OrnithAb, PGegResA, PoultAb, ProtozoAb, RM&VM, RefZh, RevApplEntom, S&F, SCI, SFA, SIA, SeedAb, VetBull, WeedAb, WildRev, ZooRec.
—BLDSC (9319.079000), CISTI, IDS, IE, Infotrieve, ingenta, KNAW, Linda Hall.
Published by: Wilson Ornithological Society, c/o Robert C Beason, Ed, Biology Dept, State University of New York, 1 College Circle, Geneseo, NY 14454. TEL 716-245-5310, FAX 716-245-5007, http://www.ummz.lsa.umich.edu/birds/wilsonbull.html, http://www.ummz.lsa.umich.edu/birds/wos.html. Ed. Robert Beason. Circ: 3,500 (paid). **Subscr. to:** Ornithological Societies of North America, Business Office, Box 1897, Lawrence, KS 66044-7099. TEL 785-843-1235, FAX 785-843-1274, osna@allenpress.com.

598 USA ISSN 1042-511X
WINGING IT; the monthly newsletter of the American Birding Association. Text in English. 1989. m. USD 36 domestic to individuals; USD 45 foreign to individuals; USD 41 domestic to libraries; USD 50 foreign to libraries; USD 18 domestic to students; USD 27 foreign to students; includes Birding & A Bird's Eye View. adv. illus. reprints avail. **Document type:** *Newsletter.*
Indexed: WildRev.
Published by: American Birding Association, PO Box 6599, Colorado Springs, CO 80934. TEL 719-578-1614, 800-850-2473, FAX 719-578-1480, member@aba.org, http://www.americanbirding.org. Ed. Matthew L Pelikan.

598 USA
WINGS ON THE NET. Text in English. w. **Document type:** *Newsletter.* **Description:** Full of interesting articles and sites on the net that pertain to birding.
Media: Online - full text.
Address: birding.guide@miningco.com. Ed. Christine Tarski.

598 AUS ISSN 1036-7810
QL671 CODEN: WINSEF
WINGSPAN. Text in English. 1969. q. AUD 68 domestic to individual members; AUD 79 in Asia & the Pacific to individual members; AUD 88 elsewhere to institutional members; AUD 108 domestic to institutional members; AUD 117 in Asia & the Pacific to institutional members; AUD 126 elsewhere to institutional members (effective 2004). back issues avail. **Document type:** *Magazine, Consumer.*
Formerly (until 1991): R A O U Newsletter (0817-5748)
Indexed: SFA, WildRev, ZooRec.
—BLDSC (9319.417647), IE, Infotrieve. **CCC.**
Published by: Birds Australia, 415 Riversdale Rd, Hawthorn East, VIC 3123, Australia. TEL 61-3-98822622, FAX 61-3-98822677, mail@birdsaustralia.com.au, http://www.birdsaustralia.com.au/wingspan.html. Ed. Leonard Young. Circ: 5,500.

598 GBR
WORLD BIRDWATCH. Text in English. 1979. q. GBP 25, USD 41 (effective 2001). bk.rev. back issues avail. **Document type:** *Newsletter.* **Description:** Reports on world bird conservation.
Formerly: International Council for Bird Preservation Newsletter (0144-4476)
Indexed: KWIWR, RefZh, WildRev.
Published by: BirdLife International, Wellbrook Ct, Girton Rd, Cambridge, CB3 ONA, United Kingdom. TEL 44-1223-277318, FAX 44-1223-277200, birdlife@birdlife.org.uk, http://www.wing-wbsj.or.jp/birdlife/world2.htm, http://www.birdlife.net. Ed. Richard Thomas. Circ: 9,500. **Dist. in Americas by:** Smithsonian Institution Press, PO Box 960, Herndon, VA 22070-0960. TEL 703-435-7064, 703-689-0660.

WORLD OF BIRDS WILDLIFE SANCTUARY CC, SOUTH AFRICA. NEWSLETTER. see *CONSERVATION*

WP-MAGAZIN. see *PETS*

598 JPN ISSN 0910-4488
YACHO/WILD BIRDS. Text in Japanese. 1934. m. JPY 5,000 (effective 2003). 50 p./no.; **Document type:** *Bulletin, Academic/Scholarly.*
Published by: Nihon Yacho no Kai/Wild Bird Society of Japan, 1-47-1 Hatsudai, Shibuya-ku, Tokyo, 151-0061, Japan. TEL 81-3-5358-3510, FAX 81-3-5358-3608, hensyu@wbsj.org. Ed. Noriko Izawa.

598 JPN
YACHOEN DAYORI/YATOMI WILD BIRD SANCTUARY NEWS. Text in Japanese. 1976. 2/yr.
Published by: Aichiken Yatomi Yachoen Jimusho/Aichi Prefecture, Yatomi Wild Bird Sanctuary Office, 2-10 Ueno, Kaifu-gun, Yatomimachi, Aichi-ken 498, Japan.

598 JPN ISSN 0910-2388
YAMAGUCHI YACHO/JOURNAL OF THE WILD BIRDS OF YAMAGUCHI. Text in Japanese. a. membership.
Published by: Nihon Yacho no Kai, Yamaguchiken Shibu/Wild Bird Society of Japan, Yamaguchi Prefecture Branch, c/o Mr Ogawa, Iwanagashimogo, Mine-gun, Shuho-cho, Yamaguchi-ken 754-0513, Japan.

598 JPN
➤ **YAMASHINA INSTITUTE FOR ORNITHOLOGY. JOURNAL/YAMASHINA CHORUI KENKYUJO KENKYU HOKOKU.** Text in English, Japanese. 1952. s-a. (s.a. no.1-13; irreg. no.14-44; 3/yr. no.45-74). JPY 10,000 (effective 2003). bk.rev. charts; illus. 50 p./no.; back issues avail. **Document type:** *Journal, Academic/Scholarly.* **Description:** Covers original reports and reviews on scientific study of birds, including bird protection.
Former titles (until 1978): Yamashina Institute for Ornithology. Miscellaneous Reports (0044-0183); (until 1964): Yamashina Institute for Ornithology and Zoology. Miscellaneous Reports
Indexed: BIOSIS Prev, BiolAb, JPI, RefZh, ZooRec.
—BLDSC (4917.503000).
Published by: Yamashina Institute for Ornithology/Yamashina Chorui Kenkyujo, 115 Konoyama, Abiko, Chiba 270-1145, Japan. TEL 81-471-82-1101, FAX 81-471-82-1106, journal@yamashina.or.jp. Ed. Satoshi Yamagishi. Circ: 1,000.

598 GBR
YORKSHIRE NATURALISTS' UNION. BIRD REPORT. Text in English. a. GBP 8 to members (effective 2001). **Document type:** *Journal, Academic/Scholarly.*
Published by: Yorkshire Naturalists' Union, University of Bradford, Bradford, W Yorks BD7 1DP, United Kingdom. TEL 44-1274-234212, FAX 44-1274-234231, m.r.d.seaward@bradford.ac.uk. Ed. M R D Seaward. Circ: 800 (paid).

598 ZMB ISSN 0378-4533
ZAMBIAN ORNITHOLOGICAL SOCIETY. NEWSLETTER. Text in English. 1971. m. USD 30. bibl. index. back issues avail. **Document type:** *Newsletter.* **Description:** Bird records, announcements, occasional reviews.
Indexed: SFA, WildRev.
Published by: Zambian Ornithological Society, PO Box 33944, Lusaka, Zambia. Ed. C Beel. Circ: 200.

598 ZMB
ZAMBIAN ORNITHOLOGICAL SOCIETY. OCCASIONAL PAPERS. Text in English. 1979. irreg., latest vol.3, 1991. price varies. **Document type:** *Monographic series.*
Published by: Zambian Ornithological Society, PO Box 33944, Lusaka, Zambia. Circ: 500.

BIOLOGY—Physiology

see also MEDICAL SCIENCES

612.044 USA ISSN 1097-9743
A S E P NEWSLETTER. Text in English. m. back issues avail. **Document type:** *Newsletter.* **Description:** Covers news, opinions, excercise physiology professionals, and events that shape exercise physiology.
Media: Online - full text.
Published by: American Society of Exercise Physiologists, College of St Scholastica, 1200 Kenwood Ave, Duluth, MN 55811. TEL 218-723-6297, FAX 218-723-6472, tboone2@css.edu, http://www.css.edu/users/tboone2/asep/toc.htm. Ed., R&P, Adv. contact Tommy Boone.

571 BGR ISSN 0323-9950
CODEN: APPBDI
ACTA PHYSIOLOGICA ET PHARMACOLOGICA BULGARICA. Text in English. 1974. q. USD 58 foreign (effective 2005). reprints avail. **Document type:** *Journal, Academic/Scholarly.* **Description:** Publishes original experimental studies, theoretical papers and reviews in the area of clinical physiology and pharmacology.
Supersedes: Bulgarska Akademiia na Naukite, Sofia, Institut po Fiziologiia. Izvestiia
Indexed: ABSML, BSLBiol, BiolAb, CIN, ChemAb, ChemTitl, DSA, ExcerpMed, IndMed, MEDLINE, RefZh.
—BLDSC (0650.900000), CASDDS, CISTI, GNLM, IE, ingenta, KNAW, Linda Hall.
Published by: Bulgarska Akademiya na Naukite, Institut po Fiziologiya/Bulgarian Academy of Sciences, Institute of Physiology, Akad Boncheva 23, Sofia, 1113, Bulgaria. TEL 359-2-9792151, FAX 359-2-719109, iph@bio.bas.bg, http://www.bio.bas.bg/iph. Circ: 456. **Dist. by:** Sofia Books, ul Silivria 16, Sofia 1404, Bulgaria. TEL 359-2-9586257, info@sofiabooks-bg.com, http://www.sofiabooks-bg.com.

B

571 HUN ISSN 0231-424X
QP1 CODEN: APHHDU
ACTA PHYSIOLOGICA HUNGARICA. Text in English. 1950. q. USD 312 (effective 2006). adv. bk.rev. bibl.; charts; illus.; abstr. index. 120 p./no.; back issues avail. **Document type:** *Journal, Academic/Scholarly.* **Description:** Publishes new research papers in experimental medical sciences, covering physiology, pathophysiology and pharmacology.
Formerly (until 1982): Academiae Scientiarum Hungaricae. Acta Physiologica (0001-6756)
Related titles: Microfilm ed.: (from PMC); Online - full text ed.: ISSN 1588-2683 (from EBSCO Publishing, Swets Information Services).
Indexed: ASCA, AbHyg, AgrForAb, AnBrAb, BIOSIS Prev, BiolAb, CIN, ChemAb, ChemTitl, CurCont, DBA, ExcerpMed, HortAb, ISR, IndMed, IndVet, MEDLINE, MSB, NSCI, NutrAb, OrnHort, PN&I, PoultAb, RA&MP, RRTA, SCI, SoyAb, TriticAb, VetBull.
—BLDSC (0652.500000), CASDDS, CISTI, GNLM, IDS, IE, Infotrieve, ingenta, KNAW, Linda Hall. **CCC.**
Published by: (Magyar Tudomanyos Akademia/Hungarian Academy of Sciences), Akademiai Kiado Rt. (Subsidiary of: Wolters Kluwer N.V.), Prielle Kornelia U. 19, Budapest, 1117, Hungary. TEL 36-1-4648282, FAX 36-1-4648221, journals@akkrt.hu, http://www.akkrt.hu. Ed. Emil Monos.

571 ARG ISSN 0327-6309
CODEN: APTLEZ
➤ **ACTA PHYSIOLOGICA PHARMACOLOGICA ET THERAPEUTICA LATINOAMERICANA**; fisiologia, farmacologia, bioquimica y ciencias afines. Text in English, French, Portuguese, Spanish; Abstracts in English, Spanish. 1950. q. USD 140. adv. charts; illus. index. **Document type:** *Journal, Academic/Scholarly.* **Description:** Publishes reports of original research on all aspects of physiology, pharmacology, immunology, biochemistry, biophysics, endocrinology, biology, neuroscience, microbiology, toxicology and therapeutics.
Former titles (until 1990): Acta Physiologica et Pharmacologica Latino Americana (0326-6656); (until 1984): Acta Physiologica Latinoamericana (0001-6764)
Related titles: Microfilm ed.
Indexed: BiolAb, CIN, ChemAb, ChemTitl, CurCont, DSA, ExcerpMed, ISR, IndMed, MEDLINE, NutrAb, SCI.
—BLDSC (0653.500000), CASDDS, CISTI, GNLM, IE, Infotrieve, ingenta, KNAW, Linda Hall.
Published by: Asociacion Latinoamericana de Ciencias Fisiologicas, Serrano, 669, Capital Federal, Buenos Aires 1414, Argentina. TEL 54-114-8557204, FAX 54-114-8562751, apptla@drwebsa.com.ar, http://www.drwebsa.com.ar/apptla. Ed., Adv. contact Dr. Enri S Borda. Circ: 1,000. **Co-sponsor:** Asociacion Latinoamericana de Farmacologia.

571 GBR ISSN 0001-6772
QP1 CODEN: APSCAX
➤ **ACTA PHYSIOLOGICA SCANDINAVICA.** Text in English. 1940. m. EUR 209 combined subscription in Europe to individuals (print & online eds.); USD 234 combined subscription in the Americas to individuals & Caribbean (print & online eds.); GBP 139 combined subscription elsewhere to individuals (print & online eds.); GBP 386 combined subscription in Europe to institutions print & online eds.; USD 734 combined subscription in the Americas to institutions & Caribbean (print & online eds.); GBP 437 combined subscription elsewhere to institutions print & online eds. (effective 2006); includes supplement. adv. abstr.; bibl.; charts; illus. back issues avail.; reprint service avail. from PSC. **Document type:** *Journal, Academic/Scholarly.* **Description:** Provides readers with original reports on physiology and biological pharmacology.
Formerly: Skandinavisches Archiv fur Physiologie
Related titles: Microform ed.: (from PQC); Online - full text ed.: ISSN 1365-201X. GBP 367 in Europe to institutions; USD 697 in the Americas to institutions & Caribbean; GBP 415 elsewhere to institutions (effective 2006) (from Blackwell Synergy, EBSCO Publishing, Gale Group, IngentaConnect, O C L C Online Computer Library Center, Inc., Swets Information Services).
Indexed: AMED, ASCA, ASFA, AnBrAb, BIOBASE, BIOSIS Prev, BiolAb, CIN, CISA, ChemAb, ChemTitl, CurCont, DBA, DSA, DentInd, ExcerpMed, IABS, ISR, IndMed, IndVet, Inpharma, MEDLINE, NSCI, NutrAb, PE&ON, PN&I, PoultAb, RRTA, Reac, SCI, SFA, SIA, THA, VetBull, WildRev, ZooRec.
—BLDSC (0654.800000), CASDDS, CISTI, GNLM, IDS, IE, Infotrieve, ingenta, KNAW, Linda Hall. **CCC.**
Published by: (Scandinavian Physiological Society), Blackwell Publishing Ltd., 9600 Garsington Rd, Oxford, OX4 2ZG, United Kingdom. TEL 44-1865-776868, FAX 44-1865-714591, customerservices@oxon.blackwellpublishing.com, http://www.blackwellpublishing.com/journals/APS. Ed. J Henriksson. Pub. Allen Stevens. R&P Sophie Savage. Adv. contact Jenny Applin. Circ: 1,300.

571 GBR ISSN 0302-2994
QP1 CODEN: APSSAD
ACTA PHYSIOLOGICA SCANDINAVICA. SUPPLEMENTUM. Text in English. 1940. irreg. USD 222 combined subscription in the Americas to individuals & Caribbean (print & online eds.); EUR 198 combined subscription in Europe to individuals (in the Eurozone) print & online eds.; GBP 132 combined subscription elsewhere to individuals print & online eds.; USD 696 combined subscription in the Americas to institutions & Caribbean (print & online eds.); GBP 366 combined subscription in Europe to institutions print & online eds.; GBP 414 combined subscription elsewhere to institutions print & online eds. (effective 2005); included with subscr. to Acta Physiologica Scandinavica. adv. **Document type:** *Academic/Scholarly.*
Formerly: Skandinavisches Archiv fur Physiologie. Supplementum
Related titles: Online - full text ed.: GBP 348 in Europe to institutions; USD 660 in the Americas to institutions; GBP 393 elsewhere to institutions (effective 2005).
Indexed: BIOBASE, CIN, ChemAb, ChemTitl, DSA, ExcerpMed, IABS, IndMed, MEDLINE, NutrAb, SFA, WildRev, ZooRec.
—BLDSC (0655.000000), CASDDS, CISTI, IE, Infotrieve, ingenta, KNAW, Linda Hall. **CCC.**
Published by: (Scandinavian Physiological Society), Blackwell Publishing Ltd., 9600 Garsington Rd, Oxford, OX4 2ZG, United Kingdom. TEL 44-1865-776868, FAX 44-1865-714591, customerservices@oxon.blackwellpublishing.com, http://www.blackwellpublishing.com. Pub. Allen Stevens. R&P Sophie Savage. Adv. contact Jenny Applin.

ADVANCES IN ELECTROMAGNETIC FIELDS IN LIVING SYSTEMS. see *BIOLOGY—Biophysics*

573.6 NLD
ADVANCES IN ORGAN BIOLOGY. Text in English. irreg., latest vol.9. price varies. **Document type:** *Monographic series, Academic/Scholarly.* **Description:** Summarizes new knowledge by researchers seeking to unravel the complex mechanisms of the maintenance and termination of pregnancy. Chapters are devoted to the best studied animal models of parturition.
—BLDSC (0709.559000).
Published by: Elsevier BV (Subsidiary of: Elsevier Science & Technology), Radarweg 29, Amsterdam, 1043 NX, Netherlands. TEL 31-20-4853911, FAX 31-20-4852457, nlinfo-f@elsevier.nl, http://www.elsevier.nl. Ed. E E Bittar TEL 608-262-0784.

612.007 USA ISSN 1043-4046
CODEN: APEDF5
➤ **ADVANCES IN PHYSIOLOGY EDUCATION.** Text in English. 1989. a. USD 35 domestic to non-members; USD 40 in Canada & Mexico to non-members; USD 45 elsewhere to non-members; USD 55 domestic to institutions; USD 60 in Canada & Mexico to institutions; USD 65 elsewhere to institutions; free to members print & online eds. (effective 2006). adv. bibl.; charts; illus. back issues avail. **Document type:** *Journal, Academic/Scholarly.* **Description:** Concerned with issues of education in physiology at all educational levels, covering scholarly essays on the direction and scope of physiology training, as well as practical aids to teaching.
Related titles: Online - full text ed.: ISSN 1522-1229. 2001. free (effective 2006) (from EBSCO Publishing, HighWire Press).
Indexed: ASCA, CIJE, IndMed, MEDLINE, PEI, RefZh.
—BLDSC (0710.045000), CISTI, IDS, Infotrieve. **CCC.**
Published by: American Physiological Society, 9650 Rockville Pike, Bethesda, MD 20814-3991. TEL 301-634-7164, FAX 301-634-7241, mreich@aps.faseb.org, info@the-aps.org, http://advan.physiology.org/, http://www.the-aps.org. Ed. Dee U Silverthorn. adv.: B&W page USD 1,250, color page USD 2,345. Circ: 11,790 (controlled).

➤ **AFRICAN JOURNAL OF BIOMEDICAL RESEARCH.** see *MEDICAL SCIENCES*

571 USA ISSN 0002-9513
QP1 CODEN: AJPHAP
➤ **AMERICAN JOURNAL OF PHYSIOLOGY (CONSOLIDATED).** (Consolidates papers published in all 7 American Journal of Physiology specialty journals.) Text in English. 1898. m. USD 2,280 domestic to non-members; USD 2,410 in Canada & Mexico to non-members; USD 2,655 elsewhere to non-members; USD 3,435 domestic to institutions; USD 3,565 in Canada & Mexico to institutions; USD 3,810 elsewhere to institutions; USD 2,395 combined subscription domestic to non-members print & online eds.; USD 2,525 combined subscription in Canada & Mexico to non-members print & online eds.; USD 2,770 combined subscription elsewhere to non-members print & online eds.; USD 885 combined subscription domestic to members print & online eds.; USD 1,015 combined subscription in Canada & Mexico to members print & online eds.; USD 1,260 combined subscription elsewhere to members print & online eds.; USD 3,595 combined subscription domestic to institutions print & online eds.; USD 3,725 combined subscription in Canada & Mexico to institutions print & online eds.; USD 3,970 combined subscription elsewhere to institutions print & online eds. (effective 2006). adv. bibl.; charts; illus. index, cum.index. back issues avail.; reprint service avail. from PQC,ISI. **Document type:** *Journal, Academic/Scholarly.* **Description:** Includes seven sections: Cell physiology, Endocrinology and metabolism, Gastrointestinal and liver physiology, Heart and circulatory physiology, Lung celluar and molecular physiology, Regulatory, integrative and comparative physiology, Renal physiology.
Related titles: Microform ed.: (from PMC, PQC); Online - full text ed.: A J P Online. USD 1,965 to individuals; USD 2,945 to institutions (effective 2006) (from HighWire Press).
Indexed: AEA, ASFA, AbHyg, AgBio, Agr, AnBrAb, B&AI, BIOSIS Prev, BibAg, BiolAb, CIN, CPA, CRFR, ChemAb, ChemTitl, CurCont, DBA, DSA, DentInd, FPA, ForAb, GSI, HelmAb, HortAb, IABS, ISR, IndMed, IndVet, KWIWR, Kidney, MEDLINE, MSB, MaizeAb, NSCI, NemAb, NutrAb, PBA, PN&I, PoultAb, ProtozoAb, RA&MP, RM&VM, RRTA, RefZh, RevApplEntom, S&F, SAA, SCI, SFA, SIA, SSCI, SoyAb, TDB, VetBull, WeedAb, WildRev, ZooRec.
—BLDSC (0834.000000), CASDDS, CISTI, GNLM, IDS, IE, Infotrieve, ingenta, KNAW, Linda Hall. **CCC.**
Published by: American Physiological Society, 9650 Rockville Pike, Bethesda, MD 20814-3991. TEL 301-634-7164, FAX 301-634-7241, info@the-aps.org, http://ajpcon.physiology.org/, http://www.the-aps.org. adv.: B&W page USD 775, color page USD 1,125. Circ: 2,500.

571.6 USA ISSN 0363-6143
QH631
➤ **AMERICAN JOURNAL OF PHYSIOLOGY: CELL PHYSIOLOGY.** Text in English. 1977. m. USD 425 domestic to non-members; USD 465 in Canada & Mexico to non-members; USD 505 elsewhere to non-members; USD 640 domestic to institutions; USD 680 in Canada & Mexico to institutions; USD 720 elsewhere to institutions; USD 445 combined subscription domestic to non-members print & online eds.; USD 485 combined subscription in Canada & Mexico to non-members print & online eds.; USD 525 combined subscription elsewhere to non-members print & online eds.; USD 180 combined subscription domestic to members print & online eds.; USD 220 combined subscription in Canada & Mexico to members print & online eds.; USD 260 combined subscription elsewhere to members print & online eds.; USD 675 combined subscription domestic to institutions print & online eds.; USD 715 combined subscription in Canada & Mexico to institutions print & online eds.; USD 755 combined subscription elsewhere to institutions print & online eds. (effective 2006). adv. back issues avail.; reprint service avail. from PQC. **Document type:** *Journal, Academic/Scholarly.* **Description:** Provides original, innovative work about normal and abnormal cell functions. Stringently reviewed, thorough and thought-provoking papers are published on the structure and function of cell membranes, contractile systems, and cellular organelles. Audience: Cell biologists, Physiologists, Biochemists and Biophysicists.
Related titles: Microform ed.: (from PQC); Online - full text ed.: A J P: Cell Physiology Online. ISSN 1522-1563. USD 360 to non-members; USD 545 to institutions (effective 2006) (from EBSCO Publishing, HighWire Press).
Indexed: ASCA, AbHyg, B&AI, BBCI, BIOBASE, BiolAb, CTA, ChemAb, CurCont, DentInd, ExcerpMed, IABS, ISR, IndMed, IndVet, Inpharma, KWIWR, MEDLINE, NutrAb, PE&ON, PEI, Reac, SCI, TDB, VetBull.

—CISTI, IDS, IE, Infotrieve. **CCC.**
Published by: American Physiological Society, 9650 Rockville Pike, Bethesda, MD 20814-3991. TEL 301-634-7164, FAX 301-634-7241, mreich@aps.faseb.org, info@the-aps.org, http://intl-ajpcell.physiology.org/, http://www.the-aps.org. Ed. Dennis Brown. adv.: B&W page USD 980, color page USD 2,075. Circ: 3,467 (paid).

573.4 USA ISSN 0193-1849
QP187.A1
➤ **AMERICAN JOURNAL OF PHYSIOLOGY: ENDOCRINOLOGY AND METABOLISM.** Text in English. 1977. m. USD 295 domestic to non-members; USD 335 in Canada & Mexico to non-members; USD 355 elsewhere to non-members; USD 445 domestic to institutions; USD 485 in Canada & Mexico to institutions; USD 505 elsewhere to institutions; USD 320 combined subscription domestic to non-members print & online eds.; USD 360 combined subscription in Canada & Mexico to non-members print & online eds.; USD 380 combined subscription elsewhere to non-members print & online eds.; USD 125 combined subscription domestic to members print & online eds.; USD 165 combined subscription in Canada & Mexico to members print & online eds.; USD 195 combined subscription elsewhere to members print & online eds.; USD 465 combined subscription domestic to institutions print & online eds.; USD 505 combined subscription in Canada & Mexico to institutions print & online eds.; USD 525 combined subscription elsewhere to institutions print & online eds. (effective 2006). back issues avail.; reprint service avail. from PQC. **Document type:** *Journal, Academic/Scholarly.* **Description:** Examines organisms at all levels of endocrine and metabolic systems development, from the subcellular and molecular to the level of whole animal.
Supersedes in part (in 1980): American Journal of Physiology: Endocrinology, Metabolism and Gastrointestinal Physiology (0363-6100)
Related titles: Microform ed.: (from PQC); Online - full text ed.: A J P: Endocrinology and Metabolism Online. ISSN 1522-1555. USD 260 to non-members; USD 385 to institutions (effective 2006) (from EBSCO Publishing, HighWire Press).
Indexed: ASCA, AbHyg, AnBrAb, B&AI, BBCI, BIOBASE, BiolAb, CTA, ChemAb, CurCont, DSA, DentInd, ExcerpMed, IABS, ISR, IndMed, IndVet, Inpharma, KWIWR, MEDLINE, NutrAb, PE&ON, PEI, Reac, SCI, TDB, VetBull.
—CISTI, IDS, IE, Infotrieve. **CCC.**
Published by: American Physiological Society, 9650 Rockville Pike, Bethesda, MD 20814-3991. TEL 301-634-7164, FAX 301-634-7241, info@the-aps.org, http://ajpendo.physiology.org/, http://www.the-aps.org. Eds. J E Pessin, Michael M Mueckler. Circ: 3,553 (paid).

573.3 USA ISSN 0193-1857
QP145
➤ **AMERICAN JOURNAL OF PHYSIOLOGY: GASTROINTESTINAL AND LIVER PHYSIOLOGY.** Text in English. 1977. m. USD 325 domestic to non-members; USD 365 in Canada & Mexico to non-members; USD 385 elsewhere to non-members; USD 480 domestic to institutions; USD 520 in Canada & Mexico to institutions; USD 540 elsewhere to institutions (effective 2006); USD 335 combined subscription domestic to non-members print & online eds. (effective 2005); USD 375 combined subscription in Canada & Mexico to non-members print & online eds.; USD 395 combined subscription elsewhere to non-members print & online eds.; USD 125 combined subscription domestic to members print & online eds.; USD 165 combined subscription in Canada & Mexico to members print & online eds.; USD 185 combined subscription elsewhere to members print & online eds.; USD 510 combined subscription domestic to institutions print & online eds.; USD 550 combined subscription in Canada & Mexico to institutions print & online eds.; USD 570 elsewhere to institutions print & online eds. (effective 2006). abstr. back issues avail. **Document type:** *Journal, Academic/Scholarly.* **Description:** Presents original papers dealing with normal or abnormal function of the alimentary canal and its accessory organs including the salivary glands, pancreas, gallbladder, and liver.
Supersedes in part (in 1980): American Journal of Physiology: Endocrinology, Metabolism and Gastrointestinal Physiology (0363-6100)
Related titles: Online - full text ed.: A J P: Gastrointestinal and Liver Physiology Online. ISSN 1522-1547. USD 280 to non-members; USD 415 to institutions (effective 2006) (from EBSCO Publishing, HighWire Press).
Indexed: ASCA, AbHyg, B&AI, BBCI, BIOBASE, BiolAb, ChemAb, CurCont, DSA, DentInd, ExcerpMed, IABS, ISR, IndMed, IndVet, Inpharma, KWIWR, MEDLINE, NutrAb, PE&ON, Reac, SCI, TDB, VetBull.
—CISTI, IDS, IE, Infotrieve. **CCC.**

Published by: American Physiological Society, 9650 Rockville Pike, Bethesda, MD 20814-3991. TEL 301-634-7164, FAX 301-634-7241, info@the-aps.org, http://intl-ajpgi.physiology.org/, http://www.the-aps.org. Ed. Marshall Montrose. Circ: 3,588 (paid).

573.1 USA ISSN 0363-6135
QP101.2
➤ **AMERICAN JOURNAL OF PHYSIOLOGY: HEART AND CIRCULATORY PHYSIOLOGY.** Text in English. 1977. m. USD 595 domestic to non-members; USD 635 in Canada & Mexico to non-members; USD 695 elsewhere to non-members; USD 885 domestic to institutions; USD 925 in Canada & Mexico to institutions; USD 985 elsewhere to institutions; USD 620 combined subscription domestic to non-members print & online eds.; USD 660 combined subscription in Canada & Mexico to non-members print & online eds.; USD 720 combined subscription elsewhere to non-members print & online eds.; USD 245 combined subscription domestic to members print & online eds.; USD 285 combined subscription in Canada & Mexico to members print & online eds.; USD 345 combined subscription elsewhere to members print & online eds.; USD 935 combined subscription domestic to institutions print & online eds.; USD 975 combined subscription in Canada & Mexico to institutions print & online eds.; USD 1,035 combined subscription elsewhere to institutions print & online eds. (effective 2006). abstr. back issues avail.; reprint service avail. from PQC. **Document type:** *Journal, Academic/Scholarly.* **Description:** Presents experimental and theoretical studies of cardiovascular function at all levels of organization ranging from the intact animal to the cellular, subcellular, and molecular levels.
Related titles: CD-ROM ed.; Microform ed.: (from PQC); Online - full text ed.: A J P: Heart and Circulatory Physiology Online. ISSN 1522-1539. USD 510 to non-members; USD 760 to institutions (effective 2006) (from EBSCO Publishing, HighWire Press).
Indexed: ASCA, AbHyg, B&AI, B&BAb, BBCI, BIOBASE, BiolAb, ChemAb, ChemoAb, CurCont, DentInd, ExcerpMed, IABS, ISR, IndMed, IndVet, Inpharma, KWIWR, MEDLINE, NutrAb, PE&ON, PEI, Reac, RefZh, SCI, TDB, VetBull.
—CISTI, IDS, IE, Infotrieve. **CCC.**
Published by: American Physiological Society, 9650 Rockville Pike, Bethesda, MD 20814-3991. TEL 301-634-7164, FAX 301-634-7241, dharder@mcw.edu, info@the-aps.org, http://intl-ajpheart.physiology.org/, http://www.the-aps.org. Eds. Brenda B Rauner, Alberto Nasjletti. Circ: 3,623 (paid).

571 USA ISSN 1040-0605
QP121.A1 CODEN: APLPE7
➤ **AMERICAN JOURNAL OF PHYSIOLOGY: LUNG CELLULAR AND MOLECULAR PHYSIOLOGY.** Text in English. 1989. m. USD 290 domestic to non-members; USD 330 in Canada & Mexico to non-members; USD 370 elsewhere to non-members; USD 435 domestic to institutions; USD 475 in Canada & Mexico to institutions; USD 515 elsewhere to institutions; USD 305 combined subscription domestic to non-members print & online eds.; USD 345 combined subscription in Canada & Mexico to non-members print & online eds.; USD 385 combined subscription elsewhere to non-members print & online eds.; USD 120 combined subscription domestic to members print & online eds.; USD 160 combined subscription in Canada & Mexico to members print & online eds.; USD 200 combined subscription elsewhere to members print & online eds.; USD 455 combined subscription domestic to institutions print & online eds.; USD 495 combined subscription in Canada & Mexico to institutions print & online eds.; USD 535 combined subscription elsewhere to institutions print & online eds. (effective 2006). abstr. back issues avail. **Document type:** *Journal, Academic/Scholarly.* **Description:** Presents original investigative and theoretical papers dealing with molecular, cellular, and morphological aspects of normal and abnormal function and response of respiratory cell components of the respiratory system.
Related titles: Online - full text ed.: A J P: Lung Cellular and Molecular Physiology Online. ISSN 1522-1504. USD 245 to non-members; USD 365 to institutions (effective 2006) (from EBSCO Publishing, HighWire Press).
Indexed: ASCA, BBCI, BIOBASE, CurCont, ExcerpMed, IABS, ISR, IndMed, Inpharma, MEDLINE, PE&ON, PEI, Reac, RefZh, SCI.
—CISTI, GNLM, IDS, IE, Infotrieve. **CCC.**
Published by: American Physiological Society, 9650 Rockville Pike, Bethesda, MD 20814-3991. TEL 301-634-7164, FAX 301-634-7241, info@the-aps.org, http://intl-ajplung.physiology.org/, http://www.the-aps.org. Ed. Asrar B Malik. Circ: 3,559 (paid and controlled).

571 USA ISSN 0363-6119
QP33
➤ **AMERICAN JOURNAL OF PHYSIOLOGY: REGULATORY, INTEGRATIVE AND COMPARATIVE PHYSIOLOGY.** Text in English. 1977. m. USD 410 domestic to non-members; USD 450 in Canada & Mexico to non-members; USD 490 elsewhere to non-members; USD 620 domestic to institutions; USD 660 in Canada & Mexico to institutions; USD 700 elsewhere to institutions; USD 425 combined subscription domestic to non-members print & online eds.; USD 465 combined subscription in Canada & Mexico to non-members print & online eds.; USD 505 combined subscription elsewhere to non-members print & online eds.; USD 155 combined subscription domestic to members print & online eds.; USD 195 combined subscription in Canada & Mexico to members print & online eds.; USD 235 combined subscription elsewhere to members print & online eds.; USD 640 combined subscription domestic to institutions print & online eds.; USD 680 combined subscription in Canada & Mexico to institutions print & online eds.; USD 720 combined subscription elsewhere to institutions print & online eds. (effective 2006). abstr. back issues avail.; reprint service avail. from PQC. **Document type:** *Journal, Academic/Scholarly.* **Description:** Presents original articles that emphasize relationships between organ systems and control of physiological processes in the whole organism, and articles on comparative physiology.
Related titles: Microform ed.: (from PQC); Online - full text ed.: A J P: Regulatory, Integrative and Comparative Physiology Online. ISSN 1522-1490. USD 350 to non-members; USD 530 to institutions (effective 2006) (from EBSCO Publishing, HighWire Press).
Indexed: ASCA, AbHyg, B&AI, B&BAb, BBCI, BIOBASE, BiolAb, CTA, ChemAb, ChemoAb, CurCont, DentInd, ExcerpMed, IABS, ISR, IndMed, IndVet, Inpharma, KWIWR, MEDLINE, NutrAb, PE&ON, PEI, Reac, SCI, TDB, VetBull.
—CISTI, IDS, IE, Infotrieve. **CCC.**
Published by: American Physiological Society, 9650 Rockville Pike, Bethesda, MD 20814-3991. TEL 301-634-7164, FAX 301-634-7241, info@the-aps.org, http://intl-ajpregu.physiology.org/, http://www.the-aps.org. Ed. Pontus B Persson. Circ: 3,256 (paid).

573.49 USA
QP249
➤ **AMERICAN JOURNAL OF PHYSIOLOGY: RENAL PHYSIOLOGY.** Text in English. 1977. m. USD 295 domestic to non-members; USD 335 in Canada & Mexico to non-members; USD 355 elsewhere to non-members; USD 445 domestic to institutions; USD 485 in Canada & Mexico to institutions; USD 505 elsewhere to institutions; USD 320 combined subscription domestic to non-members print & online eds.; USD 360 combined subscription in Canada & Mexico to non-members print & online eds.; USD 380 combined subscription elsewhere to non-members print & online eds.; USD 145 combined subscription domestic to members print & online eds.; USD 185 combined subscription in Canada & Mexico to members print & online eds.; USD 205 combined subscription elsewhere to members print & online eds.; USD 465 combined subscription domestic to institutions print & online eds.; USD 505 combined subscription in Canada & Mexico to institutions print & online eds.; USD 525 combined subscription elsewhere to institutions print & online eds. (effective 2006). abstr. back issues avail.; reprint service avail. from PQC. **Document type:** *Journal, Academic/Scholarly.* **Description:** Covers subject matter relating to the kidney, urinary tract, and epithelial cell layers. Also covers body fluid volume control and composition.
Formerly (until 1997): American Journal of Physiology: Renal, Fluid and Electrolyte Physiology (0363-6127)
Related titles: Microform ed.: (from PQC); Online - full text ed.: A J P: Renal Physiology Online. ISSN 1522-1466. USD 260 to non-members; USD 385 to institutions (effective 2006) (from EBSCO Publishing, HighWire Press).
Indexed: ASCA, AbHyg, B&AI, BBCI, BIOBASE, BiolAb, ChemAb, CurCont, DentInd, ExcerpMed, IABS, ISR, IndMed, IndVet, Inpharma, KWIWR, MEDLINE, NutrAb, PE&ON, Reac, SCI, TDB, VetBull.
—CISTI, IDS, IE. **CCC.**
Published by: American Physiological Society, 9650 Rockville Pike, Bethesda, MD 20814-3991. TEL 301-634-7164, FAX 301-634-7241, info@the-aps.org, http://intl-ajprenal.physiology.org/, http://www.the-aps.org. Ed. Jeff M Sands. Circ: 3,830 (paid).

612 ZAF
ANATOMIESE VERENIGING VAN SUIDER-AFRIKA. KONGRESVERRIGTINGE/ANATOMICAL SOCIETY OF SOUTHERN AFRICA. PROCEEDINGS OF ANNUAL CONGRESS. Text in Afrikaans, English. 197?. a., latest 1994, 24th, Pretoria. price varies. **Document type:** *Proceedings.*

B

Published by: Anatomiese Vereniging van Suider-Afrika/ Anatomical Society of Southern Africa, c/o Dr HB Groenwald, Dept. Anatomie Fakulteit Veerartsenykunde, Privaatsak X04, Onderstepoort, Pretoria 0110, South Africa.

571 DEU ISSN 0340-2061
QL951 CODEN: ANEMDG

➤ **ANATOMY AND EMBRYOLOGY.** Text in English. 1892. bi-m. EUR 1,698 combined subscription to institutions print & online eds. (effective 2005). adv. bibl.; charts; illus. back issues avail.; reprint service avail. from ISI. **Document type:** *Journal, Academic/Scholarly.* **Description:** Publishes original and review articles on the morphology and developmental biology of vertebrates, with an emphasis on mammals.
Former titles: Journal of Anatomy and Embryology; Zeitschrift fuer Anatomie und Entwicklungsgeschichte (0044-2232)
Related titles: Microform ed.: (from PQC); Online - full text ed.: ISSN 1432-0568 (from EBSCO Publishing, ProQuest Information & Learning, Springer LINK, Swets Information Services).
Indexed: ASCA, AgBio, AnBrAb, BIOBASE, BIOSIS Prev, BiolAb, ChemAb, CurCont, DSA, DentInd, ExcerpMed, HelmAb, IABS, ISR, IndMed, IndVet, Inpharma, MEDLINE, NSCI, PN&I, PoultAb, ProtozoAb, RA&MP, Reac, RefZh, SCI, VetBull, ZooRec.
—BLDSC (0900.030000), CASDDS, CISTI, GNLM, IDS, IE, Infotrieve, ingenta, Linda Hall. **CCC.**
Published by: Springer-Verlag (Subsidiary of: Springer Science+Business Media), Tiergartenstr 17, Heidelberg, 69121, Germany. TEL 49-6221-3450, FAX 49-6221-345229, http://link.springer.de/link/service/journals/00429/index.htm. Adv. contact Stephan Kroeck TEL 49-30-827875739. **Subscr. in the Americas to:** Springer-Verlag New York, Inc., Journal Fulfillment, PO Box 2485, Secaucus, NJ 07096-2485. TEL 800-777-4643, 201-348-4033, FAX 201-348-4505, journals@springer-ny.com, http://www.springer-ny.com; **Subscr. to:** Springer GmbH Auslieferungsgesellschaft, Haberstr 7, Heidelberg 69126, Germany. TEL 49-6221-345-0, FAX 49-6221-345-4229, subscriptions@springer.de.

571.8 USA ISSN 0278-4661
HQ768

➤ **ANNUAL EDITIONS: HUMAN DEVELOPMENT.** Text in English. 1974. a., latest 2003, 32nd ed. USD 20.31 per vol. (effective 2004). illus. **Document type:** *Journal, Academic/Scholarly.* **Description:** Contains a variety of carefully selected articles from the public press, including magazines, newspapers, and journals. Coverage include genetic and parental influences on development, development during infancy and early childhood and many others.
Formerly (until 1981): Annual Editions. Readings in Human Development (0090-5348)
Published by: McGraw-Hill - Dushkin (Subsidiary of: McGraw-Hill Higher Education), 2460 Kerper Blvd, Dubuque, IA 52001. TEL 800-243-6532, customer.service@mcgraw-hill.com, http://www.dushkin.com/text-data/catalog/0072862297.mhtml. Ed. Dr. Karen L. Freiberg. Pub. Ian Nielsen. R&P Cheryl Greenleaf.

571 USA ISSN 0066-4278
QP1 CODEN: ARPHAD

➤ **ANNUAL REVIEW OF PHYSIOLOGY.** Text in English. 1939. a., latest vol.66, 2004. USD 197 to institutions print or online ed.; USD 236 combined subscription to institutions print & online eds. (effective 2006). bibl.; charts; abstr. index, cum.index. back issues avail.; reprint service avail. from PSC. **Document type:** *Academic/Scholarly.* **Description:** Synthesizes and filters primary research to identify the principal contributions in the field of physiology.
Related titles: Microfilm ed.: (from PQC); Online - full content ed.: ISSN 1545-1585. USD 189 (effective 2005) (from HighWire Press); Online - full text ed.: (from bigchalk, EBSCO Publishing, H.W. Wilson, O C L C Online Computer Library Center, Inc., ProQuest Information & Learning, Swets Information Services).
Indexed: ASCA, ASFA, AbHyg, Agr, AnBrAb, B&AI, B&BAb, BIOBASE, BIOSIS Prev, BiolAb, CIN, CTA, ChemAb, ChemTitl, ChemoAb, CurCont, DSA, DentInd, EntAb, ExcerpMed, FoSS&M, GSI, GenetAb, IABS, ISR, IndMed, IndVet, Inpharma, JDDR, MEDLINE, MRD, NSA, NutrAb, PEI, PsycInfo, PsycholAb, Reac, SCI, SSCI, THA, ZooRec, e-psyche.
—BLDSC (1527.000000), CASDDS, CISTI, GNLM, IDS, IE, Infotrieve, ingenta, KNAW, Linda Hall. **CCC.**
Published by: Annual Reviews, 4139 El Camino Way, Palo Alto, CA 94303-0139. TEL 650-493-4400, 800-523-8635, FAX 650-424-0910, service@annualreviews.org, http://arjournals.annualreviews.org/loi/physiol, http://www.annualreviews.org. Ed. Joseph Hoffman. R&P Laura Folkner.

612 DEU ISSN 0920-5268
CODEN: AAPAED

➤ **APPLIED CARDIOPULMONARY PATHOPHYSIOLOGY**; the interface between laboratory and clinical practice. Abbreviated title: A C P. Text in English. 1988. q. EUR 260, USD 212 to institutions (effective 2003). **Document type:** *Academic/Scholarly.*
Related titles: Microform ed.: (from PQC); Online - full text ed.: (from EBSCO Publishing, Gale Group, IngentaConnect).
Indexed: ASCA, CurCont, EngInd, ExcerpMed, ISR, Inpharma, MEDLINE, PE&ON, Reac, SCI.
—BLDSC (1571.921330), CASDDS, CISTI, Ei, GNLM, IDS, IE, Infotrieve, ingenta. **CCC.**
Published by: Pabst Science Publishers, Am Eichengrund 28, Lengerich, 49525, Germany. TEL 49-5484-308, FAX 49-5484-550, pabst.publishers@t-online.de, http://www.pabst-publishers.de.

➤ **ARCHIVES ITALIENNES DE BIOLOGIE**; journal of neuroscience. see *MEDICAL SCIENCES—Psychiatry And Neurology*

571 NLD ISSN 1381-3455
QP1 CODEN: APBIF5

➤ **ARCHIVES OF PHYSIOLOGY AND BIOCHEMISTRY.** Text in English, French. 1885. 5/yr. GBP 363, USD 599 combined subscription to institutions print & online eds. (effective 2006). adv. charts; illus. index, cum.index. Supplement avail.; back issues avail.; reprint service avail. from PSC. **Document type:** *Journal, Academic/Scholarly.* **Description:** Publishes original research papers relating to the various parts of the physiological and biochemical sciences.
Former titles (until 1995): Archives Internationales de Physiologie, de Biochimie et de Biophysique (0778-3124); (until 1991): Archives Internationales de Physiologie et de Biochimie (0003-9799); (until 1955): Archives Internationales de Physiologie (0301-4541); (until 1904): Laboratoire de Leon Fredericq. Travaux (0774-1871)
Related titles: Microfilm ed.: (from PMC); Online - full text ed.: GBP 345, USD 569 to institutions (effective 2006) (from EBSCO Publishing, IngentaConnect, O C L C Online Computer Library Center, Inc., Swets Information Services).
Indexed: ASFA, AbHyg, AgBio, AnBrAb, BBCI, BIOBASE, BIOSIS Prev, BiolAb, CIN, CPA, ChemAb, CurCont, DSA, ESPM, ExcerpMed, FCA, HelmAb, HortAb, IABS, ISR, IndMed, IndVet, Inpharma, MEDLINE, NutrAb, PE&ON, PEI, PN&I, Reac, RefZh, SCI, SIA, SoyAb, TDB, VetBull, ZooRec.
—BLDSC (1639.570000), CASDDS, CISTI, GNLM, IDS, IE, Infotrieve, ingenta, KNAW, Linda Hall. **CCC.**
Published by: Taylor & Francis The Netherlands (Subsidiary of: Taylor & Francis Group), Schipolweg 107 C, PO Box 447, Leiden, 2316 XC, Netherlands. TEL 31-715-243080, FAX 31-715-234571, infoho@swets.nl, http://www.tandf.co.uk/journals/titles/13813455.asp, http://www.tandf.co.uk/swets.asp. Ed. Jurgen Eckel. R&P J van der Valk. adv.: page EUR 300; trim 175 x 228.

571 AUS
CODEN: PAPPCH

AUSTRALIAN PHYSIOLOGICAL AND PHARMACOLOGICAL SOCIETY. PROCEEDINGS (ONLINE EDITION). Text in English. 1970. 2/yr. adv. bk.rev. **Document type:** *Proceedings.*
Former titles: Australian Physiological and Pharmacological Society. Proceedings (Print Edition) (0067-2084); Australian Physiological Society. Proceedings
Media: Online - full content.
Indexed: BiolAb, ChemAb.
—BLDSC (6655.500000), CASDDS, CISTI, GNLM, KNAW.
Published by: Australian Physiological and Pharmacological Society (APPS), c/o Dr Craig Neylon, Department of Anatomy & Cell Biology, University of Melbourne, Melbourne, VIC 3010, Australia. FAX 61-6-2492687, http://www.apps.org.au/Proceedings/. Ed. I McCance. Adv. contact C E Hill. page AUD 330. Circ: 550.

573.8 USA ISSN 1047-5125
CODEN: ANSYEL

➤ **AUTONOMIC NERVOUS SYSTEM.** Text in English. 1991. irreg., latest 1996. price varies. **Document type:** *Monographic series, Academic/Scholarly.*
Indexed: e-psyche.
—BLDSC (1835.053000). **CCC.**
Published by: Taylor & Francis Inc. (Subsidiary of: Taylor & Francis Group), 325 Chestnut St, Ste 800, Philadelphia, PA 19016. TEL 215-625-8900, FAX 215-625-2940, info@taylorandfrancis.com, http://www.taylorandfrancis.com.

573.8 GBR ISSN 1471-2202
RC321 CODEN: BNMEA6

➤ **B M C NEUROSCIENCE.** (BioMed Central) Text in English. 2000. m. free (effective 2006). adv. **Document type:** *Journal, Academic/Scholarly.* **Description:** Publishes original research articles in all aspects of cellular, tissue-level, organismal, functional and developmental aspects of the nervous system.
Media: Online - full content (from EBSCO Publishing, National Library of Medicine).
Indexed: BIOSIS Prev, BiolAb, ExcerpMed, MEDLINE, NSCI.
—Infotrieve. **CCC.**
Published by: BioMed Central Ltd. (Subsidiary of: Current Science Ltd), Middlesex House, 34-42 Cleveland St, London, W1T 4LB, United Kingdom. TEL 44-20-76319131, FAX 44-20-76319923, info@biomedcentral.com, http://www.biomedcentral.com/bmcneurosci/. Ed. Peter Newmark. Adv. contact Deborah Cockerill.

571 GBR ISSN 1472-6793
QP1 CODEN: BPMHCV

➤ **B M C PHYSIOLOGY.** Text in English. 2000. m. free (effective 2006). adv. **Document type:** *Journal, Academic/Scholarly.* **Description:** Publishes original research articles in cellular, tissue-level, organismal, functional, and developmental aspects of physiological processes.
Media: Online - full content (from EBSCO Publishing, National Library of Medicine).
Indexed: BIOSIS Prev, BiolAb, ExcerpMed, MEDLINE, ZooRec.
—Infotrieve. **CCC.**
Published by: BioMed Central Ltd. (Subsidiary of: Current Science Ltd), Middlesex House, 34-42 Cleveland St, London, W1T 4LB, United Kingdom. TEL 44-20-76319131, FAX 44-20-76319923, info@biomedcentral.com, http://www.biomedcentral.com/bmcphysiol/. Ed. Peter Newmark. Adv. contact Deborah Cockerill.

571.1 GBR ISSN 1359-1533

BABRAHAM INSTITUTE. CORPORATE PLAN. Text in English. 1995. irreg. price varies. stat.; charts; illus. back issues avail. **Document type:** *Corporate.* **Description:** Presents a five-year plan for the institute that includes discussion of the mission statement, research strategy, education and training programs, and institute structure and finance.
Published by: Babraham Institute, Babraham Institute, Babraham Hall, Babraham, Cambridge, CB2 4AT, United Kingdom. TEL 44-1223-496000, FAX 44-1223-496020, babraham.contact@bbsrc.ac.uk, http://www.babraham.ac.uk. Eds. Caroline Edmonds, Mary Read, Richard Dyer. Pub. Caroline Edmonds. Circ: 1,500 (controlled).

571.1 GBR ISSN 1354-8425

BABRAHAM INSTITUTE. REPORT. Text in English. 1960. a. price varies. illus. **Document type:** *Corporate.*
Former titles (until 1994): Institute of Animal Physiology and Genetics Research. Report (0959-5783); Institute of Animal Physiology. Report (0065-4507)
Related titles: Online - full text ed.
Indexed: AnBrAb.
—BLDSC (1854.610700).
Published by: Babraham Institute, Babraham Institute, Babraham Hall, Babraham, Cambridge, CB2 4AT, United Kingdom. TEL 44-1223-496000, FAX 44-1223-496020, babraham.contact@bbsrc.ac.uk, http://www.babraham.ac.uk. Eds. Don Powell, Mary Read. Pub. Caroline Edmonds. Circ: 1,500.

BABRAHAM PUBLICATIONS. see *BIOLOGY—Biochemistry*

573.6 USA ISSN 0523-6754
CODEN: BIRSB5

BIOLOGY OF REPRODUCTION. SUPPLEMENT. Text in English. 1969. a. back issues avail. **Document type:** *Academic/Scholarly.*
Related titles: ◆ Supplement to: Biology of Reproduction. ISSN 0006-3363.
Indexed: BiolAb.
—CISTI, IE, Infotrieve. **CCC.**
Published by: Society for the Study of Reproduction, 1619 Monroe St., Madison, WI 53711-2063. TEL 608-256-2777, FAX 608-256-4610, ssr@ssr.org, http://www.ssr.org.

BIOLOGY OF SPORT; a quarterly journal of sport and exercise sciences. see *MEDICAL SCIENCES—Sports Medicine*

THE BREAST JOURNAL. see *MEDICAL SCIENCES—Obstetrics And Gynecology*

612.664 USA ISSN 1556-8253

▼ **BREASTFEEDING MEDICINE.** Text in English. forthcoming 2006 (Spr.). q. USD 425, USD 449 to institutions; USD 499, USD 523 combined subscription to institutions print & online eds. (effective 2006).
Related titles: Online - full text ed.: ISSN 1556-8342. forthcoming 2006 (Spr.). USD 399 (effective 2006).
Published by: Mary Ann Liebert, Inc. Publishers, 140 Huguenot St 3rd Fl, New Rochelle, NY 10801-5215. TEL 914-740-2100, FAX 914-740-2101, 800-654-3237, info@liebertpub.com, http://www.liebertpub.com.

BUREIN SAIENSU/BRAIN SCIENCE. see *MEDICAL SCIENCES—Psychiatry And Neurology*

BUREIN SAIENSU SAIZENSEN/FRONTIERS OF BRAIN SCIENCE. see *MEDICAL SCIENCES—Psychiatry And Neurology*

571 JPN ISSN 0387-9666

BYOTAI SEIRI (TOKYO)/JOURNAL OF PATHOLOGICAL PHYSIOLOGY. Text in Japanese. 1964. irreg.
Published by: Tokyo Hokenkai, Byotai Seiri Kenkyujo/Tokyo Hokenkai Foundation, Pathological Physiology Laboratory, 47-11 Kumano-cho, Itabashi-ku, Tokyo, 173-0025, Japan.

612 JPN ISSN 0917-6225

BYOTAI SEIRI TO SHINDAN CHIRYO/SANWA KAGAKU CO. MEDICAL REPORT. Text in Japanese. 1980. s-a.
Published by: Sanwa Kagaku Kenkyujo/Sanwa Kagaku Co., Ltd., 35 Higashi-Sotobori-cho, Higashi-ku, Nagoya-shi, Aichi-ken 461-0017, Japan.

571 GBR ISSN 0951-077X
CODEN: CESSDT

CAMBRIDGE TEXTS IN THE PHYSIOLOGICAL SCIENCES. Text in English. 1979. irreg. price varies. **Document type:** *Monographic series.*
Indexed: BiolAb.

Published by: Cambridge University Press, The Edinburgh Bldg, Shaftesbury Rd, Cambridge, CB2 2RU, United Kingdom. TEL 44-1223-312393, FAX 44-1223-315052, information@cambridge.org, http://publishing.cambridge.org/series/ctps, http://www.cup.cam.ac.uk/. R&P Linda Nicol TEL 44-1223-325757.

571 CAN ISSN 0008-4212
QP1 CODEN: CJPPA3

➤ **CANADIAN JOURNAL OF PHYSIOLOGY AND PHARMACOLOGY/JOURNAL CANADIEN DE PHYSIOLOGIE ET PHARMACOLOGIE.** Text mainly in English; Text occasionally in French. 1929. m. CND 167 domestic to individuals; USD 167 foreign to individuals; CND 498 domestic to institutions; USD 498 foreign to institutions (effective 1999). adv. bibl.; illus. index. back issues avail.; reprint service avail. from PQC. **Document type:** *Academic/Scholarly.*

Formerly (until 1964): Canadian Journal of Biochemistry and Physiology (0576-5544); Which supersedes in part (in 1954): Canadian Journal of Medical Sciences (0316-4403); Which was formerly (until 1951): Canadian Journal of Research. Section E: Medical Sciences (0366-743X)

Related titles: Microfiche ed.: (from MML); Microform ed.: (from MML, PMC, PQC); Online - full text ed.: ISSN 1205-7541 (from bigchalk, EBSCO Publishing, Gale Group, IngentaConnect, Micromedia ProQuest, O C L C Online Computer Library Center, Inc., ProQuest Information & Learning, Swets Information Services).

Indexed: ASCA, AbHyg, AgBio, AgrForAb, AnBrAb, AnalAb, ApicAb, BIOBASE, BIOSIS Prev, BioDAb, BiolAb, CBCARef, CIN, ChemAb, ChemTitl, CurCont, DBA, DSA, DentInd, DokArb, ExcerpMed, FPA, ForAb, HortAb, IABS, ISR, IndMed, IndVet, Inpharma, MEDLINE, MS&D, NSCI, NutrAb, OrnHort, PE&ON, PN&I, PoultAb, ProtozoAb, RA&MP, RM&VM, RRTA, Reac, RefZh, SCI, SIA, SoyAb, TDB, THA, VITIS, VetBull, WeedAb, WildRev.

—BLDSC (3034.300000), CASDDS, CINDOC, CISTI, GNLM, IDS, IE, Infotrieve, ingenta, Linda Hall. **CCC.**

Published by: N R C Research Press, Building M 55, Ottawa, ON K1A 0R6, Canada. TEL 613-993-0362, 800-668-1222, FAX 613-952-7656, research.journals@nrc.ca, pubs@nrc-cnrc.gc.ca, http://pubs.nrc-cnrc.gc.ca/cgi-bin/rp/rp2_desc_e?cjpp. Ed. Bruce P Dancik. Adv. contact Judy Heyman. B&W page CND 675; trim 11 x 8.5. Circ: 854.

571 GBR ISSN 0379-864X
QP455 CODEN: CHSED8

➤ **CHEMICAL SENSES.** Text in English. 1974. 9/yr. GBP 534, USD 961, EUR 840 to institutions; GBP 562, USD 1,012, EUR 843 combined subscription to institutions print & online eds. (effective 2006). adv. bk.rev. illus. index. 96 p./no.; back issues avail.; reprint service avail. from PSC. **Document type:** *Journal, Academic/Scholarly.* **Description:** International forum for chemoreception research at morphological, biochemical, physiological and psychophysical levels. Covers development and specific application of new methods.

Formerly (until 1980): Chemical Senses and Flavour (0302-2471)

Related titles: Online - full text ed.: ISSN 1464-3553. GBP 506, USD 911, EUR 759 to institutions (effective 2006) (from EBSCO Publishing, Gale Group, HighWire Press, IngentaConnect, O C L C Online Computer Library Center, Inc., Ovid Technologies, Inc., Oxford University Press Online Journals, ProQuest Information & Learning, Swets Information Services).

Indexed: ASCA, ASFA, AgBio, AnBeAb, AnBrAb, B&BAb, BioCN&I, CIN, CRFR, ChemAb, ChemTitl, ChemoAb, CurCont, EntAb, ExcerpMed, FS&TA, HortAb, ISR, IndMed, IndVet, Inpharma, MEDLINE, MaizeAb, NSA, NSCI, NemAb, NutrAb, PGegResA, PGrRegA, PN&I, PotatoAb, PoultAb, PsycInfo, PsycholAb, RA&MP, RM&VM, Reac, RevApplEntom, SCI, SFA, SIA, SSCI, SoyAb, TDB, VITIS, VetBull, ZooRec, e-psyche.

—BLDSC (3151.510000), CASDDS, CISTI, GNLM, IDS, IE, Infotrieve, ingenta, Linda Hall. **CCC.**

Published by: (European Chemoreception Organization), Oxford University Press, Great Clarendon St, Oxford, OX2 6DP, United Kingdom. TEL 44-1865-556767, FAX 44-1865-556646, jnl.orders@oup.co.uk, http://chemse.oxfordjournals.org/, http://www.oxfordjournals.org/. Pub. David Prosser. R&P Fiona Bennett. adv.: B&W page USD 415, B&W page GBP 230; trim 216 x 279. Circ: 560. **Co-sponsor:** Association for Chemoreception Sciences.

571 CHN ISSN 0258-6428

➤ **CHINESE JOURNAL OF PHYSIOLOGICAL SCIENCES.** Text in English. 1985. q. USD 145 domestic to individuals; USD 165 foreign to individuals; USD 245 domestic to institutions; USD 265 foreign to institutions (effective 1999). adv. 96 p./no.; **Document type:** *Academic/Scholarly.*

Related titles: ♦ Chinese ed.: Shengli Xuebao. ISSN 0371-0874.

—CISTI, GNLM, KNAW.

Published by: (Shanghai Institute of Physiology), Kexue Chubanshe/Science Press, 16 Donghuang Cheng Genbei Jie, Beijing, 100717, China. TEL 86-10-64000246, FAX 86-10-64030255. Circ: 6,000. **Overseas dist. by:** Science Press New York Ltd.

571 TWN ISSN 0304-4920
QP1 CODEN: CJPHDG

CHINESE JOURNAL OF PHYSIOLOGY/CHUNG-KUO SHENG LI HSUEH TSA CHIH. Text in English. 1927. q. TWD 2,000, USD 80 to individuals; TWD 3,000, USD 120 to institutions (effective 2005). adv. abstr.; bibl.; charts; illus. **Document type:** *Journal, Academic/Scholarly.* **Description:** Contains original papers concerned with all fields of physiology, pharmacology, anatomy, and biochemistry.

Indexed: BIOSIS Prev, BiolAb, CIN, ChemAb, ChemTitl, CurCont, ExcerpMed, ISR, IndMed, MEDLINE, SCI.

—BLDSC (3180.550000), CASDDS, GNLM, IDS, IE, Infotrieve, ingenta, KNAW.

Published by: Chinese Physiological Society/Chung-kuo Sheng Li Hsueh Hui, c/o Dr. Eminy H.Y. Lee, Ph.D., Institute of Biomedical Sciences, Academia Sinica, Taipei, 115, Taiwan. TEL 886-2-27899125, FAX 886-2-27822835, eminy@ibms.sinica.edu.tw, http://www.ibms.sinica.edu.tw/~cjp/welcome.html. Ed. Eminy H. Y. Lee. Circ: 1,000.

612.8 JPN ISSN 0300-0338

CHOKAKU GENGO SHOGAI/COMMUNICATION DISORDER RESEARCH. Text in Japanese; Summaries in English. 1972. q. JPY 4,000.

Indexed: e-psyche.

Published by: Chokaku Gengo Shogai Kenkyukai/Research Association of Communication Disorder, Tokyo Gakugei Daigaku Tokushu Kyoiku Shisetsu, 1-1 Nukui-Kita-Machi 4-chome, Koganei-shi, Tokyo-to 184-0015, Japan.

571 AUS ISSN 0305-1870
RM1 CODEN: CEXPB9

➤ **CLINICAL AND EXPERIMENTAL PHARMACOLOGY & PHYSIOLOGY.** Text in English. 1974. m. GBP 592 combined subscription in Australia & New Zealand to institutions print & online eds.; USD 1,573 combined subscription in the Americas to institutions & Caribbean, print & online eds.; GBP 971 combined subscription elsewhere to institutions print & online eds. (effective 2006). adv. back issues avail.; reprint service avail. from PQC. **Document type:** *Academic/Scholarly.* **Description:** Compiles original contributions relating to the broad fields of pharmacology and physiology.

Incorporates: Australian Society for Medical Research. Proceedings (0067-2130); Which superseded (1961-1965): Medical Research (0311-9556)

Related titles: Online - full text ed.: ISSN 1440-1681. GBP 562 in Australia & New Zealand to institutions; USD 1,494 in the Americas to institutions & Caribbean; GBP 922 elsewhere to institutions (effective 2006) (from Blackwell Synergy, EBSCO Publishing, Gale Group, IngentaConnect, O C L C Online Computer Library Center, Inc., Ovid Technologies, Inc., Swets Information Services); Supplement(s): Clinical and Experimental Pharmacology & Physiology. Supplement. ISSN 0143-9294. 1974.

Indexed: ASCA, AbHyg, AgBio, AgrForAb, AnBrAb, BIOBASE, BIOSIS Prev, BioCN&I, BiolAb, CIN, CTA, ChemAb, ChemTitl, CurCont, DBA, DSA, DentInd, ExcerpMed, HortAb, IABS, ISR, IndMed, IndVet, Inpharma, MEDLINE, NSCI, NutrAb, PE&ON, PEI, PN&I, ProtozoAb, RA&MP, Reac, SCI, SoyAb, TDB, THA, VetBull, WeedAb.

—BLDSC (3286.252000), CASDDS, CISTI, GNLM, IDS, IE, Infotrieve, ingenta, KNAW, Linda Hall. **CCC.**

Published by: (Australasian Society of Clinical and Experimental Pharmacologists), Blackwell Publishing Asia (Subsidiary of: Blackwell Publishing Ltd.), 550 Swanston St, Carlton South, VIC 3053, Australia. TEL 61-383591011, FAX 61-383591120, subs@blackwellpublishingasia.com, http://www.blackwellpublishing.com/journals/CEP. Ed. Dr. Warwick P Anderson. Adv. contact Kathryn O'Brien. B&W page AUD 1,012, color page AUD 2,057; trim 210 x 275. Circ: 650. **Subscr. to:** PO Box 378, Carlton South, VIC 3053, Australia.

➤ **CLINICAL DYSMORPHOLOGY.** see *BIOLOGY*

➤ **CLINICAL PHYSIOLOGY AND FUNCTIONAL IMAGING.** see *MEDICAL SCIENCES*

571 USA

CLINICAL PHYSIOLOGY SERIES. Text in English. 1977. irreg. price varies. **Document type:** *Monographic series, Academic/Scholarly.* **Description:** Series is designed as a bridge between basic science and clinical medicine.

Published by: American Physiological Society, 9650 Rockville Pike, Bethesda, MD 20814-3991. TEL 301-634-7164, FAX 301-634-7241, info@the-aps.org, http://www.faseb.org/aps, http://www.the-aps.org.

571.1 AUS

COMMONWEALTH SCIENTIFIC AND INDUSTRIAL RESEARCH ORGANISATION. DIVISION OF LIVESTOCK INDUSTRIES. DIVISIONAL INFORMATION SHEETS. Text in English. 1969. irreg. free. **Document type:** *Government.*

Former titles (until 2000): Commonwealth Scientific and Industrial Research Organisation. Division of Animal Production. Divisional Information Sheets; (until 1993): C S I R O Division of Animal Production. Technical Report; (until 1975): C S I R O Division of Animal Physiology. Technical Report (0084-9014)

Published by: C S I R O, Division of Livestock Industries, Public Affairs & Communication, Delivery Centre, Locked Bag 1, Blacktown, NSW 2148, Australia. TEL 61-2-98402700, FAX 61-2-98402940, catherine.young@li.csiro.au, http://www.li.csiro.au. R&P Pat Wilson TEL 61-2-98402741.

575.1 AUS

COMMONWEALTH SCIENTIFIC AND INDUSTRIAL RESEARCH ORGANIZATION. DIVISION OF ANIMAL PRODUCTION. DIVISIONAL INFORMATION. Text in English. irreg. **Document type:** *Corporate.*

Former titles (until 1993): C S I R O Division of Animal Production. Research Report (0155-7742); (until 1976): C S I R O Division of Animal Physiology. Report (0069-7281)

Indexed: BiolAb.

—CISTI.

Published by: C S I R O, Division of Livestock Industries, Public Affairs & Communication, Delivery Centre, Locked Bag 1, Blacktown, NSW 2148, Australia. TEL 61-2-98402700, FAX 61-2-98402940, p.wilson@prospect.anprod.csiro.au, catherine.young@li.csiro.au, http://www.anprod.csiro.au, http://www.li.csiro.au. Ed., R&P Pat Wilson TEL 61-2-98402741.

571 USA ISSN 1095-6433
QP33 CODEN: CBPAB5

➤ **COMPARATIVE BIOCHEMISTRY AND PHYSIOLOGY. PART A: MOLECULAR & INTEGRATIVE PHYSIOLOGY.** Text and summaries in English, French, German. 1961. 12/yr. EUR 5,336 in Europe to institutions; JPY 708,900 in Japan to institutions; USD 5,971 elsewhere to institutions (effective 2006). adv. bk.rev. bibl.; charts; illus. back issues avail. **Document type:** *Journal, Academic/Scholarly.* **Description:** Presents original research on the biochemistry and physiology of animals.

Former titles (until 1997): Comparative Biochemistry and Physiology. Part A: Physiology (1096-4940); (until 1994): Comparative Biochemistry and Physiology. Part A: Comparative Physiology (0300-9629)

Related titles: Microfiche ed.: (from MIM); Microfilm ed.: (from PQC); Online - full text ed.: (from EBSCO Publishing, Gale Group, IngentaConnect, ScienceDirect, Swets Information Services).

Indexed: AEA, ASCA, ASFA, AbHyg, AgBio, Agr, AnBeAb, AnBrAb, ApicAb, B&BAb, BBCI, BIOBASE, BIOSIS Prev, BibAg, BioCN&I, BiolAb, CPA, CRFR, ChemAb, CurCont, DSA, DentInd, ESPM, EntAb, ExcerpMed, FCA, FS&TA, ForAb, GenetAb, HerbAb, HortAb, IABS, ISR, IndMed, IndVet, Inpharma, KWIWR, MEDLINE, MaizeAb, NSCI, NemAb, NutrAb, OceAb, PBA, PE&ON, PN&I, PotatoAb, PoultAb, ProtozoAb, RA&MP, RM&VM, RRTA, Reac, RefZh, RevApplEntom, S&F, SAA, SCI, SFA, SIA, SeedAb, SoyAb, TriticAb, VetBull, WeedAb, WildRev, ZooRec.

—BLDSC (3363.751000), CISTI, GNLM, IE, Infotrieve, ingenta, Linda Hall. **CCC.**

Published by: Elsevier Inc. (Subsidiary of: Elsevier Science & Technology), 360 Park Ave. S, New York, NY 10010-1710. TEL 212-633-3730, 888-437-4636, usinfo-f@elsevier.com, http://www.elsevier.com/locate/cbpa. Eds. Patrick J. Walsh, Thomas P Mommsen. adv.: B&W page USD 550, color page USD 1,350. Circ: 2,000. **Subscr. outside the Americas to:** Elsevier BV, PO Box 211, Amsterdam 1000 AE, Netherlands. TEL 31-20-485-3757, FAX 31-20-485-3432.

➤ **COMPARATIVE BIOCHEMISTRY AND PHYSIOLOGY. PART B: BIOCHEMISTRY & MOLECULAR BIOLOGY.** see *BIOLOGY—Biochemistry*

▼ ➤ **COMPARATIVE BIOCHEMISTRY AND PHYSIOLOGY. PART D: GENOMICS AND PROTEOMICS.** see *BIOLOGY—Biochemistry*

571.3 IND ISSN 0379-0436
QH540 CODEN: CPECDM

COMPARATIVE PHYSIOLOGY AND ECOLOGY. Text in English. 1976. q. USD 28.

Indexed: ASFA, BioCN&I, BiolAb, CRFR, ChemAb, CurCont, ESPM, EntAb, ExcerpMed, FCA, GenetAb, HGA, HortAb, ISR, IndVet, OceAb, PoultAb, RiceAb, S&F, SCI, VetBull, WeedAb.

—CASDDS, CISTI, Linda Hall. **CCC.**

Published by: Impex India, M-S Premier Publication, 863 Sadarpura, Behind Syndicate Bank, Jodhpur, Rajasthan 342 003, India.

571 GBR ISSN 0143-2044
QC277.9 CODEN: CRLED9

➤ **CRYO-LETTERS.** Variant title: CryoLetters. Text in English. 1979. bi-m. GBP 55, EUR 85, USD 100 to individuals; GBP 150, EUR 225, USD 275 to institutions (effective 2005). adv. bk.rev. index. Supplement avail. **Document type:** *Newsletter, Academic/Scholarly.* **Description:** Contains original research reports, authoritative reviews, technical developments and commissioned book reviews of studies involving low temperature techniques in the investigation of physical chemical, biological and ecological problems, or the effects produced by low temperatures in a wide variety of scientific and technical processes.

Related titles: Online - full text ed.: ISSN 1742-0644 (from EBSCO Publishing, Gale Group, IngentaConnect).

Indexed: ASCA, AgBio, Agr, AgrForAb, AnBrAb, BIOBASE, BIOSIS Prev, BibAg, BioCN&I, BiolAb, CIN, CPA, ChemAb, ChemTitl, CurCont, FCA, ForAb, HerbAb, HortAb, IABS, ISR, IndVet, Inpharma, MaizeAb, OrnHort, PBA, PGegResA, PGrRegA, PHN&I, PN&I, PlantSci, PotatoAb, PoultAb, RA&MP, RM&VM, RPP, Reac, RefZh, RevApplEntom, RiceAb, S&F, SCI, SFA, SIA, SeedAb, SoyAb, VITIS, VetBull, WeedAb, ZooRec.

—BLDSC (3490.133000), CASDDS, CISTI, IDS, IE, Infotrieve, ingenta. **CCC.**
Published by: CryoLetters, c/o Royal Veterinary College, Dept. of Veterinary Basic Sciences, Royal College St, London, NW1 0TU, United Kingdom. FAX 44-20-73881027, cryoletters@rvc.ac.uk, http://www.cryoletters.org/, http://www.rvc.ac.uk. Ed., Pub., R&P, Adv. contact P F Watson. Circ: 250 (paid).

➤ **CURRENT MEDICAL LITERATURE. G H AND GROWTH FACTORS.** (Growth Hormone) see *MEDICAL SCIENCES*

➤ **CURRENT OPINION IN NEUROBIOLOGY.** see *MEDICAL SCIENCES—Psychiatry And Neurology*

➤ **DREAMING.** see *PSYCHOLOGY*

571 610 GBR ISSN 1477-741X
THE E S H R E MONOGRAPHS. (European Society for Human Reproduction and Embryology) Text in English. a. **Document type:** *Journal, Academic/Scholarly.*
Related titles: Online - full text ed.: ISSN 1477-8378 (from EBSCO Publishing, HighWire Press).
Indexed: ExcerpMed.
Published by: (European Society of Human Reproduction and Embryology BEL), Oxford University Press, Great Clarendon St, Oxford, OX2 6DP, United Kingdom. TEL 44-1865-556767, FAX 44-1865-556646, http://eshremonographs.oupjournals.org.

B

571 EGY ISSN 0301-8660
QH301
➤ **EGYPTIAN JOURNAL OF PHYSIOLOGICAL SCIENCE/AL-MAGALLAT AL-MISSRIYAT LIL-'LUM AL-FISIULUGIYYAT.** Text in English; Summaries in Arabic, English. 1974. 3/yr. USD 112 (effective 2003). abstr.; charts; illus. back issues avail.; reprint service avail. from IRC. **Document type:** *Journal, Academic/Scholarly.*
Formerly: Egyptian Journal of Physiology
Indexed: AgBio, AnBrAb, BiolAb, CIN, CPA, ChemAb, ChemTitl, DSA, FCA, HelmAb, HerbAb, HortAb, IndVet, MaizeAb, NutrAb, OrnHort, PBA, PGrRegA, PotatoAb, ProtozoAb, RA&MP, RM&VM, RPP, RevApplEntom, S&F, SIA, SeedAb, SoyAb, TriticAb, VetBull, WeedAb.
—BLDSC (3664.417000), CASDDS, CISTI, GNLM, IE, Linda Hall.
Published by: (Egyptian Physiological Society, Research Department), National Information and Documentation Centre (NIDOC), Tahrir St., Dokki, Awqaf P.O., Giza, Egypt. TEL 20-2-3371696, FAX 20-2-3371746, http://derp.sti.sci.eg/data/0129.htm. Ed. Dr. H Hamed. Circ: 1,000.

➤ **ELECTROMYOGRAPHY AND CLINICAL NEUROPHYSIOLOGY.** see *MEDICAL SCIENCES—Psychiatry And Neurology*

➤ **ENDOCRINE.** see *MEDICAL SCIENCES—Endocrinology*

➤ **ENDOTHELIUM.** see *BIOLOGY—Abstracting, Bibliographies, Statistics*

▼ ➤ **EQUINE AND COMPARATIVE EXERCISE PHYSIOLOGY;** the international journal of animal exercise physiology, biomechanics and nutrition. see *SPORTS AND GAMES—Horses And Horsemanship*

➤ **EUROPEAN JOURNAL OF ANATOMY.** see *MEDICAL SCIENCES*

571 DEU ISSN 1439-6319
QP1 CODEN: EJAPCK
➤ **EUROPEAN JOURNAL OF APPLIED PHYSIOLOGY.** Text in English. 18/yr. EUR 3,598 combined subscription to institutions print & online eds. (effective 2005). adv. reprint service avail. from ISI,PSC. **Document type:** *Journal, Academic/Scholarly.* **Description:** Contains articles with an emphasis on environmental and work physiology.
Former titles (until vol.81, no.3): European Journal of Applied Physiology and Occupational Physiology (0301-5548); (until 1973): Internationale Zeitschrift fuer Angewandte Physiologie Einschliesslich Arbeitsphysiologie (0020-9376); Which incorporated (1928-1954): Arbeitsphysiologie (0365-0863); (1937-1944): Luftfahrtmedizin (0368-7651)
Related titles: Microform ed.: (from PQC); Online - full text ed.: ISSN 1439-6327 (from EBSCO Publishing, Springer LINK, Swets Information Services).
Indexed: AMED, ASCA, BIOSIS Prev, BiolAb, CIN, CISA, ChemAb, ChemTitl, CurCont, ESPM, ErgAb, ExcerpMed, FoSS&M, H&SSA, HRIS, ISR, IndMed, Inpharma, MEDLINE, NSCI, NutrAb, PE&ON, PEI, Reac, RefZh, SCI, SIA, SSCI, SportS, TDB, THA.
—BLDSC (3829.722450), CASDDS, CISTI, GNLM, IDS, IE, Infotrieve, ingenta. **CCC.**
Published by: Springer-Verlag (Subsidiary of: Springer Science+Business Media), Tiergartenstr 17, Heidelberg, 69121, Germany. TEL 49-6221-3450, FAX 49-6221-345229, http://link.springer.de/link/service/journals/00421/index.htm. Ed. Dr. P E di Prampero. Adv. contact Stephan Kroeck TEL 49-30-827875739. **Subscr. in the Americas to:** Springer-Verlag New York, Inc., Journal Fulfillment, PO Box 2485, Secaucus, NJ 07096-2485. TEL 201-348-4033, FAX 201-348-4505, journals@springer-ny.com, http://www.springer-ny.com; **Subscr. to:** Springer GmbH Auslieferungsgesellschaft, Haberstr 7, Heidelberg 69126, Germany. TEL 49-6221-345-0, FAX 49-6221-345-4229, subscriptions@springer.de.

➤ **EUROPEAN JOURNAL OF MORPHOLOGY;** incorporating European archives & biology. see *BIOLOGY*

➤ **EXCERPTA MEDICA. SECTION 1: ANATOMY, ANTHROPOLOGY, EMBRYOLOGY & HISTOLOGY.** see *BIOLOGY—Abstracting, Bibliographies, Statistics*

➤ **EXCERPTA MEDICA. SECTION 2: PHYSIOLOGY.** see *MEDICAL SCIENCES—Abstracting, Bibliographies, Statistics*

➤ **EXCERPTA MEDICA. SECTION 21: DEVELOPMENTAL BIOLOGY AND TERATOLOGY.** see *BIOLOGY—Abstracting, Bibliographies, Statistics*

571.1 GBR ISSN 0958-0670
QP1 CODEN: EXPHEZ
➤ **EXPERIMENTAL PHYSIOLOGY.** Text in English. 1908. bi-m. GBP 85, EUR 128 combined subscription in Europe to individuals print & online eds.; USD 158 combined subscription in the Americas to individuals print & online eds.; GBP 93 combined subscription elsewhere to individuals print & online eds.; GBP 428 combined subscription in Europe to institutions print & online eds.; USD 791 combined subscription in the Americas to institutions & Caribbean (print & online eds.); GBP 471 combined subscription elsewhere to institutions print & online eds. (effective 2006). adv. bk.rev. Supplement avail.; back issues avail.; reprint service avail. from PSC. **Document type:** *Journal, Academic/Scholarly.* **Description:** Contains research papers on all aspects of experimental physiology from molecular to animal studies.
Former titles (until 1989): Quarterly Journal of Experimental Physiology and Cognate Medical Sciences (0144-8757); (until 1980): Quarterly journal of experimental physiology and cognate medical sciences (0033-5541); (until 1937): Quarterly journal of experimental physiology (0370-2901)
Related titles: Microform ed.: (from PMC, PQC); Online - full text ed.: ISSN 1469-445X. GBP 407 in Europe to institutions; USD 751 in the Americas to institutions & Caribbean; GBP 447 elsewhere to institutions (effective 2006) (from Blackwell Synergy, EBSCO Publishing, Gale Group, HighWire Press, IngentaConnect, O C L C Online Computer Library Center, Inc., Swets Information Services).
Indexed: ASCA, AgBio, AnBrAb, BIOBASE, BIOSIS Prev, BiolAb, CIN, ChemAb, ChemTitl, CurCont, DSA, ExcerpMed, HelmAb, HortAb, IABS, ISR, IndMed, IndVet, Inpharma, MEDLINE, NSCI, NemAb, NutrAb, PE&ON, PEI, PN&I, PoultAb, RA&MP, RRTA, Reac, RefZh, RiceAb, SAA, SCI, THA, TriticAb, VetBull.
—BLDSC (3840.040000), CASDDS, CISTI, GNLM, IDS, IE, Infotrieve, ingenta, KNAW, Linda Hall. **CCC.**
Published by: (Physiological Society), Blackwell Publishing Ltd., 9600 Garsington Rd, Oxford, OX4 2ZG, United Kingdom. TEL 44-1865-776868, FAX 44-1865-714591, customerservices@oxon.blackwellpublishing.com, http://www.blackwellpublishing.com/journals/EPH. Ed. John Coote. Circ: 750.

➤ **F E M S YEAST RESEARCH.** see *BIOLOGY—Microbiology*

571 UKR
QP1 CODEN: FIZHDO
FIZIOLOGICHNYI ZHURNAL/FIZIOLOGICHNYI ZHURNAL; nauchno-teoreticheskii zhurnal. Text in Ukrainian; Summaries in English. 1955. bi-m. USD 135 in United States (effective 2004). bk.rev. illus. index.
Former titles: Fiziologicheskii Zhurnal (Kiev) (0201-8489); (until 1978): Fiziologichnyi Zhurnal (0015-3311)
Indexed: BIOSIS Prev, BiolAb, ChemAb, Djerelo, ExcerpMed, INIS AtomInd, ISR, IndMed, MEDLINE, NSCI, PoultAb, RefZh, VetBull.
—CASDDS, CISTI, East View, GNLM, KNAW, Linda Hall. **CCC.**
Published by: Natsional'na Akademiya Nauk Ukrainy, Instytut Fiziolohii im. Bohomol'tsya/National Academy of Sciences of Ukraine, Bogomoletz Institute of Physiology, vul Bogomol'tsya 4, Kyiv, 01024, Ukraine. fiziol_z@serv.biph.kiev.ua. Ed. Ph N Serkov. **US dist. addr.:** East View Information Services, 3020 Harbor Ln. N., Minneapolis, MN 55447. TEL 763-550-0961, FAX 763-559-2931, eastview@eastview.com, http://www.eastview.com.

571 RUS ISSN 0131-1646
QP34.5 CODEN: FICHDB
FIZIOLOGIYA CHELOVEKA. Text in Russian. 1975. bi-m. RUR 1,380 for 6 mos. domestic; USD 324 in North America (effective 2004). illus. **Document type:** *Journal, Academic/Scholarly.* **Description:** Publishes studies on the physiology of work, speech, and sport, emphasizing their relationship to the physiology of the brain and the neurophysiology of psychological activity.
Related titles: Online - full text ed.; ♦ English Translation: Human Physiology. ISSN 0362-1197.
Indexed: BIOSIS Prev, BiolAb, CIN, ChemAb, ChemTitl, IAA, IndMed, MEDLINE, RefZh.
—CASDDS, CISTI, East View, GNLM, KNAW, Linda Hall. **CCC.**
Published by: (Rossiiskaya Akademiya Nauk/Russian Academy of Sciences), Izdatel'stvo Nauka, Profsoyuznaya ul 90, Moscow, 117864, Russian Federation. TEL 7-095-3347151, FAX 7-095-4202220, secret@naukaran.ru, http://www.maik.ru/cgi-bin/list.pl?page=chelfiz, http://www.naukaran.ru. **Dist. by:** M K - Periodica, ul Gilyarovskogo 39, Moscow 129110, Russian Federation. TEL 7-095-2845008, FAX 7-095-2813798, info@periodicals.ru, http://www.mkniga.ru.

571 UKR ISSN 0532-9310
QK710 CODEN: FBKRAT
FIZIOLOGIYA I BIOKHIMIYA KUL'TURNYKH RASTENII/PHYSIOLOGY AND BIOCHEMISTRY OF CULTIVATED PLANTS; nauchno-teoreticheskii zhurnal. Text in Russian; Summaries in English, Russian, Ukrainian. 1969. bi-m. UAK 31.80 domestic; USD 97.04 foreign (effective 2001). abstr. 92 p./no.; **Description:** Covers fundamental aspects of theoretical and experimental plant physiology and biochemistry, physiological genetics and genetic engineering. Publishes the results of original research, reviews, short communications, and methodological articles concerning the aforementioned subjects as well as cell and molecular biology, biotechnology and ecology. Also includes information on conferences, congresses and symposia.
Media: Large Type (10 pt.).
Indexed: BiolAb, CIN, CPA, CTFA, ChemAb, ChemTitl, Djerelo, FCA, HerbAb, HortAb, INIS AtomInd, ISR, MaizeAb, PBA, PGrRegA, PotatoAb, RA&MP, RPP, RefZh, RiceAb, S&F, SCI, SeedAb, SoyAb, TriticAb, WeedAb.
—BLDSC (0390.250000), IE, Linda Hall.
Published by: (Natsional'na Akademiya Nauk Ukrainy, Instytut Fiziolohii Roslyn ta Henetyky), Izdatel'stvo Logos, Vul Vasyl'kivs'ka 31-17, Kiev, Ukraine. TEL 380-44-2630114, FAX 380-44-2635150, plant@ifrg.freenet.kiev.ua. Ed. V V Morgun. **Dist. by:** M K - Periodica, ul Gilyarovskogo 39, Moscow 129110, Russian Federation; **Dist. in U.S. by:** Victor Kamkin Inc., 220 Girard St, Ste 1, Gaithersburg, MD 20877.

FRONTIER RESEARCH PROGRAM. NEWSLETTER. see *MEDICAL SCIENCES—Psychiatry And Neurology*

GENE. see *BIOLOGY—Biotechnology*

571 SVK ISSN 0231-5882
QP1 CODEN: GPBIE2
➤ **GENERAL PHYSIOLOGY AND BIOPHYSICS.** Text in English. 1982. q. USD 240 (effective 2003). bk.rev. back issues avail. **Document type:** *Journal, Academic/Scholarly.* **Description:** Publishes original scientific studies within the sphere of general physiology, biophysics and biochemistry at the cellular and molecular levels, along with papers relating the progress and development of the respective research techniques and methods.
Indexed: ASCA, AgBio, AnBrAb, BBCI, BIOSIS Prev, BiolAb, CIN, CPA, ChemAb, ChemTitl, CurCont, DSA, ExcerpMed, HortAb, ISR, IndMed, IndVet, Inpharma, MEDLINE, NutrAb, OrnHort, PBA, PE&ON, PoultAb, RA&MP, Reac, RefZh, S&F, SCI, VetBull, ZooRec.
—BLDSC (4106.725000), CASDDS, CISTI, GNLM, IDS, IE, Infotrieve, ingenta, KNAW.
Published by: Slovenska Akademia Vied, Ustav Molekularnej Fyziologie a Genetiky/Slovak Academy of Sciences, Institute of Molecular Physiology and Genetics, Vlarska 5, Bratislava, 83334, Slovakia. TEL 421-2-54772111, FAX 421-2-54773666, gpb@savba.sk, usrdtylo@savba.sk, http://www.gpb.sav.sk/, http://www.umfg.sav.sk. Ed. Branislav Uhrik. **Dist. by:** Raud D. Print, Gwerkovej 6, Bratislava 85104, Slovakia; Karger Libri AG, Petersgraben 15, Basel 11 4000, Switzerland.

571 JPN
GIFU DAIGAKU IGAKUBU HANSHA KENKYU SHISETSU GYOSEKISHU/GIFU UNIVERSITY. SCHOOL OF MEDICINE. INSTITUTE OF EQUILIBRIUM RESEARCH. BULLETIN. Text in English, Japanese. 1974. every 3 yrs.
Published by: (Hansha Kenkyu Shisetsu Hansha Seirigaku Bumon), Gifu Daigaku, Igakubu/Gifu University, School of Medicine, 40 Tsukasa-Machi, Gifu-shi, 500-8705, Japan. TEL 81-58-265-1241 ext 2300, FAX 81-58-267-2954.

571 GBR ISSN 0897-7194
QP552.G76 CODEN: GRFAEC
➤ **GROWTH FACTORS.** Text in English. 1989. q. GBP 680, USD 888 combined subscription to institutions print & online eds. (effective 2006). reprint service avail. from PSC. **Document type:** *Journal, Academic/Scholarly.* **Description:** Dedicated to the communication of significant basic and clinical research on the expression, structure, function and use of growth factors on cells, in animals, and in cancer treatment.
Related titles: CD-ROM ed.: ISSN 1026-7964. 1995; Microform ed.; Online - full text ed.: ISSN 1029-2292. GBP 646, USD 844 to institutions (effective 2006) (from EBSCO Publishing, Gale Group, IngentaConnect, O C L C Online Computer Library Center, Inc., Swets Information Services).
Indexed: AIDS&CR, ASCA, AnBrAb, BBCI, BIOBASE, ChemAb, CurCont, DSA, ExcerpMed, FS&TA, IABS, ISR, IndMed, Inpharma, MEDLINE, OGFA, Reac, SCI.
—BLDSC (4223.032950), CISTI, GNLM, IE, Infotrieve, ingenta, KNAW. **CCC.**

Published by: Taylor & Francis Ltd (Subsidiary of: Taylor & Francis Group), 4 Park Sq, Milton Park, Abingdon, OX14 4RN, United Kingdom. TEL 44-1235-828600, FAX 44-1235-829000, info@tandf.co.uk, http://www.tandf.co.uk/journals/titles/08977194.asp. Ed. Tony Burgess. **Subscr. in N. America to:** Taylor & Francis Inc., Customer Services Dept, 325 Chestnut St, 8th Fl, Philadelphia, PA 19106. TEL 215-625-8900, 800-354-1420, FAX 215-625-8914, customerservice@taylorandfrancis.com; **Subscr. to:** Journals Customer Service, Rankine Rd, Basingstoke, Hants RG24 8PR, United Kingdom. TEL 44-1256-813000, FAX 44-1256-330245, enquiry@tandf.co.uk.

➤ **H F S P WORKSHOP.** see *MEDICAL SCIENCES*

571 USA ISSN 0072-9876
➤ **HANDBOOK OF PHYSIOLOGY.** Text in English. 1959. irreg. price varies. **Document type:** *Monographic series, Academic/Scholarly.* **Description:** Provides a comprehensive but critical presentation of the state of knowledge in the various fields of functional biology.
Indexed: BiolAb.
—CCC.
Published by: American Physiological Society, 9650 Rockville Pike, Bethesda, MD 20814-3991. TEL 301-634-7164, FAX 301-634-7241, info@the-aps.org, http://www.the-aps.org.

571 JPN ISSN 0385-5716
➤ **HEIKO SHINKEI KAGAKU/EQUILIBRIUM RESEARCH.** Text in Japanese; Summaries in English. 1957. bi-m. JPY 10,000. back issues avail. **Document type:** *Academic/Scholarly.* **Description:** Contains review and original articles on vestibular neuroscience and medicine.
Indexed: ExcerpMed.
—BLDSC (3794.509700), GNLM. **CCC.**
Published by: Nihon Heiko Shinkeika Gakkai/Japan Society for Equilibrium Research, 30 Kawabata-higashi Marutamachi-dori, Sakyo-ku, Kyoto-shi, 606-8395, Japan. TEL 81-75-751-0068, FAX 81-75-751-0068, js-er@mbox.kyoto-inet.or.jp. Ed. Yu Yoshimoto. Circ: 2,000.

571 JPN ISSN 0916-0337
HEIKO SHINKEI KAGAKU. SUPPLEMENT/EQUILIBRIUM RESEARCH. SUPPLEMENT. Text in Japanese; Summaries in English. 1987. irreg.
Indexed: ExcerpMed.
—BLDSC (3794.509710).
Published by: Nihon Heiko Shinkeika Gakkai/Japan Society for Equilibrium Research, 30 Kawabata-higashi Marutamachi-dori, Sakyo-ku, Kyoto-shi, 606-8395, Japan. TEL 81-75-751-0068, FAX 81-75-751-0068, js-er@mbox.kyoto-inet.or.jp.

571 JPN ISSN 0916-3786
CODEN: COPBEY
HIKAKU SEIRI SEIKAGAKU/COMPARATIVE PHYSIOLOGY AND BIOCHEMISTRY. Text in English, Japanese. 1979. q. JPY 6,000 membership (effective 2005). adv. **Document type:** *Journal, Academic/Scholarly.*
Former titles (until 1989): Dobutsu Seiri (0289-6583); Nihon Dobutsu Seiri Gakkai Nyusu
Indexed: CIN, ChemAb, ChemTitl.
—CASDDS.
Published by: Nihon Hikaku Seiri Seikagakkai/Japanese Society for Comparative Physiology and Biochemistry, c/o Iwasaki Masayuki, Fukuoka University, Department of Earth System Science, 8-19-1 Nanakuma, Jonan-ku, Fukuoka 817-0180, Japan. TEL 81-426-772579, FAX 81-426-772559, jscpb-admin@umin.ac.jp, http://wwwsoc.nii.ac.jp/jscpb/. Circ: 700.

HUMAN BRAIN MAPPING. see *MEDICAL SCIENCES—Psychiatry And Neurology*

HUMAN DEVELOPMENT. see *MEDICAL SCIENCES*

HUMAN PHYSIOLOGY. see *MEDICAL SCIENCES*

HUMAN REPRODUCTION UPDATE. see *BIOLOGY—Abstracting, Bibliographies, Statistics*

616.178059 USA ISSN 1077-3975
➤ **IN VITRO REPORT.** Text in English. 1950. q. USD 55 domestic; USD 70 foreign (effective 2003). adv. 12 p./no. 2 cols./p.; back issues avail. **Document type:** *Newsletter, Academic/Scholarly.* **Description:** Contains news and notes about branches, sections, committees, and members of the society, placement service, notice of events of interest, and short articles.
Formerly (until 1994): T C A Report (0163-772X)
Related titles: Online - full content ed.
Published by: Society for In Vitro Biology, 13000-F York Rd, Ste 304, Charlotte, NC 28278. TEL 704-588-1923, FAX 704-588-5193, sivb@sivb.org, http://www.sivb.org/InVitroReport/. Ed. Martha S. Wright. Adv. contact Michele Schultz. Circ: 1,500.

571.1 IND ISSN 0255-7150
CODEN: ICAPDG
➤ **INDIAN JOURNAL OF COMPARATIVE ANIMAL PHYSIOLOGY.** Text in English. 1983. s-a. INR 45, USD 20 to individuals; INR 100, USD 50 to institutions. **Document type:** *Academic/Scholarly.*
Indexed: CIN, ChemAb, ChemTitl, SFA, WildRev, ZooRec.
—CASDDS, CISTI.
Published by: Indian Society for Comparative Animal Physiologists, Dept. of Zoology, Sri Venkateswara University, Tirupati, Andhra Pradesh 517 502, India. TEL 91-8574-24166, FAX 91-8574-24111. Ed. P Venkateswara Rao. Circ: 300.

612 IND ISSN 0367-8350
QP1 CODEN: IJPLAN
INDIAN JOURNAL OF PHYSIOLOGY AND ALLIED SCIENCES. Text in English. 1947. q.
Indexed: BIOSIS Prev, BiolAb.
—BLDSC (4420.000000), CISTI, IE.
Published by: The Physiology Society of India, 92, Acharya Prafulla Chandra Rd, Culcutta, West Bengal 700 009, India.

571 IND ISSN 0019-5499
QP1 CODEN: IJPPAZ
➤ **INDIAN JOURNAL OF PHYSIOLOGY AND PHARMACOLOGY.** Text in English. 1957. q. USD 100 (effective 2003). adv. bk.rev. bibl.; charts; illus. index. back issues avail. **Document type:** *Academic/Scholarly.*
Related titles: CD-ROM ed.
Indexed: ApMecR, BIOSIS Prev, BiolAb, CIN, ChemAb, ChemTitl, ExcerpMed, ExtraMED, IndMed, MEDLINE, RM&VM, VetBull.
—BLDSC (4420.130000), CASDDS, CISTI, GNLM, IE, Infotrieve, ingenta, KNAW, Linda Hall.
Published by: Association of Physiologists and Pharmacologists of India, Department of Physiology, All India Institute of Medical Sciences, Ansari Nagar, New Delhi, 110 029, India. TEL 91-11-6594812, FAX 91-11-6862663, TELEX 31-73042 AIMS IN, rambij@medinst.ernet.in. Ed., Pub., R&P, Adv. contact D Ghosh TEL 91-11-6963826. Circ: 20,000. **Subscr. to:** Scientific Publishers, 5-A New Pali Rd., Near Hotel Taj Hari Mahal, PO Box 91, Jodhpur, Rajasthan 342 003, India. info@scientificpub.com, http://www.scientificpub.com.

571 IND ISSN 0972-6292
➤ **INDIAN PACING AND ELECTROPHYSIOLOGY JOURNAL.** Text in English. 2001. q. free (effective 2005). back issues avail. **Document type:** *Journal, Academic/Scholarly.*
Media: Online - full text.
Indexed: ExcerpMed.
Published by: Indian Pacing and Electrophysiology Group, 419, 9th Main, Banashankri II State, Bangalore, India. TEL 91-80-560070, http://www.ipej.org, http://www.ipej.org/. Ed. Johnson Francis.

612 611 GBR
INSIDE THE HUMAN BODY. Text in English. 1999. w. GBP 1.70 newsstand/cover (effective 2000). **Document type:** *Magazine, Consumer.* **Description:** Provides a comprehensive and up-to-date collection of everything one ever wanted to know about the human body - how it works, what can go wrong, and how it is treated.
Published by: Bright Star Publishing plc, 179 Dalling Rd, London, W6 0ES, United Kingdom. subs@midsubs.com, http://www.brightstar.co.uk. **Subscr. to:** Hammersmith, PO Box 2822, London W6 0BR, United Kingdom. TEL 44-20-8735-1200, FAX 44-20-8746-2556. **Dist. by:** Comag, Tavistock Works, Tavistock Rd, W Drayton, Middx UB7 7QX, United Kingdom. TEL 44-1895-444055, FAX 44-1895-433602.

INTEGRATIVE PHYSIOLOGICAL AND BEHAVIORAL SCIENCE. see *MEDICAL SCIENCES—Psychiatry And Neurology*

573.156 USA ISSN 0742-7719
INTERNATIONAL BLOOD/PLASMA NEWS. Text in English. 1983. m. USD 400 in North America; USD 430 elsewhere (effective 2005). back issues avail.
—CCC.
Published by: Marketing Research Bureau, 284 Racebrook Rd, Orange, CT 04677. TEL 203-799-0298, FAX 203-891-8855, mrb_ibpn@earthlink.net, http://www.marketingresearchbureau.com/ibpn.htm.

571 HUN ISSN 0539-1113
INTERNATIONAL UNION OF PHYSIOLOGICAL SCIENCES. NEWSLETTER. Text in Hungarian. 1964. irreg. USD 3. **Document type:** *Newsletter.*
Published by: International Union of Physiological Sciences, c/o A Kovach, Experimental Research Dept, Semmelweis Medical Univ, Ulloi Ut 78-A, Budapest, 1082, Hungary. http://www.iups.org. Circ: 15,000.

INVERTEBRATE NEUROBIOLOGY. see *BIOLOGY—Abstracting, Bibliographies, Statistics*

571 JPN ISSN 0021-521X
QP1 CODEN: JJPHAM
➤ **JAPANESE JOURNAL OF PHYSIOLOGY.** Text in English. 1951. bi-m. USD 80 to individuals; USD 160 to institutions (effective 2004). **Document type:** *Journal, Academic/Scholarly.*
Formerly (until 1945): Japanese Journal of Medical Sciences, Part 3. Biophysics (0368-3737); Superseded in part (in 1927): Journal of Biophysics (0368-1432); Japanese Journal of Medical Sciences
Related titles: Online - full text ed.: (from J-Stage).
Indexed: ASCA, ASFA, BIOBASE, BIOSIS Prev, BiolAb, CIN, ChemAb, ChemTitl, CurCont, DSA, DentInd, ExcerpMed, IABS, INIS AtomInd, ISR, IndMed, Inpharma, MEDLINE, NSCI, NutrAb, PE&ON, Reac, RefZh, SCI, SSCI, THA, ZooRec.
—BLDSC (4658.000000), CASDDS, CISTI, GNLM, IDS, IE, Infotrieve, ingenta, KNAW, Linda Hall. **CCC.**
Published by: Physiological Society of Japan, 3-30-10, Hongo, Bunkyo-ku, Tokyo, 113-0033, Japan. TEL 86-3-38151624, FAX 86-3-38151603, jjp@nv-med.com, http://wwwsoc.nii.ac.jp/psj/jjp/jjphome.html, http://wwwsoc.nii.ac.jp/psj/public/. Ed. Akinori Noma. Circ: 1,600. **Dist. by:** Business Center for Academic Societies Japan, 5-16-19 Honkomagome, Bunkyo-ku, Tokyo 113-0021, Japan. TEL 81-3-58145811, 81-3-58145822.

➤ **JOURNAL OF ANIMAL MORPHOLOGY AND PHYSIOLOGY.** see *BIOLOGY*

B

571.1 DEU ISSN 0931-2439
SF95 CODEN: ZTTFAA
➤ **JOURNAL OF ANIMAL PHYSIOLOGY AND ANIMAL NUTRITION/ZEITSCHRIFT FUER TIERPHYSIOLOGIE UND TIERERNAEHRUNG.** Text in English; Summaries in English, German. 1859. bi-m. EUR 290, GBP 193 combined subscription in Europe to individuals print & online eds.; USD 358 combined subscription in the Americas to individuals & Caribbean (print & online eds.); GBP 213 combined subscription elsewhere to individuals print & online eds.; GBP 648 combined subscription in Europe to institutions print & online eds.; USD 1,200 combined subscription in the Americas to institutions & Caribbean (print & online eds.); GBP 714 combined subscription elsewhere to institutions print & online eds. (effective 2006). bk.rev. abstr.; bibl.; charts; illus. index. back issues avail. **Document type:** *Journal, Academic/Scholarly.* **Description:** Publishes research in the fields of animal physiology, physiology and biochemistry of nutrition, animal feeding, feed technology, and food preservation.
Former titles (until 1985): Zeitschrift fuer Tierphysiologie, Tierernaehrung und Futtermittelkunde (0044-3565); (until 1944): Zeitschrift fuer Tierernaehrung und Futtermittelkunde (0373-0069); (until 1938): Landwirtschaftlichen Versuchs-Stationen (0368-7457)
Related titles: ◆ Online - full text ed.: Journal of Animal Physiology and Animal Nutrition Online. ISSN 1439-0396.
Indexed: AEA, ASCA, ASFA, AgrForAb, AnBrAb, B&BAb, BIOSIS Prev, BiolAb, CIN, ChemAb, ChemTitl, CurCont, DBA, DSA, ESPM, ExcerpMed, FCA, FPA, FS&TA, FaBeAb, FoVS&M, ForAb, GenetAb, HGA, HerbAb, HortAb, ISR, IndVet, KWIWR, MEDLINE, MaizeAb, NutrAb, PN&I, PollutAb, PotatoAb, PoultAb, ProtozoAb, PsycholAb, RA&MP, RM&VM, RPP, RefZh, RevApplEntom, SCI, SFA, SIA, SeedAb, SoyAb, TriticAb, VetBull, WeedAb, WildRev, ZooRec.
—BLDSC (4936.600000), CASDDS, CISTI, GNLM, IDS, IE, Infotrieve, ingenta. **CCC.**
Published by: Blackwell Verlag GmbH (Subsidiary of: Blackwell Publishing Ltd.), Kurfuerstendamm 57, Berlin, 10707, Germany. TEL 49-30-32790634, FAX 49-30-32790610, verlag@blackwell.de, http://www.blackwellpublishing.com/journals/JPN, http://www.blackwell.de. Eds. Ellen Kienzle, Manfred Stangassinger, Martin Verstegen. Circ: 400 (paid and controlled).

571.1 DEU ISSN 1439-0396
SF95
JOURNAL OF ANIMAL PHYSIOLOGY AND ANIMAL NUTRITION ONLINE. Text in English, German. 10/yr. GBP 616 in Europe to institutions; USD 1,139 in the Americas to institutions & Caribbean; GBP 678 elsewhere to institutions (effective 2006). **Document type:** *Academic/Scholarly.*
Media: Online - full text (from Blackwell Synergy, EBSCO Publishing, Gale Group, IngentaConnect, O C L C Online Computer Library Center, Inc., Swets Information Services). **Related titles:** ◆ Print ed.: Journal of Animal Physiology and Animal Nutrition. ISSN 0931-2439.
Published by: Blackwell Verlag GmbH (Subsidiary of: Blackwell Publishing Ltd.), Kurfuerstendamm 57, Berlin, 10707, Germany. TEL 49-30-32790665, FAX 49-30-32790610, abo@blackwis.de, http://www.blackwell.de.

573.6 USA ISSN 0890-0108
➤ **JOURNAL OF ANIMAL SCIENCE. SUPPLEMENT. BIENNIAL SYMPOSIUM ON ANIMAL REPRODUCTION.** Text in English. irreg., latest vol.76, no.3, 1997. USD 20 (effective 1999). **Document type:** *Monographic series, Academic/Scholarly.*
Formerly: Journal of Animal Science. Supplement (0075-4129)
Indexed: IndMed.
Published by: American Society of Animal Science, 1111 N Dunlap Ave, Savoy, IL 61874. TEL 217-356-9050, FAX 217-938-4119, asas@assochq.org, http://www.asas.org.

571.43 612 USA ISSN 1065-8483
CODEN: JABOEG

➤ **JOURNAL OF APPLIED BIOMECHANICS.** Abbreviated title: J A B. Text in English. 1985. q. USD 52 domestic to individuals; USD 62 foreign to individuals; USD 208 domestic to institutions; USD 218 foreign to institutions; USD 73 combined subscription domestic to individuals print & online eds.; USD 83 combined subscription foreign to individuals print & online eds.; USD 291 combined subscription domestic to institutions print & online eds.; USD 301 combined subscription foreign to institutions print & online eds. (effective 2005). adv. bk.rev. bibl.; charts; stat.; illus. index. back issues avail.; reprint service avail. from PSC. **Document type:** *Journal, Academic/Scholarly.* **Description:** Designed to stimulate and communicate research and theory on the forces affecting human movement in sport exercise and rehabilitation.

Formerly (until 1992): International Journal of Sport Biomechanics (0740-2082)

Related titles: Online - full text ed.: ISSN 1543-2688. USD 62 to individuals; USD 250 to institutions (effective 2005) (from EBSCO Publishing).

Indexed: AMED, AS&TI, ASCA, CINAHL, CurCont, EngInd, ErgAb, ExcerpMed, FoSS&M, IBR, IBZ, Inpharma, PEI, Reac, SSCI, SportS.

—BLDSC (4940.653000), GNLM, IDS, IE, Infotrieve, ingenta. **CCC.**

Published by: (International Society of Biomechanics), International Association for the Philosophy of Sport/Human Kinetics, PO Box 5076, Champaign, IL 61825-5076. TEL 217-351-5076, FAX 217-351-1549, orders@hkusa.com, http://www.humankinetics.com. Ed. Thomas S. Buchanan. Pub. Rainer Martens. R&P Cheri Banks TEL 217-351-5076 ext 2275. Adv. contact Chad Hoffman. B&W page USD 300. Circ: 1,173 (paid). **Co-sponsor:** International Society for the Biomechanics of Sport.

571 USA ISSN 8750-7587
QP1 CODEN: JAPHEV

➤ **JOURNAL OF APPLIED PHYSIOLOGY.** Text in English. 1948. m. USD 725 domestic to non-members; USD 775 in Canada & Mexico to non-members; USD 825 elsewhere to non-members; USD 1,090 domestic to institutions; USD 1,140 in Canada & Mexico to institutions; USD 1,190 elsewhere to institutions; USD 760 combined subscription domestic to non-members print & online eds.; USD 810 combined subscription in Canada & Mexico to non-members print & online eds.; USD 860 combined subscription elsewhere to non-members print & online eds.; USD 325 combined subscription domestic to members print & online eds.; USD 375 combined subscription in Canada & Mexico to members print & online eds.; USD 425 combined subscription elsewhere to members print & online eds.; USD 1,140 combined subscription domestic to institutions print & online eds.; USD 1,190 combined subscription in Canada & Mexico to institutions print & online eds.; USD 1,240 combined subscription elsewhere to institutions print & online eds. (effective 2006). adv. bibl.; charts; illus. index, cum.index: vols.1-39 (1948-1975). back issues avail.; reprint service avail. from PQC. **Document type:** *Journal, Academic/Scholarly.* **Description:** Presents original papers that deal with normal or abnormal function in four areas: respiratory physiology, environmental physiology, exercise physiology, and temperature regulation.

Former titles (until 1985): Journal of Applied Physiology: Respiratory, Environmental and Exercise Physiology (0161-7567); (until 1977): Journal of Applied Physiology (0021-8987)

Related titles: Microform ed.: (from PQC); Online - full text ed.: Journal of Applied Physiology Online. ISSN 1522-1601. USD 625 to individuals; USD 935 to institutions (effective 2006) (from EBSCO Publishing, HighWire Press).

Indexed: AEA, AMED, ASCA, ASFA, AbAn, AbHyg, AgBio, AgeL, AnBrAb, B&AI, BIOBASE, BIOSIS Prev, BiolAb, CIN, CISA, ChemAb, ChemTitl, CivEngAb, CurCont, DBA, DSA, DentInd, ESPM, ErgAb, ExcerpMed, FoSS&M, H&SSA, HortAb, IAA, IABS, ISR, IndMed, IndVet, Inpharma, Inspec, MEDLINE, MaizeAb, NSCI, NutrAb, PE&ON, PEI, PN&I, PoultAb, RA&MP, RRTA, Reac, RevApplEntom, SCI, SFA, SIA, SSCI, SoyAb, SportS, TDB, TriticAb, VetBull, WeedAb, WildRev, ZooRec.

—BLDSC (4946.000000), CASDDS, CISTI, GNLM, IDS, IE, Infotrieve, ingenta, KNAW, Linda Hall. **CCC.**

Published by: American Physiological Society, 9650 Rockville Pike, Bethesda, MD 20814-3991. TEL 301-634-7164, FAX 301-634-7241, mreich@the-aps.org, info@the-aps.org, http://www.the-aps.org/publications/specialcalls/pub_sc2.html. Ed. Gary C Sieck. adv.: B&W page USD 1,090, color page USD 2,030. Circ: 3,286 (paid and free).

571 USA ISSN 0021-9541
QP1 CODEN: JCLLAX

➤ **JOURNAL OF CELLULAR PHYSIOLOGY.** Text in English. 1932. m. (in 4 vols., 3 nos./vol.). USD 7,250 domestic to institutions; USD 7,394 in Canada & Mexico to institutions; USD 7,478 elsewhere to institutions; USD 7,975 combined subscription domestic to institutions print & online eds.; USD 8,119 combined subscription in Canada & Mexico to institutions print & online eds.; USD 8,203 combined subscription elsewhere to institutions print & online eds. (effective 2006). adv. abstr.; bibl.; charts. back issues avail.; reprints avail. **Document type:** *Journal, Academic/Scholarly.* **Description:** Presents research papers concerned with physiology and pathology at the cellular level, including the biochemical and biophysical mechanisms concerned in the regulation of cellular growth, differentiation, and function.

Formerly (until 1965): Journal of Cellular and Comparative Physiology (0095-9898)

Related titles: Microform ed.: (from PQC); Online - full content ed.: ISSN 1097-4652. 1996. USD 7,250 to institutions (effective 2006); Online - full text ed.: (from EBSCO Publishing, Swets Information Services, Wiley InterScience).

Indexed: ASCA, AbHyg, AgBio, AnBrAb, B&AI, BBCI, BIOBASE, BIOSIS Prev, BiolAb, CIN, ChemAb, ChemTitl, CurCont, DSA, DentInd, ExcerpMed, IABS, ISR, IndMed, IndVet, Inpharma, MEDLINE, NSCI, NutrAb, PE&ON, ProtozoAb, RA&MP, Reac, RefZh, SCI, SSCI.

—BLDSC (4955.020000), CASDDS, CISTI, GNLM, IDS, IE, Infotrieve, ingenta, KNAW, Linda Hall. **CCC.**

Published by: (Wistar Institute of Anatomy and Biology), John Wiley & Sons, Inc., 111 River St, Hoboken, NJ 07030-5774. TEL 201-748-6000, FAX 201-748-5915, uscs-wis@wiley.com, http://www3.interscience.wiley.com/cgi-bin/jhome/31010, http://www.wiley.com. Ed. Gary S Stein. adv.: B&W page GBP 640, color page GBP 1,515; trim 210 x 279. Circ: 1,400. **Subscr. outside the Americas to:** John Wiley & Sons Ltd., The Atrium, Southern Gate, Chichester, West Sussex PO19 8SQ, United Kingdom. TEL 44-1243-843335, 0800-243407, FAX 44-1243-843232, cs-journals@wiley.co.uk.

612 USA ISSN 0892-5070

JOURNAL OF CLINICAL ELECTROPHYSIOLOGY. Text in English. 1989. s-a. **Document type:** *Journal, Academic/Scholarly.*

—BLDSC (4958.396000). **CCC.**

Published by: American Physical Therapy Association, 1111 N Fairfax St, Alexandria, VA 22314-1488. TEL 703-684-2782, FAX 703-706-3169, subscriptions@apta.org, http://www.apta.org.

573.8 DEU ISSN 0340-7594
QP1 CODEN: JCPADN

➤ **JOURNAL OF COMPARATIVE PHYSIOLOGY A**; sensory, neural, and behavioral physiology. Text in English. 1924. m. EUR 3,298 combined subscription to institutions print & online eds. (effective 2005). adv. charts; illus. cum.index. reprint service avail. from ISI. **Document type:** *Journal, Academic/Scholarly.* **Description:** Concerned with invertebrates, vertebrates, and non-human mammals, particularly with the sense organs, neural processes, as well as with the experimental analysis of behavior.

Which superseded in part (in 1974): Journal of Comparative Physiology (0302-9824); Which was formerly (until 1972): Zeitschrift fuer Vergleichende Physiologie (0044-362X)

Related titles: Microform ed.: (from PMC, PQC); Online - full text ed.: ISSN 1432-1351 (from EBSCO Publishing, Springer LINK, Swets Information Services).

Indexed: ASCA, ASFA, AbHyg, AgBio, Agr, AgrForAb, AnBeAb, AnBrAb, ApicAb, B&BAb, BIOBASE, BIOSIS Prev, BibAg, BioCN&I, BiolAb, CIN, CRFR, ChemAb, ChemTitl, ChemoAb, CurCont, DSA, DentInd, EntAb, ExcerpMed, ForAb, GenetAb, HelmAb, IABS, ISR, IndMed, IndVet, Inpharma, MEDLINE, NSA, NSCI, NutrAb, PBA, PN&I, PoultAb, RM&VM, RPP, Reac, RefZh, RevApplEntom, SCI, SFA, SIA, SSCI, SoyAb, TDB, VetBull, WeedAb, WildRev, ZooRec, e-psyche.

—BLDSC (4963.210000), CASDDS, CISTI, GNLM, IDS, IE, Infotrieve, ingenta, Linda Hall. **CCC.**

Published by: Springer-Verlag (Subsidiary of: Springer Science+Business Media), Tiergartenstr 17, Heidelberg, 69121, Germany. TEL 49-6221-3450, FAX 49-6221-345229, http://link.springer.de/link/service/journals/00359/index.htm. Ed. Dr. Friedrich G Barth. Adv. contact Stephan Kroeck TEL 49-30-827875739. **Subscr. in the Americas to:** Springer-Verlag New York, Inc., Journal Fulfillment, PO Box 2485, Secaucus, NJ 07096-2485. TEL 800-777-4643, 201-348-4033, FAX 201-348-4505, journals@springer-ny.com, http://www.springer-ny.com; **Subscr. to:** Springer GmbH Auslieferungsgesellschaft, Haberstr 7, Heidelberg 69126, Germany. TEL 49-6221-345-0, FAX 49-6221-345-4229, subscriptions@springer.de.

571 DEU ISSN 0174-1578
QP33 CODEN: JPBPDL

➤ **JOURNAL OF COMPARATIVE PHYSIOLOGY B**; biochemical, systemic, and environmental physiology. Text in English. 1924. 8/yr. EUR 1,928 combined subscription to institutions print & online eds. (effective 2005). adv. charts; illus. cum.index. reprint service avail. from ISI. **Document type:** *Journal, Academic/Scholarly.* **Description:** Provides information from the molecular level up to the organismic levels of animals, including comparative aspects of metabolism and enzymology, physiology of body fluids, and muscular physiology.

Formerly (unitl 1978): Journal of Comparative Physiology. B. Systematic and Environmental Physiology (0340-7616); Which superseded in part (in 1974): Journal of Comparative Physiology (0302-9824); Which was formerly (until 1972): Zeitschrift fuer Vergleichende Physiologie (0044-362X)

Related titles: Microform ed.: (from PMC, PQC); Online - full text ed.: ISSN 1432-136X (from EBSCO Publishing, Springer LINK, Swets Information Services).

Indexed: ASCA, ASFA, AgBio, Agr, AgrForAb, AnBeAb, AnBrAb, ApicAb, BIOBASE, BIOSIS Prev, BiolAb, CIN, ChemAb, ChemTitl, CurCont, DSA, ESPM, EntAb, ExcerpMed, ForAb, HelmAb, IABS, ISR, IndMed, IndVet, Inpharma, MEDLINE, NSA, NemAb, NutrAb, PN&I, PoultAb, ProtozoAb, Reac, RevApplEntom, S&F, SCI, SFA, SIA, VetBull, WildRev, ZooRec.

—BLDSC (4963.211000), CASDDS, CISTI, GNLM, IDS, IE, Infotrieve, ingenta, Linda Hall. **CCC.**

Published by: Springer-Verlag (Subsidiary of: Springer Science+Business Media), Tiergartenstr 17, Heidelberg, 69121, Germany. TEL 49-6221-3450, FAX 49-6221-345229, http://link.springer.de/link/service/journals/00360/index.htm. Ed. Dr. Gerhard Heldmaier. Adv. contact Stephan Kroeck TEL 49-30-827875739. **Subscr. in the Americas to:** Springer-Verlag New York, Inc., Journal Fulfillment, PO Box 2485, Secaucus, NJ 07096-2485. TEL 800-777-4643, 201-348-4033, FAX 201-348-4505, journals@springer-ny.com, http://www.springer-ny.com; **Subscr. to:** Springer GmbH Auslieferungsgesellschaft, Haberstr 7, Heidelberg 69126, Germany. TEL 49-6221-345-0, FAX 49-6221-345-4229, subscriptions@springer.de.

573.8 GBR ISSN 0307-5095

➤ **JOURNAL OF ELECTROPHYSIOLOGICAL TECHNOLOGY.** Text in English. 1949. q. GBP 10; GBP 20 foreign. adv. bk.rev. abstr.; bibl.; charts; illus. index. **Document type:** *Journal, Academic/Scholarly.* **Description:** Publishes original articles and reviews on all technical and clinical aspects of human neurophysiology, particularly EEG, EPs and EMG.

Formerly: Electrophysiological Technologists' Association. Proceedings and Journal (0013-4597)

Indexed: ExcerpMed, IndMed, e-psyche.

—BLDSC (4976.150000), CISTI, GNLM.

Published by: Electrophysiological Technologists' Association, c/o E.E.G. Department, St Bartholomew's Hospital, W Smithfield, London, EC1A 7BE, United Kingdom. TEL 44-171-601-8859, FAX 44-171-601-7875. Eds. C R Green, R Pottinger. R&P Christopher Green. Adv. contact L O'Neill. Circ: 700.

➤ **JOURNAL OF EVOLUTIONARY BIOCHEMISTRY AND PHYSIOLOGY.** see *BIOLOGY—Biochemistry*

612.044 USA ISSN 1097-9751
QP301

➤ **JOURNAL OF EXERCISE PHYSIOLOGY - ONLINE.** Abbreviated title: J E P. Text in English. 1998. q. free (effective 2005). bk.rev. back issues avail. **Document type:** *Journal, Academic/Scholarly.* **Description:** Includes scientific research by exercise physiologists in such areas as body composition, environmental exercise physiology, exercise and health, fitness and training, research design and statistics, and much more.

Media: Online - full text.

Indexed: ExcerpMed, PEI.

Published by: American Society of Exercise Physiologists, College of St Scholastica, 1200 Kenwood Ave, Duluth, MN 55811. TEL 218-723-6297, FAX 218-723-6472, tboone2@css.edu, http://www.css.edu/users/tboone2/asep/fldr/fldr.htm. Ed., R&P, Adv. contact Tommy Boone.

➤ **JOURNAL OF FERTILITY COUNSELLING.** see *MEDICAL SCIENCES*

571 USA ISSN 0022-1295
QP1 CODEN: JGPLAD

➤ **JOURNAL OF GENERAL PHYSIOLOGY.** Text in English. 1918. m. (in 2 vols., 6 nos./vol.), latest vol.120. USD 575 in US & Canada to institutions; USD 675 elsewhere to institutions; USD 1,060 in US & Canada to institutions print and online eds.; USD 1,160 elsewhere to institutions print and online eds. (effective 2003). adv. bibl.; illus.; charts; abstr. index. 90 p./no. 2 cols./p.; back issues avail.; reprint service avail. from PQC,ISI. **Document type:** *Journal, Academic/Scholarly.* **Description:** Articles that elucidate basic biological, chemical, or physical mechanisms of broad physiological significance.

Related titles: Microform ed.: (from PQC); Online - full text ed.: (from EBSCO Publishing, HighWire Press).

Indexed: ASCA, ASFA, AbHyg, AnBrAb, B&AI, B&BAb, BIOBASE, BIOSIS Prev, BiolAb, CIN, ChemAb, ChemTitl, ChemoAb, CurCont, ExcerpMed, GSI, IABS, ISR, IndMed, IndVet, Inpharma, Inspec, MEDLINE, NSCI, NutrAb, PBA, PE&ON, PEI, RM&VM, Reac, RefZh, RevApplEntom, SCI, SFA, SeedAb, TDB, VetBull, WeedAb, WildRev, ZooRec.

—BLDSC (4989.000000), CASDDS, CISTI, GNLM, IDS, IE, Infotrieve, ingenta, Linda Hall. **CCC.**

B

Published by: (Society of General Physiologists), Rockefeller University Press, 1114 First Ave, New York, NY 10021-8325. TEL 212-327-8522, FAX 212-327-8513, JGP@rockefeller.edu, rupcd@rockefeller.edu, www.jgp.org/, http://www.jgp.org. Ed. Dr. Olaf S Andersen. R&P Laura Smith TEL 212-327-8025. Adv. contact Lorna Peterson TEL 212-327-8880. B&W page USD 545, color page USD 1,945; trim 7.75 x 10.25. Circ: 1,790 (paid).

573.679 USA ISSN 1083-3021
CODEN: JMBNFU
➤ **JOURNAL OF MAMMARY GLAND BIOLOGY AND NEOPLASIA.** Text in English. 1996. q. EUR 364, USD 365, GBP 233 combined subscription to institutions print & online eds. (effective 2005). adv. reprint service avail. from PSC. **Document type:** *Journal, Academic/Scholarly.* **Description:** Publishes concise state-of-the-art research papers and reviews on all aspects of the biology and pathology of the mammary gland.
Related titles: Online - full text ed.: ISSN 1573-7039 (from EBSCO Publishing, Gale Group, IngentaConnect, Kluwer Online, O C L C Online Computer Library Center, Inc., Ovid Technologies, Inc., ProQuest Information & Learning, Springer LINK, Swets Information Services).
Indexed: AbHyg, AgBio, AnBrAb, BibLing, CurCont, DSA, ExcerpMed, ISR, IndMed, IndVet, Inpharma, MEDLINE, PE&ON, Reac, RefZh, SCI, VetBull.
—BLDSC (5011.020000), CISTI, GNLM, IDS, IE, Infotrieve, ingenta. **CCC.**
Published by: Plenum US (Subsidiary of: Springer Science+Business Media), 233 Spring St, New York, NY 10013. TEL 212-460-1500, FAX 212-460-1575, service@springer-ny.com, http://springerlink.metapress.com/openurl.asp?genre=journal&issn=1083-3021, http://www.springeronline.com. Eds. Gary C Chamness, Kermit L Carraway.

573.8 USA ISSN 0022-3034
QP351 CODEN: JNEUBZ
➤ **JOURNAL OF NEUROBIOLOGY**; an international journal. Text in English. 1969. 14/yr. USD 4,595 domestic to institutions; USD 4,763 in Canada & Mexico to institutions; USD 4,861 elsewhere to institutions; USD 5,055 combined subscription domestic to institutions print & online eds.; USD 5,223 combined subscription in Canada & Mexico to institutions print & online eds.; USD 5,321 combined subscription elsewhere to institutions print & online eds. (effective 2006). adv. bk.rev. back issues avail.; reprint service avail. from PQC. **Document type:** *Journal, Academic/Scholarly.* **Description:** Covers neuroscience from molecular, genetic and cellular approaches. Vertebrate and invertebrate nervous systems are examined at the levels of the individual cell, the ensemble, and overall behavior.
Related titles: Microform ed.: (from PQC); Online - full text ed.: ISSN 1097-4695. USD 4,595 to institutions (effective 2006) (from EBSCO Publishing, Swets Information Services, Wiley InterScience).
Indexed: ASCA, ASFA, AbHyg, AgBio, AnBrAb, ApicAb, B&BAb, BIOBASE, BIOSIS Prev, BioCN&I, BiolAb, ChemAb, ChemTitl, ChemoAb, CurCont, DentInd, ExcerpMed, HelmAb, IABS, ISR, IndMed, IndVet, Inpharma, MEDLINE, NSA, NSCI, NemAb, NutrAb, PE&ON, PGrRegA, PoultAb, Reac, RevApplEntom, S&F, SCI, SFA, THA, VetBull, WildRev, ZooRec, e-psyche.
—BLDSC (5021.450000), CASDDS, CISTI, GNLM, IDS, IE, Infotrieve, ingenta, Linda Hall. **CCC.**
Published by: John Wiley & Sons, Inc., 111 River St, Hoboken, NJ 07030-5774. TEL 800-825-7550, FAX 201-748-5915, uscs-wis@wiley.com, http://www3.interscience.wiley.com/cgi-bin/jhome/31737, http://www.wiley.com. Eds. Darcy B Kelley, Eduardo Macagno. adv.: B&W page USD 1,080, color page EUR 2,420; trim 8.25 x 11. Circ: 600 (paid). **Subscr. outside the Americas to:** John Wiley & Sons Ltd., The Atrium, Southern Gate, Chichester, West Sussex PO19 8SQ, United Kingdom. TEL 44-1243-779777, FAX 44-1243-775878, cs-journals@wiley.co.uk.

573.8 USA ISSN 0022-3077
QP351 CODEN: JONEA4
➤ **JOURNAL OF NEUROPHYSIOLOGY.** Text in English. 1938. m. USD 830 domestic to non-members; USD 890 in Canada & Mexico to non-members; USD 950 elsewhere to non-members; USD 1,235 domestic to institutions; USD 1,295 in Canada & Mexico to institutions; USD 1,355 elsewhere to institutions; USD 865 combined subscription domestic to non-members print & online eds.; USD 925 combined subscription in Canada & Mexico to non-members print & online eds.; USD 985 combined subscription elsewhere to non-members print & online eds.; USD 325 combined subscription domestic to members print & online eds.; USD 385 combined subscription in Canada & Mexico to members print & online eds.; USD 445 combined subscription elsewhere to members print & online eds.; USD 1,300 combined subscription domestic to institutions print & online eds.; USD 1,360 combined subscription in Canada & Mexico to institutions print & online eds.; USD 1,420 combined subscription elsewhere to institutions print & online eds. (effective 2006). adv. abstr.; charts; illus. Index. back issues avail.; reprint service avail. from PQC. **Document type:** *Journal, Academic/Scholarly.* **Description:** Presents original articles on the function of the nervous system. Articles report on investigations that use the techniques of electro-physiology, experimental neuroanatomy, electron microscopy and tissue culture.
Related titles: Microfilm ed.: (from PMC, PQC); Online - full text ed.: Journal of Neurophysiology Online. ISSN 1522-1598. 1966. USD 710 to non-members; USD 1,060 to institutions (effective 2006) (from EBSCO Publishing, HighWire Press).
Indexed: ASCA, ASFA, B&BAb, BIOBASE, BIOSIS Prev, BiolAb, CMCI, CTA, ChemAb, ChemTitl, ChemoAb, CurCont, DBA, DentInd, ExcerpMed, IABS, ISR, IndMed, Inpharma, MEDLINE, NSA, NSCI, NutrAb, PsycInfo, PsycholAb, Reac, RefZh, SCI, SFA, SSCI, ZooRec, e-psyche.
—BLDSC (5022.000000), CASDDS, CISTI, GNLM, IDS, IE, Infotrieve, ingenta, KNAW, Linda Hall. **CCC.**
Published by: American Physiological Society, 9650 Rockville Pike, Bethesda, MD 20814-3991. TEL 301-634-7164, FAX 301-634-7241, info@the-aps.org, http://www.jn.org, http://www.the-aps.org. Eds. Brenda B Rauner, Eve Marder, Peter L Strick. adv.: B&W page USD 790, color page USD 1,885. Circ: 2,002 (paid).

599.9 JPN ISSN 1345-3475
➤ **JOURNAL OF PHYSIOLOGICAL ANTHROPOLOGY AND APPLIED HUMAN SCIENCE.** Text in English. 1982. m. **Document type:** *Journal, Academic/Scholarly.* **Description:** Contains original articles, reviews, reports, technical reports and brief communications.
Former titles (until 1999): Applied Human Science (1341-3473); (until 1984): Annals of Physiological Anthropology (0287-8429); Seiri Jinruigaku Konwakai Kaishi
Related titles: Online - full content ed.: ISSN 1347-5355. free (effective 2005); Online - full text ed.: (from J-Stage).
Indexed: BIOSIS Prev, BiolAb, ErgAb, ExcerpMed, IndMed, MEDLINE.
—BLDSC (5037.800000), GNLM, IE, Infotrieve, ingenta, KNAW. **CCC.**
Published by: Nihon Seiri Jinrui Gakkai/Japan Society of Physiological Anthropology, c/o International Academic Printing Co. Ltd., 3-8-8 Tkadanobaba, Shinjyuku-ku, Tokyo, 169-0075, Japan. TEL 81-3-53896218, FAX 81-3-33682822, iwanaga@dergo2.tech.chiba-u.ac.jp, jspa-post@bunken.co.jp, http://www.jstage.jst.go.jp/browse/jpa/-char/en, http://www.jspa.net/. Ed. Tetsuo Katsuura.

571 GBR ISSN 0022-3751
QP1 CODEN: JPHYA7
➤ **THE JOURNAL OF PHYSIOLOGY.** Text in English. 1878. s-m. (plus proceedings 5/yr.). GBP 282, EUR 424 combined subscription in Europe to individuals print & online eds.; USD 508 combined subscription in the Americas to individuals & Caribbean, print & online eds.; GBP 302 combined subscription elsewhere to individuals print & online eds.; GBP 2,196 combined subscription in Europe to institutions print & online eds.; USD 4,057 combined subscription in the Americas to institutions & Caribbean, print & online eds.; GBP 2,415 combined subscription elsewhere to institutions print & online eds. (effective 2006). adv. bibl.; charts; illus. index, cum.index. back issues avail.; reprint service avail. from PSC. **Document type:** *Journal, Academic/Scholarly.* **Description:** Covers physiological research in vertebrates: respiration, circulation, excretion, reproduction, digestion and homeostasis. Emphasis is on neurophysiology and muscle contraction.
Related titles: Microform ed.: (from PMC, PQC); Online - full text ed.: ISSN 1469-7793. GBP 2,085 in Europe to institutions; USD 3,854 in the Americas to institutions & Caribbean; GBP 2,294 elsewhere to institutions (effective 2006) (from Blackwell Synergy, EBSCO Publishing, Gale Group, HighWire Press, IngentaConnect, O C L C Online Computer Library Center, Inc., Swets Information Services).
Indexed: ASCA, ASFA, AbHyg, AgBio, AnBrAb, ApicAb, B&AI, BIOBASE, BIOSIS Prev, BiolAb, CIN, CRFR, CTA, ChemAb, ChemTitl, CurCont, DBA, DSA, DentInd, ErgAb, ExcerpMed, HelmAb, IABS, ISR, IndMed, IndVet, Inpharma, Inspec, MEDLINE, MSB, NSCI, NemAb, NutrAb, PE&ON, PEI, PN&I, PoultAb, ProtozoAb, RM&VM, Reac, RefZh, RevApplEntom, SAA, SCI, SFA, SIA, SSCI, SoyAb, TDB, VetBull, WildRev, ZooRec, e-psyche.
—BLDSC (5039.000000), CASDDS, CISTI, GNLM, IDS, IE, Infotrieve, ingenta, Linda Hall. **CCC.**
Published by: (Physiological Society, London), Blackwell Publishing Ltd., 9600 Garsington Rd, Oxford, OX4 2ZG, United Kingdom. TEL 44-1865-776868, FAX 44-1865-714591, customerservices@oxon.blackwellpublishing.com, http://www.blackwellpublishing.com/journals/TJP. Ed. Stewart Sage. Circ: 3,100.

➤ **JOURNAL OF PHYSIOLOGY (PARIS).** see *MEDICAL SCIENCES—Psychiatry And Neurology*

➤ **JOURNAL OF PHYSIOLOGY AND BIOCHEMISTRY.** see *MEDICAL SCIENCES*

571 POL ISSN 0867-5910
QP1 CODEN: JPHPEI
➤ **JOURNAL OF PHYSIOLOGY AND PHARMACOLOGY.** Text in English. 1950. q. PLZ 125 domestic to individuals; USD 100 foreign to individuals; PLZ 250 domestic to institutions; USD 200 foreign to institutions (effective 2005). bk.rev. illus. back issues avail.; reprints avail. **Document type:** *Journal, Academic/Scholarly.* **Description:** Publishes papers which fall within the range of basic and applied physiology, pathophysiology and pharmacology.
Formerly (until 1991): Acta Physiologica Polonica (0044-6033)
Related titles: Online - full text ed.: free (effective 2005) (from EBSCO Publishing).
Indexed: ASCA, AgrAg, AgrLib, ApicAb, BIOSIS Prev, BiolAb, CIN, ChemAb, ChemTitl, CurCont, ExcerpMed, IndMed, Inpharma, Inspec, MEDLINE, NutrAb, PE&ON, Reac, RefZh, VITIS, VetBull.
—BLDSC (5039.500000), CASDDS, CISTI, GNLM, IE, Infotrieve, ingenta, KNAW, Linda Hall.
Published by: Polskie Towarzystwo Fizjologiczne/Polish Physiological Society, Jagiellonian University School of Medicine, Institute of Physiology, Grzegorzecka 16, Krakow, 31531, Poland. TEL 48-12-4211006, FAX 48-12-4222014, redjpp@cm-uj.krakow.pl, http://www.jpp.krakow.pl. Ed. Jan Bugajski. Circ: 600. **Dist. by:** Ars Polona, Krakowskie Przedmiescie 7, Warsaw, Poland. TEL 48-22-9263914, FAX 48-22-9265334, arspolona@arspolona.com.pl, http://www.arspolona.com.pl.

571 EGY ISSN 1110-7448
JOURNAL OF UNION OF ARAB BIOLOGISTS. PHYSIOLOGY AND ALGAE. Text in English. 1999. a. **Document type:** *Journal, Academic/Scholarly.*
—BLDSC (4910.569500).
Published by: Union of Arab Biologists, Faculty of Science, Cairo University, Cairo University Campus, Cairo, Egypt. info@egsz.org, http://derp.sti.sci.eg/data/0349.htm, http://www.egsz.org.

B

573.8 NLD ISSN 0957-4271
QP471 CODEN: JVEREH
➤ **JOURNAL OF VESTIBULAR RESEARCH: EQUILIBRIUM AND ORIENTATION**; an international journal of experimental and clinical vestibular science. Text in English. 1991. bi-m. EUR 658, USD 787 combined subscription print & online eds. (effective 2006). adv. bk,rev. back issues avail. **Document type:** *Journal, Academic/Scholarly.* **Description:** Includes experimental and observational studies and theoretical papers based on the current knowledge of vestibular science.
Related titles: Online - full text ed.: (from EBSCO Publishing, Gale Group, IngentaConnect, O C L C Online Computer Library Center, Inc., Swets Information Services).
Indexed: ASCA, BIOBASE, BioEngAb, BrCerAb, C&ISA, CerAb, CorrAb, E&CAJ, EMA, ESPM, ExcerpMed, FoSS&M, IAA, IABS, IndMed, Inspec, M&TEA, MBF, MEDLINE, METADEX, NSA, NSCI, PsycInfo, PsycholAb, SSCI, WAA, e-psyche.
—BLDSC (5072.340000), AskIEEE, CISTI, GNLM, IDS, IE, Infotrieve, ingenta, KNAW. **CCC.**
Published by: I O S Press, Nieuwe Hemweg 6B, Amsterdam, 1013 BG, Netherlands. TEL 31-20-6883355, FAX 31-20-6203419, info@iospress.nl, order@iospress.nl, http://www.iospress.nl/html/09574271.php. Eds. Joseph M Furman, Robert H Schor. R&P Ms. Carry Koolbergen TEL 31-20-6382189. Adv. contact Ms. Jolijn van Eunen. Circ: 350. **Subscr. in Australasia and the Far East to:** Kinokuniya Co. Ltd., Shinjuku 3-chome, Shinjuku-ku, Tokyo 160-0022, Japan. FAX 81-3-3439-1094, journal@kinokuniya.co.jp, http://www.kinokuniya.co.jp; **Subscr.in the Americas to:** I O S Press, Inc, 4502 Rachael Manor Dr., Fairfax, VA 22032-3631. iosbooks@iospress.com.

➤ **JUJIE SHUSHUXUE ZAZHI/JOURNAL OF REGIONAL ANATOMY AND OPERATIVE SURGERY.** see *MEDICAL SCIENCES—Surgery*

573.7 NLD ISSN 0968-0160
RD561 CODEN: KNEEF2
➤ **THE KNEE.** Text in English. 1994. 6/yr. EUR 128 in Europe to individuals; JPY 17,100 in Japan to individuals; USD 144 elsewhere to individuals; EUR 406 in Europe to institutions; JPY 54,100 in Japan to institutions; USD 455 elsewhere to institutions (effective 2006). adv. back issues avail. **Document type:** *Academic/Scholarly.* **Description:** Publishes studies on the clinical treatment and fundamental biomechanical characteristics of the knee.
Related titles: Microfilm ed.: (from PQC); Online - full text ed.: (from EBSCO Publishing, Gale Group, IngentaConnect, ScienceDirect, Swets Information Services).
Indexed: ExcerpMed, FoSS&M, MEDLINE.
—BLDSC (5099.863500), CISTI, GNLM, IDS, IE, Infotrieve, ingenta. **CCC.**
Published by: Elsevier BV (Subsidiary of: Elsevier Science & Technology), Radarweg 29, Amsterdam, 1043 NX, Netherlands. TEL 31-20-4853911, FAX 31-20-4852457, nlinfo-f@elsevier.nl, http://www.elsevier.com/locate/knee, http://www.elsevier.nl. Eds. Michael Ries, Simon Donell.

➤ **LOOSE CONNECTIONS.** see *SOCIAL SERVICES AND WELFARE*

573.25 USA ISSN 0362-3181
RC756 CODEN: LBHDD7
➤ **LUNG BIOLOGY IN HEALTH AND DISEASE.** Text in English. 1976. irreg., latest vol.166, 2002. price varies. adv. **Document type:** *Monographic series, Academic/Scholarly.*
Indexed: BIOSIS Prev, BiolAb, CIN, ChemAb, ChemTitl, MSB.
—BLDSC (5307.240000), CASDDS, CISTI, IE, ingenta. **CCC.**
Published by: Marcel Dekker Inc. (Subsidiary of: Taylor & Francis Group), 270 Madison Ave, New York, NY 10016-0602. TEL 212-696-9000, FAX 212-685-4540, journals@dekker.com, http://www.dekker.com. Ed. Sukhamay Lahiri. Pub. Russell Dekker. R&P Julia Mulligan. Adv. contact Eridania Perez.

➤ **MAMMARY GLAND.** see *BIOLOGY—Abstracting, Bibliographies, Statistics*

▼ new title ➤ refereed ✶ unverified ♦ full entry avail.

616.992 573 DEU ISSN 1018-7243
MECHANISMS OF B CELL NEOPLASIA. Text in English. 1983. irreg., latest vol.14, 2000. price varies. **Document type:** *Monographic series, Academic/Scholarly.*
Indexed: BIOSIS Prev.
Published by: Springer-Verlag (Subsidiary of: Springer Science+Business Media), Haber Str 7, Heidelberg, 69126, Germany. TEL 49-6221-3450, FAX 49-6221-229, subscriptions@springer.de, http://www.springer.de.

571 USA ISSN 1573-3882
▼ **METABOLOMICS.** Text in English. 2005. q. USD 255, EUR 228, GBP 152 (effective 2005). **Document type:** *Journal, Academic/Scholarly.*
Related titles: Online - full content ed.: ISSN 1573-3890. forthcoming 2005; Online - full text ed.: (from EBSCO Publishing, Kluwer Online, Springer LINK).
—CCC.
Published by: Plenum US (Subsidiary of: Springer Science+Business Media), 233 Spring St, New York, NY 10013. TEL 212-460-1500, FAX 212-460-1575, service@springer-ny.com, http://springerlink.metapress.com/openurl.asp?genre=journal&issn=1573-3882, http://www.springeronline.com. Ed. Dr. Royston Goodacre.

571 USA ISSN 1521-4605
CODEN: MPSEF6
➤ **METHODS IN PHYSIOLOGY SERIES.** Text in English. 1994. irreg., latest vol.2, 1994. price varies. back issues avail. **Document type:** *Monographic series, Academic/Scholarly.*
Indexed: ChemAb, ChemTitl.
Published by: American Physiological Society, 9650 Rockville Pike, Bethesda, MD 20814-3991. TEL 301-634-7164, FAX 301-634-7241, info@the-aps.org, http://www.faseb.org/aps, http://www.the-aps.org.

573.1 NLD ISSN 0168-1745
➤ **MICROCIRCULATION REVIEW.** Text in English. 1982. irreg., latest vol.1, 1982. price varies. **Document type:** *Monographic series, Academic/Scholarly.*
—CISTI.
Published by: Springer-Verlag Dordrecht (Subsidiary of: Springer Science+Business Media), Van Godewijckstraat 30, Dordrecht, 3311 GX, Netherlands. TEL 31-78-6576050, FAX 31-78-6576474, http://www.springeronline.com.

573.8 UKR ISSN 0028-2561
QP361 CODEN: NEFZB2
➤ **NEIROFIZIOLOGIYA/NEUROPHYSIOLOGY.** Text in Russian, Ukrainian; Summaries in English. 1969. bi-m. USD 112 foreign (effective 2004). bk.rev. illus. **Document type:** *Journal, Academic/Scholarly.* **Description:** Presents new findings in all branches of neuroscience. Covers problems of molecular and cellular neurophysiology, neurochemistry, neuropharmacology, neuromuscular physiology, functional neuromorphology, physiology of neuronal networks and centers, etc.
Related titles: ♦ English Translation: Neurophysiology. ISSN 0090-2977.
Indexed: BiolAb, CIN, ChemAb, ChemTitl, DentInd, Djerelo, ExcerpMed, INIS AtomInd, IndMed, MEDLINE, NSCI, e-psyche.
—CASDDS, CISTI, GNLM, KNAW, Linda Hall. **CCC.**
Published by: Natsional'na Akademiya Nauk Ukrainy, Instytut Fiziolohii im. Bohomol'tsya/National Academy of Sciences of Ukraine, Bogomoletz Institute of Physiology, vul Bogomol'tsya 4, Kyiv, 01024, Ukraine. TEL 380-44-2530745, FAX 380-44-2562000, fiziol_z@serv.biph.kiev.ua, http://www.biph.kiev.ua. Ed. P G Kostyuk. Circ: 900. **US dist. addr.:** East View Information Services, 3020 Harbor Ln. N., Minneapolis, MN 55447. TEL 800-477-1005, FAX 800-800-3839, eastview@eastview.com, http://www.eastview.com.

571.878 USA ISSN 0197-4580
QP376 CODEN: NEAGDO
➤ **NEUROBIOLOGY OF AGING.** Text in English. 1980. 12/yr. USD 322 to individuals; USD 299 in United States to individuals; USD 2,110 to institutions; USD 1,955 in United States to institutions; USD 138 to students; USD 128 in United States to students (effective 2006). adv. abstr.; illus. index. Supplement avail.; back issues avail.; reprint service avail. from PQC,ISI. **Document type:** *Journal, Academic/Scholarly.* **Description:** Fosters better understanding and treatment of functional changes associated with aging.
Related titles: Microfilm ed.: (from PQC); Online - full text ed.: (from EBSCO Publishing, Gale Group, IngentaConnect, ScienceDirect, Swets Information Services).
Indexed: ASCA, AbHyg, AgBio, BIOBASE, BIOSIS Prev, BiolAb, CIN, ChemAb, ChemTitl, ChemoAb, CurCont, ExcerpMed, FPA, ForAb, HelmAb, IABS, ISR, IndMed, Inpharma, MEDLINE, NSA, NSCI, NemAb, NutrAb, PE&ON, PN&I, PsycInfo, PsycholAb, RA&MP, Reac, RevApplEntom, SCI, SSCI, TDB, THA, e-psyche.
—BLDSC (6081.311000), CASDDS, CISTI, GNLM, IDS, IE, Infotrieve, ingenta, KNAW. **CCC.**
Published by: Elsevier Inc. (Subsidiary of: Elsevier Science & Technology), 360 Park Ave. S, New York, NY 10010-1710. TEL 212-989-5800, 888-437-4636, FAX 212-633-3990, usinfo-f@elsevier.com, http://www.elsevier.com/locate/neuaging. Ed. Paul D Coleman. adv.: B&W page USD 945, color page USD 2,075. Circ: 467 (paid and free).

➤ **NEUROBIOLOGY OF DISEASE.** see *MEDICAL SCIENCES—Psychiatry And Neurology*

612 ISR ISSN 1683-5506
CODEN: NLEIBT
➤ **NEUROBIOLOGY OF LIPIDS.** Text in English. 2002. irreg. free (effective 2005). **Document type:** *Journal, Academic/Scholarly.* **Description:** Provides online-only peer-reviewed publication of the results and conclusions of original research in neuroscience of lipids with a particular emphasis on novel findings in biochemistry, biophysics and physiology of cholesterol, other lipids and lipoproteins and their role in neural and synaptic development, regeneration, plasticity, circuitry, signaling, behavior, aging, degeneration, clinical neurology and transplantation.
Media: Online - full content.
Address: PO Box 1665, Rehovot, 76100, Israel. alexeikoudinov@neurobiologyoflipids.org, editorialoffice@neurobiologyoflipids.org, http://neurobiologyoflipids.org. Ed., Pub., R&P, Adv. contact Alexei R Koudinov.

573.8 USA ISSN 1539-2791
QP376 CODEN: NEURKS
➤ **NEUROINFORMATICS.** Text and summaries in English. 2002. q. USD 395 domestic to institutions; USD 410 foreign to institutions; USD 435 combined subscription domestic to institutions print & online eds.; USD 450 combined subscription foreign to institutions print & online eds. (effective 2004). bk.rev. illus. back issues avail. **Document type:** *Journal, Academic/Scholarly.* **Description:** Neuroinformatics publishes original articles and reviews with an emphasis on data structure and software tools related to analysis, modeling, integration, and sharing in all areas of neuroscience research.
Related titles: Online - full text ed.: USD 115 to individuals; USD 370 to institutions (effective 2004) (from EBSCO Publishing, Gale Group, IngentaConnect, Ovid Technologies, Inc., Swets Information Services).
Indexed: B&BAb, BioEngAb, CMCI, ExcerpMed, NSA, NSCI.
—BLDSC (6081.373530), CISTI, IE. **CCC.**
Published by: Humana Press, Inc., 999 Riverview Dr, Ste 208, Totowa, NJ 07512. TEL 973-256-1699, FAX 973-256-8341, humana@humanapr.com, http://humanapress.com/journals.pasp. Ed. Giorgio Ascoli. Pub. Thomas B. Lanigan Jr. R&P Wendy A. Warren. Adv. contacts John Chasse, Thomas B. Lanigan Jr.

573.8 USA ISSN 0893-2336
RC337 CODEN: NUROE8
➤ **NEUROMETHODS.** Text and summaries in English. 1985. irreg., latest vol.38, 2002. price varies; price varies. back issues avail. **Document type:** *Monographic series, Academic/Scholarly.* **Description:** Presents detailed methods and techniques for neuroscientists.
Formerly: Neuromethods. Series 1: Neurochemistry (1048-6089)
Indexed: BIOSIS Prev, CIN, ChemAb, ChemTitl, e-psyche.
—BLDSC (6081.503500), CISTI, IE, ingenta. **CCC.**
Published by: Humana Press, Inc., 999 Riverview Dr, Ste 208, Totowa, NJ 07512. TEL 973-256-1699, FAX 973-256-8341, humana@humanapr.com, http://humanapress.com/journals.pasp. Eds. Alan Boulton, James Baker. Pub. Thomas B. Lanigan Jr.

➤ **NEUROPHYSIOLOGY.** see *BIOLOGY—Abstracting, Bibliographies, Statistics*

➤ **NEUROPSYCHOBIOLOGY**; international journal of experimental and clinical research in biological psychiatry, pharmacopsychiatry, biological psychology, pharmacopsychology and pharmacoelectroencephalography. see *MEDICAL SCIENCES—Psychiatry And Neurology*

573.8 JPN ISSN 1340-4806
NIHON AJI TO NIOI GAKKAISHI/JAPANESE JOURNAL OF TASTE AND SMELL RESEARCH. Text in Japanese. 1994. q. **Document type:** *Journal, Academic/Scholarly.*
—BLDSC (4658.866200).
Published by: Nihon Aji to Nioi Gakkai/Japanese Association for the Study of Taste and Smell, Department of Behavioral Physiology, Faculty of Human Sciences, Osaka University, 1-2 Yamadaoka, Suita, Osaka 565-0871, Japan. TEL 81-6-68798049, FAX 81-6-68798050, jasts@hus.osaka-u.ac.jp, http://epn.hal.kagoshima-u.ac.jp/JASTS/jastsk.html. Ed. Noriyo Suzuki.

612.4 JPN ISSN 0916-1104
NIHON DAEKISEN GAKKAISHI/JAPAN SALIVARY GLAND SOCIETY. JOURNAL. Text in English, Japanese. 1959. a.
—BLDSC (4805.870000), IE, ingenta.
Published by: Nihon Daekisen Gakkai, 1604 Shimo-Sakunobe, Takatsu-ku, Kawasaki-shi, Kanagawa-ken 213-0033, Japan.

NIHON SEIRI JINRUI GAKKAISHI/JAPANESE JOURNAL OF PHYSIOLOGICAL ANTHROPOLOGY. see *BIOLOGY—Abstracting, Bibliographies, Statistics*

571 JPN ISSN 0031-9341
CODEN: NISEAV
NIHON SEIRIGAKU ZASSHI/PHYSIOLOGICAL SOCIETY OF JAPAN. JOURNAL. Text in Japanese; Summaries in English. 1937. m. JPY 1,000 per issue. adv. bk.rev. stat. cum.index.
Related titles: Microform ed.
Indexed: ASCA, BiolAb, ChemAb, DentInd, ExcerpMed, INIS AtomInd, IndMed, MEDLINE.
—CASDDS, CISTI, GNLM.
Published by: Nihon Seiri Gakkai, 30-10 Hongo 3-chome, Bunkyo-ku, Tokyo, 113-0033, Japan. TEL 81-3-3815-1624, FAX 81-3-5684-2539. Ed. Akimichi Kaneko. Circ: 3,500 (paid).

571 JPN ISSN 0911-2057
NIHON SHIKKAN MODERU DOBUTSU KENKYUKAI KIROKU/JAPANESE ASSOCIATION OF ANIMAL MODELS FOR HUMAN DISEASES. PROCEEDINGS. Text in Japanese; Summaries in English. 1985. a. **Document type:** *Proceedings.*
Published by: Nihon Shikkan Moderu Dobutsu Kenkyukai, Wakayama Kenritsu Ika Daigaku, Dai 2 Seirigaku Kyoshitsu, 9, 9 Bancho, Wakayama-shi, Wakayama-ken 640, Japan.

571 JPN ISSN 0446-6578
CODEN: NTAZAD
NIHON TAISHITSUGAKU ZASSHI/JAPANESE JOURNAL OF CONSTITUTIONAL MEDICINE. Text in Japanese; Summaries in English. 1932. a. adv. **Document type:** *Academic/Scholarly.*
—BLDSC (4651.462000), CASDDS.
Published by: Nihon Taishitsu Gakkai/Japanese Society of Constitutional Medicine, c/o Kumamoto Daigaku Igakubu, Fuzoku Iden Igaku Kenkyu Shisetsu, 24-1 kuhon-Ji 4-chome, Kumamoto-shi, 862-0976, Japan. Ed. Hiromichi Okuda. Adv. contact Norio Fujiki.

NO NO IGAKU SEIBUTSUGAKU KONWAKAI SHOROKU/ABSTRACTS OF CONFERENCE ON MEDICINE AND BIOLOGY OF THE BRAIN. see *BIOLOGY—Abstracting, Bibliographies, Statistics*

THE NOETIC JOURNAL; an international forum on the cosmology of consciousness. see *PHYSICS*

571 USA ISSN 1547-6278
QH491
▼ ➤ **ORGANOGENESIS.** Text in English. 2004. q. USD 80 combined subscription in US & Canada to individuals print & online eds.; USD 130 combined subscription elsewhere to individuals print & online eds.; USD 450 combined subscription in US & Canada to institutions print & online eds.; USD 500 combined subscription elsewhere to institutions print & online eds. (effective 2005). **Document type:** *Journal, Academic/Scholarly.*
Related titles: Online - full text ed.: ISSN 1555-8592.
Indexed: ExcerpMed.
Published by: Landes Bioscience, 810 S Church St, Georgetown, TX 78626. TEL 512-863-7762, 800-736-9948, FAX 512-863-0081, info@landesbioscience.com, http://www.landesbioscience.com/journals/organogenesis/index.php.

571 JPN ISSN 0387-494X
OSAKA SHIKA DAIGAKU SEIRIGAKU KYOSHITSU RONBUNSHU/OSAKA DENTAL UNIVERSITY. DEPARTMENT OF PHYSIOLOGY. COLLECTION OF PAPERS. Text in English, Japanese. irreg.
Published by: Osaka Shika Daigaku, Seirigaku Kyoshitsu, 1-47, Kyobashi, Higashi-ku, Osaka-shi, 540, Japan.

PAKISTAN JOURNAL OF PATHOLOGY. see *MEDICAL SCIENCES*

PANCREATIC AND SALIVARY SECRETION. see *BIOLOGY—Abstracting, Bibliographies, Statistics*

612 NLD ISSN 0928-4680
CODEN: PTHOE7
➤ **PATHOPHYSIOLOGY.** Text in English. 1994. 4/yr. EUR 227 in Europe to individuals; JPY 30,100 in Japan to individuals; USD 254 to individuals except Europe and Japan; EUR 453 in Europe to institutions; JPY 60,200 in Japan to institutions; USD 507 to institutions except Europe and Japan (effective 2006). back issues avail.; reprints avail. **Document type:** *Academic/Scholarly.* **Description:** Publishes original interdisciplinary papers on the etiology, development and elimination of pathological processes.
Incorporates (1995-1999): Physiological Medicine
Related titles: Microform ed.: (from PQC); Online - full text ed.: (from EBSCO Publishing, Gale Group, IngentaConnect, ScienceDirect, Swets Information Services).
Indexed: ChemAb, ChemTitl, ExcerpMed, MEDLINE.
—BLDSC (6412.834000), CASDDS, CISTI, GNLM, IE, Infotrieve, ingenta, KNAW. **CCC.**
Published by: (International Society for Pathophysiology), Elsevier BV (Subsidiary of: Elsevier Science & Technology), Radarweg 29, Amsterdam, 1043 NX, Netherlands. TEL 31-20-4853911, FAX 31-20-4852457, nlinfo-f@elsevier.nl, http://www.elsevier.com/locate/pathophys, http://www.elsevier.nl. Eds. Dr. D N Granger, H-C Scholle, Dr. O. Hanninen.

➤ **PFLUEGERS ARCHIV/EUROPEAN JOURNAL OF PHYSIOLOGY**; European journal of physiology. see *MEDICAL SCIENCES*

573.8 CZE ISSN 0862-8408
QP1 CODEN: PHRSEJ
➤ **PHYSIOLOGICAL RESEARCH.** Text in English. 1952. bi-m. EUR 265 in Europe; USD 275 elsewhere (effective 2005). bk.rev. charts; illus. index. 140 p./no. 2 cols./p.; back issues avail.; reprints avail. **Document type:** *Journal, Academic/Scholarly.* **Description:** Publishes articles on normal and pathological physiology, biochemistry, biophysics, pharmacology, toxicology, cell biology, experimental medicine, endocrinology and cardiovascular diseases.
Formerly (until 1991): Physiologia Bohemoslovaca (0369-9463)
Related titles: Online - full text ed.: free (effective 2005) (from ProQuest Information & Learning).
Indexed: ASCA, BIOBASE, BIOSIS Prev, BiolAb, CIN, CISA, ChemAb, ChemTitl, CurCont, DSA, DentInd, ExcerpMed, IABS, ISR, IndMed, IndVet, Inpharma, MEDLINE, NSCI, NutrAb, PE&ON, PN&I, PsycholAb, Reac, RefZh, SCI, VITIS, VetBull, e-psyche.
—BLDSC (6484.950000), CASDDS, CISTI, GNLM, IDS, IE, Infotrieve, ingenta. **CCC.**
Published by: Akademie Ved Ceske Republiky, Fyziologicky Ustav/Czech Academy of Sciences, Institute of Physiology, Videnska 1083, Prague 2, 14220, Czech Republic. TEL 420-2-410621612, FAX 420-2-41062164, ohysres@biomed.cas.cz, http://www.biomed.cas.cz/physiolres. Ed. Dr. J Kunes. Circ: 250. **Subscr. to:** Myris Trade, V Stihlach 1311, PO Box 2, Prague 4 14201, Czech Republic. TEL 420-2-34035200, FAX 420-2-34035207, myris@myris.cz, http://www.myris.cz.

571 USA ISSN 0031-9333
QP1 CODEN: PHREA7
➤ **PHYSIOLOGICAL REVIEWS.** Text in English. 1921. q. USD 270 domestic to non-members; USD 290 in Canada & Mexico to non-members; USD 310 elsewhere to non-members; USD 410 domestic to institutions; USD 430 in Canada & Mexico to institutions; USD 450 elsewhere to institutions; USD 295 combined subscription domestic to non-members print & online eds.; USD 315 combined subscription in Canada & Mexico to non-members print & online eds.; USD 335 combined subscription elsewhere to non-members print & online eds.; USD 125 combined subscription domestic to members print & online eds.; USD 145 combined subscription in Canada & Mexico to members print & online eds.; USD 165 combined subscription elsewhere to members print & online eds.; USD 425 combined subscription domestic to institutions print & online eds.; USD 445 combined subscription in Canada & Mexico to institutions print & online eds.; USD 465 combined subscription elsewhere to institutions print & online eds. (effective 2006). adv. bibl.; charts; illus. cum.index: 1936-1951, 1952-1966, 1967-1981. back issues avail.; reprint service avail. from PQC. **Document type:** *Journal, Academic/Scholarly.* **Description:** Contains invited critical reviews of physiological topics, as well as reviews in biochemistry, nutrition, general physiology, biophysics, and neuroscience.
Related titles: Microfilm ed.: (from PMC, PQC); Online - full text ed.: Physiological Reviews Online. ISSN 1522-1210. USD 235 to non-members; USD 350 to institutions (effective 2006) (from EBSCO Publishing, Gale Group, HighWire Press, Northern Light Technology, Inc., O C L C Online Computer Library Center, Inc.); Supplement(s): Physiology of Cystic Fibrosis. USD 60 to institutions (effective 2002).
Indexed: ASCA, ASFA, AnBrAb, B&AI, BIOBASE, BIOSIS Prev, BiolAb, CTA, ChemAb, ChemTitl, CurCont, DBA, DSA, DentInd, ExcerpMed, FoSS&M, GSI, IABS, ISR, IndMed, Inpharma, MEDLINE, NSA, NutrAb, PEI, Reac, RefZh, SCI, SFA, SSCI, TDB, WeedAb, WildRev, ZooRec.
—BLDSC (6485.000000), CASDDS, CISTI, GNLM, IDS, IE, Infotrieve, ingenta, Linda Hall. **CCC.**
Published by: American Physiological Society, 9650 Rockville Pike, Bethesda, MD 20814-3991. TEL 301-634-7164, FAX 301-634-7241, info@the-aps.org, http://physrev.physiology.org, http://www.the-aps.org. Ed. Susan L Hamilton. R&P Penny Ripka. adv.: B&W page USD 750, color page USD 1,985. Circ: 3,352 (paid).

571 USA ISSN 0031-9376
QP1 CODEN: PYSOAP
➤ **THE PHYSIOLOGIST.** Text in English. 1958. bi-m. USD 60 domestic to non-members; USD 65 in Canada & Mexico to non-members; USD 70 elsewhere to non-members; USD 95 domestic to institutions; USD 100 in Canada & Mexico to institutions; USD 105 elsewhere to institutions; free to members print & online eds. (effective 2006). adv. charts; illus. back issues avail.; reprint service avail. from PQC. **Document type:** *Newsletter, Academic/Scholarly.* **Description:** Contains articles on the society's affairs and announcements, as well as articles of importance to physiologists that are not suitable for other society publications.
Related titles: Microform ed.: (from PQC); Online - full text ed.: free (effective 2006) (from EBSCO Publishing).
Indexed: BiolAb, CIJE, ChemAb, DentInd, ExcerpMed, IAA, IndMed, MEDLINE, RefZh, SFA.
—BLDSC (6487.200000), CISTI, GNLM, IE, Infotrieve, ingenta, Linda Hall. **CCC.**
Published by: American Physiological Society, 9650 Rockville Pike, Bethesda, MD 20814-3991. TEL 301-634-7164, FAX 301-634-7241, info@the-aps.org, http://www.faseb.org/aps/tphys.htm, http://www.the-aps.org. Ed. Dr. Martin Frank. adv.: B&W page USD 1,135, color page USD 2,230. Circ: 9,764 (paid).

571 USA ISSN 1548-9213
QP1 CODEN: NEPSEY
➤ **PHYSIOLOGY.** Text in English. 1986. bi-m. USD 160 domestic to non-members; USD 165 in Canada & Mexico to non-members; USD 170 elsewhere to non-members; USD 230 domestic to institutions; USD 235 in Canada & Mexico to institutions; USD 240 elsewhere to institutions; USD 160 combined subscription domestic to non-members print & online eds.; USD 165 combined subscription in Canada & Mexico to non-members print & online eds.; USD 170 combined subscription elsewhere to non-members print & online eds.; USD 250 combined subscription domestic to institutions print & online eds.; USD 255 combined subscription in Canada & Mexico to institutions print & online eds.; USD 260 combined subscription elsewhere to institutions print & online eds.; free to members print & online eds. (effective 2006). adv. charts; illus. index. back issues avail.; reprint service avail. from PQC. **Document type:** *Journal, Academic/Scholarly.* **Description:** Designed to keep physiologists informed about current developments in their field.
Formerly (until 2004): News in Physiological Sciences (0886-1714)
Related titles: Microfiche ed.; Microform ed.: (from PQC); Online - full text ed.: Physiology Online. ISSN 1548-9221. USD 130 to non-members; USD 200 to institutions (effective 2006) (from EBSCO Publishing, HighWire Press).
Indexed: ASCA, AgBio, AnBrAb, B&BAb, BIOSIS Prev, BioEngAb, BiolAb, BiolDig, CIN, ChemAb, ChemTitl, CurCont, ISR, IndVet, Inpharma, NSCI, NemAb, NutrAb, PEI, Reac, S&F, SCI, SSCI.
—BLDSC (6488.050000), CASDDS, CISTI, GNLM, IDS, IE, Infotrieve, ingenta, KNAW, Linda Hall. **CCC.**
Published by: American Physiological Society, 9650 Rockville Pike, Bethesda, MD 20814-3991. TEL 301-634-7164, FAX 301-634-7241, mreich@aps.faseb.org, info@the-aps.org, http://nips.physiology.org/, http://www.the-aps.org. Ed. Walter Boron. adv.: B&W page USD 1,250, color page USD 2,345. Circ: 9,909. **Subscr. to:** Subscription Department. **Co-publisher:** International Union of Physiological Sciences.

➤ **PHYSIOLOGY**; Royal Australasian College of Dental Surgeons. Lecture notes in physiology. see *MEDICAL SCIENCES—Dentistry*

573.8 USA ISSN 0031-9384
QP351 CODEN: PHBHA4
➤ **PHYSIOLOGY & BEHAVIOR.** Text in English. 1966. 15/yr. EUR 3,941 in Europe to institutions; JPY 523,100 in Japan to institutions; USD 4,408 to institutions except Europe and Japan; EUR 370 in Europe to qualified personnel; JPY 49,300 in Japan to qualified personnel; USD 414 to qualified personnel except Europe and Japan (effective 2006). adv. bk.rev. charts; illus.; stat. index. back issues avail.; reprint service avail. from PQC. **Document type:** *Journal, Academic/Scholarly.* **Description:** Publishes original research contributions in the areas of neural control of eating, drinking, body composition and body fluids; hormonal control of behavior; sleep activity; rhythms; taste and olfaction; and learning and memory.
Related titles: Microfiche ed.: (from MIM); Microfilm ed.: (from PQC); Online - full text ed.: (from EBSCO Publishing, Gale Group, IngentaConnect, ScienceDirect, Swets Information Services).
Indexed: AEA, ASCA, ASFA, AbHyg, AgBio, Agr, AnBeAb, AnBrAb, ApicAb, B&BAb, BIOBASE, BIOSIS Prev, BibInd, BiolAb, CIS, ChemAb, ChemTitl, ChemoAb, CurCont, DSA, DentInd, ExcerpMed, FS&TA, HelmAb, HortAb, IABS, IBR, IPsyAb, ISR, IndMed, IndVet, Inpharma, MEDLINE, MaizeAb, NSCI, NutrAb, OrnHort, PE&ON, PEI, PHN&I, PN&I, PotatoAb, PoultAb, ProtozoAb, PsycInfo, PsycholAb, RA&MP, RASB, RM&VM, RRTA, Reac, RevApplEntom, S&F, SCI, SFA, SIA, SSCI, SoyAb, THA, TriticAb, VITIS, VetBull, WAE&RSA, WildRev, ZooRec, e-psyche.
—BLDSC (6488.100000), CASDDS, CISTI, GNLM, IDS, IE, Infotrieve, ingenta. **CCC.**
Published by: (International Behavioral Neuroscience Society), Elsevier Inc. (Subsidiary of: Elsevier Science & Technology), 360 Park Ave. S, New York, NY 10010-1710. TEL 212-633-3730, 888-437-4636, usinfo-f@elsevier.com, http://www.elsevier.com/locate/physbeh. Eds. Dr. Jaap M Koolhass, Dr. Stephen C Woods. adv.: B&W page USD 550, color page USD 1,350. Circ: 1,800.

571 JPN ISSN 0370-9612
QH188 CODEN: PEJAE6
PHYSIOLOGY AND ECOLOGY JAPAN. Text in English. 1947. s-a. USD 30 to individuals; USD 60 to institutions. bk.rev. back issues avail. **Description:** Covers all fields of physiology and ecology.
Indexed: BiolAb.
—CISTI.
Published by: Physiology and Ecology Japan Editorial Office/Seiri Seitai Kankokai, Kyoto Daigaku Rigakubu Dobutsugaku Kyoshitsu, Kitashirakawa, Sakyo-ku, Kyoto-shi, 606, Japan. FAX 075-751-6149, TELEX J-5422302-SCIKYU. Ed. Hiroya Kawanabe. Circ: 700.

PHYSIOLOGY CANADA. see *MEDICAL SCIENCES*

570.1 PAK ISSN 1728-9491
PHYSIOLOGY. PROCEEDINGS. Text in English. 1985. m. GBP 300 (effective 2005). **Document type:** *Proceedings, Academic/Scholarly.*
Published by: (Society of Physiologist), International Press, P O Box 17700, Karachi, 75300, Pakistan. TEL 92-21-4947486, FAX 92-21-4989257, light_68@hotmail.com. Ed. Dr. M A Raza.

571 ZAF ISSN 1022-1220
PHYSIOLOGY SOCIETY OF SOUTHERN AFRICA. PROCEEDINGS. Text in English. 1993. a. **Document type:** *Proceedings.*
Published by: Physiology Society of Southern Africa, c/o University of Pretoria, Faculty of Medicine, Dept. of Physiology, Pretoria, 0002, South Africa.

571 USA ISSN 1099-5862
➤ **PROFESSIONALIZATION OF EXERCISE PHYSIOLOGY**; an international electronic journal for exercise physiologists. Text in English. 1998. m. free (effective 2005). bk.rev. back issues avail. **Document type:** *Journal, Academic/Scholarly.* **Description:** Focuses on articles that provide a rationale for the professionalization and increased awareness of exercise physiology as a developing profession.
Media: Online - full text.
Published by: College of St. Scholastica, Department of Exercise Physiology, 1200 Kenwood Ave., Duluth, MN 55811. TEL 218-723-6297, tboone2@css.edu, http://www.css.edu/users/tboone2/asep/fldr/pro1a.htm. Ed., R&P, Adv. contact Tommy Boone.

B

573.8 GBR ISSN 0301-0082
QP356 CODEN: PGNBA5
➤ **PROGRESS IN NEUROBIOLOGY.** Text in English. 1973. 18/yr. EUR 2,926 in Europe to institutions; JPY 388,700 in Japan to institutions; USD 3,272 to institutions except Europe and Japan (effective 2006). back issues avail. **Document type:** *Academic/Scholarly.* **Description:** Reviews advances in the field of neurobiology, with coverage of all relevant disciplines.
Related titles: Microfilm ed.: (from PQC); Online - full text ed.: (from EBSCO Publishing, Gale Group, IngentaConnect, ScienceDirect, Swets Information Services).
Indexed: ASCA, AnBeAb, BIOBASE, BIOSIS Prev, BiolAb, CIN, CTA, ChemAb, ChemTitl, ChemoAb, CurCont, ExcerpMed, IABS, ISR, IndMed, Inpharma, MEDLINE, NSA, NSCI, NutrAb, PE&ON, PsycholAb, Reac, SCI, SFA, THA, WildRev, ZooRec, e-psyche.
—BLDSC (6870.300000), CASDDS, CISTI, GNLM, IDS, IE, Infotrieve, ingenta, Linda Hall. **CCC.**
Published by: Pergamon (Subsidiary of: Elsevier Science & Technology), The Boulevard, Langford Ln, East Park, Kidlington, Oxford OX5 1GB, United Kingdom. TEL 44-1865-843000, FAX 44-1865-843010, http://www.elsevier.com/locate/pneurobio. Ed. M J Zigmond. **Subscr. to:** Elsevier BV, PO Box 211, Amsterdam 1000 AE, Netherlands. TEL 31-20-485-3757, FAX 31-20-485-3432, nlinfo-f@elsevier.nl, http://www.elsevier.nl.

➤ **PSYCHOPHYSIOLOGY**; an international journal. see *MEDICAL SCIENCES—Psychiatry And Neurology*

571 ITA ISSN 1128-7713
QUADERNI DI CINESIOLOGIA. Text in Italian. 1971. q. **Document type:** *Journal, Academic/Scholarly.*
Formerly (until 1980): Cinesiologia (0392-3436)
Published by: Edizioni Quattroventi, Piazza Rinascimento 4, Urbino, PS 61029, Italy. TEL 39-072-22588, FAX 39-072-2320998, info@edizioniquattroventi.it, http://www.edizioniquattroventi.it. Ed. Osvaldo Cappellini.

RECENT RESEARCH DEVELOPMENT IN COMPARATIVE BIOCHEMISTRY AND PHYSIOLOGY. see *BIOLOGY—Biochemistry*

571 IND
RECENT RESEARCH DEVELOPMENTS IN PHYSIOLOGY. Text in English. a. **Document type:** *Academic/Scholarly.*
—BLDSC (7305.087588).
Published by: Research Signpost, T.C. 37/661 (2), Fort P.O., Trivandrum, Kerala, India.

REDOX REPORT (ONLINE). see *PHARMACY AND PHARMACOLOGY*

REFERATIVNYI ZHURNAL. BIOLOGIYA. FIZIOLOGIYA I MORFOLOGIYA CHELOVEKA I ZHIVOTNYKH. see *BIOLOGY—Abstracting, Bibliographies, Statistics*

REFERATIVNYI ZHURNAL. FIZIOLOGIYA CHELOVEKA I ZHIVOTNYKH. ENDOKRINNAYA SISTEMA, RAZMNOZHENIE, LAKTATSIYA. see *BIOLOGY—Abstracting, Bibliographies, Statistics*

REFERATIVNYI ZHURNAL. FIZIOLOGIYA CHELOVEKA I ZHIVOTNYKH. KROV', LIMFA, KROVOOBRASHCHENIE, DYKHANIE, POCHKI. see *BIOLOGY—Abstracting, Bibliographies, Statistics*

REFERATIVNYI ZHURNAL. FIZIOLOGIYA CHELOVEKA I ZHIVOTNYKH. NEIROFIZIOLOGIYA, SENSORNYE SISTEMY, V N D, NERVNO-MYSHECHNAYA SISTEMA. see *BIOLOGY—Abstracting, Bibliographies, Statistics*

REFERATIVNYI ZHURNAL. FIZIOLOGIYA CHELOVEKA I ZHIVOTNYKH. OBMEN VESHCHESTV, PITANIE, PISHCHEVARENIE. see *BIOLOGY—Abstracting, Bibliographies, Statistics*

REFERATIVNYI ZHURNAL. FIZIOLOGIYA CHELOVEKA I ZHIVOTNYKH. OBSHCHIE PROBLEMY, VOZRASTNAYA FIZIOLOGIYA. see *BIOLOGY—Abstracting, Bibliographies, Statistics*

REFERATIVNYI ZHURNAL. FIZIOLOGIYA I BIOKHIMIYA RASTENII. see *BIOLOGY—Abstracting, Bibliographies, Statistics*

RENIN, ANGIOTENSIN & KININS. see *BIOLOGY—Abstracting, Bibliographies, Statistics*

REPRODUCTION. ABSTRACT SERIES. see *BIOLOGY—Abstracting, Bibliographies, Statistics*

573.6 GBR ISSN 1477-0415
CODEN: JRFSAR

➤ **REPRODUCTION. SUPPLEMENT.** Text in English. 1966. irreg., latest vol.58. price varies. back issues avail. **Document type:** *Monographic series, Academic/Scholarly.*
Formerly (until 2001): Journal of Reproduction and Fertility. Supplement (0449-3087)
Related titles: ◆ Supplement to: Journal of Reproduction and Fertility. ISSN 0022-4251.
Indexed: AgBio, Agr, AnBrAb, BIOSIS Prev, BiolAb, CIN, ChemAb, ChemTitl, DSA, IndMed, MEDLINE, NutrAb, SFA, WildRev, ZooRec.
—BLDSC (7713.597830), CASDDS, CISTI, IE, ingenta, KNAW, Linda Hall. **CCC.**
Published by: Society for Reproduction and Fertility, 22 Newmarket Rd, Cambridge, CB5 8DT, United Kingdom. TEL 44-1223-351809, FAX 44-1223-359754, reproduction@srf-reproduction-journal.org, http://www.srf-reproduction.org/. Adv. contact Mrs. C H Clarke. **Dist. by:** Portland Press Ltd., Commerce Way, Colchester CO2 8HP, United Kingdom. TEL 44-1206-796-351, FAX 44-1206-799-331, sales@portland-services.com.

➤ **REPRODUCTIVE MEDICINE AND BIOLOGY.** see *MEDICAL SCIENCES*

573.6 USA ISSN 0890-6238
RA1224.2 CODEN: REPTED

➤ **REPRODUCTIVE TOXICOLOGY.** Text in English. 1988. 8/yr. EUR 1,249 in Europe to institutions; JPY 166,000 in Japan to institutions; USD 1,397 to institutions except Europe and Japan; EUR 218 in Europe to qualified personnel; JPY 29,100 in Japan to qualified personnel; USD 246 to qualified personnel except Europe and Japan (effective 2006). adv. back issues avail. **Document type:** *Journal, Academic/Scholarly.* **Description:** Publishes original research on the influence of chemical and physical agents on reproduction, focusing on the application of in vitro, animal and clinical research to the practice of clinical medicine.
Related titles: Microfilm ed.: (from PQC); Online - full text ed.: (from EBSCO Publishing, Gale Group, IngentaConnect, ScienceDirect, Swets Information Services).
Indexed: ASCA, ASFA, AbHyg, AgBio, AnBrAb, BIOBASE, BIOSIS Prev, BiolAb, CIN, ChemAb, ChemTitl, CurCont, DSA, ESPM, ExcerpMed, Faml, H&SSA, HelmAb, HortAb, IABS, ISR, IndMed, IndVet, Inpharma, LHB, MEDLINE, NRN, NutrAb, PE&ON, PN&I, ProtozoAb, RA&MP, RM&VM, Reac, RevApplEntom, RiskAb, S&F, SCI, SSCI, SoyAb, TDB, ToxAb, VetBull, WeedAb.
—BLDSC (7713.706500), CASDDS, CISTI, GNLM, IDS, IE, Infotrieve, ingenta, KNAW. **CCC.**
Published by: (Reproductive Toxicology Center), Elsevier Inc. (Subsidiary of: Elsevier Science & Technology), 360 Park Ave. S, New York, NY 10010-1710. TEL 212-633-3730, 888-437-4636, usinfo-f@elsevier.com, http://www.elsevier.com/locate/reprotox. Ed. Thomas B Knudsen. adv.: B&W page USD 1,065, color page USD 1,270. Circ: 1,400 (paid).

573.2 NLD ISSN 1569-9048
CODEN: RPNEAV

➤ **RESPIRATORY PHYSIOLOGY & NEUROBIOLOGY.** Text in Dutch. 1966. 15/yr. EUR 2,053 in Europe to institutions; JPY 272,600 in Japan to institutions; USD 2,296 to institutions except Europe and Japan; EUR 116 in Europe to qualified personnel; JPY 15,400 in Japan to qualified personnel; USD 131 to qualified personnel except Europe and Japan (effective 2006). illus. reprints avail. **Document type:** *Journal, Academic/Scholarly.* **Description:** For researchers in respiratory, pulmonary and circulatory physiology.
Formerly (until 2002): Respiration Physiology (0034-5687)
Related titles: Microform ed.: (from PQC); Online - full text ed.: (from EBSCO Publishing, Gale Group, IngentaConnect, ScienceDirect, Swets Information Services).
Indexed: ASCA, AbHyg, AnBrAb, BIOBASE, BIOSIS Prev, BiolAb, CIN, CISA, ChemAb, ChemTitl, CurCont, DentInd, ExcerpMed, IABS, ISR, IndMed, IndVet, Inpharma, MEDLINE, NSCI, PN&I, PoultAb, Reac, SCI, SFA, THA, VetBull, WildRev, ZooRec.
—BLDSC (7777.662250), CASDDS, CISTI, GNLM, IDS, IE, ingenta, KNAW, Linda Hall. **CCC.**
Published by: Elsevier BV (Subsidiary of: Elsevier Science & Technology), Radarweg 29, Amsterdam, 1043 NX, Netherlands. TEL 31-20-4853911, FAX 31-20-4852457, editor@rpnb.org, nlinfo-f@elsevier.nl, http://www.elsevier.com/locate/resphysiol, http://www.elsevier.nl. Ed. P Scheid. **Subscr. to:** PO Box 211, Amsterdam 1000 AE, Netherlands. TEL 31-20-485-3757, FAX 31-20-485-3432.

612 USA ISSN 0892-1253
QP1

REVIEW OF MEDICAL PHYSIOLOGY. Text in English. 1963. biennial, latest 2005. USD 49.95 per issue (effective 2005). **Document type:** *Monographic series, Academic/Scholarly.*
—BLDSC (7792.400000), CISTI.
Published by: McGraw-Hill Companies, Inc., 2 Penn Plaza, New York, NY 10121. TEL 212-512-2000, customer.service@mcgraw-hill.com, http://www.mcgraw-hill.com. Ed. Dr. William F Ganong.

571 USA ISSN 0303-4240
QP1 CODEN: RPBEA5

➤ **REVIEWS OF PHYSIOLOGY, BIOCHEMISTRY AND PHARMACOLOGY.** Text in English. 1974. irreg., latest vol.150, 2004. price varies. reprint service avail. from ISI. **Document type:** *Monographic series, Academic/Scholarly.* **Description:** Aims to filter, highlight and review the latest developments in these rapidly advancing fields.
Formerly: Ergebnisse der Physiologie, Biologischen Chemie und Experimentellen Pharmakologie (0080-2042)
Related titles: Online - full text ed.: ISSN 1617-5786 (from Swets Information Services).
Indexed: ASCA, BBCI, BIOSIS Prev, BiolAb, CIN, ChemAb, ChemTitl, ISR, IndMed, MEDLINE, SCI.
—BLDSC (7794.020000), CASDDS, CISTI, GNLM, IDS, IE, Infotrieve, ingenta, KNAW, Linda Hall. **CCC.**
Published by: Springer-Verlag New York, Inc. (Subsidiary of: Springer Science+Business Media), 233 Spring St, New York, NY 10013. TEL 212-460-1500, 800-777-4643, FAX 212-473-6272, http://www.springer-ny.com.

➤ **REVISTA BRASILEIRA DE MASTOLOGIA.** see *MEDICAL SCIENCES—Oncology*

571 ROM ISSN 1223-4974
CODEN: RMEPDZ

ROMANIAN JOURNAL OF PHYSIOLOGY; physiological sciences. Text in English, French, German, Russian, Spanish. 1974. q. bk.rev. charts; illus. index. **Document type:** *Journal, Academic/Scholarly.*
Former titles (until 1993): Revue Roumaine de Physiologie (1220-840X); (until 1990): Physiologie (1011-6206); Which superseded in part (in 1975): Revue Roumaine de Morphologie et de Physiologie (0377-4953); Which was formed by the merger of (1953-1974): Revue Roumaine de Physiologie (0035-399X); (1974-1974): Revue Roumaine de Morphologie et d'Embryologie (0377-4945); Which was formed by the merger of (1953-1974): Morfologia Normala si Patologia (0027-1063); (1953-1974): Revue Roumaine d'Embryologie et de Cytologie. Serie de Cytologie (0556-8056); (1953-1974): Revue Roumaine d'Embryologie (0300-063X); Which was formerly (until 1972): Revue Roumaine d'Embryologie et de Cytologie. Serie d'Embryologie (0035-4007); All of which superseded in part (in 1964): Revue des Sciences Medicales (0484-8632); Which superseded in part (in 1954): La Science dans la Republique Populaire Roumaine (1220-4757)
Related titles: Online - full text ed.
Indexed: BiolAb, CIN, ChemAb, ChemTitl, ExcerpMed, IndMed, MEDLINE.
—BLDSC (8019.639000), CASDDS, CISTI, GNLM, KNAW, Linda Hall.
Published by: (Academia de Stiinte Medicale), Editura Academiei Romane/Publishing House of the Romanian Academy, Calea 13 Septembrie 13, Sector 5, Bucharest, 76117, Romania. TEL 40-21-4119008, FAX 40-21-4103983, edacad@ear.ro, http://www.ear.ro. Ed. P Groza. Circ: 600. **Dist. by:** Rodipet S.A., Piata Presei Libere 1, sector 1, PO Box 33-57, Bucharest 3, Romania. TEL 40-21-2224126, 40-21-2226407, rodipet@rodipet.ro.

571 RUS ISSN 0869-8139
QP1 CODEN: FZLZAM

➤ **ROSSIISKII FIZIOLOGICHESKII ZHURNAL IM. SECHENOVA/SECHENOV PHYSIOLOGICAL JOURNAL.** Text in Russian; Summaries in English. 1917. m. USD 444 foreign (effective 2004). bk.rev. bibl.; charts; illus. index. **Document type:** *Journal, Academic/Scholarly.*
Former titles (until 1996): Fiziologicheskii Zhurnal im. Sechenova (1027-3646); (until 1992): Fiziologicheskii Zhurnal S.S.S.R. im. Sechenova (0015-329X); (until 1932): Russkii Fiziologicheskii Zhurnal im. Sechenova (1560-8220)
Indexed: AnBrAb, BiolAb, ChemAb, DentInd, ExcerpMed, IAA, IndMed, MEDLINE, NutrAb, PoultAb, PsycInfo, PsycholAb, RASB, RefZh, SCI, SSCI, VetBull, e-psyche.
—CASDDS, CISTI, East View, GNLM, Linda Hall. **CCC.**
Published by: (Rossiiskaya Akademiya Nauk/Russian Academy of Sciences), Izdatel'stvo Nauka, Sankt-Peterburgskoe Otdelenie, Mendeleevskaya liniya 1, St Petersburg, 199034, Russian Federation. TEL 7-812-3286291. Ed. Y V Natochin. Circ: 2,000. **Dist. by:** M K - Periodica, ul Gilyarovskogo 39, Moscow 129110, Russian Federation. TEL 7-095-2845008, FAX 7-095-2813798, info@periodicals.ru, http://www.mkniga.ru.

571 JPN ISSN 0285-3299
CODEN: SGKHEB

SEIRIGAKU GIJUTSU KENKYUKAI HOKOKU/REPORT OF PHYSIOLOGICAL TECHNOLOGY. Text in Japanese. 1979. a.
Indexed: CIN, ChemAb, ChemTitl.
—CASDDS.
Published by: Okazaki Kokuritsu Kyodo Kenkyu Kiko, Seirigaku Kenkyujo/Okazaki National Research Institutes, National Institute for Physiological Sciences, 38 Saigo-Naka-Myodaiji, Okazaki-shi, Aichi-ken 444-0000, Japan.

571 JPN ISSN 0913-0322
CODEN: SGHOEH

SEIRIGAKU KENKYUJO GIJUTSUKA HOKOKU/NATIONAL INSTITUTE FOR PHYSIOLOGICAL SCIENCES. TECHNICAL DIVISION. ANNUAL REPORT. Text in Japanese. 1986. a.
Indexed: ChemAb.
—CASDDS.
Published by: Okazaki Kokuritsu Kyodo Kenkyu Kiko, Seirigaku Kenkyujo/Okazaki National Research Institutes, National Institute for Physiological Sciences, 38 Saigo-Naka-Myodaiji, Okazaki-shi, Aichi-ken 444-0000, Japan.

571 JPN

SEIRIGAKU KENKYUJO NENPO/NATIONAL INSTITUTE FOR PHYSIOLOGICAL SCIENCES. ANNUAL REPORT. Text in English, Japanese. 1980. a.
Published by: Okazaki Kokuritsu Kyodo Kenkyu Kiko, Seirigaku Kenkyujo/Okazaki National Research Institutes, National Institute for Physiological Sciences, 38 Saigo-Naka-Myodaiji, Okazaki-shi, Aichi-ken 444-0000, Japan.

571 JPN

SEIRIKEN SAKYURA/OKAZAKI NATIONAL RESEARCH INSTITUTES. NATIONAL INSTITUTE FOR PHYSIOLOGICAL SCIENCES. CIRCULAR. Text in Japanese. 1978. a.
Published by: Okazaki Kokuritsu Kyodo Kenkyu Kiko, Seirigaku Kenkyujo/Okazaki National Research Institutes, National Institute for Physiological Sciences, 38 Saigo-Naka-Myodaiji, Okazaki-shi, Aichi-ken 444-0000, Japan.

571.978 GBR ISSN 1044-579X
RC261.A1 CODEN: SECBE7

➤ **SEMINARS IN CANCER BIOLOGY.** Text in English. 1989. 6/yr. EUR 180 in Europe to individuals; JPY 19,300 in Japan to individuals; USD 181 elsewhere to individuals; EUR 555 in Europe to institutions; JPY 59,900 in Japan to institutions; USD 493 elsewhere to institutions (effective 2006). adv. reprints avail. **Document type:** *Academic/Scholarly.* **Description:** Dedicated to keeping scientists informed of developments in the field of molecular oncology. Each issue is thematic in approach, devoted to an important topic of interest to cancer biologists, from the underlying genetic and molecular causes of cellular transformation and cancer to the molecular basis of potential therapies.
Related titles: Online - full text ed.: ISSN 1096-3650. USD 520 (effective 2002) (from EBSCO Publishing, Gale Group, IngentaConnect, O C L C Online Computer Library Center, Inc., ScienceDirect, Swets Information Services).
Indexed: AIDS&CR, ASCA, B&BAb, BIOSIS Prev, ChemAb, ChemTitl, CurCont, ExcerpMed, GenetAb, HGA, ISR, IndMed, Inpharma, MEDLINE, OGFA, PE&ON, Reac, SCI.
—BLDSC (8239.448340), CASDDS, CISTI, GNLM, IDS, IE, Infotrieve, ingenta, KNAW. **CCC.**
Published by: Academic Press (Subsidiary of: Elsevier Science & Technology), 24-28 Oval Rd, London, NW1 7DX, United Kingdom. TEL 44-20-72674466, FAX 44-20-74822293, apsubs@acad.com, http://www.elsevier.com/locate/semcancer. Ed. E Klein. R&P Catherine John. Adv. contact Nik Screen.

571 CHN ISSN 0559-7765
QP1 CODEN: SLKHA8

➤ **SHENGLI KEXUE JINZHAN/PROGRESS IN PHYSIOLOGICAL SCIENCES.** Text in Chinese; Abstracts in English. 1957. q. USD 20 (effective 1999). adv. bk.rev. **Document type:** *Academic/Scholarly.* **Description:** Covers physiology, biochemistry, molecular biology, pharmacology, biophysics, pathophysiology and nutrition.
Related titles: Online - full text ed.: (from East View Information Services).
Indexed: CIN, ChemAb, ChemTitl, ExtraMED, IndMed, MEDLINE.
—BLDSC (6873.490000), CASDDS, GNLM, IE, Infotrieve, ingenta, Linda Hall.
Published by: Neuroscience Research Institute, Beijing Medical University, 38 Xueyuan Rd, Beijing, 100083, China. TEL 86-1-6209-1150, FAX 86-1-6202-9252, hanjs@iname.com. Ed. Han Jisheng. Adv. contact Lazhi Feng. Circ: 3,000 (paid).

571 CHN ISSN 0371-0874
QP1 CODEN: SLHPAH
➤ **SHENGLI XUEBAO/ACTA PHYSIOLOGICA SINICA.** Text in Chinese; Summaries in English. 1927.-bi-m. CNY 112.80 (effective 2004). adv. **Document type:** *Journal, Academic/Scholarly.* **Description:** Contains mostly original research papers on physiology. Also includes short communications and reviews.
Related titles: Online - full text ed.; ♦ English ed.: Chinese Journal of Physiological Sciences. ISSN 0258-6428.
Indexed: BIOSIS Prev, BiolAb, ChemAb, ChemTitl, ExcerpMed, IndMed, MEDLINE, PsycholAb, RefZh.
—BLDSC (0655.500000), CASDDS, CISTI, GNLM, IE, Infotrieve, ingenta, Linda Hall.
Published by: (Zhongguo Kexueyuan, Shanghai Shengming Kexue Xinwen Zhongxin/Chinese Academy of Sciences, Shanghai Information Center for Life Science), Kexue Chubanshe/Science Press, 16 Donghuang Cheng Genbei Jie, Beijing, 100717, China. TEL 86-10-64000246, FAX 86-10-64030255, bwei@sibs.ac.cn, http://www.actaps.com.cn/index_c.htm, http://www.sciencep.com/. Circ: 7,000. **Dist. by:** China International Book Trading Corp, 35 Chegongzhuang Xilu, Haidian District, PO Box 399, Beijing 100044, China. TEL 86-10-68412045, FAX 86-10-68412023, cibtc@mail.cibtc.com.cn, http://www.cibtc.com.cn.

154.6 USA ISSN 1096-214X
CODEN: SROLAE
SLEEP RESEARCH (LOS ANGELES, 1998). Text in English. 1998. irreg. free. back issues avail. **Document type:** *Journal, Academic/Scholarly.*
Media: Online - full content. **Related titles:** Print ed.
Indexed: ExcerpMed, e-psyche.
Published by: (World Federation of Sleep Research Societies), WebSciences International, 1251 Westwood Blvd., Los Angeles, CA 90024-4811. sro@sro.org, info@websciences.org, http://www.sro.org, http://www.websciences.org/.

616.178059 USA
QH585
➤ **SOCIETY FOR IN VITRO BIOLOGY. PROCEEDINGS.** Text in English. irreg. price varies. **Document type:** *Proceedings, Academic/Scholarly.* **Description:** Publishes the proceedings of various meetings and specific topics of interest to tissue culture researchers.
Formerly: Tissue Culture Association. Proceedings of the Annual Meeting (0272-6564)
Published by: Society for In Vitro Biology, 13000-F York Rd, Ste 304, Charlotte, NC 28278. TEL 704-588-1923, FAX 704-588-5193, sivb@sivb.org, http://www.sivb.org.

612 301 GBR ISSN 0954-7800
CODEN: SHBSE6
➤ **SOCIETY FOR THE STUDY OF HUMAN BIOLOGY. SYMPOSIUM SERIES.** Text in English. 1960. irreg. price varies. **Document type:** *Proceedings, Academic/Scholarly.*
Formerly (until 1986): Society for the Study of Human Biology. Symposia (0081-153X)
Indexed: BIOSIS Prev, BiolAb.
—BLDSC (8585.040000), CASDDS, IE, ingenta. **CCC.**
Published by: (Society for the Study of Human Biology), Cambridge University Press, The Edinburgh Bldg, Shaftesbury Rd, Cambridge, CB2 2RU, United Kingdom. TEL 44-1223-312393, FAX 44-1223-315052, information@cambridge.org, http://www.cup.cam.ac.uk/. R&P Linda Nicol TEL 44-1223-325757. Circ: 200.

573.8 GBR ISSN 0899-0220
QP450 CODEN: SMOREZ
➤ **SOMATOSENSORY AND MOTOR RESEARCH.** Text in English. 1983. q. GBP 416, USD 686 combined subscription to institutions print & online eds. (effective 2006). adv. charts; illus. index. back issues avail.; reprint service avail. from PQC,PSC. **Document type:** *Journal, Academic/Scholarly.* **Description:** Original research on somatic sensation and its neural mechanisms. Experimental and descriptive studies.
Formerly: Somatosensory Research (0736-7244)
Related titles: Online - full text ed.: ISSN 1369-1651. GBP 395, USD 652 to institutions (effective 2006) (from EBSCO Publishing, Gale Group, IngentaConnect, O C L C Online Computer Library Center, Inc., Swets Information Services).
Indexed: ASCA, ASFA, BIOBASE, BIOSIS Prev, BiolAb, ChemAb, CurCont, ExcerpMed, IABS, ISR, IndMed, Inpharma, MEDLINE, NSA, NSCI, PsycInfo, PsycholAb, Reac, RefZh, SCI, SSCI, ZooRec, e-psyche.
—BLDSC (8327.809150), CASDDS, CISTI, GNLM, IDS, IE, Infotrieve, ingenta, KNAW. **CCC.**
Published by: Taylor & Francis Ltd (Subsidiary of: Taylor & Francis Group), 4 Park Sq, Milton Park, Abingdon, OX14 4RN, United Kingdom. TEL 44-1235-828600, FAX 44-1235-829000, info@tandf.co.uk, http://www.tandf.co.uk/journals/titles/08990220.asp. Ed. Dr. Thomas A Woolsey. Circ: 500. **Subscr. to:** Journals Customer Service, Rankine Rd, Basingstoke, Hants RG24 8PR, United Kingdom. TEL 44-1256-813000, FAX 44-1256-330245, enquiry@tandf.co.uk.

➤ **STUDIES IN FERTILITY AND STERILITY.** see *MEDICAL SCIENCES*

612 NLD ISSN 0926-9738
STUDIES IN HUMAN BIOLOGY. Text in English. 1990. irreg., latest vol.2, 1990. price varies. **Document type:** *Monographic series.*
—KNAW.
Published by: Springer-Verlag Dordrecht (Subsidiary of: Springer Science+Business Media), Van Godewijckstraat 30, Dordrecht, 3311 GX, Netherlands. TEL 31-78-6576050, FAX 31-78-6576474, http://www.springeronline.com. Ed. Kenneth M Weiss.

571 GBR ISSN 0969-8116
➤ **STUDIES IN PHYSIOLOGY.** Text in English. 1993. irreg., latest vol.4, 2000. prices varies. **Document type:** *Monographic series, Academic/Scholarly.*
—CISTI.
Published by: Portland Press Ltd. (Subsidiary of: Biochemical Society), 3rd Fl, Eagle House, 16 Procter St, London, WC1V 6NX, United Kingdom. TEL 44-20-72804110, FAX 44-20-72804169, sales@portland-services.com, http://www.portlandpress.com, http://www.portlandpress.com/books/. R&P Adam Marshall. **Subscr. to:** Commerce Way, Colchester CO2 8HP, United Kingdom. TEL 44-1206-796351, FAX 44-1206-799331.

➤ **TOKYO SHIKA DAIGAKU SEIRIGAKU KYOSHITSU GYOSEKISHU/TOKYO DENTAL COLLEGE. DEPARTMENT OF PHYSIOLOGY. BIBLIOGRAPHY.** see *BIOLOGY—Abstracting, Bibliographies, Statistics*

▼ ➤ **UKRAINICA BIOORGANICA ACTA/BIOORGANIC CHEMISTRY JOURNAL/ZHURNAL BIOORHANICHNOI KHIMII.** see *BIOLOGY—Genetics*

571 ITA ISSN 0392-8470
UNIVERSITA DI FERRARA. ANNALI. SEZIONE 1: ANATOMIA UMANA. Text in Italian. 1951. a. price varies.
Published by: (Universita degli Studi di Ferrara), Casa Editrice Leo S. Olschki, Viuzzo del Pozzetto 8, Florence, 50126, Italy. TEL 39-055-6530684, FAX 39-055-6530214, celso@olschki.it, http://www.olschki.it.

571 ITA ISSN 0373-5915
UNIVERSITA DI FERRARA. ANNALI. SEZIONE 13: ANATOMIA E FISIOLOGIA COMPARATA. Text in Italian. 1956. a. price varies.
Published by: (Universita degli Studi di Ferrara), Casa Editrice Leo S. Olschki, Viuzzo del Pozzetto 8, Florence, 50126, Italy. TEL 39-055-6530684, FAX 39-055-6530214, celso@olschki.it, http://www.olschki.it.

573.8 ITA ISSN 0373-5923
UNIVERSITA DI FERRARA. ANNALI. SEZIONE 6: FISIOLOGIA E CHIMICA BIOLOGICA. Text in Italian. 1952. a. price varies.
Published by: (Universita degli Studi di Ferrara), Casa Editrice Leo S. Olschki, Viuzzo del Pozzetto 8, Florence, 50126, Italy. TEL 39-055-6530684, FAX 39-055-6530214, http://www.olschki.it.

571 RUS
VESTNIK MOLODYCH UCHENYCH. NAUKI O ZHIZNI. Text in Russian. 2002. s-a. **Document type:** *Journal, Academic/Scholarly.*
Formerly: Vestnik Molodych Uchenych. Fiziologiya
Related titles: Online - full text ed.: ISSN 1609-5464. 2000.
Published by: Redaktsiya Zhurnala Vestnik Molodych Uchenych, 1-ya Krasnoarmeiskaya Ul., dom 1, Sankt-Peterburg, 198005, Russian Federation. vmusidorov@mail.ru, vmu@peterlink.ru, http://www.informika.ru/text/magaz/science/vys/PHYSIO/main.html. Ed. M Sidorov. **Co-sponsors:** Ministerstvo Obrazovaniya i Nauki Rossiiskoi Federatsii/Ministry of Education and Science of the Russian Federation; Sovet Rektorov Vuzov Sankt-Peterburga; Rossiiskaya Akademiya Nauk, Sankt-Peterburgskii Nauchnyi Tsentr.

571 POL ISSN 0860-9063
WYZSZA SZKOLA PEDAGOGICZNA IM. KOMISJI EDUKACJI NARODOWEJ W KRAKOWIE. ROCZNIK NAUKOWO-DYDAKTYCZNY. PRACE FIZJOLOGICZNE. Text in Polish. 1988. irreg., latest vol.2, 1991. price varies.
Published by: (Wyzsza Szkola Pedagogiczna im. Komisji Edukacji Narodowej w Krakowie), Wydawnictwo Naukowe W S P, Ul Karmelicka 41, Krakow, 31128, Poland. TEL 33-78-20.
Co-sponsor: Ministerstwo Edukacji Narodowej.

612 610 CHN ISSN 1001-165X
ZHONGGUO LINCHUANG JIEPOUXUE ZAZHI/CHINESE JOURNAL OF CLINICAL ANATOMY. Text in Chinese. 1983. bi-m. CNY 72 domestic; USD 30.60 foreign (effective 2005). **Document type:** *Journal, Academic/Scholarly.*
Related titles: Online - full text ed.: (from East View Information Services, WanFang Data Corp.).
Published by: Zhongguo Jiepou Xuehui, Diyijun Yidaxue, Jiepouxue Jiaoyanshi, Guangzhou, 510515, China. TEL 86-20-85148203, FAX 86-20-85148202, chjcana@fimmu.edu.cn, http://zglcjpxzz.periodicals.net.cn/. **Dist. by:** China International Book Trading Corp, 35 Chegongzhuang Xilu, Haidian District, PO Box 399, Beijing 100044, China. TEL 86-10-68412045, FAX 86-10-68412023, cibtc@mail.cibtc.com.cn, http://www.cibtc.com.cn.

571 CHN ISSN 1000-6834
QP1 CODEN: ZYSZE2
➤ **ZHONGGUO YINGYONG SHENGLIXUE ZAZHI/CHINESE JOURNAL OF APPLIED PHYSIOLOGY.** Text in Chinese; Abstracts and contents page in English. 1985. q. CNY 40 domestic; USD 28.53 foreign (effective 2002). adv. **Document type:** *Academic/Scholarly.* **Description:** Covers environmental physiology, pathophysiology, clinical physiology, cellular physiology, molecular physiology, ergonomics, work and exercise physiology, medical engineering and veterinary physiology.
Related titles: Online - full text ed.: (from East View Information Services).
Indexed: IndMed, MEDLINE.
—BLDSC (3180.294400), CASDDS, IE, Infotrieve, ingenta.
Published by: (Zhongguo Shengli Xuehui/Chinese Association for Physiological Sciences), Zhongguo Yingyong Shenglixue Zazhi Bianjibu, One Da Li Dao, Tianjin, 300050, China. TEL 86-22-84655184, FAX 86-22-3314818. Ed. Lu Yongda. Adv. contact Dengyun Xu TEL 86-22-28256563. page USD 500. Circ: 4,000 (paid). **Dist. outside China by:** China International Book Trading Corp, 35 Chegongzhuang Xilu, Haidian District, PO Box 399, Beijing 100044, China.

➤ **ZHURNAL EVOLYUTSIONNOI BIOKHIMII I FIZIOLOGII.** see *BIOLOGY—Biochemistry*

573.8 RUS ISSN 0044-4677
CODEN: ZVNDAM
➤ **ZHURNAL VYSSHEI NERVNOI DEYATEL'NOSTI.** Text in Russian; Summaries in English. 1951. bi-m. RUR 1,060 for 6 mos. domestic; USD 282 foreign (effective 2004). bk.rev. index. **Document type:** *Journal, Academic/Scholarly.*
Indexed: ASCA, BIOSIS Prev, BiolAb, CCMJ, CIN, ChemAb, ChemTitl, CurCont, DentInd, ExcerpMed, ISR, IndMed, Inpharma, MEDLINE, NSCI, PsycholAb, RASB, Reac, RefZh, SCI, SSCI, ZooRec, e-psyche.
—CASDDS, CISTI, East View, GNLM, IDS, Infotrieve, KNAW, Linda Hall. **CCC.**
Published by: (Rossiiskaya Akademiya Nauk, Otdelenie Fiziologii im. I.P. Pavlova), Izdatel'stvo Nauka, Profsoyuznaya ul 90, Moscow, 117864, Russian Federation. TEL 7-095-3347151, FAX 7-095-4202220, secret@naukaran.ru, http://www.maik.ru/cgi-bin/list.pl?page=jourvnd, http://www.naukaran.ru. **Dist. by:** M K - Periodica, ul Gilyarovskogo 39, Moscow 129110, Russian Federation. TEL 7-095-2845008, FAX 7-095-2813798, info@periodicals.ru, http://www.mkniga.ru.

➤ **13C IGAKU/SOCIETY FOR THE MEDICAL APPLICATION OF CARBON THIRTEEN. BULLETIN.** see *MEDICAL SCIENCES*

BIOLOGY—Zoology

see also PETS ; VETERINARY SCIENCE

594 USA
A M S NEWS. (American Malacological Society, Inc.) Text in English. 1960. s-a. USD 40 to individuals members; USD 45 to institutions members; USD 15 to students members (effective 2002). bk.rev. back issues avail. **Document type:** *Newsletter.* **Description:** Focuses on the study of mollusks.
Formerly: A M U News (1041-5300)
Indexed: ZooRec.
—Linda Hall.
Published by: American Malacological Society, Inc., c/o Susan B. Cook, Consortium for Oceanographic Research & Education, 4201 Wilson Blvd, Ste 420, Washington, DC 20005. voltzowj2@scranton.edu, http://erato.acnatsci.org/ams/publications/amb.html. Circ: 800.

597.9 GBR ISSN 0142-5145
A S R A JOURNAL. Text in English. 1979. a. membership.
Indexed: ASFA, ESPM.
Published by: Association for the Study of Reptilia and Amphibia, Cotswold Wild Life Park, Burford, Oxfordshire OX8 4JW, United Kingdom. Ed. Jenny Swainston. Circ: 500.

597.9 GBR ISSN 0261-992X
A S R A MONOGRAPHS. (Association for the Study of Reptilia and Amphibia) Text in English. 1981. irreg.
—BLDSC (1746.334360).
Published by: Association for the Study of Reptilia and Amphibia, Cotswold Wild Life Park, Burford, Oxfordshire OX8 4JW, United Kingdom.

A T C C ANIMAL VIRUSES AND ANTISERA, CHLAMYDIAE, AND RICKETTSIAE. see *BIOLOGY—Microbiology*

590 USA
A Z A COMMUNIQUE. Text in English. 1959. m. USD 125 to non-members (effective 2005). adv. stat. **Document type:** *Newsletter, Trade.*
Former titles: A A Z P A Communique; A A Z P A Newsletter (0001-0308)
Indexed: RefZh.
Published by: American Zoo and Aquarium Association, 8403 Colesville Rd, Ste 710, Silver Spring, MD 20910. TEL 301-562-0777, FAX 301-562-0888, mmoretti@aza.org, http://www.aza.org. Ed. Tim Lewthwaite. Circ: 6,300.

590.73 USA
QL76
A Z A MEMBERSHIP DIRECTORY. Text in English. 1930. a. USD 100 to non-members; USD 45 to members; USD 75 to libraries (effective 2000). adv. stat. index. **Document type:** *Directory.*
Former titles: Zoological Parks & Aquariums in the Americas; Zoos and Aquariums in the Americas (0740-7610)
Published by: American Zoo and Aquarium Association, 8403 Colesville Rd, Ste 710, Silver Spring, MD 20910. TEL 301-562-0777, FAX 301-562-0888, mmoretti@aza.org, www.aza.org. Ed., Pub., Adv. contact Tim Lewthwaite. Circ: 3,800.

590 ZAF ISSN 1021-9102
CODEN: AARDEW
AARDVARK. Text mainly in English; Text occasionally in Afrikaans. 1970. 2/yr. USD 40 to members (effective 1993). bk.rev. **Document type:** *Newsletter.*
Formerly (until July, 1990): Zoological Society of South Africa Newsletter
Indexed: ZooRec.
Published by: Zoological Society of Southern Africa, Kaffrarian Museum, PO Box 1434, King William's Town, 5600, South Africa. TEL 27-433-24506, FAX 27-431-21569. Ed. Pierre Swaneroel. Circ: 800.

B

590 TWN ISSN 1026-3810
ACADEMIA SINICA. INSTITUTE OF ZOOLOGY. MONOGRAPH SERIES. Text in English. irreg.
Published by: Academia Sinica, Institute of Zoology/Chung Yang Yen Chiu Yuan, Tung Wu Hsueh Yen Chiu So, Nankang, Taipei, 11529, Taiwan. TEL 886-2-27899550, FAX 886-2-27858059, http://www.sinica.edu.tw/zool.

590 HUN ISSN 1217-8837
QL1
➤ **ACADEMIAE SCIENTIARUM HUNGARICA. ACTA ZOOLOGICA.** Text in English. 1954. q. USD 88 (effective 2001). adv. illus. index. 96 p./no.; back issues avail. **Document type:** *Academic/Scholarly.* **Description:** Publishes original papers in zoological taxonomy and systematics, zoogeography, animal ecology, community ecology, population genetics, population biology, biodiversity studies and nature conservation.
Former titles: Acta Zoologica Hungarica (0236-7130); (until 1983): Academiae Scientiarum Hungaricae. Acta Zoologica (0001-7264)
Indexed: ASCA, ASFA, AgrForAb, B&BAb, BIOSIS Prev, BioCN&I, BiolAb, ChemAb, CurCont, EntAb, FPA, ForAb, HGA, HelmAb, HerbAb, HortAb, I&DA, ISR, KWIWR, NemAb, OrnHort, PotatoAb, RM&VM, RPP, RevApplEntom, S&F, SPPI, SeedAb, WeedAb, ZooRec.
—BLDSC (0672.700500), CISTI, IDS, Linda Hall. **CCC.**
Published by: Magyar Termeszettudomanyi Muzeum, Baross utca 13, Budapest, 1088, Hungary. TEL 36-1-2677100, FAX 36-1-3171669, perego@zoo.zoo.nhmus.hu, http://actazool.nhmus.hu. Ed., R&P, Adv. contact I Matskasi TEL 36-1-2677100. Circ: 250.

➤ **ACAROLOGY BULLETIN.** see *BIOLOGY—Entomology*

➤ **ACTA AGRICULTURAE SLOVENICA.** see *AGRICULTURE—Crop Production And Soil*

595.4 JPN ISSN 0001-5202
CODEN: AACHBY
➤ **ACTA ARACHNOLOGICA.** Text in English, French, German, Japanese; Abstracts in English. 1936. s-a. JPY 7,000; JPY 5,000 to students (effective 2003). bk.rev. charts; illus. 90 p./no.; **Document type:** *Academic/Scholarly.*
Indexed: Agr, BIOBASE, BIOSIS Prev, BioCN&I, BiolAb, ForAb, HortAb, JPI, RM&VM, RefZh, RevApplEntom, RiceAb, WeedAb, ZooRec.
—BLDSC (0596.000000), CASDDS, CISTI, IE, ingenta. **CCC.**
Published by: Nihon Kumo Gakkai/Arachnological Society of Japan, c/o Kazuhiro Tanaka, Miyagi Gakuin Women's University, 9-1-1, Sakuragaoka, Aoba-ku, Sendai-shi, 981-8557, Japan. TEL 86-22-2776154, FAX 86-22-2776186. Ed. Nobuo Tsurusaki. Circ: 600.

590 POL ISSN 0001-530X
QL1 CODEN: ABCZAQ
ACTA BIOLOGICA CRACOVIENSIA. ZOOLOGIA. Text in English. 1958. a., latest vol.43, 2001. price varies. charts; illus. index. **Document type:** *Academic/Scholarly.* **Description:** Original research papers. Forum for zoologists involved in investigating function and structure of animals from cell level.
Indexed: ASCA, AgrAg, AgrLib, AnBrAb, BIOSIS Prev, BiolAb, ChemAb, CurCont, IBR, IndVet, KWIWR, SCI, VetBull, ZooRec.
—BLDSC (0602.420000), CASDDS, CISTI, IE, ingenta, KNAW, Linda Hall.
Published by: (Polska Akademia Nauk, Oddzial w Krakowie, Komisja Biologiczna), Polska Akademia Nauk, Oddzial w Krakowie, ul sw Jana 28, Krakow, 31018, Poland. TEL 48-12-4224853, FAX 48-12-4222791. Circ: 780.

599.4 POL ISSN 1508-1109
QL737.C5
➤ **ACTA CHIROPTEROLOGICA;** international journal of bat biology. Text in English. 1999. s-a. EUR 40 to individuals; EUR 80 to institutions (effective 2005). bk.rev. abstr.; charts; illus.; maps. back issues avail. **Document type:** *Journal, Academic/Scholarly.*
Related titles: Online - full text ed.: (from Gale Group, IngentaConnect).
Indexed: BIOSIS Prev, BiolAb, CurCont, GEOBASE, RefZh, VITIS, ZooRec.
—BLDSC (0611.030000).
Published by: Polska Akademia Nauk, Muzeum i Instytut Zoologii/Polish Academy of Sciences, Museum & Institute of Zoology, ul Wilcza 64, Warsaw, 00679, Poland. TEL 48-22-6293221, FAX 48-22-6296302, acta.chiropterologica@miiz.waw.pl, libr@miiz.waw.pl, http://www.museum-bourges.net/html/revues/acta.html, http://www.miiz.waw.pl. Ed. W Bogdanowicz. Adv. contact M Pilot. Circ: 400.

591 AUT ISSN 0721-1635
QL401
ACTA CONCHYLIORUM. Text in English, German. 1981. irreg.
Published by: Club Conchylia e V., Martinigasse 26, Vienna, 1220, Austria. TEL 43-1-47654-3307, FAX 43-1-47654-3342. Ed. Wolfgang Fischer.

595.7 SCG ISSN 0354-9410
QL462 CODEN: AEJGAP
ACTA ENTOMOLOGICA SERBICA. Text in English; Summaries in Serbian. 1971. s-a. bk.rev. **Document type:** *Journal, Academic/Scholarly.*
Formerly: Acta Entomologica Iugoslavica (0350-5510)
Indexed: ASFA, BioCN&I, BiolAb, CPA, FCA, ForAb, HerbAb, HortAb, NutrAb, OrnHort, PBA, RA&MP, RRTA, RefZh, RevApplEntom, S&F, TriticAb, WeedAb, ZooRec.
—Linda Hall.
Published by: Entomological Society of Serbia, c/o Dr Ljubodrag Mihajlovic, Sumarski fakultet Univerziteta u Beogradu, Kneza Viseslava 1, Belgrade, 11030. mljuba@eunet.yu, http://entomoloskodrustvo.tripod.com/acta. Ed. Dr. Ljubodrag R Mihajlovic.

571.9 DEU ISSN 0873-9749
QL750 CODEN: AECTDW
➤ **ACTA ETHOLOGICA.** Text in English. 1998. 2/yr. EUR 128 combined subscription to institutions print & online eds. (effective 2005). back issues avail. **Document type:** *Journal, Academic/Scholarly.* **Description:** Publishes original contributions, reviews, short notes and commentaries in the entire field of the behavioral biology of both humans and other animals.
Related titles: Microform ed.; ◆ Online - full text ed.: Acta Ethologica Online. ISSN 1437-9546.
Indexed: BIOBASE, ZooRec.
—BLDSC (0615.547700), CISTI, IE, Infotrieve. **CCC.**
Published by: (Instituto Superior de Psicologia Aplicada PRT), Springer-Verlag (Subsidiary of: Springer Science+Business Media), Tiergartenstr 17, Heidelberg, 69121, Germany. TEL 49-6221-3450, FAX 49-6221-345229, http://link.springer.de/link/service/journals/10211/index.htm. Ed. Rui Oliveira. Adv. contact Stephan Kroeck TEL 49-30-827875739. **Subscr. in the Americas to:** Springer-Verlag New York, Inc., Journal Fulfillment, PO Box 2485, Secaucus, NJ 07096-2485. TEL 800-777-4643, 201-348-4033, FAX 201-348-4505, journals@springer-ny.com, http://www.springer-ny.com; **Subscr. to:** Springer GmbH Auslieferungsgesellschaft, Haberstr 7, Heidelberg 69126, Germany. TEL 49-6221-345-0, FAX 49-6221-345-4229, subscriptions@springer.de.

597 POL ISSN 0137-1592
CODEN: AIPSCJ
➤ **ACTA ICHTHYOLOGICA ET PISCATORIA.** Text in English; Summaries in English, Polish. 1970. s-a. price varies. bk.rev. **Document type:** *Journal, Academic/Scholarly.*
Related titles: Online - full text ed.: 2002. free (effective 2005).
Indexed: ASFA, AgBio, AgrAg, AgrForAb, AgrLib, AnBrAb, CRFR, ChemAb, DSA, ESPM, FCA, ForAb, HelmAb, IndVet, NutrAb, OceAb, PoultAb, ProtozoAb, RDA, RM&VM, RefZh, RevApplEntom, S&F, SFA, SIA, VetBull, WAE&RSA, WildRev, ZooRec.
—CASDDS, CISTI, Linda Hall.
Published by: Akademia Rolnicza w Szczecinie/Agricultural University of Szczecin, Dzial Wydawnictw, Ul Doktora Judyma 22, Szczecin, 71466, Poland. TEL 48-91-4541639, FAX 48-91-4541642, TELEX 0425494 AR, fizj@demeter.zoo.ar.szczecin.pl, http://www.aiep.pl/index.html. Ed. Wieslaw F Skrzypczak.

590 SWE ISSN 0072-4807
QL1 CODEN: ARSZAE
ACTA REGIAE SOCIETATIS SCIENTIARUM ET LITTERARUM GOTHOBURGENSIS. ZOOLOGICA. Text in Multiple languages. 1967. irreg., latest vol.15, 1994. price varies. **Document type:** *Monographic series.*
Supersedes in part: Goeteborgs Kungliga Vetenskaps- och Vitterhets-Samhaelle. Handlingar
Indexed: ASFA, BiolAb, ESPM, ZooRec.
—CISTI, Linda Hall.
Published by: Kungliga Vetenskaps- och Vitterhets-Samhaelle, c/o Goeteborgs Universitetsbibliotek, PO Box 222, Goeteborg, 40530, Sweden. TEL 46-31-7731733, FAX 46-31-163797. Circ: 700.

590 CZE ISSN 1211-376X
QL1 CODEN: ASZBEM
ACTA SOCIETATIS ZOOLOGICAE BOHEMICAE. Text and summaries in English, French, German. 1934. q. bk.rev. charts; illus. index. **Document type:** *Journal, Academic/Scholarly.* **Description:** Devoted to the zoology of invertebrates and vertebrates (morphology, anatomy, physiology, bionomics, ecology, phylogeny, taxonomy, zoogeography).
Former titles (until 1993): Acta Societatis Zoologicae Bohemoslovacae (0862-5247); (until 1990): Ceskoslovenska Spolecnost Zoologicka. Vestnik (0042-4595)
Indexed: ASFA, AbHyg, BIOSIS Prev, BioCN&I, BiolAb, ChemAb, EntAb, FCA, ForAb, HelmAb, HerbAb, HortAb, IndVet, NemAb, NutrAb, PHN&I, PoultAb, ProtozoAb, RM&VM, RevApplEntom, S&F, SeedAb, VetBull, WeedAb, ZooRec.
—CASDDS, CISTI, KNAW, Linda Hall.
Published by: Ceska Zoologicka Spolecnost/Czech Zoological Society, Vinicna 7, Prague 2, 128 44, Czech Republic. chalupsk@natur.cuni.cz, http://www.natur.cuni.cz/il1/zoospol/. Circ: 1,100. **Dist. in Western countries by:** Kubon & Sagner Buchexport - Import GmbH, Postfach 340180, Munich 8000, Germany.

591 VEN ISSN 0798-118X
ACTA TERRAMARIS. Text in Spanish. 1989. m.
Published by: Fundacion Terramar, Universidad Simon Bolivar, Apdo 89000, Caracas, 1080, Venezuela.

599 POL ISSN 0001-7051
QL700 CODEN: ATRLAF
➤ **ACTA THERIOLOGICA.** Text and summaries in English. 1954. q. EUR 67 foreign to institutions (effective 2005). adv. bk.rev. bibl.; illus. index. 144 p./no. 1 cols./p.; back issues avail. **Document type:** *Journal, Academic/Scholarly.* **Description:** Covers all aspects of mammalian biology. Publishes original research reports and short communications.
Related titles: Supplement(s): ISSN 1509-4537. 1983.
Indexed: AEA, ASCA, AgBio, AgrAg, AgrLib, AnBrAb, BIOBASE, BIOSIS Prev, BiolAb, ChemAb, CurCont, DSA, FCA, ForAb, GEOBASE, HerbAb, IABS, ISR, IndVet, KWIWR, MEDLINE, NutrAb, OTA, PN&I, RM&VM, RPP, RefZh, S&F, SCI, SFA, SPPI, VetBull, WLR, WildRev, ZooRec.
—BLDSC (0665.000000), CASDDS, CISTI, IDS, IE, Infotrieve, ingenta, KNAW, Linda Hall.
Published by: Polska Akademia Nauk, Zaklad Badania Ssakow/Polish Academy of Sciences, Mammal Research Institute, Ul Gen. Waszkiewicza 1, Bialowieza, 17230, Poland. TEL 48-85-6812278, FAX 48-85-6812289, acta@bison.zbs.bialowieza.pl, http://bison.zbs.bialowieza.pl. Ed. Zdzislaw Pucek. R&P, Adv. contact Agata Jaroszewicz. Circ: 650. **Dist. by:** Ars Polona, Krakowskie Przedmiescie 7, Warsaw, Poland. TEL 48-22-9263914, FAX 48-22-9265334, arspolona@arspolona.com.pl, http://www.arspolona.com.pl.

590.7 POL ISSN 1230-0527
QL1
ACTA UNIVERSITATIS LODZIENSIS: FOLIA ZOOLOGICA. Text in Polish; Summaries in Multiple languages. 1955-1974; N.S. 1981. irreg. **Document type:** *Academic/Scholarly.*
Formerly (until 1992): Acta Universitatis Lodziensis: Folia Zoologica et Anthropologica (0208-6166); Supersedes in part: Uniwersytet Lodzki. Zeszyty Naukowe. Seria 2: Nauki Matematyczno-Przyrodnicze (0076-0366)
Indexed: ZooRec.
—CISTI, KNAW, Linda Hall.
Published by: Wydawnictwo Uniwersytetu Lodzkiego/Lodz University Press, ul Jaracza 34, Lodz, 90262, Poland. TEL 331671. **Dist. by:** Ars Polona, Krakowskie Przedmiescie 7, Warsaw, Poland.

590 POL ISSN 0554-9051
QL1
ACTA UNIVERSITATIS WRATISLAVIENSIS. PRACE ZOOLOGICZNE. Text in Polish; Summaries in English. 1962. irreg. price varies. **Document type:** *Academic/Scholarly.*
Indexed: AgrLib, BIOSIS Prev, ZooRec.
—KNAW, Linda Hall.
Published by: (Uniwersytet Wroclawski), Wydawnictwo Uniwersytetu Wroclawskiego Spolka z o.o., Pl Uniwersytecki 9-13, Wroclaw, 50-137, Poland. TEL 48-71-441006, FAX 48-71-402735. Ed. Andrzej Witkowski. Circ: 250.

590 GBR ISSN 0001-7272
QL1 CODEN: AZOSAT
➤ **ACTA ZOOLOGICA**; international journal for zoology. Text in English, French, German. 1920. q. GBP 62, EUR 93 combined subscription in Europe to individuals print & online eds.; USD 114 combined subscription in the Americas to individuals &Caribbean, print & online eds.; GBP 68 combined subscription elsewhere to individuals print & online eds.; GBP 462 combined subscription in Europe to institutions print & online eds.; USD 853 combined subscription in the Americas to institutions & Caribbean, print & online eds.; GBP 508 combined subscription elsewhere to institutions print & online eds. (effective 2006). adv. bibl.; charts; illus. back issues avail.; reprint service avail. from PSC. **Document type:** *Journal, Academic/Scholarly.* **Description:** Publishes original contributions in the fields of animal organization, structure and function.
Incorporates (1911-1980): Zoon (0346-508X); Which was formerly (until 1969): Zoologiska Bidrag fraan Uppsala (0373-0964)
Related titles: Microform ed.: (from PQC); ♦ Online - full text ed.: Acta Zoologica Online. ISSN 1463-6395.
Indexed: ASCA, ASFA, AnBeAb, AnBrAb, ApEcolAb, BIOBASE, BIOSIS Prev, BioCN&I, BiolAb, ChemAb, CurCont, ESPM, EntAb, ExcerpMed, GEOBASE, HGA, HelmAb, IABS, ISR, IndVet, RM&VM, RefZh, RevApplEntom, SCI, SFA, VetBull, WildRev, ZooRec.
—BLDSC (0672.650000), CISTI, IDS, IE, Infotrieve, ingenta, Linda Hall. **CCC.**
Published by: (Kongelige Danske Videnskabernes Selskab/Royal Danish Academy of Sciences and Letters DNK, Kungliga Vetenskapsakademien/Royal Swedish Academy of Sciences SWE), Blackwell Publishing Ltd., 9600 Garsington Rd, Oxford, OX4 2ZG, United Kingdom. TEL 44-1865-776868, FAX 44-1865-714591, customerservices@oxon.blackwellpublishing.com, http://www.blackwellpublishing.com/journals/AZO. Eds. Dr. Graham Budd, Per Ahlberg. Pub. Sue Hewitt. R&P Sophie Savage. Adv. contact Jenny Applin. Circ: 251.

591.9499 BGR ISSN 0324-0770
QL298.B8 CODEN: AZBUD7
ACTA ZOOLOGICA BULGARICA. Text in English. 1975. 3/yr. USD 75 (effective 2001). bk.rev. illus. reprint service avail. from IRC. **Document type:** *Academic/Scholarly.*
Supersedes: Bulgarska Akademiia na Naukite, Sofia. Zoologicheski Institut S Muzei. Izvestiia (0068-3981)
Indexed: AgBio, AnBrAb, BIOSIS Prev, BSLBiol, BioCN&I, BiolAb, FCA, ForAb, HelmAb, HerbAb, HortAb, IndVet, NemAb, PotatoAb, PoultAb, ProtozoAb, RM&VM, RefZh, RevApplEntom, S&F, TDB, TriticAb, VetBull, ZooRec.
—BLDSC (0672.750000), CASDDS, CISTI, KNAW, Linda Hall.
Published by: (Bulgarska Akademiya na Naukite/Bulgarian Academy of Sciences, Zoologicheski Institut), Akademichno Izdatelstvo Prof. Marin Drinov/Prof. Marin Drinov Academic Publishing House, Akad G Bonchev 6, Sofia, 1113, Bulgaria. Circ: 520. **Dist. by:** Pensoft Publishers, Akad G Bonchev 6, Sofia 1113, Bulgaria. TEL 359-2-716451, FAX 359-2-704508, pensoft@mbox.infotel.bg.

590 POL ISSN 0065-1710
QL1 CODEN: AZCRAY
➤ **ACTA ZOOLOGICA CRACOVIENSIA.** Text in English. 1956. q. EUR 62 foreign (effective 2005). adv. bibl.; charts; illus. back issues avail. **Document type:** *Journal, Academic/Scholarly.* **Description:** Covers biology, systematics, palaeontology of terrestrial animals.
Related titles: Online - full text ed.: (from IngentaConnect).
Indexed: AgrAg, AgrLib, BIOSIS Prev, BiolAb, EntAb, RefZh, ZooRec.
—CISTI.
Published by: Polska Akademia Nauk, Instytut Systematyki i Ewolucji Zwierzat/Polish Academy of Sciences, Institute of Systematics and Evolution of Animals, ul Slawkowska 17, Krakow, 31-016, Poland. TEL 48-12-4221901, FAX 48-12-4224294, bochenski@isez.pan.krakow.pl, http://www.isez.pan.krakow.pl/journals/journals.htm. Eds. Zdzislawa Stebnicka, Zygmunt Bochenski. R&P Zbigniew M Bochenski. Adv. contact Ewa Zychowska. Circ: 500. **Dist. by:** Ars Polona, Krakowskie Przedmiescie 7, Warsaw, Poland. TEL 48-22-9263914, FAX 48-22-9265334, arspolona@arspolona.com.pl, http://www.arspolona.com.pl.

590 FIN ISSN 0001-7299
QH7 CODEN: AZFEAA
➤ **ACTA ZOOLOGICA FENNICA.** Text in English. 1926. irreg. (1-4/yr.). EUR 44 combined subscription to individuals print & online eds.; EUR 34 to individuals online ed.; EUR 88 combined subscription to institutions print & online eds.; EUR 66 to institutions online ed.. abstr.; charts; illus.; maps. cum.index: nos.1-50, 51-100, 101-150. 2 cols./p.; back issues avail. **Document type:** *Journal, Academic/Scholarly.* **Description:** Contains monographs and collections of papers from symposia and conference proceedings connected with Finnish and other North European research.
Indexed: ASFA, AnBeAb, ApEcolAb, BIOSIS Prev, BiolAb, ESPM, EntAb, HGA, IBR, KWIWR, OceAb, RefZh, RevApplEntom, SFA, WildRev, ZooRec.
—BLDSC (0673.000000), CISTI, IE, ingenta, KNAW, Linda Hall. **CCC.**
Published by: Finnish Zoological and Botanical Publishing Board, P Rautatiekatu 13, University of Helsinki, P O Box 17, Helsinki, 00014, Finland. TEL 358-9-19128805, FAX 358-9-19128806, sekj@helsinki.fi, http://www.sekj.org/ActaZool.html, http://www.sejk.org. Ed., R&P Krzysztof Raciborski. Circ: 850. **Distr. by:** Tiedekirja OY - Vetenskapsbokhandeln.

590 ARG ISSN 0065-1729
QL1 CODEN: AZOLA8
ACTA ZOOLOGICA LILLOANA. Text in Spanish; Summaries in English. 1943. irreg., latest vol.45, no.2, 2000. bk.rev. charts; bibl.; illus.; abstr. back issues avail. **Document type:** *Monographic series, Academic/Scholarly.*
Indexed: ASFA, BIOSIS Prev, BiolAb, ChemAb, EntAb, RefZh, ZooRec.
—BLDSC (0674.000000), CASDDS, CISTI, Linda Hall.
Published by: Fundacion Miguel Lillo, Miguel Lillo, 251, San Miguel de Tucuman, Tucuman 4000, Argentina. TEL 54-0381-4239960, FAX 54-0381-4330868, fmlinfonoa@tucbbs.com.ar, http://www.lillo.org.ar. Ed. Jose A Haedo Rossi.

591.972 MEX ISSN 0065-1737
CODEN: AZMEEF
ACTA ZOOLOGICA MEXICANA; nueva serie. Text in English, German, Spanish. 1965-1971 (vol.10, no.4); N.S.. irreg. (approx. 4/yr.), latest vol.88. USD 32 (effective 2003). index. 250 p./no.; back issues avail. **Document type:** *Journal, Academic/Scholarly.*
Indexed: ASFA, BIOSIS Prev, BioCN&I, BiolAb, EntAb, ForAb, HortAb, MaizeAb, RM&VM, RRTA, RefZh, RevApplEntom, S&F, SFA, SeedAb, WAE&RSA, WeedAb, WildRev, ZooRec.
Published by: Instituto de Ecologia, Apartado Postal 63, Xalapa, VERACRUZ 91000, Mexico. TEL 228-842-1800, FAX 228-818-7809, azm@ecologia.edu.mx, libros@ecologia.edu.mx, http://www.ecologia.edu.mx. Ed. Pedro Reyes Castillo.

590 GBR ISSN 1463-6395
QL1
ACTA ZOOLOGICA ONLINE. Text in English. q. GBP 439 in Europe to institutions; USD 811 in the Americas to institutions & Caribbean; GBP 483 elsewhere to institutions (effective 2006). **Document type:** *Academic/Scholarly.*
Media: Online - full text (from Blackwell Synergy, EBSCO Publishing, Gale Group, IngentaConnect, O C L C Online Computer Library Center, Inc., ScienceDirect, Swets Information Services). **Related titles:** Microform ed.: (from PQC); ♦ Print ed.: Acta Zoologica. ISSN 0001-7272.
Published by: Blackwell Publishing Ltd., 9600 Garsington Rd, Oxford, OX4 2ZG, United Kingdom. TEL 44-1865-776868, FAX 44-1865-714591, customerservices@oxon.blackwellpublishing.com, http://www.blackwellpublishing.com.

591.951249 TWN ISSN 1019-5858
QL307.2
➤ **ACTA ZOOLOGICA TAIWANICA/DONGWU XUEKAN.** Text in Chinese, English. 1988. 2/yr. exchange basis. **Document type:** *Academic/Scholarly.* **Description:** Contains original research on any aspects of zoological science from worldwide.
Indexed: ASFA, BIOSIS Prev, BiolAb, ESPM, SFA, ZooRec.
—BLDSC (0675.010000), CISTI.
Published by: (Department of Zoology), National Taiwan University, College of Science, PO Box 23-13, Taipei, 106, Taiwan. TEL 886-2-23630231, FAX 886-2-2363-6837, ctyen@ccms.ntu.edu.tw, http://www.zo.ntu.edu.tw/publish/index.htm. Ed., R&P Tai Sheng Chiu. Circ: 500 (controlled).

➤ **ADMINISTRATION OF THE MARINE MAMMAL PROTECTION ACT OF 1972 (UNITED STATES, FISH AND WILDLIFE SERVICE).** see *CONSERVATION*

599.8 USA ISSN 0587-4416
CODEN: ADPYA
➤ **ADVANCES IN PRIMATOLOGY.** Text in English. irreg., latest 2001. price varies. back issues avail. **Document type:** *Monographic series, Academic/Scholarly.*
—KNAW.
Published by: Springer-Verlag New York, Inc. (Subsidiary of: Springer Science+Business Media), 233 Spring St, New York, NY 10013. TEL 212-460-1500, FAX 212-460-1575, service@springer-ny.com, http://www.springer-ny.com.

590 GBR
ADVOCATES FOR ANIMALS. ANNUAL REPORT. Text in English. 1912. a. free. adv. bk.rev. back issues avail.
Formerly (until 1990): Scottish Society for Prevention of Vivisection. Annual Report
Published by: Advocates for Animals, 10 Queensferry St, Edinburgh, EH2 4PG, United Kingdom. TEL 44-131-225-6039, FAX 44-131-220-6377, advocates.animals@virgin.net. Pub. Les Ward. Circ: 10,000.

590 ZAF ISSN 1681-5556
Q85 CODEN: ANMUA9
➤ **AFRICAN INVERTEBRATES**; a journal of biodiversity research. Text in English, French, German; Summaries in English. 1906. a. price varies. cum.index. back issues avail. **Document type:** *Academic/Scholarly.* **Description:** Research articles on systematic zoology, mainly entomology, arachnology, malacology, and lower invertebrates.
Formerly (until 2001): Natal Museum. Annals (0304-0798)
Indexed: AnthLit, BiolAb, IBR, ISAP, SFA, ZooRec.
—BLDSC (0732.513350), IE.
Published by: Natal Museum, Private Bag 9070, Pietermaritzburg, KwaZulu-Natal 3200, South Africa. TEL 37-33-3451404, FAX 27-33-3450561, dbarracl@nmsa.org.za. R&P D Barraclough. Circ: 320.

597.9 ZAF
CODEN: HAAJA4
AFRICAN JOURNAL OF HERPETOLOGY. Text in English. 1965. s-a. USD 40 foreign (effective 2004). adv. bk.rev. **Document type:** *Journal, Academic/Scholarly.* **Description:** Serves as an outlet for original research on the biology of African amphibians and reptiles.
Formerly: Herpetological Association of Africa. Journal (0441-6651)
Indexed: BIOSIS Prev, BiolAb, SFA, WildRev, ZooRec.
Published by: Herpetological Association of Africa, c/o Liz Scott, Secret., Dept of Herpetology, Transvaal Museum, P.O. Box 413, Pretoria, 0001, South Africa. TEL 27-12-3227632, haasec@freemail.absa.co.za, http://www.herplit.com/contents/Africa.html, http://www.wits.ac.za/haa. Ed. W R Branch. Circ: 500.

599 ZAF
CODEN: AFSNEY
AFRICAN SMALL MAMMAL NEWSLETTER. Text in English. a. **Document type:** *Newsletter.*
Indexed: SFA, WildRev, ZooRec.
Address: c/o GN Bronner, Ed, Dept of Mammals, Transvaal Museum, PO Box 413, Pretoria, 0001, South Africa.

591.68 ZAF ISSN 1562-7020
QL337.S65 CODEN: SAJZDH
➤ **AFRICAN ZOOLOGY.** Text and summaries in English. 1965. s-a. ZAR 215 domestic to institutions; USD 90 foreign to institutions (effective 2001). adv. charts; illus. **Document type:** *Academic/Scholarly.* **Description:** Publishes original research articles and brief discussions on research in the field of zoology in Africa, especially ecology, ethology, physiology and taxonomy.
Former titles (until 2000): South African Journal of Zoology / Suid-Afrikaanse Tydskrif vir Dierkunde (0254-1858); (until 1979): Zoologica Africana (0044-5096)
Related titles: Online - full text ed.: (from EBSCO Publishing).
Indexed: ASCA, ASFA, AbAn, Agr, AnBeAb, ApEcolAb, ApicAb, BIOSIS Prev, BioCN&I, BiolAb, CRFR, ChemAb, CurCont, DSA, ESPM, EntAb, FCA, ForAb, GEOBASE, GenetAb, HGA, HelmAb, HerbAb, INIS AtomInd, ISAP, ISR, IndVet, KWIWR, NutrAb, OceAb, PGegResA, PoultAb, ProtozoAb, RM&VM, RPP, RevApplEntom, S&F, SCI, SFA, SIA, SeedAb, TDB, VetBull, WLR, WildRev, ZooRec.
—BLDSC (0735.123500), CISTI, IDS, IE, ingenta, KNAW, Linda Hall.
Published by: (Zoological Society of Southern Africa), South African Bureau for Scientific Publications, PO Box 11663, Pretoria, Hatfield 0028, South Africa. TEL 27-12-4202016, FAX 27-12-320-7803, africanzoology@up.ac.za, african.zoology@up.ac.za, http://www.up.ac.za/academic/acadorgs/zssa/. Eds. A N Hodgson, R T F Bernard. Adv. contact R T F Bernard. Circ: 600.

592.57 IND
AFRO-ASIAN NEMATOLOGY NETWORK. Text in English. 1992. s-a. membership.
Published by: Afro-Asian Society of Nematologists, c/o Narendra Deva University of Agriculture & Technology, Narendra Nagar (Kumarganj), Faizabad, Uttar Pradesh 224 229, India. Eds. B A Oteifa, M Mashkoor Alam.

AGRICOLTURA E ZOOTECNICA BIOLOGICA. see *AGRICULTURE*

AKADEMIA ROLNICZA W SZCZECINIE. ROZPRAWY. see *AGRICULTURE*

590 JPN
AKAMATA/OKINAWA HERPETOLOGICAL SOCIETY. RESEARCH REPORT. Text in Japanese. a.
Indexed: ZooRec.
Published by: Okinawa Ryosei Hachurui Kenkyukai/Okinawa Herpetological Society, Okinawa Kenritsu Hakubutsukan, Shiyurionaka-cho, Naha-shi, Okinawa-ken 903-0823, Japan.

599.657 CAN ISSN 0835-5851
➤ **ALCES**; a journal devoted to the biology and management of moose. Text in English. 1963. q. CND 38 (effective 2005); USD 30 (effective 2003). charts; illus. back issues avail. **Document type:** *Academic/Scholarly.* **Description:** Original research relating in the broadest sense to the biology and management of moose.
Formerly (until 1981): North American Moose Conference. Proceedings (0836-8716)

Related titles: Microfiche ed.; Online - full text ed.: (from Gale Group).
Indexed: AnBrAb, CPerI, DSA, EnvAb, FPA, ForAb, HelmAb, HerbAb, IndVet, KWIWR, NutrAb, PoultAb, RPP, RRTA, RevApplEntom, S&F, SFA, VetBull, WeedAb, WildRev, ZooRec.
—BLDSC (0786.716000), CISTI, IE, ingenta, Linda Hall. **CCC.**
Address: Lakehead University Bookstore, 855 Oliver Rd, Thunder Bay, ON P7B 5E1, Canada. TEL 807-343-8528, FAX 807-346-7796, http://www.lakeheadu.ca/~alceswww/alces.html. Eds. Dr. Arthur R Rodgers, Gerald Redmond. R&P M Lankester. Circ: 300.

590 HUN ISSN 0002-5658
QL1 CODEN: ALLKAS
ALLATTANI KOZLEMENYEK/ZOOLOGICAL PROCEEDINGS. Text in Hungarian; Summaries in English, German, Russian. 1902. q. USD 30. bk.rev. bibl.; charts; illus.
Indexed: BiolAb, CurCont.
—CISTI, KNAW, Linda Hall.
Published by: Magyar Biologiai Tarsasag/Hungarian Biological Society, Fo utca 68, Budapest, 1027, Hungary. Ed. I Andrassy.

597.62 FRA ISSN 0753-4973
CODEN: ALTSES
➤ **ALYTES**; international journal of batrachology. Text in English, French, Spanish. 1982. q. **Document type:** *Academic/Scholarly.*
Indexed: ASFA, BIOSIS Prev, BiolAb, ESPM, RefZh, ZooRec.
—BLDSC (0806.254400), IE, ingenta, Linda Hall.
Published by: International Society for the Study and Conservation of Amphibians, c/o Laboratoire des Reptiles et Amphibiens, Museum National d'Histoire Naturelle, 25 rue Cuvier, Paris, 75005, France. Ed. Alain Dubois.

➤ **AMEMBOA**; news and results on Thai heteroptera. see *BIOLOGY*

595.4 USA
AMERICAN ARACHNOLOGY. Text in English. 1973. irreg.
—BLDSC (0810.340000).
Published by: American Arachnological Society, c/o Norman I Platnick, Division of Invertebrate Zoology, American Museum of Natural History, Central Park W at 79th St, New York, NY 10024. TEL 212-769-5612, FAX 212-769-5277, http://www.americanarachnology.org.

594 USA ISSN 1072-2440
AMERICAN CONCHOLOGIST. Text in English. 1973. q. USD 20 (effective 1999). adv. bk.rev. back issues avail. **Document type:** *Academic/Scholarly.*
Formerly (until 1987): Conchologists of America Bulletin (0747-105X)
Indexed: ZooRec.
Published by: Conchologists of America, Inc., 1222 Holsworth Ln, Louisville, KY 40222-6616. TEL 502-423-0469, amconch@ix.netcom.com, http://www.coa.acnatsci.org./conchnet/. Ed. Lynn Scheu. Adv. contact Howard Roux. Circ: 1,400 (paid).

599.8 USA ISSN 0275-2565
QL737.P9 CODEN: AJPTDU
➤ **AMERICAN JOURNAL OF PRIMATOLOGY.** Text in English. 1981. 13/yr. USD 2,599 domestic to institutions; USD 2,755 in Canada & Mexico to institutions; USD 2,846 elsewhere to institutions; USD 2,859 combined subscription domestic to institutions print & online eds.; USD 3,015 combined subscription in Canada & Mexico to institutions print & online eds.; USD 3,106 combined subscription elsewhere to institutions print & online eds. (effective 2006). adv. bk.rev. bibl.; charts; illus. index. back issues avail. **Document type:** *Journal, Academic/Scholarly.* **Description:** Examines topics relevant to the study of primates, including all aspects of their anatomy, behavior, development, ecology, evolution, genetics, nutrition, physiology, reproduction, systematics, conservation, husbandry, and use in biomedical research.
Related titles: Microform ed.: (from PQC); Online - full text ed.: ISSN 1098-2345. USD 2,599 to institutions (effective 2006) (from EBSCO Publishing, Swets Information Services, Wiley InterScience); Supplement(s): ISSN 0736-7880. 1982.
Indexed: ASCA, AbAn, AgrForAb, AnBeAb, AnBrAb, AnthLit, ApEcolAb, B&BAb, BIOBASE, BIOSIS Prev, BiolAb, CIN, ChemAb, ChemTitl, CurCont, DSA, ESPM, ExcerpMed, FoVS&M, ForAb, GEOBASE, GSI, GenetAb, HGA, HelmAb, IABS, IBSS, ISR, IndMed, IndVet, Inpharma, MEDLINE, NutrAb, PGegResA, ProtozoAb, PsycInfo, PsycholAb, RM&VM, RRTA, Reac, RevApplEntom, SCI, SFA, SIA, SSCI, SeedAb, TDB, VetBull, WildRev, ZooRec, e-psyche.
—BLDSC (0834.400000), CASDDS, IDS, IE, ingenta, Linda Hall. **CCC.**
Published by: John Wiley & Sons, Inc., 111 River St, Hoboken, NJ 07030-5774. TEL 201-748-6000, FAX 201-748-5915, uscs-wis@wiley.com, http://www.interscience.wiley.com/jpages/0275-2565/, http://www.wiley.com. Ed. Linda M Fedigan. adv.: B&W page GBP 640, color page GBP 1,515; trim 174 x 254. Circ: 650. **Subscr. outside the Americas to:** John Wiley & Sons Ltd., The Atrium, Southern Gate, Chichester, West Sussex PO19 8SQ, United Kingdom. TEL 44-1243-843335, 0800-243407, FAX 44-1243-843232, cs-journals@wiley.co.uk.

594 USA ISSN 0740-2783
QL401
➤ **AMERICAN MALACOLOGICAL BULLETIN.** Text in English. 1931; N.S. 1982. 2/yr. USD 60 to individuals members; USD 65 to institutions members; USD 20 to students members (effective 2004). index. **Document type:** *Bulletin, Academic/Scholarly.* **Description:** Contains notable contributions in malacological research.
Former titles (until 1982): American Malacological Union. Bulletin (0096-5537); (until 1970): American Malacological Union. Annual Reports (0096-9486)
Indexed: ASCA, ASFA, BIOSIS Prev, BiolAb, CurCont, ESPM, OceAb, SPPI, ZooRec.
—BLDSC (0841.300000), IDS, IE, Infotrieve, ingenta, Linda Hall.
Published by: American Malacological Society, Inc., c/o Susan B. Cook, Consortium for Oceanographic Research & Education, 4201 Wilson Blvd, Ste 420, Washington, DC 20005. TEL 570-941-4378, voltzowj2@scranton.edu, http://erato.acnatsci.org/ams/publications/amb.html. Ed., R&P Dr. Janice Voltzow. Circ: 800.

590.74 USA ISSN 0003-0082
QL1 CODEN: AMUNAL
➤ **AMERICAN MUSEUM NOVITATES.** Short title: Notivates. Text in English. 1921. irreg., latest no.3332, 2001, Apr. price varies. bibl.; illus.; maps. back issues avail. **Document type:** *Monographic series, Academic/Scholarly.* **Description:** Contains brief professional research papers in paleontology and zoology, primarily systematics and evolutionary biology.
Related titles: Online - full text ed.: (from BioOne, C S A, O C L C Online Computer Library Center, Inc.).
Indexed: AESIS, ASFA, Agr, ApicAb, BIOSIS Prev, BiolAb, CurCont, ESPM, EntAb, KWIWR, RefZh, RevApplEntom, ZooRec.
—CISTI, Linda Hall.
Published by: American Museum of Natural History Library, Scientific Publications Distribution, Central Park W at 79th St, New York, NY 10024-5192. TEL 212-769-5545, FAX 212-769-5009, scipubs@amnh.org, http://nimidi.amnh.org. Ed. Brenda Jones. Circ: 1,000.

590.74 USA ISSN 0003-0090
QH1 CODEN: BUMNAE
➤ **AMERICAN MUSEUM OF NATURAL HISTORY. BULLETIN.** Text in English. 1881. irreg., latest no.262, 2001. price varies. bibl.; illus.; maps. back issues avail.; reprint service avail. from PQC. **Document type:** *Monographic series, Academic/Scholarly.* **Description:** Professional basic monographs in paeontology and zoology, primarily on systematics and evolutionary biology.
Related titles: Microform ed.: (from PMC, PQC); Online - full text ed.: 2000 (from BioOne, C S A, O C L C Online Computer Library Center, Inc.).
Indexed: AESIS, ASCA, ASFA, AbAn, BIOSIS Prev, BioCN&I, BiolAb, CurCont, EntAb, FPA, ForAb, ISR, OceAb, PBA, PGegResA, RASB, RefZh, RevApplEntom, S&F, SCI, SFA, WildRev, ZooRec.
—BLDSC (2390.000000), CASDDS, CISTI, IE, ingenta, Linda Hall.
Published by: American Museum of Natural History Library, Scientific Publications Distribution, Central Park W at 79th St, New York, NY 10024-5192. TEL 212-769-5545, FAX 212-769-5009, scipubs@amnh.org, http://nimidi.amnh.org. Ed. Brenda Jones. Circ: 1,200.

597 USA ISSN 0748-0539
AMERICAN SOCIETY OF ICHTHYOLOGISTS AND HERPETOLOGISTS. SPECIAL PUBLICATION. Text in English. 1984. irreg.
Indexed: ZooRec.
—Linda Hall.
Published by: American Society of Ichthyologists and Herpetologists, c/o Maureen Donnelly, Secretary, Florida International University, College Of Arts & Science, Dept of Biological Sciences, North Miami, FL 33181 . TEL 305-919-5651, FAX 305-919-5964, donnelly@fiu.edu.

599 USA ISSN 0569-8219
CODEN: AMAMBL
➤ **AMERICAN SOCIETY OF MAMMALOGISTS. SPECIAL PUBLICATIONS.** Text in English. 1967. irreg., latest vol.11. price varies. **Document type:** *Monographic series, Academic/Scholarly.*
Indexed: BIOSIS Prev, BiolAb, MA.
—BLDSC (8372.348000), CISTI.
Published by: American Society of Mammalogists, c/o Dr H Duane Smith, Secretary-Treas, Monte L Bean Life Science Museum, Brigham Young University, Provo, UT 84602-0200. TEL 801-378-2492.

590.73 USA
QL77.5
AMERICAN ZOO AND AQUARIUM ASSOCIATION. PROCEEDINGS. Text in English. a. USD 80 to non-members; USD 45 to members; USD 50 to libraries (effective 2005). illus. **Document type:** *Proceedings.*
Formerly: American Association of Zoological Parks and Aquariums. Annual Conference. Proceedings (0090-4473)
Indexed: BiolAb, KWIWR, SFA, WildRev, ZooRec.
—BLDSC (1082.452100).
Published by: American Zoo and Aquarium Association, 8403 Colesville Rd, Ste 710, Silver Spring, MD 20910. TEL 301-562-0777, FAX 301-562-0888, mmoretti@aza.org, http://www.aza.org/AZAPublications/. Ed., Pub., Adv. contact Tim Lewthwaite.

590 USA ISSN 1088-0402
QL76.5.U6
AMERICAN ZOO AND AQUARIUM ASSOCIATION. REGIONAL CONFERENCE PROCEEDINGS. Text in English. 1973. a., latest 2003. USD 45 per issue to members; USD 80 per issue to non-members (effective 2005).
Former titles (until 199?): A A Z P A Regional Conference Proceedings (0731-0439); (until 198?): A A Z P A Regional Workshop Proceedings (0731-0420); (until 1976): A A Z P A Regional Conference Proceedings (0731-0412); (until 1974): Consolidated Proceedings of the Regional A A Z P A Conferences (0731-0404)
Indexed: ZooRec.
—BLDSC (7336.578000).
Published by: American Zoo and Aquarium Association, 8403 Colesville Rd, Ste 710, Silver Spring, MD 20910-3314. TEL 301-562-0777, 800-929-4242, FAX 301-562-0888, http://www.aza.org.

597.8 NLD ISSN 0173-5373
QL640 CODEN: AMREEH
➤ **AMPHIBIA - REPTILIA.** Text in English, French, German, Spanish. 1980. q. EUR 110 in North America to individuals; USD 138 elsewhere to individuals; EUR 372 combined subscription in North America to institutions print & online eds.; USD 465 combined subscription elsewhere to institutions print & online eds. (effective 2006). adv. bk.rev. illus. back issues avail.; reprint service avail. from PSC. **Document type:** *Journal, Academic/Scholarly.* **Description:** Publishes herpetologic research reflecting the most up-to-date information on systematics and taxonomy, as well as behavior, physiology, and ecology.
Related titles: Online - full content ed.; Online - full text ed.: ISSN 1568-5381. EUR 372 in North America to institutions; USD 465 elsewhere to institutions (effective 2006) (from EBSCO Publishing, Gale Group, IngentaConnect, Kluwer Online, O C L C Online Computer Library Center, Inc., Springer LINK, Swets Information Services).
Indexed: ASFA, BIOSIS Prev, BiolAb, CurCont, ESPM, FPA, ForAb, GEOBASE, HelmAb, ISR, RM&VM, RefZh, SCI, ZooRec.
—BLDSC (0859.452500), CISTI, IDS, IE, Infotrieve, ingenta, Linda Hall. **CCC.**
Published by: (Societas Europaea Herpetologica/European Herpetological Society), Brill Academic Publishers, PO Box 9000, Leiden, 2300 PA, Netherlands. TEL 31-71-53-53-500, FAX 31-71-53-17-532, cs@brill.nl, http://www.brill.nl/m_catalogue_sub6_id7101.htm. Eds. Gunter Gollmann, L Luiselli. Adv. contact F S Geuze. **Subscr. in N. America to:** PO Box 605, Herndon, VA 20172. TEL 703-661-1585, 800-337-9255, FAX 703-661-1501, cs@brillusa.com. **Distr. outside N. America by:** c/o Turpin Distribution, Stratton Business Park, Pegasus Drive, Biggleswade, BEDFORDSHIRE SG 18 8TQ, United Kingdom. TEL 44-1767-604-954, FAX 44-1767-601-640, brill@turpin-distribution.com.

597.9 ARG ISSN 0326-8489
CODEN: ARPTEJ
AMPHIBIA & REPTILIA. Variant title: Amphibia & Reptilia (Conservacion). Text in Spanish. 1986. q.
Indexed: SFA, WildRev, ZooRec.
Published by: Fundacion Vida Silvestre Argentina, Avda. Leandro N. Alem, 968, Capital Federal, Buenos Aires 1001, Argentina.

597.9 USA ISSN 1083-446X
QL640
AMPHIBIAN & REPTILE CONSERVATION. Text in English. 1996. q. USD 25 domestic to individuals; USD 40 foreign to individuals; USD 50 domestic to institutions; USD 65 foreign to institutions (effective 2003).
Related titles: Online - full text ed.: ISSN 1525-9153. free (effective 2005) (from National Library of Medicine).
Indexed: BiolAb, ZooRec.
Address: 2525 Iowa Ave, Modesto, CA 95358-9467. editor@herpetofauna.org, http://www.pubmedcentral.gov/tocrender.fcgi?journal=218&action=archive. Ed. Craig Hassapakis.

591.5 GBR ISSN 0003-3472
QL750 CODEN: ANBEA8
➤ **ANIMAL BEHAVIOUR.** Text in English. 1953. 12/yr. EUR 1,066 in Europe to institutions; JPY 115,100 in Japan to institutions; USD 947 elsewhere to institutions (effective 2006). adv. bk.rev. illus. Index. reprints avail. **Document type:** *Journal, Academic/Scholarly.* **Description:** Contains critical reviews, original papers, and research articles about all aspects of animal behavior for biologists and veterinarians.
Formerly (until 1958): British Journal of Animal Behaviour (0950-5601)
Related titles: Microform ed.: (from PMC, PQC); Online - full text ed.: ISSN 1095-8282. USD 1,002 (effective 2002) (from EBSCO Publishing, Gale Group, IngentaConnect, O C L C Online Computer Library Center, Inc., ScienceDirect, Swets Information Services).

Indexed: AEA, ASCA, ASFA, AcaI, AgBio, Agr, AgrForAb, AnBeAb, AnBrAb, ApEcolAb, ApicAb, B&AI, BIOBASE, BIOSIS Prev, BibAg, BioCN&I, BiolAb, CDA, CRFR, ChemAb, CurCont, DSA, ESPM, EntAb, ExcerpMed, FS&TA, ForAb, GEOBASE, GSI, HelmAb, HortAb, IABS, ISR, IndMed, IndVet, Inpharma, KWIWR, MEDLINE, MLA-IB, NemAb, NutrAb, OceAb, OrnHort, PHN&I, PN&I, PoultAb, ProtozoAb, PsycInfo, PsycholAb, RM&VM, Reac, RevApplEntom, S&F, SAA, SCI, SFA, SIA, SSCI, SeedAb, SoyAb, VetBull, WAE&RSA, WeedAb, WildRev, ZooRec, e-psyche.
—BLDSC (0902.950000), CASDDS, CISTI, GNLM, IDS, IE, Infotrieve, ingenta, Linda Hall. **CCC.**
Published by: (Association for the Study of Animal Behaviour), Academic Press (Subsidiary of: Elsevier Science & Technology), 24-28 Oval Rd, London, NW1 7DX, United Kingdom. TEL 44-20-72674466, FAX 44-20-74822293, apsubs@acad.com, http://www.elsevier.com/locate/anbehav. Ed. L. Barrett. **Subscr. to:** Harcourt Publishers Ltd., Foots Cray High St, Sidcup, Kent DA14 5HP, United Kingdom. TEL 44-20-8300-3322, FAX 44-20-8309-0807. **Co-sponsor:** Animal Behaviour Society.

590.7 ESP ISSN 1578-665X
QL1 CODEN: ABCNCQ
➤ **ANIMAL BIODIVERSITY AND CONSERVATION.** Text in English, Spanish; Abstracts in English. 1958. s-a. EUR 21.04 domestic to individuals; EUR 23.44 in Europe to individuals; EUR 24.04 elsewhere to individuals; EUR 66.11 domestic to institutions; EUR 68.52 in Europe to institutions; EUR 69.12 elsewhere to institutions (effective 2004). adv. bibl.; charts; illus.; stat. **Document type:** *Journal, Academic/Scholarly.* **Description:** Disseminates zoological research.
Former titles (until 2000): Miscel.lania Zoologica (0211-6529); (until 1979): Miscelanea Zoologica (0540-3278)
Related titles: Online - full text ed.: free (effective 2005).
Indexed: ASFA, AcoustA, AgrForAb, Agrind, AnBrAb, ApEcolAb, B&AI, B&BAb, BIOSIS Prev, BehAb, BioCN&I, BiolAb, ESPM, EntAb, EnvInd, ForAb, GEOBASE, GenetAb, HGA, HelmAb, HerbAb, IECT, IndVet, MaizeAb, NemAb, NutrAb, PGegResA, PoultAb, RDA, RM&VM, RRTA, RefZh, RevApplEntom, S&F, SFA, SoyAb, WAE&RSA, WildRev, ZooRec.
—BLDSC (0902.971800), CINDOC, CISTI.
Published by: Museu de Ciencies Naturals de la Ciutadella, Museu de Zoologia, Passeig Picasso s/n, Barcelona, 08003, Spain. TEL 34-93-3196912, FAX 34-93-3104999, museuciencies@mail.bcn.es, http://bcnweb13.bcn.es:81/NASApp/wprmuseuciencies/Museu.GeneradorPagines?idioma=3&seccio=11_1, http://www.museuzoologia.bcn.es. Adv. contact Anna Omedes. Circ: 1,500.

591.9492 NLD ISSN 1570-7555
QL1 CODEN: NEJZAL
➤ **ANIMAL BIOLOGY.** Text in English. 1872. q. USD 438 combined subscription in the Americas print & online eds.; EUR 438 combined subscription elsewhere print & online eds. (effective 2006). charts; illus.; stat. back issues avail. **Document type:** *Journal, Academic/Scholarly.* **Description:** Publishes studies with an experimental or functional approach to topics in behavioral and physiological ecology, ecological and functional morphology, environmental physiology and biosystematics.
Former titles (until 2003): Netherlands Journal of Zoology (0028-2960); (until 1968): Archives Neerlandaise de Zoologie (0365-5164)
Related titles: Microform ed.: (from SWZ); Online - full content ed.; Online - full text ed.: ISSN 1570-7563. USD 394 in the Americas; EUR 315 elsewhere (effective 2006) (from EBSCO Publishing, Gale Group, IngentaConnect, Kluwer Online, O C L C Online Computer Library Center, Inc., Springer LINK, Swets Information Services).
Indexed: ASCA, ASFA, AgBio, AgrForAb, AnBeAb, AnBrAb, ApEcolAb, BIOSIS Prev, BioCN&I, BiolAb, CRFR, ChemAb, CurCont, ESPM, EntAb, ForAb, GEOBASE, GenetAb, HGA, ISR, IndVet, NutrAb, PoultAb, RM&VM, RevApplEntom, SCI, SFA, VetBull, WildRev, ZooRec.
—BLDSC (0902.971900), CISTI, IDS, IE, ingenta, Linda Hall.
Published by: (Nederlands Dierkundige Vereniging), Brill Academic Publishers, PO Box 9000, Leiden, 2300 PA, Netherlands. TEL 31-71-53-53-500, FAX 31-71-53-17-532, njz@morf.edc.wau.nl, cs@brill.nl, http://www.brill.nl/m_catalogue_sub6_id11129.htm. Ed. M. Muller. Adv. contact F S Geuze. **Subscr. to:** PO Box 605, Herndon, VA 20172. TEL 703-661-1585, 800-337-9255, FAX 703-661-1501, cs@brillusa.com. **Dist. by:** c/o Turpin Distribution, Stratton Business Park, Pegasus Drive, Biggleswade, BEDFORDSHIRE SG 18 8TQ, United Kingdom. TEL 44-1767-604-954, FAX 44-1767-601-640, brill@turpin-distribution.com.

➤ **ANIMAL GENETICS.** see *BIOLOGY—Genetics*

590 USA ISSN 0164-9531
➤ **ANIMAL KEEPERS' FORUM.** Text in English. 1974. m. USD 35 in US & Canada to individuals; USD 50 elsewhere to individuals; USD 100 in US & Canada to institutions; USD 35 to libraries (effective 2003). adv. bk.rev. bibl.; illus.; charts. index. 48 p./no.; back issues avail.; reprints avail. **Document type:** *Journal, Academic/Scholarly.* **Description:** Contains articles on exotic animal husbandry, research, and exhibit design.
Indexed: SFA, WLR, WildRev, ZooRec.
Published by: American Association of Zoo Keepers, Inc., 3601 S W 29th St., Ste 133, Topeka, KS 66614. TEL 785-273-9149, 800-242-4519, FAX 913-273-1980, akfeditor@zk.kscoxmail.com, aazkoffice@zk.kscoxmail.com, http://www.aazk.org. Ed., R&P, Adv. contact Susan D Chan TEL 785-273-9149. page USD 210; 5 x 8. Circ: 2,900.

➤ **ANIMAL LAB NEWS.** see *VETERINARY SCIENCE*

➤ **ANIMAL NATURAL HISTORY SERIES.** see *SCIENCES: COMPREHENSIVE WORKS*

590 FRA ISSN 1627-3583
CODEN: AZOOAH
➤ **ANIMAL RESEARCH.** Text and summaries in English, French. 1952. bi-m. EUR 334 combined subscription domestic print & online eds.; EUR 388 combined subscription in the European Union print & online eds; EUR 418 combined subscription elsewhere print & online eds. (effective 2005). adv. bk.rev. charts; illus. index. reprint service avail. from ISI. **Document type:** *Academic/Scholarly.* **Description:** Publishes original articles, reviews, short notes and national and international symposia proceedings on general or comparative zootechny.
Formerly (until 2000): Annales de Zootechnie (0003-424X)
Related titles: Online - full text ed.: Animal Research Online. ISSN 1627-3591 (from EBSCO Publishing, Swets Information Services).
Indexed: AEA, ASCA, ASFA, AgBio, AgrForAb, AnBrAb, BIOSIS Prev, BibAg, BiolAb, CIN, ChemAb, ChemTitl, CurCont, DSA, FCA, FS&TA, FoVS&M, ForAb, HerbAb, HortAb, ISR, IndVet, MaizeAb, NutrAb, PBA, PGegResA, PN&I, PoultAb, RM&VM, RiceAb, S&F, SCI, SFA, SIA, SoyAb, TriticAb, VetBull, WAE&RSA, WildRev, ZooRec.
—BLDSC (0905.076250), CASDDS, CISTI, IDS, IE, ingenta, Linda Hall. **CCC.**
Published by: (France. Institut National de la Recherche Agronomique (INRA)), E D P Sciences, 17 Ave du Hoggar, Parc d'Activites de Courtaboeuf, BP 112, Cedex A, Les Ulis, F-91944, France. TEL 33-1-69187575, FAX 33-1-69860678, subscribers@edpsciences.org, http://www.edpsciences.org/journal/index.cfm?edpsname=animres. Ed. Michel Doreau. Circ: 2,000.

059 ITA ISSN 0391-7746
ANIMALIA. Text in Italian. 1974. a.
Indexed: AnBeAb, EntAb.
Published by: Universita degli Studi di Catania, Istituto di Biologia Animale, Via Androne 81, Catania, Italy. http://www.unict.it.

590 POL ISSN 0003-4541
QL1 CODEN: AZOGAR
➤ **ANNALES ZOOLOGICI.** Text in Multiple languages. 1922. q. EUR 100 to individuals; EUR 200 to institutions (effective 2005). charts; abstr.; bibl.; illus.; maps. index. 160 p./no. 2 cols./p.; back issues avail. **Document type:** *Journal, Academic/Scholarly.*
Related titles: Online - full text ed.: (from Gale Group, IngentaConnect).
Indexed: ASFA, AgrAg, AgrForAb, AgrLib, AnBrAb, BIOSIS Prev, BioCN&I, BiolAb, CurCont, ESPM, ForAb, HortAb, NemAb, OrnHort, PBA, PGegResA, ProtozoAb, RM&VM, RefZh, RevApplEntom, S&F, TDB, ZooRec.
—CISTI, Linda Hall.
Published by: Polska Akademia Nauk, Muzeum i Instytut Zoologii/Polish Academy of Sciences, Museum & Institute of Zoology, ul Wilcza 64, Warsaw, 00679, Poland. TEL 48-22-6293221, FAX 48-22-6296302, libr@miiz.waw.pl, http://www.miiz.waw.pl. Ed. Dariusz Iwan. Pub., Adv. contact Katarzyna Wisniewska. Circ: 500.

590 FIN ISSN 0003-455X
QL1 CODEN: AZOFAO
➤ **ANNALES ZOOLOGICI FENNICI.** Text in English. 1964. q. EUR 44 combined subscription to individuals printed and online editions; EUR 34 to individuals online edition; EUR 10 newsstand/cover to individuals; EUR 88 combined subscription to institutions printed and online editions; EUR 66 to institutions online edition; EUR 20 newsstand/cover to institutions (effective 2005). charts; illus.; stat.; maps. index. 2 cols./p.; back issues avail. **Document type:** *Journal, Academic/Scholarly.* **Description:** Contains research reports and reviews on ecology, conservation biology, game and fisheries research of general interests, ecological physiology, faunistics and systematics.
Supersedes in part (1932-1964): Societatis Zoologicae-Botanicae Fennicae Vanamo. Annales Zoologici (0365-8627); Supersedes in part (1946-1964): Societatis Zoologicae-Botanicae Fennicae Vanamo. Archivum (0365-7280)
Related titles: Online - full text ed.: EUR 51 (effective 2003).
Indexed: ASCA, ASFA, AgBio, AgrForAb, AnBeAb, AnBrAb, ApEcolAb, BIOBASE, BIOSIS Prev, BiolAb, CPA, CRFR, ChemAb, CurCont, ESPM, EntAb, EnvAb, EnvInd, ExcerpMed, FPA, ForAb, GEOBASE, HGA, HelmAb, HerbAb, HortAb, I&DA, IABS, ISR, IndVet, KWIWR, MaizeAb, NutrAb, OrnHort, PBA, PGegResA, PGrRegA, PoultAb, RA&MP, RDA, RM&VM, RPP, RRTA, RefZh, RevApplEntom, S&F, SCI, SFA, SeedAb, VITIS, VetBull, WAE&RSA, WeedAb, WildRev, ZooRec.
—BLDSC (1004.250000), CASDDS, CISTI, IDS, IE, Infotrieve, ingenta, Linda Hall.
Published by: Finnish Zoological and Botanical Publishing Board, P Rautatiekatu 13, University of Helsinki, P O Box 17, Helsinki, 00014, Finland. TEL 358-9-19128805, FAX 358-9-19128806, sekj@helsinki.fi, http://www.sekj.org/ActaZool.html, http://www.sejk.org. Eds. Philip T.B. Starks, Juha Merila. R&P Krzysztof Raciborski. Circ: 800. **Dist. by:** Tiedekirja OY - Vetenskapsbokhandeln.

➤ **ANNALS OF ANIMAL SCIENCE.** see *ANIMAL WELFARE*

590 IND ISSN 0003-5009
QL1 CODEN: AZLGAC
ANNALS OF ZOOLOGY. Text in English. 1955. q. USD 32. bk.rev.
Indexed: BiolAb, ChemAb, SFA.
—CASDDS, CISTI.
Published by: Academy of Zoology, Khandari Rd., Agra, Uttar Pradesh 282 002, India. Ed. Beni Charan Mahendra. Circ: 1,800.

590 580 SVK ISSN 0570-202X
QL1 CODEN: AZBTAZ
ANNOTATIONES ZOOLOGICAE ET BOTANICAE. Text in English. irreg., latest vol.222, 2000. price varies. **Document type:** *Monographic series, Academic/Scholarly.*
Indexed: BIOSIS Prev, BiolAb, ZooRec.
Published by: (Slovenske Narodne Muzeum, Prirodovedne Muzeum/Slovak National Museum, Natural History Museum), Slovenske Narodne Muzeum, Narodne Muzejne Centrum, Vajanskeho nabr 2, Bratislava, 81436, Slovakia. TEL 421-2-52961973, FAX 421-2-52966653, nmc@snm.sk. Ed. Vladimir Jansky.

599.9 FRA ISSN 0761-3032
GN476.76
ANTHROPOZOOLOGICA. Text in French. 1984. s-a. adv.
Related titles: ♦ Supplement(s): Anthropozoologica Numero Special. ISSN 0994-7213.
Indexed: AnthLit, IAB, RefZh, ZooRec.
Published by: (L'Homme et l'Animal, Societe de Recherche Interdisciplinaire), H.A.S.R.I., c/o Laboratoire d'Anatomie Comparee, Museum National d'Histoire Naturelle, 55 rue Buffon, Paris, 75005, France. TEL 33-1-40793310, FAX 33-1-40793314. Ed. Jean Denis Vigne. Adv. contact Christine Lefevre.

599.9 FRA ISSN 0994-7213
ANTHROPOZOOLOGICA NUMERO SPECIAL. Text in French. 1987. irreg.
Related titles: ♦ Supplement to: Anthropozoologica. ISSN 0761-3032.
Published by: (L'Homme et l'Animal, Societe de Recherche Interdisciplinaire), H.A.S.R.I., c/o Laboratoire d'Anatomie Comparee, Museum National d'Histoire Naturelle, 55 rue Buffon, Paris, 75005, France. TEL 33-1-40793310, FAX 33-1-40793314.

590.724 USA ISSN 0892-7936
QL85
➤ **ANTHROZOOS;** a multidisciplinary journal on the interactions of people and animals. Text in English. 1987. q. USD 60 domestic to individuals; USD 70 foreign to individuals; USD 80 domestic to institutions; USD 90 foreign to institutions (effective 2005). adv. bk.rev. abstr.; illus. index. back issues avail.; reprints avail. **Document type:** *Academic/Scholarly.* **Description:** Explore impact of animals on human health and culture.
Indexed: ASCA, AgeL, Agr, ArtHuCI, BibAg, CurCont, EPB, EnvAb, FamI, FoVS&M, IAB, IndVet, KWIWR, NutrAb, PsycInfo, PsycholAb, RDA, RRTA, SAA, SCI, SFA, SOPODA, SSCI, VetBull, WildRev, e-psyche.
—BLDSC (1546.670000), CIS, CISTI, IDS, IE, Infotrieve, ingenta. **CCC.**
Published by: Purdue University Press, 30 Amberwood Pkwy, PO Box 388, Ashland, OH 44805. TEL 800-427-6553, FAX 419-281-6883, pupress@purdue.edu, http://www.vetmed.ucdavis.edu/CCAB/anthro~1.htm, http://www.thepress.purdue.edu. Ed. Anthony L Podberscek. Circ: 350.

590 ITA ISSN 0391-5522
APITALIA; notiziario quindicinale d'informazioni. Text in Italian. 1974. s-m. adv. bk.rev. index. back issues avail. **Document type:** *Bulletin.*
Published by: Federazione Apicoltori Italiani, Corso Vittorio Emanuele II, 101, Rome, RM 00186, Italy. TEL 39-6-6877175, FAX 39-6-6852287, TELEX 612533. Ed. Raffaele Cirone. Circ: 20,000.

591.5 NLD ISSN 0168-1591
SF756.7 CODEN: AABSEV
➤ **APPLIED ANIMAL BEHAVIOUR SCIENCE.** Text in English. 1975. 24/yr. EUR 2,048 in Europe to institutions; JPY 272,200 in Japan to institutions; USD 2,291 to institutions except Europe and Japan (effective 2006). adv. bk.rev. bibl.; illus.; abstr. index. back issues avail.; reprints avail. **Document type:** *Journal, Academic/Scholarly.* **Description:** Deals with the behaviour of domesticated and utilized animals.
Formerly (until 1985): Applied Animal Ethology (0304-3762)
Related titles: Microform ed.: (from PQC); Online - full text ed.: (from EBSCO Publishing, Gale Group, IngentaConnect, ScienceDirect, Swets Information Services).

B

▼ new title ➤ refereed ✶ unverified ♦ full entry avail.

Indexed: AEA, ASCA, ASFA, AbHyg, AgBio, Agr, AgrForAb, AnBeAb, AnBrAb, BIOBASE, BIOSIS Prev, BibAg, BioCN&I, BiolAb, CurCont, DSA, FCA, FPA, FoVS&M, ForAb, GEOBASE, HelmAb, HerbAb, HortAb, IAB, IABS, ISR, IndVet, KWIWR, MEDLINE, MaizeAb, NutrAb, OrnHort, PBA, PN&I, PoultAb, ProtozoAb, PsyScBA&T, PsycInfo, PsycholAb, RDA, RM&VM, RRTA, SAA, SCI, SFA, SIA, SSCI, SoyAb, TriticAb, VITIS, VetBull, WAE&RSA, WildRev, ZooRec, e-psyche.
—BLDSC (1571.446000), CISTI, IDS, IE, Infotrieve, ingenta. **CCC.**
Published by: Elsevier BV (Subsidiary of: Elsevier Science & Technology), Radarweg 29, Amsterdam, 1043 NX, Netherlands. TEL 31-20-4853911, FAX 31-20-4852457, nlinfo-f@elsevier.nl, http://www.elsevier.com/locate/applanim, http://www.elsevier.nl. Eds. H Gonyou, P Jensen.

597.9 NLD ISSN 1570-7539
▼ ➤ **APPLIED HERPETOLOGY.** Text in English. 2003. q. USD 88 in the Americas to individuals; EUR 70 elsewhere to individuals; USD 275 combined subscription in the Americas to institutions print & online eds.; EUR 220 combined subscription elsewhere to institutions print & online eds. (effective 2006). back issues avail.; reprint service avail. from PSC. **Document type:** *Journal, Academic/Scholarly.* **Description:** Presents research on amphibians and reptiles with a focus on biodiversity, conservation, environmental monitoring, farming, natural products development and wildlife management.
Related titles: Online - full text ed.: ISSN 1570-7547. USD 248 in the Americas to institutions; EUR 198 elsewhere to institutions (effective 2006) (from EBSCO Publishing, Gale Group, IngentaConnect, Kluwer Online, O C L C Online Computer Library Center, Inc., Springer LINK, Swets Information Services).
—BLDSC (1572.935000), IE.
Published by: Brill Academic Publishers, PO Box 9000, Leiden, 2300 PA, Netherlands. TEL 31-71-53-53-500, FAX 31-71-53-17-532, cs@brill.nl, l, http://www.brill.nl. Ed. M.J. Tyler. Adv. contact F S Geuze. **Subscr. in N. America to:** PO Box 605, Herndon, VA 20172. TEL 703-661-1585, 800-337-9255, FAX 703-661-1501, cs@brillusa.com. **Distr. outside N. America by:** c/o Turpin Distribution, Stratton Business Park, Pegasus Drive, Biggleswade, BEDFORDSHIRE SG 18 8TQ, United Kingdom. TEL 44-1767-604-954, FAX 44-1767-601-640, brill@turpin-distribution.com.

➤ **AQUA**; journal of ichthyology & aquatic biology. see *BIOLOGY*

➤ **AQUACULTURE ASIA.** see *AGRICULTURE*

➤ **AQUACULTURE INTERNATIONAL.** see *FISH AND FISHERIES*

597.073 NLD ISSN 0003-729X
CODEN: AQUUA2
HET AQUARIUM. Text in Dutch. 1930. m. (11/yr). EUR 31.75 domestic; EUR 45 in Europe; EUR 50 elsewhere (effective 2005). adv. bk.rev. charts; illus. index. **Document type:** *Bulletin.* **Description:** Covers aquariums, aquatic plants and animals, terraria, reptiles, amphibians, ponds, bog plants, insects, and more.
Indexed: BiolAb, ZooRec.
Published by: Nederlandse Bond "Aqua-Terra", Havenstraat 83, Hilversum, 1211 KH, Netherlands. TEL 31-15-2140175, FAX 31-15-2140179, redactie@nbat.nl, info@nbat.nl, http://www.nbat.nl. Circ: 12,000 (paid and controlled).

590 577.27 USA ISSN 1535-6868
TD427.Z43
AQUATIC INVADERS; digest of the National Aquatic Nuisance Species Clearinghouse. Text in English. 1990. q., latest vol.14, 2003. USD 30 domestic; USD 37.50 in Canada & Mexico; USD 44 elsewhere (effective 2003). Website rev. abstr.; illus.; maps; bibl. Index. 16 p./no. 2 cols./p.; back issues avail. **Document type:** *Newsletter, Academic/Scholarly.* **Description:** Presents summaries of research, meetings, legislation, and sightings of important aquatic nuisance species to encourage and facilitate communication among stakeholders.
Former titles: Dreissena! (1534-9748); (until 1994): Dreissena Polymorpha Information Review (1065-8408)
Published by: National Aquatic Nuisance Species Clearinghouse (Subsidiary of: New York Sea Grant Institute), Morgan II, SUNY College at Brockport, Brockport, NY 14420-2928. TEL 585-395-2638, FAX 585-395-2466, ZMussel@Cornell.edu, zmussel@cornell.edu, http://www.aquaticinvaders.org. Ed., R&P Diane J. Oleson. Pub. Charles R O'Neill Jr.

591.76 USA ISSN 0167-5427
➤ **AQUATIC MAMMALS.** Text in English. 1972. 3/yr. USD 95 to individuals; USD 190 to libraries (effective 2004). bk.rev. illus. back issues avail.; reprints avail. **Document type:** *Journal, Academic/Scholarly.* **Description:** Contains scientific papers dealing with all aspects of the science, conservation, care, and medicine of marine and aquatic mammals.
Related titles: Online - full text ed.: free (effective 2004) (from EBSCO Publishing, Gale Group, IngentaConnect).
Indexed: ASFA, BIOSIS Prev, BiolAb, ESPM, IndVet, KWIWR, M&TEA, OceAb, ProtozoAb, SFA, VetBull, WildRev, ZooRec.
—BLDSC (1582.390000), CISTI, IE, ingenta.
Published by: Western Illinois University Regional Center, 3561 60th St, Moline, IL 61265. TEL 309-762-9481. Ed. Jeanette Thomas. Circ: 300.

➤ **AQUAWORLD MAGAZINE**; the aquarium world. see *FISH AND FISHERIES*

590 FIN ISSN 0570-5177
CODEN: AQZOA9
AQUILO. SERIE ZOOLOGICA. Text in English. 1950. s-a. price varies. back issues avail. **Document type:** *Proceedings.*
Indexed: ASFA, BiolAb, ChemAb, ZooRec.
—BLDSC (1583.120000).
Published by: Societas Amicorum Naturae Ouluensis, Department of Zoology, University of Oulu, Linnanmaa, Oulu, 90570, Finland. Ed. Eino Erkinaro. Circ: 350. **Dist. by:** Akateeminen Kirjakauppa, PL 10128, Helsinki 00101, Finland.

595.4 URY ISSN 0254-5578
CODEN: ARCNE4
➤ **ARACNOLOGIA.** Text in English, French, Portuguese, Spanish; Summaries in English. 1983. irreg., latest vol.27, 1998. illus.; stat. cum.index every 10 nos. **Document type:** *Bulletin, Academic/Scholarly.* **Description:** Aims to communicate original scientific articles on arachnia.
Indexed: RevApplEntom, ZooRec.
—Linda Hall.
Published by: Instituto de Investigaciones Biologicas Clemente Estable, Division Zoologia Experimental, Av. Italia, 3318, Montevideo, 11610, Uruguay. TEL 4871616, rmc@iibce.edu.uy. Ed. Roberto M Capocasale. Circ: 200.

➤ **EL ARCA.** see *BIOLOGY—Genetics*

➤ **ARCHAEOFAUNA.** see *ARCHAEOLOGY*

591.9561 FRA ISSN 0299-3600
CC79.5.A5 CODEN: ARZOEK
ARCHAEOZOOLOGIA; revue international d'archeozoologie. Text mainly in English; Text occasionally in French; Summaries in English, French. 1987. 2/yr. **Document type:** *Proceedings.* **Description:** Devoted to the publication of papers presented at the International Congress of Archaeozoology. Of interest to archaeozoologists, and other archaeological scientists and zoologists.
Indexed: AnthLit, BrArAb, IAB, NumL, ZooRec.
—BLDSC (1595.151500), ingenta.
Published by: Pensee Sauvage Editions, B.P. 141, Grenoble, 38002, France. TEL 76-87-13-03, FAX 76-46-27-25.

594 DEU ISSN 0003-9284
CODEN: AMKUAQ
➤ **ARCHIV FUER MOLLUSKENKUNDE.** Text in English, German, Spanish; Summaries in English, German, Spanish. 1869. 2/yr. EUR 50 domestic; EUR 55.20 foreign (effective 2005). abstr. index. back issues avail.; reprints avail. **Document type:** *Journal, Academic/Scholarly.* **Description:** Contains papers on systematics and taxonomy of mollusks.
Indexed: ASFA, BIOSIS Prev, BiolAb, ChemAb, ESPM, ForAb, GEOBASE, IBR, PBA, PGegResA, RefZh, ZooRec.
—BLDSC (1621.000000), CISTI, IE, ingenta, Linda Hall.
Published by: (Senckenbergische Naturforschende Gesellschaft), E. Schweizerbart'sche Verlagsbuchhandlung, Johannesstr 3A, Stuttgart, 70176, Germany. TEL 49-711-3514560, FAX 49-711-35145699, mail@schweizerbart.de, http://www.schweizerbart.de/j/archiv-fuer-molluskenkunde. Ed. Ronald Janssen. Circ: 600 (paid).

597 DEU ISSN 0944-1921
SH1 CODEN: ARFMEG
➤ **ARCHIVE OF FISHERY AND MARINE RESEARCH/ARCHIV FUER FISCHEREI UND MEERESFORSCHUNG.** Text in English. 1994. 3/yr. EUR 199; EUR 80 per issue (effective 2004). adv. bk.rev. charts; illus.; maps. **Document type:** *Journal, Academic/Scholarly.* **Description:** Publishes scientific contributions on aquatic environment, ecotoxicology, fishery technology, aquatic pollution, and the biology, physiology and chemistry of fish and shellfish.
Formed by the merger of (1948-1994): Archiv fuer Fischereiwissenschaft (0003-9063); (1958-1994): Fischereiforschung (0428-4984); (1925-1994): Meeresforschung (0341-6836); Which was formerly (until 1977): Deutsche Wissenschaftliche Kommission fuer Meeresforschung. Berichte (0373-0921)
Indexed: ASFA, BIOSIS Prev, BiolAb, ChemAb, CurCont, ESPM, ExcerpMed, FS&TA, GEOBASE, HelmAb, ISR, M&GPA, NutrAb, RM&VM, RefZh, RevApplEntom, S&F, SCI, SFA, SWRA, WildRev, ZooRec.
—BLDSC (1634.278400), CASDDS, CISTI, IDS, IE, ingenta, Linda Hall. **CCC.**
Published by: Bundesforschungsanstalt fuer Fischerei, Palmaille 9, Hamburg, 22767, Germany. TEL 49-40-389050, FAX 49-40-38905200, ish@bfa-fisch.de, http://www.bfa-fish.de/iud/iud-d/index.html, http://www.bfa-fisch.de. adv.: page EUR 307; 175 x 240. Circ: 300. **Co-sponsor:** Deutsche Wissenschaftliche Kommission fuer Meeresforschung/German Scientific Commission for Marine Research.

596 GBR ISSN 0003-9969
RK1 CODEN: AOBIAR
➤ **ARCHIVES OF ORAL BIOLOGY.** Text in English, French, German. 1959. 12/yr. EUR 140 in Europe to individuals; JPY 18,600 in Japan to individuals; USD 158 to individuals except Europe and Japan; EUR 2,483 in Europe to institutions; JPY 329,600 in Japan to institutions; USD 2,776 to institutions except Europe and Japan (effective 2006). adv. bk.rev. charts; illus. index. back issues avail. **Document type:** *Journal, Academic/Scholarly.* **Description:** Publishes research results on every aspect of the oral and dental tissues and bone from the entire range of vertebrates.
Related titles: Microfilm ed.: (from PQC); Online - full text ed.: (from EBSCO Publishing, Gale Group, IngentaConnect, ScienceDirect, Swets Information Services).
Indexed: ASCA, AbAn, AbHyg, AgBio, AnBrAb, BIOBASE, BIOSIS Prev, BiolAb, CIN, CTD, ChemAb, ChemTitl, CurCont, DSA, DentInd, ExcerpMed, HortAb, IABS, ISR, IndMed, IndVet, Inpharma, MEDLINE, MS&D, MSB, MaizeAb, NRN, NSCI, NutrAb, PE&ON, PHN&I, RA&MP, RM&VM, RPP, Reac, RevApplEntom, SAA, SCI, SIA, SSCI, SoyAb, TDB, TriticAb, VITIS, VetBull.
—BLDSC (1638.475000), CASDDS, CISTI, GNLM, IDS, IE, Infotrieve, ingenta, KNAW, Linda Hall. **CCC.**
Published by: Pergamon (Subsidiary of: Elsevier Science & Technology), The Boulevard, Langford Ln, East Park, Kidlington, Oxford OX5 1GB, United Kingdom. TEL 44-1865-843000, FAX 44-1865-843010, http://www.elsevier.com/locate/archoralbio. Eds. Dr. G. R. Holland, Dr. Paul M. Speight. Circ: 1,250. **Subscr. to:** Elsevier BV, PO Box 211, Amsterdam 1000 AE, Netherlands. TEL 31-20-485-3757, FAX 31-20-485-3432, nlinfo-f@elsevier.nl, http://www.elsevier.nl.

594 ITA ISSN 0394-3399
➤ **ARGONAUTA**; international journal of malacology. Text in English. 1985. q. USD 50 foreign. bk.rev. illus. **Document type:** *Academic/Scholarly.* **Description:** Devoted to molluscan biology and taxonomy.
Indexed: SFA, ZooRec.
Published by: Associazione Malacologica Internazionale, Casella Postale 322, Acilia, RM 00126, Italy. TEL 39-6-5259331. Ed. Gabriella Raybaudi Massilia.

590 GBR
ARKFILE. Text in English. q. **Document type:** *Newsletter.*
Published by: Royal Zoological Society of Scotland, Scottish National Zoological Park, 134 Corstorphine Rd, Edinburgh, EH12 6TS, United Kingdom. TEL 44-131-334-9171, FAX 44-131-316-4050. Ed. Amanda Alabaster. Circ: 100,000.

590 BRA ISSN 0066-7870
QL1 CODEN: ARQZA4
➤ **ARQUIVOS DE ZOOLOGIA.** Text in English, Portuguese, Multiple languages. 1940. irreg. USD 25 per vol. (effective 2004). back issues avail. **Document type:** *Monographic series, Academic/Scholarly.*
Indexed: BIOSIS Prev, BiolAb, RefZh, RevApplEntom, ZooRec.
—BLDSC (1695.900000), CISTI, Linda Hall.
Published by: Universidade de Sao Paulo, Museu de Zoologia, Caixa Postal 42494, Sao Paulo, SP 04218-970, Brazil. TEL 55-11-61658090, FAX 55-11-61658113, biblmz@usp.br. Ed. Hussam Zaher. Circ: 800 (controlled).

590 NLD ISSN 1384-5950
ARTIS. Text in Dutch. 1955. bi-m. bk.rev. illus. index. **Document type:** *Consumer.*
Former titles (until 1996): Dieren (0168-6631); (until 1984): Artis (0004-3834)
Indexed: BHA.
—CISTI.
Published by: (Zoological Society Amsterdam), Koninklijk Zoologisch Genootschap Natura Artis Magistra, Instandhouding van de Diergaarde, Stichting, J Plantage Kerklaan 40, Amsterdam, 1018 CZ, Netherlands. redactie@artis.nl. Ed. G van der Sijde. Circ: 30,000.

590 ESP ISSN 1698-0476
▼ **ARXUS DE MISCEL - LANIA ZOOLOGICA.** Text in English, Spanish, Catalan. 2003. a. free (effective 2005). **Document type:** *Journal, Academic/Scholarly.* **Description:** Publishes manuscripts on faunistics, chorology, phenology, morphology and descriptive ecology. The articles consist mainly of analysis and discussion of results.
Media: Online - full text.
Published by: Museu de Ciencies Naturals de la Ciutadella, Museu de Zoologia, Passeig Picasso s/n, Barcelona, 08003, Spain. TEL 34-93-3196912, FAX 34-93-3104999, museuciencies@mail.bcn.es, http://bcnweb13.bcn.es:81/NASApp/wprmuseuciencies/Museu.GeneradorPagines?idioma=3&seccio=11_2, http://www.museuzoologia.bcn.es.

590 JPN
ASA DOBUTSU KOEN SHIIKU KIROKUSHU/ASA ZOOLOGICAL PARK OF HIROSHIMA. RECORD OF BREEDING. Text in Japanese. 1974. biennial. **Document type:** *Bulletin.*
Published by: Hiroshimashi Dobutsuen Kyokai/Hiroshima City Zoological Park Society, Hiroshimashi Asa Dobutsu Koen, Dobutsuen, Asacho, Asa Kita-ku, Hiroshima-shi, Hiroshima-ken 731-33, Japan. Ed. Hiroshi Morimoto.

597 PHL ISSN 0116-6514
ASIAN FISHERIES SCIENCE. Text in English. 1987. 4/yr. USD 15 to individual members; USD 27 to non-members; USD 38 to institutional members; USD 60 to non-members (effective 2000). adv. **Description:** Covers all aspects of Asian fisheries and aquaculture research.
Indexed: ASFA, ESPM, FS&TA, SFA, ZooRec.
—BLDSC (1742.417600), IE, ingenta.
Published by: (WorldFish Center MYS), Asian Fisheries Society (Subsidiary of: WorldFish Center), M.C.P.O. 2631, Makati City, 0718, Philippines. R&P Sandra Child TEL 60-4-6414623. adv.: page USD 200.

597.9 USA ISSN 1051-3825
QL661.A1 CODEN: AHEREO
ASIATIC HERPETOLOGICAL RESEARCH. Text in English. 1990. a.
Indexed: ZooRec.
—BLDSC (1742.756992).
Published by: Asiatic Herpetological Research Society, Museum of Vertebrate Zoology, University of California, Berkeley, CA 94720. asiaherp@uclink.berkeley.edu.

597.9 ESP ISSN 1130-6939
ASOCIACION HERPETOLOGICA ESPANOLA. BOLETIN. Text in Spanish. 1988. s-a.
Formerly (until 1990): B O. H E (1133-5726)
Indexed: IECT, ZooRec.
—CINDOC.
Published by: Asociacion Herpetologica Espanola, Dpto. Biologia Animal, Facultad Biologia (Vertebrats), Universidad de Barcelona, Av Diagonal, 645, Barcelona, 08028, Spain. TEL 34-3-4021455, FAX 34-3-4035740.

590.7 EGY
ASSIUT UNIVERSITY. FACULTY OF SCIENCE. BULLETIN: E. ZOOLOGY. Text in English. irreg.
Indexed: ZooRec.
Published by: Assiut University, Faculty of Science, c/o Dr. Muhammad Bahey, Assiut, Egypt. TEL 20-88-411376, FAX 20-88-342708, http://www.aun.eun.eg.

590 EGY ISSN 1110-7359
ASSIUT UNIVERSITY. FACULTY OF SCIENCE. BULLETIN. SECTION E. ZOOLOGY. Text in English. 1988. s-a. free (effective 2004). **Document type:** *Bulletin, Academic/Scholarly.*
Supersedes in part (in 1988): Assiut University. Faculty of Science. Bulletin. Section C. Biology and Geology (1010-2698); Which was formerly (until 1982): Assiut University. Faculty of Science. Bulletin. Section B. Biological and Geological Studies (0254-6256); Which superseded in part (in 1979): Assiut University. Science and Technology. Bulletin (0379-3389)
Published by: Assiut University, Faculty of Science, c/o Dr. Muhammad Bahey, Assiut, Egypt. TEL 20-88-411376, FAX 20-88-342708, science@aun.edu.eg, sup@aun.eun.eg, http://derp.sti.sci.eg/data/0299.htm, http://www.aun.eun.eg. Ed. Dr. Muhammad Bahey-El-Din Hasan Mazen.

ASSOCIATION POUR LA PROMOTION DE LA PROTECTION DES INVERTEBRES. CAHIERS. see *BIOLOGY—Entomology*

594 ITA
ASSOCIAZIONE MALACOLOGICA INTERNAZIONALE. NOTIZIARIO. Text in Italian. 3/yr. included with Argonauta. adv. **Document type:** *Newsletter.*
Published by: Associazione Malacologica Internazionale, Casella Postale 322, Acilia, RM 00126, Italy. TEL 39-6-5259331. Adv. contact Roberto Ubaldi.

590 DNK ISSN 0067-0227
CODEN: ATREAS
➤ **ATLANTIDE REPORT. SCIENTIFIC RESULTS OF THE DANISH EXPEDITION TO THE COASTS OF TROPICAL WEST AFRICA 1945-46.** Text in English, French. 1950. irreg., latest vol.14, 1988. price varies. back issues avail. **Document type:** *Monographic series, Academic/Scholarly.*
Indexed: BiolAb, SFA, ZooRec.
Published by: Apollo Books, Kirkeby Sand 19, Stenstrup, 5771, Denmark. TEL 45-62-26-37-37, FAX 45-62-26-37-80, apollobooks@vip.cybercity.dk. Eds. Joergen Knudsen, Torben Wolff.

597.9 ESP ISSN 1138-6126
ATLAS DE ANATOMIA ANIMAL. Text in Spanish. 1998. irreg.
Media: Online - full text.
Indexed: ZooRec.
Published by: Universidade de Vigo, Laboratorio de Anatomia Animal, Anatolab, Vigo, 36200, Spain. TEL 34-986812000, http://anatolab.uvigo.es/.

AUSTASIA AQUACULTURE. see *FISH AND FISHERIES*

AUSTASIA AQUACULTURE TRADE DIRECTORY. see *FISH AND FISHERIES*

599.8 AUS
➤ **AUSTRALASIAN PRIMATOLOGY.** Text in English. 1986. q. AUD 25 to members; AUD 35 to institutions; AUD 15 to students. adv. bk.rev. **Document type:** *Bulletin, Academic/Scholarly.* **Description:** Presents papers and short communications in all areas of primatology.
Formerly: Australian Primatology (0817-9573)
Indexed: ZooRec.
—BLDSC (1796.110000).
Published by: Australasian Primate Society, PO Box 500, One Tree Hill, SA 5114, Australia. TEL 61-8-82807670, gc00274@dany.snetad.cpg.com.au. Ed. Greaeme Crook. Circ: 150.

594.1477 AUS ISSN 1324-1753
AUSTRALASIAN SHELL NEWS. Text in English. 1953. q. USD 25 (effective 2003). adv. bk.rev. 12 p./no.; back issues avail. **Document type:** *Newsletter.* **Description:** Discusses malacology.
Former titles (until 1994): Australian Shell News (0310-1304); (until 197?): Australian Newsletter
Indexed: ASFA, RefZh, ZooRec.
Published by: Malacological Society of Australasia, Division of Invertebrate Zoology, Australian Museum, 6 College St, Sydney, NSW 2000, Australia. TEL 61-2-3206275, FAX 61-2-3206050, desb@austmus.org.au, alisonm@amsg.Austmus.gov.au. Ed. J Stanisic. Circ: 500.

591.994 AUS ISSN 0004-959X
QL1 CODEN: AJZOAS
➤ **AUSTRALIAN JOURNAL OF ZOOLOGY.** Text in English. 1953. bi-m. AUD 150 combined subscription in Australia & New Zealand to individuals print & online eds.; USD 150 combined subscription elsewhere to individuals print & online eds.; AUD 760, USD 645 combined subscription in Australia & New Zealand to institutions print & online eds. (effective 2004). adv. Index. 120 p./no.; back issues avail. **Document type:** *Journal, Academic/Scholarly.* **Description:** Covers all branches of zoology including anatomy, physiology, genetics, behavior, ecology, and zoogeography.
Related titles: Microform ed.: (from PQC); Online - full text ed.: AUD 135 in Australia & New Zealand to individuals; USD 120 elsewhere to individuals; AUD 680 in Australia & New Zealand to institutions; USD 580 elsewhere to institutions (effective 2004) (from EBSCO Publishing, Gale Group, O C L C Online Computer Library Center, Inc., Swets Information Services).
Indexed: ASCA, ASFA, AbHyg, AgBio, AgrForAb, AnBeAb, AnBrAb, ApEcolAb, B&BAb, BIOBASE, BIOSIS Prev, BioCN&I, BiolAb, CIN, CRFR, ChemAb, ChemTitl, CurCont, DSA, ESPM, EntAb, EnvAb, ExcerpMed, FPA, ForAb, GEOBASE, GenetAb, HGA, HelmAb, HerbAb, HortAb, IABS, ISR, IndVet, KWIWR, MEDLINE, NutrAb, OceAb, PBA, PGegResA, PN&I, PoultAb, ProtozoAb, RM&VM, RPP, RevApplEntom, S&F, SCI, SFA, SIA, SPPI, TDB, TriticAb, VetBull, WeedAb, WildRev, ZooRec.
—BLDSC (1813.000000), CASDDS, CIS, CISTI, IDS, IE, Infotrieve, ingenta, Linda Hall. **CCC.**
Published by: (C S I R O Australia), C S I R O Publishing, 150 Oxford St, PO Box 1139, Collingwood, VIC 3066, Australia. TEL 61-3-96627622, FAX 61-3-96627611, ajz@publish.csiro.au, publishing@csiro.au, http://www.publish.csiro.au/journals/ajz. Circ: 500.

599 AUS ISSN 0310-0049
CODEN: AUMACY
➤ **AUSTRALIAN MAMMALOGY.** Text in English. 1972. s-a. AUD 54 (effective 2001). bk.rev. **Document type:** *Journal, Academic/Scholarly.*
Indexed: ASI, ApicAb, BIOSIS Prev, BiolAb, SFA, WildRev, ZooRec.
—BLDSC (1814.060000), IE, ingenta, Linda Hall.
Published by: Australian Mammal Society Inc., GPO Box 2200, Canberra, ACT 2601, Australia. TEL 61-2-9850-8208, FAX 61-2-9850-9686, http://www.australianmammals.org.au. Ed. Mark Eldridge. Circ: 680.

590.73 AUS ISSN 0067-1975
QH1 CODEN: RAUMAJ
➤ **AUSTRALIAN MUSEUM. RECORDS.** Key Title: Records of the Australian Museum. Text in English. 1890. 3/yr., latest vol.54, 2002. AUD 220 domestic includes subscriptionto Records Supplements; AUD 200 foreign includes subscriptionto Records Supplements (effective 2002). abstr.; bibl.; illus.; maps. 160 p./no.; back issues avail. **Document type:** *Journal, Academic/Scholarly.* **Description:** Original research in zoology, geology and anthropology in Australia, Southwest Pacific and Indian Ocean areas.
Related titles: Online - full content ed.; Online - full text ed.: (from EBSCO Publishing); ♦ Supplement(s): Australian Museum, Sydney. Records Supplements. ISSN 0812-7387.
Indexed: AESIS, ASFA, BIOSIS Prev, BiolAb, CurCont, ESPM, RefZh, SFA, SPPI, SWRA, WildRev, ZooRec.
—BLDSC (7315.000000), CISTI, IE, ingenta, Linda Hall.
Published by: Australian Museum, 6 College St, Sydney, NSW 2010, Australia. TEL 61-2-93206200, FAX 61-2-93206073, editor@austmus.gov.au, editor@amsg.austmus.gov.au, http://www.amonline.net.au/publications/, http://www.austmus.gov.au. Ed., R&P Shane F McEvey.

590.73 AUS ISSN 0812-7387
CODEN: RAMSEZ
➤ **AUSTRALIAN MUSEUM, SYDNEY. RECORDS SUPPLEMENTS.** Text in English. 1890. irreg., latest vol.28, 2003. AUD 220 domestic included in subscription to Australian Museum Records; AUD 200 foreign included in subscription to Australian Museum Records. abstr.; bibl.; illus.; maps. back issues avail. **Document type:** *Monographic series, Academic/Scholarly.* **Description:** Contains monographs in zoology, geology and anthropology in Australia, Southwest Pacific and the Indian Ocean.
Formerly (until 1983): Australian Museum, Sydney. Memoirs (0067-1967)
Related titles: ♦ Supplement to: Australian Museum. Records. ISSN 0067-1975.
Indexed: AESIS, BIOSIS Prev, BiolAb, SFA, WildRev, ZooRec.
—BLDSC (7315.100000), CISTI, Linda Hall.
Published by: Australian Museum, 6 College St, Sydney, NSW 2010, Australia. TEL 61-2-93206200, FAX 61-2-93206073, editor@amsg.austmus.gov.au, http://www.amonline.net.au/publications, http://www.austmus.gov.au. Ed. Shane F McEvey.

590.73 AUS ISSN 1031-8062
CODEN: TRAMEU
➤ **AUSTRALIAN MUSEUM. TECHNICAL REPORTS.** Text in English. 1988. irreg., latest vol.18, 2003. not avail. on subscr.. bibl.; charts; illus. back issues avail. **Document type:** *Monographic series, Academic/Scholarly.* **Description:** Publishes Australian Museum catalogues, lists, and databases.
Indexed: ZooRec.
—Linda Hall.
Published by: Australian Museum, 6 College St, Sydney, NSW 2010, Australia. TEL 61-2-93206200, FAX 61-2-93206073, editor@austmus.gov.au, http://www.austmus.gov.au.

591.994 AUS ISSN 0067-2238
QL1 CODEN: AUZOA3
AUSTRALIAN ZOOLOGIST. Text in English. 1914. irreg. AUD 50; includes Australian Zoological Reviews. adv. bk.rev.
Indexed: ASFA, BIOSIS Prev, BiolAb, EPB, GEOBASE, SFA, WildRev, ZooRec.
—BLDSC (1825.000000), CISTI, IE, ingenta, Linda Hall.
Published by: Royal Zoological Society of New South Wales, PO Box 20, Mosman, NSW 2088, Australia. TEL 61-2-99697336. Ed. Dan Lunney. Circ: 1,450.

590 GBR ISSN 1470-2061
SF481
➤ **AVIAN AND POULTRY BIOLOGY REVIEWS.** Text in English. 1987. 4/yr. GBP 306, USD 493 combined subscription to institutions print & online eds. (effective 2006). adv. **Document type:** *Journal, Academic/Scholarly.* **Description:** Covers the entire scope of scientific enquiries pertaining to avian species, including fundamental biological research.
Former titles (until 2000): Poultry and Avian Biology Reviews (1357-048X); (until vol.6, 1995): Poultry Science Reviews (0964-6604); (until 1992): Critical Reviews in Poultry Biology (0889-4434)
Related titles: Online - full text ed.: GBP 245, USD 394 (effective 2006).
Indexed: AEA, AgBio, Agr, AnBrAb, BIOSIS Prev, CurCont, FS&TA, FoVS&M, ISR, IndVet, NutrAb, PoultAb, ProtozoAb, RM&VM, S&F, SCI, VetBull.
—BLDSC (1837.884000), CISTI, IDS, IE, Infotrieve, ingenta, Linda Hall. **CCC.**
Published by: Science and Technology Letters, PO Box 314, St Albans, Herts AL1 4ZG, United Kingdom. scilet@scilet.com, http://www.scilet.com/bioandbiosafety/pab.htm. Eds. Mary Ann Ottinger, Murray R Bakst. **Dist. by:** Extenza - Turpin.

590 JPN ISSN 1346-5880
CODEN: ADJHDO
AZABU DAIGAKU ZASSHI/AZABU UNIVERSITY. JOURNAL. Text in English, Japanese; Summaries in English. 1954-1979; resumed 1980. a. per issue exchange basis. **Document type:** *Bulletin, Academic/Scholarly.*
Former titles (until 2001): Azabu Daigaku Juigakubu Kenkyu Hokoku (0389-1836); Azabu Veterinary College. Bulletin
Indexed: AbHyg, BiolAb, DSA, HortAb, IndVet, NutrAb, PN&I, RA&MP, RM&VM, RPP, SAA, SoyAb, VetBull.
—CASDDS.
Published by: Azabu Daigaku/Azabu University, Center for Science Information Services, 1-17-71 Fuchinobe, Sagamihara, Kanagawa 229-8501, Japan. TEL 81-42-7547111, FAX 81-42-7547659, senta@azabu-u.ac.jp, http://www.azabu-u.ac.jp/. Circ: 800.

333.95416 GBR ISSN 0265-3656
B B C WILDLIFE. Text in English. 1963. m. GBP 26.70 domestic; GBP 41.35 in Europe; GBP 43.90 elsewhere; GBP 3.10 newsstand/cover (effective 2004). adv. bk.rev. charts; illus. index. back issues avail. **Document type:** *Magazine, Consumer.* **Description:** Features articles covering animals, plants, conservation and environment issues, in a general-interest format.
Formerly (until 1983): Wildlife (0003-3618)
Related titles: Microfilm ed.: (from PQC).
Indexed: BiolAb, BiolDig, EIA, EPB, EnerInd, EnvAb, GEOBASE, KWIWR, SFA, WBA, WMB.
—BLDSC (1871.360700), CISTI, IE. **CCC.**

B

▼ new title ➤ refereed ✶ unverified ♦ full entry avail.

Published by: B B C Worldwide Ltd., 80 Wood Ln, London, W12 0TT, United Kingdom. TEL 44-20-84331070, FAX 44-20-84332231, wildlife.magazine@bbc.co.uk, bbcworldwide@bbc.co.uk, http://www.bbcmagazines.com/wildlife/. Ed. Rosamund Kidman Cox. Pub. Heather Aylott. Adv. contact Lillian Betty. Circ: 117,859. **Subscr. to.:** BBC Wildlife Subscriptions, PO Box 279, Sittingbourne, Kent ME9 8DF, United Kingdom. TEL 44-1795-414718, FAX 44-1795-414725. **Dist. by:** Frontline, Park House, 117 Park Rd, Peterborough, Cambs PE1 2TS, United Kingdom. TEL 44-1733-555161, FAX 44-1733-562788.

590 POL ISSN 0137-6683
QL284
➤ **BADANIA FIZJOGRAFICZNE NAD POLSKA ZACHODNIA. SERIA C. ZOOLOGIA.** Text in Polish; Summaries in English. 1948. a., latest vol.49, 2002. price varies. bibl.; abstr.; charts; illus. **Document type:** *Bulletin, Academic/Scholarly.*
Supersedes in part (in 1974): Badania Fizjograficzne nad Polska Zachodnia. Seria B. Biologia (0373-7497)
Indexed: AgrLib, ZooRec.
—BLDSC (1856.208000).
Published by: (Poznanskie Towarzystwo Przyjaciol Nauk, Wydzial Matematyczno-Przyrodniczy), Poznanskie Towarzystwo Przyjaciol Nauk/Poznan Society for the Advancement of the Arts and Sciences, ul Sew Mielzynskiego 27-29, Poznan, 61725, Poland. TEL 48-61-8527441, FAX 48-61-8522205, wydawnictwo@ptpn.poznan.pl, http://www.ptpn.poznan.pl. Ed. Zofia Michalska. Circ: 250. **Dist. by:** Ars Polona, Krakowskie Przedmiescie 7, Warsaw, Poland. TEL 48-22-9263914, FAX 48-22-9265334, arspolona@arspolona.com.pl, http://www.arspolona.com.pl.

590 BGD ISSN 0304-9027
QL334.B34 CODEN: BJZOA5
➤ **BANGLADESH JOURNAL OF ZOOLOGY.** Text in English. 1973. s-a. BDT 800; USD 40 foreign. adv. bk.rev. illus. **Document type:** *Academic/Scholarly.* **Description:** Publishes research papers on all branches of zoology, both pure and applied.
Indexed: AgBio, AgrForAb, AnBrAb, BIOSIS Prev, BioCN&I, BiolAb, ForAb, HelmAb, HerbAb, HortAb, I&DA, IndVet, NemAb, NutrAb, PBA, PGegResA, PHN&I, RevApplEntom, RiceAb, S&F, SFA, SeedAb, VetBull, WAE&RSA, WeedAb, ZooRec.
—BLDSC (1861.710000), CISTI, IE, ingenta, Linda Hall.
Published by: Zoological Society of Bangladesh, c/o Dept. of Zoology, University of Dhaka, Dhaka, 1000, Bangladesh. TEL 880-2-9666120, FAX 880-2-865583, zooldu@citechco.net. Ed. S M H Kabir. Circ: 600.

590 USA ISSN 1066-0712
➤ **BANISTERIA.** Text in English. 1992. s-a.
Published by: Virginia Natural History Society, P O Box 62, Hampden-Sydney, VA 23943. Eds. Dr. Joseph C Mitchell, Dr. Steven M Roble.

590 ESP ISSN 1576-9720
BARBASTELLA. Text in Spanish. 2000. a. EUR 3 per issue (effective 2005). **Document type:** *Journal, Academic/Scholarly.*
Published by: (Universidad de Alcala de Henares, Departamento de Biologia Animal), Universidad de Alcala de Henares, Servicio de Publicaciones, Colegio Mayor de San Ildefonso, Plaza San Diego, Alcala de Henares, Madrid, Spain. TEL 34-918-854468, FAX 34-918-855161, suscripcion.public@uah.es, http://www.uah.es/servi/publicaciones. Ed. Carlos Ibanez.

594 NLD ISSN 0005-6219
QL401 CODEN: BSTRAD
BASTERIA. Text in Dutch, English, French, German. 1936. s-a. bk.rev. charts; illus. index, cum.index every 5 yrs. **Document type:** *Proceedings.*
Related titles: Microfiche ed.: (from IDC).
Indexed: ASFA, BIOSIS Prev, BiolAb, ESPM, ZooRec.
—BLDSC (1866.000000), CISTI, IE, ingenta, Linda Hall.
Published by: Nederlandse Malacologische Vereniging/Dutch Malacological Society, c/o R G Moolenbeek, Zoologisch Museum, Mauritskade 57, PO Box 94766, Amsterdam, 1090 GT, Netherlands. TEL 31-20-5256294, FAX 31-20-5255402, info@spirula.nl, http://www.spirula.nl/publicaties/basteria.htm. Ed. E Gittenberger. Circ: 600.

599.4 GBR ISSN 0269-8501
BAT NEWS. Text in English. 1990. q. GBP 16; GBP 20 foreign. adv. bk.rev. **Document type:** *Newsletter.* **Description:** Contains news, "living with bats" feature, Bat Group information, and conference reports.
Indexed: RefZh.
Published by: The Bat Conservation Trust, 15 Cloisters House, 8 Battersea Park Rd, London, SW8 4RG, United Kingdom. enquiries@bats.org.uk, http://www.bats.org.uk. adv.: color page GBP 500. Circ: 3,800.

599.4 USA ISSN 0005-6227
BAT RESEARCH NEWS. Text in English. 1960. q. USD 18 domestic to individuals; USD 22 foreign to individuals; USD 30 worldwide to institutions (effective 2000). adv. bk.rev. abstr.; bibl.; charts; illus. cum.index every 5 yrs. **Document type:** *Newsletter.*
Media: Duplicated (not offset). **Related titles:** Online - full content ed.
Indexed: BIOSIS Prev, BiolAb, RefZh, SFA, WLR, WildRev, ZooRec.
Address: 8578 Us Highway 11., Potsdam, NY 13676-3215. TEL 315-267-2259, FAX 315-267-3170, horstgr@potsdam.edu. Circ: 800.

599.4 USA ISSN 1049-0043
QL737.C5 CODEN: BATSEU
BATS. Text in English. 1983. q. USD 30 membership. bk.rev. 20 p./no.; **Document type:** *Newsletter.*
Related titles: Online - full text ed.
Indexed: SFA, WildRev, ZooRec.
Published by: Bat Conservation International, PO Box 162603, Austin, TX 78716. TEL 512-327-9721, FAX 512-327-9724, http://www.batcon.org. Ed., R&P Sara McCabe. Circ: 15,000.

599.78 USA ISSN 0885-615X
BEAR NEWS✶. Text in English. 1983. q. USD 25 (effective 2000). adv. bk.rev. back issues avail. **Document type:** *Newsletter, Consumer.* **Description:** Conservation of 8 species of wild bears and bear habitat around the world.
Indexed: EnvAb.
Published by: Great Bear Foundation, PO Box 9383, Missoula, MT 59807-9383. gbf@greatbear.org. Ed. Mary Hawver. R&P, Adv. contact Charles Jankel TEL 406-829-9378. Circ: 2,000; 5,000 (paid).

590 NLD
QL1 CODEN: BUFOAG
➤ **BEAUFORTIA BULLETIN ZOOLOGICAL MUSEUM**; series of miscellaneous publications. Text in English, French, German. 1951. irreg., latest vol.52, 2002. EUR 100 per vol. (effective 2003). illus. 70 p./no. 2 cols./p.; back issues avail. **Document type:** *Monographic series, Academic/Scholarly.* **Description:** Publishes research in taxonomy and systematics.
Formerly (until 2000): Beaufortia (0067-4745)
Indexed: ASFA, BIOSIS Prev, BiolAb, RefZh, SFA, ZooRec.
—BLDSC (1871.800000), CISTI, IE, Linda Hall. **CCC.**
Published by: Universiteit van Amsterdam, Instituut voor Biodiversiteit en Ecosysteem Dynamica, PO Box 94766, Amsterdam, 1090 GT, Netherlands. TEL 31-20-525-6904, FAX 31-20-525-5402, weerdt@science.uva.nl, weerdt@science.uva.na, http://www.ibed.bio.uva.nl. Eds. Rob W M van Soest, Wallie H de Weerdt. Circ: 600.

599.8 USA ISSN 0148-3781
BEHAVIORAL PRIMATOLOGY. Text in English. 1977. irreg., latest vol.1, 1977. USD 59.95 per issue (effective 2006). **Document type:** *Monographic series, Academic/Scholarly.*
Published by: Lawrence Erlbaum Associates, Inc., 10 Industrial Ave, Mahwah, NJ 07430-2262. TEL 201-258-2200, FAX 201-236-0072, http://www.leaonline.com.

591.5 NLD ISSN 0005-7959
BF671 CODEN: BEHAA8
➤ **BEHAVIOUR**; an international journal of behaviourial biology. Text in English, German. 1947. m. USD 938 combined subscription in the Americas print & online eds.; EUR 750 combined subscription elsewhere print & online eds. (effective 2006). bibl.; charts; illus. cum.index: vols.1-132. back issues avail.; reprint service avail. from PSC. **Document type:** *Journal, Academic/Scholarly.* **Description:** Covers the scientific study of animal behavior.
Related titles: Microform ed.: (from PMC, SWZ); Online - full content ed.: 1999; Online - full text ed.: ISSN 1568-539X. USD 844 in the Americas; EUR 675 elsewhere (effective 2006) (from EBSCO Publishing, Gale Group, IngentaConnect, Kluwer Online, O C L C Online Computer Library Center, Inc., Ovid Technologies, Inc., Springer LINK, Swets Information Services).
Indexed: AEA, ASCA, ASFA, AbAn, AgBio, AnBeAb, AnBrAb, ApEcolAb, BIOSIS Prev, BioCN&I, BiolAb, ChemAb, CurCont, DSA, ESPM, EntAb, FCA, FS&TA, ForAb, HelmAb, HortAb, ISR, IndVet, KWIWR, MEDLINE, MLA, MLA-IB, NemAb, NutrAb, PHN&I, PN&I, PoultAb, ProtozoAb, PsycInfo, PsycholAb, RASB, RM&VM, RevApplEntom, SCI, SFA, SSCI, TDB, VetBull, WildRev, ZooRec, e-psyche.
—BLDSC (1876.650000), CISTI, IDS, IE, Infotrieve, ingenta, Linda Hall. **CCC.**
Published by: Brill Academic Publishers, PO Box 9000, Leiden, 2300 PA, Netherlands. TEL 31-71-53-53-500, FAX 31-71-53-17-532, cs@brill.nl, http://www.brill.nl/m_catalogue_sub6_id8582.htm. Ed. J G van Rhijn. Adv. contact F S Geuze. **Subscr. in N. America to:** PO Box 605, Herndon, VA 20172. TEL 703-661-1585, 800-337-9255, FAX 703-661-1501, cs@brillusa.com. **Distr. outside N. America by:** c/o Turpin Distribution, Stratton Business Park, Pegasus Drive, Biggleswade, BEDFORDSHIRE SG 18 8TQ, United Kingdom. TEL 44-1767-604-954, FAX 44-1767-601-640, brill@turpin-distribution.com.

591.9493 BEL ISSN 0777-6276
QL401
➤ **BELGIAN JOURNAL OF ZOOLOGY.** Text in English, French; Summaries in English. 1863. 2/yr. EUR 50 to non-members (effective 2005). bk.rev. bibl.; charts; illus. **Document type:** *Academic/Scholarly.*
Former titles (until 1990): La Societe Royale Zoologique de Belgique. Annales (0049-1136); (until 1922): La Societe Royale Zoologique et Malacologique de Belgique. Annales (0770-1209); (until 1903): La Societe Royale Malacologique. Annales (0770-125X)
Indexed: ASCA, ASFA, AgBio, AnBrAb, BIOSIS Prev, BioCN&I, BiolAb, CurCont, ESPM, EntAb, FS&TA, ForAb, GEOBASE, HelmAb, HerbAb, I&DA, ISR, IndVet, PHN&I, PoultAb, RM&VM, RefZh, RevApplEntom, RiceAb, S&F, SCI, SFA, VetBull, ZooRec.
—BLDSC (1888.023380), CISTI, IDS, IE, ingenta, KNAW, Linda Hall.
Published by: Societe Royale Zoologique de Belgique/Koninklijke Belgische Vereniging voor Dierkunde, Limburgs Universitair Centrum, Dept SBG, Diepenbeek, 3590, Belgium. TEL 32-11-26-83-09, FAX 32-11-26-83-01, http://webhost.ua.ac.be/rbzs/bjz. Ed. Dr. Ronny Blust. Circ: 850.

590 DEU ISSN 0067-6098
BERLINER TIERPARK-BUCH. Text in German. 1957. irreg., latest vol.26, 1974. price varies. **Document type:** *Monographic series.*
Published by: Tierpark Berlin, Am Tierpark 41, Berlin, 10319, Germany.

590 IND ISSN 0303-3821
BHARTIYA KRISHI ANUSANDHAN PATRIKA; quarterly research journal of plant and animal sciences. Text in Hindi; Summaries in English. 1973. q. INR 400 domestic; USD 50 foreign (effective 2004). back issues avail. **Document type:** *Academic/Scholarly.* **Description:** The research papers of agriculture, animal, dairy, foods & home sciences in Hindi language with abstracts in English are published in this journal.
Indexed: AEA, AgrForAb, AnBrAb, CPA, ChemAb, DSA, FCA, HerbAb, HortAb, I&DA, IndVet, MaizeAb, NutrAb, OrnHort, PBA, PGegResA, PGrRegA, PHN&I, PotatoAb, RA&MP, RDA, RPP, RRTA, RevApplEntom, RiceAb, S&F, SIA, SeedAb, SoyAb, TDB, TriticAb, WAE&RSA, WeedAb.
Published by: Agricultural Research Communication Centre, 1130 Sadar Bazar, Post Office Marg, Karnal, Haryana 132 001, India. TEL 91-184-255080. Ed. R L Rajput.

590 GBR ISSN 0952-4622
QL765 CODEN: BIOAE7
➤ **BIOACOUSTICS**; the international journal of animal sound and its recording. Text in English. 1988. 3/yr. GBP 69, USD 119 to individuals; GBP 149, USD 239 to institutions (effective 2004). adv. abstr.; bibl.; charts; illus.; maps. back issues avail. **Document type:** *Journal, Academic/Scholarly.* **Description:** Collects research papers and articles on all aspects of wildlife recording.
Indexed: ASFA, AnBeAb, BIOSIS Prev, BiolAb, CurCont, ESPM, GEOBASE, OceAb, PsycInfo, PsycholAb, RefZh, SFA, WildRev, ZooRec, e-psyche.
—BLDSC (2066.679000), IE, Infotrieve, ingenta, Linda Hall. **CCC.**
Published by: (British Library, National Sound Archive), A B Academic Publishers, PO Box 42, Bicester, Oxon OX26 6NW, United Kingdom. jrnls@abapubl.demon.co.uk, http://www.zi.ku.dk/zi/bioacoustics/homepage.html. Eds. A N Popper, Peter K McGregor.

597 NLD
➤ **BIOCHEMISTRY & MOLECULAR BIOLOGY OF FISHES.** Text in English. 1991. irreg., latest vol.5, 1995. price varies. illus. back issues avail. **Document type:** *Monographic series, Academic/Scholarly.* **Description:** Examines ichthyological research into the biochemistry and molecular biology of fish.
Indexed: CIN, ChemAb, ChemTitl, ZooRec.
Published by: Elsevier BV (Subsidiary of: Elsevier Science & Technology), Radarweg 29, Amsterdam, 1043 NX, Netherlands. TEL 31-20-4853911, FAX 31-20-4852457, nlinfo-f@elsevier.nl, http://www.elsevier.nl. Eds. P W Hochachka, T P Mommsen.

590 ITA ISSN 1126-5221
QL1 CODEN: RBSVA9
BIOLOGIA E CONSERVAZIONE DELLA FAUNA. Text in Italian; Summaries in English, Italian. 1997. irreg. **Document type:** *Monographic series, Academic/Scholarly.*
Formed by the merger of (1976-1997): Ricerche di Biologia della Selvaggina. Supplemento (1121-3973); Which was formerly (1939-1976): Ricerche di Zoologia Applicata alla Caccia. Supplemento (0375-149X); (1976-1997): Ricerche di Biologia della Selvaggina (0375-0736); Which was formerly (1930-1976): Ricerche di Zoologia Applicata alla Caccia (0044-5061)
Indexed: BIOSIS Prev, BiolAb, KWIWR, RefZh, SFA, WildRev, ZooRec.
—BLDSC (2072.793000), CISTI.
Published by: Istituto Nazionale per la Fauna Selvatica, Via Ca Fornacetta, 9, Ozzano Dell'emilia, BO 40064, Italy. TEL 39-51-6512111, FAX 39-51-796628, infsammi@iperbole.bologna.it. Ed. Mario Spagnesi. Circ: 2,000.

590 ITA ISSN 1123-4245
BIOLOGIA MARINA MEDITERRANEA. Text in English, Italian. 1994. q. price varies. **Description:** Publishes the minutes of the conferences and symposia of the society.
Indexed: ESPM, ZooRec.

B

—BLDSC (2072.818000).
Published by: Societa Italiana di Biologia Marina, c/o Dipteris, Universita di Genova, Via Balbi 5, Genoa, 16126, Italy. TEL 010-2465315, FAX 010-2465315, sibmzool@unige.it, http://www.ulisse.it/~sibm/stampa.htm.

590 SVK ISSN 1335-6380
CODEN: BLOAAO
➤ **BIOLOGIA. SECTION ZOOLOGY.** Text in English. 1946. s-a. USD 138 for 3 sections (effective 2005). adv. bk.rev. charts; illus. index. 120 p./no.; back issues avail. **Document type:** *Journal, Academic/Scholarly.* **Description:** Presents original experimental and descriptive works in basic biological research in zoology (taxonomy, study of vertebrates and invertebrates, physiology).
Formerly (until 1994): Biologia. B: Zoologia (0862-1136); Supersedes in part (in 1969): Biologia (0006-3088)
Related titles: ♦ Series: Biologia. Section Botany. ISSN 1335-6372; ♦ Biologia. Section: Cellular and Molecular Biology. ISSN 1335-6399.
Indexed: ASFA, BioDAb, BiolAb, CPA, ChemAb, CurCont, ESPM, IndMed, MaizeAb, RefZh, SAA, SFA, TriticAb, VetBull, WildRev, ZooRec.
—BLDSC (2072.700000), CASDDS, CISTI, GNLM, IDS, IE, ingenta, KNAW, Linda Hall.
Published by: (Slovenska Akademia Vied, Ustav Zoologie/Slovak Academy of Sciences, Institute of Zoology), Slovak Academic Press Ltd., Nam Slobody 6, PO Box 57, Bratislava, 81005, Slovakia. biologia.zoo@savba.sk, http://www.zoo.sav.sk/biologia.htm. Eds. Maria Kazimirova, Frantisek Hindak. **Dist. abroad by:** Slovart G.T.G. s.r.o., Krupinska 4, PO Box 152, Bratislava 85299, Slovakia. TEL 421-2-63839472, FAX 421-2-63839485, http://www.slovart-gtg.sk.

➤ **BIOLOGICAL SOCIETY OF WASHINGTON. PROCEEDINGS.** see *BIOLOGY*

593 NLD
BIOLOGY OF INLAND WATERS. Text in English. 1998. irreg. price varies. **Document type:** *Academic/Scholarly.*
Published by: Backhuys Publishers BV, Postbus 321, Leiden, 2300 AH, Netherlands. TEL 31-71-517-0208, FAX 31-71-517-1856, backhuys@backhuys.com, http://www.backhuys.com. Ed. Koen Martens. Circ: 300.

590 CHL ISSN 0716-2898
QH91
BIOTA. Text in English, Spanish. 1986. irreg.
Indexed: ESPM.
—CISTI.
Published by: Universidad de Los Lagos, Instituto Profesional de Osorno, Casilla 933, Osorno, Chile.

598.07234 USA ISSN 1541-5309
QL677.5
BIRD WATCHER; the official birders newsletter of the national geographic society. Text in English. 2001. bi-m.
Published by: National Geographic Society, 1145 17th St, NW, Washington, DC 20036. TEL 800-647-5463, http://www.nationalgeographic.com. Ed. Mel Baughman.

591.9969 USA ISSN 0893-312X
CODEN: BMBZEB
BISHOP MUSEUM BULLETINS IN ZOOLOGY. Text in English. 1922. irreg., latest vol.3, 1998. price varies. reprint service avail. from PQC. **Description:** Covers zoology of Hawaii and the Pacific Basin.
Supersedes in part (in 1987): Bernice P. Bishop Museum Bulletin (0005-9439)
Indexed: BIOSIS Prev, ZooRec.
—CISTI, Linda Hall.
Published by: (Bernice Pauahi Bishop Museum), Bishop Museum Press, 1525 Bernice St, Box 19000 A, Honolulu, HI 96817. TEL 808-847-3511, FAX 808-841-8968. Circ: 300.

590 PRT ISSN 0523-7904
CODEN: BCGNAS
➤ **BOCAGIANA.** Text in Portuguese, English. 1959. irreg. per issue exchange basis. reprints avail. **Document type:** *Bulletin, Academic/Scholarly.*
Indexed: ASFA, BIOSIS Prev, BiolAb, ESPM, SFA, WildRev, ZooRec.
Published by: Camara Municipal do Funchal, Museo Municipal do Funchal Historia Natural, Rua da Mouraria 31, Funchal, Madeira 9004-546, Portugal. TEL 351-291-229761, FAX 351-291-225180, ciencia@mail.cm-funchal.pt. Ed., R&P Manuel Jose Biscoito. Adv. contact Alexandra Telo. Circ: 750.

590 BRA ISSN 0101-3580
QL242 CODEN: BOZOD9
BOLETIM DE ZOOLOGIA✶. Text in English, French, Portuguese. 1937. a. per issue exchange basis.
Supersedes in part (since 1976): Boletim de Zoologia e Biologia Marinha. Nova Serie (0067-9623)
Indexed: ASFA, BiolAb, ESPM, ZooRec.
—Linda Hall.
Published by: Universidade de Sao Paulo, Departamento de Zoologia, Centro, Caixa Postal 8191, Sao Paulo, SP 01065-970, Brazil. Ed. Walter Narchi. Circ: 500. **Co-sponsor:** Instituto de Biologia Marinha.

590 ITA ISSN 0366-2403
CODEN: BOZAAW
➤ **BOLLETTINO DI ZOOLOGIA AGRARIA E DI BACHICOLTURA.** Text in English, French, German, Italian; Summaries in English, Italian. 1928. 3/yr. EUR 40 domestic; EUR 50 foreign (effective 2004). back issues avail. **Document type:** *Monographic series, Academic/Scholarly.*
Indexed: AgBio, BIOSIS Prev, BioCN&I, BioDAb, BiolAb, FPA, ForAb, HortAb, MaizeAb, OrnHort, PBA, PHN&I, RPP, RefZh, RevApplEntom, TriticAb, VITIS, WeedAb, ZooRec.
Published by: Universita degli Studi di Milano, Istituto di Entomologia Agraria, Via Giovanni Celoria, 2, Milan, MI 20133, Italy. TEL 39-02-58356751, FAX 39-02-58356748, entom@mailserver.unimi.it. Ed. Luciano Suss. Circ: 160.

590 DEU ISSN 0006-7172
QL1 CODEN: BZOBAN
➤ **BONNER ZOOLOGISCHE BEITRAEGE.** Text in English, French, German. 1950. 4/yr. bk.rev. charts; illus.; maps. back issues avail. **Document type:** *Journal, Academic/Scholarly.* **Description:** Publishes original papers, reviews, and scientific notes covering the whole field of zoology, with emphasis on biodiversity, biogeography, history of zoology, morphology, phylogenetics, and taxonomy.
Indexed: ASFA, BIOSIS Prev, BiolAb, ESPM, KWIWR, RefZh, SFA, WildRev, ZooRec.
—BLDSC (2247.700000), CISTI, IE, ingenta, Linda Hall. **CCC.**
Published by: Zoologisches Forschungsinstitut und Museum Alexander Koenig, Adenauerallee 160, Bonn, 53113, Germany. TEL 49-228-91220, FAX 49-228-9122212, info.zfmk@uni-bonn.de, http://www.museumkoenig.uni-bonn.de. Ed. Michael Schmitt. Circ: 350.

590 DEU ISSN 0302-671X
CODEN: BZMNAF
BONNER ZOOLOGISCHE MONOGRAPHIEN. Text in English, French, German. 1971. irreg., latest vol.51, 2002. price varies. back issues avail. **Document type:** *Monographic series, Academic/Scholarly.*
Indexed: ASFA, BIOSIS Prev, BiolAb, RefZh, SFA, WildRev, ZooRec.
—CISTI, Linda Hall. **CCC.**
Published by: Zoologisches Forschungsinstitut und Museum Alexander Koenig, Adenauerallee 160, Bonn, 53113, Germany. TEL 49-228-91220, FAX 49-228-9122212, info.zfmk@uni-bonn.de, http://www.museumkoenig.uni-bonn.de. Ed. Dr. Karl-L Schuchmann. Circ: 150.

590 DEU ISSN 0174-3384
QH5
BRAUNSCHWEIGER NATURKUNDLICHE SCHRIFTEN. Text in German; Summaries in English. 1980. a. EUR 15 (effective 2001). back issues avail. **Document type:** *Proceedings, Academic/Scholarly.*
Indexed: ASFA, BIOSIS Prev, BiolAb, ESPM, EntAb, GEOBASE, IBR, RefZh, SFA, ZooRec.
Published by: Staatliches Naturhistorisches Museum, Pockelsstr 10, Braunschweig, 38106, Germany. TEL 49-531-3914351, FAX 49-531-3914370, museum@snhm.niedersachsen.de. Ed. Jurgen Hevers.

BRAZILIAN JOURNAL OF VETERINARY RESEARCH AND ANIMAL SCIENCE. see *VETERINARY SCIENCE*

590 USA ISSN 0006-9698
QL1 CODEN: BRVRAG
BREVIORA. Text in English. 1952. irreg. (3-6/yr.). price varies. bibl.; charts; illus. back issues avail. **Document type:** *Academic/Scholarly.*
Indexed: ASFA, BiolAb, ESPM, SFA, ZooRec.
—CISTI, Linda Hall.
Published by: Harvard University, Museum of Comparative Zoology, 26 Oxford St, Cambridge, MA 02138. TEL 617-495-3045, FAX 617-495-5667, http://www.mcz.harvard.edu. Ed. Kenneth J Boss. Circ: 700.

595.4 GBR ISSN 0524-4994
QL451 CODEN: BACBBR
➤ **BRITISH ARACHNOLOGICAL SOCIETY. BULLETIN.** Text in English. 1969. 3/yr. GBP 20 domestic; GBP 24 foreign (effective 2005). bk.rev. charts; illus.; stat. index. **Document type:** *Journal, Academic/Scholarly.* **Description:** Covers all aspects of biology of arachnids other than mites.
Supersedes: British Spider Study Group. Bulletin
Indexed: ASFA, Agr, BioCN&I, BiolAb, EntAb, ForAb, NutrAb, RM&VM, RefZh, RevApplEntom, S&F, SFA, WildRev, ZooRec.
—BLDSC (2412.550000), IE, ingenta, Linda Hall.
Published by: British Arachnological Society, c/o Ian Dawson, 100 Hayling Ave, Little Paxton, St Neots, Cambs PE19 6HQ, United Kingdom. TEL 44-1480-471064, info@britishspiders.org.uk, http://www.britishspiders.org.uk/html/bas.php?page=bultn&menu=publ. Circ: 700 (controlled).

595.4 GBR ISSN 0959-2261
CODEN: NBASE6
BRITISH ARACHNOLOGICAL SOCIETY. NEWSLETTER. (Dist. by: R Snazell (email: rsnazell@ite.ac.uk)) Text in English. 1971. 3/yr. looseleaf. GBP 15 domestic to individuals; GBP 18 foreign to individuals; GBP 20 domestic to institutions; GBP 24 foreign to institutions (effective 2005); (includes subscr. to British Arachnological Society. Bulletin). bk.rev.; Website rev. illus.; bibl.; maps. 2 cols./p.; back issues avail.; reprints avail. **Document type:** *Newsletter, Academic/Scholarly.*
Description: Contains general news and information.
Former titles (until Oct. 1984): The Secretary's Newsletter; (until Jul. 1981): The Secretary's New Letter
Indexed: BioCN&I, HerbAb, HortAb, NutrAb, RM&VM, RefZh, RevApplEntom, S&F, WeedAb, ZooRec.
—BLDSC (6106.396700).
Published by: British Arachnological Society, c/o Ian Dawson, 100 Hayling Ave, Little Paxton, St Neots, Cambs PE19 6HQ, United Kingdom. TEL 44-1480-471064, info@britishspiders.org.uk, http://www.britishspiders.org.uk. Circ: 650 (paid); 30 (controlled).

B

590 GBR ISSN 1475-1739
➤ **BRITISH MYRIAPOD AND ISOPOD GROUP. BULLETIN.** Text in English. 1972. a., latest vol.18, 2002. GBP 10 (effective 2003). bk.rev. back issues avail. **Document type:** *Journal, Academic/Scholarly.* **Description:** Keeps professional and amateur workers in the area of insects with more than six legs informed of current research and discoveries.
Formerly (until 2001): British Myriapod Group. Bulletin (0267-2154)
Indexed: ZooRec.
Published by: British Myriapod and Isopod Group, Rathgar, Exeter Rd, Ivybridge, Devon PL21 0BD, United Kingdom. TEL 44-1752-892703, h.j.read@btinternet.com, http://www.bmig.ac.uk. Eds. A D Barber, H J Read. R&P A D Barber.

590 GBR
BRITISH SOCIETY OF ANIMAL SCIENCE NEWSLETTER. Abbreviated title: B S A S Newsletter. Text in English. 1999. irreg. (3-4 yr.), latest no.5. back issues avail. **Document type:** *Newsletter, Academic/Scholarly.*
Media: Online - full content.
Published by: British Society of Animal Science, PO Box 3, Penicuik, Midlothian, Scotland EH26 0RZ, United Kingdom. TEL 44-131-4454508, FAX 44-131-5353120, bsas@ed.sac.ac.uk, http://www.bsas.org.uk/publs/newslttr.htm.

590 GBR
BRITISH SOCIETY OF ANIMAL SCIENCE. PROCEEDINGS. Text in English. a. **Document type:** *Proceedings, Academic/Scholarly.*
Related titles: Online - full content ed.
Published by: British Society of Animal Science, PO Box 3, Penicuik, Midlothian, Scotland EH26 0RZ, United Kingdom. TEL 44-131-4454508, FAX 44-131-5353120, bsas@ed.sac.ac.uk, http://www.bsas.org.uk/.

590.941 GBR ISSN 0958-0956
CODEN: BRWIEW
BRITISH WILDLIFE. Text in English. 1989. bi-m. GBP 23.95 in United Kingdom; GBP 25 rest of Europe; GBP 30 elsewhere rest of Europe (effective 2000). adv. bk.rev. illus. back issues avail. **Document type:** *Consumer.* **Description:** Covers British natural history, wildlife and environment.
Indexed: BIOBASE, IABS, PlantSci, ZooRec.
—BLDSC (2348.134500), IE, ingenta, Linda Hall. **CCC.**
Published by: British Wildlife Publishing, Lower Barn, Rooks Farm, Rotherwick, Basingstoke., Hook, Hants RG27 9BG, United Kingdom. TEL 44-1256-760663, FAX 44-1256-760501, brit.wildlife@clara.net. Ed., Pub., R&P Andrew Branson. Adv. contact Anne Branson. B&W page GBP 275; trim 140 x 200. Circ: 7,500 (paid).

590 USA ISSN 0068-2780
BROOKFIELD BANDARLOG. Text in English. 1949. irreg. membership.
—Linda Hall.
Published by: Chicago Zoological Society, Zoological Park, Brookfield, IL 60513. TEL 312-485-0263. Ed. George B Rabb.

590.73 USA ISSN 8756-3479
BROOKFIELD ZOO BISON. Text in English. 1966. s-a. USD 10. **Document type:** *Consumer.*
Formerly (until 1983): Brookfield Bison
Indexed: BiolDig.
—Linda Hall.
Published by: Chicago Zoological Society, Zoological Park, Brookfield, IL 60513. TEL 312-485-0263. Circ: 30,000.

590 USA ISSN 0108-0326
BRYOZOA (YEAR). Text in English. 1980. a. USD 40 to individuals; USD 10 to libraries. **Description:** Includes membership list, recent publications, and news items.
Published by: International Bryozoology Association, c/o Department of Geology, University of Illinois, Urbana, IL 61801. TEL 217-333-3833, FAX 217-244-4996. Ed. Daniel B Blake. Circ: 250.

590 IND ISSN 0970-0765
QL1 CODEN: BPAAS:A
➤ **BULLETIN OF PURE & APPLIED SCIENCES. SECTION A: ZOOLOGY.** Text in English. 1982. s-a. INR 300, USD 50 (effective 2005). adv. bk.rev. 100 p./no.; back issues avail.; reprints avail. **Document type:** *Journal, Academic/Scholarly.* **Description:** Research papers related to Zoological Science.
Supersedes in part (in 1983): Bulletin of Pure & Applied Sciences (0970-4604)
Media: Large Type (11 pt.).
Indexed: ZooRec.
—CISTI, Linda Hall. **CCC.**
Published by: A.K. Sharma, Ed. & Pub., 19-A, D D A Flats, Mansarover Park, Shahdara, New Delhi, 110 032, India. TEL 91-11-2117408, bulletin@mantraonline.com, ajaykumarsharma1955@yahoo.com. Ed., Pub., R&P, Adv. contact A K Sharma. B&W page INR 1,000, B&W page USD 50, color page INR 2,000, color page USD 100. Circ: 600.

590.73 AUS ISSN 0084-8182
BULLETIN OF ZOO MANAGEMENT. Text in English. 1969. a. free. bk.rev.
Published by: Royal Zoological Society of South Australia Inc., Zoological Gardens, Frome Road, Adelaide, SA 5000, Australia. Ed. David Langdon. Circ: 250 (controlled).

590 GBR ISSN 0007-5167
CODEN: BZONAP
➤ **BULLETIN OF ZOOLOGICAL NOMENCLATURE.** Text in English. 1943. q. GBP 123, USD 220 (effective 2003). **Document type:** *Academic/Scholarly.*
Indexed: ASFA, AnBrAb, BIOSIS Prev, BiolAb, ESPM, HelmAb, IndVet, NemAb, ProtozoAb, RM&VM, RefZh, RevApplEntom, RiceAb, SFA, WildRev, ZooRec.
—BLDSC (2926.000000), CISTI, IE, Infotrieve, ingenta, Linda Hall.
Published by: International Commission on Zoological Nomenclature, c/o Natural History Museum, Cromwell Rd, London, United Kingdom. TEL 44-20-7942-5653, iczn@nhm.ac.uk, http://www.iczn.org. Ed. A Wakeham-Dawson. Circ: 250 (paid). **Co-sponsor:** International Trust for Zoological Nomenclature.

➤ **C S A ANIMAL BEHAVIOR ABSTRACTS.** (Cambridge Scientific Abstracts) see *BIOLOGY—Abstracting, Bibliographies, Statistics*

590 BEL ISSN 0778-7103
CAHIERS D'ETHOLOGIE. Variant title: Cahiers d'Ethologie Fondamentale et Appliquee, Animale et Humaine. Text in French; Abstracts in English. 1981. q. EUR 30 domestic to individuals; EUR 45 in the European Union to individuals; EUR 50 elsewhere to individuals; EUR 75 domestic to institutions; EUR 87 in the European Union to institutions; EUR 90 elsewhere to institutions (effective 2002). **Description:** Devoted to fundamental and applied animal and human ethology.
Formerly (until 1991): Cahiers d'Ethologie Appliquee (0770-3767)
Related titles: ◆ Supplement(s): Cahiers d'Ethologie Appliquee, Animale et Humaine. Collection Enquetes et Dossiers. ISSN 0771-0305.
Indexed: BIOSIS Prev, BiolAb, RefZh, ZooRec.
Published by: Universite de Liege, Institut de Zoologie, Laboratoire d'Ethologie et de Psychologie Animale, Quai Ed Van Beneden 22, Liege, B-4020, Belgium. TEL 32-4-366-5081, FAX 32-4-366-5113, http://www.ulg.ac.be/museezoo/caheth.htm. Ed. Jean-Claude Ruwet.

590 BEL ISSN 0771-0305
CAHIERS D'ETHOLOGIE APPLIQUEE, ANIMALE ET HUMAINE. COLLECTION ENQUETES ET DOSSIERS. Text in French. 1981. s-a.
Related titles: ◆ Supplement to: Cahiers d'Ethologie. ISSN 0778-7103.
Indexed: ESPM.
Published by: Universite de Liege, Institut de Zoologie, Laboratoire d'Ethologie et de Psychologie Animale, Quai Ed Van Beneden 22, Liege, B-4020, Belgium. TEL 32-4-366-5081, FAX 32-4-366-5113, http://www.ulg.ac.be/museezoo/. Ed. Jean-Claude Ruwet.

597 USA ISSN 0575-3317
SH351.S3 CODEN: COFRAS
➤ **CALIFORNIA COOPERATIVE OCEANIC FISHERIES INVESTIGATIONS REPORTS.** Text in English; Abstracts in English, Spanish. 1959. a. free. back issues avail. **Document type:** *Academic/Scholarly.*
Indexed: ASCA, ASFA, CurCont, ESPM, Inspec, OceAb, PollutAb, SFA, WildRev, ZooRec.
—BLDSC (3012.100000), CISTI, IDS, IE, ingenta, Linda Hall.
Published by: California Cooperative Oceanic Fisheries Investigations, Scripps Institution of Oceanography, University of California, La Jolla, CA 92093-0227. TEL 619-534-4236, FAX 619-534-6500, TELEX 188929, http://www.calcofi.org/. Ed. Julie Olfe. R&P Kevin Hill. Circ: 1,200 (controlled).

597 799.1 USA ISSN 0008-1078
SK373 CODEN: CAFGAX
CALIFORNIA FISH AND GAME. Text in English. 1914. q. USD 15 domestic; USD 20 foreign (effective 2005). bk.rev. bibl.; illus. index. reprint service avail. from PQC.
Related titles: Microform ed.: (from PQC).
Indexed: ASCA, ASFA, AgBio, AnBrAb, BIOSIS Prev, BiolAb, CRFR, CalPI, ChemAb, CurCont, EPB, ESPM, EnvAb, FPA, ForAb, GEOBASE, HelmAb, HerbAb, IndVet, KWIWR, NemAb, NutrAb, OceAb, PN&I, S&F, SCI, SFA, SWRA, SeedAb, VetBull, WildRev, ZooRec.
—BLDSC (3013.000000), IDS, IE, ingenta, Linda Hall.
Published by: Department of Fish and Game, 1416 Ninth St, Sacramento, CA 95814. TEL 916-653-7664, http://www.dfg.ca.gov/coned/journal/index.html, http://www.delta.dfg.ca.gov/jobs/voluntr.html. Circ: 1,000.

591 CAN ISSN 0008-4301
QL1 CODEN: CJZOAG
➤ **CANADIAN JOURNAL OF ZOOLOGY/JOURNAL CANADIEN DE ZOOLOGIE.** Text mainly in English; Text occasionally in French. 1929. m. CND 332 combined subscription domestic to individuals Print & online eds.; USD 332 combined subscription foreign to individuals Print & online eds.; CND 1,265 combined subscription domestic to institutions Print & online eds.; USD 1,265 combined subscription foreign to institutions Print & online eds. (effective 2005). adv. bibl.; charts; illus. index. back issues avail.; reprint service avail. from PQC. **Document type:** *Journal, Academic/Scholarly.*
Formerly (until 1950): Canadian Journal of Research. Section D: Zoological Sciences (0366-7413); Which superseded in part (in 1935): Canadian Journal of Research (0366-6581)
Related titles: Microfiche ed.: (from MML); Microform ed.: (from MML, PMC, PQC); Online - full text ed.: ISSN 1480-3283 (from bigchalk, EBSCO Publishing, Gale Group, IngentaConnect, Micromedia ProQuest, O C L C Online Computer Library Center, Inc., ProQuest Information & Learning, Swets Information Services).
Indexed: ABIPC, AEA, ASCA, ASFA, AbHyg, AgBio, Agr, AgrForAb, AnBeAb, AnBrAb, ApEcolAb, ApicAb, B&AI, B&BAb, BIOBASE, BIOSIS Prev, BibAg, BioCN&I, BioDAb, BiolAb, CBCARef, CIN, CPA, CRFR, CZA, ChemAb, ChemTitl, CurCont, DSA, EPB, ESPM, EZ&PSA, EngInd, EntAb, EnvAb, EnvInd, ExcerpMed, FCA, FPA, ForAb, GEOBASE, GSI, GenetAb, HGA, HelmAb, HerbAb, HortAb, I&DA, IABS, ISR, IndVet, KWIWR, M&GPA, MEDLINE, MLA-IB, MSB, MaizeAb, NSCI, NemAb, NutrAb, OceAb, OrnHort, PBA, PGegResA, PGrRegA, PHN&I, PN&I, PotatoAb, PoultAb, ProtozoAb, RA&MP, RM&VM, RPP, RefZh, RevApplEntom, S&F, SCI, SFA, SIA, SPPI, SWRA, SeedAb, TDB, VetBull, WTA, WeedAb, WildRev, ZooRec.
—BLDSC (3037.000000), CASDDS, CIS, CISTI, GNLM, IDS, IE, Infotrieve, ingenta, Linda Hall. **CCC.**
Published by: N R C Research Press, Building M 55, Ottawa, ON K1A 0R6, Canada. TEL 613-993-9084, FAX 613-952-7656, research.journals@nrc.ca, http://pubs.nrc-cnrc.gc.ca/cgi-bin/rp/rp2_desc_e?cjz. Eds. Dr. A S M Saleuddin, Dr. K G Davey, Bruce P Dancik. Adv. contact Judy Heyman. B&W page CND 675; trim 11 x 8.5. Circ: 1,125.

590 DEU ISSN 0176-3997
CODEN: CAROEJ
CAROLINEA; Beitraege zur Naturkundlichen Forschung in Suedwestdeutschland. Text in German; Summaries in English, French. 1864. a. charts; illus. back issues avail. **Document type:** *Journal, Academic/Scholarly.* **Description:** Natural history of animals and plants in South-West Germany.
Formerly (until 1982): Beitraege zur Naturkundlichen Forschung in Suedwestdeutschland (0005-8122)
Indexed: ASFA, BIOSIS Prev, BiolAb, ESPM, IBR, RefZh, VITIS, ZooRec.
—Linda Hall.
Published by: Staatliches Museum fuer Naturkunde Karlsruhe, Erbprinzenstr 13, Karlsruhe, 76133, Germany. TEL 49-721-1752111, FAX 49-721-1752110, hhoefer_smnk@compuserve.com, http://www.smnk.de. Ed. Siegfried Rietschel. Circ: 150.

594.1477 USA ISSN 0084-862X
CATALOG OF DEALERS' PRICES FOR MARINE SHELLS. Text in English, Latin. 1965. a. USD 19.50 (effective 2001). reprint service avail. from PQC. **Description:** Provides information on the value of shells.
Published by: Of Sea & Shore Publications, PO Box 219, Port Gamble, WA 98364. TEL 360-297-2426, FAX 360-297-2426, ofseashr@sinclair.net. Ed. Thomas C Rice. Circ: 500.

597.8 USA
CODEN: CAPBAY
CATALOGUE OF AMERICAN AMPHIBIANS AND REPTILES. Text in English. 1963. irreg. (approx. 20/yr). looseleaf. USD 20 to individual members (effective 2003); USD 35 to institutional members (effective 1999). back issues avail. **Document type:** *Catalog, Academic/Scholarly.*
Indexed: BiolAb, SFA, WildRev, ZooRec.
Published by: Society for the Study of Amphibians and Reptiles, PO Box 253, Marceline, MO 64658-0253. http://www.ssarherps.org. Ed. Robert Powell. R&P Theodora Pinou TEL 203-432-5028. Circ: 900.

591.9436 AUT ISSN 1018-6093
CATALOGUS FAUNAE AUSTRIAE. Text in German. irreg. price varies. 64 p./no.; back issues avail. **Document type:** *Monographic series, Academic/Scholarly.* **Description:** Catalogs all animal life in Austria.
Indexed: BiolAb.
Published by: Verlag der Oesterreichischen Akademie der Wissenschaften, Postgasse 7/4, Vienna, W 1011, Austria. TEL 43-1-515813402, FAX 43-1-515813400, verlag@oeaw.ac.at, http://verlag.oeaw.ac.at.

597.9 USA ISSN 0892-0761
CATESBEIANA. Text in English. s-a.
Indexed: ZooRec.
Published by: Virginia Herpetological Society, Liberty University, Dept. of Biology, 1971 University Blvd, Lynchburg, VA 24502. http://fwie.fw.vt.edu/VHS/. Ed. Shelly Miller.

597 IND ISSN 0254-380X
CENTRAL MARINE FISHERIES RESEARCH INSTITUTE. TECHNICAL AND EXTENSION SERIES. Text in English. 1978. q.
Indexed: ESPM, PollutAb, ZooRec.
—BLDSC (5375.299000), IE, ingenta.
Published by: Central Marine Fisheries Research Institute, Dr. Salim Ali Rd., PO Box 1603, Cochin, Kerala 682 014, India. TEL 91-489-394867, FAX 91-484-394909.

597 BRA ISSN 0104-6411
CENTRO DE PESQUISA E EXTENSAO PESQUEIRA DO NORDESTE. BOLETIM TECNICO-CIENTIFICO. Text in Portuguese; Abstracts in English, Portuguese. 1993. s-a. BRL 15 (effective 2002); exchange basis. abstr.; bibl.; charts; maps. **Document type:** *Bulletin, Academic/Scholarly.*
Indexed: ZooRec.
Published by: Centro de Pesquisa e Extensao Pesqueira do Nordeste/Research and Extension Fishery Center for the Northeast Region, Rua Samuel Hardman, s-n, Tamandare, PE 55578-000, Brazil. TEL 55-81-6621166, FAX 55-81-5274090, adias@cepene.ibama.gov.br. Ed. Antonio Fernandes Dias.
Dist. by: Edicoes IBAMA, Diretoria de Gestao Estrategica, SAIN Av L4 Norte, Brasilia 70800-200, Brazil. TEL 61-316-1065, editora@ibama.gov.br, http://www.ibama.gov.br/edicoes/.

594.5 GBR ISSN 0260-681X
CEPHALOPOD NEWSLETTER. Text in English. 1977. s-a. GBP 7. bk.rev. abstr.; bibl. back issues avail.
Address: c/o Dr. J.R. Senior, Dept. of Adult Education, 32 Old Elvet, Durham, DH1 3JB, United Kingdom. Ed. Dr. Marion Nixon. Circ: 400.

590 USA ISSN 0747-9840
CHAMP CHANNELS. Text in English. 1983. 4/yr. USD 9; USD 10 foreign. bk.rev. illus. back issues avail. **Description:** Examines the subject of the Lake Champlain and Loch Ness monsters.
Published by: Lake Champlain Phenomena Investigation, Champlain, NY 12866. TEL 518-587-7638. Ed. Joseph W Zarzynski. Circ: 200.

597.9 USA ISSN 1088-7105
CHELONIAN RESEARCH MONOGRAPHS. Text in English. 1996. irreg. **Document type:** *Monographic series.* **Description:** Covers chelonian research, particularly conservation and biology.
Indexed: ASFA, BIOSIS Prev, OceAb, ZooRec.
Published by: Chelonian Research Foundation, 168 Goodrich St, Lunenberg, MA 01462. TEL 978-582-9668, 978-534-9440, FAX 978-582-6279, 978-840-8184, http://www.chelonian.org. Ed. Anders G J Rhodin.

590.73 GBR
CHESTER ZOO LIFE. Text in English. 1962. q. membership. bk.rev. 3 cols./p.; **Description:** News items and informational articles on exhibits and events at the Chester Zoo, with announcements of members' meetings, activities, and lists of new arrivals and births.
Former titles (until 2001): Chester Zoo News (0300-4988); (until 1986): Chez Nous; Our Zoo News
Related titles: Online - full content ed.
Published by: North of England Zoological Society, Zoological Gardens, Upton by Chester, Ches CH2 1LH, United Kingdom. TEL 44-1244-380280, FAX 44-1244-371273, marketing@chesterzoo.co.uk, http://www.chesterzoo.org.uk/zoolife/zoolife.html. Ed., R&P Pat Cade. Circ: 1,000.

597.9 USA ISSN 0009-3564
QL640 CODEN: CHSBAU
CHICAGO HERPETOLOGICAL SOCIETY. BULLETIN. Text in English. 1966. m. USD 22 domestic to individuals; USD 34 foreign to individuals; USD 38 domestic to institutions; USD 50 foreign to institutions (effective 2000). adv. bk.rev. charts; illus. back issues avail. **Document type:** *Bulletin.* **Description:** Concerned with the biology, captive care and husbandry of reptiles and amphibians. Features include articles, editorials, news of research, letters to the editor and book reviews and advertisements.
Formerly: Reptile Review
Indexed: BiolAb, RefZh, SFA, WildRev, ZooRec.
Published by: Chicago Herpetological Society, Publications Secretary, Chicago Academy of Sciences, 2060 N Clark St, Chicago, IL 60614. TEL 773-281-1850, FAX 312-549-5199, http://www.chicagoherp.org/. Ed. Michael Dloogatch TEL 773-782-2026. R&P Marcia Rybak TEL 310-456-8332. Adv. contact Ralph Shepstone. Circ: 900 (paid).

599.3593 DEU ISSN 0341-5414
CHINCHILLA POST. Text in German. 1956. bi-m. EUR 46 (effective 2002). adv. **Document type:** *Magazine, Trade.* **Description:** Reports on keeping and breeding chinchillas.
Published by: Landbuch Verlagsgesellschaft mbH, Kabelkamp 6, Hannover, 30179, Germany. TEL 49-511-67806-0, FAX 49-511-67806220, info@landbuch.de, http://www.chinchilla.com, http://www.landbuch.de. Ed. Georg Steinhuebl. Adv. contact Ute Hiensch. page EUR 365. Circ: 2,400.

597 JPN ISSN 0577-9316
CHIRIBOTAN/MALACOLOGICAL SOCIETY OF JAPAN. NEWSLETTER. Text in Japanese. 1960. q. JPY 7,500; includes Venus.
Indexed: AnBrAb, NutrAb, RevApplEntom, ZooRec.
Published by: Nihon Kairui Gakkai/Malacological Society of Japan, c/o National Science Museum, 3-23-1 Hiyakunin-cho, Shinjuku-ku, Tokyo, 169-0073, Japan. Eds. Eiji Tsuchida, Masatoyo Okamoto. Circ: 900.

599.4 590.752 333.95 BRA ISSN 1413-4403
➤ **CHIROPTERA NEOTROPICAL.** Text in English, Portuguese, Spanish; Summaries in English. 1998. s-a. free. illus. **Document type:** *Newsletter, Academic/Scholarly.* **Description:** Disseminates issues relating to the biology, ecology, and conservation of neotropical bats, those fascinating mammals of the order Chiroptera.
Related titles: E-mail ed.; Online - full content ed.
Indexed: ZooRec.
Published by: Universidade de Brasilia, Departamento de Zoologia, Brasilia, 70910-900, Brazil. TEL 55-61-3072265, FAX 55-61-274114, chiroptera@uol.com.br, zoo@unb.br, http://www.unb.br/ib/zoo/chiroptera. Circ: 700. **Co-sponsor:** Conservation International do Brasil.

590 PRT ISSN 0870-1695
QH301.C52 CODEN: CBESE7
CIENCIA BIOLOGICA: ECOLOGIA E SISTEMATICA. Variant title: Ciencia Biologica: Ecology and Systematics. Text in English, Portuguese. 1972. irreg.
Indexed: ESPM, NutrAb, ProtozoAb, ZooRec.
Published by: Universidade de Coimbra, Departamento de Zoologia, Largo Marques de Pombal, Coimbra, 3004-517, Portugal. TEL 351-39-834729, FAX 351-39-826798, zoologia@cnc.cj.uc.pt, http://www.fct.uc.pt.

590 BEL ISSN 0777-2491
➤ **COLLOQUES D'HISTOIRE DES CONNAISSANCES ZOOLOGIQUES.** Text in French, English. 1990. a., latest vol.14, 2003. price varies. abstr.; bibl.; charts; illus.; maps. back issues avail. **Document type:** *Academic/Scholarly.* **Description:** Presents a multidisciplinary approach to the history of both wild and domestic animals with respect to the human-animal relationship. The audience consists of scholars, professionals, and a general readership interested in the field.
Indexed: ZooRec.
Published by: Universite de Liege, Seminaire d'Histoire des Connaissances Zoologiques, Pl du 20 Aout, 7, Liege, 4000, Belgium. TEL 32-4-3665579, FAX 32-4-366-5723, liliane.bodson@ulg.ac.be. Ed. Liliane Bodson. Circ: 210 (paid); 40 (controlled).

➤ **COMMISSION FOR THE CONSERVATION OF ANTARCTIC MARINE LIVING RESOURCES. REPORT OF THE MEETING OF THE SCIENTIFIC COMMITTEE.** see *EARTH SCIENCES—Oceanography*

➤ **COMMUNITY ECOLOGY**; an interdisciplinary journal reporting progress in community and population studies. see *BIOLOGY—Botany*

590.724 USA ISSN 1532-0820
SF77 CODEN: LBASAE
➤ **COMPARATIVE MEDICINE (MEMPHIS).** Text in English. 1950. bi-m. USD 180 domestic; USD 195 in Canada & Mexico; USD 220 elsewhere (effective 2005). adv. charts; illus. index. back issues avail. **Document type:** *Journal, Academic/Scholarly.* **Description:** Covers comparative medicine and laboratory animal science with articles about animal models, animal behavior, animal biotechnology and related topics.
Former titles (until 2000): Laboratory Animal Science (0023-6764); (until 1971): Laboratory Animal Care (0094-5331); (until 1963): Animal Care Panel. Proceedings (0097-076X)
Related titles: Microform ed.: (from PMC); Online - full text ed.: (from EBSCO Publishing).
Indexed: AEA, ASCA, AbHyg, AgBio, Agr, AnBrAb, BIOBASE, BIOSIS Prev, BiolAb, CIN, ChemAb, ChemTitl, CurCont, DBA, DSA, DentInd, ExcerpMed, FoVS&M, HelmAb, IABS, ISR, IndMed, IndVet, Inpharma, JDDR, MEDLINE, NutrAb, PN&I, PoultAb, ProtozoAb, RM&VM, RPP, RRTA, Reac, RefZh, RevApplEntom, SAA, SCI, SFA, SoyAb, TDB, VetBull, WildRev, ZooRec.
—BLDSC (3363.790200), CASDDS, CISTI, GNLM, IDS, IE, KNAW.
Published by: American Association for Laboratory Animal Science, 9190 Crestwyn Hills Drive, Memphis, TN 38125-8538. TEL 901-754-8620, info@aalas.org, http://www.aalas.org. Ed. Robert O Jacoby. Circ: 3,000 (paid).

592.3 USA ISSN 1525-2647
QL386 CODEN: JHSWE4
➤ **COMPARATIVE PARASITOLOGY.** Text in English. 1934. s-a. USD 55 domestic; USD 57 in Canada & Mexico; USD 60 elsewhere (effective 2003). bk.rev. back issues avail. **Document type:** *Journal, Academic/Scholarly.* **Description:** It is devoted to all phases of parasitology and fields related to parasites and parasitic diseases.
Former titles (until Jan. 2000): Helminthological Society of Washington. Journal (1049-233X); (until 1990): Helminthological Society of Washington. Proceedings (0018-0130)
Related titles: Online - full text ed.: (from BioOne, C S A, O C L C Online Computer Library Center, Inc.).
Indexed: ASCA, AbHyg, AgBio, Agr, AgrForAb, BIOBASE, BIOSIS Prev, BibAg, BioCN&I, BiolAb, CurCont, EntAb, ExcerpMed, HelmAb, IABS, ISR, IndVet, NemAb, NutrAb, PN&I, PoultAb, ProtozoAb, RM&VM, RefZh, RevApplEntom, S&F, SCI, SFA, SIA, SPPI, TDB, VetBull, WildRev, ZooRec.
—BLDSC (3363.790950), CISTI, IDS, IE, ingenta, Linda Hall.
Published by: Helminthological Society of Washington, c/o Allen Press, Inc, PO Box 1897, Lawrence, KS 66044-8897. TEL 785-843-1235, FAX 785-843-1274, iscp@allenpress.com, http://www.gettysburg.edu/~shendrix/helmsoc.html, http://www.allenpress.com. Ed. Willis A Reid. Circ: 1,100. **Subscr. to:** Allen Press Inc., PO Box 1897, Lawrence, KS 66044.

594.1477 ITA ISSN 0394-0152
QL401
➤ **LA CONCHIGLIA/SHELL**; international shell magazine. Text in Italian, English. 1969. q. EUR 41.32 domestic; EUR 58.81 foreign (effective 2003). adv. bk.rev.; video rev. bibl.; illus. index. 64 p./no.; Supplement avail.; back issues avail.; reprints avail. **Document type:** *Magazine, Academic/Scholarly.* **Description:** Presents papers on taxonomy, ethology, and environmental issues related to malacology. Lists events, shows and symposia.
Related titles: CD-ROM ed.; English ed.
Indexed: RefZh, ZooRec.
Published by: Evolver S.r.l., Via Cesare Federici, 1, Rome, RM 00147, Italy. TEL 39-06-5132536, FAX 39-06-5132796, conchiglia@evolver.it, http://www.evolver.it. Ed., Adv. contact Maria Antonietta Fontana. R&P Paolo Angioy. B&W page USD 500; trim 600 x 870. Circ: 1,500. **Subscr. to:** Via Focilide, 31, Rome, RM 00125, Italy.

➤ **CONCHOLOGICAL SOCIETY SPECIAL PUBLICATION.** see *BIOLOGY*

590 BRA
CONGRESSO BRASILEIRO DE ZOOLOGIA E CONGRESSO LATINO-AMERICANO DE ZOOLOGIA. RESUMOS. Text in Portuguese. irreg., latest 1992, 12th, Belem. **Document type:** *Abstract/Index.*
Published by: (Brazil. Conselho Nacional de Desenvolvimento Cientifico e Tecnologico), Museu Paraense Milio Goeldi, Comercio, Caixa Postal 399, Belem, PA 66017-970, Brazil. TEL 091-228-2341, FAX 091-929-1412. **Co-sponsors:** Sociedade Brasileira de Zoologia; Universidade Federal do Para.

CONNAISSANCE DES INVERTEBRES. see *BIOLOGY—Entomology*

597.9 USA ISSN 1094-2246
➤ **CONTEMPORARY HERPETOLOGY.** Text in English. 1997. irreg. free. **Document type:** *Academic/Scholarly.* **Description:** Publishes articles covering all aspects of herpetology, including ecology, ethology, systematics, conservation biology, and physiology.
Media: Online - full text.
Indexed: ZooRec.
Published by: (Department of Herpetology), California Academy of Sciences, Golden Gate Park, San Francisco, CA 94118. TEL 415-750-7041, FAX 415-750-7013, jslowins@cas.calacademy.org, http://alpha.selu.edu/ch/. Ed., R&P Joseph Slowinski.

591 BRA ISSN 1516-7259
QL242
CONTRIBUICOES AVULSAS SOBRE A HISTORIA NATURAL DO BRASIL. SERIE ZOOLOGIA. Text in Portuguese. 1999. irreg.
Indexed: ZooRec.
Published by: Universidade Federal Rural do Rio de Janeiro, Instituto de Biologia, BR-465, Km 7, Seropedica, Rio de Janeiro, 23851-970, Brazil. http://www.ufrrj.br/institutos/ib/inicio.htm.

590 NLD ISSN 1383-4517
QL1
➤ **CONTRIBUTIONS TO ZOOLOGY/BIJDRAGEN TOT DE DIERKUNDE.** Text in English, French, German; Summaries in English. 1848. q. EUR 115 per issue (effective 2003). adv. bk.rev. abstr.; illus.; maps. index. 70 p./no.; reprints avail. **Document type:** *Journal, Academic/Scholarly.*
Formerly (until vol.65, 1995): Bijdragen tot de Dierkunde (0067-8546)
Indexed: ASCA, ASFA, BIOSIS Prev, BiolAb, CurCont, ESPM, ISR, KWIWR, RefZh, SCI, SFA, SSCI, WLR, WildRev, ZooRec.
—BLDSC (3461.490000), CISTI, IDS, IE, ingenta, Linda Hall.
Published by: Universiteit van Amsterdam, Commissie voor de Artis Bibliotheek, Plantage Middenlaan 45A, Amsterdam, 1018 DC, Netherlands. vonk@Sscience.uva.nl, http://www.uba.uva.nl/ctz/. Eds. F R Schram, R Vonk TEL 31-20-5256282. R&P, Adv. contact R Vonk TEL 31-20-5256282. B&W page EUR 100; 16 x 21. Circ: 400. **Subscr. to:** Contributions to Zoology, PO Box 94766, Amsterdam 1090 ST, Netherlands. **Co-sponsor:** Koninklijk Zoologisch Genootschap Natura Artis Magistra.

597 USA ISSN 0045-8511
QL1 CODEN: COPAAR
➤ **COPEIA.** Text in English. 1913. q. USD 85 to individuals; USD 135 to institutions (effective 2005). adv. bk.rev. illus. index. back issues avail.; reprints avail. **Document type:** *Journal, Academic/Scholarly.* **Description:** Serves as a publication outlet for scientific publications in ichthyology and herpetology. Includes news of members and their activities, and a summary of the annual meetings.
Related titles: Microform ed.: (from PQC); Online - full text ed.: (from BioOne, C S A, O C L C Online Computer Library Center, Inc., ProQuest Information & Learning).
Indexed: ASCA, ASFA, AgBio, AnBeAb, AnBrAb, ApEcolAb, B&AI, BIOBASE, BIOSIS Prev, BiolAb, BiolDig, BrGeoL, CRFR, ChemAb, Copeia, CurCont, ESPM, ForAb, GEOBASE, GenetAb, HGA, HelmAb, IABS, ISR, IndVet, M&TEA, NutrAb, OceAb, PGrRegA, ProtozoAb, RM&VM, RiceAb, SCI, SFA, SPPI, SWRA, VetBull, WildRev, ZooRec.
—BLDSC (3466.000000), IDS, IE, Infotrieve, ingenta, Linda Hall.
Published by: American Society of Ichthyologists and Herpetologists, c/o Karen Hickey, Allen Press Inc, Box 1897, Lawrence, KS 66044-8897. TEL 785-843-1235, 800-627-0629, FAX 785-843-1274, orders@allenpress.com, http://www.utexas.edu.depts/asih/, http://www.allenpress.com. Ed. Robert Kenley. R&P Dean Hendrickson. Circ: 3,600 (controlled).

595.384 USA ISSN 1023-8174
CRAYFISH NEWS; the official newsletter of the International Association of Astacology. Text in English. 1973. q. USD 40 for 2 yrs. to individuals; USD 80 for 2 yrs. to institutions (effective 2003). bk.rev. back issues avail. **Document type:** *Proceedings, Academic/Scholarly.* **Description:** Discusses crayfish biology, ecology and aquaculture.
Published by: International Association of Astacology, c/o IAA Secretariat, Rm 123, Swingle Hall, Auburn University, Auburn, AL 36849-5419. TEL 334-844-9123, FAX 334-844-9208, daniewh@acesag.auburn.edu. Ed. Glen Whisson. Pub., R&P Jay V Huner. Circ: 400.

CROCODILE SPECIALIST GROUP. NEWSLETTER. see *CONSERVATION*

595.3 GBR ISSN 0168-6356
CODEN: CRISD2
CRUSTACEAN ISSUES. Text in English. 1983. irreg., latest vol.10, 1995. price varies. **Document type:** *Monographic series, Academic/Scholarly.* **Description:** Covers specific subjects of crustacean research.
Indexed: BIOSIS Prev, ZooRec.
—BLDSC (3490.110000), CISTI, IE, ingenta. **CCC.**
Published by: Taylor & Francis Ltd (Subsidiary of: Taylor & Francis Group), 4 Park Sq, Milton Park, Abingdon, OX14 4RN, United Kingdom. TEL 44-1235-828600, FAX 44-1235-829000, info@tandf.co.uk, http://www.tandf.co.uk/books/. Ed. Dr. Ronald Vonk. **Dist. in U.S. by:** Ashgate Publishing Co, Old Post Rd, Brookfield, VT 05036. TEL 800-535-9544.

595.3 NLD ISSN 0011-216X
QL435.A1 CODEN: CRUSAP
➤ **CRUSTACEANA**; international journal of crustacean research. Text and summaries in English, French, German. 1960. 11/yr. USD 794 combined subscription in the Americas print & online eds.; EUR 635 combined subscription elsewhere print & online eds. (effective 2006). bk.rev. abstr.; charts; illus. cum.index: vols.1-68. back issues avail.; reprint service avail. from PSC. **Document type:** *Journal, Academic/Scholarly.* **Description:** Papers on taxonomy, ecology, physiology, anatomy, genetics and biometry in crustacean research.
Related titles: Microform ed.: (from SWZ); Online - full content ed.; Online - full text ed.: ISSN 1568-5403. USD 715 in the Americas; EUR 572 elsewhere (effective 2006) (from EBSCO Publishing, Gale Group, IngentaConnect, Kluwer Online, O C L C Online Computer Library Center, Inc., Springer LINK, Swets Information Services); ♦ Supplement(s): Crustaceana. Supplements. ISSN 0167-6563.
Indexed: ASCA, ASFA, AgBio, AnBrAb, BIOBASE, BIOSIS Prev, BiolAb, CurCont, ESPM, EntAb, FPA, ForAb, GEOBASE, HelmAb, IABS, ISR, IndVet, NutrAb, OceAb, PGegResA, ProtozoAb, RM&VM, RefZh, RevApplEntom, S&F, SCI, SFA, SPPI, SWRA, SoyAb, VetBull, WildRev, ZooRec.
—BLDSC (3490.120000), IDS, IE, Infotrieve, ingenta, Linda Hall. **CCC.**
Published by: (Universiteit van Amsterdam, Zoologisch Museum), Brill Academic Publishers, PO Box 9000, Leiden, 2300 PA, Netherlands. TEL 31-71-53-53500, FAX 31-71-53-17532, jcvvk@rulsfb.leidenuniv.nl, cs@brill.nl, http://www.brill.nl/m_catalogue_sub6_id7188.htm. Ed. J.C. von Vaupel Klein. R&P Elizabeth Venekamp. **Subscr. in N. America to:** PO Box

605, Herndon, VA 20172. TEL 703-661-1585, 800-337-9255, FAX 703-661-1501, cs@brillusa.com. **Distr. outside N. America by:** c/o Turpin Distribution, Stratton Business Park, Pegasus Drive, Biggleswade, BEDFORDSHIRE SG 18 8TQ, United Kingdom. TEL 44-1767-604-954, FAX 44-1767-601-640, brill@turpin-distribution.com.

595.3 NLD ISSN 0167-6563
QL435.A1 CODEN: CRUSBQ
➤ **CRUSTACEANA. SUPPLEMENTS**; international journal of Crustacean research. Text in Dutch. 1968. irreg., latest vol.16, 1990. price varies. back issues avail. **Document type:** *Monographic series, Academic/Scholarly.*
Related titles: ◆ Supplement to: Crustaceana. ISSN 0011-216X.
Indexed: BiolAb, ISR, ZooRec.
—Linda Hall.
Published by: Brill Academic Publishers, PO Box 9000, Leiden, 2300 PA, Netherlands. TEL 31-71-53-53-500, FAX 31-71-53-17-532, cs@brill.nl, http://www.brill.nl. R&P Elizabeth Venekamp. **Subscr. in N. America to:** PO Box 605, Herndon, VA 20172. TEL 703-661-1585, 800-337-9255, FAX 703-661-1501, cs@brillusa.com. **Distr. outside N. America by:** c/o Turpin Distribution, Stratton Business Park, Pegasus Drive, Biggleswade, BEDFORDSHIRE SG 18 8TQ, United Kingdom. TEL 44-1767-604-954, FAX 44-1767-601-640, brill@turpin-distribution.com.

590 USA ISSN 0736-7023
QL89
CRYPTOZOOLOGY. Text in English. 1982. a. free to members. adv. bk.rev. back issues avail. **Document type:** *Journal, Academic/Scholarly.* **Description:** Zoological, historical, philosophical and psychological aspects of crytozoology.
Indexed: SFA, ZooRec.
—Linda Hall.
Published by: International Society of Cryptozoology, PO Box 43070, Tucson, AZ 85733. TEL 520-884-8369, FAX 520-884-8369, iscz@azstarnet.com, http://www.internationalsocietyofcryptozoology.org/Publications/Journal/Default.aspx, http://www.izoo.org/isc. Ed. J Richard Greenwell. Circ: 800.

597.9 ARG ISSN 0326-551X
CUADERNOS DE HERPETOLOGIA. Text in English, Portuguese, Spanish. 1984. irreg. **Document type:** *Monographic series.*
Indexed: ASFA, ZooRec.
Published by: Asociacion Herpetologica Argentina, Fundacion Miguel Lillo, Miguel Lillo 251, San Miguel de Tucuman, 4000, Argentina. http://www.unt.edu.ar/AHA/AHA1.htm.

591.972 MEX ISSN 0188-9508
QL225
CUADERNOS MEXICANOS DE ZOOLOGIA. Text in Spanish. irreg. MXP 100.
Published by: Sociedad Mexicana de Zoologia, Apdo. 101-13, Mexico City, DF 04530, Mexico. Eds. Hector Espinosa Perez, Ma Eugenia Moncayo Lopez.

590 CUB
CUBA. CENTRO DE INFORMACION Y DOCUMENTACION AGROPECUARIO. BOLETIN DE RESENAS. SERIE: MEJORAMIENTO ANIMAL. Abstracts in English. 1974. irreg. per issue exchange basis.
Formerly: Cuba. Centro de Informacion y Divulgacion Agropecuario. Boletin de Resenas. Serie: Genetica y Reproduccion
Indexed: Agrind.
Published by: Centro de Informacion y Documentacion Agropecuario, Gaveta Postal 4149, Havana, 4, Cuba.

CUBAN JOURNAL OF AGRICULTURAL SCIENCE. see *AGRICULTURE*

590 JPN ISSN 1345-5834
CODEN: HRYZAJ
CURRENT HERPETOLOGY/JAPANESE JOURNAL OF HERPETOLOGY. Text in English, Japanese. 1964. s-a.
Former titles (until 1999): Hachu Ryoseiruigaku Zasshi/Japanese Journal of Herpetology/Acta Herpetologica Japonica (0285-3191); (until 1964): Hachuruigaku Zasshi/Acta Herpetologica Japonica (0285-3183)
Indexed: BIOSIS Prev, BiolAb, RefZh, ZooRec.
Published by: Nihon Hachu Ryoseirui Gakkai/Herpetological Society of Japan, Department of Zoology, Faculty of Science, Kyoto University, Kitashirakawa-Oiwakecho, Sakyo-ku, Kyoto 606-8502, Japan. tom@zoo.zool.kyoto-u.ac.jp, http://zoo.zool.kyoto-u.ac.jp/herp/publications.html.

599 USA ISSN 0899-577X
QL700
➤ **CURRENT MAMMALOGY.** Text in English. 1987. irreg., latest vol.2, 1990. USD 292 per vol. (effective 2005). back issues avail. **Document type:** *Monographic series, Academic/Scholarly.*
—CISTI, KNAW. **CCC.**
Published by: Springer-Verlag New York, Inc. (Subsidiary of: Springer Science+Business Media), 233 Spring St, New York, NY 10013. TEL 212-460-1500, FAX 212-460-1575, service@springer-ny.com, http://www.springer-ny.com. **Dist. by:** Journal Fulfillment, PO Box 2485, Secaucus, NJ 07096-2485.

592.57 IND ISSN 0971-0116
CURRENT NEMATOLOGY. Text in English. 1990. s-a. INR 200 domestic to individuals; USD 100 foreign to individuals; INR 1,000 domestic to institutions; USD 200 foreign to institutions (effective 2003). adv. **Document type:** *Academic/Scholarly.*
Indexed: AgrForAb, BioCN&I, CPA, FCA, FPA, ForAb, HelmAb, HerbAb, HortAb, NemAb, OrnHort, PBA, PHN&I, PotatoAb, RA&MP, S&F, SeedAb, TriticAb, WeedAb, ZooRec.
—BLDSC (3500.550000). **CCC.**
Published by: Bioved Research Society, c/o Brijesh K. Dwivedi General Secretary, Teliarganj, U.P., 133/42, MLN Rd, Allahabad, Uttar Pradesh 211 002, India. bioved2003@yahoo.com. Ed. B K Dwivedi. adv.: color page INR 3,000.

CURRENT PRIMATE REFERENCES. see *BIOLOGY—Abstracting, Bibliographies, Statistics*

CYPRIS; international ostracoda newsletter. see *PALEONTOLOGY*

CZECH JOURNAL OF ANIMAL SCIENCE. see *AGRICULTURE—Poultry And Livestock*

597 DEU ISSN 0724-7435
D C G INFORMATIONEN. Text in German. 1970. m. EUR 32 membership; EUR 25 to students (effective 2005). adv. bk.rev. bibl. index. back issues avail. **Document type:** *Journal, Academic/Scholarly.*
Indexed: SFA, ZooRec.
Published by: Deutsche Cichliden-Gesellschaft e.V., Parkstr 21a, Bielefeld, 33719, Germany. TEL 49-521-3369958, FAX 49-521-3369958, praesident@dcg-online.de, http://www.dcg-online.de/dHTML/files/dcgDcgInfos.html. Ed. Rainer Stawikowski. Circ: 3,000.

590.752 GBR ISSN 0141-4259
DEER. Text in English. 1966. 3/yr.
Indexed: AnBrAb, ForAb, HerbAb, IndVet, RRTA, S&F, VetBull, WAE&RSA, ZooRec.
—BLDSC (3541.200000), IE, ingenta.
Published by: The British Deer Society, Fordingbridge, Hampshire SP6 1EF, United Kingdom. TEL 44-1425-655434, FAX 44-1425-655433, h.q@bds.org.uk, http://www.bds.org.uk.

DEFENDERS. see *CONSERVATION*

590 NLD ISSN 0923-9308
➤ **DEINSEA**; Annual of the Natural History Museum Rotterdam. Text in English, French, German. 1994. a., latest vol.9, 2003. EUR 70 per vol. (effective 2005). bk.rev. illus. 120 p./no. 2 cols./p.; back issues avail.; reprints avail. **Document type:** *Journal, Academic/Scholarly.* **Description:** Publishes original research papers on topics in zoology/paleontology.
Related titles: Online - full text ed.
Indexed: RefZh, ZooRec.
—BLDSC (3546.304000).
Published by: Natuurmuseum Rotterdam/Natural History Museum, Rotterdam, Westzeedijk 345, Postbus 23452, Rotterdam, 3001 KL, Netherlands. TEL 31-10-436-4222, FAX 31-10-436-4399, deinse@nmr.nl, http://www.nmr.nl. Circ: 500 (paid and controlled).

508 560 USA ISSN 0070-3753
DENVER MUSEUM OF NATURAL HISTORY. PROCEEDINGS. Text in English. 1955-1966 (no.16); resumed 1991. irreg. price varies. **Document type:** *Proceedings.*
Formerly: Colorado Museum of Natural History
Indexed: ZooRec.
Published by: Denver Museum of Natural History, 2001 Colorado Blvd, Denver, CO 80205-5798. TEL 303-370-6444, FAX 303-331-6492. R&P Cheri Jones.

597.92 USA ISSN 0191-3875
QL666.C584
DESERT TORTOISE COUNCIL. PROCEEDINGS OF SYMPOSIUM. Text in English. 1976. a. USD 15 to non-members; USD 10 to members. **Document type:** *Proceedings.*
Indexed: ZooRec.
Published by: Desert Tortoise Council, 3273, Beaumont, CA 92223-1202. Ed. Breck Bartholomew. R&P Ed Larue. Circ: 600.

594 DEU ISSN 0418-8861
DEUTSCHE MALAKOZOOLOGISCHE GESELLSCHAFT. MITTEILUNGEN. Text and summaries in German, English. 1962. irreg., latest vol.70, 2003. EUR 14 per issue domestic; EUR 17.70 per issue foreign (effective 2005). back issues avail. **Document type:** *Monographic series, Academic/Scholarly.* **Description:** Contains papers on faunistics as well as short papers on all fields of malacozoology.
Indexed: BIOSIS Prev, BiolAb, WildRev, ZooRec.
Published by: (Senckenbergische Naturforschende Gesellschaft), E. Schweizerbart'sche Verlagsbuchhandlung, Johannesstr 3A, Stuttgart, 70176, Germany. TEL 49-711-3514560, FAX 49-711-3514569, mail@schweizerbart.de, http://www.schweizerbart.de/j/mitt-deutsche-malakozoologische-gesellschaft. Ed. Fritz F Steininger. Circ: 400 (paid). **Co-sponsor:** Deutsche Malakozoologische Gesellschaft.

590 DEU ISSN 0070-4342
CODEN: VDZGAN
DEUTSCHE ZOOLOGISCHE GESELLSCHAFT. VERHANDLUNGEN. Text in German. a. price varies. **Document type:** *Proceedings, Academic/Scholarly.*
Indexed: ASFA, AnBrAb, BiolAb, ChemAb, RefZh, RevApplEntom.
—CASDDS, CISTI, KNAW, Linda Hall. **CCC.**
Published by: (Deutsche Zoologische Gesellschaft), Elsevier GmbH, Urban & Fischer Verlag (Subsidiary of: Elsevier Science & Technology), Loebdergraben 14a, Jena, 07743, Germany. FAX 49-3641-626500, marketing.journals@urbanfischer.de, http://www.urbanfischer.de/journals. **Subscr. to:** Nature Publishing Group, Brunel Rd, Houndmills, Basingstoke, Hamps RG21 6XS, United Kingdom. TEL 44-1256-329242, FAX 44-1256-812358, subscriptions@nature.com.

597 NLD ISSN 0167-9309
SH1 CODEN: DAFSDF
➤ **DEVELOPMENTS IN AQUACULTURE AND FISHERIES SCIENCE.** Text in Dutch. 1976. irreg., latest vol.33, 2002. price varies. back issues avail. **Document type:** *Monographic series, Academic/Scholarly.*
Indexed: AEA, ASFA, B&BAb, BIOSIS Prev, ESPM, OceAb, ZooRec.
—BLDSC (3579.064000), CASDDS, CISTI, IE, ingenta. **CCC.**
Published by: Elsevier BV (Subsidiary of: Elsevier Science & Technology), Radarweg 29, Amsterdam, 1043 NX, Netherlands. TEL 31-20-4853911, FAX 31-20-4852457, nlinfo-f@elsevier.nl, http://www.elsevier.nl.

597 NLD ISSN 0924-5316
➤ **DEVELOPMENTS IN ENVIRONMENTAL BIOLOGY OF FISHES.** Text in English. 1981. irreg., latest vol.23, 2004. price varies. **Document type:** *Monographic series, Academic/Scholarly.*
Indexed: BIOSIS Prev, ZooRec.
—BLDSC (3579.071420), IE, ingenta. **CCC.**
Published by: Springer-Verlag Dordrecht (Subsidiary of: Springer Science+Business Media), Van Godewijckstraat 30, Dordrecht, 3311 GX, Netherlands. TEL 31-78-6576050, FAX 31-78-6576474, http://www.springeronline.com. Ed. David L G Noakes.

➤ **DISEASE INFORMATION (ONLINE EDITION).** see *VETERINARY SCIENCE*

590 808.803 USA
DISNEY'S ANIMAL KINGDOM. Text in English. 10/yr. USD 12 (effective 1999). **Document type:** *Consumer.*
Published by: Disney Publishing Worldwide Inc., 114 Fifth Ave, New York, NY 10011-5690. TEL 212-633-4400.

590 JPN ISSN 0916-8419
QL750 CODEN: DSKEEN
DOBUTSU SHINRIGAKU KENKYU/JAPANESE JOURNAL OF ANIMAL PSYCHOLOGY. Text in English, Japanese; Summaries in English. 1947. s-a. JPY 2,000 newsstand/cover (effective 2005). adv. Index. back issues avail. **Document type:** *Journal, Academic/Scholarly.*
Formerly (until 1990): Dobutsu Shinrigaku Nenpo - Annual of Animal Psychology (0003-5130)
Indexed: BIOSIS Prev, BiolAb, JPI, PsycInfo, PsycholAb, ZooRec, e-psyche.
—**CCC.**
Published by: Nihon Dobutsu Shinri Gakkai/Japanese Society for Animal Psychology, 3-9-8, Hachobori, Chuoh-ku, Tokyo, 104-0032, Japan. dousin@psy.flet.keio.ac.jp, http://wwwsoc.nii.ac.jp/jsap2/zassi.html. Circ: 500 (controlled).

590 JPN ISSN 0288-4887
CODEN: DOBUBT
DOBUTSU TO DOBUTSUEN/ANIMALS AND ZOOS. Text in Japanese. 1949. m. JPY 3,700, USD 64 (effective 2000). **Document type:** *Academic/Scholarly.*
Indexed: SFA, WildRev, ZooRec.
Published by: Tokyo Dobutsuen Kyokai/Tokyo Zoological Park Society, Ueno Dobutsuen, 9-83 Ueno Park, Taito-ku, Tokyo, 110-0007, Japan. TEL 81-3-3828=8235, FAX 81-3-3828-8237, http://www.tzps.or.jp/edu. Ed. Masaru Saito.

590 JPN ISSN 0386-7498
QL77.5 CODEN: DSZAEI
DOBUTSUEN SUIZOKUKAN ZASSHI/JAPANESE ASSOCIATION OF ZOOLOGICAL GARDENS AND AQUARIUMS. JOURNAL. Text in Japanese; Summaries in English, Japanese. 1959. q.
Indexed: AgBio, AnBrAb, DSA, HelmAb, IndVet, PN&I, PoultAb, RRTA, VetBull, WAE&RSA, ZooRec.
Published by: Nihon Dobutsuen Suizokukan Kyokai/Japanese Association of Zoological Gardens and Aquariums, Vella Heights Okachimachi 402, 4-23-10 Taito, Taito-ku, Tokyo, 110-0016, Japan.

DOCUMENTS SCIENTIFIQUES ET TECHNIQUES - I R D. see *EARTH SCIENCES—Oceanography*

DODO; journal of the wildlife conservation trusts. see *CONSERVATION*

590 CHN ISSN 1000-0739
QL351 CODEN: DFXUEB
➤ **DONGWU FENLEI XUEBAO/ACTA ZOOTAXONOMICA SINICA.** Text in Chinese; Summaries in English. 1964. q. CNY 88 (effective 2004). adv. **Document type:** *Journal, Academic/Scholarly.* **Description:** Contains theses on zootaxonomy, its theory and practice, scientific notes and academic discussions.
Related titles: Online - full content ed.: (from WanFang Data Corp.); Online - full text ed.: (from East View Information Services).
Indexed: AgBio, AnBrAb, ApicAb, BioCN&I, BiolAb, ForAb, HelmAb, HortAb, IndVet, PoultAb, ProtozoAb, RA&MP, RM&VM, RefZh, RevApplEntom, S&F, TDB, VetBull, ZooRec.
—BLDSC (0675.030000), CISTI, Linda Hall.
Published by: (Zhongguo Kexueyuan, Dongwusuo/Chinese Academy of Sciences, Institute of Zoology), Kexue Chubanshe/Science Press, 16 Donghuang Cheng Genbei Jie, Beijing, 100717, China. yangn@panda.ioz.ac.cn, http://dwfl.periodicals.net.cn/default.html, http://www.sciencep.com/. Circ: 6,000. **Dist. by:** China International Book Trading Corp, 35 Chegongzhuang Xilu, Haidian District, PO Box 399, Beijing 100044, China. TEL 86-10-68412045, FAX 86-10-68412023, cibtc@mail.cibtc.com.cn, http://www.cibtc.com.cn.

590 CHN ISSN 0001-7302
QL1 CODEN: TWHPA3
➤ **DONGWU XUEBAO/ACTA ZOOLOGICA SINICA.** Text in Chinese; Summaries in English. 1935. bi-m. USD 150 to individuals; USD 180 to institutions (effective 2004). adv. charts; illus.; maps. **Document type:** *Journal, Academic/Scholarly.* **Description:** Contains original theses on zoology, including taxonomy, faunistics, morphology, ecology, and experimental zoology. Also includes information about research progress and discussions among various schools of research and academic viewpoints.
Related titles: Online - full content ed.: (from WanFang Data Corp.); Online - full text ed.: (from East View Information Services).
Indexed: ASFA, BIOSIS Prev, BioCN&I, BiolAb, CIN, ChemAb, ChemTitl, CurCont, ESPM, ISR, IndVet, KWIWR, PN&I, PoultAb, ProtozoAb, RefZh, SCI, SFA, VetBull, WildRev, ZooRec.
—CASDDS, CISTI, KNAW, Linda Hall.
Published by: (Zhongguo Kexueyuan, Dongwu Yanjiusuo/Chinese Academy of Sciences, Institute of Zoology), Kexue Chubanshe/Science Press, 16 Donghuang Cheng Genbei Jie, Beijing, 100717, China. TEL 86-10-64000246, FAX 86-10-64030255, zool@panda.ioz.ac.cn, http://www.actazool.org/. Ed. Zu Wang Wang. Circ: 11,000. **Dist. by:** China International Book Trading Corp, 35 Chegongzhuang Xilu, Haidian District, PO Box 399, Beijing 100044, China. TEL 86-10-68412045, FAX 86-10-68412023, cibtc@mail.cibtc.com.cn, http://www.cibtc.com.cn.

591 CHN ISSN 1000-1786
QL1 CODEN: DOJIE2
DONGWUXUE JIKAN. Text in Chinese. 1981. **Description:** Ecosystem of crop field for research on ecology, pest management, etc.
Indexed: ASFA, ESPM, OceAb.
Published by: (Zhongguo Kexueyuan Dongwu Yanjiusuo), Kexue Chubanshe/Science Press, 16 Donghuang Cheng Genbei Jie, Beijing, 100717, China. csb@scichina.com, http://www.sciencep.com/.

590 CHN ISSN 0254-5853
QL1 CODEN: DOYADI
➤ **DONGWUXUE YANJIU/ZOOLOGICAL RESEARCH.** Text mainly in Chinese; Abstracts in English; Text occasionally in English. 1980 (Feb.). bi-m. CNY 90 domestic; CNY 410 foreign (effective 2005). adv. bk.rev. abstr. 80 p./no.; back issues avail. **Document type:** *Journal, Academic/Scholarly.* **Description:** Reports on the latest achievements and development on zoology and biomedicine, emphasizing evolution, ecology and ethnology, and biomedical animal model.
Related titles: ♦ CD-ROM ed.: Chinese Academic Journals Full-Text Database. Science & Engineering, Series A. ISSN 1007-8010; Online - full content ed.: 2005. free (effective 2005) (from WanFang Data Corp.); Online - full text ed.: (from East View Information Services).
Indexed: AEA, ASFA, AbHyg, AgBio, AgrForAb, AnBrAb, ApEcolAb, BIOSIS Prev, BioCN&I, BiolAb, CPA, ChemAb, DSA, ESPM, EntAb, FCA, ForAb, HelmAb, HerbAb, HortAb, IndVet, NutrAb, OrnHort, PGegResA, PHN&I, PN&I, PoultAb, ProtozoAb, RA&MP, RM&VM, RPP, RRTA, RefZh, RevApplEntom, S&F, SFA, SIA, SeedAb, TDB, VetBull, WildRev, ZooRec.
—BLDSC (9520.060000), CASDDS, CISTI, IE, ingenta, Linda Hall.
Published by: Zhongguo Kexueyuan, Kunming Dongwu Yanjiusuo/Chinese Academy of Sciences, Kunming Institute of Zoology, 32 Jiaochangdong Lu, Kunming, 650223, China. TEL 86-871-5199026, FAX 86-871-5191823, zoores@mail.kiz.ac.cn, http://www.bioline.org.br/zr, http://www.kiz.ac.cn. Ed. Wei-zhi Ji. R&P Fan Shan. Adv. contact Zi-yun Deng. Circ: 1,100 (paid and controlled). **Dist. by:** China International Book Trading Corp, 35 Chegongzhuang Xilu, Haidian District, PO Box 399, Beijing 100044, China. TEL 86-10-68412045, FAX 86-10-68412023, cibtc@mail.cibtc.com.cn, http://www.cibtc.com.cn.

590 CHN ISSN 0250-3263
QL1 CODEN: TWHCDZ
➤ **DONGWUXUE ZAZHI/CHINESE JOURNAL OF ZOOLOGY.** Text in Chinese. 1957. bi-m. CNY 84 (effective 2004). adv. bk.rev. **Document type:** *Journal, Academic/Scholarly.* **Description:** Aims to exchange information, experience, knowledge, and research results in zoology. Contains articles on research development, academic activities, experimental techniques, and news briefs.
Related titles: Online - full text ed.: (from East View Information Services, WanFang Data Corp.).
Indexed: AEA, AbHyg, AgBio, AnBrAb, BioCN&I, ChemAb, DSA, FCA, ForAb, HelmAb, HortAb, IndVet, NemAb, NutrAb, PBA, PN&I, PoultAb, ProtozoAb, RA&MP, RDA, RM&VM, RefZh, RevApplEntom, RiceAb, S&F, TDB, VetBull, WeedAb, ZooRec.
—BLDSC (3180.700000), CASDDS, CISTI, IE, ingenta, Linda Hall.
Published by: (Zhongguo Kexueyuan, Dongwu Yanjiusuo/Chinese Academy of Sciences, Institute of Zoology, Zhongguo Dongwu Xuehui), Kexue Chubanshe/Science Press, 16 Donghuang Cheng Genbei Jie, Beijing, 100717, China. TEL 86-10-64000246, FAX 86-10-64030255, journal@panda.ioz.ac.cn, http://dwzxz.periodicals.net.cn/default.html, http://www.sciencep.com/. **Dist. by:** China International Book Trading Corp, 35 Chegongzhuang Xilu, Haidian District, PO Box 399, Beijing 100044, China. TEL 86-10-68412045, FAX 86-10-68412023, cibtc@mail.cibtc.com.cn, http://www.cibtc.com.cn.

590 FRA ISSN 1256-7779
QL640
DUMERILIA. Text in English, French. 1994. irreg.
Indexed: ASFA, ZooRec.
Published by: (Association des Amis du Laboratoire des Reptiles et Amphibiens du Museum National d'Histoire Naturelle), A A L R A M, 25 rue Cuvier, Paris, 75005, France. TEL 33-1-40793487, reptamph@mnhn.fr, ohler@cimrs1.mnhn.fr. Ed. Roger Bour. **Subscr. in US to:** AALRAM, c/o Patricia B Zug, Div of Amphibians & Reptiles, National Museum of Nat History, NHB Mail Stop 162, Washington, DC 20560.

590.73 ZAF ISSN 0012-723X
QH1 CODEN: DMNOAM
➤ **DURBAN MUSEUM NOVITATES.** Text in English. 1952. a., latest vol.27. ZAR 40, USD 20 (effective 2003). bk.rev. back issues avail. **Document type:** *Journal, Academic/Scholarly.* **Description:** Original and review articles on taxonomy, systematics, and biogeography, particularly relating to the zoology of Southeastern Africa.
Indexed: ASFA, AgrForAb, BIOSIS Prev, BioCN&I, BiolAb, ESPM, ForAb, HerbAb, HortAb, IBR, ISAP, PBA, PoultAb, RA&MP, RefZh, RevApplEntom, S&F, ZooRec.
—BLDSC (3632.000000), CISTI, Linda Hall.
Published by: Durban Natural Science Museum, PO Box 4085, Durban, KwaZulu-Natal 4000, South Africa. TEL 27-31-3112247, FAX 27-31-3112242, davida@crsu.durban.gov.za. Ed. David Allan. Circ: 280 (controlled).

590 DNK ISSN 0109-1190
DYR I NATUR OG MUSEUM. Text in Danish. 1984. 2/yr. DKK 50 (effective 2002). illus. back issues avail.
Published by: Zoologisk Museum, Universitetsparken 15, Copenhagen Oe, 2100, Denmark. TEL 45-35-321000, FAX 45-35-321010, jfredskov@zmuc.ku.dk. Ed. Torben Wolff.

599.7 USA
EASTERN PUMA NETWORK NEWS. Text in English. 1983. q. looseleaf. USD 16 (effective 2000). bk.rev. stat. 8 p./no.; back issues avail. **Document type:** *Newsletter, Consumer.* **Description:** For research network of volunteers interested in proving the existence of the eastern sub-species of felis concolor couguar and felis concolor niger. Publishes news of puma, panther and mountain lion sightings.
Published by: Eastern Puma Network, PO Box 3562, Baltimore, MD 21214. TEL 410-254-2517, FAX 410-254-2517, epuma@flash.net, http://members.nbci.com/eprnnews/information.htm. Ed. John Lutz. R&P Jon Vinroot. Circ: 400; 253 (paid).

590 USA
ECDYSIAST. Text in English. 1981. s-a. membership. **Document type:** *Newsletter.*
Media: Duplicated (not offset).
Published by: Crustacean Society, 810 E 10th St, Box 1897, Lawrence, KS 66044. TEL 913-843-1221. Circ: 800.

593.9 NLD ISSN 0168-6100
QL381 CODEN: ECSTD6
ECHINODERM STUDIES. Text in English. 1983. biennial. price varies. **Document type:** *Academic/Scholarly.*
Indexed: BIOSIS Prev, ZooRec.
—BLDSC (3647.364500), CASDDS. **CCC.**
Published by: A A Balkema (Subsidiary of: Taylor & Francis The Netherlands), PO Box 1675, Rotterdam, 3000 BR, Netherlands. FAX 31-10-413-5947, sales@balkema.nl, http://www.balkema.nl. **Dist. in U.S. by:** Ashgate Publishing Co, Old Post Rd, Brookfield, VT 05036. TEL 800-535-9544.

597 DNK ISSN 0906-6691
QL624 CODEN: EFFIEW
➤ **ECOLOGY OF FRESHWATER FISH.** Text in English; Summaries in Spanish. 1992. q. USD 588 combined subscription in the Americas to institutions & Caribbean (print & online eds.); GBP 350 combined subscription elsewhere to institutions print & online eds. (effective 2006). adv. bk.rev. illus. reprint service avail. from PSC. **Document type:** *Academic/Scholarly.* **Description:** Publishes original articles on all aspects of fish ecology and fishery sciences in lakes, rivers and estuaries.
Related titles: Online - full text ed.: ISSN 1600-0633. USD 522 in the Americas to institutions & Caribbean; GBP 311 elsewhere to institutions (effective 2005) (from Blackwell Synergy, EBSCO Publishing, Gale Group, IngentaConnect, O C L C Online Computer Library Center, Inc., Swets Information Services).
Indexed: ASFA, AnBrAb, ApEcolAb, B&BAb, BIOSIS Prev, BiolAb, CurCont, ESPM, ForAb, GEOBASE, GenetAb, HGA, HelmAb, I&DA, ISR, IndVet, S&F, SCI, SFA, SWRA, VetBull, ZooRec.
—BLDSC (3650.043100), CISTI, IDS, IE, ingenta, Linda Hall. **CCC.**
Published by: Blackwell Munksgaard (Subsidiary of: Blackwell Publishing Ltd.), Rosenoerns Alle 1, PO Box 227, Copenhagen V, 1502, Denmark. TEL 45-77-333333, FAX 45-77-333377, info@mks.blackwellpublishing.com, http://www.blackwellpublishing.com/journals/EFF, http://www.munksgaard.dk/. Eds. Asbjorn Vollestad, David C Heins, Javier Lobon-Cervia.

➤ **ECOTROPICA.** see *BIOLOGY—Botany*

590 JPN ISSN 0389-1445
➤ **EDAPHOLOGIA.** Text in English, French, German, Japanese; Abstracts in English. 1967. 2/yr. JPY 6,000 to individuals; JPY 9,000 to institutions; JPY 4,000 to students. 50 p./no.; back issues avail. **Document type:** *Journal, Academic/Scholarly.*
Indexed: Agrind, ZooRec.
—BLDSC (3659.747093), IE, ingenta. **CCC.**
Published by: Nihon Dojo Dobutsu Gakkai/Japanese Society of Soil Zoology, Graduate School of Environment & Information Sciences, Yokohama National University, 79-7 Tokiwadai, Yokohama, 240-8501, Japan. TEL 81-43-265-3274, FAX 81-43-266-2481, kanekono@ynu.ac.jp, http://wwwsoc.nii.ac.jp/jssz/index.html. Ed. Shoichi Yoshida. R&P Yasunori Hagino. Circ: 300.

590 EGY ISSN 1110-5321
EGYPTIAN GERMAN SOCIETY FOR ZOOLOGY. JOURNAL. A, COMPARATIVE ZOOLOGY/MAGALLAT AL-GAM'IYYAT AL-MISRIYYAT AL-ALMAANIYYAT LI-'LM AL-HAYYAWAAN. 'ILM AL-FISYULUGIA AL-MUQARAN. Text in English. 1986. s-a. **Document type:** *Journal, Academic/Scholarly.*
Published by: Cairo University, Faculty of Science - Egyptian German Society for Zoology, PO Box 144, Orman - Giza, Cairo, Egypt. TEL 20-2-5676701, FAX 20-2-2625396, info@egsz.org, http://derp.sti.sci.eg/data/0373.htm, http://www,egsz.org.

590 EGY ISSN 1110-533X
EGYPTIAN GERMAN SOCIETY FOR ZOOLOGY. JOURNAL. B, ANATOMY AND EMBRYOLOGY/MAGALLAT AL-GAM'IYYAT AL-MISRIYYAT AL-ALMAANIYYAT LI-'LM AL-HAYYAWAAN. AL-TASRIH WA 'LM AL-AGINAT. Text in English. 1986. s-a.
Published by: Cairo University, Faculty of Science - Egyptian German Society for Zoology, PO Box 144, Orman - Giza, Cairo, Egypt. TEL 20-2-5676701, FAX 20-2-2625396, info@egsz.org, http://derp.sti.sci.eg/data/0234.htm, http://www,egsz.org.

590 EGY ISSN 1110-5348
EGYPTIAN GERMAN SOCIETY FOR ZOOLOGY. JOURNAL. C, HISTOLOGY AND HISTOCHEMISTRY. Text in English. 1986. s-a.
—BLDSC (4735.790000), IE.
Published by: Cairo University, Faculty of Science - Egyptian German Society for Zoology, PO Box 144, Orman - Giza, Cairo, Egypt. TEL 20-2-5676701, FAX 20-2-2625396, info@egsz.org, http://www,egsz.org.

592 EGY ISSN 1110-5356
EGYPTIAN GERMAN SOCIETY FOR ZOOLOGY. JOURNAL. D, INVERTEBRATE ZOOLOGY AND PARASITOLOGY/MAGALLAT AL-GAM'IYYAT AL-MISRIYYAT AL-ALMAANIYYAT LI-'LM AL-HAYYAWAAN. 'ILM AL-HAYWAN AL-FAQQARY WA AL-TUFAYLIAT. Text in English. 1986. s-a. **Document type:** *Journal, Academic/Scholarly.*
Published by: Cairo University, Faculty of Science - Egyptian German Society for Zoology, PO Box 144, Orman - Giza, Cairo, Egypt. TEL 20-2-5676701, FAX 20-2-2625396, info@egsz.org, http://derp.sti.sci.eg/data/0375.htm, http://www,egsz.org.

595.7 EGY ISSN 1110-5364
EGYPTIAN GERMAN SOCIETY FOR ZOOLOGY. JOURNAL. E, ENTOMOLOGY/MAGALLAT AL-GAM'IYYAT AL-MISRIYYAT AL-ALMAANIYYAT LI-'LM AL-HAYYAWAAN. 'ILM AL-HASHARAT. Text in English. 1986. s-a. **Document type:** *Journal, Academic/Scholarly.*
—BLDSC (4735.790000).

Published by: Cairo University, Faculty of Science - Egyptian German Society for Zoology, PO Box 144, Orman - Giza, Cairo, Egypt. TEL 20-2-5676701, FAX 20-2-2625396, info@egsz.org, http://derp.sti.sci.eg/data/0376.htm, http://www,egsz.org.

590 636 EGY ISSN 1110-2594
EGYPTIAN JOURNAL OF RABBIT SCIENCE. Text in English. 1991. s-a. **Document type:** *Journal, Academic/Scholarly.*
Indexed: AgBio, AgrForAb, AnBrAb, DSA, FPA, HerbAb, HortAb, IndVet, MaizeAb, OrnHort, PoultAb, RA&MP, RM&VM, SIA, SoyAb, TriticAb, WAE&RSA.
Published by: Zagazig University, Faculty of Agriculture, Banha Branch, Mushtuhur, Zagazig, Egypt. TEL 20-55-323490, 20-55-345452, http://derp.sti.sci.eg/data/0217.htm. Ed. Dr, E A Afifi.

551.46 EGY ISSN 1110-6344
EGYPTIAN JOURNAL OF ZOOLOGY. Text in English. 1997. s-a. **Document type:** *Journal, Academic/Scholarly.*
Supersedes in part (in 1996): Zoological Society A.R. Egypt. Proceedings (1110-1350); Which was formerly (until 1963): The Zoological Society of Egypt (1110-144X)
Indexed: ZooRec.
Published by: Zoological Society A.R. Egypt, Cairo University, Dept of Zoology, Faculty of Science, Gamiat El-Qahira St, Cairo, Egypt. TEL 20-2-5676638, FAX 20-2-5272556, http://derp.sti.sci.eg/data/0185.htm. Ed. Abdel-Hafezh H Muhammad.

590 JPN ISSN 0424-7086
QL461 CODEN: ESDBAK
➤ **EISEI DOBUTSU/MEDICAL ENTOMOLOGY AND ZOOLOGY.** Text in English, Japanese. 1950. q. JPY 5,000, USD 45 membership (effective 2004); subscr. incld. with membership. back issues avail. **Document type:** *Journal, Academic/Scholarly.* **Description:** Publishes original articles and research notes concerning entomology and zoology in medical and related fields.
Indexed: ASFA, AbHyg, AgBio, AgrForAb, AnBrAb, BIOSIS Prev, BioCN&I, BiolAb, ChemAb, DBA, ForAb, HelmAb, IndVet, NutrAb, PHN&I, PN&I, PoultAb, ProtozoAb, RA&MP, RM&VM, RefZh, RevApplEntom, RiceAb, S&F, SIA, SPPI, TDB, VetBull, WeedAb.
—BLDSC (5527.330000), CASDDS, CISTI, IE, ingenta. **CCC.**
Published by: Nippon Eisei Dobutsu Gakkai/Japan Society of Medical Entomology and Zoology, c/o Department of Infectious Disease Control, Oita Medical University, 1-1 Idaigaoka, Hasama-machi, Oita, 879-5593, Japan. http://wwwmez.med.uoeh-u.ac.jp/~mez/. Circ: 1,000.

➤ **ELAINMAAILMA (2003).** see *PETS*

597.85 DEU ISSN 0943-2485
ELAPHE. Text in German. 1979. q. membership. **Document type:** *Magazine, Academic/Scholarly.*
Incorporates (19??-1992): Deutsche Gesellschaft fuer Herpetologie und Terrarienkunde. Rundbrief (0177-218X)
Indexed: RefZh, ZooRec.
—BLDSC (3670.154000).
Published by: Deutsche Gesellschaft fuer Herpetologie und Terrarienkunde e.V., Postfach 1421, Rheinbach, 53351, Germany. TEL 49-2225-703333, FAX 49-2225-703338, gs@dght.de, http://www.dght.de/zeitschriften/elaphe/elaphe.htm.

599.67 USA ISSN 1535-0592
QL737.P98
ELEPHANT MANAGERS ASSOCIATION. JOURNAL. Text in English. 3/yr. USD 65 to institutions; USD 75 foreign to institutions. adv. back issues avail. **Document type:** *Trade.* **Description:** Features original articles and new items of interest to the elephant keeping profession.
Published by: Elephant Managers Association, c/o Chuck Doyle, One Conservation Pl, Syracuse, NY 13204. orders@allenpress.com, http://www.indyzoo.com/ema, http://www.allenpress.com. Ed., R&P Deborah Olson. Adv. contact Eric Sampson. **Subscr. to:** Allen Press Inc., PO Box 1897, Lawrence, KS 66044.

590 GRC ISSN 1106-2134
ELLENIKO ZOOLOGIKO ARHEIO/HELLENIC ZOOLOGICAL ARCHIVES. Text in Greek. 1993. biennial. **Document type:** *Journal, Academic/Scholarly.*
Indexed: ESPM, ZooRec.
Published by: Ellenike Zoologike Etaireia/Hellenic Zoological Society, c/o Zoological Museum, Department of Biology, University of Athens, Panepistimioupolis, Athens, GR-157 84, Greece.

590.752 AUS
ENDANGERED SPECIES. Text in English. 1999. q. AUD 70 (effective 2000). illus.
Indexed: ZooRec.
Address: GPO Box 696, Hobart, TAS 7001, Australia. http://www.endspecies.com. Ed. Terry Sellards.

595.7 BRA ISSN 0328-0381
ENTOMOLOGIA Y VECTORES. Text in Multiple languages. 1994. m.
Indexed: AbHyg, AgBio, BIOSIS Prev, BioCN&I, BiolAb, CPA, DSA, FPA, ForAb, HelmAb, HortAb, I&DA, IndVet, MaizeAb, NutrAb, OrnHort, PGegResA, PN&I, PoultAb, ProtozoAb, RA&MP, RM&VM, RRTA, S&F, SoyAb, TDB, TriticAb, VetBull, ZooRec.
Published by: Universidade Gama Filho, Rua Manoel Vitorino 553, Piedade, Rio de Janeiro, RJ 20748-900, Brazil. TEL 55-21-25997100, http://web.ugf.br.

597 NLD ISSN 0378-1909
QL614 CODEN: EBFID3
➤ **ENVIRONMENTAL BIOLOGY OF FISHES.** Text in English. 1976. m. EUR 1,858, USD 1,888, GBP 1,228 combined subscription to institutions print & online eds. (effective 2005). bk.rev. reprint service avail. from PSC. **Document type:** *Journal, Academic/Scholarly.* **Description:** Publishes original studies of the ecology, life history, epigenetics, behavior, physiology, morphology, systematics and evolution of marine and freshwater fishes.
Related titles: Microform ed.: (from PQC); Online - full text ed.: ISSN 1573-5133 (from EBSCO Publishing, Gale Group, IngentaConnect, Kluwer Online, O C L C Online Computer Library Center, Inc., Springer LINK, Swets Information Services).
Indexed: AEA, ASCA, ASFA, AgBio, AnBeAb, AnBrAb, ApEcolAb, ArtHuCI, BIOBASE, BIOSIS Prev, BibLing, BioCN&I, BiolAb, CJA, CRFR, ChemAb, CurCont, EPB, ESPM, EnvAb, EnvEAb, ExcerpMed, ForAb, GEOBASE, HelmAb, HortAb, I&DA, IABS, ISR, IndVet, NutrAb, OceAb, PollutAb, RM&VM, RefZh, S&F, SCI, SFA, SPPI, SWRA, VetBull, WRCInf, WildRev, ZooRec.
—BLDSC (3791.405000), CASDDS, CINDOC, CISTI, IDS, IE, Infotrieve, ingenta, Linda Hall. **CCC.**
Published by: Springer-Verlag Dordrecht (Subsidiary of: Springer Science+Business Media), Van Godewijckstraat 30, Dordrecht, 3311 GX, Netherlands. TEL 31-78-6576050, FAX 31-78-6576474, http://springerlink.metapress.com/openurl.asp?genre=journal&issn=0378-1909, http://www.springeronline.com. Ed. David L G Noakes.

599.665 USA ISSN 0149-0672
SF277
EQUUS. Text in English. 1977. m. USD 24 domestic; USD 36 foreign; USD 5.99 newsstand/cover (effective 2005). adv. bk.rev. illus. index. back issues avail.; reprint service avail. from PQC. **Document type:** *Magazine, Trade.* **Description:** Provides the latest information from the world's top veterinarians, equine researchers, riders and trainers on understanding and influencing equine behavior, recognizing the warning signs of illness and disease, and solving riding and training problems.
Related titles: Microform ed.: (from PQC).
Indexed: F&GI, SPI, SportS, ZooRec.
—CISTI. **CCC.**
Published by: Primedia Enthusiast Media (Subsidiary of: Primedia Consumer Media & Magazine Group), 656 Quince Orchard Rd, Gaithersburg, MD 20878. TEL 301-977-3900, FAX 301-990-9015, equuslts@aol.com, information@primedia.com, http://www.equisearch.com/magazines/Equus/, http://www.primedia.com. Ed. Laurie Prinz. Adv. contact Bob Kliner. B&W page USD 4,155, color page USD 6,640. Circ: 150,404 (paid).

590 636 FRA ISSN 0397-6572
CODEN: ETHNEJ
ETHNOZOOTECHNIE. Text in French. 1972. s-a. EUR 27 (effective 2003). back issues avail. **Document type:** *Monographic series, Academic/Scholarly.* **Description:** Studies relations among humans, animals and environment in ancient and modern societies. Considers the history and future of the raising of domesticated animals.
Indexed: AnBrAb, IAB, IndVet, NutrAb, PN&I, PoultAb, RDA, RRTA, RefZh, RevApplEntom, S&F, VetBull, WAE&RSA, ZooRec.
—BLDSC (3815.210000), IE, ingenta.
Published by: Societe d'Ethnozootechnie, 16 bis bd. Cote Blatin, Clermont-Ferrand, 63000, France. TEL 33-4-73915824. Pub. Bernard Denis.

590 636 FRA
ETHNOZOOTECHNIE. HORS-SERIE. Text in French. irreg.
Indexed: ZooRec.
Published by: Societe d'Ethnozootechnie, 16 bis bd. Cote Blatin, Clermont-Ferrand, 63000, France. TEL 33-4-73915824.

591.5 DEU ISSN 0179-1613
QL750 CODEN: ETHOEM
➤ **ETHOLOGY.** Text in English. 1937. m. EUR 125 combined subscription in Europe to individuals print & online eds.; USD 194 combined subscription in the Americas to individuals & Caribbean (print & online eds.); GBP 83 combined subscription elsewhere to individuals print & online eds.; GBP 939 combined subscription in Europe to institutions print & online eds.; USD 1,579 combined subscription in the Americas to institutions & Caribbean (print & online eds.); GBP 1,033 combined subscription elsewhere to institutions print & online eds. (effective 2006). bk.rev. illus.; stat. index. back issues avail.; reprint service avail. from PSC. **Document type:** *Journal, Academic/Scholarly.* **Description:** Contains contributions from all branches of behavior research on all species of animals, both in the field and in the laboratory.
Formerly: Zeitschrift fuer Tierpsychologie (0044-3573)
Related titles: ◆ Online - full text ed.: Ethology Online. ISSN 1439-0310; ◆ Supplement(s): Advances in Ethology. ISSN 0931-4202.
Indexed: ASCA, ASFA, AgBio, Agr, AnBeAb, AnBrAb, ApicAb, BIOBASE, BIOSIS Prev, BioCN&I, BiolAb, CurCont, DSA, ESPM, EntAb, ForAb, GEOBASE, HerbAb, IABS, IPsyAb, ISR, IndMed, IndVet, Inpharma, MEDLINE, MLA, MLA-IB, NutrAb, PN&I, PoultAb, ProtozoAb, PsycInfo, PsycholAb, RM&VM, Reac, RefZh, RevApplEntom, SCI, SFA, SIA, SPPI, SSCI, VetBull, WildRev, ZooRec, e-psyche.
—BLDSC (3815.240000), CISTI, IDS, IE, Infotrieve, ingenta. **CCC.**
Published by: (Ethologische Gesellschaft e.V. CHE), Blackwell Verlag GmbH (Subsidiary of: Blackwell Publishing Ltd.), Kurfuerstendamm 57, Berlin, 10707, Germany. TEL 49-30-32790634, FAX 49-30-32790610, verlag@blackwell.de, http://www.blackwellpublishing.com/journals/ETH, http://www.blackwell.de. Ed. Michael Taborsky. Circ: 650.

591.5 ITA ISSN 0394-9370
QL750 CODEN: EEEVEP
➤ **ETHOLOGY ECOLOGY & EVOLUTION.** Text and summaries in English. 1890. q. EUR 70 combined subscription to individuals print & online; EUR 240 combined subscription to institutions print & online (effective 2005). bk.rev. illus.; abstr. index, cum.index. 100 p./no.; back issues avail.; reprint service avail. from ISI. **Document type:** *Journal, Academic/Scholarly.* **Description:** Publishes research and review articles on all aspects of animal behavior. Emphasizes the gain in understanding of the function, ecology, or evolution of behavior.
Formerly (until 1989): Monitore Zoologico Italiano - Italian Journal of Zoology (0026-9786)
Indexed: ASCA, ASFA, AgrForAb, AnBeAb, AnBrAb, ApEcolAb, ApicAb, BIOBASE, BIOSIS Prev, BioCN&I, BiolAb, ChemAb, CurCont, ESPM, EntAb, FS&TA, ForAb, GEOBASE, GenetAb, HGA, HerbAb, IABS, ISR, IndVet, NutrAb, PBA, PHN&I, PN&I, PoultAb, RM&VM, RPP, RefZh, RevApplEntom, S&F, SCI, SFA, SSCI, SoyAb, VetBull, WAE&RSA, WildRev, ZooRec.
—BLDSC (3815.270000), CASDDS, CISTI, IDS, IE, Infotrieve, ingenta, Linda Hall. **CCC.**
Published by: Universita degli Studi di Firenze, Dipartimento di Biologia Animale e Genetica, Via Romana 17, Florence, FI 50125, Italy. TEL 39-055-2288201, FAX 39-055-222565, eee@fi.cnr.it, eee@csfet.fi.cnr.it, http://www.unifi.it/unifi/dbag/eee. Ed. Francesco Dessi Fulgheri. Circ: 400.

591.5 ITA ISSN 1120-6705
ETHOLOGY ECOLOGY & EVOLUTION. SPECIAL ISSUE. Text in English. irreg.
Indexed: ZooRec.
Published by: Universita degli Studi di Firenze, Dipartimento di Biologia Animale e Genetica, Via Romana 17, Florence, FI 50125, Italy. TEL 39-055-2288201, FAX 39-055-222565.

591.5 DEU ISSN 1439-0310
QL750
ETHOLOGY ONLINE. Text in English. m. GBP 892 in Europe to institutions; USD 1,500 in the Americas to institutions & Caribbean; GBP 981 elsewhere to institutions (effective 2006). **Document type:** *Academic/Scholarly.*
Media: Online - full text (from Blackwell Synergy, EBSCO Publishing, Gale Group, IngentaConnect, O C L C Online Computer Library Center, Inc., Swets Information Services).
Related titles: ◆ Print ed.: Ethology. ISSN 0179-1613.
Published by: Blackwell Verlag GmbH (Subsidiary of: Blackwell Publishing Ltd.), Kurfuerstendamm 57, Berlin, 10707, Germany. TEL 49-30-32790665, FAX 49-30-32790610, abo@blackwis.de, http://www.blackwell.de.

591.5 ESP ISSN 1130-3204
QL750 CODEN: ETOLEE
➤ **ETOLOGIA.** Text in English, Spanish. 1989. a., latest vol.10, 2002. EUR 33.06 to individuals; EUR 72.12 to institutions; EUR 12.02 to members (effective 2004). adv. bibl.; charts; illus. 60 p./no.; back issues avail. **Document type:** *Bulletin, Academic/Scholarly.* **Description:** Covers the field of animal behavior research, both theoretical and applied.
Related titles: Online - full text ed.: 1999. free (effective 2005).
Indexed: ASFA, AgrForAb, AnBeAb, BIOBASE, EntAb, ForAb, HerbAb, IECT, NutrAb, RevApplEntom, S&F, SeedAb, WildRev, ZooRec, e-psyche.
—BLDSC (3816.344089), CINDOC.
Published by: Sociedad Espanola de Etologia, Museu de Zoologia, Ap Correos 594, Barcelona, 08080, Spain. TEL 34-93-3196912, FAX 34-93-3104999, recercamuseuciencies@mail.bcn.es, http://webs.uvigo.es/c04/webc04/etologia/SEEesp.html, http://www.etologia.org. Eds. J C Senar, L Arias de Reyna. R&P, Adv. contact Maria Luisa Arroyo. Circ: 4,000.

590 ESP ISSN 1135-6588
ETOLOGUIA. Text in Spanish. 1986. a. **Document type:** *Bulletin.*
Former titles (until 1994): Guia del Etologo (1135-657X); (until 1990): Sociedad Espanola de Etologia. Boletin Interior (1135-6561)
Indexed: IECT, e-psyche.
Published by: (Sociedad Espanola de Etologia), Universidad de Extremadura, Servicio de Publicaciones, Plaza de Caldereros, 2, Caceres, 10071, Spain. TEL 34-927-257041, FAX 34-927-257046, publicac@unex.es, http://www.pcid.es/uex/Principal.htm.

597 571.9 GBR ISSN 0108-0288
SH171
➤ **EUROPEAN ASSOCIATION OF FISH PATHOLOGISTS. BULLETIN.** Text in English. 1979. bi-m. free to members (effective 2005). adv. bk.rev. 50 p./no. 2 cols./p.; back issues avail. **Document type:** *Bulletin, Academic/Scholarly.* **Description:** Contains short articles on fish, shellfish pathology.
Indexed: AgBio, AnBrAb, BioCN&I, CurCont, ESPM, FoVS&M, ForAb, HelmAb, HortAb, IndVet, NutrAb, OrnHort, PBA, ProtozoAb, RM&VM, RRTA, RefZh, RevApplEntom, TDB, VetBull, WAE&RSA, ZooRec.
—BLDSC (2505.718000), IE, ingenta.
Published by: European Association of Fish Pathologists, c/o F R S Marine Lab., Victoria Rd, PO Box 101, Aberdeen, AB11 9DB, United Kingdom. TEL 44-1224-295615, FAX 44-1224-295667, brunodw@marlab.ac.uk, http://www.eafp.org. Ed. Dr. A Barnes. Circ: 1,300 (paid).

591.5 USA ISSN 1090-5138
BF1 CODEN: EHBEFF
➤ **EVOLUTION AND HUMAN BEHAVIOR.** Text in English. 1979. 6/yr. USD 364 to individuals; USD 337 in United States to individuals; USD 916 to institutions; USD 850 in United States to institutions (effective 2006). back issues avail.; reprints avail. **Document type:** *Journal, Academic/Scholarly.* **Description:** Publishes new studies on ethological and sociobiological theories using comparative data, experimental results and literature reviews.
Formerly (until 1997): Ethology and Sociobiology (0162-3095)
Related titles: Microform ed.: (from PQC); Online - full text ed.: (from EBSCO Publishing, Gale Group, IngentaConnect, ScienceDirect, Swets Information Services).
Indexed: ASCA, AnthLit, ArtHuCI, CurCont, ExcerpMed, FamI, IBSS, ISR, MEDLINE, PCI, PRA, PsycInfo, PsycholAb, RefZh, SCI, SFA, SOPODA, SSA, SSCI, SociolAb, WildRev, ZooRec, e-psyche.
—BLDSC (3834.225000), IDS, IE, Infotrieve, ingenta. **CCC.**
Published by: Elsevier Inc. (Subsidiary of: Elsevier Science & Technology), 360 Park Ave. S, New York, NY 10010-1710. TEL 212-633-3730, 888-437-4636, usinfo-f@elsevier.com, http://www.elsevier.com/locate/ens. Eds. M Daly, M Wilson.

595.42 NLD ISSN 0168-8162
QL458 CODEN: EAACEM
➤ **EXPERIMENTAL & APPLIED ACAROLOGY.** Text in Dutch. 1985. m. EUR 1,548, USD 1,578, GBP 1,018 combined subscription to institutions print & online eds. (effective 2005). adv. bk.rev. illus. index. back issues avail.; reprint service avail. from ISI,PSC. **Document type:** *Journal, Academic/Scholarly.* **Description:** Brings together basic and applied research on various acarine groups, so that acarologists may more easily keep abreast of developments in related fields.
Related titles: Online - full text ed.: ISSN 1572-9702 (from bigchalk, EBSCO Publishing, Gale Group, IngentaConnect, Kluwer Online, O C L C Online Computer Library Center, Inc., Ovid Technologies, Inc., ProQuest Information & Learning, Springer LINK, Swets Information Services).
Indexed: ASCA, AbHyg, AgBio, Agr, AgrForAb, ApEcolAb, ApicAb, BIOBASE, BIOSIS Prev, BibLing, BioCN&I, BiolAb, CIN, ChemAb, ChemTitl, CurCont, DBA, EPB, ESPM, EntAb, ExcerpMed, FCA, FS&TA, FaBeAb, ForAb, GEOBASE, GenetAb, HGA, HerbAb, HortAb, IABS, ISR, IndMed, IndVet, MEDLINE, MaizeAb, OrnHort, PBA, PHN&I, PotatoAb, PoultAb, ProtozoAb, RA&MP, RM&VM, RPP, RefZh, RevApplEntom, S&F, SCI, SFA, SIA, TDB, TriticAb, VITIS, VetBull, WildRev, ZooRec.
—BLDSC (3838.620000), CASDDS, CISTI, GNLM, IDS, IE, Infotrieve, ingenta, Linda Hall. **CCC.**
Published by: Springer-Verlag Dordrecht (Subsidiary of: Springer Science+Business Media), Van Godewijckstraat 30, Dordrecht, 3311 GX, Netherlands. TEL 31-78-6576050, FAX 31-78-6576474, http://springerlink.metapress.com/openurl.asp?genre=journal&issn=0168-8162, http://www.springeronline.com. Eds. Frans Jongejan, J Bruin, Leo P S van der Geest. Circ: 1,000.

590 NOR ISSN 0014-8881
QL289 CODEN: FUNAAO
FAUNA. Text in Norwegian; Summaries in English. 1948. q. NOK 220 to individual members; NOK 270 to institutional members (effective 2005). adv. bk.rev. charts; illus. cum.index. back issues avail. **Document type:** *Magazine, Academic/Scholarly.*
Indexed: ASFA, BIOSIS Prev, BiolAb, ESPM, KWIWR, RefZh, SFA, SWRA, ZooRec.
—BLDSC (3897.820000), CISTI, IE, ingenta, Linda Hall. **CCC.**
Published by: Norsk Zoologisk Forening/Norwegian Zoological Society, PO Box 102, Blindern, Oslo, 0314, Norway. nzf@zoologi.no, http://www.zoologi.no/fauna.htm. Ed. Christian Steel. Circ: 1,700.

590 USA ISSN 1093-135X
QL1
FAUNA. Text in English. 1997. bi-m. USD 24.95; USD 4.95 newsstand/cover (effective 2001). adv. **Document type:** *Magazine, Consumer.* **Description:** Filled with enthusiasm for rare and beautiful amphibians and reptiles, bizarre insects and arachnids, and just plain weird and exotic wildlife and places.
Indexed: BiolDig.
Published by: Fauna, Inc., PO Box 476, Pleasant Grove, UT 84062-0476. TEL 801-766-4149, 888-285-5748, FAX 801-285-5748, http://www.faunamagazine.com. Ed. Louis Porras. Adv. contact Bob Smith. B&W page USD 1,350, color page USD 1,750; trim 7.875 x 10.75.

593 NLD
FAUNA DES MARINEN MIOZAENS VON KEVELAER (NIEDERRHEIN). Text in German. 1997. irreg., latest vol.3, 2001. price varies. **Document type:** *Academic/Scholarly.*
Published by: Backhuys Publishers BV, Postbus 321, Leiden, 2300 AH, Netherlands. TEL 31-71-517-0208, FAX 31-71-517-1856, backhuys@backhuys.com, http://www.backhuys.com. Ed. Guenter Wienrich. Circ: 200.

591.945 ITA ISSN 0430-1226
CODEN: FIITA
FAUNA D'ITALIA; repertorio generale delle specie animali esistenti in Italia. Text in Italian. 1956. s-a. price varies. back issues avail.
Indexed: BiolAb, ZooRec.
Published by: (Unione Zoologica Italiana), Il Sole 24 Ore Edagricole, Via Goito 13, Bologna, BO 40126, Italy. TEL 39-051-62267, FAX 39-051-490200, abbona@gce.it, http://www.edagricole.it. Circ: 2,000. **Co-sponsor:** Accademia Nazionale Italiana di Entomologia.

590 GRC ISSN 1105-8269
FAUNA GRAECIAE. Text in English, Greek. 1984. irreg. **Document type:** *Monographic series, Academic/Scholarly.*
Indexed: ESPM, ZooRec.
Published by: Ellenike Zoologike Etaireia/Hellenic Zoological Society, c/o Zoological Museum, Department of Biology, University of Athens, Panepistimioupolis, Athens, GR-157 84, Greece.

591.946 ESP
FAUNA IBERICA. Text in Spanish. 1990. irreg., latest vol.10, 1998. price varies. **Document type:** *Monographic series.*
Published by: Museo Nacional de Ciencias Naturales, Jose Gutierrez Abascal, 2, Madrid, 28006, Spain. TEL 34-1-4111328, FAX 34-1-5645078. Ed. M Angeles Ramos.

591.9481 NOR ISSN 1502-4873
QL289 CODEN: FNSAD3
➤ **FAUNA NORVEGICA.** Text in English; Summaries in Norwegian. 1980. a. NOK 70 to non-members; NOK 50 to members. adv. bk.rev. cum.index every 3 yrs. back issues avail. **Document type:** *Academic/Scholarly.*
Formerly (until 2000): Fauna Norvegica Series A. Norwegian Fauna Except Entomology and Ornithology (0332-768X)
Indexed: ASFA, AnBeAb, ApEcolAb, BIOSIS Prev, BiolAb, ESPM, EntAb, GEOBASE, IBR, KWIWR, WildRev, ZooRec.
—BLDSC (3899.257500), CISTI, ingenta, Linda Hall. **CCC.**
Published by: Norsk Entomologisk Forening, c/o Egil Michaelsen, Kurlandveien 35, Sarpsborg, 1727, Norway. TEL 47-73-58-05-00, FAX 47-73-91-54-33, kjetil.bevanger@nina.nina.no. Ed. Thrine Moen Heggberget. R&P, Adv. contact Kjetil Bevanger. Circ: 700.

591.993 SAU
FAUNA OF ARABIA. Text in English. irreg.
Formerly (until 1998): Fauna of Saudi Arabia
Indexed: ZooRec.
—BLDSC (3897.927000), ingenta.
Published by: National Commission for Wildlife Conservation and Development, PO Box 61681, Riyadh, 11575, Saudi Arabia. Eds. Friedhelm Krupp, Volker Mahnert.

590 AUS
FAUNA OF AUSTRALIA. Text in English. 1987. irreg., latest vol.5, 1997. **Document type:** *Monographic series.* **Description:** Provides an authoritative synthesis of the primary literature and other available information for animal groups present in continental Australia and its external territories.
Published by: Australian Biological Resources Study, GPO Box 787, Canberra, ACT 2601, Australia. TEL 61-2-62509506, FAX 61-2-62509555, abrs@ea.gov.au, http://www.deh.gov.au/biodiversity/abrs.

591.993 NZL ISSN 0111-5383
QL340
FAUNA OF NEW ZEALAND. Text in English. 1982. irreg., latest vol.47, no.43, 2003. price varies. bibl.; illus. back issues avail. **Document type:** *Monographic series.* **Description:** Describes systematic taxonomy of New Zealand invertebrates.
Indexed: ASFA, BIOSIS Prev, BioCN&I, BiolAb, EntAb, ForAb, RevApplEntom, ZooRec.
—BLDSC (3899.254000), Linda Hall.
Published by: Manaaki Whenua Press, 40, Lincoln, 8152, New Zealand. TEL 64-3-3256700, FAX 64-3-3252127, mwpress@landcare.cri.nz, http://www.landcare.cri.nz/mwpress, http://www.landcare.cri.nz/mwpress/. Ed. Trevor Crosby. Pub., R&P Greg Comfort TEL 64-3-3256700. Circ: 400.

591.947 IND
FAUNA OF RUSSIA AND NEIGHBORING COUNTRIES. Text in English. irreg. **Document type:** *Monographic series, Academic/Scholarly.*
Related titles: ♦ Translation of: Fauna Rossii i Sopredel'nykh Stran. ISSN 1026-5619.
Published by: Amerind Publishing Company Pvt. Ltd, N-56, Connaught Circus, New Delhi, 11001, India. TEL 91-11-3310106, FAX 91-11-3322639.

591.947 ISR
FAUNA OF THE U.S.S.R. Text in English. irreg.
Published by: Israel Program for Scientific Translations, P O Box 7145, Jerusalem, Israel.

591.95694 ISR
FAUNA PALAESTINA. Text in English. 1975. irreg., latest 1999. price varies. adv. **Document type:** *Monographic series.* **Description:** Covers the fauna of the region, concentrating on specific orders of insects, arachnids, molluscs and fish.
Published by: Israel Academy of Sciences and Humanities, 43 Jabotinski St, P O Box 4040, Jerusalem, 91040, Israel. TEL 972-2-5676233, FAX 972-2-5666059, tami@academy.ac.il, http://www.academy.ac.il. Ed. Zofia Lasman. Adv. contact Tami Korman. Circ: 700.

591.9438 POL ISSN 0303-4909
➤ **FAUNA POLSKI/FAUNA POLONIAE.** Text in Polish; Summaries in English. 1973. irreg., latest vol.23, 2004. USD 40 per vol. (effective 2005). back issues avail. **Document type:** *Monographic series, Academic/Scholarly.*
Indexed: BIOSIS Prev, ZooRec.
—CISTI.
Published by: Polska Akademia Nauk, Muzeum i Instytut Zoologii/Polish Academy of Sciences, Museum & Institute of Zoology, ul Wilcza 64, Warsaw, 00679, Poland. TEL 48-22-6293221, FAX 48-22-6296302, fauna@miiz.waw.pl, libr@miiz.waw.pl, http://www.miiz.waw.pl. Ed. P Wegrzynowicz. Circ: 600.

590 RUS ISSN 1026-5619
FAUNA ROSSII I SOPREDEL'NYKH STRAN. Text in Russian. 1911. irreg. **Document type:** *Monographic series, Academic/Scholarly.*
Former titles (until 1993): Fauna S S S R. Novaya Seriya; (until 1935): Fauna S S S R i Sopredel'nykh Stran; (until 1929): Fauna Rossii i Sopredel'nykh Stran
Related titles: ♦ English Translation: Fauna of Russia and Neighboring Countries.
Indexed: ZooRec.
Published by: Rossiiskaya Akademiya Nauk, Zoologicheskii Institut/Russian Academy of Sciences, Zoological Institute, Universitetskaya nab 1, St Petersburg, 199034, Russian Federation. TEL 7-812-3280011, FAX 7-812-3282941, admin@zin.ru, http://www.zin.ru.

590.9438 POL ISSN 0071-4089
➤ **FAUNA SLODKOWODNA POLSKI.** Text in Polish. 1935. irreg., latest vol.33, 2001. price varies. **Document type:** *Monographic series, Academic/Scholarly.* **Description:** Presents a group of animals of Polish freshwater fauna and provides information about their biology and ecology.
—BLDSC (3899.370000).
Published by: Polskie Towarzystwo Hydrobiologiczne, Ul Stefana Banacha 2, Warsaw, 02097, Poland. TEL 48-22-8224625, FAX 48-22-8224704, igor@hydro.biol.uw.edu.pl. Ed. Andrzej Piechocki. Circ: 245 (paid). **Co-publisher:** Uniwersytet Lodzki. **Co-sponsor:** Komitet Badan Naukowych/Committee of Scientific Research.

590 FRA ISSN 0428-0709
FAUNE DE MADAGASCAR. Text in French, English. 1956. irreg. back issues avail. **Document type:** *Monographic series, Academic/Scholarly.* **Description:** Identification guides on the fauna of Madagascar (both vertebrates and invertebrates).
Indexed: ZooRec.
Published by: Museum National d'Histoire Naturelle, 57 Rue Cuvier, Paris, 75231 Cedex 05, France. TEL 33-1-40793777, http://www.mnhn.fr. **Co-publisher:** Institut de Recherche pour le Developpement (I R D).

580 590 FRA ISSN 1286-4994
➤ **FAUNE ET FLORE TROPICALES.** Text in French, English. irreg. **Document type:** *Monographic series, Academic/Scholarly.*
Former titles (until 1967): Faune Tropicale (0152-674X); (until 1961): Faune de l'Union Francaise (0152-6731); Faune de l'Empire Francais
Indexed: ZooRec.
Published by: Museum National d'Histoire Naturelle, 57 Rue Cuvier, Paris, 75231 Cedex 05, France. TEL 33-1-40793777, diff.pub@mnhn.fr, http://www.mnhn.fr/publication/fft/indexan.html. **Co-sponsor:** Institut de Recherche pour le Developpement (I R D).

590 FRA ISSN 1626-6641
FAUNE SAUVAGE; bulletin technique et juridique de l'Office National de la Chasse et de la Faune Sauvage. Text in French. 1974. m. EUR 50.31 domestic; EUR 53.36 foreign (effective 2003). bk.rev. back issues avail. **Document type:** *Bulletin, Consumer.*
Former titles (until 1999): Office National de la Chasse. Bulletin Mensuel (0151-4806); (until 1976): Office National de la Chasse. Bulletin (0376-6136)
Related titles: Supplement(s): Office National de la Chasse. Fiche Technique. ISSN 1624-5636. 1981.
Indexed: RefZh.

B

Published by: Office National de la Chasse et de la Faune Sauvage, 85 bis Av de Wagram, Paris, 75017, France. TEL 33-1-44151693, FAX 33-1-47637913, http://www.oncfs.gouv.fr.

590 DEU ISSN 0430-1285
QH540 CODEN: FOEMA7
FAUNISTISCH-OEKOLOGISCHE MITTEILUNGEN. Text in German. 1952. irreg. price varies. **Document type:** *Monographic series, Academic/Scholarly.*
Formerly (until 1966): Faunistische Mitteilungen aus Norddeutschland (0933-6559)
Indexed: ASFA, BIOSIS Prev, BiolAb, ESPM, IBR, IBZ, RefZh, ZooRec.
Published by: (Faunistisch-Oekologische Arbeitsgemeinschaft), Wachholtz Verlag GmbH, Rungestr 4, Neumuenster, 24537, Germany. TEL 49-4321-906276, FAX 49-4321-906275, info@wachholtz.de, http://www.wachholtz.de.

590 USA ISSN 0015-0754
QL1 CODEN: FLDZAK
FIELDIANA: ZOOLOGY. Text in English. 1895. irreg. price varies. bibl.; charts; illus.; stat. back issues avail.; reprint service avail. from PQC. **Document type:** *Monographic series, Academic/Scholarly.* **Description:** Covers taxonomic, morphologic, evolutionary and zoogeographic studies involving Field Museum collections and research in the field.
Former titles (until 1943): Field Museum of Natural History. Zoological Series. Publication (0895-0237); (until 1909): Field Columbian Museum. Zoological Series. Publication (0097-3904)
Related titles: Microfiche ed.: (from BHP).
Indexed: ASFA, B&BAb, BIOSIS Prev, BiolAb, ChemAb, EntAb, GenetAb, HGA, RefZh, SFA, WildRev, ZooRec.
—BLDSC (3925.100000), CISTI, IE, ingenta, Linda Hall.
Published by: Field Museum, Roosevelt Rd at Lake Shore Dr, Chicago, IL 60605-2496. TEL 312-922-9410, FAX 312-427-7269. Circ: 600.

FINLANDS NATUR. see *BIOLOGY—Botany*

597 GBR ISSN 1467-2960
SH1 CODEN: FFIIAK
➤ **FISH AND FISHERIES.** Text in English. 2000. q. GBP 109, EUR 164 combined subscription in Europe to individuals print & online eds.; USD 202 combined subscription in the Americas to individuals & Caribbean (print & online eds.); GBP 120 combined subscription elsewhere to individuals print & online eds.; GBP 380 combined subscription in Europe to institutions print & online eds.; USD 701 combined subscription in the Americas to institutions & Caribbean (print & online eds.); GBP 417 combined subscription elsewhere to institutions print & online eds. (effective 2006). reprint service avail. from PSC. **Document type:** *Journal, Academic/Scholarly.* **Description:** The purpose of the journal is to provide critical overviews of major physiological, molecular, ecological and evolutionary issues in the study of fish, and to establish a forum for debate of issues of global concern in world fisheries, by publishing cutting edge reviews and discussion of internationally important topics of relevance.
Related titles: Online - full text ed.: ISSN 1467-2979. GBP 361 in Europe to institutions; USD 665 in the Americas to institutions & Caribbean; GBP 396 elsewhere to institutions (effective 2006) (from Blackwell Synergy, EBSCO Publishing, Gale Group, IngentaConnect, O C L C Online Computer Library Center, Inc., Swets Information Services).
Indexed: ASFA, ApEcolAb, B&BAb, BIOBASE, BIOSIS Prev, CurCont, EPB, ESPM, GEOBASE, OceAb, PollutAb, RefZh, SWRA, ToxAb, WRCInf, ZooRec.
—BLDSC (3934.864150), IE, Infotrieve, ingenta. **CCC.**
Published by: Blackwell Publishing Ltd., 9600 Garsington Rd, Oxford, OX4 2ZG, United Kingdom. TEL 44-1865-776868, FAX 44-1865-714591, customerservices@oxon.blackwellpublishing.com, http://www.blackwellpublishing.com/journals/FAF. Eds. Paul J B Hart, Tony J Pitcher. Pub. Elaine Stott. R&P Sophie Savage. Adv. contact Jenny Applin.

➤ **FISH & FISHERIES WORLDWIDE.** see *BIOLOGY—Abstracting, Bibliographies, Statistics*

590 597 USA ISSN 1040-2411
SH221
FISH AND WILDLIFE RESEARCH. Text in English, German. 1986. irreg., latest vol.7, 1990. price varies. **Document type:** *Journal, Academic/Scholarly.*
Indexed: ESPM.
Published by: U.S. Fish and Wildlife Service, Dept of the Interior, 1849 C St N W, Washington, DC 20240. TEL 800-344-9453, http://www.fws.gov. **Dist. by:** NTIS, 5285 Port Royal Rd, Springfield, VA 22161. info@ntis.gov.

597 NLD ISSN 0920-1742
CODEN: FPBIEP
➤ **FISH PHYSIOLOGY & BIOCHEMISTRY.** Text in English. 1986. 4/yr. EUR 455, USD 410, GBP 298 combined subscription to institutions print & online eds. (effective 2005). illus. Index. back issues avail.; reprint service avail. from PSC. **Document type:** *Journal, Academic/Scholarly.* **Description:** Publishes original research papers in all aspects of the physiology and biochemistry of fishes.
Related titles: Online - full text ed.: ISSN 1573-5168 (from EBSCO Publishing, Gale Group, IngentaConnect, Kluwer Online, O C L C Online Computer Library Center, Inc., Ovid Technologies, Inc., Springer LINK, Swets Information Services).
Indexed: ASCA, ASFA, AgBio, AnBrAb, B&BAb, BBCI, BIOBASE, BIOSIS Prev, BibLing, BiolAb, CIN, CRFR, ChemAb, ChemTitl, CurCont, ESPM, ExcerpMed, GenetAb, ISR, IndVet, MaizeAb, NSCI, NutrAb, OceAb, PN&I, RefZh, RevApplEntom, SCI, SFA, SWRA, SoyAb, TDB, VetBull, WildRev, ZooRec.
—BLDSC (3935.126000), CASDDS, CINDOC, CISTI, IDS, IE, Infotrieve, ingenta. **CCC.**
Published by: Springer-Verlag Dordrecht (Subsidiary of: Springer Science+Business Media), Van Godewijckstraat 30, Dordrecht, 3311 GX, Netherlands. TEL 31-78-6576050, FAX 31-78-6576474, http://springerlink.metapress.com/openurl.asp?genre=journal&issn=0920-1742, http://www.springeronline.com. Ed. H J Th Goos.

597 IRL ISSN 0332-4338
FISHERIES BULLETIN. Text in English. 1981. irreg. free. bk.rev. **Document type:** *Government.*
Indexed: BiolAb, RefZh, ZooRec.
Published by: Marine Institute, Fisheries Research Centre, 80 Harcourt St, Dublin, 2, Ireland. TEL 353-1-8210111, FAX 353-1-8205078. Circ: 350.

FISHERIES OCEANOGRAPHY. see *FISH AND FISHERIES*

FISHERIES OCEANOGRAPHY ONLINE. see *FISH AND FISHERIES*

592.57 USA ISSN 0360-7550
CODEN: FPNCAT
FLORIDA. DEPARTMENT OF AGRICULTURE AND CONSUMER SERVICES. NEMATOLOGY CIRCULAR. Text in English. 1962. bi-m. looseleaf. free. **Document type:** *Government.*
Indexed: BioCN&I, BiolAb, NemAb, OrnHort, RPP, RevApplEntom, WeedAb, ZooRec.
Published by: Department of Agriculture and Consumer Services, Division of Plant Industry, 1911 S W 34th St, Box 147100, Gainesville, FL 32614-7100. TEL 904-372-3505, FAX 904-955-2301. R&P Denise Feiber.

596 POL ISSN 1506-7629
FOLIA MALACOLOGICA. Text in English. 1987. q. EUR 97 foreign (effective 2005). **Description:** Reports contributions in malacological research, concerning both recent and Quaternary molluscs.
Former titles (until 1994): Akademia Gorniczo-Hutnicza im. Stanislawa Staszica. Zeszyty Naukowe. Folia Malacologica (1507-3386); (until 1990): Stanislaw Staszic Academy of Mining and Metallurgy. Scientific Bulletins. Folia Malacologica (0860-6307)
Indexed: ZooRec.
Published by: Stowarzyszenie Malakologow Polskich/Association of Polish Malacologists, Fredry 10, Poznan, 61-701, Poland. TEL 4861-529327, FAX 4861-530234, polmal@hum.amu.edu.pl, http://hum.amu.edu.pl/~polmal/smp/logo.htm. **Dist. by:** Ars Polona, Krakowskie Przedmiescie 7, Warsaw, Poland. TEL 48-22-9263914, FAX 48-22-9265334, arspolona@arspolona.com.pl, http://www.arspolona.com.pl.

590 CZE ISSN 0139-9713
CODEN: FMRZEX
FOLIA MUSEI RERUM NATURALIUM BOHEMIAE OCCIDENTALIS. ZOOLOGICA. Text in Czech. 1971. s-a. **Document type:** *Academic/Scholarly.*
Indexed: SFA, WildRev, ZooRec.
Published by: Zapadoceske Muzeum, Kopeckeho sady 2, Plzen, 30135, Czech Republic. TEL 42-19-7236541, FAX 42-19-7236541, zpcm@pm.cesnet.cz.

FOLIA PARASITOLOGICA. see *MEDICAL SCIENCES—Communicable Diseases*

599.8 CHE ISSN 0015-5713
QL737.P9 CODEN: FPRMAB
➤ **FOLIA PRIMATOLOGICA**; international journal of primatology. Text in English, French, German. 1963. bi-m. CHF 888 in Europe to institutions; CHF 908.40 elsewhere to institutions; CHF 956 combined subscription in Europe to institutions print & online eds.; CHF 976.40 combined subscription elsewhere to institutions print & online eds. (effective 2006). adv. bk.rev. bibl.; charts; illus. index. back issues avail. **Document type:** *Journal, Academic/Scholarly.* **Description:** Discusses various aspects of the study of primates.
Related titles: Microform ed.; Online - full text ed.: ISSN 1421-9980. CHF 846 to institutions (effective 2006) (from bigchalk, EBSCO Publishing, Northern Light Technology, Inc., O C L C Online Computer Library Center, Inc., ProQuest Information & Learning, Swets Information Services).
Indexed: AICP, ASCA, AbAn, AgrForAb, AnBeAb, AnthLit, ApEcolAb, BIOBASE, BIOSIS Prev, BiolAb, ChemAb, CurCont, DSA, DentInd, ESPM, ForAb, HortAb, IBSS, ISR, IndMed, IndVet, MEDLINE, NutrAb, PHN&I, ProtozoAb, PsycInfo, PsycholAb, S&F, SCI, SFA, SSCI, SeedAb, VetBull, WildRev, ZooRec, e-psyche.
—BLDSC (3973.580000), CASDDS, CISTI, GNLM, IDS, IE, Infotrieve, ingenta, KNAW, Linda Hall. **CCC.**
Published by: (European Federation for Primatology), S. Karger AG, Allschwilerstr 10, Basel, 4009, Switzerland. TEL 41-61-3061111, FAX 41-61-3061234, karger@karger.ch, http://www.karger.com/FPR, http://www.karger.ch. Ed. R H Crompton. adv.: page USD 1,185. Circ: 850.

➤ **FOLIA UNIVERSITATIS AGRICULTURAE STETINENSIS. ZOOTECHNICA.** see *AGRICULTURE—Poultry And Livestock*

596 CZE ISSN 0139-7893
QL1 CODEN: FOZODJ
➤ **FOLIA ZOOLOGICA.** Text and summaries in English. 1938. q. EUR 190 in Europe; USD 230 elsewhere (effective 2005). bk.rev. charts; illus.; tr.lit. index. back issues avail.; reprints avail. **Document type:** *Journal, Academic/Scholarly.* **Description:** Comprehensive articles on the results of original research on vertebrates, e.g. mammalogy, ornithology, ichthyology and morphology. Includes research papers, review papers, short communications and monographs.
Incorporates (in 1998): Akademie Ved Ceske Republiky. Ustav v Brne. Prirodovedne Prace (Acta Scientiarum Naturalium Academiae Scientiarum Bohemicae - Brno) (1210-9681); Which was formerly (until 1993): Ceskoslovenska Akademie Ved. Ustav v Brne. Prirodovedne Prace (0032-8758); (1955-1967): Ceskoslovenska Akademie Ved. Brnenska Zakladna. Prace (0369-8556); Folia Zoologica was formerly (until 1955): Zoologicke a Entomologicke Listy (Folia Zoologica et Entomologica (0044-5142); (until 1951): Entomolgicke Listy (Folia Entomologica)
Related titles: Online - full text ed.: (from ProQuest Information & Learning).
Indexed: ASCA, ASFA, AgBio, AnBrAb, BIOBASE, BIOSIS Prev, BioCN&I, BiolAb, CurCont, DSA, ESPM, FCA, FPA, ForAb, GEOBASE, HelmAb, HerbAb, HortAb, IABS, ISR, IndVet, KWIWR, MaizeAb, NutrAb, OrnHort, PGegResA, PN&I, PoultAb, ProtozoAb, RPP, RRTA, RefZh, S&F, SCI, SFA, SIA, TriticAb, VetBull, WildRev, ZooRec.
—BLDSC (3974.320000), CISTI, IDS, IE, ingenta, Linda Hall. **CCC.**
Published by: Akademie Ved Ceske Republiky, Ustav Biologie Obratlovcu/Academy of Sciences of the Czech Republic, Institute of Vertebrate Biology, Kvetna 8, Brno, 60365, Czech Republic. TEL 420-5-43422518, FAX 420-5-43211346, penaz@brno.cas.cz, http://www.ivb.cz/folia/pdf_obsah.htm, http://www.ivb.cz/pubser_en.htm. Ed. Milan Penaz. Circ: 400.

596 CZE ISSN 1213-1164
FOLIA ZOOLOGICA MONOGRAPHS. Text in English, Czech. 1998. irreg. **Document type:** *Monographic series.*
Indexed: ZooRec.
Published by: Akademie Ved Ceske Republiky, Ustav Biologie Obratlovcu/Academy of Sciences of the Czech Republic, Institute of Vertebrate Biology, Kvetna 8, Brno, 60365, Czech Republic. TEL 420-5-43422522, FAX 420-5-43211346, penaz@brno.cas.cz.

590 DEU ISSN 0233-1179
FORTSCHRITTE DER FISCHEREIWISSENSCHAFT. Text in German. 1982. a. **Document type:** *Academic/Scholarly.*
Indexed: ESPM.
Published by: Institut fuer Gewaesseroekologie und Binnenfischerei Berlin, Muggelseedamm 310, Berlin, 12587, Germany.

595.44 USA
FORUM MAGAZINE. Text in English. q.
Indexed: ZooRec.
Published by: American Tarantula Society, Box 756, Carlsbad, NM 88221-0756. membership@atshq.org, http://www.atshq.org/.

FOSSILIUM CATALOGUS: ANIMALIA. see *PALEONTOLOGY*

590 POL ISSN 0015-9301
QL1 CODEN: FRGFAH
➤ **FRAGMENTA FAUNISTICA.** Text in English, Polish. 1930. s-a. EUR 40 to individuals; EUR 60 to institutions (effective 2005). bibl.; charts; illus.; abstr. index. back issues avail. **Document type:** *Journal, Academic/Scholarly.*
Indexed: ASFA, AgrAg, AgrLib, BIOSIS Prev, BioCN&I, BiolAb, ForAb, HelmAb, HerbAb, HortAb, I&DA, NemAb, NutrAb, OrnHort, PBA, PoultAb, RM&VM, RPP, RefZh, RevApplEntom, S&F, ZooRec.
—BLDSC (4032.030000), CISTI, IE, Linda Hall.
Published by: Polska Akademia Nauk, Muzeum i Instytut Zoologii/Polish Academy of Sciences, Museum & Institute of Zoology, ul Wilcza 64, Warsaw, 00679, Poland. TEL 48-22-6293221, FAX 48-22-6296302, jolawyt@miiz.waw.pl, libr@miiz.waw.pl, http://www.miiz.waw.pl. Ed., Adv. contact J Dr. Wytwer. Circ: 500.

595.384 USA
FRESHWATER CRAYFISH; a journal of astacology. Text in English. 1972. biennial, latest vol.13, 2002. price varies. **Document type:** *Monographic series, Academic/Scholarly.*
Indexed: ZooRec.
Published by: International Association of Astacology, c/o IAA Secretariat, Rm 123, Swingle Hall, Auburn University, Auburn, AL 36849-5419. TEL 334-844-9123, FAX 334-844-9208, daniewh@acesag.auburn.edu.

590 GBR ISSN 1742-9994
▼ ➤ **FRONTIERS IN ZOOLOGY.** Text in English. 2004. irreg. free (effective 2006). **Document type:** *Journal, Academic/Scholarly.* **Description:** Covers all aspects of animal life.
Media: Online - full text (from National Library of Medicine).
Published by: BioMed Central Ltd. (Subsidiary of: Current Science Ltd), Middlesex House, 34-42 Cleveland St, London, W1T 4LB, United Kingdom. TEL 44-20-76319131, FAX 44-20-76319923, info@biomedcentral.com, http://www.frontiersinzoology.com/home/, http://www.biomedcentral.com. Ed. Jurgen Heinze.

591.9489 DNK ISSN 0416-704X
➤ **GALATHEA REPORT**; scientific results of the Danish deep-sea expedition round the world 1950-52. Text in English. 1956. irreg., latest vol.18, 2000. price varies. **Document type:** *Monographic series, Academic/Scholarly.*
Indexed: ZooRec.
Published by: Apollo Books, Kirkeby Sand 19, Stenstrup, 5771, Denmark. TEL 45-62-26-37-37, FAX 45-62-26-37-80, apollobooks@vip.cybercity.dk. Ed. Torben Wolff.

590 FRA ISSN 1622-7662
QL1 CODEN: GFSAER
➤ **GAME AND WILDLIFE SCIENCE.** Text in English; Abstracts in English, French. 1974. q. EUR 56.41 in the European Union; EUR 60.98 elsewhere; EUR 38.11 in the European Union to students; EUR 45.73 elsewhere to students (effective 2003). bk.rev. abstr. 96 p./no. 1 cols./p.; back issues avail.; reprints avail. **Document type:** *Journal, Academic/Scholarly.*
Description: Publishes original papers on game and wildlife (birds and mammals). Concerned with all scientific disciplines and geographical regions dealing with these animals, but focuses on papers that contribute to species habitat conservation and management.
Former titles (until 1999): Gibier Faune Sauvage - Game and Wildlife (0761-9243); (until 1983): France. Office National de la Chasse. Bulletin Special Scientifique (1148-6538)
Related titles: Online - full text ed.
Indexed: AnBrAb, BIOSIS Prev, BiolAb, FCA, ForAb, HelmAb, HerbAb, HortAb, IndVet, NutrAb, OrnHort, PN&I, PoultAb, RA&MP, RefZh, RevApplEntom, RiceAb, S&F, SFA, SeedAb, TriticAb, VetBull, WAE&RSA, WeedAb, WildRev, ZooRec.
—BLDSC (4068.807000), IE, ingenta. **CCC.**
Published by: Office National de la Chasse et de la Faune Sauvage, 85 bis Av de Wagram, Paris, 75017, France. TEL 33-1-44151693, FAX 33-1-47637913, http://www.oncfs.gouv.fr. Eds. Marcel Birkan TEL 33-1-44151717, Pierre Migot. Pub. Gerard Tendron. R&P Marcel Birkan TEL 33-1-44151717. Circ: 229 (paid).

598.417 JPN
GAN NO SHINPOJUMU/SYMPOSIUM ON WILD GEESE. Text in Japanese. irreg. **Description:** Reprints of articles on geese from other periodicals.
Published by: Gan o Hogosurukai/Japanese Association for Wild Geese Protection, c/o Mr Kurechi, 16 Kawaminami Minamimachi, kurihara-gun, Wakayanagimachi, Miyagi-ken 989-5502, Japan. TEL 81-228-32-2004, FAX 81-228-32-3294, hgh02256@nifty.ne.jp.

GAN NO TAYORI/GOOSE LETTER. see *CONSERVATION*

598.417 JPN
GANKAMOKA NO CHORUI NO CHOSA HOKOKUSHO/ANNUAL CENSUS ON WILD GEESE, DUCKS AND SWANS IN JAPAN ADVOCATED BY THE MINISTRY OF THE ENVIRONMENT. Text in Japanese. a.
Published by: Kankyocho, Shizen Kankyokyolan/Ministry of the Environment, Nature Conservation Bureau, 2-2 Kasumigaseki 1-chome, Chiyoda-ku, Tokyo, 100-0013, Japan. TEL 81-3-5521-8284, FAX 81-3-3581-7090.

590 PRT ISSN 0253-0597
GARCIA DE ORTA: SERIE DE ZOOLOGIA. Text in Portuguese. 1953. irreg., latest vol.23, 1999. price varies. back issues avail. **Document type:** *Academic/Scholarly.*
Supersedes in part (in 1973): Garcia de Orta (0016-4569)
Indexed: ASFA, BIOSIS Prev, BiolAb, ESPM, HelmAb, IndVet, ProtozoAb, RM&VM, RevApplEntom, SOPODA, VetBull, WildRev, ZooRec.
—BLDSC (4069.990000).
Published by: Instituto de Investigacao Cientifica Tropical, Rua da Junqueira, 30, Lisbon, 1349-007, Portugal. TEL 351-21-3622621, FAX 351-21-3631460, iict@iict.pt. Circ: 1,000. **Subscr. to:** Centro de Documentacao e Informacao, Rua de Jau, 47, Lisbon 1300, Portugal. TEL 351-21-3644846, FAX 351-21-3628218.

590 551.46 CHL ISSN 0717-652X
QH119 CODEN: GBCZAO
GAYANA. Text in English, Spanish. 199?. a., latest vol.65, 2001. USD 23.60 (effective 2005). adv. **Document type:** *Directory, Abstract/Index.*
Formed by the merger of (1961-1998): Gayana: Zoologia (0016-531X); (1992-1998): Gayana: Oceanologia (0716-9655); Which was formerly (1971-1992): Gayana: Miscelanea (0374-7999)
Related titles: Online - full text ed.: ISSN 0717-6538. 2000. free (effective 2005) (from SciELO).
Indexed: ASFA, ApicAb, BIOSIS Prev, BiolAb, ESPM, EntAb, OceAb, ZooRec.
—CISTI, Linda Hall.
Published by: Universidad de Concepcion, Facultad de Ciencias Naturales y Oceanograficas, Casilla 160-C, Concepcion, Chile. TEL 56-41-203059, FAX 56-41-244805, gayana@udec.cl, http://udec.cl/gayana, http://www.udec.cl/~natul/botanica/gayana/gayana.html. Ed., R&P Andres O Angulo. Adv. contact Alberto P Larrain. Circ: 1,000.

590 CZE
➤ **GAZELLA. ANNUAL REPORT AND SCIENTIFIC ARTICLES.** Text and summaries in Czech, English. 1969. a. per issue exchange basis. **Document type:** *Bulletin, Academic/Scholarly.*
Formerly: Zoologicka Zahrada v Praze. Vyrocni Zprava
Indexed: KWIWR, SFA, WildRev.
Published by: Zoologicka Zahrada v Praze/Zoological Garden of Prague, U Trojskeho Zamku 3-120, Prague 7, 171 00, Czech Republic. TEL 420-2-90007332, FAX 420-2-6890369, zoo@zoo.cz. Ed. Evzen Kus.

594 URY ISSN 0037-8607
CODEN: CSMLA5
GAZETA DE BAIXADA✶ . Text in Spanish. 1961. s-a. looseleaf. UYP 300, USD 2. bk.rev. bibl.; charts; illus. index, cum.index.
Indexed: ZooRec.
Published by: Sociedad Malacologica del Uruguay, Casilla 1401, Montevideo, Uruguay. Circ: 300.

599 JPN ISSN 1340-9409
➤ **GEIKEN TSUSHIN.** Text in Japanese. 1947. 4/yr. per issue exchange basis. 28 p./no.; **Document type:** *Newsletter, Academic/Scholarly.*
Published by: Nihon Geirui Kenkyusho/Institute of Cetacean Research, 4-5 Toyomi-cho, Chuo-ku, Tokyo, 104-0055, Japan. TEL 83-1-35366521, FAX 83-1-35366522. Ed. Kazuo Yamamura. Circ: 1,500.

590 JPN ISSN 0388-3752
GENSEI DOBUTSUGAKU ZASSHI/JAPANESE JOURNAL OF PROTOZOOLOGY. Text in English, Japanese. 1968. a.
Published by: Nihon Gensei Dobutsu Gakkai/Japan Society of Protozoology, Gifu Daigaku Igakubu Seikagaku Kyoshitsu, 40 Tsukasa-Machi, Gifu-shi, 500-8076, Japan.

590 JPN ISSN 0911-0461
GIFU FURUSATO TO DOBUTSU TSUSHIN/MAMMALS' NEWSLETTER IN HOMELAND GIFU. Text in Japanese. 1984. bi-m. **Document type:** *Newsletter.*
Published by: Gifuken Honyu Dobutsu Chosa Kenkyukai/Gifu Prefecture Mammalian Research Society, Takano, Mugi-gun, Mugegawa-cho, Gifu-ken 501-2604, Japan.

590 BRA ISSN 0103-6076
QL242 CODEN: GOZOEV
GOELDIANA ZOOLOGIA. Text in Portuguese. 1990. irreg., latest vol.19, 1993. BRL 1.50 domestic; USD 2 foreign (effective 2000).
Indexed: ZooRec.
Published by: Conselho Nacional de Desenvolvimento Cientifico e Tecnologico, Museu Paraense Emilio Goeldi, Comercio, Caixa Postal 399, Belem, PA 66017-970, Brazil. TEL 091-274-2195, FAX 091-274-1811, mgdoc@musu-goeldi.br.

598.417 JPN
GOOSE STUDY. Text in Japanese. 1990. 2/yr. JPY 2,000 (effective 1999 & 2000). bibl. **Document type:** *Bulletin.*
Description: Contains reports of research work by the Association members as well as reviews of scientific studies on goose species published in other languages.
Published by: Gan o Hogosurukai/Japanese Association for Wild Geese Protection, c/o Mr Kurechi, 16 Kawaminami Minamimachi, kurihara-gun, Wakayanagimachi, Miyagi-ken 989-5502, Japan. TEL 81-228-32-2004, FAX 81-228-32-3294, hgh02256@nifty.ne.jp. Ed. Yoshihiko Miyabayashi. Circ: 300.

599.884 USA
GORILLA. Text in English. 1976. s-a. USD 25; USD 30 foreign (effective 2000). bk.rev. back issues avail. **Document type:** *Newsletter, Consumer.* **Description:** Reports of the results and progress of ongoing study of gorilla behavior and interspecies communication, with other topics relating to the preservation and captive maintenance of gorillas.
Indexed: WildRev, e-psyche.
Published by: Gorilla Foundation, PO Box 620530, Woodside, CA 94062. TEL 650-216-6450, FAX 650-365-7906, hanabiko@earthlink.net, koko@koko.org, http://www.gorilla.org, http://www.koko.org. Ed. Dr. Francine Patterson. R&P Kevin Connelly. Circ: 30,000.

595.7 DEU
GORILLA JOURNAL. Text in English. s-a.
Indexed: ZooRec.
Published by: Berggorilla & Regenwald Direkthilfe, Lerchestr. 5, Muelheim, 45473, Germany. angela.meder@t-online.de.

GRAELLSIA; revista de zoologia. see *BIOLOGY*

GRASDUINEN. see *BIOLOGY—Botany*

597.005 CAN
GUELPH ICHTHYOLOGY REVIEWS. Text in English. 2001. irreg. **Document type:** *Journal, Academic/Scholarly.* **Description:** Aims to publish insightful papers that lead to new interpretations and increased understanding of fishes.
Media: Online - full content.
Published by: University of Guelph, Axelrod Institute of Ichthyology, 50 Stone Rd E, Guelph, ON N1G 2W1, Canada. TEL 519-824-4120 ext 8217, FAX 519-763-3906, gir@uoguelph.ca, http://gir.uoguelph.ca/, http://www.axelfish.uoguelph.ca/. Ed. David L G Noakes.

578.77 551.46 NLD ISSN 0928-2440
➤ **GUIDES TO THE IDENTIFICATION OF THE MICROINVERTEBRATES OF THE CONTINENTAL WATERS OF THE WORLD.** Variant title: Zooplankton Guides. Text in English. 1992. irreg., latest vol.20, 2003. price varies. illus. back issues avail. **Document type:** *Monographic series, Academic/Scholarly.* **Description:** Offers zooplankton guides for the scientific community.
Indexed: BIOSIS Prev, ZooRec.
—BLDSC (4229.281500).
Published by: Backhuys Publishers BV, Postbus 321, Leiden, 2300 AH, Netherlands. TEL 31-71-517-0208, FAX 31-71-517-1856, backhuys@backhuys.com, http://www.backhuys.com. Ed. H J Dumont. Pub. Wil Peters. Circ: 450 (paid).

B

596 CHN ISSN 1000-3118
QE841 CODEN: VEPAAU
➤ **GUJIZHUI DONGWU XUEBAO/VERTEBRATA PALASIATICA.** Text in Chinese; Summaries in English. 1957. q. CNY 120 (effective 2004). adv. **Document type:** *Academic/Scholarly.*
Description: Publishes research papers and brief notes on vertebrate paleontology, especially on vertebrates found in Asia.
Former titles (until 1973): Gujizhui Dongwu Yu Gurenlei (0042-4404); (until 1960): Vertebrata PalAsiatica (1000-9418)
Related titles: Online - full text ed.: (from East View Information Services, WanFang Data Corp.).
Indexed: AICP, AnthLit, RefZh, ZooRec.
—BLDSC (9216.500000), CISTI, IE, ingenta, Linda Hall.
Published by: (Zhongguo Kexueyuan, Gujizhui Dongwu yu Gurenlie Yanjiusuo/Chinese Academy of Sciences, Institute of Vertebrate Paleontology and Paleoanthropology), Kexue Chubanshe/Science Press, 16 Donghuang Cheng Genbei Jie, Beijing, 100717, China. TEL 86-10-64000246, FAX 86-10-64030255, bjs@ivpp.ac.cn, http://gjzdwxb.periodicals.net.cn/default.html, http://www.sciencep.com/. Circ: 10,000. **Dist. by:** China International Book Trading Corp, 35 Chegongzhuang Xilu, Haidian District, PO Box 399, Beijing 100044, China. TEL 86-10-68412045, FAX 86-10-68412023, cibtc@mail.cibtc.com.cn, http://www.cibtc.com.cn.

➤ **GULF AND CARIBBEAN RESEARCH.** see *EARTH SCIENCES—Oceanography*

597 JPN ISSN 0388-788X
SH171 CODEN: GYKEDT
➤ **GYOBYO KENKYU/FISH PATHOLOGY.** Text in English, Japanese. 1966. q. subscr. incld. with membership. adv. bk.rev. back issues avail. **Document type:** *Journal, Academic/Scholarly.* **Description:** Publishes research articles, short communications and reviews on disease phenomena of fishes and shellfishes.
Indexed: ASCA, ASFA, AgBio, AgrForAb, AnBrAb, BIOSIS Prev, BioCN&I, BiolAb, CIN, CRFR, ChemAb, ChemTitl, CurCont, ESPM, FoVS&M, HelmAb, HortAb, ISR, IndVet, MBA, NutrAb, OceAb, ProtozoAb, RA&MP, RM&VM, RPP, RefZh, RevApplEntom, SCI, SFA, SIA, TDB, VetBull, WildRev, ZooRec.
—BLDSC (3935.120000), CASDDS, IDS, IE, Infotrieve, ingenta. **CCC.**
Published by: Nihon Gyobyo Gakkai/Japanese Society of Fish Pathology, Tokyo University of Fisheries, Laboratory Genetics and Biochemistry, Konan 4-5-7, Minato-ku, Tokyo, 108-8477, Japan. hirono@tokyo-u-fish.ac.jp. Ed. K Muroga. R&P T Nakai. Adv. contact I Hirono. Circ: 1,000. **Dist. by:** Business Center for Academic Societies Japan, 5-16-19 Honkomagome, Bunkyo-ku, Tokyo 113-0021, Japan. TEL 81-3-58145811.

597.9 JPN ISSN 1345-5826
HACHU RYOSEIRUI GAKKAIHO/HERPETOLOGICAL SOCIETY OF JAPAN. BULLETIN. Text in Japanese. 1999. s-a. **Document type:** *Bulletin, Academic/Scholarly.*
Related titles: Online - full content ed.
Indexed: BIOSIS Prev, BiolAb, ZooRec.
Published by: Nihon Hachu Ryoseirui Gakkai/Herpetological Society of Japan, Department of Zoology, Faculty of Science, Kyoto University, Kitashirakawa-Oiwakecho, Sakyo-ku, Kyoto 606-8502, Japan. tom@zoo.zool.kyoto-u.ac.jp, http://zoo.zool.kyoto-u.ac.jp/herp/publications.html.

HACQUETIA. see *BIOLOGY—Botany*

639.2 CHN ISSN 1000-7075
SH214.54 CODEN: HSYAEN
HAIYANG SHUICHAN YANJIU/MARINE FISHERIES RESEARCH. Text in Chinese. 1980. q. **Document type:** *Journal, Academic/Scholarly.*

Related titles: Online - full text ed.: (from East View Information Services).
Indexed: ESPM.
Published by: Zhongguo Shuichan Kexue Yanjiuyuan, Huanghai Shuichan Yanjiusuo/Chinese Academy of Fishery Sciences, Yellow Sea Fisheries Research Institute, 106, Nanjing Road, Qingdao, 266071, China. TEL 86-532-5833580, FAX 86-532-5811514, liusl@ysfri.ac.cn, http://www.ysfri.ac.cn/xue.htm, http://www.ysfri.ac.cn/main-main.htm.

590 FRA ISSN 0397-765X
HALIOTIS. Text in English. 1971. a.
Indexed: ESPM, RefZh, ZooRec.
—BLDSC (4240.400000), IE, ingenta.
Published by: Societe Francaise de la Malacologie, 55 rue Buffon, Paris, 75005, France. Ed. Serge Gofas.

597.98 IND ISSN 0972-205X
CODEN: HAMAE7
➤ **HAMADRYAD;** journal of the centre for herpetology. Text in English. biennial. INR 250 SAARC to individuals; USD 40 elsewhere to individuals; INR 500 SAARC to institutions; USD 55 elsewhere to institutions (effective 2005). bk.rev. back issues avail.; reprints avail. **Document type:** *Journal, Academic/Scholarly.*
Indexed: RefZh, SFA, WildRev, ZooRec.
—BLDSC (4241.201000), ingenta.
Published by: Centre for Herpetology, Madras Crocodile Bank Trust, Mamallapuram, Post Bag 4, Chennai, Tamil Nadu 603 104, India. TEL 91-4114-272447, FAX 91-4114-242511, mcbtindia@vsnl.net, http://www.herplit.com/contents/Hamadryad.html. Ed., Pub., R&P Indraneil Das TEL 91-4114-46332. Adv. contact Harry Andrews.

595 DEU ISSN 0072-9612
QL1.H23 CODEN: MHZMA4
➤ **HAMBURGISCHES ZOOLOGISCHES MUSEUM UND INSTITUT. MITTEILUNGEN.** Text in German, English, French. 1883. a. price varies. **Document type:** *Academic/Scholarly.* **Description:** Covers all aspects of biodiversity, evolution, taxonomy, phylogeny and biogeography.
Indexed: ASFA, BIOSIS Prev, BiolAb, ESPM, NemAb, PoultAb, RM&VM, RefZh, RevApplEntom, S&F, SFA, WildRev, ZooRec.
—Linda Hall.
Published by: Universitaet Hamburg, Zoologisches Institut und Museum, Martin-Luther-King-Platz 3, Hamburg, 20146, Germany. TEL 49-40-428382287, FAX 49-40-428383937, fb4a007@rrz-cip-1.rrz.uni-hamburg.de, http://www.rrz.uni-hamburg.de/biologie/zim/eng/zeitsche.htm. Eds. Bernhard Hausdorf, Hans Georg Andres, Horst Wilkens. Circ: 600.

594 USA ISSN 0073-0807
QL401 CODEN: OPMOAN
➤ **HARVARD UNIVERSITY. MUSEUM OF COMPARATIVE ZOOLOGY. DEPARTMENT OF MOLLUSKS. OCCASIONAL PAPERS ON MOLLUSKS.** Text in English. 1945. irreg., latest vol.6, no.82, 2002. price varies. back issues avail. **Document type:** *Monographic series, Academic/Scholarly.*
Indexed: ASFA, BIOSIS Prev, BiolAb, ZooRec.
—Linda Hall.
Published by: Harvard University, Museum of Comparative Zoology, 26 Oxford St, Cambridge, MA 02138. TEL 617-495-3045, FAX 617-495-5667, http://www.mcz.harvard.edu. Ed. Kenneth J Boss. Circ: 225.

594.1477 USA ISSN 0017-8624
QL401 CODEN: HWSNAM
HAWAIIAN SHELL NEWS. Text in English. 1952. m. USD 30; USD 31 in Canada & Mexico; USD 33 elsewhere. adv. bk.rev. charts; illus.; maps; stat. **Description:** Nonscientific educational journal of events, opinions and problems in the shell world.
Media: Online - full text.
Indexed: ASFA, BiolAb, CTO, ESPM, ZooRec.
—Linda Hall.
Published by: Hawaiian Malacological Society, PO Box 22130, Honolulu, HI 96823-2130. g.-b.cook@juno.com, http://www.hits.net/~hsn. Ed. Dwayne Minton. Adv. contact Olive Schoenberg Dole.

592.3 SVK ISSN 0440-6605
QL392 CODEN: HMTGA4
➤ **HELMINTHOLOGIA.** Text in English. 1959. 4/yr. USD 156 foreign (effective 2005). adv. bk.rev. illus. index. 60 p./no.; **Document type:** *Journal, Academic/Scholarly.* **Description:** For physicians, students of medicine, and other scientific and specialized workers engaged in parasitology.
Indexed: ABSML, ASCA, AbHyg, AgBio, AnBrAb, BIOSIS Prev, BioCN&I, BiolAb, CIN, ChemAb, ChemTitl, CurCont, ExcerpMed, FCA, ForAb, HelmAb, HerbAb, HortAb, IndVet, MaizeAb, NemAb, NutrAb, PN&I, PoultAb, ProtozoAb, RA&MP, RDA, RM&VM, RPP, RefZh, RevApplEntom, S&F, SFA, SIA, TDB, VetBull, WeedAb, WildRev, ZooRec.
—BLDSC (4285.900000), CASDDS, CISTI, IDS, IE, ingenta.
Published by: (Slovenska Akademia Vied, Parazitologicky Ustav/Slovak Academy of Sciences, Parasitological Institute), Slovak Academic Press Ltd., Nam Slobody 6, PO Box 57, Bratislava, 81005, Slovakia. sap@sappress.sk, http://www.sappress.sk. Ed., Adv. contact Pavol Dubinsky. R&P Milan Rybos. Circ: 700. **Dist. by:** Slovart G.T.G. s.r.o., Krupinska 4, PO Box 152, Bratislava 85299, Slovakia. TEL 421-2-63839472, FAX 421-2-63839485, http://www.slovart-gtg.sk.

➤ **HELMINTHOLOGICAL ABSTRACTS.** see *BIOLOGY—Abstracting, Bibliographies, Statistics*

597.7 AUS ISSN 0725-1424
CODEN: HRPFEK
HERPETOFAUNA. Text in English. 1967. s-a. AUD 40 for 3 yrs.. bk.rev.
Indexed: SFA, WildRev, ZooRec.
—BLDSC (4300.280000), CISTI, IE, ingenta.
Published by: Australasian Affiliation of Herpetological Societies, Royal Exchange, PO Box R 307, Sydney, NSW 2000, Australia. Ed. G Swan. Circ: 1,200.

597.9 DEU ISSN 0172-7761
CODEN: HERFE7
HERPETOFAUNA. Text in German, Latin. 1979. irreg. adv. bk.rev. abstr.; bibl.; charts; illus.; maps. back issues avail. **Document type:** *Academic/Scholarly.*
Related titles: E-mail ed.; Fax ed.; Online - full text ed.
Indexed: ZooRec.
Published by: Herpetofauna-Verlags GmbH, Postfach 1110, Weinstadt, 71365, Germany. http://www.herpetofauna.de. Ed. H P Fuchs. adv.: B&W page MRK 750, color page MRK 900; trim 148 x 211. Circ: 1,800.

597.9 USA ISSN 0018-0831
QL640 CODEN: HPTGAP
➤ **HERPETOLOGICA.** Text in English. 1936. q. USD 50 membership (effective 2004). bk.rev. illus. index. back issues avail.; reprint service avail. from PQC. **Document type:** *Journal, Academic/Scholarly.* **Description:** Publishes original research papers and essays dealing with the biology of amphibians and reptiles.
Related titles: Microfilm ed.: (from PQC); Online - full text ed.: (from BioOne, C S A); ♦ Supplement(s): Herpetological Monograph. ISSN 0733-1347.
Indexed: ASCA, ASFA, AnBeAb, ApEcolAb, BIOBASE, BIOSIS Prev, BiolAb, CIS, ChemAb, CurCont, ESPM, GEOBASE, IABS, ISR, RM&VM, SCI, SFA, SPPI, SSCI, WildRev, ZooRec.
—BLDSC (4300.300000), CISTI, IE, Infotrieve, ingenta, Linda Hall.
Published by: Herpetologists League, c/o Christopher Phillips, Illinois Natural History Survey, 607 E Peabody, Champaign, IL 61820. TEL 217-244-7077, FAX 217-333-4949, chrisp@inhs.uiuc.edu, http://www.inhs.uiuc.edu/cbd/HL/Titles.html, http://www.inhs.uiuc.edu/cbd/HL/HL.html. Ed. Alicia Mathis. Circ: 2,000 (paid).

597.9 GBR ISSN 1473-0928
CODEN: BBHSEB
➤ **HERPETOLOGICAL BULLETIN.** Text in English. q. GBP 25, USD 50 to individual members; GBP 45, USD 90 to institutional members; GBP 18, USD 36 to students (effective 2005). adv. bk.rev. illus. back issues avail. **Document type:** *Bulletin, Academic/Scholarly.* **Description:** Publishes a range of articles concerned with herpetology. These include full length papers, etters from readers, society news and other items of general herpetological interest. Emphasis is placed on natural history, captive breeding and husbandry, veterinary and behavioural articles.
Former titles (until 2000): British Herpetological Society. Bulletin (0260-5805); (until 1980): British Herpetological Society. Newsletter
Indexed: BIOBASE, RefZh, SFA, WildRev, ZooRec.
—BLDSC (4300.326000), IE, ingenta, Linda Hall.
Published by: British Herpetological Society, c/o Zoological Society of London, Regents Park, London, NW1 4RY, United Kingdom. TEL 44-20-84529578, herpbulletin@thebhs.org, http://www.thebhs.org/. Ed. Peter Stafford. Circ: 900.

597.9 GBR ISSN 0268-0130
CODEN: HEJOES
➤ **HERPETOLOGICAL JOURNAL.** Text in English. 1948. q. GBP 25, USD 50 to individual members; GBP 18, USD 36 to students; GBP 45, USD 90 to institutional members (effective 2005). adv. bk.rev. back issues avail. **Document type:** *Journal, Academic/Scholarly.* **Description:** Publishes a range of features concerned with reptile and amphibian biology.
Formerly (until 1985): British Journal of Herpetology (0007-1056)
Indexed: ASCA, BIOBASE, CurCont, HelmAb, IABS, RefZh, SFA, WeedAb, WildRev, ZooRec.
—BLDSC (4300.328000), CASDDS, CISTI, IDS, IE, ingenta, Linda Hall.
Published by: British Herpetological Society, c/o Zoological Society of London, Regents Park, London, NW1 4RY, United Kingdom. TEL 44-20-84529578, herpjournal@thebhs.org, http://biology.bangor.ac.uk/~bss166/HJ/, http://www.thebhs.org/. Ed. Wolfgang Wuster. Circ: 900.

597.9 USA ISSN 0733-1347
QL640 CODEN: HEMOE9
➤ **HERPETOLOGICAL MONOGRAPH.** Variant title: Herpetological Monographs. Text in English. 1982. a., latest vol.18, 2004. price varies. **Document type:** *Monographic series, Academic/Scholarly.*
Related titles: Online - full text ed.: (from BioOne, C S A); ♦ Supplement to: Herpetologica. ISSN 0018-0831.
Indexed: ASFA, BIOBASE, BIOSIS Prev, BiolAb, CurCont, ISR, SCI, SFA, WildRev, ZooRec.
—BLDSC (4300.329000), CISTI, IE, Infotrieve, ingenta, Linda Hall.
Published by: Herpetologists League, c/o Christopher Phillips, Illinois Natural History Survey, 607 E Peabody, Champaign, IL 61820. TEL 423-929-6929, FAX 423-929-5958, chrisp@inhs.uiuc.edu, http://www.inhs.uiuc.edu/cbd/HL/Titles.html, http://www.inhs.uiuc.edu/cbd/HL/HL.html. Ed., R&P Darrel Frost.

597.9 USA ISSN 1069-1928
QL640
➤ **HERPETOLOGICAL NATURAL HISTORY.** Text in English. 1993. s-a. USD 25 per vol. to individuals; USD 50 per vol. to institutions (effective 2004). bk.rev. illus. back issues avail. **Document type:** *Journal, Academic/Scholarly.* **Description:** Presents observations on ecology, behavior, evolution, life history, paleontology, conservation of amphibians and reptiles.
Indexed: BIOSIS Prev, BiolAb, WildRev, ZooRec.
—BLDSC (4300.329500).
Published by: La Sierra University, Department of Biology, Riverside, CA 92515. TEL 909-785-2140, herpnathist@hotmail.com, http://www.hnh.no-frills.net/. Ed. Hinrich Kaiser. Circ: 300.

597.9 USA ISSN 0018-084X
QL640 CODEN: HEPRBU
➤ **HERPETOLOGICAL REVIEW.** Text in English. 1967. q. USD 60 to individual members; USD 115 to institutional members; USD 30 to students (effective 2004); includes subscr. to Journal of Herpetology. adv. bk.rev. abstr.; bibl.; charts; illus.; stat. back issues avail.; reprints avail. **Document type:** *Journal, Academic/Scholarly.*
Formerly: Ohio Herpetological Society Newsletter
Related titles: Online - full text ed.: (from bigchalk, Northern Light Technology, Inc., ProQuest Information & Learning).
Indexed: BIOBASE, BIOSIS Prev, BiolAb, BiolDig, IABS, RefZh, SFA, WildRev, ZooRec.
—BLDSC (4300.330000), CISTI, IE, Infotrieve, ingenta, Linda Hall. **CCC.**
Published by: Society for the Study of Amphibians and Reptiles, PO Box 253, Marceline, MO 64658-0253. ssar@herplit.com, http://www.ssarherps.org. Ed. Robert Hansen TEL 559-323-7170. Circ: 2,500 (paid).

597.85 AUT ISSN 1013-4425
QL640 CODEN: HRTZEW
➤ **HERPETOZOA.** Text and summaries in English, German. 1988. s-a. EUR 30 domestic; USD 30 foreign (effective 2003). adv. bk.rev. bibl.; charts; illus.; stat. 96 p./no. 2 cols./p.; back issues avail. **Document type:** *Journal, Academic/Scholarly.* **Description:** Covers all aspects of herpetology.
Indexed: RefZh, ZooRec.
Published by: Oesterreichische Gesellschaft fuer Herpetologie, Naturhistorisches Museum, Vienna, W 1014, Austria. TEL 43-1-52177286, FAX 43-1-52177286, heinz.grillitsch@nhm-wien.ac.at. Ed., Pub., Adv. contact Heinz Grillitsch. B&W page EUR 440; trim 170 x 245. Circ: 550 (paid).

597.98 IND
HERPINSTANCE. Text in English. s-a. INR 70 SAARC; USD 6 elsewhere (effective 2004). **Document type:** *Newsletter.*
Published by: Centre for Herpetology, Madras Crocodile Bank Trust, Mamallapuram, Post Bag 4, Chennai, Tamil Nadu 603 104, India. TEL 91-4114-272447, FAX 91-4114-242511, mcbtindia@vsnl.net, http://www.herplit.com/contents/Hamadryad.html.

597.9 GBR ISSN 0953-2021
THE HERPTILE. Text in English. 1974. irreg.
Indexed: ZooRec.
—BLDSC (4300.340000), IE, ingenta.
Published by: International Herpetological Society, c/o Mrs. Carol Friend, 15 Barnett Ln, Wordsley, West Midland DY8 5PZ, United Kingdom. membership@international-herp-society.co.uk, http://www.international-herp-society.co.uk.

590 DEU ISSN 0721-6874
HESSISCHE FAUNISTISCHE BRIEFE. Text in German. 1981. q. EUR 15 (effective 2003). adv. bk.rev. **Document type:** *Journal, Academic/Scholarly.*
Indexed: RefZh, ZooRec.
Published by: Naturwissenschaftlicher Verein Darmstadt e.V., Bessungerstr 125-C, Darmstadt, 64295, Germany. TEL 49-6151-133288. Ed. Michael Hoellwarth. Circ: 500.

599 JPN ISSN 0389-8148
HIGUMA/HOKKAIDO BROWN BEAR. Text in Japanese. 1976. a. JPY 500.
Published by: Noboribetsu Kuma Bokujo/Noboribetsu Bear Park, 224 Noboribetsuonsen-cho, Noboribetsu-shi, Hokkaido 059-0551, Japan.

590 IND ISSN 0970-2903
QL1
➤ **HIMALAYAN JOURNAL OF ENVIRONMENT AND ZOOLOGY.** Text in English. 1987. s-a. INR 400 domestic; USD 30 foreign (effective 2003). adv. bk.rev. 100 p./no.; back issues avail. **Document type:** *Journal, Academic/Scholarly.* **Description:** Covers fields of zoology, biology, ethnobiology, and environmental sciences.
Indexed: ASFA, ESPM, EntAb, PollutAb, WRCInf, ZooRec.
—Linda Hall.
Published by: Indian Academy of Environmental Sciences, c/o Dept. of Zoology, Gurukula Kangri University, Hardwar, Uttar Pradesh 249 404, India. TEL 91-1334-215940, FAX 91-1334-216366, joshi_bd@rediffmail.com. Eds. B D Joshi, P C Joshi. R&P B D Joshi. adv.: page INR 2,000. Circ: 200.

590 JPN
HIROSHIMASHI ASA DOBUTSU KOEN NENPO/ASA ZOOLOGICAL PARK OF HIROSHIMA. ANNUAL REPORT. Text in Japanese. 1971. a. **Document type:** *Corporate.*
Published by: Hiroshimashi Asa Dobutsuen Kyokai/Asa Zoological Park of Hiroshima, Dobutsuen, Asacho, Asakita-ku, Hiroshima-shi, Hiroshima-ken 731-33, Japan. Ed. Hiroshi Morimoto.

590 ESP ISSN 1133-1232
CODEN: HANIE2
HISTORIA ANIMALIUM. Text in Spanish. 1946. irreg. price varies. **Document type:** *Journal, Academic/Scholarly.*
Former titles (until 1988): Universidad de Barcelona. Publicaciones del Departamento de Zoologia (0210-4814); (until 1976): Revista de Biologia Aplicada
Indexed: AnBrAb, BIOSIS Prev, BiolAb, ESPM, PoultAb.
—CINDOC.
Published by: (Universitat de Barcelona, Facultat de Biologia), Universitat de Barcelona, Servei de Publicacions, Gran Via Corts Catalanes 585, Barcelona, 08007, Spain. TEL 34-93-4021100, http://www.publicacions.ub.es.

594 JPN ISSN 0912-1900
HITACHIOBI. Text in Japanese. 1974. irreg.
Published by: Tokyo Kairui Dokokai/Tokyo Malacological Society, 4-40-9 Yamato-cho, Nakano-ku, Tokyo, 165-0034, Japan. Ed. S Kato.

590.73 ITA
HOBBY ZOO. Text in Italian. 1983. m. free. adv. 128 p./no.; **Document type:** *Magazine, Consumer.*
Published by: Gruppo Editoriale Olimpia SpA, Via E Fermi 24, Loc Osmannoro, Sesto Fiorentino, FI 50129, Italy. TEL 39-055-30321, FAX 39-055-3032280, http://www.edolimpia.it. Ed. Renato Cacciapuoti. Adv. contact Adolfo Somigliana TEL 39-031-301059. color page EUR 1,400; 210 x 275. Circ: 14,000 (free).

590 JPN ISSN 0285-3760
HOKURIKU JOURNAL OF ZOOTECHNICAL SCIENCE. Text in Japanese. 1951. s-a. JPY 600. back issues avail.
Published by: Japan Zootechnical Society, Hokuriku Branch, c/o Department of Animal Husbandry, Faculty of Agriculture, Niigata University, Niigata, 950-21, Japan. TEL 025-262-6662, FAX 025-263-1659. Ed. K Yamamoto. Circ: 800.

HONYU DOBUTSU SHIKEN BUNKAKAI KAIHO/MAMMALIAN MUTAGENICITY STUDY GROUP COMMUNICATIONS. see *BIOLOGY—Genetics*

599 JPN ISSN 0385-437X
QL700 CODEN: HONKE4
HONYURUI KAGAKU/MAMMALIAN SCIENCE. Text in English, Japanese. s-a. membership.
Indexed: BIOSIS Prev, BiolAb, ZooRec.
—BLDSC (5357.600000).
Published by: Nihon Honyurui Gakkai/Mammalogical Society of Japan, Nihon Gakkai Jimu Senta, 16-9 Honkomagome 5-chome, Bunkyo-ku, Tokyo, 113-0021, Japan.

597 DNK ISSN 0109-2510
SH171
I C E S IDENTIFICATION LEAFLETS FOR DISEASES AND PARASITES OF FISH AND SHELLFISH/FICHES D'IDENTIFICATION DES MALADIES ET PARASITES DES POISSONS, CRUSTACES ET MOLLUSQUES. (International Council for the Exploration of the Sea) Text in English, French. 1984. irreg., latest vol.56, 1999. price varies. back issues avail. **Document type:** *Monographic series, Academic/Scholarly.*
Indexed: ASFA, ESPM, ZooRec.
Published by: International Council for the Exploration of the Sea, H. C. Andersens Boulevard 44-46, Copenhagen K, 1553, Denmark. TEL 45-33-386700, FAX 45-33-934215, info@ices.dk, http://www.ices.dk/products/idleaflets.asp. Ed. Sharon E. McGladdery. Circ: 500. **Subscr. to:** C.A. Reitzels Boghandel & Forlag A/S, Noerregade 20, Copenhagen K 1165, Denmark.

597 MYS ISSN 0115-4435
I C L A R M CONFERENCE PROCEEDINGS. Text in English. 1979. irreg. price varies. abstr.; bibl.; illus. index. back issues avail. **Document type:** *Proceedings.*
Indexed: ASFA, CivEngAb, CurCont, ESPM, SFA.
—CINDOC, CISTI.
Published by: WorldFish Center, PO Box 500 GPO, Penang, 10670, Malaysia. TEL 60-4-641-4623, FAX 60-4-643-4463, http://www.cgiar.org/iclarm/. Circ: 800.

I G B BERICHTE. see *BIOLOGY*

590.724 USA ISSN 1084-2020
QL55 CODEN: IJLOAC
➤ **I L A R JOURNAL.** Text in English. 1957. q. USD 60 domestic to individuals; USD 75 foreign to individuals; USD 550 combined subscription domestic to institutions print & online eds.; USD 600 foreign to institutions print & online eds.; USD 25 domestic to students; USD 35 foreign to students (effective 2005 - 2006). bibl.; illus. back issues avail. **Document type:** *Journal, Academic/Scholarly.* **Description:** Contains articles on animal models and issues of interest to animal care and use committees as well as information on alternatives, adjuncts and refinements to the use of animals.
Former titles: I L A R News (0018-9960); Information on Laboratory Animals for Research
Indexed: Agr, BibAg, ChemAb, CurCont, ExcerpMed, FoVS&M, IndVet, MEDLINE, RefZh, SFA, VetBull, WildRev, ZooRec.
—BLDSC (4364.040000), CISTI, IE, Infotrieve, ingenta. **CCC.**
Published by: Institute for Laboratory Animal Research, The Keek Center of the National Academies, 500 Fifth St, NW, Washington, DC 2001. TEL 202-334-2590, FAX 202-334-1687, ILARJ@nas.edu, ilarj@nas.edu, http://www.ilarjournal.com, http://dels.nas.edu/ilar/. Circ: 3,500.

590 USA ISSN 0741-5362
CODEN: ISNWEB
THE I S C NEWSLETTER. Text in English. q. USD 42 to individuals; USD 65 to institutions (effective 2000); includes receipt of Cryptozoology annually. **Document type:** *Newsletter.* **Description:** News on cryptozoology, including field reports, references, new books and interviews.
Indexed: SFA.
Published by: International Society of Cryptozoology, PO Box 43070, Tucson, AZ 85733. TEL 520-884-8369, FAX 520-884-8369, iscz@azstarnet.com, http://www.izoo.org/isc. Ed. J Richard Greenwell. Circ: 800.

590 USA
I W R C PROCEEDINGS. Text in English. 1991. a. price varies. back issues avail. **Document type:** *Proceedings.* **Description:** Publishes papers presented at the annual IWRC conference.
Published by: International Wildlife Rehabilitation Council, PO Box 8187, San Jose, CA 95155. TEL 707-864-1761, FAX 707-864-3106, iwrc@inreach.com, office@iwrc-online.org, http://www.iwrc-online.org.

590 USA
I W R C SKILLS SEMINARS. Text in English. irreg., latest vol.10. price varies. illus. back issues avail. **Document type:** *Monographic series, Trade.* **Description:** Covers various aspects on rehabilitating wild birds and animals.
Published by: International Wildlife Rehabilitation Council, PO Box 8187, San Jose, CA 95155. TEL 707-864-1761, FAX 707-864-3106, iwrc@inreach.com, office@iwrc-online.org, http://www.iwrc-online.org.

594 ESP ISSN 0212-3010
CODEN: IBERDZ
IBERUS. Text in Spanish. 1981. a. **Document type:** *Academic/Scholarly.*
Related titles: Supplement(s): Iberus. Suplemento. ISSN 1138-638X. 1988.
Indexed: ASFA, BIOSIS Prev, BiolAb, ESPM, IECT, ZooRec.
—CINDOC.
Published by: Sociedad Espanola de Malacologia, c/o Museo Nacional de Ciencias Naturales, Jose Gutierrez Abascal, 2, Madrid, 28006, Spain. Ed. Angel Guerra Sierra. **Non-members subscr. to:** Backhuys Publishers BV, Postbus 321, Leiden 2300 AH, Netherlands.

597 DEU ISSN 0936-9902
CODEN: IEFRES
ICHTHYOLOGICAL EXPLORATION OF FRESHWATERS; international journal for field-orientated ichthyology. Text in German. 1990. q. EUR 100 to individuals; EUR 180 to institutions (effective 2005). index. back issues avail. **Document type:** *Journal, Academic/Scholarly.* **Description:** Publishes papers resulting from field work in ichthyology and the documentation of the biodiversity of freshwater fishes.
Indexed: ASFA, EPB, ESPM, RefZh, SFA, ZooRec.
—BLDSC (4361.950950), IE, ingenta. **CCC.**
Published by: Verlag Dr. Friedrich Pfeil, Wolfratshauser Str 27, Munich, 81379, Germany. TEL 49-89-7428270, FAX 49-89-7242772, info@pfeil-verlag.de, http://www.pfeil-verlag.de/04biol/e9902.html. Ed. Maurice Kottelat. Circ: 500 (paid and controlled).

597 JPN ISSN 1341-8998
QL614 CODEN: GYOZA7
➤ **ICHTHYOLOGICAL RESEARCH.** Text in English. 1950. q. EUR 228 combined subscription to institutions print & online eds. (effective 2005). adv. bk.rev. abstr.; bibl.; charts; illus.; stat. index. **Document type:** *Journal, Academic/Scholarly.* **Description:** Publishes research papers on original work, either descriptive or experimental, that advances the understanding of the diversity of fishes.
Supersedes in part (in 1995): Gyoruigaku Zasshi / Japanese Journal of Ichthyology (0021-5090)
Related titles: Online - full text ed.: ISSN 1616-3915 (from EBSCO Publishing, Springer LINK, Swets Information Services).
Indexed: ASCA, ASFA, Agrind, AnBrAb, B&BAb, BIOSIS Prev, BiolAb, CRFR, ChemAb, CurCont, ESPM, GenetAb, HGA, ISR, IndVet, JPI, OceAb, RefZh, SCI, SFA, SPPI, VetBull, ZooRec.
—BLDSC (4655.350000), CISTI, IDS, IE, Infotrieve, ingenta, Linda Hall. **CCC.**
Published by: (Ichthyological Society of Japan/Nihon Gyorui Gakkai), Springer-Verlag Tokyo (Subsidiary of: Springer Science+Business Media), 3-13 Hongo 3-chome, Bunkyo-ku, Tokyo, 113-0033, Japan. TEL 81-3-38120331, FAX 81-3-38187454, http://link.springer.de/link/service/journals/10228/index.htm, http://www.springer-tokyo.co.jp/. Ed. S Kimura. Adv. contact Stephan Kroeck TEL 49-30-827875739. Circ: 700. **Subscr. in the Americas to:** Springer-Verlag New York, Inc., Journal Fulfillment, PO Box 2485, Secaucus, NJ 07096-2485. TEL 800-777-4643, 201-348-4033, FAX 201-348-4505, journals@springer-ny.com, http://www.springer-ny.com; **Subscr. to:** Springer GmbH Auslieferungsgesellschaft, Haberstr 7, Heidelberg 69126, Germany. TEL 49-6221-345-0, FAX 49-6221-345-4229, subscriptions@springer.de.

591.98 BRA ISSN 0073-4721
QL1 CODEN: IHZOAY
➤ **IHERINGIA. SERIE ZOOLOGIA.** Text in English, French, German, Italian, Portuguese, Spanish; Abstracts in English. 1957. q. exchange agreements with other institutions. bibl.; illus.; charts; stat. back issues avail. **Document type:** *Journal, Academic/Scholarly.* **Description:** Original research articles on all aspects of zoology in South America, with a focus on Brazil.
Related titles: Online - full text ed.: free (effective 2005).
Indexed: ASFA, AnBrAb, ApicAb, B&BAb, BIOSIS Prev, BioCN&I, BiolAb, EntAb, ForAb, GenetAb, HGA, HelmAb, HerbAb, HortAb, IndVet, NemAb, NutrAb, OrnHort, PBA, PGegResA, PHN&I, RM&VM, RevApplEntom, RiceAb, S&F, SFA, SeedAb, VetBull, WeedAb, WildRev, ZooRec.
—CISTI. **CCC.**
Published by: (Museu de Ciencias Naturais), Fundacao Zoobotanica do Rio Grande do Sul, Caixa Postal 1188, Porto Alegre, RS 90690-000, Brazil. TEL 55-51-33202000, FAX 55-51-33363281, galileo@pampa.tche.br, biblioteca@fzb.rs.gov.br, http://www.scielo.br/isz, http://www.fzb.rs.gov.br. Ed. Maria Helena M Galileo. Circ: 600.

➤ **IN VITRO CELLULAR & DEVELOPMENTAL BIOLOGY - ANIMAL.** see *MEDICAL SCIENCES*

590 IND ISSN 0537-0744
QL309
INDIA. ZOOLOGICAL SURVEY. ANNUAL REPORT. Text in English. a.
Published by: Zoological Survey of India, 34 Chittaranjan Ave., Kolkata, West Bengal 700 012, India.

590 IND
INDIA. ZOOLOGICAL SURVEY. NEWSLETTER. Text in English. 197?. irreg.
Published by: Zoological Survey of India, 34 Chittaranjan Ave., Kolkata, West Bengal 700 012, India.

591 IND
INDIA. ZOOLOGICAL SURVEY. RECORDS. Text in English. q. INR 81, USD 9.
Indexed: SFA, ZooRec.
Published by: Zoological Survey of India, 34 Chittaranjan Ave., Kolkata, West Bengal 700 012, India.

597 IND ISSN 0970-6011
SH1 CODEN: IJFIAW
➤ **INDIAN JOURNAL OF FISHERIES.** Text in English. 1962. q. looseleaf. INR 400 domestic; USD 56 foreign (effective 2002). bk.rev. charts; illus. index. **Document type:** *Academic/Scholarly.*
Formed by the merger of (1962-1965): Indian Journal of Fisheries. Section A (0970-5996); (1962-1965): Indian Journal of Fisheries. Section B (0970-6003); Both of which superseded in part (1954-1962): Indian Journal of Fisheries (0537-2003)
Indexed: ASFA, BiolAb, ChemAb, ESPM, FS&TA, NutrAb, SFA, SWRA, ZooRec.
—CISTI, Linda Hall.
Published by: (Central Marine Fisheries Research Institute), Scientific Publishers, 5-A New Pali Rd., Near Hotel Taj Hari Mahal, PO Box 91, Jodhpur, Rajasthan 342 003, India. TEL 91-291-2433323, FAX 91-291-2512580, info@scientificpub.com, http://www.scientificpub.com. Ed. K J Mathew. Circ: 500. **Dist. by:** H P C Publishers Distributors Pvt. Ltd., 4805 Bharat Ram Rd, 24 Darya Ganj, New Delhi 110 002, India.

591.954 IND ISSN 0971-104X
QL1 CODEN: IJZLA5
INDIAN JOURNAL OF ZOOLOGICAL SPECTRUM. Text in English. 1974. 6/yr. INR 60 to individuals; INR 100 to institutions. adv. bk.rev. bibl.; illus. back issues avail.

▼ new title ➤ refereed ✶ unverified ♦ full entry avail.

Formerly (until 1990): Indian Journal of Zoology (0302-7562)
Indexed: BiolAb, ChemAb, CurCont.
—CASDDS, CISTI, Linda Hall.
Published by: Saifia College of Science & Technology, Department of Zoology, Bhopal, Madhya Pradesh, India. Ed. Masroor Ali Khan. adv.: page INR 500. Circ: 500.

597 USA ISSN 0736-0460
QL623
➤ **INDO-PACIFIC FISHES.** Text in English. 1982. irreg. price varies. reprint service avail. from PQC. **Document type:** *Journal, Academic/Scholarly.* **Description:** Revisions of general or higher categories of fish in the Indo-West Pacific region.
Indexed: ASFA, ESPM, SFA, ZooRec.
Published by: (Bishop Museum, Division of Ichthyology), Bishop Museum Press, 1525 Bernice St, Box 19000 A, Honolulu, HI 96817. TEL 808-848-4135. Eds. Helen Randall, Dr. John Randall.

594 JPN ISSN 0288-1527
INSTITUTE OF MALACOLOGY OF TOKYO. BULLETIN. Text in English. 1979. s-a. JPY 5,000 to members (effective 1999). **Document type:** *Academic/Scholarly.*
Indexed: ZooRec.
Published by: Institute of Malacology of Tokyo/Tokyo Nantai Dobutsugaku Kenkyujo, 6-36 Midori-cho 3-chome, Tanashi-shi, Tokyo-to 188-0002, Japan. TEL 81-424-63-0851, FAX 81-424-61-1752. Ed., R&P Sadao Kosuge.

599.935 KEN
INSTITUTE OF PRIMATE RESEARCH. ANNUAL REPORT. Text in English. 1981. a.
Published by: Institute of Primate Research, Karen, PO Box 24481, Nairobi, Kenya. FAX 254-2-882546, TELEX 254-2-22892.

590.74 BRA ISSN 0073-9901
RM739 CODEN: MIBUAH
INSTITUTO BUTANTAN. MEMORIAS. Text and summaries in English, Portuguese. 1918. biennial. USD 20 (effective 1997). index, cum.index: 1918-1989. **Document type:** *Consumer.* **Description:** Reports on the institute's activities.
Indexed: AbHyg, BiolAb, ChemAb, IndMed, IndVet, MEDLINE, TDB, VetBull, ZooRec.
—BLDSC (5659.000000), CASDDS, CISTI, GNLM.
Published by: Instituto Butantan, Av. Vital Brasil 1500, Sao Paulo, SP 05503-900, Brazil. TEL 55-11-8137222, FAX 55-11-8151505, TELEX BUTA BR 011-83325. Ed. Eva Maria A Kelen. Circ: 800 (controlled).

590 GBR ISSN 1540-7063
QL1 CODEN: AMZOAF
➤ **INTEGRATIVE AND COMPARATIVE BIOLOGY.** Text in English. 1961. 6/yr. GBP 300, USD 549, EUR 450, GBP 316, USD 578, EUR 474 to institutions (effective 2006). adv. bk.rev. charts; illus. index. back issues avail.; reprint service avail. from PQC. **Document type:** *Journal, Academic/Scholarly.* **Description:** Contains papers from symposia dealing with a wide variety of zoological disciplines.
Formerly (until 2002): American Zoologist (0003-1569)
Related titles: Microfilm ed.: (from PQC); Online - full text ed.: ISSN 1557-7023. GBP 284, USD 520, EUR 426 to institutions (effective 2006) (from bigchalk, BioOne, C S A, Gale Group, H.W. Wilson, Northern Light Technology, Inc., O C L C Online Computer Library Center, Inc., ProQuest Information & Learning).
Indexed: ASCA, ASFA, AgBio, Agr, AnBeAb, AnBrAb, ApEcolAb, B&AI, BIOSIS Prev, BiolAb, BiolDig, CIN, CPA, CRFR, ChemAb, ChemTitl, CurCont, DSA, EPB, ESPM, EntAb, FCA, GSI, HGA, HelmAb, HortAb, ISR, IndVet, Inpharma, KWIWR, MEDLINE, NSCI, NemAb, NutrAb, PBA, PGegResA, PoultAb, ProtozoAb, RM&VM, Reac, RevApplEntom, SCI, SFA, VetBull, WildRev, ZooRec.
—BLDSC (0858.400000), CASDDS, CISTI, GNLM, IDS, IE, ingenta, Linda Hall. **CCC.**
Published by: (Society for Integrative and Comparative Biology USA), Oxford University Press, Great Clarendon St, Oxford, OX2 6DP, United Kingdom. TEL 44-1865-556767, FAX 44-1865-556646, jnl.orders@oup.co.uk, enquiry@oup.co.uk, http://www.oxfordjournals.org/. Ed. John Edwards. Circ: 6,300.

599.78 USA ISSN 1064-1564
INTERNATIONAL BEAR NEWS. Text in English. 1968. q. looseleaf. USD 50 (effective 2005). bk.rev. back issues avail. **Document type:** *Newsletter, Academic/Scholarly.* **Description:** Studies of bear biology and management.
Published by: International Association for Bear Research and Management, c/o Joseph Clark, IBA Secretary, USGS-SAFL, University of Tennessee, 274 Ellington Hall, Knoxville, TN 37996. TEL 865-974-4790, FAX 865-974-3555, ibanews@bearbiology.com, http://www.bearbiology.com/bearnewsmenu.html. Ed. Teresa Delorenzo. Circ: 800 (paid).

590 ESP ISSN 0377-368X
SH351.T8 CODEN: RICTEA
INTERNATIONAL COMMISSION FOR THE CONSERVATION OF ATLANTIC TUNAS. REPORT. Text in English. 1970. biennial (in 2 vols.). free to qualified personnel; USD 26.
Related titles: Microfiche ed.: (from CIS); French ed.; Spanish ed.
Indexed: ASFA, IIS, SFA, ZooRec.
—BLDSC (7523.946000).
Published by: International Commission for the Conservation of Atlantic Tunas (ICCAT), Secretariat, Calle Corazon de Maria, 8, Sixth Floor, Madrid, 28002, Spain. TEL 34-91-4165600, FAX 34-91-4152612, info@iccat.es, http://www.iccat.es. Ed. P M Miyake.

578.65 TUR ISSN 0074-3860
INTERNATIONAL CONGRESS OF PARASITOLOGY. PROCEEDINGS. Text in Turkish. 1964. quadrennial. price varies. **Document type:** *Proceedings.* **Description:** Publishes research in parasitology presented at the International Congress.
Published by: World Federation of Parasitologists, c/o Dr. M. Ziya Alkan, Secretary, Dept. of Parisitology, Medical Faculty of Ege University, Bornova-izmir, 35100, Turkey. TEL 90-232-339-8290, FAX 90-232-388-1347, alkan@med.ege.edu.tr, http://www.who.int/ina-ngo/ngo/, http://crew.med.uoeh-u.ac.jp/~welcome.

599.8 DEU ISSN 0074-3895
INTERNATIONAL CONGRESS OF PRIMATOLOGY. PROCEEDINGS. Text in German. 1967. biennial. **Document type:** *Proceedings.*
Indexed: BiolAb.
Published by: International Primatological Society, c/o Dr. H.-J. Kuhn, German Primate Center, Kellnerweg 4, Goettingen, 37077, Germany.

599.9 USA ISSN 1064-3826
➤ **INTERNATIONAL DIRECTORY OF PRIMATOLOGY.** Text in English. 1992. biennial. price varies. adv. bk.rev. stat. **Document type:** *Directory, Academic/Scholarly.*
Published by: Wisconsin Primate Research Center, 1220 Capitol Ct, Madison, WI 53715-1299. TEL 608-263-3512, FAX 608-263-4031, hamel@primate.wisc.edu, http://www.primate.wisc.edu/pin/idp/.

➤ **INTERNATIONAL JOURNAL OF ACAROLOGY.** see *BIOLOGY—Entomology*

592.57 GBR ISSN 1368-8774
➤ **INTERNATIONAL JOURNAL OF NEMATOLOGY.** Text in English. 1991 (June). s-a. USD 80 per vol. in North America to individuals; GBP 45 per vol. elsewhere to individuals; USD 140 per vol. in North America to libraries; GBP 75 per vol. elsewhere to libraries (effective 2005). **Document type:** *Journal, Academic/Scholarly.* **Description:** Devoted to the publication of original research papers on all aspects of plant, soil, freshwater, marine and invertebrate nematology.
Formerly (until 1996): Afro - Asian Journal of Nematology (0963-6420)
Indexed: AEA, AgBio, AgrForAb, BioCN&I, CPA, FCA, FPA, ForAb, HelmAb, HortAb, I&DA, MaizeAb, NemAb, OrnHort, PBA, PGegResA, PHN&I, PotatoAb, RA&MP, RPP, RiceAb, S&F, SIA, SeedAb, SoyAb, TriticAb, WAE&RSA, WeedAb, ZooRec.
—BLDSC (4542.371700), IE. **CCC.**
Published by: (Afro-Asian Society of Nematologists IND), Novacrystal Publishing, 24 Brantwood Rd, Luton, Beds LU1 1JJ, United Kingdom. TEL 44-1582-726724, rsiddiqi@dialstart.net, http://www.ifns.org/membership/aasn.html. Ed., Pub. M R Siddiqi.

➤ **INTERNATIONAL JOURNAL OF ORAL BIOLOGY.** see *MEDICAL SCIENCES—Dentistry*

599.8 USA ISSN 0164-0291
QL737.P9 CODEN: IJPRDA
➤ **INTERNATIONAL JOURNAL OF PRIMATOLOGY.** Text in English. 1980. bi-m. EUR 975, USD 995, GBP 608 combined subscription to institutions print & online eds. (effective 2005). adv. bk.rev. back issues avail.; reprint service avail. from PSC. **Document type:** *Journal, Academic/Scholarly.* **Description:** Disseminates current research in fundamental primatology, with laboratory and field studies adressing both primate biology and conservation.
Related titles: Microfilm ed.: (from PQC); Online - full text ed.: ISSN 1573-8604 (from EBSCO Publishing, Gale Group, IngentaConnect, Kluwer Online, O C L C Online Computer Library Center, Inc., Springer LINK, Swets Information Services).
Indexed: ASCA, AgrForAb, AnBeAb, AnthLit, ApEcolAb, B&BAb, BIOBASE, BibLing, BiolAb, CPA, ChemAb, CurCont, DSA, ESPM, FoVS&M, ForAb, GEOBASE, GenetAb, HGA, HelmAb, IABS, IBSS, ISR, IndVet, NutrAb, PGegResA, ProtozoAb, PsycInfo, PsycholAb, RA&MP, RPP, RefZh, S&F, SCI, SFA, SIA, SSCI, SeedAb, TDB, VetBull, WildRev, ZooRec, e-psyche.
—BLDSC (4542.484000), CASDDS, CISTI, IDS, IE, Infotrieve, ingenta, Linda Hall. **CCC.**
Published by: Plenum US (Subsidiary of: Springer Science+Business Media), 233 Spring St, New York, NY 10013. TEL 212-460-1500, FAX 212-460-1575, service@springer-ny.com, http://springerlink.metapress.com/openurl.asp?genre=journal&issn=0164-0291, http://www.springeronline.com. Ed. Russell H Tuttle.

590 PAK ISSN 1811-9778
▼ ➤ **INTERNATIONAL JOURNAL OF ZOOLOGICAL RESEARCH.** Text in English. 2005. q. USD 350 (effective 2005). **Document type:** *Journal, Academic/Scholarly.* **Description:** Publishes on all branches of zoology: anatomy, physiology, genetics, reproductive biology, developmental biology, parasitology, morphology, behaviour, ecology, zoogeography, systematics and evolution. In general, the emphasis is on the fauna of the Australasian region.
Related titles: Online - full text ed.: ISSN 1811-9786. free (effective 2005).
Published by: Asian Network for Scientific Information, 308-Lasani Town, Sargodha Rd, Faislabad, 38090, Pakistan. TEL 92-41-2001145, FAX 92-41-731433, http://www.ansinet.org/c4p.php?j_id=ijzr, http://www.ansinet.net.

599.2 CZE
INTERNATIONAL STUDBOOK EQUUS PRZEWALSKI. Text in Czech, English. 1960. a. free to qualified personnel. reprints avail.
Related titles: Supplement(s): General Studbook.
Published by: Zoologicka Zahrada v Praze/Zoological Garden of Prague, U Trojskeho Zamku 3-120, Prague 7, 171 00, Czech Republic. TEL 420-2-90007332, FAX 420-2-6890369, zoo@zoo.cz. Ed. Evzen Kus.

595.5 GBR ISSN 1561-0721
SH381.A1
INTERNATIONAL WHALING COMMISSION. ANNUAL REPORT. Text in English. 1950. a. GBP 15, USD 25, EUR 30 (effective 2000). illus.; stat. back issues avail. **Document type:** *Corporate.*
Former titles (until 1999): International Whaling Commission. Report (0143-8700); (until 1977): International Commission on Whaling. Report (0074-9591)
Related titles: Microfiche ed.: (from CIS).
Indexed: ASFA, BiolAb, CIS, ESPM, IIS, OceAb, SFA, WildRev, ZooRec.
—BLDSC (1312.001000), IE, ingenta.
Published by: International Whaling Commission, The Red House,135 Station Rd, Impington, Cambs CB4 9NP, United Kingdom. TEL 44-1223-233971, FAX 44-1223-232876, secretariat@iwcoffice.org, http://www.iwcoffice.org. Ed. G P Donovan TEL 44-1223-233971. Circ: 500.

590 USA
INTERNATIONAL WILDLIFE REHABILITATION COUNCIL. INDIVIDUAL PAPERS. Text in English. irreg. price varies. back issues avail. **Document type:** *Monographic series, Academic/Scholarly.* **Description:** Discusses the rehabilitation of specific birds and mammals.
Published by: International Wildlife Rehabilitation Council, PO Box 8187, San Jose, CA 95155. TEL 707-864-1761, FAX 707-864-3106, iwrc@inreach.com, office@iwrc-online.org, http://www.iwrc-online.org.

INTERNATIONAL WOLF; the quarterly publication of the International Wolf Center. see *CONSERVATION*

590.73 GBR ISSN 0020-9155
INTERNATIONAL ZOO NEWS. Text in English. 1951. 8/yr. GBP 45 domestic; GBP 48, USD 80 foreign (effective 2005). adv. bk.rev. bibl.; illus.; stat. a.index. back issues avail. **Document type:** *Newsletter.* **Description:** Exchange of news, information and ideas between zoos worldwide.
Indexed: RefZh, SFA, WildRev, ZooRec.
—BLDSC (4552.550000), IE, ingenta.
Address: 80 Cleveland Rd, Chichester, W Sussex PO19 7AF, United Kingdom. TEL 44-1243-782803, ngouldizn@aol.com. Ed., R&P Nicholas Gould. Circ: 500.

590.73 GBR ISSN 0074-9664
QL76 CODEN: IZYBAE
➤ **INTERNATIONAL ZOO YEARBOOK.** Text in English. 1960. a. GBP 69 domestic; EUR 116, USD 126 foreign (effective 2004). adv. index, cum.index. back issues avail. **Document type:** *Directory, Academic/Scholarly.* **Description:** Constitutes an international forum for the exchange of information amongst zoos. Reflects zoos' unique opportunities for research and data collection as well as their role in conservation of biodiversity. It portrays the increasing public awareness of the need for conservation of species and habitats.
Indexed: AnBrAb, BIOSIS Prev, BiolAb, DSA, IndVet, KWIWR, SFA, VetBull, WildRev, ZooRec.
—BLDSC (4552.600000), IE, ingenta, Linda Hall. **CCC.**
Published by: Zoological Society of London, Regents Park, London, NW1 4RY, United Kingdom. TEL 44-20-74496281, FAX 44-20-74496411, yearbook@zsl.org, http://www.zsl.org/news/n_0000001315.asp. Eds. Fiona A Fisken TEL 44-20-7449-6282, Peter J S Olney. R&P Fiona A Fisken TEL 44-20-7449-6282. adv.: B&W page GBP 800, B&W page USD 1,300; trim 133 x 192. Circ: 1,000 (controlled).

592 USA ISSN 1077-8306
QL362 CODEN: TAMSAJ
➤ **INVERTEBRATE BIOLOGY.** Text in English. 1880. q. USD 187 combined subscription in the Americas to institutions & Caribbean, print & online eds.; GBP 114 combined subscription elsewhere to institutions print & online eds. (effective 2006); USD 38 membership (effective 2005). adv. bk.rev. bibl.; illus. index, cum.index: vols.1-80 (1880-1961). back issues avail.; reprint service avail. from PSC. **Document type:** *Journal, Academic/Scholarly.* **Description:** It publishes papers on all aspects of the biology of invertebrates-protozoans and metazoans, aquatic and terrestrial, free-living and symbiotic.
Formerly (until 1995): American Microscopical Society. Transactions (0003-0023)
Related titles: Microfilm ed.: (from PMC); Online - full text ed.: ISSN 1744-7410. USD 178 in the Americas to institutions & Caribbean; GBP 108 elsewhere to institutions (effective 2006) (from Blackwell Synergy, EBSCO Publishing, Gale Group, IngentaConnect, O C L C Online Computer Library Center, Inc.).
Indexed: ABIPC, ASCA, ASFA, AgBio, Agr, AnBeAb, AnBrAb, B&AI, BIOSIS Prev, BioCN&I, BiolAb, ChemAb, CurCont, DSA, ESPM, EntAb, ForAb, HGA, HelmAb, ISR, IndMed, IndVet, Inpharma, MEDLINE, NemAb, PE&ON, PHN&I, ProtozoAb, RM&VM, Reac, RefZh, RevApplEntom, S&F, SCI, SFA, VetBull, WildRev, ZooRec.
—BLDSC (4557.703195), CASDDS, CISTI, GNLM, IDS, IE, Infotrieve, ingenta, KNAW, Linda Hall. **CCC.**
Published by: (American Microscopical Society), Blackwell Publishing, Inc. (Subsidiary of: Blackwell Publishing Ltd.), Commerce Place, 350 Main St, Malden, MA 02148. TEL 781-388-8206, 800-835-6770, FAX 781-388-8232, http://www.invertebratebiology.org, http://www.blackwellpublishing.com. Eds. Elizabeth J Balser, Patrick D Reynolds. Circ: 1,200. **Co-sponsor:** American Society of Zoologists, Division of Invertebrate Zoology.

592 DEU ISSN 1354-2516
QL364 CODEN: INNEFP
➤ **INVERTEBRATE NEUROSCIENCE.** Text in English. 1995. q. (in 1 vol., 4 nos./vol.). EUR 360 combined subscription to institutions print & online eds. (effective 2005). adv. **Document type:** *Journal, Academic/Scholarly.* **Description:** Publishes articles on invertebrate neuroscience, including studies of molecular biology, development, neurogenetics, neurotoxicology and neuronal networks.
Related titles: Online - full text ed.: ISSN 1439-1104 (from EBSCO Publishing, Springer LINK, Swets Information Services).
Indexed: ASFA, BIOSIS Prev, BiolAb, CIN, ChemAb, ChemTitl, CurCont, EntAb, ExcerpMed, HelmAb, IndMed, Inpharma, MEDLINE, NSA, OceAb, Reac, RevApplEntom, ZooRec.
—BLDSC (4557.703530), CASDDS, CISTI, IDS, IE, Infotrieve, ingenta, Linda Hall. **CCC.**
Published by: Springer-Verlag (Subsidiary of: Springer Science+Business Media), Tiergartenstr 17, Heidelberg, 69121, Germany. TEL 49-6221-3450, FAX 49-6221-345229, http://link.springer.de/link/service/journals/10158/index.htm. Ed. Dr. Mark G Darlison. Adv. contact Stephan Kroeck TEL 49-30-827875739. **Subscr. in the Americas to:** Springer-Verlag New York, Inc., Journal Fulfillment, PO Box 2485, Secaucus, NJ 07096-2485. TEL 800-777-4643, 201-348-4033, FAX 201-348-4505, journals@springer-ny.com, http://www.springer-ny.com; **Subscr. to:** Springer GmbH Auslieferungsgesellschaft, Haberstr 7, Heidelberg 69126, Germany. TEL 49-6221-345-0, FAX 49-6221-345-4229, subscriptions@springer.de.

592 ISR ISSN 0792-4259
CODEN: IRDEE2
➤ **INVERTEBRATE REPRODUCTION AND DEVELOPMENT.** Text in English, French. 1979. bi-m. USD 450 to non-members; USD 125 to members (effective 2005). adv. bk.rev. bibl.; charts; illus. index. back issues avail.; reprint service avail. from PQC. **Document type:** *Academic/Scholarly.* **Description:** Papers on the sexual, reproductive and developmental biology of invertebrates.
Former titles (until 1989): International Journal of Invertebrate Reproduction and Development (0168-8170); (until 1984): International Journal of Invertebrate Reproduction (0165-1269)
Indexed: ASCA, ASFA, AgBio, Agr, AnBrAb, B&BAb, BIOBASE, BIOSIS Prev, BibAg, BioCN&I, BiolAb, CIN, ChemAb, ChemTitl, CurCont, ESPM, ExcerpMed, ForAb, GenetAb, HGA, HelmAb, IABS, ISR, IndVet, Inpharma, NemAb, PHN&I, ProtozoAb, RM&VM, Reac, RevApplEntom, S&F, SCI, SSCI, VetBull, WeedAb, ZooRec.
—BLDSC (4557.703600), CASDDS, CISTI, IDS, IE, Infotrieve, ingenta, Linda Hall. **CCC.**
Published by: (Mario Negri Sud Research Institute, School for Scientific Communication USA, International Society for Invertebrate Reproduction), Balaban Publishers, International Science Services, P O Box 2039, Rehovot, 76120, Israel. TEL 972-8-947-6216, FAX 972-8-946-7632, balabanm@netvision.net.il, http://sun.science.wayne.edu/~jram/isir.htm.

590 ITA ISSN 1824-307X
▼ ➤ **INVERTEBRATE SURVIVAL JOURNAL.** Abbreviated title: I S J. Text in English. 2004. irreg. free (effective 2005). **Document type:** *Journal, Academic/Scholarly.* **Description:** Devoted to innovative studies on the basic defense mechanisms in invertebrates, in particular with a view to identifying biotechnologies able to act against derived diseases and related economic damage.
Media: Online - full text.
Published by: Universita degli Studi di Modena e Reggio Emilia, Via Universita 4, Modena, 41100, Italy. TEL 39-059-2055111, http://www.isj.unimo.it/.

590 AUS
INVERTEBRATE SYSTEMATICS (ONLINE EDITION). Text in English. bi-m. AUD 160 domestic to individuals; USD 145 foreign to individuals; AUD 800 domestic to institutions; USD 700 foreign to institutions (effective 2005). back issues avail. **Document type:** *Journal, Academic/Scholarly.*
Formerly (until 2001): Invertebrate Taxonomy (Online Edition) (1445-4572)
Media: Online - full text (from EBSCO Publishing, Gale Group, O C L C Online Computer Library Center, Inc., Swets Information Services). **Related titles:** Microfiche ed.: (from PQC); ♦ Print ed.: Invertebrate Systematics (Print Edition). ISSN 1445-5226.
Published by: C S I R O Publishing, 150 Oxford St, PO Box 1139, Collingwood, VIC 3066, Australia. TEL 61-3-96627629, FAX 61-3-96627611, publishing@csiro.au, http://www.publish.csiro.au/journal/is. Ed. Camilla Myers.

571.3 AUS ISSN 1445-5226
QL362.5 CODEN: ISNYAD
➤ **INVERTEBRATE SYSTEMATICS (PRINT EDITION);** Australian journal of scientific research. Text in English. 1971. bi-m. AUD 180 combined subscription domestic to individuals print & online eds.; USD 180 combined subscription foreign to individuals print & online eds.; AUD 890 combined subscription domestic to institutions print & online eds.; USD 790 combined subscription foreign to institutions print & online eds. (effective 2005). adv. index. back issues avail. **Document type:** *Journal, Academic/Scholarly.* **Description:** Covers taxonomy and systematics of invertebrates of the southern hemisphere and Indo-Pacific Region.
Former titles (until 2001): Invertebrate Taxonomy (Print Edition) (0818-0164); (until 1987): Australian Journal of Zoology, Supplementary Series (0310-9089)
Related titles: Microfiche ed.: (from PQC); ♦ Online - full text ed.: Invertebrate Systematics (Online Edition).
Indexed: ASFA, AgBio, AgrForAb, BIOBASE, BIOSIS Prev, BioCN&I, BiolAb, CurCont, ESPM, EntAb, FCA, FPA, ForAb, GEOBASE, HelmAb, HortAb, IABS, ISR, IndVet, OrnHort, PBA, PGegResA, RM&VM, RPP, RevApplEntom, S&F, SCI, SIA, VITIS, VetBull, ZooRec.
—BLDSC (4557.703670), CISTI, IDS, IE, ingenta, Linda Hall. **CCC.**
Published by: (C S I R O Australia), C S I R O Publishing, 150 Oxford St, PO Box 1139, Collingwood, VIC 3066, Australia. TEL 61-3-96627629, FAX 61-3-96627611, publishing.is@csiro.au, publishing@csiro.au, http://www.publish.csiro.au/journals/is. Circ: 500. **Co-sponsor:** Australian Academy of Science.

597 CHL ISSN 0716-1328
SH237
INVESTIGACION PESQUERA. Text in Spanish; Summaries in English. 1965. a. USD 10. abstr.; bibl.; charts; stat. **Document type:** *Academic/Scholarly.*
Formed by the 1984 merger of: Instituto de Fomento Pesquero. Serie Investigacion Pesquera (0716-4920); Instituto de Fomento Pesquero. Serie Informes Pesqueros (0716-4939); Both of which were formed by the 1974 merger of: Instituto de Fomento Pesquero. Publicacion (0080-6153); Instituto de Fomento Pesquero. Circular (0716-4912); Instituto de Fomento Pesquero. Boletin Cientifico (0374-8200)
Media: Duplicated (not offset).
Indexed: ASFA, BiolAb, ESPM, SFA.
—CISTI.
Published by: Instituto de Fomento Pesquero, Casilla 8-V, Valparaiso, Chile. Ed. Zaida Young U. Circ: 600.

591.95694 ISR ISSN 0021-2210
QL1 CODEN: IJZOAE
➤ **ISRAEL JOURNAL OF ZOOLOGY.** Text in English. 1951. q. USD 340 (effective 2002). adv. charts; illus. index. **Document type:** *Journal, Academic/Scholarly.* **Description:** Publishes research and review articles in all fields of zoology, with special emphasis on the fauna of terrestrial and marine environments in Israel, the Near East, the Red Sea and Eastern Mediterranean region.
Related titles: Online - full content ed.; Online - full text ed.: (from EBSCO Publishing).
Indexed: ASCA, ASFA, AbHyg, AgBio, AnBeAb, AnBrAb, ApEcolAb, B&BAb, BIOSIS Prev, BioCN&I, BiolAb, ChemAb, CurCont, ESPM, EntAb, FCA, ForAb, GEOBASE, GenetAb, HGA, HelmAb, HerbAb, HortAb, I&DA, ISR, IndVet, KWIWR, MEDLINE, PGegResA, PN&I, PhilInd, PoultAb, RM&VM, RRTA, RevApplEntom, RiceAb, S&F, SCI, SFA, TDB, VITIS, VetBull, WeedAb, WildRev, ZooRec.
—BLDSC (4583.818000), CISTI, GNLM, IDS, IE, Infotrieve, ingenta, Linda Hall. **CCC.**
Published by: Laser Pages Publishing Ltd., P O Box 35409, Jerusalem, 91352, Israel. laserpages@netmedia.net.il, http://www.sciencefromisrael.com. Eds. A Allan Degen, Micha Ilan. R&P Rachel Lichtensztajn. Adv. contact Elcya Weiss. Circ: 325.

590 ITA ISSN 1121-4120
ISTITUTO NAZIONALE PER LA FAUNA SELVATICA. DOCUMENTI TECNICI. Text in Italian. 1986. irreg. per issue exchange basis. **Document type:** *Monographic series.*
Published by: Istituto Nazionale per la Fauna Selvatica, Via Ca Fornacetta, 9, Ozzano Dell'emilia, BO 40064, Italy. TEL 39-51-6512111, FAX 39-51-796628, infsammi@iperbole.bologna.it. Ed. Mario Spagnesi. Circ: 2,000.

591.945 GBR ISSN 1125-0003
QL1
ITALIAN JOURNAL OF ZOOLOGY. Text and summaries in English. 1930. q. GBP 100, USD 165 combined subscription to institutions print & online eds. (effective 2006). adv. bk.rev. **Document type:** *Journal, Academic/Scholarly.*
Formerly (until 1996): Bollettino di Zoologia (0373-4137)
Related titles: Online - full text ed.: GBP 95, USD 156 to institutions (effective 2006).
Indexed: ASCA, ASFA, AgBio, AnBrAb, B&BAb, BiolAb, CIN, ChemAb, ChemTitl, CurCont, ESPM, EntAb, ForAb, GEOBASE, GenetAb, HGA, HelmAb, HortAb, IndVet, NutrAb, ProtozoAb, RM&VM, RRTA, RevApplEntom, S&F, SFA, TDB, VetBull, WeedAb, ZooRec.
—BLDSC (4588.341620), CASDDS, CISTI, IDS, IE, ingenta.
Published by: (Universita degli Studi di Modena e Reggio Emilia, Dipartimento di Biologia Animale ITA, Unione Zoologica Italiana ITA), Taylor & Francis Ltd (Subsidiary of: Taylor & Francis Group), 4 Park Sq, Milton Park, Abingdon, OX14 4RN, United Kingdom. info@tandf.co.uk, http://www.tandf.co.uk/journals. Circ: 500 (controlled).

597 ZAF ISSN 0251-1258
QL614 CODEN: ICHBB7
➤ **J L B SMITH INSTITUTE OF ICHTHYOLOGY. ICHTHYOLOGICAL BULLETIN.** Text in English. 1956. irreg., latest vol.70, 2001. USD 30 (effective 2001); includes Special Publications. abstr.; bibl. cum.index. back issues avail. **Document type:** *Bulletin, Academic/Scholarly.* **Description:** Discusses latest research conducted on a wide variety of topics pertaining to fish.
Formerly (until 1972): Ichthyological Bulletin (0073-4381)
Indexed: ASFA, BIOSIS Prev, BiolAb, ESPM, OceAb, RefZh, SFA, WildRev, ZooRec.
Published by: J L B Smith Institute of Ichthyology, Private Bag 1015, Grahamstown, East Cape 6140, South Africa. TEL 27-46-6361002, FAX 27-46-6222403, TELEX 244219 SA, ihphp.heemstra@ru.ac.za, http://www.ru.ac.za/affiliates/JLB/. Ed., R&P Phillip C Heemstra. Circ: 1,000 (controlled). **Co-sponsors:** South African National Research Foundation; South Africa Department of Arts, Culture, Science and Technology.

597 ZAF ISSN 0075-2088
QL614 CODEN: SPSIEF
➤ **J L B SMITH INSTITUTE OF ICHTHYOLOGY. SPECIAL PUBLICATION.** Text in English. 1967. irreg., latest vol.66, 2001. USD 30 (effective 2001); includes Ichthyological Bulletin. abstr.; bibl.; charts; illus.; stat. index. back issues avail. **Document type:** *Academic/Scholarly.* **Description:** Publishes short original research papers on fish systematics, zoogeography, ecology and biology.
Indexed: ASFA, BIOSIS Prev, BiolAb, ESPM, OceAb, RefZh, SFA, WildRev, ZooRec.
—Linda Hall.
Published by: J L B Smith Institute of Ichthyology, Private Bag 1015, Grahamstown, East Cape 6140, South Africa. TEL 27-46-6361002, FAX 27-46-6222403. R&P Phillip C Heemstra. Circ: 1,000 (controlled). **Co-sponsors:** South African National Research Foundation; South Africa Ministry of Arts, Culture, Science, and Technology.

➤ **J N C C REPORTS.** see *CONSERVATION*

591.5 JPN
JAPAN ETHOLOGICAL SOCIETY. NEWSLETTER. Text in Japanese. 1983. s-a. bk.rev. **Document type:** *Newsletter.*
Published by: Nippon Dobutsu Kodo Gakkai/Japan Ethological Society, Daigaku Rigakubu Dobutsugaku Kyoshitsu, Kita-Shirakawaoiwake-cho, Sakyo-ku, Kyoto-shi, 606-8224, Japan. Ed. Yoshihisa Mori.

JAPAN SOCIETY OF MEDICAL ENTOMOLOGY AND ZOOLOGY. see *BIOLOGY—Entomology*

599.74 JPN
JAPANESE PELAGIC INVESTIGATION ON FUR SEALS. Text in Japanese. 1958. a. free to qualified personnel.
Published by: National Research Institute of Far Seas Fisheries, 5-7-1 Ori-Do, shimizu-shi, Shizuoka-ken 424-0902, Japan. TEL 0543-340-715, FAX 0543-359-642. Circ: 100.

590 JPN
JAPANESE SOCIETY OF ANIMAL SCIENCE. ANNUAL MEETING. Text in English, Japanese. a. **Document type:** *Academic/Scholarly.*

B

▼ *new title* ➤ *refereed* ✶ *unverified* ♦ *full entry avail.*

—BLDSC (1087.924450).
Published by: Japanese Society of Animal Science/Nihon Chikusan Gakkai, 201 Nagatani Corporas, Ikenohata 2-9-4, Taito-ku, Tokyo, 110-0008, Japan. TEL 81-3-3828-8409, FAX 81-3-3828-7649, http://wwwsoc.nacsis.ac.jp/jszs/index.html.

590 AUT ISSN 1562-9430
QL1
JOANNEA ZOOLOGIE. Text and summaries in German, English. 1972. a. price varies. bk.rev. illus.; tr.lit. index. **Document type:** *Journal, Academic/Scholarly.*
Former titles (until 1999): Landesmuseum Joanneum. Zoologie. Mitteilungen (1027-3174); (until 1995): Landesmuseum Joanneum. Abteilung fuer Zoologie. Mitteilungen (1018-6069)
Indexed: ZooRec.
—BLDSC (5857.676000).
Published by: Landesmuseum Joanneum, Raubergasse 10, Graz, St 8010, Austria. TEL 43-316-80179760, FAX 43-316-80179800, juliana.madler@stmk.gv.at, http://www.museum-joanneum.steiermark.at. Eds. Juliana Madler, Karl Adlbauer TEL 43-316-80179761. R&P Karl Adlbauer TEL 43-316-80179761. Circ: 600.

594 AUS ISSN 0021-7719
CODEN: JCNYAE
JOURNAL DE CONCHYLIOLOGIE. Text and summaries in English, French, Multiple languages. 1850. q. price varies. bk.rev. abstr.; bibl.; charts; illus. index, cum.index.
—Linda Hall.
Address: Ed. Dr. P.H. Fischer, 18/55 Prince Albert St, Mosman, NSW 2088, Australia.

591.994 IND ISSN 0253-7214
QL1 CODEN: JAZODX
➤ **JOURNAL OF ADVANCED ZOOLOGY;** J. Adv. Zool. Text in English. 1980. s-a. INR 300, USD 50 (effective 2000). adv. bk.rev. abstr.; bibl. 75 p./no. 2 cols./p.; back issues avail. **Document type:** *Journal, Academic/Scholarly.*
Indexed: ASFA, AgBio, AgrForAb, AnBrAb, BIOSIS Prev, BioCN&I, BiolAb, CPA, CurCont, ForAb, HelmAb, HortAb, IndVet, NutrAb, OrnHort, PBA, PHN&I, ProtozoAb, RA&MP, RM&VM, RPP, RevApplEntom, S&F, SIA, SoyAb, TDB, VetBull, ZooRec.
—BLDSC (4918.947900), CISTI, IDS, IE, ingenta.
Published by: Association for the Advancement of Zoology, 305-C, Azadnagar Colony, P.O. Sheopuri, Gorakhpur, Uttar Pradesh 273 016, India. TEL 91-551-320925, FAX 91-551-344832, geag@nde.vsnl.net.in. Ed. S P Tripathi. Pub., R&P, Adv. contact S.P. Tripathi. Circ: 200 (paid); 250 (controlled). **Dist. by:** Central News Agency, 23-90, Connaught Circus, New Delhi 110 001, India.

591.96 BEL ISSN 0776-7943
QL336
JOURNAL OF AFRICAN ZOOLOGY. Text in English, French. 1911. bi-m. USD 149 in North America. charts; illus. index. **Document type:** *Journal, Academic/Scholarly.*
Former titles (until vol.108, 1994): Revue de Zoologie Africaine (0251-074X); (until 1974): Revue de Zoologie et de Botanique Africaines (0035-1814)
Indexed: ASFA, BioCN&I, BiolAb, ESPM, ForAb, GEOBASE, HelmAb, HortAb, IndVet, MaizeAb, NemAb, NutrAb, PoultAb, ProtozoAb, RevApplEntom, S&F, SFA, SoyAb, TDB, WAE&RSA, ZooRec.
—CISTI, Linda Hall.
Published by: (Musee Royal de l'Afrique Centrale/Koninklijk Museum voor Midden-Afrika), Editions AGAR a.s.b.l., Venelle du Bois de Saras 39, Wavre, 1300, Belgium. http://www.biol.ucl.ac.be/ecol/JAZ/JAZ.HomePage.html. Ed. Dr. H M Andre.

JOURNAL OF ANIMAL ECOLOGY. see *BIOLOGY*

JOURNAL OF ANIMAL PHYSIOLOGY AND ANIMAL NUTRITION/ZEITSCHRIFT FUER TIERPHYSIOLOGIE UND TIERERNAEHRUNG. see *BIOLOGY—Physiology*

JOURNAL OF ANIMAL PHYSIOLOGY AND ANIMAL NUTRITION ONLINE. see *BIOLOGY—Physiology*

590 IND ISSN 0971-2119
CODEN: JANREH
➤ **JOURNAL OF APPLIED ANIMAL RESEARCH.** Text in English; Summaries in Hindi. 1992. q. USD 100 (effective 2003). adv. bk.rev. illus. reprints avail. **Document type:** *Journal, Academic/Scholarly.* **Description:** Publishes original research work on all aspects of biological sciences applied to domestic and wild animals.
Indexed: AEA, ASCA, AgBio, AgrForAb, AnBrAb, BIOSIS Prev, BiolAb, CIN, ChemAb, ChemTitl, CurCont, DSA, FPA, FS&TA, ForAb, HelmAb, HerbAb, HortAb, IndVet, MaizeAb, NutrAb, PBA, PN&I, PotatoAb, PoultAb, ProtozoAb, RA&MP, RDA, RM&VM, RPP, RevApplEntom, RiceAb, S&F, SIA, SoyAb, TDB, TriticAb, VetBull, WAE&RSA.
—BLDSC (4939.920000), CASDDS, IDS, IE, ingenta. **CCC.**
Published by: Garuda Scientific Publications, 151 Janakpuri, Izatnagar, 243 122, India. TEL 91-581-2302923, FAX 91-581-2550147, jaarindia@yahoo.com. Ed. D K Agrawal. R&P, Adv. contact Shashi Agrawal.

597 DEU ISSN 0175-8659
QL614 CODEN: ZAICEL
➤ **JOURNAL OF APPLIED ICHTHYOLOGY/ZEITSCHRIFT FUER ANGEWANDTE ICHTHYOLOGIE.** Text in English. 1984. 6/yr., latest vol.18, no.6, 2002. EUR 309 combined subscription in Europe to individuals print & online eds.; USD 346 combined subscription in the Americas to individuals & Caribbean (print & online eds.); GBP 206 combined subscription elsewhere to individuals print & online eds.; GBP 455 combined subscription in Europe to institutions print & online eds.; USD 842 combined subscription in the Americas to institutions & Caribbean (print & online eds.); GBP 501 combined subscription elsewhere to institutions print & online eds. (effective 2006). bk.rev. **Document type:** *Journal, Academic/Scholarly.* **Description:** Publishes articles by scientists of international repute on ichthyology, aquaculture, marine fisheries, environmental toxicology using fishes as test organisms, and basic research on fish management.
Related titles: ♦ Online - full text ed.: Journal of Applied Ichthyology Online. ISSN 1439-0426.
Indexed: AEA, ASCA, ASFA, AgBio, AgrForAb, AnBrAb, B&BAb, BIOSIS Prev, BiolAb, CIN, CRFR, ChemAb, ChemTitl, CurCont, DBA, DSA, ESPM, FS&TA, GEOBASE, HelmAb, HortAb, ISR, IndVet, MaizeAb, NemAb, NutrAb, OceAb, PGegResA, PotatoAb, PoultAb, ProtozoAb, RM&VM, RefZh, RevApplEntom, SCI, SFA, SWRA, SoyAb, TriticAb, VetBull, WAE&RSA, WildRev, ZooRec.
—BLDSC (4942.620000), CASDDS, CINDOC, CISTI, IDS, IE, Infotrieve, ingenta, Linda Hall. **CCC.**
Published by: Blackwell Verlag GmbH (Subsidiary of: Blackwell Publishing Ltd.), Kurfuerstendamm 57, Berlin, 10707, Germany. TEL 49-30-32790634, FAX 49-30-32790610, verlag@blackwell.de, http://www.blackwellpublishing.com/journals/JAI, http://www.blackwell.de. Ed. H Rosenthal. Circ: 340.

597 DEU ISSN 1439-0426
QL614
JOURNAL OF APPLIED ICHTHYOLOGY ONLINE. Text in English. bi-m. GBP 432 in Europe to institutions; USD 800 in the Americas to institutions & Caribbean; GBP 476 elsewhere to institutions (effective 2006). **Document type:** *Academic/Scholarly.*
Media: Online - full text (from Blackwell Synergy, EBSCO Publishing, Gale Group, IngentaConnect, O C L C Online Computer Library Center, Inc., Swets Information Services). **Related titles:** ♦ Print ed.: Journal of Applied Ichthyology. ISSN 0175-8659.
Published by: Blackwell Verlag GmbH (Subsidiary of: Blackwell Publishing Ltd.), Kurfuerstendamm 57, Berlin, 10707, Germany. TEL 49-30-32790665, FAX 49-30-32790610, abo@blackwis.de, http://www.blackwell-science.com/~cgilib/jnlpage.bin?Journal=XJAI&File=XJAI&Page=aims; http://www.blackwell.de.

590.7 IND ISSN 0970-9304
SF84
JOURNAL OF APPLIED ZOOLOGICAL RESEARCHES. Text in English. 1990. s-a. INR 150 domestic to individuals; USD 40 foreign to individuals; INR 500 domestic to institutions; USD 100 foreign to institutions (effective 2003).
Indexed: AgBio, AgrForAb, AnBrAb, BioCN&I, CPA, DSA, FCA, FPA, ForAb, HelmAb, HerbAb, HortAb, I&DA, IndVet, MaizeAb, NemAb, NutrAb, OrnHort, PBA, PGegResA, PGrRegA, PHN&I, PN&I, PotatoAb, PoultAb, ProtozoAb, RA&MP, RDA, RM&VM, RPP, RiceAb, S&F, SIA, SeedAb, SoyAb, TDB, TriticAb, VetBull, WAE&RSA, WeedAb.
—BLDSC (4947.140000).
Published by: Applied Zoologists Research Association, C/o Dr. Anand Prakash, General Secretary (AZRA), Division of Entomology, Central Rice Research Institute, Cuttack, Orissa 753 006, India.

JOURNAL OF AQUATIC SCIENCES. see *FISH AND FISHERIES*

595.4 USA ISSN 0161-8202
QL451 CODEN: JARCDP
➤ **JOURNAL OF ARACHNOLOGY.** Text in English, French, Portuguese, Spanish. 1973. 3/yr. USD 40 to individuals; USD 125 to institutions; USD 25 to students (effective 2004). bk.rev. cum.index: vols.1-10. back issues avail. **Document type:** *Journal, Academic/Scholarly.* **Description:** Devoted to the study of Arachnida.
Related titles: Online - full text ed.: (from BioOne, C S A, O C L C Online Computer Library Center, Inc.).
Indexed: ASCA, ASFA, Agr, BIOSIS Prev, BioCN&I, BiolAb, CurCont, EntAb, ISR, RM&VM, RefZh, RevApplEntom, S&F, SCI, SoyAb, VITIS, WeedAb, ZooRec.
—BLDSC (4947.172000), CISTI, IDS, IE, Infotrieve, ingenta, Linda Hall.
Published by: American Arachnological Society, c/o Norman I Platnick, Division of Invertebrete Zoology, American Museum of Natural History, Central Park W at 79th St, New York, NY 10024. TEL 212-769-5612, FAX 212-769-5277, http://www.americanarachnology.org/JOA.html. Circ: 600 (paid).

599.6362 IND ISSN 0971-6777
➤ **JOURNAL OF CAMEL PRACTICE AND RESEARCH.** Text in English. 1994. s-a. INR 750 domestic to individuals; USD 75 foreign to individuals (effective 2001). adv. bk.rev. 100 p./no. 2 cols./p.; back issues avail. **Document type:** *Academic/Scholarly.* **Description:** Publishes manuscripts, postgraduate theses abstracts, news and other information related to the new and old world camelids.
Indexed: AbHyg, AgBio, AgrForAb, AnBrAb, DSA, FoVS&M, HelmAb, HerbAb, HortAb, IndVet, NutrAb, PBA, PN&I, ProtozoAb, RDA, RM&VM, RevApplEntom, S&F, SIA, TDB, VetBull, WAE&RSA.
—BLDSC (4954.742400), IE, ingenta.
Published by: Camel Publishing House, 67 Gandhi Nagar West, Near Lalgarh Palace, Bikaner, Rajasthan 334 001, India. TEL 91-151-521282, FAX 91-151-209286, tkedjcpr@datainfosys.net. Ed., R&P T.K. Gahlot TEL 91-151-527029. Adv. contact T K Gahlot. B&W page USD 850, color page USD 1,400; trim 11 x 8.5. Circ: 750.

590 GBR ISSN 1561-0713
QL737.C4
➤ **THE JOURNAL OF CETACEAN RESEARCH AND MANAGEMENT.** Text in English. 1999. 3/yr. GBP 75, EUR 120, USD 140 to individuals; GBP 110, EUR 175, USD 200 to institutions; GBP 25, EUR 45, USD 45 per issue (effective 2004); (subscr. includes The Journal of Cetacean Research and Management. Supplement). index. 2 cols./p.; back issues avail. **Document type:** *Journal, Academic/Scholarly.* **Description:** Publishes papers on those matters of most importance to the conservation and management of whales, dolphins and porpoises, and in particular papers that are relevant to the tasks of the IWC Scientific Committee.
Related titles: Supplement(s): GBP 45, EUR 70, USD 80 per issue (effective 2004).
Indexed: ASFA, B&BAb, BIOSIS Prev, BiolAb, ESPM, OceAb, ZooRec.
—BLDSC (4955.120000), IE, ingenta.
Published by: International Whaling Commission, The Red House,135 Station Rd, Impington, Cambs CB4 9NP, United Kingdom. TEL 44-1223-233971, FAX 44-1223-232876, secretariat@iwcoffice.org, http://www.iwcoffice.org/publications/JCRM.htm. Ed., R&P G P Donovan TEL 44-1223-233971.

594 GBR ISSN 0022-0019
QL401
➤ **JOURNAL OF CONCHOLOGY.** Text in English. 1874. s-a. GBP 32 domestic to members with magazine; GBP 35 foreign to members with magazine; GBP 37 domestic to non-members; GBP 40 foreign to non-members; GBP 42, GBP 45 domestic to non-members with magazine (effective 2003). bk.rev. bibl.; charts; illus.; maps. cum.index every 3 yrs. 2 cols./p.; back issues avail. **Document type:** *Journal, Academic/Scholarly.* **Description:** Contains scientific papers on all aspects of the study of Mollusca, and communications on Molluscan Topics of worldwide interests.
Related titles: Microform ed.: (from PQC).
Indexed: ASCA, ASFA, BIOSIS Prev, BioCN&I, BiolAb, CurCont, ESPM, ForAb, HelmAb, ISR, S&F, SCI, WeedAb, ZooRec.
—BLDSC (4965.000000), CISTI, IE, Infotrieve, ingenta.
Published by: Conchological Society of Great Britain and Ireland, c/o Mr. M.D. Weideli, 35 Bartlemy Rd, Newbury, Berks RG14 6LD, United Kingdom. TEL 44-1635-42190, FAX 44-1635-820904, membership@conchsoc.org, Mike_Weideli@compuserve.com, http://www.conchsoc.org. Ed. P G Oliver. Circ: 800.

595.3 USA ISSN 0278-0372
QL435.A1 CODEN: JCBIDB
➤ **JOURNAL OF CRUSTACEAN BIOLOGY.** Text in English. 1981. q. USD 105 in North America; USD 125 elsewhere (effective 2004). bk.rev. back issues avail. **Document type:** *Academic/Scholarly.* **Description:** Provides international exchange of information among persons interested in any aspect of crustacean studies.
Related titles: Online - full text ed.: (from BioOne, C S A, O C L C Online Computer Library Center, Inc.).
Indexed: ASCA, ASFA, AgBio, AnBrAb, BIOBASE, BIOSIS Prev, BiolAb, BiolDig, ChemAb, CurCont, ESPM, EntAb, GenetAb, HelmAb, IABS, ISR, IndVet, MSCT, NutrAb, OceAb, ProtozoAb, RM&VM, RefZh, SCI, SFA, VetBull, ZooRec.
—BLDSC (4965.680000), CASDDS, IDS, IE, Infotrieve, ingenta, Linda Hall.
Published by: Crustacean Society, 810 E 10th St, Box 1897, Lawrence, KS 66044. TEL 913-843-1221, FAX 913-843-1274, http://www.vims.edu/tcs/. Ed. Arthur G Humes. Circ: 1,100.

595.7 PAK ISSN 1812-5670
▼ ➤ **JOURNAL OF ENTOMOLOGY.** Text in English. 2004. q. USD 350 (effective 2005). **Document type:** *Journal, Academic/Scholarly.* **Description:** Publishes articles within the broadest bounds in the field of entomology.
Related titles: Online - full text ed.: ISSN 1812-5689. free (effective 2005).
Published by: Asian Network for Scientific Information, 308-Lasani Town, Sargodha Rd, Faislabad, 38090, Pakistan. TEL 92-41-2001145, FAX 92-41-731433, http://www.ansinet.org/c4p.php?j_id=je, http://www.ansinet.net.

➤ **JOURNAL OF ETHNOBIOLOGY.** see *ANTHROPOLOGY*

➤ **JOURNAL OF ETHNOBIOLOGY AND ETHNOMEDICINE.** see *MEDICAL SCIENCES*

591.5 JPN ISSN 0289-0771
QL750 CODEN: JOETE8
➤ **JOURNAL OF ETHOLOGY.** Text in English. 1983. s-a. (in 1 vol., 2 nos./vol.). EUR 173.10 combined subscription to institutions print & online eds. (effective 2005). **Document type:** *Journal, Academic/Scholarly.* **Description:** Contains scientific papers of ethology and related research areas.
Related titles: Online - full text ed.: ISSN 1439-5444 (from EBSCO Publishing, Springer LINK, Swets Information Services).
Indexed: ASCA, ASFA, Agr, AnBeAb, AnBrAb, BIOBASE, BIOSIS Prev, BioCN&I, BiolAb, CurCont, EntAb, ForAb, IABS, IndVet, NutrAb, PN&I, RM&VM, RefZh, RevApplEntom, SFA, WildRev, ZooRec.
—BLDSC (4979.602500), IDS, IE, Infotrieve, ingenta. **CCC.**
Published by: (Nippon Dobutsu Kodo Gakkai/Japan Ethological Society), Springer-Verlag Tokyo (Subsidiary of: Springer Science+Business Media), 3-13 Hongo 3-chome, Bunkyo-ku, Tokyo, 113-0033, Japan. TEL 81-3-38120331, FAX 81-3-38187454, http://link.springer.de/link/service/journals/10164/index.htm, http://www.springer-tokyo.co.jp/. Ed. Kazuki Tsuji. Adv. contact Stephan Kroeck TEL 49-30-827875739. **Subscr. in the Americas to:** Springer-Verlag New York, Inc., Journal Fulfillment, PO Box 2485, Secaucus, NJ 07096-2485. TEL 800-777-4643, 201-348-4033, FAX 201-348-4505, journals@springer-ny.com, http://www.springer-ny.com; **Subscr. to:** Springer GmbH Auslieferungsgesellschaft, Haberstr 7, Heidelberg 69126, Germany. TEL 49-6221-345-0, FAX 49-6221-345-4229, subscriptions@springer.de.

590 IND ISSN 0972-0030
JOURNAL OF EXPERIMENTAL ZOOLOGY INDIA. Text in English. 1998. s-a. INR 500 domestic to institutions; USD 70 foreign to institutions (effective 2004). adv. **Document type:** *Journal, Academic/Scholarly.*
Indexed: AbHyg, AgrForAb, AnBrAb, BIOSIS Prev, BioCN&I, BiolAb, DSA, FCA, FPA, ForAb, HelmAb, HerbAb, HortAb, IndVet, NemAb, OrnHort, PBA, PGrRegA, PHN&I, PotatoAb, PoultAb, ProtozoAb, RA&MP, RPP, RefZh, S&F, SIA, SeedAb, SoyAb, TDB, WeedAb.
—BLDSC (4983.005000).
Published by: P.R. / Yadhav, Ed. & Pub., Department of Zoology, D.A.V. (PG) College, Muzaffarnagar, Uttar Pradesh 251 001, India. TEL 91-131-2404278, FAX 91-131-431035, yadavpry@rediffmail.com. Ed., Pub. P.R. Yadav. adv.: page INR 2,000, page USD 200.

590.724 USA ISSN 1548-8969
QL1 CODEN: JEZOAO
➤ **JOURNAL OF EXPERIMENTAL ZOOLOGY PART A: COMPARATIVE EXPERIMENTAL BIOLOGY.** Variant title: Comparative Experimental Biology. Text in English. 1904. m. USD 6,550 domestic to institutions; USD 6,766 in Canada & Mexico to institutions; USD 6,892 elsewhere to institutions; USD 7,205 combined subscription domestic to institutions print & online eds.; USD 7,421 combined subscription in Canada & Mexico to institutions print & online eds.; USD 7,547 combined subscription elsewhere to institutions print & online eds. (effective 2006); Subscr. includes Journal of Experimental Zoology Part B: Molecular and Developmental Evolution. adv. abstr.; bibl.; charts; illus. index. back issues avail.; reprints avail. **Document type:** *Journal, Academic/Scholarly.*
Description: Reports the results of original research of an experimental or analytical nature in zoology, including investigations of all levels of biological organization, from the molecular to the organismal.
Supersedes in part (until 2003): The Journal of Experimental Zoology (0022-104X)
Related titles: Microform ed.: (from PMC, PQC, SWZ); Online - full content ed.: ISSN 1552-499X. 1998. USD 6,550 to institutions (effective 2006); Online - full text ed.: (from EBSCO Publishing, Swets Information Services, Wiley InterScience); ♦ Series: Journal of Experimental Zoology Part B: Molecular and Developmental Evolution. ISSN 1552-5007; ♦ Supplement(s): Journal of Experimental Zoology. Supplement. ISSN 1059-8324.
Indexed: ASCA, ASFA, AgBio, AnBrAb, B&AI, BIOBASE, BIOSIS Prev, BioCN&I, BiolAb, CIN, CRFR, CTA, ChemAb, ChemTitl, CurCont, DSA, EntAb, ExcerpMed, HelmAb, HortAb, IABS, ISR, IndMed, IndVet, Inpharma, KWIWR, MEDLINE, MaizeAb, NSCI, NemAb, NutrAb, PBA, PGegResA, PHN&I, PN&I, PoultAb, ProtozoAb, RM&VM, Reac, RefZh, RevApplEntom, S&F, SCI, SFA, SIA, TriticAb, VetBull, WildRev, ZooRec.
—BLDSC (4983.007000), CASDDS, CISTI, GNLM, IDS, IE, ingenta, Linda Hall.
Published by: John Wiley & Sons, Inc., 111 River St, Hoboken, NJ 07030-5774. TEL 201-748-6000, FAX 201-748-5915, jez@yale.edu, uscs-wis@wiley.com, http://www.interscience.wiley.com/jpages/0022-104X/, http://www.wiley.com. Ed. Francis Ruddle. adv.: B&W page GBP 640, color page GBP 1,515; trim 210 x 279. Circ: 1,200.

572 590 USA ISSN 1552-5007
JOURNAL OF EXPERIMENTAL ZOOLOGY PART B: MOLECULAR AND DEVELOPMENTAL EVOLUTION. Variant title: Molecular and Developmental Evolution. Text in English. m. USD 5,995 domestic to institutions; USD 6,175 in Canada & Mexico to institutions; USD 6,328 elsewhere to institutions; USD 6,595 combined subscription domestic to institutions print & online eds.; USD 6,775 combined subscription in Canada & Mexico to institutions print & online eds.; USD 6,928 combined subscription elsewhere to institutions print & online eds. (effective 2005); Included with a subscription to Journal of Experimental Zoology Part A: Comparative Experimental Biology. back issues avail. **Document type:** *Journal, Academic/Scholarly.*
Supersedes in part (until 2003): The Journal of Experimental Zoology (0022-104X)
Related titles: Online - full text ed.: ISSN 1552-5015. USD 5,995 to institutions (effective 2005); Included with a subscription to Journal of Experimental Zoology Part A: Comparative Experimental Biology (from EBSCO Publishing, Swets Information Services, Wiley InterScience); ♦ Series: Journal of Experimental Zoology Part A: Comparative Experimental Biology. ISSN 1548-8969; Supplement(s):.
Indexed: CurCont, SCI.
—BLDSC (4963.000000), ingenta.
Published by: John Wiley & Sons, Inc., 111 River St, Hoboken, NJ 07030-5774. TEL 201-748-6000, FAX 201-748-5915, uscs-wis@wiley.com, http://www.interscience.wiley.com/jpages/0022-104X:1/, http://www.wiley.com, http://www3.interscience.wiley.com/journalfinder.html. Ed. Gunter P Wagner.

590.724 USA ISSN 1059-8324
CODEN: JSEEDO
➤ **JOURNAL OF EXPERIMENTAL ZOOLOGY. SUPPLEMENT.** Text in English. 1987. irreg. (approx a.), latest 2002. price varies. back issues avail. **Document type:** *Academic/Scholarly.*
Related titles: ♦ Supplement to: Journal of Experimental Zoology Part A: Comparative Experimental Biology. ISSN 1548-8969.
Indexed: IndMed, MEDLINE, SFA, WildRev, ZooRec.
—CISTI.
Published by: John Wiley & Sons, Inc., 111 River St, Hoboken, NJ 07030-5774. TEL 201-748-6000, FAX 201-748-5915, uscs-wis@wiley.com, http://www.wiley.com. **Subscr. outside the Americas to:** John Wiley & Sons Ltd., The Atrium, Southern Gate, Chichester, West Sussex PO19 8SQ, United Kingdom. TEL 44-1243-843335, 0800-243407, FAX 44-1243-843232.

597 GBR ISSN 0022-1112
QL614 CODEN: JFIBA9
➤ **JOURNAL OF FISH BIOLOGY.** Text in English. 1969. m. (plus supp.). GBP 1,499 combined subscription in Europe to institutions print & online eds.; USD 2,772 combined subscription in the Americas to institutions & Caribbean (print & online eds.); GBP 1,650 combined subscription elsewhere to institutions print & online eds. (effective 2006). adv. bk.rev. illus. Index. reprints avail. **Document type:** *Journal, Academic/Scholarly.* **Description:** Covers all aspects of fish and fisheries biological research, both freshwater and marine.
Related titles: Online - full text ed.: ISSN 1095-8649. GBP 1,424 in Europe to institutions; USD 2,634 in the Americas to institutions & Caribbean; GBP 1,568 elsewhere to institutions (effective 2006) (from Blackwell Synergy, EBSCO Publishing, Gale Group, IngentaConnect, O C L C Online Computer Library Center, Inc., ScienceDirect, Swets Information Services).
Indexed: AEA, ASCA, ASFA, AgBio, AnBeAb, AnBrAb, ApEcolAb, B&BAb, BIOBASE, BIOSIS Prev, BioCN&I, BiolAb, CIN, CRFR, ChemAb, ChemTitl, CurCont, EIA, ESPM, EnvAb, EnvInd, ExcerpMed, FS&TA, ForAb, GEOBASE, GenetAb, HGA, HelmAb, HortAb, I&DA, IABS, ISR, IndVet, MEDLINE, MSB, NutrAb, OceAb, OrnHort, PoultAb, ProtozoAb, RA&MP, RDA, RM&VM, RRTA, RefZh, RevApplEntom, S&F, SCI, SFA, SIA, SWRA, SoyAb, VetBull, WAE&RSA, WRCInf, WeedAb, WildRev, ZooRec.
—BLDSC (4984.280000), CASDDS, CISTI, IDS, IE, Infotrieve, ingenta, Linda Hall. **CCC.**
Published by: (Fisheries Society of the British Isles), Blackwell Publishing Ltd., 9600 Garsington Rd, Oxford, OX4 2ZG, United Kingdom. TEL 44-1865-776868, FAX 44-1865-714591, customerservices@oxon.blackwellpublishing.com, http://www.blackwellpublishing.com/journals/JFB. Ed. J F Craig.

597.8 587.9 USA ISSN 1529-9651
SF997.5.R4
➤ **JOURNAL OF HERPETOLOGICAL MEDICINE AND SURGERY.** Text in English. 1992. q. USD 115 in North America to individuals; USD 130 elsewhere to individuals; USD 145 in North America to institutions; USD 160 elsewhere to institutions (effective 2005). adv. back issues avail. **Document type:** *Journal, Academic/Scholarly.* **Description:** Aims to improve reptilian and amphibian husbandary and veterinary care through education, exchange of ideas and research.
Formerly (until 2000): Association of Reptilian and Amphibian Veterinarians. Bulletin (1076-3139)
Indexed: DBA, RefZh, WildRev, ZooRec.
—BLDSC (4998.070000).
Published by: (Association of Reptilian and Amphibian Veterinarians), Allen Press Inc., PO Box 1897, Lawrence, KS 66044. TEL 785-843-1235, FAX 785-843-1274, arav@allenpress.com, http://www.arav.org/Journals/J053TI.htm, http://www.allenpress.com. Ed. Thomas H Boyer.

597.9 USA ISSN 0022-1511
QL640 CODEN: JHERAH
➤ **JOURNAL OF HERPETOLOGY.** Text in English. 1958. q. USD 60 to individual members; USD 115 to institutional members; USD 30 to students (effective 2004); includes subscr. to Herpetological Review. bk.rev. charts; illus. index. back issues avail.; reprints avail. **Document type:** *Journal, Academic/Scholarly.*
Former titles (until 1967): Ohio Herpetological Society. Journal (0473-9868); (until 1959): Ohio Herpetological Society. Tri-Monthly Report (1557-122X)
Related titles: Online - full text ed.: (from bigchalk, BioOne, C S A, H.W. Wilson, Northern Light Technology, Inc., O C L C Online Computer Library Center, Inc., ProQuest Information & Learning).
Indexed: ASCA, ASFA, AgrForAb, AnBeAb, ApEcolAb, B&AI, B&BAb, BIOBASE, BIOSIS Prev, BiolAb, BiolDig, CPA, ChemAb, CurCont, ESPM, ForAb, GenetAb, HelmAb, HerbAb, HortAb, IABS, ISR, IndVet, OrnHort, PGegResA, ProtozoAb, RM&VM, RefZh, RevApplEntom, S&F, SCI, SFA, SPPI, SeedAb, VetBull, WildRev, ZooRec.
—BLDSC (4998.100000), CASDDS, CISTI, IDS, IE, Infotrieve, ingenta, Linda Hall. **CCC.**
Published by: Society for the Study of Amphibians and Reptiles, PO Box 253, Marceline, MO 64658-0253. bsullivan@asu.edu, ssar@herplit.com, http://www.ssarherps.org. Ed. Brian K Sullivan TEL 602-543-6022. Circ: 2,500 (paid).

597 RUS ISSN 0032-9452
SH1 CODEN: JITHAZ
JOURNAL OF ICHTHYOLOGY. Text in English. 1961. 9/yr. USD 3,159 in North America; USD 3,635 elsewhere (effective 2004). adv. bk.rev. bibl.; charts; illus. index. **Document type:** *Journal, Academic/Scholarly.* **Description:** Covers fisheries management, fish culture, aquaculture, physiology and biochemistry of both marine and freshwater fish.
Formerly (until 1970): Problems of Ichthyology (0193-5119)
Related titles: Microform ed.: (from PQC); ♦ Translation of: Voprosy Ikhtiologii. ISSN 0042-8752.
Indexed: ASFA, AnBrAb, B&BAb, BiolAb, ESPM, NutrAb, OceAb, SFA, SWRA, WildRev, ZooRec.
—BLDSC (0415.120000), CISTI, IE, Infotrieve, ingenta. **CCC.**
Published by: (Rossiiskaya Akademiya Nauk/Russian Academy of Sciences), M A I K Nauka - Interperiodica, Profsoyuznaya ul 90, Moscow, 117997, Russian Federation. TEL 7-095-3347420, FAX 7-095-3360666, compmg@maik.ru, http://www.maik.rssi.ru/journals/ichth.htm, http://www.maik.ru. Ed. Nikolai V Parin. **Subscr. to:** Interperiodica, PO Box 1831, Birmingham, AL 35201-1831. TEL 205-995-1567, 800-633-4931, FAX 205-995-1588.

592 USA ISSN 0022-2011
SB942 CODEN: JIVPAZ
➤ **JOURNAL OF INVERTEBRATE PATHOLOGY.** Text in English. 1959. 9/yr. EUR 773 in Europe to individuals; JPY 80,800 in Japan to individuals; USD 609 to individuals except Europe and Japan; EUR 1,629 in Europe to institutions; JPY 170,200 in Japan to institutions; USD 1,284 to institutions except Europe and Japan (effective 2006). adv. bibl.; charts; illus. index. back issues avail. **Document type:** *Academic/Scholarly.*
Description: Presents original research articles and notes on the induction and pathogenesis of diseases of invertebrates.
Formerly (until 1964): Journal of Insect Pathology (0095-9049)
Related titles: Online - full text ed.: ISSN 1096-0805. USD 1,332 (effective 2002) (from EBSCO Publishing, Gale Group, IngentaConnect, O C L C Online Computer Library Center, Inc., ScienceDirect, Swets Information Services).
Indexed: AEA, ASCA, ASFA, AbHyg, AgBio, Agr, AgrForAb, AnBrAb, ApicAb, BIOBASE, BIOSIS Prev, BibAg, BioCN&I, BiolAb, CIN, CPA, ChemAb, ChemTitl, CurCont, DBA, DSA, ESPM, EntAb, ExcerpMed, FCA, ForAb, GenetAb, HGA, HelmAb, HerbAb, HortAb, ISR, IndMed, IndVet, MBA, MEDLINE, MaizeAb, NemAb, OceAb, OrnHort, PBA, PHN&I, PotatoAb, ProtozoAb, RM&VM, RPP, RefZh, RevApplEntom, S&F, SCI, SFA, SIA, SPPI, SeedAb, SoyAb, TDB, TriticAb, VITIS, VetBull, WeedAb, ZooRec.
—BLDSC (5007.950000), CASDDS, CISTI, GNLM, IDS, IE, Infotrieve, ingenta, Linda Hall. **CCC.**
Published by: Academic Press (Subsidiary of: Elsevier Science & Technology), 525 B St, Ste 1900, San Diego, CA 92101-4495. TEL 619-231-6616, 800-894-3434, FAX 619-699-6422, apsubs@acad.com, http://www.elsevier.com/locate/jip, http://www.academicpress.com. Ed. B. A. Federici.

597.9 USA ISSN 1540-773X
QL653.K3
JOURNAL OF KANSAS HERPETOLOGY. Text in English. 2002 (Mar.). q. free to members. adv. **Document type:** *Magazine, Trade.*
Published by: Kansas Herpetological Society, 5438 SW 12th Terrace #4, Topeka, KS 66604. http://www.ku.edu/~khs/. Ed. Travis W. Taggart.

B

▼ new title ➤ refereed ✶ unverified ♦ full entry avail.

599 USA ISSN 1064-7554
QL708.5 CODEN: JMEVEY
➤ **JOURNAL OF MAMMALIAN EVOLUTION.** Text in English. 1993. q. EUR 329, USD 330, GBP 233 combined subscription to institutions print & online eds. (effective 2005). adv. bk.rev. reprint service avail. from PSC. **Document type:** *Journal, Academic/Scholarly.* **Description:** Investigates all aspects of the comparative and evolutionary biology of mammals, with contributions from specialists in the fields of paleontology, molecular biology, comparative anatomy, developmental biology and cytogenics.
Related titles: Microfilm ed.: (from PQC); Online - full text ed.: ISSN 1573-7055 (from EBSCO Publishing, Gale Group, IngentaConnect, Kluwer Online, O C L C Online Computer Library Center, Inc., Springer LINK, Swets Information Services).
Indexed: ASFA, BIOSIS Prev, BibLing, BiolAb, GenetAb, HGA, RefZh, WildRev, ZooRec.
—BLDSC (5010.880000), CISTI, IE, Infotrieve, ingenta. **CCC.**
Published by: (Society for the Study of Mammalian Evolution), Plenum US (Subsidiary of: Springer Science+Business Media), 233 Spring St, New York, NY 10013. TEL 212-460-1500, FAX 212-460-1575, service@springer-ny.com, http://springerlink.metapress.com/openurl.asp?genre=journal&issn=1064-7554, http://www.springeronline.com. Ed. Mark S Springer.

599 JPN ISSN 1341-7738
JOURNAL OF MAMMALIAN OVA RESEARCH. Text in English, Japanese. 1984. s-a. membership.
Former titles (until 1991): Honyu Dobutsu Ranshi Gakkaishi (0916-7625); (until 1990): Honyu Dobutsu Ranshi Kenkyukaishi (0289-5439)
Related titles: Online - full content ed.: ISSN 1347-5878; Online - full text ed.: (from J-Stage).
—**CCC.**
Published by: Honyu Dobutsu Ranshi Gakkai/Japanese Society of Mammalian Ova Research, Nihon Daigaku Nojuigakubu Jui Serigaku Kyoshitsu, 1866 Kameino, Fujisawa-shi, Kanagawa-ken 252-0813, Japan. http://jmor.jstage.jst.go.jp/.

599 USA ISSN 0022-2372
QL700 CODEN: JOMAAL
➤ **JOURNAL OF MAMMALOGY.** Text in English. 1919. q. free to members; USD 195 (effective 2005). adv. bk.rev. bibl.; charts; illus. index. back issues avail.; reprint service avail. from PQC. **Document type:** *Journal, Academic/Scholarly.* **Description:** It publishes original research on both terrestrial and marine mammals. All aspects of the biology of mammals, including paleontology, are covered in the worldwide scope of this journal.
Related titles: Microform ed.: (from PMC, PQC); Online - full text ed.: ISSN 1545-1542 (from bigchalk, BioOne, C S A, EBSCO Publishing, JSTOR (Web-based Journal Archive), Northern Light Technology, Inc., O C L C Online Computer Library Center, Inc., ProQuest Information & Learning).
Indexed: ASCA, ASFA, AnBrAb, AgBio, Agr, AnBeAb, AnBrAb, ApEcolAb, B&AI, B&BAb, BIOBASE, BIOSIS Prev, BibAg, BioCN&I, BiolAb, BiolDig, CurCont, DSA, ESPM, FPA, ForAb, GEOBASE, GSI, GenetAb, HGA, HelmAb, HerbAb, HortAb, I&DA, IABS, ISR, IndMed, IndVet, KWIWR, MA, MEDLINE, NutrAb, OceAb, PGegResA, PN&I, RM&VM, RPP, RefZh, RevApplEntom, S&F, SCI, SFA, SPPI, SSCI, SeedAb, TDB, VetBull, WLR, WeedAb, WildRev, ZooRec.
—BLDSC (5011.000000), CISTI, GNLM, IE, Infotrieve, ingenta, Linda Hall.
Published by: American Society of Mammalogists, c/o Dr H Duane Smith, Sec -Treas, Monte L Bean Life Science Museum, Brigham Young University, Provo, UT 84602-0200. TEL 801-378-2492, asm@allenpress.com, asm@aibs.org, http://www.mammalogy.org/pubjom/index.html. Ed. David M Leslie. R&P H Duane Smith. Adv. contact Cheryl A Schmidt. **Subscr. to:** Allen Press Inc., PO Box 1897, Lawrence, KS 66044. TEL 785-843-1235, FAX 785-843-1274.

594 USA ISSN 1053-6388
CODEN: JMAMEL
JOURNAL OF MEDICAL AND APPLIED MALACOLOGY/ REVISTA DE MALACOLOGIA MEDICA Y APLICADA. Text in English, Spanish. 1989. a. USD 50 to non-members. abstr.; bibl.; charts; illus.; stat. back issues avail. **Document type:** *Journal, Academic/Scholarly.* **Description:** Contains original research on mollusks that are of medical, veterinary, agricultural and economic importance.
—CISTI.
Published by: International Society for Medical and Applied Malacology/Sociedad Internacional de Malacologia Medica y Aplicada, University of Michigan, Museum of Zoology, Mollusk Division, 1109 Geddes Ave, Ann Arbor, MI 48109-1079. TEL 734-764-0470, FAX 734-763-4080, fpaper@umich.edu. Circ: 200.

599.8 DNK ISSN 0047-2565
QL737.P9 CODEN: JMPMAO
➤ **JOURNAL OF MEDICAL PRIMATOLOGY.** Text in English. 1972. bi-m. USD 773 combined subscription in the Americas to institutions & Caribbean (print & online eds.); GBP 460 combined subscription elsewhere to institutions print & online eds. (effective 2006). adv. bk.rev. abstr.; charts; illus.; stat. reprint service avail. from PSC,ISI. **Document type:** *Journal, Academic/Scholarly.*
Related titles: Online - full text ed.: ISSN 1600-0684. USD 734 in the Americas to institutions & Caribbean; GBP 437 elsewhere to institutions (effective 2006) (from Blackwell Synergy, EBSCO Publishing, Gale Group, IngentaConnect, O C L C Online Computer Library Center, Inc., Swets Information Services).
Indexed: AIDS Ab, ASCA, AbAn, AbHyg, AgBio, AnBrAb, BIOSIS Prev, BiolAb, CIN, ChemAb, ChemTitl, CurCont, DSA, ExcerpMed, FoVS&M, HelmAb, ISR, IndMed, IndVet, Inpharma, MEDLINE, MaizeAb, NutrAb, ProtozoAb, RM&VM, Reac, SCI, SoyAb, TDB, TriticAb, VetBull, ZooRec.
—BLDSC (5017.082000), CASDDS, CISTI, GNLM, IDS, IE, Infotrieve, ingenta, KNAW. **CCC.**
Published by: Blackwell Munksgaard (Subsidiary of: Blackwell Publishing Ltd.), Rosenoerns Alle 1, PO Box 227, Copenhagen V, 1502, Denmark. TEL 45-77-333333, FAX 45-77-333377, info@mks.blackwellpublishing.com, http://www.blackwellpublishing.com/journals/JMP, http://www.munksgaard.dk/. Ed. Jorg W. Eichberg. Adv. contact Alex Speke. Circ: 500.

594 GBR ISSN 0260-1230
QL401 CODEN: JMSTDT
➤ **JOURNAL OF MOLLUSCAN STUDIES.** Text in English. 1893. q. GBP 267, USD 454, EUR 401 to institutions; GBP 281, USD 478, EUR 422 combined subscription to institutions print & online eds. (effective 2006). adv. bk.rev. index. back issues avail.; reprint service avail. from PSC. **Document type:** *Journal, Academic/Scholarly.* **Description:** Presents neurophysiological and behavioral research using molluscs as experimental material and natural populations.
Formerly (until 1976): Malacological Society of London. Proceedings (0025-1194)
Related titles: Online - full text ed.: ISSN 1464-3766. GBP 253, USD 430, EUR 380 to institutions (effective 2006) (from EBSCO Publishing, Gale Group, HighWire Press, IngentaConnect, O C L C Online Computer Library Center, Inc., Ovid Technologies, Inc., Oxford University Press Online Journals, ProQuest Information & Learning, Swets Information Services).
Indexed: ASCA, ASFA, AgBio, AnBrAb, ArtHuCI, BIOBASE, BIOSIS Prev, BioCN&I, BiolAb, CurCont, ESPM, FCA, GEOBASE, HelmAb, HortAb, IABS, ISR, IndVet, NemAb, NutrAb, OceAb, PotatoAb, RevApplEntom, RiceAb, S&F, SCI, SFA, TDB, TriticAb, WeedAb, ZooRec.
—BLDSC (5020.820000), IDS, IE, Infotrieve, ingenta, Linda Hall. **CCC.**
Published by: (Malacological Society of London), Oxford University Press, Great Clarendon St, Oxford, OX2 6DP, United Kingdom. TEL 44-1865-556767, FAX 44-1865-556646, jnl.orders@oup.co.uk, http://mollus.oxfordjournals.org/, http://www.oxfordjournals.org/. Ed. D G Reid. Pub. Cathy Kennedy. R&P Fiona Bennett. adv.: B&W page GBP 230, B&W page USD 415; trim 216 x 279. Circ: 500. **U.S. subscr. to:** Oxford University Press, 2001 Evans Rd, Cary, NC 27513. jnlorders@oup-usa.org.

592.57 USA ISSN 0022-300X
QL386.A1 CODEN: JONEB5
➤ **JOURNAL OF NEMATOLOGY.** Text in English. 1969. q. bk.rev. abstr.; bibl.; charts; illus. index. back issues avail. **Document type:** *Journal, Academic/Scholarly.* **Description:** Presents original scientific papers on research of animal-parasitic, free-living, and plant-parasitic nematodes.
Incorporates (1987-1988): Annals of Applied Nematology (0898-7939)
Indexed: AEA, ASCA, ASFA, AbHyg, AgBio, Agr, AgrForAb, ApicAb, B&AI, B&BAb, BIOSIS Prev, BibAg, BioCN&I, BiolAb, CIN, CPA, CTFA, ChemAb, ChemTitl, CurCont, DBA, DSA, ExcerpMed, FCA, FPA, ForAb, GenetAb, HGA, HelmAb, HerbAb, HortAb, I&DA, IABS, ISR, IndVet, MaizeAb, NemAb, OrnHort, PBA, PGegResA, PGrRegA, PHN&I, PlantSci, PotatoAb, PoultAb, RA&MP, RM&VM, RPP, RefZh, RevApplEntom, RiceAb, S&F, SCI, SFA, SIA, SeedAb, SoyAb, TOSA, TriticAb, VITIS, WAE&RSA, WeedAb, WildRev, ZooRec.
—BLDSC (5021.399000), CASDDS, CISTI, IDS, IE, Infotrieve, ingenta, Linda Hall. **CCC.**
Published by: Society of Nematologists, PO Box 1897, Lawrence, KS 66044-8897. TEL 785-843-1235, FAX 785-843-1274, socnema@yahoo.com, http://www.ianr.unl.edu/son/jon.htm. Ed. Bradley Hyman TEL 909-787-5911. Circ: 1,145 (paid).

595.74 ESP ISSN 1029-2020
JOURNAL OF NEUROPTEROLOGY. Text in English. 1998. a. back issues avail.
Related titles: Online - full text ed.
Indexed: AgrForAb, BioCN&I, EntAb, HortAb, S&F, ZooRec.
—CINDOC.
Published by: International Association for Neuropterology, c/o V.J. Monserrat, Ed., Madrid, 28040, Spain. artmad@bio.ucm.es, http://www.ucm.es/info/zoo/JofN.htm.

590.7 IND ISSN 0253-7230
CODEN: JSREDL
JOURNAL OF SCIENTIFIC RESEARCH. Text in English. 1978. q. INR 25, USD 25. adv. bibl.; illus.
Indexed: AESIS, ZooRec.
—BLDSC (5059.900000), CASDDS, CISTI. **CCC.**
Published by: Saifia College, Department of Zoology, Saifia College, Bhopal, Madhya Pradesh 462 001, India. Ed. M A Qayyum. Circ: 750.

594.1477 USA ISSN 0730-8000
SH370.A1 CODEN: JSHRDA
➤ **JOURNAL OF SHELLFISH RESEARCH.** Text in English. 1981. s-a. USD 75 to individual members; USD 175 to institutions (effective 2005). bk.rev. illus. index, cum.index: 1930-1972. 400 p./no.; back issues avail.; reprints avail. **Document type:** *Journal, Academic/Scholarly.* **Description:** Contains original papers dealing with all aspects of shellfish research.
Formerly: National Shellfisheries Association. Proceedings (0077-5711)
Related titles: Online - full text ed.: (from Gale Group).
Indexed: AEA, ASCA, ASFA, AbHyg, AgBio, AnBrAb, B&BAb, BIOBASE, BIOSIS Prev, BiolAb, ChemAb, CurCont, EPB, ESPM, FPA, ForAb, GEOBASE, HelmAb, HortAb, IABS, ISR, IndVet, MBA, NutrAb, OceAb, ProtozoAb, RM&VM, RRTA, RefZh, RevApplEntom, RiceAb, S&F, SCI, SFA, SoyAb, TDB, TriticAb, VetBull, WAE&RSA, ZooRec.
—BLDSC (5064.100000), CASDDS, CINDOC, CISTI, IDS, IE, Infotrieve, ingenta, Linda Hall. **CCC.**
Published by: National Shellfisheries Association, Inc., c/o University of Connecticut, Marine Science Dept, Groton, CT 06340. TEL 860-405-9282, FAX 860-405-9153, sandra.shumway@uconn.edu, http://www.shellfish.org/pubs/jsr.htm. Ed., R&P Sandra E Shumway. Circ: 950.

590 EGY ISSN 1110-5372
JOURNAL OF UNION OF ARAB BIOLOGISTS CAIRO. A. ZOOLOGY. Text in English. 1994. a. **Document type:** *Journal, Academic/Scholarly.*
—BLDSC (4910.567000).
Published by: Union of Arab Biologists, Faculty of Science, Cairo University, Cairo University Campus, Cairo, Egypt. info@egsz.org, http://derp.sti.sci.eg/data/0222.htm, http://www.egsz.org.

579.9 615.49 BRA ISSN 1678-9199
QL100 CODEN: JVTOFG
➤ **JOURNAL OF VENOMOUS ANIMALS AND TOXINS INCLUDING TROPICAL DISEASES.** Text in English. 1995. 3/yr. free (effective 2005). adv. bk.rev. abstr.; bibl.; charts; illus.; maps. index. back issues avail. **Document type:** *Academic/Scholarly.* **Description:** Devoted to research on different aspects of toxins, venomous animals, their products and derivatives.
Formerly (until 2001): Journal of Venomous Animals and Toxins (Print Edition) (0104-7930)
Media: Online - full text. **Related titles:** CD-ROM ed.: ISSN 1678-9180 (from SciELO).
Indexed: ASFA, AbHyg, BIOSIS Prev, BioCN&I, BiolAb, CIN, ChemAb, ChemTitl, DSA, ESPM, EntAb, ExcerpMed, HelmAb, IABS, INIS AtomInd, IndVet, ProtozoAb, RM&VM, RPP, RevApplEntom, TDB, ToxAb, TriticAb, VetBull, WildRev, ZooRec.
—BLDSC (5072.285000), CASDDS.
Published by: Universidade Estadual Paulista "Julio de Mesquita Filho" , Centro de Estudos de Venenos e Animais Peconhentos/Center for the Study of Venoms and Venomous Animals, Caixa Postal 577, Botucatu, Sao Paulo, SP 18618-000, Brazil. TEL 55-14-38116054, jvat@cevap.org.br, cevap@cevap.org.br, http://www.scielo.br/scielo.php?script=sci_serial&pid=1678-9199&lng=en&nrm=iso, http://www.cevap.org.br. Ed., R&P, Adv. contact Dr. Benedito Barraviera TEL 55-14-38153963. page USD 60. Circ: 1,300.
Co-sponsor: Microsoft Informatica Ltda.

590 USA ISSN 1071-2232
SF996.45
➤ **JOURNAL OF WILDLIFE REHABILITATION.** Text in English. 1978. q. USD 40 domestic to individual members; USD 50 foreign to individual members; USD 52 domestic to institutions; USD 62 foreign to institutions; USD 30 domestic to libraries; USD 40 foreign to libraries (effective 2005). adv. bk.rev. illus. index. back issues avail.; reprints avail. **Document type:** *Journal, Academic/Scholarly.* **Description:** Dedicated to the dissemination of information related to the field of wildlife rehabilitation.
Formerly (until 1993): Wildlife Journal (0893-6560)
Indexed: ASCA, FoVS&M, SFA, WildRev, ZooRec.
—BLDSC (5072.630500), IDS, IE, ingenta.
Published by: International Wildlife Rehabilitation Council, PO Box 8187, San Jose, CA 95155. TEL 408-271-2685, FAX 408-271-9285, journal@iwrc-online.org, office@iwrc-online.org, http://www.iwrc-online.org/journal/journal.html. Ed. Marianne Skoczek. adv.: B&W page USD 350. Circ: 1,800 (paid).

590.7 IND ISSN 0253-7273
QL1 CODEN: JZRED2
JOURNAL OF ZOOLOGICAL RESEARCH. Text in English. 1977. s-a. INR 30, USD 15 to individuals; INR 60, USD 40 to institutions (effective 1999). adv. bk.rev. back issues avail. **Document type:** *Newspaper.*
Indexed: BiolAb, ChemAb.
—CASDDS, CISTI.
Published by: Rajjab Khan Ed. & Pub., Orchha House, Fauladi Kalam Marg, Chhatarpur, Madhya Pradesh 471 001, India. Circ: 200.

590.7 DEU ISSN 0947-5745
QL351 CODEN: JZSEF9
➤ **JOURNAL OF ZOOLOGICAL SYSTEMATICS AND EVOLUTIONARY RESEARCH.** Text in English, French, German; Summaries in French, German, Spanish. 1963. 4/yr., latest vol.40, no.4, 2002. EUR 164 combined subscription in Europe to individuals print & online eds.; USD 176 combined subscription in the Americas to individuals & Caribbean, print & online eds.; GBP 109 combined subscription elsewhere to individuals print & online eds.; GBP 520 combined subscription in Europe to institutions print & online eds.; USD 874 combined subscription in the Americas to institutions & Caribbean, print & online eds.; GBP 572 combined subscription elsewhere to institutions print & online eds. (effective 2006). bk.rev. illus. index. back issues avail.; reprint service avail. from ISI. **Document type:** *Journal, Academic/Scholarly.* **Description:** Provides an international forum for papers on zoological systematics and evolutionary research.
Formerly (until 1994): Zeitschrift fuer Zoologische Systematik und Evolutionsforschung (0044-3808)
Related titles: ♦ Online - full text ed.: Journal of Zoological Systematics and Evolutionary Research Online. ISSN 1439-0469; Supplement(s): Fortschritte in der Zoologischen Systematik und Evolutionsforschung.
Indexed: ASCA, ASFA, AgBio, AnBrAb, ApicAb, B&BAb, BIOBASE, BIOSIS Prev, BioCN&I, BiolAb, CurCont, ESPM, EntAb, ForAb, GEOBASE, GenetAb, HGA, ISR, IndVet, NemAb, RM&VM, RefZh, RevApplEntom, SCI, SFA, WildRev, ZooRec.
—BLDSC (5072.780700), CASDDS, CISTI, IDS, IE, Infotrieve, ingenta, Linda Hall. **CCC.**
Published by: Blackwell Verlag GmbH (Subsidiary of: Blackwell Publishing Ltd.), Kurfuerstendamm 57, Berlin, 10707, Germany. TEL 49-30-32790634, FAX 49-30-32790610, verlag@blackwell.de, http://www.blackwellpublishing.com/journals/JZS, http://www.blackwell.de. Ed. Wilfried Westheide. Circ: 400.

590.7 DEU ISSN 1439-0469
JOURNAL OF ZOOLOGICAL SYSTEMATICS AND EVOLUTIONARY RESEARCH ONLINE. Text in English, French, German. 4/yr. GBP 494 in Europe to institutions; USD 830 in the Americas to institutions & Caribbean; GBP 543 elsewhere to institutions (effective 2006). **Document type:** *Academic/Scholarly.*
Media: Online - full text (from Blackwell Synergy, EBSCO Publishing, Gale Group, IngentaConnect, O C L C Online Computer Library Center, Inc., Swets Information Services). **Related titles:** ♦ Print ed.: Journal of Zoological Systematics and Evolutionary Research. ISSN 0947-5745.
Published by: Blackwell Verlag GmbH (Subsidiary of: Blackwell Publishing Ltd.), Kurfuerstendamm 57, Berlin, 10707, Germany. TEL 49-30-32790679, FAX 49-30-32790610, abo@blackwis.de, http://www.blackwell.de.

590.724 GBR ISSN 0952-8369
QL1 CODEN: JOZOEU
➤ **JOURNAL OF ZOOLOGY.** Text in English. 1987. m. USD 1,050 in North America to institutions; GBP 660 elsewhere to institutions; USD 1,185 combined subscription in North America to institutions print & online eds.; GBP 745 combined subscription elsewhere to institutions print & online eds. (effective 2005). adv. back issues avail.; reprint service avail. from PQC. **Document type:** *Journal, Academic/Scholarly.* **Description:** Publishes original papers in zoology as well as research reviews and reports of scientific meetings held by the Zoological Society of London.
Formed by the 1987 merger of: Journal of Zoology. Series A (0269-364X); Journal of Zoology. Series B (0268-196X); Incorporates (1833-1984): Zoological Society of London. Transactions (0084-5620); Both A & B superseded in part (in 1984): Journal of Zoology (0022-5460); Which was formerly (until 1965): Zoological Society of London. Proceedings (0370-2774); Which was formed by the 1944 merger of: Zoological Society of London. Proceedings. Series A; Zoological Society of London. Proceedings. Series B
Related titles: Microform ed.; Online - full text ed.: ISSN 1469-7998. USD 980 in North America to institutions; GBP 620 elsewhere to institutions (effective 2005) (from EBSCO Publishing, O C L C Online Computer Library Center, Inc., Swets Information Services).
Indexed: AEA, ASCA, ASFA, AbAn, AgBio, AgrForAb, AnBeAb, AnBrAb, ApEcolAb, ApicAb, B&AI, B&BAb, BIOBASE, BIOSIS Prev, BioCN&I, BiolAb, CRFR, CurCont, DSA, ESPM, EngInd, FPA, ForAb, GEOBASE, GenetAb, HGA, HelmAb, HerbAb, I&DA, IABS, ISR, IndVet, KWIWR, MEDLINE, NemAb, NutrAb, OceAb, PGegResA, PN&I, PoultAb, ProtozoAb, RDA, RRTA, RefZh, RevApplEntom, RiceAb, S&F, SCI, SFA, SSCI, SeedAb, TDB, VetBull, WAE&RSA, WildRev, ZooRec.
—BLDSC (5072.790000), CASDDS, CISTI, IDS, IE, Infotrieve, ingenta, KNAW, Linda Hall. **CCC.**
Published by: (Zoological Society of London), Blackwell Publishing Ltd., 9600 Garsington Rd, Oxford, OX4 2ZG, United Kingdom. TEL 44-1865-776868, FAX 44-1865-714591, customerservices@oxon.blackwellpublishing.com, http://www.blackwellpublishing.com. Eds. Ian Boyd, John Gittleman, Juliet Clutton-Brock, Robert Elwood. Circ: 1,200.

594 JPN ISSN 0912-2192
KAI NAKAMA/HANSHIN SHELL CLUB. REPORT. Text in Japanese. 1967. irreg. JPY 3,000 to members (effective 1999).
Published by: Hanshin Kairui Danwakai/Hanshin Shell Club, Kikuchi Kairui Kenkyujo, 1-41 Ohama-cho, Nishinomiya-shi, Hyogo-ken 662-0957, Japan.

590 POL ISSN 0075-5230
KATALOG FAUNY PASOZYTNICZEJ POLSKI. Text in Polish. 1970. irreg., latest 1998. price varies. **Document type:** *Catalog.*
Indexed: ZooRec.
Published by: Polskie Towarzystwo Parazytologiczne/Polish Parasitological Society, Ul Twarda 51-55, Warsaw, 00818, Poland. TEL 48-22-6206226, FAX 48-22-6206227. Ed. Bozena Grabda-Kazubska. R&P Bozena Grabda Kazubska TEL 48-22-6978961.

590 POL ISSN 0453-3623
➤ **KATALOG FAUNY POLSKI/CATALOGUS FAUNAE POLONIAE.** Text in Polish. 1960. irreg., latest vol.59, 2002. USD 10 per vol. (effective 2005). bibl. back issues avail. **Document type:** *Catalog, Academic/Scholarly.*
Indexed: BiolAb, RevApplEntom, ZooRec.
Published by: Polska Akademia Nauk, Muzeum i Instytut Zoologii/Polish Academy of Sciences, Museum & Institute of Zoology, ul Wilcza 64, Warsaw, 00679, Poland. TEL 48-22-6293221, FAX 48-22-6296302, libr@miiz.waw.pl, http://www.miiz.waw.pl. Ed. M Mroczkowski. Circ: 500.

➤ **KAUPIA**; Darmstaedter Beitraege zur Naturgeschichte. see *SCIENCES: COMPREHENSIVE WORKS*

590 DEU ISSN 0375-5290
QL76
KOELNER ZOO. ZEITSCHRIFT. Summaries in English. 1958. q. EUR 3 newsstand/cover (effective 2005). adv. back issues avail. **Document type:** *Magazine, Consumer.*
Formerly (until 1971): Freunde des Koelner Zoo (0532-6958)
Indexed: BiolAb, IBR, IBZ, KWIWR, RefZh, ZooRec.
—BLDSC (9442.800000).
Published by: Aktiengesellschaft Zoologischer Garten, Riehler Str 173, Cologne, 50735, Germany. TEL 49-221-7785-0, FAX 49-221-7785111, direction@zoo-koeln.de, http://www.zoo-koeln.de. Ed. W Kaumanns.

595.7 JPN ISSN 1346-0943
KOGANE. Text in English, Japanese. 2000. s-a. JPY 5,000 membership (effective 2005). **Document type:** *Journal, Academic/Scholarly.* **Description:** Conducts research on Scarabaeidae (beetles) and promotes the exchange of information and views among members and with other academic associations.
Indexed: EntAb, ZooRec.
—BLDSC (5100.846270).
Published by: Koganemushi-Kenkyukai/Japanese Society of Scarabaeoideans, c/o Shinya Kawai, 4-16-3, Simouma, Setagaya-ku, Tokyo, 154-0002, Japan. kogane@kawamo.co.jp, http://www.kawamo.co.jp/kogane.

595.3 JPN ISSN 0287-3478
KOKAKURUI NO KENKYU/CRUSTACEAN RESEARCH. Text in English, Japanese. 1963. a. **Document type:** *Academic/Scholarly.*
Indexed: ASFA, ESPM, SFA, ZooRec.
—BLDSC (3490.117500).
Published by: Nihon Kokakurui Gakkai/Carcinological Society of Japan, University of Fisheries, Dept of Aquatic Bioscience, 4-5-7 Ko-Unan, Minato-ku, Tokyo, 108-0075, Japan. TEL 81-3-5463-0535, FAX 81-3-5463-0684.

590 KOR ISSN 1226-5071
QH301 CODEN: KJBSFZ
KOREAN JOURNAL OF BIOLOGICAL SCIENCES. Text in English, Korean. 1959. q. KRW 30,000, USD 40. back issues avail.
Formerly (until 1997): Korean Journal of Zoology (0440-2510)
Indexed: AgBio, AnBrAb, BIOSIS Prev, BioCN&I, BiolAb, CIN, CPA, ChemAb, DSA, FCA, ForAb, HerbAb, HortAb, IndVet, NemAb, NutrAb, PBA, PGegResA, PHN&I, PotatoAb, ProtozoAb, RA&MP, RM&VM, RPP, RevApplEntom, RiceAb, S&F, SeedAb, TDB, VetBull, WeedAb, ZooRec.
—BLDSC (5113.519000), CASDDS, CISTI, IE, ingenta, Linda Hall.
Published by: Korean Association of Biological Sciences, c/o Department of Zoology, Seoul National University, Seoul, 151, Korea, S. Circ: 500.

590 KOR ISSN 1018-192X
THE KOREAN JOURNAL OF SYSTEMATIC ZOOLOGY. Text in English, Korean; Summaries in English. 1985. s-a. USD 20 to non-members; USD 23 to institutions. **Document type:** *Academic/Scholarly.* **Description:** Publishes original papers on theory and practice of systematic biologies, including classification, phylogeny and evolution in all animal kingdom.
Indexed: BIOSIS Prev, BiolAb, ZooRec.
—BLDSC (5113.574750).
Published by: (Korean Federation of Science and Technology Societies, Slovakia. Ministry of Education KEN), Korean Society of Systematic Zoology, c/o Byung-Hoon Lee, Pub., Dept. of Biology Education, Jeonbuk National University, Jeonju, 560756, Korea, S. TEL 0654-702783. **Subscr. to:** c/o Byung Lae Choe, Ed. Dept. of Biology, Sung Kyun Kwan University, Suwon 440746, Korea, S.. TEL 0331-290-5316, FAX 0331-290-5362.

599.5 JPN ISSN 0913-2244
KUJIRA/WEST JAPAN WHALES SOCIETY. NEWS. Text in Japanese. 1986. a.
Published by: Nishinihon Kujira Kenkyukai/West Japan Whales Society, Suisan Daigakko, 1944 Nagatahon-Machi, Shimonoseki-shi, Yamaguchi-ken 759-6533, Japan.

594 JPN ISSN 0911-985X
KYUSHU NO KAI/SHELLS OF KYUSHU. Text in Japanese. s-a.
Published by: Kyushu Kairui Danwakai, c/o Mr Kinzo Matsubayashi, 720 Hinamigo, Nishisonogi-gun, Togitsu-cho, Nagasaki-ken 851-2108, Japan.

590.724 GBR ISSN 0023-6772
SF405.5 CODEN: LBANAX
➤ **LABORATORY ANIMALS.** Text in English. 1966. q. GBP 137 combined subscription in Europe to institutions print & online; USD 234 combined subscription in United States to institutions print & online; GBP 142 combined subscription elsewhere to institutions print & online (effective 2005). adv. bk.rev. charts; illus. index. **Document type:** *Journal, Academic/Scholarly.* **Description:** Provides an international forum for the publication of research carried out by scientists primarily concerned with the care, welfare and science of laboratory animals.
Related titles: Online - full text ed.: USD 211 in United States; GBP 123 elsewhere (effective 2005) (from EBSCO Publishing, Gale Group, IngentaConnect, O C L C Online Computer Library Center, Inc., ProQuest Information & Learning, Swets Information Services).
Indexed: AEA, ASCA, AbHyg, AgBio, Agr, AnBrAb, BIOBASE, BIOSIS Prev, BibAg, BiolAb, CIN, ChemAb, ChemTitl, CurCont, DSA, ExcerpMed, FoVS&M, HelmAb, HortAb, IABS, ISR, IndMed, IndVet, Inpharma, MEDLINE, NutrAb, PBA, PE&ON, PN&I, PoultAb, ProtozoAb, RA&MP, RM&VM, RPP, Reac, RefZh, SCI, SFA, SIA, SoyAb, TDB, VetBull, WAE&RSA, WildRev, ZooRec.
—BLDSC (5138.600000), CASDDS, CISTI, GNLM, IDS, IE, Infotrieve, ingenta, Linda Hall. **CCC.**
Published by: (Laboratory Animal Science Association), Royal Society of Medicine Press Ltd., 1 Wimpole St, London, W1M 8AE, United Kingdom. TEL 44-20-72902921, FAX 44-20-72902929, publishing@rsm.ac.uk, http://www.roysocmed.ac.uk/pub/la.htm. Ed. T H Morris. R&P Caroline McLaughlin. Circ: 1,700. **Subscr. addr.:** PO Box 9002, London W1A 0ZA, United Kingdom. TEL 44-20-7290-2927, 44-20-7290-2928, FAX 44-20-7290-2929, rsmjournals@rsm.ac.uk.

590 NLD ISSN 0023-7051
CODEN: SPPRER
➤ **LACERTA.** Text in Dutch. 1942. bi-m. USD 75 (effective 1998). adv. bk.rev. charts; illus.; maps. index. **Document type:** *Bulletin, Academic/Scholarly.*
Indexed: BiolAb, ZooRec.
—CISTI.
Published by: Nederlandse Vereniging voor Herpetologie en Terrariumkunde/Dutch Society for Herpetology, c/o PD Gorseman, Prins Hendrikstraat 55, Zwijndrecht, 3331 XR, Netherlands. TEL 31-78-620-9299, FAX 31-78-620-9298. Ed. H A J in den Bosch. Circ: 1,900 (paid).

599 BRA ISSN 1676-7497
THE LATIN AMERICAN JOURNAL OF AQUATIC MAMMALS. Abbreviated title: L A J A M. Text in Multiple languages. 2002. s-a. **Document type:** *Journal, Academic/Scholarly.* **Description:** Publishes research on aquatic mammals in Latin America.
Indexed: ASFA, ESPM.
—BLDSC (5160.069000).
Published by: Sociedade Latinoamericana de Especialistas em Mamiferos Aquaticos, Fundacao Instituto Oswaldo Cruz, Departamento de Endemias, Laboratorio de Ecologia, Rua Leopoldo Bulhoes 1480, Terreo, Manguinhos, Rio de janeiro, RJ 21045-900, Brazil. http://www.solamac.net/.

LIBRARY NEWS FOR ZOOS AND AQUARIUMS. see *LIBRARY AND INFORMATION SCIENCES*

LINNEAN SOCIETY. OCCASIONAL PUBLICATIONS. see *CONSERVATION*

590 580 550 AUS ISSN 0370-047X
CODEN: PLSWAQ
➤ **LINNEAN SOCIETY OF NEW SOUTH WALES. PROCEEDINGS.** Text in English. 1875. a. AUD 80 (effective 2001). bk.rev. index. **Document type:** *Proceedings, Academic/Scholarly.*
Indexed: AESIS, ASFA, Agr, BIOSIS Prev, BiolAb, ChemAb, CurCont, FCA, FPA, ForAb, HerbAb, RPP, RevApplEntom, S&F, SFA, SPPI, ZooRec.
—BLDSC (6750.000000), CISTI, IE, ingenta, KNAW, Linda Hall.
Published by: Linnean Society of New South Wales, PO Box 137, Matraville, NSW 2036, Australia. TEL 61-2-9662-6196, FAX 61-2-9662-6196, linnsoc@acay.com.au, http://www.acay.com.au/~linnsoc/welcome.html. Ed., R&P M L Augee. Circ: 600 (paid).

590 GBR ISSN 0024-4082
QH1 CODEN: ZJLSA7
➤ **LINNEAN SOCIETY. ZOOLOGICAL JOURNAL**; an international journal. Text in English. m. GBP 1,213 combined subscription in Europe to institutions print & online eds.; USD 2,243 combined subscription in the Americas to institutions & Caribbean, print & online eds.; GBP 1,335 combined subscription elsewhere to institutions print & online eds. (effective 2006). adv. illus. index. reprints avail. **Document type:** *Journal, Academic/Scholarly.* **Description:** Examines zoology with an emphasis on the diversity, systematics, interrelationships, and habits of animals both living and extinct.
Formerly: Linnean Society of London. Journal
Related titles: Microfiche ed.: (from BHP); Online - full text ed.: ISSN 1096-3642. GBP 1,152 in Europe to institutions; USD 2,130 in the Americas to institutions & Caribbean; GBP 1,268 elsewhere to institutions (effective 2006) (from Blackwell Synergy, EBSCO Publishing, Gale Group, IngentaConnect, O C L C Online Computer Library Center, Inc., ScienceDirect, Swets Information Services).
Indexed: ASCA, ASFA, AgrForAb, AnBeAb, ApEcolAb, B&BAb, BIOSIS Prev, BioCN&I, BiolAb, ChemAb, CurCont, ESPM, EntAb, ForAb, GenetAb, HGA, HelmAb, HortAb, ISR, IndVet, NutrAb, OrnHort, PHN&I, RefZh, RevApplEntom, S&F, SCI, SFA, SPPI, TDB, VetBull, WildRev, ZooRec.
—BLDSC (9519.700000), CISTI, IDS, IE, Infotrieve, ingenta, Linda Hall. **CCC.**
Published by: (Linnean Society of London), Blackwell Publishing Ltd., 9600 Garsington Rd, Oxford, OX4 2ZG, United Kingdom. TEL 44-1865-776868, FAX 44-1865-714591, customerservices@oxon.blackwellpublishing.com, http://www.blackwellpublishing.com/journals/ZOJ. Ed. J P Thorpe.

597.9 NLD ISSN 1571-9006
CODEN: LSEEED
LITTERATURA SERPENTIUM. Text in Dutch, English. N.S. 2002. q. EUR 25 (effective 2005). adv. bk.rev. cum.index: vols.1-10. **Document type:** *Consumer.* **Description:** Publishes articles and information by and for amateur herpetologists.
Formed by the merger of: Litteratura Serpentium (English Edition) (0926-3527); Litteratura Serpentium (Nederlandse Edition) (0926-3586); Which were formerly (until 1982): Litteratura Serpentium (0926-3594)
Indexed: ZooRec.
Published by: European Snake Society, c/o Jan-Cor Jacobs, WA Vultostraat 62, Utrecht, 3523 TX, Netherlands. TEL 31-30-280115, http://www.snakesociety.nl. Eds. Dieter Vancraeynest, Marcel van der Voort. adv.: B&W page EUR 50. Circ: 400.

591.9861 COL ISSN 0085-2899
QL244 CODEN: LZNAAN
LOZANIA; acta zoologica colombiana. Text in English, French, German, Spanish. 1952. irreg. USD 10; or exchange basis. bibl.; illus. **Document type:** *Monographic series.*
Indexed: BiolAb, VITIS.
—CISTI.
Published by: Universidad Nacional de Colombia, Instituto de Ciencias, PO Box 7495, Bogota, CUND, Colombia. TEL 57-1-3165305, FAX 57-1-3165365, http://www.icn.unal.edu.co. Ed. F Gary Stiles. R&P Jaime Uribe M. Circ: 1,000.

599 NLD ISSN 0024-7634
CODEN: LUTAAI
➤ **LUTRA.** Text in Dutch, English, French, German; Summaries in English. 1960. s-a. EUR 17.50 (effective 2005). bk.rev. charts; illus. **Document type:** *Journal, Academic/Scholarly.* **Description:** Presents papers on mammalogy as relating to Europe, with an emphasis on the Netherlands and Belgium.
Indexed: BIOSIS Prev, BiolAb, KWIWR, RefZh, SFA, WildRev, ZooRec.
—BLDSC (5308.130000), IE, ingenta.
Published by: (Vereniging voor Zoogdierkunde en Zoogdierbescherming/Society for the Study and Protection of Mammals), Bureau V Z Z, Oude Kraan 8, Arnhem, 6811 LJ, Netherlands. TEL 31-26-3705318, FAX 31-26-3704038, lutra@vzz.nl, zoogdier@vzz.nl, http://www.vzz.nl/lutra/lutra.htm. Circ: 800.

599 CZE ISSN 0024-7774
LYNX; novitates mammaliologicae. Text in Czech, German, Russian, Slovak. 1962. irreg. price varies. bk.rev. bibl. cum.index. **Document type:** *Academic/Scholarly.*
Indexed: BIOSIS Prev, BiolAb, KWIWR, ZooRec.
Published by: (Prirodovedecke Muzeum), Narodni Muzeum, Vaclavske nam 68, Prague, 11579, Czech Republic. TEL 420-2-24497350, FAX 420-2-22246047. Ed. Oetr Benda.

599.8 CHE
MADAGASCAR PRIMATES. Variant title: Lemur News. Text in English. a. USD 15 (effective 2000). **Document type:** *Newsletter.*
Indexed: ZooRec.
Published by: (Species Survival Commission - Primate Specialist Group), International Union for Conservation of Nature and Natural Resources, Rue Mauverney 28, Gland, 1196, Switzerland. TEL 41-22-9990001, FAX 41-22-9990002, mail@hq.iucn.org. **Subscr. to:** Conservation International, 1015 18th St, N W, Ste 1000, Washington, DC 20036.

590 HUN ISSN 0076-2474
QL262
MAGYARORSZAG ALLATVILAGA/FAUNA HUNGARIAE. Text in Hungarian. 1960. irreg., latest vol.173, 2000. price varies. back issues avail. **Document type:** *Academic/Scholarly.*
Indexed: BiolAb.
Published by: Magyar Termeszettudomanyi Muzeum, Baross utca 13, Budapest, 1088, Hungary. TEL 36-1-2101330, FAX 36-1-371669, http://www.nhmus.hu.

594 USA ISSN 0076-2997
QL401 CODEN: MALAAJ
➤ **MALACOLOGIA.** Text in English, French, German, Russian, Spanish. 1962. irreg., latest vol.40, 1998. Index. **Document type:** *Journal, Academic/Scholarly.* **Description:** Covers the morphology, ecology, evolution, fossil record, classification, distribution, physiology, biochemistry, cytology, genetics and parasitism of mollusks.
Indexed: ASCA, ASFA, AgBio, AnBrAb, BIOSIS Prev, BiolAb, ChemAb, CurCont, ESPM, ForAb, HelmAb, HortAb, ISR, MEDLINE, OceAb, RevApplEntom, S&F, SCI, SPPI, SSCI, TDB, WAE&RSA, ZooRec.
—BLDSC (5354.100000), CASDDS, IE, Infotrieve, ingenta, Linda Hall.
Published by: Institute of Malacology, University of Michigan, Museum of Zoology, Mollusk Division, 1109 Geddes Ave, Ann Arbor, MI 48109-1079. TEL 734-764-0470, FAX 734-763-4080, fpaper@umich.edu, http://www.ummz.lsa.umich.edu/mollusks/index.html. Circ: 700.

594 USA ISSN 0076-3004
QL401 CODEN: MLGRBL
MALACOLOGICAL REVIEW; international journal for biology of mollusks. Text in English; Text occasionally in French, Spanish, German. 1968. a. USD 20 domestic to individuals; USD 23 foreign to individuals; USD 32 domestic to institutions; USD 35 foreign to institutions (effective 2004). bk.rev. abstr. index. Supplement avail.; back issues avail. **Document type:** *Journal, Academic/Scholarly.* **Description:** Publishes original research and review articles on all aspects of the biology and paleontology of mollusks.
Indexed: ASFA, AnBrAb, BIOSIS Prev, BiolAb, HelmAb, SFA, ZooRec.
—BLDSC (5354.150000), CISTI, IE, Linda Hall.
Published by: Society for Experimental and Descriptive Malacology, PO Box 3037, Ann Arbor, MI 48106. TEL 734-764-0470. Ed. J B Burch. Circ: 600. **Subscr. to:** PO Box 792, St. Peters, MO 63376.

594.005 GBR ISSN 1365-3725
MALACOLOGICAL SOCIETY OF LONDON. BULLETIN. Text in English. 1983. s-a. GBP 45 to individual members; GBP 25 to students members (effective 2004). **Document type:** *Bulletin, Academic/Scholarly.* **Description:** Publishes less formal (than those in the Journal) articles on molluscs; news, correspondence and opinion on malacological topics; reports of meetings; book notices and reviews; a diary of future malacological-related meetings; information on other Society publications; and Society notices.
Published by: (Malacological Society of London), University of Manchester, School of Biological Sciences, c/o Bill Bailey, Ed., G.30A Stopford Building, Oxford Rd, Manchester, M13 9PT, United Kingdom. TEL 44-161-2755632, FAX 44-161-2755586, billbailey@man.ac.uk, http://www.sunderland.ac.uk/~es0mda/jms.htm#Bulletin, http://www.sbs.man.ac.uk, http://www.biomed.man.ac.uk. Ed. S E R Bailey TEL 44-161-2753861. **Subscr. to:** Kingston University, School of Life Sciences, c/o Dr R. Cook, Membership Secretary, Penrhyn Rd, Kingston upon Thames, Surrey KT1 2EE, United Kingdom. TEL 44-20-85472000 ext 2901, FAX 44-20-85477562, r.cook@kingston.ac.uk.

594 HUN ISSN 0230-0648
QL401
➤ **MALAKOLOGIAI TAJEKOZTATO/MALACOLOGICAL NEWSLETTER.** Text in English, Hungarian. 1981. a. **Document type:** *Newsletter, Academic/Scholarly.*
Indexed: ZooRec.
Published by: Matra Muzeum, Kossuth utca 40, Gyongyos, 3200, Hungary. mmuseum@monornet.hu. Ed., Pub. Levente Fukoh. Circ: 300 (controlled).

599 GBR ISSN 0305-1838
QL700 CODEN: MMLRAI
➤ **MAMMAL REVIEW.** Text in English. 1970. q. GBP 44, EUR 66 combined subscription in Europe to individuals print & online eds.; USD 81 combined subscription in the Americas to individuals & Caribbean, print & online eds.; GBP 48 combined subscription elsewhere to individuals print & online eds.; GBP 314 combined subscription in Europe to institutions print & online eds.; USD 580 combined subscription in the Americas to institutions & Caribbean, print & online eds.; GBP 345 combined subscription elsewhere to institutions print & online eds. (effective 2006). adv. back issues avail.; reprint service avail. from PSC,ISI. **Document type:** *Journal, Academic/Scholarly.* **Description:** Carries reviews of, and reports on, all aspects of mammalogy.
Related titles: Microform ed.: (from PQC); ♦ Online - full text ed.: Mammal Review Online. ISSN 1365-2907.
Indexed: AEA, ASCA, ASFA, AgrForAb, AnBeAb, AnBrAb, ApEcolAb, BIOSIS Prev, BiolAb, CurCont, ESPM, EnvAb, FCA, FPA, ForAb, GEOBASE, HerbAb, HortAb, ISR, IndVet, KWIWR, NutrAb, PN&I, PoultAb, RefZh, S&F, SCI, SFA, VetBull, WAE&RSA, WildRev, ZooRec.
—BLDSC (5356.800000), CISTI, IDS, IE, Infotrieve, ingenta, Linda Hall. **CCC.**
Published by: (Mammal Society), Blackwell Publishing Ltd., 9600 Garsington Rd, Oxford, OX4 2ZG, United Kingdom. TEL 44-1865-776868, FAX 44-1865-714591, customerservices@oxon.blackwellpublishing.com, http://www.blackwellpublishing.com/journals/MAM. Ed. Dr. Robbie McDonald. Pub. Sue Hewitt. R&P Sophie Savage. Adv. contact Jenny Applin. Circ: 1,500.

599 GBR ISSN 1365-2907
➤ **MAMMAL REVIEW ONLINE.** Text in English. 1999. q. EUR 29 in Europe to individuals; USD 36 in the Americas to individuals & Caribbean; GBP 20 elsewhere to individuals; GBP 298 in Europe to institutions; USD 551 in the Americas to institutions & Caribbean; GBP 328 elsewhere to institutions (effective 2006). **Document type:** *Academic/Scholarly.*
Media: Online - full text (from Blackwell Synergy, EBSCO Publishing, Gale Group, IngentaConnect, O C L C Online Computer Library Center, Inc., Swets Information Services). **Related titles:** Microform ed.: (from PQC); ♦ Print ed.: Mammal Review. ISSN 0305-1838.
Published by: Blackwell Publishing Ltd., 9600 Garsington Rd, Oxford, OX4 2ZG, United Kingdom. TEL 44-1865-776868, FAX 44-1865-714591, customerservices@oxon.blackwellpublishing.com, http://www.blackwellpublishing.com.

599 GBR ISSN 0141-3392
MAMMAL SOCIETY. OCCASIONAL PUBLICATION. Text in English. 1977. irreg., latest vol.16. price varies. **Document type:** *Monographic series.*
Indexed: ZooRec.
—BLDSC (6225.792400).
Published by: Mammal Society, 15 Cloisters Business Centre,, 8 Battersea Park Roa, London, SW8 4BG, United Kingdom. TEL 44-171-498-4358.

599 JPN ISSN 1343-4152
QL700
MAMMAL STUDY. Text in English. 1952. s-a.
Formerly (until 1996): Mammalogical Society of Japan. Journal (0914-1855)
Related titles: Online - full text ed.: ISSN 1348-6160 (from J-Stage).
Indexed: BIOSIS Prev, BiolAb.
—BLDSC (5356.900000).
Published by: Nihon Honyu Dobutsu Gakkai/Mammalogical Society of Japan, Nihon Gakkai Jimu Senta, 16-9 Honkomagome 5-chome, Bunkyo-ku, Tokyo, 113-0021, Japan.

599 FRA ISSN 0025-1461
QL700 CODEN: MAMLAN
➤ **MAMMALIA**; journal de morphologie, biologie, systematique des mammiferes. Text in English, French. 1936. q. adv. bk.rev. charts; illus. back issues avail. **Document type:** *Academic/Scholarly.*
Indexed: ASCA, ASFA, AbHyg, AgrForAb, AnBrAb, BIOBASE, BIOSIS Prev, BiolAb, CurCont, DSA, FCA, ForAb, GEOBASE, HelmAb, HerbAb, HortAb, IABS, ISR, IndVet, KWIWR, MEDLINE, NutrAb, PBA, PGegResA, RefZh, RiceAb, S&F, SCI, SFA, SeedAb, TDB, VetBull, WildRev, ZooRec.
—BLDSC (5357.000000), CISTI, IDS, IE, Infotrieve, ingenta, Linda Hall. **CCC.**
Published by: (Museum National d'Histoire Naturelle, Mammiferes et Oiseaux), Museum National d'Histoire Naturelle, 57 Rue Cuvier, Paris, 75231 Cedex 05, France. TEL 33-1-40793777, http://www.mnhn.fr. Ed. Jean Dorst. Adv. contact F Petter. Circ: 670 (controlled).

599 DEU ISSN 1616-5047
QL700 CODEN: MBAICV
➤ **MAMMALIAN BIOLOGY.** Text in English, German. 1926. 6/yr. EUR 333 to institutions; EUR 387 in Europe to institutions; JPY 51,400 in Japan to institutions; USD 416 to institutions except Europe and Japan (effective 2006). adv. bk.rev. illus. index. back issues avail.; reprint service avail. from ISI. **Document type:** *Journal, Academic/Scholarly.* **Description:** Covers all aspects of mammalian biology, including anatomy, morphology, palaeontology, taxonomy, systematics, molecular biology, physiology, neurobiology, ethology, genetics, reproduction, development, evolutionary biology, domestication, ecology, faunistics, wildlife biology, conservation biology, and the biology of zoo mammals.
Formerly (until 2001): Zeitschrift fuer Saeugetierkunde (0044-3468)
Related titles: Online - full text ed.: (from EBSCO Publishing, Gale Group, IngentaConnect, O C L C Online Computer Library Center, Inc., ScienceDirect, Swets Information Services).
Indexed: ASCA, AgBio, AnBrAb, BIOBASE, BIOSIS Prev, BiolAb, CurCont, DSA, ForAb, GEOBASE, HerbAb, IABS, ISR, IndVet, KWIWR, NutrAb, S&F, SCI, SFA, SPPI, VetBull, WeedAb, WildRev, ZooRec.
—BLDSC (5357.250000), CISTI, IDS, IE, Infotrieve, ingenta, Linda Hall. **CCC.**

Published by: (Deutsche Gesellschaft fuer Saeugetierkunde), Elsevier GmbH, Urban & Fischer Verlag (Subsidiary of: Elsevier Science & Technology), Loebdergraben 14a, Jena, 07743, Germany. TEL 49-3641-626430, FAX 49-3641-626432, info@urbanfischer.de, http://www.elsevier.com/locate/mammbiol, http://www.urbanfischer.de. Eds. Dr. Dieter Kruska, Dr. Peter Langer. R&P Martin Huber TEL 49-3641-626430. Adv. contact Sabine Schroeter TEL 49-3641-626445. B&W page EUR 320, color page EUR 1,265; trim 170 x 240. Circ: 700 (paid and controlled). **Non-German speaking countries subscr. to:** Nature Publishing Group, Brunel Rd, Houndmills, Basingstoke, Hamps RG21 6XS, United Kingdom. TEL 44-1256-302629, FAX 44-1256-476117

599 USA ISSN 0076-3519
QL700 CODEN: MLNSBP
➤ **MAMMALIAN SPECIES.** Text in English. 1969. irreg. USD 30 (effective 2005). back issues avail. **Document type:** *Academic/Scholarly.* **Description:** Covers 25-35 individual species accounts each year. Summarizes current understanding of the biology of an individual species.
Related titles: Online - full text ed.: ISSN 1545-1410 (from BioOne, C S A, O C L C Online Computer Library Center, Inc., ProQuest Information & Learning).
Indexed: ASFA, AnBeAb, ApEcolAb, BIOSIS Prev, BiolAb, ESPM, KWIWR, MA, SFA, WildRev, ZooRec.
—Linda Hall.
Published by: American Society of Mammalogists, PO Box 1897, Lawrence, KS 66044-8897. TEL 801-378-2492, 785-843-1235, FAX 785-843-1274, http://www.mammalogy.org. Ed. Virginia Hayssen. Circ: 1,400.

590 RUS ISSN 0130-1667
MAMMOLOGIYA. Text in Russian. q. USD 115 in United States.
—East View.
Published by: Izdatel'stvo Kabur, Verkhnyi Predtechenskii per 8, Moscow, 123242, Russian Federation. TEL 7-095-2054785, FAX 7-095-2054785. Ed. E G Pinkhosevich. **US dist. addr.:** East View Information Services, 3020 Harbor Ln. N., Minneapolis, MN 55447. TEL 612-550-0961.

597 USA ISSN 1045-3555
MARINE FISH MONTHLY. Text in English. 1985. m. USD 22 domestic; USD 28 in Canada; USD 38 elsewhere. adv. bk.rev. illus. Index. reprints avail. **Description:** For hobbyists and collectors of marine fish.
Published by: Publishing Concepts Corp., 3243 Hwy 61 E, Luttrell, TN 37779. TEL 423-992-3892, FAX 423-992-5259, http://www.seahorses.com/fish_mag/mfm.htm. Circ: 32,420.

590 FRA ISSN 1168-3430
MARINE LIFE. Text in Multiple languages. 1979. irreg.
Formerly (until 1979): Vie Marine (0223-422X)
Indexed: ASFA, ESPM, PollutAb, RefZh, SWRA, ZooRec.
Published by: Institut Oceanographique Paul Ricard, BP 308, Marseille, 13309 Cedex 14, France. TEL 33-4-91111061, FAX 33-4-91111557, http://www.institut-paul-ricard.org.

599 USA ISSN 0824-0469
QL713.2 CODEN: MMSCEC
➤ **MARINE MAMMAL SCIENCE.** Text in English. 1985. q. USD 110 in North America; USD 120 elsewhere (effective 2001). adv. bk.rev. illus. back issues avail.; reprints avail. **Document type:** *Journal, Academic/Scholarly.* **Description:** Presents original research and observations on marine mammals, their evolution, form, function, husbandry, health, populations, and ecological relationships.
Indexed: ASCA, ASFA, AnBeAb, AnBrAb, ApEcolAb, BIOBASE, BIOSIS Prev, BiolAb, CurCont, DSA, EPB, ESPM, GEOBASE, HelmAb, IABS, ISR, IndVet, NutrAb, OceAb, RRTA, RefZh, RevApplEntom, SCI, SFA, VetBull, WLR, WildRev, ZooRec.
—BLDSC (5376.170000), CISTI, IDS, IE, Infotrieve, ingenta, Linda Hall. **CCC.**
Published by: Society for Marine Mammalogy, c/o Allen Press, Inc, Box 1897, Lawrence, KS 66044-8897. TEL 785-843-1235, FAX 785-843-1274, sfmm@allenpress.com, http://www.marinemammalogy.org.

597.9 639.9 GBR ISSN 0839-7708
QL666.C536
➤ **MARINE TURTLE NEWSLETTER.** Text in English. 1976. q. free (effective 2002). bk.rev.; music rev.; software rev.; Website rev. bibl. 2 cols./p.; back issues avail. **Document type:** *Newsletter, Academic/Scholarly.* **Description:** Provides a forum for exchange of information about all aspects of marine turtle biology and conservation. Alerts interested people to particular threats to marine turtles, as they arise.
Related titles: Online - full content ed.; Spanish ed.: Noticiero de Tortugas Marinas. ISSN 1463-9335. 1976.
Indexed: ASFA, ESPM, OceAb, ZooRec.
Published by: Marine Turtle Research Group, School of Biological Sciences, University of Wales Swansea, Singleton Park, Swansea, SA2 8PP, United Kingdom. TEL 44-1792-205678 ext 4411, FAX 44-1792-295447, MTN@swan.ac.uk, http://www.seaturtle.org/mtn. Eds. Annette Broderick, Brendan Godley. Circ: 2,500.

597.9 USA ISSN 0025-4231
QL653.M3 CODEN: MHSBB5
MARYLAND HERPETOLOGICAL SOCIETY. BULLETIN. Text in English. 1965. q. USD 50 domestic; USD 60 foreign (effective 2004). adv. bk.rev. bibl.; charts; illus.; stat. back issues avail. **Document type:** *Bulletin.* **Description:** Publishes research on amphibians and reptiles.
Related titles: Microfilm ed.
Indexed: BIOSIS Prev, BiolAb, SFA, WLR, WildRev, ZooRec.
—CISTI, Linda Hall.
Published by: (Natural History Society of Maryland, Inc.), Maryland Herpetological Society, 2643 N Charles St, Baltimore, MD 21218. TEL 410-557-6879, http://herplit.com/contents/BMHS.html, http://www.reptileinfo.com/herpsoc/mdherp.html. Ed., Adv. contact Herbert S Harris Jr. R&P Herbert Harris. Circ: 300 (paid).

590 ARG ISSN 0327-9383
QL700
MASTOZOOLOGIA NEOTROPICAL. Text in Spanish. 1994. bi-m. back issues avail.
Related titles: Online - full text ed.: ISSN 1666-0536. 2000; ♦ Supplement(s): Mastozoologia Neotropical. Publicaciones Especiales. ISSN 0329-1006.
Indexed: ZooRec.
—BLDSC (5390.292000).
Published by: Sociedad Argentina para el Estudio de los Mamiferos, Unidad de Zoologia y Ecologia Animal, CC 507, Mendoza, 5500, Argentina. mnsarem@lab.cricyt.edu.ar, http://lab1.cricyt.edu.ar/mn/indice.htm. Ed. Carlos E Borghi.

590 ARG ISSN 0329-1006
MASTOZOOLOGIA NEOTROPICAL. PUBLICACIONES ESPECIALES. Text in Spanish. 1997. irreg.
Related titles: ♦ Supplement to: Mastozoologia Neotropical. ISSN 0327-9383.
Published by: Sociedad Argentina para el Estudio de los Mamiferos, Unidad de Zoologia y Ecologia Animal, CC 507, Mendoza, 5500, Argentina. mnsarem@lab.cricyt.edu.ar, http://lab1.cricyt.edu.ar/mn/indice.htm. Ed. Carlos E Borghi.

592.3 CAN ISSN 0380-9633
CODEN: MGDLAK
➤ **MEGADRILOGICA.** Text in English, French, Spanish; Summaries in Multiple languages. 1968. irreg., latest vol.9, 2003. USD 36 per vol. 12 nos.; USD 5 per issue (effective 2005). bibl. 2 cols./p.; back issues avail. **Document type:** *Journal, Academic/Scholarly.*
Indexed: BIOSIS Prev, BibAg, BiolAb, ForAb, ZooRec.
—CISTI, Linda Hall. **CCC.**
Published by: Oligochaetology Laboratory, 18 Broadview Court, Kitchener, ON N2A 2X8, Canada. TEL 519-896-4728, FAX 519-826-7024, john.reynolds1@sympatico.ca. Ed. Dr. John W Reynolds. Circ: 1,000 (paid).

590 DEU ISSN 0934-6643
MERTENSIELLA. Text in English, German. 1988. irreg., latest vol.11, 1999. price varies. illus. **Document type:** *Monographic series, Academic/Scholarly.*
Related titles: ♦ Supplement to: Salamandra. ISSN 0036-3375.
Indexed: ZooRec.
—BLDSC (5682.281963).
Published by: Deutsche Gesellschaft fuer Herpetologie und Terrarienkunde e.V., Postfach 1421, Rheinbach, 53351, Germany. TEL 49-2225-703333, FAX 49-2225-703338, gs@dght.de, http://www.dght.de. Circ: 2,000.

597 JPN ISSN 0287-6108
MIE UNIVERSITY. FISHERIES RESEARCH LABORATORY. REPORT/MIE DAIGAKU SUISAN KENKYUJO HOKOKU. Text in English. 1978. irreg.
Related titles: Japanese ed.
Indexed: ASFA.
Published by: Mie Daigaku, Suisan Kenkyujo/Mie University, Fisheries Research Laboratory, 4190-172 Wagu, Shima-cho, Shima-gun, Mie-ken 517-0703, Japan. Ed. Washiro Kida. Circ: 500.

590 ITA ISSN 1121-9181
➤ **MIGRATORI ALATI;** rivista di gestione dell'ambiente e della fauna. Text in Italian. 1978. bi-m. EUR 16.50; EUR 4.50 per issue (effective 2002). adv. bk.rev. **Document type:** *Academic/Scholarly.*
Formerly (until 1986): Migratori Acquatici (1121-9173)
Published by: R G F di Realini Gianfranco e C. s.a.s., Via Cascine, 4, Ispra, VA 21027, Italy. rgfrealini@interfree.it, http://www.rgf.iscool.net. Ed. Gianfranco Realini. Circ: 5,000. **Subscr. to:** Via Lomazzo 47, Milan, MI 20154, Italy.

590 DEU ISSN 0076-8839
MILU: WISSENSCHAFTLICHE UND KULTURELLE MITTEILUNGEN AUS DEM TIERPARK BERLIN. Text in German. 1960. irreg., latest vol.3, 1973. index.
Indexed: KWIWR, ZooRec.
Published by: Tierpark Berlin, Am Tierpark 41, Berlin, 10319, Germany. Ed. H Dathe.

594 JPN ISSN 0912-1390
MITAMAKI/SAGAMI SHELL CLUB. NEWS. Text in Japanese. 1967. irreg.
Published by: Sagami Kairui Dokokai/Sagami Shell Club, Yokosukashi Shizen Hakubutsukan, 95 Fukadadai, Yokosuka-shi, Kanagawa-ken 238-0016, Japan.

590 DEU
QL1 CODEN: MTZMAK
➤ **MITTEILUNGEN AUS DEM MUSEUM FUER NATURKUNDE IN BERLIN - FOSSIL RECORDS.** Text and summaries in English, French, German. 1998. s-a. EUR 268 in Europe; CHF 408 in Switzerland & Liechtenstein; USD 344 elsewhere; EUR 295 combined subscription in Europe print & online eds.; CHF 449 combined subscription in Switzerland & Liechtenstein for print & online eds.; USD 379 combined subscription elsewhere print & online eds. (effective 2006). charts; illus. index. **Document type:** *Journal, Academic/Scholarly.*
Formerly (until 2005): Mitteilungen aus dem Museum fuer Naturkunde in Berlin - Zoologische Reihe (1435-1935); Which was formed by the merger of (1977-1998): Annalen fuer Ornithologie (0232-5519); (1901-1998): Mitteilungen aus dem Zoologischen Museum in Berlin (0373-8493); Which was formerly (1898-1900): Mitteilungen aus der Zoologischen Sammlung des Museums fuer Naturkunde in Berlin (0233-1519)
Related titles: Online - full text ed.: ISSN 1522-2373. EUR 268 in Europe; CHF 408 in Switzerland & Liechtenstein; USD 344 elsewhere (effective 2006) (from Wiley InterScience).
Indexed: ASFA, BiolAb, ESPM, IBR, RefZh, ZooRec.
—BLDSC (5860.345000), CISTI, IE, ingenta, Linda Hall. **CCC.**
Published by: Wiley - V C H Verlag GmbH & Co. KGaA (Subsidiary of: John Wiley & Sons, Inc.), Boschstr 12, Weinheim, 69469, Germany. TEL 49-6201-6060, FAX 49-6201-606328, adsales@wiley-vch.de, subservice@wiley-vch.de, http://www3.interscience.wiley.com/cgi-bin/jhome/109865047, http://www.wiley-vch.de. Ed. Ulrich Zeller. R&P Claudia Rutz. Adv. contact Aenne Anders TEL 49-6201-606552. **Subscr. in the Americas to:** John Wiley & Sons, Inc., 111 River St, Hoboken, NJ 07030-5774. TEL 201-748-6645, FAX 201-748-6088, subinfo@wiley.com; **Subscr. outside Germany, Austria & Switzerland to:** John Wiley & Sons Ltd., The Atrium, Southern Gate, Chichester, West Sussex PO19 8SQ, United Kingdom. TEL 44-1243-779777, FAX 44-1243-775878.

578 GBR
▼ **MOLLUSC WORLD.** Text in English. 2003 (Mar.). 3/yr. GBP 23 to individuals; GBP 32 domestic to institutional members & Ireland; GBP 37 elsewhere to institutional members; GBP 10 to students (effective 2003). **Document type:** *Magazine, Academic/Scholarly.* **Description:** Contain articles on many aspects of Conchology, such as finds, ecology, mollusc rearing, field meeting reports, biographical notes of past collectors, identification, cultural uses of shells, literature and poetry.
Incorporates (1961-2003): The Conchological Newsletter (0573-2336)
Published by: Conchological Society of Great Britain and Ireland, c/o Mr. M.D. Weideli, 35 Bartlemy Rd, Newbury, Berks RG14 6LD, United Kingdom. TEL 44-1635-42190, FAX 44-1635-820904, membership@conchsoc.org, Mike_Weideli@compuserve.com, http://www.conchsoc.org/newsletter.htm. Ed. R Hill.

594 AUS ISSN 1323-5818
QL401 CODEN: JMLAA2
➤ **MOLLUSCAN RESEARCH.** Text in English. 1957. 3/yr. AUD 100 in Australia & New Zealand online edition; AUD 110 in Australia & New Zealand print and online edition; USD 75 elsewhere online edition; USD 85 elsewhere print and online edition (effective 2003). bk.rev. back issues avail. **Document type:** *Journal, Academic/Scholarly.*
Formerly (until vol.15, 1994): Malacological Society of Australia. Journal (0085-2988)
Related titles: Online - full text ed.: (from EBSCO Publishing, Gale Group, O C L C Online Computer Library Center, Inc., Swets Information Services).
Indexed: ASFA, BioCN&I, BiolAb, ESPM, RefZh, SFA, ZooRec.
—IE. **CCC.**
Published by: (Malacological Society of Australasia, Division of Invertebrate Zoology), C S I R O Publishing, 150 Oxford St, PO Box 1139, Collingwood, VIC 3066, Australia. TEL 61-3-96627500, 61-3-96627644, FAX 61-3-96627555, 61-3-96627611, desb@austmus.gov.au, publishing@csiro.au, http://www.publish.csiro.au/journals/mr. Eds. Dr. F E Wells, Dr. Winston Ponder. Circ: 650.

599.8 JPN ISSN 0026-9794
MONKEY/MONKI. Text in Japanese. 1957. bi-m. JPY 3,000 (effective 2001). bk.rev.; film rev. bibl.; charts; illus. **Document type:** *Academic/Scholarly.*
Published by: Japan Monkey Centre/Nihon Monki Senta, 26 Kanrin, Inuyama-shi, Aichi-ken 484-0081, Japan. TEL 81-568-61-2327, FAX 81-568-62-6823. Ed., R&P Mitsuo Iwamoto. Circ: 2,000 (controlled).

595.34 USA ISSN 0722-5741
MONOCULUS; copepod newsletter. Text in English. 1980. s-a.
Related titles: Online - full text ed.: ISSN 1543-0731.
Published by: World Association of Copepodologists, c/o Janet W. Reid, Div. of Science & Learning, Virginia Museum of Natural History, Martinsville, VA 24112. TEL 276-656-6719, FAX 276-656-6701, http://www.copepoda.uconn.edu/newsletter. Ed. Janet W. Reid.

B

▼ *new title* ➤ *refereed* ✶ *unverified* ♦ *full entry avail.*

598.1 ESP ISSN 1130-8443
MONOGRAFIAS DE HERPETOLOGIA. Text in Spanish. 1989. irreg. back issues avail.
Indexed: IECT, ZooRec.
—CINDOC.
Published by: Asociacion Herpetologica Espanola, c/o Museo Nac. de Ciencias Naturales, Jose Gutierrez Abascal, 2, Madrid, 28006, Spain. lizana@gugu.usal.es, http://www.herplit.com/contents/Monografia.html.

590 POL ISSN 0137-2173
CODEN: MGFPA8
➤ **MONOGRAFIE FAUNY POLSKI.** Text in Polish, English, French, German. 1973. irreg., latest vol.21, 1995. price varies. bibl. **Document type:** *Monographic series, Academic/Scholarly.*
Indexed: AgrLib, BIOSIS Prev, BiolAb, ZooRec.
—CISTI.
Published by: Polska Akademia Nauk, Instytut Systematyki i Ewolucji Zwierzat/Polish Academy of Sciences, Institute of Systematics and Evolution of Animals, ul Slawkowska 17, Krakow, 31-016, Poland. TEL 48-12-4221901, FAX 48-12-4224294, http://www.isez.pan.krakow.pl. R&P Jozef Razowski. Circ: 600.

B

599.8 USA ISSN 0740-9729
CODEN: MONPD5
➤ **MONOGRAPHS IN PRIMATOLOGY.** Text in English. 1983. irreg., latest vol.14. price varies. **Document type:** *Monographic series, Academic/Scholarly.*
Indexed: BIOSIS Prev, BiolAb.
—CISTI.
Published by: John Wiley & Sons, Inc., 111 River St, Hoboken, NJ 07030-5774. TEL 201-748-6000, 800-825-7550, FAX 201-748-5915, uscs-wis@wiley.com, http://www.wiley.com.

594 NLD ISSN 0162-8321
CODEN: MMMOEI
MONOGRAPHS OF MARINE MOLLUSCA. Text in English. 1978. irreg., latest vol.5, 2003. price varies. back issues avail. **Document type:** *Monographic series, Academic/Scholarly.*
Indexed: ASFA, BIOSIS Prev, BiolAb, ESPM, ZooRec.
—Linda Hall.
Published by: Backhuys Publishers BV, Postbus 321, Leiden, 2300 AH, Netherlands. TEL 31-71-517-0208, FAX 31-71-517-1856, backhuys@backhuys.com, http://www.backhuys.com. Ed. Mike Ruijsenaars. Circ: 300.

590 RUS ISSN 0134-8647
MOSKOVSKII GOSUDARSTVENNYI UNIVERSITET IM. M.V. LOMONOSOVA. ZOOLOGICHESKII MUZEI. SBORNIK TRUDOV. Text in Russian. 1961. irreg. **Document type:** *Academic/Scholarly.*
Indexed: ZooRec.
—Linda Hall.
Published by: Moskovskii Gosudarstvennyi Universitet im. M.V. Lomonosova, Zoologicheskii Muzei/M.V. Lomonosov Moscow State University, Muzeum of Zoology, ul Bol'shaya Nikitskaya, dom 6, Moscow, 103009, Russian Federation. TEL 7-095-2038923, olr@zoomus.bio.msu.su, http://www.deol.ru/culture/museum/zoom/index.htm.

590 BEL ISSN 0379-1785
QL337.C6 CODEN: MRAZBN
MUSEE ROYAL DE L'AFRIQUE CENTRALE. ANNALES - SCIENCES ZOOLOGIQUES. SERIE IN 8/KONINKLIJK MUSEUM VOOR MIDDEN-AFRIKA. ANNALEN - ZOOLOGISCHE WETENSCHAPPEN. REEKS IN 8. Text in French. 1948. irreg., latest vol.278, 1996. price varies. charts; illus. **Document type:** *Monographic series.*
Indexed: BiolAb, ForAb, RefZh, RevApplEntom, ZooRec.
Published by: Musee Royal de l'Afrique Centrale/Koninklijk Museum voor Midden-Afrika, Steenweg op Leuven 13, Tervuren, 3080, Belgium. TEL 32-2-7695299, FAX 32-2-767-0242.

591.96 BEL ISSN 0778-466X
MUSEE ROYAL DE L'AFRIQUE CENTRALE. DOCUMENTATION ZOOLOGIQUE/KONINKLIJK MUSEUM VOOR MIDDEN-AFRIKA. ZOOLOGISCHE DOCUMENTATIE. Text in French. 1961. irreg., latest vol.23, 1993. **Document type:** *Monographic series.* **Description:** Scholarly publications relating to the fauna of Africa and neighboring areas.
Indexed: BiolAb, ZooRec.
Published by: Musee Royal de l'Afrique Centrale/Koninklijk Museum voor Midden-Afrika, Steenweg op Leuven 13, Tervuren, 3080, Belgium. TEL 32-2-7695299, FAX 32-2-767-0242.

MUSEO CIVICO DI STORIA NATURALE DI FERRARA. STAZIONE DI ECOLOGIA. QUADERNI. see *BIOLOGY—Entomology*

MUSEO CIVICO DI STORIA NATURALE DI VERONA. BOLLETTINO. BOTANICA ZOOLOGIA. see *BIOLOGY—Botany*

590 ARG ISSN 0372-4638
QL1 CODEN: LURZAF
MUSEO DE LA PLATA. REVISTA. SECCION ZOOLOGIA. Text in Spanish. 1890. irreg.
Supersedes in part (in 1936): Museo de La Plata. Revista (0375-1147)
Indexed: ESPM, ZooRec.
—CISTI.
Published by: Universidad Nacional de La Plata, Facultad de Ciencias Naturales y Museo, Avenidas 60 y 122, La Plata, Buenos Aires, Argentina. TEL 54-221-4258252, facultad@museo.fcnym.unlp.edu.ar.

590.73 PRT ISSN 0871-4843
QL1 CODEN: AMBOEZ
➤ **MUSEU BOCAGE. ARQUIVOS.** Text in English; Summaries in English, French, Portuguese, Spanish. 1930; N.S. 1965; N.S. 1987. irreg. per issue exchange basis only. charts; illus. index. back issues avail.; reprints avail. **Document type:** *Journal, Academic/Scholarly.*
Formed by the 1987 merger of: Museu Bocage. Arquivos. Serie A (0254-0444); Museu Bocage. Arquivos. Series B, Notas (0254-0452); Museu Bocage. Arquivos. Serie C, Supplementos (0254-0460); Museu Bocage. Arquivos. Serie D, Extensao Cultural e Ensino (0870-0540); Which supersedes (in 1981): Museu Bocage. Arquivos (0027-3988); Which was formerly titled (until 1965): Revista Portugesa de Zoologia e Biologia Geral (0484-8136); (until 1957): Museu Bocage. Arquivos (0374-1087)
Indexed: ASFA, BiolAb, SFA, WildRev, ZooRec.
—CISTI.
Published by: Museu Bocage, Rua da Escola Politechnica 58, Lisbon, 1200, Portugal. TEL 351-213921833, FAX 351-213969784. Eds. C Almaca, Maria da Graca Ramalhinho.

590 ESP ISSN 1695-8950
CODEN: TMZODN
➤ **MUSEU DE CIENCES NATURALS. MONOGRAFIES.** Text in English, Spanish; Summaries in Catalan, English, Spanish. 1917-1957; N.S. 1979. a. price varies. **Document type:** *Monographic series, Academic/Scholarly.*
Former titles (until 2003): Institut Botanic de Barcelona. Treballs (0210-8062); (until 2000): Museu de Zoologia. Treballs (0211-0687); Which superseded (in 1979): Museo de Zoologia. Trabajos. Nueva Serie Zoologica (0211-0695); Which was formerly (until 1956): Museo de Ciencias Naturales de Barcelona. Trabajos. Nueva Serie Zoologica (0211-0709); (until 1937): Museu de Ciencies Naturals de Barcelona. Treballs (0211-0717); (until 1918): Musei Barcinonensis Scientiarum Naturalium Opera
Indexed: ASFA, AcoustA, Agrind, B&AI, BehAb, BiolAb, ESPM, EnvInd, IBR, IECT, MSCT, WildRev, ZooRec.
—CINDOC.
Published by: Museu de Ciencies Naturals de la Ciutadella, Museu de Zoologia, Passeig Picasso s/n, Barcelona, 08003, Spain. TEL 34-93-3196912, FAX 34-93-3104999, museuciencies@mail.bcn.es, http://www.museuzoologia.bcn.es.

590.74 PRT ISSN 0870-3876
DP702.M11 CODEN: BMMFA2
➤ **MUSEU MUNICIPAL DO FUNCHAL. BOLETIM.** Text in Portuguese, English. 1945. a. per issue exchange basis. illus.; maps; stat. back issues avail. **Document type:** *Bulletin, Academic/Scholarly.*
Related titles: Diskette ed.; Supplement(s): Museu Municipal do Funchal. Boletim. Suplemento. ISSN 0872-2560.
Indexed: ASFA, BIOSIS Prev, BiolAb, ESPM, SFA, WildRev, ZooRec.
—BLDSC (2139.000000).
Published by: Camara Municipal do Funchal, Museu Municipal do Funchal Historia Natural, Rua da Mouraria 31, Funchal, Madeira 9004-546, Portugal. TEL 351-291-229761, FAX 351-291-225180, ciencia@mail.cm-funchal.pt. Ed., R&P Manuel Jose Biscoito. Adv. contact Alexandra Telo. Circ: 750.

591 BRA ISSN 0080-312X
QL1 CODEN: BMJZAD
MUSEU NACIONAL. BOLETIM. ZOOLOGIA. Text in Portuguese; Summaries in English; Text occasionally in French, German. 1942. irreg., latest vol.596, 2002. exchange only. bibl.; charts.
Supersedes in part (1923-1941): Museu Nacional. Boletim (0100-1507)
Indexed: ASFA, AgrForAb, BIOSIS Prev, BioCN&I, BiolAb, ForAb, HelmAb, HerbAb, PBA, PGegResA, RevApplEntom, S&F, TDB, WeedAb, WildRev, ZooRec.
—CISTI, Linda Hall.
Published by: Museu Nacional, Quinta da Boa Vista, Sao Cristovao, Rio de Janeiro, RJ 20940-040, Brazil. TEL 55-21-25688262, FAX 55-21-25681352, museu@mn.ufrj.br, http://www.acd.ufjr.br/~museuhp/homep.htm.

590.7 BRA
MUSEU PARAENSE EMILIO GOELDI. BOLETIM. NOVA SERIE ZOOLOGIA. Text mainly in Portuguese; Text occasionally in English, French. 1957; N.S. 1984. s-a. BRL 12 per issue domestic; USD 15 per issue foreign (effective 2000). abstr.; bibl.; illus. **Description:** Original papers in zoological research.
Formerly (until 1983, no.124): Museu Paraense Emilio Goeldi. Boletim. Nova Serie: Zoologia (0077-2232)
Indexed: BIOSIS Prev, BiolAb, ForAb, IndVet, RDA, RM&VM, RefZh, S&F, TDB, VetBull, WAE&RSA, WildRev, ZooRec.
—BLDSC (2143.500000), Linda Hall.
Published by: Conselho Nacional de Desenvolvimento Cientifico e Tecnologico, Museu Paraense Emilio Goeldi, Comercio, Caixa Postal 399, Belem, PA 66017-970, Brazil. TEL 091-274-2195, FAX 091-274-1811, mgdoc@musu-goeldi.br. Circ: 1,000.

MUSEUM HEINEANUM. ABHANDLUNGEN UND BERICHTE. see *BIOLOGY—Botany*

MUSEUM NATIONAL D'HISTOIRE NATURELLE. MEMOIRES. see *SCIENCES: COMPREHENSIVE WORKS*

590.74 FRA ISSN 1280-9551
QL1 CODEN: BMNADT
➤ **MUSEUM NATIONAL D'HISTOIRE NATURELLE. ZOOSYSTEMA.** Text and summaries in French, English. 1895. q. EUR 75 to individuals; EUR 150 to institutions (effective 2002). 250 p./no.; **Document type:** *Academic/Scholarly.* **Description:** Examines the inventory and analyzes and interprets animal biodiversity. Publishes original zoological research, particularly in the areas of systematics and related fields, including comparative, functional and evolutionary morphology; phylogeny; biogeography; taxonomy; and nomenclature.
Former titles (until 1997): Museum National d'Histoire Naturelle. Bulletin - Section A (Zoologie et Ecologie Animales) (0181-0626); (until 1979): Museum National d'Histoire Naturelle. Bulletin (Zoologie) (0300-9386); Which superseded in part (in 1972): Museum National d'Histoire Naturelle. Bulletin (1148-8425); Which was formerly (until 1907): Museum National d'Histoire. Bulletin (0027-4070)
Related titles: Online - full text ed.: ISSN 1638-9387. 2000. free (effective 2005).
Indexed: ASFA, AgBio, BIOSIS Prev, BioCN&I, BiolAb, CurCont, ESPM, ForAb, HelmAb, IndVet, ProtozoAb, RM&VM, RefZh, RevApplEntom, S&F, SFA, TDB, VetBull, WildRev, ZooRec.
—BLDSC (9531.860000), CISTI, IE, ingenta, Linda Hall.
Published by: Museum National d'Histoire Naturelle, 57 Rue Cuvier, Paris, 75231 Cedex 05, France. TEL 33-1-40793777, zoosyst@mnhn.fr, http://www.mnhn.fr/publication/zoosyst/azoosyst.html.

570.74 USA ISSN 0027-4100
QL1 CODEN: MCZBA4
MUSEUM OF COMPARATIVE ZOOLOGY. BULLETIN. Text in English. 1863. irreg. (3-4/yr.). price varies. bibl.; illus. back issues avail.; reprints avail. **Document type:** *Bulletin, Academic/Scholarly.* **Description:** Publishes natural sciences research papers.
Formerly: Harvard University. Museum of Comparative Zoology. Bulletin
Related titles: Microfilm ed.: (from BHP).
Indexed: BIOSIS Prev, BiolAb, RefZh, SFA, WildRev, ZooRec.
—CISTI, Linda Hall.
Published by: Harvard University, Museum of Comparative Zoology, 26 Oxford St, Cambridge, MA 02138. TEL 617-495-3045, FAX 617-495-5667, http://www.mcz.harvard.edu. Ed. Kenneth J Boss. Circ: 1,000.

590.74 AUS
Q93
➤ **MUSEUM VICTORIA. MEMOIRS.** Text in English. 1906. irreg. (1-2/yr), latest vol.58, no.2. AUD 50 (effective 2002). **Document type:** *Journal, Academic/Scholarly.*
Former titles: Museum of Victoria. Memoirs (0814-1827); (until 1984): National Museum of Victoria. Memoirs (0083-5986); (until 1946): National Museum Melbourne. Memoirs (0311-9548)
Indexed: AESIS, AICP, BIOSIS Prev, IBR, SFA, WildRev, ZooRec.
—KNAW, Linda Hall.
Published by: Museum Board of Victoria, GPO Box 666E, Melbourne, VIC 3001, Australia. TEL 61-3-8341-7777, FAX 61-3-8341-7778, http://www.museum.vic.gov.au/. Ed., R&P Gary Poore. Circ: 600.

599.4 DEU ISSN 0580-3896
QL737.C5
➤ **MYOTIS**; international journal of bat research. Text in English, German. 1963. a. EUR 13 (effective 2003). bk.rev. charts; illus.; maps. back issues avail. **Document type:** *Journal, Academic/Scholarly.* **Description:** Publication devoted to scientific research on bats. Covers biology, behavior, reproduction, and conservation of all types in different areas.
Indexed: BIOSIS Prev, BiolAb, RefZh, WildRev, ZooRec.
—CISTI.
Published by: Zoologisches Forschungsinstitut und Museum Alexander Koenig, Adenauerallee 160, Bonn, 53113, Germany. TEL 49-228-9122216, FAX 49-228-216979, info.zfmk@uni-bonn.de. Ed. Dr. Rainer Hutterer. Circ: 300.

599.5 NOR ISSN 1025-2045
QL713.25
N A M M C O. ANNUAL REPORT. Text in English. 1995. a.
Indexed: ASFA, ESPM.
Published by: North Atlantic Marine Mammal Commission, Polar Environmental Centre, Tromso, 9296, Norway. TEL 47-77-750180, FAX 47-77-750181, nammco-sec@nammco.no, http://www.nammco.no.

599.5 NOR ISSN 1560-2206
N A M M C O. SCIENTIFIC PUBLICATIONS. (North Atlantic Marine Mammal Commission) Text in English. 1998. a. **Document type:** *Monographic series.*
Indexed: ASFA, ESPM, ZooRec.
—BLDSC (6015.332370), IE.
Published by: North Atlantic Marine Mammal Commission, Polar Environmental Centre, Tromso, 9296, Norway. TEL 47-77-750180, FAX 47-77-750181, nammco-sec@nammco.no, http://www.nammco.no.

597 MYS ISSN 0116-290X
SH321
NAGA. Text in English. 1978. q. USD 20 (effective 2005). adv. bk.rev. bibl.; stat. back issues avail. **Document type:** *Journal, Academic/Scholarly.* **Description:** Carries news and articles on tropical aquatic resource research.
Formerly (until 1985): I C L A R M Newsletter (0115-4575)
Related titles: Online - full text ed.: free (effective 2005).
Indexed: AEA, ASFA, AgBio, AnBrAb, CTO, ESPM, FS&TA, I&DA, IPP, IndVet, NutrAb, PGegResA, PN&I, PoultAb, RDA, RM&VM, RRTA, RefZh, RiceAb, S&F, SFA, SIA, WAE&RSA, ZooRec.
—BLDSC (6013.240050), CISTI, IE, ingenta.
Published by: WorldFish Center, PO Box 500 GPO, Penang, 10670, Malaysia. TEL 60-4-626-1606, FAX 60-4-626-5530, http://www.worldfishcenter.org/naga/nagainfo.htm. adv.: B&W page USD 450. Circ: 5,500.

590.74 NLD ISSN 0459-1801
CODEN: ZOBJAX
NATIONAAL NATUURHISTORISCH MUSEUM. ZOOLOGISCHE BIJDRAGEN. Key Title: Zoologische Bijdragen. Text in Dutch, English, German; Summaries in English. 1955. irreg., latest vol.40, 1994. price varies. back issues avail. **Document type:** *Monographic series.*
Formerly: Rijksmuseum van Natuurlijke Historie. Zoologische Bijdragen
Indexed: BIOSIS Prev, BiolAb, SFA, WildRev, ZooRec.
—KNAW.
Published by: Nationaal Natuurhistorisch Museum, Postbus 9517, Leiden, 2300 RA, Netherlands. inform@nnm.nl. Pub. Haan Moll. Circ: 800. **Subscr. to:** Backhuys Publishers - Universal Book Services, PO Box 321, Leiden 2300 AH, Netherlands.

590.73 NLD ISSN 0024-0672
QL1 CODEN: ZMRHAP
NATIONAAL NATUURHISTORISCH MUSEUM. ZOOLOGISCHE MEDEDELINGEN. Key Title: Zoologische Mededelingen. Text mainly in English; Text occasionally in French, German. 1915. s-a. price varies. charts; illus. back issues avail. **Document type:** *Academic/Scholarly.*
Formerly: Rijksmuseum van Natuurlijke Historie. Zoologische Mededelingen
Indexed: ASFA, BIOSIS Prev, BioCN&I, BiolAb, ESPM, RM&VM, RefZh, RevApplEntom, SFA, WildRev, ZooRec.
—BLDSC (9526.000000), IE, ingenta, KNAW.
Published by: Nationaal Natuurhistorisch Museum, Postbus 9517, Leiden, 2300 RA, Netherlands. R&P C Vanachterberg. Circ: 800. **Subscr. to:** Backhuys Publishers - Universal Book Services, PO Box 321, Leiden 2300 AH, Netherlands. TEL 31-71-5171208.

590.73 NLD ISSN 0024-1652
QL1 CODEN: ZVRHAK
NATIONAAL NATUURHISTORISCH MUSEUM. ZOOLOGISCHE VERHANDELINGEN. Key Title: Zoologische Verhandelingen. Text in English; Text occasionally in French, German; Summaries in English. 1948. irreg., latest vol.322, 1998. price varies. back issues avail. **Document type:** *Academic/Scholarly.*
Formerly: Rijksmuseum van Natuurlijke Historie. Zoologische Verhandelingen
Indexed: BIOSIS Prev, BiolAb, ESPM, IndVet, RM&VM, RefZh, RevApplEntom, S&F, SFA, WildRev, ZooRec.
—BLDSC (9527.000000), CISTI, IE, ingenta, KNAW.
Published by: Nationaal Natuurhistorisch Museum, Postbus 9517, Leiden, 2300 RA, Netherlands. R&P C Vanachterberg. Circ: 800. **Subscr. to:** Backhuys Publishers - Universal Book Services, PO Box 321, Leiden 2300 AH, Netherlands.

590.74 JPN ISSN 0385-2423
QL325 CODEN: BMAZD5
NATIONAL SCIENCE MUSEUM. BULLETIN. SERIES A: ZOOLOGY/KOKURITSU KAGAKU HAKUBUTSUKAN KENKYU HOKOKU. A RUI: DOBUTSUGAKU. Text in English. 1939. q. illus.
Supersedes in part (in 1975): National Science Museum. Bulletin (0028-0119)
Indexed: Agr, BIOSIS Prev, BiolAb, EntAb, HelmAb, RefZh, SFA, ZooRec.
—CISTI.
Published by: Monbusho, Kokuritsu Kagaku Hakubutsukan/ Ministry of Education, Science and Culture, National Science Museum, 7-20 Ueno-Koen, Taito-ku, Tokyo, 110-0007, Japan.

594.1477 USA
NATIONAL SHELLFISHERIES ASSOCIATION. QUARTERLY NEWSLETTER. Text in English. q. free (effective 2003).
Related titles: Online - full text ed.
—CINDOC.
Published by: National Shellfisheries Association, Inc., c/o University of Connecticut, Marine Science Dept, Groton, CT 06340. TEL 860-405-9282, FAX 860-405-9153, cdavis@midcoast.com, http://www.shellfish.org/pubs/qnl.htm. Ed. Chris Davis.

590 DEU
NATUR UND TIERSCHUTZ KALENDER DES DEUTSCHEN TIERSCHUTZBUNDES. Text in German. 1896. a. EUR 2.30 (effective 2002). **Document type:** *Yearbook, Consumer.*
Published by: Johann Michael Sailer Verlag GmbH & Co. KG, Aeusserer Laufer Platz 17, Nuernberg, 90403, Germany. FAX 49-911-5396912, sailer@sailer-verlag.de, http://www.sailer-verlag.de. Ed. Bobby Kastenhuber. Circ: 150,000.

599 GBR
NATURAL ENVIRONMENT RESEARCH COUNCIL. SEA MAMMAL RESEARCH UNIT. SCIENTIFIC REPORT. Text in English. irreg.
Published by: Natural Environment Research Council, Sea Mammal Research Unit, Gatty Marine Laboratory, University of St Andrews, St Andrews, KY16 8LB, United Kingdom. TEL 44-1334-462630, FAX 44-1334-462632, http://smub.st-and.ac.uk/.

590 900 USA ISSN 0890-6882
NATURAL HISTORY INVENTORY OF COLORADO. Text in English. 1979. irreg. bibl.; illus.; maps. back issues avail.
Indexed: ZooRec.
Published by: University of Colorado Museum, University of Colorado, Campus 315, Boulder, CO 80309. TEL 303-492-7359, FAX 303-735-0128, skwu@spot.colorado.edu. Eds. Shi Kuei Wu, Tim Hogan.

NATURAL HISTORY OF THE NATIONAL PARKS OF HUNGARY. see *CONSERVATION*

NATURALIA PATAGONICA. SERIE CIENCIAS BIOLOGICAS. see *BIOLOGY*

NATURFORSCHENDE GESELLSCHAFT DER OBERLAUSITZ. BERICHTE. see *BIOLOGY—Botany*

NATURFOTO; Magazin fuer Tier- und Naturfotografie. see *PHOTOGRAPHY*

595.7 DEU ISSN 0939-7736
NATURHISTORISCHER VEREIN DER RHEINLANDE UND WESTFALENS. ARBEITSGEMEINSCHAFT RHEINISCHER KOLEOPTEROLOGEN. MITTEILUNGEN. Text in German. 1991. irreg. **Document type:** *Monographic series, Academic/Scholarly.*
Indexed: ASFA, ESPM, ZooRec.
Published by: Naturhistorischer Verein der Rheinlande und Westfalens e.V., Arbeitsgemeinschaft Rheinischer Koleopterologen, Strombergstr. 22a, Bornheim, 53332, Germany. TEL 49-2227-925594, FAX 49-2227-925595, frank.koehler@online.de, http://www.koleopterologie.de.

590.74 AUT ISSN 0255-0105
QL1 CODEN: ANMBEO
➤ **NATURHISTORISCHES MUSEUM IN WIEN. ANNALEN. SERIE B: BOTANIK UND ZOOLOGIE.** Text in English, French, German. 1886. a. price varies. abstr.; illus.; maps. back issues avail. **Document type:** *Academic/Scholarly.*
Supersedes in part (in 1980): Naturhistorisches Museum in Wien. Annalen (0083-6133)
Indexed: ASFA, BIOSIS Prev, BioCN&I, BiolAb, ESPM, ForAb, RefZh, RevApplEntom, SFA, SPPI, WildRev, ZooRec.
—CISTI, KNAW, Linda Hall.
Published by: Naturhistorisches Museum in Wien, Burgring 7, Postfach 417, Vienna, W 1014, Austria. TEL 43-1-52177-497, FAX 43-1-52177-229, ernst.vitek@nhm-wien.ac.at, http://www.nhm-wien.ac.at. Ed., Adv. contact Ernst Vitek.

590 DEU ISSN 0173-7481
CODEN: AVNHAV
➤ **NATURWISSENSCHAFTLICHER VEREIN IN HAMBURG. ABHANDLUNGEN.** Text in German. 1937. irreg. price varies. bk.rev. bibl.; illus. index. reprint service avail. from ISI. **Document type:** *Monographic series, Academic/Scholarly.*
Supersedes in part: Naturwissenschaftlicher Verein in Hamburg. Abhandlungen und Verhandlungen (0301-2697)
Indexed: BiolAb, ChemAb, ZooRec.
—CISTI, Linda Hall.
Published by: Verlag Goecke und Evers, Sportplatzweg 5, Keltern-Weiler, 75210, Germany. TEL 49-7236-7174, FAX 49-7236-7325, books@goeckeevers.de, http:// www.goeckeevers.de.

590 DEU ISSN 0173-749X
Q49
➤ **NATURWISSENSCHAFTLICHER VEREIN IN HAMBURG. VERHANDLUNGEN.** Text in German. 1937. irreg. EUR 50 (effective 2003). adv. bk.rev. bibl.; illus. index. **Document type:** *Proceedings, Academic/Scholarly.* **Description:** Contains scientific papers on all fields of natural history and the history of science.
Supersedes in part (in 1980): Naturwissenschaftlicher Verein in Hamburg. Abhandlungen und Verhandlungen (0301-2697); Which was formed by the merger of (1846-1937): Abhandlungen aus dem Gebiete der Naturwissenschaften (0933-9337); (1840-1937): Naturwissenschaftlicher Verein in Hamburg. Verhandlungen (0933-9353); Which was formerly (until 1877): Naturwissenschaftlicher Verein zu Hamburg. Uebersicht der Aemter-Verteilung und Wissenschaftlichen Taetigkeit (0933-9558); (until 1866): Naturwissenschaftlicher Verein in Hamburg. Jahresbericht ueber die Verhandlungen (0933-9612)
Indexed: BiolAb, ZooRec.
—CISTI, Linda Hall.
Published by: (Naturwissenschaftlicher Verein in Hamburg), Verlag Goecke und Evers, Sportplatzweg 5, Keltern-Weiler, 75210, Germany. TEL 49-7236-7174, FAX 49-7236-7325, books@goeckeevers.de, http://www.goeckeevers.de.

➤ **NATURWISSENSCHAFTLICHER VEREIN WUPPERTAL. JAHRESBERICHTE;** Heft 52. see *BIOLOGY—Botany*

594 USA ISSN 0028-1344
QL401 CODEN: NUTLA5
➤ **NAUTILUS (SANIBEL);** a quarterly devoted to the interests of malacologists. Text in English. 1886. q. USD 35 domestic to individuals; USD 40 foreign to individuals; USD 72 domestic to institutions; USD 77 foreign to institutions (effective 2005). adv. bk.rev. bibl.; charts; illus. index. back issues avail.; reprints avail. **Document type:** *Journal, Academic/Scholarly.* **Description:** It publishes papers on all aspects of the biology and systematics of mollusks. Manuscripts describing original, unpublished research, as well as review articles, will be considered.
Formerly: Conchologists' Exchange
Indexed: ASFA, BIOSIS Prev, BiolAb, CurCont, ESPM, ISR, OceAb, S&F, SPPI, ZooRec.
—BLDSC (6063.100000), CISTI, IDS, IE, Infotrieve, ingenta, Linda Hall.
Published by: Bailey-Matthews Shell Museum, 3075 Sanibel Captiva Rd, PO Box 1580, Sanibel, FL 33957. TEL 239-395-2233, FAX 239-395-6706, nautilus@shellmuseum.org, http://www.shellmuseum.org/nautilus.html. Ed., R&P Dr. Jose H Leal. Circ: 540 (paid). **Subscr. to:** Allen Press Inc., PO Box 1897, Lawrence, KS 66044.

592.57 BRA ISSN 0102-2997
QL391.N4 CODEN: NEBRET
➤ **NEMATOLOGIA BRASILEIRA.** Text in Portuguese, English. 1974. s-a. USD 30 to members (effective 2003). adv. bk.rev. **Document type:** *Journal, Academic/Scholarly.*
Formerly (until 1983): Sociedade Brasileira de Nematologia. Publicacao (0101-7020)
Indexed: AgBio, AgrForAb, BIOSIS Prev, BioCN&I, BiolAb, CPA, FCA, FPA, ForAb, HerbAb, HortAb, I&DA, MaizeAb, NemAb, OrnHort, PBA, PGegResA, PotatoAb, PoultAb, RA&MP, RPP, RefZh, RiceAb, S&F, SIA, SeedAb, SoyAb, WeedAb, WildRev, ZooRec.
—BLDSC (6075.493000), CASDDS.
Published by: Sociedade Brasileira de Nematologia, A Norte (P Piloto), Caixa Postal 02372, Brasilia, DF 70849-970, Brazil. TEL 55-61-3403660, FAX 55-61-3403660, recar@cenargen.embrapa.br. Ed. Regina M D Gomes Carneiro. Adv. contact Wilson R T Navaretti.

➤ **NEMATOLOGICAL ABSTRACTS.** see *BIOLOGY—Abstracting, Bibliographies, Statistics*

592.57 NLD ISSN 1388-5545
F1236 CODEN: NMATFJ
➤ **NEMATOLOGY;** international journal of fundamental and applied nematological research. Text in English, French, German. 1999. bi-m. USD 769 combined subscription in the Americas to institutions print & online eds.; EUR 615 combined subscription elsewhere to institutions print & online eds. (effective 2006). bk.rev. charts; illus. index. back issues avail.; reprint service avail. from PSC. **Document type:** *Journal, Academic/Scholarly.* **Description:** Covers methodology, morphological, biochemical and molecular taxonomy and systematics of soil, plant, insect and marine nematodes.
Formed by the merger of (1956-1999): Nematologica (0028-2596); (1978-1999): Fundamental and Applied Nematology (1164-5571); Which was formerly: Revue de Nematologie (0183-9187)
Related titles: Microform ed.: (from SWZ); Online - full text ed.: ISSN 1568-5411. USD 692 in the Americas to institutions; EUR 554 elsewhere to institutions (effective 2006) (from EBSCO Publishing, Gale Group, IngentaConnect, Kluwer Online, O C L C Online Computer Library Center, Inc., Springer LINK, Swets Information Services).
Indexed: ASCA, ASFA, AgBio, Agr, AgrForAb, AnBeAb, AnBrAb, BIOBASE, BIOSIS Prev, BioCN&I, BiolAb, CPA, ChemAb, CurCont, DBA, ESPM, EntAb, ExcerpMed, FCA, FPA, ForAb, GEOBASE, HelmAb, HerbAb, HortAb, I&DA, IABS, ISR, IndVet, MBA, MaizeAb, NemAb, NutrAb, OrnHort, PBA, PGegResA, PGrRegA, PlantSci, PotatoAb, RA&MP, RM&VM, RPP, RevApplEntom, RiceAb, S&F, SCI, SIA, SeedAb, SoyAb, TriticAb, VITIS, WAE&RSA, WeedAb, ZooRec.
—BLDSC (6075.500670), CASDDS, CISTI, IDS, IE, Infotrieve, ingenta, Linda Hall. **CCC.**

Published by: Brill Academic Publishers, PO Box 9000, Leiden, 2300 PA, Netherlands. TEL 31-71-53-53-500, FAX 31-71-53-17-532, cs@brill.nl, http://www.brill.nl/m_catalogue_sub6_id8548.htm. Eds. David Hunt, Roger Cook. R&P Elizabeth Venekamp. **Subscr. in N. America to:** PO Box 605, Herndon, VA 20172. TEL 703-661-1585, 800-337-9255, FAX 703-661-1501, cs@brillusa.com. **Distr. outside N. America by:** c/o Turpin Distribution, Stratton Business Park, Pegasus Drive, Biggleswade, BEDFORDSHIRE SG 18 8TQ, United Kingdom. TEL 44-1767-604-954, FAX 44-1767-601-640, brill@turpin-distribution.com.

592 USA
NEMATOLOGY NEWSLETTER. Text in English. 1995. q. membership. back issues avail. **Document type:** *Newsletter.* **Description:** Discusses research in the field of nematology and news of the society.
Published by: Society of Nematologists, PO Box 1897, Lawrence, KS 66044-8897. TEL 785-843-1235, FAX 785-843-1274, http://www.ianr.unl.edu/son/.

592.57 USA ISSN 0099-5444
QL391.N4 CODEN: NMTPAT
➤ **NEMATROPICA.** Text in Multiple languages. 1971. s-a. **Document type:** *Journal, Academic/Scholarly.* **Description:** It is an international scientific journal of tropical and subtropical nematology. Contributions describing nematological research in temperate regions, however, will be considered if they are of general interest.
Indexed: AgBio, Agr, AgrForAb, BIOSIS Prev, BioCN&I, BiolAb, CPA, CurCont, FCA, FPA, ForAb, HerbAb, HortAb, I&DA, MaizeAb, NemAb, NutrAb, OrnHort, PBA, PGegResA, PHN&I, PotatoAb, RA&MP, RPP, RiceAb, S&F, SIA, SeedAb, SoyAb, TriticAb, VITIS, WAE&RSA, WeedAb, ZooRec.
—BLDSC (6075.501000), IE, Infotrieve, ingenta.
Published by: Organization of Nematologists of Tropical America, c/o Peggy King, Secretary of ONTA, Department of Plant Pathology, Auburn University, Auburn, AL 36849-5409. TEL 334-844-4714, FAX 334-844-1948, pking@acesag.auburn.edu, http://www.ifas.ufl.edu. Ed. L W Duncan.

594 USA ISSN 0085-3887
QL1 CODEN: NOPHD2
➤ **NEMOURIA**; occasional Papers of the Delaware Museum of Natural History. Variant title: Delaware Museum of Natural History. Occasional Papers. Text in English. 1970. irreg., latest vol.44, 2000. USD 8.50 per issue domestic (effective 2005). back issues avail. **Document type:** *Journal, Academic/Scholarly.* **Description:** Publishes research papers on natural history, especially in the fields of malacology and ornithology.
Indexed: BIOSIS Prev, BiolAb, MLA, ZooRec.
—Linda Hall.
Published by: Delaware Museum of Natural History, PO Box 3937, Wilmington, DE 19807. TEL 302-658-9111, FAX 302-658-2610, jwoods@delmnh.org, http://www.delmnh.org. Ed., R&P Jean L Woods TEL 302-658-911 x 314. Circ: 100 (paid).

590 ARG ISSN 0548-1686
QL235 CODEN: NTRPAY
NEOTROPICA. Text in English, Spanish. 1954. a.
Indexed: BIOSIS Prev, BioCN&I, BiolAb, FCA, HelmAb, HerbAb, MaizeAb, NutrAb, ProtozoAb, RPP, S&F, WeedAb, ZooRec.
—BLDSC (6075.660000), IE, ingenta.
Published by: Sociedad Zoologica del Plata, Casilla de Correos 745, La Plata, Argentina. FAX 54-222-4350189.

599.8 CHE ISSN 1413-4705
QL737.P9
NEOTROPICAL PRIMATES. Text in English. 1993. a. **Document type:** *Newsletter, Academic/Scholarly.*
Indexed: RevApplEntom, ZooRec.
—BLDSC (6075.660300).
Published by: (Species Survival Commission - Primate Specialist Group), International Union for Conservation of Nature and Natural Resources, Rue Mauverney 28, Gland, 1196, Switzerland. TEL 41-22-9990001, FAX 41-22-9990002, mail@hq.iucn.org. **Subscr. to:** Conservation International, 1015 18th St, N W, Ste 1000, Washington, DC 20036.

NETTAI DOSHOKUBUTSU TOMO NO KAI KAIHO/NEWS OF THE TROPICAL PLANTS AND ANIMALS. see *BIOLOGY—Botany*

590 639.2 THA ISSN 0115-8503
NETWORK OF AQUACULTURE CENTRES IN ASIA-PACIFIC. NEWSLETTER. Text in English. 1982. q. free.
Indexed: ESPM.
Published by: Network of Aquaculture Centres in Asia-Pacific, PO Box 1040, Bangkok, 10903, Thailand. TEL 66-2-5611728, FAX 66-2-5611727, naca@enaca.org, http://www.enaca.org.

THE NEW YORK STATE CONSERVATIONIST. see *CONSERVATION*

590.993 NZL ISSN 0301-4223
QL340 CODEN: NZJZAW
➤ **NEW ZEALAND JOURNAL OF ZOOLOGY.** Text in English. 1974. q. NZD 200, USD 135 combined subscription to individuals print & online eds.; NZD 425, USD 305 combined subscription to institutions print & online eds. (effective 2006). adv. back issues avail. **Document type:** *Journal, Academic/Scholarly.* **Description:** Publishes papers on all aspects of Zoology in the Pacific and Antarctic regions.
Related titles: Online - full text ed.: NZD 170, USD 115 to individuals; NZD 360, USD 260 to institutions (effective 2006) (from EBSCO Publishing).
Indexed: ASCA, ASFA, AbHyg, AgBio, AgrForAb, AnBeAb, AnBrAb, ApEcolAb, BIOSIS Prev, BioCN&I, BiolAb, CRFR, CurCont, DSA, ESPM, EntAb, EnvAb, FCA, FPA, ForAb, GEOBASE, GenetAb, HGA, HelmAb, HerbAb, HortAb, INIS AtomInd, ISR, IndVet, KWIWR, NemAb, NutrAb, OceAb, PHN&I, PoultAb, ProtozoAb, RM&VM, RRTA, RevApplEntom, S&F, SFA, SIA, SPPI, TDB, TriticAb, VetBull, WeedAb, ZooRec.
—BLDSC (6095.300000), CASDDS, CISTI, IDS, IE, ingenta, Linda Hall. **CCC.**
Published by: R S N Z Publishing, PO Box 598, Wellington, New Zealand. TEL 64-4-4727421, FAX 64-4-4731841, sales@rsnz.org, http://www.rsnz.govt.nz/publish/nzjz/. Ed. C M King. Circ: 300. **Subscr. in the Americas to:** R S N Z Publishing, PO Box 7075, Lawrence, KS 66044-7075. TEL 785-843-1235, FAX 785-843-1274, sir@allenpress.com.

590 JPN ISSN 0285-385X
NIHON DOBUTSU GAKKAI CHUGOKU SHIKOKU SHIBU KAIHO/ZOOLOGICAL SOCIETY OF JAPAN. CHUGOKU - SHIKOKU BRANCH. PROCEEDINGS. Text in English, Japanese. 1947. a. membership. **Document type:** *Proceedings.*
Published by: Nihon Dobutsu Gakkai, Chugoku Shikoku Shibu/Zoological Society of Japan, Chugoku - Shikoku Branch, Hiroshima Daigaku Rigakubu Dobutsugaku Kyoshitsu, 1-3-1 Kagami-yama, Higashi Hiroshima-shi, Hiroshima-ken 739-8526, Japan.

590 JPN
NIHON DOBUTSUEN SUIZOKUKAN NENPO/JAPANESE ASSOCIATION OF ZOOLOGICAL GARDENS AND AQUARIUMS. ANNUAL REPORT. Text in Japanese. 1951. a.
Published by: Nihon Dobutsuen Suizokukan Kyokai/Japanese Association of Zoological Gardens and Aquariums, Vella Heights, Okachimachi 402, 4-23-10 Taito, Taito-ku, 110-8567, Japan.

NIHON GYORUI GAKKAI NENKAI KOEN YOSHI/ICHTHYOLOGY SOCIETY OF JAPAN. ADVANCE ABSTRACTS FOR THE ANNUAL MEETING. see *BIOLOGY—Abstracting, Bibliographies, Statistics*

NIHON JIKKEN DOBUTSU GAKKAI SOKAI KOEN YOSHISHU/JAPANESE ASSOCIATION FOR LABORATORY ANIMAL SCIENCE. ABSTRACTS OF GENERAL MEETING. see *BIOLOGY—Abstracting, Bibliographies, Statistics*

590.724 JPN ISSN 0913-2139
NIHON JIKKEN DOBUTSU GIJUTSUSHA KYOKAI HOKKAIDO SHIBU KAISHI/JAPANESE ASSOCIATION FOR EXPERIMENTAL ANIMAL TECHNOLOGISTS. HOKKAIDO BRANCH. JOURNAL. Text in Japanese. 1977. a.
Published by: Nihon Jikken Dobutsu Gijutsusha Kyokai, Hokkaido Shibu/Japanese Association for Experimental Animal Technologists, Hokkaido Branch, Hokkaido Daigaku Igakubu Fuzoku Dobutsu Jikken Shisetsu, Nishi 7-chome, Kita 15-jo, Kita-ku, Sapporo-shi, Hokkaido 060, Japan.

594 JPN
NIHON KABUTOGANI O MAMORU KAI KAIHO/HORSESHOE CRAB. Text in Japanese. 1979. a. membership.
Published by: Nihon Kabutogani o Mamoru Kai/Japanese Horseshoe Crab Observation Association, Kabutogani Hogo Senta, 1950-3 Yokoshima, Kasaoka-shi, Okayama-ken 714-0043, Japan.

599.8 JPN
NIHON MONKI SENTA NENPO/JAPAN MONKEY CENTRE. ANNUAL REPORT. Text in Japanese. 1988. a. **Document type:** *Proceedings, Academic/Scholarly.* **Description:** Covers news relating to the Center and its activities, including the museum, the zoological garden, and education and research functions. Includes proceedings of the Annual Meeting of Primate Study.
Published by: Japan Monkey Centre/Nihon Monki Senta, 26 Kanrin, Inuyama-shi, Aichi-ken 484-0081, Japan. TEL 81-568-61-2327, FAX 81-568-62-6823. Ed., R&P Mitsuo Iwamoto. Circ: 500.

NIHON MUKIN SEIBUTSU NOTO BAIOROJI GAKKAI SOKAI NITTEI TO SHOROKU/JAPANESE ASSOCIATION OF GERMFREE LIFE AND GNOTOBIOLOGY. ABSTRACTS OF MEETING. see *BIOLOGY—Abstracting, Bibliographies, Statistics*

590 JPN
NIHON OYO DOBUTSU KONCHU GAKKAI KYUSHU SHIBU KAIHO/DELPHAX. Text in Japanese. a.
Published by: Nihon Oyo Dobutsu Konchu Gakkai, Kyushu Shibu/Japanese Society of Applied Entomology and Zoology, Kyushu Branch, Kyushu Nogyo Shikenjo Chiiki Kiban Kenkyubu, 2421 Suya, Kikuchi-gun, Nishigoshi-machi, Kumamoto-ken 861-1102, Japan.

599.8 JPN
NIHON REICHORUI GAKKAI TAIKAI YOKOSHU/PRIMATE SOCIETY OF JAPAN. PREPRINTS OF THE ANNUAL MEETING. Text in English, Japanese. 1985. a. **Document type:** *Academic/Scholarly.*
Published by: Nihon Reichorui Gakkai/Primate Society of Japan, Kyoto Daigaku Reichorui Kenkyujo, Inuyama Kanrin, Inuyama-shi, Aichi-ken 484, Japan. Ed. Osamu Takenaka.

592.57 JPN ISSN 0919-343X
NIHON SENCHU GAKKAI NYUSU/JAPAN NEMATOLOGY NEWS. Text in Japanese. 1972. s-a.
Formerly (until 1993): Nihon Senchu Kenkyukai Nyusu (0911-7350)
Published by: Nihon Senchu Gakkai/Japanese Nematological Society, National Agriculture Research Center, Kannondai, Tsukuba-shi, Ibaraki-ken 305-0856, Japan. TEL 81-298-38-8839, FAX 81-298-38-8837, kshimz@narc.affrc.go.jp. Ed. N Minagawa.

592.57 JPN ISSN 0919-6765
NIHON SENCHU GAKKAISHI/JAPANESE JOURNAL OF NEMATOLOGY. Text in English, Japanese. 1972. s-a. USD 35. **Document type:** *Academic/Scholarly.*
Formerly: Nihon Senchu Kenkyukaishi (0388-2357)
Indexed: AgBio, AgrForAb, Agrind, BioCN&I, FCA, ForAb, HelmAb, HerbAb, HortAb, MaizeAb, NemAb, OrnHort, PBA, PGegResA, PotatoAb, RA&MP, RPP, RevApplEntom, RiceAb, S&F, SoyAb, TriticAb, WeedAb, ZooRec.
—BLDSC (4656.637000). **CCC.**
Published by: Nihon Senchu Gakkai/Japanese Nematological Society, National Agriculture Research Center, Kannondai, Tsukuba-shi, Ibaraki-ken 305-0856, Japan. TEL 81-298-38-8840, FAX 81-298-38-8837, minaga@narc.affrc.go.jp. R&P N Minagawa.

NIPPON DOBUTSU KODO GAKKAI TAIKAI HAPPYO YOSHISHU/JAPAN ETHOLOGICAL SOCIETY. ABSTRACTS OF MEETING. see *BIOLOGY—Abstracting, Bibliographies, Statistics*

590 GBR ISSN 0078-0952
NOMENCLATOR ZOOLOGICUS. Text in English. 1939. irreg., latest vol.9, 1996. GBP 100 (effective 2000). **Document type:** *Academic/Scholarly.* **Description:** Records of bibliographic origins of published generic and subgeneric names in zoology.
Published by: Zoological Society of London, Regents Park, London, NW1 4RY, United Kingdom. TEL 44-20-74496281, FAX 44-20-74496411, yearbook@zsl.org.

590 NOR ISSN 0802-0833
NORGES TEKNISK-NATURVITENSKAPELIGE UNIVERSITET. VITENSKAPSMUSEET. RAPPORT. ZOOLOGISK SERIE. Text in Norwegian. 1974. irreg. price varies.
Formerly (until 1987): Kongelige Norske Vitenskapelige Selskab. Museum Rapport. Zoologisk Serie
Indexed: ASFA.
Published by: Norges Teknisk-Naturvitenskapelige Universitet, Vitenskapmuseet/Norwegian University of Science and Technology, Museum of Natural History and Archaeology, Trondheim, 7491, Norway. TEL 47-73-59-21-45, FAX 47-73-59-22-23, http://www.ntnu.no/vmuseet/zoolavd/zooserie.html.

591.97 USA ISSN 0078-1304
QL155 CODEN: XIWFAS
➤ **NORTH AMERICAN FAUNA.** Text in English. 1889. irreg. **Document type:** *Monographic series, Academic/Scholarly.* **Description:** Publishes high-quality original scientific and review articles and reports.
Related titles: Microfiche ed.: 1889 (from BHP); Microform ed.: 1889 (from NTI); Online - full text ed.: 1889; ◆ Series of: Biological Science Report. ISSN 1081-292X.
Indexed: BIOSIS Prev, BiolAb, SFA, WildRev, ZooRec.
—CISTI, Linda Hall.
Published by: U.S. Department of the Interior, National Biological Service, C St between 18th & 19th Sts N W, Washington, DC 20240. **Orders to:** U.S. Fish and Wildlife Service, Publications Unit, MS 130, Webb Bldg, 4401 N Fairfax Dr, Arlington, VA 22203.

➤ **NORTH AMERICAN JOURNAL OF AQUACULTURE.** see *FISH AND FISHERIES*

597 CAN ISSN 1028-9127
NORTH PACIFIC ANADROMOUS FISH COMMISSION. BULLETIN. Text in English. 1998. irreg.
Indexed: RefZh.
—CISTI.
Published by: North Pacific Anadromous Fish Commission, 889 W Pender St, Ste 502, Vancouver, BC V6C 3B2, Canada. TEL 604-775-5550, FAX 604-775-5577, secretariat@npafc.org, http://www.npafc.org.

NORTHEASTERN NATURALIST. see *BIOLOGY—Botany*

596 USA ISSN 1051-1733
CODEN: NNATEP
➤ **NORTHWESTERN NATURALIST**; a journal of vertebrate biology. Text in English. 1920. 3/yr. USD 25 to individuals; USD 60 to institutions; USD 15 to students (effective 2005). adv. bk.rev. charts; illus.; stat. cum.index every 10 yrs. back issues avail.; reprint service avail. from PQC. **Document type:** *Academic/Scholarly.* **Description:** Publishes original contributions dealing with the biology of terrestrial vertebrates of northwestern North America.
Formerly (until 1989): Murrelet (0027-3716)
Related titles: Microform ed.: (from PQC); Online - full text ed.: (from BioOne, C S A).
Indexed: ASFA, BiolAb, ESPM, EntAb, SFA, SWRA, WLR, WildRev, ZooRec.
—CISTI, Linda Hall.
Published by: Society for Northwestern Vertebrate Biology, c/o Julie Grialou, 18304 Highway 20, Winthrop, WA 98862. TEL 509-996-2402, http://www.snwvb.org. Ed. Burr Betts. Circ: 600. **Dist. by:** Allen Press Inc.. TEL 785-843-1235, FAX 785-843-1274.

590 MWI ISSN 0251-1924
QH195.M47 CODEN: NYALEA
NYALA. Text in English. 1975. s-a. USD 12. adv. bk.rev. **Document type:** *Academic/Scholarly.*
Indexed: SFA, WildRev, ZooRec.
Published by: Wildlife Society of Malawi, c/o Museums of Malawi, PO Box 30360, Blantyre, Malawi. Ed. Cornell Dudley. Circ: 625.

OCEANOGRAPHIC RESEARCH INSTITUTE. SPECIAL PUBLICATION. see *EARTH SCIENCES—Oceanography*

594.1477 USA ISSN 0030-0055
CODEN: OSSHDM
OF SEA AND SHORE. Text in English. 1970. q. USD 20 domestic; USD 25 elsewhere (effective 2001). adv. bk.rev. illus. index. reprint service avail. from PQC. **Description:** Covers all aspects of shell collection.
Related titles: Microfilm ed.: (from PQC).
Indexed: RefZh, ZooRec.
—CISTI, Linda Hall.
Published by: Of Sea & Shore Publications, PO Box 219, Port Gamble, WA 98364. TEL 360-297-2426, FAX 360-297-2426, ofseashr@sinclair.net. Ed. Thomas C Rice.

590 USA
OF THE WORLD SERIES. Text in English. 1986. a. USD 27.95. bibl. index. **Description:** Book series on all kinds of wild animals and insects.
Published by: Facts on File, Inc. (Subsidiary of: W R C Media Inc.), 132 W 31st St, 17th Fl, New York, NY 10001. TEL 212-967-8800.

333.95416 USA ISSN 0085-4468
CODEN: OFWRBD
OHIO FISH AND WILDLIFE REPORT. Text in English. 1971. irreg., latest vol.12, 1995. free. **Document type:** *Monographic series, Government.*
Formed by the merger of: Ohio Fish Monographs (0078-4028); Ohio Game Monographs (0078-4036); Supersedes: Game Research in Ohio (0473-9442)
Indexed: BIOSIS Prev, BiolAb, SFA, WLR, WildRev, ZooRec.
Published by: Ohio Department of Natural Resources, Division of Wildlife, 1840 Belcher Dr, Columbus, OH 43224-1329. TEL 614-265-6300. Circ: 1,000.

OPERA LILLOANA. see *BIOLOGY—Botany*

590 HUN ISSN 0473-1034
QL1 CODEN: OPUZAS
OPUSCULA ZOOLOGICA. Text in English, German. 1956. s-a. USD 12. charts; illus.; stat.
Indexed: BiolAb, S&F, ZooRec.
—CISTI, Linda Hall.
Published by: Universitas Budapestinensis, Institutum Zoosystematicum et Oecologicum, Puskin utca 3, Budapest, 1088, Hungary. Eds. A Berczik, I Andrassy. Circ: 800.

590 CHE ISSN 1010-5220
QL461 CODEN: OZFLEJ
➤ **OPUSCULA ZOOLOGICA FLUMINENSIA.** Text in German. 1984. irreg. (approx. 14/yr.). price varies. adv. bk.rev. **Document type:** *Academic/Scholarly.* **Description:** Original research papers in the field of invertebrate zoology and entomology, with emphasis on taxonomic revisions and descriptions of new taxa, mostly insects.
Indexed: ASFA, ChemAb, EntAb, ZooRec.
—BLDSC (6277.212000).
Published by: Flumserberg Scientific Publishers, Casa d'Uors, Postfach 34, Flumserberg Bergh, 8896, Switzerland. TEL 081-332214. Ed. Dr. B Kiauta. Circ: 600.

590 GBR ISSN 0030-6053
QL81.5 CODEN: ORYXAM
➤ **ORYX**; journal of fauna and flora international. Text in English. 1903-1913; N.S. 1921; N.S. 1950. q. GBP 280 to institutions; USD 456 in North America to institutions; GBP 300 combined subscription to institutions print & online eds.; USD 488 combined subscription in North America to institutions print & online eds. (effective 2006). adv. bk.rev. bibl.; charts; illus. index. back issues avail. **Document type:** *Journal, Academic/Scholarly.* **Description:** Aims to provide a comprehensive view of the conservation of wild species of fauna and flora.
Formerly (until 1950): Society for the Restoration of the Fauna of the Empire. Journal
Related titles: Online - full text ed.: Oryx Online. ISSN 1365-3008. 1999. GBP 265 to institutions; USD 435 in North America to institutions (effective 2006) (from Blackwell Synergy, EBSCO Publishing, Gale Group, IngentaConnect, O C L C Online Computer Library Center, Inc., Swets Information Services).
Indexed: ASFA, AgrForAb, AnBrAb, ApEcolAb, BIOBASE, BIOSIS Prev, BiolAb, BiolDig, CurCont, EPB, ESPM, EnvAb, FCA, FPA, ForAb, GEOBASE, HerbAb, HortAb, IABS, ISR, IndIslam, IndVet, KWIWR, MaizeAb, OrnHort, PBA, PGegResA, PHN&I, PoultAb, RDA, RPP, RRTA, RefZh, RiceAb, S&F, SCI, SFA, SeedAb, TDB, VetBull, WAE&RSA, WeedAb, WildRev, ZooRec.
—BLDSC (6296.700000), CIS, IDS, IE, Infotrieve, ingenta, Linda Hall. **CCC.**
Published by: (Flora and Fauna International), Cambridge University Press, The Edinburgh Bldg, Shaftesbury Rd, Cambridge, CB2 2RU, United Kingdom. TEL 44-1223-312393, FAX 44-1223-315052, journals@cambridge.org, http://uk.cambridge.org/journals/journal_catalogue.asp?historylinks=ALPHA&mnemonic=ORX. Ed. Martin Fisher. Adv. contact Rebecca Curtis TEL 44-1223-325757. Circ: 3,200. **Subscr. to:** Cambridge University Press, 100 Brook Hill Dr, West Nyack, NY 10994. TEL 845-353-7500, FAX 845-353-4141, journals_subscriptions@cup.org

590 CHE ISSN 1026-2881
QL737.P98
PACHYDERM. Text in English. 2/yr. **Document type:** *Newsletter.*
Indexed: PLESA, RefZh, ZooRec.
—BLDSC (6328.292000).
Published by: (Species Survival Commission - African Elephant and Rhino Specialist Group), International Union for Conservation of Nature and Natural Resources, Rue Mauverney 28, Gland, 1196, Switzerland. TEL 41-22-9990001, FAX 41-22-9990002, mail@hq.iucn.org. **Subscr. to:** WWF Regional Office, PO Box 62440, Nairobi, Kenya.

591.95491 PAK ISSN 1013-3461
QL1 CODEN: PKCZEK
➤ **PAKISTAN CONGRESS OF ZOOLOGY. PROCEEDINGS.** Text in English. 1980. a., latest vol.19, 1999. PKR 3,000 domestic; USD 185 foreign (effective 2005). adv. 400 p./no. 1 cols./p.; back issues avail.; reprints avail. **Document type:** *Proceedings, Academic/Scholarly.* **Description:** Proceedings of Pakistan Congress of Zoology.
Indexed: AEA, ASFA, AgBio, AgrForAb, AnBrAb, BioCN&I, CIN, ChemAb, ChemTitl, EntAb, FCA, FPA, ForAb, HelmAb, HerbAb, HortAb, IndVet, MaizeAb, NutrAb, PBA, PHN&I, ProtozoAb, RA&MP, RDA, RM&VM, RPP, RevApplEntom, RiceAb, S&F, SeedAb, TDB, TriticAb, WAE&RSA, WeedAb, WildRev, ZooRec.
—BLDSC (6848.575000), CASDDS.
Published by: Zoological Society of Pakistan, c/o School of Biological Sciences, University of the Punjab, New Campus, Lahore, 54590, Pakistan. TEL 92-42-9231248, 92-42-9230980, FAX 92-42-9230966, arshak@brain.net.pk, http://www.zspk.com. Eds. Abdul Rauf Shakoori, Dr. Muzaffer Ahmad. R&P, Adv. contact Abdul Rauf Shakoori. page INR 5,000; 4.5 x 6. Circ: 300.

592.57 PAK ISSN 0255-7576
QL391.N4 CODEN: PJNEE5
➤ **PAKISTAN JOURNAL OF NEMATOLOGY.** Text in English. 1983. s-a. PKR 100, USD 43 (effective 2000). adv. back issues avail.; reprint service avail. from PQC,ISI. **Document type:** *Academic/Scholarly.*
Indexed: AgrForAb, BIOSIS Prev, BioCN&I, BiolAb, CPA, FCA, FPA, ForAb, HelmAb, HerbAb, HortAb, I&DA, MaizeAb, NemAb, OrnHort, PBA, PotatoAb, PoultAb, RA&MP, RPP, RevApplEntom, RiceAb, S&F, SIA, SoyAb, TriticAb, WeedAb, ZooRec.
—BLDSC (6341.600000), IE, ingenta.
Published by: Pakistan Society of Nematologists, National Nematological Research Centre, University of Karachi, Karachi, 75270, Pakistan. TEL 92-21-4963373, FAX 92-21-4963373, maq@nema.khi.erum.com.pk, mag@nema.khi.erum.com.pk. Ed. Abdul Ghoffar. R&P, Adv. contact M A Maqbool. Circ: 600 (controlled).

591.95491 PAK ISSN 0030-9923
QL1 CODEN: PJZOAN
➤ **PAKISTAN JOURNAL OF ZOOLOGY.** Text in English. 1969. q. PKR 3,500 domestic; USD 215 foreign; PKR 1,000 newsstand/cover domestic; USD 60 newsstand/cover foreign (effective 2005). adv. bk.rev. charts; illus.; stat. index. 100 p./no. 2 cols./p.; back issues avail. **Document type:** *Journal, Academic/Scholarly.* **Description:** Publishes articles on all aspects of animal life.
Related titles: Microfilm ed.; Supplement(s): Pakistan Journal of Zoology. Supplementary Series. PKR 300 domestic; USD 65 foreign (effective 2005).
Indexed: ASFA, AbHyg, AgBio, AgrForAb, AnBrAb, ApicAb, BIOSIS Prev, BioCN&I, BiolAb, ChemAb, ChemTitl, CurCont, DSA, ESPM, EntAb, EnvAb, FCA, FPA, FS&TA, ForAb, GEOBASE, GenetAb, HGA, HelmAb, HerbAb, HortAb, IndMed, IndVet, MaizeAb, NemAb, NutrAb, OrnHort, PBA, PHN&I, PotatoAb, PoultAb, ProtozoAb, RA&MP, RDA, RM&VM, RPP, RefZh, RevApplEntom, RiceAb, S&F, SFA, SIA, SWRA, SeedAb, SoyAb, TDB, TOSA, TriticAb, VITIS, VetBull, WAE&RSA, WTA, WeedAb, WildRev, ZooRec.
—BLDSC (6343.015000), CASDDS, CISTI, IE, Infotrieve, ingenta, Linda Hall. **CCC.**
Published by: Zoological Society of Pakistan, c/o School of Biological Sciences, University of the Punjab, New Campus, Lahore, 54590, Pakistan. TEL 92-42-9231248, 92-42-9230980, FAX 92-42-9230966, arshak@brain.net.pk, http://www.zspk.com/Pakistan%20Journal%20of%20Zoology.htm. Eds. Abdul Rauf Shakoori, Dr. Muzaffer Ahmad. adv.: page INR 10,000; 8 x 6. Circ: 500 (paid and controlled).

597 DEU ISSN 0724-6331
CODEN: PICHEK
PALAEO ICHTHYOLOGICA. Text in English, French, German. 1983. irreg., latest vol.6. abstr.; bibl.; charts; illus. back issues avail. **Document type:** *Monographic series.* **Description:** Neontological and paleontological works on systematics, ecology, and stratigraphy of fishes.
Indexed: SFA, ZooRec.
Published by: Verlag Dr. Friedrich Pfeil, Wolfratshauser Str 27, Munich, 81379, Germany. info@pfeil-verlag.de, http://www.pfeil-verlag.de. Ed. Friedrich H Pfeil. Circ: 500.

590 BRA ISSN 0031-1049
QL1 CODEN: PAZOAS
➤ **PAPEIS AVULSOS DE ZOOLOGIA.** Text in Multiple languages. 1941. irreg., latest vol.41. USD 15 (effective 2004). illus. index. back issues avail. **Document type:** *Monographic series, Academic/Scholarly.* **Description:** Publishes original contributions in systematics, paleontology, evolutionary biology, ecology, taxonomy, anatomy, behavior, functional morphology, molecular biology, ontogeny, faunistic and empirical studies that explore principles and methods of systematics.
Related titles: Online - full text ed.: free (effective 2005).
Indexed: ABIPC, ASFA, AgrForAb, BIOSIS Prev, BiolAb, ESPM, ForAb, PGegResA, PoultAb, RM&VM, RefZh, RevApplEntom, S&F, SFA, ZooRec.
—BLDSC (6358.100000), CISTI, Linda Hall.
Published by: Universidade de Sao Paulo, Museu de Zoologia, Caixa Postal 42494, Sao Paulo, SP 04218-970, Brazil. TEL 55-11-61658090, FAX 55-11-61658113, biblmz@usp.br, http://www.scielo.br/paz.htm. Ed. Hussam Zaher. Circ: 800 (paid and controlled).

591.5 USA ISSN 0738-4394
QL750
PERSPECTIVES IN ETHOLOGY. Text in English. 1973. irreg., latest vol.13, 2004. price varies. back issues avail. **Document type:** *Monographic series.*
Indexed: Agr, BIOSIS Prev, ZooRec.
—CISTI, KNAW. **CCC.**
Published by: Springer-Verlag New York, Inc. (Subsidiary of: Springer Science+Business Media), 233 Spring St, New York, NY 10013. TEL 212-460-1500, FAX 212-460-1575, service@springer-ny.com, http://www.springer-ny.com.

596 NLD ISSN 0169-7277
CODEN: PVSCD5
PERSPECTIVES IN VERTEBRATE SCIENCE. Text in English. 1980. irreg., latest vol.6, 1989. price varies. **Document type:** *Monographic series, Academic/Scholarly.*
Indexed: BIOSIS Prev.
—CASDDS, CISTI. **CCC.**
Published by: Springer-Verlag Dordrecht (Subsidiary of: Springer Science+Business Media), Van Godewijckstraat 30, Dordrecht, 3311 GX, Netherlands. TEL 31-78-6576050, FAX 31-78-6576474, http://www.springeronline.com.

590 BRA ISSN 0373-8418
QL1 CODEN: PQZOA4
PESQUISAS: PUBLICACOES DE ZOOLOGIA. Key Title: Pesquisas. Zoologia. Text in Portuguese. 1957. irreg. per issue exchange basis. **Document type:** *Academic/Scholarly.*
Supersedes in part (in 1960): Instituto Anchietano de Pesquisas. Pesquisas (0480-1873)
—CISTI.
Published by: (Universidade do Vale do Rio dos Sinos, Instituto Anchietano de Pesquisas), Unisinos, Av Unisinos, 950, Sao Leopoldo, RS 93022-000, Brazil. TEL 55-51-5908239, FAX 55-51-5908238.

▼ new title ➤ refereed ✶ unverified ♦ full entry avail.

590 USA ISSN 1522-2152
QL1 CODEN: PBZOF6
➤ **PHYSIOLOGICAL AND BIOCHEMICAL ZOOLOGY.** Abbreviated title: P B Z. Text in English. 1928. bi-m. USD 84 combined subscription to individuals print & online eds.; USD 572 combined subscription to institutions print & online eds.; USD 19 per issue to individuals; USD 103 per issue to institutions (effective 2006). adv. bk.rev. bibl.; charts; illus. Index. 120 p./no.; back issues avail.; reprint service avail. from PQC,ISI. **Document type:** *Journal, Academic/Scholarly.* **Description:** Provides an outlet for research in environmental and adaptational physiology and biochemistry. Explores comparative physiology, as well as physiological ecology.
Formerly (until 1999): Physiological Zoology (0031-935X)
Related titles: Microform ed.: (from PMC, PQC); Online - full text ed.: ISSN 1537-5293. USD 515 to institutions (effective 2006) (from EBSCO Publishing, Florida Center for Library Automation, Gale Group).
Indexed: ASCA, ASFA, AgBio, AgrForAb, AnBrAb, ApicAb, B&AI, B&BAb, BIOBASE, BIOSIS Prev, BioCN&I, BiolAb, CIN, CRFR, ChemAb, ChemTitl, CurCont, DSA, ESPM, EntAb, ExcerpMed, ForAb, GEOBASE, GenetAb, HGA, HelmAb, IABS, ISR, IndMed, IndVet, Inpharma, MEDLINE, MaizeAb, NutrAb, OceAb, PHN&I, PN&I, PollutAb, PoultAb, ProtozoAb, RM&VM, Reac, RefZh, RevApplEntom, S&F, SCI, SFA, SIA, SSCI, SoyAb, VetBull, WeedAb, WildRev, ZooRec.
—BLDSC (6484.510000), CASDDS, CISTI, IDS, IE, Infotrieve, ingenta, Linda Hall. **CCC.**
Published by: (Society for Integrative and Comparative Biology), University of Chicago Press, Journals Division, Journals Division, PO Box 37005, Chicago, IL 60637. TEL 773-753-3347, 877-705-1878, FAX 773-753-0811, 877-705-1879, subscriptions@press.uchicago.edu, http://www.journals.uchicago.edu/PBZ. Ed. James W Hicks. adv.: page USD 450; trim 8.5 x 11. Circ: 1,000 (paid).

591.98 ARG ISSN 0326-1441
CODEN: PHSAC2
➤ **PHYSIS.** (In 3 sections: Section A (ISSN 0325-0342), Section B (ISSN 0325-0350), Section C (ISSN 0325-0369)) Text mainly in Spanish; Text occasionally in English, French; Summaries in English, Spanish. 1912. s-a. ARS 40 domestic; USD 100 foreign; USD 22.50 per issue (effective 2003). bk.rev. charts; illus. cum.index: 1912-1982. 178 p./no.; back issues avail. **Document type:** *Bulletin, Academic/Scholarly.* **Description:** Devoted to zoology and botany (systematics, physiology, distribution, ecology, histology, embryology and anatomy) mainly of South America.
Indexed: ASFA, BIOSIS Prev, BioCN&I, BiolAb, CurCont, ESPM, ForAb, HelmAb, MathR, NemAb, PBA, PGegResA, SFA, SeedAb, ZooRec.
—CISTI.
Published by: Asociacion Argentina de Ciencias Naturales, Ave. Angel Gallardo, 470, Capital Federal, Buenos Aires C1405DJR, Argentina. TEL 54-11-49828370, FAX 54-11-49824494, physis@macn.gov.ar, physis@muanbe.gov.ar, http://www.latbook.com, http://www.nisc.com. Ed. Cristina Scioscia. Circ: 550.

➤ **PISCIUM CATALOGUS.** see *PALEONTOLOGY*

590 CUB ISSN 0138-6476
QH109.C9 CODEN: PECCEB
POEYANA. Text in Spanish; Abstracts in English. 1964. 15/yr. USD 75 (effective 2000). bibl.; charts; illus. **Document type:** *Academic/Scholarly.*
Formerly (until 1974): Serie Poeyana (0032-2229); Formed by the 1970 merger of: Poeyana. Serie A (0554-4068); Poeyana. Serie B (0554-4076)
Indexed: BiolAb, RevApplEntom, SFA, WildRev, ZooRec.
Published by: Academia de Ciencias de Cuba, Instituto de Ecologia y Sistematica, Carretera de Varona Km3 1/2, Capdevila, Havana, Cuba. TEL 53-7-448419, FAX 53-7-338054, ecologia@ceniai.cu. Circ: 2,000.

594 NZL ISSN 0032-2377
POIRIERIA. Text in English. 1962. s-a. membership. adv. bk.rev. **Document type:** *Academic/Scholarly.* **Description:** Provides information relevant to mollosc shell and related aspects of marine biology.
Indexed: ZooRec.
—Linda Hall. **CCC.**
Published by: Auckland Museum and Institute, Conchology Section, Private Bag 92018, Auckland, New Zealand. Ed., Adv. contact Glenys Stace. Circ: 200.

590 BRA ISSN 0104-6950
QL1
PONTIFICIA UNIVERSIDADE CATOLICA DO RIO GRANDE DO SUL. MUSEU DE CIENCIAS E TECNOLOGIA. COMUNICACOES. SERIE ZOOLOGIA. Variant title: Museu de Ciencias e Tecnologia da P U C R G S. Comunicacoes. Serie Zoologia. Text in Portuguese. 1971. s-a. BRL 11 (effective 2002).
Formerly (until 1994): Museu de Ciencias da P U C R S. Comunicacoes. Serie Zoologia (0100-3380); Which superseded in part (in 1988): Museu de Ciencias da P U C R S. Comunicacoes (0100-4573)
Indexed: ASFA, ESPM, ZooRec.
—CISTI.
Published by: Pontificia Universidade Catolica do Rio Grande do Sul. Museu de Ciencias e Tecnologia, Av Ipiranga 6681, Predio 40, Porto Alegre, RS 90619-900, Brazil. TEL 55-512-3203597, http://www.mct.pucrs.br/. Ed. Jeter J Bertoletti. **Subscr. to:** Av Ipiranga 6681, Predio 33, Caixa Postal 1429, Porto Alegre, RS 90619-900, Brazil. edipucrs@pucrs.br, http://www.pucrs.br/edipucrs.

590 PRT ISSN 0871-326X
CODEN: POZOES
PORTUGALIAE ZOOLOGICA. Text in Portuguese. 1990. irreg. **Document type:** *Monographic series.*
Indexed: ESPM, ZooRec.
Published by: Universidade de Lisboa, Faculdade de Ciencias. Departamento de Zoologia e Antropologia, Campo Grande, Edificio C5, Lisbon, 1749-016, Portugal. TEL 351-21-7500000, FAX 351-21-7500169, info.fcul@fc.ul.pt, http://www.fc.ul.pt.

593.6 JPN ISSN 0918-726X
PRECIOUS CORALS & OCTOCORAL RESEARCH. Text in English. 1993. s-a. JPY 6,000 (effective 1999). adv.
Indexed: ZooRec.
Published by: Nihon Nantai Dobutsu Gakkai/Laboratory for Biological, Economic and Technological Research of Organic Jewelry, 6-36 Midori-cho 3-chome, Tanashi-shi, Tokyo-to 188-0002, Japan. TEL 81-424-63-0851, FAX 81-424-61-1752. Ed., R&P, Adv. contact Sadao Kosuge.

PRIMATE EYE. see *ANTHROPOLOGY*

599.9 DEU ISSN 0343-3528
QL737.P9
PRIMATE REPORT. Text in German. irreg. price varies. **Document type:** *Monographic series, Academic/Scholarly.*
Indexed: ZooRec.
—BLDSC (6612.923300), GNLM, IE, ingenta.
Published by: Verlag Erich Goltze GmbH und Co. KG, Hans-Boeckler-Str 7, Goettingen, 37079, Germany. TEL 49-551-506760, FAX 49-551-5067622. Ed. A Spiegel.

599.8 JPN ISSN 0032-8332
QL737.P9 CODEN: PRMTBU
➤ **PRIMATES**; journal of primatology. Text in English. 1957. q. EUR 270 combined subscription to institutions print & online eds. (effective 2005). bk.rev. abstr.; charts; illus.; stat. **Document type:** *Journal, Academic/Scholarly.* **Description:** Provides a forum for all aspects of primates in relation to humans and other animals.
Related titles: Online - full text ed.: (from EBSCO Publishing, ProQuest Information & Learning, Springer LINK, Swets Information Services).
Indexed: AbAn, AgrForAb, AnBeAb, AnBrAb, AnthLit, ApEcolAb, B&BAb, BIOSIS Prev, BiolAb, CurCont, ESPM, FoVS&M, ForAb, GEOBASE, GenetAb, HGA, HelmAb, HortAb, IBSS, ISR, IndVet, NemAb, NutrAb, PGegResA, ProtozoAb, PsycInfo, PsycholAb, SCI, SFA, SSCI, SeedAb, TDB, VetBull, WildRev, ZooRec.
—BLDSC (6612.925000), CASDDS, CISTI, IDS, IE, ingenta, Linda Hall. **CCC.**
Published by: Springer-Verlag Tokyo (Subsidiary of: Springer Science+Business Media), 3-13 Hongo 3-chome, Bunkyo-ku, Tokyo, 113-0033, Japan. TEL 81-3-38120331, FAX 81-3-38187454, http://link.springer-ny.com/link/service/journals/10329/index.htm, http://www.springer-tokyo.co.jp/. Ed. Toshisada Nishida. Adv. contact Stephan Kroeck TEL 49-30-827875739. Circ: 600. **Subscr. in N & S America to:** Springer-Verlag New York, Inc., 233 Spring St, New York, NY 10013. TEL 212-460-1500, 800-777-4643, FAX 212-473-6272, orders@springer-ny.com, http://www.springer-ny.com.

591 JPN
PROBLEMS IN MODERN ZOOLOGY. Text in Japanese. irreg.?. **Document type:** *Monographic series.*
Published by: Zoological Society of Japan/Nihon Dobutsu Gakkai, Toshin Bldg 2F, 2-27-2 Hongo, Bunkyo-ku, Tokyo, 113-0033, Japan. TEL 81-3-38145461, FAX 81-3-38146216. Ed. Seiichiro Kawashima.

PROTOZOOLOGICAL ABSTRACTS. see *BIOLOGY—Abstracting, Bibliographies, Statistics*

590 POL ISSN 0033-247X
CODEN: PZOOAC
PRZEGLAD ZOOLOGICZNY. Text in Polish; Abstracts and contents page in English. 1957. q. PLZ 16 (effective 2000). adv. bk.rev. bibl.; illus. index. **Document type:** *Academic/Scholarly.*
Indexed: ASFA, AgrLib, BIOSIS Prev, BiolAb, ChemAb, ESPM, IndVet, RefZh, VetBull, ZooRec.
—CASDDS, CISTI, Linda Hall.
Published by: Polskie Towarzystwo Zoologiczne, ul Sienkiewicza 21, Wroclaw, 50335, Poland. TEL 48-71-225041, FAX 48-71-222817. Ed., Adv. contact Romuald J Pomorski. R&P Jerzy Turzanski. Circ: 1,420. **Dist. by:** ORPAN, Palac Kultury i Nauki, Warsaw 00901, Poland.

590 PAK ISSN 1016-1597
CODEN: PUJZEN
➤ **PUNJAB UNIVERSITY JOURNAL OF ZOOLOGY.** Text in English. 1931-1947; N.S. 1967; N.S. 1983. a. INR 500 domestic; USD 50 foreign (effective 2004). bk.rev. back issues avail. **Document type:** *Academic/Scholarly.* **Description:** Contains research papers in different disciplines of life sciences, such as entomology, parasitology, microbiology, genetic engineering, paleontology and physiology.
Formerly (until 1983): University of the Punjab. Department of Zoology. Bulletin. New Series (0079-8045)
Indexed: AgBio, AgrForAb, AnBrAb, BIOSIS Prev, BioCN&I, BiolAb, DSA, ESPM, EntAb, FCA, FPA, ForAb, HelmAb, HerbAb, HortAb, IndVet, MaizeAb, NutrAb, PBA, PHN&I, PoultAb, RA&MP, RDA, RM&VM, RPP, RefZh, RevApplEntom, SFA, SWRA, TDB, VetBull, WeedAb, WildRev, ZooRec.
—BLDSC (7160.330500), CASDDS, CISTI. **CCC.**
Published by: University of the Punjab, Department of Zoology, Quaid-e-Azam Campus, Lahore, 54590, Pakistan. TEL 92-42-5864028, FAX 92-42-5868711. Ed. Tanveer Akhtar. Circ: 300.

591.959 SGP ISSN 0217-2445
CODEN: RBUZEZ
➤ **RAFFLES BULLETIN OF ZOOLOGY.** (No issues were published in 1971-1987) Text in English. 1988 (vol.36). s-a. (Jan. & Jul.). bk.rev. back issues avail. **Document type:** *Bulletin, Academic/Scholarly.* **Description:** Publishes articles on systematics, faunistics, ecology and other aspects of zoology in tropical Southeast Asia.
Former titles (until 1970): National Museum. Bulletin; (until 1960): Raffles Museum. Bulletin
Indexed: ASCA, ASFA, AgrForAb, AnBrAb, BIOSIS Prev, BioCN&I, BiolAb, CurCont, ESPM, EntAb, ForAb, GenetAb, HGA, HortAb, ISR, NemAb, OrnHort, RevApplEntom, S&F, SCI, SFA, WeedAb, ZooRec.
—BLDSC (7242.652000), IDS, IE, ingenta.
Published by: Raffles Museum of Biodiversity Research, National University of Singapore, Department of Biological Sciences, Block S6, Level 3, Faculty of Science, Science Drive 2, Singapore, 117600, Singapore. dbsbox7@nus.edu.sg, dbsns@nus.edu.sg, http://rmbr.nus.edu.sg/rbz/. Ed. Peter Ng. Circ: 100. **Dist. by:** Backhuys Publishers - Universal Book Services, PO Box 321, Leiden 2300 AH, Netherlands.

➤ **RAY SOCIETY PUBLICATIONS.** see *BIOLOGY—Botany*

599 ISR ISSN 0334-1461
QL729.I75
RE'EM. Text in Hebrew. a. **Description:** Articles on mammals found in Israel.
Indexed: IHP.
Published by: (Israel Mammal Information Center), Society for the Protection of Nature in Israel, 4 Hashefela St, Tel Aviv, 66183, Israel. TEL 972-3-375063. Eds. B Shalmon, D Simon.

REFERATIVNYI ZHURNAL. IKHTIOLOGIYA. see *BIOLOGY—Abstracting, Bibliographies, Statistics*

REFERATIVNYI ZHURNAL. ZOOLOGIYA. see *BIOLOGY—Abstracting, Bibliographies, Statistics*

590 RUS
REFERATIVNYI ZHURNAL. ZOOLOGIYA NAZEMNYKH POZVONOCHNYKH: OBSHCHIE VOPROSY. GERPETOLOGIYA. Text in Russian. 1992. m. USD 145 foreign (effective 2006). **Document type:** *Academic/Scholarly.*
Related titles: CD-ROM ed.; Online - full text ed.
Published by: Vserossiiskii Institut Nauchnoi i Tekhnicheskoi Informatsii (VINITI), Ul Usievicha 20, Moscow, 125190, Russian Federation. TEL 7-095-1526441, FAX 7-095-9430060, dir@viniti.ru, http://www.viniti.ru. Ed. Yurii Arskii. **Dist. by:** Informnauka Ltd., Ul Usievicha 20, Moscow 125190, Russian Federation. alfimov@viniti.ru.

REFERATIVNYI ZHURNAL. ZOOLOGIYA NAZEMNYKH POZVONOCHNYKH: ORNITOLOGIYA. see *BIOLOGY—Abstracting, Bibliographies, Statistics*

REFERATIVNYI ZHURNAL. ZOOLOGIYA NAZEMNYKH POZVONOCHNYKH: TERIOLOGIYA, OKHOTOVEDENIE, ZOOPARKI. see *BIOLOGY—Abstracting, Bibliographies, Statistics*

REFERATIVNYI ZHURNAL. ZOOLOGIYA OBSHCHAYA. ZOOLOGIYA BESPOZVONOCHNYKH. see *BIOLOGY—Abstracting, Bibliographies, Statistics*

REFERATIVNYI ZHURNAL. ZOOPARAZITOLOGIYA. see *BIOLOGY—Abstracting, Bibliographies, Statistics*

599 JPN ISSN 0912-4047
REICHORUI KENKYU/PRIMATE RESEARCH. Text in English, Japanese. 1985. s-a. JPY 3,000 per issue.
Related titles: Online - full text ed.: ISSN 1880-2117 (from J-Stage).
Indexed: ZooRec.
—BLDSC (6612.923500). **CCC.**
Published by: Nihon Reichorui Gakkai/Primate Society of Japan, Kyoto Daigaku Reichorui Kenkyujo, Inuyama Kanrin, Inuyama-shi, Aichi-ken 484, Japan.

REPTILE & AMPHIBIAN HOBBYIST. see *PETS*

597.9 CAN
REPTILE LIFE. Text in English. 1996. q. CND 23.75 (effective 2000). adv. bk.rev. back issues avail. **Document type:** *Consumer.*
Published by: Wise & Wright Publishers, 100-1039 17th Ave S W, P O Box 214, Calgary, AB T2T 0B2, Canada. TEL 270-7377, FAX 244-2431. Ed. Jonathan Wright. Adv. contact Pat Wise.

597.9 USA ISSN 1068-1965
REPTILES; a guide to keeping reptiles and amphibians. Text in English. 1993. m. USD 14.99 (effective 2005). adv. bk.rev. illus. Index. reprints avail. **Document type:** *Magazine, Consumer.* **Description:** Explores all topics related to reptiles, including nutrition, health care, housing, and breeding.
Indexed: ZooRec.
Published by: Fancy Publications Inc. (Subsidiary of: Bowtie, Inc.), 3 Burroughs, Irvine, CA 92618. TEL 949-855-8822, FAX 949-855-3045, reptiles@fancypubs.com, http://www.animalnetwork.com/reptiles/default.asp. Ed. Russ Case. Circ: 50,000 (paid). **Dist. in UK by:** Comag, Tavistock Works, Tavistock Rd, W Drayton, Middx UB7 7QX, United Kingdom. TEL 44-1895-444055, FAX 44-1895-433602.

REPTILES U S A. see *PETS*

597.9 GBR ISSN 0966-7911
REPTILIAN. Text in English. 1992. m. GBP 3.50 per issue (effective 2005). adv. bk.rev. illus. reprints avail. **Document type:** *Magazine, Consumer.*
Published by: C - View Media, PO Box 1006, Southampton, Hamps SO19 7TS, United Kingdom. TEL 44-870-3213764, FAX 44-870-3216268, editor@cviewmedia.com, Info@cviewmedia.com, http://www.cviewmedia.com/. Ed., Pub. Tom Burgess. R&P, Adv. contact Chris Newman.

594 ESP ISSN 1576-933X
RESENAS MALACOLOGICAS. Text in Spanish. 1981. irreg. **Document type:** *Monographic series.*
—CINDOC.
Published by: Sociedad Espanola de Malacologia, c/o Museo Nacional de Ciencias Naturales, Jose Gutierrez Abascal, 2, Madrid, 28006, Spain. Ed. Angel A Luove del Villar.

597 NLD ISSN 0960-3166
QL614 CODEN: RFBFEA
➤ **REVIEWS IN FISH BIOLOGY AND FISHERIES.** Text in English. q. EUR 638, USD 648, GBP 418 combined subscription to institutions print & online eds. (effective 2005). bk.rev. back issues avail.; reprint service avail. from PSC. **Document type:** *Academic/Scholarly.* **Description:** Publishes review articles on varied aspects of fish and fisheries biology. The subject matter is focused on such topics as evolutionary biology, zoogeography, taxonomy (including biochemical taxonomy and stock identification), genetic manipulation, physiology, functional morphology, behavior, ecology, fisheries assessment, development, exploitation and conservation.
Related titles: Online - full text ed.: ISSN 1573-5184 (from EBSCO Publishing, Gale Group, IngentaConnect, Kluwer Online, O C L C Online Computer Library Center, Inc., Ovid Technologies, Inc., Springer LINK, Swets Information Services).
Indexed: ASCA, ASFA, AgBio, AnBeAb, AnBrAb, ApEcolAb, B&BAb, BIOSIS Prev, BibLing, CurCont, EPB, ESPM, GEOBASE, HelmAb, ISR, IndVet, M&GPA, NutrAb, OceAb, RDA, RRTA, RefZh, S&F, SCI, SFA, VetBull, WAE&RSA, WildRev, ZooRec.
—BLDSC (7790.568000), CISTI, IDS, IE, Infotrieve, ingenta. **CCC.**
Published by: Springer-Verlag Dordrecht (Subsidiary of: Springer Science+Business Media), Van Godewijckstraat 30, Dordrecht, 3311 GX, Netherlands. TEL 31-78-6576050, FAX 31-78-6576474, http://springerlink.metapress.com/openurl.asp?genre=journal&issn=0960-3166, http://www.springeronline.com. Ed. Jennifer L Nielsen.

590 BRA ISSN 0101-8175
QL242
REVISTA BRASILEIRA DE ZOOLOGIA. Text in English. q.
Related titles: Online - full text ed.: free (effective 2005).
Indexed: ASFA, AgBio, AgrForAb, AnBeAb, AnBrAb, ApEcolAb, B&BAb, BIOSIS Prev, BioCN&I, BiolAb, CPA, ESPM, EntAb, FCA, FPA, ForAb, GenetAb, HelmAb, HerbAb, HortAb, IndVet, MaizeAb, NutrAb, OceAb, OrnHort, PBA, PGegResA, PHN&I, PN&I, PoultAb, ProtozoAb, RA&MP, RRTA, S&F, SIA, SeedAb, TDB, VetBull, WeedAb, ZooRec.
—BLDSC (7845.802000).
Published by: Sociedade Brasileira de Zoologia, Av Corifeu de Azevedo Marques, 2720, Sao Paulo, 20520, Brazil.

REVISTA CUBANA DE CIENCIA AGRICOLA. see *AGRICULTURE*

597 ARG ISSN 0327-6090
REVISTA DE ICTIOLOGIA. Text in Spanish. 1991. s-a. **Document type:** *Journal, Academic/Scholarly.*
Indexed: ESPM.
Published by: Universidad Nacional de Nordeste, Facultad de Ciencias Veterinarias, Instituto de Ictiologia del Nordeste, Rectorado, 25 de Mayo 868, Corrientes, 3400, Argentina. TEL 54-3783-425064, FAX 54-3783-424678, http://www.unne.edu.ar/home.php.

REVISTA DE INVESTIGACION Y DESARROLLO PESQUERO. see *FISH AND FISHERIES*

590 MEX ISSN 0188-1884
REVISTA DE ZOOLOGIA. Text and summaries in English, Spanish. 1996 (no.2). s-a. MXP 55, USD 12 (effective 2000). **Description:** Covers paleontology, ecology, taxonomy, physiology, ornithology and other fields related to zoology.
Indexed: ASFA, ESPM.
Published by: Universidad Nacional Autonoma de Mexico, Escuela Nacional de Estudios Profesionales Iztacala, c/o Museo de las Ciencias Biologicas, Mexico, Ave. DE LOS BARRIOS S/N,, Tlalnepantla, Los Reyes Ixtacala, MEX 54090, Mexico. TEL 52-5-6231386, FAX 52-5-6231212, http://www.iztacala.unam.mx/. Ed. Tizoc Adrian Altamirano Alvarez.

597.9 ESP ISSN 0213-6686
➤ **REVISTA ESPANOLA DE HERPETOLOGIA.** Abbreviated title: Rev. Esp. Herp. Text in Spanish, English; Summaries in English. 1986. a., latest vol.15, 2001. USD 35 (effective 1999). bk.rev. Index. 150 p./no.; back issues avail. **Document type:** *Journal, Academic/Scholarly.* **Description:** Focuses on amphibian and reptile research in the fields of zoology, biology, natural history, and taxonomy.
Related titles: Online - full text ed.
Indexed: IECT, ZooRec.
—BLDSC (7854.003500), CINDOC.
Published by: Asociacion Herpetologica Espanola, Dpto. Biologia Animal, Facultad Biologia (Vertebrats), Universidad de Barcelona, Av Diagonal, 645, Barcelona, 08028, Spain. TEL 34-3-4021455, FAX 34-3-4035740, lizana@gugu.usal.es. Eds. Albert Montori Faura, Gustavo A Llorente. Pub. Albert Montori Faura. **Subscr. to:** Dpto. Biologia Animal, Facultad Biologa, Univerisdad de Salamanca, Salmanaca E-37071, Spain. TEL 34-923-294596, FAX 34-923-294515, valentin@gugu.usal.es, enriqu.ay@argen.net.

➤ **REVISTA VETERINARIA Y ZOOTECNICA DE CALDAS.** see *VETERINARY SCIENCE*

595.4 FRA ISSN 0398-4346
REVUE ARACHNOLOGIQUE. Text in English, French; Summaries in French. 1977. irreg., latest vol.12, 1998. back issues avail.
Indexed: BIOSIS Prev, BiolAb, RefZh, ZooRec.
Address: rue du Ruisseau, Solignac-sur-Loire, 43370, France. Ed. J.C. Ledoux. Pub. J C Ledoux.

590 ROM ISSN 0377-8142
CODEN: RRBADA
REVUE ROUMAINE DE BIOLOGIE. SERIE BIOLOGIE ANIMALE. Text in English, French, German, Russian, Spanish. 1956. s-a. bk.rev. abstr.; charts; illus. index. **Document type:** *Academic/Scholarly.*
Supersedes in part (in 1976): Revue Roumaine de Biologie (0250-6572); Which was formed by the 1975 merger of: Revue Roumaine de Biologie. Serie Zoologie (0035-3922); Revue Roumaine de Biologie. Serie Botanique (0035-3914); Both of which supersede (in 1964): Revue de Biologie (0484-8462)
Related titles: Online - full text ed.
Indexed: ASFA, AnBrAb, BiolAb, ChemAb, ChemTitl, DSA, ESPM, ExcerpMed, HelmAb, NemAb, NutrAb, ProtozoAb, RefZh, S&F, SFA, ZooRec.
—CASDDS, CISTI, GNLM, KNAW, Linda Hall.
Published by: (Academia Romana, Institutul de Stiinte Biologice), Editura Academiei Romane/Publishing House of the Romanian Academy, Calea 13 Septembrie 13, Sector 5, Bucharest, 76117, Romania. TEL 40-21-4119008, FAX 40-21-4103983, edacad@ear.ro. Ed. Mihai Bacescu.

590 CHE ISSN 0035-418X
QL1 CODEN: RSZOA6
➤ **REVUE SUISSE DE ZOOLOGIE/SWISS JOURNAL OF ZOOLOGY.** Text in English, French, German, Italian; Abstracts in English. 1893. q. CHF 225 domestic; CHF 230 foreign (effective 2003). adv. bibl.; charts; illus. index. **Document type:** *Journal, Academic/Scholarly.* **Description:** Contains 0riginal papers in the fields of biogeography, systematics, ecology, ethology, morphology, comparative anatomy and physiology.
Related titles: Microfiche ed.: (from IDC).
Indexed: ASCA, ASFA, AgBio, AgrForAb, AnBrAb, BIOSIS Prev, BioCN&I, BiolAb, CRFR, ChemAb, CurCont, EntAb, ForAb, HelmAb, HerbAb, HortAb, ISR, IndVet, KWIWR, MEDLINE, MaizeAb, OrnHort, PBA, PoultAb, RM&VM, RefZh, RevApplEntom, S&F, SCI, SFA, SPPI, TDB, TriticAb, WeedAb, WildRev, ZooRec.
—BLDSC (7953.400000), CASDDS, CISTI, GNLM, IDS, IE, Infotrieve, ingenta, Linda Hall.
Published by: Museum d'Histoire Naturelle de Geneve, B.P. 6434, Geneva 6, 1211, Switzerland. TEL 41-22-4186333, FAX 41-22-4186301, volker.mahnert@mhn.ville-ge.ch, http://www.ville-ge.ch/musinfo/mhng/publications/revues.htm. Ed., R&P, Adv. contact Volker Mahnert. Circ: 250.

➤ **RHEINISCHE FRIEDRICH-WILHELMS-UNIVERSITAET. INSTITUT FUER TIERZUCHTWISSENSCHAFT. ARBEITEN.** see *AGRICULTURE—Poultry And Livestock*

590 POL ISSN 0137-1657
CODEN: RNZOD8
ROCZNIKI NAUKOWE ZOOTECHNIKI. Text in English, Polish; Summaries in English, German, Polish, Russian. 1974. q. USD 35 foreign (effective 2005). back issues avail. **Document type:** *Journal, Academic/Scholarly.* **Description:** Covers breeding, feeding and feed science, technology, ethology and animal production economics.
Related titles: CD-ROM ed.; Online - full text ed.
Indexed: AEA, AgBio, AgrAg, AgrLib, AnBrAb, BiolAb, DSA, FCA, FS&TA, HerbAb, IndVet, MaizeAb, NutrAb, PBA, PHN&I, PN&I, PotatoAb, PoultAb, RA&MP, RefZh, S&F, SFA, SIA, SeedAb, SoyAb, TriticAb, VetBull, WAE&RSA, WildRev.
—BLDSC (8015.703000), CASDDS, CISTI, IE, ingenta.
Published by: Instytut Zootechniki/Institute of Animal Production, ul Sarego 2, Krakow, 31047, Poland. TEL 48-12-2588111, FAX 48-12-2588150, roczniki@izoo.krakow.pl, izooinfo@izoo.krakow.pl, http://www.izoo.krakow.pl. Ed. Mariusz Pietras. Circ: 450.

590 RUS
ROSSIISKAYA AKADEMIYA NAUK. ZOOLOGICHESKII INSTITUT. OPREDELITELI ZHYVOTNYKH/KEYS TO THE FAUNA OF THE U S S R. Text in Russian. 1927. irreg.
Formerly (until 1991): Opredeliteli po Faune S S S R
Published by: Rossiiskaya Akademiya Nauk, Zoologicheskii Institut/Russian Academy of Sciences, Zoological Institute, Universitetskaya nab 1, St Petersburg, 199034, Russian Federation. TEL 7-812-3280011, FAX 7-812-3282941, admin@zin.ru, http://www.zin.ru.

590 RUS ISSN 0206-0477
ROSSIISKAYA AKADEMIYA NAUK. ZOOLOGICHESKII INSTITUT. TRUDY/RUSSIAN ACADEMY OF SCIENCES. ZOOLOGICAL INSTITUTE. PROCEEDINGS. Text in Russian. 1932. irreg. **Document type:** *Academic/Scholarly.*
Indexed: AbHyg, AnBrAb, BioCN&I, ESPM, HelmAb, NemAb, ProtozoAb, ZooRec.
—CISTI, Linda Hall.
Published by: Rossiiskaya Akademiya Nauk, Zoologicheskii Institut/Russian Academy of Sciences, Zoological Institute, Universitetskaya nab 1, St Petersburg, 199034, Russian Federation. TEL 7-812-3280011, FAX 7-812-3282941, admin@zin.ru, http://www.zin.ru.

592.52 AUS ISSN 1327-4007
ROTIFER NEWS; a newsletter for rotiferologist throughout the world. Text in English. 1972. irreg. (1-2/yr.; s-a. before Feb. 1992), latest 33, Dec. 2000. AUD 10 in Australia & New Zealand; USD 10 elsewhere (effective 2001). bk.rev. illus. 28 p./no.; back issues avail. **Document type:** *Newsletter, Academic/Scholarly.* **Description:** Includes articles and research on Rotifera.
Published by: Murray-Darling Freshwater Research Centre, PO Box 921, Albury, NSW 2640, Australia. TEL 61-2-60582300, FAX 61-2-60431626, shielr@mdfre.canberra.edu.au. Ed. Russell J Shiel. Circ: 250.

590 GBR
ROYAL ZOOLOGICAL SOCIETY OF SCOTLAND. ANNUAL REPORT. Text in English. a. **Document type:** *Proceedings.*
—BLDSC (1426.800000).
Published by: Royal Zoological Society of Scotland, Scottish National Zoological Park, 134 Corstorphine Rd, Edinburgh, EH12 6TS, United Kingdom. TEL 44-131-334-9171, FAX 44-131-316-4050. Ed. Dr. David Waugh.

590.73 GBR
ROYAL ZOOLOGICAL SOCIETY OF SCOTLAND. ZOO GUIDE. Text in English. 1958. irreg. GBP 2.75. adv. **Document type:** *Directory.*
Published by: Royal Zoological Society of Scotland, Scottish National Zoological Park, 134 Corstorphine Rd, Edinburgh, EH12 6TS, United Kingdom. TEL 44-131-334-9171, FAX 44-131-316-4050. Circ: 100,000.

597.9 RUS ISSN 1026-2296
RUSSIAN JOURNAL OF HERPETOLOGY. Text in Russian. 1993. 3/yr. (in 1 vol., 3 nos./vol.). USD 60 foreign to individuals; USD 120 foreign to institutions (effective 2004). **Description:** Publishes basic and applied research on recent and fossil amphibians and reptiles.
Indexed: RefZh, WildRev, ZooRec.
—BLDSC (8052.709970).
Published by: Izdatel'stvo Folium, Dmitrovskoe shosse 58, Moscow, 127238, Russian Federation. TEL 7-095-4825544, 7-095-4825590, rjh@folium.ru, info@folium.ru, http://www.folium.ru/en/journals/rjh. Ed. I S Daresvsky. **Distr. in US by:** Bibliomania!, PO Box 58355, Salt Lake City, UT 84158. breck@herplit.com.

597 JPN ISSN 0285-287X
RYOSEI HACHURUI KENKYUKAISHI/NIPPON HERPETOLOGICAL JOURNAL. Text in Japanese; Summaries in English. 1975. irreg. JPY 1,000 per issue.
Published by: Nippon Ryosei Hachurui Kenkyukai/Nippon Herpetological Society, c/o Mr Kinebuchi, 2140 Katabata, Uchino, Niigata-shi, Niigata-ken 950-21, Japan.

B

593 USA
S C A M I T NEWSLETTER. Text in English. m. USD 30 to individuals; USD 60 to institutions. **Document type:** *Newsletter, Academic/Scholarly.* **Description:** Discusses marine invertebrate taxonomy and related issues.
Related titles: Online - full text ed.
Published by: Southern California Association of Marine Invertebrate Taxonomists, Attn: Leslie Harris, The Natural History Museum, 900 Exposition Blvd., Los Angeles, CA 90007. TEL 213-763-3234, FAX 213-746-2999, dcadien@lacsd.org, http://www.scamit.org.

590 DEU ISSN 0323-8563
➤ **SAEUGETIERKUNDLICHE INFORMATIONEN.** Text in German. 1977. a. **Document type:** *Journal, Academic/Scholarly.* **Description:** Presents scholarly and research articles on a wide variety of mammals.
Indexed: ZooRec.
Published by: Druck- und Verlagshaus Frisch, Sophienstr 55-57, Eisenach, 99817, Germany. TEL 49-3691-237611, FAX 49-3691-75076, druckerei.frisch@t-online.de, http://www.th-online.de/firmen/frisch.

590 DEU ISSN 0036-2344
CODEN: STKMBC
SAEUGETIERKUNDLICHE MITTEILUNGEN. Text in English, French, German. 1953. q. bk.rev. bibl.; illus. index.
Indexed: AnBrAb, BiolAb, IndVet, KWIWR, VetBull, ZooRec.
—CISTI, Linda Hall.
Address: Postfach 1153, Delligsen, 31069, Germany. Ed. G Kirk. Circ: 400.

597.85 DEU ISSN 0036-3375
QL640 CODEN: SALAAH
SALAMANDRA; Zeitschrift fuer Herpetologie und Terrarienkunde. Text in German; Abstracts in English. 1965. 4/yr. EUR 60 membership (effective 2005). bk.rev. abstr.; bibl.; charts; illus. index. **Document type:** *Journal, Academic/Scholarly.*
Related titles: ◆ Supplement(s): Mertensiella. ISSN 0934-6643.
Indexed: BIOSIS Prev, BiolAb, RefZh, ZooRec.
—BLDSC (8070.560000), CISTI, IE, ingenta, Linda Hall.
Published by: Deutsche Gesellschaft fuer Herpetologie und Terrarienkunde e.V., Postfach 1421, Rheinbach, 53351, Germany. TEL 49-2225-703333, FAX 49-2225-703338, gs@dght.de, http://www.dght.de/zeitschriften/salamandra/salamandra.htm. Ed. Dr. Klaus Henle. Circ: 4,500.

597 IRL
SALMON RESEARCH AGENCY OF IRELAND INCORPORATED. ANNUAL REPORT. Text in English. a.
Published by: Salmon Research Agency of Ireland Incorporated, Funrance, Newport, Mayo, Ireland. TEL 353-098-41107.

597 FRA ISSN 0220-1429
SAUMONS. Text in French. q.
Published by: Association Nationale de Defense des Rivieres a Saumons, 1 place Edouard Renard, Paris, 75012, France. Ed. Rene Richard.

597.9 DEU ISSN 0176-9391
CODEN: SAUREF
➤ **SAURIA**; Herpetologie und Terraristik. Text in German; Summaries in English. 1979. q. EUR 28 (effective 2005). adv. bk.rev. bibl.; charts; illus.; abstr.; maps. index. 48 p./no. 2 cols./p.; back issues avail. **Document type:** *Newsletter, Academic/Scholarly.*
Indexed: RefZh, SFA, WildRev, ZooRec.
Published by: Terrariengemeinschaft Berlin e.V., Planetenstr 45, Berlin, 12057, Germany. TEL 49-30-6847140, abo@sauria.de, http://www.sauria.de. Ed. Mirko Barts. Pub., R&P Dr. Manfred Buhle. Adv. contact Mrs. Barbara Buhle. Circ: 1,700.

594 DEU ISSN 0936-2959
SCHRIFTEN ZUR MALAKOZOOLOGIE AUS DEM HAUS DER NATUR CISMAR. Text in English, German. 1989. irreg. (1-2/yr.). bk.rev. bibl.; illus.; maps. back issues avail. **Document type:** *Monographic series, Academic/Scholarly.*
Indexed: ZooRec.
Published by: Haus der Natur Cismar, Baederstr 26, Groemitz, 23743, Germany. TEL 49-4366-1288, FAX 49-4366-1288, vwiese@hausdernatur.de. Ed., Pub. Vollrath Wiese. Circ: 300 (paid).

591.5 SGP
THE SCIENCE AND CULTURE SERIES - ETHOLOGY. Text in English. 2000. irreg., latest 2000. price varies. **Document type:** *Monographic series, Academic/Scholarly.*
Related titles: ◆ Series: The Science and Culture Series - Advanced Scientific Culture; ◆ The Science and Culture Series - Astrophysics; ◆ The Science and Culture Series - Environmental Sciences; ◆ The Science and Culture Series - Materials Science; ◆ The Science and Culture Series - Mathematics; ◆ The Science and Culture Series - Medicine; ◆ The Science and Culture Series - Nuclear Strategy and Peace Technology; ◆ The Science and Culture Series - Physics; ◆ The Science and Culture Series - Spectroscopy.
Published by: World Scientific Publishing Co. Pte. Ltd., 5 Toh Tuck Link, Singapore, 596224, Singapore. TEL 65-466-5775, FAX 65-467-7667, wspc@wspc.com.sg, series@wspc.com.sg, http://www.wspc.com.sg/books/series/scse_series.shtml, http://www.worldscientific.com. Ed. A Zichichi. **Dist. by:** World Scientific Publishing Co., Inc., 1060 Main St, River Edge, NJ 07661. TEL 201-487-9655, 800-227-7562, FAX 201-487-9656, 888-977-2665; World Scientific Publishing Ltd., 57 Shelton St, London WC2H 9HE, United Kingdom. TEL 44-20-78360888, FAX 44-20-78362020.

599.5 JPN ISSN 0917-0537
QL737.C4 CODEN: SRCTEG
➤ **SCIENTIFIC REPORTS OF CETACEAN RESEARCH/NIHON GEIRUI KENKYUSHO KENKYU HOKOKU.** Text in English. 1990. a. JPY 5,000 (effective 2001). **Document type:** *Bulletin, Academic/Scholarly.*
Supersedes (in Sep. 1990): Whales Research Institute, Tokyo, Japan. Scientific Reports (0083-9086)
Indexed: ASFA, BiolAb, ESPM, SFA, ZooRec.
—Linda Hall.
Published by: Institute of Cetacean Research/Nihon Geirui Kenkyusho, Suisan Bldg, 4-18 Toyomi-cho, Chuo-ku, Tokyo, 104-0055, Japan. TEL 81-3-3536-6521, FAX 81-3-3536-6522. Ed., R&P, Adv. contact Seiji Ohsumi. Circ: 750.

➤ **SEA GRANT ABSTRACTS**; publications from the nation's Sea Grant programs. see *BIOLOGY—Abstracting, Bibliographies, Statistics*

597 USA
SEINE. Text in English. 1997. bi-m. USD 15 in North America; USD 17 elsewhere (effective 2005). adv. bk.rev. **Document type:** *Newsletter, Consumer.* **Description:** Includes news and feature articles on ecology, icthyology, and live maintenance and study of North American fishes.
Published by: Society on North American Fishes, 123 W Mt Airy Ave, Philadelphia, PA 19119. TEL 215-247-0384, FAX 215-247-0384, rbruce@eclipse.net. Ed. Bruce Gebhardt.

590 DEU ISSN 0037-2102
QH5 CODEN: SBBOAG
➤ **SENCKENBERGIANA BIOLOGICA.** Text and summaries in German, English. 1919. s-a. EUR 56 domestic; EUR 64.10 foreign (effective 2005). abstr.; bibl. index. back issues avail.; reprints avail. **Document type:** *Journal, Academic/Scholarly.* **Description:** Contains papers on zoology and botany.
Indexed: ASFA, BIOSIS Prev, BioCN&I, BiolAb, ChemAb, ESPM, EntAb, ForAb, IBR, PoultAb, RefZh, RevApplEntom, S&F, SFA, VITIS, WildRev, ZooRec.
—BLDSC (8240.000000), CISTI, IE, Infotrieve, ingenta, Linda Hall. **CCC.**
Published by: (Deutsche Forschungsgemeinschaft, Senckenbergische Naturforschende Gesellschaft), E. Schweizerbart'sche Verlagsbuchhandlung, Johannesstr 3A, Stuttgart, 70176, Germany. TEL 49-711-3514560, FAX 49-711-35145699, mail@schweizerbart.de, http://www.schweizerbart.de/j/senckenbergiana-biologica. Eds. G Storch, M Grasshoff, W Naessig. Circ: 900.

597.3 USA
SHARK FEAR, SHARK AWARENESS. Text in English. 1994. 2/yr. USD 3 per issue. bk.rev. back issues avail. **Document type:** *Newsletter.* **Description:** Studies the shark's predatory nature, and the sociological impact of their nature on human society.
Published by: Society of Shark Fear, 1420 N W Gilman Blvd, Ste 2400, Issaquah, WA 98027-7001. Ed. Darin Johnson. Circ: 5,000 (paid).

597.3 GBR ISSN 1361-7397
SHARK NEWS. Text in English. 1994. 3/yr. GBP 5 per issue (effective 2001). **Document type:** *Newsletter.* **Description:** Provides a forum for the exchange of information on all aspects of chondrichthyan conservation matters.
Related titles: Online - full text ed.
Indexed: SFA, ZooRec.
Published by: (I U C N, Shark Specialist Group), Nature Conservation Bureau Ltd., 36 Kingfisher Ct, Hambridge Rd, Newbury, Berks RG14 5SJ, United Kingdom. TEL 44-1635-550380, FAX 44-1635-550230, post@naturebureau.co.uk. Eds. Merry Camhi, Sarah Fowler. Circ: 1,500 (controlled).

594.1477 USA ISSN 0085-607X
SHELLER'S DIRECTORY OF CLUBS, BOOKS, PERIODICALS AND DEALERS. Text in English. 1968. a. USD 6.95 (effective 2000). adv. reprint service avail. from PQC. **Document type:** *Directory.*
Published by: Of Sea & Shore Publications, PO Box 219, Port Gamble, WA 98364. TEL 360-297-2426, FAX 360-297-2426, ofseashr@sinclair.net. Ed. Thomas C Rice. Circ: 500.

SHEZHI/JOURNAL OF SNAKE. see *MEDICAL SCIENCES*

594 JPN ISSN 0917-7159
SHIBUKITSUBO/NIIGATA SHELL CLUB. REPORT. Text in Japanese. irreg.
Published by: Niigata Kaiyukai/Niigata Shell Club, c/o Mr Murayama, 301-2 Nakazawa 4-chome, Nagaoka-shi, Niigata-ken 940-0853, Japan.

599 CHN ISSN 1000-1050
➤ **SHOULEI XUEBAO/ACTA THERIOLOGICA SINICA.** Text in Chinese; Summaries in English. 1981. q. CNY 48 (effective 2004). adv. bk.rev. **Document type:** *Journal, Academic/Scholarly.* **Description:** Contains original theses on basic theories and applications of mammalian zoology. Includes taxonomy, morphology, ecology, physiology, biochemistry, paleontology and evolution, raising, domestication, natural protection, hunting, and prevention of cruelty.
Related titles: Online - full text ed.: (from East View Information Services, WanFang Data Corp.).
Indexed: BIOSIS Prev, BiolAb, GEOBASE, RefZh, ZooRec.
Published by: (Zhongguo Kexueyuan, Xibei Gaoyuan Shengwu Yanjiusuo/Chinese Academy of Sciences, Northwest Institute of Plateau Biology), Kexue Chubanshe/Science Press, 16 Donghuang Cheng Genbei Jie, Beijing, 100717, China. TEL 86-10-64000246, FAX 86-10-64030255, slxb@mail.nwipb.ac.cn, http://sleixb.periodicals.net.cn/default.html, http://www.sciencep.com/. Ed. Wang Zuwang. Circ: 5,500. **Dist. by:** China International Book Trading Corp, 35 Chegongzhuang Xilu, Haidian District, PO Box 399, Beijing 100044, China. TEL 86-10-68412045, FAX 86-10-68412023, cibtc@mail.cibtc.com.cn, http://www.cibtc.com.cn.

590 JPN
SHUKAN ASAHI HYAKKA/WEEKLY ASAHI ENCYCLOPEDIA. Text in Japanese. 1975. w.
Published by: Asahi Shimbun Publishing Co., 5-3-2 Tsukiji, Chuo-ku, Tokyo, 104-8011, Japan. Ed. Tsuyosi Nogami. **Order to:** Oversea Courier Service Co. Ltd., 9 Shibaura 2-chome, Minato-ku, Tokyo 108-0023, Japan.

597 ZAF ISSN 1684-4130
QL614
▼ **SMITHIANA BULLETIN.** Text in English. 2003. irreg. free (effective 2005). **Document type:** *Bulletin, Academic/Scholarly.*
Media: Online - full text.
Indexed: ASFA, ESPM.
Published by: National Research Foundation, South African Institute for Aquatic Biodiversity, PO Box 2600, Pretoria, 0001, South Africa. TEL 27-12-4814000, FAX 27-12-3491179, http://www.bioline.org.br/sm.

590 USA ISSN 0081-0282
QL1 CODEN: SMCZBU
SMITHSONIAN CONTRIBUTIONS TO ZOOLOGY. Text in English. 1969. irreg., latest vol.611, 2001. price varies. reprint service avail. from PQC. **Document type:** *Monographic series.*
Indexed: AESIS, ASFA, AbHyg, BIOSIS Prev, BioCN&I, BiolAb, ESPM, EntAb, ForAb, GenetAb, HGA, OceAb, RM&VM, RefZh, RevApplEntom, SFA, WildRev, ZooRec.
—BLDSC (8311.620000), CISTI, ingenta, Linda Hall. **CCC.**
Published by: Smithsonian Institution Press, PO Box 37012, Washington, DC 20013-7012. TEL 202-633-3017, schol.press@si.edu, http://www.si.edu/publications/. Circ: 2,000.

590.7 URY ISSN 0255-4402
SOCIEDAD ZOOLOGICA DEL URUGUAY. BOLETIN. Text in Spanish. 1971. s-a.
Indexed: ZooRec.
—Linda Hall.
Published by: Sociedad Zoologica del Uruguay, Facultad de Ciencias, Igua 4225, Malvin Norte, Montevideo, 11400, Uruguay. http://www.inetwork.com.uy/szu/.

598 PRT ISSN 0870-7308
SOCIEDADE PORTUGUESA DE MALACOLOGIA. PUBLICACOES OCASIONAIS. Text in Multiple languages. 1982. s-a. **Document type:** *Monographic series.*
Indexed: ESPM.
Published by: Sociedade Portuguesa de Malacologia, Largo da Princesa 24, 1o Esq, Lisbon, 1400, Portugal.

598 ITA ISSN 0394-7149
QL401
➤ **SOCIETA ITALIANA DI MALACOLOGIA. BOLLETTINO MALACOLOGICO.** Text in English, French, Italian, Spanish; Summaries in English. 1965. 3/yr. free to members (effective 2003). adv. bk.rev. index. 100 p./no.; back issues avail. **Document type:** *Academic/Scholarly.* **Description:** Principally, but not exclusively, dedicated to the recent and fossilized mollusks fauna of the Mediterranean, Europe and West Africa.
Former titles (until 1980): Unione Malacologica Italiana. Bollettino Malacologico (0394-7130); (until 1979): Conchiglie (0588-9758)
Indexed: ASFA, BIOSIS Prev, BiolAb, ZooRec.
—BLDSC (2239.090000), IE, ingenta, Linda Hall.
Published by: Societa Italiana di Malacologia, c/o Acquario Civico, Viale Gadio, 2, Milan, 20121, Italy. FAX 39-091-6713568, http://www.aicon.com/sim/. Ed. Daniele Bedulli. Adv. contact Riccardo Giannuzzi Savelli. Circ: 1,000.

598 ITA ISSN 1121-3604
SOCIETA ITALIANA DI MALACOLOGIA. LAVORI. Text in Italian, English, French, Spanish. 1964. irreg. price varies.
Formerly (until 1984): Societa Malacologica Italiana. Lavori (1121-3590)

Published by: Societa Italiana di Malacologia, c/o Acquario Civico, Viale Gadio, 2, Milan, 20121, Italy. FAX 39-091-6713568, http://www.aicon.com/sim/.

598 ITA ISSN 1121-161X
SOCIETA ITALIANA DI MALACOLOGIA. NOTIZIARIO. Text in Italian. 1983. 3/yr. free to members (effective 2003). adv. bk.rev. **Document type:** *Newsletter.* **Description:** An internal bulletin of the Societa Italiana di Malocologia, it covers topics on malacology, but also general matters about the life and functioning of the organization.
Indexed: ZooRec.
—BLDSC (6174.268100).
Published by: Societa Italiana di Malacologia, c/o Acquario Civico, Viale Gadio, 2, Milan, 20121, Italy. FAX 39-091-6713568, http://www.aicon.com/sim/. Ed. Daniele Bedulli. Adv. contact Riccardo Giannuzzi Savelli.

590 570 FRA ISSN 0758-3818
SOCIETE DES SCIENCES NATURELLES DE L'OUEST DE LA FRANCE. BULLETIN. Text in French. 1891. q. EUR 32 domestic; EUR 40 foreign. illus.; maps. back issues avail. **Document type:** *Bulletin.*
Indexed: ZooRec.
Published by: Societe des Sciences Naturelles de l'Ouest de la France (S S N O F), 12 rue Voltaire, Nantes, 44000, France. TEL 33-2-40692819. Circ: 550 (controlled).

590 636 FRA ISSN 1151-1737
SOCIETE D'ETHNOZOOTECHNIE. LETTRE. Text in French. 1981. q. EUR 27 (effective 2003). **Document type:** *Academic/Scholarly.*
Published by: Societe d'Ethnozootechnie, 16 bis bd. Cote Blatin, Clermont-Ferrand, 63000, France. TEL 33-4-73915824. Pub. Francois Spindler.

SOCIETE D'HISTOIRE NATURELLE DE COLMAR. BULLETIN. see *BIOLOGY—Botany*

597.9 FRA ISSN 0754-9962
SOCIETE HERPETOLOGIQUE DE FRANCE. BULLETIN. Text in French. 1977. q.
Indexed: BIOSIS Prev, BiolAb, ZooRec.
Published by: Societe Herpetologique de France, 2 Place Jussieu, Paris, 75320, France.

594 CHE ISSN 0259-9678
SOCIETE INTERNATIONALE DE CONCHYLIOLOGIE. BULLETIN. Text in French. 1979. q.
Indexed: ZooRec.
Published by: Societe Internationale de Conchyliologie, Musee d'Histoire Naturelle, Case Postale 6434, Geneve 6, CH-1211, Switzerland. FAX 41-22-4186301. Ed. Dr. Yves Finet.

590 FRA ISSN 0750-6848
CODEN: BSLBBS
SOCIETE LINNEENNE DE BORDEAUX. BULLETIN. Text in French; Summaries in English. 1971. q. EUR 35 (effective 2004). bk.rev. back issues avail. **Document type:** *Bulletin, Academic/Scholarly.*
Formed by the merger of (1965-1971): Societe Linneenne de Bordeaux. Actes. Serie A (0365-6896); (1965-1971): Societe Linneenne de Bordeaux. Actes. Serie B (0365-6918); Both of which superseded in part (1826-1965): Societe Linneenne de Bordeaux. Actes (0365-6934); Which was formerly (until 1830): Societe Linneenne de Bordeaux. Bulletin d'Histoire Naturelle (1154-9963)
Indexed: ASFA, BIOSIS Prev, BiolAb, RefZh, VITIS, ZooRec.
—Linda Hall.
Published by: Societe Linneenne de Bordeaux, 1 Place Bardineau, Bordeaux, 33000, France. TEL 33-5-56379782, 33-5-56444818, pelobates@wanadoo.fr, http://perso.wanadoo.fr/linneenne-bordeaux/. Ed. Michel Laguerre. Circ: 600.

591.944 FRA ISSN 0037-962X
QL1 CODEN: BZOFAZ
➤ **SOCIETE ZOOLOGIQUE DE FRANCE. BULLETIN;** evolution et zoologie. Text mainly in French; Text occasionally in English, German. 1876. q. EUR 80 to non-members (effective 2003). bk.rev. illus. index. **Document type:** *Academic/Scholarly.*
Related titles: Microfiche ed.: (from BHP, IDC); Microform ed.: (from BHP).
Indexed: ASCA, ASFA, AbHyg, AgBio, AgrForAb, AnBrAb, BIOSIS Prev, BioCN&I, BiolAb, ChemAb, CurCont, DSA, ExcerpMed, FCA, ForAb, HelmAb, HortAb, ISR, IndVet, MaizeAb, NutrAb, ProtozoAb, RM&VM, RefZh, RevApplEntom, S&F, SCI, SFA, SeedAb, VetBull, WeedAb, WildRev, ZooRec.
—BLDSC (2758.000000), CASDDS, CISTI, IE, Infotrieve, ingenta, KNAW, Linda Hall.
Published by: Societe Zoologique de France, 195 rue Saint Jacques, Paris, 75005, France. TEL 33-1-40793110. Ed. Jean-Loup d'Hondt. Circ: 650.

590 FRA ISSN 0750-747X
➤ **SOCIETE ZOOLOGIQUE DE FRANCE. MEMOIRES.** Text in French; Text occasionally in English; Summaries in English, French. 1888. irreg. price varies. index. back issues avail. **Document type:** *Academic/Scholarly.*
Indexed: SFA.
Published by: Societe Zoologique de France, 195 rue Saint Jacques, Paris, 75005, France. TEL 33-1-40793110. Ed. Jean-Loup d'Hondt.

599 USA
SOCIETY FOR MARINE MAMMALOGY NEWSLETTER (ONLINE EDITION). Abbreviated title: S M M Newsletter. Text in English. q. **Document type:** *Newsletter, Academic/Scholarly.*
Formerly (until Spring 2002): Society for Marine Mammalogy Newsletter (Print Edition)
Media: Online - full content.
Indexed: RefZh.
Published by: Society for Marine Mammalogy, c/o Randall Wells, Chicago Zoological Society, c/o Mote Marine Laboratory, 1600 Thompson Pkwy, Sarasota, FL 34236. TEL 941-388-4441, ext 454, FAX 941-388-4223, rwells@mote.org, http://www.marinemammalogy.org/news.htm. Ed. Randall Wells.

SOUTH AFRICAN JOURNAL OF WILDLIFE RESEARCH/SUID-AFRIKAANSE TYDSKRIF VIR NATUURNAVORSING. see *CONSERVATION*

SOUTHEAST ASIAN FISHERIES DEVELOPMENT CENTER. AQUACULTURE DEPARTMENT. REPORT. see *FISH AND FISHERIES*

SOUTHEASTERN NATURALIST. see *BIOLOGY—Botany*

▼ **SPARKY.** see *CHILDREN AND YOUTH—For*

590 JPN ISSN 1342-1670
QL352
➤ **SPECIES DIVERSITY;** an international journal for taxonomy, systematics, speciation, biogeography, and life historical research of animals. Text in English. 1965. q. JPY 10,000 to non-members; JPY 7,000 to members (effective 2003); includes Species Diversity and Taxas. back issues avail. **Document type:** *Journal, Academic/Scholarly.* **Description:** Aims to facilitate the international exchange of information about animal species diversity. Publishes original articles and reviews on animal biology in the fields of taxonomy, systematics, speciation, biogeography, and life history research to promote the study of biodiversity.
Supersedes in part (in 1996): Dobutsu Bunrui Gakkaishi - Japanese Society of Systematic Zoology. Proceedings (0287-0223)
Related titles: ◆ Japanese ed.: Taxa. ISSN 1342-2367.
Indexed: BiolAb, JPI, ZooRec.
Published by: Japanese Society of Systematic Zoology/Dobutsu Bunrui Gakkai, c/o Dept of Zoology, National Science Museum, 23-1 Hiyakunin-cho 3-chome, Shinjuku-ku, Tokyo, 169-0073, Japan. TEL 81-3-3364-2311, FAX 81-3-3364-7104, tomokuni@kakaku.go.jp, fujita@kahaku.go.jp, http://wwwsoc.nii.ac.jp/jssz2/index-e.html, http://wwwsoc.nii.ac.jp/jssz2/spdiv/index.html. Ed. Masaaki Tomokuni. Pub. Masatsune Takeda. Circ: 500.

594 NLD ISSN 1566-063X
SPIRULA. Text in Dutch. 1999. 6/yr. bk.rev. cum.index. **Document type:** *Newsletter.*
Incorporates (1934-2001): Nederlandse Malacologische Vereniging. Correspondentieblad (0923-5701)
Indexed: ZooRec.
Published by: Nederlandse Malacologische Vereniging/Dutch Malacological Society, c/o R G Moolenbeek, Zoologisch Museum, Mauritskade 57, PO Box 94766, Amsterdam, 1090 GT, Netherlands. TEL 31-20-5256294, FAX 31-20-5255402, info@spirula.nl, http://www.spirula.nl/publicaties/spirula.htm. Circ: 600.

590 DEU ISSN 0341-8391
QL1 CODEN: SPIXD9
➤ **SPIXIANA;** journal of zoology. Text in English, French, German. 1950. 3/yr. EUR 62.31 domestic; EUR 65.37 foreign (effective 2004). bk.rev. 100 p./no. 2 cols./p.; back issues avail. **Document type:** *Journal, Academic/Scholarly.*
Formerly (until 1976): Zoologischen Staatssammlung Muenchen. Veroeffentlichungen. (0077-2135)
Related titles: ◆ Supplement(s): Spixiana Supplemente. ISSN 0177-7424.
Indexed: ASFA, BIOSIS Prev, BiolAb, DIP, ESPM, EntAb, IBR, KWIWR, RefZh, SFA, WildRev, ZooRec.
—BLDSC (8417.350000), CISTI, IE, ingenta. **CCC.**
Published by: Zoologische Staatssammlung Muenchen, Muenchhausenstr 21, Munich, 81247, Germany. TEL 49-89-81070, FAX 49-89-8107300, http://www.zsm.mwn.de. Ed. Martin Baehr. Pub., R&P Friedrich Pfeil TEL 49-89-742827-0. Circ: 450 (controlled).

590 DEU ISSN 0177-7424
QL1 CODEN: SPSUDG
SPIXIANA SUPPLEMENTE. Text in English, French, German. 1957. irreg., latest vol.29, 2004. price varies. back issues avail. **Document type:** *Monographic series, Academic/Scholarly.*
Formerly (until 1978): Opuscula Zoologica (0030-4158)
Related titles: ◆ Supplement to: Spixiana. ISSN 0341-8391.
Indexed: BIOSIS Prev, BiolAb, EntAb, RefZh, ZooRec.
—CISTI. **CCC.**
Published by: Zoologische Staatssammlung Muenchen, Muenchhausenstr 21, Munich, 81247, Germany. TEL 49-89-81070, FAX 49-89-8107300, juliane.diller@zsm.mwn.de, http://www.pfeil-verlag.de/04biol/d7424.html, http://www.zsm.mwn.de. Ed. Martin Baehr.

590 DEU ISSN 0375-2135
QL1 CODEN: SMTFBL
STAATLICHES MUSEUM FUER TIERKUNDE DRESDEN. FAUNISTISCHE ABHANDLUNGEN. Text in English, French, German. 1963. a. price varies. bk.rev. back issues avail. **Document type:** *Academic/Scholarly.* **Description:** Focuses on the faunistics of Arachnida, Insecta and Vertebrata.
Indexed: ASFA, BIOSIS Prev, BiolAb, HGA, IBR, KWIWR, RefZh, SFA, WildRev, ZooRec.
—CISTI, Linda Hall.
Published by: Staatliche Naturhistorische Sammlungen Dresden, Museum fuer Tierkunde, Augustusstr 2, Dresden, 01067, Germany. tk@snsd.de, http://www.snsd.de/mtd_info.htm. Ed. Rainer Emmrich. Circ: 400.

594 DEU ISSN 0070-7260
QL401 CODEN: SMTMB8
➤ **STAATLICHES MUSEUM FUER TIERKUNDE DRESDEN. MALAKOLOGISCHE ABHANDLUNGEN.** Text in English, German. 1964. a. price varies. bk.rev. back issues avail. **Document type:** *Monographic series, Academic/Scholarly.* **Description:** Explores taxonomy, systematics, morphology, bionomics, ecology, zoogeography and faunistics of Mollusca.
Indexed: BIOSIS Prev, BiolAb, RefZh, ZooRec.
—CISTI, Linda Hall.
Published by: Staatliche Naturhistorische Sammlungen Dresden, Museum fuer Tierkunde, Koenigsbruecker Landstr 159, Dresden, 01109, Germany. TEL 49-351-8926326, FAX 49-351-8926327, tk@snsd.de, http://www.snsd.de/mtd_info.htm. Ed. Katrin Schniebs. Circ: 250.

596 DEU ISSN 0375-5231
CODEN: ZASMAT
STAATLICHES MUSEUM FUER TIERKUNDE DRESDEN. ZOOLOGISCHE ABHANDLUNGEN. Text in English, French, German. 1961. a. price varies. bk.rev. back issues avail. **Document type:** *Academic/Scholarly.* **Description:** Explores taxonomy, systematics, morphology, bionomics, ecology and zoogeography of Vertebrata.
Indexed: BIOSIS Prev, BiolAb, IBR, KWIWR, RefZh, SFA, WildRev, ZooRec.
—BLDSC (9520.800000), CISTI, IE, ingenta, Linda Hall.
Published by: Staatliche Naturhistorische Sammlungen Dresden, Museum fuer Tierkunde, Augustusstr 2, Dresden, 01067, Germany. tk@snsd.de, http://www.snsd.de/mtd_info.htm. Ed. Rainer Emmrich. Circ: 700.

590 DNK ISSN 0375-2909
QL1 CODEN: STRUB3
STEENSTRUPIA; journal on systematic zoology and zoogeography. Text and summaries in English. 1970. s-a. DKK 350 (effective 2002). back issues avail. **Document type:** *Journal, Academic/Scholarly.*
Indexed: ASFA, B&BAb, BIOSIS Prev, BiolAb, IBR, RefZh, ZooRec.
—BLDSC (8464.109500), CISTI, Linda Hall.
Published by: Zoologisk Museum, Universitetsparken 15, Copenhagen Oe, 2100, Denmark. TEL 45-35-321000, FAX 45-35-321010, dejacobsen@zmuc.ku.dk, http://www.zmuc.dk/commonweb/STENSTR.HTM. Ed. Danny Eibye-Jacobsen.

590 USA ISSN 0894-8968
STRANGE MAGAZINE. Text in English. 1987. s-a. USD 21.95; USD 28.95 foreign (effective 1998). bk.rev. back issues avail. **Document type:** *Consumer.* **Description:** Investigates cryptozoology, paranormal phenomena, and other topics worldwide.
Related titles: Online - full text ed.
Address: 11772 Parklawn Dr., Rockville, MD 20852-2533. TEL 301-460-4789, FAX 301-460-1959, strange1@strangemag.com, http://www.strangemag.com/. Ed. Mark Chorvinsky. Circ: 25,000.

590 POL ISSN 0082-5565
STUDIA SOCIETATIS SCIENTIARUM TORUNENSIS. SECTIO E. ZOOLOGIA. Text in Polish; Summaries in English, French, German. 1948. irreg., latest vol.10, no.5, 1987. price varies. **Document type:** *Monographic series.*
Indexed: AgrLib, BiolAb.
—CISTI.
Published by: Towarzystwo Naukowe w Toruniu, Ul Wysoka 16, Torun, 81100, Poland. TEL 48-56-23941. Ed. Melityna Gromadska.

591.7 NLD ISSN 0165-0521
QL235 CODEN: SNFEDP
➤ **STUDIES ON NEOTROPICAL FAUNA AND ENVIRONMENT.** Text in English. 1956. 3/yr. GBP 409, USD 676 combined subscription to institutions print & online eds. (effective 2006). adv. charts; illus. reprint service avail. from PSC. **Document type:** *Journal, Academic/Scholarly.* **Description:** Examines the ecology, systematics and the distribution of neotropical fauna.
Formerly (until 1976): Studies on the Neotropical Fauna (0375-2410)

B

Related titles: Microform ed.: (from SWZ); Online - full text ed.: ISSN 1744-5140. GBP 389, USD 642 to institutions (effective 2006) (from EBSCO Publishing, Gale Group, IngentaConnect, O C L C Online Computer Library Center, Inc., Swets Information Services).
Indexed: ASCA, ASFA, AgrForAb, AnBeAb, AnBrAb, ApEcolAb, BIOBASE, BIOSIS Prev, BioCN&I, BiolAb, CurCont, EPB, ESPM, EntAb, FPA, ForAb, HelmAb, HerbAb, HortAb, IndVet, OrnHort, PGegResA, ProtozoAb, RM&VM, RRTA, RefZh, RevApplEntom, S&F, SFA, SeedAb, TDB, WeedAb, WildRev, ZooRec.
—BLDSC (8491.155200), IDS, IE, Infotrieve, ingenta, Linda Hall. **CCC.**
Published by: Taylor & Francis The Netherlands (Subsidiary of: Taylor & Francis Group), Schipolweg 107 C, PO Box 447, Leiden, 2316 XC, Netherlands. TEL 31-715-243080, FAX 31-715-234571, pub@swets.nl, http://www.tandf.co.uk/journals/titles/01650521.asp, http://www.tandf.co.uk/swets.asp. Eds. A Zillikens, J Adis, W Engels. R&P J van der Valk. Adv. contact Miranda Mauritz. page EUR 300; trim 210 x 297.

B

590 JPN ISSN 0389-6838
SUZUKURI/ASA ZOOLOGICAL PARK NEWS. Text in Japanese. 1972. q. JPY 200 per issue. **Document type:** *Newsletter.*
Published by: Hiroshimashi Dobutsuen Kyokai/Hiroshima City Zoological Park Society, Hiroshimashi Asa Dobutsu Koen, Dobutsuen, Asacho, Asa Kita-ku, Hiroshima-shi, Hiroshima-ken 731-33, Japan. Ed. Hiroshi Morimoto.

590.73794985 USA
SYDNEY'S KOALA CLUB NEWS. Text in English. 1974. bi-m. USD 19 (effective 2001). **Document type:** *Newsletter.*
Description: Animal stories and information about the San Diego Zoo and San Diego Wild Animal Park for children.
Formerly: Koala Club News
Published by: Zoological Society of San Diego, PO Box 120551, San Diego, CA 92112-0551. TEL 619-234-3153, http://www.sandiegozoo.org. Ed. Karen E Worley. Circ: 135,000. **Subscr. to:** Membership Department.

591.941 NLD ISSN 0082-1101
CODEN: SBFSDH
➤ **SYNOPSES OF THE BRITISH FAUNA.** Text in English. 1970-1981; N.S. 1984. irreg., latest vol.12, 2001. price varies. illus. back issues avail. **Document type:** *Monographic series, Academic/Scholarly.* **Description:** Takes a close look at British animal species.
Indexed: ASFA, BiolAb, ESPM, ZooRec.
—BLDSC (8586.225000), CISTI, Linda Hall.
Published by: (Linnean Society of London GBR), Backhuys Publishers BV, Postbus 321, Leiden, 2300 AH, Netherlands. TEL 31-71-517-0208, FAX 31-71-517-1856, backhuys@backhuys.com, http://www.backhuys.com.

➤ **SYSTEMATIC AND APPLIED ACAROLOGY.** see *BIOLOGY—Entomology*

➤ **SYSTEMATIC AND APPLIED ACAROLOGY SPECIAL PUBLICATIONS.** see *BIOLOGY—Entomology*

590 JPN ISSN 1342-2367
➤ **TAXA.** Variant title: Takusa. Text in Japanese. 1965. 2/yr. JPY 7,000 membership; includes Species Diversity. back issues avail. **Document type:** *Journal, Academic/Scholarly.*
Description: Publishes original articles and reviews on animal biology in the fields of taxonomy, systematics, speciation, biogeography, and life history research to promote the study of biodiversity.
Supersedes in part (in 1996): Dobutsu Bunrui Gakkaishi - Japanese Society of Systematic Zoology. Proceedings (0287-0223)
Related titles: ♦ English ed.: Species Diversity. ISSN 1342-1670.
Indexed: ZooRec.
Published by: Dobutsu Bunrui Gakkai/Japanese Society of Systematic Zoology, c/o Dept of Zoology, National Science Museum, 23-1 Hiyakunin-cho 3-chome, Shinjuku-ku, Tokyo, 169-0073, Japan. TEL 81-3-3364-2311, FAX 81-3-3364-7104, kikuchi@server2.edhs.ynu.ac.jp, fujita@kahaku.go.jp, http://wwwsoc.nii.ac.jp/jssz2/index.html. Ed. Tomohiko Kikuchi.

590.752 USA ISSN 0199-2988
QL63
TAXIDERMY REVIEW✶. Text in English. 1976. bi-m. USD 10. adv. bk.rev. illus.; tr.lit. back issues avail.
Formerly: Wide World of Taxidermy
Address: 15011 Hollyvale Dr, Houston, TX 77062-2908. TEL 303-623-3965. Ed. Joseph Kish. Circ: 2,700.

591.9768 USA ISSN 0886-1269
SK449
TENNESSEE WILDLIFE. Text in English. 1977. bi-m. USD 10 (effective 2000). **Document type:** *Government.* **Description:** Reports about Tennessee wildlife and related articles and information.
Indexed: SFA, WildRev.
Published by: Wildlife Resources Agency, PO Box 40747, Nashville, TN 37204. TEL 615-781-6504, FAX 615-741-4606, http://www.state.tn.us/twra. Ed. Dave Woodward. R&P Cheri Irwin. Circ: 70,000 (paid and controlled).

590 DEU
TERRA; Faszination Unserer Erde. Text in German. q. EUR 31 domestic; EUR 39 foreign; EUR 8.20 newsstand/cover (effective 2003). **Document type:** *Magazine, Consumer.*
Published by: Tecklenborg Verlag, Siemenstr 4, Steinfurt, 48565, Germany. TEL 49-2552-92002, FAX 49-2552-920160, info@tecklenborg-verlag.de, http://www.tecklenborg-verlag.de.

THALASSIA SALENTINA. see *BIOLOGY—Botany*

590 CHE ISSN 1017-1576
DAS TIER; internationale Tier-Zeitschrift. Text in German. 1960. m. CHF 66; CHF 74 foreign (effective 1997). illus. index. back issues avail. **Document type:** *Academic/Scholarly.*
Description: Discusses new findings in zoology.
Formerly (until 1982): Grzimeks Tier, Sielmanns Tierwelt (0721-2569); Which was formed by the merger of (1960-1981): Tier (0040-7291); (1977-1981): Sielmanns Tierwelt (0344-8614); Which was formerly: Tier-Park (0170-4648)
Published by: Hallwag AG, Nordring 4, Bern, 3001, Switzerland. TEL 41-31-3323131, FAX 41-31-3314133, leserservice.hallwag@hallweb.ch. Circ: 87,712.

590 DEU
TIER BILD. Text in German. 2002. 6/yr. EUR 1.20 newsstand/cover (effective 2003). adv. **Document type:** *Magazine, Consumer.*
Published by: Axel Springer Verlag AG, Axel-Springer-Platz 1, Hamburg, 20350, Germany. TEL 49-40-34700, FAX 49-40-34725540, www.tierbild.bild.t-online.de, http://www.asv.de. Ed. Claus Strunz. Adv. contact Andrea Ehlbeck. color page EUR 10,000.

590 DEU
TIERE - FREUNDE FUERS LEBEN. Text in German. m. EUR 26.40; CHF 51.60 in Switzerland; EUR 1.99 newsstand/cover (effective 2002). adv. **Document type:** *Magazine, Consumer.*
Description: Contains articles and photos on a wide variety of animals and pets.
Published by: Panini Verlags GmbH, Ravensstr 48, Nettetal, 41334, Germany. TEL 49-711-947680, FAX 49-711-94768830, info@panini-dino.de, http://www.panini-media.de. Ed. Gaby Kaercher. Adv. contact Petra Sonnenfroh-Kost. page EUR 3,500; trim 210 x 280. Circ: 86,903 (paid).

590 DEU
TIERE IN UNSERER WELT. Text in German. 1998. q. EUR 4 newsstand/cover (effective 2003). adv. **Document type:** *Magazine, Consumer.*
Published by: OZ Verlag GmbH, Roemerstr 90, Rheinfelden, 79618, Germany. TEL 49-7623-964-0, FAX 49-7623-96464200, vollmar@oz-bpv.de, http://www.oz-verlag.com. adv.: B&W page EUR 1,150, color page EUR 1,500. Circ: 35,000 (paid and controlled).

590 DEU
TIERE UNSERE BESTEN FREUNDE. Text in German. 1998. q. EUR 4 newsstand/cover (effective 2003). adv. **Document type:** *Magazine, Consumer.*
Published by: OZ Verlag GmbH, Roemerstr 90, Rheinfelden, 79618, Germany. TEL 49-7623-964-0, FAX 49-7623-96464200, vollmar@oz-bpv.de, http://www.oz-verlag.com. adv.: B&W page EUR 1,150, color page EUR 1,500. Circ: 28,000 (paid and controlled).

590 DEU ISSN 0040-7305
CODEN: TRRHAS
➤ **DAS TIERREICH;** eine Zusammenstellung und Kennzeichnung der rezenten Tierformen. Text in English, French, German. 1897. irreg., latest vol.113, 1999. price varies. bibl.; illus. back issues avail. **Document type:** *Monographic series, Academic/Scholarly.*
Indexed: ZooRec.
—Linda Hall. **CCC.**
Published by: Walter de Gruyter GmbH & Co. KG, Genthiner Str. 13, Berlin, 10785, Germany. TEL 49-30-260050, FAX 49-30-26005251, wdg-info@degruyter.de, http://www.degruyter.de. Eds. H Wermuth, Maximilian Fischer. Circ: 250.

590.73 JPN
TOKYOTO TAMA DOBUTSU KOEN JIGYO GAIYO/TAMA ZOOLOGICAL PARK. ANNUAL REPORT. Text in Japanese. 1973. a.
Published by: Tokyoto Tama Dobutsu Koen/Tama Zoological Park, 1-1 Hodokubo 7-chome, Hino-shi, Tokyo-to 191-0042, Japan.

069 ZAF ISSN 0255-0172
CODEN: TMMOER
TRANSVAAL MUSEUM. MONOGRAPHS. Text in English. 1983. irreg., latest vol.12, 2001. price varies. bibl. index. **Document type:** *Monographic series.* **Description:** Contains contributions in archaeology, zoology, and systematics in particular.
Indexed: BIOSIS Prev, ZooRec.
—BLDSC (9026.687000), KNAW.
Published by: Transvaal Museum, PO Box 413, Pretoria, 0001, South Africa. TEL 27-12-3227632, FAX 27-12-3227939, http://www.nfi.co.za/tmpage.html. Ed. A Dreyer. R&P Anita Dreyer.

591 MAR
TRAVAUX DE L'INSTITUT SCIENTIFIQUE. SERIE ZOOLOGIE. Text in French. irreg.
Published by: Universite Mohammed V, Institut Scientifique, Ave Ibn Batouta, BP 703, Rabat-Agdal, Rabat, 10106, Morocco. TEL 212-37-774548, FAX 212-37-774540.

597 ESP ISSN 1130-6130
TREBALLS D'ICTIOLOGIA I HERPETOLOGIA. Text in Spanish. 1984. irreg.
Formerly (until 1989): Societat Catalana d'Ictiologia i Herpetologia. Treballs (0213-0165)
Published by: Sociedad Catalana de Ictiologia y Herpetologia, Museo de Zoologia, Apartado 593, Barcelona, 08080, Spain.

591.994 IDN ISSN 0082-6340
QH186
TREUBIA; a journal of zoology of the Indo-Australian archipelago. Text in English. 1915. irreg. price varies. index. **Document type:** *Academic/Scholarly.*
Indexed: BIOSIS Prev, BiolAb, ZooRec.
—Linda Hall.
Published by: Indonesian Institute of Sciences, R & D Centre for Biology, Jalan Juanda 18, Bogor, Indonesia. TEL 62-251-321038, FAX 62-251-325854. Circ: 500.

591.748 ITA ISSN 0394-6975
QL109 CODEN: TRZOEP
➤ **TROPICAL ZOOLOGY.** Text in English. 1890. 2/yr. EUR 100 combined subscription for print & online eds. (effective 2004). index. 200 p./no.; back issues avail.; reprint service avail. from ISI. **Document type:** *Journal, Academic/Scholarly.*
Description: Publishes original papers in the field of experimental and descriptive zoology and zoogeography concerning tropical areas with particular attention to Africa.
Formerly (until 1988): Monitore Zoologico Italiano. Supplemento (0374-9444)
Indexed: ASCA, ASFA, BIOSIS Prev, BioCN&I, BiolAb, ChemAb, CurCont, ForAb, HGA, IndVet, NutrAb, PGegResA, RM&VM, RefZh, RevApplEntom, S&F, SFA, SeedAb, WeedAb, WildRev, ZooRec.
—BLDSC (9057.010000), CISTI, IDS, IE, ingenta. **CCC.**
Published by: (Consiglio Nazionale delle Ricerche, Istituto per lo Studio degli Ecosistemi), Edizioni Polistampa, Via Santa Maria 27, Florence, FI 50125, Italy. TEL 39-055-2337702, FAX 39-055-229430, tz@fi.cnr.it, info@polistampa.com, http://riviste.neteditor.it/tz, http://www.polistampa.com. Eds. Giuseppe Messina, Lorenzo Chelazzi, Stefano Taiti. Circ: 1,000.

590 ITA ISSN 1121-919X
TROPICAL ZOOLOGY. SPECIAL ISSUE. Text in English. 1993. irreg. **Document type:** *Monographic series.*
Indexed: ASFA, ApEcolAb, ESPM, EntAb, GenetAb, ZooRec.
Published by: Consiglio Nazionale delle Ricerche, Istituto per lo Studio degli Ecosistemi, Via Romana 17, Florence, 50125, Italy. tz@fi.cnr.it.

590 580 USA ISSN 0082-6782
QL1 CODEN: TSZBAN
➤ **TULANE STUDIES IN ZOOLOGY AND BOTANY.** Text in English. 1953. irreg., latest vol.31, 1999. price varies. back issues avail. **Document type:** *Monographic series, Academic/Scholarly.*
Formerly (until 1968): Tulane Studies in Zoology (0090-9246)
Indexed: ASFA, BIOSIS Prev, BiolAb, ESPM, SFA, WildRev, ZooRec.
—CISTI, Linda Hall.
Published by: Tulane University, Museum of Natural History, Bldg. A-3, Wild Boar Rd, Belle Chasse, LA 70037. TEL 504-394-1711, FAX 504-394-5045, editor@museum.tulane.edu, http://www.museum.tulane.edu/pubs/tszb.html. Ed., R&P Henry L Bart. Circ: 800.

597 599.5 TUR ISSN 1303-2712
➤ **TURKISH JOURNAL OF FISHERIES AND AQUATIC SCIENCES.** Text in English. 2001. s-a. free (effective 2005). back issues avail. **Document type:** *Journal, Academic/Scholarly.* **Description:** Covers original research papers, short communications, technical notes and reviews on all aspects of fisheries and aquatic sciences.
Media: Online - full text.
Indexed: ASFA, AgBio, AnBrAb, ESPM, HelmAb, HortAb, IndVet, ProtozoAb, RM&VM, WAE&RSA.
Published by: Central Fisheries Research Institute, PO Box 129, Trabzon, 61001, Turkey. TEL 90-462-3411052, FAX 90-462-3411157, info@trjfas.org, trjfas@gul.net.tr, http://www.trjfas.org/. Ed. Vedat UzunLu.

591.9561 TUR ISSN 1300-0179
QL1 CODEN: TJZOE3
➤ **TURKISH JOURNAL OF ZOOLOGY/TURK ZOOLOJI DERGISI.** Text and summaries in English; Abstracts in Turkish. 1976. 4/yr. USD 100 (effective 2004). **Document type:** *Journal, Academic/Scholarly.*
Formerly (until 1994): Doga Turkish Journal of Zoology - Doga Turk Zooloji Dergisi (1011-0895)
Related titles: Online - full text ed.: ISSN 1303-6114. free (effective 2005) (from EBSCO Publishing).

Indexed: AgBio, AgrForAb, AnBrAb, BIOSIS Prev, BioCN&I, BiolAb, FPA, FS&TA, ForAb, GEOBASE, HelmAb, HerbAb, HortAb, I&DA, IndVet, NemAb, NutrAb, OrnHort, PHN&I, PotatoAb, PoultAb, ProtozoAb, RA&MP, RM&VM, RPP, RevApplEntom, RiceAb, S&F, SIA, TDB, TriticAb, VetBull, WeedAb, ZooRec.
—BLDSC (9072.498000), CASDDS, CISTI, IE, ingenta, Linda Hall.
Published by: Scientific and Technical Research Council of Turkey - TUBITAK/Turkiye Bilimsel ve Teknik Arastirma Kurumu, Ataturk Bulvari No. 221, Kavaklidere, Ankara, 06100, Turkey. TEL 90-312-468-5300, FAX 90-312-426-8073, bdym@tubitak.gov.tr, http://journals.tubitak.gov.tr/zoology/index.php, http://www.tubitak.gov.tr. Eds. Aykut Kence, Can Bilgin.

597.92   USA   ISSN 1526-3096
TURTLE AND TORTOISE NEWSLETTER. Text in English. s-a. free (effective 2002). Document type: Newsletter.
Related titles: Online - full content ed.
Indexed: ASFA, ZooRec.
—Linda Hall.
Published by: Chelonian Research Foundation, 168 Goodrich St, Lunenberg, MA 01462. http://www.chelonian.org/ttn/. Eds. Allen Salzberg, Heather Kalb.

333.95416   USA
SK361
U.S. FISH AND WILDLIFE SERVICE. DIVISION OF FEDERAL AID. SPORT FISH AND WILDLIFE RESTORATION PROGRAM UPDATE. Text in English. a. Document type: Government.
Formed by the merger of: Federal Aid in Sport Fish Restoration Program; Federal Aid in Wildlife Restoration Program; Which both superseded in part: Federal Aid in Sport Fish and Wildlife Restoration Programs; Which had former titles (until 1990): Federal Aid in Fish and Wildlife Restoration (0092-9697); (until 1952): Federal Aid in Wildlife Restoration (0196-4038)
—CISTI.
Published by: U.S Fish & Wildlife Service, Division of Federal Aid, Arlington Sq Rm 140, 4401 N Fairfax Dr, Arlington, VA 22203. TEL 703-358-2156, FAX 703-358-1837, FederalAid@fws.gov, http://federalaid.fws.gov/.

590   MEX
UNIVERSIDAD AUTONOMA DE NUEVO LEON. FACULTAD DE CIENCIAS BIOLOGICAS. PUBLICACIONES TECNICAS. Text in Spanish. 198?. irreg.
Published by: Universidad Autonoma de Nuevo Leon, Facultad de Ciencias Biologicas, Av Pedro de Alba y Manuel L Barragan, Ciudad Universitaria, San Nicolas de los Garza, NL 66450, Mexico. TEL 52-81-89294110, FAX 52-81-83762813, http://www.uanl.mx/bacs/fcb/.

590   ESP   ISSN 0213-313X
UNIVERSIDAD DE NAVARRA. PUBLICACIONES DE BIOLOGIA. SERIE ZOOLOGIA. Text in Spanish. 1980. irreg. price varies.
Indexed: IECT, WildRev, ZooRec.
—CINDOC.
Published by: Universidad de Navarra, Servicio de Publicaciones, Apartado 177, Pamplona, Navarra 31080, Spain. TEL 94-25-2700.

591.972   MEX   ISSN 0185-2590
UNIVERSIDAD NACIONAL AUTONOMA DE MEXICO. INSTITUTO DE BIOLOGIA. ANALES: SERIE ZOOLOGIA. Text in English, French, Spanish; Summaries in English, French, Spanish. 1967. s-a. MXP 100, USD 30 per issue (effective 2000). adv. abstr.; charts; illus.; stat. back issues avail. Document type: Monographic series. Description: Publishes articles in the area of Zoology.
Supersedes in part: Universidad Nacional Autonoma de Mexico. Instituto de Biologia. Anales (0076-7174)
Indexed: ASFA, BIOSIS Prev, BiolAb, IndVet, MaizeAb, PHN&I, ProtozoAb, RevApplEntom, RiceAb, ZooRec.
—CISTI, Linda Hall.
Published by: Universidad Nacional Autonoma de Mexico, Instituto de Biologia, Ciudad Universitaria, Apdo Postal 70-233, Mexico City, DF 04510, Mexico. TEL 52-5-622-5690, FAX 52-5-622-5687, javierd@mail.ibiologia.unam.mx, http://www.ibiologia.unam.mx. Ed. Alfonso N Garcia Aldrete. Adv. contact Javier Dominguez Galicia. Circ: 1,500.

590   ARG   ISSN 0327-4853
UNIVERSIDAD NACIONAL DE SALTA. FACULTAD DE CIENCIAS NATURALES. CATEDRA MANEJO DE FAUNA. PUBLICACIONES TECNICAS. Text in Spanish. 1990. irreg. Document type: Monographic series.
Indexed: ESPM.
Published by: Universidad Nacional de Salta, Facultad de Ciencias Naturales, Buenos Aires 177, Salta, 4400, Argentina. TEL 54-387-4311371, info@unsa.edu.ar, http://www.unsa.edu.ar.

590   FRA   ISSN 1144-5955
UNIVERSITE DE CLERMONT-FERRAND II. ANNALES SCIENTIFIQUES. SERIE BIOLOGIE ANIMALE. Text in French. 1963. irreg. price varies. back issues avail.
Formerly (until 1985): Universite de Clermont-Ferrand II. Faculte des Sciences. Annales. Biologie Animale (0069-4681)
Published by: Universite Blaise Pascal, Faculte des Sciences, Aubiere, Cedex 63177, France. Circ: 250.

590   NLD   ISSN 0165-9464
QL1   CODEN: BZMAAA
UNIVERSITEIT VAN AMSTERDAM. ZOOLOGISCH MUSEUM. BULLETIN. Key Title: Bulletin - Zoologisch Museum, Universiteit van Amsterdam. Text in English, French, German. 1966. irreg. price varies. Document type: Bulletin, Academic/Scholarly.
Indexed: ASFA, BIOSIS Prev, BiolAb, RefZh, SFA, ZooRec.
—CISTI.
Published by: Universiteit van Amsterdam, Zoologisch Museum, PO Box 94766, Amsterdam, 1090 AT, Netherlands. TEL 31-20-5257234, FAX 31-20-5255402, spoel@bio.uva.nl. Ed. S van der Spoel.

597 639.2   USA
UNIVERSITY OF MAINE. SEA GRANT PUBLICATION. Text in English. irreg.
Published by: Maine Sea Grant Program, University of Maine, Coburn Hall, Orono, ME 04469-5715. TEL 207-581-1435, FAX 207-581-1426, umseagrant@maine.edu, http://www.seagrant.umaine.edu.

590.73774   USA   ISSN 0076-8405
QL1   CODEN: MUZPA2
➤ UNIVERSITY OF MICHIGAN. MUSEUM OF ZOOLOGY. MISCELLANEOUS PUBLICATIONS. Text in English. 1916. irreg., latest vol.191. price varies. back issues avail. Document type: Monographic series, Academic/Scholarly. Description: Contains in-depth monographic, systematic, anatomical, behavioral, and faunal studies, as well as U.M.M.Z.-type specimen catalogues.
Indexed: BIOSIS Prev, BiolAb, HelmAb, IndVet, RefZh, RevApplEntom, SFA, ZooRec.
—CISTI, Linda Hall.
Published by: University of Michigan, Museum of Zoology, 1109 Geddes Ave, Ann Arbor, MI 48109-1079. TEL 734-764-0476, FAX 734-763-4080, fpaper@umich.edu, http://www.ummz.lsa.umich.edu. Ed. J B Burch. R&P Fritz Paper TEL 734-764-0470. Circ: 400.

590.73774   USA   ISSN 0076-8413
QL1   CODEN: MUZOAX
➤ UNIVERSITY OF MICHIGAN. MUSEUM OF ZOOLOGY. OCCASIONAL PAPERS. Key Title: Occasional Papers of the Museum of Zoology, University of Michigan. Text in English. 1913. irreg., latest vol.733. price varies. cum.index. back issues avail. Document type: Monographic series, Academic/Scholarly. Description: Original studies based on museum collection of material.
Related titles: Microfiche ed.: (from BHP).
Indexed: ASFA, BIOSIS Prev, BiolAb, ESPM, RefZh, RevApplEntom, SFA, ZooRec.
—CISTI, Linda Hall.
Published by: University of Michigan, Museum of Zoology, 1109 Geddes Ave, Ann Arbor, MI 48109-1079. TEL 734-764-0476, FAX 734-763-4080, fpaper@umich.edu, http://www.ummz.lsa.umich.edu. Ed. J B Burch. R&P Fritz Paper TEL 734-764-0470. Circ: 400.

590.73774   USA   ISSN 1053-6477
                           CODEN: SPUZE8
UNIVERSITY OF MICHIGAN. MUSEUM OF ZOOLOGY. SPECIAL PUBLICATIONS. Text in English. 1990. irreg., latest vol.2. price varies. back issues avail. Document type: Monographic series, Academic/Scholarly. Description: Contains subjects beyond the scope of the regular series.
Indexed: BIOSIS Prev.
—CISTI, Linda Hall.
Published by: University of Michigan, Museum of Zoology, 1109 Geddes Ave, Ann Arbor, MI 48109-1079. TEL 734-764-0476, FAX 734-763-4080, fpaper@umich.edu, http://www.ummz.lsa.umich.edu. Ed. J B Burch. R&P Fritz Paper TEL 734-764-0470.

593   FJI   ISSN 1018-2896
UNIVERSITY OF THE SOUTH PACIFIC. MARINE STUDIES PROGRAMME. TECHNICAL REPORT. Text in English. 1991. irreg. Document type: Monographic series.
Indexed: ESPM.
Published by: University of the South Pacific, Marine Studies Programme, Marine Studies, Box 1168, Suva, Fiji. FAX 679-301-490, bulai_n@usp.ac.fj, http://www.sidsnet.org/pacific/usp/marine/.

UNIVERSITY OF WASHINGTON. SCHOOL OF AQUATIC AND FISHERY SCIENCES. TECHNICAL REPORT. see BIOLOGY

590   POL   ISSN 0554-8136
UNIWERSYTET IM. ADAMA MICKIEWICZA. ZOOLOGIA. Text in Polish; Summaries in English. 1962. irreg., latest vol.38, 1993. price varies. Document type: Monographic series, Academic/Scholarly. Description: Every volume contains current research results of one author in the field of zoology, including Ph.D. works and monographs.
Formerly: Uniwersytet im. Adama Mickiewicza w Poznaniu. Wydzial Biologii i Nauk o Ziemi. Prace. Seria Zoologia (0208-6484)
Indexed: AgrLib, ZooRec.
—CISTI.

Published by: (Uniwersytet im. Adama Mickiewicza w Poznaniu/Adam Mickiewicz University), Wydawnictwo Naukowe Uniwersytetu im. Adama Mickiewicza/Adam Mickiewicz University Press, Nowowiejskiego 55, Poznan, 61-734, Poland. TEL 48-61-527380, FAX 48-61-527701. Pub. Maria Jankowska. R&P Malgorzata Bis. Circ: 380.

597   JPN   ISSN 0388-5461
UO/FISHES. Text in English, Japanese; Summaries in English. 1948. irreg. membership.
Indexed: SFA.
Published by: Uo no Kai/Japanese Society of Ichthyologists, Ito Gyogaku Kenkyu Shinko Zaidan, 26-11 Kami-Meguro 1-chome, Meguro-ku, Tokyo, 153-0051, Japan.

599   USA   ISSN 1537-6176
QL737.C27
URSUS. Text in English. 1968. s-a. (May & Nov.). USD 50 membership (effective 2005). Document type: Journal, Academic/Scholarly. Description: Includes a variety of articles on all aspects of bear management and research worldwide.
Formerly (until 1998): Bears - Their Biology and Management
Related titles: Online - full text ed.: (from C S A).
—BLDSC (9124.740020).
Published by: International Association for Bear Research and Management, c/o Joseph Clark, IBA Secretary, USGS-SAFL, University of Tennessee, 274 Ellington Hall, Knoxville, TN 37996. TEL 865-974-4790, FAX 865-974-3555, http://www.ursusjournal.com/, http://www.bearbiology.com. Ed. Richard B Harris,.

590   IND   ISSN 0256-971X
QL1
➤ UTTAR PRADESH JOURNAL OF ZOOLOGY. Text and summaries in English. 1981. 3/yr. INR 100, USD 20 to individuals; INR 200, USD 30 to institutions. adv. bk.rev. back issues avail. Document type: Academic/Scholarly.
Indexed: AEA, AgBio, AgrForAb, AnBrAb, BIOSIS Prev, BioCN&I, BiolAb, CPA, DSA, FCA, FPA, ForAb, HelmAb, HerbAb, HortAb, IndVet, MaizeAb, NemAb, NutrAb, OrnHort, PBA, PHN&I, PotatoAb, PoultAb, ProtozoAb, RA&MP, RDA, RPP, RefZh, RevApplEntom, RiceAb, S&F, SIA, SeedAb, SoyAb, TDB, TriticAb, VetBull, WAE&RSA, WeedAb, ZooRec.
—BLDSC (9135.619000), IE, ingenta.
Published by: Uttar Pradesh Zoological Society, c/o PG Dept. of Zoology, Muzaffarnagar, 251 001, India. TEL 91-131-409053, FAX 91-131-402510. Circ: 225.

599.742   SWE   ISSN 1102-6111
VAARE ROVDJUR. Text in Swedish. 1984. q. SEK 200 domestic to members; SEK 250 elsewhere to members (effective 2004). adv. bk.rev. Document type: Newsletter. Description: News and research related to carnevores in Sweden.
Formerly (until 1991): Information fraan Foereningen Vaara Rovdjur (0283-1619); Incorporates (1984-1992): Canis Lupus (0283-9474)
Published by: Svenska Rovdjursfoereningen, PO Box 144, Leksand, 79324, Sweden. TEL 46-8-4414117, info@rovdjur.se, http://www.rovdjur.se/modules.php?name=Content&pa=showpage&pid=17. Eds. Tatjana Kontio TEL 46-8-6424704, Bjoern Ljunggren TEL 46-13-52577. Circ: 4,000.

594   USA   ISSN 0042-3211
                           CODEN: VLGHAL
➤ VELIGER. Text in English. 1958. q. USD 40 in North America to individuals; USD 50 elsewhere to individuals; USD 82 in North America to institutions; USD 92 elsewhere to institutions (effective 1999). bk.rev. reprint service avail. from ISI. Document type: Journal, Academic/Scholarly. Description: International journal devoted to disseminating information about mollusks and promoting the science of malacology.
Indexed: ASCA, ASFA, BIOSIS Prev, BioCN&I, BiolAb, CurCont, ESPM, HelmAb, ISR, OceAb, RefZh, SCI, SFA, SPPI, SSCI, SWRA, ZooRec.
—BLDSC (9154.300000), CISTI, IDS, IE, Infotrieve, ingenta, Linda Hall.
Published by: California Malacozoological Society, Inc, Santa Barbara Museum of Natural History, Dept of Invertebrate Zoology, 2559 Puesta del Sol Rd, Santa Barbara, CA 93105. TEL 805-682-4711, FAX 805-963-9679, inverts@sbnature.org, http://www.sbnature.org. Ed. Barry Roth. Circ: 650 (paid).

594   JPN   ISSN 0042-3580
                           CODEN: KRZSA2
VENUS: JAPANESE JOURNAL OF MALACOLOGY/KAIRUIGAKU ZASSHI. Text in English, Japanese. 1928. q. JPY 7,500 membership (effective 2004); subscr. incld. with membership. bk.rev. illus. Index. Document type: Journal, Academic/Scholarly.
Indexed: ASFA, AgBio, AnBrAb, BIOSIS Prev, BiolAb, ESPM, ForAb, NutrAb, S&F, SFA, ZooRec.
—CISTI. CCC.
Published by: Nihon Kairui Gakkai/Malacological Society of Japan, c/o National Science Museum, 3-23-1 Hiyakunin-cho, Shinjuku-ku, Tokyo, 169-0073, Japan. msj_manager@hotmail.com, http://wwwsoc.nii.ac.jp/msj5/. Ed. Akihiko Inaba. Circ: 900.

B

▼ new title   ➤ refereed   * unverified   ◆ full entry avail.

590 UKR ISSN 0084-5604
CODEN: VEZOAK
VESTNIK ZOOLOGII/VISNYK ZOOLOGII/ZOOLOGICAL RECORD. Text in Russian; Summaries in English. 1967. bi-m. USD 120 foreign (effective 2004). abstr.
Indexed: ASFA, AgrForAb, AnBrAb, BIOSIS Prev, BioCN&I, BiolAb, ChemAb, Djerelo, ESPM, FCA, ForAb, HelmAb, HerbAb, HortAb, IndVet, NemAb, NutrAb, OrnHort, PHN&I, PN&I, PotatoAb, PoultAb, ProtozoAb, RM&VM, RefZh, RevApplEntom, S&F, SFA, TDB, TriticAb, VetBull, WeedAb, ZooRec.
—BLDSC (0033.150000), CASDDS, East View, KNAW, Linda Hall. **CCC.**
Published by: Natsional'na Akademiya Nauk Ukrainy, Instytut Zoolohii im. I.I. Shmal'hauzena, Vul Khmiel'nits'kogo 15, Kiev, 252601, Ukraine. TEL 38-44-2255365. Ed. V A Topachevskii. **Dist. by:** M K - Periodica, ul Gilyarovskogo 39, Moscow 129110, Russian Federation. TEL 7-095-2845008, FAX 7-095-2813798, info@periodicals.ru, http://www.mkniga.ru.

VETERINARSKI ARHIV. see *VETERINARY SCIENCE*

590 DEU ISSN 0179-1281
VIVARIUM, DARMSTADTS TIERGARTEN; the Darmstadt animal park Vivarium informs. Text in German. 1973. irreg. adv. back issues avail. **Document type:** *Newsletter.*
Published by: Vivarium Darmstadts Tiergarten, Schnampelweg 4, Darmstadt, 64287, Germany. FAX 49-6151-132932. Ed. Hartmut Wilke. Circ: 3,500.

VOGELKUNDLICHE BERICHTE AUS NIEDERSACHSEN. see *BIOLOGY—Ornithology*

597 RUS ISSN 0042-8752
QL614 CODEN: VOIKAR
VOPROSY IKHTIOLOGII. Text in Russian. 1961. bi-m. RUR 1,160 for 6 mos. domestic (effective 2004). bk.rev. index. **Document type:** *Journal, Academic/Scholarly.* **Description:** Covers fisheries management, fish culture, aquaculture, physiology and biochemistry of both marine and freshwater fish.
Related titles: Online - full text ed.; ♦ English Translation: Journal of Ichthyology. ISSN 0032-9452.
Indexed: ASFA, BIOSIS Prev, BiolAb, CIN, ChemAb, ESPM, RefZh, SFA, ZooRec.
—CASDDS, CISTI, East View, Linda Hall. **CCC.**
Published by: (Rossiiskaya Akademiya Nauk/Russian Academy of Sciences, Rossiiskaya Akademiya Nauk, Otdelenie Obshchei Biologii), Izdatel'stvo Nauka, Profsoyuznaya ul 90, Moscow, 117864, Russian Federation. TEL 7-095-3347151, FAX 7-095-4202220, secret@naukaran.ru, http://www.maik.rssi.ru/cgi-bin/list.pl?page=ikhtiol, http://www.naukaran.ru.

594 USA ISSN 1053-637X
QL401
WALKERANA; transactions of the P O E T S society. Text in English, Spanish. 1980. irreg. USD 20 domestic to individuals; USD 23 foreign to individuals; USD 40 domestic to institutions; USD 43 foreign to institutions (effective 1999). bibl.; charts; illus. back issues avail. **Document type:** *Academic/Scholarly.* **Description:** Publishes original research and review articles and monographs on mollusks.
Indexed: ZooRec.
Published by: Society for Experimental and Descriptive Malacology, PO Box 3037, Ann Arbor, MI 48106. TEL 313-747-2189. Ed. John B Burch. Circ: 200.

590 CAN
QL79.C2
WATERS. Text in English. 1956. q. CND 12; USD 15 in United States; USD 18 elsewhere (effective 1999). adv. charts; illus. **Document type:** *Newsletter, Academic/Scholarly.*
Former titles (until 1997): Aqua Scene (1203-1712); (until 1995): Sea Pen (0700-9275); (until 1976): Vancouver Public Aquarium Newsletter (0042-2495)
Indexed: SFA.
Published by: (Vancouver Aquarium Marine Science Centre), Canada Wide Magazines & Communications Ltd., P O Box 3232, Vancouver, BC V6B 3X8, Canada. TEL 604-659-3474, FAX 604-659-3515, information@vanaqua.org, http://www.vanaqua.org. Ed., R&P Anmarie Tomascik. Adv. contact Jackie Roqers. Circ: 18,000.

596 USA ISSN 0511-7542
QL1
WESTERN FOUNDATION OF VERTEBRATE ZOOLOGY. OCCASIONAL PAPERS. Text in English. 1968. irreg. price varies. back issues avail. **Document type:** *Monographic series.* **Description:** Consists of short papers reporting original research in vertebrate zoology.
Indexed: BiolAb, ZooRec.
Published by: Western Foundation of Vertebrate Zoology, 439 Calle San Pablo, Camarillo, CA 93012-8506. TEL 805-388-9944.

596 USA ISSN 0511-7550
QL605 CODEN: PWFVA2
WESTERN FOUNDATION OF VERTEBRATE ZOOLOGY. PROCEEDINGS. Text in English. 1963. irreg. price varies. back issues avail. **Document type:** *Proceedings.* **Description:** Contains articles on the biological and systematic phases of vertebrate zoology.
Indexed: BIOSIS Prev, BiolAb, ZooRec.
Published by: Western Foundation of Vertebrate Zoology, 439 Calle San Pablo, Camarillo, CA 93012-8506. TEL 805-388-9944.

590 USA ISSN 1527-0904
QH1 CODEN: WNANF5
WESTERN NORTH AMERICAN NATURALIST. MONOGRAPHS. Text in English. 1939. irreg., latest vol.1, no.1, 2002. USD 20 per issue (effective 2005). bk.rev. illus. index, cum.index: 1939-1990. back issues avail. **Document type:** *Monographic series, Academic/Scholarly.*
Formerly (until 2002): Great Basin Naturalist (0017-3614)
Indexed: ASCA, ASFA, AgBio, Agr, AgrForAb, AnBeAb, AnBrAb, ApEcolAb, BIOBASE, BIOSIS Prev, BioCN&I, BiolAb, CPA, CRFR, CurCont, ESPM, ExcerpMed, FCA, FPA, ForAb, HelmAb, HerbAb, HortAb, I&DA, IndVet, NemAb, NutrAb, OrnHort, PBA, PGegResA, PGrRegA, PlantSci, PoultAb, ProtozoAb, RA&MP, RPP, RRTA, RefZh, RevApplEntom, S&F, SFA, SWRA, SeedAb, TDB, TriticAb, VetBull, WeedAb, WildRev, ZooRec.
—BLDSC (9301.505000), CASDDS, IDS, IE, ingenta, Linda Hall. **CCC.**
Published by: Brigham Young University, Monte L. Bean Life Science Museau, c/o Richard L. Baumann, Editor, 290 MLBM, Provo, UT 84602. TEL 801-378-6688, FAX 801-422-3733, WNAN-BYU@email.byu.edu, http://www.wnan.byu.edu. Ed. Richard W Baumann TEL 801-378-5492. R&P Joanne Y Abel. Circ: 550.

594 USA ISSN 0361-1175
QL401 CODEN: ARWMDW
WESTERN SOCIETY OF MALACOLOGISTS. ANNUAL REPORT. Key Title: Annual Report - Western Society of Malacologists. Text in English. 1968. a. USD 20 (effective 2005). illus.
Formerly: Western Society of Malacologists. Echo; Abstracts and Proceedings of the Annual Meeting
Indexed: BiolAb, ZooRec.
Published by: Western Society of Malacologists, c/o Dr Henry Chaney, 1633 Posilipo Ln, Santa Barbara, CA 93108. Ed. Dr. Hans Bertsch. Circ: 250.

599.5 USA
WHALING ACCOUNT. Text in English. 1965-1991; resumed 1992. irreg. (2-3/yr.). USD 35 (effective 2000). bk.rev. **Document type:** *Newsletter.*
Published by: Whaling Museum Society, Inc., PO Box 25, Cold Spring, NY 11724. TEL 516-367-3418. Ed. Ann M Gill. Circ: 1,000.

590 POL ISSN 1731-8068
SF55.P7
WIADOMOSCI ZOOTECHNICZNE. Text in Polish. 1963. q. USD 30 foreign (effective 2005). **Document type:** *Bulletin, Academic/Scholarly.*
Formerly (until 2003): Instytut Zootechniki. Biuletyn Informacyjny (0209-2492)
Indexed: AEA, AgBio, AgrAg, AgrLib, AnBrAb, BIOSIS Prev, BiolAb, CPA, DSA, FCA, HerbAb, HortAb, IndVet, MaizeAb, NutrAb, PBA, PGegResA, PHN&I, PN&I, PotatoAb, PoultAb, ProtozoAb, RA&MP, RM&VM, RPP, RRTA, RefZh, S&F, SIA, SoyAb, TriticAb, VetBull, WAE&RSA, WeedAb.
—CISTI.
Published by: Instytut Zootechniki/Institute of Animal Production, ul Sarego 2, Krakow, 31047, Poland. TEL 48-12-2588111, FAX 48-12-2588150, wiad-zoot@izoo.krakow.pl, izooinfo@izoo.krakow.pl, http://www.izoo.krakow.pl. Ed. Franciszek Palowski.

333.95416 CHE ISSN 0250-3832
WILDBIOLOGIE. Text in German. 1978. q. CHF 43 domestic; CHF 50 foreign (effective 2001). back issues avail. **Document type:** *Journal, Academic/Scholarly.* **Description:** Provides information on wild animals in Europe, including biology, behaviour, ecology and protection of the environment.
Formerly (until 1992): Wildtiere - Wildbiologie
Indexed: KWIWR.
Published by: Infodienst Wildbiologie & Oekologie, Strickhofstr 39, Zuerich, 8057, Switzerland. TEL 41-1-6356131, FAX 41-1-6356819, wild@wild.unizh.ch, http://www.wild.unizh.ch. Ed. Barbara Falk. Circ: 2,200.

333.95416 DNK ISSN 0909-6396
SK351 CODEN: WIBIFS
➤ **WILDLIFE BIOLOGY.** Text in English. 1995. q. DKK 600 (effective 2004). bk.rev. 80 p./no. 2 cols./p.; back issues avail. **Document type:** *Journal, Academic/Scholarly.* **Description:** Publishes high-quality practical and theoretical research from all areas of wildlife science, with the primary task of creating the scientific basis for the enhancement of conservation and management practices for wildlife species and their environments. Promotes the discussion of important issues.
Formed by the merger of (1945-1995): Danish Review of Game Biology (0374-7344); (1988-1995): Finnish Game Research (0783-4365); Which was formerly (1948-1988): Riistatieteelisiaa Jukaisuja (0015-2447); (1979-1988): Swedish Wildlife Research (0349-5116); Which was formerly (1955-1978): Viltrevy (0505-611X)
Indexed: AEA, ASFA, AbHyg, AgBio, AnBeAb, AnBrAb, ApEcolAb, B&BAb, BIOBASE, BIOSIS Prev, BiolAb, CurCont, DSA, ESPM, FCA, ForAb, GenetAb, HGA, HelmAb, HerbAb, HortAb, IABS, IndVet, KWIWR, NutrAb, OrnHort, PBA, PGegResA, PN&I, PoultAb, ProtozoAb, RPP, RRTA, RevApplEntom, S&F, SFA, TriticAb, VetBull, WLR, WeedAb, WildRev, ZooRec.
—BLDSC (9317.273000), IE, ingenta, Linda Hall. **CCC.**
Published by: Nordisk Kollegium for Viltforskning/Nordic Council for Wildlife Research, c/o Henning Noer, Kaloe, Grenaavej 12, Roende, 8410, Denmark. TEL 45-85-201541, FAX 45-89-201515, jb@dmu.dk, hn@dmu.dk, http://www.wildlifebiology.com/. Eds. Jan Bertelsen, Jon E. Swenson TEL 47-64-948530. Circ: 1,000.

590 USA ISSN 0736-6094
Z6674
WILDLIFE DISEASE REVIEW. Text in English. 1983. m. USD 225; USD 255 foreign. index.
Address: P.O. Box 1522, Ft. Collins, CO 80522. TEL 303-484-6267, FAX 303-482-6184, TELEX 820567. Ed. B Zimmerman. Circ: 150.

333.95416 USA ISSN 0084-0173
QL1 CODEN: WLMOAF
➤ **WILDLIFE MONOGRAPHS.** Text in English. 1958. irreg., latest vol.150, 2002. price varies. 2 cols./p.; back issues avail. **Document type:** *Monographic series, Academic/Scholarly.*
Related titles: Online - full text ed.: (from ProQuest Information & Learning).
Indexed: BIOSIS Prev, BiolAb, CurCont, EIA, EPB, EnerInd, ForAb, HerbAb, ISR, IndVet, KWIWR, MASUSE, NutrAb, PoultAb, RRTA, S&F, SCI, SFA, VetBull, W&CBA, WLA, WildRev, ZooRec.
—BLDSC (9317.450000), CASDDS, CISTI, IE, Infotrieve, ingenta, Linda Hall.
Published by: The Wildlife Society, 5410 Grosvenor Ln, Ste 200, Bethesda, MD 20814. TEL 301-897-9770, FAX 301-530-2471, tws@wildlife.org, http://www.wildlife.org. Ed. Todd K Fuller. Circ: 7,000.

333.954 GBR ISSN 1460-4493
WILDLIFE OF BRITAIN. Text in English. 1998. w. GBP 1.60 newsstand/cover (effective 2000). **Document type:** *Consumer.* **Description:** Helps readers become aware of wildlife in the garden and countryside.
Published by: Bright Star Publishing plc, 179 Dalling Rd, London, W6 0ES, United Kingdom. subs@midsubs.com, http://www.brightstar.co.uk. **Dist. by:** Comag, Tavistock Works, Tavistock Rd, W Drayton, Middx UB7 7QX, United Kingdom. TEL 44-1895-444055, FAX 44-1895-433602.

WILDLIFE REHABILITATION. see *CONSERVATION*

333.95416 AUS ISSN 1035-3712
QL338 CODEN: WRESEX
➤ **WILDLIFE RESEARCH.** Text in English. 1956. bi-m. AUD 140 combined subscription in Australia & New Zealand to individuals print & online eds.; USD 160 combined subscription elsewhere to individuals print & online eds.; AUD 888 combined subscription in Australia & New Zealand to institutions print & online eds.; USD 795 combined subscription elsewhere to institutions print & online eds. (effective 2004). adv. charts; illus. Index. 110 p./no.; back issues avail. **Document type:** *Journal, Academic/Scholarly.* **Description:** Covers biology and management of wild vertebrates, primarily in Australia.
Former titles (1974-1990): Australian Wildlife Research (0310-7833); (1956-1973): C S I R O Wildlife Research (0007-9103)
Related titles: Microform ed.: (from PQC); Online - full text ed.: AUD 130 in Australia & New Zealand to individuals; USD 125 elsewhere to individuals; AUD 790 in Australia & New Zealand to institutions; USD 715 elsewhere to institutions (effective 2004) (from EBSCO Publishing, O C L C Online Computer Library Center, Inc., Swets Information Services).
Indexed: AEA, AESIS, ASCA, ASFA, AgBio, AgrForAb, AnBrAb, ApEcolAb, B&BAb, BIOBASE, BIOSIS Prev, BioCN&I, BiolAb, CurCont, DSA, EIA, ESPM, EnerInd, EnvAb, FCA, FPA, ForAb, GEOBASE, GenetAb, HGA, HelmAb, HerbAb, HortAb, I&DA, IABS, ISR, IndVet, KWIWR, MaizeAb, NutrAb, PGegResA, PN&I, PoultAb, ProtozoAb, RA&MP, RM&VM, RPP, RevApplEntom, S&F, SCI, SFA, SeedAb, TDB, TriticAb, VetBull, WAE&RSA, WeedAb, WildRev, ZooRec.
—BLDSC (9317.466500), CASDDS, CIS, CISTI, IDS, IE, Infotrieve, ingenta, Linda Hall. **CCC.**
Published by: (C S I R O Australia), C S I R O Publishing, 150 Oxford St, PO Box 1139, Collingwood, VIC 3066, Australia. TEL 61-3-96627622, FAX 61-3-96627611, wr@publish.csiro.au, publishing@csiro.au, http://www.publish.csiro.au/journals/wr. Circ: 650.

333.95416 USA
WILDLIFE RESEARCH REPORT. Text in English. irreg., latest no.90-91.
Published by: Wildlife Resources Agency, PO Box 40747, Nashville, TN 37204. TEL 615-781-6502, FAX 615-741-4606.

333.95416 USA ISSN 0091-7648
CODEN: WLSBA6

➤ **WILDLIFE SOCIETY BULLETIN**; perspectives on wildlife conservation and sustainable use. Text in English. 1973. q. USD 110 in North America to institutions; USD 125 elsewhere to institutions (effective 2003). adv. bk.rev.; software rev. bibl.; illus.; stat. index. 2 cols./p.; back issues avail.; reprint service avail. from PQC. **Document type:** *Bulletin, Academic/Scholarly.* **Description:** Disseminates scientific research and management information relating to all phases of wildlife science and management.
Related titles: Online - full text ed.: (from C S A, ProQuest Information & Learning).
Indexed: AEA, ASCA, ASFA, AgBio, Agr, AgrForAb, AnBrAb, ApEcolAb, BIOBASE, BIOSIS Prev, BibAg, BioCN&I, BiolAb, CIS, CurCont, EIA, EPB, ESPM, EnerInd, ExcerpMed, FCA, FPA, ForAb, GEOBASE, GSI, GenetAb, HGA, HelmAb, HerbAb, HortAb, IAB, IABS, ISR, IndVet, KWIWR, MaizeAb, NutrAb, OrnHort, PBA, PGegResA, PHN&I, PN&I, PlantSci, PollutAb, PoultAb, RDA, RM&VM, RPP, RRTA, RevApplEntom, RiceAb, S&F, SCI, SFA, SIA, SSCI, SWRA, SeedAb, SoyAb, TDB, TriticAb, VetBull, W&CBA, WAE&RSA, WLA, WeedAb, WildRev, ZooRec.
—BLDSC (9317.488000), CISTI, IE, Infotrieve, ingenta, Linda Hall.
Published by: The Wildlife Society, 5410 Grosvenor Ln, Ste 200, Bethesda, MD 20814. TEL 301-897-9770, FAX 301-530-2471, tws@wildlife.org, http://www.wildlife.org. Ed. Warren Ballard. R&P Yanin Walker. Circ: 6,400.

➤ **WILDLIFE WORLDWIDE.** see *BIOLOGY—Abstracting, Bibliographies, Statistics*

599.773 USA
WOLF! MAGAZINE. Text in English. 1982. q. USD 22.50; USD 29 in Canada & Mexico; USD 37.50 elsewhere (effective 2000). adv. bk.rev. **Description:** Contains accounts concerning wolves, reintroduction, wolves in captivity, recent research, recolonization, current events in the wolf world, wolf logs, and more.
Published by: North American Wildlife Park Foundation Inc., 4004E 800 N, Battle Ground, IN 47920. TEL 765-567-2265, FAX 765-567-4299, wolfpark@wolfpark.org, http://www.wolfpark.org/. Pub. Erich Klinghammer. Adv. contact Holly Jaycox Di Maio.

590.73 USA
WOLF PARK NEWS. Text in English. 1979. q. USD 20; USD 20 foreign (effective 1999). adv. bk.rev.; film rev. abstr.; illus.; stat. **Document type:** *Newsletter.* **Description:** Contains information for members of Wolf Park of events, programs, activities of animals and general park news.
Formerly (until 1985): Predator
Indexed: BiolDig.
Published by: North American Wildlife Park Foundation Inc., 4004E 800 N, Battle Ground, IN 47920. TEL 765-567-2265, FAX 765-567-4299, wolfpark@wolfpark.org, http://www.wolfpark.org/. Ed., R&P, Adv. contact Amanda Shaod. Circ: 2,000.

590 NLD
➤ **WORLD ANIMAL SCIENCE.** (Consists of: Series A, Basic Information; Series B, Disciplinary Approach; Series C, Production System Approach) Text in English. 1981. irreg., latest vol.10, 1996. price varies. back issues avail. **Document type:** *Monographic series, Academic/Scholarly.* **Description:** Provides zoologists with a complete, coherent, up-to-date picture of the entire field of animal production science.
—BLDSC (9352.912330).
Published by: Elsevier BV (Subsidiary of: Elsevier Science & Technology), Radarweg 29, Amsterdam, 1043 NX, Netherlands. TEL 31-20-4853911, FAX 31-20-4852457, nlinfo-f@elsevier.nl, http://www.elsevier.nl. Eds. Dr. A Neimann-Soerensen, Dr. D E Tribe.

595.3 NLD
WORLD DIRECTORY OF CRUSTACEA COPEPODA OF INLAND WATERS. Text in English. 2002. irreg. price varies. **Document type:** *Academic/Scholarly.*
Published by: Backhuys Publishers BV, Postbus 321, Leiden, 2300 AH, Netherlands. TEL 31-71-517-0208, FAX 31-71-517-1856, backhuys@backhuys.com, http://www.backhuys.com. Eds. Bernard Dussart, Danielle Defaye. Circ: 300.

599.32 FRA ISSN 1257-5011
WORLD RABBIT SCIENCE. Text in French. 1992. q. adv. bibl.; illus.
Formed by the merger of (1980-1992): Journal of Applied Rabbit Research (0738-9760); (1983-1992): Cuni - Sciences (0984-7847)
Indexed: AEA, AgBio, AgrForAb, AnBrAb, DSA, FS&TA, HerbAb, HortAb, IndVet, MaizeAb, NutrAb, PN&I, PoultAb, ProtozoAb, RDA, RM&VM, RPP, SoyAb, TOSA, TriticAb, VetBull, WAE&RSA.
—BLDSC (9358.560000), CISTI, IE, ingenta.
Published by: Association Francaise de Cuniculture, BP 50, Lempdes, 63370, France. TEL 33-4-73920152, FAX 33-4-73928680, asfrcuni@easynet.fr, http://www.rabbit-science.com. Ed. F Lebas. Circ: 1,500.

590 SGP ISSN 1793-0898
WORLD SCIENTIFIC SERIES IN 20TH CENTURY BIOLOGY. Text in English. 1996. irreg., latest vol.5. price varies. **Document type:** *Monographic series, Academic/Scholarly.* **Description:** Publishes the ground-breaking works of Nobel Laureates in the life sciences and medicine.
Published by: World Scientific Publishing Co. Pte. Ltd., 5 Toh Tuck Link, Singapore, 596224, Singapore. TEL 65-466-5775, FAX 65-467-7667, wspc@wspc.com.sg, series@wspc.com.sg, http://www.wspc.com.sg/books/series/wsscb_series.shtml, http://www.worldscientific.com. **Dist. by:** World Scientific Publishing Co., Inc., 1060 Main St, River Edge, NJ 07661. TEL 201-487-9655, 800-227-7562, FAX 201-487-9656, 888-977-2665; World Scientific Publishing Ltd., 57 Shelton St, London WC2H 9HE, United Kingdom. TEL 44-20-78360888, FAX 44-20-78362020.

658.567 USA ISSN 1090-560X
WORM DIGEST; worms deepening our connection to food and soil. Text in English. 1993. q. USD 12 domestic; USD 16 in Canada & Mexico; USD 20 elsewhere; USD 3.50 newsstand/cover (effective 2000). adv. bk.rev. illus. back issues avail. **Document type:** *Newsletter, Consumer.* **Description:** Reports on worms, worm composting and worm technologies for organic waste utilization and soil enrichment.
Related titles: Online - full text ed.
Published by: Edible City Resource Center, PO Box 544, Eugene, OR 97440-0544. TEL 541-485-0456, FAX 541-485-0456, mail@wormdigest.org, http://www.wormdigest.org/. Ed., R&P, Adv. contact S Zorba Frankel. page USD 300. Circ: 8,500.

WYOMING WILDLIFE MAGAZINE. see *CONSERVATION*

WYOMING WILDLIFE NEWS. see *CONSERVATION*

590 POL ISSN 0239-7994
WYZSZA SZKOLA PEDAGOGICZNA IM. KOMISJI EDUKACJI NARODOWEJ W KRAKOWIE. ROCZNIK NAUKOWO-DYDAKTYCZNY. PRACE ZOOLOGICZNE. Text in Polish; Summaries in English, Russian. 1967. irreg. bibl.; illus.
Published by: (Wyzsza Szkola Pedagogiczna im. Komisji Edukacji Narodowej w Krakowie), Wydawnictwo Naukowe W S P, Ul Karmelicka 41, Krakow, 31128, Poland. TEL 33-79-20.

597 576.5 USA ISSN 1545-8547
QL638.C94
▼ ➤ **ZEBRAFISH.** Text in English. 2004. bi-m. USD 471 domestic to institutions; USD 535 foreign to institutions; USD 562 combined subscription domestic to institutions print & online eds.; USD 619 combined subscription foreign to institutions print & online eds. (effective 2006). adv. **Document type:** *Journal, Academic/Scholarly.* **Description:** Focuses on zebrafish, which has many valuable features as a model organism for study of vertebrate development.
Related titles: Online - full content ed.: ISSN 1557-8542. USD 436 worldwide to institutions (effective 2006).
Indexed: RefZh.
—BLDSC (9439.835000), IE, Linda Hall.
Published by: Mary Ann Liebert, Inc. Publishers, 140 Huguenot St 3rd Fl, New Rochelle, NY 10801-5215. TEL 914-740-2100, FAX 914-740-2101, 800-654-3237, info@liebertpub.com, http://www.liebertpub.com/ZEB/default1.asp. Ed. Paul Collodi.

597.073 NLD ISSN 0166-8706
HET ZEE-AQUARIUM. Text in Dutch. 1949. bi-m. EUR 35.20 (effective 2005). adv. bk.rev. charts; illus. **Document type:** *Journal, Academic/Scholarly.*
Formerly (until 1979): Kor (1382-2306)
Published by: Nederlandse en Belgische Bond van Zee-Aquarium-Verenigingen (NBBZ), c/o John Franken, Ebra 200, Uithoorn, 1423 BA, Netherlands. TEL 31-297-522702, infolijn@nbbz.nl, http://www.nbbz.nl. Ed. Dennis Bakker. R&P John Franken. Adv. contact Jan Harbers TEL 31-6-22479931. color page EUR 348; 200 x 290. Circ: 2,000 (paid).

597.9 DEU ISSN 0946-7998
ZEITSCHRIFT FUER FELDHERPETOLOGIE. Text in German. 1994. a. EUR 24 domestic; EUR 27 foreign (effective 2002). **Document type:** *Monographic series, Academic/Scholarly.*
Formed by the merger of (1987-1994): Jahrbuch fuer Feldherpetologie (0931-6949); (1984-1994): Feldherpetologie (1438-4051)
Indexed: ASFA, ZooRec.
—CISTI.
Published by: Laurenti Verlag, Diemelweg 7, Bielefeld, 33649, Germany. TEL 49-5241-9619303, FAX 49-5241-9619304, verlag@laurenti.de, http://www.laurenti.de/ZfF/ZfF-Haupt.html. Eds. Burkhard Thiesmeier, Martin Schluepmann.

597 DEU ISSN 0939-6330
ZEITSCHRIFT FUER FISCHKUNDE. Text in German. 1991. biennial. bk.rev. **Document type:** *Journal, Academic/Scholarly.* **Description:** Contains information about all areas of ichthyology.
Indexed: ASFA, ESPM, IBR, SFA, ZooRec.
Published by: Verlag Natur und Wissenschaft, Postfach 170209, Solingen, 42624, Germany. TEL 49-212-819878, FAX 49-212-816216. Ed. Harro Hieronimus.

590 TWN ISSN 0253-9187
ZHONGGUO XUMU XUEHUI HUIZHI/CHINESE SOCIETY OF ANIMAL SCIENCE. JOURNAL. Text in Chinese. 1972. s-a. **Document type:** *Journal, Academic/Scholarly.*
Indexed: AEA, ASFA, AgBio, AnBrAb, DSA, ESPM, FS&TA, HortAb, I&DA, IndVet, MaizeAb, NutrAb, PN&I, PoultAb, RM&VM, RRTA, S&F, SIA, SoyAb, VetBull, WAE&RSA, WRCInf.
—BLDSC (4729.330310), IE.
Published by: Zhongguo Xumu Xuehui/Chinese Society of Animal Science, Xinhua Zhen Muchang, Tainan, Taiwan. TEL 886-6-5911211, FAX 886-6-5911754, http://www.csas.org.tw/.

ZIVA/LIVE; casopis pro biologickou praci. see *BIOLOGY*

590.73 BEL ISSN 1373-6906
QL77.A6 CODEN: ZOOAB4
ZOO (ANVERS). Text in French. 1935. q. bk.rev. charts; illus. index. **Description:** News of recent arrivals at the zoo, scientific activities undertaken by zoo staff, as well as educational and cultural activities and other items of interest to a general audience, and especially our members.
Former titles (until 1995): Zoo Anvers Planckendael (0779-4517); (until 1992): Zoo Anvers (0044-5029)
Related titles: Dutch ed.: Zoo Antwerpen. ISSN 0774-5729. 1935.
Indexed: BiolAb, IndVet, SFA, WildRev, ZooRec.
—CISTI.
Published by: Societe Royale de Zoologie d'Anvers/Koninklijke Maatschappij voor Dierkunde van Antwerpen, Koningin Astridplein 26, Antwerp, 2018, Belgium. TEL 32-3-2024540, FAX 32-3-2310018. Ed. F J Daman. R&P I Segers. Circ: 37,000.

590.73 USA ISSN 0733-3188
QL77.5 CODEN: ZOBIDX
➤ **ZOO BIOLOGY.** Text in English. bi-m. USD 1,695 domestic to institutions; USD 1,767 in Canada & Mexico to institutions; USD 1,809 elsewhere to institutions; USD 1,865 combined subscription domestic to institutions print & online eds.; USD 1,937 combined subscription in Canada & Mexico to institutions print & online eds.; USD 1,979 combined subscription elsewhere to institutions print & online eds. (effective 2006). adv. bk.rev. back issues avail. **Document type:** *Journal, Academic/Scholarly.* **Description:** Concerned with reproduction, demographics behavior, medicine, husbandry, management, conservation, and all empirical aspects of the exhibition and maintenance of wild animals in wildlife parks, zoos, and aquariums.
Related titles: Microform ed.: (from PQC); Online - full text ed.: ISSN 1098-2361. USD 1,695 to institutions (effective 2006) (from EBSCO Publishing, Swets Information Services, Wiley InterScience).
Indexed: AEA, ASCA, ASFA, AbAn, AgBio, Agr, AgrForAb, AnBeAb, AnBrAb, ApEcolAb, BIOSIS Prev, BiolAb, CIN, ChemAb, ChemTitl, CurCont, DSA, ESPM, FPA, FoVS&M, ForAb, HelmAb, HerbAb, ISR, IndVet, MEDLINE, NutrAb, PHN&I, PN&I, PoultAb, ProtozoAb, PsycInfo, PsycholAb, RA&MP, RM&VM, RefZh, RevApplEntom, SCI, SFA, SIA, VetBull, WildRev, ZooRec, e-psyche.
—BLDSC (9516.100000), CASDDS, CISTI, IDS, IE, ingenta, Linda Hall. **CCC.**
Published by: John Wiley & Sons, Inc., 111 River St, Hoboken, NJ 07030-5774. TEL 201-748-6000, FAX 201-748-5915, uscs-wis@wiley.com, http://www3.interscience.wiley.com/cgi-bin/jhome/35728, http://www.wiley.com. Ed. Dan Wharton. adv.: B&W page GBP 640, color page GBP 1,515; trim 152 x 229. Circ: 600. **Subscr. outside the Americas to:** John Wiley & Sons Ltd., The Atrium, Southern Gate, Chichester, West Sussex PO19 8SQ, United Kingdom. TEL 44-1243-843335, 0800-243407, FAX 44-1243-843232, cs-journals@wiley.co.uk.

590.73 DEU
ZOO - NACHRICHTEN; Allwetterzoo - Nachrichten. Text in German. 1980. 2/yr. adv. bk.rev. back issues avail. **Document type:** *Magazine, Consumer.* **Description:** Reports and news about animals and events at the Allwetterzoo.
Published by: Westfaelischer Zoologischer Garten Muenster GmbH, Sentruper Str 315, Muenster, 48161, Germany. TEL 49-251-89040, FAX 49-251-890490. Ed. Ilona Zuehlke. Circ: 5,000.

590.73 USA ISSN 0276-3303
QL76
ZOO VIEW. Text in English. q. USD 7 (effective 2000). back issues avail. **Description:** Educates on exotic animals and promotes interest in the Los Angeles Zoo.
Published by: Greater Los Angeles Zoo Association, 5333 Zoo Dr, Los Angeles, CA 90027-1498. TEL 323-644-4783. Ed., R&P Claire Peeler. Circ: 42,000 (paid).

590 USA ISSN 0737-9005
ZOOBOOKS. Text in English. 1980. m. USD 20.95 (effective 2005). illus. **Document type:** *Magazine, Consumer.* **Description:** Examines wildlife and their habitats for children 5-12.
Related titles: Online - full text ed.
Indexed: ICM, RGYP.
Published by: Wildlife Education Ltd., 12233 Thatcher Ct, Poway, CA 92064. TEL 858-513-7600, FAX 858-513-7660, animals@zoobooks.com, http://www.zoobooks.com. Ed., Pub. Ed Shadek. R&P Sally Mercer. Circ: 275,000 (paid).

▼ new title ➤ refereed ✶ unverified ♦ full entry avail.

590   VEN   ISSN 0798-7811
➤ **ZOOCRIADEROS/ZOOBREEDERS JOURNAL.** Text in English; Summaries in Multiple languages. 1996. 3/yr. USD 50 (effective 2004). adv. bk.rev. bibl.; illus. Index. back issues avail.; reprints avail. **Document type:** *Journal, Academic/Scholarly.*
Related titles: CD-ROM ed.; E-mail ed.; Online - full text ed.
Indexed: ASFA, ApEcolAb, BIOBASE, BiolAb, ESPM, EntAb, ZooRec.
Published by: Centro de Investigacion y Reproduccion de Especies Silvestres, Apartado Postal 397, Merida, 5101, Venezuela. cires@ciens.ula.ve, http://www.ciens.ula.ve/~cires. Ed. Hector Fernando Aguilar. Adv. contact Lieselotte Hoeger de Aguilar. Circ: 3,000.

590   DEU
DER ZOOFREUND. Text in German. 1971. q. bk.rev. **Document type:** *Newsletter, Consumer.*
Published by: Zoofreunde Hannover e.V., Adenauerallee 3, Hannover, 30175, Germany. TEL 49-511-28074158, FAX 49-511-28074168. Ed. Frank-Dieter Busch. R&P Frank Dieter Busch.

590   USA   ISSN 0163-416X
ZOOGOER. Text in English. 1963. bi-m. USD 40 to members; USD 30 to members seniors (effective 2005). adv. bk.rev. illus. **Document type:** *Consumer.* **Description:** Articles, news, and photography pertaining to wildlife conservation, natural history and animal behavior.
Formerly: Spots and Stripes (0038-8424)
Published by: Friends of the National Zoo, National Zoological Park, Washington, DC 20008. TEL 202-673-4711, FAX 202-673-4738, susan@fonz.org, http://nationalzoo.si.edu/ Publications/ZooGoer, http://www.fonz.org. Ed. Susan Lumpkin. Pub. Clinton A Fields. R&P Robert Moll. Adv. contact Joyce Rains. color page USD 2,000. Circ: 25,000 (paid).

590   DEU   ISSN 0044-5088
    CODEN: ZLGAAA
ZOOLOGICA; Originalabhandlungen aus dem Gebiet der Zoologie. Text in English, German. 1888. 2/yr. EUR 90 per issue domestic; EUR 95.20 per issue foreign (effective 2005). **Document type:** *Journal, Academic/Scholarly.*
Indexed: BiolAb, SFA, ZooRec.
—CISTI. **CCC.**
Published by: E. Schweizerbart'sche Verlagsbuchhandlung, Johannesstr 3A, Stuttgart, 70176, Germany. TEL 49-711-3514560, FAX 49-711-35145699, mail@schweizerbart.de, http://www.schweizerbart.de/j/ zoologica. Eds. F Schaller, W Funke.

590   ESP   ISSN 1130-4251
    QL293
ZOOLOGICA BAETICA. Text in Spanish. 1989. a. price varies. **Document type:** *Monographic series, Academic/Scholarly.*
Indexed: ASFA, BioCN&I, EntAb, GEOBASE, HortAb, IECT, NemAb, NutrAb, RevApplEntom, ZooRec.
—CINDOC.
Published by: (Universidad de Granada, Departamento de Biologia Animal, Ecologia y Genetica), Editorial Universidad de Granada, Antiguo Colegio Maximo, Campus de Cartuja, Granada, 18071, Spain. TEL 34-958-246220, FAX 34-958-243931, comunicacion@editorialugr.com, http://www.editorialugr.com. Ed. Felipe Pascual Torres.

591.9438   POL   ISSN 0044-510X
QL1   CODEN: ZOPOAG
➤ **ZOOLOGICA POLONIAE**; Archivum Societatis Zoologorum Poloniae. Text in English; Summaries in Polish. 1935. q. PLZ 15 domestic; USD 20 foreign (effective 2000). adv. charts; illus. index. **Document type:** *Academic/Scholarly.*
Related titles: Microfilm ed.
Indexed: AgrAg, AgrLib, BiolAb, ChemAb, IndVet, RefZh, SFA, VetBull, WildRev, ZooRec.
—CASDDS, CISTI, KNAW, Linda Hall.
Published by: Polskie Towarzystwo Zoologiczne, ul Sienkiewicza 21, Wroclaw, 50335, Poland. TEL 48-71-225041, FAX 48-71-222817. Ed. Antoni Ogorzalek. R&P Jerzy Turzanski. Circ: 700.

591.3   GBR   ISSN 0300-3256
QL1   CODEN: ZLSCA8
➤ **ZOOLOGICA SCRIPTA**; an international journal of evolutionary zoology. Text in English. 1920. q. GBP 125, EUR 188 combined subscription in Europe to individuals print & online eds.; USD 232 combined subscription in the Americas to individuals & Caribbean, print & online eds.; GBP 138 combined subscription elsewhere to individuals print & online eds.; EUR 977 combined subscription in Europe to institutions print & online eds.; USD 1,804 combined subscription in the Americas to institutions & Caribbean, print & online eds.; GBP 1,074 combined subscription elsewhere to institutions print & online eds. (effective 2006). adv. charts; illus. index. back issues avail. **Document type:** *Academic/Scholarly.* **Description:** Publishes original research in the areas of taxonomy, phylogeny, and biogeography.
Supersedes (in 1971): Arkiv for Zoologi (0004-2110)

Related titles: Microfilm ed.: (from PQC); Online - full text ed.: ISSN 1463-6409. GBP 928 in Europe to institutions; USD 1,714 in the Americas to institutions & Caribbean; GBP 1,020 elsewhere to institutions (effective 2006) (from Blackwell Synergy, EBSCO Publishing, Gale Group, IngentaConnect, O C L C Online Computer Library Center, Inc., Swets Information Services).
Indexed: ASCA, ASFA, AgBio, AnBrAb, BIOBASE, BIOSIS Prev, BioCN&I, BiolAb, CurCont, EntAb, ForAb, HelmAb, IABS, ISR, IndVet, NemAb, RM&VM, RefZh, RevApplEntom, S&F, SCI, ZooRec.
—BLDSC (9519.300000), CISTI, IDS, IE, Infotrieve, ingenta, Linda Hall. **CCC.**
Published by: (Norwegian Academy of Science and Letters NOR), Blackwell Publishing Ltd., 9600 Garsington Rd, Oxford, OX4 2ZG, United Kingdom. TEL 44-1865-776868, FAX 44-1865-714591, customerservices@oxon.blackwellpublishing.com, http://www.blackwellpublishing.com/journals/ZSC. Ed. Per Sundberg. Pub. Elaine Stott. R&P Sophie Savage. Adv. contact Jenny Applin. B&W page GBP 370, color page GBP 895. Circ: 287. **Co-sponsor:** Kungliga Vetenskapsakademien/ Royal Swedish Academy of Sciences.

➤ **ZOOLOGICAL RECORD.** see *BIOLOGY—Abstracting, Bibliographies, Statistics*

590.73   USA   ISSN 1053-802X
Z699.5.Z66
ZOOLOGICAL RECORD SEARCH GUIDE. Text in English. 1985. irreg., latest 2002/2003. USD 125 per issue (effective 2003). **Description:** Full Guide on Searching the Zoological Record Database in all formats. Includes an overview of the editorial policies, coverage criteria, controlled vocabulary listing, search tips and procedures.
—Linda Hall.
Published by: Thomson BIOSIS (Subsidiary of: Thomson I S I), 3501 Market St, Philadelphia, PA 19104. TEL 215-231-7500, 800-523-4806, FAX 215-587-2016, zoorec@york.biosis.org, info@biosis.org, http://www.biosis.org/products_services/ zrsg.html.

ZOOLOGICAL RECORD SERIAL SOURCES. see *BIOLOGY—Abstracting, Bibliographies, Statistics*

590   JPN   ISSN 0289-0003
QL1   CODEN: ZOSCEX
➤ **ZOOLOGICAL SCIENCE**; an international journal. Text in English. 1984. m. free to members (effective 2004). adv. bk.rev. illus. back issues avail.; reprint service avail. from PQC. **Document type:** *Journal, Academic/Scholarly.* **Description:** Original and review articles on all aspects of zoology.
Formed by the merger of (1927-1983): Annotationes Zoologicae Japonenses (0003-5092); (1890-1983): Dobutsugaku Zasshi - Zoological Magazine (0044-5118)
Related titles: Microform ed.: (from PQC); Online - full text ed.: free (effective 2004) (from EBSCO Publishing, J-Stage).
Indexed: ASCA, ASFA, AbHyg, AgBio, AgrForAb, AnBeAb, AnBrAb, ApicAb, BIOSIS Prev, BioCN&I, BiolAb, CIN, CTA, ChemAb, ChemTitl, CurCont, DSA, ESPM, EntAb, ForAb, GenetAb, HGA, HelmAb, HortAb, IABS, INIS AtomInd, ISR, IndVet, Inpharma, MEDLINE, MSB, NSCI, NemAb, NutrAb, OceAb, PGegResA, PHN&I, PN&I, PoultAb, ProtozoAb, RA&MP, RM&VM, RPP, Reac, RefZh, RevApplEntom, RiceAb, S&F, SCI, SFA, SIA, VetBull, ZooRec.
—BLDSC (9520.150000), CASDDS, CISTI, IDS, IE, Infotrieve, ingenta, Linda Hall. **CCC.**
Published by: Zoological Society of Japan/Nihon Dobutsu Gakkai, Toshin Bldg 2F, 2-27-2 Hongo, Bunkyo-ku, Tokyo, 113-0033, Japan. TEL 81-3-38145461, FAX 81-3-38146216, zsocj@a1.rimnet.ne.jp, http://www.jstage.jst.go.jp/browse/zsj/ _vols, http://www.soc.nii.ac.jp/zsj/zsj.html. Ed. Hitoshi Michibata. Circ: 3,400.

590   IND   ISSN 0373-5893
    CODEN: PZSIAE
➤ **ZOOLOGICAL SOCIETY, CALCUTTA. PROCEEDINGS**; proceedings of the perspective in biodiversity. Text in English. 1948. s-a. INR 500; USD 100 foreign (effective 1999). adv. bk.rev. **Document type:** *Proceedings, Academic/Scholarly.* **Description:** Publishes original articles containing new facts on any discipline of zoology, or new interpretation of existing knowledge.
Related titles: Diskette ed.
Indexed: BIOSIS Prev, BiolAb, CurCont, ZooRec.
—CISTI.
Published by: Zoological Society Calcutta, 35 Ballygunge Circular Rd., Kolkata, West Bengal 700 019, India. TEL 91-33-4753680, FAX 91-33-4764419. Ed. B R Maiti. Pub. R C Basu. R&P, Adv. contact R.C. Basu. Circ: 600; 600 (paid).

591.954   IND   ISSN 0049-8769
QL1   CODEN: JZSIAG
ZOOLOGICAL SOCIETY OF INDIA. JOURNAL. Text in English. 1948. s-a. INR 60, USD 15 (effective 2000). adv. bk.rev. charts; illus. **Document type:** *Academic/Scholarly.*
Indexed: ASFA, BiolAb, ESPM, SFA, ZooRec.
—CISTI, Linda Hall.

Published by: Zoological Society of India, Department of Zoology, Utkal University, Bhubaneswar, Orissa 751 004, India. Circ: 400. **Dist. by:** H P C Publishers Distributors Pvt. Ltd., 4805 Bharat Ram Rd, 24 Darya Ganj, New Delhi 110 002, India. TEL 91-11-325-4402, FAX 91-11-686-3511.

590   GBR   ISSN 0084-5612
QL1   CODEN: SZSLAM
➤ **ZOOLOGICAL SOCIETY OF LONDON. SYMPOSIA.** Text in English. 1960. irreg., latest vol.70, 1996. price varies. reprint service avail. from ISI. **Document type:** *Proceedings, Academic/Scholarly.*
Indexed: AnBrAb, BIOSIS Prev, BiolAb, ChemAb, IndVet, SFA, VetBull, WildRev, ZooRec.
—BLDSC (8585.080000), CASDDS, CISTI, IE, Linda Hall. **CCC.**
Published by: Oxford University Press, Great Clarendon St, Oxford, OX2 6DP, United Kingdom. TEL 44-1865-556767, FAX 44-1865-556646, enquiry@oup.co.uk, http://www.oup-usa.org/ catalogs/general/series/.

590   TWN   ISSN 1021-5506
QL307.2   CODEN: ZOSTEG
➤ **ZOOLOGICAL STUDIES.** Summaries in Chinese. 1962. q. USD 60 to individuals; free to institutions (effective 2001). 150 p./no.; reprint service avail. from ISI. **Document type:** *Journal, Academic/Scholarly.* **Description:** Publishes original research papers covering major issues in Zoology.
Formerly (until 1994): Academia Sinica. Institute of Zoology. Bulletin (0001-3943)
Indexed: ASFA, AgBio, AgrForAb, AnBrAb, BIOSIS Prev, BioCN&I, BiolAb, CIN, ChemAb, ChemTitl, CurCont, ESPM, EntAb, ForAb, GenetAb, HGA, HelmAb, HerbAb, HortAb, ISR, IndVet, MathR, NutrAb, OceAb, PBA, PN&I, ProtozoAb, RM&VM, RevApplEntom, RiceAb, S&F, SCI, SFA, TDB, VetBull, WildRev, ZooRec.
—BLDSC (9520.250000), CASDDS, CISTI, IDS, IE, ingenta, Linda Hall.
Published by: Academia Sinica, Institute of Zoology/Chung Yang Yen Chiu Yuan, Tung Wu Hsueh Yen Chiu So, Nankang, Taipei, 11529, Taiwan. TEL 886-2-27899529, 886-2-27899550, FAX 886-2-27899529, 886-2-27858059, zoolstud@gate.sinica.edu.tw, http://www.sinica.edu.tw/zool. Circ: 700 (controlled).

591.954   IND   ISSN 0255-9587
QL309
ZOOLOGICAL SURVEY OF INDIA. BULLETIN. Text in English. 1978. q. price varies. back issues avail.
Indexed: AbHyg, RevApplEntom.
—CISTI, Linda Hall.
Published by: Zoological Survey of India, 34 Chittaranjan Ave., Kolkata, West Bengal 700 012, India. Circ: 400.

591.954   IND   ISSN 0379-3540
ZOOLOGICAL SURVEY OF INDIA. MEMOIRS. Text in English. 1907. irreg. price varies. back issues avail.
Indexed: BiolAb, RevApplEntom, ZooRec.
Published by: Zoological Survey of India, 34 Chittaranjan Ave., Kolkata, West Bengal 700 012, India. Circ: 450.

591.954   IND
ZOOLOGICAL SURVEY OF INDIA. NEWS. Text in English. 1978. 2/yr. back issues avail.
Indexed: RevApplEntom.
Published by: Zoological Survey of India, 34 Chittaranjan Ave., Kolkata, West Bengal 700 012, India. Circ: 600.

590   RUS   ISSN 0044-5134
    CODEN: ZOLZAT
➤ **ZOOLOGICHESKII ZHURNAL.** Text in Russian. 1916. m. RUR 820 for 6 mos. domestic; USD 378 foreign (effective 2004). bk.rev. index. **Document type:** *Journal, Academic/Scholarly.* **Description:** Publishes articles on all trends of investigations of the animal world including systematics, morphology, histology, cytology, ontogenetics, ecology, ecological physiology, zoogeography, conservation, and use of the animal world.
Related titles: ◆ Partial English translation(s): Entomological Review. ISSN 0013-8738.
Indexed: ASCA, ASFA, AgBio, AgrForAb, AnBrAb, BIOSIS Prev, BioCN&I, BiolAb, ChemAb, CurCont, DSA, ESPM, FCA, FPA, ForAb, GenetAb, HGA, HelmAb, HerbAb, HortAb, ISR, IndVet, MaizeAb, NemAb, NutrAb, PBA, PGegResA, PHN&I, PN&I, PotatoAb, ProtozoAb, RA&MP, RM&VM, RRTA, RefZh, RevApplEntom, S&F, SCI, SFA, SIA, SeedAb, TriticAb, VetBull, WeedAb, WildRev, ZooRec.
—CASDDS, CISTI, East View, IDS, KNAW, Linda Hall. **CCC.**
Published by: (Rossiiskaya Akademiya Nauk/Russian Academy of Sciences, Rossiiskaya Akademiya Nauk, Otdelenie Obshchei Biologii), Izdatel'stvo Nauka, Profsoyuznaya ul 90, Moscow, 117864, Russian Federation. TEL 7-095-3347151, FAX 7-095-4202220, secret@naukaran.ru, http://www.maik.ru/cgi-bin/list.pl?page=zool, http://www.naukaran.ru. **Dist. by:** M K - Periodica, ul Gilyarovskogo 39, Moscow 129110, Russian Federation. TEL 7-095-2845008, FAX 7-095-2813798, info@periodicals.ru, http://www.mkniga.ru.

590 AUT ISSN 0252-1911
CODEN: VZGOD7

➤ **ZOOLOGISCH-BOTANISCHE GESELLSCHAFT IN OESTERREICH. VERHANDLUNGEN.** Text in German; Abstracts in English. 1851. a. EUR 51 (effective 2003). bk.rev. **Document type:** *Journal, Academic/Scholarly.*
Former titles (until 1977): Zoologisch-Botanische Gesellschaft, Vienna. Verhandlungen (0084-5647); (until 1918): Kaiserlich-Koniglichen Zoologisch-Botanischen Gesellschaft in Wien. Verhandlungen (1025-4749)
Indexed: ASFA, BiolAb, CPA, ForAb, HerbAb, HortAb, I&DA, NemAb, OrnHort, PBA, PGegResA, RM&VM, RRTA, RefZh, RevApplEntom, S&F, SeedAb, WAE&RSA, WeedAb, ZooRec.
—CISTI, Linda Hall.
Published by: Zoologisch-Botanische Gesellschaft in Oesterreich, Althanstr. 14, Postfach 267, Vienna, 1091, Austria. TEL 43-1-427754313, FAX 43-1-42779542, wolfgang.punz@univie.ac.at, http://www.univie.ac.at/zoobot. Circ: 1,000.

590 AUT ISSN 0084-5639
QH301

ZOOLOGISCH - BOTANISCHE GESELLSCHAFT, VIENNA. ABHANDLUNGEN. Text in German; Abstracts in English. 1901. irreg., latest vol.32, 2002. price varies. **Document type:** *Monographic series, Academic/Scholarly.*
Indexed: IndVet, RRTA, RefZh, S&F, ZooRec.
—Linda Hall.
Published by: Zoologisch-Botanische Gesellschaft in Oesterreich, Althanstr. 14, Postfach 267, Vienna, 1091, Austria. TEL 43-1-427754313, FAX 43-1-42779542, wolfgang.punz@univie.ac.at, http://www.univie.ac.at/zoobot.

590 DEU ISSN 0044-5169
QL1 CODEN: ZOGAAV

➤ **DER ZOOLOGISCHE GARTEN.** Text and summaries in English, German. 1929. 6/yr. EUR 114 in Europe to individuals; JPY 14,000 in Japan to individuals; USD 111 elsewhere to individuals; EUR 237 to institutions in Germany, Austria, Switzerland; EUR 259 in Europe to institutions; JPY 33,700 in Japan to institutions; USD 281 elsewhere to institutions (effective 2006). adv. bk.rev. abstr.; bibl.; charts; illus. Index. reprint service avail. from ISI. **Document type:** *Journal, Academic/Scholarly.* **Description:** Covers all aspects of zoological gardens from animal care to management.
Indexed: AnBrAb, BIOSIS Prev, BiolAb, IndVet, KWIWR, ProtozoAb, SFA, VetBull, WildRev, ZooRec.
—BLDSC (9522.500000), CISTI, IE, ingenta, Linda Hall. **CCC.**
Published by: (Verband Deutscher Zoodirektoren), Elsevier GmbH, Urban & Fischer Verlag (Subsidiary of: Elsevier Science & Technology), Loebdergraben 14a, Jena, 07743, Germany. TEL 49-3641-626430, FAX 49-3641-626432, info@urbanfischer.de, http://www.elsevier.com/locate/zoolgart, http://www.urbanfischer.de/journals. Ed. Wolfgang Grummt TEL 49-30-51531104. R&P Martin Huber TEL 49-3641-626430. Adv. contact Sabine Schroeter TEL 49-3641-626445. B&W page EUR 485, color page EUR 1,430; trim 170 x 240. Circ: 650 (paid and controlled).
Non-German speaking countries subscr. to: Nature Publishing Group, Brunel Rd, Houndmills, Basingstoke, Hamps RG21 6XS, United Kingdom. TEL 44-1256-302629, FAX 44-1256-476117, NatureReviews@nature.com
Co-sponsor: International Union of Directors of Zoological Gardens.

590 DEU ISSN 0044-5231
CODEN: ZOANA6

➤ **ZOOLOGISCHER ANZEIGER.** Text in English. 1878. 4/yr. EUR 140 in Europe to individuals; JPY 17,700 in Japan to individuals; USD 137 to individuals except Europe and Japan; EUR 409 to institutions; EUR 474 in Europe to institutions; JPY 63,500 in Japan to institutions; USD 514 to institutions except Europe and Japan (effective 2006). adv. bibl.; charts; illus. index. reprint service avail. from ISI. **Document type:** *Journal, Academic/Scholarly.* **Description:** Develops an understanding of the organismic world from an evolutionary standpoint.
Incorporates (1886-1995): Zoologische Jahrbuecher. Abteilung fuer Systematik, Oekologie und Geographie der Tiere (0044-5193)
Related titles: Microform ed.: (from SWZ); Online - full text ed.: (from EBSCO Publishing, Gale Group, IngentaConnect, O C L C Online Computer Library Center, Inc., ScienceDirect, Swets Information Services); Supplement(s): Zoologischer Anzeiger. Supplement.
Indexed: ASCA, ASFA, AgBio, AnBrAb, BIOSIS Prev, BioCN&I, BiolAb, ChemAb, CurCont, ESPM, EntAb, ForAb, GEOBASE, HelmAb, ISR, IndVet, NutrAb, PoultAb, RPP, RevApplEntom, S&F, SCI, SFA, VetBull, WildRev, ZooRec.
—BLDSC (9528.000000), CASDDS, CISTI, IDS, IE, Infotrieve, ingenta, Linda Hall. **CCC.**
Published by: Elsevier GmbH, Urban & Fischer Verlag (Subsidiary of: Elsevier Science & Technology), Loebdergraben 14a, Jena, 07743, Germany. TEL 49-3641-626430, FAX 49-3641-626432, journals@urbanfischer.de, http://www.elsevier.com/locate/zoolanz, http://www.urbanfischer.de/journals. Eds. Edmund Gittenberger, Geoff A. Boxshall. R&P Martin Huber TEL 49-3641-626430. Adv. contact Sabine Schroeter TEL 49-3641-626445. B&W page EUR 400, color page EUR 1,345; trim 210 x 280. Circ: 325 (paid and controlled).
Non-German speaking countries subscr. to: Nature Publishing Group, Brunel Rd, Houndmills, Basingstoke, Hamps RG21 6XS, United Kingdom. TEL 44-1256-302629, FAX 44-1256-476117, subscriptions@nature.com; **Subscr. to:** Postfach 100537, Jena 07705, Germany. TEL 49-3641-626444, FAX 49-3641-626443.

590 DEU ISSN 0944-2006
QL1 CODEN: ZOLGEA

➤ **ZOOLOGY.** Text in English. 1886. 4/yr. EUR 140 in Europe to individuals; JPY 17,700 in Japan to individuals; USD 137 to individuals except Europe and Japan; EUR 409 to institutions; EUR 474 in Europe to institutions; JPY 63,500 in Japan to institutions; USD 514 to institutions except Europe and Japan (effective 2006). adv. bk.rev. bibl.; charts; illus. index. reprint service avail. from ISI. **Document type:** *Journal, Academic/Scholarly.* **Description:** Takes a system-oriented approach to the study of animals while placing particular emphasis on the comparative aspects of animal biology.
Supersedes (in 1993): Zoologische Jahrbuecher. Abteilung fuer Allgemeine Zoologie und Physiologie der Tiere (0044-5185); Zoologische Jahrbuecher. Abteilung fuer Anatomie und Ontogenie der Tiere (0044-5177)
Related titles: Online - full text ed.: (from EBSCO Publishing, Gale Group, IngentaConnect, O C L C Online Computer Library Center, Inc., ScienceDirect, Swets Information Services).
Indexed: ASCA, AgBio, AnBrAb, ApicAb, BIOSIS Prev, BioCN&I, BiolAb, CIN, ChemAb, ChemTitl, CurCont, ForAb, HelmAb, ISR, IndVet, NSCI, NemAb, NutrAb, PoultAb, ProtozoAb, RefZh, RevApplEntom, S&F, SCI, SFA, SIA, SSCI, VITIS, VetBull, ZooRec.
—BLDSC (9529.330000), CASDDS, CISTI, IDS, IE, Infotrieve, ingenta, Linda Hall. **CCC.**
Published by: Elsevier GmbH, Urban & Fischer Verlag (Subsidiary of: Elsevier Science & Technology), Loebdergraben 14a, Jena, 07743, Germany. TEL 49-3641-626430, FAX 49-3641-626432, info@urbanfischer.de, http://www.elsevier.com/locate/zoology, http://www.urbanfischer.de/journals. Ed. J Matthias Starck. R&P Martin Huber TEL 49-3641-626430. Adv. contact Sabine Schroeter TEL 49-3641-626445. B&W page EUR 400, color page EUR 1,345; trim 210 x 280. Circ: 325 (paid and controlled). **Non-German speaking countries subscr. to:** Nature Publishing Group, Brunel Rd, Houndmills, Basingstoke, Hamps RG21 6XS, United Kingdom. TEL 44-1256-302629, FAX 44-1256-476117

591.956 DEU ISSN 0939-7140
QL334.M53 CODEN: ZMEAEB

➤ **ZOOLOGY IN THE MIDDLE EAST.** Text in English. 1986. 3/yr. EUR 48 to individuals; EUR 98 to institutions (effective 2005). adv. abstr.; bibl.; charts; illus.; maps. 120 p./no. 1 cols./p.; back issues avail.; reprints avail. **Document type:** *Journal, Academic/Scholarly.* **Description:** Covers the whole scope of zoology in the Middle East.
Indexed: ASFA, AnBrAb, BIOSIS Prev, BioCN&I, BiolAb, EntAb, FCA, GEOBASE, HelmAb, HerbAb, HortAb, RefZh, S&F, SFA, TDB, WLR, WildRev, ZooRec.
—**CCC.**
Published by: Kasparek Verlag, Moenchhofstr 16, Heidelberg, 69120, Germany. TEL 49-6221-475069, FAX 49-6221-471858, kasparek@t-online.de, http://www.kasparek-verlag.de. Eds. Max Kasparek, Ragnar Kinzelbach.

➤ **ZOOMORPHOLOGY**; an international journal of comparative and functional morphology. see *BIOLOGY*

590.73 USA ISSN 0044-5282
QL1 CODEN: ZONOA

ZOONOOZ. Text in English. 1926. m. USD 68 in city membership; USD 79 elsewhere membership (effective 2005). adv. bk.rev. charts; illus. index. reprints avail. **Document type:** *Magazine, Academic/Scholarly.*
—Linda Hall.
Published by: Zoological Society of San Diego, PO Box 120551, San Diego, CA 92112-0551. TEL 619-234-3153, http://www.sandiegozoo.org. Ed., R&P Thomas L Scharf. Circ: 250,000.

590 IND ISSN 0971-6378

ZOOS' PRINT JOURNAL. Text in English. 1986. m. INR 200 domestic; INR 225 foreign (effective 2005). bk.rev. **Document type:** *Journal.* **Description:** Publishes on all aspects of zoocraft and wildlife from India.
Indexed: AbHyg, AgrForAb, AnBrAb, BIOBASE, BioCN&I, CPA, DSA, FCA, FPA, ForAb, HelmAb, HerbAb, HortAb, IndVet, OrnHort, PBA, PGegResA, PN&I, PoultAb, ProtozoAb, RA&MP, RM&VM, RPP, S&F, SIA, TDB, WAE&RSA, WeedAb.
—BLDSC (9531.700000).
Published by: Zoo Outreach Organisation, PO Box 1683, Coimbatore, Tamil Nadu 641 004, India. TEL 91-422-2561087, FAX 91-422-2563269, herpinvert@vsnl.com, zooreach@vsnl.com, http://www.zooreach.org/Publications/ZoosPrint/Journal/ZP-JournalInfo.htm. Ed. Sanjay Molur. Pub. Nandini Rangaswamy.

590.73 USA

ZOOSLETTER. Text in English. 1961. bi-m. membership. adv. bk.rev. illus. **Document type:** *Newsletter.*
Formerly: Zoo's Letter (0044-5304)
Published by: Indianapolis Zoological Society, Inc., 1200 W Washington St, Indianapolis, IN 46222. TEL 317-638-8072. Ed. Vaughn Bidwell. Adv. contact Meg Beasley. Circ: 40,000.

590 RUS ISSN 0320-9180

ZOOSYSTEMATICA ROSSICA. Text in English. 1993. s-a. USD 35 to individuals; USD 51 to institutions (effective 2004). illus. 200 p./no. 2 cols./p.; back issues avail. **Document type:** *Journal, Academic/Scholarly.* **Description:** Focuses on new taxa, taxonomy revisions. synonymic notes, phylogenetic reconstructions, and compelling new faunistic records on animals from throughout the world. Provides a forum for zoologists in Russia and neighboring countries.
Indexed: AEA, BioCN&I, ForAb, HelmAb, HortAb, IndVet, NemAb, PBA, PotatoAb, PoultAb, ProtozoAb, RA&MP, RM&VM, RPP, RefZh, RevApplEntom, S&F, VetBull, ZooRec.
—East View.
Published by: Rossiiskaya Akademiya Nauk, Zoologicheskii Institut/Russian Academy of Sciences, Zoological Institute, Universitetskaya nab 1, St Petersburg, 199034, Russian Federation. TEL 7-812-3280011, FAX 7-812-3282941, admin@zin.ru, http://www.zin.ru/journals/zsr/index.html. Ed. I M Kerzhner.

590.12 NZL ISSN 1175-5326

➤ **ZOOTAXA.** Text in English. 2001. irreg. **Document type:** *Journal, Academic/Scholarly.* **Description:** Aims for the rapid publication of papers and monographs on all aspects of zootaxonomy.
Related titles: Online - full text ed.: ISSN 1175-5334.
Published by: Magnolia Press, PO Box 41383, Auckland, 1030, New Zealand. zootaxa@mapress.com, magnolia@mapress.com, http://www.mapress.com/zootaxa. Ed. Zhi-Qiang Zhang.

BIOPHYSICS

see *BIOLOGY—Biophysics*

BIOTECHNOLOGY

see *BIOLOGY—Biotechnology*

BIRTH CONTROL

see also *POPULATION STUDIES*

613.9 340.5 GBR

A L R A NEWSLETTER. Text in English. q. GBP 15 to members (effective 2000). adv. bk.rev. **Document type:** *Newsletter.* **Description:** Presents a pro-choice forum for the association.
Former titles (until 1995): Breaking Chains (0309-7978); (until 1977): A L R A Newsletter
Published by: Abortion Law Reform Association, 2-12 Pentonville Rd, London, N1 9FP, United Kingdom. TEL 020-7278-5539, FAX 020-7278-5236, alra@mailbox.co.uk, http://www.alramailbox.co.uk. Ed. Jane Roe. Circ: 2,000.

613.942 USA

A V S C NEWS✶. Text in English. 1963. q. membership. illus.; stat. **Document type:** *Newsletter.* **Description:** Reports news and information related to family planning and reproductive health worldwide.
Formerly: A V S News (0001-2904)
Indexed: CLFP.
Published by: (Association for Voluntary Surgical Contraception), A V S C International, 440 9th Ave Frnt 2, New York, NY 10001-1620. TEL 212-561-8000, FAX 212-779-9439, info@avsc.org, http://www.avsc.org. Ed. Karen Landovitz. R&P Pamela Beyer Harper TEL 212-561-8043. Circ: 8,000.

338.96 KEN ISSN 0250-698X

AFRICA LINK. Text in English, French. 1971. s-a. free. bk.rev. **Document type:** *Newsletter.* **Description:** Covers the activities of the family planning associations in Sub-Saharan Africa. Addresses sexual and reproductive health issues.
Related titles: Online - full text ed.: (from Gale Group, O C L C Online Computer Library Center, Inc.); ♦ French ed.: Africa Link. Edition Francaise. ISSN 1012-5019.
Indexed: CWI.
—BLDSC (0732.160800).
Published by: Africa Regional Office, Planned Parenthood Federation, Madison Insurance House, Upper Hill, PO Box 30234, Nairobi, Kenya. TEL 254-2-720280, FAX 254-2-726596, info@ippfaro.org. Ed. Justice Pobi. R&P Kodjo Efu. Circ: 3,000 (controlled).

338.96 KEN ISSN 1012-5019

AFRICA LINK. EDITION FRANCAISE. Text in French. 1988. s-a.
Media: Duplicated (not offset). **Related titles:** ♦ English ed.: Africa Link. ISSN 0250-698X.
Published by: Africa Regional Office, Planned Parenthood Federation, Madison Insurance House, Upper Hill, PO Box 30234, Nairobi, Kenya.

ASIAN AND PACIFIC WOMEN'S RESOURCE AND ACTION SERIES. see *WOMEN'S INTERESTS*

▼ new title ➤ refereed ✶ unverified ♦ full entry avail.

301.426 PAN
BOLETIN CONCIENCIA. Text in Spanish. 1967. s-a. free. adv. illus. **Document type:** *Bulletin.*
Formerly: Conciencia
Published by: Asociacion Panamena para el Planeamiento de la Familia, Apdo. Postal 4637, Panama City, 5, Panama. TEL 507-2607005, FAX 507-2362979, aplafa@sinfo.net. Ed., Adv. contact Monica Fabrega. Pub. Alfonso Lavergne. Circ: 5,000.

613.9 ATG
CARIBBEAN FAMILY PLANNING AFFILIATION. ANNUAL REPORT. Text in English. 1981. a. free to qualified personnel. **Description:** Report on the year's activities in family life education and family planning.
Published by: (International Planned Parenthood Federation, Western Hemisphere Region), Caribbean Family Planning Affiliation Limited, Airport and Factory Rds., PO Box 419, St John's, Antigua. FAX 809-462-1187. Circ: 2,000.

613.9 312 USA
CELEBRATE LIFE (STAFFORD). Text in English. 1978. bi-m. USD 12.95 (effective 1998). adv. bk.rev. index. **Document type:** *Consumer.* **Description:** Covers abortion, euthanasia, life and family issues from a pro-life perspective.
Formerly (until 1994): All About Issues (0733-1231)
Published by: American Life League, Inc., 1179 Courthouse Rd, Box 1350, Stafford, VA 22555. TEL 504-659-4171, FAX 504-659-2586, clmag@all.org. Eds. Cathy Kenyon, Rich Gelina. Pub. Judie Brown. Circ: 130,000.

301.426 IND
CENTRE CALLING. Text in English. 1966. m. free. bk.rev.
Published by: Department of Family Welfare, Kotla Rd., P O Box 5410, New Delhi, 110 002, India. Ed. Uma Shankar Mishra. Circ: 40,000. **Subscr. to:** Editor, P O Box 5410, New Delhi 110 002, India.

CHOICES; sexual and reproductive health and rights in Europe. see *POPULATION STUDIES*

363.96 USA ISSN 1550-8900
▼ **CONCEIVE MAGAZINE (FLORIDA).** Text in English. 2004. q. USD 19.20 domestic; USD 27.20 in Canada; USD 39.20 elsewhere; USD 4.99 newsstand/cover domestic; USD 6.99 newsstand/cover in Canada; USD 9.99 newsstand/cover elsewhere (effective 2005). adv. **Document type:** *Magazine, Consumer.*
Published by: Conceive Magazine, 7512 Dr. Phillips Blvd, Ste 50, PMB 205, Orlando, FL 32819. TEL 800-758-0770, FAX 407-299-5484, http://www.conceivemagazine.com/. Ed. Beth Weinhouse. Pub. Kim Hahn. adv.: color page USD 11,980, B&W page USD 10,782; trim 8.125 x 10.75. Circ: 140,000.

613.943 USA ISSN 0010-7824
RG136.A1 CODEN: CCPTAY
➤ **CONTRACEPTION.** Text in English. 1970. 12/yr. USD 287 to individuals; USD 287 in United States to individuals; USD 845 to institutions; USD 845 in United States to institutions (effective 2006). adv. bibl.; charts; illus.; abstr. s-a. index. back issues avail.; reprint service avail. from PQC. **Document type:** *Journal, Academic/Scholarly.* **Description:** Presents research reports in clinical and experimental contraception.
Related titles: Microfilm ed.: (from PQC); Online - full text ed.: (from EBSCO Publishing, Gale Group, IngentaConnect, ScienceDirect).
Indexed: ASCA, AbHyg, AgrForAb, AnBrAb, BIOBASE, BIOSIS Prev, BibRep, BiolAb, CIN, CLFP, CTFA, ChemAb, ChemTitl, CurCont, DBA, DSA, ESPM, ExcerpMed, FCA, FPA, Faml, ForAb, H&SSA, HelmAb, HortAb, IABS, INI, IPA, ISR, IndMed, Inpharma, JW-WH, MEDLINE, NutrAb, PE&ON, PopulInd, ProtozoAb, RA&MP, RAPRA, RDA, RM&VM, Reac, RefZh, SCI, SSCI, SeedAb, TDB, WAE&RSA.
—BLDSC (3425.750000), CASDDS, CINDOC, CISTI, GNLM, IDS, IE, Infotrieve, ingenta, KNAW. **CCC.**
Published by: Elsevier Inc. (Subsidiary of: Elsevier Science & Technology), 360 Park Ave. S, New York, NY 10010-1710. TEL 212-633-3730, 888-437-4636, usinfo-f@elsevier.com, http://www.elsevier.com/locate/contraception. Ed. Dr. Daniel R Mishell Jr. **Subscr. to:** Elsevier BV, PO Box 211, Amsterdam 1000 AE, Netherlands. TEL 31-20-485-3757, FAX 31-20-485-3432.

301.426 613.9 GBR
CONTRACEPTIVE EDUCATION BULLETIN. Text in English. 1976. q. GBP 15; GBP 18 foreign (effective 2001). adv. bk.rev.; Website rev. bibl. 6 p./no. 3 cols./p.; **Document type:** *Bulletin.* **Description:** Contains news, information, and commentary about contraception, reproductive health and sexual health issues.
Supersedes (in 1996): Family Planning Today (0309-1112); Which supersedes: Family Planning (0014-7338)
Indexed: BiolAb, CLFP, MEDLINE, RASB.
—**CCC.**
Published by: Family Planning Association, 2-12, Pentonville Rd, London, N1 9FP, United Kingdom. TEL 44-20-7837-5432, FAX 44-20-7837-3042, joannac@fpa.org.uk, http://www.fpa.org.uk. Ed., R&P Joanna Clarke-Jones TEL 44-20-7923-5721. Circ: 5,000.

613.9 USA ISSN 0091-9721
RG136.A1
CONTRACEPTIVE TECHNOLOGY. Text in English. every 3 yrs., latest vol.18, 2004. USD 59.95 per edition (effective 2004). **Document type:** *Monographic series, Academic/Scholarly.*
Related titles: CD-ROM ed.
—BLDSC (3425.770000).
Published by: Ardent Media, Inc. (Subsidiary of: Irvington Publishers, Inc.), 522 E. 82nd St, Ste.1, New York, NY 10028. FAX 212-861-0998.

613.9 USA ISSN 0274-726X
CODEN: UGMRAZ
CONTRACEPTIVE TECHNOLOGY UPDATE. Text in English. 1980. m. USD 449 with CME credits; USD 75 newsstand/cover (effective 2006). bk.rev. back issues avail.; reprints avail. **Document type:** *Newsletter, Trade.* **Description:** Addresses the needs of family planning professionals and is oriented toward clinical information.
Incorporates (1993-1999): Women's Health Center Management (1082-863X); Incorporates (1989-1991): Reproductive Technology Update (1050-8740)
Related titles: Microfilm ed.: (from PQC); Online - full text ed.: (from EBSCO Publishing, Florida Center for Library Automation, Gale Group, Northern Light Technology, Inc., O C L C Online Computer Library Center, Inc.).
Indexed: CINAHL, CLFP.
—BLDSC (3425.773000), IE, Infotrieve, ingenta. **CCC.**
Published by: Thomson American Health Consultants, Inc. (Subsidiary of: Thomson Corporation, Healthcare Information Group), 3525 Piedmont Rd, N E, Bldg 6, Ste 400, Atlanta, GA 30305. TEL 404-262-5511, 800-688-2421, FAX 404-262-7837, 800-284-3291, customerservice@ahcpub.com, http://www.ahcpub.com. Pub. Brenda L Mooney TEL 404-262-5403. Circ: 1,710.

DZIECKO. see *WOMEN'S HEALTH*

301.4 EGY
E P F P R. (Egyptian Population and Family Planning Review) Text in Arabic, English. 1968. 2/yr. EGP 5, USD 30 (effective 1999). bk.rev. bibl.; stat. **Document type:** *Academic/Scholarly.*
Indexed: PopulInd.
Published by: Cairo University, Institute of Statistical Studies and Research, Tharwat St., Orman, Cairo, Egypt. FAX 20-2-3482533. Ed. Ibrahim Farag Eissa. Circ: 400.

613.9 USA ISSN 1092-2687
EDUCATOR'S UPDATE. Text in English. 1996. bi-m. USD 24. bk.rev.; video rev. bibl.; illus. reprints avail.
Published by: (Education Department), Planned Parenthood Federation of America, Inc., 434 W. 33rd St., Flr. 12, New York, NY 10001-2600. library@ppfa.org, http://www.plannedparenthood.org/library/PPFA-LIBRARY/EdUpIndex.htm. Ed. Gloria A Roberts. Circ: 150.

613.9 EGY ISSN 1110-1156
THE EGYPTIAN POPULATION AND FAMILY PLANNING REVIEW. Text in English. s-a. **Document type:** *Journal, Academic/Scholarly.*
Published by: Institute of Statistical Studies and Research, Cairo University, 5 Sarwat Str, Orman, Giza, Egypt. TEL 20-2-5679070, FAX 20-2-3482533, http://derp.sti.sci.eg/data/0142.htm. Ed. Dr. Ebrahim Farag Eisa.

301.426 COL
ESTUDIOS DE PLANIFICACION FAMILIAR. Text in Spanish. 1975 (vol.9). 2/yr.
Published by: Asociacion Colombiana para el Estudio Cientifico de la Poblacion, Canal Ramirez-Antares, Carrera 18, 33-95, Bogota, CUND, Colombia. Ed. Dr. Guillermo Lopez Escobar.

613.943 GBR ISSN 1362-5187
CODEN: ECRCFK
➤ **EUROPEAN JOURNAL OF CONTRACEPTION AND REPRODUCTIVE HEALTH CARE.** Text in English. 1996. q. GBP 171, USD 283 combined subscription to institutions print & online eds. (effective 2006). adv. reprint service avail. from PSC. **Document type:** *Journal, Academic/Scholarly.* **Description:** Publishes original research papers as well as review papers and other appropriate educational material.
Related titles: Online - full text ed.: ISSN 1473-0782. GBP 162, USD 269 to institutions (effective 2006) (from EBSCO Publishing, Gale Group, IngentaConnect, O C L C Online Computer Library Center, Inc., ProQuest Information & Learning, Swets Information Services).
Indexed: CurCont, ExcerpMed, INI, IndMed, MEDLINE.
—BLDSC (3829.728227), CASDDS, CISTI, GNLM, IE, Infotrieve, ingenta. **CCC.**
Published by: (European Society of Contraception), Taylor & Francis Ltd (Subsidiary of: Taylor & Francis Group), 4 Park Sq, Milton Park, Abingdon, OX14 4RN, United Kingdom. TEL 44-1235-828600, FAX 44-1235-829000, info@tandf.co.uk, http://www.tandf.co.uk/journals/titles/13625187.asp. Ed. George Creatsas. Circ: 800 (paid).

613.9 BGD
F P A B HIGHLIGHTS. Text in English. 1978. q. 4 p./no.; back issues avail. **Document type:** *Newsletter.*
Published by: Family Planning Association of Bangladesh, 2 Naya Paltan, Dhaka, 2, Bangladesh. TEL 88-2-316134, 88-2-8311423, 88-2-8319343, FAX 88-2-8313008, TELEX 632379 IFIC BJ, fpab1@citechoo.net. Eds. Ahmad Neaz, M Emamul Haque. Pub. Ahmad Neaz. Circ: 1,000.

301.426 TWN
F P A C MONTHLY REPORT✶. Text in Chinese, English. 1961. m. free.
Published by: Family Planning Association of China, No1, Ln 160, Fuhsing S. Rd Sec 2, Taipei, 106, Taiwan.

301.4 PAK
F P A P ANNUAL REPORT. Text in English. 1964. a. **Document type:** *Corporate.*
Former titles: F P A P Biennial Report (0071-3759)
Published by: Family Planning Association of Pakistan, 3-A Temple Rd., Lahore, Pakistan. Circ: 1,000 (controlled).

613.9 PHL
THE F P O P BULLETIN. Text in English. 1969. q. free. **Document type:** *Bulletin.*
Published by: Family Planning Organization of the Philippines, 50 Dona Magdalina Hemady Ave, New Manila, Quezon City, Philippines. TEL 721-71-01, FAX 721-40-67. Ed. Javier Gil C Montemayor. Circ: 2,000.

613.9 FJI
FAMILY PLANNING ASSOCIATION OF FIJI. NEWS. Text in English. 1976 (no.37). bi-m. charts; illus.
Published by: Family Planning Association of Fiji, PO Box 619, Suva, Fiji.

301.42 IND ISSN 0377-7774
FAMILY PLANNING ASSOCIATION OF INDIA. REPORT. Text in English. 1950. a. free. illus.
Published by: Family Planning Association of India, Bajaj Bhavan, Nariman Point, Mumbai, Maharashtra 400 021, India. TEL 91-22-202-9080, FAX 91-22-202-9038, fpai@giasbm01.vsnl.net.in. Ed., R&P Jyoti Moodbidri. Circ: 2,000.

301.42 KEN
FAMILY PLANNING ASSOCIATION OF KENYA. ANNUAL REPORT. Key Title: Annual Report - Family Planning Association of Kenya. Text in English. 1971. a. free. illus. **Document type:** *Corporate.*
Published by: Family Planning Association of Kenya, Harabee P, Haile Selassie Ave., PO Box 30581, Nairobi, Kenya. Ed. Inzoberi John. Circ: 2,000.

362.8 NPL ISSN 0303-4755
HQ766.5.N37
FAMILY PLANNING ASSOCIATION OF NEPAL. ANNUAL REPORT. Text in English. 1960. a. free. stat. **Description:** Provides information on the programs and activities of the FPAN throughout the year.
Published by: Family Planning Association of Nepal, P O Box 486, Katmandu, Nepal. TEL 977-1-524440, FAX 977-1-524211, TELEX 2307 FPAN NP. Circ: 75.

362.8 NPL
FAMILY PLANNING ASSOCIATION OF NEPAL. NEWSLETTER. Text in English. 1973. bi-m. free. **Document type:** *Newsletter.* **Description:** Provides news and information of the association.
Published by: Family Planning Association of Nepal, P O Box 486, Katmandu, Nepal. TEL 977-1-524440, FAX 977-1-524211.

362.8 USA ISSN 0095-3121
HQ766.5.U5
FAMILY PLANNING PROGRAMS IN OKLAHOMA; annual statistical report. Text in English. 1971. a. illus. **Document type:** *Government.*
Published by: Department of Health, Maternal and Child Health Service, 1000 N E 10th St, Oklahoma City, OK 73117-1299. TEL 405-271-4476. Circ: 450.

613.94 GMB ISSN 0796-0174
THE GAMBIA FAMILY PLANNING ASSOCIATION NEWSLETTER. Text in English. 1972. q. free. adv. **Document type:** *Newsletter.* **Description:** Reports on workshops, training programs, resource development and association activities.
Former titles: Family Planning Association of the Gambia; (until 1987): What's On
Published by: Gambia Family Planning Association, PO Box 325, Banjul, Gambia. TEL 220-370325, FAX 220-392463, gfpa@commit.gm. Ed., Pub. Yankubba Dibba. Circ: 150.

613.9 GRD
GRENADA PLANNED PARENTHOOD ASSOCIATION. ANNUAL REPORT. Text in English. a. **Document type:** *Corporate.*
Published by: Grenada Planned Parenthood Association, Scott St., St. George's, Grenada. FAX 809-440-8057. Circ: 300.

613.9 CHN ISSN 1001-3490
GUOWAI YIXUE (JIHUA SHENGYU FENCE)/FOREIGN MEDICAL SCIENCES (FAMILY PLANNING). Text in Chinese. 1982. bi-m. CNY 24 domestic; USD 11.60 foreign (effective 2005). **Document type:** *Journal, Academic/Scholarly.*

Related titles: Online - full text ed.: (from East View Information Services).
Published by: Tianjin Yixue Keji Qingbao Yanjiusuo/Tianjin Medical Science and Technology Information Institute, 131 Chengdu Dao, Heping-qu, Tianjin, 300050, China. TEL 86-22-23302570, fcjsfc@163.com, http://gwyx-jh.periodicals.net.cn/. Ed. Yu Aifeng. **Dist. by:** China International Book Trading Corp, 35 Chegongzhuang Xilu, Haidian District, PO Box 399, Beijing 100044, China. TEL 86-10-68412045, FAX 86-10-68412023, cibtc@mail.cibtc.com.cn, http://www.cibtc.com.cn.

613.9 362.1 USA ISSN 1096-7699
HQ766.5.U5
THE GUTTMACHER REPORT ON PUBLIC POLICY. Text in English. 1998. bi-m. USD 35 domestic to individuals; USD 45 domestic to institutions (effective 2004). charts; illus.; stat. reprints avail. **Document type:** *Bulletin, Academic/Scholarly.* **Description:** Review of reproductive health and public policy.
Formed by the merger of (1968-1998): Washington Memo (0739-4179); (1990-1998): State Reproductive Health Monitor (1046-6703)
Related titles: Online - full text ed.: (from Gale Group).
Indexed: PAIS.
—Infotrieve. **CCC.**
Published by: Alan Guttmacher Institute, 120 Wall St, 21st Fl, New York, NY 10005. TEL 212-248-1111, FAX 212-248-1951, info@guttmacher.org, http://www.guttmacher.org/journals/tgr_archive.html. Ed. Cory Richards. R&P Kaylynn Chiarello. Circ: 3,000 (paid).

GYNECOLOGIE OBSTETRIQUE ET FERTILITE. see *MEDICAL SCIENCES—Obstetrics And Gynecology*

HANDLING PREGNANCY AND BIRTH CASES. see *LAW—Family And Matrimonial Law*

301.426 IND ISSN 0253-6803
RA529
HEALTH AND POPULATION: PERSPECTIVES AND ISSUES. Text in English. 1972. q. USD 60 (effective 2000). adv. bk.rev. **Document type:** *Academic/Scholarly.* **Description:** Focuses on family planning.
Formed by the merger of: N I H A E Bulletin (0378-6196); Journal of Population Research (0377-0478); Which was formerly: National Institute of Family Planning. Newsletter
Related titles: CD-ROM ed.
Indexed: AbHyg, BAS, ESPM, ExcerpMed, ExtraMED, H&SSA, JDDR, MEDLINE, PopulInd, TDB.
Published by: National Institute of Health and Family Welfare, New Mehrauli Rd., Munirka, New Delhi, 110 067, India. Ed. Somnath Roy. Circ: 1,000. **Dist. by:** H P C Publishers Distributors Pvt. Ltd., 4805 Bharat Ram Rd, 24 Darya Ganj, New Delhi 110 002, India. TEL 91-11-325-4401, FAX 91-11-686-3511.

613.9 USA ISSN 0194-8032
HQ767
HEARTBEAT (ORLANDO). Text in English. 1978. q. USD 25; includes Pulse. adv. bk.rev. charts; illus.
Published by: Institute for Women and Children, 4680 Lake Underhill Rd, Orlando, FL 32807. TEL 407-277-1942, FAX 407-381-0907. Circ: 4,000.

613.9 IDN
I P P A NEWSLETTER. Text in English. 1977. q. IDR 8,000, USD 5. stat. **Document type:** *Newsletter.* **Description:** Discusses methods used to curtail population growth.
Indexed: CLFP.
Published by: Indonesian Planned Parenthood Association, Jalan Hang Jebat 111-F3, Kebayaran Baru, PO Box 18, Jakarta, 12120, Indonesia. TEL 62-21-715905, FAX 62-21-7394088. Ed. Kustiniyati Muchtar. Circ: 2,000.

363.96 612.6 GBR
I P P F ANNUAL REPORT. Text in English, French, Spanish; Summaries in Japanese, German. 1974. a. free. illus. **Document type:** *Corporate.*
Former titles: I P P F in Action; International Planned Parenthood Federation. Annual Report (0307-6857)
Related titles: Online - full content ed.
Published by: International Planned Parenthood Federation, Regent's College, Inner Circle, Regent's Park, London, SW1 4NS, United Kingdom. TEL 44-20-7487-7900, FAX 44-20-7487-7950, info@ippf.org, http://www.ippf.org.

325 613.9 GBR ISSN 0019-0357
RG136 CODEN: IPPMAY
I P P F MEDICAL BULLETIN. Text in English, French, Spanish. 1966. bi-m. free to qualified personnel (effective 2005). **Document type:** *Bulletin, Academic/Scholarly.* **Description:** Provides up-to-date information on clinical aspects and developments in the field of family planning practice.
Related titles: Online - full content ed.; Online - full text ed.: (from Gale Group, O C L C Online Computer Library Center, Inc.); French ed.: Bulletin Medicale de l'I P P F. ISSN 0306-7815. 1966; Spanish ed.: Boletin Medico de I P P F. ISSN 0306-7823. 1966.
Indexed: AbHyg, DSA, ExcerpMed, Inpharma, MEDLINE, NutrAb, PE&ON, ProtozoAb, Reac, TDB.
—BLDSC (4567.450000), GNLM. **CCC.**
Published by: International Planned Parenthood Federation, Regent's College, Inner Circle, Regent's Park, London, SW1 4NS, United Kingdom. TEL 44-20-7487-7900, FAX 44-20-7487-7950, TELEX 919573 IPEPEE G, info@ippf.org, http://www.ippf.org/medical/bulletin/index.htm. Circ: 30,000 (controlled).

I U S S P NEWSLETTER/U I E S P BULLETIN DE LIAISON. see *POPULATION STUDIES*

I U S S P PAPERS/U I E S P DOCUMENTS DE L'UNION. see *POPULATION STUDIES*

363.46 USA ISSN 1538-6643
INFORMATION PLUS REFERENCE SERIES. ABORTION; an eternal social and moral issue. Text in English. 1980. biennial, latest 2004. USD 40 per issue (effective 2004). **Document type:** *Monographic series, Academic/Scholarly.*
Related titles: Online - full content ed.; ♦ Series of: Information Plus Reference Series.
Published by: Gale Group (Subsidiary of: Thomson Corporation), 27500 Drake Rd, Farmington Hills, MI 48331-3535. TEL 248-699-4253, 800-877-4253, FAX 248-699-8035, 800-414-5043, galeord@gale.com, http://www.galegroup.com.

613.94 ECU
INFORME ANUAL DE LAS ACTIVIDADES DE LAS UNIDADES OPERATIVAS DE SALUD EN EL PROGRAMA DE PLANIFICACION FAMILIAR DEL MINISTERIO DE SALUD. Text in Spanish. a.
Published by: Ministerio de Salud Publica, Departamento Nacional de Poblacion, Quito, Pichincha, Ecuador.

301.426 IND
INSTITUTE OF ECONOMIC RESEARCH. PUBLICATIONS ON FAMILY PLANNING. Text in English. irreg. price varies.
Published by: Institute of Economic Research, Director, Vidyagiri, Dharwar, Karnataka 580 004, India. FAX 836-41001.

INTERNATIONAL FAMILY PLANNING PERSPECTIVES. see *MEDICAL SCIENCES—Obstetrics And Gynecology*

INTERNATIONAL POPULATION CONFERENCE. PROCEEDINGS. see *POPULATION STUDIES*

363.96 USA
➤ **J A M A CONTRACEPTION NEWSLINE.** (Journal of the American Medical Association) Text in English. 1998. w. back issues avail. **Document type:** *Academic/Scholarly.*
Media: Online - full text.
Published by: American Medical Association, J A M A Information Centers, 515 N State St, Chicago, IL 60610. TEL 312-464-5000, 800-262-2350, FAX 312-464-4181, contraception@ama-assn.org, http://www.ama-assn.org/special/contra/contra.htm.

301.426 JPN ISSN 0911-0755
J O I C F P NEWS. Text in English. 1974. m. free. bk.rev. **Document type:** *Newsletter, Academic/Scholarly.* **Description:** Reports on reproductive health and family planning activities in Japan and the world, with a focus on the Integrated Project, promoted worldwide by JOICFP.
—BLDSC (4672.195750).
Published by: Japanese Organization for International Cooperation in Family Planning Inc., Hoken Kaikan Shinkan Bldg, 1-10 Ichi-Gayata-Machi, Shinjuku-ku, Tokyo, 162-0843, Japan. TEL 81-3-3268-5875, FAX 81-3-3235-7090, joicfp@i.bekkoame.ne.jp, info@joicfp.or.jp, http://www.bekkoame.ne.jp/i/joicfp. Ed. Yasuo Kon. Circ: 5,000.

301.426 USA ISSN 0891-0030
JOHNS HOPKINS UNIVERSITY. POPULATION INFORMATION PROGRAM. POPULATION REPORTS. SERIES C. FEMALE STERILIZATION. Text in Arabic, English, French, Portuguese, Spanish. 1973. irreg., latest vol.9, 1985. looseleaf. free to qualified personnel. bibl.; charts; illus.; stat. cum.index. back issues avail.
Former titles (until 1976): Johns Hopkins University. Population Information Program. Population Reports. Series C. Sterilization (Female) (0091-9268); (until 1973): George Washington University. Population Information Program. Population Reports. Series C. Sterilization (Female)
Indexed: IndMed, PopulInd.
Published by: Johns Hopkins University, Population Information Program, 624 N Broadway, Baltimore, MD 21205. TEL 301-955-8200. Ed. Ward Rinehart. Circ: (controlled).

613.94 610 USA ISSN 0891-0049
JOHNS HOPKINS UNIVERSITY. POPULATION INFORMATION PROGRAM. POPULATION REPORTS. SERIES D. MALE STERILIZATION. Text in English, French, Portuguese, Spanish. 1973. irreg., latest vol.4, 1983. looseleaf. free to qualified personnel. illus.; charts; bibl.; stat. back issues avail.
Former titles (until 1976): Johns Hopkins University. Population Information Program. Population Reports. Series D. Sterilization (Male) (0093-4488); (until 1973): George Washington University. Population Information Program. Population Reports. Series D. Sterilization (Male)
Indexed: IndMed, MEDLINE, PopulInd.
Published by: Johns Hopkins University, Population Information Program, 624 N Broadway, Baltimore, MD 21205. TEL 301-955-8200. Ed. Ward Rinehart. Circ: (controlled).

613.9 GBR ISSN 1471-1893
CODEN: BJFPDD
➤ **JOURNAL OF FAMILY PLANNING AND REPRODUCTIVE HEALTH CARE.** Text in English. 1975. q. GBP 45 domestic to individuals; GBP 50 foreign to individuals; GBP 90 domestic to institutions; GBP 110 foreign to institutions (effective 2003). adv. bk.rev. illus. **Document type:** *Journal, Academic/Scholarly.* **Description:** Presents original papers and review articles by leading authorities on all aspects of reproductive health care.
Formerly (until 2000): British Journal of Family Planning (0144-8625)
Related titles: Online - full text ed.: (from EBSCO Publishing, Gale Group, IngentaConnect).
Indexed: ASCA, BiolAb, BrNI, CINAHL, CLFP, CurCont, ExcerpMed, FamI, INI, IndMed, MEDLINE, SSCI.
—BLDSC (4983.722500), GNLM, IDS, IE, ingenta, KNAW. **CCC.**
Published by: Faculty of Family Planning and Reproductive Health Care, 11 Cornwall Ter, London, NWI 4QP, United Kingdom. journal@ffprhc.org.uk, http://www.catchword.com/ffp/14711893/contp1-1.htm, http://www.ffprhc.org.uk/. Circ: 11,000.

➤ **JOURNAL OF FAMILY WELFARE.** see *MEDICAL SCIENCES—Obstetrics And Gynecology*

➤ **JOURNAL OF PRENATAL & PERINATAL PSYCHOLOGY & HEALTH.** see *MEDICAL SCIENCES—Obstetrics And Gynecology*

613.9 IDN ISSN 0216-0269
KABAR. Text in Indonesian. 1980. q. IDR 9,600, USD 6.
Indexed: SPPI.
Published by: Indonesian Planned Parenthood Association, Jalan Hang Jebat 111-F3, Kebayaran Baru, PO Box 18, Jakarta, 12120, Indonesia. TEL 62-21-715905, FAX 62-21-7394088. Circ: 5,000.

613.9 338 GBR
KEY NOTE MARKET ASSESSMENT. CONTRACEPTIVES. Variant title: Contraceptives Market Assessment. Text in English. 1993. irreg., latest 2000, Feb. GBP 730 per issue (effective 2002). **Document type:** *Trade.* **Description:** Provides an overview of the UK contraceptives market, including industry structure, market size and trends, developments, prospects, and major company profiles.
Former titles (until 2000): Key Note Market Report: Contraceptives; Key Note Report: Contraceptives (1352-6561)
Related titles: CD-ROM ed.; Online - full text ed.
Published by: Key Note Ltd., Field House, 72 Oldfield Rd, Hampton, Mddx TW12 2HQ, United Kingdom. TEL 44-20-8481-8750, FAX 44-20-8783-0049, info@keynote.co.uk, http://www.keynote.co.uk.

179 306.874 USA ISSN 0882-116X
L F L REPORTS. Text in English. 1981. irreg. donation. bk.rev. back issues avail. **Document type:** *Newsletter.* **Description:** Focuses on the issue of abortion from a non-religious, libertarian pro-life perspective, and the philosophical foundation of parental obligation.
Published by: Libertarians for Life, 13424 Hathaway Dr., Wheaton, MD 20906. TEL 301-460-4141, DORIS.GORDON@IAD.BLKCAT.COM, http://www.cris.com/~bwjass/lfl. Ed. John Walker. Circ: 1,000.

613.9 DEU ISSN 0945-4586
LEBENSFORUM. Text in German. 1985. q. EUR 3 newsstand/cover (effective 2005). bk.rev. back issues avail. **Document type:** *Magazine, Consumer.* **Description:** Information about new fertility techniques, abortions, debate about bioethics and the ethical questions of abortion.
Formerly (until 1993): A L f A - Rundbrief (0931-3613)
Published by: Aktion Lebensrecht fuer Alle e.V., Ottmarsgaesschen 8, Augsburg, 86152, Germany. TEL 49-821-512031, FAX 49-821-156407, bgs@alfa-ev.de, http://www.alfa-ev.com. Ed. Jochen Beuckers. Circ: 5,000.

MALAYSIAN JOURNAL OF REPRODUCTIVE HEALTH. see *MEDICAL SCIENCES—Obstetrics And Gynecology*

618 IDN ISSN 0216-4027
MANTAP: MAJALAH ILMAIH P K M I/INDONESIAN ASSOCIATION FOR SECURE CONTRACEPTION. JOURNAL. Text mainly in Indonesian; Text occasionally in English. 1981. q. USD 200. reprint service avail. from IRC. **Document type:** *Academic/Scholarly.*
Published by: Perkumpulan Kontrasepsi Mantap Indonesia (PKMI)/Indonesian Association for Secure Contraception, Jalan Kramat Sentiong 49 A, Jakarta, 10450, Indonesia. TEL 62-21-3155122, FAX 62-21-3155125. Ed. Azrul Azwar. Circ: 1,000.

304.6 BOL
MONOGRAFIAS DE POBLACION Y DESARROLLO. Text in Spanish. 1974. irreg., latest vol.23, 1985. price varies. **Document type:** *Monographic series, Academic/Scholarly.*

B

▼ new title ➤ refereed ∗ unverified ♦ full entry avail.

Published by: Centro de Investigaciones Sociales, Casilla 6931 - C.C., La Paz, Bolivia. TEL 591-2-352931. Ed. Antonio Cisneros.

301.42 IND ISSN 0077-4944
N I F P GENERAL SERIES. Text in English. 1965. irreg., latest vol.22, 1977.
Published by: National Institute of Health and Family Welfare, New Mehrauli Rd., Munirka, New Delhi, 110 067, India. Ed. S Pramanik. Circ: 3,000.

301.42 IND ISSN 0077-4952
N I F P MANUAL SERIES. Text in English. 1966. irreg. free or on exchange basis.
Published by: National Institute of Health and Family Welfare, New Mehrauli Rd., Munirka, New Delhi, 110 067, India. Ed. S Pramanik. Circ: 3,000.

301.42 IND ISSN 0077-4960
N I F P MONOGRAPH SERIES. Text in English. 1966. irreg., latest vol.19, 1973. free.
Published by: National Institute of Health and Family Welfare, New Mehrauli Rd., Munirka, New Delhi, 110 067, India. Ed. S Pramanik. Circ: 3,000.

B

301.42 IND ISSN 0077-4979
N I F P REPORT SERIES. Text in English. 1966. irreg., latest vol.12, 1973. on exchange basis.
Published by: National Institute of Health and Family Welfare, New Mehrauli Rd., Munirka, New Delhi, 110 067, India. Ed. S Pramanik. Circ: 3,000.

301.42 IND ISSN 0077-4987
N I F P TECHNICAL PAPER SERIES. Text in English. 1966. irreg., latest vol.17, 1973. on exchange basis.
Published by: National Institute of Health and Family Welfare, New Mehrauli Rd., Munirka, New Delhi, 110 067, India. Ed. S Pramanik. Circ: 3,000.

613.9 618 616.95 USA ISSN 0270-3637
NETWORK (DURHAM). Text in English. 1979. q. free to qualified personnel. back issues avail. **Document type:** *Newsletter, Academic/Scholarly.* **Description:** Covers contraceptive methods, concern for maternal and child mortality; AIDS; sexually transmitted diseases.
Related titles: Online - full text ed.: (from Florida Center for Library Automation, Gale Group, O C L C Online Computer Library Center, Inc.); French ed.; Spanish ed.
Indexed: CINAHL, CWI, PAIS.
Published by: Family Health International, PO Box 13950, Research Triangle Park, NC 27709. TEL 919-544-7040, FAX 919-544-7261, http://www.fhi.org. Ed. Nash Herndon. Circ: 65,000 (controlled).

NEW PARENT. see *MEDICAL SCIENCES—Obstetrics And Gynecology*

613.9 DNK
NYHEDSBREV - FORENINGEN SEX & SAMFUND. Text in Danish. 1994. irreg. (4-6/yr). free. bk.rev. back issues avail. **Document type:** *Newsletter, Consumer.* **Description:** Information and articles about sexual and reproductive health and rights.
Former titles (until 2004): Nyhedsbrev - Foreningen Sex og Samfund (Print) (1396-8165); (until 1996): Nyhedsbrev - Foreningen for Familieplanlaegning. Sex og Samfund (1396-8157); Incorporates (1997-1998): Nyt fra Foreningen Sex & Samfund
Media: Online - full content.
Published by: Foreningen Sex og Samfund/Danish Family Planning Association, Rosenoernsalle 12,1, Copenhagen V, 1634, Denmark. TEL 45-33-931010, FAX 45-33-931009, info@sexogsamfund.dk, http://www.sexogsamfund.dk/Default.asp?ID=974. Eds. Katja Iversen, Bjarne B Christensen. Circ: 6,000.

ON THE ISSUES; the progressive woman's quarterly. see *WOMEN'S INTERESTS*

301.426 IND
ORISSA FAMILY PLANNING BULLETIN. Text in English. 1971. m. free. charts.
Published by: State Family Welfare Bureau, Directorate of Family Welfare, Bhubaneswar, Orissa, India. Ed. Dr. N N Parida. Circ: 1,200.

OUTLOOK (SEATTLE); reproductive health. see *PUBLIC HEALTH AND SAFETY*

613.9 AUS ISSN 1323-675X
➤ **OVULATION METHOD RESEARCH AND REFERENCE CENTRE OF AUSTRALIA. BULLETIN.** Text in English. 1974. q. AUD 30 (effective 2003). bk.rev. cum.index every 2 yrs. back issues avail. **Document type:** *Bulletin, Academic/Scholarly.* **Description:** Covers philosophy and theology of marriage, scientific research into reproductive biology pertaining to natural family planning, and the teaching of natural family planning.
Formerly (until vol.22, no.1, 1995): Natural Family Planning Council of Victoria. Bulletin (0312-7567)
Published by: Ovulation Method Research and Reference Centre of Australia, Billings Family Life Centre, Melbourne, 27 Alexandra Parade, Fitzroy North, VIC 3068, Australia. TEL 61-3-94811722, FAX 61-3-94824208, billings@ozemail.com.au, http://www.woomb.org. Ed. John J Billings. R&P J J Billings TEL 61-3-94811722. Circ: 3,000.

613.9 USA
OVULATION METHOD TEACHERS ASSOCIATION (PUBLICATION). Text in English. 1975. q. looseleaf. USD 10. adv. bk.rev. back issues avail. **Description:** Covers ovulation method of natural family planning and related health issues.
Published by: Ovulation Method Teachers Association, PO Box 10 1780, Anchorage, AK 99510-1780. TEL 907-343-4623, FAX 907-344-8606. Circ: 500.

PASSAGES (WASHINGTON, D.C.) (ONLINE EDITION). see *CHILDREN AND YOUTH—About*

PERSPECTIVAS INTERNACIONALES EN PLANIFICACION FAMILIAR. see *MEDICAL SCIENCES—Obstetrics And Gynecology*

PERSPECTIVES INTERNATIONALES SUR LE PLANNING FAMILIAL. see *MEDICAL SCIENCES—Obstetrics And Gynecology*

PERSPECTIVES ON SEXUAL AND REPRODUCTIVE HEALTH. see *MEDICAL SCIENCES—Obstetrics And Gynecology*

613.94 IND
PLANNED PARENTHOOD. Text in English. 1953. m. free. **Document type:** *Bulletin.*
Related titles: Microfilm ed.: (from PQC).
Published by: Family Planning Association of India, Bajaj Bhavan, Nariman Point, Mumbai, Maharashtra 400 021, India. TEL 91-22-202-9080, FAX 91-22-202-9038, fpai@giasbm01.vsnl.net.in, http://www.fpaindia.com/. Ed., R&P Jaishree Kochavara. Circ: 5,000.

613.94 USA
PLANNED PARENTHOOD TODAY; news from the most trusted advocate for reproductive choice. Text in English. q. illus. **Description:** Reports on topics of reproductive freedom and other issues affecting the health of women.
Published by: Planned Parenthood Federation of America, Inc., 434 W. 33rd St., Flr. 12, New York, NY 10001-2600. TEL 212-541-7800, members_services@ppfa.org, http://www.ppfa.org. Ed. Danielle T Leigh. **Subscr. to:** PPFA, PO Box 4447, New York, NY 10164-0359. TEL 212-261-4677.

POPULATION REPORTS (ENGLISH EDITION). see *POPULATION STUDIES*

POPULATION REPORTS (FRENCH EDITION). see *POPULATION STUDIES*

POPULATION REPORTS (PORTUGUESE EDITION). see *POPULATION STUDIES*

POPULATION REPORTS (SPANISH EDITION). see *POPULATION STUDIES*

PRO FAMILIA MAGAZIN; die Zeitschrift fuer Sexualpaedagogik, Sexualberatung und Familienplanung. see *PSYCHOLOGY*

363.46 USA
PRO-LIFE ACTION NEWS. Text in English. 1981. q. USD 10 donation (effective 2000). adv. bk.rev. **Document type:** *Newspaper.* **Description:** Includes material relating to pro-life activism such as protests and sidewalk counseling.
Published by: Pro-Life Action League, 6160 N Cicero Ave, Ste 600, Chicago, IL 60646. TEL 773-777-2900, FAX 773-777-3061, scheidl@ibm.net, http://www.prolifeaction.org. Ed., Adv. contact Ann Scheidler. Circ: 7,500.

613.9 USA
PULSE (ORLANDO). Text in English. q. USD 29 includes Heartbeat.
Published by: Institute for Women and Children, 4680 Lake Underhill Rd, Orlando, FL 32807. TEL 407-277-1942, FAX 407-381-0907.

305 GBR ISSN 1367-5486
REAL LIVES. Text in English. 1997. irreg. **Document type:** *Magazine, Consumer.*
Related titles: Online - full text ed.: (from Gale Group, O C L C Online Computer Library Center, Inc.).
Published by: International Planned Parenthood Federation, South Asia Regional Office, Regent's College, Inner Circle, Regent's Park, London, NW1 4NS, United Kingdom. TEL 44-20-7487-7977, FAX 44-20-7487-7970, sarinfo@ippf.org, http://ippfnet.ippf.org. Ed. Dr. Indira Kapoor.

RENKOUXUE YU JIHUA SHENGYU/POPULATION SCIENCE AND FAMILY PLANNING. see *POPULATION STUDIES*

REPORTER ON HUMAN REPRODUCTION & THE LAW; cases, statutes and materials on law and life sciences. see *LAW*

612.6 CHN ISSN 1001-7844
REPRODUCTION AND CONTRACEPTION. Text in English. 1989. q. USD 20 newsstand/cover (effective 2005). back issues avail. **Document type:** *Journal, Academic/Scholarly.*
Related titles: Online - full content ed.: (from WanFang Data Corp.); Online - full text ed.: (from East View Information Services); ♦ Chinese ed.: Shengzhi yu Biyun. ISSN 0253-357X.
—BLDSC (7713.598350).
Published by: Shanghai Jihua Shengyu Kexue Yanjiusuo, 2140 Xietu Lu, Shanghai, 200032, China. randc@sippr.stc.sh.cn, http://www.randc.cn/. R&P Lixi Wang. Circ: 500 (paid); 100 (controlled).

RESUMENES SOBRE POBLACION DOMINICANA. see *POPULATION STUDIES*

613.9 CHN ISSN 0253-357X
RG136.A1 CODEN: SCYYDZ
SHENGZHI YU BIYUN. Text in Chinese. 1980. bi-m. CNY 60 domestic; USD 25.20 foreign (effective 2005). 200 p./no.; **Document type:** *Journal, Academic/Scholarly.* **Description:** Covers birth control related issues in China.
Related titles: Online - full text ed.: (from East View Information Services, WanFang Data Corp.); ♦ English ed.: Reproduction and Contraception. ISSN 1001-7844.
Indexed: CIN, ChemAb, ChemTitl.
—BLDSC (7713.598300), CASDDS, GNLM, IE, Infotrieve, ingenta.
Published by: Shanghai Jihua Shengyu Kexue Yanjiusuo, 2140 Xietu Lu, Shanghai, 200032, China. randc@sippr.stc.sh.cn, http://www.randc.cn/. Circ: 4,000. **Dist. by:** China International Book Trading Corp, 35 Chegongzhuang Xilu, Haidian District, PO Box 399, Beijing 100044, China. TEL 86-10-68412045, FAX 86-10-68412023, cibtc@mail.cibtc.com.cn, http://www.cibtc.com.cn.

SINGAPORE JOURNAL OF OBSTETRICS & GYNAECOLOGY. see *MEDICAL SCIENCES—Obstetrics And Gynecology*

618 614 USA
U.S. CENTERS FOR DISEASE CONTROL. ABORTION SURVEILLANCE. ANNUAL SUMMARY. Text in English. a. free. **Document type:** *Academic/Scholarly.*
Formerly: Abortion Surveillance
Indexed: CLFP.
Published by: U.S. Department of Health and Human Services, Centers for Disease Control and Prevention, 1600 Clifton Rd, Atlanta, GA 30333. TEL 404-639-3311, 800-311-3435, http://www.cdc.gov.

WOMEN'S GLOBAL NETWORK FOR REPRODUCTIVE RIGHTS. NEWSLETTER. see *WOMEN'S HEALTH*

613.9 USA
WORLD FEDERATION OF HEALTH AGENCIES FOR THE ADVANCEMENT OF VOLUNTARY SURGICAL CONTRACEPTION. COMMUNIQUE✶. Text in Arabic, English, French, Spanish. 2/yr. free. illus.
Published by: World Federation of Health Agencies for the Advancement of Voluntary Surgical Contraception, 440 9th Ave, FRNT 2, New York, NY 10001-1620. TEL 212-351-2525, FAX 212-599-0959, TELEX 425604 AVS UI. Ed. Lynn Bakamjian. Circ: 5,500.

363.96 CHN ISSN 1004-8189
ZHONGGUO JIHUA ZHENGYUXUE ZAZHI/CHINESE JOURNAL OF FAMILY PLANNING. Text in Chinese. 1992 (Oct.). m. **Document type:** *Academic/Scholarly.*
Related titles: Online - full text ed.: (from East View Information Services).
—BLDSC (3180.327700), IE, ingenta.
Published by: (Guojia Jihua Shengyu Weiyuanhui/State Commission of Family Planning of the People's Republic of China), Zhongguo Jihua Zhengyuxue Zazhi, 12 Dahuisi Road, Beijing, 100081, China. TEL 86-10-62185784. Ed. Yaohua Zhu. **Dist. by:** China International Book Trading Corp, 35 Chegongzhuang Xilu, Haidian District, PO Box 399, Beijing 100044, China. TEL 86-10-68412045, FAX 86-10-68412023, cibtc@mail.cibtc.com.cn, http://www.cibtc.com.cn.

613.9 CHN ISSN 1671-878X
ZHONGGUO SHENGYU JIANKANG ZAZHI/CHINESE JOURNAL FOR HEALTH OF WOMEN IN CHILDBIRTH. Text in Chinese. 1990. bi-m. CNY 24 (effective 2004). **Document type:** *Journal, Academic/Scholarly.*
Formerly: Zhongguo Yousheng Youyu/Journal of Improving Birth Outcome and Child Development of China (1007-3434)
Related titles: Online - full text ed.: (from WanFang Data Corp.).
Address: Haidian-qu, 38, Xueyuan Lu, Beijing, 100083, China. TEL 38-10-82802942, FAX 38-10-82801141, bianjb@ncmih.bjmu.edu.cn, http://zgsyjkzz.periodicals.net.cn/gyjs.asp?ID=699482. **Dist. by:** China International Book Trading Corp, 35 Chegongzhuang Xilu, Haidian District, PO Box 399, Beijing 100044, China. TEL 86-10-68412045, FAX 86-10-68412023, cibtc@mail.cibtc.com.cn, http://www.cibtc.com.cn.

BIRTH CONTROL—Abstracting, Bibliographies, Statistics

613.9 GBR ISSN 0140-5314
HQ767.5.G7
GREAT BRITAIN. GOVERNMENT STATISTICAL SERVICE. ABORTION STATISTICS. Text in English. 1974. irreg.
Document type: *Government.*
—BLDSC (6237.634000).
Published by: (Puerto Rico. Department of Health USA, Great Britain. Statistics Division), Government Statistical Service, SD2, Rm 804, Hannibal House, Elephant and Castle, London, SE1 6TE, United Kingdom. TEL 0171-972-2193. **Orders to:** Department of Health and Social Security (Leaflets), PO Box 21, Stanmore, Mddx HA7 1AY, United Kingdom.

301 USA ISSN 0095-3105
HQ767.5.U5
NEBRASKA STATISTICAL REPORT OF ABORTIONS. Text in English. a. free. **Document type:** *Government.*
Published by: Data Management, PO Box 95007, Lincoln, NE 68509. TEL 402-471-2871, mark.miller@hhss.state.ne.us, http://www.hhs.state.ne.us. Ed. Mark Miller.

301.426 016 IND ISSN 0028-4327
NEW BOOKS ON FAMILY PLANNING. Text in English. 1968. bi-m. per issue exchange basis. bibl.
Media: Duplicated (not offset).
Published by: National Institute of Health and Family Welfare, New Mehrauli Rd., Munirka, New Delhi, 110 067, India. Circ: 1,250 (controlled).

613.9 SEN
SENEGAL. MINISTERE DE L'ECONOMIE, DES FINANCES ET DU PLAN. ENQUETE SUR LA PLANIFICATION FAMILIALE. Text in French. 1990. irreg. XOF 5,000; XOF 7,000 foreign (effective 1998). **Document type:** *Government.*
Published by: Ministere de l'Economie des Finances et du Plan, Direction de la Prevision et de la Statistique, BP 116, Dakar, Senegal. TEL 221-21-03-01. Pub. Ibrahima Sarr.

613.94 618.88 DNK ISSN 1397-2812
STATISTIK OM PRAEVENTION OG ABORTER (YEAR). (Included in the series: Vitalstatistik) Text in Danish; Summaries in English. 1993. a.
Formerly (until 1997): Statistik om Praevention og Aborter (1395-7104); Which was formed by the merger of (1975-1993): Statistik om Praevention og Aborter (0106-7729); Which was formerly (until 1978): Statistik om Legale Aborter (0106-7281); (1988-1993): Medicinsk Foedsels- og Misdannelsesstatistik (0904-1966); Which was formed by the merger of (1973-1988): Medicinsk Foedselsstatistik (0107-7597); (1984-1988): Misdannelsesregisteret (0109-5331)
Related titles: ◆ Series of: Sundhedsstatistikken (Year). ISSN 0909-4156.
Published by: Sundhedsstyrelsen/Danish Board of Health, Islands Brygge 67, PO Box 1881, Copenhagen S, 2300, Denmark. TEL 45-72-227400, FAX 45-72-227411, sst@sst.dk, http://www.sst.dk. **Subscr. to:** Statens Informationt, PO Box 1003, Copenhagen K 1009, Denmark.

618 USA ISSN 0094-0933
U.S. CENTERS FOR DISEASE CONTROL. ABORTION SURVEILLANCE. Text in English. 1969. q. free. stat.
Document type: *Government.*
Supersedes (in 1972): U.S. Centers for Disease Control. Abortion Surveillance Report (0300-6972)
Published by: U.S. Department of Health and Human Services, Centers for Disease Control and Prevention, 1600 Clifton Rd, Atlanta, GA 30333. TEL 404-639-3311, 800-311-3435, http://www.cdc.gov. Circ: (controlled).

BOATS AND BOATING

see SPORTS AND GAMES—Boats And Boating

BOTANY

see BIOLOGY—Botany

BUDDHISM

see RELIGIONS AND THEOLOGY—Buddhist

BUILDING AND CONSTRUCTION

see also ARCHITECTURE ; BUILDING AND CONSTRUCTION—Carpentry And Woodwork ; BUILDING AND CONSTRUCTION—Hardware ; ENGINEERING—Civil Engineering ; HEATING, PLUMBING AND REFRIGERATION ; HOUSING AND URBAN PLANNING

A A M A INDUSTRY STATISTICAL REVIEW AND FORECAST. see *BUILDING AND CONSTRUCTION—Abstracting, Bibliographies, Statistics*

690 USA
A A M A SCOPE. Text in English. 1985. 3/yr. back issues avail.
Document type: *Trade.*
Formerly: A A M A Quarterly Review
Published by: American Architectural Manufacturers Association, 1827 Walden Office Sq, Ste 550, Schaumburg, IL 60173-4268. TEL 847-303-5664, FAX 847-303-5774, webmaster@AAMANET.org, http://www.AAMANET.org. R&P Pamela Lierman. Circ: 12,000.

690 USA
A A M A UPDATE. Text in English. 1975. m. free (effective 2004).
Document type: *Newsletter.*
Published by: American Architectural Manufacturers Association, 1827 Walden Office Sq, Ste 550, Schaumburg, IL 60173-4268. TEL 847-303-5664, FAX 847-303-5774, webmaster@AAMANET.org, http://www.AAMANET.org. R&P A S Coorlim.

692.8 USA ISSN 1062-3698
A B C TODAY. Text in English. 1953. s-w. USD 42 to members; USD 60 to non-members (effective 2001). adv. bk.rev.; software rev. back issues avail. **Document type:** *Trade.*
Description: Covers the latest legislative, legal and regulatory happenings that affect the construction industry. It looks at niche markets, economic forecasts, and award winning construction projects.
Former titles: A B C Newsline (0888-014X); (until 1985): Merit Shop Scoop (0279-9464)
Related titles: Supplement(s): Computers in Construction; Surety Bonding Supplement; Metal Building Today; Guide to Construction Insurance.
Published by: Associated Builders & Contractors, Inc., 4250 N Fairfax Dr, Arlington, VA 22203. TEL 703-812-2063, FAX 703-812-8203. Ed., R&P Lisa A Nardone TEL 703-812-2063. Pub. Robert Hepner. Adv. contact Robert H Kruhm. B&W page USD 1,975; trim 16 x 10.75. Circ: 22,000 (paid).

690 GBR
A B I - B C I S HOUSE REBUILDING COST INDEX. (Association for British Insurers - Building Cost Information Service) Text in English. 1993. m. GBP 87.50 (effective 2001). **Document type:** *Bulletin.* **Description:** Updates B.C.I.S. house rebuilding cost figures published annually in the Guide to House Rebuilding Costs for Insurance Valuation.
Related titles: ◆ Issued with: B C I S Guide to House Rebuilding Costs. ISSN 1350-9500.
—BLDSC (0549.393600).
Published by: Building Cost Information Service Ltd., Royal Institution of Chartered Surveyors, Parliment Sq, 12 Great George St, London, SW1P 3AD, United Kingdom. TEL 44-20-7222-7000, FAX 44-20-7695-1501. **Co-sponsor:** Association for British Insurers.

690 346 DNK ISSN 1603-4546
A B L O NYT; andels- og ejerboligbladet. (Andelsbolighavernes Lands-Organisation) Text in Danish. 1987. 5/yr. DKK 160 (effective 2004). adv. illus. **Document type:** *Trade.*
Formerly (until 2002): Andels- og Ejerboligbladet (0909-1254)
Published by: Landsforeningen af Private Andels- & Ejerboligforeninger i Danmark, Ringstedvej 503, Bjaeverskov, 4632, Denmark. TEL 45-70-200599, FAX 45-56-872529, info@ablo.dk, http://www.ablo.dk. Ed. Allan Tyllesen. Circ: 9,000 (controlled).

691.3 USA ISSN 0065-7875
TA439
A C I MANUAL OF CONCRETE PRACTICE. Text in English. 1967. a. (in 6 vols.). USD 709.50 to non-members (effective 2005).
—BLDSC (0576.650000), CISTI. **CCC.**
Published by: American Concrete Institute, PO Box 9094, Farmington, MI 48333. TEL 248-848-3700, FAX 248-848-3701, webmaster@aci-int.org, http://www.aci-int.org.

690 USA ISSN 0889-325X
TA439.A36 CODEN: AMAJEF
➤ **A C I MATERIALS JOURNAL.** Text in English. 1929. bi-m. USD 142 domestic; USD 150 foreign (effective 2005). adv. illus. index. reprint service avail. from PQC. **Document type:** *Academic/Scholarly.* **Description:** Focuses on properties, uses, research, and handling of materials used in concrete.
Supersedes in part (Mar. 1987): American Concrete Institute. Journal (0002-8061)
Related titles: Microfiche ed.; Microfilm ed.; Online - full text ed.: (from EBSCO Publishing).
Indexed: AS&TI, ASCA, ASFA, BrCerAb, C&ISA, CIN, CRIA, CRICC, CerAb, ChemAb, ChemTitl, CivEngAb, ConcrAb, CorrAb, CurCont, E&CAJ, EEA, EMA, ESPM, EngInd, GeotechAb, H&SSA, HRIS, IAA, ICEA, ISR, M&TEA, MBF, METADEX, MSCI, SCI, WAA.
—BLDSC (0576.655000), CASDDS, CISTI, Ei, IDS, IE, Infotrieve, ingenta, Linda Hall. **CCC.**
Published by: American Concrete Institute, PO Box 9094, Farmington, MI 48333. TEL 248-848-3700, FAX 248-848-3701, webmaster@aci-int.org, http://www.aci-int.org. Ed. Rebecca A Hartford. Circ: 11,700.

691 USA ISSN 0889-3241
TA680 CODEN: ASTJEG
➤ **A C I STRUCTURAL JOURNAL.** Text in English. 1929. bi-m. USD 142 domestic; USD 150 foreign (effective 2005). adv. charts; illus. index, cum.index: 1905-1959, 1960-1989 (publications); vols. 1-78 (proceedings). back issues avail.; reprint service avail. from PQC. **Document type:** *Academic/Scholarly.* **Description:** Focuses on the structural design and analysis of concrete elements and structures.
Supersedes in part (Mar. 1987): American Concrete Institute. Journal (0002-8061)
Related titles: Microform ed.: (from PQC); Online - full text ed.: (from ProQuest Information & Learning).
Indexed: AJEE, AS&TI, ASCA, ASFA, ApMecR, BrCerAb, C&ISA, CRIA, CRICC, CerAb, ChemAb, CivEngAb, ConcrAb, CorrAb, CurCont, E&CAJ, EEA, EMA, ESPM, EngInd, ExcerpMed, GeotechAb, H&SSA, HRIS, IAA, ICEA, ISMEC, ISR, Inspec, JOF, M&TEA, MBF, METADEX, MSCI, RefZh, SCI, SoftAbEng, SolStAb, WAA.
—BLDSC (0576.821000), CASDDS, CISTI, Ei, IDS, IE, ingenta, Linda Hall. **CCC.**
Published by: American Concrete Institute, PO Box 9094, Farmington, MI 48333. TEL 248-848-3700, FAX 248-848-3701, webmaster@aci-int.org, http://www.aci-int.org. Ed. Rebecca A Hartford. Circ: 17,400.

➤ **A D S C MEMBERSHIP DIRECTORY.** see *BUSINESS AND ECONOMICS—Trade And Industrial Directories*

690 USA
A D S C PRODUCTS AND SERVICES GUIDE. Text in English. a. USD 25; USD 35 foreign (effective 1998). adv. bk.rev.
Document type: *Catalog.*
Published by: Association of Drilled Shaft Contractors, 14180 Dallas Pkwy, Ste 510, Dallas, TX 75254. TEL 214-343-2091, FAX 214-343-2384, http://www.adsc-iafd.com. Ed. Scot Litke. Circ: 1,800.

690 USA
A D S C TECHNICAL LIBRARY CATALOG. Text in English. s-a. free. **Document type:** *Catalog.*
Related titles: Online - full text ed.
Published by: Association of Drilled Shaft Contractors, 14180 Dallas Pkwy, Ste 510, Dallas, TX 75254. TEL 214-343-2091, FAX 214-343-2384, http://www.adsc-iafd.com.

A F E NEWSLINE. see *ENGINEERING*

690 USA
A G C NEWS SERVICE. Text in English. w. free to members (effective 2005). **Document type:** *Newspaper, Trade.*
Published by: Associated General Contractors of Houston, PO Box 662, Houston, TX 77092-8717. http://www.agchouston.org. Ed. Coleen Ludwig. Circ: 1,500 (controlled).

692.8 USA
A G C - OHIO. Text in English. 1991. bi-m. USD 20 (effective 1995). adv. back issues avail. **Document type:** *Trade.*
Description: Contains up-to-date information on industry trends, safety, and legislative issues. Written for the general contractor and owners-buyers of construction services.
Published by: Associated General Contractors of Ohio, 1755 Northwest Blvd, Columbus, OH 43212. TEL 614-486-6446, FAX 614-486-6498. Ed. Rich Hobbs. Adv. contact Mindy Meyer. page USD 745; trim 10.88 x 8.38. Circ: 3,000.

690 GBR
A M E C TIMES. Text in English. 1981. 6/yr. free. **Document type:** *Newspaper.*
Published by: A M E C p.l.c., Sandiway House, Hartfod, Northwich, Ches CW8 2YA, United Kingdom. TEL 44-1606-881091, FAX 44-1606-883996, steve.howarth@amec.co.uk, http://www.amec.co.uk. Ed. Steve Howarth. Circ: 25,000.

690 AUT
A P A - JOURNAL. BAU. Text in German. w. EUR 380 combined subscription for print & online eds. (effective 2003). **Document type:** *Journal, Trade.*
Related titles: Online - full text ed.
Published by: Austria Presse Agentur, Gunoldstr 14, Vienna, W 1190, Austria. TEL 43-1-360600, FAX 43-1-360603099, kundenservice@apa.at, http://www.apa.at.

690 FRA
A PROPOS (AURILLAC)✶. Text in French. q. adv.
Published by: Chambre Syndicale des Entrepreneurs du Batiment et des Travaux Publics du Central, Av. Georges-Pompidou, Aurillac, 15000, France.

A R T B A TRANSPORTATION OFFICIALS AND ENGINEERS DIRECTORY, STATE AND FEDERAL TRANSPORTATION AGENCY PERSONNEL. see *TRANSPORTATION—Roads And Traffic*

A S C. (Architects Standard Catalogue) see *ARCHITECTURE*

690 VEN
A - Z DE LA CONSTRUCCION Y LA DECORACION. Text in Spanish. 1975. a.

Published by: Publicaciones Araguaney, Edificio Lec piso 3, Calle 8, La Urbina, Caracas, DF 1073, Venezuela.

690 658 AUT
A3 BAU; das oesterreichische Baumagazin. Text in German. 1975. 10/yr. EUR 38 domestic; EUR 52 foreign; EUR 19 to students (effective 2005). adv. **Document type:** *Magazine, Trade.*
Published by: A3 Wirtschaftsverlag GmbH, Hagenauertalstr 40, Giesshuebl, N 2372, Austria. TEL 43-2236-425280, FAX 43-2236-26311, bau@a3verlag.com, a3@a3verlag.com, http://www.a3verlag.com. Ed. Heinz Honies. Adv. contact Peter Mayer. page EUR 6,970; trim 185 x 250. Circ: 15,226 (controlled).

690 DNK ISSN 1395-7953
AALBORG UNIVERSITET. INSTITUTTET FOR BYGNINGSTEKNIK. R. Text in Multiple languages. 1975. irreg., latest vol.307, 2003. price varies. illus. back issues avail. **Document type:** *Monographic series, Academic/Scholarly.*
Former titles (until 1994): Aalborg Universitetscenter. Instituttet for Bygningsteknik. R (0902-7513); (until 1984): Aalborg Universitetscenter. Instituttet for Bygningsteknik. Report (0105-7421)
Published by: Aalborg Universitet, Instituttet for Bygningsteknik/Aalborg University, Department of Building Technology and Structural Engineering, Sohngaardsholmvej 57, Aalborg, 9000, Denmark. TEL 45-96-358080, FAX 45-98-148243, http://www.civil.auc.dk/i6.

B

690 DNK ISSN 1395-8232
AALBORG UNIVERSITET. INSTITUTTET FOR BYGNINGSTEKNIK. U. Text in Danish. 1976. irreg., latest vol.210, 2002. price varies. illus. **Document type:** *Academic/Scholarly.*
Former titles (until 1994): Aalborg Universitetscenter. Instituttet for Bygningstechnik. U (0902-8005); (until 1984): Aalborg Universitetscenter. Instituttet for Bygningsteknik. Note (0105-8185)
Published by: Aalborg Universitet, Instituttet for Bygningsteknik/Aalborg University, Department of Building Technology and Structural Engineering, Sohngaardsholmvej 57, Aalborg, 9000, Denmark. TEL 45-96-358080, FAX 45-98-148243, http://www.civil.auc.dk/i6.

690 NLD ISSN 0926-9894
AANNEMER. Text in Dutch. 1990. 11/yr. EUR 147; EUR 71.50 to students (effective 2005). adv. illus. **Document type:** *Trade.* **Description:** Covers business and technical aspects of the contracting profession.
Formerly (until 1991): BouwWereld - Aannemer (0926-9886)
Related titles: ◆ Supplement(s): BouwSpecialist.
—IE, Infotrieve.
Published by: Reed Business Information bv (Subsidiary of: Reed Business), Hanzestraat 1, Doetinchem, 7006 RH, Netherlands. TEL 31-314-349911, FAX 31-314-343839, info@reedbusiness.nl, http://www.reedbusiness.nl. Ed. Peter de Winter TEL 31-314-349510. Pub. Pascal van Sluijs. Adv. contact Nienke Kool TEL 31-314-349369. B&W page EUR 2,460, color page EUR 3,882; trim 240 x 320. Circ: 6,513.

ACCESS CONTROL & SECURITY INTEGRATION BUYERS' GUIDE. see *BUSINESS AND ECONOMICS—Trade And Industrial Directories*

ACCESS CONTROL & SECURITY SYSTEMS. see *CRIMINOLOGY AND LAW ENFORCEMENT—Security*

690 GBR ISSN 1352-7517
ACCESS INTERNATIONAL. Text in English. 1994. 10/yr. USD 90 (effective 2001). adv. 60 p./no.; back issues avail.; reprints avail. **Document type:** *Magazine, Trade.* **Description:** Serves users and buyers of access equipment.
Published by: K H L Group Ltd., Southfields, Southview Rd, Wadhurst, E Sussex TN5 6TP, United Kingdom. TEL 44-1892-784088, FAX 44-1892-784086, mail@khl.com, www.accessindustry.com, http://www.khl.com. Ed. Murray Pollok. Pub. James King. R&P Peter Watkinson. Adv. contact Jon Williams. Circ: 500 (paid); 8,000 (controlled).

620.1 690 GBR
ACCESS YEARBOOK (YEAR). Text in English. a. GBP 39.95, USD 60 (effective 2001). **Document type:** *Directory.*
Published by: K H L Group Ltd., Southfields, Southview Rd, Wadhurst, E Sussex TN5 6TP, United Kingdom. TEL 44-1892-784088, FAX 44-1892-784086, mail@khl.com, http://www.khl.com. Pub. James King. R&P Peter Watkinson.

ACTA STRUCTILIA; wetenskaplijke tydskrif. see *ARCHITECTURE*

690 USA ISSN 1547-5719
ADDITIONS & DECKS. Variant title: Woman's Day Additions & Decks. Text in English. a. USD 4.99 newsstand/cover (effective 2005). adv. illus.; tr.lit. reprints avail. **Document type:** *Magazine, Consumer.* **Description:** Provides a guide to all aspects of planning and building an extension or a deck.
Published by: Hachette Filipacchi Media U.S., Inc. (Subsidiary of: Hachette Filipacchi Medias S.A.), 1633 Broadway, New York, NY 10019. TEL 212-767-6751, 212-767-6000, FAX 212-767-5612, http://www.hfmus.com. Ed. Olivia Monjo. adv.: B&W page USD 31,530, color page USD 45,050; trim 7.88 x 10.5. Circ: 350,000 (paid).

ADOBE JOURNAL. see *ARCHITECTURE*

691 GBR ISSN 0951-7197
CODEN: VMHSE2
➤ **ADVANCES IN CEMENT RESEARCH.** Text in English. 1987. q. GBP 131 domestic; GBP 170 foreign (effective 2004). bk.rev. **Document type:** *Journal, Academic/Scholarly.* **Description:** Deals with the fundamentals of cement science and includes original papers on current research on cements from all parts of the world.
Related titles: Online - full text ed.: (from EBSCO Publishing).
Indexed: BrCerAb, C&ISA, CIN, CRIA, CRICC, CerAb, ChemAb, ChemTitl, CivEngAb, CorrAb, CurCont, E&CAJ, EMA, EngInd, IAA, ICEA, Inspec, M&TEA, MBF, METADEX, MSCI, SolStAb, WAA.
—BLDSC (0703.320000), CASDDS, CISTI, Ei, IDS, IE, Infotrieve, ingenta, Linda Hall. **CCC.**
Published by: Thomas Telford Ltd., Thomas Telford House, 1 Heron Quay, London, E14 4JD, United Kingdom. TEL 44-20-76652460, FAX 44-20-75389620, journals@thomastelford.com, http://www.cement-research.com, http://www.t-telford.co.uk/. Eds. Fred Glasser, Simon Fullalove TEL 44-20-76652448. Circ: 300.

690 USA
ADVANTAGE (SPRINGFIELD). Variant title: I L M D A Advantage. Text in English. 1932. m. adv. **Document type:** *Magazine, Trade.*
Formerly: Illinois Building News (0019-1914)
Published by: Illinois Lumber and Material Dealers Association, Inc., 932 S Spring St, Springfield, IL 62704. TEL 217-544-5405, 800-252-8641, FAX 217-544-4206, ilmda@ilmda.com, http://www.ilmda.com. Ed. Barry Johnson. Pub. Mary Murphy. Adv. contact Trisha Beaty. Circ: 1,000 (paid).

AECWORKFORCE. see *OCCUPATIONS AND CAREERS*

692.8 FRA ISSN 0001-9666
AFFICHES D'ALSACE ET DE LORRAINE - MONITEUR DES SOUMISSIONS ET DES VENTES DE BOIS DE L'EST. Text in French. 1919. s-w. adv. bk.rev. bibl. index. **Document type:** *Newspaper.*
Published by: Affiches Moniteur, 1 bis rue de Bouxwiller, B.P. 238-R6, Strasbourg, Cedex 67006, France. TEL 88-21-59-79, FAX 88-23-56-24. Ed., Adv. contact Gilbert Bretillon. Circ: 11,000.

691 ZAF
AFRICAN BUILDING CONTRACTOR. Short title: A B C. Text in English. bi-m. adv. illus. **Document type:** *Trade.* **Description:** For informal building contractors. Aims to encourage black building entrepreneurs, and improve the skills of the black builder.
Published by: Emden Publishing Co., PO Box 1123, Pinegowrie, Transvaal 2123, South Africa. TEL 27-11-886-0208, FAX 27-11-789-5223. Ed. Dennis Bird. Circ: 12,000.

690 CAN
AGGREGATES & ROAD BUILDING CONTRACTOR. Text in English. 1987. 8/yr. CND 35 domestic; USD 60 in United States (effective 1999). adv. **Document type:** *Trade.*
Former titles: Canadian Aggregates and Road Building Contractor; (until 1993): Canadian Aggregates (0836-799X)
Published by: Franmore Communications Inc., 4999 St Catherines St W, Ste 215, Westmount, PQ H3Z 1T3, Canada. TEL 514-487-9868, FAX 514-487-9276. Ed., Pub. Robert L Consediwe. Adv. contact Tony Buttino. B&W page CND 3,129; trim 10.88 x 8.13. Circ: 12,500.

690 658 USA ISSN 1552-3071
AGGREGATES MANAGER. Text in English. 1996. bi-m. free to qualified personnel (effective 2005). adv. back issues avail. **Document type:** *Magazine, Trade.*
Former titles (until 2003): AggMan (1539-8366); (until 2001): Aggregates Manager (1087-3015)
Published by: James Informational Media, Inc., 2720 S River Rd, Ste 126, Des Plaines, IL 60018. TEL 847-391-9070, 800-957-9305, FAX 847-391-9058, kirk@jiminc.com, http://www.aggman.com, http://www.jiminc.com. Ed. Ruth W Stidger. Pub. Michael Porcaro.

690 USA ISSN 1046-7947
TH4911
AGRICULTURAL BUILDING COST GUIDE (YEAR). Text in English. a. USD 52 (effective 1998). **Description:** Aims to assist insurance, appraisal, and assessment industries to estimate the replacement cost of agricultural buildings in the U.S.
Published by: E.H. Boeckh, Ed. & Pub. (Subsidiary of: Thomson Publishing Corp.), 2885 S Calhoun Rd, Box 510291, New Berlin, WI 53151-0291. TEL 414-780-2800, FAX 414-780-0306. R&P E H Boeckh.

690 620.1 MDG
AKORA SOA; revue technique sur la qualite des materiaux et du batiment. Text in French. q. MGF 12, USD 2. **Document type:** *Proceedings.*
Published by: Centre d'Information et de Documentation Scientifique et Technique, BP 6224, Antananarivo, 101, Madagascar. TEL 33288. Ed. Juliette Ratsimandrava.

AKTIV. see *FORESTS AND FORESTRY—Lumber And Wood*

690 SWE ISSN 1401-4149
AKTUELLA BYGGEN. Text in Swedish. 1989. 6/yr. SEK 695 (effective 2003). adv. **Document type:** *Journal.*
Former titles (until 1995): Bygg- och Fastighetsutveckling (1101-6922); (until 1990): Bygg-guiden (1100-3782); (until 1989): Stockholms Bygg-guide; Incorporates (1990-1991): Aktuella Byggen (1101-4636)
Published by: Medact Press AB, Hangoevaegen 19, PO Box 114, Stockholm, 11574, Sweden. TEL 46-8-50624400, FAX 46-8-50624499, http://www.medact.se/t_byggen/index.asp. Ed. Anders Frankson TEL 46-8-50624432. Adv. contact David Modin TEL 46-8-50624427. B&W page SEK 18,400, color page SEK 23,700; 194 x 260.

690 USA ISSN 0002-4155
ALABAMA BUILDER✶. Text in English. 1958. m. membership. adv. tr.lit.
Published by: Home Builders Association of Alabama, Inc., PO Box 1431, Montgomery, AL 36102-1431. Ed. Teresa Owens. Circ: 3,000.

▼ **THE ALABAMA ROADBUILDER.** see *TRANSPORTATION—Roads And Traffic*

ALBERTA CONSTRUCTION SERVICE & SUPPLY DIRECTORY. see *BUSINESS AND ECONOMICS—Trade And Industrial Directories*

ALL OF HOUSING/KATEI-BAN HYAKKA SERIES. see *HOUSING AND URBAN PLANNING*

690 DEU ISSN 0002-5801
ALLGEMEINE BAUZEITUNG. Text in German. 1930. w. EUR 109.72; EUR 4.20 newsstand/cover (effective 2004). adv. bk.rev. abstr.; charts; illus.; pat.; stat.; tr.lit. back issues avail. **Document type:** *Newspaper, Trade.*
Published by: Patzer Verlag GmbH und Co. KG, Koenigsallee 65, Berlin, 14193, Germany. TEL 49-30-8959030, FAX 49-30-89590317, abz@patzer-verlag.de, http://www.abznet.de, http://www.patzerverlag.de. Ed. Rainer Oschuetz. Pub. Ulrich Patzer. Adv. contact Kirsten Koschitzki TEL 49-511-6740840. B&W page EUR 14,572.80, color page EUR 25,502.40. Circ: 32,583 (paid and controlled).

643.7 DEU ISSN 0943-061X
ALTHAUS MODERNISIEREN; der Ratgeber fuer besseres Wohnen. Text in German. 1973. bi-m. EUR 2.50 newsstand/cover (effective 2004). adv. bk.rev. **Document type:** *Magazine, Trade.*
Formerly (until 1992): Althaus Modernisierung (0343-1762)
Related titles: ◆ Supplement(s): Dachausbau.
Published by: Fachschriften Verlag GmbH, Hoehenstr 17, Fellbach, 70736, Germany. TEL 49-711-52061, FAX 49-711-5206223, info@fachschriften.de, http://www.fachschriften.de/publikationen/althaus.htm. Ed. Kurt Jeni. Pub. Ottmar Strebel. Adv. contact Wolfgang Loges. B&W page EUR 5,400, color page EUR 8,910; trim 187 x 247. Circ: 69,532 (paid and controlled).

690 USA
AMERICAN BUILDER MAGAZINE. (Published in several regional editions) Text in English. m. adv. reprints avail. **Document type:** *Trade.* **Description:** Contains material of interest to regional residential building professionals, including architects, builders, designers, developers, remodelers, subcontractors, and suppliers.
Indexed: AIAP.
Published by: Transcontinental Publishing Inc., 27003, Scottsdale, AZ 85255-0133. TEL 602-331-8900, transpub@aol.com. Pub. Richard T Hyers Sr. Circ: (controlled).

691.3 USA ISSN 0065-7646
AMERICAN CEMENT DIRECTORY; directory of cement companies and personnel, United States, Canada, Mexico, Central and South America. Text in English. 1909. a. USD 71 (effective 1999). adv. index. **Document type:** *Directory.*
Published by: Bradley Pulverizer Co., 123 S Third St, PO Box 1318, Allentown, PA 18105-1318. TEL 610-434-5191, FAX 610-770-9400, http://www.bradleypulv.com/cement.html. Ed., R&P David J Fronheiser. Adv. contact Irene Lepage. Circ: 800.

625.84 691 USA ISSN 0517-0745
AMERICAN CONCRETE INSTITUTE. COMPILATION. Text in English. 1962. irreg. price varies.
—CISTI.
Published by: American Concrete Institute, PO Box 9094, Farmington, MI 48333. TEL 248-848-3700, FAX 248-848-3701, webmaster@aci-int.org, http://www.aci-int.org.

691 USA ISSN 0193-2527
AMERICAN CONCRETE INSTITUTE. PUBLICATION SP. Text in English. 1958. irreg., latest vol.219, 2004. price varies.
Indexed: CIN, ChemAb, ChemTitl.
—BLDSC (0576.800000), CISTI, ingenta. CCC.
Published by: American Concrete Institute, PO Box 9094, Farmington, MI 48333. TEL 248-848-3700, FAX 248-848-3701, bkstore@concrete.org, http://www.concrete.org.

690 GBR
AMERICAN CONSTRUCTION CATALOG. Text in English. 1995. a. USD 55. Document type: Catalog.
Published by: Data Distribution Publications, Apex House, London Rd, Northfleet, Gravesend, Kent DA11 9JA, United Kingdom. TEL 01322-277788, FAX 01322-569627.

720 690 USA
AMERICAN CONTRACTOR. (Published in several local editions) Text in English. m. adv. reprints avail. Document type: Trade. Description: Contains articles and features of interest to regional commercial construction professionals, including architects, contractors, designers, developers, engineers, government officials, subcontractors, and suppliers.
Formerly: America's Architects and Engineers
Published by: Transcontinental Publishing Inc., 27003, Scottsdale, AZ 85255-0133. TEL 602-331-8900, transpub@aol.com. Pub. Richard T Hyers Sr. Circ: (controlled).

AMERICAN INSTITUTE OF BUILDING DESIGN NEWSLETTER. see ARCHITECTURE

▼ AMERICAN PRIDE COUNTRY HOME PLANS. see HOME ECONOMICS

690 USA ISSN 0146-7557
TA1
➤ THE AMERICAN PROFESSIONAL CONSTRUCTOR. Text in English. 1973. s-a. USD 100 domestic; USD 125 foreign (effective 2005). adv. charts; illus.; stat. 3 cols./p.; back issues avail.; reprints avail. Document type: Journal, Academic/Scholarly. Description: Publishes articles on technical and management issues for the professional constructor.
—BLDSC (0853.270000), IE, ingenta.
Published by: American Institute of Constructors, 466, 94th Ave N, St. Petersburg, FL 33702. TEL 727-578-0317, admin@aicnet.org, http://www.aicnet.org. Ed. Shima Clarke. R&P, Adv. contact Cheryl Harris. Circ: 1,100.

690 USA ISSN 0065-9940
AMERICAN RAILWAY BRIDGE AND BUILDING ASSOCIATION. PROCEEDINGS✱ . Text in English. 1969 (vol.74). a. USD 30. adv. Document type: Proceedings.
Published by: American Railway Engineering and Maintenance-of-Way Association, 8201 Corporate Dr, Ste 1125, Landover, MD 20785. TEL 301-459-3200, FAX 301-459-8077, http://www.arema.org. Circ: 800.

AMERICAN SOCIETY FOR TESTING AND MATERIALS. COMPILATION OF A S T M STANDARDS IN BUILDING CODES. see ENGINEERING—Engineering Mechanics And Materials

690 USA
AMERICA'S BEST-SELLING HOME PLANS. Text in English. 1999. q. USD 23.50; USD 6.99 newsstand/cover (effective 2000). adv. Document type: Magazine, Consumer. Description: Presents home designs and plans containing the most sought out special features.
Published by: HomeStyles Publishing & Marketing, Inc., 213 E. 4th St., 4th Fl., St. Paul, MN 55101-1603. TEL 651-602-5000, 888-626-2026, FAX 651-602-5001, eenglund@homestyles.com, http://www.homestyles.com. Ed. Eric Englund. Pub. Diana Jasan. R&P Roger Heegaard. adv.: B&W page USD 3,910, color page USD 4,830; trim 8 x 10.75. Circ: 53,200 (paid).

ANCIENT MONUMENTS SOCIETY TRANSACTIONS. see ARCHITECTURE

690 GBR
ANGLIA BUILDER. Text in English. 1988. q. GBP 17 outside East Anglia. adv. stat. back issues avail. Document type: Trade.
Published by: B C Publications, 16C Market Pl, Diss, Norfolk IP22 3AB, United Kingdom. FAX 44-1379-650480. Ed., Pub., R&P Brian Chester. Adv. contact Margaret Chester.

338.43624 DNK ISSN 0904-3616
ANLAEG BRUTTO. Variant title: V og S Priser, Anlaeg Brutto. Text in Danish. 1972. a. DKK 1,360 (effective 1998).
Former titles (until 1988): V og S Priser. Anlaeg (0105-421X)
Published by: V & S Byggedata, 551 Frederikssundvej 194, Broenshoej, 2700, Denmark. TEL 45-38-60-77-55, FAX 45-38-60-77-44, bygdat@vs-byggedata.dk, bygdat@vs.byggedata.dk, http://www.vs-byggedata.dk.

338.43624 DNK ISSN 0904-3594
ANLAEG NETTO. Variant title: V & S Priser, Anlaeg Netto. Text in Danish. 1990. a. DKK 1,410 (effective 1999).

Published by: V & S Byggedata, 551 Frederikssundvej 194, Broenshoej, 2700, Denmark. TEL 45-38-60-77-11, FAX 45-38-60-77-55, bygdat@vs-byggedata.dk, bygdat@vs.byggedata.dk. Ed. Carl Friis Skovsen.

690 NOR ISSN 0003-3715
ANLEGGSMASKINEN. Text in Norwegian. 1960. 10/yr. NOK 385 (effective 2002). adv. bk.rev. illus.; stat. index.
—CCC.
Published by: Maskinentreprenoerenes Forbund/Association of Contractors and Plantowners of Norway, Fred. Olsens gt. 3, Oslo, 0152, Norway. TEL 47-22-40-41-90, FAX 47-22-33-01-11, http://www.anleggsmaskinen.no. Ed. Odd Eigil Sjoeseth TEL 47-22-40-41-94. Adv. contact Berit Kjoeloe TEL 47-22-40-41-92. color page NOK 13,250. Circ: 8,400.

690 FRA ISSN 1270-9840
TH2 CODEN: AITBAK
ANNALES DU BATIMENT ET DES TRAVAUX PUBLICS. Text in French; Summaries in English, French, German, Spanish. 1936. 10/yr. adv. bk.rev. abstr.; charts; illus. index, cum.index every 5 yrs.
Formerly (until 1997): Institut Technique du Batiment et des Travaux Publics. Annales (0020-2568)
Indexed: ApMecR, BrCerAb, CISA, ChemAb, ConcrAb, EngInd, INIS AtomInd.
—CISTI, Linda Hall.
Published by: Societe d'Editions du Batiment et des Travaux Publics, 7, rue de la Perouse, Paris, Cedex 16 75784, France. Ed. Jacques Rene Kramer. Circ: 5,500. Subscr. to: 6-14 rue La Perouse, Paris Cedex 16 75784, France.

ANNUAL BOOK OF A S T M STANDARDS. see ENGINEERING—Engineering Mechanics And Materials

ANNUAL BOOK OF A S T M STANDARDS. VOLUME 04.01. CEMENT; LIME; GYPSUM. see ENGINEERING—Engineering Mechanics And Materials

ANNUAL BOOK OF A S T M STANDARDS. VOLUME 04.02. CONCRETE AND AGGREGATES (INCLUDING MANUAL OF AGGREGATE AND CONCRETE TESTING). see ENGINEERING—Engineering Mechanics And Materials

ANNUAL BOOK OF A S T M STANDARDS. VOLUME 04.05. CHEMICAL-RESISTANT NONMETALLIC MATERIALS; VITRIFIED CLAY PIPE; CONCRETE PIPE; FIBER-REINFORCED CEMENT PRODUCTS; MORTARS AND GROUTS; MASONRY. see ENGINEERING—Engineering Mechanics And Materials

ANNUAL BOOK OF A S T M STANDARDS. VOLUME 04.06. THERMAL INSULATION; ENVIRONMENTAL ACOUSTICS. see ENGINEERING—Engineering Mechanics And Materials

ANNUAL BOOK OF A S T M STANDARDS. VOLUME 04.08. SOIL AND ROCK (I): D420 - D5779. see ENGINEERING—Engineering Mechanics And Materials

ANNUAL BOOK OF A S T M STANDARDS. VOLUME 08.04. PLASTIC PIPE AND BUILDING PRODUCTS. see ENGINEERING—Engineering Mechanics And Materials

ANNUAL BOOKS OF A S T M STANDATDS. VOLUME 04.09. SOIL AND ROCK (II): D5780 - LATEST; GEOSYNTHETICS. see ENGINEERING—Engineering Mechanics And Materials

338.3 USA
APARTMENT AND CONDOMINIUM PERSONAL PROPERTY COST GUIDE. Text in English. a. USD 30 (effective 1998).
Published by: E.H. Boeckh, Ed. & Pub. (Subsidiary of: Thomson Publishing Corp.), 2885 S Calhoun Rd, Box 510291, New Berlin, WI 53151-0291. TEL 414-780-2800, 800-285-1288, FAX 414-780-0306. R&P E H Boeckh.

APARTMENT NEWS. see REAL ESTATE

690 USA
APPLICATOR. Text in English. 1977. 3/yr. USD 35 (effective 1999). adv. Document type: Trade. Description: Contains articles on application, techniques and problems in the sealant, waterproofing and restoration industry.
Published by: Sealant, Waterproofing and Restoration Institute, 2841 Main St, Kansas City, MO 64108. TEL 816-472-7974, FAX 816-472-7765, info@swrionline.org, http://www.swrionline.org. Ed., Adv. contact Sheila Navis. Pub. Ken Bowman. Circ: 800 (controlled).

AQUA: THE BUSINESS MAGAZINE FOR THE SPA AND POOL INDUSTRY. see BUSINESS AND ECONOMICS—Marketing And Purchasing

690 LBN ISSN 1015-8316
ARAB CONSTRUCTION WORLD INTERNATIONAL/ALAM AL-INSA'AT AL-'ARABIYYA AD-DUWALIYYAT. Text in English. 1981. 6/yr. latest vol.20. USD 50 in the Middle East; USD 60 elsewhere (effective 2001). adv. bk.rev. tr.lit. 3 cols./p.; back issues avail. Document type: Journal, Trade. Description: Covers articles of interest to importers, wholesalers, contractors, and distributors serving the building and road construction industries of the Middle East, Africa and other countries.
Formerly (until 1990): Arab Construction World (0255-8572)
Indexed: CRIA, ConcrAb.
Published by: Chatila Publishing House, Chouran, P O Box 135121, Beirut, 1102-2802, Lebanon. TEL 961-1-352413, 961-1-746869, FAX 961-1-352419, 961-1-802950, info@chatilapublishing.com, http://www.chatilapublishing.com. Eds. Ms. Joumana Sabbagh, Riyadh Chehab. Pub. Fathi Chatila. Adv. contact Mona Chatila. Circ: 10,353.

ARBOUW JOURNAAL. see OCCUPATIONAL HEALTH AND SAFETY

690 ITA ISSN 1594-9540
ARCHAEDILIA. Abbreviated title: A e. Text in Italian, English. 2002. 3/yr. EUR 34 domestic; EUR 52 foreign (effective 2004). Document type: Magazine, Trade. Description: It covers the building industry, interior and exterior decoration, materials, etc.
Published by: Gruppo Editoriale Faenza Editrice SpA, Via Pier de Crescenzi 44, Faenza, RA 48018, Italy. TEL 39-0546-670411, FAX 39-0546-660440, info@faenza.com, http://www.faenza.com.

ARCHITECT & BUILDER. see ARCHITECTURE

693.7722 693.96 ZAF ISSN 1027-6785
ARCHITECT & SPECIFIER. Text in English. 1994. q. illus.
Document type: Trade.
Formerly (until 1997): Aluminium and Glass in Building (1024-3453)
Indexed: ISAP.
Published by: A A A M S A, PO Box 15852, Verwoerdburg, Pretoria 0140, South Africa. Ed. Hans A Schefferlie. adv.: color page ZAR 5,000. Circ: 7,000 (controlled).

691 728 GBR
ARCHITECT, BUILDER, CONTRACTOR & DEVELOPER. Abbreviated title: A B C & D. Text in English. 1988. m. GBP 19 (effective 2000). adv. bk.rev.; software rev. charts; illus.; pat. back issues avail. Document type: Trade. Description: Covers developments in the British building materials and construction industries for architects and other building professionals.
Published by: Ascent Publishing Ltd., Sugar Brook Ct, Aston Rd, Bromsgrove, Worcs B60 3EX, United Kingdom. TEL 44-1527-834400, FAX 44-1527-574388. Ed. Emma Home. Adv. contact Mark Hargreaves. Circ: 24,344 (controlled).

ARCHITECTS CATALOG. see BUSINESS AND ECONOMICS—Trade And Industrial Directories

692 USA ISSN 0066-6157
TH435
ARCHITECTS, CONTRACTORS & ENGINEERS GUIDE TO CONSTRUCTION COSTS. Text in English. 1968. a. USD 49.95 (effective 2005). adv. Document type: Trade.
Published by: A C & E Publishing Co., 6129 Beard Ave S, Minneapolis, MN 55410. TEL 612-920-9699. Ed., Pub., R&P, Adv. contact Donald S Roth.

ARCHITECTS' JOURNAL. see ARCHITECTURE

ARCHITECT'S JOURNAL FOCUS; products in practice. see ARCHITECTURE

ARCHITECTURAL REVIEW. see ARCHITECTURE

690 720 004.22 GBR ISSN 1361-326X
NA968
ARCHITECTURAL TECHNOLOGY. Text in English. 1989. bi-m. free to qualified personnel. bk.rev.; software rev. 20 p./no. 2 cols./p.; back issues avail. Document type: Magazine, Trade. Description: Official publication of BIAT. Provides articles on architectural technology, updates on technical and practical news, and news of the institute. For architectural and technical professionals within the construction industry.
Formerly (until Sep. 1995): B I A T Bulletin
Indexed: ArchI, BrTechI.
—BLDSC (1600.750500).
Published by: British Institute of Architectural Technologists, 397 City Rd, London, EC1V 1NH, United Kingdom. TEL 44-20-7278-2206, FAX 44-20-7837-3194, info@biat.org.uk, http://www.biat.org.uk. Ed. Hugh Morrison. R&P, Adv. contact Adam Endacott. Circ: 7,000 (paid and controlled).

ARCHITECTURE. see ARCHITECTURE

ARCHITECTURE AND BUILDING INDUSTRY. see ARCHITECTURE

ARCHITECTURE BOSTON. see ARCHITECTURE

B

ARCHITEKTUR & BAU FORUM. see *ARCHITECTURE*

ARCHITEKTUR UND BAUFORUM NEWSLETTER. see *ARCHITECTURE*

ARCHIVOLTA; architektura, wnetrza, inwestycje, konstrukcje, technologie, materialy. see *ARCHITECTURE*

690 DEU ISSN 0949-7153
ARCONIS; Wissen zum Planen und Bauen und zum Baumarkt. Text in German. 1996. q. EUR 32; EUR 10 newsstand/cover (effective 2004). adv. **Document type:** *Journal, Trade.*
Description: Publishes articles and reports on construction science and technology, developments in building physics and construction materials, ecological construction, as well as legal and economic questions concerning all parts of building.
Formerly (until 1996): I R B Aktuell (0724-3065)
Related titles: ◆ Supplement(s): Baulit Bauschaeden.
Indexed: DIP, IBR, IBZ.
Published by: (Fraunhofer Informationszentrum Raum und Bau), Fraunhofer I R B Verlag, Nobelstr 12, Stuttgart, 70569, Germany. TEL 49-711-9702500, FAX 49-711-9702508, irb@irbdirekt.de, http://www.irbdirekt.de. Ed., R&P, Adv. contact Elke Nuermberger. Pub. Hans Kindt. B&W page EUR 980. Circ: 1,240 (paid).

B

AREA DEVELOPMENT - CANADIAN ISSUE. see *HOUSING AND URBAN PLANNING*

AREA DEVELOPMENT SITE & FACILITY PLANNING. see *HOUSING AND URBAN PLANNING*

690 USA
ARIZONA CONSTRUCTION REPORTS. Text in English. m. USD 24. **Description:** Provides building permit and housing start statistics.
Published by: (Arizona Real Estate Center), Arizona State University, Center for Business Research, College of Business, Box 874406, Tempe, AZ 85287-4406. TEL 602-965-3961, FAX 602-965-5458, asucbr@asuvm.inre.asy.edu.

ARKHITEKTURA I STROITEL'STVO ROSSII. see *ARCHITECTURE*

690 UKR
ARKHITEKTURA UKRAINY. Text in Ukrainian. 1953. m. RUR 24.60. **Document type:** *Academic/Scholarly.*
Formerly: Stroitel'stvo i Arkhitektura (0039-2405)
Indexed: API, CRIA, CRICC, RASB.
—Linda Hall.
Published by: Spilka Arkhitektoriv Ukrainy/Union of Architects of Ukraine, Kiev, Ukraine.

690 NLD
ARKO CATALOGUS BOUWWERELD. Text in Dutch. a. EUR 128.50 (effective 2005). adv. **Document type:** *Directory, Trade.*
Formerly: Nijgh Catalogus Bouwwereld
Published by: Arko Uitgeverij BV, Postbus 616, Nieuwegein, 3430 AP, Netherlands. TEL 31-30-6004780, FAX 31-30-6052618, verkoop@arko.nl, http://www.bouwcatalogus.nl, http://www.arko.nl. Pub. Arend Jan Kornet. Adv. contact Jaap Kries. Circ: 3,034 (paid).

ARKOS; scienza e restauro. see *ARCHITECTURE*

ARQUITETURA Y CONSTRUCAO; a revista para construir ou reformar sua casa. see *ARCHITECTURE*

690 720 ITA ISSN 0394-5944
ARREDO URBANO. Key Title: A U. Arredo Urbano. Text in Italian; Summaries in English. 1980. bi-m. USD 95. adv. bk.rev. back issues avail. **Document type:** *Magazine, Consumer.*
Description: Deals with urban design and architecture. Includes diagrams and blue prints of future construction and projects.
Related titles: ◆ Supplement(s): Arredo Urbano Bis. ISSN 0394-5952.
Published by: Istituto Nazionale dell'Arredo Urbano delle Strutture Ambientali, Via Dell' Acqua Traversa, 255, Rome, RM 00135, Italy. TEL 39-06-3310490, FAX 39-06-3313055. Ed. Renato Cecilia. Circ: 5,000.

690 720 ITA ISSN 0394-5952
ARREDO URBANO BIS; supplemento tecnico. Key Title: A U Bis. Text in Italian. 1980. q. **Description:** Deals with urban design and architecture, including diagrams and blue prints of future construction and projects.
Related titles: ◆ Supplement to: Arredo Urbano. ISSN 0394-5944.
Published by: Istituto Nazionale dell'Arredo Urbano delle Strutture Ambientali, Via Dell' Acqua Traversa, 255, Rome, RM 00135, Italy. TEL 39-06-3273990. Ed. Renato Cecilia.

690 ESP ISSN 0212-8578
ARTE Y CEMENTO. Text in Spanish. 1959. fortn. EUR 197.60 domestic; EUR 240.69 foreign (effective 2005). bk.rev. bibl.; pat.; stat.; tr.lit. index. **Document type:** *Trade.* **Description:** Oriented towards residential, industrial and commercial building industry.
Formerly (until 1959): Radar (0212-856X)
—CISTI.
Published by: Reed Business Information SA (Subsidiary of: Reed Business Information International), Zancoeta 9, Bilbao, 48013, Spain. TEL 34-944-285600, FAX 34-944-425116, rbi@rbi.es, http://www.rbi.es/nuevo/rev_ayc_numanteriores.htm. Circ: 20,000.

690 FRA ISSN 0995-0206
ARTISANS INFO B.T.P. Text in French. 1945. 4/yr. adv. **Document type:** *Bulletin, Corporate.*
Published by: C A P E B des, 7 bd. Pebre, Marseille, Cedex 8 13295, France. TEL 33-4-91774017, FAX 33-4-91765541. Ed. Roger Cecchini. Adv. contact Cecile Cigolini. Circ: 3,500.

690 620 GBR ISSN 0951-0850
TA217.O94 CODEN: GRDND6
ARUP JOURNAL. Text in English. 1966. q.
—BLDSC (1736.890000), CISTI, IE, ingenta.
Published by: Arup, 13 Fitzroy St, London, W1T 4BQ, United Kingdom. TEL 44-20-76361531, FAX 44-20-75803924, http://www.arup.com.

ASBESTOS INFORMATION ASSOCIATION - NORTH AMERICA. NEWS AND NOTES. see *MINES AND MINING INDUSTRY*

691.3 USA ISSN 1079-6983
TA683.7
ASCENT (CHICAGO). Text in English. q. free to qualified personnel. adv. back issues avail. **Document type:** *Magazine, Trade.*
Indexed: BrCerAb, C&ISA, CerAb, CorrAb, E&CAJ, EMA, IAA, M&TEA, MBF, METADEX, SolStAb, WAA.
—Linda Hall.
Published by: Precast - Prestressed Concrete Institute, 209 W Jackson Blvd, Ste 500, Chicago, IL 60604. TEL 312-786-0300, FAX 312-786-0353, info@pci.org, http://www.pci.org/publications/ascent/index.cfm.

▼ **ASIA-PACIFIC TROPICAL HOMES.** see *ARCHITECTURE*

ASIAN ARCHITECT & CONTRACTOR. see *ARCHITECTURE*

690 SGP
ASIAN BUILDING & CONSTRUCTION. Text in English. bi-m.
Published by: Trend Publishing & Promotion Centre, 529A Geylag Rd, Singapore, 389485, Singapore. TEL 65-7423313, FAX 65-742-4366. adv.: B&W page SGD 1,700, color page SGD 2,200; 271 x 190. Circ: 18,000.

690 ESP ISSN 0571-3226
ASINTO. Text in Spanish. 1954. q.
Indexed: IECT.
—CINDOC.
Published by: Asociacion de Ingenieros de Construccion y Electricidad del Arma de Ingenieros, Victoria, 2, Madrid, 28012, Spain.

625 USA ISSN 1055-9205
TE273
ASPHALT CONTRACTOR; paving America. Text in English. 1986. m. free to qualified personnel. adv. **Document type:** *Magazine, Trade.* **Description:** Serves asphalt producers, contractors, pavement maintenance contractors, dealers, manufacturers and public works specifiers. Includes information on asphalt issues, equipment, techniques and products.
Related titles: Online - full text ed.: (from Gale Group, ProQuest Information & Learning).
—CCC.
Published by: Cygnus Business Media, Inc., 1233 Janesville Ave, Fort Atkinson, WI 53538-0803. TEL 920-563-1698, FAX 920-568-2244, peter.hubbard@cygnuspub.com, http://www.asphalt.com, http://www.cygnusb2b.com/. adv.: B&W page USD 1,597; trim 10 x 7. Circ: 10,000 (controlled).

695 USA
ASPHALT ROOFING MANUFACTURERS ASSOCIATION. NEWSLETTER. Text in English. 6/yr. free. **Document type:** *Newsletter.*
Published by: Asphalt Roofing Manufacturers Association, 1156 15th St NW, Ste. 900, Washington, DC 20005-1717. TEL 301-348-2012, FAX 301-348-2020. Ed., R&P Jon A Berger.

690 PRT ISSN 0870-0214
ASSOCIACAO DE EMPRESAS DE CONSTRUCAO E OBRAS PUBLICAS DO SUL. INDUSTRIA DA CONSTRUCAO; revista tecnica de construcao civil e obras publicas. Text in Portuguese. 1978. m. EUR 52.50 (effective 2005). adv. bk.rev. **Document type:** *Magazine, Trade.* **Description:** Covers building, public works, and construction economics, technology, materials, and equipment.
Published by: Associacao de Empresas de Construcao e Obras Publicas, Rua Duque de Palmela, 20, Lisbon, 1250-098, Portugal. TEL 351-21-3110200, FAX 351-21-3562816, aecops@aecops.pt, http://www.aecops.pt/. Circ: 7,500.

690 CAN ISSN 0833-8388
ASSOCIATION DE LA CONSTRUCTION DE MONTREAL ET DU QUEBEC. BULLETIN. Text in French. 1975 (vol.12). m. free. **Document type:** *Bulletin.*
Formerly (until 1986): Association de la Construction de Montreal et du Quebec. Nouvelles
Related titles: English ed.: Construction Association of Montreal and the Province of Quebec. Bulletin. ISSN 0833-8396.
Published by: Association de la Construction de Montreal et du Quebec, 4970 Place de la Savane, Montreal, PQ H4P 1Z6, Canada. TEL 514-739-2381. Ed. Jaques Theoret. Circ: 5,000.

ATARASHII ZAIRYO KOHO KIKAI KOSHUKAI KOEN GAIYO/LECTURES ON NEW MATERIALS, METHODS AND MACHINERY IN CONSTRUCTION. SUMMARIES. see *ENGINEERING—Civil Engineering*

690 USA
ATLANTA BUILDING NEWS. Text in English. 2000 (July). m. free to qualified personnel (effective 2004). adv. **Document type:** *Trade.*
Published by: (Greater Atlanta Home Builders Association), Naylor Publications, Inc., 5950 NW 1st Pl, Gainesville, FL 32607-6018. TEL 800-369-6220, http://www.atlantahomebuilders.com/Default.aspx, http://www.naylor.com, http://www.naylornetwork.com/. Pub. Shane Holt. Adv. contact John O'Neil. B&W page USD 199.50, color page USD 2,199.50; trim 7 x 9.5. Circ: 5,138.

690 CAN ISSN 0842-9588
ATLANTIC CONSTRUCTION JOURNAL. Text in English. 1988. q. CND 20.70 domestic; CND 25.68 foreign (effective 2004). adv. **Document type:** *Journal, Trade.* **Description:** Carries technical reports, equipment news, and technological advances to serve the needs of construction and related industries.
Published by: Transcontinental Specialty Publications (Subsidiary of: Transcontinental Media, Inc.), 11 Thornhill Dr, Dartmouth, NS B3B 1R9, Canada. TEL 902-468-8027, FAX 902-468-2322, acj@hfxnews.ca. Ed. Shirley McLaughlin. Pub. Don Brander TEL 902-468-8027 ext 116. Adv. contact Peter Coleman TEL 902-468-8027 ext 108. page CND 3,050; trim 16 x 10.38. Circ: 12,500.

693.6 DEU ISSN 1616-6078
AUSBAU UND FASSADE. Text in German. 1947. 11/yr. EUR 101 domestic; EUR 110 foreign; EUR 10 newsstand/cover (effective 2004). adv. **Document type:** *Magazine, Trade.*
Former titles (until 2000): Stuck - Putz - Trockenbau (0941-7583); (until 1992): Stukkateur (0177-1477); (until 1984): Stuckgewerbe (0344-8711)
Published by: (Stuckgewerbebund im Zentralverband des Deutschen Baugewerbes), C. Maurer Druck und Verlag, Schubartstr 21, Geislingen, 73312, Germany. TEL 49-7331-930196, FAX 49-7331-930190, comjr@maurer-online.de, http://www.ausbauundfassade.de, http://www.maurer-online.de. Ed., R&P Andreas Gabriel. Adv. contact Sybille Lutz. B&W page EUR 2,255, color page EUR 3,965. Circ: 7,395 (paid and controlled).

AUSTRALIA. BUREAU OF STATISTICS. BUILDING ACTIVITY, AUSTRALIA: DWELLING UNIT COMMENCEMENTS, PRELIMINARY. see *BUILDING AND CONSTRUCTION—Abstracting, Bibliographies, Statistics*

AUSTRALIA. BUREAU OF STATISTICS. BUILDING ACTIVITY, AUSTRALIAN CAPITAL TERRITORY. see *BUILDING AND CONSTRUCTION—Abstracting, Bibliographies, Statistics*

AUSTRALIA. BUREAU OF STATISTICS. ENGINEERING CONSTRUCTION ACTIVITY, AUSTRALIA. see *BUILDING AND CONSTRUCTION—Abstracting, Bibliographies, Statistics*

AUSTRALIA. BUREAU OF STATISTICS. NORTHERN TERRITORY OFFICE. BUILDING ACTIVITY, NORTHERN TERRITORY. see *BUILDING AND CONSTRUCTION—Abstracting, Bibliographies, Statistics*

AUSTRALIA. BUREAU OF STATISTICS. SOUTH AUSTRALIAN OFFICE. BUILDING ACTIVITY, SOUTH AUSTRALIA. see *BUILDING AND CONSTRUCTION—Abstracting, Bibliographies, Statistics*

AUSTRALIA. BUREAU OF STATISTICS. WESTERN AUSTRALIAN OFFICE. BUILDING APPROVALS, WESTERN AUSTRALIA. see *BUILDING AND CONSTRUCTION—Abstracting, Bibliographies, Statistics*

AUSTRALIA. BUREAU OF STATISTICS. WESTERN AUSTRALIAN OFFICE. ESTIMATED STOCKS OF DWELLING, WESTERN AUSTRALIA. see *BUILDING AND CONSTRUCTION—Abstracting, Bibliographies, Statistics*

690 AUS ISSN 1032-240X
AUSTRALIAN BUILDING CONSTRUCTION AND HOUSING. Text in English. 1907-1973; N.S. 1974. m. AUD 42 domestic; AUD 60 overseas. adv. bk.rev. charts; illus.; mkt.; stat.; tr.lit. back issues avail. **Document type:** *Trade.*
Incorporates (in July, 1988): Builder N.S.W.; Which was formerly (until 1973): Construction (0010-6674)
Published by: Master Builders Association of New South Wales, Private Bag 9, Broadway, NSW 2007, Australia. TEL 02-660-7188, FAX 02-660-4437. Ed. Jerry Grover. Circ: 10,000.

690 AUS ISSN 1030-1925
AUSTRALIAN BUILDING NEWS. Abbreviated title: A B N. Text in English. 1959-1982; resumed 1985. bi-m. USD 40. adv. bk.rev. back issues avail. **Document type:** *Trade.* **Description:** Covers industry standards and regulations, new products, seminars and exhibitions, building business, law and more.
Formerly: Building News (0045-3420)
Related titles: Online - full text ed.: Australian Building News Online. ISSN 1326-8538. 1996.
Indexed: AIAP.
Published by: Sydney Building Information Centre Ltd., Suite 22, 2 Beattie St, Balmain, NSW 2041, Australia. TEL 61-2-9818-7540, FAX 61-2-9818-7521, http://www.abn.com.au/. Ed. Jos Anstee. Pub. John Wayland. Adv. contact Murray Hunter. B&W page AUD 2,200, color page AUD 3,500. Circ: 17,370 (controlled).

691 AUS ISSN 1035-4611
AUSTRALIAN CLAY JOURNAL & CERAMIC NEWS. Text in English. 1933. bi-m. AUD 30 domestic; AUD 48 foreign (effective 2001). adv. 8 p./no.; back issues avail. **Document type:** *Journal, Trade.* **Description:** For Australian and overseas manufacturers of clay products, and of plant and equipment.
Incorporates: Australian National Clay; Formerly (until 1959): Ceramic Manufacturers Association of Australia. Journal
Indexed: BrCerAb.
Published by: Hamilton Press Pty. Ltd., PO Box 386, Manly, NSW 1655, Australia. TEL 61-2-99776046, FAX 61-2-99763190, hamiltonpress@ozemail.com.au. Ed., Pub., Adv. contact Barry McCrea. B&W page AUD 1,836, color page AUD 2,456; trim 355 x 245. Circ: 400 (paid).

691 AUS ISSN 1034-7860
AUSTRALIAN CONCRETE CONSTRUCTION. Text in English. 1988. bi-m. price varies. adv. back issues avail. **Document type:** *Trade.* **Description:** Promotes the use of concrete in all construction areas.
Indexed: BrCerAb, C&ISA, CerAb, CivEngAb, ConcrAb, CorrAb, E&CAJ, EEA, EMA, IAA, M&TEA, MBF, METADEX, RefZh, SolStAb, WAA.
Published by: (Steel Reinforcement Institute of Australia), Intermedia Group Pty. Ltd., Unit 7B, 87 Bay St., PO Box 55, Glebe, NSW 2037, Australia. TEL 61-2-96602113, FAX 61-2-96604419, http://www.intermedia.com.au. Ed. Jack Cleaver. Pub. Simon Grover. Adv. contact Pete Bromley. B&W page AUD 1,470, color page AUD 650; trim 210 x 297. Circ: 10,321.

AUSTRALIAN CONSTRUCTION LAW NEWSLETTER. see *LAW*

330 AUS ISSN 1445-2634
➤ **AUSTRALIAN JOURNAL OF CONSTRUCTION ECONOMICS AND BUILDING.** Text in English. 2001 (Aug.). s-a. AUD 24.75 newsstand/cover to non-members (effective 2003); subscr. incl. in membership. bk.rev. charts; illus.; stat. Index. 100 p./no.; back issues avail. **Document type:** *Journal, Academic/Scholarly.*
Formerly (until 2001): A I Q S Refereed Journal - A I B Papers (1329-671X)
Related titles: E-mail ed.
—BLDSC (1806.575000).
Published by: Australian Institute of Quantity Surveyors, PO Box 301, Deakin West, ACT 2600, Australia. TEL 61-2-62822222, FAX 61-2-62852427, contact@aiqs.com.au, http://www.aiqs.com.au. Ed. Alan Jeary. R&P Terry Sanders. Circ: 300. **Co-publisher:** Australian Institute of Building.

➤ **AUSZUEGE AUS DEN EUROPAEISCHEN PATENTANMELDUNGEN. TEIL 1B. GRUND- UND ROHSTOFFINDUSTRIE, BAUWESEN, BERGBAU.** see *PATENTS, TRADEMARKS AND COPYRIGHTS*

690 USA ISSN 0899-5540
TH4819.P7
AUTOMATED BUILDER; the no.1 international housing technology transfer magazine for manufacturing and marketing. Text in English. 1964. m. USD 50 in US & Canada; USD 100 elsewhere; USD 6 newsstand/cover in US & Canada; USD 12 newsstand/cover elsewhere; free to qualified personnel (effective 2005). adv. bk.rev. charts; illus.; stat.; tr.lit. 48 p./no.; back issues avail.; reprint service avail. from PQC. **Document type:** *Magazine, Trade.* **Description:** The magazine covers the manufacture of buildings, residential and commercial, which in whole or part, are fabricated in a factory and erected or assembled at the site.
Former titles (until 1988): Automation in Housing and Manufactured Home Dealer (0740-3534); Automation in Housing-Systems Building News (0362-0395); Formed by the merger of: Automation in Housing (0005-1217); Systems Building News
Related titles: Microfilm ed.
Indexed: AIAP, PROMT.
—CISTI, Linda Hall.
Published by: C M N Publications (Subsidiary of: C M N Associates, Inc.), 1445 Donlon St, Ste 16, Ventura, CA 93003-5640. TEL 805-642-9735, FAX 805-642-8820, info@automatedbuilder.com, http://www.automatedbuilder.com. Ed., Pub., R&P Don O Carlson. Adv. contact Lance Carlson. B&W page USD 5,240, color page USD 6,880; trim 8 x 10.75. Circ: 25,000 (controlled).

690 USA
AUTOMATED BUILDER ANNUAL BUYERS' GUIDE. Text in English. 1977. a. USD 12 per issue (effective 2003). adv. reprint service avail. from PQC. **Document type:** *Trade.*
Former titles: Automation in Housing and Manufactured Home Dealer Annual Buyers' Guide; Automation in Housing-Systems Building News Annual Buyers' Guide
Related titles: Microfilm ed.: (from PQC).
Published by: C M N Publications (Subsidiary of: C M N Associates, Inc.), 1445 Donlon St, Ste 16, Ventura, CA 93003-5640. TEL 805-642-9735, FAX 805-642-8820, bob@automatedbuilders.com, http://www.automatedbuilders.com. Ed., Pub., R&P Don O Carlson. Adv. contact Lance Carlson. Circ: 25,000.

AUTOMATION IN CONSTRUCTION. see *COMPUTERS—Automation*

AVANCE DE INFORMACION ECONOMICA. INDUSTRIA DE LA CONSTRUCCION. see *BUILDING AND CONSTRUCTION—Abstracting, Bibliographies, Statistics*

690 720 CAN ISSN 1202-5925
AWARD MAGAZINE. Text in English. 1986. bi-m. USD 19.95. adv. bk.rev. **Document type:** *Trade.* **Description:** Covers architectural and design trends, company and project profiles for architects, interior designers, landscape architects, general contractors, developers and engineers.
Formerly (until 1990): Award: Construction in Profile (0841-8802)
Related titles: Online - full text ed.: (from Micromedia ProQuest).
Indexed: CBCABus, CBCARef.
—CISTI.
Published by: Canada Wide Magazines & Communications Ltd., 4180 Lougheed Hwy, 4th Fl, Burnaby, BC V5C 6A7, Canada. TEL 604-299-7311, FAX 604-299-9188. Ed. Les Wiseman. Adv. contact Dan Chapman. Circ: 8,000.

AZULEJO; ceramica noble. see *CERAMICS, GLASS AND POTTERY*

690 DEU ISSN 1430-6999
B B A BAU - BERATUNG - ARCHITEKTUR; Kennziffer-Zeitschrift Architekten, Planer, Bauingenieure. Text in German. 1974. 10/yr. EUR 80 domestic; EUR 82 foreign; EUR 8.20 newsstand/cover (effective 2004). adv. **Document type:** *Journal, Trade.* **Description:** Provides practical information and solutions in the fields of architecture, building and surveying.
Former titles (until 1992): B B A Planen und Bauen (0171-1555); Planen und Bauen
Indexed: ExcerpMed.
—CCC.
Published by: Konradin Verlag Robert Kohlhammer GmbH, Ernst Mey Str 8, Leinfelden-Echterdingen, 70771, Germany. TEL 49-711-75940, FAX 49-711-7594398, info@konradin.de, http://www.bba-online.de, http://www.konradin.de. Ed. Juergen Ostrowski. Adv. contact Bettina Mayer. B&W page EUR 4,660, color page EUR 5,860; trim 190 x 270. Circ: 20,040 (paid).

690 AUT
B B B - BAUMASCHINE - BAUGERAET - BAUSTELLE; Oesterreichs einzige spezialisierte Fachzeitschrift fuer Baumaschinentechnik, Baustellenreportagen und Tiefbau. Text in German. 1965. 10/yr. EUR 30 domestic; EUR 45 foreign; EUR 4 newsstand/cover (effective 2005). adv. bk.rev. abstr.; illus. **Document type:** *Magazine, Trade.*
Formerly: Baumaschine Baugeraet Baustoff (0005-6685)
Published by: Springer Business Media Austria GmbH (Subsidiary of: Springer Science+Business Media), Inkustr 16, Klosterneuburg, 3403, Austria. TEL 43-2243-301110, FAX 43-2243-30111222, office@springer-sbm.at, http://www.springer-sbm.at/front_content.php?idcat=55. Ed. Friedrich Kovacs. Adv. contact Karl Englert. B&W page EUR 3,500, color page EUR 4,980; trim 185 x 260. Circ: 12,720 (controlled).

693 GBR ISSN 0953-1688
B C A BULLETIN. Text in English. 1986. 3/yr. back issues avail. **Document type:** *Trade.*
Formerly (until 1988): Cement and Concrete Association. Bulletin (0950-2106)
—CISTI.
Published by: British Cement Association, Century House, Telford Ave, Crowthorne, Berks RG45 6YS, United Kingdom. TEL 44-1344-762676, FAX 44-1344-761214, library@bca.org.uk, http://www.bca.org.uk.

B C A DIRECTORY OF REGISTERED CONTRACTORS (YEAR). see *BUSINESS AND ECONOMICS—Trade And Industrial Directories*

690 GBR ISSN 1350-9500
B C I S GUIDE TO HOUSE REBUILDING COSTS. (Building Cost Information Service) Text in English. 1978. a. GBP 47.50 (effective 2001). **Document type:** *Trade.*
Formerly: Guide to House Rebuilding Costs for Insurance Valuation (0261-2054)
Related titles: ♦ Includes: A B I - B C I S House Rebuilding Cost Index.
—BLDSC (1871.384150). **CCC.**
Published by: Building Cost Information Service Ltd., Royal Institution of Chartered Surveyors, Parliment Sq, 12 Great George St, London, SW1P 3AD, United Kingdom. TEL 44-20-7222-7000, FAX 44-20-7695-1501.

690 GBR ISSN 0260-6216
B C I S QUARTERLY REVIEW OF BUILDING PRICES. (Building Cost Information Service) Text in English. 1981. q. GBP 260 (effective 2001). **Document type:** *Trade.*
—CCC.
Published by: Building Cost Information Service Ltd., Royal Institution of Chartered Surveyors, Parliment Sq, 12 Great George St, London, SW1P 3AD, United Kingdom. TEL 44-20-7222-7000, FAX 44-20-7695-1501. Ed. J L N Martin. Circ: 1,600.

691 DEU ISSN 0171-8908
B D - BAUMASCHINENDIENST. Text in German. 1965. m. EUR 49; EUR 7 newsstand/cover (effective 2004). adv. illus. **Document type:** *Magazine, Trade.*
Former titles (until 1974): B D fuer Baumaschinen und Baustoffe (0171-8894); (until 1972): B D fuer Baustoffe und Baumaschinen (0171-8843); (until 1972): B D mit Baumaschinendienst (0171-8851); (until 1971): Baumaschinendienst mit Baumaschinenmarkt (0171-8835); (until 1967): Baumaschinendienst (0005-6723)
—CCC.
Published by: Krafthand Verlag Walter Schulz, Walter-Schulz-Str 1, Bad Woerishofen, 86825, Germany. TEL 49-8247-30070, FAX 49-8247-300770, info@krafthand.de, http://www.krafthand.de. adv.: B&W page EUR 3,230, color page EUR 4,730. Circ: 15,054 (paid and controlled).

B

690.028 691 ZAF
B E M SPECIFIER. Text in English. 1969. m. adv.
Former titles (until 1992): Building Equipment and Materials; Building Equipment and Materials for South Africa (0007-344X)
Published by: Communications Group, PO Box 7870, Johannesburg, 2000, South Africa. Ed. H Snow. Circ: 7,147.

690 DEU ISSN 0341-3896
B I. (Bauwirtschaftliche Informationen) Text in German. 1950. 5/w. EUR 444 (effective 2004). adv. bk.rev. **Document type:** *Newspaper, Trade.*
Published by: B I Medien GmbH, Faluner Weg 33, Kiel, 24109, Germany. TEL 49-431-535920, FAX 49-431-5359225, info@bi-online.de, http://www.bi-online.de. Ed. Rudi Grimm. Adv. contact Benno Stahn. B&W page EUR 1,293, color page EUR 1,788. Circ: 9,960 (paid and controlled).

690 DEU
B I - BAUMAGAZIN. (Bauwirtschaftliche Informationen) Text in German. m. EUR 45; EUR 5 newsstand/cover (effective 2004). adv. **Document type:** *Magazine, Trade.*
Published by: B I Medien GmbH, Faluner Weg 33, Kiel, 24109, Germany. TEL 49-431-535920, FAX 49-431-5359225, info@bi-online.de, http://www.bi-online.de. adv.: B&W page EUR 2,260, color page EUR 3,460. Circ: 11,837 (paid and controlled).

692.8 USA ISSN 0194-6587
B I D SERVICE WEEKLY. Text in English. 1954. w. USD 109.37. adv. charts; illus.; mkt.; stat.; tr.lit. index. **Description:** Contains information about construction and bidding (city, state & federal) for the Pacific area, including awarded bid results, supplies, and services.
Former titles: Building Industry Digest; Builders Report Pacific (0007-3296)
Published by: Trade Publishing Co. Ltd., 287 Mokauea St, Honolulu, HI 96819. TEL 808-848-0711, FAX 808-841-3053. Ed. Alfonso Rivera. Circ: 1,380.

690 DEU
B I - GALABAU. (Bauwirtschaftliche Informationen) Text in German. 8/yr. EUR 52; EUR 8 newsstand/cover (effective 2004). adv. **Document type:** *Magazine, Trade.*
Published by: B I Medien GmbH, Faluner Weg 33, Kiel, 24109, Germany. TEL 49-431-535920, FAX 49-431-5359225, info@bi-online.de, http://www.bi-online.de. adv.: B&W page EUR 2,110, color page EUR 3,010. Circ: 12,228 (paid and controlled).

B I S; Zeitschrift fuer Bauschaden, Grundstueckswert und gutachterliche Taetigkeit. (Bau- und Immobilien-Sachverstaendiger) see *REAL ESTATE*

690 DEU
B I - UMWELTBAU. (Bauwirtschaftliche Informationen) Text in German. bi-m. EUR 38; EUR 8 newsstand/cover (effective 2004). adv. **Document type:** *Magazine, Trade.*
Published by: B I Medien GmbH, Faluner Weg 33, Kiel, 24109, Germany. TEL 49-431-535920, FAX 49-431-5359225, info@bi-online.de, http://www.bi-online.de. adv.: B&W page EUR 2,260, color page EUR 3,460. Circ: 11,501 (paid and controlled).

690 GBR
B M I BUILDING MAINTENANCE PRICE BOOK. Text in English. 1980. a. GBP 59.50 (effective 2001). adv. bk.rev. **Document type:** *Trade.*

Formerly: B M C I S Building Maintenance Price Book (0261-2933)
—BLDSC (2116.176200).
Published by: Building Maintenance Information (Subsidiary of: Royal Institute of Chartered Surveyors), B C I S Ltd, Parliament Sq, 12 Great George St, London, SW1P 3AD, United Kingdom. TEL 44-20-7222-7000, FAX 44-20-7695-1501, BMI@bcis.co.uk, http://www.bcis.co.uk/. Ed. Alan Cowen. Adv. contact Brian Barnett. Circ: 3,000 (paid).

691 GBR ISSN 0144-9060
B M P FORECASTS. (Building Material Producers) Text in English. 1979. 3/yr. GBP 375 to non-members. **Document type:** *Trade.*
Published by: National Council of Building Material Producers, 26 Store St, London, WC1E 7BT, United Kingdom. TEL 44-171-323-3770, FAX 44-171-323-0307, ninao@building-materials.org.uk. Ed. N Ovanessian.

691 GBR ISSN 0144-9052
B M P INFORMATION. (Building Material Producers) Text in English. 1947. m. GBP 80 to non-members. **Document type:** *Trade.* **Description:** Digests news and facts about the building material trade.
Published by: National Council of Building Material Producers, 26 Store St, London, WC1E 7BT, United Kingdom. TEL 44-171-323-3770, FAX 44-171-323-0307, tblake@building-materials.org.uk. Ed. P Blake. Circ: 650.

B M P MONTHLY STATISTICAL BULLETIN. (Building Material Producers) see *BUILDING AND CONSTRUCTION—Abstracting, Bibliographies, Statistics*

690 GBR
B M P STATE OF TRADE. (Building Material Producers) Text in English. 1989. s-a. GBP 150 to non-members. **Document type:** *Trade.*
Published by: National Council of Building Material Producers, 26 Store St, London, WC1E 7BT, United Kingdom. TEL 44-171-323-3770, FAX 44-171-323-0307, ninao@building-materials.org.uk.

690 USA
B O C A BULLETIN. Text in English. 1950. bi-m. free membership (effective 2005). **Document type:** *Newsletter, Trade.*
Published by: Building Officials and Code Administrators International, 4051 W Flossmoor Rd, Country Club Hills, IL 60478-5795. TEL 708-799-2300, 888-422-7233, FAX 708-799-4981, 800-214-7167, bulletin@bocai.org, boca@bocai.org, http://www.bocai.org. Adv. contact Eileen Sandoval. Circ: 15,000 (paid and controlled).

343 USA ISSN 1055-6192
KF5701.Z95
B O C A NATIONAL PROPERTY MAINTENANCE CODE. Text in English. 1978. triennial. USD 30 to non-members; USD 20 to members (effective 1999). index. **Description:** Covers general administration, light, ventilation and occupancy limitations, plumbing facilities, rubbish and garbage, and exterior property areas.
Former titles: B O C A National Existing Structure Code (0897-0076); B O C A Basic Housing - Property Maintenance Code (0525-0110)
—CISTI.
Published by: Building Officials and Code Administrators International, 4051 W Flossmoor Rd, Country Club Hills, IL 60478-5795. TEL 708-799-2300, FAX 708-799-4981, boca@bocai.org. Ed. Paul K Heilstedt.

690 658 USA
HD1393.55
B O M A.ORG. (Building Owners and Managers Association) Text in English. 1916. 10/yr. USD 75 to non-members; USD 50 to members (effective 2005). adv. bk.rev. illus.; stat. index. reprints avail. **Document type:** *Magazine, Trade.* **Description:** Contains information on international issues that can affect the profitable operation of commercial real estate facilities. Featured also are articles on building operations, systems, and procedures, trends in commercial real estate, office building occupancy rates, etc.
Former titles: Skylines (Washington) (0892-7847); (until 1986): B O M A International Skylines (0279-2044); (until May 1981): Building Owner and Manager; Supersedes (in 1976): Skyscraper Management (0037-6647)
Published by: Building Owners and Managers Association International, 1201 New York Ave, N W, Ste 300, Washington, DC 20005. TEL 202-408-2662, FAX 202-371-0181, soppen@boma.org, http://www.boma.org. Ed. Brian Lonergan. Pub. Dora Blacknall. Adv. contact Matt Fleming. page USD 4,510. Circ: 18,500 (controlled).

691 AUS ISSN 1039-9704
B P N. (Building Products News) Text in English. 1967. bi-m. AUD 36.96 (effective 2001). adv. bk.rev. tr.lit. back issues avail. **Document type:** *Trade.* **Description:** Covers building products and materials, focusing on in-depth application stories, project overviews, news and articles by respected industry figures.
Formerly (until 1993): Building Products News (0007-358X)
Related titles: Online - full text ed.: (from Gale Group).
Published by: Reed Business Information Pty Ltd (Subsidiary of: Reed Business Information International), Locked Bag 2999, Chatswood, NSW 2067, Australia. customerservice@reedbusiness.com.au, http://www.infolink.com.au, http://www.reedbusiness.com.au. Ed., R&P Dael Climo. Pub. Paul Spotswood. Adv. contact Toni Chapman. B&W page USD 2,492, color page USD 4,045; trim 239 x 330. Circ: 24,641.

690 GBR ISSN 0265-962X
B R E NEWS OF FIRE RESEARCH. Text in English. 1972. 3/yr.
Supersedes in part (in 1984): B R E News (0144-8358); Which was formerly: B R S News (0435-1231)
—CISTI.
Contact Corp. Auth.: Building Research Establishment, Garston, Watford, Herts WD25 9XX, United Kingdom. TEL 44-1923-664000, FAX 44-1923-664787, http://www.bre.co.uk.

690 GBR ISSN 1464-7788
B R E NEWS OF RESEARCH AND INNOVATION. Text in English. 1972. q. **Document type:** *Trade.* **Description:** Keeps the industry abreast of construction innovation and research findings.
Formerly (until 1997): B R E News of Construction Research (0265-9611); Which superseded in part (in 1984): B R E News (0144-8358); Which was formerly: B R S News (0435-1231)
Indexed: AIAP.
—CISTI.
Contact Corp. Auth.: Building Research Establishment, Garston, Watford, Herts WD25 9XX, United Kingdom. TEL 44-1923-664000, FAX 44-1923-664787, http://www.bre.co.uk.

690 GBR ISSN 1364-9817
B R E REPORTS ON CD-ROM. Text in English. 1996. q. GBP 75, USD 125. **Document type:** *Trade.*
Media: CD-ROM.
Contact Corp. Auth.: Building Research Establishment, Garston, Watford, Herts WD25 9XX, United Kingdom. TEL 44-1923-664000, FAX 44-1923-664787, lynnej@construct.emap.co.uk, http://www.emapconstruct.co.uk, http://www.bre.co.uk.

690 JPN ISSN 1341-2930
B R I PROCEEDINGS. (Building Research Institute) Text in English. 1995. irreg. **Document type:** *Proceedings, Government.*
—BLDSC (2283.630000), CISTI.
Published by: Building Research Institute, Research Planning and Information Department/Kensetsusho Kenchiku Kenkyujo, 1 Tatehara, Tsukuba-shi, Ibaraki-ken 305-0802, Japan.

690 JPN ISSN 0453-4972
B R I RESEARCH PAPERS. (Building Research Institute) Text in English. 1960. irreg. per issue exchange basis. **Document type:** *Academic/Scholarly.*
—CISTI.
Published by: Building Research Institute, Research Planning and Information Department/Kensetsusho Kenchiku Kenkyujo, 1 Tatehara, Tsukuba-shi, Ibaraki-ken 305-0802, Japan. Circ: 400.

690 333.3 GBR ISSN 0953-9905
B S A ANNUAL REPORT. Text in English. 1942. a. GBP 5 (effective 1997). **Document type:** *Corporate.* **Description:** Provides review of the activities of the association, its council and committees, in relationship to domestic matters and in the context of wider developments in the fields of housing, legislation, taxation and international developments.
Former titles: Building Societies Association. Annual Report; Building Societies Association. Report of the Council (0262-8155)
Published by: Building Societies Association, 3 Savile Row, London, W1X 1AF, United Kingdom. TEL 44-20-7437-0655, FAX 44-20-7287-0109. Ed. John Murray.

690 624 GBR
B S HANDBOOK 3. SUMMARIES OF BRITISH STANDARDS FOR BUILDING. Text in English. 1979. a. GBP 420. **Document type:** *Trade.*
Published by: British Standards Institution, British Standards Institution, Breckland, Linford Wood, Milton Keynes, Bucks MK14 6LE, United Kingdom. TEL 44-1908-220022, FAX 44-1908-320856.

338.4 DNK ISSN 0107-6779
B T B. (Branchevejviser for Traelast og Byggemarkeder) Text in Danish. 1976. a. DKK 85 domestic (effective 2000). adv. illus. **Document type:** *Trade.* **Description:** Directed to Danish timber merchants and home centers.
Published by: Odsgard AS, Stationsparken 25, Glostrup, 2600, Denmark. TEL 45-43-43-29-00, FAX 45-43-43-13-28, odsgard@odsgard.dk, http://www.byggeri.dk. Ed., R&P Peter Odsgard. Circ: 5,500.

690 GBR
B T I: BUILDING, TRADE & INDUSTRY. Text in English. 1985. m. adv. **Document type:** *Magazine, Trade.* **Description:** Provides news and feature articles with analysis, industry comment, market focus, site reports, product updates, commercial vehicles and mores.
Published by: Datateam Publishing Ltd, 15a London Rd, Maidstone, Kent ME16 8LY, United Kingdom. TEL 44-1622-687031, FAX 44-1622-757646, info@datateam.co.uk, http://www.datateam.co.uk/business_publications/building_trade.htm, http://www.datateam.co.uk/home/home.htm. Circ: 12,128.

690 628 LCA ISSN 1010-5700
B T - L M & S. (Building Technology - Land Management & Safety) Text in English. 1985. q. USD 10. adv. **Document type:** *Trade.*
—CCC.
Published by: A L K I M Communication Production Company, Box MA 020, Marchand Post Office, Castries, St. Lucia. Ed., Adv. contact Albert Deterville. Circ: 5,000.

690 FRA ISSN 0299-1705
B T P MAGAZINE. Text in French. 1986. 10/yr. adv.
Address: 33 rue du Mont Valerien, St Cloud, 92210, France. TEL 33-1-47711442, FAX 33-1-49110005. Ed. Jean Cayola. Circ: 18,000.

690 DEU
B U S SYSTEME; Zeitschrift fuer moderne Gebaeudetechnik. Text in German. 1995. q. EUR 28 domestic; EUR 34 foreign; EUR 20 to students; EUR 5.50 newsstand/cover (effective 2004). adv. **Document type:** *Magazine, Trade.*
Published by: Interpublic, Luederstr 10, Berlin, 12555, Germany. TEL 49-30-67489289, FAX 49-30-6744508, Redaktion@bussysteme.de, http://www.bussysteme.de. Ed. Ursula Maria Lange. adv.: B&W page EUR 1,640, color page EUR 2,870; trim 210 x 297. Circ: 7,160 (paid and controlled).

B W P D A CONVENTION PROCEEDINGS. see *FORESTS AND FORESTRY—Lumber And Wood*

BACKBONE TECHNOLOGIES. see *BUSINESS AND ECONOMICS—Marketing And Purchasing*

690 ITA ISSN 0392-2723
BAGNO E ACCESSORI. Cover title: Bagno e Accessori International. Text in English, Italian. 1974. bi-m. EUR 36 domestic; EUR 90 foreign (effective 2005). adv. illus. **Document type:** *Magazine, Trade.* **Description:** Promotes design, production, market and distribution of bathrooms.
Indexed: BrCerAb.
Published by: Gruppo Editoriale Faenza Editrice SpA, Via Pier de Crescenzi 44, Faenza, RA 48018, Italy. TEL 39-0546-670411, FAX 39-0546-660440, info@faenza.com, http://www.faenza.com. Ed. Grazia Gamberoni. R&P Luisa Teston. Adv. contact Elvio Neri. Circ: 24,000.

BARBOUR INDEX BUILDING PRODUCT COMPENDIUM. see *INTERIOR DESIGN AND DECORATION*

691 FRA ISSN 0765-040X
BAREME DES COEFFICIENTS; cours des materiaux du batiment. Text in French. 1947. m. adv.
Published by: Editions Massin, 16-18 rue de l'Amiral Mouchez, Paris, 75686 Cedex 14 , France. TEL 33-1-45654855, FAX 33-1-45654700, http://www.massin.fr.

BARRIEREFREI; Lebensraum fuer Menschen. see *ARCHITECTURE*

690 FRA ISSN 1628-0229
B@TI-COM. Text in French. 1992. 5/yr. (15 supp. by fax or e-mail). bk.rev. **Document type:** *Newsletter.* **Description:** Contains information on "smart building", building automation, cabling.
Former titles (until 2001): Bati High-Tech. La Lettre (1167-6876); (until 1991): Lettre de Bati High Tech (1145-3621)
Related titles: Online - full text ed.; Supplement(s):.
Published by: Sarl Editions Sorlet, 8 les Belles Etentes, Ste Marguerite-sur-Mer, 76119, France. TEL 33-2-35838540, FAX 33-2-35838540, esorlet@aol.com, http://www.lettre-BHT.com. Ed. Eric Sorlet. Circ: 800.

690 FRA
BATI HIGH-TECH PRODUITS ET SERVICES★ . Text in French. 3/yr. **Document type:** *Trade.*
Address: 17 bis rue Joseph de Maistre, Paris, 75018, France. TEL 42-93-22-43, FAX 43-87-50-24. Ed. Eugene Lecanon. Circ: 20,000.

690 FRA ISSN 0223-0011
BATIMENT ARTISANAL. Text in French. 1953. m. adv.
Published by: Confederation de l'Artisanat et des Petites Entreprises du Batiment, 46 av. d'Ivry, BP 353, Paris, Cedex 13 75625, France. TEL 33-1-45824000, FAX 33-1-45824910, TELEX 201 057.

690 FRA ISSN 1266-8176
BATIMENT INFORMATION. Text in French. 6/yr. EUR 32.01 domestic; EUR 38.11 in Europe; EUR 53.35 elsewhere (effective 2002). adv. **Document type:** *Newspaper, Trade.* **Description:** For persons interested in the hiring of public work, handling, transport and quarry equipment.
Formerly (until 1995): Location Actualite (0997-380X)
Related titles: ◆ Supplement(s): Locaguide. ISSN 0990-1159.

Published by: (Societe Technique d'Editions pour l'Entreprise), Groupe Chantiers de France, Bord de Seine, 202 quai de Clichy, Clichy, 92110, France. TEL 33-1-47561723, FAX 33-1-47561432, http://www.chantiersdefrance.com. Ed. Marc Montagnon. Pub. Arlette Surchamp. Adv. contact Alice Frecaut. Circ: 7,000.

690 FRA ISSN 0223-758X
BATIMENT PARISIEN. Text in French. 1978. q.
Address: 58 rue de Rochechouart, Paris, 75009, France. TEL 48-78-41-52, FAX 45-26-09-33. Ed. M Simon. Circ: 4,000.

BATIMENT RELATIONS ELEC; le journal d'information du CFE. see *ENERGY—Electrical Energy*

691 FRA ISSN 0987-7282
BATIPRIX. Text in French. 1983. a.
Published by: Publication du Moniteur, 17 rue d'Uzes, Paris, 75002, France. TEL 1-40-13-34-32, FAX 1-40-26-33-87, TELEX UPRESSE 680876F. Ed. Gilbert Lemaire. Circ: 10,000.

690 FRA ISSN 1266-2089
BATIRAMA, LE BATISSEUR EUROPEEN. Text in French. 1993. m. EUR 89 (effective 2005). adv.
Formed by the merger of (1969-1993): Batirama (0767-9920); (1988-1993): Le Batisseur Europeen (0988-5188)
Published by: Batirama, 21 rue Baudin, Montpellier, 34000, France. TEL 67-58-61-09, FAX 67-58-26-87, http://batirama.com/. Ed. Francois Thoulouze.

620 DEU ISSN 1435-1714
BAU (BERLIN); Das bundesweite Baumagazin. Text in German. 1998. m. adv. **Document type:** *Magazine, Trade.*
Published by: Knaak Verlag, Kaiserstr 8, Berlin, 13589, Germany. TEL 49-30-3751515, FAX 49-30-3754424, peterknaak@aol.com. adv.: B&W page EUR 1,259, color page EUR 2,444. Circ: 4,750 (controlled).

660 CHE
BAU & HOLZ. Text in French, German, Italian. w. adv.
Published by: Schweizerische Bau und Holzarbeiter Verband, Strassburgstr 5, PO Box 8021, Zuerich, 8004, Switzerland. Circ: 37,000.

690 CHE
BAU FLASH. Text in German. 9/yr. adv. **Document type:** *Trade.*
Published by: Kretz AG, Postfach, Feldmeilen, 8706, Switzerland. TEL 41-1-9237656, FAX 41-1-9237657, kretz_ag@bluewin.ch. Ed. Thomas Aeschmann. Adv. contact Esther Kretz. B&W page CHF 2,750, color page CHF 3,805; trim 265 x 185. Circ: 7,500.

690 AUT
BAU IM SPIEGEL. Text in German. q.
Address: Heinestrasse 3, Vienna, W 1020, Austria. TEL 01-2143344, FAX 01-2167929. Ed. Walter Polacek. Circ: 12,600.

692.8 CHE
BAU-INFO. Text in German. fortn. CHF 529. **Document type:** *Journal, Trade.* **Description:** Provides information and details on major construction projects in Switzerland.
Published by: MVS Baumarketing AG (Subsidiary of: Springer Science+Business Media), Ruetistr 22, Schlieren, 8952, Switzerland. TEL 41-1-7385151, FAX 41-1-7385200, franco.bernasconi@mvs.ch, http://www.mvs.ch/deutsch/bauinfo.

669 DEU
BAU INFORMATION. Text in German. m.
Published by: Landesverband Bauindustrie Rheinland-Pfalz, Suedallee 31-35, Koblenz Am Rhein, 56068, Germany. TEL 0261-3703334.

690 DEU ISSN 1619-5884
BAU-JOURNAL. Text in German. 2001. m. EUR 2.50 newsstand/cover (effective 2004). adv. **Document type:** *Magazine, Trade.*
Formed by the merger of (1977-2001): Bauinformation (0342-9237); (1957-2001): Bau Aktuell (1438-5155); Which was formerly (until 1999): Bau Aktuell Rheinhessen-Pfalz (0931-394X); (until 1986): Bau Aktuell Rheinland-Pfalz (0174-4518); (until 1979): Pfaelzisches Baugewerbe (0174-4240)
Published by: Baugewerbeverband Rheinhessen-Pfalz e.V., Max-Hufschmidt-Str 11, Mainz, 55130, Germany. TEL 49-6131-983490, FAX 49-6131-9834949, bgv@bgvmz.de, http://www.bgv-rheinland-pfalz.de. adv.: page EUR 895. Circ: 3,000 (controlled).

▼ **DER BAU-RECHTS-BERATER.** see *LAW*

690 DEU ISSN 0005-643X
BAU UND BAUSTOFF. Text in German. 1964. q. adv. bk.rev. **Document type:** *Magazine, Trade.*
Published by: Gert Wohlfarth GmbH, Stresemannstr 20-22, Duisburg, 47051, Germany. TEL 49-203-305270, FAX 49-203-30527820, info@wohlfarth.de, http://www.wohlfarth.de. Ed. Wolfgang Metzmacher. Adv. contact Ulrich Miggel. B&W page EUR 2,480, color page EUR 3,380. Circ: 75,000 (controlled).

690 DEU ISSN 0933-3924
BAUAUFSICHTLICHE ZULASSUNGEN. Text in German. 1967. irreg. looseleaf. price varies. **Document type:** *Monographic series, Trade.*
Published by: Erich Schmidt Verlag GmbH & Co. (Berlin), Genthiner Str 30G, Berlin, 10785, Germany. TEL 49-30-250085-0, FAX 49-30-25008521, vertrieb@esvmedien.de, http://www.erich-schmidt-verlag.de.

690 DEU
BAUDIREKT. Text in German. m. adv. **Document type:** *Magazine, Trade.*
Published by: Baugewerbliche Verbaende Westfalen, Westfalendamm 229, Dortmund, 44141, Germany. TEL 49-231-433918, FAX 49-231-433907, asbeck@bauverbaende.de, http://www.bgv-westfalen.de. Ed. Claus Asbeck. Adv. contact Nicole Schaefer. B&W page EUR 1,070, color page EUR 1,991; trim 175 x 260. Circ: 10,500 (controlled).

690 CHE ISSN 1019-4258
BAUDOC BULLETIN. Text in German, French. 1969. 10/yr. CHF 65; CHF 7 per issue (effective 2000). adv. bk.rev. illus. **Document type:** *Bulletin, Trade.* **Description:** Discusses news and issues in the building and construction industry.
Formerly (until 1991): Docu-Bulletin (1019-424X)
Published by: Schweizer Baudokumentation, Blauen, 4223, Switzerland. TEL 41-61-7614141, FAX 41-61-7612233, webmaster@baudoc.ch, http://www.baudoc.ch/deu/baumesse/home.htm. Ed. Curt Weisser. Circ: 7,000.

690 DEU ISSN 1435-1854
BAUELEMENTE BAU; Marketingmagazin fuer Bauausstatter - Fenster - Tueren - Fassaden. Text in German. 1976. m. EUR 5.50 newsstand/cover (effective 2004). adv. **Document type:** *Magazine, Trade.*
Published by: Verlag fuer Fachpublizistik GmbH, Moerikestr 15, Stuttgart, 70178, Germany. TEL 49-711-6491031, FAX 49-711-6408972, bauelemente-bau@t-online.de. Eds. Hans U. Rohwer, Rudolf Engert. adv.: B&W page EUR 3,270, color page EUR 4,993; trim 185 x 265. Circ: 13,732 (paid).

690 DEU ISSN 0170-0138
BAUEN; fuer alle, die bauen wollen. Text in German. 1975. bi-m. EUR 3 newsstand/cover (effective 2003). adv. illus.; tr.lit. **Document type:** *Magazine, Trade.*
Formerly (until 1978): Bauen und Modernisieren (0170-4095)
Related titles: ♦ Supplement(s): Biologisch Bauen; ♦ Heizen und Energie; ♦ Hausgaerten; ♦ Bauen und Finanzieren; ♦ Champion-Varia. ISSN 1169-2979.
Published by: Fachschriften Verlag GmbH, Hoehenstr 17, Fellbach, 70736, Germany. TEL 49-711-52061, FAX 49-711-5206223, info@fachschriften.de, http://www.fachschriften.de/publikationen/bauen.htm. Ed. Hans Peter Bauer Boeckler. Pub. Ottmar Strebel. Adv. contact Wolfgang Loges. B&W page EUR 5,600, color page EUR 9,240; trim 187 x 247. Circ: 33,320 (paid and controlled).

690 DEU ISSN 0171-7952
BAUEN FUER DIE LANDWIRTSCHAFT. Text in German. 1964. 3/yr. EUR 10 newsstand/cover (effective 2004). adv. bk.rev. **Document type:** *Magazine, Trade.*
Formerly: Beton-Landbau (0005-9897)
—CCC.
Published by: (Bundesverband der Deutschen Zementindustrie e.V.), Verlag Bau und Technik GmbH, Steinhof 39, Erkrath, 40699, Germany. TEL 49-211-9249932, info@verlagbt.de, http://www.verlagbt.de. Ed. Joerg Brandt. adv.: B&W page EUR 925, color page EUR 1,540. Circ: 7,850 (controlled).

BAUEN IN STAHL/CONSTRUIRE EN ACIER/COSTRUIRE IN ACCIAIO. see *ARCHITECTURE*

690 DEU
BAUEN IN UND UM BREMEN. Text in German. 1970. 3/yr. adv. 24 p./no. 3 cols./p.; **Document type:** *Magazine, Trade.* **Description:** Covers the construction trade industry in and around Bremen.
Published by: Carl Ed. Schuenemann KG, Zweite Schlachtpforte 7, Bremen, 28195, Germany. TEL 49-421-3690372, FAX 49-421-3690334, zeitschriften@schuenemann-verlag.de, http://www.schuenemann-verlag.de. Adv. contact Juergen Thiele. B&W page DEM 1,600, color page DEM 2,600; trim 185 x 260. Circ: 6,000.

691 DEU
BAUEN & BAUSTOFFE. Text in German. 1965. q. adv. **Document type:** *Magazine, Trade.*
Published by: Gert Wohlfarth GmbH, Stresemannstr 20-22, Duisburg, 47051, Germany. TEL 49-203-305270, FAX 49-203-30527820, info@wohlfarth.de, http://www.wohlfarth.de. adv.: B&W page EUR 2,480, color page EUR 3,380. Circ: 75,000 (controlled).

690 CHE ISSN 1424-4241
BAUEN UND BEWIRTSCHAFTEN. Text in German. 2000. bi-m. CHF 100 domestic; CHF 115 foreign (effective 2001). adv. illus.; mkt.; stat.; tr.lit. back issues avail. **Document type:** *Magazine, Trade.*
Published by: Verlag Bauen und Bewirtschaften, Spielhof 14a, Glarus, 8750, Switzerland. TEL 41-55-6453755, FAX 41-55-6402171, bbverlag@smile.ch. Ed., Pub. Peter Laternser. Adv. contact Jose Andre Rupprig TEL 41-55-6453755. B&W page CHF 4,350, color page CHF 6,100; trim 184 x 264.

BAUEN UND SIEDELN. see *HOUSING AND URBAN PLANNING*

690 CHE ISSN 1424-0106
BAUEN UND WOHNEN HEUTE. Text in German. 1986. a. CHF 18.50 (effective 2000). adv. **Document type:** *Magazine, Consumer.* **Description:** Contains ideas, advice and examples of various renovation and design plans for homes.
Published by: Etzel-Verlag AG, Knonauerstr 56, Cham, 6330, Switzerland. TEL 41-41-7855085, FAX 41-41-7855088, info@etzel-verlag.ch, http://www.etzel-verlag.ch/html/bwhhome.htm. Ed. Esther Kall. adv.: B&W page CHF 3,860; trim 184 x 278. Circ: 20,000 (paid and controlled).

690 DEU ISSN 0343-1444
BAUFACHBLATT. Text in German. 1970. 10/yr. adv. **Document type:** *Journal, Trade.*
Published by: Service-GmbH der Bauwirtschaft Suedbaden, Postfach 143, Freiburg, 79001, Germany. TEL 49-761-703020. adv.: B&W page EUR 620, color page EUR 1,160. Circ: 2,000 (controlled).

690 DEU ISSN 0005-6626
BAUGESCHAEFT UND BAUUNTERNEHMER. Text in German. 1966. q. EUR 40 (effective 2001). adv. bk.rev. stat.; tr.lit. **Document type:** *Journal, Trade.*
Published by: Zeitungs- und Zeitschriftenverlag Heinrichs, Brueggekamp 1, Barsinghausen, 30890, Germany. TEL 49-5105-2289. Ed., Pub. Gerhard Heinrichs.

690 DEU ISSN 1611-2768
BAUGEWERBE - MITTEILUNGEN. Text in German. 1976. m. **Document type:** *Magazine, Trade.*
Former titles (until 1999): Baugewerbe - Mitteilungen Westfalen (0343-0375); (until 1976): Baugewerbliche Mitteilungen fuer Westfalen (0343-0383)
Published by: Baugewerbeverband Westfalen, Westfalendamm 229, Dortmund, 44141, Germany. TEL 49-231-433918, FAX 49-231-433907, info@bauverbaende.de, http://www.bgv-westfalen.de. Circ: 7,400.

690 DEU ISSN 0173-5365
BAUHANDWERK; Ausbau und Modernisierung. Text in German. 1979. m. EUR 96.60 domestic; EUR 100.20 foreign; EUR 66 to students; EUR 12.50 newsstand/cover (effective 2005). adv. bk.rev. **Document type:** *Magazine, Trade.* **Description:** Trade publication for the building industry, featuring restoration, renovation and modernization of existing buildings and houses as well as extensions and additions. Lists new products, materials and appliances.
Incorporates (1990-1998): BauSanierung (0939-4680)
Published by: Bauverlag BV GmbH (Subsidiary of: Springer Science+Business Media), Avenwedderstr 55, Guetersloh, 33311, Germany. TEL 49-5241-802119, FAX 49-5241-809582, ulrike.mattern@springer-sbm.com, http://www.baunetz.de/bau/bhw/, http://www.bauverlag.de. Ed. Burkhard Froehlich. adv.: B&W page EUR 3,620, color page EUR 5,420; trim 186 x 270. Circ: 15,893 (paid and controlled).

690 DEU ISSN 0949-7544
DER BAUHERR; das Magazin fuer Massivbau und Fertighaus. Text in German. 1996. bi-m. EUR 20; EUR 3.50 newsstand/cover (effective 2003). adv. **Document type:** *Magazine, Trade.*
Published by: Compact Verlag GmbH, Zuericher Str 29, Munich, 81476, Germany. TEL 49-89-7451610, FAX 49-89-756095, info@compactverlag.de, http://www.derbauherr.de, http://www.compact-verlag.de. Ed. Stephanie Hutschenreuter. Adv. contact Claudia Koksch. B&W page EUR 6,800, color page EUR 10,300. Circ: 59,683 (paid and controlled).

690 DEU
BAUHERREN-BERATER; planen - bauen - wohnen. Text in German. 1977. a. free per issue. adv. **Document type:** *Magazine, Consumer.*
Published by: Fachschriften Verlag GmbH, Hoehenstr 17, Fellbach, 70736, Germany. TEL 49-711-52061, FAX 49-711-5206223, info@fachschriften.de, http://www.fachschriften.de/publikationen/bberater.htm. Ed. Wolfgang Grasreiner. Adv. contact Carmen Greiner. B&W page EUR 9,750, color page EUR 16,185; trim 187 x 247. Circ: 200,000 (controlled).

690 DEU ISSN 0720-7468
BAUHERREN-RATGEBER. Text in German. 1981. 3/w. adv. **Document type:** *Trade.*
Related titles: ♦ Supplement(s): Ausbau und Raumideen; ♦ Die Neuen Kuechen; ♦ Die Neuen Baeder; ♦ Kamine und Kacheloefen.
Published by: Fachschriften Verlag GmbH, Hoehenstr 17, Fellbach, 70736, Germany. TEL 49-711-52061, FAX 49-711-5206223. Adv. contact Wolfgang Kriwan.

B

690 DEU ISSN 0937-1826
BAUIDEE; das Spezial-Magazin fuer Haus und Garten. Text in German. 1988. q. EUR 4.90 newsstand/cover (effective 2005). adv. **Document type:** *Magazine, Consumer.* **Description:** Ideas and tips for building and construction.
Related titles: ♦ Online - full text ed.: Bauidee Online.
Published by: Heinrich Bauer Verlag, Burchardstr 11, Hamburg, 20077, Germany. TEL 49-40-30190, FAX 49-40-30191043, kommunikation@hbv.de, http://www.bauidee.de. Ed. Ute Stahmann. Adv. contact Dorothee Uhlig. page EUR 7,500. Circ: 88,000 (paid). **Dist. in UK by:** Powers International Ltd., 100 Rochester Row, London SW1P 1JP, United Kingdom. TEL 44-20-7630-9966, FAX 44-20-7630-9922; **Dist. in US by:** GLP International, PO Box 9868, Englewood, NJ 07631-6868. TEL 201-871-1010.

690 DEU
BAUIDEE ONLINE. Text in German. bi-m. adv. **Document type:** *Consumer.*
Media: Online - full text. **Related titles:** ♦ Print ed.: Bauidee. ISSN 0937-1826.
Published by: Heinrich Bauer Verlag, Burchardstr 11, Hamburg, 20077, Germany. http://www.bauidee.de.

690 DEU ISSN 0940-7367
BAUINDUSTRIE AKTUELL. Text in German. m. **Document type:** *Trade.*
Incorporated (in 1986): Baukonjunkturspiegel (0343-141X); Formerly (until 1986): Bauindustriebrief (0343-7795)
Published by: Hauptverband der Deutschen Bauindustrie, Kurfurstenstr. 129, Berlin, 10785, Germany. TEL 49-30-21286-0.

690 DEU ISSN 0005-6650
TA3 CODEN: BANGAS
BAUINGENIEUR; Zeitschrift fuer das gesamte Bauwesen. Text in German; Abstracts in English. 1908. 11/yr. EUR 327 domestic; EUR 346 foreign; EUR 33.50 newsstand/cover (effective 2005). adv. bk.rev. bibl.; charts; illus. index. back issues avail.; reprint service avail. from ISI. **Document type:** *Magazine, Trade.* **Description:** Provides articles covering the theory and practice of engineering construction, building practices, computers in building, and building management.
Formerly (until 1920): Armierter Beton (0174-8130)
Related titles: Microform ed.: (from PQC); Online - full text ed.
Indexed: ApMecR, ChemAb, CivEngAb, ConcrAb, DokStr, EngInd, ExcerpMed, GeotechAb, ICEA, METADEX, SoftAbEng.
—BLDSC (1867.000000), CISTI, IE, Infotrieve, ingenta, Linda Hall. **CCC.**
Published by: Springer V D I Verlag GmbH & Co. KG, Heinrichstr 24, Duesseldorf, 40239, Germany. TEL 49-211-61030, FAX 49-221-6103148, bauingenieur@technikwissen.de, anzeigen@technikwissen.de, info@technikwissen.de, http://www.technikwissen.de/bauingenieur. Ed. Thomas Burska-Erler. Adv. contact Manfred Maas. B&W page EUR 2,340, color page EUR 3,495; trim 185 x 270. Circ: 4,903 (paid and controlled).

690 AUT
BAUJOURNAL. Text in German. 1989. 9/yr. adv. bk.rev. **Document type:** *Journal, Trade.*
Published by: Baujournal Fachzeitschriften GmbH, c/o Kurt Sommersacher, Rohrbach, W 8151, Austria. TEL 43-3123-399660, FAX 43-3123-3996626, mail@bewerb.com, http://www.baujournal.at, http://www.bewerb.com. Ed., Adv. contact Kurt Sommersacher.

690 DEU
BAUKAMMER BERLIN. Text in German. q. EUR 10 per issue (effective 2004). adv. **Document type:** *Magazine, Trade.*
Published by: (Baukammer Berlin), C B Verlag Carl Boldt, Baseler Str 80, Berlin, 12205, Germany. TEL 49-30-8337087, FAX 49-30-8339125, mail@cb-verlag.de. adv.: B&W page EUR 1,025, color page EUR 1,745. Circ: 3,650 (controlled).

690 DEU ISSN 1610-3785
BAUMAGAZIN. Text in German. 1997. m. EUR 50.50 domestic; EUR 63 foreign; EUR 5 newsstand/cover (effective 2004). adv. **Document type:** *Magazine, Trade.*
Formerly (until 2001): Sueddeutsches Baumagazin (1439-5592)
Published by: S B M Verlag GmbH, Hauptstr 1, Betzigau/Kempten, 87488, Germany. TEL 49-831-522040, FAX 49-831-5220450, info@sbm-verlag.de, http://www.sbm-verlag.de. adv.: B&W page EUR 2,650, color page EUR 4,240. Circ: 12,777 (paid and controlled).

690 DEU
BAUMAGAZIN.DE. Text in German. w. **Document type:** *Trade.* **Description:** Contains building designs, materials recommendations, insurance and financing information, safety procedures and products, and new ideas and trends in home design and layout.
Media: Online - full text.
Published by: Netpoint GmbH, Fritz-Kohl-Str 24, Mainz, 55122, Germany. TEL 49-6131-3285400, FAX 49-6131-3285499, info@baumagazin.de, media@netpoint.de, http://www.baumagazin.de, http://www.netpoint.de. Ed. Petra Witzl. Adv. contact Ralf Witzl.

690 DEU
▼ **BAUMARKT UND BAUWIRTSCHAFT.** Text in German. 2004. m. EUR 178.80 domestic; EUR 198 foreign; EUR 16.50 newsstand/cover (effective 2004). adv. back issues avail. **Document type:** *Magazine, Trade.* **Description:** Covers business and technical questions in connection with underground and surface engineering and road building.
Formed by the merger of (1957-2004): Baumarkt (0341-2717); Which incorporated (1973-1978): Bauanalysis (0340-0271); (1947-2004): Bauwirtschaft (1433-0148); Which was formerly: Bauwirtschaft. Ausgabe A (0341-3810)
Indexed: ExcerpMed, KES.
—CISTI, Linda Hall.
Published by: Bauverlag BV GmbH (Subsidiary of: Springer Science+Business Media), Avenwedderstr 55, Guetersloh, 33311, Germany. TEL 05241-802332, FAX 05241-73055, http://www.baunetz.de/bau/bmbw/00101fh_.htm. Eds. A Langer, Volker Horschig. adv.: B&W page EUR 3,880, color page EUR 5,590; trim 186 x 270. Circ: 15,835 (paid and controlled).

691 DEU
BAUMASCHINEN-INSERAT. Text in German. 2000. m. EUR 260 (effective 2004). adv. **Document type:** *Newspaper, Trade.*
Published by: Baumaschinen-Inserat Druck- und Verlags GmbH, Niederhoechstaedter Str 64, Kronberg, 61476, Germany. TEL 49-6173-96660, FAX 49-6173-966610, info@baumaschinen-inserat.de, http://www.baumaschinen-inserat.de. adv.: B&W page EUR 6,450.50, color page EUR 6,780.50. Circ: 10,000 (paid and controlled).

690 DEU ISSN 0005-6715
BAUMASCHINEN- UND BAUGERAETE-HANDEL. Text in German. 1966. q. EUR 40 (effective 2001). adv. bk.rev. stat.; tr.lit. **Document type:** *Journal, Trade.* **Description:** Covers all aspects of the building machinery and equipment trade.
Published by: Zeitungs- und Zeitschriftenverlag Heinrichs, Brueggekamp 1, Barsinghausen, 30890, Germany. TEL 49-5105-2289. Ed., Pub. Gerhard Heinrichs.

BAUMEISTER; Zeitschrift fuer Architektur. see *ARCHITECTURE*

690 DEU ISSN 0179-2563
BAUMETALL; Klempnertechnik im Hochbau. Text in German. 1985. bi-m. EUR 68.40 domestic; EUR 78.40 foreign; EUR 9.90 newsstand/cover (effective 2004). adv. **Document type:** *Magazine, Trade.* **Description:** Supports the applications of metals in structural engineering.
Published by: Technischer Fachverlag GmbH, Forststr 131, Stuttgart, 70193, Germany. TEL 49-711-63672-0, FAX 49-711-6367211, haselbachm@aol.com. Ed. Manfred Haselbach. Adv. contact Annette Haselbach. B&W page EUR 1,760, color page EUR 2,510. Circ: 5,534 (paid).

690 DEU
BAUNETZ BAUKATALOG. Text in German. 1929. a. EUR 31 (effective 2005). adv. **Document type:** *Catalog, Trade.* **Description:** Entries provide product information for the architect, planner, master craftsman, specialist engineer and building contractor.
Former titles: Bertelsmann Baukatalog (0723-5895); Bauwelt Katalog (0067-4664)
Published by: Bauverlag BV GmbH (Subsidiary of: Springer Science+Business Media), Avenwedderstr 55, Guetersloh, 33311, Germany. TEL 49-5241-802119, FAX 49-5241-809582, ulrike.mattern@springer-sbm.com, http://www.baunetz.de/baukatalog/, http://www.bauverlag.de. Circ: 34,961.

690 531 DEU ISSN 0171-5445
TH6014 CODEN: BAUPDP
BAUPHYSIK. Text in German. 1979. bi-m. EUR 228.04 in Europe to institutions; CHF 404 to institutions in Switzerland & Liechtenstein; USD 264 elsewhere to institutions; EUR 250.84 combined subscription in Europe to institutions print & online eds.; CHF 445 combined subscription to institutions in Switzerland & Liechtenstein; print & online eds.; USD 291 combined subscription elsewhere to institutions print & online eds. (effective 2006). adv. **Document type:** *Journal, Trade.* **Description:** Covers topics such as the problems of thermal insulation, humidity control, acoustics, fire design, lighting and micro-climate control relating to buildings.
Related titles: Online - full text ed.: ISSN 1437-0980. EUR 228.04 in Europe to institutions; CHF 404 to institutions in Switzerland & Liechtenstein; USD 264 elsewhere to institutions (effective 2006) (from EBSCO Publishing, Swets Information Services, Wiley InterScience).
Indexed: AcoustA, ExcerpMed, IBuildSA, INIS AtomInd, RefZh.
—BLDSC (1867.800000), CASDDS, CISTI, IE, Infotrieve, ingenta, Linda Hall. **CCC.**
Published by: Ernst und Sohn, Buehringstr 10, Berlin, 13086, Germany. TEL 49-30-47031200, FAX 49-30-47031240, marketing@ernst-und-sohn.de, http://www.wiley-vch.de/ernstsohn. Ed. H P Luehr. adv.: B&W page EUR 1,350, color page EUR 2,220. Circ: 2,894 (paid and controlled). **Subscr. in the Americas to:** John Wiley & Sons, Inc., 111 River St, Hoboken, NJ 07030-5774. TEL 201-748-6645, FAX 201-748-6088, subinfo@wiley.com; **Subscr. to:** Wiley - V C H Verlag GmbH & Co. KGaA, Boschstr 12, Weinheim 69469, Germany. TEL 49-6201-606147, FAX 49-6201-606117.

690 720 DEU ISSN 0938-1694
BAUPLAN - BAUORGA; internationale technisch-wirtschaftliche Zeitschrift. Text in German. 1980. 6/yr. adv. bk.rev. **Document type:** *Trade.*
Published by: Verlag Heinrich Graefen GmbH, Im Dreispitz 30, Duisburg, 47249, Germany. TEL 49-203-702672, FAX 49-203-702672. Circ: 8,000.

690 DEU
BAUPRAXIS. Text in German. w. adv. **Document type:** *Trade.* **Description:** Provides a wide variety of sources and products for building and construction companies and contractors.
Media: Online - full text.
Published by: Marketing-Werbe-Service GmbH, Pippinger Str 159a, Munich, 81247, Germany. TEL 49-89-891233-0, FAX 49-89-89123330, redaktion@baupraxis.de, service@mws.de, http://www.baupraxis.de, http://www.mws.de. Ed., Pub. Claus-Peter Wiegner.

690 DEU ISSN 0930-1895
BAUPRAXIS-ZEITUNG. Abbreviated title: B P Z. Text in German. 1983. 11/yr. EUR 67.20 domestic; EUR 72.60 foreign; EUR 5.80 newsstand/cover (effective 2004). adv. back issues avail. **Document type:** *Newspaper, Trade.* **Description:** Presents data on the building industry, construction technology, processes, machinery, materials and components.
Formerly (until 1985): Baupraxis-Zeitung, Baupraxis (0724-7931); Which was formed by the merger of (1957-1983): Baupraxis (0005-6766); (1972-1983): Baupraxis-Zeitung (0341-4973); Which was formed by the merger of (1965-1972): B P Z - Baupraxis Zeitung (0341-4981); (1948-1972): Bau und Bauindustrie (0341-5031)
Published by: Konradin Verlag Robert Kohlhammer GmbH, Ernst Mey Str 8, Leinfelden-Echterdingen, 70771, Germany. TEL 49-711-75940, FAX 49-711-7594399, bpz.redaktion@konradin.de, info@konradin.de, http://www.konradin.de. Ed. Peter Schaeuble. Adv. contact Bettina Mayer. B&W page EUR 4,185, color page EUR 5,435; trim 190 x 270. Circ: 20,057 (paid and controlled).

690 CHE
BAUPROJEKT. Text in French, German, Italian. a. **Document type:** *Directory, Trade.*
Related titles: CD-ROM ed.; Online - full text ed.
Published by: MVS Baumarketing AG (Subsidiary of: Springer Science+Business Media), Ruetistr 22, Schlieren, 8952, Switzerland. TEL 41-1-7385151, FAX 41-1-7385200, franco.bernasconi@mvs.ch, http://www.mvs.ch. Circ: 50,000 (controlled).

690 DEU ISSN 0340-7489
BAURECHT; Zeitschrift fuer das gesamte oeffentliche und zivile Baurecht. Short title: BauR. Text in German. 1970. m. EUR 189; EUR 19.50 newsstand/cover (effective 2005). adv. **Document type:** *Magazine, Trade.*
Indexed: DIP, DokStr, IBR, IBZ.
—IE, Infotrieve. **CCC.**
Published by: Werner-Verlag GmbH (Subsidiary of: Wolters Kluwer Deutschland GmbH), Heddesdorfer Str 31, Neuwied, 56564, Germany. TEL 49-2631-801338, FAX 49-2631-801420, info@werner-verlag.de, http://www.werner-verlag.de. Eds. Hans Dieter Upmeier, Hermann Korbion. adv.: B&W page EUR 1,500; trim 140 x 200.

690 340 DEU ISSN 0941-2182
BAURECHT FUER DAS LAND BRANDENBURG. Text in German. 1992. irreg. looseleaf. price varies. **Document type:** *Monographic series, Trade.*
Published by: Erich Schmidt Verlag GmbH & Co. (Berlin), Genthiner Str 30G, Berlin, 10785, Germany. TEL 49-30-250085-0, FAX 49-30-25008521, vertrieb@esvmedien.de, http://www.erich-schmidt-verlag.de.

690 340 DEU ISSN 0940-7952
BAURECHT FUER DAS LAND MECKLENBURG - VORPOMMERN. Text in German. 1992. irreg. looseleaf. price varies. **Document type:** *Monographic series, Trade.*
Published by: Erich Schmidt Verlag GmbH & Co. (Berlin), Genthiner Str 30G, Berlin, 10785, Germany. TEL 49-30-250085-0, FAX 49-30-25008521, vertieb@esvmedien.de, http://www.erich-schmidt-verlag.de.

690 340 DEU ISSN 0941-2190
BAURECHT FUER DAS LAND SACHSEN-ANHALT. Text in German. 1992. irreg. looseleaf. price varies. **Document type:** *Monographic series, Trade.*
Published by: Erich Schmidt Verlag GmbH & Co. (Berlin), Genthiner Str 30G, Berlin, 10785, Germany. TEL 49-30-250085-0, FAX 49-30-25008521, vertrieb@esvmedien.de, http://www.erich-schmidt-verlag.de.

690 340 DEU ISSN 0941-2204
BAURECHT FUER DAS LAND THUERINGEN. Text in German. 1992. irreg. looseleaf. price varies. **Document type:** *Monographic series, Trade.*
Published by: Erich Schmidt Verlag GmbH & Co. (Berlin), Genthiner Str 30G, Berlin, 10785, Germany. TEL 49-30-250085-0, FAX 49-30-25008521, vertrieb@esvmedien.de, http://www.erich-schmidt-verlag.de.

690 340 DEU ISSN 0941-2212
BAURECHT FUER DEN FREISTAAT SACHSEN. Text in German. 1992. irreg. looseleaf. price varies. **Document type:** *Monographic series, Trade.*
Published by: Erich Schmidt Verlag GmbH & Co. (Berlin), Genthiner Str 30G, Berlin, 10785, Germany. TEL 49-30-250085-0, FAX 49-30-25008521, vertrieb@esvmedien.de, http://www.erich-schmidt-verlag.de.

690 DEU
BAURECHT TEXTE CD. Text in German. base vol. plus updates 2/yr. EUR 35 base vol(s). per vol.; EUR 25 updates per issue (effective 2005). **Document type:** *Trade.*
Media: CD-ROM.
Published by: Verlag C.H. Beck oHG, Wilhelmstr 9, Munich, 80801, Germany. TEL 49-89-38189338, FAX 49-89-38189398, abo.service@beck.de, http://www.beck.de.

343.078624 DEU
BAURECHT UND BAUPRAXIS. Text in German. m. EUR 118 (effective 2004). adv. **Document type:** *Journal, Trade.*
Published by: Deutscher Anwaltverlag GmbH, Wachsbleiche 7, Bonn, 53111, Germany. TEL 49-228-919110, FAX 49-228-9191123, kontakt@anwaltverlag.de, http://www.anwaltverlag.de. adv.: B&W page EUR 990; trim 186 x 260. Circ: 5,000 (paid and controlled).

690 340 AUT ISSN 1434-1832
KJJ3067.A15 CODEN: BABLFM
➤ **BAURECHTLICHE BLAETTER.** Variant title: B B L. Text in German. 1998. bi-m. EUR 78 to institutions (effective 2005). adv. **Document type:** *Journal, Academic/Scholarly.*
Description: Covers all aspects of planning and building law.
Related titles: Online - full text ed.
Indexed: DIP, IBR, IBZ.
—IE. **CCC.**
Published by: Springer-Verlag Wien (Subsidiary of: Springer Science+Business Media) journals@springer.at, http://www.springer.at/baubl. Eds. D Jahnel, K Giese. R&P Angela Foessl TEL 43-1-3302415517. Adv. contact Michael Katzenberger TEL 43-1-3302415220. B&W page EUR 770, color page EUR 1,386; 170 x 250. **Subscr. in the Americas to:** Springer-Verlag New York, Inc., Journal Fulfillment, PO Box 2485, Secaucus, NJ 07096-2485. TEL 800-777-4643, 201-348-4033, FAX 201-348-4505, journals@springer-ny.com, http://www.springer-ny.com.

➤ **BAUSTATISTISCHES JAHRBUCH.** see *BUILDING AND CONSTRUCTION—Abstracting, Bibliographies, Statistics*

691 DEU ISSN 1439-5606
BAUSTOFF PARTNER. Text in German. 1999. m. EUR 51 domestic; EUR 64 foreign; EUR 5 newsstand/cover (effective 2004). adv. **Document type:** *Magazine, Trade.*
Published by: S B M Verlag GmbH, Hauptstr 1, Betzigau/Kempten, 87488, Germany. TEL 49-831-522040, FAX 49-831-5220450, info@sbm-verlag.de, http://www.sbm-verlag.de/bp. adv.: B&W page EUR 2,174, color page EUR 2,743. Circ: 8,252 (paid).

690 DEU ISSN 0721-7854
BAUSTOFF-TECHNIK; Fachzeitschrift fuer Baustoffe und Baustoff-Anwendung. Text in German. 1982. m. EUR 36 domestic; EUR 54.60 foreign; EUR 3 newsstand/cover (effective 2004). adv. **Document type:** *Magazine, Trade.*
Published by: Gert Wohlfarth GmbH, Stresemannstr 20-22, Duisburg, 47051, Germany. TEL 49-203-305270, FAX 49-203-30527820, info@wohlfarth.de, http://www.wohlfarth.de. Ed. Wilfried Behr. Pub. Gert Wohlfarth. adv.: B&W page EUR 2,060, color page EUR 3,592. Circ: 4,182 (paid and controlled).

690 DEU ISSN 0005-6804
BAUSTOFF- UND BAUBEDARFSGROSSHANDEL. Text in German. 1966. q. EUR 40 (effective 2001). adv. bk.rev. stat.; tr.lit. **Document type:** *Journal, Trade.* **Description:** Contains information on wholesale trade with building materials.
Published by: Zeitungs- und Zeitschriftenverlag Heinrichs, Brueggekamp 1, Barsinghausen, 30890, Germany. TEL 49-5105-2289. Ed., Pub. Gerhard Heinrichs.

691 DEU ISSN 0005-6448
BAUSTOFFMARKT; Fachzeitschrift fuer den Baustoff-, Heimwerker- und Keramik-markt. Text in German. 1969. m. EUR 84 domestic; EUR 108.60 foreign; EUR 7 newsstand/cover (effective 2004). adv. **Document type:** *Magazine, Trade.*
Published by: (Bundesverband Deutscher Baustoffhaendler e.V.), Gert Wohlfarth GmbH, Stresemannstr 20-22, Duisburg, 47051, Germany. TEL 49-203-305270, FAX 49-203-30527820, info@wohlfarth.de, http://www.wohlfarth.de. Ed. Wilfried Behr. Pub. Gert Wohlfarth. adv.: B&W page EUR 2,190, color page EUR 3,840. Circ: 5,849 (paid).

690 DEU ISSN 0179-2857
BAUSUBSTANZ; Fachmagazin fuer Bauwerkserhaltung. Text in German. 10/yr. **Document type:** *Trade.*
Published by: Meininger Verlag GmbH, Maximilianstr 7-17, Neustadt, 67433, Germany. TEL 49-6321-8908-0, FAX 49-6321-890873. Ed. Thomas Wieckhorst. Circ: 14,526.

690 DEU ISSN 0932-8351
BAUTECHNIK. Text in German. 1924. m. EUR 330.84 in Europe to institutions; CHF 624 to institutions in Switzerland & Liechtenstein; USD 394 elsewhere to institutions; EUR 363.92 combined subscription in Europe to institutions print & online eds.; CHF 687 combined subscription to institutions in Switzerland & Liechtenstein; print & online eds.; USD 434 combined subscription elsewhere to institutions print & online eds. (effective 2006). adv. **Document type:** *Journal, Trade.*
Description: Theory and practice in civil engineering, building technology and related fields, developments in building machinery and construction methods, reviews, and technical reports.
Formed by 1983 merger of: Bautechnik. Ausgabe A (0341-1052); Bautechnik. Ausgabe B (0340-5044)
Related titles: Online - full text ed.: ISSN 1437-0999. EUR 330.84 in Europe to institutions; CHF 624 to institutions in Switzerland & Liechtenstein; USD 394 elsewhere to institutions (effective 2006) (from EBSCO Publishing, Swets Information Services, Wiley InterScience); ♦ Supplement(s): Stahlbau. ISSN 0038-9145.
Indexed: BrCerAb, C&ISA, CerAb, CivEngAb, CorrAb, E&CAJ, EEA, EMA, EngInd, GeotechAb, IAA, IMMAb, M&TEA, MBF, METADEX, SolStAb, WAA.
—CISTI, Ei, IE, Linda Hall.
Published by: Ernst und Sohn, Buehringstr 10, Berlin, 13086, Germany. TEL 49-30-47031200, FAX 49-30-47031240, marketing@ernst-und-sohn.de, http://www.wiley-vch.de/ernstsohn. Ed. Doris Greiner Mai. adv.: B&W page EUR 2,550, color page EUR 3,990. Circ: 3,422 (paid). **Subscr. in the Americas to:** John Wiley & Sons, Inc., 111 River St, Hoboken, NJ 07030-5774. TEL 201-748-6645, FAX 201-748-6088, subinfo@wiley.com; **Subscr. to:** Wiley - V C H Verlag GmbH & Co. KGaA, Boschstr 12, Weinheim 69469, Germany. TEL 49-6201-606147, FAX 49-6201-606117.

690 DEU ISSN 0170-9267
CODEN: BABADL
BAUTENSCHUTZ UND BAUSANIERUNG; Zeitschrift fuer Bauinstandhaltung und Denkmalpflege. Short title: B und B. Text in German; Summaries in English, German. 1977. 8/yr. EUR 113.50 domestic; EUR 122 foreign; EUR 18 newsstand/cover (effective 2004). adv. bk.rev. index. reprints avail. **Document type:** *Magazine, Trade.*
Indexed: AIAP, CEABA, CIN, ChemAb, ChemTitl, RefZh.
—BLDSC (1870.320000), CASDDS, CISTI, IE, ingenta. **CCC.**
Published by: Verlagsgesellschaft Rudolf Mueller GmbH & Co. KG, Stolberger Str 84, Cologne, 50933, Germany. TEL 49-221-54970, FAX 49-221-5497326, red.bautenschutz@rudolf-mueller.de, service@rudolf-mueller.de, http://www.rudolf-mueller.de. Ed. Christian Anger. Adv. contact Dagmar Weyand. B&W page EUR 2,800, color page EUR 4,720; trim 188 x 267. Circ: 6,750 (paid).

690 DEU ISSN 0945-6562
BAUVORHABEN. Text in German. 1950. m. **Document type:** *Magazine, Trade.*
Formerly (until 1993): Berliner BauVorhaben (0943-7835)
Published by: Vogel Baumedien GmbH, Bluecherstr 31A, Berlin, 10961, Germany. TEL 49-30-695950-0, FAX 49-30-69595090, info@baumedien.de, http://www.baumedien.de. Ed. Iris Kopf. Adv. contact Gernot Wetzel TEL 49-30-69595041. Circ: 2,000 (paid and controlled).

690 330 DEU ISSN 0170-9097
BAUWIRTSCHAFT IM ZAHLENBILD. Text in German. s-a. **Document type:** *Bulletin, Trade.*
Published by: Hauptverband der Deutschen Bauindustrie, Kurfurstenstr. 129, Berlin, 10785, Germany. TEL 49-30-21286-0.

690 DEU
BAUWISSEN AKTUELL; das Handbuch fuer den Bauherrn. Text in German. a. EUR 9.90 newsstand/cover (effective 2002). adv. **Document type:** *Magazine, Trade.*
Published by: Kaenguru Verlag und Medienservice GmbH, Hans-Boeckler-Str. 10, Langenfeld, 40764, Germany. TEL 49-2173-39929-0, FAX 49-2173-3992910, anzeigen@kaenguru-medien.de, http://www.kaenguru-medien.de. Adv. contact Hagen Knippen. B&W page EUR 5,500, color page EUR 7,320; trim 148 x 193. Circ: 60,000 (paid and controlled).

690.24 DEU ISSN 0938-7331
DAS BAYERISCHE KAMINKEHRER-HANDWERK. Text in German. m. adv. **Document type:** *Magazine, Trade.*
Published by: Landesinnungsverband fuer das Bayerische Kaminkehrerhandwerk, Pettenkoferstr 31, Munich, 80366, Germany. TEL 49-89-5441390, FAX 49-89-54413925, bfv@schornstein.com, http://www.liv-info.de. adv.: B&W page EUR 530, color page EUR 730. Circ: 2,475 (controlled).

960 USA
BERGER BUILDING & DESIGN COST FILE. UNIT PRICES. VOL. 1: GENERAL CONSTRUCTION TRADES. Text in English. a.
Formed by the 1981 merger of: Berger Design Cost File; Berger Building Cost File; Which was formerly: Building Cost File (0091-3499)
Published by: Building Cost File, Inc., 2906 Anthony St, Wantagh, NY 11793-2330.

690 USA
BERGER BUILDING & DESIGN COST FILE. UNIT PRICES. VOL. 2: MECHANICAL AND ELECTRICAL TRADES. Text in English. a.
Formed by the 1981 merger of: Berger Design Cost File; Berger Building Cost File; Which was formerly: Building Cost File (0091-3499)
Published by: Building Cost File, Inc., 2906 Anthony St, Wantagh, NY 11793-2330.

692.5 DNK ISSN 0909-0452
BESKRIVELSESTEKSTER. Variant title: V & S Priser, Beskrivelsestekster. Text in Danish. 1994. a. DKK 1,410 (effective 1999).
Published by: V & S Byggedata, 551 Frederikssundvej 194, Broenshoej, 2700, Denmark. TEL 45-38-60-77-11, FAX 45-38-60-77-55, bygdat@vs-byggedata.dk, bygdat@vs.byggedata.dk. Ed. Carl Friis Skovsen.

BEST NEW SMALL HOME DESIGNS. see *ARCHITECTURE*

720 USA
BEST OF BETTER HOMES AND GARDENS HOME PLANS. Text in English. 6/yr. USD 4.99 newsstand/cover domestic; USD 6.60 newsstand/cover in Canada (effective 2003). **Document type:** *Magazine, Consumer.*
Published by: Meredith Corp., 1716 Locust St, Des Moines, IA 50309-3023. TEL 515-284-3000, 800-556-9184, FAX 515-284-3657, http://www.meredith.com.

690 333.33 USA
BEST SELLERS COLLECTIONS. Text in English. 4/yr. USD 15 (effective 2000). **Document type:** *Trade.* **Description:** Contains house design sketches and data of most popular homes, and short informational articles.
Published by: Drawing Board Atlanta, Inc., PO Box 15556, Atlanta, GA 30333-0556. TEL 404-624-3999, FAX 404-624-4063, dbahomeplans@mindspring.com, sales@drawingboardatlanta.com. Ed., Pub., R&P, Adv. contact Phillip Andrew Jessup. Circ: 5,000.

690 USA
BEST SELLING HOME PLANS FROM HOME MAGAZINE. Text in English. 7/yr. free (effective 2004). adv. **Document type:** *Magazine, Consumer.*
Published by: Hanley-Wood, LLC (Subsidiary of: J.P. Morgan Chase & Co.), One Thomas Circle, NW, Ste 600, Washington, DC 20005-5701. TEL 202-452-0800, FAX 202-785-1974, jvaughan@hanleywood.com, http://www.hanleywood.com. adv.: color page USD 17,500; trim 8 x 10.5.

691.3 BEL
BETON. Text in Dutch, French. 1969. 5/yr. bk.rev. index. back issues avail. **Document type:** *Trade.* **Description:** For the precast concrete industry.
Published by: FeBe - Federation de l'Industrie du Beton/Federatie van de Betonindustrie, Rue Volta 12, Bruxelles, 1050, Belgium. TEL 32-2-735-8015, FAX 32-2-734-7795, mail@febe.be, http://www.beton.be/Febenew/Templates/beton.htm. Ed. W Simons. Circ: 8,000 (controlled).

691.3 DEU ISSN 0005-9846
TA680 CODEN: BTONAH
BETON. Text in German; Summaries in English, French. 1951. m. EUR 225; EUR 115 to students; EUR 25 newsstand/cover (effective 2005). adv. bk.rev. illus. index. **Document type:** *Magazine, Trade.*
Formerly (until 1957): Beton-Zement-Markt (0723-8568)
Indexed: ConcrAb, DokStr, ICEA, KES, RefZh, SoftAbEng.
—BLDSC (1942.680000), CISTI, IE, Infotrieve, ingenta, Linda Hall. **CCC.**
Published by: (Bundesverband der Deutschen Zementindustrie e.V.), Verlag Bau und Technik GmbH, Steinhof 39, Erkrath, 40699, Germany. TEL 49-211-9249932, FAX 49-211-9249955, info@verlagbt.de, http://www.verlagbt.de/verlag/beton/index.php?navtext=Beton. Ed. Stefan Deckers. Adv. contact Elmar Rump. B&W page EUR 2,300, color page EUR 3,905. Circ: 6,461 (paid and controlled).

691.3 RUS ISSN 0005-9889
TA680 CODEN: BTZBA2
BETON I ZHELEZOBETON. Contents page in English, French, German. 1955. bi-m. USD 98 foreign (effective 2005). bk.rev. bibl.; charts; illus. index. **Document type:** *Journal, Trade.*
Related titles: ♦ English Translation: Russian Journal of Concrete and Reinforced Concrete.
Indexed: ApMecR, CIN, CRIA, CRICC, ChemAb, ChemTitl, CivEngAb, ConcrAb, EEA, EngInd, ICEA, RASB, RefZh, SoftAbEng.
—CASDDS, CISTI, East View, Linda Hall.
Published by: Redaktsiya Zhurnala Beton i Zhelezobeton, Georgievskii per, d 1, str 3, 3-i etazh, Moscow, 119826, Russian Federation. TEL 7-095-2926205, magbeton@rambler.ru. Ed. R L Serykh. Circ: 14,700. **Dist. by:** Informnauka Ltd., Ul Usievicha 20, Moscow 125190, Russian Federation. alfimov@viniti.ru.

620.135 DEU ISSN 0342-7617
BETON-KALENDER. Text in German. 1906. a. EUR 159 (effective 2005). **Document type:** *Journal, Trade.*
Related titles: CD-ROM ed.

Published by: Ernst und Sohn, Buehringstr 10, Berlin, 13086, Germany. TEL 49-30-47031200, FAX 49-30-47031240, marketing@ernst-und-sohn.de, http://www.wiley-vch.de/ ernstsohn. Ed. Josef Eibl. Circ: 18,000.

691.3 DEU ISSN 0005-9900
TA680 CODEN: BESTAI
BETON- UND STAHLBETONBAU. Text in German. 1901. m. EUR 330.84 in Europe to institutions; CHF 588 to institutions in Switzerland & Liechtenstein; USD 384 elsewhere to institutions; EUR 363.92 in Europe to institutions print & online eds.; CHF 647 to institutions in Switzerland & Liechtenstein; print & online eds.; USD 423 elsewhere to institutions print & online eds. (effective 2006). adv. bk.rev. charts; illus. index. back issues avail. **Document type:** *Journal, Trade.*
Description: Deals specifically with problems related to concrete and reinforced concrete construction methods.
Related titles: Online - full text ed.: ISSN 1437-1006. EUR 330.84 in Europe to institutions; CHF 588 to institutions in Switzerland & Liechtenstein; USD 384 elsewhere to institutions (effective 2006) (from EBSCO Publishing, Swets Information Services, Wiley InterScience).
Indexed: ApMecR, BrCerAb, C&ISA, CerAb, ChemAb, CivEngAb, ConcrAb, CorrAb, E&CAJ, EMA, EngInd, ExcerpMed, GeotechAb, HRIS, IAA, ICEA, M&TEA, MBF, METADEX, SoftAbEng, SolStAb, WAA.
—CISTI, Ei, IE, Infotrieve, Linda Hall. **CCC.**
Published by: Ernst und Sohn, Buehringstr 10, Berlin, 13086, Germany. TEL 49-30-47031200, FAX 49-30-47031240, marketing@ernst-und-sohn.de, http://www.wiley-vch.de/publish/dt/journals/alphabeticIndex/2093/, http://www.wiley-vch.de/ernstsohn. Ed. Konrad Bergmeister. Adv. contact Fred Doischer. B&W page EUR 2,550, color page EUR 3,990. Circ: 3,477 (paid and controlled). **Subscr. in the Americas to:** John Wiley & Sons, Inc., 111 River St, Hoboken, NJ 07030-5774. TEL 201-748-6645, FAX 201-748-6088, subinfo@wiley.com; **Subscr. to:** Wiley - V C H Verlag GmbH & Co. KGaA, Boschstr 12, Weinheim 69469, Germany. TEL 49-6201-606147, FAX 49-6201-606117.

691.3 SWE ISSN 1101-9190
BETONG. Text in Swedish. 1957. q. SEK 320 in Scandinavia; SEK 450 elsewhere; SEK 95 per issue (effective 2004). **Document type:** *Trade.*
Formerly (until 1990): Nordisk Betong (0029-1307)
Indexed: ConcrAb.
—CISTI, Linda Hall.
Published by: Svenska Betongfoereningen/Swedish Concrete Association, Stockholm, 10044, Sweden. TEL 46-8-56410239, FAX 46-8-56410214, http://www.betong.se. Ed. Roger Andersson TEL 46-8-56410214.

691.3 NOR ISSN 0804-8177
BETONGINDUSTRIEN. Text in Norwegian. 1969. q. NOK 200 (effective 2002). adv. bk.rev.
Former titles (until 1994): Betongprodukter (0332-8384); (until 1970): Betongproduktinformasjon (0804-9246)
Published by: (Betongindustriens Landsforening), Bygg og Anlegg Media AS, Essensdropgt. 3, PO Box 5486, Majorstuen, Oslo, 0305, Norway. TEL 47-23-08-75-00, FAX 47-23-08-75-55. Ed. Per Helge Pedersen TEL 47-23-08-75-56. Adv. contact Mette Istad TEL 47-23-08-75-58. B&W page NOK 8,800, color page NOK 13,300; 185 x 260. Circ: 3,480.

691.3 FIN ISSN 1235-2136
BETONI. Text in Finnish. 1992. q. EUR 46 (effective 2005). adv. bk.rev. charts; illus. 80 p./no.; **Document type:** *Bulletin, Trade.* **Description:** Provides information about concrete architecture, concrete technologies, research, industry conditions, and new developments.
Formed by the merger of (1962-1992): Betonituote (0005-9919); (1977-1992): Tiedotuslehti - Suomen Betoniyhdistys-Finska Betongfoereningen (0356-3332); (1981-1992): Betoni ja Laatu (0785-8396); Which was formerly (until 1989): B L T (0358-3473)
Related titles: Online - full text ed.
Indexed: BrCerAb, C&ISA, CRIA, CerAb, ChemAb, CivEngAb, ConcrAb, CorrAb, E&CAJ, EMA, IAA, ICEA, M&TEA, MBF, METADEX, SoftAbEng, SolStAb, WAA.
—BLDSC (1944.100000), Linda Hall.
Published by: Suomen Betonitieto Oy/Finnish Concrete Industry Association, Unioninkatu 14, P O Box 11, Helsinki, 00131, Finland. TEL 358-9-6962360, FAX 358-9-1299291, http://www.betoni.com, http://www.betoni.fi. Ed. Maritta Koivisto. Adv. contact Sami Hortanen. B&W page EUR 1,720, color page EUR 2,950; 210 x 297. Circ: 16,000.

691 NLD ISSN 0166-137X
BETONIEK. Text in Dutch. 1970. 10/yr. EUR 20; EUR 2.75 newsstand/cover (effective 2005). **Document type:** *Trade.*
Published by: E N C I Media, Postbus 3532, 's Hertogenbosch, 5203 DM, Netherlands. TEL 31-73-6401231, FAX 31-73-6401284, encimedia@enci.nl, http://www.enci.nl. Circ: 4,000.

691.3 DEU ISSN 0409-2740
BETONTECHNISCHE BERICHTE✶. Text in German. 1960. irreg. index, cum.index. **Document type:** *Monographic series.*
Indexed: DokStr.
—Linda Hall.

Published by: (Verein Deutscher Zementwerke e.V.), Verlag Bau und Technik GmbH, Steinhof 39, Erkrath, 40699, Germany. info@verlagbt.de, http://www.verlagbt.de. Ed. Gert Wischers. Circ: 1,500.

691 DEU ISSN 1439-7706
BETONWERK INTERNATIONAL; Fachzeitschrift fuer die Betonindustrie. Abbreviated title: B W I. Text in English, German. 1993. bi-m. EUR 48 domestic; EUR 64 foreign; EUR 16 newsstand/cover (effective 2004). adv. 220 p./no.; back issues avail.; reprints avail. **Document type:** *Magazine, Trade.* **Description:** Covers all aspects of the concrete industry worldwide.
Formerly (until 1998): B D B Report (0944-9043)
Related titles: English ed.: Concrete Plant International. ISSN 1437-9023. 1998.
Published by: Ad-Media Verlag GmbH, Industriestr 180, Cologne, 50999, Germany. TEL 49-2236-962390, FAX 49-2236-962396, info@ad-media.de, http://www.bwi-web.de, http://www.ad-media.de. Ed. Stefan Rath. Pub., Adv. contact Gerhard Kloeckner. B&W page EUR 2,290, color page EUR 3,650. Circ: 18,253 (controlled).

691 DEU ISSN 0373-4331
TH1491 CODEN: BWFTAB
BETONWERK UND FERTIGTEIL-TECHNIK; concrete precasting plant and technology. Text in English, German; Summaries in French. 1934. m. EUR 198 domestic; EUR 216 foreign; EUR 132 to students; EUR 18.50 newsstand/cover (effective 2004). adv. bk.rev. charts; illus.; stat. index. **Document type:** *Journal, Trade.* **Description:** Trade publication for the concrete building and manufacturing industry. Covers construction, quality control, production, prefabrication, pipes and shafts, industry news, events, announcements, and positions available.
Formerly (until 1972): Betonstein-Zeitung (0005-9927)
Indexed: BrCerAb, C&ISA, CRIA, CerAb, ChemAb, CivEngAb, ConcrAb, CorrAb, DokStr, E&CAJ, EMA, EngInd, ExcerpMed, IAA, IBR, ICEA, M&TEA, MBF, METADEX, RefZh, SoftAbEng, SolStAb, WAA.
—BLDSC (1946.100000), CASDDS, CISTI, Ei, IE, Infotrieve, ingenta, Linda Hall. **CCC.**
Published by: Bauverlag BV GmbH (Subsidiary of: Springer Science+Business Media), Avenwedderstr 55, Guetersloh, 33311, Germany. TEL 49-5241-802119, FAX 49-5241-809582, bft@bauverlag.de, ulrike.mattern@springer-sbm.com, http://www.bft-online.info/de, http://www.bauverlag.de. Ed. Holger Karutz. Adv. contact Norbert Mayer. B&W page EUR 2,110, color page EUR 3,190. Circ: 8,125 (paid and controlled).

BETTER HOMES AND GARDENS BUILDING & REMODELING. see *ARCHITECTURE*

BETTER HOMES AND GARDENS GARDEN, DECK AND LANDSCAPE. see *GARDENING AND HORTICULTURE*

643.7 USA ISSN 1051-0427
TH4816
BETTER HOMES AND GARDENS HOME PRODUCTS GUIDE. Text in English. 1989. s-a. USD 4.99 newsstand/cover domestic; CND 6.50 newsstand/cover in Canada (effective 2003). adv. illus. **Document type:** *Magazine, Consumer.*
Description: Covers materials homeowners need to build or remodel a home.
Published by: Meredith Corp., 1716 Locust St, Des Moines, IA 50309-3023. TEL 515-284-3000, 800-556-9184, FAX 515-284-3657, http://www.betterhomesandgardens.com, http://www.meredith.com. Pub. Steve Levinson. Adv. contact Peggy Leib. B&W page USD 28,880, color page USD 41,500; trim 10.5 x 8. Circ: 450,000 (paid).

690 ISR
BETUMAN. Text in Hebrew. bi-m. free.
Published by: Paz Co. Ltd., P O Box 434, Haifa, 31003, Israel. TEL 04-567111. Ed. Zvi Dvorsky.

690 USA
▼ **BID INFORMATION NEWSLETTER.** Text in English. 2004. m. free. **Document type:** *Newsletter, Government.* **Description:** Details the current projects for which CDB will be accepting bids.
Related titles: Online - full content ed.
Published by: Capital Development Board, 3rd Fl, Stratton Bldg, 401 S Spring St, Springfield, IL 62706. TEL 217-782-2864, FAX 217-782-8625, http://www.cdb.state.il.us/.

797.2 GBR ISSN 1472-7641
BIG BLUE BOOK. Text in English. 2001. a. **Document type:** *Directory, Trade.*
Published by: Archant Specialist Ltd. (Subsidiary of: Archant), The Mill, Bearwalden Business Park, Royston Rd, Wendens Ambo, Essex CB11 4GB, United Kingdom. TEL 44-1799-544200, farine.clarke@archant.co.uk, http://www.archant.co.uk/.

690 USA
BIG BUILDER. Text in English. q. USD 29.95 domestic; USD 35.95 in Canada; USD 192 elsewhere (effective 2005). illus. **Document type:** *Magazine, Trade.* **Description:** Explores the management, financial and operating concerns of corporate builders.

Published by: Hanley-Wood, LLC (Subsidiary of: J.P. Morgan Chase & Co.), One Thomas Circle, NW, Ste 600, Washington, DC 20005-5701. TEL 202-452-0800, FAX 202-785-1974, http://www.hanleywood.com. Eds. John McManus, Boyce Thompson. Pub. Warren P. Nesbitt. Circ: 176,500 (controlled).

690 DEU
BIOLOGISCH BAUEN. Text in German. a. EUR 5 newsstand/cover (effective 2003). adv. **Document type:** *Magazine, Consumer.*
Related titles: ♦ Supplement to: Bauen. ISSN 0170-0138.
Published by: Fachschriften Verlag GmbH, Hoehenstr 17, Fellbach, 70736, Germany. TEL 49-711-52061, FAX 49-711-5206223, info@fachschriften.de, http://www.fachschriften.de/publikationen/biobauen.htm. Ed. Wolfgang Grasreiner. Adv. contact Claudia Pastor. B&W page EUR 2,850, color page EUR 4,731; trim 187 x 247. Circ: 50,000 (paid).

BIRU SHINBUN/BUILDING NEWSPAPER. see *ENGINEERING—Civil Engineering*

690 ISR ISSN 0334-0430
BISDEH HABNIYA. Text in Hebrew. 1955. a. ILS 120, USD 40.
Published by: Technion - Israel Institute of Technology, National Building Research Institute, Technion City, Haifa, 32000, Israel. TEL 972-4-8292242, FAX 972-4-8324534. Ed. Joab H Rektor.

690 SWE ISSN 1402-7151
BLICKPUNKT BYGG & FASTIGHET. Text in Swedish. 1995. 8/yr. SEK 416 (effective 2004). adv. **Document type:** *Trade.*
Related titles: Online - full text ed.
Published by: Active Media AB, Arabygatan 82, Vaexjoe, 35246, Sweden. TEL 46-470-711865, FAX 46-470-13042, http://www.byggfast.com. Eds. Lars Harrysson, Tina Jukas. Pub. Lars Harrysson. Adv. contact Johnny Lindman.

BLUEPRINTS. see *ARCHITECTURE*

692.8 NOR ISSN 0332-7582
BO. Text in Norwegian. 1951. q. NOK 150 (effective 2002). adv.
Formerly (until 1963): B B L Informasjon (0333-0028)
Published by: Norske Boligbyggelags Landsforbund, P. O. Box 452, Sentrum, Oslo, 0104, Norway. TEL 47-22-40-39-20, FAX 47-22-40-38-50, http://www.nbbl.no. Ed. Kaare Andre Nilsen TEL 47-22-40-38-73. Adv. contact Aase Johnsen TEL 47-71-25-57-00. B&W page NOK 17,000, color page NOK 24,000; 175 x 260. Circ: 20,730.

BODEN, WAND, DECKE. see *INTERIOR DESIGN AND DECORATION*

690 USA
BOECKH BUILDING CODE MODIFIER. Text in English. bi-m. USD 119 (effective 1998).
Published by: E.H. Boeckh, Ed. & Pub. (Subsidiary of: Thomson Publishing Corp.), 2885 S Calhoun Rd, Box 510291, New Berlin, WI 53151-0291. TEL 414-780-2800, 800-285-1288, FAX 414-780-0306. R&P E H Boeckh.

BOECKH BUILDING COST INDEX. see *BUILDING AND CONSTRUCTION—Abstracting, Bibliographies, Statistics*

690 SWE ISSN 0281-5060
BOFAST; bostads- och fastighetsbranschens maanadstidning. Text in Swedish. 1983. 11/yr. SEK 380 (effective 2001). adv. bk.rev. 52 p./no. 5 cols./p.; back issues avail. **Document type:** *Magazine, Trade.* **Description:** Covers all issues concerning real estate: housing politics, caretaking, architecture, financial, technical and social aspects of renting, owning, and developing units in multistory houses. For employees of municipal housing companies.
Related titles: Online - full text ed.
Published by: SABO Foerlags AB, Vasagatan 8-10, Box 474, Stockholm, 10129, Sweden. TEL 46-8-4415375, FAX 46-8-4415389, info@bofast.net, info@sabo.se, http://www.bofast.net, http://www.sabo.se. Ed. Charlotta Lundstroem. Pub. Gisela Lindstrand. Adv. contact Tommy Flink. B&W page SEK 19,500, color page SEK 24,800; trim 187 x 259. Circ: 24,800.

690 340 ITA ISSN 0392-3789
BOLLETTINO DI LEGISLAZIONE TECNICA. Text in Italian. 1933. m. EUR 82 (effective 2003). **Description:** Since 1933 publishes laws, decrees, national and local rules and regulations about civil engineering and construction, with comments and notes.
Incorporates (in 1990): Legislazione e Normativa delle Costruzioni (0392-503X); Formerly (until 1943): Raccolta delle Leggi che Riguardano l'Ingegneria (1594-5073)
Related titles: Online - full text ed.: ISSN 1721-4890.
Published by: Legislazione Tecnica Srl, Via dell'Architettura 16, Rome, 00144, Italy. TEL 39-06-5921743, FAX 39-06-5921068, http://www.legislazionetecnica.it.

690 GBR
BOOK OF BRITISH EXCELLENCE✶. Text in English. a. free to qualified personnel. adv. **Document type:** *Directory.* **Description:** Lists British construction products and contains company profiles. Distributed by embassies, architects, and building consultants throughout the European Community.
Published by: Custom Publishing Ltd. (Subsidiary of: Glendower Holdings Ltd.), Hatchways House, Burrows Cross, Gomshall, Surrey GUF 9QF, United Kingdom. TEL 44-1483-202001, FAX 44-1483-202847. Ed. John Bailey. Pub. Mike Gazzard. Adv. contact Ian Mitchell. page GBP 1,950. Circ: 150,000 (controlled).

690 658 USA
BOSS MAGAZINE; the construction industries' guide to greater wealth. Text in English. 1999. bi-m. USD 55 (effective 2002).
Published by: Reid Publishing, PO Box 1294, Clemson, SC 29633. TEL 864-654-3997, FAX 864-654-3996, ngreid@mindspring.com. Pub. Norman Reid. Circ: 5,200.

690 720 NLD ISSN 0366-2330
NA6.D8
BOUW. Text in Dutch. 1946. 11/yr. EUR 189.74 (effective 2005). adv. bk.rev. illus. back issues avail. **Document type:** *Journal, Trade.* **Description:** For the house building, industrial and commercial building industries, and persons in related fields, including planning, architecture and building technology.
Indexed: AIAP, API, BHA, CISA, ELLIS, IBuildSA, KES, RASB.
—BLDSC (2264.300000), CISTI, IE, Infotrieve, ingenta.
Published by: Reed Business Information bv (Subsidiary of: Reed Business), Hanzestraat 1, Doetinchem, 7006 RH, Netherlands. info@reedbusiness.nl, http://www.reedbusiness.nl. Ed. Hans Mulder. Pub. Pascal van Sluijs. Adv. contact Cor van Nek. B&W page EUR 2,135, color page EUR 3,688; trim 297 x 225. Circ: 4,750.

691 624 NLD ISSN 0166-6363
BOUWEN MET STAAL. Text in Dutch. 1967. bi-m. EUR 49.75 domestic; EUR 70 foreign (effective 2004). adv. bk.rev. bibl. index. back issues avail. **Document type:** *Journal, Trade.* **Description:** Offers technical and scientific information for the design and construction in steel of structural, architectural, and civil engineering projects.
—IE, Infotrieve.
Published by: Stichting Bouwen met Staal, Postbus 190, Zoetermeer, 2700 AD, Netherlands. TEL 31-79-3531277, FAX 31-79-3531278, bms@bouwenmetstaal.nl, http://www.bouwenmetstaal.nl. Circ: 5,000.

690 NLD ISSN 0165-2648
BOUWKOSTEN. Text in Dutch. 1972. m. looseleaf. **Document type:** *Monographic series, Trade.* **Description:** Cost information for total cost information during all stages of construction of housing and utility building.
Published by: Reed Business Information bv (Subsidiary of: Reed Business), Hanzestraat 1, Doetinchem, 7006 RH, Netherlands. TEL 31-314-349911, FAX 31-314-343839, info@reedbusiness.nl, http://www.reedbusiness.nl. Ed. W Pasman.

690 BEL ISSN 1376-3490
BOUWKRONIEK; weekblad voor bouw en industrie. Text in Dutch. 1921. w. EUR 269.33 domestic; EUR 368 in Netherlands; EUR 392 elsewhere (effective 2005). adv. charts; illus. 32 p./no.; **Document type:** *Magazine, Trade.* **Description:** Presents information for the building and construction industry.
Indexed: KES.
Published by: NV Drukkerij de Bouwkroniek, Kerkstraat 55, Dilbeek, 1701, Belgium. TEL 32-2-513-8295, FAX 32-2-511-7015, bouwkroniek@bouwkroniek.be, http://www.bouwkroniek.be. Ed. Paul Darmont. R&P Jan van Hoorick. adv.: color page EUR 2,210, B&W page EUR 794; 185 x 260. Circ: 12,000.

621.9 NLD ISSN 0006-8373
BOUWMACHINES. Text in Dutch. 1965. 16/yr. EUR 163.77 (effective 2005). adv. charts; illus.; stat. **Document type:** *Journal, Trade.* **Description:** Aimed at building contractors in housing and public buildings, earth-moving projects, highways and waterways, dredging works.
Incorporates (1994-1999): Sloop en Recycling (1381-480X)
Indexed: ExcerpMed.
—IE, Infotrieve.
Published by: Reed Business Information bv (Subsidiary of: Reed Business), Hanzestraat 1, Doetinchem, 7006 RH, Netherlands. info@reedbusiness.nl, http://www.reedbusiness.nl. Ed. Peter Tomberg. Adv. contact Cor van Nek. B&W page EUR 2,211, color page EUR 3,349; trim 285 x 215. Circ: 5,820.

690 NLD ISSN 0925-6466
BOUWMANAGEMENT EN TECHNISCH BEHEER. Text in Dutch. 1990. irreg., latest vol.16, 1997. price varies. back issues avail. **Document type:** *Monographic series.* **Description:** Discusses technical and management issues in construction.
—KNAW.
Published by: (Onderzoeksinstituut OTB), Delft University Press (Subsidiary of: Technische Universiteit Delft/Delft University of Technology), PO Box 98, Delft, 2600 MG, Netherlands. TEL 31-15-278-3254, FAX 31-15-2781661, dup@dup.tudelft.nl.

690 NLD ISSN 0166-641X
BOUWMARKT (DOETINCHEM). Text in Dutch. 1961. 10/yr. EUR 299; EUR 145 to students (effective 2005). adv. **Document type:** *Journal, Trade.* **Description:** Aimed at the financial departments of building contractors, architects, and engineering firms.
—Infotrieve.
Published by: Reed Business Information bv (Subsidiary of: Reed Business), Postbus 4, Doetinchem, 7000 BA, Netherlands. TEL 31-314-349911, FAX 31-314-343991, webwinkel.bouw&infra@reedbusiness.nl, info@reedbusiness.nl, http://www.productonline.reedbusiness.nl/product.asp?catalog%5Fname=RBI&category%5Fname=&product%5Fid=811%28Octopus%29, http://www.reedbusiness.nl. Eds. Boudewijn Messink, Wil Kuhlmann. Pub. Henk Klein Gunnewiek. Adv. contact Nienke Kool TEL 31-314-349369. B&W page EUR 588, color page EUR 1,141; trim 297 x 210. Circ: 1,110.

690 NLD ISSN 1385-5972
BOUWPLANNEN. A: GRONINGEN, FRIESLAND, DRENTHE. Text in Dutch. 1958. w. EUR 2,050 (effective 2005). back issues avail. **Document type:** *Trade.* **Description:** Publishes information on current and scheduled construction projects (commercial, industrial, offices and public works) in the Netherlands.
Formerly (until 1997): Bouwtips Editie A: Groningen, Friesland, Drenthe (0165-6457)
Published by: Reed Business Information bv (Subsidiary of: Reed Business), Postbus 4, Doetinchem, 7000 BA, Netherlands. TEL 31-314-349494, 31-314-349548, http://www.bouwplannen.net/producten/producten.asp.

690 NLD ISSN 1385-5980
BOUWPLANNEN. B: OVERIJSSEL, GELDERLAND, UTRECHT, FLEVOLAND. Text in Dutch. 1958. w. EUR 2,050 (effective 2005). back issues avail. **Document type:** *Trade.* **Description:** Publishes information on current and scheduled construction projects (commercial, industrial, offices and public works) in the Netherlands.
Formerly (until 1997): Bouwtips Editie B: Overijssel, Gelderland, Utrecht, Flevoland (0165-6503)
Published by: Reed Business Information bv (Subsidiary of: Reed Business), Postbus 4, Doetinchem, 7000 BA, Netherlands. TEL 31-314-349494, 31-314-349548, http://www.bouwplannen.net/producten/producten.asp.

690 NLD ISSN 1385-5999
BOUWPLANNEN. C: NOORD-HOLLAND EN ZUID-HOLLAND. Text in Dutch. 1958. w. EUR 2,050 (effective 2005). back issues avail. **Document type:** *Trade.* **Description:** Publishes information on current and scheduled construction projects (commercial, industrial, offices and public works) in the Netherlands.
Formerly (until 1997): Bouwtips Editie C: Noord-Holland en Zuid-Holland (0165-6554)
Published by: Reed Business Information bv (Subsidiary of: Reed Business), Postbus 4, Doetinchem, 7000 BA, Netherlands. TEL 31-314-349494, 31-314-349548, http://www.bouwplannen.net/producten/producten.asp.

690 NLD ISSN 1385-948X
BOUWPLANNEN. D: NOORD-BRABANT, LIMBURG, ZEELAND. Text in Dutch. 1958. w. EUR 2,050 (effective 2005). back issues avail. **Document type:** *Trade.* **Description:** Publishes news of current and scheduled construction projects (commercial, industrial, offices and public works) in the Netherlands.
Formerly (until 1997): Bouwtips Editie D: Zeeland, Noord-Brabant, Limburg (0165-6600)
Published by: Reed Business Information bv (Subsidiary of: Reed Business), Postbus 4, Doetinchem, 7000 BA, Netherlands. TEL 31-314-349494, 31-314-349548, http://www.bouwplannen.net/producten/producten.asp.

690 340 NLD ISSN 0165-1528
KKM3059.A48
BOUWRECHT. Text in Dutch. 1964. m. EUR 196.50 (effective 2003). adv. **Document type:** *Trade.*
Related titles: CD-ROM ed.; Online - full text ed.
—IE, Infotrieve.
Published by: (Stichting Instituut voor Bouwrecht), Kluwer B.V. (Subsidiary of: Wolters Kluwer N.V.), Postbus 23, Deventer, 7400 GA, Netherlands. TEL 31-570-673449, FAX 31-570-691555, juridisch@kluwer.nl, http://www.kluwer.nl.

690 NLD ISSN 0026-5942
BOUWWERELD. Text in Dutch. 1905. 22/yr. EUR 207; EUR 86.50 to students (effective 2005). adv. bk.rev. charts; illus.; mkt. index. **Document type:** *Journal, Trade.* **Description:** Technical and practical information for designers, architects and building contractors.
Formerly: Vakblad voor de Bouwbedrijven
Related titles: Online - full text ed.
Indexed: ExcerpMed, IBuildSA, KES.
—IE, Infotrieve.
Published by: Reed Business Information bv (Subsidiary of: Reed Business), Postbus 4, Doetinchem, 7000 BA, Netherlands. TEL 31-314-349911, FAX 31-314-343991, bouwwereld@reedbusiness.nl, info@reedbusiness.nl, http://www.bouwwereld100.nl/Home.asp, http://www.reedbusiness.nl. Ed. Peter de Winter TEL 31-314-349510. Pub. Pascal van Sluijs. adv.: B&W page EUR 2,908, color page EUR 4,396; trim 230 x 310. Circ: 11,240.

750 GBR ISSN 0307-9325
TH1301
BRICK BULLETIN. Text in English. 1947. 3/yr.
Related titles: Online - full content ed.
Indexed: C&ISA, CerAb, CorrAb, E&CAJ, EMA, SolStAb, WAA.
—BLDSC (2283.920000), CISTI, IE, ingenta.
Published by: Brick Development Association, Woodside House, Winkfield, Windsor, Berkshire SL4 2DX, United Kingdom. TEL 44-1344-885651, FAX 44-1344-890129, brick@brick.org.uk, http://www.brick.org.uk/bulletin/Bulletin.htm.

691.4 USA ISSN 0743-0043
BRICK IN ARCHITECTURE. Text in English. 1975. 5/yr. illus.
Published by: Brick Industry Association, 11490 Commerce Park Dr, Reston, VA 20191-1525. TEL 703-620-0010, FAX 703-620-3928, http://www.brickinfo.org/.

BRIDGE BUILDER. see *ENGINEERING—Civil Engineering*

690 GBR ISSN 0960-7870
BRITISH BRICK SOCIETY. INFORMATION. Text in English. 1973. 3/yr.
Published by: British Brick Society, The Honorary Secretary, 9 Bailey Close, High Wycombe, Buckinghamshire HP13 6QA, United Kingdom. TEL 44-1494-520299, michael@mhammett.freeserve.co.uk, http://www.britishbricksoc.free-online.co.uk/index.htm.

691 GBR
BRITISH CEMENT ASSOCIATION. INTERIM TECHNICAL NOTE. Text in English. 1971. irreg. back issues avail. **Document type:** *Bulletin, Trade.*
Formerly (until 1988): Cement and Concrete Association. Interim Technical Note (0268-9618)
Published by: British Cement Association, Century House, Telford Ave, Crowthorne, Berks RG45 6YS, United Kingdom. TEL 44-1344-762676, FAX 44-1344-761214, library@bca.org.uk, http://www.bca.org.uk.

690 GBR ISSN 0950-9615
BRITISH MASONRY SOCIETY. PROCEEDINGS. Text in English. 1986. irreg.
—BLDSC (6666.650000), CISTI, Linda Hall.
Published by: British Masonry Society, Shermanbury, Church Rd, Whyteleafe, Surrey CR3 0AR, United Kingdom. TEL 44-20-8660-3653, FAX 44-20-8668-6983, http://www.masonry.org.uk.

BRONX REALTOR NEWS. see *REAL ESTATE*

BUDOWNICTWO GORNICZE I TUNELOWE. see *MINES AND MINING INDUSTRY*

690 720 POL ISSN 1644-745X
BUDOWNICTWO, TECHNOLOGIE, ARCHITEKTURA. Text in Polish. 1998. q.
Formerly (until 2002): Polski Cement (1505-3261)
Published by: Spolka Cement - Wapno - Beton, ul Lubelska 29, Krakow, 30003, Poland. cwb@polskicement.com.pl, http://www.polskicement.com.pl. Circ: 3,500.

643.7 POL ISSN 1507-2789
BUDUJEMY DOM. Text in Polish. 1999. m. PLZ 108.90 domestic; EUR 65 in Europe; EUR 87 elsewhere (effective 2005). **Document type:** *Magazine, Consumer.*
Published by: A V T- Korporacja Sp. z o. o., ul Burleska 9, Warsaw, 01939, Poland. TEL 48-22-5689941, FAX 48-22-5689944, redakcja@ep.com.pl, http://www.budujemydom.pl, http://www.avt.pl. Ed. Ernest Jagodzinski.

690 GBR ISSN 0958-7438
BUILD & DESIGN PROFESSIONAL. Text in English. q.
Address: Bergius House, Clifton St, Glasgow, G3 7LA, United Kingdom. TEL 041-331-1022, FAX 041-331-1395. Ed. M Travers. Circ: 10,500.

690 GBR ISSN 0958-2681
BUILD - IT. Text in English. m. GBP 36 domestic; GBP 45 in Europe; GBP 60 foreign; GBP 2.75 newsstand/cover. adv. illus. **Document type:** *Consumer.* **Description:** Features homes that have been designed, built, or remodeled by laypersons. Includes advice from the experts.
Published by: Inside Communications Ltd., One Canada Square, Canary Wharf, London, E14 5AP, United Kingdom. FAX 44-1732-4849394, ic@insidecom.co.uk, http://www.insidecom.co.uk. Ed., R&P Martyn Hocking. Pub. Sue Woodward. Adv. contact Rachel Fallan. Circ: 21,007 (paid).
Dist. by: Comag, Tavistock Works, Tavistock Rd, W Drayton, Middx UB7 7QX, United Kingdom. TEL 44-1895-444055, FAX 44-1895-433602.

B

▼ new title ➤ refereed ✶ unverified ♦ full entry avail.

690 USA
BUILD IT!. Text in English. 1992. s-a.
Published by: New York Times Company Magazine Group, Inc., 1120 Avenue of the Americas, New York, NY 10036.

690 NZL ISSN 0110-4381
BUILD MAGAZINE. Text in English. a.
—CISTI.
Published by: Building Research Association of New Zealand, Porirua Moonshine Rd, Judgeford, Private Bag 50908, Porirua, New Zealand. TEL 64-4-2357600, FAX 64-4-2356070, branz@branz.org.nz, http://www.branz.org.nz/branz/publications/build.htm.

690 USA ISSN 0744-1193
HD9715.U5
BUILDER (WASHINGTON); NAHB, the voice of America's housing industry . Text in English. 1942. m. USD 29.95 domestic (effective 2005); USD 35.95 in Canada (effective 2004); USD 192 elsewhere (effective 2005). adv. bk.rev. illus.; tr.lit. reprints avail. **Document type:** *Magazine, Trade.* **Description:** Provides information for builders, architects, dealers and subcontractors.
Former titles: N A H B Builder; Builder (Washington) (0162-0533); N A H B Journal-Scope (0098-2865); Which was formed by the merger of: N A H B Journal (0027-5832); N A H B Washington Scope (0027-5840)
Related titles: Microform ed.: (from PQC); Online - full text ed.: (from bigchalk, Florida Center for Library Automation, Gale Group, H.W. Wilson, O C L C Online Computer Library Center, Inc., ProQuest Information & Learning).
Indexed: ABIn, AIAP, API, BPI, LRI, PROMT, SRI, Search.
—IE, Infotrieve.
Published by: (National Association of Home Builders), Hanley-Wood, LLC (Subsidiary of: J.P. Morgan Chase & Co.), One Thomas Circle, NW, Ste 600, Washington, DC 20005-5701. TEL 202-452-0800, FAX 202-785-1974, http://www.hanleywood.com. Ed. Boyce Thompson. Pub. Warren Nesbitt. adv.: B&W page USD 10,838; trim 10 x 7. Circ: 160,696.

690 USA
BUILDER AND DEVELOPER; the biggest professional home builders magazine in the USA serving California, Arizona, Nevada and the west. Text in English. 1990 (Nov.). 11/yr. free q (effective 2005). adv. back issues avail. **Document type:** *Magazine, Trade.*
Published by: Peninsula Publishing, 1602 Monrovia Ave, Newport Beach, CA 92663. TEL 949-631-0308, FAX 949-631-2475, http://www.bdmag.com. Eds. Katie Pegler, Nick Slevin. Pub. Nick Slevin. Adv. contact Rona Fiedler. B&W page USD 4,965; trim 8.75 x 11.75. Circ: 13,027 (controlled).

690 USA ISSN 1079-2910
BUILDER & REMODELER. Text in English. 1982. m. USD 12 (effective 2005). adv. bk.rev. illus. **Document type:** *Magazine, Trade.*
Formerly (until Sep. 1990): Builder; Supersedes: Long Island Builder (0024-6247)
Indexed: AIAP, BldManAb, T&II.
Published by: Sheahan Publications, Inc., PO Box 826, Westhampton, NY 11978. TEL 631-288-5400, FAX 631-288-5420, journal01@aol.com, http://www.sheahanpub.com/builder/index.htm. Ed., Pub. Denis Sheahan. Circ: 15,000.

692.8 USA
BUILDER ARCHITECT. Variant title: Builder / Architect. Text in English. 1938. m. adv. illus. **Document type:** *Magazine, Trade.* **Description:** Business-to-business magazine, reaching professionals in the residential building industry. Provides compelling local market editorial with informative national features and columns delivering a truly unique perspective for industry leaders.
Former titles: Builder-Architect for Arizona Home and Apartment Builders (0891-0332); (until 1983): Builder Architect-Contractor Engineer (0193-7472); Which was formed by the merger of: Builder-Architect (0007-327X); Arizona-New Mexico Contractor and Engineer (0004-1580)
Published by: Sunshine Media, Inc., 1540 E Maryland Ave, Phoenix, AZ 85014. TEL 602-277-3372, FAX 602-285-1485, info@sunshinemedia.com, http://www.builderarchitect.com, http://www.sunshinemedia.com. Ed. Marie Tupot Stock. adv.: B&W page USD 1,000, color page USD 1,535. Circ: 3,300.

BUILDER INSIDER. see *ARCHITECTURE*

690 USA ISSN 0887-4190
BUILDER NEWS. Text in English. 1960. m. USD 495 membership (effective 2005). adv. **Document type:** *Magazine.*
Published by: Home Builders Association of Greater St. Louis, 10104 Old Olive St, St. Louis, MO 63141. TEL 314-994-7700, FAX 314-432-7185, stlhba@stlnet.com, http://www.stlhba.com/builder. Ed. Shelly Stengel. Pub. Patrick Sullivan. Adv. contact Tracy Chiesa. B&W page USD 725. Circ: 1,550 (paid and controlled).

690 USA
BUILDERS ASSOCIATION NEWS. Text in English. 1954. m. USD 45 (effective 2005). adv. stat.; tr.lit. 28 p./no.; **Document type:** *Magazine, Trade.*
Published by: Builders Association of Fort Worth & Tarrant County, 6464 Brentwood Stair Rd, Ste 100, Fort Worth, TX 76112-3242. fortworthbuilders.org. Circ: 1,025 (controlled).

690 747 USA ISSN 1079-4891
NA7205
BUILDER'S BEST HOME PLANS. Text in English. 1991. q. USD 4.95 per issue. illus. **Document type:** *Trade.* **Description:** Features new home plans.
Formerly: Builder's Best Home Designs (1055-3460)
Published by: Hanley-Wood, LLC (Subsidiary of: J.P. Morgan Chase & Co.), One Thomas Circle, NW, Ste 600, Washington, DC 20005-5701. TEL 202-452-0800, FAX 202-785-1974, tjackson@hanleywood.com, http://www.hanley-wood.com, http://www.hanleywood.com. Ed. Bob Hoffman. Circ: 85,000.

004.16 USA
BUILDERS' COMPUTER NEWSLETTER. Text in English. 1982. 12/yr. bk.rev.
Published by: American Newsfeatures Syndicate, 113 Wattenbarger Rd, Sweetwater, TN 37874-6135. TEL 800-484-4074, FAX 423-337-0222. Ed. Ray Burr. Circ: 92,171.

690.0299 USA
BUILDERS JOURNAL. Text in English. q. adv. abstr.; tr.lit. 60 p./no.; **Document type:** *Journal, Trade.*
Formerly: South Carolina Builder
Published by: Home Builders Association of South Carolina, 223 E Park Ave, Greenville, SC 29601. TEL 864-233-2589, FAX 864-233-2094, vbmgraphics@mindspring.com, http://www.buildersc.com, http://www.builderjournalsc.com. Ed., R&P Leigh Miller. Pub., Adv. contact Van Miller TEL 864-233-2589. Circ: 6,000 (controlled).

690 GBR
BUILDERS' MERCHANT NEWS. Text in English. 1977. m. GBP 47; GBP 59 foreign (effective 1999). **Document type:** *Trade.* **Description:** Covers building materials, their distribution, and their sale.
Published by: B & M Publications (London) Ltd., Hereford House., Bridle Path, Croydon, Surrey CR9 4NL, United Kingdom. TEL 44-20-86804200, FAX 44-20-86808400, b&m@bmpublications.co.uk, info@hvpmag.co.uk. Ed. Tony Jackson. Pub. David Wilson. Circ: 7,591 (controlled).

690 GBR ISSN 0268-1323
HD9715.G7
BUILDERS MERCHANTS JOURNAL; the business journal for building supplies distributions. Text in English. 1920. m. GBP 82 domestic; GBP 98, USD 157 foreign (effective 2004). adv. bk.rev. charts; illus.; mkt. index. **Document type:** *Trade.* **Description:** Provides information, industry news, exhibition coverage and specialist features for the builders' merchants market.
Former titles (until 1985): Builders and Timber Merchant (0262-6063); (until 1982): Builders and Home Improvement Merchants Journal (0262-6055); (until 1978): Builders Merchants Journal (0007-3288); (until 1964): Builders Merchants Journal and Builders Ironmonger
Related titles: Online - full text ed.: (from EBSCO Publishing, LexisNexis, ProQuest Information & Learning).
Indexed: ABIn.
Published by: Faversham House Group Ltd., Faversham House, 232a Addington Rd, South Croydon, Surrey CR2 8LE, United Kingdom. TEL 44-20-86517100, FAX 44-20-86517117. Circ: 7,533.

690 CAN ISSN 1185-3654
BUILDING; the newsmagazine for Canada's development industry. Text in English. 1952. bi-m. CND 36.38 domestic; USD 55 in United States; USD 60 elsewhere (effective 2000). adv. bk.rev. charts; illus.; mkt.; tr.lit. index. reprint service avail. from PQC. **Document type:** *Trade.* **Description:** For developers, contractors, architects, engineers and property managers. Covers residential, commercial-industrial, retail, and institutional development.
Formerly (until 1991): Canadian Building (0008-3070); Incorporates: Real Estate Development Annual
Related titles: Microfiche ed.: (from MML); Microform ed.: (from MML, PQC); Online - full text ed.: (from Micromedia ProQuest, ProQuest Information & Learning).
Indexed: ABIn, AIAP, CBCABus, CBPI, RICS.
—CISTI. **CCC.**
Published by: Crailer Communications, 360 Dupont St, Toronto, ON M5R 1V9, Canada. TEL 416-966-9944, FAX 416-966-9946, info@building.ca, http://www.building.ca. Ed. John Fennell. Pub. Jack Ruttle. R&P Sheri Craig. Adv. contact Lisa Thorsteinson. B&W page CND 2,900, color page CND 3,950; trim 10.5 x 8. Circ: 14,000.

BUILDING; the voice of the industry. see *ARCHITECTURE*

BUILDING. see *ARCHITECTURE*

690 ZAF
BUILDING AFRICA. Text in English. 2001 (Aug.). m. ZAR 280 domestic; USD 70 in Africa; USD 150 elsewhere (effective 2002). adv. **Description:** Covers projects and developments in the building and construction industry as well as new services and products.
Published by: Brooke Pattrick Publications, PO Box 422, Bedfordview, Transvaal 2008, South Africa. TEL 27-11-622-4666, FAX 27-11-616-7196, bestbook@brookepattrick.co.za, http://www.brookepattrick.com/building_africa.html. Ed. Marian Giesen.

694 340 AUS
BUILDING AND CONSTRUCTION CONTRACTS IN AUSTRALIA: LAW AND PRACTICE. Text in English. 1990. 2 base vols. plus q. updates. looseleaf. AUD 1,540 (effective 2004). **Document type:** *Trade.* **Description:** Provides thorough discussion of general principles of contract law, with analysis of the four main Australian building and engineering contracts.
Published by: Lawbook Co. (Subsidiary of: Thomson Legal & Regulatory Ltd.), PO Box 3502, Rozelle, NSW 2039, Australia. lbccustomer@thomson.com.au, http://onlineecom01.thomson.com.au/thomson/Catalog.asp?EES_CMD=SI&EES_ID=100244, http://www.lawbookco.com.au/. Eds. John Dorter, John Sharkey.

690 GBR
HD9715.G7
BUILDING & CONSTRUCTION INDEX. Text in English. 1923. a. GBP 74 (effective 2000). adv. bk.rev. **Document type:** *Directory, Trade.* **Description:** A buyers' guide for builders, architects, engineers, surveyors, contractors, merchants, and government departments.
Former titles: Sell's Building and Construction Index (0966-0399); Sell's Building Index (0080-8717)
Published by: C M P Information Ltd. (Subsidiary of: United Business Media), Sovereign House, Sovereign Way, Tonbridge, Kent TN9 1RW, United Kingdom. TEL 44-1732-362666, FAX 44-1732-367301, enquiries@cmpinformation.com, http://www.cmpinformation.com. Ed. Gwen Young. R&P Sarah Walker. Adv. contact Elaine Soni TEL 44-1732-377423. Circ: 1,500.

690 340 AUS ISSN 0815-6050
BUILDING AND CONSTRUCTION LAW JOURNAL. Text in English. 1985. q. AUD 475 (effective 2004). back issues avail. **Document type:** *Journal, Academic/Scholarly.* **Description:** Covers changes and direction of law in the building industry.
Indexed: ILP.
—BLDSC (2359.332300), IE, ingenta.
Published by: Lawbook Co. (Subsidiary of: Thomson Legal & Regulatory Ltd.), PO Box 3502, Rozelle, NSW 2039, Australia. LRA.Service@thomson.com, http://onlineecom01.thomson.com.au/thomson/Catalog.asp?EES_CMD=SI&EES_ID=100240, http://www.lawbookco.com.au. Ed. John Dorter.

690 CAN ISSN 1186-1398
BUILDING & CONSTRUCTION TRADES TODAY; the independent, twice-seasonal newspaper linking trade contractors and trades people with general contractors, builders, designers, suppliers, owners and regulators. Text in English. 1991. 8/yr. CND 24.95; CND 2 newsstand/cover (effective 2004). adv. **Document type:** *Newspaper, Trade.* **Description:** Focuses on project stories, both residential and non-residential in the Greater Toronto area and north into cottage country.
Published by: Heisey Publishing, c/o 29 Bernard Ave, Toronto, ON M5R 1R3, Canada. TEL 416-944-1217, FAX 416-944-0133, hize@compuserve.com. Ed. Olia Mishchenko. Pub. Alan Heisey. Adv. contacts Alan Heisey, John Pierre. B&W page CND 1,860; trim 14.75 x 10.38. Circ: 3,500.

690 GBR ISSN 0360-1323
TH1 CODEN: BUSCBC
➤ **BUILDING AND ENVIRONMENT.** Text in English, French, German. 1965. 12/yr. EUR 1,659 in Europe to institutions; JPY 220,100 in Japan to institutions; USD 1,855 to institutions except Europe and Japan; EUR 231 in Europe to qualified personnel; JPY 30,600 in Japan to qualified personnel; USD 258 to qualified personnel except Europe and Japan (effective 2006). adv. bk.rev. charts; illus. back issues avail. **Document type:** *Journal, Academic/Scholarly.* **Description:** Publishes building and architectural research, applications in building design and construction, environmental behavior of buildings, components and materials.
Formerly (until 1976): Building Science (0007-3628)
Related titles: Microfilm ed.: (from PQC); Online - full text ed.: (from EBSCO Publishing, Gale Group, IngentaConnect, ScienceDirect, Swets Information Services).
Indexed: AEA, AIAP, AJEE, API, ASCA, BibInd, BrCerAb, BrTechI, C&ISA, Cadscan, CerAb, ChemAb, CivEngAb, CorrAb, CurCont, E&CAJ, EEA, EIA, EMA, EPB, ESPM, EnerRev, EngInd, EnvAb, EnvEAb, FLUIDEX, GEOBASE, IAA, IBuildSA, ICEA, ISMEC, JOF, LeadAb, M&TEA, MBF, METADEX, PollutAb, SolStAb, VITIS, WAA, Zincscan.
—BLDSC (2359.355000), CISTI, Ei, IDS, IE, Infotrieve, ingenta, Linda Hall. **CCC.**
Published by: Pergamon (Subsidiary of: Elsevier Science & Technology), The Boulevard, Langford Ln, East Park, Kidlington, Oxford OX5 1GB, United Kingdom. TEL 44-1865-843000, FAX 44-1865-843010, http://www.elsevier.com/locate/buildenv. Ed. E Mathews. Circ: 1,000.
Subscr. to: Elsevier BV, PO Box 211, Amsterdam 1000 AE, Netherlands. TEL 31-20-485-3757, FAX 31-20-485-3432, nlinfo-f@elsevier.nl, http://www.elsevier.nl.

690 MYS
BUILDING & INVESTMENT. Text in English. bi-m. MYR 120 domestic; SGD 100 in Singapore; BIF 100 in Burundi; USD 100 elsewhere (effective 2000). adv. **Description:** Covers all aspects of Malaysian building industry, including new projects, export opportunities, conferences, exhibitions, business tours and other related activities.
Published by: B & I Marketing, 32-2A Jl Pandan, 3-2 Pandan Jaya, Kuala Lumpur, 55100, Malaysia. TEL 60-3-9858223, FAX 60-3-9857409, bni@tm.net.my, http://www.buildersnet.com.my/b&i. Ed. Joane Hou. Adv. contact Eric Tan. B&W page MYR 1,900, B&W page SGD 1,200, B&W page USD 80, color page MYR 3,000, color page SGD 1,800, color page USD 1,200; trim 210 x 290.

BUILDING AND WOOD. see *LABOR UNIONS*

690 HKG
BUILDING ANNUAL. Text in Chinese. a. adv.
Published by: Wealth Trade Press Ltd., Flat D, 15-F, Sun Kai Mansion, 38 Hennessy Rd, Wanchai, Hong Kong, Hong Kong. TEL 852-2527-1282, FAX 852-2865-6529. adv.: B&W page HKD 7,000, color page HKD 7,000.009; trim 210 x 280. Circ: 30,000.

690 AUS ISSN 1440-7019
BUILDING AUSTRALIA. Text in English. 8/yr. AUD 79.20 domestic; AUD 90 in Asia & the Pacific; AUD 115 elsewhere (effective 2004). adv. **Description:** Provides reports and analysis of key issues, major policy developments, and innovations in technology important to the building industry.
Published by: Intermedia Group Pty. Ltd., Unit 7B, 87 Bay St., PO Box 55, Glebe, NSW 2037, Australia. TEL 61-2-96602113, FAX 61-2-96604419, http://www.intermedia.com.au. Ed. Rachael Bernstone. Pub. Simon Grover. Adv. contact David McLeod. B&W page AUD 4,250; trim 210 x 297. Circ: 10,736.

690 USA
BUILDING BUSINESS AND APARTMENT MANAGEMENT. Text in English. 1936. m. USD 48 to non-members; free (effective 2005). adv. charts; illus.; stat. **Document type:** *Magazine, Trade.*
Formerly: Bildor (0006-2448)
Published by: Building Industry Association of Southeastern Michigan, 30375 Northwestern Hwy, Ste 100, Farmington Hills, MI 48334-3233. TEL 248-862-1016, FAX 248-862-1051, susanas@builders.org, http://www.buildern.org. Ed., R&P, Adv. contact Susan Adler. Circ: 12,000 (paid and free).

690 340 AUS
BUILDING CODE OF AUSTRALIA. Text in English. irreg. (in 2 vols.). **Document type:** *Trade.*
Related titles: ♦ CD-ROM ed.: Building Code of Australia on CD-ROM; Online - full content ed.: AUD 249; AUD 162 renewals (effective 2003).
Published by: (Australian Building Codes Board), CanPrint Communications Pty Ltd., 16 Nyrang Street, Fyshwick, ACT 2609, Australia. TEL 61-2-62938383, FAX 61-2-62938388, abcb@canprint.com.au, http://www.canprint.com.au/. **Subscr. to:** Standards Australia International Ltd., GPO Box 5420, Sydney, NSW 2001, Australia. TEL 61-2-82066010, 1300-654646, FAX 61-82066020, 1300-6549 49, sales@standards.com.au.

343.07869 AUS
BUILDING CODE OF AUSTRALIA - LOOSELEAF UPDATING SERVICE. Text in English. irreg., latest vol.8, 1995. looseleaf. price varies. **Document type:** *Government.*
Published by: Law Press (Victoria), 52-58 Chetwynd St, West Melbourne, VIC 3003, Australia. TEL 61-3-93208686, FAX 61-3-93208699.

343.07869 AUS
BUILDING CODE OF AUSTRALIA ON CD-ROM. Abbreviated title: B C A. Text in English. irreg. AUD 262; AUD 162 renewals (effective 2003). **Document type:** *Trade.*
Media: CD-ROM. **Related titles:** Online - full content ed.: AUD 249; AUD 162 renewals (effective 2003); ♦ Print ed.: Building Code of Australia.
Published by: (Australian Building Codes Board), Standards Australia International Ltd., 286, Sussex St (cnr Bathurst St), Sydney, NSW 2000, Australia. TEL 61-2-82066000, FAX 61-2-82066001, bca.sales@standards.com.au, mail@standards.com.au, http://www.standards.com.au/. **Subscr. to:** GPO Box 5420, Sydney, NSW 2001, Australia. TEL 61-2-82066010, 1300-654646, FAX 61-82066020, 1300-6549 49, sales@standards.com.au.

692.8 917.306 USA
BUILDING CONCERNS. Text in English. 1980. q. USD 45. adv. bk.rev. back issues avail. **Document type:** *Newsletter.*
Description: Details national news of relevance. Presents major corporation and chapters' reports as well as members in the news.
Published by: National Association of Minority Contractors, 666 11th St, N W, Ste 520, Washington, DC 20001. TEL 202-347-8259, FAX 202-628-1876. Ed. Samuel Carradine. Circ: 4,000.

692 USA ISSN 0068-3531
TH435
BUILDING CONSTRUCTION COST DATA (YEAR). Text in English. 1942. a., latest vol.63, 2005. USD 115.95 (effective 2005). index. **Description:** Provides over 20,000 cost entries for estimating.
Related titles: CD-ROM ed.
—CCC.
Published by: R.S. Means Company Inc. (Subsidiary of: Reed Construction Data, Associated Construction Publications), 63 Smiths Lane, P O Box 800, Kingston, MA 02364-9988. TEL 781-585-7880, 800-334-3509, FAX 800-632-6732, http://www.rsmeans.com/bookstore/detail.asp?sku=60015.

690.028 691 AUS ISSN 1031-3745
BUILDING CONSTRUCTION MATERIALS & EQUIPMENT. Abbreviated title: B C M E. Text in English. 1959. m. adv. **Document type:** *Magazine, Trade.* **Description:** Covers all aspects of building and construction in Australia, including materials, standards, and design.
Former titles (until 1984): Australia - New Zealand Building Construction Materials and Equipment (0811-0670); (until 1983): Australia - New Zealand Building Materials and Equipment (0811-0662); (until 1980): Building Materials and Equipment (0007-3512)
Related titles: Online - full text ed.
Indexed: ABIX, CISA.
Published by: The Federal Publishing Company, 180 Bourke Rd, Alexandria, NSW 2015, Australia. TEL 61-2-93536666, FAX 61-2-93530101, bcme@fpc.com.au, contactus@fpc.com.au, http://www.bcme.com.au/, http://www.fpc.com.au. Ed. Carmel Prasad. Pub. Michael Hannan. R&P Mark Marshall. Adv. contact Nick Nicholson. Circ: 17,059.

690 USA ISSN 0192-7590
BUILDING CONSTRUCTION NEWS; a publication of the building construction industry in Northern Ohio. Text in English. 1979 (vol.4). m. USD 12; free to qualified personnel. adv. bk.rev.
Published by: Builders Exchange, Inc., 981 Keynote Circle, Cleveland, OH 44131-1842. Ed. Gregg Mazurek. Circ: (controlled).

692.5 AUS ISSN 1320-4300
BUILDING COST GUIDE. HOUSING. NEW SOUTH WALES. Text in English. 1977. q.
Former titles (until 1989): Cordell's Building Cost Guide. Housing, New Construction. New South Wales (0816-8822); (until 1985): Cordell's Building Cost Guide. Housing Alterations and Additions. NSW and ACT (0155-6843)
Published by: Cordell Building Information Services (Subsidiary of: Cordell Construction Information Services Pty. Ltd.), Level 10, 10 Help St, Chatswood, NSW 2067, Australia. TEL 61-2-99345555, FAX 61-2-99345501, info@rcd.com.au, http://www.reedconstructiondata.com.au.

690 GBR
BUILDING COST INFORMATION SERVICE. DIGESTS. Text in English. q. GBP 45 (effective 2001).
Published by: Building Cost Information Service Ltd., Royal Institution of Chartered Surveyors, Parliment Sq, 12 Great George St, London, SW1P 3AD, United Kingdom. TEL 44-20-7222-7000, FAX 44-20-7695-1501.

690 GBR
BUILDING COST INFORMATION SERVICE. ELEMENTAL ANALYSIS. Text in English. a. GBP 260 (effective 2001).
Published by: Building Cost Information Service Ltd., Royal Institution of Chartered Surveyors, Parliment Sq, 12 Great George St, London, SW1P 3AD, United Kingdom. TEL 44-20-7222-7000, FAX 44-20-7695-1501.

690 GBR
BUILDING COST INFORMATION SERVICE. INDICES & FORECASTS. Text in English. q. GBP 260 (effective 2001). **Document type:** *Trade.*
Published by: Building Cost Information Service Ltd., Royal Institution of Chartered Surveyors, Parliment Sq, 12 Great George St, London, SW1P 3AD, United Kingdom. TEL 44-20-7222-7000, FAX 44-20-7695-1501.

690 GBR
BUILDING COST INFORMATION SERVICE. LABOUR, HOURS & WAGES. Text in English. a. GBP 260 (effective 2001).
Published by: Building Cost Information Service Ltd., Royal Institution of Chartered Surveyors, Parliment Sq, 12 Great George St, London, SW1P 3AD, United Kingdom. TEL 44-20-7222-7000, FAX 44-20-7695-1501.

690 GBR
BUILDING COST INFORMATION SERVICE. SURVEYS OF TENDER PRICES. Text in English. q. GBP 260 (effective 2001).
Published by: Building Cost Information Service Ltd., Royal Institution of Chartered Surveyors, Parliment Sq, 12 Great George St, London, SW1P 3AD, United Kingdom. TEL 44-20-7222-7000, FAX 44-20-7695-1501.

BUILDING DESIGN. see *ARCHITECTURE*

690 USA ISSN 0007-3407
TH1
BUILDING DESIGN & CONSTRUCTION; the magazine for the building team . Text in English. 1950. m. USD 119 domestic; USD 164.90 in Canada; USD 159.90 in Mexico; USD 241.90 elsewhere; USD 10 newsstand/cover domestic; USD 15 newsstand/cover foreign (effective 2005). adv. charts; illus.; tr.lit. index. back issues avail.; reprint service avail. from PQC. **Document type:** *Magazine, Trade.* **Description:** Provides information for nonresidential building owners, contractors, engineers and architects. Includes design innovations, industry news, law, emerging technology, and financing.
Formerly (until 1958): Building Construction
Related titles: Microfiche ed.: (from CIS); Online - full text ed.: (from EBSCO Publishing, Factiva, Florida Center for Library Automation, Gale Group, H.W. Wilson, LexisNexis, Northern Light Technology, Inc., O C L C Online Computer Library Center, Inc., ProQuest Information & Learning).
Indexed: ABIn, AIAP, Archl, BPI, BusI, CRIA, ConcrAb, ICEA, LRI, SRI, Search, SoftAbEng, T&II.
—BLDSC (2359.715000), CISTI, IE, Infotrieve, ingenta, Linda Hall. **CCC.**
Published by: Reed Business Information (Subsidiary of: Reed Business), 2000 Clearwater Dr, Oak Brook, IL 60525. TEL 630-288-8000, FAX 630-288-8155, bpodgory@reedbusiness.com, http://www.bdcnetwork.com, http://www.reedbusiness.com. Ed. Robert Cassidy. Pub. Dean Horowitz TEL 630-288-8152. adv.: B&W page USD 9,885. Circ: 76,006 (controlled). **Subscr. to:** Reed Business Information, PO Box 9020, Maple Shade, NJ 08052-9020. TEL 303-470-4466, FAX 303-470-4691.

338.4 690 AUS ISSN 0007-3431
BUILDING ECONOMIST. Text in English. 1961. q. AUD 75 (effective 2003). adv. bk.rev.; software rev. charts; illus. 60 p./no.; back issues avail. **Document type:** *Journal, Trade.*
Incorporates: Quantity Surveyor (0048-6108)
Related titles: Online - full text ed.: (from R M I T Publishing).
Indexed: API, BldManAb, PAIS, RICS.
—BLDSC (2359.750000), CISTI, IE, ingenta.
Published by: Australian Institute of Quantity Surveyors, PO Box 301, Deakin West, ACT 2600, Australia. TEL 61-2-62822222, FAX 61-2-62852427, aiqs@compuserve.com, contact@aiqs.com.au, http://www.aiqs.com.au. Ed., R&P Ian Blyth. Adv. contact Ann Patterson. Circ: 3,300.

690 GBR ISSN 0969-8213
BUILDING ENGINEER. Text in English. 1925. m. adv. bk.rev. illus. **Description:** For professionals specializing in the technology of building.
Former titles (until 1993): Architect and Surveyor (0308-8596); (until 1977): A and S (0308-4930); (until 1975): Architect and Surveyor (0003-8431)
Indexed: API, BldManAb, BrCerAb, BrTechI, C&ISA, CerAb, CorrAb, E&CAJ, EMA, IAA, M&TEA, MBF, METADEX, RICS, SolStAb, WAA.
—BLDSC (2359.780000), IE, ingenta. **CCC.**
Published by: Association of Building Engineers, Lutyens House, Billing Brook Rd, Weston Favell, Northants, United Kingdom. TEL 44-845-1261058, FAX 44-1604-784220, editor@abe.org.uk, building.engineers@abe.org.uk, subscriptions@abe.org.uk, http://www.abe.org.uk/journal.jsp. adv.: B&W page GBP 575; bleed 210 x 297. Circ: 5,000.

690 GBR
BUILDING FOR LEISURE. Text in English. 1990. 8/yr. GBP 20 (effective 1999). adv. back issues avail. **Document type:** *Trade.* **Description:** Covers all aspects of the public and private sector leisurebuild market.
Published by: Stable Publishing, S B C House, Restmor Way, Wallington, Surrey SM6 7AH, United Kingdom. TEL 44-181-288-1080, FAX 44-181-288-1099. Ed. Richard Lafferty. Pub. Toby Filby. Adv. contact Paul Turner. color page GBP 1,775; trim 213 x 265. Circ: 11,706 (controlled).

690 AUS ISSN 1322-6754
BUILDING IN AUSTRALIA. Text in English. 1981. biennial. AUD 1,950 (effective 2000). **Document type:** *Corporate.*
Description: Reports on the medium- to long-term prospects for building activity.
Published by: B I S Shrapnel Pty. Ltd., 8th Fl., 181 Miller St, North Sydney, NSW 2060, Australia. TEL 61-2-9959-5924, FAX 61-2-9959-5795, jlewis@bis.com, http://www.bis.com.au. Ed. Robert Mellor. Circ: 300.

691 ITA
BUILDING IN ITALY (ONLINE EDITION). Text in Italian. 1990. a. (in 2 vols.). adv. **Document type:** *Catalog, Trade.*
Former titles: Building in Italy (Print Edition); Catalogo Edile
Media: Online - full content. **Related titles:** CD-ROM ed.; Online - full text ed.
Published by: BE-MA Editrice Srl, Via Teocrito 50, Milan, MI 20128, Italy. http://www.buildinginitaly.com. Ed. Gaetano Bertini Malgarini. Circ: 4,000.

690 ZAF ISSN 0378-9020
BUILDING INDUSTRIES FEDERATION. ANNUAL REPORT. Text in English. 1904. a. free. **Document type:** *Corporate.*
Description: Annual overview of the Executive Director - financial year June to May.

B

▼ new title ➤ refereed ✶ unverified ♦ full entry avail.

Published by: Building Industries Federation, PO Box 1619, Halfway House, 1685, South Africa. TEL 27-11-8051985, FAX 27-11-3151644, http://www.bifsa.org.za. Circ: 6,000 (controlled).

690 USA
BUILDING INDUSTRY. Text in English. 1954. m. USD 25 in state; USD 30 domestic; USD 40 foreign (effective 2005).
Document type: *Magazine, Trade.*
Formerly: Building History
Published by: Trade Publishing Co. Ltd., 287 Mokauea St, Honolulu, HI 96819. editorial@tradepublishing.com, http://www.buildingindustryhawaii.com. Ed. Jim Crabtree. Pub. Carl Hebenstreit. Circ: 4,750.

690 AUS ISSN 1320-0100
BUILDING INDUSTRY CONNECTION. Text in English. 1990. q. AUD 39.95 domestic; AUD 69 foreign (effective 2001). adv. bk.rev.; software rev. charts; illus.; mkt.; stat.; tr.lit. 96 p./no.; **Document type:** *Trade.* **Description:** Provides a reference for licensed builders, designers and specifiers, discussing issues such as new technology, standards, and business.
Published by: Connection Magazines Pty. Ltd., 118 Atkinson St, Oakleigh, VIC 3166, Australia. TEL 61-3-9564-2100, FAX 61-3-9568-4955, http://www.build.com.au. Ed. Ronald Wyers. Pub. Jeff Patchell. R&P David Beer TEL 61-3-9564-2125. Adv. contact Peter Harris TEL 61-3-9564-2103. page AUD 6,980; trim 205 x 276. Circ: 51,732.

690 AUS
BUILDING INDUSTRY PROSPECTS. Text in English. m. AUD 1,480 (effective 2000). **Document type:** *Bulletin.* **Description:** Provides regular monitoring of developments affecting the building industry with detailed numerical forecasts of dwelling and non-dwelling.
Published by: B I S Shrapnel Pty. Ltd., 8th Fl., 181 Miller St, North Sydney, NSW 2060, Australia. TEL 61-2-9959-5924, FAX 61-2-9959-5795, jlewis@bis.com, http://www.bis.com.au. Ed. Robert Mellor. Circ: 450.

693 658.8 GBR ISSN 1467-0984
BUILDING INTELLIGENCE. Text in English. 1983. m. GBP 180 domestic. adv. charts; illus.; stat. back issues avail. **Document type:** *Trade.*
Former titles (until 1999): Building Economist (1357-6763); (until Jan. 1995): Building Market Report (0267-2561)
Indexed: API.
Published by: Builder Group plc., Exchange Tower, 2 Harbour Exchange Sq, London, E14 9GE, United Kingdom. TEL 44-20-7560-4000, FAX 44-20-7560-4404. Ed. Alistair Stewart. Pub. Pam Barker. Adv. contact Ben Greenish. Circ: 552.
Subscr. to: Building, Freepost (LE6522), Leicstter LE87 4DH, United Kingdom. TEL 44-1858-468811.

BUILDING LAW MONTHLY. see *LAW*

690.029 USA ISSN 1541-681X
TH1092
BUILDING MATERIALS DIRECTORY. Text in English. a. USD 14 (effective 1999). **Document type:** *Directory.* **Description:** Lists all manufacturers of building materials complying with UL standards.
Published by: Underwriters Laboratories Inc., Publications, 33 Pfingsten Rd, Northbrook, IL 60062-2096. TEL 847-272-8800, FAX 847-272-0472.

690 USA ISSN 0007-3490
TH3301 CODEN: BUOMAL
BUILDING OPERATING MANAGEMENT; the national magazine for commercial and institutional buildings construction, renovation, facility mangement. Text in English. 1954. m. USD 55 (effective 2005). adv. bk.rev. illus.; tr.lit. Index. reprint service avail. from PQC. **Document type:** *Magazine, Trade.*
Formerly: Building Maintenance and Modernization
Related titles: Microform ed.: (from PQC); Online - full text ed.: (from ProQuest Information & Learning).
Indexed: ABIn, CIJE, IMI, MEDLINE, RefZh.
—CASDDS, CISTI, Linda Hall.
Published by: Trade Press Publishing Corp., 2100 W Florist Ave, Milwaukee, WI 53209. TEL 414-228-7701, FAX 414-228-1134, http://www.facilitiesnet.com/bom, http://www.tradepress.com. Eds. Edward Sullivan, D Yake. Pub. Brad Ehlert. R&P Tim Rowe TEL 414-228-7701 ext 515. adv.: B&W page USD 10,200, color page USD 12,185. Circ: 70,054 (paid and controlled).

BUILDING PERMIT ACTIVITY IN FLORIDA. see *PUBLIC ADMINISTRATION*

BUILDING PERMITS LAW BULLETIN. see *HOUSING AND URBAN PLANNING*

690 USA
BUILDING PLANNED LIST✶. Text in English. 1967. m. USD 100 per issue. charts; stat.
Published by: Live Leads Corp., 35 W 76th St 4, New York, NY 10023-1521. Ed. Thomas Szabo. Circ: 150.

674 691 USA ISSN 0742-5694
BUILDING PRODUCTS DIGEST. Text in English. 1982. m. USD 18 (effective 2005). adv. bk.rev. **Document type:** *Magazine, Trade.* **Description:** Covers industry news, how-to, new products, new literature, association news, business trends for home centers, lumber and building material retailers and wholesalers and wood treaters in 13 southern states.
Published by: Cutler Publishing, Inc., 4500 Campus Dr, Ste 480, Newport Beach, CA 92660. TEL 949-852-1990, FAX 949-852-0231, http://www.building-products.com. Ed. David Koenig. Pubs. Alan Oakes, David Cutler. Adv. contact Chuck Casey. Circ: 12,000 (controlled).

BUILDING PRODUCTS FILE. see *BUSINESS AND ECONOMICS—Trade And Industrial Directories*

690 HKG
BUILDING PRODUCTS FINDER. Text in English. 1979. a. HKD 200. **Document type:** *Trade.*
Published by: China Trend Building Press Ltd, Rm. 901 C C Wu Building, 302 Hennessy Rd, Wanchai, Hong Kong, Hong Kong. TEL 852-2802-6299. Ed. Bobo Chan.

693 ZAF
BUILDING PRODUCTS NEWS. Text in English. 19??-1995; N.S. 1999. m. ZAR 96 domestic; ZAR 182 in Namibia; ZAR 204 elsewhere (effective 2000). illus. **Document type:** *Trade.* **Description:** Reports on technical and marketing news and developments in the building-products industry.
Published by: T M L Business Publishing (Subsidiary of: Times Media Ltd.), PO Box 182, Pinegowrie, Gauteng 2123, South Africa. TEL 27-11-789-2144, FAX 27-11-789-3196, estellev@tmltrade.co.za. Adv. contact Wendy Ansell.

690 AUS
BUILDING REGULATION AUSTRALIA. Text in English. 2 base vols. plus updates 6/yr. looseleaf. AUD 545 (effective 2000). adv.
Supersedes (in 1992): Regulation of Building Standards N S W
Published by: LexisNexis Butterworths (Subsidiary of: LexisNexis Asia Pacific), Tower 2, 475-495 Victoria Ave, Chatswood, NSW 2067, Australia. TEL 61-2-94222189, FAX 61-2-94222406, http://www.lexisnexis.com.au/aus/default.asp. R&P Deanne Castellino. Adv. contact Mary Greenfield.

690 GBR ISSN 0961-3218
TH1 CODEN: BREIEA
➤ **BUILDING RESEARCH AND INFORMATION**; the international journal of research, development and demonstration. Text in English; Text occasionally in French. 1970. bi-m. GBP 739, USD 1,221 combined subscription to institutions print & online eds. (effective 2006). adv. bk.rev. illus. reprint service avail. from PSC. **Document type:** *Journal, Academic/Scholarly.* **Description:** Covers all aspects of building research and technology.
Formerly: Batiment International, Building Research and Practice (0182-3329); Which was formed by the 1970 merger of: Building Research and Practice (0306-9931); Batiment International (0373-4277)
Related titles: Online - full text ed.: ISSN 1466-4321. GBP 702, USD 1,160 to institutions (effective 2006) (from EBSCO Publishing, Gale Group, IngentaConnect, O C L C Online Computer Library Center, Inc., Swets Information Services).
Indexed: AIAP, API, ASCA, BldManAb, BrCerAb, C&ISA, CRIA, CRICC, CerAb, CivEngAb, CorrAb, DIP, E&CAJ, EMA, ESPM, EngInd, H&SSA, IAA, IBR, IBZ, IBuildSA, ICEA, ISMEC, Inspec, JOF, M&TEA, MBF, METADEX, PRA, RICS, SUSA, SolStAb, WAA.
—BLDSC (2363.527000), CISTI, Ei, IDS, IE, Infotrieve, ingenta, Linda Hall. **CCC.**
Published by: (International Council for Building Research, Studies and Documentation (CIB)), Routledge (Subsidiary of: Taylor & Francis Group), 4 Park Sq, Milton Park, Abingdon, Oxon OX14 4RN, United Kingdom. TEL 44-1235-828600, FAX 44-1235-829000, info@routledge.co.uk, http://www.tandf.co.uk/journals/titles/09613218.html, http://www.routledge.com. Ed. Richard Lorch. Circ: 4,000. **Subscr. in US & Canada to:** Customer Services Dept, Rankine Rd, Basingstoke, Hants RG24 8PR, United Kingdom. TEL 44-1256-813000, FAX 44-1256-330245.

➤ **BUILDING RESEARCH ESTABLISHMENT. FIRE NOTES.** see *FIRE PREVENTION*

690 624 720 SVK ISSN 1335-8863
CODEN: STVCA2
BUILDING RESEARCH JOURNAL. Text in English. 1953. q. USD 84 foreign (effective 2005). bk.rev. bibl.; charts; illus. index, cum.index. 64 p./no.; **Document type:** *Journal, Academic/Scholarly.* **Description:** Deals with the problems of building mechanics, as well as various building materials, construction theories, elasticity and plasticity theories.
Formerly (until 1994): Stavebnicky Casopis (0039-078X)
Indexed: ApMecR, CRIA, CRICC, ChemAb, ConcrAb, EngInd, GeotechAb, ICEA.
—CISTI, Linda Hall.
Published by: (Slovenska Akademia Vied/Slovak Academy of Sciences, Ustav Stavebnictva a Architektury/Institute of Construction and Architecture), Slovak Academic Press Ltd., Nam Slobody 6, PO Box 57, Bratislava, 81005, Slovakia. usarate@savba.sk, sap@sappress.sk, http://www.sappress.sk. Eds. Alexander Tesar, Jan Sladek. Circ: 1,250.

690 HKG ISSN 1562-4722
BUILDING REVIEW. Text in Chinese, English. 1976. m. HKD 480 (effective 1999). adv. **Document type:** *Trade.* **Description:** Covers architectural project, interior features, products and technology, company profiles, trade reports and more.
Published by: Building Review Publishing Co., 8-F, Shiu Fung Commercial Bldg, 51-53 Johnston Rd, Wanchai, Hong Kong, Hong Kong. TEL 852-2527-1282, FAX 852-2865-6529, brpublishing@ctimail.com. Ed. Tammy Tong. Pub. Peter Lee. Adv. contact Fiona Fung. B&W page HKD 8,800, color page HKD 11,600; bleed 280 x 210. Circ: 30,000.

690 352.9 USA
TH1
BUILDING SAFETY JOURNAL. Text in English. 1933. bi-m. USD 50 (effective 2004). adv. cum.index. back issues avail. **Document type:** *Magazine, Trade.* **Description:** Publishes articles on earthquake damage, fires, architecture and building officials and inspectors. Education section offers seminars to individuals interested in being certified with ICBO as building inspectors, plumbing inspectors.
Formerly (until 2004): Building Standards (0270-1197); Incorporates (1945-2003): Southern Building (0038-3864)
Indexed: CivEngAb, EEA, EngInd.
—CISTI, Ei, Linda Hall.
Published by: International Conference of Building Officials, 5360 Workman Mill Rd, Whittier, CA 90601-2298. TEL 562-699-0541, FAX 562-699-9721, http://www.iccsafe.org, http://www.icbo.org. Eds. Gregory A Layne, Sebastian Kunnappilly. Circ: 19,000 (paid).

690 USA
BUILDING SCIENCES. Text in English. 1974. bi-m. USD 35 to non-members (effective 2000). **Document type:** *Newsletter.* **Description:** Covers building industry issues. Includes Institute's activities, calendar of events and industry briefs.
Published by: National Institute of Building Sciences, 1090 Vermont Ave, N W, Ste 700, Washington, DC 20005-4905. TEL 202-289-7800. R&P Neil Sandler.

295 690 AUS
BUILDING SERVICE (B C A) N S W. Text in English. 1974. 2 base vols. plus q. updates. looseleaf. AUD 655 (effective 2004). **Document type:** *Trade.* **Description:** Contains the Building Code of Australia annotated with commentary, and all essential information relating to building standards and regulation in New South Wales.
Formerly (until 1993): Local Government Ordinance 70 "Building" (New South Wales) (0727-7997)
Published by: Lawbook Co. (Subsidiary of: Thomson Legal & Regulatory Ltd.), PO Box 3502, Rozelle, NSW 2039, Australia. LRA.Service@thomson.com, http://onlineecom01.thomson.com.au/thomson/Catalog.asp?EES_CMD=SI&EES_ID=100243, http://www.lawbookco.com.au. Ed. Colin MacLeman.

343.07869 AUS
BUILDING SERVICE NEW SOUTH WALES - FULL SERVICE. Text in English. 8-10 updates/yr), 4 base vols. plus irreg. updates. looseleaf. AUD 799 (effective 2004). **Document type:** *Trade.* **Description:** Contains comprehensive coverage of construction and building regulation in NSW, full text of the Building Code of Australia plus administrative legislation and related material including extracts of the Environmental Planning & Assessment Act 1979 and Local Government Act 1993, checklists and regulation advisory notes, and detailed commentary on each significant clause and any recent amendments.
Published by: Lawbook Co. (Subsidiary of: Thomson Legal & Regulatory Ltd.), PO Box 3502, Rozelle, NSW 2039, Australia. LRA.Service@thomson.com, http://onlineecom01.thomson.com.au/thomson/Catalog.asp?EES_CMD=SI&EES_ID=100242, http://www.lawbookco.com.au/. Ed. Colin MacLeman.

690 600 GBR ISSN 0143-6244
TH1 CODEN: BSETDF
➤ **BUILDING SERVICES ENGINEERING RESEARCH & TECHNOLOGY**; an international journal. Variant title: B S E R & T. Text in English. 1980. q. GBP 72 in Europe to individuals; USD 126 in North America to individuals; GBP 76 elsewhere to individuals; GBP 166 in Europe to institutions; USD 339 in North America to institutions; GBP 200 elsewhere to institutions; GBP 100 in developing nations; GBP 50 per issue in Europe; USD 100 per issue in North America; GBP 55 per issue elsewhere (effective 2006); subscr. includes online access. adv. bk.rev. charts; illus. index. back issues avail.; reprints avail. **Document type:** *Journal, Academic/Scholarly.* **Description:** Reports on the latest research providing you with an invaluable guide to recent developments in the field.
Related titles: Microfilm ed.: (from PQC); Online - full text ed.: ISSN 1477-0849 (from EBSCO Publishing, IngentaConnect, O C L C Online Computer Library Center, Inc., ProQuest Information & Learning, Swets Information Services).
Indexed: ABIn, BldManAb, BrCerAb, C&ISA, CerAb, CivEngAb, CorrAb, E&CAJ, EMA, EngInd, ErgAb, GasAb, IAA, IBuildSA, ICEA, Inspec, M&TEA, MBF, METADEX, SolStAb, WAA.
—BLDSC (2365.670000), AskIEEE, CISTI, Ei, IE, Infotrieve, ingenta, Linda Hall. **CCC.**

B

Published by: (Chartered Institution of Building Services), Hodder Arnold Journals (Subsidiary of: Hodder Headline plc.), 338 Euston Rd, London, NW1 3BH, United Kingdom. TEL 44-20-78736000, FAX 44-20-78736367, arnoldjournals@hodder.co.uk, http://www.bsertjournal.com, http://www.hodderarnoldjournals.com/. adv.: B&W page GBP 370; trim 189 x 246. Circ: 500. **Subscr. to:** Extenza - Turpin, Pegasus Dr, Stratton Business Park, Biggleswade, Beds SG18 8TQ, United Kingdom. TEL 44-1462-488900, FAX 44-1462-480947, subscriptions @turpinltd.com.

➤ **BUILDING SERVICES JOURNAL.** see *HEATING, PLUMBING AND REFRIGERATION*

➤ **BUILDING SOCIETIES ACT OF 1986 PRACTICE MANUAL.** see *LAW*

690   JAM
BUILDING SOCIETIES ASSOCIATION OF JAMAICA FACTBOOK. Text in English. 1974. a. free. **Document type:** *Trade.* **Description:** Statistical presentation of annual financial performances in the building society movement.
Published by: Building Societies Association of Jamaica Ltd., 17 Belmont Rd, PO Box 141, Kingston, 10, Jamaica. TEL 809-96-83855. Ed. Gayon Clarke. Circ: 500.

333.33   GBR
BUILDING SOCIETY ANNUAL ACCOUNTS MANUAL. Text in English. base vol. plus irreg. updates. looseleaf. GBP 115 to non-members; GBP 85 to members. **Document type:** *Trade.* **Description:** Provides updated commentary and analysis on the Building Societies Regulations of 1992, the Building Societies Act of 1986, the Companies Act of 1985, and other material on accounting standards of interest to building societies.
Published by: Building Societies Association, 3 Savile Row, London, W1X 1AF, United Kingdom. TEL 44-20-7437-0655, FAX 44-20-7287-0109. **Co-sponsor:** Council of Mortgage Lenders.

BUILDING SOCIETY LEAGUE TABLES (FINANCIAL). see *REAL ESTATE*

BUILDING SOCIETY LEAGUE TABLES (OPERATIONAL). see *REAL ESTATE*

BUILDING SOCIETY PEER GROUPS (FINANCIAL). see *REAL ESTATE*

BUILDING SOCIETY PEER GROUPS (OPERATIONAL). see *REAL ESTATE*

BUILDING SOCIETY TAXATION MANUAL. see *LAW—Estate Planning*

690 352.9   USA
TH1
BUILDING STANDARDS TODAY. Text in English. 1933. bi-m. included in subscr. to Building Standards. back issues avail. **Document type:** *Newsletter, Trade.*
Formerly: Building Standards Newsletter (1048-2555) —Linda Hall.
Published by: International Conference of Building Officials, 5360 Workman Mill Rd, Whittier, CA 90601-2298. TEL 562-699-0541, FAX 562-699-9721, http://www.icbo.org. Eds. Gregory A Layne, Sebastian Kunnappilly. Circ: 16,000.

690   USA
BUILDING STOCK DATABASE. Abbreviated title: B S D. Text in English. base vol. plus a. updates. **Document type:** *Trade.* **Description:** Provides history and forecast of existing space for every US county by 15 types of nonresidential and residential property categories.
Published by: F.W. Dodge, Real Estate Group (Subsidiary of: McGraw-Hill Construction Information Group), 24 Hartwell Ave, Lexington, MA 02173. TEL 800-591-4462, FAX 781-860-6884, info@mcgraw-hill.com, http://www.mag.fwdodge.com/ realestate/aboutbsd.htm, http://fwdodge.construction.com/ Analytics/.

691   USA   ISSN 0749-6133
TA676
BUILDING STONE MAGAZINE. Text in English. 1960. bi-m. USD 65 domestic; USD 120 foreign; USD 17 to qualified personnel (effective 2000). adv. bk.rev. **Document type:** *Trade.*
Formerly: Building Stone News (0007-3679)
Indexed: AIAP.
Published by: Building Stone Institute, PO Box 507, Purdys, NY 10578-0507. TEL 914-232-5725, FAX 914-232-5259. Ed. Dorothy Kender. Circ: 12,266.

690   USA   ISSN 1079-7459
BUILDING SYSTEMS MAGAZINE. Text in English. 1980. bi-m. USD 20 (effective 2004). adv. bk.rev. tr.lit. **Document type:** *Magazine, Trade.*
Former titles: Building Systems Builder (1064-5896); (until 1992): Builder - Dealer (0892-824X); (until 1987): Log Home and Alternative Housing Builder (0279-6368)
Related titles: Supplement(s): Building Product Suppliers Directory; Housing Manufacturers Directory.

Published by: Home Buyer Publications, Inc. (Subsidiary of: Active Interest Media), 4200 T Lafayette Center Dr, Chantilly, VA 20151. TEL 703-222-9411, FAX 703-222-3209, http://www.buildingsystems.com/. Ed. Charles Bevier. Pub. Tom Kupferer. Adv. contact Judy Medley. Circ: 18,000.

BUILDING TARGETED PROJECTS. see *ENERGY*

690   IRL
BUILDING TECHNOLOGY. Text in English. 1993. irreg., latest vol.7, 1997. **Document type:** *Newsletter.* **Description:** Provides information to architects and engineers committed to furthering energy-conscious and environmentally responsible design among the building professions.
Media: Online - full text.
Published by: Energy Research Group, Univ. College Dublin, School of Architecture, Richview, Clonskeagh, Dublin, 14, Ireland. TEL 353-1-269-2750, FAX 353-1-283-8908, erg@erg.ucd.ie, http://erg.ucd.ie/sectors/rue/ rue_newsletters.html.

690   USA
BUILDING TRADES EMPLOYERS' ASSOCIATION OF THE CITY OF NEW YORK. UPDATE✶ ; matters of interest to the building industry. Text in English. 197?. 10/yr. membership. charts; illus.
Supersedes (1933-1974): Building Trades Employers' Association of the City of New York. News and Opinion
Published by: Building Trades Employers Association of the City of New York, 44 W 28th St, 12 Fl, New York, NY 10001-4212. TEL 212-697-2860. Circ: 1,800.

BUILDING TRADESMAN. see *LABOR UNIONS*

690 305.4   USA   ISSN 1545-9292
▼ **BUILDING WOMEN.** Text in English. 2003 (Sum.). q. USD 40 to non-members; free to members (effective 2003). adv.
Published by: National Association of Home Builders, Women's Council, 1201 15th Street, NW, Washington, DC 20005. TEL 202-266-8200, 800-368-5242, FAX 202-266-8559, http://www.nahb.org. Ed. Judy Tibbs. Pub. Amy Larrabee. Adv. contact Marlene Adams.

690 658   USA   ISSN 0007-3725
                                   CODEN: BUILEQ
BUILDINGS; the source for facilities decision-makers. Text in English. 1906. m. USD 70 domestic; USD 85 in Canada; USD 125 elsewhere (effective 2005). adv. illus. index. back issues avail.; reprints avail. **Document type:** *Magazine, Trade.* **Description:** Covers the facilities construction and management of commercial and institutional buildings. Forecasts trends of the year to come.
Related titles: Microform ed.: (from PQC); Online - full text ed.: (from bigchalk, EBSCO Publishing, Florida Center for Library Automation, Gale Group, H.W. Wilson, Northern Light Technology, Inc., O C L C Online Computer Library Center, Inc., ProQuest Information & Learning, The Dialog Corporation).
Indexed: ABIn, AIAP, AgeL, BPI, BrCerAb, C&ISA, CerAb, CorrAb, E&CAJ, EEA, EMA, EngInd, IAA, M&TEA, MBF, METADEX, SolStAb, T&II, WAA.
—BLDSC (2366.035000), CASDDS, CISTI, IE, ingenta, Linda Hall. **CCC.**
Published by: Stamats Buildings Media, Inc., 615 Fifth St., SE, Cedar Rapids, IA 52401. TEL 319-364-6167, FAX 319-364-4278, info@buildings.com, http://www.buildings.com. Ed., R&P Linda K Monroe. Pub. Tony Dellamaria. Adv. contact Gail Utt. Circ: 72,000. (controlled)

690   USA
▼ **BUILDINGS PRODUCT CONNECTION.** Text in English. 2003. bi-m. USD 30; USD 6 per issue (effective 2004). adv. **Document type:** *Trade.*
Published by: Northwestern Lumber Association, 1405 Lilac Dr N, Ste 130, Minneapolis, MN 55422-4505. TEL 763-595-4054, FAX 763-595-4060, nlassn@nlassn.org, http://www.nlassn.org/. Ed. Beth Stoll TEL 763-595-5054. Adv. contact Pam Feldman TEL 763-595-4057. B&W page USD 1,100, color page USD 1,555; trim 8.5 x 11. Circ: 2,800 (paid).

634.9   AUS
BUILT ENVIRONMENT INNOVATION & CONSTRUCTION TECHNOLOGY. Variant title: Innovation Online. Text in English. 1989. bi-m. AUD 42 (effective 1998). adv. bibl.; charts. **Document type:** *Trade.*
Former titles: (until Oct. 2000): Building Innovation and Construction Technology (Online); (until 1998): Building Innovation and Construction Technology (Print) (1322-8935); (until 1994): Focus (1032-9315); Which was formed by the merger of (1976-1989): Rebuild (0312-620X); (1986-1989): Building Technology (0818-5042)
Media: Online - full content.
Indexed: ABIX, AESIS, BrCerAb, CRIA, CRICC, FPA, ForAb. —CISTI, Linda Hall.
Published by: C S I R O, Division of Building Construction and Engineering, PO Box 606, Rozelle, NSW 2039, Australia. TEL 61-2-98184111, FAX 61-2-98184738, TELEX AA 33766, http://www.dbce.csiro.au. Ed. June Cummings. Pub. J Grover. R&P V York. Adv. contact John Andrews. Circ: 10,000.

690   FRA   ISSN 1148-5531
BULLETIN EUROPEEN DU MONITEUR. Text in French. 1990. w. **Document type:** *Bulletin.*
Published by: Groupe Moniteur, 17 rue d'Uzes, Paris, 75002, France. FAX 33-1-40135121. Ed. Michel Levron. Circ: 650.

693   ROM   ISSN 1454-9956
BURSA CONSTRUCTIILOR. Text in Romanian. 1997. q. ROL 315,000 (effective 2002). adv. **Document type:** *Magazine, Trade.*
Published by: Ring Media, Str. Popa Tatu nr. 71, sector 1, Bucharest, Romania. TEL 40-21-3154356, FAX 40-21-3124556.

690 330   THA
BUSINESS & CONSTRUCTION MAGAZINE. Text in Thai. m. adv.
Published by: Business & Construction Magazine Co. Ltd., Srinakarin, 198-31 Soi Anamai, Bangkok, 10250, Thailand. FAX 2-3229324. Ed. Supreeya Sukkasang. Adv. contact Weerapol Rakthorn. Circ: 40,000.

690 658.8   GBR   ISSN 1468-361X
BUSINESS RATIO. BUILDERS MERCHANTS. Text in English. 1974. a. GBP 275 (effective 2001). charts; stat. **Document type:** *Trade.*
Former titles: (until 1999): Business Ratio Plus: Builders Merchants (1357-1613); (until 1994): Business Ratio Report. Builders Merchants (0261-7501)
Published by: The Prospect Shop Ltd., Field House, 72 Oldfield Rd, Hampton, Middx TW12 2HQ, United Kingdom. TEL 44-20-8461-8730, 44-20-8481-8720, FAX 44-20-8783-1940, info@theprospectshop.co.uk.

BUSINESS RATIO. BUILDING & CIVIL ENGINEERING. INTERMEDIATE. see *ENGINEERING—Civil Engineering*

BUSINESS RATIO. BUILDING & CIVIL ENGINEERING. MAJOR. see *ENGINEERING—Civil Engineering*

690 330.9   GBR   ISSN 1470-6814
BUSINESS RATIO. CONSTRUCTIONAL STEELWORK MANUFACTURERS. Text in English. 1978. a. GBP 275 (effective 2001). charts; stat. **Document type:** *Trade.* **Description:** Analyses and compares the financial performance of leading companies. Provides industry performance summaries, trends, and forecasts.
Former titles: (until 2000): Business Ratio Plus: Constructional Steelwork Manufacturers (1355-8641); (until 1994): Business Ratio Report: Constructional Steelwork Manufacturers (0261-7730)
Published by: The Prospect Shop Ltd., Field House, 72 Oldfield Rd, Hampton, Middx TW12 2HQ, United Kingdom. TEL 44-20-8461-8730, 44-20-8481-8720, FAX 44-20-8783-1940, info@theprospectshop.co.uk.

BUSINESS RATIO PLUS: HEATING & VENTILATING CONTRACTORS. see *HEATING, PLUMBING AND REFRIGERATION*

691 658.8   GBR   ISSN 1357-8308
BUSINESS RATIO PLUS: READY MIXED CONCRETE & AGGREGATES INDUSTRY. Text in English. 1973. a. charts; stat. **Document type:** *Trade.*
Formerly (until 1994): Business Ratio Report. Ready Mixed Concrete and Aggregates (0261-9466)
Published by: The Prospect Shop Ltd., Field House, 72 Oldfield Rd, Hampton, Middx TW12 2HQ, United Kingdom. TEL 44-20-8461-8730, 44-20-8481-8720, FAX 44-20-8783-1940, info@theprospectshop.co.uk.

690 658.8   GBR   ISSN 1472-7323
BUSINESS RATIO REPORT. HOUSEBUILDERS. INTERMEDIATE (YEAR). Text in English. 1978. a. GBP 275 (effective 2001). charts; stat. **Document type:** *Trade.*
Former titles: (until 2000): Business Ratio. Housebuilders. Intermediate (1468-3679); (until 1999): Business Ratio Plus. Housebuilders. Intermediate (1357-0420); (until 1994): Business Ratio Report. Housebuilders. Intermediate (0960-9431); Which supersedes in part (in 1990): Business Ratio Report. Housebuilders (0261-8435)
Published by: The Prospect Shop Ltd., Field House, 72 Oldfield Rd, Hampton, Middx TW12 2HQ, United Kingdom. TEL 44-20-8461-8730, 44-20-8481-8720, FAX 44-20-8783-1940, info@theprospectshop.co.uk.

690   GBR   ISSN 1472-7676
BUSINESS RATIO REPORT. HOUSEBUILDERS. MAJOR (YEAR). Text in English. 1978. a. GBP 275 (effective 2001).
Former titles: (until 2000): Business Ratio. Housebuilders. Major (1468-3652); (until 1999): Business Ratio Plus. Housebuilders. Major (1356-6091); (until 1994): Business Ratio Report. Housebuilders - Major (0960-944X); Which supersedes in part (in 1990): Business Ratio Report. Housebuilders (0261-8435)
Published by: The Prospect Shop Ltd., Field House, 72 Oldfield Rd, Hampton, Middx TW12 2HQ, United Kingdom. TEL 44-20-8461-8730, 44-20-8481-8720, FAX 44-20-8783-1940, info@theprospectshop.co.uk.

B

693.1 ITA
BUSINESS STONE. Text in Italian. 1992. bi-m. USD 60 foreign (effective 2000). bk.rev. mkt.; stat.; tr.lit. back issues avail. **Document type:** *Journal, Trade.* **Description:** Italian and economic news for the stone and technology field. Covers a broad range of information that concern the natural stone sector.
Former titles (until 2001): Business Stone Work; Business Stone (1124-0032)
Published by: (Italian Consortium for Marble), Ever s.n.c. di Emilia Gallini & C., Galleria Gandhi, 15, Rho, MI 20017, Italy. TEL 39-02-93900740, FAX 39-02-93900727, bstone@tin.it, http://www.bstone.it. Ed. Emilia Gallini. Adv. contact Emiliano Lazzaroni. Circ: 3,800.

016.69 DNK
BY OG BYG - AARSBERETNING. Text in Danish. 1949. a. free. illus. **Document type:** *Government.*
Former titles: S B I - Aarsberetning (0107-900X); (until 1979): Denmark. Statens Byggeforskningsinstitut. Aarsberetning
Indexed: IMMAb.
Published by: Statens Byggeforskningsinstitut/Danish Building and Urban Research, Dr Neergaards Vej 15, PO Box 119, Hoersholm, 2970, Denmark. TEL 45-45-865533, FAX 45-45-867535, by-og-byg@by-og-byg.dk, info@by-og-byg.dk, http://www.by-og-byg.dk.

690 DNK ISSN 1600-8057
BY OG BYG ANVISNING. Text in Danish. 195?. irreg. price varies. back issues avail. **Document type:** *Monographic series, Trade.*
Formerly (until 2000): S B I - Anvisning (0106-6757)
Published by: Statens Byggeforskningsinstitut/Danish Building and Urban Research, Dr Neergaards Vej 15, PO Box 119, Hoersholm, 2970, Denmark. TEL 45-45-865533, FAX 45-45-867535, info@by-og-byg.dk, http://www.by-og-byg.dk.

690 DNK ISSN 1600-8022
BY OG BYG DOKUMENTATION. Text in Danish. 2000. irreg. price varies. back issues avail. **Document type:** *Monographic series, Trade.*
Media: Online - full content. **Related titles:** Print ed.
Published by: Statens Byggeforskningsinstitut/Danish Building and Urban Research, Dr Neergaards Vej 15, PO Box 119, Hoersholm, 2970, Denmark. TEL 45-45-865533, FAX 45-45-867535, info@by-og-byg.dk, http://www.by-og-byg.dk.

016.69 DNK ISSN 1600-8030
BY OG BYG RESULTATER. Text in Danish. 2000. irreg., latest vol.37, 2004. price varies. back issues avail. **Document type:** *Monographic series, Trade.*
Formed by the merger of (1980-2000): S B I - Medddelelse (0107-4180); (1959-2000): S B I - Rapport (0573-9985); Which was formerly (until 1959): Statens Byggeforskningsinstitut. Rapport
Related titles: Online - full text ed.: ISSN 1600-8049.
—BLDSC (2938.180000), CISTI, ingenta.
Published by: Statens Byggeforskningsinstitut/Danish Building and Urban Research, Dr Neergaards Vej 15, PO Box 119, Hoersholm, 2970, Denmark. TEL 45-45-865533, FAX 45-45-867535, by-og-byg@by-og-byg.dk, info@by-og-byg.dk, http://www.by-og-byg.dk.

338.4 DNK
BYG-TEK; trade magazine for the building industry. Text in Danish. 1968. m. DKK 380 domestic (effective 2000). adv. **Document type:** *Trade.*
Formerly: Byg-Tek og Byggeri; Formed by the 1990 merger of: Byg-Teknik; Byggeri (0107-1866); Formerly: Anlaegsteknik; Moderne Jordflytning (0026-8623)
Published by: Odsgard AS, Stationsparken 25, Glostrup, 2600, Denmark. TEL 45-43-43-29-00, FAX 45-43-43-13-28, odsgard@odsgard.dk, http://www.byggeri.dk. Ed. Peter Odsgard. adv.: B&W page DKK 37,065, color page DKK 40,105; trim 370 x 256. Circ: 25,000 (controlled).

690 SWE ISSN 0281-658X
TH4
BYGG & TEKNIK. Text in Swedish. 1909. 8/yr. SEK 316 domestic; SEK 436 in Scandinavia; SEK 516 elsewhere (effective 2001). adv. illus. **Document type:** *Magazine, Trade.* **Description:** Devoted to Swedish building technology, architecture and engineering.
Former titles (until 1984): Byggnadskonst (0007-7593); (until 1966): Tidning for Byggnadskonst
Indexed: ChemAb.
Published by: Foerlags AB Bygg & Teknik, Fack 19099, Stockholm, 10432, Sweden. TEL 46-8-612-17-50, FAX 46-8-612-54-81, http://www.byggteknikforlaget.se. Ed. Stig Dahlin. Adv. contact Roland Dahlin. B&W page SEK 11,000, color page SEK 15,800; trim 185 x 270. Circ: 6,700 (controlled).

690 SWE
▼ **BYGGAREN.** Text in Swedish. 2005. 6/yr. SEK 250 domestic; SEK 325 foreign (effective 2005). adv. **Document type:** *Magazine, Trade.*
Published by: Foerlags AB Verkstadstidningen, Raasundevaegen 166, PO Box 2082, Solna, 16902, Sweden. TEL 46-8-51493400, FAX 46-8-51493409, http://www.byggaren.se, http://www.vtf.se. Ed. Lars Cyrus TEL 46-8-51493420. Adv. contact Thomas af Kleen TEL 46-851493422. B&W page SEK 11,300, color page SEK 17,900; 190 x 269.

690 DNK ISSN 0007-750X
BYGGEINDUSTRIEN/DANISH BUILDING INDUSTRY. Text in Danish. 1950. 8/yr. DKK 852 (effective 2004). adv. illus. **Document type:** *Journal, Trade.* **Description:** Provides comprehensive reports and authoritative comment on the industrial and advanced building trades.
—CISTI.
Published by: TechMedia A/S, Naverland 35, Glostrup, 2600, Denmark. TEL 45-43-242628, FAX 45-43-242626, info@techmedia.dk, http://www.techmedia.dk/html/medieinfo/bim.asp. Eds. Poul W Udengaard, Finn Asnaes. Adv. contact Finn Andersen TEL 45-43-242655. B&W page DKK 14,000, color page DKK 17,600; trim 185 x 265. Circ: 2,700 (controlled).

690 NOR ISSN 0332-7086
BYGGEINDUSTRIEN. Text in Norwegian. 1968. m. NOK 595. adv. **Document type:** *Trade.*
Published by: B A Media A-S, Postboks 128, Blindern, Oslo, 0314, Norway. TEL 47-22-96-59-22, FAX 47-22-46-00-25. Ed. Per Helge Pedersen. Circ: 10,000.

690 NOR ISSN 0333-3477
BYGGENYTT. Text in Norwegian. 1955. m. (20/yr.). NOK 480 (effective 2002). adv. bk.rev.
Incorporated (1959-1991): Bygningsartikler (0333-3655); Formerly (until 1962): Ukens Byggenytt (0801-311X)
Published by: Publicatio AS, PO Box 5023, Majorstua, Oslo, 0301, Norway. TEL 47-22-87-12-00, FAX 47-22-87-12-01, post@byggenytt.no, http://www.byggenytt.no. Ed. Bjoerner Toenne TEL 47-22-87-12-04. Circ: 10,000.

BYGGEPLADS DANMARK. see *ARCHITECTURE*

690 624 DNK ISSN 1397-7997
BYGGERI; oekonomisk-teknisk tidsskrift for bygge- og boligforhold. Text in Danish. 10/yr. DKK 300 domestic; DKK 360 foreign (effective 2000). adv. illus. back issues avail. **Document type:** *Trade.*
Formerly: Byggeforum (0107-9514)
Published by: Odsgard AS, Stationsparken 25, Glostrup, 2600, Denmark. TEL 45-43-43-29-00, FAX 45-43-43-13-28, odsgard@odsgard.dk, http://www.byggeri.dk. Ed. Tove Malzer. Pub. Peter Odsgard. Adv. contact Preben Fich. B&W page DKK 12,820, color page DKK 17,620; trim 262 x 176. Circ: 9,680 (controlled).

690 DNK ISSN 0906-1037
BYGGERIET. Text in Danish. 1991. m. adv.
Formed by the merger of (1958-1990): Murermesteren (0027-3651); (1958-1990): Byggehaandvaerket (0007-7496)
Published by: Byggeriets Arbejdsgivere, Kejsergade 2, Copenhagen K, 1195, Denmark. Ed. Kurt Jensen. Circ: 2,000.

690 DNK ISSN 1602-6187
BYGGETEKNIK; viden til vaekst. Text in Danish. 2002. 14/yr. adv. **Document type:** *Trade.*
Formed by the merger of (1994-2002): Byggeteknik. Vest (1602-4796); Which was formerly (until 2001): Byggeteknik. Jylland og Fyn (1396-0024); (1994-2002): Byggeteknik. Oest (1602-480X); Which was formerly (until 2001): Byggeteknik. Sjaelland og Oeerne (1396-0032)
Related titles: Online - full text ed.
Published by: FagbladsGruppen A/S, Birk Centerpark 36, Herning, 7400, Denmark. TEL 45-96-265299, FAX 45-96-265296, mail@byggeteknik.dk, http://www.byggeteknik.dk, http://www.fbg.dk. Ed. Bjarne Madsen. Adv. contact John Rasmussen. page DKK 27,432. Circ: 28,500 (controlled and free).

690 SWE ISSN 1101-8437
BYGGFAKTA PROJEKTNYTT. Text in Swedish. 1989. 8/yr. adv. 80 p./no. 4 cols./p.; **Document type:** *Magazine, Trade.*
Incorporates (1981-1998): Byggvarunytt (0280-1019)
Published by: Reed Business Information Sweden AB (Subsidiary of: Reed Business Information International), Loejtnansgatan 9, Ljusdal, 82781, Sweden. TEL 46-8-651552500, FAX 46-8-651552585, jbn@byggfakta.se, info@reedbusiness.se, http://www.reedbusiness.se. Ed., Pub., Adv. contact Jan Nilsson. B&W page SEK 20,400, color page SEK 24,300; trim 185 x 270. Circ: 23,100 (controlled).

690 NOR ISSN 0332-6152
BYGGHERREN. Text in Norwegian. 1974. 12/yr. adv.
—CCC.
Published by: (Byggherreforeningen), Byggherreforlaget AS, Graaterudveien 1, Drammen, 3036, Norway. Ed. Anders Thomassen. Adv. contact Knut Syversen TEL 47-69-30-82-30. B&W page NOK 14,700, color page NOK 18,300; 185 x 270. Circ: 6,981.

690 SWE ISSN 1104-5981
TH4
BYGGINDUSTRIN; organ foer byggentreprenoererna. Text in Swedish. 1931. 40/yr. SEK 1,045; SEK 499 to students (effective 2001). adv. bk.rev. charts; illus.; stat. index. 40 p./no.; **Document type:** *Magazine, Trade.*
Former titles (until 1994): Tidningen Byggindustrin (0349-3733); (until vol.6, 1980): Byggindustrin; (until 1980): Byggnadsindustrin; (until 1971): Byggnadsindustrin med Nyhetsextra; (until 1936): Stockholms Byggmaestarefoerening. Meddelande
Related titles: Supplement(s): Arets Byoggen.
Indexed: CISA, GeotechAb, IBuildSA.
Published by: Byggfoerlaget, Fack 5456, Stockholm, 11481, Sweden. TEL 46-8-665-36-75, FAX 46-8-667-72-78, morgan@byggindustrin.com, http://www.byggindustrin.com. Ed. Morgan Andersson. R&P H P Moeller TEL 46-8-665 3660. Adv. contact Gun Arvidsson TEL 46-8-665-3666. B&W page SEK 24,000, color page SEK 28,000; trim 194 x 267. Circ: 16,100.

690 NOR ISSN 0332-7221
BYGGMESTEREN. Text in Norwegian. 1926. 11/yr. NOK 370. adv.
Formerly (until 1952): Bygg- og Tomrermesteren (0802-5274)
Indexed: API, INIS AtomInd.
Published by: Byggforlaget A S, Postboksboks 5475, Majorstua, Oslo Pl., 0305, Norway. TEL 22-961150, FAX 22-697364. Ed. Per B Lotherington. Circ: 10,000.

BYGGREFERAT; nordiskt litteraturindex. see *BUILDING AND CONSTRUCTION—Abstracting, Bibliographies, Statistics*

338.4369 DNK ISSN 0108-0229
BYGNINGSDELE. Variant title: V & S Priser, Bygningsdele. Text in Danish. 1982. a. DKK 1,410 (effective 1999).
Published by: V & S Byggedata, 551 Frederikssundvej 194, Broenshoej, 2700, Denmark. TEL 45-38-60-77-11, FAX 45-38-60-77-55, bygdat@vs-byggedata.dk, bygdat@vs.byggedata.dk, http://www.vs-byggedata.dk.

338.4 690 DNK ISSN 0106-3715
TA645 CODEN: BYMEAF
BYGNINGSSTATISKE MEDDELELSER. Text in Danish, English. 1929. irreg. (approx. 4/yr.). DKK 230. bibl.; charts; illus.
Indexed: ApMecR, ConcrAb.
—CISTI, Linda Hall.
Published by: Dansk Selskab for Bygningsstatik, Bygning 118, Lundtoftevej 100, Lyngby, 2800, Denmark. Ed. L Pilegaard Hansen. Circ: 950.

690 RUS ISSN 0007-7690
TH9 CODEN: BYSTAM
BYULLETEN' STROITEL'NOI TEKHNIKI. Text in Russian. 1944. m. USD 198 (effective 1998). charts; illus. index.
Indexed: ChemAb, RefZh.
—CISTI, Linda Hall.
Published by: Gosstroi, Moscow, Russian Federation. Ed. V I Sichov. Circ: 26,400.

690 COL
C A M A C O L. ASAMBLEA NACIONAL. DOCUMENTO. (Camara Colombiana de la Construccion) Text in Spanish. 1957. a. USD 20. adv. **Document type:** *Trade.*
Published by: Camara Colombiana de la Construccion (CAMACOL), Presidencia Nacional, Carrera 10, 19-65 Piso 10, PO Box 28588, Bogota, DE, Colombia. TEL 57-1-234-5186. Circ: 10,000.

690 USA ISSN 0883-7880
C A M MAGAZINE. Text in English. 1980. m. USD 36 (effective 1999). adv. **Document type:** *Magazine, Trade.* **Description:** Provides a forum on new construction industry technology and practices, current information on new construction projects, products and services, and information on industry personnel changes and advancements.
Formerly (until 198?): Exchanger (0274-7898)
Published by: Construction Association of Michigan, 1625 S. Woodward Ave., Box 3204, Bloomfield Hill, MI 48302-3204. TEL 248-972-1000, FAX 248-972-1001, http://www.cam-online.com/. Ed. Phyllis L Brooks. Pub. Curt Hacias. Adv. contact Amanda Tackett. B&W page USD 990, color page USD 1,650; bleed 7.75 x 10. Circ: 4,460 (controlled).

C & D RECYCLER; serving the dynamic construction and demolition materials recycling market. (Construction and Demolition) see *ENVIRONMENTAL STUDIES—Waste Management*

C & D RECYCLER EQUIPMENT & SERVICES BUYERS' GUIDE. see *ENVIRONMENTAL STUDIES—Waste Management*

691 SWE ISSN 0282-6283
C B I INFORMERAR. Text in Swedish. 1985. irreg., latest 1997. SEK 50 per issue (effective 2001). **Document type:** *Academic/Scholarly.* **Description:** Covers research on cement and concrete.
Formerly: C B I Rekommendationer-Recommendations (0348-2790)
Published by: Cement- och Betong Institutet/Swedish Cement and Concrete Research Institute, Drottning Kristinas Vaeg 26, Stockholm, 100 44, Sweden. cbi@cbi.se, http://www.cbi.se. Ed. Richard McCarthy.

690 SWE ISSN 0349-2060
C B I NYTT. (Cement- och Betonginstitutet) Text in Swedish. 1974. q. free. **Description:** News about activities at the institute.
Published by: Cement- och Betong Institutet/Swedish Cement and Concrete Research Institute, Drottning Kristinas Vaeg 26, Stockholm, 100 44, Sweden. TEL 46-8-696-11-00, FAX 46-8-24-31-37, http://www.cbi.se. Eds. Gunilla Teofilusson, Johan Silfverband.

691 SWE ISSN 0346-8240 CODEN: CBIRDN
C B I RAPPORTER - REPORTS. Text in English, Swedish; Summaries in English. 1974. irreg. (approx. 6/yr.). SEK 100 (effective 2002). back issues avail.
Incorporates (1945-1988): CBI Forskning - Research (0346-6906)
Indexed: ConcrAb, Englnd.
—BLDSC (3095.600000), CISTI, Linda Hall.
Published by: Cement- och Betong Institutet/Swedish Cement and Concrete Research Institute, Drottning Kristinas Vaeg 26, Stockholm, 100 44, Sweden. TEL 46-8-696-11-00, FAX 46-8-24-31-37, http://www.cbi.se.

691.3 BEL
C B R ANNUAL REPORT. Text in English, French, Dutch. a.
Published by: CBR Group, Chaussee de la Hulpe, 185, Bruxelles, B-1170, Belgium. TEL 32-2-678-3353, FAX 32-2-678-3355, communication@cbrgroup.com, http://www.cbrgroup.com. Pub. Catherine Akexandre.

690 USA ISSN 1059-406X
HD9715.A1
C B R CONSTRUCTION BUSINESS REVIEW. Text in English. 1991. bi-m. USD 89.95 domestic; USD 119.95 foreign; USD 15 newsstand/cover (effective 2004). adv. **Document type:** *Journal, Trade.*
Indexed: ConcrAb.
—CISTI.
Published by: H L K Global Communications, Inc., 8133 Leesburg Pike, Ste 750, Vienna, VA 22182. TEL 703-734-0017, 800-922-7123, FAX 703-734-2908. Ed. Fred Maavenzadeh. Pub. Robin L Olsen. Adv. contact Levi K Gain.

690 332 USA ISSN 1078-2435
C F M A BUILDING PROFITS. Text in English. 1988. bi-m. USD 135 membership (effective 2005). adv. charts; illus. 100 p./no.; back issues avail.; reprints avail. **Document type:** *Magazine, Trade.* **Description:** Features industry news and technical articles in the field of construction financial management.
Published by: Construction Financial Management Association, 29 Emmons Dr, Ste F 50, Princeton, NJ 08540-1413. TEL 609-452-8000, FAX 609-452-0474, info@cfma.org, http://www.cfma.org/pubs/bpgen.asp. Ed., R&P Paula A Wristen. Adv. contact Ron Kress. B&W page USD 1,450. Circ: 7,000.

C H L ANNUAL EQUIPMENT GUIDE AND C H L MONTHLY EQUIPMENT GUIDE. (Contractors Hot Line) see *PUBLISHING AND BOOK TRADE*

621 USA
C H L EQUIPMENT GUIDE. (Contractors Hot Line) Text in English. a. adv.
Published by: Heartland Communications Group, Inc., PO Box 1052, Fort Dodge, IA 50501. TEL 515-955-1600, 800-673-4763, FAX 800-247-2000.

690 ESP
C I C PRODUCTOS. Text in Spanish. 3/yr. free to qualified personnel.
Published by: Centro Informativo de la Construccion, Ave de Manoferas, 44, 3a Plana, Madrid, 28050, Spain. TEL 34-91-2972000, FAX 34-91-2972154, redaccion@cicinformacion.com, http://www.cicinformacion.com/. Circ: 20,000 (paid).

690 GBR
C I I G BULLETIN. (Construction Industry Information Group) Text in English. irreg. **Description:** Provides useful information for the construction industry.
Indexed: Inspec.
Published by: C I I G, 26 Store St, London, WC1 E7BT, United Kingdom.

C I R I A ANNUAL REPORT. see *ENGINEERING—Civil Engineering*

C I R I A NEWS. see *ENGINEERING—Civil Engineering*

C I R I A REPORT. see *ENGINEERING—Civil Engineering*

C I R I A TECHNICAL NOTE. see *ENGINEERING—Civil Engineering*

690 USA
C M ADVISOR. Text in English. 1983. bi-m. membership. adv. bk.rev. back issues avail. **Document type:** *Newsletter, Trade.* **Description:** Focuses on current issues affecting construction managers and association events.
Published by: Construction Management Association of America, 7918 Jones Branch Dr., Ste. 540, Mclean, VA 22102. TEL 703-356-2622, FAX 703-356-6388, info@cmaanet.org, cmaa@iamdigex.net, http://www.cmaanet.org, http://www.access.digex/~cmaa/. Ed., Adv. contact Bruce D'Agostino.

691.3 USA
C M NEWS. Text in English. 1962. m. free to qualified personnel. adv. bk.rev. abstr.; charts; illus.; stat.; tr.lit. **Document type:** *Newsletter, Trade.* **Description:** Covers subjects related to manufacture and marketing of concrete masonry products.
Former titles: Concrete Masonry News; C - M News; C - M Newsletter; C - M News (0007-8662)
Indexed: ConcrAb.
Published by: National Concrete Masonry Association, 13750 Sunrise Valley Dr., Herndon, VA 20171-4662. TEL 703-713-1900, FAX 703-713-1910, ncma@ncma.org, http://www.ncma.org, http://ncma.org. Adv. contact Heidi Lorence. B&W page USD 1,760, color page USD 2,560. Circ: 5,000.

C P A CONSTRUCTION NICHE BUILDER. see *BUSINESS AND ECONOMICS—Public Finance, Taxation*

690 USA ISSN 0163-5018
C S I NEWSDIGEST✶. Text in English. m. membership. adv. **Description:** Targeted towards CSI members, covers member news - technical and educational, calendar of events, and employment.
Published by: Construction Specifications Institute, 289 - 266 Elmwood Ave, Buffalo, NY 14222. FAX 703-684-0465, csi@csinet.org. Ed. Sharon Hammel. Circ: 19,000.

C S I R BUILDING TECHNOLOGY. COMPLETE LIST OF PUBLICATIONS. see *BUILDING AND CONSTRUCTION—Abstracting, Bibliographies, Statistics*

070.43 USA
C W A NEWS (BUFFALO GROVE). Text in English. 1953. q. free with membership. **Document type:** *Newsletter, Trade.* **Description:** Covers news of interest to and activities of the association.
Formerly: Construction Writers Association. Newsletter (0069-9217)
Published by: Construction Writers Association, PO Box 5586, Buffalo, IL 60089-5586. TEL 847-398-7756, office@constructionwriters.org, http://www.constructionwriters.org. Circ: 750.

690 FRA ISSN 0241-6794
CAHIERS TECHNIQUES DU BATIMENT. Text in French. 1970. 9/yr. illus.
Former titles (until 1975): Cahiers Techniques du Moniteur; Urbat (0049-5697)
Published by: Groupe Moniteur, 17 rue d'Uzes, Paris, 75002, France. FAX 33-1-40135111, TELEX 680 876F.

690 USA
▼ **CALIFORNIA BUILDER.** Text in English. 2003. bi-m. free to qualified personnel (effective 2004). adv. **Document type:** *Magazine, Trade.*
Related titles: Online - full content ed.
Published by: California Building Industry Association, 1215 K St, Ste 1200, Sacramento, CA 95814. TEL 916-443-7933, FAX 916-443-1960, http://www.californiabuildermagazine.com/, http://www.cbia.org/. Ed. John Frith. Pub. Robert Rivinius. Adv. contact Mark Simpson. B&W page USD 1,650, color page USD 2,500; bleed 7.25 x 9.75.

690 USA ISSN 0045-3900
TA1
CALIFORNIA BUILDER & ENGINEER. Text in English. 1893. s-m. USD 96 domestic; USD 126 in Canada; USD 166 elsewhere (effective 2005). adv. bk.rev. illus.; stat.; tr.lit. **Document type:** *Magazine, Trade.* **Description:** Regional trade publication serving heavy construction industries of California and Hawaii.
Related titles: Online - full text ed.: (from Gale Group, ProQuest Information & Learning).
—CCC.
Published by: Reed Construction Data, Associated Construction Publications (Subsidiary of: Reed Business Information), 30 Technology Pkwy, Ste 100, Norcross, GA 30092. TEL 770-417-4000, FAX 770-417-4138, lfaulkner@reedbusiness.com, acp@reedbusiness.com, http://www.reedbusiness.com/index.asp?layout=theListProfile&theListID=693&groupID=38&industryid=38, http://www.acppubs.com/. Ed. Loren Faulkner TEL 909-328-1920. Pub. John Weatherhead. Circ: 8,500.

690 USA
CALIFORNIA BUILDER AND ENGINEER. BUYERS GUIDE & DIRECTORY. Text in English. a. USD 35 per issue (effective 2004). **Document type:** *Directory, Trade.*
Published by: Reed Construction Data, Associated Construction Publications (Subsidiary of: Reed Business Information), 30 Technology Pkwy, Ste 100, Norcross, GA 30092. TEL 770-417-4122, FAX 800-930-3003, http://www.acppubs.com/.
Subscr. to: Reed Business Information, PO Box 9020, Maple Shade, NJ 08052-9020. TEL 303-470-4466, 800-446-6551, FAX 303-470-4691, http://www.pubservice.com/CH.htm.

690 USA
CALIFORNIA CONSTRUCTION. Text in English. m. USD 40 (effective 2004). **Document type:** *Magazine, Trade.* **Description:** Provides comprehensive news about the California construction market.
Former titles (until 2003): California Construction Link (1546-9956); F. W. Dodge California Construction Link (1537-5064)
Related titles: Online - full text ed.: (from EBSCO Publishing).
—CCC.
Published by: Mcgraw-Hill Construction Dodge (Subsidiary of: McGraw-Hill Construction Information Group), 1333 S Mayflower Ave, 3rd Fl, Monrovia, CA 91016-4066. TEL 626-932-6160, http://california.construction.com, http://www.dodgeconstructionpublications.com. Ed. Paul Napolitano TEL 626-932-6169. Pub. Roylin Downs TEL 626-932-6160.

CALIFORNIA CONSTRUCTION LAW MANUAL. see *LAW*

690 340 USA ISSN 1055-9469
CALIFORNIA CONSTRUCTION LAW REPORTER. Text in English. 1991. m. looseleaf. USD 175. index. **Document type:** *Newsletter.*
Published by: Shepard's (Subsidiary of: LexisNexis North America), 555 Middle Creek Pkwy, Colorado Springs, CO 80921. TEL 800-743-7393, customer_service@shepards.com, http://www.shepards.com, http://www.lexisnexis.com/shepards/. Ed. James Acret.

690 USA
▼ **CALIFORNIA CONTRACTOR**; the newspapers for profit-conscious entrepreneurs. Text in English. 2004. m. adv. **Document type:** *Newspaper, Trade.*
Published by: United Contractors of America, Inc., 1119 Colorado Ave, Ste 15, Santa Monica, CA 90401. TEL 310-393-0601, FAX 310-393-0606, info@californiacontractor.us, http://www.californiacontractor.com. Ed. Herb Chase. Pubs. Herb Chase, Terry Cassel. Adv. contact Terry Cassel. B&W page USD 2,570; trim 10.25 x 12.5. Circ: 27,168 (controlled).

343.078 USA
CALIFORNIA MECHANICS' LIEN LAW AND CONSTRUCTION INDUSTRY PRACTICE. Text in English. 1990. latest 1996, 6th ed., 2 base vols. plus irreg. updates. looseleaf. USD 205 (effective 2003).
Published by: Michie Company (Subsidiary of: LexisNexis North America), 701 E Water St, Charlottesville, VA 22902-5389. TEL 434-972-7600, 800-446-3410, FAX 434-972-7677, http://www.michie.com. Eds. Harry M Marsh, Robert C Clifford.

CALIFORNIA STATE CONTRACTS REGISTER. see *BUSINESS AND ECONOMICS*

690 COL
CAMARA COLOMBIANA DE LA CONSTRUCCION. BOLETIN MENSUAL DE ESTADISTICA✶. Text in Spanish. 1973. m. charts; stat. **Document type:** *Bulletin.*
Indexed: RASB.
Published by: Camara Colombiana de la Construccion (CAMACOL), Presidencia Nacional, Carrera 10, 19-65 Piso 10, PO Box 28588, Bogota, DE, Colombia.

690 COL
CAMARA COLOMBIANA DE LA CONSTRUCCION. BOLETIN TRIMESTRIAL✶. Text in Spanish. 1973. q. charts; stat. **Document type:** *Bulletin.*
Published by: Camara Colombiana de la Construccion (CAMACOL), Presidencia Nacional, Carrera 10, 19-65 Piso 10, PO Box 28588, Bogota, DE, Colombia.

690 COL ISSN 0120-5102
CAMARA COLOMBIANA DE LA CONSTRUCCION. REVISTA. Key Title: Revista Camacol. Text in Spanish. 1978. q. COP 25,500, USD 30 (effective 1994). adv. charts; illus.; stat. cum.index: no.1-49. **Document type:** *Trade.* **Description:** Analysis of construction and public works, legislation, finance and marketing, and macroeconomics.
Published by: Camara Colombiana de la Construccion (CAMACOL), Presidencia Nacional, Carrera 10, 19-65 Piso 10, PO Box 28588, Bogota, DE, Colombia. TEL 57-1-217-7166, FAX 57-1-211-9559. Ed. Alberto Vasquez Restrepo. Circ: 25,000.

691 PAN
CAMARA PANAMENA DE LA CONSTRUCCION. LISTA DE PRECIOS DE MATERIALES DE CONSTRUCCION. Text in Spanish. 1961. s-a. USD 30. adv. **Document type:** *Bulletin.* **Description:** Lists local prices of construction materials and equipment rentals.
Published by: Camara Panamena de la Construccion, Apdo. 6793, Panama City, 5, Panama. TEL 507-265-2500, FAX 507-265-2571. Adv. contact Irene Quintana. Circ: 500.

CAMBRIDGE URBAN AND ARCHITECTURAL STUDIES. see *HOUSING AND URBAN PLANNING*

CANADA. STATISTICS CANADA. ASPHALT ROOFING/PAPIER-TOITURE ASPHALTE. see *BUILDING AND CONSTRUCTION—Abstracting, Bibliographies, Statistics*

B

▼ new title ➤ refereed ✶ unverified ♦ full entry avail.

CANADA. STATISTICS CANADA. BUILDING PERMITS/PERMIS DE BATIR. see *BUILDING AND CONSTRUCTION—Abstracting, Bibliographies, Statistics*

CANADA. STATISTICS CANADA. BUILDING PERMITS, ANNUAL SUMMARY/PERMIS DE BATIR, SOMMAIRE ANNUEL. see *BUILDING AND CONSTRUCTION—Abstracting, Bibliographies, Statistics*

CANADA. STATISTICS CANADA. CAPITAL EXPENDITURE PRICE STATISTICS/CANADA. STATISTIQUE CANADA. STATISTIQUES DES PRIX DE LA CONSTRUCTION RAPPORT TRIMESTRIEL. see *BUILDING AND CONSTRUCTION—Abstracting, Bibliographies, Statistics*

CANADA. STATISTICS CANADA. CAPITAL EXPENDITURES BY TYPE OF ASSET. see *BUILDING AND CONSTRUCTION—Abstracting, Bibliographies, Statistics*

CANADA. STATISTICS CANADA. HOMEOWNER REPAIR AND RENOVATION EXPENDITURE/CANADA. STATISTIQUE CANADA. DEPENSES SUR LES REPARATIONS ET RENOVATIONS EFFECTUEES PAR LES PROPRIETAIRES DE LOGEMENT AU CANADA. see *BUILDING AND CONSTRUCTION—Abstracting, Bibliographies, Statistics*

B

CANADA. STATISTICS CANADA. MINERAL WOOL INCLUDING FIBROUS GLASS INSULATION/CANADA. STATISTIQUE CANADA. LAINE MINERALE Y COMPRIS LES ISOLANTS EN FIBRE DE VERRE. see *BUILDING AND CONSTRUCTION—Abstracting, Bibliographies, Statistics*

692.8 CAN ISSN 1498-8941
CANADIAN CONTRACTOR; the magazine for builders and renovators. Text in English. 2000. q. free to qualified personnel. adv. **Document type:** *Magazine, Trade.* **Description:** Focused on bringing relevant, in depth information to contractors, renovators and builders in the residential and light commercial building industry in Canada.
Related titles: Online - full text ed.: (from Micromedia ProQuest, ProQuest Information & Learning).
Indexed: ABIn.
Published by: Rogers Media Publishing Ltd, One Mount Pleasant Rd, 11th Fl, Toronto, ON M4Y 2Y5, Canada. TEL 416-764-2000, FAX 416-764-3941, http://www.canadiancontractormagazine.com, http://www.rogers.com. Ed. Robert Gerlsbeck. Pub. Steve Payne.

690.028 CAN
CANADIAN EQUIPMENT RENTALS. Text in English. 2000. q. free to qualified personnel. adv. **Document type:** *Magazine, Trade.* **Description:** Provides information for Canadian contractors about the business of renting and leasing equipment.
Related titles: ◆ Supplement to: Heavy Construction News. ISSN 0017-9426.
Published by: Rogers Media Publishing Ltd, One Mount Pleasant Rd, 11th Fl, Toronto, ON M4Y 2Y5, Canada. TEL 416-764-2000, FAX 416-764-3941, http://www.econstruction.ca/cer, http://www.rogers.com. Ed. Russell Noble. Adv. contact Krista Bradley.

690.028 CAN ISSN 0832-6533
CANADIAN HEAVY EQUIPMENT GUIDE. Text in English. 1986. 9/yr. CND 37.45 domestic; CND 45 in United States. adv. **Description:** Describes new products and industry developments. Industry experts explain the best way to use and maintain heavy equipments.
Published by: Baum Publications Ltd., 201-2323 Boundary Rd, Vancouver, BC V5M 4V8, Canada. TEL 604-291-9900, FAX 604-291-1906, admin@baumpub.com, http://www.baumpub.com. Ed. Len Webster. Adv. contact John F Bleuler. B&W page USD 5,366, color page USD 6,551. Circ: 31,093.

690 CAN ISSN 1495-5709
CANADIAN HOMES AND COTTAGES. Text in English. 1989. 6/yr. CND 31.78 domestic; CND 59.92 foreign (effective 2005). adv. bk.rev. 112 p./no.; back issues avail. **Document type:** *Consumer.* **Description:** Covers building and renovation for residential projects.
Former titles (until 2000): Homes and Cottages (1187-0974); (until 1990): In-Home Show News (1186-6160)
Published by: In-Home Show Ltd., 2650 Meadowvale Blvd., Unit 4, Mississauga, ON L5N 6M5, Canada. TEL 905-567-1440, FAX 905-567-1442, info@homesandcottages.com, http://homesandcottages.com. Ed. Janice E Naisby. Pub., Adv. contact Steven Griffin. Circ: 64,000.

695 CAN ISSN 1489-2367
CANADIAN ROOFING CONTRACTOR & DESIGN. Text in English. q. adv.
Formerly: Canadian Roofing Contractor (0829-3511)
—CISTI.
Published by: Perks Publications Inc., 1735 Bayly St, Ste 7A, Pickering, ON L1W 3G7, Canada. TEL 416-831-4711, FAX 416-831-4725. Ed. Tanja Nowotny. Adv. contact Cathie Fedak. B&W page USD 1,230; trim 11 x 8.5. Circ: 6,000.

690 CHE ISSN 0376-6926
CANTIERI. Text in Italian. m.
Published by: Swiss Society of Builders, Muehlerain 31, Haegendorf, 4614, Switzerland. TEL 062-462215. Ed. Ruedi Moser. Circ: 7,052.

690 ITA ISSN 0393-8220
CANTIERI STRADE COSTRUZIONI. Text in Italian. 1984. m. EUR 80 domestic; EUR 105 in Europe; EUR 130 elsewhere (effective 2005). adv. **Document type:** *Magazine, Trade.* **Description:** Technical and economic news for the building industry.
Indexed: RefZh.
Published by: Gesto Editore Srl, Via Mercato 28, Milan, MI 20121 , Italy. TEL 39-02-8051511, FAX 39-02-89013553, gesto@gestoeditore.it, http://www.http://www.modainitaly.it. Ed. Ferdinando Tagliabue.

690 USA
CAPSULE REPORT. Text in English. m. free to members. **Document type:** *Newsletter, Trade.*
Published by: Master Builders' Association of Western PA/AGC, 2270 Noblestown Rd, Pittsburgh, PA 15205. TEL 412-922-3912, FAX 412-922-3729, jramage@mbawpa.org, http://www.mbawpa.org. Ed. Jon O'Brian.

690 AUS
CARPENTER AND JOINER. Text in English. 1960. irreg.
Published by: (Building Workers' Industrial Union of Australia, Victorian Branch), Industrial Printing and Publicity Co. Ltd., 122 Dover St, Richmond, VIC 3121, Australia. Ed. A Zeeno.

691.3 NLD ISSN 0008-8811
CEMENT; vakblad voor de betonwereld. Text in Dutch. 1949. 8/yr. EUR 80 domestic; EUR 83 in Belgium; EUR 125 elsewhere; EUR 25 to students; EUR 12 newsstand/cover (effective 2005). adv. bk.rev. abstr.; charts; illus. index, cum.index every 5 yrs. **Document type:** *Trade.*
Indexed: CRIA, ConcrAb, ExcerpMed, HRIS, RefZh.
—CISTI, IE, Infotrieve.
Published by: E N C I Media, Postbus 3532, 's Hertogenbosch, 5203 DM, Netherlands. TEL 31-73-6401250, FAX 31-73-6401299, http://www.vakbladcement.nl. Ed. C S Kleinman TEL 31-73-6401231. adv.: B&W page EUR 1,110; 185 x 259. Circ: 3,428.

691.5 HRV ISSN 0008-882X CODEN: CEZAA7
CEMENT; casopis industrije cementa jugoslavije. Text in Croatian; Summaries in English, French. 1957. irreg. USD 20. adv. bk.rev. charts; illus. index.
Indexed: CRIA, CRICC, ChemAb, ConcrAb.
—CASDDS.
Published by: J U C E M A/Association of the Yugoslav Cement and Asbestos-Cement Producers, Prilaz JNA 30, Zagreb, 41000, Croatia. FAX 41-278-101, TELEX 21406 YU CEMA. Ed. S Zuliani. Circ: 650.

692.8 USA ISSN 1533-5178
HD9622.A1
CEMENT AMERICAS. Text in English. 1998. bi-m. free to qualified personnel (effective 2003). adv. back issues avail.; reprints avail. **Document type:** *Magazine, Trade.*
Related titles: Online - full text ed.: (from bigchalk, Florida Center for Library Automation, ProQuest Information & Learning); Supplement(s): Cement Americas Buyers' Guide.
Indexed: ABIn.
—CCC.
Published by: Primedia Business Magazines & Media, Inc. (Subsidiary of: Primedia, Inc.), 330 N Wabash Ave, Ste 2300, Chicago, IL 60611. TEL 312-595-1080, FAX 312-595-0296, inquiries@primediabusiness.com, http://www.cementamericas.com, http://www.primediabusiness.com. Circ: 6,000.

691 GBR ISSN 0958-9465
TA418.9.C6 CODEN: CCOCEG
➤ **CEMENT AND CONCRETE COMPOSITES.** Text in English. 1979. 10/yr. EUR 1,058 in Europe to institutions; JPY 140,600 in Japan to institutions; USD 1,185 to institutions except Europe and Japan (effective 2006). adv. bk.rev. back issues avail.; reprint service avail. from PQC. **Document type:** *Journal, Academic/Scholarly.* **Description:** Designed to reflect current developments and advances being made in the general field of cement-concrete composites technology and in the production, use and performance of cement-based construction materials in general.
Formerly (until 1990): International Journal of Cement Composites and Lightweight Concrete (0262-5075); Formed by the 1981 merger of: International Journal of Cement Composites (0142-095X); International Journal of Lightweight Concrete (0142-0968)
Related titles: Microform ed.: (from PQC); Online - full text ed.: (from EBSCO Publishing, Gale Group, IngentaConnect, ScienceDirect, Swets Information Services).
Indexed: ASCA, ASFA, ApMecR, BrCerAb, C&ISA, CIN, CRIA, CRICC, CerAb, ChemAb, ChemTitl, CivEngAb, ConcrAb, CorrAb, E&CAJ, EMA, ESPM, EngInd, H&SSA, HRIS, IAA, ICEA, Inspec, JOF, M&TEA, MBF, METADEX, MSCI, RAPRA, RICS, SWRA, SolStAb, WAA.
—BLDSC (3098.986000), CASDDS, CISTI, Ei, IDS, IE, Infotrieve, ingenta, Linda Hall. **CCC.**
Published by: Pergamon (Subsidiary of: Elsevier Science & Technology), The Boulevard, Langford Ln, East Park, Kidlington, Oxford OX5 1GB, United Kingdom. TEL 44-1865-843000, FAX 44-1865-843010, http://www.elsevier.com/locate/cemconcomp. Ed. R. N. Swamy. Circ: 550. **Subscr. to:** Elsevier BV, PO Box 211, Amsterdam 1000 AE, Netherlands. nlinfo-f@elsevier.nl, http://www.elsevier.nl.

691 GBR ISSN 0008-8846
TA434 CODEN: CCNRAI
➤ **CEMENT AND CONCRETE RESEARCH.** Text in English, French, German, Russian. 1971. 12/yr. EUR 2,525 in Europe to institutions; JPY 335,400 in Japan to institutions; USD 2,825 elsewhere to institutions; EUR 335 in Europe to qualified personnel; JPY 44,600 in Japan to qualified personnel; USD 375 elsewhere to qualified personnel (effective 2006). adv. bk.rev. back issues avail. **Document type:** *Journal, Academic/Scholarly.* **Description:** Covers research in cement, cement composites, concrete and other allied materials.
Incorporates (1993-1999): Advanced Cement Based Materials (1065-7355)
Related titles: Microfilm ed.: (from PQC); Online - full text ed.: (from EBSCO Publishing, Gale Group, IngentaConnect, ScienceDirect, Swets Information Services).
Indexed: ASCA, ASFA, ApMecR, BrCerAb, C&ISA, CCI, CIN, CRIA, CRICC, CerAb, ChemAb, ChemTitl, CivEngAb, ConcrAb, CorrAb, CurCont, E&CAJ, EMA, ESPM, EngInd, ExcerpMed, H&SSA, HRIS, IAA, ICEA, INIS AtomInd, ISR, Inspec, JOF, M&TEA, MBF, METADEX, MSCI, PetrolAb, RefZh, SCI, SWRA, SoftAbEng, SolStAb, WAA, WRCInf.
—BLDSC (3098.990000), CASDDS, CISTI, Ei, IDS, IE, Infotrieve, ingenta, Linda Hall, PADDS. **CCC.**
Published by: Pergamon (Subsidiary of: Elsevier Science & Technology), The Boulevard, Langford Ln, East Park, Kidlington, Oxford OX5 1GB, United Kingdom. TEL 44-1865-843000, FAX 44-1865-843010, cemcon@psu.edu, http://www.elsevier.com/locate/cemconres. Ed. Karen Scrivener. Circ: 1,500. **Subscr. to:** Elsevier BV, PO Box 211, Amsterdam 1000 AE, Netherlands. TEL 31-20-485-3757, FAX 31-20-485-3432, nlinfo-f@elsevier.nl, http://www.elsevier.nl.

691 DEU
CEMENT INTERNATIONAL. Text in German. 2002. bi-m. EUR 198 domestic; EUR 208 foreign; EUR 98 to students; EUR 35 newsstand/cover (effective 2004). adv. **Document type:** *Magazine, Trade.* **Description:** Reports on the properties, practical application and all aspects of the manufacture of cements and binders.
Published by: Verlag Bau und Technik GmbH, Steinhof 39, Erkrath, 40699, Germany. TEL 49-211-9249932, FAX 49-211-9249955, info@verlagbt.de, http://www.verlagbt.de. Ed. Stefan Deckers. Adv. contact Guenther Jung. B&W page EUR 1,460, color page EUR 2,450; trim 210 x 297. Circ: 3,816 (paid and controlled).

690 USA
CEMENT: LATIN AMERICAN INDUSTRIAL REPORT✶. (Avail. for each of 22 Latin American countries) Text in English. 1985. a. USD 435; per country report.
Published by: Aquino Productions, P O Box 15760, Stamford, CT 06901-0760. Ed. Andres C Aquino.

691.5 GBR ISSN 0008-8889
CEMENT SPECIAL. Text in English. 1961. q. free. charts; illus.; stat.
Published by: Lafarge Aluminous Cement Co., Fondu Works, 730 London Rd, Box 13, Grays, Essex RM20 3NJ, United Kingdom. Circ: 10,000.

693 BEL ISSN 1018-5852
CEMENT STANDARDS OF THE WORLD. Text in English. 1948. irreg., latest 1991. **Document type:** *Trade.* **Description:** Details of cement standards in 112 countries and imported standards used in those countries which do not have their own.
Indexed: ConcrAb.
Published by: Cembureau, Rue d'Arlon 55, Brussels, 1040, Belgium. TEL 32-2-2341011, FAX 32-2-2304720.

691.5 POL ISSN 1425-8129 CODEN: CMWGAW
CEMENT, WAPNO, BETON. Text in Polish. 1929. bi-m. EUR 121 foreign (effective 2005). adv. bk.rev. charts; illus.; mkt.; tr.lit. index.
Former titles (until 1996): Cement, Wapno, Gips (0008-8897); (until 1950): Cement (0366-7057)
Indexed: CEABA, CRIA, ChemAb, ConcrAb.
—CASDDS, CISTI.
Published by: Spolka Cement - Wapno - Beton, ul Lubelska 29, Krakow, 30003, Poland. cwb@polskicement.com.pl, http://www.polskicement.com.pl. Circ: 700. **Dist. by:** Ars Polona, Krakowskie Przedmiescie 7, Warsaw, Poland. TEL 48-22-9263914, FAX 48-22-9265334, arspolona@arspolona.com.pl, http://www.arspolona.com.pl.

691 ARG
CEMENTO. Text in Spanish. 1967. q. free. adv. bk.rev. bibl.; charts; illus. **Document type:** *Bulletin.* **Description:** Promotes and disseminates information about Portland cement and its applications.
Formerly (until 1994): Boletin del Cemento Portland (0523-9095)

Indexed: CRIA, CRICC.
Published by: Instituto del Cemento Portland Argentino, San Martin, 1137, Capital Federal, Buenos Aires C1004AAW, Argentina. TEL 54-114-5767828, FAX 54-114-5767199, biblos@icpa.com.ar. Eds. Roberto Torrent, Ignacio Carlos A. Brunatti. Pub., Adv. contact Analia Wlazlo. R&Ps Ignacio Carlos A. Brunatti, Roberto Torrent. B&W page USD 1,600, color page USD 2,300; trim 280 x 200. Circ: 5,000.

691   ESP   ISSN 0008-8919
TA680   CODEN: CMHOAF
CEMENTO - HORMIGON; revista tecnica. Text in Spanish. 1929. m. EUR 145 domestic; EUR 190 in Europe and Latinamerica; EUR 210 elsewhere (effective 2005). adv. bk.rev. abstr.; bibl.; charts; illus.; stat. index. Document type: Trade.
Supersedes (in 1936): Cemento (1139-3343)
Indexed: CIN, ChemAb, ChemTitl, IECT, RefZh.
—CASDDS, CINDOC, CISTI, IE, Infotrieve. CCC.
Published by: Ediciones Cemento S.L., Maignon, 26, Barcelona, 08024, Spain. TEL 34-93-2844318, FAX 34-93-2108082, edicem@arrakis.es, http://www.cemento-hormigon.com/. Ed. Patricio Palomar. Pub., Adv. contact Carlos Palomar. Circ: 4,000.

CENSO DA CONSTRUCAO. see BUILDING AND CONSTRUCTION—Abstracting, Bibliographies, Statistics

690   IND
CENTRAL BUILDING RESEARCH INSTITUTE. BUILDING RESEARCH NOTE. Text in English. 1963; N.S. 1982. irreg. INR 5 (effective 2003). Document type: Newsletter, Academic/Scholarly. Description: Each issue covers a specific topic of research at the CBRI.
Formerly (until 1982): Central Building Research Institute. Building Digest (0557-319X)
Published by: Central Building Research Institute, C B R I, C S I R-INDIA, Roorkee, Uttaranchal, India. TEL 91-1332-272243, FAX 91-1332-272272, director@cbrimail.com, http://www.cbri.org. Ed. A K Agarwal.

CENTRAL BUILDING RESEARCH INSTITUTE. PUBLICATIONS INDEX. see BUILDING AND CONSTRUCTION—Abstracting, Bibliographies, Statistics

690   ESP   ISSN 1576-1118
CENTRO DE INFORMATIVO DE LA CONSTRUCTION.
Abbreviated title: C I C. Text in Spanish. 1963. m. adv. bk.rev. Document type: Trade.
Formerly (until 1997): C I C Informacion (0211-9919)
Indexed: IECT.
—CINDOC.
Published by: Centro Informativo de la Construccion, Ave de Manoferas, 44, 3a Plana, Madrid, 28050, Spain. TEL 34-91-2972000, FAX 34-91-2972154, redaccion@cicinformacion.com, http://www.tecnipublicaciones.com/sumarios/default.asp, http://www.cicinformacion.com/. Ed. Ferran Cabellos Romero. adv.: color page EUR 1,720; trim 215 x 105. Circ: 20,000.

CERAMAGAZINE; le magazine des professionnels du carreau et de la pierre naturelle. see ARCHITECTURE

691   ITA   ISSN 0392-4890
CERAMICA PER L'EDILIZIA INTERNATIONAL. Cover title: C E Ceramica per l'Edilizia International. Text in English, Italian. 1967. q. EUR 42 domestic; EUR 96 foreign (effective 2004). illus. Document type: Magazine, Trade. Description: Provides information on manufacturing companies, distributors, products, technologies, events, and initiatives in the ceramic building materials sector.
Formerly (until vol.13, no.59, 1979): Ceramica Italiana nell'Edilizia (0009-028X)
Related titles: ◆ Supplement(s): Fashion Ceramic Tiles. ISSN 1123-8135.
Indexed: BrCerAb, C&ISA, CerAb, CorrAb, E&CAJ, EMA, SolStAb, WAA.
Published by: Gruppo Editoriale Faenza Editrice SpA, Via Pier de Crescenzi 44, Faenza, RA 48018, Italy. TEL 39-0546-670411, FAX 39-0546-660440, info@faenza.com, http://www.faenza.com. Ed. Alda Hauner. R&P Luisa Teston. Adv. contact Elvio Neri. Circ: 16,000.

690   BEL
CHAMBRE SYNDICALE DE LA CONSTRUCTION. BULLETIN.
Text in French. 22/yr. adv. Document type: Bulletin.
Address: Gallerie de la Sauvenier 5, Liege, 4000, Belgium. Circ: 2,400.

690   FRA   ISSN 0009-1596
CHANTIERS COOPERATIFS. Text in French. 1948. m. adv. bibl.; illus.
Published by: Federation Nationale des Cooperatives Ouvrieres de Production du Batiment des Travaux Publics et des Activites Annexes, 88 rue de Courcelles, Paris, 75008, France. TEL 33-1-55651220, FAX 33-1-55651229. Ed. Didier Durr. Pub. Maurice Lemainque.

690   FRA   ISSN 0397-4650
CHANTIERS DE FRANCE; l'officiel des materiels de travaux publics et de batiment. Text in French. 1962. 10/yr. EUR 56.41 domestic; EUR 83.85 in Europe; EUR 129.58 elsewhere (effective 2002). adv. charts; illus.; tr.lit. Document type: Newspaper, Trade.
—CISTI.
Published by: (Societe Technique d'Editions pour l'Entreprise), Groupe Chantiers de France, Bord de Seine, 202 quai de Clichy, Clichy, 92110, France. TEL 33-1-47561723, FAX 33-1-47561432, http://www.chantiersdefrance.com. Ed., Pub. Arlette Surchamp. Adv. contact Sophie Yon. Circ: 10,000.

690 200   FRA   ISSN 0009-160X
LES CHANTIERS DU CARDINAL. Text in French. 1963. q. adv. illus. Document type: Bulletin. Description: Presents construction and maintenance of churches in Ile-de-France.
Published by: Chantiers du Cardinal, 106 rue du Bac, Paris, Cedex 7 75341, France. TEL 33-1-42224686. Ed. Jean Thizon. Circ: 60,000.

690   FRA   ISSN 1149-1051
CHARPENTE - METALLERIE - SERRURERIE. Short title: C M S. Text in French. 1972. bi-m. adv. Document type: Trade. Description: Provides a technical review of metalwork and PVC in the building trade.
Former titles: Charpente - Menuiserie - Serrurerie; (until 1989): Nouveau Journal de Charpente, Menuiserie, Metallique, Serrurerie (0291-8366)
Published by: Edial Editions, 126 rue du Temple, Paris, 75003, France. TEL 33-1-44788778, FAX 33-1-44788779, cms.redaction@edial.fr, http://www.edial.fr. Ed. Jan Meyer. Pub. Nicole Bergmann. Adv. contact Thierry Meunier. Circ: 10,000.

690   AUS   ISSN 1324-0900
CHARTERED BUILDING PROFESSIONAL. Text in English. 1972. q. AUD 20 domestic; AUD 30 foreign (effective 2000). adv. Document type: Newsletter. Description: Provides new about the institute and matters relevant to the building profession in Australia.
Formerly (until May 1995): Chartered Builder (0311-1903); Which incorporated (1988-1990): A I B Newsletter (1032-8467)
Indexed: BldManAb.
Published by: Australian Institute of Building, 217 Northbourne Ave, Turner, ACT 2612, Australia. FAX 61-2-6248-9030. Ed., Adv. contact David Green. R&P Don Debus TEL 61-2-6247-7433. Circ: 3,000 (controlled)

CHARTERED INSTITUTE OF BUILDING. CONSTRUCTION INFORMATION QUARTERLY. see BUILDING AND CONSTRUCTION—Abstracting, Bibliographies, Statistics

CHARTERED INSTITUTE OF PUBLIC FINANCE AND ACCOUNTANCY. DIRECT SERVICE ORGANISATION STATISTICS. ACTUALS. see BUILDING AND CONSTRUCTION—Abstracting, Bibliographies, Statistics

CHECKLIST SUPPLEMENT AND ILLUSTRATIVE FINANCIAL STATEMENTS FOR CONSTRUCTION CONTRACTORS. see BUSINESS AND ECONOMICS—Accounting

690   USA
CHICAGO HOME BOOK. Text in English. a. USD 39.95 (effective 2001). Description: A comprehensive, hand-on guide to building, decorating, furnishing and landscaping in the Chicago area.
Published by: The Ashley Group, 1350 E Touhy Ave, Des Plaines, IL 60018. TEL 847-390-2821, FAX 847-390-2902, pcasper@cahners.com, http://www.homebook.com, http://www.theashleygroup.com. Ed., Pub. Paul A Casper. Circ: 20,000.

690   USA   ISSN 1085-1879
CHICAGO METRO CONSTRUCTION NEWS WEEKLY (ENGINEERING EDITION). Text in English. 1995. w. adv. Document type: Newsletter, Trade. Description: Provides information on what jobs are coming up for bid or negotiation.
Related titles: Online - full text ed.
Published by: Mcgraw-Hill Construction Dodge (Subsidiary of: McGraw-Hill Construction Information Group), 148 Princeton-Hightstown Rd, Hightstown, NJ 08520. TEL 800-393-6343, http://www.dodgeconstructionpublications.com.

690   USA   ISSN 1085-1887
CHICAGO METRO CONSTRUCTION NEWS WEEKLY (GENERAL BUILDING EDITION). Text in English. 1995. w. adv. Document type: Newsletter, Trade. Description: Provides information on what jobs are coming up for bid or negotiation.
Related titles: Online - full text ed.
Published by: Mcgraw-Hill Construction Dodge (Subsidiary of: McGraw-Hill Construction Information Group), 148 Princeton-Hightstown Rd, Hightstown, NJ 08520. TEL 800-393-6343, http://www.dodgeconstructionpublications.com.

691   JPN   ISSN 1341-6731
                                        CODEN: COKHFS
CHICHIBU ONODA KENKYU HOKOKU/ONODA CEMENT COMPANY. JOURNAL OF RESEARCH. Text in English. q.?.
Formerly (until vol.45, 1994): Onoda Kenkyu Hokoku (0385-9665)
Indexed: BrCerAb.

—CISTI.
Published by: Onoda Cement Co. Ltd., 2-4-2 Osaku, Sakura-shi, Chiba-ken 285-0802, Japan.

CHIESA OGGI. see ARCHITECTURE

CHILE. INSTITUTO NACIONAL DE ESTADISTICAS. EDIFICACION. see BUILDING AND CONSTRUCTION—Abstracting, Bibliographies, Statistics

CHINESE MARKETS FOR BUILDING MATERIALS. see BUSINESS AND ECONOMICS—Marketing And Purchasing

690   BEL   ISSN 0009-6032
LA CHRONIQUE. Text in French. 1945. w. BEF 7,650 (effective 2000). adv.
Published by: S.A. Orena, Bd Lambermont 140, Bruxelles, 1030, Belgium. TEL 32-2-216-2065, FAX 32-2-245-2837. Circ: 21,900.

690   FRA
CHRONIQUE DES TRAVAUX PUBLICS ET PARTICULIERS. Text in French. w.
Address: 268 bd. Clemenceau, Marcq-en-Baroeul, 59707, France. TEL 20-72-87-14, FAX 20-45-93-28, TELEX 810 946. Ed. Gerard Ferlin. Circ: 3,750.

CHURCH BUSINESS. PRODUCTS & TECHNOLOGY. see RELIGIONS AND THEOLOGY

690   GBR
CI-NET EUROPEAN CONSTRUCTION FORECAST. Text in English. a. GBP 195. Document type: Trade.
Published by: National Council of Building Material Producers, 26 Store St, London, WC1E 7BT, United Kingdom. TEL 44-171-323-3770, FAX 44-171-323-0307, awilen@building-materials.org.uk. Ed. A Wilen.

691   FRA   ISSN 0397-006X
TA2   CODEN: CBPCDD
CIMENTS, BETONS, PLATRES, CHAUX. Text in English, French. 1903. bi-m. adv. bk.rev. abstr.; bibl.; charts; illus. index. Document type: Trade. Description: Covers cement, gypsum and lime.
Formerly (until 1974): Revue des Materiaux de Construction et de Travaux Publics (0035-2144)
Indexed: A&ATA, BrCerAb, CRIA, CRICC, ChemAb, ConcrAb, ExcerpMed, INIS AtomInd, RefZh.
—BLDSC (3198.405000), CASDDS, CISTI, IE, Infotrieve, ingenta, Linda Hall. CCC.
Published by: Septima, 14 rue Falguiere, Paris, 75015, France. TEL 33-01-44384800, FAX 33-01-44384809, abo@septima.fr, http://www.batiactu.com. Ed. C Boisaubert. adv.: B&W page EUR 719.56, color page EUR 1,428.45; bleed 210 x 295. Circ: 1,650.

CITY COMMERCIAL - RESIDENTIAL CODES. see HOUSING AND URBAN PLANNING

690 621.3   USA
CITY OF CHICAGO BUILDING CODE. Text in English. 1951. a. USD 217 (effective 2001). adv. Document type: Government. Description: Presents a compilation of Chicago regulations governing structural and mechanical requirements for new and existing construction.
Published by: Index Publishing Corporation, 415 N State St, Chicago, IL 60610. TEL 312-644-7800, FAX 312-644-4255. Ed. Joanne Reed. Pub., R&P, Adv. contact Linda Seggelke TEL 312-644-6977. Circ: 2,037.

690   USA
CLARK REPORTS. Text in English. 1962. 3/w. price varies. Document type: Newsletter.
Published by: Reed Construction Market Data Group, 30 Technology Pkwy., S., Ste.1 00, Norcross, GA 30092. TEL 800-322-0255, info@clarkreports.com, http://www.clarkereports.com.

CLASSIC HOUSE PLANS. see INTERIOR DESIGN AND DECORATION

647.9   USA
CLEANING & MAINTENANCE MANAGEMENT. Text in English. 1927. m. USD 74 (effective 2005). adv. charts; illus. index. back issues avail. Document type: Magazine, Trade. Description: Aimed at directors, managers, administrators, supervisors and executives in charge of institutional, industrial and commercial building cleaning services.
Former titles: Cleaning Management (1051-5720); National Custodian (0027-9099)
Indexed: P&BA, RILM.
—CCC.
Published by: N T P Media, 13 Century Hill Dr, Latham, NY 12110-2197. TEL 518-783-1281, FAX 518-783-1386, emeehan@ntpmedia.com, csanford@ntpinc.com, http://cmmonline.com, http://www.ntpinc.com. Ed. Eileen Meehan. Pubs. Kevin Hart, Matt Gallinger. Adv. contact Micah Ogburn. B&W page USD 3,550, color page USD 4,685; trim 7.8 x 10.8. Circ: 40,000 (controlled).

B

690.24 GBR
CLEANING MAINTENANCE AND SUPPORT SERVICES. Text in English. 1953. m. (11/yr.). GBP 69; GBP 95 foreign (effective 1999). adv. illus. **Document type:** *Trade.*
Former titles: Cleaning Maintenance; Cleaning Maintenance and Big Buildings Management (0143-0963); Which incorporated: Buildings Maintenance and Services (0308-5651)
Indexed: PROMT, RICS, WTA.
Published by: Turret R A I plc, Armstrong House, 38 Market Sq, Uxbridge, Middx UB8 1TG, United Kingdom. TEL 44-1895-454545, FAX 44-1895-454647. Ed. Neil Nixon. Circ: 13,000.

690 331.8 USA ISSN 0009-8779
CLEVELAND CITIZEN. Text in English. 1891. m. USD 7 (effective 2005). adv. back issues avail. **Document type:** *Newspaper.* **Description:** Contains news of interest to union members in the building & construction trades.
Related titles: Microfilm ed.
Published by: (Cleveland Building and Construction Trades Council), Citizen Publishing Co., Inc., 2012 W 25th St, Ste 900, Cleveland, OH 44113. TEL 216-861-4283, FAX 216-861-4282, citizenpub@citizenpublishing.com. Ed., R&P William G Obbagy. Adv. contact Terri A Andrisin. page USD 756. Circ: 10,600. Wire service: AP.

690 697 ITA ISSN 1124-2612
CLIMA CASA; piu comfort alla vita di ogni giorno. Text in Italian. 1995. m. adv. **Description:** Covers the residential air-conditioning and heating industry.
Related titles: ♦ Supplement to: R C I. Riscaldamento Climatizzazione Idronica. ISSN 1120-8457.
Published by: Tecniche Nuove SpA, Via Eritrea 21, Milan, MI 201, Italy. TEL 39-02-390901, FAX 39-02-7570364, info@tecnichenuove.com, http://www.tecnichenuove.com. Ed. Enzo Guaglione. Pub. Giuseppe Nardella. Adv. contact Sergio Savona. Circ: 30,000.

690 NLD ISSN 0010-0064
COBOUW; vakdagblad voor de bouwwereld. Text in Dutch. 1856. d. (Mon.-Fri.). EUR 498 domestic; EUR 833 foreign (effective 2005). adv. illus. **Document type:** *Newspaper, Trade.* **Description:** News on the Dutch building and construction fields: civil and utility building, earth and soil removal, road and waterway works.
Incorporates (1976-2002): Renovatie en Onderhoud (0922-4114)
Indexed: KES.
—IE.
Published by: Sdu Uitgevers bv, Postbus 20025, The Hague, 2500 EA, Netherlands. TEL 31-70-3789911, FAX 31-70-3854321, cobouw@sdu.nl, sdu@sdu.nl, http://www.cobouw.nl, http://www.sdu.nl/. Ed. Irwin Kraal. Pub. Nic Louis. Circ: 16,560. **Subscr. to:** Postbus 20014, The Hague 2500 EA, Netherlands. TEL 31-70-3789880, FAX 31-70-3789783.

COCKSHAW'S CONSTRUCTION LABOR NEWS & OPINION. see *BUSINESS AND ECONOMICS—Labor And Industrial Relations*

690 340 USA ISSN 0735-9330
KFO459.A1
CODE NEWS. Text in English. 1981. bi-m. looseleaf. USD 175. **Document type:** *Newsletter.* **Description:** Covers construction law and building code enforcement in Ohio.
Published by: Banks - Baldwin Law Publishing Co., PO Box 318063, Cleveland, OH 44131-8063. TEL 216-520-5600, FAX 216-520-5655. Ed. David S Collins.

690 FRA ISSN 0758-7317
CODE PERMANENT: CONSTRUCTION ET URBANISME. Text in French. 2 base vols. plus m. updates. looseleaf. EUR 250 base vol(s). (effective 2004). **Description:** For architects, lawyers, decorators, entrepreneurs, appraisers, construction companies and building supervisors whose work involves urbanization.
Published by: Editions Legislatives, 80 Avenue de la Marne, Montrouge, Cedex 92546, France. TEL 33-1-40923636, FAX 33-1-40923663, infocom@editions-legislatives.fr, http://www.editions-legislatives.fr. Pub. Michel Vaillant.

CODES & STANDARDS. see *HOUSING AND URBAN PLANNING*

690 USA ISSN 1546-9964
COLORADO CONSTRUCTION. Text in English. w. USD 40 (effective 2004). adv. **Document type:** *Newsletter, Trade.*
Former titles (until 2003): F W Dodge Colorado Construction (1537-5072); (until 198?): Colorado Construction Weekly (1071-0264); Colorado Construction News (1041-1976); (until 198?): Construction Bulletin and Trades Report. Colorado (0889-5287)
Related titles: Online - full text ed.: (from LexisNexis, ProQuest Information & Learning).
—CCC.
Published by: Mcgraw-Hill Construction Dodge (Subsidiary of: McGraw-Hill Construction Information Group), 2000 S Colorado Blvd, Tower 1, Ste #2000, Denver, CO 80222. TEL 303-756-9995, 800-393-6343, FAX 303-756-4465, http://www.coloradoconstructionmag.com/, http://www.dodgeconstructionpublications.com. Ed. Kim Shadwell TEL 303-584-6724. Adv. contact Phil Kummer TEL 303-584-6717.

690 ITA ISSN 1127-1922
COME RISTRUTTURARE LA CASA. Text in Italian. 1998. bi-m. EUR 16 domestic; EUR 46 foreign (effective 2004). **Document type:** *Magazine, Consumer.* **Description:** All about home improvements and remodeling.
Published by: Gruppo Editoriale Faenza Editrice SpA, Via Pier de Crescenzi 44, Faenza, RA 48018, Italy. TEL 39-0546-670411, FAX 39-0546-660440, info@faenza.com, http://www.faenza.com.

690 622 USA
COMIMEX✱. Text in English. 1991. m. adv.
Published by: Construccion Mexicana, Inc., 4913 SW 75th Ave, Miami, FL 33155-4440. TEL 305-670-4818, FAX 305-670-4820. Ed. Martha Oliveros. Circ: 8,384.

690 720 USA ISSN 1527-5604
TH4311
COMMERCIAL BUILDING. Text in English. 1999; N.S. 2001 (Oct.). m. free. adv. **Document type:** *Magazine, Trade.* **Description:** Covers business, management and legal/code issues, as well as concrete/steel structural systems, roofing, electrical systems, interior construction, mechanical systems, computers/software and tools/equipment.
Published by: Zweig White Information Services, 5900 Windward Pkwy, Ste 450, Alpharetta, GA 30005 . TEL 770-664-2812, FAX 770-664-7319, http://www.commbuilding.com/, http://www.mercormedia.com/. Pub. Daniel Pels. Adv. contact Tony Arnone TEL 312-867-9812.

690 USA
▼ **COMMERCIAL BUILDING PRODUCTS.** Text in English. 2003. bi-m. free in US & Canada to qualified personnel; USD 70 elsewhere (effective 2005); USD 24 per issue (effective 2004). adv. **Document type:** *Magazine, Trade.*
Published by: ConSource LLC, 1300 S Grove Ave, Ste 105, Barrington, IL 60010. TEL 847-382-8100, FAX 847-304-8603, jlosh@cbpmagazine.com, http://www.cbpmagazine.com. Pub. Jim Losh TEL 847-382-8100 ext 111. Adv. contact Tom Kavooras TEL 847-382-8100 ext 113. B&W page USD 5,560; trim 10.5 x 13.2. Circ: 52,000.

690 USA
COMMERCIAL, INSTITUTIONAL, LIGHT INDUSTRIAL BUILDING COST GUIDE. Text in English. q. USD 103 (effective 1999). **Description:** Aims to assist insurance, appraisal, and assessment industries to estimate the replacement cost of commercial, institutional, and light industrial buildings in the U.S.
Published by: E.H. Boeckh, Ed. & Pub. (Subsidiary of: Thomson Publishing Corp.), 2885 S Calhoun Rd, Box 510291, New Berlin, WI 53151-0291. TEL 414-780-2800, FAX 414-780-0306, http://www.boeckh.com. R&P E H Boeckh.

690 USA
COMMERCIAL SQUARE FOOT BUILDING COSTS. Text in English. 1991. a. USD 54.95 (effective 2001). **Document type:** *Trade.* **Description:** Provides buildings cost data for preliminary planning and conceptual estimating. "Square Foot Cost" section has complete building costs by square foot of floor area for 65 different building occupancies. "Functional Assembly Costs" section contains details on alternative components. Also includes ADA and landscape sections.
Published by: Saylor Publications, Inc., 9420 Topanga Canyon Blvd, Ste 203, Chatsworth, CA 91311. TEL 818-718-5966, FAX 818-718-8024, saylor@pacificnet.net. Ed., R&P Stanley J Strychaz.

690.028 ITA ISSN 1594-8161
IL COMMERCIO EDILE. Text in Italian. 1980. m. (in 2 vols.). EUR 45 domestic; EUR 85, EUR 125 in Europe (effective 2005). adv. **Document type:** *Magazine, Trade.* **Description:** Deals with machinery and equipment used in the building industry.
Formerly (until 2002): Il Commercio Edile. Materiali e Tecnologie (1129-5597); Which superseded in part (in 1999): Il Commercio Edile (1126-8808)
Published by: Tecniche Nuove SpA, Via Eritrea 21, Milan, MI 201, Italy. TEL 39-02-390901, FAX 39-02-7570364, commercioedile@tecnichenuove.com, info@tecnichenuove.com, http://www.tecnichenuove.com/epages/tecnichenuove.storefront/4309d7a9010431202740c0a80105058c/Product/Variation/CE&2D2. Ed. Roberto Anghinoni. Pub. Giuseppe Nardella. Adv. contact Sergio Savona. Circ: 15,000.

681.3 DEU ISSN 0932-5875
COMPUTER SPEZIAL. Text in German. 1986. 2/yr. adv. **Document type:** *Magazine, Trade.*
Published by: Bauverlag BV GmbH (Subsidiary of: Springer Science+Business Media), Avenwedderstr 55, Guetersloh, 33311, Germany. TEL 49-5241-802119, FAX 49-5241-809582, ulrike.mattern@springer-sbm.com, http://www.bauverlag.de. adv.: B&W page EUR 5,380, color page EUR 7,310. Circ: 79,298 (controlled).

690 NZL ISSN 1174-8540
CONCRETE; journal of the cement & concrete association of New Zealand. Variant title: New Zealand Concrete. Text in English. 1957. bi-m. NZD 72. adv. bk.rev. illus.; stat.; tr.lit. index. back issues avail. **Document type:** *Trade.* **Description:** Covers research, development and marketing of concrete, concrete products, allied services, and company news and contains profiles on prominent industry personalities.
Formerly (until 1999): New Zealand Concrete Construction (0549-0219)
Indexed: CRIA, CRICC, ChemAb, ConcrAb, EngInd, HRIS, JOF.
—BLDSC (3399.675000), CISTI, IE, ingenta. **CCC.**
Published by: (Cement and Concrete Research Association of New Zealand), A G M Publishing Ltd., Newmarket, Private Bag 99 915, Auckland, 1031, New Zealand. TEL 64-9-8464068, FAX 64-9-8468742. Ed. Barbara Glenie. Pub., R&P Robin Beckett. Adv. contact Stephaniie Watson. Circ: 1,300.

691 624 GBR ISSN 0010-5317
TA680 CODEN: CCRTAA
CONCRETE (LONDON). Text in English. 1966. 10/yr. GBP 115 domestic; GBP 145 in Europe; GBP 160 elsewhere (effective 2005). adv. bk.rev. charts; illus. index. reprint service avail. from PQC. **Document type:** *Journal, Trade.* **Description:** Features technical articles on developments in concrete materials and technology, project reports, news of conferences and events, and concrete society activities.
Incorporates: Concrete Works International (0262-4761); Which was formerly (until 1982): Precast Concrete (0010-5325); (until 1970): Concrete Building and Concrete Products; Formed by the merger of (1906-1966): Concrete and Construction Engineering (0366-550X); (1962-1966): Structural Concrete (0585-4369); Which was formerly: Reinforced Concerete News
Related titles: Microform ed.: (from PQC); Online - full text ed.: (from ProQuest Information & Learning).
Indexed: ABIn, AIAP, API, ApMecR, BrTechI, CRIA, CRICC, ChemAb, CivEngAb, ConcrAb, ESPM, EngInd, ExcerpMed, GeotechAb, H&SSA, HRIS, ICEA, M&TEA, PROMT, SWRA, SoftAbEng.
—BLDSC (3399.600000), CASDDS, CISTI, Ei, IE, Infotrieve, ingenta, Linda Hall. **CCC.**
Published by: The Concrete Society, Riverside House, 4 Meadows Business Park, Station Approach, Blackwater, Camberley, Surrey GU17 9AB, United Kingdom. TEL 44-1276-607140, FAX 44-1276-607141, subscriptions@concrete.org.uk, concsoc@concrete.org.uk, http://www.concrete.org.uk/cj_subscriptions.asp. Ed. Neil Watson. R&P Nick Clarke. Adv. contact Mrs. Jackie Louch TEL 44-1939-251502. Circ: 6,500 (paid).

691.3 USA
CONCRETE & MASONRY CONSTRUCTION PRODUCTS. Text in English. 2002. bi-m. free to qualified personnel (effective 2005). adv. **Document type:** *Newspaper, Trade.* **Description:** Contains information on services and products available to concrete and masonry contractors.
Published by: Hanley-Wood, LLC (Subsidiary of: J.P. Morgan Chase & Co.), One Thomas Circle, NW, Ste 600, Washington, DC 20005-5701. TEL 202-452-0800, FAX 202-785-1974, tjackson@hanleywood.com, http://www.hanleywood.com. adv.: color page USD 5,190; trim 9.8 x 12.5. Circ: 35,000 (paid and controlled).

666.893 691 USA ISSN 1545-4193
CONCRETE CONCEPTS. Text in English. 2002. 8/m. adv. **Document type:** *Magazine, Trade.* **Description:** Covers the critical issues contractors face, such as finding ways to work smarter, providing quality workmanship and maintaining solid safety programs to help control overhead.
Related titles: Online - full text ed.: (from Gale Group, ProQuest Information & Learning).
—CCC.
Published by: Cygnus Business Media, Inc., 33 Inverness Center Pkwy, 2nd Fl, Birmingham, AL 35242. TEL 205-988-9708, 800-366-0676, FAX 205-987-3237, http://www.concreteconcepts.com, http://www.cygnusb2b.com/. Ed. Ashley Kizzire. Pub. Ed Bauer. adv.: B&W page USD 2,928; trim 7.875 x 10.75.

691.3 USA ISSN 1533-7316
TA680 CODEN: ABCCET
CONCRETE CONSTRUCTION. Text in English. 1956. m. USD 30 domestic; USD 39 in Canada & Mexico; USD 93 elsewhere (effective 2005). adv. bk.rev. charts; illus.; tr.lit. cum.index. back issues avail.; reprints avail. **Document type:** *Magazine, Trade.* **Description:** Contains information on the design, placement, specification and utilization of concrete.
Former titles (until Nov.1999): Aberdeen's Concrete Construction (1051-5526); (until 1990): Concrete Construction (0010-5333)
Related titles: Microfilm ed.: (from PQC); Online - full text ed.: (from Florida Center for Library Automation, Gale Group, H.W. Wilson, O C L C Online Computer Library Center, Inc., ProQuest Information & Learning).
Indexed: AS&TI, CRIA, CRICC, CivEngAb, ConcrAb, EEA, EngInd, HRIS, ICEA, ISMEC, ISR, JOF, SoftAbEng.

—BLDSC (3401.100000), CASDDS, CISTI, Ei, IE, ingenta, Linda Hall. **CCC.**
Published by: Hanley-Wood, LLC (Subsidiary of: J.P. Morgan Chase & Co.), 426 S Westgate St, Addison, IL 60101. TEL 630-543-0870, FAX 630-543-3112, http://www.concreteconstruction.net, http://www.hanleywood.com. Ed. William D Palmer Jr. TEL 303-823-8284. Circ: 73,580 (paid).

691.3 IND ISSN 0010-5341
CONCRETE CONSTRUCTION AND ARCHITECTURE. Text in English. 1968. m. INR 40. adv.
Published by: Pandeya Publications, Block F, 105-C New Alipore, Kolkata, West Bengal 700 053, India. Ed. L K Pandeya. Adv. contact O N Pandeya. B&W page INR 500, color page INR 1,100; trim 280 x 220.

693 666.893 GBR ISSN 1475-9438 CODEN: CEPAET
CONCRETE ENGINEERING. Text in English. 1985. q. GBP 40 domestic; GBP 44, EUR 70 foreign (effective 2003). adv. back issues avail. **Document type:** *Journal, Trade.* **Description:** Manufacture, production, application, appearance, and function of concrete and concrete repair from international authors.
Former titles (until 2001: Concrete Engineering International (1460-5856); (until 1997): Construction Repair (0967-0726); (until 1992): International Journal of Construction Maintenance and Repair (0959-5090); (until 1990): Construction Repair (0951-0346); (until 1987): Construction Repair and Maintenance (0268-3288)
Indexed: AIAP, BioDAb, CRIA, Englnd, WSCA.
—BLDSC (3401.280000), CISTI, Ei, IE, ingenta, Linda Hall. **CCC.**
Published by: The Concrete Society, Riverside House, 4 Meadows Business Park, Station Approach, Blackwater, Camberley, Surrey GU17 9AB, United Kingdom. TEL 44-1276-607140, FAX 44-1276-607141, subscriptions@concrete.org.uk, concsoc@concrete.org.uk, http://www.concrete.org.uk. Ed., R&P Nick Clarke. Adv. contact Mrs. Jackie Louch TEL 44-1939-251502. Circ: 4,500.

691.3 JPN ISSN 0919-3979
CONCRETE ENGINEERING NEWS✶. Text in Japanese. 1968. q. **Document type:** *Trade.*
Formerly (until 1992): Doro to Konkurito - Road and Concrete (0285-6018)
Published by: Japan Cement Association, c/o JCA Secretariat, Shuwa-sakurabashi Bldg., 4-5-4, Hatchobori, Chuo-ku, Tokyo, 104-0032, Japan. TEL 81-3-35232704, FAX 81-3-35232700, international@jcassoc.or.jp, http://www.jcassoc.or.jp/index.html. Circ: 2,600.

691.3 AUS
CONCRETE IN AUSTRALIA. Text in English. q. adv. **Document type:** *Trade.* **Description:** Contains news items and articles of interest to persons in the building and construction industry.
Published by: (Concrete Institute of Australia), Engineers Australia Pty. Ltd., 2 Ernest St, PO Box 588, Crows Nest, NSW 2065, Australia. TEL 61-2-94381533, FAX 61-2-94385934, ea.editorial@eol.ieaust.org.au, http://members.australis.net.au/~engineer. Ed. Bob Jackson. Adv. contact Maria Mamone. Circ: 2,000.

691.3 USA
TA680 CODEN: CIDCD2
➤ **CONCRETE INTERNATIONAL.** Text in English. 1979. m. USD 139 (effective 2005). adv. bk.rev.; software rev.; video rev. abstr. 88 p./no.; back issues avail. **Document type:** *Journal, Academic/Scholarly.* **Description:** Publishes current reports on concrete, products, and materials related to concrete.
Formerly: Concrete International - Design and Construction (0162-4075)
Related titles: Fax ed.; Microfiche ed.
Indexed: AJEE, AS&TI, BrCerAb, C&ISA, CIN, CRIA, CRICC, CerAb, ChemAb, ChemTitl, CivEngAb, ConcrAb, CorrAb, E&CAJ, EEA, EMA, Englnd, HRIS, IAA, JOF, M&TEA, MBF, METADEX, SolStAb, WAA.
—BLDSC (3402.050000), CASDDS, CISTI, Ei, IE, ingenta, Linda Hall. **CCC.**
Published by: American Concrete Institute, PO Box 9094, Farmington, MI 48333. TEL 248-848-3700, FAX 248-848-3701, webmaster@aci-int.org, http://www.aci-int.org. Ed. Rex C Donahey. Pub. Ward R Malisch. Adv. contact Jeff Rhodes. B&W page USD 2,470, color page USD 3,690; trim 8.13 x 10.88. Circ: 20,000.

691.3 USA
CONCRETE MASONRY DESIGNS. Text in English. q. adv. back issues avail. **Document type:** *Magazine, Trade.*
Published by: National Concrete Masonry Association, 13750 Sunrise Valley Dr., Herndon, VA 20171-4662. TEL 703-713-1900, FAX 703-713-1910, ncma@ncma.org, http://ncma.org. adv.: color page USD 4,000; bleed 8.5 x 10.75.

666.893 USA
▼ **CONCRETE MONTHLY**; news from the cement and concrete industries. Text in English. 2003. m. USD 27 domestic; USD 65 foreign; free to qualified personnel (effective 2005). adv. **Document type:** *Newspaper, Trade.*
Published by: Publications & Communications, Inc., 11675 Jollyville Rd Ste 150, Austin, TX 78759. TEL 512-250-9023, FAX 512-331-3900, concretemonthly@pcinews.com, subscriptions@pcinews.com, http://www.concretemonthly.com/, http://www.pcinews.com/. Ed. Larry Storer TEL 254-399-6484. Adv. contacts Dennis Carter, Gary Pittman. B&W page USD 2,500. Circ: 20,000 (paid).

693 USA ISSN 1093-6483
CONCRETE OPENINGS; magazine of the concrete sawing & drilling association. Text in English. 1975. q. free. adv. charts; illus.; stat.; tr.lit. 76 p./no. 3 cols./p.; back issues avail. **Document type:** *Trade.* **Description:** Includes information on techniques used in concrete sawing and drilling.
Indexed: ConcrAb, METADEX.
—Linda Hall.
Published by: Concrete Sawing and Drilling Association, 11001 Danka Way N., Ste. 1, St Petersburg, FL 33716-3724. TEL 614-798-2252, FAX 614-798-2255, http://www.csda.org. Ed., Adv. contact Cherryl O'Brien TEL 614-798-2252. Pub. Patrick O'Brien. B&W page USD 2,250, color page USD 2,940; trim 11 x 8.5. Circ: 13,000 (controlled).

639.5 USA ISSN 0045-8015
CONCRETE PIPE NEWS. Text in English. 1952. q. USD 15. charts; illus. **Document type:** *Trade.* **Description:** Contains articles about the installation of concrete pipe throughout the world & stories about both innovative & standard installations.
Indexed: ConcrAb.
—Linda Hall.
Published by: American Concrete Pipe Association, 222 Las Colinas Blvd W, Ste 641, Irving, TX 75039-5423. TEL 703-821-1990, FAX 703-821-3054, http://www.concrete-pipe.org. Ed., R&P Mike Saubert. Circ: 12,000.

691 USA ISSN 1528-0187
THE CONCRETE PRODUCER. Text in English. 1983. m. free domestic to qualified personnel; USD 33 in Canada & Mexico; USD 93 elsewhere (effective 2005). adv. charts; illus.; tr.lit. Index. back issues avail. **Document type:** *Magazine, Trade.* **Description:** For producers of concrete products in the major concrete producing market segments: ready mixed concrete, precast and prestressed concrete and concrete block, tile and pipe, pavers and architectural precast.
Formerly (until 1997): Aberdeen's Concrete Trader (1055-0356)
Related titles: Online - full text ed.: (from Florida Center for Library Automation, Gale Group, H.W. Wilson).
Indexed: AS&TI, Englnd.
—**CCC.**
Published by: Hanley-Wood, LLC (Subsidiary of: J.P. Morgan Chase & Co.), 426 S Westgate St, Addison, IL 60101. TEL 630-543-0870, FAX 630-543-3112, http://www.theconcreteproducer.com/, http://www.hanleywood.com. Pub. Patrick J. Carroll. adv.: B&W page USD 3,750, color page USD 4,710. Circ: 20,017 (controlled).

691.3 USA ISSN 0010-5368
TA680
CONCRETE PRODUCTS. Text in English. 1947. m. USD 36 in US & Canada; USD 84 elsewhere; free to qualified personnel (effective 2005). adv. charts; illus.; stat.; tr.lit. back issues avail.; reprints avail. **Document type:** *Magazine, Trade.* **Description:** Provides news of legislative and regulatory affairs, updates on new products, equipment and technology, and reports on major construction projects affecting concrete mix, product design, fabrication and delivery.
Supersedes in part: Rock Products (0035-7464); Which incorporated (1896-1924): Cement and Engineering News (0096-0152)
Related titles: Microfilm ed.: (from PQC); Online - full text ed.: (from bigchalk, EBSCO Publishing, Gale Group, H.W. Wilson, Northern Light Technology, Inc., O C L C Online Computer Library Center, Inc., ProQuest Information & Learning).
Indexed: ABIn, AS&TI, CRIA, CRICC, ConcrAb, PROMT.
—BLDSC (3402.800000), CISTI, IE, ingenta, Linda Hall. **CCC.**
Published by: Primedia Business Magazines & Media, Inc. (Subsidiary of: Primedia, Inc.), 330 N Wabash Ave, Ste 2300, Chicago, IL 60611. TEL 312-595-1080, FAX 312-840-8455, dmarsh@primediabusiness.com, inquiries@primediabusiness.com, http://www.concreteproducts.com, http://www.primediabusiness.com. Ed. Don Marsh. Pub. Scott Bieda. Circ: 19,500 (controlled).
Subscr. to: PO Box 12993, Overland Park, KS 66282-2993. TEL 800-441-0294, FAX 913-967-1331.

691.3 USA
CONCRETE PUMPING. Text in English. q. free (effective 2002). **Document type:** *Magazine, Trade.*
Published by: American Concrete Pumping Association, 676 Enterprise Dr, Ste B, Lewis Center, OH 43035. TEL 614-431-5618, FAX 614-431-6944, christi@cosncretepumpers.com, http://www.concretepumpers.com/magazine.asp.

691 GBR ISSN 0010-5376
CONCRETE QUARTERLY. Text in English. 1947. q. bk.rev. illus. reprint service avail. from PQC. **Document type:** *Trade.*
Related titles: ♦ Issued with: Architects' Journal. ISSN 0003-8466.
Indexed: BldManAb, BrCerAb, ConcrAb, GeotechAb, HRIS, ICEA, JOF.
—CISTI, Linda Hall.
Published by: British Cement Association, Century House, Telford Ave, Crowthorne, Berks RG45 6YS, United Kingdom. TEL 44-1344-762676, FAX 44-1344-761214, library@bca.org.uk, http://www.bca.org.uk. Ed. George Perkin. Circ: 18,500.

691 620 USA ISSN 1055-2936
TA680
CONCRETE REPAIR BULLETIN. Text in English. 1988. bi-m. free to members. adv. charts; illus.; stat.; tr.lit. index. back issues avail. **Document type:** *Bulletin, Trade.* **Description:** Aimed at contractors, engineers, manufacturers and anyone concerned with the repair of concrete.
Indexed: BrCerAb, C&ISA, CerAb, CivEngAb, ConcrAb, CorrAb, E&CAJ, EMA, IAA, M&TEA, MBF, METADEX, SolStAb, WAA.
—Linda Hall.
Published by: International Concrete Repair Institute, 3166 S. River Rd., Ste. 132, Des Plaines, IL 60018-4260. TEL 703-450-0116, FAX 703-450-0119, concrepair@aol.com, http://www.icri.org/bulletin/index.asp. Ed. Debbie Stover. Pub. Milt Collins. R&P, Adv. contact Sally Collins. Circ: 11,000.

B

691.3 GBR ISSN 0305-1986 CODEN: CSTRDR
CONCRETE SOCIETY TECHNICAL REPORT. Text in English. 1970 (no.2). irreg., latest vol.53, 1999. price varies. **Document type:** *Monographic series.* **Description:** Features technical articles on developments in concrete materials, design and construction, project reports, news of conferences and events, and concrete society activities.
Indexed: ConcrAb, HRIS, IMMAb.
—BLDSC (3404.400000), CISTI, IE, ingenta. **CCC.**
Published by: The Concrete Society, Riverside House, 4 Meadows Business Park, Station Approach, Blackwater, Camberley, Surrey GU17 9AB, United Kingdom. TEL 44-1276-607140, FAX 44-1276-607141, subscriptions@concrete.org.uk, http://www.concrete.org.uk. Ed., R&P Nick Clarke.

691.3 USA
CONCRETE TECHNOLOGY TODAY. Text in English. 1980. 3/yr. USD 2 per issue (effective 2003). bk.rev. cum.index: 1980-1999. back issues avail. **Document type:** *Newsletter.* **Description:** Highlights practical uses of concrete technology for decision makers in design, management, or construction of building projects.
Related titles: CD-ROM ed.; Online - full text ed.
Published by: Portland Cement Association, 5420 Old Orchard Rd, Skokie, IL 60077-1083. TEL 847-966-6200, FAX 847-966-8389, steve_kosmatka@portcement.org, http://www.portcement.org. Ed. Jamie Farny. R&P Carlyn Fleck. Circ: 18,000.

691.3 GBR ISSN 0069-8288
THE CONCRETE YEARBOOK. Text in English. 1924. a. GBP 66 domestic; GBP 81 foreign (effective 1999). adv. reprint service avail. from PQC. **Document type:** *Directory, Trade.* **Description:** Directory of information on every aspect of the UK concrete and construction industries, their associated materials, products and services.
Published by: Emap Construct Ltd. (Subsidiary of: Emap Business Communications Ltd.), 151 Rosebery Ave, London, EC1R 4GB, United Kingdom. TEL 44-20-7505-8600, FAX 44-20-7505-6610, http://www.emapconstruct.co.uk. Ed. Diane McKenzie. Pub. Jane Taylor. R&P Russell Blackmore. Adv. contact Sue Boyle. Circ: 1,200.

690 USA
CONNECTICUT CONSTRUCTION HIGHLIGHTS OF THE WEEK. Text in English. 1984. w. back issues avail. **Document type:** *Newsletter.* **Description:** Covers state and national construction news for construction industry readers.
Published by: Connecticut Construction Industries Association, Inc., 912 Silas Deane Hwy, Wethersfield, CT 06109. TEL 860-529-6855, FAX 860-563-0616. Ed. Brian Holmes. Circ: 650 (controlled).

669.142 USA ISSN 1076-5522
THE CONNECTION. Text in English. 1971. q. membership. adv. **Document type:** *Newsletter.*
Published by: National Institute of Steel Detailing, Inc., 7700 Edgewater Drive, Ste 670, Oakland, CA 94621-3022. TEL 510-568-3741, FAX 510-568-3781, http://www.nisd.org. Ed. Ronald R Montes. R&P, Adv. contact Valerie Montes. B&W page USD 250. Circ: 375 (paid).

CONSERVATORY INDUSTRIES. see *CERAMICS, GLASS AND POTTERY*

690 ESP ISSN 0210-4601
CONSTRUC; revista tecnica de la construccion. Text in Spanish. 1952. q. EUR 67 (effective 2005). bk.rev.
Related titles: CD-ROM ed.; Diskette ed.
Published by: Ediciones Construc s.l., Rda Del General Mitre, 107, Barcelona, 08022, Spain. TEL 34-93-4175419, FAX 34-93-2115741, informacion@construc.es, ediconst@teleline.es, http://www.construc.es/, http://www.teleline.es/personal/ediconst. Ed., Pub. Juan Farre Sierra. Adv. contact Roberto Escobiar. Circ: 40,000.

690 BRA ISSN 0102-0501
CONSTRUCAO MINAS CENTRO OESTE. Text in Portuguese. 1977. m. USD 154 (effective 2000). adv. charts; illus.; stat. **Document type:** *Directory.*
Published by: Editora Pini Ltda., Rua Anhaia 964, Bom Retiro, SP 01130-900, Brazil. TEL 55-11-32248811. Ed. Mario Sergio Pini. Adv. contact Luiz Carlos F Oliveira.

690 BRA ISSN 0102-051X
CONSTRUCAO NORTE NORDESTE. Text in Portuguese. 1973. m. USD 154 (effective 2000). adv. bk.rev. illus. **Document type:** *Directory.*
Published by: Editora Pini Ltda., Rua Anhaia 964, Bom Retiro, SP 01130-900, Brazil. TEL 55-11-32248811. Ed. Mario Sergio Pini. Adv. contact Luiz Carlos F Oliveira.

690 624 BRA ISSN 0102-0528
CONSTRUCAO REGIAO SUL. Text in Portuguese. 1968. m. USD 154 (effective 2000). adv. bk.rev. charts; illus.; tr.lit. **Document type:** *Directory.*
Published by: Editora Pini Ltda., Rua Anhaia 964, Bom Retiro, SP 01130-900, Brazil. TEL 55-11-32248811. Ed. Mario Sergio Pini. Adv. contact Luiz Carlos F Oliveira.

B

690 624 BRA ISSN 0100-1671
CONSTRUCAO RIO DE JANEIRO. Text in Portuguese. 1970. m. USD 154 (effective 2000). adv. bk.rev. charts; illus.; stat.; tr.lit. **Document type:** *Directory.*
Published by: Editora Pini Ltda., Rua Anhaia 964, Bom Retiro, SP 01130-900, Brazil. TEL 55-11-32248811. Ed. Mario Sergio Pini. Adv. contact Luiz Carlos F Oliveira.

690 BRA ISSN 0010-6631
CONSTRUCAO SAO PAULO. Text in Portuguese. 1948. w. USD 580 (effective 2000). adv. bk.rev. illus.; mkt.; stat. **Document type:** *Directory.*
Published by: Editora Pini Ltda., Rua Anhaia, 964, Bom Retiro, Sao Paulo, SP 01130-900, Brazil. TEL 55-11-2248811. Ed. Mario Sergio Pini. Adv. contact Luiz Carlos F Oliveira.

690 ESP ISSN 1575-7447
CONSTRUCCION ALIMARKET. Text in Spanish. 1999. m. (11/yr.). EUR 142 domestic; EUR 290 in Europe; EUR 594 elsewhere (effective 2005). adv. mkt.; maps; pat.; stat.; charts; illus. Index. **Document type:** *Magazine, Trade.*
Related titles: CD-ROM ed.; Fax ed.; Online - full text ed.
Published by: Publicaciones Alimarket S.A., Albasanz 14 3o, Madrid, 28037, Spain. TEL 34-91-3274340, FAX 34-91-3274522, informa@alimarket.es, http://www.alimarket.es. Ed. Jose L Varea. R&P Carlos Guerrero. Adv. contact Isabel Bajo. color page EUR 1,298.19. Circ: 8,000.

690 USA ISSN 0192-4230
CONSTRUCCION PAN-AMERICANA. Text in Spanish. 1972. m. USD 30; free to qualified personnel. illus. back issues avail. **Document type:** *Trade.* **Description:** Covers major construction stories and reviews heavy equipment. Covers industry developments in the Americas, along with symposia and other important events.
Published by: International Construction Publishing Inc., 4913 S W 75th Ave, Miami, FL 33155. TEL 305-668-4999, FAX 305-668-7774, info@cpa-mpa.com, http://www.cpa-mpa.com. Ed. Juan Escalante. Circ: 14,405 (controlled).

CONSTRUCCION PAN-AMERICANA INTERNATIONAL BUYER'S GUIDE. see *BUSINESS AND ECONOMICS—Trade And Industrial Directories*

691 MEX ISSN 0187-7895
TA680 CODEN: CNTTEX
CONSTRUCCION Y TECNOLOGIA. Text in Spanish. 1963. m. USD 40 (effective 2000 & 2001). adv. bk.rev. index. **Document type:** *Trade.* **Description:** Contains practical and quality technological reports on cement and concrete useful for application to work done in Mexico.
Formerly: Revista I M C Y C (0034-9607)
Indexed: ApMecR, BrCerAb, C&ISA, CRIA, CRICC, CerAb, CivEngAb, ConcrAb, CorrAb, E&CAJ, EMA, IAA, ICEA, M&TEA, MBF, METADEX, SoftAbEng, SolStAb, WAA.
—CISTI, Linda Hall.
Published by: Instituto Mexicano del Cemento y del Concreto, A.C., Insurgentes Sur, No. 1846, Mexico City, DF 01030, Mexico. TEL 52-5-662-06356, FAX 52-5-661-3282. Ed. Raul Huerta Martinez. Circ: 10,000.

690 600 USA ISSN 1522-3302
CONSTRUCTECH. Text in English. m. USD 39.95 (effective 2001). adv. **Document type:** *Magazine, Trade.* **Description:** Dedicated to helping construction community-builders, owners, land developers, contractors, subcontractors, financial management, and other project management personnel understand the technology solutions being offered by hardware and software companies.
Related titles: Online - full text ed.
Published by: Specialty Publishing Co., 135 E Saint Charles Rd, Carol Stream, IL 60188. TEL 630-933-0844, FAX 630-933-0845, http://www.specialtypub.com. Ed. Bob Rakow. Pub. Peggy Smedley. Adv. contact Robert Parzy.

690 GBR ISSN 1465-3788
TH213.7.G7
CONSTRUCTING THE FUTURE. Text in English. q. free. **Document type:** *Trade.* **Description:** Keeps the industry abreast of construction innovations and research findings.
Former titles (until 1998): B R E News of Research and Innovation; B R E News of Construction Research
Related titles: Online - full text ed.
Indexed: CRIA, RICS.
—BLDSC (3420.843000), CISTI. **CCC.**
Contact Corp. Auth.: Building Research Establishment, Garston, Watford, Herts WD25 9XX, United Kingdom. TEL 44-1923-664000, FAX 44-1923-664787, crc@construct.emap.co.uk, http://www.bre.co.uk/bre/newslets/BRE_news/news_intro.html. Ed. Tom Harvey.

690 BEL
CONSTRUCTION. Text in French. 1944. w. adv. Supplement avail. **Document type:** *Trade.* **Description:** Provides relevant technical, social, economic and fiscal information for the construction industry.
Published by: National Confederation of Building Contractors/Confederation Nationale de la Construction, Rue du Lombard 34-42, Brussels, 1000, Belgium. TEL 32-2-545-5719, FAX 32-2-545-5908. Pub. Robert de Meulenaere. Adv. contact Christian Nekkebroeck. Circ: 8,950.

690 IRL
CONSTRUCTION. Text in English. m. (10/yr.). adv. bk.rev. **Document type:** *Trade.*
Published by: (Construction Industry Federation of Ireland), Dyflin Publications Ltd., 99 S Circular Rd., Dublin, 8, Ireland. TEL 353-1-4167900, FAX 353-1-4167903, construction@dyflin.ie. Adv. contact Joe Connolly. B&W page EUR 1,800, color page EUR 2,200; trim 210 x 297. Circ: 5,000.

690 USA ISSN 0010-6704
CONSTRUCTION (NORCROSS). Text in English. 1933. fortn. USD 96 domestic; USD 126 in Canada; USD 166 elsewhere; USD 10 newsstand/cover (effective 2005). adv. illus. **Document type:** *Journal, Trade.* **Description:** Reports on the contracts awarded, low bids and proposed work. Also contains field stories stressing equipment, methods, personalities, highway construction, earth moving, land development projects, utility construction, industrial building construction and public works activities underway or completed in Maryland, Washington DC, virginia, West Virginia and North Carolina.
Related titles: Online - full text ed.: (from EBSCO Publishing, Gale Group, ProQuest Information & Learning).
Indexed: ChemAb, EngInd.
Published by: Reed Construction Data, Associated Construction Publications (Subsidiary of: Reed Business Information), 30 Technology Pkwy, Ste 100, Norcross, GA 30092. TEL 800-486-0014, FAX 800-930-3003, acp@reedbusiness.com, http://www.acppubs.com/. Ed. Christina Fisher. Pub., Adv. contact John Weatherhead. B&W page USD 1,153, color page USD 1,653. Circ: 8,457 (controlled).

690 620 CAN ISSN 0700-9178
CONSTRUCTION ALBERTA NEWS. Text in English. 1974. s-w. CND 235. adv. **Document type:** *Trade.*
Published by: Construction Alberta News Ltd., 10536 106th St, Edmonton, AB T5H 2X8, Canada. TEL 403-424-1146, FAX 403-425-5886. Ed., Pub. Don Coates. Adv. contact Jack Turner. Circ: 4,125 (controlled).

690 USA
CONSTRUCTION ANALYSIS SYSTEM. Abbreviated title: C A S. Text in English. base vol. plus m. updates. **Document type:** *Trade.* **Description:** Provides detailed project-level information on contract value, square feet, project type, number of dwelling units, framing type, number of stories, and ownership type.
Published by: F.W. Dodge, Real Estate Group (Subsidiary of: McGraw-Hill Construction Information Group), 24 Hartwell Ave, Lexington, MA 02173. TEL 800-591-4462, FAX 781-860-6884, info@mcgraw-hill.com, http://www.mag.fwdodge.com/realestate/aboutcas.htm, http://fwdodge.construction.com/Analytics/.

690 624 NLD ISSN 0950-0618
TA401 CODEN: CBUMEZ
➤ **CONSTRUCTION AND BUILDING MATERIALS.** Text in English. 1987. 10/yr. EUR 850 in Europe to institutions; JPY 113,000 in Japan to institutions; USD 951 to institutions except Europe and Japan (effective 2006). bk.rev. abstr. back issues avail. **Document type:** *Academic/Scholarly.* **Description:** Covers the development, application and performance of materials in all aspects of major project architecture and civil engineering.
Related titles: Microform ed.: (from PQC); Online - full text ed.: (from EBSCO Publishing, Florida Center for Library Automation, Gale Group, IngentaConnect, ScienceDirect, Swets Information Services).
Indexed: ASCA, B&BAb, BioDAb, BrCerAb, CRIA, CRICC, CivEngAb, ConcrAb, EngInd, HRIS, ICEA, Inspec, MSCI, RAPRA, RefZh, WSCA.
—BLDSC (3420.950900), CISTI, Ei, IDS, IE, Infotrieve, ingenta. **CCC.**
Published by: Elsevier BV (Subsidiary of: Elsevier Science & Technology), Radarweg 29, Amsterdam, 1043 NX, Netherlands. TEL 31-20-4853911, FAX 31-20-4852457, nlinfo-f@elsevier.nl, http://www.elsevier.com/locate/conbuildmat, http://www.elsevier.nl. Ed. M C Forde.

343.078 USA
CONSTRUCTION AND DESIGN LAW. Text in English. 1984. 5 base vols. plus irreg. updates. looseleaf. USD 400. **Description:** Analyzes issues surrounding contracts, torts, insurance, suretyship, real estate finance, and more.
Published by: (National Institute of Construction Law, Inc.), LexisNexis (Subsidiary of: LexisNexis North America), PO Box 7587, Charlottesville, VA 22906-7587. TEL 804-972-7600, 800-562-1197, FAX 804-972-7666, llp.customer.support@lexis-nexis.com, http://www.lexislawpublishing.com. Ed. Patton Boggs.

690 340 GBR
CONSTRUCTION AND ENGINEERING PRECEDENTS. Text in English. 1998. 2 base vols. plus updates 2/yr. looseleaf. GBP 400 (effective 2006). **Document type:** *Journal, Trade.*
Published by: Sweet & Maxwell Ltd., 100 Avenue Road, London, NW3 3PF, United Kingdom. TEL 44-20-74491111, FAX 44-20-74491144, customer.services@sweetandmaxwell.co.uk, http://www.sweetandmaxwell.co.uk. **Subscr. to:** Cheriton House, North Way, Andover, Hants SP10 5BE, United Kingdom.

690 IRL ISSN 0376-7213
CONSTRUCTION AND PROPERTY NEWS. Text in English. 1973. m. adv. bk.rev. illus. **Document type:** *Newspaper, Trade.*
Published by: Jemma Publications Ltd., Marino House, 52 Glasthule Rd., Sandycove, Co. Dublin, Ireland. TEL 353-1-2800000, FAX 353-1-2801818. Ed. Maev Martin. Adv. contact Claire Keay. B&W page EUR 1,590, color page EUR 2,165; trim 243 x 345. Circ: 3,930.

690 353.55 USA ISSN 1084-3906
CONSTRUCTION AND PUBLIC WORKS - ASIA. Text in English. 1994. bi-m. **Document type:** *Trade.*
—**CCC.**
Published by: Primedia Business Magazines & Media, Inc. (Subsidiary of: Primedia, Inc.), 9800 Metcalf Ave, Overland Park, KS 66212-2216. TEL 913-341-1300, inquiries@primediabusiness.com, http://www.primediabusiness.com.

CONSTRUCTION & SURETY LAW NEWSLETTER. see *LAW*

CONSTRUCTION BRIEFINGS. see *LAW*

690 USA
CONSTRUCTION BULLETIN (ATLANTA). Text in English. 1984. s-w. USD 1,079. adv. back issues avail. **Document type:** *Bulletin.*
Related titles: Online - full text ed.
Published by: Construction Market Data, Inc., 4126 Pleasantdale Rd, Ste A8, Atlanta, GA 30340. TEL 800-949-0276, FAX 770-613-5978. Ed. David Fullem. Circ: 4,500.

690 USA ISSN 0010-6720
CONSTRUCTION BULLETIN (NORCROSS). Text in English. 1893. w. USD 209 domestic; USD 239 in Canada; USD 279 elsewhere; USD 10 newsstand/cover domestic (effective 2005). adv. stat.; tr.lit. back issues avail.; reprints avail. **Document type:** *Magazine, Trade.* **Description:** Serves heavy, highway and non-residential construction industry in MN, ND and SD.
Related titles: Online - full text ed.: (from EBSCO Publishing, Gale Group).
Published by: Reed Construction Data, Associated Construction Publications (Subsidiary of: Reed Business Information), 30 Technology Pkwy, Ste 100, Norcross, GA 30092. TEL 800-486-0014, FAX 800-930-3003, http://www.acppubs.com/. Ed. George Rekela. Pub. John Weatherhead. adv.: B&W page USD 1,198, color page USD 1,698. Circ: 4,000 (paid).
Subscr. to: Reed Business Information.

690 USA
▼ **CONSTRUCTION BUSINESS OWNER**; the magazine for growing contractors. Text in English. 2004 (Aug.). m. free domestic to qualified personnel; USD 125 foreign (effective 2005). adv. **Document type:** *Magazine, Trade.* **Description:** Designed to meet the business management needs of small to mid-sized construction business owners.
Published by: Cahaba Media Group, 1900 28th Ave South, Ste 110, Birmingham, AL 35209. TEL 205-212-9402, 800-765-4603, FAX 205-212-9452, http://www.constructionbusinessowner.com/. Ed. Tambra McKerley. Pub. Walter B Evans Jr. Adv. contact Lisa Freeman. B&W page USD 3,694; trim 7.875 x 10.5.

692.8 CAN ISSN 0228-8788
CODEN: COCAFZ
CONSTRUCTION CANADA. Text in English, French. 1959. bi-m. adv. illus.; tr.lit. **Document type:** *Magazine, Trade.* **Description:** Covers construction products, technology, building science for architects, engineers, specifiers and project managers.
Formerly (until 1980): Specification Associate (0038-691X)
—BLDSC (3421.025000), CISTI. **CCC.**

Published by: (Construction Specifications Canada), Kenilworth Media Inc., 710 -15 Wertheim Court, Richmond Hill, ON L4B 3H7, Canada. TEL 905-771-7333, 877-738-7624, FAX 905-771-7336, publisher@kenilworth.com, http://www.kenilworth.com. adv.: B&W page CND 2,135, color page CND 3,225; trim 10.75 x 8.25. Circ: 8,016.

690 368.014 USA ISSN 0272-4561
KF901.A15
CONSTRUCTION CLAIMS MONTHLY; devoted exclusively to the problems of construction contracting. (Includes: Focus on Construction Claims) Text in English. 1979. m. looseleaf. USD 317 in US & Mexico; USD 321 elsewhere; USD 347 combined subscription print & online eds. (effective 2005). index. **Document type:** *Magazine.* **Description:** Designed to help one avoid construction claims, settle claims quickly when they arise, and win disputes that require legislation.
Related titles: E-mail ed.: ISSN 1545-7451. USD 287 (effective 2005).
—CCC.
Published by: Business Publishers, Inc., 8737 Colesville Rd., Flr. 10, Silver Spring, MD 20910-3976. TEL 800-274-6737, bpinews@bpinews.com, custserv@bpinews.com, http://www.bpinews.com. Ed. Bruce M Jervis.

CONSTRUCTION CLIENT NEWSLETTER. see *BUSINESS AND ECONOMICS—Accounting*

690 AUS ISSN 1324-9525
CONSTRUCTION CONTRACTOR. Text in English. 1968. m. AUD 138.60 (effective 2001). adv. **Document type:** *Trade.* **Description:** A news magazine for the construction industry with articles relating to civil engineering, earthmoving, public works and commercial and industrial building.
Former titles (until 1995): Thomson's Construction Australia (1030-7036); (until 1986): Construction Equipment News (0007-8247)
Related titles: Online - full text ed.: (from Gale Group).
Indexed: ABIX.
—CISTI.
Published by: Reed Business Information Pty Ltd (Subsidiary of: Reed Business Information International), Locked Bag 2999, Chatswood, NSW 2067, Australia. http://www.reedbusiness.com.au. Ed. Chris Day. Pub. Paul Spotswood. Adv. contact Silvana Jovanovic. Circ: 8,925.

690 AUS
CONSTRUCTION CONTRACTOR YEARBOOK. Text in English. a. AUD 149 (effective 1999). adv. **Document type:** *Trade.* **Description:** Comprehensive reference guide for the Australian construction industry offering a specifications guide and directory listings covering equipment dealers, associations and institutions, suppliers and more.
Formerly: Construction Contractor Specification Guide
Published by: Reed Business Information Pty Ltd (Subsidiary of: Reed Business Information International), Locked Bag 2999, Chatswood, NSW 2067, Australia. customerservice@reedbusiness.com.au, http://www.reedbusiness.com.au. Ed. Chris Day. Pub. John Nuutinen. Adv. contact Ashley Day.

CONSTRUCTION CONTRACTS LAW REPORT. see *LAW*

690 720 USA
CONSTRUCTION CRITERIA BASE ONLINE. Text in English. 1987. m. **Document type:** *Trade.* **Description:** Contains guide specifications, codes, standard regulations and other criteria related to building, design and construction, primarily federal.
Formerly: Construction Criteria Base (CD-ROM)
Media: Online - full content.
Published by: National Institute of Building Sciences, 1090 Vermont Ave, N W, Ste 700, Washington, DC 20005-4905. TEL 202-289-7800, FAX 202-289-1092, ccb@nibs.org, http://www.ccb.org/.

690 USA ISSN 1084-9696
CONSTRUCTION DATA & NEWS COVERING SACRAMENTO✶. Text in English. w. adv. **Document type:** *Newsletter, Trade.*
Related titles: Online - full text ed.
Published by: McGraw-Hill Companies, Inc., Princeton Rd S 2, Box 689, Hightstown, NJ 08520-0689. TEL 800-325-2030.

690 USA
CONSTRUCTION DATA & NEWS COVERING WASHINGTON & ALASKA✶. Text in English. w. adv. **Document type:** *Newsletter, Trade.*
Related titles: Online - full text ed.
Published by: McGraw-Hill Companies, Inc., Princeton Rd S 2, Box 689, Hightstown, NJ 08520-0689. TEL 800-325-2030.

690 USA ISSN 1550-1396
CONSTRUCTION DIGEST; serving Indiana, Illinois, Ohio, Kentucky, Eastern Missouri, and West Virginia. Text in English. s-m. adv.
Formed by the merger of: Construction Digest (East Ed.) (0194-2476); Construction Digest (West Ed.) (0740-7777); Both of which superseded in part: Construction Digest (0010-6739)
Related titles: Online - full text ed.: (from Gale Group, ProQuest Information & Learning).
Published by: Reed Construction Data, Associated Construction Publications (Subsidiary of: Reed Business Information), 30 Technology Pkwy, Ste 100, Norcross, GA 30092. TEL 800-486-0014, FAX 770-417-4138, http://www.acppubs.com/. Eds. Tom Hale TEL 317-293-6860, Greg Sitek TEL 205-633-1789. Pub. John Weatherhead TEL 770-417-4120. Adv. contact John Ziegler.

690 USA ISSN 0194-8903
CONSTRUCTION DIMENSIONS MAGAZINE. Text in English. 1974. m. USD 34 in US & Canada to members; USD 40 in US & Canada to non-members; USD 50 elsewhere (effective 2005). adv. bk.rev. abstr.; stat.; tr.lit. index. **Document type:** *Magazine, Trade.*
Incorporates: G D C I Drywall; Which was formerly: Drywall Newsmagazine (0300-7197)
—CISTI.
Published by: Association of the Wall and Ceiling Industries International, 803 W Broad St, Ste 600, Falls Church, VA 22046-3108. TEL 703-534-3800, FAX 703-534-8307, info@awciu.org, http://www.awci.org. Ed., R&P Laura Porinchak. Pub. Steven Etkin. Adv. contact Brent Stone. B&W page USD 1,990, color page USD 2,940. Circ: 22,500 (paid and free).

338 USA ISSN 1521-8171
CONSTRUCTION DISTRIBUTION. Text in English. bi-m. **Document type:** *Magazine, Trade.*
Related titles: Online - full text ed.: (from Gale Group, ProQuest Information & Learning).
—CCC.
Published by: Cygnus Business Media, Inc., 1233 Janesville Ave, Fort Atkinson, WI 53538-0803. TEL 800-547-7377, FAX 920-563-1702, http://www.constructiondist.com/, http://www.cygnusb2b.com/. Ed. Tom Hammel TEL 800-547-7377 ext 661. Pub. Joe Drochak TEL 800-547-7377 ext 606. Circ: 16,000. **Subscr. to:** PO Box 470, Fort Atkinson, WI 53538.

690 SGP ISSN 0218-1258
CONSTRUCTION ECONOMICS REPORT. Text in English. 1988. q. SGD 164.80 domestic to construction companies; USD 412 domestic other institutions; USD 500 foreign; SGD 54 newsstand/cover domestic to construction companies; SGD 146.70 newsstand/cover domestic other institutions; USD 140 newsstand/cover foreign other institutions (effective 2001). **Document type:** *Government.*
Published by: Building and Construction Authority, 5 Maxwell Rd, No 08-00 MND Complex Tower Block, Singapore, 069110, Singapore. TEL 65-3257720, FAX 65-3254800, http://www.bca.gov.sg/. Circ: 1,000.

690 GBR
CONSTRUCTION EMPLOYERS FEDERATION. BULLETIN. Text in English. m. **Document type:** *Bulletin.*
Formerly: Federation of Building and Civil Engineering Contractors. Federation Bulletin
Published by: Construction Employers Federation Ltd., 143 Malone Rd, Belfast, Co Antrim BT9 6SU, United Kingdom. TEL 44-2890-877143, FAX 44-2890-877155, mail@cefni.co.uk, http://www.constructionfocus.co.uk. Ed. Tony Doran.

690.028 USA ISSN 0192-3978
TA1
CONSTRUCTION EQUIPMENT. Text in English. 1949. 13/yr. USD 99.90 domestic; USD 151.90 in Canada; USD 141.90 in Mexico; USD 246.90 elsewhere; USD 10 per issue domestic; USD 15 per issue foreign; free to qualified personnel (effective 2005). adv. charts; illus.; stat.; tr.lit. index. reprint service avail. from PQC. **Document type:** *Magazine, Trade.* **Description:** Provides detailed coverage of heavy equipment and trucks. Concerned with management, purchasing, maintenance, used and new product evaluation, as well as with trends in industry, government and the economy.
Former titles: Construction Equipment Magazine (0010-6763); Construction Equipment and Materials Magazine
Related titles: Online - full text ed.: (from EBSCO Publishing, Florida Center for Library Automation, Gale Group, Northern Light Technology, Inc., O C L C Online Computer Library Center, Inc., ProQuest Information & Learning); ♦ Supplement(s): Construction Equipment Specifications Guide.
Indexed: ABIn, BusI, ConcrAb, EngInd, ICEA, SoftAbEng, T&II.
—IE, Infotrieve, Linda Hall. **CCC.**
Published by: Reed Business Information (Subsidiary of: Reed Business), 2000 Clearwater Dr, Oak Brook, IL 60525. TEL 630-288-8140, 630-288-8185, http://www.constructionequipment.com, http://www.reedbusiness.com. Ed. Rod Sutton. Pub. Rick Blesi TEL 630-288-8140. adv.: B&W page USD 11,540, color page USD 14,535; trim 10.5 x 7.88. Circ: 80,000 (controlled). **Subscr. to:** Reed Business Information, PO Box 9020, Maple Shade, NJ 08052-9020. TEL 303-470-4466, FAX 303-470-4691.

690.028 634.9 622 USA
CONSTRUCTION EQUIPMENT BUYERS' GUIDE. Text in English. 191?. a. incl. with subscr. to Construction Equipment. adv. reprints avail. **Document type:** *Directory.*
Related titles: ♦ Supplement(s): Construction Equipment Specifications Guide.
Published by: Reed Business Information (Subsidiary of: Reed Business), 2000 Clearwater Dr, Oak Brook, IL 60525. TEL 630-288-8140, FAX 630-320-7145, http://www.constructionequipment.com/, http://www.reedbusiness.com. Circ: 80,000.

690.028 USA ISSN 0010-6755
HD9715.U5
CONSTRUCTION EQUIPMENT DISTRIBUTION. Text in English. 1936. m. USD 71.40 to non-members; USD 35.70 to members (effective 2004). adv. **Document type:** *Magazine, Trade.*
Published by: Associated Equipment Distributors, 615 W 22nd St, Oak Brook, IL 60521. TEL 630-574-0650, FAX 630-574-0132, aedonline@aol.com, http://www.aednet.org. Ed., Pub. Pam Gruebnau. Circ: 4,200 (paid).

690.028 USA ISSN 1058-787X
CONSTRUCTION EQUIPMENT GUIDE (MIDATLANTIC EDITION). Text in English. 1957. fortn. USD 65; free to qualified personnel (effective 2005). adv. tr.lit. **Document type:** *Newspaper, Trade.* **Description:** Provides current construction news, new and used equipment, auctions and projects.
Published by: Edwin M. McKeon, Ed. & Pub., 470 Maryland Dr, Fort Washington, PA 19034. TEL 215-885-2900, 800-523-2200, FAX 215-885-2910, cmongeau@constructionequipguide.com, http://www.constructionequipmentguide.com. Ed. Beth Baker. Circ: 27,256.

690.028 USA ISSN 1081-7034
CONSTRUCTION EQUIPMENT GUIDE (MIDWEST EDITION). Text in English. bi-w. USD 65; free to qualified personnel (effective 2005). **Document type:** *Newspaper, Trade.*
Published by: Edwin M. McKeon, Ed. & Pub., 470 Maryland Dr, Fort Washington, PA 19034. TEL 215-885-2900, 800-523-2200, FAX 215-885-2910, cmongeau@constructionequipguide.com, http://www.constructionequipmentguide.com. Circ: 29,106.

690.028 USA
CONSTRUCTION EQUIPMENT GUIDE (NORTHEAST EDITION). Text in English. fortn. USD 65; free to qualified personnel (effective 2005). **Document type:** *Newspaper, Trade.* **Description:** Provides current construction news, new and used equipment, auctions and projects.
Published by: Edwin M. McKeon, Ed. & Pub., 470 Maryland Dr, Fort Washington, PA 19034. TEL 215-885-2900, FAX 215-885-2910, cmongeau@constructionequipguide.com, http://www.constructionequipmentguide.com.

690.028 USA ISSN 1058-6474
CONSTRUCTION EQUIPMENT GUIDE (SOUTHEAST EDITION). Text in English. bi-w. USD 60 (effective 2005). **Document type:** *Newspaper, Trade.*
Published by: Edwin M. McKeon, Ed. & Pub., 470 Maryland Dr, Fort Washington, PA 19034. TEL 215-885-2900, 800-523-2200, FAX 215-885-2910, cmongeau@constructionequipguide.com, http://www.constructionequipmentguide.com. Ed. Craig Mongeau. Pub. Ted McKeon. Circ: 26,641.

690.028 USA
CONSTRUCTION EQUIPMENT SPECIFICATIONS GUIDE. Text in English. a. free (effective 2004). charts; illus. **Document type:** *Directory, Trade.* **Description:** Provides technical specifications for all types of construction equipment.
Media: Online - full text. **Related titles:** ♦ Supplement to: Construction Equipment. ISSN 0192-3978; ♦ Supplement to: Construction Equipment Buyers' Guide.
Published by: Reed Business Information (Subsidiary of: Reed Business), 2000 Clearwater Dr, Oak Brook, IL 60525. TEL 630-288-8140, FAX 630-288-8145, http://www.constructionequipment.com, http://www.reedbusiness.com.

690 GBR ISSN 0964-0665
CONSTRUCTION EUROPE. Text in English. 1990. m. USD 140 (effective 2001). adv. bk.rev. **Document type:** *Magazine, Trade.* **Description:** Reports on the effects of the single European market on Europe's construction industry and general construction related information.
Published by: K H L Group Ltd., Southfields, Southview Rd, Wadhurst, E Sussex TN5 6TP, United Kingdom. TEL 44-1892-784088, FAX 44-1892-784086, mail@khl.com, http://www.constructioneurope.com, http://www.khl.com. Ed. Chris Sleight TEL 44-1892-784088. Pub. James King. R&P Peter Watkinson. Adv. contact David Stowe. B&W page GBP 2,295, color page GBP 3,115; trim 210 x 297. Circ: 13,899.

690 USA
▼ **CONSTRUCTION EXECUTIVE.** Text in English. 2003. m. USD 65 to non-members; USD 45 to members (effective 2005). **Document type:** *Magazine, Trade.*
Published by: Associated Builders & Contractors, Inc., 4250 N Fairfax Dr, Arlington, VA 22203. TEL 703-812-2063, FAX 703-812-8203, nardone@abc.org, gotquestions@abc.org, http://www.abc.org/. Ed. Lisa A Nardone TEL 703-812-2063. Adv. contact Donald R Berry TEL 908-852-7466. Circ: 23,000 (paid).

▼ *new title* ➤ *refereed* ✶ *unverified* ♦ *full entry avail.*

THE CONSTRUCTION FOREMAN'S GUIDE TO O S H A REGULATIONS. (Occupational Health and Safety Administration) see *OCCUPATIONAL HEALTH AND SAFETY*

690 720 GBR ISSN 0267-7768
TH15
CONSTRUCTION HISTORY. Text in English. 1985. a. GBP 70 domestic; GBP 75 foreign. abstr. back issues avail. **Document type:** *Academic/Scholarly.*
Formerly: Construction Science
Indexed: AIAP, API, AmH&L, BHA, HistAb, IBR, IBZ.
—BLDSC (3421.294000), IE, ingenta. **CCC.**
Published by: Chartered Institute of Building, Englemere, Kings Ride, Ascot, Berks SL5 7TB, United Kingdom. TEL 44-1344-630700, FAX 44-1344-630777, pharlow@ciob.org.we. Eds. Christopher Powell, Robert Thorne.

338.4 USA ISSN 0069-9187
CONSTRUCTION IN HAWAII. Text in English. 1967. a. free. back issues avail. **Description:** Reports all facets of construction activities in Hawaii in the previous year, and includes industry forecast.
Formerly: Housing Activity in Hawaii
Published by: Bank of Hawaii, Economics Department, PO Box 2900, Honolulu, HI 96846. TEL 808-537-8307, FAX 808-536-9433, http://www.boh.com/econ/. Ed. Paul H Brewbaker. Circ: 8,000.

690 IND
CONSTRUCTION INDUSTRIES AND TRADE ANNUAL. Text in English. 1968. a. adv. **Document type:** *Trade.*
Formerly: Construction Industries and Trade Journal (0010-6828)
Published by: Ad International, Sayajiganj, Baroda, Gujarat 390 005, India. TEL 64158. Ed. Parshuram Bldg. Adv. contact C M Pandit. Circ: 4,200.

CONSTRUCTION INDUSTRIES OF MASSACHUSETTS DIRECTORY; a directory and catalog of highway and heavy construction in New England. see *BUSINESS AND ECONOMICS—Trade And Industrial Directories*

690 332 USA
CONSTRUCTION INDUSTRY ANNUAL FINANCIAL SURVEY. Text in English. 1989. a. USD 149 (effective 2001). adv. back issues avail. **Document type:** *Trade.* **Description:** Construction industry's only financial performance report. Includes financial data, accounting methods, insurance issues, and corporate policies and procedures.
Published by: Construction Financial Management Association, 29 Emmons Dr, Ste F 50, Princeton, NJ 08540-1413. TEL 609-452-8000, FAX 609-452-0417. Ed., R&P Brian Summers. adv.: B&W page USD 1,550. Circ: 2,000.

690 GBR
CONSTRUCTION INDUSTRY COUNCIL. NEWSLETTER. Text in English. **Document type:** *Newsletter.* **Description:** Serves the construction industry, emphasising the significance of the built environment to the nation.
Media: Online - full text.
Published by: Construction Industry Council, 26 Store St, London, WC1E 7BT, United Kingdom. TEL 44-171-637-8692, FAX 44-171-580-6140, gwatts@cic.org.uk, http://www.cic.org.uk/About/about-cic.htm. Ed. Graham Watts.

690 SGP
CONSTRUCTION INDUSTRY DEVELOPMENT BOARD. CONSTRUCTION PROJECT LISTING. Text in English. w. SGD 123.60, USD 123.60 (effective 1999). **Document type:** *Government.*
Media: Fax.
Published by: Building Construction Authority, 9 Maxwell Rd, No 03-00, Annexe A, MND Complex, Singapore, 069112, Singapore. TEL 65-225-6711, FAX 65-225-7301, cidb_enguiry@cidb.gov.sg, http://www.cidb.gov.sg.

CONSTRUCTION INDUSTRY LAW LETTER. see *LAW*

690 SGP
CONSTRUCTION INFONET. Text in English. irreg. SGD 500 Non Construction-Related Companies; SGD 400 Construction-Related Companies (effective 2001). **Document type:** *Trade.* **Description:** Contains articles on the Singapore's construction industry, including quarterly reports, reviews and outlook, manppower situation, statistics and project information, and more.
Media: Online - full content.
Published by: Building and Construction Authority, 5 Maxwell Rd, No 08-00 MND Complex Tower Block, Singapore, 069110, Singapore. TEL 65-3257720, FAX 65-3254800, http://www.bca.gov.sg/ceru/onlineconstat.html.

658 IRL ISSN 0790-0724
CONSTRUCTION INFORMATION SERVICES REPORT. Text in English. 1972. w. adv. **Document type:** *Magazine, Trade.* **Description:** Provides advance market information to the construction and allied trades industries in Ireland.
Published by: Newmarket Information Ltd., 66 Ranelagh, Dublin, 6, Ireland. TEL 353-1-4910043, FAX 353-1-4910092, info@newinfo.ie, http://www.newinfo.ie. Circ: 2,500 (controlled).

690 CAN ISSN 1203-2743
CONSTRUCTION INNOVATION/INNOVATION EN CONSTRUCTION. Text in English, French. 1995. q. free. back issues avail. **Document type:** *Journal, Trade.* **Description:** Provides news of recent research results, product evaluations, code developments and conference highlights to Canada's construction practitioners.
Formed by the merger of (1989-1995): Building Performance News (0843-6487); (1992-1995): C C M C News (1188-0783); (1989-1995): Materials News (1188-4096); Which was formerly (until 1992): I R C Materials News (0840-9986); (1988-1995): Structures News (1188-407X); Which was formerly (until 1991): I R C Structures News (0840-8599); (1957-1995): N B C - N F C News (0848-600X); Which was formerly (until 1989): N B C News N F C (0380-8599); (until 1975): National Building Code News (0700-1495); (until 1973): N B C News (0027-612X)
Related titles: Online - full text ed.: ISSN 1480-5642.
—CISTI, Linda Hall.
Published by: National Research Council of Canada, Institute for Research in Construction, 1200 Montreal Rd, Bldg M-23A, Ottawa, ON K1A 0R6, Canada. TEL 613-993-9960, FAX 613-952-4040, jane.swartz@nrc.ca, Irc.Client-Services@nrc.ca, http://www.nrc.ca/irc/newsletter/toc.html. Ed. Jane Swartz.

690 GBR ISSN 1471-4175
➤ **CONSTRUCTION INNOVATION**; information, process, management. Text in English. 1992. q. GBP 92 in Europe to individuals; USD 167 in North America to individuals; GBP 98 elsewhere to individuals; GBP 246 in Europe to institutions; USD 429 in North America to institutions; GBP 253 elsewhere to institutions (effective 2006); Subscr. includes online access. adv. 288 p./no.; back issues avail.; reprints avail. **Document type:** *Journal, Academic/Scholarly.* **Description:** Covers all aspects of successful IT/process development and implementation. Reports on construction innovations in information, process, technology and management.
Formerly (until March 2001): International Journal of Construction Information Technology (0968-0365)
Related titles: Online - full text ed.: ISSN 1477-0857 (from EBSCO Publishing, Gale Group, IngentaConnect, O C L C Online Computer Library Center, Inc., ProQuest Information & Learning, Swets Information Services).
Indexed: BrCerAb, C&ISA, CerAb, CorrAb, E&CAJ, EMA, IAA, M&TEA, MBF, METADEX, WAA.
—BLDSC (3421.309390), CISTI, IE, Infotrieve, ingenta, Linda Hall. **CCC.**
Published by: Hodder Arnold Journals (Subsidiary of: Hodder Headline plc.), 338 Euston Rd, London, NW1 3BH, United Kingdom. TEL 44-20-78736000, FAX 44-20-78736367, arnoldjournals@hodder.co.uk, http://www.arnoldpublishers.com/journals/pages/con_inn/14714175.htm, http://www.hodderarnoldjournals.com/. Eds. Jack Goulding, Martin Skitmore, Mustafa Alshawi. adv.: B&W page GBP 370; trim 189 x 246. **Subscr. to:** Extenza - Turpin, Pegasus Dr, Stratton Business Park, Biggleswade, Beds SG18 8TQ, United Kingdom. TEL 44-1462-488900, FAX 44-1462-480947, subscriptions @turpinltd.com.

➤ **CONSTRUCTION INSURANCE: COVERAGES AND DISPUTES.** see *INSURANCE*

➤ **CONSTRUCTION LABOR NEWS.** see *BUSINESS AND ECONOMICS—Labor And Industrial Relations*

➤ **CONSTRUCTION LABOR REPORT.** see *BUSINESS AND ECONOMICS—Labor And Industrial Relations*

690 USA
CONSTRUCTION: LATIN AMERICAN INDUSTRIAL REPORT✶. (Avail. for each of 22 Latin American countries) Text in English. 1985. a. USD 435; per country report.
Published by: Aquino Productions, P O Box 15760, Stamford, CT 06901-0760. Ed. Andres C Aquino.

690 340 GBR ISSN 0963-6706
CONSTRUCTION LAW. Text in English. 10/yr. GBP 199 domestic; GBP 219 foreign (effective 2003). bk.rev. stat. **Document type:** *Trade.* **Description:** Focuses on the legal issues that arise in management in the construction industry.
Published by: Eclipse Group Ltd. (Subsidiary of: LexisNexis UK (Scottish Office)), 18-20 Highbury Place, London, N5 1QP, United Kingdom. TEL 44-20-7354-5858, FAX 44-20-7226-8618. Ed. Nicholas Barrett. Pub. Andrew S Brode. R&P David J Martin TEL 44-171-354-6711.

690 340 USA
CONSTRUCTION LAW. Text in English. 1986. 6 base vols. plus irreg. updates. looseleaf. USD 830 base vol(s). (effective 2002). **Description:** This is for any lawyer who prepares construction contracts or litigates construction disputes. You receive expert guidance on handling every aspect of the construction process, from the initial bid, to drafting and performance of the contract, to subsequent claims, disputes, and litigation. Use the sources of sample forms, contracts, and agreements to sucessfully represent any client involved in a construction project.
Related titles: CD-ROM ed.
Published by: Matthew Bender & Co., Inc. (Subsidiary of: LexisNexis North America), 1275 Broadway, Albany, NY 12204. international@bender.com, http://bender.lexisnexis.com. Ed. Steven Stein.

690 340 GBR ISSN 0267-2359
K3
CONSTRUCTION LAW JOURNAL. Text in English. 1984. 8/yr. GBP 562, EUR 845 in Europe; GBP 585, USD 1,063 elsewhere; GBP 281, EUR 423 in Europe to students; GBP 293, USD 532 elsewhere to students (effective 2006). adv. reprint service avail. from WSH. **Document type:** *Journal, Academic/Scholarly.* **Description:** Concentrates on providing current information to the construction industry, including changes in case law and legislation.
Related titles: Online - full text ed.
Indexed: CLI, ELJI, LJI, LRI, RICS.
—BLDSC (3421.328000), IE, ingenta.
Published by: Sweet & Maxwell Ltd., 100 Avenue Road, London, NW3 3PF, United Kingdom. TEL 44-20-74491111, FAX 44-20-74491144, customer.services@sweetandmaxwell.co.uk, http://www.sweetandmaxwell.co.uk. Adv. contact Jackie Wood.

CONSTRUCTION LAW REPORTS. see *LAW*

CONSTRUCTION LAW REPORTS. see *LAW*

690 340 GBR
CONSTRUCTION LAW SERVICE. Text in English. 1999. q. GBP 985; GBP 1,836 overseas (effective 2005). **Description:** Provides the legal information requirements of construction lawyers in private practice and industry.
Media: CD-ROM.
Published by: Sweet & Maxwell Ltd., 100 Avenue Road, London, NW3 3PF, United Kingdom. TEL 44-20-74491111, FAX 44-20-74491144, customer.services@sweetandmaxwell.co.uk, http://www.sweetandmaxwell.co.uk.

CONSTRUCTION LAW UPDATE. see *LAW*

690 340 USA ISSN 0272-0116
KF1950.A15
CONSTRUCTION LAWYER. Text in English. q. USD 40 to individuals; USD 25 to qualified personnel (effective 2005). bk.rev.; software rev. 48 p./no. 2 cols./p.; back issues avail. **Document type:** *Newsletter.* **Description:** Legal developments in the construction industry. Serves as a clearinghouse of information on programs related to The construction industry and to provide training programs for lawyers and concerned laypersons.
Related titles: Online - full text ed.
Indexed: CLI, LRI.
Published by: (American Bar Association, Forum Committee on the Construction Industry), A B A Publishing, 750 N Lake Shore Dr, Chicago, IL 60611. TEL 312-988-5000, FAX 312-988-6081, service@abanet.org, http://www.abanet.org/abapubs/periodicals/constlaw2.html. Ed. Adrian L Bastianelli. Circ: 6,400. **Subscr. to:** P O Box 10892, Chicago, IL 60610-0892. TEL 800-825-2221, FAX 312-988-5568.

690 340 USA ISSN 0279-1102
KF901.A75
CONSTRUCTION LITIGATION REPORTER; recent decisions of national significance. Text in English. 1979. m. looseleaf. USD 655 (effective 2005). bibl. index. back issues avail. **Document type:** *Newsletter, Trade.* **Description:** Legal developments and summaries of cases affecting construction law.
Published by: Thomson West (Subsidiary of: Thomson Corporation, The), 610 Opperman Dr, Eagan, MN 55123-1396. TEL 651-687-8000, 800-328-4880, FAX 651-687-6674, customer.service@westgroup.com, http://www.westgroup.com/store/product.asp?product%5Fid=14047937&catalog%5Fname=wgstore, http://west.thomson.com. Ed. Mark Schneier.

690 658 GBR ISSN 0268-2478
CONSTRUCTION MANAGEMENT✶. Text in English. 1983. bi-m. adv.
Indexed: BldManAb.
Published by: Adscope Ltd, Middlesex House, 29-45 High St, Edgware, HA8 7UU, United Kingdom. Ed. E Foster. Circ: 9,600.

690 GBR ISSN 0144-6193
CODEN: CMECF3
➤ **CONSTRUCTION MANAGEMENT AND ECONOMICS.** Text in English. 1983. m. GBP 1,662, USD 2,745 combined subscription to institutions print & online eds. (effective 2006). adv. bk.rev. reprint service avail. from PSC. **Document type:** *Journal, Academic/Scholarly.* **Description:** Focuses on research, case studies and innovative practice in the building industry; subjects include architecture, building, civil engineering, economics, management, planning and surveying.
Incorporates (1986-198?): International Journal of Construction Management and Technology; Formerly: Journal of Construction Industry Economics and Management
Related titles: Online - full text ed.: ISSN 1466-433X. GBP 1,579, USD 2,608 to institutions (effective 2006) (from EBSCO Publishing, Gale Group, IngentaConnect, O C L C Online Computer Library Center, Inc., Swets Information Services).

Indexed: ABIn, API, BldManAb, BrCerAb, C&ISA, CerAb, CivEngAb, CorrAb, DIP, E&CAJ, EMA, ESPM, EngInd, GEOBASE, IAA, IBR, IBZ, IBuildSA, ICEA, M&TEA, MBF, METADEX, RASB, RICS, RiskAb, SUSA, SolStAb, WAA.
—BLDSC (3421.358100), CISTI, IE, Infotrieve, ingenta, Linda Hall. **CCC.**
Published by: Routledge (Subsidiary of: Taylor & Francis Group), 4 Park Sq, Milton Park, Abingdon, Oxon OX14 4RN, United Kingdom. TEL 44-1235-828600, FAX 44-1235-829000, info@routledge.co.uk, http://www.tandf.co.uk/journals/titles/01446193.asp, http://www.routledge.com. Ed. Dr. Will P Hughes. **Subscr. to:** Taylor & Francis Ltd, Journals Customer Service, Rankine Rd, Basingstoke, Hants RG24 8PR, United Kingdom. TEL 44-1256-813000, FAX 44-1256-330245, enquiry@tandf.co.uk.

690 GBR ISSN 1360-3566
TH1
CONSTRUCTION MANAGER. Text in English. 1963. m. GBP 50; GBP 60 foreign (effective 1999). adv. bk.rev. reprint service avail. from PQC. **Document type:** *Trade.* **Description:** Contains articles on technical and management aspects of building, together with reports on conferences and seminars.
Former titles (until 1995): Chartered Builder (0957-8773); Building Technology and Management (0007-3709)
Related titles: Microform ed.: (from PQC).
Indexed: API, BrTechI, CISA, IBuildSA, ICEA, Inspec, RICS, SoftAbEng, WSCA.
—BLDSC (3421.358600), CISTI, IE, ingenta, Linda Hall. **CCC.**
Published by: (Chartered Institute of Building), Englemere Services Ltd., Englemere, Kings Ride, Ascot, Berks SL5 7TB, United Kingdom. TEL 44-1344-23355, FAX 44-1344-23467. Ed. Connal Vickers. R&P Julian Barlow. Adv. contact Steve Brand. Circ: 25,000.

690 CAN ISSN 0832-5804
CONSTRUCTION MANITOBA. Text in English. 1987. q. CND 12. adv. **Description:** Covers the construction industry in the province of Manitoba.
Published by: (Winnipeg Construction Association), Sanford Evans Communications Ltd., 1077 Church Ave, P O Box 398, Winnipeg, MB R3C 3B1, Canada. TEL 204-775-0201, FAX 204-783-7488. Ed. G Greasley. Circ: 1,064.

690 USA
CONSTRUCTION MARKET DATA. Text in English. w. USD 200 (effective 1999). **Document type:** *Newspaper.* **Description:** Covers heavy and general engineering construction, bid calls, bid openings, contract awards, and more.
Published by: Construction Market Data, Inc., 8878 Barrons Blvd., Littleton, CO 80129-2345. TEL 510-636-2480, FAX 510-636-2492. Ed., Pub. William B Wallace. Circ: 5,000 (paid).

690 KOR
CONSTRUCTION MATERIAL PRICES/WOLGAN KONSOL MULKA. Text in Korean. 1970. m. KRW 9,000, USD 12. adv.
Published by: Construction Association of Korea, 71-2 Nonhyun dong, Kangnam-ku, Seoul, 135701, Korea, S. Ed. Suh Joo Whan. Circ: 2,000.

691 389 USA
CONSTRUCTION METRICATION. Text in English. q. **Document type:** *Newsletter, Trade.*
Published by: National Institute of Building Sciences, 1090 Vermont Ave, N W, Ste 700, Washington, DC 20005-4905. TEL 202-289-7800, FAX 202-289-1092, nibs@nibs.org, http://www.nibs.orgge.

690 GBR
CONSTRUCTION MIDLANDS. Text in English. 10/yr.
Address: Sta Bldgs, Maclure Rd, Rochdale, Lancs OL11 1DN, United Kingdom. TEL 0706-58880, FAX 071-0706-59403. Ed. J McClelland. Circ: 11,600.

690 GBR
CONSTRUCTION MONITOR. Text in English. 10/yr. free. **Document type:** *Newsletter, Government.* **Description:** Provides information about the construction industry in the U.K., including health, legal, financial and governmental aspects. Includes calendar of events.
Formerly (until 1994): Euronews Construction
Related titles: ♦ Issued with: Building. ISSN 0007-3318.
—BLDSC (3421.720000).
Published by: Department of Environment, Rm. C1-01a, 2 Marsham St., London, SW1P 3EB, United Kingdom. TEL 44-171-276-6600, FAX 44-171-276-3826. Ed. David Broyd. Circ: 35,000.

624 USA
CONSTRUCTION MONTHLY ONLINE; the unlimited information source for the construction industry. Short title: C M Online. Text in English. m.
Media: Online - full text.
Published by: Franklin Publishing (Birmingham), 3132 Valley Park Drive, Birmingham, AL 35243. TEL 205-969-0085, 800-999-5314, FAX 205-969-0088, cadams@wwisp.com, http://www.constmonthly.com/. Ed. Chuck Adams.

690 GBR ISSN 0010-6860
CONSTRUCTION NEWS. Text in English. 1871. w. GBP 72; GBP 1.45 newsstand/cover; GBP 95 in Europe; GBP 125 elsewhere (effective 1999). adv. bk.rev. illus. **Document type:** *Trade.* **Description:** For the contractor market. Covers the entire industry from boardroom to site office. Presents financial news, analyses and legal reports in an easily digestible form.
Related titles: Online - full text ed.: (from ProQuest Information & Learning); ♦ Supplement(s): Construction News Products. ISSN 0267-5137.
Indexed: AIAP, API, BMT, BldManAb, BrTechI, CISA, FLUIDEX, RICS.
—BLDSC (3421.750000), CISTI.
Published by: Emap Construct Ltd. (Subsidiary of: Emap Business Communications Ltd.), 151 Rosebery Ave, London, EC1R 4GB, United Kingdom. TEL 44-20-7505-6600, FAX 44-20-7505-3535, http://www.emapconstruct.co.uk. Ed. John Pullin. Pub. Geoff Hall. Adv. contact Simon Elgar. **Dist. by:** Seymour Distribution Ltd, 86 Newman St, London W1T 3EX, United Kingdom. FAX 44-207-396-8002, enquiries@seymour.co.uk.

690 USA ISSN 0160-5607
TH1
CONSTRUCTION NEWS. Text in English. 1934. s-m. USD 96 domestic; USD 126 in Canada; USD 166 elsewhere; USD 10 newsstand/cover (effective 2005). adv. bk.rev. **Document type:** *Magazine, Trade.* **Description:** Covers Arkansas, Oklahoma, western Tennessee, Mississippi, Louisiana.
Related titles: Online - full text ed.: (from EBSCO Publishing, Gale Group).
Indexed: AIAP, FLUIDEX, RICS.
—CCC.
Published by: Reed Construction Data, Associated Construction Publications (Subsidiary of: Reed Business Information), 30 Technology Pkwy, Ste 100, Norcross, GA 30092. TEL 800-486-0014, FAX 800-930-3003, http://www.reedbusiness.com/index.asp?layout=theListProfile&theListID=697&groupid=38&industryid=38, http://www.acppubs.com/. Ed. Lisa Doyle. Pub., Adv. contact John Weatherhead. B&W page USD 1,415, color page USD 1,915. Circ: 6,200 (controlled).

690 GBR ISSN 0267-5137
CONSTRUCTION NEWS PRODUCTS. Text in English. 1983. bi-m. **Document type:** *Directory, Trade.*
Related titles: ♦ Supplement to: Construction News. ISSN 0010-6860.
Published by: Emap Construct Ltd. (Subsidiary of: Emap Business Communications Ltd.), 151 Rosebery Ave, London, EC1R 4GB, United Kingdom. TEL 44-20-7505-6600, FAX 44-20-7505-3535, TELEX 299973-ITP-LM-G, http://www.emapconstruct.co.uk. Ed. D Taylor. Circ: 41,000. **Subscr. to:** PO Box 1584, Birmingham, AL 35201-1584.

690 USA ISSN 1086-6191
CONSTRUCTION NEWS WEEKLY, COVERING NEW ORLEANS & VICINITY. Text in English. 1995. w. adv. **Document type:** *Newsletter, Trade.* **Description:** Provides information on what jobs are coming up for bid or negotiation.
Related titles: Online - full text ed.
Published by: Mcgraw-Hill Construction Dodge (Subsidiary of: McGraw-Hill Construction Information Group), 148 Princeton-Hightstown Rd, Hightstown, NJ 08520. TEL 800-393-6343, http://www.dodgeconstructionpublications.com.

690 USA ISSN 1550-0888
CONSTRUCTION NEWS WEEKLY COVERING NORTH AND SOUTH DAKOTA. Variant title: McGraw Hill Construction Dodge Construction News Weekly Covering North and South Dakota. Text in English. w. USD 40 (effective 2004). adv. **Document type:** *Newsletter, Trade.* **Description:** Provides information on what jobs are coming up for bid or negotiation.
Former titles: F.W. Dodge Construction News Weekly Covering North and South Dakota (1095-0885); (until 1997): Dakota Construction News Weekly Covering North and South Dakota (1088-3533)
Related titles: Online - full text ed.
Published by: Mcgraw-Hill Construction Dodge (Subsidiary of: McGraw-Hill Construction Information Group), 148 Princeton-Hightstown Rd, Hightstown, NJ 08520. TEL 800-393-6343, http://www.dodgeconstructionpublications.com.

690 USA ISSN 1086-6132
CONSTRUCTION NEWS WEEKLY, COVERING NORTHERN MISSISSIPPI. Text in English. 1995. w. adv. **Document type:** *Newsletter, Trade.* **Description:** Provides information on what jobs are coming up for bid or negotiation.
Related titles: Online - full text ed.
Published by: Mcgraw-Hill Construction Dodge (Subsidiary of: McGraw-Hill Construction Information Group), 148 Princeton-Hightstown Rd, Hightstown, NJ 08520. TEL 800-393-6343, http://www.dodgeconstructionpublications.com.

690 USA ISSN 1089-4829
CONSTRUCTION NEWS WEEKLY, COVERING RHODE ISLAND, EASTERN CONNECTICUT AND BRISTOL COUNTY MASSACHUSETTS. Text in English. w. adv. **Document type:** *Newsletter, Trade.* **Description:** Provides information on what jobs are coming up for bid or negotiation.
Formerly (until 199?): Rhode Island Construction News Weekly Covering Rhode Island, Eastern Connecticut and Bristol County Massachusetts (1086-5268)
Related titles: Online - full text ed.
Published by: Mcgraw-Hill Construction Dodge (Subsidiary of: McGraw-Hill Construction Information Group), 148 Princeton-Hightstown Rd, Hightstown, NJ 08520. TEL 800-393-6343, http://www.dodgeconstructionpublications.com.

690 USA ISSN 1095-1016
CONSTRUCTION NEWS WEEKLY, COVERING ROANOKE, VIRGINIA AND VICINITY. Text in English. w. adv. **Document type:** *Newsletter, Trade.* **Description:** Provides information on what jobs are coming up for bid or negotiation.
Formerly (until 199?): Virginia Construction Weekly, Covering Roanoke and Vicinity (1086-5349)
Related titles: Online - full text ed.
Published by: Mcgraw-Hill Construction Dodge (Subsidiary of: McGraw-Hill Construction Information Group), 148 Princeton-Hightstown Rd, Hightstown, NJ 08520. TEL 800-393-6343, http://www.dodgeconstructionpublications.com.

690 USA ISSN 1086-6175
CONSTRUCTION NEWS WEEKLY, COVERING SHREVEPORT & VICINITY. Text in English. 1995. w. adv. **Document type:** *Newsletter, Trade.* **Description:** Provides information on what jobs are coming up for bid or negotiation.
Related titles: Online - full text ed.
Published by: Mcgraw-Hill Construction Dodge (Subsidiary of: McGraw-Hill Construction Information Group), 148 Princeton-Hightstown Rd, Hightstown, NJ 08520. TEL 800-393-6343, http://www.dodgeconstructionpublications.com.

B

690 USA ISSN 1086-6124
CONSTRUCTION NEWS WEEKLY, COVERING SOUTHERN MISSISSIPPI. Text in English. 1995. w. adv. **Document type:** *Newsletter, Trade.* **Description:** Provides information on what jobs are coming up for bid or negotiation.
Related titles: Online - full text ed.
Published by: Mcgraw-Hill Construction Dodge (Subsidiary of: McGraw-Hill Construction Information Group), 148 Princeton-Hightstown Rd, Hightstown, NJ 08520. TEL 800-393-6343, http://www.dodgeconstructionpublications.com.

690 USA ISSN 1085-1852
CONSTRUCTION NEWS WEEKLY, COVERING SOUTHERN WISCONSIN. Text in English. 1995. w. adv. **Document type:** *Newsletter, Trade.* **Description:** Provides information on what jobs are coming up for bid or negotiation.
Related titles: Online - full text ed.
Published by: Mcgraw-Hill Construction Dodge (Subsidiary of: McGraw-Hill Construction Information Group), 148 Princeton-Hightstown Rd, Hightstown, NJ 08520. TEL 800-393-6343, http://www.dodgeconstructionpublications.com.

690 USA ISSN 1085-8210
CONSTRUCTION NEWS WEEKLY, COVERING THE BRONX, MANHATTAN, & STATEN ISLAND. Text in English. 1995. w. adv. **Document type:** *Newsletter, Trade.* **Description:** Provides information on what jobs are coming up for bid or negotiation.
Related titles: Online - full text ed.
Published by: Mcgraw-Hill Construction Dodge (Subsidiary of: McGraw-Hill Construction Information Group), 148 Princeton-Hightstown Rd, Hightstown, NJ 08520. TEL 800-393-6343, http://www.dodgeconstructionpublications.com.

690 USA ISSN 1086-6221
CONSTRUCTION NEWS WEEKLY, COVERING THE RIO GRANDE VALLEY. Text in English. 1995. w. adv. **Document type:** *Newsletter, Trade.* **Description:** Provides information on what jobs are coming up for bid or negotiation.
Related titles: Online - full text ed.
Published by: Mcgraw-Hill Construction Dodge (Subsidiary of: McGraw-Hill Construction Information Group), 148 Princeton-Hightstown Rd, Hightstown, NJ 08520. TEL 800-393-6343, http://www.dodgeconstructionpublications.com.

690 USA ISSN 1086-6140
CONSTRUCTION NEWS WEEKLY, COVERING THE STATE OF MISSISSIPPI. Text in English. 1995. w. adv. **Document type:** *Newsletter, Trade.* **Description:** Provides information on what jobs are coming up for bid or negotiation.
Related titles: Online - full text ed.
Published by: Mcgraw-Hill Construction Dodge (Subsidiary of: McGraw-Hill Construction Information Group), 148 Princeton-Hightstown Rd, Hightstown, NJ 08520. TEL 800-393-6343, http://www.dodgeconstructionpublications.com.

690 USA ISSN 1550-0861
CONSTRUCTION NEWS WEEKLY COVERING THE STATE OF NEBRASKA. Variant title: McGraw Hill Construction Dodge Construction News Weekly Covering the State of Nebraska. Text in English. w. USD 40 (effective 2004). adv. **Document type:** *Newsletter, Trade.* **Description:** Provides information on what jobs are coming up for bid or negotiation.
Former titles (until 200?): F.W. Dodge Construction News Weekly Covering the State of Nebraska (1094-1029); (until 199?): Construction News Weekly Covering Nebraska (1085-5777)
Related titles: Online - full text ed.

Published by: Mcgraw-Hill Construction Dodge (Subsidiary of: McGraw-Hill Construction Information Group), 148 Princeton-Hightstown Rd, Hightstown, NJ 08520. TEL 800-393-6343, http://www.dodgeconstructionpublications.com.

690 USA ISSN 1095-0915
CONSTRUCTION NEWS WEEKLY, COVERING THE STATE OF VERMONT. Text in English. w. adv. **Document type:** *Newsletter, Trade.* **Description:** Provides information on what jobs are coming up for bid or negotiation.
Formerly (until 199?): Dodge Construction News Weekly Covering Vermont (1085-8199)
Related titles: Online - full text ed.
Published by: Mcgraw-Hill Construction Dodge (Subsidiary of: McGraw-Hill Construction Information Group), 148 Princeton-Hightstown Rd, Hightstown, NJ 08520. TEL 800-393-6343, http://www.dodgeconstructionpublications.com.

690 USA ISSN 1086-6248
CONSTRUCTION NEWS WEEKLY, COVERING WESTERN MISSOURI. Text in English. 1992. w. adv. **Document type:** *Newsletter, Trade.* **Description:** Provides information on what jobs are coming up for bid or negotiation.
Related titles: Online - full text ed.
Published by: Mcgraw-Hill Construction Dodge (Subsidiary of: McGraw-Hill Construction Information Group), 148 Princeton-Hightstown Rd, Hightstown, NJ 08520. TEL 800-393-6343, http://www.dodgeconstructionpublications.com.

690 USA ISSN 1086-6108
CONSTRUCTION NEWS WEEKLY COVERING WESTERN OKLAHOMA. Text in English. 1995. w. adv. **Document type:** *Newsletter, Trade.* **Description:** Provides information on what jobs are coming up for bid or negotiation.
Related titles: Online - full text ed.
Published by: Mcgraw-Hill Construction Dodge (Subsidiary of: McGraw-Hill Construction Information Group), 148 Princeton-Hightstown Rd, Hightstown, NJ 08520. TEL 800-393-6343, http://www.dodgeconstructionpublications.com.

690 USA ISSN 0892-3337
CONSTRUCTION NEWS WEST✱. Text in English. w. adv. **Document type:** *Newsletter, Trade.*
Formerly: Construction Week (0744-1568)
Related titles: Online - full text ed.
Published by: McGraw-Hill Companies, Inc., Princeton Rd S 2, Box 689, Hightstown, NJ 08520-0689. TEL 800-325-2030.

690 GBR
CONSTRUCTION NORTH. Text in English. 6/yr. USD 10 (effective 1999). adv. **Document type:** *Trade.*
Published by: Wealthstream Ltd., Sta Bldgs, Maclure Rd, Rochdale, Lancs OL11 1DN, United Kingdom. TEL 01706-658-880, FAX 01706-659-403, steph-wealthstream@btinternet.com, http://www.wealthstream.co.uk. Ed. Mac Greenwood. R&P, Adv. contact Steph Wilks. Circ: 10,600.

690 GBR
THE CONSTRUCTION PLANT - HIRE ASSOCIATION BULLETIN. Text in English. 10/yr. membership. **Document type:** *Trade.* **Description:** Contains information relating to plant hire companies in the U.K.
Published by: Construction Plant - Hire Association Bulletin, 28 Eccleston St, London, SW1W 9PY, United Kingdom. TEL 44-171-730-7117, FAX 44-171-730-7110. Ed., R&P Linda Malcolm.

690 SGP
CONSTRUCTION PROJECT LISTING. Text in English. w. SGD 123.60 (effective 2001). **Document type:** *Trade.*
Media: Fax.
Published by: Building and Construction Authority, 5 Maxwell Rd, No 08-00 MND Complex Tower Block, Singapore, 069110, Singapore. TEL 65-3257720, FAX 65-3254800, http://www.bca.gov.sg/.

CONSTRUCTION REVIEW. see *BUILDING AND CONSTRUCTION—Abstracting, Bibliographies, Statistics*

368.1 USA
CONSTRUCTION RISK MANAGEMENT. Text in English. 1984. q. looseleaf. USD 270 (effective 2003). **Document type:** *Journal, Trade.* **Description:** Covers insurance and risk-management considerations for contracting organizations of any type.
Published by: International Risk Management Institute, Inc., 12222 Merit Dr, Ste 1450, Dallas, TX 75251-2276. TEL 972-960-7693, FAX 972-371-5120, info@irmi.com, http://www.irmi.com. Eds. Ann Rudd, Jack P Gibson. R&P Paul Murray TEL 972-687-9313.

692.8 USA
CONSTRUCTION SCHEDULES: ANALYSIS, EVALUATION AND INTERPRETATION OF SCHEDULES IN LITIGATION. Text in English. 1983. irreg., latest 1998, 2nd ed. USD 75 (effective 2003). **Description:** In keeping with the focus on claims prevention and the contractors' desire that all involved work together to achieve the personal and professional goals of every stakeholder, this periodical focuses on and analyzes the impact of this goal on scheduling.
Published by: Michie Company (Subsidiary of: LexisNexis North America), 701 E Water St, Charlottesville, VA 22902-5389. TEL 434-972-7600, 800-446-3410, FAX 434-972-7677, http://www.michie.com. Eds. H Murray Hohns, Michael T Callahan.

690.028 USA ISSN 1542-2828
CONSTRUCTION SITE NEWS. Abbreviated title: C.S.N. Text in English. m. USD 69 (effective 2002). adv. **Document type:** *Magazine, Trade.* **Description:** Provides current equipment and industry information for all construction site needs.
Published by: Grand View Media Group, Inc. (Subsidiary of: EBSCO Industries, Inc.), 200 Croft St., # 1, Birmingham, AL 35242-1824. TEL 888-431-2877, webmaster@grandviewmedia.com, http://www.grandviewmedia.com. Ed. Ashley Kizzire. Pub. Tim Garmon. adv.: page USD 3,800; trim 8 x 10.875.

690 USA ISSN 0010-6925
TH425 CODEN: COSPAJ
CONSTRUCTION SPECIFIER; for commercial and industrial construction. Text in English. 1950. m. USD 48 domestic; USD 58 in Canada (effective 2004). adv. bk.rev. illus. index. reprints avail. **Document type:** *Magazine, Trade.* **Description:** Covers technology, materials and law, in non-residential commercial construction.
Related titles: ♦ Supplement(s): Modern Materials.
Indexed: AIAP, ArchI, BrCerAb, C&ISA, CerAb, CivEngAb, ConcrAb, CorrAb, E&CAJ, EEA, EMA, EngInd, IAA, M&TEA, MBF, METADEX, Search, SolStAb, WAA.
—BLDSC (3421.865000), CISTI, Ei, IE, ingenta, Linda Hall. **CCC.**
Published by: Construction Specifications Institute, 289 - 266 Elmwood Ave, Buffalo, NY 14222. TEL 866-572-5633, FAX 866-572-5677, info@constructionspecifier.com, csi@csinet.org, http://www.constructionspecifier.com/, http://www.csinet.org. Ed. Anthony Capken. Pub. Ellen Kral. adv.: color page USD 5,085. Circ: 26,408 (paid).

690 AUS
CONSTRUCTION SUPERVISOR. Text in English. 1967. bi-m. AUD 0.30 per issue.
Indexed: BldManAb.
Published by: (Australian Institute of Construction Supervisors), Percival Publishing Co. Pty. Ltd., 862-870 Elizabeth St, Waterloo Dc, NSW 2017, Australia.

▼ **CONSTRUCTION SUPERVISOR'S SAFETY BULLETIN.** see *OCCUPATIONAL HEALTH AND SAFETY*

690 330 USA
CONSTRUCTION SURVEY. Text in English. m. USD 30 (effective 2000). **Document type:** *Trade.* **Description:** Conducts a nationwide survey of 200 construction firms regarding their current conditions and expectations for the coming months.
Related titles: Online - full text ed.: free.
Published by: Dun & Bradstreet, Economic Analysis Department (Subsidiary of: Dun & Bradstreet Corporation), c/o Judy Webb, 3 Sylvan Way, Parsippany, NJ 07054. FAX 973-254-4063, http://www.dnb.com. R&P Judy Webb.

690 ZAF ISSN 1607-9612
CONSTRUCTION WORLD. Text in English. ZAR 219.45 (effective 2001).
Published by: Primedia Publishing, 366 Pretoria Ave, Ferndale, Randburg, Transvaal 2194, South Africa. TEL 27-11-787-5725, FAX 27-11-787-5776, http://www.primemags.co.za.

690 FRA ISSN 0010-6976
CONSTRUCTIONS EQUIPEMENTS POUR LES LOISIRS. Text in French; Summaries in English, German. 1961. bi-m. adv. bk.rev. bibl.; charts; illus. cum.index. **Document type:** *Trade.*
Published by: Techno-Loisirs, 3 rue Sivel, Paris, 75014, France. Ed. Georges E Caille. Circ: 7,000.

690 USA ISSN 0162-6191
TA201
CONSTRUCTOR; the construction management magazine. Text in English. 1919. m. USD 15 to members; USD 250 to non-members (effective 2005). adv. bk.rev. tr.lit.; illus. index. back issues avail.; reprints avail. **Document type:** *Magazine, Trade.* **Description:** Contains feature material on markets, equipment, manpower and money.
Related titles: Online - full text ed.
Indexed: BldManAb, ConcrAb, HRIS, ICEA, SoftAbEng.
—BLDSC (3423.000000), CISTI, IE, ingenta, Linda Hall.
Published by: (Associated General Contractors of America), A G C, 333 John Carlyle St, Ste 200, Alexandria, VA 22314-5745. TEL 703-837-5355, 703-548-3118, FAX 703-548-3119, info@agc.org, http://www.agc.org/page.ww?section=CONSTRUCTOR+Magazine&name=About+CONSTRUCTOR+Magazine. Eds. Benjamin Harring, Mark Shaw. Pub. Mark Kelly. adv.: B&W page USD 5,100, color page USD 5,300. Circ: 43,780 (paid and controlled).

690 ARG ISSN 0010-7018
CONSTRUCTOR. Text in Spanish. 1901. w. ARS 96, USD 96 for 6 mos.. adv. bk.rev.
Indexed: HRIS.
Published by: Constructor s.r.l., Hipolito Yrigoyen, 615 Piso 7, Capital Federal, Buenos Aires 1086, Argentina. TEL 54-114-3430716, FAX 54-114-3319368. Ed. Marcelo Daniel Donadio. Circ: 15,000.

690 ESP ISSN 1135-402X
CONSTRUCTORS. Text in Spanish. 1977. 11/yr. adv. bk.rev. **Document type:** *Magazine, Trade.*
Formerly (until 1994): Gremi de Constructors d'Obres de Barcelona i Comarques. Revista
Published by: (Gremi de Constructors d'Obres de Catalunya), Editorial Interpress' S.L., C. Benedicto Mateo 8-10, Bjs., Barcelona, 08034, Spain. TEL 34-93-2800522, FAX 34-93-2054620, interpress@ctu.es, http://www.editiner.com. Ed. J Fernandez Martorell. Circ: 5,000.

690 PRT
CONSTRUDATA; relatorio semanal dos projetos de construcao. Text in Portuguese. 1990. w. adv. stat. back issues avail. **Document type:** *Newsletter.* **Description:** Provides sales leads for contractors, sub-contractors, suppliers and other contruction or post-contruction related companies.
Related titles: Diskette ed.
Published by: Construdata S.A., Rua Eira, 1, Alges de Cima, Lisbon, 1495, Portugal. TEL 351-1-4103435, FAX 351-1-4109677, construdata@mail.telepac.pt. Ed. Jose Geada. Circ: 5,000.

690 ESP ISSN 1577-824X
CONSTRUINTER. Text in Spanish. 2001. m. bk.rev.; Website rev. mkt. **Document type:** *Magazine, Trade.*
Related titles: Online - full text ed.: ISSN 1577-9858. 2001.
Published by: Editorial Interpress' S.L., C. Benedicto Mateo 8-10, Bjs., Barcelona, 08034, Spain. TEL 34-93-2800522, FAX 34-93-2054620, redaccion@construinter.com, interpress@ctu.es, http://www.construinter.com/, http://www.editiner.com. Ed. J Fernandez Martorell.

690 CAN ISSN 0833-0239
CONSTRUIRE. Text in French. 1986. bi-m. CND 28.43, USD 60. adv. back issues avail. **Document type:** *Trade.* **Description:** Focuses on major construction projects within the renovation, building materials, research and development projects, professional continuing education, and health and security sectors on project sites.
Incorporated (1988-1990): Contact C S S T (1182-1558)
Indexed: AIAP.
—CISTI.
Published by: Association de la Construction de Montreal et du Quebec, 4970 Place de la Savane, Montreal, PQ H4P 1Z6, Canada. TEL 514-739-2381, FAX 514-739-8933, acqprov@total.net. Ed. Christiane Rioux. Adv. contact Pierre Leduc. B&W page CND 2,075, color page CND 2,675; trim 10.88 x 8.13. Circ: 18,683 (controlled). **Dist. by:** 7875 Trans Rd, St Laurent, PQ H4S 1L3, Canada.

690 MAR ISSN 0851-0210
CONSTRUIRE; hebdomadaire du batiment et des travaux publics du Maroc. Text in French. 1940. w. MAD 340 domestic; MAD 440 foreign. adv. **Document type:** *Trade.* **Description:** Covers the construction and public works sector in Morocco.
Indexed: AIAP.
Published by: Societe Nouvelle Construire, 25 rue d'Azilal, Casa Bandoeng, B P 10902, Casablanca, Morocco. Ed. Bouchaib Talal.

690 CHE ISSN 0010-7034
CONSTRUIRE. Text in French. m. CHF 30. adv. illus.; stat.
Indexed: AIAP.
Published by: Federation Romande de Metiers du Batiment, 10 rue de Beaumont, Case Postale 339, Geneva 25, 1211, Switzerland. Ed. P Schuetz. Circ: 2,565. **Co-sponsor:** Groupement Romand des Maitres Ferblantiers et Appareilleurs.

CONSUMER HOME AND GARDEN. see *GARDENING AND HORTICULTURE*

691 720 USA ISSN 1527-7690
TA426
CONTEMPORARY STONE & TILE DESIGN. Text in English. 1995. q. free domestic qualified professionals (effective 2005). adv. back issues avail. **Document type:** *Magazine, Trade.* **Description:** Promotes the benefits of natural stone to a readership of architects, interior designers, specifiers and consumers.
Formerly (until 199?): Contemporary Stone Design (1522-2233)
Related titles: Online - full text ed.: (from Florida Center for Library Automation, Gale Group, ProQuest Information & Learning).
Indexed: ABIn.
Published by: B N P Media, 755 W Big Beaver Rd, Ste 1000, Troy, MI 48084-4903. TEL 248-362-3700, FAX 248-362-0317, cstd@bnpmedia.com, http://www.stoneworld.com, http://www.bnpmedia.com/. Adv. contact Janelle Minghine. B&W page USD 2,840, color page USD 3,875. Circ: 19,000 (controlled).

B

692.8 GBR
HD9715.G72
CONTRACT JOURNAL. Text in English. 1879. w. GBP 109 domestic; GBP 184, USD 276 in United States; GBP 226, USD 339 elsewhere (effective 2000). adv. bk.rev. charts; illus.; mkt.; pat.; tr.lit. **Document type:** *Trade.* **Description:** Trade journal for management within building and civil engineering companies, plant wirers, quantity surveyors and subcontractors.
Former titles (until 1979): U K Plant Hire Guide (0307-2630); Contract Journal (0010-7859)
Related titles: Microfilm ed.; Online - full text ed.: (from EBSCO Publishing, Gale Group, H.W. Wilson, LexisNexis, O C L C Online Computer Library Center, Inc., ProQuest Information & Learning).
Indexed: API, BPI, BldManAb, CISA, F&EA, HRIS, ICEA, RICS, SoftAbEng.
—BLDSC (3425.800000), Ei. **CCC.**
Published by: Reed Business Information Ltd. (Subsidiary of: Reed Business), Quadrant House, The Quadrant, Brighton Rd, Sutton, Surrey SM2 5AS, United Kingdom. TEL 44-20-86523500, FAX 44-208-652-8977, 44-20-86528932, http://www.contractjournal.co.uk/home/Default.asp?type=0&liSectionID=12, http://www.reedbusiness.co.uk/. Ed. David Nunn TEL 44-20-8652-4643. Adv. contact Steve Beard TEL 44-20-8652-4652. Circ: 45,000. **Subscr. to:** Quadrant Subscription Services, PO Box 302, Haywards Heath, W Sussex RH16 3YY, United Kingdom. TEL 44-1444-475603, FAX 44-1444-445447, rbi.subscriptions@qss-uk.com.

692.8 USA
CONTRACT LAWSUITS: TRIAL STRATEGIES AND TECHNIQUES. Text in English. 1989 (2nd ed.). latest 1989, 2nd ed., base vol. plus irreg. updates. USD 85 (effective 2003). 565 p./no.
Published by: Michie Company (Subsidiary of: LexisNexis North America), 701 E Water St, Charlottesville, VA 22902-5389. TEL 434-972-7600, 800-446-3410, FAX 434-972-7677, http://www.michie.com. Ed. Edward J. Imwinkelried.

690 USA ISSN 0897-7135
CONTRACTOR; the newsmagazine of mechanical contracting. Text in English. 1954. m. adv. charts; illus.; stat.; tr.lit. back issues avail.; reprint service avail. from PQC. **Document type:** *Magazine, Trade.* **Description:** For air conditioning, heating, fire protection, piping, refrigeration, plumbing, contractors.
Related titles: Microfilm ed.; Online - full text ed.: (from bigchalk, EBSCO Publishing, Florida Center for Library Automation, Gale Group, Northern Light Technology, Inc., O C L C Online Computer Library Center, Inc., ProQuest Information & Learning); Supplement(s): Radiant Living; Opportunities in the Air.
Indexed: ABIn, T&II.
—CISTI. **CCC.**
Published by: Penton Media, Inc. (Subsidiary of: Pittway Company), 1300 E 9th St, Cleveland, OH 44114-1503. http://www.contractormag.com, http://www.penton.com. Ed. Bob Miodonski. adv.: B&W page USD 6,860, color page USD 8,550; trim 14.75 x 11. Circ: 50,377 (controlled). **Subscr. to:** PO Box 901979, Cleveland, OH 44190-1979.

690 USA ISSN 1523-9047
CONTRACTOR TOOLS AND SUPPLIES. Text in English. bi-m. adv. **Document type:** *Magazine, Trade.*
Published by: Pfingsten Publishing, L L C, 6000 Lombardo Center Dr, Ste 420, Seven Hills, OH 44131. TEL 216-328-8926, 888-772-8926, FAX 216-328-9452, info@pfpublish.com, http://www.pfpub.com.

CONTRACTOR'S BUSINESS STRATEGIST. see *BUSINESS AND ECONOMICS—Management*

690 CAN
CONTRACTOR'S DESK; serving the building industry. Text in English. 1994. bi-m. CND 15; CND 23 in United States; CND 30 elsewhere. adv. bk.rev. **Document type:** *Magazine, Trade.* **Description:** Dedicated to the advancement of construction innovations by means of education, research and service.
Related titles: Diskette ed.
Published by: Nationwide Promotions Limited, 12 Dawn Dr, Burnside Industrial Park, Dartmouth, NS B3B 1H9, Canada. TEL 902-468-5253, FAX 902-468-5697, cdesk@accesscable.net, cxna@netcom.ca. Ed. Bill Harris. Adv. contact Dave Boutilier TEL 902-468-6871. B&W page CND 1,733, color page CND 2,533; trim 10.63 x 8.13. Circ: 3,500 (paid); 11,500 (controlled).

692.8 USA
CONTRACTORS EQUIPMENT GUIDE. Text in English. 1959. bi-w. USD 70. **Document type:** *Trade.* **Description:** Advertises new and used construction equipment and related services.
Address: 50 Central Ave, Box 324, Needham, MA 02194-2914. TEL 781-449-1250, 800-225-8448, FAX 781-449-7768. Ed., Pub. John J LaCamera Jr. adv.: page USD 1,025. Circ: 30,000.

658 USA ISSN 0192-6330
CONTRACTORS HOT LINE. Text in English. w. USD 109 in United States; USD 119 in Canada; USD 130 in Mexico (effective 1999). **Description:** Brings together buyers and sellers of new and used construction equipment nationwide.
Published by: Heartland Construction Group, Inc., 1003 Central Ave, Fort Dodge, IA 50501. TEL 515-955-1600, 888-247-2002, FAX 515-955-6636, ch1@contractorshotline.com, ceg@contractorshotline.com, http//:www.contractorshotline.com, http://www.contractorshotline.com. Circ: 50,000.

690 THA
CONTRACTORS MAGAZINE. Text in Thai. m. adv.
Published by: Nirapai Turakij, Charansanidwong Bangkoknoi, 1909-376 Soi Ruampattana, Bangkok, 10700, Thailand. TEL 02-4355888, FAX 02-4357958. Ed. Rattapol Khanchit. Adv. contact Jiraphorn Nirapai.

690 HKG
CONTRACTORS SOURCING GUIDE. Text in Chinese, English. 1997. a. HKD 200; HKD 200 newsstand/cover. **Document type:** *Trade.* **Description:** Presents articles about construction site equipment, plants and construction material.
Published by: China Trend Building Press Ltd, Rm. 901 C C Wu Building, 302 Hennessy Rd, Wanchai, Hong Kong, Hong Kong. TEL 852-2802-6299. Ed. Bobo Chan. Circ: 15,000.

690 AUS
CORDELL WEEKLY CONSTRUCTION REPORTS. (In 7 Sections: Commercial; Community; Civil Engineering; Industrial; Flats & Units; Housing; Mining) Text in English. 1972. w. price varies. **Document type:** *Trade.*
Formerly: Cordell Construction Reports
Related titles: Online - full text ed.
Published by: Cordell Building Information Services (Subsidiary of: Cordell Construction Information Services Pty. Ltd.), PO Box 124, St Leonards, NSW 2065, Australia. TEL 61-2-99345555, FAX 61-2-99345501, info@cordell.com.au, http://www.cordell.com.au. Ed. Rob Wild. R&P Katharina Bauer. Circ: 6,500.

690 AUS ISSN 1320-4319
CORDELL'S BUILDING COST GUIDE. COMMERCIAL AND INDUSTRIAL. Text in English. 1971. q. AUD 430. adv. **Document type:** *Trade.*
Former titles: Cordell's Building Cost Guide. New Construction; Cordell's Building Cost Book and Estimating Guide. New South Wales (0311-2497); Cordell's Building Price Book and Estimating Guide. New South Wales
Published by: Cordell Building Information Services (Subsidiary of: Cordell Construction Information Services Pty. Ltd.), PO Box 124, St Leonards, NSW 2065, Australia. TEL 61-2-99345555, FAX 61-2-99345501, info@cordell.com.au, http://www.cordell.com.au. Ed. Rob Wild. R&P Katharina Bauer. Circ: 6,000.

690 AUS ISSN 1320-4653
CORDELL'S BUILDING COST GUIDE. HOUSING. Text in English. q. AUD 430. **Document type:** *Trade.*
Formerly: Cordell's Cost Guide. Housing Alterations and Additions
Published by: Cordell Building Information Services (Subsidiary of: Cordell Construction Information Services Pty. Ltd.), PO Box 124, St Leonards, NSW 2065, Australia. TEL 61-2-99345555, FAX 61-2-99345501, info@cordell.com.au, http://www.cordell.com.au. Ed. Rob Wild. R&P Katharina Bauer.

690 AUS ISSN 0311-7472
CORDELL'S PRICE INDEX OF BUILDING MATERIALS. Text in English. fortn. AUD 430. **Document type:** *Trade.*
Published by: Cordell Building Information Services (Subsidiary of: Cordell Construction Information Services Pty. Ltd.), PO Box 124, St Leonards, NSW 2065, Australia. TEL 61-2-99345555, FAX 61-2-99345501, info@cordell.com.au, http://www.cordell.com.au. Ed. Rob Wild. R&P Katharina Bauer.

690 AUS
CORDELL'S WHO'S WHO IN BUILDING: ARCHITECTS. Text in English. a. **Document type:** *Trade.*
Formerly: Cordell's Who's Who in Building: Non-Housing
Published by: Cordell Building Information Services (Subsidiary of: Cordell Construction Information Services Pty. Ltd.), PO Box 124, St Leonards, NSW 2065, Australia. TEL 61-2-99345555, FAX 61-2-99345501, info@cordell.com.au, http://www.cordell.com.au. Ed. Rob Wild. R&P Katharina Bauer.

690 AUS
CORDELL'S WHO'S WHO IN BUILDING: BUILDERS. Text in English. a. **Document type:** *Trade.*
Formerly: Cordell's Who's Who in Building: Housing
Published by: Cordell Building Information Services (Subsidiary of: Cordell Construction Information Services Pty. Ltd.), PO Box 124, St Leonards, NSW 2065, Australia. TEL 61-2-99345555, FAX 61-2-99345501, info@cordell.com.au, http://www.cordell.com.au. Ed. Rob Wild. R&P Katharina Bauer.

690 721 AUS
CORDELL'S WHO'S WHO IN BUILDING: DEVELOPERS. Text in English. a. **Document type:** *Directory.*
Formerly: Cordell's Who's Who in Design Specifying
Published by: Cordell Building Information Services (Subsidiary of: Cordell Construction Information Services Pty. Ltd.), PO Box 124, St Leonards, NSW 2065, Australia. TEL 61-2-99345555, FAX 61-2-99345501, info@cordell.com.au, http://www.cordell.com.au. Ed. Rob Wild. R&P Katharina Bauer.

690 USA
CORNERSTONE (HOUSTON). Text in English. 2002. q. free domestic to members (effective 2005). adv. **Document type:** *Magazine.*
Published by: Associated General Contractors of Houston, PO Box 662, Houston, TX 77001. TEL 713-843-3700, FAX 713-843-3777, tamara.b@agchouston.org, http://www.agchouston.org. adv.: B&W page USD 1,339; trim 8.375 x 10.875. Circ: 3,000 (paid and controlled).

B

690 ESP
CORREO DE LA CONSTRUCCION. Text in Spanish. 22/yr. EUR 40 domestic; EUR 84 foreign (effective 2005). adv. Website rev. **Document type:** *Newspaper, Newspaper-distributed.*
Published by: Ediciones Roda, S.L., Corcega 204 bajos, Tda. 2, Barcelona, 08036, Spain. TEL 34-93-419-2881, FAX 34-93-419-2463, correo@edicionesroda.es, http://www.edicionesroda.es/principal-cc.htm. Ed. Antonio Castro. Adv. contact Carlos Castro. Circ: 16,500.

690 ITA ISSN 1121-6336
COSTRUIRE. Text in Italian. 1982. m. (11/yr). EUR 47 domestic; EUR 99 foreign (effective 2004). adv. **Document type:** *Magazine, Consumer.* **Description:** Covers the building construction industry in Italy.
Formerly (until 1987): Costruire per Abitare (1121-6328)
Indexed: AIAP.
Published by: Editrice Abitare Segesta SpA, Corso Monforte 15, Milan, MI 20122, Italy. TEL 39-02-76090, FAX 39-02-76090301, redazione@costruire.it, http://www.costruire.it. Ed. Leonardo Fiori. Adv. contact Alessandra Fedele. Circ: 34,794.

690 ITA ISSN 1722-3644
▼ **COSTRUIRE IMPIANTI.** Text in Italian. 2003. m. EUR 55 (effective 2004). **Document type:** *Magazine, Consumer.*
Published by: Editrice Abitare Segesta SpA, Corso Monforte 15, Milan, MI 20122, Italy. TEL 39-02-76090, FAX 39-02-76090301, redazione@costruire.it, http://www.costruire.it.

690 ITA ISSN 0010-9657
COSTRUTTORI ROMANI. Text in Italian. 1965; N.S. 1990 (vol.4, no.9). m. free. adv. bk.rev. charts; illus. **Document type:** *Bulletin.*
Published by: Associazione dei Costruttori Edili di Roma e Provincia, Via di Villa Patrizi, 11, Rome, RM 00161, Italy. TEL 39-06-4403886, FAX 39-06-4403885. Ed. Piero Sacchetti. Adv. contact Fabio Cauli. Circ: 5,000.

COSTRUZIONI; tecnica ed organizzazione dei cantieri. see *ENGINEERING—Civil Engineering*

COSTRUZIONI METALLICHE; rivista dei tecnici dell'acciaio. see *ENGINEERING—Civil Engineering*

693 USA
COUNCIL NEWS AND VIEWS. Text in English. 1995. 5/yr. free. **Document type:** *Newsletter.* **Description:** Promotes the trade of masonry in general and cryptic masonry in particular.
Published by: Grand Council, R. & S.M. of Ohio, 1231 E 286th St, Euclid, OH 44132. TEL 216-732-9098, FAX 216-261-3961, ohiorsm@aol.com. Ed. Merlyn E Meredith. Circ: 1,500.

690 352.9 USA
COUNCIL OF AMERICAN BUILDING OFFICIALS. ONE AND TWO FAMILY DWELLING CODE. Text in English. 1971. a. USD 40 to non-members; USD 30 to members (effective 2000). Supplement avail. **Document type:** *Proceedings, Trade.*
Formerly (until 1983): International Conference of Building Officials. One and Two Family Dwelling Code
Published by: (Council of American Building Officials), International Conference of Building Officials, 5360 Workman Mill Rd, Whittier, CA 90601-2298. TEL 562-699-0541, FAX 562-699-9721, http://www.icbo.org.

COUNCIL ON TALL BUILDINGS AND URBAN HABITAT. COLLECTED PAPERS. see *HOUSING AND URBAN PLANNING*

COUNCIL ON TALL BUILDINGS AND URBAN HABITAT. PROCEEDINGS. see *HOUSING AND URBAN PLANNING*

▼ *new title* ➤ *refereed* ✶ *unverified* ♦ *full entry avail.*

690 747 USA ISSN 1532-8732
NA7205
COUNTRY LIVING DREAM HOMES. Text in English. 1988-1989; resumed 1994. s-a. USD 3.95 newsstand/cover. adv. illus.
Document type: *Consumer.* **Description:** Offers house plans and ideas for the best in farm houses, fantasy cottages, classic Colonials, and Victorian homes.
Related titles: Online - full text ed.: (from EBSCO Publishing).
Published by: Hearst Corporation, Hearst Special Publications, 1790 Broadway, New York, NY 10019. TEL 212-830-2910, FAX 212-586-3455, http://www.hearstcorp.com. Ed. Pamela Abrahams. Pub. Brian J Doyle. Adv. contact Phil Decarlo. Circ: 250,000 (paid).

690 720 USA
COUNTRYPOLITAN HOMES & PLANS. Text in English. 1992. q. USD 19.50; USD 4.99 newsstand/cover (effective 2000). adv.
Document type: *Magazine, Consumer.* **Description:** Features homes that combine warmth of the country with the amenities of today's most innovative designs.
Published by: HomeStyles Publishing & Marketing, Inc., 213 E. 4th St., 4th Fl., St. Paul, MN 55101-1603. TEL 651-602-5000, FAX 651-602-5001, kbaruth@homestyles.com, http://www.homestyles.com. Ed. Eric Englund. R&P Roger Heegaard. Adv. contact Shelley Junker. B&W page USD 3,910, color page USD 4,830; trim 8 x 10.75. Circ: 59,000.

690 USA ISSN 1089-3466
COUNTRY'S BEST LOG HOMES. Text in English. 1996. bi-m. USD 19.95 domestic; USD 20.96 elsewhere; USD 3.99 per issue (effective 2003). **Document type:** *Magazine, Consumer.*
Description: Covers milled log homes; includes design, buy, build, maintain and decorate information.
Published by: Sovereign Media, 453 Carlisle Dr, Herndon, VA 20170-4819. TEL 703-964-0361, FAX 703-964-0366.

CRANE HOT LINE. see *MACHINERY*

690.028 USA ISSN 1070-0188
TJ1363
CRANE WORKS. Text in English. 1992. bi-m. free to qualified personnel. adv. back issues avail.; reprints avail. **Document type:** *Magazine, Trade.* **Description:** Covers the how-to of crane and rigging operations. Focuses on safety standards, procedures of crane operations, and information on the latest equipment and technology.
Indexed: BrCerAb, C&ISA, CerAb, CorrAb, E&CAJ, EMA, IAA, M&TEA, MBF, METADEX, SolStAb, WAA.
—Linda Hall.
Published by: Zweig White Information Services, 204 West Kansas, Ste 103, Independence, MO 64050. TEL 816-254-8735, FAX 816-254-2128, http://www.mercormedia.com/ME2/Audiences/default.asp. Ed., Pub. Michael Scheibach. Circ: 9,834. **Subscr. to:** Box 510, Fayette, MO 65248. TEL 660-248-3256, subs@mercormedia.com.

690.028 GBR ISSN 0260-745X
CRANES TODAY HANDBOOK. Text in English. 1974. a. GBP 63 domestic; GBP 75 in Europe; USD 125 in US & Canada; GBP 78 elsewhere (effective 1999). adv. **Document type:** *Trade.*
Published by: Wilmington Publishing Ltd. (Subsidiary of: Wilmington Group Plc), Maidstone Rd, Footscray, Sidcup, Kent DA14 5HZ, United Kingdom. TEL 44-1322-277788, FAX 44-1322-276474, cranestoday@wilmington.co.uk. Ed. Phil Bishop. Pub., R&P John Hopley. Adv. contact Alistair Newton. Circ: 5,000. **Subscr. to:** WDIS, PO Box 200, Ruislip, Mddx HA4 0SY, United Kingdom. TEL 44-20-8841-8545, FAX 44-20-8841-9676.

CUNZHEN JIANSHE/TOWN OR VILLAGE DEVELOPMENT. see *ARCHITECTURE*

692.8 USA ISSN 0161-7257
TH435
CURRENT CONSTRUCTION COSTS. Text in English. 1963. a. USD 69.95 (effective 2001). **Document type:** *Trade.*
Description: Contains unit construction costs with Open Shop and Union installation costs, as well as material cost and man-hours. Also includes assembly costs, square foot building costs, location factors, and indexes.
Published by: Saylor Publications, Inc., 9420 Topanga Canyon Blvd, Ste 203, Chatsworth, CA 91311. TEL 818-718-5966, FAX 818-718-8024. Ed., R&P Stanley J Strychaz. Circ: 8,000.

CURRENT CONSTRUCTION REPORTS: EXPENDITURES FOR RESIDENTIAL IMPROVEMENTS AND REPAIRS. see *HOUSING AND URBAN PLANNING*

CURRENT CONSTRUCTION REPORTS: HOUSING COMPLETIONS. see *HOUSING AND URBAN PLANNING*

CURRENT CONSTRUCTION REPORTS: HOUSING STARTS. see *HOUSING AND URBAN PLANNING*

CURRENT CONSTRUCTION REPORTS: HOUSING UNITS AUTHORIZED BY BUILDING PERMITS; states and selected metropolitan areas. see *HOUSING AND URBAN PLANNING*

CURRENT CONSTRUCTION REPORTS: NEW RESIDENTIAL CONSTRUCTION IN SELECTED METROPOLITAN AREAS. see *HOUSING AND URBAN PLANNING*

CURRENT CONSTRUCTION REPORTS: VALUE OF NEW CONSTRUCTION PUT IN PLACE. see *HOUSING AND URBAN PLANNING*

690 USA ISSN 1055-3479
NA7208
CUSTOM HOME. Text in English. 1991. 7/yr. USD 24 in US & Canada; USD 92 elsewhere; free to qualified personnel (effective 2005). adv. illus. back issues avail. **Document type:** *Magazine, Trade.* **Description:** Contains features on every facet of custom home building and design.
Incorporates (1976-1999): Custom Builder (0895-2493)
Related titles: Online - full text ed.: (from Gale Group); Supplement(s): Custom Home Outdoors. 2002.
—BLDSC (3506.116700), CISTI, IE, ingenta.
Published by: Hanley-Wood, LLC (Subsidiary of: J.P. Morgan Chase & Co.), One Thomas Circle, NW, Ste 600, Washington, DC 20005-5701. TEL 202-452-0800, FAX 202-785-1974, tjackson@hanleywood.com, http://www.customhomeonline.com, http://www.hanleywood.com. Ed. Leslie Ensor. Pub. Michael Boyle. Circ: 40,000 (paid and free).

CYPRUS. DEPARTMENT OF STATISTICS AND RESEARCH. CONSTRUCTION AND HOUSING STATISTICS. see *BUILDING AND CONSTRUCTION—Abstracting, Bibliographies, Statistics*

690 POL
CODEN: CZTEAY
CZASOPISMO TECHNICZNE. SERIA B: BUDOWNICTWO. Text in Polish; Contents page in Multiple languages. 1877; N.S. 1961. irreg. PLZ 20 (effective 2000). bk.rev. charts; illus. index. **Document type:** *Academic/Scholarly.*
Supersedes in part: Czasopismo Techniczne (0011-4561); Which was formerly (until 1883): Dzwignia (1230-2791)
Indexed: ChemAb.
—CASDDS, Linda Hall.
Published by: Politechnika Krakowska, Ul Warszawska 24, Krakow, 31155, Poland. TEL 48-12-6374289, FAX 48-12-6374289, TELEX 322468 PK PL. Ed. Elzbieta Nachlik. Adv. contact Ewa Malochleb. Circ: 12,000.

D B - DEUTSCHE BAUZEITUNG; Fachzeitschrift fuer Architekten und Bauingenieure. see *ARCHITECTURE*

D C A NEWS. see *PETROLEUM AND GAS*

D E M M. (Digest of Equipment, Materials and Management) see *ENGINEERING*

690 DEU ISSN 1438-7778
D I B T MITTEILUNGEN. Text in German. 1970. bi-m. EUR 110.28 in Europe to institutions; CHF 204 to institutions in Switzerland & Liechtenstein; USD 128 elsewhere to institutions; EUR 121.31 combined subscription in Europe to institutions print & online eds.; CHF 225 combined subscription to institutions in Switzerland & Liechtenstein; print & online eds.; USD 141 combined subscription elsewhere to institutions print & online eds. (effective 2006). **Document type:** *Journal, Trade.*
Formerly: Institut fuer Bautechnik. Mitteilungen (0172-3006)
Related titles: Online - full text ed.: ISSN 1437-1030. EUR 110.28 in Europe to institutions; CHF 204 to institutions in Switzerland & Leichtenstein; USD 128 elsewhere to institutions (effective 2006) (from EBSCO Publishing, Swets Information Services, Wiley InterScience).
Indexed: RefZh.
—CISTI, IE, Infotrieve. **CCC.**
Published by: (Institut fuer Bautechnik), Ernst und Sohn, Buehringstr 10, Berlin, 13086, Germany. TEL 49-30-47031200, FAX 49-30-47031240, marketing@ernst-und-sohn.de, http://www.wiley-vch.de/ernstsohn. Circ: 3,000. **Subscr. in the Americas to:** John Wiley & Sons, Inc., 111 River St, Hoboken, NJ 07030-5774. TEL 201-748-6645, FAX 201-748-6088, subinfo@wiley.com; **Subscr. to:** Wiley - V C H Verlag GmbH & Co. KGaA, Boschstr 12, Weinheim 69469, Germany. TEL 49-6201-606405, FAX 49-6201-606184.

691.2 DEU ISSN 0178-3343
D N I. (Die Naturstein Industrie) Text in German. 1965. 8/yr. adv. **Document type:** *Trade.* **Description:** Magazine of the German stone industry and its associations.
Formerly (until 1979): Naturstein-Industrie (0028-1034)
Indexed: DokStr, RefZh.
Published by: Stein-Verlag Baden-Baden GmbH, Josef Herrmann Str 1-3, Iffezheim, 76473, Germany. TEL 49-7229-606-0, FAX 49-7229-60610. Ed. Gabriela Schulz. Pub. Wilhelm Joesch. R&P Jutta Senn. Adv. contact Alfons John. Circ: 7,800.

690 DEU ISSN 0174-5336
D S B. (Die Schweizer Baustoff-Industrie) Text in French, German. 1969. 9/yr. adv. **Document type:** *Trade.*
Indexed: RefZh.
Published by: Stein-Verlag Baden-Baden GmbH, Josef Herrmann Str 1-3, Iffezheim, 76473, Germany. TEL 49-7229-606-0, FAX 49-7229-60610. Ed. Joachim Zeitner. Pub. Wilhelm Joesch. R&P Jutta Senn. Adv. contact Alfons John. Circ: 2,600.

DACH UND GRUEN; Fachmagazin fuer Bauwerksbegruenung Dach - Fassade - Innenraum. see *GARDENING AND HORTICULTURE*

695 CHE
DACH UND WAND; Schweizerischer Dachdeckmeister-Zeitung. Text in French, German. 1907. m. CHF 55. **Document type:** *Trade.* **Description:** Covers all aspects of roofing.
Published by: (Schweizerischer Dachdeckermeister Verband), Verlag Dach und Wand, Lindenstr 4, Uzwil, 9240, Switzerland. TEL 073-517244.

691 AUT
DACH UND WAND ABDICHTUNG. Text in German. m. EUR 48 domestic; EUR 69 foreign (effective 2005). adv. bk.rev. illus. **Document type:** *Magazine, Trade.*
Formerly: Oesterreichische Dachdecker- und Pflasterer-Zeitung (0029-8999)
Published by: (Bundes- und Landesinnungen der Dachdecker und Pflasterer), Oesterreichischer Wirtschaftsverlag GmbH (Subsidiary of: Sueddeutscher Verlag GmbH), Wiedner Hauptstr 120-124, Vienna, W 1051, Austria. TEL 43-1-546640, FAX 43-1-54664406, office@wirtschaftsverlag.at, http://www.wirtschaftsverlag.at. Ed. Birgit Tegtbauer. Adv. contact Rudolf Reiter. B&W page EUR 1,736, color page EUR 2,480; trim 185 x 255. Circ: 4,200 (paid and controlled).

695 DEU ISSN 1618-9612
DACHBAU-MAGAZIN. Text in German. 1952. m. EUR 81.90 domestic; EUR 93.55 foreign; EUR 7.50 newsstand/cover (effective 2004). adv. back issues avail. **Document type:** *Magazine, Trade.*
Formerly (until 2002): Der Dachdeckermeister (0343-382X)
Published by: Verlag F.H. Kleffmann GmbH, Herner Str 299, Bochum, 44809, Germany. TEL 49-234-95391-0, FAX 49-234-9539130, service@kleffmann-verlag.de, http://www.dachbau-magazin.de, http://www.kleffmann-verlag.de. adv.: B&W page EUR 2,410, color page EUR 4,220; trim 182 x 268. Circ: 14,858 (paid and controlled).

690 DEU ISSN 0172-1003
DAS DACHDECKER-HANDWERK; Zeitschrift fuer Wand-, Dach- und Abdichtungs-Technik. Short title: D D H. Text in German. 1949. s-m. EUR 163.50 domestic; EUR 186 foreign; EUR 11 newsstand/cover (effective 2004). adv. back issues avail. **Document type:** *Magazine, Trade.*
Former titles (until 1978): Das Dachdecker-Handwerk (0341-5422); (until 1971): Deutsches Dachdecker-Handwerk (0012-124X)
—IE.
Published by: (Zentralverband des Dachdeckerhandwerks e.V), Verlagsgesellschaft Rudolf Mueller GmbH & Co. KG, Stolberger Str 84, Cologne, 50933, Germany. TEL 49-221-54970, FAX 49-221-5497326, red.ddh@rudolf-mueller.de, service@rudolf-mueller.de, http://www.rudolf-mueller.de. Ed. Elke Herbst. Adv. contact Charles Greene. B&W page EUR 3,370, color page EUR 5,560; trim 188 x 267. Circ: 11,484 (paid).

690 DEU
DAEMM JOURNAL; Informationszeitung ueber den Nutzen des Daemmens fuer Mensch und Umwelt. Text in German. 1988. irreg. **Document type:** *Newspaper, Trade.*
Published by: Gesamtverband Daemmstoffindustrie, Carl-Benz-Str 7, Frankfurt Am Main, 60314, Germany. TEL 49-69-40893995, FAX 49-69-40143722, info@gdi-daemmstoffe.de, http://www.gdi-daemmstoffe.de. Circ: 800,000.

690 CAN ISSN 0317-3178
DAILY COMMERCIAL NEWS AND CONSTRUCTION RECORD. Text in English. 1929. d. (5/w..). CND 662.33; CND 846 foreign. adv.
Formerly: Daily Commercial News and Building Record (0317-316X)
Related titles: Online - full text ed.: (from Micromedia ProQuest).
Indexed: CBCABus, CBPI.
—CISTI.
Published by: Daily Commercial News (Subsidiary of: Southam Inc.), 280 Yorkland Blvd, North York, ON M2J 4Z6, Canada. TEL 416-494-4990, FAX 416-756-2767. Ed. Scott Button. Pub. Ian Hardy. Adv. contact Dave Watson. Circ: 4,600.

690 KOR
THE DAILY CONSTRUCTION NEWS. Text in Korean. d. **Document type:** *Newspaper.*
Formerly: Construction Association of Korea. Construction News Service
Published by: Construction Association of Korea, 71-2 Nonhyun dong, Kangnam-ku, Seoul, 135701, Korea, S.

692.8 USA ISSN 0011-5401
DAILY CONSTRUCTION SERVICE. Text in English. 1919. d. (Mon.-Fri.). USD 1,619 (effective 2005). adv. bk.rev. m. index. **Document type:** *Newspaper, Trade.* **Description:** Detailed descriptions of construction projects out for bid.
Published by: Construction Market Data, Inc., 4126 Pleasantdale Rd, Ste A8, Atlanta, GA 30340. TEL 800-949-0276, FAX 770-613-5978, http://www.cmdg.com. Ed., Adv. contact William B Wallace. page USD 750; trim 11 x 8.5. Circ: 2,500 (paid).

690 USA
DAILY CONSTRUCTION SERVICE - SOUTHERN CALIFORNIA. Text in English. d. (Mon.-Fri.). USD 1,185 (effective 2005). **Document type:** *Newspaper, Trade.*

Published by: Reed Construction Data, Associated Construction Publications (Subsidiary of: Reed Business Information), 30 Technology Pkwy, Ste 100, Norcross, GA 30092. TEL 770-417-4000, marketing@reedbusiness.com, http://www.reedconstructiondata.com. Eds. Brian Mulligan, Scott McGillvray. Pub. William B Wallace. Circ: 1,000 morning (paid).

690 USA
DAILY JOURNAL OF COMMERCE (GRETNA). Text in English. 1922. d. (Mon.-Fri.). USD 456; USD 300 for 6 mos.; USD 1.75 newsstand/cover (effective 2005). **Document type:** *Newspaper, Trade.*
Published by: Dolan Media Co., 118 Terry Pkwy, Gretna, LA 70056. TEL 504-368-8900, FAX 504-368-8999, mark.singletary@nopg.com, http://www.djc-gp.com/, http://www.dolanmedia.com/. Ed. Milton Lacoste. Pub. D Mark Singletary. Adv. contact Gary Laquin. Circ: 11,300 morning (paid).

690 USA ISSN 1084-970X
DAILY PACIFIC BUILDER. Text in English. 1895. d. (5/w..). USD 16 newsstand/cover (effective 2004). adv. charts; illus.; stat. **Document type:** *Newspaper, Trade.* **Description:** Provides sales leads.
Published by: Mcgraw-Hill Construction Dodge (Subsidiary of: McGraw-Hill Construction Information Group), 1333 S Mayflower Ave, 3rd Fl, Monrovia, CA 91016-4066. TEL 626-932-6161, 800-393-6343, FAX 626-932-6163, http://www.dodgeconstructionpublications.com. Ed. Paul Napolitano TEL 626-932-6169. Adv. contact Susan Miller TEL 877-887-7175. Circ: 2,000.

690 JPN ISSN 0914-3890
DAINIPPON KOBOKU K.K. GIJUTSU SHIRYO/DAI NIPPON CONSTRUCTION CO., LTD. TECHNICAL MATERIALS. Text in Japanese. 1963. a.
Published by: Dainippon Koboku K.K. Komu Honbu, 6-8 Usa-Minami 1-chome, Gifu-shi, 500-8367, Japan.

695 NLD ISSN 1381-2874
DAKENRAAD. Text in Dutch. 1994. bi-m. illus. **Document type:** *Trade.* **Description:** Provides information for contractors and architects who build, install, repair, and design roofs.
Published by: Arko Uitgeverij BV, Postbus 616, Nieuwegein, 3430 AP, Netherlands. TEL 31-30-605-1090, gerlings@arko.nl, http://www.arko.nl. Ed. A van den Hout. Pub. Marc Gerlings. Circ: 3,000.

693.5 DNK ISSN 0109-758X
DANSK BETON/DANISH CONCRETE. Text in Danish. 1972. q. adv. illus. **Document type:** *Trade.*
Formerly (until 1984): Dansk Beton Industri (0901-3091)
Published by: (Dansk Beton Industriforening), Parita Grafik A/S, Broendbytoften 11, Broendby, 2600, Denmark. TEL 45-36-38-25-25, FAX 45-36-16-25-20. Ed. Jan Broch Nielsen. Adv. contact Bjoern Quistgaard. B&W page DKK 7,200, color page DKK 13,600; trim 171 x 247. Circ: 6,800. **Co-sponsors:** Dansk Betonforening; Dansk Betonelementforening; Dansk Fabriksbetonforening.

690 USA ISSN 1552-9495
DAVISON'S FENCE BLUE BOOK. Text in English. 1866. a. USD 125 domestic (effective 2005). adv. 400 p./no. 3 cols./p.; **Document type:** *Magazine, Trade.*
Published by: Davison Publishing Co., Inc., 3452 Lake Lynda Dr, Ste 363, Orlando, FL 32817. TEL 407-380-8900, FAX 407-380-5222, info@davisonpublishing.com, http://www.davisonpublishing.com. adv.: B&W page USD 1,900. Circ: 10,000 (paid and controlled).

368 GBR
DAYWORK RATES UPDATING SERVICE. Text in English. 1986. irreg. GBP 150 (effective 2001). **Document type:** *Trade.*
Formerly: Building Cost Information Service Guide to Daywork Rates (0950-3250)
Published by: Building Cost Information Service Ltd., Royal Institution of Chartered Surveyors, Parliment Sq, 12 Great George St, London, SW1P 3AD, United Kingdom. TEL 44-20-7222-7000, FAX 44-20-7695-1501.

691 USA ISSN 1092-7395
DEALER & APPLICATOR. Text in English. 1971. 9/yr. USD 35 domestic; USD 45 foreign (effective 2005). adv. **Document type:** *Magazine, Trade.*
Formerly (until 1997): Custom Applicator (0011-4111)
Published by: Vance Publishing Corp., 400 Knightsbridge Pkwy, Lincolnshire, IL 60069. TEL 847-634-2600, 800-255-5113, FAX 847-634-4379, http://www.dealerandapplicator.com, http://www.vancepublishing.com. Ed. Rob Wiley. Circ: 16,000.

690 USA
DEAR BUILDER. Text in English. 2001. m. back issues avail. **Document type:** *Newsletter.* **Description:** Dedicated to providing readers with home building, maintenance, and improvement information available anywhere.
Media: E-mail. **Related titles:** Online - full text ed.
Published by: Infomedia Group, Inc., Box 444, Mendham, NJ 07945. contact@dearbuilder.com, http://www.dearbuilder.com/. Ed. Alan Isabelle.

690 ESP
DECOLETAJE. Text in Spanish. q. EUR 57 domestic; EUR 76 in Europe; USD 76 elsewhere (effective 2004). **Document type:** *Magazine, Trade.*
Published by: Metal Spain, Hermosilla 38, 1B, Madrid, 28001, Spain. TEL 34-91-5765609, FAX 34-91-5782924, magazine@metalspain.co, http://www.metalspain.com.

690 ITA ISSN 1128-7543
DEDALO. Text in Italian. 1974. 10/yr. adv. **Description:** Informs on projects, works in progress, and construction industry trends.
Formerly (until 1984): Nuova Edilizia Lombarda (1128-7535)
Published by: Assimpredil, Via S. Maurilio 21, Milan, 20123, Italy. TEL 39-02-88129501, FAX 39-02-8056802, http://www.assimpredilance.it. Circ: 10,000.

690 USA ISSN 1085-813X
DELAWARE VALLEY WEEKLY CONSTRUCTION REVIEW, COVERING LEHIGH VALLEY. Text in English. w. adv. **Document type:** *Newsletter, Trade.* **Description:** Provides information on what jobs are coming up for bid or negotiation.
Related titles: Online - full text ed.
Published by: Mcgraw-Hill Construction Dodge (Subsidiary of: McGraw-Hill Construction Information Group), 148 Princeton-Hightstown Rd, Hightstown, NJ 08520. TEL 800-393-6343, http://www.dodgeconstructionpublications.com.

690 NLD ISSN 1386-1077
DELFT MARITIEM. Text in Dutch. 1995. irreg., latest vol.7, 1997. price varies. **Document type:** *Monographic series.*
Published by: Delft University Press (Subsidiary of: Technische Universiteit Delft/Delft University of Technology), PO Box 98, Delft, 2600 MG, Netherlands. TEL 31-15-2785121, FAX 31-15-2781661, dup@dup.tudelft.nl.

DEMOLICION Y RECICLAJE; tecnicas de demolicion y recuperacion de materiales. see *ENGINEERING—Engineering Mechanics And Materials*

690 USA ISSN 1522-5690
DEMOLITION; the voice of the demolition industry. Text in English. 1973. bi-m. USD 40 (effective 2005). adv. 56 p./no. 3 cols./p.; back issues avail.; reprints avail. **Document type:** *Magazine, Trade.* **Description:** Contains articles that discuss technical aspects of structural demolition and salvage and disposal of contents.
Formerly: Demolition Age (0362-7772)
—CISTI.
Published by: National Association of Demolition Contractors, 16 N Frankin St, Ste 203, Doylestown, PA 18901-4949. TEL 215-348-8282, 800-541-2412, FAX 215-348-8422, info@demolitionmagazine.com, http://www.demolitionmagazine.com. Ed. Michael R Taylor. adv.: B&W page USD 1,700. Circ: 4,700 (paid and free).

690 GBR
DEMOLITION & DISMANTLING. Text in English. q. **Description:** Received by demolition companies, construction organizations, manufacturers and distributors of machinery, plants and vehicles.
Address: Computer House, 65 Mortimer Rd, Mitcham, CR4 3HS, United Kingdom. TEL 081-648-9286, FAX 081-685-9473. Ed. John Bergen. Circ: 4,000.

690 628.4 GBR ISSN 1465-9778
DEMOLITION & RECYCLING INTERNATIONAL. Text in English. 1999. bi-m. GBP 27 in United Kingdom; GBP 43.95 foreign (effective 2001). adv. bk.rev. charts; illus.; maps; mkt.; stat.; tr.lit. back issues avail. **Document type:** *Trade.*
Published by: K H L Group Ltd., Southfields, Southview Rd, Wadhurst, E Sussex TN5 6TP, United Kingdom. TEL 44-1892-784088, FAX 44-1892-784086, mail@khl.com, http://www.khl.com. Ed. Paul Marsden. Pub. James King. R&P Peter Watkinson. Adv. contact David Stowe. B&W page GBP 1,470, color page GBP 2,000; trim 210 x 297. Circ: 500 (paid); 7,000 (controlled).

343.489078 DNK ISSN 0108-9803
DENMARK. BOLIGMINISTERIET. BUILDING REGULATIONS. Text in Danish. 1977. irreg.
Published by: Boligministeriet/Ministry of Housing and Building, Slotholmsgade 1-3, Departmentets 4 kontor, Copenhagen K, 1216, Denmark.

690 USA
DENVER DAILY JOURNAL. Text in English. 1897. d. (Mon.-Fri.). USD 1,944 (effective 2005). adv. charts; illus.; stat. **Document type:** *Newspaper, Trade.* **Description:** Provides sales leads for Denver construction industry.
Related titles: Microfiche ed.
Published by: Mcgraw-Hill Construction Dodge (Subsidiary of: McGraw-Hill Construction Information Group), 200 SW Michigan St., Ste. 100, Seattle, WA 98106-3906. http://www.dodgeconstructionpublications.com. Pub. Al Slattery. Adv. contact Diana Murphy. Circ: 10,000.

DESIGN - BUILD; serving design-builders and owners in the worldwide, nonresidential construction market. see *ENGINEERING—Civil Engineering*

690 721 USA ISSN 1086-9433
TH1
DESIGN - BUILD BUSINESS. Text in English. 1935. m. USD 66; free to qualified personnel (effective 2004). adv. bk.rev. back issues avail.; reprints avail. **Document type:** *Magazine, Trade.* **Description:** Presents features, news, project examples, of interest to builders, architects, designers and remodelers.
Former titles (until 1996): Sun - Coast Architect - Builder (0744-8872); Formed by the merger of: Western Building Design (0192-1568); Pacific Coast Builder (0192-1703)
Related titles: Online - full text ed.: (from ProQuest Information & Learning).
Published by: McKellar Publications, Inc., 221 E. Glenoaks Blvd., Ste. 120, Glendale, CA 91207-2122. TEL 818-241-0250, FAX 818-241-4406. Ed. Paula Doyle. Pub. Kirk Moen. adv.: B&W page USD 8,306, color page USD 9,601. Circ: 52,000 (controlled).

DESIGN COST DATA; the cost estimating magazine for architects, builders and specifiers. see *ARCHITECTURE*

690 USA
DESIGN INDEX. Text in English. a. USD 59.95 (effective 2001). **Description:** A reference sourcebook for local commercial and residential design professionals.
Formerly: Chicago - Midwest Design Index
Published by: The Ashley Group, 1350 E Touhy Ave, Des Plaines, IL 60018. TEL 847-390-2821, FAX 847-390-2902, pcasper@cahners.com, http://www.theashleygroup.com/designindex.html. Ed., Pub. Paul A Casper.

691 USA
DESIGN MANUAL. Text in English. s-a. USD 25 per issue.
Published by: Steel Deck Institute, PO Box 25, Fox River Grove, IL 60021-0025. TEL 847-462-1930, FAX 847-462-1940, http://www.sdi.org. R&P Steven Roehrig.

DESIGN TRENDS. see *ARCHITECTURE*

643.7 USA
DESIGNER SHOWCASE. Text in English. a. adv. **Document type:** *Magazine, Consumer.*
Published by: Hanley-Wood, LLC (Subsidiary of: J.P. Morgan Chase & Co.), One Thomas Circle, NW, Ste 600, Washington, DC 20005-5701. TEL 202-452-0800, FAX 202-785-1974, http://www.hanleywood.com. adv.: color page USD 17,500; trim 8 x 10.5.

DESIGNER'S BEST HOME PLANS. see *ARCHITECTURE*

DETAIL; Zeitschrift fuer Architektur & Baudetail. see *ARCHITECTURE*

690 USA ISSN 1085-1895
DETROIT METRO CONSTRUCTION NEWS WEEKLY. Text in English. 1995. w. adv. **Document type:** *Newsletter, Trade.* **Description:** Provides information on what jobs are coming up for bid or negotiation.
Related titles: Online - full text ed.
Published by: Mcgraw-Hill Construction Dodge (Subsidiary of: McGraw-Hill Construction Information Group), 148 Princeton-Hightstown Rd, Hightstown, NJ 08520. TEL 800-393-6343, http://www.dodgeconstructionpublications.com.

690 DEU
DEUTSCHE BAUINDUSTRIE - JAHRESBERICHT. Text in German. a. **Document type:** *Bulletin, Trade.*
Published by: Hauptverband der Deutschen Bauindustrie, Kurfurstenstr. 129, Berlin, 10785, Germany. TEL 49-30-21286-0.

DEUTSCHER BAUKATALOG. see *ARCHITECTURE*

690 DEU ISSN 0939-8791
DEUTSCHES BAUBLATT. Text in German. m.
Supersedes (1974-1988): Baugeraetemarkt
Address: Im Bondorf 30, Linz, 53545, Germany. TEL 08387-399-0, FAX 038387-299-33, TELEX 541121. Ed. Martin A Schmitt. Circ: 28,500. **Dist. by:** Buchdruckerei Holzer, Fridolin Holzer Str 22, Postfach 159, Weiler-Simmerberg 88171, Germany.

690 333.333 USA ISSN 0888-6067
DEVELOPMENT (HERNDON). Text in English. 1969. q. USD 65 to non-members; USD 50 to members; USD 5 newsstand/cover (effective 2005). adv. bk.rev. tr.lit. **Document type:** *Magazine, Trade.* **Description:** Covers the full range of commercial real estate.
Formerly: N A I O P News
Indexed: AIAP.
Published by: National Association of Industrial and Office Properties, 2201 Cooperative Way, Ste 300, Herndon, VA 20171. TEL 703-904-7100, FAX 703-904-7942, turner@naiop.org, http://www.naiop.org. Ed., R&P Sheila Kelly Vertino. Pub. Shirley A Maloney. adv.: B&W page USD 2,365, color page USD 3,375; trim 8.375 x 11. Circ: 25,000 (paid).

B

▼ new title ➤ refereed ✶ unverified ♦ full entry avail.

690 DEU
DAS DICKE DEUTSCHE BAUBUCH; Alles ueber gute Einfamilienhaeuser. Text in German. 1998. a. EUR 14.50 domestic; EUR 17 foreign (effective 2003). adv. **Document type:** *Directory, Trade.*
Published by: biz Verlag GmbH Berlin, Tschaikowskistr. 40-42, Berlin, 13156, Germany. TEL 49-30-437380, FAX 49-30-43738111, info@biz-verlag.de, http://www.biz-verlag.de/baubuch/index-high.html. Ed. Doris Neumann. Pub., Adv. contact Peter Neumann. page EUR 6,214.

349 FRA ISSN 0012-2467
DICTIONNAIRE PERMANENT: CONSTRUCTION ET URBANISME. Text in French. 1962. 3 base vols. plus m. updates. looseleaf. EUR 330 base vol(s). (effective 2004). bibl. index, cum.index. **Description:** Examines judicial problems encountered in construction and urbanization.
Published by: Editions Legislatives, 80 Avenue de la Marne, Montrouge, Cedex 92546, France. TEL 33-1-40923636, FAX 33-1-40923663, infocom@editions-legislatives.fr, http://www.editions-legislatives.fr. Ed. Christine Vignes Basques. Pub. Michel Vaillant. Circ: 9,000.

B

690 621.8 USA
DIRECTIONAL DRILLING. Text in English. 1996. bi-m. Free to qualified subscribers.. adv. **Document type:** *Magazine, Trade.* **Description:** Covers news and events about the horizontal directional drilling construction industry.
Published by: Benjamin Media, Inc., 1770 Main St, Box 190, Peninsula, OH 44264. TEL 330-467-7588, FAX 330-468-2289, ttmag@ttmag.com, http://www.directionaldrilling.com, http://www.ttmag.com. Pub. Robert Krzys. Adv. contact Kelley Dadich.

DIRECTIVOS CONSTRUCCION. see *REAL ESTATE*

690 IND
DIRECTORY OF BUILDERS AND CONTRACTORS. Text in English. 1987. irreg. USD 20. adv. charts; illus. **Document type:** *Directory.* **Description:** Regional listing of names, addresses and telephone numbers of builders and property developers, civil, electrical, sanitary and painting contractors.
Published by: Architects Publishing Corp. of India, 51 Sujata, Ground Fl., Rani Sati Marg, Malad East, Mumbai, Maharashtra 400 097, India. TEL 91-22-883-4442. Ed. A K Gupta. Circ: 5,000.

DIRECTORY OF BUILDING CODES & REGULATIONS. see *HOUSING AND URBAN PLANNING*

690 USA
DIRECTORY OF LICENSED PRODUCTS. Text in English. 1961. a. free. **Document type:** *Directory.*
Published by: Air Movement and Control Association, 30 W University Dr, Arlington, IL 60004. TEL 708-394-0150, FAX 708-253-0088. Ed. Mark Stevens. Circ: 12,000.

DIRECTORY OF MANUFACTURERS & DEALERS OF BUILDING INDUSTRY. see *BUSINESS AND ECONOMICS—Trade And Industrial Directories*

690 BRA ISSN 0012-3358
DIRIGENTE CONSTRUTOR. Text in Portuguese. 1964. m. USD 70. adv. bk.rev. charts; illus.; stat. index, cum.index.
Published by: Editora Visao Ltda., Rua Alvaro de Carvalho, 354, Centro, Sao Paulo, SP 01050-070, Brazil. TEL 256-5011, FAX 258-1919. Ed. Hamilton Lucas de Oliviera. Circ: 23,889.

343.078 USA
DISCOVERY IN CONSTRUCTION LITIGATION. Text in English. 1994. w/ current supplement), latest 1994, base vol. plus irreg. updates. USD 115 (effective 2003). **Description:** Explores aspects of discovery such as litigation support systems, privileges, and alternative dispute resolution; includes interrogatories and requests, appendices with sample forms, lists of documents and discovery rules.
Published by: Michie Company (Subsidiary of: LexisNexis North America), 701 E Water St, Charlottesville, VA 22902-5389. TEL 434-972-7600, 800-446-3410, FAX 434-972-7677, http://www.michie.com. Eds. Barry B Bramble, Frank M Rapoport, Michael T Callahan.

690 USA
DISTINCTIVE WOOD HOMES✶. Text in English. 2001. q. USD 9.99 newsstand/cover (effective 2001). adv. **Document type:** *Magazine, Consumer.*
Published by: Goodman Media Group, Inc., 250 W 57th St, Ste 710, New York, NY 10107-0799. TEL 212-541-7100, FAX 212-245-1241. Ed. Roland Sweet. Pub. Jason Goodman.

690 USA ISSN 0897-6236
NA7205
DISTINGUISHED HOME PLANS. Text in English. 1985. q. USD 23.50; USD 5.98 newsstand/cover; CND 9.25 newsstand/cover in Canada (effective 2000). adv. **Document type:** *Magazine, Consumer.* **Description:** Contains executive home plans that offer the ultimate in elegance.
Published by: HomeStyles Publishing & Marketing, Inc., 213 E. 4th St., 4th Fl., St. Paul, MN 55101-1603. TEL 651-602-5000, 888-626-2026, FAX 651-602-5001, http://www.homestyles.com. Ed. Sara Freund. R&P Roger Heegaard. Adv. contact Shelley Junker. B&W page USD 3,910, color page USD 4,830; trim 8 x 10.75. Circ: 52,500.

728 USA
DISTINGUISHED HOME PLANS & PRODUCTS - CUSTOM HOME PLANS GUIDE. Text in English. 1950. q. USD 1.75. adv.
Formerly: Distinguished Home Plans and Products
Published by: Master Plan Service, Inc., c/o National Home Plan, 37 Mountain Ave, Springfield, NJ 07087. Ed. Kenneth Miller. Circ: 70,000.

690 USA ISSN 0012-4281
TA1
DIXIE CONTRACTOR. Text in English. 1926. s-m. USD 96 domestic; USD 126 in Canada; USD 166 elsewhere (effective 2005). adv. illus.; tr.lit. back issues avail. **Document type:** *Magazine, Trade.*
Related titles: Online - full text ed.: (from Gale Group, ProQuest Information & Learning).
—CCC.
Published by: Reed Construction Data, Associated Construction Publications (Subsidiary of: Reed Business Information), 30 Technology Pkwy, Ste 100, Norcross, GA 30092. TEL 770-417-4122, 800-322-6996, FAX 800-895-8661, sdhudson@reedbusiness.com, http://www.acppubs.com, http://www.acppubs.com/. Ed. Steve Hudson TEL 678-297-7999. Pub., Adv. contact John Weatherhead. B&W page USD 1,663, color page USD 2,163. Circ: 8,500 (controlled).

690 BEL ISSN 0771-176X
DOBBIT MAGAZINE (FRENCH EDITION); la seule revue Belge de bricolage pour le consommateur. Text in French. 1982. 10/yr. EUR 31 (effective 2005). adv. illus.; tr.lit. **Document type:** *Consumer.* **Description:** Offers tips and information for consumers interested in do-it-yourself renovating, remodeling, gardening, and landscaping.
Related titles: Dutch ed.: Dobbit Magazine (Dutch Edition). ISSN 0771-1719.
Published by: Professional Media Group, Torhoutsesteenweg 226 bus 2/6, Zedelgem, B-8210, Belgium. TEL 32-50-240404, FAX 32-50-240445, info@pmgroup.be, http://www.dobbit.be/?lang=f, http://www.pmgroup.be. Ed. Wim Depondt. Circ: 25,000 (paid).

690 BEL ISSN 0774-1421
DOBBIT PROFESSIONAL (FRENCH EDITION). Text in French. 1987. 11/yr. EUR 68 (effective 2005). adv. illus.; tr.lit. Supplement avail. **Document type:** *Trade.* **Description:** Covers new products, techniques, and marketing news for the building materials distribution professional.
Related titles: Dutch ed.: Dobbit Professional (Dutch Edition). ISSN 0774-1413.
Published by: Professional Media Group, Torhoutsesteenweg 226 bus 2/6, Zedelgem, B-8210, Belgium. TEL 32-50-240404, FAX 32-50-240445, info@pmgroup.be, http://www.retail-diy.be/?lang=f, http://www.pmgroup.be. Ed. Inez Costenoble. adv.: color page EUR 2,025; trim 297 x 210. Circ: 7,500 (controlled).

690 USA ISSN 1071-5037
DODGE CONSTRUCTION NEWS. CHICAGO✶. Text in English. 1946. d. (Mon.-Fri.). USD 1,680 (effective 2004). adv. charts; illus.; mkt.; stat.; tr.mk. **Document type:** *Newspaper, Trade.* **Description:** Classified, legal and display ads for Chicago construction projects.
Former titles: Chicago Dodge Construction News (0012-480X); Chicago Construction News
Published by: Mcgraw-Hill Construction Dodge (Subsidiary of: McGraw-Hill Construction Information Group), 130 E Randolph St, Ste 400, Chicago, IL 60601-6213. TEL 312-233-7470, 800-393-6343, FAX 312-233-7430, http://www.dodgeconstructionpublications.com. Ed. Craig Barner TEL 312-233-7471. Adv. contact Mamie DiGangi TEL 312-233-7473.

690 USA ISSN 1085-8121
DODGE CONSTRUCTION NEWS. CONNECTICUT. Text in English. 1992. w. adv. **Document type:** *Newsletter, Trade.* **Description:** Provides information on what jobs are coming up for bid or negotiation.
Related titles: Online - full text ed.
Published by: Mcgraw-Hill Construction Dodge (Subsidiary of: McGraw-Hill Construction Information Group), 148 Princeton-Hightstown Rd, Hightstown, NJ 08520. TEL 800-393-6343, http://www.dodgeconstructionpublications.com.

690 USA
DODGE CONSTRUCTION NEWS. LOS ANGELES EDITION. Text in English. 1865. d. USD 1,392. adv. charts; illus.; stat. **Document type:** *Trade.* **Description:** Classified, legal and display ads for Los Angeles construction projects.
Published by: Mcgraw-Hill Construction Dodge (Subsidiary of: McGraw-Hill Construction Information Group), 148 Princeton-Hightstown Rd, Hightstown, NJ 08520. TEL 800-393-6343, http://www.dodgeconstructionpublications.com. Circ: 4,250.

690 USA
F.W. DODGE CONSTRUCTION NEWS WEEKLY COVERING ALBANY. Text in English. 1993. w. adv. **Document type:** *Newsletter, Trade.* **Description:** Provides information on what jobs are coming up for bid or negotiation.
Formerly (until 199?): Dodge Construction News Weekly Covering Albany (1085-8148)
Related titles: Online - full text ed.
Published by: Mcgraw-Hill Construction Dodge (Subsidiary of: McGraw-Hill Construction Information Group), 148 Princeton-Hightstown Rd, Hightstown, NJ 08520. TEL 800-393-6343, http://www.dodgeconstructionpublications.com.

690 USA
F.W. DODGE CONSTRUCTION NEWS WEEKLY COVERING AUSTIN. Text in English. 1995. w. adv. **Document type:** *Newsletter, Trade.* **Description:** Provides information on what jobs are coming up for bid or negotiation.
Formerly (until 199?): Construction News Weekly Covering Austin - San Antonio (1086-6167)
Related titles: Online - full text ed.
Published by: Mcgraw-Hill Construction Dodge (Subsidiary of: McGraw-Hill Construction Information Group), 148 Princeton-Hightstown Rd, Hightstown, NJ 08520. TEL 800-393-6343, http://www.dodgeconstructionpublications.com.

690 USA ISSN 1095-094X
F.W. DODGE CONSTRUCTION NEWS WEEKLY COVERING BALTIMORE, MARYLAND. Variant title: Construction News Weekly Covering Baltimore, Maryland. Text in English. w. adv. **Document type:** *Newsletter, Trade.* **Description:** Provides information on what jobs are coming up for bid or negotiation.
Formerly (until 199?): Baltimore Construction News (1086-5330)
Related titles: Online - full text ed.
Published by: Mcgraw-Hill Construction Dodge (Subsidiary of: McGraw-Hill Construction Information Group), 148 Princeton-Hightstown Rd, Hightstown, NJ 08520. TEL 800-393-6343, http://www.dodgeconstructionpublications.com.

690 USA
F.W. DODGE CONSTRUCTION NEWS WEEKLY COVERING BATON ROUGE. Text in English. 1995. w. adv. **Document type:** *Newsletter, Trade.* **Description:** Provides information on what jobs are coming up for bid or negotiation.
Formerly (until 199?): Construction News Weekly Covering Baton Rouge & Vicinity (1086-6213)
Related titles: Online - full text ed.
Published by: Mcgraw-Hill Construction Dodge (Subsidiary of: McGraw-Hill Construction Information Group), 148 Princeton-Hightstown Rd, Hightstown, NJ 08520. TEL 800-393-6343, http://www.dodgeconstructionpublications.com.

690 USA ISSN 1089-943X
F.W. DODGE CONSTRUCTION NEWS WEEKLY COVERING BEAUMONT, TX - LAKE CHARLES, LA. Text in English. w. adv. **Document type:** *Newsletter, Trade.* **Description:** Provides information on what jobs are coming up for bid or negotiation.
Related titles: Online - full text ed.
Published by: Mcgraw-Hill Construction Dodge (Subsidiary of: McGraw-Hill Construction Information Group), 148 Princeton-Hightstown Rd, Hightstown, NJ 08520. TEL 800-393-6343, http://www.dodgeconstructionpublications.com.

690 USA ISSN 1085-8202
F.W. DODGE CONSTRUCTION NEWS WEEKLY COVERING BROOKLYN & QUEENS. Text in English. 1995. w. adv. **Document type:** *Newsletter, Trade.* **Description:** Provides information on what jobs are coming up for bid or negotiation.
Related titles: Online - full text ed.
Published by: Mcgraw-Hill Construction Dodge (Subsidiary of: McGraw-Hill Construction Information Group), 148 Princeton-Hightstown Rd, Hightstown, NJ 08520. TEL 800-393-6343, http://www.dodgeconstructionpublications.com.

690 USA ISSN 1095-1482
F.W. DODGE CONSTRUCTION NEWS WEEKLY COVERING BUFFALO, NEW YORK AND VICINITY. Text in English. 1994. w. adv. **Document type:** *Newsletter, Trade.* **Description:** Provides information on what jobs are coming up for bid or negotiation.
Formerly (until 199?): Construction News Weekly Covering Buffalo & Vicinity (1085-8156)
Related titles: Online - full text ed.
Published by: Mcgraw-Hill Construction Dodge (Subsidiary of: McGraw-Hill Construction Information Group), 148 Princeton-Hightstown Rd, Hightstown, NJ 08520. TEL 800-393-6343, http://www.dodgeconstructionpublications.com.

690 USA ISSN 1085-195X
F.W. DODGE CONSTRUCTION NEWS WEEKLY, COVERING CENTRAL AND SOUTHERN ILLINOIS. Key Title: Weekly Construction News, Covering Central & Southern Illinois. Text in English. w. adv. **Document type:** *Newsletter, Trade.* **Description:** Provides information on what jobs are coming up for bid or negotiation.
Related titles: Online - full text ed.
Published by: Mcgraw-Hill Construction Dodge (Subsidiary of: McGraw-Hill Construction Information Group), 148 Princeton-Hightstown Rd, Hightstown, NJ 08520. TEL 800-393-6343, http://www.dodgeconstructionpublications.com.

690   USA   ISSN 1094-107X
F.W. DODGE CONSTRUCTION NEWS WEEKLY COVERING CENTRAL INDIANA. Text in English. 1992. w. adv. **Document type:** *Newsletter, Trade.* **Description:** Provides information on what jobs are coming up for bid or negotiation.
Formerly (until 199?): Dodge Building Review Covering Central Indiana (1085-1925)
Related titles: Online - full text ed.
Published by: Mcgraw-Hill Construction Dodge (Subsidiary of: McGraw-Hill Construction Information Group), 148 Princeton-Hightstown Rd, Hightstown, NJ 08520. TEL 800-393-6343, http://www.dodgeconstructionpublications.com.

690   USA   ISSN 1095-0974
F.W. DODGE CONSTRUCTION NEWS WEEKLY COVERING CENTRAL NEW JERSEY. Text in English. w. adv. **Document type:** *Newsletter, Trade.* **Description:** Provides information on what jobs are coming up for bid or negotiation.
Formerly (until 199?): Weekly Construction Review Covering Central New Jersey (1085-8237)
Related titles: Online - full text ed.
Published by: Mcgraw-Hill Construction Dodge (Subsidiary of: McGraw-Hill Construction Information Group), 148 Princeton-Hightstown Rd, Hightstown, NJ 08520. TEL 800-393-6343, http://www.dodgeconstructionpublications.com.

690   USA   ISSN 1086-6183
F.W. DODGE CONSTRUCTION NEWS WEEKLY, COVERING DALLAS & VICINITY. Key Title: Construction News Weekly, Covering Dallas & Vicinity. Text in English. 1995. w. adv. **Document type:** *Newsletter, Trade.* **Description:** Provides information on what jobs are coming up for bid or negotiation.
Related titles: Online - full text ed.
Published by: Mcgraw-Hill Construction Dodge (Subsidiary of: McGraw-Hill Construction Information Group), 148 Princeton-Hightstown Rd, Hightstown, NJ 08520. TEL 800-393-6343, http://www.dodgeconstructionpublications.com.

690   USA   ISSN 1095-1024
F.W. DODGE CONSTRUCTION NEWS WEEKLY COVERING EASTERN MASSACHUSETTS. Text in English. w. adv. **Document type:** *Newsletter, Trade.* **Description:** Provides information on what jobs are coming up for bid or negotiation.
Formerly (until 199?): Massachusetts Construction News Weekly, Covering Eastern Massachusetts (1085-3812)
Related titles: Online - full text ed.
Published by: Mcgraw-Hill Construction Dodge (Subsidiary of: McGraw-Hill Construction Information Group), 148 Princeton-Hightstown Rd, Hightstown, NJ 08520. TEL 800-393-6343, http://www.dodgeconstructionpublications.com.

690   USA   ISSN 1095-0591
F.W. DODGE CONSTRUCTION NEWS WEEKLY COVERING EASTERN MISSOURI. Text in English. 1993. w. adv. **Document type:** *Newsletter, Trade.* **Description:** Provides information on what jobs are coming up for bid or negotiation.
Formerly (until 1997): Weekly Construction News Covering Eastern Missouri (1085-1844)
Related titles: Online - full text ed.
Published by: Mcgraw-Hill Construction Dodge (Subsidiary of: McGraw-Hill Construction Information Group), 148 Princeton-Hightstown Rd, Hightstown, NJ 08520. TEL 800-393-6343, http://www.dodgeconstructionpublications.com.

690   USA   ISSN 1086-6116
F.W. DODGE CONSTRUCTION NEWS WEEKLY COVERING EASTERN OKLAHOMA. Key Title: Construction News Weekly, Covering Eastern Oklahoma. Text in English. w. adv. **Document type:** *Newsletter, Trade.* **Description:** Provides information on what jobs are coming up for bid or negotiation.
Related titles: Online - full text ed.
Published by: Mcgraw-Hill Construction Dodge (Subsidiary of: McGraw-Hill Construction Information Group), 148 Princeton-Hightstown Rd, Hightstown, NJ 08520. TEL 800-393-6343, http://www.dodgeconstructionpublications.com.

690   USA   ISSN 1086-623X
F.W. DODGE CONSTRUCTION NEWS WEEKLY COVERING GREATER KANSAS CITY. Key Title: Construction News Weekly Covering Kansas City. Text in English. 1992. w. adv. **Document type:** *Newsletter, Trade.* **Description:** Provides information on what jobs are coming up for bid or negotiation.
Related titles: Online - full text ed.
Published by: Mcgraw-Hill Construction Dodge (Subsidiary of: McGraw-Hill Construction Information Group), 148 Princeton-Hightstown Rd, Hightstown, NJ 08520. TEL 800-393-6343, http://www.dodgeconstructionpublications.com.

690   USA   ISSN 1086-6159
F.W. DODGE CONSTRUCTION NEWS WEEKLY COVERING HOUSTON. Key Title: Construction News Weekly Covering Houston. Text in English. w. adv. **Document type:** *Newsletter, Trade.* **Description:** Provides information on what jobs are coming up for bid or negotiation.
Related titles: Online - full text ed.
Published by: Mcgraw-Hill Construction Dodge (Subsidiary of: McGraw-Hill Construction Information Group), 148 Princeton-Hightstown Rd, Hightstown, NJ 08520. TEL 800-393-6343, http://www.dodgeconstructionpublications.com.

690   USA
F.W. DODGE CONSTRUCTION NEWS WEEKLY COVERING JACKSONVILLE AND VICINITY. Text in English. w. adv. **Document type:** *Newsletter, Trade.* **Description:** Provides information on what jobs are coming up for bid or negotiation.
Formerly (until 199?): Florida Construction News Covering Jacksonville & Vicinity (1085-2247)
Related titles: Online - full text ed.
Published by: Mcgraw-Hill Construction Dodge (Subsidiary of: McGraw-Hill Construction Information Group), 148 Princeton-Hightstown Rd, Hightstown, NJ 08520. TEL 800-393-6343, http://www.dodgeconstructionpublications.com.

690   USA   ISSN 1088-3711
F.W. DODGE CONSTRUCTION NEWS WEEKLY COVERING LONG ISLAND∗ . Key Title: Construction News Weekly Covering Long Island. Text in English. 1995. w. adv. **Document type:** *Newsletter, Trade.* **Description:** Provides information on what jobs are coming up for bid or negotiation.
Related titles: Online - full text ed.
Published by: Mcgraw-Hill Construction Dodge (Subsidiary of: McGraw-Hill Construction Information Group), 148 Princeton-Hightstown Rd, Hightstown, NJ 08520. TEL 800-393-6343, http://www.dodgeconstructionpublications.com.

690   USA   ISSN 1095-1431
F.W. DODGE CONSTRUCTION NEWS WEEKLY COVERING METROPOLITAN PHILADELPHIA AND DELAWARE. Text in English. w. adv. **Document type:** *Newsletter, Trade.* **Description:** Provides information on what jobs are coming up for bid or negotiation.
Formerly (until 199?): Delaware Valley Weekly Construction Review, Covering Metro Philadelphia & Delaware (1086-5357)
Related titles: Online - full text ed.
Published by: Mcgraw-Hill Construction Dodge (Subsidiary of: McGraw-Hill Construction Information Group), 148 Princeton-Hightstown Rd, Hightstown, NJ 08520. TEL 800-393-6343, http://www.dodgeconstructionpublications.com.

690   USA   ISSN 1094-1096
F.W. DODGE CONSTRUCTION NEWS WEEKLY COVERING MINNESOTA AND WESTERN WISCONSIN. Text in English. 1991. w. adv. **Document type:** *Newsletter, Trade.* **Description:** Provides information on what jobs are coming up for bid or negotiation.
Formerly (until 199?): Minnesota Construction News (1085-5785)
Related titles: Online - full text ed.
Published by: Mcgraw-Hill Construction Dodge (Subsidiary of: McGraw-Hill Construction Information Group), 148 Princeton-Hightstown Rd, Hightstown, NJ 08520. TEL 800-393-6343, http://www.dodgeconstructionpublications.com.

690   USA   ISSN 1095-0990
F.W. DODGE CONSTRUCTION NEWS WEEKLY COVERING NORFOLK & VICINITY. Text in English. w. adv. **Document type:** *Newsletter, Trade.* **Description:** Provides information on what jobs are coming up for bid or negotiation.
Formerly (until 199?): Virginia Construction Weekly Covering Norfolk & Vicinity (1086-5233)
Related titles: Online - full text ed.
Published by: Mcgraw-Hill Construction Dodge (Subsidiary of: McGraw-Hill Construction Information Group), 148 Princeton-Hightstown Rd, Hightstown, NJ 08520. TEL 800-393-6343, http://www.dodgeconstructionpublications.com.

690   USA   ISSN 1085-1860
CODEN: SDBNAR
F.W. DODGE CONSTRUCTION NEWS WEEKLY, COVERING NORTHEAST WISCONSIN - UPPER PENINSULA. Text in English. w. adv. **Document type:** *Newsletter, Trade.* **Description:** Provides information on what jobs are coming up for bid or negotiation.
Related titles: Online - full text ed.
Published by: Mcgraw-Hill Construction Dodge (Subsidiary of: McGraw-Hill Construction Information Group), 148 Princeton-Hightstown Rd, Hightstown, NJ 08520. TEL 800-393-6343, http://www.dodgeconstructionpublications.com.

690   USA   ISSN 1095-0826
F.W. DODGE CONSTRUCTION NEWS WEEKLY COVERING NORTHERN INDIANA. Text in English. 1992. w. adv. **Document type:** *Newsletter, Trade.* **Description:** Provides information on what jobs are coming up for bid or negotiation.
Formerly (until 1997): Dodge Building Review Covering Northern Indiana (1085-1933)
Related titles: Online - full text ed.
Published by: Mcgraw-Hill Construction Dodge (Subsidiary of: McGraw-Hill Construction Information Group), 148 Princeton-Hightstown Rd, Hightstown, NJ 08520. TEL 800-393-6343, http://www.dodgeconstructionpublications.com.

690   USA   ISSN 1095-1040
F.W. DODGE CONSTRUCTION NEWS WEEKLY COVERING NORTHERN NEW JERSEY. Text in English. w. adv. **Document type:** *Newsletter, Trade.* **Description:** Provides information on what jobs are coming up for bid or negotiation.
Formerly (until 199?): Weekly Construction Review Covering Northern New Jersey (1085-8229)
Related titles: Online - full text ed.

Published by: Mcgraw-Hill Construction Dodge (Subsidiary of: McGraw-Hill Construction Information Group), 148 Princeton-Hightstown Rd, Hightstown, NJ 08520. TEL 800-393-6343, http://www.dodgeconstructionpublications.com.

690   USA   ISSN 1099-2944
F.W. DODGE CONSTRUCTION NEWS WEEKLY COVERING PITTSBURGH, PENNSYLVANIA AND VICINITY. Text in English. w. adv. **Document type:** *Newsletter, Trade.* **Description:** Provides information on what jobs are coming up for bid or negotiation.
Formerly (until 199?): Dodge Construction News Weekly Covering Pittsburgh and Vicinity (1087-0938)
Related titles: Online - full text ed.
Published by: Mcgraw-Hill Construction Dodge (Subsidiary of: McGraw-Hill Construction Information Group), 148 Princeton-Hightstown Rd, Hightstown, NJ 08520. TEL 800-393-6343, http://www.dodgeconstructionpublications.com.

690   USA   ISSN 1095-1008
F.W. DODGE CONSTRUCTION NEWS WEEKLY COVERING RICHMOND, VIRGINIA AND VICINITY. Text in English. w. adv. **Document type:** *Newsletter, Trade.* **Description:** Provides information on what jobs are coming up for bid or negotiation.
Formerly (until 199?): Virginia Construction Weekly, Covering Richmond & Vicinity (1085-8180)
Related titles: Online - full text ed.
Published by: Mcgraw-Hill Construction Dodge (Subsidiary of: McGraw-Hill Construction Information Group), 148 Princeton-Hightstown Rd, Hightstown, NJ 08520. TEL 800-393-6343, http://www.dodgeconstructionpublications.com.

690   USA   ISSN 1095-144X
F.W. DODGE CONSTRUCTION NEWS WEEKLY COVERING ROCHESTER, NEW YORK AND VICINITY. Text in English. 1994. w. adv. **Document type:** *Newsletter, Trade.* **Description:** Provides information on what jobs are coming up for bid or negotiation.
Formerly (until 199?): Construction News Weekly Covering Rochester & Vicinity (1085-8164)
Related titles: Online - full text ed.
Published by: Mcgraw-Hill Construction Dodge (Subsidiary of: McGraw-Hill Construction Information Group), 148 Princeton-Hightstown Rd, Hightstown, NJ 08520. TEL 800-393-6343, http://www.dodgeconstructionpublications.com.

690   USA
DODGE CONSTRUCTION NEWS WEEKLY COVERING SOUTHERN CALIFORNIA INCLUDING NEVADA. Text in English. w. adv. **Document type:** *Newsletter, Trade.* **Description:** Provides information on what jobs are coming up for bid or negotiation.
Related titles: Online - full text ed.
Published by: Mcgraw-Hill Construction Dodge (Subsidiary of: McGraw-Hill Construction Information Group), 148 Princeton-Hightstown Rd, Hightstown, NJ 08520. TEL 800-393-6343, http://www.dodgeconstructionpublications.com.

690   USA   ISSN 1094-1045
F.W. DODGE CONSTRUCTION NEWS WEEKLY COVERING SOUTHERN INDIANA. Text in English. 1992. w. adv. **Document type:** *Newsletter, Trade.* **Description:** Provides information on what jobs are coming up for bid or negotiation.
Formerly (until 199?): Dodge Building Review Covering Southern Indiana (1085-1917)
Related titles: Online - full text ed.
Published by: Mcgraw-Hill Construction Dodge (Subsidiary of: McGraw-Hill Construction Information Group), 148 Princeton-Hightstown Rd, Hightstown, NJ 08520. TEL 800-393-6343, http://www.dodgeconstructionpublications.com.

690   USA   ISSN 1095-0958
F.W. DODGE CONSTRUCTION NEWS WEEKLY COVERING SOUTHERN NEW JERSEY AND DELAWARE. Text in English. w. adv. **Document type:** *Newsletter, Trade.* **Description:** Provides information on what jobs are coming up for bid or negotiation.
Formerly (until 199?): Weekly Construction Review Covering Southern New Jersey & Delaware (1085-8245)
Related titles: Online - full text ed.
Published by: Mcgraw-Hill Construction Dodge (Subsidiary of: McGraw-Hill Construction Information Group), 148 Princeton-Hightstown Rd, Hightstown, NJ 08520. TEL 800-393-6343, http://www.dodgeconstructionpublications.com.

690   USA   ISSN 1094-1053
F.W. DODGE CONSTRUCTION NEWS WEEKLY COVERING ST. LOUIS, MISSOURI AND VICINITY. Text in English. w. adv. **Document type:** *Newsletter, Trade.* **Description:** Provides information on what jobs are coming up for bid or negotiation.
Formerly (until 199?): Weekly Construction News Covering St. Louis & Vicinity (1085-1828)
Related titles: Online - full text ed.
Published by: Mcgraw-Hill Construction Dodge (Subsidiary of: McGraw-Hill Construction Information Group), 148 Princeton-Hightstown Rd, Hightstown, NJ 08520. TEL 800-393-6343, http://www.dodgeconstructionpublications.com.

B

▼ *new title*   ➤ *refereed*   ∗ *unverified*   ◆ *full entry avail.*

690 USA ISSN 1095-1458
F.W. DODGE CONSTRUCTION NEWS WEEKLY COVERING SYRACUSE, NEW YORK & VICINITY. Text in English. 1994. w. adv. **Document type:** *Newsletter, Trade.* **Description:** Provides information on what jobs are coming up for bid or negotiation.
Formerly (until 199?): Construction News Weekly Covering Syracuse & Vicinity (1085-8172)
Related titles: Online - full text ed.
Published by: Mcgraw-Hill Construction Dodge (Subsidiary of: McGraw-Hill Construction Information Group), 148 Princeton-Hightstown Rd, Hightstown, NJ 08520. TEL 800-393-6343, http://www.dodgeconstructionpublications.com.

690 USA ISSN 1095-1474
F.W. DODGE CONSTRUCTION NEWS WEEKLY COVERING THE HUDSON VALLEY, NEW YORK. Text in English. 1993. w. adv. **Document type:** *Newsletter, Trade.* **Description:** Provides information on what jobs are coming up for bid or negotiation.
Formerly (until 199?): Construction News Weekly Covering the Hudson Valley (1086-525X)
Related titles: Online - full text ed.
Published by: Mcgraw-Hill Construction Dodge (Subsidiary of: McGraw-Hill Construction Information Group), 148 Princeton-Hightstown Rd, Hightstown, NJ 08520. TEL 800-393-6343, http://www.dodgeconstructionpublications.com.

690 USA ISSN 1095-1466
F.W. DODGE CONSTRUCTION NEWS WEEKLY COVERING THE NORTH SHORE, MASSACHUSETTS. Text in English. w. adv. **Document type:** *Newsletter, Trade.* **Description:** Provides information on what jobs are coming up for bid or negotiation.
Formerly (until 199?): Massachusetts Construction News Weekly Covering the North Shore (1086-5276)
Related titles: Online - full text ed.
Published by: Mcgraw-Hill Construction Dodge (Subsidiary of: McGraw-Hill Construction Information Group), 148 Princeton-Hightstown Rd, Hightstown, NJ 08520. TEL 800-393-6343, http://www.dodgeconstructionpublications.com.

690 USA ISSN 1095-0966
F.W. DODGE CONSTRUCTION NEWS WEEKLY COVERING THE SOUTH SHORE, MASSACHUSETTS. Text in English. w. adv. **Document type:** *Newsletter, Trade.* **Description:** Provides information on what jobs are coming up for bid or negotiation.
Formerly (until 199?): Massachusetts Construction News Weekly Covering the South Shore (1086-5314)
Related titles: Online - full text ed.
Published by: Mcgraw-Hill Construction Dodge (Subsidiary of: McGraw-Hill Construction Information Group), 148 Princeton-Hightstown Rd, Hightstown, NJ 08520. TEL 800-393-6343, http://www.dodgeconstructionpublications.com.

690 USA ISSN 1094-6160
F.W. DODGE CONSTRUCTION NEWS WEEKLY COVERING THE STATE OF ALABAMA. Text in English. w. adv. **Document type:** *Newsletter, Trade.* **Description:** Provides information on what jobs are coming up for bid or negotiation.
Formerly (until 199?): Alabama Construction News Weekly Covering the State of Alabama (1085-2204)
Related titles: Online - full text ed.
Published by: Mcgraw-Hill Construction Dodge (Subsidiary of: McGraw-Hill Construction Information Group), 148 Princeton-Hightstown Rd, Hightstown, NJ 08520. TEL 800-393-6343, http://www.dodgeconstructionpublications.com.

690 USA ISSN 1094-1037
F.W. DODGE CONSTRUCTION NEWS WEEKLY COVERING THE STATE OF ARKANSAS. Text in English. 1992. w. adv. **Document type:** *Newsletter, Trade.* **Description:** Provides information on what jobs are coming up for bid or negotiation.
Formerly (until 199?): Arkansas Construction News Weekly (1086-6256)
Related titles: Online - full text ed.
Published by: Mcgraw-Hill Construction Dodge (Subsidiary of: McGraw-Hill Construction Information Group), 148 Princeton-Hightstown Rd, Hightstown, NJ 08520. TEL 800-393-6343, http://www.dodgeconstructionpublications.com.

690 USA ISSN 1094-6152
F.W. DODGE CONSTRUCTION NEWS WEEKLY COVERING THE STATE OF GEORGIA. Variant title: Construction News Weekly Covering the State of Georgia. Text in English. w. adv. **Document type:** *Newsletter, Trade.* **Description:** Provides information on what jobs are coming up for bid or negotiation.
Formerly (until 199?): Dodge Construction News Weekly Covering Georgia (1085-2220)
Related titles: Online - full text ed.
Published by: Mcgraw-Hill Construction Dodge (Subsidiary of: McGraw-Hill Construction Information Group), 148 Princeton-Hightstown Rd, Hightstown, NJ 08520. TEL 800-393-6343, http://www.dodgeconstructionpublications.com.

690 USA ISSN 1094-1061
F.W. DODGE CONSTRUCTION NEWS WEEKLY COVERING THE STATE OF IOWA. Text in English. w. adv. **Document type:** *Newsletter, Trade.* **Description:** Provides information on what jobs are coming up for bid or negotiation.
Formerly (until 199?): Iowa Construction News (1069-1820)
Related titles: Online - full text ed.
Published by: Mcgraw-Hill Construction Dodge (Subsidiary of: McGraw-Hill Construction Information Group), 148 Princeton-Hightstown Rd, Hightstown, NJ 08520. TEL 800-393-6343, http://www.dodgeconstructionpublications.com.

690 USA ISSN 1096-4533
F.W. DODGE CONSTRUCTION NEWS WEEKLY COVERING THE STATE OF KANSAS, EXCLUDING KANSAS CITY. Text in English. w. adv. **Document type:** *Newsletter, Trade.* **Description:** Provides information on what jobs are coming up for bid or negotiation.
Formerly (until 1996): Construction News Weekly Covering Kansas (1087-4070)
Related titles: Online - full text ed.
Published by: Mcgraw-Hill Construction Dodge (Subsidiary of: McGraw-Hill Construction Information Group), 148 Princeton-Hightstown Rd, Hightstown, NJ 08520. TEL 800-393-6343, http://www.dodgeconstructionpublications.com.

690 USA ISSN 1095-0923
F.W. DODGE CONSTRUCTION NEWS WEEKLY COVERING THE STATE OF MAINE. Text in English. w. adv. **Document type:** *Newsletter, Trade.* **Description:** Provides information on what jobs are coming up for bid or negotiation.
Formerly (until 199?): Maine Construction News Weekly (1086-5292)
Related titles: Online - full text ed.
Published by: Mcgraw-Hill Construction Dodge (Subsidiary of: McGraw-Hill Construction Information Group), 148 Princeton-Hightstown Rd, Hightstown, NJ 08520. TEL 800-393-6343, http://www.dodgeconstructionpublications.com.

690 USA ISSN 1095-0982
F.W. DODGE CONSTRUCTION NEWS WEEKLY COVERING THE STATE OF NEW HAMPSHIRE. Text in English. w. adv. **Document type:** *Newsletter, Trade.* **Description:** Provides information on what jobs are coming up for bid or negotiation.
Formerly (until 199?): New Hampshire Construction News Weekly (1086-5284)
Related titles: Online - full text ed.
Published by: Mcgraw-Hill Construction Dodge (Subsidiary of: McGraw-Hill Construction Information Group), 148 Princeton-Hightstown Rd, Hightstown, NJ 08520. TEL 800-393-6343, http://www.dodgeconstructionpublications.com.

690 USA ISSN 1099-2952
F.W. DODGE CONSTRUCTION NEWS WEEKLY COVERING THE STATE OF WEST VIRGINIA. Text in English. 1995. w. adv. **Document type:** *Newsletter, Trade.* **Description:** Provides information on what jobs are coming up for bid or negotiation.
Formerly (until 199?): Weekly Construction News Covering West Virginia (1087-0962)
Related titles: Online - full text ed.
Published by: Mcgraw-Hill Construction Dodge (Subsidiary of: McGraw-Hill Construction Information Group), 148 Princeton-Hightstown Rd, Hightstown, NJ 08520. TEL 800-393-6343, http://www.dodgeconstructionpublications.com.

690 USA ISSN 1095-1490
F.W. DODGE CONSTRUCTION NEWS WEEKLY COVERING WASHINGTON D.C. Text in English. w. adv. **Document type:** *Newsletter, Trade.* **Description:** Provides information on what jobs are coming up for bid or negotiation.
Formerly (until 199?): Washington, D.C. Construction News (1086-5322)
Related titles: Online - full text ed.
Published by: Mcgraw-Hill Construction Dodge (Subsidiary of: McGraw-Hill Construction Information Group), 148 Princeton-Hightstown Rd, Hightstown, NJ 08520. TEL 800-393-6343, http://www.dodgeconstructionpublications.com.

690 USA ISSN 1094-5415
F.W. DODGE CONSTRUCTION NEWS WEEKLY COVERING WEST CENTRAL FLORIDA. Text in English. w. adv. **Document type:** *Newsletter, Trade.* **Description:** Provides information on what jobs are coming up for bid or negotiation.
Formerly (until 199?): Florida Construction News Covering West Central Florida (1085-2263)
Related titles: Online - full text ed.
Published by: Mcgraw-Hill Construction Dodge (Subsidiary of: McGraw-Hill Construction Information Group), 148 Princeton-Hightstown Rd, Hightstown, NJ 08520. TEL 800-393-6343, http://www.dodgeconstructionpublications.com.

690 USA ISSN 1095-1032
F.W. DODGE CONSTRUCTION NEWS WEEKLY COVERING WESTERN MASSACHUSETTS. Text in English. w. adv. **Document type:** *Newsletter, Trade.* **Description:** Provides information on what jobs are coming up for bid or negotiation.
Formerly (until 199?): Massachusetts Construction News Weekly, Covering Western Massachusetts (1086-5306)
Related titles: Online - full text ed.
Published by: Mcgraw-Hill Construction Dodge (Subsidiary of: McGraw-Hill Construction Information Group), 148 Princeton-Hightstown Rd, Hightstown, NJ 08520. TEL 800-393-6343, http://www.dodgeconstructionpublications.com.

690 USA ISSN 1096-8377
F.W. DODGE CONSTRUCTION NEWS WEEKLY COVERING WESTERN NORTH CAROLINA. Text in English. w. adv. **Document type:** *Newsletter, Trade.* **Description:** Provides information on what jobs are coming up for bid or negotiation.
Formerly (until 199?): Weekly Construction Review Covering Western North Carolina (1085-827X)
Related titles: Online - full text ed.
Published by: Mcgraw-Hill Construction Dodge (Subsidiary of: McGraw-Hill Construction Information Group), 148 Princeton-Hightstown Rd, Hightstown, NJ 08520. TEL 800-393-6343, http://www.dodgeconstructionpublications.com.

690 USA ISSN 1085-1909
DODGE CONSTRUCTION NEWS WEEKLY, COVERING WESTERN PENNSYLVANIA. Text in English. 1995. w. adv. **Document type:** *Newsletter, Trade.* **Description:** Provides information on what jobs are coming up for bid or negotiation.
Related titles: Online - full text ed.
Published by: Mcgraw-Hill Construction Dodge (Subsidiary of: McGraw-Hill Construction Information Group), 148 Princeton-Hightstown Rd, Hightstown, NJ 08520. TEL 800-393-6343, http://www.dodgeconstructionpublications.com.

690 USA ISSN 1088-3541
DODGE CUSTOM NEWSLETTER COVERING WAL MART. Text in English. w. adv. **Document type:** *Newsletter, Trade.* **Description:** Provides information on what jobs are coming up for bid or negotiation.
Related titles: Online - full text ed.
Published by: Mcgraw-Hill Construction Dodge (Subsidiary of: McGraw-Hill Construction Information Group), 148 Princeton-Hightstown Rd, Hightstown, NJ 08520. TEL 800-393-6343, http://www.dodgeconstructionpublications.com.

690 USA
DODGE PIPELINE. Text in English. base vol. plus q. updates. USD 31,900 for 110 markets and five property types; USD 15,000 for one property type (effective 2002). **Document type:** *Trade.* **Description:** Provides detailed information on commercial construction projects that enables users to gauge potential over-supply as well as to monitor competitive projects as they progress through the planning cycle.
Media: CD-ROM.
Published by: F.W. Dodge, Real Estate Group (Subsidiary of: McGraw-Hill Construction Information Group), 24 Hartwell Ave, Lexington, MA 02173. TEL 800-591-4462, FAX 781-860-6884, info@mcgraw-hill.com, http://www.mag.fwdodge.com/realestate/aboutpip.htm, http://fwdodge.construction.com/Analytics/.

690 USA
DODGE REPAIR & REMODEL COST BOOK; the sourcebook - labor and material costs for residential and light commercial construction. Text in English. 1986. a. USD 59.95 (effective 1998). **Description:** Contains over 10,000 component costs categorized by C.S.I. 16-division format. Labor and material costs as well as productivity rates are constantly researched.
Former titles (until 1992): Repair and Remodelling Quarterly; (until 1988): Dodge Remodelling and Retrofit Cost Data
Published by: Marshall & Swift, 911 Wilshire Vlvd, Los Angeles, CA 90017-3409. TEL 800-544-2678, FAX 213-683-9043. Ed. Fred Atkinson. Circ: 3,000.

690 USA ISSN 1087-0997
F.W. DODGE WEEKLY CONSTRUCTION NEWS, COVERING CINCINNATI & VICINITY. Key Title: Weekly Construction News, Covering Cincinnati & Vicinity. Text in English. 1995. w. adv. **Document type:** *Newsletter, Trade.* **Description:** Provides information on what jobs are coming up for bid or negotiation.
Related titles: Online - full text ed.
Published by: Mcgraw-Hill Construction Dodge (Subsidiary of: McGraw-Hill Construction Information Group), 148 Princeton-Hightstown Rd, Hightstown, NJ 08520. TEL 800-393-6343, http://www.dodgeconstructionpublications.com.

690 USA ISSN 1088-1425
F.W. DODGE WEEKLY CONSTRUCTION NEWS, COVERING CLEVELAND, AKRON, CANTON. Text in English. 1993. w. adv. **Document type:** *Newsletter, Trade.* **Description:** Provides information on what jobs are coming up for bid or negotiation.
Formerly (until 1995): Weekly Construction News Covering Northeast Ohio (1085-1836)
Related titles: Online - full text ed.
Published by: Mcgraw-Hill Construction Dodge (Subsidiary of: McGraw-Hill Construction Information Group), 148 Princeton-Hightstown Rd, Hightstown, NJ 08520. TEL 800-393-6343, http://www.dodgeconstructionpublications.com.

690 USA ISSN 1087-0970
F.W. DODGE WEEKLY CONSTRUCTION NEWS, COVERING COLUMBUS & VICINITY. Key Title: Weekly Construction News, Covering Columbus & Vicinity. Text in English. 1995. w. adv. **Document type:** *Newsletter, Trade.* **Description:** Provides information on what jobs are coming up for bid or negotiation.
Related titles: Online - full text ed.

B

Published by: Mcgraw-Hill Construction Dodge (Subsidiary of: McGraw-Hill Construction Information Group), 148 Princeton-Hightstown Rd, Hightstown, NJ 08520. TEL 800-393-6343, http://www.dodgeconstructionpublications.com.

690 USA ISSN 1087-0989
F.W. DODGE WEEKLY CONSTRUCTION NEWS, COVERING DAYTON & VICINITY. Key Title: Weekly Construction News, Covering Dayton & Vicinity. Text in English. 1995. w. adv. **Document type:** *Newsletter, Trade.* **Description:** Provides information on what jobs are coming up for bid or negotiation.
Related titles: Online - full text ed.
Published by: Mcgraw-Hill Construction Dodge (Subsidiary of: McGraw-Hill Construction Information Group), 148 Princeton-Hightstown Rd, Hightstown, NJ 08520. TEL 800-393-6343, http://www.dodgeconstructionpublications.com.

690 USA ISSN 1087-1012
F.W. DODGE WEEKLY CONSTRUCTION NEWS, COVERING EASTERN KENTUCKY. Key Title: Weekly Construction News, Covering Eastern Kentucky. Text in English. w. adv. **Document type:** *Newsletter, Trade.* **Description:** Provides information on what jobs are coming up for bid or negotiation.
Related titles: Online - full text ed.
Published by: Mcgraw-Hill Construction Dodge (Subsidiary of: McGraw-Hill Construction Information Group), 148 Princeton-Hightstown Rd, Hightstown, NJ 08520. TEL 800-393-6343, http://www.dodgeconstructionpublications.com.

690 USA ISSN 1087-1020
F.W. DODGE WEEKLY CONSTRUCTION NEWS, COVERING LEXINGTON & VICINITY. Key Title: Weekly Construction News, Covering Lexington & Vicinity. Text in English. 1995. w. adv. **Document type:** *Newsletter, Trade.* **Description:** Provides information on what jobs are coming up for bid or negotiation.
Related titles: Online - full text ed.
Published by: Mcgraw-Hill Construction Dodge (Subsidiary of: McGraw-Hill Construction Information Group), 148 Princeton-Hightstown Rd, Hightstown, NJ 08520. TEL 800-393-6343, http://www.dodgeconstructionpublications.com.

690 USA ISSN 1085-8261
F.W. DODGE WEEKLY CONSTRUCTION REVIEW, COVERING EASTERN NORTH CAROLINA. Key Title: Weekly Construction Review, Covering Eastern North Carolina. Text in English. 1995. w. adv. **Document type:** *Newsletter, Trade.* **Description:** Provides information on what jobs are coming up for bid or negotiation.
Related titles: Online - full text ed.
Published by: Mcgraw-Hill Construction Dodge (Subsidiary of: McGraw-Hill Construction Information Group), 148 Princeton-Hightstown Rd, Hightstown, NJ 08520. TEL 800-393-6343, http://www.dodgeconstructionpublications.com.

643.7 747 RUS
DOM. Text in Russian. bi-m.
Published by: Izdatel'skii dom Gefest, B Semenovskaya 40, Moscow, 105023, Russian Federation. TEL 7-095-3662890, FAX 7-095-3662434. Ed. Yu S Stolyarov. **US dist. addr.:** East View Information Services, 3020 Harbor Ln. N., Minneapolis, MN 55447. TEL 612-550-0961.

690 POL ISSN 1506-6444
DOM (WARSAW, 1994). Text in Polish. 1994. w. **Document type:** *Consumer.*
Former titles (until 1997): Dom i Budownictwo (1506-6436); (until 1995): Gazeta o Domu (1232-1745)
Related titles: ◆ Supplement to: Gazeta Wyborcza. ISSN 0860-908X.
Published by: Agora S.A., ul Czerska 8/10, Warsaw, 00732, Poland. TEL 48-22-6994301, FAX 48-22-6994603, http://www.gazeta.pl.

690 POL ISSN 1505-3016
DOM DLA KOWALSKICH. Text in Polish. 1999. q. **Document type:** *Magazine, Trade.*
Published by: Wydawnictwo Murator Sp. z o.o., ul Kamionkowska 45, Warsaw, 03812, Poland. TEL 48-22-5905000, FAX 48-22-5905444, wydawnictwo@murator.com.pl, http://www.murator.com.pl.

690 POL ISSN 1427-2830
DOM DOSTEPNY. Text in Polish. 1996. a. **Document type:** *Journal, Trade.*
Published by: Wydawnictwo Murator Sp. z o.o., ul Kamionkowska 45, Warsaw, 03812, Poland. TEL 48-22-5905000, FAX 48-22-5905444, wydawnictwo@murator.com.pl, http://www.murator.com.pl.

690 POL ISSN 1233-8443
DOM LETNI. Text in Polish. 1995. a. **Document type:** *Magazine, Trade.*
Published by: Wydawnictwo Murator Sp. z o.o., ul Kamionkowska 45, Warsaw, 03812, Poland. TEL 48-22-5905000, FAX 48-22-5905444, wydawnictwo@murator.com.pl, http://www.murator.com.pl.

690 USA
DOOR AND ACCESS SYSTEMS. Text in English. 1990. q. **Document type:** *Trade.* **Description:** Covers garage door systems, rolling doors, grilles, and electronics.
Former titles: Garage Door Business; (until Jan. 1996): Door and Access Systems
Published by: Door & Access Systems Manufacturers Association, 1300 Sumner Ave, Cleveland, OH 44115-2851. TEL 216-241-7333, FAX 216-241-0105. Ed. Tom Wadsworth. Circ: 12,000 (controlled).

690 USA
DOOR & OPERATOR INDUSTRY. Text in English. bi-m. free. adv. index. **Description:** Provides news and information about the door and operator industry with a particular emphasis on the door and operator dealer.
Published by: International Door Association, P O Box 246, W. Milton, OH 45383. TEL 513-698-4188. Ed. Christopher S Long.

690 USA
DOOR & WINDOW MANUFACTURER. Abbreviated title: D W M. Text in English. m. (combined issues in Jan./Feb). USD 40 foreign; free domestic to qualified personnel (effective 2005). back issues avail. **Document type:** *Magazine, Trade.*
Published by: Key Communications, Inc., PO Box 569, Garrisonville, VA 22463. TEL 540-720-5584, http://www.dwmmag.com/, http://www.key-com.com/. Ed., Pub. Tara Taffera. Circ: 25,005 (controlled). **Subscr. to:** CirTec, 4 1/2 W. Wilson St, Ste C6, Batavia, IL 60510. FAX 630-482-3051.

338.4769 658 USA
DOOR & WINDOW RETAILING✶. Text in English. 1989. bi-m. USD 15. adv. **Document type:** *Trade.* **Description:** Provides news, technical reports, product descriptions, marketing concepts, trends, opinion and interviews about door and window marketing.
Former titles (until 1993): Door and Window Business; (until 1991): Door and Window Retailing
Published by: Jervis and Associates, 14255 Us Highway 1., # 200, Juno Beach, FL 33408-1490. TEL 908-850-8100. Ed. John H Jervis. Adv. contact Linda Callindritto. Circ: 16,000.

DOORS AND HARDWARE. see *BUILDING AND CONSTRUCTION—Hardware*

DROGOWNICTWO. see *ENGINEERING—Civil Engineering*

THE DROP CLOTH. see *PAINTS AND PROTECTIVE COATINGS*

690 352.9 USA ISSN 1055-4505
KF5701.Z95
DWELLING CONSTRUCTION UNDER THE UNIFORM MECHANICAL CODE. Text in English. 1991. triennial. USD 25.75 to non-members; USD 19.35 to members (effective 2000). **Document type:** *Trade.*
Published by: International Conference of Building Officials, 5360 Workman Mill Rd, Whittier, CA 90601-2298. TEL 562-699-0541, FAX 562-699-9721, http://www.icbo.org.

620 GBR
E & C BULLETIN. (Engineering & Construction) Text in English. 3/yr.
Published by: Kvaerner Engineering & Construction, 68 Hammersmith Rd, London, W14 8YW, United Kingdom. TEL 44-20-7339-1000, FAX 44-20-7339-1100, http://www.kvaerner.com/eandc/, http://www.kvaerner.com/EandC.

690 DEU ISSN 1611-8642
E B - ENERGIEEFFIZIENTES BAUEN. Text in German. 2000. q. EUR 28 domestic; EUR 44 foreign; EUR 9 newsstand/cover (effective 2005). adv. **Document type:** *Magazine, Trade.*
Published by: EnergieEffizientes Bauen Verlags GmbH, Kernerweg 18, Urbach, 73660, Germany. TEL 49-7181-885150, FAX 49-7181-884639, info@eb-magazin.de, http://www.eb-magazin.de. Ed., Adv. contact Gerhard Paulus. B&W page EUR 2,100, color page EUR 3,675; trim 180 x 270. Circ: 7,978 (paid and controlled).

690 AUS ISSN 0311-4783
E B S NOTES ON THE SCIENCE OF BUILDING. Text in English. 1949. irreg. price varies. illus. cum.index.
Former titles (until 1973): C E B S Notes on the Science of Building (0311-0427); Notes on the Science of Building (0300-371X)
Indexed: ARI.
—CISTI. **CCC.**
Published by: (Australia. Experimental Building Station), AusInfo, GPO Box 1920, Canberra Mc, ACT 2610, Australia. TEL 61-2-62633541, FAX 61-2-62634909. Circ: 6,000.

692.8 USA ISSN 0896-3169
CODEN: GNTKAC
E C A MAGAZINE. Text in English. 1957. m. USD 10. adv. bk.rev.
Formerly (until 1963): E G C A Magazine (Engineering and Grading Contractors Association)
Published by: Engineering Contractors' Association, 8310 Florence Ave, Downey, CA 90240. TEL 213-861-0929, FAX 213-923-6179. Ed. John Simpson. Circ: 2,034.

E N R; the construction weekly. (Engineering News Record) see *ENGINEERING—Civil Engineering*

690 USA
EARTH (LOS ANGELES). Text in English. 1955. q. USD 20. adv. charts; illus. reprint service avail. from PQC. **Document type:** *Trade.* **Description:** Earthmoving and heavy construction in Southern California.
Related titles: Microform ed.: (from PQC).
Published by: Shepherd Media Group, PO Box 6789, Los Angeles, CA 90022. TEL 310-463-4043, FAX 310-699-0491. Ed. David J Byrnes. R&P Frank Weir. Circ: 5,200 (controlled).

THE EARTHMOVER AND CIVIL CONTRACTOR. see *ENGINEERING—Civil Engineering*

690.24 FRA
ECHO DES CONCIERGES; bulletin des loges. Text in French. m. (10/yr.; double nos. for Jul.-Aug., Sep.-Oct.). adv.
Address: 17 rue du Dragon, Paris, 75006, France. Circ: 15,000.

B

690 USA ISSN 1055-8284
ECONOMIC HOME OWNER✶. Text in English. 1991. q. USD 29.99. adv. Supplement avail. **Document type:** *Consumer.* **Description:** Provides helpful information on a variety of topics relating to home repair, with information on industry trends.
Published by: Publishing & Business Consultants, 4427 W Slauson Ave, Los Angeles, CA 90043-2717. TEL 213-732-3477, FAX 213-732-9123. Ed. Andeson Napoleon Atia. Circ: 120,000.

690 AUT ISSN 1605-4628
ECOSOPHIA. Variant title: Ecosophia Newsletter. Text in German. 199?. m. adv. **Document type:** *Trade.*
Media: Online - full text.
Published by: Ecosophia Kommunikation, Laxenburgerstr 12-5, Wiener Neudorf, 2351, Austria. TEL 43-2236-62364-0, FAX 43-2236-623643, planung.verlag@ecosophia.at, http://www.ecosophia.at. Ed. Pia Bauer. Pub. Karl Keindl.

ECUADOR. INSTITUTO NACIONAL DE ESTADISTICA Y CENSOS. ENCUESTA ANUAL DE EDIFICACIONES. see *BUILDING AND CONSTRUCTION—Abstracting, Bibliographies, Statistics*

690 ARG ISSN 0328-0950
HD9715.A72
EDIFICACION, PERMISOS PARA CONSTRUCCIONES PRIVADAS. Text in Spanish. 1991. a., latest vol.7, 1997. ARS 15, USD 45 (effective 1999). **Document type:** *Government.*
Published by: Instituto Nacional de Estadistica y Censos, Avda. Presidente Julio A. Roca, 615 P B, Capital Federal, Buenos Aires 1067, Argentina. TEL 54-114-3499662, FAX 54-114-3499621, ces@indec.mecon.ar, http://www.indec.mecon.ar.

690 ITA
EDILIZIA (MILAN). Text in Italian. 6/yr. EUR 55 (effective 2005). **Document type:** *Magazine, Trade.*
Published by: De Lettera Editore, Via Tabino 25, Milan, MI 20131, Italy. http://www.delettera.it. Ed. Fiorino Ivan de Lettera. Circ: 8,000.

690 720 ITA
EDILIZIA (TURIN). Text in Italian. 22/yr.
Address: Via San Francesco da Paola, 37, Turin, TO 10123, Italy. TEL 39-011-540796. Ed. Ezio Gianotti. Circ: 4,000.

690 ITA ISSN 0422-5619
EDILIZIA POPOLARE. Text in Italian. 1954. bi-m. EUR 48 domestic; EUR 77 foreign (effective 2005). adv. bk.rev.; play rev. abstr.; bibl.; charts; illus.; stat.
Indexed: API.
Published by: (Associazione Nazionale fra gli Istituti Autonomi e Consorzi Case Popolari), Edizioni Edilizia Popolare, Via Cavour 179A, Rome, RM, Italy. TEL 39-06-47865460, FAX 39-06-47865444, edil.pop@agora.stm.it, http://www.federcasa.it/edilpop/index.htm. Ed. Enzo Collio.

690 ESP ISSN 0213-6287
EDITECO. Text in Spanish. 1986. 11/yr.
Address: Plaza Republica del Ecuador, 6, Madrid, 28016, Spain. TEL 34-91-2509943, FAX 34-91-4582606. Ed. Angel Bengoechea. Circ: 8,500.

696 333.79 USA
Z5943.E5
THE EFFICIENT HOUSE SOURCEBOOK; an annotated bibliography and directory of helpful organizations. Text in English. 1987. irreg., latest 1992. USD 15. bk.rev. **Document type:** *Directory, Bibliography.* **Description:** Comprehensive annotated survey of literature on home energy conservation, including design, renovation and retrofitting. Also lists government, non-profit and other organizations providing educational materials on energy efficiency.
Formerly (until 1992): Resource-Efficient Housing (1063-0112)
Published by: Rocky Mountain Institute, 1739 Snowmass Creek Rd, Snowmass, CO 81654-9199. TEL 970-927-3851, FAX 970-927-4178. Ed. Robert Sardinsky.

EHIMEKEN KENSETSU KENKYUJO KENKYUJOHO/EHIMEKEN CONSTRUCTION LABORATORY. REPORT. see *ENGINEERING—Civil Engineering*

▼ *new title* ➤ *refereed* ✶ *unverified* ◆ *full entry avail.*

643.7 USA
EICHLER NETWORK NEWSLETTER. Text in English. 1993. q. free to qualified personnel; USD 12 (effective 2005). bk.rev. back issues avail. **Document type:** *Newsletter, Consumer.* **Description:** Focuses on interior and exterior maintenance issues affecting the Eichler home, blended with historical retrospectives on the architecture, the late builder, and key figures from his staff; and feature stories on the homeowners and the pleasures of owning an Eichler.
Related titles: Online - full text ed.; Supplement(s): Eichler Network Home Maintenance Directory; House of Questions.
Published by: The Eichler Network, P O Box 22635, San Francisco, CA 94122. TEL 415-668-0954, FAX 415-661-1416, marty@eichlernetwork.com, http://www.eichlernetwork.com. Pub. Marty Arbunich. Circ: 15,000 (paid and free).

692.8 DEU
EINFAMILIENHAEUSER. Text in German. 1993. a. EUR 5 newsstand/cover (effective 2003). adv. **Document type:** *Magazine, Consumer.*
Published by: City-Post Verlagsgesellschaft mbH, Lessingstr 14, Munich, 80336, Germany. TEL 49-89-5990810, FAX 49-89-59908133, anzeigen@cpz.de, http://www.cpz.de. Adv. contact Sebastian Schmidt. B&W page EUR 5,100, color page EUR 8,100; trim 180 x 270. Circ: 72,000 (paid and controlled).

B

645 DEU
DAS EINFAMILIENHAUS. Text in German. 1982. bi-m. EUR 2.90 newsstand/cover (effective 2003). adv. **Document type:** *Magazine, Consumer.*
Published by: City-Post Verlagsgesellschaft mbH, Lessingstr 14, Munich, 80336, Germany. TEL 49-89-5990810, FAX 49-89-59908133, anzeigen@cpz.de, http://www.cpz.de/pub/pub_deh.htm. adv.: B&W page EUR 5,100, color page EUR 8,100; trim 180 x 270. Circ: 62,530 (paid and controlled).

690 CHE ISSN 1422-8467
DAS EINFAMILIENHAUS; das schweizer Magazin fuer Bauen, Wohnen, Haus und Garten. Text in German. 1977. bi-m. CHF 89 for 2 yrs. (effective 2003). adv. **Document type:** *Magazine, Consumer.*
Published by: Etzel-Verlag AG, Knonauerstr 56, Cham, 6330, Switzerland. TEL 41-41-7855085, FAX 41-41-7855088, info@etzel-verlag.ch, http://www.das-einfamilienhaus.ch. Ed. Christine Vollmer. Pub. Thomas Staehli. Adv. contact Sarah Eggerschwiler. B&W page CHF 4,070; trim 199 x 278. Circ: 73,451.

690 RUS ISSN 0013-3116
EKONOMIKA STROITEL'STVA. Text in Russian. 1959. m. USD 107 foreign (effective 2003). index.
Address: Troitskii 2-i per 6-a, str 9, Moscow, 129090, Russian Federation. TEL 7-095-2843295. **Dist. by:** M K - Periodica, ul Gilyarovskogo 39, Moscow 129110, Russian Federation. TEL 7-095-2845008, FAX 7-095-2813798, info@periodicals.ru, http://www.mkniga.ru; **Dist. in U.S. by:** Victor Kamkin Inc., 220 Girard St, Ste 1, Gaithersburg, MD 20877. TEL 301-881-1637, http://www.kamkin.com.

ELECTRICAL CONSTRUCTION MATERIALS DIRECTORY. see *ENGINEERING—Electrical Engineering*

690 DEU ISSN 0934-5914
ELEMENT UND BAU. Text in German. 1982. bi-m. EUR 9.50 newsstand/cover (effective 2003). adv. **Document type:** *Magazine, Trade.*
Formerly (until 1988): Element und Fertigbau
Indexed: INIS AtomInd.
Published by: Dr. Harnisch Verlagsgesellschaft GmbH, Blumenstr 15, Nuernberg, 90402, Germany. TEL 49-911-20180, FAX 49-911-2018100, e+b@harnisch.com, service@harnisch.com, http://www.harnisch.com/element_bau/index.htm. Ed. Armin Koenig. Pub. Benno Keller. adv.: B&W page EUR 2,135, color page EUR 3,335; trim 171 x 256. Circ: 6,400 (paid).

690 USA ISSN 0013-614X
ELEVATOR CONSTRUCTOR. Text in English. 1906. m. free membership. **Document type:** *Newspaper, Trade.*
Published by: International Union of Elevator Constructor Companies, 7154 Colombia Gateway Rd, Columbia, MD 21046. TEL 410-953-6150, FAX 410-953-6169, http://www.iuec.org. Ed., Pub. James Chapman. Circ: 17,500 (controlled).

690 GBR ISSN 1029-6840
ELEVATOR TECHNOLOGY. Text in English. 1996. irreg.
—BLDSC (3730.450000).
Published by: International Association of Elevator Engineers, PO Box 4372, Brentwood, Essex CM14 4PW, United Kingdom. TEL 44-1268-711560, FAX 44-1268-711567, http://www.elevcon.com.

690 USA ISSN 0013-6158
TJ1370
ELEVATOR WORLD. Text in English. 1953. m. USD 75 domestic; USD 110 foreign (effective 2005). adv. bk.rev. charts; illus.; pat.; tr.lit. index. back issues avail.; reprints avail. **Document type:** *Magazine, Trade.* **Description:** Covers the technical and business aspects of the elevator and escalator industry and related fields.
Related titles: Online - full text ed.: ISSN 1557-525X.
Indexed: BrCerAb, C&ISA, CISA, CerAb, CivEngAb, CorrAb, E&CAJ, EEA, EMA, EngInd, HRIS, IAA, M&TEA, MBF, METADEX, RefZh, SolStAb, WAA.
—BLDSC (3730.500000), Ei, IE, Infotrieve, ingenta, Linda Hall. **CCC.**
Published by: Elevator World, Inc., PO Box 6507, Mobile, AL 36660-6507. TEL 251-479-4514, 800-730-5093, FAX 251-479-7043, editorial@elevator-world.com, http://www.elevator-world.com/. Eds. Robert S Caporale, Stacie B Hyman. Pub. Ricia Sturgeon-Hendrick. Adv. contact Bruce T Mackinnon. Circ: 6,200 (paid).

690 USA
ELEVATOR WORLD SOURCE DIRECTORY. Text in English. a., latest 2001-2002. adv. **Document type:** *Directory, Trade.* **Description:** Contains suppliers, manufacturers, products, consultants, contractors, associations and publications.
Related titles: CD-ROM ed.; Online - full text ed.
Published by: Elevator World, Inc., PO Box 6507, Mobile, AL 36660-6507. TEL 251-479-4514, 800-730-5093, FAX 251-479-7043, editorial@elevator-world.com, http://www.elevator-world.com/2-membr.shtml. adv.: page USD 2,315.

EMDEN'S CONSTRUCTION LAW. see *LAW*

690 ESP ISSN 0210-2145
EME DOS - AGENDA DE LA CONSTRUCCION. Text in Spanish. 1976. q. EUR 77 (effective 2005). adv. **Description:** Provides prices of materials.
Published by: EmeDos, Rosello, 184 4o 1o, Barcelona, 08008, Spain. TEL 34-93-4510981, FAX 34-93-4512363, info@emedos.es, http://www.emedos.es/.

620.005 BRA ISSN 0103-7358
O EMPREITEIRO. Text in Portuguese, Spanish. 1961. m. USD 60. adv. bk.rev. illus. **Document type:** *Magazine, Trade.*
Related titles: Online - full text ed.; Special ed(s).: 500 Largest Construction & Engineering Companies in Brazil.
Published by: Editora Univers Ltda., Rua Diogo Moriera 124, Sao Paolo, SP CEP 05423-904, Brazil. TEL 55-11-3039-8982, FAX 55-11-3039-8983, oempreiteiro@editoraunives.com.br, jyoung@editoraunivers.com.br, http://www.minerios.com.br. Ed., Pub. Joseph Young. Adv. contact Irene Carvalho. color page USD 3,986. Circ: 10,000.

ENCUESTA TRIMESTRAL SOBRE LA INDUSTRIA DE LA CONSTRUCCION. see *BUILDING AND CONSTRUCTION—Abstracting, Bibliographies, Statistics*

ENERGY AND BUILDINGS. see *ENERGY*

690 720 USA ISSN 0741-3629
CODEN: EDUDEA
ENERGY DESIGN UPDATE; the monthly newsletter on energy-efficient housing. Text in English. 1982. m. USD 337, USD 397 (effective 2005). charts; illus.; pat.; stat. back issues avail. **Document type:** *Newsletter.* **Description:** Covers new products, research, and techniques for building energy-efficient, high-quality, and healthful houses. Includes discussion of mechanical systems, major appliances, and an objective look at products' promotional claims.
Related titles: Online - full text ed.: (from EBSCO Publishing).
—CISTI. **CCC.**
Published by: Aspen Law & Business (Subsidiary of: Wolters Kluwer N.V.), 1185 Ave of the Americas, 37th Fl, New York, NY 10036. TEL 212-597-0210, FAX 212-597-0336, holladay@sover.net, http://www.aspenpub.com. Ed. Martin Holladay.

ENERGY IN BUILDING AND INDUSTRY. see *ENERGY*

693.832 GBR ISSN 0969-885X
ENERGY IN BUILDINGS AND INDUSTRY. Text in English. 1982. m.
Formerly (until 1993): Energy in Buildings (0263-3299)
—**CCC.**
Published by: Industrial Trade Journals Ltd., Stakes House, Quebec Sq, Westerham, Kent TN16 1TD, United Kingdom. TEL 44-1959-564212, FAX 44-1959-562325.

690 GBR ISSN 0969-9988
TH438 CODEN: ECMGE6
➤ **ENGINEERING, CONSTRUCTION AND ARCHITECTURAL MANAGEMENT.** Text in English. 1994. bi-m. EUR 1,554.04 in Europe; USD 1,489 in North America; AUD 2,869 in Australasia; GBP 1,086.41 in the UK & elsewhere (effective 2006). bk.rev. bibl.; illus. index. reprint service avail. from PSC. **Document type:** *Journal, Academic/Scholarly.* **Description:** Publishes research in all areas of construction: building, civil engineering, major infrastructure and maintenance and includes construction management, project management, the management of construction companies and architectural practices..
Related titles: Online - full text ed.: ISSN 1365-232X. GBP 88 in Europe to individuals; USD 140 in North America to individuals; GBP 88 elsewhere to individuals; GBP 409 in Europe to institutions; USD 648 in North America to institutions; GBP 409 elsewhere to institutions (effective 2002) (from Blackwell Synergy, EBSCO Publishing, Emerald Group Publishing Limited, Gale Group, IngentaConnect, O C L C Online Computer Library Center, Inc., ProQuest Information & Learning, Swets Information Services).
Indexed: ABIn, API, BrCerAb, C&ISA, CerAb, CivEngAb, CorrAb, E&CAJ, EMA, ESPM, IAA, ICEA, Inspec, M&TEA, MBF, METADEX, RiskAb, SolStAb, WAA.
—BLDSC (3758.609000), CISTI, IE, Infotrieve, ingenta, Linda Hall. **CCC.**
Published by: (Loughborough University of Technology, Department of Civil and Building Engineering), Emerald Group Publishing Limited, 60-62 Toller Ln, Bradford, W Yorks BD8 9BY, United Kingdom. TEL 44-1274-777700, FAX 44-1274-785200, infomation@emeraldinsight.com, http://www.emeraldinsight.com/ecam.htm. Ed. Ronald McCaffer. Pub. Claire Jones.

690 624 ESP
ENTORNO. Text in Spanish. 6/yr.
Indexed: AIAP.
Address: Avda Baron de Carcer, 37, Valencia, 46001, Spain. TEL 34-96-3525369, FAX 34-96-4252880.

624 DNK ISSN 0109-4890
ENTREPRENOEREN. Text in Danish. 1971. 10/yr. DKK 250. adv.
Published by: Entreprenoerforeningen/Danish Contractors Association, Noerre Voldgade 106, Copenhagen K, 1015, Denmark. TEL 45-33-138801, FAX 45-33-132450, TELEX 27049. Ed. Joern Damgaard. Circ: 5,935.

690 711 USA ISSN 1062-3957
TA401
ENVIRONMENTAL BUILDING NEWS; newsletter on environmentally responsible design and construction. Text in English. 1992. m. USD 99 in North America to individuals; USD 129 elsewhere to individuals; USD 199 in North America to institutions; USD 229 elsewhere to institutions (effective 2005). bk.rev. bibl.; illus. index. back issues avail.; reprints avail. **Document type:** *Newsletter, Trade.* **Description:** Offers building contractors and architects practical, in-depth insight into environmentally responsible building materials, technologies, and construction methods. Also reviews new products and reports on news in the field.
Related titles: CD-ROM ed.; Online - full text ed.
Indexed: EPB, EnvAb.
—BLDSC (3791.405800), CISTI. **CCC.**
Published by: BuildingGreen, Inc., 122 Birge St Ste 30, Brattleboro, VT 05301-3206. TEL 802-257-7300, FAX 802-257-7304, ebn@buildinggreen.com, http://www.buildinggreen.com. Ed. Nadav Malin. Pub. Daniel Woodbury. Circ: 3,400 (paid).

690 USA ISSN 1095-8932
TH1
ENVIRONMENTAL DESIGN & CONSTRUCTION. Text in English. 1997. bi-m. free domestic to qualified personnel; USD 32 domestic (effective 2005). **Document type:** *Magazine, Trade.* **Description:** Covers all aspects of environmentally sound building design and construction including recycled building products, energy efficiency, alternative energy sourges, indoor air quality, and systems of waste disposal and re-use.
Related titles: Online - full text ed.: (from bigchalk, EBSCO Publishing, Florida Center for Library Automation, Gale Group, O C L C Online Computer Library Center, Inc., ProQuest Information & Learning).
Indexed: ABIn, BrCerAb, C&ISA, CerAb, CorrAb, E&CAJ, EMA, IAA, M&TEA, MBF, METADEX, SolStAb, WAA.
—Linda Hall. **CCC.**
Published by: (Environmental Design & Construction), B N P Media, 755 W Big Beaver Rd, Ste 1000, Troy, MI 48084-4903. TEL 248-362-3700, FAX 248-362-0317, http://www.edcmag.com, http://www.bnpmedia.com/. Ed. Michele Hucal. Pub. Diana Brown. Circ: 18,000 (paid and controlled).

690 721 HUN ISSN 0013-9661
EPITES- EPITESZETTUDOMANY/ARCHITECTONICS AND ARCHITECTURE. Text in Hungarian; Summaries in English. 1957. q. USD 88 (effective 2006). adv. bk.rev. illus.; abstr. 90 p./no.; back issues avail. **Document type:** *Journal, Academic/Scholarly.* **Description:** Studies contributed by the committee of the Department of Technological Sciences of Hungarian Academy of Sciences, on the fields of architectonics and architecture.
Formerly (until 1968): Epites- es Kozlekedestudomanyi Kozlemenyek (0423-278X)
Related titles: Online - full text ed.: ISSN 1588-2764.
Indexed: BHA, HBB.
—Linda Hall.
Published by: (Budapest University of Technology and Monuments), Akademiai Kiado Rt. (Subsidiary of: Wolters Kluwer N.V.), Prielle Kornelia U. 19, Budapest, 1117, Hungary. TEL 36-1-4648282, FAX 36-1-4648221, journals@akkrt.hu, http://www.akkrt.hu. Ed. J Szabo.

691 HUN ISSN 0013-970X
TP785 CODEN: EPITAA
EPITOANYAG. Text in Hungarian; Summaries in English, German, Hungarian, Russian. 1949. q. HUF 2,000, USD 20. adv. bk.rev. abstr.; charts; illus. index. **Description:** Serves the cement and lime, structural ceramics, ceramic houseware, high-tech ceramics, inorganic heat and sound insulation, glass, natural stone and gravel, and concrete industries.
Indexed: BrCerAb, C&ISA, CIN, CRIA, CerAb, ChemAb, ChemTitl, ConcrAb, CorrAb, E&CAJ, EMA, HBB, HistAb, SolStAb, WAA.
—BLDSC (3794.300000), CASDDS, CISTI, Linda Hall.
Published by: Szilikatipari Tudomanyos Egyesulet, Fo utca 68, Budapest, 1027, Hungary. TEL 36-1-2019360. Ed. Ilona Wojnarovits. R&P Jozsef Talaber. adv.: B&W page USD 180, color page USD 450. Circ: 2,700. **Dist. by:** Kultura, PO Box 149, Budapest 1389, Hungary.

690.028 BEL ISSN 0775-2075
EQUIPMENT CONSTRUCTION. Text in Dutch, French. 1987. 11/yr. **Document type:** *Trade.*
Published by: Benefalux S.A., Avenue Montjoie, 226, Bruxelles, 1080, Belgium. TEL 32-2-345-0191, FAX 32-2-347-2038.

977 622 USA ISSN 0897-5159
TH900
EQUIPMENT ECHOES. Text in English. 1986. q. USD 22 in US & Canada; USD 27 foreign (effective 2000). adv. bk.rev. charts; illus.; tr.lit. back issues avail. **Document type:** *Journal, Academic/Scholarly.* **Description:** Deals with historical construction equipments.
Published by: Historical Construction Equipment Association, 16623 Liberty Hi Rd, Bowling Green, OH 43402-9309. TEL 419-352-5616, FAX 419-352-6086, hcca@wcnet.org. Ed. Donald W Frantz. R&Ps Donald W Frantz, Thomas Berry. Adv. contact Elaine Angel. B&W page USD 200. Circ: 4,300 (paid).

690 CAN ISSN 0710-2720
EQUIPMENT JOURNAL. Text in English. 1966. 17/yr. CND 28, USD 35 (effective 2000). adv. **Document type:** *Newspaper, Trade.* **Description:** Features news of the construction industry such as roadbuilding, general construction and natural resources. Contains the latest information available to assist in determining industry decisions.
Published by: Pace Publishing Limited, 5160 Explorer Dr, Unit 6, Mississauga, ON L4W 4T7, Canada. TEL 905-629-7500, 800-667-8541, FAX 905-629-7988, equipmentjournal@globalserve.net, http://www.equipmentjournal.com, http://www.equipmentjournalonline.com. Ed. Michael Anderson. Pub., R&P John Baker. Adv. contact J Scott Smith. B&W page CND 1,531, color page CND 2,097. Circ: 25,005.

690 GBR
EQUIPMENT NEWS. Text in English. fortn. GBP 50 in Europe; GBP 75 elsewhere. **Document type:** *Trade.*
Published by: Construction Publications Ltd., 2-6 Boundary Row, London, SE1 8HN, United Kingdom. TEL 44-171-410-6611, FAX 44-171-522-9648.

690.028 USA ISSN 0891-141X
EQUIPMENT TODAY. Text in English. 1966. m. (plus a. product issue). USD 71 domestic; USD 91 in Canada & Mexico; USD 139 elsewhere (effective 2005). adv. illus. **Document type:** *Magazine, Trade.* **Description:** Provides contractors with information on equipment selection, application, maintenance, safety and new products.
Formerly: Equipment Guide News (0149-5240); Which incorporated: Reporter of Construction Equipment (0034-480X)
Related titles: Online - full text ed.: (from Gale Group).
—CCC.
Published by: Cygnus Business Media, Inc., 1233 Janesville Ave, Fort Atkinson, WI 53538-0803. TEL 800-547-7377, FAX 920-563-1698, becky.schultz@cygnusb2b.com, http://www.equipmenttoday.com. Ed. Becky Shultz. Pub. Kris Flitcroft. Circ: 83,000 (controlled).

690.028 USA ISSN 1057-7262
TH900
EQUIPMENT WORLD. Text in English. 1972. m. free to qualified personnel. adv. illus. **Document type:** *Magazine, Trade.* **Description:** Provides information and insight needed to make business decisions when buying, renting, leasing, selling or using equipment from earthmovers to pickup trucks.
Incorporates (in 1992): Equipment Management (0733-3056); Which was formerly (until 1982): Heavy Duty Equipment Maintenance - Management (0734-2640); (until 1979): E.M. (Heavy Duty Equipment and Maintenance); Incorporates (in 1989): Contractor's Market Center (0884-3376)
Related titles: Online - full text ed.: Equipment World Online.
Indexed: ABIn, BrCerAb, C&ISA, CerAb, CorrAb, E&CAJ, EMA, IAA, M&TEA, MBF, METADEX, SolStAb, WAA.
—Linda Hall.
Published by: Randall Publishing Company, 3200 Rice Mine Rd, Tuscaloosa, AL 35406. TEL 800-633-5953, FAX 205-752-0930, tjackson@equipmentworld.com, tkillgore@randallpub.com, http://www.equipmentworld.com, http://www.randallpub.com, http://www.equipment.com. Eds. Tom Jackson, Marcia Gruver. Pub. Dan Tidwell. adv.: B&W page USD 11,350, color page USD 13,930; trim 8.125 x 10.875. Circ: 82,000 (controlled and free).

ESTADISTICA DEL CEMENTO. see *BUILDING AND CONSTRUCTION—Abstracting, Bibliographies, Statistics*

ESTATISTICAS DA CONSTRUCAO DE EDIFICIOS. see *BUILDING AND CONSTRUCTION—Abstracting, Bibliographies, Statistics*

690 BEL ISSN 1010-7185
EUROPEAN CEMENT ASSOCIATION. EUROPEAN ANNUAL REVIEW. Text in English, French. 1951; N.S. 1979. a., latest vol.18, 1997. USD 200 (effective 1999). **Document type:** *Trade.* **Description:** Annual round-up of the European Cement Association.
Formerly (until 1979): Cement Market and Outlook
Published by: (European Cement Association), Cembureau, Rue d'Arlon 55, Brussels, 1040, Belgium. TEL 32-2-2341011, FAX 32-2-2304720.

EUROPEAN CEMENT ASSOCIATION. WORLD STATISTICAL REVIEW. see *BUILDING AND CONSTRUCTION—Abstracting, Bibliographies, Statistics*

690 GBR ISSN 1367-8140
EUROPEAN CONSTRUCTION INSTITUTE. PUBLICATION. Text in English. 1991. irreg.
—BLDSC (7059.765000), ingenta.
Published by: European Construction Institute, Loughborough University, Sir Frank Gibb Annexe, West Park, Loughborough, Leicestershire LE11 3TU, United Kingdom. TEL 44-0-1509-223526, eci@lboro.ac.uk.

690 GBR
EUROPEAN EQUIPMENT INDEX. Text in English. a. USD 60 (effective 2001). **Document type:** *Directory.*
Published by: K H L Group Ltd., Southfields, Southview Rd, Wadhurst, E Sussex TN5 6TP, United Kingdom. TEL 44-1892-784088, FAX 44-1892-784086, mail@khl.com, http://www.constructioneurope.com, http://www.khl.com. Adv. contact David Stowe.

EVALUATING YOUR FIRM'S INJURY & ILLNESS RECORD. CONSTRUCTION INDUSTRIES. see *OCCUPATIONAL HEALTH AND SAFETY*

692.8 USA ISSN 0014-3995
TA730.A3
EXCAVATING CONTRACTOR✶. Text in English. 1905. m. free to qualified personnel. adv. bk.rev. abstr.; charts; illus.; stat. index. reprint service avail. from PQC.
Formerly: Excavating Engineer
Related titles: Microform ed.: 1905 (from PQC).
—Linda Hall.
Published by: Cummins Publishing Co., 6557 Forest Park Dr, Troy, MI 48098-1954. TEL 313-358-4900. Ed. R J Stevens. Circ: 35,000.

690 USA
EXTERIOR CONTRACTOR. Text in English. 2002 (Nov.). 4/yr. **Document type:** *Magazine, Trade.* **Description:** Provides information for specialty contracting firms involved in roofing, siding, decking and window replacement projects.
Published by: Jervis and Associates, 14255 Us Highway 1., # 200, Juno Beach, FL 33408-1490. http://www.exteriorcontractor.com. Ed. John H Jervis.

690 AUT
F G W SCHRIFTENREIHE. Text in German. 1958. irreg., latest vol.158, 2004. price varies. adv. **Document type:** *Monographic series, Trade.*
Published by: Forschungsgesellschaft fuer Wohnen Bauen und Planen, Loewengasse 47, Vienna, W 1030, Austria. TEL 43-1-71262510, FAX 43-1-712625121, office@fgw.at, http://www.fgw.at. Adv. contact Wolfgang Amann.

691 CHE ISSN 1562-3610
F I B BULLETIN. Text in English. 1976. 5/yr. **Document type:** *Bulletin, Trade.*
Formerly (until 1991): Comite Euro-International du Beton. Bulletin d'Information (0378-9489)
—BLDSC (2512.530000), CISTI, IE, ingenta.
Published by: Federation Internationale du Beton/International Federation for Structural Concrete, Case Postale 88, Lausanne, 1015, Switzerland. TEL 41-21-6932747, FAX 41-21-6935884, fib@epfl.ch, http://fib.epfl.ch/publications/fib.

690 658 USA ISSN 1545-2891
HD9715.A1
F M I QUARTERLY. (Fails Management Institute) Text in English. q. USD 240 (effective 2003).
Formerly (until 2003): Contractors Management Journal (1089-9332)
Published by: F M I Corp., 5151 Glenwood Ave. Ste. 100, Raleigh, NC 27612-3267. TEL 919-787-8400, FAX 919-785-9320, quarterly_info@fminet.com, http://www.fminet.com. Ed. Alison Carrara. Pub. Jerry Jackson.

F UND I-BAU; Bauen mit Systemen. see *ARCHITECTURE*

690 USA
FABRICATORS HOTLINE. Text in English. m. USD 14.95 (effective 2005). **Document type:** *Magazine, Trade.*
Published by: Heartland Communications, Inc., 1003 Central Ave., Fort Dodge, IA 50501. TEL 515-955-1600, FAX 515-955-3753, ads@imtproduction.com, http://www.industrialgroup.com. Circ: 10,000 (paid and controlled).

▼ **FABULOUS FLOORS.** see *INTERIOR DESIGN AND DECORATION*

FACHBUCHVERZEICHNIS BAUWESEN - ARCHITEKTUR (YEAR). see *BUILDING AND CONSTRUCTION—Abstracting, Bibliographies, Statistics*

692.8 GBR ISSN 0263-2772
TS177 CODEN: FCILEC
FACILITIES. Text in English. 1983. 6/yr. EUR 8,709.79 in Europe; USD 8,859 in North America; AUD 10,609 in Australasia; GBP 6,001.91 in UK & elsewhere (effective 2006). bk.rev. charts; illus. back issues avail.; reprint service avail. from PSC. **Document type:** *Journal, Academic/Scholarly.* **Description:** Covers the multidisciplinary topics of people, property and process management.
Related titles: Online - full text ed.: (from EBSCO Publishing, Emerald Group Publishing Limited, Gale Group, IngentaConnect, O C L C Online Computer Library Center, Inc., ProQuest Information & Learning, Swets Information Services).
Indexed: ABIn, CJA, EmerIntel, Emerald, ErgAb, Inspec.
—BLDSC (3863.430000), AskIEEE, Ei, IE, Infotrieve, ingenta. **CCC.**
Published by: Emerald Group Publishing Limited, 60-62 Toller Ln, Bradford, W Yorks BD8 9BY, United Kingdom. TEL 44-1274-777700, FAX 44-1274-785200, help@emeraldinsight.com, infomation@emeraldinsight.com, http://www.emeraldinsight.com/fm.htm. Ed. Edward Finch. **Subscr. addr. in N America:** Emerald Group Publishing Ltd., 44 Brattle St, 4th Fl, Cambridge, MA 02138. TEL 617-497-2175, 888-622-0075, FAX 617-354-6875.

720 690 USA ISSN 1049-2925
TH4311
FACILITIES PLANNING HANDBOOK. Text in English. a., latest vol.3. adv. **Document type:** *Trade.*
Address: PO Box 1568, Orinda, CA 94563. TEL 925-254-1744, FAX 925-254-1093, fmdm@fmdata.com. Ed., R&P, Adv. contact Lee Ingalls TEL 925-254-6386.

690 USA
FAMILY STYLE HOME PLANS; homes to fit your family. Text in English. 1994. q. USD 15; USD 3.98 newsstand/cover (effective 2000). adv. **Document type:** *Magazine, Consumer.* **Description:** Contains top-selling homes designed for families. Features homes with game rooms, media rooms, computer alcoves and interactive family spaces.
Published by: HomeStyles Publishing & Marketing, Inc., 213 E. 4th St., 4th Fl., St. Paul, MN 55101-1603. TEL 651-602-5000, FAX 651-602-5001, http://www.homestyles.com. Ed. Josh Kimball. Adv. contact Shelley Junker. B&W page USD 3,910, color page USD 4,830; trim 8 x 10.75. Circ: 74,100.

690 DEU ISSN 0941-7796
FASSADE. Text in German. 1969. 9/yr. EUR 51.20 domestic; EUR 54.25 foreign; EUR 7.80 newsstand/cover (effective 2004). adv. back issues avail. **Document type:** *Magazine, Trade.*
Formerly (until 1992): Maler- und Lackiererhandwerk (0343-4079)
Published by: Verlag F.H. Kleffmann GmbH, Herner Str 299, Bochum, 44809, Germany. TEL 49-234-95391-0, FAX 49-234-9539130, service@kleffmann-verlag.de, http://www.kleffmann-verlag.de. adv.: B&W page EUR 1,834, color page EUR 2,935. Circ: 7,308 (paid and controlled).

690 DEU ISSN 0948-1214
FASSADENTECHNIK. Text in German. 1995. bi-m. EUR 68 domestic; EUR 73 in Europe; EUR 81 elsewhere; EUR 15 newsstand/cover (effective 2005). adv. **Document type:** *Magazine, Trade.*
Published by: Cubus Medien Verlag GmbH, Eppendorfer Baum 25, Hamburg, 20249, Germany. TEL 49-40-28096750, FAX 49-40-28096752, cubus@fassadentechnik.de, http://www.fassadentechnik.de. Ed. Martin Jung. Adv. contact Kirsten Jung. B&W page EUR 2,175, color page EUR 3,645; trim 175 x 262. Circ: 6,913 (paid).

690 333.33 USA
FAVORITE HOMES. Text in English. 4/yr. USD 15 (effective 2000). **Document type:** *Trade.* **Description:** Contains house design sketches and data of architect-selected homes, and short informational articles.
Published by: Drawing Board Atlanta, Inc., PO Box 15556, Atlanta, GA 30333-0556. TEL 404-624-3999, FAX 404-624-4063, dbahomeplans@mindspring.com, sales@drawingboardatlanta.com. Ed., Pub., R&P, Adv. contact Phillip Andrew Jessup. Circ: 5,000.

690 ESP
FEDERACION DE ENTIDADES EMPRESARIALES DE LA CONSTRUCCION DE BARCELONA. BOLETIN. Text in Spanish. 12/yr.
Published by: Federacion de Entidades Empresariales de la Construccion de Barcelona, Via Layetana 28, Barcelona, 08003, Spain. TEL 3-310-67-12.

690 GBR
FENCING NEWS. Text in English. 1981. bi-m. GBP 35 (effective 1999). adv. **Document type:** *Trade.* **Description:** Features news and views from around the UK an abroad, profiles - company and personal, appointments, products - developments, news and inventions, quality and training matters, technical and safety items, new or impending legislation and information technology.
Published by: Grendon Publications Ltd., PO Box 1, Atherstone, Warks CV9 1BE, United Kingdom. TEL 44-1827-711722, FAX 44-1827-718081, fn@zipmail.co.uk, http://www.internet-uk.net/fencing-news.htm. Ed. Bob Jennings. Adv. contact Paul Carter. B&W page GBP 629, color page GBP 938; trim 265 x 180. Circ: 3,500.

690 USA ISSN 0895-450X
FENESTRATION; a magazine for manufacturers & distributors of windows, doors, & other fenestration products. Text in English. 1987. 10/yr. USD 15 domestic; USD 21 foreign (effective 2000). **Document type:** *Magazine, Trade.* **Description:** Contains informations for manufacturers and distributors of windows, doors and other fenestration products.
—CCC.
Published by: Ashlee Publishing Co., Inc., 18 E 41st St, 20th Fl, New York, NY 10017-6222. TEL 212-376-7722, FAX 212-376-7723, publisher@ashlee.com, http://www.ashlee.com. Eds. Joel Bruinooge, Morgan O'Rourke. Pub. Jordan Wright. Circ: 16,500 (controlled).

690 DEU
FERTIG HAEUSER MAGAZIN. Text in German. 2/yr. EUR 2.50 newsstand/cover (effective 2003). adv. **Document type:** *Magazine, Consumer.*
Published by: Zwei M GmbH, Theodor-Althoff-Str 39, Essen, 45133, Germany. TEL 49-201-87126920, FAX 49-201-87126912. adv.: B&W page EUR 5,120, color page EUR 6,920. Circ: 70,000 (paid and controlled).

690 DEU ISSN 0720-745X
FERTIGHAEUSER. Text in German. 1981. a. EUR 8 newsstand/cover (effective 2003). adv. **Document type:** *Magazine, Consumer.*
Related titles: ♦ Supplement to: Hausbau. ISSN 0934-8026.
Published by: Fachschriften Verlag GmbH, Hoehenstr 17, Fellbach, 70736, Germany. TEL 49-711-52061, FAX 49-711-5206223, info@fachschriften.de, http://www.fachschriften.de/publikationen/fertighaeuser.htm. Ed. Paul Daleiden. Adv. contact Barbara Hoof. B&W page EUR 6,130, color page EUR 10,176; trim 187 x 247. Circ: 80,000 (paid and controlled).

690 381 ITA ISSN 0393-8050
LE FIERE; rassegna periodica tecnica di documentazione e informazione. Text in Italian. 1968. irreg. price varies. adv. charts; illus. index. back issues avail. **Document type:** *Magazine, Trade.* **Description:** Reports on fairs and meetings.
Formerly (until 1981): Edilizia alle Fiere (0013-0877)
Published by: Casa Editrice la Fiaccola, Via Conca del Naviglio 37, Milan, MI 20123, Italy. TEL 39-02-89421350, FAX 39-02-89421484, http://www.fiaccola.it. Ed. Pasquale Satalino. Pub. Giuseppe Saronni. Adv. contact Mauro Nartelli. Circ: 39,873.

FIJI. BUREAU OF STATISTICS. CENSUS OF BUILDING AND CONSTRUCTION. see *BUILDING AND CONSTRUCTION—Abstracting, Bibliographies, Statistics*

FINANCIAL MANAGEMENT AND ACCOUNTING FOR THE CONSTRUCTION INDUSTRY. see *BUSINESS AND ECONOMICS—Accounting*

FINANCIAL SURVEY. BRICK & TILE MANUFACTURERS AND DISTRIBUTORS. see *BUSINESS AND ECONOMICS—Trade And Industrial Directories*

FINANCIAL SURVEY. BUILDERS MERCHANTS. see *BUSINESS AND ECONOMICS—Trade And Industrial Directories*

FINANCIAL SURVEY. BUILDING CONTRACTORS; company data for success. see *BUSINESS AND ECONOMICS—Trade And Industrial Directories*

FINANCIAL SURVEY. PLANT HIRE; company data for success. see *BUSINESS AND ECONOMICS—Trade And Industrial Directories*

FINLAND. TILASTOKESKUS. RAKENNUSKUSTANNUSINDEKSI (KUUKAUSITILASTO)/STATISTICS FINLAND. BUILDING COST INDEX. see *BUILDING AND CONSTRUCTION—Abstracting, Bibliographies, Statistics*

FIREPLACE YEARBOOK. see *INTERIOR DESIGN AND DECORATION*

691 DEU
FLIESEN MAGAZIN; fuer Handwerk und Handel. Text in German. bi-m. adv. **Document type:** *Magazine, Trade.*
Published by: Menzel Medien, Fasanenweg 7, Offenau, 74254, Germany. TEL 49-7136-970255, FAX 49-7136-970257, info@fliesenmagazin.de, http://www.fliesenmagazin.de.

698.9 645.1 ZAF
FLOORS BUYERS GUIDE. Text in English. a.
Published by: Schalk Burger Publications, Kirkness Park Centre, C Hertzog & Beves Sts, Monument Park, Pretoria 0105, South Africa. TEL 27-12-6622014, FAX 27-12-6622030, office@floors.co.za. Circ: 5,000.

690 USA ISSN 0015-3923
FLORIDA BUILDER MAGAZINE✶; the magazine of Florida residential and commercial construction. Text in English. 1946. bi-m. USD 18. adv. bk.rev. **Document type:** *Trade.*
Address: 1776 N Pine Island Rd, Ste 216, Fort Lauderdale, FL 33322-5223. TEL 813-835-4689. Ed. Joan B Antoine. Adv. contact Duane Williams. Circ: 10,125.

FLORIDA CONSTRUCTION LAW MANUAL. see *LAW—Corporate Law*

343.078 USA
FLORIDA CONSTRUCTION LIEN MANUAL. Text in English. 1974. w/ current supplement), latest 1974, 5 base vols. plus irreg. updates. looseleaf. USD 375 (effective 2003). **Description:** This all-inclusive work provides answers regarding abandoned construction, priority of payment among lienors, and performance necessary for lien. It also gives clear analysis of lienable services and materials, priority among lienors, lender responsibility, performance requirements, lien foreclosure procedures, personal money judgments, equitable liens, surety's defenses, payment bonds, interpleader proceedings, discharge of liens, attorney's fees, self-help, replevin, and criminal liability.
Published by: Michie Company (Subsidiary of: LexisNexis North America), 701 E Water St, Charlottesville, VA 22902-5389. TEL 434-972-7600, 800-446-3410, FAX 434-972-7677, http://www.michie.com. Ed. Stephen B Rakusin.

690 USA ISSN 1085-2255
FLORIDA CONSTRUCTION NEWS COVERING NORTHWEST FLORIDA. Text in English. w. adv. **Document type:** *Newsletter, Trade.* **Description:** Provides information on what jobs are coming up for bid or negotiation.
Related titles: Online - full text ed.
Published by: Mcgraw-Hill Construction Dodge (Subsidiary of: McGraw-Hill Construction Information Group), 148 Princeton-Hightstown Rd, Hightstown, NJ 08520. TEL 800-393-6343, http://www.dodgeconstructionpublications.com.

690 USA ISSN 1085-2239
FLORIDA CONSTRUCTION NEWS COVERING ORLANDO & VICINITY. Text in English. w. adv. **Document type:** *Newsletter, Trade.* **Description:** Provides information on what jobs are coming up for bid or negotiation.
Related titles: Online - full text ed.
Published by: Mcgraw-Hill Construction Dodge (Subsidiary of: McGraw-Hill Construction Information Group), 148 Princeton-Hightstown Rd, Hightstown, NJ 08520. TEL 800-393-6343, http://www.dodgeconstructionpublications.com.

690 USA ISSN 1084-9548
FLORIDA CONSTRUCTION NEWS WEEKLY COVERING MIAMI & VICINITY. Text in English. 1995. w. adv. **Document type:** *Newsletter, Trade.* **Description:** Provides information on what jobs are coming up for bid or negotiation.
Related titles: Online - full text ed.
Published by: Mcgraw-Hill Construction Dodge (Subsidiary of: McGraw-Hill Construction Information Group), 148 Princeton-Hightstown Rd, Hightstown, NJ 08520. TEL 800-393-6343, http://www.dodgeconstructionpublications.com.

690 USA ISSN 1084-9564
FLORIDA CONSTRUCTION NEWS WEEKLY COVERING WEST PALM BEACH AND VICINITY. Text in English. 1995. w. adv. **Document type:** *Newsletter, Trade.* **Description:** Provides information on what jobs are coming up for bid or negotiation.
Related titles: Online - full text ed.
Published by: Mcgraw-Hill Construction Dodge (Subsidiary of: McGraw-Hill Construction Information Group), 148 Princeton-Hightstown Rd, Hightstown, NJ 08520. TEL 800-393-6343, http://www.dodgeconstructionpublications.com.

690 USA ISSN 0191-4618
FLORIDA FORUM. Text in English. 1961. m. USD 24; free to qualified personnel (effective 2005). adv. bk.rev. charts; illus.; stat. index. **Document type:** *Magazine, Trade.* **Description:** Written for roofing, sheet metal and air conditioning contractors, builders, general contractors, manufacturers and distributors. Includes F.W. Dodge Construction reports, legislative updates, Association news, industry meetings and events and people and products.
Published by: (Florida Roofing, Sheet Metal & Air Conditioning Contractors Association, Inc.), F R S A, 4111 Metric Dr, Winter Park, FL 32792. TEL 407-671-3772, FAX 407-679-0010, frsa@floridaroof.com, http://www.floridaroof.com. Ed. Steve Munnell. R&P Bonnie B Pierce. Adv. contact Alberto Duenas. B&W page USD 1,310. Circ: 4,500 (free).

▼ **FLORIDA KITCHEN & BATH**; creative ideas, design trends and exciting products for informed consumers, homebuilders, designers and remodeling professionals. see *INTERIOR DESIGN AND DECORATION*

690 USA
FOCUS ON N A R I. Text in English. 1982. m. membership only. adv. **Document type:** *Newsletter, Trade.* **Description:** Features and technical articles on the remodeling industry, and association news.
Formerly (until 1997): N A R I Focus
Published by: National Association of the Remodeling Industry, 780 Lee St, Ste 200, Des Plaines, IL 60016. TEL 847-298-9200, 800-611-6274, FAX 877-685-6274, info@nari.org, http://www.nari.org. Ed., Pub. Susan Maney. R&P, Adv. contact Jennifer McKain. Circ: 7,500 (controlled).

FORM & FUNCTION. see *ARCHITECTURE*

690 658.3 DNK ISSN 0902-9303
FORMANDSBLADET. Text in Danish. 1974. 11/yr. adv.
Published by: Dansk Formands Forening, Prags Boulevard 45, Copenhagen S, 2400, Denmark. TEL 45-32-96-56-22, FAX 45-32-96-58-22. Ed. Per Ysbaek Nielsen.

690 DNK ISSN 1600-8065
FORSK. Text in Danish. 1988. q. free (effective 2004). **Document type:** *Newsletter, Trade.*
Former titles (until 2000): Information om Byggeri og Planlaegning (1396-1667); (until 1995): S B I Information fra Statens Byggeforskningsinstitut (0904-3373)
Related titles: E-mail ed.
Published by: Statens Byggeforskningsinstitut/Danish Building and Urban Research, Dr Neergaards Vej 15, PO Box 119, Hoersholm, 2970, Denmark. TEL 45-45-865533, FAX 45-45-867535, info@by-og-byg.dk, http://www.by-og-byg.dk.

690 USA ISSN 0274-5186
TA775
FOUNDATION DRILLING; serving contractors, deep foundation design engineers, and manufacturers and suppliers of drilled foundation and anchored earth retention systems equipment and services throughout the world. Text in English. 1980. 8/yr. USD 75 domestic; USD 95 foreign (effective 2005). adv. bk.rev. **Document type:** *Magazine, Trade.* **Description:** For the foundation drilling and anchored earth retention industries worldwide. Includes feature articles, news departments, insurance, personnel and management reports, and a calendar of monthly events.
—Linda Hall.
Published by: Association of Drilled Shaft Contractors, 14180 Dallas Pkwy, Ste 510, Dallas, TX 75254. TEL 214-343-2091, FAX 214-343-2384, adsc@adsc-iafd.com, http://www.adsc-iafd.com. Ed. Scot Litke. Adv. contact Ted Ledgard. Circ: 2,000 (paid).

690 NLD ISSN 1385-514X
QE605
FRAGBLAST; the international for blasting and fragmentation. Text in Dutch. 1997. q. GBP 221, USD 365 combined subscription to institutions print & online eds. (effective 2006). reprint service avail. from PSC. **Document type:** *Journal, Academic/Scholarly.* **Description:** Serves as a means of communication for engineers, scientists, and practitioners developing and utilizing explosives in construction and resource removal.
Related titles: Online - full text ed.: GBP 210, USD 347 to institutions (effective 2006) (from EBSCO Publishing, Gale Group, IngentaConnect, O C L C Online Computer Library Center, Inc., Swets Information Services).
Indexed: C&ISA, E&CAJ, GEOBASE, IAA.
—BLDSC (4030.793000), Linda Hall. **CCC.**
Published by: Taylor & Francis The Netherlands (Subsidiary of: Taylor & Francis Group), Schipolweg 107 C, PO Box 447, Leiden, 2316 XC, Netherlands. TEL 31-715-243080, FAX 31-715-234571, pub@swets.nl, infoho@swets.nl, http://www.tandf.co.uk/journals/titles/1385514X.asp, http://www.tandf.co.uk/swets.asp. Ed. H P Rossmanith.

690 747 ITA ISSN 0393-4969
FRAMES ARCHITETTURA DEI SERRAMENTI; rivista internazionale degli infissi e dei sistemi di chiusura nell'edilizia. Text in English, Italian. 1983. 6/yr. EUR 34 domestic; EUR 83 foreign (effective 2004). adv. bk.rev. 96 p./no.; back issues avail. **Document type:** *Magazine, Trade.* **Description:** For those interested in the role of window frames in architectural design. Contains technical research, news of innovations in the sector, and news on new products and designs.
Formerly: Frames Porte e Finestre
Indexed: AIAP.
Published by: Gruppo Editoriale Faenza Editrice SpA, Via Pier de Crescenzi 44, Faenza, RA 48018, Italy. TEL 39-0546-670411, FAX 39-0546-660440, info@faenza.com, http://www.faenza.com. Ed. Fabrizio Bianchetti. R&P Luisa Teston. Adv. contact Elvio Neri. B&W page EUR 2,710, color page EUR 3,040; 22.5 x 31. Circ: 20,000.

FRANCE. MINISTERE DE L'EQUIPEMENT, DES TRANSPORTS, DU LOGEMENT, DU TOURISME ET DE LA MER. STATISTIQUES DE LA CONSTRUCTION. see *BUILDING AND CONSTRUCTION—Abstracting, Bibliographies, Statistics*

690 FRA
FRANCHE COMTE BATIMENT ET TRAVAUX PUBLICS. Text in French. 4/yr.

Address: B.P. 1239, Besancon, 25004, France. TEL 81-83-25-11, FAX 81-83-17-70.

690 JPN
FUDO GIJUTSU KENKYU HOKOKUSHU/FUDO TECHNICAL RESEARCH REPORTS. Text in Japanese. 1981. a. **Document type:** *Academic/Scholarly.*
Published by: Fudo Kensetsu K.K. Chuo Kenkyujo/Fudo Construction Co., Ltd., Central Research Institute, 2-1 Taito 1-chome, Taito-ku, Tokyo, 110-0016, Japan.

690 CHN
FUJIAN JIANCAI/FUJIAN CONSTRUCTIONAL MATERIAL. Text in Chinese. q. CNY 6.
Published by: Fujian Sheng Jiancai Kexue Yanjiusuo, No61, Liuqiao Yangqiao Lu, Fuzhou, Fujian 350002, China. TEL 713994. Ed. Hu Yucai. **Dist. overseas by:** Jiangsu Publications Import & Export Corp., 56 Gao Yun Ling, Nanjing, Jiangsu, China.

FUKUSHIMAKEN KENSETSU GIJUTSU. FUKUKEN/ FUKUSHIMA ASSOCIATION OF CONSTRUCTION. NEWS. see *ENGINEERING—Civil Engineering*

690 333.33 USA
FULL COLLECTION. Text in English. 1989. a. USD 45 (effective 2000). adv. **Document type:** *Trade.* **Description:** Contains house design sketches and data.
Published by: Drawing Board Atlanta, Inc., PO Box 15556, Atlanta, GA 30333-0556. TEL 404-624-3999, FAX 404-624-4063, dbahomeplans@mindspring.com, sales@drawingboardatlanta.com. Ed., Pub., R&P, Adv. contact Phillip Andrew Jessup. Circ: 1,000.

690 DEU ISSN 1619-3822
FUSSBODENBAU MAGAZIN; Estrichtechnik - Industriefussboden - Klebetechnik. Text in German. 1984. bi-m. adv. **Document type:** *Magazine, Trade.*
Formerly (until 2002): Estrich Technik (0949-3352)
Published by: Menzel Medien, Fasanenweg 7, Offenau, 74254, Germany. TEL 49-7136-970255, FAX 49-7136-970257, info@fussbodenbau-magazin.de, http://www.fussbodenbau.de. adv.: B&W page EUR 1,040, color page EUR 1,680. Circ: 1,938 (paid and controlled).

690 DEU ISSN 1434-8063
G & H - GEBAEUDETECHNIK UND HANDWERK. Text in German. 1998. m. EUR 63 domestic; EUR 84 foreign (effective 2005). adv. **Document type:** *Magazine, Trade.*
Published by: Henrich Publikationen GmbH, Talhofstr 24b, Gilching, 82205, Germany. TEL 49-8105-38530, FAX 49-8105-385311, info@verlag.henrich.de, http://www.guh-elektro.de, http://www.henrich.de. Ed. Elmo Schwandke. Adv. contact Claus Mayer. B&W page EUR 3,600; trim 184 x 255. Circ: 37,566 (paid and controlled).

G I - GESUNDHEITS INGENIEUR; Haustechnik - Bauphysik - Umwelttechnik. see *PUBLIC HEALTH AND SAFETY*

GARDENING & DECK DESIGN. see *GARDENING AND HORTICULTURE*

GARDENING & OUTDOOR LIVING. see *GARDENING AND HORTICULTURE*

647.9 DEU ISSN 1430-2748
GEBAEUDE MANAGEMENT; Immobilien Facilities Services. Text in German. 1995. 10/yr. EUR 53 domestic; EUR 59 foreign; EUR 6.30 newsstand/cover (effective 2003). adv. **Document type:** *Journal, Trade.*
Related titles: E-mail ed.; Online - full text ed.
Published by: Deutscher Fachverlag GmbH, Mainzer Landstr 251, Frankfurt Am Main, 60326, Germany. TEL 49-69-759501, FAX 49-69-75952999, heidrun.dangl@dfv.de, info@dfv.de, http://www.dfv.de. Adv. contact Andreas Schaefer. B&W page EUR 4,081, color page EUR 5,338. Circ: 8,278 (controlled).

GEBOUWBEHEER. see *BUSINESS AND ECONOMICS—Management*

GEODRILLING INTERNATIONAL. see *ENGINEERING—Civil Engineering*

690 ITA
GEOMETRI INFORMAZIONE. Text in Italian. 1979. m. USD 23.
Published by: Chiandetti Editore s.r.l., Via Vittorio Veneto, 106, Reana Del Roiale, UD 33010, Italy.

690 USA ISSN 1552-8693
GEORGIA BUILDER. Text in English. 6/yr. USD 18 (effective 2005).
Published by: Association Publishing Inc., 2117 Smith Ave, Chesapeake, VA 23320. TEL 757-420-2434, FAX 757-424-5954, http://www.statebuildermagazines.com. Ed. Carolyn Berry. Pubs. Joyce F Hearn, Sandra Amidon. Circ: 12,000.

690 ITA
GEOTEC. Text in Italian. 1988. 9/yr. **Document type:** *Trade.*
Formerly: Georama
Published by: Professional Press s.r.l., Piazzale Francesco Baracca, 10, Milan, MI 20123, Italy. TEL 02-48-19-43-20, FAX 02-48-01-11-00. Ed. Andrea Bonalanza. Pub. Enrico Bassi. Circ: 18,000.

GERMANY. STATISTISCHES BUNDESAMT. AUSGEWAEHLTE ZAHLEN FUER DIE BAUWIRTSCHAFT. see *BUILDING AND CONSTRUCTION—Abstracting, Bibliographies, Statistics*

GERMANY. STATISTISCHES BUNDESAMT. FACHSERIE 17, PREISE, REIHE 5: KAUFWERTE FUER BAULAND. see *BUILDING AND CONSTRUCTION—Abstracting, Bibliographies, Statistics*

GERMANY. STATISTISCHES BUNDESAMT. FACHSERIE 4, PRODUZIERENDES GEWERBE, REIHE 5: BAUGEWERBE. see *BUILDING AND CONSTRUCTION—Abstracting, Bibliographies, Statistics*

GERMANY. STATISTISCHES BUNDESAMT. FACHSERIE 5, BAUTAETIGKEIT UND WOHNUNGEN, REIHE 1: BAUTAETIGKEIT. see *BUILDING AND CONSTRUCTION—Abstracting, Bibliographies, Statistics*

GERMANY. STATISTISCHES BUNDESAMT. FACHSERIE 5, BAUTAETIGKEIT UND WOHNUNGEN, REIHE 2: BEWILLIGUNGEN IM SOZIALEN WOHNUNGSBAU. see *BUILDING AND CONSTRUCTION—Abstracting, Bibliographies, Statistics*

GERMANY. STATISTISCHES BUNDESAMT. FACHSERIE 5, BAUTAETIGKEIT UND WOHNUNGEN, REIHE 3: BESTAND AN WOHNUNGEN. see *BUILDING AND CONSTRUCTION—Abstracting, Bibliographies, Statistics*

690 CHE
GESUND BAUEN UND WOHNEN. Text in German. a. CHF 12.30 (effective 2000). adv. **Document type:** *Magazine, Consumer.* **Description:** Contains information on ecological and environmental building materials and plans.
Published by: Etzel-Verlag AG, Knonauerstr 56, Cham, 6330, Switzerland. TEL 41-41-7855085, FAX 41-41-7855088, info@etzel-verlag.ch, http://www.etzel-verlag.ch/html/gbhome.htm. Ed. Esther Kall. adv.: B&W page CHF 3,690; trim 184 x 278. Circ: 17,500 (paid).

690 USA
GETAWAY CABINS & COTTAGES. Text in English. 1998. q. USD 3.98 newsstand/cover (effective 2000). adv. illus. **Document type:** *Magazine, Consumer.* **Description:** Offers a variety of getaway homes that range from log homes and small cabins to comfortable second homes.
Former titles: Getaway Homes; Getaway Houses
Published by: HomeStyles Publishing & Marketing, Inc., 213 E. 4th St., 4th Fl., St. Paul, MN 55101-1603. TEL 651-602-5000, 888-626-2026, FAX 651-602-5001, http://www.homestyles.com. Ed. Sara Freund. Adv. contact Shelley Junker. B&W page USD 3,910, color page USD 4,830; trim 8 x 10.75. Circ: 67,600.

691 NLD ISSN 1386-596X
GEVELRAAD. Text in Dutch. 1997. 5/yr. illus. **Document type:** *Trade.* **Description:** Provides management information for persons working with building facades.
Published by: Arko Uitgeverij BV, Postbus 616, Nieuwegein, 3430 AP, Netherlands. TEL 31-30-605-1090, gerlings@arko.nl, http://www.arko.nl. Ed. N Hendriks. Pub. Marc Gerlings. Circ: 4,000.

690 NLD ISSN 0921-4550
GEZOND BOUWEN EN WONEN. Text in Dutch. 1987. bi-m. EUR 48 (effective 2003).
Incorporates (1982-1987): V I B A Tijdschrift (0169-2062) —Infotrieve.
Published by: Uitgeverij Lakerveld BV, Mangaanstraat 50, Postbus 43250, The Hague, 2504 AG, Netherlands. FAX 31-70-321-8744, http://www.gbw.vwg.net/artikelen/artikelinfo/openartikels.htm.

GIJUTSU KENKYUJO SHOHO/INSTITUTE OF TECHNOLOGY AND DEVELOPMENT. TECHNICAL REPORTS. see *ENGINEERING—Civil Engineering*

GIJUTSU KENKYUJOHO/TECHNICAL RESEARCH INSTITUTE. TECHNICAL REPORTS. see *ENGINEERING—Civil Engineering*

691 ITA ISSN 1123-8259
IL GIORNALE DEL MARMO/INTERNATIONAL STONE MAGAZINE. Text in Italian. 1965. bi-m. EUR 39 domestic; EUR 77 foreign (effective 2004). adv. **Document type:** *Magazine, Trade.*
Related titles: Online - full text ed.: ISSN 1593-2273. 1999.
Published by: Gruppo Editoriale Faenza Editrice SpA, Via Pier de Crescenzi 44, Faenza, RA 48018, Italy. TEL 39-0546-670411, FAX 39-0546-660440, info@faenza.com, http://www.faenza.com. Ed. Carlo Montani. Adv. contact Elvio Neri. Circ: 6,000.

690 ITA
GIORNALE DEL RIVENDITORE EDILE. Text in Italian. 12/yr.
Published by: National Federation of Building Materials Traders, Via Trezzo d'Adda 16, Milan, MI 20144, Italy. TEL 2-42-39-446, FAX 2-48-95-28-89. Ed. Giorgio Panciroli. Circ: 11,000.

690 ITA
IL GIORNALE DEL SERRAMENTO; tecnologia del serramento e degli accessori. Short title: G D S. Text in Italian. 1988. 7/yr. EUR 25 domestic; EUR 47 foreign (effective 2004). adv. illus. **Document type:** *Magazine, Trade.*
Published by: Gruppo Editoriale Faenza Editrice SpA, Via Pier de Crescenzi 44, Faenza, RA 48018, Italy. TEL 39-0546-670411, FAX 39-0546-660440, info@faenza.com, http://www.faenza.com. Ed. Stefania Battaglia. R&P Luisa Teston. Adv. contact Elvio Neri. Circ: 16,000.

690 ITA
GIORNALE DELL'EDILIZIA ITALIANA. Text in Italian. 11/yr.
Address: Via Trezzo d'Adda 16, Milan, MI 20144, Italy. TEL 39-02-4239446, FAX 39-02-44952889. Ed. Giorgio Panciroli. Circ: 35,000.

GLASS & GLAZING PRODUCTS. see *CERAMICS, GLASS AND POTTERY*

691 JPN
GLASS BLOCK AND BRICK✶. Text in Japanese. 1961. s-a. per issue exchange basis.
Published by: Nippon Electric Glass Co. Ltd./Nippon Denki Garasu K.K., 7-1 Seiran 2-chome, Otsu-shi, Shiga-ken 520-0833, Japan.

GLASS DIGEST; trade magazine serving the flat glass, architectural metal and allied products industry. see *CERAMICS, GLASS AND POTTERY*

690 GBR
GLOBAL CEMENT REPORT. Text in English. 1994. biennial. GBP 195 (effective 1998). adv. **Document type:** *Trade.*
Published by: Tradeship Publications Ltd., Old Kings Head Ct, 15 High St, Dorking, Surrey RH4 1AR, United Kingdom. TEL 44-1306-740363, FAX 44-1306-740660, tradeship@dial.pipex.com, http://www.cemnet.co.uk. Ed., Adv. contact David Hargreaves.

690 334.5 SWE ISSN 1102-6804
GODA GRANNAR. Text in Swedish. 1954. q. adv.
Formerly (until 1991): Fasaden (0345-3251)
Published by: Svenska Bostaeder, PO Box 95, Vaellingby, 16212, Sweden. TEL 46-8-59861000, svenska bostader@svebo.se, http://www.svebo.se/godagrannar.

643 DNK ISSN 0281-3041
GOER SAA HAER✶. Variant title: Goer Saa Haer i Hemmet. Text in Danish. 1981. 14/yr. SEK 42.50 per issue. adv. 68 p./no. 4 cols./p.; **Document type:** *Consumer.*
Published by: Bonnier Publications AS, Strandboulevarden 130, Copenhagen Oe, 2100, Denmark. TEL 45-39-17-20-00, FAX 45-39-29-01-99. Ed. Freddy Nielskov. Pub. Lars Engstroem. adv.: color page SEK 22,800; trim 185 x 250. Circ: 56,400 (paid).

796.352029 USA
GOLF COURSE BUILDERS ASSOCIATION OF AMERICA. DIRECTORY. Text in English. a. USD 15 (effective 2000). adv. **Document type:** *Directory, Trade.*
Formerly: Golf Course Builders of America Directory
Published by: Golf Course Builders Association of America, 727 "O" St, Lincoln, NE 68508. TEL 404-476-4444, FAX 404-476-4444, gcbaa@aol.com, http://www.gcbaa.org. Ed. Lee Hetrick. Adv. contact Susan Monk. Circ: 3,500.

690 621.9 CHN ISSN 1000-1212
GONGCHENG JIXIE/CONSTRUCTION MACHINERY & EQUIPMENT. Text in Chinese. 1964. m. USD 50.40 foreign; CNY 8 newsstand/cover domestic; USD 4.20 newsstand/cover foreign (effective 2001). adv.
Related titles: Online - full content ed.: (from WanFang Data Corp.); Online - full text ed.: (from East View Information Services).
Published by: Tianjin Gongcheng Jixie Yanjiusuo, Dingzigu 3-Hao Lu, Tianjin, 300131, China. TEL 86-22-26371751, FAX 86-22-26370666, tjricmmd@public.tjuc.com.cn. Ed. Wen-Yuan Xu. adv.: B&W page USD 500, color page USD 1,000; trim 258 x 185. **Dist. outside of China by:** China International Book Trading Corp, 35 Chegongzhuang Xilu, Haidian District, PO Box 399, Beijing 100044, China. TEL 86-10-68412045, FAX 86-10-68412023, cibtc@mail.cibtc.com.cn, http://www.cibtc.com.cn.

690 CHN ISSN 1000-8993
TH4
➤ **GONGYE JIANZHU/INDUSTRIAL CONSTRUCTION.** Text in Chinese. 1964. m. CNY 60; CNY 48 foreign. adv. bk.rev. **Document type:** *Academic/Scholarly.*
Related titles: Microfiche ed.; Online - full text ed.: (from East View Information Services).
Indexed: Englnd.
—Linda Hall.

B

Published by: Yejin-bu, Jianzhu Yanjiu Zongyuan/Ministry of Metallurgical Industry, Central Research Institute of Construction, 33 Xitucheng Lu, Haidian-qu, Beijing, 100088, China. TEL 86-10-6222-5599, FAX 86-10-6222-5938. Ed. Fan Xisheng. Adv. contact Wang Shuting. color page USD 1,500; trim 187 x 260. Circ: 8,000 (controlled). **Dist. overseas by:** China International Book Trading Corp, 35 Chegongzhuang Xilu, Haidian District, PO Box 399, Beijing 100044, China.

690 GBR ISSN 1368-0080
GOOD PRACTICE CASE STUDY. Text in English. 1989. irreg., latest vol.236, 1997.
—BLDSC (4201.350700). **CCC.**
Published by: (Great Britain. Department of Environment), Construction Research Communications Ltd., 151 Rosebery Ave, London, EC1R 4QX, United Kingdom. TEL 44-171-505-6622, FAX 44-171-505-6606, TELEX 923 220, http://www.bre.co.uk.

624 HRV ISSN 1330-3945
GRADITELJ. Text in Croatian. 1993. bi-m. **Document type:** *Journal, Trade.*
Published by: Europska Strucna Naklada d.o.o., Dordiceva 10, Zagreb, 10000, Croatia. TEL 385-1-430416, FAX 385-1-425496. Ed. Nenad Lihtar.

GRADJEVINAR. see *ENGINEERING—Civil Engineering*

GREAT BRITAIN. DEPARTMENT OF THE ENVIRONMENT. PRICE ADJUSTMENT FORMULAE FOR CONSTRUCTION CONTRACTS: MONTHLY BULLETIN OF INDICES. see *BUILDING AND CONSTRUCTION—Abstracting, Bibliographies, Statistics*

GREECE. NATIONAL STATISTICAL SERVICE. BUILDING ACTIVITY STATISTICS. see *BUILDING AND CONSTRUCTION—Abstracting, Bibliographies, Statistics*

GREECE. NATIONAL STATISTICAL SERVICE. REVISED PRICE INDICES OF NEW BUILDING DWELLINGS CONSTRUCTION (YEAR). see *BUILDING AND CONSTRUCTION—Abstracting, Bibliographies, Statistics*

690.028 USA
GREEN SHEET (NORCROSS). Text in English. m. (Second Saturday of month). free (effective 2004); Included with Michigan Contractor & Builder. **Description:** A used equipment trader publication for contractors in Upper Michigan, Wisconsin, and Minnesota.
Published by: Reed Construction Data, Associated Construction Publications (Subsidiary of: Reed Business Information), 30 Technology Pkwy, Ste 100, Norcross, GA 30092. TEL 770-417-4120, FAX 770-417-4138, http://www.acppubs.com/. Pub. John Weatherhead TEL 770-417-4120. Circ: 13,000.

338.4769 DNK ISSN 0907-1040
GROENLAND. Variant title: V & S Priser, Groenland. Text in Danish. 1992. a. DKK 1,410 (effective 1999).
Published by: V & S Byggedata, 551 Frederikssundvej 194, Broenshoej, 2700, Denmark. TEL 45-38-60-77-11, FAX 45-38-60-77-55, bygdat@vs-byggedata.dk, bygdat@vs.byggedata.dk. Ed. Carl Friis Skovsen.

GROUND ENGINEERING YEARBOOK. see *BUSINESS AND ECONOMICS—Trade And Industrial Directories*

669 FRA
GROUPE DES CHAMBRES SYNDICALES DU BATIMENT ET DES TRAVAUX PUBLICS DU DEPARTEMENT DE L'OISE. MONTHLY REVIEW. Text in French. m.
Published by: Groupe des Chambres Syndicales du Batiment et des Travaux Publics du Departement de l'Oise, 19 Pl. Georges Clemenceau, Beauvais, 60000, France. TEL 774128, TELEX 430306.

DER GRUNDSTEIN. see *LABOR UNIONS*

690 BRA
GUIA DE FORNECEDORES DA CONSTRUCAO. Text in Portuguese. 1998. m. BRL 48, USD 192 (effective 1999). adv. back issues avail. **Document type:** *Trade.* **Description:** Covers building and contruction, architecture and civil engineering.
Related titles: Online - full text ed.
Published by: Editora Guia de Fornecedores Ltda., Av Doutor Adolfo Pinto, 109 Andar 4, B Funda, Sao Paulo, SP 01156-050, Brazil. TEL 55-11-3924-9655, FAX 55-11-826-9789, arteguia@hipernet.com.br, http://www.editoraguia.com.br. Ed. Eduardo David Airton. Adv. contact Camila Nunez. page USD 3,917; trim 14.25 x 10.5. Circ: 15,000.

690 FRA
GUIDE DE L'ENTREPRENEUR DU BATIMENT ET DES TRAVAUX PUBLICS✶. Text in French. 6/yr. **Description:** Practical advice and prices of materials for the building trade.
Published by: Editions S E R I P, c/o Office de Justification de la Diffusion, 40 bd. Malesherbes, Paris, 75008, France. TEL 48-81-91-91. Ed. Yves de Kerautem. Circ: 57,250.

690 FRA
GUIDE PRATIQUE DE L'ENTREPRENEUR - BOIS - ALU - P V C✶. Text in French. 6/yr.
Published by: Editions S E R I P, c/o Office de Justification de la Diffusion, 40 bd. Malesherbes, Paris, 75008, France. TEL 48-81-91-91, FAX 48-81-81-77. Ed. Regine Heurteur. Circ: 13,000.

690 FRA ISSN 1254-4019
GUIDE PRATIQUE DE L'ENTREPRENEUR - MACONNERIE✶. Text in French. 6/yr.
Published by: Editions S E R I P, c/o Office de Justification de la Diffusion, 40 bd. Malesherbes, Paris, 75008, France. TEL 48-81-91-91, FAX 48-81-81-77. Ed. Reni Giacomo. Circ: 15,000.

690 BHR ISSN 1560-0416
GULF CONSTRUCTION. Text in English. 1980. m. BHD 35,000, USD 95; BHD 3,000 newsstand/cover (effective 2001). adv. charts; illus.; stat.; tr.lit. 100 p./no. 3 cols./p.; **Description:** Distributed to decision-makers and executives in construction-related companies, architects, engineers, contractors, public works authorities, importers of plant equipment, building materials and plant hire companies.
Related titles: Online - full text ed.
Published by: Al Hilal Publishing & Marketing Group, Exhibition Ave, PO Box 224, Manama, Bahrain. TEL 973-293131, FAX 973-293400, hilalmg@traderarabic.net, hilalcirc@tradearabia.net, http://www.gulfconstructiononline.com. Ed. Bina Prabhu Goveas. Pub. A M Abdul Rahman. adv.: B&W page USD 2,015, color page USD 2,890; trim 210 x 282. Circ: 12,485.

690 GBR ISSN 0266-2736
GULF CONSTRUCTION & SAUDI ARABIA REVIEW DIRECTORY. Text in English. 1985. a. **Document type:** *Directory, Trade.*
Published by: Hilal International (UK) Ltd., Crescent Ct, 102 Victor Rd, Teddington, Midds TW11 8SS, United Kingdom. TEL 44-20-8943-3630.

690 USA
H B A OPTIONS. (Home Builders Association) Text in English. 1982. bi-w. free to members. adv. **Document type:** *Newsletter, Consumer.*
Formerly: H B A Newsletter
Published by: Home Builders Association of Greater St. Louis, 10104 Old Olive St, St. Louis, MO 63141. TEL 314-994-7700, FAX 314-432-7185, questions@hbastl.com, stlhba@stlnet.com, http://www.stlhba.com. Ed. Shelly Stengel. Pub. Patrick Sullivan. Adv. contact Tracy Chiesa. B&W page USD 725, color page USD 925. Circ: 1,500 (controlled and free).

690 614.85 GBR
H S E INFORMATION SHEET. CONSTRUCTION INFORMATION SHEET. Text in English. irreg., latest no.46, 1997.
Formerly (until no.46): H S E Information Sheet. Construction Steet
—BLDSC (4335.321700).
Published by: Health and Safety Executive, Broad Ln, Sheffield, S3 7HQ, United Kingdom. TEL 44-114-2892000, FAX 44-114-2892500, public.enquiries@hse.gov.uk, http://www.hse.gov.uk.

690.029 DNK ISSN 0107-5454
HAANDBOG FOR BYGNINGSINDUSTRIEN. Text in Danish. 1931. biennial. DKK 422 domestic (effective 2000). adv. **Document type:** *Catalog.*
Published by: Nyt Nordisk Forlag-Arnold Busck A-S, Koebmagergade 49, Copenhagen K, 1150, Denmark. FAX 45-33-73-35-76, nnf@nytnordiskforlag.dk, http://www.nytnordiskforlag.dk. Circ: 8,200.

620 DEU ISSN 1430-7715
HAEUSER HEUTE. Text in German. 1996. q. EUR 1.20 newsstand/cover (effective 2003). adv.
Published by: Publikom Z Verlagsgesellschaft mbH, Frankfurter Str 168, Kassel, 34121, Germany. TEL 49-561-2031742, FAX 49-561-2032745, publikom_z@dierichs.de, http://www.publikom-z.de. adv.: B&W page EUR 7,200, color page EUR 8,650. Circ: 128,112 (paid and controlled).

690 CHE ISSN 1422-8483
HAEUSER MODERNISIEREN. Text in German. 1988. q. CHF 54 for 2 yrs. (effective 2000). adv. **Document type:** *Magazine, Consumer.* **Description:** Provides information and advice on the renovation and modernization of homes and apartments.
Published by: Etzel-Verlag AG, Knonauerstr 56, Cham, 6330, Switzerland. TEL 41-41-7855085, FAX 41-41-7855088, info@etzel-verlag.ch, http://www.haeuser-modernisieren.ch/html/hmhome.htm. Ed. Esther Kall. adv.: B&W page CHF 3,790; trim 199 x 278. Circ: 19,400 (paid).

690 666 USA
HANDBOOK FOR CERAMIC TILE INSTALLATION. Text in English. 1963. a. USD 3 (effective 2000). illus. **Document type:** *Trade.* **Description:** Presents architects and builders with ceramic tile installation standards.
Related titles: CD-ROM ed.: USD 5 (effective 2000).
Published by: Tile Council of America, Inc., 100 Clemson Research Blvd, Anderson, SC 29625-6548. TEL 864-646-8453, FAX 864-646-2821, info@tileusa.com, http://www.tileUSA.com. Ed., R&P Robert Daniels. Circ: 60,000; 55,000 (paid).

690 DEU ISSN 0017-7202
HANDBUCH DES BAUHERRN; bauen - modernisieren - einrichten. Text in German. 1964. s-a. EUR 16 (effective 2005). **Document type:** *Directory, Trade.*
Published by: Springer BauMedien GmbH Heinze (Subsidiary of: Springer Science+Business Media), Bremer Weg 184, Celle, 29223, Germany. TEL 49-5141-500, FAX 49-5141-50104, info@heinze.de, http://www.heinze.de. Ed. Juergen Wolf. Circ: 600,000.

692.8 CHE
DAS HANDBUCH DES BAUHERRN. Text in German. a. free to qualified personnel. **Document type:** *Journal, Trade.* **Description:** Provides a source of information and advice for building and construction contractors and companies.
Published by: MVS Baumarketing AG (Subsidiary of: Springer Science+Business Media), Ruetistr 22, Schlieren, 8952, Switzerland. TEL 41-1-7385151, FAX 41-1-7385200, franco.bernasconi@mvs.ch, http://www.mvs.ch/deutsch/handbuch/index.htm. Circ: 50,085 (controlled).

690 DEU
HANDBUCH FUER DAS DACHBAUHANDWERK. Text in German. 1987. a. EUR 28.80 (effective 2004). adv. **Document type:** *Directory, Trade.*
Formerly: Handbuch fuer den Dachdeckermeister
Published by: Verlag F.H. Kleffmann GmbH, Herner Str 299, Bochum, 44809, Germany. TEL 49-234-95391-0, FAX 49-234-9539130, service@kleffmann-verlag.de, http://www.kleffmann-verlag.de. adv.: B&W page EUR 640, color page EUR 840. Circ: 1,036 (paid and controlled).

690 DEU
HANDBUCH FUER DAS MALER- UND LACKIERERHANDWERK. Text in German. 1952. a. EUR 29.80 (effective 2004). adv. **Document type:** *Directory, Trade.*
Published by: Verlag F.H. Kleffmann GmbH, Herner Str 299, Bochum, 44809, Germany. TEL 49-234-95391-0, FAX 49-234-9539130, service@kleffmann-verlag.de, http://www.kleffmann-verlag.de. adv.: B&W page EUR 1,100, color page EUR 1,720. Circ: 3,605 (paid and controlled).

690 DEU
HANDBUCH FUER KLEMPNERARBEITEN. Text in German. 1994. a. EUR 28.80 (effective 2004). adv. **Document type:** *Directory, Trade.*
Published by: Verlag F.H. Kleffmann GmbH, Herner Str 299, Bochum, 44809, Germany. TEL 49-234-95391-0, FAX 49-234-9539130, service@kleffmann-verlag.de, http://www.kleffmann-verlag.de. adv.: B&W page EUR 300, color page EUR 420. Circ: 783 (paid and controlled).

690 DEU
HANDBUCH FUER ROLLADEN UND SONNENSCHUTZSYSTEME. Text in German. 2000. a. EUR 29.80 (effective 2004). **Document type:** *Directory, Trade.*
Published by: Verlag F.H. Kleffmann GmbH, Herner Str 299, Bochum, 44809, Germany. TEL 49-234-95391-0, FAX 49-234-9539130, service@kleffmann-verlag.de, http://www.kleffmann-verlag.de.

HARD HAT MAGAZINE. see *BUSINESS AND ECONOMICS—Labor And Industrial Relations*

338.4 USA ISSN 0279-1242
HARD HAT NEWS. Text in English. 1979. fortn. free to qualified personnel. adv. **Document type:** *Magazine, Trade.* **Description:** Covers heavy construction and roadbuilding industries.
Published by: Lee Publications, Inc., 6113 State Hwy 5, Palatine Bridge, NY 13428. TEL 515-673-3237, 800-836-2888, FAX 518-673-2381, http://www.hardhat.com. Ed. M Hilton. Pub. Frederick W Lee. Adv. contact Larry Price. B&W page USD 700, color page USD 995. Circ: 23,355.

690 DEU ISSN 0017-8403
HAUS UND GRUND; das Magazin fuer Haus-, Wohnungs und Grundeigentuemer. Text in German. 1915. m. EUR 16.87 (effective 2002). adv. bk.rev. illus.; stat. index. **Document type:** *Magazine, Consumer.*
Published by: Haus und Grund Verlag GmbH, Elisabethstr 4, Dortmund, 44139, Germany. TEL 49-231-95830, FAX 49-231-958395, verlag@haus-und-grund.com, http://www.haus-und-grund.com. Ed. Henning Dreis. Circ: 110,200 (controlled).

690 340 DEU ISSN 0171-8533
HAUS- UND GRUNDBESITZ IN RECHT UND PRAXIS. Text in German. 1978. irreg. looseleaf. **Document type:** *Proceedings.*
Published by: Rudolf Haufe Verlag GmbH & Co. KG, Hindenburgstr 64, Freiburg Im Breisgau, 79102, Germany. TEL 49-761-3683-0, FAX 49-761-3683236. Eds. Guenther Reinisch, Julius Schoenhofer.

690 DEU
HAUS UND WOHNUNG; das Ratgeber-Magazin fuer Haus, Wohnung und Garten. Text in German. 1962. m. EUR 3.90 newsstand/cover (effective 2005). adv. bk.rev. charts; illus. index. 65 p./no.; **Document type:** *Magazine, Consumer.*
Formerly: Magazin fuer Haus und Wohnung (0024-9769)
Published by: Huss-Medien GmbH, Am Friedrichshain 22, Berlin, 10407, Germany. TEL 49-30-421510, FAX 49-30-42151232, verlag.wirtschaft@hussberlin.de, http://www.huss-medien.de. Ed. Birgit Holtz. Pub. Wolfgang Huss. Adv. contact Jessica Wiese TEL 49-30-42151404. B&W page EUR 7,800, color page EUR 4,950; trim 185 x 250. Circ: 110,000 (paid and controlled).

690 DEU ISSN 0934-8026
HAUSBAU; bauen und Fertighaus. Text in German. 1963. bi-m. EUR 3.50 newsstand/cover (effective 2003). adv. bk.rev. illus.; mkt.; tr.lit. **Document type:** *Magazine, Trade.* **Description:** News about house building and renovation.
Former titles (until 1986): Bauen und Fertighaus (0005-6510); Fertig Bauen (0430-3253)
Related titles: ♦ Supplement(s): Fertighaeuser. ISSN 0720-745X; ♦ HausTest.
Published by: Fachschriften Verlag GmbH, Hoehenstr 17, Fellbach, 70736, Germany. TEL 49-711-52061, FAX 49-711-5281424, info@fachschriften.de, http://www.fachschriften.de/publikationen/hausbau.htm. Ed. Paul Daluden. Pub. Guenter Bayer. Adv. contact Barbara Hoof. B&W page EUR 6,130, color page EUR 10,176; trim 187 x 247. Circ: 73,259 (controlled).

690 DEU
HAUSTECH. Text in German. a. adv. **Document type:** *Magazine, Consumer.*
Published by: Fachschriften Verlag GmbH, Hoehenstr 17, Fellbach, 70736, Germany. TEL 49-711-52061, FAX 49-711-5281424, info@fachschriften.de, http://www.fachschriften.de/publikationen/haustech.htm. Ed. Wolfgang Grasreiner. Adv. contact Claudia Pastor. B&W page EUR 8,950, color page EUR 14,442. Circ: 160,000 (controlled).

690 DEU
HAUSTEST. Text in German. a. EUR 6.80 newsstand/cover (effective 2003). adv. **Document type:** *Magazine, Consumer.*
Related titles: ♦ Supplement to: Hausbau. ISSN 0934-8026.
Published by: Fachschriften Verlag GmbH, Hoehenstr 17, Fellbach, 70736, Germany. TEL 49-711-52061, FAX 49-711-5206223, info@fachschriften.de, http://www.fachschriften.de/publikationen/haustest.htm. Ed. Paul Daleiden. Adv. contact Barbara Hoof. B&W page EUR 5,280, color page EUR 8,765; trim 187 x 247. Circ: 60,000 (paid).

690 USA
HAWAII BUILDING GUIDE (DIRECTORY). Text in English. 1954. a. USD 20; free to qualified personnel. adv. **Document type:** *Directory.*
Formerly: Building Industry Digest of Hawaii
Published by: Trade Publishing Co. Ltd., 287 Mokauea St, Honolulu, HI 96819. TEL 808-848-0711. Ed. John Black. Circ: 4,500.

690 362 USA
▼ **HEALTHCARE BUILDING IDEAS.** Text in English. 2004. bi-m. free to qualified personnel (effective 2005). **Document type:** *Magazine, Trade.* **Description:** Covers the design, construction and maintenance of healthcare facilities.
Published by: D & D Communications Group LLC http://www.healthcarebuildingideas.com/default.asp. Ed. Shannon Powers-Jones TEL 803-396-8516. Pub. David Corson.

HEALTHCARE CONSTRUCTION MONITOR. see *HEALTH FACILITIES AND ADMINISTRATION*

HEARTLAND REAL ESTATE BUSINESS; the Midwest's real estate source. see *REAL ESTATE*

692.8 CAN ISSN 0017-9426
HEAVY CONSTRUCTION NEWS. Text in English. 1957. fortn. free to qualified personnel (effective 2005). adv. bibl.; charts. index. **Document type:** *Magazine, Trade.* **Description:** Focuses on business prospects, site stories, maintenance and new products.
Related titles: Microfiche ed.: (from MML); Microform ed.: (from MML); Online - full text ed.; ♦ Supplement(s): Canadian Equipment Rentals.
Indexed: CBCABus, CBPI.
—CISTI. **CCC.**
Published by: Rogers Media Publishing Ltd, One Mount Pleasant Rd, 11th Fl, Toronto, ON M4Y 2Y5, Canada. TEL 416-764-2000, FAX 416-764-3941, http://www.econstruction.ca, http://www.rogers.com. Ed. Jim Barnes. Pub. Craig Coulter. Circ: 23,000.

690.028 USA ISSN 1522-4643
HEAVY EQUIPMENT NEWS. Text in English. 199?. m. adv. **Document type:** *Magazine, Trade.* **Description:** Designed for contractors in the highway, heavy construction, building, mining, aggregate and other specialized construction industries.
Published by: Grand View Media Group, Inc. (Subsidiary of: EBSCO Industries, Inc.), 200 Croft St., # 1, Birmingham, AL 35242-1824. TEL 888-431-2877, webmaster@grandviewmedia.com, http://www.grandviewmedia.com. adv.: page USD 6,000; trim 8 x 10.875.

690.028 USA
HEAVY EQUIPMENT NEWS ANNUAL DIRECTORY. Text in English. 1999. a. **Document type:** *Directory, Trade.* **Description:** Provides information and contact sources for construction companies across the country.
Published by: Grand View Media Group, Inc. (Subsidiary of: EBSCO Industries, Inc.), 200 Croft St., # 1, Birmingham, AL 35242-1824. TEL 888-431-2877, webmaster@grandviewmedia.com, http://www.grandviewmedia.com.

690 DEU
HEINZEBAUOFFICE. Text in German. 2/yr. **Document type:** *Magazine, Trade.*
Published by: Springer BauMedien GmbH Heinze (Subsidiary of: Springer Science+Business Media), Bremer Weg 184, Celle, 29223, Germany. TEL 49-5141-500, FAX 49-5141-50104, info@heinze.de, http://www.heinze.de.

HERON. see *ENGINEERING—Civil Engineering*

338.3 USA
HIGH - VALUED DWELLING COST GUIDE. Text in English. a. USD 52 (effective 1998).
Published by: E.H. Boeckh, Ed. & Pub. (Subsidiary of: Thomson Publishing Corp.), 2885 S Calhoun Rd, Box 510291, New Berlin, WI 53151-0291. TEL 414-780-2800, 800-285-1288, FAX 414-780-0306. R&P E H Boeckh.

HIGHWAY BUILDER. see *ENGINEERING—Civil Engineering*

690 ZAF ISSN 1607-9604
HIRE SOUTH AFRICA. Text in English. 1989. 11/yr. ZAR 348 domestic; ZAR 434 foreign (effective 2003). **Description:** Contains news and articles about members, to developments in the hire industry and to coverage of the latest plant and equipment on the market.
Published by: (Contractors Plant Hire Association), Primedia Publishing, 366 Pretoria Ave, Ferndale, Randburg, Transvaal 2194, South Africa. TEL 27-11-787-5725, FAX 27-11-787-5776, http://www.cpha.co.za/hiresa.htm. Ed. Allyson Koekhove.

690 DEU ISSN 0342-5169
HOCH- UND TIEFBAU; die Fachzeitschrift der Bauwirtschaft. Text in German. 1948. 9/yr. EUR 45 domestic; EUR 55 foreign; EUR 6 newsstand/cover (effective 2002). adv. **Document type:** *Magazine, Trade.*
Related titles: Online - full text ed.
Published by: H E Verlag fuer Fachinformation GmbH & Co. KG, Heerstr 5, Meinerzhagen, 58540, Germany. TEL 49-2354-7799-0, FAX 49-2354-779977, http://www.htbau.de. Ed. Susanne Wieland TEL 49-8193-1263. Adv. contact Imke Ridder. B&W page EUR 2,500, color page EUR 4,000; trim 187 x 260. Circ: 12,098 (paid and controlled).

693 DEU
HOELZ- UND OEKO-HAEUSER. Text in German. a. EUR 6 domestic; EUR 7.50 foreign (effective 2003). adv. **Document type:** *Directory, Trade.*
Published by: biz Verlag GmbH Berlin, Tschaikowskistr. 40-42, Berlin, 13156, Germany. TEL 49-30-437380, FAX 49-30-43738111, info@biz-verlag.de, http://www.biz-verlag.de. Ed. Doris Neumann. Pub., Adv. contact Peter Neumann. page EUR 6,214. Circ: 76,211 (paid and controlled).

690 DEU ISSN 1860-8841
HOLZBAU; das Fachmagazin fuer den Holzhausbau. Text in German. 1999. bi-m. EUR 60 domestic; EUR 65 foreign; EUR 30 to students (effective 2005). adv. **Document type:** *Magazine, Trade.*
Former titles (until 2005): Die Neue Quadriga (1612-104X); (until 1999): Quadriga (1434-1875)
Related titles: Online - full text ed.
Published by: Verlag Kastner & Zeeb, Schlosshof 2-6, Wolnzach, 85283 , Germany. TEL 49-8442-92530, FAX 49-8442-2289, info@quadriga-news.de, verlag@kastner.de, http://www.quadriga-news.de, http://www.kastner.de. Ed., Pub. Eduard Kastner. Adv. contact Ina Helstab. B&W page EUR 1,980, color page EUR 3,420; trim 175 x 258.5. Circ: 12,049 (paid and controlled).

690 DEU ISSN 1439-1945
HOLZB!TS; Holzhaus & Business. Text in German. 1999. bi-m. EUR 6.20 newsstand/cover (effective 2002). adv. **Document type:** *Magazine, Trade.*
Published by: Fachschriften Verlag GmbH, Hoehenstr 17, Fellbach, 70736, Germany. TEL 49-711-52061, FAX 49-711-5281424, info@fachschriften.de, http://www.fachschriften.de. Ed. Paul Daleiden. Adv. contact Claudia Pastor. B&W page EUR 2,000, color page EUR 3,200. Circ: 7,000 (paid and controlled).

HOME; the remodeling and decorating resource. see *ARCHITECTURE*

690 CAN ISSN 0840-4348
HOME BUILDER MAGAZINE. Text in English. 1987. bi-m. CND 30 domestic; USD 30 in United States; CND 84 elsewhere (effective 2000). adv. back issues avail.; reprints avail. **Document type:** *Trade.* **Description:** Covers new home construction and renovation markets in Canada.
—CISTI.
Published by: Work-4 Projects Ltd., 4819 St Charles Blvd, Pierrefonds, PQ H9H 3C7, Canada. TEL 514-620-2200, FAX 514-620-6300, homebuilder@work4.ca. Ed. Frank O'Brien. R&P Ady Artzy. Adv. contact Cheryl Carvery. B&W page CND 4,110, color page CND 5,210. Circ: 23,088 (controlled).

690 USA ISSN 1550-5715
HOME BUILDING. Variant title: Woman's Day Home Building. Text in English. 2000. a. USD 4.99 per issue (effective 2005). adv. **Document type:** *Magazine, Consumer.*
Published by: Hachette Filipacchi Media U.S., Inc. (Subsidiary of: Hachette Filipacchi Medias S.A.), 1633 Broadway, New York, NY 10019. http://www.hfmus.com. Ed. Olivia Monjo. adv.: B&W page USD 28,890, color page USD 41,275. Circ: 450,000.

B

HOME CHANNEL NEWS. see *BUSINESS AND ECONOMICS*

643 USA
HOME CHANNEL NEWS NEWSFAX. Variant title: H C N Newsfax. Newsfax. Text in English. 1992. w. USD 189 (effective 2005). **Document type:** *Trade.* **Description:** Contains weekly summary on developments in the U.S. retail home improvement market.
Formerly: National Home Center News Newsfax (1079-638X)
Media: Fax. **Related titles:** E-mail ed.; Online - full text ed.: (from Gale Group).
Published by: Lebhar-Friedman, Inc., 425 Park Ave, New York, NY 10022. TEL 212-756-5000, info@lf.com, http://www.homechannelnews.com/, http://www.lf.com.

THE HOME HANDYMAN. see *HOW-TO AND DO-IT-YOURSELF*

643.7 USA
HOME MAGAZINE'S BEST KITCHEN & BATH. Text in English. s-a. available at newsstands and not by subscription. **Document type:** *Consumer.*
Related titles: Online - full text ed.
Published by: Hachette Filipacchi Media U.S., Inc. (Subsidiary of: Hachette Filipacchi Medias S.A.), 1633 Broadway, New York, NY 10019. TEL 212-767-6000, http://www.homemag.com/, http://www.hfmus.com. Ed. Timothy A Drew. Circ: 123,420.

690 ZAF ISSN 1023-2451
HOME OWNER BUILDING & IMPROVEMENTS BUYERS GUIDE. Text in English. 1994. a. ZAR 88 (effective 1998). adv. illus. **Document type:** *Consumer.*
Published by: Avonwold Publishing Co. (Pty) Ltd., Avonwold House, 24 Baker St, Rosebank, Johannesburg, 2196, South Africa. TEL 27-11-788-1610, FAX 27-11-880-2732.

690 USA ISSN 1040-547X
NA7205
HOME PLANNER. Text in English. 1989. bi-m. USD 49.95; USD 4.99 newsstand/cover (effective 2005). adv. **Document type:** *Magazine, Consumer.* **Description:** Contains home plans, showing detailed exterior illustrations, floor plans, and planning pointers. Also contains in-depth how-to advice.
Published by: Home Planners, LLC (Subsidiary of: Hanley-Wood, LLC), 3275 W Ina Rd, Ste 220, Tucson, AZ 85741-2153. TEL 888-846-8188, http://www.homeplanners.com. Circ: 100,000.

747 GBR ISSN 0266-3910
HOME PLUS. Text in English. 1983. q.
Related titles: ♦ Supplement to: Practical Householder. ISSN 0079-4813.
Published by: Nexus Media Ltd. (Subsidiary of: Highbury House Communications PLC), Nexus House, Azalea Dr, Swanley, Kent BR8 8HU, United Kingdom. TEL 44-1442-66551, FAX 44-1322-661257.

690 USA
HOME REMODELING NEW PRODUCT IDEAS. Text in English. a. USD 3.99 newsstand/cover (effective 2005). adv. illus. **Document type:** *Magazine, Consumer.* **Description:** Offers home remodeling strategies; reports on new products and tools.
Formerly: Woman's Day Home Improvements
Published by: Hachette Filipacchi Media U.S., Inc. (Subsidiary of: Hachette Filipacchi Medias S.A.), 1633 Broadway, New York, NY 10019. http://www.hfmmag.com, http://www.hfmus.com. Ed. Carol Gatto. Pub. Jim Fraguela. adv.: B&W page USD 31,530, color page USD 45,050; trim 7.88 x 10.5. Circ: 400,000 (paid).

690 USA
HOMEBUILDER✶. Text in English. 1980. m. USD 21. adv.
Published by: Thompson Publications, Inc., 2781 W Hannon Hill Dr, Tallahassee, FL 32308-8916. TEL 904-681-3583, FAX 904-224-1359. Ed. Paul M Thompson. Circ: 22,000.

690 747 GBR ISSN 1464-1054
HOMEBUILDING & RENOVATING; designing, building & renovating your own home. Text in English. m. GBP 26.50 domestic; GBP 38 in Europe; GBP 62 in Canada; GBP 67 elsewhere; GBP 2.75 newsstand/cover (effective 2000). adv. illus.; mkt.; stat. back issues avail. **Document type:** *Consumer.* **Description:** Deals with all aspects of creating or renovating a unique home.
Formerly (until 1997): Individual Homes (0960-0868)
Related titles: Online - full text ed.
Published by: Ascent Publishing Ltd., Sugar Brook Ct, Aston Rd, Bromsgrove, Worcs B60 3EX, United Kingdom. TEL 44-1527-834400, FAX 44-1527-834499, indhomes@ascentpub.demon.co.uk, customerservice@centaur.co.uk, http://www.homebuidling.co.uk, http://www.homebuilding.co.uk. Ed. Michael Holmes. Pub., R&P Peter Harris. Adv. contact Liam Bray. page GBP 1,725; trim 230 x 297. Circ: 18,500 (paid); 2,000 (controlled). **Dist. by:** Comag Specialist Division, Tavistock Works, Tavistock Rd, W Drayton, Mddx UB7 7QX, United Kingdom.

690 GBR ISSN 1740-3421
TH4805
HOMES. Text in English. 1996. m. illus. **Document type:** *Trade.* **Description:** Covers all aspects of housing construction.
Formerly (until 2002): Building Homes (1362-038X)
Related titles: ♦ Supplement to: Building. ISSN 0007-3318.
Indexed: API, BrTechI.
—BLDSC (4326.176491), IE, Infotrieve. **CCC.**
Published by: Builder Group plc., 7th Floor, Anchorage House, 2 Clove Crescent, London, London E14 2BE, United Kingdom. TEL 44-20-75604000, FAX 44-20-75604026.

690 747 AUS ISSN 0817-4296
HOMES & LIVING. Text in English. 1981. q. (plus 3 annuals: Renovations, Yearbook and Gardens & Outdoor Living). AUD 30 (effective 1999). adv. bk.rev. index. back issues avail. **Document type:** *Magazine, Consumer.* **Description:** Features homes, gardens for builders, decorators, renovators.
Formerly (until 1984): W.A. Homes and Living (0817-430X)
Published by: H B M Management Publishing, PO Box 449, Leederville, W.A. 6903, Australia. TEL 61-8-92278334, FAX 61-8-92278337. Ed. Jennie Fitzhardige. Pub., R&P Ron Tan. Adv. contact Caroline Shanley. Circ: 50,000.

690 USA ISSN 0897-621X
NA7205
HOMESTYLES HOME PLANS. Text in English. 1986. q. USD 19.50; USD 4.99 newsstand/cover (effective 2000). adv. **Document type:** *Magazine, Consumer.* **Description:** Focuses on designs for move-up homes, homes with special amenities, homes for empty nesters, and homes inspired by European design.
Published by: HomeStyles Publishing & Marketing, Inc., 213 E. 4th St., 4th Fl., St. Paul, MN 55101-1603. TEL 651-602-5000, 888-626-2026, FAX 651-602-5001, http://www.homestyles.com. Ed. Josh Kimball. R&P Roger Heegaard. Adv. contact Shelley Junker. B&W page USD 3,910, color page USD 4,830; trim 8 x 10.75. Circ: 62,800.

HONG KONG ARCHITECTS & DESIGNERS CATALOGUE (YEAR). see *ARCHITECTURE*

338.4 HKG
HONG KONG BUILDER DIRECTORY (YEAR)✶. Text in Chinese, English. a. HKD 595; USD 100 foreign. adv. illus. **Document type:** *Directory.* **Description:** Covers construction products and services, building professionals, and relevant government departments.
Published by: T P L Corporation Ltd., Blcok C, 10th FL, Sea View Estate 2-8 Watson Rd, North Point, Hong Kong. TEL 852-25668381, FAX 852-25080255. adv.: B&W page HKD 8,150, color page HKD 10,900; trim 210 x 280. Circ: 8,000.

HONG KONG. BUILDING DEVELOPMENT DEPARTMENT. BUILDING STATISTICS. see *STATISTICS*

HONG KONG SPECIAL ADMINISTRATIVE REGION OF CHINA. CENSUS AND STATISTICS DEPARTMENT. QUARTERLY REPORT OF EMPLOYMENT AND VACANCIES AT CONSTRUCTION SITES. see *BUILDING AND CONSTRUCTION—Abstracting, Bibliographies, Statistics*

HONG KONG SPECIAL ADMINISTRATIVE REGION OF CHINA. CENSUS AND STATISTICS DEPARTMENT. REPORT ON ANNUAL SURVEY OF BUILDING, CONSTRUCTION AND REAL ESTATE SECTORS. see *BUILDING AND CONSTRUCTION—Abstracting, Bibliographies, Statistics*

691.3 ESP ISSN 1133-1380
HORMIGON PREPARADO. Text in Spanish. 1987. bi-m. **Document type:** *Trade.* **Description:** For public works engineers, architects, technical schools, and concrete companies.
Indexed: IECT.
—CINDOC.
Published by: (Asociacion Nacional Espanola de Fabricas de Hormigon Preparado), Ediciones Metyel, S.L., Antonio Gonzalez Porras, 35 2o, Madrid, 28019, Spain. TEL 34-91-4690240, FAX 34-91-4690304. Ed., Adv. contact Francisco Carmona. Circ: 6,000 (paid).

691 ESP ISSN 0439-5689
TA87 CODEN: HOACBE
➤ **HORMIGON Y ACERO.** Text in Spanish. 1964. 4/yr. bk.rev. **Document type:** *Academic/Scholarly.*
Indexed: IECT, RefZh.
—CINDOC.
Published by: Asociacion Tecnica Espanola del Pretensado, Apartado 19002, Madrid, 28080, Spain. TEL 34-91-7660703, FAX 34-91-7660703.

➤ **HOSPITAL SURVEY AND CONSTRUCTION ACT WITH ADMENDMENTS.** see *LAW—Constitutional Law*

690 647.9 USA
▼ **HOSPITALITY CONSTRUCTION.** Text in English. forthcoming 2006 (Jan.). bi-m. **Document type:** *Magazine, Trade.*
Published by: D & D Communications Group LLC, 425 Tribble Gap Rd, Ste 103, PO Box 1589, Cumming, GA 30040. TEL 770-781-2511, FAX 770-781-6303. Ed. Chelsie Butler.

690 CHE
HOTEL UND GASTRO PLUS. Text in German. 3/yr. **Document type:** *Directory, Trade.*
Published by: MVS Baumarketing AG (Subsidiary of: Springer Science+Business Media), Ruetistr 22, Schlieren, 8952, Switzerland. TEL 41-1-7385151, FAX 41-1-7385200, franco.bernasconi@mvs.ch, http://www.mvs.ch. Circ: 27,000 (controlled).

HOUSE. see *ARCHITECTURE*

690 747 USA ISSN 1532-8597
NA7205
HOUSE BEAUTIFUL HOME BUILDING. Text in English. 1935. s-a. USD 3.50 newsstand/cover (effective 2005). adv. illus. back issues avail. **Document type:** *Magazine, Consumer.* **Description:** Offers design ideas for individuals and families planning to custom build a home.
Formerly: House Beautiful Building Manual (0018-6430)
Indexed: AIAP.
Published by: Hanley-Wood, LLC (Subsidiary of: J.P. Morgan Chase & Co.), 3275 W Ina Rd, Ste 220, Tucson, AZ 85741. TEL 520-544-8206, FAX 520-544-8224, http://www.hearstspecials.com, http://www.hanleywood.com. adv.: B&W page USD 22,050, color page USD 31,495; trim 10.75 x 8. Circ: 325,000 (paid).

690 GBR ISSN 0951-1334
HOUSE BUILDER; management journal of a 3 billion pound industry. Text in English. 1941. m. GBP 66; GBP 99 foreign. adv. tr.lit. **Document type:** *Trade.*
Indexed: API, RICS.
—BLDSC (4334.620000), IE, ingenta.
Published by: (House-Builders' Federation), Housebuilder Publications Ltd., 82 New Cavendish St, London, W1M 8AD, United Kingdom. TEL 44-171-580-5588, FAX 44-171-323-0890. Ed. Ben Roskrow. Pub., R&P Alan Dawson. Adv. contact Alan Levett. Circ: 18,134 (controlled).
Co-sponsor: National House Building Council.

690 USA
HOUSE MAGAZINE; the northeast builder's trade journal. Text in English. 1993. bi-m. USD 18. adv. charts; illus.; stat.; tr.lit. back issues avail. **Document type:** *Magazine, Trade.* **Description:** Covers the residential construction industry in the northeastern U.S. Includes new products and innovative building systems.
Formerly: VT Builder Magazine
Published by: Patrick Gass & Co., Inc., PO Box 235, Jericho, VT 05465. TEL 802-899-4838, FAX 802-899-1709. Ed. Richard A Mindell. Adv. contact Richard Mindell. Circ: 25,000.

354.35 AUS
HOUSING. Text in English. 1948. bi-m. AUD 45 to non-members (effective 1998). adv. bk.rev. **Document type:** *Trade.* **Description:** Covers housing industry nationally; new products, new developments, economic research, management and marketing coverage.
Former titles: Housing Victoria - Tasmania (1035-9265); Housing Victoria; Housing Products and Costing Guide; Housing Australia (0046-8096)
Published by: (Housing Industry Association), H.I.A. Publishing Pty. Ltd., 70 Jolimont St, Jolimont, VIC 3002, Australia. TEL 61-3-92808200, FAX 61-3-92808205. Ed. Kevin Randall. R&P Penny Brown. Adv. contact Keith Park. Circ: 30,000.

690 333.33 GBR ISSN 1359-4672
HOUSING FINANCE REVIEW. Text in English. 1952. q. free. charts; stat. cum.index: 1973-1994. **Document type:** *Bulletin.*
Former titles: Nationwide Building Society. House Prices; Nationwide Anglia Building Society. House Prices (0263-3639); Nationwide Anglia Building Society. Occasional Bulletin; Cooperative Permanent Building Society. Occasional Bulletin
Indexed: BldManAb.
Published by: Nationwide Building Society, Planning Department, Nationwide House, Pipers Way, Swindon, Wilts SN38 1XX, United Kingdom. FAX 44-1793-455903, http://www.nationwide.co.uk. Ed. P J Sanderson. Circ: 50,000.

690 USA ISSN 1044-0402
HOUSTON BUILDER. Text in English. 1943. m. USD 12 domestic to members (effective 2005). **Document type:** *Magazine, Trade.*
Contact Owner: Greater Houston Builders Association, 9511 W. Sam Houston Pkwy., N., Houston, TX 77064. TEL 281-970-8970, FAX 281-970-8971, http://www.ghba.org. Circ: 2,000 (paid).

690.764 659.1 USA
▼ **HOUSTON HOUSINGUIDE.** Text in English. 2003. q. adv. **Document type:** *Magazine, Consumer.*
Published by: Naylor Publications, Inc., 5950 NW 1st Pl, Gainesville, FL 32607-6018. TEL 800-369-6220, shall@naylor.com, http://www.naylornetwork.com/. Pub. Kathleen Gardner. adv.: B&W page USD 1,356, color page USD 2,537; trim 8.5 x 11.

696 HRV ISSN 1330-3953
HRVATSKI INSTALATER. Text in Croatian. 1993. bi-m. **Document type:** *Journal, Trade.*
Published by: Europska Strucna Naklada d.o.o., Dordiceva 10, Zagreb, 10000, Croatia. TEL 385-1-430416, FAX 385-1-425496, esn@esn.tel.hr. Ed. Nenad Lihtar.

HUNGARY. KOZPONTI STATISZTIKAI HIVATAL. BERUHAZASI, EPITOIPARI, LAKASEPITESI EVKONYV. see *BUILDING AND CONSTRUCTION—Abstracting, Bibliographies, Statistics*

690 SWE ISSN 0018-7968
HUSBYGGAREN. Text in Swedish. 1959. 6/yr. SEK 200; SEK 70 per issue (effective 2004). adv. bk.rev. abstr.; charts; illus.; pat.; stat.; tr.mk. index. **Document type:** *Magazine, Trade.*
Published by: Svenska Byggingenjoerers Riksfoerbund (SBR), Folkungsgatan 122, Box 4415, Stockholm, 10269, Sweden. TEL 46-8-4621790, FAX 46-8-4622033, husbyggaren@swipnet.se, bygging@bygging.se, http://www.bygging.se. Ed. Margot Granvik TEL 46-8-7430473. Adv. contact Roland Maartenson TEL 46-8-6447960. B&W page SEK 11,400, color page SEK 19,800; trim 175 x 255. Circ: 6,888.

338.4769 DNK ISSN 0904-3632
HUSBYGNING BRUTTO. Variant title: V & S Priser, Husbygning Brutto. Text in Danish. 1974. a. DKK 1,410 (effective 1999).
Formerly (until 1989): V og S Priser, Husbygning (0105-4201)
Published by: V & S Byggedata, 551 Frederikssundvej 194, Broenshoej, 2700, Denmark. TEL 45-38-60-77-11, FAX 45-38-60-77-55, bygdat@vs-byggedata.dk, bygdat@vs.byggedata.dk.

338.436 DNK ISSN 0904-3624
HUSBYGNING NETTO. Variant title: V & S Priser, Husbygning Netto. Text in Danish. 1987. a. DKK 1,410 (effective 1999).
Formerly (until 1989): V og S Priser, Netto (0902-2791)
Published by: V & S Byggedata, 551 Frederikssundvej 194, Broenshoej, 2700, Denmark. TEL 45-38-60-77-11, FAX 45-38-60-77-55, bygdat@vs-byggedata.dk, bygdat@vs.byggedata.dk. Ed. Carl Friis Skovsen.

690 338 GBR
HUTCHINS' U K BUILDING COSTS HANDBOOK (YEAR). Text in English. a. **Document type:** *Directory, Trade.*
Formerly (until 2002): Hutchins' Small and Major Works. U K Building Costs Handbook (Year)
—BLDSC (4337.860200).
Published by: International Property and Construction Consultants, Franklin + Andrews, Sea Containers House, 20 Upper Ground, London, SE1 9LZ, United Kingdom.

HUTTLINGER'S PIPELINE REPORT. see *PETROLEUM AND GAS*

690 NOR ISSN 1504-0119
▼ **HYTTE-FRITID.** Text in Norwegian. 2003. bi-m. NOK 299 (effective 2005). adv. **Document type:** *Magazine, Consumer.* **Description:** For the cottage owner.
Published by: Vanebo Fagpresse AS, PO Box 130, Kirkenaer, 2260, Norway. TEL 47-62-941000, FAX 47-62-941010, firmapost@vanebo.no, http://www.vanebo.no. Ed. Kjertil Vasby Bruaroey. Adv. contact Heidi Torstensen TEL 47-22-096939.

690 USA
TP882
I E E E CEMENT INDUSTRY TECHNICAL CONFERENCE. PROCEEDINGS. Text in English. 1959. a. USD 188 per vol.; USD 94 per vol. to members (effective 2004). **Document type:** *Proceedings, Trade.* **Description:** Development and application of electrical systems specifically related to the manufacture of cement.
Former titles (until 1995): I E E E Cement Industry Technical Conference. Conference Record (1079-9931); (until 1994): I E E E Cement Industry Technical Conference. Record of Conference Papers (1050-3854); (until 1986): I E E E Cement Industry (0731-4884); (until 1980): I E E E Cement Industry Technical Conference (0731-4906); (until 1977): I E E E - C I T Conference (0731-4892); (until 1976): I E E E Cement Industry Technical Conference (0731-4876); (until 1967): Cement Industry Technical Conference (0731-4868); (until 1965): Cement Conference (0731-485X)
Related titles: CD-ROM ed.; Microfiche ed.; Online - full text ed.: (from I E E E).

Indexed: Inspec.
—BLDSC (4362.932500). **CCC.**
Published by: Institute of Electrical and Electronics Engineers, Inc., 3 Park Ave, 17th Fl, New York, NY 10016-5997. TEL 212-419-7900, 800-678-4333, FAX 212-752-4929, customer.service@ieee.org, http://www.ieee.org. **Co-sponsor:** Industry Applications Society.

I E Q STRATEGIES; a guide to the practical control of indoor air problems. (Indoor Environmental Quality) see *ENVIRONMENTAL STUDIES—Pollution*

690 PHL ISSN 1027-0582
➤ **I F A W P C A INFORMATION SERVICES.** Text in English. 1992. m. 12 p./no.; back issues avail. **Document type:** *Bulletin, Academic/Scholarly.* **Description:** Contains research on construction, new technologies, and construction projects in the Asia-Pacific region.
Published by: International Federation of Asian and Western Pacific Contractors' Associations, Padilla Bldg, 3rd Fl., Ortigas Commercial Center, Emerald Ave., Pasig, Manila, Philippines. TEL 632-631-2782, FAX 632-631-2773, ifawpca@mozcom.com, http://www.ifawpca.org. Circ: 100.

690 620 PHL ISSN 1027-0590
I F A W P C A NEWSLETTER. Text in English. q. adv. back issues avail.
Published by: International Federation of Asian and Western Pacific Contractors' Associations, Padilla Bldg, 3rd Fl., Ortigas Commercial Center, Emerald Ave., Pasig, Manila, Philippines. TEL 632-631-2782, FAX 632-631-2773, TELEX 29083 IFAWPCA PH, ifawpca@mozcom.com, http://www.ifawpca.org. Ed. Rodante D Marcoleta. R&P Rodante Marcoleta. adv.: B&W page USD 200; trim 9.5 x 6.5.

330 DEU ISSN 1435-2745
I F O STUDIEN ZUR BAU- UND WOHNUNGSWIRTSCHAFT. Text in German. 1974. irreg., latest vol.20, 1998. **Document type:** *Monographic series.* **Description:** Research results of the Department of Construction and Housing in Germany.
Formerly: I F O Studien zur Bauwirtschaft (0170-5687)
Published by: I F O Institut fuer Wirtschaftsforschung, Poschingerstr 5, Munich, 81679, Germany. TEL 49-89-9224-0, FAX 49-89-985369, ifo@ifo.de, http://www.ifo.de. Circ: 400.

690.028 USA
I - O. Text in English. 1991. m. free. adv. **Document type:** *Trade.* **Description:** For those involved in the purchase, sale or related services of used construction eqipment.
Published by: Construction Media Group Inc., PO Box 6132, Indianapolis, IN 46206-6132. TEL 317-329-3100, http://www.hardhattrader.com/index.asp. Pub. John White. R&P, Adv. contact Cyndi Veach. Circ: 100,000.

691 USA
ILLINOIS DEALER DIRECTORY AND BUYER'S GUIDE* . Text in English. 1932. a. USD 20. adv.
Formerly: Illinois Directory and Suppliers Listing (0073-4799)
Published by: Illinois Lumber and Material Dealers Association, Inc., 932 S Spring St, Springfield, IL 62704. ilmda@ilmda.com. Circ: 750.

690 333.33 DEU ISSN 0940-7987
IMMOBILIEN MANAGER. Text in German. 1992. 10/yr. EUR 99 domestic; EUR 110 foreign; EUR 13 newsstand/cover (effective 2004). adv. **Document type:** *Magazine, Trade.*
Published by: Verlagsgesellschaft Rudolf Mueller GmbH & Co. KG, Stolberger Str 84, Cologne, 50933, Germany. TEL 49-221-54970, FAX 49-221-5497326, red.immobilienmanager@rudolf-mueller.de, service@rudolf-mueller.de, http://www.rudolf-mueller.de. Ed. Christof Hardebusch. Pub. Andreas Schiller. Adv. contact Olaf Huetten. B&W page EUR 4,825, color page EUR 6,700; trim 164 x 250. Circ: 16,730 (paid).

690 ITA ISSN 1128-5850
LE IMPRESE EDILI. Text in Italian. 1990. m. EUR 12.40 domestic; EUR 35 in Europe; EUR 60 elsewhere (effective 2005). adv. **Document type:** *Magazine, Trade.* **Description:** Informs on new products and technologies in the construction and building industry.
Formerly (until 1999): Le Imprese (1126-8778)
Published by: Tecniche Nuove SpA, Via Eritrea 21, Milan, MI 201, Italy. TEL 39-02-390901, FAX 39-02-7570364, imprese.edili@tecnichenuove.com, info@tecnichenuove.com, http://www.tecnichenuove.com/epages/tecnichenuove.storefront/430a01830a4a94862740c0a80105060c/Product/View/IMP&2D3. Ed. Roberto Anghinoni. Pub. Giuseppe Nardella. Adv. contact Sergio Savona. Circ: 17,000.

IMPROVE YOUR CONSTRUCTION BUSINESS SERIES. see *BUSINESS AND ECONOMICS—Labor And Industrial Relations*

691.3 ITA
INBETON. Text in Italian, English. 1957. 5/yr. EUR 30 (effective 2005). **Document type:** *Magazine, Trade.*
Former titles: Precast; Produrre: La Qualita dei Manufatti in Calcestuzzo (0390-6124)
Published by: BE-MA Editrice Srl, Via Teocrito 50, Milan, MI 20128, Italy. TEL 39-02-252071, FAX 39-02-27000692, http://www.bema.it. Ed. Dal Lago.

INCOME - EXPENSE ANALYSIS: CONVENTIONAL APARTMENTS. see *REAL ESTATE*

INCOME - EXPENSE ANALYSIS: FEDERALLY ASSISTED APARTMENTS. see *REAL ESTATE*

INCOME - EXPENSE ANALYSIS: SHOPPING CENTERS, OPEN AND ENCLOSED. see *REAL ESTATE*

690 IND
INDIAN ARCHITECT & BUILDER. Text in English. 1987. m. USD 70. adv. **Description:** Contains construction activities, international news briefs and interviews with leading architects and engineers.
Formerly: Building and Construction
Indexed: AIAP.
Published by: IPFonline Ltd., 33 D'Silva Rd, Mylapore, Chennai, 600 004, India. TEL 91-44-4661698, FAX 91-44-4661617. Ed. Sarayu Ahuja. Pub. R V Pandit. adv.: B&W page INR 7,000, color page INR 12,500; trim 205 x 280. Circ: 35,000.

691 IND
INDIAN CEMENT INDUSTRY DESKBOOK. Text in English. 1977. biennial. INR 175, USD 55 (effective 2000). adv. bk.rev. abstr.; charts; illus. **Document type:** *Trade.*
Related titles: Microform ed.: (from PQC).
Published by: Technical Press Publications, Eucharistic Congress Bldg. No.1, 5/1 Convent St, Colaba, Mumbai, Maharashtra 400 039, India. TEL 91-22-2021446, FAX 91-22-2871499. adv.: B&W page INR 1,750, color page INR 2,250; trim 18 x 23. Circ: 6,400.

INDIAN CONCRETE JOURNAL. see *ENGINEERING—Civil Engineering*

690 IND ISSN 0971-1244
INDIAN CONSTRUCTION; journal of the builders' association of India. Text in English. 1968. m. INR 500, USD 60 (effective 2000). adv. bk.rev. abstr. **Document type:** *Bulletin, Trade.*
Formerly (until 1979): Builders' Association of India. Bulletin (0304-9507)
Indexed: CRIA, CRICC.
Published by: Builders' Association of India, Commerce Centre, J. Dadajee (Tardeo) Rd., Mumbai, Maharashtra 400 034, India. Circ: 7,000.

690 USA
INDIANA BUILDER MAGAZINE. Text in English. 1990. m. USD 28. adv. **Document type:** *Trade.*
Published by: ProTec Publishing, PO Box 404, Spencer, IN 47460-0404. TEL 812-332-1693, FAX 812-332-0117. Ed. C Dale Risch. Adv. contact Mike Burns. B&W page USD 900, color page USD 1,250; trim 11 x 8.5. Circ: 12,444.

INDICES DE PRECIOS DE LOS INSUMOS BASICOS DE LA INDUSTRIA DE LA CONSTRUCCION. see *BUILDING AND CONSTRUCTION—Abstracting, Bibliographies, Statistics*

690 ITA ISSN 1123-8208
L'INDUSTRIA DEI LATERIZI. Text in Italian; Summaries in English. 1950. bi-m. EUR 32 domestic; EUR 62 foreign (effective 2004). bk.rev. charts; mkt.; stat. **Document type:** *Magazine, Trade.* **Description:** Presents an up-to-date on technological issues.
Formed by the 1990 merger of: Refrattari e Laterizi (0391-3848); Industria Italiana dei Laterizi (0019-7610)
Indexed: BrCerAb, ChemAb.
Published by: (Associazione Nazionale degli Industriali dei Laterizi), Gruppo Editoriale Faenza Editrice SpA, Via Pier de Crescenzi 44, Faenza, RA 48018, Italy. TEL 39-0546-670411, FAX 39-0546-660440, info@faenza.com, http://www.faenza.com. Ed. Giovanni Biffi. Adv. contact Elvio Neri. Circ: 3,300.

690 ITA ISSN 0579-4900
L'INDUSTRIA DELLE COSTRUZIONI. Text in English, Italian. 1967. bi-m. EUR 50 (effective 2005). adv. bk.rev. back issues avail. **Document type:** *Magazine, Trade.*
Indexed: AIAP, API.
—BLDSC (4438.530000), IE, ingenta.
Published by: (Associazione Nazionale Costruttori Edili), Edilstampa (Subsidiary of: Associazione Nazionale Costruttori Edili), Via Guattani 24, Rome, 00161, Italy. TEL 39-06-84567403, FAX 39-06-44232981, edilstampa@ance.it, http://www.edilstampa.ance.it. Circ: 9,000.

690 ITA ISSN 0019-7637
TA680 CODEN: IICEAW
INDUSTRIA ITALIANA DEL CEMENTO. Text in English, Italian. 1930. m. (11/yr.). EUR 65 domestic; EUR 98 foreign (effective 2004). adv. bk.rev. charts; illus.; stat. index. back issues avail.; reprints avail. **Document type:** *Magazine, Trade.*
Indexed: CRIA, ConcrAb, Englnd, METADEX, RefZh.
—BLDSC (4439.000000), CINDOC, CISTI, Ei, IE, ingenta, Linda Hall.
Published by: Associazione Italiana Tecnica Economica del Cemento, Piazza G Marconi 25, Rome, 00144, Italy. TEL 39-06-54210237, FAX 39-06-5915408, http://www.aitecweb.com. Circ: 10,000.

691 BEL ISSN 0775-8413
INDUSTRIE CIMENTIERE BELGE/BELGISCHE CEMENTNIJVERHEID. Text and summaries in Dutch, French. 1976. a. free. stat. **Document type:** *Bulletin.* **Description:** Annual report of activity.
Related titles: Microform ed.
Published by: Federation de l'Industrie Cimentiere Belge/Federatie van de Belgische Cementnijverheid, Rue Volta 8, Brussels, 1050, Belgium. TEL 32-2-6455211, FAX 32-2-6400670, info@febelcem.be, http://www.febelcem.be. Ed. J.P. Jacobs. Circ: 1,500.

690 DEU ISSN 0935-2023
INDUSTRIEBAU. Text in German. 1955. bi-m. EUR 97.20 domestic; EUR 106.20 foreign; EUR 86.40 to students; EUR 19 newsstand/cover (effective 2004). adv. bk.rev. bibl.; charts; illus.; pat.; tr.lit. **Document type:** *Magazine, Trade.*
Formerly: Zentralblatt fuer Industriebau (0044-4227)
Indexed: CISA, ExcerpMed.
—IE, Infotrieve. **CCC.**
Published by: (Arbeitsgemeinschaft Industriebau e.V.), Callwey Verlag, Streitfeldstr 35, Munich, 81673, Germany. TEL 49-89-4360050, FAX 49-89-436005113, redaktion@industriebau-online.de, a.hagenkord@callwey.de, http://www.industriebau-online.de, http://www.callwey.de. Ed. Karin Kronthaler. Adv. contact Thomas Schumann TEL 49-89-436005120. B&W page EUR 1,960, color page EUR 3,310; trim 175 x 250. Circ: 3,039 (paid).

691 AUS
INFO-LINK S E ASIA. Text in English. q. USD 35 (effective 1998). adv. **Description:** Profiles new and existing products in the construction industry for architects, interior designers, builders and construction companies.
Published by: Reed Business Information Pty Ltd (Subsidiary of: Reed Business Information International), Locked Bag 2999, Chatswood, NSW 2067, Australia. TEL 61-2-9422-2999, FAX 61-2-9422-2844, http://www.infolink.com.au/. Adv. contact Christopher Watson. Circ: 27,700.

691 AUS
INFO-LINK THE BOOK. Text in English. a. AUD 114.99 domestic; AUD 137 in New Zealand; AUD 155 elsewhere (effective 2005). adv. **Document type:** *Directory, Trade.* **Description:** Contains over 15,000 product listings in the architecture, interior design and building industries.
Related titles: CD-ROM ed.: AUD 53.90 (effective 2000); Online - full text ed.
Published by: Reed Business Information Pty Ltd (Subsidiary of: Reed Business Information International), Locked Bag 2999, Chatswood, NSW 2067, Australia. customerservice@reedbusiness.com.au, http://www.infolink.com.au/publications.asp#book, http://www.reedbusiness.com.au. Circ: 10,472.

690 CUB
INFORMACION CONSTRUCCION* . Text in Spanish. 1975. bi-m. per issue exchange basis. illus.
Published by: Comite Estatal de la Construccion, Centro Tecnico Superior de la Construccion, Ministry of Construction, Avda. Carlos M. de Cespedes y Calle 35, Havana, Cuba. Ed. Regino Gayoso.

690 VEN
INFORMADOR DE LA CONSTRUCCION Y DE LA INDUSTRIA. Text in Spanish. 1957. a. USD 150. adv.
Published by: Publicaciones Sangar, C.A., Apdo. 2323 (1010A), Caracas, Venezuela. TEL 626853. Ed. Coral Garcia de Hernandez. Circ: 10,000.

690 DEU
INFORMATION SOURCES IN ARCHITECTURE AND CONSTRUCTION. Text in English. irreg., latest vol.2, 1995. USD 110 in North America (effective 2001). bibl. **Document type:** *Directory, Bibliography.* **Description:** Helps reference librarians identify key sources of primary information in architecture and construction.
Related titles: ♦ Series: Information Sources for the Press and Broadcast Media; ♦ Information Sources in Chemistry; ♦ Information Sources in Finance and Banking; ♦ Information Sources in the Life Sciences; ♦ Information Sources in Grey Literature; ♦ Information Sources in Physics; ♦ Guides to Information Sources Series; ♦ Information Sources in Development Studies; ♦ Information Sources in Engineering; ♦ Information Sources in Environmental Protection; ♦ Information Sources in Law; ♦ Information Sources in Official Publications.
Published by: K.G. Saur Verlag GmbH (Subsidiary of: Gale Group), Ortlerstr 8, Munchen, 81373, Germany. TEL 49-89-769020, FAX 49-89-76902150, info@saur.de, http://www.saur.de. Ed. Valerie Nurcombe.

690 DEU ISSN 1616-170X
INFORMATIONSDIENST OEFFENTLICHES BAURECHT. Text in German. bi-m. EUR 61; EUR 14.50 newsstand/cover (effective 2005). **Document type:** *Bulletin, Trade.*

Published by: Werner-Verlag GmbH (Subsidiary of: Wolters Kluwer Deutschland GmbH), Berliner Allee 11A, Duesseldorf, 40212, Germany. TEL 49-211-38798-0, FAX 49-211-383104, info@werner-verlag.de, http://www.werner-verlag.de.

690 CHE
INFORMATOR. Text in French, German. 1976. 6/yr. CHF 9 per issue. **Document type:** *Trade.*
Published by: Informator Verlags AG, Buhlmatt 9, Kleinwangen, 6277, Switzerland. TEL 41-41-9103823, FAX 41-41-9105956. Ed. Yolanda Allenspach. Circ: 30,000.

690 POL ISSN 1234-8368
INFORMATOR BUDOWLANY. Text in Polish. 1995. a. EUR 21 foreign (effective 2005). **Document type:** *Directory, Trade.*
Published by: Wydawnictwo Murator Sp. z o.o., ul Kamionkowska 45, Warsaw, 03812, Poland. TEL 48-22-5905000, FAX 48-22-5905444, wydawnictwo@murator.com.pl, http://www.murator.com.pl. **Dist. by:** Ars Polona, Krakowskie Przedmiescie 7, Warsaw, Poland. TEL 48-22-9263914, FAX 48-22-9265334, arspolona@arspolona.com.pl, http://www.arspolona.com.pl.

B

690 POL ISSN 1506-9575
INFORMATOR USLUG BUDOWLANYCH. Text in Polish. 1999. a. adv. **Document type:** *Directory, Trade.*
Published by: Wydawnictwo Murator Sp. z o.o., ul Kamionkowska 45, Warsaw, 03812, Poland. TEL 48-22-5905000, FAX 48-22-5905444, wydawnictwo@murator.com.pl, http://www.murator.com.pl. adv.: page PLZ 10,000.

690 ESP ISSN 0020-0883
CODEN: ICOMA6
INFORMES DE LA CONSTRUCCION; revista de informacion tecnica. Text in Spanish; Summaries in English. 1948. bi-m. EUR 65.61 domestic; EUR 109.38 foreign (effective 2003). adv. bk.rev. bibl.; charts; illus. cum.index: nos.1-100. back issues avail. **Document type:** *Trade.* **Description:** Technical and scientific articles explaining the complete process of the construction field.
Indexed: AIAP, API, ApMecR, BrCerAb, C&ISA, CerAb, ChemAb, CivEngAb, ConcrAb, CorrAb, E&CAJ, EEA, EMA, GeotechAb, IAA, IBR, IECT, M&TEA, MBF, METADEX, RILM, RefZh, SolStAb, WAA.
—CINDOC, IE, Infotrieve, Linda Hall.
Published by: Consejo Superior de Investigaciones Cientificas, Instituto de Ciencias de la Construccion Eduardo Torroja, C Serrano Galvache, s-n, Madrid, 28033, Spain. TEL 34-91-3020440, FAX 34-91-3020700, director.ietcc@csic.es, http://www.csic.es/torroja, http://www.ietcc.csic.es. Circ: 2,500.

INGEGNERI ARCHITETTI COSTRUTTORI. see *ENGINEERING—Civil Engineering*

DER INGENIEUR. see *ENGINEERING*

INGENIOEREN/ENGINEER. see *ENGINEERING*

690 624 TUR
INSAAT DUNYASI/CONSTRUCTION WORLD - INTERNATIONAL CONTRACTING AND TRADE MAGAZINE; uluslararasi muteahhitlik ve ticaret mecmuasi. Text in Turkish. 1982. m. TRL 10,000,000; USD 60 foreign. adv. **Document type:** *Trade.* **Description:** Contains Corporate news and news about he development in asphalt, bulding construction, architecture, construction materials and working machinese; information and reference sources of contractors.
Published by: Halic Uluslararasi Yayincilik Ltd. Sti., Cumhuriyet Cad., Istanbul, Babil Sok 9-10, Harbiye, 80230, Turkey. TEL 90-212-2272564, FAX 90-212-2584524, insaat@bilseim.com.tr, http://www.bilseim.com.tr. Ed. M Vasfi Pakman. Pub. Mustafa Ustun. Adv. contact N Nizih Kazankaya. Circ: 7,000.

690 ESP ISSN 0212-8519
INSTALACIONES DEPORTIVAS XXI; revista de la construccion deportiva materiales y accesorios. Text in Spanish. 1974. bi-m. EUR 99.84 domestic; EUR 111.86 foreign (effective 2003). adv. bk.rev. charts; illus. **Document type:** *Trade.* **Description:** Covers the building industry, equipment, maintenance, materials and accessories for sport installations.
Published by: Reed Business Information SA (Subsidiary of: Reed Business Information International), Zancoeta 9, Bilbao, 48013, Spain. TEL 34-944-285600, FAX 34-944-425116, rbi@rbi.es, http://www.rbi.es. Ed. Marcel Lleal. Adv. contact Manuel Masip. Circ: 4,000.

690 720 ROM ISSN 1223-8120
INSTITUTUL POLITEHNIC DIN IASI. BULETINUL. SECTIA 6: CONSTRUCTII, ARHITECTURA. Text in English, French, German, Italian, Russian, Spanish. 1946. q. per issue exchange basis. adv. bk.rev. bibl.
Formerly: Institutul Politehnic din Iasi. Buletinul. Sectia 5: Constructii, Imbunatatiri Funciare; Which was formed by the merger of: Institutul Politehnic Iasi. Buletinul. Sectia 5: Constructii, Arhitectura; And: Institutul Politehnic din Iasi. Buletinul. Sectia VI: Imbunatatiri Funciare
Related titles: Series of: Institutul Politehnic din Iasi. Buletinul.
Indexed: ApMecR, ChemAb, MathR.
Published by: Institutul Politehnic din Iasi "Gh Asachi", Bd Copou 11, Iasi, 6600, Romania. TEL 40-81-46577, FAX 40-81-47923. Eds. Alfred Braier, Hugo Rosman. Circ: 450.

INSTYTUT TECHNIKI BUDOWLANEJ. PRACE. see *ENGINEERING—Civil Engineering*

693 333.7916 GBR ISSN 1478-8667
INSULATION; the energy efficiency newsletter. Text in English. 1957. bi-m. GBP 83 domestic; GBP 98 foreign (effective 2005). adv. bk.rev. back issues avail. **Document type:** *Newsletter, Trade.* **Description:** Covers products and services which will lead to building energy efficient commercial, industrial, and domestic properties.
Former titles (until 2002): Essential Energy Efficiency (1476-6701); (until 2001): Insulation (Rickmansworth) (1464-0112); (until 1988): Insulation Journal (0950-1940); (until 1980): Insulation (Wheathampstead) (0020-4552)
Related titles: Online - full text ed.: (from Gale Group).
—BLDSC (4531.318000), CISTI, IE, Infotrieve.
Published by: Complete Circulation and Marketing Ltd., Unit 8, Netherhall Yard, Mill Ln, Newick, Lewes BN8 4JL, United Kingdom. c.dann@completecircmktg.co.uk. Ed. Mark Corliss. Pub., Adv. contact Colin C Dann. B&W page GBP 767; trim 210 x 297. Circ: 2,000 (paid). **Subscr. to:** W D I S Ltd., Units 12 & 13, Cranleigh Garden Industrial Estate, Southall, Mddx UB8 2DB, United Kingdom. TEL 44-20-8606-7300, FAX 44-20-8606-7301.

690 696 USA
INSULATION CONTRACTORS MONTHLY. Text in English. 1980. m. membership. adv. bk.rev.
Formerly: I C A A News
Published by: Insulation Contractors Association of America, 1321 Duke St, Alexandria, VA 22313-6237. TEL 703-739-0356, FAX 703-739-0412. Circ: 1,000.

693.83 USA ISSN 1097-4458
TH1715.A1
INSULATION OUTLOOK. Text in English. 1956. m. USD 45 (effective 2004). adv. bk.rev. charts; illus.; stat.; tr.lit. back issues avail. **Document type:** *Magazine, Trade.* **Description:** Concerns commercial and industrial insulation industries.
Former titles (until 1994): Outlook (Alexandria) (0898-5766); Insulation Outlook (0270-3963); N I C A Outlook (0047-8881)
Published by: National Insulation Association, 99 Canal Center Plaza, Ste 222, Alexandria, VA 22314. TEL 703-683-6480, FAX 703-549-4838, gfellows@insulation.org, http://www.insulation.org. adv.: B&W page USD 1,421, color page USD 2,472; trim 10.88 x 8.25. Circ: 5,199 (paid and controlled).

690 GBR
INTELLIGENT BUILD & DESIGN INNOVATIONS. Text in English. s-a. GBP 19.95 per issue; free to qualified personnel (effective 2005). adv. **Document type:** *Journal, Trade.* **Description:** Contains articles from some of the leading decision makers at the cutting edge of technological developments and modern architecture.
Published by: S P G Media Ltd. (Subsidiary of: Sterling Publishing Group Plc.), Brunel House, 55-57 North Wharf Rd, London, W2 1LA, United Kingdom. TEL 44-20-79159600, FAX 44-20-77242089, info@sterlingpublications.com, http://www.ibdi.info/, http://www.spgmedia.com/. Ed. Priya Rehal TEL 44-20-79159728. Pub. Mr. Sam Raingill TEL 44-20-79159729. Adv. contact Tanvir Choudhury TEL 44-20-79159940. B&W page GBP 5,100, color page GBP 5,900.

690 USA ISSN 0888-0387
INTERIOR CONSTRUCTION. Text in English. 1956. bi-m. USD 35 to non-members (effective 2005). adv. back issues avail. **Document type:** *Magazine, Trade.*
Former titles (until vol.29, 1985): Inside Contracting (0193-2586); (until 1979): Sound Ideas (0038-1837)
Published by: Ceilings & Interior Systems Construction Association, 1500 Lincoln Hwy, Ste 202, St Charles, IL 60174. TEL 630-584-1919, FAX 630-584-2003, info@cisca.org, http://cisca.org/publications, http://www.cisca.org. Ed. Bill Spilman. Pub., Adv. contact Bonnie Luck. Circ: 2,500 (paid and controlled).

625 693.5 USA ISSN 1087-9862
INTERLOCKING CONCRETE PAVEMENT MAGAZINE. Text in English. 1994. q. adv. bk.rev. charts; illus.; stat.; tr.lit. 24 p./no. 3 cols./p.; back issues avail. **Document type:** *Magazine, Trade.* **Description:** Reports industry news on concrete pavers, precast concrete paving slabs, and related segmental concrete products.
Published by: Interlocking Pavement Institute, 1444 Eye St, N W, Ste 700, Washington, DC 20005-2210. TEL 202-712-9023, FAX 202-408-0285, ICPI@bostromdc.com, http://www.icpi.org. Ed., R&P David R Smith TEL 202-712-9036. Adv. contact Sarah Major. B&W page USD 2,075, color page USD 3,245; trim 11 x 8.5. Circ: 20,000 (controlled).

692.8 USA
INTERMOUNTAIN CONTRACTOR; building and engineering construction news. Text in English. 1950. m. USD 40 (effective 2005). adv. bk.rev. charts; illus.; stat. **Document type:** *Magazine, Trade.* **Description:** Provides comprehensive local coverage on general building, heavy/highway, design, engineering and industrial construction news throughout Utah and Idaho.
Former titles: Intermountain Contractor News Weekly (1099-7687); (until 199?): Intermountain Contractor (0020-5656)
Related titles: Online - full text ed.: (from EBSCO Publishing, LexisNexis, ProQuest Information & Learning).
Indexed: ABIn.
—CCC.
Published by: Mcgraw-Hill Construction Dodge (Subsidiary of: McGraw-Hill Construction Information Group), 425 West 1700 S, Salt Lake City, UT 84115. TEL 801-974-2830, FAX 801-972-8975, http://intermountain.construction.com, http://www.dodgeconstructionpublications.com. Ed. Candice Macfarlane TEL 801-974-2830. Adv. contact Don Fulton TEL 801-974-2936. B&W page USD 840, color page USD 1,360. Circ: 4,500 (paid and free).

690 GBR
INTERNATIONAL ASIAN BUILDING PRODUCTS CATALOGUE. Text in English. 1985. a. USD 55. **Document type:** *Catalog.*
Published by: Data Distribution Publications, Apex House, London Rd, Northfleet, Gravesend, Kent DA11 9JA, United Kingdom. TEL 01322-277788, FAX 01322-569627.

690 USA
INTERNATIONAL BUILDING CODE. Text in English. 1999. irreg., latest 2003. USD 86 per issue to non-members; USD 69 per issue to members; USD 96.50 to non-members for looseleaf ed.; USD 76 per issue to members for looseleaf ed. (effective 2005). **Document type:** *Trade.*
Formed by the merger of (19??-1999): Standard Building Code (1050-6241); Which was formerly (until 1976): Southern Standard Building Code; (19??-1999): B O C A National Building Code (0897-0068); Which was formerly (until 1987): B O C A Basic/National Building Code; (until 1981): B O C A Basic Building Code
Related titles: CD-ROM ed.: International Building Code on I-Quest CD-ROM. USD 81 per issue to non-members for single user; USD 65 per issue to members for single user (effective 2005); ♦ Series of: International Codes; Supplement(s): International Building Code. Supplement. USD 13 per issue to non-members; USD 10 per issue to members (effective 2005).
Published by: International Code Council, 5203 Leesburg Pike, Ste 600, Falls Church, VA 22041. TEL 703-931-4533, FAX 703-379-1546, webmaster@iccsafe.org, http://www.iccsafe.org.

690 USA
INTERNATIONAL BUILDING CODE COMMENTARY. Variant title: I B C Commentary. Text in English. irreg., latest 2003. USD 170.50 combined subscription to non-members for vol.1 & 2; USD 136.50 combined subscription to members for vol.1 & 2 (effective 2005). **Document type:** *Trade.*
Published by: International Code Council, 5203 Leesburg Pike, Ste 600, Falls Church, VA 22041. TEL 703-931-4533, FAX 703-379-1546, webmaster@iccsafe.org, http://www.iccsafe.org.

690 GBR ISSN 0959-6038
INTERNATIONAL CEMENT REVIEW. Text in English. m. GBP 135, USD 240. **Document type:** *Trade.* **Description:** News featuring trading and technical developments from around the world.
Indexed: CRIA, CRICC, RefZh.
—BLDSC (4538.416500), IE, ingenta.
Published by: Tradeship Publications Ltd., Old Kings Head Ct, 15 High St, Dorking, Surrey RH4 1AR, United Kingdom. TEL 44-1306-740363, FAX 44-1306-740660, tradeship@dial.pipex.com, http://www.cement.co.uk, http://www.cemnet.co.uk. Ed. David Hargreaves. Circ: 4,109.

690 352.9 USA ISSN 0896-9752
KF5701.Z9
INTERNATIONAL CONFERENCE OF BUILDING OFFICIALS. ANALYSIS OF REVISIONS TO THE (YEAR) UNIFORM CODES. Text in English. triennial. USD 16.95 to non-members; USD 12.75 to members (effective 2000). **Document type:** *Proceedings, Trade.*
Formerly: International Conference of Building Officials. Analysis of Revisions to the Uniform Building Code
Published by: International Conference of Building Officials, 5360 Workman Mill Rd, Whittier, CA 90601-2298. TEL 562-699-0541, FAX 562-699-9721, http://www.icbo.org.

690 352.9 USA
INTERNATIONAL CONFERENCE OF BUILDING OFFICIALS. BUILDING DEPARTMENT ADMINISTRATION. Text in English. 1973. irreg. USD 49.50 to non-members; USD 45 to members (effective 2000). **Document type:** *Proceedings, Trade.*
Published by: International Conference of Building Officials, 5360 Workman Mill Rd, Whittier, CA 90601-2298. TEL 562-699-0541, FAX 562-699-9721, http://www.icbo.org.

690 352.9 USA ISSN 0579-3769
INTERNATIONAL CONFERENCE OF BUILDING OFFICIALS. CODE CHANGES COMMITTEE. ANNUAL REPORT. Text in English. bi-m. free (effective 2000). **Document type:** *Proceedings, Corporate.*
Published by: International Conference of Building Officials, 5360 Workman Mill Rd, Whittier, CA 90601-2298. TEL 562-699-0541, FAX 562-699-9721, http://www.icbo.org.

690 352.9 USA ISSN 0896-9728
KF5701.Z95
INTERNATIONAL CONFERENCE OF BUILDING OFFICIALS. DWELLING CONSTRUCTION UNDER THE UNIFORM BUILDING CODE. Text in English. triennial. USD 12.45 to members; USD 16.55 to non-members (effective 2000). **Document type:** *Proceedings, Trade.*
—CISTI.
Published by: International Conference of Building Officials, 5360 Workman Mill Rd, Whittier, CA 90601-2298. TEL 562-699-0541, FAX 562-699-9721, http://www.icbo.org.

690 352.9 USA
INTERNATIONAL CONFERENCE OF BUILDING OFFICIALS. EVALUATION REPORTS. Text in English. a. USD 170 (effective 2000). Supplement avail. **Document type:** *Trade.*
Related titles: CD-ROM ed.: USD 150 to non-members; USD 125 to members (effective 2000).
Published by: International Conference of Building Officials, 5360 Workman Mill Rd, Whittier, CA 90601-2298. TEL 562-699-0541, FAX 562-699-9721, http://www.icbo.org.

690 352.9 USA
INTERNATIONAL CONFERENCE OF BUILDING OFFICIALS. PLAN REVIEW MANUAL. Text in English. triennial. USD 33.90 to non-members; USD 25.50 to members (effective 2000). **Document type:** *Proceedings, Trade.*
Published by: International Conference of Building Officials, 5360 Workman Mill Rd, Whittier, CA 90601-2298. TEL 562-699-0541, FAX 562-699-9721, http://www.icbo.org.

690 352.9 USA ISSN 0896-971X
KF5701.Z95
INTERNATIONAL CONFERENCE OF BUILDING OFFICIALS. UNIFORM CODE FOR THE ABATEMENT OF DANGEROUS BUILDINGS. Text in English. triennial. USD 13.15 to non-members; USD 9.95 to members (effective 2000). **Document type:** *Proceedings, Trade.*
—CISTI.
Published by: International Conference of Building Officials, 5360 Workman Mill Rd, Whittier, CA 90601-2298. TEL 562-699-0541, FAX 562-699-9721, http://www.icbo.org.

690 352.9 USA ISSN 0501-1213
KF5701.Z95
INTERNATIONAL CONFERENCE OF BUILDING OFFICIALS. UNIFORM HOUSING CODE. Text in English. 1955. triennial. USD 13.15 to non-members; USD 9.95 to members (effective 2000). **Document type:** *Proceedings, Trade.*
—CISTI.
Published by: International Conference of Building Officials, 5360 Workman Mill Rd, Whittier, CA 90601-2298. TEL 562-699-0541, FAX 562-699-9721, http://www.icbo.org.

690 352.9 USA ISSN 0896-9671
KF5708.Z95
INTERNATIONAL CONFERENCE OF BUILDING OFFICIALS. UNIFORM MECHANICAL CODE. Text in English. triennial. USD 42 to non-members; USD 33.60 to members (effective 2000). **Document type:** *Proceedings, Trade.*
—CISTI.
Published by: International Conference of Building Officials, 5360 Workman Mill Rd, Whittier, CA 90601-2298. TEL 562-699-0541, FAX 562-699-9721, http://www.icbo.org.

INTERNATIONAL CONSTRUCTION. see *ENGINEERING—Civil Engineering*

INTERNATIONAL CONSTRUCTION LAW REVIEW. see *LAW—International Law*

690 CHE ISSN 1020-0142
INTERNATIONAL CONSTRUCTION MANAGEMENT SERIES. Text in English. 1994. irreg., latest vol.6, 1995. CHF 15, USD 12. **Document type:** *Monographic series.*
Published by: (International Labour Office), I L O Publications, 4 route des Morillons, Geneva 22, 1211, Switzerland. TEL 41-22-799-6111, FAX 41-22-799-6358. Ed. Derek Miles. **Dist. in US by:** I L O Publications Center, 9 Jay Gould Court, Ste. CT, PO Box 753, Waldorf, MD 20604. TEL 301-638-3152, FAX 301-843-0159, ilopubs@tasco1.com.

690.028 GBR ISSN 0967-8034
INTERNATIONAL CRANES. Text in English; Summaries in French, German, Spanish. 1992. m. USD 140 (effective 2001). adv. bk.rev. back issues avail. **Document type:** *Magazine, Trade.* **Description:** For buyers and users of cranes and lifting equipment worldwide.
Published by: K H L Group Ltd., Southfields, Southview Rd, Wadhurst, E Sussex TN5 6TP, United Kingdom. TEL 44-1892-784088, FAX 44-1892-784086, cranes@khl.com, mail@khl.com, http://www.craneworld.com, http://www.khl.com. Ed. Ben Shaw. Pub. James King. R&P Peter Watkinson. Adv. contact John Aushi. Circ: 15,133.

INTERNATIONAL DIRECTORY OF BUILDING AND CONSTRUCTION MATERIALS & SUPPLIES IMPORTERS. see *BUSINESS AND ECONOMICS—Trade And Industrial Directories*

INTERNATIONAL DIRECTORY OF CONSTRUCTION AND BUILDING EQUIPMENT IMPORTERS. see *BUSINESS AND ECONOMICS—Trade And Industrial Directories*

690 USA ISSN 1536-2213
TH151
INTERNATIONAL ENERGY CONSERVATION CODE (YEAR). Text in English. 1998. triennial, latest 2003. USD 29 per issue to non-members; USD 23 per issue to members; USD 37 per issue to non-members for looseleaf ed.; USD 29.50 per issue to members for looseleaf ed. (effective 2005). **Document type:** *Trade.* **Description:** Encourages energy conservation through efficiency in envelope design, mechanical systems, lighting systems, and the use of new materials and techniques.
Formerly: Model Energy Code
Related titles: ◆ Series of: International Codes; Supplement(s): International Energy Conservation Code. Supplement. USD 8 per issue to non-members; USD 6 per issue to members (effective 2005).
Published by: International Code Council, 5203 Leesburg Pike, Ste 600, Falls Church, VA 22041. TEL 703-931-4533, FAX 703-379-1546, webmaster@iccsafe.org, http://www.iccsafe.org.

➤ 690 GBR ISSN 1466-5115
INTERNATIONAL JOURNAL OF COMPUTER INTEGRATED DESIGN AND CONSTRUCTION. Abbreviated title: C I D A C. Text in English. 1999. q. GBP 70 to individuals; GBP 85.25 to individuals for Print & Online Eds.; GBP 140 to institutions; GBP 158.75 to institutions for Print & Online Eds. (effective 2000). **Document type:** *Academic/Scholarly.* **Description:** Provides a forum for the dissemination of information related to the use of computers and associated technologies in the integration of the design and construction processes.
Related titles: Online - full content ed.: GBP 47 to individuals; GBP 94 to institutions.
—BLDSC (4542.174650).
Published by: (Loughborough University, Department of Civil & Building Engineering), S E T O (Subsidiary of: Institution of Structural Engineers), 11 Upper Belgrave St, London, SW1X 8BH, United Kingdom. TEL 44-20-7235-4535, FAX 44-20-7235-4294, lorans@istructe.org.uk. Ed. C J Anumba.

➤ 624 USA ISSN 1550-3984
INTERNATIONAL JOURNAL OF CONSTRUCTION EDUCATION AND RESEARCH. Text in English. 1997. 3/yr. free (effective 2005). bk.rev. **Document type:** *Journal, Academic/Scholarly.* **Description:** Provides construction educators and practitioners with access to information, ideas, and materials for improving and updating their understanding of the construction industry and construction education.
Formerly (until 2004): Journal of Construction Education (1522-8150)
Media: Online - full content.
Published by: Associated Schools of Construction, Rm. 427 Langford Bldg A, Department of Construction Science, Texas A & M University, College Station, TX 77843-3137. TEL 409-458-4782, FAX 409-862-1572, jce@taz.tamu.edu, http://www.ascjournal.ascweb.org/, http://ascweb.org/jce. Ed., Pub., R&P Kenneth C Williamson III. Circ: 750.

➤ **INTERNATIONAL JOURNAL OF LOW ENERGY AND SUSTAINABLE BUILDINGS.** see *ENGINEERING—Civil Engineering*

➤ 690 GBR ISSN 0956-0599
INTERNATIONAL JOURNAL OF SPACE STRUCTURES. Text in English. 1985. 4/yr. GBP 211; GBP 230 combined subscription print & online eds. (effective 2006). bk.rev. index. **Document type:** *Journal, Academic/Scholarly.* **Description:** Provides an international forum for the interchange of information on all aspects of analysis, design and construction of space structures.
Formerly (until 1988): Space Structures (0266-3511)
Related titles: Online - full text ed.: GBP 202 (effective 2006) (from EBSCO Publishing, Gale Group, IngentaConnect, Swets Information Services).
Indexed: ApMecR, B&BAb, BrCerAb, C&ISA, CerAb, CivEngAb, CorrAb, E&CAJ, EEA, EMA, EngInd, IAA, ISMEC, M&TEA, MBF, METADEX, RASB, SolStAb, WAA.
—BLDSC (4542.660000), CISTI, Ei, IE, ingenta. **CCC.**
Published by: Multi-Science Publishing Co. Ltd., 5 Wates Way, Brentwood, Essex CM15 9TB, United Kingdom. TEL 44-1277-244632, FAX 44-1277-223453, sciencem@hotmail.com, http://www.multi-science.co.uk/space.htm. Ed. H Nooshin.

➤ **INTERNATIONAL JOURNAL OF VENTILATION.** see *HEATING, PLUMBING AND REFRIGERATION*

690 NLD ISSN 0020-7853
TK1
INTERNATIONAL LIGHTING REVIEW. Text in English. 1949. 3/yr. bk.rev. charts; illus. index, cum.index. **Document type:** *Journal, Trade.* **Description:** Reports on lighting applications worldwide.
Related titles: French ed.: Revue Internationale de l'Eclairage. ISSN 0035-3388. 1949; German ed.: Internationale Licht Rundschau. ISSN 0165-9863. 1949; Spanish ed.: Revista Internacional de Luminotecnica. ISSN 0167-7608. 1949.
Indexed: API, CISA, ErgAb, HRIS, IBuildSA
—BLDSC (4543.000000), CISTI, IE, ingenta, Linda Hall.
Published by: (Philips Lighting B.V.), Foundation Prometheus, Postbus 721, Eindhoven, 5600 AS, Netherlands. TEL 31-40-275-5779, FAX 31-40-275-7800, lighting.ilr@chv.lighting.philips.com, http://www.lightingreview.com. Ed. J F Caminada. Circ: 32,000 (controlled).

690 GBR
INTERNATIONAL MIDDLE EAST BUILDING PRODUCTS CATALOGUE. Text in English. 1976. a. USD 55. **Document type:** *Catalog.*
Formerly: Middle East Construction Catalogue - Building Products Edition
Published by: Data Distribution Publications, Apex House, London Rd, Northfleet, Gravesend, Kent DA11 9JA, United Kingdom. TEL 01322-277788, FAX 01322-569627. Circ: 7,000.

INTERNATIONAL PLUMBING CODE. see *HEATING, PLUMBING AND REFRIGERATION*

343 USA ISSN 1085-1151
K3542
INTERNATIONAL PRIVATE SEWAGE DISPOSAL CODE. Text in English. 1995. irreg., latest 2003. USD 22 to non-members; USD 18 to members (effective 2005). Index. **Document type:** *Trade.* **Description:** Covers administration, definitions, general regulations, site evaluation and requirements, materials, soil absorption systems, pressure distribution systems, tanks, mound systems, cesspools, and inspections.
Related titles: ◆ Series of: International Codes.
Published by: International Code Council, 5203 Leesburg Pike, Ste 600, Falls Church, VA 22041. TEL 703-931-4533, FAX 703-379-1546, webmaster@iccsafe.org, http://www.iccsafe.org.

690 USA
INTERNATIONAL RESIDENTIAL CODE FOR ONE- AND TWO-FAMILY DWELLINGS. Text in English. irreg., latest 2003. USD 62 per issue to non-members; USD 49.50 per issue to members; USD 75.50 per issue to non-members for looseleaf ed.; USD 57 per issue to members for looseleaf ed. (effective 2005). **Document type:** *Trade.*
Former titles: International One and Two-Family Dwelling Code; C A B O One and Two Family Dwelling Code
Related titles: ◆ Series of: International Codes.
Published by: International Code Council, 5203 Leesburg Pike, Ste 600, Falls Church, VA 22041. TEL 703-931-4533, FAX 703-379-1546, webmaster@iccsafe.org, http://www.iccsafe.org.

691 FIN
INTERNATIONAL TRADE CONFERENCE OF WORKERS OF THE BUILDING, WOOD AND BUILDING MATERIALS INDUSTRIES. (BROCHURE). Text in Finnish. irreg., latest vol.7, 1975. **Document type:** *Proceedings.*
Published by: Trade Unions International of Workers of the Building Wood and Building Materials Industries, PL 281, Helsinki, 00101, Finland.

INTERNATIONAL UNION OF BRICKLAYERS AND ALLIED CRAFTSMEN. JOURNAL. see *LABOR UNIONS*

INTERNATIONAL WELDING ENGINEERING. see *METALLURGY—Welding*

690 DEU ISSN 0947-4498
TH3401
INTERNATIONALE ZEITSCHRIFT FUER BAUINSTANDSETZEN/ INTERNATIONAL JOURNAL FOR RESTORATION OF BUILDINGS AND MONUMENTS. Text in English, German. 1995. 6/yr. EUR 105; EUR 19 newsstand/cover (effective 2005). adv. bk.rev.; Website rev. abstr. 100 p./no.; back issues avail.; reprints avail. **Document type:** *Magazine, Trade.*
Indexed: A&ATA, BrCerAb, C&ISA, CerAb, CivEngAb, CorrAb, E&CAJ, EMA, IAA, M&TEA, MBF, METADEX, SolStAb, WAA.
—BLDSC (4542.537000), CISTI, IE, ingenta, Linda Hall.
Published by: (Fraunhofer-Informationszentrum Raum und Bau), Aedificatio Verlag GmbH, Wintererstr 78, Freiburg, 79104, Germany. TEL 49-761-8818650, FAX 49-761-8818651, office@aedificat.de, http://www.aedificat.de. Ed. F H Wittmann. Adv. contact B Harzer. Circ: 1,500.

IRELAND. CENTRAL STATISTICS OFFICE. EARNINGS AND HOURS WORKED IN CONSTRUCTION. see *BUILDING AND CONSTRUCTION—Abstracting, Bibliographies, Statistics*

IRELAND. CENTRAL STATISTICS OFFICE. INDEX OF EMPLOYMENT IN CONSTRUCTION. see *BUILDING AND CONSTRUCTION—Abstracting, Bibliographies, Statistics*

IRISH BUILDING MAGAZINE. see *ARCHITECTURE*

690 696 697 IRL ISSN 0791-0878
IRISH BUILDING SERVICES NEWS. Text in English. 1961. m. adv. back issues avail. **Document type:** *Trade.* **Description:** Provides dedicated coverage of the heating, ventilation, air conditioning, refrigeration, instruments & controls, building management, sanitary ware, plumbing, maintenance and environmental industries.

B

▼ *new title* ➤ *refereed* ✳ *unverified* ◆ *full entry avail.*

Former titles (until 1988): Irish H & V News (0790-2786); (until 1983): H & V News (0332-2335); (until 1980): Irish H & V News (0332-2327); (until 1971): Irish Plumbing and Heating Engineer (0332-2289); (until 1964): Irish Plumbing and Heating Contractor (0332-2270)
Indexed: IBuildSA.
Published by: Pressline Ltd., Carraig Court, Georges Ave, Blackrock, Co. Dublin, Ireland. TEL 353-01-2885001, FAX 353-01-2886966, bsnews@pressline.ie, pressl@iol.ie, http://ireland.iol.ie/~pressl/BSNews.htm, http://www.iol.ie/~pressl/. Adv. contact Joe Warren. B&W page EUR 1,800, color page EUR 2,200; trim 210 x 299. Circ: 3,200.

690   IRL   ISSN 0791-9786
IRISH CONSTRUCTION INDUSTRY. Text in English. 1990. 12/yr. EUR 87.60 (effective 2002). adv. **Document type:** *Magazine, Trade.*
Published by: Commercial Publications Ltd., Idrone Mews, Idrone Ln., Blackrock, Co. Dublin, Ireland. TEL 353-1-2833233, FAX 353-1-2833254, info@irishconstruction.com, http://www.irishconstruction.com. adv.: B&W page EUR 1,620, color page EUR 1,895; trim 210 x 297. Circ: 3,800.

338.47624   IRL   ISSN 1393-6719
IRISH CONSTRUCTION TIMES. Text in English. 1997. m. adv. **Document type:** *Magazine, Trade.*
Formerly (until 1998): Construction Times (1393-5771)
Address: 25a Phibsboro Pl., Phibsboro, Dublin, 7, Ireland. TEL 353-1-8603555, FAX 353-1-8603100. adv.: color page EUR 2,286. Circ: 15,000 (controlled).

690   DEU   ISSN 0938-1899
ISOLIER-TECHNIK. Text in German. 1976. bi-m. EUR 32 domestic; EUR 40 foreign (effective 2002). adv. **Document type:** *Magazine, Trade.*
Former titles (until 1989): Damm-Technik (0933-792X); (until 1987): Dammtechnik, Isolierung (0930-391X); (until 1985): Isolierung, Dammtechnik (0178-9112); (until 1985): Isolierung (0172-7834)
Indexed: RefZh.
—IE, Infotrieve.
Published by: Lambda Verlag GmbH, Hauptstr. 6, Gars am Inn, 83536, Germany. TEL 49-8073-2550, FAX 49-8073-2535, info@isolier-technik.de, http://www.isolier-technik.de. adv.: page EUR 1,440; trim 176 x 260.

ISRAEL. CENTRAL BUREAU OF STATISTICS. CONSTRUCTION IN ISRAEL/HA-BINUI BE-YISRAEL. see *BUILDING AND CONSTRUCTION—Abstracting, Bibliographies, Statistics*

690   ITA   ISSN 0393-8069
ITALIAN BUILDING AND CONSTRUCTION. Text in English. 1978. q. EUR 50 domestic; EUR 100 foreign (effective 2004). adv. index. back issues avail. **Document type:** *Magazine, Trade.* **Description:** Promotes the Italian building and construction industry.
Indexed: RefZh.
Published by: Casa Editrice la Fiaccola, Via Conca del Naviglio 37, Milan, MI 20123, Italy. TEL 39-02-89421350, FAX 39-02-89421484, http://www.fiaccola.it. Ed. Giuseppe Saronni. Adv. contact Mauro Nartelli. Circ: 30,000.

ITALIAN HOME NEWS. see *INTERIOR DESIGN AND DECORATION*

ITALY. ISTITUTO NAZIONALE DI STATISTICA. STATISTICHE DELL'ATTIVITA EDILIZIA. see *BUILDING AND CONSTRUCTION—Abstracting, Bibliographies, Statistics*

ITALY. ISTITUTO NAZIONALE DI STATISTICA. STATISTICHE DELLE OPERE PUBBLICHE. see *BUILDING AND CONSTRUCTION—Abstracting, Bibliographies, Statistics*

690   RUS   ISSN 1019-6390
CODEN: IVUAEZ
▶ **IZVESTIYA VYSSHIKH UCHEBNYKH ZAVEDENII. STROITEL'STVO.** Text in Russian; Contents page in English. m. RUR 240; USD 150 foreign (effective 2000). adv. **Document type:** *Journal, Academic/Scholarly.*
Formerly (until 1992): Izvestiya Vysshikh Uchebnikh Zavedenii. Arkhitektura y Stroitel'stvo (0536-1052)
Indexed: RefZh.
—CASDDS, CISTI, East View, Linda Hall.
Published by: Novosibirskii Gosudarstvennyi Universitet Arkhitektury y Stroitel'stva, Leningradskaya ul 113, Novosibirsk, 630008, Russian Federation. TEL 7-3832-662859, FAX 7-3832-660991, rektor@ngasu.nsk.su. Ed. V G Sebeshev. Pub. Arkady P Yanenko. Adv. contact Valerian V Fedorov. **US dist. addr.:** East View Information Services, 3020 Harbor Ln. N., Minneapolis, MN 55447. TEL 612-550-0961.

690   JPN   ISSN 0914-4528
J A C I C REPORT/J A C I C JOHO. Text in Japanese. 1986. q. JPY 1,000 per issue.
Published by: Japan Construction Information Center/Nihon Kensetsu Joho Sogo Senta, 10-20 Akasaka 7-chome, Minato-ku, Tokyo, 107-0052, Japan.

691.3   JPN
J C I TRANSACTIONS. Text in English. 1978. a. **Document type:** *Academic/Scholarly.*
Indexed: CRIA, CRICC, ConcrAb.
Published by: Nihon Konkurito Kogaku Kyokai/Japan Concrete Institute, Sohgo Hanzomon Bldg., 12F, 1-7 Koji-Machi, Chiyoda-ku, Tokyo, 102-0083, Japan. TEL 81-3-3263-1571, FAX 81-3-3263-2115, chii@jci-net.or.jp, info@jci-net.or.jp, http://www.jci-net.or.jp. Ed. Hiroshi Yamshita. Circ: 1,800.

690   JPN
J S S C BULLETIN. (Japanese Society of Steel Construction) Text in Japanese. q. **Document type:** *Journal, Academic/Scholarly.* **Description:** Contains information on topical projects, new products or methods, and overseas news for members.
Published by: Nihon Kokozo Kyokai/Japanese Society of Steel Construction, Yotsuya-Mitsubishi Bldg, 9F, 3-2-1 Yotsuya, Shinjuku-ku, Tokyo, 160-0004, Japan. TEL 81-3-59191535, FAX 81-3-59191536, JSSC-INFO@jssc.or.jp, http://www.jssc.or.jp/

690   JPN
J S S C JOURNAL OF CONSTRUCTIONAL STEEL. (Japanese Society of Steel Construction) Text in Japanese. a. **Document type:** *Journal, Academic/Scholarly.* **Description:** Proceedings of the annual Steel Structure Symposium.
Published by: Nihon Kokozo Kyokai/Japanese Society of Steel Construction, Yotsuya-Mitsubishi Bldg. 9F, 3-2-1 Yotsuya, Shinjuku-ku, Tokyo, 160-0004, Japan. TEL 81-3-59191535, FAX 81-3-59191536, JSSC-INFO@jssc.or.jp, http://www.jssc.or.jp/.

690   JPN
J S S C TECHNICAL REPORT∗ /J S S C REPOTO. Text in Japanese. 1986. irreg. **Description:** Contains articles on the achievements of the activities of JSSC committees such as researches studies and standardization activities.
Published by: Nihon Kokozo Kyokai/Japanese Society of Steel Construction, Yotsuya-Mitsubishi Bldg. 9F, 3-2-1 Yotsuya, Shinjuku-ku, Tokyo, 160-0004, Japan. TEL 81-3-59191535, FAX 81-3-59191536, JSSC-INFO@jssc.or.jp, http://www.jssc.or.jp/.

353.55   JAM
JAMAICA. MINISTRY OF CONSTRUCTION (WORKS). JAMAICA BUDGET (YEAR). Text in English. a. **Document type:** *Government.*
Published by: Ministry of Construction (Works), Kingston, Jamaica.

623   GBR
JANE'S NAVAL CONSTRUCTION AND RETROFIT MARKETS. Text in English. m. GBP 1,250, USD 1,999, AUD 3,250 (effective 2004). **Document type:** *Trade.* **Description:** Includes information on the availability of second hand hulls, manufacturers of naval weapons and equipment and ship designs on offer.
Media: Online - full content. **Related titles:** CD-ROM ed.: GBP 1,165, USD 1,865, AUD 3,030 (effective 2004).
Published by: Jane's Information Group, Sentinel House, 163 Brighton Rd, Coulsdon, Surrey CR5 2YH, United Kingdom. TEL 44-20-87003700, FAX 44-20-87631006, info@janes.co.uk, http://jnc.janes.com/, http://www.janes.com.

691   JPN   ISSN 0911-8985
JAPAN CONCRETE INSTITUTE. TRANSACTIONS. Text in English. 1979. a. JPY 10,000 newsstand/cover (effective 2004). **Document type:** *Academic/Scholarly.* **Description:** Consists of the translated versions of some 60-70 out of the total 400+ papers published in the JCI Annual Conference Proceedings and Concrete Research and Technology.
Indexed: EEA.
—BLDSC (8973.650000), CISTI. CCC.
Published by: Nihon Konkurito Kogaku Kyokai/Japan Concrete Institute, Sohgo Hanzomon Bldg, 12F, 1-7 Koji-Machi, Chiyoda-ku, Tokyo, 102-0083, Japan. TEL 81-3-3263-1571, FAX 81-3-3263-2115, info@jci-net.or.jp, http://www.jci-net.or.jp.

690   JPN
JAPAN'S CONSTRUCTION TODAY. Text in English. a. per issue exchange basis. **Document type:** *Bulletin.*
Published by: Overseas Construction Association of Japan/Kaigai Kensetsu Kyokai, 24-2 Haccho-Bori 2-chome, Chuo-ku, Tokyo, 104-0032, Japan. TEL 81-3-3553-1631, FAX 81-3-3551-0148. Ed., R&P Yoshio Yokoyama.

JIANZHU ANQUAN/CONSTRUCTION SAFETY. see *OCCUPATIONAL HEALTH AND SAFETY*

690   CHN   ISSN 1007-9629
JIANZHU CAILIAO XUEBAO/JOURNAL OF BUILDING MATERIALS. Text in Chinese. 1998. q. **Document type:** *Journal, Academic/Scholarly.*
Related titles: Online - full text ed.: (from East View Information Services, WanFang Data Corp.).
Indexed: C&ISA, E&CAJ, IAA.
—BLDSC (4954.610390).

Published by: Tongji Daxue, Cailiao Kexue yu Gongcheng Xueyuan, 1239, Xiping Lu, Shanghai, 200092, China. TEL 86-21-65981597, FAX 86-21-65983585, jcxb@mail.tongji.edu.cn, http://jzclxb.periodicals.net.cn/default.html.

690   CHN   ISSN 1002-3232
JIANZHU GONGREN/CONSTRUCTION WORKERS. Variant title: Builders Monthly. Text in Chinese. 1980. m. USD 2.50 (effective 2000); USD 20 foreign. adv.
Published by: Beijing Shi Jianzhu Gongcheng Zonggongsi/Beijing Construction Engineering Company, No 19 Nanlishi Lu, Fuxingmenwai, Beijing, 100045, China. TEL 86-10-6801-5033, FAX 86-10-6803-3576. Ed. Peng Shenghao. R&P Qingxiang Xu TEL 86-10-6803-3966. Adv. contact Xu Qingxiang. B&W page USD 500, color page USD 1,400. Circ: 120,000 (paid).

690   CHN   ISSN 1001-019X
JIANZHU GUANLI XIANDAIHUA/CONSTRUCTION MANAGEMENT MODERNIZATION. Text in Chinese. 1985. q. CNY 4.50 newsstand/cover (effective 2000); USD 0.54 newsstand/cover. adv. **Document type:** *Academic/Scholarly.*
Related titles: Online - full text ed.: (from East View Information Services).
Published by: Harbin Jianzhu Daxue/Harbin University of Architecture and Engineering, 66 Xi Dazhi St, Harbin, Heilongjiang 150006, China. TEL 86-451-6281155, FAX 86-451-6282276, guanke@sunzo.hrbucea.edu.an. Ed. Guan Ke. R&P Ke Guan. Adv. contact Yue Yu. color page USD 500. Circ: 4,000.

690   CHN   ISSN 1000-6869
JIANZHU JIEGOU XUEBAO/JOURNAL OF BUILDING STRUCTURES. Text in Chinese. bi-m. USD 2.30 per issue.
Related titles: Online - full text ed.: (from East View Information Services).
Indexed: C&ISA, E&CAJ, EEA, EngInd, IAA.
—CISTI.
Contact Dist.: China International Book Trading Corp/Zhongguo Guoji Tushu Maoyi Zonggongsi, 35 Chegongzhuang Xilu, Haidian District, PO Box 399, Beijing, 100044, China. TEL 86-10-68412045, FAX 86-10-68412023, cibtc@mail.cibtc.com.cn, http://www.cibtc.com.cn.

690 720   CHN   ISSN 1000-4726
JIANZHU JISHU/ARCHITECTURAL TECHNOLOGY. Text in Chinese. 1970. m. USD 5.60; USD 25 in Hong Kong; USD 50 elsewhere (effective 2000). adv.
Related titles: Online - full text ed.: (from East View Information Services).
—BLDSC (1601.994250).
Published by: Beijing Jianzhu Gongcheng Zonggongsi/Beijing Architectural Engineering Corporation, 19 Nanlishi Lu, Fuxingmenwai, Beijing, 100045, China. TEL 86-10-6801-5033, FAX 86-10-6803-3576. Ed. Peng Shenghao. R&P Qingsiang Xu TEL 86-10-6803-3966. Adv. contact Xu Qingxiang. page USD 1,000. Circ: 70,000.

JIANZHU JISHU JI SHEJI/ARCHITECTURE TECHNOLOGY & DESIGN. see *ARCHITECTURE*

JOBSITE - TOOLS AND MATERIALS FOR THE FLOORCOVERING PROFESSIONAL. see *INTERIOR DESIGN AND DECORATION*

692   USA   ISSN 1533-1768
JOBSITE - TOOLS AND MATERIALS FOR THE PAINTING & WALLCOVERING PROFESSIONAL. Text in English. bi-m. adv.
Published by: Trades Publishing, Inc, 24 Arnett Ave, 200, Lambertville, NJ 08530. TEL 609-397-5601, FAX 609-397-5640, editor@jobsitemagazine.com. Ed. David Cane. Pub. Troy Bausinger. Circ: 45,000.

JOBSITE - TOOLS AND MATERIALS FOR THE PLUMBING PROFESSIONAL. see *HEATING, PLUMBING AND REFRIGERATION*

JORDAN. DEPARTMENT OF STATISTICS. CONSTRUCTION STATISTICS. see *BUILDING AND CONSTRUCTION—Abstracting, Bibliographies, Statistics*

690   USA
THE JOURNAL (WARM SPRINGS); the magazine for manufactured housing professionals. Text in English. 1980. m. Free to qualified subscribers. adv. **Document type:** *Journal, Trade.* **Description:** Covers news and trends affecting the manufactured housing industry.
Published by: J & S Publishing, P O Box 288, Manchester, GA 31816. TEL 706-655-2333, 800-869-0471, FAX 706-655-3402, news@journalmfdhousing.com, http://www.journalmfdhousing.com/. Pub. Jim Visser. adv.: B&W page USD 1,843; trim 10.25 x 11.875.

690   CAN   ISSN 0047-2115
JOURNAL CONSTRUCTO. Text in French. 1963. s-w. CND 299. adv. **Document type:** *Newspaper, Trade.*
Related titles: Microfilm ed.: (from BNQ).

Published by: Groupe Constructo (Subsidiary of: Kerwil Publications Ltd.), 1500 boul Jules Poitras, Ste 200, St Laurent, PQ H4N 1X7, Canada. TEL 514-745-5720, FAX 514-339-2267. Ed., Adv. contact Johanne Rouleau. Pub. Guy Choiniere.

690 CHE ISSN 0021-776X
JOURNAL DE LA CONSTRUCTION DE LA SUISSE ROMANDE. Text in French. 1926. m. CHF 85 (effective 2000). adv. bk.rev. **Document type:** *Journal, Trade.* **Description:** Trade publication for the construction industry, covering buildings, roads, association news, exhibitions, new products, etc.
Indexed: CISA.
Address: Case Postale 74, Saint-Sulpice, 1025, Switzerland. TEL 41-21-6959520, FAX 41-21-6959550, http://www.jcsr.ch. Ed. Solange Giovanna. adv.: B&W page CHF 2,080, color page CHF 3,640; trim 185 x 267. Circ: 10,000.

690 FRA ISSN 1148-554X
JOURNAL DU CHAUFFAGE ET DU SANITAIRE. Text in French. 1989. 8/yr.
Published by: Groupe Moniteur, 17 rue d'Uzes, Paris, 75002, France. FAX 33-1-40135111. Ed. Michele Fourret. Circ: 17,000.

691 CAN ISSN 0831-0122
JOURNAL INDUSTRIEL DU QUEBEC. Text in English. 1985. 10/yr. CND 25. adv. **Description:** Provides information on various products needed in the industry. For executive management and purchasers.
Published by: Rogers Media Publishing Ltd, One Mount Pleasant Rd, 11th Fl, Toronto, ON M4Y 2Y5, Canada. TEL 416-764-2000, FAX 416-764-3941, http://www.rogers.com. Circ: 25,000 (controlled).

693 JPN ISSN 1346-8014
TA680 CODEN: JACTBX
▼ ➤ **JOURNAL OF ADVANCED CONCRETE TECHNOLOGY.** Text in English. 2003. 3/yr. USD 90 to individuals; USD 150 to institutions (effective 2004). **Document type:** *Journal, Academic/Scholarly.* **Description:** Reports on original scientific research works on concrete technology, covering pertinent topics on materials, structures and environments.
Related titles: Online - full content ed.: ISSN 1347-3913. USD 60 to individuals; USD 30 to students (effective 2004); Online - full text ed.: (from J-Stage).
Indexed: BrCerAb, C&ISA, CerAb, CorrAb, E&CAJ, EEA, EMA, IAA, M&TEA, MBF, METADEX, WAA.
—BLDSC (4918.945760), CISTI, IE, Linda Hall.
Published by: Nihon Konkurito Kogaku Kyokai/Japan Concrete Institute, Sohgo Hanzomon Bldg, 12F, 1-7 Koji-Machi, Chiyoda-ku, Tokyo, 102-0083, Japan. TEL 81-3-3263-1571, FAX 81-3-3263-2115, info@jci-net.or.jp, http://www.j-act.org/, http://www.jci-net.or.jp. Ed. H Mihashi.

➤ **JOURNAL OF ASIAN ARCHITECTURE AND BUILDING ENGINEERING.** see *ARCHITECTURE*

624.2 USA ISSN 1084-0702
TG1 CODEN: JBENF2
➤ **JOURNAL OF BRIDGE ENGINEERING.** Text in English. 1996. bi-m. USD 422 domestic to institutions; USD 469 combined subscription domestic to institutions print & online eds.; USD 446 foreign to institutions; USD 493 combined subscription foreign to institutions print & online eds. (effective 2005). bk.rev. back issues avail. **Document type:** *Magazine, Academic/Scholarly.* **Description:** Provides an international communication forum for the exchange of information among practicing bridge engineers, constructors, and researchers. Devoted exclusively to bridge engineering, reports on both the theory and the practice of the structural design, inspection, construction, and performance of bridges.
Related titles: CD-ROM ed.: USD 60 to members for CD and online eds.; USD 272 to institutions for CD and online eds. (effective 2001); Online - full text ed.: (from EBSCO Publishing, Swets Information Services).
Indexed: AS&TI, BrCerAb, C&ISA, CerAb, CivEngAb, CorrAb, E&CAJ, EEA, EMA, ESPM, EngInd, H&SSA, HRIS, IAA, ICEA, M&TEA, MBF, METADEX, RiskAb, SWRA, SolStAb, WAA.
—CISTI, IE, Infotrieve, Linda Hall. **CCC.**
Published by: American Society of Civil Engineers, 1801 Alexander Bell Dr, Reston, VA 20191-4400. TEL 703-295-6300, 800-548-2723, FAX 703-295-6222, http://www.pubs.asce.org/journals/be.html, http://www.asce.org. Ed. Dennis R. Mertz. **Subscr. to:** PO Box 79342, Baltimore, MD 21279-0342.

690 333.332 GBR ISSN 1742-8262
▼ **JOURNAL OF BUILDING APPRAISAL.** Text in English. 2005 (Jan.). q. GBP 160 in Europe; USD 295 in United States; GBP 175 elsewhere (effective 2005). **Document type:** *Journal, Academic/Scholarly.* **Description:** Deals with building condition, defects, repair and maintenance and addresses the issues confronting professionals responsible for the appraisal and refurbishment of the built environment.
Related titles: Online - full text ed.: ISSN 1744-9545 (from IngentaConnect).
Published by: Palgrave Macmillan Ltd. (Subsidiary of: Macmillan Publishers Ltd.), Houndmills, Basingstoke, Hants RG21 6XS, United Kingdom. TEL 44-1256-329242, FAX 44-1256-810526, journal-info@palgrave.com, http://www.palgrave-journals.com/. Ed. Malcolm Hollis.

690 SGP ISSN 1609-9451
➤ **JOURNAL OF CONSTRUCTION RESEARCH.** Abbreviated title: J C R. Text in English. 2002. s-a. SGD 49, USD 29, EUR 26 to individuals; SGD 144 combined subscription per issue to institutions print & online eds.; USD 85, EUR 77 combined subscription to institutions print & online eds. (effective 2006). back issues avail. **Document type:** *Journal, Academic/Scholarly.* **Description:** Its goal is to investigate and expand the frontiers of knowledge that cover business decision making applications of scholarly construction research, that is, of construction operations, management, economics and engineering services.
Related titles: Online - full content ed.; Online - full text ed.: (from EBSCO Publishing, O C L C Online Computer Library Center, Inc., Swets Information Services).
Indexed: BrCerAb, C&ISA, CerAb, CorrAb, E&CAJ, EMA, ESPM, H&SSA, IAA, M&TEA, MBF, METADEX, RiskAb, SolStAb, WAA.
—BLDSC (4965.188000), IE, ingenta. **CCC.**
Published by: (Hong Kong Institute of Real Estate HKG), World Scientific Publishing Co. Pte. Ltd., 5 Toh Tuck Link, Singapore, 596224, Singapore. TEL 65-466-5775, FAX 65-467-7667, wspc@wspc.com.sg, http://www.worldscinet.com/journals/jcr/jcr.shtml, http://www.worldscientific.com. Ed. Raymond Y C Tse. **Subscr. to:** Farrer Rd, PO Box 128, Singapore 912805, Singapore. sales@wspc.com.sg. **Dist. by:** World Scientific Publishing Co., Inc., 1060 Main St, River Edge, NJ 07661. TEL 201-487-9655, 800-227-7562, FAX 201-487-9656, 888-977-2665.; World Scientific Publishing Ltd., 57 Shelton St, London WC2H 9HE, United Kingdom. TEL 44-20-78360888, FAX 44-20-78362020, sales@wspc.co.uk.

➤ **JOURNAL OF FINANCIAL MANAGEMENT OF PROPERTY AND CONSTRUCTION.** see *REAL ESTATE*

690 USA ISSN 1056-828X
THE JOURNAL OF LIGHT CONSTRUCTION (NATIONAL ED.). Text in English. 1986. m. USD 39.95 domestic; USD 50.95 foreign (effective 2005).
Formed by the 1991 merger of: The Journal of Light Construction (Eastern Ed.) (1049-6033); The Journal of Light Construction (Midwest Ed.) (1050-2629); The Journal of Light Construction (Western Ed.) (1050-2637); All of which supersedes (in 1989): The Journal of Light Construction (1040-5224); Which was formerly (until 1988): New England Builder (0889-6526)
Related titles: Online - full content ed.; Online - full text ed.: (from Gale Group).
—BLDSC (5010.471300), CISTI.
Published by: Hanley-Wood, LLC (Subsidiary of: J.P. Morgan Chase & Co.), 186 Allen Brook Ln, Williston, VT 05495. TEL 802-879-3335, FAX 802-879-9384, jlc-editorial@hanleywood.com, http://www.jlconline.com/cgi-bin/jlconline.storefront, http://www.hanleywood.com. **Subscr. to:** J L C Subscriptions, PO Box 420235, Palm Coast, FL 32142-0235. TEL 800-375-5981.

690 USA ISSN 1050-2610
JOURNAL OF LIGHT CONSTRUCTION (NEW ENGLAND ED.). Text in English. 1982. m. USD 59.95 domestic; USD 50.95 foreign (effective 2004). adv. bk.rev.; software rev. illus. 100 p./no.; back issues avail.; reprints avail. **Document type:** *Journal, Trade.* **Description:** Provides practical information on building technology and business management for residential and light-commercial building contractors.
Supersedes in part (in 1989): Journal of Light Construction (1040-5224); Which was formerly (until 1988): New England Builder (0889-6526)
Related titles: CD-ROM ed.: USD 179.95 archive ed. (effective 2000 - 2001); Online - full text ed.: (from Gale Group).
Indexed: Search.
—BLDSC (5010.471300), CISTI.
Published by: Hanley-Wood, LLC (Subsidiary of: J.P. Morgan Chase & Co.), 186 Allen Brook Ln, Williston, VT 05495. TEL 802-879-3335, FAX 802-879-9384, djackson@hanley-wood.com, tjackson@hanleywood.com, http://jlconline.com, http://www.hanleywood.com. Ed. Dan Jackson. Pub. Rick Strachan. Circ: 64,148 (paid).

JOURNAL OF MEDIA ECONOMICS. see *COMMUNICATIONS*

JOURNAL OF REAL ESTATE AND CONSTRUCTION. see *REAL ESTATE*

JOURNAL OF WOOD SCIENCE. see *FORESTS AND FORESTRY—Lumber And Wood*

690 DEU ISSN 1433-6316
JUNGE HAEUSER; Bauideen fuer Einsteiger. Text in German. 1997. bi-m. EUR 1 newsstand/cover (effective 2003). adv. **Document type:** *Magazine, Consumer.*
Published by: Fachschriften Verlag GmbH, Hoehenstr 17, Fellbach, 70736, Germany. TEL 49-711-52061, FAX 49-711-5206223, info@fachschriften.de, http://www.fachschriften.de/publikationen/jungehaeuser.htm. Ed. Wolfgang Grasreiner. Adv. contact Barbara Hoof. B&W page EUR 5,280, color page EUR 8,765; trim 187 x 247. Circ: 70,081 (paid and controlled).

690 ISR
KABLAN UVONEH/CONTRACTOR AND BUILDER. Text in Hebrew. 1952. q. ILS 36.80. illus.
Published by: Contractors and Builders Center in Israel, 43 Hatarese Blvd., Tel Aviv, 62492, Israel. TEL 03-440560. Ed. Elnakam Artzieli. Circ: 3,500.

690 USA ISSN 1069-3297
KELLER'S CONSTRUCTION REGULATORY UPDATE. Text in English. 1993. m. looseleaf. USD 159 (effective 2005). **Document type:** *Newsletter, Trade.* **Description:** Provides news related to construction specific DOT, EPA and OSHA regulatory activities.
Published by: J.J. Keller & Associates, Inc., 3003 W Breezewood Ln, P O Box 368, Neenah, WI 54957-0368. TEL 877-564-2333, FAX 800-727-7516, sales@jjkeller.com, http://www.jjkeller.com. Pub. John J Keller.

B

690 JPN ISSN 0286-4630
KENCHIKU KENKYU SHIRYO/BUILDING RESERCH DATA. Text in Japanese. 1997 (Nov., no.92). irreg. **Document type:** *Academic/Scholarly.*
Published by: Kensetsusho Kenchiku Kenkyujo/Building Research Institute (Subsidiary of: Ministry of Construction), 1 Tachihara, Tsukuba-shi, Ibaraki-ken 305, Japan. TEL 81-298-64-2151, FAX 81-298-64-2909, www-adm@kenken.go.jp, http://www.kenken.go.jp/.

720 JPN ISSN 0286-4622
KENCHIKU KENKYUJO NENPO/BUILDING RESEARCH INSTITUTE. ANNUAL REPORT. Abbreviated title: B R I. Annual Report. Text in Japanese. 1967. a. **Document type:** *Academic/Scholarly.*
Indexed: INIS AtomInd.
—BLDSC (1118.480000).
Published by: Kensetsusho Kenchiku Kenkyujo/Building Research Institute (Subsidiary of: Ministry of Construction), 1 Tachihara, Tsukuba-shi, Ibaraki-ken 305, Japan. TEL 81-298-64-2151, FAX 81-298-64-2909, www-adm@kenken.go.jp, http://www.kenken.go.jp/.

690 JPN
KENSETSU HAKUSHO/WHITE PAPER OF CONSTRUCTION WORKS. Text in Japanese. 1949. a. JPY 2,700 (effective 2000). **Document type:** *Government.*
Published by: Ministry of Land, Infrastructure and Transport, 2-1-3, Kasumigaseki, Chiyoda-ku, Tokyo, 100-8918, Japan. TEL 81-3-5253-8111, http://www.mlit.go.jp/.

690 621.9 JPN
KENSETSU KIKAI DOKO CHOSA HOKOKU/ANNUAL REPORT OF CONSTRUCTION MACHINERY AND EQUIPMENT. Text in Japanese. 1978. a. **Document type:** *Government.*
Published by: Tsusho Sangyosho, Kikai Joho Sangyokyoku/Ministry of International Trade and Industry, Machinery and Information Industries Bureau, 3-1 Kasumigaseki 1-chome, Chiyoda-ku, Tokyo, 100-0013, Japan.

690 621.9 JPN ISSN 0388-4066
KENSETSU KIKAIKA KENKYUJO NENPO/CONSTRUCTION METHOD AND MACHINERY RESEARCH INSTITUTE. ANNUAL REPORT. Text in Japanese. 1965. a. **Document type:** *Academic/Scholarly.*
Published by: Nihon Kensetsu Kikaika Kyokai, Kensetsu Kikaika Kenkyujo/Japan Construction Mechanization Association, Construction Method and Machinery Research Institute, 3154 Obuchi, Fuji-shi, Shizuoka-ken 417-0801, Japan. FAX 81-545-35-3719. Ed. Hidesuke Nakashima.

690 621.9 JPN
KENSETSU KIKAIKAI KENKYUJO SEINO SHIKEN HOKOKU/JAPANESE CONSTRUCTION METHOD AND MACHINERY RESEARCH INSTITUTE. REPORT OF PERFORMANCE TESTS. Text in Japanese. 1964. irreg. JPY 500. **Document type:** *Academic/Scholarly.*
Published by: Nihon Kensetsu Kikaika Kyokai, Kensetsu Kikaika Kenkyujo/Japan Construction Mechanization Association, Construction Method and Machinery Research Institute, 3154 Obuchi, Fuji-shi, Shizuoka-ken 417-0801, Japan. TEL 81-545-35-0212, FAX 81-545-35-3719.

KENSETSU KOGAKU KENKYU SHINKOKAI NENPO/SOCIETY FOR THE PROMOTION OF CONSTRUCTION ENGINEERING. ANNUAL REPORT. see *ENGINEERING—Civil Engineering*

KENSETSU KOJI SAIGAI BOSHI TEIANSHU/PROPOSALS FOR INDUSTRIAL SAFETY OF CONSTRUCTION. see *OCCUPATIONAL HEALTH AND SAFETY*

KENSETSU NO KIKAIKA/CONSTRUCTION MECHANIZATION. see *MACHINERY*

KENSETSU TOKEI GEPPO/MONTHLY OF CONSTRUCTION STATISTICS. see *BUILDING AND CONSTRUCTION—Abstracting, Bibliographies, Statistics*

690 JPN
KENSETSUSHO KINKI CHIHO KENSETSUKYOKU. JIGYO GAIYO✶ /MINISTRY OF CONSTRUCTION. KINKI REGIONAL CONSTRUCTION BUREAU. ANNUAL REPORT. Text in Japanese. a. JPY 2,000.
Published by: Kinki Kensetsu Kyokai/Kinki Association of Construction, c/o Ministry of Construction, 2-1 Kasumigaseki, Chiyoda-ku, Tokyo, 100-0013, Japan.

691.4 PRT ISSN 0871-780X
KERAMICA. Text in Portuguese. 1975. q. **Document type:** *Magazine, Trade.* **Description:** Trade review of the construction ceramics industry.
Formerly (until 1989): Associacao Portuguesa de Industriais da Ceramica de Construcao. Boletim Informativo (0871-9225)
Published by: Associacao Portuguesa de Industriais da Ceramica de Construcao, Rua Coronel Veiga Simao, Edif C, Coimbra, 3020-053, Portugal. TEL 351-239-497600, FAX 351-239-497601, info@apicer.pt.

690 GBR
KEY NOTE MARKET REPORT: BRICKS & TILES. Variant title: Bricks & Tiles. Text in English. irreg., latest 2001, July. GBP 340 per issue (effective 2002). **Document type:** *Trade.* **Description:** Provides an overview of a specific UK market segment and includes executive summary, market definition, market size, industry background, competitor analysis, current issues, forecasts, company profiles, and more.
Formerly: Key Note Report: Bricks and Tiles (0951-9114)
Related titles: CD-ROM ed.; Online - full text ed.
Indexed: CRIA.
Published by: Key Note Ltd., Field House, 72 Oldfield Rd, Hampton, Mddx TW12 2HQ, United Kingdom. TEL 44-20-8481-8750, FAX 44-20-8783-0049, info@keynote.co.uk, http://www.keynote.co.uk. Ed. Lyndsey Barker.

690 GBR ISSN 1365-6716
KEY NOTE MARKET REPORT: BUILDERS' MERCHANTS. Variant title: Builders' Merchants Market Report. Text in English. irreg., latest 2001, Oct. GBP 340 per issue (effective 2002). **Document type:** *Trade.* **Description:** Provides an overview of a specific UK market segment and includes executive summary, market definition, market size, industry background, competitor analysis, current issues, forecasts, company profiles, and more.
Formerly (until 1996): Key Note Report: Builders' Merchants (0952-5351)
Published by: Key Note Ltd., Field House, 72 Oldfield Rd, Hampton, Mddx TW12 2HQ, United Kingdom. TEL 44-20-8481-8750, FAX 44-20-8783-0049, info@keynote.co.uk, http://www.keynote.co.uk. Ed. Jenny Baxter.

690 GBR
KEY NOTE MARKET REPORT: BUILDING CONTRACTING. Variant title: Building Contracting Market Report. Text in English. irreg., latest 2001, June. GBP 340 per issue (effective 2002). **Document type:** *Trade.* **Description:** Provides an overview of a specific UK market segment and includes executive summary, market definition, market size, industry background, competitor analysis, current issues, forecasts, company profiles, and more.
Formerly: Key Note Report: Building Contracting (0269-901X)
Related titles: CD-ROM ed.; Online - full text ed.
Published by: Key Note Ltd., Field House, 72 Oldfield Rd, Hampton, Mddx TW12 2HQ, United Kingdom. TEL 44-20-8481-8750, FAX 44-20-8783-0049, info@keynote.co.uk, http://www.keynote.co.uk. Ed. Peter Witney.

690 GBR ISSN 1461-3379
KEY NOTE MARKET REPORT: BUILDING MATERIALS. Variant title: Building Materials Market Report. Text in English. irreg., latest 2001, April. GBP 340 per issue (effective 2002). **Document type:** *Trade.* **Description:** Provides an overview of a specific UK market segment and includes executive summary, market definition, market size, industry background, competitor analysis, current issues, forecasts, company profiles, and more.
Formerly (until 1997): Key Note Report: Building Materials
Related titles: CD-ROM ed.; Online - full text ed.
—CCC.
Published by: Key Note Ltd., Field House, 72 Oldfield Rd, Hampton, Mddx TW12 2HQ, United Kingdom. TEL 44-20-8481-8750, FAX 44-20-8783-0049, info@keynote.co.uk, http://www.keynote.co.uk. Ed. Jacob Howard.

690 GBR ISSN 1365-6708
KEY NOTE MARKET REPORT: BUILDING SOCIETIES. Variant title: Building Societies. Text in English. irreg., latest vol.10, 1996, July. GBP 340 per issue (effective 2002). **Document type:** *Trade.* **Description:** Provides an overview of a specific UK market segment and includes executive summary, market definition, market size, industry background, competitor analysis, current issues, forecasts, company profiles, and more.
Formerly (until 1996): Key Note Report: Building Societies
Related titles: CD-ROM ed.; Online - full text ed.
Published by: Key Note Ltd., Field House, 72 Oldfield Rd, Hampton, Mddx TW12 2HQ, United Kingdom. TEL 44-20-8481-8750, FAX 44-20-8783-0049, info@keynote.co.uk, http://www.keynote.co.uk. Ed. Phillippa Smith.

353.55 GBR ISSN 1368-3276
KEY NOTE MARKET REPORT: HOUSEBUILDING. Variant title: Housebuilding. Text in English. irreg., latest 2001, Sept. GBP 340 per issue (effective 2002). **Document type:** *Trade.* **Description:** Provides and overview of a specific UK market segment and includes executive summary, market definition, market size, industry background, competitor analysis, current issues, forecasts, company profiles, and more.
Formerly (until 1997): Key Note Report: Housebuilding (0954-4372)
Related titles: CD-ROM ed.; Online - full text ed.
Published by: Key Note Ltd., Field House, 72 Oldfield Rd, Hampton, Mddx TW12 2HQ, United Kingdom. TEL 44-20-8481-8750, FAX 44-20-8783-0049, info@keynote.co.uk, http://www.keynote.co.uk. Ed. Emily Pattullo.

690 GBR
KEY NOTE MARKET REPORT: INSULATION PRODUCTS. Variant title: Insulation Products. Text in English. irreg., latest 1993, Oct. GBP 340 per issue (effective 2002). **Document type:** *Trade.* **Description:** Provides and overview of a specific UK market segment and includes executive summary, market definition, market size, industry background, competitor analysis, current issues, forecasts, company profiles, and more.
Formerly: Key Note Report: Insulation Products (0951-3566)
Related titles: CD-ROM ed.; Online - full text ed.
Published by: Key Note Ltd., Field House, 72 Oldfield Rd, Hampton, Mddx TW12 2HQ, United Kingdom. TEL 44-20-8481-8750, FAX 44-20-8783-0049, info@keynote.co.uk, http://www.keynote.co.uk.

690 GBR ISSN 1359-2580
KEY NOTE MARKET REVIEW: U K CONSTRUCTION INDUSTRY. Text in English. 1989. irreg., latest 2001, Apr. GBP 565 per issue (effective 2002). **Document type:** *Trade.* **Description:** Provides an overview of the UK construction industry, including industry structure, market size and trends, developments, prospects, and major company profiles.
Formerly (until 1992): Market Review. U.K. Construction Industry (0960-4243)
Related titles: CD-ROM ed.; Online - full text ed.
—CCC.
Published by: Key Note Ltd., Field House, 72 Oldfield Rd, Hampton, Mddx TW12 2HQ, United Kingdom. TEL 44-20-8481-8750, FAX 44-20-8783-0049, info@keynote.co.uk, http://www.keynote.co.uk/showReport.asp?report=Constructi1152. Ed. Emma Wiggin.

KIRSH'S CONSTRUCTION LIEN CASE FINDER. see *LAW*

643.3 USA ISSN 0730-2487
TT197
KITCHEN & BATH BUSINESS. Cover title: K B B. Text in English. 1955. m. USD 79 domestic; USD 94 in Canada; USD 139 elsewhere; USD 10 newsstand/cover; free to qualified personnel (effective 2005). adv. charts; illus. index. **Document type:** *Magazine, Trade.* **Description:** Covers the residential kitchen and bathroom market.
Formerly: Kitchen Business (0023-1932)
Related titles: Online - full text ed.: (from EBSCO Publishing, Gale Group, O C L C Online Computer Library Center, Inc., ProQuest Information & Learning).
Indexed: ABIn.
—CCC.
Published by: V N U Business Publications (Subsidiary of: V N U Business Media), 770 Broadway, New York, NY 10003-9595. bmcomm@vnuinc.com, http://www.kbbonline.com/, http://www.vnubusinessmedia.com/. Eds. Bill Partsch TEL 646-654-4412, Christina Trauthwein TEL 646-654-4481. Pub. Lyle C Landon. Adv. contact Michelle Finn TEL 312-583-5607. B&W page USD 7,740, color page USD 9,950; trim 8.125 x 10.875. Circ: 50,051 (paid). **Subscr. to:** PO Box 1124, Skokie, IL 60076-8124.

643.7 USA
KITCHEN BATH SPECIALIST. Text in English. m.
Published by: Kasmar Publications, Inc., PO Box 12638, Palm Desert, CA 92255. TEL 760-773-2874, 800-253-9992, FAX 760-773-2876, info@kasmarpub.com, http://www.kasmarpublications.com. Ed. Greg Rohl.

690 JPN
KOKUDO KENSETSU NO GENKYO/PRESENT STATE OF LAND CONSTRUCTION. Text in Japanese. 1949. a. **Document type:** *Government.*
Published by: Ministry of Land, Infrastructure and Transport, 2-1-3, Kasumigaseki, Chiyoda-ku, Tokyo, 100-8918, Japan. TEL 81-3-5253-8111, http://www.mlit.go.jp/.

KOKYO. see *ENGINEERING—Civil Engineering*

690 CHE
KOMMUNAL KATALOG; Nachschlagewerk fuer Behoerden und Einkaeufer. Text in German. 1976. a. CHF 25. adv. bk.rev. **Document type:** *Catalog.*
Published by: Vogt-Schild AG, Zuchwilerstr 21, Solothurn 1, 4501, Switzerland. TEL 41-32-6247474, FAX 065-247235. Ed. Marianne Flury. Adv. contact Hansruedi Spiri. B&W page CHF 2,600, color page CHF 3,700; trim 260 x 185. Circ: 5,000.

KOMPASS PROFESSIONNEL. BATIMENT ET GENIE CIVIL, MANUTENTION - LEVAGE, BOIS - MEUBLES. see *BUSINESS AND ECONOMICS—Trade And Industrial Directories*

691.3 JPN ISSN 0387-1061
TA680 CODEN: KOKODX
➤ **KONKURITO KOGAKU/CONCRETE JOURNAL.** Text in Japanese; Summaries in English. 1963. m. adv. bk.rev. abstr.; bibl.; charts; illus. Index. **Document type:** *Journal, Academic/Scholarly.* **Description:** Covers various aspects of concrete materials, design, building, and technology.
Formerly: Konkurito Jaanaru (0023-3544)
Indexed: BrCerAb, C&ISA, CerAb, ChemAb, ChemTitl, CivEngAb, ConcrAb, CorrAb, E&CAJ, EMA, IAA, INIS AtomInd, M&TEA, MBF, METADEX, SolStAb, WAA.
—CASDDS, CISTI, Linda Hall. **CCC.**
Published by: Nihon Konkurito Kogaku Kyokai/Japan Concrete Institute, Sohgo Hanzomon Bldg, 12F, 1-7 Koji-Machi, Chiyoda-ku, Tokyo, 102-0083, Japan. TEL 81-3-3263-1571, FAX 81-3-3263-2115, info@jci-net.or.jp, http://www.jci-net.or.jp/bulletin/index.html. Circ: 9,000.

➤ **KONKURITO KOGAKU RONBUNSHU/CONCRETE RESEARCH AND TECHNOLOGY.** see *ENGINEERING—Civil Engineering*

690 JPN
KONOIKEGUMI GIJUTSU KENKYU HAPPYOKAI RONBUNSHU/KONOIKE CONSTRUCTION CO. PROCEEDINGS OF ANNUAL MEETING. (Not avail. to general public) Text in Japanese. 1975. a. for qualified personnel only. **Document type:** *Academic/Scholarly.*
Published by: Konoikegumi Gijutsu Kenkyujo/Konoike Construction Co., Ltd., Research Institute of Technology, 20-1 Sakura 1-chome, Tsukuba-shi, Ibaraki-ken 305-0003, Japan.

690 JPN ISSN 0914-6229
TA4
KONOIKEGUMI GIJUTSU KENKYU HOKOKU/KONOIKE CONSTRUCTION CO. TECHNICAL RESEARCH REPORTS. Text and summaries in English, Japanese. 1988. a.
Published by: Konoikegumi Gijutsu Kenkyujo/Konoike Construction Co., Ltd., Research Institute of Technology, 20-1 Sakura 1-chome, Tsukuba-shi, Ibaraki-ken 305-0003, Japan.

960 DEU ISSN 0344-4570
DER KONSTRUKTEUR. Text in German. 1970. 10/yr. EUR 88 domestic; EUR 102 foreign; EUR 8 newsstand/cover (effective 2004). adv. charts; illus. **Document type:** *Magazine, Trade.*
Published by: Verlag fuer Technik und Wirtschaft GmbH & Co., Lise-Meitner-Str 2, Mainz, 55129, Germany. TEL 49-6131-992-0, FAX 49-6131-992100, info@vfmz.de, http://www.industrie-service.de. Ed. Michael Doeppert. Adv. contact Michael Spahn. B&W page EUR 4,700, color page EUR 5,930; trim 185 x 265. Circ: 25,000.

690 DEU ISSN 0947-9333
KONSTRUKTION UND ENGINEERING; die Fachzeitung fuer Konstrukteure und Entwickler. Text in German. 1977. m. EUR 71 domestic; EUR 89 foreign; EUR 6 newsstand/cover (effective 2005). adv. **Document type:** *Magazine, Trade.* **Description:** Presents information on the newest trends and developments in products and processes, case studies on the implementation of components and systems, as well as successful organizational aspects of design engineering management.
Former titles (until 1994): Konstruktion und Elektronik (0177-7459); Konstruktion, Entwicklung und Design; Konstruktion und Design (0344-6034)
Published by: Verlag Moderne Industrie AG & Co. KG, Justus-von-Liebig-Str 1, Landsberg, 86899, Germany. TEL 49-8191-1250, FAX 49-8191-125211, ke@mi-verlag.de, info@mi-verlag.de, http://www.k-e.de/ke, http://www.mi-verlag.de. Ed. Franz Graf. Adv. contact Gabriele Claus. B&W page EUR 5,060, color page EUR 6,440; trim 190 x 270. Circ: 24,528 (paid and controlled).

690 DNK ISSN 0907-3574
KONSTRUKTOEREN. Text in Danish. 1981. 11/yr. membership. adv. illus. **Description:** Deals with union matters, news about building and construction.
Former titles (until 1989): Bygningskonstruktoerernes Fagblad (0905-0736); (until 1988): Bygningskonstruktoerernes Medlemsorientering (0109-5692); D B
Published by: Konstruktoerforeningen/Danish Association of Construction Architects, Ny Vestergade 13, Copenhagen K, 1471, Denmark. TEL 45-33-36-41-50, FAX 45-33-36-41-60, redaktionen@kf.dk, http://www.kf.dk/bladet/index-blad.html. Ed. Anne Wegeberg. adv.: B&W page DKK 8,330; 245 x 175. Circ: 4,076.

690 DEU
KRAN UND BUEHNE. Text in German. 6/yr. adv. **Document type:** *Trade.* **Description:** For users and buyers of cranes and access equipment.

Published by: K H L (King Haller Ltd.) International, Georgenstr 61B, Munich, 80799, Germany. TEL 49-89-55028266, FAX 49-89-55028266, mail@khl.com, http://www.khl.com. Ed. Tim Whiteman. Adv. contact Hans Haller.

KUNST UND STADT. see *ARCHITECTURE*

KUWAIT. CENTRAL STATISTICAL OFFICE. ANNUAL SURVEY OF ESTABLISHMENTS - CONSTRUCTION/KUWAIT. AL-IDARAH AL-MARKAZIYYAH LIL-IHSA'. AL-BAHTH AL-SANAWI LIL-MANSHAAT - AL-TASHYID WAL-BINA'. see *BUILDING AND CONSTRUCTION—Abstracting, Bibliographies, Statistics*

KUWAIT. CENTRAL STATISTICAL OFFICE. CONSTRUCTION STATISTICS RESULTS/KUWAIT. AL-IDARAH AL-MARKAZIYYAH LIL-IHSA'. NATA'IJ IHSA'AT AL-TASHYID WAL-BINA'. see *BUILDING AND CONSTRUCTION—Abstracting, Bibliographies, Statistics*

KYORYO NENKAN/STEEL BRIDGE YEARBOOK. see *ENGINEERING—Civil Engineering*

690 USA
L B M JOURNAL. Short title: B M R. Text in English. 1984. m. free to qualified personnel (effective 2005). adv. **Document type:** *Magazine, Trade.*
Former titles: Building Material Dealer (1522-0230); Building Material Retailer; Supersedes: Retail Lumberman (0034-608X); Northwestern Lumberman (0092-0681); Which was formerly: Northwestern and Mississippi Valley Lumberman (0091-6390); Which was formed by the merger of: Northwestern Lumber Dealer (0029-3504); Mississippi Valley Lumberman (0026-6426)
—Linda Hall.
Published by: Custom Bulit Publishing LLC, 9505 161st St W, Lakeville, MN 55044. TEL 952-892-7793, FAX 952-892-7816, http://www.lbmjournal.com/. Ed. Greg Brooks TEL 812-944-6354. Pub. Rick Schumacher. Adv. contact Jodie Cook. Circ: 27,000 (controlled).

690 333.33 USA
LARGER HOMES COLLECTION. Text in English. 1989. a., latest vol.10, 1999. adv. illus.; mkt.; tr.lit. **Document type:** *Magazine, Trade.*
Published by: Drawing Board Atlanta, Inc., PO Box 15556, Atlanta, GA 30333-0556. TEL 404-624-3999, FAX 404-624-4063, sales@drawingboardatlanta.com, http://www.drawingboardatlanta.com. Ed., Pub., R&P, Adv. contact Phillip Andrew Jessup. B&W page USD 500; trim 6.75 x 10. Circ: 1,000 (paid).

353.55 ITA ISSN 1122-2506
LAVORI PUBBLICI. Text in Italian. 1989. m. EUR 75 (effective 2005). **Document type:** *Magazine, Trade.*
Published by: Grafill Srl, Via Principe di Palagonia 87-91, Palermo, 90145, Italy. TEL 39-091-6823069, FAX 39-091-6823313, editore@grafill.it, http://www.grafill.it.

691 GBR ISSN 0960-6823
LAXTON'S BUILDING PRICE BOOK (YEAR). Text in English. 1828. a., latest 2004, 176th ed. GBP 105, USD 165 per vol. (effective 2004). adv. stat. **Document type:** *Directory, Trade.* **Description:** Provides 250,000 pricing elements for construction cost estimating.
Former titles: Laxton's National Building Price Book (0960-6815); Laxton's Building Price Book (0305-6589)
—BLDSC (5161.900000).
Published by: Butterworth - Heinemann (Subsidiary of: Elsevier Ltd., Books Division), Linacre House, Jordan Hill, Oxford, OX2 8DP, United Kingdom. TEL 44-1865-310366, FAX 44-1865-310898, duncan.enright@repp.co.uk, http://www.bh.com. Ed. V B Johnson. Circ: 3,000 (paid).

LEASING PROFESSIONAL NEWSLETTER. see *BUSINESS AND ECONOMICS—Small Business*

338.47624 SWE ISSN 0345-7133
LEVERANSTIDNINGEN ENTREPRENAD. Text in Swedish. 1970. 22/yr. SEK 605 domestic; SEK 915 in Scandinavia (effective 2004). adv. illus. **Document type:** *Newspaper, Trade.*
Formed by the merger of (1931-1970): Svensk Leveranstidning; (1968-1970): Entreprenad (0013-9025)
Indexed: RefZh.
Published by: Svensk Leveranstidning AB, Hemvaernsgatan 11, PO Box 6054, Solna, 17106, Sweden. TEL 46-8-56488630, FAX 46-8-897005, tidningen@entreprenad.com, http://www.entreprenad.com. Eds. Lars-Olof Eriksson TEL 46-8-56488642, Goeran Bergstrand TEL 46-8-56488637. Adv. contact Raija Kouhia TEL 46-8-56488636. B&W page SEK 25,850, color page SEK 29,700; trim 250 x 350. Circ: 16,000 (controlled).

LIBYA. CENSUS AND STATISTICS DEPARTMENT. REPORT OF THE SURVEY OF LICENSED CONSTRUCTION UNITS. see *BUILDING AND CONSTRUCTION—Abstracting, Bibliographies, Statistics*

392.8 DNK ISSN 0024-287X
LICITATIONEN; dagbladet for bygge- og anlaegsvirksomhed. Text in Danish. 1908. 5/w. DKK 2,695 domestic; DKK 4,962 elsewhere (effective 2003). adv. **Document type:** *Newspaper, Trade.* **Description:** Aimed at all parts of the building and construction industry. Contains information about Danish and European tenders.
Formerly: Haandvaerkets Dagblad
Related titles: Online - full content ed.
Published by: Aller Business AS, Marielundsvej 46 D, Herlev, 2730, Denmark. TEL 45-44-858899, FAX 45-44-858887, licitationen@licitationen.dk, info@allerbusiness.dk, http://www.licitationen.dk, http://www.allerbusiness.dk. Ed. Klaus Toettrup. adv.: page DKK 15,500; 266 x 365. Circ: 6,100.

690 LIE
LIECHTENSTEINER BAU- UND HAUSZEITUNG. Text in German. m. **Document type:** *Newspaper, Trade.*
Address: Postfach 983, Vaduz, 9490, Liechtenstein. TEL 423-2301740, FAX 423-2375601. Ed. Norman Kaufmann. Circ: 10,000.

LIFTING & TRANSPORTATION INTERNATIONAL. see *TRANSPORTATION—Trucks And Trucking*

690 621.3 USA ISSN 1069-0050
LIGHTING ANSWERS. Text in English. 1993. irreg. (approx. 1-3/yr.). USD 8 per issue. bibl.; charts; illus. back issues avail. **Document type:** *Newsletter.* **Description:** Presents educational information about specific lighting technology issues and topics, such as fluorescent lamps or building controls, in a question-and-answer format.
Published by: Rensselaer Polytechnic Institute, Lighting Research Center, 21 Union St, Troy, NY 12180. TEL 518-276-8716, FAX 518-276-2999, lrc@rpi.edu, http://www.lrc.rpi.edu. Ed. Russell Leslie. R&P Kevin Heslin.

691.3 USA ISSN 0075-9457
LIGHTWEIGHT CONCRETE INFORMATION SHEETS. Text in English. 1952. irreg. free. cum.index: 1952-1988. back issues avail. **Document type:** *Trade.* **Description:** Information on ceramic lightweight aggregate which is used in concrete, concrete masonry, asphalt, horticulture, roof tile and insulation.
Published by: Expanded Shale, Clay and Slate Institute, 2225 E Murray Holladay Rd, Ste 102, Salt Lake City, UT 84117. TEL 801-272-7070, FAX 801-272-3377. Ed. John P Ries. Circ: 20,000.

690 FRA ISSN 0990-1159
LOCAGUIDE; du BTP et de la manutention. Text in French. a. FRF 150 domestic; FRF 200 in Europe; FRF 270 elsewhere (effective 2000). adv. **Document type:** *Newspaper, Trade.* **Description:** Lists addresses for drilling, pumping, sawing, cutting, air compression, concrete and other construction-related businesses.
Related titles: ♦ Supplement to: Batiment Information. ISSN 1266-8176.
Published by: (Societe Technique d'Editions pour l'Entreprise), Groupe Chantiers de France, Bord de Seine, 202 quai de Clichy, Clichy, 92110, France. TEL 33-1-47561723, FAX 33-1-47561432. Pub. Arlette Surchamp. Adv. contact Sophie Yon. Circ: 10,000.

LOCAL AUTHORITY BUILDING & MAINTENANCE. see *PUBLIC ADMINISTRATION—Municipal Government*

690 USA
LODGING: AN INDUSTRY OVERVIEW. Text in English. a. USD 395. **Description:** Examines the transition of the lodging industry and its impact on related industries such as construction, banking, insurance, transportation services, tourism and furniture. Also analyzes the major trends of globalization, segmentation and consolidation.
Published by: Dun & Bradstreet Information Services (Murray Hill) (Subsidiary of: Dun & Bradstreet, Inc.), 103 John F Kennedy Pkwy., Short Hills, NJ 07078-2708. TEL 908-665-5224, FAX 908-771-7599. Ed. Robert Porreca.

690 USA ISSN 1536-3252
LOG & TIMBER STYLE. Text in English. 2001. bi-m. USD 16.97; USD 3.95 newsstand/cover (effective 2001). adv. **Document type:** *Consumer.*
Published by: Wiesner Publishing, LLC, 7009 S Potomac St, Ste 200, Centennial, CO 80112. TEL 303-397-7600, FAX 303-397-7619, http://www.wiesnerpublishing.com.

690 USA ISSN 1061-5857
LOG CABIN NEWS; the quarterly newsletter of the Log Cabin Society of Michigan. Text in English. 1989 (Spring). q. USD 25 (effective 2005). adv. bk.rev. back issues avail. **Document type:** *Newsletter, Consumer.* **Description:** Promotes awareness of log cabins in Michigan and elsewhere for their historical value, encourages restoration of existing log cabins and construction of new ones, and presents news of related activities and festivals.
Published by: Log Cabin Society of Michigan, 3505 Rock Edwards Dr, Sodus, MI 49126-8700. TEL 269-925-3836, logcabincrafts@qtm.net, http://www.qtm.net/logcabincrafts. Ed., Pub., Adv. contact Virginia Handy. Circ: 200; 350 (paid).

690 USA ISSN 1097-7929
LOG HOME DESIGN IDEAS. Text in English. 1994. 9/yr. USD 23.95 domestic; USD 39.99 in Canada; USD 48.99 elsewhere (effective 2003). adv. back issues avail. **Document type:** *Magazine, Consumer.* **Description:** Provides design ideas, styles, techniques with log homes for owners and people who are interested in log homes.
Published by: Log Home Design Ideas, LLC, 4125 Lafayette Center Dr., Ste. 100, Chantilly, VA 20151-1242. webmaster@lhdi.com, http://www.lhdi.com. **Subscr. to:** PO Box 420235, Palm Coast, FL 32142-0235. TEL 877-235-2233.

643.1 690 USA ISSN 1041-830X
TH4840
LOG HOME LIVING. Text in English. 1989. m. USD 19.95 domestic; USD 29.95 in Canada; USD 47 in Mexico; USD 65 elsewhere; USD 3.99 newsstand/cover domestic; USD 4.99 newsstand/cover in Canada (effective 2005). adv. back issues avail. **Document type:** *Magazine, Consumer.* **Description:** For people who own or want to own contemporary log homes.
Incorporates: Log Home Plans
Related titles: ♦ Supplement(s): Log Home Living Annual Buyer's Guide.
Published by: Home Buyer Publications, Inc. (Subsidiary of: Active Interest Media), 4125 Lafayette Center Dr. Ste. 100, Chantilly, VA 20151. editor@loghomeliving.com, http://www.loghomeliving.com, http://www.homebuyerpubs.com/. Ed. Michael McCarthy. Adv. contact Elaine Nosaka. B&W page USD 6,160, color page USD 8,105. Circ: 140,000 (paid).

B

690 USA ISSN 1552-8731
LOUISIANA BUILDER. Text in English. 6/yr. USD 18 (effective 2005). **Description:** Covers issues of interest to the state building industry, including state and national legislation, taxes, financing and local association activities and events.
Published by: Association Publishing Inc., 2117 Smith Ave, Chesapeake, VA 23320. TEL 757-420-2434, FAX 757-424-5954, http://www.statebuildermagazines.com. Ed. Joan Stanus. Pubs. Joyce F Hearn, Sandra Amidon. Circ: 5,200.

692.8 USA ISSN 0195-7074
LOUISIANA CONTRACTOR. Text in English. 1953. m. (plus a. Directory). USD 40 (effective 2005). adv. tr.lit. **Document type:** *Magazine, Trade.* **Description:** Provides local, in-depth and comprehensive coverage on heavy engineering, highway, building and industrial construction news in Louisiana.
Formerly: Contractors Magazine
Related titles: Online - full text ed.: (from EBSCO Publishing, LexisNexis, ProQuest Information & Learning).
Indexed: ABIn.
—CCC.
Published by: Mcgraw-Hill Construction Dodge (Subsidiary of: McGraw-Hill Construction Information Group), 2900 Westfork Dr Ste 345, Baton Rouge, LA 70827. TEL 225-292-8980, 800-786-8980, FAX 225-292-5089, 800-786-5089, http://www.louisianacontractor.com/, http://www.dodgeconstructionpublications.com. Ed. Sam Barnes TEL 225-292-8980 ext 20. Pub. Kevin Rhodes TEL 225-292-8980 ext 15. Adv. contact Robin Elliott TEL 504-482-1004. B&W page USD 1,195, color page USD 1,745; trim 8.125 x 10.875. Circ: 5,300 (paid and controlled).

LOW BIDDER. see *TRANSPORTATION—Roads And Traffic*

647.9 USA ISSN 1098-5697
LUSTRE. Text in English. 1997. bi-m. USD 48 (effective 2005). adv. illus. **Document type:** *Magazine, Trade.*
Related titles: Online - full text ed.: (from Gale Group, ProQuest Information & Learning).
—CCC.
Published by: Cygnus Business Media, Inc., 3 Huntington Quadrangle, Ste 301N, Melville, NY 11747-3601. TEL 631-856-2700, FAX 631-845-7109, TimMurphy@cygnuspub.com, http://www.lustremag.com. Ed. Lorraine DePasque. Pub. Steve Feldman. Adv. contact Hope Reiner. Circ: 4,000 (paid).

LUXEMBOURG. SERVICE CENTRAL DE LA STATISTIQUE ET DES ETUDES ECONOMIQUES. INDICATEURS RAPIDES. SERIE A2: INDICES DES PRIX DE LA CONSTRUCTION. see *BUILDING AND CONSTRUCTION—Abstracting, Bibliographies, Statistics*

LUXEMBOURG. SERVICE CENTRAL DE LA STATISTIQUE ET DES ETUDES ECONOMIQUES. INDICATEURS RAPIDES. SERIE G: AUTORISATIONS DE BATIR - BATIMENTS, LOGEMENTS ET VOLUME BATI. see *BUILDING AND CONSTRUCTION—Abstracting, Bibliographies, Statistics*

690 USA
LUXURY HOME BUILDER. Text in English. 6/yr. free to qualified personnel (effective 2005); Included with Professional Builder. adv. **Document type:** *Magazine, Trade.* **Description:** Serves the custom home builder.
Formerly: Luxury Home Ideas

Published by: Reed Business Information (Subsidiary of: Reed Business), 2000 Clearwater Dr, Oak Brook, IL 60525. TEL 630-288-8180, FAX 630-288-8179, hmccune@reedbusiness.com, http://www.housingzone.com/, http://www.reedbusiness.com. Ed. Heather McCune TEL 630-288-8190. adv.: color page USD 5,500. Circ: 45,000 (paid). **Subscr. to:** Reed Business Information, PO Box 9020, Maple Shade, NJ 08052-9020. TEL 303-470-4466, 800-446-6551, FAX 303-470-4691, http://www.pubservice.com/CH.htm.

LUXURY HOME DESIGN. see *INTERIOR DESIGN AND DECORATION*

LUXURY POOLS; the registry of America's greatest pool builders. see *LEISURE AND RECREATION*

693.7 DEU ISSN 1436-0446
CODEN: MLVBAD
M & T - METALLHANDWERK. Text in German. 1899. m. EUR 97.50 domestic; EUR 117 foreign; EUR 12 newsstand/cover (effective 2004). adv. bk.rev. pat. **Document type:** *Journal, Trade.*
Former titles: M & T - Metallhandwerk & Technik (0934-3199); Which incorporated (in 1995): Metallverarbeitung (0026-0908); Metallhandwerk and Metalltechnik (0026-0789); Metallhandwerk
Indexed: CIN, ChemAb, ChemTitl, CivEngAb.
—CASDDS, CISTI, Linda Hall. **CCC.**
Published by: (Bundesverband Metall), Charles Coleman Verlag GmbH & Co. KG, Wahmstr 56, Luebeck, 23552, Germany. TEL 49-451-79933-0, FAX 49-451-7993399, coleman@rudolf-mueller.de, http://www.rudolf-mueller.de. Ed. Dietrich Muhs. Pub. Guenter Sandscheper. Adv. contact Ulrich Claussen. B&W page EUR 3,320, color page EUR 4,370. Circ: 19,754 (controlled).

691 USA
M C A A INFO. Text in English. m. **Document type:** *Trade.*
Published by: Mason Contractors Association of America, 33 S. Roselle Rd., Schaumburg, IL 60193-1646. TEL 630-705-4200, FAX 630-705-4209. Pub. Michael Adelizzi.

691 USA
M C MAGAZINE; the voice of manufactured concrete products industry. Text in English. 1995. q. adv. tr.lit. 78 p./no.; **Document type:** *Magazine, Trade.*
Published by: National Precast Concrete Association, 10333 N Meridian St, Ste 272, Indianapolis, IN 46290-1081. TEL 317-571-9500, 800-366-7731, FAX 317-571-0041, npca@precast.org, http://www.precast.org. Ed. Ron Hyink. Pub. Ty E Gable. Adv. contact Brenda C Mayaleri. Circ: 8,500.

393 SWE
M E - TIDNINGEN. Text in Swedish. 1957. m. (10/yr.). SEK 240. adv. bk.rev. abstr.; charts; illus.; stat.; tr.lit. **Document type:** *Trade.*
Former titles: Maskinentreprenoeren (0284-7140); (until 1986): S E R - Tidningen (0037-2080)
Published by: Maskinentreprenoernas Foerlags AB/Swedish Earth Moving Machine Owners Association, Fack 1609, Stockholm, 11186, Sweden. TEL 46-8-762-70-65, FAX 46-8-611-85-41. Ed. Dag Af Ekenstam. Pub. Nils Jakobsson. Adv. contact Christer Holmquist. B&W page SEK 11,250, color page SEK 18,250; trim 270 x 185. Circ: 6,900.

690 CHE
M O P✶. Text in German. 5/yr. **Document type:** *Trade.*
Published by: Weka Verlag AG, c/o Tobias Landau, Froebelstr 33, Zurich, 8032, Switzerland. Circ: 3,000.

MAANSIIRTO/EARTHMOVING; maa- ja vesirakennusteknillinen aikakauslehti. see *ENGINEERING—Civil Engineering*

MACAO. DIRECCAO DOS SERVICOS DE ESTATISTICA E CENSOS. INDICES E PRECOS DOS MATERIAS DE CONSTRUCAO/MACAO. CENSUS AND STATISTICS DEPARTMENT. INDEXES AND PRICES OF CONSTRUCTION MATERIALS. see *BUILDING AND CONSTRUCTION—Abstracting, Bibliographies, Statistics*

MACAO. DIRECCAO DOS SERVICOS DE ESTATISTICA E CENSOS. RECENSEAMENTO A CONSTRUCAO/MACAO. CENSUS AND STATISTICS DEPARTMENT. CONSTRUCTION SURVEY. see *BUILDING AND CONSTRUCTION—Abstracting, Bibliographies, Statistics*

690.028 ITA ISSN 1594-7041
MACCHINE EDILI. Text in Italian. 1980. m. EUR 45 domestic (effective 2004). **Document type:** *Magazine, Trade.*
Formerly (until 2002): Il Commercio Edile. Macchine e Attrezzature (1129-5600); Which superseded in part (in 1999): Il Commercio Edile (1126-8808)
Published by: Tecniche Nuove SpA, Via Eritrea 21, Milan, MI 201, Italy. TEL 39-02-390901, FAX 39-02-7570364, macchine.edili@tecnichenuove.com, info@tecnichenuove.com, http://www.tecnichenuove.com.

MADERA Y BOSQUES. see *FORESTS AND FORESTRY—Lumber And Wood*

690 FRA ISSN 0987-7444
MAGAZINE DE LA CONSTRUCTION✶. Text in French. 1980. 10/yr. **Document type:** *Trade.*
Former titles (until 1987): Entrepreneur Magazine (0767-4791); (until 1986): Guide Pratique de l'Entrepreneur du Batiment et de Travaux Publics. Magazine (0755-4915)
Published by: Editions S E R I P, c/o Office de Justification de la Diffusion, 40 bd. Malesherbes, Paris, 75008, France. TEL 48-81-91-91. Ed. Alain Morvan. Circ: 36,000.

666.89 620.136 GBR ISSN 0024-9831
TA680 CODEN: MCORAV
➤ **MAGAZINE OF CONCRETE RESEARCH.** Text in English. 1949. 10/yr. ((feb-Jun, Aug-Dec)). GBP 300 domestic; GBP 375 foreign (effective 2004). adv. bk.rev. abstr.; bibl.; illus. reprint service avail. from PQC. **Document type:** *Journal, Academic/Scholarly.* **Description:** Publishes original research on the behavior of concrete and its constituent materials, both in the laboratory and in structures.
Related titles: Online - full text ed.: (from EBSCO Publishing).
Indexed: AJEE, ASCA, BldManAb, BrCerAb, C&ISA, CIN, CRIA, CRICC, CerAb, ChemAb, ChemTitl, CivEngAb, ConcrAb, CorrAb, CurCont, E&CAJ, EEA, EMA, EngInd, GeotechAb, HRIS, IAA, ICEA, ISR, Inspec, JOF, M&TEA, MBF, METADEX, MSCI, RAPRA, SCI, SoftAbEng, SolStAb, WAA.
—BLDSC (5333.000000), CASDDS, CISTI, Ei, IDS, IE, Infotrieve, ingenta, Linda Hall. **CCC.**
Published by: Thomas Telford Ltd., Thomas Telford House, 1 Heron Quay, London, E14 4JD, United Kingdom. TEL 44-20-76652460, FAX 44-20-75389620, journals@thomastelford.com, http://www.concrete-research.com, http://www.t-telford.co.uk/. Eds. Peter Hewlett, Simon Fullalove TEL 44-20-76652448. Circ: 3,000.

690 ITA
MAGAZZINO EDILE. Text in Italian. 6/yr.
Address: Viale Don Minzoni, 51, Bresso, MI 20091, Italy. TEL 39-02-6108119. Ed. Paolo Benna. Circ: 8,250.

690.24 USA ISSN 1072-3560
MAINTENANCE SOLUTIONS. Text in English. 1993. m. free to qualified personnel (effective 2005). adv. **Document type:** *Magazine, Trade.* **Description:** Covers maintenance management, i.e., directors, managers, supervisors and other professionals responsible for the physical maintenance, engineering systems support and housekeeping functions in commercial and institutional buildings.
Related titles: Online - full text ed.: (from Northern Light Technology, Inc., ProQuest Information & Learning).
Published by: Trade Press Publishing Corp., 2100 W Florist Ave, Milwaukee, WI 53209. TEL 414-228-7701, FAX 414-228-1134, dan.hounsell@tradepress.com, http://www.tradepress.com. Ed. Dan Hounsell. Pub., Adv. contact Brian Terry. R&P Tim Rowe TEL 414-228-7701 ext 515. B&W page USD 7,025, color page USD 9,005; trim 10.625 x 14.375. Circ: 35,000 (controlled).

647.9 USA ISSN 0025-0929
MAINTENANCE SUPPLIES. Text in English. 1956. m. (9/yr.). free to qualified personnel; USD 66 domestic; USD 88 in Canada & Mexico (effective 2005). adv. bk.rev. charts; illus. index. **Document type:** *Magazine, Trade.*
Related titles: Online - full text ed.: (from Gale Group, ProQuest Information & Learning).
—CCC.
Published by: Cygnus Business Media, Inc., 3 Huntington Quadrangle, Ste 301N, Melville, NY 11747-3601. TEL 631-845-2700, FAX 631-845-2723, richard.dipaolo@cygnuspub.com, http://www.maintenancesuppliesmag.com, http://www.cygnusb2b.com. Ed. Richard DiPaolo TEL 618-845-2700 ext 217. Pub. Tracy Aston TEL 205-380-1431. Circ: 16,500 (controlled).

690 FRA ISSN 0244-1136
MAISON ET TRAVAUX; le magazine deco qui me comprend. Text in French. 1978. 6/yr. EUR 23 domestic; EUR 32 foreign (effective 2005). adv. index.
Supersedes (in 1981): Batiguide (0151-573X)
Published by: Presse Pratique Parisienne, 16-18 rue de l'Amiral Mouchez, Paris, Cedex 14 75686, France. TEL 33-1-45654848, FAX 33-1-45654700, TELEX 240-918 TRACE, http://www.maison-travaux.fr. Ed. Patrick de Montalivet. Adv. contact Jean Massin. Circ: 190,204.

MAISONS & AMBIANCES. see *INTERIOR DESIGN AND DECORATION*

MALEREN; organ for malermestrenes landsforbund. see *PAINTS AND PROTECTIVE COATINGS*

691 ESP ISSN 0210-1513
MANIPULACION DE MATERIALES EN LA INDUSTRIA. Short title: M A N I P. Text in Spanish. 1972. m. adv.
Published by: Publicaciones Internacionales S.A., Paseo Castellana, 210, Madrid, 28046, Spain. Ed. Tomas Blas Abascal. Circ: 2,000 (controlled).

690 CAN ISSN 0714-3222
MANITOBA - WINNIPEG BUILDING & CONSTRUCTION TRADES COUNCIL YEARBOOK. Text in English. 1971. a.
Published by: (Manitoba - Winnipeg Building & Construction Trades Council), Naylor Communications Ltd. (Winnipeg), 100 Sutherland Ave, Winnipeg, MB R2W 3C7, Canada. TEL 204-947-0222. Ed. Janis Connolly. Circ: 2,250.

690 USA ISSN 1086-4962
MANUFACTURED STRUCTURES NEWSLETTER✶. Text in English. 1969. m. looseleaf. USD 115 in US & Canada; USD 135 elsewhere (effective 1999). **Document type:** *Newsletter, Trade.* **Description:** Covers conferences, industry news releases, regulatory and marketing news for all types of industrialized-modular, plus HUD-code manufactured homes and buildings in the US, Canada and internationally.
Formerly: Manufactured Housing Newsletter (0197-1816)
Published by: Hal Carlson, Ed & Pub. PO Box 865, Hershey, PA 17033-0865. TEL 970-285-7540, FAX 970-285-7540, halc@gj.net. R&P Hal Carlson.

690 ITA ISSN 1121-7456
MAPPA DEI FORNITORI. Text in Italian. 1990. a. EUR 11.88 (effective 2005). **Document type:** *Directory, Trade.*
Related titles: ◆ Supplement to: TSport. ISSN 1121-6913.
Published by: Editoriale Tsport Srl, Via Antonio Saluzzo 16, Milan, MI 20162, Italy. TEL 39-02-6438282, FAX 39-02-64749554, info@tsport.it, http://www.tsport.it.

MAQUINARIA Y EQUIPO. see *MACHINERY*

MARYLAND BUILDER. see *HOUSING AND URBAN PLANNING*

690 721 UZB ISSN 1026-3551
TH4
MASKAN; arkhitektura i stroitel'stvo Uzbekistana, Kazakhstana, Azerbaidzana, Kyrgyzstana, Tadzjikistana, Turkmenistana. Text in Uzbek. 1966. m. charts; illus. index.
Formerly (until no.9, 1991): Stroitel'stvo i Arkhitektura Uzbekistana (0039-243X)
Indexed: ChemAb, RASB.
—Linda Hall.
Address: Ul Gazety Pravda 41, Tashkent, 700000, Uzbekistan.

691 USA ISSN 0025-4681
TH1199
MASONRY. Text in English. 1961. 6/yr. USD 24 domestic; USD 30 in Canada; USD 32 in Mexico (effective 2005). adv. bk.rev. illus. **Document type:** *Magazine, Trade.*
—CISTI.
Published by: (Mason Contractors Association of America), Lionheart Publishing, Inc., 506 Roswell St, Ste 220, Marietta, GA 30060-4101. TEL 770-431-0867, FAX 770-432-6969, jen@lionhrtpub.com, lpi@lionhrtpub.com, http://www.masonrymagazine.com, http://www.lionhrtpub.com. Pub. Michael Adelizzi. Adv. contact Marvin Diamond. B&W page USD 1,360, color page USD 2,305. Circ: 16,000 (paid and free).

691 USA
TH1199 CODEN: AMMCEK
MASONRY CONSTRUCTION. Text in English. 1988. irreg. USD 30 domestic; USD 39 in Canada & Mexico; USD 93 elsewhere (effective 2005). adv. bk.rev. charts; illus.; stat.; tr.lit. Index. reprints avail. **Document type:** *Magazine, Trade.* **Description:** Complete and authoritative source of information about the masonry construction industry.
Former titles: Aberdeen's Magazine of Masonry Construction (1055-4408); (until 1990): Magazine of Masonry Construction (0898-6088)
Related titles: Online - full text ed.: (from Florida Center for Library Automation, Gale Group, H.W. Wilson, O C L C Online Computer Library Center, Inc.).
Indexed: AS&TI, B&BAb, BrCerAb, C&ISA, CRIA, CRICC, CerAb, ConcrAb, CorrAb, E&CAJ, EMA, EngInd, SolStAb, WAA.
—CISTI, IE, Linda Hall. **CCC.**
Published by: Aberdeen Group (Subsidiary of: Hanley-Wood, LLC), 426 S Westgate St, Addison, IL 60101. TEL 630-543-0870, FAX 630-543-3112, cschierhorn@wocnet.com, http://www.masonryconstruction.com, http://www.worldofmasonry.com. Ed. Rick Yelton. Circ: 30,000 (paid).

MASONRY INTERNATIONAL; journal of the British Masonry Society. see *ARCHITECTURE*

690 624 USA ISSN 0741-1294
CODEN: MSJUET
➤ **THE MASONRY SOCIETY JOURNAL.** Text in English. 1981. irreg. (1-2/yr), latest vol.20, 2002. USD 55 in North America; USD 60 elsewhere (effective 2003). bk.rev. back issues avail. **Document type:** *Journal, Academic/Scholarly.* **Description:** Technical masonry research. Includes masonry design for architects and engineers.
Indexed: C&ISA, CerAb, CorrAb, E&CAJ, EEA, EMA, SolStAb, WAA.
—CISTI.
Published by: Masonry Society, 3970 Broadway St, Ste 201 D, Boulder, CO 80304-1135. TEL 303-939-9700, FAX 303-541-9215, info@masonrysociety.org, http://www.masonrysociety.org/tmsjournalmain.htm. Ed. Benson P Shing. Circ: 2,500.

690 AUS ISSN 1039-4532
MASTER BUILDER. Text in English. 1949. 6/yr. AUD 48; AUD 60 foreign. adv. bk.rev.
Formerly (until 1992): Australian Builder (0004-878X)
—BLDSC (5389.550000).
Published by: Master Builders Association of Victoria, 332-334 Albert St, East Melbourne, VIC 3002, Australia. TEL 03-419-4555, FAX 03-417-7006. Ed. Giselle Grynbaum. Circ: 5,246.

690 GBR ISSN 0025-4991
MASTER BUILDERS' JOURNAL. Text in English. 1955. m. GBP 19.70. adv. bk.rev. illus.; tr.lit. **Document type:** *Trade.*
Related titles: Online - full text ed.
Published by: (Federation of Master Builders), Construction Industry Services Ltd., Gordon Fisher House 14-15, Great James St, London, WC1N 3DP, United Kingdom. TEL 44-71-242-7583, FAX 44-71-404-0296, BRIX@fmb.org.uk, http://www.fmb.org.uk/frames/buildersinfo/allbuilders/publications/masterbuilder/masterbuilder.html. Ed. Ray Briggs. Circ: 21,000.

690 USA
MASTER PLAN FOR PROFESSIONAL HOME REMODELING. Text in English. 1997. a. free to homeowners. adv. **Document type:** *Consumer.* **Description:** Includes features about the remodeling industry to help homeowners successfully complete a remodeling project.
Published by: National Association of the Remodeling Industry, 780 Lee St, Ste 200, Des Plaines, IL 60016. TEL 847-298-9200, 800-611-6274, FAX 877-685-6274, info@nari.org, http://www.nari.org. R&P Susan Maney.

691 ESP ISSN 0465-2746
TP875 CODEN: MCUAAA
MATERIALES DE CONSTRUCCION. Text in English, Spanish. 1949. q. EUR 51.50 domestic; EUR 66.97 foreign (effective 2005). adv. bk.rev.
Indexed: A&ATA, BrCerAb, C&ISA, CEABA, CIN, CerAb, ChemAb, ChemTitl, CivEngAb, ConcrAb, CorrAb, E&CAJ, EMA, EngInd, IAA, ICEA, IECT, M&TEA, MBF, METADEX, MSCI, SoftAbEng, SolStAb, WAA.
—BLDSC (5393.700000), CASDDS, CINDOC, Ei, IDS, IE, ingenta, Linda Hall. **CCC.**
Published by: Consejo Superior de Investigaciones Cientificas, Instituto de Ciencias de la Construccion Eduardo Torroja, C Serrano Galvache, s-n, Madrid, 28033, Spain. TEL 34-91-3020440, FAX 34-91-3020700, matercnstrucc@ietcc.csic.es, materconstruc@ietcc.csic.es, http://www.csic.es/torroja, http://www.ietcc.csic.es. Ed. Francisca Puertas. Circ: 1,000.

690 ITA ISSN 1126-3946
MATERIALI EDILI. Text in Italian. 1994. bi-m. adv. **Document type:** *Magazine, Trade.*
Published by: Alberto Greco Editore, Viale Espinasse 141, Milan, MI 20156, Italy. TEL 39-02-300391, FAX 39-02-30039300, age@gruppodg.com, http://www.ageditore.com. adv.: page EUR 2,900; 230 x 300.

692.8 FRA ISSN 1359-5997
CODEN: MCMSBP
➤ **MATERIALS AND STRUCTURES/MATERIAUX ET CONSTRUCTIONS.** Text in English, French. 1959. 10/yr. EUR 378 (effective 2003). adv. reprints avail. **Document type:** *Journal, Academic/Scholarly.* **Description:** Presents technical papers on the properties and performance of building materials and structures in laboratory and service conditions; the standardization of test methods between countries; and the application of such results to the structural use of materials in building and civil engineering applications.
Former titles (until 1986): Materiaux et Constructions (0025-5432); (until 1967): R I L E M. Bulletin (0534-7157)
Related titles: Online - full text ed.
Indexed: AESIS, ASCA, ApMecR, BrCerAb, C&ISA, CIN, CRIA, CRICC, CerAb, ChemAb, ChemTitl, ConcrAb, CorrAb, CurCont, E&CAJ, EEA, EMA, ESPM, EngInd, H&SSA, IAA, ICEA, ISMEC, JOF, M&TEA, MBF, METADEX, MSCI, SolStAb, WAA.
—BLDSC (5394.103000), CASDDS, CISTI, Ei, IE, Infotrieve, ingenta, Linda Hall. **CCC.**
Published by: (International Union of Testing and Research Laboratories for Materials and Structures (RILEM)), R I L E M Publications S.A.R.L., 157 Rue des Blains, Bagneux, 92220, France. TEL 33-1-45361020, FAX 33-1-45366320, ms@rilem.net, http://www.rilem.net. Ed. M Brusin.

690 POL ISSN 0137-2971
MATERIALY BUDOWLANE. Text in Polish. 1974. m. PLZ 168 domestic; EUR 83 foreign (effective 2005). adv. 124 p./no.; **Document type:** *Magazine, Trade.*
Published by: Wydawnictwo SIGMA - N O T Sp. z o.o., ul Ratuszowa 11, PO Box 1004, Warsaw, 00950, Poland. TEL 48-22-8180918, FAX 48-22-6192187, informacja@sigma-not.pl, http://www.sigma-not.pl. Ed. Krystyna Wisniewska TEL 48-22-8262027. adv.: B&W page PLZ 2,600, color page PLZ 5,600. Circ: 10,000. **Dist. by:** Ars Polona, Krakowskie Przedmiescie 7, Warsaw, Poland. TEL 48-22-9263914, FAX 48-22-9265334, arspolona@arspolona.com.pl, http://www.arspolona.com.pl.

691 FRA
MATERIAUX DE CONSTRUCTION ET PRODUITS DE CARRIERES. Text in French. 4/yr.
Address: 3 rue Alfred Roll, Paris, 75017, France. TEL 33-1-44014701, FAX 33-1-40540328, TELEX 641 394 F. Ed. Olivier Guinet. Circ: 2,800.

690 NLD
MATERIEELKRANT. Text in Dutch. 1966. 11/yr. EUR 171.72 (effective 2005). adv. bk.rev. illus. **Document type:** *Trade.* **Description:** Information on building, construction and transportation machinery and tools.
Former titles: Grondverzet en Bouwtransport (0920-8380); (until 1980): Machinepark (0165-4012)
Indexed: ExcerpMed.
—IE, Infotrieve.
Published by: Sdu Uitgevers bv, Postbus 34, The Hague, 2516 BC, Netherlands. sdu@sdu.nl, http://www.sdu.nl/. Ed. Wim D Mol. Pub. Harry Schram. adv.: B&W page EUR 3,125; trim 262 x 338. Circ: 6,548. **Subscr. to:** Postbus 20014, The Hague 2500 EA, Netherlands. TEL 31-70-3789880, FAX 31-70-3789783.

691 721 DEU ISSN 1432-3427
DAS MAUERWERK. Text in German. 1997. bi-m. EUR 119.63 in Europe to institutions; CHF 194 to institutions in Switzerland & Liechtenstein; USD 144 elsewhere to institutions; EUR 131.59 combined subscription in Europe to institutions print & online eds.; CHF 214 combined subscription to institutions in Switzerland & Liechtenstein; print & online eds.; USD 159 combined subscription elsewhere to institutions print & online eds. (effective 2006). **Document type:** *Journal, Trade.* **Description:** Forum for the exchange of knowledge and experience pertaining to buildings from all over Europe.
Related titles: Online - full text ed.: ISSN 1437-1022. EUR 119.63 in Europe to institutions; CHF 194 to institutions in Switzerland & Liechtenstein; USD 144 elsewhere to institutions (effective 2006) (from EBSCO Publishing, Swets Information Services, Wiley InterScience).
—**CCC.**
Published by: Ernst und Sohn, Buehringstr 10, Berlin, 13086, Germany. TEL 49-30-47031200, FAX 49-30-47031240, marketing@ernst-und-sohn.de, http://www.wiley-vch.de/ernstsohn, http://www.wiley-vch.de/ernstsohn. Ed. Peter Schubert. **Subscr. in the Americas to:** John Wiley & Sons, Inc., 111 River St, Hoboken, NJ 07030-5774. TEL 201-748-6645, FAX 201-748-6088, subinfo@wiley.com; **Subscr. to:** Wiley - V C H Verlag GmbH & Co. KGaA, Boschstr 12, Weinheim 69469, Germany. TEL 49-6201-606147, FAX 49-6201-606117.

691 721 DEU ISSN 0170-4958
MAUERWERK-KALENDER. Text in German. 1976. a. EUR 109 (effective 2005). **Document type:** *Directory, Trade.*
Published by: Ernst und Sohn, Buehringstr 10, Berlin, 13086, Germany. TEL 49-30-47031200, FAX 49-30-47031240, marketing@ernst-und-sohn.de, http://www.wiley-vch.de/ernstsohn. Eds. Hans-Joerg Irmschler, Peter Schubert. **Subscr. to:** Wiley - V C H Verlag GmbH & Co. KGaA, Boschstr 12, Weinheim 69469, Germany. TEL 49-6201-606405, FAX 49-6201-606184.

MEALEY'S LITIGATION REPORTS: CONSTRUCTION DEFECTS. see *LAW—Civil Law*

691 USA ISSN 0894-4342
TH435
MEANS ASSEMBLIES COST DATA (YEAR). Text in English. 1976. a. USD 128.95.
Former titles: Means Assemblies Costs; Means Systems Costs
Published by: R.S. Means Company Inc. (Subsidiary of: Reed Construction Data, Associated Construction Publications), 63 Smiths Lane, P O Box 800, Kingston, MA 02364-9988. TEL 800-334-3509, FAX 617-585-7466. Ed. Philip R Waier.

691 USA ISSN 1075-0274
TA682.26
MEANS CONCRETE AND MASONRY COST DATA. Text in English. 1982. a. USD 74.95. bk.rev. charts; stat. back issues avail. **Document type:** *Trade.* **Description:** Includes cost facts for every concrete estimating problem, from complicated formwork to lavish brickwork.
Former titles (until 1994): Means Concrete Cost Data (Year) (1075-0533); (until 1987): Concrete and Masonry Cost Data (0739-8298)
Published by: R.S. Means Company Inc. (Subsidiary of: Reed Construction Data, Associated Construction Publications), 63 Smiths Lane, P O Box 800, Kingston, MA 02364-9988. TEL 617-585-7880, 800-334-3509, FAX 617-585-7466. Ed. Philip R Waier. Circ: 3,000.

MEANS CONSTRUCTION COST INDEXES. see *BUILDING AND CONSTRUCTION—Abstracting, Bibliographies, Statistics*

690 USA
MEANS COSTWORKS BUILDING CONSTRUCTION COST DATA. Text in English. a. USD 142.95 (effective 2005). **Document type:** *Trade.* **Description:** Covers unit costs for more than 23,500 building components, including information on the latest construction methods and materials, estimating reference tables, typical square foot costs for 160 buildings, and trade labor crew and equipment costs.
Media: CD-ROM.
Published by: R.S. Means Company Inc. (Subsidiary of: Reed Construction Data, Associated Construction Publications), 63 Smiths Lane, P O Box 800, Kingston, MA 02364-9988. TEL 781-585-7880, 800-334-3509, FAX 800-632-6732.

692 USA ISSN 1075-0789
TH435
MEANS FACILITIES CONSTRUCTION COST DATA. Text in English. 1986. a. **Document type:** *Trade.*
Formerly (until 1994): Means Facilities Cost Data (0888-6709)
Published by: R.S. Means Company Inc. (Subsidiary of: Reed Construction Data, Associated Construction Publications), 63 Smiths Lane, P O Box 800, Kingston, MA 02364-9988. TEL 617-585-7880, 800-448-8182, FAX 617-585-7466. Ed. Philip R Waier.

690 USA ISSN 0893-5602
TH435
MEANS HEAVY CONSTRUCTION COST DATA. Text in English. a. USD 82.95. **Description:** Provides current unit and systems prices for thousands of heavy construction installations.
Published by: R.S. Means Company Inc. (Subsidiary of: Reed Construction Data, Associated Construction Publications), 63 Smiths Lane, P O Box 800, Kingston, MA 02364-9988. TEL 800-334-3509, FAX 617-585-7466.

B

690 USA
MEANS INTERIOR COST DATA (YEAR). Text in English. 1984. a. USD 79.95.
Formerly: Interior Cost Data (Year) (8755-7541)
Published by: R.S. Means Company Inc. (Subsidiary of: Reed Construction Data, Associated Construction Publications), 63 Smiths Lane, P O Box 800, Kingston, MA 02364-9988. TEL 800-334-3509, FAX 617-585-7466. Ed. Roger Grant.

331.11 USA ISSN 1529-6164
HD4966.B92
MEANS LABOR RATES FOR THE CONSTRUCTION INDUSTRY. Text in English. 1973. a. USD 174.95.
Formerly (until 1988): Labor Rates for the Construction Industry (0098-3608)
—**CCC.**
Published by: R.S. Means Company Inc. (Subsidiary of: Reed Construction Data, Associated Construction Publications), 63 Smiths Lane, P O Box 800, Kingston, MA 02364-9988. TEL 800-334-3509, FAX 617-585-7466. Ed. Philip R Waier.

690 USA ISSN 0896-7601
TH4315
MEANS LIGHT COMMERCIAL COST DATA (YEAR). Text in English. a. USD 72.95. charts; illus.
Published by: R.S. Means Company Inc. (Subsidiary of: Reed Construction Data, Associated Construction Publications), 63 Smiths Lane, P O Box 800, Kingston, MA 02364-9988. TEL 800-334-3509.

690 USA
TH435
MEANS MECHANICAL COST DATA (YEAR). Text in English. 1978. a. USD 79.95.
Former titles: Mechanical Cost Data (0748-2698); Mechanical and Electrical Cost Data (0193-1954)
—CISTI. **CCC.**
Published by: R.S. Means Company Inc. (Subsidiary of: Reed Construction Data, Associated Construction Publications), 63 Smiths Lane, P O Box 800, Kingston, MA 02364-9988. TEL 800-334-3509, FAX 617-585-7466. Ed. Melville J Mossman.

690 USA
TH435
MEANS OPEN SHOP BUILDING CONSTRUCTION COST DATA (YEAR). Text in English. 1985. a. USD 76.95.
Formerly: Open Shop Building Construction Cost Data (Year) (0883-8127)
Published by: R.S. Means Company Inc. (Subsidiary of: Reed Construction Data, Associated Construction Publications), 63 Smiths Lane, P O Box 800, Kingston, MA 02364-9988. TEL 800-334-3509, FAX 617-585-7466. Ed. Philip R Waier.

691 USA ISSN 0898-5006
TH3411
MEANS REPAIR AND REMODELING COST DATA (YEAR). Text in English. 1980. a. USD 79.95.
Formerly: Repair and Remodeling Cost Data (0271-5945)
—CISTI.
Published by: R.S. Means Company Inc. (Subsidiary of: Reed Construction Data, Associated Construction Publications), 63 Smiths Lane, P O Box 800, Kingston, MA 02364-9988. TEL 617-585-7880, FAX 617-585-7466. Ed. Philip R Waier.

691 USA ISSN 0738-1239
TH435
MEANS RESIDENTIAL COST DATA. Text in English. 1982. a. USD 72.95.
Formerly: Residential - Light Commercial Cost Data (0733-6403)
Published by: R.S. Means Company Inc. (Subsidiary of: Reed Construction Data, Associated Construction Publications), 63 Smiths Lane, P O Box 800, Kingston, MA 02364-9988. TEL 617-585-7880, FAX 617-585-7466. Ed. Philip R Waier.

▼ new title ➤ refereed ✶ unverified ♦ full entry avail.

691 USA ISSN 1064-5128
TH435
MEANS SITE WORK AND LANDSCAPE COST DATA (YEAR). Text in English. 1982. a. USD 82.95. **Description:** Covers every aspect of modern site work estimating: exploration, pollution control, soil retention, hidden utilities, security, and site enhancement.
Formerly (until 1992): Means Site Work Cost Data (0734-8479)
Published by: R.S. Means Company Inc. (Subsidiary of: Reed Construction Data, Associated Construction Publications), 63 Smiths Lane, P O Box 800, Kingston, MA 02364-9988. TEL 800-334-3509, FAX 617-585-7466.

690 GBR
MECHAID. Text in English. 1994. bi-m. GBP 24 (effective 1999). adv. back issues avail. **Document type:** *Trade.* **Description:** For buyers and specifiers of tools plants and equipment.
Related titles: Online - full text ed.
Published by: Special T Publishing Ltd., 41 High St, Oakham, Morcott, Rutland LE15 9DN, United Kingdom. TEL 44-1572-747472, FAX 44-1572-747576, mechaid@mechaid.com, http://www.mechaid.com. Ed. Mike Wyatt. Pub. Richard Hacker. Adv. contact Steve Liverman. B&W page GBP 950, color page GBP 1,300. Circ: 6,500 (controlled).

621 600 USA
MECHANICAL CONTRACTOR LITERATURE SHOWCASE. Text in English. s-a. adv. tr.lit. **Document type:** *Trade.*
Published by: Penton Media, Inc. (Subsidiary of: Pittway Company), 2700 S River Rd, Ste 109, Des Plaines, IL 60018. TEL 847-799-3101, FAX 847-299-3018, http://www.pentonmedia.com. Circ: 52,572.

692.8 USA
MECHANICAL CONTRACTORS ASSOCIATION OF AMERICA. STATISTICAL SURVEY REPORT✶ . Text in English. s-a. USD 40 to non-members; USD 20 to members.
Published by: Mechanical Contractors Association of America, 1385 Piccard Dr, Rockville, MD 20850. TEL 301-869-5800.

690.837 FIN ISSN 1456-6257
MEIDAN MOKKI. Text in Finnish. 1997. 8/yr. EUR 69.60 domestic; EUR 72 in Europe; EUR 77.60 elsewhere (effective 2005). adv. **Document type:** *Magazine, Consumer.* **Description:** Specializes in cabin style holiday living.
Published by: A-Lehdet Oy, Risto Rytin tie 33, Helsinki, 00081, Finland. TEL 358-9-75961, FAX 358-9-7598600, a-tilaus@a-lehdet.fi, http://www.a-lehdet.fi/lehdet/lehti/meidan_mokki/. Ed. Paeivie Anttila. Adv. contact Matti Sahravuo TEL 358-9-7596385. color page EUR 4,100; 187 x 241. Circ: 52,132 (controlled).

690 FIN ISSN 1455-2825
MEIDAN TALO. Text in Finnish. 1960. m. EUR 90.80 domestic; EUR 93 in Europe; EUR 102.90 elsewhere (effective 2005). adv. **Document type:** *Magazine, Consumer.* **Description:** Provides an information bank for the builder and decorator; full of practical instructions for one family house, a cottage, or a terrace house.
Former titles (until 1997): Meidan Talo ja Koti (1237-1130); (until 1992): Meidan Talo (1978) (0356-6110); (until 1978): Rakennusviesti (0355-5062)
Published by: A-Lehdet Oy, Risto Rytin tie 33, Helsinki, 00081, Finland. TEL 358-9-75961, FAX 358-9-7598600, a-tilaus@a-lehdet.fi, http://www.a-lehdet.fi/lehdet/lehti/meidan_talo/. Ed. Timo Paasky. Adv. contact Matti Sahravuo TEL 358-9-7596385. color page EUR 4,700; 187 x 241. Circ: 78,275 (controlled).

MEKHANIZATSIYA STROITEL'STVA. see *ENGINEERING—Civil Engineering*

MERCHANT MAGAZINE. see *FORESTS AND FORESTRY—Lumber And Wood*

690 658 ZAF
MERKELS' BUILDERS' PRICING AND MANAGEMENT MANUAL. Text in English. 1948. a. price varies. adv. **Document type:** *Directory, Trade.*
Published by: T M L Business Publishing (Subsidiary of: Times Media Ltd.), PO Box 182, Pinegowrie, Gauteng 2123, South Africa. TEL 27-11-789-2144, FAX 27-11-789-3196. Circ: 2,000.

690 338 DNK ISSN 0904-1559
MESTER TIDENDE. Text and summaries in Danish. 1987. m. DKK 350 (effective 2003). adv. **Document type:** *Trade.*
Published by: Aller Business AS, Marielundsvej 46 D, Herlev, 2730, Denmark. TEL 45-44-858899, FAX 45-44-858887, mt@mestertidende.dk, info@allerbusiness.dk, http://www.mestertidende.dk, http://www.allerbusiness.dk. adv.: page DKK 44,500. Circ: 37,648.

690 669 USA ISSN 8756-2014
METAL CONSTRUCTION NEWS. Text in English. 1980. m. free domestic to qualified personnel; USD 45 in Canada & Mexico; USD 125 elsewhere (effective 2005). adv. **Document type:** *Magazine, Trade.*
Formerly: Metal Building News (0274-8843)
Indexed: BrCerAb, C&ISA, CerAb, CorrAb, E&CAJ, EMA, IAA, M&TEA, MBF, METADEX, WAA.
—Linda Hall.
Published by: Modern Trade Communications, Inc., 7450 Skokie Blvd, Skokie, IL 60077. TEL 847-674-2200, FAX 847-674-3676, mcn@moderntrade.com, http://www.metalconstructionnews.com, http://www.moderntrade.com. Ed., R&P Shawn L Zuver. adv.: B&W page USD 3,620, color page USD 5,545. Circ: 32,664 (controlled).

693 USA ISSN 1085-8474
METAL HOME DIGEST. Text in English. bi-m. free domestic to qualified personnel; USD 45 in Canada & Mexico; USD 125 elsewhere (effective 2005). adv. **Document type:** *Magazine, Trade.* **Description:** Focuses on residential steel framing and the metal roofing and siding markets.
Indexed: BrCerAb, C&ISA, CerAb, CorrAb, E&CAJ, EMA, IAA, M&TEA, MBF, METADEX, SolStAb, WAA.
—Linda Hall.
Published by: Modern Trade Communications, Inc., 7450 Skokie Blvd, Skokie, IL 60077. TEL 847-674-2200, FAX 847-674-3676, mhd@moderntrade.com, http://www.metalhomedigest.com. Ed., R&P Shawn L Zuver. Pub. Sam W Milnark. adv.: B&W page USD 3,615, color page USD 5,305; trim 8.125 x 10.875. Circ: 30,000 (controlled).

695 USA ISSN 1533-8711
METAL ROOFING. Text in English. 2001. bi-m. USD 29.98; USD 4.95 newsstand/cover; free to qualified personnel (effective 2004). adv. **Document type:** *Magazine, Trade.* **Description:** Aimed at contractors involved in the installation of metal roofing on residential and commercial structures. Features include industry news; eye catching metal roofing projects; an engineer's technology journal; product news; plus periodic features, and more.
Published by: Krause Publications, Inc. (Subsidiary of: F & W Publications, Inc.), 700 E State St, Iola, WI 54990-0001. TEL 715-445-2214, 800-258-0929, FAX 715-445-4087, info@krause.com, http://www.krause.com. Ed. Scott Tappa. Pub. Bill Bright TEL 715-445-2214 ext 308. Adv. contact Randy Graper TEL 715-445-2214 ext 380. B&W page USD 3,679, color page USD 5,070; trim 7.75 x 10.5. Circ: 25,292 (controlled and free).

669.717 DEU ISSN 0947-9430
METALLBAU UND ALUMINIUM - KURIER. Text in German. 1995. m. EUR 97.20 domestic; EUR 108 foreign; EUR 64 to students; EUR 11.50 newsstand/cover (effective 2005). **Document type:** *Journal, Trade.*
Formed by the merger of (1990-1994): Metallbau (0938-7579); (1984-1994): Aluminium - Kurier (0175-6273)
Indexed: CivEngAb.
—Linda Hall. **CCC.**
Published by: Bauverlag BV GmbH (Subsidiary of: Springer Science+Business Media), Avenwedderstr 55, Guetersloh, 33311, Germany. TEL 49-5241-802119, FAX 49-5241-809582, ulrike.mattern@springer-sbm.com, http://www.bauverlag.de. Ed. Stefan Elgass. Circ: 25,200 (paid and controlled).

METALMAG; the magazine for metal contruction professionals. see *METALLURGY*

MICHERON BINIYA, ENERGIA VESHERUTIM NIVCHARIM. see *ENERGY*

343.078 USA
MICHIGAN CONSTRUCTION LIENS. Text in English. 1995. a. USD 105 (effective 2003). 500 p./no.
Published by: Michie Company (Subsidiary of: LexisNexis North America), 701 E Water St, Charlottesville, VA 22902-5389. TEL 434-972-7600, 800-446-3410, FAX 434-972-7677, http://www.michie.com. Ed. John F Rohe.

690 USA ISSN 1087-092X
MICHIGAN CONSTRUCTION NEWS WEEKLY, COVERING THE SOUTHERN PENINSULA BEYOND DETROIT. Text in English. 1995. w. adv. **Document type:** *Newsletter, Trade.* **Description:** Provides information on what jobs are coming up for bid or negotiation.
Related titles: Online - full text ed.
Published by: Mcgraw-Hill Construction Dodge (Subsidiary of: McGraw-Hill Construction Information Group), 148 Princeton-Hightstown Rd, Hightstown, NJ 08520. TEL 800-393-6343, http://www.dodgeconstructionpublications.com.

690 USA
MICHIGAN CONSTRUCTOR. Text in English. 1994. 3/yr. adv. **Document type:** *Magazine, Trade.* **Description:** Covers how responsible AGC members are building Michigan's infrastructure.
Related titles: French ed.: Rapport Trimestriel Sur le Commerce Agroalimentaire, Faits Saillants. ISSN 1480-0780. 1997.
Published by: (Michigan Chapter A G C), Naylor Publications, Inc., 5950 NW 1st Pl, Gainesville, FL 32607-6018. TEL 800-369-6220, http://mi.agc.org/Member_Services/Publications.asp, http://www.naylor.com. Pub. Steve Harmon. adv.: B&W page USD 1,339.50; trim 8.375 x 10.875. Circ: 4,000.

692.8 USA ISSN 1553-3816
MICHIGAN CONTRACTOR & BUILDER; engineering and construction. Text in English. 1907. w. USD 169 domestic; USD 199 in Canada; USD 239 elsewhere (effective 2005). adv. bk.rev. back issues avail.; reprints avail. **Document type:** *Magazine, Trade.* **Description:** Devoted to Michigan's heavy construction industry. Reports maintenance, operating, legal and legislative information of significance to contractors and public officials.
Formerly: Daily Construction Report (0744-0626)
Related titles: Online - full text ed.: (from ProQuest Information & Learning).
Indexed: MMI.
Published by: Reed Construction Data, Associated Construction Publications (Subsidiary of: Reed Business Information), 30 Technology Pkwy, Ste 100, Norcross, GA 30092. TEL 770-417-4122, FAX 800-930-3003, acp@reedbusiness.com, http://www.acppubs.com, http://www.acppubs.com/. Ed. Aram Kalousdian. Pub. John Weatherhead TEL 770-417-4120. adv.: B&W page USD 800, color page USD 1,300. Circ: 2,237 (paid). **Subscr. to:** Reed Business Information, Reed Construction Data Regional Publications, P O Box 15426, N. Hollywood, CA 91615-5426. TEL 818-487-4529, FAX 818-487-4550.

MICHIGAN MASTER PLUMBER & MECHANICAL CONTRACTOR; a monthly magazine for Michigan's plumbing, heating, cooling industry. see *HEATING, PLUMBING AND REFRIGERATION*

690 USA ISSN 1548-6567
▼ **MID-ATLANTIC CONSTRUCTION.** Text in English. 2004 (Mar.). bi-m. USD 20 (effective 2004).
Related titles: Online - full text ed.: (from ProQuest Information & Learning).
—**CCC.**
Published by: McGraw-Hill Companies, Inc., 1221 Ave of the Americas, New York, NY 10020. TEL 212-512-2000, http://www.midatlantic.construction.com, http://www.mcgraw-hill.com. Ed., Pub. Heather Hatfield.

693 USA ISSN 1522-7294
MIDWEST CONSTRUCTION. Text in English. 1998. m. USD 40 (effective 2005). **Document type:** *Magazine, Trade.* **Description:** Provides news, features, people and projects around the Illinois, Indiana and Wisconsin region.
Related titles: Online - full text ed.: (from LexisNexis, ProQuest Information & Learning).
Indexed: ABIn.
—**CCC.**
Published by: Mcgraw-Hill Construction Dodge (Subsidiary of: McGraw-Hill Construction Information Group), 130 E Randolph St, Ste 400, Chicago, IL 60601-6213. TEL 312-233-7470, 800-257-0993, 800-393-6343, FAX 312-233-7430, craig_barner@mcgraw-hill.com, http://www.midwestconstructionmag.com/, http://www.dodgeconstructionpublications.com. Ed. Craig Barner TEL 312-233-7471. Adv. contact Mamie DiGangi TEL 312-233-7473.

692.8 USA ISSN 0026-3044
MIDWEST CONTRACTOR MAGAZINE. (In 2 editions: North & South) Text in English. 1901. s-m. USD 96 domestic; USD 126 in Canada; USD 166 elsewhere (effective 2005). adv. bk.rev. illus. **Document type:** *Magazine, Trade.* **Description:** Articles and information on bids-awards, planned work, business methods, new products and literature, legislation, association meetings, and manufacturer-distributor news pertaining to the engineered construction and public works industries in Iowa, Kansas, Nebraska, and western and northeastern Missouri.
Formerly (until 1929): Western Contractor (0097-4218); Which incorporated (1909-1912): Cement Record (0099-4928)
Related titles: Online - full text ed.: (from Gale Group, ProQuest Information & Learning).
Published by: Reed Construction Data, Associated Construction Publications (Subsidiary of: Reed Business Information), 30 Technology Pkwy, Ste 100, Norcross, GA 30092. TEL 770-417-4114, 800-322-6996, FAX 770-417-4002, 800-895-8661, acp@reedbusiness.com, http://www.acppubs.com, http://www.acppubs.com/. Eds. Curt Grandia TEL 515-226-0273, Greg Sitek TEL 205-633-1789. Pub. John Weatherhead TEL 770-417-4120. Adv. contact Tammy Henderson. B&W page USD 1,285, color page USD 1,735. Circ: 7,491 (paid and free).

690 CHE
MIGROS-MAGAZIN. Text in German. w. CHF 48 membership (effective 2005). adv. **Document type:** *Magazine, Consumer.*
Formerly (until 2004): Wir Brueckenbauer
Published by: Migros-Genossenschafts-Bund, Postfach 1751, Zuerich, 8031, Switzerland. TEL 41-44-2723030, FAX 41-44-2773590, redaktion@migrosmagazin.ch, verlag@migrosmagazin.ch, http://www.migrosmagazin.ch. Ed. Hans Schneeberger. Pub. Jean Pierre Pfister. Adv. contact Bernd Maulaz. B&W page CHF 19,988, color page CHF 30,903; trim 205 x 290. Circ: 1,754,899.

338.4769 DNK ISSN 0908-3855
MILJOE. Variant title: V & S Priser, Miljoe. Text in Danish. 1994. a. DKK 1,360 (effective 1998).

B

Published by: V & S Byggedata, 551 Frederikssundvej 194, Broenshoej, 2700, Denmark. TEL 45-38-60-77-11, FAX 45-38-60-77-55. Ed. Carl Friis Skovsen.

690 SWE ISSN 1650-4925
MILJOEFORSKNING (STOCKHOLM). Text in Swedish. 1958. 6/yr. SEK 345 (effective 2001). **Document type:** *Journal, Academic/Scholarly.*
Incorporates (1990-2000): Ett Gott Raad (1101-0967); Former titles (until 2001): Byggforskning (1102-3686); (until vol.5, 1991): Tidskriften Byggforskning (0349-8093); (until 1980): Fraan Byggforskningen (0429-2928)
Published by: FORMAS/Swedish Research Council for Environment, Agricultural Sciences and Spatial Planning, Birger Jarls Torg 5, Box 1206, Stockholm, 11182, Sweden. TEL 46-8-775-40-00, FAX 46-8-775-40-10, info@formas.se, http://www.formas.se. Ed. Birgitta Bruzelius.

MILLION DOLLAR PROJECT PLANNED LIST. see *ARCHITECTURE*

690 USA ISSN 0895-7304
MILLWORK MANUFACTURING. Text in English. 1985. bi-m. USD 15 per issue. adv.
Published by: Associations Publications, Inc., PO Box1480, Collierville, TN 38027-1480. TEL 901-853-7470. Ed. Joyce Powell. Circ: 6,620.

690 USA
MILLWORK PRODUCTS GUIDE. Text in English. a.
Published by: National Sash and Door Jobbers Association, 10225 Robert Trent Jones Pkwy, New Port Richey, FL 34655-4649.

MINNESOTA P - H - C CONTRACTOR MAGAZINE. see *HEATING, PLUMBING AND REFRIGERATION*

690 USA ISSN 1552-8723
MISSISSIPPI BUILDER. Text in English. 6/yr. USD 18 (effective 2005).
Published by: Association Publishing Inc., 2117 Smith Ave, Chesapeake, VA 23320. TEL 757-420-2434, FAX 757-424-5954, http://www.statebuildermagazines.com. Ed. Lorie Gomez. Pubs. Joyce F Hearn, Sandra Amidon. Circ: 4,000.

MITGLIEDERINFORMATION. see *ARCHITECTURE*

690 ISR ISSN 0333-7502
MIVNIM. Text in Hebrew. m. ILS 300, USD 75. adv. **Document type:** *Trade.* **Description:** For the construction industry in Israel.
Indexed: IHP.
Published by: Merav Publishing Industries Ltd., 27 Soutine St, Tel Aviv, 64684, Israel. TEL 972-3-5211900, FAX 972-3-5211902, merav@trendline.co.il, http://www.merav.co.il. Ed. Eilat Elgor. Adv. contact David Keizelman. B&W page USD 1,085, color page USD 1,704; trim 25 x 18. Circ: 15,000.

388.3 USA ISSN 0733-6497
TL297
MOBILE - MANUFACTURED HOME BLUE BOOK✶. Text in English. 2/yr. USD 100. back issues avail. **Document type:** *Directory.*
Formerly (until 1982): Mobile Home Blue Book (0733-6489)
Published by: National Market Reports, Inc., 29 N Wacker Dr, Chicago, IL 60606-3297. TEL 312-855-0137, FAX 312-855-0137. Ed. Gary Dillow. Pub., R&P George Stanton.

333.33 USA ISSN 1081-7808
HD9715.7.U6
MOBILE - MANUFACTURED HOUSING COST GUIDE. Text in English. 198?. a. USD 38.
Published by: E.H. Boeckh, Ed. & Pub. (Subsidiary of: Thomson Publishing Corp.), 2885 S Calhoun Rd, Box 510291, New Berlin, WI 53151-0291. TEL 414-780-2800, 800-285-1288, FAX 414-780-0306. R&P E H Boeckh.

690 USA
MODERN HOMES. Text in English. 1999. bi-m. free domestic to members industry (effective 2005). adv. 34 p./no. 3 cols./p.; **Document type:** *Magazine, Trade.*
Formerly: In Focus
Published by: Manufactured Housing Institute, 2101 Wilson Blvd, Ste 610, Arlington, VA 22201-3062. TEL 703-558-0400, FAX 703-558-0401, kami@mfghome.org, http://www.manufacturedhousing.org. Eds. Bruce A Savage, Kami Watson. adv.: B&W page USD 4,340, color page USD 4,774. Circ: 19,000 (controlled).

693.71 USA ISSN 0026-8445
TA472
MODERN STEEL CONSTRUCTION. Text in English. 1944. m. free domestic to qualified personnel; USD 36 foreign (effective 2005). illus.
Supersedes (in 1961): Steel Construction Digest
Indexed: AIAP, ApMecR, BrCerAb, C&ISA, CerAb, CivEngAb, CorrAb, E&CAJ, EEA, EMA, EngInd, HRIS, IAA, M&TEA, MBF, METADEX, S&VD, SolStAb, WAA.
—BLDSC (5897.500000), CISTI, Ei, IE, Infotrieve, ingenta, Linda Hall.

Published by: American Institute of Steel Construction, Inc., 1 E. Wacker Dr., Chicago, IL 60601-1802. TEL 312-670-5407, FAX 312-670-5403, http://www.aisc.org/. Ed. Scott Melnick. Circ: 35,000.

690 624 ITA ISSN 0390-1025
MODULO. Text in Italian. 1975. m. (10/yr.). EUR 70 (effective 2005). **Document type:** *Magazine, Trade.* **Description:** Covers technology and design for quality in building.
Indexed: AIAP.
Published by: BE-MA Editrice Srl, Via Teocrito 50, Milan, MI 20128, Italy. TEL 39-02-252071, FAX 39-02-27000692, segreteria@bema.it, http://www.bema.it. Ed. Giuseppe Biondo.

691 USA
▼ **MOLD & MOISTURE MANAGEMENT**; the magazine for moisture prevention and remediation. Text in English. 2005. q. USD 30; free to qualified personnel (effective 2005). adv. **Document type:** *Magazine, Trade.* **Description:** Dedicated to preventing and curing moisture problems in all types of structures.
Published by: Key Communications, Inc., PO Box 569, Garrisonville, VA 22463. TEL 540-720-5584, FAX 540-720-5687, info@moldmag.com, http://www.moldmag.com, http://www.key-com.com/. Ed. Megan Headley. Pub. Debra Levy. adv.: B&W page USD 2,700, color page USD 4,045; trim 8 x 10.75. Circ: 28,000 (paid and controlled).

LE MONITEUR DES TRAVAUX PUBLICS ET DU BATIMENT. see *ENGINEERING—Civil Engineering*

624 621.9 FRA ISSN 0998-4577
LE MONITEUR - MATERIELS ET CHANTIERS. Text in French. 1921. 9/yr. adv. bk.rev.
Incorporates: Equipement Mecanique, Carrieres et Materiaux; Which was formerly: Equipment Mecanique des Chantiers (0013-9882)
Related titles: ♦ Supplement to: Le Moniteur des Travaux Publics et du Batiment. ISSN 0026-9700.
Published by: Groupe Moniteur, 17 rue d'Uzes, Paris, 75002, France. FAX 33-1-42333819. Ed. Michel Roche. Circ: 15,000.

691 ESP ISSN 0212-7091
MONITOR✶. Text in Spanish. 1888. m. **Document type:** *Trade.*
Formerly (until 1983): Monitor de Obras Publicas (0540-651X)
Published by: Agrupacion Nacional de Constructores de Obras Publicas, Serrano, 174, Madrid, 28002, Spain. TEL 34-91-5630504, FAX 34-91-5634758, ptello@seopan.es. Ed. Paloma Tello Lucini. Circ: 8,000.

690 USA
MONITOR (SKOKIE). Text in English. m.
Published by: Portland Cement Association, 5240 Old Orchard Rd, Skokie, IL 60077-1083. TEL 708-966-6200. Ed. Bill Toal.

690 RUS ISSN 0027-0040
CODEN: MSRYA9
MONTAZHNYE I SPETSIAL'NYE RABOTY V STROITEL'STVE. Text in Russian. 1941. m. USD 151. bk.rev. bibl.; charts; illus.
Indexed: BrCerAb, C&ISA, CerAb, ChemAb, CivEngAb, CorrAb, E&CAJ, EMA, EngInd, M&TEA, MBF, METADEX, RASB, RefZh, SolStAb, WAA.
—East View, Linda Hall. **CCC.**
Published by: Izdatel'stvo Stroizdat, Komsomol'skii pr-t 42, Moscow, 119826, Russian Federation. TEL 7-095-2516967, FAX 7-095-2459780. Ed. I G Shumilina. **US dist. addr.:** East View Information Services, 3020 Harbor Ln. N., Minneapolis, MN 55447. TEL 612-550-0961.

302.23029 USA ISSN 0844-3459
TH4818.W6
MUIR'S ORIGINAL LOG HOME GUIDE FOR BUILDERS & BUYERS. Text in English. 1978. q. CND 12, USD 12 domestic; USD 25 foreign. adv. bk.rev. charts; illus.; tr.lit. Supplement avail.; back issues avail. **Description:** Covers developments in the log home industry. Contains how-to articles on buying as well as (or in place of) building a log house in North America.
Formerly: Log Home Guide for Builders and Buyers (0707-5006); Incorporates: Log Home Decor for Builders and Buyers
Indexed: AIAP.
—**CCC.**
Published by: Muir Publishing Co., Inc., 164 Middle Creek Rd, Cosby, TN 37722. TEL 800-345-5647, FAX 615-487-3249. Ed. Allan T Muir. adv.: B&W page USD 6,325, color page USD 7,900. Circ: 175,000.

690 333.33 USA ISSN 0146-0919
MULTI-HOUSING NEWS. Cover title: M H N. Text in English. 1966-1991; resumed 1992. m. USD 80 domestic; USD 125 in Canada; USD 240 elsewhere (effective 2004). adv. illus. **Document type:** *Magazine, Trade.* **Description:** Covers finance, marketing, sales and other developments affecting the multi-unit building and management industry.
Formerly: Apartment Construction News (0003-6358)
Related titles: Online - full text ed.: (from EBSCO Publishing, Florida Center for Library Automation, Gale Group, O C L C Online Computer Library Center, Inc., ProQuest Information & Learning).
Indexed: ABIn, AgeL.
—**CCC.**

Published by: V N U Business Publications (Subsidiary of: V N U Business Media), 770 Broadway, New York, NY 10003-9595. pwatson@multi-housingnews.com, bmcomm@vnuinc.com, http://www.multi-housingnews.com/, http://www.vnubusinessmedia.com/. Ed. Bryant Roussseau. Pub. Peter Watson TEL 646-654-4488. adv.: B&W page USD 9,000, color page USD 10,940. Circ: 26,476 (controlled).
Subscr. to: PO Box 1055, Skokie, IL 60076.

MUR; arkitektur og byggeteknikk. see *ARCHITECTURE*

690 DNK ISSN 0908-164X
MURERNES FAGBLAD. Text in Danish. 1990. m. **Document type:** *Trade.*
Supersedes in part (in 1996): Byg og Trae (0906-2653); Which was formed by the merger of (1970-1990): Blik og Roer (0901-3296); (1974-1990): Bygning og Trae (0901-3989); (1927-1990): Murernes Fagblad (0107-7589); (1955-1990): Trae (0903-1499)
Published by: Specialarbejderforbundet i Danmark, Kampmannsgade 4, Copenhagen V, 1790, Denmark. TEL 45-33-14-21-40, FAX 45-33-97-24-60.

690 USA ISSN 1555-2500
NA7115.3
▼ **MY HOUSE IN THE MOUNTAIN STATES.** Text in English. 2005 (Jan./Feb.). bi-m. USD 9.95 (effective 2004). adv. **Document type:** *Magazine, Consumer.* **Description:** Covers construction & design of affluent homes in the mountain states, including topics such as materials, furnishings, techniques, trends, and business advise.
Published by: McGraw-Hill Companies, Inc., 1221 Ave of the Americas, New York, NY 10020. TEL 212-512-2000, customer.service@mcgraw-hill.com, http://www.myhousemag.com/, http://www.mcgraw-hill.com. Ed. Mindy Pantiel. Pub. Al Slattery. Adv. contact Jennifer Sweeney. color page USD 4,700.

381.45 USA ISSN 1078-8824
HD9715.7.U62
N A D A MANUFACTURED HOUSING APPRAISAL GUIDE. Text in English. 3/yr. USD 100 (effective 1999). adv.
Former titles (until 1993): N.A.D.A. Mobile - Manufactured Housing Appraisal Guide (0742-9274); N.A.D.A. Mobile Home Appraisal Guide (0095-6538)
Published by: (National Automobile Dealers Association), N.A.D.A. Appraisal Guides, PO Box 7800, Costa Mesa, CA 92628-7800. TEL 800-966-6232, FAX 714-556-8715. Ed., R&P, Adv. contact Lenny Sims TEL 714-556-8511. Pub. Don Christy Jr.

690 USA
N A H B REMODELOR. Text in English. 1988. bi-m. **Document type:** *Newsletter.* **Description:** Covers remodelling issues, technical advice and council news.
Published by: (Remodelors Council), National Association of Home Builders, 1201 15th St, N W, Washington, DC 20005-2800. TEL 202-822-0200, FAX 202-861-2170. Ed. Christopher P Nicholson. Circ: 5,000.

N A: NUEVA ARCHITECTURA CON ARCILLA COCIDA. see *ARCHITECTURE*

690 USA
N A R I REMODELER'S JOURNAL. Text in English. 1997. q. membership. adv. bk.rev. **Description:** Includes features and technical articles on the remodeling industry, association news, and business management issues.
Published by: National Association of the Remodeling Industry, 780 Lee St, Ste 200, Des Plaines, IL 60016. TEL 847-298-9200, 800-611-6274, FAX 877-685-6274, info@nari.org, http://www.nari.org. Ed. Susan Maney. R&P Jennifer McKain. Circ: 7,500 (controlled).

690 USA ISSN 1081-6569
THE N A W I C IMAGE; for today's women in construction. Text in English. 1971. m. USD 35 to non-members; USD 55 foreign (effective 2001). adv. stat.; tr.lit. **Document type:** *Trade.* **Description:** Covers financial, legal, educational and career issues relating to women in construction.
Published by: National Association of Women in Construction, 327 S Adams St, Fort Worth, TX 76104. TEL 817-877-5551, FAX 817-877-0324, nawic@onamp.net, http://www.nawic.org. Ed., R&P Leona Priya Dalavai. Pub. Dede Hughes. Adv. contact Kara Roberson. page USD 1,000; trim 11 x 8.5. Circ: 6,500 (paid).

N B O ABSTRACTS. see *BUILDING AND CONSTRUCTION—Abstracting, Bibliographies, Statistics*

N C B ABSTRACTS. see *BUILDING AND CONSTRUCTION—Abstracting, Bibliographies, Statistics*

690 IND
N C B NEWSLETTER; a quarterly information carrier of NCB's services to the industry. Text in English. 1999. q. adv. **Description:** Provides information on cement industry. Mainly for cement producers, construction engineers, concrete technologists, quality control specialists, consultants and scientists interested in cement concrete.
Indexed: CRIA.

B

Published by: National Council for Cement and Building Materials, P-21 South Ext. Part-II, Ring Rd., New Delhi, 110 049, India. TEL 91-129-246174, FAX 91-129-242100, 91-11-6258868, nccbm@giasdl01.vsnl.net.in. Ed. C. Rajkumar. Pub. S.C. Rastogi. adv.: color page INR 10,000, color page USD 350.

N C S B C S NEWS. see *HOUSING AND URBAN PLANNING*

695 GBR
N F R C ROOFING INDUSTRY DIRECTORY. Text in English. 1979. a. adv. **Document type:** *Directory, Trade.*
Formerly: N F R C Yearbook
Published by: (National Federation of Roofing Contractors), B P G (Bourne) Ltd., 2 West St, Bourne, Lincs PE10 9NE, United Kingdom. TEL 0778-393747, FAX 0778-425453. Ed. S McLoughlin. Adv. contact Rod Plowe.

690 USA ISSN 1049-7579
CODEN: NBSSES
N I S T BUILDING SCIENCE SERIES. Text in English. irreg. price varies. **Document type:** *Monographic series, Government.*
Description: Presents research results on test methods and performance criteria related to structural and environmental functions, durability and safety.
Formerly: U.S. National Bureau of Standards. Building Science Series (0083-1794)
Indexed: BrCerAb, C&ISA, CerAb, CivEngAb, CorrAb, E&CAJ, EMA, IAA, Inspec, M&TEA, MBF, METADEX, SolStAb, WAA, WSCA.
—CISTI, Ei.
Published by: U.S. National Institute of Standards and Technology, 100 Bureau Dr, Gaithersburg, MD 20899. TEL 301-975-6478. **Subscr. to:** National Technical Information Service, Government Research Center, 5285 Port Royal Rd, Springfield, VA 22161. TEL 703-605-6060, 800-363-2068, http://www.ntis.gov.

N R C A MEMBERSHIP DIRECTORY. see *BUSINESS AND ECONOMICS—Trade And Industrial Directories*

691.3 USA ISSN 0077-5355
CODEN: NRMCAO
N R M C A PUBLICATION. Text in English. 1931. irreg., latest vol.144, 1973. price varies.
Indexed: ConcrAb.
Published by: National Ready Mixed Concrete Association, 900 Spring St, Silver Spring, MD 20910. TEL 301-587-1400. Ed. R D Gaynor. Circ: 2,000.

THE N S P I BUSINESS OWNERS. see *PHYSICAL FITNESS AND HYGIENE*

N S S E A MEMBERSHIP DIRECTORY. see *EDUCATION—School Organization And Administration*

N T I S ALERTS: BUILDING INDUSTRY TECHNOLOGY. see *BUILDING AND CONSTRUCTION—Abstracting, Bibliographies, Statistics*

690 SCG ISSN 0350-2619
NASE GRADEVINARSTVO. Text in Serbian; Summaries in English. 1947. bi-m. abstr.; bibl.; illus.; stat. 24 p./no. 2 cols./p.;
Related titles: ◆ Supplement to: Masinstvo. ISSN 0461-2531.
Indexed: ConcrAb, GeotechAb.
Published by: Savez Inzenjera i Tehnicara Srbije, Kneza Milosa 7, Belgrade, 11000. TEL 381-11-3237363, sits@yuonline.net, http://www.sits.org.yu. Ed. Joza Tucakov. Adv. contact Ivanka Vuletic. Circ: 1,000.

690 IND
NATIONAL BUILDING. Text in English. s-a. INR 66, USD 23.76. **Document type:** *Government.*
Published by: Government of India, Department of Publications, Civil Lines, New Delhi, 110 054, India.

NATIONAL BUILDING SERVICE. see *LAW*

690 IND ISSN 0255-8165
NATIONAL BUILDINGS CONSTRUCTION CORPORATION. BULLETIN. Text and summaries in English. 1973. q. free. **Document type:** *Bulletin.*
Published by: National Buildings Construction Corporation Limited, NBCC House, Lodi Rd., New Delhi, 110 003, India. TEL 690314, TELEX 31-66665 NBCC IN. Ed. V Grover. Circ: 2,000.

690 IND ISSN 0027-8815
NATIONAL BUILDINGS ORGANISATION. JOURNAL. Text in English. 1955. s-a. INR 10, USD 3.60. adv. bk.rev. charts; illus.; stat.
Indexed: AIAP, API, CRIA, CRICC.
—CISTI.
Published by: National Buildings Organisation, G Wing, Nirman Bhavan, Maulana Azad Rd., New Delhi, 110 011, India. Ed. S Pratap. Circ: 750.

NATIONAL CONFERENCE OF STATES ON BUILDING CODES AND STANDARDS. ANNUAL CONFERENCE PROCEEDINGS. see *HOUSING AND URBAN PLANNING*

692.5 USA ISSN 0547-5511
NATIONAL CONSTRUCTION ESTIMATOR. Text in English. a. USD 47.50 (effective 2004). **Description:** Provides estimated prices for every common building material, manhours, recommended crew, and labor cost for installation.
Published by: Craftsman Book Company, 6058 Corte del Cedro, Box 6500, Carlsbad, CA 92018. TEL 800-829-8123, http://www.craftsman-book.com/tne32/tne32_nep/nce.html.

666.8 IND
NATIONAL COUNCIL FOR CEMENT AND BUILDING MATERIALS. ANNUAL REPORT. Text in English. a. illus. **Document type:** *Corporate.*
Formerly: Cement Research Institute of India. Annual Report
Indexed: ConcrAb.
Published by: National Council for Cement and Building Materials, 34th Kilometer Stone, Delhi-Mathura Rd. (NA-2), Ballabgarh, Haryana 121 004, India. TEL 91-129-242051, FAX 91-129-242100.

690 USA ISSN 1092-602X
TK435
(YEAR) NATIONAL ELECTRICAL ESTIMATOR. Text in English. 1985. a. USD 47.75 (effective 2001). reprints avail. **Document type:** *Trade.* **Description:** Covers manhours, labor, and material costs for installing electrical in residential, commercial, and industrial construction.
Formerly: Electrical Construction Estimator (1041-729X)
Related titles: CD-ROM ed.; Diskette ed.; Online - full text ed.
Published by: Craftsman Book Company, 6058 Corte del Cedro, Box 6500, Carlsbad, CA 92018. TEL 760-438-7828, 800-829-8123, FAX 760-438-0398, http://www.craftsman-book.com. Ed., R&P Laurence Jacobs. Pub. Gary Moselle. Adv. contact Bill Grote. Circ: 5,000 (paid).

690.028 USA
NATIONAL EQUIPMENT DIGEST CARD DECK. Abbreviated title: N.E.D. Card Deck. Text in English. q. adv. **Document type:** *Journal, Trade.* **Description:** Acts as a buying source for contractors in the concrete and heavy construction industries.
Published by: Grand View Media Group, Inc. (Subsidiary of: EBSCO Industries, Inc.), 200 Croft St., # 1, Birmingham, AL 35242-1824. TEL 888-431-2877, webmaster@grandviewmedia.com, http://www.grandviewmedia.com. adv.: B&W page USD 2,200, color page USD 2,600; 3 x 5.

690 JPN
NATIONAL FEDERATION OF CONSTRUCTION WORKERS' UNIONS. ZENKENSOREN. Text in Japanese. bi-w.
Published by: National Federation of Construction Workers' Unions, 7-15 Takadanobaba 2-chome, Shinjuku-ku, Tokyo, 169-0075, Japan.

NATIONAL FIRE CODE OF CANADA (YEAR). see *FIRE PREVENTION*

690 USA
NATIONAL INSTITUTE OF BUILDING SCIENCES. ANNUAL REPORT TO THE PRESIDENT. Text in English. 1978. a. **Document type:** *Corporate.*
Published by: National Institute of Building Sciences, 1090 Vermont Ave, N W, Ste 700, Washington, DC 20005-4905. TEL 202-289-7800. R&P Neil Sandler. Circ: 2,000.

670.29 USA
NATIONAL PRECAST CONCRETE ASSOCIATION. MEMBERSHIP DIRECTORY & BUYER'S GUIDE. Text in English. a. USD 300 to non-members. adv. **Document type:** *Directory, Trade.* **Description:** Lists over 800 producers and associate members of the Association; over 250 precast concrete products.
Formerly: Directory of Membership & Precast Concrete Products
Published by: National Precast Concrete Association, 10333 N Meridian St, Ste 272, Indianapolis, IN 46290-1081. TEL 317-253-0486, 800-366-7731, FAX 317-259-7230, npca@precast.org, http://www.precast.org. Ed. Ron Hyink. Pub. Ty E Gable. Adv. contact Brenda C Mayaleri.

690 AUS ISSN 1037-9908
NATIONAL PRECASTER. Text in English. 3/yr. **Document type:** *Newsletter, Trade.*
Indexed: BrCerAb, C&ISA, CerAb, CorrAb, E&CAJ, EMA, IAA, M&TEA, MBF, METADEX, SolStAb, WAA.
Published by: National Precast Concrete Association Australia, 8-10 Palmer St, North Parramatta, NSW 2151, Australia. TEL 61-2-98908853, FAX 61-2-98908854, info@npcaa.com.au.

690 USA
NATIONAL SASH AND DOOR JOBBERS ASSOCIATION. BULLETIN. Text in English. irreg. **Document type:** *Bulletin.*
Published by: National Sash and Door Jobbers Association, 10225 Robert Trent Jones Pkwy, New Port Richey, FL 34655-4649.

690 USA
NATIONAL SASH AND DOOR JOBBERS ASSOCIATION. NEWSLETTER. Text in English. m. **Document type:** *Newsletter.*
Published by: National Sash and Door Jobbers Association, 10225 Robert Trent Jones Pkwy, New Port Richey, FL 34655-4649.

691 USA
NATIONAL TERRAZZO AND MOSAIC ASSOCIATION. DIRECTORY✱. Text in English. a. **Document type:** *Directory.*
Published by: National Terrazzo and Mosaic Association, 110 E Market St, Ste 200A, Leesburg, VA 20176-3122. TEL 312-635-7744.

690 USA ISSN 8750-6580
NATION'S BUILDING NEWS. Text in English. 1985. 8/yr. free to members (effective 2005). adv. **Document type:** *Newspaper, Trade.* **Description:** Covers all aspects of the housing industry, including national regulatory, technological, and legislative new.
Related titles: ◆ Online - full content ed.: Nations Building News Online.
Published by: (National Association of Home Builders), Naylor Publications, Inc., 5950 NW 1st Pl, Gainesville, FL 32607-6018. TEL 800-369-6220, http://www.naylor.com. Ed. Tim Ahern. adv.: B&W page USD 11,999.50, color page USD 13,499.50; trim 10.875 x 15.5. Circ: 160,000.

504 USA
NATIONS BUILDING NEWS ONLINE. Text in English. w. free (effective 2003). **Document type:** *Newsletter, Trade.* **Description:** Gives you an insider's look at all the important news and developments affecting the housing industry.
Media: Online - full content. **Related titles:** ◆ Print ed.: Nation's Building News. ISSN 8750-6580.
Published by: National Association of Home Builders, 1201 15th St, N W, Washington, DC 20005-2800. TEL 202-266-8200, 800-368-5242, FAX 202-266-8559, tahern@nahb.com, http://www.nahb.org.

691.2 GBR ISSN 1356-5443
NATURAL STONE SPECIALIST. Text in English. 1965. m. GBP 38 domestic; GBP 43 foreign (effective 2005). adv. bk.rev. abstr.; illus.; tr.lit. **Document type:** *Magazine, Trade.* **Description:** Covers all aspects of dimensional stone industry from extraction to finished products in construction, memorial masonry, restoration, and sculpture.
Formerly: Stone Industries (0039-1778)
Indexed: A&ATA, AESIS, C&ISA, CerAb, CorrAb, E&CAJ, EMA, Englnd, SolStAb, WAA.
—CISTI, Ei.
Published by: Q M J Publishing Ltd., 7 Regent St, Nottingham, NG1 5BS, United Kingdom. TEL 44-115-9411315, FAX 44-115-9484035, nss@qmj.co.uk, http://www.naturalstonespecialist.com/, http://www.qmj.co.uk/. Ed. Eric Bignell TEL 44-115-9453898. Adv. contact Margaret Beaman TEL 44-1903-884146. B&W page GBP 735, color page GBP 950. Circ: 2,500 (paid).

690 DEU ISSN 0028-1026
NATURSTEIN; Fachzeitschrift fuer die gesamte Naturwerkstein-Wirtschaft. Text in German; Summaries in English. 1946. m. EUR 94.50 domestic; EUR 108.40 foreign; EUR 9.80 newsstand/cover (effective 2002). adv. bk.rev. charts; illus.; stat. index. **Document type:** *Magazine, Trade.* **Description:** Devoted to stone-masonry. Covers stone and wood sculpture, stone-industry, technology, restoration, architecture, building authorities, and cemeteries worldwide. Includes association news, international news, and positions available.
—CCC.
Published by: Ebner Verlag GmbH, Karlstr 41, Ulm, 89073, Germany. TEL 49-731-1520168, FAX 49-731-68503, gl@ebnerverlag.de, http://www.natursteinonline.de, http://www.ebnerverlag.de. Ed. Barbara Hollaender. adv.: B&W page EUR 2,040, color page EUR 3,300. Circ: 7,079.

690 NLD ISSN 0165-6368
NATUURSTEEN. Text in Dutch. 1949. m. adv. **Document type:** *Trade.* **Description:** Independent trade publication for the natural stone industrie in the Netherlands and Belgium.
Published by: Wijlhuizen Vaktijdschriften, Wilhelminasingel 4, Nijmegen, 6524 AK, Netherlands. TEL 31-24-3605253, FAX 31-24-3605210. Ed. Peter Vorstenbosch. Pub., R&P Yvo Wijlhuizen. Adv. contact Erwin Dewolff. Circ: 5,700.

690 ALB ISSN 1010-4003
T4
NDERTUESI/CONSTRUCTEUR. Text in Albanian. q. USD 6.15.
Published by: Ministria e Ndertimit/Ministere de la Construction, Tirana, Albania. TELEX 4208.

690 624 ITA
UN NEMICO INFILTRATO/INFILTRATED ENEMY. Text in English, Italian. 1998. a. EUR 44 (effective 2003). adv. 302 p./no.; back issues avail. **Document type:** *Monographic series, Trade.* **Description:** Offers plans, completed and still in progress, technical data, tables and the most innovative methods for dealing with humidity-related problems.
Published by: Antonio Zoppas Editore S.r.l., Via Calvi 27, Conegliano, TV 31015, Italy. TEL 39-0438-411908, FAX 39-0438-31539, anzoppas@tmn.it, http://www.ulisselibri.com. Adv. contact Mies Cesarina. B&W page EUR 2,118, color page EUR 3,357; trim 208 x 296. Circ: 30,000.

B

307.14 KEN
TA401
NETWORK OF AFRICAN COUNTRIES ON COST-EFFECTIVE BUILDING TECHNOLOGIES. Text in English. 1989. biennial. free. **Document type:** *Newsletter.* **Description:** Compiles and disseminates information, case studies and data on low-cost innovations in local building materials and construction technology. It is a medium for information exchange and facilitator for acquisition of suitable technologies and know-how by needy countries.
Formerly: Journal of the Network of African Countries on Local Building Materials and Technologies (1012-9812)
Published by: United Nations Centre for Human Settlements (Habitat), PO Box 30030, Nairobi, Kenya. TEL 254-2-623067, FAX 254-2-624060. Eds. Baris Der Petrossian, Rainer Nordberg.

690 DEU ISSN 1439-6351
NEUE ZEITSCHRIFT FUER BAURECHT UND VERGABERECHT. Key Title: NZBau. Text in German. 2000. m. EUR 218 domestic; EUR 238.50 foreign; EUR 20.50 newsstand/cover (effective 2005). **Document type:** *Journal, Trade.*
Published by: Verlag C.H. Beck oHG, Wilhelmstr 9, Munich, 80801, Germany. TEL 49-89-38189338, FAX 49-89-38189398, abo.service@beck.de, http://www.beck.de.

690 AUT ISSN 0253-0198
NEUES VOM BAU. Text in German. 1955. bi-m. bk.rev. **Document type:** *Magazine, Trade.*
Indexed: RASB.
Address: Hasnerstrasse 36, Linz, O 4020, Austria. TEL 43-732-656062, FAX 43-732-666683. Ed. Rudolf Steininger. Circ: 14,500.

690 GBR ISSN 0956-9081
NEW BUILDER. Abbreviated title: N B. Text in English. w. GBP 65; GBP 115 foreign.
Indexed: WSCA.
—CCC.
Published by: Builder Group, 1 Millharbour, London, E14 9RA, United Kingdom. Ed. Simon Middelboe.

658 IRL
NEW BUSINESS REPORT. Text in English. fortn. **Document type:** *Newsletter, Trade.* **Description:** Provides information on all new foreign investment, industrial, commercial and tourism construction projects planned in Ireland.
Published by: Newmarket Information Ltd., 66 Ranelagh, Dublin, 6, Ireland. TEL 353-1-4910043, FAX 353-1-4910092, info@newinfo.ie, http://www.newinfo.ie.

NEW CALEDONIA. INSTITUT DE LA STATISTIQUE ET DES ETUDES ECONOMIQUES. INDICE ET INDEX DU B T P. see *BUILDING AND CONSTRUCTION—Abstracting, Bibliographies, Statistics*

690 USA ISSN 0028-470X
NEW ENGLAND CONSTRUCTION. Text in English. 1936. s-m. USD 96 domestic; USD 126 in Canada; USD 166 elsewhere; USD 10 newsstand/cover (effective 2005). adv. illus. 90 p./no. 3 cols./p.; **Document type:** *Magazine.* **Description:** News and articles pertaining to heavy, highway, and non-residential building construction.
Related titles: Online - full text ed.: (from Gale Group, ProQuest Information & Learning).
—CCC.
Published by: Reed Construction Data, Associated Construction Publications (Subsidiary of: Reed Business Information), 30 Technology Pkwy, Ste 100, Norcross, GA 30092. TEL 770-417-4114, 800-322-6996, FAX 770-417-4002, 800-895-8661, acp@reedbusiness.com, http://www.acppubs.com/. Ed. Paul Fournier TEL 978-433-1966. Pub. John Weatherhead TEL 770-417-4120. adv.: B&W page USD 1,138, color page USD 1,638. Circ: 10,500 (controlled).

690 USA
NEW JERSEY SHORE BUILDERS ASSOCIATION BULLETIN BOARD; voice of the Jersey Shore building industry. Text in English. 1952. m. USD 10 (effective 2005). adv. bk.rev. **Document type:** *Magazine, Trade.*
Published by: New Jersey Shore Builders Association, 190 Oberlin Ave., N, Lakewood, NJ 08701. TEL 732-364-2828, FAX 732-605-2577. Ed. Robert Bolderman. Circ: 400 (controlled).

690 330 USA
NEW PLANT REPORT. Text in English. 1981. m. USD 1,800 (effective 2001). stat. **Document type:** *Corporate.* **Description:** Covers current announcements of U.S. and foreign corporate expansion plans, acquisitions, facility construction and facility closings; focus is on manufacturing industries.
Media: Diskette. **Related titles:** E-mail ed.; Print ed.
Published by: Conway Data, Inc., 6625 The Corners Pkwy, Ste 200, Norcross, GA 30092. TEL 770-446-6996, FAX 770-263-8825, http://www.conway.com. Ed. Ron Starner. Pub. Mckinley Conway.

690 JPN ISSN 0917-0782
NEW SETSUBI SHIZAI JOHO/INFORMATION ON NEW EQUIPMENTS. Text in Japanese. 1990. m.
Published by: Nikkan Kogyo Shimbun, Ltd., 14-1 Nihonbashikoamicho, Chuo-ku, Tokyo, 103-8548, Japan.

690 USA
NEW SMALL HOMES; home plans under 2,000 square feet. Cover title: Small Homes. Text in English. 1998. q. USD 15; USD 3.98 newsstand/cover (effective 2000). adv. **Document type:** *Magazine, Consumer.* **Description:** Contains homes which accomodate family living within a compact area.
Published by: HomeStyles Publishing & Marketing, Inc., 213 E. 4th St., 4th Fl., St. Paul, MN 55101-1603. TEL 651-602-5000, 888-626-2026, FAX 651-602-5001, http://www.homestyles.com. Ed. Sara Freund. Adv. contact Shelley Junker. B&W page USD 3,910, color page USD 4,830; trim 8 x 10.75. Circ: 81,900.

721 692.8 GBR ISSN 0968-0098
TA684
NEW STEEL CONSTRUCTION✶. Text in English. bi-m. GBP 70; (foreign GBP 90) (effective 1998). adv. bk.rev. bibl.; illus.; pat.; tr.lit. index. back issues avail. **Document type:** *Trade.* **Description:** Information for the constructional steelwork industry.
Formed by the 1993 merger of: Steel Construction Today (0950-9216); Steel Construction (0950-6039); Which was formerly (1985-1986): B S C A News (0950-6020)
Indexed: RICS.
—BLDSC (6088.766200), CISTI, IE, ingenta.
Published by: (Steel Construction Institute), Kingslea Press Ltd., 137 Newhall St., Birmingham, West Midlands B3 1SF, United Kingdom. TEL 44-1902-771134, FAX 44-1902-771195. Ed. John Rawson. Pub. Phil Walder. Adv. contact John Waters. page GBP 858; trim 178 x 254. Circ: 10,000. **Co-sponsor:** British Constructional Steelwork Association Ltd.

NEW YORK APARTMENT LAW INSIDER. see *REAL ESTATE*

690 340 USA
NEW YORK BUILDING LAWS MANUAL✶. Text in English. 1911. irreg. (amended 1993), latest 1990. looseleaf. USD 65. adv.
Published by: New York Society of Architects, 299 Broadway Rm 206, New York, NY 10007-1901. TEL 212-675-6646. Circ: 1,000.

NEW YORK CITY BUILDING CODE. see *LAW*

690 USA ISSN 1547-545X
NEW YORK CONSTRUCTION; serving the entire construction industry in New York, New Jersey and Connecticut. Text in English. 1953. w. USD 40 (effective 2005). adv. charts; illus.; mkt. **Document type:** *Magazine, Trade.* **Description:** Provides news, features, people and projects around the New York, New Jersey and Connecticut's region.
Formerly: New York Construction News (0028-7164)
Related titles: Online - full text ed.: (from EBSCO Publishing, LexisNexis, ProQuest Information & Learning).
Indexed: ABIn.
—CCC.
Published by: Mcgraw-Hill Construction Dodge (Subsidiary of: McGraw-Hill Construction Information Group), News 2 Penn Plz, 9th Fl, New York, NY 10121-2298. TEL 212-904-4775, 800-393-6343, http://newyork.construction.com, http://www.dodgeconstructionpublications.com. Ed. Natalie Keith. Adv. contact Ann Green. B&W page USD 1,285, color page USD 1,885; trim 10.88 x 8.5. Circ: 6,200.

NEW ZEALAND BUILDING ECONOMIST; current construction costs. see *ARCHITECTURE*

690 NZL ISSN 1174-863X
NEW ZEALAND HOME & ENTERTAINING. Text in English. 1936. bi-m. NZD 7.95 newsstand/cover. adv. charts; illus.; tr.lit. **Document type:** *Magazine, Consumer.* **Description:** Covers state of the art in New Zealand design. Includes domestic and commercial architecture, interior design, renovations, landscaping, and furnishings.
Former titles (until 1999): New Zealand Home and Building (0110-098X); (until 1975): Home and Building (0018-392X)
Indexed: INZP.
—CCC.
Published by: A C P New Zealand, 17B Hargreaves St, College Hill, Pasonby, Auckland, 1036, New Zealand. TEL 64-9-3735408, FAX 64-9-3089498. Circ: 30,000.

690 NGA
NIGERIA. NATIONAL INTEGRATED SURVEY OF HOUSEHOLDS. BUILDING AND CONSTRUCTION SURVEY. Text in English. a. **Document type:** *Government.*
Supersedes: Nigeria. Federal Office of Statistics. Building and Construction Survey
Published by: (Nigeria. National Integrated Survey of Households), Federal Office of Statistics, Dissemination Division, c/o Mrs. M.T. Osita, 36-38 Broad St, PMB 12528, Lagos, Nigeria. TEL 234-1-2601710-4.

690 JPN ISSN 0286-021X
NIHON KOKUDO KAIHATSU K.K. GIJUTSU KENKYU HOKOKU/JAPAN DEVELOPMENT AND CONSTRUCTION CORP. TECHNICAL REPORT. Text in Japanese. 1981. a. **Document type:** *Academic/Scholarly.*
Published by: Nihon Kokudo Kaihatsu K.K., Gijutsu Kenkyujo/Japan Development and Construction Corp., Technical Research Institute, 4036-1 Nakatsu, Aiko-gun, Aikawa-machi, Kanagawa-ken 243-0303, Japan.

NIKKEI DIGITAL KENSETSU. see *ARCHITECTURE—Computer Applications*

690 JPN ISSN 1344-901X
NIKKEI HOME BUILDER. Text in Japanese. 1999. m. JPY 20,000 (effective 2000). adv. back issues avail. **Document type:** *Trade.* **Description:** Offers practical information for technical experts in the field of house building, providing information that is essential for house-building experts in keeping up with the changes in market needs.
Published by: Nikkei Business Publications Inc. (Subsidiary of: Nihon Keizai Shimbun, Inc.), 2-7-6 Hirakawa-cho, Chiyoda-ku, Tokyo, 102-8622, Japan. TEL 81-3-5210-8311, FAX 81-3-5210-8530, info@nikkeibpnyc.com, info@nikkeibp-america.com, http://www.nikkeipb.com. Ed. Kazutaka Yonemori. Pub. Shoji Tanabe. Adv. contact Akira Sakaguchi. B&W page JPY 260,000, color page JPY 390,000; trim 208 x 280. Circ: 20,000. **Dist. in America by:** Nikkei Business Publications America Inc., 575 Fifth Ave, 20th Fl, New York, NY 10017.

B

NISSAN KENSETSU. GIJUTSU HONBU. GIJUTSU REPOTO/NISSAN CONSTRUCTION. TECHNICAL DEPARTMENT. TECHNICAL REPORT. see *ENGINEERING—Civil Engineering*

690 JPN
NISSAN KENSETSU. GIJUTSU HONBU. TEKUNIKARU REPOTO/NISSAN CONSTRUCTION. TECHNOLOGICAL REPORT. Text in Japanese. 1980. q. **Document type:** *Trade.*
Published by: Nissan Kensetsu K.K., Gijutsu Honbu, 2-6 Minami-Aoyama 1-chome, Minato-ku, Tokyo, 107-0062, Japan.

690 332 ITA
NOLEGGIO. Text in Italian. 2001. bi-m. EUR 25 domestic (effective 2004). **Document type:** *Magazine, Trade.*
Published by: Tecniche Nuove SpA, Via Eritrea 21, Milan, MI 201, Italy. TEL 39-02-390901, FAX 39-02-7570364, noleggio@tecnichenuove.com, info@tecnichenuove.com, http://www.tecnichenuove.com.

691 SWE ISSN 1402-5728
➤ **NORDIC JOURNAL OF BUILDING PHYSICS**; acta physica aedificiorum. Text in English. 1997. irreg. free (effective 2005). **Document type:** *Journal, Academic/Scholarly.* **Description:** Focuses on problems related to heat, air and moisture applied to buildings and building construction.
Media: Online - full text.
Published by: (Avdelningen foer Byggnadsteknik/Division of Building Technology), Kungliga Tekniska Hoegskolan, Institutionen foer Byggvetenskap/Royal Institute of Technology, Department of Civil Engineering and Architectural Engineering, Brinellvaegen 34, Stockholm, 10044, Sweden. bphys@ce.kth.se, bphys@byv.kth.se, http://www.byv.kth.se/avd/byte/bphys/. Ed., R&P Per Levin. **Co-sponsor:** Swedish Council for Building Research.

➤ **NORGES LANDBRUKSHOEGSKOLE. INSTITUTT FOR TEKNISKE FAG. RAPPORTER/AGRICULTURAL UNIVERSITY OF NORWAY. DEPARTMENT OF AGRICULTURAL ENGINEERING. RESEARCH REPORTS.** see *AGRICULTURE*

690 USA
NORTH AMERICAN BUILDING MATERIAL DISTRIBUTION ASSOCIATION. CHANNELS. Text in English. bi-m. USD 50 to members. adv. **Document type:** *Newsletter.*
Former titles: North American Building Material Distribution Association. Journal; National Building Materials Distributors. Journal
Published by: North American Building Material Distribution Association, 401 N Michigan Ave, Chicago, IL 60611-4274. TEL 312-321-6845, FAX 312-644-0310, nbmda@sba.com, http://www.nbmda.org. Ed. Kevin Grommonley. Pub. Kevin Gammonley. R&P Keven Gammonley. Adv. contact Chris Mundschenk.

691.3 USA ISSN 1046-7270
TP880.N7
NORTH AMERICAN CEMENT DIRECTORY INCLUDING MEXICO AND THE CARIBBEAN. Text in English. 1987. a. **Document type:** *Directory.*
Formerly (until 1989): North American Cement Directory (1048-3853)
Published by: Primedia Business Magazines & Media, Inc. (Subsidiary of: Primedia, Inc.), 330 N Wabash Ave, Ste 2300, Chicago, IL 60611.

693.1 USA ISSN 1053-2366
NORTH AMERICAN MASONRY CONFERENCE. PROCEEDINGS. Text in English. 1978. every 4 yrs. **Document type:** *Proceedings.*
—BLDSC (6848.291000).
Published by: (North American Masonry Conference), Masonry Society, 3970 Broadway St, Ste 201 D, Boulder, CO 80304-1135. TEL 303-939-9700, FAX 303-541-9215, info@masonrysociety.org, http://www.masonrysociety.org.

690 USA ISSN 1552-8685
NORTH CAROLINA BUILDER. Text in English. 11/yr. USD 30 (effective 2005).
Published by: Association Publishing Inc., 2117 Smith Ave, Chesapeake, VA 23320. TEL 757-420-2434, FAX 757-424-5954, http://www.statebuildermagazines.com. Ed. Terri Denison. Pubs. Joyce F Hearn, Sandra Amidon. Circ: 16,000.

NORTHEAST REAL ESTATE BUSINESS. see *REAL ESTATE*

690 GBR
NORTHERN BUILDER. Text in English. 1989. bi-m. GBP 1.50 per issue (effective 2000). adv. **Document type:** *Trade.*
Description: Covers in depth all sections of the building industry and its allied trades and professions in Northern Ireland.
Published by: Northern Builder Ltd., Unit 22, Lisburn Enterprise Centre, Ballinderry Rd Industrial Estate, Ballinderry Rd, Lisburn, BT28 2SA, United Kingdom. TEL 44-1846-663390, FAX 44-1846-666242, info@northerbuilder.co.uk, www.northernbuilder.co.uk. Ed. Alan Bailie. R&P, Adv. contact Barry Gibson. B&W page GBP 660, color page GBP 950. Circ: 5,000 (controlled).

690 USA ISSN 1546-9794
NORTHWEST CONSTRUCTION. Text in English. 1998. m. USD 40 (effective 2005). **Document type:** *Magazine, Trade.*
Description: Services the construction and related industries of Washington, Oregon, and Alaska.
Formerly: Construction Data & News
Related titles: Online - full text ed.
Published by: McGraw-Hill Companies, Inc., 3100 N. Central Ave., Ste. 155, Phoenix, AZ 85012. TEL 602-631-3073, FAX 602-631-3076, customer.service@mcgraw-hill.com, http://northwest.construction.com, http://www.mcgraw-hill.com. Ed. Sheila Bacon. Pub. Karen Heck. Circ: 6,500 (paid and controlled).

690 USA ISSN 1085-1941
NORTHWEST ILLINOIS CONSTRUCTION NEWS WEEKLY. Text in English. 1992. w. adv. **Document type:** *Newsletter, Trade.*
Description: Provides information on what jobs are coming up for bid or negotiation.
Related titles: Online - full text ed.
Published by: Mcgraw-Hill Construction Dodge (Subsidiary of: McGraw-Hill Construction Information Group), 148 Princeton-Hightstown Rd, Hightstown, NJ 08520. TEL 800-393-6343, http://www.dodgeconstructionpublications.com.

690 ESP ISSN 1138-4166
NOTA DE COYUNTURA, CONSTRUCCION. Text in Spanish. 1998. bi-m.
Related titles: Online - full text ed.
Indexed: IECT.
—CINDOC.
Published by: Ministerio de Fomento, Centro de Publicaciones, Paseo de la Castellana, 67, Madrid, 28029, Spain. TEL 34-91-5976187, FAX 34-91-5976186, cpublic@mfom.es, http://www.mfom.es/estadisticas/.

690.028 RUS
NOVYE PROMYSHLENNYE KATALOGI. STROITEL'NYE, DOROZHNYE I KOMMUNAL'NYE MASHINY I OBORUDOVANIE. STROITEL'NYE MATERIALY. Text in Russian. m. USD 355 in United States.
Published by: Rossiiskii N.I.I. Problem Transporta, Lubyanskii pr 5, Moscow, 101820, Russian Federation. TEL 7-095-9254609, FAX 7-095-2002203. **US dist. addr.:** East View Information Services, 3020 Harbor Ln. N., Minneapolis, MN 55447. TEL 612-550-0961.

690 DEU
NR 1. Text in German. 1973. a. **Document type:** *Bulletin.*
Published by: A B G Frankfurt Holding, Elbestr 48, Frankfurt Am Main, 60329, Germany. TEL 49-69-2608-0, FAX 49-69-2608333. Eds. Katie Hoeser, Petra Stoelting. Circ: 46,000.

690 USA ISSN 1542-0744
EL NUEVO CONSTRUCTOR. Text in Spanish. 2002 (Fall). 6/yr. free. **Document type:** *Magazine, Trade.* **Description:** Provides how-to training articles and information aimed at Hispanics working in the residential construction industry.
Published by: Hanley-Wood, LLC (Subsidiary of: J.P. Morgan Chase & Co.), One Thomas Circle, NW, Ste 600, Washington, DC 20005-5701. TEL 202-452-0800, FAX 202-785-1974, tjackson@hanleywood.com, http://www.elnuevoconstructor.com, http://www.hanleywood.com. Pub. Rick Strachan.

690 ITA ISSN 1592-1387
IL NUOVO BAGNO. Text in Italian. 1980. q. price varies. adv. **Document type:** *Catalog, Consumer.*
Published by: Di Baio Editore SpA, Via Luigi Settembrini 11, Milan, MI 20124, Italy. TEL 39-02-674951, FAX 39-02-67495228, http://www.dibaio.com. Ed. Giuseppe Maria Jonghi Lavarini.

690 ITA ISSN 0029-6325
IL NUOVO CANTIERE. Text in Italian. 1966. m. EUR 39 domestic; EUR 109 in Europe; EUR 117 elsewhere (effective 2005). adv. back issues avail. **Document type:** *Magazine, Trade.* **Description:** Presents current events, technology trends and market data on the building sector.
Formerly: Cantiere (0008-5715)
Published by: Tecniche Nuove SpA, Via Eritrea 21, Milan, MI 201, Italy. TEL 39-02-390901, FAX 39-02-7570364, nuovocantiere@tecnichenuove.com, info@tecnichenuove.com, http://www.tecnichenuove.com/epages/tecnichenuove.storefront/4309d7a9010431202740c0a80105058c/Product/View/NC&2D3. Ed. Roberto Anghinoni. Circ: 6,727.

NYA BYGGREGLER. see *BUILDING AND CONSTRUCTION—Abstracting, Bibliographies, Statistics*

624 CUB ISSN 1028-2149
O B R A S; la revista cubana de la construccion. Text in Esperanto. 1997. 3/yr. illus.
Published by: Centro de Informacion de la Construccion (CIC), Avd Carlos M de Cespedes y 35, Havana, Cuba. TEL 53-7-81-6998, 53-7-81-4934, FAX 53-7-33-5585, ctecnico@cenial.inf.cu. Circ: 4,000.

O T B WERKDOCUMENTEN. see *PUBLIC ADMINISTRATION*

691 NLD ISSN 1384-1173
O T BOUWSTENEN. Text in Dutch. 1996. irreg., latest vol.39, 1998. price varies. **Document type:** *Monographic series.*
Description: Discusses the use and manufacture of stone used in construction.
—KNAW.
Published by: Delft University Press (Subsidiary of: Technische Universiteit Delft/Delft University of Technology), PO Box 98, Delft, 2600 MG, Netherlands. TEL 31-15-278-3254, FAX 31-15-2781661, dup@dup.tudelft.nl.

690 MEX ISSN 0185-464X
OBRAS. Text in Spanish. 1973. m. USD 48 in US & Canada; USD 53 in Latin America; USD 57 in Europe. adv. illus.
Document type: *Trade.* **Description:** Covers the construction industry in Mexico.
Related titles: Online - full text ed.: ISSN 1605-4768. 1997.
Indexed: AIAP.
Published by: Grupo Editorial Expansion (Subsidiary of: Capital Cities - A B C, Inc.), SALAMANCA 35, Col Roma, Mexico City, DF 06700, Mexico. servicioaclientes@expansion.com.mx, http://www.obrasweb.com, http://www.gee.com.mx. Ed. Enrique Chao. Adv. contact Elena Bayardo. Circ: 10,623.

690 340 DEU ISSN 1432-623X
▼ **OEFFBAUR**; Monatsinformation zum Oeffentlichen Baurecht. Text in German. 2004. m. EUR 156 domestic; EUR 176.50 foreign; EUR 14.50 newsstand/cover (effective 2005).
Document type: *Journal, Trade.*
Published by: Verlag C.H. Beck oHG, Wilhelmstr 9, Munich, 80801, Germany. TEL 49-89-38189340, FAX 49-89-38189398, abo.service@beck.de, http://www.beck.de.

691 AUT
DER OESTERREICHISCHE BAUSTOFFMARKT; Fachblatt fuer den Baustoffhandel und die Baumaerkte. Text in German. 8/yr. EUR 66.70 domestic; EUR 81.30 foreign (effective 2005). adv.
Document type: *Journal, Trade.* **Description:** Covers all aspects of the building and construction industry.
Published by: Verlag Lorenz, Ebendorferstr 10, Vienna, W 1010, Austria. TEL 43-1-40566950, FAX 43-1-4068693, baustoff@verlag-lorenz.at, office@verlag-lorenz.at, http://www.verlag-lorenz.at/bm/baustoff.htm. Ed. Alois Froestl. Adv. contact Renate Kaspar. B&W page EUR 2,230, color page EUR 3,635; trim 185 x 264. Circ: 5,000 (paid and controlled).

690 AUT
OESTERREICHISCHE BAUWIRTSCHAFT; Das Magazin fuer Technik, Planung und Wirtschaft am Bau. Text in German. 1997. 10/yr. EUR 36 domestic; EUR 52 foreign; EUR 4 newsstand/cover (effective 2005). adv. illus.; mkt.; maps; tr.lit.
Document type: *Magazine, Trade.*
Related titles: Fax ed.; Online - full text ed.
Published by: Springer Business Media Austria GmbH (Subsidiary of: Springer Science+Business Media), Inkustr 16, Klosterneuburg, 3403, Austria. TEL 43-2243-301110, FAX 43-2243-30111222, office@springer-sbm.at, http://www.springer-sbm.at. Ed. Helmut Nussbaumer. Adv. contact Johan Grasser. B&W page EUR 3,224, color page EUR 4,730; trim 185 x 255. Circ: 9,350 (controlled).

690 AUT ISSN 0029-8891
TH3
OESTERREICHISCHE BAUZEITUNG. Text in German. 1962. w. EUR 130 domestic; EUR 205 foreign (effective 2005). adv. bk.rev. illus. **Document type:** *Newspaper, Trade.*
Indexed: CISA.
Published by: Oesterreichischer Wirtschaftsverlag GmbH (Subsidiary of: Sueddeutscher Verlag GmbH), Wiedner Hauptstr 120-124, Vienna, W 1051, Austria. TEL 43-1-546640, FAX 43-1-54664406, office@wirtschaftsverlag.at, http://www.wirtschaftsverlag.at. Ed. Gisela Gary. Adv. contact Robert Huber. B&W page EUR 3,045, color page EUR 4,350; trim 185 x 255. Circ: 9,892 (paid and controlled).

690 AUT ISSN 0029-9499
DER OESTERREICHISCHE SPENGLER UND KUPFERSCHMIED; offizielles Fachorgan der Bundesinnung. Text in German. 1947. m. adv. bk.rev. abstr.; illus.; stat.; tr.lit. index. **Document type:** *Magazine, Trade.*
Published by: Landesinnung Wien der Spengler und Kupferschmiede, Gruengasse 27, Vienna, W 1050, Austria. TEL 43-1-5873769, FAX 43-1-5870539, http://wien.spenglerinnung.at. Ed. Irmtraud Strohmayer. Circ: 2,000.

690 FRA ISSN 0294-0752
OFFICE DES PRIX DU BATIMENT - EDITION MACONNERIE PEINTURE. Text in French. 1975. 4/yr.
Address: 468 rue de la Croix Verte, BP 1061, Montpellier, Cedex 1 34007, France. TEL 67-41-01-52, FAX 67-52-49-27. Ed. Guy Dumons. Circ: 19,364.

690 FRA ISSN 1268-1393
L'OFFICIEL HEBDO; le journal des cuisinistes, des bainistes et des electromenagistes. Text in French. 1953. w. adv. back issues avail. **Document type:** *Newspaper.*
Former titles (until 1994): Officiel des Cuisinistes, des Bainistes et des Electromenagistes (1269-0538); Lettre des Cuisinistes, des Bainistes et des Electromenagistes (0988-4343)
Related titles: ◆ Supplement(s): Officiel Magazine (Montpellier). ISSN 1270-1602.
Published by: Officiel S.A., 26 allee Jules Milhau, Montpellier, Cedex 2 34265, France. TEL 33-04-67588228, FAX 33-04-67923886, sodiep@cuisirama.com, http://www.cuisirama.com, http://www.officielnet.com. Circ: 4,500.

618.13 FRA ISSN 1270-1602
OFFICIEL MAGAZINE (MONTPELLIER); revue de l'equipement de la cuisine et de la salle de bains. Text in French. 1996. m. included with subscription to L'Officiel Hebdo. **Document type:** *Magazine, Trade.*
Related titles: ◆ Supplement to: L' Officiel Hebdo. ISSN 1268-1393.
Published by: Officiel S.A., 26 allee Jules Milhau, Montpellier, Cedex 2 34265, France. TEL 33-04-67588228, FAX 33-04-67923886, info@officielnet.com, http://www.officielnet.com. Adv. contact Laurent Ventura. Circ: 3,500.

690 USA ISSN 1552-8707
OHIO BUILDER. Text in English. 1981. 6/yr. USD 18 (effective 2005). adv.
Published by: Association Publishing Inc., 2117 Smith Ave, Chesapeake, VA 23320. TEL 757-420-2434, FAX 757-424-5954, http://www.statebuildermagazines.com. Ed. Joan Stanus. Pubs. Joyce F Hearn, Sandra Amidon. adv.: B&W page USD 869, color page USD 1,189; trim 11 x 8.5. Circ: 9,000.

690 JPN
OKINAWAKEN KENSETSU GIJUTSU SENTA SHIKEN NENPO/OKINAWA CONSTRUCTION TECHNOLOGICAL CENTER. ANNUAL REPORT. Text in Japanese. a.
Published by: Okinawaken Kensetsu Gijutsu Senta/Okinawa Construction Technological Center, 7-13 Yori-Miya 1-chome, Naha-shi, Okinawa-ken 902-0064, Japan.

729 USA ISSN 0094-0178
TH3401
OLD HOUSE JOURNAL. Text in English. 1973. 6/yr. USD 21.97 domestic; USD 31.97 in Canada; USD 51.97 elsewhere (effective 2005). adv. bk.rev. illus. index. back issues avail.; reprints avail. **Document type:** *Magazine, Consumer.*
Description: How-to and technical data on restoration, plus period house styles, decorating and products for the pre-1939 home.
Related titles: Online - full text ed.
Indexed: A&ATA, AIAP, API, GardL, IHTDI, RGPR.
Published by: Restore Media LLC, 1000 Potomac St, N W, Ste 102, Washington, DC 20007. TEL 202-339-0744, FAX 202-339-0749, OHJ@palmcoastd.com, http://www.oldhousejournal.com/. Ed. Gordon Bock. Pub. Michael J. Tucker. Circ: 100,000 (paid).

729 691 USA ISSN 1077-2332
TH455
OLD-HOUSE JOURNAL RESTORATION DIRECTORY. Text in English. 1976. a. USD 14.95; USD 12.95 for subscr. to Old-House Journal. adv. illus. **Document type:** *Directory.*
Description: Extensively indexed listing of over 1,500 companies that provide restoration and renovation products and special services.
Former titles: Old-House Journal Directory; Old-House Journal Catalog (0271-7220); Old-House Journal Buyers' Guide
Published by: Hanley-Wood, LLC (Subsidiary of: J.P. Morgan Chase & Co.), One Thomas Circle, NW, Ste 600, Washington, DC 20005-5701. TEL 202-452-0800, FAX 202-785-1974, tjackson@hanleywood.com, http://www.hanleywood.com. Ed., Pub. Patricia Poore. R&P Lucy Oliver. Adv. contact Rebecca Bernie. Circ: 20,000.

B

691 CAN
ON THE LEVEL. Text in English. a.
Published by: Canadian Masonry Contractors' Association, 360 Superior Blvd, Mississauga, ON L5T 2N7, Canada. TEL 416-564-6622, FAX 416-564-5744.

690 NLD
ONDERNEMINGSANALYSES BOUW. Text in Dutch. a.
Description: Financial and economic information on the construction industry in the Netherlands.
Formerly (until 1992): Fact and Figures Bouw (Year) (0927-1260)
Published by: Reed Business Information bv (Subsidiary of: Reed Business), Postbus 16400, Den Haag, 2500 BK, Netherlands. TEL 31-70-3624800, FAX 31-70-3605606. Ed. H Stevens.

690 USA
OPTIONS; for today's fine homes. Text in English. 2000. bi-m. free to qualified personnel (effective 2005). adv. **Document type:** *Magazine, Trade.*
Published by: Peninsula Publishing, 1602 Monrovia Ave, Newport Beach, CA 92663. TEL 949-631-0308, FAX 949-631-2475, http://www.optionsmag.com/. Eds. Katie Pegler, Nick Slevin. Pub. Nick Slevin. Adv. contact Rona Fiedler. color page USD 4,900; trim 8.75 x 11.75. Circ: 25,000 (controlled).

OPUS DESIGN FILE. see *BUSINESS AND ECONOMICS—Trade And Industrial Directories*

690 720 ITA
ORDINE DEGLI INGEGNERI DELLA PROVINCIA DI PALERMO. BOLLETTINO. Text in Italian. 6/yr. **Document type:** *Bulletin.*
Published by: Ordine degli Ingegneri della Provincia di Palermo, Via Franceso Gristi 120, Milan, MI 90139, Italy. TEL 91-58-14-21. Ed. Roberta Messina.

690 USA ISSN 1552-874X
OREGON BUILDER. Text in English. 6/yr. USD 18 (effective 2003).
Published by: Association Publishing Inc., 2117 Smith Ave, Chesapeake, VA 23320. TEL 757-420-2434, FAX 757-424-5954, http://www.statebuildermagazines.com. Ed. Stacey Klemenc. Pubs. Joyce F Hearn, Sandra Amidon. Circ: 5,000.

690 CHE
ORGANE DU SYNDICAT DU BATIMENT ET DU BOIS. Text in French. 6/yr.
Address: 28 Avenue de Sevelin, Lausanne 20, 1000, Switzerland. TEL 021-6262627, FAX 021-6262628. Ed. Serge Baehler. Circ: 26,000.

ORNAMENTAL & MISCELLANEOUS METAL FABRICATOR. see *METALLURGY*

690 AUS ISSN 0728-7275
OWNER BUILDER MAGAZINE; the australasian home builders magazine. Text in English. 1981. bi-m. AUD 34.50 domestic; AUD 54 in New Zealand; AUD 64 elsewhere (effective 2004). adv. bk.rev. back issues avail. **Document type:** *Magazine, Consumer.* **Description:** "How to" build your own home or extensions; includes encouragement and inspirational stories of owner-builders in Australia.
Indexed: Pinpoint.
Published by: Russell Andrews & Association Pty. Ltd., 66 Broadway, Dunolly, VIC 3472, Australia. TEL 61-3-546899, FAX 61-3-54681899, obmag@iinet.net.au, http://www.byohouse.com.au/obmag/. Ed. Russell Andrews. Circ: 15,100.

691.3 USA ISSN 0887-9672
TA680 CODEN: PCIJEE
➤ **P C I JOURNAL.** Text in English. 1956. bi-m. USD 38 domestic; USD 53 foreign (effective 2001). adv. bk.rev. abstr.; charts; illus.; tr.lit. index, cum.index: 1956-1981. 160 p./no.; back issues avail. **Document type:** *Magazine, Academic/Scholarly.* **Description:** Reports on current research, design, construction and innovations in the use of precast and prestressed concrete.
Formerly (until 1982): Prestressed Concrete Institute Journal (0032-793X)
Related titles: Microfilm ed.: (from PQC).
Indexed: ASCA, ASFA, CRIA, CRICC, CivEngAb, ConcrAb, CurCont, EEA, ESPM, EngInd, GeotechAb, H&SSA, HRIS, ICEA, JOF, MSCI, SoftAbEng.
—BLDSC (6413.612000), CISTI, Ei, IDS, IE, Infotrieve, ingenta, Linda Hall.
Published by: Precast - Prestressed Concrete Institute, 209 W Jackson Blvd, Ste 500, Chicago, IL 60604. http://www.pci.org. R&P George D Nasser. Adv. contact Christine Beckmann. B&W page USD 1,240, color page USD 2,600; bleed 8.25 x 11.125. Circ: 8,300 (paid and controlled).

690 620 USA ISSN 0030-8544
TH1
PACIFIC BUILDER AND ENGINEER. Text in English. 1902. s-m. USD 96 domestic; USD 126 in Canada; USD 166 elsewhere; USD 10 newsstand/cover (effective 2005). adv. bk.rev. illus.; mkt.; tr.lit. index, cum.index. reprints avail. **Document type:** *Magazine, Trade.*
Related titles: Microform ed.: 1902 (from PQC); Online - full text ed.: (from Gale Group, ProQuest Information & Learning).
Indexed: RASB.
—Linda Hall. **CCC.**
Published by: Reed Construction Data, Associated Construction Publications (Subsidiary of: Reed Business Information), 30 Technology Pkwy, Ste 100, Norcross, GA 30092. TEL 800-322-6996, FAX 800-895-8661, acp@reedbusiness.com, http://www.acppubs.com, http://www.acppubs.com/. Ed. Carl Molesworth TEL 360-757-1949. Pub. John Weatherhead TEL 770-417-4120. Adv. contact John Weatherhead. B&W page USD 2,079, color page USD 2,579. Circ: 11,000 (controlled).

PAINTING AND WALLCOVERING CONTRACTOR. see *PAINTS AND PROTECTIVE COATINGS*

690 GBR ISSN 1361-1666
PANEL INDUSTRY MONITOR. Text in English. 1988. 10/yr. GBP 225; GBP 370 foreign. back issues avail. **Document type:** *Newsletter.* **Description:** Serves executive managers int he global wood based panel industry; examines markets, capacity, company and product developments.
Published by: Data Transcripts, PO Box 14, Dorking, Surrey RH5 4YN, United Kingdom. TEL 44-1306-884473. Ed. Ward Williams.

690 790.1 GBR
GV401
PANSTADIA INTERNATIONAL QUARTERLY REPORT; the definitive journal for the sports facility industry worldwide. Text in English. 1993. q. GBP 100 domestic; USD 180 foreign (effective 2005). adv. bk.rev. tr.lit.; stat. back issues avail. **Document type:** *Journal, Trade.* **Description:** Publishes a mix of articles on the sports facility market, including new products, services and innovations, case studies of new stadia-arenas or rebuilt, and educational articles on all aspects of the planning, building, fitting-out, and management of stadia and arenas world-wide.
—BLDSC (6357.476500), ingenta.
Published by: Panstadia Publishing Company Ltd., The Stadium Centre II, Hall Farm House, 9 High St, Castle Donington, Derby, Derbys DE74 2PP, United Kingdom. TEL 44-1332-814555, FAX 44-1332-814745, enquiries@panstadia.com, sales@panstadia.com, http://www.panstadia.com. Ed. Tony Chakraborty. Pub. Julian A Radley. R&P, Adv. contact Katie L Else TEL 44-1332-814745. color page GBP 4,832; trim 210 x 297. Circ: 52,000.

PAPUA NEW GUINEA. NATIONAL STATISTICAL OFFICE. BUILDING STATISTICS. see *BUILDING AND CONSTRUCTION—Abstracting, Bibliographies, Statistics*

690 FRA ISSN 1153-026X
PARIS LE JOURNAL. Text in French. 1977. m. free (effective 2005). bk.rev. **Document type:** *Magazine, Consumer.*
Formerly: Ville de Paris (0220-8156)
Published by: Association pour l'Information Municipale, Hotel de Ville, Paris R.p., 75196, France. TEL 33-1-42767530, FAX 33-1-427610445. Ed. Patrice de Clinchamps. Circ: 1,100,000.

PARKING NEWS; B P A - parking news. see *TRANSPORTATION—Roads And Traffic*

PEOPLE & PROFITS; Bill Lee's tips, tactics and how-to's for the building supply, hardware and home center industry. see *BUSINESS AND ECONOMICS—Marketing And Purchasing*

690 USA ISSN 1081-9592
PERMANENT BUILDINGS AND FOUNDATIONS; the business news magazine for the concrete builder. Text in English. 1989. 8/yr. USD 40 domestic; USD 52 in Canada & Mexico; USD 75 elsewhere; USD 5 newsstand/cover (effective 2000). adv. bk.rev. back issues avail. **Document type:** *Trade.* **Description:** Covers new products, business management, techniques, and trends in permanent building for residential or commercial use. For general and concrete contractors and home builders.
Formerly: Foundations
Related titles: Online - full text ed.
Published by: R.W. Nielsen Company, 5245 N Kensington, PO Box 11067, Kansas City, MO 64119. TEL 816-453-0590, 800-748-7690, FAX 816-453-0591, http://www.pbf.org. Ed., Pub., R&P Roger W Nielsen. Adv. contact Bill Edson. B&W page USD 3,377; trim 10.75 x 8. Circ: 30,000.

PERSPECTIVE. see *ARCHITECTURE*

PERSPECTIVE (INDIANAPOLIS). see *REAL ESTATE*

PHILIPPINE ARCHITECTURE, ENGINEERING & CONSTRUCTION RECORD. see *ARCHITECTURE*

PILELINE ONLINE; the magazine for foundation, engineering and construction professionals. see *ENGINEERING—Civil Engineering*

LA PISCINA. see *ARCHITECTURE*

690 ESP ISSN 0210-6868
PISCINAS XXI; revista de la construccion, mantenimiento, equipo y accesorios de la piscina. Text in Spanish. 1976. 8/yr. EUR 132.60 domestic; EUR 147.62 foreign (effective 2003). adv. back issues avail. **Document type:** *Trade.* **Description:** Covers building, maintenance and equipment for swimming pools, spas and saunas.
Published by: Reed Business Information SA (Subsidiary of: Reed Business Information International), Zancoeta 9, Bilbao, 48013, Spain. TEL 34-944-285600, FAX 34-944-425116, rbi@rbi.es, http://www.rbi.es. Ed. Marcel Lleal. Pub. Manuel Masip. Adv. contact Eduardo Lazaro. Circ: 6,000.

690 FRA ISSN 1287-5007
PISCINES & SPAS. Text in French. 1967. 5/yr. adv. charts; illus.; stat.; tr.lit. **Description:** Review specializing in construction and equipping.
Former titles (until 1998): Piscines - Spas Magazine (0295-5725); Piscines (0032-0285)
Published by: Editions Christian Ledoux S.A., 155 av. de Paris, Villejuif, Cedex 94807, France. TEL 46-77-70-70, FAX 46-77-32-55, TELEX 260 808 F TXFRA. Ed. Charlotte Le Baron. Circ: 40,000. **Subscr. to:** Praxs s.a., 68 rue des Bruyeres, Les Lilas 93260, France.

PLAISIRS DE VIVRE/LIVING IN STYLE. see *INTERIOR DESIGN AND DECORATION*

PLANERA BYGGA BO. see *HOUSING AND URBAN PLANNING*

PLANNING. see *ARCHITECTURE*

PLANNING AND DEVELOPMENT SERVICE NEW SOUTH WALES. see *LAW*

690.028 GBR
PLANT & EQUIPMENT GUIDE; the standard reference for new and used construction equipment values. Text in English. 1969. m. looseleaf. GBP 175 domestic; GBP 225 foreign (effective 1999). mkt. **Document type:** *Directory.* **Description:** Provides information guide to used plant and equipment prices.
Published by: Emap Construct Ltd. (Subsidiary of: Emap Business Communications Ltd.), 151 Rosebery Ave, London, EC1R 4GB, United Kingdom. TEL 44-20-7505-6606, FAX 44-20-7505-6610. Circ: 500 (paid).

PLANT MANAGERS JOURNAL. see *BUSINESS AND ECONOMICS—Management*

690 GBR
PLANT WORLD. Text in English. 1981. bi-w. GBP 35 (effective 1999). adv. **Document type:** *Trade.*
Formerly: World Plant
Published by: Sheen Publishing Ltd., Sheen Publishing Ltd, 50 Queens Rd, Buckhurst Hill, Essex IG9 5DD, United Kingdom. TEL 44-181-504-1661, FAX 44-181-505-4336. Ed. Carole Titmuss. Pubs. Carole Titmuss, Tony Prior. Adv. contact Sandie Handworker. Circ: 12,000.

690 IRL
PLANTMAN MAGAZINE; the plant, construction and quarrying magazine. Text in English. 1970. m. adv. **Document type:** *Magazine, Trade.* **Description:** Aims at major operators in the civil engineering field and covers publications for the plant, construction and quarrying industries.
Address: 1 The Green, Kingswood Heights, Dublin, 24, Ireland. info@plantmanmagazine.com, http://www.plantmanmagazine.com. Ed., R&P Patrick Murphy. adv.: color page EUR 1,600; trim 210 x 297. Circ: 4,750 (controlled).

PLASTERER AND CEMENT MASON. see *LABOR UNIONS*

690 668.4 GBR ISSN 0147-2429
PLASTICS IN BUILDING CONSTRUCTION. Text in English. 1976. m. GBP 456 combined subscription to institutions print & electronic eds. in Europe, Middle East, Africa & Australasia; USD 661 combined subscription elsewhere to institutions print & electronic eds. (effective 2004). bk.rev. stat. back issues avail.; reprints avail. **Document type:** *Newsletter.* **Description:** Reports on the news and information pertaining to polymeric products used in building and construction.
Related titles: E-mail ed.; Online - full content ed.: ISSN 1531-1988. 1999; Online - full text ed.: (from Swets Information Services).
Indexed: BrCerAb, C&ISA, CerAb, CivEngAb, CorrAb, E&CAJ, EMA, EngInd, IAA, M&TEA, MBF, METADEX, RAPRA, SolStAb, WAA.
—BLDSC (6531.910000), CISTI, IE, Infotrieve, ingenta, Linda Hall. **CCC.**
Published by: Sage Publications Ltd. (Subsidiary of: Sage Publications, Inc.), 1 Oliver's Yard, 55 City Rd, London, EC1 1SP, United Kingdom. TEL 44-20-73248500, FAX 44-20-73248600, info@sagepub.co.uk, http://www.sagepub.co.uk/journal.aspx?pid=105733. Ed. James P Harrington. Circ: 90 (paid).

POLISH CONSTRUCTION REVIEW. see *BUSINESS AND ECONOMICS—Investments*

B

POLITECHNIKA GDANSKA. ZESZYTY NAUKOWE. BUDOWNICTWO LADOWE. see *ENGINEERING—Civil Engineering*

POLITECHNIKA LODZKA. ZESZYTY NAUKOWE. BUDOWNICTWO. see *ENGINEERING—Civil Engineering*

690 624 POL ISSN 0137-2297
POLITECHNIKA WARSZAWSKA. PRACE NAUKOWE. BUDOWNICTWO. Text in Polish. 1953. irreg., latest no.133, 1999. **Document type:** *Academic/Scholarly.*
Formerly (until 1968): Politechnika Warszawska. Zeszyty Naukowe. Budownictwo (0509-7002)
—Linda Hall.
Published by: Oficyna Wydawnicza Politechniki Warszawskiej/Publishing House of the Warsaw University of Technology, ul Polna 50, Warsaw, 00644, Poland. bgpw@bg.pw.edu.pl, http://www.wpw.pw.edu.pl.

690 USA ISSN 0363-5864
PORTLAND CEMENT ASSOCIATION. RESEARCH AND DEVELOPMENT BULLETIN. Text in English. 1953. irreg. USD 15 (effective 2004).
Formerly: Portland Cement Association Development Department. Bulletin (0554-7407)
—CISTI, Linda Hall.
Published by: Portland Cement Association, 5240 Old Orchard Rd, Skokie, IL 60077-1083. TEL 847-966-6200, FAX 847-966-8389, info@cement.org, http://www.portcement.org.

690 ESP ISSN 0032-5600
POTENCIA; revista tecnica de maquinaria para obras publicas, construccion y excavacion. Text in Spanish. 1964. 13/yr. EUR 143.75 domestic; EUR 228 in Europe (effective 2004). adv. bibl.; illus.; tr.lit. **Document type:** *Magazine, Trade.*
Related titles: ◆ Supplement to: Power Engineering International. ISSN 1069-4994.
Indexed: IECT.
—CCC.
Published by: Goodman Business Press S.A., Goya 115, 4to. dcha., Madrid, 28009, Spain. TEL 34-91-3096310, FAX 34-91-4018090, info@goodman-bp.com, http://www.goodman-bp.com. Ed. Greg Reed. Pub. Marsha Robertson. R&P Brian Taylor. Adv. contact Jane Harrod. Circ: 12,000. **Co-publisher:** PennWell Corp.

690 CAN ISSN 0226-9597
PRACTICAL HOMES. Text in English. 1955. a., latest vol.30, 1996. CND 3.50 newsstand/cover (effective 2000). adv. charts. back issues avail. **Document type:** *Catalog.* **Description:** Features floor plans and architectural designs for houses by top Canadian designers.
Published by: Giroux Publishing, 102 Ellis St, Penticton, BC V2A 4L5, Canada. TEL 604-493-0942, FAX 604-493-7526, plan@westhomeplanners.com. Ed. Michael A Giroux. Adv. contact Michael Giroux. page CND 1,858; trim 10.5 x 8.13. Circ: 10,000.

747 GBR ISSN 0079-4813
PRACTICAL HOUSEHOLDER. Text in English. 1955. m. USD 23.40; GBP 32.20 in Europe; GBP 47.20 elsewhere. adv.
Incorporates: New Homemaker (0144-1620); Practical Home-Building and Decorating (0032-6402)
Related titles: ◆ Supplement(s): Home Plus. ISSN 0266-3910.
Indexed: Pinpoint.
Published by: Nexus Media Ltd. (Subsidiary of: Highbury House Communications PLC), Nexus House, Azalea Dr, Swanley, Kent BR8 8HU, United Kingdom. TEL 44-1442-66551, FAX 44-1442-66998. Ed. John McGowan. R&P Tony Debell. Adv. contact Paul Barrett. B&W page GBP 1,095. Circ: 76,778.

PRACTICE PERIODICAL ON STRUCTURAL DESIGN AND CONSTRUCTION. see *ENGINEERING—Civil Engineering*

643.7 USA ISSN 1539-9540
PREMIER HOMES. Text in English. 2002. a. USD 8.95 newsstand/cover (effective 2003).
Published by: Home Planners, LLC (Subsidiary of: Hanley-Wood, LLC), 3275 W Ina Rd, Ste 220, Tucson, AZ 85741-2153. TEL 888-846-8188, http://www.homeplanners.com.

690 USA ISSN 0741-9023
PRESERVATION TECH NOTES. Text in English. 1984. irreg.
Indexed: AIAP.
Published by: U.S. Department of the Interior, National Park Service, Heritage Preservation Services, 1849 C Street NW, Washington, DC 20240. TEL 202-208-6843, nps_hps-info@nps.gov, http://www2.cr.nps.gov/tps/technotes/tnhome.htm, http://www2.cr.nps.gov/welcome.htm. **Subscr. to:** U.S. Government Printing Office, Superintendent of Documents, 732 N Capitol St, NW, Washington, DC 20401. TEL 866-512-1800.

PRESS RELEASE - BUILDING SOCIETIES ASSOCIATION. see *BUILDING AND CONSTRUCTION—Abstracting, Bibliographies, Statistics*

PREVISIONS GLISSANTES DETAILLEES EN PERSPECTIVES SECTORIELLES (VOL.28): BATIMENTS D'ACTIVITE. see *BUSINESS AND ECONOMICS—Economic Situation And Conditions*

PREVISIONS GLISSANTES DETAILLEES EN PERSPECTIVES SECTORIELLES (VOL.30): MATERIAUX DE CONSTRUCTION I. see *BUSINESS AND ECONOMICS—Economic Situation And Conditions*

PREVISIONS GLISSANTES DETAILLEES EN PERSPECTIVES SECTORIELLES (VOL.31): MATERIAUX ET COMPOSANTS DE CONSTRUCTION II. see *BUSINESS AND ECONOMICS—Economic Situation And Conditions*

PREVISIONS GLISSANTES DETAILLEES EN PERSPECTIVES SECTORIELLES (VOL.5): CONSTRUCTION DE MACHINES. see *BUSINESS AND ECONOMICS—Economic Situation And Conditions*

690 ITA
PREZZI INFORMATIVI PER OPERE EDILI. Text in Italian. 1985. 4/yr. EUR 122 (effective 2005). **Document type:** *Directory, Trade.* **Description:** Provides price guidelines for the building industry.
Published by: Maggioli Editore, Via del Carpino 8/10, Santarcangelo di Romagna, RN 47822, Italy. TEL 39-0541-628111, FAX 39-0541-622020, editore@maggioli.it, http://www.maggioli.it. Ed. Roberto Passoni. Circ: 6,000. **Co-publisher:** Passoni Editore.

690 CAN
PRO-CONTRACTOR. Text in English. q. CND 12 (effective 2005). **Document type:** *Magazine, Trade.* **Description:** Provides a communication outlet for businesses and individuals involved in construction and building industry in Alberta.
Address: 104, 524-17 Ave S W, Calgary, AB, Canada. TEL 403-209-6505, FAX 403-209-6508, info@procontractor.ca, http://www.procontractor.ca.

690 DEU ISSN 0944-2065
PRO FERTIGHAUS; der gute Weg zum Eigenheim. Text in German. 1993. bi-m. EUR 1 newsstand/cover (effective 2003). adv. **Document type:** *Magazine, Consumer.*
Published by: Fachschriften Verlag GmbH, Hoehenstr 17, Fellbach, 70736, Germany. TEL 49-711-52061, FAX 49-711-5206223, info@fachschriften.de, http://www.fachschriften.de/publikationen/profertighaus.htm. Ed. Paul Daleiden. Adv. contact Barbara Hoof. B&W page EUR 5,481, color page EUR 9,098; trim 187 x 247. Circ: 68,082 (paid and controlled).

690 POL ISSN 0555-2966
PROBLEMY ROZWOJU BUDOWNICTWA/PROBLEMS OF BUILDING GROWTH. Text in Polish; Contents page in English, French, German, Russian. 1963. q. PLZ 120 (effective 2000). bk.rev. **Document type:** *Newspaper.*
Formerly (until 1969): Problemy Inwestowania i Rozwoju (0032-9517)
Related titles: Microfiche ed.
Published by: Instytut Gospodarki Mieszkaniowej, Ul. Filtrowa 1, Warsaw, 00-925, Poland. TEL 48-22-8250683, FAX 48-22-8250683, igm@warman.com.pl. Ed. Inga Ogonowska. Pub., R&P Ryszard Uchman. Adv. contact Zofia Karsznia. Circ: 2,000.

690 USA ISSN 1072-0561
TH1
PROFESSIONAL BUILDER. Text in English. 1936. 17/yr. (plus "Construct", published 6 times per yr.). USD 109.90 domestic; USD 179.90 in Canada; USD 164.90 in Mexico; USD 292.90 elsewhere; USD 10 newsstand/cover domestic; free to qualified personnel (effective 2005); Includes Luxury Home Builder. adv. bk.rev. charts; illus.; mkt.; tr.lit. reprints avail. **Document type:** *Magazine, Trade.* **Description:** Covers the residential and light commercial construction and remodeling industries, featuring legislation, news, market data, merchandising, technology, design, land development, financing and new products.
Former titles (until 1993): Professional Builder and Remodeler (1053-6353); (until 1990): Professional Builder (0885-8020); (until 1985): Professional Builder and Apartment Business (0361-5316); (until 1972): Professional Builder (0033-0043); (until 1967): Practical Builder
Related titles: CD-ROM ed.; Microfiche ed.: (from CIS); Online - full text ed.: (from EBSCO Publishing, Florida Center for Library Automation, Gale Group, H.W. Wilson, Northern Light Technology, Inc., O C L C Online Computer Library Center, Inc., ProQuest Information & Learning).
Indexed: ABIn, BPI, BrCerAb, BusI, C&ISA, CerAb, CorrAb, E&CAJ, EIA, EMA, EnvAb, IAA, M&TEA, MBF, METADEX, SRI, Search, SolStAb, T&II, WAA.
—BLDSC (6857.300000), CIS, CISTI, IE, ingenta, Linda Hall. **CCC.**
Published by: Reed Business Information (Subsidiary of: Reed Business), 2000 Clearwater Dr, Oak Brook, IL 60525. TEL 630-288-8180, FAX 630-288-8179, dhorowitz@reedbusiness.com, http://www.housingzone.com/pb/, http://www.reedbusiness.com. Eds. Heather McCune TEL 630-288-8190, Roy Diez. Pub. Dean Horowitz TEL 630-288-8180. adv.: B&W page USD 7,865, color page USD 11,130. Circ: 127,277 (paid and controlled).

690 USA
PROFESSIONAL BUILDER'S HOME PLAN DATABASE CD-ROM. Text in English. a. USD 54.95 (effective 1999). **Document type:** *Directory.* **Description:** Provides an extensive source to help new-home builders, architects, designers and consumers find and select the new-house plans that best fit their needs.
Media: CD-ROM.
Published by: HomeStyles Publishing & Marketing, Inc., 213 E. 4th St., 4th Fl., St. Paul, MN 55101-1603. TEL 612-602-5000, 888-626-2026, http://www.homestyles.com. Circ: 3,000 (paid).

690 GBR ISSN 0967-2605
PROFESSIONAL BUILDERS MERCHANT. Abbreviated title: P B M. Text in English. 1992. 10/yr. GBP 27; GBP 35 in Ireland; GBP 39 elsewhere. **Document type:** *Trade.*
Published by: Hamerville Magazines Ltd., Regal House, Regal Way, Watford, Herts WD2 4YJ, United Kingdom. TEL 44-1923-237799, FAX 44-1923-246901.

721.822 USA
▼ **PROFESSIONAL DOOR DEALER.** Text in English. 2003. bi-m. USD 12.99 domestic; USD 29.95 foreign (effective 2005). adv. **Document type:** *Magazine, Trade.* **Description:** Focused on providing more of the news, features and essential knowledge required to run the businesses of today.
Related titles: Online - full text ed.
Published by: Virgo Publishing, Inc., 3300 N. Central Ave., Ste 300, Phoenix, AZ 85012. TEL 480-990-1101, FAX 480-990-0819, cs@vpico.com, http://www.professionaldoordealer.com/, http://www.vpico.com. Ed. Amy Campbell TEL 480-990-1101 ext 1598. Pub. Mike Saxby TEL 480-990-1104 ext 1666. adv.: B&W page USD 2,204; trim 8.125 x 10.875. Circ: 15,000.

690 USA ISSN 1521-9135
TH4816
PROFESSIONAL REMODELER. Text in English. 1997. bi-m. USD 77.90 domestic; USD 97 in Canada; USD 128.50 elsewhere; USD 15 newsstand/cover domestic; USD 20 newsstand/cover foreign (effective 2004). adv. **Document type:** *Magazine, Trade.* **Description:** Source of industry information for remodelers, buyers and specifiers in top metro markets. Articles vocer innovative construction techniques and the latest management ideas that will increase the remodeler's quality, reduce costs and shorten the time needed to successfully complete each job.
Related titles: Online - full text ed.: (from EBSCO Publishing, Gale Group, H.W. Wilson, O C L C Online Computer Library Center, Inc., ProQuest Information & Learning).
Indexed: BPI.
Published by: Reed Business Information (Subsidiary of: Reed Business), 2000 Clearwater Dr, Oak Brook, IL 60525. TEL 630-288-8180, FAX 630-288-8179, dhorowitz@reedbusiness.com, http://www.housingzone.com/pr/index.asp, http://www.reedbusiness.com. Eds. Heather McCune TEL 630-288-8190, Rod Sutton. Circ: 65,000 (paid).

695 USA ISSN 0896-5552
TH2430
PROFESSIONAL ROOFING. Text in English. 1962. m. USD 30 in North America; USD 70 elsewhere (effective 2005). back issues avail.; reprints avail. **Document type:** *Magazine, Trade.* **Description:** Examines commercial, industrial and residential roofing issues through features, columns, and technical articles.
Formerly (until 1988): Roofing Spec (0199-7742)
—BLDSC (6864.214000), CISTI.
Published by: National Roofing Contractors Association, O'Hare International Center, 10255 W Higgins Rd, Ste 600, Rosemont, IL 60018-5607. TEL 847-299-9070, FAX 847-299-1183, bailey@nrca.net, nrca@nrca.net, http://www.professionalroofing.net, http://www.narca.net. Ed. Ambika Bailey. Pub. Carl Good. Adv. contact Jeff Jarvis. Circ: 20,000 (controlled).

690 USA
PROFESSIONAL SERVICES BULLETIN. Text in English. m. back issues avail. **Document type:** *Bulletin, Government.* **Description:** Provides the official advertisement to secure design services for CDB.
Related titles: Online - full content ed.
Published by: Capital Development Board, 3rd Fl, Stratton Bldg, 401 S Spring St, Springfield, IL 62706. TEL 217-782-2864, FAX 217-782-8625, http://www.cdb.state.il.us/.

690 ZAF
PROFESSIONS AND PROJECTS REGISTER. Text in English. 1988. a. ZAR 212 (effective 1998). **Document type:** *Trade.* **Description:** Details for architects, quantity purveyors, engineers and land surveyors in the housing construction and engineering industries, including all major projects in Southern Africa.
Published by: Avonwold Publishing Co. (Pty) Ltd., Avonwold House, 24 Baker St, Rosebank, Johannesburg, 2196, South Africa. TEL 27-11-788-1610, FAX 27-11-880-2732. Ed. E T Braby. Circ: 6,250.

338.476 NZL ISSN 1173-9916
PROGRESSIVE BUILDING. Text in English. bi-m.

Published by: A G M Publishing Ltd., Newmarket, Private Bag 99 915, Auckland, 1031, New Zealand. TEL 64-9-8464068, FAX 64-9-8468742, agm@agm.co.nz, http://www.agm.co.nz. Ed. Steve Bohling. Pub. Robin Beckett.

690 IRL
PROJECT MANAGEMENT. Text in English. bi-m. adv. **Document type:** *Magazine, Trade.*
Published by: Tara Publishing Co. Ltd., Poolbeg House, 1-2 Poolbeg St, Dublin, 2, Ireland. TEL 353-1-6719244, FAX 353-1-2413020, pm@tarapublishingco.com, info@tarapublishingco.com. Ed. Ruth Walton. Adv. contact Bernard Potter. B&W page EUR 1,700, color page EUR 2,000.

PROJECT PLANNING AND CONTROL FOR CONSTRUCTION. see *HOUSING AND URBAN PLANNING*

PROJECT RUSSIA/PROEKT ROSSIYA; journal on architecture, urbanism, design, technology. see *ARCHITECTURE*

690 GBR
PROJECT SCOTLAND. Text in English. 1970. m. GBP 58.50 domestic; GBP 65 foreign (effective Oct. 2002). adv. **Document type:** *Trade.*
Incorporates: Cope in Scotland
Published by: Peebles Media Group, Bergius House, Clifton St, Glasgow, G3 7LA, United Kingdom. TEL 44-141-567-6000, FAX 44-141-353-2336, projectscotland@peeblesmedia.com, info@peeblesmedia.com, http://www.peeblesmedia.com/ps/index.htm. Ed. Mike Travers. Adv. contact Mark Griston. Circ: 6,100.

690 MEX
PROMACASA. Text in Spanish. 1971. m. adv.
Address: Av Cuauhtemoc 1486, 401C, Mexico City, DF, Mexico. Ed. Rafael Cordova. Circ: 8,000.

PROMOZIONE SICUREZZA. see *LABOR UNIONS*

690 RUS ISSN 0033-118X
TH4 CODEN: PMSTAO
PROMYSHLENNOE STROITEL'STVO. Contents page in English, German. 1923. m. RUR 27. adv. charts; illus.; stat. index.
Indexed: ChemAb, EngInd, GeotechAb, RASB.
—CASDDS, CISTI.
Published by: Gosstroi, Tret'yakovskii pr-t 1, kom 2, Moscow K-12, Russian Federation. Ed. P I Karalov. Circ: 12,000.

690 VEN
PRONTUARIO TECNICO DE LA CONSTRUCCION. Text in Spanish. 1975. a. adv.
Published by: Prontuario Tecnico Comercial, Ave. Miquel Angel, Prolonga Lion el Casquillito, Resd. Hilton, Ofc 1, PO Box, Colinas de Bello Monte, Caracas, DF 1050, Venezuela.

PROPERTIES. see *REAL ESTATE*

691 USA ISSN 1055-3444
PROSALES. Text in English. 1989. m. USD 36 domestic; USD 52 in Canada; USD 192 elsewhere; free to qualified personnel (effective 2005). illus. **Document type:** *Magazine, Trade.* **Description:** Helps building product dealers, distributors, and wholesalers better understand the needs of their professional customers, home builders and remodeling contractors.
Related titles: Online - full text ed.: (from Florida Center for Library Automation, Gale Group).
Published by: Hanley-Wood, LLC (Subsidiary of: J.P. Morgan Chase & Co.), One Thomas Circle, NW, Ste 600, Washington, DC 20005-5701. TEL 202-452-0800, FAX 202-785-1974, tjackson@hanleywood.com, http://www.prosalesmagazine.com, http://www.hanleywood.com. Ed. Lisa Clift. Pubs. Nellie Callahan, Rick Strachan. Circ: 36,000 (controlled).

690 CAN
PROVEN AND POPULAR HOME PLANS. Text in English. 1994. a. CND 5.95 (effective 2000). adv. **Document type:** *Catalog.* **Description:** Features designs from Canada's top home designers and editorial features on the latest housing innovations.
Published by: Giroux Publishing, 102 Ellis St, Penticton, BC V2A 4L5, Canada. TEL 604-493-0942, FAX 604-493-7526, plan@westhomeplanners.com. Ed. Michael A Giroux. Pub. G T Giroux. Adv. contact Dennis Thatchuk. Circ: 10,000 (controlled).

PUBLIC SECTOR PROPERTY. see *BUSINESS AND ECONOMICS—Marketing And Purchasing*

690 SGP
PUBLIC SECTOR STANDARD CONDITIONS OF CONTRACT (YEAR). Text in English. irreg., latest 1999. SGD 21.60 per issue domestic; USD 50 per issue foreign (effective 2001). reprints avail. **Document type:** *Trade.*
Published by: Building and Construction Authority, 5 Maxwell Rd, No 08-00 MND Complex Tower Block, Singapore, 069110, Singapore. TEL 65-3257720, FAX 65-3254800, http://www.bca.gov.sg/.

690 SGP
PUBLIC SECTOR STANDARD CONDITIONS OF CONTRACT FOR DESIGN AND BUILD (YEAR). Text in English. irreg., latest 2001. SGD 21.60 per issue domestic; USD 50 per issue foreign (effective 2001). **Document type:** *Trade.*
Published by: Building and Construction Authority, 5 Maxwell Rd, No 08-00 MND Complex Tower Block, Singapore, 069110, Singapore. TEL 65-3257720, FAX 65-3254800, http://www.bca.gov.sg/.

PUBLIC WORKS RESEARCH INSTITUTE. JOURNAL OF RESEARCH. see *ENGINEERING—Civil Engineering*

690 CAN ISSN 0829-6359
PUBLIQUIP. Text in English. 1983. m. CND 35, USD 50. adv. back issues avail. **Document type:** *Trade.*
Formerly: Publiquip - Roucam
Published by: Publiquip Inc., 10595 Louis H. Lafontaine, Anjou, PQ H1J 2E8, Canada. TEL 514-351-1110. Ed., Pub. Gilles Chevigny. Adv. contact Michel Levasseur. Circ: 38,500.

674 690 DNK ISSN 0106-2018
PUFF; fagtidsskrift for traelast- og byggemarkeder. Text in Danish. 1977. 11/yr. DKK 410 domestic (effective 2000). adv. **Document type:** *Trade.*
Published by: Odsgard AS, Stationsparken 25, Glostrup, 2600, Denmark. TEL 45-43-43-29-00, FAX 45-43-43-13-28. Ed. Peter Odsgard. Adv. contact Michael Staal. B&W page DKK 8,915, color page DKK 12,495; trim 262 x 185. Circ: 1,950.

690 624 JPN ISSN 0387-1983
PURESUTORESUTO KONKURITO/JOURNAL OF PRESTRESSED CONCRETE. Text in Japanese. 1959. bi-m.
Indexed: ConcrAb, INIS AtomInd.
—BLDSC (5042.225000).
Published by: Puresutoresuto Konkurito Gijutsu Kyokai/Japan Prestressed Concrete Engineering Association, 4-6 Tsukudo-cho, Shinjuku-ku, Tokyo, 162-0821, Japan.

Q P A STATISTICAL YEARBOOK. see *BUILDING AND CONSTRUCTION—Abstracting, Bibliographies, Statistics*

690.2 USA ISSN 0098-9207
TH4816
QUALIFIED REMODELER. Text in English. 1975. a. free to qualified personnel. adv. illus. reprints avail. **Document type:** *Magazine, Trade.* **Description:** Emphasizes on the ways to improve contractors' business management skills and provides them with resources and information needed for long-term success.
Incorporates (1985-1991): Kitchen and Bath Concepts (8750-9504)
Related titles: Online - full text ed.: (from EBSCO Publishing, Gale Group, ProQuest Information & Learning).
—CCC.
Published by: Cygnus Business Media, Inc., 1233 Janesville Ave, Fort Atkinson, WI 53538-0803. roger.stanley@cygnusb2b.com, http://qrmagazine.com. Ed. Patrick O'Toole. Pub. Tom Drozda. adv.: B&W page USD 10,185, color page USD 11,450. Circ: 85,000 (paid and controlled).

691.3 GBR ISSN 1357-7336
QUALITY CONCRETE. Text in English. 1982. m. GBP 30, USD 50. adv. bk.rev. **Document type:** *Trade.* **Description:** For people who batch, mix, pump, transport, pour and compact concrete.
Formerly (until 1995): Quality Concrete Plant and Production (0264-0236)
Indexed: BrCerAb, C&ISA, CRIA, CRICC, CerAb, CivEngAb, ConcrAb, CorrAb, E&CAJ, EMA, EngInd, IAA, M&TEA, MBF, METADEX, SolStAb, WAA.
—CISTI, Linda Hall.
Published by: Hayden Jeffery Ed. & Pub., 12 Grimsdells Ln, Amersham, Bucks HP6 6HF, United Kingdom. TEL 44-1494-726273, FAX 44-1494-726273. Circ: 5,200.

690 ITA
QUARRY AND CONSTRUCTION/CAVE E COSTRUZIONI. Text in Italian. 1962. m. EUR 52 (effective 2005). adv. illus. **Document type:** *Magazine, Trade.* **Description:** Contains information on the Italian construction industry.
Formerly: Frantoio
Published by: Edizioni P E I s.r.l., Strada Naviglio Alto 46, Parma, PR 43100, Italy. FAX 39-0521-773572, info@quarry-construction.it, http://www.quarry-construction.it, http://www.edizionipei.it. Ed. Carlo Cagozzi. Adv. contact Brunetta Damenti. Circ: 50,000.

690 GBR
QUARRY PRODUCT ASSOCIATION. Text in English. a. free. **Document type:** *Corporate.*
Formerly: B A C M I in (Year)
Published by: British Aggregate Construction Materials Industries, 156 Buckingham Palace Rd, London, SW1W 9TR, United Kingdom. TEL 0171-730-8194, FAX 0171-730-4355.

690 CAN ISSN 0709-0692
QUART DE ROND. Text in French. 1959. 8/yr. CND 36. adv. **Document type:** *Trade.*
—CISTI.
Published by: Building Materials Retailer Association of Quebec, 474 Place Trans, Longueuil, PQ J4G 1N8, Canada. TEL 514-646-5842, FAX 514-646-6171, admacq@accent.net, http://www.quart-de-rond.qc.ca. Ed. Gabriel Pollender. Adv. contact Claude Dagenais. B&W page CND 1,970, color page CND 2,820; trim 10.88 x 8.13. Circ: 5,200.

690 CAN
QUEBEC HABITATION. Text in French. 1987. 6/yr. CND 17.33. adv.
Published by: Association Provinciale des Constructeurs d'Habitations du Quebec, 5930 Louis H Lafontaine, Anjou, PQ H1M 1S7, Canada. TEL 514-353-9960, FAX 514-353-4825. Adv. contact Pierre Moreau. B&W page CND 1,445. Circ: 15,000.

692.8 FRA ISSN 1015-4531
R I L E M NEWS. (Reunion Internationale des Laboratoires d'Essais et des Recherches sur les Materiaux et les Construc) Text in English. 1986. irreg.
Published by: R I L E M Publications S.A.R.L., 157 Rue des Blains, Bagneux, 92220, France. TEL 33-1-45361020, FAX 33-1-45366320.

692.8 FRA ISSN 1461-1147
R I L E M PROCEEDINGS. (Reunion Internationale des Laboratoires d'Essais et des Recherches sur les Materiaux et les Construc) Text in English. irreg.
Published by: R I L E M Publications S.A.R.L., 157 Rue des Blains, Bagneux, 92220, France. TEL 33-1-45361020, FAX 33-1-45366320.

692.8 FRA ISSN 1369-4448
R I L E M REPORT. (Reunion Internationale des Laboratoires d'Essais et des Recherches sur les Materiaux et les Construc) Text in English. 1991. irreg. price varies.
—BLDSC (7971.462000), IE, ingenta. **CCC.**
Published by: R I L E M Publications S.A.R.L., 157 Rue des Blains, Bagneux, 92220, France. TEL 33-1-45361020, FAX 33-1-45366320, http://www.rilem.net/reports.php.

693.83 USA ISSN 0033-7129
R S I. (Roofing, Siding, Insulation) Text in English. 1945. m. USD 44 domestic; USD 55 in Canada & Mexico; USD 78 elsewhere; USD 5 newsstand/cover domestic; USD 7 newsstand/cover in Canada & Mexico; USD 12 newsstand/cover elsewhere (effective 2005). adv. charts; illus.; tr.lit. back issues avail. **Document type:** *Magazine, Trade.* **Description:** Focuses on sales promotion, industry news, trends and new products.
Incorporates: Solar Contractor
Related titles: Microform ed.: (from PQC); Online - full text ed.: (from EBSCO Publishing, Factiva, ProQuest Information & Learning).
Indexed: ABIn, Cadscan, CivEngAb, LeadAb, PROMT, Zincscan.
—CISTI. **CCC.**
Published by: Advanstar Communications, Inc., 7500 Old Oak Blvd, Cleveland, OH 44130-3369. TEL 440-891-2767, FAX 440-891-2727, mrusso@advanstar.com, info@advanstar.com, http://www.rsimag.com, http://www.advanstar.com. Ed. Michael Russo. Pub. Sean Carr. R&P Jerry N Mix TEL 800-225-4569. Adv. contact Mary Ellen Galvin. Circ: 23,814 (paid and controlled). **Subscr. to:** Advanstar Marketing Services, Customer Service Department, 131 West, First St, Duluth, MN 55802. TEL 218-723-9200, 800-598-6008, FAX 218-723-9437.

624 FIN ISSN 0033-9121
RAKENNUSLEHTI. Text in Finnish. 1966. 41/yr. EUR 108 in Europe; EUR 126 rest of world (effective 2004). adv. bk.rev. **Document type:** *Magazine, Trade.* **Description:** Publishes current trade news in Finland and abroad, reviews and presentations of new products and information on trends in construction.
Incorporates: Rakennustuotanto (0355-5526)
Published by: Suomen Rakennuslehti Oy, Mannerheimintie 40, Helsinki, 00100, Finland. TEL 358-9-584-44-00, FAX 358-9-584-44-600, sampsa.heila@rakennuslehti.fi, http://www.rakennuslehti.fi/lehdet. Ed. Sampsa Heila. Adv. contact Hannu Virtanen. B&W page EUR 9,310, color page EUR 10,374; trim 310 x 410. Circ: 26,689.

690 721 FIN ISSN 0048-6663
RAKENNUSTAITO/FINNISH CONSTRUCTION MAGAZINE. Text in Finnish. 1905. s-m. (10/yr.). EUR 62 (effective 2005). adv. bk.rev. illus. index. **Document type:** *Magazine, Trade.* **Description:** Contains information about construction sites, production, materials, methods, projects and companies.
Published by: (Rakennusmestarien Keskusliitto/Central Association of Construction Engineers), Rakennustieto Oy, Runebergienkatu 5 i, PO Box 1004, Helsinki, 00101, Finland. TEL 358-9-5495570, FAX 358-9-5495320, http://www.rakennustieto.fi. Ed. Riitta Ollila TEL 358-9-54955405. Adv. contact Stina Laehde. B&W page EUR 1,790, color page EUR 2,980; trim 270 x 180. Circ: 12,000. **Co-sponsor:** Rakennustietosaatio.

690 FIN ISSN 0355-8614
RAKENTAJA. Text in Finnish. 1924. 24/yr. EUR 25.25 (effective 2005). adv. bk.rev. **Document type:** *Trade.*
Related titles: Microfiche ed.

Published by: Rakennusliitto/Construction Trade Union of Finland, Siltasaarenkatu 4, PO Box 307, Helsinki, 00530, Finland. TEL 358-9-77021, FAX 358-9-7702241, http://www.rakennusliitto.fi. Ed. Markku Salomaa. Circ: 93,000.

620 DEU ISSN 1431-4576
RATGEBER BAUEN. Text in German. 1990. q. EUR 2.50 newsstand/cover (effective 2002). adv. **Document type:** *Magazine, Consumer.*
Formerly (until 1996): Planen, Bauen und Wohnen (0938-3557)
Related titles: Online - full text ed.
Published by: Kaenguru Verlag und Medienservice GmbH, Hans-Boeckler-Str. 10, Langenfeld, 40764, Germany. TEL 49-2173-39929-0, FAX 49-2173-3992910, anzeigen@kaenguru-medien.de, http://www.kaenguru-medien.de. adv.: B&W page EUR 5,120, color page EUR 6,920. Circ: 70,000 (paid and controlled).

690 DEU ISSN 0173-9220
RATIONELL REINIGEN. Text in German. m. EUR 79 domestic; EUR 93.40 foreign; EUR 6.90 newsstand/cover (effective 2002). adv. bk.rev. **Document type:** *Magazine, Trade.*
Formerly: Gebaeudigereiniger-Handwerk (0016-5727)
—IE, Infotrieve.
Published by: (Bundesinnungsverband des Gebaeudereiniger-Handwerks), Hans Holzmann Verlag GmbH, Gewerbestr 2, Bad Woerishofen, 86825, Germany. TEL 49-8247-35401, FAX 49-8247-354170, redrr@holzmannverlag.de, http://www.rationell-reinigen.de/index.html, http://www.holzmannverlag.de. Ed. Peter Hartmann. Adv. contact Claudia Baur. Circ: 17,500.

690 AUS ISSN 0810-8064
RAWLINSONS AUSTRALIAN CONSTRUCTION HANDBOOK (YEAR). Text in English. 1983. a. AUD 210 (effective 2000). adv. back issues avail. **Description:** Provides prices for all stages of the building construction process, for feasibility studies, estimating, budgeting, cost control and contract management.
Published by: Rawlhouse Publishing Pty. Ltd., 1141 Hay St, West Perth, W.A. 6005, Australia. TEL 61-8-93218951, FAX 61-8-94811914, info@rawlhouse.com, http://www.rawlhouse.com/. Ed., Adv. contact Iain Baillie. R&P Christine Morriss. Circ: 3,250.

690 AUS ISSN 1039-5350
RAWLINSONS CONSTRUCTION COST GUIDE. Text in English. 1993. a., latest 2000, 8th ed. AUD 125 domestic (effective 2000). **Document type:** *Directory, Trade.* **Description:** Covers smaller construction projects in the $100,000 to $750,000 range, including regional Indices for all states, building price indices, building costs per square metre together with elemental costs, estimating comparative costs providing estimating rates for the various components of a building, detailed prices for all trades and services, typical Renovations items applicable to kitchens and bathrooms, and Labour Constants for many of the major items of work.
Published by: Rawlhouse Publishing Pty. Ltd., 1141 Hay St, West Perth, W.A. 6005, Australia. TEL 61-8-93218951, FAX 61-8-94811914, info@rawlhouse.com, http://www.rawlhouse.com/.

RAWLINSONS NEW ZEALAND CONSTRUCTION HANDBOOK. see *BUSINESS AND ECONOMICS—Trade And Industrial Directories*

690 USA
READY TO BUILD HOME PLANS. Text in English. 1997. m. USD 4.99 newsstand/cover (effective 2005). **Document type:** *Magazine, Consumer.*
Published by: The Garlinghouse Company (Subsidiary of: Active Interest Media), 4125 Lafayette Center Dr, Ste 100, Chantilly, VA 20151. TEL 703-547-4154, 800-235-5700, FAX 703-222-9705, info@garlinghouse.com, http://www.garlinghouse.com/. Circ: 83,000 (paid).

REAL ESTATE DIRECTORY OF MANHATTAN. see *REAL ESTATE*

690 USA ISSN 1079-1272
REAL ESTATE NEW YORK. Text in English. 1982. 10/yr. USD 79.95 domestic; USD 170 foreign (effective 2005). adv. software rev. charts; mkt.; stat.; tr.lit. back issues avail. **Document type:** *Magazine, Trade.* **Description:** Contains timely news coverage of commercial office, retail, industrial & multi-family real estate markets in New York City, Long Island, Westchester, Southern Connecticut and Northern New Jersey.
Formerly (until 1994): Better Buildings (0744-530X)
Related titles: Online - full text ed.
Indexed: AIAP.
Published by: Real Estate Media Inc. (Subsidiary of: A L M), 520 8th Ave., New York, NY 10018-6507. TEL 212-929-6900, 212-929-6900, jschein@remediainc.com, http://www.renymag.com, http://www.remediainc.com. adv.: B&W page USD 2,625, color page USD 4,120; trim 10 x 7. Circ: 15,206.

REAL ESTATE NEWS AND BUYERS GUIDE. see *REAL ESTATE*

REALTY AND BUILDING. see *REAL ESTATE*

REALTY REPORT. see *REAL ESTATE*

690 DEU
RECHTSPRECHUNG ZUM PRIVATEN BAURECHT. Text in German. 1954. base vol. plus m. updates. looseleaf. cum.index: 1954-1977. **Document type:** *Bulletin.*
Formerly: Rechtsprechung der Bau-Ausfuehrung (0034-1371)
Published by: Werner-Verlag GmbH (Subsidiary of: Wolters Kluwer Deutschland GmbH), Heddesdorfer Str 31, Neuwied, 56564, Germany. TEL 49-211-38798-0, FAX 49-211-383104. Ed. Reiner Hochstein.

690 ITA ISSN 1126-3938
RECUPERARE L'EDILIZIA. Text in Italian. 1998. q. adv. **Document type:** *Magazine, Trade.*
Published by: Alberto Greco Editore, Viale Espinasse 141, Milan, MI 20156, Italy. TEL 39-02-300391, FAX 39-02-30039300, age@gruppodg.com, http://www.ageditore.com. adv.: page EUR 2,900; 230 x 300.

RECYCLING - DEMOLIZIONI & RICICLAGGIO. see *ENVIRONMENTAL STUDIES—Waste Management*

690 USA
REED FIRST SOURCE. Text in English. 1992. a. free to qualified personnel (effective 2005). **Document type:** *Directory, Trade.* **Description:** Provides A/E/C professionals free access to the industry's most comprehensive, up-to-date library of formatted commercial building product information, plus manufacturers' addresses, telephone numbers, trade names, and regional distributors.
Supersedes in part (in 200?): BuildSource Product Finder (1496-5356); Former titles: First Source (1549-3318); (until 2000): First Source for Products (1528-4786)
Related titles: Online - full content ed.
Published by: Reed Construction Data, 30 Technology Pkwy South, Ste 100, Norcross, GA 30092. TEL 800-395-1988, FAX 800-444-1059, contactus@firstsourceonl.com, http://www.ReedFirstSource.com, http://www.reedfirstsource.com.

REFERATIVNYI ZHURNAL. PROCHNOST' KONSTRUKTSII I MATERYALOV. see *BUILDING AND CONSTRUCTION—Abstracting, Bibliographies, Statistics*

690 FRA ISSN 1764-0709
REFLETS ET NUANCES. Text in French. 5/yr. adv. illus.
Published by: U N P V F, 9 rue la Perouse, Paris, Cedex 16 75784, France. TEL 40-69-53-71, FAX 40-70-01-74, TELEX 611 975 F. Ed. Raphae'l Filpo.

690 GBR
REFURBISHMENT PROJECTS. Text in English. 1986. bi-m. GBP 18 (effective 1999). adv. **Document type:** *Trade.*
Formerly: Refurbishment Products
Published by: Sheen Publishing Ltd., Sheen Publishing Ltd, 50 Queens Rd, Buckhurst Hill, Essex IG9 5DD, United Kingdom. TEL 44-181-504-1661, FAX 44-181-505-4336, TELEX 296620-SHEEN-G. Ed. Tony Prior. Pub. Carole Titmuss. Adv. contact Lesley Porter. Circ: 8,100.

690 USA ISSN 1086-5241
THE REGIONAL ALLIANCE CONSTRUCTION NEWS WEEKLY. Text in English. w. adv. **Document type:** *Newsletter, Trade.* **Description:** Provides information on what jobs are coming up for bid or negotiation.
Related titles: Online - full text ed.
Published by: Mcgraw-Hill Construction Dodge (Subsidiary of: McGraw-Hill Construction Information Group), 148 Princeton-Hightstown Rd, Hightstown, NJ 08520. TEL 800-393-6343, http://www.dodgeconstructionpublications.com.

690 USA ISSN 0885-8039
TH4816
REMODELING. Text in English. 1985. m. USD 24.95 domestic; USD 39.95 in Canada; USD 192 elsewhere; free to qualified personnel (effective 2005). adv. bk.rev. charts; illus.; stat.; tr.lit. back issues avail.; reprint service avail. from PQC. **Document type:** *Magazine, Trade.* **Description:** Provides current news and information for the residential remodeling market.
Formerly: Remodeling World (0745-2152); Incorporates (1948-1987): Remodeling Contractor (Washington); Which was formerly (until 1983): Home Improvement Contractor (0146-5996); (until 1976): Home Improvements (0018-4063); (until 1969): Building Specialties and Home Improvements
Related titles: Microform ed.: (from PQC); Online - full text ed.: Remodeling Online (from Florida Center for Library Automation, Gale Group).
Published by: Hanley-Wood, LLC (Subsidiary of: J.P. Morgan Chase & Co.), One Thomas Circle, NW, Ste 600, Washington, DC 20005-5701. TEL 202-452-0800, FAX 202-785-1974, tjackson@hanleywood.com, http://www.remodelingmagazine.com, http://www.hanleywood.com. Ed. Sal Alfano. Pub. Rick Strachan. adv.: B&W page USD 10,770, color page USD 12,670. Circ: 82,456 (controlled).

690 USA ISSN 1552-8677
REMODELING MAGAZINE. Text in English. q. USD 12 (effective 2003).
Published by: Association Publishing Inc., 2117 Smith Ave, Chesapeake, VA 23320. TEL 757-420-2434, FAX 757-424-5954, http://www.statebuildermagazines.com. Ed. Stacey Klemenc. Pubs. Joyce F Hearn, Sandra Amidon. Circ: 160,000.

643.7 USA
REMODELING NEWS (NORTHERN - CENTRAL NEW JERSEY EDITION). Text in English. 1987. m. USD 24.95 domestic; USD 34.95 foreign (effective 2005). adv. bk.rev. **Document type:** *Magazine, Trade.* **Description:** Provides professional builders and remodeling contractors with business information, product knowledge and how-to techniques. Geared to residential remodeling, custom building and light construction industries.
Former titles: Building & Remodeling News (Northern - Central New Jersey Edition) (1077-2030); (until 1994): Remodeling News (Northern - Central New Jersey Edition) (1053-1505); Which superseded in part: Remodeling News (1043-2183)
Related titles: Regional ed(s).: Remodeling News (Baltimore - Washington, DC Edition); Remodeling News (Greater Boston - New England Edition); Remodeling News (Greater Philadelphia - Delaware Edition); Remodeling News (Long Island - Metro New York Edition); Remodeling News (Westchester, Rockaland, Putnam, Orange, Fairfield & New Haven Edition).
Published by: J S D Communications, 600-C Lake St, Ramsey, NJ 07446-1245. TEL 201-327-1600, FAX 201-327-3185, renee@opcenter.net, http://www.remodelingnews.com. Ed. Renee Rewiski. Pub. Jim Duffy. Adv. contact Don Smith. Circ: 75,000 (controlled).

690 USA
REMODELING - REPAIR CONSTRUCTION COSTS. Text in English. 1991. a. USD 54.95 (effective 2001). **Document type:** *Trade.* **Description:** Helps one choose the best labor costs for the job using a unique grading system.
Published by: Saylor Publications, Inc., 9420 Topanga Canyon Blvd, Ste 203, Chatsworth, CA 91311. TEL 818-718-5966, FAX 818-718-8024, http://www.saylor.com. Ed., R&P Stanley J Strychaz.

690 USA ISSN 1535-0347
REMOTE SITE & EQUIPMENT MANAGEMENT. Text in English. 2001. bi-m. free domestic to qualified personnel; USD 44 domestic; USD 60 foreign (effective 2005). adv. **Document type:** *Magazine, Trade.*
Related titles: ◆ Supplement(s): Short-Range Wireless.
—CCC.
Published by: Webcom Communications Corp., 7355 E Orchard Rd, Ste 100, Greenwood Village, CO 80111. TEL 720-528-3770, 800-803-9488, FAX 720-528-3771, johncg@infowebcom.com, http://www.remotemagazine.com, http://www.infowebcom.com.

643.7 CAN
RENOVATION AND DECOR MAGAZINE. Text in English. 1990. 2/yr. adv. **Document type:** *Consumer.*
Former titles: Renovation Magazine; Professional Renovation Magazine (1182-0470)
Published by: Homes Publishing Group, 178 Main St, Unionville, ON L3R 2G9, Canada. TEL 905-479-4663, FAX 905-479-4482. Ed. Patrick Tivey. R&P M Rosset. Adv. contact Kathleen Kelly. Circ: 75,000.

690 AUT
RENOVATION UND DOMIZIL; das Magazin fuer Hausbau, Umbau und Wohnkultur. Text in German. 6/yr. EUR 12 domestic; EUR 17 foreign; EUR 4 newsstand/cover (effective 2005). adv. **Document type:** *Magazine, Trade.*
Formerly: Renovation
Published by: Springer Business Media Austria GmbH (Subsidiary of: Springer Science+Business Media), Inkustr 16, Klosterneuburg, 3403, Austria. TEL 43-2243-301110, FAX 43-2243-30111222, office@springer-sbm.at, http://www.springer-sbm.at. Ed. Wolfgang Kadrnoska. Adv. contacts Ernst Wottowa, Josef Malek. B&W page EUR 4,220, color page EUR 5,970; trim 185 x 260. Circ: 40,000 (paid and controlled).

690 DNK ISSN 1396-6820
RENOVERING & DRIFT - BRUTTO. Variant title: V & S Priser. Renovering og Drift - Brutto. Text in Danish. 1989. a. DKK 1,410 (effective 1999). **Document type:** *Trade.*
Published by: V & S Byggedata, 551 Frederikssundvej 194, Broenshoej, 2700, Denmark. TEL 45-38-60-77-11, FAX 45-38-60-77-55, bygdat@vs-byggedata.dk, bygdat@vs.byggedata.dk.

338.4769 DNK ISSN 1396-6812
RENOVERING OG DRIFT - NETTO. Variant title: V & S Priser, Renovering og Drift - Netto. Text in Danish. 1989. a. DKK 1,410 (effective 1999).
Supersedes in part (in 1997): Renovering og Drift (0905-9814); Which was formerly (until 1991): Drift og Vedligehold (0904-3608)
Published by: V & S Byggedata, 551 Frederikssundvej 194, Broenshoej, 2700, Denmark. TEL 45-38-60-77-11, FAX 45-38-60-77-55, bygdat@vs-byggedata.dk. Ed. Carl Friis Skovsen.

643.7 DEU
RENOVIEREN; neue Ideen fuer alte Haeuser. Text in German. 1998. 6/yr. EUR 12; EUR 2.50 newsstand/cover (effective 2003). adv. **Document type:** *Magazine, Consumer.* **Description:** Contains information and advice on renovating and reconstructing old houses.
Published by: Besser Bauen Verlag GmbH, Herdweg 20, Stuttgart, 70174, Germany. TEL 49-711-163874-0, FAX 49-711-16387450, renovieren@besserbauen.de, info@besserbauen.de, http://www.trendmedien.com/4renovieren/4_f.htm, http://www.besserbauen.de. Ed. Klaus Vetterle. adv.: B&W page EUR 5,000, color page EUR 7,000. Circ: 41,000 (paid and controlled).

690.028 USA ISSN 1531-2348
RENTSMART!; solutions for the construction professional. Text in English. 1997. bi-m. free to qualified personnel. adv. bk.rev. charts; illus.; stat. back issues avail. **Document type:** *Trade.* **Description:** Informs professionals in construction how to get the most from rental equipment. Reviews new equipment.
Related titles: Online - full text ed.: RentSmart Online.
Published by: Randall Publishing Company, RentSmart!, 3200 Rice Mine Rd, Tuscaloosa, AL 35406. TEL 800-633-5953, FAX 205-750-8070, rbushery@randallpub.com, http://www.randallpub.com, http://www.rentsmartonline.com. Ed. Marcia Gruver. Pub., Adv. contact Jim Longton. B&W page USD 4,610; trim 10.88 x 8.13. Circ: 50,876 (controlled).

690 USA ISSN 1549-1986
REPLACEMENT CONTRACTOR. Text in English. 2002. 7/yr. USD 29.95 domestic; USD 39.95 in Canada; USD 49.95 elsewhere (effective 2005). **Document type:** *Magazine, Trade.*
Published by: Hanley-Wood, LLC (Subsidiary of: J.P. Morgan Chase & Co.), One Thomas Circle, NW, Ste 600, Washington, DC 20005-5701. TEL 202-452-0800, FAX 202-785-1974, http://www.omeda.com/rcon/, http://www.hanleywood.com. Eds. Jim Cory, Sal Alfano. Circ: 22,500.

690 747 FRA ISSN 1246-354X
REPONSES BAIN. Abbreviated title: R B. Text in French. 1993. 6/yr. adv.
Published by: S 4 E Publications, 40 rue Guy Moquet, BP 120, Champigny-sur-Marne, Cedex 94501, France. TEL 1-48-84-91-91, FAX 1-48-81-81-77. Ed. Marianne Tournier. Adv. contact Christelle Granger. Circ: 8,000.

690 GBR ISSN 0034-5105
RESALE WEEKLY. Text in English. 1964. w. GBP 8.50. adv.
Published by: Moffat Publishing Co. Ltd., 1-23 Queen's Rd W, Plaistow, London, E13 OAP, United Kingdom. Ed. J W Branch. Circ: 9,500.

690 FRA ISSN 1157-576X
RESEAUX (SAINT CLOUD)/NETWORK. Text in French. 1990. 8/yr. adv. **Document type:** *Corporate.* **Description:** Covers materials used in all forms of pipework and aerial wires: water, electricity, gas and phone.
Indexed: IIFP.
Published by: Reseaux - Com, 33 rue du Mont Valerien, St Cloud, 92210, France. TEL 33-1-47711203, FAX 33-1-46029176. Ed. Terone Bouche. Circ: 10,000.

690 USA ISSN 1053-2986
TH4815.8
RESIDENTIAL BUILDING COST GUIDE (YEAR). Text in English. a. USD 52 (effective 1998). **Description:** Aims to assist the insurance, appraisal, and assessment industries to estimate the replacement cost of homes in the U.S.
Published by: E.H. Boeckh, Ed. & Pub. (Subsidiary of: Thomson Publishing Corp.), 2885 S Calhoun Rd, Box 510291, New Berlin, WI 53151-0291. TEL 414-780-2800, FAX 414-780-0306. R&P E H Boeckh.

692.8 USA
RESIDENTIAL CONSTRUCTION COSTS. Text in English. 1982. a. USD 69.95 (effective 2001). **Document type:** *Trade.* **Description:** Contains unit construction costs for residential construction, open shop and union installation costs, as well as material cost and man-hours. Also includes assembly costs, location factors and indexes.
Published by: Saylor Publications, Inc., 9420 Topanga Canyon Blvd, Ste 203, Chatsworth, CA 91311. TEL 818-718-5966, FAX 818-718-8024, http://www.saylor.com. Ed., R&P Stanley J Strychaz. Circ: 4,000.

690 USA
RESIDENTIAL SQUARE FOOT BUILDING COSTS (YEAR). Text in English. 1993. a. USD 34.95 (effective 2001). **Document type:** *Trade.* **Description:** Provides single-family building cost data that can be used for conceptual estimating, planning, appraisal and insurance placement. The "Square Foot Cost" section has complete building costs by square foot of floor area for six different classes of construction. Also includes sections on functional assembly and landscape costs.
Published by: Saylor Publications, Inc., 9420 Topanga Canyon Blvd, Ste 203, Chatsworth, CA 91311. TEL 818-718-5966, FAX 818-718-8024. Ed., R&P Stanley J Strychaz.

690 ZAF
RESOURCE QUANTITIES AND PRICING GUIDE. Variant title: Build Aid Building and Pricing Guide. Text in English. 1993. a. ZAR 140 (effective 1999). adv. charts; illus.; mkt.; tr.lit. back issues avail. **Document type:** *Directory, Trade.* **Description:** Aimes at general building industry in terms of domestic market. Includes product information and pricing guide.
Related titles: E-mail ed.; Online - full text ed.
Published by: Alexander Wynn Publications (Pty) Ltd., Block B, Huringham Office Park, PO Box 979, Cramerview, Johannesberg 2060, South Africa. TEL 27-11-7810211, FAX 27-11-781-0214, apple@aad.co.za. Ed. Kirsten Forrester. Pub. Kristen Forrester. R&P Graham Alexander. Adv. contact Gordon Alexander. B&W page ZAR 5,500, color page ZAR 7,500; trim 210 x 297.

690 USA
RESTON SERIES IN CONSTRUCTION TECHNOLOGY✶. Text in English. 1971. irreg. price varies. adv. bk.rev.
Published by: Reston Publishing Company, Inc., c/o Prentice Hall, 240 Frisch Ct, Paramus, NJ 07652-5240. Ed. Alice Barr.

690 USA
RETAIL CONSTRUCTION; the journal for architecture, design, construction and facilities operation. Text in English. 2002. bi-m. free to qualified personnel; USD 50; USD 10 per issue (effective 2005). adv. **Document type:** *Magazine, Trade.* **Description:** Focuses specifically on the design, construction, renovation and operation of retail businesses - from malls and strip centers to free standing structures and power centers, from restaurants and groceries to major deparment stores and big-box discount stores. Designed to meet the needs of the retail executives who are responsible for the design, construction and operation of from two dozen to thousands of units.
Related titles: Online - full content ed.
Published by: D & D Communications Group LLC, 425 Tribble Gap Rd, Ste 103, PO Box 1589, Cumming, GA 30040. TEL 770-781-2501, 877-598-9156, FAX 770-781-6303, info@retailconstructionmag.com, http://www.retailconstructionmag.com. Ed. Dave Doucette. Pub. David Corson. adv.: B&W page USD 2,475, color page USD 3,400; trim 8 x 10.75. **Subscr. to:** PO Box 1589, Cumming, GA 30028.

691 ARG
REVISTA A C O M A C. Text in Spanish. m. adv. stat.
Published by: Asociacion de Comerciantes en Materiales para Construccion y Afines, Viamonte, 2160, Capital Federal, Buenos Aires 1056, Argentina. Ed. Oscar M Leguizamon.

690 BRA
REVISTA DE PRECOS PARA CONSTRUCAO DE PREDIOS✶. Text in Portuguese. 1962. m. adv.
Published by: Editora Revista de Precos Ltda., Av. N. Sa de Copacabana, 749 gr. 801, Rio De Janeiro, RJ 220550, Brazil. TEL 55-21-2356397, FAX 55-21-2356923. Ed. Tatiana Salme Lowjagin. Pub. Sila Bardo Do Couto. Adv. contact Luiz Antonio de Souza e Silva. B&W page USD 1,080, color page USD 1,732. Circ: 16,000.

LA REVISTA DEL VIDRIO, FACHADAS Y VENTANAS. see *CERAMICS, GLASS AND POTTERY*

690 PAN
REVISTA PANAMENA DE LA CONSTRUCCION. Text in Spanish. 1961. m. USD 20. adv. **Document type:** *Trade.* **Description:** Covers many aspects of construction including permits, legal issues, and new technology.
Formerly (until 1984): Camara Panamena de la Construccion. Boletin Informativo
Published by: Camara Panamena de la Construccion, Apdo. 6793, Panama City, 5, Panama. TEL 507-265-2500, FAX 507-265-2571. Ed. Eduardo Rodriguez Jr. Adv. contact Diamar Aparicio. Circ: 1,500.

690 ROM ISSN 1583-3186
CODEN: RRMEB7
➤ **REVISTA ROMANA DE MATERIALE/ROMANIAN JOURNAL OF MATERIALS.** Text in Romanian, English. 1971. q. ROL 5,000, USD 100 (effective 2003). 80 p./no.; back issues avail. **Document type:** *Journal, Trade.* **Description:** News on research, design, technologies and new manufacturing processes in the fields of ceramics, glass, composites, binders-concretes, natural stone.
Formerly (until 2002): Materiale de Constructi (0253-0201)
Indexed: ChemAb.
—BLDSC (7870.512500), CISTI, Linda Hall.
Published by: Procema S A, Calea Grivitei nr 136, Sector 1, Bucarest, 78122, Romania. TEL 40-21-2229352, FAX 40-21-2228349, procgriv@unicom.ro, http://www.procema.ro. Ed. Ion Teoreanu.

690 FRA ISSN 0397-9296
REVUE TECHNIQUE DU BATIMENT ET DES CONSTRUCTIONS INDUSTRIELLES. Text in French. 1953. bi-m. bk.rev. bibl.; illus. **Document type:** *Magazine, Trade.*
Formerly (until 1958): Revue Technique du Batiment (0048-8186)
Published by: Diffusions et Relations Officielles, 50 rue Championnet, Paris, 75018, France. TEL 33-1-42541414, FAX 33-1-42522894. Ed. Jacqueline Mehr. Adv. contact Emmanuelle Mehr. Circ: 20,030.

690 USA
THE RHODE ISLAND BUILDER REPORT. Text in English. 1951. 12/yr. membership. adv. bk.rev. **Document type:** *Newsletter.* **Description:** For the residential construction industry.
Formerly: Rhode Island Builder
Published by: Rhode Island Builders Association, 450 Veterans Memorial Pkwy 301, East Providence, RI 02914-5380. TEL 401-438-7400, FAX 401-438-7446. Ed. Paul F Eno. Pub. Roger R Warren. Adv. contact Janet Kortick. Circ: 3,400 (controlled).

690 ITA ISSN 0393-4411
RIABITA. Text in Italian. 1985. 9/yr. EUR 40 domestic; EUR 50 foreign (effective 2005). adv. **Document type:** *Magazine, Consumer.* **Description:** Covers reconstruction, renovation and maintenance of private and public buildings.
Published by: Rima Editrice, Viale Sarca 243, Milan, MI 20126, Italy. TEL 39-02-66103539, FAX 39-02-66103558, rima@rimaedit.it, http://www.rimaedit.it/riabita.htm. adv.: color page EUR 3,590; 310 x 240. Circ: 19,300.

690.028 ITA
LA RIVENDITA; il nuovo commercio dei prodotti e delle attrezzature per l'edilizia. Text in Italian. 1997. bi-m. EUR 35 (effective 2005). illus. **Document type:** *Magazine, Trade.* **Description:** Informs on advances in the building and construction industry with special attention given to new products.
Published by: BE-MA Editrice Srl, Via Teocrito 50, Milan, MI 20128, Italy. TEL 39-02-252071, FAX 39-02-27000692, segreteria@bema.it, http://www.bema.it.

690 340 ITA ISSN 0485-2435
RIVISTA GIURIDICA DELL'EDILIZIA. Text in Italian. 1958. bi-m. EUR 129.11 in the European Union; EUR 193.67 elsewhere (effective 2002). adv. **Description:** Offers commentary on legislation and administrative practices regarding urbanization and building.
Related titles: CD-ROM ed.
Indexed: IBR, IBZ.
—IE.
Published by: Casa Editrice Dott. A. Giuffre (Subsidiary of: LexisNexis Europe and Africa), Via Busto Arsizio, 40, Milan, MI 20151, Italy. TEL 39-02-28089200, FAX 39-02-38009582, giuffre@giuffre.it, http://www.giuffre.it. Eds. Giuseppe Guarino, Maria Alessandra Sandulli. Circ: 6,200.

RIVISTA TRIMESTRALE DEGLI APPALTI; rivista di dottrina-legislazione-giurisprudenza. see *LAW—Corporate Law*

690 USA
ROCK & DIRT. Text in English. 1949. 36/yr. USD 48 domestic; USD 168 foreign (effective 2001). adv. illus. **Document type:** *Trade.*
Related titles: Online - full text ed.; ♦ Spanish ed.: Rock & Dirt en Espanol.
Published by: T A P Publishing Co., P O Box 489, Crossville, TN 38557. TEL 931-484-5137, 800-251-6776, FAX 931-484-2532, 800-423-9030, subs@rockanddirt.com, http://www.rockanddirt.com/. Pub. Michael D Stone. Adv. contact Barbara Patterson. Circ: 172,000.

690.028 USA
ROCK & DIRT EN ESPANOL. Text in Spanish. 1992. m. **Document type:** *Magazine, Trade.* **Description:** Covers all types of new and used heavy equipment, related products and services.
Related titles: ♦ English ed.: Rock & Dirt.
Published by: T A P Publishing Co., P O Box 489, Crossville, TN 38557. TEL 931-484-5137, 800-251-6776, FAX 931-484-2532, 800-423-9030, subs@rockanddirt.com, http://www.rdespanol.com.

693 622 USA ISSN 0747-3605
TN950 CODEN: ROPRA5
ROCK PRODUCTS; the aggregate industry's journal of applied technology. Text in English. 1897. m. free domestic to qualified personnel; USD 36 domestic; USD 58 in Canada; USD 79 elsewhere (effective 2005). adv. illus.; tr.lit.; pat. index. 72 p./no. 3 cols./p.; back issues avail.; reprint service avail. from PQC. **Document type:** *Magazine, Trade.* **Description:** Provides news, product information, case history articles and operating tips for producers of construction aggregates - crushed stone, sand and gravel, Portland cement, lime, gypsum, other non-metallic materials and recycled construction materials,.
Related titles: Microform ed.: (from PQC); Online - full text ed.: (from EBSCO Publishing, Northern Light Technology, Inc., O C L C Online Computer Library Center, Inc., ProQuest Information & Learning); ♦ Supplement(s): Rock Products Cement Edition.
Indexed: AESIS, CRIA, CRICC, ChemAb, ConcrAb, EngInd, ExcerpMed, PROMT.
—BLDSC (8002.000000), CASDDS, Ei, Infotrieve, ingenta, Linda Hall. **CCC.**

Published by: Primedia Business Magazines & Media, Inc. (Subsidiary of: Primedia, Inc.), 330 N Wabash Ave, Ste 2300, Chicago, IL 60611. TEL 312-595-1080, FAX 312-840-8455, rmarkley@primemediabusiness.com, inquiries@primediabusiness.com, http://www.rockproducts.com, http://www.primediabusiness.com. Ed. Rick Markley. Pub. Scott Bieda. Circ: 19,000 (controlled).
Subscr. to: 2104 Harvell Circle, Bellevue, NE 68005. TEL 402-505-7173, 866-505-7173, FAX 402-293-0741.

693 622 USA
ROCK PRODUCTS CEMENT EDITION. Text in English. 1993. bi-m. included into Rock Products. **Document type:** *Trade.* **Description:** Provides cement industry personnel the latest information on market news, developing technologies, and new products.
Related titles: ♦ Supplement to: Rock Products. ISSN 0747-3605.
Indexed: ConcrAb, EngInd.
Published by: Primedia Business Magazines & Media, Inc. (Subsidiary of: Primedia, Inc.), 330 N Wabash Ave, Ste 2300, Chicago, IL 60611. TEL 312-595-1080, FAX 312-595-0296, inquiries@primediabusiness.com, http://www.primediabusiness.com. Circ: 5,000 (controlled).

B

690 FIN
ROCKWORLD. Text in English. 4/yr. **Document type:** *Magazine, Trade.*
Published by: Sanoma Magazines Finland Corporation, Hoylaamotie 1 D, P.O. Box 100, Helsinki, 00040, Finland. TEL 358-9-1201, FAX 358-9-1205171, info@sanomamagazines.fi, http://www.sanomamagazines.fi. Circ: 23,000 (controlled).

690 USA
ROCKY MOUNTAIN CONSTRUCTION. Text in English. s-m. USD 96 (effective 2005). tr.lit. **Document type:** *Journal, Trade.* **Description:** Covering Arizona, Colorado, Nevada, New Mexico, Utah and Wyoming, it is aimed at those engaged in engineering (highway and heavy), non-residential building construction, and allied fields relating to construction or requiring the use of construction equipment.
Formed by the merger of: Rocky Mountain Counstruction (North Edition) (0192-3943); Rocky Mountain Counstruction (South Edition) (0192-3951)
Published by: Reed Construction Data, Associated Construction Publications (Subsidiary of: Reed Business Information), 30 Technology Pkwy, Ste 100, Norcross, GA 30092. TEL 770-417-4114, FAX 770-417-4138, hwagner@reedbusiness.com, http://www.reedconstructiondata.com/product/CA375522.html?industryid=22315, http://www.acppubs.com/. Ed. Hol Wagner TEL 303-295-0630. Pub. John Weatherhead TEL 770-417-4120. Circ: 11,000 (controlled).

690 USA
ROCKY MOUNTAIN CONSTRUCTION. ANNUAL BUYERS GUIDE & DIRECTORY. Text in English. a. USD 35 per issue (effective 2004). **Document type:** *Directory, Consumer.*
Published by: Reed Construction Data, Associated Construction Publications (Subsidiary of: Reed Business Information), 30 Technology Pkwy, Ste 100, Norcross, GA 30092. TEL 770-417-4122, 800-322-6996, FAX 770-417-4138, 800-895-8661.

690 DEU ISSN 1612-6599
ROLLLADEN - TORE - SONNENSCHUTZSYSTEME. Text in German. 1966. m. EUR 90.90 domestic; EUR 102.50 foreign; EUR 8 newsstand/cover (effective 2004). adv. **Document type:** *Magazine, Trade.*
Formerly (until 2003): Der Rolladen - Jalousiebauer (0344-8088)
Published by: Verlag F.H. Kleffmann GmbH, Herner Str 299, Bochum, 44809, Germany. TEL 49-234-95391-0, FAX 49-234-9539130, service@kleffmann-verlag.de, http://www.kleffmann-verlag.de. Ed. M Scholz. adv.: B&W page EUR 2,240, color page EUR 3,910. Circ: 9,828 (paid and controlled).

695 GBR
ROOFING. Text in English. 1950. m. GBP 35. adv. bk.rev. illus.; tr.lit. **Description:** Covers roofing products, their manufacturers, distributors and suppliers.
Formerly: Roofing Contractor (0035-8193)
Indexed: BrCerAb, RICS.
—CISTI.
Published by: (National Federation of Roofing Contractors), B P G (Bourne) Ltd., 2 West St, Bourne, Lincs PE10 9NE, United Kingdom. TEL 0778-393747, FAX 0778-425453. Ed. S McLoughlin. Circ: 13,250.

695 GBR
ROOFING, CLADDING AND INSULATION. Text in English. 10/yr. GBP 35 (effective 1999). adv. **Document type:** *Trade.*
Indexed: CoppAb, METADEX.
Published by: Unity Media Communications Ltd., Stakes House, Quebec Sq, Westerham, Kent TNB16 1UN, United Kingdom. TEL 44-1959-565690, FAX 44-1959-564390. Ed. Martin James. Pub. Colin Wilkinson. Adv. contact Mike Pinkney. Circ: 8,000.

695 720 USA ISSN 1098-1519
TH2391
ROOFING CONTRACTOR. Text in English. 1981. 12/yr. free to qualified personnel (effective 2004). adv. bk.rev. charts; illus.; stat. index. back issues avail. **Document type:** *Magazine, Trade.* **Description:** Covers all aspects of the roofing industry.
Formerly (until 1997): Roofer (0279-4616)
Related titles: Microfiche ed.; Online - full text ed.: (from Florida Center for Library Automation, Gale Group, O C L C Online Computer Library Center, Inc.).
—CCC.
Published by: B N P Media, 2401 W Big Beaver Rd, 7th Fl., Troy, MI 48084. TEL 248-244-6252, http://www.roofingcontractor.com, http://www.bnpmedia.com/. Ed. Jo Delorenzo. Pub. Jill Nash. Adv. contacts Jill Nash, Marcia Wright. B&W page USD 4,925, color page USD 5,670. Circ: 27,205 (controlled). **Subscr. to:** PO Box 3212, Northbrook, IL 60065. TEL 847-291-5224, FAX 847-291-4816.

695 NLD ISSN 0924-705X
ROOFING HOLLAND✶. Text in Dutch. 1991. 11/yr. adv. back issues avail. **Document type:** *Trade.*
Published by: Mandate Publishers BV, Kerkemeer la, Akersloot, 1921 XT, Netherlands. TEL 31-2513-20500, mandate@dakweb.nl, http://www.dakweb.nl. Ed. M van Lieshout. Pub. D Lindeman. Circ: 14,000 (controlled).

695.029 USA ISSN 1538-0130
ROOFING MATERIALS AND SYSTEMS DIRECTORY. Text in English. a. USD 20 (effective 1999). **Document type:** *Directory.* **Description:** Lists all manufacturers of roofing materials and equipment complying with UL standards.
Published by: Underwriters Laboratories Inc., Publications, 33 Pfingsten Rd, Northbrook, IL 60062-2096. TEL 847-272-8800, FAX 847-272-0472.

690 GBR ISSN 1369-5630
ROYAL INSTITUTION OF CHARTERED SURVEYORS. CONTRACTS IN USE. Text in English. a. **Document type:** *Bulletin.*
—BLDSC (3426.312000). **CCC.**
Published by: Royal Institution of Chartered Surveyors, RICS Contact Centre, Surveyor Court, Westwood Way, Coventry, CV4 8JE, United Kingdom. TEL 44-207-222-7000, FAX 44-207-334-3811.

690 630 USA ISSN 0888-3025
RURAL BUILDER. Text in English. 1967. 7/yr. USD 29.98; USD 4.50 newsstand/cover; free to qualified personnel (effective 2004). adv. bk.rev. charts; illus. **Document type:** *Magazine, Trade.* **Description:** For contractors, suppliers, and builders servicing non-urban America.
Formerly (until 1986): Farm Building News (0014-7869)
—CISTI. **CCC.**
Published by: Krause Publications, Inc. (Subsidiary of: F & W Publications, Inc.), 700 E State St, Iola, WI 54990-0001. TEL 715-445-2214, 800-258-0929, FAX 715-445-4087, ruralbuilder@krause.com, info@krause.com, http://www.krause.com. Ed. Scott Tappa. Pub. Bill Bright TEL 715-445-2214 ext 308. Adv. contact Randy Graper TEL 715-445-2214 ext 380. B&W page USD 5,802, color page USD 7,192; trim 7.75 x 10.5. Circ: 26,099 (controlled and free).

691.3 693.5 NLD
RUSSIAN JOURNAL OF CONCRETE AND REINFORCED CONCRETE. Text in English. 1988. q. USD 250 (effective 1999). **Document type:** *Academic/Scholarly.* **Description:** Includes papers of interest to the international construction industry. Excludes papers of only local interest and those dealing with management and economics of the Russian construction industry.
Formerly (until Dec. 1991): Soviet Journal of Concrete and Reinforced Concrete (0970-244X)
Related titles: ♦ Translation of: Beton i Zhelezobeton. ISSN 0005-9889.
Indexed: CRIA, CRICC, JOF, METADEX.
—BLDSC (0420.760800), CISTI. **CCC.**
Published by: (State Committee on Construction RUS), A A Balkema (Subsidiary of: Taylor & Francis The Netherlands), PO Box 1675, Rotterdam, 3000 BR, Netherlands. FAX 31-10-413-5947, sales@balkema.nl, http://www.balkema.nl.

691 ZAF ISSN 0038-2027
S A BUILDER. Short title: S.A. Builder - Bouer. Text in English. 1923. m. ZAR 110 (effective 2000). adv. bk.rev. charts; illus. index. **Document type:** *Trade.*
Indexed: ISAP.
Published by: (Building Industries Federation), Malnor (Pty) Ltd., Private Bag X20, Auckland Park, Johannesburg 2006, South Africa. TEL 27-11-7263081, FAX 27-11-7263017, malnor@iafrica.com. Ed. Jo Prince. R&P Ken Nortje. adv.: B&W page ZAR 4,775, color page ZAR 5,825; trim 210 x 297. Circ: 8,300.

690 DEU ISSN 0036-102X
S B/CONSTRUCCION DE INSTALLACIONES DEPORTIVAS Y PISCINAS/EQUIPEMENT SPORTIF ET PISCINES/SPORTS FACILITIES AND SWIMMING POOLS. (Sportstaettenbau und Baederanlagen) Text in English, French, German, Spanish. 1967. bi-m. EUR 42; EUR 9 newsstand/cover (effective 2005). adv. bk.rev. abstr.; illus. 90 p./no.; back issues avail. **Document type:** *Journal, Trade.* **Description:** Contains information on sports facilities of all kinds and developments in sports equipment.
Indexed: SportS.
Published by: (International Association for Sports and Leisure Facilities), S B 67 Verlagsgesellschaft mbH, Postfach 320340, Cologne, 50797, Germany. TEL 49-2238-963322, FAX 49-2238-963323. Ed. Frieder Roskam. Adv. contact Claudia Barz. page EUR 1,300; trim 210 x 297. Circ: 4,870 (paid and controlled).

690 CHE
S E L EDILIZIA SVIZZERA. Text in Italian. 24/yr.
Published by: Gewerkschaft Bau und Holz, Postfach, Zuerich, 8021, Switzerland. TEL 01-2951636, FAX 01-2951799. Circ: 30,000.

690 FRA
S N S O BULLETIN. Text in French. 12/yr. **Document type:** *Bulletin.*
Address: 8 rue Catulle Mendes, Paris, 75017, France. TEL 46-22-18-65. Ed. Sylvie Touchard Cantie. Circ: 5,000.

690 FRA ISSN 1274-2740
SAGERET ILE DE FRANCE; annuaire national du batiment et des travaux publics. Text in French. 1809. a. FRF 3,000 (effective 1998). adv. **Document type:** *Directory.*
Formerly (until 1995): Sageret: Annuaire General du Batiment et des Travaux Publics (1162-0250)
Published by: Sageret, 7 rue Plumet, Paris, 75015, France. FAX 42-73-04-47, TELEX UJE 1111-699559. Circ: 60,000.

690 USA ISSN 1045-3792
ST. LOUIS CONSTRUCTION NEWS & REVIEW. Text in English. 1969. bi-m. USD 27; free to qualified personnel (effective 2005). adv. charts; illus.; stat.; tr.lit. back issues avail.; reprints avail. **Document type:** *Newspaper, Trade.* **Description:** Covers construction, architecture and engineering.
Published by: Finan Publishing Company, Inc., 107 W. Pacific Ave., St. Louis, MO 63119. TEL 314-961-6644, FAX 314-961-4809, cpreusse@finan.com, http://ww.stlconstruction.com. Ed. Peter Downs. Pub. Thomas J. Finan. Adv. contact Gene Keevan. B&W page USD 1,570, color page USD 2,370. Circ: 7,800 (paid and controlled).

690 JPN
SAISHIN NO SEKO GIJUTSU/LATEST CONSTRUCTION TECHNOLOGY. Text in Japanese. 1985. a.
Published by: (Doboku Seko Kenkyu linkai), Doboku Gakkai/Japan Society of Civil Engineers, Mu-banchi, Yotsuya 1-chome, Shinjuku-ku, Tokyo, 160-0004, Japan.

SAITAMA DAIGAKU KOGAKUBU KENSETSUKEI KENKYU HOKOKU/SAITAMA UNIVERSITY. FACULTY OF ENGINEERING. DEPARTMENT OF CONSTRUCTION. RESEARCH REPORT. see *ENGINEERING—Civil Engineering*

690 BEL
SANILEC (DUTCH EDITION); vakblad voor het installatiebedrijf. Text in Dutch. 9/yr. (plus 20 e-mails). EUR 68 (effective 2005). adv. **Description:** Discusses the construction materials market, along with new products and techniques.
Related titles: ♦ French ed.: Sanilec (French Edition).
Published by: Professional Media Group, Torhoutsesteenweg 226 bus 2/6, Zedelgem, B-8210, Belgium. TEL 32-50-240404, FAX 32-50-240445, info@pmgroup.be, http://www.pmgroup.be. adv.: color page EUR 2,400.

690 BEL
SANILEC (FRENCH EDITION); revue professionelle pour l'entreprise d'installation. Text in French. 1995. 9/yr. (plus 20 e-mails). EUR 56 (effective 2005). adv. illus. **Document type:** *Trade.* **Description:** Discusses the construction materials market, along with new products and techniques.
Related titles: ♦ Dutch ed.: Sanilec (Dutch Edition).
Published by: Professional Media Group, Torhoutsesteenweg 226 bus 2/6, Zedelgem, B-8210, Belgium. TEL 32-50-240404, FAX 32-50-240445, info@pmgroup.be, http://www.sanilec.be/?lang=f, http://www.pmgroup.be. Ed. Filip Werniers. adv.: color page EUR 2,400; trim 297 x 210. Circ: 12,000 (controlled).

720 RUS
SANKT-PETERBURGSKAYA PANORAMA. Text in Russian. 1936. m. bibl.; charts; illus. index.
Former titles (until Oct. 1991): Leningradskaya Panorama (0233-7010); (until 1982): Stroitel'stvo i Arkhitektura Leningrada (0039-2413)
Indexed: AIAP, API, ChemAb, RASB.
Address: Nevskii pr-t 53, St Petersburg, 191025, Russian Federation. TEL 7-812-1131523. Circ: 6,000.

690.24 USA
SCAFFOLD INDUSTRY. Text in English. 1972. m. USD 25 to members; USD 65 to non-members (effective 2005). adv. **Document type:** *Magazine, Trade.*

Formerly: Scaffold Industry Association Newsletter
Published by: Scaffold Industry Association, PO Box 20574, Phoenix, AZ 85036-0574. TEL 602-257-1144, FAX 602-257-1166, sia@scaffold.org, http://www.scaffold.org/displaycommon.cfm?an=3. Ed., R&P Gary W Larson. Adv. contact Jon Sperber.

690 USA
SCAFFOLD INDUSTRY ASSOCIATION. (YEAR) DIRECTORY AND HANDBOOK. Text in English. 1980. a. USD 125 per issue (effective 2005). adv. illus. **Document type:** *Directory.* **Description:** Provides articles, news, and information tailored specifically for the access industry.
Published by: Scaffold Industry Association, PO Box 20574, Phoenix, AZ 85036-0574. TEL 602-257-1144, FAX 602-257-1166, sia@scaffold.org, http://www.scaffold.org. Ed. Gary W Larson. Adv. contact Jon Sperber. Circ: 2,000.

698.9 645.1 ZAF
SCHALK BURGER'S FLOORS IN AFRICA. Variant title: Floors in Africa. Text in English. 1985. every 6 wks. adv. illus. **Document type:** *Consumer.*
Former titles (until vol.13, 1995): Schalk Burger's Southern Africa Floorcovering Journal; (until vol.12, no.3, 1994): Schalk Burger's S.A. Floor Covering Journal; (until 1988): S.A. Floor Covering Journal (0258-9958)
Published by: Schalk Burger Publications, PO Box 25260, Monument Park, Pretoria 0105, South Africa. TEL 27-12-6622014, FAX 27-12-6622030, office@floors.co.za. Ed. Liezel van der Merwe.

690.24 DEU ISSN 0943-4593
SCHORNSTEINFEGERHANDWERK. Text in German. 1884. m. EUR 6.80 newsstand/cover (effective 2004). adv. bk.rev. illus. **Document type:** *Magazine, Trade.* **Description:** Discusses the work of chimney sweeps.
Published by: Bundesverband des Schornsteinfegerhandwerks, Westerwaldstr 6, St. Augustin, 53757, Germany. TEL 49-2241-34070, FAX 49-2241-340710, schornziv@aol.com, ziv@schornsteinfeger.de, http://verband.schornsteinfeger.de. adv.: B&W page EUR 1,137, color page EUR 1,537; trim 180 x 256. Circ: 13,000 (paid and controlled).

690 CHE ISSN 0036-7303
SCHWEIZER BAUBLATT. Text in German. 1889. s-w. CHF 350 domestic; CHF 498 foreign (effective 2000). adv. bk.rev. illus.; pat.; stat.; tr.lit. **Document type:** *Journal, Trade.*
Published by: Schueck Soehne AG, Bahnhofstr 24, Rueschlikon, 8803, Switzerland. TEL 41-1-7247777, FAX 41-1-7247877.

690 CHE
SCHWEIZER BAUPRODUKTE-INDEX. Text in German, French. a. **Document type:** *Directory, Trade.* **Description:** Provides building and contruction products and services information.
Related titles: CD-ROM ed.; Online - full text ed.
Published by: MVS Baumarketing AG (Subsidiary of: Springer Science+Business Media), Ruetistr 22, Schlieren, 8952, Switzerland. TEL 41-1-7385151, FAX 41-1-7385200, franco.bernasconi@mvs.ch, http://www.mvs.ch/Deutsch/sbi/index.htm.

690 CHE ISSN 0376-6853
SCHWEIZER BAUWIRTSCHAFT/GIORNALE SVIZZERO DEGLI IMPRESARI COSTRUTTORI/JOURNAL SUISSE DES ENTREPRENEURS. Text in French, German, Italian. 1911. w. CHF 216. adv. bibl.; charts; illus.; tr.lit. **Document type:** *Trade.*
Formerly: Hoch- und Tiefbau (0046-7677)
Indexed: CISA, GeotechAb.
Published by: (Schweizerischer Baumeisterverband), AG Verlag Hoch- und Tiefbau, Postfach, Zuerich, 8023, Switzerland. FAX 41-1-2610324. Ed. Rene Mueller.

SCHWEIZER JOURNAL. see *ARCHITECTURE*

690 DEU ISSN 0343-4958
SCHWIMMBAD UND SAUNA; das Magazin fuer Schwimmbaeder, Whirlpools, Saunas und Solarien. Text in German. 1969. bi-m. EUR 4.50 newsstand/cover (effective 2002). adv. tr.lit. **Document type:** *Magazine, Trade.*
Published by: Fachschriften Verlag GmbH, Hoehenstr 17, Fellbach, 70736, Germany. TEL 49-711-52061, FAX 49-711-5281424, schwimmbad@fachschriften.de, info@fachschriften.de, http://www.schwimmbad-und-sauna.de, http://www.fachschriften.de. Ed. Karl-Heinz Linderich. Pub. Guenter Bayer. Adv. contact Wolfgang Kriwan. B&W page EUR 3,700, color page EUR 6,364; trim 184 x 276. Circ: 197,627 (controlled).

690 624 GBR ISSN 0085-6002
TH61
SCOTTISH BUILDING & CIVIL ENGINEERING YEAR BOOK. Text in English. 1960. a. USD 30. adv. **Document type:** *Trade.*
Media: Duplicated (not offset).
Published by: Edinburgh Pictorial Ltd., House, Edinburgh, Smith's Pl, Edinburgh, EH6 8NU, United Kingdom. TEL 44-131-554-1551, FAX 44-131-555-2965. Ed. C C Cumming. R&P, Adv. contact Cathie Gowans. Circ: 3,000.

691 USA
SCREENING INDUSTRY. Text in English. 1974. q. **Document type:** *Newsletter.*
Formerly: Screening News
Published by: (Screen Manufacturers Association), Fitzgerald Corporation, 2850 S Ocean Blvd, Apt 114, Palm Beach, FL 33480-5535. TEL 561-533-0991, FAX 561-533-7466. Ed. Frank S Fitzgerald. Circ: 1,000.

690 JPN ISSN 0389-1879
SEKO/ARCHITECTURAL PRODUCT ENGINEERING. Variant title: Kenchiku no Gijutsu. Text in Japanese. 1966. m. adv.
Published by: Shokokusha Publishing Co. Ltd., 25 Saka-Machi, Shinjuku-ku, Tokyo, 160-0002, Japan. TEL 81-3-3359-3231, FAX 81-3-3357-3961. Ed. Kiyoshi Kamahara. Adv. contact Toshio Takahashi. B&W page JPY 120,000, color page JPY 400,000. Circ: 50,000.

690 640 CAN ISSN 0833-1103
NA7241
SELECT HOME DESIGNS. Text in English. 1983. a. CND 9.95 (effective 1998). adv. bk.rev. **Document type:** *Catalog.* **Description:** New home designs and information on new home construction and products.
Published by: Planners Plus Enterprises Ltd., 611 Alexander St, Ste 301, Vancouver, BC V6A 1E1, Canada. TEL 604-879-4144, FAX 604-251-3212. Ed., Adv. contact Brian Thorn. color page CND 6,980. Circ: 85,000.

690 RUS ISSN 0201-4211
SEL'SKOE STROITEL'STVO. Text in Russian. m. USD 119.95 in United States.
Indexed: RASB, RefZh.
—CISTI, East View.
Published by: Minsel'khozprod Rossiiskoi Federatsii, Per Krasina 16, Moscow, 123056, Russian Federation. TEL 7-095-2543940. Ed. V V Akhlomov. **US dist. addr.:** East View Information Services, 3020 Harbor Ln. N., Minneapolis, MN 55447. TEL 612-550-0961.

620.1 JPN ISSN 0916-3182
SEMENTO, KONKURITO RONBUNSHU. Variant title: C A J Proceedings of Cement & Concrete. Text in English, Japanese. 1947. a. JPY 3,500. abstr.
Formed by the 1989 merger of (1947-1988): Semento Gijutsu Nenpo (0370-9914); Cement Association of Japan. Review of the General Meeting. Technical Session (0386-0825); Which was formerly (1957-1963): Japan Cement Engineering Association. Review of the General Meeting (0365-3617)
—CISTI. **CCC.**
Published by: Japan Cement Association, c/o JCA Secretariat, Shuwa-sakurabashi Bldg., 4-5-4, Hatchobori, Chuo-ku, Tokyo, 104-0032, Japan.

658.2 648 USA ISSN 0279-0548
TX955
SERVICES. Text in English. 1981. m. USD 30 domestic; USD 54 foreign (effective 2000). adv. back issues avail. **Document type:** *Trade.* **Description:** Articles on the janitorial industry, from cleaning to security services, both management and technical in every issue.
Published by: Building Service Contractors Association International, 10201 Lee Hwy, Ste 225, Fairfax, VA 22030. TEL 703-359-7090, FAX 703-352-0493, http://www.bscai.org. Ed., Pub., R&P Donald E Tepper. adv.: B&W page USD 2,190, color page USD 3,415; trim 8.125 x 10.875. Circ: 612 (paid); 17,841 (controlled). **Subscr. to:** PO Box 850756, Braintree, MA 02185-9908.

SERVICIO REFERATIVO DE LA CONSTRUCCION. see *BUILDING AND CONSTRUCTION—Abstracting, Bibliographies, Statistics*

691 CHN ISSN 1002-3046
TA401 CODEN: ZHOYEU
SHANDONG JIAN-CAI XUEYUAN XUEBAO/SHANDONG UNIVERSITY OF BUILDING MATERIALS. JOURNAL. Text in Chinese. 1987. q. CNY 4.50 newsstand/cover. **Document type:** *Journal, Academic/Scholarly.*
—BLDSC (4874.727000), IE, ingenta.
Published by: Shandong Jianzhu Cailiao Gongye Xueyuan/Shandong University of Building Materials, Jiwei Lu 106-hao, Jinan, 250022, China. TEL 86-531-7963250 ext 5452. Ed. Wei Xu. **Dist. by:** China International Book Trading Corp, 35 Chegongzhuang Xilu, Haidian District, PO Box 399, Beijing 100044, China. TEL 86-10-68412045, FAX 86-10-68412023, cibtc@mail.cibtc.com.cn, http://www.cibtc.com.cn.

690 CHN ISSN 1005-6637
SHANGHAI JIANSHE KEJI/SHANGHAI CONSTRUCTION SCIENCE AND TECHNOLOGY. Text in Chinese. 1980. bi-m. CNY 7, USD 3 newsstand/cover (effective 2002). **Description:** Reflects the newest information on plan, design, construction project, building materials, municipal engineering, traffic, residence, real estate, public utility, environment protection and horticulture etc of Shanghai construction systems, and publishes those papers on science & technology fruits, focal project construction and management soft science etc. This magazine sets up the columns of plan & design, municipal engineering & traffic, construction technique, residential construction, real estate, building materials, public utility, horticulture & Green Belt, environment health & protection, decoration, management, important events of Shanghai construction science & technology.
Published by: Shanghai Jianshe Keji Qingbao Zhongxin Zhan/Institute of Scientific and Technical Information of Shanghai, 75 Wanping Nan-Lu, Shanghai, 200032, China. TEL 86-21-64387445, FAX 86-21-64387445, http://www.istis.sh.cn/istis/kjqk1/jskj.htm. Ed. Chen Zhengqian. **Dist. by:** China International Book Trading Corp, 35 Chegongzhuang Xilu, Haidian District, PO Box 399, Beijing 100044, China. TEL 86-10-68412045, FAX 86-10-68412023, cibtc@mail.cibtc.com.cn, http://www.cibtc.com.cn.

690 USA ISSN 0164-6559
SHELTER; building a future for dealers and distributors of building products. Text in English. 1962. m. (combined issues in Jan./Feb.). free to qualified personnel; USD 35 domestic; USD 40 foreign (effective 2005). adv. illus.; stat.; tr.lit. **Document type:** *Magazine, Trade.*
Formerly: N S D J A Digest (National Sash and Door Jobbers Association)
Indexed: AIAP.
Published by: Key Communications, Inc., PO Box 569, Garrisonville, VA 22463. TEL 540-720-5584, FAX 540-720-5687, http://www.sheltermagazine.com/, http://www.key-com.com/. Ed. Samantha Carpenter. Pub. Debra Levy. adv.: page USD 2,700, color page USD 4,045. Circ: 34,555 (paid and controlled). **Subscr. to:** CirTec, 4 1/2 W. Wilson St, Ste C6, Batavia, IL 60510. FAX 630-482-3051.

SHIGONG JISHU/CONSTRUCTION TECHNOLOGY. see *ARCHITECTURE*

629 JPN ISSN 0289-8330
SHIMIZU KENSETSU KENKYU HOKOKU/SHIMIZU CONSTRUCTION TECHNICAL RESEARCH REPORT. Text in Japanese; Summaries in English, Japanese. 1962. s-a. per issue exchange basis. **Document type:** *Bulletin.* **Description:** Contains selected original papers of Shimizu Corporation's research engineers.
Indexed: CivEngAb, INIS AtomInd.
—Linda Hall. **CCC.**
Published by: Shimizu Kensetsu K.K., Gijutsu Kenkyujo/Shimizu Corporation, Institute of Technology, 4-17 Ecchujima 3-chome, Koto-ku, Tokyo, 135-0044, Japan. TEL 03-3643-4311, FAX 03-3643-7260. Ed. Muneo Kawamura. Circ: 600.

690 JPN ISSN 0912-7518
SHIMIZU TECHNICAL RESEARCH BULLETIN. Text in English. 1982. a. per issue exchange basis. **Document type:** *Bulletin.* **Description:** Contains original papers of the company's research engineers.
Indexed: CivEngAb, EEA, METADEX.
—CISTI. **CCC.**
Published by: Shimizu Corporation, Institute of Technology, 4-17 Ecchujima 3-chome, Koto-ku, Tokyo, 135-0044, Japan. TEL 03-3643-4311, FAX 03-3643-7260. Ed. Muneo Kawamura. Pub. Hiroshi Yamahara. Circ: 300.

SHIP, PORT, AND OFFSHORE TECHNOLOGY. see *TRANSPORTATION—Ships And Shipping*

690 CHN
SHOUDU JIANSHE BAO/CAPITAL CONTRUCTION NEWS. Text in Chinese. 1993. 3/w. CNY 6.50 per month (effective 2004). adv. **Document type:** *Newspaper, Government.*
Related titles: Online - full content ed.
Published by: Beijing Ribao Baoye Jituan/Beijing Daily Newspaper Group, 20, Jianguomen Dajie, Beijing, 100734, China. TEL 86-10-65136157, FAX 86-10-65282630, sdjsb@263.net, http://www.bjd.com.cn/sdjsb/965/965.htm. **Dist. by:** China International Book Trading Corp, 35 Chegongzhuang Xilu, Haidian District, PO Box 399, Beijing 100044, China. TEL 86-10-68412045, FAX 86-10-68412023, cibtc@mail.cibtc.com.cn, http://www.cibtc.com.cn.

691 CHN ISSN 1001-6171
TP875
SHUINI JISHU/CEMENT TECHNOLOGY. Text in Chinese. bi-m. CNY 300. adv.
Related titles: Online - full text ed.: (from East View Information Services).
Published by: Tianjin Shuini Gongye Sheji Yanjiuyuan/Tianjin Design Academy for Cement Industry, Yin He Qiao Li, Beijiao (North Star Suburb), Tianjin 300400, China. TEL 86-22-26391311, FAX 86-22-26390071, TELEX 23264 FRHTC CN. Ed. Zhu Zupei. Adv. contact Shen Ying. Circ: 10,000.

B

690   DEU
THE SHUTTERS AND BLINDS EXPERT; magazine for building details. Text in English. 2000. bi-m. **Document type:** *Journal, Trade.*
Published by: Verlag F.H. Kleffmann GmbH, Herner Str 299, Bochum, 44809, Germany. TEL 49-234-95391-0, FAX 49-234-9539130, service@kleffmann-verlag.de, http://www.kleffmann-verlag.de.

690   DEU
SICHERHEITS-MAGAZIN. Text in German. 1953. 2/yr. adv. **Document type:** *Magazine, Trade.*
Published by: Gert Wohlfarth GmbH, Stresemannstr 20-22, Duisburg, 47051, Germany. TEL 49-203-305270, FAX 49-203-30527820, info@wohlfarth.de, http://www.wohlfarth.de. adv: B&W page EUR 2,480, color page EUR 4,280; trim 178 x 258. Circ: 50,000 (controlled).

SIL'S'KE BUDIVNYTSTVO. see *AGRICULTURE*

690   SGP   ISSN 0218-3153
SINGAPORE SOURCE BOOK FOR ARCHITECTS & DESIGNERS. Text in English. 1989. a. USD 60. adv. **Description:** Provides a comprehensive catalogue of building and decorative products and services.
Published by: Times Media Pte Ltd, Directories Division, 1 New Industrial Rd, Times Centre, Singapore, 536196, Singapore. TEL 65-2848844, FAX 65-2850161, ttdmktg@cop.tpl.com.sg, http://www.timesbiz.com.sg. Pub., R&P Leslie Lim. Adv. contact Joseph Liang.

690   DEU   ISSN 0943-3880
SISTA AKTUELL. Text in German. 1984. 4/yr. free. **Document type:** *Magazine, Trade.* **Description:** Information on sealing windows and concrete building elements with connecting sealant.
Published by: Wegra Verlag GmbH, Frankfurterstr 10, Tamm, 71732, Germany. TEL 49-7141-23030, FAX 49-7141-230323, wegra@t-online.de. Circ: 15,000.

690   GBR
                       TH57
SITE RECORDER; for all invloved in site inspections. Text in English. 1882. m. GBP 30 to non-members (effective 2003). adv. bk.rev. tr.lit. **Document type:** *Journal, Trade.* **Description:** Concerns the control of building quality performance and standards.
Former titles (until June 2003): On-Site (1478-3355); (until June 2002): On-Site News (1476-7147); (until 2002): Clerk of Works (1464-4002); (until 1982): Institute of Clerks of Works. Journal (0020-2789); (until 1966): Institute of Clerks of Works of Great Britain Incorporated. Journal (0368-248X); (until 1947): Incorporated Clerks of Works Association of Great Britain. Journal (0368-2447)
Indexed: ConcrAb.
—BLDSC (8286.424750).
Published by: Institute of Clerks of Works of Great Britain, 1st and 2nd Floors, The Old House, The Lawns, 33 Thorpe Rd, Petersborough, PE3 6AD, United Kingdom. TEL 44-1733-564033, FAX 44-1733-564632, info@icwbg.com, info@icwgb.co.uk, http://www.icwgb.com/journal.htm. Ed. Rachel L Morris TEL 44-1733-865772. Circ: 4,500.

SOLIDSURFACE; the journal of the solid surface industry. see *INTERIOR DESIGN AND DECORATION*

THE SOURCE (PRINCETON). see *BUSINESS AND ECONOMICS—Trade And Industrial Directories*

SOUTH AFRICA. STATISTICS SOUTH AFRICA. BUILDING PLANS PASSED AND BUILDINGS COMPLETED. see *BUILDING AND CONSTRUCTION—Abstracting, Bibliographies, Statistics*

SOUTH AFRICA. STATISTICS SOUTH AFRICA. CENSUS OF CONSTRUCTION. see *BUILDING AND CONSTRUCTION— Abstracting, Bibliographies, Statistics*

SOUTH AFRICA. STATISTICS SOUTH AFRICA. STATISTICAL RELEASE. BUILDING INDUSTRY ADVISORY COUNCIL CONTRACT PRICE ADJUSTMENT PROVISIONS - WORKGROUP INDICES (HAYLETT). see *BUILDING AND CONSTRUCTION—Abstracting, Bibliographies, Statistics*

SOUTH AFRICA. STATISTICS SOUTH AFRICA. STATISTICAL RELEASE. BUILDING PLANS PASSED AND BUILDINGS COMPLETED. see *BUILDING AND CONSTRUCTION— Abstracting, Bibliographies, Statistics*

SOUTH AFRICA. STATISTICS SOUTH AFRICA. STATISTICAL RELEASE. BUILDING STATISTICS - PRIVATE SECTOR. see *BUILDING AND CONSTRUCTION—Abstracting, Bibliographies, Statistics*

690   ZAF
SOUTH AFRICAN CONSTRUCTION WORLD. Text in English. 1982. m. ZAR 60. back issues avail.
Formerly: South African Construction News
Indexed: ISAP.

Published by: Phase Four (Pty) Ltd., PO Box 784279, Sandton, Transvaal 2146, South Africa. TEL 011-444-4566, FAX 011-444-7888. Ed. Arthur Tassell. Circ: 5,100.

SOUTH AFRICAN HOME OWNER. see *ARCHITECTURE*

690   ZAF
SOUTH AFRICAN HOMES AND PLANS; resource quantities and pricing guide. Text in English. 1999. a. ZAR 120; ZAR 19.50 foreign (effective 2000). adv. illus. **Document type:** *Consumer.* **Description:** Aimed at potential home owners, especially those interested in buying readymade houseplans designed by professionals.
Published by: Alexander Wynn Publications (Pty) Ltd., Block B, Huringham Office Park, PO Box 979, Cramerview, Johannesberg 2060, South Africa. TEL 27-11-7810211, FAX 27-11-781-0214, apple@aad.co.za. Ed., Pub. Kirstein Forrester. R&P Graham Alexander. Adv. contact Gordon Alexander. color page ZAR 6,000; trim 210 x 297. Circ: 10,000 (paid).

690   AUS   ISSN 0157-938X
SOUTH AUSTRALIAN BUILDER. Text in English. 1976. m. AUD 40 (effective 1999). adv. **Document type:** *Trade.* **Description:** Contains Advice, news, statistics and features for the building and construction of industries.
Formed by the merger of (1966-1975): South Australian Master Builder; (1939-1976): Builder (0007-3245); Which was formerly: Building & Construction
Indexed: ARI.
Published by: Master Builders Association of South Australia, 47 South Terrace, Adelaide, SA 5000, Australia. TEL 61-08-8410-1961, FAX 61-08-8410-4502, buildsa@mbasa.com.au, http://www.mbasa.com.au. Ed. David Callan. R&P, Adv. contact Paul Vincent. B&W page AUD 825, color page AUD 1,075; trim 210 x 295. Circ: 2,000 (controlled).

690   GBR
SOUTH WEST BUILDING AND CONSTRUCTION. Text in English. 1997. m. free. adv. bk.rev.; software rev. illus.; tr.lit. back issues avail. **Document type:** *Trade.* **Description:** Covers new work, new products, contracts, commentary and related news.
Published by: Tindle Group, Hollytrees, Tuckermarsh, Bere Alston, Yelverton, Devon PL20 7HB, United Kingdom. TEL 44-1822-840202, FAX 44-1822-840990, paul@internet-today.co.uk. Ed. Paul White. adv: B&W page GBP 700, color page GBP 800. Circ: 10,000.

690   SGP
SOUTHEAST ASIA BUILDING*. Text in English. 1974. m. USD 105. adv. bk.rev.
Formerly (until 1988): Southeast Asian Building Annual
Indexed: AIAP.
Published by: Q T F Publications, 08-01 Block A, SLF Complex, 510 Thomson Rd, Singapore, 298135, Singapore. FAX 65-2225587. Ed. Margie T Logarta. Adv. contact Sherry Kang. B&W page USD 1,150, color page USD 1,350; trim 275 x 205. Circ: 6,500.

690   USA   ISSN 1546-9808
SOUTHEAST CONSTRUCTION (FLORIDA EDITION). Text in English. m. USD 40 (effective 2004). **Document type:** *Magazine, Trade.* **Description:** Provides local, in-depth and comprehensive coverage on heavy engineering, highway, building and industrial construction news in Florida.
Published by: Mcgraw-Hill Construction Dodge (Subsidiary of: McGraw-Hill Construction Information Group), 4901 Vineland Rd, Ste 310, Orlando, FL 32811. TEL 407-226-2200, 800-393-6343, FAX 407-226-2207, http:// www.southeastconstructionmag.com/, http:// www.dodgeconstructionpublications.com. Ed. Scott Judy. Pub. Kevin Rhodes TEL 225-292-8980 ext 15. Adv. contact Jim Van Natta TEL 407-977-4397.

690 624   USA
SOUTHERN BUILDING CODE CONGRESS. STANDARD BUILDING CODE. Text in English. triennial.
Published by: Southern Building Code Congress, International, 900 Montclair Rd, Birmingham, AL 35213. TEL 205-591-1853, FAX 205-592-7001.

690   USA
SOUTHERN BUILDING CODE CONGRESS. STANDARD GAS CODE. Text in English. triennial.
Published by: Southern Building Code Congress, International, 900 Montclair Rd, Birmingham, AL 35213. TEL 205-591-1853, FAX 205-592-7001.

690 621   USA
SOUTHERN BUILDING CODE CONGRESS. STANDARD MECHANICAL CODE. Text in English. triennial.
Published by: Southern Building Code Congress, International, 900 Montclair Rd, Birmingham, AL 35213. TEL 205-591-1853, FAX 205-592-7001.

690 616.15   USA
SOUTHERN BUILDING CODE CONGRESS. STANDARD PLUMBING CODE. Text in English. triennial.

Published by: Southern Building Code Congress, International, 900 Montclair Rd, Birmingham, AL 35213. TEL 205-591-1853, FAX 205-592-7001.

690   USA
SOUTHERN HOME PLANS. Variant title: Traditional Southern Home Plan. Text in English. 1998. q. USD 19.90; USD 4.99 newsstand/cover (effective 2000). adv. **Document type:** *Magazine, Consumer.* **Description:** Dedicated to the glories of Southern architecture, featuring a variety of homes from columned estates to cozy homes with front porches.
Formerly: Southern Home Planning
Published by: HomeStyles Publishing & Marketing, Inc., 213 E. 4th St., 4th Fl., St. Paul, MN 55101-1603. TEL 651-602-5000, 888-626-2026, FAX 651-602-5001, http:// www.homestyles.com. Ed. Sara Freund. Adv. contact Shelley Junker. B&W page USD 3,910, color page USD 4,830; trim 8 x 10.75. Circ: 59,000.

624 622   USA   ISSN 1064-6914
SOUTHWEST CONTRACTOR. Text in English. 1938. m. USD 40 (effective 2004). adv. 85 p./no.; back issues avail.; reprints avail. **Document type:** *Magazine, Trade.* **Description:** Covers the commercial, highway, and industrial construction industry.
Incorporates: Southwest Builder
Related titles: Online - full text ed.: (from EBSCO Publishing, LexisNexis).
—CCC.
Published by: Mcgraw-Hill Construction Dodge (Subsidiary of: McGraw-Hill Construction Information Group), 3110 N Central Ave, Ste 155, Phoenix, AZ 85012 . TEL 800-393-6343, http://southwest.construction.com, www.dodgeconstructionpublications.com, http:// www.fwdodge.com. Ed. Kelly Wendel TEL 602-631-3069. Pub. Mark Kelly TEL 602-631-3080. Adv. contact Erica Lange TEL 602-631-3066. B&W page USD 1,050, color page USD 1,250; trim 11 x 8.5. Circ: 5,600 (controlled).

690 643.7   USA
▼ **SPACES OF KANSAS CITY.** Text in English. 2003. s-a. adv. **Document type:** *Magazine, Consumer.* **Description:** Delivers the latest trends in building, remodeling and home interiors.
Published by: Grand Communications, 1729 Grand Blvd, Kansas City, MO 64108. TEL 816-234-4173, FAX 816-234-4123. Pub. Bill Gaier TEL 816-234-4194. Adv. contact Michelle Jolles. page USD 2,730; trim 8.875 x 10.875. Circ: 60,000.

SPAIN. MINISTERIO DE LA VIVIENDA. ESTADISTICA DE LA INDUSTRIA DE LA CONSTRUCCION. see *BUILDING AND CONSTRUCTION—Abstracting, Bibliographies, Statistics*

690   USA
SPEC-DATA PROGRAM*; concise manufacturer's product literature in C S I format and proprietary specification on specific products. Text in English. 1966. q. USD 250 to non-members. adv. **Description:** Technical data on products available in commercial, industrial and institutional markets.
Former titles: Spec-Data Manu-Spec System; Spec-Data System
Published by: Construction Specifications Institute, 289 - 266 Elmwood Ave, Buffalo, NY 14222. FAX 703-684-0465, csi@csinet.org. Circ: 12,600.

SPEC-DATA PROGRAM INDEX. see *BUILDING AND CONSTRUCTION—Abstracting, Bibliographies, Statistics*

691   GBR   ISSN 0950-6632
SPECIALIST BUILDING FINISHES. Text in English. 1967. q. GBP 12. adv. illus. **Document type:** *Newsletter.*
Incorporates: Modern Plastering (0026-8267)
Published by: (Federation of Plastering and Drywall Contractors), Phebrury Publications Ltd., 2 Bovingdon Close, Bovingdon, Hemel Hempstead, Herts HP3 0QU, United Kingdom. TEL 44-1442-832908. Ed. Peter Hancocks. Circ: 5,000.

690   ITA
SPECIALIZZATA. Text in Italian. 1990. m. (10/yr.). EUR 70 (effective 2005). **Document type:** *Magazine, Trade.* **Description:** Provides information on the latest technology in the sectors of civil engineering, residential and industrial building.
Formerly: Impermeabilizzare
Published by: BE-MA Editrice Srl, Via Teocrito 50, Milan, MI 20128, Italy. TEL 39-02-252071, FAX 39-02-27000692, segreteria@bema.it, http://www.bema.it. Ed. Dario Marabelli.

690   GBR   ISSN 0081-3567
SPECIFICATION; building methods and products. Text in English. 1898. a. GBP 75. adv. **Document type:** *Directory.* **Description:** Provides a primer for students of architecture and persons involved in building procurement.
Related titles: CD-ROM ed.
Published by: E MAP - Architecture, 33-39 Bowling Green Ln, London, EC1R 0DA, United Kingdom. TEL 44-171-837-1212, FAX 44-171-833-8072. Ed. Alan Williams. Circ: 20,000.

690 621.3 USA ISSN 1067-2451
SPECIFIER REPORTS. Text in English. 1991. irreg. (approx. 4/yr.). looseleaf. USD 30 per issue. bibl.; charts; illus. back issues avail. **Document type:** *Newsletter.* **Description:** Publishes product-specific performance data and general technical information for lighting products marketed in the U.S., including electronic ballasts, compact fluorescent lamps, reflectors and power reducers.
Published by: Rensselaer Polytechnic Institute, Lighting Research Center, 21 Union St, Troy, NY 12180. TEL 518-276-8716, FAX 518-276-2999, lrc@rpi.edu, http://www.lrc.rpi.edu. Ed. Russell Leslie. R&P Kevin Heslin.

690 ZAF
SPECIFILE BUILDING COMPENDIUM. Text in Afrikaans, English. 1976. a. ZAR 95. adv. **Description:** Lists addresses and phone numbers of manufacturers of building products, descriptions of their specific products.
Published by: Communications Group Specifile, Information Services Division, Handel Rd & Northern Pkwy, PO Box 7870, Johannesburg, 2000, South Africa. FAX 011-835-1943, TELEX 4-82735 SA. Ed. V Shapiro. Circ: 5,500.

690 ZAF
SPECIFILE NEWS AND PRODUCT UPDATE. Text in English. 1980. bi-m. back issues avail. **Document type:** *Trade.*
Published by: Communications Group, PO Box 7870, Johannesburg, 2000, South Africa. Circ: 2,500.

690 GBR ISSN 1467-1697
SPECIFY. Text in English. 1980. bi-m. GBP 20. adv. bk.rev. back issues avail. **Document type:** *Magazine, Trade.* **Description:** Covers news and views on all aspects of the construction industry in Northern Ireland.
—CCC.
Published by: Greer Publications, 5B Edgewater Business Park, Belfast Harbour Estate, Belfast, BT3 9JQ, United Kingdom. TEL 44-28-9078-3200, FAX 44-28-9078-3210, http://www.ulsterbusiness.com/greer. Ed. Eddie O'Gorman. Adv. contact Jackie Stott. Circ: 4,500.

690 USA
SPECTEXT; coordinated 16 division master guide specification in C S I format and style. Text in English. 1979. q. price varies.
Published by: Construction Sciences Research Foundation, 202 Wyndhurst Ave, Baltimore, MD 21210. TEL 410-323-8489. Circ: 2,200.

690 GBR ISSN 0306-3046
TH435
SPON'S ARCHITECTS' & BUILDERS' PRICE BOOK. Text in English. 1873. a. GBP 130 per issue (effective Sep. 2005). adv. stat. **Document type:** *Directory.* **Description:** Essential work for those involved in the pricing of construction works.
—BLDSC (8419.050000). **CCC.**
Published by: Spon Press (Subsidiary of: Taylor & Francis Ltd), 11 New Fetter Ln, London, EC4P 4EE, United Kingdom. TEL 44-20-7583-9855, FAX 44-20-7842-2300, http://www.pricebooks.co.uk/books/ab.asp, http://www.efnspon.com. Circ: 13,000.

690 GBR ISSN 0267-4181
SB472.565
SPON'S LANDSCAPE & EXTERNAL WORKS PRICEBOOK. Text in English. 1972. a. GBP 95 per issue (effective Sep. 2005). illus. **Document type:** *Directory.*
Former titles: Spon's Landscape Pricebook (0144-8404); Spon's Landscape Handbook (0306-3054)
—BLDSC (8419.060500).
Published by: Spon Press (Subsidiary of: Taylor & Francis Ltd), 11 New Fetter Ln, London, EC4P 4EE, United Kingdom. TEL 44-20-7583-9855, FAX 44-20-7842-2300, http://www.pricebooks.co.uk/books/ext.asp, http://www.efnspon.com.

690 621.3 GBR ISSN 0305-4543
TH6010
SPON'S MECHANICAL & ELECTRICAL SERVICES PRICE BOOK. Text in English. 1968. a. GBP 125 per issue (effective Sep. 2005). **Document type:** *Directory.*
Published by: Spon Press (Subsidiary of: Taylor & Francis Ltd), 11 New Fetter Ln, London, EC4P 4EE, United Kingdom. TEL 44-20-7583-9855, FAX 44-20-7842-2300, http://www.pricebooks.co.uk/books/me.asp, http://www.efnspon.com.

SPORT- BAEDER- FREIZEITBAUTEN; aquatic, sports and recreations buildings. see *SPORTS AND GAMES*

690 SWE ISSN 1650-772X
STAALBYGGNAD. Text in Swedish. 2001. a., latest vol.3, 2003. SEK 50 (effective 2003). adv. back issues avail. **Document type:** *Trade.*
Published by: Staalbyggnadsinstitutet/Swedish Institute of Steel Construction, Banergatan 54, PO Box 54, Stockholm, 11592, Sweden. TEL 46-8-6610180, FAX 46-8-6610305, info@sbi.se, http://www.sbi.se.

STADIA; the international review of sports venue design, operations & technology. see *ARCHITECTURE*

STADIA WORLD; the annual guide to design and build of stadia and arenas. see *ARCHITECTURE*

690 669 DEU ISSN 0176-3083
STAHLBAU - NACHRICHTEN. Text in German. bi-m. bk.rev.; software rev.; Website rev. 60 p./no. 3 cols./p.; **Document type:** *Journal, Trade.*
Published by: (Deutscher Stahlbau-Verband), Verlagsgruppe Wiederspahn, Biebricher Allee 11B, Wiesbaden, 65187, Germany. TEL 49-611-846515, FAX 49-611-801252, info@mixedmedia-konzepts.de.

STAR PERFORMERS BUILDING & CONSTRUCTION. see *BUSINESS AND ECONOMICS—Trade And Industrial Directories*

STATE BAR OF WISCONSIN. CONSTRUCTION AND PUBLIC CONTRACT LAW SECTION. NEWSLETTER. see *LAW*

STATE COMMERCIAL - RESIDENTIAL CODES. see *HOUSING AND URBAN PLANNING*

691 CAN ISSN 0380-6898
STATISTICS CANADA. MANUFACTURING, CONSTRUCTION AND ENERGY DIVISION. CEMENT. Text in English. 1931. m. stat. **Description:** Contains data on production, shipments and end of month stocks of Portland, masonry and other cement in Canada.
Related titles: Online - full content ed.: ISSN 1481-5311.
—CISTI.
Published by: (Statistics Canada, Manufacturing, Construction and Energy Division), Statistics Canada, Statistical Reference Centre, Rm. 1500, Main Bldg, Holland Ave, Ottawa, ON K1A 0T6, Canada. TEL 613-951-8116, 800-263-1136, infostats@statcan.ca, http://www.statcan.ca:8096/bsolc/english/bsolc?catno=44-001-X.

STATISTIK AUSTRIA. WOHNEN. see *BUILDING AND CONSTRUCTION—Abstracting, Bibliographies, Statistics*

690 DEU ISSN 0949-2275
STAVEBNI MATERIALY. Text in Czech. q. **Document type:** *Trade.*
Published by: Stein-Verlag Baden-Baden GmbH, Josef Herrmann Str 1-3, Iffezheim, 76473, Germany. TEL 49-7229-606-0, FAX 49-7229-60610. Pub. Wilhelm Joesch. R&P Jutta Senn.

690 331.88 CZE ISSN 0039-0798
STAVEBNIK✶ ; ctrnactideni pracujicich ve stavebnictvi. Text in Czech. 1897. s-m. USD 22.30.
Published by: Stavba - Odborovy Svaz Ceske Republiky, Senovazne nam 23, Prague, 11282, Czech Republic. Ed. Ladislav Jencik. Circ: 25,000.

690 NLD ISSN 1380-9393
STEDEBOUW EN ARCHITECTUUR. Text in Dutch. 1984. m. illus. **Document type:** *Trade.* **Description:** Each volume covers a specific subject in home design and construction, such as roofing, lumber, and construction methods.
Published by: Arko Uitgeverij BV, Postbus 616, Nieuwegein, 3430 AP, Netherlands. TEL 31-30-605-1090, gerlings@arko.nl, http://www.arko.nl. Ed. W Beemster. Pub. Marc Gerlings. Circ: 9,000.

669.142 AUS ISSN 1447-5359
TS350
STEEL AUSTRALIA. Text in English. 1972. q. AUD 110 domestic; AUD 100 foreign (effective 2004). adv. bk.rev. charts; illus.; tr.lit. cum.index. 30 p./no.; back issues avail. **Document type:** *Magazine, Consumer.* **Description:** Aimed at engineers; covers use of fabricated steel in construction.
Former titles (until Sep. 2002): Construct in Steel (1030-2581); (until Aug. 1987): Steel Fabrication Journal (0311-015X)
Indexed: ARI, ApMecR, RefZh.
—Linda Hall.
Published by: Australian Steel Institute, PO Box 6366, North Sydney, NSW 2059, Australia. TEL 61-2-99296666, FAX 61-2-99555406, enquiries@steel.org.au, http://www.steel.org.au/html/bookshop/steelmag.html. Ed., R&P Mr. Chris Chaseling. Adv. contact Ms. Anita Kavieris. Circ: 2,500.

690 669.142 ZAF
STEEL CONSTRUCTION. Text in English. bi-m. ZAR 40 (effective 2000). adv. **Document type:** *Trade.* **Description:** Covers all aspects of the steel sector of the building industry.
Indexed: ISAP.
Published by: Southern African Institute of Steel, PO Box 1338, Johannesburg, 2000, South Africa. TEL 27-11-838-1665, FAX 27-11-834-4301, info@saisc.co.za, saisc@iafrica.com, http://www.saisc.co.za. Ed., Adv. contact Sandra Townsend.

693.71 AUS ISSN 0049-2205
STEEL CONSTRUCTION. Text in English. 1967. s-a. AUD 110 domestic; AUD 100 foreign (effective 2004). **Document type:** *Academic/Scholarly.* **Description:** Provides technical literature on steel design mainly for the structural engineer.
Indexed: ARI, ApMecR.
—BLDSC (8462.550000), Linda Hall.
Published by: Australian Steel Institute, PO Box 6366, North Sydney, NSW 2059, Australia. TEL 61-2-99296666, FAX 61-2-99555406, enquiries@steel.org.au, http://www.steel.org.au. Ed. Dr. Peter Kneen. R&P Arun Syam. Circ: 4,500.

STEEL DESIGN/CONSTRUCTION METALLIQUE. see *ARCHITECTURE*

691.2 DEU ISSN 0940-6905
STEIN; Das Magazin fuer den Natursteinmarkt. Text in German. 1884. m. EUR 108 domestic; EUR 115.20 foreign; EUR 68.40 domestic to students; EUR 75.60 foreign to students; EUR 10.50 newsstand/cover (effective 2004). adv. bk.rev. bibl.; illus.; stat. index. **Document type:** *Magazine, Trade.*
Supersedes (1971-1990): Steinmetz und Bildhauer
Indexed: DIP, IBR, IBZ.
Published by: Callwey Verlag, Streitfeldstr 35, Munich, 81673, Germany. TEL 49-89-4360050, FAX 49-89-436005113, redaktion@stein-netz.de, a.hagenkord@callwey.de, http://www.stein-netz.de, http://www.callwey.de. Ed. Willy Hafner. Adv. contact Beate Muck. B&W page EUR 2,128, color page EUR 3,388. Circ: 6,844 (paid).

690 DEU ISSN 0942-7538
TN950.A1
STEINTIME; bauen mit Naturstein. Text in German. 1992. s-a. **Document type:** *Journal, Trade.*
Indexed: IBR, IBZ.
Published by: Callwey Verlag, Streitfeldstr 35, Munich, 81673, Germany. TEL 49-89-4360050, FAX 49-89-436005113, a.hagenkord@callwey.de, http://www.stein-netz.de, http://www.callwey.de. Circ: 30,000.

690 SWE ISSN 0346-1866
STEN; the Scandinavian stone industries magazine. Text in Swedish. 1939. q. SEK 280 (effective 1998). **Description:** Directed to architects and building contractors in the Scandinavian countries.
Published by: Sveriges Stenindustrifoerbund/Swedish Stone Industries Federation, Fack 167, Kristianstad, 29122, Sweden. TEL 46-44-20-97-80, FAX 46-44-20-96-75. Ed. Christer Kjellen. Pub. Kurt Johansson. adv.: B&W page SEK 8,740, color page SEK 12,250; trim 260 x 190. Circ: 8,300 (controlled). **Co-sponsor:** Stenindustriens Landssammenslutning, Norge.

609 TUR ISSN 1300-3399
➤ **STESISAT MUHENDISLIGI.** Text in Turkish; Summaries in English, Turkish. 1992. m. adv. back issues avail. **Document type:** *Bulletin, Academic/Scholarly.*
Related titles: Fax ed.
Published by: Chamber of Mechanical Engineers, Sumer Sokak, Demirtepe 36-1-A, Ankara, 06440, Turkey. TEL 90-312-231-3159, FAX 90-312-231-3165, yayin@mmo.org.tr, http://www.mmo.org.tr. Ed. Ali Ekbar Gakar. Pub. Mehmet Sopance. Adv. contact Ayten Yildir. **Dist. by:** Sakizagaci Sok 16, Istanbul 80080, Turkey.

690 336.2 DEU
STEUER-BRIEF FUER DAS BAU- UND BAUNEBENGEWERBE. Text in German. m. EUR 5.80 per issue (effective 2005). **Document type:** *Journal, Trade.*
Formerly: Steuer-Brief fuer das Baugewerbe (0946-4603)
Published by: Deubner Verlag GmbH & Co. KG, Oststr 11, Cologne, 50996, Germany. TEL 49-221-9370180, FAX 49-221-93701890, kundenservice@deubner-verlag.de, http://www.vrp.de.

693.1 720 ITA
STONE & STEIN. Text in English, German, Italian. 1990. s-a. free.
Formerly (unti 1996): Marmo In
Published by: (Italian Consortium for Marble), Ever s.n.c. di Emilia Gallini & C., Galleria Gandhi, 15, Rho, MI 20017, Italy. TEL 39-02-93900740, FAX 39-02-93900727, bstone@tin.it, http://www.bstone.it.

691 USA
STONE BUSINESS. Text in English. m. free (effective 2002). adv. **Document type:** *Magazine, Trade.* **Description:** Aims to enhance the demand for stone by providing architects, designers, builders, fabricators and installers with a greater understanding of stone's versatility in residential and commercial architecture.
Published by: Stone Business Magazine, PO Box 709, Orinda, CA 94563. TEL 925-386-0058, FAX 925-386-0183, dave@stonebusiness.net, http://www.stonebusiness.net. Ed. Emerson Schwartzkopf. Pub. Dave Anderson. adv.: B&W page USD 2,130; trim 8.125 x 10.875.

625.82029 GBR
STONE FEDERATION HANDBOOK. Text in English. biennial. free. adv. **Document type:** *Directory, Trade.* **Description:** Lists members of the Stone Federation of Great Britain and indicates their specific interests.
Published by: (Stone Federation of Great Britain), Herald House Ltd., 96 Dominion Rd, Worthing, BN14 8JP, United Kingdom. TEL 44-1903-821082, FAX 44-1903-821081. Ed. Jane Buxey. Adv. contact Margaret Beaman.

B

▼ *new title* ➤ *refereed* ✶ *unverified* ♦ *full entry avail.*

690 USA ISSN 1525-4909
TA426
STONE MAGAZINE; the trade magazine for specifiers, fabricators, and suppliers of dimensional stone. Text in English. 1985. 12/yr. USD 50 domestic; USD 55 in Canada & Mexico; USD 60 elsewhere (effective 1999). adv. bk.rev. back issues avail. **Document type:** *Trade.* **Description:** Contains dimensional stone industry trends and events. Features articles on quarrying, installation, fabrication and cutting techniques, sales and marketing, finance, equipment and new products.
Formerly: Dimensional Stone Magazine (0883-0258)
—CCC.
Published by: Ashlee Publishing Co., Inc., 18 E 41st St, 20th Fl, New York, NY 10017-6222. TEL 212-376-7722, FAX 212-376-7723, ashleep@aol.com, http://www.stonemag.com. adv.: B&W page USD 1,935, color page USD 2,665; 10 x 7. Circ: 15,000 (controlled).

691 USA
STONE, SAND & GRAVEL REVIEW. Text in English. 1999. bi-m. USD 48 (effective 2004). adv. **Document type:** *Magazine, Trade.* **Description:** Designed to provide a communication forum for the aggregates industry by which to facilitate the exchange of information on industry technology, trends, developments and concerns.
Published by: (National Stone, Sand & Gravel Association), Naylor Publications, Inc., 5950 NW 1st Pl, Gainesville, FL 32607-6018. TEL 800-369-6220, http://www.naylor.com. Pub. Chris Hodges TEL 800-369-6220 ext 3368. adv.: B&W page USD 2,029.50; trim 8.375 x 10.875.

STONE WORLD. see *MINES AND MINING INDUSTRY*

690 FRA ISSN 0183-455X
STORES ET FERMETURES. Text in French. 7/yr. **Description:** Treats windows, awnings, locks, shutters, blinds.
Published by: Creations Editions Productions Publicitaires, 70, rue Amelot, Paris, 75011, France. TEL 33-01-43383056, FAX 33-1-43465818.

690 RUS
STROITEL'NAYA GAZETA. Text in Russian. w. USD 189.95 in United States.
Related titles: Microfiche ed.: (from EVP).
Published by: Izdatel'stvo Stroitel'naya Gazeta, Furkasovskii per 12-5, Moscow, 101973, Russian Federation. TEL 7-095-9251629, FAX 7-095-9232542, stroy@glasnet.ru. Ed. P A Degtyarev. **US dist. addr.:** East View Information Services, 3020 Harbor Ln. N., Minneapolis, MN 55447. TEL 612-550-0961.

STROITEL'NAYA MEKHANIKA I RASCHET SOORUZHENII. see *ENGINEERING—Engineering Mechanics And Materials*

691 BGR
STROITELNI MATERIALI I SILIKATNA PROMISHLENOST. Text in Bulgarian. 1960. m. BGL 4.10, USD 18.
Indexed: A&ATA, BSLGeo, ChemAb.
Published by: Ministerstvo na Stroezhite i Arkhitekturata, Sofia, Bulgaria. Circ: 2,500. **Dist. by:** Hemus, 6 Rouski Blvd., Sofia 1000, Bulgaria.

STROITEL'NOE VEDOMOSTI; gazeta dlya stroitelei, proektirovshchikov, rabotnikov stroindustrii i zastroishchikov. see *ARCHITECTURE*

693 RUS ISSN 0585-430X
CODEN: STRMAC
STROITEL'NYE MATERYALY. Text in Russian. 1955. m. USD 247 foreign (effective 2005). **Document type:** *Journal, Trade.* **Description:** Covers high-priority aspects of development, production and use of building materials in modern construction.
Indexed: BrCerAb, C&ISA, CerAb, CivEngAb, CorrAb, E&CAJ, EMA, M&TEA, MBF, METADEX, RASB, RefZh, SolStAb, WAA.
—CASDDS, CISTI, East View, Linda Hall. **CCC.**
Address: Ul Krzhizhanovskogo 13, ofis 507-b, Moscow, 117818, Russian Federation. Ed. M G Rublevskaya. **US dist. addr.:** East View Information Services, 3020 Harbor Ln. N., Minneapolis, MN 55447. TEL 800-477-1005, FAX 800-800-3839, eastview@eastview.com, http://www.eastview.com.

690 BGR ISSN 0562-1852
STROITELSTVO. Text in Bulgarian; Summaries in German, Russian. 1954. bi-m. USD 60 foreign (effective 2005). **Document type:** *Journal, Academic/Scholarly.*
Indexed: BSLGeo, BSLIndus, BSLMath, CISA, ChemAb, EEA, GeotechAb, RASB, RefZh.
—CASDDS.
Published by: University of Architecture, Building and Geodesy, 1 Hristo Smirnenski Blvd, Sofia, 1421, Bulgaria. TEL 359-2-661967, FAX 359-2-656863. Circ: 3,997. **Dist. by:** Sofia Books, ul Silivria 16, Sofia 1404, Bulgaria. TEL 359-2-9586257, info@sofiabooks-bg.com, http://www.sofiabooks-bg.com. **Co-sponsor:** Nauchno-Tekhnicheski Suiuz po Stroitelstvo/Scientific-Technical Union of Building.

STROITEL'STVO GRADAT/CONSTRUCTION & CITY. see *HOUSING AND URBAN PLANNING*

690 BLR
STROITEL'STVO I NEDVIZHIMOST'. Text in Russian. 1995. w. **Document type:** *Newspaper, Trade.*
Related titles: Online - full content ed.: ISSN 1606-7053. 2000.
Published by: Izdatel'stvo Nestor, A/ya 563, Minsk, 220113, Belarus. nestorpb@nestor.minsk.by, http://www.nestor.minsk.by.

STRUCTURAL CONCRETE. see *ENGINEERING—Civil Engineering*

STRUCTURAL MOVER. see *ENGINEERING—Civil Engineering*

692 620 GBR ISSN 0263-080X
TA630
STRUCTURAL SURVEY. Text in English. 1983. 5/yr. EUR 4,066.16 in Europe; USD 4,169 in North America; AUD 4,759 in Australasia; GBP 2,848.16 in UK & elsewhere (effective 2006). bk.rev. abstr. back issues avail.; reprint service avail. from PSC. **Document type:** *Bulletin.* **Description:** Only journal in its field to offer access to comments and advice on all aspects of the inspection and survey of buildings.
Related titles: CD-ROM ed.; Online - full text ed.: (from EBSCO Publishing, Emerald Group Publishing Limited, Gale Group, IngentaConnect, O C L C Online Computer Library Center, Inc., ProQuest Information & Learning, Swets Information Services).
Indexed: ABIn, API, BrCerAb, C&ISA, CerAb, CorrAb, E&CAJ, EMA, EmerIntel, ICEA, RICS, SolStAb, WAA.
—BLDSC (8478.610000), CISTI, IE, Infotrieve, ingenta. **CCC.**
Published by: Emerald Group Publishing Limited, 60-62 Toller Ln, Bradford, W Yorks BD8 9BY, United Kingdom. TEL 44-1274-777700, FAX 44-1274-785200, infomation@emeraldinsight.com, http://www.emeraldinsight.com/ss.htm. Ed. Mike Hoxley. **Subscr. addr. in N American:** Emerald Group Publishing Ltd., 44 Brattle St, 4th Fl, Cambridge, MA 02138. TEL 617-497-2175, 888-622-0075, FAX 617-354-6875.

690 GBR ISSN 1353-5331
SUBCON. Text in English. 1993. bi-m. adv. **Document type:** *Magazine, Trade.* **Description:** Reports on news and trends of interest to subcontractors.
Related titles: Online - full text ed.: (from LexisNexis).
Indexed: METADEX.
Published by: Centaur Publishing, St Giles House, 50 Poland St, London, W1V 4AX, United Kingdom. TEL 44-20-7970-4000, lrahman@centaur.co.uk, http://www.centaur.co.uk. adv.: B&W page GBP 1,890, color page GBP 2,100.

690 DEU
SUEDDEUTSCHE BAUWIRTSCHAFT. Text in German. 1951. m. adv. bk.rev. charts; illus.; stat.; tr.lit. **Document type:** *Magazine, Trade.*
Published by: Verlag Sueddeutsche Bauwirtschaft, Wilhelm-Hertz-Str 14, Stuttgart, 70192, Germany. TEL 49-711-2573333, FAX 49-711-2573422. Ed., Pub. Horst Kimmich. adv.: B&W page EUR 1,025, color page EUR 1,745; trim 180 x 250. Circ: 5,000 (paid and controlled).

690 USA ISSN 0745-354X
SUN BELT BUILDING JOURNAL. Text in English. 1976. m. USD 11. adv. bk.rev.
Published by: Sun Belt Publishing Co., 5125 N 16th St, Phoenix, AZ 85016. TEL 602-264-3500. Ed. Jerry Rockwell. Circ: 8,263.

690 USA
SUNSET 250 BEST SELLING HOME PLANS. Text in English. 1998. a. USD 4.99 newsstand/cover (effective 2004). adv. **Document type:** *Magazine, Consumer.*
Published by: Sunset Publishing Corp., 80 Willow Rd, Menlo Park, CA 94025-3691. TEL 650-321-3600, FAX 650-327-7537, http://www.sunset.com. Pub. Tom Marshall TEL 212-522-9058. adv.: B&W page USD 4,180, color page USD 4,830; trim 8 x 10.5. Circ: 100,000.

692.8 USA
SUPERINTENDING FOR CONTRACTORS: HOW TO BRING JOBS IN ON TIME, ON BUDGET. Text in English. 1987. irreg. USD 34.95. charts; illus.
Formerly (until 1991): Superintending for the General Contractor
Published by: R.S. Means Company Inc. (Subsidiary of: Reed Construction Data, Associated Construction Publications), 63 Smiths Lane, P O Box 800, Kingston, MA 02364-9988. TEL 617-585-7880.

338.4 IRN ISSN 0301-7478
SURVEY OF CONSTRUCTION ACTIVITIES OF THE PRIVATE SECTOR IN URBAN AREAS OF IRAN. Text in Persian, Modern. q. free. illus.; stat.
Published by: (Iran. Economic Statistics Department), Bank Markazi Jomhouri Islami Iran/Central Bank of the Islamic Republic of Iran, P O Box 11365-8531, Tehran, Iran. FAX 98-21-390323.

691 SWE ISSN 0284-432X
SVERIGES BYGG- OCH INSTALLATIONSVAROR; huvudleverantoerer - tillverkare. Text in Swedish. 1987. a.
Published by: Svensk Byggtjaenst/Swedish Building Centre, Sankt Eriksgatan 117, 9, Stockholm, 11387, Sweden. TEL 46-8-4571000, FAX 46-8-4571199, http://www.byggtjanst.se.

SVERIGES LANTBRUKSUNIVERSITET. INSTITUTIONEN FOER JORDBRUKETS BIOSYSTEM OCH TEKNOLOGI. SPECIALMEDDELANDE/SWEDISH UNIVERSITY OF AGRICULTURAL SCIENCES. DEPARTMENT OF AGRICULTURAL BIOSYSTEMS AND TECHNOLOGY. SPECIAL REPORT. see *AGRICULTURE*

SWEDEN. STATISTISKA CENTRALBYRAAN. STATISTISKA MEDDELANDEN. SERIE BO, BOSTAEDER OCH BYGGNADER. see *BUILDING AND CONSTRUCTION—Abstracting, Bibliographies, Statistics*

690 SWE ISSN 1650-576X
HC380.E5
SWEDISH RESEARCH FOR SUSTAINABILITY. Text in English. 1994. 4/yr. free. **Document type:** *Academic/Scholarly.*
Formerly (until 2001): Swedish Building Research (1400-6995); Which was formed by the merger of (1976-1994): Synopses of Swedish Building Research (0347-9935); (1976-1994): Newsletter of Swedish Building Research (1102-3554); Which was formerly (until 1990): Swedish Building Research News (0349-0254)
Indexed: EnvAb, IBuildSA.
—BLDSC (8574.210000), CISTI.
Published by: FORMAS/Swedish Research Council for Environment, Agricultural Sciences and Spatial Planning, Birger Jarls Torg 5, Box 1206, Stockholm, 11182, Sweden. TEL 46-8-775-40-00, FAX 46-8-775-40-10, kerstin.franklin@formas.se, http://www.formas.se. Ed. Kerstin Franklin TEL 46-8-775-40-45.

690 CAN ISSN 1497-7893
SWEET'S CATALOGUE FILE, CANADIAN CONSTRUCTION. Text in English, French. 1966. a. free to qualified personnel. **Document type:** *Catalog, Trade.*
Former titles (until 2001): Sweet's Canadian Construction Catalogue (1190-9072); (until 1988): Sweet's Canadian Construction Catalogue File (0082-0431)
Related titles: CD-ROM ed.: Sweetsource.
—CISTI.
Published by: McGraw-Hill Information Systems Company of Canada, 270 Yorkland Blvd, North York, ON M2J 1R8, Canada. TEL 416-496-3100, FAX 416-496-3123, http://www.sweets.com, http://sweets.construction.com. Ed. Breda Murphy. Circ: 7,000 (controlled).

720 624 USA ISSN 1529-9929
SWEET'S DIRECTORY. Text in English. a. USD 69.95 (effective 2004). illus.
Published by: Mcgraw-Hill Construction Sweets (Subsidiary of: McGraw-Hill Construction Information Group), 2 Penn Plaza 10th Fl, New York, NY 10121. TEL 800-442-2258, FAX 866-227-9393, sweets_customerservice@mcgraw-hill.com, http://sweets.construction.com/.

690 USA
SWEET'S GENERAL BUILDING AND RENOVATION FILE. Text in English. 1906. a. USD 350 (effective 2000). **Document type:** *Catalog.*
Formerly: Sweet's General Building Catalog File
Published by: Mcgraw-Hill Construction Sweets (Subsidiary of: McGraw-Hill Construction Information Group), 2 Penn Plaza 10th Fl, New York, NY 10121. TEL 212-904-4450, FAX 212-904-2348. Pub. Howard Mager Jr. Circ: 27,000 (controlled).

690 USA
SWEET'S HOMEBUILDING & REMODELING FILE. Text in English. a. free to qualified personnel (effective 2000). **Document type:** *Catalog.*
Published by: Mcgraw-Hill Construction Sweets (Subsidiary of: McGraw-Hill Construction Information Group), 2 Penn Plaza 10th Fl, New York, NY 10121. TEL 212-904-4450, FAX 212-904-2348. Pub. Howard Mager Jr. Circ: 29,000 (controlled).

690 USA
SWEET'S INTERNATIONAL BUILDING PRODUCTS CATALOG FILE. Text in English. a. free to qualified personnel. **Document type:** *Catalog.*
Formerly: Sweet's International Construction File
Published by: Mcgraw-Hill Construction Sweets (Subsidiary of: McGraw-Hill Construction Information Group), 2 Penn Plaza 10th Fl, New York, NY 10121. TEL 212-904-4450, FAX 212-904-2348. Pub. Howard Mager Jr. Circ: 10,000.

690 USA
SWEET'S INTERNATIONAL PRODUCTLINE✶. Text in English. 1993. q. adv. **Description:** Provides the latest up-to-date information on building product materials for the international market.
Published by: Mcgraw-Hill Construction Sweets (Subsidiary of: McGraw-Hill Construction Information Group), 2 Penn Plaza 10th Fl, New York, NY 10121. TEL 212-904-4750, FAX 212-904-4302. Ed. Jeff Elliott. Circ: (controlled).

690 USA
SWEET'S PRODUCTLINE. Text in English. q. adv. back issues avail. **Description:** Provides up-to-date information, in a 4-color format, on building products.

Published by: Mcgraw-Hill Construction Sweets (Subsidiary of: McGraw-Hill Construction Information Group), 2 Penn Plaza 10th Fl, New York, NY 10121. TEL 212-904-4750, FAX 212-904-4302. Ed. Jeff Elliott. Pub. Gloria Glowacki. Circ: 25,000 (controlled).

SWEET'S STRUCTURAL & CIVIL PRODUCTS SOURCEBOOK. see *ENGINEERING—Civil Engineering*

797.2 725.74 GBR ISSN 1351-7791
SWIMMING POOL NEWS. Text in English. 1962. bi-m. adv. bk.rev. **Document type:** *Magazine, Trade.* **Description:** Covers design and construction technology for pools and saunas.
Published by: Archant Specialist Ltd. (Subsidiary of: Archant), The Mill, Bearwalden Business Park, Royston Rd, Wendens Ambo, Essex CB11 4GB, United Kingdom. TEL 44-1799-544200, spn.edit@swimmingpoolnews.co.uk, farine.clarke@archant.co.uk, http://www.swimmingpoolnews.co.uk, http://www.archant.co.uk/. Ed. Christina Connor. adv.: color page GBP 860; trim 210 x 297.

690 CHE
SWISSBAU SPECIAL. Text in German. a. free to qualified personnel. **Document type:** *Journal, Trade.*
Published by: MVS Baumarketing AG (Subsidiary of: Springer Science+Business Media), Ruetistr 22, Schlieren, 8952, Switzerland. TEL 41-1-7385151, FAX 41-1-7385200, franco.bernasconi@mvs.ch, http://www.mvs.ch. Circ: 15,000 (controlled).

690 FRA ISSN 0989-2583
SYCODES INFORMATIONS. Text in French. 1989. 6/yr. adv.
Published by: Agency of Quality Construction, 9 bd. Malesherbes, Paris, 75008, France. TEL 33-1-44510351, FAX 33-1-47428171. Ed. Michel Ternier. Adv. contact Francoise Daudin. Circ: 5,000.

690 628.5 USA
T A B JOURNAL. (Testing and Balancing) Text in English. 1988. q. USD 24 (effective 1999). tr.lit. back issues avail. **Document type:** *Trade.* **Description:** Case studies and technical articles on testing and balancing.
Related titles: Online - full text ed.
Indexed: EngInd.
Published by: American Air Balance Council, 1518 K St, N W, 503, Washington, DC 20005. TEL 202-737-0207, FAX 202-638-4833, aabchq@aol.com, http://www.aabchq. Ed. Brian Hutchins.

666.893 553.62 USA
T A C A CONVEYOR. Text in English. 2002. bi-m. adv.
Published by: (Texas Aggregates and Concrete Association), Rector - Duncan & Associates, 314 Highland Mall Blvd, Ste 510, Austin, TX 78752. TEL 512-454-5262, FAX 512-451-9556, wbrowning@rector-duncan.com, http://www.rector-duncan.com/. adv.: B&W page USD 525; trim 8.5 x 11.

T B M. (Tunnel Business Magazine) see *ENGINEERING—Civil Engineering*

690 720 FIN ISSN 1459-1839
▼ **T M RAKENNUSMAAILMA.** Variant title: Tekniikan Maailma Rakennusmaailma. Text in Finnish. 2003. q. EUR 20.40 (effective 2005). adv. **Document type:** *Magazine, Consumer.*
Related titles: ♦ Supplement to: T M. Tekniikan Maailma. ISSN 0355-4287.
Published by: Yhtyneet Kuvalehdet Oy/United Magazines Ltd., Maistraatinportti 1, Helsinki, 00015, Finland. TEL 358-9-15661, FAX 358-9-145650, http://www.kuvalehdet.fi/. Ed. Martti Merilinna. adv.: page EUR 5,130.

690 NLD
T N O BUILDING AND CONSTRUCTION RESEARCH. ANNUAL REPORT. Text in Dutch, English. 1954. a. free. bibl.; charts; illus. **Document type:** *Corporate.*
Formerly: Institute T N O for Building Materials and Building Structures. Annual Report
Published by: T N O, Building and Construction Research, PO Box 49, Delft, 2600 AA, Netherlands. TEL 31-15-2842000, FAX 31-15-2843990, TELEX 38270, info@bouw.tno.nl, http://www.tno.nl/instit/bouw/home.html. Circ: 2,500.

693 ITA
T R E - ANNUAL LAPIDEI; formazione geologica e primi usi dei lapidei. Marmi del Nord Italia con schede tecniche. (Territorio Restauro Edilizia) Text in English, Italian. 1996. a. USD 36 foreign (effective 2003). adv. bk.rev. 96 p./no.; back issues avail. **Document type:** *Monographic series, Trade.*
Published by: Antonio Zoppas Editore S.r.l., Via Calvi 27, Conegliano, TV 31015, Italy. TEL 39-0438-411908, FAX 39-0438-31539, anzoppas@tmn.it, http://www.ulisselibri.com. Ed. Antonio Zoppas. Adv. contact Mies Cesarina. B&W page EUR 878, color page EUR 1,266; trim 296 x 208. Circ: 29,000 (paid); 1,000 (controlled).

690.028 ITA
T R E - EUROPEAN BUILDING MAGAZINE. (Territorio - Restauro - Edilizia) Text in Italian, English. 1991. q. EUR 29 domestic; EUR 42 foreign (effective 2003). adv. bk.rev. illus.; maps. index. 92 p./no.; back issues avail. **Document type:** *Magazine, Trade.* **Description:** Covers European architecture, construction, civil engineering projects, and urban planning.
Published by: Antonio Zoppas Editore S.r.l., Via Calvi 27, Conegliano, TV 31015, Italy. TEL 39-0438-411908, FAX 39-0438-31539, anzoppas@tmn.it, http://www.ulisselibri.com. Ed., Pub. Antonio Zoppas. Adv. contact Mies Cesarina. B&W page EUR 1,834, color page EUR 2,918; trim 296 x 208. Circ: 13,000 (paid); 12,000 (controlled).

690 JPN ISSN 0387-2254
CODEN: TKGJAW
TAISEI KENSETSU GIJUTSU KENKYUJOHO/TAISEI TECHNICAL RESEARCH REPORT. Text in Japanese; Summaries in English, Japanese. 1968. a.
Indexed: CIN, ChemAb, ChemTitl, CivEngAb, EEA.
—CASDDS. **CCC.**
Published by: Taisei Kensetsu K.K., Gijutsu Kenkyujo/Taisei Corp., Technology Research Center, 344-1 Nase-cho, Totsuka-ku, Yokohama-shi, Kanagawa-ken 245-0051, Japan. TEL 81-45-814-7223, FAX 81-45-814-7254. Ed. Yamada Masaaki. Pub. Matsumoto Toshio.

690 JPN ISSN 0285-5445
TAISEI QUARTERLY. Text in Japanese; Summaries in English. 1961. q.
Published by: Taisei Kensetsu K.K., 25-1 Nishi-Shinjuku 1-chome, Shinjuku-ku, Tokyo, 160-0023, Japan.

690 JPN ISSN 0374-4663
TA630 CODEN: TGKHAI
TAKENAKA GIJUTSU KENKYU HOKOKU/TAKENAKA TECHNICAL RESEARCH REPORT. Text in Japanese. 1966. s-a. free. back issues avail.
Indexed: EEA, EngInd, INIS AtomInd, Inspec, JTA, RefZh.
—BLDSC (8601.077000), AskIEEE, Linda Hall. **CCC.**
Published by: (Takenaka Komuten Gijutsu Kenkyujo/Takenaka Technical Research Laboratory), Takenaka Komuten Co. Ltd., 1-13 Hon-Machi 4-chome, Chuo-ku, Osaka-shi, 541-0053, Japan.

343.07869 690.5 DEU ISSN 0935-7211
TASCHENLEXIKON BAU- UND ARCHITEKTENRECHTLICHER ENTSCHEIDUNGEN. Text in German. 1978. irreg. price varies. **Document type:** *Monographic series, Trade.*
Published by: Erich Schmidt Verlag GmbH & Co. (Berlin), Genthiner Str 30G, Berlin, 10785, Germany. TEL 49-30-250085-0, FAX 49-30-25008521, vertrieb@esvmedien.de, http://www.erich-schmidt-verlag.de.

690 AUS
TASMANIAN MASTER BUILDER. Text in English. 1963. q. AUD 60 (effective 2002). adv. bk.rev. **Document type:** *Trade.*
Formerly: Tasmanian Building Journal
Published by: Master Builders' Association of Tasmania, PO Box 992 K, Hobart, TAS 7001, Australia. TEL 61-3-62343810, FAX 61-3-62343860. Ed. Wesley Phillips. Adv. contact Wesley Philips. color page AUD 1,000. Circ: 900.

690 USA ISSN 1096-360X
TH4805
TAUNTON'S FINE HOMEBUILDING. Text in English. 1980. bi-m. USD 37.95 in US & Canada; USD 45.95 elsewhere; USD 7.99 newsstand/cover domestic; USD 8.99 newsstand/cover in Canada (effective 2005). adv. bk.rev. illus. reprints avail. **Document type:** *Magazine, Trade.* **Description:** Provides professional-level information on residential building and remodeling with in-depth technique articles.
Formerly (until 1991): Fine Homebuilding (0273-1398)
Indexed: AIAP, API, AS&TI, ASIP, BRI, CBRI, EEA, IHTDI, Search.
—BLDSC (3927.752000), CISTI, IE, ingenta.
Published by: Taunton Press, Inc., 63 South Main St, PO Box 5506, Newtown, CT 06470-5506. TEL 203-426-8171, 800-477-8727, FAX 203-270-6751, fh@taunton.com, http://www.finehomebuilding.com, http://www.taunton.com. Ed. Kevin Ireton. Pub. Jon Miller. Adv. contacts Owen McMamara, Jeff Dwight. B&W page USD 13,080, color page USD 18,310; trim 8.88 x 10.88. Circ: 300,000 (paid). **Dist. by:** Curtis Circulation Co., 730 River Road, New Milford, NJ 07646.

690 BRA ISSN 0104-1053
TECHNE. Text in Portuguese. 1992. bi-m. USD 54 (effective 2000). adv. **Document type:** *Directory.*
Published by: Editora Pini Ltda., Rua Anhaia, 964, Bom Retiro, Sao Paulo, SP 01130-900, Brazil. TEL 55-11-2248811. Ed. Mario Sergio Pini. Adv. contact Luiz Carlos F Oliveira.

690 ISR ISSN 0792-0776
TECHNION - ISRAEL INSTITUTE OF TECHNOLOGY. RESEARCH REPORTS. Text in English. biennial. free.
Published by: Technion - Israel Institute of Technology, National Building Research Institute, Technion City, Haifa, 32000, Israel. TEL 972-4-8292242, FAX 972-4-8324534, TELEX 46406-TECON-IL. Ed. Monica Paciuk.

690 DEU ISSN 1439-3875
TECHNISCHE UNIVERSITAET BRAUNSCHWEIG. INSTITUT FUER BAUSTOFFE, MASSIVBAU UND BRANDSCHUTZ. MATERIALPRUEFANSTALT FUER DAS BAUWESEN. SCHRIFTENREIHE. Text in German. 1963. irreg. (approx. 6/yr.). price varies. **Document type:** *Monographic series, Academic/Scholarly.*
Former titles (until 1998): Technische Universitaet Braunschweig. Institut fuer Baustoffe, Massivbau und Brandschutz. Amtliche Materialpruefanstalt fuer das Bauwesen (1439-3867); (until 1989): Technische Universitaet Braunschweig. Institut fuer Baustoffe, Massivbau und Brandschutz. Schriftenreihe (0178-5796); (until 1978): Institut fuer Baustoffkunde und Stahlbetonbau. Schriftenreihe (0178-580X)
Published by: Technische Universitaet Braunschweig, Institut fuer Baustoffe Massivbau und Brandschutz, Beethovenstr 52, Braunschweig, 38106, Germany. TEL 49-531-3915400, FAX 49-531-3915900, o.dienelt@tu-bs.de, http://www.ibmb.tu-bs.de.

690 AUT
TECHNOPRESS BAU MAGAZIN; Oesterreichs Baufachzeitschrift fuer Hoch- und Ausbaupraxis in Planung, Produktentscheidung und Ausfuehrung. Text in German. 1974. bi-m. EUR 25 domestic; EUR 37.50 foreign; EUR 4 newsstand/cover (effective 2005). adv. bk.rev. abstr.; illus. **Document type:** *Magazine, Trade.*
Formerly: Bau Magazin
Published by: Springer Business Media Austria GmbH (Subsidiary of: Springer Science+Business Media), Inkustr 16, Klosterneuburg, 3403, Austria. TEL 43-2243-301110, FAX 43-2243-30111222, office@springer-sbm.at, http://www.springer-sbm.at. Ed. Alexander Riell. Adv. contact Ernst Wottowa. B&W page EUR 4,030, color page EUR 5,680; trim 185 x 260. Circ: 12,650 (paid and controlled).

B

690 USA
TECHOME BUILDER; the builder's guide to technology. Text in English. 2001. 9/yr. free domestic to qualified personnel; USD 95 foreign (effective 2005). adv. **Document type:** *Magazine, Trade.* **Description:** Provides builders with essential information and advice on how to leverage technology to increase productivity. competitive edge, and profits and how to incorporate technology products and services effectively in new homes and remodeling products. Features builder and industry news, product news and analysis, builder profiles and how-to stories.
Published by: E H Publishing, Inc., 111 Speen St, Ste 200, Framingham, MA 01701-2000. TEL 508-663-1500, FAX 508-663-1599, http://www.techomebuilder.com/, http://www.ehonline.com. Eds. Charles Wardell, Jason Knott TEL 508-358-3400 ext 226. adv.: color page USD 5,500; trim 10.25 x 12. Circ: 20,000.

690 ITA ISSN 0040-1803
TECNICA E RICOSTRUZIONE. Text in Italian. 1946. bi-m. adv. bk.rev. illus.; mkt.
Published by: Ordine degli Ingegneri della Provincia di Catania, Via Vincenzo Giuffrida, 202, Catania, CT 95128, Italy. Ed. Sebastiano Quatarone.

691 ESP ISSN 1578-1224
TECNO ROCA; revista profesional de la piedra natural. Text in Spanish. 1999. 6/yr. EUR 50 domestic; EUR 73.20 in Europe (effective 2004). **Document type:** *Magazine, Trade.*
Published by: Goodman Business Press S.A., Goya 115, 4to. dcha., Madrid, 28009, Spain. TEL 34-91-3096310, FAX 34-91-4018090, info@goodman-bp.com, http://www.goodman-bp.com.

690 VEN ISSN 0798-9601
➤ **TECNOLOGIA Y CONSTRUCCION.** Text in Spanish. 1985. s-a. VEB 1,500, USD 20 to individuals; VEB 2,000, USD 25 to institutions. abstr.; bibl.; charts; maps. index. **Document type:** *Academic/Scholarly.*
Published by: Instituto de Desarrollo Experimental de la Construccion, Apartado Postal 47169, Caracas, DF 1041-A, Venezuela. TEL 58-2-6931269, FAX 58-2-6931183. Ed. Maria Elena Hobaica.

690 ESP ISSN 1136-0062
NA673
TECTONICA. Text in Spanish. 1996. q. back issues avail.
Related titles: Ed.: Tectonica (English Edition). ISSN 1576-8589. 2000.
—CINDOC.
Published by: ATC Ediciones, S.L., P. del Prado, 24 6o. Izq., Madrid, 28014, Spain. TEL 34-91-4200066, FAX 34-91-14297706, tectonica@tectonica.es, http://www.tectonica.es/. Ed. Berta Blasco. Circ: 15,000.

691 DNK ISSN 0040-2141
TEGL. Text in Danish. 1897. q. DKK 180 domestic (effective 2000). adv. bk.rev. charts; illus.; tr.lit.
Indexed: ChemAb.
—BLDSC (8763.537000).
Published by: Murerfagets Oplysningsraad/Information Council of the Masons Association, Lille Strandstraede 20 C, Copenhagen K, 1254, Denmark. TEL 45-33-32-22-30, FAX 45-33-32-22-97, info@muro.dk, http://www.muro.dk. Ed. Soeren Boegh. Circ: 10,500.

▼ new title ➤ refereed ✶ unverified ♦ full entry avail.

690 RUS
TEKHNOLOGIYA. SERIYA. RESURSOSBEREGAYUSHIE PROTSESSY, OBORUDOVANIE, MATERIALY. Text in Russian. q. USD 89 in United States.
Published by: V.I.M.I., Volokolamskoe shosse 77, Moscow, 123584, Russian Federation. TEL 7-095-4911306, FAX 7-095-4916820. **US dist. addr.:** East View Information Services, 3020 Harbor Ln. N., Minneapolis, MN 55447. TEL 612-550-0961.

690 669 JPN
TEKKOTSU/STEEL FRAME. Text in Japanese. 1983. s-a.
Published by: Tekkotsu Kensetsugyo Kyokai/Japan Steel Constructors Association, 2-18 Ginza 2-chome, Chuo-ku, Tokyo, 104-0061, Japan.

690 SGP
TENDERS ESTIMATING DATA SERVICE. Text in English. 1988. s-a. USD 103 in Singapore; USD 200 elsewhere.
Published by: Construction Industry Development Board, Annexe A MND Complex, 9 Maxwell Rd 03-00, Singapore, 069112, Singapore. TEL 65-2256711, FAX 65-2257301, cidb_enquiry@cidb.gov.sg, http://www.cidb.gov.sg. Circ: 200.

691 USA
TENNESSEE CONCRETE MAGAZINE. Text in English. 2001. 3/yr. free to members (effective 2004). **Document type:** *Magazine, Trade.*
Published by: (Tennessee Ready Mixed Concrete Association), Naylor Publications, Inc., 5950 NW 1st Pl, Gainesville, FL 32607-6018. TEL 800-369-6220, http://www.naylor.com. Pub. Shane Holt.

690 USA ISSN 1084-9580
TENNESSEE CONSTRUCTION NEWS WEEKLY. KNOXVILLE & VICINITY. Text in English. 1995. w. adv. **Document type:** *Newsletter, Trade.* **Description:** Provides information on what jobs are coming up for bid or negotiation.
Related titles: Online - full text ed.
Published by: Mcgraw-Hill Construction Dodge (Subsidiary of: McGraw-Hill Construction Information Group), 148 Princeton-Hightstown Rd, Hightstown, NJ 08520. TEL 800-393-6343, http://www.dodgeconstructionpublications.com.

690 USA ISSN 1084-9572
TENNESSEE CONSTRUCTION NEWS WEEKLY. MEMPHIS & VICINITY. Text in English. 1995. w. adv. **Document type:** *Newsletter, Trade.* **Description:** Provides information on what jobs are coming up for bid or negotiation.
Related titles: Online - full text ed.
Published by: Mcgraw-Hill Construction Dodge (Subsidiary of: McGraw-Hill Construction Information Group), 148 Princeton-Hightstown Rd, Hightstown, NJ 08520. TEL 800-393-6343, http://www.dodgeconstructionpublications.com.

690 USA ISSN 1084-9556
TENNESSEE CONSTRUCTION NEWS WEEKLY. NASHVILLE & VICINITY. Text in English. 1995. w. adv. **Document type:** *Newsletter, Trade.* **Description:** Provides information on what jobs are coming up for bid or negotiation.
Related titles: Online - full text ed.
Published by: Mcgraw-Hill Construction Dodge (Subsidiary of: McGraw-Hill Construction Information Group), 148 Princeton-Hightstown Rd, Hightstown, NJ 08520. TEL 800-393-6343, http://www.dodgeconstructionpublications.com.

729.7 USA ISSN 0040-3806
TERRAZZO TOPICS✶. Text in English. 1970 (vol.59). 10/yr. membership. **Document type:** *Newsletter.* **Description:** Covers activities of the association.
Formerly: Terrazzo Trends
Published by: National Terrazzo and Mosaic Association, 110 E Market St, Ste 200A, Leesburg, VA 20176-3122. Circ: 1,500.

690 USA ISSN 0164-8012
TEXAS BUILDER. Text in English. 1989. bi-m. USD 12. adv. **Document type:** *Trade.*
Published by: Oliver Publications, PO Box 8619, Ft. Worth, TX 76124-0619. TEL 817-451-8951. Ed. Rene Adams. Pub. Becky Oliver. Circ: 10,000 (paid).

690 USA ISSN 1077-1867
TEXAS CONSTRUCTION. Text in English. 1993. m. USD 40 (effective 2004). adv. **Document type:** *Magazine, Trade.* **Description:** Focuses on Texas construction and industrial markets.
Related titles: Online - full text ed.: (from LexisNexis, ProQuest Information & Learning).
Indexed: ABIn.
—CCC.
Published by: Mcgraw-Hill Construction Dodge (Subsidiary of: McGraw-Hill Construction Information Group), 1341 W Mockingbird Ln Ste 1104E, Dallas, TX 75247. TEL 214-688-5090, 800-794-7305, 800-393-6343, FAX 214-688-5091, http://www.txconstruction.com/, http://www.dodgeconstructionpublications.com. Ed. Mark Rea TEL 214-688-5198. Adv. contact Joan Callahan TEL 215-688-5096. Circ: 6,300.

TEXAS CONSTRUCTION LAW MANUAL. see *LAW*

690 USA ISSN 1521-7000
TEXAS CONSTRUCTION NEWS WEEKLY COVERING FORT WORTH AND VICINITY. Text in English. 1995. w. adv. **Document type:** *Newsletter, Trade.* **Description:** Provides information on what jobs are coming up for bid or negotiation.
Formerly (until 199?): Construction News Weekly Covering Fort Worth and Vicinity (1086-6205)
Related titles: Online - full text ed.
Published by: Mcgraw-Hill Construction Dodge (Subsidiary of: McGraw-Hill Construction Information Group), 148 Princeton-Hightstown Rd, Hightstown, NJ 08520. TEL 800-393-6343, http://www.dodgeconstructionpublications.com.

692.8 USA ISSN 0192-9216
TEXAS CONTRACTOR. Text in English. 1923. s-m. USD 96 (effective 2004). adv. **Document type:** *Magazine, Trade.* **Description:** Aimed at Texas contractors of highways and heavy construction, engineers, contractors, material producers, officials, architects, distributors, and manufacturers.
Related titles: Online - full text ed.: (from Gale Group, ProQuest Information & Learning).
—CCC.
Published by: Reed Construction Data, Associated Construction Publications (Subsidiary of: Reed Business Information), 30 Technology Pkwy, Ste 100, Norcross, GA 30092. TEL 770-417-4120, 800-322-6996, FAX 770-417-4138, 800-895-8661, http://www.cmdg.com, http://www.acppubs.com/ . Ed. Liz Moucka TEL 972-872-9700. Pub. John Weatherhead TEL 770-417-4120. Circ: 7,050.

▼ **TEXAS REAL ESTATE BUSINESS.** see *REAL ESTATE*

TEXTE ZUM UMWELTTECHNIK UND OEKOLOGIE IM BAUWESEN. see *ENVIRONMENTAL STUDIES*

THAI BUILDERS DIRECTORY. see *BUSINESS AND ECONOMICS—Trade And Industrial Directories*

643.7 USA ISSN 1086-2633
TH4805
THIS OLD HOUSE. Text in English. 1995. 10/yr. USD 15.96 domestic; USD 25.96 in Canada; USD 8.94 per issue (effective 2005). adv. illus.; tr.lit. back issues avail.; reprints avail. **Document type:** *Magazine, Consumer.* **Description:** Covers the renovation and maintenance of old houses.
Incorporates (in 2001): Today's Homeowner Solutions (1532-1851); Which was formerly (until 2001): Today's Homeowner (1089-4810); (until 1996): Home Mechanix (8755-0423); (until 1984): Mechanix Illustrated (0025-6587); Which incorporated: Electronics Illustrated (0013-5178)
Related titles: Online - full text ed.: (from EBSCO Publishing, O C L C Online Computer Library Center, Inc., ProQuest Information & Learning).
Indexed: MASUSE, RGPR.
—CISTI.
Published by: Time4 Media, Inc. (Subsidiary of: Time, Inc), 1185 Ave of the Americas, 27th Fl, New York, NY 10035. TEL 212-522-9465, 800-898-7237, FAX 212-522-9435, http://www.thisoldhouse.com. Ed. Donna Sapolin. Adv. contact Richard Berenson. B&W page USD 26,470, color page USD 37,800. Circ: 672,754 (paid). **Subscr. to:** PO Box 83078, Birmingham, AL 35282-8772.

TIDINGS (SILVER SPRING). see *EDUCATION—School Organization And Administration*

690 338.769 SWE ISSN 0346-2692
TIDNINGEN BYGGKONTAKT. Text in Swedish. 1972. 25/yr. SEK 450 (effective 1998). adv.
Published by: Produktionsgruppen Ekonomisk Foervaltning AB, Fack 4152, Nacka, 13104, Sweden. TEL 46-8-448-25-50, FAX 46-8-448-25-77. Ed. Anders Enquist. Adv. contact Mats Eriksson. B&W page SEK 16,000, color page SEK 20,500; trim 360 x 252. Circ: 9,800.

690 DEU ISSN 0944-8780
TIEFBAU. Text in German. 1889. m. EUR 42; EUR 21 to students; EUR 4 newsstand/cover (effective 2006). adv. bk.rev. **Document type:** *Newspaper, Trade.*
Formerly: Tiefbauberufsgenossenschaft (0340-952X)
Indexed: CISA, DokStr, GeotechAb, RefZh.
—CINDOC, IE, Infotrieve. **CCC.**
Published by: Erich Schmidt Verlag GmbH & Co. (Berlin), Genthiner Str 30G, Berlin, 10785, Germany. TEL 49-30-2500850, FAX 49-30-250085305, vertrieb@esvmedien.de, http://www.tiefbaubg.de, http://www.esv.info. Ed. M. Bandmann. Adv. contact Helmut Lanzinger TEL 49-89-8299600. B&W page EUR 3,290, color page EUR 5,270; trim 185 x 260. Circ: 34,623.

690 338.4 747 FIN ISSN 0356-3987
TIKKURILAN VIESTI. Text in Finnish. 1929. s-a. free. back issues avail. **Document type:** *Trade.*
Related titles: Swedish ed.: Dickursby Meddelanden. ISSN 0356-3995.
Published by: Tikkurila Oy, Kuninkaalantie 1, PL 53, Vantaa, 01301, Finland. TEL 358-0-857731, FAX 358-0-8577-6934. Ed. Visa Pekkarinen. Circ: 30,000.

TILE & DECORATIVE SURFACES; the voice of America's tile market. see *CERAMICS, GLASS AND POTTERY*

TILE NEWS. see *CERAMICS, GLASS AND POTTERY*

TILING NEWS. see *CERAMICS, GLASS AND POTTERY*

690 USA ISSN 1061-9860
TH1101
TIMBER FRAMING. Text in English. 1985. q. USD 25 domestic; USD 30 in Canada; USD 40 elsewhere (effective 2000). adv. bk.rev. index. back issues avail. **Document type:** *Trade.* **Description:** Reports on the guild's work and membership activities with articles about history, house design, engineering, mechanical systems, traditional building, timber framing abroad, and forest preservation for builders, owners, and designers.
Formerly: Timber Framers News
Published by: Timber Framers Guild of North America, PO Box 1075, Bellingham, WA 98227. TEL 360-733-4001, FAX 360-733-4002, tfguild@telcomplus.net, joel@tfguild.org, http://www.tfguild.org. Ed., Pub., R&P, Adv. contact Ken Rower.

690 USA
TH4818.W6
TIMBER HOME LIVING. Text in English. 1991. bi-m. USD 19.95 domestic; USD 26.97 foreign; USD 3.99 newsstand/cover (effective 2005). adv. 100 p./no.; back issues avail. **Document type:** *Magazine, Consumer.* **Description:** A consumer guide to buying and building timber frame homes.
Formerly: Timber Frame Homes (1054-1136)
Related titles: Online - full text ed.
Published by: Home Buyer Publications, Inc. (Subsidiary of: Active Interest Media), 4125 Lafayette Center Dr. Ste. 100, Chantilly, VA 20151. TEL 703-222-9111, FAX 703-222-3209, http://www.timberhomeliving.com/index.cfm. Ed. Michael McCarthy. Adv. contact Elaine Nosaka. B&W page USD 4,478, color page USD 5,839. Circ: 45,000 (paid).

TIMES (BETHLEHEM). see *HOUSING AND URBAN PLANNING*

690 JPN ISSN 0910-917X
TODA KENSETSU GIJUTSU KENKYU HOKOKU/TODA TECHNICAL RESEARCH REPORT. Text in English, Japanese. 1974. a.
—CCC.
Published by: Toda Kensetsu K.K., Gijutsu Kenkyujo/Toda Corp., Technical Research Laboratory, 315 Kaname, Tsukuba-shi, Ibaraki-ken 300-2622, Japan.

690 USA
TODAY'S LIFESTYLES HOME PLANS. Text in English. 1994. q. USD 23.50 (effective 2000). adv. **Document type:** *Magazine, Consumer.* **Description:** Contains home plans and informative articles for the way we live today.
Published by: HomeStyles Publishing & Marketing, Inc., 213 E. 4th St., 4th Fl., St. Paul, MN 55101-1603. TEL 651-602-5000, 888-626-2026, FAX 651-602-5001, http:// www.homestyles.com. Ed. Josh Kimball. Adv. contact Shelley Junker. B&W page USD 3,910, color page USD 4,830; trim 8 x 10.75. Circ: 54,400.

690 JPN
TOKEN GEPPO/TOKEN MONTHLY. Text in Japanese; Summaries in English, Japanese. 1951. m. JPY 300 per issue.
Published by: Tokyo Kensetsugyo Kyokai/Associated General Contractors of Tokyo, 5-1 Haccho-Bori 2-chome, Chuo-ku, Tokyo, 104-0032, Japan.

690 JPN ISSN 0285-4546
TOKYU KENSETSU GIJUTSU KENKYUJOHO/TOKYU CONSTRUCTION TECHNICAL REPORTS. Text in Japanese; Summaries in English, Japanese. 1973. a.
Published by: Tokyu Kensetsu K.K., Gijutsu Kenkyujo/Tokyu Construction Co., Ltd., Technological Research Institute, 1-16-14 Shibuya, Shibuya-ku, Tokyo, 150-0002, Japan.

690 669 JPN
TOMOEGUMI TEKKOJO GIHO/TOMOEGUMI IRON WORKS TECHNICAL REPORT. Text in Japanese; Summaries in English, Japanese. 1988. a.
Published by: Tomoegumi Tekkojo, 2-10 Ginza 6-chome, Chuo-ku, Tokyo, 104-0061, Japan.

690 DEU
TOOL; Werkzeug-Praxis Rests & Tipps. Text in German. a. EUR 3 newsstand/cover (effective 2002). adv. **Document type:** *Magazine, Consumer.*
Published by: Fachschriften Verlag GmbH, Hoehenstr 17, Fellbach, 70736, Germany. TEL 49-711-52061, FAX 49-711-5281424, info@fachschriften.de, http:// www.fachschriften.de. Ed. Elmar Haag Schwilk. Adv. contact Wolfgang Loges. B&W page EUR 5,200, color page EUR 8,632. Circ: 60,000 (controlled).

690 USA ISSN 1534-2425
TOOLS OF THE TRADE. Variant title: Hanley-Wood's Tools of the Trade. Text in English. 5/yr. USD 19.80; USD 24.80 in Canada; USD 39.80 elsewhere. illus. **Document type:** *Magazine, Trade.* **Description:** Source for tool-buying pros who work in commercial and residential construction and remodeling.
Formerly (until 1998): J L C's Tools of the Trade (1068-0039)

Related titles: Online - full text ed.: (from Gale Group).
Indexed: BHA.
Published by: Hanley-Wood, LLC (Subsidiary of: J.P. Morgan Chase & Co.), One Thomas Circle, NW, Ste 600, Washington, DC 20005-5701. TEL 202-452-0800, FAX 202-785-1974, tjackson@hanleywood.com, http://www.hanleywood.com. Circ: 80,000 (paid).

690.029 USA
TOP 400 CONTRACTORS SOURCEBOOK. Text in English. 1974. a. USD 25. adv. **Document type:** *Directory.* **Description:** Provides rankings and overviews of the top 400 contractors for eight major industry sectors.
Supersedes (in 1998): E N R Contractors Sourcebook and Directory; Which was formed by the 1996 merger of: E N R Directory of Contractors - Midwest (1065-2205); E N R Directory of Contractors - Northeast (1065-2191); E N R Directory of Contractors - South (1065-2213); E N R Directory of Contractors - West (1065-2183); All of which superseded (in 1992): E N R Directory of Contractors (0098-6453); Incorporated: E N R Directory of Construction Information Resources (1077-2154); Which superseded (1978-1993): Directory of Construction Associations (0193-2764)
Related titles: Online - full text ed.; ♦ Supplement to: E N R. ISSN 0891-9526.
Published by: Engineering News-Record (Subsidiary of: McGraw-Hill Construction Information Group), Two Penn Plaza, 9th Fl, New York, NY 10121-2298. TEL 212-904-4591, FAX 212-904-4093, http://www.enr.com.

THE TOP 500 DESIGN FIRMS SOURCEBOOK. see *ENGINEERING*

TOP CONTACTS. see *BUSINESS AND ECONOMICS—Trade And Industrial Directories*

690 658 GBR
TOP SOCIETY. Text in English. 1978. q. free. adv. back issues avail. **Document type:** *Newsletter.*
Published by: National Merchant Buying Society, 3 Chancery Pl, Millstone Ln, Leicester, LE1 5JN, United Kingdom. TEL 44-116-253-0531, FAX 44-116-251-7589. Ed. Denis Gray. Adv. contact Laura Gray. Circ: 2,500 (controlled).

690 JPN ISSN 1340-3249
➤ **TOYO CONSTRUCTION TECHNICAL RESEARCH REPORTS.** Text in English, Japanese. 1976. a. free. **Document type:** *Academic/Scholarly.*
Formerly: Gijutsu Kenkyujo Hokoku - Technical Research Institute. Report (0911-338X)
—CCC.
Published by: Toyo Kensetsu K.K. Gijutsu Kenkyujo, Gijutsu Kenkyujo/Toyo Construction Co., Ltd., Technical Research Institute, Kowa-Hitotsubashi Bldg, 3-7-1 Kanda-Nishiki cho, Chiyoda ku, Tokyo, 101-0054, Japan. TEL 81-3-3296-4631, FAX 81-3-3296-4633. Circ: 300.

690.028 388.324 USA
TRACK AND TIRE. Text in English. 1991. 17/yr. USD 19.95. **Document type:** *Trade.* **Description:** Contractors source for equipments, parts, tires and related services.
Address: 29829 Greenfield Rd, Ste 101, Southfield, MI 48076-2201. TEL 800-872-2574, FAX 313-557-4156. Ed. John H Osborne. adv.: B&W page USD 485; 9.75 x 6.25. Circ: 30,100 (controlled).

690 DEU
THE TRADE WITH BUILDING MATERIALS/HANDEL MIT BAUMATERIAL. Text in English, German. q. EUR 40 (effective 2001). adv. **Document type:** *Magazine, Trade.*
Published by: Zeitungs- und Zeitschriftenverlag Heinrichs, Brueggekamp 1, Barsinghausen, 30890, Germany. TEL 49-5105-2289. Ed., Pub. Gerhard Heinrichs.

720 690 USA ISSN 1541-8634
TRADELINE EXCLUSIVE REPORTS. Text in English. 1982. irreg. USD 149 (effective 2005). bk.rev.; software rev. cum.index: 1982-1994. 16 p./no. 2 cols./p.; back issues avail. **Document type:** *Journal, Trade.* **Description:** Reports on recently completed buildings in the areas of health care, R & D, corporate, institutional, and high-tech construction. Highlights facilities management tools and strategies.
Former titles (until 2002): F M Data Monthly (1096-4436); (until 1997): Facilities Planning News (1045-7089)
Media: Online - full content.
Published by: Tradeline, Inc., PO Box 1568, Orinda, CA 94563. TEL 925-254-1744, FAX 925-254-1093, fmdm@fmdata.com, http://www.tradelineinc.com. Ed. Lysa Lewallen. Adv. contact Derek Westfall. Circ: 8,500 (paid and free).

690 USA ISSN 0898-0284
TRADITIONAL BUILDING. Text in English. 1988. bi-m. USD 21.95 (effective 2005). adv. bk.rev. 200 p./no.; **Document type:** *Magazine, Trade.* **Description:** Reviews products and materials for builders and restorers of historical buildings, and includes source lists for hard-to-find items.
Indexed: AIAP.
Published by: Historical Trends Corporation, 69A Seventh Ave, Brooklyn, NY 11217. TEL 718-636-0788, FAX 718-636-0750, htcstaff@traditional-building.com, http://www.traditional-building.com. Ed., Pub. Clem Labine. Adv. contact Danielle Wren. B&W page USD 2,905, color page USD 3,400. Circ: 25,650 (paid and controlled).

690 USA ISSN 1088-114X
TRADITIONAL HOME RENOVATION STYLE; the before & after magazine. Variant title: Renovation Style. Text in English. 1995. bi-m. USD 19.95; USD 4.95 newsstand/cover (effective 2004). adv. 128 p./no.; **Document type:** *Magazine, Consumer.* **Description:** Provides inspiration for anyone's dream home. If offers creative details, affordable options and simple solutions for renovating. decorating, architecture and landscaping.
Published by: Meredith Corp., 1716 Locust St, Des Moines, IA 50309-3023. TEL 515-284-3000, 800-556-9184, FAX 515-284-3657, renostyl@meredith.com, http://www.meredith.com. Eds. Ann Omvig Maine, Luann Brandsen. Pubs. Mark J Josephson, Robin Holstein. adv.: B&W page USD 29,370, color page USD 42,070. Circ: 300,000 (paid). **Dist. in UK by:** Seymour Distribution Ltd, 86 Newman St, London W1T 3EX, United Kingdom. FAX 44-207-396-8002, enquiries@seymour.co.uk.

690 DEU ISSN 0179-8006
TROCKENBAU AKUSTIK. Text in German. 1984. 10/yr. EUR 105.50 domestic; EUR 115 foreign; EUR 13 newsstand/cover (effective 2004). adv. index. **Document type:** *Magazine, Trade.*
Indexed: RefZh.
Published by: Verlagsgesellschaft Rudolf Mueller GmbH & Co. KG, Stolberger Str 84, Cologne, 50933, Germany. TEL 49-221-54970, FAX 49-221-5497326, red.trockenbau@rudolf-mueller.de, service@rudolf-mueller.de, http://www.rudolf-mueller.de. Ed. Thomas Gruening. Adv. contact Thomas Fuengerlings. B&W page EUR 3,670, color page EUR 6,055; trim 188 x 267. Circ: 14,730 (paid).

690 RUS
TA680 CODEN: TSMTAC
TSEMENT I EGO PRIMENENIE. Text in Russian. 1901. bi-m. USD 168 foreign (effective 2003). adv. bk.rev. illus.
Formerly: Tsement (0041-4867)
Indexed: CIN, CRIA, CRICC, ChemAb, ChemTitl, ConcrAb, RASB, RefZh.
—CASDDS, CISTI, Linda Hall. **CCC.**
Published by: Stroiizdat, S.- Peterburgskoe Otdeleniye, Volkhovsky per 3, St Petersburg, 199053, Russian Federation. Ed. Nataliya Tushenkova. Adv. contact N A Surovtseva. Circ: 2,300. **Dist. by:** M K - Periodica, ul Gilyarovskogo 39, Moscow 129110, Russian Federation. TEL 7-095-2845008, FAX 7-095-2813798, info@periodicals.ru, http://www.mkniga.ru.

TUNNELLING ACTIVITIES IN JAPAN. see *ENGINEERING—Civil Engineering*

▼ **TUNNELLING & TRENCHLESS CONSTRUCTION.** see *ENGINEERING—Civil Engineering*

TURKEY. DEVLET ISTATISTIK ENSTITUSU. BINA INSAAT ISTATISTIKLERI/TURKEY. STATE INSTITUTE OF STATISTICS. BUILDING CONSTRUCTION STATISTICS. see *BUILDING AND CONSTRUCTION—Abstracting, Bibliographies, Statistics*

TURKEY. STATE INSTITUTE OF STATISTICS. QUARTERLY BUILDING CONSTRUCTION COST INDEX. see *BUILDING AND CONSTRUCTION—Abstracting, Bibliographies, Statistics*

TURKISH CONSTRUCTION CATALOG. see *ENGINEERING—Civil Engineering*

690 POL ISSN 0867-1915
TYGODNIK BUDOWLANY. Text in Polish. 1990. w. PLZ 200; PLZ 4.50 newsstand/cover (effective 1998). **Description:** For building contractors, producers of building materials, municipal and local administration offices, members of builidng and craft chambers and for whose that are bound with the building industry by their profession.
Published by: Centralny Osrodek Informacji Budownictwa, Ul Bartycka 26, Warsaw, 00716, Poland. TEL 48-22-6511389, FAX 48-22-404551. Ed. Iza Sas. adv.: B&W page PLZ 1,200, color page PLZ 1,800. Circ: 5,000.

U I T B B BULLETIN. see *LABOR UNIONS*

691 FRA
U N I C E M ANNUAIRE OFFICIEL. Text in French. 1945. a. adv. **Document type:** *Directory.*
Published by: (Union Nationale des Industries de Carrieres et Materiaux de Construction), Union Francaise d'Annuaires Professionnels, 130 av. des Bouleaux, B.P. 36, Trappes, Cedex 78192, France. TEL 33-1-30138200, FAX 33-1-30138211, info@essor-contacts.tm.fr, http://www.essor-contacts.tm.fr. Circ: 5,000.

690 USA
U S COURT AND TRACK BUILDERS ASSOCIATION NEWSLINE. Text in English. q. USD 25; USD 35 foreign (effective 2001). bk.rev. **Document type:** *Newsletter, Trade.* **Description:** Covers the design and building of tennis courts and tracks. Reviews new products and companies.
Published by: U S Tennis Court & Track Builders Association, 3225 Ellicott Mills Dr, Ste N, Ellicott City, MD 21043-4547. TEL 410-418-4800, FAX 410-418-4875, info@ustcba.com, http://www.ustctba.com. Ed. Carol T Shaner. Circ: 750 (paid).

691 USA ISSN 0041-7661
U.S. GLASS, METAL & GLAZING. Variant title: U S Glass. Text in English. 1966. m. USD 45; USD 6 per issue (effective 2005). adv. bk.rev. charts; illus.; stat.; tr.lit. back issues avail. **Document type:** *Magazine, Trade.* **Description:** Covers manufacturing and marketing segments and wholesale, retail trade relating to flat glass, auto glass, architectural metal and related products.
Related titles: Online - full text ed.
—CISTI, Linda Hall.
Published by: Key Communications, Inc., PO Box 569, Garrisonville, VA 22463. TEL 540-720-5584, FAX 540-720-5687, usglass@glass.com, http://www.glass.com, http://www.key-com.com/. Ed. Ellen Chilcoat. Pub. Debra Levy. Adv. contact Penny Stacey. B&W page USD 2,445, color page USD 3,995. Circ: 25,000 (controlled).

690 GBR
ULSTER BUILDER AND ALLIED TRADES JOURNAL. Text in English. 1946. m. GBP 2.20.
Address: c/o William H. Guilfoyle, 27 Dunlambert Park, Belfast, BT15 3NJ, United Kingdom.

690 665 USA ISSN 1090-400X
UNDERGROUND FOCUS; the magazine of below-ground damage prevention. Text in English. 1986. bi-m. USD 20; USD 35 in Canada; USD 55 elsewhere. adv. tr.lit. **Document type:** *Trade.* **Description:** Covers placement and protection of below ground facilities. Includes new products, news briefs, accident file, trench cave-ins, and contractor's view.
Indexed: BrCerAb, C&ISA, CerAb, CivEngAb, ConcrAb, CorrAb, E&CAJ, EMA, IAA, M&TEA, MBF, METADEX, SolStAb, WAA.
—Linda Hall.
Published by: Canterbury Communications, Inc., PO Box 638, Spooner, WI 54801. TEL 715-635-7975, FAX 715-635-7977, ufmagazine@underspace.com, http://www.underspace.com. Ed., Pub. R.N. Rosencrans. R&P R N Rosencrans. Adv. contact Scott Landes. Circ: 25,000.

UNDERNEATH IT ALL. see *ENGINEERING*

669 FRA
UNION DEPARTEMENTALE DES SYNDICATS D'ENTREPRENEURS ET D'ARTISANS DU BATIMENT ET DES TRAVAUX PUBLICS DE LA HAUTE-GARONNE. OFFICIEL DU BATIMENT. Text in French. m.
Published by: Union Departementale des Syndicats d'Entrepreneurs et d'Artisans du Batiment et des Travaux Publics de la Haute-Garonne, 11 bd. des Recollets, Toulouse, Cedex 31078, France.

691 FRA
UNION NATIONALE DES ENTREPRENEURS PLATRIERS-PLAQUISTES, STAFFEURS ET STUCATEURS. BULLETIN. Text in French. 1987. s-a. membership. adv. **Document type:** *Bulletin.*
Published by: Union Nationale des Entrepreneurs Platriers-Plaquistes Staffeurs et Stucateurs, 33 av. Kleber, Paris, Cedex 16 75784, France.

UNITED NATIONS. DEPARTMENT OF INTERNATIONAL ECONOMIC AND SOCIAL AFFAIRS. STATISTICAL OFFICE. CONSTRUCTION STATISTIC YEARBOOK. see *BUILDING AND CONSTRUCTION—Abstracting, Bibliographies, Statistics*

690 ROM ISSN 1224-6026
TH4
UNIVERSITATEA POLITEHNICA DIN TIMISOARA. BULETINUL STIINTIFIC. SERIA CONSTRUCTII ARHITECTURA. Text in English, French, German, Romanian. 1920. s-a. USD 20 (effective 2000). bk.rev. **Document type:** *Bulletin.*
Formerly: Institutul Politehnic Timisoara. Buletinul Stiintific si Tehnic. Seria Constructii (0373-4374); Which superseded in part: Institutul Politehnic din Timisoara. Buletinul de Stiinta si Tehnic (0563-5594)
—CISTI, Linda Hall.
Published by: Universitatea Politehnica din Timisoara, Piata Victoriei 2, Timisoara, 1900, Romania. TEL 40-56-200349, FAX 40-56-190321. Ed. Marin Ivan. Circ: 500.

690 USA
UNIVERSITY OF ILLINOIS. SCHOOL OF ARCHITECTURE - BUILDING RESEARCH COUNCIL. COUNCIL NOTES. Text in English. 1945. irreg. back issues avail. **Document type:** *Trade.* **Description:** Provides practical consumer-oriented advice on home planning, construction, and maintenance.
Formerly: University of Illinois. Small Homes Council. Building Research Council. Circulars (0073-5396)
—Linda Hall.

B

▼ *new title* ➤ *refereed* ✶ *unverified* ♦ *full entry avail.*

Published by: (Building Research Council), University of Illinois at Urbana-Champaign, School of Architecture, One E St Mary s Rd, Champaign, IL 61820. TEL 217-333-1801, 800-336-0616, FAX 217-244-2204. Ed. James R Anderson. Circ: 3,900.

690 USA ISSN 0073-5426
UNIVERSITY OF ILLINOIS. SCHOOL OF ARCHITECTURE - BUILDING RESEARCH COUNCIL. TECHNICAL NOTES. Text in English. 1945. irreg., latest vol.18, 1990. **Document type:** *Academic/Scholarly.* **Description:** Contains semitechnical reports on specific building problems.
—Linda Hall.
Published by: (Building Research Council), University of Illinois at Urbana-Champaign, School of Architecture, One E St Mary s Rd, Champaign, IL 61820. TEL 217-333-1801, 800-336-0616, FAX 217-244-2204. Ed. James R Anderson.

690 ZAF ISSN 0258-9265
HC905.A1
UNIVERSITY OF STELLENBOSCH. BUREAU FOR ECONOMIC RESEARCH. BUILDING AND CONSTRUCTION. Key Title: Building and Construction (Stellenbosch). Text in English. 1969. q. ZAR 890 (effective Jul. 2003). stat. cum.index. **Document type:** *Journal, Academic/Scholarly.* **Description:** Discusses current conditions, problems and opportunities in the building and construction sectors.
Former titles (until 1986): Report on Business Conditions in the Building Industry (0586-4941); Building Survey (0045-3447)
Related titles: Online - full text ed.
Indexed: ISAP.
Published by: Universiteit Stellenbosch, Bureau for Economic Research/Stellenbosch University, University, Private Bag 5050, Stellenbosch, 7599, South Africa. TEL 27-21-8872810, FAX 27-21-8899225, hhman@maties.sun.ac.za, http://www.journals.co.za/ej/ejour_build.html, http://www.sun.ac.za/. Ed. C H Martin. Circ: 600.

UNIVERSITY OF TECHNOLOGY, SYDNEY. FACULTY OF DESIGN ARCHITECTURE AND BUILDING HANDBOOK. see *ARCHITECTURE*

690 DEU
UNTERNEHMERBRIEF BAUWIRTSCHAFT. Text in German. 1987. m. EUR 180 (effective 2004). **Document type:** *Journal, Trade.*
Former titles: Finanz- und Steuer-Ratgeber Bauwirtschaft (0949-9067); (until 1993): Finanz- und Steuer-Ratgeber Baugewerbe (0939-8465)
Published by: (Institut fuer Wirtschaftspublizistik), Vogel Verlag und Druck GmbH & Co. KG, Max-Planck-Str 7-9, Wuerzburg, 97064, Germany. TEL 49-931-4180, FAX 49-931-4182100, marliese_bernhardt@vogel-medien.de, http://www.vogel-medien.de. **Subscr. to:** DataM-Services GmbH, Fichtestr 9, Wuerzburg 97074, Germany. TEL 49-931-417001, FAX 49-931-4170499, swestenberger@datam-services.de, http://www.datam-services.de.

UNTERRICHT ARBEIT UND TECHNIK. see *EDUCATION—Teaching Methods And Curriculum*

690 USA
▼ **UPSCALE REMODELING.** Text in English. forthcoming 2006. q. **Document type:** *Magazine, Trade.*
Published by: Hanley-Wood, LLC (Subsidiary of: J.P. Morgan Chase & Co.), One Thomas Circle, NW, Ste 600, Washington, DC 20005-5701. TEL 202-452-0800, FAX 202-785-1974, http://www.hanleywood.com.

URB.A0. (Assiste par Ordinateur) see *ARCHITECTURE*

690 PRT
URBANISMO E CONSTRUCAO. Text in Portuguese. 26/yr.
Address: Repoliek, APDO, 9002, Amadora, 2700, Portugal. TEL 495-97-69, FAX 496-08-14. Ed. Mario Pedro.

690 USA ISSN 0042-1383
UTAH CONSTRUCTION REPORT. Text in English. 1958. q. charts; stat. **Document type:** *Trade.*
Published by: University of Utah, Bureau of Economic and Business Research, 1645 E Campus Center Dr, Rm 401, Salt Lake City, UT 84112-9302. TEL 801-581-6333, FAX 801-581-3354, bureau@business.utah.edu, http://www.business.utah.edu/bebr/. Ed. R Thayne Robson TEL 801-581-7274. R&P R. Thayne Robson TEL 801-581-7274. Circ: 2,400.

690 USA
UTILITY CONSTRUCTION AND MAINTENANCE. Text in English. 1990. 4/yr. USD 12 domestic; USD 18 in Canada; USD 35 elsewhere. **Document type:** *Magazine, Trade.* **Description:** Focuses on construction, maintenance, and equipment for managers in the utilities, public works, municipalities. Includes CATV operators and related contractors.
Published by: Practical Communications, Inc., 220 N. Smith St., # 228, Palatine, IL 60067-8500. Eds. Alan Richter, Alan Richter. Pubs. Alan Richter, Judith Chance. R&P Alan Richter. Adv. contact James Queenan. Circ: 25,500 (controlled).

V & S GENERALBESKRIVELSE. see *BUSINESS AND ECONOMICS—Marketing And Purchasing*

V & S GENERALBESKRIVELSE. SUPPLEMENT. see *BUSINESS AND ECONOMICS—Marketing And Purchasing*

V & S REGLER FOR OPMAALING AF BYGGERI. see *BUSINESS AND ECONOMICS—Marketing And Purchasing*

V W D - BAUWIRTSCHAFT. see *BUSINESS AND ECONOMICS—Investments*

690 333 NLD
VASTGOEDMARKT. Text in Dutch. m. (11/yr.). EUR 396 domestic; EUR 435 foreign (effective 2005). adv. **Document type:** *Trade.* **Description:** Covers the housing and office construction markets in the Netherlands.
Published by: Sdu Uitgevers bv, Postbus 20025, The Hague, 2500 EA, Netherlands. TEL 31-70-3789911, FAX 31-70-3854321, vgm@sdu.nl, sdu@sdu.nl, http://www.vastgoedmarkt.nl, http://www.sdu.nl/. Ed. Ruud de Wit. Pub. Ronald Elward. Circ: 10,126. **Subscr. to:** Postbus 20014, The Hague 2500 EA, Netherlands. TEL 31-70-3789880, FAX 31-70-3789783.

620.0046 658.202 DNK ISSN 1398-2451
VEDLIGEHOLD DRIFT OG TEKNOLOGI; tidskrift for olie, gas, el, byg, anlaeg, rullende materiel, transport, luft, vand, land, uddannelse, miljoe. Text in Danish. 1998. 8/yr. DKK 525 (effective 2004). adv.
Published by: (Danske Vedligeholdsforening), Scanpublisher A-S, Emiliekildevej 35, Klampenborg, 2930, Denmark. TEL 45-39-908000, FAX 45-39-908280, info@scanpublisher.dk, http://www.scanpublisher.dk. Ed. Svend Aage West. Adv. contact Klavs Vejborg. B&W page DKK 11,575, color page DKK 17,500; trim 184 x 268. Circ: 4,000.

690 DEU ISSN 1612-9555
VERBAND DER PRIVATEN BAUSPARKASSEN. JAHRBUCH. Text in German. 1950. a. **Document type:** *Magazine, Trade.*
Formerly (until 1993): Privates Bausparwesen (0085-5154)
Published by: Verband der Privaten Bausparkassen e.V., Klingelhoeferstr 4, Berlin, 10785, Germany. TEL 49-30-590091500, FAX 49-30-590091501, bausparkassen@vdpb.de, http://www.bausparkassen.de.

690 DEU ISSN 0507-6714
VEREIN DEUTSCHER ZEMENTWERKE. FORSCHUNGSINSTITUT DER ZEMENTINDUSTRIE. TAETIGKEITSBERICHT. Text in English. 1948. triennial. free. **Document type:** *Trade.*
Related titles: German ed.
Published by: Verein Deutscher Zementwerke e.V., Tannenstr 2, Duesseldorf, 40476, Germany. TEL 49-211-45781, FAX 49-211-4578296, info@vdz-online.de, http://www.vdz-online.de. Circ: 2,000.

690 AUS
VICTORIA BUILDING LEGISLATION SERVICE - UPDATES. Text in English. irreg., latest 1995, Feb. looseleaf. price varies. **Document type:** *Government.*
Published by: Law Press (Victoria), 52-58 Chetwynd St, West Melbourne, VIC 3003, Australia. TEL 61-3-93208686, FAX 61-3-93208699.

VILLAAEGAREN. see *REAL ESTATE*

690 USA ISSN 1552-8715
VIRGINIA BUILDER. Text in English. 1988. 9/yr. USD 24 to non-members (effective 2005). adv. **Document type:** *Trade.* **Description:** Features recent and upcoming HBAV events, lobbying efforts, educational programs, information on national building trends and products, and calendar listings.
Published by: Association Publishing Inc., 2117 Smith Ave, Chesapeake, VA 23320. TEL 757-420-2434, FAX 757-424-5954, http://www.statebuildermagazines.com. Ed. Carolyn Berry. Pubs. Joyce F Hearn, Sandra Amidon. R&P Joyce F Hearn. Adv. contact Dee Coates. B&W page USD 1,300, color page USD 1,850; trim 10.875 x 8.375. Circ: 6,500.

VIRGINIA POLYTECHNIC INSTITUTE AND STATE UNIVERSITY. SARDO PALLET AND CONTAINER RESEARCH LABORATORY. LABORATORY REPORT. see *FORESTS AND FORESTRY—Lumber And Wood*

690 IND ISSN 0042-7217
VISWASILPI*. Text in Telugu. 1970 (vol.3). m. INR 3. adv. bk.rev.; film rev.; play rev. illus.
Published by: Cherravuru Nagabhushanacharyulu, V.B. Bhavan, P.O. Guntur, Dist., Narasaraopet, Andhra Pradesh, India. Circ: 1,000.

690 DEU
VOITH ANNUAL REPORT. Text in German. a. **Document type:** *Corporate.*
Published by: J.M. Voith Aktiengesellschaft, Postfach 1940, Heidenheim, 89509, Germany. TEL 49-7321-372864, FAX 49-7321-377000, info@voith.de, http://www.voith.de.

690 USA
THE VOLATILE WORLD OF THE CONSTRUCTION INDUSTRY. Text in English. 1991. a. USD 395. **Description:** Examines all facets of the construction industry and its impact on the overall economy. Also analyzes different types of construction companies and their financial condition by geographic region.
Published by: Dun & Bradstreet Information Services (Murray Hill) (Subsidiary of: Dun & Bradstreet, Inc.), 103 John F Kennedy Pkwy., Short Hills, NJ 07078-2708. TEL 908-665-5224, FAX 908-771-7599. Ed. Mark Smith.

VOLKSHUISVESTINGSBELEID EN WONINGMARKT. see *HOUSING AND URBAN PLANNING*

690 AUT
VORSCHAU. Text in German. 1969. a. stat. index. **Document type:** *Bulletin, Trade.*
Published by: Forschungsgesellschaft fuer Wohnen Bauen und Planen, Loewengasse 47, Vienna, W 1030, Austria. TEL 43-1-71262510, FAX 43-1-712625121, office@fgw.at, http://www.fgw.at. Ed. Wolfgang Amann. Circ: (controlled).

690 VEN
VOZ DE LA CONSTRUCCION*. Text in Spanish. 1962. m.
Published by: Editor Ferga C.A., Edif. Halven, Ave. Universidad esq Monroy, Apdo 16044, Caracas, DF 1011-A, Venezuela. TEL 562-28-96, TELEX 21381 CABIC VC. Ed. Eduardo Arcila Farias. Circ: 5,000.

691 USA ISSN 0043-0161
TH8120
WALLS & CEILINGS. Text in English. 1938. m. USD 42 domestic; USD 54.94 in Canada; USD 78 elsewhere (effective 2005). adv. bk.rev. charts; illus.; stat.; tr.lit. **Document type:** *Magazine, Trade.* **Description:** For contractors, specifiers, manufacturers, architects and suppliers engaged in drywall, lath, plaster, metal framing, ceiling systems, exterior insulation, acoustics and fireproofing.
Formerly: Plastering Industries
Related titles: Online - full text ed.: (from Florida Center for Library Automation, Gale Group, O C L C Online Computer Library Center, Inc.).
—CCC.
Published by: B N P Media, 755 W Big Beaver Rd, Ste 1000, Troy, MI 48084-4903. TEL 248-362-3700, FAX 248-362-0317, wyattj@bnp.com, http://www.bnpmedia.com/. Ed. Nick Moretti. Pub. Amy Tuttle. adv.: B&W page USD 2,025, color page USD 3,025. Circ: 30,000 (paid and controlled).

WATERSHAPES. see *ARCHITECTURE*

WEEKEND PROPERTY HOME FINDER. see *REAL ESTATE*

690 USA ISSN 1087-0954
WEEKLY CONSTRUCTION NEWS, COVERING TOLEDO & VICINITY. Text in English. 1995. w. adv. **Document type:** *Newsletter, Trade.* **Description:** Provides information on what jobs are coming up for bid or negotiation.
Related titles: Online - full text ed.
Published by: Mcgraw-Hill Construction Dodge (Subsidiary of: McGraw-Hill Construction Information Group), 148 Princeton-Hightstown Rd, Hightstown, NJ 08520. TEL 800-393-6343, http://www.dodgeconstructionpublications.com.

690 USA ISSN 1087-1004
WEEKLY CONSTRUCTION NEWS, COVERING WESTERN KENTUCKY. Text in English. 1995. w. adv. **Document type:** *Newsletter, Trade.* **Description:** Provides information on what jobs are coming up for bid or negotiation.
Related titles: Online - full text ed.
Published by: Mcgraw-Hill Construction Dodge (Subsidiary of: McGraw-Hill Construction Information Group), 148 Princeton-Hightstown Rd, Hightstown, NJ 08520. TEL 800-393-6343, http://www.dodgeconstructionpublications.com.

690 USA ISSN 1087-0946
WEEKLY CONSTRUCTION NEWS, COVERING YOUNGSTOWN & VICINITY. Text in English. w. adv. **Document type:** *Newsletter, Trade.* **Description:** Provides information on what jobs are coming up for bid or negotiation.
Related titles: Online - full text ed.
Published by: Mcgraw-Hill Construction Dodge (Subsidiary of: McGraw-Hill Construction Information Group), 148 Princeton-Hightstown Rd, Hightstown, NJ 08520. TEL 800-393-6343, http://www.dodgeconstructionpublications.com.

690 USA ISSN 1085-8253
WEEKLY CONSTRUCTION REVIEW, COVERING CENTRAL PENNSYLVANIA. Text in English. w. adv. **Document type:** *Newsletter, Trade.* **Description:** Provides information on what jobs are coming up for bid or negotiation.
Related titles: Online - full text ed.
Published by: Mcgraw-Hill Construction Dodge (Subsidiary of: McGraw-Hill Construction Information Group), 148 Princeton-Hightstown Rd, Hightstown, NJ 08520. TEL 800-393-6343, http://www.dodgeconstructionpublications.com.

690 USA
WEST VIRGINIA CONSTRUCTION NEWS. Text in English. 1937. bi-m. USD 8 (effective 2004). adv. bk.rev. **Document type:** *Magazine, Trade.* **Description:** Includes Articles, commentary, news items, and announcements on the legislative, economic, and regulatory issues affecting the building, highway, and heavy utility contracting industries in the state.
Published by: Contractors Association of West Virginia, 2114 Kanawha Blvd E, Charleston, WV 25311. TEL 304-342-1166, FAX 304-342-1074, cawv@cawv.org. Ed. Michael L Clowser. Adv. contact Lorie Johnson. Circ: 1,500.

690 USA ISSN 0043-3535
WESTERN BUILDER; building and engineering construction news of Wisconsin, upper Michigan, northern Illinois. Text in English. 1911. w. USD 135 (effective 2005). adv. bk.rev. illus. **Document type:** *Magazine, Trade.* **Description:** Serves the heavy, highway, and non-residential construction industry in Wisconsin, the Upper Peninsula of Michigan, and Northern Illinois.
Related titles: Online - full text ed.: (from Gale Group, ProQuest Information & Learning).
—Linda Hall. **CCC.**
Published by: Reed Construction Data, Associated Construction Publications (Subsidiary of: Reed Business Information), 30 Technology Pkwy, Ste 100, Norcross, GA 30092. TEL 800-486-0014, FAX 800-930-3003, bgantenbein@reedbusiness.com, http://www.acppubs.com/pub_wb.html. Ed. Barry Gantenbein TEL 262-521-1646. Pub. John Weatherhead TEL 770-417-4120. Circ: 4,450 (paid and free). **Subscr. to:** Reed Business Information, Reed Construction Data Regional Publications, P O Box 15426, N. Hollywood, CA 91615-5426. TEL 818-487-4529, 877-902-9762, FAX 818-487-4550.

690 USA
WESTERN BUILDER. ANNUAL BUYERS GUIDE & DIRECTORY. Text in English. a. USD 35 per issue (effective 2004). **Document type:** *Directory, Trade.* **Description:** An equipment guide with a cross-referenced listing of manufacturers, area distributors, and their lines.
Published by: Reed Construction Data, Associated Construction Publications (Subsidiary of: Reed Business Information), 30 Technology Pkwy, Ste 100, Norcross, GA 30092. TEL 770-417-4122, http://www.acppubs.com/. Ed. Barry Gantenbein TEL 262-521-1646. **Subscr. to:** Reed Business Information, Reed Construction Data Regional Publications, P O Box 15426, N. Hollywood, CA 91615-5426. TEL 818-487-4529, 877-902-9762, FAX 818-487-4550.

▼ **WESTERN REAL ESTATE BUSINESS.** see *REAL ESTATE*

690 USA ISSN 0164-5803
WESTERN ROOFING - INSULATION - SIDING. Text in English. 1978. bi-m. USD 12 (effective 2003). adv. bk.rev. **Document type:** *Journal, Trade.*
Related titles: Microform ed.
Published by: (Western State Roofing Contractors Association), Dodson Publications Inc., 546 Court St, Reno, NV 89501-1711. TEL 775-333-1080, FAX 775-333-1081, info@westernroofing.net, http://www.westernroofing.net. Ed., Pub., R&P, Adv. contact Marc Dodson. Circ: 20,300 (controlled).

690 GBR ISSN 0142-9094
WHAT'S NEW IN BUILDING. Text in English. 1978. m. GBP 48, USD 90. adv. **Document type:** *Trade.*
Related titles: Online - full text ed.: (from Gale Group, LexisNexis, ProQuest Information & Learning).
Indexed: ABIn.
—**CCC.**
Published by: Morgan-Grampian (Construction Press) Ltd. (Subsidiary of: Morgan-Grampian plc), Morgan-Grampian House, 30 Calderwood St, London, SE18 6QH, United Kingdom. TEL 0181-855-7777, FAX 0181-316-3169. Ed. Janice Purath. Adv. contact Ian Witham. Circ: 30,000.

698.9 643.7 USA
WHO'S WHO IN THE WALL AND CEILING INDUSTRY. Text in English. a. **Document type:** *Directory, Trade.*
Published by: Association of the Wall and Ceiling Industries International, 803 W Broad St, Ste 600, Falls Church, VA 22046-3108. TEL 703-534-8307, FAX 703-534-8307. Ed., R&P Laura Porinchak. Pub. Steven Etkin. Adv. contact Brent Stone.

338.476 690 USA ISSN 1525-1195
WINDOW & DOOR. Text in English. 1993. bi-m. free to qualified personnel (effective 2003). adv. **Document type:** *Magazine, Trade.* **Description:** Serves fabricators and manufacturers of windows and doors. Reports the latest industry developments, technical information, management strategies, and new product information.
Former titles (until 1999): Window & Door Fabricator (1087-2272); D W G Fabricator; (until 1995): D and W Fabricator
Published by: (National Glass Association), Jervis and Associates, 14255 Us Highway 1., # 200, Juno Beach, FL 33408-1490. nga@glass.org, http://www.windowanddoor.net/, http://ourworld.compuserve.com/homepages/nga. Ed. John Swanson. Pub. Nicole Harris. Adv. contact Mike Gribbin. color page USD 2,090. Circ: 8,000.

338.476 GBR ISSN 1361-1941
WINDOW FABRICATOR AND INSTALLER. Abbreviated title: W F I. Text in English. 1988. 10/yr. GBP 27; GBP 35 in Ireland; GBP 39 elsewhere. **Document type:** *Trade.*
Formerly (until 1995): Professional Window Fabricator and Installer (1357-4590)
Published by: Hamerville Magazines Ltd., Regal House, Regal Way, Watford, Herts WD2 4YJ, United Kingdom. TEL 44-1923-237799, FAX 44-1923-246901.

WINDOW INDUSTRIES. see *CERAMICS, GLASS AND POTTERY*

690 666 GBR
WINDOW TRADE NEWS. Text in English. 10/yr. **Document type:** *Trade.*
Address: 33-39 Bowling Green Ln, London, EC1R 0DA, United Kingdom. TEL 44-171-837-1212, FAX 44-171-278-4003. Ed. Peter Taylor. Circ: 6,210.

690 CAN ISSN 1206-1972
WINDOW WORLD. Text in English. 1996. 6/yr. CND 30 domestic; USD 30 in United States; USD 84 elsewhere (effective 2000). adv. back issues avail.; reprints avail. **Document type:** *Trade.* **Description:** Delivers coverage of news and technical and marketing information to small and medium window and door manufacturers in Canada and the United States.
Published by: Work-4 Projects Ltd., 4819 St Charles Blvd, Pierrefonds, PQ H9H 3C7, Canada. TEL 514-620-2200, FAX 514-620-6300, work4@total.net. Ed. Frank O'Brien. Pub. Nachmi Artzy. R&P, Adv. contact Ady Artzy. B&W page CND 1,925, color page CND 3,075; trim 10.75 x 8.25. Circ: 5,600.

690 DEU
WIR VOM BAU. Text in German. 1982. m. EUR 7.88; EUR 0.66 newsstand/cover (effective 2001). **Document type:** *Magazine, Trade.*
Published by: Werkschriften Verlag GmbH, Bachstr 14-16, Heidelberg, 69121, Germany. TEL 49-6221-6446-0, FAX 49-6221-644640, info@haefner-verlag.de, http://www.haefner-verlag.de. Circ: 1,900 (paid).

690 USA
WISCONSIN BADGER BUILDER. Text in English. 1984. bi-m. free to members (effective 2003). adv. **Document type:** *Magazine, Trade.* **Description:** Provides economic and industrial trend information for the home building industry. Includes input and feedback by members, advertisers, and affiliated businesses.
Formerly: Badger Builder
Published by: (Wisconsin Builders Association), Trails Media Group, Inc., 1131 Mills St., PO Box 317, Black Earth, WI 53515. TEL 608-767-8000, 800-236-8088, FAX 608-767-5444, info@wistrails.com, http://www.trailsmediagroup.com. Ed. Christine Schwanke. Pub. Scott Klug. adv.: B&W page USD 1,385, color page USD 1,800; 7.125 x 9.75. Circ: 6,500 (paid).

690 CHE
DAS WOHNEN. Text in German. m.
Published by: Schweizerischer Verband fuer Wohnungs Wesen, Bucheggstr 107, Zuerich, 8057, Switzerland. TEL 1-284240.

WOHNEN PLUS; Fachmagazin der gemeinnuetzigen Bauvereinigungen. see *HOUSING AND URBAN PLANNING*

340 690 DEU ISSN 0344-8738
➤ **DER WOHNUNGSEIGENTUEMER.** Text in German. 1971. q. EUR 13.50; EUR 4.50 newsstand/cover (effective 2003). adv. cum.index: 1971-1982, 1983-1984, 1985-1986, 1987-1988. back issues avail.; reprints avail. **Document type:** *Journal, Academic/Scholarly.*
Published by: Haus und Grund Verlag und Service GmbH, Mohrenstr 33, Berlin, 10117, Germany. TEL 49-30-202160, FAX 49-30-2021-6555, zv@haus-und-grund.net, http://www.haus-und-grund.net. Ed. Volker Bielefeld. adv.: B&W page EUR 1,180, color page EUR 1,570. Circ: 8,400.

690 DEU ISSN 0043-7166
WOHNUNGSEIGENTUM. Text in German. 1949. m. adv. bk.rev.
Formerly: Eigenwohner
Published by: Verlag der Eigenwohner GmbH, Tangstedter Landstr 83, Hamburg, 22415, Germany. Circ: 6,910.

690 KOR
WOLGAN KORE KAGIOK. Text in Korean. m.
Published by: Construction Association of Korea, 71-2 Nonhyun dong, Kangnam-ku, Seoul, 135701, Korea, S. TEL 2-5476101, FAX 2-5276979.

WOMAN'S DAY HOME REMODELING. see *ARCHITECTURE*

WOOD/BOIS. see *FORESTS AND FORESTRY—Lumber And Wood*

WOOD DESIGN & BUILDING. see *FORESTS AND FORESTRY—Lumber And Wood*

691 GBR ISSN 0263-6050
TP875 CODEN: WOCEDR
WORLD CEMENT. Text in English. 1928. m. GBP 104, USD 210 (effective 1998). adv. bk.rev. charts; illus.; pat. back issues avail. **Document type:** *Trade.*
Former titles: World Cement Technology (0308-8855); Cement Technology (0008-8854); Cement and Lime Manufacture
Related titles: Online - full text ed.: (from Gale Group).
Indexed: BrCerAb, BrTechI, C&ISA, CIN, CRIA, CRICC, ChemAb, CivEngAb, ConcrAb, E&CAJ, EngInd, ExcerpMed, M&TEA, PROMT, SolStAb.
—BLDSC (9353.075000), CASDDS, CISTI, Ei, IE, Infotrieve, ingenta, Linda Hall.
Published by: Palladian Publications Ltd., 15 South St, Farnham, Surrey GU9 7QU, United Kingdom. TEL 44-1252-718999, FAX 44-1252-718992, mail@palladian-publications.com. Ed. Paul Maxwell Cook. Adv. contact Rod Hardy. Circ: 3,500.

693 BEL ISSN 1013-9532
WORLD CEMENT DIRECTORY. Text in English. 1958. irreg. USD 1,200 (effective 1999). adv. illus. **Document type:** *Directory.* **Description:** Provides information on the international cement industry; covers company management, locations of plants and their access to ports, number and types of kilns, fuel used, and production and capacity figures.
Published by: (European Cement Association), Cembureau, Rue d'Arlon 55, Brussels, 1040, Belgium. TEL 32-2-2341011, FAX 32-2-2304720. Circ: 1,500.

690 GBR
WORLD CRANE GUIDE. Text in English. a. USD 60 (effective 2001). **Document type:** *Directory.*
Published by: K H L Group Ltd., Southfields, Southview Rd, Wadhurst, E Sussex TN5 6TP, United Kingdom. TEL 44-1892-784088, FAX 44-1892-784086, cranes@khl.com, mail@khl.com, http://www.craneworld.com, http://www.khl.com. R&P Peter Watkinson.

690 USA ISSN 1054-5115
WORLD FENCE NEWS. Text in English. 1983. m. USD 24.95 (effective 1998). **Document type:** *Newspaper, Trade.* **Description:** Contains current information on events, trends, products and services that affect the fence industry.
Address: 6101 W Courtyard Dr, 3 115, Austin, TX 78730-5029. TEL 512-349-2536. Ed., R&P Rick Henderson. Pub. Rodger D Duke. adv.: B&W page USD 1,910, color page USD 2,635; trim 14.25 x 10.75. Circ: 12,600.

WORLDWIDE DIRECTORY OF CONSULTANTS AND CONTRACTORS. see *BUSINESS AND ECONOMICS—Trade And Industrial Directories*

690 334 DEU
WUERTTEMBERGISCHE BAU-BERUFSGENOSSENSCHAFT. JAHRESBERICHT. Text in German. a. **Document type:** *Trade.*
Published by: Wuerttembergische Bau-Berufsgenossenschaft, Friedrich-Gerstlacher-Str 15, Boeblingen, 71032, Germany. TEL 07031-6250. Ed. Petra Krisa.

690 690 DEU ISSN 0172-2514
WUERTTEMBERGISCHE BAU-BERUFSGENOSSENSCHAFT. MITTEILUNGEN. Text in German. 1960. 4/yr. adv. bk.rev. charts; illus. **Document type:** *Trade.* **Description:** Covers safety and health protection in the building industry. Features accident prevention, safety rules, reports of events, lists of courses in safety, forthcoming events and exhibitions.
Formerly: Bau (0005-6413)
Indexed: CISA.
Published by: Wuerttembergische Bau-Berufsgenossenschaft, Friedrich-Gerstlacher-Str 15, Boeblingen, 71032, Germany. TEL 49-7031-625-0, FAX 49-7031-625-100. Ed. Horst Haun. Circ: 24,000.

YAPI; aylik kultur, sanat ve mimarlik dergisi. see *ARCHITECTURE*

YOUR HOME. see *HOUSING AND URBAN PLANNING*

307.1 690 CZE ISSN 1212-1711
ZAKLADANI. Text in Czech. 1989. q. CZK 288 (effective 2003). **Document type:** *Journal, Trade.*
—BLDSC (9426.005000).
Published by: Zakladani Staveb, K Jezu 1, PO Box 21, Prague 4, 14301, Czech Republic. TEL 42-2-44004111, FAX 42-2-41773713, propagace@zakladani.cz, http://www.zakladani.cz/casopis/!new/casopis.html.

ZBORNIK ISTRAZIVACKIH RADOVA IZ OBLASTI MATERIJALA I KONSTRUKCIJA U GRADJEVINARSTVU. see *ENGINEERING—Civil Engineering*

690 AUT ISSN 0514-2946
TA680 CODEN: ZMBEA4
ZEMENT UND BETON. Text in German. 1953. q. EUR 20 domestic; EUR 30 foreign (effective 2005). adv. bk.rev. abstr.; illus. **Document type:** *Magazine, Trade.* **Description:** Trade journal for innovation and application in the area of cement and concrete.
Indexed: CIN, CRIA, CRICC, ChemAb, ChemTitl.
—CASDDS, CISTI, Linda Hall.
Published by: Zement und Beton Handels- und Werbegesellschaft mbH, Reisnerstrasse 53, Vienna, W 1030, Austria. TEL 43-1-7146685-0, FAX 43-1-714668526, zement@zement-beton.co.at. Ed., R&P Ernst Roubin. Adv. contact Frank Huber. Circ: 4,500.

B

692.8 JPN ISSN 0044-4006
ZENKEN JOURNAL/ZENKEN JANARU. Text in Japanese. 1962. m. JPY 1,200. stat. index.
Published by: Associated General Contractors of Japan Inc./Zenkoku Kensetsu Gyomukai, 2-5-1 Haccho-Bori, Chuo-ku, Tokyo, 104-0032, Japan. Eds. Yashio Murata, Yasuo Takata. Circ: 10,000.

ZHILISHCHNOE I KOMMUNAL'NOE KHOZYAISTVO. see *BUSINESS AND ECONOMICS—Production Of Goods And Services*

690 RUS ISSN 0044-4472
ZHILISHCHNOE STROITEL'STVO. Text in Russian. 1958. m. USD 145. bk.rev. bibl. index.
Indexed: RASB, RefZh.
—CISTI, East View, Linda Hall.
Published by: Izdatel'stvo po Stroitel'stvu, Dolgorukovskaya ul 23-a, Moscow, 101442, Russian Federation. TEL 7-095-9782737, FAX 7-095-9762036. Circ: 12,600. **US dist. addr.:** East View Information Services, 3020 Harbor Ln. N., Minneapolis, MN 55447. TEL 612-550-0961.

B

690 621 CHN ISSN 1001-7151
ZHONGGUO DIANTI/CHINA ELEVATOR. Text in Chinese; Abstracts in English. 1985. bi-m. CNY 192 (effective 2000); USD 180 foreign. adv. **Document type:** *Journal, Trade.*
Description: Provides comprehensive elevator, escalator, passenger converyor, parking system publication concerned with technology and market.
Formerly: Elevator Bulletin
Published by: China Elevator Association, 61 Jinguang Ave, Langfang, Hebei 065000, China. TEL 86-316-2311446, FAX 86-316-2311447, chinaem@public.lfptt.he.cn, http://www.cea-net.org/chinaelevator. Ed. Kerong Peng. R&P Zengjian Li. Adv. contact Li Zengjian. color page USD 1,500. Circ: 5,300 (paid); 200 (controlled). **Co-sponsor:** China Academy of Building Research, Institute of Building Mechanization.

690 CHN
ZHONGGUO JIANCAI BAO/CHINA BUILDING MATERIALS NEWS. Text in Chinese. 1986. d. (6/week). CNY 148.80 (effective 2004). **Document type:** *Newspaper, Trade.*
Related titles: Online - full content ed.
Published by: Jingji Ribao Baoye Jituan/Economic Daily Newspaper Group, Xicheng-qu, 3, Nanlishi Lu, 5F, Longfanxizilou, Beijing, 100037, China. TEL 86-10-68047006, FAX 86-10-68030975, http://www.chinabmb.com/cbmdaily. **Dist. by:** China International Book Trading Corp, 35 Chegongzhuang Xilu, Haidian District, PO Box 399, Beijing 100044, China. TEL 86-10-68412045, FAX 86-10-68412023, cibtc@mail.cibtc.com.cn, http://www.cibtc.com.cn.

690 CHN
ZHONGGUO JIANSHE BAO/CHINA CONSTRUCTION NEWS. Text in Chinese. 1986. d. (6/week). CNY 239.40 (effective 2004). **Document type:** *Newspaper, Trade.*
Address: Baiwanzhuang Jianbuyuan, Beijing, 100037, China. TEL 86-10-68311589, FAX 86-10-68394407, xwzx@chinajsb.cn, http://www.chinajsb.cn/. **Dist. by:** China International Book Trading Corp, 35 Chegongzhuang Xilu, Haidian District, PO Box 399, Beijing 100044, China. TEL 86-10-68412045, FAX 86-10-68412023, cibtc@mail.cibtc.com.cn, http://www.cibtc.com.cn.

690 CHN
ZHONGGUO JIANZHUYE NIANJIAN/CHINA BUILDING INDUSTRY ALMANAC. Text in Chinese. 1985. a. CNY 60 (effective 1999).
Published by: Zhongguo Jianzhu Gongye Chubanshe, Xijiao, Baiwanzhuang, Beijing, China. TEL 86-10-6839-3529, FAX 86-10-6834-8830.

690 USA
▼ **50 PLUS BUILDER.** Text in English. 2005. q. free to qualified personnel (effective 2005). adv. **Document type:** *Magazine, Trade.* **Description:** Business management publication for homebuilders, developers, architects and designers who build new homes for the 50 plus age demographics.
Related titles: Online - full text ed.: 50PlusBuilder.com.
Published by: Peninsula Publishing, 1602 Monrovia Ave, Newport Beach, CA 92663. TEL 949-631-0308, FAX 949-631-2475, nslevin@50plusbuilder.com, http://www.50plusbuilder.com/. Eds. Melinda Sheckells, Nick Slevin. Pub. Nick Slevin. Adv. contact Rona Fiedler. B&W page USD 4,300; trim 8.75 x 11.75.

747 DEU
▼ **250 UMBAU-IDEEN.** Text in German. 2003. a. EUR 3.80 newsstand/cover (effective 2004). adv. **Document type:** *Magazine, Consumer.*
Published by: City-Post Verlagsgesellschaft mbH, Lessingstr 14, Munich, 80336, Germany. TEL 49-89-5990810, FAX 49-89-59908133, anzeigen@cpz.de, http://www.cpz.de. adv.: B&W page EUR 5,250, color page EUR 8,100; trim 180 x 270. Circ: 100,000 (paid and controlled).

BUILDING AND CONSTRUCTION—Abstracting, Bibliographies, Statistics

690.021 USA
A A M A INDUSTRY STATISTICAL REVIEW AND FORECAST. Text in English. 1970. a. USD 100 (effective 2004). back issues avail. **Document type:** *Trade.*
Published by: American Architectural Manufacturers Association, 1827 Walden Office Sq, Ste 550, Schaumburg, IL 60173-4268. TEL 847-303-5664, FAX 847-303-5774, webmaster@AAMANET.org, http://www.AAMANET.org. R&P Pamela Lierman. Adv. contact Janice Charletta. Circ: 514.

690.021 AUS ISSN 0818-3511
AUSTRALIA. BUREAU OF STATISTICS. BUILDING ACTIVITY, AUSTRALIA: DWELLING UNIT COMMENCEMENTS, PRELIMINARY. Text in English. 1953. q. AUD 18.50 per issue (effective 2003). **Document type:** *Government.* **Description:** Contains estimates of the number of dwelling units commenced for both private and public sectors, in originally and seasonally adjusted terms.
Published by: Australian Bureau of Statistics, PO Box 10, Belconnen, ACT 2616, Australia. TEL 61-2-6252-5249, FAX 61-2-6252-6778, http://www.abs.gov.au.

690.021 AUS ISSN 1031-0169
AUSTRALIA. BUREAU OF STATISTICS. BUILDING ACTIVITY, AUSTRALIAN CAPITAL TERRITORY. Text in English. 1961. q. AUD 20 (effective 2003). **Document type:** *Government.* **Description:** Contains number of dwelling units and value of residential buildings, value of alterations and additions to residential buildings, and value of non-residential building.
Published by: Australian Bureau of Statistics, PO Box 10, Belconnen, ACT 2616, Australia. TEL 61-2-6207-0326, FAX 61-2-6207-0282, http://www.abs.gov.au.

690.021 AUS
AUSTRALIA. BUREAU OF STATISTICS. DIRECTORY OF CONSTRUCTION STATISTICS. Text in English. 2000. irreg., latest 2000. AUD 58 (effective 2002). **Document type:** *Government.*
Published by: Australian Bureau of Statistics, PO Box 10, Belconnen, ACT 2616, Australia. TEL 61-2-6252-5249, FAX 61-2-6252-6778, http://www.abs.gov.au.

690.21 AUS
AUSTRALIA. BUREAU OF STATISTICS. ENGINEERING CONSTRUCTION ACTIVITY, AUSTRALIA. Text in English. 1994. q. AUD 22 (effective 2003). **Document type:** *Government.* **Description:** Covers value of engineering construction work done, value of commencements and value of work yet to be done.
Supersedes in part: Australia. Bureau of Statistics. Building and Construction Activity, Australia (1322-8730); Which was formed by the merger of (1948-1994): Building Activity, Australia (0728-375X); (1989-1994): Construction Activity at Constant Prices, Australia (1033-9809); (1991-1994): Engineering Construction Activity, Autralia (1037-3993); Which was formerly (1987-1991): Engineering Construction Survey, Australia (0819-7989)
Published by: Australian Bureau of Statistics, PO Box 10, Belconnen, ACT 2616, Australia. TEL 61-2-6252-5249, FAX 61-2-6252-6778, http://www.abs.gov.au.

690.021 AUS ISSN 0729-2031
AUSTRALIA. BUREAU OF STATISTICS. NORTHERN TERRITORY OFFICE. BUILDING ACTIVITY, NORTHERN TERRITORY. Text in English. 1956. q. AUD 20 (effective 2003). **Document type:** *Government.* **Description:** Contains number of dwelling units and value of residential buildings, value of alterations and additions to residential buildings, and value of non-residential buildings.
Published by: Australian Bureau of Statistics, Northern Territory Office, 5th Fl., 81 Smith St, Darwin, N.T. 0800, Australia. TEL 61-8-8943-2110, FAX 61-8-8981-1218, http://www.abs.gov.au.

690.021 AUS
AUSTRALIA. BUREAU OF STATISTICS. PRIVATE SECTOR CONSTRUCTION INDUSTRY, AUSTRALIA. Text in English. 1979. irreg., latest 1997. AUD 22 (effective 2003). **Document type:** *Government.*
Formerly: Australia. Bureau of Statistics. Construction Industry Survey: Private Sector Construction Establishments, Details of Operations, Australia
Published by: Australian Bureau of Statistics, PO Box 10, Belconnen, ACT 2616, Australia. TEL 61-2-6252-5249, FAX 61-2-6252-6778, http://www.abs.gov.au.

690.021 AUS
AUSTRALIA. BUREAU OF STATISTICS. PRIVATE SECTOR CONSTRUCTION INDUSTRY, AUSTRALIA, PRELIMINARY. Text in English. 1978. irreg., latest 1996. AUD 22 (effective 2002). **Document type:** *Government.* **Description:** Number of establishments operating during the year, employment, wages and salaries, components of turnover, stocks, purchases and selected expenses.
Formerly: Construction Industry, Australia: Summary of Private Sector Operations
Published by: Australian Bureau of Statistics, PO Box 10, Belconnen, ACT 2616, Australia. TEL 61-6-2525249, FAX 61-6-2526778, http://www.abs.gov.au.

690.021 AUS ISSN 0726-1896
AUSTRALIA. BUREAU OF STATISTICS. SOUTH AUSTRALIAN OFFICE. BUILDING ACTIVITY, SOUTH AUSTRALIA. Text in English. 1980. q. AUD 20 (effective 2003). charts. **Document type:** *Government.* **Description:** Contains information about the number and value of residential building commenced and completed.
Published by: Australian Bureau of Statistics, South Australian Office, GPO Box 2272, Adelaide, SA 5001, Australia. TEL 61-8-82377582, FAX 61-8-8237-7566, http://www.abs.gov.au.

690.021 AUS ISSN 0727-2278
AUSTRALIA. BUREAU OF STATISTICS. WESTERN AUSTRALIAN OFFICE. BUILDING APPROVALS, WESTERN AUSTRALIA. Text in English. 1944. m. AUD 21 (effective 2003). **Document type:** *Government.* **Description:** Contains number of dwelling units and value of residential buildings approved for both private and public sectors.
Published by: Australian Bureau of Statistics, Western Australian Office, PO Box K 881, Perth, W.A. 6001, Australia. TEL 61-8-9360-5307, FAX 61-8-9360-5955, http://www.abs.gov.au.

690.021 AUS ISSN 1031-7120
HD7379.W47
AUSTRALIA. BUREAU OF STATISTICS. WESTERN AUSTRALIAN OFFICE. ESTIMATED STOCKS OF DWELLING, WESTERN AUSTRALIA. Text in English. 1986. a. AUD 20 (effective 2000). **Document type:** *Government.*
Description: Contains estimates of population and private dwellings.
Formerly: Estimated Stocks of Dwellings in Census Collection Districts and Statistical Local Areas, Western Australia
Published by: Australian Bureau of Statistics, Western Australian Office, PO Box K 881, Perth, W.A. 6001, Australia. TEL 61-8-9360-5307, FAX 61-8-9360-5955, http://www.abs.gov.au.

690.021 MEX ISSN 0187-4950
HD9715.C5
AVANCE DE INFORMACION ECONOMICA. INDUSTRIA DE LA CONSTRUCCION. Text in Spanish. 1986. q. MXP 48, USD 16.
Published by: Instituto Nacional de Estadistica, Geografia e Informatica, Secretaria de Programacion y Presupuesto, Prol. Heroe de Nacozari 2301 Sur, Puerta 11, Acceso, Aguascalientes, 20270, Mexico. TEL 52-4-918-1948, FAX 52-4-918-0739, http://www.inegi.gob.mx. Circ: 800.

690.021 GBR ISSN 0144-9036
B M P MONTHLY STATISTICAL BULLETIN. (Building Material Producers) Text in English. 1974. m. GBP 200 to non-members; free to members. **Document type:** *Bulletin.*
Description: Presents statistics of the building material production trade, housing starts, completions, and renovations.
Published by: National Council of Building Material Producers, 26 Store St, London, WC1E 7BT, United Kingdom. TEL 44-171-323-3770, FAX 44-171-323-0307, ninao@building-materials.org.uk. Ed. N Ovanessian. Circ: 250.

690.021 CHE ISSN 1423-5277
BAU- UND WOHNBAUSTATISTIK IN DER SCHWEIZ. Text in French, German. 1996. a. CHF 20 (effective 2001). **Document type:** *Government.*
Formed by the merger of (1987-1996): Wohnbautaetigkeit in der Schweiz (1018-2292); (1986-1996): Bautaetigkeit und Bauvorhaben in der Schweiz (0491-8398)
Published by: Bundesamt fuer Statistik, Espace de l'Europe 10, Neuchatel, 2010, Switzerland. TEL 41-32-7136011, FAX 41-32-7136012, information@bfs.admin.ch, http://www.admin.ch/bfs.

690.021 DEU ISSN 0084-7739
BAUSTATISTISCHES JAHRBUCH. Text in German. 1960. a. **Document type:** *Trade.*
Published by: Hauptverband der Deutschen Bauindustrie, Kurfurstenstr. 129, Berlin, 10785, Germany. TEL 49-30-21286-0.

BELGIUM. INSTITUT NATIONAL DE STATISTIQUE. INDUSTRIE ET CONSTRUCTION. CONSTRUCTION ET LOGEMENT. see *HOUSING AND URBAN PLANNING—Abstracting, Bibliographies, Statistics*

BELGIUM. NATIONAAL INSTITUUT VOOR DE STATISTIEK. INDUSTRIE EN BOUWNIJVERHEID. BOUWNIJVERHEID EN HUISVESTING. see *HOUSING AND URBAN PLANNING—Abstracting, Bibliographies, Statistics*

016.69 USA
BOECKH BUILDING COST INDEX. Text in English. 6/yr. USD 119 (effective 1998). **Document type:** *Abstract/Index.*
Published by: E.H. Boeckh, Ed. & Pub. (Subsidiary of: Thomson Publishing Corp.), 2885 S Calhoun Rd, Box 510291, New Berlin, WI 53151-0291. TEL 414-780-2800, 800-285-1288, FAX 414-780-0306. R&P E H Boeckh.

016.69 SWE ISSN 0345-1941
BYGGREFERAT; nordiskt litteraturindex. Text in Danish, English, Finnish, Norwegian, Swedish. 1972. 4/yr. SEK 1,190 (effective 2002). bk.rev. abstr. **Document type:** *Abstract/Index.*
Description: Abstracts articles and books in the construction and building fields.

Published by: BYGGDOK, Institutet foer Byggdokumentation/ Swedish Institute of Building Documentation, Sankt Eriksgatan 46, Stockholm, 11234, Sweden. TEL 47-08-617 74 50, FAX 47-08-617 74 60, info@byggdok.se. Ed. Boerje Hoeglander. Pub. Arne Winerdal. Circ: 600.

016.69 ZAF
C S I R BUILDING TECHNOLOGY. COMPLETE LIST OF PUBLICATIONS. Text in English. 1980. a. ZAR 45.
Document type: *Bibliography.* **Description:** Comprehensive listing of research publications in building and construction.
Supersedes: National Building Research Institute. Complete List of N B R I Publications (0077-3581)
Related titles: Diskette ed.
Published by: C S I R, Building Technology/W N N R Boutegnologie, PO Box 395, Pretoria, 0001, South Africa.

695.021 CAN ISSN 0380-5786
CANADA. STATISTICS CANADA. ASPHALT ROOFING/PAPIER-TOITURE ASPHALTE. Text in English, French. 1932. m. CND 47; USD 47 foreign. back issues avail. **Description:** Covers production and shipments, domestic and export of asphalt roofing shingles, sidings, tar and asphalt felts and sheathing.
Related titles: Microform ed.: (from MML); Online - full text ed.
—CISTI.
Published by: Statistics Canada, Operations and Integration Division, Circulation Management, Jean Talon Bldg, 2 C12, Tunney's Pasture, Ottawa, ON K1A 0T6, Canada. TEL 613-951-7277, 800-267-6677, FAX 613-951-1584, http://www.statcan.ca. Circ: 250.

690.021 CAN ISSN 0318-8809
CANADA. STATISTICS CANADA. BUILDING PERMITS/PERMIS DE BATIR. Text in English, French. 1922. m. CND 186; USD 189 foreign (effective 1999). **Document type:** *Government.*
Description: Statistics of building permits issued by municipalities; number of new dwelling units by type; value of residential, commercial, governmental and institutional building construction for individual municipalities, metropolitan areas, census divisions and provinces.
Related titles: Microform ed.: (from MML); Online - full text ed.: ISSN 1480-7475.
Published by: Statistics Canada, Operations and Integration Division, Circulation Management, Jean Talon Bldg, 2 C12, Tunney's Pasture, Ottawa, ON K1A 0T6, Canada. TEL 613-951-7277, 800-267-6677, FAX 613-951-1584, http://www.statcan.ca.

690.021 CAN ISSN 0575-7975
CANADA. STATISTICS CANADA. BUILDING PERMITS, ANNUAL SUMMARY/PERMIS DE BATIR, SOMMAIRE ANNUEL. Text in English, French. 1966. a. CND 62 domestic; USD 62 foreign (effective 1999). **Document type:** *Government.* **Description:** Provides the number and value of building permits issued in more than 1600 Canadian municipalities. Includes data analysis and definitions.
Related titles: Microform ed.: (from MML); Online - full text ed.
Published by: Statistics Canada, Operations and Integration Division, Circulation Management, Jean Talon Bldg, 2 C12, Tunney's Pasture, Ottawa, ON K1A 0T6, Canada. TEL 613-951-7277, 800-267-6677, FAX 613-951-1584, http://www.statcan.ca.

690.021 CAN ISSN 1499-9889
CANADA. STATISTICS CANADA. CAPITAL EXPENDITURE PRICE STATISTICS/CANADA. STATISTIQUE CANADA. STATISTIQUES DES PRIX DE LA CONSTRUCTION RAPPORT TRIMESTRIEL. (Catalogue 62-008) Text in English, French. 1974. q. CND 5.60, USD 6.70.
Former titles (until 2001): Canada. Statistics Canada. Construction Price Statistics (0833-238X); (until 1985): Canada. Statistics Canada. Construction Price Statistics. Monthly Bulletin (0319-8243); Canada. Statistics Canada. Construction Price Statistics. Quarterly Report (0319-8251)
—CISTI.
Published by: Statistics Canada, Communications Division, 3rd Fl, R H Coats Bldg, Ottawa, ON K1A 0A6, Canada.

690.021 CAN ISSN 1201-057X
CANADA. STATISTICS CANADA. CAPITAL EXPENDITURES BY TYPE OF ASSET. (Catalogue 64-201) Text in English, French. 1951. a. CND 39, USD 47 domestic; USD 55 foreign.
Description: Presents data on the total value of construction put in place. Includes current and constant dollars for new and repair construction and the type of structure by sector and province.
Formerly (until 1992): Canada. Statistics Canada. Construction in Canada (0527-4974)
—CISTI.
Published by: Statistics Canada, Publications Sales and Services, Ottawa, ON K1A 0T6, Canada. TEL 613-951-7277, FAX 613-951-1584.

690.021 CAN ISSN 1206-3835
CANADA. STATISTICS CANADA. HOMEOWNER REPAIR AND RENOVATION EXPENDITURE/CANADA. STATISTIQUE CANADA. DEPENSES SUR LES REPARATIONS ET RENOVATIONS EFFECTUEES PAR LES PROPRIETAIRES DE LOGEMENT AU CANADA. Text in English. 1987. a. CND 31; USD 31 foreign. adv. **Document type:** *Government.*
Formerly (until 1995): Canada. Statistics Canada. Homeowner Repair and Renovation Expenditure in Canada (0840-8106)
Related titles: Online - full text ed.
Published by: Statistics Canada, Operations and Integration Division, Circulation Management, Jean Talon Bldg, 2 C12, Tunney's Pasture, Ottawa, ON K1A 0T6, Canada. TEL 613-951-7277, 800-267-6677, FAX 613-951-1584, http://www.statcan.ca. Adv. contact Kathryn Bonner.

690.021 CAN ISSN 0229-6098
HD9623.C2
CANADA. STATISTICS CANADA. MINERAL WOOL INCLUDING FIBROUS GLASS INSULATION/CANADA. STATISTIQUE CANADA. LAINE MINERALE Y COMPRIS LES ISOLANTS EN FIBRE DE VERRE. Text in English, French. 1950. m. CND 62; USD 62 foreign (effective 1999). **Document type:** *Government.* **Description:** Covers production and factory shipments of mineral wool including fibrous glass insulation used in construction.
Related titles: Microform ed.: (from MML).
Published by: Statistics Canada, Operations and Integration Division, Circulation Management, Jean Talon Bldg, 2 C12, Tunney's Pasture, Ottawa, ON K1A 0T6, Canada. TEL 613-951-7277, 800-267-6677, FAX 613-951-1584, http://www.statcan.ca.

690.021 BRA ISSN 0103-6882
CENSO DA CONSTRUCAO. Text in Portuguese. 1985. quinquennial. **Document type:** *Government.* **Description:** Presents data on the number of construction establishments, employed persons, salaries and wages, withdrawals and other payments, construction costs, operational revenue, gross production value, and construction costs and expenditures.
Published by: Fundacao Instituto Brasileiro de Geografia e Estatistica, Centro de Documentacao e Disseminacao de Informacoes, Rua General Canabarro, 706 Andar 2, Maracana, Rio de Janeiro, RJ 20271-201, Brazil. TEL 55-21-264-5424, FAX 55-21-2841959.

016.69 IND
CENTRAL BUILDING RESEARCH INSTITUTE. PUBLICATIONS INDEX. Text in English. irreg. free. **Document type:** *Bibliography.* **Description:** List of all available CBRI publications.
Formerly: Central Building Research Institute. List of Publications (0557-322X)
Related titles: Diskette ed.
Published by: Central Building Research Institute, C B R I, C S I R-INDIA, Roorkee, Uttaranchal, India. TEL 91-1332-272243, FAX 91-1332-272272, director@cbrimail.com, http://www.cbri.org.

016.69 GBR ISSN 1469-4891
CHARTERED INSTITUTE OF BUILDING. CONSTRUCTION INFORMATION QUARTERLY. Text in English. 1976. q. GBP 88 to non-members; GBP 38 to members; GBP 120 to institutions (effective 2005). reprint service avail. from PQC.
Document type: *Abstract/Index.* **Description:** Aims to communicate construction innovation to the widest audience of industry stakeholders.
Incorporates: Building Management Abstracts (0308-9665); Former titles (until 1999): Construction Information File - C I F; (until 1992): Technical Information Service - T I S (0262-6632); Which was formed by the merger of (1971-1982): Chartered Institute of Building. Estimating Information Service (0308-8073); (1971-1982): Chartered Institute of Building. Site Management Information Service (0308-8081); (1977-1982): Chartered Institute of Building. Maintenance Information Service (0140-9665); (1979-1982): Chartered Institute of Building. Surveying Information Service (0143-649X)
Related titles: Online - full text ed.: (from Swets Information Services).
—BLDSC (3421.309370), CISTI.
Published by: Chartered Institute of Building, Englemere, Kings Ride, Ascot, Berks SL5 7TB, United Kingdom. TEL 44-1344-630700, FAX 44-1344-630777, sjwilson@ciob.org.uk, http://www.ciob.org.uk/ciob/siteRoot/Information/Publications.aspx. Ed. Caroline Collier TEL 31-1636-700021. Circ: 4,500.

690.021 GBR
CHARTERED INSTITUTE OF PUBLIC FINANCE AND ACCOUNTANCY. DIRECT SERVICE ORGANISATION STATISTICS. ACTUALS. Text in English. 1982. a. GBP 105. back issues avail.
Former titles: Chartered Institute of Public Finance and Accountancy. Direct Labour Organisation Statistics. Actuals; Chartered Institute of Public Finance and Accountancy. Direct Labour Statistics. Actuals (0263-2977)
Published by: (Statistical Information Service), Chartered Institute of Public Finance and Accountancy, 3 Robert St, London, WC2N 6RL, United Kingdom. TEL 44-20-7543-5800, FAX 44-20-7543-5700, http://www.cipfa.org.uk.

690.021 CHL
CHILE. INSTITUTO NACIONAL DE ESTADISTICAS. EDIFICACION. Text in Spanish. 1980. a. CLP 2,000; USD 13.50 in United States; USD 15.90 elsewhere.
Published by: Instituto Nacional de Estadisticas, Casilla 498, Correo 3, Ave. Bulnes, 418, Santiago, Chile. TEL 56-2-6991441, FAX 56-2-6712169.

690.021 USA ISSN 0010-6917
CONSTRUCTION REVIEW. Text in English. 1955. q. USD 18 domestic; USD 30 foreign (effective 2005). charts; mkt.; stat. cum.index. back issues avail.; reprint service avail. from CIS.
Document type: *Magazine, Government.* **Description:** Compiles most federal government statistics on construction and building products.
Related titles: Microfiche ed.: (from CIS); Microform ed.: (from MIM, PQC); Online - full text ed.: (from EBSCO Publishing, Florida Center for Library Automation, Gale Group, H.W. Wilson, Northern Light Technology, Inc., O C L C Online Computer Library Center, Inc., ProQuest Information & Learning, The Dialog Corporation).
Indexed: ABIn, AmStI, BPI, BldManAb, BusI, ConcrAb, HongKongiana, IUSGP, PAIS, PROMT, RASB, T&II.
—CISTI, Linda Hall.
Published by: U.S. International Trade Administration, Basic Industries Division, Herbert C Hoover Bldg, ITA Rm H4039, 14th St and Constitution Ave, Washington, DC 20230. TEL 202-482-0134, FAX 202-482-0382. Ed. Patrick H MacAuley. Circ: 1,500 (paid). **Subscr. to:** U.S. Government Printing Office, Superintendent of Documents, PO Box 371954, Pittsburgh, PA 15250-7954. TEL 202-512-1800, FAX 202-512-2250.

690.021 CYP
HD9715.C95
CYPRUS. DEPARTMENT OF STATISTICS AND RESEARCH. CONSTRUCTION AND HOUSING STATISTICS. Text in English, Greek. a. CYP 6 (effective 1999). **Document type:** *Government.* **Description:** Presents statistical data on the construction industry and housing.
Formerly: Cyprus. Department of Statistics and Research. Construction and Housing Report (0253-8725)
Published by: Ministry of Finance, Department of Statistics and Research, 13 Andreas Araouzos St, Nicosia, 1444, Cyprus. TEL 357-2-309318, FAX 357-2-374830, cydsr@cytanet.com.cy, http://www.pio.gov.cy/dsr.

624.09489 690.09489 DNK ISSN 0108-5549
DENMARK. DANMARKS STATISTIK. BYGGE- OG ANLAEGSVIRKSOMHED. Text in Danish. 1983. triennial. price varies. **Document type:** *Government.*
Supersedes in part (1976-1983): Statistiske Efterretninger A (0105-306X); (1976-1983): Statistiske Efterretninger B (0105-3078); Which both superseded in part (1909-1976): Statistiske Efterretninger (0039-0674)
Related titles: ♦ Series of: Denmark. Danmarks Statistik. Statistiske Efterretninger. Indhold. ISSN 1396-8173.
Published by: Danmarks Statistik, Sejroegade 11, Copenhagen Oe, 2100, Denmark. TEL 45-39-173917, FAX 45-39-173939.

690.021 ECU
ECUADOR. INSTITUTO NACIONAL DE ESTADISTICA Y CENSOS. ENCUESTA ANUAL DE EDIFICACIONES. Text in Spanish. a. USD 10.92 newsstand/cover (effective 2001). stat.
Document type: *Government.*
Related titles: Diskette ed.
Published by: Instituto Nacional de Estadistica y Censos, Juan Larrea N15-36 y Jose Riofrio, Quito, Ecuador. TEL 593-2-529858, FAX 593-2-509836, inec1@ecnet.ec, http://www.inec.gov.ec.

690.021 MEX ISSN 0186-9035
ENCUESTA TRIMESTRAL SOBRE LA INDUSTRIA DE LA CONSTRUCCION. Text in Spanish. q. MXP 6.50, USD 2.
Published by: Instituto Nacional de Estadistica, Geografia e Informatica, Secretaria de Programacion y Presupuesto, Prol. Heroe de Nacozari 2301 Sur, Puerta 11, Acceso, Aguascalientes, 20270, Mexico. TEL 52-4-918-1948, FAX 52-4-918-0739, http://www.inegi.gob.mx.

666.24021 ESP
ESTADISTICA DEL CEMENTO. Text in Spanish. a.
Published by: Ministerio de Industria, Paseo Castellana, 160, Madrid, 28046, Spain. FAX 259-84-80.

690.021 PRT ISSN 0871-9969
ESTATISTICAS DA CONSTRUCAO DE EDIFICIOS. Text in Portuguese. 1970. a. EUR 10 (effective 2005). stat.
Document type: *Government.*
Superses in part (in 1990): Estatisticas da Construcao e da Habitacao - Statistiques du Batiment et de l'Habitation (0377-2225)
Published by: Instituto Nacional de Estatistica, Ave. Antonio Jose de Almeida 2, Lisbon, 1000-043, Portugal. TEL 351-21-8426100, FAX 351-21-8426380, ine@ine.pt, http://www.ine.pt/. Circ: 500.

609.021 BEL ISSN 0777-611X
EUROPEAN CEMENT ASSOCIATION. WORLD STATISTICAL REVIEW. Key Title: World Statistical Review - Cembureau. Text in English. 1959. a. USD 200 (effective 1999).
Description: Presents data on cement production, imports, exports and consumption.
Formerly: European Cement Association. Statistical Review
Published by: (European Cement Association), Cembureau, Rue d'Arlon 55, Brussels, 1040, Belgium. TEL 32-2-2341011, FAX 32-2-2304720.

B

▼ new title ➤ refereed ✶ unverified ♦ full entry avail.

690.021 DEU ISSN 0343-6403
FACHBUCHVERZEICHNIS BAUWESEN - ARCHITEKTUR (YEAR). Text in German. 1900. a. **Document type:** *Trade.*
Published by: Rossipaul Kommunikation GmbH, Menzinger Str 37, Munich, 80638, Germany. TEL 49-89-179106-0, FAX 49-89-17910622. Ed. Angela Sendlinger. Circ: 30,000.

690.021 FJI ISSN 0259-6016
FIJI. BUREAU OF STATISTICS. CENSUS OF BUILDING AND CONSTRUCTION. Text in English. a., latest 1994. USD 5 (effective 2000). **Document type:** *Government.*
Published by: Bureau of Statistics, c/o Librarian, Govt. Bldg. 5, PO Box 2221, Suva, Fiji. TEL 679-315-822, FAX 679-303-656.

FINLAND. TILASTOKESKUS. KESAMOKIT/FINLAND. STATISTICS FINLAND. FREE-TIME RESIDENCES/FINLAND. STATISTIKCENTRALEN. FRITIDSHUS. see *HOUSING AND URBAN PLANNING—Abstracting, Bibliographies, Statistics*

690.021 330 FIN ISSN 1236-9942
FINLAND. TILASTOKESKUS. MAARAKENNUSKUSTANNUSINDEKSI. Text in Finnish, Swedish. 1969. m. EUR 63; EUR 9 per issue (effective 2005). stat. **Document type:** *Government.*
Incorporates (1991-2003): Finland. Tilastokeskus. Maarakennusalan ja Metsaalan Konekustannusindeksi (0788-9984); Former titles (until 1993): Finland. Tilastokeskus. Tie- ja Maarakennuskustannusindeksi (0784-8188); (until 1988): Indeksetiedotus T R (0355-2411)
Published by: Tilastokeskus/Statistics Finland, Tyopajakatu 13, Statistics Finland, Helsinki, 00022, Finland. TEL 358-9-17341, FAX 358-9-17342750, http://www.stat.fi/.

FINLAND. TILASTOKESKUS. RAKENNUKSET, ASUNNET JA ASUINOLOT. see *HOUSING AND URBAN PLANNING—Abstracting, Bibliographies, Statistics*

690.021 FIN ISSN 0784-8196
FINLAND. TILASTOKESKUS. RAKENNUSKUSTANNUSINDEKSI (KUUKAUSITILASTO)/STATISTICS FINLAND. BUILDING COST INDEX. (Subseries of Finland. Tilastokeskus. Indeksitiedotus) Text in English, Finnish, Swedish. 1968. m. EUR 68; EUR 10 per issue (effective 2005). **Document type:** *Government.*
Supersedes (in 1988): Finland. Tilastokeskus. Indeksitiedotus RK, Rakennuskustannukset (0355-239X)
Related titles: Online - full text ed.: ISSN 1795-4282.
Published by: Tilastokeskus/Statistics Finland, Tyopajakatu 13, Statistics Finland, Helsinki, 00022, Finland. TEL 358-9-17341, FAX 358-9-17342750, http://www.stat.fi/.

690.021 330 FIN ISSN 0786-0994
FINLAND. TILASTOKESKUS. RAKENNUSKUSTANNUSINDEKSI. (VUOSITILASTO)/ STATISTICS FINLAND. BUILDING COST INDEX. Text in English, Finnish, Swedish. 1988. a. stat. **Document type:** *Government.*
Supersedes in part (in 1988): Finland. Tilastokeskus. R K. Rakennuskustannusindeksi (0355-239X)
Published by: Tilastokeskus/Statistics Finland, Tyopajakatu 13, Statistics Finland, Helsinki, 00022, Finland. TEL 358-9-17341, FAX 358-9-17342750, http://www.stat.fi/.

690.021 FIN ISSN 0784-8390
HD9715.F5
FINLAND. TILASTOKESKUS. RAKENTAMINEN/FINLAND. STATISTICS FINLAND. BUILDING. Text in English, Finnish, Swedish. 1968. 32/yr. EUR 262 (effective 2005). stat. **Document type:** *Government.*
Formerly (until 1988): Finland. Tilastokeskus. R A. Rakentaminen (0355-2314)
Published by: Tilastokeskus/Statistics Finland, Tyopajakatu 13, Statistics Finland, Helsinki, 00022, Finland. TEL 358-9-17341, FAX 358-9-17342750, http://www.stat.fi/.

FINLAND. TILASTOKESKUS. RAKENTAMINEN JA ASUMINEN: VUOSIKIRJA/FINLAND. STATISTICS FINLAND. CONSTRUCTION AND HOUSING. YEARBOOK. see *HOUSING AND URBAN PLANNING—Abstracting, Bibliographies, Statistics*

690.021 FRA ISSN 1274-8668
FRANCE. MINISTERE DE L'EQUIPEMENT, DES TRANSPORTS, DU LOGEMENT, DU TOURISME ET DE LA MER. STATISTIQUES DE LA CONSTRUCTION. Text in French. 4/yr. **Document type:** *Government.*
Formerly: France. Direction du Batiment, des Travaux Publics et de la Conjoncture. Statistiques de la Construction (0338-4160)
Related titles: Microfiche ed.
Published by: (France. Ministere de l'Urbanisme et du Logement), Documentation Francaise, 29-31 quai Voltaire, Paris, Cedex 7 75344, France. FAX 33-1-40157230.

690.021 DEU ISSN 0072-1719
GERMANY. STATISTISCHES BUNDESAMT. AUSGEWAEHLTE ZAHLEN FUER DIE BAUWIRTSCHAFT. Text in German. m. **Document type:** *Government.*
Indexed: RASB.
Published by: Statistisches Bundesamt, Gustav-Stresemann-Ring 11, Wiesbaden, 65180, Germany. TEL 49-611-75-1, FAX 49-611-724000, http://www.statistik-bund.de.

692.021 DEU ISSN 0720-4124
HD651.A1
GERMANY. STATISTISCHES BUNDESAMT. FACHSERIE 17, PREISE, REIHE 5: KAUFWERTE FUER BAULAND. Text in German. q. **Document type:** *Government.*
Supersedes: Germany (Federal Republic, 1949-) Statistisches Bundesamt. Preise, Loehne, Wirtschaftsrechnungen. Reihe 5: Preise und Preisindizes fuer Bauwerke und Bauland (0072-3908)
Indexed: RASB.
Published by: Statistisches Bundesamt, Gustav-Stresemann-Ring 11, Wiesbaden, 65180, Germany. TEL 49-611-75-1, FAX 49-611-724000, http://www.statistik-bund.de.

690.021 DEU
GERMANY. STATISTISCHES BUNDESAMT. FACHSERIE 4, PRODUZIERENDES GEWERBE, REIHE 5: BAUGEWERBE. (Consists of three subseries: Reihe 5.1: Beschaeftigung, Umsatz und Geraetbestand der Betriebe im Baugewerbe; Reihe 5.2: Beschaeftigung, Umsatz und Investitionen der Unternehmen im Baugewerbe; Reihe 5.3: Kostenstruktur der Unternehmen im Baugewerbe) Text in German. a. price varies. **Document type:** *Government.*
Formerly: Germany (Federal Republic, 1949-) Statistisches Bundesamt. Fachserie 4, Reihe 5: Beschaeftigung, Umsatz, Investitionen und Kosten Struktur im Baugewerbe (0072-1727)
Published by: Statistisches Bundesamt, Gustav-Stresemann-Ring 11, Wiesbaden, 65180, Germany. TEL 49-611-75-1, FAX 49-611-724000, http://www.statistik-bund.de.

690.021 DEU ISSN 0072-1735
HD9715 .G33
GERMANY. STATISTISCHES BUNDESAMT. FACHSERIE 5, BAUTAETIGKEIT UND WOHNUNGEN, REIHE 1: BAUTAETIGKEIT. Text in German. a. **Document type:** *Government.*
Indexed: RASB.
Published by: Statistisches Bundesamt, Gustav-Stresemann-Ring 11, Wiesbaden, 65180, Germany. TEL 49-611-75-1, FAX 49-611-724000, http://www.statistik-bund.de.

690.021 DEU ISSN 0072-1743
HD7339.A3
GERMANY. STATISTISCHES BUNDESAMT. FACHSERIE 5, BAUTAETIGKEIT UND WOHNUNGEN, REIHE 2: BEWILLIGUNGEN IM SOZIALEN WOHNUNGSBAU. Text in German. a. **Document type:** *Government.*
Indexed: RASB.
Published by: Statistisches Bundesamt, Gustav-Stresemann-Ring 11, Wiesbaden, 65180, Germany. TEL 49-611-75-1, FAX 49-611-724000, http://www.statistik-bund.de.

690.021 DEU ISSN 0072-1751
HD9715.G3
GERMANY. STATISTISCHES BUNDESAMT. FACHSERIE 5, BAUTAETIGKEIT UND WOHNUNGEN, REIHE 3: BESTAND AN WOHNUNGEN. Text in German. a. **Document type:** *Government.*
Indexed: RASB.
Published by: Statistisches Bundesamt, Gustav-Stresemann-Ring 11, Wiesbaden, 65180, Germany. TEL 49-611-75-1, FAX 49-611-724000, http://www.statistik-bund.de.

690.021 GBR ISSN 0964-4571
GREAT BRITAIN. DEPARTMENT OF THE ENVIRONMENT. PRICE ADJUSTMENT FORMULAE FOR CONSTRUCTION CONTRACTS: MONTHLY BULLETIN OF INDICES. Text in English. m. GBP 110 (effective 1998). stat. back issues avail. **Document type:** *Government.* **Description:** Enables tenderers to price building work.
Formed by the 1984 merger of: Monthly Bulletin Construction Indices for Use with National Economic Development Office Price Adjustment Formulae (0262-0642); Price Adjustment Formulae for Building Contracts: Bulletin of Indices (0262-0634)
—BLDSC (6612.865100).
Published by: (Great Britain. Department of Environment), Stationery Office, 51 Nine Elms Ln, London, SW8 5DA, United Kingdom. TEL 44-20-7873-0011, FAX 44-20-7873-8247. Circ: 2,800 (paid). **Subscr. to:** PO Box 276, London SW8 5DT, United Kingdom. TEL 44-20-7873-8499, FAX 44-20-7873-8222.

690.021 GBR
HD7333.A3
GREAT BRITAIN. DEPARTMENT OF THE ENVIRONMENT, TRANSPORT AND THE REGIONS. HOUSING AND CONSTRUCTION STATISTICS. Text in English. 1972. 8/yr. GBP 65 (effective 1998). **Document type:** *Government.*
Supersedes: Great Britain. Department of the Environment. Housing and Construction Statistics (0308-9819)
Indexed: RASB.
—CCC.
Published by: Department for Transport, Local Government and the Regions, TSR5 Branch, Zone 2/18, Great Minster House, 76 Marsham St, London, SW1P 4DR, United Kingdom. TEL 44-20-7944-6642, publicity@detr.gov.uk, http://www.dtlr.gov.uk/. Circ: 2,300. **Subscr. to:** H.M.S.O., Publications Centre, PO Box 276, London SW8 5DT, United Kingdom. TEL 44-20-7873-9090, 44-870-600-5522, FAX 44-20-7873-8200, 44-870-600-5533. **Co-sponsor:** Scottish Development Department, Welsh Office.

690.021 GRC ISSN 0256-7970
HD7357.5.A3
GREECE. NATIONAL STATISTICAL SERVICE. BUILDING ACTIVITY STATISTICS. Text in Greek. 1977. a., latest 1994. back issues avail. **Document type:** *Government.*
Published by: National Statistical Service of Greece, Statistical Information and Publications Division/Ethniki Statistiki Ypersia tes Ellados, 14-16 Lykourgou St, Athens, 101 66, Greece. TEL 30-1-3289-397, FAX 30-1-3241-102, http://www.statistics.gr, http://www.statistics.gr/Main_eng.asp.

690.021 GRC
GREECE. NATIONAL STATISTICAL SERVICE. REVISED PRICE INDICES OF NEW BUILDING DWELLINGS CONSTRUCTION (YEAR). Text in English, Greek. 1983. decennial. USD 4. back issues avail. **Document type:** *Government.*
Published by: National Statistical Service of Greece, Statistical Information and Publications Division/Ethniki Statistiki Ypersia tes Ellados, 14-16 Lykourgou St, Athens, 101 66, Greece. TEL 30-1-3289-397, FAX 30-1-3241-102.

690.021 HKG
HONG KONG SPECIAL ADMINISTRATIVE REGION OF CHINA. CENSUS AND STATISTICS DEPARTMENT. AVERAGE WHOLESALE PRICES OF SELECTED BUILDING MATERIALS. Text in Chinese. m. free. stat. back issues avail. **Document type:** *Government.*
Related titles: Online - full content ed.; English ed.
Published by: Census and Statistics Department/Zhengfu Tongjichu, Building, Construction and Real Estate Statistics Section, 15/F Chuang's Hung Hom Plaza, 83 Whuhu St, Hung Hom, Kowloon, Hong Kong. TEL 852-2882-4684, FAX 852-2805-6153, bcre_1@censtatd.gov.hk, http://www.info.gov.hk/censtatd, http://www.statisticalbookstore.gov.hk. **Dist. by:** Government Publications Centre, Low Block, Ground Fl, Queensway Government Offices, 66 Queensway, Hong Kong, Hong Kong. TEL 852-2537-1910, FAX 852-2523-7195.

690.021 HKG
HONG KONG SPECIAL ADMINISTRATIVE REGION OF CHINA. CENSUS AND STATISTICS DEPARTMENT. QUARTERLY REPORT OF EMPLOYMENT AND VACANCIES AT CONSTRUCTION SITES. Text in Chinese, English. 1976. q. HKD 88; HKD 22 newsstand/cover (effective 2002). stat. **Document type:** *Government.* **Description:** Presents up-to-date statistics on number of construction sites, manual workers engaged and vacancies of manual workers at building and construction sites in both private and public sectors. Also contains an analysis of the above statistics with respect to type of site, end-use of construction projects and employment size of site. These statistics provide an indication of labor demand of construction sites, and are very useful for labor market monitoring and economic analysis.
Formerly: Employment, Wages and Material Prices in the Construction Industry
Related titles: Online - full text ed.
Published by: Census and Statistics Department/Zhengfu Tongjichu, Employment Statistics Section, 20/F Wanchai Tower, 12 Harbour Rd, Wan Chai, Hong Kong. TEL 852-2582-5076, FAX 852-2827-2296, es_2@censtatd.gov.hk, http://www.info.gov.hk/censtatd/eng/public/pub_list/ES/qsevcs_index.html, http://www.statisticalbookstore.gov.hk. **Subscr. to:** Information Services Department, Publications Sales Section, 4/F, Murray Bldg, Garden Rd, Hong Kong, Hong Kong. TEL 852-2842-8844, FAX 852-2598-7482, puborder@isd.gcn.gov.hk, http://www.info.gov.hk/isd/book_e.htm. **Dist. by:** Government Publications Centre, Low Block, Ground Fl, Queensway Government Offices, 66 Queensway, Hong Kong, Hong Kong. TEL 852-2537-1910, FAX 852-2523-7195.

690.021 HKG
HONG KONG SPECIAL ADMINISTRATIVE REGION OF CHINA. CENSUS AND STATISTICS DEPARTMENT. REPORT ON ANNUAL SURVEY OF BUILDING, CONSTRUCTION AND REAL ESTATE SECTORS. Text in Chinese, English. 1983. a., latest 1999. HKD 30 newsstand/cover (effective 2001). stat. back issues avail. **Document type:** *Government.* **Description:** Contains statistics on the structure and operating characteristics of the building and civil engineering construction industry; architectural, surveying and project engineering services; real estate development, real estate leasing, brokerage and maintenance management services.
Formerly: Annual Survey of Building, Contruction and Real Estate Sectors
Related titles: Online - full content ed.
Published by: Census and Statistics Department/Zhengfu Tongjichu, Building, Construction and Real Estate Statistics Section, 15/F Chuang's Hung Hom Plaza, 83 Whuhu St, Hung Hom, Kowloon, Hong Kong. TEL 852-2882-4684, FAX 852-2805-6153, bcre_1@censtatd.gov.hk, http://www.info.gov.hk/censtatd, http://www.statisticalbookstore.gov.hk. **Subscr. to:** Information Services Department, Publications Sales Section, 4/F, Murray Bldg, Garden Rd, Hong Kong, Hong Kong. TEL 852-2842-8844, puborder@isd.gcn.gov.hk, http://www.info.gov.hk/isd/book_e.htm. **Dist. by:** Government Publications Centre, Low Block, Ground Fl, Queensway Government Offices, 66 Queensway, Hong Kong, Hong Kong. TEL 852-2537-1910, FAX 852-2523-7195.

690.021 HKG
HONG KONG SPECIAL ADMINISTRATIVE REGION OF CHINA. CENSUS AND STATISTICS DEPARTMENT. REPORT ON THE QUARTERLY SURVEY OF CONSTRUCTION OUTPUT. Text in Chinese, English. 1984. q. HKD 40; HKD 10 newsstand/cover (effective 2001). stat. **Document type:** *Government.* **Description:** Contains statistics on the value of construction work performed by building and civil engineering establishments.
Published by: Census and Statistics Department/Zhengfu Tongjichu, Building, Construction and Real Estate Statistics Section, 15/F Chuang's Hung Hom Plaza, 83 Whuhu St, Hung Hom, Kowloon, Hong Kong. TEL 852-2882-4684, FAX 852-2805-6153, bcre_1@censtatd.gov.hk, http://www.info.gov.hk/censtatd/eng/public/pub_list/BCRE/qsco_index.html, http://www.statisticalbookstore.gov.hk. **Subscr. to:** Information Services Department, Publications Sales Section, 4/F, Murray Bldg, Garden Rd, Hong Kong, Hong Kong. TEL 852-2842-8844, FAX 852-2598-7482, puborder@isd.gcn.gov.hk, http://www.info.gov.hk/isd/book_e.htm. **Dist. by:** Government Publications Centre, Low Block, Ground Fl, Queensway Government Offices, 66 Queensway, Hong Kong, Hong Kong. TEL 852-2537-1910, FAX 852-2523-7195.

690.021 HUN
HUNGARY. KOZPONTI STATISZTIKAI HIVATAL. BERUHAZASI, EPITOIPARI, LAKASEPITESI EVKONYV. Text in Hungarian. a. HUF 438. stat. **Document type:** *Government.*
Former titles: Hungary. Kozponti Statisztikai Hivatal. Lakasstatisztikai Evkonyv (0236-9524); Hungary. Kozponti Statisztikai Hivatal. Lakasepites es Megszunes (0209-5513)
Published by: Kozponti Statisztikai Hivatal, Marketing Oszta'ly, Keleti Karoly utca 5-7, Budapest, 1024, Hungary. TEL 36-1-345-6000, FAX 36-1-345-6699, http://www.ksh.hu.

690.021 CRI
INDICES DE PRECIOS DE LOS INSUMOS BASICOS DE LA INDUSTRIA DE LA CONSTRUCCION. Text in Spanish. m. free. charts; stat. **Document type:** *Government.* **Description:** Reports on the amount of raw materials consumed by the construction industry during the previous month, comparing these figures with those of the preceding months over a one-year period.
Published by: Ministerio de Economia Industria y Comercio, Area de Estadistica y Censos, Apdo 10163, San Jose, 1000, Costa Rica. TEL 506-258-0033, FAX 506-223-0813.

690.021 IRL ISSN 1393-7103
IRELAND. CENTRAL STATISTICS OFFICE. CENSUS OF BUILDING AND CONSTRUCTION. Text in English. 1986. a. charts; stat. **Document type:** *Government.*
Formerly (until 1998): Ireland. Central Statistics Office. Census of Building and Construction. Results for Private Firms with 20 or More Persons Engaged (0791-296X)
Related titles: Online - full text ed.
Published by: Central Statistics Office/Eire, An Phriomh-Oifig Staidrimh, Skehard Rd., Cork, Ireland. TEL 353-21-4535000, FAX 353-21-4535555, information@cso.ie, http://www.cso.ie/releasespublications/pr_construct.htm.

690.021 IRL ISSN 1393-5143
HD4966.C68
IRELAND. CENTRAL STATISTICS OFFICE. EARNINGS AND HOURS WORKED IN CONSTRUCTION. Text in English. 198?. q. charts; stat. **Document type:** *Government.*
Description: Estimates of the average hours worked and average earnings per hour and per week of each of the main categories of employee in private-sector construction firms employing ten or more persons.
Formerly (until 1997): Ireland. Central Statistical Office. Building and Construction: Average Earnings and Hours Worked - For Private Firms with 10 or More Persons Engaged (0791-2951)
Media: Duplicated (not offset). **Related titles:** Online - full text ed.
Published by: Central Statistics Office/Eire, An Phriomh-Oifig Staidrimh, Skehard Rd., Cork, Ireland. TEL 353-21-4535000, FAX 353-21-4535555, information@cso.ie, http://www.cso.ie/releasespublications/pr_construct.htm.

690.021 IRL ISSN 1393-5178
HD5768.I7
IRELAND. CENTRAL STATISTICS OFFICE. INDEX OF EMPLOYMENT IN CONSTRUCTION. Text in English. m. **Document type:** *Government.* **Description:** Measures changes in the employment levels of private construction firms employing five or more persons.
Former titles (until 1997): Ireland. Central Statistics Office. Building and Construction. Monthly Index of Employment in Private Firms with Five or More Persons Engaged. (0791-2943); (until 1985): Ireland. Central Statistics Offive. Building and Construction. Provisional Index of Employment for Private Firms with Five or More Persons Engaged (0791-2935); Ireland. Central Statistics Office. Building Employment Index
Media: Duplicated (not offset). **Related titles:** Online - full text ed.
Published by: Central Statistics Office/Eire, An Phriomh-Oifig Staidrimh, Skehard Rd., Cork, Ireland. TEL 353-21-4535000, FAX 353-21-4535555, information@cso.ie, http://www.cso.ie/releasespublications/pr_construct.htm.

690.021 ISR ISSN 0069-9195
ISRAEL. CENTRAL BUREAU OF STATISTICS. CONSTRUCTION IN ISRAEL/HA-BINUI BE-YISRAEL. Text in Hebrew. 1960. irreg., latest 1997. ILS 30. **Document type:** *Government.*
Related titles: Diskette ed.
Published by: Central Bureau of Statistics, PO Box 13015, Jerusalem, 91130, Israel. TEL 972-2-6553364, FAX 972-2-6521340.

690.021 ITA
ITALY. ISTITUTO NAZIONALE DI STATISTICA. STATISTICHE DELL'ATTIVITA EDILIZIA. Text in Italian. 1955. a.
Supersedes in part: Italy. Istituto Centrale di Statistica. Annuario Statistico dell'Attivita Edilizia e delle Opere Pubbliche (0075-1804)
Published by: Istituto Nazionale di Statistica, Via Cesare Balbo 16, Rome, 00184, Italy. FAX 39-06-46735198.

690.021 ITA
ITALY. ISTITUTO NAZIONALE DI STATISTICA. STATISTICHE DELLE OPERE PUBBLICHE. Text in Italian. 1955. a. **Document type:** *Government.*
Supersedes in part: Italy. Istituto Centrale di Statistica. Annuario Statistico dell'Attivita Edilizia e delle Opere Pubbliche (0075-1804)
Published by: Istituto Nazionale di Statistica, Via Cesare Balbo 16, Rome, 00184, Italy. FAX 39-06-46735198.

690.021 JOR
JORDAN. DEPARTMENT OF STATISTICS. CONSTRUCTION STATISTICS. Text in Arabic, English. 1987. a. USD 15 (effective 2000). **Document type:** *Government.*
Published by: Department of Statistics, P O Box 2015, Amman, Jordan. TEL 962-6-842171, FAX 962-6-833518.

016.693 THA ISSN 0125-1759
TA444
JOURNAL OF FERROCEMENT. Text in English. 1976. q. USD 22 in Asia to individuals; USD 36 elsewhere to individuals; USD 40 in Asia to institutions; USD 70 elsewhere to institutions (effective 2005). adv. bk.rev. abstr.; illus. Index. reprint service avail. from PQC. **Document type:** *Academic/Scholarly.* **Description:** Covers concrete, cement, low-cost composite materials and related topics.
Former titles: N Z F C M A Bulletin; N Z F C M A Newsletter
Related titles: Microfilm ed.: (from PQC).
Indexed: ApMecR, BrCerAb, C&ISA, CRIA, CerAb, CivEngAb, CorrAb, E&CAJ, EMA, EngInd, IAA, ISMEC, M&TEA, MBF, METADEX, RefZh, SolStAb, WAA.
—BLDSC (4984.030000), CISTI, Ei, IE, Infotrieve, ingenta, Linda Hall.
Published by: International Ferrocement Information Center, Asian Institute of Technology, Kluang Luant, PO Box 4, Pathumthani, 12120, Thailand. TEL 66-2-5245864, FAX 66-2-5245870, geoferro@ait.ac.th, http://www.sce.ait.ac.th/ific/journal.asp.

690.021 JPN ISSN 0916-653X
KENSETSU TOKEI GEPPO/MONTHLY OF CONSTRUCTION STATISTICS. Text in Japanese. 1973. m. JPY 980 per issue.
Published by: Kensetsu Bukka Chosakai/Construction Prices Investigation Institute, 11-8 Nihonbashiodenma-cho, Chuo-ku, Tokyo, 103-0011, Japan.

690.021 KWT
KUWAIT. CENTRAL STATISTICAL OFFICE. ANNUAL SURVEY OF ESTABLISHMENTS - CONSTRUCTION/KUWAIT. AL-IDARAH AL-MARKAZIYYAH LIL-IHSA'. AL-BAHTH AL-SANAWI LIL-MANSHAAT - AL-TASHYID WAL-BINA'. Text in Arabic, English. 1983. a., latest 1995. **Document type:** *Government.*
Published by: Central Statistical Office/Al-Idarah al-Markaziyyah lil-Ihsa', P O Box 26188, Safat, 13122, Kuwait. TEL 965-2428200, FAX 965-2430464.

690.021 KWT
KUWAIT. CENTRAL STATISTICAL OFFICE. CONSTRUCTION STATISTICS RESULTS/KUWAIT. AL-IDARAH AL-MARKAZIYYAH LIL-IHSA'. NATA'IJ IHSA'AT AL-TASHYID WAL-BINA'. Text in Arabic, English. 1979. a., latest 1995. **Document type:** *Government.*
Published by: Central Statistical Office/Al-Idarah al-Markaziyyah lil-Ihsa', P O Box 26188, Safat, 13122, Kuwait. TEL 965-2428200, FAX 965-2430464.

690 CHE
LEERWOHNUNGSBESTAND IN DER SCHWEIZ. STICHTAG 1. JUNI (YEAR)/LOGEMENTS VACANTS EN SUISSE DENOMBRES AU 1ER JUIN (YEAR). Text in French, German. 1988. a. CHF 7 (effective 2001). **Document type:** *Government.*
Formerly: Leerwohnungszaehlung 1. Juni (Year)
Published by: Bundesamt fuer Statistik, Espace de l'Europe 10, Neuchatel, 2010, Switzerland. TEL 41-32-7136011, FAX 41-32-7136012, information@bfs.admin.ch, http://www.admin.ch/bfs.

690.021 LBY ISSN 0075-9279
LIBYA. CENSUS AND STATISTICS DEPARTMENT. REPORT OF THE SURVEY OF LICENSED CONSTRUCTION UNITS. Text in Arabic, English. 1967. a. free. **Document type:** *Government.*
Published by: Secretariat of Planning, Census and Statistics Department, P O Box 600, Tripoli, Libya.

690.021 LUX ISSN 1012-6597
LUXEMBOURG. SERVICE CENTRAL DE LA STATISTIQUE ET DES ETUDES ECONOMIQUES. INDICATEURS RAPIDES. SERIE A2: INDICES DES PRIX DE LA CONSTRUCTION. Text in French. s-a. looseleaf. **Document type:** *Government.*
Published by: Service Central de la Statistique et des Etudes Economiques, 13, rue Erasme, Luxembourg, L-1468, Luxembourg. TEL 352-478-4233, FAX 352-464-289, statec.post@statec.etat.lu, http://www.statec.public.lu.

690.021 LUX
LUXEMBOURG. SERVICE CENTRAL DE LA STATISTIQUE ET DES ETUDES ECONOMIQUES. INDICATEURS RAPIDES. SERIE B2: INDICES DE L'ACTIVITE DANS LA CONSTRUCTION. Text in French. m. looseleaf. **Document type:** *Government.*
Published by: Service Central de la Statistique et des Etudes Economiques, 13, rue Erasme, Luxembourg, L-1468, Luxembourg. TEL 352-478-4233, FAX 352-464-289, statec.post@statec.etat.lu, http://www.statec.public.lu.

690.021 LUX ISSN 1012-666X
LUXEMBOURG. SERVICE CENTRAL DE LA STATISTIQUE ET DES ETUDES ECONOMIQUES. INDICATEURS RAPIDES. SERIE G: AUTORISATIONS DE BATIR - BATIMENTS, LOGEMENTS ET VOLUME BATI. Text in French. m. looseleaf. **Document type:** *Government.*
Published by: Service Central de la Statistique et des Etudes Economiques, 13, rue Erasme, Luxembourg, L-1468, Luxembourg. TEL 352-478-4233, FAX 352-464-289, statec.post@statec.etat.lu, http://www.statec.public.lu.

690.021 MAC
MACAO. DIRECCAO DOS SERVICOS DE ESTATISTICA E CENSOS. INDICES E PRECOS DOS MATERIAS DE CONSTRUCAO/MACAO. CENSUS AND STATISTICS DEPARTMENT. INDEXES AND PRICES OF CONSTRUCTION MATERIALS. Text in Chinese, Portuguese. 1992. q. free. **Document type:** *Government.*
Published by: Direccao dos Servicos de Estatistica e Censos, Rua Inacio Baptista, No. 4-6, P.O. Box 3022, Macau. TEL 853-3995311, FAX 853-307825, info@dsec.gov.mo, http://www.dsec.gov.mo/.

690.021 MAC
MACAO. DIRECCAO DOS SERVICOS DE ESTATISTICA E CENSOS. RECENSEAMENTO A CONSTRUCAO/MACAO. CENSUS AND STATISTICS DEPARTMENT. CONSTRUCTION SURVEY. Text in Chinese, Portuguese. 1991. a. **Document type:** *Government.*
Published by: Direccao dos Servicos de Estatistica e Censos, Rua Inacio Baptista, No. 4-6, P.O. Box 3022, Macau. TEL 853-3995311, FAX 853-307825, info@dsec.gov.mo, http://www.dsec.gov.mo/.

690.021 MYS ISSN 0127-8576
MALAYSIA. DEPARTMENT OF STATISTICS. SPECIAL RELEASE 2 - FOR BUILDING WORKS, PENINSULAR MALAYSIA/MALAYSIA. JABATAN PERANGKAAN. SIARAN KHAS 2 - UNTUK KERJA-KERJA PEMBINAAN, SEM. MALAYSIA. Text in English, Malay. 1982. m. MYR 2 per issue (effective 1999). **Document type:** *Government.*
Published by: Department of Statistics/Jabatan Perangkaan, Jalan Cenderasari, Kuala Lumpur, 50514, Malaysia. TEL 60-3-294-4264, FAX 60-3-291-4535, jpmeto@po.jaring.my, http://www.statistics.gov.my.

690.021 MYS
MALAYSIA. DEPARTMENT OF STATISTICS. SPECIAL RELEASE 2 - FOR BUILDING WORKS, SABAH/MALAYSIA. JABATAN PERANGKAAN. SIARAN KHAS 2 - UNTUK KERJA-KERJA PEMBINAAN, SABAH. Text in English, Malay. m. MYR 3 per issue (effective 1999). **Document type:** *Government.*
Published by: Department of Statistics/Jabatan Perangkaan, Jalan Cenderasari, Kuala Lumpur, 50514, Malaysia. TEL 60-3-294-4264, FAX 60-3-291-4535, jpmeto@po.jaring.my, http://www.statistics.gov.my.

690.021 MYS
MALAYSIA. DEPARTMENT OF STATISTICS. SPECIAL RELEASE 2 - FOR BUILDING WORKS, SARAWAK/MALAYSIA. JABATAN PERANGKAAN. SIARAN KHAS 2 - UNTUK KERJA-KERJA PEMBINAAN, SARAWAK. Text in English, Malay. m. MYR 2 per issue (effective 1999). **Document type:** *Government.*
Published by: Department of Statistics/Jabatan Perangkaan, Jalan Cenderasari, Kuala Lumpur, 50514, Malaysia. TEL 60-3-294-4264, FAX 60-3-291-4535, jpmeto@po.jaring.my, http://www.statistics.gov.my.

690.021 USA ISSN 0361-9591
MEANS CONSTRUCTION COST INDEXES. Text in English. q. USD 198. charts; stat.

B

Published by: R.S. Means Company Inc. (Subsidiary of: Reed Construction Data, Associated Construction Publications), 63 Smiths Lane, P O Box 800, Kingston, MA 02364-9988. TEL 800-334-3509, FAX 617-585-7466.

016.69   IND   ISSN 0027-6138
N B O ABSTRACTS. Text in English. 1956. m. per issue exchange basis. bk.rev.; film rev. stat. cum.index.
Media: Duplicated (not offset).
Published by: National Buildings Organisation, G Wing, Nirman Bhavan, Maulana Azad Rd., New Delhi, 110 011, India. Ed. S Protar. Circ: 500.

016.691   IND   ISSN 0972-3420
TA680
N C B ABSTRACTS. Text in English. 1968. q. INR 200 domestic; USD 30 foreign (effective 2005). abstr. **Document type:** Abstract/Index. **Description:** Summarizes recent research in cement, concrete, and other building materials.
Formerly (until 2000): C R I Abstracts (0576-9922)
Published by: National Council for Cement and Building Materials, A-135, Defence Colony, New Delhi, 110 024, India. TEL 91-129-5241963, FAX 91-129-5242100, info@cementresearch.com, http://www.ncbindia.com. Circ: 600.

016.691   IND   ISSN 0972-3439
N C B CURRENT CONTENTS. Text in English. 1969. bi-m. INR 200 domestic; USD 30 foreign (effective 2005). **Document type:** Abstract/Index.
Formerly (until 2000): C R I Current Contents (0970-7891)
Indexed: CRIA.
Published by: National Council for Cement and Building Materials, A-135, Defence Colony, New Delhi, 110 024, India. TEL 91-129-5241963, FAX 91-129-5242100, info@cementresearch.com, http://www.ncbindia.com. Circ: 450.

016.69   USA
N T I S ALERTS: BUILDING INDUSTRY TECHNOLOGY. Text in English. s-m. USD 241.50 in North America; USD 316.25 foreign (effective 2005). index. back issues avail. **Document type:** Newsletter, Bibliography. **Description:** Contains summaries of the latest Government sponsored studies and their findings. Covers titles received by NTIS in architectural design, environmental engineering, building equipment and maintenance, and related fields.
Former titles: Abstract Newsletter: Building Industry Technology (0163-1500); Weekly Abstract Newsletter: Building Industry Technology; Weekly Government Abstracts. Building Industry Technology; Weekly Government Abstracts. Building Technology
Related titles: Microform ed.: (from NTI).
Published by: U.S. Department of Commerce, National Technical Information Service, 5285 Port Royal Rd, Springfield, VA 22161. TEL 703-605-6000, info@ntis.gov, http://www.ntis.gov.

690.021   NCL   ISSN 0984-2594
NEW CALEDONIA. INSTITUT DE LA STATISTIQUE ET DES ETUDES ECONOMIQUES. INDICE ET INDEX DU B T P. Text in French. 1983. m. charts; stat. 8 p./no.; **Document type:** Directory, Government.
Formerly (unitl 198?): New Caledonia. Institut Territorial de la Statistique et des Etudes Economiques. Index Batiment, Indice des Couts des Materiaux de Construction (0758-0347)
Published by: Institut de la Statistique et des Etudes Economiques, BP 823, Noumea, 98845, New Caledonia. TEL 687-283156, FAX 687-288148, dp@itsee.nc, http://www.isee.nc/. Ed. Gerard Baudchon.

690.021   NZL
NEW ZEALAND. STATISTICS NEW ZEALAND. BUILDING CONSENTS ISSUED. Text in English. m. stat. **Document type:** Government. **Description:** Contains details of the number, value and region of both residential and non-residential building consents by building type.
Published by: Statistics New Zealand/Te Tari Tatau, PO Box 2922, Wellington, New Zealand. TEL 64-4-495-4600, FAX 64-4-473-2626, info@stats.govt.nz, http://www.stats.govt.nz.

690.021   NZL
NEW ZEALAND. STATISTICS NEW ZEALAND. VALUE OF BUILDING WORK PUT IN PLACE. Text in English. q. stat. **Document type:** Government. **Description:** Provides summary of the value of construction work done, broken down by building type and region.
Published by: Statistics New Zealand/Te Tari Tatau, PO Box 2922, Wellington, New Zealand. TEL 64-4-495-4600, FAX 64-4-473-2626, info@stats.govt.nz, http://www.stats.govt.nz.

690.021   NOR   ISSN 0550-7162
HA1501
NORWAY. STATISTISK SENTRALBYRAA. BYGGEAREALSTATISTIKK. Text in Norwegian; Text occasionally in Norwegian Nynorsk. 1967. q.
Related titles: Online - full text ed.; ◆ Series of: Norges Offisielle Statistikk. ISSN 0300-5585.
Published by: Statistisk Sentralbyraa/Statistics Norway, Kongensgate 6, Postboks 8131, Dep, Oslo, 0033, Norway. TEL 47-21-090000, FAX 47-21-094973, ssb@ssb.no, http://www.ssb.no/emner/10/09/byggeareal/. Ed. John Egil Bjoerke TEL 47-62-885400.

016.69   SWE   ISSN 0281-7276
NYA BYGGREGLER. Text in Swedish. 1968. 6/yr. SEK 1,190 (effective 2002). bk.rev. reprints avail. **Document type:** Abstract/Index. **Description:** News about building regulations and standards in Sweden.
Formerly (until 1984): Nya Byggnormer (0280-7815)
Published by: BYGGDOK, Institutet foer Byggdokumentation/ Swedish Institute of Building Documentation, Sankt Eriksgatan 46, Stockholm, 11234, Sweden. TEL 47-08-617 74 50, FAX 47-08-617 74 60, info@byggdok.se. Ed. Gerard Lingre. Pub. Arne Winerdal. Circ: 400 (paid).

OSNOVNYE POKAZATELI INVESTITSIONNOI I STROITEL'NOI DEYATEL'NOSTI V ROSSIISKOI FEDERATSII/MAIN INDICATORS OF CONSTRUCTION AND INVESTMENT ACTIVITIES IN THE RUSSIAN FEDERATION. see BUSINESS AND ECONOMICS—Abstracting, Bibliographies, Statistics

690.021   PNG   ISSN 0479-4826
PAPUA NEW GUINEA. NATIONAL STATISTICAL OFFICE. BUILDING STATISTICS. Text in English. 1963. q. PGK 12 domestic; PGK 20 foreign (effective 2005). **Document type:** Government. **Description:** Covers building construction activity in urban areas. Contains the number and values of dwellings and other types of buildings, by ownership, building type and provinces. Also includes tables on the value of repairs, additions and replacements, and employment in the building industry.
Formerly: Building (0033-5339)
Published by: National Statistical Office, Waigani, National Capital District, PO Box 337, Port Moresby, Papua New Guinea. TEL 675-3011200, FAX 675-3251869, http://www.nso.gov.pg/. Ed. Francis K Kasau. Circ: 250.

690.021   GBR   ISSN 0261-6416
PRESS RELEASE - BUILDING SOCIETIES ASSOCIATION. Text in English. 1978. m. GBP 54. **Document type:** Trade. **Description:** Provides all the information supplied in the B.S.A. monthly figures press release on mortgage lending and savings; includes a commentary.
Related titles: Fax ed.: GBP 125.
Published by: Building Societies Association, 3 Savile Row, London, W1X 1AF, United Kingdom. TEL 44-20-7437-0655, FAX 44-20-7734-6416, publications@bsa.org.uk, http://www.bsa.org.uk/. Ed. John Murray.

690.021   GBR
Q P A STATISTICAL YEARBOOK. Text in English. a. GBP 20. **Document type:** Trade.
Published by: Quarry Products Association, 156 Buckingham Palace Rd, London, SW1W 9TR, United Kingdom. TEL 0171-730-8194, FAX 0171-730-4355.

REFERATIVNYI ZHURNAL. EKONOMIKA STROITEL'STVA. see BUSINESS AND ECONOMICS—Abstracting, Bibliographies, Statistics

016.69   RUS   ISSN 0203-5154
REFERATIVNYI ZHURNAL. PROCHNOST' KONSTRUKTSII I MATERYALOV. Text in Russian. 1953. m. USD 376 foreign (effective 2005). **Document type:** Journal, Abstract/Index.
Related titles: CD-ROM ed.; Online - full text ed.
—East View.
Published by: Vserossiiskii Institut Nauchnoi i Tekhnicheskoi Informatsii (VINITI), Ul Usievicha 20, Moscow, 125190, Russian Federation. TEL 7-095-1526441, FAX 7-095-9430060, dir@viniti.ru, http://www.viniti.ru. **Dist. by:** Informnauka Ltd., Ul Usievicha 20, Moscow 125190, Russian Federation. alfimov@viniti.ru.

016.69   DEU
SAMMLUNG BAUAUFSICHTLICH EINGEFUEHRTE TECHNISCHE BAUBESTIMMUNGEN. Abbreviated title: S T B. Text in German. base vol. plus updates 4/yr. EUR 254 (effective 2005). **Document type:** Journal, Trade. **Description:** Provides a reference source for rules and regulations relating to the building and construction industries.
Published by: Beuth Verlag GmbH, Burggrafenstr 6, Berlin, 10787, Germany. TEL 49-30-26012260, FAX 49-30-26011260, postmaster@beuth.de, http://www.beuth.de.

016.69   DEU
SAMMLUNG BAUAUFSICHTLICH EINGEFUEHRTE TECHNISCHE BAUBESTIMMUNGEN CD-ROM. Text in German. base vol. plus updates 4/yr. EUR 280 (effective 2005). **Document type:** Trade.
Media: CD-ROM.
Published by: Beuth Verlag GmbH, Burggrafenstr 6, Berlin, 10787, Germany. TEL 49-30-26012260, FAX 49-30-26011260, postmaster@beuth.de, http://www.beuth.de.

016.69   DEU
SCHRIFTTUM BAUWESEN: GESAMTAUSGABE. Text in German. 1976. m. adv. bk.rev. abstr. **Document type:** Trade.
Former titles: Literaturinformationdienst Schrifttum Bauwesen: Gesamtausgabe (0175-6214); (until 1983): Literaturinformationdienst Schrifttum Bauwesen: Standardprofildienst Gesamtausgabe (0722-060X); (until 1981): Schrifttum Bauwesen: Gesamtausgabe (0343-4494); Schrifttumkartei Bauwesen (0036-6994); Schrifttumkartei Beton (0036-7001)

Published by: (Fraunhofer Informationszentrum Raum und Bau, I R B), Fraunhofer I R B Verlag, Nobelstr 12, Stuttgart, 70569, Germany. TEL 49-711-9702500, FAX 49-711-9702507, irb@irbdirekt.de, http://www.irbdirekt.de.

016.69   CUB
SERVICIO REFERATIVO DE LA CONSTRUCCION✱. Cover title: S R Construccion. Text in Spanish. 1967. bi-m. per issue exchange basis. **Document type:** Abstract/Index.
Formerly: Revista Referativo de la Construccion (0035-0427)
Published by: Comite Estatal de la Construccion, Centro Tecnico Superior de la Construccion, Ministry of Construction, Avda. Carlos M. de Cespedes y Calle 35, Havana, Cuba. Ed. Angel Fernandez Chavez. Circ: 3,000.

690.021   ZAF
SOUTH AFRICA. STATISTICS SOUTH AFRICA. BUILDING PLANS PASSED AND BUILDINGS COMPLETED. Text in English. a., latest 1997. ZAR 30 (effective 2000). **Document type:** Government.
Former titles (until Aug. 1998): South Africa. Central Statistical Service. Building Plans Passed and Buildings Completed; South Africa. Department of Statistics. Building Plans and Buildings Completed
Published by: Statistics South Africa/Statistieke Suid-Afrika, Private Bag X44, Pretoria, 0001, South Africa. TEL 27-12-310-8911, FAX 27-12-310-8500, info@statssa.pwv.gov.za, http://www.statssa.gov.za.

690.021   ZAF
SOUTH AFRICA. STATISTICS SOUTH AFRICA. CENSUS OF CONSTRUCTION. Text in English. triennial. ZAR 20 (effective 2000). **Document type:** Government.
Formerly (until Aug. 1998): South Africa. Central Statistical Service. Census of Construction
Published by: Statistics South Africa/Statistieke Suid-Afrika, Private Bag X44, Pretoria, 0001, South Africa. TEL 27-12-310-8911, FAX 27-12-310-8500, info@statssa.pwv.gov.za, http://www.statssa.gov.za.

SOUTH AFRICA. STATISTICS SOUTH AFRICA. STATISTICAL RELEASE. ACTUAL AND ANTICIPATED CONSTRUCTION EXPENDITURE OF THE PUBLIC SECTOR BY REGION. see BUSINESS AND ECONOMICS—Abstracting, Bibliographies, Statistics

690.021   ZAF
SOUTH AFRICA. STATISTICS SOUTH AFRICA. STATISTICAL RELEASE. BUILDING INDUSTRY ADVISORY COUNCIL CONTRACT PRICE ADJUSTMENT PROVISIONS - WORKGROUP INDICES (HAYLETT). Text in English. m. ZAR 410 per issue (effective 2000). **Document type:** Government.
Formerly (until Aug. 1998): South Africa. Central Statistical Service. Statistical Release. Building Industry Advisory Council Contract Price Adjustment Provisions - Workgroup Indices (Haylett)
Published by: Statistics South Africa/Statistieke Suid-Afrika, Private Bag X44, Pretoria, 0001, South Africa. TEL 27-12-310-8911, FAX 27-12-310-8500, info@statssa.pwv.gov.za, http://www.statssa.gov.za.

690.021   ZAF
SOUTH AFRICA. STATISTICS SOUTH AFRICA. STATISTICAL RELEASE. BUILDING PLANS PASSED AND BUILDINGS COMPLETED. Text in English. a. **Document type:** Government.
Formerly (until Aug. 1998): South Africa. Central Statistical Service. Statistical Release. Building Plans Passed and Buildings Completed
Published by: Statistics South Africa/Statistieke Suid-Afrika, Private Bag X44, Pretoria, 0001, South Africa. TEL 27-12-310-8911, FAX 27-12-310-8500, info@statssa.pwv.gov.za, http://www.statssa.gov.za.

690.021   ZAF
SOUTH AFRICA. STATISTICS SOUTH AFRICA. STATISTICAL RELEASE. BUILDING STATISTICS - PRIVATE SECTOR. Text in English. m. free. **Document type:** Government.
Formerly (until Aug. 1998): South Africa. Central Statistical Service. Statistical Release. Building Statistics - Private Sector; Supersedes: South Africa. Central Statistical Service. Statistical News Release. Building Statistics - Private Sector - Building Plans Passed and Buildings Completed - Summary Statistics - Preliminary
Published by: Statistics South Africa/Statistieke Suid-Afrika, Private Bag X44, Pretoria, 0001, South Africa. TEL 27-12-310-8911, FAX 27-12-310-8500, info@statssa.pwv.gov.za, http://www.statssa.gov.za.

690.021   ZAF
SOUTH AFRICA. STATISTICS SOUTH AFRICA. STATISTICAL RELEASE. CENSUS OF CONSTRUCTION. Text in English. irreg., latest 1994. **Document type:** Government.
Formerly (until Aug. 1998): South Africa. Central Statistical Service. Statistical Release. Census of Construction
Published by: Statistics South Africa/Statistieke Suid-Afrika, Private Bag X44, Pretoria, 0001, South Africa. TEL 27-12-310-8911, FAX 27-12-310-8500, info@statssa.pwv.gov.za, http://www.statssa.gov.za.

690.021 ESP ISSN 0561-4902
SPAIN. MINISTERIO DE LA VIVIENDA. ESTADISTICA DE LA INDUSTRIA DE LA CONSTRUCCION. Text in Spanish. a.
Related titles: Series: Spain. Ministerio de la Vivienda. Documentos Informativos.
Published by: Ministerio de la Vivienda, Secretaria General Tecnica, Madrid, Spain.

016.69 USA
SPEC-DATA PROGRAM INDEX*✶*. Text in English. 1968. a. **Document type:** *Directory, Abstract/Index.* **Description:** Listing of building products and manufacturers in the SPEC-DATA Program.
Former titles: Spec-Data Manu-Spec Program Index; Spec-Data Manu-Spec System Index; Spec-Data Manu-Spec Index
Related titles: Microfiche ed.
Published by: Construction Specifications Institute, 289 - 266 Elmwood Ave, Buffalo, NY 14222. FAX 703-684-0465, csi@csinet.org. Ed. Carol E Duke. Circ: 22,000.

690.021 AUT
STATISTIK AUSTRIA. WOHNEN. Text in German. 1956. a. EUR 27.62. **Document type:** *Government.* **Description:** Presents statistics on the reconstruction of homes and on the stock of occupied dwellings.
Former titles: Austria. Statistisches Zentralamt. Wohnen; Austria. Statistisches Zentralamt. Wohnungsdaten (1013-5626); Austria. Statistisches Zentralamt. Die Wohnbautaetigkeit (0067-2300)
Related titles: ♦ Series of: Beitraege zur Oesterreichischen Statistik. ISSN 0067-2319.
Published by: Statistik Austria, Guglgasse 13, Vienna, W 1110, Austria. TEL 43-1-711280, FAX 43-1-711287728, info@statistik.gv.at, http://www.statistik.at. Circ: 400.

690.021 SGP
SURVEY OF THE CONSTRUCTION INDUSTRY (YEAR). Text in English. 1997. a. SGD 32.50 domestic; USD 45 foreign (effective 2001). **Document type:** *Government.* **Description:** Serves as a useful guide to industry planners and players, as well as researchers undertaking special studies on the local construction industry. Subjects covered are: structure; performance; gross income and expenditure components; small, medium, and large contractors; and foreign and local contractors.
Formerly: Census of the Construction Industry (Year)
Published by: Building and Construction Authority, 5 Maxwell Rd, No 08-00 MND Complex Tower Block, Singapore, 069110, Singapore. TEL 65-3257720, FAX 65-3254800, http://www.bca.gov.sg/.

690.021 SWE ISSN 0085-6991
SWEDEN. STATISTISKA CENTRALBYRAAN. STATISTISKA MEDDELANDEN. SERIE BO, BOSTAEDER OCH BYGGNADER. Text in Swedish; Summaries in English. 1966. irreg. SEK 980.
Published by: Statistiska Centralbyraan/Statistics Sweden, Publishing Unit, Orebro, 70189, Sweden. Circ: 1,375.

690.021 TUR ISSN 1013-5529
HA1911
TURKEY. DEVLET ISTATISTIK ENSTITUSU. BINA INSAAT ISTATISTIKLERI/TURKEY. STATE INSTITUTE OF STATISTICS. BUILDING CONSTRUCTION STATISTICS. Text in English, Turkish. 1969. a., latest covers 1991-1996. USD 60 (effective 1998). **Document type:** *Government.* **Description:** Provides statistical information on building construction and occupancy, including regional data.
Published by: Devlet Istatistik Enstitusu/State Institute of Statistics, Necatibey Caddesi 114, Ankara, 06100, Turkey. TEL 90-312-4185027, FAX 90-312-4170432, yayin@die.gov.tr, http://www.die.gov.tr. Circ: 1,151.

690.021 TUR ISSN 1300-6754
TURKEY. STATE INSTITUTE OF STATISTICS. QUARTERLY BUILDING CONSTRUCTION COST INDEX. Text in English, Turkish. 1992. a. USD 45 (effective 1996). **Document type:** *Government.*
Published by: Devlet Istatistik Enstitusu/State Institute of Statistics, Necatibey Caddesi 114, Ankara, 06100, Turkey. TEL 90-312-4185027, FAX 90-312-4170432.

690.021 USA
U.S. BUREAU OF THE CENSUS. (YEAR) ECONOMIC CENSUS. CONSTRUCTION. (Issued in 3 series: Geographic Area Series, Industry Series, and Special Report Series.) Text in English. 1930. quinquennial. **Document type:** *Government.*
Formerly: Census of Construction Industries: Final Reports (0082-934X)
Related titles: ♦ CD-ROM ed.: Economic Census CD-ROM Series; Online - full text ed.
Published by: U.S. Bureau of the Census (Subsidiary of: U.S. Department of Commerce), Customer Services, Washington, DC 20233. TEL 301-457-4100, FAX 301-457-4714, http://www.census.gov.

690.021 USA ISSN 0257-9073
UNITED NATIONS. DEPARTMENT OF INTERNATIONAL ECONOMIC AND SOCIAL AFFAIRS. STATISTICAL OFFICE. CONSTRUCTION STATISTIC YEARBOOK. Text in English. 1982. a.
Published by: (Department of International Economic and Social Affairs (DIESA), Statistical Office), United Nations Publications, Rm DC2-853, United Nations Bldg, 2 United Nations Plaza, New York, NY 10017. TEL 212-963-8302, 800-253-9646, FAX 212-963-3489, publications@un.org, http://www.un.org/publications, http://www.un.org/Pubs.

BUILDING AND CONSTRUCTION—Carpentry And Woodwork

A I T I M BOLETIN DE INFORMACION TECNICA. see *FORESTS AND FORESTRY—Lumber And Wood*

A W I NEWSBRIEFS. see *ARCHITECTURE*

694 USA ISSN 0895-9005
AMERICAN WOODTURNER. Text in English. 1986. q. USD 25; USD 30 in Canada; USD 40 elsewhere. adv. bk.rev. illus. **Document type:** *Trade.*
Indexed: IHTDI.
Published by: American Association of Woodturners, 75 5th St W., Ste. 222, Saint Paul, MN 55102-7704. TEL 651-484-9094, FAX 651-484-1724, aaa@citilink.com, http://www.RTPnet.org/~aaw. Ed. Dick Burrows. Circ: 7,600 (paid).

AMERICAN WOODWORKER. see *HOW-TO AND DO-IT-YOURSELF*

694 AUS
AUSTRALASIAN FURNISHING INDUSTRY NEWS. Text in English. 10/yr. AUD 60 in Australia & New Zealand; AUD 80 elsewhere. adv. **Document type:** *Trade.* **Description:** Contains editorials on timbers, wood machinery, veneers, laminates, MDF particle boards spray equipment, cabinet hardware and handtools.
Formerly: Australasian Cabinetmaker and Timber Trade Journal; Which incorporated: Australian Shop and Office Fittings Today
Published by: (Cabinetmakers Association of Western Australia), Furnishing Publications Pty. Ltd., Courtyard Monash Homaker Centre, 1207 Prices Hwy, Clayton, VIC 3168, Australia. TEL 61-3-9562-9177, FAX 61-3-9562-9477. Ed., Pub., R&P, Adv. contact Keith Dunn. **Co-sponsors:** Victorian Cabinet Manufacturing Industry Association; Kitchen and Allied Trades Association of Newcastle.

694 AUS ISSN 0818-0261
AUSTRALIAN WOODWORKER. Text in English. 1985. bi-m. AUD 34 domestic; AUD 48 in New Zealand; AUD 55 in Asia & the Pacific; AUD 60 elsewhere (effective 2004). adv. bk.rev. back issues avail. **Document type:** *Magazine, Consumer.* **Description:** Directed toward the professional and serious amateur woodworker.
Published by: Skills Publishing Pty. Ltd., PO Box 514, Hazelbrook, NSW 2779, Australia. TEL 61-2-4759-2844, FAX 61-2-4759-3721, aww@skillspublish.com.au, http://www.skillspublish.com.au/Awwcurrent.htm. Ed. Steven Burrows. Pub., R&P Art Burrows. Adv. contact Peter Douglas. B&W page AUD 1,795, color page AUD 2,495; trim 205 x 275. Circ: 19,210.

694 DEU ISSN 0005-6545
BAUEN MIT HOLZ. Text in German. 1899. m. EUR 112.80 domestic; EUR 138.60 foreign; EUR 12 newsstand/cover (effective 2004). adv. bk.rev. abstr.; bibl.; charts; illus.; pat.; stat.; tr.lit. index. **Document type:** *Magazine, Trade.*
Indexed: RefZh.
—IE, Infotrieve. **CCC.**
Published by: Bruderverlag Albert Bruder GmbH, Bismarckstr 21, Karlsruhe, 76133, Germany. TEL 49-721-913880, FAX 49-721-9138897, info@bruderverlag.de, http://www.rudolf-mueller.de. Ed. Klaus Fritzen. Adv. contact Berthold Hasenfraz. B&W page EUR 2,465, color page EUR 4,280. Circ: 8,808 (paid).

BERGISCHE HANDWERK. see *ART*

BEST WEEKEND WOODWORKING PROJECTS. see *HOW-TO AND DO-IT-YOURSELF*

BETTER HOMES AND GARDENS WOOD. see *HOW-TO AND DO-IT-YOURSELF*

BUILD HOME VICTORIA'S BEST PROJECT & KIT HOMES. see *INTERIOR DESIGN AND DECORATION*

694 GBR ISSN 1467-9108
BUSINESS RATIO. JOINERY MANUFACTURERS. Text in English. 1978. a. GBP 275 (effective 2001). charts; stat. **Document type:** *Trade.*
Former titles (until 1999): Business Ratio Plus: Joinery Manufacturers (1357-1346); (until 1994): Business Ratio Report. Joinery Manufacturers (0261-8591)
Published by: The Prospect Shop Ltd., Field House, 72 Oldfield Rd, Hampton, Middx TW12 2HQ, United Kingdom. TEL 44-20-8461-8730, 44-20-8481-8720, FAX 44-20-8783-1940, info@theprospectshop.co.uk.

694 SWE ISSN 0007-7569
BYGGNADSARBETAREN. Text in Swedish. 1949. 18/yr. SEK 297 (effective 2004). adv. bk.rev.; play rev. charts; illus.; mkt.; stat.; tr.lit. index. **Document type:** *Magazine, Trade.*
Incorporates (1940-1957): Murarnas Fackblad
Related titles: Online - full text ed.
Published by: Svenska Byggnadsarbetarefoerbundet, Hagagatan 2, Stockholm, 10632, Sweden. TEL 46-8-7284900, FAX 46-8-7284980, redaktionen@byggnadsarbetaren.nu, forbundet@byggnads.se, http://www.byggnadsarbetaren.nu, http://www.byggnads.se. Ed., Pub. Kenneth Petterson TEL 46-8-7284970. Adv. contact Andreas Melchert. color page SEK 35,600; trim 185 x 270. Circ: 168,000.

C T B A INFO. see *FORESTS AND FORESTRY—Lumber And Wood*

CANADIAN HOME WORKSHOP; the do-it-yourself magazine. see *HOW-TO AND DO-IT-YOURSELF*

694 USA ISSN 0008-6843
HD6350.C2
THE CARPENTER. Text in English. 1881. bi-m. USD 10 to non-members; free to members (effective 2005). adv. illus. **Document type:** *Magazine, Trade.* **Description:** Directed to people who follow carpentry and its allied trades.
Published by: United Brotherhood of Carpenters and Joiners of America, 50 F St NW, Flr. 3, Washington, DC 20001-1530. TEL 202-546-6206, FAX 202-547-8979, http://www.carpenters.org/carpentermag. Ed., Pub. Andris J Silins. adv.: B&W page USD 13,600, color page USD 17,650; bleed 6.875 x 9.75. Circ: 530,000 (controlled).

694 USA
THE CARPENTER'S FORUM. Text in English. 1990. q. adv. **Document type:** *Magazine, Trade.* **Description:** Provides news and information to union carpenters in Northern Illinois, Southeastern Wisconsin and Northeastern Iowa.
Related titles: Online - full content ed.
Published by: Chicago Regional Council of Carpenters, 12 E Erie St, 10th Fl, Chicago, IL 60611-2796. TEL 312-787-3076, FAX 312-951-1540, gtenner@carpentersunion.org, http://www.carpentersunion.org/. adv.: color page USD 3,600; trim 8.5 x 11. Circ: 46,218.

694 FRA
CHARPENTE - MENUISERIE - PARQUETS; le magazine des metiers du bois. Text in French. 1910. m. (10/yr.). adv. bk.rev. charts; illus. index.
Former titles: Nouveau Journal de Charpente - Menuiserie - Parquets (0029-4675); (until 1959): Nouveau Journal de Charpente - Menuiserie (1141-1945)
Published by: Edial Editions, 126 rue du Temple, Paris, 75003, France. TEL 33-1-44788778, FAX 33-1-44788779, cmp.redaction@edial.fr, http://www.edial.fr. Ed. Serge Van Den Broucke. Pub. Nicole Bergmann. Adv. contact Damien Adrover. Circ: 10,000.

CHIP CHATS. see *ARTS AND HANDICRAFTS*

698.3 USA
CLASSIFIED EXCHANGE. Text in English. m. USD 50; USD 100 foreign (effective 1999). **Document type:** *Trade.*
Published by: Miller Publishing Corporation, 1235 Sycamore View Rd, Memphis, TN 38134. TEL 901-372-8166, FAX 901-373-6180, editor@millerpublishing.com, http://www.millerpublishing.com. Ed. Joanne Avanzi. Circ: 21,000.

694 USA
CONCRETE HOMES. Text in English. 2000. q. USD 15; USD 4.95 newsstand/cover (effective 2001). adv. **Document type:** *Consumer.*
Published by: Publications & Communications, Inc., 505 Cypress Creek Rd, Ste B, Cedar Park, TX 78613-4429. TEL 512-250-9023, FAX 512-331-3900. Ed. Katherine Lagomansino. Pub. Brona Stockton.

694 USA ISSN 0010-6968
CONSTRUCTIONEER; news-photo coverage of construction in New York, Pennsylvania, New Jersey, Delaware. Text in English. 1945. s-m. USD 96 domestic; USD 126 in Canada; USD 166 elsewhere; USD 10 newsstand/cover (effective 2005). adv. charts; illus.; tr.lit. **Document type:** *Magazine, Trade.* **Description:** Covers the construction industry in New York, Pennsylvania, New Jersey and Delaware. Include articles on equipment and product applications and methods of contractors specializing in all forms of heavy construction. Also comprehensive bid and award news, new products, people in the industry, and the latest government-related developments.
Related titles: Online - full text ed.: (from EBSCO Publishing, Gale Group, ProQuest Information & Learning).
Indexed: ConcrAb.
—Linda Hall. **CCC.**

B

Published by: Reed Construction Data, Associated Construction Publications (Subsidiary of: Reed Business Information), 30 Technology Pkwy, Ste 100, Norcross, GA 30092. TEL 800-486-0014, FAX 800-930-3003, acp@reedbusiness.com, http://www.acppubs.com/. Ed. Matthew Phair TEL 914-271-5692. Pub., Adv. contact John Weatherhead. B&W page USD 1,915, color page USD 2,415. Circ: 11,400 (controlled). **Subscr. to:** Reed Business Information, PO Box 9020, Maple Shade, NJ 08052-9020. TEL 303-470-4466, FAX 303-470-4691.

CONTRACTOR'S BUSINESS MANAGEMENT REPORT. see *BUSINESS AND ECONOMICS—Accounting*

698.3 USA ISSN 1055-6729
CREATIVE WOODWORKS AND CRAFTS. Text in English. 1988. 8/yr. USD 29.97 domestic; USD 37.97 in Canada; USD 45.97 elsewhere (effective 2005). adv. illus. reprints avail. **Document type:** *Magazine, Consumer.* **Description:** Concentrates on woodworking - woodcrafting, scrolling, carving, Intarsia painting, plus other techniques.
Published by: All American Crafts, Inc., 7 Waterloo Rd, Stanhope, NJ 07874-2621. TEL 973-347-6900, 800-877-5527, FAX 973-347-6909, editors@allamericancrafts.com, http://www.woodworksandcrafts.com/, http://www.allamericancrafts.com. Ed. Robert Becker. Pub. Jerry Cohen. Circ: 95,000 (paid and controlled). **Dist. by:** Kable, 641 Lexington Ave, New York, NY 10022. TEL 212-705-4600.

694 USA ISSN 1058-403X
HD9773.U4
CUSTOM WOODWORKING BUSINESS. Text in English. 1991. m. USD 50; free to members (effective 2005). adv. **Document type:** *Magazine, Trade.* **Description:** Covers the business, design and technical needs of custom woodworking operations.
Related titles: Online - full text ed.
Published by: Vance Publishing Corp., PO Box 1400, Lincolnshire, IL 60069. TEL 800-343-2016, hmkuhl@aol.com, http://www.vancepublishing.com. Ed. Helen Kuhl. Pub. Harry Urban. adv.: color page USD 6,520. Circ: 56,734 (controlled).

D D S - DAS MAGAZIN FUER MOEBEL UND AUSBAU; Fachzeitschrift fuer die Holz- und Kunststoffverarbeitung. see *INTERIOR DESIGN AND DECORATION—Furniture And House Furnishings*

684.1 ITA ISSN 0393-330X
DATALIGNUM. Text in English, German, Italian. 1982. m. (10/yr.). EUR 52 (effective 2004). adv. bk.rev. **Document type:** *Magazine, Trade.*
Published by: Milla International S.r.l., Via Stefano Ussi, 4, Milan, MI 20125, Italy. TEL 39-2-66101160, FAX 39-2-66100433. Ed. Pietro Stroppa. R&P, Adv. contact Silvia Buchi. Circ: 9,000.

DEREVOOBRABATYVAYUSHCHAYA PROMYSHLENNOST'/ WOOD PROCESSING INDUSTRY. see *FORESTS AND FORESTRY—Lumber And Wood*

DOEHETZELF. see *HOME ECONOMICS*

694 SVK ISSN 0012-6144
CODEN: DRVOAT
DREVO/WOOD. Text in Slovak, Czech; Summaries in English, German, Russian. 1946. m. USD 36. bk.rev. charts; illus.; pat. index. **Document type:** *Academic/Scholarly.* **Description:** Covers wood and wood products application.
Indexed: ABIPC, BioDAb, CIN, CISA, ChemAb, ChemTitl, FPA, ForAb, RefZh.
—CASDDS, CISTI, Linda Hall.
Published by: Statny Drevarsky Vyskumny Ustav/State Forest Products Research Institute, Lamacska cesta 1, Bratislava, 83330, Slovakia. TEL 421-7-59376-132, FAX 421-7-54772-063. Ed. Monika Tothova. R&P Stanislav Florek. adv.: B&W page USD 580. Circ: 3,000.

694 POL ISSN 1644-3985
TA401 CODEN: PITDAL
➤ **DREWNO/WOOD;** prace naukowe, doniesienia, komunikaty. Text in Polish, English; Abstracts and contents page in English. 1954. s-a. PLZ 20 per issue (effective 2003). bibl.; illus. **Document type:** *Academic/Scholarly.* **Description:** Articles presenting the results of research works in the field of wood technology.
Formerly (until 2003): Instytut Technologii Drewna. Prace (0032-6240)
Indexed: AgrAg, AgrLib, ChemAb, FPA, ForAb, RefZh.
—BLDSC (3623.551670), CASDDS, CISTI.
Published by: Instytut Technologii Drewna/Wood Technology Institute, ul Winiarska 1, Poznan, 60654, Poland. TEL 48-61-8492401, FAX 48-61-8224372, office@itd.poznan.pl, http://www.itd.poznan.pl. Ed. Ewa G Ratajczak. Circ: 300.

694.2 USA ISSN 1099-9647
F C I: FLOOR COVERING INSTALLER. Key Title: Floor Covering Installer. Text in English. m. **Document type:** *Trade.* **Description:** Provides floor covering installers and contractors with how-to and management information.
Related titles: Online - full text ed.: (from Florida Center for Library Automation, Gale Group, O C L C Online Computer Library Center, Inc.).
Published by: B N P Media, 22801 Ventura Blvd, Ste 115, Woodland Hills, CA 91364-1222. TEL 818-224-8035, FAX 818-224-8042, http://www.fcimag.com, http://www.bnp.com/.

694 DNK ISSN 1602-4931
FAGBLADET TIB. (Trae-Industri-Byg i Danmark) Text in Danish. 1997. m.
Formerly (until 2001): Trae og Byg (1397-033X); Which was formed by the merger of (1990-1996): Byg og Trae (0906-2653); (1991-1996): Trae (0906-5601)
Published by: Forbundet Trae-Industri-Byg i Danmark, Mimersgade 41, Copenhagen N, 2200, Denmark. TEL 45-35-31-95-99, FAX 45-35-31-94-50, fagbladet@tib.dk, http://www.tib.dk/default.asp?ID=150. Ed. Steen-Lynge Pedersen.

FINE TOOL JOURNAL. see *ANTIQUES*

694 USA ISSN 0361-3453
TT180
FINE WOODWORKING. Text in English. 1975. bi-m. USD 34.95 in US & Canada; USD 41.95 elsewhere (effective 2005). adv. bk.rev. illus. Index. reprints avail. **Document type:** *Magazine, Consumer.* **Description:** Contains articles on making beautiful, practical things out of wood, covering the gamut of furniture styles and projects.
Incorporates (in 1998): Home Furniture (1095-0907); Which superseded (in 1997): Taunton's Home Furniture (1095-1059); (1994-1996): Fine Woodworking's Home Furniture (1076-8327)
Indexed: ASIP, ArtInd, BHA, DAAI, IHTDI, MELSA.
—BLDSC (3927.775000), IE, ingenta.
Published by: Taunton Press, Inc., 63 South Main St, PO Box 5506, Newtown, CT 06470-5506. TEL 203-426-8171, 800-477-8727, FAX 203-426-3434, fw@taunton.com, http://www.taunton.com/finewoodworking/index.asp. Adv. contact Linda Abbett. B&W page USD 11,020, color page USD 15,090; trim 7.63 x 9.75. Circ: 295,000 (paid). **Dist. by:** Eastern News Distributors Inc., 3360 Industrial Rd., Harrisburg, PA 17110-2933; **Dist. in UK by:** Comag, Tavistock Works, Tavistock Rd, W Drayton, Middx UB7 7QX, United Kingdom.

694 USA ISSN 1079-087X
FRAME BUILDING NEWS. Text in English. 1987. 5/yr. USD 22.50 domestic; USD 57.97 in Canada; USD 63.97 elsewhere; free to qualified personnel (effective 2004). adv. **Document type:** *Magazine, Trade.* **Description:** Provides news, features, technical articles, and advertising of special interest to National Frame Builders Association members and the contractors and engineers involved in designing and erecting post-frame and other types of low-rise buildings.
Published by: (National Frame Builders Association), Krause Publications, Inc. (Subsidiary of: F & W Publications, Inc.), 700 E State St, Iola, WI 54990-0001. TEL 715-445-2214, 800-258-0929, FAX 715-445-4087, framebuildingnews@krause.com, info@krause.com, http://www.krause.com/static/construction.htm. Ed. Scott Tappa. Pub. Bill Bright TEL 715-445-2214 ext 308. Adv. contact Randy Graper TEL 715-445-2214 ext 380. B&W page USD 4,230, color page USD 5,621; trim 7.75 x 10.5. Circ: 17,835 (controlled and free).

▼ **FRAMING MONTHLY;** the educations resource for the custom framer. see *ART*

698.3 GBR ISSN 1365-4292
FURNITURE & CABINETMAKING; for the wood craftsman. Text in English. 1996. 10/yr. GBP 39, USD 76; GBP 2.95 newsstand/cover (effective 1999). adv. illus. **Document type:** *Consumer.* **Description:** Covers the craft of furniture and cabinetmaking in all aspects, including projects, features, news and information on tools, materials and equipment.
Published by: (Guild of Master Craftsmen), G M C Publications Ltd., 166 High St, Lewes, E Sussex BN7 1XU, United Kingdom. TEL 44-1273-477374, FAX 44-1273-487692. Ed. Paul Richardson. Pub. Alan Phillips. Adv. contact Linda Grace. Circ: 25,000. **Dist. by:** Comag, Tavistock Works, Tavistock Rd, W Drayton, Middx UB7 7QX, United Kingdom. TEL 44-1895-444055, FAX 44-1895-433602.

694.2 DEU ISSN 0939-4192
FUSSBODENTECHNIK. Text in German. 1952. bi-m. EUR 16 newsstand/cover (effective 2004). adv. bk.rev. abstr.; charts; illus.; pat.; tr.mk. index. **Document type:** *Magazine, Trade.*
Supersedes in part (in 1989): B T H - Fussboden-Zeitung (0933-2855); Which was formerly (until 1987): Fussboden-Zeitung (0342-6181); (until 1975): Teppich- und Fussboden-Zeitung (0342-6149); (until 1972): Fussboden-Zeitung (0016-3236)
Indexed: A&ATA, KES, RAPRA, TTI.
Published by: S N Verlag Michael Steinert, An der Alster 21, Hamburg, 20099, Germany. TEL 49-40-2484540, FAX 49-40-2803788, bth@snfachpresse.de, http://www.sn-verlag.de. adv.: B&W page EUR 2,065, color page EUR 3,180. Circ: 9,536 (paid and controlled).

684.0805 GBR ISSN 0967-0009
GOOD WOODWORKING. Text in English. 1992. 13/yr. GBP 24.99 in United Kingdom; GBP 2.60 newsstand/cover; GBP 46 in Europe; GBP 66 rest of world (effective 2000). adv. bk.rev. charts; illus.; mkt.; tr.lit. **Document type:** *Consumer.* **Description:** Aims to inform readers about what is happening in the woodworking world. Contains projects, news, and product tests.
Related titles: Online - full text ed.
—CCC.
Published by: Future Publishing Ltd., Beauford Court, 30 Monmouth St, Bath, Avon BA1 2BW, United Kingdom. TEL 44-1225-442244, FAX 44-1225-732248, phil.davy@futurenet.co.uk, http://www.futurenet.com, http://www.futurenet.com/futureonline. Ed. Phil Davy. Pub., R&P James Penwell. Adv. contact Nicky Marsh. Circ: 22,000 (paid).

354.8 USA
GOVERNMENT ACCOUNTING AND AUDITING DISCLOSURE MANUAL. Text in English. base vol. plus a. updates. looseleaf. USD 175; USD 245 foreign (effective 1998). Supplement avail. **Document type:** *Trade.* **Description:** Covers all aspects of disclosure and reporting requirements for the financial statements of state and local governments.
Published by: W G & L Financial Reporting & Management Research (Subsidiary of: R I A), 395 Hudson St, New York, NY 10014. TEL 212-367-6300, FAX 212-367-6718. Eds. Allan B Afterman, Rowan H Jones. **Subscr. to:** The Park Square Bldg., 31 St James Ave, Boston, MA 02116-4112. TEL 800-950-1207.

645 ITA
GUIDA: ANNUARIO DEI FORNITORI DELL'INDUSTRIA DEL MOBILE. Text in English, Italian. a. EUR 25 domestic; EUR 50 foreign (effective 2004). **Description:** Lists firms in the woodworking machinery field.
Related titles: CD-ROM ed.
Published by: Industria del Mobile s.r.l., Via Giambologna 21, Milan, 20136, Italy. TEL 39-02-8394780, FAX 39-02-8372547, idm@idm.net, http://www.idm.net.

694 FRA
GUIDE PRATIQUE DE L'ENTREPRENEUR - MENUISERIE✶. Text in French. 6/yr. **Description:** Studies carpentry and joinery.
Published by: Editions S E R I P, c/o Office de Justification de la Diffusion, 40 bd. Malesherbes, Paris, 75008, France. TEL 48-81-91-91, FAX 48-81-81-77. Ed. Regine Heurteur. Circ: 13,000.

H O B - DIE HOLZBEARBEITUNG. see *FORESTS AND FORESTRY—Lumber And Wood*

694 USA ISSN 0897-022X
HARDWOOD FLOORS. Text in English. 1988. 7/yr. USD 36 domestic; USD 60 foreign; free to qualified personnel (effective 2005). adv. **Document type:** *Magazine, Trade.* **Description:** Geared towards floor covering contractors, retailers, builders and interior designers. Includes association news and issues facing the industry.
Published by: (National Wood Flooring Association), Athletic Business Publications, Inc., 4130 Lien Rd, Madison, WI 53704-3602. TEL 608-249-0186, FAX 608-249-1153, editors@hardwoodmag.com, editors@athleticbusiness.com, http://www.nwfa.org/member/mag.aspx. Ed. Kim Whalgren. Pub., Adv. contact Kris Thimmesch. Circ: 24,285 (controlled).

HARDWOOD PLYWOOD & VENEER NEWS. see *FORESTS AND FORESTRY—Lumber And Wood*

694 DEU ISSN 0945-1994
TS840
HOLZ; Zeitschrift fuer Moebelhersteller, Laden- und Innenausbau. Text in German. 1947. bi-m. adv. bk.rev. illus.; tr.lit. index. **Document type:** *Magazine, Trade.*
Former titles (until 1993): Holz-Kunststoff (0933-4580); Holz-Kunststoff-Moebelfertigung (0341-0331); Holz-Kunststoff (0018-375X)
Related titles: Supplement(s): A K Holz.
Indexed: RefZh.
Published by: Holz-Verlag GmbH und Co. KG, Postfach 1260, Mering, 86407, Germany. TEL 49-8233-32761, FAX 49-8233-32762. Ed. Manfred Kittel. adv.: B&W page EUR 2,100, color page EUR 2,700; trim 185 x 270. Circ: 7,922 (paid).

694 DEU ISSN 0723-4856
HOLZBAU - REPORT. Text in German. 1976. m. looseleaf. membership. adv. bk.rev. back issues avail. **Document type:** *Trade.*
Published by: Landesinnungsverband des Bayerischen Zimmererhandwerks, Eisenacher Str 17, Munich, 80804, Germany. TEL 49-89-36085-0, FAX 49-89-36085100. Ed., R&P Wolfgang Strauss. Circ: 4,000. **Subscr. to:** Josef M. Greska GmbH, Morassistr 26, Munich 80469, Germany.
Co-sponsor: Verbaende des Bayerischen Zimmerer- und Holzbaugewerbes.

694 DEU ISSN 1430-788X
HOLZPRAXIS EXKLUSIV; Informationen fuer das Holz- und Kunststoffverarbeitende Handwerk. Text in German. 1987. 3/yr. free. **Document type:** *Magazine, Trade.*
Formerly (until 1995): Holz Praxis (0943-3864)
Published by: Wegra Verlag GmbH, Frankfurterstr 10, Tamm, 71732, Germany. TEL 49-7141-23030, FAX 49-7141-230323, wegra@t-online.de. Circ: 50,000.

HOME IMPROVEMENT RETAILING. see *BUILDING AND CONSTRUCTION—Hardware*

694 NLD ISSN 0923-5574
HET HOUTBLAD; vaktijdschrift voor het houtvak en de bouwsector. Text in Dutch. 8/yr. EUR 60 (effective 2005). adv. bk.rev. tr.lit. back issues avail. **Document type:** *Magazine, Trade.* **Description:** For architects, housing associations, building inspectors, construction firms, wood traders and the furniture industry.
Former titles (until 1989): Vorm en Techniek in Hout (0922-3185); (until 1988): Houttechniek (0166-0195); (until 1979): Houtconstructeur (0922-3274)
—IE, Infotrieve.
Published by: (Centrum Hout/Timber Information Center), Het Houtblad B.V., Postbus 1375, Almere, 1300 BJ, Netherlands. TEL 31-36-5327331, FAX 31-36-5329708, houtblad@centrum-hout.nl, http://www.houtblad.nl. Circ: 16,500.

I C S CLEANING SPECIALIST. (Installation and Cleaning Specialist) see *INTERIOR DESIGN AND DECORATION—Furniture And House Furnishings*

684.1 ITA ISSN 0019-753X
INDUSTRIA DEL MOBILE. Text in Italian, English. 1959. 10/yr. EUR 80 domestic; EUR 160 foreign (effective 2004). adv. illus.
Related titles: CD-ROM ed.; Special ed(s).: Industria del Mobile. Directory.
Published by: Industria del Mobile s.r.l., Via Giambologna 21, Milan, 20136, Italy. TEL 39-02-8394780, FAX 39-02-8372547, idm@idm.net, http://www.idm.net. Circ: 6,000.

694 GBR
INDUSTRIAL WOODWORKER. Text in English. 1991. m. GBP 25; GBP 60 foreign. adv. software rev. illus.; tr.lit. back issues avail. **Document type:** *Trade.* **Description:** Aimed at professional trade woodworkers, joiners, furniture manufacturers, door and window manufacturers, cabinet makers, etc.
Published by: Willowe Magazines Ltd., Whitton Ct, Leintwardine, Nr. Craven Arms, Shrops SY7 CL5, United Kingdom. TEL 44-1797-227300, FAX 44-1797-222445. Ed. John Emslie. Pub., Adv. contact Bill Lowe. color page GBP 995; trim 270 x 360. Circ: 13,000 (controlled).

694 CHE
INDUSTRIEL SUR BOIS. Text in French. 1923. m. CHF 60 (effective 2001). adv. 64 p./no. 3 cols./p.; back issues avail. **Document type:** *Journal, Trade.*
Published by: Federation Romande des Entreprises de Menuiserie, Ebenisterie, Charpentes, des Fabriques de Meubles et des Parquetereurs, Case Postale 193, Le Mont-sur-Lausanne, CH-1052, Switzerland. TEL 41-21-6521553, FAX 41-21-6521565, frm@frm-bois-romand.ch, http://www.frm-bois-romand.ch. Ed. Daniel Vaucher. Adv. contact Corinne Meylan. B&W page CHF 1,320, color page CHF 2,850; trim 185 x 262. Circ: 2,600.

694 GBR
INSTITUTE OF CARPENTERS JOURNAL. Text in English. 1900. q. membership. bk.rev. back issues avail. **Document type:** *Trade.* **Description:** Reports on membership and industry news.
Published by: Institute of Carpenters, 12 Valley Gardens, Downend, Bristol, Glos BS16 6SF, United Kingdom. TEL 44-115-949-0641, FAX 44-115-949-1664. Ed. David R Winson. Circ: 2,800 (controlled).

694 DEU
INTERN (TAUBERBISCHOFSHEIM). Text in English, French, German, Italian, Spanish. s-a. **Document type:** *Consumer.*
Published by: Michael Weinig AG, Weinigstr 2-4, Tauberbischofsheim, 97941, Germany. TEL 49-9341-860, weinig@t-online.de, http://www.weinig.com. Ed., R&P Rudi Walz. Circ: 3,000.

INTERNATIONAL DIRECTORY OF WOODWORKING EQUIPMENT AND TOOLS IMPORTERS. see *BUSINESS AND ECONOMICS—Trade And Industrial Directories*

694 AUT ISSN 0020-9422
HD9750.1
INTERNATIONALER HOLZMARKT; Holztechnische Weltschau. Text in German. 1909. 6/yr. EUR 88; EUR 25 newsstand/cover (effective 2005). adv. mkt. **Document type:** *Magazine, Trade.*
Incorporates (1958-1999): Holz im Handwerk (0018-3776)
Indexed: KES.
—CINDOC.
Published by: Verlag Dr. A. Schendl GmbH & Co. KG, Geblergasse 95, Vienna, 1170, Austria. TEL 43-1-484178525, FAX 43-1-4841785966, holzmarkt@schendl.at, http://www.internationalerholzmarkt.at. Ed. Marianne Schroetter. Adv. contact Renate Storz. B&W page EUR 2,226, color page EUR 2,698; trim 220 x 290. Circ: 5,275 (paid and controlled).

▼ **JAERN, BYGG, FAERG/BUILDING MATERIAL AND HARDWARE TRADE JOURNAL.** see *BUSINESS AND ECONOMICS—Marketing And Purchasing*

691 USA
JOBSITE - TOOLS AND MATERIALS FOR THE FRAMING AND DRYWALL PROFESSIONAL. Text in English. 1999. bi-m. adv. **Document type:** *Magazine, Trade.*
Formerly: Jobsite (Interior & Exterior Wall Edition) (1526-5021)
Published by: Trades Publishing, Inc, 24 Arnett Ave, 200, Lambertville, NJ 08530. TEL 609-397-5601, FAX 609-397-5640, editor@jobsitemagazine.com, http://www.jobsitemagazine.com/frd.html. Ed. David Cane. Pub. Troy Bausinger. Circ: 60,000.

684 USA ISSN 1049-9547
JOINERS' QUARTERLY; the journal of timber framing and traditional building. Text in English. 1983. q. USD 24 domestic; USD 28 in Canada; USD 35 elsewhere; USD 6.50 newsstand/cover (effective 2000). adv. bk.rev.; software rev. charts; illus.; tr.lit. cum.index: 1994-1997, no. 3. back issues avail. **Document type:** *Trade.* **Description:** Deals with timber frame construction and design, log building, scribe-rule, architecture, sustainable building, historical building techniques and natural house building, and straw, clay, thatch, strawbale, and forestry practices.
Published by: Fox Maple Press, Inc., Coin Hill Rd, PO Box 249, Brownfield, ME 04010. TEL 207-935-3720, FAX 207-935-4575, foxmaple@nxi.com, http://www.nxi.com, http://www.joinersquaterly.com. Ed., Pub., R&P, Adv. contact Steve Chappell. B&W page USD 680, color page USD 1,280; trim 10.88 x 8.13. Circ: 6,000 (paid).

JOURNAL OF AMERICAN ORGANBUILDING. see *MUSIC*

KEY NOTE MARKET REPORT: TIMBER & JOINERY. see *FORESTS AND FORESTRY—Lumber And Wood*

IL LEGNO. see *FORESTS AND FORESTRY—Lumber And Wood*

643.1 649 USA
LOG HOME LIVING ANNUAL BUYER'S GUIDE. Text in English. 1984. a. USD 9.95 newsstand/cover (effective 2002). adv. **Document type:** *Directory, Consumer.* **Description:** Comprehensive guide to building and maintaining a log home. Includes six industry directories: Yellow pages of the Log Home Industry; Log Home Floor Plan; Products & Services Guide; Producers Directory; Suppliers Marketplace; Log Home Bookstore.
Related titles: ♦ Supplement to: Log Home Living. ISSN 1041-830X.
Published by: Home Buyer Publications, Inc. (Subsidiary of: Active Interest Media), 4200 T Lafayette Center Dr, Chantilly, VA 20151. TEL 703-222-9411, FAX 703-222-3209, http://www.loghomeliving.com, http://www.homebuyerpubs.com/. Ed. Peter Lobred. Pub. Tom Kupferer. Adv. contact Julie Puckett. B&W page USD 7,106.

694 FRA ISSN 1766-4381
MAISON BRICOLAGE ET DECORATION. Text in French. 1985. m. adv. **Document type:** *Magazine, Consumer.*
Former titles (until 2004): Maison Bricolage (1625-6778); (until 2000): Idees Maison Bricolages (1292-6744); (until 1999): Maison Bricolages (0769-3702)
Published by: Publications Bonnier Hachette (Subsidiary of: Hachette Filipacchi Medias S.A.), 20 Rue de Billancourt, Boulogne-Billancourt, 92100, France. Ed. Philippe Loison. Pub., Adv. contact Daniel Bonnier. Circ: 120,704.

694.2 BEL
MENUISERIE; revue professionelle pour tous les specialistes de la menuiserie bois, PVC et aluminium. Text in French. 1994. 11/yr. (plus 20 e-mails). EUR 68 (effective 2005). adv. illus.; tr.lit. **Document type:** *Trade.* **Description:** Covers all new-product, marketing, and construction aspects of working with wood, along with vinyl and aluminum products.
Related titles: ♦ Dutch ed.: Schrijnwerk.
Published by: Professional Media Group, Torhoutsesteenweg 226 bus 2/6, Zedelgem, B-8210, Belgium. TEL 32-50-240404, FAX 32-50-240445, info@pmgroup.be, http://www.menuis.be/?lang=f, http://www.pmgroup.be. Ed. Patrick Vermaut. adv.: color page EUR 2,575; trim 297 x 210. Circ: 15,106 (controlled).

NATIONAL ASSOCIATION OF HOME AND WORKSHOP WRITERS NEWSLETTER. see *JOURNALISM*

694 FRA
OFFICIEL DU BOIS (EDITION ROUGE). Text in French. 1930. w. adv.
Formerly: Bois National (Edition Rouge)
Published by: Societe "le Bois National", 3 rue Claude Odde, St Etienne, Cedex 1 42007, France. TEL 77-74-39-99, FAX 77-93-11-26, TELEX 300 818.

698.3 USA
PALLET DIGEST. Text in English. bi-m.
Published by: Dixie Publications, 257 N Main St, Box 489, Wadley, GA 30477. TEL 912-252-5237, FAX 912-252-1140. Ed. Jack D Smith.

694 USA
PANEL WORLD BUYERS' GUIDE. Text in English. a. USD 10 (effective 2001). **Document type:** *Directory, Trade.* **Description:** Lists manufacturers, equipment suppliers, products and services of the panel and veneer industry.
Related titles: CD-ROM ed.: USD 150 (effective 2001).
Published by: Hatton-Brown Publishers, Inc., 225 Hanrick St, Montgomery, AL 36104. TEL 334-834-1170, FAX 334-834-4525, mail@panelworldmag.com, mail@hattonbrown.com, http://www.panelworldmag.com, http://www.hattonbrown.com/.

694 NLD ISSN 1385-2019
PARKETBLAD. Text in Dutch. 1995. m. EUR 61 domestic; EUR 66 in Belgium; EUR 83 elsewhere (effective 2005). adv. illus. back issues avail. **Document type:** *Journal, Trade.* **Description:** Covers parquet business.
Published by: Uitgeverij Lakerveld BV, Turfschipper 53, Postbus 160, Wateringen, 2290 AD, Netherlands. TEL 31-174-315000, FAX 31-174-315001, uitgeverij@lakerveld.nl, http://www.parketblad.nl, http://www.lakerveld.nl. Ed. Gerben J Sas. Pub. Ad van Gaalen. adv.: B&W page EUR 1,010, color page EUR 2,100; trim 185 x 268. Circ: 2,119.

694 USA ISSN 0884-8823
TT180
POPULAR WOODWORKING. Text in English. 1981. 7/yr. USD 19.96 domestic; USD 35.96 foreign; USD 4.99 newsstand/cover (effective 2005). adv. bk.rev. illus. back issues avail. **Document type:** *Magazine, Consumer.*
Former titles (until 1985): Popular Woodworker (0743-6203); (until 1984): Pacific Woodworker (0277-576X)
Indexed: IHTDI, MASUSE.
Published by: F & W Publications, Inc., 4700 E Galbraith Rd, Cincinnati, OH 45236. TEL 513-531-2690, FAX 513-891-7196, popwood@fwpubs.com, http://www.popwood.com/, http://www.fwpublications.com. Ed., Pub. Steve Shanesy. adv.: B&W page USD 5,340. Circ: 190,000 (paid). **Dist. in UK by:** Seymour Distribution Ltd, 86 Newman St, London W1T 3EX, United Kingdom. TEL 44-20-73968000, FAX 44-20-73968002.

694 USA
POPULAR WOODWORKING: TOOL BUYING GUIDE (YEAR). Text in English. 2000. a. USD 5.99 newsstand/cover (effective 2001). adv. **Document type:** *Consumer.*
Published by: F & W Publications, Inc., 4700 E. Galbraith Rd., Cincinnati, OH 45236-6708. TEL 513-531-2222, http://www.popwood.com. Ed. Steve Shanesy.

694 GBR ISSN 0032-6488
CODEN: PRPSDA
PRACTICAL WOODWORKING. Text in English. 1966. m. GBP 12 domestic; GBP 34.50 in Europe; GBP 36.50 in United States; GBP 40 elsewhere; GBP 2.75 newsstand/cover (effective 2004). adv. bk.rev. illus. index. **Document type:** *Magazine, Consumer.*
Indexed: GdIns, Pinpoint, WBA, WMB.
—**CCC.**
Published by: Highbury Leisure Publishing Ltd (Subsidiary of: Highbury House Communications PLC), Berwick House, 8-10 Knoll Rise, Orpington, Kent BR6 0EL, United Kingdom. TEL 44-1322-660070, FAX 44-1322-616319, mark.chisholm@nexusmedia.com, http://www.hhc.co.uk/practicalwood. Ed. Mark Chisholm. Pub. Tony Debell. R&P, Adv. contact Reza Zaman. color page GBP 835; trim 215 x 295. Circ: 26,636. **Dist. by:** Comag, Tavistock Works, Tavistock Rd, W Drayton, Middx UB7 7QX, United Kingdom. TEL 44-1895-433600, FAX 44-189-543-3606.

694 GBR
PROFESSIONAL BUILDER; small builders and contractors business magazine. Text in English. 1972. m. (11/yr.). GBP 30; GBP 35 in Ireland; GBP 39 elsewhere (effective 1999). adv. bk.rev. illus. **Document type:** *Trade.*
Former titles: Professional Builder and House Remodeller (0263-7936); B J - Builder's Journal (0260-5120); Builder and Decorator
Published by: Hamerville Magazines Ltd., Regal House, Regal Way, Watford, Herts WD2 4YJ, United Kingdom. TEL 44-1923-237799, FAX 44-1923-246901. Ed. Terry Smith. Pub., R&P Brian Shannon. Adv. contact Andy Costin. Circ: 105,050.

PROFESSIONAL REFINISHING; the magazine of the wood restoration industry. see *INTERIOR DESIGN AND DECORATION—Furniture And House Furnishings*

634.9 674 FIN ISSN 0355-953X
PUUMIES. Text in Finnish. 1955. 10/yr. EUR 47 domestic; EUR 53 foreign (effective 2005). adv. bk.rev. **Document type:** *Magazine, Trade.*
Published by: Puumiesten Liitto ry/Association of Finnish Woodworking Technicians and Engineers, Keskustie 20 D, Jyvaeskylae, 40100, Finland. TEL 358-14-215636, FAX 358-14-215652, toimitus@puumies.fi, http://www.puumies.fi. Ed. Ritva Varis. adv.: B&W page EUR 1,450, color page EUR 2,300; 186 x 270. Circ: 3,050.

B

▼ new title ➤ refereed ✶ unverified ♦ full entry avail.

RENOVATOR'S SUPPLY. see *INTERIOR DESIGN AND DECORATION*

698.3 GBR ISSN 1368-4752
THE ROUTER. Text in English. 1997. 10/yr. GBP 19.95, USD 39.95; GBP 2.95 newsstand/cover (effective 1998). adv. **Document type:** *Consumer.* **Description:** Includes projects, features, news and information on tools, materials and equipment.
Published by: (Guild of Master Craftsmen), G M C Publications Ltd., 166 High St, Lewes, E Sussex BN7 1XU, United Kingdom. TEL 44-1273-477374, FAX 44-1273-478606. Ed. Alan Goodsell. Pub. Alan Phillips. Adv. contact Linda Grace. Circ: 25,000. **Dist. by:** Comag, Tavistock Works, Tavistock Rd, W Drayton, Middx UB7 7QX, United Kingdom. TEL 44-1895-433055, FAX 44-1895-433602.

698.3 GBR ISSN 0968-266X
ROUTING; using the world's most versatile power tool. Text in English. 1993. q. GBP 17.70 domestic; GBP 27.48 foreign; GBP 2.95 newsstand/cover. **Document type:** *Trade.* **Description:** Discusses woodworking techniques and projects using a router for readers of all abilities.
Published by: Nexus Media Ltd. (Subsidiary of: Highbury House Communications PLC), Nexus House, Azalea Dr, Swanley, Kent BR8 8HU, United Kingdom. TEL 44-1322-660070, FAX 44-1322-667633. Ed. Neil Mead. **Subscr. in N. America to:** Wise Owl Worldwide Publications, 5674 El Camino Real., Ste. D, Carlsbad, CA 92008-7130. TEL 310-375-6258; **Subscr. to:** Tower House, Tower House, Sovereign Park, Market Harborough, Leics LE16 9EF, United Kingdom. TEL 44-1858-435322. **Dist. by:** Comag, Tavistock Works, Tavistock Rd, W Drayton, Middx UB7 7QX, United Kingdom. TEL 44-1895-444055, FAX 44-1895-433602.

S I A; skogsindustriarbetaren. see *FORESTS AND FORESTRY—Lumber And Wood*

694.2 BEL
SCHRIJNWERK; vakblad voor wie profesioneel actief is in hout-, PVC- en aluminiumschrijnwerk. Text in Dutch. 1994. 11/yr. (plus 20 e-mails). EUR 68 (effective 2005). adv. illus.; tr.lit. **Document type:** *Trade.* **Description:** Covers all new-product, marketing, and construction aspects of working with wood, along with vinyl and aluminum products.
Related titles: ♦ French ed.: Menuiserie.
Published by: Professional Media Group, Torhoutsesteenweg 226 bus 2/6, Zedelgem, B-8210, Belgium. TEL 32-50-240404, FAX 32-50-240445, info@pmgroup.be, http://www.swerk.be/?lang=n, http://www.pmgroup.be. Ed. Yan Hoffman. adv.: color page EUR 2,575; trim 297 x 210. Circ: 15,400 (controlled).

SCHWEIZER HOLZ-BOERSE; Fachblatt fuer alle Gebiete der Holzwirtschaft. see *FORESTS AND FORESTRY*

694 CHE
SCHWEIZER HOLZBAU. Text in German. 1934. m. CHF 85 (effective 2000). adv. illus. **Document type:** *Trade.*
Formerly (until 1982): Holzbau (0018-3814)
Indexed: CISA.
Published by: Hoch- und Tiefbau Verlag AG, Postfach 7039, Zuerich, 8023, Switzerland. TEL 0258-8333, FAX 0261-0324. Ed. Walter Bogusch. Adv. contact Alexander Eugster. Circ: 8,100.

694 CHE ISSN 0036-7753
SCHWEIZERISCHE SCHREINERZEITUNG. Text in French. 1889. w. CHF 128 to non-members. adv. bk.rev. abstr.; mkt.; illus.; stat.; tr.lit. index. **Document type:** *Trade.*
Indexed: CISA.
Published by: Verband Schweizerischer Schreinermeister und Moebelfabrikanten, Schmelzbergstr 56, Zuerich, 8044, Switzerland. TEL 01-2678100, FAX 01-2878152. Ed. Alois Bohnet. Circ: 10,400.

694 GBR ISSN 1368-2830
SELFBUILD; build and design a home of your own. Variant title: SelfBuild & Design. Text in English. 1997. m. GBP 33 domestic; GBP 44.50 foreign; GBP 2.75 newsstand/cover (effective 2000). adv. illus. **Document type:** *Consumer.* **Description:** All aspects of designing and building your own home.
Published by: Waterways World Ltd., The Well House, High St, Burton-on-Trent, Staffs DE14 1JQ, United Kingdom. TEL 44-1283-742950, FAX 44-1283-742966, ww@wellhouse.easynet.co.uk. Ed. Ross Stokes. Adv. contact David Melville. Circ: 20,000 (paid). **Dist. by:** Comag, Tavistock Works, Tavistock Rd, W Drayton, Middx UB7 7QX, United Kingdom. TEL 44-1895-444055, FAX 44-1895-433602.

694 ITA ISSN 0392-8063
SERRAMENTI E FALEGNAMERIA. Text in Italian. 1979. m. (9/yr.). adv. **Document type:** *Magazine, Trade.*
Related titles: ♦ Supplement(s): Rapporto Congiunturale.
Published by: Alberto Greco Editore, Viale Espinasse 141, Milan, MI 20156, Italy. TEL 39-02-300391, FAX 39-02-30039300, age@gruppodg.com, http://www.ageditore.com. adv.: page EUR 3,200; 210 x 297. Circ: 8,500.

694 USA ISSN 1062-9696
TT180
SHOPNOTES. Text in English. 1992. bi-m. USD 24 domestic; CND 45 in Canada; USD 34 elsewhere (effective 2005). illus. reprints avail. **Document type:** *Consumer.* **Description:** For woodworking hobbyists.
Indexed: IHTDI.
Published by: August Home Publishing Co., 2200 Grand Ave, Des Moines, IA 50312-5306. TEL 515-282-7000, FAX 515-883-1695, shopnotes@shopnotes.com, http://www.augusthome.com. Ed. Tim Robertson. Pub. Donald B Peschke. R&P Julia Fish. Circ: 165,000.

SIGNS CANADA. see *ART—Computer Applications*

THIS OLD HOUSE GUIDE TO INTERIORS. see *INTERIOR DESIGN AND DECORATION*

694 NLD ISSN 0040-7933
TIMMERFABRIKANT. Text in Dutch. 1951. m. adv. illus.; stat. **Document type:** *Trade.*
Published by: (Nederlandse Bond van Timmerfabrikanten), Wijlhuizen Vaktijdschriften, Wilhelminasingel 4, Nijmegen, 6524 AK, Netherlands. TEL 31-24-3605253, FAX 31-24-3605210. Ed. Peter Vorstenbosch. Pub., R&P Yvo Wijlhuizen. Adv. contact Erwin Dewolff. Circ: 1,400 (paid).

694 AUT
TISCHLER JOURNAL. Text in German. 1962. m. EUR 70 domestic; EUR 113 foreign (effective 2005). adv. bk.rev. illus. **Document type:** *Magazine, Trade.*
Formerly: Der Tischler (0040-8131)
Published by: (Bundesinnung und Landesinnung der Tischler Oesterreichs), Oesterreichischer Wirtschaftsverlag GmbH (Subsidiary of: Sueddeutscher Verlag GmbH), Wiedner Hauptstr 120-124, Vienna, W 1051, Austria. TEL 43-1-546640, FAX 43-1-54664406, office@wirtschaftsverlag.at, http://www.wirtschaftsverlag.at. Ed. Harald Siebenbuerger. Adv. contact Michael Stich. B&W page EUR 2,351, color page EUR 3,359; trim 185 x 255. Circ: 7,525 (paid and controlled).

694 USA
TOOLS & SHOPS. Variant title: Fine Woodworking's Tools & Shops. Text in English. 2001. a. USD 6.95 newsstand/cover; USD 7.95 newsstand/cover in Canada (effective 2002). adv. **Document type:** *Magazine, Consumer.* **Description:** Contains articles and features on woodworking tools and shops.
Published by: Taunton Press, Inc., 63 South Main St, PO Box 5506, Newtown, CT 06470-5506. TEL 203-426-8171, 800-477-8727, FAX 203-426-3434, http://www.taunton.com. Ed. Timothy D Schreiner.

694 GBR ISSN 0954-0156
TRADITIONAL WOODWORKING; the magazine for all woodworkers. Text in English. 1988. m. GBP 31.20 in United Kingdom; GBP 42.50 in Europe; GBP 53.80 elsewhere; GBP 2.60 newsstand/cover (effective 2000). adv. bk.rev. tr.lit. index. back issues avail. **Document type:** *Consumer.* **Description:** Discusses techniques and features projects for the amateur and professional woodworker. Reviews woodworking tools.
Published by: Waterways World Ltd., The Well House, High St, Burton-on-Trent, Staffs DE14 1JQ, United Kingdom. TEL 44-1283-742950, FAX 44-1283-742966, ww@wellhouse.easynet.co.uk. Ed. Kidd Alan. Pub. Peter Johns. Adv. contact Rod Straw. Circ: 20,000 (paid). **Dist. by:** Comag, Tavistock Works, Tavistock Rd, W Drayton, Middx UB7 7QX, United Kingdom. TEL 44-1895-444055, FAX 44-1293-415009.

694 DNK ISSN 0041-0624
TRAE NYT. Text in Danish. 1966. 11/yr. DKK 234 (effective 2004). adv. bk.rev. charts; illus. **Document type:** *Magazine, Trade.* **Description:** Provides information to members of the wood-working industry through articles about new products in wood-working machines, workshop methods, storage and internal transport, semimanufactures and accessories for the furniture industry.
Related titles: Online - full text ed.
Published by: TechMedia A/S, Naverland 35, Glostrup, 2600, Denmark. TEL 45-43-242628, FAX 45-43-242626, info@techmedia.dk, http://www.techmedia.dk. Ed. Peter Friis TEL 45-43-242616. Adv. contact Finn Anker Jensen TEL 45-43-242647. B&W page DKK 17,900, color page DKK 22,400; trim 175 x 257. Circ: 6,229 (controlled).

694 674 DNK ISSN 0107-9360
TRAE NYTS LEVERANDOERREGISTER. Text in Danish. 1976. a. adv. **Document type:** *Directory, Trade.*
Published by: TechMedia A/S, Naverland 35, Glostrup, 2600, Denmark. TEL 45-43-242628, FAX 45-43-242626, info@techmedia.dk, http://www.techmedia.dk. Ed. Erik Kuhlman. Circ: 15,521.

698.3 ITA ISSN 0393-4373
VERNICIATURA DEL LEGNO. Short title: V d L. Text in Italian. 1982. bi-m. EUR 50 domestic; EUR 100 foreign (effective 2005). adv. bk.rev. abstr.; tr.lit. index. **Document type:** *Magazine, Trade.*
Indexed: RefZh, WSCA.
Published by: Rivista del Colore SpA, Palazzo Larice Edificio M, Via Torri Bianche 3, Vimercate, MI 20059, Italy. TEL 39-039-629041, FAX 39-039-62904208, info@larivistadelcolore.com, http://www.larivistadelcolore.com. Ed., R&P Danilo O Malavolti. Adv. contact Francesco Stucchi. Circ: 4,100.

694 USA
VESTERHEIM WOODWORKING NEWSLETTER; newsletter for woodworkers in the Norwegian-American tradition. Text in English. q. USD 35 in United States; USD 39 in Canada & Mexico; USD 40 elsewhere (effective 2001). bk.rev. back issues avail. **Document type:** *Newsletter.* **Description:** For woodcarvers in any of several Norwegian woodcarving and knife-making traditions. Includes history, instruction, events, awards, personal experiences, and information on classes.
Published by: Vesterheim Norwegian-American Museum, PO Box 379, Decorah, IA 52101. TEL 319-382-9681, FAX 319-382-8828, vesterheim@vesterheim.org, http://www.vesterheim.org. Ed. Bob Mischka. R&P Charles Langton.

VICTORIAN HOMES. see *INTERIOR DESIGN AND DECORATION*

694 GBR ISSN 0042-5842
VIEWPOINT (LONDON, 1970). Text in English. 1970. q. free. adv. bk.rev. **Document type:** *Trade.*
Incorporates: U C A T T Journal; Woodworkers and Painters Journal (0049-7940)
Published by: Union of Construction Allied Trades and Technicians, UCATT House, 177 Abbeville Rd, London, SW4 9RL, United Kingdom. Ed. A Vedeille. Circ: 80,000.

694 NLD ISSN 1381-9763
VLOER TECHNISCH MAGAZINE. Text in Dutch. 1985. bi-m. EUR 25; EUR 5.50 per issue (effective 2003).
Former titles (until 1992): VTM (0926-0455); (until 1989): Vloer Info (0925-2703)
—Infotrieve.
Published by: Wijlhuizen Vaktijdschriften, Wilhelminasingel 4, Nijmegen, 6524 AK, Netherlands. TEL 31-24-3605253, FAX 31-24-3605210, info@wijlhuizen.com. Ed. Marcel Debets.

698.3 USA ISSN 1544-7022
WEEKEND WOODCRAFTS. Text in English. N.S. 1998. bi-m. USD 19.97; USD 5.99 newsstand/cover (effective 2005). adv. back issues avail. **Document type:** *Magazine, Consumer.* **Description:** Includes a wide variety of woodworking projects with easy-to-follow instructions. Targets all skill levels.
Published by: E G W Publishing Co., 1041 Shary Circle, Concord, CA 94518. TEL 925-671-9852, FAX 925-671-0692, editor@weekendwoodcrafts.com, support@egw.com, http://www.weekendwoodcrafts.com, http://www.egw.com. Eds. Robert Joseph, Robert Joseph. Adv. contacts Rickie Wilson TEL 800-777-1164 ext 1208, Rickie Wilson. B&W page USD 2,000, color page USD 2,800; trim 8 x 10.5. Circ: 100,000 (paid).

694 DEU
WEINIG INFO. Text in Chinese, English, French, German, Italian, Japanese, Spanish. 1960. s-a. **Document type:** *Corporate.*
Published by: Michael Weinig AG, Weinigstr 2-4, Tauberbischofsheim, 97941, Germany. TEL 49-9341-860, FAX 49-9341-7080, weinig@t-online.de, http://www.weinig.com. Ed., R&P Rudi Walz. Circ: 70,000.

WHERE TO BUY HARDWOOD PLYWOOD, VENEER AND ENGINEERED HARDWOOD FLOORING. see *FORESTS AND FORESTRY—Lumber And Wood*

698.3 USA
WOOD FINISHING QUARTERLY. Text in English. 1981. q. free. adv.
Published by: Dakota County Area Vocational Technical Institute, Wood Finishing Trade Program, 1300 E 145th St, Rosemount, MN 55068. TEL 651-423-8472. Ed. Dan McGraw. Circ: 10,000.

WOOD NEWS; products-processes machines. see *FORESTS AND FORESTRY—Lumber And Wood*

698.3 USA ISSN 1097-8054
WOOD STROKES & WOODCRAFTS. Text in English. 1992. bi-m. USD 19.97 domestic; USD 31.97 foreign; USD 5.99 newsstand/cover (effective 2005). adv. back issues avail. **Document type:** *Magazine, Consumer.*
Formerly (until 1996): Wood Strokes and Weekend Woodcrafts (1089-5906); Which was formed by the merger of: Wood Strokes (1069-6962); Weekend Woodcrafts (1058-9821)
Published by: E G W Publishing Co., 1041 Shary Circle, Concord, CA 94518. TEL 925-671-9852, 800-777-1164, FAX 925-671-0692, editor@weekendwoodcrafts.com, support@egw.com, http://www.weekendwoodcrafts.com/, http://www.egw.com. Ed. Sandra Wagner. Adv. contact Rickie Wilson TEL 800-777-1164 ext 1208. color page USD 3,718. Circ: 33,000 (paid).

698.3 GBR ISSN 0965-9463
WOODCARVING. Text in English. 1992. bi-m. GBP 21.50, USD 41.95; GBP 3.25 newsstand/cover. adv. illus. **Document type:** *Consumer.* **Description:** Covers the craft of woodcarving by promoting interaction among carvers, as well as providing projects, designs, and tool reviews.
Indexed: ABM, IHTDI.
Published by: (Guild of Master Craftsmen), G M C Publications Ltd., 166 High St, Lewes, E Sussex BN7 1XU, United Kingdom. TEL 44-1273-477374, FAX 44-1273-478606. Ed. Nick Hough. Pub. A E Phillips. Adv. contact Linda Grace. B&W page GBP 800, color page GBP 1,080; trim 298 x 210. Circ: 25,000. **Dist. by:** Comag, Tavistock Works, Tavistock Rd, W Drayton, Middx UB7 7QX, United Kingdom. TEL 44-1895-444055, FAX 44-1895-433602.

694 USA ISSN 1553-2461
TT185
▼ **WOODCRAFT MAGAZINE.** Text in English. 2005 (Jan.). bi-m. USD 38.95 in US & Canada; USD 7.99 newsstand/cover (effective 2005). adv. **Document type:** *Magazine, Consumer.*
Published by: Dovetail Media Inc, 5225 Rosemar Rd, P O Box 7020, Parkersburg, WV 26102-7020. TEL 304-485-2647, FAX 304-420-9840, http://www.WoodcraftMagazine.com. Ed. A J Hamler. Adv. contacts Andrew Bondi, Ruth Goodwin.

694 USA ISSN 0894-5403
WOODSHOP NEWS. Text in English. 1986. m. USD 21.95 domestic; USD 33.95 foreign (effective 2005). adv. illus. reprints avail. **Document type:** *Magazine, Trade.* **Description:** News for and about people who work with wood.
Indexed: RefZh.
Published by: Soundings Publications, L L C, 10 Bokum Rd, Essex, CT 06426. TEL 860-767-8227, FAX 860-767-0645, http://www.woodshopnews.com, http://www.soundingspub.com. Ed. Tod Riggio. Pub. Glenn C Mallory. Adv. contact Spencer Isola TEL 847-295-0051. Circ: 90,000 (paid).

694 USA ISSN 0164-4114
WOODSMITH. Text in English. 1979. bi-m. USD 28 domestic; CND 46 in Canada; USD 32 elsewhere (effective 2005); USD 4.95 newsstand/cover (effective 2002). illus. 36 p./no.; back issues avail. **Document type:** *Magazine, Consumer.* **Description:** Guides woodworking hobbyists.
Indexed: IHTDI.
Published by: August Home Publishing Co., 2200 Grand Ave, Des Moines, IA 50312-5306. TEL 515-282-7000, FAX 515-282-6741, woodsmith@woodsmith.com, http://www.woodsmith.com, http://www.augusthome.com. Ed. Terry Strohman. Pub. Donald B Peschke. R&P Doug Hicks TEL 515-875-7170. Circ: 325,000.

694.6 GBR ISSN 1367-4420
THE WOODTURNER. Text in English. 1997. q. GBP 18; GBP 3 newsstand/cover (effective 1999). **Document type:** *Consumer.* **Description:** For the woodworker who enjoys new project ideas, tips, techniques, and reviews.
Published by: Nexus Media Ltd. (Subsidiary of: Highbury House Communications PLC), Nexus House, Azalea Dr, Swanley, Kent BR8 8HU, United Kingdom. TEL 44-1322-660070, FAX 44-1322-667633. Ed. Nick Hunton. **Subscr. in N. America to:** Wise Owl Worldwide Publications, 5674 El Camino Real., Ste. D, Carlsbad, CA 92008-7130. TEL 310-375-6258; **Subscr. to:** Tower Publishing Services Ltd., Tower House, Sovereign Park, Market Harborough, Leics LE16 9EF, United Kingdom. TEL 44-1858-438823, FAX 44-1858-434958. **Dist. by:** Comag, Tavistock Works, Tavistock Rd, W Drayton, Middx UB7 7QX, United Kingdom. TEL 44-1895-444055, FAX 44-1895-433602.

698 GBR ISSN 0958-9457
WOODTURNING. Text in English. 1990. m. GBP 41.40 domestic; USD 51.75 foreign (effective 2004). adv. bk.rev. illus. reprints avail. **Document type:** *Consumer.* **Description:** Covers the craft of woodturning. Includes information on tools, materials, and equipment.
Indexed: ABM, IHTDI.
Published by: (Guild of Master Craftsmen), G M C Publications Ltd., 166 High St, Lewes, E Sussex BN7 1XU, United Kingdom. TEL 44-1273-478449, FAX 44-1273-478606, mags@thegmcgroup.com, http://www.thegmcgroup.com/. Ed. Mark Baker. Pub. A E Phillips. Adv. contact Linda Grace. Circ: 31,311. **Dist. by:** Royal Mail International, C/o Smart Mail, 140, 58th Street, Ste 2B, Brooklyn, NY 11220.

WOODWORK. see *HOW-TO AND DO-IT-YOURSELF*

694 GBR
THE WOODWORKER & WOODTURNER. Text in English. 1901. m. GBP 38.40 domestic; EUR 52.50 in Europe; USD 90 in United States; GBP 63.50 elsewhere (effective 2004). adv. bk.rev. charts; illus. index. back issues avail.; reprints avail. **Document type:** *Magazine, Consumer.* **Description:** Appeals to beginner and expert woodworkers alike with new projects, how-to advice, and product reviews.
Former titles (until Nov.2004): The Woodworker (0043-776X); Woodworker Annual (0084-1196)
Indexed: GdIns, IHTDI, Pinpoint.
—BLDSC (9346.808050), IE, ingenta.
Published by: Highbury Leisure Publishing Ltd (Subsidiary of: Highbury House Communications PLC), Berwick House, 8-10 Knoll Rise, Orpington, Kent BR6 0EL, United Kingdom. TEL 44-1689-887200, FAX 44-1689-886666, info@nexusmedia.com, http://www.getwoodworking.com, http://www.hhc.co.uk/. Ed. Mark Ramuz. **Subscr. in the US to:** Wise Owl Worldwide Publications, 5674 El Camino Real., Ste. D, Carlsbad, CA 92008-7130. info@wiseowlmagazines.com, http://www.wiseowlmagazines.com/.

WOODWORKER'S JOURNAL; the voice of the woodworking community. see *HOW-TO AND DO-IT-YOURSELF*

684 USA ISSN 1080-0042
WOODWORKERS WEST. Text in English. 1988. bi-m. USD 12 domestic; USD 18 in Canada (effective 2001). adv. 72 p./no. 2 cols./p.; back issues avail. **Document type:** *Magazine, Consumer.* **Description:** Covers the people and events within the woodworking community in the western US. Includes news, shows, exhibits, clubs, classes and profiles.
Formerly: Southern California Woodworker (0898-3550)
Related titles: Online - full text ed.
Published by: Goldman Communications, PO Box 452058, Los Angeles, CA 90045. TEL 310-398-5931, editor@woodwest.com, http://www.woodwest.com. Ed., Pub., R&P, Adv. contact Ronald Goldman TEL 310-216-9265. 1/4 page USD 150; trim 5 x 3.5. Circ: 10,000.

694 CAN ISSN 0838-4185
WOODWORKING; Canada's leading magazine serving the producers of wood and wood products. Text in English. 1987. 7/yr. USD 35 domestic; USD 59.50 in United States; USD 65 elsewhere (effective 2005). adv. charts; illus.; stat.; tr.lit. back issues avail. **Document type:** *Magazine, Trade.* **Description:** Directed to makers of furniture, kitchen cabinets, millwork and for sawmill operators.
Related titles: Online - full text ed.: (from bigchalk, Northern Light Technology, Inc.).
Indexed: CBCABus, DAAI.
Published by: C L B Media, Inc. (Subsidiary of: Canada Law Book Inc.), 240 Edward St, Aurora, ON L4G 3S9, Canada. TEL 905-727-0077, FAX 905-727-0017, http://www.woodworkingcanada.com, http://www.clbmedia.ca. Ed. Kerry Knudsen. Pub. Blair Tullis. Circ: 11,168 (controlled).

694 USA
▼ **WOODWORKING (CINCINNATI).** Text in English. 2004 (Feb.). s-a. **Document type:** *Magazine, Trade.*
Published by: F & W Publications, Inc., 4700 E Galbraith Rd, Cincinnati, OH 45236. TEL 513-531-2690, FAX 513-531-0798, http://www.fwpublications.com. Ed. Steve Shanesy. Circ: 11,000.

694 USA
▼ **WOODWORKING AT HOME**; the DVD magazine for craftsmen. Text in English. 2003 (Jan.). 7/yr. USD 33.95 (effective 2003). **Document type:** *Magazine, Consumer.* **Description:** Contains 90 minutes of step by step guide to woodworking projects and techniques.
Media: Optical Disk - DVD. **Related titles:** Online - full content ed.
Published by: SoftWerks International Inc., 2413 W Algonquin Rd, PO Box 425, Algonquin, IL 60102. TEL 847-854-2381, FAX 847-854-2382, http://www.woodworkingathome.com/Mag/introducing.htm.

694 DEU ISSN 0342-6521
DER ZIMMERMANN. Text in German. m. EUR 55.20 domestic; EUR 63 foreign; EUR 6.90 newsstand/cover (effective 2004). adv. **Document type:** *Magazine, Trade.*
—CCC.
Published by: Bruderverlag Albert Bruder GmbH, Bismarckstr 21, Karlsruhe, 76133, Germany. TEL 49-721-913880, FAX 49-721-9138897, info@bruderverlag.de, http://www.rudolf-mueller.de. Ed. Peter Kuebler. Adv. contact Berthold Hasenfraz. B&W page EUR 2,130, color page EUR 3,945. Circ: 10,623 (paid).

BUILDING AND CONSTRUCTION—Hardware

APPLIANCE MAGAZINE. see *ENGINEERING—Electrical Engineering*

683 GBR ISSN 0959-986X
ARCHITECTURAL IRONMONGERY JOURNAL. Variant title: A I Journal. Text in English. 1973. q. adv. charts; illus.; pat.; stat.; tr.lit. back issues avail. **Document type:** *Trade.* **Description:** Features articles, legal page, Eurostandards update and product news. Readers generally include merchant and manufacturing buyers and senior management, as well as companies, architects and other specifiers.
Formerly (until 1990): G A I News (0951-7456)
Published by: Guild of Architectural Ironmongers, Editorial, 89 Great Eastern St, London, EC2A 3HY, United Kingdom. TEL 44-20-7729-0586, 44-20-7790-3431, FAX 44-20-7729-7765, radams@geapr.co.uk. Ed. Robin Adams. Pub., Adv. contact Peter Spill. B&W page GBP 1,070, color page GBP 1,320; trim 181 x 270. Circ: 4,500 (controlled).

683 SGP ISSN 0254-1149
ASIAN SOURCES HARDWARES. Text in English. 1976. m. USD 75 (effective 2005). adv. **Document type:** *Trade.* **Description:** Covers home center products, auto parts & accessories, machinery and industrial supplies.
Related titles: CD-ROM ed.; Online - full text ed.
Indexed: HongKongiana.
Published by: Global Sources, c/o Media Data Systems Pte Ltd, PO Box 0203, Raffles City, 911707, Singapore. TEL 65-65472800, FAX 65-65472888, service@globalsources.com, http://www.globalsources.com/MAGAZINE/BUYERS/HWBR.HTM?pi_proj=GSOLHP. Ed. Romeo E Udanga. Pub. Spenser Au. Circ: 21,200.

683 AUS ISSN 0004-9255
AUSTRALIAN HARDWARE JOURNAL. Text in English. 1886. m. AUD 68 domestic; USD 124 foreign (effective 2000). adv. bk.rev. illus.; mkt.; stat. **Document type:** *Trade.*
Related titles: Online - full text ed.
Indexed: ABIX.
Published by: Glenvale Publications, 4 Palmer Ct, Mt Waverley, VIC 3149, Australia. TEL 61-3-9544-2233, FAX 61-3-9543-1150, glenvale@glenv.com.au, samc@glenv.com.au. Ed. Betty Tanddo. Adv. contact Gary Bedford. B&W page AUD 2,080, color page AUD 2,520. Circ: 6,343.

B H F DIRECTORY. see *BUSINESS AND ECONOMICS—Trade And Industrial Directories*

683 DEU ISSN 0005-6480
BAUBESCHLAG MAGAZIN. Text in German. 1953. m. adv. **Document type:** *Magazine, Trade.*
Formerly: Baubeschlag Magazin mit Praktikus; Incorporates (in 1974): Praktikus (0171-3361)
Published by: Gert Wohlfarth GmbH, Stresemannstr 20-22, Duisburg, 47051, Germany. TEL 49-203-305270, FAX 49-203-30527820, info@wohlfarth.de, http://www.wohlfarth.de. Ed. Thorsten Schmidt. adv.: B&W page EUR 1,946, color page EUR 3,326. Circ: 23,000.

683 DEU ISSN 0067-4583
BAUBESCHLAG-TASCHENBUCH. Text in German. 1952. a. adv. bk.rev. **Document type:** *Magazine, Trade.*
Published by: Gert Wohlfarth GmbH, Stresemannstr 20-22, Duisburg, 47051, Germany. TEL 49-203-305270, FAX 49-203-30527820, info@wohlfarth.de, http://www.wohlfarth.de. Pub. Gert Wohlfarth. Circ: 5,600.

683 ESP
BRICOLAGE DISTRIBUCION. Text in Spanish. 4/yr.
Address: Via Augusta, 59, 8o Of. 812, Barcelona, 08006, Spain. TEL 3-237-88-65, FAX 3-415-86-88. Ed. Salvador Beltran Nunez. Circ: 10,000.

683 USA ISSN 0007-2710
TS2301.B8
BRUSHWARE. Text in English. 1898. bi-m. USD 35; USD 70 foreign (effective 1998). adv. bk.rev. illus.; stat. **Document type:** *Trade.*
—CISTI, Linda Hall.
Address: Centaur South, 5515 Dundee Rd, Huddleston, VA 24104. TEL 540-297-1517, FAX 540-297-1519. Ed. Leslie W Neff. Pub., R&P, Adv. contact Carl H Wurzer. Circ: 1,800 (paid).

683.3 CAN ISSN 1203-1771
CANADIAN LOCKSMITH; the technical news magazine for the locksmith and security industry. Text in English. 1982. 5/yr. CND 42 (effective 1997). adv. back issues avail. **Document type:** *Trade.*
Address: 137 Vaughan Rd, Toronto, ON M6C 2L9, Canada. TEL 416-653-2199, FAX 416-656-3048, tclarsin@interlog.com. Ed. Arnold Sintnicolaas. Circ: 500.

621.88 TWN
CHINESE FASTENER & WIRE. Text in Chinese. s-a. USD 30 (effective 2001). adv. **Document type:** *Magazine, Trade.* **Description:** Publishes information on fasteners, wires and springs for the domestic market of mainland China.
Published by: Fastener World, Inc., 469 Yu Ping Rd, Tainan, Taiwan. TEL 886-6-2954000, FAX 886-6-2953939, fastener@www.fastener-world.com.tw, http://www.fastener-world.com.tw/English/cfwdm.htm. adv.: B&W page USD 700, color page USD 1,050.

683 FRA ISSN 0988-1433
CONFEDERATION SERVICE✶. Text in French. m. (11/yr.).
Former titles (until 1987): Cahiers Confederation Service (0767-4996); Confederation Service (0242-1585)
Address: 91 rue de Miromesnil, Paris, 75008, France. TEL 45-61-99-44, FAX 42-25-77-52, TELEX 650 680 F. Ed. M Passebosc. Circ: 3,500.

D I Y SUPERSTORE INTERNATIONAL. (Do It Yourself) see *HOW-TO AND DO-IT-YOURSELF*

B

683 GBR ISSN 0967-2257
D I Y TRADE BUYERS' GUIDE; the year book for the D I Y, hardware trades, housewares and garden equipment industries. (Do It Yourself) Text in English. 1908. a. GBP 75 domestic; GBP 93 in Europe (effective 1999). index.
Document type: *Directory, Trade.* **Description:** Contains classified lists covering D.I.Y. hardware, housewares, and garden trades detailing manufacturers, wholesalers, retailers, and trade names.
Former titles: Benn's Guide (Year) (0954-8548); Benn's Hardware Directory and D I Y Buyers Guide (0261-1465); Benn's Hardware Directory (0067-5725)
Published by: C M P Information Ltd. (Subsidiary of: United Business Media), Sovereign House, Sovereign Way, Tonbridge, Kent TN9 1RW, United Kingdom. TEL 44-1732-362666, FAX 44-1732-367301, enquiries@cmpinformation.com, http://www.cmpinformation.com. R&P Sarah Walker. Circ: 1,500.

D I Y WEEK. (Do It Yourself) see *HOW-TO AND DO-IT-YOURSELF*

DIRECTORY OF AUTOMOTIVE AFTERMARKET SUPPLIERS (YEAR). see *BUSINESS AND ECONOMICS—Trade And Industrial Directories*

DO-IT-YOURSELF RETAILING; serving hardware, home center & building material retailers. see *HOW-TO AND DO-IT-YOURSELF*

683 USA ISSN 0361-5294
TS200
DOORS AND HARDWARE. Text in English. 1936. m. USD 69 in US & Canada; USD 109 elsewhere (effective 2005). adv. illus.; tr.lit. index. **Document type:** *Magazine, Trade.*
Description: Designed primarily for the door and architectural hardware wholesale commercial markets.
Incorporates (in 1975): American Society of Architectural Hardware Consultants. News and Views (0044-7935); Formerly (until May 1975): Hardware Consultant (0017-7687)
Related titles: Online - full text ed.: (from Gale Group).
Published by: Door and Hardware Institute, 14150 Newbrook Dr Ste 200, Chantilly, VA 20151. TEL 703-222-2010, FAX 703-222-2410, publications@dhi.org, http://www.dhi.org. Ed. Jesse Madden. Adv. contacts Molly Long, Cathy DeCenzo. Circ: 13,000 (paid and controlled).

683 DEU
EISENWAREN ZEITUNG; Markt fuer Werkzeuge, Beschlaege, Heimwerken & Garten. Text in German. 1948. 11/yr. EUR 6 newsstand/cover (effective 2005). adv. bk.rev. illus. **Document type:** *Journal, Trade.*
Formerly: E Z Eisenwaren (0945-5345); Which superseded in part (in 1992): E Z - Eisenwaren und Hausrat (0938-2011); Which was formerly (until 1989): Eisenwaren- und Hausrat-Zeitung (0931-5411); (until 1986): Eisenwaren-Zeitung (0013-2861)
Published by: (Fachverband des Deutschen Eisenwaren- und Hausrathandels/Federation of German Hardware and Houseware Retailers), Eisenwaren-Zeitung GmbH, Eichendorffstr 3, Duesseldorf, 40474, Germany. TEL 49-211-4705062, FAX 49-211-4705064, info@ez-hz.de, http://www.ez-hz.de. Ed. Norbert Krylow. adv.: B&W page EUR 2,208, color page EUR 3,905; trim 185 x 260. Circ: 6,002.

683 GBR
EUROPEAN DIRECTORY OF SUSTAINABLE AND ENERGY EFFICIENT BUILDING - COMPONENTS SERVICES MATERIALS. Text in English. 1993. a. GBP 59.50, USD 90. adv. **Document type:** *Directory.* **Description:** Contains a wide range of contributions providing an overview of current practices in energy efficient design and construction.
Formerly: European Directory of Energy Efficient Building - Components Services Materials (1352-0172)
—BLDSC (3829.689575), CISTI.
Published by: Earthscan / James & James, 8-12 Camden High St, London, NW1 0JH, United Kingdom. TEL 44-20-7387-8558, FAX 44-20-7387-8998, EDSEEB@jxj.com, http://www.jxj.com/. Eds. John Goulding, Owen Lewis. Pub. Edward Milford. Adv. contact Ian Malim. B&W page GBP 2,795, color page GBP 3,495.

683 USA ISSN 0746-2441
TJ1320
FASTENER TECHNOLOGY INTERNATIONAL. Text in English. 1977. bi-m. USD 35 in US & Canada; USD 70 elsewhere; USD 8 newsstand/cover; free to qualified personnel (effective 2005). adv. pat. **Document type:** *Magazine, Trade.*
Formerly (until 1983): Fastener Technology (0272-7331)
Indexed: BrCerAb, C&ISA, CerAb, CivEngAb, CorrAb, E&CAJ, EMA, IAA, M&TEA, MBF, METADEX, SolStAb, WAA.
—CISTI, IE, Linda Hall.
Published by: Initial Publications Inc., 3869 Darrow Rd, Ste 109, Stow, OH 44224. TEL 330-686-9544, FAX 330-686-9563, info@fastenertech.com, http://www.fastenertech.com. Ed. Michael J McNulty. Pub. John L Jones. Circ: 13,000 (controlled).

621.88 TWN
FASTENER WORLD. Text in English, Chinese. bi-m. USD 80 (effective 2001). adv. **Document type:** *Magazine, Trade.*
Description: Covers news about the fastener industry, including management, manufacturing equipment and tooling and information technology.
Related titles: English ed.: USD 70 (effective 2001).
Published by: Fastener World, Inc., 469 Yu Ping Rd, Tainan, Taiwan. TEL 886-6-2954000, FAX 886-6-2953939, fastener@www.fastener-world.com.tw, http://www.fastener-world.com.tw/English/fwdm.htm. adv.: B&W page USD 950, color page USD 1,600.

680 USA
FASTENING. Text in English. 1995. q. **Document type:** *Trade.*
Indexed: METADEX.
Published by: McGuire Fasteners, Inc., 27081 N. 96th Way, Scottsdale, AZ 85262-8441. mmcguire@mail.fastening.com, http://www.fastening.com. Ed., Pub. Mike McGuire. Circ: 28,000.

683 ITA
FERRAMENTA & CASALINGHI. Text in Italian. 1965. m. free.
Document type: *Magazine, Trade.*
Published by: Edizioni Collins Sas, Via Giovanni Pezzotti, 4, Milan, MI 20141, Italy. TEL 39-02-8372897, FAX 39-02-58103891, collins@collins.com, http://www.netcollins.com. Circ: 17,000 (controlled and free).

683 ESP
FERRETERIA ACTUALIDAD. Text in Spanish. 6/yr.
Address: Via Augusta, 59 8o, Of. 812, Barcelona, 08006, Spain. TEL 3-237-88-65, FAX 3-415-86-88. Ed. Salvador Beltran Nunez. Circ: 10,000.

683 ESP ISSN 0212-8276
FERRETICA. Text in Spanish. 9/yr. USD 100.
Address: Mazustegui, 21 4o planta, Bilbao, Vizcaya 48006, Spain. TEL 415-90-22, FAX 416-27-43. Ed. Teresa del Hoyo. Circ: 5,200.

683 ITA
FINESTRA INTERNATIONAL. Text in English, French, Spanish. 1986. 4/yr. EUR 65 domestic; EUR 99 foreign (effective 2005). adv. **Document type:** *Trade.*
Indexed: METADEX.
Published by: Reed Business Information Spa (Subsidiary of: Reed Business Information International), Viale G. Richard 1/A, Milan, 20143, Italy. TEL 39-02-818301, FAX 39-02-81830406, info@reedbusiness.it, http://www.winglass.reedbusiness.it/ita/rivista.asp?idContainer=282&idContent=4854, http://www.reedbusiness.it. adv.: B&W page EUR 1,430, color page EUR 2,050; bleed 297 x 214. Circ: 7,500.

683 CAN
GUIDE DES CENTRES ET DES QUINCAILLERIES DU QUEBEC. Text in English. 1993. a.
Published by: Les Productions CT Enr., 1048 rue d' Avaugour, Chicoutimi, PQ G7H 2T1, Canada. TEL 418-696-4805, FAX 514-359-0836. Ed. Martine Breton. adv.: B&W page CND 1,030, color page CND 1,330; trim 10.88 x 8.25. Circ: 3,000.

683 GBR ISSN 1466-6170
HARDWARE & BUILDING MATERIALS WORLD BUYERS' GUIDE. Text in English. 1999. a. GBP 180, USD 290 (effective 1999). adv. **Document type:** *Directory.* **Description:** Covers manufacturers, importers, exporters of hardware and building materials world wide.
Related titles: Large type ed. 8 pt.
Published by: Global Promotions, 1 Tobin Close, London, NW3 3DY, United Kingdom. TEL 44-171-586-1720, FAX 44-171-483-2684, sang@globalnet.co.uk. Ed., Adv. contact Mr. R.S.C. Iengar. B&W page USD 300, color page USD 450; trim 18 x 26. Circ: 4,500 (paid); 500.

683 GBR ISSN 0266-0539
HARDWARE AND GARDEN REVIEW. Text in English. 1968. m. GBP 65 domestic; GBP 84, USD 134 foreign (effective 2004). adv. bk.rev. back issues avail. **Document type:** *Trade.*
Description: Provides coverage of the housewares, do-it-yourself, and gardening market for the independent retailer.
Former titles: Hardware Review (0017-7733); Hardware Trades Review
Indexed: B&I.
Published by: Faversham House Group Ltd., Faversham House, 232a Addington Rd, South Croydon, Surrey CR2 8LE, United Kingdom. TEL 44-20-86517100, FAX 44-20-86517117. Ed. Susanna Clark. Pub. Colin Petty. Adv. contact Dominic Moon. Circ: 14,970 (controlled).

683 CAN ISSN 0847-9968
HARDWARE & HOME CENTRE MAGAZINE. Variant title: Centre Magazine. Text in English. 1977. 8/yr. CND 29.91 domestic; USD 51.95 in United States; USD 54.95 elsewhere (effective 2005). adv. **Document type:** *Magazine, Trade.* **Description:** Brings up-to-date news on the industry, latest products, merchandising, buying skills and ways of increasing profit.
(until 1988): Hardware, Home, Building Supply Centre (0847-995X); (until 1986): Centre (0703-4598)
Related titles: Online - full text ed.: (from Micromedia ProQuest).
Published by: Business Information Group, 12 Concorde Pl, Ste 800, Toronto, ON M3C 4J2, Canada. TEL 416-442-5600, 800-668-2374, FAX 416-442-2191, http://www.centremagazine.com, http://www.businessinformationgroup.ca. Circ: 17,358.

683 CAN ISSN 1199-2786
HARDWARE MERCHANDISING; the information source for home improvement retailers. Text in English. 1888. 9/yr. CND 42.80 (effective 2001). adv. illus.; mkt.; stat.; tr.lit. **Document type:** *Magazine, Trade.* **Description:** Offers news, information, business building tips for hardware, building supply and home centre retailers.
Former titles (until 1993): Hardware Merchandising, Building Supply Dealer (0831-0807); (until 1985): Hardware and Housewares Merchandising (0827-1429); (until 1984): Hardware Merchandising (0017-7717)
Related titles: Microfiche ed.: (from MML); Microfilm ed.: (from MML); Microform ed.: (from MML); Online - full text ed.: (from Micromedia ProQuest, ProQuest Information & Learning).
Indexed: ABIn, CBCABus.
Published by: Rogers Media Publishing Ltd, One Mount Pleasant Rd, 11th Fl, Toronto, ON M4Y 2Y5, Canada. TEL 416-764-2000, FAX 416-764-3941, http://www.hardwaremerch.com, http://www.rogers.com. Ed. Robert Gerlsbeck. Pub. Steve Payne. Circ: 15,000.

683 ZAF
HARDWARE RETAILER. Text in English. 1985. m. ZAR 60. adv. illus. **Document type:** *Trade.*
Published by: Complete Publishing (Pty.) Ltd., PO Box 87745, Houghton, Johannesburg 2041, South Africa. TEL 27-11-7892112, FAX 27-11-789-5347. Circ: 6,584.

683 GBR
HARDWARE TODAY. Text in English. m. free. adv. bk.rev. illus.; stat. **Document type:** *Trade.*
Formerly: N F I Bulletin (0027-6502)
Indexed: FS&TA, NutrAb, WAE&RSA.
—BLDSC (6109.073500), ingenta.
Published by: Indices Publications Ltd., 14-16 Church St, Rickmansworth, Herts WD3 1RQ, United Kingdom. TEL 44-1923-711434, FAX 44-1923-896063. Ed. John Morgan. Pub., R&P Michael I Weedon. Adv. contact Kevin Toole. B&W page GBP 695, color page GBP 1,130; trim 210 x 297. Circ: 11,000.

683 TWN
HARDWARE WORLD. Text in Chinese, English. s-a. USD 30 (effective 2001). adv. **Document type:** *Magazine, Trade.*
Description: Covers market trends, companies and the latest technologies in the Taiwan hardware industry.
Published by: Fastener World, Inc., 469 Yu Ping Rd, Tainan, Taiwan. TEL 886-6-2954000, FAX 886-6-2953939, fastener@www.fastener-world.com.tw, http://www.fastener-world.com.tw/english/hwdm.htm. adv.: B&W page USD 900, color page USD 1,350.

683 694 CAN ISSN 1204-3044
HOME IMPROVEMENT RETAILING. Text in English. 1995. bi-m. CND 69 domestic; CND 90 foreign (effective 2000). adv.
Document type: *Trade.*
Published by: Powershift Communications Inc., 245 Fairview Mall Dr, Ste 501, North York, ON M2J 4T1, Canada. TEL 416-494-1066, FAX 416-494-2536. Ed. Joseph Hornyak. Adv. contact Dante Piccinin. B&W page CND 3,515, color page CND 4,545; trim 10.88 x 8.13.

HONG KONG ENTERPRISE. see *GIFTWARE AND TOYS*

683 HKG ISSN 1021-8882
HONG KONG HOUSEHOLD. Text in English. 1983. s-a. HKD 300 for 2 yrs. in Hong Kong; USD 54 for 2 yrs. in Asia except Japan; USD 72 for 2 yrs. elsewhere (effective 2000). adv. illus.; stat. back issues avail. **Document type:** *Trade.*
Description: Provides a one-stop source for all sorts of household and hardware products.
Related titles: Online - full content ed.
Indexed: HongKongiana.
Published by: Hong Kong Trade Development Council, 38th Fl Office Tower, Convention Plaza, 1 Harbour Rd, Wanchai, Hong Kong. TEL 852-2584-4333, publications@tdc.org.hk, hktdc@tdc.org.hk, http://www.tdc.org.hk/prodmag/house/house.htm. Ed. K S Chan. Adv. contact Wengi Yuen. color page HKD 13,500; 213 x 280. Circ: 40,000.

683 AUS
INSIDE AUSTRALIAN HARDWARE. Text in English. 1989. bi-m. AUD 25 domestic; AUD 50 foreign (effective 2000). adv. stat.; tr.lit. back issues avail. **Document type:** *Trade.* **Description:** Provides information for hardware and garden centre retailers and suppliers on new products, industry statistics and development, coverage of conferences and trade shows, personnel profiles and appointments.
Published by: Hardware Publications, 1st Fl 512 S Pine Rd, Everton Park, QLD 4053, Australia. TEL 61-7-3355-4155, FAX 61-7-3354-1933, hardpub@powerup.com.au. Adv. contacts Hugh Banney, Ken Head TEL 61-3-9579-4395. B&W page AUD 1,460, color page AUD 1,880; trim 276 x 210. Circ: 5,933 (paid and controlled).

INTERNATIONAL DIRECTORY OF HAND TOOLS AND POWER TOOLS IMPORTERS. see *BUSINESS AND ECONOMICS—Trade And Industrial Directories*

INTERNATIONAL DIRECTORY OF MACHINE TOOLS AND ACCESSORIES IMPORTERS. see *BUSINESS AND ECONOMICS—Trade And Industrial Directories*

INTERNATIONAL DIRECTORY OF PLUMBING SUPPLIES, SANITARY WARE, PIPES & FITTINGS IMPORTERS. see *BUSINESS AND ECONOMICS—Trade And Industrial Directories*

INTERNATIONAL DIRECTORY OF SCREWS, NUTS, BOLTS AND FASTENERS IMPORTERS. see *BUSINESS AND ECONOMICS—Trade And Industrial Directories*

683 IRL ISSN 0790-276X
IRISH HARDWARE. Text in English. 1938. m. adv. bk.rev. tr.lit. **Document type:** *Trade.* **Description:** Contains news and information for persons involved in the hardware retail trade.
Former titles (until 1984): Hardware and Allied Trader (0790-0880); (until 1983): Irish Hardware and Allied Trader (0047-1461); (until 1943): Hardware and Allied Trader (0790-0872)
Published by: (Irish Hardware and Building Materials Association), Jemma Publications Ltd., Marino House, 52 Glasthule Rd., Sandycove, Co. Dublin, Ireland. TEL 353-1-2800000, FAX 353-1-2801818, sales@jemma.ie. Adv. contact Patrick A Bowles. B&W page EUR 1,510, color page EUR 1,870; trim 210 x 297. Circ: 1,697.

ISENKRAMBRANCHEN. see *INTERIOR DESIGN AND DECORATION—Furniture And House Furnishings*

▼ **JAERN, BYGG, FAERG/BUILDING MATERIAL AND HARDWARE TRADE JOURNAL.** see *BUSINESS AND ECONOMICS—Marketing And Purchasing*

KETENS IN KAART. see *HOW-TO AND DO-IT-YOURSELF*

683.3 USA ISSN 0193-3191
LOCKSMITH GAZETTE; the magazine of professional locksmithing. Text in English. 1977. q. USD 16. adv. bk.rev. **Document type:** *Trade.*
Address: PO Box 14321, Columbus, OH 43214. Ed. Victor Fanberg. Circ: 3,500.

683.3 USA ISSN 1050-2254
TS519
LOCKSMITH LEDGER INTERNATIONAL. Text in English. 1939. m. USD 41 (effective 2005). adv. charts; illus.; mkt.; pat.; tr.lit.; tr.mk. index. reprints avail. **Document type:** *Magazine, Trade.* **Description:** Technical news magazine of the physical and electronic security industry.
Former titles (until 1988): Locksmith Ledger (0273-625X); Locksmith Ledger and Security Register (0024-5720)
Related titles: Online - full text ed.: (from Gale Group, ProQuest Information & Learning).
—CCC.
Published by: Cygnus Business Media, Inc., 100 Colony Park Dr, Suite 230, Cumming, GA 30040. TEL 770-886-0800, FAX 770-889-7703, http://www.securityinfowatch.com. Ed. Gale Johnson. Circ: 13,600 (paid).

LOCKSMITH LEDGER - INTERNATIONAL DIRECTORY. see *CRIMINOLOGY AND LAW ENFORCEMENT—Security*

683 ESP
MENAJE TOTAL. Text in Spanish. 6/yr.
Address: Via Augusta, 59 8o Of 812, Barcelona, 08006, Spain. TEL 3-237-11-98. Ed. Salvador Beltran Nunez. Circ: 25,000.

683 GBR
NATURAL STONE DIRECTORY. Text in English. 1968. biennial. GBP 35 (effective 2000). **Document type:** *Directory.* **Description:** Lists all quarries and stone available in the U.K. and Ireland, as well as imported materials. Provides information on suppliers of related equipment and services for specifiers and users of stone.
—BLDSC (6041.500000).
Published by: Herald House Ltd., 96 Dominion Rd, Worthing, BN14 8JP, United Kingdom. TEL 01903-821082, FAX 01903-215904.

683 NZL ISSN 0028-8160
NEW ZEALAND HARDWARE JOURNAL✶ . Text in English. 1971 (vol.16). m. NZD 8. adv. bk.rev. illus. **Document type:** *Trade.*
Related titles: Online - full text ed.
Indexed: ABIX.
—CCC.
Published by: (New Zealand Wholesale Hardware Guilds' Federation), Marketplace Press Ltd, P.O. Box 28-372, Remuera, Auckland, New Zealand. TEL 64-9-3664576, FAX 64-9-3664580, http://www.marketplacepress.co.nz. Circ: 1,000.
Co-sponsor: N.Z. Retail Hardware Federation.

683 ESP ISSN 0213-0823
NUEVA FERRETERIA; revista para los profesionales de la ferreteria y afines. Text in Spanish. 1985. m. EUR 100.57 domestic; EUR 132.55 foreign (effective 2004). adv.
Related titles: ◆ Supplement(s): Catalogo Expoferro.
Published by: Tecnipublicaciones Espana, S.L., Avda de Manoteras 44, 3a Planta, Madrid, 28050, Spain. TEL 34-91-2972000, FAX 34-91-2972154, tp@tecnipublicaciones.com, http://www.tecnipublicaciones.com. adv.: B&W page EUR 750, color page EUR 981; bleed 210 x 285. Circ: 85,000.

683 ITA ISSN 0394-3216
NUOVA FINESTRA; serramenti e componenti per l'edilizia. Text in Italian. 1977. 11/yr. EUR 79 domestic; EUR 119 foreign (effective 2005). adv. bk.rev. **Document type:** *Magazine, Trade.* **Description:** Covers all aspects of windows design and manufacture.
Formerly (until 1979): Finestra (0394-3224)
Published by: Reed Business Information Spa (Subsidiary of: Reed Business Information International), Viale G. Richard 1/A, Milan, 20143, Italy. TEL 39-02-818301, FAX 39-02-81830406, info@reedbusiness.it, http://www.winglass.reedbusiness.it/eng/rivista.asp?idContainer=300&idContent=6843, http://www.reedbusiness.it. adv.: B&W page EUR 1,150, color page EUR 1,690; bleed 297 x 210. Circ: 7,300.

683 AUT
DER OESTERREICHISCHER BAUSTOFFMARKT. Text in German. 8/yr. EUR 66.70 domestic; EUR 81.30 foreign (effective 2005). adv. **Document type:** *Magazine, Trade.*
Published by: Verlag Lorenz, Ebendorferstr 10, Vienna, W 1010, Austria. TEL 43-1-40566950, FAX 43-1-4068693, baustoff@verlag-lorenz.at, office@verlag-lorenz.at, http://www.verlag-lorenz.at/bm/. Ed. Alois Froestl. Adv. contact Alexandra Lehrer. B&W page EUR 2,230, color page EUR 3,635; trim 185 x 264. Circ: 5,500 (paid and controlled).

683 CHE ISSN 0031-5923
PERSPECTIVE. Text in French, German. 1912. s-m. CHF 85; CHF 89 foreign (effective 1998). adv. bk.rev. illus.; stat.; tr.lit. **Document type:** *Trade.* **Description:** Trade journal covering the hardware industry: tools, fittings, appliances, machinery, housewares, glass, camping equipment.
Formerly: Eisenwarenhandel
Related titles: Online - full text ed.: (from Northern Light Technology, Inc.).
Indexed: BusI.
Published by: Association of Swiss Ironmongers, Talstr 66, Zuerich, 8001, Switzerland. TEL 41-1-2242084, FAX 41-1-2242088. Ed. Christoph Rotermund. Adv. contact Ursula Merkle. Circ: 2,000.

683 GBR ISSN 1470-9600
RETAIL INTERIORS. Text in English. 1957. m. GBP 36 to individuals; GBP 43 in Europe to individuals; GBP 70 elsewhere to individuals (effective 1999). adv. bk.rev. illus. **Document type:** *Journal, Trade.*
Former titles (until 2000): S E N: Shop Equipment & Shopfitting News (0037-4172); (until 1961): Shop Equipment News
—CCC.
Published by: Emap Maclaren Ltd. (Subsidiary of: Emap Business Communications Ltd.), c/o EMAP Communications, Scriptor Court, 155 Farringdon Rd, London, EC1R 3AD, United Kingdom. TEL 44-20-78416600, raym@maclaren.emap.co.uk, tracey.bigmore@emap.com, http://www.emap.com. Ed. Ray Moloney. Adv. contact Tony Patman. Circ: 9,801.

683 DEU ISSN 0179-1591
SCHLOSS & BESCHLAG-MARKT; Wirtschaftsfachmagazin fuer die Eisenwaren- und Sicherheitsbranche. Text in German. 1986. m. EUR 50.40 domestic; EUR 68.40 foreign; EUR 4.20 newsstand/cover (effective 2005). adv. **Document type:** *Magazine, Trade.*
Formerly (until 1985): Fachtechnikinformation (0342-2720)
Published by: Gert Wohlfarth GmbH, Stresemannstr 20-22, Duisburg, 47051, Germany. TEL 49-203-305270, FAX 49-203-30527820, info@wohlfarth.de, http://www.schloss-und-beschlagmarkt.de, http://www.wohlfarth.de. Ed. Uwe Hennig. Pub. Gert Wohlfarth. adv.: B&W page EUR 1,750, color page EUR 2,950; trim 178 x 264. Circ: 2,120 (paid and controlled).

683 CHE
SCHWEIZER BAUSTOFF INDUSTRIE. Text in German. 8/yr. **Document type:** *Trade.*
Address: Buberbergplatz 9, Bern, 3001, Switzerland. TEL 41-31-3262626, FAX 41-31-3262629. Circ: 2,700.

683 USA ISSN 1045-831X
TH9739
SECURITY SALES; technology for security installation and service. Text in English. 1979. m. (plus Factbook in Dec.). USD 96 domestic; USD 140 foreign; free to qualified personnel (effective 2005). adv. bk.rev. illus.; mkt. back issues avail. **Document type:** *Magazine, Trade.* **Description:** Practical applications, features and new technology developments for the security alarm dealer.
Former titles (until 1988): A I D (Agoura Hills) (0885-7784); (until 1987): Alarm Installer and Dealer (0195-8178)
Related titles: Online - full content ed.; Supplement(s): Security Sales Annual Fact Book.
Published by: (National Alarm Association of America), Bobit Business Media, 3520 Challenger St, Torrance, CA 90503. TEL 310-533-2400, FAX 310-533-2500, http://securitysales.com, http://www.bobit.com. Ed. Scott Goldfine. Pub. Michael Zawinski. Circ: 25,021 (controlled).

683 ITA
SERRAMENTI+DESIGN. Text in Italian. 1990. m. EUR 43 domestic; EUR 85 in Europe; EUR 120 elsewhere (effective 2005). adv. **Document type:** *Magazine, Trade.*
Formerly: S E C Serramenti e Componenti (1120-7876)
Published by: Tecniche Nuove SpA, Via Eritrea 21, Milan, MI 201, Italy. TEL 39-02-390901, FAX 39-02-7570364, sec@tecnichenuove.com, info@tecnichenuove.com, http://www.tecnichenuove.com/epages/tecnichenuove.storefront/430a2ddc02615c0c2740c0a8010505b2/Product/View/SEC&2D3. Ed. Marco Di Marzio. Circ: 6,090.

683 TWN
TAIWAN HARDWARE. Text in English. s-a. USD 50 in Americas, Europe & Africa; USD 40 elsewhere (effective 2000). adv. **Description:** Lists suppliers of hardware products from Taiwan.
Published by: China Economic News Service, 555 Chunghsiao E. Rd Sec 4, Taipei, 110, Taiwan. TEL 886-2-2642-2629, FAX 886-2-2642-7422, webmaster@www.cens.com, http://www.cens.com. adv.: B&W page TWD 35,000, color page TWD 40,000.

683 FRA
TECHNIQUES NOUVELLES; Menuiserie - Miroiterie - Metallerie. Variant title: T N Menuiserie - Miroiterie - Metallerie. Text in French. 1967. 10/yr. adv. **Document type:** *Trade.*
Formerly: T N Serrurerie - Miroiterie
Address: Imp des Tuileries, BP 27, Florensac, 34510, France. TEL 33-4-67777175, FAX 33-4-67777567. Ed. Jacques Salasc. Adv. contact Claude Ricart. Circ: 6,000; 6,000 (controlled).

683 USA
TOOLS & HARDWARE: LATIN AMERICAN INDUSTRIAL REPORT✶ . (Avail. for each of 22 Latin American countries) Text in English. 1985. a. USD 435; per country report.
Published by: Aquino Productions, P O Box 15760, Stamford, CT 06901-0760.

683 USA
TOP DRAWER✶ . Text in English. 196?. q. free.
Published by: Axia Incorporated, 801 Travis St No.1400, Houston, TX 77002-5727. TEL 312-654-3350. Ed. Ethel C Stahnke. Circ: 2,000.

VAKBLAD MIX; voor de doe-het-zelf en ijzerwaren- en tuinhandel. see *HOW-TO AND DO-IT-YOURSELF*

683 TUR ISSN 1301-0026
YAPI MALZEME & TEKNIK. Text in Turkish. 1996. m. USD 100 (effective 2001). adv. 150 p./no. 3 cols./p.; **Document type:** *Trade.*
Published by: Ihlas Magazine Group, Ihlas Holding Mrk. Binasi, 29 Ekim Cad. 23, Yenibosna - Istanbul, 34530, Turkey. TEL 90-212-4542530, FAX 90-212-4542555, bsensoz@img.com.tr, imga@img.com.tr, http://www.img.com.tr. Ed. Ahmet Kizil. Pub. Ferruh Isik. R&P Muhsin Yilmaz. Adv. contact Ms. Bahar Sensoz. page USD 2,000; 21.8 x 30. Circ: 16,000.

BUSINESS AND ECONOMICS

see also ADVERTISING AND PUBLIC RELATIONS ; BUSINESS AND ECONOMICS—Accounting ; BUSINESS AND ECONOMICS—Banking And Finance ; BUSINESS AND ECONOMICS—Banking And Finance—Computer Applications ; BUSINESS AND ECONOMICS—Chamber Of Commerce Publications ; BUSINESS AND ECONOMICS—Computer Applications ; BUSINESS AND ECONOMICS—Cooperatives ; BUSINESS AND ECONOMICS—Domestic Commerce ; BUSINESS AND ECONOMICS—Economic Situation And Conditions ; BUSINESS AND ECONOMICS—Economic Systems And Theories, Economic History ; BUSINESS AND ECONOMICS—International Commerce ; BUSINESS AND ECONOMICS—International Development And Assistance ; BUSINESS AND ECONOMICS—Investments ; BUSINESS AND ECONOMICS—Labor And Industrial Relations ; BUSINESS AND ECONOMICS—Macroeconomics ; BUSINESS AND ECONOMICS—Management ; BUSINESS AND ECONOMICS—Marketing And Purchasing ; BUSINESS AND ECONOMICS—Office Equipment And Services ; BUSINESS AND ECONOMICS—Personnel Management ; BUSINESS AND ECONOMICS—Production Of Goods And Services ; BUSINESS AND ECONOMICS—Public Finance, Taxation ; BUSINESS AND

B

▼ new title ➤ refereed ✶ unverified ◆ full entry avail.

ECONOMICS—*Small Business* ; *BUSINESS AND ECONOMICS—Trade And Industrial Directories* ; *CONSUMER EDUCATION AND PROTECTION* ; *INSURANCE* ; *LABOR UNIONS* ; *OCCUPATIONS AND CAREERS* ; *REAL ESTATE* ; *see also specific industries*

A A P E X TODAY. (Automotive Aftermarket Products Expo) see *MEETINGS AND CONGRESSES*

330   AUS   ISSN 1037-8286
A B A R E RESEARCH REPORTS. Text in English. 1969. irreg. (8-15/yr.). **Document type:** *Monographic series, Government.* **Description:** Contains economic and commodity analyses.
Former titles (until Apr., 1989): Australian Bureau of Agricultural and Resource Economics. Occasional Paper (1031-6698); (until 1987): Bureau of Agricultural Economics. Occasional Paper (0815-1458)
Related titles: Online - full content ed.
Indexed: AESIS, ASFA, AgBio, AnBrAb, DSA, FCA, FPA, FS&TA, ForAb, HerbAb, HortAb, IndVet, NutrAb, PBA, PHN&I, RRTA, S&F, SIA, TriticAb, VetBull, WAE&RSA.
—BLDSC (0537.724475), CISTI, IE. **CCC.**
Published by: Australian Bureau of Agricultural and Resource Economics, GPO Box 1563, Canberra, ACT 2601, Australia. TEL 61-2-62722000, FAX 61-2-62722001, sales@abare.gov.au, http://www.abareconomics.com. Ed., R&P Andrew Wright TEL 61-2-62722290.

330   MWI
A B A TODAY. Text in English. 1982. m.
Published by: African Businessmen's Association of Malawi, PO Box 5861, Limbe, Malawi. Ed. Rex Chalera.

A B C'S OF MAKING MONEY ONLINE. see *COMPUTERS— Internet*

A C C A DOCKET. see *LAW—Corporate Law*

330   PHL
A D B BUSINESS OPPORTUNITIES. Text in English. m. USD 10 newsstand/cover (effective 2005). **Description:** Covers proposed projects, advance action on procurement, consultant recruitment and retroactive financing, procurement notices, and contract awards.
Former titles (until 1990): Asian Development Bank. Proposed Projects, Procurement Notices and Contracts Awarded; (until 1989): Asian Development Bank. Proposed Projects and Contracts Awarded; (until 1988): Asian Development Bank. Operational Information on Proposed Projects (0115-6209)
Related titles: Microfiche ed.: (from CIS); Online - full content ed.
Indexed: CRIA, IIS, IPP.
Published by: Asian Development Bank, Publications Unit, P.O. Box 789, Manila, 0980, Philippines. TEL 63-2-6362648, adbpub@adb.org, http://www.adb.org/Business/Opportunities/default.asp.

330   FRA
A D R E S. ANNALES D'ECONOMIE ET DE STATISTIQUE. (Association pour le Developpement de la Recherche en Economie et en Statistique) Text in French. q.
Related titles: Online - full text ed.
Published by: Association pour le Developpement de la Recherche en Economie et en Statistique, INSEE, c/o Bruno Crepon, Boulevard Gabriel Peri 15, Malakoff Cede, 92245, France. http://www.adres.prd.fr/annales/index.htm.

330   AUT
A K AKTUELL. Text in German. 5/yr. **Document type:** *Bulletin, Trade.*
Published by: A K Aktuell, Maximilianstr 7, Innsbruck, T 6020, Austria. TEL 43-5222-5340, FAX 43-5222-53401290, ak@tirol.com. Ed. Elmar Schiffkorn. Circ: 200,000.

330   FRA
A LA BARRE DE L'ENTREPRISE. Text in French. 1957. q. adv.
Published by: A la Barre de l'Entreprise, 24-26 rue Hamelin, Paris, 75116, France. Circ: 2,000.

330   USA   ISSN 0892-1067
A O I BUSINESS VIEWPOINT. Text in English. 1960. bi-m. USD 17 (effective 2000). adv. **Document type:** *Consumer.*
Published by: Associated Oregon Industries, Inc., 1149 Court St, N E, Salem, OR 97301-4030. TEL 503-588-0050, FAX 503-588-0052, aoi@aoi.org, http://www.aoi.org. Ed., Pub. Donna C Lewis. R&P Kathleen Hall. Adv. contact Jennifer O'Brien.

A P S REVIEW DOWNSTREAM TRENDS. see *PETROLEUM AND GAS*

A P S REVIEW GAS MARKET TRENDS. see *PETROLEUM AND GAS*

330   SGP   ISSN 0217-4472
HC441.A1
➤ **A S E A N ECONOMIC BULLETIN.** Abbreviated title: A E B. Text in English. 1984. 3/yr. (Apr., Aug. & Dec.). SGD 61 to individuals in Singapore, Malaysia & Brunei; USD 54 to individuals in Asia, Australia, New Zealand & Japan; USD 68 elsewhere to individuals; SGD 97 to institutions in Singapore, Malaysia & Brunei; USD 100 to institutions in Asia, Australia, New Zealand & Japan; USD 126 elsewhere to institutions (effective 2005). adv. bk.rev. abstr.; bibl.; charts; stat.; illus. index. 130 p./no.; back issues avail.; reprint service avail. from SCH. **Document type:** *Bulletin, Academic/Scholarly.*
Description: Current economic issues pertaining to the countries of the Association of Southeast Asian Nations: Indonesia, Philippines, Thailand, Malaysia, Singapore, Brunei, Vietnam, Laos, Cambodia and Myanmar. Also covers ASEAN's relations with its major trade partners: the USA, Japan, EU, East Asia, and Australasia, and its relationships with the world political economy.
Related titles: Microform ed.: (from PQC); Online - full text ed.: (from Chadwyck-Healey Inc., EBSCO Publishing, Florida Center for Library Automation, Gale Group, O C L C Online Computer Library Center, Inc., ProQuest Information & Learning).
Indexed: ABIn, APEL, BAS, DIP, FPA, HRA, HortAb, IBR, IBSS, IBZ, JEL, PAIS, PCI, PHN&I, PRA, PerIslam, RASB, RDA, SPAA, WAE&RSA.
—BLDSC (1739.952000), IE, Infotrieve, ingenta.
Published by: Institute of Southeast Asian Studies, 30 Heng Mui Keng Terrace, Pasir Panjang, Singapore, 119614, Singapore. FAX 65-67756259, pubsunit@iseas.edu.sg, http://www.iseas.edu.sg/.

330   DEU
A S U - B J U NEWS. (Arbeitsgemeinschaft Selbstaendiger Unternehmer - Bundesverband Junger Unternehmer) Text in German. 1983. m. EUR 4.90 newsstand/cover (effective 2004). adv. **Document type:** *Magazine, Trade.*
Published by: (Arbeitsgemeinschaft Selbstaendiger Unternehmer e.V.), Dr. Breitsohl Verlagsgesellschaft mbH, Loeffelstr 1, Stuttgart, 70597, Germany. TEL 49-711-7696370, FAX 49-711-76963729, news@breitsohl.de, info@breitsohl.de, http://www.asu-bju-news.de, http://www.breitsohl.de. Ed. Kirsten Goetze. adv.- B&W page EUR 2,700, color page EUR 3,700. Circ: 14,670 (paid and controlled). **Co-sponsor:** Bundesverband Junger Unternehmer.

A W A - AKTUELLER WIRTSCHAFTSDIENST FUER APOTHEKER. see *PHARMACY AND PHARMACOLOGY*

A W H P ACTION. see *PHYSICAL FITNESS AND HYGIENE*

330   GBR   ISSN 1362-9603
ABERYSTWYTH ECONOMIC RESEARCH PAPERS. Text in English. irreg. **Document type:** *Monographic series.*
—BLDSC (0539.127000), ingenta.
Published by: University of Wales, School of Management and Business, Penglais, Aberystwyth, SY23 3DD, United Kingdom. http://www.aber.ac.uk/~ecowww.

ABORIGINAL BUSINESS MAGAZINE. see *ETHNIC INTERESTS*

ABORIGINAL ONTARIO; open for business. see *ETHNIC INTERESTS*

330   TWN   ISSN 1018-161X
HB9
➤ **ACADEMIA ECONOMIC PAPERS/JINGJI LUNWEN. ZHONGYANG YANJIUYUAN JINGJI YANJIUSUO.** Text in Chinese, English. 1973. q. USD 30 (effective 2003). bk.rev. abstr.; charts; illus. 150 p./no.; back issues avail.; reprints avail. **Document type:** *Journal, Academic/Scholarly.*
Indexed: APEL, BAS, JEL.
—BLDSC (0570.469200).
Published by: Academia Sinica, Institute of Economics, 128 Yen-Chiu-Yuan Rd. Sec.2, Nankang-qu, Taipei, 11529, Taiwan. TEL 886-2-2782-2791, FAX 886-2-2785-3946, eclcb@econ.sinica.edu.tw, http://www.sinica.edu.tw/econ/publish. Ed. Chung-Ming Kuan. R&P Min Hui Hsu TEL 886-2-27822791 ext 614. Circ: 2,000.

330   USA
ACCEPTABLE IDENTIFICATION AND CLASSIFICATION OF GOODS AND SERVICES MANUAL. Text in English. base vol. plus s-a. updates. looseleaf. USD 104 (effective 2001). **Document type:** *Government.* **Description:** Lists goods and services by their appropriate classification under the classification system of the Nice (International) Agreement.
Published by: U.S. Government Printing Office, 732 N Capitol St NW, Washington, DC 20401. TEL 202-512-1800, FAX 202-512-2250, http://www.gpo.gov.

330   GBR   ISSN 0958-5206
HF5601
➤ **ACCOUNTING, BUSINESS AND FINANCIAL HISTORY;** an international and comparative review. Text in English. 1990. 3/yr. GBP 288, USD 475 combined subscription to institutions print & online eds. (effective 2006). back issues avail.; reprint service avail. from PSC. **Document type:** *Academic/Scholarly.*
Description: Analyzes past developments in business and finance history; explains present structure and practices; and aims to create a platform for solving current problems and predicting future developments.
Related titles: Online - full text ed.: ISSN 1466-4275. GBP 274, USD 451 to institutions (effective 2006) (from EBSCO Publishing, Gale Group, IngentaConnect, O C L C Online Computer Library Center, Inc., Swets Information Services).
Indexed: ABIn, AmH&L, DIP, HistAb, IBR, IBSS, IBZ, IndIslam, JEL.
—BLDSC (0573.592300), IE, Infotrieve, ingenta. **CCC.**
Published by: Routledge (Subsidiary of: Taylor & Francis Group), 4 Park Sq, Milton Park, Abingdon, Oxon OX14 4RN, United Kingdom. TEL 44-1235-828600, FAX 44-1235-829000, info@routledge.co.uk, http://www.tandf.co.uk/journals/routledge/09585206.html, http://www.routledge.com. Eds. J R Edwards, Trevor Boyns. R&P Sally Sweet. Circ: 600. **Subscr. in US & Canada to:** Taylor & Francis Inc., Customer Services Dept, 325 Chestnut St, 8th Fl, Philadelphia, PA 19106. TEL 800-354-1420, FAX 215-625-8914; **Subscr. to:** Taylor & Francis Ltd, Journals Customer Service, Rankine Rd, Basingstoke, Hants RG24 8PR, United Kingdom. TEL 44-1256-813000, FAX 44-1256-330245, enquiry@tandf.co.uk.

330   HUN   ISSN 0001-6373
HB9.M28   CODEN: AOECDR
ACTA OECONOMICA; Periodical of the Hungarian Academy of Sciences. Text in English. 1966. q. USD 300 (effective 2006). adv. bk.rev. charts; abstr.; bibl. 120 p./no.; back issues avail.; reprints avail. **Document type:** *Journal, Academic/Scholarly.*
Description: Publishes articles on East European and Hungarian economic development, policy, management system and planning, and reforms. Includes issues of world economics and trade.
Related titles: Online - full text ed.: ISSN 1588-2659 (from EBSCO Publishing, Gale Group, IngentaConnect, Swets Information Services).
Indexed: ASCA, BAS, CurCont, GEOBASE, IBR, IBSS, IBZ, JEL, KES, PAIS, RASB, RRTA, SSCI, WAE&RSA.
—IDS, IE, Infotrieve. **CCC.**
Published by: (Magyar Tudomanyos Akademia/Hungarian Academy of Sciences), Akademiai Kiado Rt. (Subsidiary of: Wolters Kluwer N.V.), Prielle Kornelia U. 19, Budapest, 1117, Hungary. TEL 36-1-4648282, FAX 36-1-4648221, journals@akkrt.hu, http://www.akkrt.hu. Ed. Adam Torok.

330   CZE   ISSN 1212-3285
HB9
➤ **ACTA UNIVERSITATIS BOHEMIAE MERIDIONALES/ SCIENTIFIC JOURNAL FOR ECONOMICS, MANAGEMENT AND TRADE;** vedecky casopis pro ekonomiku, rizeni a obchod. Text in Czech; Abstracts in English. 1998. s-a. **Document type:** *Journal, Academic/Scholarly.*
Indexed: DSA, FCA, HortAb, NutrAb, PHN&I, PN&I, PotatoAb, PoultAb, RRTA, WAE&RSA.
—CISTI.
Published by: Jihoceska Univerzita v Ceskych Budejovicich , Zemedelska Fakulta/University of South Bohemia in Ceske Budejovice, Faculty of Agriculture, Studentska 13, Ceske Budejovice, 370 05, Czech Republic. wolkova@zf.jcu.cz, http://www.zf.jcu.cz. Ed. Jiri Kares.

330.07   POL   ISSN 0208-6018
HB3
ACTA UNIVERSITATIS LODZIENSIS: FOLIA OECONOMICA. Text in Polish; Summaries in Multiple languages. 1975. irreg. **Document type:** *Academic/Scholarly.* **Description:** Research on political economy, econometrics and statistics, accounting, informatics, planning and economic policy, marketing, foreign trade and more.
Supersedes in part (in 1980): Uniwersytet Lodzki. Zeszyty Naukowe. Seria 3: Nauki Ekonomiczne i Socjologiczne (0076-0374)
Indexed: IBSS, RASB, RefZh.
—KNAW.
Published by: Wydawnictwo Uniwersytetu Lodzkiego/Lodz University Press, ul Jaracza 34, Lodz, 90262, Poland. TEL 331671. **Dist. by:** Ars Polona, Krakowskie Przedmiescie 7, Warsaw, Poland.

330   POL   ISSN 0208-5305
HB9
ACTA UNIVERSITATIS NICOLAI COPERNICI. NAUKI HUMANISTYCZNO-SPOLECZNE. EKONOMIA. Text in Polish. 1972. irreg. price varies. **Document type:** *Academic/Scholarly.*
Formerly (until 1973): Uniwersytet Mikolaja Kopernika w Toruniu. Nauki Humanistyczno-Spoleczne. Zeszyty Naukowe. Ekonomia (0208-5380)
Indexed: AgrLib, RASB.
Published by: Uniwersytet Mikolaja Kopernika/Nicolaus Copernicus University, Wydawnictwo, ul Gagarina 39, Torun, 87100, Poland. TEL 48-56-14295. **Dist. by:** Osrodek Rozpowszechniania Wydawnictw Naukowych PAN, Palac Kultury i Nauki, Warsaw 00901, Poland.

330 FIN ISSN 1455-2647
ACTA UNIVERSITATIS OULUENSIS. SERIES G. OECONOMICA. Text in Multiple languages. 1997. irreg. price varies.
Document type: *Monographic series, Academic/Scholarly.*
Published by: Oulun Yliopisto, Julkaisupalvelut/University of Oulu. Publications Committee, Pentti Kaiteran Katu 1, PO Box 8000, Oulu, 90014, Finland. TEL 358-8-5531011, FAX 358-8-5534112, university.of.aulu@aulu.fi, http://www.kirjasto.oulu.fi/english/julkaisutoiminta/acta/, http://www.oulu.fi. Eds. Seppo Eriksson TEL 358-8-5532903, Olli Vuolteenaho TEL 358-8-5375302. R&P Olli Vuolteenaho TEL 358-8-5375302.

300 HUN ISSN 1219-6762
ACTA UNIVERSITATIS SZEGEDIENSIS. ACTA OECONOMICA. Text in Hungarian; Summaries in English, German. 1959-1988; N.S. 1996. irreg., latest vol.1, 1996. exchange basis. **Document type:** *Monographic series, Academic/Scholarly.* **Description:** Discusses problems of post-war Hungarian economy, with special regard to the transition period beginning with 1989. Also deals with the history of the Hungarian economy.
Supersedes (1959-1988): Acta Universitatis Szegediensis de Attila Jozsef Nominatae. Sectio Oeconomico-Politica (0554-5374)
Published by: (Szegedi Tudomanyegyetem, Allam- es Jogtudomanyi Kar, Gazdasagtudomanyi Kar/University of Szeged, Faculty of Law, Department of Economics), Szegedi Tudomanyegyetem/University of Szeged, c/o E Szabo, Exchange Librarian, Dugonics ter 13, PO Box 393, Szeged, 6701, Hungary. TEL 36-62-544009, FAX 36-62-420895, kati@lib.juris.u-szeged.hu, Eneh.Szabo@bibl.u-szeged.hu, http://www.u-szeged.hu. Ed. Karoly Toth. Circ: 400.

330 POL
ACTA UNIVERSITATIS WRATISLAVIENSIS. EKONOMIA. Text in Polish; Summaries in English, German. 1993. irreg. price varies. **Document type:** *Academic/Scholarly.*
Published by: (Uniwersytet Wroclawski), Wydawnictwo Uniwersytetu Wroclawskiego Spolka z o.o., Pl Uniwersytecki 9-13, Wroclaw, 50-137, Poland. TEL 48-71-441006, FAX 48-71-402735. Ed. Leon Olszewski. Circ: 300.

ACTA UNIVERSITATIS WRATISLAVIENSIS. PRZEGLAD PRAWA I ADMINISTRACJI. see *PUBLIC ADMINISTRATION*

330 FRA ISSN 0752-5192
ACTION COMMERCIALE. Text in French. 1982. 11/yr. adv.
Published by: Informations Marketing Editions Specialisees (IMES), 105 rue Anatole France, Levallois-Perret, 92300, France. TEL 33-1-41342800, FAX 33-1-47481035. Ed. Dominique Vialard. Adv. contact Thierry Frontere. Circ: 15,000.
Subscr. to: Action Commerciale, B.P. 43, Massy 91302, France.

330 USA
ACTUALIDAD ECONOMICA EN CD-ROM. Text mainly in Spanish. 1996. a. **Document type:** *Academic/Scholarly.*
Description: Publishes the full text of the weekly Spanish business magazine Actualidad Economica.
Media: CD-ROM (from Chadwyck-Healey Inc.).
Published by: ProQuest Information & Learning, 300 N Zeeb Rd., PO Box 1346, Ann Arbor, MI 48106-1346. FAX 703-683-7589, info@il.proquest.com, http://www.chadwyck.com.

330 CAN ISSN 0001-771X
HB3
ACTUALITE ECONOMIQUE. Text in English. 1925. q. CND 60 (effective 1998). adv. bk.rev. bibl.; charts. index, cum.index: 1925-1950, 1950-1960, 1960-1970, 1980-1990. **Document type:** *Academic/Scholarly.*
Related titles: Online - full text ed.: (from Micromedia ProQuest, ProQuest Information & Learning).
Indexed: ABIn, AmH&L, CBCARef, CBPI, CPerI, ELLIS, HistAb, IBR, IBSS, ILD, JEL, PAIS, PCI, PdeR, RASB, RefZh, SSCI. —BLDSC (0677.105000), CISTI, IE, Infotrieve, ingenta.
Published by: (Societe Canadienne de Science Economique), Ecole des Hautes Etudes Commerciales, 3000 Chemin de la Cote Sainte Catherine, Montreal, PQ H3T 2A7, Canada. TEL 514-340-6437. Ed. Paul Lanoie. Circ: 1,200.

▼ **ACUMEN JOURNAL OF SCIENCES.** see *BIOLOGY—Biotechnology*

338 ROM ISSN 1220-6156
ADEVARUL ECONOMIC. Text in Romanian. 1992. w. **Document type:** *Magazine, Trade.*
Published by: Editura Adevarul, Piata Presei Libere nr. 1, sector 1, Bucharest, Romania. TEL 40-21-2242893, FAX 40-21-2244030, publi@adevarul.kappa.ro.

330 USA ISSN 1088-016X
ADVANCE (SAN FRANCISCO)✶. Text in Spanish. 1989. bi-m. USD 12; USD 2 newsstand/cover (effective 1997). adv. bk.rev.; film rev.; music rev.; play rev.; software rev.; tel.rev.; video rev. charts; illus.; stat.; tr.lit. back issues avail.
Document type: *Consumer.* **Description:** Covers different issues of today's business world, such as computers and technology, especially for business people and college students.
Formerly (until 1996): Avance Hispano (1088-0151)
Address: c/o Meza T Meza, Ed., 4230 Mission St, San Francisco, CA 94112-1520. TEL 415-647-8029, FAX 415-821-4127, mtm@aol.com. Ed., Pub., Adv. contact Marco T Meza. page USD 2,500; trim 10 x 8. Circ: 35,000.

330 USA
ADVANCE NEWS JOURNAL. Text in English. 1978. w. USD 18, USD 25; USD 0.75 newsstand/cover (effective 2000). adv.
Document type: *Newspaper, Trade.*
Incorporates: McAllen News Journal (1082-5479)
Published by: Advance Publishing Company, 1101 N Cage, Twin Palm Plaza, Ste C1, Pharr, TX 78577. TEL 956-783-0036. Ed., Pub., Adv. contact Gregg Wendorf. Circ: 4,000,000 (paid); 3,500 (controlled).

330 USA ISSN 1048-1559
HG6001
ADVANCES IN FUTURES AND OPTIONS RESEARCH. Text in English. 1986. a., latest vol.10, 1998. price varies. back issues avail. **Document type:** *Monographic series, Academic/Scholarly.*
—BLDSC (0707.400000), ingenta. **CCC.**
Published by: J A I Press Inc. (Subsidiary of: Elsevier Science & Technology), 360 Park Ave S, New York, NY 10010-1710. TEL 212-989-5800, FAX 212-633-3990, usinfo-f@elsevier.com, http://www.elsevier.com/wps/find/bookdescription.cws_home/BS_AFOR/description#description. Eds. G Pennacchi, P P Boyle, P Ritchken.

330 OMN
AL-ADWA'. Text in Arabic. s-m.
Indexed: PerIslam.
Published by: Oman Publishing House, P O Box 580, Muscat, Oman. TEL 704353, TELEX 3376. Ed. Habib Muhammad Nasib. Circ: 15,600.

330 RUS
AFANASII BIRZHA. Text in Russian. 1996. w. **Document type:** *Newspaper, Consumer.*
Published by: Afanasii-Birzha, Vagzhanova 7, of 201, Tver', 170000, Russian Federation. TEL 7-0822-489898, 7-0822-557208, afanasy@online.tver.ru, http://194.87.239.38. Ed. Marina Znamerovskaya. Circ: 16,000.

AFRICA REPORT. see *POLITICAL SCIENCE*

▼ **AFRICA WEEK**; networking intelligence. see *POLITICAL SCIENCE*

330 NGA ISSN 1116-4875
HB74.9.A35
AFRICAN JOURNAL OF ECONOMIC POLICY. Text in English. 1992. s-a. USD 20 in Africa to individuals; USD 40 elsewhere to individuals; USD 30 in Africa to institutions; USD 60 elsewhere to institutions (effective 2004). back issues avail.
Document type: *Academic/Scholarly.*
Related titles: Online - full text ed.: (from International Network for the Availability of Scientific Publications, African Journals Online).
Published by: University of Ibadan, Trade Policy Research and Training Programme, Department of Economics, Ibadan, Nigeria. http://www.inasp.info/ajol/journals/ajep/about.html. Ed. Abiodun Bankole.

332 TZA ISSN 0856-6372
HD2917
AFRICAN JOURNAL OF FINANCE AND MANAGEMENT. Text in English. 1992. s-a. TZS 4,800 domestic; USD 28 foreign (effective 2003). adv. **Document type:** *Academic/Scholarly.*
Description: Contains in-depth articles and reports on topics in finance and management, accounting, insurance, social security, and related areas.
Formerly (until Jan. 1997): I F M Journal of Finance and Management (0856-4086)
Related titles: Online - full text ed.: (from International Network for the Availability of Scientific Publications, African Journals Online).
Published by: Institute of Finance Management, Library, PO Box 3918, Dar Es Salaam, Tanzania. TEL 255-51-112931, ifm@costech.gn.apc.org, http://www.inasp.info/ajol/journals/ajfm/about.html. Ed. M L Arora. Circ: 2,000.

AFRICAN REVIEW OF BUSINESS AND TECHNOLOGY. see *TECHNOLOGY: COMPREHENSIVE WORKS*

330 DEU
AFRIKA STUDIEN. Text in German. 1964. irreg., latest vol.127, 1999. **Document type:** *Monographic series.*
Indexed: AgrForAb.
Published by: Weltforum Verlag, Hohenzollernplatz 3, Bonn, 53173, Germany. TEL 49-228-368243-0, FAX 49-228-3682439. Circ: 500.

AGENDA BOSTON; special events resource directory. see *MEETINGS AND CONGRESSES*

AGENDA CHICAGO; special events resource directory. see *MEETINGS AND CONGRESSES*

330 ITA ISSN 0065-4264
AGENDA DEL DIRIGENTE DI AZIENDA✶. Text in Italian. a.
Published by: Editoriale Emme Elle s.r.l., Via Reno, 30, Rome, RM 00198, Italy.

AGENDA NEW YORK; special events resource directory. see *MEETINGS AND CONGRESSES*

AGENDA NORTHERN CALIFORNIA; special events resource directory. see *MEETINGS AND CONGRESSES*

AGENDA SOUTHERN CALIFORNIA; special events resource directory. see *MEETINGS AND CONGRESSES*

AGENDA VENUES. see *MEETINGS AND CONGRESSES*

AGENDA WASHINGTON; special events resource directory. see *MEETINGS AND CONGRESSES*

330 070 ESP
AGRUPACION DE PERIODISTAS DE INFORMACION ECONOMICA. INFORME. Text in Spanish. 1975. a.
Published by: Agrupacion de Periodistas de Informacion Economica, Pz Callao, 4, Madrid, 28013, Spain. info@apie.es, http://www.apie.es/.

332.6327 USA
AHEAD; the newsletter of ForecastCenter.com. Text in English. 2000. irreg. abstr.; stat. 3 p./no.; back issues avail. **Document type:** *Newsletter, Corporate.* **Description:** Provides a focal point for forecasts beyond the current year and serves as a resource and community for understanding change.Topics include business, finance, etc.
Media: E-mail.
Published by: ForecastCenter.com LLC, 23 Prescott Dr, Marlboro, NJ 07746-1351. TEL 732-972-2570, FAX 732-536-9430, mail@forecastcenter.com, http://www.forecastcenter.com/ahead.htm. Ed., Pub., R&P Irving Leveson.

330 EGY ISSN 1110-1008
AIN SHAMS UNIVERSITY. ECONOMIC AND BUSINESS REVIEW. Text in English. 1973. q. EGP 12 (effective 2003).
Document type: *Academic/Scholarly.*
Published by: Ain Shams University, Faculty of Commerce, Abbassia, Cairo, Egypt. TEL 20-2-2615602, FAX 20-2-2615603, http://derp.sti.sci.eg/data/0102.htm. Ed. Dr. Muhammad Abdel-Mugid.

AIRCRAFT FINANCE. see *TRANSPORTATION—Air Transport*

AIRCRAFT LIENS & DETENTION RIGHTS. see *TRANSPORTATION—Air Transport*

AIRLINE BUSINESS REPORT. see *TRANSPORTATION—Air Transport*

330 JPN
AJIKEN TOPIC REPORT. Text in Japanese. 1994. irreg. free.
Document type: *Bulletin.* **Description:** Intends to offer prompt commentary and analyses of emerging problems in developing countries.
Published by: Institute of Developing Economies/Ajia Keizai Kenkyusho, 3-2-2 Wakaba, Mihana-ku, Chiba-shi, Chiba 261-8545, Japan. TEL 81-43-299-9536, FAX 84-43-299-9724, info@ide.go.jp, http://www.ide.go.jp. Circ: 2,000.

330 JPN ISSN 1341-3406
DS1
➤ **AJIKEN WORLD TRENDS.** Key Title: Ajiken Warudo, Torendo. Text in Japanese. 1995. m. JPY 10,620 (effective 2003). bk.rev. illus.; stat. **Document type:** *Academic/Scholarly.*
Description: Contains articles, reports, and photo essays with information on developing countries. Subject areas include business, economics, political science, agriculture, sociology, environmental studies, history, and law.
Formed by the 1995 merger of: Ajiken News - Ajiken Nyusu (0389-0007); Ajiken Trends - Ajiken Torendo (0386-1287)
Indexed: RASB.
Published by: Institute of Developing Economies/Ajia Keizai Kenkyusho, 3-2-2 Wakaba, Mihana-ku, Chiba-shi, Chiba 261-8545, Japan. TEL 81-43-299-9536, FAX 84-43-299-9724, info@ide.go.jp, http://www.ide.go.jp. Circ: 600.

330 POL ISSN 0324-8445
HB9 CODEN: PNAWDL
AKADEMIA EKONOMICZNA IM. OSKARA LANGEGO WE WROCLAWIU. PRACE NAUKOWE. Text in Polish. 1956. irreg. price varies. adv. bk.rev. illus. **Document type:** *Monographic series, Academic/Scholarly.*
Formerly (until 1974): Wyzsza Szkola Ekonomiczna we Wroclawiu. Prace Naukowe (0524-4560)
Related titles: Microform ed.; ♦ Series of: Akademia Ekonomiczna im. Oskara Langego we Wroclawiu. Prace Naukowe. Seria: Monografie i Opracowania. ISSN 0239-8532.
Indexed: AgrLib, CIN, ChemAb, ChemTitl, RASB. —BLDSC (6589.060000), CASDDS, IE, ingenta.
Published by: Akademia Ekonomiczna im. Oskara Langego we Wroclawiu, ul Komandorska 118-120, Wroclaw, 53345, Poland. TEL 48-71-3680100, FAX 48-71-3672778, www@ae.wroc.pl, http://www.ae.wroc.pl. Ed. Krzysztof Jajuga.

330 POL ISSN 0239-8532
AKADEMIA EKONOMICZNA IM. OSKARA LANGEGO WE WROCLAWIU. PRACE NAUKOWE. SERIA: MONOGRAFIE I OPRACOWANIA. Text in Polish. 1981. irreg. price varies. **Document type:** *Monographic series, Academic/Scholarly.*
Related titles: ◆ Series: Akademia Ekonomiczna im. Oskara Langego we Wroclawiu. Prace Naukowe. ISSN 0324-8445.
Indexed: RASB.
Published by: Akademia Ekonomiczna im. Oskara Langego we Wroclawiu, ul Komandorska 118-120, Wroclaw, 53345, Poland. TEL 48-71-3680100, FAX 48-71-3672778. Ed. Alicja Ziolkowska.

330 POL ISSN 1230-1477
AKADEMIA EKONOMICZNA, KRAKOW. RECTOR'S LECTURES. Key Title: Rector's Lectures. Text in English, Polish. 1992. irreg. price varies. back issues avail. **Document type:** *Academic/Scholarly.*
Published by: (Akademia Ekonomiczna, Krakow), Wydawnictwo Akademii Ekonomicznej w Krakowie, Ul Rakowicka 27, Krakow, 31-510, Poland. TEL 48-12-2935742, FAX 48-12-2935098, wydaw@ae.krakow.pl, http://www.ae.krakow.pl. Circ: 120.

330 POL ISSN 0208-7944
HB9 CODEN: ZAEKDO
➤ **AKADEMIA EKONOMICZNA, KRAKOW. ZESZYTY NAUKOWE.** Text in Polish; Summaries in English. 1955. irreg. price varies. back issues avail. **Document type:** *Academic/Scholarly.*
Formerly: Wyzsza Szkola Ekonomiczna. Zeszyty Naukowe (0075-5125)
Indexed: AgrLib, ChemAb.
—CASDDS.
Published by: (Akademia Ekonomiczna, Krakow), Wydawnictwo Akademii Ekonomicznej w Krakowie, Ul Rakowicka 27, Krakow, 31-510, Poland. TEL 48-12-2935009, FAX 48-12-2935010, wydaw@ae.krakow.pl, http://www.ae.krakow.pl. Circ: 120.

330 POL ISSN 0209-1674
➤ **AKADEMIA EKONOMICZNA, KRAKOW. ZESZYTY NAUKOWE. SERIA SPECJALNA: MONOGRAFIE.** Text in Polish; Summaries in English. 1961. irreg. price varies. back issues avail. **Document type:** *Monographic series, Academic/Scholarly.*
Formerly: Wyzsza Szkola Ekonomiczna, Krakow. Zeszyty Naukowe. Seria Specjalna: Monografie
Published by: (Akademia Ekonomiczna, Krakow), Wydawnictwo Akademii Ekonomicznej w Krakowie, Ul Rakowicka 27, Krakow, 31-510, Poland. TEL 48-12-2935009, FAX 48-12-2935010, TELEX 0325414, akademia@ae.krakow.pl, http://www.ae.krakow.pl. Circ: 500.

330 POL
AKADEMIA EKONOMICZNA, POZNAN. ZESZYTY NAUKOWE. SERIA 2. PRACE HABILITACYJNE. Text in Polish. 1957. irreg. price varies. **Document type:** *Monographic series, Academic/Scholarly.*
Formerly: Akademia Ekonomiczna, Poznan. Zeszyty Naukowe. Seria 2. Prace Habilitacyjne i Doktorskie (0079-4554)
Indexed: FS&TA, RefZh.
Published by: (Akademia Ekonomiczna w Poznaniu), Wydawnictwo Akademii Ekonomicznej w Poznaniu, al Niepodleglosci 10, Poznan, 60967, Poland. TEL 48-61-8543154, FAX 48-61-8543159, info@wydawnictwo-ae.pl, http://www.wydawnictwo-ae.pl. Ed. Antoni Sobczak. Circ: 250.

330 POL ISSN 1641-2168
HB54 CODEN: ZNANSDH
AKADEMIA EKONOMICZNA W POZNANIU. ZESZYTY NAUKOWE. Text in Polish. 1961. irreg. price varies. **Document type:** *Academic/Scholarly.*
Former titles (until 2000): Akademia Ekonomiczna w Poznaniu. Zeszyty Naukowe. Seria 1 (0208-4902); (until 1974): Wyzsza Szkola Ekonomiczna w Poznaniu. Zeszyty Naukowe. Seria 1 (0079-4546)
Indexed: FS&TA, RASB, RefZh, ZentMath.
—BLDSC (9512.142500), CASDDS.
Published by: (Akademia Ekonomiczna w Poznaniu), Wydawnictwo Akademii Ekonomicznej w Poznaniu, al Niepodleglosci 10, Poznan, 60967, Poland. TEL 48-61-8543154, FAX 48-61-8543159, info@wydawnictwo-ae.pl, http://www.wydawnictwo-ae.pl. Ed. Antoni Sobczak. Circ: 300.

330 GEO ISSN 1512-0961
HC10
AKADEMIYA NAUK GRUZII. IZVESTIYA. SERIYA EKONOMICHESKAYA. Text in Russian. q.
Indexed: RefZh.
Published by: Georgian Academy of Sciences, Rustaveli pr 52, Tbilisi, 380008, Georgia. TEL 995-32-997593, FAX 995-32-998823, http://www.acnet.ge.

330.07 DEU
AKTIV WIRTSCHAFTSZEITUNG. Text in German. fortn. **Document type:** *Newspaper, Consumer.*
Published by: Institut der Deutschen Wirtschaft, Gustav-Heinemann-Ufer 84-88, Cologne, 50968, Germany. TEL 49-221-49811, FAX 49-221-4981592, redaktion@aktiv-wirtschaftszeitung.de, welcome@iwkoeln.de, http://www.div-aktiv.de, http://www.iwkoeln.de.

330 TUR ISSN 1301-0131
AKTUEL PARA. Text in Turkish. 1994. w. **Document type:** *Magazine, Trade.*
Formerly (until 1996): Para (1300-803X)
Published by: 1 Numara Hearst Yayincilik, Sabah Tesisleri, Tesvikiye Caddesi 123, Tesvikiye, Istanbul, 80200, Turkey. TEL 90-212-3158000, FAX 90-212-3159272, para@birnumara.com.tr, http://para.birnumara.com.tr/w/, http://www.birnumara.com.tr.

330 DEU ISSN 0943-5085
AKTUELLER E G - FOERDERBRIEF FUER BETRIEBE, BERATER UND BEHOERDEN. Text in German. 1993. m. EUR 148 domestic; EUR 154 foreign (effective 2005). **Document type:** *Newsletter, Trade.* **Description:** Provides comprehensive explanations on EC supported programs, open and forthcoming tenders, news for companies, consultants and authorities.
Published by: Europa-Kontakt Informations- und Verlagsgesellschaft mbH, Breite Str 29, Berlin, 10178, Germany. TEL 49-30-203084070, FAX 49-30-203084077, eu.kontakt@t-online.de, http://www.europa-kontakt.de.

650 USA ISSN 1542-8974
HC107.A4
ALABAMA BUSINESS. Text in English. 1930. q. free. stat. back issues avail. **Document type:** *Newsletter.* **Description:** Contains regular features including an economic forecast, housing affordability index, and key economic indicators.
Former titles: Alabama Business and Economic Indicators (1055-4645); (until 1990): Alabama Business (0002-4163); (until 1955): University of Alabama Business News (0735-8725); Incorporating (1955-1973): Alabama Retail Trade (0002-4333)
Related titles: Microfiche ed.: (from CIS); Online - full text ed.
Indexed: PAIS, SRI.
Published by: University of Alabama, Center for Business and Economic Research, PO Box 870221, Tuscaloosa, AL 35487-0221. TEL 205-348-6191, FAX 205-348-2951, http://cber.cba.ua.edu/publi.html#publi2, http://cber.cba.us.edu. Ed. Annette Watters. Circ: 3,750.

ALABAMA LIBERTY. see *POLITICAL SCIENCE*

338.0029 USA ISSN 8756-4092
ALASKA BUSINESS MONTHLY. Text in English. 1985. m. USD 21.95. adv. stat.; illus. index. back issues avail.; reprints avail. **Document type:** *Trade.* **Description:** Promotes economic growth in Alaska through coverage of people, issues and trends affecting the state's business sector.
Related titles: Online - full text ed.: (from Florida Center for Library Automation, Gale Group, Northern Light Technology, Inc., O C L C Online Computer Library Center, Inc., ProQuest Information & Learning, The Dialog Corporation).
Indexed: ABIn, BusDate.
Published by: Alaska Business Publishing Co., PO Box 241288, Anchorage, AK 99524-1288. TEL 907-276-4373, FAX 907-279-2900, http://www.akbizmag.com/. Ed., R&P Ron Dalby. Pub. Vern McCorkle. Adv. contact Jim Martin. Circ: 10,000.

330 CAN ISSN 1703-6305
▼ **ALBERTA CANCER BOARD. BUSINESS PLAN.** Text in English. 2005. a. **Document type:** *Corporate.*
Related titles: Online - full content ed.
Published by: Alberta Cancer Board, Provincial Office, Ste 1220, Standard Life Centre, 10405 Jasper Ave, Edmonton, AB T5J 3N4, Canada. TEL 780-412-6300, FAX 780-412-6326, info@cancerboard.ab.ca, http://www.cancerboard.ab.ca/.

330 CAN ISSN 1708-4075
ALBERTA FINANCE ANNUAL REPORT. Text in English. 19??. a. **Document type:** *Government.*
Supersedes in part (in 2002): Treasury Annual Report (1207-5477); Which was formerly (until 1994): Alberta. Alberta Treasury. Ministry Overview & Annual Report (1200-7412); (until 1992): Alberta. Alberta Treasury. Annual Report (0381-386X)
Related titles: Online - full content ed.
Published by: Alberta Finance Ministry, Rm 426, Terrace Bldg, 9515 - 107 St., Edmonton, AB T5K 2C3, Canada. http://www.finance.gov.ab.ca/publications/annual_repts/finance/index.html.

330 CAN ISSN 1700-2567
ALBERTA FINANCE MINISTRY. ACTIVITY REPORT. Text in English. 2000. q. **Document type:** *Government.*
Related titles: Online - full content ed.
Published by: Alberta Finance Ministry, Rm 426, Terrace Bldg, 9515 - 107 St., Edmonton, AB T5K 2C3, Canada. TEL 780-427-3035, FAX 780-427-1147, http://www.finance.gov.ab.ca/publications/budget/index.html.

330 CAN ISSN 1708-4083
ALBERTA REVENUE ANNUAL REPORT. Text in English. a. **Document type:** *Government.*
Supersedes in part (in 2001): Treasury Annual Report (1207-5477); Which was formerly (until 1994): Alberta. Alberta Treasury. Ministry Overview & Annual Report (1200-7412); (until 1992): Alberta. Alberta Treasury. Annual Report (0381-386X)
Related titles: Online - full content ed.
Published by: Alberta Finance Ministry, Rm 426, Terrace Bldg, 9515 - 107 St., Edmonton, AB T5K 2C3, Canada. TEL 780-427-3035, FAX 780-427-1147, http://www.finance.gov.ab.ca/publications/annual_repts/finance/index.html.

330 CAN ISSN 1207-2591
ALBERTA VENTURE. Text in English. 1983. 10/yr. CND 21.39 domestic; CND 35.70 in United States; CND 54 elsewhere (effective 2004). **Document type:** *Magazine, Consumer.* **Description:** Serves as an authoritative information source for Alberta's business community.
Former titles (until 1995): Venture (0843-7904); (until 1989): Alberta Venture (0828-3206)
Indexed: CPerI.
—CCC.
Address: #201, 10350-124 St, Edmonton T5N 3V9, AB T5N 3V9, Canada. TEL 780-990-0839, FAX 780-425-4921, admin@albertaventure.com, http://www.albertaventure.com. Ed. Tracy Hyatt.

330 ECU
ALFA-GAMMA. Text in Spanish. m.
Address: Apdo 5391, Guayaquil, Guayas, Ecuador. Ed. Maria A Game de Gomendirrutia. Circ: 5,000.

330 USA
ALL ABOUT NET PROFITS. Text in English. bi-w. free. **Document type:** *Trade.* **Description:** Presents articles on business and marketing.
Media: Online - full text.
Address: editor@ABCmarketing.com, http://www.abcmarketing.com/.

ALLEN CONFIDENTIAL. see *HOUSING AND URBAN PLANNING*

340 363.5 USA ISSN 1525-2159
ALLEN LETTER. Text in English. 1990. m. looseleaf. USD 124.95 (effective 2001). bk.rev. bibl.; illus.; mkt.; stat.; tr.lit. **Document type:** *Newsletter.* **Description:** Serves owner and property managers of manufactured home communities across the US and Canada.
Published by: P M N Publishing, PO Box 47024, Indianapolis, IN 46247. TEL 317-888-7156, FAX 317-888-2056, gallen@manufactured-housing.net, http://www.mfdhousing.com. Ed. George Allen. Pub. Susan McCarty. Circ: 500; 300 (paid); 200 (controlled).

600 ITA ISSN 1594-5332
ALLESTIRE; politica-tecnica-economia per mostre fiere congressi vetrine negozi stand. Text in Italian. 1984. 6/yr. EUR 25.82 domestic; EUR 41.32 foreign (effective 2005). adv. illus. **Document type:** *Magazine, Trade.* **Description:** Covers political, technical and economic matters relating to the holding of exhibitions and trade fairs.
Published by: Edinterni Srl, Viale Andrea Doria 35, Milan, MI 20124, Italy. TEL 39-02-66988188, FAX 39-02-66988190, redazione@edinterni.it, http://www.edinterni.com. Circ: 8,000.

331.125 GBR
ALODIS; the service for self-employed professionals. Text in English. 2001. m. **Document type:** *Magazine, Consumer.* **Description:** Covers self-employment with topics that include: taxes, specialist software, personal assistants, training and grants, marketing advice and practical solutions to business problems.
Published by: Mongrels, The Turnmill, 63 Clerkenwell Rd, London, EC1M 5NP, United Kingdom. TEL 44-20-7959-3133, 44-20-7014-1611, partnerships@mongrel.com, http://www.alodis.co.uk/alodis/home/default.asp?cookie%5Ftest=1, http://www.mongrel.com/. Eds. Andrew Erskine TEL 44-20-7959-3209, Julia Hutchison. Circ: 210,000.

330 FRA ISSN 0247-3739
ALTERNATIVES ECONOMIQUES. Text in French. 1980. m. EUR 29.70 domestic; EUR 40.40 in Europe; EUR 40.40 French speaking Africa; EUR 54.10 elsewhere (effective 2002). adv. bk.rev. **Document type:** *Newspaper, Consumer.* **Description:** Provides economic and social news.
Incorporates (1977-1985): L' Economie en Question (0221-1300); Which was formerly (until 1979): Pour la Lutte (0151-8615)
Related titles: Supplement(s): Alternatives Economiques. Hors-Serie. ISSN 1252-4999.
Indexed: AltPI, PAIS, PerIslam, RASB.
—BLDSC (0803.683000), IE, ingenta.
Address: 28 rue du Sentier, Paris, 75002, France. TEL 33-01-44882890, FAX 33-01-40284358, http://www.alternatives-economiques.fr. Circ: 100,000.

338.27492605 GBR ISSN 1464-7753
ALUMINIUM EXTRUSION MARKETS. Text in English. 1996. m. 8 p./no.; **Document type:** *Newsletter, Trade.* **Description:** Covers the extrusions industries of Europe, North America and Asia.

Supersedes in part (in 1998): Aluminium Products Monthly (1364-1239)
Indexed: BrCerAb, CerAb, CorrAb, EMA, M&TEA, MBF, METADEX, WAA.
—CCC.
Published by: Metal Bulletin plc, 16 Lower Marsh, London, SE1 7RJ, United Kingdom. TEL 44-20-78279977, FAX 44-20-78276441, http://www.metalbulletin.com/research/mbsb_aem.asp.

338.47669722 GBR ISSN 1464-8857
ALUMINIUM FLAT ROLLED MARKETS. Text in English. 1996. m. 12 p./no.; **Document type:** *Newsletter, Trade.*
Description: Reports on the flat rolled industries of Europe, North America and Asia.
Supersedes in part (until 1998): Aluminium Products Monthly (1364-1239)
—CCC.
Published by: Metal Bulletin plc, 16 Lower Marsh, London, SE1 7RJ, United Kingdom. TEL 44-20-78279977, FAX 44-20-78276441, http://www.metalbulletin.com/research/mbsb_afrm.asp.

334 NLD ISSN 0002-6999
AMBT EN PLICHT. Text in Dutch. 1970 (vol.18). m. bk.rev. bibl. **Document type:** *Bulletin, Consumer.*
Published by: (Gereformeerd Maatschappelijk Verbond), Bureau G.M.V., Postbus 547, Zwolle, 8000 AM, Netherlands. TEL 038-4218649, FAX 038-4218629, gmv@worldonline.nl, http:www.gmv.nl. Ed. W I Meyer. R&P J Westert.

330 CHL
AMERICA ECONOMIA. Text in Portuguese, Spanish. 1986. s-m. CLP 39.60 domestic; USD 50 in North America; USD 150 elsewhere (effective 2002). **Description:** Covers business and finance in Latin America.
Related titles: Online - full text ed.
Indexed: PAIS.
Published by: AmericaEconomia, Av Apoquinado 4499, Piso 10, Santiago, Chile. TEL 56-2-2909400, FAX 56-2-2066005, http://www.americaeconomia.com. Pub. Ian Mc Cluskey. Circ: 100,000.

330 USA ISSN 1540-1200
AMERICAN ACADEMY OF BUSINESS, CAMBRIDGE. JOURNAL. Text in English. 2001. 2/yr. USD 192 in North America; USD 258 elsewhere (effective 2004). adv. **Document type:** *Journal, Academic/Scholarly.* **Description:** Publishes articles of interest to members of the business community and provides leadership in introducing new concepts to its readership.
Related titles: Online - full text ed.: (from EBSCO Publishing, ProQuest Information & Learning).
Indexed: ABIn.
—BLDSC (4683.680000).
Published by: American Academy of Business, Cambridge, 995 Weeping Willow Way, Hollywood, FL 33019. FAX 954-923-4057, drsenguder@aol.com, http://www.jaabc.com/journal.htm. Eds., Pubs. Jean Gordon, Turan Senguder.

AMERICAN BUSINESS LAW JOURNAL. see *LAW—Corporate Law*

330 USA ISSN 0743-2348
➤ **AMERICAN BUSINESS REVIEW.** Text in English. 1983. s-a. illus. reprints avail. **Document type:** *Academic/Scholarly.*
Related titles: Online - full text ed.: (from bigchalk, EBSCO Publishing, Northern Light Technology, Inc., O C L C Online Computer Library Center, Inc., ProQuest Information & Learning).
Indexed: ABIn.
Published by: University of New Haven, School of Business, 17 Tulip Dr., Glen Cove, NY 11542-1441. Ed. Robert Rainish TEL 203-932-7363.

➤ **AMERICAN FIREWORKS NEWS.** see *ENGINEERING—Chemical Engineering*

330 USA ISSN 0034-5407
HC101
AMERICAN INSTITUTE FOR ECONOMIC RESEARCH. RESEARCH REPORTS. Text in English. 1934. s-m. USD 59. bk.rev. charts; stat. index.
Published by: American Institute for Economic Research, PO Box 1000, Great Barrington, MA 01230. TEL 413-528-1216, FAX 413-528-0103. Ed. Lawrence Pratt. Circ: 8,000.

330 USA ISSN 1522-0419
HF1
AMERICAN INTERNATIONAL COLLEGE. JOURNAL OF BUSINESS. Text in English. 199?. a.
Related titles: Online - full text ed.: (from Florida Center for Library Automation, Gale Group).
Published by: American International College, 1000 State St, Springfield, MA 01109-3189. inquiry@www.aic.edu, http://www.aic.edu.

330 301 USA ISSN 0002-9246
H1 CODEN: AJESA3
➤ **AMERICAN JOURNAL OF ECONOMICS AND SOCIOLOGY.** Text in English. 1941. 5/yr., latest vol.61, no.5, 2002. USD 51 combined subscription in the Americas to individuals & Caribbean, print & online eds.; EUR 63 combined subscription in Europe to individuals print & online eds.; GBP 42 combined subscription elsewhere to individuals print & online eds.; USD 183 combined subscription in the Americas to institutions & Caribbean, print & online eds.; GBP 147 combined subscription elsewhere to institutions print & online eds. (effective 2006). bk.rev. stat.; abstr.; illus. index. reprint service avail. from NTI,PQC,ISI. **Document type:** *Journal, Academic/Scholarly.* **Description:** Presents an interdisciplinary synthesis in social sciences and philosophy, studying economic, social, and political problems of representative democratic societies. Articles based on empirical research.
Related titles: Microfiche ed.: (from PQC); Microfilm ed.: (from PQC); Online - full text ed.: ISSN 1536-7150. USD 174 in the Americas to institutions & the Caribbean; GBP 139 elsewhere to institutions (effective 2006) (from Blackwell Synergy, EBSCO Publishing, Florida Center for Library Automation, Gale Group, H.W. Wilson, IngentaConnect, O C L C Online Computer Library Center, Inc., Swets Information Services).
Indexed: ABCPolSci, ABIn, ABS&EES, AC&P, APEL, ASCA, Acal, AgeL, AmH&L, ArtHuCI, BAS, BPIA, BRI, CBRI, CIJE, CJA, CPM, CREJ, CurCont, DIP, EIP, ERA, ESPM, ETA, EnerInd, FS&TA, FamI, HRA, HistAb, IBR, IBSS, IBZ, IMFL, IPSA, IndIslam, JEL, KES, MEA, MEA&I, MEDLINE, PAIS, PRA, PSA, PSI, PopulInd, RASB, RHEA, RRTA, RiskAb, SEA, SENA, SOMA, SOPODA, SPAA, SRRA, SSA, SSCI, SSI, SUSA, SWA, SWR&A, SociolAb, TEA, V&AA, WAE&RSA, WorkRelAb.
—BLDSC (0824.350000), CISTI, IDS, IE, Infotrieve, ingenta. CCC.
Published by: (Robert Schalkenbach Foundation), Blackwell Publishing, Inc. (Subsidiary of: Blackwell Publishing Ltd.), Commerce Place, 350 Main St, Malden, MA 02148. TEL 781-388-8206, FAX 781-388-8232, subscrip@blackwellpub.com, http://www.blackwellpublishing.com/journals/AJES. Ed. Laurence S Moss. Circ: 2,200. **Co-sponsor:** Francis Neilson Fund.

➤ **AMERICAN PHARMACEUTICAL REVIEW.** see *PHARMACY AND PHARMACOLOGY*

➤ **AMERICA'S FUTURE.** see *POLITICAL SCIENCE*

➤ **AMERICA'S LOCAL BUSINESS NEWS NETWORK.** see *COMPUTERS—Internet*

330 ESP ISSN 0213-7569
HB9
ANALES DE ESTUDIOS ECONOMICOS Y EMPRESARIALES. Text in Spanish. 1986. irreg., latest vol.11, 1996. **Document type:** *Monographic series, Academic/Scholarly.*
—CINDOC.
Published by: Universidad de Valladolid, Secretariado de Publicaciones, Juan Mambrilla, 14, Valladolid, 47003, Spain. TEL 34-83-294499, FAX 34-83-290300.

330 ESP ISSN 0214-4646
ANALISE EMPRESARIAL. Text in Spanish. 3/yr.
Address: Pi y Margall, 72 bajo, Apartado 1331, Vigo, Pontevedra 36202, Spain. TEL 86-29-94-48, FAX 86-20-56-04. Ed. Alfonso Rivas Fraga. Circ: 3,000.

330 340 ITA ISSN 1720-951X
ANALISI GIURIDICA DELL'ECONOMIA. Text in Italian. 2002. s-a. EUR 41 domestic to individuals; EUR 74 foreign to individuals; EUR 63 domestic to institutions print & online eds.; EUR 113 foreign to institutions print & online eds. (effective 2004).
Related titles: Online - full text ed.
Published by: Societa Editrice Il Mulino, Strada Maggiore 37, Bologna, 40125, Italy. TEL 39-051-256011, FAX 39-051-256034, riviste@mulino.it, http://www.mulino.it.

330 URY
ANALISIS; administracion contabilidad economia. Text in Spanish. 1992. s-a. price varies.
Published by: Fundacion de Cultura Universitaria, Casilla de Correo Central, Veinticinco De Mayo, 568, Montevideo, 11003, Uruguay. TEL 598-2-9161152, FAX 598-2-9152549, fcuventa@multi.com.uy, http://www.fcu.com.uy.

330 RUS
ANALITICHESKOE OBOZRENIE. Text in Russian. 1995. w. USD 1,695 in the Americas (effective 2000).
Published by: Agentstvo Praim, Khvostov per., 11a, Moscow, 103062, Russian Federation. TEL 7-095-2361011. **Dist. by:** East View Information Services, 3020 Harbor Ln. N., Minneapolis, MN 55447. TEL 763-550-0961, FAX 763-559-2931.

330 CHN
ANHUI SHANGBAO/ANHUI BUSINESS DAILY. Text in Chinese. 1984. d. CNY 10.50, USD 4.40 per month (effective 2004). **Document type:** *Newspaper, Trade.*
Related titles: Online - full content ed.

Published by: Anhui Ribao Baoye Jituan, 206, Jinzhai Lu, Hefei, 230061, China. TEL 86-551-2832510, FAX 86-551-2832587. **Dist. by:** China International Book Trading Corp, 35 Chegongzhuang Xilu, Haidian District, PO Box 399, Beijing 100044, China. TEL 86-10-68412045, FAX 86-10-68412023, cibtc@mail.cibtc.com.cn, http://www.cibtc.com.cn.

330 POL ISSN 0459-9586
ANNALES UNIVERSITATIS MARIAE CURIE-SKLODOWSKA. SECTIO H. OECONOMIA. Text and summaries in English, French, German, Polish. 1967. a. price varies. **Document type:** *Academic/Scholarly.*
Indexed: HortAb, IBSS, PotatoAb, PoultAb, RASB.
Published by: Uniwersytet Marii Curie-Sklodowskiej w Lublinie, Wydawnictwo, pl M Curie Sklodowskiej 5, Lublin, 20031, Poland. TEL 48-81-375304, FAX 48-81-336699. Ed. Ryszard Orlowski. Circ: 350.

354.35 DEU ISSN 0570-1864
HT390
➤ **ANNALS OF REGIONAL SCIENCE**; international journal of urban, regional and environmental research and policy. Text in English. 1967. q. EUR 478 combined subscription to institutions print & online eds. (effective 2005). adv. bk.rev. cum.index every 5 yrs. back issues avail.; reprint service avail. from PSC. **Document type:** *Journal, Academic/Scholarly.*
Description: Promotes high quality scholarship on important theoretical and empirical issues in regional science and urban studies.
Related titles: Online - full text ed.: ISSN 1432-0592 (from EBSCO Publishing, ProQuest Information & Learning, Springer LINK, Swets Information Services).
Indexed: ABCPolSci, ABIn, AIAP, ASCA, AgeL, BibInd, CREJ, CurCont, EI, ESPM, ForAb, GEOBASE, IBR, IBSS, IBZ, JEL, PAIS, PSA, PopulInd, RASB, RDA, RiskAb, SSCI, SUSA, WAE&RSA.
—BLDSC (1043.650000), CISTI, IDS, IE, Infotrieve, ingenta, CCC.
Published by: Springer-Verlag (Subsidiary of: Springer Science+Business Media), Tiergartenstr 17, Heidelberg, 69121, Germany. TEL 49-6221-3450, FAX 49-6221-345229, http://link.springer.de/link/service/journals/00168/index.htm. Eds. B Johansson, R R Stough, T J Kim. Adv. contact Stephan Kroeck TEL 49-30-827875739. Circ: 1,100. **Subscr. in the Americas to:** Springer-Verlag New York, Inc., Journal Fulfillment, PO Box 2485, Secaucus, NJ 07096-2485. TEL 800-777-4643, 201-348-4033, FAX 201-348-4505, journals@springer-ny.com, http://www.springer-ny.com; **Subscr. to:** Springer GmbH Auslieferungsgesellschaft, Haberstr 7, Heidelberg 69126, Germany. TEL 49-6221-345-0, FAX 49-6221-345-4229, subscriptions@springer.de.

➤ **THE (YEAR) ANNOTATED BANKRUPTCY AND INSOLVENCY ACT.** see *LAW*

330 FRA
ANNUAIRE DES ADMINISTRATEURS ET DES SOCIETES. Text in French. 1978 (vol.62). a.
Formerly: Annuaire Desfosses
Published by: D A F S A, 42 rue Emeriau, Paris, 75015, France. FAX 40-60-51-51.

330 FRA ISSN 1169-4475
ANNUAIRE DES DOCTEURS EN SCIENCES ECONOMIQUES. Key Title: Annuaire - A N D E S E. Text in French. 1954. a. **Document type:** *Directory.*
Formerly (until 1991): Association Nationale des Docteurs es Sciences Economiques. Annuaire (1152-7528)
Published by: (Association Nationale des Docteurs en Sciences Economiques), Editions de L' Andese, 2 rue Jacques Daguerre, Rueil - Malmaison, 92565, France. TEL 33-1-47143914, FAX 33-1-47143990. Ed. Rene Le Moal.

ANNUAIRE TELEXPORT; les exportateurs et importateurs francais. see *BUSINESS AND ECONOMICS—Chamber Of Commerce Publications*

330 170 100 USA ISSN 1055-5455
HF5387
➤ **ANNUAL EDITIONS: BUSINESS ETHICS.** Text in English. 1989. a., latest 2004, 16th ed. USD 20.31 per vol. (effective 2004). illus. **Document type:** *Academic/Scholarly.*
Description: Presents different perspectives on understanding basic concepts and concerns of business ethics and to provide ideas on how to incorporate these concepts into the policies and decision-making processes of businesses.
Published by: McGraw-Hill - Dushkin (Subsidiary of: McGraw-Hill Higher Education), 2460 Kerper Blvd, Dubuque, IA 52001. TEL 800-243-6532, customer.service@mcgraw-hill.com, http://www.dushkin.com. Ed. John E Richardson. Pub. Ian Nielsen. R&P Cheryl Greenleaf.

330 USA ISSN 1092-776X
HC101
➤ **ANNUAL EDITIONS: ECONOMICS.** Text in English. 1971. a., latest 2002, 32nd ed. USD 20.31 per vol. (effective 2004). illus. **Document type:** *Academic/Scholarly.*
Formerly: Annual Editions: Readings in Economics (0090-4430)

B

Published by: McGraw-Hill - Dushkin (Subsidiary of: McGraw-Hill Higher Education), 2460 Kerper Blvd, Dubuque, IA 52001. TEL 800-243-6532, customer.service@mcgraw-hill.com, http://www.dushkin.com/text-data/catalog/0072548452.mhtml. Ed. Don Cole. Pub. Ian Nielsen. R&P Cheryl Greenleaf.

338.04 USA ISSN 1520-3956
ANNUAL EDITIONS: ENTREPRENEURSHIP. Text in English. 2000. a., latest 2002, 4th ed. USD 20.31 per vol. (effective 2004). **Document type:** *Academic/Scholarly.* **Description:** Informative anthology of current newspaper, magazine, and journal articles, explores the entrepreneurial process from idea to harvest. Selections are culled from such sources as Forbes, Fortune, Business Week, and Harvard Business Review.
Published by: McGraw-Hill - Dushkin (Subsidiary of: McGraw-Hill Higher Education), 2460 Kerper Blvd, Dubuque, IA 52001. TEL 800-243-6532, customer.service@mcgraw-hill.com, http://www.dushkin.com/text-data/catalog/0072529113.mhtml. Ed. Robert W Price.

ANNUAL EDITIONS: INTERNET AND BUSINESS. see *COMPUTERS—Internet*

330 ITA
ANNUARIO NAZIONALE DEI DOTTORI COMMERCIALISTI. Text in Italian. 1980. a. **Document type:** *Directory, Trade.*
Published by: Consiglio Nazionale dei Dottori Commercialisti, Piazza della Repubblica 59, Rome, 00187, Italy. FAX 39-06-47863349, 39-06-478631, http://www.cndc.it. Ed. Francesco Serao. Adv. contact Luciano Alcaro Menichini. Circ: 40,000.

ANTITRUST & COMMERCE REPORT. see *LAW—Corporate Law*

ANTITRUST LAW AND ECONOMICS REVIEW. see *LAW—Corporate Law*

330 ARG
ANUARIO DE LA ECONOMIA ARGENTINA/ARGENTINE ECONOMY ANNUAL. Text in English, Spanish. 1961. a. USD 350. adv. **Document type:** *Newsletter, Corporate.*
Published by: Consejo Tecnico de Inversiones S.A., Tucuman, 834 1o, Capital Federal, Buenos Aires 1049, Argentina. FAX 54-114-3224887. Ed. Jose Luis Blanco. Pub. Daniel Sticco. Adv. contact Marta Ortega.

330 301 IND ISSN 0378-4568
ANVESAK. Text in English. 1972. s-a. INR 40, USD 20. adv. bk.rev. **Document type:** *Academic/Scholarly.*
Indexed: FCA, I&DA, PAA&I, RDA, S&F, SoyAb, WAE&RSA.
Published by: Sardar Patel Institute of Economics and Social Research, Spiesr Thaltej Rd., Ahmedabad, Gujarat 380 084, India. TEL 91-79-441598. Ed. G V S N Murty. Circ: 200.

▼ **ANWALTSPRAXIS WIRTSCHAFTSRECHT.** see *LAW*

APERTURA. see *POLITICAL SCIENCE*

DIE APOTHEKENWELT. see *PHARMACY AND PHARMACOLOGY*

330 USA ISSN 0003-6595
APPALACHIA; journal of the Appalachian regional commission. Text in English. 1967. 3/yr. free (effective 2004). bk.rev. charts; illus.; stat. cum.index. back issues avail.; reprints avail. **Document type:** *Magazine, Government.* **Description:** Devoted to regional development.
Formerly: Appalachian Digest
Related titles: Microfiche ed.
Indexed: Agr, AmH&L, BRI, BiolAb, CBRI, CIJE, EPB, EnvAb, HistAb, IUSGP, PAIS, SportS, Telegen.
—BLDSC (1569.040000), IE, ingenta.
Published by: U.S. Appalachian Regional Commission, 1666 Connecticut Ave N W, Suite 700, Washington, DC 20009-1068. TEL 202-884-7799, info@arc.gov, http://www.arc.gov/index.do?nodeId=4. Ed. Diane Bowker Smith. Circ: 20,000.

APPLAUSE; the international live music business monthly. see *MUSIC*

330 IND ISSN 0570-4839
APPLIED ECONOMIC PAPERS. Text in English. 1961. s-a. bk.rev. charts.
Published by: Osmania University, Department of Commerce, Hyderabad, Andhra Pradesh 500 007, India.

330 GBR ISSN 0003-6846
HB1 CODEN: APPEBP
➤ **APPLIED ECONOMICS.** Text in English. 1969. 21/yr. GBP 3,553, USD 5,863 combined subscription to institutions print & online eds. (effective 2006); Includes Applied Financial Economics and Applied Economics Letters.. adv. charts; illus. Index. back issues avail.; reprint service avail. from PQC,ISI,PSC. **Document type:** *Journal, Academic/Scholarly.* **Description:** Encourages economic analysis to economics problems in the private and public sectors.
Related titles: Online - full text ed.: ISSN 1466-4283. 1999. GBP 3,375, USD 5,570 to institutions (effective 2006) (from EBSCO Publishing, Florida Center for Library Automation, Gale Group, IngentaConnect, Northern Light Technology, Inc., O C L C Online Computer Library Center, Inc., Swets Information Services); ◆ Supplement(s): Applied Financial Economics. ISSN 0960-3107; ◆ Applied Economics Letters. ISSN 1350-4851.
Indexed: ABIn, AEA, AHCMS, APEL, ASCA, AgeL, AnBrAb, BAS, BPI, BPIA, CIS, CJA, CPM, CREJ, CurCont, DSA, ESPM, Emerald, FCA, FPA, FamI, ForAb, GEOBASE, HortAb, I&DA, IBR, IBSS, IBZ, ILD, IndVet, JCQM, JEL, MaizeAb, NutrAb, PAIS, PCI, PHN&I, PN&I, PRA, PotatoAb, PoultAb, RASB, RDA, RRTA, RevApplEntom, RiceAb, RiskAb, S&F, SIA, SSCI, SoyAb, T&II, TDB, TriticAb, VetBull, WAE&RSA, e-psyche.
—BLDSC (1571.970000), CISTI, IDS, IE, Infotrieve, ingenta. **CCC.**
Published by: Routledge (Subsidiary of: Taylor & Francis Group), 4 Park Sq, Milton Park, Abingdon, Oxon OX14 4RN, United Kingdom. TEL 44-1235-828600, FAX 44-1235-829000, econjournals@gwmail.warwick.ac.uk, info@routledge.co.uk, http://www.tandf.co.uk/journals/routledge/00036846.html, http://www.routledge.com. Eds. Lucio Sarno, Mark Taylor. **Subscr. in N America to:** Taylor & Francis Inc., Customer Services Dept, 325 Chestnut St, 8th Fl, Philadelphia, PA 19106. TEL 800-354-1420, FAX 215-625-8914; **Subscr. to:** Taylor & Francis Ltd, Journals Customer Service, Rankine Rd, Basingstoke, Hants RG24 8PR, United Kingdom. TEL 44-1256-813000, FAX 44-1256-330245, enquiry@tandf.co.uk.

330 GBR ISSN 1350-4851
➤ **APPLIED ECONOMICS LETTERS.** Text in English. 1994. 15/yr. GBP 642, USD 1,042 combined subscription to institutions print & online eds. (effective 2006). adv. back issues avail.; reprint service avail. from PSC. **Document type:** *Journal, Academic/Scholarly.* **Description:** Publishes short accounts of new and original research within two months of receipt.
Related titles: Online - full text ed.: ISSN 1466-4291. GBP 610, USD 990 (effective 2006) (from EBSCO Publishing, Gale Group, IngentaConnect, O C L C Online Computer Library Center, Inc., Swets Information Services); ◆ Supplement to: Applied Economics. ISSN 0003-6846.
Indexed: ASCA, AgBio, AgrForAb, AnBrAb, CJA, CurCont, FamI, GEOBASE, HerbAb, HortAb, IBR, IBSS, IBZ, IndVet, JEL, MaizeAb, NutrAb, PHN&I, PN&I, PoultAb, RASB, RDA, RRTA, RiceAb, S&F, SIA, SSCI, SoyAb, TDB, TriticAb, VetBull, WAE&RSA.
—BLDSC (1571.972000), IDS, IE, Infotrieve, ingenta. **CCC.**
Published by: Routledge (Subsidiary of: Taylor & Francis Group), 4 Park Sq, Milton Park, Abingdon, Oxon OX14 4RN, United Kingdom. TEL 44-1235-828600, FAX 44-1235-829000, econjournals@gwmail.warwick.ac.uk, info@routledge.co.uk, http://www.tandf.co.uk/journals/routledge/13504851.html, http://www.routledge.com. Eds. Lucio Sarno, Mark Taylor. R&P Ms. Sarah King. **Subscr. in N America to:** Taylor & Francis Inc., Customer Services Dept, 325 Chestnut St, 8th Fl, Philadelphia, PA 19106. TEL 800-354-1420, FAX 215-625-8914; **Subscr. to:** Taylor & Francis Ltd, Journals Customer Service, Rankine Rd, Basingstoke, Hants RG24 8PR, United Kingdom. TEL 44-1256-813000, FAX 44-1256-330245, enquiry@tandf.co.uk.

330 GBR ISSN 1744-6546
▼ ➤ **APPLIED FINANCIAL ECONOMICS LETTERS.** Text in English. 2005. 6/yr. GBP 249, USD 405 combined subscription to institutions print & online eds. (effective 2006). **Document type:** *Journal, Academic/Scholarly.*
Related titles: Online - full text ed.: ISSN 1744-6554. GBP 237, USD 385 to institutions (effective 2006) (from EBSCO Publishing, Gale Group, IngentaConnect).
—BLDSC (1572.556000).
Published by: Routledge (Subsidiary of: Taylor & Francis Group), 4 Park Sq, Milton Park, Abingdon, Oxon OX14 4RN, United Kingdom. TEL 44-1235-828600, FAX 44-1235-829000, journals@routledge.com, http://www.tandf.co.uk/journals/titles/17446546.asp, http://www.routledge.com. Ed. Mark Taylor.

➤ **ARAB - AMERICAN BUSINESS**; the magazine for a culture of success. see *ETHNIC INTERESTS*

330 GBR
ARAB - BRITISH BUSINESS. Text in English. 50/yr. free to members. **Document type:** *Bulletin.*
Published by: Arab - British Chamber of Commerce, 6 Belgrave Sq, London, SW1X 8PH, United Kingdom. TEL 44-171-235-4363, FAX 44-171-235-1748, abb@abccbims.force9.co.uk. Ed. Sakina Daudjee.

ARAB WORLD AGRIBUSINESS/AL-ZIRA'AH FI-L-ALAM AL-ARABI. see *AGRICULTURE*

330 CAN ISSN 0830-8888
ARABUSINESS INTERNATIONAL. Text in Arabic, English. 1986. 24/yr. USD 72 domestic; USD 100 foreign. adv.
Published by: Allam Arabic Publishing & Advertising Co., 370 Queen St E, Toronto, ON M5A 1T1, Canada. TEL 416-861-0238, FAX 416-861-0238, TELEX 416-861-0238. Ed. Salah Allam.

330 DEU ISSN 1619-4365
ARBEIT, INNOVATION UND NACHHALTIGKEIT. Text in German. irreg., latest vol.4, 2004. price varies. **Document type:** *Monographic series, Academic/Scholarly.*
Published by: Rainer Hampp Verlag, Meringerzellerstr 10, Mering, 86415, Germany. TEL 49-8233-4783, FAX 49-8233-30755, Rainer_Hampp_Verlag@t-online.de, http://www.hampp-verlag.de.

ARBEIT UND OEKOLOGIE BRIEFE. see *ENVIRONMENTAL STUDIES*

331 DEU ISSN 0947-2967
ARBEIT UND TECHNIK. Text in German. 1995. irreg., latest vol.27, 2004. price varies. **Document type:** *Monographic series, Academic/Scholarly.*
Published by: Rainer Hampp Verlag, Meringerzellerstr 10, Mering, 86415, Germany. TEL 49-8233-4783, FAX 49-8233-30755, Rainer_Hampp_Verlag@t-online.de, http://www.hampp-verlag.de.

330 USA
ARBOR NEWS. Text in English. m. free. **Document type:** *Newsletter, Trade.*
Published by: Gleaner Life Insurance Society, 5200 US 223 W, Adrian, MI 49221-7894. TEL 517-263-2244, FAX 517-265-7745, gleaner@gleaner.com, http://www.gleanerlife.com/. Ed. Jennifer Allman. Circ: 1,200 (free).

330 DEU ISSN 0342-6270
ARCHIV UND WIRTSCHAFT; Zeitschrift fuer das Archivwesen der Wirtschaft. Text in German. 1967. q. EUR 8 newsstand/cover (effective 2004). adv. bk.rev.; film rev. bibl.; illus. index. back issues avail. **Document type:** *Journal, Trade.*
Indexed: DIP, IBR, IBZ, RefZh.
Published by: Vereinigung Deutscher Wirtschaftsarchivare e.V., Commerzbank AG, Historische Dokumentation, Kaiserplatz 1, Frankfurt Am Main, 60261, Germany. TEL 49-69-13623616, FAX 49-69-13623422, detlef_krause@commerzbank.com, http://www.wirtschaftsarchive.de. R&P, Adv. contact Detlef Krause. B&W page EUR 370; trim 136 x 200. Circ: 550 (paid and controlled).

ARCHIVUM TREBONENSE. see *HISTORY—History Of Europe*

330 POL
➤ **ARGUMENTA OECONOMICA CRACOVIENSIA.** Text in English. 2001. irreg. price varies. 200 p./no. 1 cols./p.; **Document type:** *Academic/Scholarly.*
Published by: (Akademia Ekonomiczna, Krakow), Wydawnictwo Akademii Ekonomicznej w Krakowie, Ul Rakowicka 27, Krakow, 31-510, Poland. TEL 48-12-2935009, FAX 48-12-2935010, wydaw@ae.krakow.pl, http://www.ae.krakow.pl. Circ: 350.

330 DEU
ARGUMENTE ZU UNTERNEHMENSFRAGEN. Text in German. m. **Document type:** *Academic/Scholarly.*
Published by: (Institut der Deutschen Wirtschaft), Deutscher Instituts Verlag GmbH, Gustav-Heinemann-Ufer 84-88, Cologne, 50968, Germany. TEL 49-221-4981452, FAX 49-221-4981445.

330 LBN
L'ARGUS DE L'ECONOMIE LIBANAISE. Text in French. 1966. m. USD 300 (effective 2001). **Document type:** *Bulletin.* **Description:** Survey of economic developments in Lebanon, including trade and industry, finance and taxation, public works and reconstruction, transports and communications, labor and social affairs.
Published by: Bureau of Lebanese and Arab Documentation - Argus, Sodeco St, P O Box 165403, Beirut, Lebanon. TEL 961-1-219113.

330 FRA ISSN 0752-4471
ARGUS DU FONDS DE COMMERCE ET DE L'INDUSTRIE✶. Text in French. 1982. 6/yr.
Published by: Groupe ICF, Tour Centre Affaire, Avenir Ouest, Nanterre, Cedex 92025, France. TEL 42-94-97-74. Ed. Marie Jose Plumas. Circ: 30,000.

ARIBA B2B UPDATE. see *COMPUTERS—Internet*

ARIBA MAGAZINE; the magazine for business-to-business ecommerce. see *COMPUTERS—Internet*

338 EST ISSN 1406-1252
ARIELU. Text in Estonian. 1994. m. EEK 360 (effective 2002). adv. **Document type:** *Magazine, Trade.* **Description:** Contains articles and information on economic issues of interest to entrepreneurs.
Published by: Inreko Press, Ahtri 6, Tallinn, 10151, Estonia. TEL 372-631-1568, FAX 372-631-1181, arielu@inrekopress.ee, http://www.inrekopress.ee/AE/index.html. Ed. Margit Aedla. adv.: page EEK 17,900; 210 x 297.

330 USA ISSN 0273-6950
ARIZONA BUSINESS GAZETTE. Text in English. 1880. w. (Thu.). USD 30 (effective 2005). adv. **Document type:** *Newspaper, Trade.*

Related titles: Online - full text ed.: (from Gale Group, Northern Light Technology, Inc., The Dialog Corporation).
Indexed: ABIn, BusDate, T&II.
—**CCC.**
Published by: Phoenix Newspapers, Inc., PO Box 1950, Phoenix, AZ 85001. TEL 602-271-7373, FAX 602-271-7363, luci.scott@pni.com, http://www.azcentral.com/abgnews/. Ed. Luci Scott. Adv. contact Tom Bianco. Circ: 15,123. Wire service: AP.

330 USA
ARIZONA ECONOMIC INDICATORS (TUCSON). Text in English. 1984. s-a. USD 17 domestic; USD 23 foreign (effective 2000). **Description:** Presents historical data for some 530 measures of economic activity for the state of Arizona and its counties. Provides useful information for both public and private sector professionals.
Published by: University of Arizona, College of Business and Public Administration, Economic and Business Research Program, McClelland Hall 204, Tucson, AZ 85721. TEL 520-621-2155, FAX 520-621-2150, pmontoya@bpa.arizona.edu. Ed. Diana Hunter. Circ: 1,000.

330 USA
ARIZONA ECONOMIC TRENDS. Text in English. q. free. **Document type:** *Government.* **Description:** Provides an update and analysis of state and county employment and economic data, as well as information on state and national programs and policies that affect the nation's and Arizona's labor markets.
Indexed: SRI.
Published by: Arizona Department of Economic Security, Research Administration, Site Code 733A, Box 6123, Phoenix, AZ 85005. TEL 602-542-3871, FAX 602-542-6474. Ed. Brent Fine. Circ: 4,500.

330 650 USA ISSN 0004-1742
HC107.A8 CODEN: ABRVBM
➤ **ARKANSAS BUSINESS AND ECONOMIC REVIEW.** Text in English. 1933. q. free in N. America only. charts; illus.; stat. cum.index. **Document type:** *Academic/Scholarly.*
Formerly: Arkansas Business Bulletin
Related titles: Microfiche ed.: (from CIS); Online - full text ed.: (from EBSCO Publishing, Florida Center for Library Automation, Gale Group, O C L C Online Computer Library Center, Inc., ProQuest Information & Learning, The Dialog Corporation).
Indexed: ABIn, BPIA, BusI, Inspec, ManagCont, PAIS, PMA, SRI, T&II.
Published by: (Bureau of Business and Economic Research), University of Arkansas, College of Business Administration, 301 Business Administration Building, Fayetteville, AR 72701. TEL 501-575-4151, FAX 501-575-7687, sbarger@comp.uark.edu. Ed., R&P Craig T Schulman. Circ: 3,900.

330 USA ISSN 1053-6582
ARKANSAS BUSINESS JOURNAL. Text in English. 1984. w. USD 29.95 for 6 mos. in state; USD 54.95 in state; USD 84.95 out of state; USD 1 newsstand/cover (effective 2005). **Document type:** *Newspaper, Trade.*
Related titles: Online - full content ed.; Online - full text ed.: (from bigchalk, Gale Group, O C L C Online Computer Library Center, Inc., ProQuest Information & Learning).
—**CCC.**
Published by: Arkansas Business Publishing Group, 122 E Second St, Little Rock, AR 72203. TEL 501-372-1443, 888-322-6397, FAX 501-375-7933, info@abpg.com, http://www.abpg.com, http://www.arkansasbusiness.com/news/print_editions/arkbiz.asp. Ed. Gwen Moritz. Pub. Jeff Ankins. Adv. contact Shawn Hecher. Circ: 3,000 (paid).

ART MATERIALS RETAILER. see *ART*

330 IND ISSN 0004-3559
HC431
➤ **ARTHA VIJNANA.** Text in English. 1959. q. INR 300, USD 75 (effective 2000). adv. bk.rev. charts; stat. Annual Index. back issues avail. **Document type:** *Academic/Scholarly.*
Indexed: BAS, CREJ, EIP, ForAb, I&DA, IBSS, ILD, KES, PAA&I, PAIS, RASB, RDA, RRTA, RiceAb, S&F, S&MA, TOSA, WAE&RSA.
—BLDSC (1733.750000), Infotrieve.
Published by: Gokhale Institute of Politics and Economics, c/o V.S. Chire, 846 Shivajinagar, Deccan Gymkhana, Pune, Maharashtra 411 004, India. TEL 91-20-5650287, 91-20-5654288, 91-20-5675008, FAX 91-20-5652579, 91-20-5675600, gipe@vsnl.com. Ed. V.S. Chitre. Circ: 200; 250 (paid).

330 IND
ARTHA VIJNANA REPRINT SERIES. Text in English. 1975. irreg., latest vol.15, 1991. price varies.
Published by: Gokhale Institute of Politics and Economics, c/o V.S. Chire, 846 Shivajinagar, Deccan Gymkhana, Pune, Maharashtra 411 004, India. TEL 91-20-5654288.

330 IND ISSN 0004-3575
ARTHANITI. Text in English. 1957. s-a. INR 15, USD 4. bk.rev. charts; stat.
Indexed: BAS, IBR, JEL.

Published by: University of Calcutta, Department of Economics, 56-A Barrackapore Trunk Rd., Kolkata, West Bengal 700 050, India. Ed. Amlan Datta. Circ: 400.

330 IND ISSN 0970-7654
ARTHIK PRASANGA; an economic and commercial quarterly journal in Bengali. (Aapra) Text in English. 1952-1985; resumed 1988. q. INR 30, USD 10 (effective 2001). adv. bk.rev. charts; illus.; pat.; stat.; tr.lit.; tr.mk. 24 p./no. 1 cols./p.; back issues avail.; reprints avail. **Document type:** *Newspaper.*
Published by: Economic Studies & Journals Publishing Co., 2 Private Rd., Dum Dum, Kolkata, West Bengal 700 074, India. TEL 91-33-5512288, FAX 91-33-551-3635. Ed., Pub. Gautam Mukherjee. R&P, Adv. contact Shounak Lahiri. page INR 2,000; 18.5 x 11.5. Circ: 24,000.

330 ITA
ARTIGIANATO DI SICILIA. Text in Italian. 1965. m.
Published by: Associazione Artigiani Provincia di Palermo, Artigianato di Sicilia, Via Roma, 391, Palermo, PA 90133, Italy. Circ: 20,000.

ARZNEIMITTEL ZEITUNG. see *PHARMACY AND PHARMACOLOGY*

ARZT UND WIRTSCHAFT. see *MEDICAL SCIENCES*

330 GBR
ASHTON BUSINESS SCHOOL. POLICY SUPPORT SERIES. Text in English. irreg.
—BLDSC (6543.327622).
Published by: (Aston University, Aston Business School), Bostock Marketing Group Limited, 7 Holt Court North, Heneage St West, Aston Science Park, Birmingham, B7 4AX, United Kingdom. TEL 44-121-333-6006, FAX 44-121-333-6800, bmg@bostock.co.uk, http://www.bostock.co.uk.

330 SGP
ASIA 21. Text in English. m. SGD 64.27 in the Middle East and Asia Pacific; USD 72 elsewhere. **Document type:** *Consumer.* **Description:** Devoted to introducing breakthrough business concepts from ASEAN and Japan. Covers the spectrum from business and management matters to environmental, gender and cultural concerns.
Published by: (P H P Institute JPN), P H P International Pte. Ltd., 331 North Bridge Rd, 03-04 Odeon Towers, Singapore, 188720, Singapore. TEL 65-3333455, FAX 65-3333265, http://www.php.co.jp. Ed. Catherine Khoo. **Subscr. outside Asia Pacific & Middle East to:** PHP Institute of America, 420 Lexington Ave, Ste 646, New York, NY 10170. TEL 212-949-8022, FAX 212-949-8243.

ASIA BUSINESS LAW REVIEW. see *LAW*

ASIA ENVIRONMENTAL BUSINESS JOURNAL. see *ENVIRONMENTAL STUDIES*

ASIA ENVIRONMENTAL REVIEW; the business report for environmental decision-makers with operations in Asia . see *ENVIRONMENTAL STUDIES*

330 SGP ISSN 1019-2239
HF3751
ASIA INC. Text in English. 1992. m. USD 15 in Taiwan; USD 29 in Japan; SGD 30 in Singapore; USD 8 in Philippines; USD 9 in Indonesia & Thailand; BND 30 in Brunei Darussalam; USD 14 in Australia, Korea & Malaysia; USD 20 in elsewhere in Asia; USD 22 in US & China; USD 21 in United Kingdom; USD 23 elsewhere (effective 2005). adv. **Document type:** *Magazine, Trade.* **Description:** Covers Asian business, economic and political issues, travel, leisure and self-improvement.
Related titles: Online - full text ed.: (from Factiva).
Indexed: ManagCont, T&II.
Published by: Asia Inc. Ltd., 150 Cecil St. # 13-00, Singapore, 069543, Singapore. TEL 65-62328622, FAX 65-62328630, http://www.asia-inc.com/. adv.: B&W page USD 6,780, color page USD 8,800; trim 204 x 266. Circ: 75,000.

330 GBR
ASIA INTELLIGENCE WIRE. Text in English. d. **Document type:** *Newspaper, Trade.*
Media: Online - full content.
Published by: Financial Times Information Ltd., Fitzroy House, 13-17 Epworth St, London, EC2A 4DL, United Kingdom. TEL 44-20-7825-8000, FAX 44-20-7608-2032, http://www.ft.com.

330 JPN
ASIA MARKET REVIEW. Abbreviated title: A M R. Text in Japanese. s-a. JPY 92,400 (effective 2002). **Document type:** *Magazine, Trade.*
Published by: Jukagaku Kogyo Tsushinsha/Heavy & Chemical Industry News Agency, 2-36 Jinbo-cho, Kanda, Chiyoda-ku, Tokyo, 101-0051, Japan. TEL 81-3-3230-3531, FAX 81-3-3264-0728, fcnews@jkn.co.jp, http://www.amr-mag.com/, http://www.jkn.co.jp/.

330 320 CAN
ASIA PACIFIC BULLETIN. Text in English. m.
Media: Online - full text. **Related titles:** E-mail ed.
Published by: Asia Pacific Foundation of Canada, 666-999 Canada Place, Vancouver, BC V6C 3E1, Canada. http://www.asiapacificbusiness.ca/apbn/bulletin.cfm.

330 GBR ISSN 1360-2381
HF3820.5
➤ **ASIA PACIFIC BUSINESS REVIEW.** Text in English. 1994. q. GBP 270, USD 410 combined subscription to institutions print & online eds. (effective 2006). adv. bk.rev. index. back issues avail.; reprint service avail. from PSC. **Document type:** *Journal, Academic/Scholarly.* **Description:** Concentrates on the way the economic transformation of the Pacific Rim has reshaped the global economy, explaining and investigating the rise of Far Eastern businesses and their international competitiveness.
Formerly (until 1995): Journal of Far Eastern Business (1351-0363)
Related titles: Online - full text ed.: GBP 257, USD 403 to institutions (effective 2006) (from EBSCO Publishing, Gale Group, IngentaConnect, O C L C Online Computer Library Center, Inc., Swets Information Services).
Indexed: ABIn, APEL, BAS, ESPM, Emerald, GEOBASE, IBSS, JEL, M&MA, RefZh, RiskAb.
—BLDSC (1742.257600), IE, Infotrieve, ingenta. **CCC.**
Published by: Routledge (Subsidiary of: Taylor & Francis Group), 4 Park Sq, Milton Park, Abingdon, Oxon OX14 4RN, United Kingdom. TEL 44-1235-828600, FAX 44-1235-829000, info@routledge.co.uk, http://www.tandf.co.uk/journals/titles/13602381.asp, http://www.routledge.com. Eds. Chris Rowley, Malcolm Warner. adv.: B&W page GBP 195, B&W page USD 285.

330 658 SGP
ASIA - PACIFIC BUSINESS SERIES. Text in English. 2000. irreg., latest vol.2, 2001. price varies. **Document type:** *Monographic series, Academic/Scholarly.*
Published by: World Scientific Publishing Co. Pte. Ltd., 5 Toh Tuck Link, Singapore, 596224, Singapore. TEL 65-466-5775, FAX 65-467-7667, wspc@wspc.com.sg, series@wspc.com.sg, http://www.wspc.com.sg/books/series/apbs_series.shtml, http://www.worldscientific.com. Eds. Lane Kelly, Richard Brislin. **Dist. by:** World Scientific Publishing Co., Inc., 1060 Main St, River Edge, NJ 07661. TEL 201-487-9655, 800-227-7562, FAX 201-487-9656, 888-977-2665; World Scientific Publishing Ltd., 57 Shelton St, London WC2H 9HE, United Kingdom. TEL 44-20-78360888, FAX 44-20-78362020, sales@wspc.co.uk.

330.995 AUS
ASIA PACIFIC ECONOMIC OUTLOOK. Text in English. a. AUD 18,000 (effective 2000). charts; stat. **Document type:** *Corporate.* **Description:** Supplies an overview of the prospects for the 14 major Asia-Pacific economies.
Published by: B I S Shrapnel Pty. Ltd., 8th Fl., 181 Miller St, North Sydney, NSW 2060, Australia. TEL 61-2-9959-5924, FAX 61-2-9959-5795, nhatcher@bis.com, http://www.bis.com.au. Ed. Nigel Hatcher. Circ: 200 (paid).

330 320 CAN
ASIA PACIFIC FOUNDATION OF CANADA. APSUMMIT SERIES. Text in English. irreg.
Media: Online - full text.
Published by: Asia Pacific Foundation of Canada, 666-999 Canada Place, Vancouver, BC V6C 3E1, Canada. http://www.asiapacific.ca/analysis/pubs/index.cfm#1.

330 320 CAN
ASIA PACIFIC FOUNDATION OF CANADA. EVENT REPORTS. Text in English. irreg.
Media: Online - full text.
Published by: Asia Pacific Foundation of Canada, 666-999 Canada Place, Vancouver, BC V6C 3E1, Canada. http://www.asiapacific.ca/analysis/pubs/index.cfm#1.

330 320 CAN
ASIA PACIFIC FOUNDATION OF CANADA. IMPACT REPORTS. Text in English. irreg.
Media: Online - full text.
Published by: Asia Pacific Foundation of Canada, 666-999 Canada Place, Vancouver, BC V6C 3E1, Canada. http://www.asiapacificbusiness.ca/apbn/impact/index.cfm.

330 320 CAN
ASIA PACIFIC FOUNDATION OF CANADA. ROUNDTABLE WORKSHOP REPORTS. Text in English. irreg.
Media: Online - full text.
Published by: Asia Pacific Foundation of Canada, 666-999 Canada Place, Vancouver, BC V6C 3E1, Canada. http://www.asiapacific.ca/analysis/pubs/index.cfm#1.

330 320 CAN
ASIA PACIFIC FOUNDATION OF CANADA. SURVEYS. Text in English. irreg.
Media: Online - full text.
Published by: Asia Pacific Foundation of Canada, 666-999 Canada Place, Vancouver, BC V6C 3E1, Canada. http://www.asiapacific.ca/analysis/pubs/index.cfm#1.

B

338.95 AUS ISSN 1326-8481
HC460.5.A1
➤ **ASIA PACIFIC JOURNAL OF ECONOMICS AND BUSINESS.** Text in English. 1997. s-a. AUD 55 domestic to individuals; USD 50 foreign to individuals; AUD 132 domestic to institutions; USD 120 foreign to institutions (effective 2005). **Document type:** *Journal, Academic/Scholarly.* **Description:** Aims to publish original, scholarly articles from a wide variety of disciplines, addressing economics and business-related subjects.
Indexed: JEL.
—BLDSC (1742.260682), IE, ingenta.
Published by: Curtin University of Technology, School of Economics and Finance, c/o Ms Sue Hall, GPO Box U 1987, Perth, W.A. 6845, Australia. TEL 61-8-9266-7147, FAX 61-8-9266-2378, kerri@cbs.curtin.edu.au, hallsp@cbs.curtin.edu.au, http://www.cbs.curtin.edu.au/journals/apjeb/. Ed. Ian Kerr.

330 AUS ISSN 1036-3793
DS501
ASIA PACIFIC PROFILES. Text in English. 1990. a. AUD 500; USD 500 foreign. stat. **Description:** A review of the economics of East Asia and the Pacific region with current statistics and projections.
Published by: (Asia Pacific Economics Group), Australian National University, G.P.O. Box 4, Canberra, ACT 2601, Australia. TEL 61-2-6249-4705, FAX 61-2-6257-2886. Ed. Maree Tait. **Subscr. to:** FT Newsletters and Management Reports, Asia Pacific Suite 1808, Asian House, 1 Hennessy Rd, Wanchai, Hong Kong, Hong Kong. FAX 852-25206646.

ASIA - PACIFIC REVIEW. see *POLITICAL SCIENCE—International Relations*

ASIA PACIFIC TECH MONITOR. see *TECHNOLOGY: COMPREHENSIVE WORKS*

330 GBR
ASIA PACIFIC WEEKLY FINANCIAL NEWS SUMMARY. Text in English. w. looseleaf. GBP 480; GBP 515 foreign. stat. **Document type:** *Trade.* **Description:** Covers financial and commercial news on companies in Malaysia, Singapore, Thailand, Japan, Hong Kong, Australia, and Korea.
Published by: Financial Times Information Ltd., Extel, Fitzroy House, 13-17 Epworth St, London, EC2A 4DL, United Kingdom. TEL 44-20-7608-8000, FAX 44-20-7608-2032, eic@ft.com, http://www.info.ft.com.

330 332.6 AUS ISSN 1445-4300
ASIA TODAY INTERNATIONAL. Text in English. 1983 (June). m. AUD 165 domestic; HKD 980 in Hong Kong; USD 150 elsewhere (effective 2005). adv. bk.rev. 72 p./no.; back issues avail. **Document type:** *Magazine, Trade.* **Description:** Identifies business opportunities in Asia and changes in Asian government policies affecting foreign trade, investment, taxation, economic development.
Formerly (until Sep. 2000): Asia Today (0813-2844)
Related titles: Microfiche ed.: (from PQC); Online - full content ed.: Asia Today Online; Online - full text ed.: (from LexisNexis).
Indexed: ABIX.
Published by: East Asia News and Features (Australia) Pty. Ltd., Level 29, Chifley Tower, 2 Chifley Sq., Sydney, NSW 2000, Australia. TEL 61-2-9970-6477, FAX 61-2-9913-2003, asiatoday@asiatoday.com.au, asiatoday@bigpond.com, http://www.asiatoday.com.au. Ed. Florence Chong. Pub., R&P, Adv. contact Barry Pearton. B&W page AUD 2,845, color page AUD 3,770; trim 277 x 190. Circ: 8,414 (paid and controlled). **Subscr. to:** Grosvenor Place Post Office, Box N7, Sydney, NSW 1220, Australia. **Dist. by:** Abraham Book Centre, Rm.1203, Hong Kong Plaza, 188 Connaught Rd W, Hong Kong, Hong Kong. TEL 852-2856-9484, FAX 852-2565-8749.

330 TWN ISSN 1609-1566
ASIA TRADEMART NEWS. Text in English. 2001. m. **Document type:** *Trade.*
Published by: Interface Global Taiwan Co., Ltd., PO Box 173-12, Taipei, 116, Taiwan. service@asiatrademart.com, http://www.asiatrademart.com.

330 GBR
ASIAINFO DAILY CHINA NEWS. Text in English. d. **Document type:** *Newspaper, Trade.*
Media: Online - full content.
Published by: Financial Times Information Ltd., Fitzroy House, 13-17 Epworth St, London, EC2A 4DL, United Kingdom. TEL 44-20-7825-8000, FAX 44-20-7608-2032, http://www.ft.com.

330 IND ISSN 0972-3986
ASIAN - AFRICAN JOURNAL OF ECONOMICS AND ECONOMETRICS. Text in English. 2001. s-a. USD 155 to institutions (effective 2006).
Published by: Scientific Publishers, 5-A New Pali Rd., Near Hotel Taj Hari Mahal, PO Box 91, Jodhpur, Rajasthan 342 003, India. TEL 91-291-2433323, FAX 91-291-2512580, journals@scientificpub.com, http://www.scientificpub.com/bookdetails.php?booktransid=465&bookid=461.

330 SGP ISSN 0218-9275
HD2891.85 CODEN: ACRJFV
➤ **ASIAN CASE RESEARCH JOURNAL.** Abbreviated title: A C R J. Text in English. 1997. s-a. SGD 111, USD 63, EUR 61 to individuals; SGD 148, USD 84, EUR 81 combined subscription to institutions print & online eds. (effective 2006). adv. back issues avail. **Document type:** *Journal, Academic/Scholarly.* **Description:** Aims to provide case instructors, whether academics, consultants, or company in-house trainers, with a selection of high-quality cases on Asian companies and MNCs operating in Asia-Pacific.
Related titles: Online - full text ed.: SGD 141, USD 80, EUR 77 to institutions (effective 2005) (from EBSCO Publishing, O C L C Online Computer Library Center, Inc., Swets Information Services).
Indexed: ESPM, RiskAb.
—BLDSC (1742.403532), IE, ingenta. **CCC.**
Published by: (National University of Singapore, Faculty of Business Administration), World Scientific Publishing Co. Pte. Ltd., 5 Toh Tuck Link, Singapore, 596224, Singapore. TEL 65-466-5775, FAX 65-467-7667, wspc@wspc.com.sg, http://www.worldscinet.com/journals/acrj/acrj.shtml, http://www.worldscientific.com. Ed. Lau Geok Theng. adv.: B&W page GBP 640, color page GBP 1,515. **Subscr. to:** Farrer Rd, PO Box 128, Singapore 912805, Singapore. sales@wspc.com.sg. **Dist. by:** World Scientific Publishing Co., Inc., 1060 Main St, River Edge, NJ 07661. TEL 201-487-9655, 800-227-7562, FAX 201-487-9656, 888-977-2665.

330 PHL ISSN 0117-0481
HC411
ASIAN DEVELOPMENT OUTLOOK. Text in English. a. USD 36 newsstand/cover (effective 2001). **Description:** Provides a broad view of economic progress in developing Asia and the Pacific, and offers analysis and assessment of recent trends.
Related titles: Online - full text ed.
Indexed: IIS.
—BLDSC (1742.407740), CISTI.
Published by: Asian Development Bank, Publications Unit, P.O. Box 789, Manila, 0980, Philippines. adbpub@adb.org, http://www.adb.org/Documents/Books/ADO/.

330.95 USA ISSN 1535-3516
HC411
ASIAN ECONOMIC PAPERS. Text in English. 2001. 3/yr. USD 44 in US & Canada to individuals; USD 64 elsewhere to individuals; USD 140 in US & Canada to institutions; USD 160 elsewhere to institutions (effective 2005). **Document type:** *Journal, Academic/Scholarly.* **Description:** Contains high quality, objective analysis of key economic issues of a particular Asian economy or of the broader Asian region.
Related titles: Online - full text ed.: ISSN 1536-0083. USD 40 to individuals; USD 126 to institutions (effective 2004); (from EBSCO Publishing, Gale Group, IngentaConnect, O C L C Online Computer Library Center, Inc., Swets Information Services).
Indexed: ABIn.
—BLDSC (1742.411000), IE.
Published by: M I T Press, 55 Hayward St, Cambridge, MA 02142-1493. TEL 617-253-5646, FAX 617-258-6779, journals-info@mit.edu, http://mitpress.mit.edu/aep. Eds. Jeffrey D Sachs, Wing Thye Woo, Yunjong Wang.

330 IND ISSN 0004-4555
HB9
ASIAN ECONOMIC REVIEW. Text in English. 1958. 3/yr. INR 210; USD 60 foreign. bk.rev. bibl.; charts; stat. **Document type:** *Academic/Scholarly.* **Description:** Publishes articles and reviews on specific economic, social projects undertaken in various developing countries as well as discussions of policy implications.
Related titles: Online - full text ed.: (from Factiva, Gale Group).
Indexed: AEA, APEL, BAS, BPIA, CREJ, CTFA, IBSS, IndIslam, JEL, PAA&I, PCI, PerIslam, RDA, RiceAb, WAE&RSA.
—BLDSC (1742.412000), CISTI.
Published by: Indian Institute of Economics, 11-6-841 Red Hills, Hyderabad, Andhra Pradesh 500 004, India. TEL 91-40-225083, TELEX 0425-6038 FAP IN. Ed. M Venkata Rao. Circ: 400.

ASIAN JOURNAL OF PUBLIC ADMINISTRATION. see *PUBLIC ADMINISTRATION*

ASIAN MEETINGS AND INCENTIVES. see *MEETINGS AND CONGRESSES*

330 320 CAN
ASIAN OUTLOOK. Text in English. q.
Media: Online - full content.
Published by: Asia Pacific Foundation of Canada, 666-999 Canada Place, Vancouver, BC V6C 3E1, Canada. http://www.asiapacificbusiness.ca/apbn/outlook.cfm.

ASIAN REVIEW OF BUSINESS AND TECHNOLOGY. see *TECHNOLOGY: COMPREHENSIVE WORKS*

330 AUS
ASIAPULSE NEWS. Text in English. 1996. irreg. **Document type:** *Trade.* **Description:** Covers Asian companies, industries, infrastructure, investments, joint ventures, and trade opportunities in 20 countries and 50 industry categories.
Media: Online - full content.
Published by: Asia Pulse Pte Ltd., Level 7, The AAP Centre, Locked Bag 21, Grosvenor Pl, Sydney, NSW 2000, Australia. TEL 61-2-9322-8634, FAX 61-2-9322-8639, asiapulse@asiapulse.com, http://www.asiapulse.com/.

330 ARG
ASOCIACION DE ECONOMISTAS ARGENTINOS. COLECCION INSTITUTO SUPERIOR. Text in Spanish. irreg., latest vol.3, 1976. charts; stat.
Published by: (Asociacion de Economistas Argentinos), Editorial el Coloquio, Junin, 735, Capital Federal, Buenos Aires 1026, Argentina.

ASPER REVIEW OF INTERNATIONAL BUSINESS AND TRADE LAW. see *LAW—Corporate Law*

330 PRT
ASSOCIACAO COMERCIAL DO PORTO. BOLETIM. Text in Portuguese. m.
Published by: Associacao Comercial do Porto, Camara de Comercio e Industria do Porto, Palacio da Bolsa, Porto, 4000, Portugal.

330 GBR
ASSOCIATION. Text in English. q. **Document type:** *Newsletter.*
Published by: Society of Association Executives, Courtleigh, Westbury Leigh, Westbury, Wilts BA13 3TA, United Kingdom. TEL 01380-830964, FAX 01380-830574. Ed. Leslie Rocker. Circ: 1,000.

ASSOCIATION LEADERSHIP. see *MEETINGS AND CONGRESSES*

330 JPN ISSN 0004-5683
ASSOCIATION OF ECONOMIC GEOGRAPHERS. ANNALS. Text in English, Japanese. 1954. s-a. JPY 1,800, USD 6. bk.rev. abstr.; bibl.; charts; illus.
—BLDSC (1028.340000). **CCC.**
Published by: Association of Economic Geographers/Keizai Chiri Gakkai, c/o Graduate School, Meiji University, 1-1 Kanda-Surugadai, Chiyoda-ku, Tokyo, 101-0062, Japan. Ed. Isamu Ota.

330 USA ISSN 1066-8691
ASSOCIATION SOURCE. Text in English. 1985. m. USD 15 (effective 1995). adv. bk.rev. **Document type:** *Trade.* **Description:** Designed for association executives and their staff members, with emphasis on feature articles relating to association management.
Formerly: Source (Casselberry) (0898-8811)
Published by: Florida Society of Association Executives, PO Box 11119, Tallahassee, FL 32302-3119. TEL 904-222-7994, FAX 904-222-6350. Ed. Tom Burchnell. Adv. contact Brian Pinsker. Circ: 1,100.

330 GBR
➤ **ASTON UNIVERSITY. PUBLIC SERVICES MANAGEMENT RESEARCH CENTRE. WORKING PAPER.** Text in English. 1984. irreg., latest vol.43, 1997. GBP 5 per vol.. **Document type:** *Academic/Scholarly.*
Formerly: Aston University. Public Sector Management Research Unit. Working Paper (0954-3554)
Published by: Aston University, Public Sector Management Research Centre, Aston Triangle, Birmingham, W Mids B4 7ET, United Kingdom. TEL 44-121-3593611, FAX 44-121-3596350, http://www.aston.ac.uk. Ed. Tony Bovaird.

330 SAU ISSN 1319-3449
HF3763
AL-ASWAQ. Key Title: Al-Aswaq as-Sa'udiat. Text and summaries in Arabic. 1995. m. SAR 160 domestic; SAR 180 foreign; SAR 10 newsstand/cover (effective 1999); USD 48. adv. charts; mkt.; stat.; tr.lit. back issues avail. **Document type:** *Consumer.* **Description:** Focusses on issues in the economic, financial and trade activities in Saudi Arabia. Comprehensively covers all local seminars and conferences dealing with present day economic realities and future developments.
Published by: (Makkah Advertising), Communications Enterprises, P O Box 4288, Jeddah, 21491, Saudi Arabia. FAX 966-2-653-0693, info@makkaahadv.com, www.makkahadv.com. Ed. Safwat J Bajunaid. Pub. Mohammed Salahuddin. R&P Salah Abu Al-Wafa TEL 966-2-651-7442. Adv. contact Salah Abu Al Wafa. B&W page SAR 11,000, color page SAR 13,000; trim 210 x 275. **Dist. by:** Saudi Distribution Co., P O Box 13195, Jeddah 21493, Saudi Arabia. TEL 966-2-653-0909, FAX 966-2-653-3191.

330 QAT
ASWAQ AL-KHALIJ. Text in Arabic. 1980. w.
Published by: Dar al-Nabaa Press Printing and Publishing, P O Box 3344, Doha, Qatar. TEL 438326, FAX 439859. Ed. Mohamed Salim Al Kuwari. Pub. Mohamed Salim al-Kuwari. Circ: 6,000.

330 GRC ISSN 1105-8536
ATHENS FINANCIAL GAZETTE. Text in English. 1987. fortn. looseleaf. USD 300 foreign. back issues avail. **Document type:** *Newsletter.* **Description:** Examines the political economy, outlook and prospects, and leading economic indicators of Greece.
Related titles: Online - full text ed.

Published by: Enimeroseis - Dioscuri Ltd., 21 Sarandapichou St, Athens, 114 71, Greece. TEL 361-5497, FAX 363-8274, eladop@enternet.gr, http://www.enternet.gr/afg. Ed. Olga Palagia. Pub., R&P Eugene Ladopoulos.

330 USA ISSN 1527-6937
HB615
ATLANTA CATALYST. Text in English. 1999. bi-m. USD 24 (effective 2001). adv. **Document type:** *Magazine, Consumer.* **Description:** Celebrates Atlanta as a city that is always changing and a mecca for those seeking both personal and professional success.
Incorporates (1997-2003): Business to Business (1527-6929)
Published by: Leader Publishing Group, Inc., 3379 Peachtree Rd, NE, Ste 300, Atlanta, GA 30326. TEL 404-888-0555, 800-256-8271, info@catalystmagazine.com, http://www.catalystmagazine.com. Ed. Kenna Simmons. Circ: 15,000 (paid).

330 CAN ISSN 0319-003X
ATLANTIC CANADA ECONOMICS ASSOCIATION. ANNUAL CONFERENCE PROCEEDINGS. Text in English. 1975 (no.4). a. price varies. charts; stat. **Document type:** *Proceedings, Academic/Scholarly.*
Related titles: Online - full text ed.
—BLDSC (0573.799000). **CCC.**
Published by: Atlantic Canada Economics Association, c/o Stephen Law, Dept of Economics, Mount Allison University, 144 Main St, Sackville, NB E4L 1A7, Canada. slaw@mta.ca, http://www.unb.ca/econ/acea. R&P Christina Fader. Circ: 150.

330 NLD ISSN 0197-4254
HB1
➤ **ATLANTIC ECONOMIC JOURNAL.** Text in English. 1973. q. EUR 200, USD 218, GBP 138 combined subscription to institutions print & online eds. (effective 2005). bk.rev. abstr.; charts; illus.; stat. 100 p./no. 1 cols./p.; back issues avail.; reprint service avail. from PSC. **Document type:** *Journal, Academic/Scholarly.*
Related titles: Microform ed.: (from PQC); Online - full text ed.: ISSN 1573-9678. USD 218 (effective 2005) (from bigchalk, EBSCO Publishing, Florida Center for Library Automation, Gale Group, Northern Light Technology, Inc., ProQuest Information & Learning, Springer LINK, The Dialog Corporation).
Indexed: ABIn, BPIA, CREJ, CurCont, ESPM, HRA, JEL, LRI, ManagCont, PAIS, PRA, RASB, RRTA, RiskAb, SSI, T&II.
—BLDSC (1765.899500), CISTI, IE, Infotrieve, ingenta. **CCC.**
Published by: (International Atlantic Economic Society USA), Springer-Verlag Dordrecht (Subsidiary of: Springer Science+Business Media), Van Godewijckstraat 30, Dordrecht, 3311 GX, Netherlands. TEL 31-78-6576050, FAX 31-78-6576474, http://springerlink.metapress.com/openurl.asp?genre=journal&issn=0197-4254, http://www.springeronline.com. Circ: 1,500.

330 CAN
ATLANTIC PROGRESS; business, politics, economics. Text in English. 1921. 8/yr. CND 25 domestic; USD 25 in United States; CND 35 overseas; CND 3.95 newsstand/cover (effective 2000). adv. **Document type:** *Consumer.* **Description:** Focuses on small and medium-sized businesses within the four Atlantic Canadian provinces. Official inflight magazine of Air Nova.
Formerly (until 1994): Commercial News (0046-6735)
Indexed: CBCARef, CBPI.
—CISTI.
Published by: (Atlantic Provinces Chamber of Commerce), Atlantic Progress Publishing, 1660 Hollis St, Ste 603, Halifax, NS B3J 1V7, Canada. TEL 902-494-0999, FAX 902-494-0998, app@app.ca, http://www.events.app.ca. Ed. David Holt. Pub. Neville J Gilfoy. R&P Paula Adamski. Adv. contact Maxwell Brennan. B&W page CND 2,566, color page CND 3,721; trim 10.75 x 8.19. Circ: 22,500. **Dist. by:** Disticor, 695 Westney Rd S., Ste. 14, Ajax, ON L1S 6M9, Canada. TEL 905-619-6565, FAX 905-619-2903.

330 USA ISSN 1092-3012
ATTAINMENT BUSINESS STARTUPS JOURNAL. Text in English. 1997. irreg. (8-10/yr). **Document type:** *Newsletter.* **Description:** Practical, how-to resources for startup businesses which focus on early phase financing, production and marketing.
Media: Online - full text.
Published by: Abiogenesis Publications, PO Box 9, Bellingham, WA 98227-0009. attainment@abiogenesis.com, http://www.abiogenesis.com/attainment. Ed. Julie Petersen.

650 305.896 USA
AU MAGAZINE✶ . Text in English. m. **Document type:** *Trade.* **Description:** Reports on the entire urban business industry by focusing not only on industry leaders, but their lesser known emerging counterparts as well.
Media: Online - full text.
Address: 1006 Lincoln Way Apt 213, Ames, IA 50010-3359. TEL 515-292-7742, sdavis@brigadoon.com, http://www.aumagazine.com. Ed. Sean Alonzo Davis.

330 658 AUS ISSN 0729-2384
AUDITOPICS✶ . Text in English. 1980. m. AUD 20. adv. bk.rev. back issues avail.
Published by: Institute of Internal Auditors, Victorian Branch, PO Box 817F, Melbourne, VIC 3001, Australia. FAX 61-3-857-4487. Ed. Jim Shaw. Circ: 600.

330 UKR
AUKTSION. Text in Russian. w. USD 235 in the Americas (effective 2000).
Published by: Redaktsiya Auktsion, A-ya 43, Nikolaev, 327024, Ukraine. TEL 31-24-30. Ed. V Gidulian. **Dist. by:** East View Information Services, 3020 Harbor Ln. N., Minneapolis, MN 55447. TEL 763-550-0961, FAX 763-559-2931.

330 DEU ISSN 0944-9337
AUSBILDER HANDBUCH. Text in German. 1994. 4 base vols. plus updates 6/yr. looseleaf. EUR 198 (effective 2005). **Document type:** *Bulletin, Trade.*
Published by: Deutscher Wirtschaftsdienst (Subsidiary of: Wolters Kluwer Deutschland GmbH), Schoenhauser Str 64, Cologne, 50968, Germany. TEL 49-221-937630, FAX 49-221-9376399, box@dwd-verlag.de, http://www.dwd-verlag.de.

AUSBILDER IN DER CHEMISCHEN INDUSTRIE. see *CHEMISTRY*

AUSTIN BOOK OF LISTS. see *PUBLISHING AND BOOK TRADE*

330 USA ISSN 0892-869X
AUSTIN BUSINESS JOURNAL. Text in English. 1981. w. (Fri.). USD 86 (effective 2005). adv. **Document type:** *Newspaper, Trade.* **Description:** Includes industry information in the following ares: real estate, demographics, health care and others.
Related titles: Microform ed.: (from PQC); Online - full text ed.: (from Florida Center for Library Automation, Gale Group, O C L C Online Computer Library Center, Inc., ProQuest Information & Learning).
Indexed: ABIn, BusDate, T&II.
—CCC.
Published by: American City Business Journals, Inc. (Austin), 111 Congress Ave, Ste 750, Austin, TX 78701. TEL 512-328-0180, FAX 512-328-7304, austin@bizjournals.com, http://austin.bcentral.com. Ed. John Egan. Pub. Lyn Chasteen. Adv. contact John Garrett. Circ: 7,800. Wire service: PR.

330 AUS
AUSTRALIA. COMMONWEALTH COMPETITIVE NEUTRALITY COMPLAINTS OFFICE. INVESTIGATIONS. Text in English. 1999. irreg. back issues avail. **Description:** Publishes investigations into competitive neutrality complaints.
Related titles: Online - full content ed.
Published by: Productivity Commission, Media and Publications Section, Locked Bag 2, Collins St E., Melbourne, VIC 8003, Australia. TEL 61-3-9653-2100, FAX 61-3-9653-2199, maps@pc.gov.au, http://www.pc.gov.au.

330 AUS
AUSTRALIA. PRODUCTIVITY COMMISSION. COMMISSION RESEARCH PAPERS. Text in English. 1996. irreg. prices varies. back issues avail. **Document type:** *Government.*
Related titles: Online - full content ed.
Published by: Productivity Commission, Media and Publications Section, Locked Bag 2, Collins St E., Melbourne, VIC 8003, Australia. FAX 61-3-9653-2199, maps@pc.gov.au, http://www.pc.gov.au. **Subscr. to:** AusInfo, GPO Box 1920, Canberra Mc, ACT 2610, Australia. TEL 61-2-6275-3442, FAX 61-2-6295-4888.

330 AUS
AUSTRALIA. PRODUCTIVITY COMMISSION. SUBMISSIONS. Text in English. 1990. irreg. back issues avail. **Document type:** *Government.*
Related titles: Online - full content ed.
Published by: Productivity Commission, Media and Publications Section, Locked Bag 2, Collins St E., Melbourne, VIC 8003, Australia. TEL 61-3-9653-2100, FAX 61-3-9653-2199, maps@pc.gov.au, http://www.pc.gov.au.

650.0715 AUS ISSN 1036-2878
AUSTRALIAN BUSINESS EDUCATION DIRECTORY✶ . Text in English. s-m. AUD 195.
Formerly: Australian Directory of Conferences, Seminars and Short Courses
Published by: Mount Wise Press Pty. Ltd., 56 Rose St, Armadale, VIC 3143, Australia. FAX 03-824-2935.

AUSTRALIAN DEFENCE BUSINESS REVIEW; the national defense industry and astrospace reporter. see *MILITARY*

330 AUS ISSN 0004-900X
HB1
➤ **AUSTRALIAN ECONOMIC PAPERS.** Text in English. 1962. q. USD 53 combined subscription in the Americas to individuals print & online eds.; AUD 54 combined subscription in Australia & New Zealand to individuals print & online eds.; EUR 54 combined subscription in Europe to individuals print & online eds.; GBP 36 combined subscription elsewhere to individuals print & online eds.; GBP 63 combined subscription in Australia & New Zealand to institutions print & online eds.; USD 175 combined subscription in the Americas to institutions print & online eds.; USD 88, GBP 62 combined subscription in developing nations to institutions print & online eds.; GBP 122 combined subscription elsewhere to institutions print & online eds. (effective 2006). adv. bibl.; charts; illus.; stat. Index. reprint service avail. from PSC. **Document type:** *Journal, Academic/Scholarly.* **Description:** Publishes papers, from leading international economists, in theoretical, empirical and policy economics.
Related titles: Online - full text ed.: ISSN 1467-8454. USD 161 in the Americas to institutions & Caribbean; GBP 111 elsewhere to institutions (effective 2005) (from Blackwell Synergy, EBSCO Publishing, Gale Group, IngentaConnect, O C L C Online Computer Library Center, Inc., Swets Information Services).
Indexed: ABIn, APEL, AusPAIS, BAS, CREJ, CurCont, ESPM, IBR, IBSS, IBZ, ILD, JEL, PAIS, PCI, RASB, RRTA, RiskAb, SSCI, WAE&RSA.
—BLDSC (1798.670000), IE, Infotrieve, ingenta. **CCC.**
Published by: (Flinders University of South Australia, Department of Economics, University of Adelaide, Department of Economics), Blackwell Publishing Asia (Subsidiary of: Blackwell Publishing Ltd.), 550 Swanston St, Carlton South, VIC 3053, Australia. TEL 61-383591011, FAX 61-383591120, subs@blackwellpublishingasia.com, http://www.blackwellpublishing.com/journals/AEPA. Ed. Daniel Leonard. Circ: 1,250.

330 AUS ISSN 0004-9018
HC601
➤ **AUSTRALIAN ECONOMIC REVIEW.** Text in English. 1968. q. GBP 168 combined subscription in Australia & New Zealand to institutions print & online eds.; USD 356 combined subscription in the Americas to institutions & the Caribbean for print & online eds.; GBP 249 combined subscription elsewhere to institutions print & online eds.; AUD 42 combined subscription in Australia & New Zealand to students print & online eds.; USD 35 combined subscription in the Americas to students & the Caribbean for print & online eds.; EUR 35 combined subscription in Europe to students print & online eds.; GBP 23 combined subscription elsewhere to students print & online eds. (effective 2006). charts; stat. **Document type:** *Journal, Academic/Scholarly.* **Description:** Contains articles on applied economic and social issues.
Related titles: Microform ed.: (from PQC); Online - full text ed.: ISSN 1467-8462. GBP 159 in Australia & New Zealand to institutions; USD 338 in the Americas to institutions & Caribbean; GBP 237 elsewhere to institutions (effective 2006) (from Blackwell Synergy, EBSCO Publishing, Gale Group, IngentaConnect, O C L C Online Computer Library Center, Inc., R M I T Publishing, Swets Information Services).
Indexed: ABIn, APEL, ArtHuCI, AusPAIS, CREJ, GEOBASE, GdIns, IBSS, ILD, JEL, PAIS, PROMT, PSA, RASB, SociolAb, WAE&RSA, WBA.
—BLDSC (1798.680000), IE, Infotrieve, ingenta. **CCC.**
Published by: (University Of Melbourne, Institute of Applied Economic and Social Research GBR), Blackwell Publishing Asia (Subsidiary of: Blackwell Publishing Ltd.), 550 Swanston St, Carlton South, VIC 3053, Australia. TEL 61-383591011, FAX 61-383591120, 61-383591120, subs@blackwellpublishingasia.com, http://www.blackwellpublishing.com/journals/AERE. Eds. Ian McDonald, Mark Wooden, Ross Williams. Circ: 900.

330 AUS
AUSTRALIAN FINANCIAL REVIEW MAGAZINE. Abbreviated title: A F R Magazine. Text in English. 1995. m. (Fri.). adv. **Document type:** *Magazine, Consumer.*
Related titles: ♦ Issued with: Australian Financial Review. ISSN 0404-2018.
Published by: Fairfax Business Media (Subsidiary of: John Fairfax Holdings Ltd.), 201 Sussex St, Sydney, NSW 2000, Australia. TEL 61-2-9282-3137, http://www.fxj.com.au/. Circ: 103,300.

AUSTRALIAN JOURNAL OF CONSTRUCTION ECONOMICS AND BUILDING. see *BUILDING AND CONSTRUCTION*

060 AUS
AUSTRALIAN ORGANISATIONS & LEADERS. Text in English. a. AUD 150 for both Print & Online editions (effective 2000). **Document type:** *Directory, Bibliography.* **Description:** Contains listing of all Australian associations with presidents, political parties, industrial relations organisations, & religious organisations.
Related titles: Online - full content ed.: AUD 95 (effective 2000).
Published by: Bookman Press Pty Ltd, Lu 10, 227 Collins St, Melbourne, VIC 3000, Australia. TEL 61-3-96542000, FAX 61-3-96542290, bookman@bookman.com.au, http://www.bookman.com.au.

AUSTRIAN ECONOMIC QUARTERLY. see *BUSINESS AND ECONOMICS—Economic Situation And Conditions*

330 USA
AUTO WEEKLY. Text in English. w. (Every Fri. afternoon). Free. **Document type:** *Consumer.* **Description:** Covers automobile sales in the North Bay, CA, area.
Related titles: Online - full content ed.
Published by: Auto Weekly, Inc., 5550 Commerce Blvd., Ste. 14, Rohnert Park, CA 94928-1637. TEL 800-540-2916, admin@autoweeklyink.com, http://www.autoweeklyink.com/. Circ: 1,500 (controlled).

AUTOFILE. see *TRANSPORTATION—Automobiles*

AUTOFILE QUARTERLY REPORT. see *TRANSPORTATION—Automobiles*

AUTOMOBILWIRTSCHAFT. see *TRANSPORTATION—Automobiles*

AUTOMOTIVE DEALERS DIGEST. see *TRANSPORTATION—Automobiles*

330 NLD ISSN 1387-6163
AVANTA. Text in Dutch. 1986. 10/yr. adv. illus. **Document type:** *Magazine, Consumer.*
Former titles (until 1997): V B Magazine: Voor Vrouwen in Business (0929-5496); (until 1993): Vrouw en Bedrijf (0920-5764)
Related titles: Online - full text ed.
—IE, Infotrieve.
Published by: Reed Business Information bv (Subsidiary of: Reed Business), Van de Sande, Bakhuyzenstraat 4, Amsterdam, 1061 AG, Netherlands. TEL 31-20-515-9222, FAX 31-20-515-9990, info@reedbusiness.nl, http://www.reedbusiness.nl.

AZERBAIJAN NEFT TESERRUFATY. see *PETROLEUM AND GAS*

330 ITA
AZIENDA E FISCO. Text in Italian. 1991. fortn. EUR 192 (effective 2005). adv. **Document type:** *Magazine, Consumer.*
Published by: IPSOA Editore (Subsidiary of: Wolters Kluwer Italia Srl), Strada 1, Palazzo F6, Milanofiori, Assago, MI 20090, Italy. TEL 39-02-82476888, FAX 39-02-82476436, http://www.ipsoa.it. Ed. Massimiliano Galioni. Adv. contact Luciano Alcaro Menichini.

330 ESP ISSN 1137-442X
H8.S7
AZKOAGA. Text in Spanish. 1986. irreg. price varies. **Document type:** *Journal, Academic/Scholarly.*
Formerly (until 1997): Sociedad de Estudios Vascos. Cuadernos de Seccion. Ciencias Sociales y Economicas (1130-555X)
Published by: Eusko Ikaskuntza/Sociedad de Estudios Vascos, Palacio Miramar, Miraconcha 48, Donostia, San Sebastian 20007, Spain. TEL 34-943-310855, FAX 34-943-213956, ei-sev@sc.ehu.es, http://www.eusko-ikaskuntza.org/.

330 USA
B 2 B QUARTERLY. Text in English. q. adv. **Document type:** *Magazine, Trade.* **Description:** Covers local business developments and issues, including personalities and profiles.
Published by: Omaha Publications, PO Box 461208, Omaha, NE 68046-1208. TEL 402-339-6624, FAX 402-592-2798, http://www.omahapublications.com/newsite/b2bquarterly.php. adv.: B&W page USD 2,210, color page USD 2,600.

330 UAE
B B G CALLING. (British Business Group) Text in English. 1988. q. free to members. **Description:** Includes articles of interests to the British Business Group community, progress and upcoming companies and activities.
Published by: Motivate Publishing, PO Box 2331, Dubai, United Arab Emirates. TEL 971-4-824060, FAX 971-4-824436, motivate@emirates.net.ae. Ed. Allen Armstrong. R&P Shawki Abd El Malik. adv.: B&W page USD 800, color page USD 970. Circ: 3,000.

650 700 USA ISSN 0005-2841
B C A NEWS. (Business Committee for the Arts) Text in English. 1968. q. USD 55; USD 65 foreign; USD 30 to non-profit organizations. illus.; stat. **Document type:** *Newsletter.* **Description:** Focuses on the alliances between business and the arts. Features interviews with business leaders, information about new business arts alliances, issues and trends.
Published by: Business Committee for the Arts, Inc., 2927 41st Ave., # 4, Long Is City, NY 11101-3304. TEL 212-664-0600, FAX 212-956-5980. Ed. Jemma Fried. Circ: 1,000.

330 AUS ISSN 1442-6544
B C A PAPERS. Text in English. 1999. 3/yr. **Description:** Covers issues such as the work place, the environment, taxation, and other Australian business related information.
Related titles: Online - full content ed.: ISSN 1444-366X.
Published by: Business Council of Australia, GPO Box 1472N, Melbourne, VIC 3001, Australia. TEL 61-3-96104222, FAX 61-3-96104223, info@bca.com.au, http://www.bca.com.au/default.asp?pnewsid=830.

330 CAN ISSN 0829-481X
B C BUSINESS. Variant title: British Columbia Business. Text in English. 1972. m. CND 15.80 domestic; CND 39.95 in United States; CND 45.95 elsewhere; CND 3.95 newsstand/cover (effective 2004). adv. **Document type:** *Magazine, Trade.* **Description:** Covers prominent business leaders and key developments in the local area. Provides data on business trends and opportunities.
Incorporated (1985-1987): Asia Pacific Business (0829-4488); Former titles (until 1983): B C Business Magazine (0384-0581); (until 1975): Business in B C (0384-0573)
Related titles: Microfiche ed.: (from MML); Microform ed.: (from MML); Online - full text ed.: (from bigchalk, EBSCO Publishing, Florida Center for Library Automation, Gale Group, Micromedia ProQuest, O C L C Online Computer Library Center, Inc., ProQuest Information & Learning, The Dialog Corporation).
Indexed: ABIn, BusDate, CBCABus, CBCARef, CBPI, CPerl, T&II.
Published by: Canada Wide Magazines & Communications Ltd., 4180 Lougheed Hwy, 4th Fl, Burnaby, BC V5C 6A7, Canada. TEL 604-299-7311, 800-663-0518, FAX 604-299-9188, cwm@canadawide.com, http://www.bcbusinessmagazine.com, http://www.canadawide.com. Ed. Bonnie Irving. Pub. Peter Legge. Adv. contact Debbie McLean. Circ: 13,000 (paid); 13,000 (controlled).

330 DEU ISSN 0937-2385
B D I HANDBUCH DER FORSCHUNGS- UND INNOVATIONSFOERDERUNG. Text in German. 1979. 3 base vols. plus bi-m. updates. looseleaf. EUR 128 (effective 2005). **Document type:** *Bulletin, Trade.*
Published by: Deutscher Wirtschaftsdienst (Subsidiary of: Wolters Kluwer Deutschland GmbH), Schoenhauser Str 64, Cologne, 50968, Germany. TEL 49-221-937630, FAX 49-221-9376399, box@dwd-verlag.de, http://www.dwd-verlag.de. Eds. C Kreklau, J von Freyend.

330 USA ISSN 1051-208X
B N A C COMMUNICATOR; topics and resources for training. (Bureau of National Affairs) Text in English. 1980. q. free to qualified personnel. adv. bk.rev. back issues avail. **Document type:** *Trade.* **Description:** Covers topics and resources for training in the areas of human resource development, safety, labor relations, and equal employment opportunity.
Published by: B N A Communications, Inc., 8300 Colesville Rd, Ste 100B, Silver Spring, MD 20910. TEL 800-233-6067, FAX 301-495-1071, http://www.bna.com/bnac, http://www.hrhub.com/storefronts/bnacommunications.html. Ed. Dorinda Capole. Pub. Rohit Patel. R&P Theresa McGrail TEL 301-294-6772. Circ: 230,000 (controlled).

330 AUS
B P ACCELERATOR. (British Petroleum) Text in English. 1932. m. free. **Document type:** *Newsletter.* **Description:** Covers BP's involvement in community and oil industry issues relating to Australia and Papua New Guinea.
Published by: B P Australia Ltd., 360 Elizabeth St, Melbourne, VIC 3001, Australia. TEL 03-2684824. Ed. N J McMaster. Circ: 3,500.

330 USA ISSN 1084-3981
HF5001
➤ **B QUEST.** Text in English. 1996. irreg. free (effective 2005). bk.rev. illus. back issues avail.; reprints avail. **Document type:** *Academic/Scholarly.* **Description:** Presents applied topics in business and economics, with contributions fromboth academicians and practitioners.
Media: Online - full text.
Published by: State University of West Georgia, Richards College of Business, 1600 Maple St, Carrollton, GA 30118-3020. TEL 770-836-6477, FAX 770-836-6774, cscott@westga.edu, http://www.westga.edu/~bquest. Ed. Dr. Carole E Scott.

330 AUS ISSN 0727-758X
B R W. Text in English. 1980. w. AUD 199 domestic (effective 2005). adv. bk.rev. charts; illus.; mkt. Index. back issues avail.; reprints avail. **Document type:** *Magazine, Trade.* **Description:** Gives an overall view of Australian business. Deals with current events, industrial relations, accounting, law, management, special events issues, personnel, agriculture and leisure.
Incorporates (1935-1987): Rydge's (0725-5640); (1985-1987): Rydge's Management and Marketing Update (0819-5951); (1984-1986): Today's Computers (0813-3611)
Related titles: Online - full text ed.
Indexed: ABIX, ABIn, AESIS, AusPAIS, Emerald, IMI, INIS AtomInd, Inspec, PAIS, PCI, WBA, WMB.
—BLDSC (2353.626000), IE, ingenta.
Published by: Fairfax Business Media (Subsidiary of: John Fairfax Holdings Ltd.), 469 La Trobe St, Melbourne 3000, NSW 3000, Australia. TEL 61-3-9603-3888, FAX 61-3-9670-4328, online@brw.fairfax.com.au, http://www.brw.com.au/, http://www.fxj.com.au/. Pub. John Fairfax. Adv. contact Michael Grenenger. page AUD 12,800; trim 275 x 220. Circ: 63,578.

B V - EUROLETTER; E G-Binnenmarkt: Tips, Trends, Termine. (Bayerische Vereinsbank) see *BUSINESS AND ECONOMICS—Banking And Finance*

330 659.1 USA
B2B E-NEWSLETTER. Text in English. s-m. USD 595 (effective 2001). **Document type:** *Newsletter.* **Description:** Provides articles, studies and surveys about business to business advertising, direct marketing and internet communications.
Media: Online - full text. **Related titles:** Fax ed.: USD 695.
Published by: Web-Based Training, Inc., 2777 Yulupac Ave, Ste 133, Santa Rosa, CA 95405. TEL 707-538-5043, B2B@Doyle.Marketing.com, http://www.DoyleMarketing.com.

330 004.678 CAN ISSN 1498-086X
BACKBONE MAGAZINE; the strength of e-business. Text in English. 2001. bi-m. CND 19.95 domestic; CND 35.95 foreign (effective 2004). adv. **Document type:** *Magazine, Consumer.* **Description:** Covers developments in e-commerce.
Published by: Publimedia Communications Inc., 200 - 1140 Homer St, Vancouver, BC V6B 2X6 , Canada. TEL 604-609-9841, 888-609-8809, FAX 604-609-9891, info@backbonemag.com, http://www.backbonemag.com. Ed. Peter Wolchak. adv.: color page CND 11,750; trim 8.25 x 10.375. **Dist. by:** Globe Distribution Services, 1210 - 1140 Pender St W, Vancouver, BC V6E 4G1, Canada. TEL 604-687-4436, FAX 604-687-8501.

BALANCE SHEETS. see *BUSINESS AND ECONOMICS—Abstracting, Bibliographies, Statistics*

330 USA ISSN 1526-145X
BALANCED SCORECARD REPORT. Text in English. bi-m. USD 295 (effective 2005). **Document type:** *Newsletter.* **Description:** Latest research and front-line implementation news from organizations using the Balanced Scorecard strategic management system.
Related titles: Online - full text ed.
—BLDSC (1860.569500). **CCC.**
Published by: Harvard Business School Publishing, 60 Harvard Way, Boston, MA 02163. TEL 617-783-7500, 800-988-0866, FAX 617-783-7555, corpcustserv@hbsp.harvard.edu, http://www.hbsp.harvard.edu. **Subscr. to:** PO Box 52623, Boulder, CO 80322-2623.

330 340 EST ISSN 1021-8149
HC243.A1
THE BALTIC REVIEW. Text in English. 1993. q. USD 50 in Europe to corporations; USD 70 in US & Canada to corporations; USD 80 elsewhere to corporations; USD 45 in Europe to individuals; USD 65 in US & Canada to individuals; USD 70 elsewhere to individuals (effective 2001). adv. **Document type:** *Magazine, Trade.* **Description:** Covers business, law and economics in Estonia, Latvia and Lithuania.
Published by: The Baltic Review, PO Box 90, Tallinn, 10501, Estonia. TEL 372-6-313170, FAX 372-6-313332, tbr@zzz.ee, http://www.zzz.ee/tbr/. Ed. Erik Terk. Pub. Vilja Savisaar. adv.: B&W page USD 1,250, color page USD 1,850. **Dist. in US by:** c/o Jenik Radon, 269 W 71 St, New York, NY 10023-3701. TEL 212-496-2700, FAX 212-724-3393, jradon@gramercy.ios.com.

330 USA ISSN 0747-1823
BALTIMORE BUSINESS JOURNAL. Text in English. 1983. w. (Fri.). USD 88 (effective 2005). adv. back issues avail. **Document type:** *Newspaper, Trade.* **Description:** Covers local business news on a weekly basis with emphasis on local finance, health care and real estate.
Related titles: Microform ed.: (from PQC); Online - full text ed.: (from Florida Center for Library Automation, Gale Group, Northern Light Technology, Inc., O C L C Online Computer Library Center, Inc., ProQuest Information & Learning, The Dialog Corporation).
Indexed: ABIn, BusDate, T&II.
—**CCC.**
Published by: American City Business Journals, Inc. (Baltimore), 111 Market Place Ste 720, Baltimore, MD 21202. TEL 410-576-1161, FAX 410-752-3112, baltimore@bizjournals.com, http://www.bizjournals.com/baltimore/. Ed. Joanna Sullivan. Pub. James Breiner. Adv. contact John Dinkel. Circ: 13,500.

330 CHL
BANCO CENTRAL DE CHILE. DOCUMENTO DE TRABAJO. Text in Spanish. irreg., latest vol.35, 1998. CLP 1,500, USD 15 (effective 1999). **Document type:** *Monographic series.*
Published by: Banco Central de Chile, Casilla 967, Santiago, Chile. TEL 56-2-670-2000, FAX 56-2-698-4847.

330 CHL ISSN 0716-2391
BANCO CENTRAL DE CHILE. ESTUDIOS MONETARIOS. Text in Spanish. 1967. irreg., latest vol.12, 1996. CLP 5,000, USD 25 (effective 1999). **Document type:** *Monographic series.*
Published by: Banco Central de Chile, Casilla 967, Santiago, Chile. TEL 56-2-670-2000, FAX 56-2-698-4847.

330 CHL ISSN 0716-2502
BANCO CENTRAL DE CHILE. SERIE DE ESTUDIOS ECONOMICOS. Text in Spanish. 1981. irreg., latest vol.41, 1997. CLP 1,500, USD 15 newsstand/cover. **Document type:** *Monographic series.*
Published by: Banco Central de Chile, Casilla 967, Santiago, Chile. TEL 56-2-670-2000, FAX 56-2-698-4847.

330 BGD
BANGLADESH ARTHANAITIKA JARIP. Text in Bengali. 1971. a. free.

Formerly (until 1974): Bangladesh Economic Survey (0070-8704)
Related titles: English ed.
Published by: Ministry of Finance, Economic Adviser's Wing, Bangladesh Secretariat Bldg No. 6, Dhaka, 1000, Bangladesh. Circ: 2,000.

336 ROM ISSN 1454-6280
BANII NOSTRI. Text in Romanian. 1999. m. adv. **Document type:** *Magazine, Trade.*
Published by: Media On S R L Romania, Str. Viesparilor nr. 19, sector 2, Bucharest, Romania. TEL 40-21-2102934, FAX 40-21-2102935, sales@investromania.ro, http://www.investromania.ro/.

330 MLT ISSN 1017-7841
➤ **BANK OF VALLETTA REVIEW.** Text in English. 1990. s-a. free. back issues avail. **Document type:** *Academic/Scholarly.*
Indexed: JEL.
Published by: Bank of Valletta, BOV Centre, High St, Sliema, SLM 16, Malta. TEL 356-313134, FAX 356-313139, spu@bov.com. Ed. Lino Briguglio. Circ: 1,000.

➤ **BANK TRAVEL MANAGEMENT.** see *TRAVEL AND TOURISM*

330 DEU ISSN 0170-6659
BANKFACHKLASSE; Praxisfaelle, Pruefungsfaelle, Aktuelles. Text in German. 1978. m. EUR 55.80; EUR 5 newsstand/cover (effective 2004). adv. **Document type:** *Magazine, Trade.*
—CCC.
Published by: Betriebswirtschaftlicher Verlag Dr. Th. Gabler GmbH (Subsidiary of: Springer Science+Business Media), Abraham-Lincoln-Str 46, Wiesbaden, 65189, Germany. TEL 49-611-78780, FAX 49-611-7878400, bankfachklasse@bertelsmann.de, gabler.service@gwv-fachverlage.de, http://www.bankfachklasse.de, http://www.gabler.de. Ed. Margaretha Hamm. Adv. contact Tanja Pfisterer. B&W page EUR 3,250, color page EUR 4,906. Circ: 17,500 (paid and controlled).

BANKRUPTCY SERVICE (LAWYERS EDITION). see *LAW—Corporate Law*

BANKS, INVESTMENT & STOCKMARKET. see *BUSINESS AND ECONOMICS—Banking And Finance*

330 MEX ISSN 0187-3601
BANMAR. Text in Spanish. 1985. m.
Indexed: ESPM.
Published by: Banco Nacional Pesquero y Portuario, Paseo de la Reforma 155 1 er Piso, Col Cuauhtemoc, Mexico City, 06500, Mexico.

BANQUES ET ENTREPRISES AU MAROC. see *BUSINESS AND ECONOMICS—Banking And Finance*

330 FRA
BAREME SOCIAL PERIODIQUE. Text in French. q. FRF 360 (effective 1997).
Published by: Groupe Liaisons S.A. (Subsidiary of: Wolters Kluwer BV), 1 Avenue Edouard Belin, Rueil Malmaison, Cedex 92856, France. TEL 33-1-41299696, FAX 33-1-41299880.

330.071 USA ISSN 1043-190X
HF1131
BARRON'S GUIDE TO GRADUATE BUSINESS SCHOOLS. Text in English. biennial, latest 13th ed. USD 16.95 per issue (effective 2003). **Document type:** *Directory, Consumer.*
Published by: Barron's Educational Series, Inc., 250 Wireless Blvd., Hauppage, NY 11788. TEL 516-434-3311, info@barronseduc.com, http://www.barronseduc.com.

330 USA ISSN 1543-3579
BATTEN BRIEFINGS. Text in English. 2002. q. USD 50 (effective 2003).
Published by: University of Virginia, Batten Institute at the Darden Graduate School of Business, 100 Darden Blvd., Charlottesville, VA 22903. TEL 434-243-4300, FAX 434-924-7104, http://www.darden.virginia.edu/batten. Ed. Elizabeth F. O'Halloran. Pub. Trienet P. Coggeshall.

BAUINDUSTRIE AKTUELL. see *BUILDING AND CONSTRUCTION*

BAUWIRTSCHAFT IM ZAHLENBILD. see *BUILDING AND CONSTRUCTION*

330 DEU
BAYER ANNUAL REPORT (UNABRIDGED VERSION). Text in English, German. 1951. a. **Document type:** *Corporate.*
Formerly: Bayer Business Report (Unabridged Version)
Published by: Bayer AG, Corporate Communications, Kaiser-Wilhelm-Allee, Leverkusen, 51368, Germany. TEL 49-214-3058992, FAX 49-214-3071985, ute.bode.ub@bayer-ag.de, http://www.bayer.com. Circ: 150,000.

650 USA ISSN 0739-1072
CODEN: BYBSA2
BAYLOR BUSINESS REVIEW. Text in English. 1949. s-a. USD 15 domestic; USD 18 foreign; free alumni. bk.rev. cum.index. reprint service avail. from PQC. **Document type:** *Magazine, Consumer.*
Supersedes (in 1983): Baylor Business Studies (0005-724X)
Related titles: Microfilm ed.: (from PQC); Online - full text ed.: (from bigchalk, EBSCO Publishing, O C L C Online Computer Library Center, Inc., ProQuest Information & Learning).
Indexed: ABIn, BPIA, BusI, KES, ManagCont, PAIS, PMA, T&II.
—BLDSC (1871.239400), IE.
Published by: Baylor University, Hankamer School of Business, BU Box 98006, Waco, TX 76798-8006. http://hsb.baylor.edu/business_review/. Ed. Judith Corwin. Circ: 1,600.

330.968 ZAF
BE IN. Text in English. 1993. 3/yr. adv. illus. **Document type:** *Trade.*
Published by: Black Enterprise Publishing and Marketing, PO Box 2185, Houghton, Johannesburg 2041, South Africa.

330 TUR ISSN 1301-0093
BEBEGIM VE BIZ. Text in Turkish. 1996. m. **Document type:** *Magazine, Trade.*
Published by: 1 Numara Hearst Yayincilik, Sabah Tesisleri, Tesvikiye Caddesi 123, Tesvikiye, Istanbul, 80200, Turkey. TEL 90-212-3158000, FAX 90-212-3159272, aktuel@birnumara.com.tr, http://www.birnumara.com.tr.

330 CHN
BEIJING CAIMAO XUEYUAN XUEBAO/BEIJING INSTITUTE OF FINANCE AND TRADE. JOURNAL. Text in Chinese. bi-m.
Published by: Beijing Caimao Xueyuan, 68 Nanxiange Jie, Guang'anmennei, Beijing, 100053, China. TEL 365938. Ed. Shi Chunnian.

330 CHN ISSN 1001-7429
BEIJING QINGGONGYE XUEYUAN XUEBAO/BEIJING INSTITUTE OF LIGHT INDUSTRY. JOURNAL. Text in Chinese. 1983. q. back issues avail. **Document type:** *Academic/Scholarly.*
Related titles: Online - full content ed.: (from WanFang Data Corp.).
Published by: Beijing Qinggongye Xueyuan/Beijing Institute of Light Industry, Fucheng Lu no.11, Haidian qu, Beijing, 100037, China. Ed. En Ming Hu.

330 CHN
BEIJING THIS MONTH. Text in English. m. CNY 150 domestic; USD 120 foreign (effective 2003). adv. **Document type:** *Magazine, Trade.* **Description:** Covers Beijing general lifestyle, including arts and culture, restaurants, historical locations and feature articles.
Related titles: Online - full content ed.
Published by: A S M Overseas Corp., Asian Games Garden, Bldg 2-6A,12 Xiaoying Lu, Chaoyang-qu, Beijing, 100101, China. TEL 86-1-64974451, FAX 86-1-64974872, icic@cbw.com, http://www.cbw.com/btm/. adv.: page CNY 23,000; 215 x 275. Circ: 70,000. **Subscr. to:** 227040, Los Angeles, CA 90022-0740.

330 CHN
BEIJING XIANDAI SHANGBAO/BEIJING MODERN BUSINESS DAILY. Text in Chinese. 2002. d. (6/week). CNY 24 per month (effective 2004). adv. **Document type:** *Newspaper, Trade.*
Published by: Beijing Ribao Baoye Jituan/Beijing Daily Newspaper Group, Zhaoyang-qu, 21, Hepingli Xi Jia, Beijing, 100013, China. FAX 86-10-84275605, http://www.bjbusiness.com.cn/. **Dist. by:** China International Book Trading Corp, 35 Chegongzhuang Xilu, Haidian District, PO Box 399, Beijing 100044, China. TEL 86-10-68412045, FAX 86-10-68412023, cibtc@mail.cibtc.com.cn, http://www.cibtc.com.cn.

330 AUT
BEIRAT FUER WIRTSCHAFTS UND SOZIALFRAGEN ✶ . Text in German. a. **Document type:** *Bulletin, Trade.*
Address: Prinz Eugen Str 20-22, Vienna, W 1040, Austria. TEL 43-1-501650, FAX 43-1-501652513.

330 DEU ISSN 0720-6682
BEITRAEGE ZUR ANGEWANDTEN WIRTSCHAFTSFORSCHUNG. Text in German. 1976. irreg., latest vol.29, 2002. price varies. **Document type:** *Monographic series, Academic/Scholarly.*
Published by: Duncker und Humblot GmbH, Carl-Heinrich-Becker-Weg 9, Berlin, 12165, Germany. TEL 49-30-7900060, FAX 49-30-79000631, info@duncker-humblot.de, http://www.duncker-humblot.de.

330 DEU ISSN 0522-6457
BEITRAEGE ZUR GANZHEITLICHEN WIRTSCHAFTS- UND GESELLSCHAFTSLEHRE. Text in German. 1966. irreg., latest vol.10, 2000. price varies. **Document type:** *Monographic series, Academic/Scholarly.*
Published by: Duncker und Humblot GmbH, Carl-Heinrich-Becker-Weg 9, Berlin, 12165, Germany. TEL 49-30-7900060, FAX 49-30-79000631, info@duncker-humblot.de, http://www.duncker-humblot.de.

330 DEU ISSN 1436-2996
BEITRAEGE ZUR PERSONAL- UND ORGANISATIONSOEKONOMIK. Text in German. irreg., latest vol.14, 2004. price varies. **Document type:** *Monographic series, Academic/Scholarly.*
Published by: Rainer Hampp Verlag, Meringerzellerstr 10, Mering, 86415, Germany. TEL 49-8233-4783, FAX 49-8233-30755, Rainer_Hampp_Verlag@t-online.de, http://www.hampp-verlag.de.

330 DEU ISSN 0170-5784
BEITRAEGE ZUR QUANTITATIVEN WIRTSCHAFTSFORSCHUNG. Text in German. 1975. irreg., latest vol.5, 1996. price varies. **Document type:** *Monographic series.*
Published by: I F O Institut fuer Wirtschaftsforschung, Poschingerstr 5, Munich, 81679, Germany. TEL 49-89-9224-0, FAX 49-89-985369, makedonski@ifo.de, http://www.ifo.de.

338 DEU ISSN 0171-1407
BEITRAEGE ZUR STRUKTURFORSCHUNG. Text in German. 1967. irreg., latest vol.187, 2001. price varies. **Document type:** *Monographic series, Academic/Scholarly.*
Formerly (until 1970): D I W - Beitraege zur Strukturforschung (0522-9472)
Published by: Duncker und Humblot GmbH, Carl-Heinrich-Becker-Weg 9, Berlin, 12165, Germany. TEL 49-30-7900060, FAX 49-30-79000631, info@duncker-humblot.de, http://www.duncker-humblot.de.

330 DEU ISSN 0522-7194
BEITRAEGE ZUR VERHALTENSFORSCHUNG. Text in German. 1959. irreg., latest vol.42, 2001. price varies. **Document type:** *Monographic series, Academic/Scholarly.*
Published by: Duncker und Humblot GmbH, Carl-Heinrich-Becker-Weg 9, Berlin, 12165, Germany. TEL 49-30-7900060, FAX 49-30-79000631, info@duncker-humblot.de, http://www.duncker-humblot.de.

330 USA ISSN 1064-7716
DK507.8
BELARUSIAN REVIEW. Text in English. 1991. q. USD 20; USD 40 foreign.
Published by: Byelorussian-American Association, PO Box 10353, Torrance, CA 90505. FAX 310-373-0793, http://www.belreview.cz/index.html.

330 BLR
BELORUSSKAYA DELOVAYA GAZETA/BELORUSSIAN BUSINESS NEWSPAPER; birzhi i banki. Text in Russian. 1992. 3/w. USD 419 foreign (effective 2005). adv. tel.rev.; video rev. mkt. back issues avail. **Document type:** *Newspaper, Consumer.* **Description:** Covers politics, culture, economy, news and analysis.
Related titles: Online - full content ed.
Published by: J S C Belorusskaya Delovaya Gazeta, ul Chkalova 12, 4 etazh, Minsk, 220039, Belarus. info@bdg.by, http://www.bdg.by. Ed. Pyotr Martsev. R&P Svetlana Kalinkina TEL 216-25-83. Adv. contact Sergey Skorakhod. B&W page USD 3,000; trim 390 x 260. Circ: 21,000 (paid). **Dist. by:** East View Information Services, 3020 Harbor Ln. N., Minneapolis, MN 55447. TEL 800-477-1005, FAX 800-800-3839, eastview@eastview.com, http://www.eastview.com.

330 BLR
BELORUSSKII RYNOK. Text in Russian. w.
Address: Ul Rabkorovskaya 17, Minsk, 220001, Belarus. TEL 375-172-2280024, 375-172-2280023, 375-172-2228029, FAX 375-172-2227641, 375-172-2227644, root@br.minsk.by, http://www.br.minsk.by. Ed. Vyacheslav Khodosovskii. Circ: 15,000.

330 USA
BENCHMARKING IN PRACTICE. Text in English. 1996. irreg. members only. **Document type:** *Newsletter, Trade.*
Published by: American Productivity & Quality Center, 123 N. Post Oak Ln., 3rd Fl., Houston, TX 77024. apqcinfo@apqc.org, http://www.apqc.org. Ed. Paige Leavitt. Circ: 1,000 (controlled and free).

330.949 DNK ISSN 0907-8274
HC357.F3
BERETNING OM DEN OEKONOMISKE UDVIKLING PAA FAEROERNE. Text in Danish. 1973. a. free. **Document type:** *Government.* **Description:** Contains reports on economic development in the Faroe Islands.
Formerly (until 1992): Oekonomiske Udvikling paa Faeroerne (0108-6464)
Published by: Statsministeriet, Raadgivende Udvalg Vedroerende Faeroerne, Christiansborg, Copenhagen K, 1218, Denmark. TEL 45-33-92-33-00, FAX 45-33-11-16-65, TELEX 27027, stm@stm.dk, http://www.statsministeriet.dk/. Circ: 500. **Subscr. to:** Prime Minister's Office, Christiansborg, Copenhagen K 1218, Denmark.

330 DEU ISSN 1612-7420
BERICHTE AUS DER FACHHOCHSCHULE. Text in German. 19??. irreg., latest vol.35, 2004. price varies. **Document type:** *Monographic series, Academic/Scholarly.*

B

▼ new title ➤ refereed ✶ unverified ♦ full entry avail.

Published by: Fachhochschule Muenster, Huefferstr 27, Muenster, 48149, Germany. TEL 49-251-830, FAX 49-251-8364015, verwaltung@fh-muenster.de, http://www.fh-muenster.de.

330 MYS
BERITA I D S DEVELOPMENT REVIEW. Text in English. m. MYR 3.50 domestic; MYR 5.50 foreign (effective 2000).
Document type: *Newsletter.* **Description:** Covers social, economic and current affairs, with updates on research programs and activities of the institute.
Published by: Institute for Development Studies (Sabah)/Institut Kajian Pembangunan (Sabah), Ste. 7 CF01 7th Fl Block C, Kompleks Karamunsing, Kota Kinabalu, Sabah 88300, Malaysia. TEL 60-88-246166, FAX 60-88-234707, TELEX IDS MA80067. Ed. Mohd Yaakub H Johari.

BERKELEY LAW AND ECONOMICS WORKING PAPERS (ONLINE EDITION). see *LAW*

BERKELEY LAW AND ECONOMICS WORKING PAPERS (PRINT EDITION). see *LAW*

330 DEU ISSN 0863-2952
BERLINER MERKUR. Text in German. 1990. m. EUR 2 newsstand/cover. adv. **Document type:** *Magazine, Trade.*
Published by: Merkur Verlag, Binzstr 18, Berlin, 13189, Germany. TEL 49-30-4725393, FAX 49-30-4732251. Ed. Uwe Riemer. Adv. contact Liane Komoll. B&W page EUR 1,680, color page EUR 3,180. Circ: 29,500 (controlled).

330.9489 DNK ISSN 1604-2603
HC351
BERLINGSKE NYHEDSMAGASIN. Text in Danish. 1985. w. DKK 1,780 (effective 2005). adv. back issues avail. **Document type:** *Magazine, Corporate.* **Description:** Contains in-depth articles about the most important events in Danish trade and industry, a summary of current news, and portraits of influential corporate executives.
Former titles (until 2004): Berlingske Tidendes Nyhedsmagasin (1602-5202); (until 2002): Boersens Nyhedsmagasin (0900-1298); Which was formed by the merger of (1982-1985): Politisk Ugebrev (0109-0909); (1978-1985): Maaneds Boersen (0105-8843); (1968-1985): Management (0025-1631)
—Linda Hall.
Published by: Berlingske Tidendes Nyhedsmagasin, Pilestraede 34, PO Box 2128, Copenhagen K, 1015, Denmark. TEL 45-33-757400, FAX 45-33-757444, redaktion@bny.dk, http://www.bny.dk. Eds. Pia Fuglsang Bach TEL 45-33-757402, Flemming Hoejbo TEL 45-33-757401. Adv. contact Anders Juul Rasmussen. color page DKK 35,000; trim 210 x 280. Circ: 15,000. **Dist. by:** Forhandlerservice.

330 CHE ISSN 0067-6128
BERNER BEITRAEGE ZUR NATIONALOEKONOMIE. Text in German, English. 1965. irreg., latest vol.88, 2002. price varies. **Document type:** *Monographic series, Academic/Scholarly.*
—CCC.
Published by: Paul Haupt AG, Falkenplatz 14, Bern, 3001, Switzerland. TEL 41-31-3012425, FAX 41-31-3014669, verlag@haupt.ch, http://www.haupt.ch.

330 USA
BERNSTEIN ON STOCK. Text in English. 1998. w. USD 280 (effective 1999). tr.lit. back issues avail. **Document type:** *Newsletter.*
Related titles: Online - full text ed.
Published by: M B H Commodity Advisors, Inc., PO Box 353, Winnetka, IL 60093-0353. TEL 847-291-1870, FAX 847-291-9435, marilyn@trade-futures.com, jake@trade-futures.com. Ed. Jacob Bernstein.

BERUFS- UND KARRIERE-PLANER. WIRTSCHAFT. see *OCCUPATIONS AND CAREERS*

330 USA ISSN 1537-1239
HD28
BEST PRACTICES; the applied business journal of the Moravian M B A. Text in English. 2002. s-a.
Published by: Moravian College, 1200 Main St., Bethlehem, PA 18018. TEL 610-807-4444, http://www.moravian.edu. Ed. Santo D. Marabella.

330 BEL
BESTUUR EN BELEID V Z W. Text in Flemish. s-m. Supplement avail. **Description:** Covers regulations, subsidies, accounting, personnel and directional leadership.
Published by: C E D Samsom (Subsidiary of: Wolters Samsom Belgie n.v.), Kouterveld 14, Diegem, 1831, Belgium. TEL 32-2-7231111.

330 VNM ISSN 1341-3066
BETONAMU KEIZAI SHUHO/VIETNAM ECONOMIC NEWS. Text in Japanese. 1995. w.
Former titles (until 1995): Betonamu Sangyo Keizai Doko (1340-3435); (until 1993): Betonamu Keizai Doko (0917-8449)
Related titles: Online - full text ed.: (from Gale Group).
Published by: Vietnam Institute for Economic Research, 28 Le Quy Don St., Q.3,, TP Hochi Minh, Viet Nam. TEL 84-8-9321335, FAX 84-8-9321370. Ed. Dr. Tran Du Lich.

330 DEU ISSN 0341-1044
BETRIEB UND PERSONAL. Text in German. 1970. m. EUR 131.80; EUR 12.90 newsstand/cover (effective 2004). adv. **Document type:** *Magazine, Trade.*
Indexed: IBR, IBZ.
—IE, Infotrieve. **CCC.**
Published by: Stollfuss Verlag GmbH & Co. KG, Dechenstr 7, Bonn, 53115, Germany. TEL 49-228-7240, FAX 49-228-72491181, info@stollfuss.de, http://www.stollfuss.de/programm/products/0400085.htm. adv.: B&W page EUR 2,250, color page EUR 3,580. Circ: 8,000 (paid and controlled).

330 DEU
BETRIEBSERGEBNISSE BUCHFUEHRENDER BETRIEBE. Text in German. 1970. a. **Document type:** *Bulletin.*
Published by: Landwirtschaftskammer Rheinland, Endenicher Allee 60, Bonn, 53115, Germany. TEL 49-228-703-223, FAX 49-228-703498. Ed. Hans Peter Rehse.

330 DEU ISSN 0172-6196
DER BETRIEBSWIRT. Text in German. 1959. q. EUR 45 (effective 2005). bk.rev. back issues avail. **Document type:** *Magazine, Trade.*
Formerly (until 1979): Der Betriebswirt. Ausgabe A (0340-854X); Incorporates (1981-1981): L B W - Fachinformation (0723-760X); Which was formed by the merger of (1976-1981): L B W - Fachinformation. Marketing (0174-1489); (1976-1981): L B W - Fachinformation. Organisation, Datenverarbeitung (0174-1497); (1976-1981): L B W - Fachinformation. Personalwirtschaft (0174-1500); (1976-1981): L B W - Fachinformation. Unternehmensfuehrung, Finanzwesen, Rechnungswesen (0174-1519); All of which superseded in part (in 1980): Literaturberater Wirtschaft (0170-6209)
Published by: Deutscher Betriebswirte Verlag GmbH, Postfach 1332, Gernsbach, 76586, Germany. TEL 49-7224-9397151, FAX 49-7224-9397251, info@betriebswirte-verlag.de, http://www.betriebswirte-verlag.de/der_betriebswirt.htm. Ed. Casimir Katz. Adv. contact Horst Wannemacher. Circ: 2,600.

330 DEU ISSN 0933-3614
BETRIEBSWIRTSCHAFTLICHES ARBEITSBUCH. Text in German. 1978. irreg. looseleaf. price varies. **Document type:** *Monographic series, Trade.*
Published by: Erich Schmidt Verlag GmbH & Co. (Berlin), Genthiner Str 30G, Berlin, 10785, Germany. TEL 49-30-250085-0, FAX 49-30-25008521, vertrieb@esvmedien.de, http://www.erich-schmidt-verlag.de.

330 IND
BETTER BUSINESS. Text in English. bi-m.
Published by: Ad International, 212 Arun Chambers, Taredo Rd., Mumbai, Maharashtra 400 034, India. Pub. R C Pandit.

330 AUS ISSN 1447-0705
BETTER BUSINESS MAGAZINE. Text in English. 2000. q. AUD 35 domestic; AUD 45 in Asia & the Pacific; AUD 50 elsewhere (effective 2004). adv.
Formerly (until 2002): Small Business Series (1443-2803)
Related titles: Online - full content ed.
Published by: Business Essentials Pty Ltd, Reply Paid 579, HAWTHORN, VIC 3122, Australia. TEL 61-3-98828333, FAX 61-3-98828017, info@be.com.au, http://www.bbmagazine.com.au/bb/. adv.: page AUD 8,500; trim 206 x 276. Circ: 34,190.

330 363.7 USA ISSN 1544-5135
HD30.255
BEYOND PINSTRIPES; preparing mbas for social and environmental stewardship. Text in English. 1998. a.
Published by: (World Resources Institute), Aspen Institute, Initiative for Social Innovation through Business, 271 Madison Ave. Ste. 606, New York, NY 10016. TEL 212-895-8000, FAX 212-895-8012, info@aspenisib.org, http://www.beyondgreypinstripes.org, http://www.aspenisib.org.

330 USA ISSN 0884-8513
BEYOND RELIEF. Text in English. 1985. irreg.
Published by: African Development Foundation, 1400 I St NW 10th Fl, Washington, DC 20005-2248. TEL 202-673-3916, FAX 202-673-8819, http://www.adf.gov/.

BIBLIOGRAPHIE DER WIRTSCHAFTSWISSENSCHAFTEN. see *BIBLIOGRAPHIES*

330 UKR
BIBLIOTECHKA BANKIRA. Text in Ukrainian. bi-m. USD 124 in the Americas (effective 2000).
Address: Ul. Streletskaya, 28, Kiev, Ukraine. TEL 212-42-91, FAX 224-23-36. **Dist. by:** East View Information Services, 3020 Harbor Ln. N., Minneapolis, MN 55447. TEL 763-550-0961, FAX 763-559-2931.

330 ROM ISSN 0067-8082
BIBLIOTHECA OECONOMICA. Text in Romanian; Summaries in English, French, Russian. 1967; N.S. 1992. irreg.
Published by: (Institutul de Cercetari Economice), Editura Academiei Romane/Publishing House of the Romanian Academy, Calea 13 Septembrie 13, Sector 5, Bucharest, 76117, Romania.

330 USA
BID MAGAZINE. Text in English. 2001 (Jun.). m. bk.rev.
Document type: *Magazine, Consumer.* **Description:** Covers the investments in emerging technologies including high tech, biotechnology, e-commerce, telecommunications and digital media space.
Published by: NexGen Publishing, 53 W 36th St Ste 606, New York, NY 10018. TEL 212-971-9111.

330.9 FRA ISSN 0755-2238
BILANS HEBDOMADAIRES. Text in French. 1945. w. looseleaf.
Description: Provides a summary of the political, economic and social news in France and the world.
Incorporates (in 1997): Lettre Financiere (0395-0905); Actualites Economiques
—CCC.
Published by: Societe Generale de Presse et d'Editions, 13 av. de l'Opera, Paris, 75001, France. TEL 33-1-40151789, FAX 33-1-40151715, TELEX SOGPRES 230023. Ed. Marianne Berard Quelin.

BILL SHIPP'S GEORGIA. see *PUBLIC ADMINISTRATION*

338 USA
BIOCENTURY EXTRA. Text in English. d. USD 2,195 combined subscription for BioCentury: The Bernstein Report on BioBusiness, BioCentury Extra, BioCentury Part II, BioCentury Quarterly Stock Reports (effective 2004). **Document type:** *Newsletter, Trade.* **Description:** Covers top stories, company news, clinical news, financial news, politics & policy, and stock indicators.
Media: E-mail.
Published by: BioCentury Publicattions Inc., PO Box 1246, San Carlos, CA 94070. https://www.biocentury.com/html/promos/bcx/, http://www.biocentury.com/.

338 USA
BIOCENTURY PART II. Text in English. w. USD 2,195 combined subscription for BioCentury: The Bernstein Report on BioBusiness, BioCentury Extra, BioCentury Part II, BioCentury Quarterly Stock Reports (effective 2004). **Document type:** *Newsletter, Trade.* **Description:** Covers industry deals, regulatory events, clinical activities, and financings.
Media: E-mail.
Published by: BioCentury Publicattions Inc., PO Box 1246, San Carlos, CA 94070. https://www.biocentury.com/html/promos/bc2/, http://www.biocentury.com/.

338 USA ISSN 1097-7201
BIOCENTURY: THE BERNSTEIN REPORT ON BIOBUSINESS. Text in English. w. USD 2,195 combined subscription for BioCentury: The Bernstein Report on BioBusiness, BioCentury Extra, BioCentury Part II, BioCentury Quarterly Stock Reports (effective 2004). **Document type:** *Newsletter, Trade.*
Description: Provides analysis, interpretation and commentary on bio-industry development, corporate performance and shareholder value.
Media: Online - full content.
Published by: BioCentury Publicattions Inc., PO Box 1246, San Carlos, CA 94070. https://www.biocentury.com/html/promos/bc1/, http://www.biocentury.com/.

BIOPHOENIX DATABASE ON CD-ROM. see *MEDICAL SCIENCES*

BIOTECH MARKET NEWS & LEGAL STRATEGIES. see *BIOLOGY—Biotechnology*

BIOTECH UNLIMITED. see *BIOLOGY—Biotechnology*

330 USA
BIOTECH UPDATE (MIAMI BEACH). Text in English. w.
Document type: *Newsletter, Trade.*
Media: E-mail.
Published by: 123Jump.com, 407 Lincoln Rd Ste 12D, Miami Beach, FL 33139. TEL 305-673-6339, FAX 305-673-6386, editorial@123jump.com, http://www.123jump.com/.

330 GBR ISSN 0956-8328
BIRKBECK COLLEGE DISCUSSION PAPERS IN ECONOMICS. Text in English. 1972. irreg. free. **Document type:** *Monographic series, Academic/Scholarly.*
Formerly (until 1987): Birkbeck College Discussion Papers (0956-831X)
Indexed: RDA.
—BLDSC (3597.914800), IE, ingenta.
Published by: (Department of Economics), University of London, Birkbeck College, Birkbeck College, 7-15 Gresse St, London, W1P 2LL, United Kingdom. TEL 44-171-631-6401, FAX 44-171-631-6416, http://www.econ.bbk.ac.uk/research/wpaper.htm/. Circ: 200.

330 USA ISSN 0889-2237
BIRMINGHAM BUSINESS JOURNAL. Text in English. 1983. w. (Fri.). USD 65 (effective 2005). adv. back issues avail.
Document type: *Newspaper.* **Description:** Contains business news, information and analysis.
Related titles: Online - full text ed.: (from Florida Center for Library Automation, Gale Group, O C L C Online Computer Library Center, Inc., ProQuest Information & Learning).
Indexed: ABIn, BusDate.

—CCC.
Address: 2140 11th Ave S., Ste. 205, Birmingham, AL 35205-2840. TEL 205-322-0000, FAX 205-322-0040, birmingham@bizjournals.com, http://birmingham.bizjournals.com/birmingham/. Ed. Jim Degraw. Pub. Tine Verciglio Savas. Adv. contact Adam Burst. Circ: 6,000 (paid and free). Wire service: PR.

330 RUS
BIRZHA. Text in Russian. w.
Published by: Nizhegorodskaya Torgovo-Promyshlennyi Dom, Ul Belinskogo 110, of 165, Nizhnii Novgorod, Russian Federation. TEL 7-8312-356286, FAX 7-8312-355848, birzha@birzha.sci-nnov.ru, http://www.birzhaplus.sandy.ru/birzha/index.htm. Ed. Vladimir Lapyrin. Circ: 20,000.

339.1 ROM ISSN 1454-8380
BIZ. Text in Romanian. 1999. s-m. adv. **Document type:** *Magazine, Trade.*
Published by: Business Media Group, Bd. Regina Maria nr. 1, bl. P5B, sector 1, ap. 10-11-12, Bucharest, Romania. TEL 40-21-3353473, FAX 40-21-3353474, subscribe@bmg.ro.

330 USA
BIZ (ADDISON). Text in English. 2000. bi-m. USD 23.95; USD 3.99 newsstand/cover (effective 2001). adv. **Document type:** *Consumer.*
Published by: C E G, Inc., 16885 Dallas Pkwy, Addison, TX 75001. TEL 972-991-3333, FAX 972-960-9555, gpetrone@biz-mag.com, http://www.biz-mag.com. Ed. Gina Petrone. Pub. Jim Meeker.

330 USA ISSN 1553-2593
BIZ A Z; the magazine for the hungry business mind. (Arizona) Text in English. 1997 (Sept). bi-m. USD 15 (effective 2003). adv. **Document type:** *Magazine, Trade.* **Description:** Provides Arizona's business leaders with idea-driven strategies that help them outsmart and outperform the competitor.
Related titles: Online - full content ed.: bizAZ.com.
Published by: bizAZ, 5151 N 16th St, Ste E 128, Phoenix, AZ 85016. TEL 602-667-3008, 877-834-4430, FAX 602-667-6441, bizaz@bizaz.com, http://www.bizaz.com. adv.: color 1/8 page USD 2,965; trim 8.375 x 10.875. Circ: 25,000.

330 CAN
BIZ - HAMILTON-HALTON BUSINESS REPORT. Text in English. 1986. q. CND 10.65. adv. bk.rev.; film rev.; play rev. back issues avail.
Formerly: Report Business Quarterly; Incorporates: Hamilton Report; Hamilton Business Report
Published by: Town Publishing Group Inc., 875 Main St W, Hamilton, ON L8S 4R1, Canada. TEL 905-522-6117, FAX 905-529-2242, townl@interlynx.net. Ed. Arthur Kelly. Pub. Wayne Narciso. Adv. contact Janice Novak. Circ: 21,000.

330 RUS ISSN 0868-6009
HD70.R9
BIZNES. Text in Russian. m.
Indexed: RASB.
—East View.
Published by: Izdatel'skii Dom Biznes, Ul Zatsepa 4-b, Moscow, 113054, Russian Federation. TEL 7-095-2350600. **US dist. addr.:** East View Information Services, 3020 Harbor Ln. N., Minneapolis, MN 55447. TEL 612-550-0961, FAX 612-559-2931.

330 UKR
BIZNES. Text in Ukrainian. w.
Indexed: RASB.
Published by: Vydavnytstvo Blits - Inform, Ul Kioto 25, Kiev, Ukraine. TEL 380-544-45-05, FAX 380-544-45-05. **US dist. addr.:** East View Information Services, 3020 Harbor Ln. N., Minneapolis, MN 55447. TEL 612-550-0961.

330 RUS ISSN 1606-1551
BIZNES DLYA VSEKH. Text in Russian. 1998. w. (48/yr.). free (effective 2004). back issues avail. **Document type:** *Consumer.*
Media: Online - full text.
Indexed: RASB.
Published by: (Rossiiskaya Assotsiatsiya Razvitiya Malogo Predprinimatel'stva), Al'yans Midiya, Bolotnaya ul 12, str 3, Moscow, 115035, Russian Federation. TEL 7-095-2345380, FAX 7-095-2345363, allmedia@allmedia.ru, http://www.businesspress.ru, http://allmedia.ru.

330 LVA ISSN 1407-3021
BIZNES I BALTIYA. Text in Russian. 1991. 3/w. USD 445 in United States. adv.
Related titles: Online - full text ed.
Address: Balasta dambis 3, Riga, 1081, Latvia. TEL 371-7033044, FAX 371-7033040, root@info.bb.neonet.lv, http://www.bb.lv. Ed. Tatyana Fast. Pub. Vladimir Gurov. Adv. contact Inara Baubele. Circ: 19,000. **US dist. addr.:** East View Information Services, 3020 Harbor Ln. N., Minneapolis, MN 55447. TEL 612-550-0961.

330 364.1 RUS ISSN 1606-1446
BIZNES I KRIMINAL. Text in Russian. 1999. w. free (effective 2004). back issues avail. **Document type:** *Consumer.*
Media: Online - full text.
Published by: Al'yans Midiya, Bolotnaya ul 12, str 3, Moscow, 115035, Russian Federation. TEL 7-095-2345380, FAX 7-095-2345363, allmedia@allmedia.ru, http://www.businesspress.ru, http://allmedia.ru.

330 RUS
BIZNES I STRAKHOVANIE. Text in Russian. m.
Indexed: RASB.
Published by: Firma Ankil, Elizavetinskii pr-d 6-1, ofis 23, Moscow, 107005, Russian Federation. TEL 7-095-2653718, FAX 7-095-2653718. Ed. Yu V Ponomarenko. **US dist. addr.:** East View Information Services, 3020 Harbor Ln. N., Minneapolis, MN 55447. TEL 612-550-0961.

330 RUS
BIZNES PRAKTIKA. Text in Russian. s-m.
Address: Ul Sovetskaya 30, Novosibirsk, 630099, Russian Federation. practica@online.nsk.su, http://www.nsk.ru/~practica.

330 UZB
BIZNES VESTNIK VOSTOKA. Abbreviated title: B V V. Text in Uzbek. w. USD 289 in United States.
Address: Matbuotcilar 32, 4 etazh, Tashkent, 700000, Uzbekistan. TEL 7-136-5856. Ed. Galina Chebakova. **US dist. addr.:** East View Information Services, 3020 Harbor Ln. N., Minneapolis, MN 55447. TEL 612-550-0961.

330 AUS
BIZREVIEW.COM.AU. Text in English. bi-m. AUD 99 (effective 2001). adv. **Document type:** *Magazine, Trade.*
Published by: Publishing Services (Australia) Pty. Ltd., 244 St Pauls Terrace, Fortitude Valley, Brisbane, QLD 4000, Australia. TEL 61-7-3854-1286, FAX 61-7-3252-4829, grahamg@bizreview.com.au, http://www.bizreview.com.au. Ed. Gardiner Graham. adv.: B&W page AUD 7,335, color page AUD 9,775; trim 275 x 205. Circ: 7,116.

330 USA
THE BIZWEB E-GAZETTE. Text in English. w. **Description:** Business related e-zine, which features articles, marketing tips and business related classifieds.
Media: Online - full text.
Published by: BizWeb E-Gazette mail@JDD-Publishing.com.

BIZWIZE. see *COMPUTERS—Internet*

330 BEL ISSN 1375-0690
BIZZ; le magazine qui se mele de vos affaires. Text in French. 1999. m. EUR 33 (effective 2004). adv. **Document type:** *Magazine, Trade.*
Related titles: Dutch ed.: ISSN 1375-0704.
Published by: Roularta Media Group, Research Park, Zellik, 1731, Belgium. TEL 32-2-4675611, FAX 32-2-4675757, communication@roularta.be, http://www.bizzmagazine.be, http://www.roularta.be. Circ: 50,888 (paid).

330 NLD ISSN 1380-8206
BIZZ; Voor ondernemers. Key Title: BiZZ. Text in Dutch. 1994. m. EUR 99.06 (effective 2005). adv. illus. **Document type:** *Trade.* **Description:** Provides topical information and practical ideas for the company manager, owner or entrepreneur.
Related titles: Online - full content ed.; Online - full text ed.: (from LexisNexis).
Published by: Reed Business Information bv (Subsidiary of: Reed Business), Planetenbaan 80-99, Maarssen, 3606 AK, Netherlands. TEL 31-346-577201, FAX 31-346-550282, bizz.info@reedbusiness.nl, http://www.productonline.reedbusiness.nl/product.asp?catalog%5Fname=RBI&category%5Fname=&product%5Fid=681%28Octopus%29, http://www.reedbusiness.nl. Ed. Arjan Kors TEL 31-346-577766. Pub. Ewald Smits. adv.: color page EUR 11,774; trim 212 x 285. Circ: 174,291.

330 305.896 USA
THE BLACK E O E JOURNAL; the employment & entrepreneur magazine. Text in English. 1991. q. USD 16; USD 3.50 newsstand/cover (effective 2003). adv. **Document type:** *Journal, Consumer.*
Published by: Olive Tree Publishing, Inc., 6845 Indiana Ave., Ste. 2, Riverside, CA 92506-4224. pburke@blackeoejournal.com, http://www.blackeoejournal.com/. adv.: B&W page USD 7,000, color 1/8 page USD 7,650; trim 8.375 x 10.875. Circ: 112,000 (paid).

650 USA ISSN 0006-4165
E185.8 CODEN: BLENDG
BLACK ENTERPRISE. Text in English. 1970. m. USD 17.95; USD 3.99 newsstand/cover (effective 2005). adv. bk.rev. illus. reprint service avail. from PQC. **Document type:** *Magazine, Trade.* **Description:** Features business service information for African American professionals and entrepreneurs.
Related titles: Microfiche ed.: (from PQC); Microfilm ed.: (from PQC); Online - full text ed.: Black Enterprise.com (from bigchalk, EBSCO Publishing, Florida Center for Library Automation, Gale Group, H.W. Wilson, LexisNexis, Northern Light Technology, Inc., O C L C Online Computer Library Center, Inc., ProQuest Information & Learning, SoftLine Information).
Indexed: ABIn, ATI, AcaI, B&I, BLI, BPI, BPIA, BRI, BusI, CBRI, ENW, IIBP, IPARL, ISAP, LRI, MASUSE, MagInd, PAIS, PCI, PMR, PSI, RGAb, RGPR, SRI, T&II, TOM, WorkRelAb.
—BLDSC (2105.925000), IE, ingenta. **CCC.**
Published by: Earl G. Graves Publishing Co., Inc., 130 Fifth Ave, New York, NY 10011. TEL 212-242-8000, FAX 212-886-9610, beeditor@aol.com, hanks@blackenterprise.com, http://www.blackenterprise.com. Ed. Alfred A Edmond. Pub. Earl G Graves. Adv. contact Dirk Caldwell TEL 212-886-9543. B&W page USD 24,885, color page USD 33,145; trim 8 x 10.88. Circ: 500,000 (paid). **Dist. in UK by:** Seymour Distribution Ltd, 86 Newman St, London W1T 3EX, United Kingdom. TEL 44-20-73968000, FAX 44-20-73968002.

BLACK HOLE; urban music magazine. see *MUSIC*

330.07 DEU ISSN 1432-301X
BLICKPUNKT WIRTSCHAFT (COLOGNE). Text in German. 1996. m. **Document type:** *Magazine, Consumer.* **Description:** Provides articles and information on business concerns.
Published by: Institut der Deutschen Wirtschaft, Gustav-Heinemann-Ufer 84-88, Cologne, 50968, Germany. TEL 49-221-49811, FAX 49-221-4981592, redaktion@aktiv-wirtschaftszeitung.de, welcome@iwkoeln.de, http://www.div-blickpunkt.de, http://www.iwkoeln.de.

BLUEPRINT SERIES. see *ENVIRONMENTAL STUDIES*

330 AUS
BLUES COUNTRY MAGAZINE. Text in English. 1991. bi-m. AUD 33 (effective 2001). adv. **Document type:** *Trade.*
Published by: Publishing Services (Australia) Pty. Ltd., 244 St Pauls Terrace, Fortitude Valley, Brisbane, QLD 4000, Australia. TEL 61-7-3854-1286, FAX 61-7-3252-4829, http://www.bluescountry.com.au. Ed. Gardiner Graham. Adv. contact David Sweedman. color page AUD 4,050, B&W page AUD 990; trim 265 x 195. Circ: 50,000.

330 658 GBR
BOARDROOM. Text in English. 1978. m. GBP 11.50. adv. bk.rev. pat.; stat.; tr.lit. **Document type:** *Trade.*
Formerly: Trade and Industry in Ireland
Published by: Ulster Magazines Ltd., 58 Rugby Rd, Belfast, Co Antrim BT7 1NT, United Kingdom. TEL 44-1232-230425, FAX 44-1232-243595. Ed. Larry Nixon. Circ: 5,000.

BODYSHOP (FRENCH EDITION). see *TRANSPORTATION—Automobiles*

330 DEU ISSN 0343-7728
BOERSEN ZEITUNG. Text in German. 5/w. (Tue.-Sat.). **Document type:** *Newspaper, Consumer.*
Formed by the merger of (1966-1972): Boersen Zeitung. Ausgabe A (0344-2551); (1966-1972): Boersen Zeitung. Ausgabe B (0344-2578); Which both superseded in part: Boersen Zeitung (0344-2594)
Published by: Herausgebergemeinschaft Wertpapier-Mitteilungen Keppler Lehmann GmbH & Co., Postfach 110932, Frankfurt Am Main, 60044, Germany. TEL 49-69-2732-0, FAX 49-69-234473. Ed. Hans Herdt.

330 ESP ISSN 0006-6249
HB9
BOLETIN DE ESTUDIOS ECONOMICOS; revista de investigacion economica. Text in Spanish. 1942. 3/yr. EUR 28.55 domestic; EUR 32.45 foreign (effective 2002). adv. bk.rev. bibl. index. **Document type:** *Journal, Academic/Scholarly.*
Formerly: Universidad de Deusto. Publicaciones. Economia
Indexed: AmH&L, BAS, BibInd, ELLIS, ExcerpMed, HistAb, IBR, PAIS, RASB, SCIMP.
—BLDSC (2203.840000), CINDOC, IE, Infotrieve.
Published by: (Asociacion de Licenciados en Ciencias Economicas), Universidad de Deusto, Apdo 1/E, Bilbao, 48080, Spain. TEL 34-94-4139162, FAX 34-94-4456817, publicaciones@deusto.es. Eds. Fernando Gomez Bezares, Susana Rodriguez Vidarte. Adv. contact Gabriela Mateos. Circ: 5,000.

330 ARG
BOLETIN INFORMATIVO. Text in Spanish. 1997. bi-w. back issues avail.
Media: Online - full text.
Published by: Universidad de Buenos Aires, Facultad de Ciencias Economicas, Ave. Cordoba No. 2122, Buenos Aires, 1120, Argentina. TEL 54-114-3744448, web@econ.uba.ar, http://www.econ.uba.ar/www/servicios/publicaciones/index.html.

BOLETIN POSGRADOS. see *SOCIAL SCIENCES: COMPREHENSIVE WORKS*

330 COL
BOLETIN UNICO DE LICITACIONES Y CONCURSO. Text in Spanish. 1995. m. COP 250,000, USD 200 (effective 2000). adv. **Document type:** *Directory.* **Description:** Provides information on open auctions in the country.
Published by: Confederacion Colombiana de Camaras de Comercio, Carrera 13 no. 27-47 of. 502, Santa Fe de Bogota, CUND, Colombia. TEL 57-1-3467055, FAX 57-1-3467517, confecamaras@inter.net.co, http://www.confecamaras.org.co. adv.: B&W page COP 1,200,000, B&W page USD 800, color page COP 1,500,000, color page USD 1,000; 215 x 280. Circ: 5,000 (paid and controlled).

659.3 ROM ISSN 1454-2773
BOOK OF LISTS. Text in English. 1998. a. **Document type:** *Directory, Trade.* **Description:** Contains facts and figures on business companies and personnel in the Romanian marketplace.
Published by: AmeriCelt Publishing SRL, Str. Principatele Unite nr. 47, sector 4, Bucharest, Romania. TEL 40-21-3372828, FAX 40-21-3372831, luminita.holban@bbw.ro, http://www.bbw.ro/bookoflists.htm.

330 MYS ISSN 0128-7397
HC448.B6
BORNEO REVIEW. Text in English. 1990. s-a. MYR 32 (effective 2000). adv. **Document type:** *Academic/Scholarly.* **Description:** Publishes research pertaining to economic, social, political and public administrative developments.
Related titles: Online - full text ed.: (from ProQuest Information & Learning).
Indexed: APEL, IBSS, RDA, WAE&RSA.
Published by: Institute for Development Studies (Sabah)/Institut Kajian Pembangunan (Sabah), Ste. 7 CF01 7th Fl Block C, Kompleks Karamunsing, Kota Kinabalu, Sabah 88300, Malaysia. TEL 60-88-246166, FAX 60-88-234707.

330 RUS
BOSS. Text in Russian. 2000. m.
Related titles: Online - full content ed.
Published by: Izdatel'stvo Biznes i Komp'iuter, a/ya 75, Moscow, 127238, Russian Federation. TEL 7-095-4887406, http://www.cfin.ru/press/boss, http://www.bizcom.ru. Ed. Aleksandr Polianskii.

330 USA ISSN 0746-4975
THE BOSTON BUSINESS JOURNAL. Text in English. 1981. w. (Fri.). USD 109 (effective 2005). adv. back issues avail. **Document type:** *Newspaper, Consumer.* **Description:** Covers the diverse and dynamic economy of Greater Boston.
Related titles: Online - full text ed.: (from CompuServe Inc., Data-Star, EBSCO Publishing, Florida Center for Library Automation, Gale Group, O C L C Online Computer Library Center, Inc., ProQuest Information & Learning, The Dialog Corporation).
Indexed: ABIn, BusDate, LRI.
—CCC.
Published by: American City Business Journals, Inc. (Boston), 200 High St Ste 4B, Boston, MA 02110. TEL 617-330-1000, FAX 617-330-1016, boston@bizjournals.com, http://boston.bizjournals.com/boston/. Ed. George Donnelly. Pub. John C Menneto. adv.: B&W page USD 3,975. Circ: 20,000.

330 USA
BOSTON SEAPORT JOURNAL. Text in English. m. adv. **Description:** Focuses on Boston business, tourism, and transportation news.
Published by: Robert Weiss Associates, 256 Marginal St, East, Boston, MA 02128-2800. TEL 617-561-4000, FAX 617-561-2821. Pub. Robert H Weiss.

330 ZAF
BOTSWANA; review - commerce, industry and tourism. Text in English. a. ZAR 30 (effective 1999).
Published by: Braby's (Subsidiary of: Associated Industries), Attn: Sue Pearson, PO Box 1426, Pinetown, 3600, South Africa. TEL 27-31-7174141, FAX 27-31-7173011.

330 BWA
BOTSWANA BUSINESS MONTH MAGAZINE. Text in English. 1988. bi-m. BWP 10.65; USD 15 foreign. adv. **Document type:** *Trade.* **Description:** Encourages investment and economic development in Botswana.
Published by: News Company Botswana Pty. Ltd., PO Box 1605, Gaborone, Botswana. TEL 267-312833, FAX 267-312774, TELEX 2631 BD. Ed. Clara Olsen. adv.: B&W page BWP 1,360, color page BWP 1,950. Circ: 500.

330 BWA
BOTSWANA BUSINESS NEWS. Text in English. 1980. m. free. **Document type:** *Newsletter, Government.* **Description:** Covers a variety of subjects related to trade and investment promotion. Reviews commercial and industrial development.
Published by: Ministry of Commerce and Industry, Department of Trade and Investment Promotion (T I P A), Private Bag 00367, Gaborone, Botswana. TEL 267-351790, FAX 267-305375, TELEX 2674 TRADE BD. Eds. Monty Letshwiti, Mukram Sheikh. Circ: 3,000.

330 CAN ISSN 1480-1574
BOTTIN DES SERVICES ET D'EXPERTISE-CONSEIL. Text in French. 1998. a. CND 39.95. **Document type:** *Directory.* **Description:** Lists approximately 500 key organizations and agencies offering expertise to firms covering all sectors of life in Quebec.
Published by: Quebec dans le Monde, C P 8503, Sainte Foy, PQ G1V 4N5, Canada. TEL 418-659-5540, FAX 418-659-4143. Ed. Denis Turcotte.

330 BMU
BOTTOM LINE. Text in English. 1991. q. free. adv. **Document type:** *Consumer.*
Published by: The Royal Gazette Ltd., 2 Par la Ville Rd, Hamilton, HM08, Bermuda. TEL 441-295-5881, FAX 441-295-9178, editor@crown.newsmedia.bm. Adv. contact Bryce McGregor. B&W page BSD 770, color page BSD 1,540.

657 CAN ISSN 0831-5477
THE BOTTOM LINE; the independent voice for Canada's accounting and financial professionals. Text in English. 1985. m. CND 84 domestic; CND 125 foreign; CND 29.95 to students (effective 2005). adv. bk.rev. back issues avail. **Document type:** *Newspaper, Trade.* **Description:** Accounting news, coverage of corporate governance and professional standards, software reviews, tax court decisions and professional development for accountants.
Related titles: Microfiche ed.; Microfilm ed.: (from MML); Microform ed.: (from MML); Online - full text ed.: (from Northern Light Technology, Inc.).
Indexed: CBCARef, CBPI, CPerI, T&II.
—CCC.
Published by: LexisNexis Butterworths Canada Inc. (Subsidiary of: LexisNexis North America), 123 Commerce Valley Dr E, Ste 700, Markham, ON L3T 7W8, Canada. TEL 905-479-2665, 800-668-6481, FAX 905-479-3758, 800-461-3275, tbl@lexisnexis.ca, info@lexisnexis.ca, http://www.lexisnexis.ca/bottomline/about.php. Pub. Gary P Rodrigues. R&P Mirella Allera. Adv. contact Warren Beesley. B&W page CND 3,640; trim 15 x 10.25. Circ: 5,300 (paid); 24,700 (controlled).

BOTTOM LINE / PERSONAL. see *CONSUMER EDUCATION AND PROTECTION*

BOTTOM LINE - YEAR BOOK. see *CONSUMER EDUCATION AND PROTECTION*

330.07 DEU ISSN 1438-9339
BRAND EINS. Text in German. 1999. 10/yr. EUR 54; EUR 37 to students; EUR 6 newsstand/cover (effective 2003). adv. back issues avail. **Document type:** *Magazine, Consumer.* **Description:** Covers all aspects of business and economics with articles and discussions.
Indexed: IBR, IBZ.
Published by: Brand Eins Verlag GmbH, Schauenburger Str 21, Hamburg, 20095, Germany. TEL 49-40-323316-0, FAX 49-40-32331620, brief@brandeins.de, verlag@brandeins.de, http://www.brandeins.de. Ed. Gabriele Fischer. Pub. Eva-Maria Buettner. Adv. contact Joachim Uetzmann TEL 49-40-32331676. color page EUR 9,900; bleed 212 x 280. Circ: 87,098 (paid). **Dist. by:** ASV Vertriebs GmbH, Suederstr 77, Hamburg 20097, Germany.

330 USA
BRANDYWINE.NET BUSINESS REPORT. Text in English. 1989. bi-w. USD 9; USD 36 foreign (effective 1999). adv. **Document type:** *Newspaper.* **Description:** Contains business, technology information news and reports.
Former titles: Chester County Business Report; Chester County Biz
Related titles: Online - full text ed.
Published by: Ad Pro, Inc., PO Box 520, Oxford, PA 19363. TEL 610-932-2444, FAX 610-932-2246, breditor@brandywine.net, http://www.chestercounty.com/brandywine.netbussiness.report. Ed. Joanne Silva. Pub. Randall Lieberman. Adv. contact Alan Turns. Circ: 6,000.

330 BRA ISSN 1414-414X
BRASIL EM EXAME. Text in Portuguese. 1971. a. adv. bk.rev. charts; illus.; stat. **Document type:** *Consumer.* **Description:** For professionals in administration, marketing, finance, human resources and industry.
Published by: Editora Abril, S.A., Av. das Nacoes Unidas, 7221, 11 andar Pinheiros, Sao Paulo, SP 05425-902, Brazil. TEL 55-11-50872112, FAX 55-11-50872100, http://www.abril.com.br/. Ed. Jose Roberto Guzzo. Circ: 6,600.

330 BRA ISSN 1516-4373
➤ **BRAZILIAN ELECTRONIC JOURNAL OF ECONOMICS.** Text in Multiple languages. 1997. s-a. free (effective 2005). back issues avail. **Document type:** *Journal, Academic/Scholarly.* **Description:** Focuses on economics of the internet, network economics, and information economics.
Media: Online - full content.
Indexed: JEL.
Published by: Universidade Federal de Pernambuco, Departamento de Economia, Grupo de Economia de Redes, Pernambuco, Brazil. beje@decon.ufpe.br, http://www.beje.decon.ufpe.br.

330 USA
BREAKAWAY: A FOCUS ON SMALL BUSINESS. Text in English. bi-m. adv. **Document type:** *Consumer.* **Description:** Provides information on practical advice on topics like workplace issues, employee benefits and health insurance, technology and equipment purchases, tax regulations, hiring and firing, and more for Wall Street Journal subscribers who work in companies with fewer than 100 employees.
Related titles: ◆ Supplement to: Wall Street Journal (Eastern Edition). ISSN 0099-9660; ◆ Supplement to: Wall Street Journal (Midwest Edition). ISSN 0163-089X; ◆ Supplement to: Wall Street Journal (Southwest Edition). ISSN 0193-225X; ◆ Supplement to: Wall Street Journal (Western Edition). ISSN 0193-2241.
Published by: Dow Jones & Company, Inc. (Chicago) (Subsidiary of: Dow Jones Company), One S Wacker Dr, Ste 2100, Chicago, IL 60606-3388. TEL 312-750-4100, FAX 312-750-4153, http://www.wsj.com.

330 USA ISSN 0889-5104
BREVARD BUSINESS NEWS; a weekly Space Coast publication. Text in English. w. **Document type:** *Newsletter, Trade.*
Address: 4300 Fortune Pl Ste D, Melbourne, FL 32904 . TEL 321-951-7777.

330 USA
BRIDGES (ST. LOUIS); linking lenders and communities. Text in English. q. back issues avail. **Document type:** *Newsletter.* **Description:** Focuses on comunity development issues in the Eighth Federal Reserve District.
Published by: Federal Reserve Bank of St. Louis, PO Box 442, St. Louis, MO 63166. TEL 314-444-8444, http://www.stls.frb.org/publications/br/.

330 GBR
BRIEFCASE BUSINESS NEWS. Text in English. 1987. 11/yr. GBP 25 to non-members (effective 2000). adv. back issues avail. **Document type:** *Bulletin.*
Published by: (Redditch & Bromsgrove Chamber of Commerce), Lily Publishing Ltd., Crossgate House, Crossgate Rd, Park Farm Industrial Estate, Redditch, Worcs B98 7SN, United Kingdom. TEL 44-1527-502503, FAX 44-1527-502811. Ed. Claire Wolfe. R&P, Adv. contact Jeannette Laight. page GBP 495; 270 x 186. Circ: 4,000.

330 USA
BRIEFING NEWSLETTER. Text in English. w. free domestic to members (effective 2005). **Document type:** *Newsletter, Trade.*
Published by: National Association of Manufacturers, 1331 Pennsylvania Ave., N.W., Ste. 1500 N. Tower, Washington, DC 20004-1790. TEL 202-637-3000, FAX 202-637-3182, manufacturing@nam.org, http://www.nam.org. Ed. Doug Kurkul. Circ: 26,500 (paid).

330 GBR ISSN 0968-7017
BRIEFING NOTES IN ECONOMICS. Text in English. 1992. irreg. GBP 7, USD 10 (effective 2002). back issues avail. **Document type:** *Journal.* **Description:** Provides a "non-technical platform" for economic research in order to reach a wider audience.
Indexed: JEL.
Published by: Richmond College, School of Business, 16 Young St, London, W8 5EH, United Kingdom. FAX 44-20-79383037, bne@richmond.ac.uk, http://www.richmond.ac.uk/bne. Ed. Parviz Dabir-Alai.

BRITAIN'S RICHEST ASIAN 200. see *BIOGRAPHY*

330 GBR
BRITISH-NORTH AMERICAN COMMITTEE PUBLICATIONS. Text in English. 1970. irreg. price varies. bibl.; charts. **Document type:** *Bulletin.* **Description:** Discusses U.K., U.S. and Canadian relations.
Formerly: British-North American Research Association. Committee Publications
Published by: British-North American Research Association, Grosvenor Gardens House 35-37, Grosvenor Gardens, London, SW1W 0BS, United Kingdom. TEL 44-171-828-6644, FAX 44-171-828-5830, safe@bnava.demon.co.uk.

330 GBR
BRITISH-NORTH AMERICAN RESEARCH ASSOCIATION. OCCASIONAL PAPERS. Text in English. 1972. irreg. price varies. bibl.; charts. **Description:** Discusses policy issues relating to U.K. economic performance in world economy.
Published by: British-North American Research Association, Grosvenor Gardens House 35-37, Grosvenor Gardens, London, SW1W 0BS, United Kingdom. TEL 44-171-828-6644, FAX 44-171-828-5830, sales@bnava.demon.co.uk.

BRITISH PLASTICS FEDERATION. BUSINESS TRENDS SURVEY. see *PLASTICS*

BROADBAND HOUSE. see *COMPUTERS—Internet*

330.9 USA
BROOKLYN BUSINESS JOURNAL. Text in English. m.
Published by: Brooklyn Journal Publications, Inc., 129 Montague St, Brooklyn, NY 11201. TEL 718-624-6033, FAX 718-624-5302.

330 USA ISSN 0890-2933
BROOM, BRUSH & MOP. Text in English. 1912. m. USD 25 domestic; USD 35 in Canada & Mexico; USD 100 elsewhere (effective 2005). adv. tr.lit.; stat. **Document type:** *Magazine, Trade.* **Description:** Covers industry news, sales analysis, market conditions, suppliers' surveys, new product news and monthly import and export figures on both raw materials and finished products.
Formerly (until 1982): Broom and Broom Corn News (0007-2400)

Published by: Rankin Publishing, 204 E Main St, PO Box 130, Arcola, IL 61910-0130. TEL 217-268-4959, 800-598-8083, FAX 217-268-4815, http://www.rankinpublishing.com/broomhome.html. Ed. Don Rankin. Pub. Linda Rankin. adv.: B&W page USD 392, color page USD 859; trim 8.5 x 11. Circ: 1,300.

330 GBR ISSN 1466-5182
BRUNEL UNIVERSITY. DEPARTMENT OF ECONOMICS AND FINANCE. DISCUSSION PAPER. Text in English. 1997. m. **Document type:** *Monographic series.*
—BLDSC (3597.090400).
Published by: Brunel University, Department of Economics and Finance, Uxbridge, Middlesex UB8 3PH, United Kingdom. TEL 44-1895-274000, http://www.brunel.ac.uk.

339 ROM ISSN 1453-5572
BUCHAREST BUSINESS WEEK. Text in English. 1997. w. **Document type:** *Magazine, Trade.* **Description:** Contains up-to-date news and information for business leaders in Romania.
Published by: AmeriCelt Publishing SRL, Str. Principatele Unite nr. 47, sector 4, Bucharest, Romania. TEL 40-21-3372828, FAX 40-21-3372831, luminita.holban@bbw.ro, http://www.bbw.ro. Circ: 21,000 (paid and controlled).

330 HUN ISSN 1219-1841
BUDAPEST BOOK OF LISTS (YEAR). Key Title: Book of Lists (Budapest). Text in Hungarian. 1993. a. HUF 599, USD 29.95 (effective 1999). **Document type:** *Directory.* **Description:** Contains 66 industry lists and key data on 1,000 Hungarian companies; includes address, phone number, key personnel, clients, revenues and more.
Related titles: Hungarian ed.: Listak Konyve. ISSN 1416-6461; ◆ Supplement to: Budapest Business Journal. ISSN 1216-7304.
Published by: New World Publishing Inc., Szent Istvan Korut 11, III emelet, Budapest, 1055, Hungary. TEL 36-1-374-3344, FAX 361-374-3345, editor@bbj.hu, http://www.ceebiz.com.

330 HUN ISSN 1216-7304
BUDAPEST BUSINESS JOURNAL. Text in Hungarian. 1992. w. (48/yr.). HUF 26,490 domestic; EUR 199 foreign (effective 2005). adv. **Document type:** *Magazine, Consumer.*
Related titles: Online - full text ed.: (from EBSCO Publishing, LexisNexis); ◆ Supplement(s): Budapest Book of Lists (Year). ISSN 1219-1841; ◆ Budapest Business Journal's Who's Who in Hungarian Telecom. ISSN 1419-2063; ◆ Who's Who in Advertising and Media; ◆ Budapest Business Journal's Who's Who in Finance. ISSN 1418-8937; ◆ Equity Central Europe. ISSN 1418-9496.
—BLDSC (2355.906600).
Published by: New World Publishing Inc., Szent Istvan Korut 11, III emelet, Budapest, 1055, Hungary. TEL 36-1-374-3344, FAX 361-374-3345, editor@bbj.hu, http://www.ceebiz.com. Ed. Miklos S Gaspar. Pub. Margaret Ann Dowling.

BUDGET SPEECH. see *PUBLIC ADMINISTRATION*

BUEROJOURNAL. see *HANDICAPPED—Visually Impaired*

330 USA ISSN 0882-2859
BUFFALO BUSINESS JOURNAL. Text in English. 1984. fortn. USD 25. adv.
Address: 465 Main St, Buffalo, NY 14203-1793. TEL 716-854-5822, FAX 716-854-3394, buffalo@bizjournals.com, http://buffalo.bizjournals.com/. Ed. Norman Myer. Circ: 15,000.

330 497.12 CAN ISSN 1706-3388
BUILDING ABORIGINAL AND NORTHERN ECONOMIES/ BATISSEURS DE L'ECONOMIE AUTOCHTONE ET DU NORD. Text in English, French. 1988. bi-m.
Former titles (until 2002): Building Aboriginal Economies (1704-3697); (until 2002): Circles of Light (1498-5799); (until 2000): Transition. Canada. Indian and Northern Affairs Canada (0840-1748)
Published by: Indian and Northern Affairs Canada/Affaires Indiennes et du Nord Canada, Terrasses de la Chaudiere, 10 Wellington, North Tower, Hull, PQ K1A 0H4, Canada. TEL 800-567-9604, infopubs@ainc-inac.gc.ca, http://www.ainc-inac.gc.ca.

BUILDING IN AUSTRALIA. see *BUILDING AND CONSTRUCTION*

BUILDING INDUSTRY PROSPECTS. see *BUILDING AND CONSTRUCTION*

330 BGR
BULGARIAN ECONOMIC OUTLOOK. Text in English. w. USD 720 foreign (effective 2002). **Document type:** *Bulletin, Trade.* **Description:** Publishes analysis, prognoses, bank information, and actual economic and political information.
Published by: Bulgarska Telegrafna Agentsia/Bulgarian Telegraph Agency, Tsarigradsko shose 49, Sofia, 1040, Bulgaria. TEL 359-2-9881719, FAX 359-2-9885463, main@bta.bg, http://www.bta-bg.net. **Dist. by:** Sofia Books, ul Silivria 16, Sofia 1404, Bulgaria. TEL 359-2-9586257, info@sofiabooks-bg.com, http://www.sofiabooks-bg.com.

BULLETIN L A R F. see *BUSINESS AND ECONOMICS—Banking And Finance*

330 GBR ISSN 0307-3378
HB1
➤ **BULLETIN OF ECONOMIC RESEARCH.** Text in English. 1949. q. EUR 60 combined subscription in Europe to individuals print & online eds.; USD 67 combined subscription in the Americas to individuals & Caribbean (print & online eds.); GBP 40 combined subscription elsewhere to individuals print & online eds.; GBP 302 combined subscription in Europe to institutions print & online eds.; GBP 61 combined subscription in Eastern Europe to institutions print & online eds.; USD 101 combined subscription in developing nations to institutions print & online eds.; USD 674 combined subscription in the Americas to institutions & Caribbean (print & online eds.); GBP 401 combined subscription elsewhere to institutions print & online eds. (effective 2006). adv. bk.rev. charts; illus. index. reprint service avail. from PSC. **Document type:** *Journal, Academic/Scholarly.* **Description:** Publishes articles across the entire field of economics, econometrics and economic history.
Formerly (until 1970): Yorkshire Bulletin of Economic and Social Research (0307-4943)
Related titles: Microform ed.: (from PQC); Online - full text ed.: ISSN 1467-8586. GBP 287 in Europe to institutions; GBP 58 in Eastern Europe to institutions; USD 96 in developing nations to institutions; USD 640 in the Americas to institutions; GBP 381 elsewhere to institutions (effective 2006) (from Blackwell Synergy, EBSCO Publishing, Gale Group, IngentaConnect, O C L C Online Computer Library Center, Inc., Swets Information Services).
Indexed: ABIn, APEL, AmH&L, BPIA, BrHumI, BusI, CCMJ, CIS, CJA, CPM, CREJ, GEOBASE, HistAb, IBR, IBSS, IBZ, ILD, JCQM, JEL, KES, MEA&I, MathR, MathSciNet, PAIS, PCI, RASB, T&II, WBA.
—BLDSC (2849.620000), CISTI, IE, Infotrieve, ingenta. **CCC.**
Published by: Blackwell Publishing Ltd., 9600 Garsington Rd, Oxford, OX4 2ZG, United Kingdom. TEL 44-1865-776868, FAX 44-1865-714591, customerservices@oxon.blackwellpublishing.com, http://www.blackwellpublishing.com/journals/BOER. Eds. Indrajit Ray, Luisa Zanchi. Circ: 650.

330 FRA ISSN 0298-511X
LE BULLETIN OFFICIEL DE LA CONCURRENCE, DE LA CONSOMMATION ET DE LA REPRESSION DES FRAUDES. Text in French. 1941. m. EUR 19.10 (effective 2005). **Document type:** *Bulletin, Government.*
Former titles (until 1985): Bulletin Officiel des Services des Prix, Concurrence et Consommation (0764-5325); (until 1984): Bulletin Officiel de la Concurrence et de la Consommation (0245-7660); (until 1980): Bulletin Officiel des Services des Prix (0397-6408)
—IE, Infotrieve.
Published by: (France. Direction Generale de la Concurrence, de la Consommation et de la Repression des Fraudes), Direction des Journaux Officiels, 26 rue Desaix, Paris, 75727 Cedex 15 , France. TEL 33-1-40587500, info@journal-officiel.gouv.fr, http://www.journal-officiel.gouv.fr.

BUREAU BRIEFS (MADISON, WI). see *TRAVEL AND TOURISM*

330 LCA ISSN 1010-5719
BUSINESS. Text in English. 1985. q. USD 10. adv.
—CCC.
Published by: A L K I M Communication Production Company, Box MA 020, Marchand Post Office, Castries, St. Lucia. Ed. Albert Deterville. Circ: 5,000.

330 USA ISSN 0894-6205
BUSINESS ACTION. Text in English. q. free to members (effective 2005). 8 p./no.; **Document type:** *Newsletter, Trade.*
Published by: San Diego Regional Chamber of Commerce, 402 W Broadway, Ste 1000, San Diego, CA 92101-3585. TEL 619-544-1300, FAX 619-744-7481, http://www.sdchamber.org. Ed. Kristine Norquist. Circ: 6,000 (free).

BUSINESS ADVICE AND FINANCIAL PLANNING. see *BUSINESS AND ECONOMICS—Banking And Finance*

BUSINESS ADVISORY CLIENT NEWSLETTER. see *BUSINESS AND ECONOMICS—Accounting*

330 CAN
THE BUSINESS ADVOCATE. Text in English. 1987. m. free.
Published by: London Chamber of Commerce, 244 Pall Mall St, P O Box 3295, London, ON N6A 5P6, Canada. TEL 519-432-7551, FAX 519-432-8063. Ed. John Redmond. Circ: 10,000.

BUSINESS ADVOCATE; a quarterly update of the litigation activities of the U.S. Chambers of Commerce. see *LAW—Corporate Law*

330 USA ISSN 1050-091X
BUSINESS ALABAMA MONTHLY. Text in English. 1986. m. USD 21.95 domestic; free domestic to qualified personnel (effective 2005). adv. **Document type:** *Magazine, Trade.* **Description:** For business owners, managers, and presidents of companies in Alabama.
Formerly (until 1987): Business Alabama (0886-3024)
Published by: P M T Publishing Inc., 3729 Cottage Hill Rd, Ste H, Mobile, AL 36609-6500. TEL 251-473-6269, FAX 205-941-1494, pmtpub@aol.com. Ed. Don Milazzo. Pub., R&P T J Potts. Circ: 15,500 (paid).

330 USA ISSN 1081-6216
BUSINESS ALERT (BROOKVILLE). Text in English. 1982. q. free. back issues avail. **Document type:** *Newsletter.*
Indexed: ISAP.
Published by: (Center for Business Research), Long Island University, C.W. Post College, 720 Northern Blvd., Brookville, NY 11548. TEL 516-299-2832, FAX 516-299-4170, cbr@titan.liunet.edu. Ed. Elizabeth Mezick. Circ: 300.

BUSINESS ALERT (FREDERICKSBURG). see *NATIVE AMERICAN STUDIES*

330 HKG
BUSINESS ALERT - CHINA. Text in English. m. USD 36 per issue foreign (effective 2000).
Published by: Hong Kong Trade Development Council, 38th Fl Office Tower, Convention Plaza, 1 Harbour Rd, Wanchai, Hong Kong. TEL 852-2584-4333, hktdc@tdc.org.hk, http://www.tdc.org.hk/.

330 HKG
BUSINESS ALERT - E U. (European Union) Text in English. 1996. bi-w. USD 40 per issue (effective 2000).
Published by: Hong Kong Trade Development Council, 38th Fl Office Tower, Convention Plaza, 1 Harbour Rd, Wanchai, Hong Kong. TEL 852-2584-4333, hktdc@tdc.org.hk, http://www.tdc.org.hk, http://www.tdc.org.hk/.

338.5 IND ISSN 0007-6430
HB1
➤ **BUSINESS ANALYST.** Text in English. 1968. 2/yr., latest vol.22, 2001. INR 300, USD 40 (effective 2001). adv. bk.rev. illus. 120 p./no. 2 cols./p.; back issues avail.; reprints avail. **Document type:** *Academic/Scholarly.* **Description:** Publishes articles and conference and seminar reports.
Related titles: Record ed.
Published by: University of Delhi, Shri Ram College of Commerce, New Delhi, 110 007, India. TEL 7257905, FAX 7256510, srcc@del2.vsnl.net.in. Ed. Chandra Shekhar Sharma. R&P L N Tara. adv.: page INR 7,000. Circ: 300.

346.07 USA
BUSINESS AND COMMERCIAL LITIGATION: A TRIAL LAWYER'S HANDBOOK. Text in English. 1995. base vol. plus a. updates. USD 110. **Description:** Contains techniques used successfully in hundreds of actual trials.
Published by: LexisNexis (Subsidiary of: LexisNexis North America), PO Box 7587, Charlottesville, VA 22906-7587. TEL 804-972-7600, 800-562-1197, FAX 804-972-7666, llp.customer.support@lexis-nexis.com, http://www.lexislawpublishing.com. Ed. Edward F Mannino.

BUSINESS & CONSTRUCTION MAGAZINE. see *BUILDING AND CONSTRUCTION*

650 330 USA ISSN 0007-6465
HC107.S7 CODEN: BSERA6
BUSINESS & ECONOMIC REVIEW. Text in English. 1954. q. free. charts; illus.; stat. Index. reprint service avail. from PQC. **Document type:** *Consumer.* **Description:** Covers business, economic, and environmental issues in South Carolina and the southeast, with some national and international topics.
Related titles: Microform ed.: (from PQC); Online - full text ed.: (from EBSCO Publishing, Northern Light Technology, Inc., ProQuest Information & Learning).
Indexed: ABIn, AgeL, BPIA, PAIS, PMA, PSI.
Published by: (Division of Research), University of South Carolina, Darla Moore School of Business, 1705 College St, Columbia, SC 29208. TEL 803-777-2510, FAX 803-777-9344, janc@darla.badm.sc.edu. Ed., R&P Jan K Collins. Circ: 5,419.

330 GBR
BUSINESS AND ECONOMICS RESEARCH DIRECTORY. Text in English. 1996. irreg., latest vol.1. GBP 145, USD 235 per vol. (effective 2002). **Document type:** *Directory.* **Description:** Lists research institutes engaged in the study of business and economics and provides related journals and periodicals.
Published by: Europa Publications Limited (Subsidiary of: Taylor & Francis Group), 11 New Fetter Ln, London, EC4P 4EE, United Kingdom. TEL 44-20-7822-4300, FAX 44-20-7842-2249, sales.europa@tandf.co.uk, http://www.europapublications.co.uk/titles/berd.html, http://www.europapublications.com. Ed. Ian Preston.

330 GBR ISSN 1365-0564
BUSINESS & FINANCE IN SCOTLAND✶. Text in English. 1974. a. adv. bk.rev. **Document type:** *Trade.*
Published by: Scottish County Press Ltd., Sherwood Industrial Estate, Bonnyrigg, Midlothian EH19 3LW, United Kingdom. TEL 44-131-663-2404, FAX 44-131-663-6863. Ed. David Young. Circ: 14,000.

BUSINESS AND NATURAL ENVIRONMENT. see *ENVIRONMENTAL STUDIES*

330 USA ISSN 1469-3569
BUSINESS AND POLITICS (ONLINE EDITION). Text in English. 3/yr. USD 35 to individuals; USD 215 to institutions (effective 2006). **Document type:** *Journal, Academic/Scholarly.*
Media: Online - full text (from EBSCO Publishing, Gale Group, IngentaConnect, O C L C Online Computer Library Center, Inc., Swets Information Services).
—CCC.
Published by: Berkeley Electronic Press, 2809 Telegraph Ave., Ste 202, Berkeley, CA 94705. TEL 510-665-1200, FAX 510-665-1201, info@bepress.com, http://www.bepress.com/bap/. Ed. Vinod K Aggarwal.

BUSINESS & PROFESSIONAL ETHICS JOURNAL. see *PHILOSOPHY*

650 USA ISSN 0007-6503
HF5001 CODEN: BUSOBE
➤ **BUSINESS AND SOCIETY**; a journal of interdisciplinary exploration. Text in English. 1960. q. USD 431, GBP 278 to institutions; USD 448, GBP 290 combined subscription to institutions print & online eds. (effective 2006). adv. bk.rev. abstr.; tr.lit.; illus. Index. back issues avail.; reprint service avail. from PQC. **Document type:** *Journal, Academic/Scholarly.* **Description:** Focuses on business and society, social issues in management, and business ethics. Covers topics that include business ethics and values. business-government relations, corporate goverence, environmental management and international dimensions of business and society relationships.
Related titles: Microform ed.: (from PQC); Online - full text ed.: ISSN 1552-4205. USD 426, GBP 275 to institutions (effective 2006) (from C S A, EBSCO Publishing, Florida Center for Library Automation, Gale Group, O C L C Online Computer Library Center, Inc., ProQuest Information & Learning, Sage Publications, Inc., Swets Information Services).
Indexed: ABIn, BPI, BPIA, BrCerAb, BusI, C&ISA, CerAb, CommAb, CompR, CorrAb, E&CAJ, EMA, ESPM, Emerald, HRA, IAA, IMI, IPSA, M&TEA, MBF, MEA&I, METADEX, ManagCont, ORMS, PAIS, PMA, PRA, QC&AS, RiskAb, SOPODA, SSA, SociolAb, T&II, V&AA, WAA, WorkRelAb.
—BLDSC (2933.225000), IE, Infotrieve, ingenta, Linda Hall. **CCC.**
Published by: (International Association for Business and Society, Research Committee), Sage Publications, Inc., 2455 Teller Rd, Thousand Oaks, CA 91320. TEL 805-499-0721, FAX 805-499-8096, info@sagepub.com, http://www.sagepub.com/journal.aspx?pid=131. Ed. John F Mahon. Pub. Sara Miller McCune. R&P Tanya Udin TEL 805-499-0721 ext 7716. Adv. contact Kirsten Beaulieu TEL 805-499-0721 ext 7160. page USD 350. Circ: 700 (paid and free). **Subscr. overseas to:** Sage Publications Ltd., 1 Oliver's Yard, 55 City Rd, London EC1 1SP, United Kingdom. TEL 44-20-73740645, FAX 44-20-73748741, subscription@sagepub.co.uk.

650 USA ISSN 0045-3609
HD60.5.U5 CODEN: BUSRAM
BUSINESS AND SOCIETY REVIEW; journal of the Center for Business Ethics at Bentley College. Text in English. 1972. q. USD 91 combined subscription in the Americas to individuals & Caribbean, print & online eds.; EUR 114 combined subscription in Europe to individuals print & online eds.; GBP 76 combined subscription elsewhere to individuals print & online eds.; USD 211 combined subscription in the Americas to institutions & Caribbean, print & online eds.; GBP 166 combined subscription elsewhere to institutions print & online eds. (effective 2006). adv. bk.rev. illus. back issues avail.; reprint service avail. from WSH,PSC. **Document type:** *Journal, Academic/Scholarly.*
Formerly (until 1974): Business and Society Review/Innovation (0092-2706); Which was formed by the merger of (1962-1972): Innovation (0537-7196); Business and Society Review (0893-4398)
Related titles: Microform ed.: (from PQC); Online - full text ed.: ISSN 1467-8594. USD 200 in the Americas to institutions & Caribbean; GBP 158 elsewhere to institutions (effective 2006) (from Blackwell Synergy, EBSCO Publishing, Gale Group, H.W. Wilson, IngentaConnect, O C L C Online Computer Library Center, Inc., Swets Information Services).
Indexed: ABIn, ATI, AgeL, BPI, BPIA, BusI, CLI, CompR, FutSurv, ILP, IPARL, LRI, M&MA, MEA&I, ManagCont, PAIS, PMA, PRA, PSI, PersLit, RI-1, RI-2, SCIMP, SSI, T&II, WorkRelAb.
—BLDSC (2933.226000), IE, Infotrieve, ingenta. **CCC.**
Published by: Blackwell Publishing, Inc. (Subsidiary of: Blackwell Publishing Ltd.), Commerce Place, 350 Main St, Malden, MA 02148. TEL 781-388-8206, FAX 781-388-8232, cbeinfo@bentley.edu, subscrip@blackwellpub.com, http://www.blackwellpublishing.com/journals/BASR. Ed. Robert E Frederick. Adv. contact Ben Harkinson. B&W page USD 350. Circ: 3,000 (paid).

330 020 GBR ISSN 0007-6538
HF5736
BUSINESS ARCHIVES. Variant title: Business Archives Principles and Practices. Business Archives Sources and History. Text in English. 1934. s-a. (Principles and Practices is published in May; Sources and History is published in Nov.). GBP 35 to individual members; GBP 55 to institutions; GBP 145 to corporations (effective 2005). adv. bk.rev. cum.index. back issues avail. **Document type:** *Journal, Academic/Scholarly.* **Description:** The May issue carries articles on the management of modern records and the administration of business archives. The articles aim to assist in quick and effective decision-making and also point to further detailed sources of information and includes a bibliography of new relevant literature. The November issue carries articles on source material for business history; lists of business records deposited in record offices and books published in the field of business and industrial history.
Formerly (until 1962): Business Archives Council. Quarterly Bulletin
—BLDSC (2933.240000), IE, ingenta.
Published by: Business Archives Council, c/o Ms F. Maccoll, Records Manager, Rio Tinto plc, 6 St James's Sq, London, SW1Y 4LD, United Kingdom. TEL 44-20-77532123, http://www.businessarchivescouncil.org.uk/publications/annualreports/, http://www.businessarchivescouncil.com/. Ed., R&P Serena Kelly TEL 44-20-7407-6110. Adv. contact J Campbell. Circ: 600.

330 025 GBR
BUSINESS ARCHIVES COUNCIL. ANNUAL CONFERENCE PROCEEDINGS. Text in English. a. GBP 45 membership. adv. **Document type:** *Proceedings.*
Published by: Business Archives Council, c/o Ms F. Maccoll, Records Manager, Rio Tinto plc, 6 St James's Sq, London, SW1Y 4LD, United Kingdom. TEL 44-20-77532123, http://www.businessarchivescouncil.org.uk/publications/annualreports/, http://www.businessarchivescouncil.com/. R&P Serena Kelly TEL 44-20-7407-6110. Adv. contact J Campbell.

330 025 GBR
BUSINESS ARCHIVES COUNCIL. NEWSLETTER. Text in English. q. GBP 35 to individual members; GBP 55 to institutional members (effective 2005). adv. back issues avail. **Document type:** *Newsletter.* **Description:** Carries topical information about exhibitions, publications, courses and Council events and services.
Formerly (until 1969): Business Archives Council: Quarterly Newsletter (0309-4200)
—BLDSC (2933.270000).
Published by: Business Archives Council, c/o Ms F. Maccoll, Records Manager, Rio Tinto plc, 6 St James's Sq, London, SW1Y 4LD, United Kingdom. TEL 44-20-77532123, http://www.businessarchivescouncil.org.uk/publications/newsletters/, http://www.businessarchivescouncil.org.uk/publications/annualreports/, http://www.businessarchivescouncil.com/. R&P Serena Kelly TEL 44-20-7407-6110. Adv. contact J Campbell.

330 USA
BUSINESS ASSET. Text in English. 1998. q.
Published by: Baumer Financial Publishing (Subsidiary of: Imagination Publishing, LLC), 820 W Jackson Blvd No 450, Chicago, IL 60607. TEL 312-627-1020, FAX 312-627-1105, baumerfpub@aol.com. Ed. Elizabeth Seymour. Circ: 25,000.

BUSINESS ASSOCIATE; partners in land conservation. see *CONSERVATION*

330 USA
BUSINESS AT HOME (ONLINE). Text in English. q. USD 9.98 (effective 1998). **Document type:** *Trade.*
Formerly: Business at Home (Print)
Media: Online - full content.
Published by: Oregon Business Media, 610 S W Broadway, 200, Portland, OR 97205-3431. TEL 503-223-0304, FAX 503-223-6544, feedback@oregonbusiness.com, http://www.gohome.com/, http://www.gohome.com/departments/.

330 CHN
BUSINESS BEIJING. Text in English. m. CNY 150 domestic; USD 120 foreign (effective 2003). adv. 40 p./no.; **Document type:** *Magazine, Trade.* **Description:** Covers business related news in Beijing and China, including other major news stories, investment information and other articles.
Published by: A S M Overseas Corp., Asian Games Garden, Bldg 2-6A,12 Xiaoying Lu, Chaoyang-qu, Beijing, 100101, China. TEL 86-1-64974451, FAX 86-1-64974872, icic@cbw.com, http://www.cbw.com/busbj/. adv.: page CNY 23,000; 215 x 275. Circ: 50,000. **Subscr. to:** 227040, Los Angeles, CA 90022-0740.

028.1 USA ISSN 0741-8132
BUSINESS BOOK REVIEW✶. Text in English. 1984. bi-m. USD 45. bk.rev. index.
Indexed: BRI, CBRI.
Published by: Corporate Support Systems, 1802 S Duncan, Champaign, IL 61821. Ed. Jagdish N Sheth. Circ: 4,000.

330 GBR
BUSINESS BULLETIN. Text in English. 1981. bi-m. GBP 25. adv. bk.rev. **Document type:** *Consumer.*
Indexed: BldManAb, RASB.
Published by: Dart Publishing, Guildhall, Dartmouth, Devon, United Kingdom. Ed. Philip K Spann. Circ: 14,000.

330 USA ISSN 1055-8217
BUSINESS CONCEPTS✶. Text in English. 1991. q. USD 29.99. adv. Supplement avail. **Document type:** *Consumer.* **Description:** Presents money making ideas and new business opportunities.
Published by: Publishing & Business Consultants, 4427 W Slauson Ave, Los Angeles, CA 90043-2717. TEL 213-732-3477, FAX 213-732-9123. Ed. Andeson Napoleon Atia. Circ: 120,000.

BUSINESS CRIMES BULLETIN. see *LAW—Criminal Law*

330 ZAF ISSN 1015-0706
BUSINESS DAY. (Published in 2 editions: National; Final (Johannesburg)) Text in English. 1985. 5/w. (Mon-Fri.). ZAR 520. adv. bk.rev.; film rev.; music rev.; play rev. illus. 10 cols./p.; back issues avail. **Document type:** *Newspaper.* **Description:** News and information of interest to the business and financial community.
Related titles: Online - full text ed.: ISSN 1563-5775. 1985.
Published by: B D F M Ltd., PO Box 1745, Saxonwold, 2132, South Africa. TEL 27-11-2803000, 27-11-280-3000, FAX 27-11-2805600, busday@tml.co.za, http://www.bday.co.za. Ed., R&P Jim Jones TEL 27-11-2805504. Pub. Alan Greenblo. Adv. contact Karen Bonsal. Circ: 40,000 (paid).

330 THA
BUSINESS DAY (BANGKOK). Text in English. d. **Document type:** *Newspaper.*
Related titles: Online - full text ed.
Published by: Business Day Company Limited, 22nd Fl, Olympia Tower, 444 Ratchadapisak Rd, Bangkok, 10320, Thailand.

330 IND
BUSINESS DEEPIKA; economic & financial weekly. Text in Malayalam. w. (Mon.). INR 440 for 2 yrs.; INR 5 newsstand/cover. adv.
Published by: Rashtra Deepika Ltd., Deepika Bldg., C.M.S. College Rd., P O Box 7, Kottayam, Kerala 686 001, India. TEL 91-481-566706, FAX 91-481-567947, TELEX 0888-203-DPKA IN. adv.: page INR 120,000. Circ: 50,000.

330 IND
BUSINESS DEEPIKA INTERNATIONAL. Text in Malayalam. w. (Mon.).
Published by: Rashtra Deepika Ltd., Deepika Bldg., C.M.S. College Rd., P O Box 7, Kottayam, Kerala 686 001, India. TEL 91-481-566706, FAX 91-481-567947. adv.: page INR 120,000.

330 USA ISSN 0895-3791
BUSINESS DIGEST✶. Variant title: Cape and Islands Business Digest. Southeastern Massachusetts - Cape and Islands Business Digest. Text in English. 1986. m. USD 28. adv. back issues avail. **Document type:** *Consumer.* **Description:** Contains local business news and issues for Cape Cod, Massachusetts.
Former titles: Business Digest of Southeastern Massachusetts - Cape Cod; Business Digest of Southeastern Massachusetts (1040-5380)
Related titles: Online - full text ed.: (from ProQuest Information & Learning).
Indexed: BusDate.
Published by: Cape & Islands Business Digest, Inc., PO Box 64, Hyannis, MA 02647-0064. TEL 508-778-5042, FAX 508-778-5063. Ed. Anthony Alva. Adv. contact Jeff Lyon. page USD 1,075; bleed 11 x 8.5. Circ: 6,500.

330 USA ISSN 1046-168X
BUSINESS DIGEST OF GREATER WATERBURY✶. Text in English. 1989. bi-m. USD 24. adv. **Description:** Tracks the movements of people within the 17 towns of the Greater Waterbury business community, new businesses, and new products and services. Includes interviews with business leaders and profiles of successful businesses.
Formerly: Greater Waterbury Business Digest
Published by: Four Stars Publishing Co., Inc., 197 Tranquility Rd, PO Box 9018, Middlebury, CT 06702-2230. TEL 203-754-9922, FAX 203-754-5192. Ed. Barbara J Mitchell. Circ: 6,300 (controlled).

330 GBR ISSN 0958-7918
BUSINESS EAST MIDLANDS. Text in English. 1986. m. GBP 19.50. adv. **Document type:** *Trade.*
Related titles: Online - full text ed.
Published by: Business Magazine Group, Adamsway, Mansfield, Notts NG18 4FP, United Kingdom. TEL 44-1623-450500, FAX 44-1623-454560. Ed. Sue Allen. Circ: 11,207.

658 USA
BUSINESS ECCOUNTANT; world business news for students. Text in English. 1999. w. back issues avail.
Media: Online - full text. **Related titles:** E-mail ed.

Address: query@businessed.net, http://www.businessed.net/, http://www.businessed.net/current_edition.htm. Ed. P A Prendergast.

330 USA ISSN 0007-666X
HC101 CODEN: BECODS
BUSINESS ECONOMICS; designed to serve the needs of people who use economics in their work. Text in English. 1965. q. USD 105 domestic; USD 110 in Canada & Mexico; USD 120 elsewhere (effective 2004). adv. bk.rev. bibl.; charts; illus.; stat. Index. back issues avail.; reprint service avail. from PQC,SCH. **Document type:** *Journal, Trade.* **Description:** Features articles on applied economics, including macro- and microeconomics, monetary and fiscal policy, short- and long-term business forecasting, interest rates, international economics, industry studies, and deregulation; statistics; changing technology and book reviews.
Related titles: CD-ROM ed.; Microform ed.: (from PQC); Online - full text ed.: ISSN 1554-432X (from bigchalk, EBSCO Publishing, Florida Center for Library Automation, Gale Group, H.W. Wilson, Northern Light Technology, Inc., O C L C Online Computer Library Center, Inc., ProQuest Information & Learning).
Indexed: ABIn, BLI, BPI, BPIA, BusI, CREJ, ChPerI, JEL, MagInd, ManagCont, PAIS, T&II, WBA, WMB, WorkRelAb.
—BLDSC (2933.455000), IE, Infotrieve, ingenta. **CCC.**
Published by: National Association for Business Economics, 1233 20th St, N W, Ste 505, Washington, DC 20036-2304. TEL 202-463-6223, FAX 202-463-6239, nabe@nabe.com, http://www.nabe.com/busecon.htm. Ed. Robert Thomas Crow. Circ: 4,700.

330 GBR ISSN 0306-5049
THE BUSINESS ECONOMIST. Text in English. 1969. 3/yr. GBP 32 in Europe; GBP 38 elsewhere (effective 2001). adv. bk.rev. back issues avail. **Document type:** *Academic/Scholarly.* **Description:** Covers developments in the UK, overseas and world economics. Discusses issues in applied economic theory and analysis of individual industries.
Indexed: CPM, Emerald, IBSS, PAIS.
—BLDSC (2933.475000), IE, Infotrieve, ingenta.
Published by: Society of Business Economists, 11 Baytree Walk, Watford, Herts WD17 4RX, United Kingdom. TEL 44-1923-237287, admin@sbe.co.uk, www.sbe.co.uk. Ed. James Hirst. R&P Marian Marshall. Adv. contact Kay Webb. Circ: 1,000.

BUSINESS EDGE. see *OCCUPATIONS AND CAREERS*

650.0711 USA ISSN 0007-6678
HF1101.U57
BUSINESS EDUCATION FORUM. Text in English. 1947. q. (Oct., Dec., Feb. & Apr.). free to members. adv. illus. Index. back issues avail.; reprint service avail. from PQC. **Document type:** *Journal, Academic/Scholarly.*
Related titles: Microform ed.: (from PQC).
Indexed: ABIn, BusEdI, CIJE, CPE, ERA, ETA, EduInd, MEA, RHEA, SEA, SENA, SOMA, TEA.
—BLDSC (2933.540000), IE, ingenta.
Published by: National Business Education Association, 1914 Association Dr, Reston, VA 20191-1596. TEL 703-860-8300, FAX 703-620-4483, nbea@nbea.org, http://www.nbea.org/marketfbef.html. Ed. Susan O'Brien. Adv. contact Noelle C Sotack. Circ: 15,300 (paid).

330 USA
BUSINESS EDUCATION GUIDE. Text in English. 1986. 3/yr. USD 10 (effective 1999). adv. **Document type:** *Directory.* **Description:** Includes articles and listings of seminars, courses, workshops and services.
Address: PO Box 2014, Neptune, NJ 07754. TEL 732-280-2244, FAX 732-681-5482, http://www.bized.com. Ed. Catherine Sims. Pub. Sky Williams. R&P Cathy Sims. Adv. contact Valerie Elyar. Circ: 75,000.

330 FRA ISSN 0982-0418
BUSINESS - ENTREPRISE. Text in French. 1986. 6/yr.
Address: 23 rue des Apennins, Paris, 75017, France. TEL 42-28-59-00, FAX 42-28-24-58. Ed. John Martial. Circ: 92,000.

330 AUS
BUSINESS ESSENTIALS MAGAZINE. Text in English. m. AUD 235, USD 249. **Document type:** *Trade.* **Description:** Covers issues relating to all facets of running a business includes the economy, tax, superannuation, succession planning, investment, modern marketing techniques and more.
Related titles: Audio cassette/tape ed.; CD-ROM ed.; Online - full text ed.
Published by: Business Essentials, 405 Riversdale Rd, Camberwell, VIC 3124, Australia. TEL 61-3-9882-8333, FAX 800-656-351, info@be.com.au, http://www.be.com.au.

330 GBR ISSN 0962-8770
HF5387 CODEN: BUETFV
➤ **BUSINESS ETHICS**; a European review. Text in English. 1992. q. EUR 129 combined subscription in Europe to individuals print & online eds.; USD 144 combined subscription in the Americas to individuals & Caribbean, print & online eds.; GBP 86 combined subscription elsewhere to individuals print & online eds.; USD 1,018 combined subscription in the Americas to institutions & Caribbean, print & online eds.; GBP 606 combined subscription elsewhere to institutions print & online eds. (effective 2006). illus. reprint service avail. from PSC. **Document type:** *Journal, Academic/Scholarly.* **Description:** Aims to enhance the quality of decision making at all levels of business throughout Europe.
Related titles: Online - full text ed.: ISSN 1467-8608. USD 967 in the Americas to institutions & Caribbean; GBP 576 elsewhere to institutions (effective 2006) (from Blackwell Synergy, EBSCO Publishing, IngentaConnect, O C L C Online Computer Library Center, Inc., Swets Information Services).
Indexed: ABIn, Emerald, IBSS, PhilInd, PsycInfo, PsycholAb, SOPODA, SSI.
—BLDSC (2933.634000), IE, Infotrieve, ingenta. **CCC.**
Published by: Blackwell Publishing Ltd., 9600 Garsington Rd, Oxford, OX4 2ZG, United Kingdom. TEL 44-1865-776868, FAX 44-1865-714591, beer@hud.ac.uk, customerservices@oxon.blackwellpublishing.com, http://www.blackwellpublishing.com/journals/BEER. Ed. Christopher Cowton TEL 44-1484-473061.

330 USA ISSN 0894-6582
BUSINESS ETHICS; the magazine of corporate responsibility. Text in English. 1987. q. USD 49 domestic; USD 59 foreign (effective 2005). adv. bk.rev. 24 p./no. 3 cols./p.; back issues avail.; reprints avail. **Document type:** *Newsletter, Trade.* **Description:** For socially responsible business and investing; offers practical advice and views for enlightened businesspeople.
Formerly: Business Ethics Magazine
Indexed: AltPI, CPM.
—BLDSC (2933.633500), IE, Infotrieve. **CCC.**
Published by: New Mountain Media LLC., PO Box 8439, Minneapolis, MN 55408-0439. TEL 612-879-0695, 800-601-9010, FAX 612-879-0699, bizethics@aol.com, http://www.business-ethics.com/. Pub. Michael Connor. adv.: page USD 3,778. Circ: 10,000 (paid and free).

BUSINESS ETHICS QUARTERLY. see *PHILOSOPHY*

330 USA ISSN 1087-4704
BUSINESS EXAMINER. Text in English. 1985. bi-w. (Mon.). USD 48; USD 2.50 newsstand/cover (effective 2005). **Document type:** *Newspaper.*
Published by: Pierce County Business Examiner, 1517 S. Fawcett Ave., Ste. 350, Tacoma, WA 98402-1807. TEL 253-404-0891, FAX 253-404-0892, mail@businessexaminer.com. Ed. George Pica. Pub. Jeff Rounce. Circ: 10,000 (paid).

330 CAN ISSN 0838-6048
BUSINESS EXAMINER (NORTH ISLAND EDITION). Text in English. m. CND 35 (effective 2003).
Supersedes in part (in 1987): Business Examiner (0838-6056)
Related titles: Online - full text ed.: (from Micromedia ProQuest); ♦ Supplement(s): Business Examiner Presents. ISSN 0841-8675.
Published by: Business Examiner Ltd., 777 Poplar St, Nanaimo, BC V9S 2H7, Canada. TEL 250-754-8344, FAX 250-753-8344, mark@businessexaminer.net, http://www.businessexaminer.net. Ed. Mark MacDonald. Circ: 11,800.

330 CAN ISSN 0836-1142
BUSINESS EXAMINER (SOUTH ISLAND EDITION). Text in English. 1984. 12/yr. CND 45 (effective 2003). adv. **Document type:** *Newspaper.*
Supersedes in part (in 1987): Business Examiner (0838-6056)
Related titles: Online - full text ed.: (from Micromedia ProQuest); ♦ Supplement(s): Business Examiner Presents. ISSN 0841-8675.
Published by: Business Examiner Ltd., 818 Broughton St, Victoria, BC V8W 1E4, Canada. TEL 250-381-3926, FAX 250-381-5606, larry@businessexaminer.net, http://www.businessexaminer.net. Pub. Bill Macadam. Circ: 12,500.

330 GBR ISSN 0262-7019
BUSINESS EXPRESS✶. Text in English. 1980. q. GBP 6.50.
Published by: Modern English Publications Ltd., Brunel Rd, Basingstoke, Hants RG21 6XT, United Kingdom. Ed. Hilary Rees Parnall. Circ: 2,000.

330 GRD
BUSINESS EYE. Text in English. bi-m.
Published by: Business Eye International, Ltd., P.O. Box 360, Young St., St. George's, Grenada. TEL 809-440-3425.

330 USA ISSN 0749-9418
BUSINESS FIRST (BUFFALO); Western New York' s business newspaper. Text in English. 1984. w. (Mon.). USD 89 (effective 2005). adv. charts; illus.; stat. back issues avail. **Document type:** *Newspaper, Trade.*
Related titles: Microform ed.: (from PQC); Online - full text ed.: (from Florida Center for Library Automation, Gale Group, O C L C Online Computer Library Center, Inc., ProQuest Information & Learning, The Dialog Corporation).
Indexed: ABIn, BusDate, LRI.
—CCC.
Published by: American City Business Journals, Inc. (Buffalo) (Subsidiary of: American City Business Journals, Inc.), 465 Main St, Buffalo, NY 14203-1793. TEL 716-854-5822, FAX 716-854-3394, buffalo@bizjournals.com, http://www.bizjournals.com/buffalo/, http://www.bizjournals.com/buffalo/services. Eds. Donna Collins, Jeff Wright. Pub. Jack Connors. Adv. contact Shelley Rohaver. Circ: 15,000 (paid). Wire service: AP.

330 USA ISSN 0748-6138
BUSINESS FIRST (LOUISVILLE); the business newspaper of Greater Louisville. Text in English. 1984. w. (Fri.). USD 85 (effective 2005). adv. back issues avail. **Document type:** *Newspaper, Trade.* **Description:** Covers regional business news.
Formerly: Louisville Business First
Related titles: Online - full text ed.: (from Gale Group, O C L C Online Computer Library Center, Inc., ProQuest Information & Learning).
Indexed: ABIn, BusDate, LRI.
—CCC.
Published by: A C B J Business Publications, Inc., 501 S 4th Ave, Ste 130, Louisville, KY 40202-2520. TEL 502-583-1731, FAX 502-587-1703, louisville@bizjournals.com, http://www.bizjournals.com/louisville. Ed., R&P Carol Timmons. adv.: color page USD 5,015. Circ: 15,000 (paid).

B

330 USA ISSN 0733-2408
HD28
➤ **BUSINESS FORUM (LOS ANGELES).** Text in English. 1975. q. USD 99 (effective 2004). adv. bk.rev. illus. Index. back issues avail.; reprint service avail. from PQC. **Document type:** *Magazine, Academic/Scholarly.* **Description:** Research articles and interpretative commentary on contemporary issues of interest to all business and economics disciplines, for business executives, academicians, and public administrators.
Formerly (until 1982): Los Angeles Business and Economics (0278-3428)
Related titles: Microform ed.: (from PQC); Online - full text ed.: (from EBSCO Publishing, Florida Center for Library Automation, Gale Group, O C L C Online Computer Library Center, Inc., ProQuest Information & Learning).
Indexed: ABIn, BPIA, Emerald, ManagCont, PAIS.
—BLDSC (2933.667000), IE, ingenta. **CCC.**
Published by: California State University, Los Angeles, School of Business & Economics, 5151 State University Dr, Los Angeles, CA 90032-8120. TEL 213-343-2806, FAX 213-343-6432, mqiomta@cslanet.calstatela.edu, http://cbe.calstatela.edu/publication/index.htm. Ed., R&P, Adv. contact Tom H Woods. Circ: 8,500 (paid and controlled).

650 GBR ISSN 0007-6791
HF11
➤ **BUSINESS HISTORY.** Text in English. 1959. q. GBP 288, USD 474 combined subscription to institutions print & online eds. (effective 2006). adv. bk.rev. illus. index. back issues avail.; reprint service avail. from PSC. **Document type:** *Journal, Academic/Scholarly.* **Description:** Publishes research articles in the field of business history, and is concerned with the long-term evolution and contemporary operation of business systems and enterprises.
Related titles: CD-ROM ed.; Microfilm ed.: (from PQC); Online - full text ed.: GBP 274, USD 465 to institutions (effective 2006) (from EBSCO Publishing, Florida Center for Library Automation, Gale Group, IngentaConnect, Northern Light Technology, Inc., O C L C Online Computer Library Center, Inc., Swets Information Services).
Indexed: ABIn, ASCA, AmH&L, ArtHuCI, BAS, BPI, BPIA, BrHumI, CurCont, DIP, GEOBASE, HistAb, IBR, IBSS, IBZ, JEL, MEA&I, PAIS, PCI, SOPODA, SSA, SSCI, SociolAb, T&II, WBA, WMB, WTA.
—BLDSC (2933.710000), IDS, IE, Infotrieve, ingenta. **CCC.**
Published by: Routledge (Subsidiary of: Taylor & Francis Group), 4 Park Sq, Milton Park, Abingdon, Oxon OX14 4RN, United Kingdom. TEL 44-1235-828600, FAX 44-1235-829000, info@routledge.co.uk, http://www.tandf.co.uk/journals/titles/00076791.asp, http://www.routledge.com. adv.: B&W page GBP 195, B&W page USD 285; trim 110 x 178.

650 USA ISSN 0007-6805
➤ **BUSINESS HISTORY REVIEW.** Text in English. 1926. q. USD 50 to individuals; USD 130 to institutions; USD 30 to students (effective 2004). adv. bk.rev. charts; illus. index, cum.index. reprints avail. **Document type:** *Journal, Academic/Scholarly.*
Formerly (until 1954): Business Historical Society. Bulletin (1065-9048)
Related titles: Microform ed.: (from PQC); Online - full text ed.: (from Chadwyck-Healey Inc., Florida Center for Library Automation, Gale Group, H.W. Wilson, JSTOR (Web-based Journal Archive), Northern Light Technology, Inc., O C L C Online Computer Library Center, Inc., ProQuest Information & Learning, The Dialog Corporation).
Indexed: ABIn, ABS&EES, ASCA, ATI, AmH&L, ArtHuCI, BAS, BPI, BRD, BRI, BusI, CBRI, CurCont, HistAb, IBR, IBSS, IBZ, JEL, KES, LRI, MAB, MEA&I, PAIS, PCI, SSCI, SSI, T&II, WorkRelAb.
—BLDSC (2933.730000), IE, Infotrieve, ingenta.

Published by: Harvard Business School Publishing, Soldier's Field Rd, Boston, MA 02163. TEL 617-495-1003, FAX 617-495-0594, bhr@hbs.edu, info@hbs.edu, http://www.hbs.edu/bhr. Eds. Jeffrey Jones, Walter A Friedman. Adv. contact Kristen Donahue. page USD 200; trim 4.75 x 7.75. Circ: 2,000 (paid and controlled).

330 IND

BUSINESS HISTORY STUDIES. Text in English. 1980. 4/yr. INR 460, USD 114 (effective 2000). adv. abstr.; bibl. index.
Published by: K.K. Roy (Private) Ltd., 55 Gariahat Rd., P O Box 10210, Kolkata, West Bengal 700 019, India. R&P M Misra TEL 91-33-475-4872. Circ: 518.

650 USA ISSN 0007-6813
HF5001
BUSINESS HORIZONS. Text in English. 1957. 6/yr. EUR 97 in Europe to individuals; JPY 12,700 in Japan to individuals; USD 107 to individuals except Europe and Japan; EUR 299 in Europe to institutions; JPY 39,600 in Japan to institutions; USD 335 to institutions except Europe and Japan (effective 2006). adv. bk.rev. charts; illus. index. reprint service avail. from PQC. **Document type:** *Magazine, Trade.* **Description:** Covers approaches to management and marketing, studies of business situations, accounting, banking, business education, and corporation activities.
Related titles: Microform ed.: (from PQC); Online - full text ed.: (from EBSCO Publishing, Florida Center for Library Automation, Gale Group, H.W. Wilson, IngentaConnect, Northern Light Technology, Inc., O C L C Online Computer Library Center, Inc., ScienceDirect, Swets Information Services).
Indexed: AAR, ABIn, ABS&EES, ADPA, APEL, ASEANManA, ATI, AgeL, BAS, BLI, BPI, BPIA, BRD, BRI, BusI, CBRI, CCR, CPM, CREJ, CurCont, DPD, EAA, Emerald, ExcerpMed, FutSurv, IBR, IMI, Inspec, KES, LRI, LogistBibl, M&MA, MEA&I, MEDLINE, MagInd, ManagCont, ORMS, PAIS, PMA, PROMT, PersLit, QAb, QC&AS, RASB, RI-1, RI-2, SCIMP, SSCI, T&DA, T&II, WorkRelAb.
—BLDSC (2933.770000), AskIEEE, IE, Infotrieve, ingenta. **CCC.**
Published by: (Indiana University, Kelley School of Business), Elsevier Inc. (Subsidiary of: Elsevier Science & Technology), 360 Park Ave. S, New York, NY 10010-1710. TEL 212-633-3730, http://www.elsevier.com/locate/bushor. Ed. Catherine M. Dalton. Circ: 3,000 (paid).

658 ZAF ISSN 1365-1560
HF3871
BUSINESS IN AFRICA INTERNATIONAL MAGAZINE. Text in English. 1992. bi-m. ZAR 330 domestic; USD 120 in US & Canada; GBP 66 in United Kingdom; USD 330 elsewhere; ZAR 15 newsstand/cover domestic; USD 10 newsstand/cover in United States; GBP 5 newsstand/cover in United Kingdom. illus. **Document type:** *Magazine, Consumer.* **Description:** Provides updates of financial, business and leisure news.
Published by: Goldcity Ventures Ltd, PO Box 1357, Rivonia, Gauteng 2128, South Africa. TEL 27-11-807-0948, FAX 27-11-807-0919. **Dist. in UK by:** MarketForce UK Ltd, 247 Tottenham Court Rd, London, Middx W1T 7AU, United Kingdom. TEL 44-20-72616996, FAX 44-207-2616951.

330 GBR

BUSINESS IN BRIEF. Text in English. 1990. m. GBP 12; GBP 25 foreign. back issues avail. **Document type:** *Bulletin.*
Published by: Community Publishers Ltd., 50 Prospect Pl, Swindon, Wilts SN1 3LG, United Kingdom. TEL 44-1793-497799, FAX 44-1793-497744. Ed. D.L. Thomas. Adv. contact D L Thomas. Circ: 14,500.

330 CAN ISSN 1193-1698

BUSINESS IN CALGARY. Text in English. 1992. m. CND 30 domestic; CND 45 foreign; CND 3.50 newsstand/cover. adv. **Document type:** *Trade.* **Description:** Discusses all issues that affect business in the Calgary area.
Address: PO Box 2400, Stn.M, Calgary, AB T2P 0W8, Canada. TEL 403-264-3270, FAX 403-264-3276. Ed. Richard Bronstein. Pub. Pat Ottmann. Adv. contact Evelyne Nykyforuk. Circ: 33,500.

330 RUS
HF3621
BUSINESS IN RUSSIA. Text in English. m.
Related titles: ♦ Russian ed.: Delovye Lyudi. ISSN 0868-9504.
—East View.
Address: B Polyanka 13, str 1, Moscow, 109180, Russian Federation. TEL 7-095-2380711, FAX 7-095-2386058, root@dl.glanet.ru. Ed. S Tsekhmistrenko. **US dist. addr.:** East View Information Services, 3020 Harbor Ln. N., Minneapolis, MN 55447. TEL 612-550-0961.

330 CAN ISSN 0849-5017

BUSINESS IN VANCOUVER. Text in English. 1989. w. CND 69.95 domestic; CND 95.95 foreign. adv. illus. **Document type:** *Newspaper.* **Description:** Covers business news in the Greater Vancouver area.
Published by: Business in Vancouver Media Group, 1155 Pender St W, Ste 500, Vancouver, BC V6E 2P4, Canada. TEL 604-688-2398, FAX 604-688-1963, news@biv.com, subscribe@biv.com, http://www.businessinvancouver.com. Ed. Ian Noble. Pub. Peter Ladner. Adv. contact Nick Hiam. Circ: 12,000 (paid).

330 GBR ISSN 0263-1067

BUSINESS IN YORKSHIRE. Text in English. 1982. m. GBP 30 (effective 2000). adv. bk.rev. **Document type:** *Magazine, Consumer.*
Published by: Business Magazine Group, Adamsway, Mansfield, Notts NG18 4FP, United Kingdom. TEL 44-1623-450500, FAX 44-1623-454560, biy@bmgroup.co.uk, http://www.bmgroup.co.uk. Ed. Lee Stokes. Circ: 11,251.

330 HKG ISSN 1468-120X

BUSINESS INDIA INTELLIGENCE. Text in English. 1994. m. GBP 895 print or online; USD 105 per issue print or online (effective 2004). Supplement avail. **Document type:** *Trade.* **Description:** Provides analyses of foreign investment and market entry strategies in India. Covers issues such as market size, investment as well as corporate strategies of multinationals and Indian business groups.
Former titles (until 1999): India Business Intelligence (1352-8335); Business South Asia (1023-9189)
Related titles: CD-ROM ed.: (from The Dialog Corporation); Online - full content ed.; Online - full text ed.: (from EBSCO Publishing).
Indexed: B&I.
—**CCC.**
Published by: Economist Intelligence Unit, 60/F Central Plaza, 18 Harbour Rd, Wanchai, Hong Kong. TEL 852-2802-7288, 852-2585-3888, FAX 852-2802-7638, 851-2802-7720, hongkong@eiu.com, http://store.eiu.com/index.asp?layout=product_home_page&product_id=420000242&, http://www.eiu.com/.

330 GBR ISSN 1464-8814

BUSINESS INFO MAGAZINE. Text in English. 1998. m. **Document type:** *Magazine, Consumer.* **Description:** Covers developments in business equipment, IT services and supplies in a consumer meets business style.
Indexed: Inspec.
Published by: Solutions Business Publishing Ltd., Woodlands, 415 Limpsfield Rd, Warlingham, Surrey CR6 9HA, United Kingdom. TEL 44-1883-629930, FAX 44-1883-629933, info@info.uk.ws, http://www.infouk.ws.

330 340 UKR ISSN 1560-4349

BUSINESS INFORM. Text in Russian, English. 1991. m. USD 120 foreign (effective 2000). adv. **Document type:** *Academic/Scholarly.* **Description:** Covers business and economics, law, and sociology.
Published by: A.G. Rystenko Ed. & Pub., PO Box 870, Kharkov, 61050, Ukraine. TEL 380-572142755, FAX 380-572-142755, chiefaobi@mail.ru, http://www.gp.kharkov.ua/aobi. R&P A G Rystenko. Adv. contact Liubov M Liburkina. page USD 500. **US dist. addr.:** East View Information Services, 3020 Harbor Ln. N., Minneapolis, MN 55447. TEL 612-550-0961.

BUSINESS INFORMATION ALERT; sources, strategies and signposts for information professionals. see *LIBRARY AND INFORMATION SCIENCES*

330 LBN ISSN 0254-4342

BUSINESS INFORMATION DIGEST. Text in English. m. free.
Published by: Middle East Airlines, c/o Sr. Manager of Market Development, Middle East Airlines HQ, P O Box 206, Beirut, Lebanon.

330 DEU ISSN 1860-1987

▼ **BUSINESS INFORMATION MANAGEMENT.** Text in German. 2004. irreg. price varies. **Document type:** *Monographic series, Academic/Scholarly.*
Published by: Fachhochschule Muenster, Huefferstr 27, Muenster, 48149, Germany. TEL 49-251-830, FAX 49-251-8364015, verwaltung@fh-muenster.de, http://www.fh-muenster.de.

330 USA ISSN 1040-7545

BUSINESS INSIGHTS. Text in English. 1982. s-a.
Published by: University of Southern Mississippi, 2701 Hardy St, Hattiesburg, MS 39406. http://www.usm.edu.

330 USA ISSN 1552-2326
HF5548.32
BUSINESS INTEGRATION JOURNAL. Variant title: B I Journasl(Business Integration Journal). Text in English. 1999. m. free to qualified personnel; USD 96 (effective 2003). adv. **Document type:** *Journal.* **Description:** Seeks to harmonize company resources, including people, processes, suppliers, customers and technology, by creating a cohesive and accessible IT infrastructure to support the needs of business users.
Formerly (until 2003): E A I Journal
Related titles: Online - full text ed.
Published by: Thomas Communications, Inc., 9330 Lyndon B Johnson Fwy., Ste. 800, Dallas, TX 75243-4310. info@bijonline.com, http://www.bijonline.com/. Ed. Tony M Brown. adv.: B&W page USD 6,460; trim 8 x 10.75.

330 USA

▼ **BUSINESS INTELLIGENCE REVIEW.** Variant title: B I Review. Text in English. 2005. q. free to qualified personnel (effective 2005). **Document type:** *Magazine, Trade.* **Description:** Focuses on providing actionable information on the strategic use of technology to make organizations more effective and responsive.
Published by: Source Media, Inc., One State St Plaza, 27th Fl, New York, NY 10004. TEL 212-803-6077, 800-221-1809, FAX 212-747-1154, custserv@sourcemedia.com, http://www.bireview.com. Circ: 118,000 (controlled).

330 IRL ISSN 0790-8636

BUSINESS IRELAND. Text in English. 1986. 4/yr. free. **Document type:** *Newsletter.* **Description:** Presents industrial and business information about Ireland for foreign readers.
Indexed: RefZh.
Published by: Irish Industrial Development Agency, Wilton Park House, Wilton Pl., Dublin, 2, Ireland. TEL 01-6686633, FAX 01-6603703. Ed. Gerry O'Shaughnessy. Circ: 15,000.

▼ **BUSINESS JET TRAVELER.** see *TRANSPORTATION—Air Transport*

330 KEN

BUSINESS JOURNAL; Kenya's retail traders & financial newspaper. Text in English, Swahili. 1978. m. KES 50. adv. illus. **Document type:** *Trade.*
Indexed: BLI, BusI, CurCont.
Published by: Kenya National Chamber of Commerce and Industry, Nairobi, Kenya. TEL 254-2-220867, FAX 254-2-340664. Ed., Adv. contact Peter G Muiruri. Circ: 12,000.

330 USA ISSN 1079-7394

THE BUSINESS JOURNAL (FRESNO). Text in English. 3/w. (Mon., Wed. & Fri.). USD 59; USD 1 per issue (effective 2005). **Document type:** *Newspaper, Trade.* **Description:** Contains business news, information and commentary, identifies market trends and focuses on new business opportunities.
Related titles: Online - full text ed.: (from EBSCO Publishing).
Published by: American City Business Journals, Inc. (Fresno), 1315 Van Ness, Ste 200, Fresno, CA 93721. TEL 559-490-3400, FAX 559-490-3531, gw@thebusinessjournal.com, lee@thebusinessjournal.com, https://www.thebusinessjournal.com. Pub. Gordon M Webster Jr. Circ: 6,200 (paid).

330 USA ISSN 1527-8611

THE BUSINESS JOURNAL (JACKSONVILLE). Text in English. 1985. w. (Fri.). USD 79 (effective 2005). **Document type:** *Newspaper, Trade.*
Formerly: Jacksonville Business Journal (0885-453X)
Related titles: Online - full text ed.: ISSN 1534-2336 (from Gale Group).
Indexed: BusDate, LRI.
—**CCC.**
Published by: American City Business Journals, Inc. (Jacksonville), 1200 Riverplace Blvd Ste 201, Jacksonville, FL 32207-1808. TEL 904-396-3502, FAX 904-396-5706, bmill@bizjournals.com, jacksonville@bizjournals.com, http://www.bizjournals.com/jacksonville/. Pub. David Sillick. Circ: 11,900.

330 USA ISSN 1530-8170

THE BUSINESS JOURNAL (KANSAS CITY); serving metropolitan Kansas City. Text in English. w. USD 90 (effective 2005).
Related titles: Online - full text ed.: (from Gale Group, O C L C Online Computer Library Center, Inc., ProQuest Information & Learning).
Indexed: ABIn.
—**CCC.**
Published by: American City Business Journals, Inc. (Kansas City), 1100 Main St., Ste. 210, Kansas City, MO 64105-5123. kansascity@bizjournals.com, http://www.bizjournals.com/kansascity/. Ed. Brian Kaberline.

330 USA ISSN 1540-1847
CODEN: CIBUFE
THE BUSINESS JOURNAL (MINNEAPOLIS - ST. PAUL). Variant title: Minneapolis - St. Paul CityBusiness with Corporate Report Minnesota. Text in English. 1999. w. USD 89 (effective 2005). adv. bk.rev. **Document type:** *Magazine, Trade.* **Description:** Contains late-breaking business news for the Twin Cities area, small-business information, and more.
Formed by the June 1999 merger of: CityBusiness (Minneapolis) (1098-5700); Which was formerly (1985-1998): Minneapolis / St. Paul CityBusiness (0883-3044); (1983-1985): Minneapolis CityBusiness (0742-809X); (1996-1999): Corporate Report (1091-4161); Which was formerly (1981-1996): Corporate Report Minesota (0279-5299); (1973-1981): Corporate report (Edina) (0190-9517); (19??-1973): Ninth Federal Reserve District. Corporate Report (0090-7952)
Related titles: Microfiche ed.: (from PQC); Online - full text ed.: (from CompuServe Inc., Data-Star, Gale Group, O C L C Online Computer Library Center, Inc., The Dialog Corporation).
Indexed: BRI, BusDate, LRI, PAIS, T&II.
—**CCC.**

B

Published by: (American City Business Journals, Inc.), CityBusiness (Subsidiary of: American City Business Journals, Inc.), 527 Marquette Ave, Ste 300, Minneapolis, MN 55402. TEL 612-288-2100, FAX 612-288-2121, bewen@bizjournals.com, twincities@amcity.com, http://www.bizjournals.com/twincities/, http://www.amcity.com/twincities. Ed. Dirk De Young TEL 612-288-2111. Pub. Lisa Bormaster. Adv. contact April Wallace TEL 612-288-2136. page USD 5,670. Circ: 12,000 (paid). **Subscr. to:** Buz Books Inc., 120 W Morehead St, Ste 100, Charlotte, NC 28202. TEL 800-486-3289.

330 USA ISSN 0895-1632
THE BUSINESS JOURNAL (PHOENIX); serving Phoenix & the Valley of the Sun. Text in English. 1980. w. USD 87 (effective 2005). adv. back issues avail. **Document type:** *Magazine, Trade.* **Description:** Covers all facets of business news about the Phoenix metropolitan area.
Former titles (until 1987): Greater Phoenix Business Journal (0890-9644); (until 1986): Phoenix Business Journal (0273-9542)
Related titles: Online - full text ed.: (from Florida Center for Library Automation, Gale Group, O C L C Online Computer Library Center, Inc., ProQuest Information & Learning, The Dialog Corporation).
Indexed: ABIn, BusDate, LRI, T&II.
—CCC.
Published by: American City Business Journals, Inc. (Phoenix), 101 N First Ave, Ste 2300, Phoenix, AZ 85003. TEL 602-230-8400, FAX 602-230-0955, phoenix@bizjournals.com, http://phoenix.bizjournals.com, http://www.bizjournals.com. Ed. Ilana Lowery TEL 602-308-6513. Pub. Don Henninger TEL 602-230-8400. Adv. contacts Sherri Conley TEL 602-308-6536, Linda Green. page USD 5,590. Circ: 15,000 (paid and free).

330 USA
BUSINESS JOURNAL (RIVERSIDE). Text in English. 2/w. USD 54 (effective 2005). **Document type:** *Newspaper.* **Description:** Helps to stay on top of the news affecting the legal and real estate communities in Riverside County.
Published by: Business Journal, 4129 Main St, Ste.209, Riverside, CA 92501. TEL 951-784-0111, FAX 951-784-6947, http://www.dailyjournal.com. Ed. Katrina Dewey.

330 USA ISSN 1047-8582
THE BUSINESS JOURNAL (YOUNGSTOWN). Variant title: Youngstown-Warren Business Journal. Text in English. 1984. s-m. USD 36 (effective 2005). adv. **Document type:** *Newspaper, Trade.*
Related titles: Online - full text ed.
Published by: Youngstown Publishing Co., PO Box 714, Youngstown, OH 44501. TEL 330-744-5023, FAX 330-744-5838, mrg@business-journal.com, info@business-journal.com, http://www.business-journal.com. Pub. Andrea Wood. Circ: 45,000 (paid and controlled).

330 USA ISSN 1548-1859
➤ **BUSINESS JOURNAL FOR ENTREPRENEURS.** Text in English. 1988. q. USD 185 domestic; USD 205 foreign (effective 2003). adv. bk.rev. tr.lit. back issues avail. **Document type:** *Academic/Scholarly.*
Published by: Franklin Publishing Company, 2723 Steamboat Circle, Arlington, TX 76006. TEL 817-548-1124, FAX 817-299-0930, http://www.franklinpublishing.net. Ed. Mrs. Maxime E Knight. Pub., R&P, Adv. contact Dr. Ludwig Otto. page USD 395; trim 8.5 x 11. Circ: 1,000 (paid).

330 USA
BUSINESS JOURNAL OF CENTRAL N Y. Text in English. 1985. w.
Related titles: Online - full text ed.
Published by: C N Y Business Review, Inc., 231 Wallton St, Syracuse, NY 13202-1230. TEL 315-472-3104, FAX 315-478-8166, editor@cnybusinessjournal.com, http://www.cnybusinessjournal.com. Ed. Charles McChesney. Circ: 8,000.

330 USA ISSN 1040-6360
THE BUSINESS JOURNAL OF UPPER EAST TENNESSEE AND SOUTHWEST VIRGINIA. Text in English. 1988. m. USD 12 (effective 2003). adv. bk.rev. **Document type:** *Consumer.*
Related titles: Microfiche ed.; Online - full text ed.
Indexed: BusDate.
Published by: Business Publishers Company, Box 643, Tri Port Complex, 2333 D Hwy 75, Blountville, TN 37617. TEL 615-323-7111, FAX 615-323-1479, http://www.bjournal.com/. Ed. Hank Hayes. Pub. Elizabeth W Pardue. adv.: B&W page USD 1,295, color page USD 1,620; trim 14 x 11. Circ: 10,000.

330 USA ISSN 0740-2899
CODEN: OEKSDJ
BUSINESS JOURNAL SERVING GREATER MILWAUKEE. Text in English. 1983. w. (Fri.). USD 92.95; USD 144.95 for 2 yrs. (effective 2005). adv. bk.rev. **Document type:** *Newspaper.* **Description:** Concentrates on business and business-related issues in Milwaukee and southeastern Wisconsin.
Related titles: Online - full text ed.: (from Florida Center for Library Automation, Gale Group, O C L C Online Computer Library Center, Inc., ProQuest Information & Learning).
Indexed: ABIn, BusDate, LRI, T&II.
—CCC.

Published by: Business Journal of Milwaukee Inc., 600 W Virginia St, Ste 500, Milwaukee, WI 53204-1551. milwaukee@bizjournals.com, http://milwaukee.bizjournals.com/milwaukee/. Pub. Mark Sabljak. Circ: 13,015 (paid).

330 LKA
BUSINESS LANKA. Text in English. 1981. q. LKR 320. adv. **Document type:** *Trade.* **Description:** Provides information on Sri Lankan exports and products for business people.
Published by: Sri Lanka Export Development Board, Trade Information Service, No. 115 Sir Chittampalam A Gardiner Mawatha, Colombo, 3, Sri Lanka. TEL 91-1-438512-5, FAX 94-1-438404, TELEX 21457 EXDEV CE. Ed. S Samarasekera. Circ: 2,000.

BUSINESS LAW ADVISORY. see *LAW*

BUSINESS LAW MONOGRAPHS. see *LAW—Corporate Law*

BUSINESS LAW REPORTS/RECUEIL DE JURISPRUDENCE EN DROIT DES AFFAIRES. see *LAW—Corporate Law*

BUSINESS LAW REVIEW. see *LAW—Corporate Law*

BUSINESS LAW TODAY. see *LAW—Corporate Law*

BUSINESS LAWYER. see *LAW—Corporate Law*

330 USA ISSN 1060-8230
BUSINESS LEADER. Text in English. 1989. m. USD 24 (effective 1998). adv. **Document type:** *Trade.* **Description:** Covers business in the Research Triangle area (greater Raleigh-Durham). Profiles leaders, gives company success stories, and provides management ideas and advice.
Formerly (until 1991): Business Digest (1058-6490)
Related titles: Microform ed.: (from PQC); Online - full text ed.: (from bigchalk, Northern Light Technology, Inc., O C L C Online Computer Library Center, Inc., ProQuest Information & Learning).
Indexed: ABIn, BusDate.
Published by: Business to Business Inc., 3801 Wake Forest Rd, Ste 102, Raleigh, NC 27609. TEL 919-872-7077, FAX 919-872-1590, editor@businessleader.com, http://www.businessleader.com. Ed. Amy Nelson. Pub., R&P Dan Davies. Adv. contact Martin Seligson. Circ: 11,000.

BUSINESS LEADER PROFILES FOR STUDENTS. see *BIOGRAPHY*

330 USA
THE BUSINESS LEDGER (EASTON); serving the business leaders of Delaware. Text in English. m. USD 20 in New Castle County; USD 35 outside New Castle County; USD 2 newsstand/cover (effective 2005). adv. **Document type:** *Newspaper.* **Description:** Provides business news in Delaware in a convenient and easy-to-read format.
Formerly: New Castle Business Ledger
Published by: Chesapeake Publishing Corp., 29088 Airpark Dr., Easton, MD 21601. TEL 401-822-1500, ledger@dca.net, http://www.ncbl.com/. Ed. W. Douglas Rainey. Pub. James B. Streit Jr. Adv. contact Melvin Butler. Circ: 12,500 (paid).

330 USA
THE BUSINESS LEDGER (OAK BROOK); the business newspaper for suburban Chicago. Text in English. 1993. bi-w. USD 40 (effective 2005). adv. bk.rev. back issues avail. **Document type:** *Newspaper.* **Description:** Covers trends, issues, industries, specific companies and business people in DuPage, N.W. Cook County and Fox Valley.
Formerly: DuPage Business Ledger (1082-8397)
—CCC.
Published by: Ledger Publishing Co., 600 Enterprise Dr, Ste 100, 100 Oak Brook, Oak Brook, IL 60523. TEL 630-571-8911, FAX 630-571-4053, bizledger@thebusinessledger.com, http://www.thebusinessledger.com/. Pub. James E Elsner. Adv. contact Jonathan Twitty. Circ: 17,000.

BUSINESS LIABILITY INSURANCE: LITIGATION, ARBITRATION AND SETTLEMENT. see *INSURANCE*

338 CAN ISSN 1493-0579
BUSINESS LONDON. Text in English. 1975. m. CND 24. adv. **Document type:** *Consumer.* **Description:** Business news in London and St. Thomas.
Former titles (until 1999): London Business Magazine (1204-5551); London Business Monthly Magazine (0820-5698); (until 1987): Western Ontario Business (0383-6193)
Related titles: Online - full text ed.
Indexed: BusDate.
Published by: Bowes Publishers Ltd., PO Box 7400, London, ON N5Y 4X3, Canada. TEL 519-472-7601, FAX 519-473-2256. Ed. Gord Delamont. Circ: 14,000.

330 GBR ISSN 1353-2855
BUSINESS MAGAZINE (READING). Variant title: Thames Valley Business Magazine. Text in English. 1993. m. GBP 35 domestic (effective 2001); Free to qualified subscribers.. adv. **Document type:** *Magazine, Trade.* **Description:** Covers business news and issues for the Thames Valley region.

Published by: Elcot Publications (South) Ltd., 1210 Parkview, Arlington Business Park, Theale, Reading, RG7 4TY, United Kingdom. TEL 44-118-9304030, FAX 44-118-9305030, busmag@elcot.co.uk, http://www.businessmag.co.uk.

330 USA
BUSINESS MARKET NEWS. Text in English. 1991. q. USD 24. bk.rev. **Document type:** *Newsletter.* **Description:** Provides economic and marketing management for business-to-business marketers.
Published by: Hemsing Advertising, 755 W Big Beaver Rd, Ste 416, Troy, MI 48084-4903. TEL 810-362-0448, FAX 810-362-3884. Ed. Jeffrey Bourque. Circ: (controlled).

330 USA
BUSINESS MATTERS. Text in English. 1903. m. USD 36 (effective 2005). **Document type:** *Newsletter, Trade.*
Formerly: Chamber Business
Published by: Reno-Sparks Chamber of Commerce, One E First St, Reno, NV 89501. TEL 775-337-3035, FAX 775-686-3038, http://www.reno-sparkschamber.org. Circ: 2,400 (paid and controlled).

B

330 USA
BUSINESS MEDIA. Text in English. 1986. q. USD 12 (effective 2000). adv. bk.rev. charts; illus.; stat. **Document type:** *Journal, Trade.* **Description:** Covers business news, business people, and business management.
Published by: Business Media Publications, 9260 Baltimore St, NE, Minneapolis, MN 55449. TEL 612-780-1018, FAX 612-780-8228. Ed., R&P Gregg Kroll. Pub. Kathy Kroll. Adv. contact Becky Zenz. Circ: 20,000.

330 USA
BUSINESS NEW HAVEN. Text in English. 1993. bi-w. **Document type:** *Magazine, Trade.*
Published by: Second Wind Media Ltd., 1221 Chapel St., New Haven, CT 06511-4701. news@businessnewhaven.com, http://www.businessnewhaven.com. Ed. Michael C Bingham. Circ: 14,000.

330 CAN ISSN 0834-020X
BUSINESS NEWS. Text in English. 1986. m. CND 35. adv. **Document type:** *Newsletter.*
Published by: St. John's Board of Trade, 10 Fort William Place, P O Box 5127, St. John's, NF A1C 5V5, Canada. TEL 709-726-2961, FAX 709-726-2003. Ed. Kyran Pittman Snair. Adv. contact David Udle. B&W page CND 615, color page CND 1,100. Circ: 1,400.

330 CZE
BUSINESS NEWS. Text in English. 1990. 5/w. CZK 3,119 per month; USD 720 (effective 2000). Supplement avail. **Document type:** *Newspaper, Consumer.* **Description:** Contains detailed information on economic developments in the Czech Republic and Slovakia, economic analysis, exchange rates, and shares.
Formerly: Ecoservice
Published by: Ceska Tiskova Kancelar/Czech News Agency, Opletalova 5, Prague, 11144, Czech Republic. TEL 420-2-22098111, FAX 420-2-24225376, obchodni@mail.ctk.cz, http://www.ctk.cz. Ed. Sylvia Maria Irglova. Circ: 170.

330 IDN
BUSINESS NEWS. Text in English. 1956. 2/w. IDR 66,000 per month. adv. **Document type:** *Bulletin.*
Related titles: Indonesian ed.
Published by: P T Business News, Jalan H Abdul Muis 70, Jakarta, 10160, Indonesia. TEL 62-21-3848207, FAX 62-21-3454280. Ed. Sanjoto Sastromihardjo. Adv. contact Heru Nuroso. B&W page USD 1,210, color page USD 3,660; trim 280 x 205. Circ: 15,000.

977.4 USA
THE BUSINESS NEWS; the voice for business in Northwest Michigan. Text in English. 1994. m. USD 10 (effective 2004). adv. **Document type:** *Magazine, Trade.* **Description:** Targets decision makers and consumers with local & regional information critical to businesses in Northwest Michigan.
Published by: West Shore Publishing, L L C, 800 Hastings St, Ste E, Traverse City, MI 49686. TEL 231-929-7919, 800-445-7123, FAX 231-959-7914, biznews@traverse.com, http://www.westshorepub.com. Ed. Gayle Neu. Pub. John Tarrant. Adv. contact Craig McIntosh. B&W page USD 1,395; trim 10.75 x 10.25. Circ: 10,000.

330 POL ISSN 1231-0573
BUSINESS NEWS FROM POLAND. Text in English, Polish. 1990. fortn. **Document type:** *Bulletin, Consumer.* **Description:** Covers Polish politics, economics, banking, finance, stock exchange, industry, legislation, transport, foreign trade.
Related titles: Online - full text ed.
Published by: Polska Agencja Prasowa (P.A.P.)/Polish Press Agency, Al Jerozolimskie 7, Warsaw, 00950, Poland. TEL 48-2-6122489, FAX 48-2-6122495, TELEX 817720 PAPEX PL, boss@ikp.atm.com.pl. Ed. Aneta Dylewska. adv.: page USD 200. Circ: 600.

330 GBR
BUSINESS NORTH EAST. Text in English. 1987. m. GBP 19.50. adv. **Document type:** *Trade.*
Related titles: Online - full text ed.

Published by: Business Magazine Group, Adamsway, Mansfield, Notts NG18 4FP, United Kingdom. TEL 44-1623-450500, FAX 44-1623-454560. Ed. Ian Fammond. Circ: 11,213.

330 GBR ISSN 0958-7926
BUSINESS NORTH WEST. Text in English. 1988. m. GBP 30 (effective 2000). adv. **Document type:** *Magazine, Consumer.* **Description:** Contains a blend of business news, features, area reviews and profiles for directors and senior management in companies located in the North West region of England.
Published by: Business Magazine Group, Adamsway, Mansfield, Notts NG18 4FP, United Kingdom. TEL 44-1623-450500, FAX 44-1623-454560, bnw@bmgroup.co.uk, http://www.bmgroup.co.uk. Ed. Michael Grumett.

658 GBR ISSN 1358-1953
BUSINESS NOW. Text in English. 1994. bi-m. **Description:** Includes tips and techniques to help managers improve their own businesss' performance.
Published by: Wyvern Publications Ltd, Link House, 8 Bartholomew's Walk, Ely, CB7 4ZD, United Kingdom. TEL 44-135-3665544, FAX 44-135-3667666, wyvern@wyvern.co.uk, http://www.wyvern.co.uk. Circ: 1,000.

B

THE BUSINESS OF FILM. see *MOTION PICTURES*

330 USA
BUSINESS OPERATIONS REPORTS. (Includes: Egypt; Nigeria; Saudi Arabia; South Africa; Baltic States (Estonia, Latvia, & Lithuania); Belarus & Ukraine; Bulgaria & Romania; Central Asia Republics (Kazakhstan, Turkmenistan, & Uzbekistan); Croatia & Slovenia; Czech Republic & Slovakia; Hungary; Poland; Russia; China; India; Indonesia; Malaysia; Philippines; Thailand; Vietnam; Taiwan; Argentina; Brazil; Mexico; Myanmar, Laos & Cambodia; Turkey; Pakistan; South Korea) Text in English. 1995. q. USD 345 (effective 2004). **Description:** Reports on business operational issues in 39 emerging markets. Coverage includes political climate, infrastructure, investment issues, land availability, labour and business services, finance, marketing and distribution.
Formerly (until 1997): Business Reports
Published by: Economist Intelligence Unit, 111 W 57th St, New York, NY 10019. TEL 212-554-0600, 800-938-4685, FAX 212-586-1182, http://www.eiu.com.

330 GBR ISSN 0265-3591
BUSINESS OPPORTUNITIES DIGEST. Text in English. m. free. **Document type:** *Newsletter, Consumer.* **Description:** Contains 20 tips on business opportunities.
Published by: Highbury Direct Publishing (Subsidiary of: Highbury House Communications PLC), Jordan House, 47 Brunswick Pl, London, N1 6EB, United Kingdom. TEL 44-20-76086500, FAX 44-20-76086704, http://www.hhc.co.uk/businessopportunitiesdigest. Adv. contact James Brown. Circ: 50,000.

330 BGR
BUSINESS OPPORTUNITIES IN BULGARIA. Text in English. 1980. 3/yr. USD 25. **Description:** Provides information on Bulgaria's economy and foreign economic relations.
Formerly (until 1997): Bulgaria - Economic Development (Year)
Published by: Bulgarska Turgovsko-Promishlena Palata/Bulgarian Chamber of Commerce and Industry, 42 Parchevich ul, Sofia, 1058, Bulgaria. TEL 359-2-9872631, FAX 359-2-9873209, bcci@bcci.bg, http://www.bcci.bg/. Circ: 3,000.

330 340 USA
BUSINESS ORGANIZATIONS: BLUE SKY REGULATIONS. Text in English. 1977. irreg. (in 4 vols.). looseleaf. USD 890 (effective 1999).
Related titles: CD-ROM ed.
Published by: Matthew Bender & Co., Inc. (Subsidiary of: LexisNexis North America), 1275 Broadway, Albany, NY 12204. international@bender.com, http://bender.lexisnexis.com. Ed. A A Sommer Jr.

330 340 USA
BUSINESS ORGANIZATIONS: FEDERAL SECURITIES EXCHANGE ACT OF 1934. Text in English. 1967. 2 base vols. plus irreg. updates. looseleaf. USD 660 base vol(s). (effective 2002). **Description:** covers the organization of the SEC, 1934 Act registration and reporting requirements, Integrated Disclosure, Proxy contests, insider trading and short-swing trading, registration and regulation of securities markets, broker-dealers, transfer ageencies.
Related titles: CD-ROM ed.
Published by: Matthew Bender & Co., Inc. (Subsidiary of: LexisNexis North America), 1275 Broadway, Albany, NY 12204. international@bender.com, http://bender.lexisnexis.com. Ed. A A Sommer Jr.

330 340 USA
BUSINESS ORGANIZATIONS: PROFESSIONAL CORPORATIONS AND ASSOCIATIONS. Text in English. 1970. irreg. (in 7 vols.). looseleaf. USD 1,070 (effective 1999). Supplement avail. **Description:** Provides information on forming, operating, and changing ownership of a professional corporation or association.
Published by: Matthew Bender & Co., Inc. (Subsidiary of: LexisNexis North America), 1275 Broadway, Albany, NY 12204. international@bender.com, http://www.bender.com, http://bender.lexisnexis.com. Ed. Berrien C Eaton Jr.

330 USA
THE BUSINESS PAPER. Text in English. w.
Published by: Greenspun Media Group, 2290 Corporate Circle Dr Ste 280, Henderson, NV 89014. TEL 702-990-2550, FAX 702-990-2526.

330 HUN ISSN 0237-3831
BUSINESS PARTNER HUNGARY. Text in English. 1986. bi-m. HUF 25,200, USD 110 (effective 2000). adv. **Document type:** *Newsletter.* **Description:** Covers Hungarian trade acts and regulations, customs foreign exchange, investments. Includes foreign trade statistics, industry tests, commodity market reports, regional investment offers.
Related titles: German ed.
Published by: Kopint - Datorg Plc, Csokonai u 3, Budapest, 1081, Hungary. TEL 36-1-3039586, FAX 36-1-303-9582, nemeth@kopdat.hu, http://www.kopdat.hu. Ed. Ilona Nemeth. R&P, Adv. contact Judit Boncz.

330 USA ISSN 1051-094X
HF3163.F7
BUSINESS PEOPLE. Variant title: Business People Magazine of Greater Fort Wayne. Text in English. 1987. m. USD 16.95; USD 3 newsstand/cover (effective 2005). adv. **Document type:** *Trade.* **Description:** Deals with issues and information affecting business professionals throughout Allen County and northeast Indiana.
Related titles: Online - full text ed.: (from O C L C Online Computer Library Center, Inc., ProQuest Information & Learning).
Indexed: ABIn.
Published by: Michiana Business Publications, Inc., 536 W Cook Rd, Fort Wayne, IN 46825-3323. info@businesspeoplemagazine.com, kerb@businesspeople.com, dcopeland@businesspeople.com. Ed. Steven R Harris. Pub. Daniel C Copeland. adv.: B&W page USD 1,115, color page USD 1,540; trim 11 x 8.5. Circ: 8,400.

330 USA ISSN 1523-6781
BUSINESS PEOPLE VERMONT. Text in English. 1984. m. USD 30 (effective 2005). adv. bk.rev. **Document type:** *Trade.* **Description:** Profiles local business people.
Formerly (until March 1999): Business Digest of Greater Burlington (8750-2305)
Related titles: Supplement(s): Business Travel Guide.
Published by: Mill Publishing, Inc., PO Box 953, Williston, VT 05495-0953. TEL 802-862-4109, FAX 802-862-9322, busydigest@vermontguides.com, http://www.vermontguides.com. Ed. Edna Tenney. Pub. Jack Tenney. R&P, Adv. contact Rebecca Awodey. Circ: 7,000 (controlled).

338 USA ISSN 0896-3703
HC107.A13
BUSINESS PERSPECTIVES. Text in English. 1963. q. free (effective 2005). stat. back issues avail. **Document type:** *Academic/Scholarly.*
Formerly: Mid-South Business Journal (0279-8174); Which superseded (in 1981): Mid-South Quarterly Business Review (0885-4696); Which was formerly (until 1971): Memphis State Business Review (0025-9209)
Related titles: Online - full text ed.: (from EBSCO Publishing, Factiva, Florida Center for Library Automation, Gale Group, Northern Light Technology, Inc., O C L C Online Computer Library Center, Inc., ProQuest Information & Learning).
Indexed: ABIn, BPIA, BusI, LRI, ManagCont, PAIS, SPAA, SRI, SUSA, T&II.
—BLDSC (2934.602000), IE, ingenta.
Published by: University of Memphis, Bureau of Business and Economic Research, Memphis, TN 38152. TEL 901-678-4158, FAX 901-678-4086, scsmith@cc.memphis.edu, http://www.people.memphis.edu/%7Ebberlib/businessperspectives.htm, http://www.peopl.memphis.edu/~bberlib/. Ed. Stephen Smith. Circ: 2,500.

330 IRL ISSN 1393-5712
BUSINESS PLUS. Text in English. 1998. m. EUR 28 domestic; EUR 33.08 in United Kingdom; EUR 43.24 elsewhere (effective 2002). adv. **Document type:** *Magazine, Trade.* **Description:** Provides readers with news and information on Irish business services and resources.
Related titles: Online - full text ed.: 2000.
Address: 88 Ranelagh Rd., Dublin, 6, Ireland. TEL 353-1-4960666, info@businessplus.ie, http://www.bizplus.ie. Ed. Nick Mulcahy. Adv. contact Siobhan O'Connell. Circ: 40,000 (paid and controlled).

330 USA
THE BUSINESS POST. Text in English. m. USD 75; free to qualified personnel (effective 2005). adv. **Document type:** *Newspaper, Trade.*
Published by: Appen Newspapers, Inc., 319 N Main St, Alpharetta, GA 30201. TEL 770-442-3278, FAX 770-475-1216, appen@northfulton.com, http://www.northfulton.com, http://www.northfulton.com/. Ed. Hatcher Hurd. Pub. Ray Appen. adv.: page USD 1,800. Circ: 15,000 (paid).

330 USA ISSN 1524-5489
THE BUSINESS PRESS. Text in English. 1995. w. USD 59 (effective 2002). adv. **Document type:** *Newspaper, Trade.* **Description:** Reports on new business developments.
Related titles: Online - full text ed.: (from O C L C Online Computer Library Center, Inc., ProQuest Information & Learning).
Indexed: ABIn.
Published by: The Business Press, 3700 Inland Empire Blvd., Ste. 450, Ontario, CA 91764. TEL 909-980-7330, FAX 909-476-9630, http://www.thebizpress.com. Ed. John Orr. Adv. contact Jeanette Jourdier.

330 CAN ISSN 1187-9114
BUSINESS PROGRAM GUIDE, ALBERTA. Text in English. 1989. a.
Published by: Alberta Venture, #201, 10350-124 St, Edmonton T5N 3V9, AB T5N 3V9, Canada. TEL 780-990-0839, admin@albertaventure.com.

330 POL ISSN 0866-9287
BUSINESS PROMOTION. Text in Polish. 1990. m.
Published by: Business Publications Ltd., PO Box 1354, Katowice, 40096, Poland. TEL 48-32-599647. Ed. Boguslaw Faciejew. Circ: 2,000.

THE BUSINESS PUBLISHER. see *PUBLISHING AND BOOK TRADE*

330 PRI ISSN 1552-6224
HF3351
BUSINESS PUERTO RICO. Text in English. 1981 (Win). 4/yr. USD 29.70 for 6 nos.. adv. illus.; stat. **Document type:** *Consumer.* **Description:** Covers economic events on the island.
Published by: Puerto Rico Almanacs, Inc., PO Box 9582, Santurce, 00908-0582, Puerto Rico. TEL 787-725-3155, FAX 787-725-3196. Ed. Connie Garcia. Circ: 13,500.

330 AUS
BUSINESS QUARTERLY. Text in English. q. reprints avail. **Description:** Focuses on the effect that government, international relations, new products and new trends will have on Australian business in the future.
Media: Online - full text.
Indexed: CPM, CPerI, M&MA.
Published by: Monash University, Public Affairs Office, Bldg. 3.1, Wellington Road, Clayton, VIC 3168, Australia. TEL 61-3-9905-2057, FAX 61-3-9905-2097, brenda.harkness@mcom.monash.edu.au, http://www.monash.edu.au/pubs/busquart/index.html. Ed. Brenda Harkness.

330 ROM
THE BUSINESS REVIEW. Text in English. w. adv. **Document type:** *Magazine, Trade.*
Published by: Business Media Group, Bd. Regina Maria nr. 1, bl. P5B, sector 1, ap. 10-11-12, Bucharest, Romania. TEL 40-21-3353473, FAX 40-21-3353474, subscribe@bmg.ro.

330 USA ISSN 1537-4254
THE BUSINESS REVIEW. Text in English. w. (Mon.). USD 84; USD 145 for 2 yrs.; USD 186 for 3 yrs.; USD 1.75 newsstand/cover (effective 2005). **Document type:** *Newspaper.*
Former titles (until 2001): Capital District Business Review (0747-3699); (until 1984): Business Review (Albany) (0192-527X)
Related titles: Online - full text ed.: (from Gale Group, O C L C Online Computer Library Center, Inc., ProQuest Information & Learning); Supplement(s): Book of Lists. 2001.
—CCC.
Published by: American City Business Journals, Inc. (Albany), 40 British American Blvd, Latham, NY 12210. albany@bizjournals.com, http://albany.bizjournals.com/albany. Circ: 10,000 (paid). Wire service: PR.

330 PHL
BUSINESS REVIEW. Text in English. bi-m. **Document type:** *Magazine, Trade.* **Description:** Contains reports on the most recent economic activities in Europe and the Philippines; addresses issues affecting business; provides information on the activities of the ECCP and its committees.
Published by: European Chamber of Commerce in the Philippines, 19/F Axa Life Center, Sen. Gil Puyat Avenue corner Tindalo Street, Makati City, Metro Manila, 1200, Philippines. TEL 63-2-8451324, FAX 63-2-8451395, info@eccp.com, http://interim.eccp.com/index.eccp.php.

330 GBR ISSN 1354-1110
HF11
BUSINESS REVIEW. Text in English. 1994. 4/yr. (Sep.-Apr.). GBP 21.95 domestic; GBP 30 in Europe; GBP 35 elsewhere (effective Sep. 2002). adv. **Document type:** *Magazine, Trade.* **Description:** Focuses on core topics, from a fresh, up-to-date perspective.
Related titles: Online - full text ed.: (from Florida Center for Library Automation, Gale Group).
—BLDSC (2934.669500).

Published by: Philip Allan Updates, Market Pl, Deddington, Banbury, Oxon OX15 0SE, United Kingdom. TEL 44-1869-338652, FAX 44-1869-338803, sales@philipallan.co.uk, http://www.philipallan.co.uk. Ed. Catherine Tate. R&P Ceri Jenkins. Circ: 18,500.

331 JPN
BUSINESS REVIEW/BIJINESU REBYU. Text in Japanese. 1953. q. JPY 800.
Indexed: JTA.
Published by: Chikura Shobo, c/o Kyobashi Daiichi Seimei Bldg, 4-12 Kyobashi 2-chome, Chuo-ku, Tokyo, 104-0031, Japan. Ed. Ikujiro Nonaka. Circ: 1,000.

330 USA ISSN 1357-0293
HF3630.2
BUSINESS RUSSIA (NEW YORK). Text in English. 1995. m. USD 90 per issue (effective 2004). **Description:** Provides information on all the issues that affect business across every part of the former Soviet Union.
Related titles: Online - full text ed.: (from EBSCO Publishing).
Published by: Economist Intelligence Unit, 111 W 57th St, New York, NY 10019. TEL 212-554-0600, 800-938-4685, FAX 212-586-1182, http://www.eiu.com.

330 USA
THE BUSINESS SALE. Text in English. 2001. irreg. USD 24 per issue domestic (effective 2004). **Document type:** *Trade.*
Published by: D.L. Perkins, LLC, 7010 S Yale, Ste 120, Tulsa, OK 74136. TEL 918-493-4900, FAX 918-493-4924, 800-634-0605, renae@thebusinessowner.com, http://www.thebusinessowner.com. Pub., R&P David L Perkins Jr. Adv. contact Renae Williams TEL 918-493-4900.

330 USA ISSN 1540-1014
BUSINESS SCENE. Text in Chinese. 2002 (Jun.). m.
Published by: Voice of America, Chinese Branch, 330 Independence Ave., S W, Rm. 2600, Washington, DC 20237. TEL 202-401-6387, FAX 202-619-3765, caijing@voa.gov, http://www.freexinwen.com/caijing. Ed. Joseph J. Chen.

330 USA
BUSINESS SENSE. Text in English. 1998. quadrennial.
Published by: Baumer Financial Publishing (Subsidiary of: Imagination Publishing, LLC), 820 W Jackson Blvd No 450, Chicago, IL 60607. TEL 312-627-1020, FAX 312-627-1105, baumerfpub@aol.com. Ed. Elizabeth Seymour. Circ: 85,000.

330 GBR ISSN 1468-0831
BUSINESS SOUTH EAST. Text in English. 1999. m. GBP 30 (effective 2000). adv. **Document type:** *Magazine, Consumer.* **Description:** Communicates news and information from authoritative and professional sources to heighten awareness of current business trends and changes in the South East region of England. Also encourages and supports the region's growth, economy and recognition.
Published by: Business Magazine Group, Adamsway, Mansfield, Notts NG18 4FP, United Kingdom. TEL 44-1623-450500, FAX 44-1623-454560, bse@bmgroup.co.uk, http://www.bmgroup.co.uk. Ed. Dan Panes.

330 GBR ISSN 0958-7934
BUSINESS SOUTH WEST. Text in English. 1980. m. GBP 19.50. adv. bk.rev. illus.
Formerly: Business West
Published by: Business Magazine Group, Adamsway, Mansfield, Notts NG18 4FP, United Kingdom. TEL 44-1623-450500, FAX 44-1623-454560. Ed. Sue Turner. Circ: 11,594.

BUSINESS SPACE REGISTER. see *REAL ESTATE*

330 420 DEU
BUSINESS SPOTLIGHT. Text in English. 2001. q. EUR 33.80; EUR 26.80 to students; EUR 9.50 newsstand/cover (effective 2004). adv. **Document type:** *Magazine, Consumer.* **Description:** Focuses on the world of business for those wishing to learn or improve their English language skills.
Published by: Spotlight Verlag GmbH & Co KG, Fraunhoferstr 22, Planegg, 82152, Germany. TEL 49-89-85681-0, FAX 49-89-85681105, business-spotlight@spotlight-verlag.de, abo@spotlight-verlag.de, http://www.business-spotlight.de, http://www.spotlight-online.de. adv.: B&W page EUR 4,199, color page EUR 6,997. Circ: 62,179 (paid).

650 IND
BUSINESS STANDARD. Text in English. 1975. m. INR 4 newsstand/cover. adv. **Document type:** *Newspaper.*
Indexed: B&I.
Published by: Anand Bazar Patrika Ltd., 6 Prafulla Sarkar St, Kolkata, West Bengal 700 001, India. TEL 033-274880, FAX 033-303240. Ed. T N Ninan. Adv. contact Gautam Gupta Bhaya. Circ: 13,808.

330 USA ISSN 1086-8488
HC101
BUSINESS STATISTICS OF THE UNITED STATES; patterns of economic change. Text in English. 1951-1951 (ceased same year); N.S. 1995. irreg., latest vol.9. USD 147 per issue (effective 2004).
Formerly (until 1991): Business Statistics (0083-2545)
Published by: Bernan Press, 4611-F Assembly Dr, Lanham, MD 20706-4391. TEL 301-459-2255, FAX 301-459-0056, bpress@bernan.com, http://www.bernan.com/Online_Catalog/Title_Page.aspx?TitleID=7705375.

330 USA
BUSINESS STRATEGIES. Text in English. 1983. 3 base vols. plus m. updates. looseleaf. USD 935 base vol(s). (effective 2004). **Description:** Provides business advisors and entrepreneurs with the necessary information to successfully start and manage a small business. It is a comprehensive blend of business law, tax law, human resources and accounting information and includes essential, yet often difficult to locate, forms for a variety of key business transactions.
Published by: C C H Inc., 2700 Lake Cook Rd, Riverwoods, IL 60015. TEL 847-267-7000, 800-449-6439, cust_serv@cch.com, http://www.cch.com. Pub. Stacey Caywood.

330 AUS
BUSINESS STRATEGIES REPORT. Text in English. 1998. w. free. **Document type:** *Newsletter.* **Description:** Provides news and tips on how to run a profitable and successful business.
Media: Online - full text.
Published by: Thirteenth (13th) Beach Marketing Services Pty. Ltd., PO Box 7252, Geelong West, VIC 3218, Australia. neigel@learningcurve.com.au, http://www.learningcurve.com.au. Ed. Nigel Rawlings.

BUSINESS STRATEGY FOR THE BIO-ENVIRONMENT. see *ENVIRONMENTAL STUDIES*

330 HUN ISSN 1588-9025
BUSINESS STUDIES. Alternating issues in Hungarian, English. 1994. s-a.
Former titles (until 2001): Publications of the University of Miskolc. Series F. Economic Sciences (1219-543X); (until 1995): University of Miskolc Bulletin. Series F. Economic Sciences (1219-1418)
Published by: Miskolci Egyetem/University of Miskolc, Miskolc, 3515, Hungary. TEL 36-46-565111, FAX 36-46-565203, pzbozsi@gold.uni-miskolc.hu, http://www.uni-miskolc.hu.

330 GBR
BUSINESS STUDIES MAGAZINE. Text in English. m. **Document type:** *Trade.*
Published by: Stanley Thornes, Ellenborough House, Wellington St, Cheltenham, Glos GL50 1YW, United Kingdom. TEL 01242-224234.

330 IRL
BUSINESS STUDIES SERIES. Text in English. 1979. irreg. price varies. **Document type:** *Monographic series.*
Published by: Irish Business and Employers Confederation, Confederation House, 84-86 Lower Baggot St., Dublin, 2, Ireland. TEL 353-1-6601011, FAX 353-1-6601717, http://www.iol.ie/ibec. Ed. Tony Donohoe.

BUSINESS TAX PLANNING. see *BUSINESS AND ECONOMICS—Public Finance, Taxation*

BUSINESS TECH. see *COMPUTERS—Internet*

330 SGP
BUSINESS TIMES. Text in English. 1976. d. (except Sun.). SGD 288 domestic; SGD 1,607 in Brunei, China, Hong Kong, India, Indonesia, Korea, Philippines, Pakistan, Sri Lanka, Thailand, Taiwan, Vietnam & Asia Pacific countries (excluding Hawaii).; USD 1,925 in Australia, Japan & New Zealand; USD 2,407 elsewhere (effective 2003). adv. bk.rev.; film rev.; music rev.; play rev.; software rev. illus.; mkt. 26 p./no. 8 cols./p.; Supplement avail.; back issues avail. **Document type:** *Newspaper.* **Description:** Singapore's business newspaper.
Related titles: Microfiche ed.; Microfilm ed.: (from PQC); Online - full text ed.; Includes: Shipping Times.
Indexed: B&I.
Published by: Singapore Press Holdings Ltd., 1000 Tea Payoh North, News Centre, Singapore, 318994, Singapore. TEL 65-63195318, 65-63196319, FAX 65-63198277, 65-63198150, btnews@sph.com.sg, http://www.asia1.com.sg/biztimes, http://www.sph.com.sg/. Ed. Patrick Daniel. Adv. contact Lawrence Loh. Circ: 31,205 (paid).

330 THA ISSN 0125-2313
BUSINESS TIMES. Text in English. 1979. w.
Related titles: Online - full text ed.: (from Northern Light Technology, Inc.).
Address: Thai Bldg, 1400 Rama IV Rd, Bangkok, 10110, Thailand.

330 NGA ISSN 0331-2585
BUSINESS TIMES; economic and business review. Text in English. 1975. w. NGN 50 newsstand/cover. illus. **Document type:** *Newspaper, Consumer.*
Related titles: Online - full text ed.: (from Northern Light Technology, Inc.).
Published by: Daily Times of Nigeria Ltd., Publications Division, New Isheri Rd., PMB 21340, Ikeja, Agidingbi, Lagos, Nigeria. TEL 234-1-4977280, FAX 234-1-4977283. Ed. Tajudeen Kunle. Circ: 100,000.

330 MYS
BUSINESS TIMES. Text in English. 1976. d. (6/w.). MYR 232.50, USD 2,464.50. back issues avail.
Related titles: Online - full text ed.
Indexed: B&I.
Published by: Financial Publications Sdn. Bhd., 31 Jalan Riong, Kuala Lumpur, 59100, Malaysia. TEL 2745444. Ed. Henry Chang. Circ: 12,000.

330 CAN ISSN 1185-1600
BUSINESS TO BUSINESS (BRACEBRIDGE). Text in English. 1989. 7/yr. CND 35, USD 50. adv.
Published by: Bracebridge Examiner Ltd., 16 Manitoba St, P O Box 1049, Bracebridge, ON P0B 1C0, Canada. TEL 705-645-8771, FAX 705-645-1718. Ed. Mike Archer. Circ: 6,034 (controlled).

THE BUSINESS - TO - BUSINESS MARKETER. see *ADVERTISING AND PUBLIC RELATIONS*

330 CAN
BUSINESS TO BUSINESS NEWS. Text in English. 1993. m. CND 24; CND 34 in United States; CND 40 elsewhere. adv.
Address: P O Box 130, Durham, ON N0G 1R0, Canada. TEL 519-369-6950, FAX 519-369-6961. Pub. Geo Benninger. Adv. contact Roseanne Vermein. B&W page CND 865.

330 IND
BUSINESS TODAY. Text in English. 1992. fortn. INR 215 domestic; USD 19.50 foreign (effective 2004). adv. **Document type:** *Magazine, Trade.*
Related titles: Online - full text ed.
Published by: Living Media India Pvt. Ltd., F-14-15, Connaught Place, New Delhi, India. TEL 91-11-23315801, FAX 91-11-23712998, wecare@intoday.com, http://www.business-today.com, http://www.indiatoday.com. Ed. Aroon Purie. adv.: B&W page INR 42,000, color page INR 160,000; trim 191 x 273. Circ: 127,378. **Subscr. to:** We Care, 1-A Hamilton House, New Delhi 110 001, India. TEL 91-11-23352870, FAX 91-11-23352874.

330 OMN
BUSINESS TODAY. Text in English. 1998. m. USD 54 (effective 1999). mkt.; stat.; tr.lit. back issues avail. **Document type:** *Consumer.*
Published by: Apex Publishing, Ruwi, P O Box 2616, Muscat, 112, Oman. TEL 968-799388, FAX 968-793316, apexoman@gto.net.om.

330 EGY
BUSINESS TODAY. Text in English. 1995. m. EGP 204; USD 60 in United States. adv. back issues avail.
Published by: International Business Associates, 1079 Corniche el-Nil, Garden City,, Cairo, Egypt. TEL 20-2-3571300, FAX 20-2-3383423, letters@businesstoday-eg.com, http://www.businesstoday-eg.com. Ed. Lyla Allan. Pub. Ann Marie Harrison. adv.: B&W page USD 2,150; trim 180 x 250. Circ: 8,000.

BUSINESS TORTS. see *LAW—Corporate Law*

330 340 USA
BUSINESS TRANSACTIONS IN EASTERN EUROPE. Text in English. 1996. 2 base vols. plus a. updates. looseleaf. USD 455 base vol(s). (effective 2003). **Description:** Includes discussion of relevant business - legal information for 12 Eastern European jurisdictions.
Published by: (Center for International Legal Studies AUT), Matthew Bender & Co., Inc. (Subsidiary of: LexisNexis North America), 1275 Broadway, Albany, NY 12204. international@bender.com, http://bender.lexisnexis.com. Eds. Christian Campbell, Stephen Breidenbach.

330 341.7 USA
BUSINESS TRANSACTIONS IN GERMANY. Text in English. 1983. 4 base vols. plus irreg. updates. looseleaf. USD 574 base vol(s). (effective 2003). **Description:** A comprehensive guide to doing business with an integral member of the world business community.
—BLDSC (2934.892000).
Published by: Matthew Bender & Co., Inc. (Subsidiary of: LexisNexis North America), 1275 Broadway, Albany, NY 12204. international@bender.com, http://bender.lexisnexis.com. Ed. Bernd Ruster.

BUSINESS TRANSACTIONS LAW. see *LAW—Corporate Law*

BUSINESS TRAVELER (USA EDITION). see *TRAVEL AND TOURISM*

BUSINESS TRAVELLER (GERMAN EDITION). see *TRAVEL AND TOURISM*

BUSINESS TRAVELLER (UK/EUROPE EDITION). see *TRAVEL AND TOURISM*

B

330 USA
BUSINESS VALUATION GUIDE. Text in English. a. USD 315 (effective 2004); includes Business Valuation Alert Newsletter. **Description:** Provides practical insights, fundamental know-how and detailed, step-by-step guidance to help professionals at all levels meet the challenges and succeed in providing business valuation services.
Related titles: Alternate Frequency ed(s).: Business Valuation Alert Newsletter. q. USD 155 (effective 2004).
Published by: C C H Inc., 2700 Lake Cook Rd, Riverwoods, IL 60015. TEL 847-267-7000, 800-449-6439, cust_serv@cch.com, http://www.cch.com. Ed. George B Hawkins.

338 GBR ISSN 1468-9162
HF5001
BUSINESS VOICE. Text in English. 1970. m. GBP 30 domestic to non-members; GBP 54 in Europe to non-members; GBP 64 elsewhere to non-members (effective 2001). adv. **Document type:** *Bulletin.*
Former titles: C B I News (0261-6661); (until 1981): C B I Members Bulletin (0140-2188)
Indexed: RAPRA.
Published by: Confederation of British Industry, Centre Point, 103 New Oxford St, London, WC1A 1DU, United Kingdom. TEL 44-20-7395-8247, FAX 44-20-7240-1578, edit@businessvoice.co.uk, http://www.cbi.org.uk. Ed. Adam Jolly. Adv. contact Toby McAra. B&W page GBP 3,400, color page GBP 4,200;.

B

336 POL ISSN 1642-6770
BUSINESS WEEK. Text in Polish. 1992. m. PLZ 182 (effective 2004). **Document type:** *Magazine, Trade.*
Formerly (until 2001): Business Week Polska (1230-1884)
Published by: Agencja Wydawniczo-Reklamowa "Wprost" sp. z o.o., Reform Plaza, Al. Jerozolimskie 123, Warszawa, 02017, Poland. TEL 48-22-5291100, FAX 48-22-8529016, redakcja@bwp.pl, http://www.bwp.pl, http://www.wprost.pl. Ed. Piotr Aleksandrowicz. Adv. contact Jolanta Gajewska.

650 USA ISSN 0007-7135
CODEN: BUWEA3
BUSINESS WEEK. Text in English. 1929. w. USD 64 domestic; CND 94.95 in Canada; USD 199 in Asia; USD 4.95 newsstand/cover domestic (effective 2005). adv. bk.rev. illus.; stat. index. back issues avail.; reprint service avail. from PQC. **Document type:** *Magazine, Trade.* **Description:** Provides comprehensive coverage of news and developments affecting the business world. Includes information on computers, finance, labor, industry, marketing, science and technology.
Related titles: Microform ed.: (from PQC); Online - full text ed.: BusinessWeek Online (from EBSCO Publishing, Florida Center for Library Automation, Gale Group, LexisNexis, Northern Light Technology, Inc., O C L C Online Computer Library Center, Inc.); ◆ Partial Chinese translation(s): Business Week. Asian Edition; ◆ International ed.: Business Week International. ISSN 0739-8409; Special ed(s).: Business Week. Industrial Edition. ISSN 0739-8395; Supplement(s): Business Week Small Biz. ISSN 1556-1232. 2004 (Summer).
Indexed: ABIPC, ABIn, ARG, ASCA, ATI, Acal, AgeL, Agr, B&I, BLI, BMT, BPI, BPIA, BRI, BrTechI, BusI, CADCAM, CBNB, CBRI, CIN, CLFP, CPerI, ChemAb, ChemTitl, CompB, CompD, CompIU, CurCont, CurPA, EIA, Emerald, EnerRev, EnvAb, FutSurv, HECAB, HlthInd, IPARL, IndBusRep, InfoSAb, Inpharma, KES, LRI, M&MA, M&TEA, MASUSE, MEA&I, MEDLINE, MagInd, ManagCont, MicrocompInd, ORMS, PAIS, PCR2, PE&ON, PMR, PRA, PersLit, QC&AS, RASB, RGAb, RGPR, RI-1, RI-2, Reac, RefZh, ResCtrInd, RoboAb, SRI, T&II, TOM, TTI, TelAb, Telegen, WBA, WMB, WorkRelAb.
—BLDSC (2934.930000), CIS, CISTI, IDS, IE, Infotrieve, ingenta. **CCC.**
Published by: McGraw-Hill Companies, Inc., 1221 Ave of the Americas, New York, NY 10020. TEL 212-512-2000, FAX 212-426-7087, bwreader@businessweek.com, http://www.businessweek.com/, http://www.mcgraw-hill.com. Pubs. Bill Cooper, William P Kupper Jr. Adv. contact Linda F Caravalho. B&W page USD 57,400, color page USD 85,000; trim 7.875 x 10.5. Circ: 1,160,000 (paid).

382 330 USA ISSN 0865-8986
BUSINESS WEEK (HUNGARIAN EDITION)✶. Variant title: Business Week (Magyar Kiadas). Text in Hungarian. 1990. bi-m. USD 1,080, HUF 2,160. adv. **Document type:** *Trade.* **Description:** Comprehensive coverage of news and developments affecting the business world.
Published by: McGraw-Hill Companies, Inc., 1221 Ave of the Americas, New York, NY 10020. TEL 212-512-3867. Eds. Forgacs Katalin, Gomori Endre. Circ: 8,000. **Dist. by:** Hirlapkiado Vallalat, Blaha Lutza ter 3, Budapest 8 1959, Hungary.

382 330 CHN
BUSINESS WEEK. ASIAN EDITION. Text in Chinese. 1986. bi-m. adv. back issues avail. **Document type:** *Trade.* **Description:** Covers economics, management, and financial subjects.
Formerly: International Business and Management - Guoji Shangye yu Guanli (1002-445X)
Related titles: ◆ Partial translation of: Business Week. ISSN 0007-7135.
Published by: (Ministry of Foreign Economic Relations and Trade, Institute of International Trade), McGraw-Hill Companies, 5-E Citic Bldg, 19 Jianwaidajie, Beijing, 100004, China. TEL 86-10-8526-2427, http://asia.businessweek.com/. Circ: 60,000. **Dist. by:** MOFERT, 28 Donghouxiang, Andingmenwai, Beijing 100710, China. TEL 421-9332.

650 USA
BUSINESS WEEK FRONTIER✶. Text in English. 1999. d. free. adv. charts; illus.; stat. **Document type:** *Newsletter, Trade.* **Description:** Offers up-to-the-minute business news covered in detail in Business Week magazine.
Media: E-mail.
Published by: McGraw-Hill Companies, Inc., 1221 Ave of the Americas, New York, NY 10020. http://frontier.businessweek.com, http://www.mcgraw-hill.com. Adv. contact Karen Christiansen TEL 212-512-6896.

330 GBR ISSN 0739-8409
BUSINESS WEEK INTERNATIONAL. Text in English. 1929. w. GBP 68; GBP 2.20 newsstand/cover (effective 2000). adv. bk.rev. **Document type:** *Magazine, Trade.*
Related titles: Microform ed.; ◆ International ed. of: Business Week. ISSN 0007-7135.
Indexed: M&MA.
—**CCC.**
Published by: McGraw-Hill, Wimbledon Bridge House, 1 Hartfield Rd, London, SW19 3RU, United Kingdom. TEL 44-208-543-1234, FAX 44-208-543-7091. Ed. Stanley Reed. adv.: B&W page USD 22,100, color page USD 33,000; trim 200 x 266. Circ: 100,000 (paid). **Dist. by:** Comag, Tavistock Works, Tavistock Rd, W Drayton, Middx UB7 7QX, United Kingdom. TEL 44-1895-444050, 44-1895-433602, 44-1895-444055, FAX 44-1895-1895-433602.

330 TWN ISSN 1021-9536
HF41
BUSINESS WEEKLY/SHANG YEH CHOU K'AN. Text in Chinese. 1987. w. (50/yr.). TWD 3,800, USD 180 domestic; TWD 4,300 foreign. adv. **Document type:** *Magazine, Trade.* **Description:** Reports on world business news.
Related titles: Online - full text ed.: (from Northern Light Technology, Inc.).
Published by: Business Weekly, Inc., 1F, no. 7, Ln 13, Yungkang St, Taipei, Taiwan. TEL 02-3121357, FAX 02-3936024, http://www.businessweekly.com.tw. Ed. Li Meng Chou. **Dist. in US by:** World Journal Bookstore, 141-07 20th Ave., Whitestone, NY 11357.

330 NGA
BUSINESS WEEKLY (LAGOS). Text in English. w. **Document type:** *Trade.*
Address: PMB 21340, Ikeja, Lagos, Nigeria.

330 GBR ISSN 0958-7942
BUSINESS WEST MIDLANDS. Text in English. 1988. m. GBP 30 (effective 2000). adv. **Document type:** *Magazine, Consumer.*
Related titles: Online - full text ed.
Published by: Business Magazine Group, Adamsway, Mansfield, Notts NG18 4FP, United Kingdom. TEL 44-1623-450500, FAX 44-1623-454560, bwm@bmgroup.co.uk, http://www.bmgroup.co.uk. Ed. Lisa Powell. Circ: 11,825.

650 USA
BUSINESS WIRE. Text in English. d.
Media: Online - full text. **Related titles:** E-mail ed.; Fax ed.
Published by: Business Wire New York, 40 E 52nd St, 14th Fl, New York, NY 10022. TEL 212-752-9600, FAX 212-752-9698, 888-381-9473, SF_sales_group@bizwire.com, http://www.businesswire.com/.

330 GBR
BUSINESS WORLD. Text in English. 1996. m.
Published by: Adetch Publishing, 194 Torrington Ave, Loventry, United Kingdom. TEL 01203-474309, FAX 01203-462694. Ed. Peter Marshall. Circ: 25,000 (controlled).

330 IND ISSN 0970-8197
BUSINESS WORLD. Text in English. 1980. fortn. INR 12 newsstand/cover. adv. **Document type:** *Trade.*
Related titles: Online - full text ed.: (from East View Information Services).
Address: 145 Atlanta, 209 Ceremonial Blvd., Nariman Point, Mumbai, Maharashtra 400 021, India. TEL 91-22-240581, TELEX 112354. Ed. T N Ninan. Adv. contact Bikash Banerjee. B&W page INR 30,000, color page INR 60,000; trim 265 x 194. Circ: 37,204.

330 GBR ISSN 0966-0313
BUSINESSAGE; passion is the essence of success. Text in English. m. GBP 18; GBP 3 newsstand/cover (effective 1999). adv. **Document type:** *Trade.* **Description:** Covers important business issues and news in the U.K.
—BLDSC (2933.176300).
Published by: BusinessAge Magazine Ltd., Newspaper House, 3rd Fl, 8-16 Great New St, London, EC4A 3BN, United Kingdom. TEL 44-171-583-9797, FAX 44-171-583-7676, mail@businessage.com, http://www.businessage.com. Ed., Pub. Tom Rubython. Adv. contact Iain McDonald. Circ: 66,841 (paid). **Dist. by:** M M C Ltd., Octagon House, White Hart Meadows, Ripley, Woking, Surrey GU23 6HR, United Kingdom. TEL 44-1483-211222, FAX 44-1483-224541.

330 USA ISSN 1049-9822
BUSINESSWEST. Text in English. 1984. m. **Description:** Offers overviews of business in the Pioneer Valley with feature articles on business news and trends.
Formerly (until 1989): The Western Massachusetts Business Journal (0891-7302)
Related titles: Online - full text ed.: (from EBSCO Publishing, O C L C Online Computer Library Center, Inc., ProQuest Information & Learning).
Indexed: ABIn.
Address: 1441 Main St, Springfield, MA 01103. TEL 413-781-8600, FAX 413-781-3930, http://www.businesswest.com.

BUYERS GUIDE TO U.S. COTTON. see *AGRICULTURE—Crop Production And Soil*

BY DESIGN; the ultimate magazine for gift basket retailers. see *GIFTWARE AND TOYS*

330 USA
A BYTE OF GODLY COUNSEL. Text in English. m. free. **Document type:** *Newsletter.* **Description:** Provides articles on a wide range of business management topics, all based on Christian principles.
Media: Online - full text.
Published by: The C12 Group, 656 Flamingo Dr., Apollo Beach, FL 33572. admin@thec12group.com, http://thec12group.com. Ed. Buck Jacobs.

330 RUS
BYULLETEN' FONDOVOGO RYNKA PREDPRIYATII TEK. Text in Russian. 1994. 36/yr. USD 1,850 in the Americas (effective 2000).
Published by: Informatsionno-Analiticheskoe Agentstvo Infotek, Kitaiskii pr., 7, Moscow, 103074, Russian Federation. TEL 7-095-9273091, FAX 7-095-2204818. **Dist. by:** East View Information Services, 3020 Harbor Ln. N., Minneapolis, MN 55447. TEL 763-550-0961, FAX 763-559-2931.

330 AUS ISSN 1329-1270
C A E R WORKING PAPER. (Centre for Applied Economic Research) Text in English. 1977. irreg. **Document type:** *Monographic series, Academic/Scholarly.*
Formerly (until 1991): University of New South Wales, Centre for Applied Economic Research. Working Papers (0157-4701)
—BLDSC (2947.361380).
Published by: University of New South Wales, Centre for Applied Economic Research, Sydney, NSW NSW 2052, Australia. TEL 61-2-93853335, FAX 61-2-93136337, caer@unsw.edu.au, http://economics.web.unsw.edu.au/research/caer.

741.67 AUS ISSN 1035-9222
C B D✶. (Corporate Business Design) Text in English. a. AUD 60 (effective 2000). illus.
Published by: Armadillo Publishers Pty. Ltd., 410 Elizabeth Street, PO Box 12358, Melbourne, VIC 8006, Australia. TEL 61-3-52896137, FAX 61-3-52896137.

338 GBR ISSN 0268-2273
C B I ANNUAL REPORT. Text in English. a. **Document type:** *Corporate.*
Published by: Confederation of British Industry, Centre Point, 103 New Oxford St, London, WC1A 1DU, United Kingdom. TEL 44-171-395-8164, FAX 44-171-240-1578.

330 GBR ISSN 0961-6330
C B I - COOPERS & LYBRAND SURVEY OF FINANCIAL SERVICES. Text in English. 1990. q. GBP 325 to non-members (effective 1999); GBP 180 to members. adv. **Document type:** *Trade.* **Description:** Covers value and volume of business, charges, costs and profitablity, employment and training, capital expenditure, and prospects. Results reflect the views of around 300 companies from banking to venture capital.
Formerly: C B I - Coopers & Lybrand Deloitte Survey of Financial Services
Published by: Confederation of British Industry, Centre Point, 103 New Oxford St, London, WC1A 1DU, United Kingdom. TEL 44-171-379-7400, FAX 44-171-240-1578. Ed. Sudhair Junankar. R&P Wendy Hayes TEL 44-171-395-8036. Adv. contact Frances Hughes.

350 GBR
C B I MONTHLY INDUSTRIAL TRENDS SURVEY. Text in English. m. GBP 665 to non-members; GBP 400 to members (effective 1999). adv. **Description:** Covers short term manufacturing trends.
Former titles: C B I Monthly Trends Survey; C B I Monthly Trends Enquiry; C B I Monthly Trends Survey; C B I Monthly Trends Enquiry
Published by: Confederation of British Industry, Centre Point, 103 New Oxford St, London, WC1A 1DU, United Kingdom. TEL 44-171-395-8164, FAX 44-171-240-1578. Ed. Adam Jolly. Adv. contact Toby McAra.

338 GBR
C B I QUARTERLY INDUSTRIAL TRENDS SURVEY. Text in English. q. GBP 255 to non-members; GBP 200 to members (effective 1999). **Description:** Provides latest trends in output, orders, employment, investment plans, stock of raw materials, costs, prices ,export orders and deliveries for each of 50 manufacturing industries.
Formerly: C B I Industrial Trends Survey (0142-6435)
—BLDSC (3095.480000).
Published by: Confederation of British Industry, Centre Point, 103 New Oxford St, London, WC1A 1DU, United Kingdom. TEL 44-171-395-8164, FAX 44-171-240-1578. R&P Wendy Hayes TEL 44-171-395-8036.

330 USA
C B M C INSIDER. Text in English. 3/yr. USD 10 (effective 2000). adv. **Description:** Contains news, information, and features about the ministry of CBMC.
Formerly: Christian Businessman
Published by: C B M C, 6650 E. Brainerd Rd., Ste. 100, Chattanooga, TN 37421-3737. TEL 423-698-4444, FAX 423-629-4434, info@cbmc.com, http://www.cbmc.com. Ed. Robert J Tamasy. Pub. Phil Downer. R&P Ginger West.

330 DEU
C D H BAYERN. Text in German. m.
Published by: Wirtschaftsverband Bayerischer Handelsvertreter und Handelsmakler, Ismaninger Str 63, Munich, 81675, Germany. TEL 471046.

330 CAN ISSN 0824-8001
HD9710.C2
C.D. HOWE INSTITUTE COMMENTARY. Text in English. 1982. irreg., latest vol.210. CND 12 per issue (effective 2005). **Description:** Commentaries on Canadian economic and social policy issues.
Related titles: Online - full text ed.: (from Gale Group, Micromedia ProQuest).
Indexed: CBCABus, CBCARef, CPerI, GSS&RPL.
—CISTI. **CCC.**
Published by: C.D. Howe Institute, 125 Adelaide St East, Toronto, ON M5C 1L7, Canada. TEL 416-865-1904, FAX 416-865-1866, publicat@cdhowe.org, http://www.cdhowe.org.

C D SICHERHEITS-MANAGEMENT. (Criminal Digest) see *CRIMINOLOGY AND LAW ENFORCEMENT—Security*

380 ESP
C E A M - REVISTA DE ECONOMIA INDUSTRIAL. Text in Spanish. 1952. q. adv. abstr.; bibl.; charts; illus. **Description:** Covers industrial economics.
Published by: Centro de Estudios y Asesoramiento Metalurgico, Jose Anselmo Clave 2, Barcelona 2, Spain. TEL 3-318-80-58, FAX 3-317-14-63, TELEX 59250 CEAM. Ed. Juan Ortega Galan.

346.066 USA ISSN 1086-3036
C E I UPDATE. Text in English. 1988. m. USD 50. bk.rev. back issues avail. **Document type:** *Newsletter.* **Description:** Focuses on principles of limited government and free enterprise. Government regulations and current economic policies are critiqued according to whether they advance or hinder economic freedom.
Published by: Competitive Enterprise Institute, 1001 Connecticut Ave, N W, Ste 1250, Washington, DC 20036-5504. TEL 202-331-1010, FAX 202-331-0640, info@cei.org, http://www.cei.org. Ed. Jonathan H Adler. Pub. Fred L Smith Jr. R&P Mark Lerner. Circ: 7,500.

330 CHN
C E O & C I O. Text in Chinese. 24/yr. adv. **Document type:** *Magazine, Trade.* **Description:** Provides pros and cons of implementing differing enterprise information systems while addressing both technical and business concerns.
Published by: I D G China, Rm. 616, Tower A, COFCO Plaza, Jianguomennei Dajie, Beijing, 100005 , China. TEL 86-10-6526-0959, FAX 86-10-6526-0866, dumin@idg.com.cn, http://www.ceocio.com.cn, http://www.idgchina.com. Ed. Jiuru Liu. Adv. contact Xianhua Shao. color page CNY 18,000; trim 205 x 270. Circ: 35,000 (paid and controlled).

330 BEL
C E P S RESEARCH REPORTS. Text in English. irreg. price varies. **Document type:** *Monographic series.*
—BLDSC (3113.696200).
Published by: Centre for European Policy Studies, Pl du Congres 1, Brussels, 1000, Belgium. TEL 32-2-2293911, FAX 32-2-2194151, http://www.ceps.be/Default.php.

330 DEU
C E S I F O BULLETIN. (Center for Economic Studies) Text in English. q.
Formerly (until 1999): C E S Journal
Related titles: Online - full text ed.
Published by: I F O Institut fuer Wirtschaftsforschung, Poschingerstr 5, Munich, 81679, Germany. http://www.cesifo.de/CESifoPortal.

330 DEU ISSN 1610-241X
HB5
C E S - I F O ECONOMIC STUDIES. (Center for Economic Studies - Ifo Institute for Economic Research) Text in English. 1955. q. bk.rev. Index. **Document type:** *Journal, Academic/Scholarly.* **Description:** Aims to bridge the gap between specialized research in economics and the interest of non-specialists.
Formerly (until 2003): I F O Studien (0018-9731)
Related titles: Online - full content ed.; Online - full text ed.: (from EBSCO Publishing, ProQuest Information & Learning).
Indexed: ABIn, DIP, IBR, IBSS, IBZ, IPSA, JEL, PAIS, SCIMP.
—IE. **CCC.**
Published by: I F O Institut fuer Wirtschaftsforschung, Poschingerstr 5, Munich, 81679, Germany. TEL 49-89-9224-0, FAX 49-89-985369, ifo@ifo.de, http://www.cesifoeconomicstudies.de/, http://www.ifo.de.
Co-publisher: Center for Economic Studies.

330 DEU ISSN 1615-245X
HC240.A1
C E S I F O FORUM; a quarterly journal on economic trends in the Federal Republic of Germany. (Center for Economic Studies) Text in English. 1978. q.
Formerly (until 2000): I F O Digest (0170-7663)
Related titles: Online - full text ed.: free (effective 2005) (from ProQuest Information & Learning).
Indexed: ABIn, CREJ, JEL, KES.
Published by: I F O Institut fuer Wirtschaftsforschung, Poschingerstr 5, Munich, 81679, Germany. TEL 49-89-9224-0, FAX 49-89-985369, ifo@ifo.de, http://www.cesifo.de/, http://www.ifo.de. Circ: 650.

330 DEU
C E S I F O WORKING PAPERS. Text in English. irreg.
Related titles: Online - full text ed.
Published by: I F O Institut fuer Wirtschaftsforschung, Poschingerstr 5, Munich, 81679, Germany. http://www.cesifo.de/CESifoPortal.

330 AUS ISSN 1325-9407
C F O. (Chief Financial Officer) Text in English. m. AUD 79 (effective 2002). **Document type:** *Magazine, Trade.*
Formerly (until 1995): Return on Information (1321-7836)
Published by: Fairfax Business Media (Subsidiary of: John Fairfax Holdings Ltd.), Level 26, 1 Market St, Sydney, NSW 2000, Australia. TEL 800-809-323, cfo@brw.fairfax.com.au, http://www.cfoweb.com.au/, http://www.fxj.com.au/. Ed. Roger Hogan. Pub. Michael Gill. Adv. contact Stewart Hopper TEL 61-2-9273-3815.

330 USA ISSN 8756-7113
HG4026 CODEN: CFOMEX
C F O; the magazine for senior financial executives. (Chief Financial Officer) Text in English. 1985. m. USD 60 domestic; USD 120 foreign; free to qualified personnel (effective 2005). adv. illus. Supplement avail.; reprint service avail. from PQC. **Document type:** *Magazine, Trade.* **Description:** Covers all matters of interest to senior financial executives, along with profiles of prominent individuals, surveys of how companies manage their working capital, and reports on government, business, and taxation trends.
Related titles: Online - full text ed.: (from EBSCO Publishing, Factiva, Florida Center for Library Automation, Gale Group, O C L C Online Computer Library Center, Inc., ProQuest Information & Learning); ♦ Regional ed(s).: C F O Europe. ISSN 1462-5601; ♦ C F O Asia; ♦ Supplement(s): e C F O.
Indexed: ABIn, ATI, BPI, CurCont, LogistBibl, SoftBase.
—BLDSC (3128.516000), IDS, IE, Infotrieve, ingenta. **CCC.**
Published by: C F O Publishing Corporation (Subsidiary of: Economist Group), 253 Summer St, Boston, MA 02210. TEL 617-345-9700, FAX 617-951-4090, juliahomer@cfopub.com, http://www.cfo.com/. Ed. Julia Homer. Pub. Kevin Quinlan. Adv. contact Lissa Short. B&W page USD 43,336, color page USD 61,908. Circ: 435,050 (controlled). **Subscr. to:** PO Box 1230, Skokie, IL 60076-9798.

333 USA
▼ **C F O I T.** (Chief Financial Officer Information Technology) Text in English. 2003. q. adv. **Document type:** *Magazine, Trade.*
Published by: C F O Publishing Corporation (Subsidiary of: Economist Group), 253 Summer St, Boston, MA 02210. TEL 617-345-9700, FAX 617-951-4090, http://www.cfo.com. Pub. Kevin Quinlan. adv.: B&W page USD 47,550, color page USD 63,173; trim 8.125 x 10.75.

C I M O S A NEWS. (C I M Open Systems Architecture) see *ENGINEERING*

330 CIV ISSN 1011-839X
HC501
C I R E S CAHIERS. Text in French. 1970. q. XOF 2,400. bk.rev. bibl.
Indexed: ASD, PAIS, RASB.
Published by: Universite Nationale de Cote d'Ivoire, Centre Ivoirien de Recherches Economiques et Sociales, 08 BP 1259, Abidjan, Ivory Coast. TEL 44-09-53, FAX 44-57-08. Ed. Paul T Perrault. Circ: 250.

330 CHE ISSN 0170-5679
C I R E T STUDIEN. Text in German, English. 1963. irreg., latest vol.53, 1999. **Document type:** *Monographic series, Trade.*
Published by: Center for International Research on Economic Tendency Surveys, KOF-ETH, ETH Zentrum, Zurich, 8092, Switzerland. TEL 41-1-6324238, FAX 41-1-6321150, info@ciret.org, http://www.ciret.org. Circ: 400.

630 USA
C L O. Text in English. 2002 (Oct.). bi-m. USD 195 domestic; USD 210 in Canada & Mexico; USD 228 elsewhere (effective 2002). adv. **Document type:** *Magazine, Trade.* **Description:** Covers solutions for enterprise productivity, including topics such as corporate training, writing to executives and officers about the importance, benefits and advancements of a properly trained workforce.
Published by: MediaTec Publishing, Inc., 444 N Michigan Ave, Chicago, IL 60611. TEL 312-828-2800, http://www.clomedia.com. Ed. Norman B Kamikow.

330 USA
C L O EXECUTIVE BRIEFINGS. (Chief Learning Officer) Text in English. s-m. free to qualified personnel. **Document type:** *Newsletter, Trade.* **Description:** Includes report on topics of interest to learning executives, as well as the latest industry news and useful extras, like stock listings for major education vendor companies.
Published by: MediaTec Publishing, Inc., 444 N Michigan Ave, Chicago, IL 60611. TEL 312-828-2800, http://www.clomedia.com/newsletters/.

B

650 AUS ISSN 1443-2943
C O B A R WORKING PAPERS. (Centre of Business Analysis and Research) Text in English. 1999. irreg. **Description:** Constitutes work in progress and encompasses research within the areas of business and management.
Media: Online - full text.
Published by: University of South Australia. Division of Business and Enterprise, Centre of Business Analysis and Research, Box 2471, Adelaide, SA 2471, Australia. TEL 61-8-8302-0053, FAX 61-8-8302-0102, cobar@unisar.edu.au, http://business.unisa.edu.au.

C P A EXAMINATION REVIEW. BUSINESS LAW AND PROFESSIONAL RESPONSIBILITIES. (Certified Public Accountant) see *LAW—Corporate Law*

330 USA
C R M BUYER. (Customer Relations Management) Text in English. 2002. m. reprints avail. **Document type:** *Magazine, Trade.*
Related titles: Online - full content ed.
Published by: NewsFactor Network, 21700 Oxnard St, Ste 2040, Woodland Hills, CA 91367. TEL 818-593-2200, FAX 818-593-2203, http://www.crmbuyer.com/, http://www.newsfactor.com/. Pub. Richard Kern.

330 USA
▼ **C S C O**; insights for the supply chain executive. Text in English. 2004. q. free to qualified personnel (effective 2005). adv. **Document type:** *Magazine, Trade.*
Published by: Helmers Publishing, Inc., 174 Concord St, Peterborough, NH 03458-0874. TEL 603-924-9631, FAX 603-924-7408, dandrews@helmers.com, http://www.cscomagazine.com, http://www.helmers.com/. Pub. David L Andrews. adv.: color page USD 7,500; trim 7.875 x 10.75. Circ: 20,000 (controlled).

CADERNOS DE POS-GRADUACAO EM DIREITO POLITICO E ECONOMICO. see *LAW*

CAHIERS D'ECONOMIE APPLIQUEE AUX SCIENCES HUMAINES. see *HUMANITIES: COMPREHENSIVE WORKS*

330 CHE
CAHIERS ECONOMIQUES. Text in French, German. 1974. a. price varies. **Document type:** *Bulletin, Academic/Scholarly.*
Formerly: Colloques Economiques
Published by: Academic Press Fribourg, Perolles 42, Fribourg, 1705, Switzerland. TEL 41-26-4264311, FAX 41-26-4264300.

330 COD ISSN 0008-0209
HC501.A1
CAHIERS ECONOMIQUES ET SOCIAUX. Text in French. 1962. q. XAF 1,000, USD 10. adv. bk.rev. abstr.; charts; mkt.; stat. index, cum.index. **Document type:** *Academic/Scholarly.*
Related titles: Microfiche ed.: (from IDC); English ed.
Indexed: ASD, CCA, IPSA, JEL, KES, PAIS, RASB, REE&TA.
Published by: Universite de Kinshasa, Institut de Recherches Economiques et Sociales, BP 257, Kinshasa, 11, Congo, Dem. Republic. Ed. Sebisogo Muhima. Circ: 1,000.

330 CHN ISSN 1671-4725
HG187.C6
CAIJING. Text in Chinese. 2000. bi-w. CNY 4 newsstand/cover (effective 2005). **Document type:** *Journal, Academic/Scholarly.*
Related titles: Online - full text ed.: (from WanFang Data Corp.).
Address: Zhaoyangmen Wei, 22, Dajie, Fanli Dasha 10-ceng, Beijing, 100020, China. TEL 86-10-65885047, FAX 86-10-65885046, money1@homeway.com.cn, http://cj.periodicals.net.cn/, http://www.caijing.com.cn/.

330 CHN ISSN 1004-4892
CAIJING LUNCONG/COLLECTED ESSAYS ON FINANCE AND ECONOMICS. Text in Chinese. 1992. bi-m. **Document type:** *Journal, Academic/Scholarly.*
Related titles: Online - full content ed.: (from WanFang Data Corp.); Online - full text ed.: (from East View Information Services).
Published by: Zhejiang Caijing Xueyuan/Zhejiang Institute of Finance and Economics, 269, Wenhua Lu, Hangzhou, 310012, China. TEL 86-571-88922750, FAX 86-571-88922748, cjlc@zufe.edu.cn, http://cjlc.periodicals.net.cn/.

CALIFORNIA REAL ESTATE REPORTER. see *REAL ESTATE*

330 692.8 USA
CALIFORNIA STATE CONTRACTS REGISTER. Text in English. 1981. s-m. (d. on the Internet). adv. **Document type:** *Government.*
Related titles: Online - full text ed.
Published by: Department of General Services, Office of Small and Minority Business, 1531 I St, 2nd Fl, Sacramento, CA 95814-2016. TEL 916-323-5478, FAX 916-442-7855, http://www.dgs.ca.gov/osmb. Circ: 6,200.

CALL CENTRE MAGAZINE; customer service management. see *COMMUNICATIONS—Telephone And Telegraph*

330 USA ISSN 0888-8671
HG2037
CALLAHAN'S CREDIT UNION DIRECTORY. Text in English. 1986. a. USD 135 (effective 1999). adv. **Document type:** *Directory.*
Related titles: Diskette ed.
Published by: Callahan & Associates, Inc., 1001 Connecticut Ave, N W, Ste 1001, Washington, DC 20036. TEL 202-223-3920, FAX 202-223-1311, callahan@creditunions.com, callahan@callahan.com, http://www.creditunions.com, http://www.callahan.com. Ed. Ray Springsteen. Pub. Chip Filson. R&P Alix Filson. Adv. contact Tanya Baker. Circ: 3,500.

382 URY
CAMARA DE COMERCIO URUGUAYO - BRITANICA. BOLETIN INFORMATIVO. Text in Spanish. 1969. m. free. stat.
Formerly: Camara de Comercio Uruguayo - Britanica. Revista (0008-1914)
Published by: Camara de Comercio Uruguayo - Britanica, Av. Libertador Brig. Gral. Lavalleja, P. 2, Of. 201, Montevideo, 11000, Uruguay. TEL 5982-98-0349, FAX 5982-90-0936. Circ: 150 (controlled).

330 338 VEN
CAMARA DE INDUSTRIALES DE CARACAS. NOTI. Text in Spanish. m. **Description:** Directed to the industrial world.
Published by: Camara de Industriales de Caracas, Edificio Camara de Industriales, piso 2, Esq. de Puente Anauco, Caracas, 1011-A, Venezuela. TEL 02-571-42-24, FAX 02-571-20-09, TELEX 24453 CAINC VC. Circ: 20,000.

330 GBR
CAMBRIDGE ECONOMIC HANDBOOKS. Text in English. irreg. price varies. **Document type:** *Monographic series.*
Indexed: IMMAb.
Published by: Cambridge University Press, The Edinburgh Bldg, Shaftesbury Rd, Cambridge, CB2 2RU, United Kingdom. TEL 44-1223-312393, FAX 44-1223-315052, information@cambridge.org, http://www.cup.cam.ac.uk/. Eds. G M Heal, P S Dasgupta. R&P Linda Nicol TEL 44-1223-325757.

330 GBR ISSN 0309-166X
HB1
➤ **CAMBRIDGE JOURNAL OF ECONOMICS.** Text in English. 1977. bi-m. GBP 295, USD 531, EUR 443 to institutions; GBP 58, USD 104, EUR 87 in developing nations to institutions; GBP 310, USD 558, EUR 465 combined subscription to institutions print & online eds. (effective 2006). adv. bk.rev. illus. Index. back issues avail.; reprint service avail. from PSC. **Document type:** *Journal, Academic/Scholarly.* **Description:** Provides a forum for the non-neoclassical approaches to economics.
Related titles: Online - full text ed.: ISSN 1464-3545. GBP 279, USD 502, EUR 419 to institutions (effective 2006) (from Chadwyck-Healey Inc., EBSCO Publishing, Gale Group, HighWire Press, IngentaConnect, O C L C Online Computer Library Center, Inc., Oxford University Press Online Journals, ProQuest Information & Learning, Swets Information Services).
Indexed: ABIn, APEL, ASCA, ArtHuCI, BAS, BrHumI, CREJ, CurCont, DIP, GEOBASE, IBR, IBSS, IBZ, ILD, JEL, PAA&I, PAIS, PCI, PSA, RASB, RDA, RRTA, SSA, SSCI, SSI, SociolAb, WAE&RSA, WBA, WMB.
—BLDSC (3015.956000), CISTI, IDS, IE, Infotrieve, ingenta. **CCC.**
Published by: (Cambridge Political Economy Society), Oxford University Press, Great Clarendon St, Oxford, OX2 6DP, United Kingdom. TEL 44-1865-556767, FAX 44-1865-556646, apn1000@econ.cam.ac.uk, jnl.orders@oup.co.uk, http://cje.oxfordjournals.org/, http://www.oxfordjournals.org/. R&P Fiona Bennett. Adv. contact Helen Pearson. B&W page USD 345, page GBP 230; trim 115 x 205. Circ: 1,750.

330 GBR ISSN 1462-4877
CAMBRIDGE STUDIES IN MODERN ECONOMIC HISTORY. Text in English. 1995. irreg., latest 2003. price varies. **Document type:** *Monographic series, Academic/Scholarly.* **Description:** Primarily concerned with the history of economic performance, output and productivity, assessing the characteristics, causes and consequences of economic growth (and stagnation) in the Western world.
—BLDSC (3015.995340).
Published by: Cambridge University Press, The Edinburgh Bldg, Shaftesbury Rd, Cambridge, CB2 2RU, United Kingdom. TEL 44-1223-312393, FAX 44-1223-315052, information@cambridge.org, http://publishing.cambridge.org/series/mech.

330 GBR ISSN 0306-7890
CAMBRIDGE UNIVERSITY. DEPARTMENT OF APPLIED ECONOMICS. OCCASIONAL PAPERS. Text in English. 1964. irreg. price varies. **Document type:** *Monographic series.*
—BLDSC (6222.200000), IE, ingenta.
Published by: Cambridge University Press, The Edinburgh Bldg, Shaftesbury Rd, Cambridge, CB2 2RU, United Kingdom. TEL 44-1223-312393, FAX 44-1223-315052, information@cambridge.org, http://publishing.cambridge.org/series/caeo.

CAMPAIGN FINANCE LAW; a summary of state campaign finance laws with quick reference charts. see *POLITICAL SCIENCE*

CAMPGROUND MANAGEMENT; The voice of the North American campground business. see *SPORTS AND GAMES—Outdoor Life*

330 320 CAN ISSN 1481-0425
CANADA ASIA COMMENTARY. Text in English. 1986. bi-m.
Former titles (until 1998): Dialogue (1184-874X); (until 1990): Asia Pacific Foundation of Canada. Newsletter (0835-832X)
Related titles: Online - full text ed.: ISSN 1481-0433. 1999.
Published by: Asia Pacific Foundation of Canada, 666-999 Canada Place, Vancouver, BC V6C 3E1, Canada. http://www.asiapacific.ca/analysis/pubs/index.cfm#2.

330 320 CAN ISSN 1206-4017
CANADA ASIA REVIEW. Text in English. 1997. a.
Related titles: Online - full text ed.: ISSN 1495-5008. 1999.
Published by: Asia Pacific Foundation of Canada, 666-999 Canada Place, Vancouver, BC V6C 3E1, Canada. http://www.asiapacific.ca/analysis/pubs/index.cfm#1.

330 CAN
CANADA. STATISTICS CANADA. ANALYTICAL STUDIES BRANCH. RESEARCH PAPER SERIES. Text in English, French. 1986. irreg., latest vol.225, 2004. free (effective 2004). **Description:** Covers agriculture, business firm dynamics, immigration, labour, language, mortality, pensions, and statistical computing and simulation.
Formerly: Canada. Statistics Canada. Analytical Studies Branch. Research Paper Series (Print Edition) (1200-5223)
Media: Online - full text.
Published by: (Statistics Canada, Analytical Studies Branch), Statistics Canada, Publications Sales and Services, Ottawa, ON K1A 0T6, Canada. TEL 613-951-8116, infostats@statcan.ca, http://www.statcan.ca:8096/bsolc/english/bsolc?catno=11F0019M.

338.4 CAN ISSN 0382-4144
CANADA. STATISTICS CANADA. MANUFACTURING INDUSTRIES OF CANADA. NATIONAL AND PROVINCIAL AREAS/CANADA. STATISTIQUE CANADA. INDUSTRIES MANUFACTURIERES DU CANADA: PROVINCES DE L'ATLANTIQUE. (Catalog 31-204) Text in English. 1972. a. CND 1.40, USD 1.70. stat. **Document type:** *Government.*
Formed by the merger of (19??-1972): Canada. Statistics Canada. Manufacturing Industries of Canada: British Columbia, Yukon and Northwest Territories (0527-5628); Which was formerly (until 1969): Manufacturing Industries of Canada. Section F: British Columbia, Yukon and Northwest Territories (0828-3303); (1920-1972): Canada. Statistics Canada. General Review of the Manufacturing Industries of Canada. Volume 1: Industries by Province (0382-4152); Which superseded in part in 1968: Manufacturing Industries of Canada. Section A: Summary for Canada (0575-8947); Which was formerly (until 1961): General Review of the Manufacturing Industries of Canada (0382-4179); (until 1949): Manufacturing Industries of Canada (0076-4248); (19??-1972): Canada. Statistics Canada. Manufacturing Industries of Canada: Atlantic Provinces (0527-558X); Which was formerly (until 1969): Manufacturing Industries of Canada. Section B: Atlantic Provinces (0828-3249); (19??-1972): Canada. Statistics Canada. Manufacturing Industries of Canada. Prairie Provinces (0527-561X); Which was formerly (until 1969): Manufacturing Industries of Canada. Section E: Prairie Provinces (0828-329X); (19??-1972): Canada. Statistics Canada. Manufacturing Industries of Canada. Quebec (0527-5598); Which was formerly (until 1969): Manufacturing Industries of Canada. Section C: Quebec (0828-3265); (until 1968): Manufacturing Industries of Canada. Section C: Province of Quebec (0828-3257); (19??-1972): Canada. Statistics Canada. Manufacturing Industries of Canada. Ontario (0527-5601); Which was formerly (until 1969): Manufacturing Industries of Canada. Section D: Ontario (0828-3281); (until 1967): Manufacturing Industries of Canada. Section D: Province of Ontario (0828-3273)
—CISTI.
Published by: Statistics Canada, Communications Division, 3rd Fl, R H Coats Bldg, Ottawa, ON K1A 0A6, Canada.

650 CAN ISSN 0008-3100
CODEN: CABUAL
CANADIAN BUSINESS. Text in English. 1928. bi-w. CND 39.95 domestic; CND 64.95 in United States; CND 129.95 overseas (effective 2005). adv. bk.rev. charts; illus.; tr.lit. Index. back issues avail.; reprints avail. **Document type:** *Magazine, Trade.* **Description:** Provides timely, topical management information on ideas, issues and opportunities for senior executives.
Former titles (until 1977): Canadian Business Magazine (0820-9529); (until 1972): Canadian Business (0820-9510); (until 1932): Commerce of the Nation; Incorporates (1981-1982): Energy (0711-6381)
Related titles: Microfiche ed.: (from MML); Microfilm ed.: (from MML); Microform ed.: (from MML); Online - full text ed.: (from bigchalk, EBSCO Publishing, Florida Center for Library Automation, H.W. Wilson, LexisNexis, Micromedia ProQuest, Northern Light Technology, Inc., O C L C Online Computer Library Center, Inc., ProQuest Information & Learning).
Indexed: ABIn, BPI, BPIA, BusI, CBCABus, CBCARef, CBPI, CPerI, Inspec, LRI, M&MA, MASUSE, MagInd, PAIS, PROMT, RASB, SRRA, SportS, T&II, WorkRelAb.
—BLDSC (3018.250000), AskIEEE, CASDDS, CISTI, IE, Infotrieve, ingenta. **CCC.**
Published by: Rogers Media Publishing Ltd, One Mount Pleasant Rd, 11th Fl, Toronto, ON M4Y 2Y5, Canada. TEL 416-764-1200, FAX 416-764-1255, http://www.canadianbusiness.com/homepage/index.jsp, http://www.rogers.com. adv.: B&W page CND 9,840, color page CND 12,300; trim 10.75 x 8. Circ: 83,000 (paid).

330 CAN ISSN 0383-9893
CANADIAN BUSINESS CONDITIONS/CONJONCTURE CANADIENNE. Text in English. **Document type:** *Journal, Trade.*
Related titles: Online - full text ed.: (from Micromedia ProQuest, ProQuest Information & Learning); French ed.: La Conjoncture Canadienne. ISSN 0834-3152.
Indexed: ABIn.
Published by: Canadian Imperial Bank of Commerce, Commerce Court, 25 King St W, Toronto, ON M5L 1A2, Canada. TEL 416-980-2211, customer.care@cibc.com, http://www.cibc.com.

330.9 CAN ISSN 0705-8330
CANADIAN BUSINESS ECONOMICS. Text in English. 1977. 4/yr. CND 42.80 domestic to individuals; USD 40 in United States to individuals; CND 64.20 domestic to institutions; USD 60 in United States to institutions; CND 10 newsstand/cover (effective 2000). **Description:** Promotes research and discussion in the fields of economics, business and public policy. Covers the Canadian economy and international economics.
Related titles: Online - full text ed.: (from Micromedia ProQuest, Northern Light Technology, Inc., ProQuest Information & Learning).
Indexed: CBCABus, CBCARef, CBPI, CPerI, JEL, PAIS, SRRA.
Published by: Canadian Association for Business Economics, 111 Sparter St, Ste 500, Ottawa, ON K1P 5B5, Canada. TEL 613-233-8891, FAX 613-233-8250, leo_de_bever@otpp.com, http://www.cabe.ca. **Subscr. to:** c/o Anne Richard, P O Box 828, Sta B, Ottawa, ON K1P 5P9, Canada. TEL 613-238-4831, FAX 613-238-7698.

330 CAN ISSN 1497-7125
CANADIAN BUSINESS FRANCHISE. Text in English. 1994. bi-m. USD 19.95 (effective 2005). **Document type:** *Magazine, Trade.*
Published by: C G B Publishing Ltd., 200-478 River Avenue, Winnipeg, MB R3L 0C8, Canada. TEL 204-235-0010, FAX 204-235-0116, cgbpublishing@shawcable.com, http://www.cgb.ca/.

300 CAN ISSN 1486-584X
CANADIAN BUSINESS FRANCHISE HANDBOOK. Text in English. 1996. a. CND 12.95 newsstand/cover (effective 2005). **Document type:** *Magazine, Trade.*
Published by: C G B Publishing Ltd., 200-478 River Avenue, Winnipeg, MB R3L 0C8, Canada. TEL 204-235-0010, FAX 204-235-0116, cgbpublishing@shawcable.com, http://www.cgb.ca/handbook.html.

330 CAN ISSN 0829-1349
CANADIAN BUSINESS LIFE. Text in English. 1981. q. CND 20. adv.
Indexed: CBPI.
Published by: Better Business Bureau, Publication Division, 44 Byward Market Sq, Ste 220, Ottawa, ON K1N 7A2, Canada. TEL 613-789-5151, FAX 613-789-7044, http://www.canadiancouncilbbb.ca. Ed. Fiorella Grossi. Adv. contact Max Lieberman. Circ: 48,000.

CANADIAN ENERDATA LTD. WEEKLY PRICE UPDATE. see *PETROLEUM AND GAS*

CANADIAN FRANCHISE GUIDE. see *LAW*

CANADIAN GAS PRICE REPORTER. see *PETROLEUM AND GAS*

338.4 CAN ISSN 1484-3773
CANADIAN INSTITUTE FOR HEALTH INFORMATION. NATIONAL HEALTH EXPENDITURE TRENDS. Text in English. 1971. a. **Description:** Provides expenditure data by source of funds and use of funds at the provincial and territorial levels and for Canada.
Formerly (until 1997): National Health Expenditures in Canada (0703-6116)
Related titles: Online - full content ed.: ISSN 1707-2298.
Published by: Canadian Institute for Health Information, 377 Dalhousie St, Ste 200, Ottawa, ON K1N 9N8, Canada. TEL 613-241-7860, FAX 613-241-8120, nhex@cihi.ca, http://www.cihi.ca.

330 CAN ISSN 0825-0383
HD28 CODEN: CJASE9
➤ **CANADIAN JOURNAL OF ADMINISTRATIVE SCIENCES/REVUE CANADIENNE DES SCIENCES DE L'ADMINISTRATION.** Text and summaries in English, French. 1984. q. CND 125 domestic; USD 125 foreign (effective 2006). adv. bk.rev. abstr. back issues avail. **Document type:** *Journal, Academic/Scholarly.* **Description:** Covers all fields of business administration, and publishes both theoretical and empirical papers.
Related titles: CD-ROM ed.; Microfiche ed.: (from MML); Online - full text ed.: (from bigchalk, EBSCO Publishing, Micromedia ProQuest, Northern Light Technology, Inc., O C L C Online Computer Library Center, Inc., ProQuest Information & Learning).
Indexed: ABIn, ASCA, CBCARef, CBPI, CPerI, CurCont, JEL, SOPODA, SRRA, SSCI, SSI.
—BLDSC (3027.880000), IDS, IE, ingenta.
Published by: (Administrative Sciences Association of Canada), Dalhousie University, Faculty of Management, Rowe Bldg, Ste 2014, 6100 University Ave, Halifax, NS B3H 3J5, Canada. TEL 902-494-3836, FAX 902-494-1483, cjas@dal.ca, http://www.mgmt.dal.ca/cjas. Eds. Iraj Fooladi, Mary R Brooks. Circ: 900 (paid).

330 USA ISSN 0008-4085
HC111
➤ **CANADIAN JOURNAL OF ECONOMICS/REVUE CANADIENNE D'ECONOMIE.** Text in English, French. 1968. q. USD 173 combined subscription in the Americas to institutions & Caribbean (print & online eds.); USD 195 combined subscription in Canada to institutions print & online eds.; GBP 120 combined subscription elsewhere to institutions print & online eds.; USD 15 combined subscription in the Americas to members print & online eds.; GBP 10 combined subscription elsewhere to members print & online eds. (effective 2006). adv. bk.rev. illus. index, cum.index: vols. 1-10. reprints avail. **Document type:** *Journal, Academic/Scholarly.* **Description:** Publishes theoretical and empirical papers in all areas of economics, along with case studies, descriptive essays, review articles, and articles devoted primarily to construction and reporting of important data.
Supersedes in part (1928-1967): Canadian Journal of Economics and Political Science (0315-4890); Which was formerly (until 1934): Contributions to Canada Economics (0383-6258)
Related titles: Microfiche ed.: (from MML); Microfilm ed.: (from MML); Online - full text ed.: ISSN 1540-5982. USD 164 in the Americas to institutions & Caribbean; USD 185 in Canada to institutions; GBP 114 elsewhere to institutions (effective 2006) (from Blackwell Synergy, EBSCO Publishing, Gale Group, IngentaConnect, JSTOR (Web-based Journal Archive), O C L C Online Computer Library Center, Inc., Swets Information Services).
Indexed: ABIn, ABS&EES, ASCA, AgeL, BAS, BPIA, CBCARef, CBPI, CLI, CPerI, CREJ, CurCont, DIP, DSA, ESPM, EnvEAb, FamI, GEOBASE, IBR, IBSS, IBZ, ILD, ILP, JEL, KES, PAIS, PCI, RASB, RDA, RRTA, RiceAb, RiskAb, SRRA, SSCI, SSI, SWA, T&II, WAE&RSA, WBA, WorkRelAb.
—BLDSC (3031.158000), CISTI, IDS, IE, Infotrieve, ingenta. **CCC.**
Published by: (Canadian Economics Association CAN), Blackwell Publishing, Inc. (Subsidiary of: Blackwell Publishing Ltd.), Commerce Place, 350 Main St, Malden, MA 02148. TEL 781-388-8206, FAX 781-388-8232, subscrip@blackwellpub.com, http://www.blackwellpublishing.com/journals/CJE. Circ: 2,600.

▼➤ **CANADIAN JOURNAL OF QUANTUUM ECONOMICS**; the journal of academic research and current affairs on quality-of-life issues. see *SOCIAL SCIENCES: COMPREHENSIVE WORKS*

➤ **CANADIAN NATURAL GAS MARKET REPORT.** see *PETROLEUM AND GAS*

330 CAN ISSN 0318-0859
CANADIAN PROCESS EQUIPMENT & CONTROL NEWS. Text in English. 1972. bi-m. adv. **Document type:** *Magazine, Trade.* **Description:** Provides information on new and existing products and applications.
Published by: Canadian Process Equipment & Control News Ltd., 29-588 Edward Ave, Richmond Hill, ON L4C 9Y6, Canada. TEL 905-770-8077, FAX 905-770-7075, cpe@cpecn.com, http://www.cpecn.com/. Ed. Laura Gardash. Pub. Rob Sommerville. Adv. contacts Peter Birchard, Rob Sommerville. B&W page CND 3,700; trim 11 x 16.5. Circ: 23,110 (controlled).

330 CAN ISSN 0383-7920
CANADIAN RENTAL SERVICE. Text in English, French. 1976. 8/yr. CND 42 domestic; CND 60 in United States; CND 98 elsewhere (effective 2005). adv. tr.lit. back issues avail. **Document type:** *Magazine, Trade.* **Description:** Covers news, features, new trends, photo stories and new products considered significant for the rental industry in Canada, for heavy or light construction machinery, general tools, party supplies and lawn and garden equipment.
Published by: Annex Publishing & Printing, Inc., 222 Argyle Ave, Delhi, ON N4B 2Y2, ON N4B 2Y2, Canada. TEL 519-582-2513, 800-265-2827, FAX 519-582-4040, sfredericks@annexweb.com, http://www.annexweb.com. Circ: 3,690.

330 CAN ISSN 1491-1396
F1001
CANADIAN SPEECHES. Text in English. 1986. bi-m. CND 85 domestic; USD 85 in United States; CND 140 elsewhere; CND 14.02 newsstand/cover (effective 2000). index. back issues avail. **Document type:** *Academic/Scholarly.* **Description:** Presents full-text of speeches about issues which reflect broad national interest.
Former titles (until 1999): Canadian Speeches: Issues of the Day (1191-0860); (until 1991): Canadian Speeches: Issues, Informed Thought (0849-9918)
Related titles: CD-ROM ed.; Microfiche ed.: (from MML); Microfilm ed.; Microform ed.: (from MML); Online - full text ed.: (from Florida Center for Library Automation, Gale Group, Micromedia ProQuest, The Dialog Corporation).
Indexed: CBCABus, CBCARef, CBPI, CPerI, SRRA.
—CCC.
Address: 194 King St, P O Box 250, Woodville, ON K0M 2T0, Canada. TEL 705-439-2580, FAX 705-439-1208, earle.gray@sympatico.ca. Ed., Pub., R&P Earle Gray. Circ: 1,000 (paid).

338.9 CAN ISSN 1497-7141
CANADIAN SUBSIDY DIRECTORY. Text in English. 1999. a. CND 69.95 combined subscription print and online eds (effective 2004). **Description:** Contains direct and indirect financial subsidies, grants and loans offered by government departments and agencies, foundations, association, and organizations.
—CISTI.
Published by: Canadian Business Publications Co., 4865 Highway 138, R.R. 1, St-Andrews West, ON K0C 2A0, Canada. TEL 819-322-5756, 866-322-3376, http://www.mgpublishing.net/.

330 USA
CANDLELIGHT. Text in English. 1994. w. USD 375 (effective 1999). tr.lit. **Document type:** *Newsletter.*
Related titles: Online - full text ed.
Published by: M B H Commodity Advisors, Inc., PO Box 353, Winnetka, IL 60093-0353. TEL 847-291-1870, FAX 847-291-9435, marilyn@trade-futures.com, jake@trade-futures.com. Ed. Marzlyn Kinney. Pub. Jake Bernstein.

330 ZAF ISSN 1028-1215
CAPE BUSINESS NEWS. Text in English. 1980. m. adv. **Description:** Covers business news in the Cape Town area.
Related titles: Online - full text ed.: ISSN 1563-5600.
Published by: Peninsula Business News (Pty) Ltd, P O Box 60567, Cape Town, 7439, South Africa. TEL 27-21-5574061, FAX 27-21-5574707, editor@cbn.co.za, http://www.cbn.co.za. Ed. Johan Moolman.

330 USA
CAPE COD BUSINESS JOURNAL✶. Text in English. m.
Published by: Tri-Coastal Publishing, Inc., PO Box 39, Orleans, MA 02653-0039. Ed. Anne B Saint. Circ: 11,000.

330 DEU ISSN 0008-5847
HB5
CAPITAL; das Wirtschaftsmagazin. Text in German. 1962. m. EUR 59.80; EUR 3 newsstand/cover (effective 2003). adv. bk.rev. charts; illus.; stat.; tr.lit. **Document type:** *Magazine, Trade.* **Description:** Covers management strategies, analyses of selected industry and business sectors, political developments and current events for business executives.
Related titles: Microfilm ed.: (from ALP).
Indexed: KES, PAIS, RASB.
—IE, Infotrieve.
Published by: Gruner und Jahr AG & Co., Am Baumwall 11, Hamburg, 20459, Germany. TEL 49-40-3703-0, FAX 49-40-37036000, capital@guj-koeln.de, ksc@guj.de, http://www.capital.de, http://www.guj.de. Ed. Ralf Dieter Brunowsky. Adv. contact Rolf Ruediger Nausch. B&W page EUR 17,850, color page EUR 24,360. Circ: 228,364 (paid).

330 FRA ISSN 1162-6704
HF5001
CAPITAL; l'essentiel de l'economie. Text in French. 1991. m. EUR 27.50 domestic (effective 2002). adv. **Document type:** *Magazine, Consumer.* **Description:** Covers areas of interest to top executives, whether macro- or microeconomic.
Published by: Prisma Presse, 6 rue Daru, Paris, 75379, France. TEL 33-1-44153000, FAX 33-1-47641042, prisma@presse-info.fr, http://www.capital.fr, http://www.prisma-presse.com. Ed. Jean Joel Gurviez. Circ: 335,708. **Subscr. to:** Service Abonnements, B 140, Sainte Genevieve Cedex 60732, France. TEL 33-3-44625202.

330 TUR ISSN 1300-5960
CAPITAL; aylik ekonomi dergisi. Text in Turkish. 1993. m. adv. **Document type:** *Magazine, Trade.*
Related titles: Online - full text ed.
Published by: D B R - Dogan Burda Rizzoli Dergi Yayyncylyk ve Pazarlama A.S., Hurriyet Medya Towers, Gunesli - Istanbul, 34212, Turkey. TEL 90-212-4103111, FAX 90-212-4103112, capital@dbr.com.tr, abone@dbr.com.tr, http://www.capital.com.tr, http://www.dbr.com.tr.

330 ESP
CAPITAL. Text in Spanish. m. EUR 24.95 domestic; EUR 55.70 in Europe; EUR 71.60 elsewhere (effective 2004). **Document type:** *Magazine, Consumer.*
Published by: G y J Espana Ediciones S.L., Albasanz, 15 Edificio A, Madrid, 28037, Spain. TEL 34-91-4369800, FAX 34-91-5751280, capital@gyj.es, http://www.gyj.es.

330 ROM ISSN 1221-3152
CAPITAL; saptamanal economic si financiar. Text in Romanian. 1992. w. ROL 360,000; ROL 46,000 per issue (effective 2001). adv. software rev.; Website rev. charts; mkt.; stat.; tr.lit. Index. **Document type:** *Magazine, Consumer.* **Description:** Covers management strategies, analyses of selected industry and business sectors, political developments and current events for business executives.
Related titles: CD-ROM ed.; Online - full text ed.
Published by: Ringier Romania, Str Fabrica de Glucoza 5, Bucharest, Romania. TEL 40-01-2030901, FAX 40-01-2425363, redactie@capital.ro, office@ringier.ro, http://www.capital.ro, http://www.ringier.ro. Eds. Andreea Rosca, Ionut Popescu. Pub. Razvan Corneteanu. R&P Andreea Rosca. Adv. contact Aurelian Amuraritei TEL 40-01-2030857. B&W page USD 2,150, color page USD 3,800; trim 400 x 270. Circ: 38,000 (paid).

330 ITA ISSN 0392-3320
HC301
CAPITAL. Text in Italian. 1979. m. EUR 42 (effective 2005). adv. illus. **Document type:** *Magazine, Consumer.* **Description:** Portrays the lifestyle of the successful businessman, with articles on personal investments, cultural topics, and current affairs.
Published by: R C S Periodici (Subsidiary of: R C S Mediagroup), Via Angelo Rizzoli, 2, Milan, MI 20132, Italy. TEL 39-2-25845413, FAX 39-2-25845444, info@periodici.rcs.it, http://www.rcsmediagroup.it/siti/periodici.php. Ed. Paulo Bonnani. Adv. contact Flavio Biondi. Circ: 70,340 (paid).

CAPITAL MAGAZINE. see *COMPUTERS—Internet*

330 RUS
CAPITAL MARKETS REPORT. Text in Russian. 48/yr.
Related titles: English ed.
Published by: Independent Business Media, Romanov per 3, Moscow, Russian Federation. TEL 7-095-2036543, FAX 7-095-2038023. **US dist. addr.:** East View Information Services, 3020 Harbor Ln. N., Minneapolis, MN 55447. TEL 612-550-0961. **Co-sponsor:** Adam Smith Institute, Skate Press Consulting Agency.

330 USA
▼ **CAPITAL REGION BUSINESS JOURNAL.** Text in English. 2005. m. USD 48 (effective 2005). **Document type:** *Magazine.* **Description:** Targets business owners and decision makers who affect the business community.
Published by: Capital Newspapers, Inc., 1901 Fish Hatchery Rd., Madison, WI 53713. TEL 800-362-8333, customerservice@capitalnewspapers.com, http://www.capitalnewspapers.com.

CAPITOL UPDATE. see *PUBLIC ADMINISTRATION*

330 GBR ISSN 1461-9318
CARDIFF BUSINESS SCHOOL. DISCUSSION PAPERS IN ECONOMICS. Text in English. 1995. irreg.
—BLDSC (9597.917500).
Published by: Cardiff Business School, Cardiff University, Aberconway Bldg, Colum Drive, Cardiff, Wales CF10 3EU, United Kingdom. TEL 44-29-20874000, FAX 44-29-20874419, http://www.cf.ac.uk.

▼ new title ➤ refereed ✶ unverified ♦ full entry avail.

B

330 USA ISSN 1552-2504
CARDIOVASCULAR BUSINESS WEEK. Text in English. w. USD 2,595 in US & Canada; USD 2,795 elsewhere; USD 2,825 combined subscription in US & Canada print & online eds.; USD 3,055 combined subscription elsewhere print & online eds. (effective 2005). **Document type:** *Newsletter, Academic/Scholarly.* **Description:** Covers business news of companies that are developing medicines and devices for the treatment of cardiovascular disease, including fiscal reports, contracts, patents and regulation.
Related titles: Online - full content ed.: ISSN 1552-2512; Online - full text ed.: (from ProQuest Information & Learning).
Published by: NewsRx, PO Box 5528, Atlanta, GA 31107-0528. TEL 800-726-4550, FAX 303-290-9025, info@newsrx.com, http://www.newsrx.com/product_descriptions/CARDIOVASCULAR_BUSINESS_WEEK.HTM.

CAREERS AND THE M B A. (Masters of Business Administration) see *OCCUPATIONS AND CAREERS*

330 PER ISSN 1605-3044
CARETAS. Text in Spanish. 1950. m.
Related titles: Online - full text ed.: ISSN 1605-3036. 1995.
Indexed: RASB.
Address: Camana 615, Of. 308, Lima, Peru. TEL 287-520, http://www.caretas.com.pe. Ed. Antonio Passano. Circ: 90,000.

330 PRI ISSN 0194-8326
CARIBBEAN BUSINESS. Text in English. 1975. w. (Thu.). USD 2 newsstand/cover; USD 42 (effective 2005). adv. tr.lit. 72 p./no.; reprints avail. **Document type:** *Newspaper, Corporate.* **Description:** Covers business, management and financial happenings and trends in the Caribbean.
Related titles: Online - full text ed.: (from EBSCO Publishing, Gale Group).
Indexed: T&II.
Published by: Casiano Communications Inc., 1700 Fernandez Juncos Ave, San Juan, 00909-2999, Puerto Rico. TEL 787-728-3000, FAX 787-268-5058, editor@casiano.com, cservice@casiano.com, http://www.puertoricowow.com, http://www.casiano.com. Eds. Elizabeth Roman, Alberto Velazquez. Adv. contact Enid Rivera. col. inch USD 96; 10.125 x 13. Circ: 45,000 (paid and free); 228,730 (paid and free).

330 ATG
CARIBBEAN HANDBOOK. Text in English. 1983. a. USD 85 (effective 2000). adv. bk.rev.
Published by: F T Caribbean, PO Box 1037, St John's, Antigua. TEL 268-462-3392, FAX 268-462-3492. Ed. Lindsay Maxwell. Pub., R&P Edna Fortescue. Circ: 12,000. **Subscr. to:** Subscription Department, 19 Mercers Rd, London N19 4PH, United Kingdom. TEL 44-20-72815746, 44-20-72817157.

CARLTON COMMUNICATIONS PLC. ANNUAL REPORT AND ACCOUNTS. see *COMMUNICATIONS—Television And Cable*

330 USA
CAROLINA BUSINESS. Text in English. 1985. m. USD 27. adv. **Description:** Contains business articles and buyer information. Emphasizes a single aspect of business each month. Includes regular listings of new Eastern North Carolina corporations, as well as a section on real estate and investments.
Published by: Taylor Publications, Inc., PO Box 12006, New Bern, NC 28561. TEL 252-633-5106, FAX 252-633-2836, info@carolinabusiness.net, http://www.carolinabusiness.net. Ed., Pub., R&P, Adv. contact Cynthia K Gaskins. B&W page USD 1,831, color page USD 2,331. Circ: 20,403 (controlled).

650 USA ISSN 0008-6932
HC101
CARROLL BUSINESS BULLETIN. Text in English. 1957. 2/yr. USD 2. bk.rev. charts; illus.
Indexed: PAIS.
Published by: John Carroll University, School of Business, University Heights, Cleveland, OH 44118. TEL 216-491-4391. Ed. Dr. Alfred Schneider. Circ: 5,500.

330 MEX ISSN 0187-7674
CARTA ECONOMICA REGIONAL. Text in Spanish. 1988. bi-m. MXP 90 domestic; USD 50 foreign (effective 2002).
Related titles: Online - full text ed.: (from Gale Group).
Indexed: PAIS.
Published by: Universidad de Guadalajara, Instituto de Estudios Economicos y Regionales, Nucleo Los Belenes, Periferico Norte 799, Edificio B-1er piso, Apdo. Postal 2-738, Zapopan, Jalisco 45000, Mexico. TEL 31-656-9480, FAX 31-656-9564, cartaeco@cea.udg.mx, http://keynes.cucea.udg.mx/~bpo27139/revistas/cartaeco/.

330 AUT
CASH FLOW. Text in German. 11/yr.
Address: Stubenring 2, Vienna, W 1010, Austria. TEL 01-5138800, FAX 01-5138808. Ed. Ferenc Papp. Circ: 50,000.

332 GBR
CASPIAN BUSINESS NEWS (INT'L ED.); the Caspian region's business weekly. Text in English. w.
Related titles: Regional ed(s).: Caspian Business News (Azerbaijan Edition).
Published by: C B N International Ltd, 78 York St, London, W1H 1DP, United Kingdom. TEL 44-207-298100, http://www.caspianbusinessnews.com.

330 GBR ISSN 0069-0937
CASS LIBRARY OF INDUSTRIAL CLASSICS★. Text in English. 1966. irreg. price varies. **Document type:** *Academic/Scholarly.*
Published by: Frank Cass Publishers (Subsidiary of: Taylor & Francis Group), Crown House, 47 Chase Side, Southgate, London, N14 5BP, United Kingdom. TEL 44-20-89202100, FAX 44-20-84478548, info@frankcass.com, http://www.frankcass.com. R&P Anna Whiston.

330 ITA
CASSAMARCA; rivista trimestrale di politica economica finanziaria istituzionale e sociale. Text in Italian. 1987. q. free. back issues avail. **Description:** Covers economic, financial and cultural topics.
Published by: Cassamarca SpA, Piazza S Leonardo, 1, Treviso, TV 31100, Italy. TEL 39-422-6541, FAX 39-422-654316. Ed. Claudio Alessandri. Circ: 4,000.

CATALOGO LEGALE. see *LAW*

CATTLE BUSINESS IN MISSISSIPPI. see *AGRICULTURE—Poultry And Livestock*

330 CYM
CAYMAN EXECUTIVE. Text in English. q. KYD 33 domestic; USD 40 foreign (effective 2000). adv.
Published by: Cayman Publishing Co. Ltd., PO Box 173 GT, Grand Cayman, Cayman Isl. TEL 345-949-5111, FAX 345-949-7033. Eds. Brian Uzzell, Colleen Webb. Adv. contact Valerie Simon.

330 USA
CECIL BUSINESS LEDGER. Text in English. 1992. m. USD 12. adv. **Description:** Contains features and news articles on topics of interest to local business owners, managers, and professionals.
Published by: Chesapeake Publishing Corp., 601 Bridge St, Elkton, MD 21922-0429. TEL 410-398-3311, FAX 410-398-4044. Pub. Jeffrey Mezzatesta. Adv. contact Gene Schwenk. B&W page USD 650; trim 15 x 11.5. Circ: 2,895.

CEMETERY DIRECTORY. see *FUNERALS*

330 USA ISSN 1062-1563
CENTER FOR URBAN POLICY RESEARCH REPORT. Key Title: CUPReport (Piscataway, N.J.). Text in English. 1990. irreg. **Document type:** *Academic/Scholarly.* **Description:** Covers the activities & events in the center, community out-reach programs, and other urban policy related issues.
Published by: Rutgers University, Center for Urban Policy Research, Civic Sq 33 Livingston Ave Ste 400, New Brunswick, NJ 08901-1982. FAX 732-932-2363, pashman@rci.rutgers.edu, http://www.policy.rutgers.edu/cupr.

CENTRAL AMERICA REPORT. see *POLITICAL SCIENCE*

CENTRAL ASIA-CAUCASUS ANALYST. see *POLITICAL SCIENCE*

330 327 GBR ISSN 1467-0291
CENTRAL ASIA NEWSFILE. Text in English. 1993. m. GBP 200 domestic; GBP 220 foreign (effective 2000). back issues avail. **Document type:** *Bulletin, Academic/Scholarly.* **Description:** News digest and analysis of current affairs in Central Asia. Aimed at business people, expatriates, decision makers and investors in the region.
Published by: Curzon Press Ltd., 15 The Quadrant, 6-8 Church Rd, Richmond, Surrey TW9 1BP, United Kingdom. TEL 44-0208-484660, FAX 44-20-83326735, publish@curzonpress.co.uk. Pub. Malcolm Campbell.

330 USA ISSN 1058-3599
CENTRAL PENN BUSINESS JOURNAL. Text in English. 1984. w. USD 59.95 (effective 2005). adv. illus.; charts; maps; stat. **Document type:** *Magazine, Trade.* **Description:** Covers the latest local business news and offers analysis of trends.
Formerly: Strictly Business
Related titles: Microform ed.: (from PQC); Online - full text ed.: (from Northern Light Technology, Inc., O C L C Online Computer Library Center, Inc., ProQuest Information & Learning).
Indexed: ABIn, BusDate.
—CCC.
Published by: Journal Publications, Inc., 101 N Second St, 2nd Fl., Harrisburg, PA 17101. http://www.journalpub.com/. Eds. Jason Klinger, Thomas Barstow. Pub. David Schankweiler. R&P Peter Burke. Adv. contact Kathy Mrksic. Circ: 12,000 (controlled).

CENTRAL RESEARCH INSTITUTE OF ELECTRIC POWER INDUSTRY. SOCIO-ECONOMIC RESEARCH CENTER. TECHNICAL REPORTS (ENGLISH EDITION). see *SOCIOLOGY*

330 382 GBR ISSN 1366-1531
CENTRE FOR RESARCH IN ECONOMIC DEVELOPMENT AND INTERNATIONAL TRADE. RESEARCH PAPER. Text in English. 198?. irreg. **Document type:** *Monographic series.*
—BLDSC (3487.284800).
Published by: The University of Nottingham, Centre for Resarch in Economic Development and International Trade, University Park, Nottingham, NG7 2RD, United Kingdom. TEL 44-115-9515151, FAX 44-115-9513666, http://www.nottingham.ac.uk.

330 300 GBR ISSN 1466-0261
CENTRE FOR SOCIAL AND ECONOMIC RESEARCH ON THE GLOBAL ENVIRONMENT. WORKING PAPER. POLICY ANALYSIS. Variant title: C S E R G E Working Paper P A. Text in English. 1994. irreg. **Document type:** *Monographic series, Academic/Scholarly.*
—BLDSC (3490.179730).
Published by: University of East Anglia, Centre for Social and Economic Research on the Global Environment, School of Environmental Sciences, Norwich, NR4 7TJ, United Kingdom. TEL 44-1603-592642, FAX 44-1603-593739, a.howe@uea.ac.uk, http://www.uea.ac.uk/env/cserge/.

330 GBR
CENTRE FOR THE STUDY OF GLOBALISATION AND REGIONALISATION. WORKING PAPER SERIES. Text in English. 1998. irreg. GBP 2 per issue (effective 2002).
Related titles: Online - full text ed.
—BLDSC (3490.182100).
Published by: University of Warwick, Centre for the Study of Globalisation and Regionalisation, Coventry, CV4 7AL, United Kingdom. TEL 44-24-76523523, FAX 44-24-76572548, http://www.warwick.ac.uk/fac/soc/csgr.

330 FRA
CENTRE NATIONAL DE LA RECHERCHE SCIENTIFIQUE. MONOGRAPHIES D'ECONOMETRIE. Text in French. 1960. irreg. price varies. adv. bk.rev. index. **Document type:** *Monographic series, Academic/Scholarly.*
Formerly (until 1985): Centre National de la Recherche Scientifique. Seminaire d'Econometrie. Monographies (0071-8270)
Published by: (France. Centre National de la Recherche Scientifique), C N R S Editions, 15 Rue Malebranche, Paris, 75005, France. TEL 33-1-53102700, FAX 33-1-53102727, http://www.cnrseditions.fr. Circ: 1,500.

CENTRE ON REGULATION AND COMPETITION. WORKING PAPERS. see *POLITICAL SCIENCE*

CENTRO DE CIENCIAS DA ECONOMIA E INFORMATICA. REVISTA. see *COMPUTERS—Information Science And Information Theory*

330 AUT
CERCLE ECONOMIQUE. Text in German. m.
Address: Elisabethstrasse 13, Vienna, W 1010, Austria. TEL 01-5877707, FAX 01-5870752. Ed. Karl Hannes Schmidt. Circ: 20,000.

330 CZE
CESKY SPOTR EBITEL. Text in Czech. a. **Document type:** *Trade.*
Published by: Strategie Praha s.r.o., Drtinova 8, Prague 5, 150 00, Czech Republic. TEL 420-2-57323578, FAX 420-2-57018362, strategie.praha@istrategie.cz, http://www.istrategie.cz.

330 PRI
CETERIS PARIBUS; revista de economia de Puerto Rico. Text in Spanish. 1991. s-a. **Document type:** *Academic/Scholarly.* **Description:** Presents recent research in social sciences from the institute.
Related titles: Online - full text ed.: free (effective 2003).
Indexed: PAIS.
Published by: Universidad de Puerto Rico, Facultad de Artes y Ciencias/University of Puerto Rico, Faculty of Arts and Sciences, Departamento de Economia, PO Box 9262, Mayaguez, 00681-9262, Puerto Rico. TEL 787-265-3840, FAX 787-265-5426, http://ceterisparibus.uprm.edu, http://econweb.uprm.edu.

658 USA ISSN 1079-6428
CHAIN STORE AGE EXECUTIVE FAX. Text in English. 1994. w. **Document type:** *Trade.*
Media: Fax. **Related titles:** Online - full text ed.: (from Florida Center for Library Automation, Gale Group, O C L C Online Computer Library Center, Inc.).
Published by: Lebhar-Friedman, Inc., 425 Park Ave, New York, NY 10022. http://www.chainstoreage.com/, http://www.lf.com.

330 ZAF
CHAIRMAN'S BRIEF★. Text in English. 1993. m. ZAR 541.50.
Published by: Andrew Levy & Associates, PO Box 1431, Rivonia, Gauteng 2128, South Africa.

330 USA ISSN 0577-5132
HC101 CODEN: CHLGBB
➤ **CHALLENGE (ARMONK)**; the magazine of economic affairs. Text in English. 1952. bi-m. USD 58 domestic to individuals; USD 79 foreign to individuals; USD 265 domestic to institutions; USD 355 foreign to institutions (effective 2006). adv. bk.rev. bibl.; charts; illus.; stat. index. back issues avail.; reprint service avail. from PSC. **Document type:** *Journal, Academic/Scholarly.* **Description:** Presents a wide range of views on national and international economic affairs in the belief that an informed dialogue can result in more rational and effective public policy.
Related titles: Microform ed.: (from PQC); Online - full text ed.: 2001 (Jan.) (from EBSCO Publishing, Florida Center for Library Automation, H.W. Wilson, O C L C Online Computer Library Center, Inc., ProQuest Information & Learning, Swets Information Services).
Indexed: ABIn, ASIP, AcaI, BAS, BPI, CurCont, DIP, IBR, IBSS, IBZ, JEL, MagInd, ManagCont, PAIS, SSI, WorkRelAb.
—BLDSC (3129.100000), IE, ingenta. **CCC.**
Published by: M.E. Sharpe, Inc., 80 Business Park Dr, Armonk, NY 10504. TEL 914-273-1800, 800-541-6563, FAX 914-273-2106, custserv@mesharpe.com, http://www.mesharpe.com/mall/results1.asp. Ed. Jeffrey Madrick. Adv. contact Barbara Ladd TEL 914-273-1800 ext 121. page USD 750; 9 x 6. Circ: 5,000.

330 FRA ISSN 0751-4417
CHALLENGES. Text in French. 1982. m. **Description:** Aims at exposing the key to financial success.
Address: 10 place de la Bourse, Paris, 75002, France. TEL 33-1-44883403, FAX 33-1-44883752. Ed. Gilles Le Gendre. Pub. Claude Perdriel. Circ: 176,500.

CHANYE YU HUANJING/INDUSTRY AND ENVIRONMENT. see *ENVIRONMENTAL STUDIES*

330 CAN ISSN 1192-4365
CHARITABLE BUSINESS. Text in English. 1992. bi-m. CND 18, USD 30. adv. bk.rev. **Document type:** *Trade.* **Description:** Covers the administration and facility management needs of charities and nonprofit organizations for executive managers, administration and property managers.
Published by: Momentum Media Management, 4040 Creditview Rd, Unit 11, P O Box 1800, Mississauga, ON L5C 3Y8, Canada. TEL 905-813-7100, FAX 905-813-7117, barwellj@momentummedia.com. Ed., R&P Jay Barwell. Adv. contact Hugh Parkinson. B&W page CND 1,915, color page CND 2,750; trim 11 x 8. Circ: 11,100 (controlled).

330 USA ISSN 1530-7530
CHARLESTON REGIONAL BUSINESS JOURNAL. Text in English. 1994. bi-w.
Published by: Setcom, Inc., Box 446, Charleston, SC 29402. TEL 843-723-7702, FAX 843-723-7060, info@crbj.com, http://www.crbj.com. Pub. William Settlemyer. Circ: 7,000.

330 USA ISSN 0887-5588
CHARLOTTE BUSINESS JOURNAL. Text in English. 1986. w. (Fri.). USD 78 (effective 2005). **Document type:** *Newspaper, Trade.*
Formerly: Business Journal Of Charlotte
Related titles: Online - full text ed.: (from O C L C Online Computer Library Center, Inc., ProQuest Information & Learning).
Indexed: BusDate, LRI.
—CCC.
Published by: American City Business Journals, Inc. (Charlotte), 120 W Morehead St, Ste 200, Charlotte, NC 28202. TEL 704-973-1100, 800-704-3757, FAX 704-973-1102, charlotte@bizjournals.com, http://www.bizjournals.com/charlotte/. Ed. Robert Morris. Pub. Jeannie Falknor. Circ: 14,500.

330 CHN ISSN 1005-4332
CHENGSHI JINGJI, QUYUE JINGJI/URBAN ECONOMY AND REGIONAL ECONOMY. Text in Chinese. 1987. m. CNY 78 (effective 2004). 80 p./no.; **Document type:** *Journal, Academic/Scholarly.*
Formerly (until 1987): Chengshi Jingji (1001-3083)
Indexed: RASB.
Published by: Zhongguo Renmin Daxue, Shubao Zilio Zhongxin/Renmin University of China, Information Center for Social Server, Dongcheng-qu, 3, Zhangzizhong Lu, Beijing, 100007, China. TEL 86-10-64039458, FAX 86-10-64015080, kyes@163.net, http://www.confucius.cn.net/bkdetail.asp?fzt=F107. **Dist. in US by:** China Publications Service, PO Box 49614, Chicago, IL 60649. TEL 312-288-3191, FAX 312-288-8570.

330 USA
CHESAPEAKE BUSINESS LEDGER. Text in English. m. free (effective 2005). **Document type:** *Newspaper.*
Published by: Chesapeake Publishing Corp., 29088 Airpark Dr., Easton, MD 21601. TEL 401-822-1500, FAX 410-770-4019, http://www.chespub.com/ledgers.htm. Ed. Richard McNey. Pub. Larry Effingham. Adv. contacts Gail Ruppe, David Fike. Circ: 4,500 (paid).

330 340 JPN ISSN 0912-7208
K3
CHIBA DAIGAKU HOGAKU RONSHU/CHIBA JOURNAL OF LAW AND POLITICS. Text in Japanese. 1969. irreg. **Document type:** *Journal, Academic/Scholarly.*
Supersedes in part (in 1986): Chiba Daigaku Hokei Kenkyu (0386-2100); Which superseded in part (1971): Chiba Daigaku Jinbun Gakubu Kiyo (0386-2089)
—BLDSC (3172.670300).
Published by: Chiba Daigaku, Hokei Gakubu, Keizai Gakka/Chiba University, Faculty of Law and Economics, Department of Economics, 1-33, Yayoi-cho, Inage-ku, Chiba-shi, Chiba 263-8522 , Japan. TEL 81-43-290-2343, FAX 81-43-290-2372, http://www.chiba-u.ac.jp/general/organization/le/index.html, http://www.chiba-u.ac.jp/e/aca/u/le/index.html.

330 JPN ISSN 0912-7216
HB9
CHIBA DAIGAKU KEIZAI KENKYU/CHIBA UNIVERSITY. ECONOMICS JOURNAL. Text in Japanese. 1969. a. **Document type:** *Journal, Academic/Scholarly.*
Supersedes in part (in 1986): Chiba Daigaku Hokei Kenkyu (0386-2100); Which supersedes in part (in 1971): Chiba Daigaku Jinbun Gakubu Kiyo (0386-2089)
—BLDSC (3653.820000).
Published by: Chiba Daigaku, Hokei Gakubu, Keizai Gakka/Chiba University, Faculty of Law and Economics, Department of Economics, 1-33, Yayoi-cho, Inage-ku, Chiba-shi, Chiba 263-8522 , Japan. TEL 81-43-290-2343, FAX 81-43-290-2372, http://www.chiba-u.ac.jp/general/organization/le/index.html, http://www.chiba-u.ac.jp/e/aca/u/le/index.html.

330 USA ISSN 1044-0844
CHICAGO ENTERPRISE. Text in English. 1986. 6/yr. free. adv. bk.rev. **Description:** Covers economic development and urban issues in Chicago area.
Related titles: Online - full text ed.: (from ProQuest Information & Learning).
Indexed: BusDate.
Published by: Commercial Club of Chicago, One First National Plaza, 2700, Chicago, IL 60603. TEL 312-853-1203, FAX 312-853-1209. Ed. David H Roeder. Circ: 9,100.

330 JPN
CHIIKI KEIZAI KENKYU/STUDIES ON REGIONAL ECONOMICS. Text in Japanese. 1990. a. **Document type:** *Monographic series, Academic/Scholarly.*
—BLDSC (3172.879094).
Published by: Hiroshima Daigaku, Keizai Gakubu/Hiroshima University, Faculty of Economics, 1-1-89, Higashisenda-machi, Naka-ku, Hiroshima 730-0053, Japan. TEL 81-82-542-6991, FAX 81-82-249-4991, http://www.eco.hiroshima-u.ac.jp/index.html.

CHILDREN'S SOCIAL & ECONOMICS EDUCATION; an international journal. see *EDUCATION*

CHILE. INSTITUTO NACIONAL DE ESTADISTICAS. ESTADISTICA Y ECONOMIA. see *STATISTICS*

CHINA COMPUTER RESELLER WORLD. see *COMPUTERS*

363.7 GBR
CHINA ENVIRONMENTAL REVIEW. Text in English. 1997. bi-m. GBP 175; GBP 150 email edition (effective 2000). **Document type:** *Trade.* **Description:** Focuses on environmental information and analysis of developments impacting business in China. Contains news and analysis of policy, legislative developments, and company activity along with market surveys and business opportunities.
Published by: Asia Environmental Trading Ltd., 55 Exhibition Rd, London, SW7 2PG, United Kingdom. TEL 44-20-7581-5277, FAX 44-20-7589-1477, aet@asianenviro.com, http://www.asianenviro.com. Ed. Dylan Tanner.

330 USA
CHINA HAND; investing, licensing and trading conditions today. Text in English. 1981. m. looseleaf. USD 2,415 print or online; USD 280 newsstand/cover print or online (effective 2004). **Description:** Covers laws and regulations full-text, including starting a new business, dealing with foreign trade corporations, plus negotiating and implementing joint ventures in the PRC.
Related titles: CD-ROM ed.: (from SilverPlatter Information, Inc., The Dialog Corporation); Online - full text ed.
Published by: Economist Intelligence Unit, 111 W 57th St, New York, NY 10019. TEL 212-554-0600, 800-938-4685, FAX 212-586-1182, http://www.eiu.com. Ed. Lois Dougan Tretiak. Circ: 1,000.

CHINA LAW & PRACTICE; documenting & analysing the Chinese legal system. see *LAW*

330 GBR
CHINA MONITOR - EUROPE/ZHONGGUO TOUSHI. Text in Chinese, English. 1993. q. GBP 80. **Document type:** *Trade.* **Description:** Designed to increase awareness of what is happening in Europe and in China, among companies on both continents. Aims to provide details of emerging trends, opportunities and change in the Chinese - European economy. Includes analysis of economic developments and business opportunities in both markets as well as assistance to companies to help them understand Chinese and European business practices.
Formerly: China Monitor (1353-6079)
Published by: Household World Ltd., 1 Ben Rhydding Rd, Ilkley, LS29 8RJ, United Kingdom. TEL 44-1943-602632, FAX 44-1943-603497, editor@chinamonitor.demon.co.uk, http://www.chinamonitor.com. Ed. Yingxian Soong. Pub., R&P Sau Wan Chan. adv.: B&W page GBP 1,900, color page GBP 2,500; trim 277 x 189. Circ: 4,500.

330 HKG
CHINA'S TOP 200. Text in English. a. HKD 640, USD 95 (effective 2001). **Document type:** *Trade.* **Description:** Contains lists of lawyers, tax advisors, accountants, business consultants, financial institutions, and corporate locations.
—BLDSC (3180.263630).
Published by: Euromoney Publications plc., 5/F Printing House, 6 Duddell Street, Central, Hong Kong. TEL 852-2842-6906, FAX 852-2810-8417, enquiries@alphk.com, http://www.euromoney.com.

330 HKG
CHINESE ECONOMIC MONTHLY. Text in Chinese. 12/yr.
Address: Manley Commercial Bldg no.1206, 367-375 Queens Rd, Central, Hong Kong, Hong Kong. TEL 5-443133, FAX 5-450774. Ed. Li Hung.

330 TWN
CHINESE ECONOMIC REVIEW/CHUNG-KUO CHING CHI P'ING LUN. Text in Chinese. 1969. q. TWD 60 newsstand/cover domestic; USD 2.50 newsstand/cover in Hong Kong; USD 3.50 newsstand/cover in Asia; USD 4.50 newsstand/cover elsewhere.
Published by: (Chinese Institute for Economic Development/Chung-kuo Ching Chi Chien She Yen Chiu Hui), Chinese Economic Review Publishers, 3F, No7, Alley 2, Szewei Ln, Chung Cheng Rd, Hsintien, Taipei Hsien, 23136, Taiwan. TEL 02-912-1811. Ed. Chou I Ping.

330 USA ISSN 1097-1475
HC426
➤ **THE CHINESE ECONOMY**; translation and studies. Text in English. 1967. bi-m. USD 149 domestic to individuals; USD 221 foreign to individuals; USD 1,180 domestic to institutions; USD 1,300 foreign to institutions (effective 2006). adv. index. back issues avail.; reprint service avail. from PSC. **Document type:** *Journal, Academic/Scholarly.* **Description:** Presents ongoing developments in the Chinese economy. Articles by China's leading economists present analyses of the functioning of the economy, the problems of reform, and debates over economic policy. Special thematic issues concentrate on a specific area of focus.
Formerly (until 1997): Chinese Economic Studies (0009-4552)
Related titles: Online - full text ed.: 2004 (Jan.) (from EBSCO Publishing, O C L C Online Computer Library Center, Inc., Swets Information Services).
Indexed: ABIn, APEL, BAS, CREJ, CurCont, DIP, IBR, IBSS, IBZ, ILD, JEL, PAIS, RASB, RRTA, SSCI, WAE&RSA.
—BLDSC (3180.277600), CISTI, IDS, IE, Infotrieve, ingenta. **CCC.**
Published by: M.E. Sharpe, Inc., 80 Business Park Dr, Armonk, NY 10504. TEL 914-273-1800, 800-541-6563, FAX 914-273-2106, custserv@mesharpe.com, http://www.mesharpe.com/mall/results1.asp. Ed. Joseph Fewsmith. Adv. contact Barbara Ladd TEL 914-273-1800 ext 121. page USD 300; trim 8 x 5.

➤ **CHINESE FILM MARKET.** see *MOTION PICTURES*

➤ **CHINESE JOURNAL OF ADMINISTRATION.** see *PUBLIC ADMINISTRATION*

330 300 FRA ISSN 1285-087X
CHRONIQUE INTERNATIONALE DE L'I R E S. (Institut de Recherches Economiques et Sociales) Text in French. 1989. bi-m.
Formerly (until 1997): Chronique Internationale (1145-1408)
Related titles: Online - full text ed.: (from ProQuest Information & Learning).
Indexed: ABIn.
Published by: Institut de Recherches Economiques et Sociales, 16 Boulevard du Mont d'Est, 9ieme etage, Noisy-le-Grand, France. TEL 33-1-4815-1922, info@ires-fr.org, http://www.ires-fr.org/files/publications/chronique%20internationale/chroniqueires.htm, http://www.ires-fr.org/files/ires/IRES.htm.

330 CHN
CHUANGYE ZHE/ENTREPRENEURS. Text in Chinese. bi-m.
Published by: Shanghai Fanyi Chuban Gongsi/Shanghai Translation Publishing Company, 597 Fuxing Zhonglu, Shanghai, 200020, China. TEL 4332298. Ed. He Congying.

▼ *new title* ➤ *refereed* ✶ *unverified* ♦ *full entry avail.*

330 CHN ISSN 1004-4582
CHUANGYEZHE/ENTREPRENEUR. Text in Chinese. 1986. m. CNY 68 domestic; USD 28.80 foreign (effective 2005).
Document type: *Journal, Academic/Scholarly.*
Published by: Guangdong Sheng Laodonghe, Shehui Baozhang Ting/Guangdong Bureau of Labour and Social Security, 316, Huanshi Zhonglu, 6F, Jinying Dasha, Guangzhou, 510060, China. TEL 86-20-83352104, FAX 86-20-83192405, http://cyz.periodicals.net.cn/, http://www.gd.lss.gov.cn/gb/molss/. **Dist. by:** China International Book Trading Corp, 35 Chegongzhuang Xilu, Haidian District, PO Box 399, Beijing 100044, China. TEL 86-10-68412045, FAX 86-10-68412023, cibtc@mail.cibtc.com.cn, http://www.cibtc.com.cn.

330 JPN ISSN 0910-8874
HD28
CHUBU UNIVERSITY. COLLEGE OF BUSINESS ADMINISTRATION AND INFORMATION SCIENCE. JOURNAL. Text in Japanese. 1985. s-a. eschange basis to libraries. bk.rev. **Description:** Contains articles, research notes, reports of association attendance.
Related titles: Japanese ed.: Keieijoho Gakubu Ronshu.
Published by: Chubu University, College of Business Administration and Information Science, Kasugai, Aichi 487-8501, Japan. TEL 81-568-51-1111, FAX 81-568-52-1505.

330 GBR
CHURCHES PURCHASING SCHEME. Text in English. 1989. s-a. adv. back issues avail. **Document type:** *Academic/Scholarly.*
Description: Provides a means of supplying a wide range of goods and services at competitive prices by negotiating bulk discounts with suppliers, primarily for churches, charities, and educational organizations.
Published by: Ecclesiastical Insurance Office, Desk Top Publishing Unit, Beaufort House, Brunswick Rd, Gloucester, Glos GL1 1JZ, United Kingdom. TEL 0452-383080, FAX 0452-383621. Adv. contact Maggie Vinson. Circ: 32,500 (controlled).

330 382 ITA ISSN 1120-4249
CINA NOTIZIE; rassegna informativa di attualita cinese. Text in Italian. 1970. bi-m. EUR 150 (effective 2005). adv. **Document type:** *Newsletter, Trade.* **Description:** Directed to Italian economic operators wishing to cooperate with Chinese partners. Supplies basic up-to-date information on fiscal, customs, legal, statistical, and monetary topics.
Published by: Camera di Commercio Italo Cinese, Via Giosue' Carducci, 18, Milan, MI 20123, Italy. TEL 39-02-862325, FAX 39-02-72000236, china-italy@planet.it, www.china-italy.com, http://www.china-italy.com. Ed. Carlo F Butti. Circ: 1,500 (paid and controlled).

330 USA ISSN 1096-8636
CINCINNATI BUSINESS COURIER; serving the Cincinnati - Northern Kentucky region. Text in English. 1984. w. (Fri.). USD 83 (effective 2005). adv. bk.rev. back issues avail.; reprint service avail. from PQC. **Document type:** *Newspaper.*
Description: Serves the general business information needs of qualified recipients in the Cincinnati metropolitan area, including Northern Kentucky.
Incorporates (1988-1996): Business Record (Cincinnati) (1068-2899); Which was formerly (until 1993): Greater Cincinnati Business Record (1044-9264)
Related titles: Microfiche ed.; Online - full text ed.: (from Florida Center for Library Automation, Gale Group, O C L C Online Computer Library Center, Inc., ProQuest Information & Learning).
Indexed: ABIn, BusDate, LRI.
Published by: A C B J Business Publications, Inc., 501 S 4th Ave, Ste 130, Louisville, KY 40202-2520. TEL 513-621-6665, FAX 513-621-2462, cincinnati@bizjournals.com, cincinnati@amcity.com, http://www.bizjournals.com/cincinnati/. Ed., R&P Rob Daumeyer. Pub. Tammy Tierney Allison. Circ: 12,800 (paid).

330 ESP
CINCO DIAS. Text in Spanish. 1978. d. (Mon.-Fri.). adv.
Document type: *Newspaper.*
Related titles: Online - full text ed.
Published by: Estructura S.A., Gran Via, 32 o Piso 2, Madrid, 28013, Spain. TEL 538-61-00, FAX 523-06-82, http://www.cincodias.es/. Circ: 26,655.

331.881 DNK ISSN 0108-0636
➤ **CIVILOEKONOMEN.** Text in Danish. 1953. 10/yr. (10/yr.). DKK 470 (effective 2004). adv. bk.rev. charts; illus.; stat. index.
Document type: *Magazine, Trade.*
Related titles: Online - full text ed.
Published by: Civiloekonomerne/Association of Danish Business Economists, Soetorvet 5, PO Box 2043, Copenhagen K, 1012, Denmark. TEL 45-33-141446, FAX 45-33-141449, info@civiloekonomerne.org, http://www.civiloekonomerne.org. Ed. Gitte S Nielsen. Circ: 16,843 (controlled).

330 USA ISSN 1059-3055
CLEVELAND ENTERPRISE. Text in English. 1991. q. USD 15.95. adv. bk.rev. **Document type:** *Trade.* **Description:** For CEOs of growing businesses in Northeast Ohio. Features Northeast Ohio businesses only.
Published by: Enterprise Development, Inc., 11000 Cedar Ave, 4th Fl, Cleveland, OH 44106. TEL 216-229-9445, FAX 216-229-3236. Ed. Barbara Mooney. Pub. Sandra K Siebenschuh. Adv. contact George Allen. B&W page USD 3,970, color page USD 5,060; trim 10.88 x 8.38. Circ: 30,000.

330 USA
CLICK MAGAZINE; the talk of Silicon Valley. Text in English. m. Free to qualified subscribers. adv. **Document type:** *Magazine, Trade.* **Description:** Covers news and issues of interest to executives in the San Francisco Bay area.
Published by: 18 Media Inc., 618 Santa Cruz Ave, Menlo Park, CA 94025. TEL 650-324-1818, FAX 650-324-1888.

THE CLUB. see *TRANSPORTATION—Air Transport*

330 USA ISSN 1060-3417
COAST BUSINESS. Text in English. 1989. bi-w. USD 22.50. adv. bk.rev. **Document type:** *Consumer.* **Description:** Covers the business news, people and opportunities in South Mississippi and surrounding counties.
Related titles: Microfilm ed.: (from PQC); Online - full text ed.: (from Northern Light Technology, Inc., O C L C Online Computer Library Center, Inc., ProQuest Information & Learning).
Indexed: ABIn, BusDate.
Published by: Ship Island Holding Co., PO Box 1209, Gulfport, MS 39502-1209. TEL 601-868-1182, FAX 601-867-2986, coastbusiness@nse.com. Ed. Lauren Thompson. Pub. Belinda Mallery. R&P Krista Bongiorno. Adv. contact Shirley Leroy. Circ: 8,000 (paid).

COCOINFO INTERNATIONAL. see *AGRICULTURE*

330 LUX ISSN 1680-2187
COHESION FUND. ANNUAL REPORT (YEAR). Text in English. 1996. a.
Related titles: French ed.: Fonds de Cohesion. Rapport Annuel. ISSN 1561-2147; Spanish ed.: Fondo de Cohesion. Informe Anual. ISSN 1680-2209; Greek ed.: Tameiou Sunohes. Etesia Ekthese. ISSN 1680-2217; Portuguese ed.: Fundo de Coesao. Relatorio Anual. ISSN 1680-2225.
Published by: European Commission, Office for Official Publications of the European Union, 2 Rue Mercier, Luxembourg, L-2985, Luxembourg. TEL 352-29291, FAX 352-2929-44637, http://europa.eu.int.

COLECCAO HORIZONTE UNIVERSITARIO. see *POLITICAL SCIENCE*

330 ESP
COLECCION TABLERO. Text in Spanish. irreg., latest vol.8, 1982.
Published by: Editorial Planeta S.A., Corsega, 273-277, Barcelona, 08008, Spain.

330 ESP
COLEGIO DE CORREDORES DE COMERCIO DE ZARAGOZA. BOLETIN DE COTIZACION OFICIAL. Text in Spanish. w.
Document type: *Academic/Scholarly.*
Published by: Colegio de Corredores de Comercio de Zaragoza/College of Business Agents of Zaragoza, San Clemente, 21 3o, Zaragoza, 50001, Spain. Ed. Gonzalo Divar Loyola.

330 USA
COLLEGE BOULEVARD NEWS. Text in English. 1984. w. USD 42. adv. illus. back issues avail.
Published by: Sun Publications, Inc., 7373 W 107th St, Ste 250, Overland, Park, KS 66212-2547. TEL 913-381-1010, FAX 913-381-9889. Ed. Steve Hale. Circ: 30,000.

368.094 COL
COLOMBIA. SUPERINTENDENCIA BANCARIA. SEGUROS Y CAPITALIZACION. Text in Spanish. 1972. a. free. **Document type:** *Government.*
Published by: Superintendencia Bancaria, Apartado Aereo 3460, Bogota, CUND, Colombia. TEL 57-1-2804060, FAX 57-1-2800864. Circ: 500.

330 USA ISSN 1062-810X
COLORADO SPRINGS BUSINESS JOURNAL. Text in English. 1989. w. (Fri.). USD 64.50; USD 1.50 newsstand/cover (effective 2005). adv. back issues avail.; reprints avail.
Document type: *Newspaper, Consumer.* **Description:** Provides local business news, and feature articles of interest to the business and professional community.
Related titles: Online - full text ed.: (from Newsbank, Inc., Northern Light Technology, Inc., O C L C Online Computer Library Center, Inc., ProQuest Information & Learning).
Indexed: ABIn, BusDate.
Address: 31 E Platte Ave, Ste 300, Colorado Springs, CO 80901. TEL 719-634-3223, FAX 719-634-5157, mail@csbj.com, http://www.csbj.com/. Pub. Lon P Matejczyk. Adv. contact Carol Wolfe. B&W page USD 2,234; trim 11.5 x 15. Circ: 1,522 (paid); 3,306 (controlled); 212 (free). Wire service: PR.

330 USA ISSN 0732-1015
HF5429.4.C6
COLORADO STATE AND COUNTY RETAIL SALES BY STANDARD INDUSTRIAL CLASSIFICATION. Text in English. 1970. q. (plus a.). USD 75 domestic; USD 90 foreign (effective 2001); subscr. includes Colorado City Retail Sales. back issues avail.
Supersedes in part: Colorado County and City Retail Sales by Standard Industrial Classification (0091-4789)
Published by: University of Colorado, Business Research Division, Campus Box 420, Boulder, CO 80309-0420. TEL 303-492-8227, FAX 303-492-3620. Circ: 60.

COLUMBIA BUSINESS LAW REVIEW. see *LAW*

330 USA ISSN 0069-6331
COLUMBIA STUDIES IN ECONOMICS. Text in English. 1968. irreg., latest vol.10, 1979. **Document type:** *Monographic series.*
Published by: Columbia University Press, 61 W 62nd St, New York, NY 10023. TEL 212-666-1000. Ed. Kate Witterberg. R&P Lisa Simmars.

650 USA
COLUMBIA UNIVERSITY GRADUATE SCHOOL OF BUSINESS. DISSERTATIONS SERIES. Text in English. irreg. price varies.
Published by: (Columbia University), Free Press, c/o Simon & Shuster, 1230 Ave of the Americas, New York, NY 10020. TEL 212-935-2000, FAX 212-605-9364.

650 USA ISSN 0748-6146
COLUMBUS BUSINESS FIRST. Text in English. 1984. w. (Fri.). USD 89 (effective 2005). 72 p./no. 4 cols./p.; **Document type:** *Newspaper.* **Description:** Contains some of each week top stories on business strategies.
Related titles: Online - full text ed.: (from Florida Center for Library Automation, Gale Group, O C L C Online Computer Library Center, Inc., ProQuest Information & Learning).
Indexed: ABIn, BusDate.
—CCC.
Published by: Business First of Columbus, 471 E Broad St, Ste 1500, Columbus, OH 43215. TEL 614-461-4040, FAX 614-365-2980, columbus@bizjournals.com, http://www.bizjournals.com/columbus/. Ed. Dominic Cappa. Circ: 12,500 (paid). Wire service: AP.

330 URY
LA COMARCA; negocios y empresas del Mercosur. Text in Spanish. m.
Published by: Comarca Ltda., Colonia, 881 Piso 7 Esc. 21, Montevideo, 11102, Uruguay. TEL 911038. Ed. Jose A Ripoll.

330 BOL ISSN 1017-8856
COMENTARIOS ECONOMICOS DE ACTUALIDAD. Abbreviated title: C E A. Text in English, Spanish. 1983. s-m. USD 120 (effective 2000). **Document type:** *Newsletter.* **Description:** Includes information, analysis and research about economic situations and conditions, investments, international commerce, macroeconomics, trade and industry, ecological development and small business.
Address: PO Box 3 12097 S M, La Paz, Bolivia. TEL 591-2-431550, FAX 591-2-432554, veceba@caoba.entelnet.bo. Ed. Guido Cespedes Argandona.

330 ARG
EL COMERCIAL. Text in Spanish. 1991. d.
Published by: Scharoner's S.A.I.C, Hipolito Yrigoyen 58, Formosa, 3600, Argentina. TEL 54-3717-431035, 54-3717-431036, redaccion@elcomercial.com.ar, http://www.elcomercial.com.ar.

COMLINE: BIOTECHNOLOGY AND MEDICAL INDUSTRY OF JAPAN. see *MEDICAL SCIENCES*

COMLINE: CHEMICAL INDUSTRY OF JAPAN. see *ENGINEERING—Chemical Engineering*

330 JPN
COMLINE: INDUSTRIAL AUTOMATION INDUSTRY OF JAPAN. Text in English. irreg. **Document type:** *Trade.*
Media: Online - full content.
Published by: O D S Corp., Kuyo Bldg, 5-10-5 Minami-Aoyama, Minato-ku, Tokyo, 107, Japan. TEL 81-3-3486-2676, http://www.ods.co.jp/. **Dist. by:** COMLINE International Corp., 10601 South DeAnza Blvd Ste 216, Cupertino, CA 95014. TEL 408-257-9956.

COMLINE: TELECOMMUNICATIONS INDUSTRY OF JAPAN. see *COMMUNICATIONS*

330 388 JPN
COMLINE: TRANSPORTATION INDUSTRY OF JAPAN. Text in English. irreg. **Document type:** *Trade.*
Media: Online - full content.
Published by: O D S Corp., Kuyo Bldg, 5-10-5 Minami-Aoyama, Minato-ku, Tokyo, 107, Japan. TEL 81-3-3486-2676, http://www.ods.co.jp/. **Dist. by:** COMLINE International Corp., 10601 South DeAnza Blvd Ste 216, Cupertino, CA 95014. TEL 408-257-9956.

330 SWE
COMMERCE✳ . Text in Swedish. bi-m. SEK 210 (effective 2000). adv. Document type: Magazine, Trade.
Published by: Mentor Online AB, Tryffelslingan 10, PO Box 72001, Lidingoe, 18172, Sweden. TEL 46-8-670-41-00, FAX 46-8-661-64-55, info@mentoronline.se. Ed. Camilla Myrsten. Adv. contact Rose-Marie Erikson. color page SEK 16,400; 210 x 297.

330 FRA
COMMERCE ET PERSPECTIVES. Text in French. 1868. 4/yr. adv.
Published by: A E C C I P, 1 rue Armand Moisant, Paris, 75015, France. TEL 43-20-98-70. Ed. Georges Guillot. Circ: 3,500.

384.33 USA
COMMERCE EXTRA. Text in English. m. free. Document type: Newsletter.
Media: Online - full text.
Address: news@outreach.com, commerce-request@lists.outreach.com, http://www.outreach.com/commercelink/issue1.html.

330 FRA ISSN 1142-4907
COMMERCE FORAIN✳ . Text in French. s-m.
Formed by the 1941 merger of: Monde Forain (1142-4893); Syndicaliste Forain (1923) (1142-4885)
Address: Z.I. de la Mollette, 20 rue de la Victoire, Le Blanc Mesnil, Cedex 93155, France. TEL 33-1-43492470, FAX 33-1-43492796. Ed. Caron Gilbert. Circ: 25,000.

330 382 DEU ISSN 0010-2857
HF296.A29
COMMERCE IN GERMANY. Text in English. 1920. 5/yr. EUR 7.70 newsstand/cover (effective 2004). adv. bk.rev. bibl.; stat. back issues avail. Document type: Magazine, Trade. Description: Provides information about the American Chamber of Commerce's various lobbying and networking activities and about important transatlantic economic developments.
Published by: American Chamber of Commerce in Germany e.V., Rossmarkt 12, Frankfurt am Main, 60311, Germany. TEL 49-69-9291040, FAX 49-69-92910411, info@amcham.de, http://www.amcham.de. adv.: B&W page EUR 2,326, color page EUR 3,553. Circ: 7,000 (paid and controlled).

330 OMN
THE COMMERCIAL. Text in Arabic, English. m. adv.
Published by: Commercial, P O Box 5002, Muscat, Oman. TEL 705972, TELEX 3189.

COMMERCIAL CRIME INTERNATIONAL. see CRIMINOLOGY AND LAW ENFORCEMENT

COMMERCIAL LAW REPORT. see LAW

381 ITA
COMMERCIO VERONESE. Text in Italian. 1971. m. free. Document type: Trade.
Published by: Associazione Commercianti della Provincia di Verona, Corso Porta Nuova, 4, Verona, VR 37122, Italy. TEL 39-045-591688, FAX 39-045-595846. Circ: 10,000.

330 CAN ISSN 1200-569X
COMMISSION DES VALEURS MOBILIERES DU QUEBEC. RAPPORT ANNUEL. Text in French. 1983. a.
Published by: Commission des Valeurs Mobilieres du Quebec, 800, square Victoria, 22e etage, C. P. 246, Tour de la Bourse, Montreal, PQ H4Z 1G3, Canada. TEL 514-940-2150, 800-361-5072, FAX 514-873-3090, http://www.cvmq.com.

330 CAN ISSN 1491-896X
COMMISSIONER OF COMPETITION (YEAR) ON THE ENFORCEMENT AND ADMINISTRATION OF THE COMPETITION ACT, CONSUMER PACKAGING AND LABELLING ACT, PRECIOUS METALS MARKING ACT, TEXTILE LABELLING ACT. ANNUAL REPORT/ COMMISSAIRE DE LA CONCURRENCE POUR L'EXERCICE SE TERMINANT LE 31 MARS (ANNEE) SUR L'APPLICATION ET L'ADMINISTRATION DES LOIS SUIVANTES, LOI SUR LA CONCURRENCE, LOI SUR L'EMBALLAGE ET L'ETIQUETAGE DES PRODUITS DE CONSOMMATION, LOI SUR LE POINCONNAGE DES METAUX PRECIEUX, LOI SUR L'ETIQUETAGE DES TEXTILES. Text in English, French. irreg.
Former titles (until 1998): Director of Investigation and Research, Competition Act. Annual Report (0837-4279); (until 1985): Director of Investigation and Research, Combines Investigation Act. Annual Report (0707-3410); (until 1975): Director of Investigation and Research. Combines Investigation Act. Report (0707-3429)
Related titles: Online - full content ed.: ISSN 1700-7003.
—CISTI.
Published by: Industry Canada, Competition Bureau, 50 Victoria St, Gatineau, PQ K1A 0C9, Canada. TEL 819-997-4282, 800-348-5358, FAX 819-997-0324, compbureau@cb-bc.gc.ca, http://competition.ic.gc.ca/epic/internet/incb-bc.nsf/en/h_ct01269e.html, http://www.cb-bc.gc.ca.

COMMITMENT. see WOMEN'S INTERESTS

330 USA
COMMITTEE ON THE STATUS OF WOMEN IN THE ECONOMICS PROFESSION. NEWSLETTER. Text in English. 3/yr. USD 20 to members (effective 2000). Document type: Newsletter. Description: Contains news of the organization and its members; lists career opportunities for women in the economics professions.
Published by: American Economic Association, Committee on the Status of Women in the Economics Profession, c/o Dr. Beth Allen, Ed., Dept of Economics, University of Minnesota, 1035 Management & Economics, 271, 19th Ave S, Minneapolis, MN 55455. TEL 612-626-8213, FAX 612-624-0209. Ed., Pub., R&P, Adv. contact Beth Allen. Subscr. to: Joan Haworth, 4901 Tower Ct, Tallahassee, FL 32303.

COMMON SENSE. see POLITICAL SCIENCE

330 FRA ISSN 0988-3851
COMMUNICATION C B NEWS. Text in French. 1986. 52/yr.
Formerly (until 1988): Communication and Business (0299-0334)
Address: 175-177 rue d'Aguesseau, Boulogne-Billancourt, 92100, France. TEL 46-04-12-12, FAX 46-04-38-52. Ed. Francoise Vidal. Circ: 8,718.

COMMUNICATIONS NEWS. see COMMUNICATIONS

330 USA
COMMUNIQUE (WASHINGTON, 1971)✳ . Text in English. 1971. bi-m. membership. bk.rev. Description: Covers seminars, conferences, member news, and promotion of the organization.
Published by: World President's Organization, Inc., 1 Canal Center Plz, Ste 105, Alexandria, VA 22314-1595. TEL 202-508-0144, FAX 202-737-0654, TELEX 4972461 WORBUS. Ed. Ann Marie Ross. Circ: 3,500.

330 USA
COMMUNITY INVESTMENTS NEWSLETTER. Text in English. 3/yr., latest vol.13, no.2, 2001.
Related titles: Online - full content ed.
Published by: Federal Reserve Bank of San Francisco, PO Box 7702, San Francisco, CA 94120. TEL 415-974-2978, sf.communityaffairs@sf.frb.org, http://www.sf.frb.org/publications/community/investments/index.html, http://www.frbsf.org.

330 DEU ISSN 1438-3810
COMPANIES AND SECTORS. Text in German. 1958. w. EUR 1,150.41 (effective 1999). reprint service avail. from SCH. Document type: Directory.
Formerly (until 1998): Handbuch der Deutschen Aktiengesellschaften (0938-2941)
Published by: Hoppenstedt Bonnier Zeitschriften GmbH, Havelstr. 9, Darmstadt, 64295, Germany. TEL 49-6151-380-0, FAX 49-6151-380-360.

330 GBR ISSN 1357-9428
COMPANY CAR POLICY U.K. Text in English. a. Document type: Corporate.
Published by: Monks Partnership Ltd., Monks Partnership, The Mill House, Royston Rd, Wendens Ambo, Saffron Walden, Essex CB11 4JX, United Kingdom. TEL 44-1799-542222, FAX 44-1799-541805, info@monkspartnership.co.uk. R&P David Atkins.

330 GBR ISSN 0966-5269
COMPANY DIGEST. Text in English. 1982. m. GBP 35, USD 70 (effective 1999). adv. bk.rev.; software rev. charts; illus. back issues avail. Document type: Bulletin.
Published by: Piton Publishing House Ltd., 79 High St, Godalming, Surrey GU7 1AW, United Kingdom. TEL 44-1483-425454, FAX 44-1483-414262, digest@companydigest.co.uk, http://www.companydigest.co.uk. Ed. Peter Tribe. Adv. contact Suzanne Kimber. page GBP 1,200. Circ: 11,200 (controlled).

330 GBR ISSN 1355-7696
COMPANY REPORTING. Text in English. m.
—IE. CCC.
Published by: Company Reporting Limited, 11 John's Place, Edinburgh, United Kingdom. TEL 44-131-561-8000, FAX 44-131-561-8001.

330 GBR
COMPANY VIEW. Text in English. m. stat. Description: Provides financial data and news on 11,000 companies worldwide..
Media: CD-ROM.
Published by: Financial Times Information Ltd., Extel, Fitzroy House, 13-17 Epworth St, London, EC2A 4DL, United Kingdom. TEL 44-20-7825-8000, FAX 44-20-7608-2032, eic@ft.com, http://www.info.ft.com.

330 GBR ISSN 1024-5294
HF1351 CODEN: COCHFM
COMPETITION AND CHANGE; the journal of global political economy. Text in English. 1996. q. GBP 46 combined subscription in North America to individuals print & online eds.; USD 57 combined subscription elsewhere to individuals print & online eds.; GBP 153 combined subscription in North America to institutions print & online eds.; USD 217 combined subscription elsewhere to institutions print & online eds. (effective 2005). reprint service avail. from PSC. Document type: Journal, Academic/Scholarly. Description: Examines the changing nature of business organization in a highly competitive global economy.
Related titles: Online - full text ed.: USD 184 to individuals; GBP 130 to institutions (effective 2005) (from EBSCO Publishing, Gale Group, IngentaConnect, O C L C Online Computer Library Center, Inc., Swets Information Services).
Indexed: BibInd, CPM, IBSS, JEL.
—BLDSC (3363.992260), IE, Infotrieve. CCC.
Published by: Maney Publishing, Hudson Rd, Leeds, W Yorks LS9 7DL, United Kingdom. TEL 44-113-2497481, FAX 44-113-2486983, maney@maney.co.uk, http://www.maney.co.uk/journals/cac. Eds. Julie Froud TEL 44-161-275-4018, Sukhdev Johal TEL 44-1784-439854.

330 USA ISSN 1545-2581
HD41
COMPETITION FORUM. Text in English. a. USD 40 per issue domestic to individuals; USD 60 per issue foreign to individuals; USD 60 per issue domestic to institutions; USD 80 per issue foreign to institutions (effective 2005).
Published by: Indiana University of Pennsylvania, International Academy of Business Disciplines, PO Box 1658, Indiana, PA 15705. TEL 754-357-5759, aaali@grove.iup.edu. Ed., R&P Abbas J Ali.

COMPETITION LAW INSIGHT; antitrust law and policy in a global market. see LAW—International Law

330 IND
COMPETITION LEADER. Text in English. 1977. m.
Address: 7 Old Court House St., Kolkata, West Bengal 700 001, India. Ed. S C Talukdar. Circ: 97,000.

330 BEL ISSN 1025-2266
COMPETITION POLICY NEWSLETTER. Text in English. 1994. 3/yr. Document type: Newsletter.
Related titles: Online - full content ed.: free.
Indexed: PAIS.
—BLDSC (3363.993180).
Published by: European Commission, Directorate-General for Competition, Rue Joseph II / Jozef II straat 70, Brussels, B-1000, Belgium. infocomp@cec.eu.int, http://europa.eu.int/comm/competition/publications/cpn/, http://europa.eu.int/comm/competition/index_en.html.

330 IND ISSN 0971-8753
COMPETITION REFRESHER. Text in English. 1984. m. INR 200; INR 21 newsstand/cover (effective 1999). adv.
Published by: (Bright Careers Institute), Competition Refresher Pvt. Ltd., 2767 Bright House, Darya Ganj, New Delhi, 110 002, India. TEL 91-11-3282226, FAX 91-11-3269227, psbright@ndf.vsnl.net. Ed. D S Phull. Pub., R&P Pritam Singh Bright. Adv. contact K C Lapsha. B&W page INR 25,000, color page INR 50,000; trim 175 x 245. Circ: 148,693 (paid).

330 IND
COMPETITION SUCCESS REVIEW. Text in English. 1964. m. INR 21 newsstand/cover.
Published by: Competition Review Pvt. Ltd., 604 Prabhat Kiran, Rajendra Place, New Delhi, 110 008, India. TEL 11-4712898, FAX 11-5754647. Ed. S K Sachdeva. adv.: B&W page INR 50,000, color page INR 100,000; trim 175 x 245. Circ: 250,000.

330.9 332.6 USA
THE (YEAR) COMPETITIVENESS REPORT ON ARGENTINA: FINANCIALS RETURNS, LABOR PRODUCTIVITY AND INTERNATIONAL GAPS. Text in English. a., latest 2000. USD 210 (effective 2001). Document type: Yearbook. Description: Analyses data drawn from 23000 firms, yielding some 600 benchmarks across 200 measures with 70 graphical gap analysis. focusing on the fundamentals: financial performance and labor productivity.
Published by: Icon Group International, Inc., 4370 La Jolla Village Dr. 4o. Fl., San Diego, CA 92122. TEL 858-546-4340, FAX 858-546-4341, http://www.icongrouponline.com/. Ed. Stephanie Winters.

330.9 332.6 USA
THE (YEAR) COMPETITIVENESS REPORT ON BRAZIL: FINANCIALS RETURNS, LABOR PRODUCTIVITY AND INTERNATIONAL GAPS. Text in English. a., latest 2000. USD 210 (effective 2001). Document type: Yearbook. Description: Analyses data drawn from 23000 firms, yielding some 600 benchmarks across 200 measures with 70 graphical gap analysis. focusing on the fundamentals: financial performance and labor productivity.
Published by: Icon Group International, Inc., 4370 La Jolla Village Dr. 4o. Fl., San Diego, CA 92122. TEL 858-546-4340, FAX 858-546-4341, http://www.icongrouponline.com/. Ed. Stephanie Winters.

330.9 332.6 USA
THE (YEAR) COMPETITIVENESS REPORT ON CANADA: FINANCIALS RETURNS, LABOR PRODUCTIVITY AND INTERNATIONAL GAPS. Text in English. a., latest 2000. USD 210 (effective 2001). **Document type:** *Yearbook.* **Description:** Analyses data drawn from 23000 firms, yielding some 600 benchmarks across 200 measures with 70 graphical gap analysis. focusing on the fundamentals: financial performance and labor productivity.
Published by: Icon Group International, Inc., 4370 La Jolla Village Dr. 4o. Fl., San Diego, CA 92122. TEL 858-546-4340, FAX 858-546-4341, http://www.icongrouponline.com/. Ed. Stephanie Winters.

330.9 332.6 USA
THE (YEAR) COMPETITIVENESS REPORT ON CHILE: FINANCIALS RETURNS, LABOR PRODUCTIVITY AND INTERNATIONAL GAPS. Text in English. a. USD 210 (effective 2001). **Document type:** *Yearbook.* **Description:** Analyses data drawn from 23000 firms, yielding some 600 benchmarks across 200 measures with 70 graphical gap analysis. focusing on the fundamentals: financial performance and labor productivity.
Published by: Icon Group International, Inc., 4370 La Jolla Village Dr. 4o. Fl., San Diego, CA 92122. TEL 858-546-4340, FAX 858-546-4341, http://www.icongrouponline.com/. Ed. Stephanie Winters.

330.9 332.6 USA
THE (YEAR) COMPETITIVENESS REPORT ON COLOMBIA: FINANCIALS RETURNS, LABOR PRODUCTIVITY AND INTERNATIONAL GAPS. Text in English. a., latest 2000. USD 210 (effective 2001). **Document type:** *Yearbook.* **Description:** Analyses data drawn from 23000 firms, yielding some 600 benchmarks across 200 measures with 70 graphical gap analysis. focusing on the fundamentals: financial performance and labor productivity.
Published by: Icon Group International, Inc., 4370 La Jolla Village Dr. 4o. Fl., San Diego, CA 92122. TEL 858-546-4340, FAX 858-546-4341, http://www.icongrouponline.com/. Ed. Stephanie Winters.

330.9 332.6 USA
THE (YEAR) COMPETITIVENESS REPORT ON LATIN AMERICA: FINANCIALS RETURNS, LABOR PRODUCTIVITY AND INTERNATIONAL GAPS. Text in English. a., latest 2000. USD 210 (effective 2001). **Document type:** *Yearbook.* **Description:** Analyses data drawn from 23000 firms, yielding some 600 benchmarks across 200 measures with 70 graphical gap analysis, focusing on the fundamentals: financial performance and labor productivity.
Published by: Icon Group International, Inc., 4370 La Jolla Village Dr. 4o. Fl., San Diego, CA 92122. TEL 858-546-4340, FAX 858-546-4341, http://www.icongrouponline.com/. Ed. Stephanie Winters.

330.9 332.6 USA
THE (YEAR) COMPETITIVENESS REPORT ON MEXICO: FINANCIALS RETURNS, LABOR PRODUCTIVITY AND INTERNATIONAL GAPS. Text in English. a., latest 2000. USD 210 (effective 2001). **Document type:** *Yearbook.* **Description:** Analyses data drawn from 23000 firms, yielding some 600 benchmarks across 200 measures with 70 graphical gap analysis. focusing on the fundamentals: financial performance and labor productivity.
Published by: Icon Group International, Inc., 4370 La Jolla Village Dr. 4o. Fl., San Diego, CA 92122. TEL 858-546-4340, FAX 858-546-4341, http://www.icongrouponline.com/. Ed. Stephanie Winters.

330.9 332.6 USA
THE (YEAR) COMPETITIVENESS REPORT ON PERU: FINANCIALS RETURNS, LABOR PRODUCTIVITY AND INTERNATIONAL GAPS. Text in English. a., latest 2000. USD 210 (effective 2001). **Document type:** *Yearbook.* **Description:** Analyses data drawn from 23000 firms, yielding some 600 benchmarks across 200 measures with 70 graphical gap analysis. focusing on the fundamentals: financial performance and labor productivity.
Published by: Icon Group International, Inc., 4370 La Jolla Village Dr. 4o. Fl., San Diego, CA 92122. TEL 858-546-4340, FAX 858-546-4341, http://www.icongrouponline.com/. Ed. Stephanie Winters.

330.9 332.6 USA
THE (YEAR) COMPETITIVENESS REPORT ON VENEZUELA: FINANCIALS RETURNS, LABOR PRODUCTIVITY AND INTERNATIONAL GAPS. Text in English. a. USD 210 (effective 2001). **Document type:** *Yearbook.* **Description:** Analyses data drawn from 23000 firms, yielding some 600 benchmarks across 200 measures with 70 graphical gap analysis. focusing on the fundamentals: financial performance and labor productivity.
Published by: Icon Group International, Inc., 4370 La Jolla Village Dr. 4o. Fl., San Diego, CA 92122. TEL 858-546-4340, FAX 858-546-4341, http://www.icongrouponline.com/. Ed. Stephanie Winters.

COMPUTER BUSINESS REVIEW. see *COMPUTERS—Computer Industry*

COMPUTERS IN HIGHER EDUCATION ECONOMICS REVIEW. see *COMPUTERS—Computer Assisted Instruction*

330 HKG
COMPUTRADE INTERNATIONAL. Text in English. 10/yr. USD 60. adv. back issues avail. **Document type:** *Trade.* **Description:** Provides information about products and market trends to developers, manufacturers and buyers of PC-related products.
Related titles: Online - full text ed.: CompuTrade Web.
Published by: Ace Marketing & Publications, Inc., 10F, Ultragrace Commercial Bldg, 5 Jordan Rd, Kowloon, Hong Kong. TEL 852-2359-3668, FAX 852-2770-5886, 886-2-23945163, service@computrade.com.tw, www.computrade.com.tw. Pub. Jack Roan. adv.: page USD 6,100; 36.5 x 26. Circ: 45,000.

330 051 320 USA
COMSTOCK'S BUSINESS - CALIFORNIA'S CAPITOL REGION. Text in English. 1989. m. USD 30; USD 3.50 newsstand/cover (effective 2005). adv. index. back issues avail. **Document type:** *Magazine, Trade.* **Description:** Publishes for top managers including CEOs, presidents, owners of companies, regional managers, government leaders, professionals and entrepreneurs. Profiles community leaders; discusses issues facing communities, and growth in the region.
Formerly: Comstock's
Published by: Comstock Publishing, Inc., 3090 Fite Cir, Ste 101, Sacramento, CA 95827-0000. TEL 916-364-1000, FAX 916-364-0280, jtcomstock@aol.com. Ed. Douglas Curley. Pub. Winnie Comstock-Carlson. Adv. contact Clayton Blakley. B&W page USD 2,620, color page USD 3,950. Circ: 40,000 (paid and controlled).

330 051 USA
COMSTOCK'S BUSINESS - SAN JOACHIN VALLEY. Text in English. m. USD 12; USD 3 newsstand/cover (effective 2001).
Published by: Comstock Publishing, Inc., 3090 Fite Cir, Ste 101, Sacramento, CA 95827-0000. TEL 916-364-1000, FAX 916-364-0280. Pub. Winnie Comstock-Carlson. Adv. contact Clayton Blakley.

330 USA
CONCEPTS IN ACTION. Text in English. q.
Published by: Deloitte & Touche, 10 Westport Rd, C 2 N, Box 820, Wilton, CT 06897. TEL 203-761-3000.

330 USA
CONCORD BUSINESS. Text in English. 1989. a. USD 2.50. adv. **Document type:** *Newspaper, Trade.* **Description:** Covers economic and financial developments in the city of Concord. Written by area businessmen, stockbrokers and bankers.
Address: PO Box 2393, Concord, NH 03301. TEL 603-224-6566. Ed. Kathleen Shean. Pub., R&P, Adv. contact James C Boyle. Circ: 5,000.

CONFERENCE AND INCENTIVE TRAVEL. see *TRAVEL AND TOURISM*

330 USA ISSN 0899-2231
CONFERENCE BOARD. ANNUAL REPORT. Text in English. 1987. a.
Published by: Conference Board, Inc., 845 Third Ave, New York, NY 10022. TEL 212-339-0345, FAX 212-980-7014, http://www.conference-board.org.

338 USA ISSN 1077-0526
HG4028.C6
CONFERENCE BOARD. CORPORATE CONTRIBUTIONS. Text in English. a. USD 180 to non-members; USD 45 to members (effective 2003). **Document type:** *Monographic series.*
Former titles (until 1989): Conference Board. Survey of Corporate Contributions (1043-5344); (until 1988): Conference Board. Annual Survey of Corporate Contributions (0146-0986); (until 1974): Conference Board. Report on Company Contributions (0069-8369)
Related titles: Microfiche ed.: (from CIS); Online - full text ed.
Indexed: PAIS, SRI.
—CISTI.
Published by: Conference Board, Inc., 845 Third Ave, New York, NY 10022. TEL 212-759-0900, FAX 212-980-7014, http://www.conference-board.org.

330 CAN ISSN 1205-1675
CONFERENCE BOARD OF CANADA. MEMBERS' BRIEFING. Text in English. irreg.
Published by: Conference Board of Canada, 255 Smyth Rd, Ste 100, Ottawa, ON K1H 8M7, Canada. TEL 613-526-3280, FAX 613-526-4857, ikm@conferenceboard.ca, http://www.conferenceboard.ca/inn/publications.htm.

330 USA ISSN 0732-572X
CONFERENCE BOARD. REPORTS. Variant title: Conference Board. Reseach Reports. Text in English. 1941. irreg. varies.
Incorporates (in 1990): Conference Board. Perspectives (1046-2988); Conference Board. Research Bulletin; Which was formerly (1975-1981): Conference Board. Information Bulletin (0197-4971)
—CCC.
Published by: Conference Board, Inc., 845 Third Ave, New York, NY 10022. TEL 212-339-0345, FAX 212-836-9740, atb@conference-board.com, http://www.conference-board.org.

330 NIC ISSN 1605-0967
CONFIDENCIAL. Text in Spanish. w.
Related titles: Online - full text ed.: ISSN 1605-0959. 1999.
Published by: Inversiones Multimedia S.A., De la Iglesia El Carmen 1c. al lago, 1/2 c. abajo., Managua, Nicaragua. TEL 505-2-268-4650, FAX 505-2-268-0129, revista@confidencial.com.ni, bodan@ibw.com.ni, http://www.confidencial.com.ni/. Ed. Oliver Bodan.

330 301 USA ISSN 0363-9460
CODEN: SCNEBK
CONFRONTATION - CHANGE REVIEW. Key Title: Confrontation - Change Literary Review. Text in English. 1976. q. USD 16 (effective 2002). adv. bk.rev.; film rev.; play rev.; software rev.; Website rev. bibl.; charts; illus.; stat. index. **Document type:** *Journal, Consumer.*
Incorporated: Journal of Applied Social and Economic Sciences
Indexed: PsycholAb.
Published by: Economic Research Center, Inc., 3955 Denlinger Rd, Dayton, OH 45426-2329. TEL 513-837-0498, FAX 513-837-5888. Ed., Adv. contact Frederick M Finney. Circ: 1,000.

330 ITA
CONGIUNTURA ECONOMICA LAZIALE. Text in Italian. m.
Indexed: PAIS.
Published by: Cassa di Risparmio di Roma, 320 Via del Corso, Rome, 00186, Italy.

CONJONCTURE ECONOMIQUE DES REGIONS DU QUEBEC EN (YEAR). see *BUSINESS AND ECONOMICS—Production Of Goods And Services*

330 ARG
CONSEJO TECNICO DE INVERSIONES. INFORME ESPECIAL. Text in English, Spanish. 1975. s-a. USD 110. adv. **Document type:** *Newspaper, Corporate.* **Description:** Current economic updates and 5-year projections.
Published by: Consejo Tecnico de Inversiones S.A., Tucuman, 834 1o, Capital Federal, Buenos Aires 1049, Argentina. FAX 54-114-3224887. Ed. Jose Luis Blanco. Pub. Daniel Sticco. Adv. contact Marta Ortega.

CONSTRUCTION DISTRIBUTION. see *BUILDING AND CONSTRUCTION*

330 USA ISSN 1526-159X
K3
CONSTRUCTION LAW AND BUSINESS. Text in English. bi-m. USD 185 (effective 2002). **Document type:** *Journal.*
Related titles: Online - full text ed.: (from EBSCO Publishing).
Published by: Aspen Publishers, Inc. (Subsidiary of: Wolters Kluwer N.V.), 111Eighth Ave., 7th Fl, New York, NY 10011. TEL 212-771-0600, FAX 212-771-0885, customer.service@aspenpubl.com, http://www.aspenpublishers.com.

CONSTRUCTION SURVEY. see *BUILDING AND CONSTRUCTION*

330 SEN
CONSTRUIRE L'AFRIQUE. Text in French. 1985. 6/yr.
Address: BP 3770, Dakar, Senegal. TEL 24-19-61, FAX 23-07-90. Ed. Cheikh Ousmane Diallo.

330 ITA ISSN 1120-9585
CONSULENZA; settimanale di informazione e commenti operativi per l'azienda. Text in Italian. 1976. w. (44/yr.). EUR 500 (effective 2005). adv. **Document type:** *Magazine, Trade.*
Related titles: Online - full text ed.: ISSN 1721-1026. 1999.
Published by: Gruppo Buffetti SpA, Via del Fosso di Santa Maura, Rome, 00169, Italy. TEL 39-06-231951. Ed. Sergio Milocco. Circ: 16,000.

330 USA ISSN 0887-0314
CONSULTING INTELLIGENCE. Text in English. 1983. bi-m. members only. adv. **Document type:** *Newsletter, Trade.* **Description:** For all independent professional consultants.
Published by: American Consultants League, 30466 Prince William St, Princess Anne, MD 21853. TEL 651-410-4869, FAX 651-410-4885, the-consultants-institute@usa.net. Ed., R&P, Adv. contact Hubert Bermont. B&W page USD 500, color page USD 500; trim 8.5 x 11. Circ: 1,000.

CONSULTING RATES AND BUSINESS PRACTICES. ANNUAL SURVEY. see *OCCUPATIONS AND CAREERS*

CONSULTING SUCCESS ONLINE. see *ADVERTISING AND PUBLIC RELATIONS*

CONSUMER CREDIT CONTROL. see *LAW*

CONSUMER PROTECTION, ANTITRUST & UNFAIR BUSINESS PRACTICES NEWSLETTER. see *CONSUMER EDUCATION AND PROTECTION*

CONSUMERS SHOULD KNOW. see *REAL ESTATE*

B

330 371.42 CAN
CONTACT TORONTO. Text in English. 1992. biennial. CND 65 to non-members; CND 45 to members. **Document type:** *Directory.*
Former titles (until 1999): Toronto Region Top Employer's Guide (1199-6579); (until 1994): Guide to the Toronto Region's Top Employers (1183-7373)
Published by: Toronto Board of Trade, 1 First Canadian Place, P O Box 60, Toronto, ON M5X 1C1, Canada. TEL 416-366-6811, http://www.bot.com. Ed. Mary de Reus.

330 FRA ISSN 1166-4231
CONTACTS A V A. (Assurances Vieillesse des Artisans) Text in French. 1963. 6/yr. bk.rev. **Document type:** *Trade.*
Description: Covers commercial, economic, and social security matters, as they affect artisans in France and the EU.
Published by: Magazine Institution d'Assurances Vieillesse des Artisans, 28 boulevard de Grenelle, Paris, Cedex 15 75737, France. TEL 33-1-44375156, FAX 33-1-44375205, ava@cancava.fr, http://www.cancava.fr. Ed. Philippe Bollecker. R&P Lucien Chauvier. Circ: 1,185,000.

CONTAINER INTELLIGENCE MONTHLY. see *TRANSPORTATION—Ships And Shipping*

CONTAINER INTELLIGENCE QUARTERLY. see *TRANSPORTATION—Ships And Shipping*

330 USA ISSN 1074-3529
HD72
➤ **CONTEMPORARY ECONOMIC POLICY.** Text in English. 1982. q. GBP 194 to institutions (effective 2005); USD 298, EUR 291 to institutions; GBP 148 academic; USD 226, EUR 222 academics; GBP 204, USD 313, EUR 306 combined subscription to institutions print & online eds.; GBP 156, USD 239, EUR 234 combined subscription academics; print & online eds. (effective 2006), adv. bk.rev. illus.; abstr. Index. back issues avail.; reprint service avail. from PSC. **Document type:** *Journal, Academic/Scholarly.*
Formerly (until 1994): Contemporary Policy Issues (0735-0007)
Related titles: Microfilm ed.: (from PQC); Online - full text ed.: ISSN 1465-7287. GBP 184, USD 282, EUR 276 to institutions; GBP 140, USD 214, EUR 210 academics (effective 2006) (from bigchalk, EBSCO Publishing, Florida Center for Library Automation, Gale Group, H.W. Wilson, HighWire Press, IngentaConnect, Northern Light Technology, Inc., O C L C Online Computer Library Center, Inc., Oxford University Press Online Journals, ProQuest Information & Learning, Swets Information Services).
Indexed: ABIn, ABS&EES, ASCA, AgeL, AmH&L, CJA, ChPerl, CurCont, EnerRev, FamI, HRA, HistAb, IBR, IBSS, IBZ, IPARL, JEL, PAIS, PRA, RI-1, RI-2, RefZh, SPAA, SSCI, SSI, SUSA, WAE&RSA, WBA, WBSS,
—BLDSC (3425.179450), CISTI, IDS, IE, Infotrieve, ingenta. **CCC.**
Published by: (Western Economic Association International), Oxford University Press (Subsidiary of: Oxford University Press), 2001 Evans Rd, Cary, NC 27513. TEL 919-677-0977, 800-852-7323, FAX 919-677-1714, info@weainternational.org, jnlorders@oup-usa.org, http://cep.oxfordjournals.org/, http://www.us.oup.com. Ed. Darwin C. Hall. Pub. Eric Staib. Adv. contact Helen Pearson. B&W page GBP 175; 145 x 210. Circ: 3,000.

➤ **THE CONTEMPORARY MIDDLE EAST/GENDAI NO CHUTO.** see *POLITICAL SCIENCE*

330 332 USA ISSN 1569-3759
CONTEMPORARY STUDIES IN ECONOMIC AND FINANCIAL ANALYSIS; an international series of monographs. Text in English. 1976. irreg., latest vol.85, 2002. price varies. charts; stat. back issues avail. **Document type:** *Monographic series, Academic/Scholarly.* **Description:** Designed to include titles covering a wide range of topics within the fields of economics and finance.
Related titles: Online - full text ed.: (from ScienceDirect).
Indexed: EngInd.
—BLDSC (3425.306000), ingenta.
Published by: J A I Press Inc. (Subsidiary of: Elsevier Science & Technology), 360 Park Ave S, New York, NY 10010-1710. TEL 212-989-5800, FAX 212-633-3990, usinfo-f@elsevier.com, http://www.elsevier.com/wps/find/bookseriesdescription.cws_home/BS_CSEFA/description. Eds. J R Aronson, R J Thornton.

330 DEU ISSN 0178-5737
CONTRASTE; Monatszeitung fuer Selbstorganisation. Text in German. 1984. 11/yr. EUR 45 (effective 2005). **Document type:** *Newspaper, Trade.*
Published by: Contraste e.V., Postfach 104520, Heidelberg, 69035, Germany. TEL 49-6221-162467, FAX 49-6221-164489, contraste@t-online.de, http://www.nadir.org/nadir/periodika/contraste, http://www.contraste.org.

330 340 ITA ISSN 1123-5047
I CONTRATTI. Text in Italian. 1993. m. (11/yr.). EUR 172 (effective 2005). adv. **Document type:** *Magazine, Consumer.*
Related titles: CD-ROM ed.: ISSN 1591-5484.
Published by: IPSOA Editore (Subsidiary of: Wolters Kluwer Italia Srl), Strada 1, Palazzo F6, Milanofiori, Assago, MI 20090, Italy. TEL 39-02-82476888, FAX 39-02-82476436, http://www.ipsoa.it. Ed. Massimiliano Galioni. Adv. contact Luciano Alcaro Menichini.

330 BRA
CONTRIBUICOES EM ECONOMIA. Text in Portuguese. 1977. irreg. illus. **Document type:** *Monographic series.*
Published by: Editora Campus Ltda. (Subsidiary of: Elsevier Science & Technology), Rua Sete de Setembro 111-16 andar, Rio De Janeiro, RJ 20150-002, Brazil. TEL 55-21-509-5340, FAX 55-21-507-1991. Ed. Claudio M Rothmuller.

330 DEU ISSN 1431-1933
CONTRIBUTIONS TO ECONOMICS. Text in German. 1989. irreg., latest vol.14, 2005. price varies. **Document type:** *Monographic series, Academic/Scholarly.*
Published by: Springer-Verlag (Subsidiary of: Springer Science+Business Media), Tiergartenstr 17, Heidelberg, 69121, Germany. TEL 49-6221-3450, FAX 49-6221-345229, subscriptions@springer.de, http://www.springer.de. Eds. M Bihn, W A Mueller.

330 USA ISSN 1093-1163
HG4001
CONTROLLER'S COST AND PROFIT REPORT. Text in English. 1979. s-m. USD 205; USD 287 foreign (effective 1998). **Document type:** *Newsletter.* **Description:** Focuses exclusively on all areas of crucial interest to chief financial officers, from taxes and legal developments to operations and compensation, giving quick access to the latest ideas and methods.
Former titles (until 1997): Controller's Cost Report (1081-9215); (until 1995): Wendell's Report for Controllers (1067-7313); (until 1993): C F O Alert (Monthly) (0894-4822); (until 1987): Corporate Controllers Report (0745-3078); (until 1982): Corporate Controller's and Treasurer's Report (0274-6107)
Related titles: Online - full text ed.: (from EBSCO Publishing, Gale Group).
Published by: W G & L Financial Reporting & Management Research (Subsidiary of: R I A), 395 Hudson St, New York, NY 10014. TEL 212-367-6300, FAX 212-367-6718. Ed. Paul J Wendell. **Subscr. to:** The Park Square Bldg., 31 St James Ave, Boston, MA 02116-4112. TEL 800-950-1207.

CONTUREN. see *LITERARY AND POLITICAL REVIEWS*

330 USA
COOPERS & LYBRAND. MONOGRAPH SERIES∗. Text in English. irreg., latest vol.3, 1995. price varies. back issues avail. **Document type:** *Monographic series.*
Indexed: ATI.
Published by: Coopers & Lybrand L.L.P., Publishing Division, 12902 Federal Systems Park Dr, Fairfax, VA 22033-4421. TEL 703-908-1527, 800-247-6553.

330 NIC
COORDINADORA REGIONAL DE INVESTIGACIONES ECONOMICAS Y SOCIALES. CUADERNOS. (In 5 series: Debates, Ensayos, Avances, Documentos, Bibliografias) Text in Spanish. 1982. irreg. **Document type:** *Academic/Scholarly.*
Published by: Coordinadora Regional de Investigaciones Economicas y Sociales, Apdo 3516, Managua, Nicaragua. Ed. Andres Serbin.

330 DNK ISSN 1398-7461
COPENHAGEN BUSINESS SCHOOL. DEPARTMENT OF INTERNATIONAL ECONOMICS AND MANAGEMENT. WORKING PAPERS. Text in English. 1999. irreg., latest 2004. back issues avail. **Document type:** *Monographic series, Academic/Scholarly.*
Media: Online - full content.
Published by: Copenhagen Business School, Department of International Economics and Management/Handelshoejskolen. Institut for International Oekonomi og Virksomhedsledelse, Porcelaenshaven 24, Frederiksberg, 2500, Denmark. TEL 45-38-152515, FAX 45-38-152500, int@cbs.dk, http://www.cbs.dk/content/view/pub/8240.

330 DNK ISSN 1601-9571
COPENHAGEN BUSINESS SCHOOL. FACULTY OF ECONOMICS AND BUSINESS ADMINISTRATION. PH.D-SERIE. Text in Danish, English. 1990. irreg. back issues avail. **Document type:** *Monographic series, Academic/Scholarly.*
Formerly (until 2001): Copenhagen Business School. Faculty of Economics and Business Administration. Ph.D. Serie (0906-6934)
Published by: Copenhagen Business School, Faculty of Economics and Business Administration/Handelshoejskolen. Erhvervsoekonomiske Fakultet, Solbjerg Plads 3, Frederiksberg, 2000, Denmark. TEL 45-38-152682, FAX 45-38-152675, http://www.cbs.dk.

380.1 DNK ISSN 1602-6004
COPENHAGEN SCHOOL OF BUSINESS. FORUM FOR ADVERTISING RESEARCH. RESEARCH PAPER. Text in Danish. 1985. irreg. back issues avail. **Document type:** *Monographic series, Academic/Scholarly.*
Former titles (2000-2002): Copenhagen School of Business. Advertising Research Group. Research Paper (1600-728X); (until 1996): Copenhagen School of Economics and Business Administration. Marketing Institute. Research Paper (0900-1808)
Published by: Copenhagen Business School, Department of Marketing/Handelshoejskolen. Institut for Afsaetningsoekonomi, Solbjerg Plads 3C, Frederiksberg C, 2000, Denmark. TEL 45-38-152100, FAX 45-38-152101, jra.markt@cbs.dk, http://www.frf.cbs.dk.

330 DNK ISSN 1396-9765
COPENHAGEN UNIVERSITY. INSTITUTE OF ECONOMICS. CENTER FOR INDUSTRIAL ECONOMICS. DISCUSSION PAPERS. Text in English. 1997. irreg.
—BLDSC (3597.121400).
Published by: Koebenhavns Universitet, Oekonomisk Institut. Center for Industri Oekonomi/Copenhagen University, Institute of Economics. Center for Industrial Economics, Noerregade 10, Copenhagen, 1017, Denmark. TEL 45-35322626, FAX 45-35322628, http://www.ku.dk.

330 USA
COPYSOURCE QUARTERLY. Text in English. 1996. q. USD 199 (effective 1999). **Document type:** *Newsletter.* **Description:** Provides a resource for producing in-house newsletters. Includes topics such as leadership and teamwork, financial planning, customer service, health and safety, personal and professional development, and sales.
Published by: Bureau of Business Practice (Subsidiary of: Aspen Publishers, Inc.), 1185 Avenue of the Americas, 37th Fl, New York, NY 10036. TEL 860-442-4365, 800-243-0876, FAX 860-437-3555, rebecca_armitage@prenhall.com, http://www.bbpnews.com. Ed. Kathy Cipriani. Pub. Peter Garabedian. R&P Kathryn Mennone.

330 COL
CORPORACION FINANCIERA COLOMBIANA. EJERCICIO. Text in Spanish. a.
Published by: Corporacion Financiera Colombiana, Carrera Nos. 26-45, Apartado Aereo 11843, Bogota, CUND, Colombia.

CORPORATE ACCOUNTABILITY & FRAUD DAILY. see *LAW—Corporate Law*

CORPORATE ACQUISITIONS AND MERGERS. see *LAW—Corporate Law*

330 USA
CORPORATE ALMANAC. Text in English. a.
Published by: Cognetics, Inc., 281 Winter St., Waltham, MA 02451-8740. Eds. Anne Haggerty, David Birch.

330 CAN
CORPORATE ELITE. Text in English. 1990. a. adv.
Published by: Financial Post Datagroup, 300-1450 Don Mills Rd, Don Mills, ON M3B 3R5, Canada. TEL 416-350-6176, FAX 416-599-6171. R&P Theresa Butcher.

330 381.1 USA
▼ **CORPORATE EVENT.** Text in English. 2005. q. USD 28 domestic; USD 38 in Canada & Mexico; USD 48 elsewhere (effective 2005). adv. **Document type:** *Magazine, Trade.* **Description:** Targets marketing directors, event managers and event producers incolved in user conferences, trade shows, dealer/distributor events, media events, VIP summits and community events. Devoted to case studies on the b2b segment of the event marketing industry.
Published by: Exhibitor Publications, Inc., 206 S Broadway, Ste 745, Rochester, MN 55904-6565. TEL 507-289-6556, 888-235-6155, FAX 507-289-5253, http://www.exhibitoronline.com/exhibitormagazine/eventmag.asp, http://www.exhibitornet.com. Eds. Whitney Archibald, Lee Knight. adv.: color page USD 3,420; trim 8.5 x 10.875. **Subscr. to:** PO Box 368, Rochester, MN 55903-0368.

330 338 USA ISSN 0361-2309
HD60.5.U5
CORPORATE EXAMINER. Text in English. 1972. 10/yr. USD 50; USD 55 in Canada & Mexico; USD 60 elsewhere (effective 2001). bk.rev. back issues avail. **Document type:** *Newsletter, Trade.*
Indexed: HRIR.
Published by: Interfaith Center on Corporate Responsibility, Rm 550, 475 Riverside Dr, New York, NY 10115-0500. TEL 212-870-2296. Ed. Diane Bratcher. Pub. Timothy Smith. Circ: 1,500.

330 CAN ISSN 1481-2185
THE CORPORATE EXECUTIVE; news Atlantic. Text in English. 1992. 6/yr. CND 18. adv. bk.rev. **Document type:** *Newspaper, Trade.* **Description:** Current business articles directed at upper management covering all of the Atlantic Canada, New England, and Europe.
Published by: Nationwide Promotions Limited, 12 Dawn Dr, Burnside Industrial Park, Dartmouth, NS B3B 1H9, Canada. TEL 902-468-5709, FAX 902-468-5697, corpexec@accesscable.net. Ed. Bill Harris. R&P, Adv. contact Dave Boutilier TEL 902-468-6871. B&W page CND 1,525, color page CND 2,325; trim 11.88 x 9.25. Circ: 12,000.

B

330 USA ISSN 1535-962X
CORPORATE EXECUTIVE; the newsletter for officers and directors of public office. Text in English. 1986. 6/yr., latest vol.15, no.3. USD 495; USD 535 foreign (effective 1999). index. back issues avail. **Document type:** *Newsletter.* **Description:** Provides ongoing legal advice on a wide range of executive compensation matters.
Related titles: Online - full content ed.: USD 495 to individuals; USD 1,195 to institutions (effective 2001).
Published by: Executive Press, PO Box 21639, Concord, CA 94521-0639. TEL 925-685-5111, http://www.thecorporatecounsel.net. Ed. Jesse M Brill.

CORPORATE FINANCE REVIEW. see *BUSINESS AND ECONOMICS—Banking And Finance*

330 USA ISSN 0163-3031
HG4057
CORPORATE FINANCE SOURCEBOOK; the guide to major capital investment sources and related financial services. Text in English. 1980. a. USD 689 per issue (effective 2005). adv. tr.lit. **Document type:** *Directory.* **Description:** Includes 18 highly specialized chapters including: venture capital, major private lenders, commercial finance, leasing, commercial banks, US-based foreign banks, investment banks, foreign investment banks in the US, business intermediaries, pension managers, master trusts, cash managers, business insurance brokers, real estate services, securities analysts, and CPAs. —CCC.
Published by: National Register Publishing (Subsidiary of: Marquis Who's Who), 562 Central Ave, New Providence, NJ 07974. TEL 800-473-7020, FAX 908-673-1189, NRPsales@marquiswhoswho.com, http://www.financesourcebook.com, http://www.nationalregisterpub.com. Circ: 10,122.

330 GBR ISSN 0964-8410
HD2741
➤ **CORPORATE GOVERNANCE (OXFORD)**; an international review. Text in English. 1992. bi-m. EUR 75 combined subscription in Europe to individuals print & online eds.; USD 84 combined subscription in the Americas to individuals & Caribbean (print & online eds.); GBP 50 combined subscription elsewhere to individuals print & online eds.; USD 1,660 combined subscription in the Americas to institutions & Caribbean (print & online eds.); GBP 940 combined subscription elsewhere to institutions print & online eds. (effective 2006). **Document type:** *Journal, Academic/Scholarly.* **Description:** Acts as a forum for the exchange of information, insights and knowledge based on both theoretical development and practical experience.
Related titles: Online - full text ed.: ISSN 1467-8683. USD 1,579 in the Americas to institutions & Caribbean; GBP 940 elsewhere to institutions (effective 2006) (from Blackwell Synergy, EBSCO Publishing, Gale Group, IngentaConnect, O C L C Online Computer Library Center, Inc., Swets Information Services).
Indexed: ABIn, APEL, CPM, CurCont, Emerald, IBSS, ILP, SSCI. —BLDSC (3472.066100), IE, Infotrieve, ingenta. **CCC.**
Published by: Blackwell Publishing Ltd., 9600 Garsington Rd, Oxford, OX4 2ZG, United Kingdom. TEL 44-1865-776868, FAX 44-1865-714591, customerservices@oxon.blackwellpublishing.com, http://www.blackwellpublishing.com/journals/CORG. Ed. Christine A Mallin TEL 44-121-4142773.

332.6 USA
CORPORATE GROWTH✶. Text in English. 1968. m. USD 198. **Description:** Covers all aspects of mergers, acquisitions, divestitures, corporate growth and development world-wide.
Related titles: Microform ed.: 1968 (from PQC).
Indexed: ABIn.
Published by: Princeton Research Institute, Western Management Center, PO Box 2702, Scottsdale, AZ 85252-2072. TEL 609-396-0305.

384 GBR
CORPORATE I T UPDATE. Text in English. m. GBP 50, USD 170 (effective 1999). **Document type:** *Trade.* **Description:** Briefing for executives who need a jargon-free update on the issues, technologies and products relevant to the corporate organizations which emerge from the rapidly changing IT and telecomms marketplaces.
Media: Online - full text.
Published by: M2 Communications Ltd., PO Box 475, Coventry, W Mids CV1 2ZW, United Kingdom. TEL 44-1203-634700, FAX 44-1203-634144, M2PW@m2.com, http://www.m2.com. Ed. Darren Ingram. **Dist. in N. America by:** Publications Resource Group, 121 Union St., Box 792, North Adams, MA 01247. TEL 413-664-6185, FAX 413-664-9343.

338.09 IND
CORPORATE OBSERVER. Text in English. 1982. q. USD 200.
Published by: Pranava Industrial Services Pvt. Ltd., 18 Sagar Tarang, Bhulabhai Desai Rd., Mumbai, Maharashtra 400 036, India. TEL 822-6236. Ed. P J Divatia.

330 GBR
CORPORATE REGISTER. Text in English. 1989. q. GBP 215 (effective Apr. 2001). bk.rev. stat.; mkt. back issues avail. **Document type:** *Directory, Trade.* **Description:** Contains contact details and biographies for directors, officers and advisers of all U.K. stock market companies.
Former titles (until Dec. 2003): PricewaterhouseCoopers Corporate Register; Price Waterhouse Corporate Register (1352-8157); (until 1995): Arthur Andersen Corporate Register; Hambro Corporate Register (0956-2893)
Related titles: CD-ROM ed.: PricewaterhouseCoopers C D Register. GBP 495 (effective 2000); Online - full text ed. —BLDSC (3472.095800).
Published by: H S Financial Publishing Ltd., City Innovation Centre, 26-31 Whiskins St, London, EC1R 0JD, United Kingdom. TEL 44-20-7278-7769, FAX 44-20-7278-9808, http://www.corporateregister.co.uk, http://www.hsfinancial.com. Ed., Pub., R&P James Ranft. Adv. contact Ray Witter TEL 44-20-7278-7769.

330 USA ISSN 0890-4278
HC107.W63
CORPORATE REPORT WISCONSIN. Text in English. 1985. m. USD 30; free to qualified personnel (effective 2005). adv. bk.rev. back issues avail.; reprints avail. **Document type:** *Magazine, Trade.* **Description:** Monthly business magazine for executives in the state of Wisconsin.
Related titles: Microform ed.; Online - full text ed.: (from ProQuest Information & Learning).
Indexed: ABIn, BusDate.
Published by: Trails Media Group, Inc., 1131 Mills St., PO Box 317, Black Earth, WI 53515. TEL 608-767-8000, 800-236-8088, FAX 608-767-5444, johnh@wistrails.com, info@wistrails.com, http://www.trailsmediagroup.com/CRW/crw.html. Ed. Paul Zukowski. Pub. Scott Klug Sr. adv.: B&W page USD 3,070, color page USD 3,745. Circ: 30,000 (controlled).

338 USA
CORPORATE RESPONSIBILITY✶. Text in English. 1972. bi-m. USD 85.
Address: 658 Counselors Way, Williamsburg, VA 23185-4059. Ed. Judith Mackey.

330 GBR
CORPORATE SOLUTIONS. Text in English. 1998. q. GBP 20; GBP 50 foreign. **Document type:** *Trade.* —BLDSC (3472.093225).
Published by: Financial Times Professional Publishing (Subsidiary of: Financial Times Group), Maple House, 149 Tottenham Court Rd, London, W1P 9LL, United Kingdom. TEL 44-20-7896-2222, FAX 44-20-7896-2276. **Subscr. to:** Quadrant Subscription Services, Rockwood House, 9-17 Perrymount Rd, Haywards Heath, W. Sussex RH16 3DH, United Kingdom.

[CORPORATE] SOLUTIONS. see *COMPUTERS—Computer Industry*

CORPORATE YELLOW BOOK; who's who at the leading U.S. companies. see *BUSINESS AND ECONOMICS—Management*

330 GBR
CORPORATION OF LONDON. SUBJECT REPORT. Text in English. irreg., latest vol.9, 1994. **Document type:** *Bulletin.*
Published by: Corporation of London, Public Relations Office, Corporation Of London, Guildhall, London, EC2P 2EJ, United Kingdom.

330 USA
CORPUS CHRISTI BAY AREA BUSINESS. Text in English. 1992. q. USD 8.95. adv. bk.rev. stat. back issues avail. **Document type:** *Trade.* **Description:** Targets business and industry decision-makers with articles on business, small-business management, trade with Mexico, and sales and personnel management.
Published by: (Corpus Christi Area Development Corporation), Woolford Publishing (Subsidiary of: Leah Woolford & Co., Inc.), 711 N Carancahua St, Ste 500, Corpus Christi, TX 78475-1301. TEL 512-883-8833, FAX 512-883-4329. Ed. Jeffrey R Woolford. Adv. contact Jeff Woolford. page USD 1,000. Circ: 6,500 (controlled). **Co-sponsor:** Corpus Christi Chamber of Commerce.

330 FRA ISSN 1621-3920
CORRESPONDANCE ECONOMIQUE; quotidien d'informations economiques et sociales. Text in French. 1945. d. adv. **Description:** Provides economic, social and financial information.
Published by: Societe Generale de Presse et d'Editions, 13 av. de l'Opera, Paris, 75001, France. TEL 33-1-40151789, FAX 33-1-40151715. Ed. Etienne Lacour. Pub. Marianne Berard Quelin.

330 ITA ISSN 1590-8100
CORRIERE TRIBUTARIO. Text in Italian. 1978. w. (48/yr.). EUR 269 (effective 2005). adv. bk.rev. index. **Document type:** *Magazine, Trade.*
Related titles: CD-ROM ed.: 1987; Online - full text ed.: (from EBSCO Publishing).
Published by: IPSOA Editore (Subsidiary of: Wolters Kluwer Italia Srl), Strada 1, Palazzo F6, Milanofiori, Assago, MI 20090, Italy. TEL 39-02-82476888, FAX 39-02-82476436, http://www.ipsoa.it. Ed. Massimiliano Galioni. Adv. contact Luciano Alcaro Menichini. Circ: 39,500.

COST SECTOR CATERING. see *FOOD AND FOOD INDUSTRIES*

330 BEL
COTE LIBRE✶. Text in French. 5/w. adv. **Document type:** *Newspaper.*
Address: Rue de Birmingham 131, Brussels, 1070, Belgium. TEL 2-5265666, FAX 2-5265526. Circ: 4,000.

COTTON ECONOMIC REVIEW. see *AGRICULTURE—Crop Production And Soil*

330 NZL
COUNTERACTION; your magazine for retail business knowledge. Text in English. m. NZD 50 domestic; NZD 67 in Australia; NZD 76 elsewhere (effective 2002). **Document type:** *Magazine, Trade.*
Published by: Adjust Media Ltd, Kereru, 18 Kauri Rd, Waikanae, New Zealand. editor@counteraction.co.nz, http://www.counteraction.co.nz. Pubs. Andre Dromgool, Nicky Cassels.

332 382 USA ISSN 1041-3553
HC10
COUNTRY FORECASTS (SYRACUSE). Text in English. 1985. s-a. (Apr. & Oct.). USD 695; USD 375 per vol. (effective 2001). back issues avail. **Description:** Contains rankings and data for over 106 countries on political, economic, and social variables; methods of data-gathering and forecasting; and assumptions underlying the forecasts.
Former titles (until 1988): Country Facts (0889-5007); Country Data Quarterly; Incorporates (1981-1988): Political Climate for International Business (0887-7637); (1986-1988): Political Risk Database (0890-4928); (1986-1988): Country Database (0890-4952)
Related titles: Diskette ed.; Online - full text ed.: (from Data-Star).
Published by: The P R S Group, Inc., PO Box 248, East Syracuse, NY 13057-0248. TEL 315-431-0511, FAX 315-431-0200, custserv@prsgroup.com, http://www.countrydata.com, http://www.prsgroup.com. R&P Mary Lou Walsh.

330 USA ISSN 1478-3614
HC151.A1
COUNTRY PROFILE. BARBADOS, BRITISH VIRGIN ISLANDS, CAYMAN ISLANDS, NETHERLANDS ANTILLES, ARUBA. Text in English. 19??. a. USD 265 per issue print or online (effective 2004). **Document type:** *Trade.*
Supersedes in part (in 2001): Country Profile. Bahamas, Barbados, Bermuda, British Virgin Islands, Netherlands Antilles, Aruba, Turks and Caicos Islands, Cayman Islands (1462-690X); Which superseded in part (in 1997): Country Profile. Belize, Bahamas, Bermuda, Cayman Islands, Turks and Caicos Islands (1367-8124); (in 1997): Country Profile. Jamaica, Barbados (1351-4164); Which was formerly (until 1993): Country Profile. Jamaica (0269-4506); (until 1986): Quarterly Economic Review. Jamaica. Annual Supplement
Related titles: Online - full text ed.: (from EBSCO Publishing).
Published by: Economist Intelligence Unit, 111 W 57th St, New York, NY 10019. TEL 212-554-0600, FAX 212-586-1181, newyork@eiu.com, http://www.eiu.com.

330 USA
COUNTRY PROFILE. BHUTAN. Text in English. a. USD 265 per issue print or online (effective 2004). **Document type:** *Trade.*
Published by: Economist Intelligence Unit, 111 W 57th St, New York, NY 10019. TEL 212-554-0600, FAX 212-586-1181, newyork@eiu.com, http://www.eiu.com.

330 USA
COUNTRY PROFILE. FIJI. Text in English. a. USD 265 per issue print or online (effective 2004). **Document type:** *Trade.*
Published by: Economist Intelligence Unit, 111 W 57th St, New York, NY 10019. TEL 212-554-0600, FAX 212-586-1181, newyork@eiu.com, http://www.eiu.com.

330 USA ISSN 1478-3630
HC154.5.A1
COUNTRY PROFILE. PUERTO RICO, BAHAMAS, BERMUDA, TURKS AND CAICOS ISLANDS. Text in English. 19??. a. USD 265 per issue print or online (effective 2004). **Document type:** *Trade.*
Supersedes in part (in 2002): Country Profile. Bahamas, Barbados, Bermuda, British Virgin Islands, Netherlands Antilles, Aruba, Turks and Caicos Islands, Cayman Islands (1462-690X); Which superseded in part (in 1998): Country Profile. Jamaica, Barbados (1351-4164); (in 1998): Country Profile. Belize, Bahamas, Bermuda, Cayman Islands, Turks and Caicos Islands (1367-8124); And (in 2002): Country Profile. Dominican Republic, Haiti, Puerto Rico (0269-512X); Which was formerly (until 1985): Quarterly Economic Review of Dominican Republic, Haiti, Puerto Rico. Annual Supplement
Related titles: Online - full text ed.: (from EBSCO Publishing).

Published by: Economist Intelligence Unit, 111 W 57th St, New York, NY 10019. TEL 212-554-0600, FAX 212-586-1181, newyork@eiu.com, http://www.eiu.com.

330 USA ISSN 1478-3487
HC154.5.A1
COUNTRY REPORT. PUERTO RICO, BAHAMAS, BERMUDA, TURKS AND CAICOS ISLANDS. Text in English. 2002. q. USD 485 print or online; USD 230 per issue print or online (effective 2004). **Document type:** *Trade.*
Supersedes in part (in 2002): Country Report. Bahamas, Barbados, Bermuda, British Virgin Islands, Netherlands Antilles, Aruba, Turks and Caicos Islands, Cayman Islands (1462-687X); Which superseded in part (in 1998): Country Report. Jamaica, Barbados, Belize, Bahamas, Bermuda, Cayman Islands, Turks and Caicos Islands (1368-9142); Which was formerly (until 1996): Country Report. Jamaica, Belize, Bahamas, Bermuda, Barbados (1460-3543); (until 1994): Country Report. Jamaica, Belize, Bahamas, Bermuda, Barbados, Cayman Islands (1354-2699); (until 1993): Country Report. Trinidad and Tobago, Guyana, Windward and Leeward Islands, Suriname, Netherlands Antilles, Aruba (1351-8674); (until 1993): Country Report. Jamaica, Belize, Bahamas, Bermuda (0269-7130); (until 1986): Quarterly Economic Review of Jamaica, Belize, Bahamas, Bermuda (0266-9617); Which superseded in part (in 1984): Quarterly Economic Review of the West Indies, Belize, Bahamas, Bermuda, Guyana (0142-3738); Which was formerly: Q E R West Indies, Belize, Bahamas, Bermuda, Guyana; (in 2002): Country Report. Dominican Republic, Haiti, Puerto Rico (1465-6396); Which was formerly (until 1998): Country Report. Cuba, Dominican Republic, Haiti, Puerto Rico (0269-5251); (until 1986): Quarterly Economic Review of Cuba, Dominican Republic, Haiti, Puerto Rico (0142-3819); Q E R Cuba, Dominican Republic, Haiti, Puerto Rico
Published by: Economist Intelligence Unit, 111 W 57th St, New York, NY 10019. newyork@eiu.com, http://www.eiu.com.

330 USA
COUNTY EXECUTIVE SUMMARY. Text in English. 1990. m. free to members (effective 2005). **Document type:** *Newsletter.*
Published by: County Executives of America, 1010 Massachusetts Ave, N W, Ste 100, Washington, DC 20001. TEL 202-289-4805, FAX 202-289-4809, http://www.countryexecutives.org. Ed. Kelly Griffin. Circ: 5,000 (controlled).

330 USA
COUP✶ ; information for development executives. Text in English. 1983. q. looseleaf. USD 100. adv. bk.rev. charts; illus.; pat.; stat.; tr.lit. index. back issues avail. **Description:** Reports on acquisitions, mergers, divestitures, venture capital, private placements, corporate financing, planning takeovers, writing investment proposals, and sources of secret business information for practitioners.
Formerly: Venture Capital
Related titles: Microfilm ed.: 1983.
Published by: Venture Capital Consultants America, 917 S Park St, Owosso, MI 48867-4422. Eds. Ben Campbell, Jeff Campbell. Circ: 3,000.

330 TUN ISSN 0330-1516
COURRIER DE L'INDUSTRIE. Text in French. 1977. q. TND 20 domestic; USD 35 foreign (effective 2001). illus.; stat.; tr.lit. back issues avail. **Document type:** *Magazine, Government.*
Published by: Agence de Promotion de l'Industrie/Industrial Promotion Agency, 63 rue de Syrie, Tunis Belvedere, 1002, Tunisia. TEL 216-1-792144, FAX 216-1-782482, TELEX 14166 TN, api@api.com.tn. Ed. Moudher Ben Salem. Circ: 2,000.

330 333.33 FRA
COURRIER DES EMPLOYES D'IMMEUBLES✶ . Text in French. 12/yr.
Address: 53 rue de Vivienne, Paris, 75002, France. TEL 42-36-69-25. Ed. Jacques Simakis. Circ: 22,000.

332 947 FRA ISSN 0590-0239
HC244.A1
COURRIER DES PAYS DE L'EST. Text in French. 1964. m. (10/yr.). EUR 110 domestic; EUR 117 in Europe; EUR 117 DOM-TOM; EUR 125 elsewhere (effective 2003). adv. bk.rev. index. **Document type:** *Government.*
Related titles: Microfiche ed.
Indexed: IBZ, KES, PAIS, PdeR, WAE&RSA.
—BLDSC (3483.080000), IE, Infotrieve, ingenta.
Published by: (Centre d'Etudes et de Documentation sur l'Ex-U R S S, la Chine et l'Europe de l'Est), Documentation Francaise, 29-31 quai Voltaire, Paris, Cedex 7 75344, France. FAX 33-1-40157230. Ed. Sophie Moati. Circ: 1,300.

330 USA ISSN 1090-1612
COURT & COMMERCIAL RECORD. Text in English. 1895. 3/w. (Mon., Wed., Fri.). USD 68 (effective 2005). **Document type:** *Newspaper, Trade.*
Formerly (until 1994): Indianapolis Commercial (1059-9649)
Published by: I B J Corp., 41 E Washington St, Ste 200, Indianapolis, IN 46204. TEL 317-636-0200, FAX 317-263-5259, indian@ibj.com, http://courtcommercialrecord.com. Ed. Rebecca Collier. Pubs. Chris Katterjohn, Glenda Russell. Circ: 845 (paid).

330 USA ISSN 0882-1992
K2
CRAIN'S DETROIT BUSINESS. Text in English. w. (Mon.). USD 59 combined subscription in state print & online eds.; USD 79 combined subscription out of state print & online eds.; USD 127 combined subscription foreign print & online eds. (effective 2005). adv. **Document type:** *Newspaper, Trade.* **Description:** Presents award-winning coverage, industry rankings and "who's who" listings of manufacturing, health care, commercial and industrial real estate, technology and finance for upper-level executives and business owners.
Related titles: Online - full text ed.: Crainsdetroit.com. USD 39 (effective 2002) (from bigchalk, EBSCO Publishing, Florida Center for Library Automation, Gale Group, H.W. Wilson, LexisNexis, Northern Light Technology, Inc., O C L C Online Computer Library Center, Inc., ProQuest Information & Learning, The Dialog Corporation).
Indexed: ABIn, B&I, BPI, BusDate, LRI, T&II.
—CCC.
Published by: Crain Communications, Inc., 1155 Gratiot Ave, Detroit, MI 48207-2997. TEL 313-446-6000, FAX 313-446-1687, dbarkholz@crain.com, http://www.crainsdetroit.com, http://www.crain.com. Ed. Mary Kramer. Pubs. Keith Crain, Keith E. Crain. adv.: B&W page USD 8,960, color page USD 9,760. Circ: 34,660 (paid). Wire service: CNS.

330 USA ISSN 8756-789X
CRAIN'S NEW YORK BUSINESS. Text in English. 1984. w. (Mon.). USD 69.95 domestic; USD 124.95 foreign; USD 3 newsstand/cover (effective 2005). adv. bk.rev. 32 p./no.; back issues avail. **Document type:** *Newspaper, Trade.* **Description:** Covers all business industry sectors including real estate, finance, advertising, hospitality, business services and technology as well as city politics in New York area.
Former titles (until 1985): Citybusiness (8756-6249); (until 1984): New York CityBusiness (8750-7056)
Related titles: Microform ed.; Online - full text ed.: USD 35 (effective 2001) (from bigchalk, EBSCO Publishing, Gale Group, H.W. Wilson, LexisNexis, Northern Light Technology, Inc., O C L C Online Computer Library Center, Inc., ProQuest Information & Learning, The Dialog Corporation).
Indexed: ABIn, B&I, BPI, BusDate, LRI, T&II.
—CCC.
Published by: Crain Communications, Inc., 1155 Gratiot Ave, Detroit, MI 48207-2997. atownsend@crain.com, http://www.crainsny.com/, http://www.crain.com. Eds. Greg David, Rance Crain. Pub. Alair Townsend. Adv. contact Vanessa Cognard. B&W page USD 17,220, color page USD 20,515. Circ: 62,000.

330 GBR ISSN 0963-1690
HD53
➤ **CREATIVITY AND INNOVATION MANAGEMENT.** Text in English. 1992. q. EUR 138 combined subscription in Europe to individuals print & online eds.; USD 155 combined subscription in the Americas to individuals & Caribbean, print & online eds.; GBP 92 combined subscription elsewhere to individuals print & online eds.; USD 815 combined subscription in the Americas to institutions & Caribbean, print & online eds.; GBP 485 combined subscription elsewhere to institutions print & online eds. (effective 2006). reprint service avail. from PSC. **Document type:** *Journal, Academic/Scholarly.* **Description:** Promotes understanding and scholarship internationally in the fields of creativity and innovation.
Related titles: Online - full text ed.: ISSN 1467-8691. USD 774 in the Americas to institutions & Caribbean; GBP 461 elsewhere to institutions (effective 2006) (from Blackwell Synergy, EBSCO Publishing, Gale Group, IngentaConnect, O C L C Online Computer Library Center, Inc., Swets Information Services).
Indexed: ABIn, CPM, Emerald, Inspec, PsycInfo, PsycholAb.
—BLDSC (3487.250400), IE, Infotrieve, ingenta. **CCC.**
Published by: Blackwell Publishing Ltd., 9600 Garsington Rd, Oxford, OX4 2ZG, United Kingdom. TEL 44-1865-776868, FAX 44-1865-714591, customerservices@oxon.blackwellpublishing.com, http://www.blackwellpublishing.com/journals/CAIM. Eds. Olaf Fisscher, Petra de Weerd-Nederhof.

330 USA ISSN 1055-8225
CREDIT & FINANCE✶ . Text in English. 1991. q. USD 29.99. adv. Supplement avail. **Document type:** *Consumer.* **Description:** Covers consumer related credit issues.
Published by: Publishing & Business Consultants, 4427 W Slauson Ave, Los Angeles, CA 90043-2717. TEL 213-732-3477, FAX 213-732-9123. Ed. Andeson Napoleon Atia. Circ: 120,000.

330 COL
CRITERIO ECONOMICO. Text in Spanish. 1965. 3/yr. per issue exchange basis. adv. bk.rev. abstr.; illus.; stat.
Former titles (until no.27, 1976): Sociedad Colombiana de Economistas. Revista; Sociedad Colombiana de Economistas. Boletin Informativo
Indexed: PAIS.
Published by: Sociedad Colombiana de Economistas, Apartado Aereo 8429, Bogota, CUND, Colombia. Circ: 2,000.

330 GBR ISSN 1742-2043
▼ ➤ **CRITICAL PERSPECTIVES ON INTERNATIONAL BUSINESS.** Text in English. 2005 (Feb.). q. EUR 760.16 in Europe; USD 879 in North America; AUD 1,199 in Australasia; GBP 531.79 elsewhere in the UK and elsewhere (effective 2006). **Document type:** *Journal, Academic/Scholarly.* **Description:** Publishes material that engages critically with the broad field of international business including, but not restricted to, issues of globalization, production and consumption, economic change, societal change, politics and power of organizations and governments, environment, etc.
Media: Online - full content. **Related titles:** Online - full text ed.: (from Emerald Group Publishing Limited).
Published by: Emerald Group Publishing Limited, 60-62 Toller Ln, Bradford, W Yorks BD8 9BY, United Kingdom. TEL 44-1274-777700, FAX 44-1274-785200, dbs.cpoib@durham.ac.uk, infomation@emeraldinsight.com, http://www.emeraldinsight.com/cpoib.htm. Eds. Dr. George Cairns, Dr. Joanne Roberts. Pub. Ms. Paula Fernandez. R&P Mr. John Eggleton.

658 HRV ISSN 1330-1179
CROMAN. Text in Croatian. 1993. m. **Document type:** *Magazine, Consumer.*
Published by: Croman d.d., Kneza Mutimira 1-IV, Zagreb, 10000, Croatia. TEL 385-1-4552671, FAX 385-1-4552547. Ed. Domagoj Zovko.

330 340.5 341.7582 GBR
CRONER'S MODEL BUSINESS CONTRACTS. Variant title: Model Business Contracts. Text in English. 1988. base vol. plus m. updates. looseleaf. GBP 293 (effective 1999). **Document type:** *Newsletter.* **Description:** Provides model forms of contracts for the purchase and sales of goods and services, in addition to building contracts, contracts of carriage, provision of financial services, and intellectual property rights protection.
Related titles: Online - full text ed.
Published by: Croner.C C H Group Ltd. (Subsidiary of: Wolters Kluwer N.V.), 145 London Rd, Kingston, Surrey KT2 6SR, United Kingdom. TEL 44-20-85473333, FAX 44-20-85472637, info@croner.co.uk, http://www.croner.co.uk.

330 URY
CRONICAS ECONOMICAS. Text in Spanish. 1981. w.
Address: Avda. del Libertador Brig. Gral. Lavalleja, Montevideo, Uruguay.

CROW'S WEEKLY MARKET REPORT OF LUMBER & PANEL PRODUCTS. see *FORESTS AND FORESTRY—Lumber And Wood*

330 USA
CT BUSINESS MAGAZINE. Text in English. 1998. 8/yr. USD 19.95; USD 4.95 newsstand/cover (effective 2001). adv. back issues avail. **Document type:** *Journal.* **Description:** Reports on the people, issues and events that shape Connecticut's economy.
Published by: Nolan Media LLC, 615 Main St, Cromwell, CT 06416. TEL 860-635-1819, FAX 860-632-7203, ctbizmag@snet.net, http://www.ctbizmag.com. Ed. Chris Brunson. R&P Ron Nolan TEL 860-635-1819. Adv. contact Clare A Bearer. B&W page USD 3,720, color page USD 5,178; trim 8 x 10.75. Circ: 2,000 (paid); 18,000 (controlled).

658 ESP ISSN 0211-4356
CUADERNOS DE CIENCIAS ECONOMICAS Y EMPRESARIALES. Text in Spanish. 1970. s-a. back issues avail. **Document type:** *Academic/Scholarly.*
Formerly (until 1977): Cuadernos de Ciencias Economicas (0211-4348)
Related titles: Online - full text ed.; ◆ Supplement(s): Papeles de Trabajo. ISSN 1132-2640.
—CINDOC.
Published by: Universidad de Malaga, Facultad de Ciencias Economicas y Empresariales, Campus de El Ejido, Malaga, 29071, Spain. TEL 34-95-2131148, FAX 34-95-2132031, cumalaga@uma.es, http://www.uma.es/revistas/revcee/. Ed. Estrella Ayala Moscoso.

330 CHL ISSN 0716-0046
➤ **CUADERNOS DE ECONOMIA**; Latin American journal of economics. Text in English, Spanish. 1963. 3/yr. looseleaf. CLP 12,000 domestic; USD 44 in Latin America; USD 54 in Europe; USD 54 in North America (effective 2005). adv. bk.rev. bibl.; charts; stat.; tr.lit. back issues avail. **Document type:** *Journal, Academic/Scholarly.* **Description:** Emphasizes Latin American economic problems, includes theoretical issues related to Latin American countries. Focuses on applied work for use in the design and evaluation of economic policies.
Related titles: Online - full text ed.: ISSN 0717-6821. 2000. free (effective 2005) (from EBSCO Publishing, Gale Group, SciELO).
Indexed: HAPI, IBR, Inspec, JEL, PAIS, RRTA, WAE&RSA.
—BLDSC (3490.662800), IE, Infotrieve, ingenta.
Published by: Pontificia Universidad Catolica de Chile, Instituto de Economia, Casilla 76, Correo, 17, Santiago, Chile. TEL 56-2-6864314, FAX 56-2-5532377, aaguirre@facea.puc.cl, http://www.cuadernosdeeconomia.cl, http://www.scielo.cl. Ed. Sebastian Claro. R&P Ana Maria Aguirre. Circ: (controlled).

▼ *new title* ➤ *refereed* ✶ *unverified* ◆ *full entry avail.*

330 VEN
HC10
CUADERNOS DE INFORMACION ECONOMICA. Text in Spanish. 1949. s-a. charts; stat.
Published by: Corporacion Venezolana de Fomento, Unidad de Estudios, Edificio Norte, Centro Simon Bolivar, Caracas, DF 1060, Venezuela.

330 ESP ISSN 1132-9386
HC381
CUADERNOS DE INFORMACION ECONOMICA. Text in Spanish. 1987. bi-m. EUR 64 domestic; EUR 100 foreign (effective 2003). bk.rev. **Document type:** *Magazine, Trade.* **Description:** Covers all economic and financial topics, both national and international.
Published by: Fundacion de las Cajas de Ahorros Confederadas para la Investigacion Economica y Social, Juan Hurtado de Mendoza, 19, Madrid, 28036, Spain. TEL 34-91-3507907, FAX 34-91-3508040, publica@funcas.ceca.es, http://www.funcas.ceca.es. Ed., R&P Fernando Gonzalez Olivares. Pub. Victorio Valle Sanchez. Adv. contact Jose Luis Echarri TEL 34-91-3507907. Circ: 2,800.

330 CUB ISSN 0864-4675
CUBA ECONOMICA. Text in Spanish. 1990. 4/yr. USD 20 in South America; USD 24 in North America; USD 28 elsewhere.
Indexed: RASB.
Published by: Ediciones Cubanas, Obispo No. 527, Apdo. 605, Havana, Cuba. Circ: 8,000.

320.97291 USA ISSN 1073-7715
F1788
CUBANEWS; the authoritative source of information on Cuba's political and business future. Text in English. 1993. m. USD 429 to individuals (effective 2000). back issues avail. **Document type:** *Newsletter.* **Description:** Reports on economic, political, and business trends in Cuba.
Related titles: Online - full text ed.: (from Florida Center for Library Automation, Gale Group).
—CCC.
Published by: Target Research LLC, 611 Pennsylvania Ave, SE, Ste 341, Washington, DC 20003. TEL 202-543-5076, FAX 202-546-8929, latinenergy@compuserve.com, http://www.cubanews.com. Ed., Pub. Jason L Feer. **Subscr. to:** PO Box 19690, Alexandria, VA 22320-0690.

CULTURE MANDALA; the bulletin of the centre for East-West cultural and economic studies. see *POLITICAL SCIENCE—International Relations*

330 USA
CURRENT BUSINESS REPORTS. SERVICE ANNUAL SURVEY. Text in English. 1966. a. **Document type:** *Government.*
Incorporates: Current Business Reports. Transportation Annual Survey; Former titles: Current Business Reports. Monthly Selected Services Receipts (0092-038X); (until 1968): Current Selected Services Report. Monthly Selected Services Receipts (0565-1018)
Published by: U.S. Bureau of the Census (Subsidiary of: U.S. Department of Commerce), Customer Services, Washington, DC 20233. TEL 310-457-4100, http://www.census.gov/econ/www/servmenu.html.

332 USA
CURRENT ISSUES IN ECONOMICS AND FINANCE. Text in English. 1995. m. abstr.
Related titles: Online - full text ed.
Indexed: ABIn, PAIS.
Published by: Federal Reserve Bank of New York, 33 Liberty St., New York, NY 10045. http://www.ny.frb.org/rmaghome/curr_iss/2000.html.

330 AUS ISSN 1035-901X
HB1
CURTIN UNIVERSITY OF TECHNOLOGY. SCHOOL OF ECONOMICS AND FINANCE. WORKING PAPER SERIES. Text in English. 1990. irreg. **Document type:** *Monographic series, Academic/Scholarly.*
—BLDSC (9350.835760), IE, ingenta.
Published by: Curtin University of Technology, School of Economics and Finance, c/o Ms Sue Hall, GPO Box U 1987, Perth, W.A. 6845, Australia. TEL 61-8-9266-7756, FAX 61-8-9266-3026.

330 USA
TS156.A1
➤ **THE CUSTOMER DRIVEN QUALITY JOURNAL.** Text in English. 1991. bi-m. USD 139 domestic to individuals; USD 179 foreign to individuals; USD 236 to institutions. adv. bk.rev. **Document type:** *Journal, Academic/Scholarly.* **Description:** Contains interviews, case studies, international news and columns covering a broad range of industries and organizations on various topics of quality and customer satisfaction.
Formerly (until 2000): The Quality Observer (1057-9583)
Indexed: ABIn, QAb.
Published by: International Customer Satisfaction Society, 3970 Chain Bridge Rd, Fairfax, VA 22030-3316. TEL 703-691-9496, FAX 903-691-9399, tqoedtr@erols.com. Ed., R&P Kay Moore. Adv. contact Mary Johnson. Circ: 25,000.

658.812 AUS
CUSTOMER MAGAZINE: CUSTOMER SERVICE MANAGEMENT. Text in English. 1996. m. USD 595 for print, CD-ROM or online ed. (effective 2002). adv. bk.rev.; software rev.; Website rev. abstr.; charts; mkt.; tr.lit.; illus.; stat. 36 p./no.; back issues avail.; reprints avail. **Document type:** *Newsletter, Trade.* **Description:** Provides information to senior managers in large private and public enterprises responsible for customer service management.
Related titles: CD-ROM ed.; E-mail ed.; Online - full content ed.
Published by: (Australian Customer Association), I I A Publishing Pty. Ltd., PO Box 861, Double Bay, NSW 2028, Australia. TEL 61-2-93440586, FAX 61-2-93440586, subs@callcentre.com.au, http://www.callcentre.com.au. Ed. Martin Grace. Pub. Frank Garvin. Adv. contact Norv Turner. color page AUD 3,300, B&W page AUD 2,600. Circ: 32,300 (controlled).

658.41205 GBR ISSN 1466-8866
CUSTOMER RELATIONSHIP MANAGEMENT. Text in English. 1997. bi-m. **Document type:** *Magazine, Trade.*
Formerly (until 1999): Corporate Strategy Director (1462-0480)
Published by: Penton Media Europe (Subsidiary of: Penton Media, Inc.), Penton House, 288-290 Worton Rd, Isleworth, Mddx TW7 6EL, United Kingdom. TEL 44-20-8232-1600, FAX 44-20-8232-1650, information@penton.com, http://www.penton.com.

658.812 AUS
CUSTOMER RELATIONSHIP MANAGEMENT MAGAZINE. Text in English. 1998. m. USD 595 for print, CD-ROM or online ed. (effective 2002). adv. bk.rev.; software rev.; Website rev. abstr.; mkt.; tr.lit.; stat. 24 p./no.; back issues avail.; reprints avail. **Document type:** *Magazine, Trade.* **Description:** Provides information for senior managers in large private and public enterprises responsible for customer relationship management.
Related titles: CD-ROM ed.; Online - full content ed.
Published by: (Australasian C R M User Group), I I A Publishing Pty. Ltd., PO Box 861, Double Bay, NSW 2028, Australia. TEL 61-2-93440586, FAX 61-2-93440718, subs@callcentre.com.au, http://www.callcentre.com.au. Ed., R&P Martin Grace. Pub. Frank Garvin. Adv. contact Norv Turner. B&W page USD 2,600, color page USD 3,300. Circ: 29,100.

659 USA
➤ **CUSTOMER SERVICE;** a journal of theory, service and practices. Text in English. 1990. s-a. USD 50. adv. back issues avail. **Document type:** *Academic/Scholarly.* **Description:** Features in-depth articles on a variety of customer service issues.
Formerly: I C S A Journal (1074-5467)
Published by: International Customer Service Association, 401 N Michigan Ave, Chicago, IL 60611-4267. TEL 312-321-6800, FAX 312-321-6869. Ed. Mark Nelson. Adv. contact Jennifer Maher. page USD 1,600. Circ: 4,000.

330 USA ISSN 1541-7735
▼ **CUSTOMRETAILER.** Text in English. 2003. m. free to qualified personnel. **Document type:** *Magazine, Trade.* **Description:** Covers the custom installed products and services industries.
Related titles: Online - full text ed.: (from H.W. Wilson, O C L C Online Computer Library Center, Inc.).
Indexed: BPI.
Published by: North American Publishing Co., 1500 Spring Garden St., Ste 1200, Philadelphia, PA 19130-4094. TEL 215-238-5300, FAX 215-238-5457, http://customretailermag.com/, http://www.napco.com. Ed. Ron Goldberg. Adv. contact Bernard Schneyer.

330 CZE ISSN 1212-074X
HB74.M3 CODEN: EKMOBF
➤ **CZECH ECONOMETRIC SOCIETY. BULLETIN.** Text mainly in English. 1965-1991; resumed 1994. q. free with membership. 120 p./no. 1 cols./p.; back issues avail. **Document type:** *Bulletin, Academic/Scholarly.* **Description:** Covers the application of mathematical methods in economics including linear and nonlinear programming, operation research methods of macro and micro-economics, and systems analysis.
Formerly (until 1991): Ekonomicko-Matematicky Obzor (0013-3027)
Indexed: Inspec, JEL, MathR, ORMS, QC&AS, SSCI.
Published by: Akademie Ved Ceske Republiky, Ustav Teorie Informace a Automatizace/Academy of Sciences of the Czech Republic, Institute of Information Theory and Automation, Pod Vodarenskou vezi 4, Prague 8, 18208, Czech Republic. TEL 420-2-66051111, FAX 420-2-86890378, utia@utia.cas.cz, http://www.utia.cas.cz. Ed. Miloslav Vosvrda. Adv. contact Eva Dostalova.

330 USA
CZECH REPUBLIC & SLOVAKIA BUSINESS REPORT WEEKLY. Text in English. w. **Document type:** *Trade.*
Media: Online - full content.
Published by: Interfax America, Inc. (Subsidiary of: Interfax Ltd.), 3025 S Parker Rd, Ste 737, Aurora, CO 80014-2925. TEL 303-825-1510, FAX 303-825-1513, america@interfax.com, http://www.interfax.com.

330 IRL ISSN 1393-290X
D C U B S RESEARCH PAPERS. Text in English. 1996. irreg., latest vol.40, 2002. **Document type:** *Monographic series, Academic/Scholarly.*
—BLDSC (7752.002000).
Published by: Dublin City University Business School, Dublin, 9, Ireland. TEL 353-1-7005000, FAX 353-1-8360830, http://www.dcu.ie/dcubs/research_papers/.

330 PHL ISSN 0116-7111
HC451
D L S U BUSINESS & ECONOMICS REVIEW. (De La Salle University) Text in English. 1983. s-a. PHP 140, USD 16. adv. bk.rev. **Document type:** *Academic/Scholarly.* **Description:** Publishes scholarly articles reflecting significant quantitative or qualitative research. Includes speeches, research reports, and "state of the art" papers.
Formerly: Journal of Business and Economics
Indexed: IPP.
—BLDSC.
Published by: De La Salle University, College of Business and Economics, 2401 Taft Ave, Manila, 1004, Philippines. TEL 632-594832, FAX 632-521-9094. Circ: 300.

D M REVIEW; covering business intelligence, integration, & analytics. (Data Management) see *COMPUTERS—Data Base Management*

330 USA
D R I - MCGRAW-HILL U S ECONOMIC OUTLOOK. Text in English. m. **Document type:** *Trade.*
Formerly: D R I - McGraw-Hill U S Executive Report
Published by: D R I - McGraw-Hill, 24 Hartwell Ave, Lexington, MA 02173. TEL 617-863-5100, FAX 617-860-6332. Ed. Cynthia Latta.

DAEDALUS. see *SOCIOLOGY*

330 SWE ISSN 0346-640X
DAGENS INDUSTRI. Variant title: Di. Text in Swedish; Summaries in English. 1976. 6/w. SEK 2,967 combined subscription domestic print & online eds; SEK 3,868 combined subscription in Scandinavia print & online eds; SEK 7,641 combined subscription elsewhere print & online eds (effective 2004). adv. 5 cols./p.; **Document type:** *Newspaper.*
Formed by the merger of (1961-1976): Elektroniknyhetarna (0345-2824); (1946-1976): Ingenjoertidningen Teknisk Information (0040-2311); (1965-1976): Modern Datateknik (0026-7686); (1968-1976): Modern Kemi (0047-7710); (1965-1976): Moderna Transporter (0026-8585); Modern Ytbehandling (0302-8321); (1962-1976): Pack-Distribution (0030-9001); Plastvaerlden (0032-132X)
Related titles: Online - full text ed.: ISSN 1402-4209.
Indexed: B&I, CBNB, P&BA.
—CISTI.
Published by: Dagens Industri AB, Torsgatan 21, Stockholm, 11390, Sweden. TEL 46-8-7288590, http://di.se/nyheter/. Ed. Gunilla Herlitz. Adv. contact Gerd Jensen. B&W page SEK 89,900, color page SEK 119,900; trim 358 x 252. Circ: 117,700.

330 NZL
DAILY AARDVARK. Text in English. d. **Document type:** *Newspaper, Trade.*
Media: Online - full content.
Address: http://www.aardvark.co.nz.

330 346.065 USA ISSN 1538-1757
DAILY BUSINESS REVIEW (BROWARD EDITION). Text in English. 1926. d. (Mon.-Fri.). USD 288; USD 308 combined subscription print & online eds. (effective 2005). adv. **Document type:** *Newspaper, Trade.* **Description:** Provides South Florida's daily business news and information on the economy and the courts.
Formerly: Broward Review (0887-4751)
Related titles: Microfilm ed.; ♦ Online - full content ed.: Daily Business Review (Online Edition); Online - full text ed.: (from Gale Group).
Published by: Daily Business Review (Subsidiary of: A L M), 633 S Andrews Ave, Fort Lauderdale, FL 33301. TEL 954-468-2600, 800-777-7300, FAX 954-468-2630, cmobley@alm.com, https://www.dailybusinessreview.com/. Ed. David V Lyons TEL 305-347-6694. Pub. T Alicia Coya. Adv. contact Anthony J DiGregorio. Circ: 9,624 (paid and controlled). Wire service: DJNS.

346.065 330 USA
DAILY BUSINESS REVIEW (ONLINE EDITION). Text in English. d. USD 129 (effective 2004). **Document type:** *Newspaper, Trade.*
Media: Online - full content. **Related titles:** Microfilm ed.; Online - full text ed.: (from Gale Group); (from Gale Group); ♦ Print ed.: Daily Business Review (Broward Edition). ISSN 1538-1757; ♦ Miami Daily Business Review. ISSN 1070-6437; ♦ Daily Business Review (Palm Beach Edition). ISSN 1538-2311.
Published by: Daily Business Review (Subsidiary of: A L M), 1 SE Third Ave, Ste 900, Miami, FL 33131. TEL 305-377-3721, 800-777-7300, http://www.dailybusinessreview.com/. Ed. David V Lyons TEL 305-347-6694. Adv. contact Anthony J DiGregorio.

346.065 330 USA ISSN 1538-2311
DAILY BUSINESS REVIEW (PALM BEACH EDITION). Text in English. 1976. d. (Mon.-Fri.). USD 219; USD 258 combined subscription print & online eds. (effective 2005). adv. bk.rev. **Document type:** *Newspaper, Trade.* **Description:** Provides South Florida's daily business news and information on the economy and the courts.
Former titles: Palm Beach Review (0884-8785); Palm Beach Review and Business Record (0199-0969); Law Review and Business Record of Palm Beach County (0164-7652)
Related titles: ♦ Online - full content ed.: Daily Business Review (Online Edition); Online - full text ed.: (from Gale Group).
Published by: Daily Business Review (Subsidiary of: A L M), 1 SE Third Ave, Ste 900, Miami, FL 33131. TEL 305-377-3721, https://www.dailybusinessreview.com/. Ed. David V Lyons TEL 305-347-6694. Adv. contact Anthony J DiGregorio. Circ: 9,624 (paid and controlled). Wire service: PR, UPI.

330 USA ISSN 0889-2431
DAILY COMMERCIAL RECORD. Text in English. 1888. d. (Mon.-Fri.). USD 202 (effective 2005). **Document type:** *Newspaper, Consumer.*
Address: 706 Main St, Dallas, TX 75202. dcr@mode14.com, http://www.dailycommercialrecord.com. Ed. E N Cates. Circ: 3,200 morning (paid).

330 USA ISSN 8750-734X
DAILY COMMERCIAL RECORDER. Text in English. 1896. d. (Mon.-Fri.). USD 1 newsstand/cover; USD 55 subscr - mailed for 3 mos.; USD 150 subscr - mailed (effective 2005). **Document type:** *Newspaper, Consumer.*
Published by: Prime Time Newspapers, 17400 Judson Rd, San Antonio, TX 78247. TEL 210-453-3300, FAX 210-736-5506, dcr@primetimenewspapers.com, http://www.primetimenewspapers.com, http://www.primetimenewspapers.com/. Ed. Tara Parker. Pub. Helen I. Lutz. Circ: 1,000 morning (paid). Wire service: UPI, LAT-WAT.

330 USA ISSN 1545-830X
THE DAILY DEAL; the journal for corporate, law & finance professionals. Text in English. 1999. d. (Mon.-Fri.). USD 249 domestic; USD 299 in Canada; USD 399 foreign (effective 2005). adv. **Document type:** *Newspaper, Trade.* **Description:** Offers essential news and analysis covering the strategies that compel companies to merge, acquire and divest, and the tactics that close the deals.
Former titles (until 2002): The Daily Deal & Silicon Valley News (1538-7291); (until 1999): The Daily Deal (1527-5345)
Related titles: E-mail ed.: The Daily Deal E-Newsletters; Online - full text ed.: The Daily Deal Digital (from LexisNexis, ProQuest Information & Learning); Other ed.: The Daily Deal Wireless.
Published by: The Deal, LLC (Subsidiary of: A L M), 105 Madison Ave, 5th Fl, New York, NY 10016. TEL 212-313-9238, epaisley@amlaw.com, dmarcus@thedeal.com, http://www.thedeal.com/. adv.: B&W page USD 4,500, color page USD 6,500. Circ: 14,000 (controlled).

DAILY JOURNAL OF COMMERCE (GRETNA). see *BUILDING AND CONSTRUCTION*

330 345.01 USA
DAILY RECORD (KANSAS CITY). Text in English. 1889. d. (Mon.- Fri.). USD 81 (effective 2000). adv. **Document type:** *Newspaper.*
Published by: Legal Communications Corp. (Subsidiary of: Dolan Media Corp.), 612 N Second St, PO Box 88910, St. Louis, MO 63188. TEL 314-421-1880. Circ: 600 (paid).

330 USA
THE DAILY RECORD (OMAHA). Text in English. 1886. d. (Mon.-Fri.). USD 84; USD 0.50 newsstand/cover (effective 2005). adv. **Document type:** *Newspaper, Trade.*
Contact: Daily Record, Inc., 3323 Leavenworth St, Omaha, NE 68105. TEL 402-345-1303, FAX 402-345-2351, record@radiks.net, http://www.omahadailyrecord.com. Pub. Ron Henningsen. Adv. contact Lynda Henningsen. col. inch USD 7.25. Circ: 2,000 morning (paid).

330 USA ISSN 0197-8055
THE DAILY RECORDER. Text in English. 1911. d. (Mon.-Fri.). USD 246; USD 0.75 newsstand/cover (effective 2005). **Document type:** *Newspaper, Consumer.*
Published by: Daily Journal Corp., 901 "H" St., Ste. 312, Sacramento, CA 95814. TEL 916-444-2355, FAX 916-444-0636, Christa_beebout@dailyjournal.com, http://www.dailyjournal.com. Circ: 1,059 morning (paid). Wire service: AP.

THE DAILY REPORTER (COLUMBUS). see *LAW*

330 USA
DAILY REPORTER (LINCOLN). Text in English. 1885. d. (Mon.-Fri.). USD 0.25 newsstand/cover; USD 14.99 (effective 2005). **Document type:** *Newspaper.*
Published by: Gant Publishing Co., PO Box 5325, Lincoln, NE 68505-0325. TEL 402-466-8521, gant@npcenter.com. Ed. Pat Seeba. Circ: 500 morning (paid).

330 346.066 USA ISSN 0743-8397
DAILY TERRITORIAL. Text in English. 1930. d. (Mon.-Fri.). USD 112.50 (effective 2005). adv. **Document type:** *Newspaper, Consumer.* **Description:** Publishes Pima County Public Records in Tucson, AZ.
Related titles: Online - full content ed.
Published by: Territorial Newspapers, 3280 E Hemisphere Lp, Ste 180, Tucson, AZ 85706. TEL 520-294-1200, FAX 520-294-4040, http://www.azbiz.com/. Circ: 1,100.

330 USA
DAILY TIPS FOR ENTREPRENEURS. Text in English. d. free. **Description:** Provides tips and ideas to help run and grow any business.
Media: Online - full text.
Published by: J C I Inc., 2459 S E TV Hwy, 461, Hillsboro, OR 97123. al@dailytips.com, http://www.dailytips.com.

330 USA ISSN 0899-4129
DALLAS BUSINESS JOURNAL. Text in English. 1977. w. (Fri.). USD 87 (effective 2005). adv. **Document type:** *Newspaper.* **Description:** Contains news and information essential to business executives, including features, data listing and how-to articles.
Supersedes in part in 1988: Dallas - Fort Worth Business Journal (8750-6084)
Related titles: Microform ed.: 1977 (from PQC); Online - full text ed.: 1977 (from Florida Center for Library Automation, Gale Group, O C L C Online Computer Library Center, Inc., ProQuest Information & Learning).
Indexed: ABIn, BusDate, LRI, T&II.
—CCC.
Published by: American City Business Journals, Inc. (Dallas), 12801 North Central Expwy, Ste 800, Dallas, TX 75243. TEL 214-696-5959, FAX 214-696-1486, dallas@bizjournals.com, http://dallas.bcentral.com/dallas/. Circ: 13,200 (paid).

DANCE RETAILER NEWS; the news magazine for the retail community. see *DANCE*

DANSK INDUSTRI EFTER 1870. see *HISTORY—History Of Europe*

330.9489 DNK ISSN 0107-8224
DEN DANSKE BANK. ORIENTERING. Text in Danish. 1976; N.S. 1990. m. free. charts; stat. **Document type:** *Bulletin.* **Description:** Discusses economic issues and trends as they affect Denmark.
Formerly: Danske Bank af 1871. Orientering
Published by: Danske Bank, Oekonomisk Afdeling, c/o Library, Holmens Kanal 2-12, Copenhagen K, 1092, Denmark. TEL 45-33-44-00-00. Ed. Joergen Birger Christensen.

DARWIN (ONLINE EDITION). see *COMPUTERS—Internet*

330 CAN
DATELINE WINNIPEG. Text in English. q. free. adv. **Document type:** *Newsletter.*
Published by: Better Business Bureau of Winnipeg & Manitoba, 301 365 Hargrave St, Winnipeg, MB R3B 2K3, Canada. TEL 204-942-7166, FAX 204-943-1489. Ed. T S Durham. Adv. contact T.S. Durham. Circ: 2,000 (controlled).

330 USA ISSN 1063-3413
DAYTON BUSINESS REPORTER✶. Text in English. 1991. bi-w. USD 28. adv. **Document type:** *Newspaper.* **Description:** Provides news and commentary about the area business community. Provides a forum for the exchange of opinions and ideas.
Related titles: CD-ROM ed.: 1991 (from ProQuest Information & Learning); Microform ed.: 1991 (from PQC); Online - full text ed.: 1991 (from ProQuest Information & Learning); ♦ Supplement(s): Acquisition.
Indexed: BusDate.
Published by: Dayton Daily News, 45 S Ludlow St, Dayton, OH 45402. http://www.daytonbusiness.com. Ed., R&P Gene Fox. Adv. contact Tina Rhodus. B&W page USD 2,122, color page USD 2,697; trim 15 x 11.38. Circ: 10,000 (controlled).
Co-publisher: Cox Ohio Publishing.

330 ESP
DE ECONOMIA; revista de temas economicos. Text in Spanish. 1948. q.
Published by: Consejo Economico Sindical Nacional, Paseo del Prado, 18, Madrid, Spain.

330 GBR ISSN 1367-3114
➤ **DE MONTFORT UNIVERSITY. LEICESTER BUSINESS SCHOOL. OCCASIONAL PAPER.** Text in English. 1992. irreg., latest vol.26. GBP 3 per issue (effective 1996). **Document type:** *Monographic series, Academic/Scholarly.*
—BLDSC (6217.497100), IE, ingenta.
Published by: (Department of Marketing), De Montfort University, Leicester Business School, Leicester, Leics LE1 9BH, United Kingdom. TEL 0116-257-8254, FAX 0116-257-7795, aacmar@dmu.ac.ukc.uk. Ed. David Crick.

330 USA
THE DEAL. Text in English. w. USD 249 (effective 2003). **Document type:** *Magazine, Trade.*
Related titles: Online - full content ed.: USD 160 (effective 2003).
Published by: The Deal, LLC (Subsidiary of: A L M), 105 Madison Ave, 5th Fl, New York, NY 10016. TEL 212-313-9238, dmarcus@thedeal.com, http://www.thedeal.com/.

▼ **THE DEALER BOOK.** see *AGRICULTURE—Agricultural Equipment*

330 UKR
DEBET-KREDYT; ukrayins'kyi bukhgalters'kyi tyzhnevyk. Text in Ukrainian. w.
Related titles: Online - full content ed.
Published by: Dilova Presa, Vul Mechnikova 10/2, Kyiv, 25203, Ukraine. TEL 38-44-2949642, debet-kredit@gc.kiev.ua, reklama@gc.kiev.ua, reklama@gc.lviv.ua, http://www.dtkt.com.ua, http://www.gc.kiev.ua/.

DECATUR FOCUS. see *HOUSING AND URBAN PLANNING*

355 GBR
DEFENCE INDUSTRY DIGEST. Text in English. 1984. m. GBP 145, USD 260. **Description:** Digests news from the defense industry.
Published by: Longman Group UK Ltd., Law Tax and Finance Division, 21-27 Lambs Conduit St, London, WC1N 3NJ, United Kingdom. TEL 44-20-7242-2548, FAX 44-207-831-8119. Ed. John Reed.

DEFENSE TECHNOLOGY BUSINESS. see *MILITARY*

330 FRA ISSN 0759-089X
DEFIS; premier magazine pratique de l'entreprise. Text in French. 1983. 11/yr. adv. bk.rev. **Document type:** *Trade.*
Address: c/o Free Lance S.A., 204 bd. Raspail, Paris, 75006, France. TEL 33-1-44105431. Ed. Marc de Jobe. Pub. Guy Singer. Circ: 60,317.

DELAWARE CAPITAL REVIEW. see *LAW*

330 USA ISSN 1093-0736
DELAWARE CAPITOL REVIEW. Text in English. 1978. w. USD 78 domestic; USD 90 in the Americas. adv. **Document type:** *Newspaper.*
Formerly: Delaware Business Review (1061-4605)
Related titles: Online - full text ed.: (from Northern Light Technology, Inc., O C L C Online Computer Library Center, Inc., ProQuest Information & Learning).
Indexed: ABIn, BusDate.
Published by: Independent Newspapers, Inc., PO Box 737, Dover, DE 19903. TEL 302-674-3600, FAX 302-741-8252. Ed. Diane Cook. Pub. Tamra Brittingham. R&P Mike Pelrine. Adv. contact Tonda Parks. Circ: 10,100.

330 RUS
DELO (IRKUTSK). Text in Russian. s-m. **Description:** Includes official information of the Irkutsk Oblast administration, as well as commentary from specialists and other detailed information on currency and credit markets and securities, and bank services.
Published by: Sibirskoe Informatsionnoe Agentstvo, Ul Kommunarov 10, A-ya 33, Irkutsk 3, 666403, Russian Federation. TEL 7-3952-347228, 7-3952-251025, 7-3952-252360, postbox@sia.irk.ru, http://www.sia.ru. Ed. Aleksandr Podkorytov.

330 BLR ISSN 0869-2696
DELO (MINSK); vostok + zapad. Text in Russian. 11/yr. USD 35 (effective 2002).
Related titles: Online - full content ed.: ISSN 1608-1404; English ed.: Belarus and Business; German ed.: Weissrussland und Unternehmen.
Indexed: RefZh.
Published by: Delo - Vostok + Zapad, Pr Masherova 11, Minsk, 220600, Belarus. TEL 375-17-2235209, FAX 375-17-2230967, http://www.delobelarus.com. Ed. Viktor Zhuk.

330 RUS
DELO (SAMARA); ekonomicheskoe obozrenie. Text in Russian. 1992. w. **Document type:** *Journal, Consumer.*
Published by: ZAO Gazetnyi Mir, Ul Eroshevskogo 3, 4 et, Samara, Russian Federation. TEL 7-8462-352194, 7-8462-345921, FAX 7-8462-346923, delo@cofe.ru. Ed. Tat'yana Gorshkova. Circ: 1,005.

330 GBR
DELOITTE AND TOUCHE SCOTTISH CHAMBERS BUSINESS SURVEY. Text in English. 1984. q. GBP 150 (effective 2000). adv. **Document type:** *Bulletin.*
Former titles: Scottish Chambers Business Survey (0954-4976); Scottish Business Survey (0267-1212)
Published by: University of Strathclyde, Fraser of Allander Institute for Research on the Scottish Economy, Curran Bldg, 100 Cathedral St, Glasgow, G4 0LN, United Kingdom. TEL 44-141-548-3958, FAX 44-141-552-8347, fai@strath.ac.uk, http://www.fraser.strath.ac.uk. Ed., R&P Brian Ashcroft.

330 RUS
DELOPROIZVODSTVO. Text in Russian. q.
Published by: Biznes Shkola Intel-Sintez, Ul Profsoyuznaya 3, Moscow, 117036, Russian Federation. TEL 7-095-1299212, FAX 7-095-1246809, http://www.top-personal.ru.

B

330 RUS ISSN 1681-7907
DELOVAYA KHRONIKA; zhurnal o biznese i den'gakh. Text in Russian. 2002 (Jan.). w. **Document type:** *Magazine, Consumer.*
Related titles: Online - full content ed.
Published by: Izdatel'stvo Ostrov, Ul Shchepkina, dom 58, str.3, Moskow, 129110, Russian Federation. TEL 7-095-9612760, FAX 7-095-9612761, ad@naostrove.ru, market@naostrove.ru, http://chronicle.ru, http://naostrove.ru. Eds. Anastasiya Lebedeva, Natalia Kosareva. Adv. contact Alla Putko TEL 7-095-9612770.

330 RUS
DELOVAYA KNIGA. Text in Russian. m. USD 125 (effective 1999). adv. bk.rev.
Published by: Delovaya Kniga Co. Ltd., Leningradskii pr-t 80-2, km 304, 404, Moscow, 125190, Russian Federation. TEL 7-095-158-1721, FAX 7-095-943-9239. Ed. S M Kasumova. Adv. contact Paul Prokazov. page USD 120. Circ: 5,000. **US dist. addr.:** East View Information Services, 3020 Harbor Ln. N., Minneapolis, MN 55447. TEL 612-550-0961.

330 KAZ
DELOVAYA NEDELYA. Text in Russian. w. USD 299 in United States. **Document type:** *Newspaper, Consumer.*
Related titles: Online - full text ed.
Address: Ul Zhybek Zholy 64, 2 etazh, Almaty, 480000, Kazakstan. TEL 327-2-50-62-72, FAX 327-2-33-91-48, rikki@kazmail.asdc.kz. Ed. Tulegan Askarov. **US dist. addr.:** East View Information Services, 3020 Harbor Ln. N., Minneapolis, MN 55447. TEL 612-550-0961.

330 RUS ISSN 1681-6013
DELOVAYA PANORAMA. Text in Russian. w. stat. **Document type:** *Newspaper, Consumer.*
Published by: Media-Stels, Pr Chernoshevvskogo 7, Petersburg, Russian Federation. TEL 7-812-3273383, dp@vp.ru. Ed. Veneamin Bereslavskii. Circ: 13,500.

330 RUS
DELOVAYA PENZA. Text in Russian. w. stat. **Document type:** *Newspaper.*
Related titles: Online - full content ed.
Published by: Redaktsiya Delovaya Penza, Ul Kirova 65/2, Penza, 440600, Russian Federation. TEL 7-8412-664092, 7-8412-665326, dp@sura.com.ru, http://dp.penza.net. Ed. M N Zivenko. Circ: 5,000.

330 UKR
DELOVAYA UKRAINA/DILOVAYA UKRAINA. Text in Ukrainian. s-w. USD 395 in United States.
Related titles: Microfilm ed.: (from EVP); Online - full text ed.
Published by: Izdatel'skii Dom Delovaya Ukraina, Pr Pobedy 50, Kiev, Ukraine. TEL 380-44-517-7355. **US dist. addr.:** East View Information Services, 3020 Harbor Ln. N., Minneapolis, MN 55447. TEL 612-550-0961.

330 RUS
DELOVOE POVOLZH'E. Text in Russian. w. USD 389 in the Americas (effective 2000).
Published by: Redaktsiya Delovoe Povolzh'e, Ul. Krasnoznamenskaya, 12, Volgograd, 400066, Russian Federation. TEL 8442-337367, FAX 8442-337367. Ed. V Teplitskii.

330 RUS
DELOVOI EKSPRESS. Text in Russian. w. USD 129.95 in United States.
Published by: Elm Press, Pryamoi per 12, A-ya 360, Moscow, 121099, Russian Federation. TEL 7-095-2412469, FAX 7-095-2053280, express@elmpress.ru. Ed. A V Sharkov. **US dist. addr.:** East View Information Services, 3020 Harbor Ln. N., Minneapolis, MN 55447. TEL 612-550-0961.

330 RUS
DELOVOI KVARTAL. Text in Russian. w. adv.
Published by: Izdatel'stvo Pul's Tsen, Ul Khokhryakova 55, Ekaterinburg, 620144, Russian Federation. TEL 7-3432-127404, 7-3432-127606, 7-3432-127777, dk@apress.ru, http://www.apress.ru/publ/dk. Ed. Igor Lazarev. adv.: page RUR 14,800; 21.5 x 28.

330 RUS
DELOVOI MIR SODRUZHESTVA. Text in Russian. 1996. bi-m. USD 165 in the Americas (effective 2000).
Related titles: ♦ Supplement to: Radikal.
Indexed: RASB.
Published by: Mezhgosudarstvennyi Ekonomicheskii Komitet, Ul. Kosygina, 13, pod.4, Moscow, 117334, Russian Federation. TEL 7-095-9388703.

330 USA
DELOVOI NOVISIBIRSK. Text in Russian. 2000 (Sep.). d. adv.
Media: Online - full content.
Published by: Medion.ru TEL 7-3832-210686, dnsk@medion.ru, info@medion.ru, http://www.dsnk.ru. adv.: online banner USD 25.

330 RUS
DELOVOI NOVOSIBIRSK. Text in Russian. d.
Media: Online - full content.
Address: dnsk@medion.ru, http://www.dnsk.ru.

330 RUS
DELOVOI PARTNER. Text in Russian. m. USD 195 in United States.
Indexed: RASB.
Published by: Izdatel'stvo Dom Infra M, Dmitrovskoe shosse 107, Moscow, 127214, Russian Federation. TEL 7-095-4857177, FAX 7-095-4855318. Ed. V M Prudnikov. **US dist. addr.:** East View Information Services, 3020 Harbor Ln. N., Minneapolis, MN 55447. TEL 612-550-0961.

330 RUS
DELOVOI PETERBURG. Text in Russian. w. USD 245 in United States.
Address: Krasnoarmeiskaya ul 33, St Petersburg, 198103, Russian Federation. TEL 812-326-97-00, FAX 812-326-97-01, contakt@delo.spb.ru. Ed. O Tret'yakov. **US dist. addr.:** East View Information Services, 3020 Harbor Ln. N., Minneapolis, MN 55447. TEL 612-550-0961.

330 RUS
DELOVOI URAL. Text in Russian. 1992. w. **Document type:** *Newspaper, Consumer.*
Published by: Gazeta Delovoi Ural, Pr Lenina 83, k 405, Chelyabinsk, 454080, Russian Federation. TEL 7-3512-656930, 7-3512-657266, 7-3512-657267, delur@chel.surnet.ru, http://www.infoural.ru. Ed. G S Lubnin. Adv. contact Irina Shtefan.

330 RUS
DELOVOI VIZIT. BYULLETEN' PROMYSHLENOI REKLAMY. Text in Russian. 1992. m. USD 170 in the Americas (effective 2000).
Published by: Reklamnoe Agentstvo Arabeska, Ul. B. Serpukhovskaya, 25, A-ya 30, Moscow, 113093, Russian Federation. TEL 7-095-2365417, FAX 7-095-2370821. Ed. E V Tulupov.

330 RUS
DELOVOI VTORNIK. Text in Russian. w. back issues avail. **Document type:** *Newsletter, Consumer.*
Address: Ul Pravdy 24, 8 et, A-ya 40, GSP 3, Moscow, 125993, Russian Federation. TEL 7-095-2573792, vtornik@adi.ru, http://www.inform.adi.ru. Ed. V Simonov. Circ: 2,997,500.

330 RUS ISSN 0868-9504
DELOVYE LYUDI. Text in Russian. 1991. m. USD 209 foreign (effective 2005). **Document type:** *Magazine, Consumer.*
Related titles: ♦ English ed.: Business in Russia.
Published by: Moskovskii Komsomolets, ul 1905 goda, dom 7, Moscow, 123995, Russian Federation. TEL 7-095-2532094, dl@mk.ru, podpiska@mk.ru, http://www.dl.mk.ru, http://www.mk.ru. Circ: 87,000. **US dist. addr.:** East View Information Services, 3020 Harbor Ln. N., Minneapolis, MN 55447. TEL 800-477-1005, FAX 800-800-3839, eastview@eastview.com, http://www.eastview.com.

330 EST ISSN 1406-2593
DELOVYE VEDOMOSTI. Text in Russian. 1996. w. adv. **Document type:** *Newspaper, Trade.*
Published by: Aripaeva Kirjastuse AS, Parnu mnt 105, Tallinn, 19094, Estonia. TEL 372-667-0066, FAX 372-667-0165, allan@mbp.ee, http://www.vedomosti.ee, http://www.mbp.ee. Ed. Allan Soon.

330.0711 USA
DELTA PI EPSILON. (YEAR) RESEARCH CONFERENCE PROCEEDINGS. Text in English. 1988. biennial. USD 15 (effective 2000). **Document type:** *Proceedings.* **Description:** Contains selected presentations at the Delta Pi Epsilon National Research Conference.
Published by: Delta Pi Epsilon Graduate Business Education Society, National Office, P O Box 4340, Little Rock, AR 72214. TEL 501-562-1233, FAX 501-562-1293.

330.0711 USA ISSN 0160-3957
DELTA PI EPSILON. SERVICE BULLETINS. Text in English. 1977. irreg., latest vol.4, 1990. price varies. **Document type:** *Bulletin.* **Description:** Designed for researchers, teachers, doctoral and master's candidates interested in conducting researches in business education.
Published by: Delta Pi Epsilon Graduate Business Education Society, National Office, P O Box 4340, Little Rock, AR 72214. TEL 501-562-1233, FAX 501-562-1293.

330 RUS
DENEZHKA. Text in Russian. m. **Document type:** *Magazine.*
Related titles: ♦ Supplement to: Spros. ISSN 1026-9444.
Published by: Informatsionno-Izdatel'skii Fond Spros, ul Varvarka 14, magazin "Spros", Moscow, 109012, Russian Federation. TEL 7-095-2984889, konfop@glasnet.ru, http://finance.spros.ru. Ed. Sergei Trukhachev. Circ: 40,000.

DENTAL ECONOMICS; revista de la gestion de la clinica dental. see *MEDICAL SCIENCES—Dentistry*

330 USA ISSN 0893-7745
THE DENVER BUSINESS JOURNAL. Text in English. 1981. w. (Fri.). USD 86 (effective 2005). adv. abstr. **Document type:** *Newspaper.*
Formerly (until 1986): Rocky Mountain Business Journal (0279-0769)
Related titles: Online - full text ed.: (from Florida Center for Library Automation, Gale Group, Northern Light Technology, Inc., O C L C Online Computer Library Center, Inc., ProQuest Information & Learning).
Indexed: ABIn, BusDate.
—CCC.
Published by: American City Business Journals, Inc. (Denver), 1700 Broadway, 515, Denver, CO 80290. TEL 303-837-3500, FAX 303-837-3535, denver@bizjournals.com, http://www.bizjournals.com/denver/. Circ: 15,000.

330 USA ISSN 1068-6681
DES MOINES BUSINESS RECORD. Text in English. 1983. w. (Mon.). USD 59 (effective 2005). adv. bk.rev. **Document type:** *Newspaper.*
Former titles (until 199?): Business Record (Des Moines) (0746-410X); (until 1983): Des Moines Daily Business Record (0745-1806)
Related titles: Online - full text ed.: (from EBSCO Publishing, Florida Center for Library Automation, Gale Group, O C L C Online Computer Library Center, Inc., ProQuest Information & Learning).
Indexed: ABIn, BusDate, T&II.
Published by: Business Publications Corp., 4521 Fleur St, Ste A-2, Des Moines, IA 50309. TEL 515-953-4822, FAX 515-288-0309, http://www.businessrecord.com. Ed. Jim Pollock. Pub. Connie Wimer. Adv. contact Janette Larkin. col. inch USD 26.58. Circ: 7,100.

330 332.1 CHL ISSN 0716-2219
HJ8584
DEUDA EXTERNA DE CHILE. Text in English, Spanish. 1977. a. CLP 4,000, USD 20 (effective 1999). **Document type:** *Government.* **Description:** Contains statement of Chilean external debt for each year with cumulative statistics.
Published by: Banco Central de Chile, Casilla 967, Santiago, Chile. TEL 56-2-670-2000, FAX 56-2-698-4847. Circ: 400.

330 DEU ISSN 0720-7026
DEUTSCHES INSTITUT FUER WIRTSCHAFTSFORSCHUNG. SONDERHEFTE. Text in German. 1948. irreg., latest vol.174, 2003. price varies. **Document type:** *Monographic series, Academic/Scholarly.*
Published by: (Deutsches Institut fuer Wirtschaftsforschung), Duncker und Humblot GmbH, Carl-Heinrich-Becker-Weg 9, Berlin, 12165, Germany. TEL 49-30-7900060, FAX 49-30-79000631, info@duncker-humblot.de, http://www.duncker-humblot.de.

330 GBR ISSN 0951-1407
DEVELOPMENTS IN ECONOMICS. Text in English. 1985. a. —BLDSC (3579.071050), IE, ingenta. **CCC.**
Published by: Causeway Press Ltd., Causeway Press Ltd, PO Box 13, Ormskirk, Lancs L39 5HP, United Kingdom. TEL 44-1695-576048, FAX 44-1695-570714.

330 IND
DHARAM NARAIN MEMORIAL LECTURE SERIES. Text in English. 1981. irreg., latest vol.7, 1988.
Published by: Institute of Economic Growth, University of Enclave, New Delhi, 110 007, India. TEL 2522201.

330 PRY
DIA. Text in Spanish. 1981. d. PYG 617,100, USD 435; PYG 2,000 newsstand/cover (effective 1997). adv. bk.rev.; film rev.; software rev.; tel.rev.; video rev. tr.lit. 32 p./no. 6 cols./p.; back issues avail. **Document type:** *Newspaper, Consumer.* **Description:** Articles of economy, business and related fields.
Formerly (until 1995): Hoy
Related titles: Online - full text ed.: ISSN 1605-0738. 1997.
Published by: Multimedia S.A., MCAL LOPEZ, 2948, Asuncion, Paraguay. TEL 595-21-6034000, FAX 595-21-606-330, eldia@infonet.com.py, http://www.eldia.com.py/. Ed. Manuel Godoy. Adv. contact Guillermo Cortes. page USD 3,300; trim 12 x 10.5. Wire service: AFP, AP.

331 PER ISSN 1682-4350
DIAGNOSTICO Y PROPUESTA. Text in Spanish. 2000. m.
Media: Online - full text.
Published by: Consorcio de Investigacion Economica y Social, C. Antero Aspillaga No. 584, San Isidro, Lima, 27, Peru. TEL 51-1-4218082, http://www.consorcio.org/diagnostico.asp.

330 BOL
DIAGRAMA ECONOMICO. Text in Spanish. m.
Address: Casilla 2762, La Paz, Bolivia. Ed. V Rodriguez.

DIALOGO SOCIAL. see *SOCIOLOGY*

DIAMOND HARVARD BUSINESS. see *BUSINESS AND ECONOMICS—Management*

330 004 600 TWN ISSN 1726-2364
▼ ➤ **DIANZI SHANGWU YANJIU/ELECTRONIC COMMERCE STUDIES.** Text in Chinese, English. 2003. q. TWD 1,200 domestic; USD 50 foreign (effective 2004 & 2005). abstr.; bibl.; charts; illus. back issues avail. **Document type:** *Journal, Academic/Scholarly.* **Description:** Publishes academic articles on electronic commerce, including management, marketing and technolog issues.

Published by: National Taipei University, Graduate Institute of Information Management, 69, Sec 2, Jian-Guo N. Road, Taipei, 10433, Taiwan. TEL 886-2-25009508, FAX 886-2-25175924, chang@atisr.org, wangson@mail.ntpu.edu.tw. Ed. Wenchang Fang.

330 PRT ISSN 0872-1696
DIARIO ECONOMICO. Text in Portuguese. 1989. d. **Document type:** *Newspaper.*
Related titles: Online - full text ed.; ◆ Supplement(s): A Industria do Norte; ◆ A I P Ambiente.
Published by: Media Capital Editora Multimedia, S.A., Rua Dr. Mario Castelhano, No.40, Queluz de Baixo, 2749-502, Portugal. TEL 351-707301001, FAX 351-214347653, http://www.de.iol.pt. Circ: 24,000. **Co-publisher:** Recoletos Compania Editorial S.A.

330 346.066 FRA ISSN 1764-0555
DICTIONNAIRE JOLY CONCURRENCE. Text in French. 2 base vols. plus s-a. updates. looseleaf. **Document type:** *Trade.*
Published by: Joly Editions, 31 rue Falguiere, Paris, 75015, France. TEL 33-1-56541600, FAX 33-1-56541647.

DICTIONNAIRE PERMANENT: DROIT DES AFFAIRES. see *LAW*

330 LVA
DIENAS BIZNESS. Text in Latvian; Summaries in English, Russian. 1992. 3/w. USD 1,180 foreign (effective 2003). adv. 28 p./no. 5 cols./p.; **Document type:** *Newspaper.*
Address: Balasta dambis 3, 1301, Riga, 1081, Latvia. TEL 371-2-464690, FAX 371-80-828287. Ed. Juris Paiders. Adv. contact Andris Morkans. Circ: 15,000. **Dist. by:** M K - Periodica, ul Gilyarovskogo 39, Moscow 129110, Russian Federation. TEL 7-095-2845008, FAX 7-095-2813798, info@periodicals.ru, http://www.mkniga.ru.

330 ECU ISSN 0012-2696
HC121
DIFUSION ECONOMICA. Text in Spanish. 1967 (vol.5). 3/yr. ECS 120, USD 6. charts; stat.
Indexed: PAIS.
Published by: Universidad de Guayaquil, Instituto de Investigaciones Economicas y Politicas, Apdo 5725, Guayaquil, Guayas, Ecuador. Ed. Enrique Salas Castilo.

DIGITAL COAST REPORTER. see *COMPUTERS—Internet*

DIGITAL TELEVISION. see *COMMUNICATIONS—Television And Cable*

330 UKR ISSN 1680-3310
DILOVYI VISNYK; business herald magazine. Text in Russian, Ukrainian. 1992. m. USD 65 domestic; USD 130 in North America (effective 2001). 36 p./no. 2 cols./p.; **Document type:** *Magazine, Corporate.*
Published by: Redaktsiya Dilovyi Visnyk, Ul. Velyka Zhytomyrs'ka, 33, Kiev, Ukraine. TEL 380-44-2122958, FAX 380-44-2123253, bhm@ucci.org.ua, http://www.uccl.org.ua. Ed. Victor Marienko. Adv. contact Antonina Samoilenko. Circ: 4,000 (paid); 4,500 (controlled).

059.956 JPN
DIME; trend magazine for business people. Text in Japanese. m. adv. **Document type:** *Magazine, Trade.*
Published by: Shogakukan Inc., 3-1 Hitotsubashi 2-chome, Chiyoda-ku, Tokyo, 101-8001, Japan. TEL 81-3-3230-5211, FAX 81-3-3264-8471, http://www.shogakukan.co.jp.

330 BOL ISSN 0012-2939
DINAMICA ECONOMICA✶. Text in Spanish. 1961. bi-m. BOB 20, USD 20. adv. bk.rev. charts; illus.
Published by: Universidad Mayor de San Andres, Facultad de Economia Juridica y Ciencias Sociales, Casilla 4787, La Paz, Bolivia. Ed. Eduarde Nava Morales Eguia. Circ: 12,000.

330 ESP
DINERO. Text in Spanish. w.
Published by: Nuevo Projecto 50, Po. Odsteuala, 36, Madrid, 28046, Spain. Ed. Rafael Navas.

330 ITA
DIPARTIMENTO DI ECONOMIA AZIENDALE. STUDI DI RAGIONERIA E DI ECONOMIA AZIENDALE. Text in Italian. 1993. irreg., latest vol.3, 1994. price varies. adv. **Document type:** *Monographic series.*
Published by: Liguori Editore srl, Via Posillipo 394, Naples, 80123, Italy. TEL 39-81-7206111, FAX 39-81-7206244, http://www.liguori.it. Pub. Guido Liguori. Adv. contact Maria Liguori.

330 DEU
DIPLOMATISCHE VERTRETUNGEN DER BUNDESREPUBLIK DEUTSCHLAND IM AUSLAND. Text in German. base vol. plus m. updates. EUR 49.90 (effective 2005). reprints avail. **Document type:** *Directory, Trade.*
Formerly: Vertretungen der Bundesrepublik Deutschland im Ausland (0431-509X)
Published by: Deutscher Wirtschaftsdienst (Subsidiary of: Wolters Kluwer Deutschland GmbH), Schoenhauser Str 64, Cologne, 50968, Germany. TEL 49-221-937630, FAX 49-221-9376399, box@dwd-verlag.de, http://www.dwd-verlag.de.

339.31 LBN ISSN 1564-7625
DIRASAT AL-HISABAT AL-QAWMIYYAT LI-MINTAQAT AL-LAGNAT AL-IQTISADIYYAT WA-AL-IGTIMA'IYYAT LI-GARBI ASIYA/UNITED NATIONS ECONOMIC AND SOCIAL COMMISSION FOR WESTERN ASIA. NATIONAL ACCOUNTS STUDIES OF THE E S C W A REGION. Text in Arabic, English. 1977. a. USD 15 (effective 2004). **Document type:** *Bulletin.* **Description:** Contains estimates and available data on gross domestic product at both current and constant prices, as well as consolidated national accounts for each member country.
Former titles: Al-Umam al-Muttahidat al-Lagnat al-Iqtisadiyyat wa-al-Igtimaiyyat li-Garbi Asiya. Dirasat al-Hisabet al-Qawmiyat (1010-965X); (until 1986): Al-Umam al-Muttahidat, al-Lagnat al-Iqtisadiyyat li-Garbi Asiya. Dirasat al-Dahl al-Qawmi (0252-7952)
Published by: United Nations, Economic and Social Commission for Western Asia, PO Box 11-8575, Beirut, Lebanon. TEL 961-1-981301, FAX 961-1-981510, webmaster-eswa@un.org, http://www.escwa.org.lb/information/publications/main.htm.

330 EGY ISSN 1110-1547
AL DIRASAT WA-AL-BUHUT AL-TIGARIYYAT/COMMERCIAL STUDIES AND RESEARCH. Text in Arabic; Abstracts in Arabic. 1981. s-a. **Document type:** *Journal, Academic/Scholarly.*
Published by: Zagazig University, Faculty of Commerce, Banha Branch, Zagazig, Egypt. TEL 20-13-225493, FAX 20-13-230860, http://derp.sti.sci.eg/data/0012.htm. Ed. Dr. Hamed Tulba Muhammad.

330 LBY
DIRASSAT✶; Libyan economic and business review. Text in Arabic, English. 1964. s-a. USD 15. charts; stat.
Indexed: ChemAb, ForAb, S&F.
Published by: University of Garyounis, Faculty of Economics and Commerce, Center of Economics and Business Research, Benghazi, Libya. Circ: 3,000.

330 ESP ISSN 0210-0908
DIRECCION Y PROGRESO. Text in Spanish. 1972. 6/yr.
Indexed: ELLIS.
—CINDOC.
Published by: Association of Business Development, Montalban, 3 6o, Madrid, 28014, Spain. TEL 1-532-22-65. Ed. B Herrero Nieto. Circ: 4,736.

DIRECTIVOS CONSTRUCCION. see *REAL ESTATE*

DIRITTO ED ECONOMIA; rivista-dibattito interdisciplinare quadrimestrale. see *LAW*

330 GBR ISSN 1360-2438
➤ **DISCUSSION PAPER IN ECONOMICS.** Text in English. irreg. **Document type:** *Academic/Scholarly.*
Formerly (until 1993): Discussion Paper in Economics and Econometrics
Indexed: MaizeAb, TriticAb, WAE&RSA.
—BLDSC (3597.933850), IE, ingenta.
Published by: University of Nottingham, Department of Economics, University Park, Nottingham, Notts NG7 2RD, United Kingdom. TEL 44-115-9515480, FAX 44-115-9514159, richard.disney@nottingham.ac.uk. Ed. R Disney. Circ: 160.

330 306.09 GBR ISSN 1366-2864
DISCUSSION PAPERS IN ECONOMIC AND SOCIAL HISTORY. Text in English. 1995. irreg., latest 2004. free (effective 2004). back issues avail. **Document type:** *Monographic series, Academic/Scholarly.*
Related titles: Online - full content ed.
—BLDSC (3597.914300).
Published by: University of Oxford, Nuffield College, New Road, Oxford, OX1 1NF, United Kingdom. TEL 44-1865-278500, FAX 44-1865-278621, Avner.Offer@nuf.ox.ac.uk, http://www.nuff.ox.ac.uk/Economics/History/.

330 GBR ISSN 1363-822X
➤ **DISCUSSION PAPERS IN PUBLIC SECTOR ECONOMICS.** Text in English. 1992. irreg. **Document type:** *Monographic series, Academic/Scholarly.*
—BLDSC (3597.949700).
Published by: (Public Sector Economics Research Centre), University of Leicester, Faculty of Social Sciences, Leicester, Leics LE1 7RH, United Kingdom. TEL 44-116-252-5368, http://www.leicester.ac.uk/. Ed. Mike Shields. Circ: 100.

330 004 GBR ISSN 1369-3905
DISCUSSION PAPERS IN QUANTITATIVE ECONOMICS & COMPUTING. Text in English. 1992. irreg. **Document type:** *Monographic series.*
—BLDSC (3597.949800), ingenta.
Published by: University of Reading, Department of Economics, Whiteknights, PO Box 218, Reading, RG6 6AA, United Kingdom.

330 AUS
DISTRIBUTION ONLINE. Text in English. w. AUD 49.50 (effective 2001). **Document type:** *Newsletter, Trade.*
Media: E-mail.
Published by: Publishing Services (Australia) Pty. Ltd., 244 St Pauls Terrace, Fortitude Valley, Brisbane, QLD 4000, Australia. TEL 61-7-3854-1286, FAX 61-7-3252-4829.

330 USA
DISTRIBUTOR'S LINK. Text in English. 1976. q. USD 30. adv. **Document type:** *Trade.*
Published by: Leo J. Coar, Ed. & Pub., 4297 Corp Sq N, Naples, FL 33942. TEL 813-643-2713, FAX 813-643-5795, linkmagazine@msn.com, http://www.linkmagazine.com. R&P Leo J Coar. Adv. contact Maryann Marzocchi. Circ: 13,000.

550 330 CHN ISSN 1003-3920
DIZHI JISHU JINGJI GUANLI/GEOLOGICAL TECHNOECONOMIC MANAGEMENT. Text in Chinese. 1979. bi-m. CNY 3 per issue domestic (effective 2000). **Document type:** *Academic/Scholarly.* **Description:** Covers the land development, business and economic issues in china.
Related titles: Online - full content ed.: (from WanFang Data Corp.); Online - full text ed.: (from East View Information Services).
Published by: Shijiazhuang Jingji Xueyuan, 302 Shijiazhuang Huai-nan Lu, Hebei, 050031, China.

330 336 USA ISSN 1520-0221
DOCUMENTARY CREDIT WORLD. Text in English. 1985. m. USD 495 (effective 2004). **Document type:** *Newsletter, Trade.* **Description:** For business persons, bankers and lawyers. Covers legislative and judicial developments concerning letter of credit practices.
Formerly (until 1997): Letter of Credit Update (0883-0487)
—CCC.
Published by: Institute of International Banking Law & Practice, 20405 Ryecroft Ct, Montgomery Village, MD 20886. TEL 301-869-9840, FAX 301-926-1265, info@iiblp.org, http://www.iiblp.org/dcw.asp. Ed. James E Byrne.

B

330 340 USA
DOING BUSINESS IN BRAZIL. Text in English. 1979. 2 base vols. plus updates 2/yr. looseleaf. USD 375 (effective 2005). **Description:** Provides analysis and description of the Brazilian government, legislature and judiciary, and detailed commentary of the principal commercial and financial laws that affect foreign investment.
Related titles: Supplement(s): Legal Letter.
Published by: Juris Publishing, Inc., 71 New St, Huntington, NY 11743-3301. TEL 631-351-5430, 800-887-4064, FAX 631-351-5712, info@jurispub.com, http://www.jurispub.com/books.asp?id=110.

330 341.7 USA
DOING BUSINESS IN CANADA. Text in English. 1984. 3 base vols. plus irreg. updates. looseleaf. USD 821 base vol(s). (effective 2003). **Description:** Written by a top Canadian law firm, the work supplies the comprehensive coverage and expert advice necessary to make informed decisions. Designed for use by both attorneys and businesspersons, this practical guide untangles the complex web of national and provincial legislation and regulation.
Published by: Matthew Bender & Co., Inc. (Subsidiary of: LexisNexis North America), 1275 Broadway, Albany, NY 12204. international@bender.com, http://bender.lexisnexis.com. Ed. Elliott Stikeman.

330 340 USA
DOING BUSINESS IN CHINA. Text in English. 1990. 3 base vols. plus updates 2/yr. looseleaf. USD 575 (effective 2005). **Description:** Examines the variety of political, economic and governmental issues affecting business in today's China.
Published by: Juris Publishing, Inc., 71 New St, Huntington, NY 11743-3301. TEL 631-351-5430, 800-887-4064, FAX 631-351-5712, info@jurispub.com, http://www.jurispub.com/books.asp?id=113. Ed. William P Streng.

330 341.7 USA
DOING BUSINESS IN FRANCE. Text in English. 1983. 2 base vols. plus irreg. updates. looseleaf. USD 550 base vol(s). (effective 2003). **Description:** Practice-oriented treatise covering taxation, banking and securities, foreign investment, auditing and accounting standards.
Published by: Matthew Bender & Co., Inc. (Subsidiary of: LexisNexis North America), 1275 Broadway, Albany, NY 12204. international@bender.com, http://bender.lexisnexis.com. Ed. Moquet Borde Dieux.

330 341.7 USA
DOING BUSINESS IN IRELAND. Text in English. 1987. base vol. plus a. updates. looseleaf. USD 220 base vol(s). (effective 2003). **Description:** Focuses on Irish business and legal climate, particularly investment incentives, taxation, employment law, export-import restrictions, intellectual property and product liability.
Published by: Matthew Bender & Co., Inc. (Subsidiary of: LexisNexis North America), 1275 Broadway, Albany, NY 12204. international@bender.com, http://bender.lexisnexis.com. Ed. Patrick Ussher.

▼ new title ➤ refereed ✶ unverified ◆ full entry avail.

B

330 341.7 USA ISSN 1057-3925
KNX1040.A13
DOING BUSINESS IN JAPAN. Text in English. 1980. 10 base vols. plus irreg. updates. looseleaf. USD 1,169 base vol(s). (effective 2003). **Description:** A major guide for your Japanese business dealings. Comprehensive and practical treatment focuses on all substantive areas, including: contracts, business organizations and regulation, employment law, securities, intellectual property, competition law and taxation.
Published by: Matthew Bender & Co., Inc. (Subsidiary of: LexisNexis North America), 1275 Broadway, Albany, NY 12204. international@bender.com, http://bender.lexisnexis.com. Ed. Zentaro Kitagawa.

330 340 USA ISSN 1068-0683
KGF333.B86
DOING BUSINESS IN MEXICO. (Includes bi-m. Legal Letter) Text in English, Spanish. 1980. 4 base vols. plus s-a. updates. looseleaf. USD 568.50 (effective 2004). **Document type:** *Trade.* **Description:** Source on legal, economic, and practical aspects affecting the conduct of business in Mexico.
Published by: Transnational Publishers, Inc., 410 Saw Mill River Rd, Ardsley, NY 10502-2615. TEL 914-693-5100, 800-914-8186, FAX 914-693-4430, info@transnationalpubs.com. Ed. Philip von Mehren.

330 341.7 USA
DOING BUSINESS IN SPAIN. Text in English. 1987. base vol. plus irreg. updates. looseleaf. USD 259 base vol(s). (effective 2003). **Description:** Guide to the business and legal environment in Spain, with coverage of foreign investment incentives, exchange controls, taxation, labor relations, business regulation and intellectual property.
Published by: Matthew Bender & Co., Inc. (Subsidiary of: LexisNexis North America), 1275 Broadway, Albany, NY 12204. international@bender.com, http://bender.lexisnexis.com. Ed. Fernando Pombo.

330 341.7 USA
DOING BUSINESS IN THE UNITED KINGDOM. Text in English. 1985. 3 base vols. plus irreg. updates. looseleaf. USD 821 base vol(s). (effective 2003). **Description:** Covers all the necessary legal background for planning business transactions and dealing with problems arising from investments and trade in the United Kingdom. Written by experienced London practitioners, this comprehensive work covers the business, private, commercial and regulatory laws of England, Scotland and Northern Ireland.
Published by: Matthew Bender & Co., Inc. (Subsidiary of: LexisNexis North America), 1275 Broadway, Albany, NY 12204. international@bender.com, http://bender.lexisnexis.com. Ed. Barbara Ford.

330 340 USA ISSN 1057-8684
KF390.B84
DOING BUSINESS IN THE UNITED STATES. Text in English. 1978. 6 base vols. plus irreg. updates. looseleaf. USD 1,491 base vol(s). (effective 2005). Supplement avail. **Description:** Provides comprehensive coverage for foreign attorneys, investors and officials who need an overview of U.S. law. It covers taxation; financing; contracts; preparation of sales agreements; corporation law; Uniform Commer cial Code; securities regulation; franchising; antitrust law; import/export law; acquisitions and mergers; regulation of banks; insurance; bankruptcy; partnerships and joint ventures; environmental laws; and intellectual and industrial property laws, including patents and trade secrets.
—CCC.
Published by: Matthew Bender & Co., Inc. (Subsidiary of: LexisNexis North America), 1275 Broadway, Albany, NY 12204. international@bender.com, http://bender.lexisnexis.com.

330 CHN ISSN 1005-8060
DONGFANG QIYEJIA/GLOBAI VIEWS. Text in Chinese. 1988. m. **Document type:** *Magazine, Trade.*
Related titles: Online - full text ed.: (from WanFang Data Corp.).
Published by: Yuanjian Zhongguo/China Media Group, 8, Hangzhoudao Zeng no.1, Hexi-qu, Tianjin, 300201, China. TEL 86-22-23025136, FAX 86-22-23025135, edit@mediagroup.com.cn, http://dfqyj.periodicals.net.cn/default.html, http://www.mediagroup.com.cn/.

330 CHN
DONGYA JINGMAO XINWEN/EAST ASIA ECONOMY AND TRADE NEWS. Text in Chinese. 1994. d. CNY 144 (effective 2004). **Document type:** *Newspaper, Trade.*
Related titles: Online - full content ed.
Published by: Dongya Jingmao Xinwenshe, 68, Renmin Dajie, Changchun, China. TEL 86-431-7816334, dyjmxw@public.cc.jl.cn, http://dyxw.com/news/. **Dist. by:** China International Book Trading Corp, 35 Chegongzhuang Xilu, Haidian District, PO Box 399, Beijing 100044, China. TEL 86-10-68412045, FAX 86-10-68412023, cibtc@mail.cibtc.com.cn, http://www.cibtc.com.cn.

330 GBR ISSN 0266-1438
DORSET BUSINESS. Text in English. 1983. bi-m. GBP 15.
Published by: Dorset Chamber of Commerce and Industry, 4 New Fields, Stinsford Rd, Nuffield, Dorset Poole, BH17 0DB, United Kingdom. TEL 01202-448800, FAX 01202-448836, dcci@blcnkdorset.co.uk. Ed. Gareth Weekes. Circ: 4,000.

330 JPN ISSN 0387-3021
HB9
DOSHISHA UNIVERSITY ECONOMIC REVIEW/DOSHISHA DAIGAKU KEIZAIGAKU RONSO. Text in Japanese. 1948. 4/yr. JPY 4,500 (effective 2002). **Document type:** *Bulletin, Academic/Scholarly.*
Related titles: Online - full content ed.
Indexed: AmH&L, HistAb.
Published by: Doshisha University, Doshisha Economic Association/Doshisha Daigaku Keizaigaku-kai, Karasuma Imadegawa, Kamikyo-ku, Kyoto-shi, 602, Japan. TEL 81-75-251-3534, FAX 81-75-251-3060, http://duels.doshisha.ac.jp:88/, http://www.econ.doshisha.ac.jp. Ed. Kunitoshi Suenaga. Circ: 2,500.

330 378 SWE ISSN 0283-636X
DROEMMEN OM ELIN. Text in Swedish. 1972. q. SEK 50 (effective 1990).
Published by: (E L I N - Ekonomfoereningen vid Universitetet i Linkoeping), Linkoeping Universitet, Institutionen foer Tema, Linkoeping, 58183, Sweden.

330 USA ISSN 0270-7713
DUN & BRADSTREET'S KEY BUSINESS RATIOS. Text in English. 1987. a. GBP 195 (effective 1998). **Document type:** *Directory.*
Formerly: Key Business Ratios
Published by: Dun & Bradstreet, Inc., Business Economics Dept, 99 Church St, New York, NY 10007. TEL 212-285-7191.

540 660 USA ISSN 0095-8808
DUPONT MAGAZINE. Text in English. 1913. bi-m. charts; illus.; tr.lit.
Indexed: ABIPC, BrCerAb, CADCAM, Englnd, FLUIDEX, GALA, IPackAb, TTI, WTA.
—BLDSC (3630.760000), CISTI, IE, ingenta, Linda Hall.
Published by: E.I. du Pont de Nemours & Co., Montchanin Bldg, N 9442, Wilmington, DE 19898. TEL 302-774-7988, FAX 302-774-2760. Ed. Jim Moore. Circ: 215,000.

330 NLD ISSN 0922-9825
DUTCH COMPANY YEARBOOK. Text in Dutch. 1988. a. **Description:** Provides financial data on the most successful businesses in the Netherlands.
Published by: Reed Business Information bv (Subsidiary of: Reed Business), Postbus 16400, Den Haag, 2500 BK, Netherlands. TEL 31-70-3624800, FAX 31-70-3605606.

DVENADTSAT' S POLOVINOI. see *CHILDREN AND YOUTH—For*

330 UKR
DZHERELO. Text in Ukrainian. q. USD 295 in the Americas (effective 2000).
Published by: Institut Problem Registratsii Informatsii, Ul. Shpaka 2, Kiev, Ukraine. TEL 441-21-97.

330 658 DEU ISSN 0938-8702
E B; Handbuch fuer Selbstaendige und Unternehmer. Text in German. 1982. m. looseleaf. back issues avail. **Document type:** *Bulletin.* **Description:** A how-to publication on starting a new business in Germany.
Formerly: Erfolgsberater
Published by: V N R Verlag fuer die Deutsche Wirtschaft AG, Theodor-Heuss-Str 2-4, Bonn, 53095, Germany. TEL 49-228-8205-0, FAX 49-228-364411. Ed. Norman Rentrop.

330.0711 AUS ISSN 1448-3696
E B E JOURNAL✶. Variant title: Economics and Business Educators Journal. Text in English. 1966. q. free to members. bk.rev. **Document type:** *Journal, Academic/Scholarly.* **Description:** Contains current relevant professional development articles on and activities for teaching Business Studies, Economics, Legal Studies and Commerce,.
Former titles (until vol.38, no.4, 2002): Economics (1328-7966); (until 1992): E C T A Com (0813-9423); (until 1983): Economics and Commercial Teachers' Association of New South Wales. Newsletter; (until 1974): Econ News; (until 1972): E T A News; Economics Teachers' Association of New South Wales. Newsletter
Indexed: AEI, CREJ, Perlslam.
Published by: Economics and Business Educators New South Wales, PO Box 67, Leichhardt, NSW 2040, Australia. TEL 61-2-95645007, FAX 61-2-95645309, ebensw@bigpond.com, http://alex.edfac.usyd.edu.au/ebe/index.html. Circ: 1,000.

330 004.678 USA
E-BUSINESS WORLD. Text in English. 1999. d. free. **Document type:** *Trade.*
Media: Online - full text.
Published by: International Data Group, One Exter Plaza, Boston, MA 02116. http://www.e-businessworld.com.

330 FRA
E-BUSINESS WORLD. Text in English. 1999. bi-m. USD 250 (effective 2000). **Description:** Presents up to the minute information on e-business issues from the perspective of the world business community.
Published by: International Chamber of Commerce, 38 Cours Albert 1er, Paris, 75008, France. TEL 33-1-49532923, FAX 33-1-49532902, pub@iccwbo.org, http://www.iccwbo.org.

E-COMMERCE LAW DAILY. see *LAW*

E-COMMERCE LAW REPORT; buying and selling on the Internet. see *COMPUTERS—Internet*

330 USA
E D I DEVELOPMENT POLICY CASE SERIES. Text in English. irreg., latest vol.9, 1994.
Published by: (Economic Development Institute), World Bank Group, 1818 H St, NW, Washington, DC 20433. TEL 202-473-1155, FAX 202-522-2627, books@worldbank.org, http://www.worldbank.org.

330 USA ISSN 1012-490X
E D I POLICY SEMINAR REPORT. (Economic Development Institute) Text in English. 1988. irreg.
Related titles: Spanish ed.: I D E Informe de un Seminario de Politica. ISSN 1012-6120.
—BLDSC (3660.585000).
Published by: World Bank Group, 1818 H St, NW, Washington, DC 20433. TEL 202-477-1234, FAX 202-676-0581, books@worldbank.org, http://www.worldbank.org.

362.10258 USA ISSN 1526-6052
E-HEALTHCARE MARKET REPORTER. Text in English. 1999. 24/yr. USD 239 for 6 mos. via email only (effective 2005). Index. 8 p./no.; back issues avail. **Document type:** *Newsletter, Consumer.* **Description:** An executive briefing delivered via email on the latest developments in the proliferation of electronic commerce among healthcare and managed care organizations.
Published by: Managed Care Information Center, 1913 Atlantic Ave, Ste F4, Manasquan, NJ 08736. TEL 888-843-6242, FAX 888-329-6242, mcic@themcic.com, http://www.healthresourcesonline.com/managed_care/24nl.htm, http://www.themcic.com.

330 USA
E I U NEWSLETTERS. (Includes Business Asia, Business Africa, Business Latin America, Business Europe, Business Eastern Europe, Business China, and Crossborder Monitor) Text in English. base vol. plus m. updates. **Document type:** *Newsletter.*
Related titles: CD-ROM ed.
Published by: Economist Intelligence Unit, 111 W 57th St, New York, NY 10019. TEL 212-554-0600, 800-938-4685, FAX 212-586-1182.

330 382 GBR ISSN 1465-3141
E M U - THE NEWS BULLETIN. (European Monetary Union) Text in English. 1998. q. **Document type:** *Trade.*
Related titles: Online - full text ed.
Published by: Eclipse Group Ltd. (Subsidiary of: LexisNexis UK (Scottish Office)), 18-20 Highbury Place, London, N5 1QP, United Kingdom. TEL 44-20-7354-5858, FAX 44-20-7226-8106, publications@irseclipse.co.uk, http://www.irseclipse.co.uk.

330 GBR ISSN 1469-0462
E-MMERCE. Text in English. 1999. bi-m. GBP 245, USD 365 (effective Aug. 2001). **Document type:** *Trade.*
Related titles: Online - full content ed.
—BLDSC (3733.539150).
Published by: Ark Financial Publishing, 4th Fl Zeeta House, 200 Upper Richmond Rd, London, SW15 2SH, United Kingdom. TEL 44-2-0785-2700, FAX 44-2-0785-9373, info@ark-goup.com, http://www.ark-group.com. Pub. Ruper Sayer.

THE E N D S REPORT. see *ENVIRONMENTAL STUDIES*

330 GBR ISSN 1369-2054
E R B E D U. WORKING PAPERS. (European Regional Business and Economic Development Unit) Text in English. irreg. **Document type:** *Monographic series.*
—BLDSC (3794.930500).
Published by: Leeds Metropolitan University, Leeds Business School, City Campus, Calverley St, Leeds, LS1 3HE, United Kingdom. http://www.lmu.ac.uk/lbs.

330 USA
E S B N ONLINE. (Entrepreneur - Small Business Newsletter) Text in English. 1996. m. **Document type:** *Trade.* **Description:** Provides pertinent business information.
Media: Online - full content.
Published by: Portrait Press, 4652 Portrait Ln, Plano, TX 75024. TEL 214-491-2460, FAX 214-491-2460, ppress@cyberhighway.net, http://www.esbnonline.com/news/.

330 300 IRL
E S R I ACCOUNTS AND BALANCE SHEET. Text in English. a. **Document type:** *Corporate.*
—BLDSC (0573.529510).
Published by: Economic and Social Research Institute, 4 Burlington Rd., Dublin, 4, Ireland. TEL 353-1-667-1525, FAX 353-1-668-6231. Ed. B J Whelan. R&P Gillian Davidson.

330 300 IRL
E S R I ANNUAL REPORT. Text in English. a. **Document type:** *Corporate.*
—BLDSC (1241.049000).

Published by: Economic and Social Research Institute, 4 Burlington Rd., Dublin, 4, Ireland. TEL 353-1-667-1525, FAX 353-1-668-6231. Ed. B J Whelan. R&P Gillian Davidson.

341.2422 DNK ISSN 1603-3566
HC240.A1
E U; beretning til folketinget vedroerende udviklingen i Den Europaeiske Union. (Europaeiske Union) Text in Danish. 1974. a., latest 2003. free. **Document type:** *Government.*
Former titles (until 2003): Beretning om Udviklingen i EU i (Year) (1601-2453); (until 2001): Beretning til Folketinget Vedrorende Udviklingen i Den Europaeiske Union (Koepenhavn, 1999) (1600-7859); (until 1998): Beretning Vedroerende Udviklingen i den Europaeiske Union (1395-8720); (until 1995): Beretning Vedroerende Udviklingen i de Europaeiske Faellesskaber (0107-2013)
Published by: Udenrigsministeriet, Kommunikationsenhed/Royal Danish Ministry of Foreign Affairs, Department of Press and Information, Asiatisk Plads 2, Copenhagen K, 1448, Denmark. TEL 45-33-920000, FAX 45-33-920710, ke@um.dk, http://www.um.dk/da/servicemenu/Publikationer/Udenrigspolitik/EU-politik/.

E U R O M A P ECONOMIC SURVEY. (European Plastics and Rubber Machinery Manufacturers Association) see *PLASTICS*

EAI JOURNAL; the resource for e-business and application integration. see *COMPUTERS—Internet*

EAI JOURNAL ONLINE. see *COMPUTERS—Internet*

330 USA ISSN 1547-240X
➤ **THE EARNINGS ANALYST.** Text in English. 1998. a. USD 25 per issue (effective 2003). **Document type:** *Journal, Academic/Scholarly.*
Published by: American Rehabilitation Economics Association, 127 N. Westwind Dr., El Cajon, CA 92020-2955. TEL 800-317-2732, FAX 619-593-9989, http://www.a-r-e-a.org/journal.shtml. Ed. Thomas R. Ireland.

330 USA
EARNINGS TICKER. Text in English. w. free. **Document type:** *Newsletter, Trade.*
Media: E-mail.
Published by: 123Jump.com, 407 Lincoln Rd Ste 12D, Miami Beach, FL 33139. TEL 305-673-6339, FAX 305-673-6386, editorial@123jump.com, http://www.123jump.com/. Ed. Boris Petrov. Pub. Manish Shah. Adv. contact Glen Sundin TEL 973-984-2432.

330 USA
EAST BAY BUSINESS TIMES. Text in English. w. (Fri). USD 79 (effective 2005). adv. **Document type:** *Newspaper, Consumer.*
Related titles: Online - full text ed.
Contact: American City Business Journals, Inc. (East Bay), 6160 Stoneridge Mall Rd Ste 300, Pleasanton, CA 94588. TEL 925-598-1830, FAX 925-598-1840, eastbay@bizjournals.com, http://eastbay.bcentral.com/eastbay/. Ed. Michael Hytha. Adv. contact Craig Johnson. color page USD 4,218. Circ: 10,000 (paid and free). Wire service: PR.

330 AUT
EAST - WEST REPORT; business information for the Central European investor. Text in English. 1992. q. **Document type:** *Trade.*
Published by: Bank Austria AG, Am Hof 2, Vienna, W 1010, Austria. TEL 01-71191-0. Eds. Alexander Vogel, Franz Himmer.

330 KEN ISSN 1011-4750
HC501
EASTERN AFRICA ECONOMIC REVIEW. Text in English. 1954-1977; N.S. 1985. s-a. USD 70. adv. bk.rev. bibl.; charts; stat. reprints avail.
Formerly (until 1969): East African Economic Review (0424-0790)
Indexed: ASD, IBSS, JEL, PAIS, PCI, RDA, RRTA, SSCI, WAE&RSA.
Published by: Kenya Literature Bureau, PO Box 30022, Nairobi, Kenya. Ed. J K Maitha. Circ: 1,000.

330 USA ISSN 0094-5056
HB1
➤ **EASTERN ECONOMIC JOURNAL.** Text in English. 1974. q. USD 50 in US & Canada to members; USD 55 elsewhere to members; USD 75 in US & Canada to libraries; USD 95 elsewhere to libraries (effective 2005). adv. bk.rev. bibl. reprint service avail. from PSC. **Document type:** *Academic/Scholarly.*
Description: Devoted to free and open intellectual inquiry from diverse philosophical perspectives in all areas of theoretical and applied research related to economics.
Related titles: Online - full text ed.: (from EBSCO Publishing, Northern Light Technology, Inc., O C L C Online Computer Library Center, Inc., ProQuest Information & Learning).
Indexed: ABIn, BPIA, CJA, JEL.
—BLDSC (3646.587900), IE, Infotrieve, ingenta.
Published by: Eastern Economic Association, Iona College, 715 North Ave, New Rochelle, NY 10801-1890. TEL 914-633-2088, FAX 914-633-2549, mlesser@iona.edu, http://www.iona.edu/eea/publications/publication.htm. Adv. contact Jenifer C Gamber. Circ: 1,000 (paid).

332 USA ISSN 1084-1431
EASTERN ECONOMIST. Text in English. 1994. w. USD 249 in North America; USD 295 elsewhere (effective 2005).
—BLDSC (3646.588200).
Published by: Matlid Publications, 2228 W Chicago Ave, Chicago, IL 60622. TEL 773-278-8662, FAX 773-278-4051, editor@easterneconomist.com, matlid@interaccess.com. **Subscr. to:** Redaktsiya Eastern Economist, Ul. Gor'kogo, 21, Kiev, Ukraine. TEL 380-44-2393899, FAX 380-44-2393880.

330 USA ISSN 0012-8775
HC244.A1
➤ **EASTERN EUROPEAN ECONOMICS**; a journal of translations. Text in English. 1962. bi-m. USD 149 domestic to individuals; USD 221 foreign to individuals; USD 1,230 combined subscription domestic to institutions print & online eds.; USD 1,350 combined subscription foreign to institutions print & online eds. (effective 2006). adv. illus. index. reprint service avail. from PSC. **Document type:** *Journal, Academic/Scholarly.* **Description:** Covers economic thought and policy in "the new Europe." Discusses problems associated with the transition to mamrket economy, including inflation, unemployment, inadequate investment and savings, and other issues.
Related titles: Online - full text ed.: 2001 (Jan.) (from EBSCO Publishing, Gale Group, O C L C Online Computer Library Center, Inc., Swets Information Services).
Indexed: ABIn, ASCA, CREJ, CurCont, GEOBASE, IBR, JEL, KES, PAIS, PCI, SSCI, WAE&RSA.
—BLDSC (3646.595000), IDS, IE, Infotrieve, ingenta. **CCC.**
Published by: M.E. Sharpe, Inc., 80 Business Park Dr, Armonk, NY 10504. TEL 914-273-1800, 800-541-6563, FAX 914-273-2106, custserv@mesharpe.com, http://www.mesharpe.com/mall/results1.asp?ACR=EEE. Ed. Josef Brada. Adv. contact Barbara Ladd TEL 914-273-1800 ext 121. page USD 300; 8 x 5.

330 USA ISSN 1074-9624
EASTERN PENNSYLVANIA BUSINESS JOURNAL. Text in English. 1989. w. USD 36 (effective 1999). adv. **Document type:** *Newspaper.* **Description:** Covers business and economic news including real estate transfers, new businesses, bankruptcies, and related subjects.
Related titles: Online - full text ed.: (from Northern Light Technology, Inc., O C L C Online Computer Library Center, Inc., ProQuest Information & Learning).
Indexed: ABIn, BusDate.
Published by: Press - Enterprise, Inc. (Bethlehem), 65 E Elizabeth Ave, Ste 700, Bethlehem, PA 18018-6806. TEL 610-807-9619, 800-328-1026, FAX 610-807-9612. Ed. G Jacob Laubach. R&P Linda Zulli Trumbauer. Adv. contact Linda Zulli-Trumbauer. B&W page USD 2,035, color page USD 2,290; 12.63 x 10.13. Circ: 12,000.

330 RUS
EBRUKA V V T/EUREKA T I T; vremya visokih tehnologii - time of high technologies. Text in Russian. m.
Published by: Moscow Center for Introduction of Scientific and Technical Achievements, Tsentr Moskva, Pr-t Mira, Moscow, 129223, Russian Federation. TEL 7-095-9747423, FAX 7-095-9747293, mailbox@eureka.ru, http://www.eureka.ru. Ed. Vladimir Borovyak. Circ: 80,000.

▼ **ECHELON**; magazine for gay and lesbian professionals. see *HOMOSEXUALITY*

330 BEL ISSN 0776-409X
L'ECHO (BRUSSELS). Text in French. 1881. 5/w. EUR 255 (effective 2005). adv. bk.rev. **Document type:** *Newspaper.*
Formerly: Echo de la Bourse
Published by: Editeco S.A., Rue de Birmingham 131, Brussels, 1070, Belgium. TEL 32-2-526-5502, FAX 32-2-526-5526, redaction@lecho.be, contact@lecho.be, http://www.lecho.be/index.jsp. Ed. F Melaet. Circ: 54,000.

330 DEU
ECHO-HANDELSJOURNAL; Fachzeitschrift fuer modernen Lebensmittelhandel. Text in German. 1952. m. EUR 1.55 newsstand/cover (effective 2005). adv. **Document type:** *Journal, Trade.*
Published by: Rewe-Verlag GmbH, Domstr 20, Cologne, 50668, Germany. TEL 49-221-149-0, FAX 49-221-1499552. Ed. Josef Rosen. adv.: B&W page EUR 5,266.31, color page EUR 8,952.72; trim 210 x 280. Circ: 51,600 (paid and controlled).

330 NLD ISSN 1383-990X
ECLAIRE. Text in Dutch. 1979. 9/yr. (includes special issue). bk.rev.
Published by: Economics Faculty Association Rotterdam (EFR), Burgmeester Oudlaan 50, Kamer C 1-15, Rotterdam, 3062 PA, Netherlands. TEL 31-10-4081146, FAX 31-10-4532928, efr@few.eur.nl. Ed. E A Kerkuijk. Circ: 3,000; 35,000.

330 ESP
ECO. Text in Spanish. 12/yr.
Address: Via La Cierva 13, Polig. del Tambre, 15890 Santiago, Madrid, Spain. TEL 81-56-38-06, FAX 81-57-26-60. Ed. Jose M Couselo. Circ: 5,000.

330.071 AUS ISSN 1320-968X
H1
ECODATE. Text in English. 1987. q. AUD 65.50 (effective 2003). back issues avail. **Document type:** *Academic/Scholarly.*
Description: Presents recent developments in Australian economics for 12th grade students.
Related titles: Online - full text ed.: (from EBSCO Publishing).
Indexed: MASUSE, WBA, WMB.
Published by: Warringal Publications, 116 Argyle St, Fitzroy, VIC 3065, Australia. TEL 61-3-94160200, FAX 61-3-94160402. Ed. Bronwyn Hession. Pub. Colin Hobbs. Circ: 2,000.

330 FRA ISSN 0296-4449
ECOFLASH; mensuel d'informations economiques et sociales. Text in French. 10/yr. **Description:** Each issue studies a sociological, economic, historical or geographical theme, with a methodological analysis and bibliography.
Published by: Centre National de Documentation Pedagogique, 29 rue de l'Ulm, Paris, Cedex 5 75230, France. TEL 33-1-46349000, FAX 33-1-46345544. Ed. Albert Cohen. **Subscr. to:** CNDP - Abonnement, B.P. 750, Sainte Genevieve Cedex 60732, France. FAX 33-3-44033013.

B

ECOMPANY.COM. see *COMPUTERS—Internet*

330 DEU
ECON BUSINESS NAVIGATOR. Variant title: Navigator. Text in German. q. **Document type:** *Magazine, Trade.*
Published by: (Econ Verlag), BurdaYukom Publishing GmbH (Subsidiary of: Hubert Burda Media Holding GmbH & Co. KG), Schleissheimer Str 141, Munich, 80797, Germany. TEL 49-89-306200, FAX 49-89-30620100, navigator@econ-list.com, info@burdayukom.de, http://www.yukom.de. Circ: 10,000 (controlled).

ECON ED AND THE FED. see *EDUCATION*

330 371 USA
ECON-EXCHANGE. Text in English. s-a. **Document type:** *Newsletter.* **Description:** Each issue discusses a single economics subject and includes three lesson plans for K-12 teachers.
Published by: Federal Reserve Bank of Richmond, Research Dept, Box 27622, Richmond, VA 23261. http://www.rich.frb.org.

330 MAR ISSN 0851-5743
DT324
ECONOMAP; daily economic and financial news bulletin. Text in French. 1976. d. MAD 3,582, USD 370 (effective 1998). adv. illus.
Published by: Maghreb Arabe Presse, 122 Avenue Allal Ben Abdellah, B P 1049, Rabat, 10000, Morocco. TEL 212-7-764083, FAX 212-7-767097, TELEX 310-44, map@map.co.ma, http://www.map.co.ma. Ed. Abdeljalil Fenjiro. Circ: 1,000.

330 GBR ISSN 0012-9682
HB1 CODEN: ECMTA7
➤ **ECONOMETRICA**; journal of the Econometric Society. Text in English. 1933. bi-m. USD 35 in developing nations to institutions print & online; GBP 301 combined subscription elsewhere to institutions print & online; USD 500 elsewhere to institutions print & online (effective 2006). adv. charts; illus. index, cum.index: vols.1-20 (1933-1952), vols.21-45 (1953-1977). reprint service avail. from PQC,PSC. **Document type:** *Journal, Academic/Scholarly.*
Related titles: Microform ed.: (from PMC, PQC); Online - full text ed.: ISSN 1468-0262. USD 33 in developing nations to institutions; GBP 286, USD 475 elsewhere to institutions (effective 2006) (from Blackwell Synergy, EBSCO Publishing, Gale Group, IngentaConnect, JSTOR (Web-based Journal Archive), O C L C Online Computer Library Center, Inc., ProQuest Information & Learning, Swets Information Services).
Indexed: ABIn, ASCA, AgeL, BAS, BPIA, Biostat, CCMJ, CIS, CMCI, CPM, CREJ, CurCont, EngInd, FamI, IBR, IBSS, IBZ, IPSA, JCQM, JEL, KES, MEA&I, MathR, MathSciNet, ORMS, PCI, PHN&I, QC&AS, RRTA, SCI, SSCI, SSI, ST&MA, T&II, WAE&RSA, ZentMath.
—BLDSC (3650.100000), CISTI, IDS, IE, Infotrieve, ingenta.
Published by: (Econometric Society), Blackwell Publishing Ltd., 9600 Garsington Rd, Oxford, OX4 2ZG, United Kingdom. TEL 44-1865-776868, FAX 44-1865-714591, econometrica@www.econometricsociety.org, customerservices@oxon.blackwellpublishing.com, http://www.blackwellpublishing.com/journal.asp?ref=0012-9682&site=1. Ed. Eddie Dekel TEL 972-3-640-9905. Circ: 6,000.

330 GBR ISSN 1368-4221
HB139
➤ **THE ECONOMETRICS JOURNAL.** Text in English. 1998. 3/yr. EUR 48 combined subscription in Europe to individuals print & online eds.; USD 54 combined subscription in the Americas to individuals & Caribbean (print & online eds.); GBP 32 combined subscription elsewhere to individuals print & online eds.; USD 234 combined subscription in the Americas to institutions & Caribbean (print & online eds.); GBP 139 combined subscription elsewhere to institutions print & online eds. (effective 2006). cum.index. reprint service avail. from PSC. **Document type:** *Journal, Academic/Scholarly.*
Description: Seeks to encourage reporting of new developments in the context of applied problems and to provide a focus for debate about alternative approaches. For theoretical econometricians, economists, and applied econometricians.
Related titles: Online - full text ed.: ISSN 1368-423X (from Blackwell Synergy, EBSCO Publishing, Gale Group, IngentaConnect, O C L C Online Computer Library Center, Inc., Swets Information Services).
Indexed: ABIn, CCMJ, IBSS, JEL, MathR, MathSciNet, RefZh.
—BLDSC (3650.112500), IE, Infotrieve. **CCC.**
Published by: (Royal Economic Society), Blackwell Publishing Ltd., 9600 Garsington Rd, Oxford, OX4 2ZG, United Kingdom. TEL 44-1865-776868, FAX 44-1865-714591, customerservices@oxon.blackwellpublishing.com, http://www.blackwellpublishing.com/journals/ECTJ. Ed. Karim Abadir.

B

330 ITA
ECONOMIA. Text in Italian. 1988. irreg., latest vol.10, 1999. price varies. adv. **Document type:** *Monographic series.*
Published by: Liguori Editore srl, Via Posillipo 394, Naples, 80123, Italy. TEL 39-81-7206111, FAX 39-81-7206244, http://www.liguori.it. Ed. Salvatore Vinci. Pub. Guido Liguori. Adv. contact Maria Liguori.

330 PER ISSN 0254-4415
HC226
➤ **ECONOMIA.** Variant title: Revista Economia. Text in Spanish. 1977. s-a. USD 30 (effective 2003). bk.rev. **Document type:** *Academic/Scholarly.*
Indexed: JEL, PAIS.
Published by: (Departamento de Economia), Pontificia Universidad Catolica del Peru, Fondo Editorial, Plaza Francia 1164, Cercado de Lima, Lima, 1, Peru. TEL 51-14-626390, FAX 51-14-611785, editorial@pucp.edu.pe, http://www.pucp.edu.pe. Eds. Jorge Rojas, Maximo Vega Centeno. Circ: 500.

330 ECU ISSN 0012-9704
HC201
ECONOMIA. Text in Spanish. 1965. s-a. USD 10. bk.rev. stat.
Description: Covers all aspects of the economy in Ecuador, past and present.
Indexed: IBSS.
Published by: Universidad Central del Ecuador, Instituto de Investigaciones Economicas, Ciudad Universitaria, Apdo 17 03 0724, Quito, Pichincha, Ecuador. TEL 593-2-525018, FAX 593-2-229481, secretar@iieuc.ecx.ec. Ed. Isaias Campana C.

330 GTM ISSN 0046-113X
HC144.A1
ECONOMIA. Text in Spanish. 3/yr. GTQ 5, USD 5. bk.rev.
Published by: Universidad de San Carlos de Guatemala, Instituto de Investigaciones Economicas y Sociales, Ciudad Universitaria, Edificio S6 3er. Nivel, Guatemala City Zona, Guatemala.

330 ARG ISSN 0325-0830
ECONOMIA. Text in Spanish. 1913. q.
Formerly (until 1972): Revista de Ciencias Economicas. Temas de Economia (0325-0822); Supersedes in part (in 1970): Revista de Ciencias Economicas (0034-7779)
Published by: Colegio de Graduados en Ciencias Economicas, Viamonte, 1582, Capital Federal, Buenos Aires 1055, Argentina.

330 JPN ISSN 0012-9712
ECONOMIA. Text in Japanese. 1950. q. per issue exchange basis. bk.rev. index. **Document type:** *Academic/Scholarly.*
Published by: Yokohama Kokuritsu Daigaku/Yokohama National University, Economic Society, 79-3 Tokiwa-Dai, Hodogaya-ku, Yokohama-shi, Kanagawa-ken 240-8501, Japan. Ed. Shinjiro Sagiwara. Circ: 1,800 (controlled).

330 650 PRT ISSN 0870-3531
HB1.A1
➤ **ECONOMIA (LISBON, 1977).** Text in English, French, Portuguese, Spanish. 1977. 2/yr. USD 20 in Europe; USD 25 elsewhere (effective 2005). adv. bk.rev. bibl.; charts; stat. **Document type:** *Academic/Scholarly.* **Description:** Essays and research on economics and management science.
Indexed: IBR, IBSS, IBZ, JEL, PAIS.
Published by: Universidade Catolica Portuguesa, Faculdade de Ciencias Economicas e Empresariais, Caminho da Palma de Cima, Lisbon, 1648-023, Portugal. TEL 351-21-7214000, FAX 351-21-7270252, http://www.fcee.ucp.pt/. Ed. Fernando Branco. Circ: 2,000.

330 ITA ISSN 1122-2417
ECONOMIA DELLA CULTURA. Text in Italian. 1991. q. EUR 50 domestic to individuals; EUR 85 foreign to individuals; EUR 64 domestic to institutions; EUR 115 foreign to institutions (effective 2004). bk.rev. back issues avail. **Document type:** *Academic/Scholarly.*
Published by: (Associazione per l'Economia della Cultura), Societa Editrice Il Mulino, Strada Maggiore 37, Bologna, 40125, Italy. TEL 39-051-256011, FAX 39-051-256034, riviste@mulino.it, http://www.mulino.it.

330 340 ITA
ECONOMIA E DIRITTO DEL TERZIARIO. Text in Italian. 1989. 3/yr. EUR 51 domestic; EUR 74 foreign (effective 2003).
Published by: Franco Angeli Edizioni, Viale Monza 106, Milan, 20127, Italy. TEL 39-02-2837141, FAX 39-02-26144793, redazioni@francoangeli.it, http://www.francoangeli.it.

330 ITA ISSN 0391-2078
HD28
ECONOMIA E POLITICA INDUSTRIALE. Text in Italian. 1974. q. EUR 68 domestic; EUR 94 foreign (effective 2003).
Indexed: IBR, IBZ, PAIS.
—BLDSC (3650.480000), IE, ingenta.
Published by: Franco Angeli Edizioni, Viale Monza 106, Milan, 20127, Italy. TEL 39-02-2837141, FAX 39-02-26144793, redazioni@francoangeli.it, http://www.francoangeli.it. Ed. Sergio Vacca.

330 BRA ISSN 0104-0618
HM35
ECONOMIA E SOCIEDADE. Text in Portuguese. 1992. s-a. BRL 15 per issue (effective 2002). **Description:** Covers contemporary political, economic and social questions.
Indexed: JEL, PAIS.
Published by: Universidade Estadual de Campinas, Instituto de Economia, Caixa Postal 6135, Campinas, SP 13083-970, Brazil. TEL 55-19-3788-5725, FAX 55-19-3289-1512, http://www.eco.unicamp.br.

330 ITA ISSN 1593-9499
➤ **ECONOMIA ED AMBIENTE;** rivista dell' A N E A T. (Associazione Nazionale degli Economisti dell' Ambiente e del Territorio) Text in Italian. 1982. bi-m. EUR 34 domestic; EUR 55 foreign (effective 2003). adv. bk.rev. index. back issues avail. **Document type:** *Journal, Academic/Scholarly.*
Published by: I.P.E.M. - C.I.S.P.E., Via di Fortezza 1, Pisa, 56125, Italy. TEL 39-050-571181, FAX 39-050-571198. Ed. Romano Molesti. R&P Silvio Truceo. Adv. contact A C Cappuccilli.

330 MEX ISSN 0185-0849
ECONOMIA INFORMA. Text in Spanish. 1974. m. MXP 230, USD 45 (effective 2000).
Indexed: PAIS.
Published by: Universidad Nacional Autonoma de Mexico, Facultad de Economia, Edif. Anexo de la Facultad, 2do. Piso, Circuito Interior, Ciudad Universitaria, Mexico, D.F., 04510, Mexico. TEL 52-5-6222137, FAX 52-5-6222131, http://herzog.economia.unam.mx/. Ed. Julio Moguel.

330 ESP ISSN 0012-9801
ECONOMIA INTERNACIONAL. Text in Spanish. 1956. m. adv. bk.rev. bibl.; stat. **Document type:** *Consumer.*
Indexed: PAIS.
Address: Balmes, 213, Barcelona, 08001, Spain. Ed. Jacinto Calm Domenech. Circ: 20,000.

330 MEX ISSN 0185-0458
HC131
ECONOMIA MEXICANA. Text in English, Spanish. 1979. s-a. MXP 70 domestic to individuals; USD 40 foreign to individuals; MXP 100 domestic to individuals; USD 95 foreign to individuals (effective 2000). adv. **Document type:** *Journal, Academic/Scholarly.* **Description:** Economic review for the analysis and discussion of the economic problems of Mexico and Latin America.
Related titles: Online - full text ed.: 2004. free (effective 2005) (from EBSCO Publishing).
Indexed: HAPI, IBR, JEL, PAIS.
Published by: (Departamento de Economia), Centro de Investigacion y Docencia Economicas, Carretera Mexico-Toluca Km. 16.5, Apdo. Postal 116-114, Mexico City, DF 01130, Mexico. TEL 52-5-7279885, FAX 52-5-7279885, ecomex@cide.edu, villagom@dis1.cide.mx, http://redalyc.uaemex.mx/redalyc/src/inicio/HomRevRed.jsp?iCveEntRev=323, http://www.cide.mx. Ed. David Mayer Foulkes. R&P Ofelia Aruti TEL 525-7279800 ext. 2207. Circ: 1,000.

330 MEX ISSN 0186-8470
ECONOMIA NACIONAL. Text in Spanish. m. MXP 350 domestic; USD 110 in Latin America; USD 95 elsewhere (effective 2001). back issues avail. **Document type:** *Academic/Scholarly.*
Related titles: Online - full content ed.: ISSN 1606-8149. 2000.
Indexed: PAIS.
Address: Plaza Necaxa No.6-304, Col. Cuahutemoc, Mexico, DF, 06500, Mexico. TEL 52-5-5140026, FAX 52-5-5255363, revista@economianacional.com.mx, http://www.economianacional.com.mx/. Eds. Roberta Soria Olivera, Miguel Almedia Delgado. Circ: 16,000.

330 900 MEX ISSN 0531-8203
HC10
ECONOMIA POLITICA. Text in Spanish. 1965. q. USD 6. bk.rev. illus.
Published by: Instituto Politecnico Nacional, Escuela Superior de Economia, Unidad Profesional Zacatenco, 07738 Mexico, Mexico, Col Lindavista, Mexico City, DF 07300, Mexico. Circ: 2,000.

330 ITA ISSN 1120-2890
ECONOMIA POLITICA; rivista di teoria e analisi. Text in Italian. 1984. 3/yr. EUR 55 domestic to individuals; EUR 84 foreign to individuals; EUR 102 domestic to institutions print & online eds.; EUR 135 foreign to institutions print & online eds. (effective 2004). adv. index. back issues avail. **Document type:** *Academic/Scholarly.*
Related titles: Online - full text ed.
Indexed: JEL.
Published by: Societa Editrice Il Mulino, Strada Maggiore 37, Bologna, 40125, Italy. TEL 39-051-256011, FAX 39-051-256034, riviste@mulino.it, http://www.mulino.it. Ed. Alberto Quadrio Curzio. Adv. contact M Luisa Vezzali. Circ: 900.

330 HND ISSN 0424-2483
HC145.A1
ECONOMIA POLITICA. Text in Spanish. 1962; N.S. 1972. irreg. USD 2. bk.rev.
Indexed: ILD, PAIS.
Published by: Universidad Nacional Autonoma de Honduras, Instituto de Investigaciones Economicas y Sociales, Ciudad Universitaria, Tegucigalpa DC, Honduras. Ed. Victor Meza. Circ: 1,000.

330 CHL ISSN 0716-0100
ECONOMIA Y ADMINISTRACION. Text and summaries in English, Spanish. 1964. s-a. CLP 6,000 domestic to individuals; USD 20 foreign to individuals; CLP 4,000 domestic to institutions; USD 12 foreign to institutions (effective 2004). adv. bk.rev. bibl.; charts; stat. index, cum.index. **Document type:** *Journal, Academic/Scholarly.*
Indexed: IBSS.
Published by: Universidad de Concepcion, Facultad de Ciencias Economicas y Administrativas, Casilla 160-C, Concepcion, Chile. TEL 56-41-204172, FAX 56-41-221866, anguerre@udec.cl, raguiler@udec.cl. Ed. Rosa Aguilera Vidal. R&P Juan Saavedra Gonzalez. Adv. contact Alexi Mondaca. Circ: 500 (paid and controlled).

330 VEN ISSN 0012-9895
H8.S7
ECONOMIA Y CIENCIAS SOCIALES✶. Text in Spanish. 1970 (vol.12). q. bibl.; charts.
Indexed: HAPI, HistAb, IPSA.
Published by: Universidad Central de Venezuela, Facultad de Ciencias Economicas y Sociales, Ciudad Universitaria, ZP 104, Los Chaguaramos, Caracas, DF 1040, Venezuela. Ed. D F Maza Zavala.

330 CUB ISSN 0252-8584
HB9 CODEN: ECDEEN
ECONOMIA Y DESARROLLO. Summaries in English, French. 1970. bi-m. CUP 300; USD 13 in North America; USD 14 in South America; USD 18 in Europe; USD 21 elsewhere. bibl.; charts; illus.; stat.
Indexed: HAPI, IBR, IBSS, PAIS, RRTA, SOPODA, WAE&RSA.
Published by: (Universidad de La Habana), Ediciones Cubanas, Obispo No. 527, Apdo. 605, Havana, Cuba. Ed. Fernando Gonzalez. Circ: 11,000.

330 CHL ISSN 0717-0033
HD4811
ECONOMIA Y TRABAJO EN CHILE. Variant title: Revista de Economia y Trabajo. Text in Spanish. 1993. s-a. USD 20 to individuals; USD 30 to institutions; USD 15 to students. **Document type:** *Academic/Scholarly.*
Published by: Programa de Economia del Trabajo, Santo Domingo, 526, Santiago, Chile. TEL 56-2-6326128, FAX 56-2-6333671. Ed. Gonzalo Rivas.

330 IND ISSN 0424-2513
HC431
ECONOMIC AFFAIRS; a quarterly journal of economics. Text in English. 1956. q. INR 200, USD 22.50 (effective 1999 & 2000). adv. bk.rev. index. reprints avail. **Document type:** *Academic/Scholarly.*
Indexed: AEA, AgrForAb, AnBrAb, BAS, CPM, DSA, FCA, ForAb, HortAb, I&DA, IBR, IBSS, IBZ, ILD, JEL, MaizeAb, NutrAb, OrnHort, PHN&I, PN&I, PotatoAb, PoultAb, RA&MP, RDA, REE&TA, RRTA, RevApplEntom, RiceAb, S&F, SIA, TriticAb, WAE&RSA, WeedAb.
—BLDSC (3651.420000), IE, ingenta.
Published by: Himansu Roy Ed. & Pub., BC-144 Sector-1, Salt Lake City, Kolkata, West Bengal 700 064, India. TEL 91-33-373034. Circ: 2,000.

330.9   GBR   ISSN 0265-0665
HC251
➤ **ECONOMIC AFFAIRS**; the journal of the IEA. Text in English. 1980. q. GBP 24, EUR 36 combined subscription in Europe to individuals print & online eds; USD 54 combined subscription in the Americas to individuals & Caribbean, print & online eds; GBP 32 combined subscription elsewhere to individuals print & online eds; GBP 125 combined subscription in Europe to institutions print & online eds.; USD 232 combined subscription in the Americas to institutions & Caribbean, print & online eds.; GBP 138 combined subscription elsewhere to institutions print & online eds; GBP 20, EUR 30 combined subscription in Europe to students print & online eds; USD 45 combined subscription in the Americas to students & Caribbean, print & online eds; GBP 27 combined subscription elsewhere to students print & online eds (effective 2006). adv. bk.rev. index. reprint service avail. from PSC. **Document type:** *Journal, Academic/Scholarly.* **Description:** Each issue presents original research articles on an economic topic, such as market analysis, government policy, or inflation.
Formerly: Journal of Economic Affairs (0260-8359)
Related titles: Online - full text ed.: ISSN 1468-0270. GBP 119 in Europe to institutions; USD 220 in the Americas to institutions & Caribbean; GBP 131 elsewhere to institutions (effective 2006) (from Blackwell Synergy, EBSCO Publishing, Gale Group, IngentaConnect, O C L C Online Computer Library Center, Inc., Swets Information Services).
Indexed: ABIn, BrHumI, CREJ, Emerald, GEOBASE, PCI, RDA, RRTA, RefZh.
—BLDSC (3651.422000), IE, Infotrieve, ingenta. **CCC.**
Published by: (Institute of Economic Affairs), Blackwell Publishing Ltd., 9600 Garsington Rd, Oxford, OX4 2ZG, United Kingdom. TEL 44-1865-776868, FAX 44-1865-714591, customerservices@oxon.blackwellpublishing.com, http://www.blackwellpublishing.com/journals/ECAF. Ed. Philip Booth. Pub. John Hayes. Adv. contact Griselda Anderson. Circ: 5,000.

330   AUS   ISSN 0313-5926
HB1
➤ **ECONOMIC ANALYSIS AND POLICY.** Text in English. 1970. 2/yr. AUD 20 to institutional members; AUD 30 to individuals; AUD 40 to institutions; AUD 10 per issue to individual members; AUD 15 per issue to individuals; AUD 20 per issue to institutions (effective 2001). adv. bk.rev. **Document type:** *Journal, Academic/Scholarly.*
Related titles: Online - full text ed.: (from R M I T Publishing).
Indexed: AusPAIS, CREJ, ESPM, JEL, PAIS, RiskAb, S&F, WAE&RSA.
—BLDSC (3651.441000), IE, ingenta. **CCC.**
Published by: Economic Society of Australia, Department of Economics, the university of Queensland, GPO Box 2434, Brisbane, QLD 4001, Australia. TEL 61-7-3365-6340, FAX 61-7-3365-7299, a.lindley@economics.uq.edu.au. Ed. Steve Harrison. R&P A. Lindley TEL 61-7-33656578. Adv. contact J. Stanford. Circ: 550.

330   SCG   ISSN 0351-286X
HD28
ECONOMIC ANALYSIS AND WORKERS MANAGEMENT✱. Text in English, Serbo-Croatian. 1967. q. USD 30 to individuals; USD 70 to institutions. adv. bk.rev. abstr.; bibl.; charts; stat.
Formerly: Ekonomska Analiza - Economic Analysis (0013-3213)
Indexed: CREJ, JEL, MEA&I, PAIS, SSCI.
Published by: Udruzenje za Ekonomiju Samoupravljanja, c/o Economists' Society of Serbia, Nusiceva 6-111, P.O. Box 490, Belgrade, 11000. Ed. Branko Horvat. Circ: 2,000.

ECONOMIC ANALYSIS OF UNITED STATES SKI AREAS. see *SPORTS AND GAMES—Outdoor Life*

330   SVN   ISSN 1580-0466
HB9
➤ **ECONOMIC AND BUSINESS REVIEW/EKONOMSKA IN POSLOVNA REVIJA**; for Central and South-Eastern Europe. Text in English. 1950. q. EUR 50 to individuals; EUR 100 to institutions (effective 2005). adv. bk.rev. bibl.; charts; stat. back issues avail. **Document type:** *Journal, Academic/Scholarly.* **Description:** Covers the disciplines of economics and business administration with a particular emphasis on the conditions and prospects of Central and South-Eastern European countries.
Former titles (until 1999): Slovenian Economic Review (0354-0731); (until 1990): Ekonomska Revija (0013-3256)
Related titles: Online - full text ed.: (from ProQuest Information & Learning).
Indexed: ABIn, IBSS, JEL, RASB.
Published by: Univerza v Ljubljani, Faculty of Economics, Kardeljeva ploscad 17, Ljubljana, SI-1000, Slovenia. ebr.editors@ef.uni-lj.si, http://miha.ef.uni-lj.si/ebr/. Eds. Danijel Pucko, Janez Prasnikar, Nevenka Hrovatin. **Subscr. to:** Mladinska Knjiga Trgovina, Slovenska 29, Ljubljana 1000, Slovenia.

338   IND   ISSN 0012-995X
ECONOMIC & BUSINESS REVIEW. Text in English. 1969. q. USD 10. adv. bk.rev.
Published by: S.S. Mohan, 31-13 East Patel Nagar, New Delhi, 110 008, India. TEL 583926. Circ: 2,100.

330   GBR   ISSN 1351-3621
➤ **ECONOMIC & FINANCIAL REVIEW.** Text in English. 1994. q. GBP 190 in Europe; GBP 205 elsewhere (effective 2005). **Document type:** *Journal, Academic/Scholarly.* **Description:** Aims to provide a forum for communication among public sector, private sector and academic economists, removing the isolation that currently exists among these groups so that new theories will be more in tune with the real workings of the economy. Covers fiscal and economic policy-making on the government level as well as issues facing market decision-makers who need to incorporate government actions into their forecasts.
Indexed: JEL.
—BLDSC (3651.451500), IE, ingenta.
Published by: European Economics and Financial Centre, 20 Guilford St, London, WC1N 1DZ, United Kingdom. TEL 44-20-72290402, FAX 44-20-72215118, eefc@eefc.com, http://www.eefc.com/efrnew.htm. Ed. H M Scobie. **Subscr. to:** Publications Department, PO Box 2498, London W2 4LE, United Kingdom.

➤ **ECONOMIC AND INDUSTRIAL DEMOCRACY**; an international journal. see *POLITICAL SCIENCE*

330.9   IND   ISSN 0012-9976
➤ **ECONOMIC AND POLITICAL WEEKLY**; a journal of current economic and political affairs. Text in English. 1966. w. INR 685 to individuals; INR 450 to students (effective 2005). adv. bk.rev. charts; stat.; illus. 80 p./no. 3 cols./p.; back issues avail.; reprints avail. **Document type:** *Academic/Scholarly.* **Description:** Deals with researches in economics and other social sciences. Aims at academicians, researches, teachers and students.
Formerly: Economic Weekly
Related titles: Microfiche ed.: (from IDC); Online - full text ed.
Indexed: APEL, ARDT, ASCA, AbHyg, AgBio, AgeL, AgrForAb, ArtHuCl, BAS, CLOSS, CTFA, CurCont, DSA, FCA, FPA, FamI, ForAb, HortAb, I&DA, ILD, IPSA, MEA&I, NutrAb, PAA&I, PAIS, PBA, PGegResA, PHN&I, PopulInd, PotatoAb, ProtozoAb, RA&MP, RDA, RI-1, RI-2, RRTA, RevApplEntom, RiceAb, S&F, SIA, SSCI, SeedAb, SoyAb, TDB, TOSA, TriticAb, WAE&RSA, WeedAb.
—BLDSC (3651.480000), IE, Infotrieve, ingenta.
Published by: The Economic and Political Weekly, Hitkari House, 284 Shahid Bhagatsingh Rd., Mumbai, Maharashtra 400 038, India. TEL 91-22-696073, FAX 91-22-696072, epw@vsnl.com, http://www.epw.org.in/showIndex.php. Ed., R&P Krishna Raj. Adv. contact Kamal G Fanibanda. B&W page USD 500, color page USD 1,000; trim 173 x 235. Circ: 14,000 (paid).

330.1   IND   ISSN 0070-8437
ECONOMIC AND SCIENTIFIC RESEARCH FOUNDATION. ANNUAL REPORT. Text in English. 1967. a. free.
Description: Features annual activities of the foundation.
Published by: Economic and Scientific Research Foundation, Federation House, New Delhi, 110 001, India. Circ: 1,000.

330   IRL
➤ **ECONOMIC AND SOCIAL RESEARCH INSTITUTE. GENERAL RESEARCH SERIES.** Text in English. 1961. irreg., latest vol.177, 2002. price varies. back issues avail. **Document type:** *Monographic series, Academic/Scholarly.*
Former titles: Economic and Social Research Institute. Publications Series. Paper (0070-8755); (until 1967, no.35): Economic Research Institute. Paper (0332-3358)
Indexed: RRTA, WAE&RSA.
Published by: The Liffey Press, Ashbrook House, 10 Main St, Raheny, Dublin, 5, Ireland. TEL 353-1-8511458, FAX 353-1-8511459. Ed. B J Whelan. Pub. David Givens. R&P Gillian Davidson. **Co-sponsor:** Economic and Social Research Institute.

330   IRL   ISSN 0790-9470
HC10
ECONOMIC AND SOCIAL RESEARCH INSTITUTE. MEDIUM TERM REVIEW. Text in English. biennial. EUR 57.14 (effective 2001). charts. **Document type:** *Corporate.* **Description:** Assesses the effects of international developments and Irish economic policies on the domestic economy in recent years.
Published by: Economic and Social Research Institute, 4 Burlington Rd., Dublin, 4, Ireland. TEL 353-1-667-1525, FAX 353-1-668-6231. Ed. B J Whelan. R&P Gillian Davidson.

330 300   IRL
ECONOMIC AND SOCIAL RESEARCH INSTITUTE. MEMORANDUM SERIES. Text in English. 1962. irreg., latest vol.187, 1994. EUR 3.81 per issue (effective 2001). **Document type:** *Monographic series, Academic/Scholarly.*
Published by: Economic and Social Research Institute, 4 Burlington Rd., Dublin, 4, Ireland. TEL 353-1-667-1525, FAX 353-1-668-6231. Ed. B J Whelan. R&P Gillian Davidson.

330   IRL
ECONOMIC AND SOCIAL RESEARCH INSTITUTE. POLICY RESEARCH SERIES. Text in English. 1979. irreg., latest vol.53, 2004. price varies. **Document type:** *Monographic series, Academic/Scholarly.*
Indexed: RRTA, WAE&RSA.
—ingenta.

Published by: Economic and Social Research Institute, 4 Burlington Rd., Dublin, 4, Ireland. TEL 353-1-6671525, FAX 353-1-6686231, admin@esri.ie, http://www.esri.ie.

330 300   IRL
ECONOMIC AND SOCIAL RESEARCH INSTITUTE. TECHNICAL SERIES. Text in English. 1986. irreg. ("Official Statistcs: Above and below the public debate" by Tim Holt), latest vol.30, 2000. EUR 5.08 domestic (effective 2001). **Document type:** *Monographic series.*
Published by: Economic and Social Research Institute, 4 Burlington Rd., Dublin, 4, Ireland. TEL 353-1-667-1525, FAX 353-1-668-6231. Ed. B J Whelan. R&P Gillian Davidson.

330 300   IRL   ISSN 0012-9984
HC257.I6
➤ **ECONOMIC AND SOCIAL REVIEW.** Text in English. 1969. q. USD 35 to individuals; USD 55 to libraries (effective 1999 - 2000). adv. bk.rev. index. **Document type:** *Academic/Scholarly.* **Description:** Publishes papers, both theoretical and applied, in all areas of social science.
Related titles: Online - full text ed.: (from ProQuest Information & Learning).
Indexed: ABIn, ASCA, ASSIA, AmH&L, BPIA, BusI, CPM, CREJ, CurCont, DIP, FamI, GEOBASE, HistAb, IBR, IBSS, IBZ, IMFL, IPSA, JEL, MEA&I, PAIS, PCI, RASB, RRTA, SSCI, ST&MA, WAE&RSA.
—BLDSC (3651.520000), IDS, IE, Infotrieve, ingenta.
Published by: Economic and Social Studies, 4 Burlington Rd., Dublin, 4, Ireland. TEL 353-1-6671525, FAX 353-1-6686231. Eds. F Barry, H Tovey. R&P C O'Regan. Circ: 450.

330   JAM   ISSN 0256-5013
HC157.J2
ECONOMIC AND SOCIAL SURVEY OF JAMAICA. Text in English. 1957. a. JMD 1,200 (effective 2002).
Formerly (until 1972): Economic Survey of Jamaica (0448-1895)
Published by: Planning Institute of Jamaica, 10-16 Grenada Way, Kingston, 5, Jamaica. TEL 876-906-4463, http://www.pioj.gov.jm.

330   DEU   ISSN 0343-754X
HC10
➤ **ECONOMIC BULLETIN.** Text in English. 1963. m. EUR 360 combined subscription for print & online eds.; EUR 36 per issue (effective 2004). adv. 56 p./no. 2 cols./p.; back issues avail. **Document type:** *Journal, Academic/Scholarly.* **Description:** Contains research articles and papers on all aspects of economics.
Related titles: Online - full text ed.: ISSN 1438-261X (from EBSCO Publishing, ProQuest Information & Learning, Springer LINK).
Indexed: ABIn, KES.
—IE, Infotrieve. **CCC.**
Published by: Deutsches Institut fuer Wirtschaftsforschung, Koenigin-Luise-Str 5, Berlin, 14195, Germany. TEL 49-30-897890, FAX 49-30-89789200, bulletin@diw.de, postmaster@diw.de, http://www.diw.de/deutsch/produkte/publikationen/bulletin/index.html. Circ: 300 (controlled).

330   LBY
ECONOMIC BULLETIN. Text in English. m.
Published by: Jamahiriya News Agency, Sharia al-Fateh, P O Box 2303, Tripoli, Libya. TEL 37106, TELEX 20841.

330   GHA   ISSN 0013-0044
ECONOMIC BULLETIN OF GHANA✱. Text in English. 1957. q. USD 5.50. **Document type:** *Bulletin.*
Indexed: JEL.
Published by: Economic Society of Ghana, c/o Dept of Economics, University of Ghana, PO Box 57, Legon, Accra, Ghana. Ed. J C Degraft Johnson.

330   USA   ISSN 0428-1276
HC108.C7
ECONOMIC COMMENTARY. Text in English. 1948. s-m. free. cum.index: 1982-1998. back issues avail. **Document type:** *Newsletter, Trade.* **Description:** Presents scholarly papers on current issues pertaining to patterns and trends in foreign and domestic banking, trade, finance, and investment.
Supersedes: Business Trends
Related titles: Online - full text ed.: (from EBSCO Publishing, Florida Center for Library Automation, Gale Group, O C L C Online Computer Library Center, Inc., ProQuest Information & Learning).
Indexed: ABIn, BLI, FiP.
Published by: Federal Reserve Bank of Cleveland, PO Box 6387, Cleveland, OH 44101. TEL 216-579-3079, FAX 216-579-3172, http://www.clevelandfed.org/. Eds. Michele Lachman, Monica Crabtree-Reuser. R&P Lee Faulhaber TEL 216-579-2961. Circ: 12,000.

330   CHE   ISSN 0251-0197
ECONOMIC COMMISSION FOR EUROPE. ANNUAL REPORT. Text in English. 1947. a. **Document type:** *Yearbook, Trade.* **Description:** Contains an outline of the proceedings and records of decisions taken at the annual session.
Related titles: French ed.: Nations Unies. Commission Economique pour l'Europe. Rapport Annuel. ISSN 0251-0189; Russian ed.: Organizatsiya Ob'edinennykh Natsii. Evropeiskaya Ekonomicheskaya Komissiya. God ovoi Doklad. ISSN 0251-0200.

▼ *new title*   ➤ *refereed*   ✱ *unverified*   ◆ *full entry avail.*

B

Indexed: RASB.
Published by: United Nations, Economic Commission for Europe (ECE), Palais des Nations, Geneva 10, 1211, Switzerland. TEL 41-22-9174444, FAX 41-22-9170505, info.ece@unece.org, http://www.unece.org.

330 USA ISSN 1539-1922
HD72
ECONOMIC DEVELOPMENT JOURNAL. Text in English. 197?. q. USD 60 to non-members; free to members (effective 2005). adv.
Former titles (until 2002): Economic Development Commentary (8755-8629); (until 1981): Commentary (Washington, D.C.) (0193-4619); Incorporates: C U E D Economic Developments (8755-8718)
Related titles: Online - full text ed.: (from EBSCO Publishing, ProQuest Information & Learning).
Indexed: ABIn.
Published by: International Economic Development Council, 734 15th Street, NW, Ste. 900, Washington, DC 20005. TEL 202-223-7800, FAX 202-223-4745, ejones@iedconline.org, mail@iedc.org, http://www.iedconline.org. Circ: 2,000.

330 USA ISSN 0424-2769
HG179
ECONOMIC EDUCATION BULLETIN. Text in English. 1960. m. USD 59 membership (effective 2005).
Indexed: DIP, IBR, IBZ, PAIS, RASB.
Published by: American Institute for Economic Research, PO Box 1000, Great Barrington, MA 01230. TEL 413-528-1216, FAX 413-528-0103, http://www.aier.org/eeb.html.

ECONOMIC, FINANCIAL AND INDUSTRY SECTOR REPORTS. see *ENGINEERING*

330 SGP ISSN 0219-9815
ECONOMIC IDEAS LEADING TO THE 21ST CENTURY/ ECONOMIC IDEAS LEADING TO THE TWENTY-FIRST CENTURY. (vol.1: The Japanese Economy) Text in English. 2000. irreg., latest vol.7, 2001, Nov. price varies. **Document type:** *Monographic series, Academic/Scholarly.* **Description:** Provides information for students, professionals and general readers on economic situations and economic theories around the world.
Published by: (Kobe University JPN), World Scientific Publishing Co. Pte. Ltd., 5 Toh Tuck Link, Singapore, 596224, Singapore. TEL 65-466-5775, FAX 65-467-7667, series@wspc.com.sg, http://www.wspc.com.sg/books/series/eil21c_series.shtml, http://www.worldscientific.com. Eds. L R Klein, V Su. **Dist. in the US by:** World Scientific Publishing Co., Inc., 1060 Main St, River Edge, NJ 07661. TEL 201-487-9655, 800-227-7562, FAX 201-487-9656, 888-977-2665, wspc@wspc.com; **Dist. by:** World Scientific Publishing Ltd., 57 Shelton St, London WC2H 9HE, United Kingdom. TEL 44-20-78360888, FAX 44-20-78362020, sales@wspc.co.uk.

330 USA ISSN 0095-2583
HB1 CODEN: ECIND6
➤ **ECONOMIC INQUIRY.** Text in English. 1962. q. GBP 184, USD 282, EUR 276 to institutions; GBP 194, USD 297, EUR 291 to institutions print & online eds. (effective 2006). adv. charts; illus.; abstr. index. back issues avail.; reprint service avail. from PQC,PSC. **Document type:** *Journal, Academic/Scholarly.* **Description:** It publishes research on all economics topics.
Formerly: Western Economic Journal (0043-3640)
Related titles: Microform ed.: (from PQC); Online - full text ed.: ISSN 1465-7295. GBP 175, USD 268, EUR 263 to institutions (effective 2006) (from bigchalk, Chadwyck-Healey Inc., EBSCO Publishing, Florida Center for Library Automation, Gale Group, H.W. Wilson, HighWire Press, IngentaConnect, Northern Light Technology, Inc., O C L C Online Computer Library Center, Inc., Oxford University Press Online Journals, ProQuest Information & Learning, Swets Information Services, The Dialog Corporation).
Indexed: ABIn, APEL, ASCA, AgeL, AmH&L, BAS, BPIA, BusI, CJA, CPM, CREJ, CurCont, DIP, ESPM, FamI, HRA, HistAb, IBR, IBSS, IBZ, IBibSS, IPARL, JEL, LRI, MEA&I, MEDLINE, PAIS, PCI, PRA, RRTA, RefZh, RiskAb, SPAA, SSCI, SSI, SUSA, T&II, V&AA, WAE&RSA, WBA.
—BLDSC (3653.660000), CISTI, IDS, IE, Infotrieve, ingenta. **CCC.**
Published by: Oxford University Press (Subsidiary of: Oxford University Press), 2001 Evans Rd, Cary, NC 27513. TEL 919-677-0977, 800-852-7323, FAX 919-677-1714, ecinquiry@econ.tamu.edu, jnlorders@oup-usa.org, http://ei.oxfordjournals.org/, http://www.us.oup.com. Ed. Dennis W. Jansen. Pub. Eric Staib. Adv. contact Helen Pearson. B&W page GBP 175, B&W page USD 255; 145 x 210. Circ: 3,550.

330 GBR ISSN 0013-0133
HB1 CODEN: ECJOAB
➤ **THE ECONOMIC JOURNAL.** Text in English. 1891. 8/yr. GBP 337 combined subscription in Europe to institutions print & online eds.; USD 515 combined subscription in the Americas to institutions & Caribbean (print & online eds.); GBP 139, USD 225 combined subscription in developing nations to institutions print & online eds.; GBP 358 combined subscription elsewhere to institutions print & online eds. (effective 2006). adv. bk.rev. illus. index, cum.index. reprint service avail. from PQC,PSC. **Document type:** *Journal, Academic/Scholarly.*
Related titles: Microfilm ed.: (from PMC, PQC); Online - full text ed.: ISSN 1468-0297. GBP 320 in Europe to institutions; USD 489 in the Americas to institutions & Caribbean; GBP 132, USD 214 in developing nations to institutions; GBP 340 elsewhere to institutions (effective 2006) (from Blackwell Synergy, EBSCO Publishing, Gale Group, IngentaConnect, JSTOR (Web-based Journal Archive), O C L C Online Computer Library Center, Inc., Swets Information Services).
Indexed: ABIn, APEL, ASCA, AmH&L, BAS, BPIA, BRI, CBRI, CJA, CPM, CREJ, CurCont, DIP, ESPM, Emerald, ExcerpMed, FamI, GEOBASE, HRIS, HistAb, IBR, IBSS, IBZ, ILD, JEL, KES, MEA&I, NutrAb, PAA&I, PAIS, PGegResA, PSI, RDA, RRTA, RefSour, RefZh, RiskAb, SCIMP, SSCI, SSI, T&II, TDB, WAE&RSA, WBA, WorkRelAb.
—BLDSC (3653.800000), CISTI, IDS, IE, Infotrieve, ingenta. **CCC.**
Published by: (Royal Economic Society), Blackwell Publishing Ltd., 9600 Garsington Rd, Oxford, OX4 2ZG, United Kingdom. TEL 44-1865-776868, FAX 44-1865-714591, customerservices@oxon.blackwellpublishing.com, http://www.blackwellpublishing.com/journals/ECOJ. Eds. Andrew Scott, Steve Machin. Circ: 7,000.

330 JPN
ECONOMIC JOURNAL OF HOKKAIDO UNIVERSITY. Text in English. a.
Published by: Hokkaido University, Graduate School of Economics and Business Administration, Kita 9, Nishi 7, Kita-ku, Sapporo, 060-0809, Japan. TEL 81-11-706-4058, FAX 81-11-706-4947, keizai@pop.econ.hokudai.ac.jp, http://www.hokudai.ac.jp/catalog/02-03/f_g/03_04/03_04_051-052.html.

330 330.1 GBR ISSN 0391-5026
HB1
ECONOMIC NOTES. Text and summaries in English. 1972. 3/yr., latest vol.31, no.3, 2002. EUR 44 combined subscription in Europe to individuals print & online eds.; USD 49 combined subscription in the Americas to individuals & Caribbean, print & online eds.; GBP 29 combined subscription elsewhere to individuals print & online eds.; USD 254 combined subscription in the Americas to institutions & Caribbean, print & online eds.; GBP 151 combined subscription elsewhere to institutions print & online eds. (effective 2006). bk.rev. bibl.; charts; stat. index, cum.index: 1972-1991. **Document type:** *Journal, Academic/Scholarly.* **Description:** Covers economic theory, methodology and international economics.
Related titles: Online - full text ed.: ISSN 1468-0300. USD 240 in the Americas to institutions & Caribbean; GBP 143 elsewhere to institutions (effective 2006) (from Blackwell Synergy, EBSCO Publishing, Gale Group, IngentaConnect, O C L C Online Computer Library Center, Inc., Swets Information Services); ♦ Italian ed.: Note Economiche. ISSN 0391-8289.
Indexed: ABIn, CurCont, GEOBASE, IBSS, JEL, ST&MA.
—BLDSC (3653.932000), IE, Infotrieve, ingenta. **CCC.**
Published by: (Monte dei Paschi di Siena), Blackwell Publishing Ltd., 9600 Garsington Rd, Oxford, OX4 2ZG, United Kingdom. TEL 44-1865-776868, FAX 44-1865-714591, customerservices@oxon.blackwellpublishing.com, http://www.blackwellpublishing.com/journals/ECNO. Ed. Alessandro Vercelli.

330 AUS
ECONOMIC OUTLOOK. Text in English. 1964. m. AUD 1,050 (effective 2000). **Document type:** *Bulletin.* **Description:** Provides analysis and forecasts of prospects for the Australian economy.
Published by: B I S Shrapnel Pty. Ltd., 8th Fl., 181 Miller St, North Sydney, NSW 2060, Australia. TEL 61-2-9959-5924, FAX 61-2-9959-5795, jlewis@bis.com.au, http://www.bis.com.au. Ed. Frank Gelber. Circ: 560.

330 JOR
ECONOMIC PERSPECTIVES. Text in Arabic. bi-w. USD 350. adv. **Document type:** *Newspaper.*
Formerly: Al-Ghad al-Iqtisadi
Published by: Media Services International, P O Box 9313, Amman, 11191, Jordan. TEL 648298, TELEX 21392, http://www.arabia.com/ep/. Ed. Osama Ash Sharif. Adv. contact Mahmoud Fares.

330 USA
ECONOMIC PERSPECTIVES (WASHINGTON, D.C.). Text in English. 4/yr. back issues avail. **Document type:** *Journal, Government.*
Media: Online - full content. **Related titles:** Arabic Translation; French Translation; Portuguese Translation; Russian Translation; Spanish Translation:.
Published by: U.S. Department of State, Bureau of International Information Programs, 301 4th St, S W, Washington, DC 20547. http://usinfo.state.gov/journals/journals.htm, http://usinfo.state.gov/homepage.htm.

330 GBR ISSN 0266-4658
HD87
➤ **ECONOMIC POLICY;** a European forum. Text in English. 1985. q. EUR 68 combined subscription in Europe to individuals print & online eds.; USD 67 combined subscription in the Americas to individuals & Caribbean, print & online eds.; GBP 45 combined subscription elsewhere to individuals print & online eds.; USD 425 combined subscription in the Americas to institutions & Caribbean, print & online eds.; GBP 280 combined subscription elsewhere to institutions print & online eds.; EUR 33 combined subscription in Europe to students print & online eds.; USD 36 combined subscription in the Americas to students & Caribbean, print & online eds.; GBP 22 combined subscription elsewhere to students print & online eds. (effective 2006). adv. illus. Index. back issues avail.; reprint service avail. from PSC. **Document type:** *Journal, Academic/Scholarly.*
Related titles: Microform ed.: (from PQC); Online - full text ed.: ISSN 1468-0327. USD 404 in the Americas to institutions & Caribbean; GBP 266 elsewhere to institutions (effective 2006) (from Blackwell Synergy, EBSCO Publishing, Gale Group, IngentaConnect, JSTOR (Web-based Journal Archive), O C L C Online Computer Library Center, Inc., Swets Information Services).
Indexed: ABIn, APEL, AgBio, BAS, CurCont, ELLIS, ESPM, Emerald, GEOBASE, IBSS, IPSA, JEL, PAIS, PCI, PGegResA, RRTA, RiskAb, SPAA, SSCI, WAE&RSA.
—BLDSC (3654.091300), IDS, IE, Infotrieve, ingenta. **CCC.**
Published by: (Ecole Normale Superieure, Departement et Laboratoire d'Economie Theorique et Appliquee FRA, Centre for Economic Policy Research, Editions de la Maison des Sciences de l'Homme FRA, European Economic Association), Blackwell Publishing Ltd., 9600 Garsington Rd, Oxford, OX4 2ZG, United Kingdom. TEL 44-1865-776868, FAX 44-1865-714591, customerservices@oxon.blackwellpublishing.com, http://www.blackwellpublishing.com/journals/ECOP. **Co-sponsor:** Editions de la Maison des Sciences de l'Homme.

330 AUS ISSN 0013-0249
HC601 CODEN: DMSPBH
➤ **THE ECONOMIC RECORD.** Text in English. 1925. q. GBP 100 combined subscription in Australia & New Zealand to institutions print & online eds.; USD 171 combined subscription in the Americas to institutions print & online eds.; GBP 133 combined subscription elsewhere to institutions print & online eds. (effective 2006). adv. bk.rev. bibl.; illus. Index. reprint service avail. from PQC,ISI. **Document type:** *Journal, Academic/Scholarly.*
Related titles: Microfilm ed.: (from PQC); Online - full text ed.: ISSN 1475-4932. GBP 95 in Australia & New Zealand to institutions; USD 162 in the Americas to institutions; GBP 116 elsewhere to institutions (effective 2006) (from Blackwell Synergy, EBSCO Publishing, Florida Center for Library Automation, Gale Group, IngentaConnect, O C L C Online Computer Library Center, Inc., ProQuest Information & Learning, R M I T Publishing, Swets Information Services).
Indexed: ABIn, APEL, ARI, ASCA, AusPAIS, BAS, BusI, CREJ, CurCont, DIP, FamI, GEOBASE, IBR, IBSS, IBZ, JEL, KES, MEA&I, PAIS, PCI, RASB, RRTA, SSCI, SWA, T&II, WAE&RSA, WBA, WTA, WorkRelAb.
—BLDSC (3654.200000), CISTI, IDS, IE, Infotrieve, ingenta. **CCC.**
Published by: (Economic Society of Australia), Blackwell Publishing Asia (Subsidiary of: Blackwell Publishing Ltd.), 550 Swanston St, Carlton South, VIC 3053, Australia. TEL 61-383591011, FAX 61-383591120, subs@blackwellpublishingasia.com, http://www.blackwellpublishing.com/journals/ECOR. Eds. Glenn Otto, Harry Bloch, Paul Miller. Circ: 3,800.

330 USA ISSN 1058-661X
ECONOMIC REFORM TODAY. Text in English. 1991. q.
Related titles: Online - full text ed.
Published by: Center for International Private Enterprise, 1615 H St, N W, Washington, DC 20062-2000. TEL 202-463-5901, FAX 202-887-3447, cipe@cipe.org, http://www.cipe.org.

330 PHL ISSN 0424-2904
HC451
ECONOMIC RESEARCH JOURNAL. Text in English. 1953. q.
Indexed: BAS.
Published by: (Faculty of the Graduate School), University of the East, Sampaloc, Manila, Philippines.

330 IDN ISSN 0125-9628
ECONOMIC REVIEW. Text in English. 1966. q. free. charts; stat. **Document type:** *Corporate.* **Description:** Serves as an informative communication media between Bank BNI and its clients.
Related titles: Microfiche ed.: (from IDC); Indonesian ed.: Majalah Tinjauan Ekonomi B.N.I. 1946. ISSN 0125-9571.
Published by: PT. Bank Negara Indonesia (Bank BNI), Jalan Jenderal Sudirman Kav 1, PO Box 2955, Jakarta, 10220, Indonesia. TEL 62-21-5728606, FAX 62-21-5728456, TELEX 65511 KBBNI IA. Ed. M Arsjad. Circ: 2,000.

330 LKA ISSN 0259-9775
HC424.A1
ECONOMIC REVIEW. Text in English. 1975. m. USD 35. **Document type:** *Academic/Scholarly.*
Indexed: RDA.

Published by: People's Bank, Research Department, Sir Chittampalam A. Gardinar Mawatha, Colombo, 2, Sri Lanka. TEL 01-327082. Ed. L Siriwardene.

330 GBR ISSN 0265-0290
ECONOMIC REVIEW. Text in English. 1982. 4/yr. (Sep.-Apr.). GBP 23.95 domestic; GBP 30 in Europe; GBP 35 elsewhere (effective Sep. 2002). adv. **Document type:** *Academic/Scholarly.*
Related titles: Online - full text ed.: (from Gale Group).
Indexed: BrHumI, Emerald, PAIS.
—BLDSC (3654.580000), IE, ingenta.
Published by: Philip Allan Updates, Market Pl, Deddington, Banbury, Oxon OX15 0SE, United Kingdom. TEL 44-1869-338652, FAX 44-1869-338803, sales@philipallan.co.uk, http://www.philipallan.co.uk. Ed. Sarah Ashton. R&P Ceri Jenkins.

330 BGD ISSN 0070-8631
ECONOMIC REVIEW✶. Text in English. 1964. a.
Published by: (Economics Association), University of Dhaka, Ramna, Dhaka, 1000, Bangladesh.

338.9 PAK ISSN 0531-8955
HC440.5.A1
ECONOMIC REVIEW. Text in English. 1970. m. PKR 600, USD 100 (effective 1999). adv. bk.rev. charts; stat. **Document type:** *Trade.*
Related titles: Online - full text ed.: (from EBSCO Publishing, Florida Center for Library Automation, Gale Group).
Indexed: BAS, BPIA, IBR, IBZ, LRI, PAIS, T&II.
Published by: Economic and Industrial Publications, Al-Masiha, 47, Abdullah Haroon Rd., P O Box 7843, Karachi, 74400, Pakistan. TEL 92-21-7728434. Ed., Pub., R&P Iqbal Haidari TEL 92-21-7728963. Adv. contact A M Khan. Circ: 50,000.

330 JPN ISSN 0013-0273
HB9
ECONOMIC REVIEW (KYOTO)/KEIZAI RONSO. Text in Japanese; Contents page in English. 1915. m. USD 50. index.
Indexed: AmH&L, HistAb, RASB.
Published by: Kyoto University, Economic Society/Kyoto Daigaku Keizai Gakkai, Sakyo-ku, Kyoto-shi, 606, Japan. Circ: 1,600.

ECONOMIC REVIEW OF THE YEAR - THE GREEK ECONOMY. see *BUSINESS AND ECONOMICS—Economic Situation And Conditions*

330.9593 THA
ECONOMIC REVIEWS. Text in English. s-a. **Description:** Summarizes and analyzes Thailand's economy.
Published by: Post Publishing Public Co. Ltd., Bangkok Post Bldg, Off Sunthorn Kosa Rd, Klong Toey, 136 Na Ranong Rd, Bangkok, 10110, Thailand. TEL 662-240-3700, FAX 662-240-3790.

330 POL ISSN 1505-4683
➤ **ECONOMIC SCIENCES.** Text in English, Polish. 1985. a. PLZ 20 domestic; USD 20 foreign (effective 2002 - 2003). abstr.; bibl.; charts; illus. back issues avail. **Document type:** *Journal, Academic/Scholarly.* **Description:** Covers organization and management, economic policy, marketing and market analysis, economics of food industry, finance and banking.
Supersedes in part (in 1998): Acta Academiae Agriculturae ac Technicae Olstenensis (1509-3727)
Indexed: AEA, AbHyg, DSA, HerbAb, NutrAb, PHN&I, PoultAb, RefZh, S&F, TriticAb, WAE&RSA, WeedAb.
—CISTI.
Published by: (Uniwersytet Warminsko-Mazurski), Wydawnictwo U W M, ul J Heweliusza 14, Olsztyn, 10724, Poland. TEL 48-89-5233661, FAX 48-89-5233438, wydawca@uwm.edu.pl, http://www.uwm.edu.pl/wydawnictwo. Ed. Tadeusz Stachowski. Pub. Zofia Gawinek.

330 AUS ISSN 0812-0439
➤ **ECONOMIC SOCIETY OF AUSTRALIA. ECONOMIC PAPERS.** Text in English. 1941; N.S. 1982. q. AUD 45 domestic to non-members; AUD 75 foreign to non-members (effective 2002). adv. bk.rev. charts; stat. back issues avail. **Document type:** *Academic/Scholarly.* **Description:** Contains papers dealing with issues in business, economics and economic policies.
Formerly: Economic Society of Australia and New Zealand. New South Wales and Victorian Branches. Economic Papers (0013-0354)
Related titles: Online - full text ed.: (from Gale Group).
Indexed: AusPAIS, IBSS.
—BLDSC (3653.977000), IE, ingenta.
Published by: Economic Society of Australia, c/o Central Council Administrator, Jane Oldroyd, PO Box 937, St Ives, NSW 2075, Australia. ecosoc@optushome.com.au, http://www.ecosoc.org.au/cesapubs.htm. Eds. Mike White, Peter Forsyth, Russell Smyth. R&P, Adv. contact Cynthia Orchard TEL 61-3-94974140. B&W page AUD 530. Circ: 1,300 (paid).

➤ **ECONOMIC SOCIOLOGY.** see *SOCIOLOGY*

330 IND ISSN 0013-0362
HC10
ECONOMIC STUDIES; a journal of economic outlook and trend. (ESJPubCo.) Text in English. 1960-1985; resumed 1988. fortn. INR 180 domestic to individuals; USD 80 foreign to individuals; INR 180 domestic to institutions; USD 60 foreign to institutions (effective 2001). adv. bk.rev. charts; illus.; pat.; stat.; tr.lit.; tr.mk. 16 p./no. 2 cols./p.; back issues avail.; reprints avail. **Document type:** *Newspaper.* **Description:** A Journal of Socio-Economic Outlook and Trend.
Indexed: BAS.
Published by: Economic Studies & Journals Publishing Co., 2 Private Rd., Dum Dum, Kolkata, West Bengal 700 074, India. TEL 91-33-5512288, FAX 91-33-551-3635. Ed. Gautam Mukherjee. R&P, Adv. contact Shounak Lahiri. page INR 8,000; 20 x 15. Circ: 28,000. **Subscr. to:** P O Box 10868, Kolkata, West Bengal 700 009, India.

330 BGD ISSN 1021-125X
ECONOMIC TIMES. Text in English. 1989. w. USD 56 (effective 2001). adv. illus.; tr.lit. 8 p./no.; back issues avail. **Document type:** *Newspaper, Trade.* **Description:** Contains comments, analysis, suggestions and social problems.
Published by: Munirul Huq Ed. & Pub., South Dhanmondi, 65-2 Laboratory Rd, Dhaka, 1205, Bangladesh. TEL 880-2-501930, FAX 880-2-8314933, 880-2-8315224, bfc@bdmail.net, ecotimes@sitlbd.net. Ed., Pub., R&P Munirul Huq TEL 880-2-505376. Circ: 6,200.

330 IRL ISSN 0332-3951
ECONOMIC TRENDS. Text in English. 1970. m. reprints avail. **Document type:** *Bulletin.* **Description:** Provides commentary with graphical summary of the current economic situation.
Published by: Irish Business and Employers Confederation, Confederation House, 84-86 Lower Baggot St., Dublin, 2, Ireland. TEL 353-1-6601011, FAX 353-1-6601717, http://www.iol.ie/ibec. Ed. David Croughan.

330 GBR ISSN 0013-0427
➤ **ECONOMICA.** Text in English. 1921. q. EUR 50 combined subscription in Europe to individuals print & online eds.; USD 55 combined subscription in the Americas to individuals & Caribbean, print & online eds.; GBP 33 combined subscription elsewhere to individuals print & online eds.; USD 299 combined subscription in the Americas to institutions & Caribbean, print & online eds.; GBP 176 combined subscription elsewhere to institutions print & online eds.; EUR 36 combined subscription in Europe to students print & online eds.; USD 40 combined subscription in the Americas to students & Caribbean, print & online eds.; GBP 24 combined subscription elsewhere to students print & online eds. (effective 2006). adv. bk.rev. charts; stat.; illus. index. back issues avail.; reprint service avail. from PSC. **Document type:** *Journal, Academic/Scholarly.*
Related titles: Online - full text ed.: ISSN 1468-0335. USD 283 in the Americas to institutions & Caribbean; GBP 167 elsewhere to institutions (effective 2006) (from Blackwell Synergy, EBSCO Publishing, Gale Group, IngentaConnect, JSTOR (Web-based Journal Archive), O C L C Online Computer Library Center, Inc., Swets Information Services).
Indexed: ABIn, APEL, AmH&L, ArtHuCI, BAS, CJA, CPM, CREJ, CurCont, DIP, EIP, ExcerpMed, FamI, GEOBASE, HistAb, IBR, IBSS, IBZ, IPSA, JEL, MEA&I, PAIS, PCI, RRTA, SCIMP, SSCI, SSI, ST&MA, WAE&RSA, WBA.
—BLDSC (3656.900000), CISTI, IDS, IE, Infotrieve, ingenta. **CCC.**
Published by: (London School of Economics and Political Science, Suntory and Toyota International Centres for Economics and Related Disciplines), Blackwell Publishing Ltd., 9600 Garsington Rd, Oxford, OX4 2ZG, United Kingdom. TEL 44-1865-776868, FAX 44-1865-714591, customerservices@oxon.blackwellpublishing.com, http://www.blackwellpublishing.com/journals/ECCA. Eds. Alan Manning, Frank Cowell, Tore Ellingsen. Circ: 3,800.

330 IDN
ECONOMICS AND FINANCE IN INDONESIA. Text in English. 1948. q.
Indexed: BAS.
Published by: University of Indonesia, Institute for Economic and Social Research, Jalan Raya Salemba 4, Jakarta, 10430, Indonesia. TEL 021-330225, FAX 021-334310. Circ: 4,000.

330 USA ISSN 1545-2921
HB1
ECONOMICS BULLETIN. Text in English. 2001. irreg. free (effective 2005). **Document type:** *Bulletin, Academic/Scholarly.* **Description:** Contains original notes, comments, preliminary results, manuscripts that keep the profession informed about ongoing research programs on economics.
Media: Online - full content.
Address: c/o John Conley, Dept. of Economics, 414 Calhoun Hall, Vanderbilt University, Nashville, TN 37235. http://www.economicsbulletin.com/. Ed. John Conley.

330 DEU ISSN 1435-6104
HD2741
➤ **ECONOMICS OF GOVERNANCE.** Text in English. 2000. 3/yr. EUR 128.80 combined subscription to institutions print & online eds. (effective 2005). reprint service avail. from PSC. **Document type:** *Journal, Academic/Scholarly.* **Description:** Aims to foster research on governance at many levels, including corporations, businesses, and non-profit organizations.
Related titles: Microform ed.; Online - full text ed.: ISSN 1435-8131 (from EBSCO Publishing, ProQuest Information & Learning, Springer LINK, Swets Information Services).
Indexed: ABIn, CJA, JEL, PSA, SociolAb.
—BLDSC (3657.011000), IE, Infotrieve, ingenta. **CCC.**
Published by: Springer-Verlag (Subsidiary of: Springer Science+Business Media), Tiergartenstr 17, Heidelberg, 69121, Germany. TEL 49-6221-3450, FAX 49-6221-345229, http://link.springer.de/link/service/journals/10101/index.htm. Eds. Dr. Amihai Glazer, Dr. Kai Konrad. Adv. contact Stephan Kroeck TEL 49-30-827875739. **Subscr. in the Americas to:** Springer-Verlag New York, Inc., Journal Fulfillment, PO Box 2485, Secaucus, NJ 07096-2485. TEL 800-777-4643, 201-348-4033, FAX 201-348-4505, journals@springer-ny.com, http://www.springer-ny.com; **Subscr. to:** Springer GmbH Auslieferungsgesellschaft, Haberstr 7, Heidelberg 69126, Germany. TEL 49-6221-345-0, FAX 49-6221-345-4229, subscriptions@springer.de.

➤ **ECONOMICS OF SCIENCE, TECHNOLOGY AND INNOVATION.** see *TECHNOLOGY: COMPREHENSIVE WORKS*

330 USA
ECONOMICS RESEARCH NETWORK. Text in English. irreg.
Media: Online - full content.
Published by: Social Science Electronic Publishing Michael_Jensen@ssrn.com, http://www.ssrn.com.

330 CAN ISSN 1188-4304
ECONOMIE ET AFFAIRES AU QUEBEC. Text in English. biennial. CND 59.95 (effective 2000). **Document type:** *Directory.* **Description:** Contains listings of chambers of commerce, major firms, and financial institutions in Quebec.
—CISTI.
Published by: Quebec dans le Monde, C P 8503, Sainte Foy, PQ G1V 4N5, Canada. TEL 418-659-5540, FAX 418-659-4143.

330.1 FRA ISSN 0070-8801
ECONOMIE ET SOCIETE. Text in French. 1970. irreg. price varies. **Document type:** *Journal, Academic/Scholarly.*
Indexed: CurCont, KES.
—**CCC.**
Published by: Editions du Seuil, 27 Rue Jacob, Paris, 75006, France. TEL 33-1-40465050, FAX 33-1-40464300, contact@seuil.com, http://www.seuil.com. Ed. Edmond Blanc.

330 FRA ISSN 0013-0567
HB3
ECONOMIES ET SOCIETES. Text in French. 1945. m. **Description:** Concentrates on the different areas of economic research.
Former titles (until 1996): Cahiers de l'I S E A (0994-8287); (until 1963): Institut de Science Economique Applique. Cahiers (0994-8279)
Indexed: ELLIS, IBSS, JEL, PAIS, RefZh.
—BLDSC (3658.450000), IE, Infotrieve, ingenta.
Published by: (Institut de Sciences Mathematiques et Economiques Appliquees), Les Presses de l'I S M E A, BP 22, Paris, Cedex 13 75622, France. TEL 33-1-55489076, FAX 33-1-55489071, http://www.ismea.org. Ed. Gerard de Bernis.

331 FRA ISSN 0068-4821
ECONOMIES ET SOCIETES. SERIE AB. ECONOMIE DU TRAVAIL. Text in French. 1960. irreg., latest 1987.
—IE, Infotrieve.
Published by: Les Presses de l'I S M E A, BP 22, Paris, Cedex 13 75622, France. TEL 33-1-55489076, FAX 33-1-55489071, http://www.ismea.org. Ed. Gerard de Bernis. Circ: 1,600.

ECONOMIES ET SOCIETES. SERIE EN. ECONOMIE DE L'ENERGIE. see *ENERGY*

330 FRA
ECONOMIES ET SOCIETES. SERIE K. ECONOMIE DE L'ENTREPRISE. Text in French. irreg.
Published by: Les Presses de l'I S M E A, BP 22, Paris, Cedex 13 75622, France. TEL 33-1-55489076, FAX 33-1-55489071, http://www.ismea.org. Ed. Gerard de Bernis.

330 FRA
ECONOMIES ET SOCIETES. SERIE W. DYNAMIQUE TECHNOLOGIQUE ET ORGANISATION. Text in French. irreg.
Published by: Les Presses de l'I S M E A, BP 22, Paris, Cedex 13 75622, France. TEL 33-1-55489076, FAX 33-1-55489071, http://www.ismea.org. Ed. Gerard de Bernis.

▼ new title ➤ refereed ✶ unverified ♦ full entry avail.

B

330   USA   ISSN 0013-063X
CODEN: ENOME9
➤ DE ECONOMIST. Text in English. 1852. q. q. EUR 358, USD 368, GBP 218 combined subscription to institutions print & online eds. (effective 2005). adv. bk.rev. bibl. index, cum.index every 10-20 yrs. reprint service avail. from PQC,PSC. **Document type:** *Journal, Academic/Scholarly.* **Description:** Publishes review articles and original studies dealing with theoretical issues in economics, as well as applied research, with a focus on Europe.
Related titles: Online - full text ed.: ISSN 1572-9982 (from EBSCO Publishing, Gale Group, IngentaConnect, Kluwer Online, O C L C Online Computer Library Center, Inc., ProQuest Information & Learning, Springer LINK, Swets Information Services).
Indexed: ABIn, BRD, BibLing, BusI, CurCont, DIP, ExcerpMed, FamI, GEOBASE, IBR, IBSS, IBZ, JEL, KES, MEA&I, PAIS, PCI, PROMT, PSA, RefZh, SOPODA, SSA, SSCI, SSI, SWA, Telegen.
—BLDSC (3659.310000), IDS, IE, Infotrieve, ingenta, KNAW. CCC.
Published by: (Royal Netherlands Economic Association NLD), Springer-Verlag New York, Inc. (Subsidiary of: Springer Science+Business Media), 233 Spring St, New York, NY 10013. TEL 212-460-1500, FAX 212-460-1575, service@springer-ny.com, http://springerlink.metapress.com/openurl.asp?genre=journal&issn=0013-063X, http://www.springer-ny.com. Circ: 3,000. **Subscr. to:** Journal Fulfillment, PO Box 2485, Secaucus, NJ 07096-2485. TEL 201-348-4033, FAX 201-348-4505, journals@springer-ny.com.

330   PRT   ISSN 0870-4236
ECONOMISTA. Text in Portuguese. 1982. q.?.
Published by: Ordem dos Economistas, Rua da Estrela No 8, Lisbon, 1200-669, Portugal. TEL 351-21-3929470, FAX 351-21-2961428, geral@ordemeconomistas.pt, http://www.ordemeconomistas.pt/. Ed. Manuela Morgado.

330   MEX
EL ECONOMISTA (PRINT); analysis - opinion - advice. Text in Spanish. 1988. d. (Mon.-Fri.). MXP 2,000 (effective 2005). adv. software rev. 64 p./no. 4 cols./p.; back issues avail. **Document type:** *Newspaper, Consumer.* **Description:** Features local and national business news.
Related titles: E-mail ed.; Online - full text ed.: El Economista (Online). ISSN 1560-7895. 1998.
Indexed: B&I.
Published by: Periodico Economista S.A. de C.V., Ave Coyoacan No 515, Col Del Valle, Mexico City, DF 03100, Mexico. TEL 52-55-53265444, FAX 52-55-56829070, rodeg@economista.com.mx, http://www.economista.com.mx/. Ed. Patricia Mercado Sanchez. Pub. Rita Varela Mayorga. Adv. contact Jesus Hernandez Flores. B&W page MXP 32,640, color page MXP 56,440; trim 310 x 250. Circ: 37,448 (controlled).

330   CUB   ISSN 1563-826X
EL ECONOMISTA DE CUBA. Text in Spanish. 1998. w. adv. **Description:** Features business and economic news and in depth articles.
Media: Online - full text.
Published by: Asociacion Nacional de Economistas y Contadores de Cuba, Calle 22 Esquina 9 No 901, Miramar Playa, La Habana, Cuba. TEL 537-293303, FAX 537-223456, anec@info.get.tur.cu, http://www.eleconomista.cubaweb.cu/. Ed. Pedro Hernandez-Sotot.

330   ESP   ISSN 0212-4386
ECONOMISTAS. Text in Spanish. 1983. q. adv.
Indexed: PAIS.
—CINDOC.
Published by: Colegio de Economistas de Madrid, Flora, 1, Madrid, 28013, Spain. TEL 34-1-5594602. Ed. Emilio Ontiveros Baeza.

ECONOMY AND SOCIETY. see *SOCIAL SCIENCES: COMPREHENSIVE WORKS*

ECONOMY AND THE FOREIGN POLICY. see *BUSINESS AND ECONOMICS—Economic Systems And Theories, Economic History*

330 952 320   JPN   ISSN 1348-9216
HC462.9
ECONOMY, CULTURE & HISTORY JAPAN SPOTLIGHT. Text in English. 1982. bi-m. JPY 6,000; JPY 1,200 newsstand/cover (effective 2004). adv. bk.rev. illus. **Document type:** *Journal, Academic/Scholarly.* **Description:** Provides in-depth, analytical, historical and cultural information on Japan's trade, business, economic issues, current events, legislation and politics.
Formerly (until 2003): Journal of Japanese Trade and Industry (0285-9556)
Related titles: Online - full text ed.
Indexed: BAS, BPI, CADCAM, EnvAb, M&MA, PAIS, RASB, RefZh, TTI, TelAb.
—IE, Infotrieve.
Published by: Japan Economic Foundation, 11th Fl, Jiji Press Bldg., 5-15-8 Ginza Chuo-Ku, Tokyo, 104-0061, Japan. TEL 81-3-55654821, FAX 81-3-55654828, info@jef.or.jp, http://www.jef.or.jp/en_act/journal.html. Circ: 35,000.

330   TWN
ECONOMY TODAY/CHIN JIH CHING CHI. Text in Chinese. m. USD 22 in Hong Kong; USD 25 in Asia; USD 28 elsewhere. adv. illus. **Description:** Covers the economic situation for businesspeople, entrepreneurs, analysts. Also includes some general interest articles.
Address: 15 Foochow St, Taipei, 10722, Taiwan. TEL 02-341-2338.

330   USA
ECONWPA. Text in English. m.
Media: Online - full content.
Published by: Washington University, Economics Department, Campus Box 1208, St. Louis, MO 63130. bparks@wuecona.wustl.edu, http://econwpa.wustl.edu/wpawelcome.html.

330   DEU
ECONY. Text in German. bi-m. adv. **Document type:** *Consumer.*
Related titles: Online - full text ed.
Published by: Manager Magazin Verlagsgesellschaft mbH, Brandstwiete 19, Hamburg, 20457, Germany. TEL 49-40-3080050, FAX 49-40-30800549, briefe@econy.de, mm_redaktion@manager-magazin.de, http://www.econy.de. Ed. Gabriele Fischer. Pub. Heinz Gerhardt. Adv. contact Christian Schlottau.

ECOS DE A L A D I. see *POLITICAL SCIENCE*

330   DEU
EDEKA HANDELS-RUNDSCHAU. Text in German. 1907. s-m. EUR 2.10 newsstand/cover (effective 2005). adv. **Document type:** *Journal, Trade.*
Published by: Edeka Verlag GmbH, New-York-Ring 6, Hamburg, 22297, Germany. TEL 49-40-63770, FAX 49-40-63772478, verlag@edeka.de, http://www.edeka.de. Ed. Gerhard Neumann. Adv. contact Peter Bartsch. page EUR 5,900; trim 280 x 416. Circ: 12,675 (paid and controlled).

330   MNG
EDIYN DZASGIYN BOLOVSROL/ECONOMIC EDUCATION. Text in Mongol. 18/yr.
Published by: Mongolian People's Revolutionary Party, Ulan Bator, Mongolia. Ed. D Surenjav. Circ: 37,000.

338   EST   ISSN 1406-4499
KJS3405.A27
EESTI MAJANDUSE TEATAJA. Text in Estonian. 1991. m. EEK 1,550 (effective 2002). **Document type:** *Journal, Trade.*
Formerly (until 1999): Eesti Valismajanduse Teataja (1021-9420)
Published by: Mainor Kirjastus, Kuhlbarsi 1, Tallinn, 10128, Estonia. TEL 372-620-7542, FAX 372-620-7545, teataja@mmk.ee, http://emt.ehk.ee. Ed. Aime Hendre.

EGYPTE - MONDE ARABE. see *POLITICAL SCIENCE*

330   USA
EINHORN NEWSLETTER. Text in English. q. **Document type:** *Newsletter.*
Published by: Einhorn Associates, 2675 N Mayfair Rd, Ste 410, Milwaukee, WI 53226-1305. TEL 414-453-4488, FAX 414-453-4831, iamtrent@yahoo.com, http://www.einhorn.com. Ed. Trent Myers.

330   ESP
EJECUTIVOS FINANCIEROS. Text in Spanish. 6/yr.
Published by: Asociacion Espanola de Ejecutivos Financieros/Spanish Association of Financial Executives, Carranza, 25 3o, Madrid, 28004, Spain. TEL 1-445-09-97. Ed. Luis G Justicia. Circ: 20,000.

330   RUS   ISSN 0131-7652
EKO; Ekonomika i Organizatsiya Promyshlennogo Proizvodstva. Text in Russian. 1970. m. USD 199 in United States. bk.rev. 192 p./no.; **Document type:** *Journal, Academic/Scholarly.* **Description:** Covers the economy and industry. Methodology includes case studies and sociological surveys.
Indexed: RefZh.
—East View.
Address: Pr-t Akad Lavrent'eva 17, Novosibirsk, 630090, Russian Federation. TEL 7-3832-341925, eco@ieie.nsc.ru, http://www.econom.nsc.ru/edo. Ed. S V Kazantsev. **US dist. addr.:** East View Information Services, 3020 Harbor Ln. N., Minneapolis, MN 55447. TEL 612-550-0961.

330   RUS
EKOLINK. Text in Russian. q.
Address: Michurinskii pr-t 8-29, kom 929, Moscow, 117192, Russian Federation. TEL 7-095-9399247, FAX 7-095-1471356. **US dist. addr.:** East View Information Services, 3020 Harbor Ln. N., Minneapolis, MN 55447. TEL 612-550-0961.

330   CZE   ISSN 1210-0714
HC267.B2
EKONOM. Variant title: Tydenik Hospodarskych Novin. Text in Czech. 1991. w. CZK 1,352 (effective 2003). adv. **Document type:** *Magazine, Trade.*
Indexed: B&I.

Published by: Economia a.s., Dobrovskeho 25, Prague 7 7, 170 55, Czech Republic. TEL 420-2-33071111, FAX 420-2-33072003, economia@economia.cz, ekonom@economia.cz, http://www.economia.cz. Ed. Zbynek Fiala. Adv. contact Lukas Polak. page CZK 173,000; trim 186 x 256.

330   IDN   ISSN 0126-155X
HC446
EKONOMI DAN KEUANGAN INDONESIA. Text in Indonesian. 1953. q.
Indexed: IBR, IBZ, PAIS.
Published by: Universitas Indonesia, Lembaga Penyelidikan Ekonomi dan Masyarakat, Fakultas Ekonomi, Jakarta, Indonesia.

330   IDN
EKONOMI DAN PEMBANGUNAN. Text in Indonesian. 1977. m.
Indexed: EI.
Published by: Lambung Mangkurat University, Faculty of Economics/Universitas Lambung Mangkurat, Fakultas Ekonomi, Jl. Lambung Mangkurat 20, Banjarmasin, Indonesia.

330   IDN   ISSN 0216-3659
HC446
EKONOMI INDONESIA. Text in English. 1971. bi-m.
Indexed: APEL.
Address: Jalan Merdeka, Timur 11-12, Jakarta, Indonesia. TEL 021-494458. Ed. Z Achmad. Circ: 20,000.

330   POL   ISSN 1505-0211
HB9
EKONOMIA MATEMATYCZNA. Text in Polish. 1997. irreg.
Indexed: MathR, MathSciNet.
Published by: (Akademia Ekonomiczna im. Oskara Langego we Wroclawiu), Wydawnictwo Akademii Rolniczej we Wroclawiu, ul Sopocka 23, Wroclaw, 50344, Poland. FAX 328-12-77, http://www.ae.wroc.pl/wydaw/Prace_n/emat/emat.html.

330   RUS
EKONOMICHESKAYA GAZETA. Text in Russian. 1994. bi-m. RUR 312 for 6 mos. (effective 2003). **Document type:** *Newspaper, Consumer.*
Published by: Izdatel'skii Dom Ekonomicheskaya Gazeta, Bumazhnyi proezd 14, Moscow, 101462, Russian Federation. TEL 7-095-2573224, FAX 7-095-2002297, akdi@akdi.ru, http://www.akdi.ru. Ed. N P Tarasenko.

330 333.7 340   RUS
EKONOMICHESKIE I PRAVOVYE VOPROSY NEDROPOL'ZOVANIYA V ROSSII. Text in Russian. 24/yr. USD 349.95 in United States.
Published by: Informatsionno-Izdatel'skii Tsentr po Geologii i Nedropol'zovaniu Geoinformmark, Goncharnaya 38, Moscow, 115172, Russian Federation. TEL 7-095-9156724. **US dist. addr.:** East View Information Services, 3020 Harbor Ln. N., Minneapolis, MN 55447. TEL 612-550-0961.

330   RUS
EKONOMICHESKIE I SOTSYAL'NYE PROBLEMY ROSSII. Text in Russian. q.
Indexed: RefZh.
Address: Nakhimovskii pr-t 51-21, Moscow, 117418, Russian Federation. TEL 7-095-1204514, FAX 7-095-4202261. **US dist. addr.:** East View Information Services, 3020 Harbor Ln. N., Minneapolis, MN 55447. TEL 612-550-0961.

330   RUS
EKONOMICHESKIE NOVOSTI ROSSII I SODRUZHESTVA/ECONOMIC NEWS FROM RUSSIA AND COMMONWEALTH. Text in Russian. 1992. bi-m. USD 215 foreign (effective 2005). **Document type:** *Newspaper, Consumer.* **Description:** The digest of business press. Presents the latest developments in the CIS countries, commentaries to new normative documents.
Published by: Ekonomicheskie Novosti/Economic News, Post Box 58, Moscow 9, 103050, Russian Federation. TEL 7-095-2993827, FAX 7-095-9210609, econews@econews.ru, http://www.econews.ru/Econews/index.html. **Dist. by:** East View Information Services, 3020 Harbor Ln. N., Minneapolis, MN 55447. TEL 800-477-1005, FAX 800-800-3839, eastview@eastview.com, http://www.eastview.com.

330   RUS
EKONOMICHESKOE DOS'E ZAKONODATEL'NOE OBESPECHENIE BIZNESA V ROSSII. Text in Russian, English. 1997. 8/yr. USD 995 in the Americas (effective 2000).
Published by: Izdatel'stvo Konseko, Ul. B. Filevskaya, 22-2, Moscow, 121309, Russian Federation. TEL 7-095-1422054, FAX 7-095-1422095.

330   MDA
EKONOMICHESKOE OBOZRENIE LOGOS PRESS. Text in Russian. w. USD 215 in the Americas (effective 2000).
Published by: Logos Press, Shtefan Chel Mare, 92, Chishinau, Kishinev, Moldova. TEL 24-98-35, FAX 24-81-39. Ed. Sergei Mishin.

330   TJK
EKONOMICHESKOE OBOZRENIE TADZHIKISTANA. Text in Russian. 24/yr. USD 399 in the Americas (effective 2000).

Published by: Redaktsiya Ekonomicheskoe Obozrenie Tadzhikistana, Bohtar, 35-1, 8 etazh, Dushanbe, Tajikistan. TEL 21-78-63, FAX 21-72-20. Ed. Umed Babahanov.

330 SVK ISSN 0013-3035
HB9
EKONOMICKY CASOPIS/JOURNAL OF ECONOMICS. Text in Slovak; Abstracts and contents page in English, Russian. 1953. bi-m. USD 130 foreign (effective 2005). bk.rev. bibl.; stat. index. **Document type:** *Journal, Academic/Scholarly.* **Description:** Presents papers directed to economic problems and mathematical solutions. For economists in production and management centers, teachers and university and specialized secondary school students.
Indexed: ASCA, BusI, CurCont, GEOBASE, IBSS, JEL, SCIMP, SSCI.
—IDS.
Published by: (Slovenska Akademia Vied, Ekonomicky Ustav), Slovak Academic Press Ltd., Nam Slobody 6, PO Box 57, Bratislava, 81005, Slovakia. sap@sappress.sk, http://www.sappress.sk. Ed. Egon Hlavaty. **Co-sponsor:** Slovenska Akademie Vied, Prognosticky Ustav.

330 510 RUS ISSN 0424-7388
HB74.M3 CODEN: EMAMBV
EKONOMIKA I MATEMATICHESKIE METODY. Text in Russian. 1965. q. USD 202.50 in United States. **Document type:** *Academic/Scholarly.*
Related titles: Online - full text ed.: (from East View Information Services).
Indexed: CIS, IBSS, RefZh, ZentMath.
—East View, KNAW.
Published by: Central Institute of Economics and Mathematics, Staromonetnyi per 35, Moscow, 117418, Russian Federation. TEL 7-095-2308298, http://ts1.cemi.rssi.ru/emm/. Ed. V L Makarov. Circ: 3,500. **US dist. addr.:** East View Information Services, 3020 Harbor Ln. N., Minneapolis, MN 55447. TEL 612-550-0961.

330 RUS
EKONOMIKA I VREMYA; ezhenedel'noe obozrenie delovoi zhizni Severa i Severa-Zapada Rossii. Text in Russian. w. RUR 77.16. adv. **Description:** Surveys business in northern Russia, focusing on the northwest.
Address: Ul Aleksandra Nevskogo 12, St Petersburg, 193167, Russian Federation. TEL 7-812-3270305, FAX 7-812-2710286, info@econ.spb.ru. Ed. Aleksandr Evseev.

335 RUS ISSN 1607-0615
EKONOMIKA I ZHIZN'. Text in Russian. 1918. w. USD 345 foreign (effective 2005). adv. illus. 32 p./no.; **Document type:** *Newspaper, Consumer.* **Description:** Main features include economy, finance and industry, real estate, business, international cooperation, education and health.
Formerly (until 1990): Ekonomicheskaya Gazeta (0013-3132)
Related titles: CD-ROM ed.; Microfilm ed.: (from EVP, PQC); Microform ed.: (from EVP, PQC); Online - full text ed.; ♦ Regional ed(s).: Ekonomika i Zhizn'. Gostinyi Ryad; ♦ Ekonomika i Zhizn'. Rus'; ♦ Ekonomika i Zhizn'. Sankt-Peterburgskii Vypusk; Ekonomika i Zhizn'. Moskovskii Vypusk; ♦ Supplement(s): E Z - Yurist; ♦ E Z - Vopros - Otvet; ♦ Vash Partner-Konsul'tant; ♦ Bukhgalterskoye Prilozheniye.
Indexed: B&I, CDSP, PROMT.
Published by: Izdatel'skii Dom Ekonomicheskaya Gazeta, Bumazhnyi proezd 14, Moscow, 101462, Russian Federation. TEL 7-095-2573153, 7-095-2512003, FAX 7-095-2002297, gazeta@ekonomika.ru, http://www.akdi.ru. Ed. Yury V Yakutin. R&P Y A Tartanov TEL 7-095-2573413. Adv. contact Lidia Vdovina TEL 7-095-2573157. B&W page USD 14,100; trim 380 x 266. Circ: 460,000. **Dist. by:** East View Information Services, 3020 Harbor Ln. N., Minneapolis, MN 55447. TEL 800-477-1005, FAX 800-800-3839, eastview@eastview.com, http://www.eastview.com.

330 RUS
EKONOMIKA I ZHIZN'. GOSTINYI RYAD. Text in Russian. w. USD 349 in the Americas (effective 2000).
Related titles: ♦ Regional ed(s).: Ekonomika i Zhizn'. ISSN 1607-0615; ♦ Ekonomika i Zhizn'. Rus'; ♦ Ekonomika i Zhizn'. Sankt-Peterburgskii Vypusk; Ekonomika i Zhizn'. Moskovskii Vypusk.
Published by: Redaktsiya Ekonomika i Zhizn', Gostinyi Ryad, Pl. Stariy Torg, 7, P.O. Box 1037, Kaluga, 248661, Russian Federation. TEL 0842-561496, FAX 0842-561496, gr@kaluga.ru. Ed. A Trusov.

330 RUS
EKONOMIKA I ZHIZN'. RUS'. Text in Russian. w. USD 349 in the Americas (effective 2000).
Related titles: ♦ Regional ed(s).: Ekonomika i Zhizn'. ISSN 1607-0615; ♦ Ekonomika i Zhizn'. Gostinyi Ryad; ♦ Ekonomika i Zhizn'. Sankt-Peterburgskii Vypusk; Ekonomika i Zhizn'. Moskovskii Vypusk.
Published by: Redaktsiya Ekonomika i Zhizn'. Rus', Ul. Krasnoryadskaya, 23, Ryazan', 390000, Russian Federation. TEL 8112-773679. Ed. I Levchenko.

330 RUS
EKONOMIKA I ZHIZN'. SANKT-PETERBURGSKII VYPUSK. Text in Russian. w. USD 454 in the Americas (effective 2000).
Related titles: ♦ Regional ed(s).: Ekonomika i Zhizn'. ISSN 1607-0615; ♦ Ekonomika i Zhizn'. Gostinyi Ryad; ♦ Ekonomika i Zhizn'. Rus'; Ekonomika i Zhizn'. Moskovskii Vypusk.
Published by: Redaktsiya Ekonomika i Zhizn'. Sankt-Peterburgskii Vypusk, Ul. A. Nevskogo, 12, St. Petersburg, 193167, Russian Federation. TEL 812-3270305, FAX 812-2710286, info@econ.spb.rug. Ed. A Evseev.

330 RUS ISSN 1609-7122
EKONOMIKA I ZHIZN'. SIBIR. Text in Russian. 1994. w. USD 545 in United States (effective 2002).
Related titles: Online - full content ed.
Published by: Redaktsiya Ekonomika i Zhizn. Sibir, a/ya 2418, P, Krasnoyarsk, 660075, Russian Federation. TEL 3912-218156, FAX 3912-211171, el@krsk.ru, eco@pressa.krasnoyarsk.su, http://www.ecolife.krsk.ru. Ed. V V Khrebtov.

330 RUS
EKONOMIKA. PREDPRINIMATEL'STVO. OKRUZHAYUSHCHAYA SREDA. Text in Russian. 1993. q. USD 130 in the Americas (effective 2000).
Published by: Izdatel'stvo M T S N T I, Ul. Kusinena, 21b, Moscow, 125252, Russian Federation. TEL 7-095-1987210, FAX 7-095-9430089. Ed. A I Kozyrev.

330 SCG ISSN 0353-443X
HD28
EKONOMIKA PREDUZECA✶ . Summaries in English. 1953. m. YUN 1,600, USD 150. adv. abstr.; bibl.; charts.
Former titles (until 1989): Ekonomika Udruzenog Rada (0350-1434); (until 1984): Ekonomika Preduzeca (0013-3078)
Published by: Savez Ekonomista Srbije, Nusiceva 6-111, P.O. Box 490, Belgrade, 11000. Ed. Jovan Rankovic. Circ: 3,000.

330 RUS ISSN 0235-2494
HD1491.R9
EKONOMIKA SEL'SKOKHOZYAISTVENNYKH I PERERABATYVAYUSHCHIKH PREDPRIYATII. Text in Russian. 1926. m. USD 120 foreign (effective 2003).
Indexed: AEA, AbHyg, AnBrAb, DSA, FCA, ForAb, HerbAb, HortAb, I&DA, IndVet, MaizeAb, NutrAb, PBA, PHN&I, PN&I, PotatoAb, PoultAb, RRTA, RefZh, RiceAb, S&F, SIA, SeedAb, SoyAb, TriticAb, VetBull, WAE&RSA.
—East View.
Address: Sadovaya-Spasskaya 18, kom 422, Moscow, 107807, Russian Federation. TEL 7-095-2072110, FAX 7-095-2072870. Ed. V A Orlov. Circ: 18,600. **Dist. by:** M K - Periodica, ul Gilyarovskogo 39, Moscow 129110, Russian Federation. TEL 7-095-2845008, FAX 7-095-2813798, info@periodicals.ru, http://www.mkniga.ru; **US dist. addr.:** East View Information Services, 3020 Harbor Ln. N., Minneapolis, MN 55447. TEL 612-550-0961.

330 370 RUS ISSN 1560-6937
EKONOMIKA. VOPROSY SHKOL'NOGO EKONOMICHESKOGO OBRAZOVANIYA. Text in Russian. 1998. q. RUR 180 domestic for 4 mos.; USD 68 foreign (effective 2005). **Document type:** *Journal, Academic/Scholarly.*
Published by: Izdatel'stvo Sibirskogo Otdeleniya Rossiiskoi Akademii Nauk/Publishing House of the Russian Academy of Sciences, Siberian Branch, Morskoi pr 2, a/ya 187, Novosibirsk, 630090, Russian Federation. TEL 7-3832-300570, FAX 7-3832-333755, psb@ad-sbras.nsc.ru, http://www-psb.ad-sbras.nsc.ru. **Dist. by:** M K - Periodica, ul Gilyarovskogo 39, Moscow 129110, Russian Federation. TEL 7-095-2845008, FAX 7-095-2813798, info@periodicals.ru, http://www.mkniga.ru.

330 SWE ISSN 0345-2646
EKONOMISK DEBATT/ECONOMIC DEBATE. Text in Swedish. 1973. 8/yr. SEK 415; SEK 300 to students; SEK 55 newsstand/cover (effective 2003). adv. index, cum.index: 1878-1926. **Document type:** *Journal, Academic/Scholarly.*
Supersedes: Nationalekonomiska Foereningens Foerhandlingar
Indexed: IBSS, INIS AtomInd.
Published by: Nationalekonomiska Foereningen/Swedish Economic Society, c/o IUI, PO Box 5501, Stockholm, 11485, Sweden. TEL 46-8-16-23-07, FAX 46-8-15-46-70, http://www.ne.su.se/ed. Eds. Anders Bjoerklund, Lennart Berg. Adv. contact Elisabeth Gustafsson. page SEK 5,300. Circ: 2,000. **Subscr. to:** I L Prenumerationsservice, Vitplistergraend 43, Haessekby 16573, Sweden.

330 FIN ISSN 0013-3183
HC337.F5
➤ **EKONOMISKA SAMFUNDETS TIDSKRIFT/JOURNAL OF THE ECONOMIC SOCIETY OF FINLAND.** Text mainly in Swedish; Summaries in English. 1913. 3/yr., latest vol.55, 2002. EUR 25 (effective 2002). adv. bk.rev. abstr.; illus.; stat. index. back issues avail. **Document type:** *Journal, Academic/Scholarly.*
Indexed: ASCA, CIS, CurCont, IBR, IBZ, ILD, JEL, PAIS, RefZh, SSCI.
—IDS.
Published by: Ekonomiska Samfundet i Finland/Economic Society of Finland, c/o Sonja Groenblom-Holmquist, Mariankan 41, Bostan 5, Tammerfors, 33200, Finland. TEL 358-40-5068021. Eds. Kenneth Snellman, Dr. Ralf Eriksson, Gunnar Rosenquist. R&P, Adv. contact Sonja Groenblom-Holmquist TEL 358-40-5068021. Circ: 1,400.

330 TUR ISSN 1300-5847
HC491.E374
EKONOMIST. Text in Turkish. 1991. w. TRL 90,000,000 domestic; EUR 320, USD 280 foreign (effective 2002). adv. **Document type:** *Magazine, Trade.*
Published by: D B R - Dogan Burda Rizzoli Dergi Yayyncylyk ve Pazarlama A.S., Hurriyet Medya Towers, Gunesli - Istanbul, 34212, Turkey. TEL 90-212-4103111, FAX 90-212-4103112, abone@dbr.com.tr, http://www.dbr.com.tr.

330 SCG ISSN 0354-5253
EKONOMIST. Abstracts and contents page in English, Russian. 1948. q.
Published by: Novinsko-Izdavacko Preduzece E-press d.o.o., Draze Pavlovica 31, Belgrade, 11000. TEL 381-11-3284034, office@ekonomist.co.yu, http://www.ekonomist.co.yu. Ed. Mijat Lakicevic.

330 HRV ISSN 1332-2788
EKONOMIST. Text in Croatian. 2000. m. **Document type:** *Magazine, Trade.*
Published by: Progres d.o.o., Varsavska 2, Zagreb, 10000, Croatia. TEL 385-1-4432301, FAX 385-1-4432889.

330 POL ISSN 0013-3205
HC337.P7
➤ **EKONOMISTA**; czasopismo poswiecone nauce i potrzebom zycia. Text in Polish; Summaries in English, Russian. 1900. bi-m. EUR 110 foreign (effective 2005). adv. bk.rev. bibl.; charts. index. back issues avail. **Document type:** *Journal, Academic/Scholarly.* **Description:** Acedemic and theoretical publication covering economic theory and practice for university professors, researchers, and students.
Indexed: AgrLib, AmH&L, HistAb, IBSS.
—IE, Infotrieve.
Published by: Polskie Towarzystwo Ekonomiczne, ul Nowy Swiat 49, Warsaw, 00042, Poland. TEL 48-22-8275031, zk@pte.pl, http://www.pte.pl/pte/nauka/main.php. Ed. Zdzislaw Sadowski. R&P W Switalski. Adv. contact Wladyslaw Switalski. B&W page USD 800. Circ: 1,300 (paid). **Dist. by:** Ars Polona, Krakowskie Przedmiescie 7, Warsaw, Poland. TEL 48-22-9263914, FAX 48-22-9265334, arspolona@arspolona.com.pl, http://www.arspolona.com.pl. **Co-sponsor:** Polska Akademia Nauk, Komitet Nauk Ekonomicznych.

330 HRV ISSN 1331-677X
EKONOMSKA ISTRAZIVANJA/ECONOMIC RESEARCH. Text in Serbo-Croatian. 1988. s-a. HRK 100 (effective 2004). bk.rev. **Document type:** *Journal.*
Formerly (until 1998): Gospodarstvo Istre (0353-2860)
Indexed: GEOBASE, JEL.
Published by: Sveuciliste u Rijeci, Fakultet Ekonomije i Turizma "Dr. Mijo Mirkovic", Preradoviceva 1, Pula, 52 100, Croatia. TEL 385-52-377000, FAX 385-52-216416, imilj@efpu.hr, ured@efpu.hr, http://www.efpu.hr/publikacije/, http://www.efpu.hr/fet. Ed. Lovre Bozina.

330 SCG ISSN 0013-323X
EKONOMSKA MISAO✶ . Text in Serbo-Croatian; Summaries in English, Russian. 1968. q. YUN 15,000, USD 140.
Indexed: JEL.
Published by: Savez Ekonomista Srbije, Nusiceva 6-111, P.O. Box 490, Belgrade, 11000. Ed. Ljubomir Madzar.

330 SCG ISSN 0013-3264
HB9
EKONOMSKI ANALI. Text in Serbo-Croatian. 1951. q. **Document type:** *Journal, Academic/Scholarly.*
Published by: Univerzitet u Beogradu, Ekonomski Fakultet, Kamenicka 6, Belgrade, 11000. TEL 381-11-3021020, FAX 381-11-639560, ekof@one.ekof.bg.ac.yu, http://www.ekof.bg.ac.yu/anali. Ed. Zarko Bulajic.

330 HRV ISSN 0424-7558
HB9
EKONOMSKI PREGLED. Text in Serbo-Croatian; Summaries in English, Russian. 1950. m. bibl.; charts. index.
Indexed: AmH&L, HistAb, IBSS, JEL.
Published by: Hrvatsko Drustvo Ekonomista/Croatian Society of Economics, Trg. J.F. Kennedya 6, Zagreb, 10000, Croatia. Circ: 1,700.

330 HRV ISSN 0353-359X
HB9
EKONOMSKI VJESNIK. Text in Croatian. 1988. s-a. HRK 60 to individuals; HRK 200 to institutions (effective 2002 - 2003).
Indexed: RRTA, RefZh, WAE&RSA.
Published by: Sveuciliste Josipa Jurja Strossmayera u Osijeku, Ekonomski Fakultet, Gajev Trg 7, Osijek, 31000, Croatia. TEL 385-31-224400, FAX 385-31-211604, http://www.efos.hr/hrv/izdjelatnost/evjesnik/. Ed. Dr. Zeljko Turkalj.

330 HRV ISSN 1331-8004
EKONOMSKOG FAKULTETA U RIJECI. ZBORNIK RADOVA/RIJEKA SCHOOL OF ECONOMICS. PROCEEDINGS. Text in Serbo-Croatian. 1971. s-a.
Former titles (until 1997): Sveuciliste u Rijeci. Ekonomski Fakultet. Zbornik Radova (1330-6308); (until 1994): Ekonomski Fakultet u Rijeci. Zbornik Radova (0353-3689); (until 1980): Sveuciliste u Zagrebu. Ekonomski Fakultet u Rijeci. Sbornik (1330-6316)

B

Indexed: JEL.
Published by: Sveuciliste u Rijeci, Ekonomski Fakultet, Ivana Filipovica 4, Rijeka, 51000, Croatia. TEL 385-51-355111, FAX 385-51-212268, zbornik@efri.hr, efri@efri.hr, http://www.efri.hr. Ed. Ivo Sever. Circ: 300.

330 USA ISSN 8750-6033
HF5001
EL PASO ECONOMIC REVIEW. Text in English. 1964. bi-m. USD 15. charts; stat. back issues avail. **Document type:** *Academic/Scholarly.*
Former titles: El Paso Business Review (0162-1041); El Paso Economic Review (0013-4031)
Indexed: PAIS.
Published by: University of Texas at El Paso, Texas Centers, Burges Hall, Rm 410, El Paso, TX 79968-0541. TEL 915-747-5036. Ed. James E Trumbly. Circ: 1,000.

338.9 SLV
EL SALVADOR: COYUNTURA ECONOMICA; boletin informativo y analisis economico. Text in Spanish. 1985. bi-m. SVC 36, USD 16.
Supersedes (1950-19??): Revista de Economia de El Salvador
Published by: (El Salvador. Instituto de Investigaciones Economicas CUB), Universidad de El Salvador, Facultad de Ciencias Economicas, Aptdo. Postal 2830, San Salvador, El Salvador. TEL 257755. Circ: 1,000.

330 FRA
ELECTRICITE DE FRANCE. DIRECTION DES ETUDES ET RECHERCHES. COLLECTION DE NOTES INTERNES. ORGANISATION, INFORMATION, ENVIRONNEMENT SOCIAL ET ECONOMIQUE. Text in French. 1992. irreg. free.
Published by: Electricite de France, Direction des Etudes et Recherches, 1 av. du General de Gaulle, Clamart, Cedex 92141, France. TEL 1-47-65-43-21, FAX 1-47-65-31-24. Ed. Jean Marie Lecoeuvre.

330 TWN
ELECTRONIC BUSINESS INFORMATION. Text in Japanese. m. adv. **Description:** Contains information for importers and OEM buyers within Japan on Taiwan and Asian produced IT products, electronic components, parts and subassemblies.
Related titles: CD-ROM ed.: Electronic Business Information/Japan Directory CD.
Published by: Arco Publications Inc., 4F, No. 5, Sec. 1, Pa-Te Rd, Taipei, Taiwan. adv.: page USD 2,000. Circ: 18,000.

330 FIN ISSN 1239-2685
HF5387
ELECTRONIC JOURNAL OF BUSINESS ETHICS AND ORGANIZATION STUDIES. Text in English. s-a. free (effective 2005). back issues avail. **Document type:** *Journal, Academic/Scholarly.*
Media: Online - full content.
Published by: University of Jyvaskyla, School of Business and Economics, B O E N, PO Box 35, Jyvaskyla, 40351, Finland. TEL 358-40-7050982, http://ejbo.jyu.fi/index.cgi?page=cover. Eds. Anna-Maija Lamsa, Tuomo Takala.

330 FRA ISSN 1298-0137
HB97.3
➤ **ELECTRONIC JOURNAL OF EVOLUTIONARY MODELING AND ECONOMIC DYNAMICS.** Text in English. 2000. s-a. free (effective 2005). bk.rev.; software rev. abstr.; charts; illus.; bibl. **Document type:** *Journal, Academic/Scholarly.* **Description:** Provides a forum for discussion in the area of evolutionary modeling. Topics covered include, but are not limited to, selection and evolutionary industry dynamics, evolutionary game theory, modeling bounded rationality and learning through evolutionary algorithms, and agent based modeling of complex adaptive systems.
Media: Online - full content.
Published by: E-JEMED, E-JEMED.IFREDE-E3i, Universite Montesquieu Bordeaux IV, Ave Leon Duguit, Pessac, 33608, France. editor@e-jemed.org, http://beagle.u-bordeaux4.fr/jemed/. Ed. Murat Yildizoglu.

330 GBR ISSN 1566-6379
ELECTRONIC JOURNAL OF INFORMATION SYSTEMS EVALUATION. Text in English. 1997. s-a. free (effective 2005). **Document type:** *Journal, Academic/Scholarly.* **Description:** It aims to publish articles and papers that provide critical perspectives on topics relevant to information systems evaluation, with an emphasis on the organizational and management implications.
Media: Online - full text.
Published by: Academic Conferences Limited, Curtis Farm, Kidmore End, Nr Reading, RG4 9AY, United Kingdom. TEL 44-1189-724148, FAX 44-1189-724691, http://www.ejise.com/index.htm.

ELEKTRO UND WIRTSCHAFT. see *ENGINEERING—Electrical Engineering*

330 USA
EMPIRE (NEW YORK, 2002); the magazine of business innovation. Text in English. 2002. m. USD 11 (effective 2003). adv. illus. **Document type:** *Magazine, Trade.* **Description:** Spotlighting Ideas, Innovation, Money & Power in New York.
Related titles: Online - full text ed.
Published by: Empire Media, Inc., 62 White St, New York, NY 10013. TEL 212-925-7070, editorial@empiremedia.com, http://www.empiremedia.com/magazine.html. Circ: 40,000 (paid and controlled).

330 USA
EMPIRE NEW YORK NEWSLETTER. Text in English. 2002. w. free (effective 2002). **Document type:** *Trade.*
Media: E-mail.
Published by: Empire Media, Inc., 62 White St, New York, NY 10013. editorial@empiremedia.com, http://www.empireny.com/subscriber/NewsletterSubscribeForm.html, http://www.empiremedia.com, http://www.empiremedia.com.

330 DEU ISSN 0377-7332
HB1.A1
➤ **EMPIRICAL ECONOMICS**; a quarterly journal of the Institute for Advanced Studies, Vienna. Text in English. 1976. q. EUR 668 combined subscription to institutions print & online eds. (effective 2005). reprints avail. **Document type:** *Journal, Academic/Scholarly.* **Description:** Papers dealing with the confrontation of relevant economic theory with observed data through the use of adequate econometric methods.
Related titles: Online - full text ed.: ISSN 1435-8921 (from EBSCO Publishing, ProQuest Information & Learning, Springer LINK, Swets Information Services).
Indexed: ABIn, GEOBASE, IAOP, IBR, IBSS, IBZ, IBibSS, JCQM, JEL, ORMS, PAIS, QC&AS, RefZh, SCIMP, ST&MA, WBSS.
—BLDSC (3737.010000), IE, Infotrieve, ingenta. **CCC.**
Published by: (Institute for Advanced Studies, Vienna AUT), Physica-Verlag GmbH und Co. (Subsidiary of: Springer-Verlag), Postfach 105280, Heidelberg, 69042, Germany. TEL 49-6221-487492, FAX 49-6221-487177, physica@springer.de, http://link.springer.de/link/service/journals/00181/index.htm. Eds. Badi H Baltagi, Baldev Raj. Adv. contact Stephan Kroeck TEL 49-30-827875739. **Subscr. in the Americas to:** Springer-Verlag New York, Inc., Journal Fulfillment, PO Box 2485, Secaucus, NJ 07096-2485. TEL 800-777-4643, 201-348-4033, FAX 201-348-4505, journals@springer-ny.com, http://www.springer-ny.com; **Subscr. to:** Springer GmbH Auslieferungsgesellschaft, Haberstr 7, Heidelberg 69126, Germany. TEL 49-6221-345-0, FAX 49-6221-345-4229, subscriptions@springer.de.

330 USA ISSN 0899-8833
EMPLOYEE OWNERSHIP REPORT. Text in English. 1981. bi-m. USD 80 domestic membership; USD 90 foreign membership (effective 2005). bk.rev. 16 p./no.; **Document type:** *Newsletter.* **Description:** Contains legal, regulatory, and financial news pertaining to employee ownership, tips on management and communication practices, research and case studies.
Formerly (until 1987): Employee Ownership
—**CCC.**
Published by: National Center for Employee Ownership, Inc., 1736 Franklin St, 8th fl, Oakland, CA 94612. TEL 510-208-1300, FAX 510-272-9510, nceo@nceo.org, http://www.nceo.org/nceo/newsletter.html. Ed. Corey Rosen. Circ: 3,000.

EMPRESA E. (Empresa Electronica) see *COMPUTERS—Internet*

330 ESP ISSN 1131-6551
EMPRESARIO. Text in Spanish. 1978. 11/yr. EUR 25 (effective 2006). adv. **Description:** Contains economic and business information.
Related titles: Supplement(s): El Empresario. Suplemento. ISSN 1698-5400. 2004.
Published by: Confederacion Espanola de la Pequena y Mediana Empresa, Diego de Leon, 50, Madrid, 28006, Spain. FAX 34-91-5645264, cepyme@cepyme.es, http://www.cepyme.es/empresario.html. Ed. Carlota Dominguez. Pub., Adv. contact Alfonso Picabia. page EUR 2,700; 210 x 280. Circ: 9,775.

ENER DATABOOK AND DATADISK. see *PETROLEUM AND GAS*

ENERGOBIZNES. see *ENERGY*

ENERGY BUSINESS REVIEW. see *ENERGY*

ENERGY ECONOMIC NEWS. see *ENERGY*

ENERGY ECONOMIST; an international analysis. see *ENERGY*

ENERGY USER NEWS DIGEST. see *ENERGY*

▼ **ENERGYBIZ.** see *ENERGY*

THE ENGINEERING ECONOMIST. see *ENGINEERING*

330 USA ISSN 0099-0043
NE2720
ENGRAVERS JOURNAL. Text in English. 1975. 12/yr. USD 49; USD 65 in Canada; USD 78 elsewhere (effective 1999). adv. illus. **Document type:** *Trade.*
Indexed: MagInd.
—Linda Hall.
Published by: Davis Farrell & Associates, Inc., PO Box 318, Brighton, MI 48116-0318. TEL 810-229-5725, FAX 810-229-8320, http://www.engraversjournal.com. Ed. Michael J Davis.

330 FRA ISSN 1167-2196
HC271
ENJEUX LES ECHOS. Text in French. 11/yr. **Description:** Provides financial and economic analysis and prospects.
Formerly (until 1992): Dynasteurs (0983-1517)
Related titles: Online - full text ed.: (from Factiva).
Published by: Echos Hera, 46 rue de la Boetie, Paris, Cedex 8 75381, France. TEL 33-1-49536565, FAX 33-1-42252640. Ed. Olivier Jay. Pub. Olivier Fleurot. Circ: 120,000.

330 ARG
ENOIKOS. Text in Spanish. 1993. q. back issues avail.
Related titles: Online - full text ed.
Published by: Universidad de Buenos Aires, Facultad de Ciencias Economicas, Ave. Cordoba No. 2122, Buenos Aires, 1120, Argentina. TEL 54-114-3744448, web@econ.uba.ar, http://www.econ.uba.ar/www/enoikos/principal.htm. Ed. Carlos A Degrossi.

ENROUTE; your complimentary in-flight magazine. see *TRAVEL AND TOURISM*

330 ARG ISSN 0325-3937
HG185.A7
ENSAYOS ECONOMICOS. Text in Spanish. 1977. q.
Indexed: PAIS.
Published by: Banco Central de la Republica Argentina, Centro de Estudios Monetarios y Bancarios, Department de Tramite General, Reconquista, 266, Buenos Aires, 1003, Argentina.

320 330 COL ISSN 0120-4483
HC196
➤ **ENSAYOS SOBRE POLITICA ECONOMICA.** Text in Spanish. 1982. s-a. USD 20; USD 10 newsstand/cover (effective 2003). **Document type:** *Journal, Academic/Scholarly.* **Description:** Contains academic articles which are original, interesting and technically correct, and which teach a lesson regarding economic problems or the economic policies necessary to remedy them.
Indexed: IBR, IBSS, PAIS.
Published by: Banco de la Republica, Subgerencia de Estudios Economicos, Calle 11, no. 4-14, Bogota, CUND, Colombia. TEL 57-1-3431111, FAX 57-1-3421804, espe@banrep.gov.co, http://www.banrep.gov.co/espe/ensayos.htm. Ed., R&P Andres Carvajal. Circ: 1,500 (paid and controlled).

330 USA
ENTERPRISE (SALT LAKE CITY). Text in English. 1971. w. USD 48. adv. illus.; stat. back issues avail. **Document type:** *Newspaper.*
Related titles: Microform ed.: (from PQC); Online - full text ed.
Indexed: BusDate.
Published by: Digest Publishing of Utah Inc., PO BOX 11778, PIONEER STA, Salt Lake City, UT 84147. TEL 801-533-0556. Ed., R&P George Gregersen. Adv. contact Kirk Dyorich. Circ: 5,700.

330 USA ISSN 1467-2227
HF5343
➤ **ENTERPRISE AND SOCIETY**; the international journal of business and history. Text in English. 1975. q. GBP 147 to institutions (effective 2005); USD 235, EUR 221 to institutions; GBP 105, USD 154, EUR 158 academics; GBP 155, USD 248, EUR 233 combined subscription to institutions print & online eds.; GBP 110, USD 162, EUR 165 combined subscription academics; print & online eds. (effective 2006). adv. bk.rev. illus. back issues avail.; reprint service avail. from PSC. **Document type:** *Journal, Academic/Scholarly.* **Description:** Articles focus on individual firms and industries and that are grounded in a broad historical framework, this journal offers a forum for debate on the historical relations between business and their large political, cultural, institutional, social, and economic contexts.
Formerly (until 2000): Business and Economic History (0894-6825)
Related titles: Online - full text ed.: ISSN 1467-2235. 2000. GBP 140, USD 224, EUR 210 to institutions; GBP 99 academics; USD 146, EUR 149 academcis (effective 2006) (from bigchalk, EBSCO Publishing, Gale Group, IngentaConnect, O C L C Online Computer Library Center, Inc., Oxford University Press Online Journals, Project MUSE, ProQuest Information & Learning, Swets Information Services).
Indexed: ABIn, AmH&L, BAS, HistAb, IBSS, JEL, PCI.
—BLDSC (3776.620250), IE, Infotrieve, ingenta. **CCC.**
Published by: (Business History Conference), Oxford University Press (Subsidiary of: Oxford University Press), 2001 Evans Rd, Cary, NC 27513. TEL 919-677-0977, 800-852-7323, FAX 919-677-1714, jnlorders@oup-usa.org, http://es.oxfordjournals.org/, http://www.us.oup.com. Ed. William J. Hausman TEL 757-221-2381. Pub. Eric Staib. R&P Fiona Willis. Adv. contact Helen Pearson. B&W page GBP 175, B&W page USD 260; 205 x 125. Circ: 800.

330 CHE
ENTREPRENDRE. Text in French. s-a. CHF 1,000 to individuals; CHF 5,000 to institutions. **Document type:** *Consumer.*

Published by: (Jeune Chambre Economique de Geneve), Bercher SA, Rue de l Athenee 34, Geneva, 1206, Switzerland. TEL 022-3473388, FAX 022-3462047. Circ: 10,000.

330 FRA ISSN 1145-5764
ENTREPRENDRE. Text in French. 1984. 11/yr. EUR 34 (effective 2005). **Document type:** *Magazine, Consumer.*
Related titles: Online - full text ed.: (from Factiva).
Address: 6 bis rue Auguste Vitu, Paris, 75015, France. TEL 33-1-45774141, FAX 33-1-45792211, redac.entreprendre@wanadoo.fr, http://www.l'express.press.fr. Ed. Bernard Mara. Circ: 78,262.

330 CAN ISSN 1188-7427
ENTREPRENDRE; le magazine des gens qui ont l'esprit d'entreprise. Text in English. 1987. m. CND 34.13 domestic; CND 59.95 in United States; CND 4.95 newsstand/cover. adv. **Document type:** *Trade.* **Description:** Targets all decision-makers in the private or public sector, education, management or labour who are interested in promoting economic growth in Quebec and other parts of Canada.
Formerly (until 1992): Club Regional de l'Entrepreneurship (0840-9145)
Published by: Editions Qualite Performante Inc., 1600 bd St Martin E, Tour B, Bureau 630, Ville de, Laval, PQ H7G 4S7, Canada. TEL 514-669-8373, 800-479-1777, FAX 514-669-9078, message@entreprendre.ca, http://www.entreprendre.ca. Ed. Jean Noel Tremblay. Pub., Adv. contact Edmond Bourque. B&W page CND 4,795, color page CND 6,495; trim 11.13 x 8.63. Circ: 20,000; 30,000 (paid).

330 MEX
ENTREPRENEUR; la autoridad para el emprendedor. Text in Spanish. 199?. m. USD 25; USD 60 in United States; USD 75 elsewhere. adv. **Document type:** *Magazine, Trade.*
Published by: Impresiones Aereas S.A. de C.V., Arquimides 5, Col Polanco, Mexico City, DF 11560, Mexico. TEL 525-726-8941, FAX 525-726-8969, entrepreneurmex@isanet.com.mx. Ed. Laura Martinez. adv.: color page USD 3,145.

330.9 COD
L'ENTREPRENEUR. Text in French. 1978. 6/yr. USD 100 (effective 1999). adv. **Document type:** *Bulletin.* **Description:** Reprints articles from different authors on the enforcement of the laws and regulations of any business and trade. Provides paragraphs on business world events in Congo and abroad; tenders, classified ads; economic aspects of Congo.
Published by: Federation des Entreprises du Congo, 10 av. des Aviateurs, BP 7247, Kinshasa, Congo, Dem. Republic. TEL 242-22286, TELEX 21071 ANEZA ZR. Ed. Athanase Matenda Kyelu. Adv. contact Joseph Mukanya.

330 USA
ENTREPRENEUR.COM. Text in English. 1996. m. USD 819.99 (effective 2005). **Document type:** *Magazine, Consumer.*
Incorporates: Bizstartups.com
Media: Online - full text (from EBSCO Publishing, Florida Center for Library Automation, Gale Group). **Related titles:** Microfiche ed.; ♦ Print ed.: Entrepreneur (Irvine). ISSN 0163-3341.
Published by: Entrepreneur Media, Inc., 2445 McCabe Way, Ste 400, Irvine, CA 92614. TEL 949-261-2325, FAX 949-261-0234, entmag@entrepreneur.com, http://www.entrepreneurmag.com. Ed. Rieva Lesonsky.

330 USA
ENTREPRENEUR'S BIZSTARTUPS.COM. Text in English. 1989. m. Free.
Formerly: Entrepreneur's Business Start-Ups (Print)
Media: Online - full content.
Published by: Entrepreneur Media, Inc., 2445 McCabe Way, Ste 400, Irvine, CA 92614. TEL 949-261-2083, FAX 949-261-0234, bsumag@entrepreneur.com, http://www.bizstartups.com. Circ: 250,000.

330 GBR ISSN 0898-5626
HC79.I53
➤ **ENTREPRENEURSHIP & REGIONAL DEVELOPMENT;** an international journal. Text in English. 1989. bi-m. GBP 292, USD 481 combined subscription to institutions print & online eds. (effective 2006). adv. reprint service avail. from PSC. **Document type:** *Journal, Academic/Scholarly.* **Description:** Focuses on the roles entrepreneurial enterprises play in regional economic growth and prosperity.
Related titles: Online - full text ed.: ISSN 1464-5114. GBP 277, USD 457 to institutions (effective 2006) (from EBSCO Publishing, Gale Group, IngentaConnect, O C L C Online Computer Library Center, Inc., Swets Information Services).
Indexed: ABIn, CurCont, GEOBASE, IBSS, JEL, SSCI.
—BLDSC (3790.547500), IE, Infotrieve, ingenta. **CCC.**
Published by: Routledge (Subsidiary of: Taylor & Francis Group), 4 Park Square, Milton Park, Abingdon, Oxon OX14 4RN, United Kingdom. TEL 44-1235-828600, FAX 44-1235-829000, info@routledge.co.uk, http://www.tandf.co.uk/journals/titles/08985626.asp, http://www.routledge.co.uk. Ed. Bengt Johannisson. **Subscr. addr. in Europe:** Taylor & Francis Ltd, Journals Customer Service, Rankine Rd, Basingstoke, Hants RG24 8PR, United Kingdom. TEL 44-1256-813000, FAX 44-1256-330245, enquiry@tandf.co.uk; **Subscr. in N. America to:** Taylor & Francis Inc., Customer Services Dept, 325 Chestnut St, 8th Fl, Philadelphia, PA 19106. TEL 800-354-1420, FAX 215-625-8914.

➤ **ENTREPRESSE.** see *JOURNALISM*

330 331 FRA ISSN 0995-4945
ENTREPRISE ET CARRIERES. Text in French. 1989. w. FRF 675 (effective 1998).
Published by: Groupe Liaisons S.A. (Subsidiary of: Wolters Kluwer BV), 1 Avenue Edouard Belin, Rueil Malmaison, Cedex 92856, France. TEL 33-1-41299696, FAX 33-1-41299880.

330 FRA ISSN 1161-2770
HF5001
ENTREPRISES ET HISTOIRE. Text in English, French. 1992. 3/yr. adv. abstr.; charts. cum.index: 1992-1998. back issues avail. **Document type:** *Academic/Scholarly.* **Description:** Deals with the business history of the 19th and 20th centuries for an audience of students and scholars of business administration and of history.
Related titles: Online - full text ed.: (from ProQuest Information & Learning).
Indexed: ABIn, AmH&L, HistAb, IBSS.
Published by: Editions E S K A, 12 avenue du 4 septembre, Paris, 75002, France. TEL 33-1-4286-5593, FAX 33-1-4260-4535, fridenso@ehess.fr, eska@eska.fr, http://www.eh.net/bhc/enterprises.htm7, http://www.eska.fr. Ed. Patrick Fridenson. Pub. Serge Kebabtchief. R&P, Adv. contact Nathalie Tomachevski. Circ: 500.

ENVIRONMENTAL AND RESOURCE ECONOMICS. see *ENVIRONMENTAL STUDIES*

ENVIRONMENTAL AND RESOURCE ECONOMICS. see *ENVIRONMENTAL STUDIES*

THE ENVIRONMENTAL BENCHMARKER AND STRATEGIST. see *ENVIRONMENTAL STUDIES*

ENVIRONMENTAL BUSINESS JOURNAL; strategic information for a changing industry. see *ENVIRONMENTAL STUDIES*

ENVIRONMENTAL DUE DILIGENCE REPORT. see *LAW*

ENVIRONMENTAL INDUSTRY YEARBOOK. see *ENVIRONMENTAL STUDIES*

ENVIRONMENTAL ISSUES IN BUSINESS TRANSACTIONS. see *ENVIRONMENTAL STUDIES*

ENVIRONMENTAL LAW IN REAL ESTATE AND BUSINESS TRANSACTIONS. see *ENVIRONMENTAL STUDIES*

330 USA ISSN 1530-4701
EPLANT. Text in English. m. **Document type:** *Journal, Trade.*
Published by: Chemical Week Associates, 110 William St 11th Fl, New York, NY 10038. TEL 212-621-4900, FAX 212-621-4690, http://www.eplantnow.com/, http://www.chemicalspecialties.com. Ed. Rick Mullin TEL 212-621-4968. Adv. contact Erin Ferriter TEL 212-621-4932.

EQUIPMENT LEASING TODAY. see *MACHINERY*

▼ **ERASMUS LAW AND ECONOMICS REVIEW.** see *LAW*

330 DEU ISSN 1436-2961
ERFOLGREICH SELBSTANDIG. Text in German. 1998. q. looseleaf. **Document type:** *Magazine, Trade.*
Published by: W R S Verlag GmbH & Co. KG (Subsidiary of: Rudolf Haufe Verlag GmbH & Co. KG), Fraunhoferstr 5, Planegg, 82152, Germany. info@wrs.de, http://www.wrs.de.

330 DNK ISSN 0109-9310
ERHVERVS-ORIENTERING STAT AMT, KOMMUNE; kommunikationstidskrift for erhverv og institution. Text in Danish. 1983. 8/yr. free. adv. illus.
Published by: Mono-Marketing A-S, Gammel Kongevej 23, Copenhagen V, 1610, Denmark. Circ: 10,000.

330 DNK ISSN 0109-792X
ERHVERVSLEDEREN; den direkte forbindelse til beslutningstagere i Danmark. Text in Danish. 1984. 6/yr. adv. illus.
Published by: Dansk Erhvervsforlag, Teglholmsgade 8, Copenhagen SV, 2450, Denmark. Circ: 60,000 (controlled).

330 CHE
ESPRESSO. Text in German. 10/yr. CHF 49; CHF 60 foreign. **Document type:** *Bulletin.*
Formerly: Professionnelle
Published by: Modapress AG, Koeschenruetistr 109, Postfach, Zuerich, 8052, Switzerland. TEL 41-1-3024044, FAX 41-1-3022022. Circ: 56,000.

ESTATISTICAS DO EMPREGO. see *BUSINESS AND ECONOMICS—Small Business*

330 340 CAN
➤ **THE ESTEY CENTRE JOURNAL OF INTERNATIONAL LAW AND TRADE POLICY.** Text in English. s-a. **Document type:** *Journal, Academic/Scholarly.*
Media: Online - full content.
Published by: The Estey Centre for Law and Economics in International Trade, Ste 820 410 22nd St E, Saskatoon, SK S7T 5T6, Canada. TEL 306-244-4800, FAX 306-244-7839, kerr.w@sk.sympatico.ca, http://128.233.58.173/estey/index.htm. Ed. William A Kerr.

330 COL ISSN 0121-4802
ESTRATEGIA ECONOMIA Y FINANCIERA. Text in Spanish. 1977. s-m. COP 95,100, USD 180; EUR 192 in Europe. adv. bk.rev.
Indexed: IBSS.
Published by: Servicios de Informacion S.A., Calle 18, 3-82 Piso 3, Apartado Aereo 53120, Bogota, CUND, Colombia. TEL 57-1-2437911, FAX 57-1-2837365, estrateg@uniandes.edu.co. Ed. Marta Lasprilla. Adv. contact Elsa Pineda. Circ: 10,000 (paid).

330 VEN ISSN 0798-9733
HC236
ESTUDIOS DE COYUNTURA. Text in Spanish. 1989. s-a. VEB 300, USD 20. bk.rev.
Published by: Universidad de Zulia, Facultad de Ciencias Economicas y Sociales, Apdo. 526, Maracaibo, 4001A, Venezuela. TEL 061-428504, FAX 061-416025. Ed. Hernan Pardo.

330 CHL ISSN 0304-2758
➤ **ESTUDIOS DE ECONOMIA.** Text in Spanish, English. 1973. s-a. adv. **Document type:** *Journal, Academic/Scholarly.*
Related titles: Online - full text ed.: free (effective 2006) (from EBSCO Publishing); English ed.
Indexed: IBSS, JEL, PAIS.
Published by: Universidad de Chile, Facultad de Ciencias Economicas y Administrativas, Ave. Ranacagua, 257, Santiago, Chile. FAX 562-634-7342, http://redalyc.uaemex.mx/redalyc/src/inicio/HomRevRed.jsp?iCveEntRev=221. Ed. Jorge Marshall. Circ: 400.

330 ARG ISSN 0425-368X
HB9
➤ **ESTUDIOS ECONOMICOS.** Text in Spanish. 1962. a. per issue exchange basis. bk.rev. bibl. back issues avail. **Document type:** *Journal, Academic/Scholarly.*
Indexed: ILD, JEL.
Published by: Universidad Nacional del Sur, Departamento de Economia, 12 de Octubre y San Juan, Bahia Blanca, Buenos Aires 8000, Argentina. TEL 54-291-4595138, FAX 54-291-4595139, reveseco@criba.edu.ar. Ed. Elena Ortiz de Guevara. R&P Ricardo Bara. Circ: 500.

330.1 BRA ISSN 0101-4161
HB9
➤ **ESTUDOS ECONOMICOS.** Text in Portuguese. 1970. q. BRL 36, USD 60 (effective 2001). adv. bk.rev. bibl.; charts; stat. index, cum.index. **Document type:** *Academic/Scholarly.* **Description:** Presents original papers in economic research.
Formerly (until 1971): Revista de Teoria e Pesquisa Economica (0101-4110)
Indexed: HAPI, IBR, JEL, PAIS.
Published by: Fundacao Instituto de Pesquisas Economicas, Departamento de Publicacoes, Pinheiros, Caixa Postal 11474, Sao Paulo, SP 05422-970, Brazil. TEL 55-11-38185867, FAX 55-11-38125471, restecon@edu.usp.br. Ed., R&P Helio Zylberstajn TEL 55-11-8185889. Adv. contact Eny Elza Ceotto. Circ: 1,000.

330 381 382 DEU ISSN 0721-7072
ETAGE; Chef-Informationen. Text in German. 1981. q. EUR 4 newsstand/cover (effective 2003). adv. bk.rev. index. back issues avail. **Document type:** *Magazine, Trade.*
Published by: Dr. Horst Kerlikowsky Verlag, Antonienstr 3, Munich, 80802, Germany. FAX 49-30-3240814. Ed., R&P Horst Kerlikowsky. Adv. contact Stephanie Porschen. B&W page EUR 1,649, color page EUR 2,799. Circ: 1,000.

330.9 FRA ISSN 0757-6714
ETAT DU MONDE; annuaire economique et geopolitique mondial. Text and summaries in French. 1981. a. price varies. back issues avail.
Related titles: CD-ROM ed.: Etat du Monde sur CD-ROM.
Indexed: RASB.
Published by: Editions La Decouverte, 9 bis rue Abel Hovelacque, Paris, 75013, France. TEL 33-1-44088400, FAX 33-1-44088419. Pub. Francois Geze. Circ: 45,000.

ETHICS & POLICY. see *SOCIOLOGY*

330 GBR
ETHICS, EXCELLENCE AND LEADERSHIP. OCCASIONAL PAPERS. Variant title: Ethics, Excellence and Leadership. Discussion Paper. Text in English. 2000. irreg. GBP 5 per issue domestic (effective 2001). **Document type:** *Academic/Scholarly.* **Description:** Addresses such issues as the qualities of command, comprehensions of corporate governance and the parameters of value-based corporate management in a global market.
—BLDSC (3814.657900).

B

Published by: St. Edmund's College, Von Hugel Institute (Subsidiary of: University of Cambridge), Cambridge, CB3 0BN, United Kingdom. TEL 44-1223-336090, FAX 44-1223-362590, vhi@st-edmunds.cam.ac.uk, http://www.st-edmunds.cam.ac.uk/vhi/research/occpaper.shtml, http://www.st-edmunds.cam.ac.uk/vhi/index.shtml.

ETHIKOS; examining ethical and compliance issues in business. see *PHILOSOPHY*

ETTELA'AT-E SIYASSI EQTESADI; mahnameh siyassi ve eqtesadi. see *POLITICAL SCIENCE*

327 330 TUR ISSN 1300-1612
DJK1
EURASIAN STUDIES. Text in English. q.
Indexed: IBSS, IndIslam, PAIS.
—BLDSC (3828.088820).
Published by: Turkish International Cooperation Agency, Akay Caddesi 6, Kucukesat, Ankara, 06640, Turkey.

330 MAC ISSN 0872-8496
➤ **EURO ASIA JOURNAL OF MANAGEMENT.** Text in English. 1991. s-a. MOP 61 domestic; USD 19.50 foreign; MOP 35 newsstand/cover (effective 2005). adv. back issues avail. **Document type:** *Journal, Academic/Scholarly.* **Description:** Provides a forum for discussion over a wide range of management issues defined in the broad sense. However, particular emphases are placed on the advancement of management theory and practice in Asia, especially, China, and the European continent.
Published by: Fundacao Macau/Macau Foundation, Av. da Amizade, 918, 16 andar, Edf. World Trade Center, Macau, Macau. TEL 853-966777, FAX 853-968658, fbacn@umac.mo or nelson.antonio@iscte.pt, fmac@macau.ctm.net, http://www.geocities.com/eajm2002/, http://www.fmac.org.mo. Eds. Bernadette Ozorio TEL 853-974757, Carlos Noronha, Leonel Miranda, Nelson Antonio, Virginia Trigo. R&P, Adv. contact Bernadette Ozorio TEL 853-974757. B&W page MOP 2,000; 16 x 23. Circ: 200.

330 DEU ISSN 0939-2734
EURO BRIEF. Text in German. m. looseleaf. EUR 75 (effective 2002). **Document type:** *Bulletin, Trade.*
Published by: Deutscher Wirtschaftsdienst (Subsidiary of: Wolters Kluwer Deutschland GmbH), Schoenhauser Str 64, Cologne, 50968, Germany. TEL 49-221-93763-0, FAX 49-221-9376399. Ed. Hermann Bohle.

EURO-CHALLENGE; international career guide for students and graduates. see *OCCUPATIONS AND CAREERS*

330 GBR
EURO EDI WEEK; electronic commerce in europe. Text in English. 1996. bi-w.
Published by: Euronewsletters Ltd., 81 Chiltley Way, Liphook, Hampshire GU30 7HE, United Kingdom. TEL 44-1428-722909, FAX 44-1428-725499, 100066.2140@compuserve.com. Ed. Freddie Dawkins.

330 677 DEU ISSN 0942-9638
EURODECOR. Text in German. 1971. 10/yr. **Document type:** *Trade.*
Former titles (until 1992): F T B-Handel (0175-6575); (until 1984): Das Farbenfachgeschaeft (0343-6047)
—CCC.
Published by: Meininger Verlag GmbH, Maximilianstr 7-17, Neustadt, 67433, Germany. TEL 49-6321-8908-0, FAX 49-6321-890873. Ed. Christoph Meininger. Circ: 9,610.

330 USA ISSN 1524-6515
EURONOMICS. Text in English. m. free. stat. back issues avail. **Document type:** *Newsletter.* **Description:** Covers economic, social and political developments in Europe and North and Latin America.
Media: Online - full text. **Related titles:** E-mail ed.
Published by: Morren Mondial Associates, Inc., HCL 69, Box 1258, Cutler, ME 04626. TEL 207-259-3444, FAX 207-259-3444, euronomics_news@europehouse.com, http://www.europehouse.com/euronomics. Ed., R&P Rick Morren. Circ: 80,000 (controlled). **Subscr. to:** Euronomics, Morren Mondial Associates Inc., Box 39606, Fl. 33339-9606, Ft. Lauderdale, FL 33339-9606. TEL 954-776-5697, FAX 954-772-7514.

336 339.5 FRA ISSN 1145-0339
EURONOVA. Text in French. 1989. m.
Published by: I N F E D, 3 rue Blaise Pascal, Veyre-Monton, 63960, France. TEL 73-69-65-94. Ed. Brigitta Sirotteau.

330 331.259 DEU ISSN 0949-8567
EUROPAEISCHER INFORMATIONSBRIEF BILDUNG UND BESCHAEFTIGUNG. Text in German. 1995. bi-m. EUR 86 domestic; EUR 96 foreign (effective 2005). **Document type:** *Newsletter, Trade.* **Description:** Contains current and background information on European policy in the field of education and employment.
Published by: Europa-Kontakt Informations- und Verlagsgesellschaft mbH, Breite Str 29, Berlin, 10178, Germany. TEL 49-30-203084070, FAX 49-30-203084077, eu.kontakt@t-online.de, http://www.europa-kontakt.de.

320.9 GBR ISSN 0966-8136
DK266.A2 CODEN: EASTER
➤ **EUROPE - ASIA STUDIES.** Text in English. 1949. 8/yr. GBP 623, USD 1,030 combined subscription to institutions print & online eds. (effective 2006). adv. bk.rev. illus. index. back issues avail.; reprint service avail. from PSC. **Document type:** *Journal, Academic/Scholarly.*
Formerly (until 1993): Soviet Studies (0038-5859)
Related titles: Microfiche ed.; Online - full text ed.: ISSN 1465-3427. GBP 592, USD 979 to institutions (effective 2006) (from EBSCO Publishing, Florida Center for Library Automation, Gale Group, IngentaConnect, JSTOR (Web-based Journal Archive), O C L C Online Computer Library Center, Inc., ProQuest Information & Learning, Swets Information Services).
Indexed: ABCPolSci, ABIn, ABS&EES, AMB, ASCA, AmH&L, ArtHuCI, BAS, BRI, BrHumI, CJA, CurCont, DIP, EIA, EnerInd, FamI, GEOBASE, HistAb, HumInd, IBR, IBSS, IBZ, IPSA, JEL, KES, LID&ISL, LRI, MASUSE, MEA&I, PAIS, PCI, PSA, PerIslam, RHEA, RRTA, SOPODA, SSA, SSCI, SSI, SociolAb, WAE&RSA, WBA, WMB.
—BLDSC (3829.461740), IDS, IE, Infotrieve, ingenta. **CCC.**
Published by: Routledge (Subsidiary of: Taylor & Francis Group), 4 Park Sq, Milton Park, Abingdon, Oxon OX14 4RN, United Kingdom. TEL 44-1235-828600, FAX 44-1235-829000, info@routledge.co.uk, http://www.tandf.co.uk/journals/titles/09668136.asp, http://www.routledge.co.uk. Ed. Roger Clarke. **Subscr. in N. America to:** Taylor & Francis Inc., Customer Services Dept, 325 Chestnut St, 8th Fl, Philadelphia, PA 19106. TEL 215-625-8900, 800-354-1420, FAX 215-625-8914, customerservice@taylorandfrancis.com; **Subscr. to:** Taylor & Francis Ltd, Journals Customer Service, Rankine Rd, Basingstoke, Hants RG24 8PR, United Kingdom. TEL 44-1256-813000, FAX 44-1256-330245.

➤ **EUROPE FOR BUSINESS TRAVELERS.** see *TRAVEL AND TOURISM*

330 DEU ISSN 1431-3006
EUROPEAN AND TRANSATLANTIC STUDIES. Text in English. 1995. irreg., latest 2004. price varies. **Document type:** *Monographic series, Academic/Scholarly.* **Description:** Presents contributions to theoretical analysis and economic policy topics in Europe and North America.
Published by: Springer-Verlag (Subsidiary of: Springer Science+Business Media), Haber Str 7, Heidelberg, 69126, Germany. TEL 49-6221-3450, FAX 49-6221-229, orders@springer.de, http://www.springer.de.

330 GBR ISSN 1469-6460
HD70.E7
EUROPEAN BUSINESS FORUM. Abbreviated title: E B F. Text in English. q. EUR 200 in Europe to institutions; USD 200 elsewhere to institutions (effective 2005). adv. **Document type:** *Magazine, Trade.* **Description:** Promotes debate and discussion between top players in the academic, business and consultancy worlds and to bring a European focus to global management issues.
Related titles: Online - full text ed.: (from EBSCO Publishing, Gale Group, O C L C Online Computer Library Center, Inc., ProQuest Information & Learning).
Indexed: ABIn.
—CCC.
Published by: Kogan Page Ltd., 120 Pentonville Rd, London, N1 9JN, United Kingdom. TEL 44-20-7278-0433, FAX 44-20-7837-6348, sophie@ebfonline.com, http://www.ebfonline.com, http://www.kogan-page.co.uk/. Adv. contact Toby McAra TEL 44-20-7833-8761.

330 GBR
EUROPEAN BUSINESS INFORMATION CONFERENCE (YEAR) PROCEEDINGS. Text in English. a. GBP 85. **Document type:** *Proceedings.*
—BLDSC (3829.551400).
Published by: T F P L Publishing, 17-18 Britton St, London, EC1M 5NQ, United Kingdom. TEL 44-171-251-5522, FAX 44-171-251-8318, central@tfpl.com, http://www.tfpl.com.

330 GBR ISSN 0955-534X
➤ **EUROPEAN BUSINESS REVIEW.** Text in English. bi-m. EUR 8,481.41 in Europe; USD 8,569 in North America; AUD 11,969 in Australasia; GBP 5,795.29 in UK & elsewhere (effective 2006). reprint service avail. from PSC. **Document type:** *Journal, Academic/Scholarly.* **Description:** Interdisciplinary focus on management and business issues in Europe.
Incorporates (1988-1996): New European (0953-1432)
Related titles: Online - full text ed.: (from EBSCO Publishing, Emerald Group Publishing Limited, Gale Group, IngentaConnect, O C L C Online Computer Library Center, Inc., ProQuest Information & Learning, Swets Information Services).
Indexed: ABIn, BrHumI, CPM, DIP, EmerIntel, Emerald, IBR, IBSS, IBZ, PerIslam, RASB, SCIMP, WMB.
—BLDSC (3829.557200), IE, Infotrieve, ingenta. **CCC.**
Published by: Emerald Group Publishing Limited, 60-62 Toller Ln, Bradford, W Yorks BD8 9BY, United Kingdom. TEL 44-1274-777700, FAX 44-1274-785200, infomation@emeraldinsight.com, http://www.emeraldinsight.com/ebr.htm. Eds. John Coleman, Dr. Richard Welford. **Subscr. addr. in N America:** Emerald Group Publishing Ltd., 44 Brattle St, 4th Fl, Cambridge, MA 02138. TEL 617-497-2175, 888-622-0075, FAX 617-354-6875.

338 LUX ISSN 0256-5846
HC241.2 CODEN: BSCCEN
EUROPEAN COMMUNITIES. ECONOMIC AND SOCIAL COMMITTEE. BULLETIN. Text in Danish, Dutch, English, French, German, Greek, Italian, Portuguese, Spanish. 1961. 3/yr. free in Luxembourg. bibl.
Indexed: ECI.
Published by: European Commission, Office for Official Publications of the European Union, 2 Rue Mercier, Luxembourg, L-2985, Luxembourg. TEL 352-29291, info-info-opoce@cec.eu.int, http://europa.eu.int. Circ: 5,000. **Dist. in the U.S. by:** Bernan Associates, Bernan, 4611-F Assembly Dr., Lanham, MD 20706-4391.

330 LUX
EUROPEAN COMMUNITIES. ECONOMIC AND SOCIAL COMMITTEE. COMMISSION DOCUMENTS. Text in English. irreg. USD 620.
Formerly: European Communities. Economic and Social Committee. Opinions and Reports (0255-0717)
Related titles: Microfiche ed.
Indexed: RASB.
—BLDSC (6272.030000).
Published by: European Commission, Office for Official Publications of the European Union, 2 Rue Mercier, Luxembourg, L-2985, Luxembourg. TEL 352-29291, info-info-opoce@cec.eu.int, http://europa.eu.int. **Dist. in the U.S. by:** Bernan Associates.

327 LUX ISSN 1011-5269
EUROPEAN COMMUNITIES. ECONOMIC AND SOCIAL CONSULTATIVE ASSEMBLY. ANNUAL REPORT. Text in Danish, Dutch, English, French, German, Greek, Italian, Portuguese, Spanish. a. USD 35. **Description:** Covers the Economic and Social Committee's work.
Formerly (until 1986): European Communities. Economic and Social Committee. Annual Report (Year) (0376-5458)
Published by: European Commission, Office for Official Publications of the European Union, 2 Rue Mercier, Luxembourg, L-2985, Luxembourg. TEL 352-29291, info-info-opoce@cec.eu.int, http://europa.eu.int. **Dist. in U.S. by:** Bernan Associates, Bernan, 4611-F Assembly Dr., Lanham, MD 20706-4391.

330 LUX ISSN 1682-0800
EUROPEAN COMPETITIVENESS REPORT. Text in English. 2001. a.
Related titles: Online - full content ed.
Published by: (European Commission, Directorate General Enterprise and Industry BEL), European Commission, Office for Official Publications of the European Union, 2 Rue Mercier, Luxembourg, L-2985, Luxembourg. entr-competit-benchmarkg@cec.eu.int, info-info-opoce@cec.eu.int, http://www.eurunion.org/publicat/index.htm.

330 NLD ISSN 0014-2921
CODEN: EERVAI
➤ **EUROPEAN ECONOMIC REVIEW.** Text in Dutch. 1969. 8/yr. EUR 52 in Europe to individuals; JPY 7,200 in Japan to individuals; USD 54 elsewhere to individuals; EUR 1,438 in Europe to institutions; JPY 190,900 in Japan to institutions; USD 1,438 elsewhere to institutions (effective 2006). adv. illus. index, cum.index: vols.1-10. back issues avail.; reprints avail. **Document type:** *Journal, Academic/Scholarly.* **Description:** Publishes theoretical and empirical papers on topics in economics.
Related titles: Microfilm ed.: (from PQC); Online - full text ed.: (from EBSCO Publishing, Gale Group, IngentaConnect, O C L C Online Computer Library Center, Inc., ScienceDirect, Swets Information Services).
Indexed: ABIn, ASCA, AgeL, ArtHuCI, BAS, BPIA, BusI, CJA, CPM, CREJ, CurCont, ELLIS, ESPM, Emerald, GEOBASE, IBSS, JEL, KES, MEA&I, ManagCont, PAIS, PCI, RRTA, RiskAb, SSCI, SSI, T&II, WAE&RSA, WBA, WMB.
—BLDSC (3829.697000), CISTI, IDS, IE, Infotrieve, ingenta. **CCC.**
Published by: (European Economic Association GBR), Elsevier BV, North-Holland (Subsidiary of: Elsevier Science & Technology), Sara Burgerhartstraat 25, Amsterdam, 1055 KV, Netherlands. TEL 31-20-485-3911, FAX 31-20-485-2457, nlinfo-f@elsevier.nl, http://www.elsevier.com/locate/eer, http://www.elsevier.nl. Eds. G A Pfann, Z. Eckstein. Pub. J Dirkmaat. **Subscr. to:** Elsevier BV, PO Box 211, Amsterdam 1000 AE, Netherlands. TEL 31-20-485-3757, FAX 31-20-485-3432, http://www.elsevier.nl.

330 GBR
EUROPEAN ENTREPRENEUR. Text in English. q.
Address: Knightsbridge House, Headley, Newbury, Berks RG15 8JY, United Kingdom. TEL 0635-269055. Ed. Peter van der Sluijs.

330 628.5 BEL
▼ **EUROPEAN INDUSTRIAL RESEARCH.** Text in English. 2003 (Jul.). q. **Document type:** *Magazine, Government.* **Description:** Provides a round up of news and views on innovative EU research.
Related titles: Online - full content ed.

Published by: European Commission, Directorate General - Joint Research Center, Public Relations Unit, SDME 10/78, Brussels, B-1049, Belgium. rtd-nmp@cec.eu.int, http://europa.eu.int/comm/research/industrial_technologies/magazine_en.html.

338.09 FRA ISSN 0258-6894
EUROPEAN INDUSTRIAL RESEARCH MANAGEMENT ASSOCIATION. CONFERENCE PAPERS. Text in Multiple languages. 1967. irreg.
—BLDSC (3666.756000), CISTI.
Published by: European Industrial Research Management Association, 34 Rue de Bassano, Paris, 75008, France. TEL 33-1-53238310, FAX 33-1-47200530, http://www.eirma.asso.fr/.

330 ITA ISSN 1824-2979
▼ ➤ **THE EUROPEAN JOURNAL OF COMPARATIVE ECONOMICS.** Text in English. 2004. irreg. free (effective 2005). **Document type:** *Journal, Academic/Scholarly.* **Description:** Publishes scientific articles on theoretical and empirical research in any field of comparative economic studies.
Media: Online - full text.
Published by: Universita Carlo Cattaneo, Corso Matteotti 222, Castellanza, VA 21053, Italy. http://eaces.liuc.it.

330 AUT ISSN 1450-2275
▼ ➤ **THE EUROPEAN JOURNAL OF ECONOMICS, FINANCE AND ADMINISTRATIVE SCIENCES.** Text in English. 2004. q. **Document type:** *Journal, Academic/Scholarly.* **Description:** It encompasses theoretical, empirical or policy oriented research articles, original research reports, reviews, short communication and scientific commentaries in the fields of economics and administrative sciences including both controversial and innovative ideas and detailed contributions from other directly related fields such as econometrics, economic development, trade and the environment, and political economy.
Media: Online - full text.
Published by: EuroJournals, Inc., PO Box 1123, Vienna, Austria. TEL 43-921-23113333, FAX 43-921-23113334, http://www.eurojournals.com. Ed. Giovanni Collini.

340 330 USA ISSN 0929-1261
K5 CODEN: EJLEEA
➤ **EUROPEAN JOURNAL OF LAW AND ECONOMICS.** Text in English. 1993. bi-m. EUR 648, USD 648, GBP 398 combined subscription to institutions print & online eds. (effective 2005). bk.rev. back issues avail.; reprint service avail. from WSH,PSC. **Document type:** *Journal, Academic/Scholarly.* **Description:** Publishes analytical studies of the impact of legal interventions into economic processes by legislators, courts and regulatory agencies, with an emphasis on the EC and EC law.
Related titles: Online - full text ed.: ISSN 1572-9990 (from EBSCO Publishing, Gale Group, IngentaConnect, Kluwer Online, O C L C Online Computer Library Center, Inc., ProQuest Information & Learning, Springer LINK, Swets Information Services).
Indexed: ABIn, BibLing, IBSS, JEL, PSA, RefZh, SOPODA.
—BLDSC (3829.730960), IE, Infotrieve, ingenta. **CCC.**
Published by: Springer-Verlag New York, Inc. (Subsidiary of: Springer Science+Business Media), 233 Spring St, New York, NY 10013. TEL 212-460-1500, FAX 212-460-1575, service@springer-ny.com, http://springerlink.metapress.com/openurl.asp?genre=journal&issn=0929-1261, http://www.springer-ny.com. Eds. Frank H Stephen, Jurgen G Backhaus. **Subscr. to:** Journal Fulfillment, PO Box 2485, Secaucus, NJ 07096-2485. TEL 201-348-4033, FAX 201-348-4505, journals@springer-ny.com.

338.83 GBR
THE EUROPEAN MERGERS & ACQUISITIONS HANDBOOK (YEARS). Text in English. a.
Published by: Euromoney Publications plc, Nestor House, Playhouse Yard, London, EC4V 5EX, United Kingdom. TEL 44-207-7798673, FAX 44-20-77798541.

330 382 GBR ISSN 1462-320X
EUROPEAN MONETARY UNION; the journal for business. Abbreviated title: E M U. Text in English. 1998. 8/yr. GBP 395; GBP 415 foreign. bk.rev. index. back issues avail. **Document type:** *Trade.* **Description:** Provides advice on technical and strategic preparations for businesses who deal with the new European single currency.
Related titles: Online - full text ed.: ISSN 1465-1386.
Published by: Eclipse Group Ltd. (Subsidiary of: LexisNexis UK (Scottish Office)), 18-20 Highbury Place, London, N5 1QP, United Kingdom. TEL 44-20-7354-5858, FAX 44-20-7226-8106, publications@irseclipse.co.uk, http://www.irseclipse.co.uk. Ed. Lynn Strongin Dodds. Pub. Andrew Brode.

330 GBR
EUROPEAN PANEL ANALYSIS GROUP. WORKING PAPER. Text in English. irreg. **Document type:** *Academic/Scholarly.*
Published by: European Panel Analysis Group (Subsidiary of: Institute for Social and Economic Research), c/o Marcia Freed Taylor, University of Essex, Wivenhoe Park, Colchester, Colchester CO4 3SQ, United Kingdom. TEL 44-1206-872387, marcia@essex.ac.uk, http://www.iser.essex.ac.uk/epag/.

EUROPEAN PHARMACEUTICAL REVIEW; the quarterly review of pharmaceutical business and technology. see *PHARMACY AND PHARMACOLOGY*

330 LUX
EUROPEAN UNION. FINANCIAL REPORT. Text in English. 1988. a.
Formerly (until 1995): European Communities. Financial Report (1016-023X)
—BLDSC (3926.966650).
Published by: European Commission, Office for Official Publications of the European Union, 2 Rue Mercier, Luxembourg, L-2985, Luxembourg. http://europa.eu.int.

EUROPEAN VOICE; a weekly view of the union. see *GENERAL INTEREST PERIODICALS—Europe*

330 BEL ISSN 0778-4899
L'EVENEMENT IMMOBILIER. Text in French. 1982. m. adv. bk.rev. illus. **Document type:** *Trade.*
Formerly (until 1991): Magazine de l'Evenement Immobilier (0773-6789)
Published by: Editions Dupuis S.A., Rue Jules Destree 52, Marcinelle, 6001, Belgium. TEL 32-71-600500, FAX 32-71-600599, TELEX 64-168 DUPUIS B. Ed. Violaine Muuls. Pub. Jean Pierre Dupuis. Circ: 30,000 (controlled).

EVENT MANAGEMENT; an international journal. see *TRAVEL AND TOURISM*

330 CHL
EVOLUCION DE LA ECONOMIA EN (YEAR) Y PERSPECTIVAS PARA (YEAR). Text in Spanish. 1990. a. CLP 1,500, USD 15 newsstand/cover.
Published by: (Consejo al Ministro de Hacienda y al Senado), Banco Central de Chile, Casilla 967, Santiago, Chile. TEL 56-2-670-2000, FAX 56-2-698-4847. Circ: 1,500.

330 ITA ISSN 1592-6656
EVOLUZIONE DEI SETTORI INDUSTRIALI. Text in Italian. 1995. q.
Published by: Centro Studi Confindustria, Viale Pasteur 6, Rome, 00144, Italy. TEL 06-5920509, FAX 06-5924819, http://www.confindustria.it.

330 BRA ISSN 0102-2881
HF5001
EXAME. Text in Portuguese. 1971. fortn. BRL 231.40 domestic; USD 172.66 foreign (effective 2005). adv. charts; illus.; stat. back issues avail. **Document type:** *Magazine, Consumer.* **Description:** For professionals in administration, marketing, finance, human resources and industry.
Formerly: Negocios em Exame
Related titles: Online - full text ed.; ♦ Supplement(s): Melhores e Maiores. ISSN 0104-3234; ♦ Info Exame. ISSN 1415-3270; ♦ Vip Exame. ISSN 0104-737X.
Indexed: B&I.
Published by: Editora Abril, S.A., Av. das Nacoes Unidas, 7221, 11 andar Pinheiros, Sao Paulo, SP 05425-902, Brazil. TEL 55-11-50872112, FAX 55-11-50872100, servicos.exame@abril.com.br, http://www.portalexame.abril.com.br/, http://www.abril.com.br/. Ed. Paulo Nogueira. adv.: page BRL 85,600. Circ: 196,160. **Subscr. to:** Rua do Curtume, Rua do Curtume, 769, Sao Paulo, SP 0506-900, Brazil. TEL 011-823-9100.

330 FRA ISSN 1141-8141
EXCELLENCE. Text in French. 4/yr.
Indexed: CINAHL.
Published by: Societe d'Edition du Personnel Territorial, BP 215, Voiron, Cedex 38506, France. TEL 76-65-71-36, FAX 76-66-12-85. Ed. Maryse Deschambures. Circ: 20,000.

330 TWN ISSN 1011-2227
EXCELLENCE BUSINESS MONTHLY. Text in Chinese. 1984. m. TWD 1,980. adv. bk.rev. **Description:** Serves as a trends analyst of the business community. Covers companies and industries, investment and money market, government policies, economic forecast and economic viewpoints.
Published by: Excellence Publications Co., 5-F No 531-1 Chung Cheng Rd, Hsin-Tien City, Taipei, 231, Taiwan. TEL 886-2-218-6988, FAX 886-2-218-6494. Ed. Angony Han. Pub. Chris J F Lin. Adv. contact Saria Chou. B&W page USD 2,900, color page USD 4,500; trim 280 x 210. Circ: 66,000.

330 ZAF ISSN 1023-0572
EXECUBRIEF (ENGLISH EDITION); solutions for business. Text in English. 1994. q. looseleaf.
Related titles: Afrikaans ed.: ISSN 1019-2387.
Published by: Coopers & Lybrand, PO Box 2536, Johannesburg, 2000, South Africa.

330 PHL
EXECUTIVE BRIEF: PHILIPPINE BUSINESS. Text in English. 6/yr. USD 60.
Published by: Leverage International (Consultants) Inc., PS Bank Bldg 5F, Ayala Ave., C.P.O. Box 2296, Makati Mm, Philippines. FAX 632-8101594.

330 USA ISSN 1051-2829
THE EXECUTIVE MEMO. Text in English. bi-w. USD 100 (effective 2001). back issues avail. **Document type:** *Trade.* **Description:** Covers regulatory and compliance information, educational opportunities, pending and enacted legislation, legal decisions, upcoming IMA events and conferences and more.
Related titles: E-mail ed.; Online - full content ed.
Published by: The Illinois Manufacturers Association, 1301 W 22nd St., Ste. 610, Oak Brook, IL 60523. TEL 630-368-5300, 800-875-4462, FAX 630-218-7467, ima@ima-net.org, http://www.ima-net.org/. Ed., Pub. Laurie Kaczmar TEL 630-368-5300 ext. 3122.

330 USA
EXECUTIVE PLANNING SUMMARY. Text in English. 1983. a. free. **Document type:** *Government.* **Description:** Overview of Missouri economy, demographics, and economic development opportunities.
Published by: Missouri Department of Economic Development, PO Box 118, Jefferson City, MO 65102. TEL 314-751-4241, FAX 314-751-7385, http://www.state.mo.us. Ed. Daniel Onunkwor. Circ: 500.

B

330 USA ISSN 0888-4110
EXECUTIVE SPEECHES. Text in English. 1986. bi-m. USD 60 domestic; USD 70 in Canada; USD 80 in Europe; USD 80 in South America; USD 94 in Asia (effective 2000). illus. Index. reprints avail. **Document type:** *Journal, Trade.* **Description:** Features the full text of 10-12 speeches by executives.
Related titles: CD-ROM ed.; Microform ed.: (from PQC); Online - full text ed.: (from bigchalk, EBSCO Publishing, Florida Center for Library Automation, Gale Group, Northern Light Technology, Inc., O C L C Online Computer Library Center, Inc., ProQuest Information & Learning).
Indexed: ABIn, PSI.
—BLDSC (3836.223850), IE, ingenta.
Published by: Executive Speaker Co., PO Box 292437, Dayton, OH 45429. TEL 937-294-8493, FAX 937-294-6044, mail@executive-speaker.com, http://www.executive-speaker.com. Ed. Robert Skovard. Pub. Robert Skovgard.

650 USA
EXECUTIVE SUITE✶. Text in English. 1991. m. USD 24. **Document type:** *Trade.* **Description:** Targets African-American business owners in the Washington, DC-Baltimore corridor.
Published by: Eric Communications, 12138 Central Ave., Ste. 301, Mitchellville, MD 20721-1932. TEL 301-277-7080, FAX 301-439-7885. Ed. James Eric. adv.: B&W page USD 600, color page USD 750. Circ: 10,000.

330 USA
EXECUTIVE SUMMARY: SOUTHEAST. Text in English. 2001 (Oct.). q. **Document type:** *Magazine, Trade.* **Description:** Showcases the technology industry based in Alabama, Florida, Georgia, Mississippi, North Carolina, South Carolina and Tennessee.
Published by: Thomas Andrew Company Publishing, 4242 Chickamauga Rd, Birmingham, AL 35213. TEL 205-868-9037, FAX 205-870-5336, tfindlay@executivesummarymag.com, http://www.executivesummarymag.com. Pub. Tom Findlay.

▼ **EXECUTIVE TRAVELER**; the elite corporate retreat and client entertainment magazine. see *TRAVEL AND TOURISM*

330 USA ISSN 1056-3008
EXECUTIVE WOMEN INTERNATIONAL. PULSE. Text in English. q. USD 8 to members (effective 2000). adv. **Document type:** *Directory, Corporate.* **Description:** Publication for member firms and their key representatives.
Formerly: Executive Women International. Times
Published by: Executive Women International, 515 S 700 E, Ste 2 A, Salt Lake City, UT 84102-2801. TEL 801-355-2800, FAX 801-355-2852, ewi@executivewomen.org, http://www.executivewomen.org. Ed. Kris Wilkerson. R&P Rose Defa. Adv. contact Tamara Spence-Burgess. Circ: 4,500 (controlled).

330 USA ISSN 0890-426X
EXIMBANK LETTER; trends in trade, project, and investment finance. Text in English. 1986. s-m. USD 288. q. index. **Document type:** *Newsletter.*
Published by: International Business Affairs Corporation, 4938 Hampden Ln, Bethesda, MD 20814-2914. TEL 301-907-8647. Ed. Richard Barovick.

330 ESP
EXPANSION. Text in Spanish. 1986. d. 43 p./no. 6 cols./p.; back issues avail. **Document type:** *Newspaper.* **Description:** Covers business and economics news.
Related titles: CD-ROM ed.: (from Chadwyck-Healey Inc.); Microfilm ed.: (from PQC); Online - full content ed.: Expansion y Empleo; Online - full text ed.; Supplement(s): Expansion & Empleo.
Indexed: B&I.
Published by: Recoletos Compania Editorial S.A (Subsidiary of: Pearson Publishing Group), Paseo Recoletos, 1 5o, Madrid, 28001, Spain. TEL 34-91-3373220, FAX 34-91-3373266, expansion@recoletos.es, http://www.expansion.com/, http://www.recoletos.es. Ed. Jesus Martinez Vazquez. Adv. contact Angel Guardiola Moreno.

330 USA
EXPANSION EN CD-ROM. Text in English. 1996. a. **Description:** Provides the complete text of the Spanish business newspaper Expansion.
Media: CD-ROM (from Chadwyck-Healey Inc.).
Published by: ProQuest Information & Learning, 300 N Zeeb Rd., PO Box 1346, Ann Arbor, MI 48106-1346. FAX 703-683-7589, info@il.proquest.com, http://www.chadwyck.com.

330 FRA ISSN 1254-3179
L'EXPANSION MANAGEMENT REVIEW; revue des responsables. Text in French. 1976. q. EUR 84.15 in the European Union; EUR 94.15 elsewhere (effective 2005).
Formerly (until 1994): Harvard l'Expansion (0397-5495)
Indexed: PdeR, SCIMP.
Published by: Groupe Express-Expansion (Subsidiary of: Socpresse), 17 rue de l'Arrivee, Paris Cede, 75733, France. TEL 33-1-53911111, http://www.lexpansion.com, http://www.groupe-expansion.com. Circ: 8,000.

EXPERTBIZ INSIGHTS. see *COMPUTERS—Internet*

330 AUS
EXPORT FINANCE AND INSURANCE CORPORATION. ANNUAL REPORT. Text in English. a. **Document type:** *Trade.*
Media: Online - full content. **Related titles:** Ed.
Published by: Export Finance and Insurance Corporation, 22 Pitts St, Sydney, NSW 2000, Australia. TEL 800-685-109, FAX 61-2-9201-5222, info@efic.gov.au, http://www.efic.gov.au/home/newspub.asp.

382.60971 CAN ISSN 1486-620X
EXPORT WISE. Text in English. 1983. q.
Formerly (until 1998): E D C Today (0839-9549)
Related titles: Online - full content ed.: ISSN 1495-6756; Online - full text ed.: (from EBSCO Publishing); ◆ French ed.: Exportateurs Avertis. ISSN 1486-6218.
Published by: Export Development Canada/Exportation et Developpement, 151 O'Connor, Ottawa, ON K1A 1K3, Canada. TEL 613-598-2500, FAX 613-237-2690, http://www.edc.ca/corpinfo/pubs/exportwise/index_e.htm.

382.6097105 CAN ISSN 1486-6218
EXPORTATEURS AVERTIS. Text in French. 1999. q.
Related titles: Print ed.: Exportateurs Avertis (En Ligne). ISSN 1495-6772; ◆ English ed.: Export Wise. ISSN 1486-620X.
Published by: Export Development Canada/Exportation et Developpement, 151 O'Connor, Ottawa, ON K1A 1K3, Canada. TEL 613-598-2500, FAX 613-237-2690, http://www.edc.ca/corpinfo/pubs/exportwise/index_f.htm.

EXPRESS; magazine for account holders of D H L International. see *COMMUNICATIONS*

EXPRESSION D'ENTREPRISE; le magazine de la communication. see *COMMUNICATIONS*

330 PRT ISSN 0870-1970
EXPRESSO. Text in Portuguese. 1973. w. EUR 60 (effective 2005). adv. back issues avail. **Document type:** *Newspaper, Consumer.*
Related titles: Microfiche ed.; Online - full text ed.
Published by: Sociedade Jornalistica e Editorial, S.A., Rua Ribeiro Sanches, 65, Lisbon, 1200-787, Portugal. TEL 351-21-4544021, FAX 351-21-4435310, http://semanal.expresso.clix.pt/capa/default.asp, http://expresso.clix.pt/. Ed. Jose Antonio Saravia. Circ: 113,500.

330 USA
▼ **EXTENDED RETAIL INDUSTRY.** Variant title: E R I. Text in English. 2005. bi-m. (m. in 2006). free to qualified personnel (effective 2005). **Document type:** *Magazine, Trade.* **Description:** Provides in-depth analysis of the effective integration of people, process and technology throughout the retail value chain.
Published by: Retail Systems Alert Group, 332, Newton U F, MA 02464-0002. info@retailsystems.com, http://www.retailsystems.com/Index.cfm?PageName=publicationseri.

330 ARG ISSN 0328-4050
H8.S7
F A C E S. (Facultad de Ciencias Economicas y Sociales) Text in Spanish. 1995. s-a. MXP 5 per issue (effective 2002).
Indexed: PSA, SociolAb.
Published by: Universidad Nacional de Mar del Plata, Facultad de Ciencias Economicas y Sociales, CC 462, Mar del Plata, 7600, Argentina. TEL 54-223-474-9696, cendocu@mdp.edu.ar, http://eco.mdp.edu.ar/faces/default.htm.

330 USA ISSN 0259-2460
F A O ECONOMIC AND SOCIAL DEVELOPMENT PAPER. (Food and Agriculture Organization) Text in English. 1978. irreg., latest vol.143. price varies. **Document type:** *Monographic series.*
Related titles: French ed.: Etudes F A O: Developpement Economique et Social. ISSN 0259-2215.
Indexed: DSA, FS&TA, NutrAb, PN&I, RDA, RiceAb, S&F, SFA, SIA, TDB, WAE&RSA.
—BLDSC (3865.627500), IE.
Published by: Food and Agriculture Organization of the United Nations, c/o Bernan Associates, 4611 F Assembly Dr, Lanham, MD 20706-4391. TEL 301-459-7666, FAX 301-459-0056.

330 USA
F & S REPORTS✶. Text in English. irreg.
Published by: Frost & Sullivan, 7550 IH 10 W., Ste 400, San Antonio, TX 78229-5811. TEL 212-233-1080. Ed. Henry M Berler.

330 USA
F D M MAGAZINE. Text in English. 1959. m. USD 60 domestic; USD 90 in Canada; USD 130 elsewhere (effective 2005). adv. **Document type:** *Magazine.*
Published by: Chartwell Communications, 1350 E. Touhy Ave., Ste. 105W, Des Plaines, IL 60018-3319. bplantz@fdmonline.com, http://www.fdmmag.com. adv.: B&W page USD 4,650, color page USD 5,175. Circ: 45,000 (controlled).

330 DEU ISSN 0071-769X
F I W - SCHRIFTENREIHE. (Forschungsinstitut fuer Wirtschaftsverfassung und Wettbewerb e.V.) Text in German. 1962. irreg., latest vol.182, 2001. price varies. adv. bk.rev. **Document type:** *Monographic series, Academic/Scholarly.*
Indexed: ELLIS.
Published by: (Forschunginstitut fuer Wirtschaftsverfassung und Wettbewerb e.V.), Carl Heymanns Verlag KG, Luxemburger Str 449, Cologne, 50939, Germany. TEL 49-221-943730, FAX 49-221-94373901, marketing@heymanns.com, http://www.heymanns.com.

F.O. LICHT'S WORLD DISTILLERIES GUIDE (YEARS). see *BEVERAGES*

330 CAN ISSN 1486-4916
F P SURVEY, PREDECESSOR, AND DEFUNCT. (Financial Post) Text in English. 1981. biennial. CND 98.95. adv. **Description:** Aids in tracing mergers, amalgamations, name changes or charter cancellations of Canadian businesses.
Former titles (until 2001): Survey of Predecessor and Defunct Companies (0832-0772); (until 1985): Financial Post Survey of Predecessor and Defunct Companies (0712-3256)
Published by: Financial Post Datagroup, 300-1450 Don Mills Rd, Don Mills, ON M3B 3R5, Canada. TEL 416-350-6507, FAX 416-350-6501, fpdg@fpdata.finpost.com. Ed. John Byrne. Circ: 6,000.

FABIAN NEWSLETTER. see *POLITICAL SCIENCE*

330 GBR
FABIAN SOCIETY. DISCUSSION PAPER. Text in English. irreg. **Document type:** *Academic/Scholarly.*
—BLDSC (3597.202300), ingenta.
Published by: Fabian Society, 11 Dartmouth St, London, SW1H 9BN, United Kingdom. TEL 44-171-222-8877, FAX 44-171-976-7153, fabian-society@geo2.poptel.org.uk, http://www.fabian-society.org.uk.

330 SCG ISSN 0354-4699
FACTA UNIVERSITATIS. SERIES ECONOMICS AND ORGANIZATION. Text in English, French, German. a., latest vol.1, no.8, 2000. **Document type:** *Journal, Academic/Scholarly.*
Indexed: RefZh.
—Linda Hall.
Published by: Univerzitet u Nishu/University of Nis, Univerzitetski Trg 2, P.O. Box 123, Nis, 18000. TEL 381-18-547970, FAX 381-18-547950, facta@ni.ac.yu, http://facta.junis.ni.ac.yu/facta/eao/eao.html, http://ni.ac.yu. Ed. Ljiljana Stankovic.

330.07 NLD ISSN 0926-2172
FACTOR D; kwartaalblad voor het economie-onderwijs en zijn didactiek. Text in Dutch. 1983. q. EUR 12 (effective 2003). **Document type:** *Academic/Scholarly.* **Description:** Covers issues relating to economics instruction and teacher education.
Formerly (until 1990): Appels en Peren (0167-8221)
Published by: Stichting Landelijke Werkgroep Economie Onderwijs (LWEO), Postbus 7442, Amsterdam, 1007 JK, Netherlands. TEL 31-20-6700270, FAX 31-20-670-0271, postbus@lweo.nl, http://www.lweo.nl.

FACTS ON FILE. YEARBOOK. see *HISTORY—History Of North And South America*

330 CZE ISSN 1212-5598
FACULTY OF AGRICULTURE IN CESKE BUDEJOVICE. COLLECTION OF SCIENTIFIC PAPERS. SERIES FOR ECONOMICS, MANAGEMENT AND TRADE. Text in Czech; Abstracts in English. 1986. s-a. **Document type:** *Journal, Academic/Scholarly.*
Former titles (until 1998): Jihoceske Univerzity v Ceskych Budejovicich. Zemedelska Fakulta. Sbornik (1211-796X); (until 1992): Vysoke Skoly Zemedelske v Praze. Agronomicka Fakulta v Ceskych Budejovicich.. Sbornik (0862-3392)
Indexed: DSA, HortAb, IndVet, PHN&I, RDA, RRTA, S&F, VetBull, WAE&RSA.
—CISTI.
Published by: Jihoceska Univerzita v Ceskych Budejovicich , Zemedelska Fakulta/University of South Bohemia in Ceske Budejovice, Faculty of Agriculture, Studentska 13, Ceske Budejovice, 370 05, Czech Republic. wolkova@zf.jcu.cz, http://www.zf.jcu.cz. Ed. Petr Hartvich.

338.88 GBR ISSN 1465-2838
FACULTY OF BUSINESS & MANAGEMENT. WORKING PAPER. Text in English. irreg. **Document type:** *Academic/Scholarly.* **Description:** Covers areas associated with teaching and research within the Faculty, including international business and management.
—BLDSC (9350.151000).
Published by: University of Lincoln, Business School, Brayford Pool, Lincoln, LN6 7TS, United Kingdom. TEL 44-1522-882000, enquiries@lincoln.ac.uk, http://www.lincoln.ac.uk.

330 GBR
FACULTY OF BUSINESS. EUROPEAN STUDIES WORKING PAPERS. Text in English. irreg.
—BLDSC (3864.675960).
Published by: University of Paisley, Faculty of Business, Department of Accounting, Economics & Languages, High St, Paisley, PA1 2BE, United Kingdom. TEL 44-141-848-3000, FAX 44-141-848-3618. Eds. J Struthers, Dr. James Sheffield, M Myant.

338 FIN ISSN 1237-2196
FAILI. Text in Finnish; Summaries in English. 1963. 4/yr. adv. bk.rev. **Document type:** *Bulletin.*
Formerly (until 1994): Liikearkisto (0356-7850)
Related titles: Online - full text ed.
Published by: Liikearkistoyhdistys r.y./Finnish Business Archives Association, P O Box 271, Helsinki, 00101, Finland. TEL 358-9-31043123, FAX 358-9-31043814, http://www.liikearkistoyhdistys.fi/julkaisut/julkaisut.htm. Ed. Pentti Laiva-Koivisto. Circ: 550.

330 FIN ISSN 0358-626X
FAKTA. Text in Finnish. 1981. m. EUR 133.80 domestic; EUR 136 in Europe; EUR 156.90 elsewhere (effective 2003). adv. bk.rev. **Document type:** *Consumer.* **Description:** Targets decision makers, business executives, upper management and senior executives, experts and business and development specialists.
Published by: A-Lehdet Oy, Risto Rytin tie 33, Helsinki, 00081, Finland. TEL 358-9-75961, FAX 358-9-7598600, a-tilaus@a-lehdet.fi, http://www.a-lehdet.fi. Ed. Timo Holtari. Circ: 30,000.

FARM BUSINESS DATA (YEAR). see *AGRICULTURE—Feed, Flour And Grain*

FAXNEWZ. see *CRIMINOLOGY AND LAW ENFORCEMENT—Security*

330 CHN ISSN 1003-0670
HC427.92
FAZHAN YANJIU/DEVELOPMENT RESEARCH. Text in Chinese. 1983. m. CNY 54 domestic; USD 34.80 foreign (effective 2005). **Document type:** *Journal, Academic/Scholarly.* **Description:** Covers social and economic development issues.
Related titles: Online - full text ed.: (from East View Information Services).
Published by: Fujian Sheng Jingji Yanjiu Zhongxin/Fujian Economics Studies Center, 8, Hualin Lu, Rm. 247, Sheng Zhengfu Bldg., Fuzhou, 350003, China. fzyjzzs@vip.sina.com, http://fzyj.periodicals.net.cn/. **Dist. by:** China International Book Trading Corp, 35 Chegongzhuang Xilu, Haidian District, PO Box 399, Beijing 100044, China. TEL 86-10-68412045, FAX 86-10-68412023, cibtc@mail.cibtc.com.cn, http://www.cibtc.com.cn.

330 USA ISSN 0889-9223
THE FED TRACKER; specializing in domestic and global money flow analysis. Key Title: Ken Coleman's The Fed Tracker. Text in English. m. USD 96; USD 110 foreign. back issues avail. **Document type:** *Newsletter.*
Formed by the 1992 merger of: Fed Tracker Reality Theory Newsletter (0739-3563); Fed Tracker Special Report (0739-5256)
Published by: Seraphim Press, 4805 Courageous Ln, Carlsbad, CA 92008. TEL 619-720-0107, FAX 619-720-4208. Ed. S R Coleman. Pub. Kenneth Coleman. Circ: 1,300.

330 USA ISSN 0195-2617
FEDERAL GRANTS MANAGEMENT HANDBOOK. Text in English. 1978. 2 base vols. plus m. updates. USD 269; USD 35 per chapter for each federal grnating agency. bk.rev. **Document type:** *Newsletter, Trade.* **Description:** Provides information to federal financial assistance recipients, it includes detailed guidance on obtaining grants, preparing to receive funds, preparing for audits, managing grant expenditures and handling grant disputes.
—CCC.
Published by: Thompson Publishing Group, Grants Management Advisory Service, 1725 K St, N W, Ste 700, Washington, DC 20006. TEL 202-739-9698, FAX 202-296-9657, gran@thompson.com, http://www.thompson.com. Ed., R&P Anne Woodworth. Pub. Daphne Musselwhite. Circ: 3,300.

330 340 USA
FEDERAL RESERVE BANK OF PHILADELPHIA. BANKING LEGISLATION AND POLICY. Text in English. q. back issues avail. **Document type:** *Government.*
Published by: Federal Reserve Bank of Philadelphia, 10 Independence Mall, Philadelphia, PA 19106. http://www.phil.frb.org/econ/blp/index.html. R&P Deron Green TEL 215-574-4102.

330 USA
FEDERAL RESERVE BANK OF PHILADELPHIA. BUSINESS OUTLOOK SURVEY. Text in English. m. stat. back issues avail. **Document type:** *Government.* **Description:** Surveys manufacturers in the Third Federal Reserve District: employment, working hours, new and unfilled orders, shipments inventories, delivery times, prices paid, and prices received.
Published by: Federal Reserve Bank of Philadelphia, 10 Independence Mall, Philadelphia, PA 19106. mike.trebing@phil.frb.org, http://www.phil.frb.org/econ/bos/index.html.

330 USA
FEDERAL RESERVE BANK OF PHILADELPHIA. RESEARCH RAP. Text in English. q. back issues avail. **Document type:** *Academic/Scholarly.*
Published by: Federal Reserve Bank of Philadelphia, 10 Independence Mall, Philadelphia, PA 19106. http://www.philfrb.org/econ/resrap/index.html, http://www.phil.frb.org.

330 USA
FEDERAL RESERVE BANK OF PHILADELPHIA. SOUTH JERSEY BUSINESS REVIEW. Text in English. 1991. q. **Description:** Surveys business activity of South Jersey businesses in the Chamber of Commerce. Covers employment, working hours, new and unfilled orders, shipments/sales, inventories, delivery times, prices paid, cost of labor/benefits, and prices received.
Published by: Federal Reserve Bank of Philadelphia, 10 Independence Mall, Philadelphia, PA 19106. http://www.phil.frb.org/econ/sj/index.html.

FEDERAL RESERVE BANK OF PHILADELPHIA. TECHNICAL BRIEFS. see *HOUSING AND URBAN PLANNING*

330 USA
FEDERAL RESERVE BANK OF RICHMOND. WORKING PAPER SERIES. Text in English. irreg. stat. back issues avail. **Document type:** *Monographic series, Academic/Scholarly.* **Description:** Includes working papers by, and in collaboration with, economists at the Federal Reserve Bank of Richmond.
Published by: Federal Reserve Bank of Richmond, Research Dept, Box 27622, Richmond, VA 23261. http://www.rich.frb.org/pubs/wpapers.

330 USA
FEDERAL RESERVE BANK OF SAN FRANCISCO. WORKING PAPERS. Text in English. irreg. stat. back issues avail. **Document type:** *Newsletter.*
Related titles: Online - full content ed.
Published by: Federal Reserve Bank of San Francisco, PO Box 7702, San Francisco, CA 94120. TEL 415-974-2978, http://www.sf.frb.org/publications/economics/papers/index.html, http://www.frbsf.org.

330 RUS
FEDERALIZM. Text in Russian. q. USD 85 in United States.
Published by: Finansovaya Korporatsiya Lugra, Nakhimovskii pr-t 32, Moscow, 117218, Russian Federation. TEL 7-095-3324506. Ed. S D Valentei. **US dist. addr.:** East View Information Services, 3020 Harbor Ln. N., Minneapolis, MN 55447. TEL 612-550-0961.

330 GBR ISSN 1354-5701
HQ1381 CODEN: FEECFE
➤ **FEMINIST ECONOMICS.** Text in English. 1995. q. GBP 321, USD 329 combined subscription to institutions print & online eds. (effective 2006). adv. bk.rev. illus. reprint service avail. from PSC. **Document type:** *Journal, Academic/Scholarly.* **Description:** A review of cross-disciplinary perspectives and intellectual traditions in economics.
Related titles: Online - full text ed.: ISSN 1466-4372. GBP 219, USD 313 to institutions (effective 2006) (from EBSCO Publishing, Gale Group, IngentaConnect, O C L C Online Computer Library Center, Inc., Swets Information Services).
Indexed: ABIn, AgeL, AltPI, BAS, BrHumI, CurCont, DIP, ERA, FamI, FemPer, IBR, IBSS, IBZ, JEL, MEA, PSA, SOPODA, SSA, SSCI, SWA, SociolAb.
—BLDSC (3905.197230), IDS, IE, Infotrieve, ingenta. **CCC.**
Published by: (International Association for Feminist Economics), Routledge (Subsidiary of: Taylor & Francis Group), 4 Park Square, Milton Park, Abingdon, Oxon OX14 4RN, United Kingdom. TEL 44-1235-828600, FAX 44-1235-829000, http://www.tandf.co.uk/journals/titles/13545701.asp. Ed. Diana Strassmann. R&P Sally Sweet. adv.: page GBP 150; trim 190 x 115. **Subscr. to:** Subscriptions, PO Box 362, Abingdon, Oxon OX14 3WB, United Kingdom. TEL 44-1235-401060, FAX 44-1235-401075.

330 BIH
FEROELEKTRO. Text in Serbo-Croatian. 1978. m. looseleaf. free. tr.lit.
Address: Trg Oktobra bb, Sarajevo, 71000, Bosnia Herzegovina. TEL 387-71-35607. Ed. Veljko Zugic. Circ: 25,000.

FERRO ALLOYS MONTHLY. see *METALLURGY*

330 HUN ISSN 0015-086X
FIGYELO; gazdasagpolitikai hetilap. Text in Hungarian. 1957. w. HUF 13,680 (effective 2004). adv. charts; illus.; stat. **Document type:** *Magazine, Trade.* **Description:** Aims to help the business community do better business by offering case studies, forecasts, and in-depth analyses.
Related titles: Online - full text ed.: ISSN 1586-0221.
Indexed: HBB, RASB, RefZh.
Published by: Sanoma Budapest Kiadoi Rt. (Subsidiary of: Sanoma Magazines Finland Corporation), Bokor Utca 15-19, Budapest, 1037, Hungary. TEL 36-1-4371100, FAX 36-1-2502303, figyelo@sanomabp.hu, info@sanomabp.hu, http://www.figyelo.hu, http://www.sanoma.hu. Adv. contact Piroska Bosanszki. page HUF 850,000; trim 200 x 267. Circ: 63,506 (paid).

330 HUN ISSN 1417-3085
FIGYELO PESTI TOZSDEK. Text in Hungarian. 1997. 2/yr. **Document type:** *Magazine, Trade.*
Published by: Sanoma Budapest Kiadoi Rt. (Subsidiary of: Sanoma Magazines Finland Corporation), Bokor Utca 15-19, Budapest, 1037, Hungary. TEL 36-1-4371100, FAX 36-1-2502303, info@sanomabp.hu, http://www.sanoma.hu. Adv. contact Piroska Bosanszki.

330 HUN
FIGYELO TOP 200. Text in Hungarian. a. HUF 4,400 (effective 2004). adv. **Document type:** *Magazine, Trade.* **Description:** Contains analyses of the top 200 Hungarian companies as well as the main economic indices and trends of the previous year and expectations for the coming year.
Published by: Sanoma Budapest Kiadoi Rt. (Subsidiary of: Sanoma Magazines Finland Corporation), Bokor Utca 15-19, Budapest, 1037, Hungary. TEL 36-1-4371100, FAX 36-1-2502303, info@sanomabp.hu, http://www.sanoma.hu. Adv. contact Piroska Bosanszki. page HUF 1,300,000; trim 205 x 285. Circ: 10,000 (paid).

332 HUN ISSN 1587-1878
FIGYELO TREND. Text in Hungarian. 2001. bi-m. adv. **Document type:** *Magazine, Trade.*
Published by: Sanoma Budapest Kiadoi Rt. (Subsidiary of: Sanoma Magazines Finland Corporation), Bokor Utca 15-19, Budapest, 1037, Hungary. TEL 36-1-4371100, FAX 36-1-2502303, info@sanomabp.hu, http://www.sanoma.hu. Adv. contact Gabriella Rakosi. page HUF 580,000; trim 200 x 267. Circ: 10,000 (controlled).

330 DEU ISSN 1616-0274
FINANCE; das Finanzmagazin fuer Unternehmer. Text in German. 2000. m. EUR 54; EUR 6 newsstand/cover (effective 2005). adv. **Document type:** *Magazine, Trade.* **Description:** Provides coverage of corporate finances and the mergers and acquisitions markets.
Published by: Frankfurter Allgemeine Zeitung GmbH, Postfach 200163, Frankfurt Am Main, 60605, Germany. TEL 49-69-75911888, FAX 49-69-75911843, info@faz-institut.de, http://www.faz-institut.de. adv.: page EUR 6,902. Circ: 25,000 (paid and controlled).

330 AUS
FINANCE AND MARKETING INTELLIGENCE SYSTEM. Text in English. d. **Document type:** *Trade.*
Media: Online - full content.
Published by: Roy Morgan Research, PO Box 2282 U, Melbourne, VIC 3001, Australia. TEL 61-3-96296888, FAX 61-3-96291250, http://www.roymorgan.com.

330 AUS
FINANCIAL REVIEW BOSS. Text in English. m. **Document type:** *Magazine, Trade.*
Related titles: ♦ Issued with: Australian Financial Review. ISSN 0404-2018.
Published by: Fairfax Business Media (Subsidiary of: John Fairfax Holdings Ltd.), 201 Sussex St, Sydney, NSW 2000, Australia. TEL 61-2-9282-2822, http://www.fxj.com.au/. Ed. Helen Trinca. Circ: 108,182.

330 UGA
FINANCIAL TIMES. Text in English. d.
Address: Plot 17-19 Sta. Rd., PO Box 31399, Kampala, Uganda. TEL 245798. Ed. Dan Salasatta.

330 BEL ISSN 0772-0890
DE FINANCIEEL ECONOMISCHE TIJD. Text in Dutch. 1968. 5/w. EUR 320; EUR 160 to students (effective 2005). adv. bk.rev. **Document type:** *Newspaper.*
Related titles: CD-ROM ed.; Online - full text ed.: (from LexisNexis).
Indexed: KES.
Published by: Uitgeversbedrijf Tijd n.v., Franklin Bldg, Posthoflei 3, Bus 9, Berchem (Antwerp), 2600, Belgium. TEL 32-3-286-0211, FAX 32-3-286-0210, contactcenter@tijd.be, http://www.tijd.be. Ed. Hans Maertens. Pub. Paul Huybrechts. Adv. contact Marc van de Guchtve. Circ: 55,000 (paid).

330 NLD ISSN 1388-4425
HET FINANCIEELE DAGBLAD. Text in Dutch; Summaries in English. 1796. d. (6/wk., Mon.-Sat.). EUR 345 (effective 2005). adv. abstr.; illus.; stat. 20 p./no. 10 cols./p.; back issues avail.; reprints avail. **Document type:** *Newspaper, Consumer.* **Description:** Publishes financial and business news from the Netherlands and Europe, and covers political issues relevant to the business community.
Incorporates (1992-1998): Netherlander (0927-5800); Former titles: Dagelijksche Beurscourant; Amsterdamsch Effectenblad
Related titles: Online - full text ed.
Indexed: CBNB, LHB.
Published by: F D Mediagroep, PO Box 216, Amsterdam, 1000 AE, Netherlands. TEL 31-20-5928888, FAX 31-20-5928800, info@fdmediagroep.nl, http://www.fd.nl/Home.asp, http://www.fdmediagroep.nl. Ed. A Bakker. R&P L Sieders. Adv. contact L. Sieders. Circ: 56,819.

B

330 MEX
EL FINANCIERO. Text in Spanish. 1981. d. **Document type:** *Newspaper.* **Description:** Daily financial newspaper published in Mexico.
Related titles: ♦ English ed.: El Financiero International Edition.
Published by: El Financiero International Inc., Lago Bolsena 176, Col Anahuac, Mexico City, DF 11320, Mexico. TEL 525-227-7600, FAX 525-227-7634, http://www.elfinaciero.com.mx. Circ: 135,000.

330 RUS ISSN 1683-9501
FINANSOVYI DIREKTOR/FINANCIAL DIRECTOR. Text in Russian. 2002. m. USD 120 (effective 2005). **Document type:** *Journal, Trade.*
Published by: Independent Media (Moscow), ul Vyborgskaya dom 16, str 1, Moscow, 125212, Russian Federation. TEL 7-095-2323200, FAX 7-095-2329265, fd@fd.ru, podpiska@imedia.ru, http://www.fd.ru, http://www.independent-media.ru. Ed. Tatiana Ischenko.

330 ITA
FINANZA E FISCO. Text in Italian. 1987. 12/yr. EUR 201.42 (effective 2005). adv. **Document type:** *Magazine, Consumer.*
Address: Via Cristoforo Colombo 436, Rome, RM 00145, Italy. TEL 39-06-5416320, FAX 39-06-5415822, redazione@tin.it, http://www.finanzaefisco.it. Ed. Eugenio Pompei. Circ: 30,000.

330 ESP ISSN 0210-4997
FINANZAS. Text in Spanish. 1960. 12/yr.
Address: Alcala, 20, Apartado 14776, Madrid, 28014, Spain. TEL 34-01-532-23-28. Ed. C Munoz Hernandez.

553.65 USA ISSN 1090-0896
FINER POINTS MAGAZINE. Text in English. 1969. q. USD 35 domestic; USD 45 in Canada & Mexico; USD 90 elsewhere (effective 2004). adv. **Document type:** *Magazine, Trade.* **Description:** Covers news on technological advancements, application development and educational programs for superabrasives such as industrial diamond, cubic boron nitride, polycrystallines, CVD, diamond -like films and other materials.
—BLDSC (3927.777500), Linda Hall.
Published by: Industrial Diamond Association of America, Inc., PO Box 29460, Columbus, OH 43229-0460. TEL 614-797-2265, FAX 614-797-2264, http://www.superabrasives.org/finer_points_magazine1.php3. adv.: B&W page USD 1,425, color page USD 1,820. Circ: 75,000 (paid and controlled).

330 FIN ISSN 0784-5197
HB1
FINNISH ECONOMIC PAPERS. Text in English. 1988. s-a. free to members; EUR 27 per vol. domestic to non-members; EUR 57 per vol. elsewhere to non-members (effective 2004). **Document type:** *Journal.*
Related titles: Online - full text ed.
Indexed: IBSS, JEL.
Published by: (Kansantaloudellinen Yhdistys/Finnish Economic Association, Ekonomiska Samfundet i Finland/Economic Society of Finland), Taloustieteellinen Seura ry/Finnish Society for Economic Research, c/o Department of Economics, RUESG, University of Helsinki, PO Box 17, Helsinki, 00014, Finland. TEL 358-9-19128761, FAX 358-9-19128742, fep@taloustieteellinenseura.fi, http://www.taloustieteellinenseura.fi/fep/. Ed. Markku Lanne.

330 FIN ISSN 1237-3052
FINNS IN BUSINESS. Text in English. 1994. a.
Related titles: ♦ Supplement to: Talouselama. ISSN 0356-5106.
Published by: Talentum Oyj, Malminkatu 30, PO Box 920, Helsinki, 00101, Finland. TEL 358-240-4240, FAX 358-240-424130, info@talentum.fi, http://www.talentum.fi.

FIRST CLASS EXECUTIVE TRAVEL. see *TRAVEL AND TOURISM*

FIRST MOVES. see *MEDICAL SCIENCES*

658.812 USA ISSN 1093-8540
FIRST-RATE CUSTOMER SERVICE. Text in English. bi-w. USD 142 domestic; USD 172 in Canada; USD 192 elsewhere (effective 2005). **Document type:** *Newsletter, Trade.*
Published by: Briefings Publishing Group (Subsidiary of: Douglas Publications, Inc.), 1101 King St, Ste 110, Alexandria, VA 22314. TEL 703-518-2343, 800-722-9221, FAX 703-684-2136, customerservice@briefings.com, http://www.briefings.com.

330 NLD
FISCAAL ADVIES. Text in Dutch. q. adv.
Published by: Reed Business Information bv (Subsidiary of: Reed Business), Van de Sande, Bakhuyzenstraat 4, Amsterdam, 1061 AG, Netherlands. TEL 31-20-515-9222, FAX 31-20-515-9990, info@reedbusiness.nl, http://www.reedbusiness.nl.

330 NLD ISSN 0925-4552
FISCAAL UP TO DATE. Text in Dutch. 1984. w. EUR 825 (effective 2003). **Document type:** *Newsletter.*
—IE, Infotrieve.
Published by: Fiscaal Up to Date BV, Postbus 125, Eindhoven, 5600 AC, Netherlands. TEL 31-40-2925950, FAX 31-40-2925 955, informatie@futd.nl, http://www.futd.nl.

B

330 USA
FISCAL NOTES. Text in English. m. stat. **Document type:** *Government.*
Media: Online - full content.
Published by: Texas Comptroller of Public Accounts, PO Box 13528, Capitol Station, Austin, TX 78711-3528 . http://www.window.state.tx.us/comptrol/fnotes/fnhome.html. Eds. Greg Mt. Joy, Suzanne Staton.

FISKERIOKONOMISKE SMASKRIFTER/PAPERS ON FISHERIES ECONOMICS. see *FISH AND FISHERIES*

330 975.9 USA ISSN 1042-590X
FLORIDA BUSINESS. Text in English. 1984. m.
Former titles (until 1988): Florida Business, Tampa Bay (0898-0772); (until 1986): Gulfcoast Business (0743-6041)
Published by: Business Journal Publishing Co., PO Box 9859, Naples, FL 33941. TEL 813-263-7525, FAX 813-263-1046.

330 340 USA
FLORIDA CORPORATIONS LAW AND PRACTICE. Text in English. 1985. irreg. (in 4 vols.). looseleaf. USD 570 (effective 1999).
Published by: Matthew Bender & Co., Inc. (Subsidiary of: LexisNexis North America), 1275 Broadway, Albany, NY 12204. international@bender.com, http://bender.lexisnexis.com.

FLORIDA MEDICAL BUSINESS. see *MEDICAL SCIENCES*

FOCUS ON BUSINESS. see *BUSINESS AND ECONOMICS—Chamber Of Commerce Publications*

330.071 GBR
FOCUS ON BUSINESS EDUCATION. Text in English. 1907. 3/yr. GBP 39 (effective 2001). adv. bk.rev. 20 p./no. 3 cols./p.; **Document type:** *Journal, Academic/Scholarly.*
Formerly (until 1986): Commercial Teacher (0010-311X)
Published by: Society of Teachers in Business Education, 28 Norlands Cresc, Chislehurst, Kent BR7 5RN, United Kingdom. editor@stbe.clara.co.uk, http://www.stbe-net. Ed. M D Drew. R&P, Adv. contact M.D. Drew. page EUR 200. Circ: 1,500.

330 340 DEU ISSN 0941-3618
FOERDERUNG DER WIRTSCHAFT IN DEN NEUEN BUNDESLAENDERN. Text in German. 1992. irreg. price varies. **Document type:** *Monographic series, Trade.*
Published by: Erich Schmidt Verlag GmbH & Co. (Berlin), Genthiner Str 30G, Berlin, 10785, Germany. TEL 49-30-250085-0, FAX 49-30-25008511, esv@esvmedien.de, http://www.erich-schmidt-verlag.de.

330 POL ISSN 0071-674X
FOLIA OECONOMICA CRACOVIENSIA. Text in Polish; Summaries in English, Russian. 1960. a. price varies. **Document type:** *Academic/Scholarly.* **Description:** Covers system-independent monetarized economy; investment rate changes; agricultural production; territorial and social differences of consumption.
Indexed: RASB.
Published by: (Polska Akademia Nauk, Oddzial w Krakowie, Komisja Nauk Ekonomicznych), Polska Akademia Nauk, Oddzial w Krakowie, ul sw Jana 28, Krakow, 31018, Poland. TEL 48-12-224853, FAX 48-12-222791. Ed. Janusz Maciaszek. Circ: 530.

330 USA
FOLIO (OKLAHOMA CITY). Text in English. bi-m. illus. **Document type:** *Newsletter, Government.*
Former titles: Oklahoma Economic Development News; Oklahoma P.E.P.; Incorporates: Oklahoma Now!
Indexed: B&I.
Published by: Department of Commerce, PO Box 26980, Oklahoma City, OK 73126-0980. FAX 405-815-5281. Ed. Tracy Alford. Circ: 7,000.

330 MEX
FONDO DE CULTURA. SERIE DE LECTURAS. Text in Spanish. 1973. irreg. price varies. adv. bk.rev. bibl. **Document type:** *Academic/Scholarly.*
Published by: Fondo de Cultura Economica, Carretera PICACHO AJUSCO 227, Col Bosques del Pedregal, Mexico City, DF 14200, Mexico. TEL 52-55-52274672, FAX 52-55-52274683. Ed. Carlos Bazdresch. Circ: 5,000.

330 RUS
FONDOVYE NOVOSTI; ezhednevnoe izdanie. Text in Russian. 1994. 260/yr. USD 1,895 in the Americas (effective 2000).
Published by: Agentstvo Praim, Khvostov per., 11a, Moscow, 103062, Russian Federation. TEL 7-095-2361011. **Dist. by:** East View Information Services, 3020 Harbor Ln. N., Minneapolis, MN 55447. TEL 763-550-0961, FAX 763-559-2931.

330 UKR
FONDOVYI RYNOK. Text in Russian. 48/yr. USD 495 in the Americas (effective 2000).
Published by: Redaktsiya Fondovyi Rynok, Ul Vladimirskaya 64, Kiev, Ukraine. TEL 221-38-03. **Dist. by:** East View Information Services, 3020 Harbor Ln. N., Minneapolis, MN 55447. TEL 763-550-0961, FAX 763-559-2931.

330 POL ISSN 1733-7291
FORBES. Text in Polish. 2001 (Apr.). m. PLZ 84 domestic (effective 2005). **Document type:** *Magazine, Consumer.* **Description:** Covers all aspects of the business and investment worlds.
Formerly (until 2005): Profit (1641-9367)
Related titles: Online - full content ed.
Published by: Axel Springer Polska, Al Jerozolimskie 181, Warsaw, 02222, Poland. TEL 48-22-6084100, FAX 48-22-6084106, asp@axelspringer.com.pl, http://www.axelspringer.com.pl. Circ: 50,000 (paid).

FORBES. see *BUSINESS AND ECONOMICS—Management*

330 JPN ISSN 0916-9903
FORBES (NIHON-BAN)/FORBES (JAPAN EDITION). Text in Japanese. 1992. m. JPY 10,800 (effective 2005). **Document type:** *Magazine, Consumer.*
Published by: Gyosei Corp. Ltd., 4-30-16 Ogikubo Suginamiku, Tokyo, 167-8088, Japan. TEL 81-3-53496666, FAX 81-3-53496677, eigyo1@gyosei.co.jp, http://www.gyosei.co.jp/forbes/forbes.html. Ed. Hideo Onozuka. Pub. Yohji Ito. Adv. contact Masakuni Saito. Circ: 100,000.

330 USA ISSN 1467-1654
FORBES GLOBAL. Text in English. 1998. bi-w. USD 59.95 (effective 2004).
Formerly (until 1999): Forbes Global Business & Finance (1462-1312)
Related titles: Online - full text ed.: (from EBSCO Publishing, Gale Group).
—BLDSC (3985.525700). **CCC.**
Published by: Forbes, Inc., 60 Fifth Ave, New York, NY 10011. TEL 212-620-0220, FAX 212-620-1873, http://www.forbes.com. Ed. Lawrence Minard.

658 057.1 RUS ISSN 1810-8660
▼ **FORBES RUSSIA.** Text in Russian. 2004 (Apr.). m. RUR 780; RUR 80 newsstand/cover (effective 2004). adv. **Document type:** *Magazine, Consumer.* **Description:** Covers a wide array of topics from the worlds of industry, finance, international business, marketing, law, taxes, science, technology, communications, investments and entrepreneurship.
Published by: ZAO Axel Springer Russia, 16/1, Dokukina St, Moscow, 129226, Russian Federation. TEL 7-095-9805252, FAX 7-095-9805255, info@axelspringer.ru, http://www.axelspringer.ru. Ed. Maxim Kashulinsky. Pub. Leonid Bershidsky. Adv. contact Svetlana Lanugova. B&W page USD 7,000, color page USD 9,300. Circ: 55,000 (paid and controlled).

330 CAN ISSN 0015-6957
F1051
FORCES. Text in English, French. 1967. q. CND 15. adv. charts; illus.; stat. cum.index every 2 yrs. **Document type:** *Magazine, Trade.*
Indexed: CPerl, PdeR.
—CISTI.
Published by: Transcontinental Media, Inc. (Subsidiary of: Transcontinental, Inc.), 1100 Blvd Rene Levesque W, 24th Fl, Montreal, PQ H3B 4X9, Canada. TEL 514-392-9000, FAX 514-392-1489, info@transcontinental.ca, http://www.revueforces.com, http://www.transcontinental-gtc.com/en/home.html. Circ: (controlled).

330 737.4 USA ISSN 0095-294X
THE FORECASTER. Text in English. 1962. 40/yr. USD 150 domestic; USD 190 foreign; USD 10 newsstand/cover (effective 2001). bk.rev. charts; mkt.; stat. back issues avail. **Document type:** *Newsletter.* **Description:** Confidential reports about future economic developments. Includes analyses of property, interest rates, speculation, gold, silver,coins, antiques, cars and travel.
Published by: Forecaster Publishing Co., Inc., 19623 Ventura Blvd, Tarzana, CA 91356. TEL 818-345-4421. Ed., R&P John Kamin.

330.9598 GBR ISSN 1463-0982
FOREIGN COMPANIES IN INDONESIA YEARBOOK. Text in English. 1998. a. GBP 240, USD 390 (effective 2000). **Document type:** *Trade.* **Description:** Provides extensive information on corporations, including contact details, senior executive personnel, companies listed by index, competitor data, and company subsidiaries.
Related titles: CD-ROM ed.: GBP 390, USD 670 (effective 2000).
—**CCC.**
Published by: Business Monitor International Ltd., Commercial Intelligence Service, 179 Queen Victoria St, London, EC4V 4DU, United Kingdom. TEL 44-20-7248-0468, FAX 44-20-7248-0467, subs@businessmonitor.com, http://www.businessmonitor.com.

330.959 GBR ISSN 1465-0266
FOREIGN COMPANIES IN PHILIPPINES YEARBOOK. Text in English. 1998. a. GBP 240, USD 390 (effective 2001). **Document type:** *Trade.* **Description:** Provides extensive information on corporations, including contact details, senior executive personnel, indexed company listings, competitor data, and company subsidiaries.
Related titles: CD-ROM ed.: GBP 390, USD 670 (effective 2001).
—**CCC.**
Published by: Business Monitor International Ltd., Commercial Intelligence Service, 179 Queen Victoria St, London, EC4V 4DU, United Kingdom. TEL 44-20-7248-0468, FAX 44-20-7248-0467, busmon@dial.pipex.com, http://www.businessmonitor.com.

FOREIGN REPRESENTATIVES IN THE U.S. YELLOW BOOK; who's who in the U.S. offices of foreign corporations, foreign nations, the foreign press and intergovernmental organizations. see *POLITICAL SCIENCE—International Relations*

330 657 USA ISSN 8756-8888
HV8079.W47
FORENSIC ACCOUNTING REVIEW✶. Text in English. 1983. m. looseleaf. USD 125; USD 155 foreign. back issues avail. **Document type:** *Newsletter.* **Description:** Digest of current incidents of corporate fraud, including insider trading, executive frauds, improper auditing, embezzlement, bank fraud and questionable accounting.
Related titles: Online - full text ed.: (from ProQuest Information & Learning).
Indexed: ABIn, CJPI.
Published by: Computer Protection Systems, Inc., 12275 Appletree Dr, Plymouth, MI 48170-3739. TEL 313-459-8787, FAX 313-459-8787. Ed. Jack Bologna.

FORTUNE C N E T TECHNOLOGY REVIEW. see *TECHNOLOGY: COMPREHENSIVE WORKS*

330 HKG
FORTUNE CHINA. Text in Chinese. 9/yr. HKD 529 in Hong Kong; USD 80 in Asia & the Pacific; USD 97 elsewhere (effective 2000).
Published by: C C I Asia-Pacific Ltd., 23/F Tianjin Bldg, 167 Connaught Rd W, Hong Kong, Hong Kong. TEL 852-2548-7801, fc-circ@cci.com.hk, http://fortunechina.com/frontpage.html, http://www.cci.com.hk.

330 NLD ISSN 0738-5587
HF5001
FORTUNE INTERNATIONAL. Text in Dutch. bi-w. adv. **Document type:** *Magazine, Consumer.*
Related titles: Online - full text ed.: (from EBSCO Publishing, Florida Center for Library Automation, Gale Group, LexisNexis, ProQuest Information & Learning).
Indexed: ABIn, Emerald, Inspec, M&MA, RAPRA, RASB, WBA, WMB.
—IE.
Published by: Time Warner Publishing BV (Subsidiary of: Time Warner, Inc.), Ottho Heldring Straat 5, Amsterdam, 1066 AZ, Netherlands. TEL 31-20-5104911, FAX 31-20-6175077, http://www.fortune.com. Ed. John Huey. Pub. Stuart Arnold. R&P Jo Mattern. Adv. contact Christopher Poleway. Circ: 860,000; 850,000 (paid).

330 332.6 USA
FORUM (NEW YORK, 1986). Text in English. s-a. membership. charts; illus. **Document type:** *Newsletter.*
Formerly: A B A Business Briefs; Which was formerly (until 1978): A L A Brief; American Lawyers Association Brief
Published by: American Businesspersons Association, 350 Fairway Dr, Ste 200, Deerfield Beach, FL 33441-1834. TEL 954-571-1877, membership@assnservices.com, http://www.aba-assn.com. Ed. B Lydia Young. Circ: 5,000.
Co-sponsors: National Association of the Professions; The Attorneys Group.

330 DEU ISSN 1438-5007
FORUM KONJUNKTUR; der internationale wirtschaftsbericht. Text in German. 1999. q. **Document type:** *Journal, Academic/Scholarly.*
Related titles: Online - full text ed.: ISSN 1616-5217. 2001.
Published by: Albert-Ludwigs-Universitaet Freiburg, WorkShop Konjunktur, Platz der Alten Synagoge 1, Freiburg, 79085, Germany. TEL 49-761-2032349, FAX 49-761-2032180, jelitto@vwl.uni-freiburg.de, http://www.vwl.uni-freiburg.de/konjunktur/.

330 DEU ISSN 0340-7705
FORUM WARE. Text in English, German. 1972. a. bk.rev.
Document type: *Journal, Academic/Scholarly.* **Description:** Devoted to the commodity and its significance for man, economy and nature. Covers study and instruction, knowledge of commodities, ecological aspects, and consumer information.
Formerly (until 1976): D G W T Informationen (0340-7713)
Indexed: RefZh.
Published by: Deutsche Gesellschaft fuer Warenkunde und Technologie, Bredeneyer Str 64c, Essen, 45133, Germany. TEL 49-201-4309575, FAX 49-201-4309576, loebert@dgwt.de, http://dgwt.de. Ed. Guenter Otto. **Co-sponsor:** Oesterreichische, und Internationale, Gesellschaft fuer Warenkunde und Technologie.

330 USA ISSN 1081-2792
FOUNDATION & CORPORATE FUNDING ADVANTAGE. Text in English. 1995. m. USD 240. **Document type:** *Newsletter.* **Description:** Listings of available grants from foundations and corporations.
Published by: Progressive Business Publications, 370 Technology Dr, Malvern, PA 19355-1315. TEL 610-695-8600, 800-220-5000, FAX 610-647-8089, editor@pbp.com, http://www.pbp.com. Ed. Susan Wade Elnicki. R&P Curt Brown. Circ: 4,110 (paid).

650 GBR
FOUNDATION FOR BUSINESS RESPONSIBILITIES. DIALOGUES. Text in English. irreg., latest vol.2, 1972.
Formerly: Industrial Educational and Research Foundation. Dialogues
Published by: Foundation for Business Responsibilities, 40 Doughty St, London, WC1N 2LF, United Kingdom.

650 GBR ISSN 0073-7410
FOUNDATION FOR BUSINESS RESPONSIBILITIES. DISCUSSION PAPER. Text in English. 1965. irreg. price varies. bk.rev.
Published by: Foundation for Business Responsibilities, 40 Doughty St, London, WC1N 2LF, United Kingdom.

650 GBR ISSN 0073-7429
FOUNDATION FOR BUSINESS RESPONSIBILITIES. OCCASIONAL PAPERS. Text in English. 1965. irreg. price varies. bk.rev.
Published by: Foundation for Business Responsibilities, 40 Doughty St, London, WC1N 2LF, United Kingdom.

658 GBR ISSN 0073-7437
FOUNDATION FOR BUSINESS RESPONSIBILITIES. RESEARCH PAPER. Text in English. 1965. irreg. price varies. bk.rev.
Published by: Foundation for Business Responsibilities, 40 Doughty St, London, WC1N 2LF, United Kingdom.

650 GBR
FOUNDATION FOR BUSINESS RESPONSIBILITIES. SEMINAR PAPERS. Text in English. 3/yr. USD 15.
Published by: Foundation for Business Responsibilities, 40 Doughty St, London, WC1N 2LF, United Kingdom.

330 USA
FOUR CORNERS BUSINESS JOURNAL. Text in English. 1993. s-m. USD 187 domestic; USD 486.20 foreign (effective 2001). adv. 28 p./no. 5 cols./p.; **Document type:** *Newspaper.* **Description:** Provides general business news and information concerning the four corners region, where Colorado, Arizona, Utah and New Mexico meet.
Related titles: Online - full text ed.
Published by: Avanti Communications, Inc., PO Box 2117, Durango, CO 81302. TEL 970-385-7883, FAX 970-259-5277, publisher@frontier.net, http://www.businessjournals.com/. Ed. Ralph Damiani. Pub. Hugh Le Vrier. Adv. contact Cindy Le Vrier. page USD 1,680; trim 16 x 10. Circ: 10,000.

330 FRA ISSN 0995-3531
FRANCE. DIRECTION GENERALE DE LA CONCURRENCE, DE LA CONSOMMATION ET DE LA REPRESSION DES FRAUDES. ACTUALITES. Text in French. m. (11/yr.). EUR 31 (effective 2003).
Published by: (France. Direction Generale de la Concurrence, de la Consommation et de la Repression des Fraudes), Imprimerie Nationale, BP 514, Douai, Cedex 59505, France. TEL 27-93-70-70, FAX 27-93-70-96. **Subscr. to:** Lavoisier, Lavoisier - Dept Abonnements, 14 rue de Provigny, Cachan 94236, France. TEL 33-1-47406700, FAX 33-1-47406702, abo@lavoisier.fr, http://www.lavoisier.fr.

330 FRA ISSN 0766-6268
HC276.3.A1
FRANCE. INSTITUT NATIONAL DE LA STATISTIQUE ET DES ETUDES ECONOMIQUES. NOTE DE CONJONCTURE. Text in French. 5/yr.
Indexed: RASB.
Published by: Institut National de la Statistique et des Etudes Economiques, 1 rue Vincent Auriol, Amiens, Cedex 1 80027, France. TEL 33-3-22927322, FAX 33-3-22979295.

330 FRA ISSN 0990-9435
CODEN: NMNPAX
FRANCE. INSTITUT NATIONAL DE LA STATISTIQUE ET DES ETUDES ECONOMIQUES. NOTE DE CONJONCTURE INTERNATIONALE. Text in French. 1988. 4/yr.
Published by: Institut National de la Statistique et des Etudes Economiques, 1 rue Vincent Auriol, Amiens, Cedex 1 80027, France. TEL 33-3-22927322, FAX 33-3-22979295, inseeactualites@insee.fr.

310 658.5 FRA
FRANCE. SERVICE D'ETUDE DES STRATEGIES ET DES STATISTIQUES INDUSTRIELLES. SOCIETES D'ETUDES ET DE CONSEILS, INGENIEURS-CONSEILS. Variant title: France. Service d'Etude des Strategies et des Statistiques Industrielles. Ingenierie, Etudes et Conseils. Text in French. 1968. a. **Description:** Statistics on engineering services in France.
Formerly: France. Service du Traitement de l'Information et des Statistiques Industrielles. Societe d'Etudes et de Conseils, Ingenieurs-Conseils
Published by: Service d'Etude des Strategies et des Statistiques Industrielles (SESSI), 20 av. de Segur, Paris, 75353, France. TEL 33-1-43194108, FAX 33-1-43194173.

330 CAN ISSN 1497-1488
FRANCHISE CANADA. Text in English. 2000. bi-m. CND 17.35 (effective 2005). **Document type:** *Magazine, Trade.* **Description:** Geared to entrepreneurs interested in acquiring a franchise. Contains top-notch editorial from leading authorities in the industry as well as tips on how to establish a successful franchise.
Published by: (Canadian Franchise Association), August Communications, 225-530 Century St, Winnipeg, MB R3H 0Y4, Canada. TEL 204-957-0265, 888-573-1136, FAX 204-957-0217, 866-957-0217, info@august.ca, http://www.august.ca.

FRANCHISE LAW JOURNAL. see *LAW*

FRANCHISE TIMES (ROSEVILLE). see *BUSINESS AND ECONOMICS—Production Of Goods And Services*

330 USA
FRANCHISE UPDATE. Text in English. q. USD 39.95.
Address: PO Box 20547, San Jose, CA 95160-0547. TEL 408-997-7795, FAX 408-997-9377, 103042.3305@compuserve.com, http://franchise-update.com. Ed. Theresa Thilgen. Circ: 10,000.

330 DEU ISSN 0067-5938
FREIE UNIVERSITAET BERLIN. OSTEUROPA-INSTITUT. WIRTSCHAFTSWISSENSCHAFTLICHE VEROEFFENTLICHUNGEN. Variant title: Wirtschaftswissenschaftliche Veroeffentlichungen. Text in German. 1954. irreg., latest vol.42, 1987. price varies. **Document type:** *Monographic series, Academic/Scholarly.*
Published by: Freie Universitaet Berlin, Osteuropa-Institut, Garystr 55, Berlin, 14195, Germany. TEL 49-30-83853380, FAX 49-30-83853788, oei@zedat.fu-berlin.de, http://www.oei.fu-berlin.de. Circ: 500.

330 ZAF
FREIGHT & TRADING WEEKLY; the shipper's newspaper. Abbreviated title: F T W. Text in English. 1973. w. adv. bk.rev. **Document type:** *Newspaper, Trade.* **Description:** Covers all aspects of international trade from an importer's and exporter's point of view.
Former titles: Freight and Container Weekly; (until 1983): F C Weekly; Which incorporated (in 1980): Southern Africa's Freighting News; Containering and Transport News
Published by: Travel and Trade Publishing (Pty) Ltd., PO Box 662, Auckland Park, Johannesburg 2006, South Africa. TEL 27-11-726-3036, FAX 27-11-726-3994, davem@nowmedia.co.za, http://rappidttp.com. Ed. Joy Orlek. Adv. contact Carmel Levinrad. B&W page ZAR 7,187.70, color page ZAR 7,403.33; trim 220 x 310. Circ: 3,493 (controlled).

330 USA
FRESNO BUSINESS JOURNAL ✶ . Text in English. 1986. w. USD 30. **Description:** Contains news about public and private companies, personality profiles, local business trends, advice and data.
Related titles: Microfilm ed.: 1986 (from LIB).
Published by: Fresno Business Journal, Inc., 1315 Van Ness Ave 200, Fresno, CA 93721-1713. TEL 209-237-0114, FAX 209-237-3540. adv.: B&W page USD 500; trim 15 x 11.5. Circ: 1,724.

330 USA ISSN 0740-7416
HB615
FRONTIERS OF ENTREPRENEURSHIP RESEARCH. Text in English. 1981. a. price varies. **Document type:** *Proceedings, Academic/Scholarly.*
—BLDSC (4042.013000).
Published by: Babson College, Arthur M. Blank Center for Entrepreneurship, Babson Park, MA 02457. TEL 781-239-4420, http://www3.babson.edu/eship/, http://www2.babson.edu.

330 USA ISSN 1527-4667
FT. WORTH BUSINESS PRESS. Text in English. 1988. w. USD 43. adv. **Document type:** *Newspaper, Trade.*
Formerly: The Business Press (1045-8697)
Related titles: Online - full text ed.: (from EBSCO Publishing, Gale Group, LexisNexis, O C L C Online Computer Library Center, Inc.).
Indexed: B&I.
Published by: Carolyn Ashford, 3509 Hulen St, Ste 201, Ft. Worth, TX 76107. TEL 817-336-8300, FAX 817-332-3038. Ed. Wayne Carter. Pub. Nick Karanges. R&P Greg Moss. Adv. contact Kathleen King. Circ: 7,500.

053.1 DEU
FUCHSBRIEFE. Text in German. 2/w. adv. **Document type:** *Newsletter, Trade.* **Description:** Provides current news and analysis of the economic and political conditions in Germany.
Related titles: E-mail ed.
Published by: Verlag Fuchsbriefe (Subsidiary of: Springer Science+Business Media), Albrechtstr 22, Berlin, 10117, Germany. TEL 49-30-28881720, FAX 49-30-28045576, http://www.fuchsbriefe.de. Ed., Pub. Ralf Vielhaber.

FUEL CELL INDUSTRY REPORT. see *ENERGY*

330 JPN ISSN 0285-2772
FUKUOKA DAIGAKU KEIZAIGAKU RONSO/FUKUOKA UNIVERSITY REVIEW OF ECONOMICS. Text in Japanese. 1949. q.
Supersedes in part (until 1956): Fukuoka Shodai Ronso (0285-2802)
—BLDSC (4054.899700).
Published by: Fukuoka Daigaku, Kenkyujo/Fukuoka University, Central Research Institute, 8-19-1 Nanakuma, Jonan-ku, Fukuoka, 814-0180, Japan.

FUNDACAO CENTRO DE PESQUISAS ECONOMICAS E SOCIAIS DO PIAUI. RELATORIO DE ATIVIDADES. see *SOCIOLOGY*

330 ESP
➤ **FUNDACION DE LAS CAJAS DE AHORROS CONFEDERADAS. DOCUMENTOS DE TRABAJO.** Text in Spanish. 1987. irreg., latest vol.158, 1999. **Document type:** *Monographic series, Academic/Scholarly.* **Description:** Publishes research conducted or promoted by the foundation.
Formerly: Confederacion Espanola de Cajas de Ahorros. Fundacion Fondo para la Investigacion Economica y Social. Documentos de Trabajo
Media: Online - full text.
Published by: Fundacion de las Cajas de Ahorros Confederadas para la Investigacion Economica y Social, Juan Hurtado de Mendoza, 19, Madrid, 28036, Spain. TEL 34-91-3507907, FAX 34-91-3508040, publica@funcas.ceca.es, http://www.funcas.ceca.es. Ed. Fernando Gonzalez Olivares. Pub. Victorio Valle Sanchez. Circ: 500.

330 ESP
FUNDACION DE LAS CAJAS DE AHORROS CONFEDERADAS. ESTUDIOS. Text in Spanish. 1987. irreg., latest vol.2, 2002. price varies. **Document type:** *Monographic series, Trade.* **Description:** Publishes research conducted or promoted by the foundation, whose results become manuals or reference works.
Formerly: Confederacion Espanola de Cajas de Ahorros. Fundacion Fondo para la Investigacion Economica y Social. Estudios
Published by: Fundacion de las Cajas de Ahorros Confederadas para la Investigacion Economica y Social, Juan Hurtado de Mendoza, 19, Madrid, 28036, Spain. TEL 34-91-3507907, FAX 34-91-3508040, publica@funcas.ceca.es, http://www.funcas.ceca.es. Ed. Fernando Gonzalez Olivares. Pub. Victorio Valle Sanchez. Circ: 2,000.

FUNK - SPOT; Radioservice des Instituts der deutschen Wirtschaft. see *COMMUNICATIONS—Radio*

330 NLD ISSN 1380-6947
FUSIE & OVERNAME; magazine about mergers and acquisitions. Short title: F & O. Text in Dutch. 1993. 10/yr. EUR 194.25 (effective 2005). adv. bk.rev. charts; illus.; stat.; mkt. 64 p./no.; back issues avail. **Document type:** *Magazine, Corporate.* **Description:** Covers issues involving all aspects of mergers and acquisitions.
Related titles: CD-ROM ed.
Published by: Reed Business Information bv (Subsidiary of: Reed Business), Postbus 16500, Den Haag, 2500 BM, Netherlands. TEL 31-70-4415255, FAX 31-70-4415919, info@reedbusiness.nl, http://www.reedbusiness.nl. adv.: B&W page EUR 916, color page EUR 1,698; trim 215 x 285. Circ: 594.

FUTURIBLES; analyse et prospective. see *SOCIOLOGY*

B

▼ new title ➤ refereed ✶ unverified ♦ full entry avail.

330   USA   ISSN 0738-9264
FUTURIFIC. (future terrific) Text in English. 1976. m. USD 80
domestic to individuals; USD 120 foreign to individuals; USD
160 domestic to institutions; USD 200 foreign to institutions
(effective 2001). adv. bk.rev.; film rev.; software rev. 32 p./no.;
back issues avail.; reprints avail. **Document type:** *Magazine,
Consumer.* **Description:** 26th years as the Newsmagazine of
the future, producing highly accurate forecasts of humanitis
future.
Published by: Futurific, Inc., Foundation for Optimism, 305
Madison Ave, Concourse 10B, New York, NY 10165. TEL
212-297-0502, 800-696-2836, keytonyc@aol.com. Ed., Adv.
contact Balint Szent-Miklosy. Pub. Balint Szent Miklosy. Circ:
10,000.

330   ESP   ISSN 1136-0593
➤ FUZZY ECONOMIC REVIEW; review of the International
Association for Fuzzy-set Management and Economy. Text in
English. 1995. s-a. EUR 60 (effective 2003). **Document type:**
Journal, Academic/Scholarly.
—BLDSC (4060.736700).
Published by: International Association for Fuzzy-Set
Management and Economy (SIGEF), Avinguda de la
Universitat 1, Reus, 43204, Spain. TEL 34-977-759800, FAX
34-977-759810, xct@fcee.urv.es, http://www.fcee.urv.es/sigef.

330   CHE   ISSN 1422-0482
H5
G D I IMPULS; Vierteljahresschrift fuer Entscheidungstraeger in
Wirtschaft und Gesellschaft. Text in German. 1982. q. CHF
120 (effective 2001). adv. bk.rev. **Document type:** *Magazine,
Trade.* **Description:** Alerts decision makers in industry and
politics to the emerging issues in their fields.
Published by: Gottlieb Duttweiler Institut, Langhaldenstr 21,
Postfach, Rueschlikon, 8803, Switzerland. TEL 41-1-7246111,
FAX 41-1-7246262, http://www.gdi.ch. Ed., Pub. Stefan Kaiser.
Circ: 3,000 (paid); 2,200 (controlled).

330   ITA   ISSN 1123-7260
G D O WEEK; il settimanale economico della distribuzione
moderna e della industria. (Grande Distribuzione Organizzata)
Text in Italian. 1970. w. EUR 80 domestic; EUR 160 foreign
(effective 2005). 84 p./no.; back issues avail. **Document type:**
Magazine, Trade.
Former titles: Grande Distribuzione e Distribuzione Organizzata
(1121-9564); (until 2001): Distribuzione Organizzata
(0394-8455); (until 1984): Droghiere. Distribuzione
Organizzata (0394-879X); (until 1983): Droghiere (0394-8781);
(until 1972): Rassegna de "Il Droghiere" (0394-8773)
Related titles: Online - full text ed.
Published by: Gruppo Editoriale A G E P E Srl, Via G Patecchio
2, Milan, MI 20141, Italy. TEL 39-02-399861, FAX
39-02-39844800, mbox@gruppoagepe.it, http://
www.gdoweek.it, http://www.agepe.it. Circ: 26,000 (controlled).

G E. DIRITTO ED ECONOMIA DELLO STATO SOCIALE. see
LAW

330   RUS
G I S - OBOZRENIE. Text in Russian. 1994. q. USD 235 in North
America (effective 2000).
Published by: Redaktiya/G I S - Obozrenie, A-ya 2, Moscow,
125124, Russian Federation. TEL 7-095-2577436. **Dist. by:**
East View Information Services, 3020 Harbor Ln. N.,
Minneapolis, MN 55447. TEL 763-550-0961, FAX
763-559-2931.

330 630   CAN
G - MAIL. Text in English. w. CND 500 (effective 2004).
Document type: *Newsletter, Trade.* **Description:** Provides a
weekly synopsis of the seed industry news, research and
related topics.
Media: E-mail.
Published by: Issues Ink, 203-897 Corydon Ave, Winnipeg, MB
R3M 0W7, Canada. TEL 204-453-1965, FAX 204-475-5247,
issues@issuesink.com, http://www.issuesink.com.

330 378   USA   ISSN 1072-7612
G S B CHICAGO. (Graduate School of Business) Text in English.
1979. 3/yr. bk.rev. **Description:** Features business-related
articles for the alumni.
Published by: University of Chicago, Graduate School of
Business, 1101 E 58th St, Chicago, IL 60637. TEL
312-702-1234, http://gsbwww.uchicago.edu/news/gsbchicago.
Ed. William S Bike. Circ: 35,000 (controlled).

330   BOL   ISSN 0016-3767
GACETA ECONOMICA. Text in Spanish. 1967. m. USD 28.80.
adv. bk.rev. bibl.; charts; illus.; stat.
Address: G Mercado, 996, PO Box 237, La Paz, Bolivia. Ed.
Arturo Valdivieso.

GAIA; oekologische Perspektiven in Natur-, Geistes- und
Wirtschaftswissenschaften. see *HUMANITIES:
COMPREHENSIVE WORKS*

330   USA
GAINESVILLE - OCALA BUSINESS. Text in English. 1987. m.
USD 18. adv. **Document type:** *Trade.*
Formerly: Business in Gainesville

Published by: Linda Young-Marks, PO Box 4649, Ocala, FL
34478. TEL 352-622-2995, FAX 904-622-9200. Ed. Vinod
Chhabra. Pub. Linda Young Marks. Adv. contact Gene
McConnell. Circ: 12,000.

GAMES RETAILER. see *GIFTWARE AND TOYS*

658.1   ESP   ISSN 1575-9237
GANAR.COM. Text in Spanish. 1999. m. **Document type:**
Magazine, Trade. **Description:** The premier business
magazine of Spain, published in print and on the Internet.
Related titles: Online - full content ed.: ISSN 1575-9245.
Published by: Recoletos Compania Editorial S.A (Subsidiary of:
Pearson Publishing Group), Paseo Recoletos, 1 5o, Madrid,
28001, Spain. TEL 34-91-3373220, FAX 34-91-3373266,
expansion@recoletos.es, http://www.ganar.com,
http://www.recoletos.es.

330   CHN   ISSN 1000-064X
GANG AO JINGJI/ECONOMICS IN HONG KONG AND MACAO.
Text in Chinese. m.
Related titles: Online - full text ed.: (from East View Information
Services).
Published by: Guangdong Sheng Shehui Kexueyuan, Gang Ao
Yanjiu Zhongxin/Guangdong Academy of Social Sciences,
Hong Kong and Macao Research Center, No 6, Xihepu,
Dongshan, Guangzhou, Guangdong 510080, China. TEL
776123. Ed. Xu Long.

330   EGY
AL-GARIDAH AT-TIGARIYYAH AL-MISRIYYAH. Text in Arabic.
1921. w.
Published by: Garidah at-Tigariyyah al-Misriyyah, 25 Sharia
Nubar Pasha, Cairo, Egypt. Circ: 7,000.

330   USA   ISSN 1053-5527
HG4501
GARY NORTH'S REMNANT REVIEW. Text in English. 1974. m.
USD 129. adv. back issues avail. **Document type:**
Newspaper. **Description:** Features topics as world politics,
reducing the national debt, downsizing the US government,
and coping with the year 2000 computer problem.
Published by: American Bureau of Economic Research, c/o
Agora, 1217 St Paul St, Baltimore, MD 21202. TEL
410-223-2510, 800-433-1528, FAX 410-223-2582. Ed. Gary
North. R&P Jody Madron. Adv. contact Douglas Cooke. Circ:
15,000.

330   BRA
GAZETA MERCANTIL DAILY NEWSPAPER. Text in Portuguese.
1920. d. USD 171 (effective 2002). **Document type:**
Newspaper. **Description:** Brazilian daily financial and
business newspaper circulated nationally.
Related titles: Online - full text ed.
Published by: Gazeta Mercantil, Rua Engenheiro Francisco Pitta
Brito 125, San Paulo, 04753-080, Brazil. TEL 55-11-55473716,
FAX 55-11-55473778, http://www.gazetamercantil.com.br.

GAZETA PRAWNA. see *LAW*

330   POL   ISSN 1505-1943
GAZETA PRZEDSIEBIORCZYCH. Text in Polish. 1994. m.
Document type: *Newspaper, Consumer.*
Formerly (until 1995): Gazeta dla Przedsiebiorczych (1505-3865)
Related titles: ◆ Supplement to: Gazeta Wyborcza. ISSN
0860-908X.
Published by: Agora S.A., ul Czerska 8/10, Warsaw, 00732,
Poland. TEL 48-22-6994301, FAX 48-22-6994603,
http://www.gazeta.pl.

GAZETA SZKOLNA. see *EDUCATION*

330 300   IRL
GEARY LECTURE SERIES. Text in English. 1967. irreg., latest
vol.29, 1999. price varies. **Document type:** *Monographic
series.*
—BLDSC (4095.500000).
Published by: Economic and Social Research Institute, 4
Burlington Rd., Dublin, 4, Ireland. TEL 353-1-667-1525, FAX
353-1-668-6231, http://www.esri.ie. Ed. B J Whelan. R&P John
Roughan. **Dist. by:** Oak Tree Press, Merrion Bldgs., Lower,
Merrion Sq, Dublin 2, Ireland. TEL 353-1-6761600, FAX
353-1-6761644.

330   JPN   ISSN 0918-0591
HF5001
GEKKAN KEIDANREN. Text in Japanese. 1953. m. USD 5. adv.
charts; illus.; stat.
Formerly (until 1992): Keidanren Geppo (0453-4484)
Indexed: RASB.
Published by: Japan Federation of Economic
Organizations/Keizai Dantai Rengokai (KEIDANREN), 9-4
Ote-Machi 1-chome, Chiyoda-ku, Tokyo, 100-0004, Japan.
TEL 81-3-3279-1411, FAX 81-3-5255-6255. Circ: 15,000.

GENERAL AVIATION BUSINESS REPORT. see
TRANSPORTATION—Air Transport

330 363.7 576.5   USA   ISSN 1552-5651
GENETICS & ENVIRONMENTAL BUSINESS WEEK. Text in
English. w. USD 2,595 in US & Canada; USD 2,795
elsewhere; USD 2,825 combined subscription in US & Canada
print & online eds.; USD 3,055 combined subscription
elsewhere print & online eds. (effective 2005). **Document
type:** *Newsletter, Academic/Scholarly.*
Related titles: Online - full content ed.: ISSN 1552-566X; Online -
full text ed.: (from ProQuest Information & Learning).
Published by: NewsRx, PO Box 5528, Atlanta, GA 31107-0528.
TEL 800-726-4550, FAX 303-290-9025, info@newsrx.com,
http://www.newsrx.com/product_descriptions/
GENETICS_AND_ENVIRONMENTAL_BUSINESS_WEEK.HTM.

THE GEORGE WASHINGTON INTERNATIONAL LAW REVIEW.
see *LAW—International Law*

GEORGETOWN JOURNAL OF INTERNATIONAL LAW. see
LAW—International Law

338   USA   ISSN 0279-3857
HC107.G4
GEORGIA BUSINESS AND ECONOMIC CONDITIONS. Text in
English. 1929. bi-m. free (effective 2000). charts; stat.
cum.index. back issues avail. **Document type:**
Academic/Scholarly.
Formerly: Georgia Business (0016-8173)
Related titles: Microfiche ed.: (from CIS).
Indexed: PAIS, SRI.
Published by: (Selig Center for Economic Growth), University of
Georgia, Terry College of Business, 535 Brooks Hall, Athens,
GA 30602. TEL 706-542-4085, FAX 706-542-3858,
http://www.selig.uga.edu. Ed. Lorena Akioka. Circ: 3,000.

330   USA   ISSN 0884-1179
HC107.G4
GEORGIA ECONOMIC OUTLOOK. Text in English. a. USD 20
(effective 2000). **Document type:** *Academic/Scholarly.*
Published by: (Selig Center for Economic Growth), University of
Georgia, Terry College of Business, 535 Brooks Hall, Athens,
GA 30602. TEL 706-542-4085, FAX 706-542-3858,
http://www.selig.uga.edu.

GERMAN BRIEF. see *PUBLIC ADMINISTRATION*

330   GBR   ISSN 1465-2188
GERMANY'S GLOBAL COMPANIES. Text in English; Summaries
in English, German. 1997. a. GBP 150; USD 260 foreign
(effective 2000). adv. stat. back issues avail. **Document type:**
Directory. **Description:** Annual review of overseas activities of
German companies, together with directory of all major
players.
Published by: Urban Publishing Co., Hampstead, PO Box 625,
London, NW3 2TZ, United Kingdom. TEL 44-2082-091722,
FAX 44-2084-554107. Ed. Tann von Hove. adv.: B&W page
USD 1,600, color page USD 3,200; trim 210 x 270. Circ:
7,500.

330   HUN   ISSN 0237-5478
GESCHAEFTSPARTNER UNGARN. Text in Hungarian.
1986-1992; resumed 1996. bi-m. HUF 25,200, USD 110
(effective 2000). adv. **Document type:** *Newsletter.*
Description: Covers Hungarian trade acts and regulations,
customs, foreign exchange, and investments. Includes foreign
trade statistics, industry tests, and market reports.
Published by: Kopint - Datorg Plc, Csokonai u 3, Budapest,
1081, Hungary. TEL 36-1-3039586, FAX 36-1-303-9582,
nermth@kopint.hu, info@kopint-datorg.hu,
http://www.kopint.hu, http://www.kopint-datorg.hu. Ed. Ilona
Nemeth. R&P, Adv. contact Judit Boncz. Circ: 1,000.

331   DEU   ISSN 0949-3867
GESCHAEFTSWELT. Text in German. 1989. m. adv. **Document
type:** *Magazine, Trade.*
Formerly (until 1994): GeschaeftsWelt - Wirtschafts- und
Finanzzeitschrift fuer Geschaeftsfreunde der Sparkassen
(0942-6396)
Published by: Deutscher Sparkassenverlag GmbH, Am
Wallgraben 115, Stuttgart, 70565, Germany. TEL 49-711-7820,
FAX 49-711-7821709, webredaktion@dsv-gruppe.de,
http://www.dsv-gruppe.de. adv.: B&W page EUR 7,000, color
page EUR 7,900. Circ: 109,905 (controlled).

330   CAN   ISSN 0701-0028
GESTION; revue internationale de gestion. Text in French. 1976.
4/yr. CND 50 (effective 1998). adv. bk.rev. **Document type:**
Trade.
Related titles: Online - full text ed.: (from Micromedia ProQuest,
ProQuest Information & Learning).
Indexed: ABIn, PdeR.
—BLDSC (4163.690000), CISTI, IE, ingenta.
Published by: Ecole des Hautes Etudes Commerciales, 3000
Chemin de la Cote Sainte Catherine, Montreal, PQ H3T 2A7,
Canada. TEL 514-340-6677, FAX 514-340-6382,
revue.gestion@hec.ca. Ed. Alain Gosselin. Circ: 6,500.

330 AUT
GEWINN; das Wirtschaftsmagazin fuer den persoenlichen Vorteil. Text in German. 1982. m. EUR 41.80 (effective 2005). adv. tel.rev. charts; illus. back issues avail. **Document type:** *Magazine, Consumer.* **Description:** Contains useful information and tips regarding careers, money matters, legal issues, taxation, real estate, business, and leisure activities.
Published by: Wailand und Waldstein GmbH, Stiftgasse 31, Vienna, W 1070, Austria. TEL 43-1-52124-0, FAX 43-1-5212430, gewinn@gewinn.vienna.at, http://www.gewinn.co.at. Eds., Pubs. Georg Wailand, Georg Waldstein. Adv. contact Raimund Jacoba. B&W page EUR 7,000, color page EUR 12,250; trim 185 x 250. Circ: 101,000 (controlled).

GEZONDHEIDSZORG, BELEID EN ORGANIZATIE. see *HEALTH FACILITIES AND ADMINISTRATION*

330 052 GBR
GILT; the elite magazine. Text in English. 1998. bi-m. GBP 2.95 newsstand/cover; USD 4.90 newsstand/cover in United States. adv. **Document type:** *Consumer.* **Description:** Provides information on the high profile business world and the personalities and lifestyles within it.
Published by: Torch Publishing plc, Irwin House, 118 Southwark St, London, SE1 0SW, United Kingdom. TEL 44-171-803-9803, FAX 44-171-803-9804, ebrodie@torchplc.com. Ed. Evelyn Brodie. Circ: 14,000 (paid). **Dist. by:** M M C Ltd., Octagon House, White Hart Meadows, Ripley, Woking, Surrey GU23 6HR, United Kingdom. TEL 44-1483-211222.

330 ITA ISSN 0017-0097
HB7 CODEN: GIAEAY
GIORNALE DEGLI ECONOMISTI E ANNALI DI ECONOMIA. Text in English, Italian. 1875. q. EUR 100 in the European Union; EUR 140 elsewhere (effective 2004). adv. bk.rev. charts. index. reprints avail. **Description:** Contains studies on Italian and international economic systems and policies. Articles which concern international economic methodologies are published in English while academic analyses of recent economic research may be in Italian.
Related titles: Microfiche ed.: (from BHP).
Indexed: CIS, CurCont, EIP, ELLIS, IBSS, JEL, PAIS, PCI, RASB, SSCI, ST&MA.
—BLDSC (4177.800000), IE, Infotrieve, ingenta.
Published by: (Universita Commerciale Luigi Bocconi), E G E A SpA, Viale Isonzo 25, Milan, MI 20135, Italy. TEL 39-02-58365751, FAX 39-02-58365753, egea.edizioni@uni-bocconi.it. Circ: 1,450.

330 ITA
GIORNALE DEI COMMERCIANTI DELLE IMPRESE TURISTICHE DEI SERVIZI. Text in Italian. 20/yr.
Published by: Coop. Edizioni Commercio, Via Messina, 19, Rome, RM 00198, Italy. TEL 06-86-83-96. Ed. Renzo Santelli. Circ: 210,000.

330 ITA
GIORNALE DEI DOTTORI COMMERCIALISTI. Text in Italian. 1968. 12/yr. adv. **Document type:** *Newspaper, Trade.*
Published by: Consiglio Nazionale dei Dottori Commercialisti, Piazza della Repubblica 59, Rome, 00187, Italy. FAX 39-06-47863349, 39-06-478631, http://www.cndc.it. Ed. Giorgio Sganga. Circ: 30,200.

330 GBR
GLASGOW CALEDONIAN UNIVERSITY. CALEDONIAN BUSINESS SCHOOL. WORKING PAPER. Text in English. s-a.
—BLDSC (9349.369120).
Published by: Glasgow Caledonian University, Division of Economics and Enterprise, Coacaddens Road, Glasgow, G4 0BA, United Kingdom. TEL 44-0141-3313319, FAX 44-0141-3313293, S.J.Bailey@gcal.ac.uk. Ed. Stephen Bailey.

GLASS INDUSTRY AGENTS & REPRESENTATIVES WORLD GUIDE. see *CERAMICS, GLASS AND POTTERY*

GLASSONLINE WEEKLY WORLD NEWS & FINANCIAL REPORTS. see *CERAMICS, GLASS AND POTTERY*

GLASSONLINE WORLD YELLOW PAGES. see *CERAMICS, GLASS AND POTTERY*

330 RUS
GLAVBUKH. Text in Russian. m. USD 215 in North America (effective 2000).
Indexed: RASB.
Published by: Izdatel'stvo Glavbukh, B Sukharevskii per 19, str 1, pod 2, Moscow, 103051, Russian Federation. TEL 7-095-2084040, FAX 7-095-2084040. **Dist. by:** East View Information Services, 3020 Harbor Ln. N., Minneapolis, MN 55447. TEL 763-550-0961, FAX 763-559-2931.

330 USA
GLOBAL ADVISOR NEWSLETTER. Text in English. 1995. q.
Media: Online - full content.
Published by: InterSol Associates, 226 N Morning Glory, Brea, CA 92621. http://www.entrepreneurs.net/intersol/newsltr.htm.

330 GBR
GLOBAL AGENDA. Text in English. irreg. **Document type:** *Newspaper, Trade.*
Media: Online - full content.
Published by: Economist Newspaper Ltd, 25 St James's St, London, SW1A 1HG, United Kingdom. http://www.economist.com/.

330 USA ISSN 1553-1392
▼ ➤ **GLOBAL BUSINESS & ECONOMICS ANTHOLOGY.** Text in English. 2005. a. USD 83 per issue (effective 2005). **Document type:** *Academic/Scholarly.*
Published by: Business & Economics Society International, 64 Holden St, Worcester, MA 01605. TEL 508-595-0089, FAX 508-756-1780, http://www.besiweb.com/Anthology.

330 GBR ISSN 1097-4954
HF5001
➤ **GLOBAL BUSINESS & ECONOMICS REVIEW.** Text in English. s-a. USD 450 to institutions; USD 545 combined subscription to institutions print & online eds. (effective 2005). **Document type:** *Journal, Academic/Scholarly.* **Description:** Covers advanced concepts and research in all aspects of business and economics. Pays special attention to the results of increasing global business activity, targeting the educated lay reader.
Related titles: Online - full text ed.: ISSN 1745-1329. USD 450 to institutions (effective 2005).
Indexed: C&ISA, E&CAJ, IAA, JEL.
—BLDSC (4195.354200). **CCC.**
Published by: (Business & Economics Society International USA), Inderscience Publishers, IEL Editorial Office, PO Box 735, Olney, Bucks MK46 5WB, United Kingdom. TEL 44-1234-240519, FAX 44-1234-240515, dkan@besiweb.com, editor@inderscience.com, http://www.besiweb.com/GBER.html, http://www.inderscience.com. Ed. Demetri Kantarelis.

330 USA ISSN 1528-8161
GLOBAL BUSINESS MAGAZINE. Text in English. 1999. m. adv. **Document type:** *Magazine, Trade.* **Description:** Provides readers with tools and strategies for doing business worldwide, with coverage of global markets, finance, transport/logistics, technology, telecommunications, risk management, business culture and travel, and innovative ideas to help companies stay on the cutting edge of global trade and investment.
Address: 733 15th St, NW, Ste 1100, Washington, DC 20005. TEL 202-737-1060, FAX 202-783-5966, info@gbmag.com, http://www.gbmag.com. Ed. Barry Lynn. Pubs. John Mooney, Patricia Steele. Adv. contact Anu Kumar. color page USD 9,825; trim 203 x 268. Circ: 86,344 (paid and controlled).

330 IND ISSN 0972-1509
HC59.15
➤ **GLOBAL BUSINESS REVIEW.** Text in English. 2000. s-a. GBP 125, USD 219 to institutions; GBP 130, USD 228 combined subscription to institutions print & online eds. (effective 2006). **Document type:** *Journal, Academic/Scholarly.* **Description:** Acts as a forum for the wider dissemination of current management and business practice and research drawn from around the globe but with an emphasis on Asian and Indian perspectives.
Related titles: Online - full text ed.: GBP 124, USD 217 to institutions (effective 2006) (from Sage Publications, Inc.).
Indexed: RefZh.
—BLDSC (4195.355300), IE, ingenta.
Published by: Sage Publications India Pvt. Ltd. (Subsidiary of: Sage Publications, Inc.), M-32 Market, Greater Kailash-I, PO Box 4215, New Delhi, 110 048, India. TEL 91-11-6444958, FAX 91-11-6472426, http://www.sagepub.com/journal.aspx?pid=138, http://www.indiasage.com/. Ed. Ajit Prasad. **Subscr. in Europe, Middle East, Africa & Australasia to:** Sage Publications Ltd., 1 Oliver's Yard, 55 City Rd, London EC1 1SP, United Kingdom. TEL 44-20-73740645, FAX 44-20-73748741, subscription@sagepub.co.uk; **Subscr. in the Americas to:** Sage Publications, Inc., 2455 Teller Rd, Thousand Oaks, CA 91320. TEL 805-499-0721, FAX 805-499-0871, journals@sagepub.com.

330 GBR
HF1414
THE GLOBAL COMPETITIVENESS REPORT. Text in English. a. CHF 800. **Document type:** *Trade.* **Description:** Aims to serve as a guide to national competitiveness.
Formerly: World Competitiveness Report (1015-5449)
—BLDSC (4195.382300), CISTI.
Published by: (World Economic Forum), Euromoney Publications plc, Nestor House, Playhouse Yard, London, EC4V 5EX, United Kingdom. TEL 44-207-7798673, FAX 44-20-77798541, contact@weforum.org, information@euromoneyplc.com.

GLOBAL ECONOMIC JUSTICE REPORT. see *POLITICAL SCIENCE—International Relations*

330 332 USA ISSN 1057-8714
HG9997
GLOBAL GUARANTY'S CREDIT ENHANCEMENT AND FINANCIAL GUARANTY DIRECTORY. Text in English. 1991. **Document type:** *Directory.*
Media: Online - full content. **Related titles:** Online - full text ed.
Published by: LexisNexis Academic & Library Solutions, 4520 East-West Hwy, Bethesda, MD 20814.3389. TEL 301-654-1550, 800-638-8380, FAX 301-657-3203, academicinfo@lexisnexis.com, http://www.lexisnexis.com/academic/.

330.1 340 USA
GLOBAL JURIST. Text in English. a. USD 35 to individuals; USD 215 to institutions (effective 2005); Subscription includes the titles in series: Global Jurist Advances, Global Jurist Frontiers and Global Jurist Topics. **Document type:** *Journal, Academic/Scholarly.* **Description:** Offers a forum for scholarly cyber-debate on issues of comparative law, law and economics, international law, law and development, and legal anthropology.
Media: Online - full content. **Related titles:** ♦ Series: Global Jurist Frontiers. ISSN 1535-1653; ♦ Global Jurist Advances. ISSN 1535-1661; ♦ Global Jurist Topics. ISSN 1535-167X.
Published by: Berkeley Electronic Press, 2809 Telegraph Ave., Ste 202, Berkeley, CA 94705. TEL 510-665-1200, FAX 510-665-1201, info@bepress.com, http://www.bepress.com/gj/. Eds. Alberto Monti, Ugo Mattei.

330 CAN
GLOBAL MARKETPLACE REPORT. AFRICA & THE MIDDLE EAST MARKETPLACE. Text in English. m. USD 425 (effective 2004). **Document type:** *Trade.*
Media: Online - full content.
Published by: World Wide Projects Inc., 206-4030 Notre-Dame W, Montreal, PQ H4C 1R1, Canada. TEL 514-935-5675, FAX 514-935-3628, mpbastien@worldwide-projects.com, http://www.worldwide-projects.com/africamlg.html.

330 CAN
GLOBAL MARKETPLACE REPORT. ASIA & THE PACIFIC MARKETPLACE. Text in English. m. USD 475 (effective 2004). **Document type:** *Trade.*
Media: Online - full content.
Published by: World Wide Projects Inc., 206-4030 Notre-Dame W, Montreal, PQ H4C 1R1, Canada. TEL 514-935-5675, FAX 514-935-3628, mpbastien@worldwide-projects.com, http://www.worldwide-projects.com/asiamlg.html.

330 CAN
GLOBAL MARKETPLACE REPORT. GLOBAL GENERAL ENGINEERING/ CONSTRUCTION & PLANT OPERATIONS MARKETPLACE. Text in English. m. USD 475 (effective 2004). **Document type:** *Trade.*
Media: Online - full content.
Published by: World Wide Projects Inc., 206-4030 Notre-Dame W, Montreal, PQ H4C 1R1, Canada. TEL 514-935-5675, FAX 514-935-3628, mpbastien@worldwide-projects.com, http://www.worldwide-projects.com/engine.html.

330 CAN
GLOBAL MARKETPLACE REPORT. GLOBAL MARKETPLACE. Text in English. m. USD 675 (effective 2004).
Media: Online - full content.
Published by: World Wide Projects Inc., 206-4030 Notre-Dame W, Montreal, PQ H4C 1R1, Canada. TEL 514-935-5675, FAX 514-935-3628, mpbastien@worldwide-projects.com, http://www.worldwide-projects.com/.

330 CAN
GLOBAL MARKETPLACE REPORT. LATIN AMERICA & CARIBBEAN MARKETPLACE. Text in English. m. USD 425 (effective 2004).
Media: Online - full content.
Published by: World Wide Projects Inc., 206-4030 Notre-Dame W, Montreal, PQ H4C 1R1, Canada. TEL 514-935-5675, FAX 514-935-3628, mpbastien@worldwide-projects.com, http://www.worldwide-projects.com/latinmlg.html.

330 CAN
GLOBAL MARKETPLACE REPORT. MINING, METAL MAKING & CONVERSION MARKETPLACE. Text in English. m. USD 375 (effective 2004). **Document type:** *Trade.*
Media: Online - full content.
Published by: World Wide Projects Inc., 206-4030 Notre-Dame W, Montreal, PQ H4C 1R1, Canada. TEL 514-935-5675, FAX 514-935-3628, mpbastien@worldwide-projects.com, http://www.worldwide-projects.com/oilhotbo.html.

330 GBR
GLOBAL TELECOMS BUSINESS YEARBOOK. Text in English. a. **Document type:** *Yearbook, Trade.*
Published by: Euromoney Institutional Investor Plc., Nestor House, Playhouse Yard, London, EC4V 5EX, United Kingdom. TEL 44-20-7779-8673, FAX 44-20-7779-8541, http://www.euromoneyplc.com.

GLOBAL TRAVELLER. see *TRAVEL AND TOURISM*

052 AUS ISSN 1328-7435
GLOBE. Text in English. 1996. q. **Document type:** *Magazine, Trade.* **Description:** Provides its readers with information, ideas and trends about communications and technology within the business context.

B

▼ new title ➤ refereed ✶ unverified ♦ full entry avail.

Published by: A C P Custom Media, Level 7, 50 Park St, Sydney, NSW 2000, Australia. TEL 61-2-9282-8019, FAX 61-2-9267-3625, custominfo@acp.com.au, http://www.custompubs.acp.com.au. Pub. Christian Hyland. Circ: 10,000 (controlled).

THE GLOBE (ROLLINSVILLE); I C O M's monthly electronic newsletter. see *ADVERTISING AND PUBLIC RELATIONS*

330 342.3 USA ISSN 1525-5379
THE GODLY BUSINESS WOMAN MAGAZINE; all women are business women. Text in English. 1999. bi-m. USD 20.65 in United States; USD 32.65 elsewhere (effective 2001). adv.
Description: Strives to address issues which are important and significant to the busy women of today. Each issue features five to ten features and regular topics that deal with the body, mind, spirit, money matters, gifts from the heart, kid's kraft korner, continuing education, tasty sensations, beauty tips, missions and puzzles.
Published by: The Godly Business Woman Magazine, PO Box 181004, Casselberry, FL 32718-1004. TEL 407-696-2805, 800-560-1090, FAX 407-695-8033, info@godlybusinesswoman.com, publisher@godlybusinesswoman.com, http://www.godlybusinesswoman.com/index.html. Pub. Kathleen Jackson.

B

GOKHALE INSTITUTE MIMEOGRAPH SERIES. see *POLITICAL SCIENCE*

GOKHALE INSTITUTE. STUDIES. see *POLITICAL SCIENCE*

GOLF MARKET TODAY. see *SPORTS AND GAMES—Ball Games*

338 CHN ISSN 1001-3024
HD2326
GONGYE JINGJI/INDUSTRIAL ECONOMY. Text in Chinese. 1978. m. CNY 127.20 (effective 2004). 104 p./no.; **Document type:** *Journal, Academic/Scholarly.*
Published by: Zhongguo Renmin Daxue, Shubao Zilio Zhongxin/Renmin University of China, Information Center for Social Server, Dongcheng-qu, 3, Zhangzizhong Lu, Beijing, 100007, China. TEL 86-10-84043003, FAX 86-10-64015080, kyes@163.net, http://www.confucius.cn.net/bkdetail.asp?fzt=F3. **Dist. in US by:** China Publications Service, PO Box 49614, Chicago, IL 60649. TEL 312-288-3191, FAX 312-288-8570; **Dist. by:** China International Book Trading Corp, 35 Chegongzhuang Xilu, Haidian District, PO Box 399, Beijing 100044, China. TEL 86-10-68412045, FAX 86-10-68412023, cibtc@mail.cibtc.com.cn, http://www.cibtc.com.cn.

382 CAN ISSN 0848-9076
GOOD NEWS. Text in English. 1980. bi-m. free. **Document type:** *Newsletter.* **Description:** Features articles on local companies that have been recently established, have recently expanded or won an award. Also contains information on seminars of interest to local companies.
Formerly (until 1988): Good News Bulletin (0835-6351)
Related titles: Online - full text ed.
Published by: Windsor-Essex County Development Commission, City Centre, Ste 215, 333 Riverside Dr W, Windsor, ON N9A 5K4, Canada. TEL 519-255-9200, FAX 519-255-9987, info@choosewindsor.com, http://www.choosewindsor.com. Ed. Wendy Stark. Circ: 1,800.

330 USA ISSN 1523-4215
GOOD STUFF (MALVERN). Text in English. 1998. m. USD 27.86 (effective 2003). 24 p./no. 1 cols./p.; **Document type:** *Newsletter.* **Description:** Collection of insights, inspiring thoughts, and anecdotes.
Published by: Progressive Business Publications, 370 Progressive Dr, Malvern, PA 19355-1315. TEL 610-695-8600, 800-220-5000, FAX 610-647-8089, editor@pbp.com, http://www.pbp.com/gst.html. Ed. Ken Dooley. R&Ps Curt Brown, Joan Rightnour.

330 RUS
GOROD N. Text in Russian. w. USD 249 in North America (effective 2000).
Indexed: RASB.
Published by: Redaktsiya Gorod N, Pr Voroshilovskii 62, Rostov-na-Donu, 344010, Russian Federation. TEL 8632-326614, FAX 8632-323524. Ed. S Stroitelev. **Dist. by:** East View Information Services, 3020 Harbor Ln. N., Minneapolis, MN 55447. TEL 763-550-0961, FAX 763-559-2931.

330 PAK ISSN 0424-2815
HC440.5.A1
GOVERNMENT COLLEGE. ECONOMIC JOURNAL. Text in English. 1966. s-a. PKR 100, USD 40 per issue (effective 2000). bk.rev. charts; stat. **Document type:** *Academic/Scholarly.*
Indexed: PAIS.
Published by: Government College, Department of Economics, Lahore, Pakistan. TEL 92-42-6824177. Ed. Mohammed Aslam. R&P Salman Ahmad. Circ: 300.

330 GBR ISSN 0268-8948
GOVERNMENT CONTRACTING REVIEW. Text in English. 1986. q. GBP 75, USD 140. **Description:** Articles on procedures, practices and policies relating to government contracting.
—CCC.
Published by: Longman Group UK Ltd., Law Tax and Finance Division, 21-27 Lambs Conduit St, London, WC1N 3NJ, United Kingdom. TEL 44-20-7242-2548, FAX 44-207-831-8119. Ed. John Reed.

330 USA
▼ **GOVERNMENT ENTERPRISE.** Text in English. 2003. bi-m. **Document type:** *Magazine, Trade.*
Related titles: Online - full content ed.
Published by: C M P Media LLC (Subsidiary of: United News & Media), 600 Community Dr, Manhasset, NY 11030. TEL 516-562-5000, FAX 516-562-5036, http://www.governmententerprise.com/, http://www.cmp.com. Ed. Bob Evans TEL 516-562-5189. Pub. Mike Friedenberg TEL 516-562-5424.

GOVERNMENT OF ALBERTA ANNUAL REPORT. see *PUBLIC ADMINISTRATION*

▼ **GRAPHIC & DESIGN BUSINESS.** see *ART*

330 314 GBR ISSN 1366-2538
GREAT BRITAIN. OFFICE FOR NATIONAL STATISTICS. CONSUMER TRENDS. Text in English. 1995. q. GBP 45 (effective 2004). stat. back issues avail. **Document type:** *Government.*
Formerly (until 1995): Business Monitor (1360-0338)
Published by: Stationery Office, 51 Nine Elms Ln, London, SW8 5DA, United Kingdom. TEL 44-20-78738787, http://www.tso.co.uk.

330 GBR ISSN 1464-2190
GREAT BRITAIN. SCOTTISH OFFICE. ECONOMIC RESEARCH PAPER. Text in English. 1995. irreg. **Document type:** *Monographic series.*
—BLDSC (3654.479500).
Published by: Scottish Office, Economic Advice and Statistics, 1-G10, Victoria Quay, Scottish Office, Leith Docks, Edinburgh, EH6 6QQ, United Kingdom. TEL 44-131-244-0445, FAX 44-131-244-0446.

GREAT LAKER; lighthouses, lake boats, travel & leisure. see *TRANSPORTATION—Ships And Shipping*

330 USA
GREATER GREENWOOD BUSINESS JOURNAL✶. Text in English. 1992. m. USD 15. bk.rev. back issues avail. **Document type:** *Newspaper.* **Description:** Presents extensive coverage of business events in greater Greenwood, Indiana. How-to tips for business owners featured regularly.
Published by: Kelly Publications, Inc., P O Box 7126, Greenwood, IN 46142-6422. TEL 317-882-8796, FAX 317-882-8830. Ed. Maggie Kelly. Pub. Publ Brian Kelly. adv.: B&W page USD 495, color page USD 795; trim 13 x 10.25. Circ: 14,000.

GREECE AND INTERNATIONAL TRANSPORT/ELLAS KAI DIEDNIS METAPHORES; monthly financial magazine. see *TRANSPORTATION*

GREEK ECONOMY IN FIGURES (YEAR). see *BUSINESS AND ECONOMICS—Abstracting, Bibliographies, Statistics*

333.72 USA ISSN 1056-490X
GREEN BUSINESS LETTER; the hands-on journal for environmentally conscious companies. Text in English. m. USD 95 (effective 2000). bk.rev. back issues avail. **Document type:** *Newsletter.* **Description:** Provides business advice for incorporating environmental concerns into all aspects of business operation. Includes product reviews and new-technology analysis.
Media: Online - full text.
Indexed: EnvAb.
—CCC.
Published by: Tilden Press Inc., 6 Hillwood Pl., Oakland, CA 94610-1810. TEL 510-451-6611, gbl@greenbiz.com, http://www.greenbiz.com. Ed. Joel Makower.

330 USA ISSN 1529-9139
GREEN@WORK. Text in English. 2000. bi-m. USD 35 domestic; USD 50 in Canada; USD 60 elsewhere (effective 2002). **Document type:** *Magazine, Consumer.* **Description:** Covers environmental and business issues; topics include corporate or social leader, outstanding corporate acts and news releases, upcoming events, cutting edge sustainable policy and executive orders from state government, news from the deregulation and alternative energy front, and more.
Related titles: Online - full content ed.
Published by: L.C. Clark Publishing Co., 840 US Hwy One, Ste 330, North Palm Beach, FL 33408. greenoffice@msn.com, http://www.greenatworkmag.com. Ed. Katie Sosnowchik. Pub. Karrie Laughlin.

330 DEU ISSN 1619-2575
DIE GROSSHANDELSKAUFLEUTE. Text in German. 1995. m. EUR 43.80 (effective 2005). adv. **Document type:** *Magazine, Trade.*
Published by: Friedrich Kiehl Verlag GmbH, Pfaustr 13, Ludwigshafen, 67063, Germany. TEL 49-621-635020, FAX 49-621-6350222, l.kurz@kiehl.de, info@kiehl.de, http://www.kiehl.de. Ed. Lothar Kurz. Pub. Ernst Kleyboldt. Adv. contact Susanna Marazzotta. page EUR 580; trim 186 x 260. Circ: 3,000 (paid).

330 DEU
GRUENDER MAGAZIN. Text in German. 2001. q. EUR 3.50 newsstand/cover (effective 2003). adv. **Document type:** *Magazine, Trade.*
Published by: M M Vg - Management Medien Verlagsgesellschaft, Luederichstr 2-4, Cologne, 51105, Germany. TEL 49-221-82958613, FAX 49-221-82958615. adv.: page EUR 6,100. Circ: 58,209 (paid and controlled).

330 GUM ISSN 1045-053X
HF4031.5
GUAM BUSINESS NEWS. Text in English. m. **Document type:** *Magazine.*
Indexed: SPPI.
Published by: Glimpses of Guam, Inc., P O Box 3191, Agana, Guam 96910, Guam. TEL 671-472-1829, FAX 671-472-2163, http://www.glimpsesofguam.com. Ed. Jonathan Needham.

GUANGDONG HUAGONG/GUANGDONG CHEMICAL INDUSTRY. see *CHEMISTRY*

330 CHN
GUANGDONG JIAGE YANJIU/GUANGDONG PRICE RESEARCH. Text in Chinese. q.
Published by: Guangdong Sheng Wujia Yanjiusuo/Guangdong Price Research Institute, Shengfu Dayuan, Dongfeng Zhonglu, Guangzhou, Guangdong 510031, China. TEL 330860. Ed. Liu Shijing.

330 VEN
GUIA INDUSTRIAL DE VENEZUELA. Text in Spanish. 1955. a. VEB 18,000 domestic; USD 30 foreign (effective 1999). adv. **Description:** Includes a list of all the industries and industrial activities of the country with the aim of augmenting sales.
Related titles: Diskette ed.; E-mail ed.; Online - full text ed.
Published by: Editorial Guia Industrial, Ave. Francisco de Miranda con Calle B de Los Ruices, Edificio Irene, Piso 1, Of. 13, Caracas, DF 1071, Venezuela. TEL 58-2-235-4551, FAX 58-2-238-6657. Ed. Jose Precedo.

GUIDE DES COUTS DE TRANSPORT. see *TRANSPORTATION*

330.071 USA
GUIDE TO DOCTORAL PROGRAMS IN BUSINESS AND MANAGEMENT. Text in English. 1985. irreg., latest 1995. USD 15 domestic; USD 20 foreign (effective 2001). **Document type:** *Directory.*
Published by: The Association to Advance Collegiate Schools of Business, 600 Emerson Rd., Ste. 300, St. Louis, MO 63141-6762. TEL 314-872-8481, FAX 314-872-8495, http://www.aacsb.edu. Ed. Cathy Soete. R&P Howard Hoskins TEL 314-872-8507.

GUIDE TO THE ECONOMIC REGULATION OF THE ELECTRICITY INDUSTRY. see *ENERGY—Electrical Energy*

GUIDE TO THE ECONOMIC REGULATION OF THE ENERGY INDUSTRIES IN THE EUROPEAN UNION. see *ENERGY*

GUIDE TO THE ECONOMIC REGULATION OF THE GAS INDUSTRY. see *PETROLEUM AND GAS*

330 UAE
GULF BUSINESS. Text in English. 1996. m. AED 160; USD 95 foreign. adv. **Description:** Provides in-depth coverage of all aspects of business, commerce, and trade, concentrating primarily on the countries of the Arab Gulf Co-operation Council.
Related titles: Online - full text ed.
Published by: Motivate Publishing, PO Box 2331, Dubai, United Arab Emirates. TEL 971-4-824060, FAX 971-4-824436, motivate@emirates.net.ae, http://www.gulfbusiness.com. Ed. George Hopkins. Pub. Ian Fairservice. R&P Shawki Abd El Malik. Adv. contact Shawki Abd Elmalik. B&W page USD 2,750, color page USD 3,450; trim 182 x 245. Circ: 19,500.

330 USA
GULF COAST BUSINESS REVIEW. Text in English. 1952. w. (Fri.). USD 95; USD 0.75 newsstand/cover (effective 2005). adv. charts; illus.; mkt.; maps; stat.; tr.lit. 60 p./no. 4 cols./p.; back issues avail. **Document type:** *Newspaper, Trade.*
Description: Covers news of interest to the Hillsborough, Pinellas, and Pasco Counties legal, financial, business and real estate communities. Includes real estate transactions, foreclosure sales, property sales, legal notices, civil actions, public records, bid proposals and summaries, and editorials related to business, law, and real estate.
Former titles (until 2004): Tampa Bay Review; (until 2002): Warfield's Tampa Bay Review (1084-5399); (until 1995): Pinellas County Review (0746-746X)

Published by: Longboat Observer Inc., 408 E. Madison St., Tampa, FL 33602. TEL 813-221-9505, 800-403-2493, FAX 813-221-9403, http://www.review.net. Pub., R&P Matt Walsh. adv.: page GBP 416; trim 17.25 x 11.375. Circ: 1,500 (paid).

330 BHR ISSN 1353-5528
GULF ECONOMIC MONITOR. Abbreviated title: G E M. Text in English. 1995. w. USD 400 (effective 2001). 22 p./no. 2 cols./p.; **Description:** It is a report specially designed to provide executives a comprehensive round up of regional business news under different sectors-construction, industries, oil and gas, travel and tourism, economy and finance, shipping and transport and tenders.
Published by: Al Hilal Publishing & Marketing Group, Exhibition Ave, PO Box 224, Manama, Bahrain. TEL 973-293131, FAX 973-293400, TELEX 8981 HILAL BN, hilalmg@traderarabic.net, hilalcirc@tradearabia.net.

GULF STATES NEWSLETTER. see *POLITICAL SCIENCE—International Relations*

330 CHN ISSN 1009-1572
GUOMIN JINGJI GUANLI/MANAGEMENT OF NATIONAL ECONOMY. Text in Chinese. 1994. m. CNY 150 (effective 2004). 192 p./no.; **Document type:** *Journal, Academic/Scholarly.*
Formerly (until 2000): Guomin Jingji Guanli yu Jihua (1005-4316)
Indexed: RASB.
Published by: Zhongguo Renmin Daxue, Shubao Zilio Zhongxin/Renmin University of China, Information Center for Social Server, Dongcheng-qu, 3, Zhangzizhong Lu, Beijing, 100007, China. TEL 86-10-64039458, FAX 86-10-64015080, kyes@163.net, http://www.confucius.cn.net/bkdetail.asp?fzt=F10. **Dist. in US by:** China Publications Service, PO Box 49614, Chicago, IL 60649. TEL 312-288-3291, FAX 312-288-8570; **Dist. by:** China International Book Trading Corp, 35 Chegongzhuang Xilu, Haidian District, PO Box 399, Beijing 100044, China. TEL 86-10-68412045, FAX 86-10-68412023, cibtc@mail.cibtc.com.cn, http://www.cibtc.com.cn.

GUOWAI YIXUE (WEISHENG JINGJI FENCE)/FOREIGN MEDICAL SCIENCES (SANITATION ECONOMICS). see *PUBLIC HEALTH AND SAFETY*

330 401 305.8956 GBR ISSN 1354-2893
GYOSEI JOURNAL. Text in English, Japanese. every 2 yrs. GBP 7.50, JPY 1,200 (effective 2003). **Document type:** *Journal, Academic/Scholarly.* **Description:** Publishes theoretical and investigative scholarship and research in business, culture and language studies by the teachers, researchers and consultants of Witan Hall and its associated institutions and collaborators.
—BLDSC (4233.919000).
Published by: Witan Hall, London Rd, Reading, Berkshire RG1 5AQ, United Kingdom. TEL 44-118-9310152, FAX 44-118-9310137, info@gyosei.ac.uk, http://www.gyosei.ac.uk/jp/about_us/gyosei_journal.html.

330 CZE ISSN 0862-9587
H N - HOSPODARSKE NOVINY. Text in Czech. 1957. w. CZK 2,848 (effective 2003). adv. **Document type:** *Newspaper, Trade.*
Formerly (until 1990): Hospodarske Noviny (0322-7774)
Related titles: Online - full text ed.: (from East View Information Services).
Published by: Economia a.s., Dobrovskeho 25, Prague 7 7, 170 55, Czech Republic. TEL 420-2-33071111, FAX 420-2-33072003, hn@economia.cz, economia@economia.cz, http://www.economia.cz. Ed. Roman Gallo. Adv. contact Lukas Polak. page CZK 96,000; trim 297 x 422.

330 USA
H R MEMO. Text in English. bi-w. Latest issue avail. to members of Illinois Manufacturers Association only; back issues avail. free online. **Document type:** *Newsletter, Trade.* **Description:** Covers the issues of employer liability and government regulations.
Media: Online - full content. **Related titles:** E-mail ed.
Published by: The Illinois Manufacturers Association, 1301 W 22nd St., Ste. 610, Oak Brook, IL 60523. TEL 630-368-5300, 800-875-4462, FAX 630-218-7467, ima@ima-net.org, http://www.ima-net.org/. Ed., Pub. Laurie Kaczmar TEL 630-368-5300 ext. 3122.

330 HUN ISSN 1217-9647
HC10
H V G; gazdasagi, politikai hirmagazin. Text in Hungarian. 1978. w. HUF 1,922, USD 102. adv. charts; illus.; stat.; tr.lit. **Document type:** *Magazine, Consumer.* **Description:** Political, economic weekly paper. Read by educated middle-aged generation in the cities.
Formerly (until 1992): Heti Vilaggazdasag (0139-1682)
Related titles: Online - full text ed.
Indexed: HBB, RASB, RILM, RefZh.
Published by: Heti Vilaggazdasag Rt., Szepvolgyi ut 35, Budapest, 1037, Hungary. TEL 361-1884329, FAX 361-1887101, sztibor@hvg.hu, http://www.hvg.hu/. Ed. Ivan Lipovecz. Adv. contact Henriette Kovacs. B&W page HUF 280,000, color page HUF 350,000. Circ: 114,000.

330 DEU ISSN 0179-2253
HD87
H W W A - REPORT. Text in German. 1971. irreg., latest vol.250, 2005. **Document type:** *Monographic series, Trade.*
Related titles: ♦ Series: Internationale Direktinvestionen. ISSN 0933-9884.
—BLDSC (4340.290000).
Published by: H W W A - Institut fuer Wirtschaftsforschung Hamburg, Informationszentrum, Neuer Jungfernstieg 21, Hamburg, 20347, Germany. TEL 49-40-428340, FAX 49-40-42834451, hwwa@hwwa.de, http://www.hwwa.de.

330 DEU ISSN 0344-2608
H Z DEUTSCHES WIRTSCHAFTSBLATT. Text in German. 1948. bi-w. adv. bk.rev.
Published by: Verlagsanstalt Handwerk, Postfach 8120, Duesseldorf, 1 4000, Germany. TEL 0211-307073, FAX 0211-307070, TELEX 08587-140. Circ: 178,833.

330 ISR
HADSHOT PENSIA. Text in Hebrew. 1968. m.
Published by: Kaliah Ltd., Rehov Ben-Yeduha 165, Tel Aviv, 63471, Israel.

330 CHN
HAINAN JISHU JINGJI XINXI. Text in Chinese. m.
Published by: Hainan Sheng Keji Qingbao Yanjiusuo/Hainan Institute of Science and Technology Information, No 89, Haifu Dadao, Haikou, Hainan 570003, China. TEL 42232. Ed. Lin Fang'an.

330 500 CHN ISSN 1006-3013
HAIXIA KEJI YU CHANYE. Text in Chinese. 1994. bi-m. CNY 6 newsstand/cover domestic (effective 2000). **Document type:** *Academic/Scholarly.*
Related titles: Online - full content ed.: (from WanFang Data Corp.); Online - full text ed.: (from East View Information Services).
Published by: Haixia Liang'an Kexue Jishu Jiaoliu Zhongxin, PO Box 2143, Beijing, 100045, China. TEL 86-1-68511566, FAX 86-1-68511827. Ed. Kun-ming Xu.

330 UKR
HALYTS'KI KONTRAKTY. Text in Ukrainian. 1990. w. UAK 324 (effective 2002). **Document type:** *Newspaper, Consumer.*
Related titles: Online - full content ed.
Published by: Dilova Presa, Vul Mechnikova 10/2, Kyiv, 25203, Ukraine. TEL 38-44-2949642, gazeta@gc.kiev.ua, reklama@gc.kiev.ua, reklama@gc.lviv.ua, http://www.kontrakty.com.ua, http://www.gc.kiev.ua/.

330 GBR
HANDBOOK OF BUSINESS TENANCIES. Text in English. 1985. base vol. plus updates 3/yr. looseleaf. GBP 350 (effective 2005). **Document type:** *Trade.*
Published by: Sweet & Maxwell Ltd., 100 Avenue Road, London, NW3 3PF, United Kingdom. TEL 44-20-74491111, FAX 44-20-74491144, customer.services@sweetandmaxwell.co.uk, http://www.sweetandmaxwell.co.uk. **Subscr. to:** Cheriton House, North Way, Andover, Hants SP10 5BE, United Kingdom.

330 DEU ISSN 0934-375X
HANDBUCH DER STEUERLICHEN BETRIEBSPRUEFUNG. Text in German. 1977. irreg. looseleaf. price varies. **Document type:** *Monographic series, Trade.*
Published by: Erich Schmidt Verlag GmbH & Co. (Berlin), Genthiner Str 30G, Berlin, 10785, Germany. TEL 49-30-250085-0, FAX 49-30-25008521, vertrieb@esvmedien.de, http://www.erich-schmidt-verlag.de.

330 DEU ISSN 0935-2279
HANDBUCH DER UNTERNEHMENSBERATUNG. Text in German. 1976. irreg. looseleaf. price varies. **Document type:** *Monographic series, Trade.*
Published by: Erich Schmidt Verlag GmbH & Co. (Berlin), Genthiner Str 30G, Berlin, 10785, Germany. TEL 49-30-250085-0, FAX 49-30-25008521, vertrieb@esvmedien.de, http://www.erich-schmidt-verlag.de.

330 POL ISSN 1230-9664
HANDEL. Text in Polish. 1993. 22/yr. EUR 80 foreign (effective 2005). **Document type:** *Magazine, Trade.*
Published by: Polskie Wydawnictwo Fachowe Sp. Z o.o. (Subsidiary of: Deutscher Fachverlag GmbH), Jadzwingow 14, Warsaw, 02-692, Poland. FAX 48-22-8536702, handel.redakcja@pwf.com.pl, pwf@pwf.com.pl, http://www.pwf.com.pl/handel/. Circ: 22,000 (paid and controlled). **Dist. by:** Ars Polona, Krakowskie Przedmiescie 7, Warsaw, Poland. TEL 48-22-9263914, FAX 48-22-9265334, arspolona@arspolona.com.pl, http://www.arspolona.com.pl.

330 AUT
HANDEL UND GEWERBE✶. Text in German. m. **Document type:** *Trade.*
Address: c/o Oesterreichischer Zeitschriften Verband, Hoerlgasse 18-5, Vienna, W 1090, Austria. Ed. Gerd Volker Weege. Circ: 4,900.

330 AUT
HANDELSAGENT. Text in German. m. EUR 25 domestic; EUR 46 foreign (effective 2005). adv. **Document type:** *Magazine, Trade.*
Formerly: H V Magazin
Published by: (Bundesgremium der Handelsagenten), Oesterreichischer Wirtschaftsverlag GmbH (Subsidiary of: Sueddeutscher Verlag GmbH), Wiedner Hauptstr 120-124, Vienna, W 1051, Austria. TEL 43-1-546640, FAX 43-1-54664406, handelsagent@wirtschaftsverlag.at, office@wirtschaftsverlag.at, http://www.wirtschaftsverlag.at/ireds-987.html. adv.: color page EUR 3,650; trim 179 x 246. Circ: 11,000 (paid and controlled).

330 DNK ISSN 0106-4363
HANDELSHOEJSKOLEN I AARHUS. INSTITUT FOR ERHVERVS- OG SAMFUNDSBESKRIVELSE. SKRIFTSERIE C. Text in Danish. 1983 (no.6). irreg. free.
Published by: Handelshoejskolen i Aarhus, Institut for Erhvervs- og Samfundsbeskrivelse/Aarhus School of Business, Department of Applied Economics, Fuglesange Alle 20, Aarhus V, 8210, Denmark. Circ: 200.

001.64 DNK ISSN 1398-067X
HANDELSHOEJSKOLEN I AARHUS. INSTITUT FOR INFORMATIONSBEHANDLING. WORKING PAPERS. Text in Multiple languages. 1979. irreg., latest 2000. price varies. illus. **Document type:** *Monographic series, Academic/Scholarly.*
Former titles (until 1996): Handelshoejskolen i Aarhus. H - ifi, Institut for Informationsbehandling (0905-1392); (until 1987): Handelshoejskolen i Aarhus. Skriftserie. Institut for Informationsbehandling. H (0902-9087); (until 1982): Handelshoejskolen i Aarhus. Skriftserie. Institut for Statistik og Datalogi. H (0106-8490)
Published by: Handelshoejskolen i Aarhus, Institut for Informationsbehandling/Aarhus School of Business, Department of Information Science, Fuglesangsalle 4, Aarhus V, 8210, Denmark. TEL 45-89-48-63-66, FAX 45-86-15-37-92.

HANDELSPRAKTIJKEN EN MEDEDINGING/PRATIQUE DU COMMERCE ET CONCURRENCE. see *LAW—Corporate Law*

330 375 DNK ISSN 0900-4505
HANDELSSKOLEN. Text in Danish. 1968. 13/yr. adv.
Formed by the merger of (1911-1967): Danske Handelsskole (0900-4483); (1941-1967): Handelsskolebladet (0900-4491)
Published by: Handelsskolernes Laererforening, Godthaabsvej 106, Copenhagen F, 2000, Denmark. Circ: 3,300.

330 CHE ISSN 1422-8971
HANDELSZEITUNG. Text in Chechen. 1861. w. CHF 218 domestic; CHF 303 foreign; CHF 4.80 newsstand/cover (effective 2005). adv. **Document type:** *Newspaper, Trade.*
Formerly (until 1994): Schweizerische Handelszeitung (1422-917X)
Published by: HandelsZeitung und Finanzrundschau AG, Seestr 344, Postfach, Zurich, CH 8027, Switzerland. TEL 41-1-2883560, http://www.handelszeitung.ch. Adv. contact Rene Grolimund. B&W page CHF 8,847.60, color page CHF 12,483.60; trim 291 x 438. Circ: 31,804 (paid and controlled).

330 DNK ISSN 0108-6987
HANDLEREN. Text in Danish. 1980. 6/yr. free. adv. illus.
Published by: Moderate Studenter ved Handelshoejskolen i Koebenhavn, Lokale 140, Julius Thomsens Plads 10, Frederiksberg C, 1925, Denmark. Ed. Anders Fauerskov.

330 DEU
HANSEATISCHE WERTPAPIERBOERSE HAMBURG. AMTLICHE KURSBLATT. Text in German. 1853. d.
Published by: Hanseatische Wertpapierboerse Hamburg, Postfach 111509, Hamburg, 20415, Germany. TEL 040-361302-0. Circ: 650.

330 USA
HARFORD BUSINESS LEDGER. Text in English. 1989. m. USD 21 in county; USD 36.75 elsewhere (effective 2005). adv. bk.rev.; software rev.; Website rev. **Document type:** *Newspaper, Trade.*
Related titles: Online - full text ed.
Indexed: BusDate.
Published by: Homestead Publishing Co., 10 Hays St., Bel Air, MD 21014-0189. TEL 410-838-4400, FAX 410-638-0357, http://www.theaegis.com. Pub. John Worthington IV. Adv. contact Marianne Pfeffer. Circ: 8,100.

330 ISR
HAROSHET; monthly review for the Israeli producer. Text in Hebrew. m. ILS 86.
Published by: Kalia Press Ltd., Rehov Ben-Yehuda 165, Tel Aviv, 63471, Israel.

330 USA ISSN 1083-5245
HARTFORD BUSINESS JOURNAL. Text in English. 1992. bi-w. USD 64.95 (effective 2005). adv. **Document type:** *Journal, Trade.* **Description:** Provides a source for business news in the Central Connecticut region.
Related titles: Online - full text ed.
—CCC.

Address: 15 Lewis St, Ste 400, Hartford, CT 06103. TEL 860-236-9998, FAX 860-570-2493, jzwiebel@hbjournal.com, http://www.hbjournal.com. Ed. Phillip Moeller. Pub. Joe Zwiebel. Adv. contact Gail Lebert.

650 USA ISSN 0017-8012
HF5001 CODEN: HABRAX
➤ **HARVARD BUSINESS REVIEW.** Text in English. 1922. m. USD 129 domestic; USD 139 in Canada & Mexico; USD 165 elsewhere (effective 2005). adv. bk.rev. charts; illus. cum.index. reprints avail. **Document type:** *Journal, Academic/Scholarly.* **Description:** Publishes research and case studies on issues in corporate strategies, management, finance, regulatory policy, technology, international trends, and related subjects.
Related titles: Microform ed.: (from PQC); Online - full text ed.: (from bigchalk, Data-Star, EBSCO Publishing, Florida Center for Library Automation, Gale Group); ♦ Japanese Translation: Diamond Harvard Business. ISSN 0385-4272.
Indexed: ABIPC, ABIn, ABS&EES, ADPA, AHCMS, APEL, ASCA, ASEANManA, ASIP, ATI, Acal, AgeL, BAS, BLI, BMT, BPI, BPIA, BRI, BusI, CADCAM, CBRI, CCR, CIJE, CPM, CommAb, CompB, CompR, CurCont, DIP, Emerald, Englnd, EnvAb, ExcerpMed, FamI, FutSurv, HECAB, IBR, IBZ, ILD, IMI, Inpharma, Inspec, JEL, KES, LII, LOIS, LogistBibl, M&MA, MEA&I, MEDLINE, MResA, MagInd, ManagCont, ORMS, PAIS, PCI, PCR2, PE&ON, PMA, PROMT, PersLit, PsycholAb, QAb, RAPRA, RASB, RGAb, RGPR, RICS, RPFIA, Reac, RefZh, RehabLit, ResCtrlnd, RoboAb, SCIMP, SSCI, T&II, TTI, TelAb, Telegen, WBA, WorkRelAb.
—BLDSC (4265.800000), CASDDS, CIS, Ei, IDS, IE, Infotrieve, ingenta. **CCC.**
Published by: (Harvard University, Graduate School of Business Administration), Harvard Business School Publishing, 60 Harvard Way, Boston, MA 02163. TEL 617-783-7500, 800-668-6780, FAX 617-783-7555, hbr_editorial@hbsp.harvard.edu, corpcustserv@hbsp.harvard.edu, http://harvardbusinessonline.hbsp.harvard.edu, http://www.hbsp.harvard.edu. Ed. Tom Stewart. Pub. Cathy Cronin. adv.: B&W page USD 29,392, color page USD 35,578; trim 8.19 x 10.75. Circ: 250,000 (paid). **Subscr. to:** PO Box 52623, Boulder, CO 80322-2623.

330 RUS
▼ **HARVARD BUSINESS REVIEW RUSSIA.** Text in Russian. 2004. m. EUR 195 (effective 2005). adv. **Document type:** *Magazine, Trade.*
Published by: Independent Media (Moscow), ul Vyborgskaya dom 16, str 1, Moscow, 125212, Russian Federation. TEL 7-095-2323200, FAX 7-095-2329265, hbr-info@imedia.ru, podpiska@imedia.ru, http://www.hbr-russia.ru, http://www.independent-media.ru. Ed. Elena Mirskaya.

650.0711 USA
HF1134
HARVARD BUSINESS SCHOOL ALUMNI BULLETIN. Text in English. 1921. q. USD 40 domestic; USD 50 foreign; free alumni (effective 2005). adv. bk.rev. charts; illus. reprints avail. **Document type:** *Bulletin.*
Formerly: Harvard Business School. Bulletin (0017-8020)
Indexed: PAIS, RASB.
—IE, Infotrieve.
Published by: Harvard University, Graduate School of Business Administration, Soldiers Field Rd, Boston, MA 02163. TEL 617-495-6554, bulletin@hbs.edu, http://www.alumni.hbs.edu/bulletin. Ed. Roger Thompson TEL 617-495-6256. Circ: 68,000 (paid and free).

330 USA ISSN 0749-5072
HARVARD BUSINESS SCHOOL. ANNUAL REPORT. Text in English. a. USD 75. adv. **Document type:** *Corporate.*
Published by: Harvard Business School, Annual Report Office, 2401 HBS Student Mail Ctr, Boston, MA 02163. TEL 617-495-5093, annreport@hbs.edu. Ed. Oliver Ryan. Adv. contact Eric Chu. Circ: 1,500 (paid).

330 320 USA ISSN 1098-1144
DS701
HARVARD CHINA REVIEW. Text in English. 1998. s-a. USD 15 to individuals; USD 50 to institutions (effective 2005).
Related titles: Online - full text ed.: (from EBSCO Publishing).
Indexed: PAIS.
Published by: Harvard China Forum, Box 380219, Cambridge, MA 02238-0219. FAX 617-249-1612, magazine@harvardchina.org, http://www.harvardchina.org/magazine/index.html. Ed. Sijin Cheng TEL 617-642-9632.

330 ESP ISSN 0210-900X
HF5001
HARVARD - DEUSTO BUSINESS REVIEW. Text in Spanish. 1980. bi-m. EUR 129.79 (effective 2003).
Indexed: PCI.
—CINDOC, IE, Infotrieve.
Published by: Ediciones Deusto S.A., Alameda Recalde, 27, 7, Bilbao, Vizcaya 48009, Spain. TEL 34-94-9022-42324, deusto-sistemas@ediciones-deusto.es.

330 USA ISSN 0073-0505
➤ **HARVARD ECONOMIC STUDIES.** Text in English. irreg., latest vol.162, 1997. price varies. adv. **Document type:** *Monographic series, Academic/Scholarly.*
Indexed: RASB.
—BLDSC (4265.890000).
Published by: Harvard University Press, 79 Garden St, Cambridge, MA 02138. TEL 617-495-2600, FAX 617-495-5898, http://www.hup.harvard.edu. R&P Mindy Koyanis TEL 617-495-2619. Adv. contact Denise Waddington.

➤ **HARVARD UNIVERSITY. JOHN M. OLIN CENTER FOR LAW, ECONOMICS, AND BUSINESS. DISCUSSION PAPER.** see *LAW*

➤ **HEALTH CARE BUSINESS DIGEST.** see *MEDICAL SCIENCES*

368.382 USA ISSN 1085-1089
RA413.5.U5
➤ **HEALTH CARE INNOVATIONS.** Text in English. 1991. bi-m. USD 50; USD 80 foreign. adv. back issues avail. **Document type:** *Academic/Scholarly.* **Description:** Highlights research and trends within managed health care.
Formerly (until 1994): A A P P O Journal (American Association of Preferred Provider Organizations) (1054-5913)
Indexed: CINAHL, IPA, MEDLINE, SWR&A.
Published by: (American Association of Preferred Provider Organizations), Health Communications, Inc., 1 Bridge Plaza, Ft. Lee, NJ 07024. TEL 201-947-5545, FAX 201-947-8406. Ed. Douglas L Elden. Circ: 23,000.

332.6 USA ISSN 1091-9716
THE HEALTH CARE M & A MONTHLY. Text in English. 1996. m. looseleaf. USD 1,995 (effective 2004). mkt.; stat. back issues avail. **Document type:** *Newsletter, Consumer.* **Description:** Provides transaction information and analysis on the health care services merger and acquisition market, including hospitals, managed care, physician groups, long-term care, home health care, behavioral care, and several others.
Related titles: Online - full content ed.: USD 5,980; USD 4,784 to educational institutions (effective 2002); Alternate Frequency ed(s).: The M & A Weekly. 1996. w. USD 5,980 domestic; USD 5,980 in Canada; USD 5,980 foreign; USD 4,784 domestic to institutions (effective Jan. 2002); ♦ Supplement(s): The Health Care M & A Report.
Published by: Irving Levin Associates, Inc., 268-1/2 Main Ave, Norwalk, CT 06851. TEL 203-846-6800, 800-248-1668, FAX 203-846-8300, info@healthcaremanda.com, general@levinassociates.com, http://www.healthcaremanda.com. Pub. Ms. Eleanor B Meredith. R&P Stephen M Monroe. Adv. contact Mrs. Gail Donovan TEL 203-966-4343. Circ: 225.

332.6 USA
THE HEALTH CARE SERVICES ACQUISITION REPORT. Text in English. 1995. a., latest 2001, 7th Edition. looseleaf. USD 495 for print or online; USD 645 combined subscription for print & online eds.; USD 316 to educational inst. (for print or online); USD 436 combined subscription to educational inst. (for print & online) (effective 2002). mkt.; stat. back issues avail. **Document type:** *Newsletter, Consumer.* **Description:** Details various acquisition multiples (price per bed, price to revenues) for the non-profit and for-profit hospital acquisition market as well as summary averages for the past five years. The bulk of the report includes transactional data on the hospital mergers and acquisitions that occurred.
Formerly (until 2000): The Hospital Acquisition Report (1088-9124)
Related titles: Online - full text ed.
Published by: Irving Levin Associates, Inc., 268-1/2 Main Ave, Norwalk, CT 06851. TEL 203-846-6800, 800-248-1668, FAX 203-846-8300, general@levinassociates.com, http://www.levinassociates.com. Pub. Ms. Eleanor B Meredith. R&P Stephen M Monroe.

▼ **HEALTH ECONOMICS, POLICY AND LAW.** see *MEDICAL SCIENCES*

HEALTH ECONOMICS RESEARCH GROUP. DISCUSSION PAPER. see *HEALTH FACILITIES AND ADMINISTRATION*

HEALTH ECONOMICS RESEARCH GROUP. RESEARCH REPORT. see *HEALTH FACILITIES AND ADMINISTRATION*

330 CHN
HEILONGJIANG JINGJIBAO/HEILONGJIANG ECONOMY. Text in Chinese. 1985. 6/w. CNY 216 (effective 2004). **Document type:** *Newspaper, Consumer.*
Address: Nangang-qu, 51, Changjiang Lu, Haerbin, Heilongjiang 150008, China. TEL 86-451-82635411, zbs11@hljjb.com, http://www.hljjb.com/index.asp. **Dist. by:** China International Book Trading Corp, 35 Chegongzhuang Xilu, Haidian District, PO Box 399, Beijing 100044, China. TEL 86-10-68412045, FAX 86-10-68412023, cibtc@mail.cibtc.com.cn, http://www.cibtc.com.cn.

330 GRC
HELLENEWS. Text in English. 1958. w. USD 125. back issues avail. **Document type:** *Newsletter.* **Description:** Contains the abridged or condensed version of the news reported in the "Express Daily Financial Newspaper", and economic information from other sources as well.
Published by: Hellenews Ltd., 39 Amaroussiou-Halandriou Rd., Maroussi, Athens, Greece. TEL 30-1-6899400, FAX 30-1-6899430, TELEX 219746, http://www.kapatel.gr/express/hellen/news1.htm. Ed., R&P John M Germanos TEL 301-6899407. Circ: 6,200.

330 FIN ISSN 0356-889X
HELSINGIN KAUPPAKORKEAKOULU. JULKAISUSARJA B. TUTKIMUKSIA. Text in English, Finnish. irreg.
—BLDSC (4286.394000).
Published by: Helsinki School of Economics, Runeberginkatu 22-24, Helsinki, 00100, Finland.

330 FIN
HELSINGIN KAUPPAKORKEAKOULU. JULKAISUSARJA E. SELVITYKSIAE. Text in English, Finnish. irreg.
Published by: Helsinki School of Economics, Runeberginkatu 22-24, Helsinki, 00100, Finland.

330 FIN ISSN 1235-5674
HELSINGIN KAUPPAKORKEAKOULU. JULKAISUSARJA W. WORKING PAPERS. Text in Finnish, English. 1980. irreg. per issue exchange basis.
Formerly (until 1993): Helsingin Kauppakorkeakoulu. Julkaisusarja F. Tyopapereita (0358-2973)
Published by: Helsinki School of Economics, Runeberginkatu 22-24, Helsinki, 00100, Finland. Circ: 100.

330 660 CHN ISSN 1003-3467
HENAN HUAGONG/HENAN CHEMICAL INDUSTRY. Text in Chinese. 1965. m. CNY 8, USD 3.40 newsstand/cover (effective 2003). adv. **Document type:** *Journal, Academic/Scholarly.*
Related titles: Online - full text ed.: (from East View Information Services).
—BLDSC (4295.107000).
Published by: Henan-sheng Huagong Yanjiusuo, 37, Jianshe Dong Lu, Zhengzhou, 450052, China. TEL 86-371-7970324, FAX 86-371-7945072, bjb@hncic.com, http://www.hncic.com/. Ed. Jia-xuan Ma. adv.: B&W page CNY 800, color page CNY 2,500. **Dist. by:** China International Book Trading Corp, 35 Chegongzhuang Xilu, Haidian District, PO Box 399, Beijing 100044, China. TEL 86-10-68412045, FAX 86-10-68412023, cibtc@mail.cibtc.com.cn, http://www.cibtc.com.cn.

HERMES INTERNATIONAL; the English magazine for Cyprus. see *GENERAL INTEREST PERIODICALS—Cyprus*

330 NPL ISSN 0259-1405
HIMALAYAN ECONOMIST. Text in English. 1972. q. USD 5. adv.
Indexed: BAS.
Published by: Parthibeshar P. Timilsima, Ed.& Pub., 21-694-1 Dillibazar, Kathmandu, Nepal. Circ: 500.

330 JPN ISSN 0917-0030
HIROSHIMA DAIGAKU KEIZAI KENKYU SOSHO. Text in Japanese. 1982. irreg. **Document type:** *Monographic series.*
—BLDSC (4315.592700).
Published by: Hiroshima Daigaku, Keizai Gakubu/Hiroshima University, Faculty of Economics, 1-1-89, Higashisenda-machi, Naka-ku, Hiroshima 730-0053, Japan. TEL 81-82-542-6991, FAX 81-82-249-4991, http://www.eco.hiroshima-u.ac.jp/index.html.

330 JPN ISSN 0386-2704
HB9
HIROSHIMA DAIGAKU KEIZAI RONSO. Text in Japanese. 1951. q. **Document type:** *Journal, Academic/Scholarly.*
Formerly (until 1977): Seikei Ronso/Journal of Politics and Economics (0488-1109)
Indexed: AmH&L.
—BLDSC (4315.596850).
Published by: Hiroshima Daigaku, Keizai Gakubu/Hiroshima University, Faculty of Economics, 1-1-89, Higashisenda-machi, Naka-ku, Hiroshima 730-0053, Japan. TEL 81-82-542-6991, FAX 81-82-249-4991, http://www.eco.hiroshima-u.ac.jp/index.html.

330 USA ISSN 0199-0349
HF3000
HISPANIC BUSINESS MAGAZINE. Text in English. 1979. m. USD 19.97 domestic; USD 39.97 in Mexico; USD 49.97 elsewhere (effective 2005). adv. bk.rev. illus. back issues avail.; reprints avail. **Document type:** *Magazine, Trade.* **Description:** Covers successful Hispanic-owned businesses, political, economic and social trends, and consumer products. Provides tips for aspiring entrepreneurs and for executives and professionals.
Related titles: Online - full text ed.: (from H.W. Wilson, O C L C Online Computer Library Center, Inc.).
Indexed: BPI, ChPerl, MagInd, PAIS, SRI.
—**CCC.**
Published by: Hispanic Business Inc., 425 Pine Ave, Santa Barbara, CA 93117-3700. TEL 805-964-4554, FAX 805-964-6139, hbinfo@hninc.com, http://www.hispanicbusiness.com/, http://www.hispanstar.com. Ed., Pub. Jesus Chavarria. adv.: page USD 13,714, color page USD 18,056. Circ: 245,000 (paid and controlled).

HISPANIC NETWORK MAGAZINE; a Latino lifesyle, business and employment magazine. see *ETHNIC INTERESTS*

330 AUS ISSN 1037-0196
HB75
➤ **HISTORY OF ECONOMICS REVIEW.** Text in English. 1981. s-a. AUD 30 in Australia & New Zealand to individuals; USD 50 elsewhere to institutions (effective 2002). bk.rev. 120 p./no.; back issues avail. **Document type:** *Academic/Scholarly.* **Description:** Contributing articles and reviews on the history of economics from an international perspective.
Related titles: Online - full text ed.: (from R M I T Publishing).
Indexed: AusPAIS, JEL.
—BLDSC (4317.992000), IE, ingenta.
Published by: History of Economic Thought Society of Australia, University of Tasmania, GPO Box 252-85, Hobart, TAS 2052, Australia. TEL 61-3-6226-2284, FAX 61-3-6223-4520, j.king@latrobe.edu.au, william.coleman@utas.edu.au, http://www.comlaw.utas.edu.au/economics/her/her.html. Ed., R&P J E King TEL 61-3-9479-1707. Circ: 120 (paid).

➤ **HITACHI KASEI TEKUNIKARU REPOTO/HITACHI CHEMICAL TECHNICAL REPORT.** see *ENGINEERING—Chemical Engineering*

330 JPN ISSN 0018-280X
HC461.A1
➤ **HITOTSUBASHI JOURNAL OF ECONOMICS.** Text in English. 1960. s-a. JPY 1,900 (effective 2001). bibl.; charts; illus.; stat.; abstr. index. 80 p./no.; **Document type:** *Journal, Academic/Scholarly.* **Description:** Presents papers that concern empirical, theoretical and-or historical aspects of the Japanese economy.
Supersedes in part (1950-1960): Hitotsubashi Academy. Annals (0439-2841)
Indexed: ABIn, APEL, ASCA, BAS, CREJ, CurCont, IBSS, JEL, KES, PAIS, PCI, RASB, SSCI.
—BLDSC (4318.935000), IE, ingenta.
Published by: (Hitotsubashi Daigaku, Hitotsubashi Gakkai/Hitotsubashi University, Hitotsubashi Academy), Sanseido Publishing Company, Ltd., 2-22-14, Misakicho, Chiyoda-ku, Tokyo, 101-8371, Japan. FAX 81-3-3230-9569, info@sanseido-publ.co.jp, http://www.sanseido-publ.co.jp/. Eds. T Iwaisako, T Mori. Circ: 1,100. **Dist. by:** Japan Publications Trading Co., Ltd., Book Export II Dept, PO Box 5030, Tokyo International, Tokyo 101-3191, Japan. TEL 81-3-32923753, FAX 81-3-32920410, infoserials@jptco.co.jp, http://www.jptco.co.jp.

300 JPN ISSN 0018-2818
H1
➤ **HITOTSUBASHI REVIEW/HITOTSUBASHI RONSO.** Text in Japanese. 1938. m. JPY 8,500 (effective 2003). bk.rev. bibl.; charts; illus.; maps; stat. index. 120 p./no.; **Document type:** *Journal, Academic/Scholarly.*
Related titles: Online - full content ed.
Indexed: AmH&L, HistAb, IBSS, RASB, VetBull.
Published by: Hitotsubashi Daigaku, Hitotsubashi Gakkai/Hitotsubashi University, Hitotsubashi Academy, 2-1 Naka, Kunitachi-shi, Tokyo-to 186-0004, Japan. Ed. Y Fukuda. Circ: 1,350. **Dist. by:** Japan Publications Trading Co., Ltd., Book Export II Dept, PO Box 5030, Tokyo International, Tokyo 101-3191, Japan. TEL 81-3-32923753, FAX 81-3-32920410, infoserials@jptco.co.jp, http://www.jptco.co.jp.

330 GBR ISSN 0073-2818
HC12
➤ **HOBART PAPERS.** Text in English. 1960. irreg. GBP 40 (effective 2002). **Document type:** *Academic/Scholarly.*
Related titles: Microfiche ed.
—CCC.
Published by: Institute of Economic Affairs, 2 Lord North St, London, SW1P 3LB, United Kingdom. TEL 44-20-77998900, FAX 44-20-77992137, iea@iea.org.uk, http://www.iea.org.uk. Ed. Colin Robinson.

330 630 USA ISSN 1533-0931
HOBBY FARMS. Text in English. 2001. s-a. USD 5.99 newsstand/cover (effective 2002). **Document type:** *Consumer.*
Published by: Bowtie, Inc., 2401 Beverly Blvd, Los Angeles, CA 90057-0900. TEL 805-461-6774, FAX 805-461-6774, pksamuel@charter.net. Ed. Kathleen Samuelson. Pub. Norman Ridker.

HOCHSCHULE FUER TECHNIK UND WIRTSCHAFT DRESDEN. BERICHTE UND INFORMATIONEN. see *TECHNOLOGY: COMPREHENSIVE WORKS*

HOCKEY BUSINESS NEWS; covering ice and inline hockey. see *SPORTS AND GAMES*

330.08 JPN ISSN 0916-4650
HB9
HOKKAIDO UNIVERSITY. ECONOMIC JOURNAL. Text in English. 1969. a. free. bk.rev. **Document type:** *Academic/Scholarly.* **Description:** Devoted to the coverage of economic developments.
Former titles (until vol.18, July 1989): Hokudai Economic Papers (0441-7410); Hokkaido Economic Papers
Indexed: BAS, RASB.
—BLDSC (3653.830000).
Published by: Hokkaido University, Faculty of Economics/Hokkaido Daigaku Keizaigakubu, North 9, West 7, Kita-ku, Sapporo, 060-0809, Japan. TEL 81-11-706-4112, FAX 81-11-706-4947. Circ: 560 (controlled).

330 NLD ISSN 0927-4375
HOLLAND MANAGEMENT REVIEW. Cover title: H M R. Text in Dutch. 1984. bi-m. adv. bk.rev. illus. cum.index. back issues avail. **Document type:** *Magazine, Trade.*
Formerly (until 1991): Harvard Holland Review (0168-9444)
—IE, Infotrieve. **CCC.**
Published by: Reed Business Information bv (Subsidiary of: Reed Business), Van de Sande, Bakhuyzenstraat 4, Amsterdam, 1061 AG, Netherlands. TEL 31-20-515-9222, FAX 31-20-515-9990, info@reedbusiness.nl, http://www.reedbusiness.nl. Ed. T Otting. Circ: 7,000.

HOLZBAU - REPORT. see *BUILDING AND CONSTRUCTION—Carpentry And Woodwork*

338 CAN ISSN 1198-5143
HOME BUSINESS REPORT. Text in English. 1990. q. CND 17.12, USD 26 (effective 2001). adv. bk.rev.; software rev. stat.; tr.lit. back issues avail. **Document type:** *Trade.* **Description:** Aimed at the growing number of persons taking on the challenge of operating busines sess from home.
Formerly: B.C. Home Business Report
Related titles: Online - full text ed.: (from Gale Group).
Indexed: CPerI.
Published by: H B Communications Group Inc., 2949 Ash St, Abbotsford, BC V2S 4G5, Canada. TEL 604-854-5530, FAX 604-854-3087, hbrcanada@aol.com. Ed. Jennifer Scott. Pub., R&P Barbara Mowat. Adv. contact Brittany Mowat. B&W page CND 3,500, color page CND 4,485; trim 11 x 8.2. Circ: 50,000. **Dist. by:** Andrew Wood, International Publishing Consultants, Forest Green Square, 16715 - 12 Yonge St., Ste. 161, New Market, ON L3X 1X4, ON L3X 1X4, Canada. TEL 905-895-3208, FAX 905-895-3208.

330 683 USA ISSN 1538-7348
HOME CHANNEL NEWS. Text in English. 1975. s-m. USD 99 (effective 2005). **Document type:** *Magazine, Consumer.*
Formerly (until 2002): National Home Center News (0192-6772)
Related titles: Online - full content ed.: 1996 (from Florida Center for Library Automation); Online - full text ed.: (from EBSCO Publishing, Gale Group, O C L C Online Computer Library Center, Inc., ProQuest Information & Learning); Supplement(s): Pro Dealer; International Hardware & D I Y News.
—CCC.
Published by: Lebhar-Friedman, Inc., 425 Park Ave, New York, NY 10022. TEL 212-756-5252, FAX 212-756-5395, info@lf.com, http://www.homechannelnews.com, http://www.lf.com. Ed. Matt Nannery. Pub. Jeffrey Arlen. Circ: 54,000 (controlled and free).

330 USA ISSN 1521-236X
HOME NETWORKING NEWS. Text in English. 1986. 12/yr., latest vol.12, 2002. USD 499 domestic; USD 799 for 2 yrs. (effective 2002). back issues avail. **Document type:** *Newsletter, Trade.* **Description:** Provides information on home networking, automation and related subsystems, covering industry trends, products, protocols and companies that affect the business of residential technology. Topics featured: Audio/video, security, lighting, automation, digital convergence, PC networking and residential gateways. Readers include: Manufacturers, distributors, telcos, cable companies, OEMs, hardware/software developers, consumer electronics firms, dealers, utilities and analysts.
Formerly (until 1997): Electronic House Intelligence Report (1092-0722)
Related titles: E-mail ed.
Published by: E H Publishing, Inc., 111 Speen St, Ste 200, Framingham, MA 01701-2000. TEL 508-358-3400, 651-275-9564, FAX 508-358-5195, 651-275-9568, http://www.homenetnews.com/. Ed. Julie Jacobson. Pub. Kenneth Moyes.

HOMECARE MAGAZINE. see *MEDICAL SCIENCES—Nurses And Nursing*

659.1 HND
HONDURAS. CONSEJO SUPERIOR DE PLANIFICACION ECONOMICA. PLAN OPERATIVO ANUAL. SECTOR INDUSTRIAL. Text in Spanish. a.
Published by: Consejo Superior de Planificacion Economica, Secretaria Tecnica, Tegucigalpa DC, Honduras.

HONDURAS. CONSEJO SUPERIOR DE PLANIFICACION ECONOMICA. PLAN OPERATIVO ANUAL. SECTOR TURISMO. see *TRAVEL AND TOURISM*

330 HKG
HONG KONG BUSINESS. Text in Chinese. 1982. m. HKD 250; HKD 30 newsstand/cover. adv. **Document type:** *Consumer.* **Description:** Covers Hong Kong, China and international business. Also contains news and features that affect businesspeople in Hong Kong.
Formerly: Hong Kong Business Today
Related titles: Online - full text ed.; ◆ Supplement(s): Hong Kong Business Annual.
Indexed: HongKongiana.
Published by: Communication Management Ltd., 1811 Hong Kong Plaza, 188 Connaught Rd W, Hong Kong, Hong Kong. FAX 852-2858-2671. Ed. Gopalan M P. Pub., R&P Lina Ross. Adv. contact Louis Shek. B&W page HKD 19,160, color page HKD 28,465; 184 x 260. Circ: 14,677.

330 HKG
HONG KONG BUSINESS ANNUAL. Text and summaries in English. 1989. a. HKD 48 domestic; USD 15 foreign; HKD 69 newsstand/cover. adv. back issues avail. **Document type:** *Magazine, Consumer.*
Related titles: ◆ Supplement to: Hong Kong Business.
Indexed: HongKongiana.
Published by: Communication Management Ltd., 1811 Hong Kong Plaza, 188 Connaught Rd W, Hong Kong, Hong Kong. TEL 852-2859-4343, FAX 852-2859-4343, cmail@cmlink.com. Ed. M P Gopalan. Pub. Lina Ross. Adv. contact Louis Shek. B&W page HKD 19,160, color page HKD 28,465; trim 210 x 286. **Dist. by:** Hg Hing Kee Book and Newspaper Agency, Unit 6 G-F, Kai Fuk Ind Ctr., Bay, 1 Wang Tung St, Kowloon Bay, Kowloon, Hong Kong. TEL 852-2759-3808, FAX 852-2759-0050.

330 HKG
HONG KONG ECONOMIC YEARBOOK. Text in Chinese. a. adv.
Published by: Economic Information & Agency, 342 Hennessy Rd 10th Fl, 10 th Fl, Wanchai, Hong Kong. TEL 852-573-8217, FAX 852-838-8304. Circ: 9,800.

330 HKG
HONG KONG JINGJI RIBAO/HONG KONG ECONOMIC TIMES. Text in Chinese. 1988. d. (Mon.-Sat.). HKD 1,800. adv. film rev.; music rev.; play rev. illus. **Document type:** *Newspaper, Consumer.* **Description:** Business newspaper that concentrates on economic news and reports. Also covers a diverse range of political, social and cultural topics.
Related titles: Supplement(s): H K Money Times; H K Information Technology Times.
Published by: E T Press/Jingji Ribao Chubanshe, Beijiao Zhahuadao 321 Hao, Heda Dasha 2 Zuo 808-809 Shi, Hong Kong, Hong Kong. TEL 852-2880-2444, FAX 852-2516-9989, etpress@hket.com, http://www.etpress.com.hk/. adv.: B&W page HKD 34,560, color page HKD 69,760; trim 208 x 140. Circ: 59,806 (paid).

HONG KONG. LEGISLATIVE COUNCIL. FINANCE COMMITTEE. REPORT. see *PUBLIC ADMINISTRATION*

330 HKG
HONG KONG SPECIAL ADMINISTRATIVE REGION OF CHINA. CENSUS AND STATISTICS DEPARTMENT. EMPLOYMENT AND VACANCIES STATISTICS (DETAILED TABLES) SERIES D. IMPORT/EXPORT TRADES. Text in Chinese, English. 1981. a., latest 2000. HKD 26 (effective 2002). stat. **Document type:** *Government.* **Description:** Contains detailed employment and vacancies statistics in respect of the import/export trades. The statistics are analyzed by district Council District and size of establishment.
Related titles: Online - full content ed.
Published by: Census and Statistics Department/Zhengfu Tongjichu, Employment Statistics Section, 20/F Wanchai Tower, 12 Harbour Rd, Wan Chai, Hong Kong. TEL 852-2582-5076, FAX 852-2827-2296, es_2@censtatd.gov.hk, http://www.info.gov.hk/censtatd/eng/public/pub_list/ES/sev_d_index.html, http://www.statisticalbookstore.gov.hk. **Subscr. to:** Government Publications Centre; Information Services Department, Publications Sales Section, 4/F, Murray Bldg, Garden Rd, Hong Kong, Hong Kong. TEL 852-2842-8844, FAX 852-2598-7482, puborder@isd.gcn.gov.hk, http://www.info.gov.hk/isd/book_e.htm.

330 USA
HOUSE OF BUSINESS. Text in English. 2000. bi-m. USD 19.99; USD 4.99 newsstand/cover (effective 2001). adv. **Document type:** *Magazine, Consumer.*
Published by: House of Business LLC, 928 Broadway, New York, NY 10010. TEL 212-358-0486, FAX 212-358-0492, editor@houseofbusinessmag.com, http://www.houseofbusinessmag.com. Ed., Pub. Scott DeGarmo.

HOUSTON BUSINESS AND TAX LAW JOURNAL. see *LAW*

330 USA
HOW TO DO BUSINESS WITH THE UNITED NATIONS✶; the complete guide to U.N. procurement. Text in English. a. **Document type:** *Trade.*
Published by: United Nations Association of the United States of America, Inc., 801 2nd Ave, New York, NY 10017-4706. Eds. Ralph L Gwerman, Sandrine Tessonneyre.

380.1029 USA ISSN 0278-372X
HD2771
HOW TO FIND INFORMATION ABOUT COMPANIES; the corporate intelligence source book. Text in English. a. (in 3 vols.). USD 395 (effective 1999). **Document type:** *Directory.* **Description:** Provides business managers worldwide with guidance on finding information about their competitors.

Published by: Washington Researchers, Ltd., 1655 Fort Myer Dr., Ste. 800, Arlington, VA 22209-3119. TEL 703-312-2863, FAX 703-527-4586, research@researchers.com, http://www.researchers.com. Ed. M Newman. R&P Ellen O'Kane.

330 020 USA ISSN 1044-9337
HD38.7
HOW TO FIND INFORMATION ABOUT DIVISIONS, SUBSIDIARIES, & PRODUCTS. Text in English. a. USD 145 (effective 1999). **Document type:** *Directory.* **Description:** Tells where to look for obscure information about a segment of a company; how to determine which government agencies, trade associations, and industry experts can be of help; and how to tap the company's competitors for information.
Published by: Washington Researchers, Ltd., 1655 Fort Myer Dr., Ste. 800, Arlington, VA 22209-3119. TEL 703-312-2863, FAX 703-527-4586, research@researchers.com, http://www.researchers.com, http://www.washingtonresearchers.com. Ed. M Newman. R&P Ellen O'Kane.

660 CHN ISSN 1008-0511
TP1
➤ **HUAGONG KEJI/SCIENCE & TECHNOLOGY IN CHEMICAL INDUSTRY.** Text in Chinese. bi-m. USD 48 (effective 2001). 64 p./no.; back issues avail. **Document type:** *Journal, Academic/Scholarly.*
Related titles: Online - full text ed.: (from East View Information Services).
—BLDSC (8134.255400), IE, ingenta.
Published by: Jilin Chemical Group Corporation, 27 East Zunyi Rd, Jilin City, Jilin Province 132021, China. TEL 86-432-3973377, FAX 86-432-3977065, hgkjcn@sina.com. Ed. Zhu Xinghao.

330 CHN ISSN 1004-9754
➤ **HUAN BOHAI JINGJI LIAOWANG/ECONOMIC OUTLOOK ROUND THE BOHAI SEA.** Text in Chinese. 1987. bi-m. CNY 48 (effective 2000); USD 18. adv. bk.rev. **Document type:** *Academic/Scholarly.* **Description:** Regional economic magazine covering Bohai Sea Rim and Pacific Ocean Rim.
Related titles: Online - full text ed.: (from East View Information Services).
Published by: Huan Bohai Diqu Jingji Xinxi Xiehui/Economic Information Association of the Bohai Sea Rim, 39 Youyi Lu, Hexi-qu, Tianjin 300201, China. TEL 86-22-2813-1745, FAX 86-22-2835-4270. Ed., R&P Kaiming Lin. Pub. Yuelong Fan. Adv. contact Xiuli Chen. B&W page CNY 1,800. Circ: 20,000 (paid).

330 CHN ISSN 1005-4901
HUANQIU SHICHANG XINXI DAOBAO/GLOBAL MARKET INFORMATION HERALD. Text in Chinese. m. **Document type:** *Academic/Scholarly.* **Description:** Analyzes Chinese and foreign market trends. Contains market studies, investment guides and interviews of prominent figures of various industries.
Published by: Zhongguo Shehui Kexueyuan, Wenxian Xinxi Zhongxin/Chinese Academy of Social Sciences, Centre for Documentation and Information, No. 5, Jianguomen-nei Dajie, Beijing, 100732, China. TEL 86-10-6523-0096, FAX 86-10-5512-6393. Ed. Huiguo Li. **Dist. overseas by:** China International Book Trading Corp, 35 Chegongzhuang Xilu, Haidian District, PO Box 399, Beijing 100044, China.

330 USA ISSN 1050-1096
HUDSON VALLEY BUSINESS JOURNAL. Text in English. 1986. fortn. USD 26 (effective 2003). adv. 40 p./no. 4 cols./p.; back issues avail. **Document type:** *Newspaper.*
Formerly (until 198?): Orange County Business Journal (1040-3000)
Related titles: Online - full text ed.: (from EBSCO Publishing).
Address: 86 E Main St, Wappinger Falls, NY 12590. TEL 845-298-6236, FAX 845-298-6238, hvbjmail@aol.com, http://www.hvbj.com. Ed., R&P Edward Klein. adv.: B&W page USD 1,320, color page USD 1,547. Circ: 15,000 (paid). **Dist. by:** Kornish-Kissen, Rte 211 E, Middletown, NY 10940. TEL 914-692-4321.

330 USA ISSN 1546-4423
HC107.N72
HUDSON VALLEY REVIEW. Text in English. 1992. q.
Published by: Marist College, School of Management, Bureau of Economic Research, 3399 North Rd., Poughkeepsie, NY 12601. TEL 845-575-3945, FAX 845-575-3640, http://www.marist.edu/management/bureau.

330 IND ISSN 0419-0432
HUKERIKAR MEMORIAL LECTURE SERIES. Text in English. 1964. irreg. price varies.
Published by: Institute of Economic Research, Director, Vidyagiri, Dharwar, Karnataka 580 004, India. FAX 836-41001.

650 GBR ISSN 1368-0765
HULL BUSINESS SCHOOL. WORKING PAPER. Key Title: Working Paper - Hull Business School. Text in English. 1997. irreg. **Document type:** *Monographic series, Academic/Scholarly.*
Published by: University of Lincoln, Business School, Brayford Pool, Lincoln, LN6 7TS, United Kingdom. TEL 44-1522-882000, enquiries@lincoln.ac.uk, http://www.lincoln.ac.uk.

330 HUN ISSN 0133-0365
HC267.A2
HUNGARIAN ECONOMY/GAZDASAGI HETILAP FIGYELO; a quarterly economic and business review. Text in English. 1972-199?; resumed. q. USD 19.50. adv. bk.rev. **Document type:** *Government.*
Indexed: KES, PROMT, RASB.
Published by: (Israel. Ministry of Industry and Trade ISR), Verzal Co. Ltd., Frangepan utca 66, Budapest 13, 1135, Hungary. TEL 36-1-118-6064, FAX 36-1-118-0524. Ed. Andras Hirschler. Circ: 11,000.

I C A UPDATE (CHICAGO). see *TRANSPORTATION—Automobiles*

I C O M NEWSLETTER. see *ADVERTISING AND PUBLIC RELATIONS*

659 USA
I C S A NEWS. Text in English. 1981. q. USD 100. back issues avail. **Document type:** *Trade.* **Description:** Communicates news, ideas and business trends in customer service for professionals. Includes association and industry news, chapter news, technology updates, management tips and new member listings.
Published by: International Customer Service Association, 401 N Michigan Ave, Chicago, IL 60611-4267. TEL 312-321-6800, FAX 312-321-6869. Ed. Kristin Stromberg. Circ: 3,500.

▼ **I D E A TRAINER SUCCESS.** see *PHYSICAL FITNESS AND HYGIENE*

330 JPN
I D E INTERNATIONAL JOINT RESEARCH PROJECT SERIES. Text in English. 1996. irreg. price varies. **Document type:** *Academic/Scholarly.* **Description:** Consists of anthologies of papers based on collaborative research between the Institute and distinguished scholars in the US, the UK, and other developed countries.
Indexed: RDA.
Published by: Institute of Developing Economies/Ajia Keizai Kenkyusho, 3-2-2 Wakaba, Mihana-ku, Chiba-shi, Chiba 261-8545, Japan. TEL 81-43-299-9536, FAX 84-43-299-9724, info@ide.go.jp, http://www.ide.go.jp. Circ: 100. **Subscr. to:** Maruzen Co., Ltd., Export Dept., PO Box 5050, Tokyo International 100-3191, Japan. FAX 81-3-3278-9256, journal@maruzen.co.jp, http://www.maruzen.co.jp.

338.91 JPN ISSN 0537-9202
➤ **I D E OCCASIONAL PAPERS SERIES.** Text in English. 1967. irreg., latest vol.38, 2002. price varies. **Document type:** *Monographic series, Academic/Scholarly.*
Formerly (until 1969): I A E A Occasional Papers
Published by: Institute of Developing Economies/Ajia Keizai Kenkyusho, 3-2-2 Wakaba, Mihana-ku, Chiba-shi, Chiba 261-8545, Japan. TEL 81-43-299-9536, FAX 84-43-299-9724, info@ide.go.jp, http://www.ide.go.jp. Circ: 100. **Subscr. to:** Maruzen Co., Ltd., Export Dept., PO Box 5050, Tokyo International 100-3191, Japan. FAX 81-3-3278-9256, journal@maruzen.co.jp, http://www.maruzen.co.jp.

330 JPN
➤ **I D E RESEARCH SERIES/KENKYU-SOSHO.** Text in Japanese. 1959. irreg., latest vol.531, 2003. price varies. **Document type:** *Academic/Scholarly.* **Description:** Covers a wide spectrum of topics on developing countries. Issues have included titles such as "Civil Society in Asia: Political Dynamics between State and Society," "Financial Crises and Regulations," and "Reexamining the Informal Sector in Africa." Subject areas include business, economics, political science, agriculture, sociology, environmental studies, history and law.
—BLDSC (4362.345500).
Published by: Institute of Developing Economies/Ajia Keizai Kenkyusho, 3-2-2 Wakaba, Mihana-ku, Chiba-shi, Chiba 261-8545, Japan. TEL 81-43-299-9536, FAX 84-43-299-9724, info@ide.go.jp, http://www.ide.go.jp. Circ: 700.

330 JPN
I D E SPOT SURVEY. Text in English. 1995. irreg. **Document type:** *Academic/Scholarly.* **Description:** Intends to respond to public demand by offering prompt analyses of emerging problems in developing countries, such as the financial crisis in East Asian countries, tensions between Iraq and the U.S., etc.
Published by: Institute of Developing Economies/Ajia Keizai Kenkyusho, 3-2-2 Wakaba, Mihana-ku, Chiba-shi, Chiba 261-8545, Japan. TEL 81-43-299-9536, FAX 84-43-299-9724, info@ide.go.jp, http://www.ide.go.jp. Circ: 1,500.

338.91 JPN
I D E SYMPOSIUM PROCEEDINGS. Text in English. 1974. a. price varies. **Document type:** *Proceedings.*
Published by: Institute of Developing Economies/Ajia Keizai Kenkyusho, 3-2-2 Wakaba, Mihana-ku, Chiba-shi, Chiba 261-8545, Japan. TEL 81-43-299-9536, FAX 84-43-299-9724, info@ide.go.jp, http://www.ide.go.jp. Circ: 100. **Subscr. to:** Maruzen Co., Ltd., Export Dept., PO Box 5050, Tokyo International 100-3191, Japan. FAX 81-3-3278-9256, journal@maruzen.co.jp, http://www.maruzen.co.jp.

330 DEU ISSN 0945-1730
I F O DOKUMENTATION. Text in German. 1993. irreg., latest vol.4, 1995. **Document type:** *Monographic series.*
Published by: I F O Institut fuer Wirtschaftsforschung, Poschingerstr 5, Munich, 81679, Germany. TEL 49-89-9224-0, FAX 49-89-985369, ifo@ifo.de, http://www.ifo.de.

330 DEU
I F O DRESDEN BERICHTET; ueber Konjunktur, Struktur, Wirtschaftspolitik. Text in German. bi-m. **Document type:** *Bulletin.*
Published by: I F O Institut fuer Wirtschaftsforschung, Poschingerstr 5, Munich, 81679, Germany. TEL 49-89-9224-0, FAX 49-89-985369, ifo@ifo.de, http://www.ifo.de.

330 DEU
I F O FORSCHUNGSBERICHTE DER ABTEILUNG ENTWICKLUNGSLAENDER. Text in German. 1965. irreg., latest vol.88, 1999. **Document type:** *Monographic series.* **Description:** Covers economic issues affecting developing nations.
Published by: (I F O Institut fuer Wirtschaftsforschung), Weltforum Verlag, Hohenzollernplatz 3, Bonn, 53173, Germany. TEL 49-228-368243-0, FAX 49-228-3682439, ifo@ifo.de. Circ: 150.

330 DEU ISSN 0947-3173
I F O IM (MONTH). Text in German. m. **Document type:** *Bulletin.*
Published by: I F O Institut fuer Wirtschaftsforschung, Poschingerstr 5, Munich, 81679, Germany. TEL 49-89-9224-0, FAX 49-89-985369, ifo@ifo.de, http://www.ifo.de.

330 DEU ISSN 0445-0736
I F O INSTITUT FUER WIRTSCHAFTSFORSCHUNG. SCHRIFTENREIHE. Text in German. 1949. irreg., latest vol.149, 2000. price varies. **Document type:** *Monographic series, Academic/Scholarly.*
Published by: (I F O Institut fuer Wirtschaftsforschung), Duncker und Humblot GmbH, Carl-Heinrich-Becker-Weg 9, Berlin, 12165, Germany. TEL 49-30-7900060, FAX 49-30-79000631, info@duncker-humblot.de, http://www.duncker-humblot.de.

330 DEU ISSN 0536-1613
I F O INSTITUT FUER WIRTSCHAFTSFORSCHUNG. SONDERSCHRIFT. Text in German. 1949. irreg., latest vol.38, 1972. price varies. **Document type:** *Monographic series, Academic/Scholarly.*
Published by: (I F O Institut fuer Wirtschaftsforschung), Duncker und Humblot GmbH, Carl-Heinrich-Becker-Weg 9, Berlin, 12165, Germany. TEL 49-30-7900060, FAX 49-30-79000631, info@duncker-humblot.de, http://www.duncker-humblot.de.

330 DEU
I F O KONJUNKTURPERSPEKTIVEN. Text in German. 1974. m. back issues avail. **Document type:** *Bulletin.*
Formerly (until 1991): Konjunkturperspektiven
Published by: I F O Institut fuer Wirtschaftsforschung, Poschingerstr 5, Munich, 81679, Germany. TEL 49-89-9224-0, FAX 49-89-985369, ifo@ifo.de, http://www.ifo.de.

330 DEU ISSN 0018-974X
HC281
I F O SCHNELLDIENST. Text in German. 1948. 2/m. EUR 96 to individuals; EUR 225 to institutions; EUR 48 to students; EUR 10 newsstand/cover (effective 2001). bk.rev. charts; stat. **Document type:** *Journal, Academic/Scholarly.*
Related titles: Online - full text ed.: (from ProQuest Information & Learning).
Indexed: ABIn, ELLIS, KES, RASB, WAE&RSA.
—BLDSC (4363.320000). **CCC.**
Published by: I F O Institut fuer Wirtschaftsforschung, Poschingerstr 5, Munich, 81679, Germany. TEL 49-89-9224-0, FAX 49-89-985369, ifo@ifo.de, http://www.ifo.de. Ed. Marga Jennewein.

330 DEU ISSN 0170-5695
I F O STUDIEN ZU HANDELS- UND DIENSTLEISTUNGSFRAGEN. Text in German. 1962. irreg., latest vol.56, 1998. price varies. **Document type:** *Monographic series.* **Description:** Research results concerning marketing and service sectors.
Formerly: I F O Institut fuer Wirtschaftsforschung. Studien zu Handelsfragen (0073-4268)
Published by: I F O Institut fuer Wirtschaftsforschung, Poschingerstr 5, Munich, 81679, Germany. TEL 49-89-9224-0, FAX 49-89-985369, ifo@ifo.de, http://www.ifo.de. Circ: 400.

330 700 DEU
I F O STUDIEN ZU KULTUR UND WIRTSCHAFT. Text in German. 1990. irreg., latest vol.24, 1999. price varies. **Document type:** *Monographic series.*
Published by: I F O Institut fuer Wirtschaftsforschung, Poschingerstr 5, Munich, 81679, Germany. TEL 49-89-9224-0, FAX 49-89-985369, ifo@ifo.de, http://www.ifo.de.

I F O STUDIEN ZUR BEVOELKERUNGSOEKONOMIE. see *POPULATION STUDIES*

330 DEU ISSN 0944-0356
I F O STUDIEN ZUR INNOVATIONSFORSCHUNG. Text in German. 1993. irreg., latest vol.4, 1997. price varies. **Document type:** *Monographic series.*
Published by: I F O Institut fuer Wirtschaftsforschung, Poschingerstr 5, Munich, 81679, Germany. TEL 49-89-9224-0, FAX 49-89-985369, ifo@ifo.de, http://www.ifo.de.

330 DEU ISSN 0176-0874
I F O STUDIEN ZUR STRUKTURFORSCHUNG. Text in German. 1983. irreg., latest vol.30, 1999. price varies. **Document type:** *Monographic series.*
Published by: I F O Institut fuer Wirtschaftsforschung, Poschingerstr 5, Munich, 81679, Germany. TEL 49-89-9224-0, FAX 49-89-985369, ifo@ifo.de, http://www.ifo.de.

363.7 DEU ISSN 0175-8330
HC240.A1
I F O STUDIEN ZUR UMWELTOEKONOMIE. Text in German. 1984. irreg., latest vol.24, 1999. price varies. **Document type:** *Monographic series.*
Published by: I F O Institut fuer Wirtschaftsforschung, Poschingerstr 5, Munich, 81679, Germany. TEL 49-89-9224-0, FAX 49-89-985369, ifo@ifo.de, http://www.ifo.de.

330 BOL
I I E REVISTA. Variant title: Revista Economica. Text in Spanish. 1945. s-a. USD 10.
Published by: Universidad Boliviana Tecnica de Oruro, Instituto de Investigaciones Economicas, Casilla 441, Oruro, Bolivia.

330 DEU
I K B DEUTSCHE INDUSTRIEBANK. GESCHAEFTSBEREICH VOLKSWIRTSCHAFT UND MARKETING. I K B - MITTEILUNGEN. Text in German. 3/yr. **Document type:** *Bulletin.*
Former titles: Deutsche Industriebank. Geschaeftsbereich Volkswirtschaft. I K B - Mitteilungen (0940-0001); Deutsche Industriebank. Volkswirtschaftliche Abteilung. V W - Mitteilungen
Published by: I K B Deutsche Industriebank AG, Wilhelm-Boetzkes-Str 1, Duesseldorf, 40474, Germany. TEL 49-211-8221-4499, FAX 49-211-8221-2766. Circ: 16,000.

I M S COMPANY PROFILES. see *PHARMACY AND PHARMACOLOGY*

I N A VJESNIK INDUSTRIJE NAFTE. see *PETROLEUM AND GAS*

330 USA
I P A REPORT. Text in English. s-a.
Indexed: PAIS.
Published by: Institute of Public Administration, 411 Lafayette St, 3rd Fl, New York, NY 10003. TEL 212-992-9899, FAX 212-995-4876, info@theipa.org, publications@thejpa.org, http://www.theipa.org/publications/ipareport.html.

330.9 BRA
I P E A SERIE P N P E. Text in Portuguese. 1982. irreg., latest vol.11, 1985. price varies.
Published by: (Programa Nacional de Pesquisa Economica), Instituto de Planejamento Economico e Social, Centro, Caixa Postal 2672, Rio De Janeiro, RJ 20001970, Brazil. TEL 021-220-5533. Ed. Hamilton N Marques. Circ: 1,000.

I R I SENTINEL. see *INSURANCE*

330 USA ISSN 1549-8204
I S A - I E E E SENSORS FOR INDUSTRY CONFERENCE. PROCEEDINGS. Text in English. 2001. a. **Document type:** *Proceedings, Academic/Scholarly.*
Published by: I E E E Service Center, 445 Hoes Ln, PO Box 1331, Piscataway, NJ 08855-1331. TEL 908-981-0060, 800-678-4333.

330 SGP ISSN 0218-2114
➤ **I S E A S CURRENT ECONOMIC AFFAIRS SERIES.** Text in English. 1991. irreg., latest vol.29, 2003. price varies. back issues avail. **Document type:** *Monographic series, Academic/Scholarly.* **Description:** Covers current economic affairs in the Asia-Pacific region.
Published by: Institute of Southeast Asian Studies, 30 Heng Mui Keng Terrace, Pasir Panjang, Singapore, 119614, Singapore. TEL 65-6870-2447, FAX 65-6775-6259, pubsunit@iseas.edu.sg, http://www.iseas.edu.sg/. R&P Mrs. Triena Ong TEL 65-6870-2449.

330 JPN
I S E R REPRINT SERIES. Text in Japanese. a. **Description:** Reprints of articles published by ISER members or by others working in association with the institute.
Published by: Institute of Social and Economic Research, Osaka University, 10-1 Mihogaoka, Ibaraki-shi, Osaka 567, Japan. TEL 06-8775111.

I-STREET MAGAZINE. see *COMPUTERS—Internet*

I T LEADERSHIP; leveraging business performance through technology. (Information Technology) see *COMPUTERS*

I T S QUARTERLY. see *TRANSPORTATION*

330 DEU ISSN 0344-919X
I W D. Text in German. 1975. w. EUR 127.28; EUR 81.68 to students (effective 2005). **Document type:** *Bulletin, Trade.*
Formed by the merger of (1951-1975): Institut der Deutschen Wirtschaft. Unternehmerbrief (0344-9181); Which was formerly (until 1973): Deutsche Industrieinstitut. Unternehmerbrief (0415-7257); (1951-1975): Institut der Deutschen Wirtschaft. Schnelldienst (0344-8975); Which was formerly (until 1973): Deutsche Industrieinstitut. Schnelldienst (0344-8983)
Published by: (Institut der Deutschen Wirtschaft), Deutscher Instituts Verlag GmbH, Gustav-Heinemann-Ufer 84-88, Cologne, 50968, Germany. TEL 49-221-4981510, FAX 49-221-4981533, div@iwkoeln.de, http://www.iwkoeln.de.

330 ISL ISSN 1670-1976
THE ICELANDIC ECONOMY. Cover title: Economic Outlook for Iceland. Text in English. 1975. s-a. **Document type:** *Government.*
Related titles: Online - full text ed.: ISSN 1670-4355. 2002; ♦ Icelandic ed.: Thjodarbuskapurinn. ISSN 1670-1968.
Published by: Fjarmalaraduneytid/Icelandic Ministry of Finance, Arnarhvall, Reykjavik, 150, Iceland. TEL 354-545-9200, FAX 354-562-8280, mail@fjr.stjr.is, http://www.ministryoffinance.is.

330 USA ISSN 8750-4022
IDAHO BUSINESS REVIEW. Text in English. 1984. w. (Mon.). USD 75 (effective 2005). adv. bk.rev. stat. back issues avail. **Document type:** *Newspaper, Trade.* **Description:** Provides current news, plus information about records and construction for business owners and managers.
Related titles: Online - full text ed.: USD 30 (effective 2005) (from Newsbank, Inc., O C L C Online Computer Library Center, Inc., ProQuest Information & Learning).
Indexed: ABIn, BusDate.
Address: 200 North Fourth St, Ste 300, Boise, ID 83702. TEL 208-336-3768, FAX 208-336-5534, info@idahobusiness.net, news@idahobusiness.net, http://www.idahobusiness.net. Ed. Steven Anderson. Pub. Rick Carpenter. Adv. contact Rocky Cook. page USD 1,335. Circ: 2,550.

330 USA
IDEA CENTRAL. Text in English. m.
Media: Online - full content.
Published by: Electronic Policy Network epn@epn.org, http://epn.org/prospect/mission.html.

330 USA
IDEA-LETTER. Text in English. 2001. m. USD 49.95; USD 8 newsstand/cover (effective 2005). **Document type:** *Newsletter.*
Published by: Small Business Marketing Ideas, 5585 Erindale Dr #203, Colorado Springs, CO 80918. TEL 877-700-1322, FAX 719-268-1323, idealetter@aol.com, http://www.idealetter.com. Ed., Pub. Barry Thomsen.

330 ESP
IDEAS EMPRESARIALES. Text in Spanish, English. 1982. 4/yr. free. adv. **Document type:** *Magazine, Academic/Scholarly.* **Description:** Business and economics studies and news.
Published by: Asociacion de Antiguos Alumnos del Instituto de Empresa, Maria de Molina, 12, Madrid, 28006, Spain. TEL 34-91-5689621, FAX 34-91-5689711, alumni@ie.edu, http://www.ideas-empresariales.com. Ed. Victoria Gimeno. Adv. contact Maria Ybarra. Circ: 19,627.

330 FRA ISSN 0180-9709
IDEES LUCRATIVES. Text in French. 10/yr.
Published by: Maison des Chevaliers de Saint Jean, 1 Place du Lycee, BP 266, Colmar, Cedex 68005, France. TEL 89-24-04-64, FAX 89-23-58-27. Ed. Jean Luc Specht. Circ: 15,000.

330 RUS
IDEI DLYA SHEFA. Text in Russian. 1995. bi-m. USD 100 in North America (effective 2000).
Published by: Interekspert, E-37, Moscow, 105037, Russian Federation. TEL 7-095-1662281, FAX 7-095-1661127. Ed. M K Petrosian. **Dist. by:** East View Information Services, 3020 Harbor Ln. N., Minneapolis, MN 55447. TEL 763-550-0961, FAX 763-559-2931.

330 JPN ISSN 0915-5732
TN860
IDEMITSU GIHO. Text in Japanese. 1958. bi-m.
Formerly (until 1989): Idemitsu Sekiyu Gijutsu (0286-4649)
—BLDSC (4362.421000).
Published by: Idemitsu Kosan Kabushiki Gaisha/Idemitsu Kosan Co., Ltd., 1-1, Marunouchi 3-chome, Chiyoda-ku, Tokyo, 100-8321, Japan. http://www.idemitsu.co.jp/gijutsu/index.html.

330 BGR ISSN 0013-2993
HC407.B9
IKONOMICHESKA MISUL. Text in Bulgarian; Summaries in English. 1956. bi-m. BGL 0.75 newsstand/cover; USD 62 foreign (effective 2002). bk.rev. charts. index. reprint service avail. from IRC. **Document type:** *Journal.* **Description:** Reflects economic theory and practice in Bulgaria and abroad; reveals the problems of Bulgarian economic reforms, transactions to market economy and specific conditions of the Bulgarian economy.
Related titles: English ed.: Economic Thought. USD 26 (effective 2002).
Indexed: BSLEcon, RASB.
Published by: (Bulgarska Akademiya na Naukite/Bulgarian Academy of Sciences, Ikonomiceski Institut), Universitetsko Izdatelstvo Sv. Kliment Okhridski/Publishing House of the Sofia University St. Kliment Ohridski, Akad G Bonchev 6, Sofia, 1113, Bulgaria. Ed. K Kiriakov. Circ: 6,220. **Dist. by:** Hemus, 6 Rouski Blvd., Sofia 1000, Bulgaria.

330 BGR ISSN 0205-3292
IKONOMICHESKI IZSLEDVANIA/STUDIES OF ECONOMICS. Text in Bulgarian; Summaries in English. 1985. 3/yr. USD 75 foreign; USD 20 per issue foreign (effective 2004). **Document type:** *Journal, Academic/Scholarly.*
Indexed: JEL, RefZh.
Published by: Bulgarska Akademiya na Naukite, Ikonomiceski Institut/Bulgarian Academy of Sciences, Institute of Economics, 3 Aksakov St., Sofia, 1040, Bulgaria. TEL 359-2-9890595, FAX 359-2-9882108, ineco@iki.bas.bg, http://www.iki.bas.bg/. Ed. Mitko Dimitrov.

330 659.1 BGR ISSN 0205-0994
IKONOMICHESKI ZHIVOT. Text in Bulgarian. 1965. w. USD 210 foreign (effective 2002). adv. bk.rev. charts; illus.; pat.; stat.; tr.lit. **Document type:** *Newspaper.* **Description:** Publishes business news for businessmen, managers, accountants, insurance and advertising agents; documents and comments by Council of Ministers, Ministry of Finance, National Statistical Institute.
Indexed: RASB.
Address: Moskovska ul 9, Sofia, 1000, Bulgaria. TEL 35-92-879506, FAX 35-92-882140. Ed. Vasil Alexiev. Adv. contact Dimistar Ivanov. Circ: 20,000. **Dist. by:** Sofia Books, ul Silivria 16, Sofia 1404, Bulgaria. TEL 359-2-9586257, info@sofiabooks-bg.com, http://www.sofiabooks-bg.com.

330 USA
THE ILLINOIS MANUFACTURERS ASSOCIATION. ANNUAL REPORTS. BENEFITS REPORT. Text in English. a. **Document type:** *Trade.* **Description:** Provides information on employee benefits packages.
Published by: The Illinois Manufacturers Association, 220 E Adams St, Springfield, IL 62701-1123. TEL 630-368-5300, 800-875-4462, FAX 630-218-7467, ima@ima-net.org, http://www.ima-net.org/.

330 USA
THE ILLINOIS MANUFACTURERS ASSOCIATION. ANNUAL REPORTS. COMPENSATION REPORT. Text in English. a. **Document type:** *Corporate.* **Description:** Covers wages, salaries, and compensation data.
Published by: The Illinois Manufacturers Association, 220 E Adams St, Springfield, IL 62701-1123. TEL 630-368-5300, 800-875-4462, FAX 630-218-7467, ima@ima-net.org, http://www.ima-net.org/.

330 USA
IMANET. Text in English. m. free domestic to members (effective 2005). **Document type:** *Newsletter, Trade.* **Description:** Contains important information concerning taxation, human resources, labor, worker(UNKNOWN CHARACTER)s compensation, unemployment compensation, government, legislative updates (from both the state and federal levels), environment, manufacturing trends and other current developments affecting industry.
Published by: Indiana Manufacturers Association, Inc., One American Sq., Ste 2400, Indianapolis, IN 46282. TEL 317-632-2474, FAX 317-231-2320, ima@imaweb.com, http://www.imaweb.com. Ed. Charlene Hickey. Circ: 5,600 (controlled).

330 ITA ISSN 1591-612X
IMPRESA ARTIGIANA. Text in Italian. 1987. d. free to members. adv. **Document type:** *Magazine, Trade.*
Related titles: Online - full text ed.
Published by: Confederazione Generale Italiana dell'Artigianato, Via di San Giovanni in Laterano, 152, Rome, RM 00184, Italy. TEL 39-06-703741, stampa@confnaz.confartigianato.it, http://www.confartigianato.it. Ed. Giovanni Vitelli. Circ: 3,000.

330 DEU ISSN 0720-9037
IMPULSE (HAMBURG). Text in German. 1980. m. EUR 43.20; EUR 5.50 newsstand/cover (effective 2003). adv. **Document type:** *Magazine, Consumer.*
Related titles: Microfilm ed.: (from ALP).
—IE, Infotrieve.
Published by: Gruner und Jahr AG & Co., Am Baumwall 11, Hamburg, 20459, Germany. TEL 49-40-3703-0, FAX 49-40-37036000, ksc@guj.de, http://www.impulse.de, http://www.guj.de. adv.: B&W page EUR 11,190, color page EUR 15,300. Circ: 156,655 (paid).

B

330 USA ISSN 1530-1575
IN BUSINESS LAS VEGAS. Text in English. 2000. w. (Fri.). USD 38 (effective 2005). **Document type:** *Magazine, Trade.*
Related titles: Online - full content ed.
Published by: Greenspun Media Group, 2290 Corporate Circle, Ste 250, Henderson, NV 89074. TEL 702-990-2545, FAX 702-383-7264, http://www.inbusinesslasvegas.com/, https://www.greenspunmedia.com/. Ed. Michael J Kelley. Pub. Bruce Spotleson.

330 ROM ISSN 1224-1342
IN REVIEW. Variant title: In Review Romania. Text in English. 1995. m. **Document type:** *Magazine, Trade.*
Published by: Business Media Group, Bd. Regina Maria nr. 1, bl. P5B, sector 1, ap. 10-11-12, Bucharest, Romania. TEL 40-21-3353473, FAX 40-21-3353474, subscribe@bmg.ro.

330 600 USA
IN TECHNOLOGY. Text in English. m.
Published by: Pittsburgh Technology Council, 2000 Technology Dr, #100, Pittsburgh, PA 15219-3110. TEL 412-687-2700. Ed. Lynne Glover.

330 305.8 USA
IN THE BLACK; the African-American business journal. Text in English. q. USD 15.80 (effective 2001). adv.
Published by: In The Black Publishing Ltd, PO Box 470847, Aurora, CO 80047-0847. TEL 303-696-7988, FAX 303-671-7335.

330 SGP ISSN 1793-0960
▼ **INCREASING RETURNS AND INFRAMARGINAL ECONOMICS.** Text in English. 2005. irreg. price varies. **Document type:** *Monographic series, Academic/Scholarly.*
Published by: World Scientific Publishing Co. Pte. Ltd., 5 Toh Tuck Link, Singapore, 596224, Singapore. TEL 65-466-5775, FAX 65-467-7667, series@wspc.com.sg, http://www.wspc.com/books/series/irie_series.shtml, http://www.worldscientific.com. Eds. James Buchanan, Yew-Kwang Ng. **Subscr. to:** Farrer Rd, PO Box 128, Singapore 912805, Singapore. TEL 65-382-5663, FAX 65-382-5919. **Dist. by:** World Scientific Publishing Co., Inc., 1060 Main St, River Edge, NJ 07661. TEL 201-487-9655, 800-227-7562, FAX 201-487-9656, 888-977-2665, wspc@wspc.com.; World Scientific Publishing Ltd., 57 Shelton St, London WC2H 9HE, United Kingdom. TEL 44-20-78360888, FAX 44-20-78362020, sales@wspc.co.uk.

380.099305 NZL ISSN 1171-8730
INDEPENDENT. Text in English. 1992. m.
Indexed: WBA.
Published by: Pauanui Publishing Ltd., 57 Fort St., Level 3, Patent House, Auckland, New Zealand. TEL 64-9-3033534, FAX 64-9-3032999.

INDEPENDENT CATERER. see *HOTELS AND RESTAURANTS*

INDEX OF ECONOMIC FREEDOM. see *POLITICAL SCIENCE*

338 IND
INDIA. MINISTRY OF HEAVY INDUSTRY. REPORT. Text in English. 1973. irreg. **Document type:** *Government.*
Published by: Ministry of Heavy Industry, New Delhi, India.

INDIAN BUSINESS AND MANAGEMENT. see *NATIVE AMERICAN STUDIES*

330 IND ISSN 0019-4670
HB1.A1
➤ **INDIAN ECONOMIC REVIEW.** Text in English. 1952; N.S. 1966. s-a. INR 300, USD 50 (effective 1999). adv. bk.rev. charts. index. **Document type:** *Academic/Scholarly.*
Indexed: BAS, CREJ, ESPM, IBSS, JEL, PAIS, PCI, RASB, RDA, RRTA, RiskAb, WAE&RSA.
—BLDSC (4396.340000), IE, Infotrieve, ingenta.
Published by: University of Delhi, Delhi School of Economics, New Delhi, 110 007, India. TEL 91-11-7257005, FAX 91-11-7257159, ier@cdedse.ernet.in. Ed. Partha Sen. Circ: 600.

330 IND ISSN 0019-5170
HB9
➤ **INDIAN JOURNAL OF ECONOMICS.** Text in English. 1916. q. USD 175 (effective 2006). bk.rev. bibl.; charts; illus.; mkt.; pat.; tr.mk. Index. back issues avail. **Document type:** *Journal, Academic/Scholarly.* **Description:** Covers articles on economic problems by author of academic standing or authoritative positions, furnishing a convenient and compact vehicle for publication of original investigations, and disseminating information about the economic activities of India and other countries.
Related titles: Microfiche ed.: (from IDC).
Indexed: BAS, CREJ, CTFA, DIP, ESPM, IBR, IBSS, IBZ, ILD, JEL, PAA&I, PAIS, PCI, RASB, RDA, RiskAb, S&MA, SSCI, TOSA.
—BLDSC (4411.700000), IE, Infotrieve, ingenta.
Published by: Scientific Publishers, 5-A New Pali Rd., Near Hotel Taj Hari Mahal, PO Box 91, Jodhpur, Rajasthan 342 003, India. TEL 91-291-2433323, FAX 91-291-2512580, info@scientificpub.com, http://www.scientificpub.com/bookdetails.php?booktransid=316&bookid=312. Circ: 500.

330 IND ISSN 0972-5784
HC431
➤ **INDIAN JOURNAL OF ECONOMICS AND BUSINESS.** Abbreviated title: I J E B. Text in English. s-a. USD 60 to institutions (effective 2006). **Document type:** *Journal, Academic/Scholarly.*
Indexed: AgBio, JEL, MaizeAb, PGegResA, PHN&I, PoultAb, WAE&RSA.
—BLDSC (4411.705000), IE.
Published by: Serials Publications, 4, B.S.S. Hall, Khyber Pass Market, Civil Lines, Delhi, 110 054, India. TEL 91-11-3811659, FAX 91-11-3812678, serials@satyam.net.in, http://www.scientificpub.com/bookdetails.php?booktransid=464&bookid=460. Ed. Kishore G Kulkarni.

330 IND ISSN 0971-0396
INDIAN SCHOOL OF POLITICAL ECONOMY. JOURNAL. Text in English. 1989. q. USD 80. **Document type:** *Academic/Scholarly.*
Indexed: BAS.
Published by: (Indian School of Political Economy), New Age International Pvt. Ltd., Journals Division, 4835-24 Ansari Rd., Darya Ganj, New Delhi, 110 002, India. TEL 91-11-326-1487, FAX 91-11-326-7437.

INDIANA AGRINEWS. see *AGRICULTURE*

650 USA ISSN 0019-6541
HC107.I6 CODEN: IBREAO
INDIANA BUSINESS REVIEW. Text in English. 1926. q. free. charts; illus.
Related titles: Microfiche ed.: (from CIS); Online - full text ed.: (from bigchalk, EBSCO Publishing, Florida Center for Library Automation, Gale Group, Northern Light Technology, Inc., O C L C Online Computer Library Center, Inc., ProQuest Information & Learning).
Indexed: ABIn, BPIA, BusDate, JEL, PAIS, PMA, SRI.
Published by: Indiana University, School of Business, 107 S Indiana Ave, Bloomington, IN 47405. TEL 812-855-5507. Ed. Morton J Marcus. Circ: 4,000.

330 USA
INDIANA JOURNAL OF COMMERCE AND INDUSTRY. Text in English. 1988. m. USD 29.95. adv. **Document type:** *Newspaper.* **Description:** Provides domestic and international business news and analysis.
Formerly: Evansville Business Journal
Related titles: Online - full text ed.
Indexed: BusDate.
Published by: R & W Publishing, Inc., PO Box 3275, Evansville, IN 47731-3275. TEL 812-425-2210, FAX 812-422-4984. Ed., R&P Barbara Stahura. Pub., Adv. contact Conrad L Roe. Circ: 12,000.

330 600 PAN
INDICADORES DE ACTIVIDADES CIENTIFICAS Y TECNOLOGICAS. Text in Spanish. biennial. PAB 1 (effective 2000). **Document type:** *Bulletin.* **Description:** Presents indications for expenses in scientific and technological activities, investigation and development, human resources, invention patents and other items of interest.
Published by: Direccion de Estadistica y Censo, Contraloria General, Apdo. 5213, Panama City, 5, Panama. TEL 507-210-4800, FAX 507-210-4801, cgrdec@contraloria.gob.pa.

330 CHL ISSN 0716-2413
INDICADORES ECONOMICOS Y SOCIALES. Text in English, Spanish. 1981. irreg., latest vol.3, 1989. CLP 19,000, USD 55 newsstand/cover. charts; stat. **Description:** Presents the development of the Chilean economy.
Published by: Banco Central de Chile, Casilla 967, Santiago, Chile. TEL 56-2-670-2000, FAX 56-2-698-4847. Circ: 1,100.

338 IDN
INDOBIZ NEWS SELECTIONS. Text in English. irreg. **Description:** Designed for businesses related to Indonesia and for people seeking information about Indonesia.
Media: Online - full text.
Published by: Indonesia Business Center Online, Internet Nusa Bhakti, Indonesia. nusa@indobiz.com, http://www.indobiz.com/news/news.htm.

330 IDN
INDONESIA BUSINESS WEEKLY. Text in English. w.
Address: Bisnis Indonesia Bldg. 5th Fl., Slipi, Jl Let Jend S Parman Kav 12, Jakarta, 11410, Indonesia. TEL 5304016, FAX 5305868.

330 PAN
INDUSTRIA. Text in Spanish. 1953. q. free. adv. **Document type:** *Newsletter.*
Published by: Sindicato de Industriales de Panama, Apdo. 6-4798, El Dorado, Panama City, 1, Panama. TEL 507-30-0169. Ed. Flor Ortega. Circ: 1,000.

330 PRT
HC391
A INDUSTRIA DO NORTE. Text in Portuguese. 1846. w. free to qualified personnel (effective 2005). adv. **Document type:** *Newspaper, Trade.* **Description:** Deals with economical, technological, and juridical themes of industry.
Former titles: Industria do Norte - Informacao (0872-6728); (until 1994): Industria do Norte (0019-7572); (until 1938): Trabalho Nacional (0870-9505); (until 1915): Industrial Portuense
Related titles: ◆ Supplement to: Diario Economico. ISSN 0872-1696.
Indexed: PAIS.
Published by: Associacao Industrial Portuense, Praca das Industrias, Apdo 3200, Lisbon, 1301-965, Portugal. TEL 351-21-3601000, FAX 351-21-3641301, aip@aip.pt, http://www.aip.pt/. Ed. Norton de Maios. Pub. Angelo Ludgero Marques. Adv. contact Ana David. Circ: 5,000.

330 VEN
INDUSTRIA VENEZOLANA. Text in Spanish. 1971. 6/yr.
Published by: Editorial Guia Industrial, Chacao, Apdo 60772, Caracas, DF 1060, Venezuela. Ed. Jose Precedo.

INDUSTRIAL & TRADE DIRECTORY. see *BUSINESS AND ECONOMICS—Trade And Industrial Directories*

330 GBR
INDUSTRIAL DEVELOPMENT ACT, 1982, ANNUAL REPORT. Text in English. a. GBP 12. **Document type:** *Government.* **Description:** Describes the powers under the Act including the powers under past legislation which the act consolidated.
Published by: Stationery Office, 51 Nine Elms Ln, London, SW8 5DA, United Kingdom. TEL 44-20-7873-0011, FAX 44-20-7873-8247, book.orders@theso.co.uk, http://www.national-publishing.co.uk. **Dist. by:** UNIPUB, 4611-F Assembly Dr., Lantham, MD 20706-4391. TEL 301-459-7666.

330 USA
INDUSTRIAL DEVELOPMENT AND THE SOCIAL FABRIC; an international series of historical monographs. Text in English. 1979. irreg., latest vol.16, 2000. price varies. back issues avail. **Document type:** *Monographic series, Academic/Scholarly.*
—BLDSC (4449.491000).
Published by: J A I Press Inc. (Subsidiary of: Elsevier Science & Technology), 360 Park Ave S, New York, NY 10010-1710. TEL 212-989-5800, FAX 212-633-3990, usinfo-f@elsevier.com, http://www.elsevier.com/wps/find/bookdescription.cws_home/BS_IDSF/description#description. Ed. John P McKay.

INDUSTRIAL INFORMATICS AND INTEGRATED MANUFACTURING BUSINESS SYSTEMS SERIES. see *ENGINEERING—Industrial Engineering*

330 USA
INDUSTRIAL NEWS (IAEGER). Text in English. 1926. w. USD 6 (effective 1999). adv. **Document type:** *Newspaper.*
Related titles: CD-ROM ed.
Published by: William A. Johnson, Ed. & Pub., PO Box 180, Iaeger, WV 24844. TEL 304-938-2142. R&P William A Johnson. Adv. contact Sheila Bailey. Circ: 2,510.

INDUSTRIAL REPORTS. see *LAW—Corporate Law*

338.09 IND
INDUSTRIAL RESEARCHER. Text in English. 1974. q. USD 200. adv.
Related titles: Online - full text ed.: (from The Dialog Corporation).
Published by: Pranava Industrial Services Pvt. Ltd., 18 Sagar Tarang, Bhulabhai Desai Rd., Mumbai, Maharashtra 400 036, India. TEL 3633236. Ed. P J Divatia. Circ: 500.

639 338 ESP ISSN 0212-7202
SH1
INDUSTRIAS PESQUERAS; revista maritima quincenal. Text in Spanish; Summaries in Spanish, English. 1927. fortn. EUR 90 domestic; EUR 120 in Europe; EUR 145 elsewhere (effective 2005). bk.rev. abstr.; bibl.; charts; illus.; stat. **Document type:** *Magazine, Trade.*
Indexed: ASFA, ESPM, IECT.
—CINDOC.
Published by: Servicios Industriales Pesqueros S.A., Policarpo Sanz, 22-3, Vigo, Pontevedra 36202, Spain. TEL 34-986-445055, FAX 34-986-430625, sipsa@arrakis.es, http://www.industriaspesqueras.com. Ed. Alfonso Paz Andrade. Adv. contact Luis Demiguel. Circ: 5,000.

330 CHE
INDUSTRIE FLASH. Text in German. 9/yr. adv. **Document type:** *Trade.*
Published by: Kretz AG, Postfach, Feldmeilen, 8706, Switzerland. TEL 41-1-9237656, FAX 41-1-9237657, kretz_ag@bluewin.ch. Ed. Rudolf Weber. Adv. contact Esther Kretz. B&W page CHF 2,870, color page CHF 3,930; trim 265 x 185. Circ: 6,900.

330 GBR
INDUSTRY AND EUROPEAN MARKET. Text in English. 6/yr. adv. **Document type:** *Newsletter, Trade.*
Address: St Faiths Ln, Norwich, Norfolk NR1 1NN, United Kingdom. TEL 44-1603-765800, FAX 44-1603-760551. Ed. Peter Mercer. Adv. contact Rob Whattam. color page GBP 1,725, B&W page GBP 1,327; bleed 183 x 257.

338.005 GBR ISSN 1366-2716
HD45
INDUSTRY AND INNOVATION; dynamics, strategies, policies. Text in English. 1993. q. GBP 285, USD 471, AUD 530 combined subscription to institutions print & online eds. (effective 2006). reprint service avail. from PSC. **Document type:** *Journal, Academic/Scholarly.* **Description:** Provides cross-disciplinary scholarship devoted to understanding the dynamics of industrial growth, change, and sustainability.
Formerly (until 1997): Journal of Industry Studies (1320-6095)
Related titles: Online - full text ed.: ISSN 1469-8390. GBP 271, USD 447, AUD 504 to institutions (effective 2006) (from EBSCO Publishing, Gale Group, IngentaConnect, O C L C Online Computer Library Center, Inc., ProQuest Information & Learning, Swets Information Services).
Indexed: ABIn, GEOBASE, IBSS, JEL.
—BLDSC (4476.287000), IE, Infotrieve, ingenta. **CCC.**
Published by: Routledge (Subsidiary of: Taylor & Francis Group), 4 Park Sq, Milton Park, Abingdon, Oxon OX14 4RN, United Kingdom. TEL 44-1235-828600, FAX 44-1235-829000, info@routledge.co.uk, http://www.tandf.co.uk/journals/titles/13662716.asp, http://www.routledge.co.uk. Eds. Henrik Sornn-Friese, Ina Drejer, Jens F Christensen, Mark Lorenzen. **Subscr. to:** Taylor & Francis Ltd, Journals Customer Service, Rankine Rd, Basingstoke, Hants RG24 8PR, United Kingdom. TEL 44-1256-813000, FAX 44-1256-330245.

▼ **INDUSTRY FOCUS.** see *INSURANCE*

330 MLT
INDUSTRY TODAY. Text in English. q. MTL 1, USD 5.50 per issue; MTL 2 per issue foreign. **Document type:** *Trade.* **Description:** Geared toward FOI members, local business organizations, institutions and public corporations, unions, local media, government agencies, diplomatic and consular representations in Malta and elsewhere, and various international trade and professional organizations.
Published by: (Malta Federation of Industry), Crest Publicity Ltd., Circle Flats, Flat 8, H. Calleja Schembri St., Msida, MSD 06, Malta. TEL 356-317821, FAX 356-319984. Ed. Edwin Calleja. Circ: 2,000.

330 USA ISSN 1520-3565
HD28
INDUSTRYWEEK (GROWING COMPANIES EDITION). Text in English. 1998. m. USD 40 domestic; USD 55 in Canada; USD 70 elsewhere; USD 4 newsstand/cover domestic; USD 6 newsstand/cover in Canada; USD 8 newsstand/cover elsewhere (effective 2000). **Document type:** *Trade.*
Related titles: Online - full text ed.
Published by: Penton Media, Inc. (Subsidiary of: Pittway Company), 1300 E 9th St, Cleveland, OH 44114-1503. http://www.penton.com, http://www.industryweek.com.

330 CAN ISSN 1194-8973
INFO - AFFAIRES. Text in English. 1989. m.
Published by: Gilles Belleau, Ed. & Pub., 71 Rue Acadie, Richibouctou, NB E4W 3V2, Canada. TEL 506-523-1123, FAX 506-523-1122. Circ: 8,000.

330 RUS
INFO BIZNES. Text in Russian. w. **Document type:** *Journal.*
Related titles: Online - full content ed.
Published by: Komputerra, 2-i Roshchinskii proezd 8, Moscow, 117419, Russian Federation. TEL 7-095-2322262, 7-095-2322263, FAX 7-095-9561938, 7-095-9562385, ibusiness@comuterra.ru, http://www.ibusiness.ru. Ed. Denis Viktorov. Pub. Andrei Krasnov. Circ: 19,000.

330 CHE
INFO-VENTE. Text in French. 11/yr.
Published by: Ligue Suisse de la Representation Commerciale, 20 rue Camille Martin, Geneva, 1203, Switzerland. TEL 022-7960711, FAX 022-730530. Ed. Joseph Schafer. Circ: 5,000.

330 338.4 ESP
INFORMACION TECNICO ECONOMICA. Text in Spanish. 1977. q.
Published by: (Asociacion de Investigacion de la Industria Papelera Espanola), Instituto Papelero Espanol, Carretera de la Coruna, Km. 7, Madrid, 28040, Spain. TEL 34-91-3070976, FAX 34-91-3572828. Circ: 800.

332 BRA
INFORMACOES F I P E. Text in Portuguese. 1980. m. USD 39 (effective 1999). adv. charts; stat. **Document type:** *Bulletin, Academic/Scholarly.*
Published by: Fundacao Instituto de Pesquisas Economicas, Departamento de Publicacoes, Pinheiros, Caixa Postal 11474, Sao Paulo, SP 05422-970, Brazil. TEL 55-11-38185867, FAX 55-11-38125471, restecon@edu.usp.br. Ed., R&P Helio Zylberstajn TEL 55-11-8185889. Adv. contact Eny Elza Ceotto.

330 PRT
INFORMADOR FISCAL. Text in Portuguese. 4/yr.
Address: Rua St. Idelfonso 42-1o, Porto, Portugal.

INFORMATION ECONOMICS AND POLICY. see *COMMUNICATIONS*

330 CAN ISSN 1195-3616
INFORMATION HIGHWAYS. Text in English. 1988. bi-m. adv. **Description:** Provides information to assist knowledge and content executives, managers, and professionals in improving knowledge performance in public and private sector organizations from a Canadian perspective.
Formerly (until 1993): Database Canada (0840-7797)
Indexed: CINAHL, CPerI, InfoSAb.
—CISTI. **CCC.**
Published by: e-Content Institute, 1999 Avenue Rd, Suite 102, Toronto, ON M5M 4A5, Canada. TEL 416-488-7372, FAX 416-488-7078, info@econtentinstitute.org, http://www.econtentinstitute.org/. Ed. Sue Bowness. Adv. contact Joanne Shinwell. B&W page CND 1,760; trim 8.25 x 10.75.

330 USA ISSN 1070-4639
HF54.52.U5
THE (YEAR) INFORMATION PLEASE BUSINESS ALMANAC & DESK REFERENCE. Variant title: Information Please Business Almanac and Sourcebook. Text in English. a. USD 21.95. maps; stat. **Description:** Provides a comprehensive reference of business addresses, media contacts, government agencies, area and zip codes, and other handy information for business professionals.
Published by: Information Please LLC (Subsidiary of: Pearson Education), 160 Gould St, Needham, MA 02494. TEL 617-832-0300, FAX 617-956-2696, info@infoplease.com, http://infoplease.com, http://www.infoplease.com/. Ed. Seth Godin.

330 016 DEU
INFORMATION SOURCES IN OFFICIAL PUBLICATIONS. Text in English. 1997. irreg. USD 95 in North America (effective 2001). bibl. **Document type:** *Directory, Bibliography.* **Description:** Helps reference librarians and other information-management professionals identify and assess key sources of primary information regarding all kinds of corporate, organizational, and governmental official publications from around the world.
Related titles: ♦ Series: Information Sources for the Press and Broadcast Media; ♦ Information Sources in Chemistry; ♦ Information Sources in Finance and Banking; ♦ Information Sources in the Life Sciences; ♦ Information Sources in Grey Literature; ♦ Information Sources in Physics; ♦ Guides to Information Sources Series; ♦ Information Sources in Architecture and Construction; ♦ Information Sources in Development Studies; ♦ Information Sources in Engineering; ♦ Information Sources in Environmental Protection; ♦ Information Sources in Law.
Published by: K.G. Saur Verlag GmbH (Subsidiary of: Gale Group), Ortlerstr 8, Munchen, 81373, Germany. TEL 49-89-769020, FAX 49-89-76902150, info@saur.de, http://www.saur.de. Ed. Valerie Nurcombe.

330 FRA ISSN 0766-6241
INFORMATIONS M M M. Text in French. 1964. 11/yr. **Document type:** *Bulletin.*
Published by: Club M M M, 26 rue Cadet, Paris, 75009, France. TEL 45-23-01-07, FAX 45-23-02-88. Ed. Brigitte Guillot. Circ: 2,000.

330 PAN
INFORMATIVO INDUSTRIAL. Text in Spanish. m. **Document type:** *Newsletter.*
Published by: Sindicato de Industriales de Panama, Apdo. 6-4798, El Dorado, Panama City, 1, Panama. TEL 507-2300169. Ed. Flor Ortega.

330 HRV ISSN 0537-6645
INFORMATOR. Text in Croatian. 1953. w. **Document type:** *Magazine, Trade.*
Published by: Informator d.d., Zelinska 3, Zagreb, 10002, Croatia. TEL 385-1-6111500, FAX 385-1-6111446, info@informator.hr, http://www.informator.hr. Ed. Ivo Buric.

330 POL ISSN 1427-6372
INFORMATOR INDYWIDUALNEGO INWESTORA. Text in Polish. 1997. q. **Document type:** *Magazine, Trade.*
Published by: Wydawnictwo Murator Sp. z o.o., ul Kamionkowska 45, Warsaw, 03812, Poland. TEL 48-22-5905000, FAX 48-22-5905444, wydawnictwo@murator.com.pl, http://www.murator.com.pl.

330 RUS
INFORMATSIONNYI BYULLETEN' STATKOMITETA SNG. Text in Russian. bi-m. USD 205 in North America (effective 2000).
Published by: Statisticheskii Komitet SNG, Myasnitskaya 39, Moscow, 103450, Russian Federation. TEL 7-095-2074180. Ed. M A Korolev. **Dist. by:** East View Information Services, 3020 Harbor Ln. N., Minneapolis, MN 55447. TEL 763-550-0961, FAX 763-559-2931.

330 PER
INFORME NEGOCIACION COLECTIVA. Text in Spanish. 1990. m. **Document type:** *Newsletter.*
Published by: Asesoramiento y Analisis Laborales S.A., Mariano Odicio, 334, Miraflores, Lima 18, Peru. TEL 469477. Ed. Luis Aparicio Valdez.

330 PER
INFORME TRIBUTARIO. Text in Spanish. 199?. m.
Related titles: Supplement(s): Analisis Tributario.
Published by: Asesoramiento y Analisis Laborales S.A., Mariano Odicio, 334, Miraflores, Lima 18, Peru. TEL 469477.

INFORPRESS CENTROAMERICANA. see *POLITICAL SCIENCE*

INFOS DE L'EXPRESSION D'ENTREPRISE. see *BUSINESS AND ECONOMICS—Management*

330 USA
THE INFOSERV LIBRARY. (Information Services) Text in English. d. Free to Members of The Illinois Manufacturers' Association. **Document type:** *Trade.* **Description:** Provides information of various topics to manufacturing and allied enterprises in Illinois.
Media: Online - full content.
Published by: The Illinois Manufacturers Association, 220 E Adams St, Springfield, IL 62701-1123. TEL 630-368-5300, 800-875-4462, FAX 630-218-7467, ima@ima-net.org, http://www.ima-net.org/.

338.9 GBR ISSN 1460-468X
INFRASTRUCTURE JOURNAL. Text in English. bi-m. GBP 395, USD 650 (effective 2002). back issues avail. **Document type:** *Journal.*
Related titles: Online - full content ed.
Published by: Torcello Publishing, 14 Kensington Ct, London, W8 5DN, United Kingdom. TEL 44-20-7938-3660, FAX 44-20-7938-3560, InfraJourn@aol.com, http://www.infrastructurejournal.com.

B

330 GBR
INFRASTRUCTURE YEARBOOK. Text in English. 1994. a. GBP 95. adv. **Document type:** *Trade.* **Description:** Detailed review of developments in private financing of infrastructure projects all over the world.
Published by: Privatisation International Ltd., Ste. 404, Butlers Wharf Business Centre, 45 Curlew St, London, SE1 2ND, United Kingdom. TEL 44-20-7378-1620, FAX 44-20-7403-7876, 100446.3646@compuserve.com. Ed. Rodney Lord. Adv. contact Diana Howarth.

380 USA ISSN 1046-9958
HD2771
INGRAM'S; Kansas city's business magazine. Text in English. 1974. m. USD 44.95; USD 3.95 newsstand/cover (effective 2005). adv. bk.rev. back issues avail.; reprints avail. **Document type:** *Magazine, Trade.* **Description:** A business publication that covers the states of Missouri and Kansas focusing on Kansas City.
Former titles: Corporate Report; (until 1989): Corporate Report - Kansas City (0273-9968); (until 1981): Outlook (0191-6815)
Related titles: Online - full text ed.: (from Gale Group, O C L C Online Computer Library Center, Inc., ProQuest Information & Learning); Supplement(s): Destination K C; The Book of Leads & Lists; Destination M O; Destination Andrew County; Destination Atchinson County; Destination Buchanan County; Destination Cass County; Destination Clay County; Destination Douglas County; Destination Franklin County; Destination Clinton County; Destination DeKalb County; Destination Jackson County; Destination Jefferson County; Destination Johnson County Missouri; Destination Johnson County Kansas; Destination Lafayette County; Destination Leavenworth County; Destination Miami County; Destination Northland; Destination Platte County; Destination Ray County; Destination Shawnee County; Destination Wyandotte County; Destination Warrensburg County.
Indexed: ABIn, BusDate, T&II.
—Linda Hall.
Published by: Show-me Publishing, Inc., 2049 Wyandotte St., Kansas City, MO 64108-1925. info@ingramsonline.com, http://www.ingramsonline.com. Ed. Jack Cashill. Pub. Joseph K Sweeney. R&P, Adv. contact Michelle Sweeney. B&W page USD 3,280, color page USD 3,795; trim 8.125 x 10. Circ: 100,000 (paid and controlled).

330 600 USA
INNOVATION✶. Text in English. 1994. w. USD 15. **Description:** Covers trends, strategies and innovations in business and technology.
Media: Online - full text.
Published by: NewsScan Inc., 1594 Wimbeldon Dr, N W, Kennesaw, GA 30144-2914. gehl@newsscan.com, http://www.newsscan.com. Eds. John Gehl, Suzanne Douglas.

330 USA
INNOVATION (ROCHESTER). Text in English. 1995. m.
Media: Online - full content.
Published by: Idea Connections, 693 E Ave, Rochester, NY 14607. http://www.innovating.com.

330 340 500 USA ISSN 1531-3468
HC79.T4
➤ **INNOVATION POLICY AND THE ECONOMY.** Text in English. 2001. a. price varies. **Document type:** *Monographic series, Academic/Scholarly.* **Description:** Provides a forum for research on the interactions between public policy and the innovation process.
Related titles: Online - full text ed.: ISSN 1537-2618 (from EBSCO Publishing, Gale Group, IngentaConnect, O C L C Online Computer Library Center, Inc., Swets Information Services).
—BLDSC (4515.482350), IE.

Published by: (National Bureau of Economic Research), M I T Press, 55 Hayward St, Cambridge, MA 02142-1493. TEL 617-253-5646, FAX 617-258-6779, journals-info@mit.edu, http://mitpress.mit.edu/catalog/item/default.asp?sid=80CF13C7-A980-4927-9750-40EC65BBFED2&ttype=4&tid=53. Ed. Adam B Jaffe.

330   FRA   ISSN 1267-4982
INNOVATIONS. Text in French. 1995. s-a. EUR 30.50 (effective 2004). **Document type:** *Journal, Academic/Scholarly.*
Published by: L' Harmattan, 5 rue de l'Ecole Polytechnique, Paris, 75005, France. TEL 33-1-43257651, FAX 33-1-43258203, http://www.editions-harmattan.fr.

330   DEU   ISSN 1860-0247
▼ **INNOVATIVE BESCHAEFTIGUNGSPOLITIK IN FORSCHUNG UND PRAXIS.** Text in German. 2005. irreg. price varies. **Document type:** *Monographic series, Academic/Scholarly.*
Published by: Verlag Dr. Kovac, Arnoldstr 49, Hamburg, 22763, Germany. TEL 49-40-3988800, FAX 49-40-39888055, info@verlagdrkovac.de, http://www.verlagdrkovac.de/15-5.htm.

330   USA
INPRACTICE. Text in English. 1996. m. USD 95 to non-members; USD 50 to members; free to qualified personnel (effective 2005). **Document type:** *Newsletter, Trade.* **Description:** Presents in-depth case studies of organizations that excel in various business processes.
Formerly: Knowledge Management Inpractice.
Published by: American Productivity & Quality Center, 123 N Post Oak Ln, Ste 300, Houston, TX 77024-7797. TEL 713-681-4020, 800-776-9676, FAX 713-681-1182, pleavitt@apqc.org, apqcinfo@apqc.org, http://www.apqc.org. Ed. Craig Henderson. Circ: 1,000 (paid and controlled).

330   DEU   ISSN 1433-2019
INPUT. Text in German. q. EUR 6.50 newsstand/cover (effective 2003). adv. **Document type:** *Magazine, Consumer.*
Published by: Verwaltungs- und Wirtschafts-Akademie Freiburg, Bertoldstr 54, Freiburg, 79098, Germany. TEL 49-761-386730, FAX 49-761-3867333, inputmagazin@onlinegroup.de, webmaster@vwa-freiburg.de, http://www.inputmagazin.de, http://www.vwa-freiburg.de. adv.: B&W page EUR 1,015, color page EUR 1,250. Circ: 4,000 (paid and controlled).

330   DEU   ISSN 0579-6415
INPUT - OUTPUT STUDIEN. Text in German. 1969. irreg., latest vol.16, 1984. price varies. **Document type:** *Monographic series.*
Published by: I F O Institut fuer Wirtschaftsforschung, Poschingerstr 5, Munich, 81679, Germany. TEL 49-89-9224-0, FAX 49-89-985369, ifo@ifo.de, http://www.ifo.de.

INQUIRY. see *EDUCATION—Higher Education*

330   USA   ISSN 1523-5521
INSIDE BUSINESS. Text in English. 1999. m. USD 19.95; USD 2.95 newsstand/cover (effective 2001). adv. **Document type:** *Magazine, Consumer.*
Related titles: Online - full text ed.: (from Florida Center for Library Automation, Gale Group).
Published by: Great Lakes Publishing Co., 1422 Euclid Ave, Cleveland, OH 44115. TEL 216-771-2833, FAX 216-781-6318, information@inside-business.com, http://www.inside-business.com. Ed. Steve Gleydura. Pub. Lute Harmon.

INSIDE MICHIGAN POLITICS. see *PUBLIC ADMINISTRATION*

330   USA
INSIDE THE VAULT. Text in English. q. **Document type:** *Newsletter.* **Description:** Educates the public on a number of economics subjects.
Published by: Federal Reserve Bank of St. Louis, PO Box 442, St. Louis, MO 63166. TEL 314-444-8444, http://www.stls.org/publications/itv.

330   USA   ISSN 1069-5184
INSIDE TUCSON BUSINESS. Text in English. 1991. w. (Mon.). USD 47.50 (effective 2005). adv. **Document type:** *Newspaper, Trade.*
Related titles: Online - full text ed.: (from EBSCO Publishing).
Published by: Territorial Newspapers, 3280 E Hemisphere Lp, Ste 180, Tucson, AZ 85706. TEL 520-294-1200, FAX 520-294-4040, http://www.azbiz.com. Ed. Rod Smith. Adv. contact David Stoler. Circ: 8,250 (controlled).

330   CAN   ISSN 1206-4238
THE INSIDEEDGE. Text in English. 1997. q. **Document type:** *Newsletter.* **Description:** Covers emerging economic and management issues, as well as research findings, networking activities, and other initiatives of the board.
Published by: Conference Board of Canada, 255 Smyth Rd, Ste 100, Ottawa, ON K1H 8M7, Canada. TEL 613-526-3280, FAX 613-526-4857, corpcomm@conferenceboard.ca, http://www.conferenceboard.ca/insidedge/.

330   332.6   CAN   ISSN 0821-0012
INSOLVENCY BULLETIN. Text in English, French. 1980. q. free. **Description:** Aimed at trustees, jurists, registrars, accountants, credit managers and those with an interest in bankruptcy and insolvency.

Supersedes in part (in 1980): Canada Corporations. Bulletin. Bankruptcy and Insolvency (0382-3288); Which was formerly (until 1976): Canada Corporations Act Bulletin (0382-327X).
Indexed: ICLPL.
Published by: Industry Canada/Industrie Canada, Distribution Services, Communications & Marketing Branch, Rm 268D, West Tower, C.D. Howe Bldg, 235 Queen St, Ottawa, ON K1A 0H5, Canada. FAX 613-954-6436. Ed. Henri Massue Monat. Circ: 2,350.

320.5322   FRA
INSTITUT DES RECHERCHES MARXISTES. ISSUES. Text in French. 1979. 4/yr. adv. bk.rev.
Former titles: S E P I R M Issues; Institut de Recherches Marxistes. Issues (0222-7762)
Published by: Espaces Marx, 64 bd. Auguste Blanqui, Paris, 75013, France. Circ: 2,000.

330   DEU   ISSN 0720-6852
INSTITUT FUER EMPIRISCHE WIRTSCHAFTSFORSCHUNG. ARBEITSPAPIERE. Text in German. 1971. irreg., latest vol.11, 1995. price varies. **Document type:** *Monographic series, Academic/Scholarly.*
Published by: (Institut fuer Empirische Wirtschaftsforschung), Duncker und Humblot GmbH, Carl-Heinrich-Becker-Weg 9, Berlin, 12165, Germany. TEL 49-30-7900060, FAX 49-30-79000631, info@duncker-humblot.de, http://www.duncker-humblot.de.

330   DEU   ISSN 0720-7239
INSTITUT FUER EMPIRISCHE WIRTSCHAFTSFORSCHUNG. VEROEFFENTLICHUNGEN. Text in German. 1968. irreg., latest vol.38, 2002. price varies. **Document type:** *Monographic series, Academic/Scholarly.*
Published by: (Institut fuer Empirische Wirtschaftsforschung), Duncker und Humblot GmbH, Carl-Heinrich-Becker-Weg 9, Berlin, 12165, Germany. TEL 49-30-7900060, FAX 49-30-79000631, info@duncker-humblot.de, http://www.duncker-humblot.de.

330   GBR   ISSN 1367-5796
INSTITUTE FOR FINANCIAL RESEARCH WORKING PAPERS. Text in English. 1995. irreg. free. **Document type:** *Monographic series.*
—BLDSC (9350.164000).
Published by: (Department of Economics), University of London, Birkbeck College, Birkbeck College, 7-15 Gresse St, London, W1P 2LL, United Kingdom. TEL 44-171-631-6401, FAX 44-171-631-6316, http://www.econ.bbk.ac.uk/research/fwpaper.htm/.

330   HUN   ISSN 1215-5241
HC10
INSTITUTE FOR WORLD ECONOMICS. WORKING PAPERS. Text in English. 1991. irreg. ((12-18/yr.)). price varies. **Document type:** *Monographic series, Academic/Scholarly.*
Related titles: Duplicated (not offset) ed.; E-mail ed.
Published by: Institute for World Economics, PO Box 936, Budapest, 1535, Hungary. TEL 36-1-2246760, FAX 36-1-2246761, vgyorgyi@vki.hu, http://www.vki.hu. Circ: 1,000.

330   GBR   ISSN 0073-909X
H11
▶ **INSTITUTE OF ECONOMIC AFFAIRS. OCCASIONAL PAPERS.** Text in English. 1963. irreg. GBP 40 (effective 2005); Subscr. includes approx. 9 publications as released during the year. **Document type:** *Monographic series, Academic/Scholarly.*
Related titles: Microfiche ed.
Indexed: RefZh.
—BLDSC (6217.450000), IE, ingenta. **CCC.**
Published by: Institute of Economic Affairs, 2 Lord North St, London, SW1P 3LB, United Kingdom. TEL 44-20-77998900, FAX 44-20-77992137, iea@iea.org.uk, http://www.iea.org.uk. Ed. Colin Robinson.

330   GBR   ISSN 0073-9103
▶ **INSTITUTE OF ECONOMIC AFFAIRS. RESEARCH MONOGRAPHS.** Text in English. 1966. irreg. GBP 40 (effective 2002). **Document type:** *Academic/Scholarly.*
Related titles: Microfiche ed.
—BLDSC (7743.080000).
Published by: Institute of Economic Affairs, 2 Lord North St, London, SW1P 3LB, United Kingdom. TEL 44-20-77998900, FAX 44-20-77992137, iea@iea.org.uk, http://www.iea.org.uk. Ed. Colin Robinson.

330   IND
INSTITUTE OF ECONOMIC GEOGRAPHY, INDIA. JOURNAL✱. Text in English. 1970. s-a. USD 4. illus.
Published by: Institute of Economic Geography, 4-1 Ashton Rd., Kolkata, West Bengal 700 020, India.

330   IND
INSTITUTE OF ECONOMIC GROWTH. WORKING PAPERS. Text in English. 1972. irreg., latest vol.157, 1993.
Published by: Institute of Economic Growth, University of Enclave, New Delhi, 110 007, India. TEL 7257101.

330   IND   ISSN 0020-2851
INSTITUTE OF ECONOMIC RESEARCH. JOURNAL. Text in English. 1966. s-a. INR 50, USD 20. adv. bk.rev. charts; illus.; stat. index. back issues avail. **Description:** Covers economic research in agriculture, housing and urban planning, population studies and social sciences.
Indexed: BAS, RDA, WAE&RSA.
Published by: Institute of Economic Research, Vidyagiri, Dharwad, Karnataka 580 004, India. FAX 836-41001. Ed. N Vajra Kumar. Circ: 200.

330   IND
INSTITUTE OF ECONOMIC RESEARCH. PUBLICATIONS ON ECONOMICS. Text in English. irreg. price varies.
Published by: Institute of Economic Research, Director, Vidyagiri, Dharwar, Karnataka 580 004, India. FAX 836-41001.

330   AUS   ISSN 1329-8100
HB1
INSTITUTE OF PUBLIC AFFAIRS. REVIEW. Text in English. 1947. q. USD 28. adv. bk.rev. back issues avail. **Document type:** *Journal, Academic/Scholarly.* **Description:** Presents analysis and comment on social, political and economic issues.
Former titles (until 1997): I P A Review (1030-4177); (until 1986): Institute of Public Affairs. Review (1030-4169); (until 1982): I P A Review (0019-0268)
Related titles: Online - full text ed.: 1947 (from EBSCO Publishing, O C L C Online Computer Library Center, Inc., ProQuest Information & Learning).
Indexed: ABIX, ABIn, AusPAIS, ChLitAb, PAIS, PCI, WBA, WMB.
Published by: Institute of Public Affairs, Level 2, 410 Collins St, Melbourne, VIC 3000, Australia. TEL 61-3-9600-4744, FAX 61-3-9602-4989, orders@ipa.org.au, http://www.ipa.org.au. Ed., R&P Ken Baker. Adv. contact Louise Cato. Circ: 7,800.

330   USA
INSTITUTE OF SOCIAL AND ECONOMIC RESEARCH. REPORTS. Text in English. 1963. irreg., latest vol.58, 1985. price varies.
Formerly: Institute of Social, Economic and Government Research. Reports (0065-5937)
Published by: University of Alaska, Institute of Social and Economic Research, 3211 Providence Dr, Anchorage, AK 99508-4614. TEL 907-786-7710, FAX 907-786-7739. Ed. Linda Leask.

330   CAN
INSTITUTE OF SOCIAL AND ECONOMIC RESEARCH. SOCIAL AND ECONOMIC PAPERS. Text in English. irreg.
Published by: Institute of Social and Economic Research, Memorial University, St. John's, NF A1C 5S7, Canada. TEL 709-737-8156, FAX 709-737-2041, iser@mun.ca, http://www.mun.ca/iser/.

330   PER   ISSN 1022-0399
INSTITUTO DE ESTUDIOS PERUANOS. DOCUMENTOS DE TRABAJO. SERIE ECONOMIA. Key Title: Serie Economia. Text in Spanish. 1985. irreg. price varies. back issues avail. **Document type:** *Monographic series, Academic/Scholarly.* **Description:** Publishes new research on the economy of Peru.
Related titles: ◆ Series of: Instituto de Estudios Peruanos. Documentos de Trabajo. ISSN 1022-0356.
Published by: (Instituto de Estudios Peruanos), I E P Ediciones (Subsidiary of: Instituto de Estudios Peruanos), Horacio Urteaga 694, Jesus Maria, Lima, 11, Peru. TEL 51-14-3326194, FAX 51-14-3326173, libreria@iep.org.pe, http://iep.perucultural.org.pe.

330   BRA   ISSN 1415-4250
HC186
INSTITUTO DE PESQUISA ECONOMICA APLICADA. BOLETIM CONJUNTURAL. Text in Portuguese. q. BRL 40; BRL 70 foreign; includes Carta de Conjuntura.
Published by: Instituto de Pesquisa Economica Aplicada, Av Presidente Antonio Carlos, 51 Andar 13, Centro, Rio De Janeiro, RJ 20020-010, Brazil. TEL 55-21-38048117, FAX 55-21-22205533, editrj@ipea.gov.br, http://www.ipea.gov.br. Circ: 700.

INSTRUCTIONAL STRATEGIES: AN APPLIED RESEARCH SERIES. see *EDUCATION—Teaching Methods And Curriculum*

INSURANCE CONFERENCE PLANNER. see *INSURANCE*

380.1029   SGP
INSURANCE WHO'S WHO IN ASIA. Text in English. a. USD 288 in Singapore & Malaysia; USD 330 elsewhere (effective 2005). **Document type:** *Directory, Trade.* **Description:** Contains more than 346 bio-data of top insurance executives from 26 countries in Asia.
Published by: Ins Communications Pte. Ltd., 57A Amoy St., Singapore, 069 883, Singapore. TEL 65-62245583, FAX 65-62241091, http://www.asiainsurancereview.com/EStore/whos-who-asia-insurance.asp.

330   USA
INTER-BUSINESS ISSUES. Text in English. 1989. m.

Published by: Central Illinois Business Publishers, Inc., 5005 N. Glen Park Place Rd., Peoria, IL 61614-4677. TEL 309-672-3060, FAX 309-672-3065. Ed., Pub. Jan Wright Vergon. Adv. contact Amy Ackerman Kinsinger.

330 USA
THE INTER-CITY EXPRESS. Text in English. 1909. s-w. (Wed. & Fri.). USD 144; USD 1 newsstand/cover (effective 2005). adv. **Document type:** *Newspaper.*
Published by: Daily Journal Corp., 915 E. First St., Los Angeles, CA 90012. TEL 213-229-5300, FAX 213-625-0945, Lisa_Churchhill@dailyjournal.com, http://www.dailyjournal.com. Ed. Lisa Churchill. Pub. Tonya Peacock. adv.: col. inch USD 4.84. Circ: 1,500 evening (paid). Wire service: SMWS, AP.

330 USA ISSN 1089-8840
◆ **INTERACTIVE TRANSACTIONS OF O R / M S.** Variant title: Interactive Transactions of Operations Research / Management Sciences. Text in English. 1996. irreg. free. **Document type:** *Journal, Academic/Scholarly.* **Description:** Contains original scholarly articles and bibliographies that provide a perspective view of the OR/MS discipline and exploit the interactivity offered by the Internet.
Media: Online - full content.
Published by: I N F O R M S, c/o Ramesh Sharda, Editor, College Of Business Administration, Oklahoma State University, Stillwater, OK 74078. TEL 405-744-5180, FAX 405-744-8850, informs@informs.org, http://orcs.bus.okstate.edu/itorms/, http://www.informs.org. Ed. Erhan Erkut.

338.071 CAN ISSN 0315-9892
INTERCOM (SASKATOON). Text in English. 2/yr. CND 20 (effective 2000). adv. **Document type:** *Bulletin.*
Indexed: CEI.
Published by: (Saskatchewan Business Teachers' Association), Saskatchewan Teachers' Federation, 2317 Arlington Ave., Saskatoon, SK S7J 2H8, Canada. stf@stf.sk.ca.

330 AUT ISSN 1615-7362
➤ **INTERDISCIPLINARY STUDIES IN ECONOMICS AND MANAGEMENT.** Text in English. 2000. irreg., latest vol.3, 2002. price varies. **Document type:** *Monographic series, Academic/Scholarly.* **Description:** Promotes basic research in the economic and social sciences.
Published by: Springer-Verlag Wien (Subsidiary of: Springer Science+Business Media) TEL 43-1-3302415-0, FAX 43-1-330242665, journals@springer.at, http://www.springer.at. R&P Angela Foessl TEL 43-1-3302415517.

330 340 RUS ISSN 1096-3030
INTERFAX. BUSINESS LAW REPORT. Text in English. w. **Description:** Provides analysis of reforms in foreign investment, currency legislation, joint venture regulation, import/export operations, tax regulations, and other areas of major legal interest.
Formerly (until 199?): Interfax Business Law Review (1072-2653)
Related titles: Online - full text ed.: (from Florida Center for Library Automation); Russian ed.
Published by: Interfax Ltd., 1-ya Tverskaya-Yamskaya 2, Moscow, 127006, Russian Federation. TEL 7-095-2500022, FAX 7-095-2501436, russia@interfax.com, http://www.interfax.ru. **Dist. elsewhere by:** Interfax America, Inc., 3025 S Parker Rd, Ste 737, Aurora, CO 80014-2925. TEL 303-368-1421, FAX 303-368-1458, america@interfax.com, http://www.interfax.com; **Dist. in Germany Austria and Switzerland by:** Interfax Deutschland GmbH; **Dist. in Western Europe by:** Interfax Europe Ltd.

330 RUS ISSN 1072-2661
INTERFAX. BUSINESS REPORT. Text in English. d. USD 2,520. **Document type:** *Consumer.* **Description:** Covers daily economic and political events affecting business, including business transactions, tenders, legislation, currency rates, statistics and stock market activity.
Related titles: Online - full text ed.; Russian ed.
Published by: Interfax Ltd., 1-ya Tverskaya-Yamskaya 2, Moscow, 127006, Russian Federation. TEL 7-095-2509840, FAX 7-095-2509727. **Dist. elsewhere by:** Interfax America, Inc., 3025 S Parker Rd, Ste 737, Aurora, CO 80014-2925. TEL 303-825-1510, 852-2537-2262, FAX 303-825-1513, 852-2537-2264, america@interfax.com, http://www.interfax.com; **Dist. in Germany, Austria and Switzerland by:** Interfax Deutschland GmbH, IndustriestraBe 6, Kronberg/Tx 61476 , Germany. TEL 49-61-7361369, FAX 49-61-7361206; **Dist. in Western Europe by:** Interfax Europe Ltd., 1st Fl, 50 Hans Crescent, Knightsbridge, London SW1X 0N, United Kingdom. TEL 44-20-7581-5550, FAX 44-20-7581-4490.

330 USA
INTERFAX. BUSINESS WOCHE. Text in English. w. **Document type:** *Trade.* **Description:** Covers political news directly impacting business activities; contracts, talks and consultations held by Western companies in the CIS; international tenders; the status of CIS currencies; and legal issues impacting the interests of foreign companies.
Related titles: German ed.

Contact Dist.: Interfax America, Inc. (Subsidiary of: Interfax Ltd.), 3025 S Parker Rd, Ste 737, Aurora, CO 80014-2925. TEL 852-2537-2262, FAX 852-2537-2264. **Dist. in Germany, Austria and Switzerland by:** Interfax Deutschland GmbH, IndustriestraBe 6, Kronberg/Tx 61476 , Germany. TEL 49-61-7361369, FAX 49-61-7361206; **Dist. in Western Europe by:** Interfax Europe Ltd., 1st Fl, 50 Hans Crescent, Knightsbridge, London SW1X 0N, United Kingdom. TEL 44-20-7581-5550, FAX 44-20-7581-4490.

330 RUS
INTERFAX. CENTRAL ASIA & CAUCASUS BUSINESS REPORT. Text in English. w. USD 1,620. **Document type:** *Consumer.* **Description:** Provides news and analysis on the economies of the eight Central Asian and Caucasus-region countries of the former Soviet Union.
Published by: Interfax Ltd., 1-ya Tverskaya-Yamskaya 2, Moscow, 127006, Russian Federation. TEL 7-095-2509840, FAX 7-095-2509727. **Dist. elsewhere by:** Interfax America, Inc., 3025 S Parker Rd, Ste 737, Aurora, CO 80014-2925. TEL 303-825-1510, 852-2537-2262, FAX 303-825-1513, 852-2537-2264, america@interfax.com, http://www.interfax.com; **Dist. in Germany, Austria and Switzerland by:** Interfax Deutschland GmbH, IndustriestraBe 6, Kronberg/Tx 61476 , Germany. TEL 49-61-7361369, FAX 49-61-7361206; **Dist. in Western Europe by:** Interfax Europe Ltd., 1st Fl, 50 Hans Crescent, Knightsbridge, London SW1X 0N, United Kingdom. TEL 44-20-7581-5550, FAX 44-20-7581-4490.

330 USA
INTERFAX. CENTRAL ASIA BUSINESS NEWS. Text in English. w.
Published by: Interfax America, Inc. (Subsidiary of: Interfax Ltd.), 3025 S Parker Rd, Ste 737, Aurora, CO 80014-2925. TEL 303-825-1510, FAX 303-825-1513, america@interfax.com, http://www.interfax.com.

330 RUS
INTERFAX. CENTRAL ASIA REPORT. Text in English. d. **Document type:** *Consumer.* **Description:** Provides the latest information on political and economic events in all Central Asian countries - Kazakhstan, Kyrgyzstan, Tajikistan, Turkmenistan, and Uzbekistan.
Formerly: Interfax. Central Asia News Service
Published by: Interfax Ltd., 1-ya Tverskaya-Yamskaya 2, Moscow, 127006, Russian Federation. TEL 7-095-2509840, FAX 7-095-2509727. **Dist. elsewhere by:** Interfax America, Inc., 3025 S Parker Rd, Ste 737, Aurora, CO 80014-2925. TEL 303-825-1510, 852-2537-2262, FAX 303-825-1513, 852-2537-2264, america@interfax.com, http://www.interfax.com; **Dist. in Germany, Austria and Switzerland by:** Interfax Deutschland GmbH, IndustriestraBe 6, Kronberg/Tx 61476 , Germany. TEL 49-61-7361369, FAX 49-61-7361206; **Dist. in Western Europe by:** Interfax Europe Ltd., 1st Fl, 50 Hans Crescent, Knightsbridge, London SW1X 0N, United Kingdom. TEL 44-20-7581-5550, FAX 44-20-7581-4490.

330 USA
INTERFAX. CHINA BUSINESS REPORT. Text in English. w. **Document type:** *Trade.* **Description:** Covers the economic and business developments of China's economic scene, government economic policy and the implementation process of reform. Also includes reports and surveys on companies and industry sectors, financial markets, as well as key economic indicators.
Contact Dist.: Interfax America, Inc. (Subsidiary of: Interfax Ltd.), 3025 S Parker Rd, Ste 737, Aurora, CO 80014-2925. TEL 852-2537-2262, FAX 852-2537-2264. **Dist. by:** Interfax Deutschland GmbH, IndustriestraBe 6, Kronberg/Tx 61476 , Germany. TEL 49-61-7361369, FAX 49-61-7361206; Interfax Europe Ltd., 1st Fl, 50 Hans Crescent, Knightsbridge, London SW1X 0N, United Kingdom. TEL 44-20-7581-5550, FAX 44-20-7581-4490.

330 USA
INTERFAX. CZECH REPUBLIC BUSINESS NEWS. Text in English. w. **Document type:** *Trade.*
Media: Online - full content.
Published by: Interfax America, Inc. (Subsidiary of: Interfax Ltd.), 3025 S Parker Rd, Ste 737, Aurora, CO 80014-2925. TEL 303-825-1510, FAX 303-825-1513, america@interfax.com, http://www.interfax.com.

330 USA
INTERFAX. CZECH REPUBLIC BUSINESS REPORT. Text in English. d. **Document type:** *Trade.* **Description:** Provides information on business, political development, market analysis and same day trading results.
Contact Dist.: Interfax America, Inc. (Subsidiary of: Interfax Ltd.), 3025 S Parker Rd, Ste 737, Aurora, CO 80014-2925. TEL 852-2537-2262, FAX 852-2537-2264. **Dist. by:** Interfax Deutschland GmbH, IndustriestraBe 6, Kronberg/Tx 61476 , Germany. TEL 49-61-7361369, FAX 49-61-7361206; Interfax Europe Ltd., 1st Fl, 50 Hans Crescent, Knightsbridge, London SW1X 0N, United Kingdom. TEL 44-20-7581-5550, FAX 44-20-7581-4490.

330 RUS ISSN 1096-3111
INTERFAX. DAILY FINANCIAL REPORT. Text in English. d. USD 2,520. **Document type:** *Trade.* **Description:** Provides reporting and analysis on the equity, commodity and financial markets of Russia and the CIS.
Related titles: Russian ed.
Published by: Interfax Ltd., 1-ya Tverskaya-Yamskaya 2, Moscow, 127006, Russian Federation. TEL 7-095-2509840, FAX 7-095-2509727. **Dist. elsewhere by:** Interfax America, Inc., 3025 S Parker Rd, Ste 737, Aurora, CO 80014-2925. TEL 303-825-1510, 852-2537-2262, FAX 303-825-1513, 852-2537-2264, america@interfax.com, http://www.interfax.com; **Dist. in Germany, Austria and Switzerland by:** Interfax Deutschland GmbH, IndustriestraBe 6, Kronberg/Tx 61476 , Germany. TEL 49-61-7361369, FAX 49-61-7361206; **Dist. in Western Europe by:** Interfax Europe Ltd., 1st Fl, 50 Hans Crescent, Knightsbridge, London SW1X 0N, United Kingdom. TEL 44-20-7581-5550, FAX 44-20-7581-4490.

330 RUS
INTERFAX. DAILY UKRAINE BUSINESS REPORT. Text in English. d. USD 1,620. **Description:** Covers political, economic and business events in Ukraine.
Published by: Interfax Ltd., 1-ya Tverskaya-Yamskaya 2, Moscow, 127006, Russian Federation. TEL 7-095-2509840, FAX 7-095-2509727. **Dist. elsewhere by:** Interfax America, Inc., 3025 S Parker Rd, Ste 737, Aurora, CO 80014-2925. TEL 303-825-1510, 852-2537-2262, FAX 303-825-1513, 852-2537-2264, america@interfax.com, http://www.interfax.com; **Dist. in Germany, Austria and Switzerland by:** Interfax Deutschland GmbH, IndustriestraBe 6, Kronberg/Tx 61476 , Germany. TEL 49-61-7361369, FAX 49-61-7361206; **Dist. in Western Europe by:** Interfax Europe Ltd., 1st Fl, 50 Hans Crescent, Knightsbridge, London SW1X 0N, United Kingdom. TEL 44-20-7581-5550, FAX 44-20-7581-4490.

INTERFAX. DIPLOMATIC PANORAMA. see *POLITICAL SCIENCE—International Relations*

330 USA ISSN 1097-8887
INTERFAX. EURASIAN BUSINESS REPORT. Text in English. w. **Description:** Covers the business information from Russian Far East from the Ural Mountains to the Kamchatka Peninsula.
Formerly (until 1997): Siberian Business Report (1096-3138)
Related titles: Russian ed.
Contact Dist.: Interfax America, Inc. (Subsidiary of: Interfax Ltd.), 3025 S Parker Rd, Ste 737, Aurora, CO 80014-2925. TEL 852-2537-2262, FAX 852-2537-2264. **Dist. in Germany, Austria and Switzerland by:** Interfax Deutschland GmbH, IndustriestraBe 6, Kronberg/Tx 61476 , Germany. TEL 49-61-7361369, FAX 49-61-7361206; **Dist. in Western Europe by:** Interfax Europe Ltd., 1st Fl, 50 Hans Crescent, Knightsbridge, London SW1X 0N, United Kingdom. TEL 44-20-7581-5550, FAX 44-20-7581-4490.

330 USA
INTERFAX. HUNGARY BUSINESS REPORT (DAILY). Text in English. d. **Document type:** *Trade.* **Description:** Covers daily political, business and financial developments and market analysis in the Republic of Hungary.
Contact Dist.: Interfax America, Inc. (Subsidiary of: Interfax Ltd.), 3025 S Parker Rd, Ste 737, Aurora, CO 80014-2925. TEL 852-2537-2262, FAX 852-2537-2264. **Dist. in Germany, Austria and Switzerland by:** Interfax Deutschland GmbH, IndustriestraBe 6, Kronberg/Tx 61476 , Germany. TEL 49-61-7361369, FAX 49-61-7361206; **Dist. in Western Europe by:** Interfax Europe Ltd., 1st Fl, 50 Hans Crescent, Knightsbridge, London SW1X 0N, United Kingdom. TEL 44-20-7581-5550, FAX 44-20-7581-4490.

330 USA
INTERFAX. HUNGARY BUSINESS REPORT (WEEKLY). Text in English. w. **Document type:** *Trade.* **Description:** Covers the week's political, business and financial developments in the Republic of Hungary, together with in-depth market analysis.
Contact Dist.: Interfax America, Inc. (Subsidiary of: Interfax Ltd.), 3025 S Parker Rd, Ste 737, Aurora, CO 80014-2925. TEL 852-2537-2262, FAX 852-2537-2264. **Dist. in Germany, Austria and Switzerland by:** Interfax Deutschland GmbH, IndustriestraBe 6, Kronberg/Tx 61476 , Germany. TEL 49-61-7361369, FAX 49-61-7361206; **Dist. in Western Europe by:** Interfax Europe Ltd., 1st Fl, 50 Hans Crescent, Knightsbridge, London SW1X 0N, United Kingdom. TEL 44-20-7581-5550, FAX 44-20-7581-4490.

330 USA
INTERFAX. POLAND BUSINESS REPORT. Text in English. d. **Document type:** *Trade.* **Description:** Covers major political and economic developments in the Republic of Poland with special emphasis on the country's business and financial markets.

B

Contact Dist.: Interfax America, Inc. (Subsidiary of: Interfax Ltd.), 3025 S Parker Rd, Ste 737, Aurora, CO 80014-2925. TEL 852-2537-2262, FAX 852-2537-2264. **Dist. Germany, Austria and Switzerland by:** Interfax Deutschland GmbH, IndustriestraBe 6, Kronberg/Tx 61476 , Germany. TEL 49-61-7361369, FAX 49-61-7361206; **Dist. in Western Europe by:** Interfax Europe Ltd., 1st Fl, 50 Hans Crescent, Knightsbridge, London SW1X 0N, United Kingdom. TEL 44-20-7581-5550, FAX 44-20-7581-4490.

330   RUS
INTERFAX. POLAND BUSINESS REVIEW. Text in English. w. **Document type:** *Trade.* **Description:** Provides business information on companies and industry sectors, weekly analysis of national financial markets, key economic indicators and economic policy outlook.
Published by: Interfax Ltd., 1-ya Tverskaya-Yamskaya 2, Moscow, 127006, Russian Federation. TEL 7-095-2509840, FAX 7-095-2509727. **Dist. elsewhere by:** Interfax America, Inc., 3025 S Parker Rd, Ste 737, Aurora, CO 80014-2925. TEL 303-825-1510, 852-2537-2262, FAX 303-825-1513, 852-2537-2264, america@interfax.com, http://www.interfax.com; **Dist. in Germany, Austria and Switzerland by:** Interfax Deutschland GmbH, IndustriestraBe 6, Kronberg/Tx 61476 , Germany. TEL 49-61-7361369, FAX 49-61-7361206; **Dist. in Western Europe by:** Interfax Europe Ltd., 1st Fl, 50 Hans Crescent, Knightsbridge, London SW1X 0N, United Kingdom. TEL 44-20-7581-5550, FAX 44-20-7581-4490.

330   RUS   ISSN 1096-3170
INTERFAX. PRESIDENTIAL BULLETIN. Text in English. d. USD 1,820. **Document type:** *Trade.* **Description:** Covers the government and presidential offices in Russia, the CIS and Baltic countries.
Related titles: Online - full text ed.: (from Florida Center for Library Automation); Russian ed.
Published by: Interfax Ltd., 1-ya Tverskaya-Yamskaya 2, Moscow, 127006, Russian Federation. TEL 7-095-2509840, FAX 7-095-2509727. **Dist. elsewhere by:** Interfax America, Inc., 3025 S Parker Rd, Ste 737, Aurora, CO 80014-2925. TEL 303-825-1510, 852-2537-2262, FAX 303-825-1513, 852-2537-2264, america@interfax.com, http://www.interfax.com; **Dist. in Germany, Austria and Switzerland by:** Interfax Deutschland GmbH, IndustriestraBe 6, Kronberg/Tx 61476 , Germany. TEL 49-61-7361369, FAX 49-61-7361206; **Dist. in Western Europe by:** Interfax Europe Ltd., 1st Fl, 50 Hans Crescent, Knightsbridge, London SW1X 0N, United Kingdom. TEL 44-20-7581-5550, FAX 44-20-7581-4490.

330   USA
INTERFAX. RUSSIA & F S U BUSINESS REPORT WEEKLY. (Former Soviet Union) Text in English. w. **Document type:** *Trade.*
Related titles: Online - full content ed.
Published by: Interfax America, Inc. (Subsidiary of: Interfax Ltd.), 3025 S Parker Rd, Ste 737, Aurora, CO 80014-2925. TEL 303-825-1510, FAX 303-825-1513, america@interfax.com, http://www.interfax.com.

330   USA
INTERFAX. RUSSIA & F S U GENERAL NEWS. (Former Soviet Union) Text in English. w. **Document type:** *Trade.*
Published by: Interfax America, Inc. (Subsidiary of: Interfax Ltd.), 3025 S Parker Rd, Ste 737, Aurora, CO 80014-2925. TEL 303-825-1510, FAX 303-825-1513, america@interfax.com, http://www.interfax.com.

330   USA
INTERFAX. RUSSIAN COMPANY NEWS. Text in English. w. **Document type:** *Trade.*
Published by: Interfax America, Inc. (Subsidiary of: Interfax Ltd.), 3025 S Parker Rd, Ste 737, Aurora, CO 80014-2925. TEL 303-825-1510, FAX 303-825-1513, america@interfax.com, http://www.interfax.com.

330   USA   ISSN 1096-3146
INTERFAX. UKRAINE BUSINESS REPORT. Text in English. w. **Document type:** *Trade.* **Description:** Provides business information on Ukraine: macro economics, securities, power, agriculture, mining, oil and gas, privatization, communications, trade and transportation.
Contact Dist.: Interfax America, Inc. (Subsidiary of: Interfax Ltd.), 3025 S Parker Rd, Ste 737, Aurora, CO 80014-2925. TEL 852-2537-2262, FAX 852-2537-2264. **Dist. by:** Interfax Deutschland GmbH, IndustriestraBe 6, Kronberg/Tx 61476 , Germany. TEL 49-61-7361369, FAX 49-61-7361206; Interfax Europe Ltd., 1st Fl, 50 Hans Crescent, Knightsbridge, London SW1X 0N, United Kingdom. TEL 44-20-7581-5550, FAX 44-20-7581-4490.

INTERFAX VREMYA; politiko-ekonomicheskii ezhenedel'nik. see *GENERAL INTEREST PERIODICALS—Russia*

330   RUS
INTERFAX. WEEKLY BUSINESS REPORT. Text in English. w. **Document type:** *Trade.* **Description:** Covers the developments in a number of industries, including transportation, telecommunications, construction, power, aerospace, chemical, high technology, automotive, health care, maritime, defense conversion, privatization, foreign trade and customs.
Published by: Interfax Ltd., 1-ya Tverskaya-Yamskaya 2, Moscow, 127006, Russian Federation. TEL 7-095-2509840, FAX 7-095-2509727. **Dist. elsewhere by:** Interfax America, Inc., 3025 S Parker Rd, Ste 737, Aurora, CO 80014-2925. TEL 303-825-1510, 852-2537-2262, FAX 303-825-1513, 852-2537-2264, america@interfax.com, http://www.interfax.com; **Dist. in Germany, Austria and Switzerland by:** Interfax Deutschland GmbH, IndustriestraBe 6, Kronberg/Tx 61476 , Germany. TEL 49-61-7361369, FAX 49-61-7361206; **Dist. in Western Europe by:** Interfax Europe Ltd., 1st Fl, 50 Hans Crescent, Knightsbridge, London SW1X 0N, United Kingdom. TEL 44-20-7581-5550, FAX 44-20-7581-4490.

330   FRA   ISSN 1564-1813
INTERGOVERNMENTAL OCEANOGRAPHIC COMMISSION. REPORTS OF GOVERNING AND MAJOR SUBSIDIARY BODIES. Text in English. 1984. irreg. **Document type:** *Monographic series.*
Related titles: Ed.: Organes Directeurs et des Principaux Organes Subsidiaires. Rapport. ISSN 1023-4306. 1984.
Published by: (Intergovernmental Oceanographic Commission USA), UNESCO Publishing, 7 place de Fontenoy, Paris, 75352, France. http://ioc.unesco.org/iocweb/IOCpub/IOCpub.htm, http://www.unesco.org/publishing.

330   USA   ISSN 1083-0898
HB1
➤ **INTERNATIONAL ADVANCES IN ECONOMIC RESEARCH.** Text in English. 1995. q. EUR 159, USD 175, GBP 110 combined subscription to institutions print & online eds. (effective 2005). abstr.; charts; illus.; stat. 125 p./no. 1 cols./p.; back issues avail.; reprints avail. **Document type:** *Journal, Academic/Scholarly.*
Related titles: Online - full text ed.: ISSN 1573-966X. USD 175 (effective 2005) (from EBSCO Publishing, Factiva, Florida Center for Library Automation, Gale Group, ProQuest Information & Learning, Springer LINK).
Indexed: ABIn, JEL.
—BLDSC (4535.600500), IE, ingenta. **CCC.**
Published by: (International Atlantic Economic Society), Springer-Verlag New York, Inc. (Subsidiary of: Springer Science+Business Media), 233 Spring St, New York, NY 10013. TEL 212-460-1500, FAX 212-460-1575, service@springer-ny.com, http://springerlink.metapress.com/openurl.asp?genre=journal&issn=1083-0898, http://www.springer-ny.com. Ed., R&P John M. Virgo. Circ: 1,000. **Subscr. to:** Journal Fulfillment, PO Box 2485, Secaucus, NJ 07096-2485. TEL 201-348-4033, FAX 201-348-4505, journals@springer-ny.com.

➤ **THE INTERNATIONAL BANKING SYSTEMS MARKET REPORT (YEAR).** see *BUSINESS AND ECONOMICS— Banking And Finance*

330   USA   ISSN 1534-4428
INTERNATIONAL BUSINESS & FINANCE DAILY. Text in English. d. USD 1,388 domestic (effective 2005 - 2006). back issues avail. **Document type:** *Newsletter, Trade.* **Description:** Provides business news and financial reporting from the United States and around the world.
Media: Online - full text (from The Bureau of National Affairs, Inc.).
—**CCC.**
Published by: The Bureau of National Affairs, Inc., 1231 25th St., NW, Washington, DC 20037. TEL 800-372-1033, 800-452-7773, FAX 800-253-0332, customercare@bna.com, http://www.bna.com/products/corplaw/ibdm.htm. **Subscr. to:** 9435 Key West Ave, Rockville, MD 20850.

332.6   GBR   ISSN 0969-5931
HD2755.5
➤ **INTERNATIONAL BUSINESS REVIEW.** Text in English. 1992. 6/yr. EUR 107 in Europe to individuals; JPY 14,000 in Japan to individuals; USD 120 to individuals except Europe and Japan; EUR 950 in Europe to institutions; JPY 126,300 in Japan to institutions; USD 1,063 to institutions except Europe and Japan (effective 2006). back issues avail.; reprints avail. **Document type:** *Journal, Academic/Scholarly.* **Description:** Publishes empirical studies with practical application, and discussions of theoretical and methodological issues in international business, especially marketing and management concerns.
Formerly (until 1993): Scandinavian International Business Review (0962-9262)
Related titles: Microform ed.: (from PQC); Online - full text ed.: (from EBSCO Publishing, Gale Group, IngentaConnect, O C L C Online Computer Library Center, Inc., ScienceDirect, Swets Information Services).
Indexed: ABIn, Emerald, IBSS, M&MA.
—BLDSC (4538.383500), IE, Infotrieve, ingenta. **CCC.**

Published by: Pergamon (Subsidiary of: Elsevier Science & Technology), The Boulevard, Langford Ln, East Park, Kidlington, Oxford OX5 1GB, United Kingdom. TEL 44-1865-843000, FAX 44-1865-843010, http://www.elsevier.com/locate/ibusrev. Ed. Pervez N Ghauri.
Subscr. to: Elsevier BV, PO Box 211, Amsterdam 1000 AE, Netherlands. TEL 31-20-485-3757, FAX 31-20-485-3432, nlinfo-f@elsevier.nl, http://www.elsevier.nl.

330   CAN   ISSN 0704-7584
INTERNATIONAL DEVELOPMENT RESEARCH CENTRE. ANNUAL REPORT/CENTRE DE RECHERCHES POUR LE DEVELOPPEMENT INTERNATIONAL. RAPPORT ANNUEL. Text in English, French. 1971. a. illus. **Document type:** *Corporate.*
Media: Online - full text.
Indexed: PotatoAb, WAE&RSA.
—CISTI. **CCC.**
Published by: International Development Research Centre/Centre de Recherches pour le developpement international, P O Box 8500, Ottawa, ON K1G 3H9, Canada. TEL 613-236-6163, FAX 613-563-2476, kmorrow@idrc.ca, http://www.idrc.ca. Ed. Robert Charbonneau.

330   GBR   ISSN 0074-4646
INTERNATIONAL ECONOMIC ASSOCIATION. PROCEEDINGS OF THE CONFERENCES AND CONGRESSES. Text in English. 1956. irreg. **Document type:** *Proceedings.*
Indexed: EngInd.
Published by: Palgrave Macmillan Ltd. (Subsidiary of: Macmillan Publishers Ltd.), Houndmills, Basingstoke, Hants RG21 6XS, United Kingdom. TEL 44-1256-329242, FAX 44-1256-810526, http://www.macmillan-press.co.uk.

330   USA   ISSN 0020-6598
HB1   CODEN: INERAE
➤ **INTERNATIONAL ECONOMIC REVIEW.** Text in English. 1960. q. USD 76 combined subscription in the Americas to individuals & Caribbean (print & online eds.); EUR 80 combined subscription in Europe to individuals print & online eds.; GBP 53 combined subscription elsewhere to individuals print & online eds.; USD 430 combined subscription in the Americas to institutions & Caribbean (print & online eds.); GBP 301 combined subscription elsewhere to institutions print & online eds.; USD 34 combined subscription in the Americas to students & Caribbean (print & online eds.); EUR 39 combined subscription in Europe to students print & online eds.; GBP 26 combined subscription elsewhere to students print & online eds. (effective 2006). adv. illus.; abstr. index, cum index. back issues avail.; reprint service avail. from PSC. **Document type:** *Journal, Academic/Scholarly.*
Related titles: Online - full text ed.: ISSN 1468-2354. USD 383 in the Americas to institutions & Caribbean; GBP 286 elsewhere to institutions (effective 2006) (from Blackwell Synergy, EBSCO Publishing, Gale Group, IngentaConnect, JSTOR (Web-based Journal Archive), O C L C Online Computer Library Center, Inc., Swets Information Services).
Indexed: ABIn, ABS&EES, APEL, ASCA, AgeL, AmStI, BAS, BPI, BPIA, BusI, CCMJ, CIS, CJA, CREJ, CurCont, IBSS, JEL, MAB, MEA&I, MathR, MathSciNet, PAIS, RASB, SSCI, SSI, T&II, WBA, ZentMath.
—BLDSC (4539.791000), CISTI, IDS, IE, Infotrieve, ingenta, Linda Hall. **CCC.**
Published by: (University of Pennsylvania, Department of Economics CAN), Blackwell Publishing, Inc. (Subsidiary of: Blackwell Publishing Ltd.), Commerce Place, 350 Main St, Malden, MA 02148. TEL 781-388-8206, FAX 781-388-8232, ier@sas.upenn.edu, subscrip@blackwellpub.com, http://www.blackwellpublishing.com/journals/IER. Eds. Charles Y Horioka, Randall Wright. Circ: 2,000. **Subscr. in Japan to:** Osaka University Institute of Social and Economic Research Association, 6-1 Mihogaoka, Ibaraki, Osaka 567-0047, Japan. **Co-sponsor:** Osaka University Institute of Social and Economic Research Association.

➤ **INTERNATIONAL GAMING & WAGERING BUSINESS.** see *SPORTS AND GAMES*

628   GBR   ISSN 1357-9282
INTERNATIONAL INSTITUTE FOR ENVIRONMENT AND DEVELOPMENT. ENVIRONMENTAL ECONOMICS PROGRAMME. DISCUSSION PAPER. Cover title: Environmental Economics Programme. Discussion Paper. Text in English. 1992. irreg., latest 1998, DP98-03. GBP 15 per issue (effective 2002). bibl.; charts; maps; stat. 25 p./no.; back issues avail. **Document type:** *Monographic series, Academic/Scholarly.* **Description:** Examines a range of issues in environmental economics including theoretic questions and applications, case studies and policy analysis. They are aimed at academics and researchers.
Formerly (until 1994): London Environmental Economics Centre. Discussion Paper
Related titles: E-mail ed.; Online - full content ed.
—BLDSC (3597.195000).
Published by: (Environmental Economics Programme), International Institute for Environment and Development, 3 Endsleigh St, London, WC1H 0DD, United Kingdom. TEL 44-207-388-2117, FAX 44-207-388-2826, mailbox@iied.org, http://www.iied.org. R&P Joshua Bishop. Adv. contact Frances Reynolds. Circ: 200 (paid).

▼ **THE INTERNATIONAL JOURNAL OF ACADEMY OF EXECUTIVES AND ADMINISTRATORS.** see *EDUCATION—Adult Education*

650 IND ISSN 0972-7302
▼ ➤ **INTERNATIONAL JOURNAL OF APPLIED BUSINESS AND ECONOMIC RESEARCH.** Text in English. 2003. m. USD 155 to institutions (effective 2006). **Document type:** *Journal, Academic/Scholarly.* **Description:** Provides a forum to both academics and decision makers to advance theory and application in the fields of business and economics. JABER publishes original research in accounting, economics, finance, management and quantitative methods, which has an international orientation.
Indexed: JEL.
Published by: Scientific Publishers, 5-A New Pali Rd., Near Hotel Taj Hari Mahal, PO Box 91, Jodhpur, Rajasthan 342 003, India. TEL 91-291-2433323, FAX 91-291-2512580, info@scientificpub.com, journals@scientificpub.com, http://www.scientificpub.com/bookdetails.php?booktransid=332&bookid=328.

330 TWN ISSN 1728-8673
➤ **INTERNATIONAL JOURNAL OF BUSINESS AND INFORMATION.** Text in English. q. **Document type:** *Journal, Academic/Scholarly.* **Description:** Covers theoretical, empirical and applied fields of business and information.
Published by: Academy of Taiwan Information Systems Research, PO Box 179-45, Taipei, 116, Taiwan. TEL 886-2-25009508, FAX 886-2-25175924, http://atisr.org/journal/, http://www.atisr.org/.

330 GBR ISSN 1477-9048
▼ **INTERNATIONAL JOURNAL OF BUSINESS GOVERNANCE AND ETHICS.** Text in English. 2003. q. USD 450 to institutions; USD 545 combined subscription to institutions print & online eds. (effective 2005). **Document type:** *Journal, Academic/Scholarly.* **Description:** Publishes high quality papers from a wide variety of disciplinary orientations on the general subject of business governance and ethics.
Related titles: Online - full text ed.: ISSN 1741-802X. USD 450 to institutions (effective 2005) (from EBSCO Publishing).
Indexed: BrCerAb, C&ISA, CerAb, CorrAb, E&CAJ, EMA, IAA, Inspec, M&TEA, MBF, METADEX, WAA.
—BLDSC (4542.155858), IE, Linda Hall.
Published by: Inderscience Publishers, IEL Editorial Office, PO Box 735, Olney, Bucks MK46 5WB, United Kingdom. TEL 44-1234-240519, FAX 44-1234-240515, ijbge@inderscience.com, http://www.inderscience.com/ijbge. Ed. Pervaiz K Ahmed. **Subscr. to:** World Trade Centre Bldg, 29 route de Pre-Bois, Case Postale 896, Geneva 15 1215, Switzerland. FAX 41-22-7910885, subs@inderscience.com.

330 AUS ISSN 1320-7156
HD28
INTERNATIONAL JOURNAL OF BUSINESS STUDIES. Text in English. 1993. s-a. AUD 35 domestic; AUD 45 foreign (effective 2000). **Document type:** *Academic/Scholarly.*
Related titles: Online - full text ed.: (from EBSCO Publishing, O C L C Online Computer Library Center, Inc., ProQuest Information & Learning).
Indexed: ABIn.
Published by: Edith Cowan University, Pearson Street, Churchlands, Perth, W.A., WU 6018, Australia. TEL 61-08-92738496, FAX 61-08-92738063, ijbs@cowan.edu.au. Circ: 100 (paid); 50 (controlled).

330 GBR ISSN 1367-3262
INTERNATIONAL JOURNAL OF BUSINESS TRANSFORMATION. Text in English. 1995. q. GBP 120; GBP 140 foreign. adv. bk.rev. illus. **Document type:** *Trade.* **Description:** Examines how the use of self-assessment leads to continuous improvement, superior competitive performance, and achievement of world-class status.
Formerly (until 1997): Self-Assessment (1356-9627)
Published by: I F S International Ltd., Wolseley Rd, Wolseley Business Park, Kempston, Beds MK42 7PW, United Kingdom. TEL 44-1234-853605, FAX 44-1234-854499. Ed. Dan M Boland. Pub. Roy L Chase. R&P, Adv. contact David Watts.

637 GBR ISSN 1471-0307
➤ **INTERNATIONAL JOURNAL OF DAIRY TECHNOLOGY ONLINE.** Text in English. q. GBP 236 in Europe to institutions; USD 437 in the Americas to institutions & Caribbean; GBP 260 elsewhere to institutions (effective 2006). **Document type:** *Journal, Academic/Scholarly.*
Media: Online - full text (from Blackwell Synergy, EBSCO Publishing, Gale Group, IngentaConnect, O C L C Online Computer Library Center, Inc., Swets Information Services). **Related titles:** ♦ Print ed.: International Journal of Dairy Technology. ISSN 1364-727X.
—CCC.
Published by: Blackwell Publishing Ltd., 9600 Garsington Rd, Oxford, OX4 2ZG, United Kingdom. TEL 44-1865-776868, FAX 44-1865-714591, customerservices@oxon.blackwellpublishing.com, http://www.blackwellpublishing.com.

330 629.8 GBR ISSN 1742-7525
▼ **INTERNATIONAL JOURNAL OF ELECTRONIC TRADE.** Text in English. forthcoming 2006. q. USD 450 to institutions; USD 545 to institutions print & online eds. (effective 2005). **Document type:** *Journal, Academic/Scholarly.*
Related titles: Online - full text ed.: ISSN 1742-7533. forthcoming 2006. USD 450 to institutions (effective 2005).
Published by: Inderscience Publishers, IEL Editorial Office, PO Box 735, Olney, Bucks MK46 5WB, United Kingdom. TEL 44-1234-240519, FAX 44-1234-240515, ijetrade@inderscience.com, info@inderscience.com, http://www.inderscience.com/ijetrade. **Subscr. to:** World Trade Centre Bldg, 29 route de Pre-Bois, Case Postale 896, Geneva 15 1215, Switzerland. FAX 41-22-7910885, subs@inderscience.com.

650 GBR ISSN 1465-7503
HB615
➤ **INTERNATIONAL JOURNAL OF ENTREPRENEURSHIP AND INNOVATION.** Text in English. 2000. q. USD 226 combined subscription in United States to institutions print & online eds.; EUR 232 combined subscription to institutions in the Eurozone; print & online eds.; GBP 153 combined subscription elsewhere to institutions print & online eds. (effective 2005). bk.rev.; Website rev. illus.; abstr. index. back issues avail. **Document type:** *Journal, Academic/Scholarly.* **Description:** Publishes papers, case studies and reviews which explore ideas and experience relating to the development and application of entrepreneurship.
Related titles: Online - full text ed.: 2000 (from EBSCO Publishing, Gale Group, IngentaConnect, Swets Information Services).
Indexed: ABIn, IBSS.
—BLDSC (4542.240500), IE, Infotrieve, ingenta.
Published by: I P Publishing Ltd., Coleridge House, 4-5 Coleridge Gardens, London, NW6 3HQ, United Kingdom. TEL 44-20-7372-2600, FAX 44-20-7372-2253, JEdmondIP@aol.com, http://www.ippublishing.com/general_entrepreneurship.htm. Ed. Gerard McElwee. R&P John Edmondson. **Subscr. to:** Extenza - Turpin, Pegasus Dr, Stratton Business Park, Biggleswade, Beds SG18 8TQ, United Kingdom. subscriptions@turpinltd.com.

330 370 IRL
▼ **INTERNATIONAL JOURNAL OF ENTREPRENEURSHIP EDUCATION.** Text in English. 2003. q. GBP 59 in United Kingdom to individuals; EUR 85 in Europe to individuals; USD 110 elsewhere to individuals; GBP 137 in United Kingdom to institutions print or online; EUR 195 in Europe to institutions print or online; USD 240 elsewhere to institutions print or online; GBP 131.25 combined subscription in United Kingdom to institutions print & online; USD 243.75 combined subscription in Europe to institutions print & online; USD 300 combined subscription elsewhere to institutions print & online (effective 2005). **Document type:** *Journal, Academic/Scholarly.* **Description:** Publishes case studies, overview articles on advances in entrepreneurship research, lectures and research papers on entrepreneurship education. Its aim is to be a primary source of entrepreneurship articles for professors and their students.
Related titles: Online - full text ed.
—BLDSC (4542.240570).
Published by: Senate Hall Academic Publishing, PO Box 8261, Shankill, Co. Dublin, Ireland. TEL 353-1-2005066, FAX 353-1-2823701, info@senatehall.com, http://www.senatehall.com/ijee/. Eds. Andrew Burke, David Audretsch, Marilyn Kourilsky.

INTERNATIONAL JOURNAL OF FORECASTING. see *BUSINESS AND ECONOMICS—Economic Situation And Conditions*

330 GBR ISSN 1744-9928
▼ ➤ **INTERNATIONAL JOURNAL OF GREEN ECONOMICS.** Text in English. 2005. q. USD 450 to institutions; USD 545 to institutions print & online eds. (effective 2005). **Document type:** *Journal, Academic/Scholarly.* **Description:** Aims to establish an effective channel of communication between policy makers, government agencies, academic and research institutions concerned with the running, involvement and impact of the economy on all sections of society.
Related titles: Online - full text ed.: ISSN 1744-9936. USD 450 to institutions (effective 2005).
Published by: Inderscience Publishers, IEL Editorial Office, PO Box 735, Olney, Bucks MK46 5WB, United Kingdom. TEL 44-1234-240519, FAX 44-1234-240515, ijge@inderscience.com, info@inderscience.com, http://www.inderscience.com/ijge. Ed. Dr. Miriam Kennet. **Subscr. to:** World Trade Centre Bldg, 29 route de Pre-Bois, Case Postale 896, Geneva 15 1215, Switzerland. FAX 41-22-7910885, subs@inderscience.com.

➤ **INTERNATIONAL JOURNAL OF HEALTH CARE FINANCE AND ECONOMICS.** see *PUBLIC HEALTH AND SAFETY*

330 GBR ISSN 1741-8496
▼ ➤ **INTERNATIONAL JOURNAL OF INFORMATION INTEGRITY.** Text in English. 2005. 4/yr. USD 450; USD 545 combined subscription print & online eds. (effective 2005). **Document type:** *Journal, Academic/Scholarly.* **Description:** Publishes research on the theoretical aspects of information integrity and the empirical effects of lack of information integrity on organizational performance and sustained survival in both the private and public arenas.
Related titles: Online - full text ed.: ISSN 1741-850X. USD 450 (effective 2005).
Published by: Inderscience Publishers, IEL Editorial Office, PO Box 735, Olney, Bucks MK46 5WB, United Kingdom. TEL 44-1234-240519, FAX 44-1234-240515, ijii@inderscience.com, info@inderscience.com, http://www.inderscience.com/ijii. Ed. Paul Prabhaker.

330 USA
INTERNATIONAL JOURNAL OF ISLAMIC FINANCIAL SERVICES. Text in English. q. members only.
Media: Online - full content.
Address: http://islamic-finance.net/journal.html. Ed. Mohammed Obaidullah.

330 AUS ISSN 1447-9524
▼ ➤ **INTERNATIONAL JOURNAL OF KNOWLEDGE, CULTURE AND CHANGE MANAGEMENT.** Text in English. 2003. a. AUD 300 (effective 2004). Index. back issues avail. **Document type:** *Monographic series, Academic/Scholarly.* **Description:** Covers liveability of organizations for insiders, and their credibility and attraction to outsiders; but also their tangible results in the form of efficiency, effectiveness and productivity. The intangibles of knowledge, culture and change management do not appear on balance sheets, but ultimately do have an enormous impact on 'bottom lines'.
Related titles: CD-ROM ed.; Online - full content ed.
Published by: Common Ground, PO Box 463, Altona, VIC 3018, Australia. kathryn@commongroundpublishing.com, ManagementJournal.Publisher-Site.com/, http://commongroundgroup.com/. Eds. Howard Dare, Mary Kalantzis. Pub. Kathryn Otte.

330 GBR ISSN 1367-5567
➤ **INTERNATIONAL JOURNAL OF LOGISTICS;** research and applications. Text in English. 1998. q. GBP 328, USD 541 combined subscription to institutions print & online eds. (effective 2006). illus. reprint service avail. from PSC. **Document type:** *Journal, Academic/Scholarly.* **Description:** Publishes work with a clear applicability to the business world. The term 'logistics' is taken in its broadest context with "articles crossing the various traditional functional boundaries of the complete supply-chain.".
Related titles: Online - full text ed.: ISSN 1469-848X. GBP 312, USD 514 to institutions (effective 2006) (from EBSCO Publishing, Gale Group, IngentaConnect, O C L C Online Computer Library Center, Inc., Swets Information Services).
Indexed: C&ISA, E&CAJ, IAA, IBR, IBZ.
—BLDSC (4542.321700), IE, Infotrieve, ingenta. **CCC.**
Published by: Taylor & Francis Ltd (Subsidiary of: Taylor & Francis Group), 4 Park Sq, Milton Park, Abingdon, OX14 4RN, United Kingdom. TEL 44-1235-828600, FAX 44-1235-829000, info@tandf.co.uk, http://www.tandf.co.uk/journals/titles/13675567.asp. Eds. Dr. Tony Whiteing, Kulwant S Pawar. **Subscr. to:** Journals Customer Service, Rankine Rd, Basingstoke, Hants RG24 8PR, United Kingdom. TEL 44-1256-813000, FAX 44-1256-330245, enquiry@tandf.co.uk.

▼ ➤ **INTERNATIONAL JOURNAL OF LOGISTICS ECONOMICS AND GLOBALISATION.** see *TRANSPORTATION*

330 389.1 GBR ISSN 1740-8849
▼ ➤ **INTERNATIONAL JOURNAL OF SERVICES AND STANDARDS.** Text in English. 2004. q. USD 450 to institutions print or online ed.; USD 545 combined subscription to institutions print & online eds. (effective 2005). **Document type:** *Journal, Academic/Scholarly.*
Related titles: Online - full text ed.: ISSN 1740-8857 (from EBSCO Publishing).
Indexed: C&ISA, E&CAJ, IAA, Inspec.
—BLDSC (4542.544687).
Published by: Inderscience Publishers, IEL Editorial Office, PO Box 735, Olney, Bucks MK46 5WB, United Kingdom. TEL 44-1234-240519, FAX 44-1234-240515, ijss@inderscience.com, info@inderscience.com, http://www.inderscience.com/ijss. Ed. Dr. Binshan Lin. **Subscr. to:** World Trade Centre Bldg, 29 route de Pre-Bois, Case Postale 896, Geneva 15 1215, Switzerland. FAX 41-22-7910885, subs@inderscience.com.

330 301 GBR ISSN 0306-8293
HB1 CODEN: ISLEBC
➤ **INTERNATIONAL JOURNAL OF SOCIAL ECONOMICS.** Text in English. 1974. m. EUR 10,721.66 in Europe; USD 10,849 in North America; AUD 13,219 in Australasia; GBP 7,393.91 in UK & elsewhere (effective 2006). bk.rev. charts; illus. reprint service avail. from PSC. **Document type:** *Journal, Academic/Scholarly.* **Description:** Contains articles that deal with socioeconomic problems. Covers socioeconomic systems, human resources policy, social indicators, environmental economics, income distribution and policy, social services, demographic trends, and ethical and religious influence.

B

▼ new title ➤ refereed ✶ unverified ♦ full entry avail.

Incorporates: International Review of Economics and Ethics (0268-392X)
Related titles: Online - full text ed.: (from EBSCO Publishing, Emerald Group Publishing Limited, Florida Center for Library Automation, Gale Group, IngentaConnect, O C L C Online Computer Library Center, Inc., ProQuest Information & Learning, Swets Information Services).
Indexed: ABIn, ABS&EES, APEL, ASSIA, BAS, BPIA, BusI, CJA, CREJ, CurCont, EIP, ERA, ETA, EmerIntel, Emerald, IBSS, ILD, IndIslam, JEL, KES, LRI, M&MA, MEA, ManagCont, PAIS, PCI, PerIslam, RASB, RDA, RHEA, SCIMP, SEA, SENA, SOMA, SSCI, SWA, T&II, TEA, WAE&RSA, WBSS.
—BLDSC (4542.555000), IDS, IE, Infotrieve, ingenta. **CCC.**
Published by: (International Institute of Social Economics), Emerald Group Publishing Limited, 60-62 Toller Ln, Bradford, W Yorks BD8 9BY, United Kingdom. TEL 44-1274-777700, FAX 44-1274-785200, infomation@emeraldinsight.com, http://www.emeraldinsight.com/ijse.htm. Ed. John C O'Brien.

330 384 USA ISSN 1553-118X
▼ ➤ **INTERNATIONAL JOURNAL OF STRATEGIC COMMUNICATION.** Text in English. forthcoming 2007 (Jan). q. **Document type:** *Journal, Academic/Scholarly.* **Description:** Aims at fostering understanding of the processes, prospects, and challenges of communication for organizations in a changing global society.
Related titles: Online - full text ed.: ISSN 1553-1198. forthcoming 2007 (Jan).
Published by: Lawrence Erlbaum Associates, Inc., 10 Industrial Ave, Mahwah, NJ 07430-2262. TEL 201-258-2200, 800-926-6579, FAX 201-236-0072, journals@erlbaum.com, http://www.leaonline.com/loi/ijsc, http://www.erlbaum.com. Eds. Betteke van Ruler, Derina Holtzhauzen, Kirk Hallahan.

330 GBR ISSN 1743-8284
▼ ➤ **INTERNATIONAL JOURNAL OF SUSTAINABLE DESIGN.** Text in English. forthcoming 2006. q. USD 450 to institutions print or online ed.; USD 545 combined subscription to institutions print & online eds. (effective 2005). **Document type:** *Journal, Academic/Scholarly.*
Related titles: Online - full text ed.: ISSN 1743-8292. forthcoming 2006.
Published by: Inderscience Publishers, IEL Editorial Office, PO Box 735, Olney, Bucks MK46 5WB, United Kingdom. TEL 44-1234-240519, FAX 44-1234-240515, ijsdes@inderscience.com, info@inderscience.com, http://www.inderscience.com/ijsdes. Ed. Joan M Alier. **Subscr. to:** World Trade Centre Bldg, 29 route de Pre-Bois, Case Postale 896, Geneva 15 1215, Switzerland. FAX 41-22-7910885, subs@inderscience.com.

330 GBR ISSN 1357-1516
➤ **INTERNATIONAL JOURNAL OF THE ECONOMICS OF BUSINESS.** Text in English. 1994. 3/yr. GBP 370, USD 595 combined subscription to institutions print & online eds. (effective 2006). adv. bk.rev. index. reprint service avail. from PSC. **Document type:** *Journal, Academic/Scholarly.* **Description:** Presents original economics that are clearly applicable to business, both private and public sector, and related public policy problems or issues.
Formerly (until vol.1, no.2, 1994): Journal of the Economics of Business (0962-1369)
Related titles: Microfiche ed.; Online - full text ed.: ISSN 1466-1829. GBP 352, USD 565 to institutions (effective 2006) (from EBSCO Publishing, Florida Center for Library Automation, Gale Group, IngentaConnect, Northern Light Technology, Inc., O C L C Online Computer Library Center, Inc., ProQuest Information & Learning, Swets Information Services).
Indexed: ABIn, DIP, IBR, IBSS, IBZ, JEL.
—BLDSC (4542.198000), IE, Infotrieve, ingenta. **CCC.**
Published by: Routledge (Subsidiary of: Taylor & Francis Group), 4 Park Square, Milton Park, Abingdon, Oxon OX14 4RN, United Kingdom. TEL 44-1235-828600, FAX 44-1235-829000, info@routledge.co.uk, http://www.tandf.co.uk/journals/routledge/13571516.asp, http://www.routledge.co.uk. Eds. Eleanor Morgan, H E Frech III. adv.: page GBP 200. **Subscr. to:** Taylor & Francis Ltd, Journals Customer Service, Rankine Rd, Basingstoke, Hants RG24 8PR, United Kingdom. TEL 44-1256-813000, FAX 44-1256-330245, enquiry@tandf.co.uk.

330 GBR ISSN 1368-6925
INTERNATIONAL LIBRARY OF CRITICAL WRITINGS IN BUSINESS HISTORY. Text in English. 1991. irreg. **Document type:** *Monographic series.*
—BLDSC (4542.905000).
Published by: Edward Elgar Publishing Ltd, Glensanda House, Montpellier Parade, Cheltenham, Glos GL50 1UA, United Kingdom. TEL 44-1242-226934, FAX 44-1242-262111, info@e-elgar.co.uk, http://www.e-elgar.co.uk.

330 GBR ISSN 1368-6933
INTERNATIONAL LIBRARY OF CRITICAL WRITINGS IN ECONOMICS. Text in English. 1990. irreg. **Document type:** *Monographic series.*
—BLDSC (4542.910000), IE.
Published by: Edward Elgar Publishing Ltd, Glensanda House, Montpellier Parade, Cheltenham, Glos GL50 1UA, United Kingdom. TEL 44-1242-226934, FAX 44-1242-262111, info@e-elgar.co.uk, http://www.e-elgar.co.uk.

338.83 GBR
INTERNATIONAL MERGERS & ACQUISITIONS (YEARS). Text in English. a., latest 2005, April, 6th Edition. GBP 115 per issue (effective 2005). **Document type:** *Yearbook, Trade.* **Description:** Provide the reader with a unique insight into the global M&A market by highlighting the opportunities as well as the pitfalls that face M&A practitioners in this ever changing market.
—BLDSC (4544.137300).
Published by: Euromoney Publications plc, Nestor House, Playhouse Yard, London, EC4V 5EX, United Kingdom. TEL 44-20-77798888, information@euromoneyplc.com, http://www.euromoney-yearbooks.com/default.asp?page=5&pcID=3705, http://www.euromoney.com, http://euromoney-yearbooks.com. Ed. Lori Nicholson. Pub. Adrian Hornbook.

330 IND
INTERNATIONAL PRESS CUTTING SERVICE: LIST OF NEW INDUSTRIES APPROVED BY GOVERNMENT. Text in English. w. INR 715, USD 85 (effective 1999). **Document type:** *Newsletter.* **Description:** Contains a list of recent government-approved industries.
Published by: International Press Cutting Service, PO Box 121, Allahabad, Uttar Pradesh 211 001, India. TEL 91-532-622392.

658 USA ISSN 1074-7877
INTERNATIONAL RESEARCH IN THE BUSINESS DISCIPLINES. Text in English. 1993. irreg., latest vol.4, 2003. price varies. back issues avail. **Document type:** *Monographic series, Academic/Scholarly.* **Description:** Provides an outlet for unique, often cutting edge, business research with an international flavor.
Related titles: Online - full text ed.: (from ScienceDirect).
—**CCC.**
Published by: J A I Press Inc. (Subsidiary of: Elsevier Science & Technology), 360 Park Ave S, New York, NY 10010-1710. TEL 212-989-5800, FAX 212-633-3990, usinfo-f@elsevier.com, http://www.elsevier.com/wps/find/bookdescription.cws_home/BS_IRBD/description#description. Ed. M Ryan.

330.071 USA ISSN 0035-354X
INTERNATIONAL REVIEW FOR BUSINESS EDUCATION/ INTERNATIONALE ZEITSCHRIFT FUER KAUFMAENNISCHES BILDUNGSWESEN/REVISTA INTERNACIONAL PARA LA ENSENANZA COMERCIAL/REVUE INTERNATIONALE POUR L'ENSEIGNEMENT COMMERCIAL/RIVISTA INTERNAZIONALE PER LA CULTURA COMMERCIALE. Text in English, French, German, Italian, Spanish. 1901. s-a. adv. bk.rev. charts. **Document type:** *Journal, Trade.*
Indexed: BusEdI.
Published by: International Society for Business Education, PO Box 20457, Carson City, NV 89721. TEL 775-882-1445, FAX 775-882-1449, secretary@siec-isbe.org, http://www.siec-isbe.org. Ed. Helen Zimmerman. R&P G L Kantin. Circ: 2,200 (paid).

330 GBR ISSN 0269-2171
HB1
➤ **INTERNATIONAL REVIEW OF APPLIED ECONOMICS.** Text in English. 1987. 5/yr. GBP 552, USD 964 combined subscription to institutions print & online eds. (effective 2006). adv. bk.rev. illus.; abstr. Index. back issues avail.; reprint service avail. from PSC. **Document type:** *Journal, Academic/Scholarly.* **Description:** Examines the practical application of economic ideas.
Related titles: Online - full text ed.: ISSN 1465-3486. GBP 524, USD 916 to institutions (effective 2006) (from bigchalk, EBSCO Publishing, Factiva, Florida Center for Library Automation, Gale Group, IngentaConnect, Northern Light Technology, Inc., O C L C Online Computer Library Center, Inc., ProQuest Information & Learning, Swets Information Services).
Indexed: ABIn, BAS, GEOBASE, IBR, IBSS, IBZ, Inspec, JEL, PAIS, RASB, RDA, TriticAb, WAE&RSA.
—BLDSC (4546.160000), IE, Infotrieve, ingenta. **CCC.**
Published by: Routledge (Subsidiary of: Taylor & Francis Group), 4 Park Sq, Milton Park, Abingdon, Oxon OX14 4RN, United Kingdom. TEL 44-1235-828600, FAX 44-1235-829000, info@routledge.co.uk, http://www.tandf.co.uk/journals/titles/02692171.asp, http://www.routledge.co.uk. **Subscr. to:** Taylor & Francis Ltd, Journals Customer Service, Rankine Rd, Basingstoke, Hants RG24 8PR, United Kingdom. TEL 44-1256-813000, FAX 44-1256-330245, enquiry@tandf.co.uk.

330 378 GBR
INTERNATIONAL REVIEW OF ECONOMICS EDUCATION. Text in English. 2001. q. **Document type:** *Journal, Academic/Scholarly.* **Description:** Focuses on improving the quality of higher education economics teaching by publishing research on curriculum design, pedagogy, assessment, innovation and evaluation. Emphasizes role of research in good professional practice.
Published by: University of Bristol, Learning and Teaching Support Network Centre for Economics, 8-10 Berkeley Sq, Bristol, BS8 1HH, United Kingdom. TEL 44-117-9287071, FAX 44-117-9287112, ltsn-econ@bristol.ac.uk, http://econltsn.ilrt.bris.ac.uk/journals.htm. Eds. Carol Johnston, Peter Davies.

330 332 GBR ISSN 1358-1937
INTERNATIONAL RISK MANAGEMENT. Text in English. 1994. m. GBP 85; GBP 95 in Europe; GBP 105 elsewhere. adv. charts; stat.; tr.lit. index. **Document type:** *Trade.*
Published by: Emap Finance (Subsidiary of: Emap Business Communications Ltd.), 33-39 Bowling Green Ln, London, EC1R 0DA, United Kingdom. TEL 44-171-505-8000, FAX 44-171-505-3185, http://www.emap.com. Ed. Mike Handley. Pub. Nick Morgan.

INTERNATIONAL STATUS REPORT ON PLASTICS INDUSTRY WORLDWIDE. see *PLASTICS*

330 NLD ISSN 0924-5170
➤ **INTERNATIONAL STUDIES IN ECONOMICS AND ECONOMETRICS.** Text in English. 1969. irreg., latest vol.37, 1997. price varies. back issues avail. **Document type:** *Monographic series, Academic/Scholarly.*
—BLDSC (4549.771000). **CCC.**
Published by: Springer-Verlag Dordrecht (Subsidiary of: Springer Science+Business Media), Van Godewijckstraat 30, Dordrecht, 3311 GX, Netherlands. TEL 31-78-6576050, FAX 31-78-6576474, http://www.springeronline.com.

➤ **INTERNATIONAL TECHNOLOGY AND BUSINESS OPPORTUNITIES. CATALOGUE.** see *TECHNOLOGY: COMPREHENSIVE WORKS*

330 341 USA
INTERNATIONAL TRADE. Text in English. q. USD 29.50 to non-members; free to members (effective 2000). adv. **Document type:** *Newspaper.*
Formed by the merger of: World Trade News; World Trade Update
Indexed: RASB.
Published by: International Trade Association, 1224 N Nokomis N E, Alexandria, MN 56308-5072. TEL 320-763-5101, FAX 320-763-9290. Ed., R&P, Adv. contact Robert Johnson. Pub. Robert G Johnson.

INTERNATIONAL TRAVELLER. see *TRAVEL AND TOURISM*

INTERNATIONALE DIREKTINVESTIONEN. see *POLITICAL SCIENCE*

330 USA
▼ **THE INTERNET JOURNAL OF INFORMATION SYSTEMS.** Text in English. 2004. irreg. free to individuals; USD 500 to institutions (effective 2005). **Document type:** *Journal, Academic/Scholarly.*
Media: Online - full content.
Published by: Internet Scientific Publications, L.L.C., 23 Rippling Creek Dr, Sugar Land, TX 77479. TEL 832-443-1193, FAX 281-240-1533, wenker@ispub.com, http://www.ispub.com/ostia/index.php?xmlFilePath=journals/ijis/front.xml.

330 USA
INTRO. Text in English. biennial. adv.
Published by: Business Publications Corp., 4521 Fleur St, Ste A-2, Des Moines, IA 50309. TEL 515-953-4822, FAX 515-953-1394. Adv. contact Jon Matejczyk.

330 GBR
INVEST IN BRITAIN ANNUAL REPORT. Text in English. 1977. a. free. charts; illus.; stat. back issues avail. **Document type:** *Government.* **Description:** Reviews activities and investments in the UK by foreign companies.
Published by: Invest in Britain Bureau, 1 Victoria St, 66-74 Victoria St, London, SW1H 0ET, United Kingdom. TEL 44-171-215-2501, FAX 44-171-215-5651. Circ: 6,000 (controlled).

330 ESP ISSN 0210-1521
INVESTIGACIONES ECONOMICAS. Text in Spanish; Summaries in English. 1986. 3/yr. EUR 25 to individuals; EUR 75 to institutions; EUR 18 to students (effective 2004). bk.rev. **Description:** Covers economic theory, history of economics and Spanish industrial and public economics.
Related titles: Online - full text ed.: ISSN 1575-4367. 1999.
Indexed: IBR, IBSS, JEL.
—CINDOC.
Published by: Fundacion SEPI, C/ Quintana 2, 3a Planta, Madrid, 28008, Spain. TEL 34-91-5488351, http://www.funep.es/invecon/.

INVESTMENT NEWS. see *BUSINESS AND ECONOMICS—Investments*

330 USA ISSN 1050-6551
HG1616.I5
INVESTMENT PERFORMANCE DIGEST. Text in English. q. USD 398 (effective 1998). back issues avail. **Document type:** *Trade.*
Published by: I D C Financial Publishing, Inc., PO Box 140, Hartland, WI 53029. TEL 414-367-7231, FAX 414-367-6497. Ed., Pub., R&P John E Rickmeier.

330 IRL ISSN 1649-248X
IRISH JOURNAL OF MANAGEMENT. Text in English. 1979. s-a.
Formerly (until 2000): Irish Business and Administrative Research (0332-1118)

Related titles: Online - full text ed.: (from EBSCO Publishing, O C L C Online Computer Library Center, Inc.).
Indexed: ABIn.
—BLDSC (4571.990000), IE.
Published by: Irish Academy of Management, University of Ulster, Northland Rd, Londonberry, BT48 7JL, Ireland.

330 USA ISSN 1072-6136
HF5003
IRWIN BUSINESS AND INVESTMENT ALMANAC. Text in English. 1977. a. USD 75.
Former titles (until 1994): Business One Irwin Business and Investment Almanac (1057-5014); (until 1991): Dow Jones-Irwin Business and Investment Almanac (0733-2610); Dow Jones-Irwin Business Almanac (0146-6534)
Indexed: ATI.
Published by: Irwin Professional Publishing, 1333 Burr Ridge Pkwy., Burr Ridge, IL 60521-6489. TEL 708-789-4000. Eds. Caroline Levine, Sumner N Levine. Circ: 7,600.

330 FJI
ISLANDS BUSINESS. Text in English. 1980. m. FJD 40, USD 45 domestic; AUD 30 S. Pacific Islands; AUD 25 in Australia; NZD 35 in New Zealand; NZD 30 to US & Micronesia; NZD 35 elsewhere (effective 2000). adv. bk.rev. **Document type:** *Trade.* **Description:** Covering Pacific Islands business, economics and politics.
Former titles: Islands Business Politics; (until 1994): Islands Business Pacific; (until 1991): Islands Business
Indexed: RDA.
Address: 46 Gordon St, PO Box 12718, Suva, Fiji. TEL 6-79-303623, FAX 6-79-303943, editor@ibi.com.fj, http://www.islandsbusiness.com. Ed. Peter Lomas. Pub. Robert Keith Reid. R&P Godfrey Scoullar. Adv. contact Roslyn Hussain. Circ: 8,500 (paid).

ISSUES IN BUSINESS ETHICS. see *PHILOSOPHY*

ISSUES IN POLITICAL ECONOMY; undergraduate student research in Economics. see *POLITICAL SCIENCE*

330 ITA ISSN 0075-1529
ISTITUTO MOBILIARE ITALIANO. ANNUAL REPORT. Text in Italian. 1932. a.
Related titles: English ed.
Published by: Istituto Mobiliare Italiano, Viale Dell' Arte, 25, Rome, RM 00144, Italy. Circ: 2,400.

330 ITA
▼ **ISTITUZIONI E SVILUPPO ECONOMICO/INSTITUTIONS AND ECONOMIC DEVELOPMENT.** Text in Italian. 2003. 3/yr. EUR 54 domestic; EUR 71 foreign (effective 2003). **Document type:** *Journal, Academic/Scholarly.*
Published by: (Universita degli Studi di Lecce, Facolta di Giurisprudenza), Franco Angeli Edizioni, Viale Monza 106, Milan, 20127, Italy. TEL 39-02-2837141, FAX 39-02-26144793, redazioni@francoangeli.it, http://www.dipe.unile.it/ise, http://www.francoangeli.it.

330 RUS
IZ RUK V RUKI; gazeta besplatnykh ob'yavlenii. Text in Russian. 1992. 260/yr. USD 795 in North America (effective 2000).
Published by: Redaktsiya Iz Ruk v Ruki, Bumazhnyi pr 14, Moscow, 125015, Russian Federation. TEL 7-095-2573049, FAX 7-095-2512841. **Dist. by:** East View Information Services, 3020 Harbor Ln. N., Minneapolis, MN 55447. TEL 763-550-0961, FAX 763-559-2931.

JANE'S DEFENCE INDUSTRY. see *MILITARY*

JANE'S INTELLIGENCE DIGEST. see *POLITICAL SCIENCE*

JANE'S NAVAL CONSTRUCTION AND RETROFIT MARKETS. see *BUILDING AND CONSTRUCTION*

338.476234 GBR
JANE'S WORLD DEFENCE INDUSTRY. Text in English. s-a. GBP 795, USD 1,265, AUD 2,070 (effective 2004). **Document type:** *Trade.* **Description:** Covers the corporate activity in the defence industry, including ownership, key personnel, workforce, recent financial performance, plants and subsidiaries, products and new technologies, and summary of recent major contracts.
Related titles: Online - full content ed.: GBP 1,250, USD 1,999, AUD 3,250 (effective 2004).
Published by: Jane's Information Group, Sentinel House, 163 Brighton Rd, Coulsdon, Surrey CR5 2YH, United Kingdom. TEL 44-20-87003700, FAX 44-20-87631006, info@janes.co.uk, http://jwdi.janes.com/, http://www.janes.com. **Dist. by:** 1340 Braddock Pl, Ste 300, Alexandria, VA 22314-1651. TEL 703-683-3700, 800-824-0768, FAX 703-836-0297, 800-836-0297; Jane's Information Group Asia, 60 Albert St, #15-01 Albert Complex, Singapore 189969, Singapore. TEL 65-331-6280, FAX 65-336-9921, info@janes.com.sg; Jane's Information Group Australia, PO Box 3502, Rozelle, NSW 2039, Australia. TEL 61-2-8587-7900, FAX 61-2-8587-7901, info@janes.thomson.com.au.

330 NLD ISSN 1569-2043
DS820.8
JAPAN. Text in English. 2001. bi-m. EUR 40.68 in the European Union; GBP 29.70 in United Kingdom; JPY 9,540 in Japan; USD 59.70 elsewhere; USD 9.95 newsstand/cover (effective 2002). adv. illus. **Document type:** *Magazine, Consumer.* **Description:** Provides coverage of Japan on everything from business and politics to arts and society.
Published by: Hotei Publishing, Royal Tropical Institute, PO Box 95001, Amsterdam, 1090 HA, Netherlands. TEL 31-20-5688330, FAX 31-20-568-8286, info@japan-mag.com, info@hotei-publishing.com, http://www.japan-mag.com. Ed. Ray Edgar. Adv. contact Petra Noordermeer.

JAPAN LUMBER JOURNAL. see *FORESTS AND FORESTRY—Lumber And Wood*

JAPAN POLICY AND POLITICS. see *POLITICAL SCIENCE*

330 USA
JAPAN WEEKLY MONITOR. Text in English. w. **Document type:** *Trade.*
Media: Online - full content.
Published by: Kyodo News International, Inc., 50 Rockefeller Plaza, Ste 803, New York, NY 10020. TEL 212-397-3723, FAX 212-397-3721, kni@kyodonews.com, http://www.kyodonews.com/.

330 AUS ISSN 1352-4739
HB9
➤ **THE JAPANESE ECONOMIC REVIEW.** Text in English. 1950. q. USD 82 combined subscription in the Americas to individuals & Caribbean (print & online eds.); EUR 86 combined subscription in Europe to individuals print & online eds.; GBP 57 combined subscription elsewhere to individuals print & online eds.; USD 203 combined subscription in the Americas to institutions & Caribbean (print & online eds.); GBP 83, USD 120 combined subscription in developing nations to institutions print & online eds.; GBP 141 combined subscription elsewhere to institutions print & online eds. (effective 2006). bk.rev. **Document type:** *Academic/Scholarly.*
Formerly (until 1995): Economic Studies Quarterly (0557-109X)
Related titles: Online - full text ed.: ISSN 1468-5876. USD 193 in the Americas to institutions & Caribbean; GBP 79, USD 114 in developing nations to institutions; GBP 134 elsewhere to institutions (effective 2006) (from Blackwell Synergy, EBSCO Publishing, Gale Group, IngentaConnect, O C L C Online Computer Library Center, Inc., Swets Information Services).
Indexed: ABIn, CCMJ, CREJ, CurCont, GEOBASE, IBSS, JEL, MathR, MathSciNet, PSA, SSCI.
—BLDSC (4650.762700), IDS, IE, Infotrieve, ingenta. **CCC.**
Published by: Blackwell Publishing Asia (Subsidiary of: Blackwell Publishing Ltd.), 550 Swanston St, Carlton South, VIC 3053, Australia. TEL 61-383591011, FAX 61-383591120, subs@blackwellpublishingasia.com, http://www.blackwellpublishing.com/journals/JERE. Eds. Makoto Yano, Nobuhiro Kiyotaki.

330 USA ISSN 1097-203X
HC461
➤ **THE JAPANESE ECONOMY**; translations and studies. Text in English. 1972. q. USD 144 domestic to individuals; USD 183 foreign to individuals; USD 864 domestic to institutions; USD 966 foreign to institutions (effective 2006). adv. back issues avail.; reprint service avail. from PSC. **Document type:** *Journal, Academic/Scholarly.* **Description:** Contains translations of economic and management material from Japanese sources, primarly scholarly journals and books. Selections are intended to reflect developments in the Japanese economy and to be of interest to those professionally concerned with this field.
Formerly (until 1997): Japanese Economic Studies (0021-4841)
Related titles: Online - full text ed.: 2004 (Apr.) (from EBSCO Publishing, O C L C Online Computer Library Center, Inc., Swets Information Services).
Indexed: ABIn, ASCA, BAS, CREJ, CurCont, ESPM, FamI, IBR, JEL, KES, PAIS, RiskAb, SSCI.
—BLDSC (4650.764200), IDS, IE, Infotrieve, ingenta. **CCC.**
Published by: M.E. Sharpe, Inc., 80 Business Park Dr, Armonk, NY 10504. TEL 914-273-1800, 800-541-6563, FAX 914-273-2106, custserv@mesharpe.com, http://www.mesharpe.com/mall/results1.asp. Ed. Walter F Hatch. Adv. contact Barbara Ladd TEL 914-273-1800 ext 121. page USD 300; trim 8 x 5.

650 JPN ISSN 1349-807X
JAPANESE RESEARCH IN BUSINESS HISTORY. Text in English. 1984. a. JPY 5,000 newsstand/cover to non-members; JPY 3,500 newsstand/cover to members (effective 2005). bk.rev. **Document type:** *Journal, Academic/Scholarly.*
Formerly (until vol.20, 2003): Japanese Yearbook on Business History (0910-2027)
Indexed: AmH&L, HistAb.
Published by: (Business History Society of Japan), Japan Business History Institute Library, Fuji Building, 3rd floor, 2-12-4 Hirakawacho, Tokyo, Chiyoda-ku 102-0093, Japan. TEL 81-3-32621090, FAX 81-3-32395090, info@jbhi.or.jp, http://www.jbhi.or.jp/.

THE JERUSALEM TIMES; bilady. see *POLITICAL SCIENCE—International Relations*

330 261.2 USA ISSN 1524-5578
JEWISH BUSINESS QUARTERLY. Text in English. 2000. q. **Document type:** *Magazine, Trade.*
Published by: E M Publishing Enterprises, Inc, 19456 Ventura Blvd, 200, Tarzana, CA 91356. TEL 818-654-0870, FAX 818-654-0874.

330 CHN ISSN 1002-851X
JIANZHU JINGJI. Text in Chinese. 1985. m.
Related titles: Online - full text ed.: (from East View Information Services).
Published by: Zhongguo Jianzhu Xuehui, Jianzhu Jingji Xueshu Weiyuanhui, No 19 Chegongzhuang Dajie, Xizhimenwai, Beijing, 100044, China. TEL 8992669. Ed. Yang Shen.

330 CHN
JINGJI CANKAO BAO/ECONOMIC INFORMATION DAILY. Text in Chinese. 1981. d. CNY 270 (effective 2004). **Document type:** *Newspaper, Consumer.*
Published by: Xinhua Tongxunshe/Xinhua News Agency, 57 Xuanwumen Xidajie, Beijing, 100803, China. TEL 86-10-63071114, http://www.xinhuanet.com/xhsjj/baokan.htm. **Dist. in US by:** China Books & Periodicals Inc, 360 Swift Ave., Ste. 48, S San Fran, CA 94080-6220; **Dist. by:** China International Book Trading Corp, 35 Chegongzhuang Xilu, Haidian District, PO Box 399, Beijing 100044, China. TEL 86-10-68412045, FAX 86-10-68412023, cibtc@mail.cibtc.com.cn, http://www.cibtc.com.cn.

330 CHN
JINGJI DAOBAO/ECONOMIC REPORTER. Text in English. d. (6/week). CNY 103.20 (effective 2004). **Document type:** *Newspaper, Trade.*
Related titles: Online - full content ed.
Published by: Dazhongbao Yejituan/Dazhong News Group, 6, Leyuan Dajie, Jinan, Shangdong 250014, China. TEL 86-531-2968989, http://www.dzwww.com/jingjidaobao/. **Dist. by:** China International Book Trading Corp, 35 Chegongzhuang Xilu, Haidian District, PO Box 399, Beijing 100044, China. TEL 86-10-68412045, FAX 86-10-68412023, cibtc@mail.cibtc.com.cn, http://www.cibtc.com.cn.

JINGJI FAZHI. see *LAW—Corporate Law*

330 CHN ISSN 1003-3580
JINGJI LUNTAN/ECONOMIC TRIBUNE. Text in Chinese. 1987. s-m. 48 p./no.; **Document type:** *Academic/Scholarly.* **Description:** Provides timely information on Chinese economic development.
Related titles: Online - full text ed.: (from East View Information Services).
Indexed: RASB.
Published by: Hebei Sheng Shehui Kexueyuan/Hebei Academy of Social Sciences, 9 Shiyi Lu, Shijiazhuang, Hebei 050051, China. TEL 86-311-3035747, FAX 86-311-3036594. Ed. Liu Peng. **Dist. overseas by:** China International Book Trading Corp, 35 Chegongzhuang Xilu, Haidian District, PO Box 399, Beijing 100044, China.

330 CHN ISSN 1005-3425
HC427.92
JINGJI PINGLUN/ECONOMIC REVIEW. Text in Chinese. 1980. bi-m. CNY 68; USD 120 foreign. 96 p./no.; **Document type:** *Academic/Scholarly.* **Description:** Contains academic researches, reports and comments on economic theories and major practical issues.
Related titles: Online - full text ed.: (from East View Information Services).
Published by: Jingji Pinglun Zazhishe, Wuhan Daxue Jingji Xueyuan, Wuhan, Hubei 430072, China. TEL 86-27-87682902, sec@whu.edu.cn. Ed. Wang Bin. Pub. Tao Meosheng. Adv. contact Wang Huiying. **Dist. overseas by:** China International Book Trading Corp, 35 Chegongzhuang Xilu, Haidian District, PO Box 399, Beijing 100044, China.

330 TWN
JINGJI RIBAO/ECONOMIC DAILY NEWS. Text in Chinese. 1967. d. USD 240 for 3 mos.. adv. **Document type:** *Newspaper.* **Description:** Contains economic, finance, trade, real estate, industry and commercial news.
Indexed: B&I.
Address: 555 Chung Hsaio E. Rd, Sec 4, Taipei, 105, Taiwan. TEL 886-2-763-8095, FAX 886-2-763-4124. Ed. Shyh Shyang Lui. adv.: B&W page TWD 250,000; trim 545 x 395. Circ: 275,000.

330 CHN
JINGJI RIBAO/ECONOMIC DAILY. Text in Chinese. d. CNY 297 (effective 2004). 12 p./no.; **Document type:** *Newspaper, Consumer.* **Description:** Covers the Chinese national economy.
Related titles: Online - full content ed.
Indexed: RASB.

Published by: Jingji Ribao Baoye Jituan/Economic Daily Newspaper Group, Xuanwen-qu, 2, Baizhifang Dongjie, Beijing, 100054, China. TEL 86-10-63539414, FAX 86-10-63539408, http://www.ced.com.cn/. **Dist. in US by:** China Books & Periodicals Inc, 360 Swift Ave., Ste. 48, S San Fran, CA 94080-6220; **Dist. outside China by:** China International Book Trading Corp, 35 Chegongzhuang Xilu, Haidian District, PO Box 399, Beijing 100044, China. TEL 86-10-68412045, FAX 86-10-68412023, cibtc@mail.cibtc.com.cn, http://www.cibtc.com.cn.

330 CHN ISSN 1004-972X
JINGJI WENTI/ECONOMIC ISSUES. Text in Chinese. 1979. m.
Related titles: Online - full text ed.: (from East View Information Services).
Indexed: CPM.
Published by: Shanxi Sheng Shehui Kexueyuan/Shanxi Academy of Social Sciences, 38 Bingzhou Nanlu, Taiyuan, Shanxi 030006, China. TEL 775841. Ed. Chen Dianmo.

330 CHN ISSN 1006-2912
JINGJI WENTI TANSUO/INQUIRY INTO ECONOMIC PROBLEMS. Text in Chinese. 1980. m. CNY 60 (effective 2004). **Document type:** *Journal, Academic/Scholarly.*
Related titles: Online - full text ed.: (from East View Information Services, WanFang Data Corp.).
—BLDSC (4516.223000).
Address: 685, Dongerhuan Lu, Kunming, Yunnan 650216, China. TEL 86-871-3849950, http://jjwtts.periodicals.net.cn/default.html. **Dist. in US by:** China Books & Periodicals Inc, 360 Swift Ave., Ste. 48, S San Fran, CA 94080-6220. TEL 415-282-2994; **Dist. by:** China International Book Trading Corp, 35 Chegongzhuang Xilu, Haidian District, PO Box 399, Beijing 100044, China. TEL 86-10-68412045, FAX 86-10-68412023, cibtc@mail.cibtc.com.cn, http://www.cibtc.com.cn.

330 CHN ISSN 1000-8330
JINGJI YU SHEHUI FAZHAN/ECONOMICS AND SOCIAL DEVELOPMENT. Text in Chinese. q.
Indexed: RASB.
Published by: Taiyuan Jishu Jingji Yanjiu Zhongxin/Taiyuan Research Center of Technology and Economics, 21 Hanxiguan, Taiyuan, Shanxi 030002, China. TEL 345385. Ed. Yang Kaishan.

330 CHN ISSN 1002-9818
JINGJI YUCE YU XINXI/ECONOMIC FORECAST AND INFORMATION. Text in Chinese. 1985. m.
Published by: Guojia Jingji Xinxi Zhongxin, Jingji Xinxi-bu/National Economic Information Center, Bureau of Economic Information, No 58 Sanlihe Lu, Beijing, 100045, China. TEL 8091733. Ed. Wu Jiapei.

330 CHN ISSN 1008-5130
JINGJI YUEKAN/ECONOMIC MONTHLY. Text in Chinese. 1985. m. CNY 120 (effective 2004). **Document type:** *Magazine, Trade.*
Related titles: Online - full text ed.: (from East View Information Services).
Published by: Jingji Ribao Baoye Jituan/Economic Daily Newspaper Group, Haidian-qu, 3, Xitucheng Lu, Beilou 6-ceng, Beijing, 100088, China. TEL 86-10-82013112-1045 ext 1026, FAX 86-10-62358406, jjykzz@yahoo.com.cn, http://bkdy.ce.cn/fenlei/t20031120_213242.shtml. **Dist. by:** China International Book Trading Corp, 35 Chegongzhuang Xilu, Haidian District, PO Box 399, Beijing 100044, China. TEL 86-10-68412045, FAX 86-10-68412023, cibtc@mail.cibtc.com.cn, http://www.cibtc.com.cn.

330 CHN ISSN 1005-474X
JINGJI ZHENGCE XINXI/INFORMATION ON ECONOMICS POLICY. Text in Chinese. 1992. s-m. CNY 108 (effective 2004). **Document type:** *Journal, Academic/Scholarly.*
Related titles: Print ed.: USD 80.20 (effective 2001).
Published by: Zhongguo Renmin Daxue, Shubao Zilio Zhongxin/Renmin University of China, Information Center for Social Server, Dongcheng-qu, 3, Zhangzizhong Lu, Beijing, 100007, China. TEL 86-10-64039458, FAX 86-10-64015080, kyes@163.net, http://www.confucius.cn.net/bkdetail.asp?fzt=X5. **Dist. in the US by:** China Publications Service, PO Box 49614, Chicago, IL 60649. TEL 312-288-3291, FAX 312-288-8570; **Dist. outside of China by:** China International Book Trading Corp, 35 Chegongzhuang Xilu, Haidian District, PO Box 399, Beijing 100044, China. TEL 86-10-68412045, FAX 86-10-68412023, cibtc@mail.cibtc.com.cn, http://www.cibtc.com.cn/.

330 CHN
JINGJI ZONGHENG. Text in Chinese. 1985. m. adv. bk.rev. **Document type:** *Academic/Scholarly.* **Description:** Covers Chinese economic reforms and economic development strategies. Reviews Chinese and foreign economic theories and thoughts.
Published by: Jilin Sheng Jingjixue Tuanti Lianhehui, 28 Xinfa Lu, Changchun, Jilin 130051, China. TEL 0431-829642, FAX 0431-826854. Ed. Zhang Weida. Circ: 7,000. **Dist. outside China by:** China International Book Trading Corp, 35 Chegongzhuang Xilu, Haidian District, PO Box 399, Beijing 100044, China.

330.9 CHN ISSN 1001-3385
JINGJISHI (BEIJING)/ECONOMICS HISTORY. Text in Chinese. 1978. bi-m. CNY 67.20 (effective 2004). 160 p./no.; **Document type:** *Journal, Academic/Scholarly.*
Indexed: RASB.
Published by: Zhongguo Renmin Daxue, Shubao Zilio Zhongxin/Renmin University of China, Information Center for Social Server, Dongcheng-qu, 3, Zhangzizhong Lu, Beijing, 100007, China. TEL 86-10-64039458, FAX 86-10-64015080, kyes@163.net, http://www.confucius.cn.net/bkdetail.asp?fzt=F7. **Dist. in US by:** China Publications Service, PO Box 49614, Chicago, IL 60649. TEL 312-288-3291, FAX 312-288-8570; **Dist. by:** China International Book Trading Corp, 35 Chegongzhuang Xilu, Haidian District, PO Box 399, Beijing 100044, China. TEL 86-10-68412045, FAX 86-10-68412023, cibtc@mail.cibtc.com.cn, http://www.cibtc.com.cn.

330 CHN ISSN 1004-4914
HC427.92
JINGJISHI (TAIYUAN)/CHINA ECONOMIST. Text in Chinese. 1986. bi-m.
Related titles: Online - full text ed.: (from East View Information Services).
Indexed: ArtHuCI.
Published by: Shanxi Jingji Guanli Xueyuan/Shanxi Institute of Economics and Management, 46, Jiefang Lu, Taiyuan, Shanxi 030002, China. TEL 227266. Ed. Zhang Chengong.

330 CHN ISSN 1002-8390
HB9
JINGJIXUE DONGTAI. Text in Chinese. 1960. m.
Published by: Zhongguo Shehui Kexueyuan, Jingji Yanjiusuo/Chinese Academy of Social Sciences, Economic Research Institute, 2 Yuetan Beixiaojie, Beijing, 100836, China. TEL 895023. Ed. Mao Tianqi.

330 CHN ISSN 1003-5656
HC427.92
JINGJIXUE JIA/ECONOMIST. Text in Chinese. bi-m. adv. 128 p./no.; **Document type:** *Academic/Scholarly.* **Description:** Encourages academic discussions about economic theories.
Related titles: Online - full text ed.: (from East View Information Services).
Indexed: ArtHuCI.
Published by: Xinan Caijing Daxue/Southwestern University of Finance and Economics, 55 Guanghua Cun, Xijiao, Chengdu, Sichuan 610074, China. TEL 86-28-7784707, FAX 86-28-784689. Ed. Liu Shibai. Adv. contact Li Jianyong. **Dist. overseas by:** China International Book Trading Corp, 35 Chegongzhuang Xilu, Haidian District, PO Box 399, Beijing 100044, China.

330 CHN ISSN 1006-169X
JINRONG YU JINGJI/FINANCE AND ECONOMICS. Text in Chinese. m.
Related titles: Online - full text ed.: (from East View Information Services).
Published by: Jiangxi Sheng Jinrong Xuehui/Jiangxi Finance Society, No 302 Zhongshan Lu, Nanchang, Jiangxi 330009, China. TEL 52965. Ed. Peng Chunhua. **Co-sponsor:** Zhongguo Renmin Yinhang Jiangxi Sheng Fenhuang Jinrong Yanjiusuo.

330 CHN
JISHU JINGJI XINXI. Text in Chinese. m.
Published by: Guangxi Jingji Weiyuanhui/Guangxi Economics Commission, 1 Minle Lu, Nanning, Guangxi 530012, China. TEL 25294. Ed. Li Guanhua.

330 JPN ISSN 0446-8147
JITSUGYO NO NIHON/BUSINESS OF JAPAN. Text in Japanese. 1897. m. JPY 5,760. adv. bk.rev. **Description:** Covers business in general, consumer affairs, as well as financial and investment trends.
Published by: Jitsugyo no Nihon Sha Ltd., 3-9 Ginza 1-chome, Chuo-ku, Tokyo, 104-0061, Japan. TEL 81-3-3562-1967, FAX 81-3-3562-3200, lebo2234@niftyserve.or.jp. Ed. Toshio Kawajiri. Pub. Yoshikazu Masuda. Adv. contact Maqaaki Ohara. B&W page JPY 480,000, color page JPY 750,000. Circ: 48,000.

330 DEU
JOB & FUTURE; das junge Wirtschaftsmagazin. Text in German. 1998. bi-m. adv. **Document type:** *Magazine, Consumer.*
Published by: Deutscher Supplement Verlag GmbH, Breslauer Str 300, Nuernberg, 90471, Germany. TEL 49-911-8003161, FAX 49-911-8003639, info@supplement-verlag.de, http://www.job-future.de, http://www.deutscher-supplement-verlag.de. adv.: B&W page EUR 3,900, color page EUR 5,200. Circ: 183,460 (controlled).

JOB OPENINGS FOR ECONOMISTS. see *OCCUPATIONS AND CAREERS*

330.1 CAN
JOHN DEUTSCH INSTITUTE FOR THE STUDY OF ECONOMIC POLICY. CONFERENCE SERIES. Text in English. 1999. irreg., latest 2003. price varies. **Document type:** *Monographic series, Academic/Scholarly.*
Published by: John Deutsch Institute for the Study of Economic Policy, Dunning Hall Room 216C, Queen's University, Kingston, ON K7L 3N6, Canada. TEL 613-533-2294, FAX 613-533-6025.

330 RUS ISSN 0869-5369
JOINT VENTURES/SOVMESTNYE PREDPRIYATIYA. Text in Russian; Summaries in English. 1990. bi-m. USD 60 (effective 1998). adv.
Indexed: RASB.
Published by: Assotsiatsiya Sovmestnykh Predpriyatii/Association of the Joint Ventures, Leningradskii pr-t 55, Moscow, 12513, Russian Federation. TEL 943-9481, FAX 148-71-14. Ed. Evgenii Minin. adv.: B&W page RUR 30,000, B&W page USD 1,750, color page RUR 83,000, color page USD 6,500. Circ: 11,000.

JOINT VENTURES: STRUCTURING ALTERNATIVES. see *LAW—Corporate Law*

330 GBR ISSN 0267-8152
JORDANS JOURNAL. Text in English. 1985. q. free (effective 2003). **Document type:** *Trade.*
Published by: Jordan Publishing Ltd., 21 St Thomas St, Bristol, BS1 6JS, United Kingdom. TEL 44-117-9230600, FAX 44-117-9250486, customerservice@jordanpublishing.co.uk, http://www.jordanpublishing.co.uk. Ed. Richard Hudson. Circ: 7,200 (controlled).

650 USA ISSN 1048-4701
JOSEPH I. LUBIN MEMORIAL LECTURES. Text in English. 1961. a. price varies. **Document type:** *Monographic series.*
Formerly (until 1984): Charles C. Moskowitz Lectures (0084-8727)
Published by: (New York University, College of Business and Public Administration), New York University Press, 70 Washington Square So, New York, NY 10012. TEL 212-998-2575, 800-996-6987, FAX 212-995-3833. Ed. Dean Daniel E Diamond. R&P Susan Conn. Circ: 2,000.

330 305.897 CAN ISSN 1481-9112
➤ **JOURNAL OF ABORIGINAL ECONOMIC DEVELOPMENT.** Text in English. 1999. s-a. CND 60 domestic; USD 60 foreign; CND 90 domestic to libraries; USD 9 foreign to libraries; CND 35 newsstand/cover (effective 2002). adv. bk.rev. charts; illus. back issues avail. **Document type:** *Journal, Academic/Scholarly.* **Description:** Features academic articles, examples from economic practicioners, book reviews and special issues geared towards anyone interested in aboriginal economic development.
Related titles: Online - full text ed.: ISSN 1481-9120.
Published by: Captus Press, York University Campus, 4700 Keele St, North York, ON M3J 1P3, Canada. TEL 416-736-5537, FAX 416-736-5793, pauline@captus.com, http://www.captus.com/information/f-aborflyer.htm. R&P Lily Chu. Adv. contact Pauline Lai. page CND 900; trim 7.5 x 9. **Co-publisher:** Council of the Advancement of Native Development Officers.

330 CAN ISSN 1192-2621
➤ **THE JOURNAL OF ACCOUNTING CASE RESEARCH.** Text in English. 1992. s-a. CND 64.20 domestic; USD 60 foreign; CND 96.30 domestic to libraries; USD 90 foreign to libraries; CND 48.15 per issue domestic; USD 45 per issue foreign (effective 2004). charts. back issues avail. **Document type:** *Journal, Academic/Scholarly.* **Description:** Provides cases which represent a variety of topics in accounting education and related fields.
Published by: Captus Press, York University Campus, 4700 Keele St, North York, ON M3J 1P3, Canada. TEL 416-736-5537, FAX 416-736-5793, pauline@captus.com, http://www.captus.com. Ed. Dr. Eldon James Gardner. R&P Lily Chu. Adv. contact Pauline Lai.

330 USA ISSN 1522-8916
HF3871
➤ **JOURNAL OF AFRICAN BUSINESS.** Abbreviated title: J A B. Text in English. 1999. s-a. USD 250 combined subscription domestic to institutions print & online eds.; USD 337.50 combined subscription in Canada to institutions print & online eds.; USD 362.50 combined subscription elsewhere to institutions print & online eds. (effective 2006). adv. 120 p./no. 1 cols./p.; back issues avail.; reprint service avail. from HAW. **Document type:** *Journal, Academic/Scholarly.* **Description:** Focuses on business and policy issues in reference to doing business in and with African nations. Features high quality, cross-functional articles from and for academics, practitioners, and policymakers interested in African business.
Related titles: Online - full text ed.: ISSN 1522-9076. free with print ed. (effective 2001) (from EBSCO Publishing, O C L C Online Computer Library Center, Inc., Swets Information Services).
Indexed: ABIn, DIP, ESPM, Emerald, GEOBASE, HRA, IBR, IBZ, JEL, PRA, RefZh, RiskAb, WTA.
—BLDSC (4919.987600), Haworth. **CCC.**
Published by: International Business Press (Subsidiary of: Haworth Press, Inc.), 10 Alice St, Binghamton, NY 13904. TEL 607-722-5857, 800-429-6784, FAX 607-771-0012, 800-895-0582, getinfo@haworthpress.com, http://www.haworthpress.com/web/JAB. Ed. Sam C Okoroafo. Pub. William Cohen. R&P Ruth Ann Heath TEL 607-722-5857 ext 316. Adv. contact Rebecca Miller-Baum TEL 607-722-5857

B

ext 337. B&W page USD 315, color page USD 550; trim 4.375 x 7.125. Circ: 99 (paid). **Subscr. to:** Haworth Press, Inc., 10 Alice St, Binghamton, NY 13904-1580. TEL 607-722-5857, 800-429-6784, FAX 607-722-1424, 800-895-0582, getinfo@haworthpress.com, http://www.haworthpress.com.

330 CAN ISSN 1499-691X
▼ ➤ **JOURNAL OF APPLIED BUSINESS AND ECONOMICS.** Text in English. 2003. s-a. CND 75, USD 50 (effective 2005). back issues avail. **Document type:** *Journal, Academic/Scholarly.* **Description:** Dedicated to the advancement and dissemination of business and economic knowledge, ongoing results of research in accordance with international scientific or scholarly standards.
Published by: North American Business Press, 1100 Memorial Ave, Ste 242, Thunder Bay, ON, Canada. TEL 804-343-8422, david.smith@lakeheadu.ca. Circ: 500 (paid).

658 USA ISSN 0892-7626
➤ **JOURNAL OF APPLIED BUSINESS RESEARCH.** Text in English. 1985. q. USD 300 to institutions (effective 2004). adv. bk.rev. abstr. 120 p./no. 1 cols./p.; back issues avail.; reprints avail. **Document type:** *Journal, Academic/Scholarly.* **Description:** Publishes articles pertaining to the scientific investigation of business and economics problems. Includes both theoretical and applied research.
Related titles: Online - full text ed.: (from EBSCO Publishing, O C L C Online Computer Library Center, Inc., ProQuest Information & Learning).
Indexed: ABIn, ATI, AgeL, BAS, BPI, IBSS, JEL, WBA.
—BLDSC (4940.660000), IE, ingenta. **CCC.**
Published by: Western Academic Press, PO Box 620760, Littleton, CO 80162. TEL 303-904-4750, FAX 303-978-0413, cluter@wapress.com, http://www.wapress.com/JABRMain.htm. Ed. Ronald C Clute. Circ: 600.

330 ARG ISSN 1514-0326
HB1
JOURNAL OF APPLIED ECONOMICS. Text in English. 1998. s-a. **Description:** Covers industrial organization, international economics, labor economics, finance, money and banking, growth, public finance, political economy, law and economics, and environmental economics.
Related titles: Online - full text ed.: (from EBSCO Publishing, ProQuest Information & Learning).
Indexed: ABIn, IBSS, JEL.
Published by: Universidad del CEMA, Av Cordoba 374, Buenos Aires, C1054AAP, Argentina. http://www.cema.edu.ar/publicaciones/jae.html. Ed. Carlos A Rodriguez.

650 USA ISSN 0021-9398
CODEN: PEASEF
➤ **THE JOURNAL OF BUSINESS (CHICAGO).** Text in English. 1922. q. USD 52 combined subscription to individuals print & online eds.; USD 258 combined subscription to institutions print & online eds.; USD 18 per issue to individuals; USD 78 per issue to institutions (effective 2006). adv. bk.rev. bibl.; illus. index, cum.index: vol.1-24 (1928-1951). 300 p./no.; back issues avail.; reprint service avail. from PQC,ISI,PSC. **Document type:** *Journal, Academic/Scholarly.* **Description:** Publishes research, analysis, and inquiry into issues of theoretical and practical importance to the business community.
Former titles (until 1954): University of Chicago. Journal of Business (0740-9168); (until 1927): The University Journal of Business (1525-6979)
Related titles: Microform ed.: (from MIM, PMC, PQC); Online - full text ed.: ISSN 1537-5374. USD 232 to institutions (effective 2006) (from EBSCO Publishing, Gale Group, JSTOR (Web-based Journal Archive), ProQuest Information & Learning).
Indexed: ABIn, APEL, ATI, AcaI, AgeL, AmH&L, BAS, BLI, BPI, BPIA, BusI, CIS, CommAb, CurCont, DIP, HistAb, IBR, IBSS, IBZ, JCQM, JEL, KES, M&MA, MCR, MEA&I, ManagCont, ORMS, PAIS, PCI, PROMT, QC&AS, RASB, SSCI, WAE&RSA.
—BLDSC (4954.650000), IDS, IE, Infotrieve, ingenta. **CCC.**
Published by: University of Chicago Press, Journals Division, Journals Division, PO Box 37005, Chicago, IL 60637. TEL 773-753-3347, 877-705-1878, FAX 773-753-0811, 877-705-1879, subscriptions@press.uchicago.edu, http://www.journals.uchicago.edu/JB, http://www.press.uchicago.edu/. Eds. Ann L McGill, Pradeep K Chintagunta, Richard H Thaler, Albert Madansky. Adv. contact Cheryl Jones. page USD 475; trim 6 x 9. Circ: 2,800 (paid).

330 USA ISSN 1528-5014
HB1
➤ **JOURNAL OF BUSINESS AND ECONOMIC PERSPECTIVES.** Text in English. 1975. s-a. USD 15 to individuals; USD 26 to libraries (effective 2003). bk.rev. back issues avail.; reprints avail. **Document type:** *Academic/Scholarly.* **Description:** Publishes empirical research on business and economic issues.
Formerly (until 1980): Business and Economics Perspectives (0887-4360)
Indexed: PAIS.
Published by: University of Tennessee at Martin, College of Business and Public Affairs, 111 Business Administration Bldg, Martin, TN 38238-5015. TEL 731-587-7226, FAX 731-587-7241. Ed. Bob G Figgins. Circ: 2,500.

650 330 USA ISSN 1063-343X
HF5001
➤ **JOURNAL OF BUSINESS AND ECONOMIC STUDIES✶.** Text in English. 1974. s-a. USD 25 (effective 2000). adv. bk.rev. charts; illus.; stat. **Document type:** *Academic/Scholarly.* **Description:** Publishes scholarly research in all areas of business and economics, practical and theoretical.
Former titles (until 1991): Northeast Journal of Business and Economics (8755-5123); (until 1983): New England Journal of Business and Economics; Rhode Island Business Quarterly (0035-4570)
Related titles: Online - full text ed.: (from EBSCO Publishing, O C L C Online Computer Library Center, Inc., ProQuest Information & Learning).
Indexed: ABIn, PAIS.
—BLDSC (4954.661020).
Published by: (Northeast Business and Economics Association), Salem State College, School of Business, 352 Lafayette St, Salem, MA 01970. TEL 978-542-7316, FAX 978-542-6027, jbes@salem.mass.edu. Ed. David Jacobson. R&P Kim Underhill. Circ: 1,000.

➤ **JOURNAL OF BUSINESS & FINANCE LIBRARIANSHIP.** see *LIBRARY AND INFORMATION SCIENCES*

➤ **JOURNAL OF BUSINESS & PSYCHOLOGY.** see *PSYCHOLOGY*

330 USA ISSN 1522-8398
HF5001 CODEN: BPUAEI
➤ **JOURNAL OF BUSINESS AND PUBLIC AFFAIRS.** Text in English. 1975. a., latest vol.25, no.1. free. adv. illus. Index. reprints avail. **Document type:** *Academic/Scholarly.* **Description:** Brings before academic, business and civil leaders current professional thought which will assist them in their professional development.
Formerly (until 1998): Business and Public Affairs (0361-7653); Which superseded (in 197?): Business Dynamics (0045-3625)
Indexed: PAIS.
—BLDSC (4954.661530).
Published by: Murray State University, College of Business and Public Affairs, PO Box 9, Murray, KY 42071. TEL 502-762-6970, FAX 502-762-3482, cbpa@murraystate.edu, http://www.murraystate.edu. Ed. W Glynn Margold. R&P Pam Dancan. Adv. contact Pam Duncan. Circ: 1,000.

650 301 NGA ISSN 0331-8583
H53.N6
JOURNAL OF BUSINESS & SOCIAL STUDIES. Text in English. 1968; N.S. 1977. s-a. NGN 20, USD 25. adv. bk.rev. charts; illus.; maps. reprint service avail. from PQC. **Document type:** *Academic/Scholarly.* **Description:** Covers African economics, agriculture and general development issues.
Related titles: Microform ed.: N.S. (from PQC).
Indexed: CCA.
Published by: (University of Lagos), Lagos University Press, Publishing Division, Akoka, PO Box 132, Yaba, Lagos State, Nigeria. Ed. Oladejo O Okediji. Circ: 1,500.

330 CYP ISSN 1012-2591
JOURNAL OF BUSINESS AND SOCIETY. Text in English. 1988. s-a. CYP 10 domestic; USD 30 foreign (effective 2004). **Document type:** *Journal, Academic/Scholarly.* **Description:** Provides a forum for the exchange of ideas among businessmen, executives, scientists, and academicians who are concerned with economic, business, social, and technological issues and practices.
Indexed: IBSS, SSA, SociolAb.
Published by: Cyprus College, 6 Diogenes St, PO Box 22006, Nicosia, 1516, Cyprus. mtramoun@cycollege.ac.cy, http://www.cycollege.ac.cy/academics/default.cfm?category=4&subcategory=32. Ed. Andreas Ge Orphanides.

658.45 USA ISSN 1050-6519
HF5717 CODEN: JBTCE9
➤ **JOURNAL OF BUSINESS AND TECHNICAL COMMUNICATION.** Text in English. 1987. q. USD 463, GBP 299 to institutions; USD 482, GBP 311 combined subscription to institutions print & online eds. (effective 2006). adv. bk.rev.; software rev. back issues avail.; reprints avail. **Document type:** *Journal, Academic/Scholarly.* **Description:** Provides information on the latest communication practices, problems, and trends in both industry and the academic world.
Formerly (until 1988): Iowa State Journal of Business and Technical Communication (0892-5720)
Related titles: Online - full text ed.: ISSN 1552-4574. USD 458, GBP 296 to institutions (effective 2006) (from C S A, EBSCO Publishing, O C L C Online Computer Library Center, Inc., ProQuest Information & Learning, Sage Publications, Inc., Swets Information Services).
Indexed: ABIn, ASCA, AbAn, CIJE, CommAb, CurCont, HRA, L&LBA, RHEA, SFSA, SOPODA, SPAA, SSCI, SUSA.
—BLDSC (4954.663000), IDS, IE, Infotrieve, ingenta. **CCC.**
Published by: Sage Publications, Inc., 2455 Teller Rd, Thousand Oaks, CA 91320. TEL 805-499-0721, 800-818-7243, FAX 805-499-8096, 800-583-2665, info@sagepub.com, http://www.sagepub.com/journal.aspx?pid=48. Ed. Dorothy Winsor. Pub. Sara Miller McCune. Adv. contact Kirsten Beaulieu TEL 805-499-0721 ext 7160. page USD 350. Circ: 400 (paid and free). **Subscr. overseas to:** Sage Publications Ltd., 1 Oliver's Yard, 55 City Rd, London EC1 1SP, United Kingdom. TEL 44-20-73740645, FAX 44-20-73748741, subscription@sagepub.co.uk.

330 FRA ISSN 1729-3618
HB3711
JOURNAL OF BUSINESS CYCLE MEASUREMENT AND ANALYSIS. Text in English. 3/yr. EUR 98, USD 112, GBP 69, JPY 13,200 (effective 2005). **Document type:** *Journal, Trade.* **Description:** Covers the theory and operation of business and economic cycle research, including both statistical measurement and analytical aspects.
Related titles: Online - full content ed.: ISSN 1729-3626. EUR 76, USD 87, GBP 53, JPY 10,400 (effective 2005); Online - full text ed.: (from EBSCO Publishing, Gale Group, IngentaConnect, Swets Information Services).
Published by: Organization for Economic Cooperation and Development, 2 Rue Andre Pascal, Paris, 75775 Cedex 16, France. TEL 33-1-45248200, FAX 33-1-45248500, http://www.oecd.org. **Dist. by:** O E C D Turpin North America, PO Box 194, Downingtown, PA 19335-0194. TEL 610-524-5361, 800-456-6323, FAX 610-524-5417, journalscustomer@turpinna.com. **Co-publisher:** Centre for International Research on Economic Tendency Surveys.

B

330 USA
➤ **JOURNAL OF BUSINESS DISCIPLINES.** Text in English. 2000. s-a. USD 25 domestic; USD 50 foreign (effective 2003). bk.rev. back issues avail. **Document type:** *Journal, Academic/Scholarly.* **Description:** Dedicated to publishing applied business articles designed to inform business practitioners and academics. Presents articles of current importance that are either empirical or theoretical in approach.
Published by: University of Indiana Southeast, Academy of Business Disciplines, 4201 Grant Line Rd., New Albany, IN 47150. TEL 812-841-2532, FAX 812-941-2672, http://149.160.29.73/author.htm. Ed. Douglas K. Barney. **Co-sponsor:** Shippensburg University, School of Business.

174 NLD ISSN 0167-4544
HF5387
➤ **JOURNAL OF BUSINESS ETHICS.** Text in English. 1982. 28/yr. EUR 1,548, USD 1,569, GBP 968 combined subscription to institutions print & online eds. (effective 2005). adv. bk.rev. illus. reprint service avail. from PSC. **Document type:** *Journal, Academic/Scholarly.* **Description:** Publishes original articles from a variety of methodological and disciplinary perspectives concerning ethical issues related to business.
Incorporates (1997-2004): Teaching Business Ethics (1382-6891); (1988-2004): International Journal of Value-Based Management (0895-8815)
Related titles: Microform ed.: (from PQC); Online - full text ed.: ISSN 1573-0697 (from Chadwyck-Healey Inc., EBSCO Publishing, Gale Group, IngentaConnect, Kluwer Online, O C L C Online Computer Library Center, Inc., ProQuest Information & Learning, Springer LINK, Swets Information Services).
Indexed: ABIn, ADPA, ASCA, ATI, AgeL, ArtHuCI, BPI, BPIA, BibLing, CJA, CPM, ChPerI, CommAb, CurCont, DIP, ESPM, Emerald, FamI, IBR, IBSS, IBZ, M&MA, ManagCont, PAIS, PCI, PRA, PhilInd, RI-1, RI-2, RiskAb, SSCI, SSI, T&II.
—BLDSC (4954.686000), IDS, IE, Infotrieve, ingenta. **CCC.**
Published by: Springer-Verlag Dordrecht (Subsidiary of: Springer Science+Business Media), Van Godewijckstraat 30, Dordrecht, 3311 GX, Netherlands. TEL 31-78-6576050, FAX 31-78-6576474, http://springerlink.metapress.com/openurl.asp?genre=journal&issn=0167-4544, http://www.springeronline.com. Eds. Deborah C Poff, Alex C Michalos.

➤ **JOURNAL OF BUSINESS FINANCE & ACCOUNTING.** see *BUSINESS AND ECONOMICS—Accounting*

330 USA ISSN 0278-6087
HB3730
JOURNAL OF BUSINESS FORECASTING METHODS AND SYSTEMS. Text in English. 1981. q. USD 85 domestic; USD 110 foreign (effective 2004). adv. bk.rev. abstr.; bibl.; charts; illus. index. back issues avail.; reprints avail. **Document type:** *Journal, Trade.* **Description:** Covers subjects such as how to prepare and use forecasts or set up a forecasting system, the problems that exist between forecasters and users and how they can be resolved, and experiences of different companies and individuals in the field. Gives forecasts of key economic variables in 47 countries.
Related titles: CD-ROM ed.; Microform ed.: (from PQC); Online - full text ed.: (from EBSCO Publishing, O C L C Online Computer Library Center, Inc.).
Indexed: ABIn, ATI, BPIA, CIS, ESPM, ManagCont, ORMS, RASB, RiskAb.
—BLDSC (4954.695000), IE, Infotrieve, ingenta. **CCC.**

Published by: Graceway Publishing Co., PO Box 670159, Flushing, NY 11367-0159. TEL 516-504-7576, 800-440-0499, FAX 516-498-2029, ibf@ibf.org, http://www.ibf.org/index.cfm?fuseaction=showObjects&objectTypeID=20. Ed., R&P Chaman L Jain TEL 718-990-7314. Adv. contact Jean McCreary. page USD 850; trim 7.5 x 9. Circ: 3,500.

JOURNAL OF BUSINESS LAW. see *LAW—Corporate Law*

330 CAN ISSN 0703-1947
JOURNAL OF BUSINESS VALUATION (YEAR). Text in English. 1973. a., latest 2004. CND 75 per issue domestic; USD 63.56 per issue foreign (effective 2005).
Published by: (The Canadian Institute of Chartered Business Valuators), Carswell (Subsidiary of: Thomson Corporation), One Corporate Plaza, 2075 Kennedy Rd, Toronto, ON M1T 3V4, Canada. TEL 416-609-8000, 800-387-5164, FAX 416-298-5094, carswell.customerrelations@thomson.com, http://www.carswell.com/description.asp?iInputType=1&stBack=selSearch%3Dkeyword%26txtSearch%3DJournal%2Bof%2Bbusiness%2Bvaluation%26NextRec%3D0%26sess.

330 USA ISSN 0883-9026
CODEN: JBVEEP
➤ **JOURNAL OF BUSINESS VENTURING.** Text in English. 1985. 6/yr. EUR 142 in Europe to individuals; JPY 19,000 in Japan to individuals; USD 160 to individuals except Europe and Japan; EUR 761 in Europe to institutions; JPY 101,000 in Japan to institutions; USD 850 to institutions except Europe and Japan (effective 2006). adv. illus. Index. back issues avail.; reprints avail. **Document type:** *Journal, Academic/Scholarly.* **Description:** Details research on entrepreneurship, either as independent start-ups or within existing corporations.
Related titles: Microform ed.: (from PQC); Online - full text ed.: (from EBSCO Publishing, Gale Group, IngentaConnect, ScienceDirect, Swets Information Services).
Indexed: ABIn, ASCA, CPM, CurCont, ESPM, Emerald, FamI, Inspec, M&MA, RASB, RefZh, RiskAb, SSCI.
—BLDSC (4954.718500), IDS, IE, Infotrieve, ingenta. **CCC.**
Published by: Elsevier Inc. (Subsidiary of: Elsevier Science & Technology), 360 Park Ave. S, New York, NY 10010-1710. TEL 212-633-3730, 888-437-4636, FAX 212-633-3990, usinfo-f@elsevier.com, http://www.elsevier.com/locate/jbusvent. Ed. S Venkataraman. Adv. contact Aretha Gaskin. B&W page USD 1,060, color page USD 2,295. Circ: 675 (paid and free). **Subscr. outside the Americas to:** Elsevier BV, PO Box 211, Amsterdam 1000 AE, Netherlands. TEL 31-20-485-3757, FAX 31-20-485-3432.

➤ **JOURNAL OF COMMERCIAL BIOTECHNOLOGY.** see *BIOLOGY—Biotechnology*

➤ **JOURNAL OF COMMON MARKET STUDIES.** see *POLITICAL SCIENCE*

330 USA ISSN 0147-5967
HB90
➤ **JOURNAL OF COMPARATIVE ECONOMICS.** Text in English. 1977. 4/yr. EUR 122 in Europe to individuals; JPY 13,200 in Japan to individuals; USD 99 to individuals except Europe and Japan; EUR 708 in Europe to institutions; JPY 73,900 in Japan to institutions; USD 576 to institutions except Europe and Japan; EUR 89 in Europe to students; JPY 9,800 in Japan to students; USD 79 to students except Europe and Japan (effective 2006). adv. bk.rev. illus. Index. back issues avail.; reprints avail. **Document type:** *Academic/Scholarly.* **Description:** Devoted to the analysis and study of contemporary, historical, and hypothetical economic systems.
Related titles: Online - full text ed.: ISSN 1095-7227 (from EBSCO Publishing, Gale Group, IngentaConnect, O C L C Online Computer Library Center, Inc., ScienceDirect, Swets Information Services).
Indexed: ABIn, ABS&EES, APEL, ASCA, BAS, BPIA, CJA, CREJ, CurCont, FamI, IBSS, JEL, PAIS, PCI, RASB, RDA, RRTA, SSCI, SSI, T&II, WAE&RSA, ZentMath.
—BLDSC (4961.890000), CISTI, IDS, IE, Infotrieve, ingenta. **CCC.**
Published by: (Association for Comparative Economic Studies), Academic Press (Subsidiary of: Elsevier Science & Technology), 525 B St, Ste 1900, San Diego, CA 92101-4495. TEL 619-231-6616, 800-894-3434, FAX 619-699-6422, apsubs@acad.com, http://www.elsevier.com/locate/jce, http://www.academicpress.com. Ed. John P Bonin.

▼ ➤ **JOURNAL OF COMPETITION LAW AND ECONOMICS.** see *LAW*

330 USA ISSN 1092-8057
HF5686.M3 CODEN: JMINEU
JOURNAL OF COST MANAGEMENT. Variant title: Cost Management. Text in English. 1987. bi-m. USD 230 (effective 2004). adv. reprint service avail. from PSC. **Document type:** *Magazine, Trade.* **Description:** Provides information to help improve cost-management systems and techniques in order to pursue more vigorous marketing and pricing strategies.
Formerly (until 1992): Journal of Cost Management for the Manufacturing Industry (0899-5141)
Related titles: Microform ed.: (from PQC); Online - full text ed.: (from ProQuest Information & Learning).
Indexed: ABIn, ATI, Emerald, IBSS, Inspec.
—BLDSC (4965.431000), Ei, IE, Infotrieve, ingenta. **CCC.**

Published by: W G & L Financial Reporting & Management Research (Subsidiary of: R I A), 395 Hudson St, New York, NY 10014. TEL 212-367-6300, FAX 212-337-4207, ria@thomson.com, http://www.riahome.com/estore/detail.asp?ID=ZMCM. Ed. Tom Pryor. Circ: 2,649.

330 USA
THE JOURNAL OF CURRENT RESEARCH IN GLOBAL BUSINESS. Text in English. 1999. s-a. USD 28 to individuals; USD 40 to institutions (effective 2003). **Description:** Aims at providing opportunities for the exchange of professional ideas, to enhance research in fields of business and global concerns, and to create a general awareness of significant accomplishments in the area of domestic and international enterprises.
Published by: Association for Global Business, PO Box 1381, Harrisonburg, VA 22803. fdamanpour@msn.com. Ed. Winston Awadzi TEL 302-857-6932.

330 NLD ISSN 0167-2681
HD28 CODEN: JEBOD9
➤ **JOURNAL OF ECONOMIC BEHAVIOR & ORGANIZATION.** Text in English. 1980. 12/yr. EUR 100 in Europe to individuals; JPY 13,300 in Japan to individuals; USD 104 to individuals except Europe and Japan; EUR 1,591 in Europe to institutions; JPY 211,200 in Japan to institutions; USD 1,780 to institutions except Europe and Japan (effective 2006). adv. bk.rev. illus. Index. back issues avail.; reprints avail. **Document type:** *Academic/Scholarly.* **Description:** Emphasizes theoretical and empirical research on economic decision, organization and behavior.
Related titles: Microform ed.: (from PQC); Online - full text ed.: (from EBSCO Publishing, Gale Group, IngentaConnect, ScienceDirect, Swets Information Services).
Indexed: ABIn, ASCA, ArtHuCI, BPIA, BusI, CJA, CREJ, CurCont, ESPM, ForAb, IBSS, Inspec, JEL, ManagCont, PCI, PsycInfo, PsycholAb, RASB, RiskAb, SSCI, T&II, e-psyche.
—BLDSC (4972.790000), AskIEEE, IDS, IE, Infotrieve, ingenta. **CCC.**
Published by: Elsevier BV, North-Holland (Subsidiary of: Elsevier Science & Technology), Sara Burgerhartstraat 25, Amsterdam, 1055 KV, Netherlands. TEL 31-20-485-3911, FAX 31-20-485-2457, nlinfo-f@elsevier.nl, http://www.elsevier.com/locate/jebo, http://www.elsevier.nl. Ed. J. B. Rosser Jr. **Subscr. to:** Elsevier BV, PO Box 211, Amsterdam 1000 AE, Netherlands. TEL 31-20-485-3757, FAX 31-20-485-3432, http://www.elsevier.nl.

330 TUR ISSN 0252-953X
JOURNAL OF ECONOMIC COOPERATION AMONG ISLAMIC COUNTRIES. Text in English. 1979. q. USD 40 to individuals; USD 60 to institutions; USD 10 newsstand/cover to individuals; USD 15 newsstand/cover to institutions (effective 2003). **Document type:** *Journal, Academic/Scholarly.*
Related titles: Online - full text ed.: (from EBSCO Publishing).
Indexed: IBSS, JEL.
—BLDSC (4972.820000).
Published by: Statistical Economic and Social Research and Training Centre for Islamic Countries, Attar Sokak, No: 4, Gaziosmanpasa, Ankara, 06700, Turkey. TEL 90-312-4686172, FAX 90-312-4673458, oicankara@sesrtcic.org, http://www.sesrtcic.org/pubs/jec/default.shtml.

▼ **JOURNAL OF ECONOMIC CRIME MANAGEMENT.** see *LAW—Criminal Law*

330.071 USA ISSN 0022-0485
H62.5.U5
➤ **THE JOURNAL OF ECONOMIC EDUCATION.** Text in English. 1969. q. USD 62 domestic to individuals; USD 76 foreign to individuals; USD 135 domestic to institutions; USD 149 foreign to institutions; USD 33.75 per issue (effective academic year 2005 - 2006). adv. bk.rev. abstr.; charts; stat.; illus. Index. back issues avail.; reprint service avail. from PSC. **Document type:** *Journal, Academic/Scholarly.* **Description:** Features original articles on innovations in and evaluations of teaching techniques, materials and programs in economics. Articles, tailored to the needs of instructors of introductory through graduate-level economics, cover content and pedagogy in a variety of mediums.
Related titles: CD-ROM ed.: (from ProQuest Information & Learning); Microform ed.; Online - full text ed.: (from bigchalk, Chadwyck-Healey Inc., EBSCO Publishing, Florida Center for Library Automation, Gale Group, H.W. Wilson, JSTOR (Web-based Journal Archive), Northern Light Technology, Inc., O C L C Online Computer Library Center, Inc., ProQuest Information & Learning).
Indexed: ABIn, ASCA, AgeL, BusEdI, CIJE, CPE, CurCont, DIP, EAA, ERA, ETA, EduInd, IBR, IBZ, JEL, MEA, PAIS, PCI, RHEA, SEA, SENA, SOMA, SSCI, TEA.
—BLDSC (4972.900000), IDS, IE, Infotrieve, ingenta. **CCC.**
Published by: (Helen Dwight Reid Educational Foundation), Heldref Publications, 1319 18th St, NW, Washington, DC 20036-1802. TEL 202-296-6267, 800-365-9753, FAX 202-293-6130, jece@heldref.org, subscribe@heldref.org, http://www.heldref.org/jecone.php. Adv. contact Chante Douglas. B&W page USD 340; trim 5 x 7.5. Circ: 936 (paid).

330 338.91 KOR ISSN 1225-651X
➤ **JOURNAL OF ECONOMIC INTEGRATION.** Text and summaries in English. 1986. q. USD 40 foreign to individuals; USD 120 foreign to institutions (effective 2005). adv. bk.rev. 200 p./no.; back issues avail. **Document type:** *Journal, Academic/Scholarly.* **Description:** Publishes articles that investigate economic issues in international economic integration.
Formerly (until 1992): Journal of International Economic Integration (1015-356X)
Related titles: Online - full content ed.; Online - full text ed.: (from EBSCO Publishing).
Indexed: JEL.
—BLDSC (4973.051000), IE, ingenta. **CCC.**
Published by: Sejong University, Center for International Economics, Kunja-Dong, Kwangjin-Gu, Seoul, 143-747, Korea, S. TEL 82-2-34083151, cie@sejong.ac.kr, hhlee@kunja.sejong.ac.kr, http://dasan.sejong.ac.kr/~cie/, http://www.sejong.ac.kr/~cie/. Ed. Myung Gun Choo. adv.: page USD 500. Circ: 250 (paid); 1,250 (controlled).

330 GBR ISSN 1350-178X
HB131
➤ **JOURNAL OF ECONOMIC METHODOLOGY.** Text in English. 1989. q. GBP 272, USD 452 combined subscription to institutions print & online eds. (effective 2006). adv. reprint service avail. from PSC. **Document type:** *Journal, Academic/Scholarly.* **Description:** Explores current and historical developments in the field of economic practice and methodological work.
Formerly (until 1994): Methodus (1018-5070)
Related titles: Online - full text ed.: ISSN 1469-9427. GBP 258, USD 429 to institutions (effective 2006) (from EBSCO Publishing, Gale Group, IngentaConnect, O C L C Online Computer Library Center, Inc., Swets Information Services).
Indexed: ABIn, DIP, IBR, IBSS, IBZ, JEL, RASB.
—BLDSC (4973.053500), IE, Infotrieve, ingenta. **CCC.**
Published by: (International Network for Economic Method), Routledge (Subsidiary of: Taylor & Francis Group), 4 Park Sq, Milton Park, Abingdon, Oxon OX14 4RN, United Kingdom. TEL 44-1235-828600, FAX 44-1235-829000, info@routledge.co.uk, http://www.tandf.co.uk/journals/titles/1350178X.asp, http://www.routledge.co.uk. Eds. D Wade Hands, John B Davis. R&P Sally Sweet. adv.: page GBP 150; trim 190 x 115. Circ: 850. **Subscr. to:** Taylor & Francis Ltd, Journals Customer Service, Rankine Rd, Basingstoke, Hants RG24 8PR, United Kingdom. TEL 44-1256-813000, FAX 44-1256-330245, enquiry@tandf.co.uk.

330 KOR ISSN 1226-4261
JOURNAL OF ECONOMIC RESEARCH. Text in English. 1996. s-a. KRW 100,000 domestic to non-members; USD 20 foreign to non-members; free to members (effective 2003). **Document type:** *Journal, Academic/Scholarly.* **Description:** Provides an outlet for publication in all theoretical and empirical aspects of economics, financial economics and related areas.
Formerly (until 1996): Hanyang Journal of Economic Studies (1226-2153)
Indexed: JEL.
—BLDSC (4973.054500), IE, ingenta.
Published by: Asia Pacific Economic Association, Hanyang University, Seoul, 133-791, Korea, S. jer@heri.re.kr. Ed. Ji-Sung Yoo.

330 GBR ISSN 0144-3585
HB1
➤ **JOURNAL OF ECONOMIC STUDIES.** Text in English. 1965; N.S. 1974. bi-m. EUR 9,884.29 in Europe; USD 9,859 in North America; AUD 12,489 in Australasia; GBP 6,817.54 in UK & elsewhere (effective 2006). bk.rev. charts; stat. reprint service avail. from PSC. **Document type:** *Journal, Academic/Scholarly.* **Description:** Maintains a sound balance between the theory and practice of economics. Covers new developments in the international monetary system, urban bias in developing countries, economic methodology, labor and regional economics, history of economic thought, finance, and dependency theory.
Formerly (until 1973): Economic Studies (0449-2420)
Related titles: Online - full text ed.: (from EBSCO Publishing, Emerald Group Publishing Limited, Gale Group, IngentaConnect, O C L C Online Computer Library Center, Inc., ProQuest Information & Learning, Swets Information Services).
Indexed: ABIn, BusI, CurCont, DIP, EmerIntel, Emerald, FPA, ForAb, IBR, IBSS, IBZ, JEL, PAIS, RASB, RDA, RRTA, SSCI, T&II, TriticAb, WAE&RSA.
—BLDSC (4973.055000), IE, Infotrieve, ingenta. **CCC.**
Published by: Emerald Group Publishing Limited, 60-62 Toller Ln, Bradford, W Yorks BD8 9BY, United Kingdom. TEL 44-1274-777700, FAX 44-1274-785200, infomation@emeraldinsight.com, http://www.emeraldinsight.com/jes.htm.

330 GBR ISSN 0950-0804
HB1
➤ **JOURNAL OF ECONOMIC SURVEYS.** Text in English. 1987. 5/yr., latest vol.16, no.5, 2002. EUR 89 combined subscription in Europe to individuals print & online eds.; USD 99 combined subscription in the Americas to individuals & Caribbean, print & online eds.; GBP 59 combined subscription elsewhere to individuals print & online eds.; GBP 377 combined subscription in Europe to institutions print & online eds.; USD 743 combined subscription in the Americas to institutions & Caribbean, print & online eds.; GBP 442 combined subscription elsewhere to institutions print & online eds.; EUR 42 combined subscription in Europe to students print & online eds.; USD 47 combined subscription in the Americas to students & Caribbean, print & online eds.; GBP 28 combined subscription elsewhere to students print & online eds. (effective 2006). adv. bk.rev. back issues avail.; reprints avail. **Document type:** *Journal, Academic/Scholarly.* **Description:** Includes surveys of topics in economics: econometrics, economic history and business economics.
Related titles: Online - full text ed.: ISSN 1467-6419. GBP 358 in Europe to institutions; USD 706 in the Americas to institutions & Caribbean; GBP 420 elsewhere to institutions (effective 2006) (from Blackwell Synergy, EBSCO Publishing, Gale Group, IngentaConnect, O C L C Online Computer Library Center, Inc., Swets Information Services).
Indexed: APEL, CurCont, GEOBASE, IBSS, JEL, SSCI.
—BLDSC (4973.065000), IE, Infotrieve, ingenta. **CCC.**
Published by: Blackwell Publishing Ltd., 9600 Garsington Rd, Oxford, OX4 2ZG, United Kingdom. TEL 44-1865-776868, FAX 44-1865-714591, customerservices@oxon.blackwellpublishing.com, http://www.blackwellpublishing.com/journals/JOES. Eds. Colin J Roberts, Donald A R George, Leslie T Oxley, Stuart T Sayer. Circ: 300.

330 IND
JOURNAL OF ECONOMICS✶ . Text in English. 1973. s-a. INR 60, USD 20. adv. bk.rev.
Indexed: JEL.
Published by: Meerut University Economics Association, Meerut University, Uttar Pradesh, Meerut, 250 005, India. Ed. O P Gupta.

339 AUT ISSN 0931-8658
HB5 CODEN: ZENOA4
➤ **JOURNAL OF ECONOMICS/ZEITSCHRIFT FUER NATIONALOEKONOMIE.** Text in English. 1930. 9/yr. (in 3 vols., 3 nos./vol.). EUR 1,098 combined subscription to institutions print & online eds. (effective 2005). adv. bk.rev. charts; illus.; abstr. index, cum.index: vol.1-15. back issues avail.; reprint service avail. from ISI. **Document type:** *Journal, Academic/Scholarly.* **Description:** Specializes in mathematical economic theory of medium- and high-level difficulty, with emphasis on microeconomic theory. Includes papers on macroeconomic topics.
Formerly (until 1986): Zeitschrift fuer Nationaloekonomie (0044-3158)
Related titles: Microform ed.: (from PQC); Online - full text ed.: ISSN 1617-7134 (from EBSCO Publishing, ProQuest Information & Learning, Springer LINK, Swets Information Services); ♦ Supplement(s): Journal of Economics. Supplement.
Indexed: ABIn, ASCA, CJA, CurCont, DIP, IBR, IBSS, IBZ, JEL, KES, MathR, PAIS, PCI, RASB, SSCI, ZentMath.
—BLDSC (4973.081000), IDS, IE, Infotrieve, ingenta. **CCC.**
Published by: Springer-Verlag Wien (Subsidiary of: Springer Science+Business Media) journals@springer.at, http://www.springer.at/jecon. R&P Angela Foessl TEL 43-1-3302415517. Adv. contact Michael Katzenberger TEL 43-1-3302415220. B&W page EUR 1,000; 120 x 190. **Subscr. in the Americas to:** Springer-Verlag New York, Inc., Journal Fulfillment, PO Box 2485, Secaucus, NJ 07096-2485. TEL 800-777-4643, 201-348-4033, FAX 201-348-4505, journals@springer-ny.com, http://www.springer-ny.com.

330 USA ISSN 0361-6576
HB1 CODEN: JOECFQ
➤ **JOURNAL OF ECONOMICS (SPRINGFIELD).** Text in English. 1975. s-a. USD 32 domestic; USD 44 foreign; USD 16 per issue (effective 2001). adv. bk.rev. back issues avail. **Document type:** *Academic/Scholarly.* **Description:** Publishes original research in the general area of economics.
Indexed: ESPM, JEL, RiskAb, SOPODA, SSA, SociolAb.
Published by: Missouri Valley Economics Association, c/o Steve Shaw, MidAmerica Nazarene University, 2030 East College Way, Olathe, KS 66062. TEL 913-782-3750 ext180, FAX 913-791-3409, http://www.cba.uni.edu/economics/joe.htm. Ed. David R Hakes. Circ: 350 (paid).

330 650 USA ISSN 0148-6195
CODEN: JEBUDR
➤ **JOURNAL OF ECONOMICS AND BUSINESS.** Text in English. 1949. 6/yr. EUR 89 in Europe to individuals; JPY 11,800 in Japan to individuals; USD 92 elsewhere to individuals; EUR 506 in Europe to institutions; JPY 67,100 in Japan to institutions; USD 565 elsewhere to institutions (effective 2006). adv. bk.rev. charts; mkt. index, cum.index. back issues avail.; reprint service avail. from PQC,ISI. **Document type:** *Journal, Academic/Scholarly.* **Description:** Provides a forum for scholarly research in applied economics, finance and related disciplines that focus on the domestic and international aspects of business and society.
Formerly (until 1972): Economic and Business Bulletin (0012-9933)
Related titles: Microform ed.: (from PQC); Online - full text ed.: (from EBSCO Publishing, Gale Group, IngentaConnect, ScienceDirect, Swets Information Services).
Indexed: ABIn, BAS, BLI, BPI, BPIA, BusI, CREJ, CurCont, Emerald, JEL, MCR, MEDLINE, ManagCont, PAIS, PCI, PMA, SSCI, T&II.
—BLDSC (4973.092000), IDS, IE, Infotrieve, ingenta. **CCC.**
Published by: (Temple University, School of Business Administration), Elsevier Inc. (Subsidiary of: Elsevier Science & Technology), 655 Ave. of the Americas, New York, NY 10010. TEL 212-989-5800, FAX 212-633-3990, jeconbus@surfer.sbm.temple.edu, usinfo-f@elsevier.com, http://www.elsevier.com/locate/jeb. Ed. Kenneth J. Kopecky. adv.: B&W page USD 1,060, color page USD 2,295. Circ: 824 (paid and free). **Subscr. outside the Americas to:** Elsevier BV, PO Box 211, Amsterdam 1000 AE, Netherlands. TEL 31-20-485-3757, FAX 31-20-485-3432.

330 USA ISSN 1533-3604
HB74.8
JOURNAL OF ECONOMICS AND ECONOMIC EDUCATION RESEARCH. Text in English. 2000. a.
Related titles: Online - full text ed.: ISSN 1533-3590.
Published by: (Academy of Economics and Economic Education), Allied Academies, 145 Travis Rd., P. O. Box 2689, Cullowhee, NC 28723. TEL 828-293-9251, FAX 828-293-9407, info@alliedacademies.org, http://www.alliedacademies.org/econ-ed/index.html. Ed. Larry R. Dale.

330 USA ISSN 1055-0925
HB1
➤ **JOURNAL OF ECONOMICS AND FINANCE.** Text in English. 1989. 3/yr. USD 25 to individual members; USD 40 domestic to institutional members; USD 55 foreign to institutional members (effective 2004). adv. 125 p./no.; back issues avail. **Document type:** *Journal, Academic/Scholarly.* **Description:** Examines economics and finance through theoretical and empirical research at higher academic levels.
Related titles: Online - full text ed.: (from EBSCO Publishing, O C L C Online Computer Library Center, Inc., ProQuest Information & Learning).
Indexed: ABIn, JEL.
—BLDSC (4973.095080), IE, ingenta.
Published by: The Academy of Economics and Finance, c/o MBA Office, 316 Combs Academic Bld., Eastern Kentucky University, Richmond, KY 40475. TEL 859-622-1775, FAX 859-622-1413, jeandf@mtsu.edu, http://www.jeandfe.org/, http://www.economics-finance.org. R&P Sally Ham Govan. Adv. contact Leland Gustafson. Circ: 375.

330 382 346 JPN ISSN 1344-770X
HC461.A1
JOURNAL OF ECONOMICS, BUSINESS AND LAW. Text in Multiple languages. 1957-1998; resumed. a. **Document type:** *Academic/Scholarly.*
Former titles: Osaka Prefecture University. Series D: Economics, Business Administration and Law (1342-3274); (until 1996): University of Osaka Prefecture. Bulletin. Series D: Economics, Business Administration and Law; University of Osaka Prefecture. Bulletin. Series D: Sciences of Economy, Commerce and Law (0473-4637)
Indexed: JEL.
—BLDSC (4973.095370).
Published by: Osaka Prefecture University/Osaka-furitsu Daigaku, 1-1 Gakuen-cho, Sakai-shi, Osaka, 599 8531, Japan. TEL 81-722-52-1161, FAX 81-722-52-6798. Ed. Asaba Yoshimasa.

339 AUT
➤ **JOURNAL OF ECONOMICS. SUPPLEMENT.** Text in English. irreg., latest vol.9, 2002. price varies. adv. **Document type:** *Monographic series, Academic/Scholarly.* **Description:** Specializes in mathematical economic theory, with emphasis on microeconomic theory. Includes papers on macroeconomic topics.
Former titles: Journal of Economics. Supplementum (Vienna) (0931-9573); (until 1986): Zeitschrift fuer Nationaloekonomie. Supplementum (0084-537X)
Related titles: ♦ Supplement to: Journal of Economics. ISSN 0931-8658.
Published by: Springer-Verlag Wien (Subsidiary of: Springer Science+Business Media) TEL 43-1-3302415-0, FAX 43-1-330242665, journals@springer.at, http://www.springer.at/jecon. Ed. Dieter Boes. R&P Angela Foessl TEL 43-1-3302415517. Adv. contact Michael Katzenberger TEL 43-1-3302415220. B&W page EUR 1,000; 120 x 190. **Subscr. to:** Springer-Verlag New York, Inc., 233 Spring St, New York, NY 10013. TEL 800-777-4643, FAX 201-348-4505, orders@springer-ny.com.

650.0711 USA ISSN 0883-2323
HF1101
➤ **JOURNAL OF EDUCATION FOR BUSINESS.** Text in English. 1924. bi-m. USD 56 domestic to individuals; USD 72 foreign to individuals; USD 106 domestic to institutions; USD 122 foreign to institutions; USD 17.67 per issue (effective academic year 2005 - 2006). adv. bk.rev. bibl.; illus. index. back issues avail.; reprint service avail. from PSC. **Document type:** *Journal, Academic/Scholarly.* **Description:** Includes business educators at the secondary, collegiate and postgraduate levels.
Formerly (until 1985): Journal of Business Education (0021-9444)
Related titles: CD-ROM ed.: (from ProQuest Information & Learning); Microform ed.; Online - full text ed.: (from bigchalk, EBSCO Publishing, Florida Center for Library Automation, Gale Group, H.W. Wilson, Northern Light Technology, Inc., O C L C Online Computer Library Center, Inc., ProQuest Information & Learning).
Indexed: ABIn, BRI, BusEdI, CBRI, CIJE, CPE, DIP, ERA, ETA, EduInd, IBR, IBZ, MEA, MRD, PAIS, RASB, RHEA, RefSour, SEA, SENA, SOMA, SWA, TEA.
—BLDSC (4973.127500), IE, Infotrieve, ingenta. **CCC.**
Published by: (Helen Dwight Reid Educational Foundation), Heldref Publications, 1319 18th St, NW, Washington, DC 20036-1802. TEL 202-296-6267, 800-365-9753, FAX 202-293-6130, jeb@heldref.org, subscribe@heldref.org, http://www.heldref.org/jeb.php. Adv. contact Chante Douglas. B&W page USD 700; trim 7 x 10. Circ: 660 (paid).

➤ **JOURNAL OF EMPLOYEE OWNERSHIP LAW AND FINANCE.** see *LAW*

330 SGP ISSN 0218-4958
HD62.7
➤ **JOURNAL OF ENTERPRISING CULTURE.** Text in English. 1993. 4/yr. SGD 347, USD 201, EUR 191 combined subscription to institutions print & online eds. (effective 2006). back issues avail. **Document type:** *Journal, Academic/Scholarly.* **Description:** Publishes conceptual, research and case based works that can be of practical value to business persons, educators, students and advocates.
Related titles: Online - full text ed.: (from EBSCO Publishing).
Indexed: ABIn, ESPM, IBSS, RiskAb.
—BLDSC (4979.292500), IE. **CCC.**
Published by: World Scientific Publishing Co. Pte. Ltd., 5 Toh Tuck Link, Singapore, 596224, Singapore. TEL 65-466-5775, FAX 65-467-7667, wspc@wspc.com.sg, http://www.worldscinet.com/jec/jec.shtml, http://www.worldscientific.com. Eds. Ravinder A Zutshi, Soke-Yin Wong, Wee-Liang Tan. **Subscr. to:** Farrer Rd, PO Box 128, Singapore 912805, Singapore. sales@wspc.com.sg. **Dist. by:** World Scientific Publishing Co., Inc., 1060 Main St, River Edge, NJ 07661. TEL 201-487-9655, 800-227-7562, FAX 201-487-9656, 888-977-2665.; World Scientific Publishing Ltd., 57 Shelton St, London WC2H 9HE, United Kingdom. TEL 44-20-78360888, FAX 44-20-78362020, sales@wspc.co.uk.

330 621.9 USA ISSN 0740-008X
HD39.4
➤ **THE JOURNAL OF EQUIPMENT LEASE FINANCING.** Text in English. 1983. s-a. USD 125 (effective 2005). **Document type:** *Journal, Academic/Scholarly.* **Description:** Covers industry trends, current leasing research, industry growth opportunities and accounting, legal, tax, and regulatory issues.
Related titles: Online - full text ed.: (from ProQuest Information & Learning).
Indexed: ATI, BLI.
Published by: Equipment Leasing Association, 4301 N Fairfax Dr, Ste 550, Arlington, VA 22203-1627. TEL 703-527-8655, FAX 703-527-2649, http://www.leasefoundation.org/JELF, http://www.elaonline.com/.

330 USA ISSN 1553-3778
▼ **JOURNAL OF FINANCE LITERATURE.** Text in English. 2005 (Win.). q. USD 50 to individuals; USD 125 to institutions (effective 2005).
Published by: Villanova University, Department of Finance, 800 Lancaster Ave, Bartley Hl, Villanova, PA 19085. TEL 610-519-4500, http://www.cf.villanova.edu/finance.htm. Ed. Jean L. Heck.

330 NLD ISSN 0304-405X
HG4501 CODEN: JFECDT
➤ **JOURNAL OF FINANCIAL ECONOMICS.** Text in English. 1974. 12/yr. EUR 98 in Europe to individuals; JPY 13,000 in Japan to individuals; USD 99 to individuals except Europe and Japan; EUR 1,862 in Europe to institutions; JPY 247,700 in Japan to institutions; USD 2,084 to institutions except Europe and Japan; EUR 69 in Europe to students; JPY 8,900 in Japan to students; USD 75 to students except Europe and Japan (effective 2006). adv. bk.rev. illus. index. back issues avail.; reprints avail. **Document type:** *Academic/Scholarly.* **Description:** Provides a forum for the publication of research in the general area of financial economics.
Related titles: Microform ed.: (from PQC); Online - full text ed.: (from EBSCO Publishing, Gale Group, IngentaConnect, ScienceDirect, Swets Information Services).
Indexed: ABIn, ASCA, ATI, BPI, BPIA, BusI, CIS, CMCI, CPM, CREJ, CurCont, ESPM, Emerald, IBSS, Inspec, JCQM, JEL, ManagCont, PCI, RefZh, RiskAb, SCIMP, SSCI, T&II, WBA.
—BLDSC (4984.240000), IDS, IE, Infotrieve, ingenta. **CCC.**
Published by: Elsevier BV, North-Holland (Subsidiary of: Elsevier Science & Technology), Sara Burgerhartstraat 25, Amsterdam, 1055 KV, Netherlands. TEL 31-20-485-3911, FAX 31-20-485-2457, jfe@jfe.rochester.edu, nlinfo-f@elsevier.nl, http://www.elsevier.com/locate/jfec, http://www.elsevier.nl. **Subscr. to:** Elsevier BV, PO Box 211, Amsterdam 1000 AE, Netherlands.

B

330 332 USA ISSN 0270-2592
HG1
➤ **JOURNAL OF FINANCIAL RESEARCH.** Text in English. 1978. q. USD 287 combined subscription in the Americas to institutions & Caribbean (print & online eds.); GBP 246 combined subscription elsewhere to institutions print & online eds. (effective 2006). adv. illus. index. back issues avail.; reprint service avail. from PQC. **Document type:** *Journal, Academic/Scholarly.*
Related titles: Microform ed.: (from PQC); Online - full text ed.: ISSN 1475-6803. USD 273 in the Americas to institutions & Caribbean; GBP 233 elsewhere to institutions (effective 2006) (from Blackwell Synergy, EBSCO Publishing, Florida Center for Library Automation, Gale Group, H.W. Wilson, IngentaConnect, Northern Light Technology, Inc., O C L C Online Computer Library Center, Inc., Swets Information Services).
Indexed: ABIn, ATI, BPI, CPM, ESPM, Emerald, JEL, RiskAb, SCIMP, SSCI.
—BLDSC (4984.265000), IDS, IE, Infotrieve, ingenta. **CCC.**
Published by: (Southern Finance Association), Blackwell Publishing, Inc. (Subsidiary of: Blackwell Publishing Ltd.), Commerce Place, 350 Main St, Malden, MA 02148. TEL 781-388-8206, FAX 781-388-8232, subscrip@blackwellpub.com, http://www.blackwellpublishing.com/journals/JFR. Ed. William T Moore. adv.: B&W page USD 200; trim 7 x 10. Circ: 1,900 (paid). **Co-sponsor:** Southwestern Finance Association.

330 USA ISSN 1572-3089
▼ ➤ **JOURNAL OF FINANCIAL STABILITY.** Text in English. 2004. 4/yr. EUR 205 in Europe to institutions; JPY 26,900 in Japan to institutions; USD 241 to institutions except Europe and Japan (effective 2006). **Document type:** *Journal, Academic/Scholarly.* **Description:** Provides an international forum for theoretical and empirical macro and micro economic and financial analysis of the causes, management, resolution and prevention of financial crises, including banking, securities market, payments and currency crises.
Related titles: Online - full text ed.: (from EBSCO Publishing, ScienceDirect, Swets Information Services).
—BLDSC (4984.267500), IE.
Published by: Elsevier Inc. (Subsidiary of: Elsevier Science & Technology), 360 Park Ave. S, New York, NY 10010-1710. TEL 212-633-3730, 888-437-4636, usinfo-f@elsevier.com, http://www.elsevier.com/locate/jfstabil. Eds. George Kaufman, Iftekhar Hasan, William Hunter. Adv. contact Tino DeCarlo.

▼ ➤ **JOURNAL OF FOREST PRODUCTS BUSINESS RESEARCH.** see *FORESTS AND FORESTRY—Lumber And Wood*

330 USA ISSN 1053-7287
HG3879
➤ **JOURNAL OF GLOBAL BUSINESS.** Text in English. 1990. s-a. USD 28 to individuals; USD 40 to institutions (effective 2005). adv. bk.rev. back issues avail. **Document type:** *Academic/Scholarly.* **Description:** Aims to provide a forum for the exchange of professional ideas, enhance research in the field of business and global concerns, and create a general awareness of significant accomplishments in the area of global enterprises.
Indexed: ABIn.
—BLDSC (4996.260000), IE, ingenta.
Published by: Association for Global Business, PO Box 1381, Harrisonburg, VA 22803. fdamanpour@msn.com, http://falcon.jmu.edu/~damanpfx. Ed., R&P Faramarz Damanpour. adv.: B&W page USD 250. Circ: 1,000.

330 GBR ISSN 0022-1821
HD1 CODEN: JIEOAF
➤ **THE JOURNAL OF INDUSTRIAL ECONOMICS.** Text in English. 1952. q. GBP 37, EUR 56 combined subscription in Europe to individuals print & online eds.; USD 70 combined subscription in the Americas to individuals & Caribbean, print & online eds.; GBP 41 combined subscription elsewhere to individuals print & online eds.; GBP 144 combined subscription in Europe to institutions print & online eds.; USD 220 combined subscription in the Americas to institutions & Caribbean, print & online eds.; GBP 156 combined subscription elsewhere to institutions print & online eds.; EUR 32 combined subscription in Europe to students & Caribbean, print & online eds.; USD 28 combined subscription in the Americas to students print & online eds.; GBP 21 combined subscription elsewhere to students print & online eds. (effective 2006). adv. bibl.; charts; illus. index. back issues avail.; reprint service avail. from PQC,PSC. **Document type:** *Journal, Academic/Scholarly.* **Description:** Publishes the analysis of modern industry, functioning of markets, behaviour of firms and policy.
Related titles: Microform ed.: (from MIM, PQC); Online - full text ed.: ISSN 1467-6451. GBP 137 in Europe to institutions; USD 210 in the Americas to institutions & Caribbean; GBP 149 elsewhere to institutions (effective 2006) (from Blackwell Synergy, EBSCO Publishing, Gale Group, IngentaConnect, JSTOR (Web-based Journal Archive), O C L C Online Computer Library Center, Inc., Swets Information Services).
Indexed: ABIn, APEL, ASCA, BAS, BPI, BPIA, BrHumI, BusI, CPM, CREJ, CurCont, EIA, Emerald, EnerInd, HRA, IBR, IBSS, IBZ, JEL, KES, M&MA, MResA, ManagCont, ORMS, PAIS, PCI, PRA, PROMT, RASB, SCIMP, SPAA, SSCI, T&II, V&AA, WBA, WorkRelAb.
—BLDSC (5005.650000), IDS, IE, Infotrieve, ingenta. **CCC.**
Published by: Blackwell Publishing Ltd., 9600 Garsington Rd, Oxford, OX4 2ZG, United Kingdom. TEL 44-1865-776868, FAX 44-1865-714591, customerservices@oxon.blackwellpublishing.com, http://www.blackwellpublishing.com/journals/JOIE. Ed. Pierre Regibeau. Circ: 1,850.

330 338 USA ISSN 1566-1679
JOURNAL OF INDUSTRY, COMPETITION AND TRADE; from theory to policy. Text in English. 2001. q. EUR 267, USD 267, GBP 180 combined subscription to institutions print & online eds. (effective 2005). adv. reprint service avail. from PSC. **Document type:** *Journal, Academic/Scholarly.* **Description:** Contains research on industry, competition and trade policy. It will investigate the microeconomic foundation of industrial strategy, innovation, competition, and trade policy and it will concentrate on the functioning of product markets, such as goods and services.
Related titles: Online - full text ed.: ISSN 1573-7012 (from EBSCO Publishing, Gale Group, IngentaConnect, Kluwer Online, O C L C Online Computer Library Center, Inc., ProQuest Information & Learning, Springer LINK, Swets Information Services).
Indexed: ABIn, BibLing, RefZh.
—BLDSC (5006.681000), IE, Infotrieve, ingenta. **CCC.**
Published by: Springer-Verlag New York, Inc. (Subsidiary of: Springer Science+Business Media), 233 Spring St, New York, NY 10013. TEL 212-460-1500, FAX 212-460-1575, service@springer-ny.com, http://springerlink.metapress.com/openurl.asp?genre=journal&issn=1566-1679, http://www.springer-ny.com. Eds. Andre Sapir, Karl Aiginger. **Subscr. to:** Journal Fulfillment, PO Box 2485, Secaucus, NJ 07096-2485. TEL 201-348-4033, FAX 201-348-4505, journals@springer-ny.com.

330 GBR ISSN 1744-1374
▼ **JOURNAL OF INSTITUTIONAL ECONOMICS.** Text in English. 2005 (June). s-a. GBP 137 to institutions; USD 246 in North America to institutions; GBP 145 combined subscription to institutions print & online eds.; USD 259 combined subscription in North America to institutions print & online eds. (effective 2006). **Document type:** *Journal.* **Description:** Studies the nature, role, and evolution of institutions in the economy.
Related titles: Online - full text ed.: ISSN 1744-1382. GBP 125 to institutions; USD 255 in North America to institutions (effective 2006) (from EBSCO Publishing).
Published by: Cambridge University Press, The Edinburgh Bldg, Shaftesbury Rd, Cambridge, CB2 2RU, United Kingdom. TEL 44-1223-312393, FAX 44-1223-315052, journals@cambridge.org, http://uk.cambridge.org/journals. Ed. Geoffrey M Hodgson. **Subscr. to:** Cambridge University Press, 100 Brook Hill Dr, West Nyack, NY 10994. TEL 845-353-7500, FAX 845-353-4141, journals_subscriptions@cup.org

330 GBR ISSN 0260-1079
HB1
➤ **JOURNAL OF INTERDISCIPLINARY ECONOMICS.** Text in English. 1984. 4/yr. GBP 129, USD 209 (effective 2005). adv. bk.rev. **Document type:** *Journal, Academic/Scholarly.*
Related titles: Microform ed.
Indexed: APEL, AmH&L, CREJ, DIP, HistAb, IBR, IBSS, IBZ, JEL, PSA, RefZh, SociolAb.
—BLDSC (5007.546000), IE, Infotrieve, ingenta. **CCC.**
Published by: A B Academic Publishers, PO Box 42, Bicester, Oxon OX26 6NW, United Kingdom. jrnls@abapubl.demon.co.uk. Ed. Ruth Taplin.

➤ **JOURNAL OF INTERDISCIPLINARY STUDIES (POMONA)**; a journal of research and innovative activities. see *ENGINEERING*

330 USA ISSN 1527-8603
HF1351
➤ **JOURNAL OF INTERNATIONAL BUSINESS AND ECONOMY.** Text in English. 2000. a., latest vol.3, 2002. USD 50 per issue domestic to individuals; USD 60 per issue foreign to individuals; USD 70 per issue domestic to institutions; USD 80 per issue foreign to institutions (effective 2003 - 2004). a.index. back issues avail. **Document type:** *Journal, Academic/Scholarly.* **Description:** Publishes theoretical and empirical articles relating to international business and economy such as international competitiveness, institutions, and cultural differences.
Published by: (Insitute of Industrial Policy Studies KOR), San Francisco State University, College of Business, 1600 Holloway Ave, San Francsico, CA 94132. TEL 415-338-1754, 415-338-0596, jkang@sfsu.edu. Eds. Edwin C Duerr, Hwy-Chang Moon, Yim-Yu Wong. Pub. Jay S Kang. **Co-publisher:** Insitute of Industrial Policy Studies.

650 GBR ISSN 0047-2506
HF1
➤ **JOURNAL OF INTERNATIONAL BUSINESS STUDIES.** Abbreviated title: J I B S. Text in English. 1970. bi-m. USD 137 combined subscription in United States to individuals; GBP 87 combined subscription elsewhere to individuals; USD 198 combined subscription in United States to institutions; GBP 126 combined subscription elsewhere to institutions (effective 2005); Combined subscr. includes print & online. adv. bk.rev. charts. back issues avail.; reprint service avail. from PQC,SCH. **Document type:** *Journal, Academic/Scholarly.* **Description:** Publishes the results of basic or applied research in international or comparative business. Also publishes important conceptual or theoretical contributions that augment knowledge in the field or advance educational methodology.
Related titles: Microform ed.: (from PQC); Online - full text ed.: ISSN 1478-6990. GBP 104 in Europe to institutions; USD 162 elsewhere to institutions (effective 2004) (from EBSCO Publishing, Florida Center for Library Automation, Gale Group, H.W. Wilson, IngentaConnect, JSTOR (Web-based Journal Archive), Micromedia ProQuest, Northern Light Technology, Inc., O C L C Online Computer Library Center, Inc., ProQuest Information & Learning, Swets Information Services).
Indexed: ABIn, ABS&EES, ADPA, APEL, ASCA, BAS, BPI, BusI, CPM, CPerI, ChPerI, CurCont, ESPM, Emerald, IBSS, JEL, M&MA, MEA&I, ManagCont, PAIS, PROMT, RASB, RiskAb, SCIMP, SSCI, T&II, WBA, WMB.
—BLDSC (5007.590000), IDS, IE, Infotrieve, ingenta. **CCC.**
Published by: (University of Western Ontario, Western Business School CAN), Palgrave Macmillan Ltd. (Subsidiary of: Macmillan Publishers Ltd.), Houndmills, Basingstoke, Hants RG21 6XS, United Kingdom. TEL 44-1256-329242, FAX 44-1256-810526, journal-info@palgrave.com, http://www.palgrave-journals.com/jibs/index.html. Ed. Arie Y Lewin. adv.: B&W page USD 400. Circ: 4,100. **Co-sponsor:** Academy of International Business.

330 JPN ISSN 0911-1247
JOURNAL OF INTERNATIONAL ECONOMIC STUDIES. Text in English. 1985. a. **Document type:** *Journal.*
Published by: Hosei University, Institute of Comparative Economic Studies/Hosei Daigaku. Hikaku Keizai Kenkyujo, 4342 Aihara-machi, Machida-shi, Tokyo, 194-0298, Japan. TEL 81-42-7832330, FAX 81-42-7832332, ices@mt.tama.hosei.ac.jp, http://www.hosei.ac.jp/hikaku2/jies.htm.

330 NLD ISSN 0022-1996
HF1 CODEN: JIECBE
➤ **JOURNAL OF INTERNATIONAL ECONOMICS.** Text in English. 1971. 6/yr. EUR 125 in Europe to individuals; JPY 17,200 in Japan to individuals; USD 130 to individuals except Europe and Japan; EUR 1,190 in Europe to institutions; JPY 157,900 in Japan to institutions; USD 1,330 to institutions except Europe and Japan (effective 2006). adv. bk.rev. charts; illus. index. back issues avail.; reprints avail. **Document type:** *Academic/Scholarly.* **Description:** Publishes analytical work in the pure theory of international trade and payment analysis.
Related titles: Microform ed.: (from PQC); Online - full text ed.: (from EBSCO Publishing, Gale Group, IngentaConnect, ScienceDirect, Swets Information Services).
Indexed: ABIn, APEL, ASCA, BAS, BPIA, BusI, CurCont, ESPM, GEOBASE, IBSS, JEL, KES, PAIS, PCI, RASB, RRTA, RiskAb, SCIMP, SSCI, SSI, T&II, WAE&RSA, WBA.
—BLDSC (5007.650000), CISTI, IDS, IE, Infotrieve, ingenta. **CCC.**
Published by: Elsevier BV, North-Holland (Subsidiary of: Elsevier Science & Technology), Sara Burgerhartstraat 25, Amsterdam, 1055 KV, Netherlands. TEL 31-20-485-3911, FAX 31-20-485-2457, nlinfo-f@elsevier.nl, http://www.elsevier.com/locate/jie, http://www.elsevier.nl. Eds. C. M. Engel, J. Eaton. **Subscr. to:** Elsevier BV, PO Box 211, Amsterdam 1000 AE, Netherlands. TEL 31-20-485-3757, FAX 31-20-485-3432, http://www.elsevier.nl.

➤ **JOURNAL OF LAW AND ECONOMICS.** see *LAW*

330 170 USA ISSN 1098-1217
➤ **THE JOURNAL OF MARKETS & MORALITY.** Variant title: Markets & Morality. Text in English. 1998. s-a. USD 25 domestic to individuals; USD 35 foreign to individuals; USD 60 domestic to institutions; USD 70 foreign to institutions (effective 2005). **Document type:** *Journal, Academic/Scholarly.* **Description:** Explores the relationship between economics and morality from the social science and theological perspectives.
Related titles: Online - full text ed.: (from EBSCO Publishing).
Indexed: JEL, SSCI.
Published by: Acton Institute for the Study of Religion and Liberty, 161 Ottawa Ave., NW, Ste. 301, Grand Rapids, MI 49503. TEL 616-454-3080, FAX 616-454-9454, info@acton.org, http://www.acton.org/publicat/m_and_m/.

➤ **JOURNAL OF MODERN AFRICAN STUDIES.** see *POLITICAL SCIENCE*

330 AUS
▼ ➤ **JOURNAL OF NEW BUSINESS IDEAS AND TRENDS.** Text in English. 2003. s-a. AUD 160 to individuals; AUD 520 to institutions (effective 2003). **Document type:** *Journal, Academic/Scholarly.* **Description:** Aims to provide a forum for disseminating vital information and knowledge regarding new business thinking.
Related titles: Online - full text ed.
Published by: U B P Consulting and Publishing, 24 Ebdent St, Ballarat, VIC 3350, Australia. TEL 61-3-53279415, FAX 61-3-53279405, j.vanbeveren@ballarat.edu.au, http://www.ubp.com.au. Ed., Pub. John Van Beveren.

➤ **JOURNAL OF ORGANIZATIONAL AND END USER COMPUTING**; the international journal of information user management. see *COMPUTERS—Microcomputers*

320 USA ISSN 0022-3808
CODEN: JLPEAR
➤ **JOURNAL OF POLITICAL ECONOMY.** Text in English. 1892. bi-m. USD 57 combined subscription to individuals print & online eds.; USD 330 combined subscription to institutions print & online eds.; USD 14 per issue to individuals; USD 61 per issue to institutions (effective 2006). adv. bk.rev. abstr.; bibl.; charts; illus.; stat. Index. reprint service avail. from PQC,WSH,ISI,PSC. **Document type:** *Journal, Academic/Scholarly.* **Description:** Presents work in traditional areas of political economics: monetary theory, fiscal policy, labor economics, planning and developments, micro- and macroeconomic theory, and international trade and finance. Also publishes analyses in related fields such as economic thought and social economics.
Related titles: Microform ed.: (from MIM, PMC, PQC); Online - full text ed.: ISSN 1537-534X. USD 297 to institutions (effective 2006) (from EBSCO Publishing, Florida Center for Library Automation, Gale Group, JSTOR (Web-based Journal Archive), ProQuest Information & Learning).
Indexed: ABCPolSci, ABIn, APEL, AgeL, AmH&L, ArtHuCI, BAS, BLI, BRD, BRI, BusI, CBRI, CJA, CPM, CREJ, CurCont, DIP, ERA, FamI, GEOBASE, HistAb, IBR, IBSS, IBZ, IPSA, IndIslam, JEL, KES, MEA&I, NutrAb, PAIS, PCI, PopulInd, RASB, RDA, RI-1, RI-2, RRTA, SCIMP, SRRA, SSCI, SSI, SWA, SociolAb, WAE&RSA.
—BLDSC (5040.850000), CISTI, IDS, IE, Infotrieve, ingenta. **CCC.**
Published by: University of Chicago Press, Journals Division, Journals Division, PO Box 37005, Chicago, IL 60637. TEL 773-753-3347, 877-705-1878, FAX 773-753-0811, 877-705-1879, subscriptions@press.uchicago.edu, http://www.journals.uchicago.edu/JPE/. Eds. Anil Kashyap, Canice Prendergast, Nancy L Stokey, Robert Shimer, Steven D Levitt. adv.: page USD 445; trim 9 x 6. Circ: 6,100.

330 USA ISSN 0890-913X
HB95
JOURNAL OF PRIVATE ENTERPRISE. Text in English. 1985. a. USD 12. bk.rev. back issues avail. **Document type:** *Academic/Scholarly.* **Description:** Brings together scholars in the fields of economics, management, entrepreneurship, marketing, finance, ethics, religion and education who have done research on topics pertaining to the American system of private enterprise.
Indexed: JEL, PAIS.
Published by: Association of Private Enterprise Education, 112 Business Administration Bldg, University of Tennessee, Martin, Martin, TN 38238. TEL 901-587-7208, FAX 901-587-7228. Ed. J R Clark. Circ: 750.

330 USA ISSN 1090-4999
HD1
JOURNAL OF REGIONAL ANALYSIS & POLICY. Text in English. 1971. s-a. USD 35 to individuals; USD 45 to institutions. bk.rev. **Document type:** *Academic/Scholarly.*
Formerly: Regional Science Perspectives (0097-1197)
Indexed: ASFA, GEOBASE, JEL.
—BLDSC (5048.650000), IE, ingenta.
Published by: (Mid-Continent Regional Science Association), University of Nebraska at Lincoln, Bureau of Business Research, 114 C B A, Lincoln, NE 68588-0408. TEL 402-472-7928. Ed. F Charles Lamphear. R&P F. Charles Lamphear. Circ: 500.

658 USA ISSN 1533-2667
HF5415.55 CODEN: JCMREQ
➤ **JOURNAL OF RELATIONSHIP MARKETING**; innovations & enhancements for customer service, relations & satisfaction. Abbreviated title: J R M. Text in English. 1995. q. USD 360 combined subscription domestic to institutions print & online eds.; USD 486 combined subscription in Canada to institutions print & online eds.; USD 522 combined subscription elsewhere to institutions print & online eds. (effective 2006). adv. 120 p./no.; back issues avail.; reprint service avail. from HAW. **Document type:** *Journal, Academic/Scholarly.* **Description:** Supplies practical, applied literary resources to professionals in a wide range of industries on customer-client service, quality enhancement, and value for services and products purchased or provided.
Formerly (until 2000): Journal of Customer Service in Marketing & Management (1069-2533)
Related titles: Microform ed.: (from PQC); Online - full text ed.: ISSN 1533-2675. free to institutions (effective 2003); free with print subs. (from EBSCO Publishing, O C L C Online Computer Library Center, Inc., Swets Information Services).
Indexed: ABIn, DIP, HRA, IBR, IBZ, M&MA, RefZh.
—BLDSC (5049.170000), Haworth. **CCC.**
Published by: Haworth Press, Inc., 10 Alice St, Binghamton, NY 13904-1580. TEL 607-722-5857, 800-429-6784, FAX 607-722-1424, 800-895-0582, getinfo@haworthpress.com, http://www.haworthpress.com/web/JRM. Ed. David Bejou. Pub. William Cohen. R&P Ruth Ann Heath TEL 607-722-5857 ext 316. Adv. contact Rebecca Miller-Baum TEL 607-722-5857 ext 337. B&W page USD 300, color page USD 525; trim 4.375 x 7.125. Circ: 246 (paid).

➤ **JOURNAL OF SOCIAL, POLITICAL AND ECONOMIC STUDIES.** see *POLITICAL SCIENCE*

➤ **JOURNAL OF SPACE COMMERCE.** see *AERONAUTICS AND SPACE FLIGHT*

330 790.1 USA ISSN 1527-0025
GV561
➤ **JOURNAL OF SPORTS ECONOMICS.** Text in English. 2000. q. USD 371, GBP 240 to institutions; USD 386, GBP 250 combined subscription to institutions print & online eds. (effective 2006). **Document type:** *Journal, Academic/Scholarly.* **Description:** Includes relevant topics in labour market research, labour-management relations, collective bargaining, wage determination, local public finance and other fields related to the economics of sport.
Related titles: Online - full text ed.: ISSN 1552-7794. USD 367, GBP 237 to institutions (effective 2006) (from EBSCO Publishing, O C L C Online Computer Library Center, Inc., Sage Publications, Inc., Swets Information Services).
Indexed: CJA, JEL, PEI, RRTA.
—BLDSC (5066.189700), IE, ingenta. **CCC.**
Published by: Sage Publications, Inc., 2455 Teller Rd, Thousand Oaks, CA 91320. TEL 805-499-0721, 800-818-7243, FAX 805-499-0871, 800-583-2665, info@sagepub.com, http://www.sagepub.com/journal.aspx?pid=188. Eds. Leo H Kahane, Todd L Idson. **Subscr. to:** Sage Publications Ltd., 1 Oliver's Yard, 55 City Rd, London EC1 1SP, United Kingdom. TEL 44-20-73740645, FAX 44-20-73748741, subscription@sagepub.co.uk.

330 USA ISSN 0094-1190
HT321 CODEN: JUECDW
➤ **JOURNAL OF URBAN ECONOMICS.** Text in English. 1974. 6/yr. EUR 130 in Europe to individuals; JPY 14,000 in Japan to individuals; USD 99 to individuals except Europe and Japan; EUR 1,321 in Europe to institutions; JPY 137,900 in Japan to institutions; USD 1,015 to institutions except Europe and Japan (effective 2006). illus. Index. back issues avail.; reprints avail. **Document type:** *Academic/Scholarly.* **Description:** Illustrates empirical, theoretical, positive, or normative approaches to urban economics.
Related titles: Online - full text ed.: ISSN 1095-9068. USD 1,065 (effective 2002) (from EBSCO Publishing, Gale Group, IngentaConnect, O C L C Online Computer Library Center, Inc., ScienceDirect, Swets Information Services).
Indexed: APEL, ASCA, AgeL, BPI, BPIA, CJA, CREJ, ChPerI, CurCont, EEA, ESPM, ExcerpMed, FamI, IBR, IBSS, IBZ, JEL, ManagCont, PAA&I, PAIS, PRA, RASB, RiskAb, SOPODA, SPAA, SRRA, SSCI, SUSA, T&II, ZentMath.
—BLDSC (5071.554000), IDS, IE, Infotrieve, ingenta. **CCC.**
Published by: Academic Press (Subsidiary of: Elsevier Science & Technology), 525 B St, Ste 1900, San Diego, CA 92101-4495. TEL 619-231-6616, 800-894-3434, FAX 619-699-6422, apsubs@acad.com, http://www.elsevier.com/locate/jue, http://www.academicpress.com. Ed. Jan K Brueckner.

330 NLD ISSN 1569-1829
➤ **JOURNAL ON CHAIN AND NETWORK SCIENCE.** Text in English. 2001. 2/yr. USD 125 to individuals; USD 250 to institutions (effective 2004). bk.rev. back issues avail.; reprints avail. **Document type:** *Journal, Academic/Scholarly.* **Description:** Articles about theory building and practice in the field of chains and networks in the light of increased complexity of the global network economy.
Indexed: FS&TA.
—BLDSC (4955.180000), IE.
Published by: Wageningen Academic Publishers, PO Box 220, Wageningen, 6700 AE, Netherlands. TEL 31-317-476516, FAX 31-317-453417, journal@wageningenacademic, http://www.sls.wageningen-ur.nl/bk/journal/index.html, http://www.wageningenacademic.com. Ed. Dr. S. W. F. Omta. Pub., R&P Mike Jacobs TEL 31-317-476516.

340 USA ISSN 0737-5468
K10
JOURNAL RECORD. Text in English. 1903. d. (Mon.-Fri.). USD 140 in county (effective 2005). adv. bk.rev. **Document type:** *Newspaper, Consumer.*
Formerly: Daily Law Journal Record (0011-5452)
Related titles: Microfiche ed.: 1903; Online - full text ed.: 1903 (from bigchalk, Gale Group, Newsbank, Inc., Northern Light Technology, Inc., ProQuest Information & Learning).
Indexed: ABIn, T&II.
Published by: (Oklahoma Farmers Union), Journal Record Publishing Co. (Subsidiary of: Dolan Media Co.), 222 N Robinson Ave, Box 26370, Oklahoma City, OK 73102. editorial@journalrecord.com, http://www.journalrecord.com. Ed., Pub. D. Mark Singletary. Adv. contact Mary Melon. col. inch USD 14.70. Circ: 3,500 (paid). Wire service: AP, NYT.

JOURNAL WIRTSCHAFTSPRAXIS. see *EDUCATION—Teaching Methods And Curriculum*

330 USA
JOURNEY (ANTIOCH). Text in English. 1991. q. USD 39.95. adv. bk.rev. **Document type:** *Newsletter, Corporate.* **Description:** Provides business managers with proven methods of improving their operating performance.
Published by: Buker, Inc., 800 Main St., Antioch, IL 60002-1542. TEL 847-855-8554, FAX 847-855-0889, nhorton@buker.com, http://www.buker.com. Ed. James W Bieal. Adv. contact Mike Stickler.

330 378 USA
JUNGLE MAGAZINE. Text in English. 7/yr. USD 24.97 (effective 2003). adv. back issues avail. **Document type:** *Magazine, Consumer.* **Description:** Takes readers behind the scenes on Wall Street and into the boardroom giving them the insights and hard-won wisdom they need to succeed.
Related titles: Online - full content ed.
Published by: Jungle Media Group, 632 Broadway, 7th Fl, New York, NY 10012. TEL 212-352-0840, FAX 212-352-9282, smcduffy@junglemediagroup.com, http://www.jdjungle.com/, http://www.junglemediagroup.com/. adv.: B&W page USD 21,575, color page USD 26,000; trim 8 x 10.875.

B

330 IND ISSN 0971-8745
JUNIOR SCIENCE REFRESHER; science magazine. Text in English. 1987. m. INR 200; INR 20 newsstand/cover. adv. **Document type:** *Academic/Scholarly.*
Published by: (Bright Careers Institute), Junior Science Refresher Pvt. Ltd., 2769 Bright House, Darya Ganj, New Delhi, 110 002, India. TEL 91-11-3276554, FAX 91-11-3269227, TELEX ND 31-76101, psbright@ndf.vsnl.net.in. Ed. D S Phull. Pub., R&P Pritam Singh Bright. Adv. contact K C Lapsha. B&W page INR 35,000, color page INR 70,000; 175 x 245. Circ: 71,758.

JUTA'S BUSINESS LAW; the quarterly law review for people in business. see *LAW—Corporate Law*

677.4743 CHN ISSN 1008-8261
JUZHI GONGYE/POLYESTER INDUSTRY. Text in Chinese. 1988. bi-m. CNY 10 newsstand/cover (effective 2005). **Document type:** *Journal, Academic/Scholarly.*
Related titles: Online - full text ed.: (from East View Information Services, WanFang Data Corp.).
Indexed: BrCerAb, C&ISA, CerAb, CorrAb, E&CAJ, EMA, IAA, M&TEA, MBF, METADEX, WAA.
—BLDSC (6547.572000), Linda Hall.
Address: 71, Anshan Road, Shahekou District, Dalian, Liaoning 116021, China. jzgydlcn@163.com, http://jzgy.periodicals.net.cn/. Ed. Shi-min Zhang.

330 332 339 KOR
K D B REPORT. Text and summaries in English. 1977. m. free.
Published by: Korea Development Bank, 10-2 Kwanch'ol-dong, Chongno-gu, C.P.O. Box 28, Seoul, Korea, S. Ed. Bong Won Lee. Circ: 2,800.

K M WORLD; creating and managing the knowledge-based enterprise. (Knowledge Management) see *COMPUTERS—Computer Graphics*

330 JPN ISSN 0387-2955
K S U ECONOMIC AND BUSINESS REVIEW. Text in English. 1974. a.
Indexed: PAIS.
Published by: Kyoto Sangyo University, Society of Economics and Business Administration/Kyoto Sangyo Daigaku, Keizai Keiei Gakkai, Motoyama, Kamigamo, Kita-ku, Kyoto, 603-8555, Japan.

330 JPN ISSN 0451-2081
KAGAWA DAIGAKU KEIZAI GAKUBU KENKYU NENPO/ANNALS OF ECONOMIC STUDIES. Text in Japanese. 1961. a. **Document type:** *Academic/Scholarly.*
—BLDSC (1031.635000).
Published by: Kagawa Daigaku, Keizai Gakubu/Kagawa University, Faculty of Economics, Kyomu, Takamatsu, Kagawa 760-8523 , Japan. TEL 81-87-832-1813, FAX 81-87-832-1820, http://www.ec.kagawa-u.ac.jp/index.html.

330 CHN
KAIFANG YUEKAN; Shanghai Xinchao Zazhi. Text in Chinese. m. **Description:** Covers the latest development in China's economic reform.
Address: 62 Henshan Lu, Shanghai, 200031, China. TEL 86-21-4313564, FAX 86-21-4315274. **Dist. overseas by:** China International Book Trading Corp, 35 Chegongzhuang Xilu, Haidian District, PO Box 399, Beijing 100044, China.

330 JPN ISSN 0449-7554
HB9
KANSAI UNIVERSITY ECONOMIC REVIEW/KANSAI DAIGAKU KEIZAI RONSHU. Text in Japanese. 1950. bi-m. bk.rev.
Indexed: ADPA, APEL.
—BLDSC (3654.950000).
Published by: Kansai University, Economic Society/Kansai Daigaku Keizai Gakkai, Senriyama, Suita, Osaka-shi, Japan.

▼ new title ➤ refereed ✶ unverified ♦ full entry avail.

330 FIN ISSN 0022-8427
HB9
KANSANTALOUDELLINEN AIKAKAUSKIRJA/FINNISH ECONOMIC JOURNAL. Text in Finnish; Summaries in English. 1905. q. EUR 27 (effective 2004). adv. bk.rev. bibl.
Document type: *Journal, Academic/Scholarly.*
Formerly (until 1929): Yhteiskuntaloudellinen Aikakauskirja
Indexed: JEL, RASB, RefZh, WBSS.
Published by: Kansantaloudellinen Yhdistys/Finnish Economic Association, c/o Merja Kauhanen, Labour Institute for Economic Research, Pitkansillanranta 3A, Helsinki, 00530, Finland. TEL 358-9-25357345, yhdist@ktyhdistys.net, http://www.ktyhdistys.net/English/association.htm. Eds. Klaus Kultti, Hannu Vartiainen. Circ: 2,000.

330 FIN ISSN 0355-7847
KANSANTALOUDELLISIA TUTKIMUKSIA/ECONOMIC STUDIES. Text in Finnish; Text occasionally in English. 1933. irreg. price varies. **Document type:** *Monographic series, Academic/Scholarly.*
Published by: Kansantaloudellinen Yhdistys/Finnish Economic Association, c/o Merja Kauhanen, Labour Institute for Economic Research, Pitkansillanranta 3A, Helsinki, 00530, Finland. TEL 358-9-25357345, yhdist@ktyhdistys.net, http://www.ktyhdistys.net.

330 USA
KANSAS BUSINESS AND ECONOMIC REVIEW. Text in English. 1948-1970; resumed 1977. s-a. **Document type:** *Trade.*
Former titles (until 2001): Kansas Business Review (Lawrence, 1977, Print Edition) (0164-8632); (until 1977): Kansas Business Review (Lawrence, 1948) (0191-4189)
Media: Online - full content.
Indexed: PAIS.
Published by: University of Kansas, Policy Research Institute, 1541 Lilac Ln, 607 Blake Hall, Lawrence, KS 66044-3177. TEL 785-864-3701, FAX 785-864-3683, pri@ku.edu, http://www.ku.edu/pri.

330 BGR
KAPITAL/CAPITAL. Text in Bulgarian. w. BGL 80 domestic; EUR 78 foreign; USD 310 elsewhere (effective 2005). **Document type:** *Newspaper, Consumer.*
Related titles: Online - full content ed.: BGL 40 domestic; USD 30 foreign (effective 2005).
Published by: Economedia, ul Ivan Vazov 20, et. 2, Sofia, Bulgaria. TEL 359-2-9376444, FAX 359-2-9376236, http://www.capital.bg.

330 UKR
KAPITAL. Text in Ukrainian. m. USD 145 in United States.
Published by: Izdatel'stvo Blits-Inform, Ul Kioto 25, Kiev, Ukraine. TEL 518-12-67. **US dist. addr.:** East View Information Services, 3020 Harbor Ln. N., Minneapolis, MN 55447. TEL 612-550-0961.

330 FIN ISSN 0451-5560
KAUPPALEHTI. Text in Finnish. 1898. d. adv. **Document type:** *Newspaper, Trade.*
Related titles: Online - full text ed.; ♦ Supplement(s): Kauppalehti Presso. ISSN 1795-3030; Kauppalehti Optio. ISSN 1238-4895. 1987.
Indexed: P&BA, RASB.
Published by: Kustannusosakeyhtio Kauppalehti, PO Box 830, Helsinki, 00101, Finland. TEL 358-9-50781, http://www.kauppalehti.fi. Ed. Hannu Leinanen. Circ: 84,068.

330 FIN ISSN 1795-3030
▼ **KAUPPALEHTI PRESSO.** Text in Finnish. 2004. w. adv.
Document type: *Newspaper.*
Related titles: Online - full text ed.: ISSN 1795-3049; ♦ Supplement to: Kauppalehti. ISSN 0451-5560.
Published by: Kustannusosakeyhtio Kauppalehti, PO Box 830, Helsinki, 00101, Finland. TEL 358-9-50781, http://presso.kauppalehti.fi/p/l/i/etusivu/index.jsp, http://www.kauppalehti.fi. Ed. Hannu Leinanen.

330 JPN ISSN 0022-9695
HC461
KEIDANREN REVIEW. Text in English. 1964. bi-m. free. adv. charts; illus.; stat.
Indexed: BAS, RASB.
Published by: Japan Federation of Economic Organizations/Keizai Dantai Rengokai (KEIDANREN), 9-4 Ote-Machi 1-chome, Chiyoda-ku, Tokyo, 100-0004, Japan. TEL 81-3-3279-1411, FAX 81-3-5255-6255, TELEX 0222 3188 KDRTOKJ. Circ: 12,000.

330 JPN ISSN 0386-9113
HD28
KEIEI SHIGAKU/JAPAN BUSINESS HISTORY REVIEW. Text in Japanese. 1967. 4/yr. JPY 4,200.
Indexed: AmH&L.
Published by: (Business History Society of Japan), University of Tokyo, Graduate School of Science, Chirigaku Kyoshitsu, 3-1, Hongo 7-chome, Bunkyo-ku, Tokyo, 113-0033, Japan.

650 JPN ISSN 0453-4557
HF41
KEIO BUSINESS REVIEW. Text in English. 1978 (vol.15). a. price varies. charts; stat. **Document type:** *Academic/Scholarly.*
Indexed: ADPA, BAS, CPM, IBSS, PAIS.
Published by: Keio University Society of Business and Commerce, c/o Faculty of Business and Commerce, Mita, Minato-ku, Tokyo, 108-0073, Japan. TEL 81-3-3453-4511. Ed. T Shimizu. **Dist. by:** Japan Publications Trading Co., Ltd., Book Export II Dept, PO Box 5030, Tokyo International, Tokyo 101-3191, Japan. TEL 81-3-32923753, FAX 81-3-32920410, infoserials@jptco.co.jp, http://www.jptco.co.jp.

330 JPN ISSN 0022-9709
HB9
➤ **KEIO ECONOMIC STUDIES.** Text in English. 1963. s-a. JPY 3,000 (effective 2003). adv. bk.rev. back issues avail.
Document type: *Journal, Academic/Scholarly.*
Indexed: APEL, BAS, CREJ, IBR, IBSS, IBZ, JEL, RASB, SSCI, WAE&RSA.
—BLDSC (5088.870000), IE, Infotrieve, ingenta.
Published by: Keio Gijuku Daigaku, Keio Keizai Gakkai/Keio University, Keio Economic Society, 2-15-45 Mita, Minato-ku, Tokyo, 108-8345, Japan. TEL 81-3-3453-4511, FAX 81-3-5427-1578, http://www.keio.ac.jp/org/kes/. Ed. Naoyuki Yoshino. R&P, Adv. contact Toshiaki Nakazawa. Circ: 800.

650 JPN ISSN 0075-5346
KEIO MONOGRAPHS OF BUSINESS AND COMMERCE. Text in Japanese. 1967. irreg. price varies. **Document type:** *Monographic series.*
Published by: Keio University Society of Business and Commerce, c/o Faculty of Business and Commerce, Mita, Minato-ku, Tokyo, 108-0073, Japan. **Dist. by:** Japan Publications Trading Co., Ltd., Book Export II Dept, PO Box 5030, Tokyo International, Tokyo 101-3191, Japan. TEL 81-3-32923753, FAX 81-3-32920410, infoserials@jptco.co.jp, http://www.jptco.co.jp.

330 JPN ISSN 0022-9725
HB9
➤ **KEIZAI KAGAKU/ECONOMIC SCIENCE.** Text mainly in Japanese; Text occasionally in English. 1951. q. bk.rev. bibl.; charts; stat. index, cum.index. 170 p./no.; back issues avail.
Document type: *Journal, Academic/Scholarly.*
—BLDSC (3655.180000).
Published by: Nagoya Daigaku, Keizaigaku kenkyuka/Nagoya University, Graduate School of Economics, Furo-cho, Chikusa-ku, Nagoya, 464-8601, Japan. TEL 81-52-789-2360, FAX 81-52-789-4924, econosci@soec.nagoya-u.ac.jp, http://www.soec.nagoya-u.ac.jp/htm/eco_sci/eco_sc.html. Ed. Masayoshi Tomosugi. Circ: 900.

330 JPN ISSN 0387-7310
KEIZAI KAGAKU RONSHU/SHIMANE UNIVERSITY. FACULTY OF LAW AND LITERATURE. MEMOIRS. Text in Japanese. 1975. a. **Document type:** *Academic/Scholarly.*
—BLDSC (4973.087000).
Published by: Shimane Daigaku, Hobungakubu/Shimane University, Faculty of Law and Literature, 1060 Nishi-Kawazu-Machi, Matsue-shi, Shimane-ken 690-0000, Japan.

330 JPN ISSN 0022-9733
HB9
KEIZAI KENKYU/ECONOMIC REVIEW (TOKYO, 1950). Text in English, Japanese. 1950. q. JPY 6,300. adv. bk.rev. bibl.; illus.; stat.
Indexed: AmH&L, HistAb, JEL, RASB.
Published by: (Hitotsubashi Daigaku/Hitotsubashi University, Keizai Kenkyujo), Iwanami Shoten, Publishers, 2-5-5 Hitotsubashi, Chiyoda-ku, Tokyo, 101-0003, Japan. FAX 81-3-239-9618. Ed. R Minami. Circ: 1,500. **Dist. overseas by:** Japan Publications Trading Co., Ltd., Book Export II Dept, PO Box 5030, Tokyo International, Tokyo 101-3191, Japan. TEL 81-3-32923753, FAX 81-3-32920410, infoserials@jptco.co.jp, http://www.jptco.co.jp.

330 JPN ISSN 0022-9741
HB9
KEIZAI SHIRIN/HOSEI UNIVERSITY ECONOMIC REVIEW. Text in Japanese. 1925. q. JPY 3,200 (effective 2001). bk.rev.
Document type: *Journal, Academic/Scholarly.*
Indexed: AmH&L, HistAb.
Published by: Hosei Daigaku, Keizai Gakkai/Hosei University, Economics Society, 4342 Aihara-Machi, Machida-shi, Tokyo-to 194-2098, Japan. TEL 81-427-83-2517, FAX 81-427-83-2611. Ed. Hajime Kiyohara.

330 JPN ISSN 0451-6265
HB9
KEIZAIGAKU KENKYU (SAPPORO)/ECONOMIC STUDIES. Text in Japanese. 1951. q. **Document type:** *Journal, Academic/Scholarly.*
—BLDSC (3655.750000).
Published by: Hokkaido University, Graduate School of Economics and Business Administration, Kita 9, Nishi 7, Kita-ku, Sapporo, 060-0809, Japan. TEL 81-11-706-4058, FAX 81-11-706-4947, keizai@pop.econ.hokudai.ac.jp, http://www.hokudai.ac.jp/catalog/02-03/f_g/03_04/03_04_051-052.html.

330 JPN ISSN 0022-975X
HB9
KEIZAIGAKU KENKYU (TOKYO)✶ /JOURNAL OF POLITICAL ECONOMY. Text in Japanese. 1931. bi-m. per issue exchange basis. bk.rev. cum.index.
Indexed: HistAb, RASB.
—BLDSC (5040.880000).
Published by: Keizai Riron Gakkai/Society of Political Economy, c/o Rikkyo Daigaku Keizaigakubu, 3 Ikebukuro, Toshima-ku, Tokyo, 171-0014, Japan. Ed. Senzo Hidemura. Circ: (controlled).

330 JPN ISSN 0453-4778
KEIZAIGAKU RONSAN/JOURNAL OF ECONOMICS. Text in Japanese. 1960. bi-m. **Document type:** *Academic/Scholarly.*
Indexed: HistAb.
Published by: Chuo Daigaku, Keizaigaku Kenkyukai/Chuo University, Economic Society, 742 Higashi-Nakano, Hachioji-shi, Tokyo-to 192-0351, Japan. Ed. Toshihiko Aono.

330 JPN ISSN 0022-9768
HB9
KEIZAIGAKU RONSHU/JOURNAL OF ECONOMICS. Text in Japanese. 1931. q. JPY 5,200. bk.rev. stat. cum.index.
Document type: *Academic/Scholarly.*
Indexed: AmH&L, CREJ, HistAb, IBSS, RASB.
Published by: (University of Tokyo/Tokyo Daigaku Soryushi Butsuri Kokusai Kenkyu Senta, School of Economics), University of Tokyo, Graduate School of Science, Chirigaku Kyoshitsu, 3-1, Hongo 7-chome, Bunkyo-ku, Tokyo, 113-0033, Japan. Circ: (controlled). **Dist. by:** Business Center for Academic Societies Japan, 5-16-19 Honkomagome, Bunkyo-ku, Tokyo 113-0021, Japan. TEL 81-3-58145811, 81-3-58145822.

330 JPN ISSN 0910-8858
HC10
KEIZAIJIN. Text in Japanese. 1947. m. **Document type:** *Bulletin.*
Published by: Kansai Economic Federation, Nakanoshima Center Bldg, 6-2-27 Nakanoshima, Kita-ku, Osaka-shi, 530-0005, Japan. TEL 81-6-441-0105, FAX 81-6-443-5347. Ed. A Sakurauchi. Circ: 2,600.

330 JPN
KEIZAIKAI. Text in Japanese. 1972. s-m. JPY 7,900. adv. bk.rev.
Formerly: Economic World
Published by: Keizaikai Co. Ltd., 11 Mori Bldg, 2-6-4 Toranomon, Minato-ku, Tokyo, 105-0001, Japan. Ed. Yuzo Yasuda. Circ: 156,000.

KEJI JINBU YU DUICE/SCIENCE & TECHNOLOGY PROGRESS AND POLICY. see *SCIENCES: COMPREHENSIVE WORKS*

330.9 USA
KENTUCKY ANNUAL ECONOMIC REPORT (YEAR). Text in English. 1972. a. single copy free. back issues avail.
Document type: *Academic/Scholarly.* **Description:** Analysis of Kentucky's economy, including trends for personal income, employment and earnings by industry.
Former titles: Commonwealth of Kentucky. Annual Economic Report (Year); Kentucky. Council of Economic Advisors. Annual Report (0270-238X)
Published by: Center for Business & Economic Research, 335BA Gatton B & E Bldg, University of Kentucky, Lexington, KY 40506-0036. TEL 606-257-7675, FAX 606-257-7671. Ed., R&P Steven N Allen. Circ: 1,800.

330 USA ISSN 0279-5388
KENTUCKY JOURNAL OF COMMERCE & INDUSTRY. Text in English. 1959. bi-w. USD 5; free to members (effective 2005). adv. **Document type:** *Newspaper, Trade.* **Description:** Covers topics of interest to the business and industry community in Kentucky.
Published by: Associated Industries of Kentucky, 2303 Greene Way, Louisville, KY 40220-4009. TEL 502-491-4737, FAX 502-491-5322, aik@aik.com. Ed. Steven P. Bullard. adv.: page USD 450. Circ: 6,000 (paid and free).

330 USA ISSN 0734-4058
HC107.K4
THE KENTUCKY JOURNAL OF ECONOMICS AND BUSINESS. Text in English. 1980. a.
Related titles: Online - full text ed.: (from ProQuest Information & Learning).
Published by: Kentucky Economic Association, c/o Tom Cate, Department of Economics, Finance, and Information Systems, Northern Kentucky University, Highland Heights, KY 41099. cate@nku.edu, http://people.morehead-st.edu/fs/t.creahan/kea.htm.

330 338 USA
THE KENTUCKY MANUFACTURER. Text in English. 1982. m. USD 25 (effective 1999). adv.
Related titles: Online - full text ed.
Indexed: BusDate.
Published by: Industrial Marketing, Inc., PO Box 4310, Lexington, KY 40544-4310. TEL 800-264-3303, FAX 606-223-6709, webmaster@industrysearch.com. Ed., R&P Kevin Kerfoot. Pub. David Zaluski. Adv. contact David Braun. Circ: 11,000.

330 KEN
KENYA. CENTRAL BUREAU OF STATISTICS. LEADING ECONOMIC INDICATOR. Text in English. 1996. m. KES 3,600 (effective 2001).

Published by: Ministry of Finance and Planning, Central Bureau of Statistics, PO Box 30266, Nairobi, Kenya. TEL 254-2-333970, 254-2-317011, FAX 254-2-333030, http://www.treasury.go.ke.cbs.

330 GBR ISSN 0142-5048
HC252.2
KEY BRITISH ENTERPRISES. Text in English. a. GBP 520 (effective 2000). **Document type:** *Directory.*
Related titles: Online - full text ed.
Published by: Dun & Bradstreet Ltd., 50-100 Holmers Farm Way, High Wycombe, Bucks HP12 4UL, United Kingdom. TEL 44-1494-423689, FAX 44-1494-422332. **Dist. by:** Current Pacific Ltd., PO Box 36-536, Northcote, Auckland, New Zealand. TEL 64-9-480-1388, FAX 64-9-480-1387, info@cplnz.com, http://www.cplnz.com.

330 GBR ISSN 1365-6740
KEY NOTE MARKET REPORT: DESIGN CONSULTANCIES. Variant title: Design Consultancies Market Report. Text in English. 1989. irreg., latest 2000, Feb. GBP 340 per issue (effective 2002). **Description:** Provides an overview of the UK design consultancies market, including industry structure, market size and trends, developments, prospects, and major company profiles.
Formerly (until 1996): Key Note Report: Design Consultancies (0957-347X)
Published by: Key Note Ltd., Field House, 72 Oldfield Rd, Hampton, Mddx TW12 2HQ, United Kingdom. TEL 44-20-8481-8750, FAX 44-20-8783-0049, info@keynote.co.uk, http://www.keynote.co.uk.

330 GBR
KEY RATES AND DATA. Text in English. a. GBP 10.50 (effective 2000). stat. **Document type:** *Trade.*
Related titles: Online - full content ed.; ♦ Series of: Croner's Reference Book for Employers. ISSN 0070-1580.
Published by: Croner.C C H Group Ltd. (Subsidiary of: Wolters Kluwer N.V.), 145 London Rd, Kingston, Surrey KT2 6SR, United Kingdom. TEL 44-20-85473333, FAX 44-20-85472637, info@croner.co.uk, http://www.croner.cch.co.uk.

650.07 USA
KEYING IN. Text in English. 1991. 4/yr. USD 70 domestic to libraries; USD 80 foreign to libraries (effective 2001); includes Business Education Forum and Yearbook. back issues avail. **Document type:** *Newsletter.*
Published by: National Business Education Association, 1914 Association Dr, Reston, VA 20191-1596. TEL 703-860-8300, FAX 703-620-4483. Pub. Janet M Treichel. R&P Noelle C Sotack.

338 NLD
KIJK OP OOST NEDERLAND. Text in Dutch. 1981. 8/yr. EUR 30 (effective 2002). adv. Website rev. illus. **Document type:** *Magazine, Consumer.*
Former titles: Dynamisch Oost Nederland (0921-3619); Dynamisch Overijssel
Published by: Uitgeverij ten Brink BV, Postbus 41, Meppel, 7940 AA, Netherlands. TEL 31-522-855306, FAX 31-522-855300, uitg@gmgroep.nl, http://www.giethoorn-tenbrink.nl. Ed. Karel Koolhoven. R&P Guus Wiggerts TEL 31-522-855305. Adv. contact Marco Neep. Circ: 10,000.

330 SAU ISSN 1018-3582
➤ **KING SAUD UNIVERSITY JOURNAL. ADMINISTRATIVE SCIENCES.** Key Title: Majallat Jami'at al-Malik Sa'ud, al-'Ulum al-Idariyyah. (Other sections avail.: Agricultural Sciences, Architecture and Planning, Arts, Computer and information Sciences, Educational Sciences and Islamic Studies, Engineering Sciences, Science) Text in Arabic, English. 1989. s-a. USD 5 (effective 2001). charts; illus. **Document type:** *Journal, Academic/Scholarly.*
Published by: King Saud University, University Libraries, P O Box 22480, Riyadh, 11495, Saudi Arabia. TEL 966-1-4676148, FAX 966-1-4676162. Ed. Khalid A. Al-Hamoudi. R&P Saad A Al-Dobaian. Circ: 3,000.

330 USA
KINKO'S IMPRESS. Text in English. 2000. irreg.
Media: Online - full text.
Address: http://www.kinkos.com. Ed. Catherine Sabino.

330 RWA
KINYAMATEKA. Text in Kinyarwanda. 1933. fortn.
Address: 5 bd de l'OUA, BP 761, Kigali, Rwanda. TEL 6164. Ed. Andre Sibomana. Circ: 11,000.

330 CHE
KMUBUSINESS MAGAZIN. Text in German. 2002. 9/yr. CHF 60 (effective 2002). adv. **Document type:** *Magazine, Trade.*
Related titles: Online - full text ed.
Published by: Mediax AG, Schneebergstr 7, Sankt Gallen, 9000, Switzerland. TEL 41-71-2264040, FAX 41-71-2264045, redaktion@kmubusiness.ch, info@mediaxag.ch, http://www.kmubusiness.ch, http://www.mediaxag.ch. adv.: page CHF 12,500; trim 225 x 300. Circ: 50,000 (paid and controlled).

KNIGHT'S GUIDE TO BEST VALUE AND PUBLIC PROCUREMENT. see *LAW*

330 ANT
KNOW HOW. Text in English. m.
Published by: Know How Group N.V., Schottegatweg Oost 56, PO Box 473, Willemstad, Curacao, Netherlands Antilles. TEL 367079, FAX 367080.

330 JPN ISSN 0075-6415
KOBE ECONOMIC AND BUSINESS RESEARCH SERIES. Text in English. 1962. irreg., latest vol.15. exchange basis. **Document type:** *Monographic series, Academic/Scholarly.*
Published by: Kobe University, Research Institute for Economics and Business Administration/Kobe Daigaku, Keizai Keiei Kenkyujo, Rokko, Nada-ku, Kobe-shi, Hyogo-ken 657-8501, Japan. TEL 81-78-8037036, FAX 81-78-8037059, kenjo@rieb.kobe-u.ac.jp, http://www.rieb.kobe-u.ac.jp/academic/ra/researchseries/research_ser-j.html. Circ: 400.

330 JPN ISSN 0075-6407
HC461
KOBE ECONOMIC AND BUSINESS REVIEW. Text in English. 1953. a., latest vol.47. exchange basis. **Document type:** *Journal, Academic/Scholarly.* **Description:** Explores business and economic issues worldwide.
Indexed: ATI, BAS, CREJ, IBSS, JEL, RASB.
Published by: Kobe University, Research Institute for Economics and Business Administration/Kobe Daigaku, Keizai Keiei Kenkyujo, Rokko, Nada-ku, Kobe-shi, Hyogo-ken 657-8501, Japan. TEL 81-78-8037036, FAX 81-78-8037059, kenjo@rieb.kobe-u.ac.jp, http://www.rieb.kobe-u.ac.jp/academic/ra/researchseries/review.html. Circ: 550.

330 JPN ISSN 0454-1111
HB9
➤ **KOBE UNIVERSITY ECONOMIC REVIEW.** Text in English. 1955. a. per issue exchange basis. **Document type:** *Academic/Scholarly.* **Description:** Publishes research and analysis in all economic topics areas by faculty members.
Indexed: APEL, BAS, CREJ, IBR, IBZ, JEL, KES.
—BLDSC (5100.611000), IE, ingenta.
Published by: Kobe University, Graduate School of Economics/Kobe Daigaku, Keizai Gakubu, Rokko-Dai-cho, Nada-ku, Kobe-shi, Hyogo-ken 657-0013, Japan. TEL 81-78-803-6854, FAX 81-78-803-7293, ekenjo2@rose.rokkodai.kobe-u.ac.jp. Eds. Kazuhiro Ohtani, Koji Shinjo. Circ: 650.

330 JPN
KOBE UNIVERSITY. RESEARCH INSTITUTE FOR ECONOMICS AND BUSINESS ADMINISTRATION. ANNALS OF ECONOMICS AND BUSINESS. Text in Japanese. irreg. **Document type:** *Monographic series, Academic/Scholarly.*
Related titles: Online - full content ed.
Published by: Kobe University, Research Institute for Economics and Business Administration/Kobe Daigaku, Keizai Keiei Kenkyujo, Rokko, Nada-ku, Kobe-shi, Hyogo-ken 657-8501, Japan. TEL 81-78-8037036, FAX 81-78-8037059, kenjo@rieb.kobe-u.ac.jp, http://www.rieb.kobe-u.ac.jp/academic/ra/researchseries/annual-j.html.

330 621.9 JPN
KOBE UNIVERSITY. RESEARCH INSTITUTE FOR ECONOMICS AND BUSINESS ADMINISTRATION. BUSINESS MACHINE SERIES. Text in Japanese. irreg. **Document type:** *Monographic series, Academic/Scholarly.*
Related titles: Online - full content ed.
Published by: Kobe University, Research Institute for Economics and Business Administration/Kobe Daigaku, Keizai Keiei Kenkyujo, Rokko, Nada-ku, Kobe-shi, Hyogo-ken 657-8501, Japan. TEL 81-78-8037036, FAX 81-78-8037059, kenjo@rieb.kobe-u.ac.jp, http://www.rieb.kobe-u.ac.jp/academic/ra/researchseries/mechanization-j.html.

330 JPN ISSN 1345-2207
KOBE UNIVERSITY. RESEARCH INSTITUTE FOR ECONOMICS AND BUSINESS ADMINISTRATION. DISCUSSION PAPER SERIES (ENGLISH EDITION). Text in English. 1975. irreg. **Document type:** *Monographic series, Academic/Scholarly.*
Formerly (until 1991): Kobe University. Research Institute for Economics and Business Administration. Discussion Paper (English Edition) (0917-2645)
Related titles: Online - full content ed.; ♦ Japanese ed.: Kobe University. Research Institute for Economics and Business Administration. Discussion Paper Series (Japanese Edition). ISSN 1345-2215.
Published by: Kobe University, Research Institute for Economics and Business Administration/Kobe Daigaku, Keizai Keiei Kenkyujo, Rokko, Nada-ku, Kobe-shi, Hyogo-ken 657-8501, Japan. TEL 81-78-8037036, FAX 81-78-8037059, kenjo@rieb.kobe-u.ac.jp, http://www.rieb.kobe-u.ac.jp/academic/ra/dp/index.html.

330 JPN ISSN 1345-2215
KOBE UNIVERSITY. RESEARCH INSTITUTE FOR ECONOMICS AND BUSINESS ADMINISTRATION. DISCUSSION PAPER SERIES (JAPANESE EDITION). Text in Japanese. 1988. irreg. **Document type:** *Monographic series, Academic/Scholarly.*
Formerly (until 1990): Kobe University. Research Institute for Economics and Business Administration. Discussion Paper (Japanese Edition) (0917-2653)
Related titles: Online - full content ed.; ♦ English ed.: Kobe University. Research Institute for Economics and Business Administration. Discussion Paper Series (English Edition). ISSN 1345-2207.
Published by: Kobe University, Research Institute for Economics and Business Administration/Kobe Daigaku, Keizai Keiei Kenkyujo, Rokko, Nada-ku, Kobe-shi, Hyogo-ken 657-8501, Japan. TEL 81-78-8037036, FAX 81-78-8037059, kenjo@rieb.kobe-u.ac.jp, http://www.rieb.kobe-u.ac.jp/academic/ra/dp/index-j.html.

330 JPN
KOBE UNIVERSITY. RESEARCH INSTITUTE FOR ECONOMICS AND BUSINESS ADMINISTRATION. MONETARY RESEARCH SERIES. Text in Japanese. irreg. **Document type:** *Monographic series, Academic/Scholarly.*
Related titles: Online - full content ed.
Published by: Kobe University, Research Institute for Economics and Business Administration/Kobe Daigaku, Keizai Keiei Kenkyujo, Rokko, Nada-ku, Kobe-shi, Hyogo-ken 657-8501, Japan. TEL 81-78-8037036, FAX 81-78-8037059, kenjo@rieb.kobe-u.ac.jp, http://www.rieb.kobe-u.ac.jp/academic/ra/researchseries/monetary-j.html.

330 JPN
KODO SEICHO KI HE NO SHOGEN. Text in Japanese. irreg., latest 1999. **Document type:** *Monographic series, Academic/Scholarly.*
—BLDSC (5100.722200).
Published by: Economist Henshubu, 3-2, Kanda-Jimbocho, Chiyoda-ku, Tokyo, 101-0051, Japan. TEL 81-3-32301661, FAX 81-3-32652993, nikkeihy@js7.so-net.ne.jp, http://www.nikkeihyo.co.jp/.

330 DNK ISSN 0906-0669
KOEBENHAVNS UNIVERSITET. OEKONOMISK INSTITUT. CYKELAFDELINGEN. MEMO. Text in Danish, English. 1958. irreg.
Former titles (until 1990): Koebenhavns Universitet. Oekonomisk Institut. Gult Memo (0904-0943); (until 1987): Koebenhavns Universitet. Oekonomiske Institut. Cyckelafdelingen. Memo (0902-0128); Supersedes in Part (in 1972): Koebenhavns Universitet. Oekonomisk Institut. Memorandum
Published by: Koebenhavns Universitet, Oekonomisk Institut (Subsidiary of: Cykelafdelingen), Studiestraede 6, Copenhagen K, 1455, Denmark.

330 DNK ISSN 0107-3664
KOEBENHAVNS UNIVERSITET. OEKONOMISK INSTITUT. MEMO. Variant title: Koebenhavns Universitet. Oekonomisk Institut. Blaat Memo. Text in Danish, English. 1958. irreg. illus.
Supersedes in part (in 1972): Koebenhavns Universitet. Oekonomiske Institut. Memorandum (0574-0045)
Published by: Koebenhavns Universitet, Oekonomisk Institut (Subsidiary of: Cykelafdelingen), Studiestraede 6, Copenhagen K, 1455, Denmark.

330 DNK ISSN 0108-2221
KOEBENHAVNS UNIVERSITET. OEKONOMISK INSTITUT. ROED SERIE. Text in Danish, English. 1981. irreg.
Published by: Koebenhavns Universitet, Oekonomisk Institut (Subsidiary of: Cykelafdelingen), Studiestraede 6, Copenhagen K, 1455, Denmark.

330 JPN ISSN 0288-6340
HB9
KOKUGAKUIN UNIVERSITY ECONOMIC REVIEW/ KOKUGAKUIN KEIZAIGAKU. Text in Japanese. 1966 (vol.15). q. JPY 2,000. bk.rev. **Document type:** *Academic/Scholarly.*
Formerly: Seikei Ronso - Faculty of Politics, Law and Economics. Journal (0582-4192)
Indexed: AmH&L, HistAb.
Published by: Kokugakuin University, Faculty of Economics, 4-10-28 Higashi, Shibuya-ku, Tokyo, Japan. TEL 03-5466-0342, FAX 03-5466-2340. Ed. Ichiro Nagai. Pub. Makoto Iki. Circ: 2,000.

330 JPN ISSN 0387-3129
HC461
KOKUMIN KEIZAI ZASSHI/JOURNAL OF ECONOMICS & BUSINESS ADMINISTRATION. Text in English. 1906. m. **Document type:** *Journal, Academic/Scholarly.*
Indexed: JEL.
Published by: Kobe University, Research Institute for Economics and Business Administration/Kobe Daigaku, Keizai Keiei Kenkyujo, Rokko, Nada-ku, Kobe-shi, Hyogo-ken 657-8501, Japan. TEL 81-78-8037036, FAX 81-78-8037059, kenjo@rieb.kobe-u.ac.jp, http://www.rieb.kobe-u.ac.jp/kokumin/index.html.

330 JPN ISSN 0389-9861
KOMAZAWA DAIGAKU KEIZAI GAKUBU KENKYU KIYO/KOMAZAWA UNIVERSITY. FACULTY OF ECONOMICS. JOURNAL. Text in Japanese. 1955. a. **Document type:** *Journal, Academic/Scholarly.*
Formerly (until 1967): Komazawa Daigaku Shokei Gakubu Kenkyu Kiyo/Kamazawa University. Faculty of Commerce and Economics. Journal (0452-3644); Which superseded in part (in 1960): Komazawa Daigaku Kenkyu Kiyo (0452-361X)

Published by: Komazawa Daigaku, Keizai Gakubu/Komazawa University, Faculty of Economics, 1-23-1 Komazawa, Setagaya-ku, Tokyo, 154-8525, Japan. TEL 81-3-34189343, http://www.komazawa-u.ac.jp/gakubu/keizai/index.html.

KOMMENTARII. see POLITICAL SCIENCE

330   RUS
KOMMERCHESKIE VESTI. Text in Russian. w. Document type: Newspaper, Consumer.
Published by: Izdatelskii Dom Kommercheskie Vesti, Ul Gagarina 8, Omsk, 644099, Russian Federation. TEL 7-3812-240053, omskbusinessnews@infomsk.ru. Ed. Marat Isangazin. Circ: 6,000.

330   RUS
KOMMERSANT. Text in Russian. 1989. d. USD 250 foreign (effective 2005); includes online ed.. Document type: Newspaper, Consumer.
Related titles: Microfiche ed.: (from EVP); Microfilm ed.: (from EVP); Online - full text ed.: USD 250 foreign (effective 2003); Regional ed(s).: Kommersant S-Peterburg.
Indexed: B&I, RASB.
Published by: Izdatel'skii Dom Kommersant, ul Vrubelya 4, str 1, Moscow, 125080, Russian Federation. TEL 7-095-9439771, FAX 7-095-9439728, kommersant@kommersant.ru, http://www.kommersant.ru. Ed. Andrey Vasilyev. Pub. Boris Berezovsky. Circ: 117,000 (paid and controlled).

330   RUS
KOMMERSANT - DEN'GI. Text in Russian. w. USD 150 foreign (effective 2004). Document type: Magazine, Consumer.
Published by: Izdatel'skii Dom Kommersant, ul Vrubelya 4, str 1, Moscow, 125080, Russian Federation. TEL 7-095-9439771, 7-095-9439750, FAX 7-095-9439728, dengi@kommersant.ru, kommersant@kommersant.ru, http://www.kommersant.ru. Ed. Sergei Yakovlev. US dist. addr.: East View Information Services, 3020 Harbor Ln. N., Minneapolis, MN 55447. TEL 763-550-0961, FAX 763-559-2931, eastview@eastview.com, http://www.eastview.com.

330   MDA
KOMMERSANT MOLDOVY. Text in Moldavian. w. USD 249 in United States.
Address: Vlaiku Pyrkelab 45, 5-i etazh, Kishinev, Moldova. TEL 0422-229662, FAX 0422-221274, kp@kp.md. Ed. Artem Varenitsa. US dist. addr.: East View Information Services, 3020 Harbor Ln. N., Minneapolis, MN 55447. TEL 612-550-0961.

330   RUS
KOMMERSANT - VLAST'. Text in Russian. w. USD 150 foreign (effective 2004). Document type: Magazine, Consumer.
Published by: Izdatel'skii Dom Kommersant, ul Vrubelya 4, str 1, Moscow, 125080, Russian Federation. TEL 7-095-9439771, 7-095-9439750, FAX 7-095-9439728, vlast@kommersant.ru, kommersant@kommersant.ru, http://www.kommersant.ru. Ed. R Artem'ev. Circ: 73,100. US dist. addr.: East View Information Services, 3020 Harbor Ln. N., Minneapolis, MN 55447. TEL 763-550-0961, FAX 763-559-2931, eastview@eastview.com, http://www.eastview.com.

330   TJK
KOMPANION. Text in Russian. 1996. w. USD 345 in North America.
Published by: Redaktsiya Kompanion, Bohtar 35-1, Dushanbe, 734002, Tajikistan. TEL 21-29-82, FAX 21-29-82. Ed. Natal'ei Bruker. Dist. by: East View Information Services, 3020 Harbor Ln. N., Minneapolis, MN 55447. TEL 763-550-0961, FAX 763-559-2931.

330   RUS
KOMPANIYA. Text in Russian. 1998. w. USD 175 in North America.
Published by: Izdatel'skii Dom Kur'er, 1-ya Tverskaya-Yamskaya ul 29, Moscow, 125047, Russian Federation. TEL 7-095-2509269, FAX 7-095-2509565. Dist. by: East View Information Services, 3020 Harbor Ln. N., Minneapolis, MN 55447. TEL 763-550-0961, FAX 763-559-2931.

332   UKR
KOMP&N'ON. Text in Russian. 1996. w. stat. Document type: Journal.
Related titles: Online - full content ed.
Published by: Kompan'on, Ul Kikvidze 39, Kiev, 252103, Ukraine. TEL 38-44-2676482, komp@maximum.com.ua, http://www.maximum.com.ua/main/. Ed. Aleksei Valer'evich Pogorelov.

KOMPASS BUSINESS SERVICES AND TRANSPORT. see BUSINESS AND ECONOMICS—Trade And Industrial Directories

KOMPASS DIRECTORY. see PLASTICS

330   FRA   ISSN 0295-7965
KOMPASS REGIONAL ECONOMIQUE ET INDUSTRIEL. ALSACE. Text in French. 1960. a. adv. Document type: Directory.
Formerly (until 1982): Inventaire Regional Economique et Industriel. Alsace (0240-4753)

Published by: Kompass France, 66 quai du Marechal Joffre, Courbevoie, Cedex 92415, France. TEL 33-1-41165100, FAX 33-1-41165156, infos@kompass-france.com, http://www.kompass.fr. Ed., Pub., R&P Bertrand Macabeo. Adv. contact Philippe Leroux.

330   FRA   ISSN 0295-7981
KOMPASS REGIONAL ECONOMIQUE ET INDUSTRIEL. AQUITAINE. Text in French. 1979. a. adv. Document type: Directory.
Formerly (until 1982): Inventaire Regional Economique et Industriel. Aquitaine (0245-1158)
Published by: Kompass France, 66 quai du Marechal Joffre, Courbevoie, Cedex 92415, France. TEL 33-1-41165100, FAX 33-1-41165156, infos@kompass-france.com, http://www.kompass.fr. Ed., Pub., R&P Bertrand Macabeo. Adv. contact Philippe Leroux.

330   FRA   ISSN 0295-7957
KOMPASS REGIONAL ECONOMIQUE ET INDUSTRIEL. AUVERGNE. Text in French. 1960. a. adv. Document type: Directory.
Formerly (until 1982): Inventaire Regional Economique et Industriel de l'Auvergne (0183-8040)
Related titles: ◆ Series of: Bibliotheque de la S E L A F. ISSN 0249-7050.
Published by: Kompass France, 66 quai du Marechal Joffre, Courbevoie, Cedex 92415, France. TEL 33-1-41165100, FAX 33-1-41165156, infos@kompass-france.com, http://www.kompass.fr. Ed., Pub., R&P Bertrand Macabeo. Adv. contact Philippe Leroux.

330   FRA   ISSN 0295-7922
KOMPASS REGIONAL ECONOMIQUE ET INDUSTRIEL. BOURGOGNE. Text in French. 1960. a. adv. Document type: Directory.
Formerly (until 1982): Inventaire Regional Economique et Industriel. Bourgogne (0245-1166)
Published by: Kompass France, 66 quai du Marechal Joffre, Courbevoie, Cedex 92415, France. TEL 33-1-41165100, FAX 33-1-41165156, infos@kompass-france.com, http://www.kompass.fr. Ed., Pub., R&P Bertrand Macabeo. Adv. contact Philippe Leroux.

330   FRA   ISSN 0759-3929
KOMPASS REGIONAL ECONOMIQUE ET INDUSTRIEL. BRETAGNE. Text in French. 1960. a. adv. Document type: Directory.
Published by: Kompass France, 66 quai du Marechal Joffre, Courbevoie, Cedex 92415, France. TEL 33-1-41165100, FAX 33-1-41165156, infos@kompass-france.com, http://www.kompass.fr. Ed., Pub., R&P Bertrand Macabeo. Adv. contact Philippe Leroux.

330   FRA   ISSN 0759-3910
KOMPASS REGIONAL ECONOMIQUE ET INDUSTRIEL. CENTRE. Text in French. 1960. a. adv. Document type: Directory.
Published by: Kompass France, 66 quai du Marechal Joffre, Courbevoie, Cedex 92415, France. TEL 33-1-41165100, FAX 33-1-41165156, infos@kompass-france.com, http://www.kompass.fr. Ed., Pub., R&P Bertrand Macabeo. Adv. contact Philippe Leroux.

330   FRA   ISSN 0295-7930
KOMPASS REGIONAL ECONOMIQUE ET INDUSTRIEL. CHAMPAGNE - ARDENNES. Text in French. 1960. a. adv. Document type: Directory.
Formerly (until 1982): Inventaire Regional Economique et Industriel. Champagne - Ardennes (0183-8059)
Published by: Kompass France, 66 quai du Marechal Joffre, Courbevoie, Cedex 92415, France. TEL 33-1-41165100, FAX 33-1-41165156, infos@kompass-france.com, http://www.kompass.fr. Ed., Pub., R&P Bertrand Macabeo. Adv. contact Philippe Leroux.

330   FRA   ISSN 0295-7949
KOMPASS REGIONAL ECONOMIQUE ET INDUSTRIEL. FRANCHE-COMTE. Text in French. 1960. a. adv. Document type: Directory.
Formerly (until 1982): Inventaire Regional Economique et Industriel. Franche-Comte (0245-1174)
Published by: Kompass France, 66 quai du Marechal Joffre, Courbevoie, Cedex 92415, France. TEL 33-1-41165100, FAX 33-1-41165156, infos@kompass-france.com, http://www.kompass.fr. Ed., Pub., R&P Bertrand Macabeo. Adv. contact Philippe Leroux.

330   FRA   ISSN 0759-3813
KOMPASS REGIONAL ECONOMIQUE ET INDUSTRIEL. ILE-DE-FRANCE. Text in French. 1930. a. adv. Document type: Directory.
Formerly (until 1982): Inventaire Regional Economique et Industriel. Ile-de-France (0759-3805); Which was formed by the merger of: Inventaire Regional Economique et Industriel de l'Ile-de-France. Petite Couronne de Paris (0152-9684); Inventaire Regional Economique et Industriel de l'Ile-de-France. Grande Couronne de Paris (0152-9676)
Published by: Kompass France, 66 quai du Marechal Joffre, Courbevoie, Cedex 92415, France. TEL 33-1-41165100, FAX 33-1-41165156, http://kompass.fr/. Ed., Pub., R&P Bertrand Macabeo. Adv. contact Philippe Leroux.

330   FRA   ISSN 0295-7795
KOMPASS REGIONAL ECONOMIQUE ET INDUSTRIEL. LANGUEDOC - ROUSSILLON. Text in French. 1960. a. adv. Document type: Directory.
Published by: Kompass France, 66 quai du Marechal Joffre, Courbevoie, Cedex 92415, France. TEL 33-1-41165100, FAX 33-1-41165156, infos@kompass-france.com, http://www.kompass.fr. Ed., Pub., R&P Bertrand Macabeo. Adv. contact Philippe Leroux.

330   FRA   ISSN 0759-4755
KOMPASS REGIONAL ECONOMIQUE ET INDUSTRIEL. LIMOUSIN, POITOU - CHARENTES. Text in French. 1960. a. adv. Document type: Directory.
Former titles (until 1981): Qui Vend Quoi? Qui Achete Quoi? Limousin, Poitou, Charentes (0184-4024); (until 1977): Annuaire des Entreprises Regionales. Limousin, Poitou - Charentes (0184-4032)
Published by: Kompass France, 66 quai du Marechal Joffre, Courbevoie, Cedex 92415, France. TEL 33-1-41165100, FAX 33-1-41165156, infos@kompass-france.com, http://www.kompass.fr. Ed., Pub., R&P Bertrand Macabeo. Adv. contact Philippe Leroux.

330   FRA   ISSN 0295-7914
KOMPASS REGIONAL ECONOMIQUE ET INDUSTRIEL. LORRAINE. Text in French. 1960. a. adv. Document type: Directory.
Formerly (until 1982): Inventaire Regional Economique et Industriel. Lorraine (0752-7187)
Published by: Kompass France, 66 quai du Marechal Joffre, Courbevoie, Cedex 92415, France. TEL 33-1-41165100, FAX 33-1-41165156, infos@kompass-france.com, http://www.kompass.fr. Ed., Pub., R&P Bertrand Macabeo. Adv. contact Philippe Leroux.

330   FRA   ISSN 0295-7787
KOMPASS REGIONAL ECONOMIQUE ET INDUSTRIEL. MIDI-PYRENEES. Text in French. 1960. a. adv. Document type: Directory.
Published by: Kompass France, 66 quai du Marechal Joffre, Courbevoie, Cedex 92415, France. TEL 33-1-41165100, FAX 33-1-41165156, infos@kompass-france.com, http://www.kompass.fr. Ed., Pub., R&P Bertrand Macabeo. Adv. contact Philippe Leroux.

330   FRA   ISSN 0295-7973
KOMPASS REGIONAL ECONOMIQUE ET INDUSTRIEL. NORD, PAS-DE-CALAIS. Text in French. 1960. a. adv. Document type: Directory.
Formerly (until 1982): Inventaire Regional Economique et Industriel du Nord et du Pas-de-Calais (0152-9692)
Published by: Kompass France, 66 quai du Marechal Joffre, Courbevoie, Cedex 92415, France. TEL 33-1-41165100, FAX 33-1-41165156, infos@kompass-france.com, http://www.kompass.fr. Ed., Pub., R&P Bertrand Macabeo. Adv. contact Philippe Leroux.

330   FRA   ISSN 0752-9309
KOMPASS REGIONAL ECONOMIQUE ET INDUSTRIEL. NORMANDIE. Text in French. 1960. a. adv. Document type: Directory.
Formerly (until 1982): Inventaire Regional Economique et Industriel. Normandie (0752-7179)
Published by: Kompass France, 66 quai du Marechal Joffre, Courbevoie, Cedex 92415, France. TEL 33-1-41165100, FAX 33-1-41165156, infos@kompass-france.com, http://www.kompass.fr. Ed., Pub., R&P Bertrand Macabeo. Adv. contact Philippe Leroux.

330   FRA   ISSN 0759-5506
KOMPASS REGIONAL ECONOMIQUE ET INDUSTRIEL. PICARDIE. Text in French. 1960. a. adv. Document type: Directory.
Formerly (until 1982): Inventaire Regional Economique et Industriel. Picardie (0245-1182)
Published by: Kompass France, 66 quai du Marechal Joffre, Courbevoie, Cedex 92415, France. TEL 33-1-41165100, FAX 33-1-41165156, infos@kompass-france.com, http://www.kompass.fr. Ed., Pub., R&P Bertrand Macabeo. Adv. contact Philippe Leroux.

330   FRA   ISSN 0759-3686
KOMPASS REGIONAL ECONOMIQUE ET INDUSTRIEL. PROVENCE, ALPES, COTE-D'AZUR, CORSE. Text in French. 1960. a. adv. Document type: Directory.
Published by: Kompass France, 66 quai du Marechal Joffre, Courbevoie, Cedex 92415, France. TEL 33-1-41165100, FAX 33-1-41165156, infos@kompass-france.com, http://www.kompass.fr. Ed., Pub., R&P Bertrand Macabeo. Adv. contact Philippe Leroux.

330   FRA   ISSN 0752-921X
KOMPASS REGIONAL ECONOMIQUE ET INDUSTRIEL. RHONE - ALPES. Text in French. 1960. a. adv. Document type: Directory.
Formerly (until 1982): Inventaire Regional Economique et Industriel. Rhone - Alpes (0752-9201); Which was formed by the merger of: Inventaire Regional Economique et Industriel. Alpes (0240-4745); Inventaire Regional Economique et Industriel. Rhone - Loire

Published by: Kompass France, 66 quai du Marechal Joffre, Courbevoie, Cedex 92415, France. TEL 33-1-41165100, FAX 33-1-41165156, infos@kompass-france.com, http://www.kompass.fr. Ed., Pub., R&P Bertrand Macabeo. Adv. contact Philippe Leroux.

330 FRA ISSN 1767-6509
KOMPASS REGIONAL. PAYS DE LA LOIRE. Text in French. 1960. a. adv. **Document type:** *Directory.*
Former titles (until 2001): Kompass Regional Economique et Industriel. Pays de la Loire (0295-7906); (until 1982): Inventaire Regional Economique et Industriel. Pays-de-la-Loire (0752-7195)
Published by: Kompass France, 66 quai du Marechal Joffre, Courbevoie, Cedex 92415, France. TEL 33-1-41165100, FAX 33-1-41165156, infos@kompass-france.com, http://www.kompass.fr. Ed., Pub., R&P Bertrand Macabeo. Adv. contact Philippe Leroux.

332 338 FRA
KOMPASS REGIONAUX. Text in French. 1960. a. (in 19 vols.). price varies. adv. charts; stat. **Document type:** *Directory.*
Formerly: Inventaires Economiques et Industriels Regionaux
Published by: Kompass France, 66 quai du Marechal Joffre, Courbevoie, Cedex 92415, France. TEL 33-1-41165100, FAX 33-1-41165156, infos@kompass-france.com, http://www.kompass.fr. Ed., Pub., R&P Bertrand Macabeo. Adv. contact Philippe Leroux.

330 634 710 DNK ISSN 0909-0703
KONGELIGE VETERINAER- OG LANDBOHOEJSKOLE. INSTITUT FOR OEKONOMI, SKOV OG LANDSKAB. SAMFUNDSVIDENSKABELIG MEMO-SERIE/SOCIAL SCIENCE RESEARCH PAPERS. Text and summaries in Danish. 1994. irreg. **Document type:** *Monographic series.*
Published by: Kongelige Veterinaer- og Landbohoejskole, Institut for Oekonomi, Skov og Landskab/Royal Veterinary and Agricultural University. Department of Economics and Natural Resources, Rolighedsvej 23, Frederiksberg C, 1958, Denmark. TEL 45-35-28-22-15, FAX 45-35-28-26-71.

330 HUN ISSN 1586-2534
KONJUNKTURBERICHTE. Text in Hungarian, German. 1994. a.
Indexed: PAIS.
Published by: Nemet-Magyar Ipari es Kereskedelmi Kamara, Loevohaz u. 30, Budapest, 1024, Hungary. TEL 36-1-345-7600, FAX 36-1-315-0638, ahkung@ahkungarn.hu, http://www.duihk.hu.

330 DEU ISSN 0722-0227
KONJUNKTURINDIKATOREN. Text in German. 1976. m. **Document type:** *Bulletin.*
Published by: I F O Institut fuer Wirtschaftsforschung, Poschingerstr 5, Munich, 81679, Germany. TEL 49-89-9224-0, FAX 49-89-985369, http://www.ifo.de.

330 RUS
KONTINENT - SIBIR; regionalnaya delovaya gazeta. Text in Russian. d. (Mon.-Fri.). back issues avail. **Document type:** *Newspaper, Consumer.*
Published by: Sibir Press, Ul Chelyuskintsev 50, Novisibirsk, 630132, Russian Federation. http://com.sibpress.ru.

330 600 RUS ISSN 0868-6378
HC340.12.Z9
KONVERSIYA/CONVERSION. Text in Russian; Summaries in English. 1990. m. RUR 360 (effective 1998). adv. index. back issues avail.
Related titles: Microfiche ed.: (from EVP).
Indexed: RASB.
—East View.
Published by: Informatsionno-analiticheskaya i Izdatel'skaya Firma (IZANA), Izmailovskii Ostrov, Ofitserskii Korpus, Moscow, 105037, Russian Federation. TEL 7-095-1654827, FAX 7-095-1660818. Ed. Dmitri V Birukov. adv.: page USD 2,000. Circ: 5,000. **US dist. addr.:** East View Information Services, 3020 Harbor Ln. N., Minneapolis, MN 55447. TEL 763-550-0961, FAX 763-559-2931, eastview@eastview.com, http://www.eastview.com.

330 DEU
KONZERN STRUKTUR - DATENBANK/GROUP STRUCTURE DATABASE. Text in German. back issues avail. **Description:** Publishes information on companies and their relationships.
Media: Online - full text. **Related titles:** Fax ed.
Published by: Hoppenstedt Bonnier Zeitschriften GmbH, Havelstr. 9, Darmstadt, 64295, Germany. TEL 49-6151-380-267, FAX 49-6151-380131, konzernstrukturen@hopp.de.

330 CAN ISSN 0842-098X
KOOTENAY BUSINESS MAGAZINE. Text in English. 1988. m. free to qualified personnel in Kootenay, Columbia, Boundary, Revelstoke; CND 9.95 elsewhere (effective 2006). **Document type:** *Magazine, Trade.* **Description:** Provides business information about the Kootenays.
Formerly: Kootenay Business Journal (0842-0580)
Published by: Koocanusa Publications Inc, Ste. 100, 100 - 7th Ave. S., Cranbrook, BC V1C 2J4, Canada. TEL 250-426-7253, 800-663-8555, FAX 250-426-4125, info@kpimedia.com, http://www.kootenaybiz.com/, http://koocanusapublications.com/. Pub., Adv. contact Keith Powell. Circ: 9,000 (controlled).

330 KOR
KOREA BUSINESS WORLD. Text in English. 1985. m. adv. **Description:** Covers business and economics in South Korea.
Indexed: BAS.
Published by: Korea Businessworld Ltd., 107-6 Banpo-dong, Seocho-ku, 4-F Suhgun Bldg, Seoul, 137040, Korea, S. TEL 02-5321464, FAX 02-5947663. Pub. Lee Kie Hong. Adv. contact Willard Chang Suk Lee. B&W page USD 3,402, color page USD 5,230; trim 275 x 205. Circ: 40,200.

330 KOR ISSN 1017-8929
KOREA ECONOMIC REPORT. Text in English. 1986. m. KRW 6,000, USD 50 domestic; USD 100 in China & the Far East; USD 108 in India & Southeast Asia; USD 120 in Middle East, Africa & S. America; USD 115 elsewhere (effective 2004). **Document type:** *Magazine, Trade.* **Description:** Covers economic policies, trade and industry issues, and foreign business activity in Korea.
Indexed: IBSS.
Published by: World Media, Inc, Ste 903, Shinsong Bldg, 25-4 Yoido-dong, Youngdungpo-gu, Seoul, 150-010, Korea, S. FAX 82-2-780-1717, ker@economicreport.co.kr, http://www.economicreport.co.kr/. Circ: 35,000.

330 KOR
KOREA ECONOMIC RESEARCH INSTITUTE. RESEARCH PAPER. INDUSTRIAL STUDIES. Text in Korean. 1995. irreg. (3-13/yr.).
Published by: Korea Economic Research Institute, Yeongdungpo-ku, 28-1 Yoido dong, Seoul, 150756, Korea, S. TEL 82-2-3771-0001, FAX 82-2-785-0270, http://www.keri.org.

330 KOR
KOREA ECONOMIC RESEARCH INSTITUTE. RESEARCH PAPER. SPECIAL PROJECTS STUDIES. Text in Korean. 1995. 5/yr.
Published by: Korea Economic Research Institute, Yeongdungpo-ku, 28-1 Yoido dong, Seoul, 150756, Korea, S. TEL 02-3771-0001, FAX 02-785-0270, http://www.keri.org.

330 KOR
KOREAN BUSINESS REVIEW✶. Text in English. 1978. m. free. adv. bk.rev.
Indexed: KES, PAIS, RASB.
Published by: Federation of Korean Industries, c/o Korean Chamber of Commerce & Industry, 45, 4-ka Namdaemun-no, CPO Box 25, Chung-ku, Seoul, Korea, S. TEL 02-780-1801, FAX 02-782-2271, TELEX K 25544 FEKOIS. Ed. Cho Kyu Hah. Adv. contact Kawk Sung Young. color page USD 2,000; trim 255 x 185. Circ: 20,000.

330 KOR ISSN 0023-3978
KOREAN ECONOMIC JOURNAL/KYONGJE NONJIP. Text in Korean. 1962. q. per issue exchange basis. bk.rev. abstr.; bibl. index. **Document type:** *Academic/Scholarly.*
Indexed: APEL, BAS.
Published by: (Institute of Economic Research), Seoul National University, San 56-1 Sinlim-dong, Kwanak-ku, Seoul, 151742, Korea, S. TEL 02-877-1629, FAX 02-888-4454. Ed. Sung Hwi Lee. Circ: 500.

330 USA ISSN 0894-6302
KOREA'S ECONOMY. Text in English. 1985. a. **Description:** Covers Korean economy, security, and trade relations with the United States.
Published by: Korea Economic Institute, 1201 F St., N.W., Suite 910, Washington, DC 20004. TEL 202-464-1982, FAX 202-464-1987, http://www.keia.org/koreaEC.htm.

330 RUS
KORINF. Text in Russian. w. USD 489.95 in United States.
Indexed: RASB.
Published by: Izdatel'skii Tsentr Korinf, Ovchinnikovskaya nab 18-1, Moscow, 113324, Russian Federation. TEL 7-095-2053004, FAX 7-095-2339946. Ed. I F Ermachenkov. **US dist. addr.:** East View Information Services, 3020 Harbor Ln. N., Minneapolis, MN 55447. TEL 612-550-0961.

330 KGZ
KORPORATIVNYI VESTNIK. Text in Russian. m. **Document type:** *Newspaper, Consumer.*
Published by: Tsentr po Korporativnomu Razvitiyu/Corporate Development Center, Chui 106, Bishkek, Kyrgyzstan. TEL 996-312-224507, 996-312-224320, 996-312-662457, FAX 996-312-661664, info@cdc.kg, http://www.kv.cdc.kg/.

330 657 POL ISSN 1428-7382
KOSZTY. Text in Polish. 1997. bi-w. PLZ 119 (effective 2001).
Published by: Grupa Wydawnicza INFOR Sp. z o.o., Ul Okopowa 58/72, Warsaw, 01042, Poland. TEL 48-22-5304208, 48-22-5304450, bok@infor.pl. Ed. Marzena Nikiel. Adv. contact Waldemar Krakowiak.

KOTTKE NATIONAL END OF SEASON SURVEY. see *SPORTS AND GAMES—Outdoor Life*

338 NOR ISSN 0452-7208
KRISTOFER LEHMKUHL FORELESNING. Text in Norwegian. 1958. a. free to conferees. **Document type:** *Journal, Academic/Scholarly.* **Description:** Presents lecture on economics and business administration.
Published by: Norges Handelshoeyskole/Norwegian School of Economics and Business Administration, Helleveien 30, Bergen, 5045, Norway. TEL 47-55-95-92-16, FAX 47-55-959100, TELEX 40642-NHH-N. Circ: 800.

332.632210 DNK ISSN 0905-4472
KURSLISTE FOR DANSKE AKTIESELSKABER OG ANPARTSSELSKABER SAMT GROENLANDSKE SELSKABER. Text in Danish. 1979. a. DKK 475.
Formerly (until 1989): Kursliste og Selskabsfortegnelse for Danske Aktieselskaber og Anpartsselskaber samt Fortegnelse over Groenlandske Selskaber, Foreninger og Filialer af Udenlandske Selskaber (0902-0233); Which was formed by the 1985 merger of: Fortegnelse over Danske Aktieselskaber, Anpartsselskaber, Filialer af Udenlandske Selskaber samt over Foreninger (0106-2085); Kursliste Verdroerende Aktier i Danske Aktieselskaber samt Anparter i Anpartsselskaber (0902-0225)
Published by: Skatteministeriet, Told og Skattestyrelsen, Oestbanegade 123, Copenhagen Oe, 2100, Denmark. TEL 45-35297300.

330 RUS
KUZBASS-INFORM. Text in Russian. 1991. m.
Published by: Institut Ekonomiki, Kemerovskii Otdel, Sovetskii pr 63, kab 59, Kemerovo, 650000, Russian Federation. TEL 25-25-77. Circ: 5,000.

330 658 SWE
KVALITETSMAGASINET. Text in Swedish. 1990. bi-m. SEK 650 (effective 2003). adv.
Formerly (until 1993): Q A Magazine (1101-3796)
Published by: A B Nordreportern, PO Box 104, Umeaa, 90103, Sweden. TEL 46-90-700900, FAX 46-90-142330, info@nordreportern.se, http://www.kvalitetsmagasinet.com, http://www.nordreportern.se. Eds. Catrin Offerman, Anders Pauser TEL 46-90-700901. Adv. contact Christian Sjoestroem.

330 300 BEL ISSN 1573-6202
▼ **KWARTAALSCHRIFT ECONOMIE**; tijdschrift voor algemeen en bedrijfseconomische vraagstukken. Text in Dutch, English, French, German. 2004. 4/yr. adv. bk.rev. charts. index. reprint service avail. from PQC. **Document type:** *Academic/Scholarly.*
Formed by the merger of (1947-2004): Economisch en Sociaal Tijdschrift (0013-0575); (1935-2003): Maandschrift Economie (0013-0486)
Related titles: Microform ed.: (from PQC).
Indexed: DIP, ELLIS, IBR, IBSS, IBZ, JEL, KES, PAIS.
—IE, Infotrieve.
Published by: (Stichting Maandschrift Economie NLD), Universitaire Faculteiten Sint Ignatius te Antwerpen/ Ruusbroecgenootschap, Prinsstraat 13, Antwerp, 2000, Belgium. TEL 32-3-2204723, FAX 32-3-220-4420, lieve.lerno@ufsia.ac.be. Ed. Bruno De Borger. Circ: 1,300.

330 JPN ISSN 0023-6055
HB9
KYOTO UNIVERSITY ECONOMIC REVIEW/KYOTO DAIGAKU KEIZAI GAKUBU KIYO. Variant title: Kyoto University. Faculty of Economics. Memoirs. Text in English. 1926. s-a.
Indexed: APEL, BAS, IBSS, JEL, PAIS, RASB.
Published by: Kyoto University, Faculty of Economics, c/o Economic Research Office, 606 Sakyo-ku, Kyoto-shi, Japan. Circ: 500. **Co-sponsor:** Imperial University of Kyoto. Department of Economics.

330.9 332 COL
L A R F REPORT. ANNUAL. Text in English. 1979. a. free. charts; illus.; stat. **Document type:** *Bulletin.* **Description:** Covers annual economic summary of the international economy and of the five member countries of the LARF: Bolivia, Colombia, Ecuador, Peru and Venezuela.
Formerly: A R F Report. Annual
Related titles: Spanish ed.
Published by: Latin American Reserve Fund/Fondo Latinoamericano de Reservas, Apartado Aereo 241523, Bogota, COND, Colombia. TEL 57-1-285-8511, FAX 57-1-288-1117. Circ: 300.

330 USA
L O H A S JOURNAL. Variant title: Natural Business LOHAS Journal. Text in English. 2000. bi-m. USD 19.95 (effective 2003). adv. **Document type:** *Journal, Trade.* **Description:** Tracks business and consumer trends involving products produced with a concern for health and the environment.
Published by: Natural Business Communications LLC, 360 Interlocken Blvd, Ste. 300, Broomfield, CO 80021-3496. TEL 303-442-8983, FAX 303-440-7741, info@lohasjournal.com, http://www.lohasjournal.com. Ed. Frank Lampe TEL 303-222-8964. Pub., Adv. contact Steven Hoffman TEL 303-222-8967. B&W page USD 3,000, color page USD 5,000; trim 8.375 x 10.875.

330 USA
▼ **L S A E RESOURCE.** Text in English. 2003. q. USD 175 membership (effective 2004). adv. **Document type:** *Newsletter.* **Description:** Contains the most current association news and organizational information.

B

Published by: (Louisiana Society of Association Executives), Naylor Publications, Inc., 5950 NW 1st Pl, Gainesville, FL 32607-6018. TEL 800-369-6220, http://www.naylor.com. Pub. Chris Hodges TEL 800-369-6220 ext 3368. adv.: B&W page USD 1,099.50; trim 8.375 x 10.875.

330 USA ISSN 1552-6461
LAB BUSINESS WEEK. Text in English. w. USD 2,595 in US & Canada; USD 2,795 elsewhere; USD 2,825 combined subscription in US & Canada print & online eds.; USD 3,055 combined subscription elsewhere print & online eds. (effective 2005). **Document type:** *Newsletter, Academic/Scholarly.*
Description: Reports the latest fiscal reports, mergers and acquisitions, patents and business trends affecting biotech and pharma companies who manufacture or market laboratory materials or equipment, including reports from the CDC and FDA.
Related titles: Online - full content ed.: ISSN 1552-647X; Online - full text ed.: (from ProQuest Information & Learning).
Published by: NewsRx, PO Box 5528, Atlanta, GA 31107-0528. TEL 800-726-4550, info@newsrx.com, http://www.newsrx.com/product_descriptions/LAB_BUSINESS_WEEK.HTM.

330 PAK ISSN 1811-5438
THE LAHORE JOURNAL OF ECONOMICS. Text in English. s-a. INR 600 domestic; USD 50 foreign (effective 2004). **Document type:** *Journal.*
Indexed: SSCI.
—BLDSC (5143.762500).
Published by: Lahore School of Economics, 105-C-2, Gulberg III, Lahore, 54660, Pakistan. TEL 92-42-5874385, FAX 92-42-5714936, nina_lse@yahoo.com, http://www.lse.edu.pk/. Eds. Salman Ahmed, Shahid Amjad Chaundhry, Viqar Ahmad.

LAMY DROIT COMMERCIAL. see *LAW—Corporate Law*

LAMY DROIT ECONOMIQUE; concurrence, distribution, consommation. see *LAW*

LAMY PROTECTION SOCIALE. see *LAW—Corporate Law*

LAMY SOCIAL. see *LAW*

338.18489 DNK ISSN 0106-1291
HD2001
LANDBRUGETS OEKONOMI/DANISH AGRICULTURAL ECONOMY. Text in Danish; Summaries in English. 1978. a. price varies.
Indexed: DSA, IndVet, PN&I, PoultAb, S&F, WAE&RSA, WeedAb.
—BLDSC (5151.130000), CISTI.
Published by: Ministeriet for Foedevarer, Landbrug og Fiskeri, Foedevareoekonomisk Institut/Ministry of Food, Agriculture and Fisheries, Danish Research Institute of Food Economics, Rolighedsvej 25, Frederiksberg C, 2000, Denmark. TEL 45-35-28-68-00, FAX 45-35-28-68-01.

330 USA ISSN 1063-925X
THE LANE REPORT; Kentucky's business news source. Text in English. 1985. m. USD 29 (effective 1997). adv. back issues avail. **Document type:** *Magazine, Consumer.* **Description:** Contains business and economic news for executives, managers, professionals and entrepreneurs in Kentucky.
Related titles: Online - full text ed.: (from Northern Light Technology, Inc.).
Indexed: BusDate.
Published by: Lane Communications Group, 201 E Main St, 1402, Lexington, KY 40507-2003. TEL 606-244-3500, FAX 606-244-3544, editorial@lanereport.com, http://www.lanereport.com. Ed. Claude Hammond. Pub. Ed Lane. R&P Steve Kress TEL 859-244-3531. Adv. contact Richard Kelly TEL 859-244-3543. B&W page USD 1,725, color page USD 1,995; trim 10.88 x 8.5. Circ: 15,000.

330 USA ISSN 1071-2186
LAS VEGAS BUSINESS PRESS. Text in English. 1993. w. (Mon.). USD 68 (effective 2005). adv. **Document type:** *Newspaper, Trade.*
Related titles: Microfilm ed.: (from LIB); Microform ed.: (from PQC); Online - full text ed.: (from EBSCO Publishing, Northern Light Technology, Inc., O C L C Online Computer Library Center, Inc., ProQuest Information & Learning).
Indexed: ABIn, BusDate.
Published by: Wick Communications, 1385 Pama Ln, Ste 111, Las Vegas, NV 89119-3849. TEL 702-871-6780, FAX 702-871-3298, editor@vegas.net. Ed. Jeff Burbank. Pub. Rod Smith. Adv. contact Chris Weir. Circ: 11,256.

330 ISR
LATA'ASYAN. Text in Hebrew. 1987. m. adv.
Published by: Manufacturers Association of Israel, 29 Hamered St, Tel Aviv, 68125, Israel. TEL 972-3-5128800, FAX 972-3-5103060, TELEX 342651. Ed. Eli Laniado. Circ: 4,000.

LATEINAMERIKA ANALYSEN. see *POLITICAL SCIENCE—International Relations*

LATIN AMERICA REPORT. see *POLITICAL SCIENCE*

LATIN AMERICAN LAW AND BUSINESS REPORT. see *LAW—Corporate Law*

330 USA
LATIN C E O; executive strategies for the Americas. (Chief Executive Officer) Text in English. 1999. m. USD 39.95; USD 4.95 newsstand/cover (effective 2001). adv. **Document type:** *Consumer.*
Published by: SouthFloridaC E O Magazine, 200 SE First St, Ste 601, Miami, FL 33131. TEL 305-379-1118, http://www.latinceo.com. Ed. J P Faber. Pub. Richard N Roffman. adv.: B&W page USD 13,160, color page USD 14,160; trim 8.125 x 10.875.

330 LVA ISSN 1407-1010
LATVIJAS EKONOMIST. Text in Latvian. m. USD 179 in United States.
Address: Elizabetes 45-47, 317 ist, Riga, Latvia. TEL 371-7332932, FAX 371-7222861. Ed. E Ogurok. **US dist. addr.:** East View Information Services, 3020 Harbor Ln. N., Minneapolis, MN 55447. TEL 612-550-0961.

LAW FOR BUSINESS. see *LAW—Corporate Law*

330 CAN
▼ **LEADING BUSINESS.** Text in English. 2003. 11/yr. free to members (effective 2004). **Document type:** *Newsletter, Trade.*
Published by: (Calgary Chamber of Commerce), RedPoint Media Group Inc., 1902K-11th St SE, Calgary, AB T2G 3G2, Canada. gdavies@redpointmedia.ca. Ed. Gary Davies TEL 403-240-9055 ext 222. Pub. Dan Bowman.

330 LBN ISSN 1727-0618
LEBANON OPPORTUNITIES. Text in English. 1997. m. USD 40 (effective 2005). **Document type:** *Newspaper, Trade.*
Related titles: Online - full text ed.: ISSN 1727-0626.
Published by: InfoPro Management, Emile Edde St., Salem Bldg., 2nd Fl., PO Box 11, Beirut, 4355, Lebanon. TEL 961-1-739777, FAX 961-1-749090, opportunities@infopro.com.lb, http://www.opportunities.com.lb/Lebanon/Default.asp. Ed., Pub. Ramzi el-Hafez.

LECTURE NOTES IN ECONOMICS AND MATHEMATICAL SYSTEMS; operations research, computer science, social science. see *MATHEMATICS*

338 DNK ISSN 0902-3704
HB9
➤ **LEDELSE & ERHVERVSOEKONOMI.** Text in Danish, Norwegian, Swedish. 1937. q. DKK 445 (effective 2004). bk.rev. bibl.; abstr.; stat. index. **Document type:** *Journal, Academic/Scholarly.*
Former titles (until 1987): Erhvervsoekonomisk Tidsskrift (0014-0147); (until 1955): Handelsvidenskabeligt Tidsskrift (0904-244X)
Related titles: Online - full text ed.
Indexed: IBSS, RASB.
Published by: Civiloekonomerne/Association of Danish Business Economists, Soetorvet 5, PO Box 2043, Copenhagen K, 1012, Denmark. TEL 45-33-141446, FAX 45-33-141449, info@civiloekonomerne.org, http://www.civiloekonomerne.org. Eds. Axel Schultz-Nielsen, Gitte S Nielsen. Circ: 17,000.

➤ **LEDGER (BOSTON).** see *EDUCATION*

330 USA ISSN 1042-0134
HC106.8
LEFT BUSINESS OBSERVER. Text in English. 1986. m. USD 22 to individuals; USD 55 to institutions (effective 2005). bk.rev. **Document type:** *Newsletter.* **Description:** Covers economics and politics worldwide, with emphasis on the US.
Related titles: Online - full text ed.: (from ProQuest Information & Learning, SoftLine Information).
Indexed: AltPI.
Published by: Doug Henwood, Ed. & Pub., 250 W 85th St, No 7J, New York, NY 10024-3217. TEL 212-874-4020, FAX 212-874-3137, http://www.leftbusinessobserver.com/. Ed., Pub., R&P Doug Henwood. Circ: 3,000 (paid).

LEGAL BUSINESS. see *LAW*

LEGAL CONNECTION: CORPORATIONS AND LAW FIRMS; a directory of publicly-held corporations and their law firms. see *LAW*

LEGALINES: COMMERCIAL LAW KEYED TO THE FARNSWORTH CASEBOOK. see *LAW—Corporate Law*

330 GBR ISSN 0967-716X
LEICESTER ECONOMIC REVIEW. Text in English. 1993. q. **Document type:** *Bulletin, Government.* **Description:** Reports on the activities of the Leicester City Council, Economic Services, and how they affect the local economy.
Published by: (Leicester. Environment and Development), Leicester City Council, Economic Services, New Walk Centre, Welford Pl, Leicester, Leics LE1 6ZG, United Kingdom. Ed. Mathe Diseko.

330 FRA ISSN 0756-5577
LETTRE DE L'O F C E. (Observatoire Francais des Conjonctures Economiques) Text in French. 1982. 10/yr. EUR 24 domestic to individuals; EUR 28.50 foreign to individuals; EUR 41 domestic to institutions; EUR 45 foreign to institutions; EUR 22.50 domestic to students (effective 2005).
Indexed: ELLIS, PAIS.
Published by: (Observatoire Francais des Conjonctures Economiques), Presses de Sciences Po, 44 rue du Four, Paris, 75006, France. TEL 33-01-44393960, FAX 33-01-45480441, info@presses.sciences-po.fr, http://www.sciences-po.fr.

330 FRA
LETTRE M M M. Text in French. 1991. w. looseleaf. back issues avail. **Description:** Looks at the global economy.
Published by: Club M M M, 26 rue Cadet, Paris, 75009, France. TEL 45-23-01-07, FAX 45-23-02-88. Ed. Edmund Ballerand.

330 CHN
LIAONING JINGJI/LIAONING ECONOMICS. Text in Chinese. m.
Published by: Liaoning Fazhan Yanjiu Zhongxin/Liaoning Development Research Center, Beiling Dajie, Shenyang, Liaoning 110032, China. Ed. Liu Mingliang.

330 658 LBR
LIBERIAN ECONOMIC AND MANAGEMENT REVIEW✶. Text in English. 1972. s-a. USD 6. adv. bk.rev. charts; stat.
Published by: (Economic and Management Research Institute), University of Liberia, College of Business and Public Administration, Monrovia, Liberia.

▼ **LIFECOACH MAGAZINE**; the exclusive guide for forward thinkers. see *PSYCHOLOGY*

330 FIN ISSN 0024-3469
HD58.5
➤ **LIIKETALOUDELLINEN AIKAKAUSKIRJA/FINNISH JOURNAL OF BUSINESS ECONOMICS.** Text mainly in English; Summaries in English; Text occasionally in Finnish, German, Swedish. 1952. q. EUR 29 domestic; EUR 37 foreign (effective 2005). bk.rev. bibl. index. back issues avail.; reprint service avail. from PQC. **Document type:** *Journal, Academic/Scholarly.* **Description:** Publishes research reports on economics and business administration.
Indexed: DIP, ForAb, IBR, IBZ, JEL, PAIS, SSCI.
—BLDSC (5215.700000), IE, ingenta.
Published by: Liiketaloustieteellinen Yhdistys Ry/Helsinki School of Economics and Business Administration, PO Box 1210, Helsinki, 00101, Finland. TEL 358-9-43131, FAX 358-9-43138678, lta@hkkk.fi, http://hkkk.fi/lta, http://www.hkkk.fi/lta. Ed. Eero Kasanen. Circ: 1,800.

330 FIN ISSN 1239-6044
LIIKETALOUS. Text in Finnish. 1956. m. (10/yr.). adv. bk.rev. charts; illus. index. **Document type:** *Magazine.*
Formerly (until 1996): Merkonomi (0026-0088)
Published by: Liiketalouden Liitto LTA, Huutokallionkatu 17, Hamina, 49408, Finland. TEL 358-400-694600, liitto@liiketaloudenliitto.fi, http://www.liiketaloudenliitto.fi. Circ: 20,000.

330 DEU
LION. Text in German. m. EUR 2 newsstand/cover (effective 2003). adv. **Document type:** *Magazine, Trade.*
Published by: Schuermann & Klagges GmbH & Co. KG, Industriestr 34, Bochum, 44894, Germany. TEL 49-234-92140, FAX 49-234-9214100, sk@skala.de, http://www.skala.de. adv.: B&W page EUR 1,900, color page EUR 3,330. Circ: 42,146 (paid and controlled).

330 DEU ISSN 0937-0862
HB5
LIST FORUM FUER WIRTSCHAFTS- UND FINANZPOLITIK. Text in German. q. EUR 51.13; EUR 12.78 newsstand/cover (effective 2003). **Document type:** *Journal, Academic/Scholarly.*
Former titles (until 1989): Listforum (0342-2623); (until 1977): List-Gesellschaft. Mitteilungen (0342-1252)
Indexed: DIP, IBR, IBZ.
Published by: List Gesellschaft e.V., Westfaelische Wilhelms-Universitaet, Am Stadtgraben 9, Muenster, 48143, Germany. TEL 49-251-8322904, FAX 49-251-8328395, mail@list-gesellschaft.de, http://www.list-gesellschaft.de. Ed. Karl-Hans Hartwig.

334.71 LTU ISSN 1392-9739
LITHUANIAN BUSINESS REVIEW. Text in English. 10/yr. LTL 69 domestic; EUR 69 in Europe; USD 63 elsewhere (effective 2002). **Document type:** *Journal.*
Published by: UAB Neolitas, Palangos 9, Kaunas, 3000, Lithuania. TEL 370-7-322525, FAX 370-7-323273, lbr@neolitas.lt, http://www.neolitas.lt/lbr. Ed. Vytautas Gaizauskas. Adv. contact Mindaugas Jukna.

330 USA
LIVINGSTON SURVEY. Text in English. s-a. stat. back issues avail. **Document type:** *Government.* **Description:** Summarizes economic forecast from economists in a variety of sectors. Includes actual releases, documentation, inflation growth rates, mean data of respondents of survey respondents and economists.
Published by: Federal Reserve Bank of Philadelphia, 10 Independence Mall, Philadelphia, PA 19106. dean.crousher@phi.frb.org, http://www.phil.frb.org/econ/liv/index.html.

LLOYD'S LIST. see *TRANSPORTATION—Ships And Shipping*

330 GBR ISSN 0269-0942
➤ **LOCAL ECONOMY.** Text in English. 1986. q. GBP 213, USD 353 combined subscription to institutions print & online eds. (effective 2006). adv. bk.rev. back issues avail.; reprint service avail. from PQC,PSC. **Document type:** *Journal, Academic/Scholarly.* **Description:** Covers economic situations and conditions, as well as cooperatives, and other related fields of business and economics.
Related titles: Microfiche ed.; Microfilm ed.; Online - full text ed.: ISSN 1470-9325. GBP 202, USD 335 to institutions (effective 2006) (from EBSCO Publishing, Gale Group, IngentaConnect, O C L C Online Computer Library Center, Inc., Swets Information Services).
Indexed: DIP, IBR, IBSS, IBZ, JEL, SWA.
—BLDSC (5290.011420), IE, Infotrieve, ingenta. **CCC.**
Published by: (South Bank Polytechnic, Local Economy Policy Unit), Routledge (Subsidiary of: Taylor & Francis Group), 4 Park Sq, Milton Park, Abingdon, Oxon OX14 4RN, United Kingdom. TEL 44-1235-828600, FAX 44-1235-829000, info@routledge.co.uk, http://www.tandf.co.uk/journals/titles/02690942.asp, http://www.routledge.co.uk. Eds. James DeFilippis, Peter North, Stuart Wilks-Heeg. Circ: 700. **Subscr. to:** Taylor & Francis Ltd, Journals Customer Service, Rankine Rd, Basingstoke, Hants RG24 8PR, United Kingdom. TEL 44-1256-813000, FAX 44-1256-330245, enquiry@tandf.co.uk.

➤ **LOGISTICS EUROPE.** see *TRANSPORTATION*

330 DEU ISSN 0172-9047
LOHN UND GEHALT; e-Entgeltabrechnung - Personalverguetung - e-Zeitwirtschaft. Text in German. 1979. 8/yr. EUR 95; EUR 17 newsstand/cover (effective 2004). adv. **Document type:** *Magazine, Trade.*
Indexed: DIP, IBR, IBZ.
—IE, Infotrieve. **CCC.**
Published by: Datakontext Fachverlag GmbH, Augustinusstr 9 d, Frechen, 50226, Germany. TEL 49-2234-966100, FAX 49-2234-966109, info@datakontext.com, http://www.datakontext-press.de/LG/lg_hauptframe.htm. Adv. contact Gabriele Beuder. B&W page EUR 1,700, color page EUR 2,975; trim 178 x 246. Circ: 7,200 (paid and controlled).

330 IND
LOKPRABHA. Text in Marathi. 1974. w. adv. bk.rev.
Address: Express Towers, Nariman Point, Mumbai, Maharashtra 400 021, India. TEL 91-22-202-2627, FAX 91-22-285-2108. Ed. Pradeep Varma. Circ: 34,401.

330 GBR
LONDON GUILDHALL UNIVERSITY. DEPARTMENT OF BUSINESS STUDIES. OCCASIONAL PAPERS. Text in English. 2001 (July). irreg. **Document type:** *Monographic series, Academic/Scholarly.* **Description:** Promotes research and discussion in business studies and related areas.
—BLDSC (3553.620000).
Published by: London Guildhall University, Dept of Business Studies, Business School, 84 Moorgate, London, EC2M 6SQ, United Kingdom. TEL 44-20-7320-1441, FAX 44-20-7320-1465. Ed. Brian Kettell.

330 GBR ISSN 0954-4763
LONDON GUILDHALL UNIVERSITY. DEPARTMENT OF ECONOMICS. WORKING PAPER. Text in English. irreg., latest vol.30, 1994. **Document type:** *Monographic series.*
Published by: London Guildhall University, Department of Economics, 117-119 Houndsditch, London, EC3A 7BU, United Kingdom. TEL 0171-320-1000, FAX 0171-320-1337. Ed. David Wilson.

330 GBR
LONDON SCHOOL OF ECONOMICS AND POLITICAL SCIENCE. CENTRE FOR ANALYSIS OF RISK AND REGULATION. Text in English. irreg. **Document type:** *Monographic series, Academic/Scholarly.*
Published by: London School of Economics and Political Science, Centre for Analysis of Risk and Regulation, Houghton Street, London, WC12A 2AE, United Kingdom. TEL 44-20-79556577, FAX 44-20-79556578, http://www.lse.ac.uk/depts/carr/publications.htm.

330 GBR
LONDON SCHOOL OF ECONOMICS AND POLITICAL SCIENCE. CENTRE FOR ANALYSIS OF RISK AND REGULATION. DISCUSSION PAPERS. Text in English. irreg. back issues avail. **Document type:** *Monographic series, Academic/Scholarly.*
Related titles: Online - full content ed.
Published by: London School of Economics and Political Science, Centre for Analysis of Risk and Regulation, Houghton Street, London, WC12A 2AE, United Kingdom. FAX 44-20-79556578, 44-20-79556578, http://www.lse.ac.uk/depts/carr/publications.htm.

LONDON SCHOOL OF ECONOMICS AND POLITICAL SCIENCE. CENTRE FOR DISCRETE & APPLICABLE MATHEMATICS. RESEARCH REPORT SERIES. see *MATHEMATICS*

330 GBR ISSN 0961-5725
LONDON SCHOOL OF ECONOMICS AND POLITICAL SCIENCE. CENTRE FOR ECONOMIC PERFORMANCE. DISCUSSION PAPER. Text in English. 1990. irreg.
—BLDSC (3597.120600), IE, ingenta.
Published by: London School of Economics and Political Science, Centre for Economic Performance, Room H102, Freepost LON 14052, London, WC2A 2BR, United Kingdom.

330 USA
LONG BEACH BUSINESS JOURNAL. Text in English. 1987. bi-w. USD 17.50. **Document type:** *Newspaper.*
Published by: South Coast Publishing, 2599 E 28th St, 212, Long Beach, CA 90806-2139. TEL 562-988-1222, FAX 562-988-1239, http://www.lbcnet.com/journal. Pub., R&P George Economides. Circ: 340,000.

330 USA ISSN 0896-4688
LONG ISLAND. Text in English. 1987. 11/yr. USD 30 (effective 2000). adv. **Description:** Focuses on issues of interest to the Long Island business community—taxes, environment, housing, economic data, government relations, transportation, labor supply, interviews and profiles, advice, small business news, viewpoints, association news and a calendar of events.
Published by: Long Island Association, 9006, Commack, NY 11725-9006. TEL 516-499-4400. Ed., R&P Gary W Wojtas. Pub. Matthew T Crosson. Circ: 10,000.

330 USA ISSN 0894-4806
LONG ISLAND BUSINESS NEWS. Text in English. 1953. w. (Fri.). USD 75 (effective 2005). adv. **Document type:** *Newspaper.*
Former titles: Long Island - Business (0893-5734); (until 1979): L I Business Review (0274-9157)
Related titles: Online - full text ed.: (from EBSCO Publishing, Florida Center for Library Automation, Gale Group, Newsbank, Inc., Northern Light Technology, Inc., O C L C Online Computer Library Center, Inc., ProQuest Information & Learning).
Indexed: ABIn, BusDate, T&II.
—**CCC.**
Published by: Long Island Commercial Review, Inc., 2150 Smithtown Ave, Ronkonkoma, NY 11779-7327. TEL 631-737-1700, FAX 631-737-1890, editor@libn.com, http://www.libn.com. Ed., Pub. Peter Mantius. Adv. contact Jaci Clement. B&W page USD 3,009, color page USD 3,604. Circ: 11,200 (paid).

330 AUS
LONG TERM FORECASTS (YEAR). Text in English. a. AUD 1,280 (effective 2000). **Document type:** *Corporate.* **Description:** Examines the medium- to long-term prospects of the Australian economy.
Published by: B I S Shrapnel Pty. Ltd., 8th Fl., 181 Miller St, North Sydney, NSW 2060, Australia. TEL 61-2-9959-5924, FAX 61-2-9959-5795, jlewis@bis.com, http://www.bis.com.au. Ed. Frank Gelber. Circ: 200.

LOSINKA. see *PUBLIC ADMINISTRATION—Municipal Government*

330 GBR
LOUGHBOROUGH ECONOMIC RESEARCH PAPERS. Text in English. irreg. free. back issues avail. **Document type:** *Academic/Scholarly.*
Formerly: Loughborough Occasional Papers in Economics
Published by: Loughborough University, Department of Economics, Loughborough University, Loughborough, Leics LE11 3TU, United Kingdom. TEL 44-1509-222729, FAX 44-1509-223910. Ed. Leigh Drake. Circ: 93.

▼ **LOWCARBIZ**; your ultimate low carb voice. see *FOOD AND FOOD INDUSTRIES*

330 DEU ISSN 0344-5216
LUEBECKISCHE BLAETTER. Text in German. 21/yr. **Document type:** *Bulletin, Trade.*
Published by: Schmidt-Roemhild Verlag, Mengstr 16, Luebeck, 23552, Germany. TEL 49-451-7031-01, FAX 49-451-7031281, eickershoff@beleke.de, http://www.schmidt-roemhild.de. Circ: 2,000 (controlled).

LUXEMBOURG. SERVICE CENTRAL DE LA STATISTIQUE ET DES ETUDES ECONOMIQUES. STATISTIQUES HISTORIQUES. see *BUSINESS AND ECONOMICS—Abstracting, Bibliographies, Statistics*

LUYOU GUANGLI/MANAGEMENT OF TOURISM. see *TRAVEL AND TOURISM*

330 RUS
LYUDI DELA; Rossiiskii analaticheskii zhurnal dlya delovykh lyudei. Text in Russian. m. adv. illus.; mkt.; stat. **Document type:** *Magazine, Consumer.* **Description:** Contains profiles of regional business leaders and other business features. Covers a wide range of topics to help inform the business professional, including market news, information on taxes, legislation, and tariffs, and a lifestyle section.
Related titles: Online - full content ed.
Published by: P S - Izdatel'stvo, Ul Kamenskaya 74, 7 et, Novisibrsk, 630091, Russian Federation. TEL 7-3832-249238, FAX 7-3832-297471. Ed. Tatyana Kuz'minykh. Adv. contacts Anna Blednova, Irina Oboroni. B&W page RUR 9,020, color page RUR 16,000.

▼ **M 2 M.** see *COMMUNICATIONS*

330 USA ISSN 1541-3284
M B A JUNGLE. (Masters in Business Administration) Text in English. 2000. 8/yr. USD 11.97 domestic; USD 16.97 in Canada; USD 39.97 elsewhere; USD 3.95 newsstand/cover domestic; USD 4.95 newsstand/cover in Canada (effective 2005). adv. **Document type:** *Magazine, Trade.* **Description:** Contains a wide variety of business and lifestyle articles for MBA students.
Related titles: ♦ Online - full content ed.: MBAJungle.com.
Published by: Jungle Interactive Media, 632 Broadway, 7th Fl, New York, NY 10012-2614. TEL 212-352-0840, 866-458-6453, FAX 212-352-9282, info@mbajungle.com, info@jungleinteractive.com, http://www.mbajungle.com, http://www.jungleinteractive.com. Ed. Bill Shapiro. Circ: 100,000 (controlled).

330 USA
M B I; the national report on minority, women-owned and disadvantaged businesses. Text in English. 1987. m. USD 299 combined subscription print & online eds. (effective 2004). index. 12 p./no. 2 cols./p.; **Document type:** *Newsletter.* **Description:** Reports on affirmative action, minority employment, government contracts and education.
Formerly: Minorities in Business Insider (1050-3463)
—**CCC.**
Published by: (Community Development Services, Inc.), C D Publications, Inc., 8204 Fenton St, Silver Spring, MD 20910-2889. TEL 301-588-6380, FAX 301-588-0519, mbi@cdpublications.com, http://www.cdpublications.com. Ed. James S Byrne. Pub., R&P Mike Gerecht.

M-BUSINESS; the voice of the next mobile economy. see *COMPUTERS—Internet*

650 TTO
M D C BUSINESS JOURNAL. (Management Development Centre) Text in English. 1976. s-a. free.
Published by: Management Development Centre, Library, Salvatori Bldg, PO Box 1301, Port-of-Spain, Trinidad, Trinidad & Tobago. TEL 809-623-1961, FAX 809-623-2111. Ed. Ingrid Jordan. Circ: 1,200.

330 USA ISSN 1540-1960
T58.6 CODEN: MQEIAI
➤ **M I S QUARTERLY EXECUTIVE**; a research journal dedicated to improving practice. Text in English. 2002 (Mar.). q. USD 125 combined subscription domestic to individuals print & online eds.; USD 145 combined subscription foreign to individuals print & online eds. (effective 2004). **Document type:** *Journal, Academic/Scholarly.* **Description:** Covers practice-based research in the information systems field.
Related titles: Online - full text ed.: ISSN 1540-1979. USD 50 to individuals; USD 395 to libraries; USD 495 to institutions (effective 2004).
Indexed: Inspec.
Published by: Indiana University, Accounting and Information Systems Department, Kelley School of Business, E. 10th St., Bloomington, IN 47405-1710. TEL 812-855-8966, FAX 812-855-4985, http://www.misqe.org/jsp/index.jsp, http://www.indiana.edu/~aisdept/. Ed. Jack Rockart. Pub. Alan Dennis.

330 IND
M M - THE INDUSTRY MAGAZINE. Text in English. m. adv. **Document type:** *Magazine, Trade.* **Description:** Features news, views and analyses on cutting edge technologies, trends in technology management and world class products. It is a trend-setter in business-to-business in India.It provides balanced mix of information pertaining to trends, applications, developments and innovations in technology and management.
Related titles: ♦ Regional ed(s).: Maschinenmarkt. ISSN 0341-5775.
Published by: Jasubhai Media Pvt. Ltd, D-222/2, TTC Industrial Area, MIDC, Nerul, Navi Mumbai, 400 706, India. TEL 91-22-7629191, FAX 91-22-7629223, editor@mm-india.com, http://www.mm-india.com/mm.

330 USA
M O D A REPORT✶. Text in English. q. USD 15.
Published by: M.O. Dickerson Associates, Inc., 2125 Reed St, Philadelphia, PA 19146-4533.

355 GBR ISSN 0951-8053
M O D NEWS. Text in English. 1987. m. GBP 69, USD 130. **Document type:** *Government.* **Description:** News service of important information concerning the Ministry of Defence, including its press releases and government reports.
—**CCC.**
Published by: (Great Britain. Ministry of Defence), Longman Group UK Ltd., Law Tax and Finance Division, 21-27 Lambs Conduit St, London, WC1N 3NJ, United Kingdom. TEL 44-20-7242-2548, FAX 44-207-831-8119. Ed. Michael Bentley.

▼ new title ➤ refereed ✶ unverified ♦ full entry avail.

338 USA ISSN 1091-0638
M R O TODAY. (Maintenance, Repair & Operations) Text in English. bi-m. **Document type:** *Trade.* **Description:** Provides information to sales and marketing professionals who sell maintenance, repair & operations supplies to the industry.
Published by: Pfingsten Publishing, L L C, 6000 Lombardo Center Dr, Ste 420, Seven Hills, OH 44131. TEL 216-328-8926, 888-772-8926, FAX 216-328-9452, info@pfpublish.com, http://www.mrotoday.com/, http://www.pfpub.com. Ed. Paul Arnold.

330 USA
M S R B MANUAL. (Municipal Security Rulemaking Board) Text in English. 1977. base vol. plus bi-m. updates. USD 430 base vol(s). (effective 2004). **Description:** Provides municipal securities professionals with complete and current information concerning the regulations and requirements that govern the conduct of a municipal securities business.
Related titles: CD-ROM ed.: USD 423 (effective 2004); Online - full text ed.: USD 423 (effective 2004).
Published by: C C H Inc., 2700 Lake Cook Rd, Riverwoods, IL 60015. TEL 847-267-7000, 800-449-6439, cust_serv@cch.com, http://www.cch.com. Pub. Stacey Caywood.

B

330 610 USA
M X; business strategies for medical technology executives. Text in English. bi-m. USD 150; free to qualified personnel (effective 2005). adv. **Document type:** *Magazine, Trade.* **Description:** Provides business news and information relevant to medical device executives.
Formerly (until 1999): Medical Device Executive Portfolio
Published by: Canon Communications LLC, 11444 W Olympic Blvd, Ste 900, Los Angeles, CA 90064-1549. TEL 310-445-4269, FAX 310-445-4299, feedback@devicelink.com, http://www.devicelink.com/mx, http://www.cancom.com. Eds. Steven Halasey, John Bethune. Pub. William F Cobert. adv.: B&W page USD 4,530, color page USD 5,925. Circ: 15,000 (controlled).

MACAO. DIRECCAO DOS SERVICOS DE ESTATISTICA E CENSOS. ESTIMATIVAS DO PRODUTO INTERNO BRUTO/MACAO. CENSUS AND STATISTICS DEPARTMENT. GROSS DOMESTIC PRODUCT ESTIMATES. see *BUSINESS AND ECONOMICS—Abstracting, Bibliographies, Statistics*

MACAO. DIRECCAO DOS SERVICOS DE ESTATISTICA E CENSOS. INQUERITO INDUSTRIAL/MACAO. CENSUS AND STATISTICS DEPARTMENT. INDUSTRIAL SURVEY. see *BUSINESS AND ECONOMICS—Abstracting, Bibliographies, Statistics*

330 650 MAC
MACAU INDUSTRY. Text in English. 1977. a. stat.
Published by: Macau Business Centre, Edificio Ribeiro, P.O. Box 138, Macau.

MACOMB COUNTY LEGAL NEWS. see *LAW*

333.33 917 USA
MADDUX BUSINESS REPORT. Text in English. 1984. m. USD 45 (effective 2005). adv. 68 p./no.; back issues avail. **Document type:** *Magazine, Consumer.*
Former titles: Maddux Report (0889-0838); Tampa Bay's Maddux Report
Published by: Maddux Report L.C., 146 2nd St N., Ste. 205, St Petersburg, FL 33701-3361. nhowe@maddux.com, http://maddux.com. Ed. Carlen Maddux. Pub., R&P, Adv. contact Nancy Howe. B&W page USD 2,550, color page USD 3,145. Circ: 15,000.

330 ITA
MADE IN; mensile di economia. Text in Italian. 1988. m. EUR 173 (effective 2005). **Document type:** *Magazine, Consumer.*
Related titles: Diskette ed.
Published by: Bergamo 15 Srl, Via Don Luigi Palazzolo 67, Bergamo, BE 24122, Italy. TEL 39-035-217848, FAX 39-035-212600, info@bergamo15.it, http://www.bergamo15.it. Ed. Mario Zambetti.

330 ITA
MADE IN BERGAMO. TRIMESTRALE DI ECONOMIA. Text in Italian. 1988. q. EUR 33 (effective 2005). adv. **Document type:** *Magazine, Consumer.*
Formerly: Made in Bergamo
Published by: Bergamo 15 Srl, Via Don Luigi Palazzolo 67, Bergamo, BE 24122, Italy. TEL 39-035-217848, FAX 39-035-212600, info@bergamo15.it, http://www.bergamo15.it. Ed. Mario Zambetti.

AL-MAGALLAH AL-QANUNIYYAH AL-IQTISADIYYAH/LAW AND ECONOMIC REVIEW. see *LAW*

MAGALLAT AL-BUHUT AL-IDARIYYAT/ADMINISTRATIVE RESEARCH REVIEW. see *PUBLIC ADMINISTRATION*

330 EGY ISSN 1110-2276
MAGALLAT AL-BUHUTH AL-TIGARIYYAT AL-MU'ASIRAT/ JOURNAL OF MODERN COMMERCIAL RESEARCHES. Text in Arabic. 1987. s-a. EGP 10 domestic; USD 10 foreign (effective 2004). **Document type:** *Journal, Academic/Scholarly.*
Published by: Assiut University, Faculty of Commerce, Souhag, Assiut, Egypt. TEL 20-93-601807, FAX 20-93-604820, http://derp.sti.sci.eg/data/0286.htm. Ed. Dr. Authman Muhammad Yasin.

330 KWT ISSN 1561-0411
➤ **MAGALLAT AL-TANMIYAT WA-AL-SIYASAT AL-IQTISADIYYAT/JOURNAL OF DEVELOPMENT AND ECONOMIC POLICIES.** Text in Arabic, English. 1998. s-a. USD 15 to individuals in Arab Countries; USD 25 elsewhere to individuals; USD 25 to institutions in Arab Countries; USD 40 elsewhere to institutions (effective 2004). **Document type:** *Journal.*
Indexed: JEL.
Published by: Al-Ma'had al-'Arabi Li-l-Tahtit/Arab Planning Institute, PO Box 5834, Safat, 13059, Kuwait. TEL 965-248-48754, FAX 965-248-42935, jodep@api.org.kw, api@api.org.kw, http://www.api-jodep.com/, http://www.arab-api.org/index.html. Ed. Essa Al-Gazali.

330 ISR
MAGAZINE OF ISRAELI INDUSTRY. Text in English, Hebrew. q. free (effective 2002). **Document type:** *Magazine, Trade.*
Address: c/o Ronen Yogev, 29 Hammered St, Tel Aviv, 68125, Israel. TEL 972-3-5142890, FAX 972-3-5142881. Ed. Ronen Yogev.

330 CAN
MAGAZINE QUEBEC ENTREPRISE. Text in English. 1992. 6/yr. CND 20.
Address: 483 Marie Claire Daveluy Rd, Boisbriand, PQ J7G 3G9, Canada. TEL 514-433-9971, FAX 514-433-0434. Ed. Daniel Boisvert. adv.: B&W page CND 2,100, color page CND 3,000; trim 10.88 x 8.13. Circ: 25,000.

330 USA ISSN 1530-0749
MAINEBIZ. Text in English. fortn. USD 39.95 (effective 2002). adv. **Document type:** *Trade.* **Description:** Contains feature stories, columns, news briefs, profiles, company rankings in a variety of industries, listings of incorporations and real estate deals, company news and calendar highlights.
Published by: Worcester Publishing, Ltd., 413 Congress St, Portland, ME 04101. TEL 207-761-8379, FAX 207-761-0732, http://www.maine-biz.com/. Ed. Scott Sutherland TEL 207-761-8379 ext. 25. Pub. Donna Brassard TEL 207-761-8379 ext. 27.

330 MWI
MALAWI DEVELOPMENT CORPORATION. ANNUAL REPORT. Text in English. 1965. a. free. **Document type:** *Corporate.* **Description:** Presents information of the accounts of the Malawi Development Corporation for the year.
Published by: Malawi Development Corporation, PO Box 566, Blantyre, Malawi. TEL 265-620100, FAX 265-620584-33, TELEX 44146. Circ: 1,000.

330 MYS
MALAYSIA. DEPARTMENT OF STATISTICS. BUSINESS EXPECTATIONS SURVEY OF LIMITED COMPANIES MALAYSIA/MALAYSIA. JABATAN PERANGKAAN. PENYIASATAN JANGKAAN PERNIAGAAN BAGI SYARIKAT-SYARIKAT BERHAD MALAYSIA. Text in English, Malay. s-a. MYR 10 per issue (effective 1999). **Document type:** *Government.*
Published by: Department of Statistics/Jabatan Perangkaan, Jalan Cenderasari, Kuala Lumpur, 50514, Malaysia. TEL 60-3-294-4264, FAX 60-3-291-4535, jpmeto@po.jaring.my, http://www.statistics.gov.my/.

MALAYSIA. DEPARTMENT OF STATISTICS. MONTHLY CONSUMER PRICE INDEX, MALAYSIA/MALAYSIA. JABATAN PERANGKAAN. INDEKS HARGA PENGGUNA, MALAYSIA. see *STATISTICS*

330 MYS ISSN 0126-5504
HC445.5.A1
MALAYSIAN BUSINESS. Text in English. 1972. s-m. MYR 70.10 in Singapore, Brunei & Darussalam; USD 104.80 in India, Thailand, China, Japan, Australia; USD 139.60 in Argentina, Brazil, Africa, USA, Canada; USD 127.90 in Middle East & Europe (effective 2005). adv. bk.rev. charts; illus. **Document type:** *Magazine, Trade.* **Description:** Covers business, investments, market analysis and technology updates, as well as political events that have an impact on business.
Related titles: Online - full text ed.: (from Florida Center for Library Automation, Gale Group, LexisNexis, ProQuest Information & Learning); (from Northern Light Technology, Inc.).
Indexed: ABIn, RASB.
Published by: Berita Publishing, No. 16-20 Jalan 4/109E, Desa Business Park, Taman Desa, Kuala Lumpur, 58100, Malaysia. TEL 60-3-7620 8111, FAX 60-3-7620 8026, http://www.malaysianbusiness.com.my/. Ed. Datuk A Kadir Jasin. adv.: B&W page MYR 4,960, color page MYR 6,290; trim 210 x 275. Circ: 25,000. **Dist. by:** New Straits Times Press (M) Bhd, Circulation Department, 31 Jln Riong, Kuala Lumpur 59100, Malaysia.

330 RUS
MALYI BIZNES ROSSII. Text in Russian. m. USD 139 in United States.
Indexed: RASB.
Address: Ul Dzerzhinskogo 50, Kursk, 305000, Russian Federation. FAX 0712-566503. **US dist. addr.:** East View Information Services, 3020 Harbor Ln. N., Minneapolis, MN 55447. TEL 612-550-0961.

332.6 USA ISSN 1525-9706
RA413
THE MANAGED CARE ACQUISITION REPORT. Text in English. 1999. a., latest 1999. looseleaf. USD 495 for print or online ed.; USD 645 combined subscription for print & online eds. (effective 2002). mkt.; stat. 180 p./no.; back issues avail. **Document type:** *Newsletter, Consumer.* **Description:** Provides transaction details on 277 publicly announced mergers and acquisitions in the managed care sector; covers HMOs, PPOs, Blue Cross, behavioral, dental, pharmacy and eye care managed care plans. There is also a 10 page introduction summarizing the acquisition market for managed care companies.
Published by: Irving Levin Associates, Inc., 268-1/2 Main Ave, Norwalk, CT 06851. TEL 203-846-6800, 800-248-1668, FAX 203-846-8300, general@levinassociates.com, http://www.levinassociates.com. Pub. Ms. Eleanor B Meredith. R&P Stephen M Monroe.

330 362 368 USA ISSN 1552-5678
MANAGED CARE BUSINESS WEEK. Text in English. w. USD 2,595 in US & Canada; USD 2,795 elsewhere; USD 2,825 combined subscription in US & Canada print & online eds.; USD 3,055 combined subscription elsewhere print & online eds. (effective 2005). **Document type:** *Newsletter, Academic/Scholarly.* **Description:** Provides the managed care company and provider executive with the important business news and fiscal trends that affect access to and provision of healthcare, including state plan changes and expansions, federal Medicare and Medicaid changes, fiscal reports from MCOs and providers, and legislative proposals that impact profitability.
Related titles: Online - full content ed.: ISSN 1552-5686; Online - full text ed.: (from ProQuest Information & Learning).
Published by: NewsRx, PO Box 5528, Atlanta, GA 31107-0528. TEL 800-726-4550, info@newsrx.com, http://www.newsrx.com/product_descriptions/MANAGED_CARE_BUSINESS_WEEK.HTM.

330 GBR ISSN 1471-9894
MANAGING ECONOMIC TRANSITION NETWORK. WORKING PAPER SERIES. Text in English. 2001 (Jan). irreg. **Document type:** *Monographic series, Academic/Scholarly.* **Description:** Brings together research in progress, conducted by academics and practitioners from across the United Kingdom for dissemination to a wider audience in order to facilitate discussion.
—BLDSC (5683.123500).
Published by: Manchester Metropolitan University, Business School, Aytoun Building, Aytoun St, Manchester, M1 3GH, United Kingdom. TEL 44-161-247-6799, FAX 44-161-247-6854, MET-Network@mmu.ac.uk, http://www.business.mmu.ac.uk/met/wps.htm.

330 GBR ISSN 1462-5571
MANAGING PARTNER. Text in English. 1998. 10/yr. GBP 315 domestic; EUR 505 in Europe; USD 475 elsewhere (effective 2004). adv. **Document type:** *Magazine, Trade.*
Related titles: Online - full content ed.: GBP 195 domestic; EUR 305 in Europe; USD 275 elsewhere (effective 2004); Online - full text ed.: (from EBSCO Publishing).
Published by: Ark Group Ltd, 86-88 Upper Richmond Rd, London, SW15 2UR, United Kingdom. TEL 44-20-87852700, FAX 44-20-87859373, info@ark-group.com, http://www.mpmagazine.com, http://www.ark-group.com. Ed. Caroline Poynton. Pub. Andreas Silbermann. Adv. contact Luis Keats.

MANCHETE. see *LITERARY AND POLITICAL REVIEWS*

MANNHEIMER BEITRAEGE ZUR OEKONOMISCHEN OEKOLOGIE. see *CONSERVATION*

330 NLD ISSN 1383-6803
MANSHOLT STUDIES (ONLINE EDITION). Text in English. 1995. irreg., latest vol.21, 2001. price varies. **Document type:** *Monographic series, Academic/Scholarly.*
Formerly (until 2001): Mansholt Studies (Print Edition); Which was formed by the merger of (1989-1995): Wageningen Economic Papers (0924-106X); (1988-1995): Wageningen Ruimtelijke Studies (0923-4373); (1988-1995): Wageningen Sociologische Studies (0923-4365); Which was formerly (1982-1988): Landbouwuniversiteit Wageningen. Vakgroepen voor Sociologie. Mededelingen (0923-4381)

Indexed: BIOSIS Prev., WAE&RSA.
Published by: (Landbouwuniversiteit Wageningen), Backhuys Publishers BV, Postbus 321, Leiden, 2300 AH, Netherlands. TEL 31-71-517-0208, FAX 31-71-517-1856, backhuys@euronet.nl, backhuys@backhuys.com, http://www.euronet.nl/users/backhuys/, http://www.backhuys.com.

382 600   USA   ISSN 1534-4878
HC79 .I55
MANTRAM. Text in English. 2001. m. USD 24.95; USD 2.95 newsstand/cover (effective 2001). adv. Index. back issues avail. **Document type:** *Magazine.* **Description:** It is designed to suit the interests of the South Asian professional in the US. It covers technologies like IT, telecom, bio-tech to HR profiles.
Published by: Mantram, LLC, 505 Thornall St., Ste 306, Edison, NJ 08837. TEL 732-516-1199 ext 207, FAX 732-516-9399, subscribe@mantramol.com, http://www.mantramol.com. Ed. Sunil Adam. R&P Ramesh Gurnani TEL 732-494-8900. Adv. contact Rahul Walia. page USD 3,000, online banner USD 300; trim 8.125 x 10.125. Circ: 15,000 (controlled).

330   IND   ISSN 0025-2921
HC431
➤ **MARGIN.** Text in English. 1968. q. INR 500 (effective 1999); INR 125 newsstand/cover; USD 110 newsstand/cover foreign (effective 1999). bk.rev. abstr.; charts; stat. back issues avail.; reprints avail. **Document type:** *Academic/Scholarly.* **Description:** Aimed at providing a focal point for dissemination of empirical information and research findings in broad areas of applied economics. A major emphasis is on policy analysis and application of modern quantitative techniques to developmental issues.
Indexed: BAS, EIP, JEL, PAA&I, REE&TA.
—BLDSC (5373.510000), IE, ingenta.
Published by: National Council of Applied Economic Research, Parisila Bhawan, 11 Indraprastha Estate, New Delhi, 110 002, India. TEL 91-11-3317860, FAX 91-11-3327164, pk.krishnaswamy@ncaer.sprintrpg.ems.vsnl.net.in. Ed. Basanta E Pradhan. Pub. P K Krishnaswamy. Circ: 300 (paid); 300 (controlled).

➤ **MARINE BUSINESS JOURNAL;** the voice of the marine industries nationwide. see *SPORTS AND GAMES—Boats And Boating*

330   ITA   ISSN 1122-8873
MARK UP; economia, produzione e politiche della distribuzione. Text in Italian. 1994. m. EUR 100 domestic; EUR 200 foreign (effective 2005). adv. **Document type:** *Magazine, Consumer.* **Description:** For entrepreneurs and managers of production, marketing, retailing and service sectors. Offers features and articles on European and international scenarios, analysis of operating profits, descriptions of market share and key factors in mass market.
Published by: Editoriale Quasar, Via Patecchio 2, Milan, MI 20141, Italy. TEL 39-02-57316011, FAX 39-02-57316191, http://www.markup.it, http://www.editorialequasar.it. Ed. Luigi Rubinelli. Pub. Giuseppe Dilettoso. Adv. contact Rosy Battaglia. Circ: 60,000 (paid).

330   GBR   ISSN 1463-0877
MARKET LEADER; the journal of the marketing society. Text in English. 1998. q. GBP 145 in United Kingdom; GBP 155 foreign (effective 2000). adv. charts; illus. back issues avail. **Document type:** *Journal.* **Description:** Aimed at senior managers and board level directors, and covers new ideas and thinking in business. It provides articles covering a range of issues, written by well known and respected business leaders.
Related titles: Online - full text ed.
—CCC.
Published by: N T C Publications Ltd. (Subsidiary of: World Advertising Research Center Ltd.), Farm Rd, Henley-on-Thames, Oxon RG9 1EJ, United Kingdom. TEL 44-1491-411000, FAX 44-1491-571188, market_leader@ntc.co.uk, http://www.warc.com. Ed. Julie Lannon. R&P Shahzia Chaudhri TEL 44-1491-418632. Adv. contact Tim Clifton. Circ: 4,200 (paid and controlled).

330   USA   ISSN 1096-8431
MARKETPLACE (APPLETON); northeast Wisconsin's business magazine. Text in English. 1989. 13/yr. USD 48; free to qualified personnel (effective 2003). adv. reprints avail. **Document type:** *Magazine, Corporate.* **Description:** Provides in-depth analysis of business news and trends in Northeast Wisconsin, and company profiles.
Formerly (until 1997): Marketplace Magazine (1054-2264)
Related titles: Microform ed.: (from PQC); Online - full text ed.: (from bigchalk, Northern Light Technology, Inc., O C L C Online Computer Library Center, Inc., ProQuest Information & Learning).
Indexed: ABIn, BusDate.
Published by: A D D Inc., PO Box 1897, Appleton, WI 54912-1897. TEL 920-735-5969, FAX 820-735-5970, marketplace@add-inc.com. Ed. Rick Berg. Pub. R&P, Adv. contact Al Wells. Circ: 15,000 (controlled).

330   USA
MARKETWISE. Text in English. 1995. 3/yr. **Document type:** *Magazine.* **Description:** Promotes economic development using success stories of creative and effective financing of low and moderate-income individuals, communities, and small businesses.
Published by: Federal Reserve Bank of Richmond, Research Dept, Box 27622, Richmond, VA 23261. http://www.rich.frb.org/cao/mwpubs.html.

330   DEU   ISSN 0948-8340
MARKT UND MITTELSTAND. Text in German. 1995. m. EUR 57 domestic; EUR 72 foreign; EUR 5 newsstand/cover (effective 2003). adv. **Document type:** *Magazine, Trade.*
Published by: Finanzen Verlagsgesellschaft mbH (Subsidiary of: Axel Springer Verlag AG), Augustenstr 10, Munich, 80333, Germany. TEL 49-89-27264262, FAX 49-89-27264328, info@marktundmittelstand.de, redaktion@finanzen.net, http://www.marktundmittelstand.de, http://www.finanzen.net. Ed. Thomas Graef. adv.: color page EUR 9,800; trim 210 x 280. Circ: 95,000 (paid and controlled).

330   DEU   ISSN 0178-8183
MARKTORIENTIERTE UNTERNEHMENSFUEHRUNG. Text in German. 1986. irreg., latest vol.25, 2001. EUR 53.30 per vol. (effective 2003). **Document type:** *Monographic series, Academic/Scholarly.*
Published by: Peter Lang GmbH Europaeischer Verlag der Wissenschaften, Eschborner Landstr 42-50, Frankfurt Am Main, 60489, Germany. TEL 49-69-7807050, FAX 49-69-78070543, zentrale.frankfurt@peterlang.com, http://www.peterlang.de. Ed. Hermann Freter.

THE MARYLAND REPORT. see *PUBLIC ADMINISTRATION*

▼ **MATHEMATICAL ECONOMICS AND GAME THEORY.** see *MATHEMATICS*

330   ISR   ISSN 0333-7839
HC415.25.A1
MAURICE FALK INSTITUTE FOR ECONOMIC RESEARCH IN ISRAEL. REPORT AND DISCUSSION PAPER SERIES. Text in English. 1964. irreg. free.
Formerly: Maurice Falk Center for Economic Research in Israel. Report. (0076-5473)
Related titles: Hebrew ed.
—BLDSC (3597.495000).
Published by: Maurice Falk Institute for Economic Research in Israel, P. Naphtali Bldg., The Hebrew University, Mt. Scopus, Jerusalem, 91905, Israel. TEL 972-2-883130, FAX 972-2-816071. Circ: 500.

330   ISR
MAZAL U'BRACHA DIAMONDS. Text in English, Hebrew. m. USD 230 (effective 2002). adv. **Document type:** *Trade.* **Description:** Provides information on all important diamond industry and market issues, covering diamond mining, manufacturing, marketing, related sectors of insurance, banking, investment, technology and more.
Formerly: Mazal U'Bracha
Published by: Tacy Ltd., PO Box 3441, Ramat Gan, 52133, Israel. TEL 972-3-5750196, FAX 972-3-5754829, office@tacy.co.il, http://212.150.188.137/Guy/bb/mainNew.asp.

330   USA
MBAJUNGLE.COM. Text in English. 2000. m. adv. **Document type:** *Trade.* **Description:** Delivers business news and information, industry overviews, company profiles, resume upload capabilities, and other resources for MBA students.
Media: Online - full content. **Related titles:** ♦ Print ed.: M B A Jungle. ISSN 1541-3284.
Published by: Jungle Interactive Media, 632 Broadway, 7th Fl, New York, NY 10012-2614. TEL 866-458-6453, info@mbajungle.com, http://www.mbajungle.com.

330   DEU
MCK WISSEN. Text in German. 2002. 3/yr. EUR 15 newsstand/cover (effective 2002). **Document type:** *Magazine, Trade.*
Published by: McKinsey & Company, Koenigsallee 60c, Duesseldorf, 40027, Germany. TEL 49-211-1364690, FAX 49-211-1364731, rolf_antrecht@mckinsey.com, http://www.mckinsey.de. Ed. Susanne Risch. Circ: 50,000 (paid and controlled).

330 340   USA
MECKLENBURG TIMES. Text in English. 1924. s-w. (Tue. & Fri.). USD 0.50 newsstand/cover; USD 51 (effective 2005). **Document type:** *Newspaper, Trade.*
Related titles: Microfiche ed.
Published by: Legal and Business Publishers, Inc., 400 Clarice Ave., Ste 100, Charlotte, NC 08204. TEL 704-377-6221, FAX 704-377-6214, themecktimes@carolina.rr.com. Ed. Kim Gibson. Pub. John Kurie. Circ: 900 (paid). Wire service: CNS, AP.

MEDIA DETAIL; vakblad voor de detailhandelaren in de consumentenelectronica. see *ELECTRONICS*

MEDICAL DEALER. see *MEDICAL SCIENCES*

681   USA   ISSN 1552-2520
MEDICAL DEVICE BUSINESS WEEK. Text in English. w. USD 2,595 in US & Canada; USD 2,795 elsewhere; USD 2,825 combined subscription in US & Canada print & online eds.; USD 3,055 combined subscription elsewhere print & online eds. (effective 2005). **Document type:** *Newsletter, Academic/Scholarly.* **Description:** Reports the latest fiscal reports, patent filings, mergers and acquisitions, and market trends for a broad spectrum of medical material and medical device marketing and manufacturing companies, including new product introductions, new contract announcements and joint ventures.
Related titles: Online - full content ed.: ISSN 1552-2539; Online - full text ed.: (from ProQuest Information & Learning).
Published by: NewsRx, PO Box 5528, Atlanta, GA 31107-0528. TEL 800-726-4550, info@newsrx.com, http://www.newsrx.com/product_descriptions/MEDICAL_DEVICE_BUSINESS_WEEK.HTM.

616.07   USA   ISSN 1552-6399
MEDICAL IMAGING BUSINESS WEEK. Text in English. w. USD 2,595 in US & Canada; USD 2,795 elsewhere; USD 2,825 in US & Canada; USD 3,055 elsewhere (effective 2005). **Document type:** *Newsletter, Academic/Scholarly.* **Description:** Covers the latest business news from these firms, including fiscal reports, patent filings, new product and contract announcements, mergers, acquisitions and joint ventures.
Related titles: Online - full content ed.: ISSN 1552-6445; Online - full text ed.: (from ProQuest Information & Learning).
Published by: NewsRx, PO Box 5528, Atlanta, GA 31107-0528. TEL 800-726-4550, info@newsrx.com, http://www.newsrx.com/product_descriptions/MEDICAL_IMAGING_BUSINESS_WEEK.HTM.

MEDICAL PATENT BUSINESS WEEK. see *PATENTS, TRADEMARKS AND COPYRIGHTS*

(YEAR) MEDICAL SERVICES DIRECTORY. see *MEDICAL SCIENCES*

MEETINGS EAST. see *TRAVEL AND TOURISM*

▼ **MEETINGS MIDAMERICA.** see *TRAVEL AND TOURISM*

MEETINGS SOUTH. see *TRAVEL AND TOURISM*

MEETINGS WEST. see *TRAVEL AND TOURISM*

338.7   IND   ISSN 0376-5423
HC438.M4
MEGHALAYA INDUSTRIAL DEVELOPMENT CORPORATION. ANNUAL REPORT. Key Title: Annual Report - Meghalaya Industrial Development Corporation. Text in English. 1972. a.
Published by: Meghalaya Industrial Development Corporation, Additional Civil Secretariat Bldg., Shillong, Meghalaya 1, India.

330   CHN   ISSN 1002-9605
MEITAN JINGJI YANJIU/COAL ECONOMICS STUDY. Text in Chinese. 1981. m. CNY 4.50; USD 6 foreign. **Description:** Covers studies on the multifarious economic problems of the coal industry, as well as related government policies and statues.
Related titles: CD-ROM ed.; Online - full text ed.: (from East View Information Services).
Published by: Zhongguo Meitan Kexue Yanjiu Zongyuan, Jingji Yanjiusuo, Hepingli, Beijing, 100013, China. TEL 86-10-6423-4338, FAX 86-10-6422-1627. Ed. Zhang Yunzhang. Circ: 10,000.

330   CHL
MEJORES DATOS. Text in Spanish. 1990. w. adv. **Description:** Features weekly business news.
Related titles: Online - full text ed.
Published by: Lomas y Cia, Ltd, Castellon No 635, Concepcion, Chile. TEL 56-41-245828, FAX 56-41-255748, diario@mejoresdatos.cl, http://www.mejoresdatos.cl/. Ed. Claudio M Pozo. R&P Cristian Seiter-Balboa.

330   DEU   ISSN 0176-5833
MEMO-FORUM; Zirkular der Arbeitsgruppe Alternative Wirtschaftspolitik. Text in German. 1983. irreg., latest vol.26, 1998. EUR 3 per issue (effective 2001). back issues avail. **Document type:** *Bulletin, Academic/Scholarly.*
Indexed: IBR, IBZ.
Published by: Arbeitsgruppe Alternative Wirtschaftspolitik, Postfach 330447, Bremen, 28334, Germany. TEL 49-421-4914480, FAX 49-421-4914488, memorandum@t-online.de, http://www.memo.uni-bremen.de. Ed. Axel Troost. Circ: 3,500.

330   USA   ISSN 0747-167X
MEMPHIS BUSINESS JOURNAL. Text in English. 1979. w. (Fri.). USD 78; USD 1.50 newsstand/cover (effective 2005). adv. bk.rev. **Document type:** *Journal, Trade.*
Formerly (until Mar. 1984): Mid-South Business (0274-8525)
Related titles: Microform ed.: (from PQC); Online - full text ed.: (from Florida Center for Library Automation, Gale Group, Northern Light Technology, Inc., O C L C Online Computer Library Center, Inc., ProQuest Information & Learning, The Dialog Corporation).

B

Indexed: ABIn, BusDate, LRI, T&II.
—CCC.
Published by: (Memphis Business Journal), American City Business Journals, Inc. (Charlotte), 120 W Morehead St, Ste 200, Charlotte, NC 28202. TEL 800-704-3757, memphis@bizjournals.com, http://www.bizjournals.com/memphis/. Ed. Bill Wellborn. Circ: 9,000 (paid and controlled).

330 ARG
EL MENHIR. Text in Spanish. 1991. irreg., latest no.4, Oct. 1993. free. adv. bk.rev. **Description:** Includes interviews, articles on Argentine and world economy written by people who work in either private or governmental institutions.
Published by: Universidad de Buenos Aires, Colegio de Economica, Olleros, 2016 Piso 6, Capital Federal, Buenos Aires 1426, Argentina. TEL 54-114-7721666, FAX 54-114-8214540. Ed. Maximiliano Montenegro. Circ: 5,000.

330 ITA
MERCATI FINANZIARI✶. Text in Italian. d.
Published by: Milano Finanza Editori SpA, Via Marco Burigozzo, 5, Milan, MI 20122, Italy. TEL 2-80-291, FAX 2-80-52-832. Ed. Lionello Cadorin. Circ: 30,000.

330 340 ITA ISSN 1590-5128
MERCATO CONCORRENZA REGOLE. Text in Italian. 1999. 3/yr. EUR 52 domestic to individuals; EUR 76 foreign to individuals; EUR 84 domestic to institutions Print & online eds.; EUR 121 foreign to institutions Print & online eds. (effective 2004).
Related titles: Online - full text ed.
Published by: Societa Editrice Il Mulino, Strada Maggiore 37, Bologna, 40125, Italy. TEL 39-051-256011, FAX 39-051-256034, riviste@mulino.it, http://www.mulino.it.

330 ESP ISSN 1138-1140
MERCURIO; revista de economia y empresa. Text in Spanish. 1997. irreg.
—CINDOC.
Published by: Universidad de Valladolid, Secretariado de Publicaciones, Juan Mambrilla, 14, Valladolid, 47003, Spain. TEL 34-83-294499, FAX 34-83-290300. **Co-sponsor:** Caja Duero.

330 USA ISSN 0742-602X
HD2746.5
MERGER AND ACQUISITION SOURCEBOOK (YEAR). Text in English. a. (plus q. updates). USD 350 (effective 2001). **Description:** Provides in depth review of 3000 plus mergers and acquisitions in the U.S. and world markets. Includes legal and financial data.
Related titles: CD-ROM ed.: USD 395 (effective 2001).
Published by: N V S T.com, Inc., 14450 N E 29th Pl., Ste.108, Bellevue, WA 98007. TEL 425-702-9733, 800-910-6878, FAX 425-702-9753, http://www.nvst.com/pnvHome.asp.

330 USA ISSN 1076-3600
HD2746.5
THE MERGER YEARBOOK. Text in English. 1980. a. USD 595. adv. charts; stat. index. back issues avail. **Document type:** *Trade.* **Description:** Listing of acquisition announcements by industry, indexed by corporate and individual targets.
Formed by the 1992 merger of: International Merger Yearbook (1052-9942); U S Merger Yearbook (1076-3619); Which was formerly (1990-1991): Domestic Merger Yearbook (1052-9934); (until 1989): Yearbook on Corporate Mergers, Joint Ventures and Corporate Policy (0732-5320)
Published by: Securities Data Publishing (Subsidiary of: Thomson Financial / I M G Media), 195 Broadway, New York, NY 10007. TEL 212-333-9202, http://www.thomsonfinancial.com. Ed. Daniel Bokser.

332.6 USA ISSN 0026-0010
HG4028.M4 CODEN: AMACDR
MERGERS & ACQUISITIONS (NEW YORK, 1965); the dealmakers' journal. Variant title: Mergers and Acquisitions Journal. Text in English. 1965. m. USD 695 domestic; USD 870 foreign (effective 2005). adv. charts; illus. index. back issues avail.; reprint service avail. from PQC. **Document type:** *Magazine, Trade.* **Description:** Provides in-depth coverage of merger techniques and strategies, corporate development, and data on US merger and acquisition activity. For financial executives and legal, accounting, and banking professionals.
Incorporated (in 1967): Mergers and Acquisitions Monthly (0543-5137)
Related titles: Microfiche ed.: (from CIS); Microform ed.: (from PQC); Online - full text ed.: (from EBSCO Publishing, Florida Center for Library Automation, Gale Group, H.W. Wilson, LexisNexis, Northern Light Technology, Inc., O C L C Online Computer Library Center, Inc., ProQuest Information & Learning).
Indexed: ABIn, ATI, B&I, BPI, BPIA, BusI, CLI, Emerald, LRI, ManagCont, PAIS, PROMT, SRI, T&II.
—BLDSC (5680.770000), IE, Infotrieve, ingenta. **CCC.**
Published by: Source Media, Inc., One State St Plaza, 27th Fl, New York, NY 10004. TEL 212-803-6077, 800-221-1809, FAX 212-747-1154, custserv@sourcemedia.com, http://www.majournal.com, http://www.sourcemedia.com. Ed. Martin Sikora. Adv. contact James MacDonald TEL 212-803-8749. Circ: 3,000 (paid).

330 USA ISSN 1532-4745
MERGERS & ACQUISITIONS - ASIA PACIFIC. Key Title: M & A Reporter Asia Pacific. Text in English. 2000. d. (Mon.-Fri.). USD 780 for 6 mos. (effective 2002). **Document type:** *Trade.* **Description:** Covers companies in the Asia-Pacific region targeted for merger or acquisition type transaction.
Media: E-mail.
Published by: Beard Group, Inc, PO Box 9867, Washington, DC 20016. TEL 240-629-3300, FAX 240-629-3360, info@beard.com, http://www.beard.com.

338.83 CAN ISSN 0843-5421
MERGERS AND ACQUISITIONS IN CANADA. Variant title: M & A. Text in English. 1986. m. CND 695 (effective 2005).
Related titles: Online - full text ed.: (from Factiva).
—CCC.
Published by: Crosbie & Company Inc., One First Canadian Pl, 9th Flr, PO Box 116, Toronto, ON M5X 1A4, Canada. TEL 416-362-7726, FAX 416-362-3447, info@crosbieco.com, http://www.crosbieco.com/M&A.html.

330 USA ISSN 1099-3428
MERGERS & ACQUISITIONS REPORT. Text in English. 1988. w. USD 1,675 domestic print & online eds.; USD 1,725 foreign print & online eds. (effective 2005). adv. **Document type:** *Newsletter, Consumer.*
Formerly (until 1996): Mergers & Restructurings (1092-1362); Incorporates (1992-199?): Mergers & Acquisitions International (1066-3525); Which incorporated (1988-1992): M & A Europe (1017-5229)
Related titles: Online - full text ed.: (from EBSCO Publishing, Florida Center for Library Automation, Gale Group, LexisNexis, O C L C Online Computer Library Center, Inc., ProQuest Information & Learning).
Indexed: ABIn, ATI, B&I.
—CCC.
Published by: Source Media, Inc., One State St Plaza, 27th Fl, New York, NY 10004. TEL 212-803-6077, 800-221-1809, FAX 212-747-1154, custserv@sourcemedia.com, http://www.mareport.com, http://www.sourcemedia.com.

MERTENS RULINGS. see *LAW*

METALMECANICA. see *METALLURGY*

METALWORKING INSIDERS' REPORT; the global newsletter on factory equipment. see *MACHINERY*

330 GBR ISSN 0026-1386
HB1.A1
➤ **METROECONOMICA;** international review of economics. Text in English, French, German, Italian. 1949. q. EUR 57 combined subscription in Europe to individuals print & online eds.; USD 64 combined subscription in the Americas to individuals & Caribbean, print & online eds.; GBP 38 combined subscription elsewhere to individuals print & online eds.; USD 549 combined subscription in the Americas to institutions & Caribbean, print & online eds.; GBP 327 combined subscription elsewhere to institutions print & online eds. (effective 2006). adv. bk.rev. bibl.; charts. index, cum.index every 10 yrs. reprint service avail. from PSC. **Document type:** *Journal, Academic/Scholarly.* **Description:** Provides essential reading for professionals and students interested in a wide spectrum of theoretical approaches to analytical economics, providing an international forum for debate among completing theories and research programs going beyond the traditional emphasis on market equilibrium/disequilibrium.
Related titles: Online - full text ed.: ISSN 1467-999X. USD 522 in the Americas to institutions & Caribbean; GBP 311 elsewhere to institutions (effective 2006) (from Blackwell Synergy, EBSCO Publishing, Gale Group, IngentaConnect, O C L C Online Computer Library Center, Inc., Swets Information Services).
Indexed: ABIn, CCMJ, CREJ, IBR, IBSS, IBZ, JEL, MathR, MathSciNet, PCI, RASB, RRTA, RefZh, WAE&RSA, ZentMath.
—BLDSC (5748.750000), IE, Infotrieve, ingenta. **CCC.**
Published by: Blackwell Publishing Ltd., 9600 Garsington Rd, Oxford, OX4 2ZG, United Kingdom. TEL 44-1865-776868, FAX 44-1865-714591, customerservices@oxon.blackwellpublishing.com, http://www.blackwellpublishing.com/journals/MECA. Ed. Heinz D Kurz TEL 43-316-380-3444. Circ: 1,800.

330 MEX
MEXICAN FORECAST; fortnightly forecast for management and investors on Mexican business and investment trends. Text in English. 1992. s-m. USD 595 (effective 1997). adv. **Document type:** *Newsletter.*
Published by: Grupo Editorial Expansion (Subsidiary of: Capital Cities - A B C, Inc.), Salamanca No. 149,, Col Roma, Mexico City, DF 06700, Mexico. TEL 525-2072066, FAX 525-5116351. Ed. Lindajoy Fenley. Pub., R&P David Estrello. Adv. contact Maria Elena Bayardo.

MEZHDUNARODNI OTNOSHENIA. see *HISTORY—History Of Europe*

MI2N; music industry news network. see *MUSIC*

330 USA ISSN 1070-6437
MIAMI DAILY BUSINESS REVIEW. Text in English. 1926. d. (Mon.-Fri.). USD 298 combined subscription print & online eds. (effective 2005). adv. **Document type:** *Newspaper, Trade.* **Description:** Provides South Florida's daily business news and information on the economy and the courts.
Formerly (until 1993): Miami Review (0888-0263)
Related titles: Microfilm ed.; ◆ Online - full content ed.: Daily Business Review (Online Edition); Online - full text ed.: (from Florida Center for Library Automation, Gale Group, ProQuest Information & Learning).
—CCC.
Published by: Daily Business Review (Subsidiary of: A L M), 1 SE Third Ave, Ste 900, Miami, FL 33131. TEL 305-377-3721, https://www.dailybusinessreview.com/. Ed. David V Lyons TEL 305-347-6694. Adv. contact Anthony J DiGregorio. Circ: 9,624 (paid and controlled). Wire service: DJNS.

330 USA ISSN 1535-5829
MIBIZ SOUTHWEST; Michigan's business advocate. Text in English. bi-w.
Published by: News One Inc., 6687 Seeco Dr, C, Kalamazoo, MI 49009. TEL 616-544-0560, FAX 616-544-0563, swinfo@mibiz.com, http://www.mibiz.com. Adv. contact Randy Sneller.

330 USA ISSN 1533-8975
MIBIZ WEST; business advocate of West Michigan. Text in English. 1988. 26/yr. USD 46 (effective 2001); free to qualified personnel. **Document type:** *Newspaper, Consumer.* **Description:** West Michigan's premier business publication serving Kent, Ottawa, Muskegon and Allegan (Grand Rapids MSA) and nine surrounding counties.
Formerly (until Jan. 2001): Shoreline Business Monthly (1085-4916)
Published by: William R. Lowry, Ed. & Pub., 6520 Schamber Dr., Ste. A, Muskegon, MI 49444-9752. TEL 231-798-4669, FAX 231-798-8335, wlowry@mibiz.com, http://www.mibiz.com/. Circ: 13,000.

THE MICHIGAN BUSINESS LAW JOURNAL. see *LAW*

330 USA ISSN 1090-8919
HB1
MICHIGAN JOURNAL OF ECONOMICS. Text in English. 1979. a. (Spring). USD 6 (effective 2004). bk.rev. back issues avail. **Document type:** *Journal, Academic/Scholarly.* **Description:** Contains 4-5 economics essays written by undergraduates.
Published by: University of Michigan, Economics Department, 154 Lorch Hall, 611 Tappan St, Ann Arbor, MI 48109-1220. TEL 734-239-2320, http://www.umich.edu/~michje/. Circ: 300.

330 CAN ISSN 1198-3558
MICRO. Text in English. 1994. q. **Document type:** *Newsletter.*
Related titles: Online - full content ed.: ISSN 1495-1991; Online - full text ed.: (from Micromedia ProQuest).
Indexed: RefZh.
Published by: Industry Canada/Industrie Canada, Distribution Services, Communications & Marketing Branch, Rm 268D, West Tower, C.D. Howe Bldg, 235 Queen St, Ottawa, ON K1A 0H5, Canada. mepa.apme@ic.gc.ca, publications@ic.gc.ca, http://strategis.ic.gc.ca/epic/internet/ineas-aes.nsf/en/h_ra01878e.html, http://www.ic.gc.ca.

330 USA ISSN 0895-1772
HD28
➤ **MID-AMERICAN JOURNAL OF BUSINESS.** Text in English. 1985. s-a. (Mar. & Sep.). USD 25 to individuals; USD 40 to institutions; USD 30 foreign (effective 2005). adv. bk.rev. bibl.; charts; illus.; stat. Index. 70 p./no. 2 cols./p.; back issues avail.; reprints avail. **Document type:** *Journal, Academic/Scholarly.* **Description:** Publishes general business articles intended for business professionals - executives, consultants, and teachers.
Formed by the merger of (1971-1985): Ball State Business Review (0749-6141); (1929-1982): Ball State Journal for Business Educators; Which was formerly (until 1965): Ball State Commerce Journal
Related titles: Microform ed.: (from PQC); Online - full text ed.: (from H.W. Wilson, O C L C Online Computer Library Center, Inc., ProQuest Information & Learning).
Indexed: ABIn, BPI, BusEdI, Emerald, PAIS, PsycInfo, PsycholAb, e-psyche.
—BLDSC (5761.313430), IE, ingenta.
Published by: Ball State University, Bureau of Business Research, 2000 W University Ave, Muncie, IN 47306-0360. TEL 765-289-1241, FAX 765-285-8024, jlane@bsu.edu, http://www.bsu.edu/majb. Ed. Ashok Gupta. R&P, Adv. contact Judy Lane. B&W page USD 250; trim 11 x 8.5. Circ: 1,800 (paid and free).

➤ **THE MIDDLE EAST.** see *LITERARY AND POLITICAL REVIEWS*

330 AUS ISSN 1035-3704
➤ **MIDDLE EAST BUSINESS AND ECONOMIC REVIEW.** Text in English. 1989. s-a. USD 40 domestic; USD 50 foreign (effective 2001). bk.rev. abstr.; charts. **Document type:** *Academic/Scholarly.* **Description:** Specializes in research related to the Middle Eastern countries in the areas of business and economics.
Indexed: IBSS, JEL.

B

—BLDSC (5761.359800), IE, ingenta.
Published by: Association for Middle East Economic Research, c/o School of Economics and Finance, U W S, Wollongong, NSW 2500, Australia. TEL 61-246-203214, FAX 61-246-266683. Eds. Mokhtar M Metwally, Satya Paul.

330 USA ISSN 0194-4525
MIDLANDS BUSINESS JOURNAL; published for the nation's industrial and agri-business heartland. Text in English. 1975. w. (Fri.). USD 60 (effective 2005). adv. **Document type:** *Newspaper.*
Published by: M B J Corporation, 1324 S. 119th St., Omaha, Douglas, NE 68144. TEL 402-330-1760, FAX 402-758-9315, lori@mbj.com, http://www.mbj.com. Ed., Pub. Robert Hoig. adv.: page USD 740. Circ: 5,200 (paid).

MIDWEST LAW REVIEW. see *LAW*

330 EGY ISSN 1110-7731
MIGALIT AL-BUHUWT AL-TUGARIYAT GAMI'AT AL-ZAQAZIQ/ZAGAZIG UNIVERSITY. JOURNAL OF COMMERCIAL RESEARCH. Text in Arabic. 1978. s-a. EGP 10 domestic; EGP 35 foreign; EGP 10 newsstand/cover domestic; EGP 25 newsstand/cover foreign (effective 2004). **Document type:** *Journal, Academic/Scholarly.*
Published by: Zagazig University, Faculty of Commerce, Banha Branch, Zagazig, Egypt. TEL 20-55-233330, FAX 20-55-343331, http://derp.sti.sci.eg/data/0023.htm. Ed. Dr. Muhammad Shawqi.

MIND MATTERS REVIEW. see *PSYCHOLOGY*

MINE DEVELOPMENT BUSINESS LEADS (MDBL). see *MINES AND MINING INDUSTRY*

MINEXTRACT. see *MINES AND MINING INDUSTRY*

330 CHN
MINGPAI SHIBAO/SPOTLIGHT TIMES. Text in Chinese. 2/w. CNY 53.04. **Document type:** *Newspaper.*
Related titles: Online - full content ed.
Published by: Jingji Ribao Baoye Jituan/Economic Daily Newspaper Group, Haidian-qu, 33, Fucheng Lu, 10F, Beijing Gongshang Daxue Zonghelou, Beijing, China. TEL 86-10-68981138, http://www.mpsb.com.cn/. **Dist. by:** China International Book Trading Corp, 35 Chegongzhuang Xilu, Haidian District, PO Box 399, Beijing 100044, China. TEL 86-10-68412045, FAX 86-10-68412023, cibtc@mail.cibtc.com.cn, http://www.cibtc.com.cn.

330 POL ISSN 1234-673X
MINISTERSTWO FINANSOW. BIULETYN SKARBOWY. Text in Polish. 1995. bi-m. EUR 44 foreign (effective 2005). **Document type:** *Bulletin.*
Published by: (Ministerstwo Finansow), Grupa Wydawnicza INFOR Sp. z o.o., Ul Okopowa 58/72, Warsaw, 01042, Poland. TEL 48-22-7613030, FAX 48-22-7613031, bok@infor.pl, http://www.infor.pl. Ed. Elzbieta Radziszewska. Adv. contact Waldemar Krakowiak. **Dist. by:** Ars Polona, Krakowskie Przedmiescie 7, Warsaw, Poland. TEL 48-22-9263914, FAX 48-22-9265334, arspolona@arspolona.com.pl, http://www.arspolona.com.pl.

330 USA ISSN 1543-1029
HD2341
▼ **MINORITY AND SMALL BUSINESS REVIEW.** Text in English. 2003 (Jan.). a. USD 10 newsstand/cover (effective 2003).
Published by: Hsi Lai University, Center for the Study of Minority and Small Business, 1409 N. Walnut Grove Ave., Rosemead, CA 91770. TEL 626-571-8811, FAX 626-571-1413, http://www.hlu.edu. Ed. Bill Y. Chen.

330 305.8 USA
MINORITY BUSINESS JOURNAL. Text in English. 1985. bi-m. USD 8.50. adv. illus. **Description:** Provides news briefs, business updates, profiles of successful minority business people, announcements and reports on conferences and trade fairs.
Published by: James D. Lewis Enterprises, 511 Junilla St, Pittsburgh, PA 15219. TEL 412-682-4386. Circ: 100,000.

MINORITY M B A. (Masters in Business Administration) see *OCCUPATIONS AND CAREERS*

330 305.8 USA
MINORITY OPPORTUNITY NEWS. Text in English. s-m. USD 50 (effective 2001).
Published by: Minority Opportunity News Inc, 2730 Stemmons, 1202 Tower West, Dallas, TX 75207. TEL 972-606-3891, FAX 214-905-5198. Pub. Thurman Jones.

330 UKR
MIR DENEG. Text in Ukrainian. m. USD 220 in United States.
Address: Ul Sh Rustaveli 39-41, Kiev, Ukraine. TEL 380-44-227-3691, FAX 380-44-227-7635. **US dist. addr.:** East View Information Services, 3020 Harbor Ln. N., Minneapolis, MN 55447. TEL 612-550-0961.

330 RUS ISSN 0131-2227
HC10
MIROVAYA EKONOMIKA I MEZHDUNARODNYE OTNOSHENIYA. Text in Russian; Contents page in English. 1957. m. USD 204 foreign (effective 2003). bk.rev. bibl.; charts; stat. index. **Document type:** *Academic/Scholarly.*
Related titles: Microfiche ed.: (from EVP); Online - full text ed.: (from East View Information Services).
Indexed: CDSP, HistAb, IBSS, IPSA, RASB, RRTA, RefZh, WAE&RSA.
Published by: Rossiiskaya Akademiya Nauk, Institut Mirovoi Ekonomiki i Mezhdunarodnykh Otnoshenii, Profsoyuznaya ul 23, Moscow, 117418, Russian Federation. TEL 7-095-1284709, imemoran@glasnet.ru. Ed. G G Diligenskii. R&P S I Litsov TEL 7-095-3347391. Circ: 4,200. **Dist. by:** M K - Periodica, ul Gilyarovskogo 39, Moscow 129110, Russian Federation. TEL 7-095-2845008, FAX 7-095-2813798, info@periodicals.ru, http://www.mkniga.ru; **Dist. in U.S. by:** Victor Kamkin Inc., 220 Girard St, Ste 1, Gaithersburg, MD 20877.

330 CAN
MISSISSAUGA BUSINESS NEWS. Text in English. 1993. m. CND 28; USD 47 in United States. adv. software rev. charts; illus.; stat.; tr.lit. back issues avail. **Document type:** *Newspaper.*
Related titles: CD-ROM ed.; Online - full text ed.
Published by: Metroland Printing, Publishing and Distributing Ltd., 3145 Wolfedale Rd, Mississauga, ON L5C 3A9, Canada. Ed. Judy Immerson. Pub. Ron Lenyk TEL 905-273-8119. Adv. contact Joe Ingham. B&W page CND 2,425; trim 15 x 10. Circ: 32,025 (controlled).

330 JPN ISSN 0026-6760
HB9
➤ **MITA GAKKAI ZASSHI/MITA JOURNAL OF ECONOMICS.** Text in Japanese. 1909. q. JPY 8,000, USD 66.70 (effective 2003). bk.rev. abstr.; charts. back issues avail. **Document type:** *Journal, Academic/Scholarly.*
Indexed: AmH&L, HistAb.
Published by: Keio Gijuku Daigaku, Keio Keizai Gakkai/Keio University, Keio Economic Society, 2-15-45 Mita, Minato-ku, Tokyo, 108-8345, Japan. TEL 81-3-3453-4511, FAX 81-3-5427-1578, http://www.keio.ac.jp/org/kes. Ed. Kenichi Tomobe. R&P, Adv. contact Toshiaki Nakazawa. **Dist. by:** Japan Publications Trading Co., Ltd., Book Export II Dept, PO Box 5030, Tokyo International, Tokyo 101-3191, Japan.

330 CZE ISSN 1211-0507
MODERNI OBEC. Text in Czech. 1994. m. CZK 960; CZK 75 newsstand/cover (effective 2003). adv. **Document type:** *Magazine, Trade.*
Published by: Economia a.s., Dobrovskeho 25, Prague 7 7, 170 55, Czech Republic. TEL 420-2-33071111, FAX 420-2-33072003, moderni.obec@economia.cz, http://www.economia.cz. Ed. Lydia Stoupova. adv.: page CZK 39,000; trim 185 x 254.

330 RUS
MODUS. Text in Russian. 1995. 20/yr. USD 145 in North America (effective 2000).
Published by: Kommercheskoe Informatsionnoe Agentstvo/Mobile, 5-i Donskoi pr 21b korp 8, Moscow, 117926, Russian Federation. TEL 7-095-9580168. Ed. P Kurkov. **Dist. by:** East View Information Services, 3020 Harbor Ln. N., Minneapolis, MN 55447. TEL 763-550-0961, FAX 763-559-2931.

330 MEX ISSN 0186-2901
MOMENTO ECONOMICO; informacion y analisis de la coyuntura mexicana. Text in Spanish. bi-m. MXP 85, USD 18 (effective 2000). back issues avail. **Description:** Examines the economy and politics of Mexico, specifically, but not exclusively.
Related titles: Online - full text ed.: Momento Economico. Boletin Electronico. ISSN 1605-5675. 1995 (from EBSCO Publishing).
Indexed: HAPI, JEL, PAIS, RASB.
Published by: Universidad Nacional Autonoma de Mexico, Instituto de Investigaciones Economicas, Torre II de Humanidades 5o Piso, Ciudad Universitaria, Mexico City, DF 04510, Mexico. TEL 52-5-6230130, FAX 52-5-6160730, alamillo@servidor.unam.mx, http://serpiente.dgsca.unam.mx/iie. Ed. Adrian Gonzales.

330 AUS ISSN 1441-5429
MONASH UNIVERSITY. DEPARTMENT OF ECONOMICS. DISCUSSION PAPERS. Text in English. 1999. irreg.
—BLDSC (3553.795000).
Published by: Monash University, Department of Economics, Clayton Campus, Wellington Rd, Clayton, VIC 3800, Australia. TEL 61-3-99054000, FAX 61-3-99054007, http://www.monash.edu.au.

330 AUS
MONASH UNIVERSITY. FACULTY OF BUSINESS AND ECONOMICS. FACULTY NEWSLETTER. Text in English. m. **Document type:** *Newsletter.* **Description:** Highlights events, awards and administration regarding the Faculty of Business and Economics at Monash University.
Related titles: Online - full text ed.
Published by: Monash University, Faculty of Business and Economics, Wellington Rd, Clayton, VIC 3168, Australia. TEL 61-3-99052327, lynne.macdonald@buseco.monash.edu.au, http://www.buseco.monash.edu.au/faculty/pubs/newsletter.

330 ITA ISSN 0391-6855
AP37
IL MONDO; il settimanale economico Italiano. Text in Italian. 1949. w. (50 issues). EUR 100 (effective 2005). adv. bk.rev. illus. Index. back issues avail.; reprints avail. **Document type:** *Magazine, Consumer.* **Description:** Reports national and international news in the world of politics, the economy, business, and culture.
Related titles: Online - full text ed.: Mondo Online; ♦ Supplement to: Corriere della Sera. ISSN 1120-4982.
Indexed: PAIS, RASB.
Published by: R C S Periodici (Subsidiary of: R C S Mediagroup), Via Angelo Rizzoli, 2, Milan, MI 20132, Italy. TEL 39-2-25845413, FAX 39-2-25845444, ilmondo@rcs.it, info@periodici.rcs.it, http://www.il mondo.rcs.it, http://www.rcsmediagroup.it/siti/periodici.php. Ed. Gianni Gambarotta. Adv. contact Flavio Biondi. Circ: 70,000 (paid). **Dist. in UK by:** Seymour Distribution Ltd, 86 Newman St, London W1T 3EX, United Kingdom. TEL 44-20-73968000, FAX 44-20-73968002.

330 USA
MONETARY AND ECONOMIC REVIEW. Text in English. 1985. m. USD 150 domestic; USD 180 foreign (effective 2002). adv. bk.rev. cum.index: 1985-1997. back issues avail. **Document type:** *Newsletter, Consumer.* **Description:** Reviews the political, governmental and central bank actions as to how they affect the economy and certain investments.
Related titles: Online - full text ed.
Published by: F A M C Inc., 375 E. Horsetooth Rd., Bldg. 2, Fort Collins, CO 80525. TEL 970-223-4962, FAX 970-223-4996, http://www.famcinc.com. Ed., Pub., Adv. contact Dr. Larry Bates. R&P Cindy Standley TEL 970-223-4962. Circ: 5,000 (paid).

330 AUT ISSN 1420-4576
MONEY TREND; Internationales Magazin fuer Muenzen und Papiergeld. Text in German. 1968. 11/yr. EUR 77 domestic; EUR 99 in Europe; EUR 143 elsewhere (effective 2005). adv. **Document type:** *Magazine, Consumer.*
Indexed: NumL.
Published by: Money Trend Verlag GmbH, Kutschkergasse 42, Vienna, N 1180, Austria. TEL 43-1-47686, FAX 43-1-4768621, vweege@webway.at, http://www.moneytrend.at. Ed. Gerd Volker Weege. Pub. Markus Weege. R&P, Adv. contact Zuzanna Stauffer. B&W page EUR 1,100, color page EUR 1,600; trim 197 x 269. Circ: 20,000 (paid and controlled).

330 CAN ISSN 1488-1349
MONEYSENSE. Text in English. 1999. bi-m.
Related titles: Online - full text ed.: (from Micromedia ProQuest, ProQuest Information & Learning).
Indexed: ABIn.
Published by: Maclean Hunter Ltd., Maclean Hunter Bldg, 777 Bay St, Ste 405, Toronto, ON M5W 1A7, Canada. TEL 416-596-5624, FAX 416-596-5866.

332.6 GBR ISSN 0960-264X
HG5431
MONEYWISE; Britain's best-selling personal finance magazine. Text in English. m. GBP 32; GBP 2.95 newsstand/cover (effective 1999). **Document type:** *Consumer.* **Description:** Contains advice, surveys and news pertaining to personal investments.
—CCC.
Published by: R D Publications Ltd., 11 Westferry Circus, Canary Wharf, London, E14 4HE, United Kingdom. TEL 44-171-715-8000, FAX 44-171-715-8725, http://www.moneywise.co.uk. Circ: 101,709. **Dist. by:** Comag, Tavistock Works, Tavistock Rd, W Drayton, Middx UB7 7QX, United Kingdom. TEL 44-1895-444055, FAX 44-1895-433602.

330 FRA ISSN 0750-3598
MONITEUR DU COMMERCE ET DE L'INDUSTRIE. Text in French. 1901. 24/yr. adv.
Address: 13 rue d' Uzes, Paris, 75002, France. TEL 45-08-95-94, FAX 42-33-78-83. Circ: 20,000.

330 RUS
MONITORING OBSHCHESTVENNOGO MNENIYA: EKONOMICHESKIE I SOTSYAL'NYE PEREMENY. Text in Russian. 1998. bi-m. USD 275 in North America (effective 2000).
Indexed: RefZh.
Published by: Aspekt Press Ltd., Ul Plekhanova 23 korp 3, Moscow, 111398, Russian Federation. TEL 7-095-3093600. Ed. Yu Levada. **Dist. by:** East View Information Services, 3020 Harbor Ln. N., Minneapolis, MN 55447. TEL 763-550-0961, FAX 763-559-2931.

330 MYS
MONOGRAPH SERIES ON MALAYSIAN ECONOMIC AFFAIRS. Text in English. 1971. irreg., latest vol.6, 1987. price varies. bibl. **Document type:** *Monographic series.*

B

Published by: (University of Malaya, Faculty of Economics & Administration), University of Malaya/Perpustakaan Universiti Malaya, Lembah Pantai, Kuala Lumpur, 59100, Malaysia. http://www.um.edu.my. Circ: 1,000.

330 USA ISSN 1531-8125
MONOGRAPHS OF THE JOURNAL OF CONSUMER RESEARCH. Abbreviated title: M J C R. (vol.1: Emotional Decisions: Trade-off Difficulty and Coping in Consumer Choice) Text in English. 2001 (Spring). irreg., latest no.1, 2001. USD 18 newsstand/cover domestic; USD 23.76 newsstand/cover in Canada; USD 22.50 newsstand/cover elsewhere (effective 2003); free with subscr. to Journal of Consumer Research. **Document type:** *Monographic series, Consumer.* **Description:** Publishes major works that generate authoritative new findings about consumer research based on large scale empirical studies or conceptual integration and model development.
—BLDSC (5915.475000). **CCC.**
Published by: University of Chicago Press, Journals Division, Journals Division, PO Box 37005, Chicago, IL 60637. TEL 773-702-3347, subscriptions@press.uchicago.edu, http://www.journals.uchicago.edu/MJCR/home.html. Adv. contact Timothy Hill TEL 773-702-8187.

650 USA ISSN 0026-9921
HC107.M9 CODEN: MBQUA9
MONTANA BUSINESS QUARTERLY. Abbreviated title: M B Q. Text in English. 1962. q. USD 35 (effective 2005). adv. index. back issues avail. **Document type:** *Academic/Scholarly.*
Related titles: Microfilm ed.: (from PQC); Online - full text ed.: (from EBSCO Publishing, Florida Center for Library Automation, Gale Group, Northern Light Technology, Inc., O C L C Online Computer Library Center, Inc., ProQuest Information & Learning).
Indexed: ABIn, BPIA, BusDate, BusI, PAIS, T&II.
—BLDSC (5928.005400), IE, ingenta.
Published by: University of Montana, Bureau of Business and Economic Research, Gallagher Business Building, 32 Campus Dr. #6840, Missoula, MT 59812-6840. TEL 406-243-5113, FAX 406-243-2086. Ed. Shannon Jahrig. R&P, Adv. contact Carolyn Schultz. Circ: 1,700. **Co-sponsor:** University of Montana, School of Business Administration.

MONTHLY REPORT ON EUROPE. see *POLITICAL SCIENCE—International Relations*

330 CAN ISSN 0835-7692
MONTREAL BUSINESS MAGAZINE. Text in English. 1988. 6/yr. adv. bk.rev. **Document type:** *Trade.* **Description:** Includes commentaries on wealth management, industry sector reports, corporate profiles, professional advice in law, accounting, and management.
Address: 215 St Jacques St W, Ste 240, Montreal, PQ H2Y 1M6, Canada. TEL 514-286-8038, FAX 514-287-7346, info@mbm-minc.com, mbminc@istar.ca. Ed. Michael Carin. R&P Mark Weller. Circ: 16,500; 16,500 (controlled).

330 RUS
MORSKIE VESTI ROSSII. Text in Russian. 1997. 24/yr. USD 215 in North America (effective 2000).
Published by: Izdatel'stvo Soross, Ul Petrovka 3-6 ofis 543, Moscow, 103775, Russian Federation. TEL 7-095-9157091. Ed. A I Kuznetsov. **Dist. by:** East View Information Services, 3020 Harbor Ln. N., Minneapolis, MN 55447. TEL 763-550-0961, FAX 763-559-2931.

052 330 RUS ISSN 0868-8400
MOSCOW MAGAZINE. Text in English. 1990. m. USD 54 domestic; USD 89 in Europe; USD 112 in North America. adv. bk.rev. illus. back issues avail. **Description:** Covers developments affecting the Soviet economy, including privatization, political and legislative changes; also provides information on business and cultural life in Moscow for foreign residents and visitors, with listings of restaurants and services.
Related titles: Russian ed.
Address: Dom Zhurnalista, Suvorovsky bulv 8-A, kom 303, Moscow, 121019, Russian Federation. TEL 203-3644, FAX 291-1787. Circ: 60,000. **Subscr. to:** PO Box 6805, Haarlem 2001 JH, Netherlands.

330 RUS ISSN 0027-1365
HB97.5
MOSKOVSKII GOSUDARSTVENNYI UNIVERSITET. VESTNIK. SERIYA 6: EKONOMIKA. Text in Russian. 1966. bi-m. USD 48 foreign (effective 2004). bk.rev. bibl. index. **Document type:** *Journal, Academic/Scholarly.*
Supersedes in part: Moskovskii Gosudarstvennyi Universitet. Vestnik. Seriya Ekonomika, Filosofiya (0579-9457)
Indexed: IBSS, RASB, RefZh.
—East View.
Published by: (Moskovskii Gosudarstvennyi Universitet im. M.V. Lomonosova, Ekonomicheskii Fakul'tet/M.V. Lomonosov Moscow State University, Department of Economics), Izdatel'stvo Moskovskogo Gosudarstvennogo Universiteta im. M. V. Lomonosova/Publishing House of Moscow State University, B Nikitskaya 5/7, Moscow, 103009, Russian Federation. TEL 7-095-2295091, FAX 7-095-2036671, kd_mgu@rambler.ru, http://www.msu.ru/depts/MSUPubl. Circ: 2,150. **Dist. by:** M K - Periodica, ul Gilyarovskogo 39, Moscow 129110, Russian Federation. TEL 7-095-2845008, FAX 7-095-2813798, info@periodicals.ru, http://www.mkniga.ru.

MOTION. see *TRAVEL AND TOURISM*

THE MOTION SYSTEM DESIGN. see *ENGINEERING—Mechanical Engineering*

MOTORSPORT & BUSINESS. see *SPORTS AND GAMES*

MULTICHANNEL NEWSDAY FAX. see *COMMUNICATIONS—Television And Cable*

330 GBR ISSN 0953-7929
MULTINATIONAL EMPLOYER. Text in English. 1984. 11/yr. GBP 175, USD 290 (effective 1999). adv. bk.rev. **Document type:** *Bulletin.* **Description:** International human resources comments.
Formerly (until 1988): Corporate Expatriate (0267-2324)
Address: PO Box 149, Farnham, Surrey GU9 8YH, United Kingdom. TEL 44-1252-726416, FAX 44-1252-713730. Ed., R&P, Adv. contact Beatrice Falzone.

330 658 MEX
MUNDO EJECUTIVO. Text in Spanish. 1979. m. MXP 470; MXP 870 Including Hecho en Mexico (effective 2001). adv. back issues avail. **Document type:** *Trade.* **Description:** Covers domestic economic general news about Mexico and the world.
Related titles: Online - full text ed.: ISSN 1563-7565.
Published by: Grupo Internacional Editorial S A de C V, Rio Nazas 34, Col. Cuahutemoc, Mexico D F, 06500, Mexico. TEL 52-5-2099930, FAX 52-5-5660564, buzon@intermundo.com.mx, http://www.intermundo.com.mx/. Ed. Ana Luisa Ochoa. Adv. contact Fabrizio Tavano. color page MXP 67,000. Circ: 31,000.

MUNICIPAL PLANNING - LAND USE BULLETIN. see *PUBLIC ADMINISTRATION—Municipal Government*

330 AUS ISSN 1440-5059
MURDOCH UNIVERSITY. DEPARTMENT OF ECONOMICS. WORKING PAPER SERIES. Text in English. 1987. irreg. AUD 5 per issue domestic; AUD 10 per issue foreign (effective 2001). **Document type:** *Monographic series.* **Description:** Provides an accessible forum for members of the Economics Programme to publish the preliminary results of their research.
Former titles (until 1998): Murdoch University. Department of Economics. Working Paper (Print) (1321-201X); (until 1993): Murdoch University. Economics Programme. Working Papers (0819-9809)
Media: Online - full text.
Published by: Murdoch University, Department of Economics, South St, Murdoch, W.A. 6150, Australia. http://pandora.nla.gov.au/nla/pandora/murdochpaper.html. Ed. Meg Jadlowkier.

380.1025 AUS
MURRAY BRIDGE BUSINESS & COMMUNITY SERVICES GUIDE. Text in English. 1990. a. free. adv. **Document type:** *Directory, Consumer.* **Description:** Provides community information and business listings.
Published by: Murray Bridge Information Centre, 3 South Tce, Murray Bridge, SA 5253, Australia. TEL 61-85-322900, FAX 61-85-322766. Ed. Beryl Price. R&P Theresa Geister TEL 61-85-323094. Adv. contact Tony Samblich.

330 BEL
MUSEE ROYAL DE L'AFRIQUE CENTRALE. DOCUMENTATION ECONOMIQUE/KONINKLIJK MUSEUM VOOR MIDDEN-AFRIKA. ECONOMISCHE DOCUMENTATIE. Text mainly in French; Text occasionally in Dutch. 1961. irreg., latest vol.9, 1995. price varies. reprints avail. **Document type:** *Monographic series.*
Indexed: PAIS.
Published by: Musee Royal de l'Afrique Centrale/Koninklijk Museum voor Midden-Afrika, Steenweg op Leuven 13, Tervuren, 3080, Belgium. TEL 32-2-7695299, FAX 32-2-767-0242.

330 GBR
THE MUSHROOM. Text in English. 2001. fortn. GBP 55 (effective 2001). **Document type:** *Trade.* **Description:** Covers topics such as job market trends, accounting, insurance & legal issues, finance, computer hardware & software, and work related subjects.
Published by: The Mushroom, 3 Aldeburgh Ave, Lemington Rise, Newcastle Upon Tyne, NE15 8TA, United Kingdom. mushroomhq@prent.freeserve.co.uk, melva@cableinet.co.uk, http://www.mushroomhq.com/.

MUSICDISH; music industry magazine. see *MUSIC*

330 CAN
MUSKOKA BUSINESS MAGAZINE✶. Text in English. 1987. s-m. USD 5. adv.
Formerly: Muskoka Focus on Business (0841-940X)
Published by: Muskoka Educational Supply Group, 11 Manitoba St, P O Box 1526, Bracebridge, ON P0B 1C0, Canada. TEL 705-645-4463, FAX 705-645-3928. Ed. Dave Opavsky. Adv. contact Gord Lomas. Circ: 3,000.

330 FRA ISSN 0985-2433
MUTATIONS. Text in French. 1987. a. free. **Document type:** *Catalog.*
Published by: Novespace, 15 rue des Halles, Paris, 75001, France. TEL 42-33-41-41, FAX 40-26-08-60. Ed. Jean Pierre Fouquet. Circ: 20,000.

330 PHL
MYANMAR BUSINESS. Text in English. m. USD 295. **Document type:** *Newsletter.* **Description:** Focuses on how to trade and invest and make business connections in Myanmar.
Published by: Options Publishing Services, 10 Garcia Villa St, San Lorenzo Village, Makati City Mm, Philippines. TEL 63-2-818-3289, FAX 63-2-819-3752, opsi@mni.sequel.net. Pub. Melva C Nath.

650.0711 USA ISSN 0148-5784
HF1101
N A B T E REVIEW. Text in English. 1973. a. USD 25 (effective 2001). bibl. back issues avail. **Document type:** *Journal.*
Indexed: BusEdI.
Published by: (National Association for Business Teacher Education), National Business Education Association, 1914 Association Dr, Reston, VA 20191-1596. TEL 703-860-8300, FAX 703-620-4483. Circ: 1,200.

330 USA ISSN 0888-949X
THE N B E R DIGEST. Text in English. m. free (effective 2005). **Document type:** *Bulletin.* **Description:** Summarizes selected Working Papers of the bureau's research. Makes research available to economists, promoting discussion and revision of Papers before their final publication.
Related titles: ◆ Online - full content ed.: The N B E R Digest Online.
Indexed: RefZh.
—BLDSC (6067.717400).
Published by: National Bureau of Economic Research, 1050 Massachusetts Ave, 3rd Fl, Cambridge, MA 02138-5398. TEL 617-868-3900, FAX 617-349-3955, subs@nber.org, http://www.nber.org/digest.

330 USA
THE N B E R DIGEST ONLINE. Text in English. m. **Document type:** *Academic/Scholarly.*
Media: Online - full content. **Related titles:** ◆ Print ed.: The N B E R Digest. ISSN 0888-949X.
Published by: National Bureau of Economic Research, 1050 Massachusetts Ave, 3rd Fl, Cambridge, MA 02138-5398. TEL 617-868-3900, FAX 617-349-3955, subs@nber.org, http://www.nber.org/digest.

330 USA ISSN 1073-2489
N B E R TECHNICAL WORKING PAPER SERIES. (National Bureau of Economic Research) Text in English. 1992. irreg. USD 150 domestic to individuals; USD 120 domestic academic; USD 200 foreign to individuals; USD 155 foreign academic; free to qualified personnel (effective 2005).
Related titles: Online - full text ed.: USD 110 to individuals; USD 70 academic (effective 2005).
—Infotrieve.
Published by: National Bureau of Economic Research, 1050 Massachusetts Ave, 3rd Fl, Cambridge, MA 02138-5398. TEL 617-868-3900, FAX 617-349-3955, http://www.nber.org.

N C STATE ECONOMIST. (North Carolina) see *AGRICULTURE—Agricultural Economics*

330 GBR
N E R A TOPICS. Text in English. 1989. irreg. free. **Document type:** *Monographic series.* **Description:** Monographs on micro-economic subjects.
Published by: National Economic Research Associates, 15 Stratford Pl, London, W8 6RB, United Kingdom. TEL 44-171-629-6787, FAX 44-171-495-3216, annie_cleghorn@nera.co.uk, http://www.nera.com. Ed. Dermot Glynn. R&P Annie Cleghorn.

371.206 USA
N G M A EBULLETIN. Text in English. m. USD 75 for membership to individuals (effective 2003); membership incls. eBulletin, Journal & News Brief. **Document type:** *Bulletin, Trade.* **Description:** Includes short, informative announcements, including new grants management jobs, NGMA events, membership opportunities, and other NGMA-related programs.
Media: E-mail.
Published by: National Grants Management Association, 11654 Plaza America Dr, #609, Reston, VA 20190-4700. TEL 703-648-9023, FAX 703-648-9024, info@ngma-grants.org, http://www.ngma-grants.org/.

371.206 USA
N G M A NEWS BRIEF. Text in English. q. USD 75 for membership to individuals (effective 2003); membership incls. eBulletin, Journal & News Brief. **Document type:** *Newsletter, Trade.* **Description:** Features articles on issues such as current statutory requirements, OMB Circulars, audit resolutions, grants streamlining, and Federal, state and local government policies and procedures.
Published by: National Grants Management Association, 11654 Plaza America Dr, #609, Reston, VA 20190-4700. TEL 703-648-9023, FAX 703-648-9024, info@ngma-grants.org, http://www.ngma-grants.org/.

N I S E R OCCASIONAL PAPERS. see *SOCIAL SCIENCES: COMPREHENSIVE WORKS*

338 USA ISSN 1540-4161
N J BIZ. Text in English. w. USD 56; USD 84 for 2 yrs.; USD 99 for 3 yrs. (effective 2005). adv. **Document type:** *Newspaper, Trade.* **Description:** Provides business news and information about New Jersey companies and the New Jersey economy.
Formerly (until 2004): The Business News New Jersey
Related titles: Online - full text ed.: (from EBSCO Publishing, O C L C Online Computer Library Center, Inc., ProQuest Information & Learning).
Published by: Snowden Publications, 104 Church St, New Brunswick, NJ 08901. TEL 732-246-7677, FAX 732-249-8886, info@njbiz.com, http://www.njbiz.com. adv.: B&W page USD 3,780, color page USD 4,380. Wire service: PR.

330 USA
N S A C I NEWS. Text in English. m. free to members.
Published by: Northwest & Schaumburg Association of Commerce and Industry, Zurich Towers, 1450 E American Lane, Ste 140, Schaumburg, IL 60173. TEL 847-517-7110, FAX 847-517-7116, staff@nsaci.org, http://www.nsaci.org. Ed., Pub. Bernadet Shanahan. Circ: 1,600.

330 SGP ISSN 0218-3269
N U S ECONOMIC JOURNAL. (National University of Singapore) Text in English. 1962. a. SGD 10 (effective 2000). adv. **Description:** Contains honor students' academic exercises, interviews with academicians & ministers, special speeches. Also discusses current economic and business issues.
Formerly (until 1990): National University of Singapore. Economics and Statistics Society. Annual Journal - Suara Ekonomi (0585-8127)
Published by: National University of Singapore, Economics and Statistics Society, c/o Department of Economics, 10 Kent Ridge Crescent, Singapore, 0511, Singapore. TEL 65-777-9117, ens_nus@asiamail.com, http://nussu.nus.edu.sg/nussu/Nclubsoc/ENS. Ed. Cadence Wong Yim Hwa. Circ: 10,000.

N V MAGAZINE; the new vision in business. (New Vision) see *ETHNIC INTERESTS*

330 USA
N W FLORIDA'S BUSINESS CLIMATE; the magazine of business for the Gulf Coast. (Nowrthwest) Variant title: Northwest Florida's Business Climate. Text in English. bi-m. USD 14.50 domestic; USD 5 newsstand/cover domestic (effective 2004). adv. **Document type:** *Magazine, Trade.* **Description:** Covers regional business issues and economic development activities of Florida's Gulf Coast, particularly Escambia County, Okaloosa County, and Santa Rosa County.
Formerly: Climate (1087-9749)
Published by: Ballinger Publishing, 41 N Jefferson St, Pensacola, FL 32501. TEL 850-433-1166, 800-596-3777, FAX 850-435-9174, info@burchellpublishing.com, http://www.climatebusiness.com/climate.asp, http://www.ballingerpublishing.com. Adv. contact Malcolm G Ballinger TEL 850-433-1166 ext 27. B&W page USD 2,105, color page USD 2,255.

330 CHN ISSN 1001-4691
HB9
NANKAI JINGJI YANJIU/NANKAI ECONOMIC STUDIES. Text in Chinese. 1985. bi-m. USD 30. **Document type:** *Monographic series.*
Related titles: Online - full text ed.: (from East View Information Services).
Published by: Nankai Daxue, Jingji Xueyuan/Nankai University, College of Economics, 94 Weijin Rd, Tianjin 300071, China. TEL 86-22-3342161, FAX 86-22-3344853. Ed. Yue Zhang. Circ: 2,000.

330 JPN ISSN 0912-6139
NANZAN KEIZAI KENKYU/NANZAN JOURNAL OF ECONOMIC STUDIES. Text in Japanese. 1952. 3/yr. free. **Document type:** *Journal, Academic/Scholarly.*
Supersedes in part (in 1986): Akademia. Keizai Keieigaku-hen (0389-844X); Which superseded in part (in 1975): Akademia (0515-8680)
—BLDSC (6015.343830).
Published by: Nanzan Daigaku, Keizai Gakkai/Nanzan University, Society of Economics, 18 Yamazato-cho, Showa-ku, Nagoya, 466-8673, Japan.

330 GBR ISSN 1460-0838
NAPIER UNIVERSITY BUSINESS SCHOOL. WORKING PAPER SERIES. Text in English. 1997. irreg. back issues avail. **Document type:** *Monographic series, Academic/Scholarly.* **Description:** Examines specific topics in business.
—BLDSC (6015.345576).
Published by: Napier University, Business School Research Bureau, Sighthill Campus, Sighthill Ct, Edinburgh, Scotland E11 4BN, United Kingdom. TEL 44-131-455-3334, FAX 44-131-455-3486, 000NapierUnivBusRes, nubsrb@napier.ac.uk, http://www.nubs.napier.ac.uk.

330 BGR ISSN 0323-9004
NARODNOSTOPANSKI ARKHIV/ARCHIVES OF NATIONAL ECONOMY. Text in Bulgarian; Summaries in Bulgarian, English, Russian. 1946. q. BGL 1,700, USD 11 (effective 1998). adv. bk.rev. **Document type:** *Academic/Scholarly.*
Indexed: BSLEcon, RASB.
Published by: Dimiter Tsenov Academy of Economics, 2 Em Chakarov ul, Svishtov, 5250, Bulgaria. TEL 359-681-40135, FAX 359-681-40071, uircornrn@cornrn.uni-svishtov.bg. Ed., R&P, Adv. contact Svetlozar Kaltchev TEL 359-631-30076. Circ: 1,700. **Dist. by:** Hemus, 6 Rouski Blvd., Sofia 1000, Bulgaria.

330 SVN ISSN 0547-3101
➤ **NASE GOSPODARSTVO/OUR ECONOMY: REVIEW OF CURRENT PROBLEMS IN ECONOMICS.** Text in English, German, Slovenian; Summaries in English, Slovenian. 1955. q. (vols.5-6). SIT 6,600 domestic; USD 85 foreign (effective 2003 - 2004). bk.rev. charts; stat. index. 220 p./no.; back issues avail. **Document type:** *Academic/Scholarly.* **Description:** Deals with current issues in economics.
Related titles: CD-ROM ed.; Online - full text ed.: (from EBSCO Publishing).
Indexed: ABIn, JEL.
Published by: Ekonomsko-Poslovna Fakulteta/Faculty of Business and Economics, Razlagova 14, Maribor, 2000, Slovenia. TEL 386-2-22900, FAX 386-2-216111, nasegospodarstvo@uni.mb.si, nase.gospodarstvo@uni.mb.si, http://epf.uni-mb.si. Ed., R&P Davor Savin TEL 386-62-2290273. Pub. Majda Bastic. Circ: 4,500. **Co-sponsor:** Ekonomski Center Maribor.

330 USA ISSN 1052-4215
NASHVILLE BUSINESS AND LIFESTYLES; Nashville, Tennessee business magazine. Text in English. 1978. m. USD 18. adv.
Formerly (until 1990): Nashville Business and Lifestyle; Which incorporates (1978-1990): Advantage (0739-5515); (1973-1990): Nashville! (0162-8410)
Related titles: Online - full text ed.: 1978 (from Gale Group, ProQuest Information & Learning).
Indexed: BusDate, T&II.
Published by: Southeast Magazines, Inc., 545 Mainstream Dr, Ste 101, Nashville, TN 37228. TEL 615-242-6992, FAX 615-242-2248. Ed. Steve Rogers. Circ: 18,500. **Subscr. to:** PO Box 24649, Nashville, TN 37202-4649.

330 USA ISSN 0889-2873
NASHVILLE BUSINESS JOURNAL. Text in English. 1985. w. (Fri.). USD 82 (effective 2005). adv. **Document type:** *Newspaper.* **Description:** Regional business magazine.
Related titles: Microform ed.: (from PQC); Online - full text ed.: ISSN 1549-3229 (from Northern Light Technology, Inc., O C L C Online Computer Library Center, Inc., ProQuest Information & Learning).
Indexed: ABIn, BusDate.
—CCC.
Published by: American City Business Journals, Inc., 120 W Morehead St, Ste 400, Charlotte, NC 28202. TEL 704-973-1000, FAX 704-973-1001, nashville@bizjournals.com, http://www.bizjournals.com/nashville. Ed. Geert DeLombaerd. Circ: 10,000 (paid).

330 330.9 LUX ISSN 0256-7601
NATIONAL ACCOUNTS E S A - AGGREGATES (YEARS). Text in English. 1977. irreg., latest 1970-1995. USD 25. **Document type:** *Monographic series.*
Formerly: Statistical Office of the European Communities. Comparison in Real Terms of E S A Aggregates
Related titles: Microfiche ed.: (from CIS).
Indexed: IIS.
Published by: European Commission, Office for Official Publications of the European Union, 2 Rue Mercier, Luxembourg, L-2985, Luxembourg. Circ: 4,100. **Dist. in the U.S. by:** Bernan Associates, Bernan, 4611-F Assembly Dr., Lanham, MD 20706-4391. TEL 301-459-0056, 800-274-4447.

330.72 USA ISSN 0898-2937
HB1
NATIONAL BUREAU OF ECONOMIC RESEARCH. WORKING PAPER SERIES. Text in English. irreg. (approx. 450/yr.). USD 870 domestic to institutions; USD 1,260 foreign to institutions; USD 1,650 domestic to corporations; USD 2,000 foreign to corporations. back issues avail. **Description:** Presents papers on economic issues ranging from corporate finance, industrial organization and taxation to monetary economics, international finance and macroeconomics.
Related titles: Online - full text ed.
Indexed: RDA, RiceAb, TriticAb, WAE&RSA.
—BLDSC (6067.719500), IE, ingenta.
Published by: National Bureau of Economic Research, 1050 Massachusetts Ave, 3rd Fl, Cambridge, MA 02138-5398. TEL 617-868-3900, FAX 617-349-3955, http://www.nber.org/wwp.html. R&P Helena Oliveira.

330 AUS ISSN 1036-4145
NATIONAL BUSINESS BULLETIN. Text in English. 1992. m. AUD 84; AUD 98 print & online eds. (effective 2004). adv. software rev.; Website rev.; video rev. charts; illus.; stat. back issues avail. **Document type:** *Magazine, Corporate.* **Description:** Written by chief executives for chief executives of top 500 companies in Australia.
Related titles: Online - full content ed.: AUD 45 (effective 2004).
Published by: National Business Magazine, PO Box 687, Darlinghurst, NSW 2010, Australia. TEL 61-2-92125588, FAX 61-2-92123709, nbb@nationalbusiness.com.au, http://www.nationalbusiness.com.au. Eds. Doug Nettleship, Thomson Philip. R&Ps Stephen Cottier, Thomson Philip. Adv. contact Stephen Cottier. B&W page AUD 5,445, color page AUD 7,095; trim 275 x 215. Circ: 55,000 (controlled).

NATIONAL DIRECTORY OF CORPORATE PUBLIC AFFAIRS. see *BUSINESS AND ECONOMICS—Trade And Industrial Directories*

371.206 USA
NATIONAL GRANTS MANAGEMENT ASSOCIATION. JOURNAL. Text in English. s-a. USD 75 for membership to individuals (effective 2003); membership incls. eBulletin, Journal & News Brief. **Document type:** *Journal, Trade.* **Description:** Covers specific grants management matters.
Published by: National Grants Management Association, 11654 Plaza America Dr, #609, Reston, VA 20190-4700. TEL 703-648-9023, FAX 703-648-9024, info@ngma-grants.org, http://www.ngma-grants.org/.

330 GBR ISSN 0027-9501
HC10 CODEN: NIERAY
NATIONAL INSTITUTE ECONOMIC REVIEW. Text in English. 1959. q. GBP 254, USD 444 to institutions; GBP 264, USD 462 combined subscription to institutions print & online eds. (effective 2006). adv. charts; stat.; illus. Index. reprints avail. **Document type:** *Journal, Academic/Scholarly.*
Related titles: Microfiche ed.; Online - full text ed.: ISSN 1741-3036. GBP 251, USD 439 to institutions (effective 2006) (from EBSCO Publishing, Florida Center for Library Automation, Gale Group, H.W. Wilson, Northern Light Technology, Inc., O C L C Online Computer Library Center, Inc., Sage Publications, Inc., Swets Information Services).
Indexed: ABIn, BPI, BPIA, BusI, CPM, CREJ, ELLIS, Emerald, IBR, IBSS, IBZ, ILD, Inspec, JEL, M&MA, PAIS, PROMT, RASB, RRTA, T&II, WAE&RSA, WBSS.
—BLDSC (6025.580000), IE, Infotrieve, ingenta. **CCC.**
Published by: (National Institute of Economic and Social Research), Sage Publications Ltd. (Subsidiary of: Sage Publications, Inc.), 1 Oliver's Yard, 55 City Rd, London, EC1 1SP, United Kingdom. TEL 44-20-73248500, FAX 44-20-73248600, info@sagepub.co.uk, http://www.sagepub.co.uk/journal.aspx?pid=105717. Ed. Martin Weale. adv.: page GBP 200. Circ: 1,700. **Subscr. in the Americas to:** Sage Publications, Inc., 2455 Teller Rd, Thousand Oaks, CA 91320. TEL 805-499-0721, FAX 805-499-0871, journals@sagepub.com.

330 301 GBR ISSN 0070-8453
NATIONAL INSTITUTE OF ECONOMIC AND SOCIAL RESEARCH, LONDON. ECONOMIC AND SOCIAL STUDIES. Text in English. 1946. irreg. price varies. index. **Document type:** *Monographic series.*
—BLDSC (3651.530000).
Published by: Cambridge University Press, The Edinburgh Bldg, Shaftesbury Rd, Cambridge, CB2 2RU, United Kingdom. TEL 44-1223-312393, FAX 44-1223-315052, information@cambridge.org, http://publishing.cambridge.org/series/esre. R&P Linda Nicol TEL 44-1223-325757.

330 GBR ISSN 0077-4928
NATIONAL INSTITUTE OF ECONOMIC AND SOCIAL RESEARCH, LONDON. OCCASIONAL PAPERS. Text in English. 1946. irreg. price varies. **Document type:** *Monographic series.*
Published by: Cambridge University Press, The Edinburgh Bldg, Shaftesbury Rd, Cambridge, CB2 2RU, United Kingdom. TEL 44-1223-312393, FAX 44-1223-315052, information@cambridge.org, http://publishing.cambridge.org/series/esro. R&P Linda Nicol TEL 44-1223-325757.

330 USA
NATIONAL SUMMARY OF DOMESTIC TRADE RECEIVABLES. Text in English. 1958. q. USD 200. charts; illus.; stat. **Document type:** *Trade.*
Published by: Credit Research Foundation, Inc., 8815 Centre Park Dr, Ste 200B, Columbia, MD 21045. TEL 410-740-5499.

330 IRL
NATIONAL UNIVERSITY OF IRELAND. ECONOMICS DEPARTMENT. WORKING PAPERS SERIES. Text in English. irreg. **Document type:** *Academic/Scholarly.*
—BLDSC (3656.972000).
Published by: National University of Ireland, Economics Department, Maynooth, Co. Kildare, Ireland. http://www.may.ie.economics. Circ: 70.

B

NATIONAL YOUTH AFFAIRS RESEARCH SCHEME REPORTS. see *CHILDREN AND YOUTH—About*

330   BLR
NATSIONALNAYA EKONOMICHESKAYA GAZETA. Text in Russian. w. **Document type:** *Newspaper, Consumer.*
Published by: Belbiznespress, Vul Kazyrouskaya 15, Minsk, 220028, Belarus. TEL 375-172-2131813, 375-172-2131804, 375-172-2131808, FAX 375-172-2131816, econ@neg.belpak.minsk.by, press.net.by/neg/current. Ed. Fedar Fedaravich Vyalikacelets. Circ: 38,960.

330   POL   ISSN 0137-1428
NAUKI EKONOMICZNE. Text in Polish; Summaries in Multiple languages. 1974. irreg., latest vol.7, 1994. price varies. **Document type:** *Monographic series, Academic/Scholarly.* **Description:** Each issue contains the Ph.D. thesis of one author.
Published by: (Uniwersytet im. Adama Mickiewicza w Poznaniu/Adam Mickiewicz University), Wydawnictwo Naukowe Uniwersytetu im. Adama Mickiewicza/Adam Mickiewicz University Press, Nowowiejskiego 55, Poznan, 61-734, Poland. TEL 48-61-527380, FAX 48-61-527701. Pub. Maria Jankowska. R&P Malgorzata Bis.

NEBRASKA CHAMBER OF COMMERCE & INDUSTRY. LEGISLATIVE REPORT. see *LAW*

330   RUS
NEDELYA. Text in Russian. 1960. 48/yr. USD 175 in North America (effective 2000).
Related titles: Microfilm ed.: (from EVP).
Published by: Redaktsiya Nedelya, Ul Tverskaya 18 korp 1, Moscow, 103791, Russian Federation. TEL 7-095-2094311. Ed. Yu A Sorokin. **Dist. by:** East View Information Services, 3020 Harbor Ln. N., Minneapolis, MN 55447. TEL 763-550-0961, FAX 763-559-2931.

NEFT', GAZ I BIZNES. see *PETROLEUM AND GAS*

330.332   ARG   ISSN 0328-8579
HF3381
NEGOCIOS. Text in Spanish. 1993. m. USD 75 (effective 2002). adv. **Document type:** *Magazine, Trade.*
Published by: Editorial Atlantida S.A., Azopardo 579, 3 piso, Capital Federal, Buenos Aires 1307, Argentina. TEL 54-11-4331-3865, FAX 54-11-4343-1362, info@atlantidadigital.com.ar, http://www.atlantida.com.ar.

330   MEX   ISSN 1606-819X
NEGOCIOS (VERACRUZ). Text in Spanish. 1999. w. back issues avail.
Media: Online - full text.
Published by: Servicios Informativos y Publicitarios de Difusion y Comunicacion, S.A. de C.V., Versalles 21-402, Col. Juarez, Mexico, D.F., 06600, Mexico. TEL 52-5-5465862, http://www.negociosdeveracruz.com.mx/. Ed. Fausto Fernandez Ponce.

330   JPN   ISSN 0388-5704
HC10
NENPO KEIZAIGAKU/HIROSHIMA ECONOMIC STUDIES. Text in Japanese. 1980. a. **Document type:** *Monographic series, Academic/Scholarly.*
Published by: Hiroshima Daigaku, Keizai Gakubu/Hiroshima University, Faculty of Economics, 1-1-89, Higashisenda-machi, Naka-ku, Hiroshima 730-0053, Japan. TEL 81-82-542-6991, FAX 81-82-249-4991, http://www.eco.hiroshima-u.ac.jp/index.html.

330   CAN   ISSN 0840-8009
NET WORTH. Text in English. 1988. m. free.
Media: Online - full text.
—CCC.
Published by: Meep Media, Inc., 335 390 Notre Dame West, Montreal, PQ H2Y 1T9, Canada. TEL 514-288-5948, FAX 514-288-3409, info@meep.com, http://www.meep.com/magazine/biz.

330   ISR
NETO. Text in Hebrew. bi-m.
Published by: Raayonote Ltd., P O Box 26051, Tel Aviv, 61260, Israel. TEL 03-204029. Ed. Shlomo Smalsky. Circ: 1,000.

330   USA
NEVADA BUSINESS JOURNAL. Text in English. 1986. bi-m. USD 44 (effective 1998). adv. **Document type:** *Trade.* **Description:** Covers Nevada business concerns and issues.
Related titles: Online - full text ed.
Address: 4386 S. Eastern Ave., Ste. B, Las Vegas, NV 89119-6052. TEL 702-735-7003, FAX 702-733-5953. Ed. Connie Brennan. Pub., R&P Stephen Brock. Adv. contact Ben Falk. B&W page USD 2,740, color page USD 3,930. Circ: 16,000.

NEVADA JOURNAL (LAS VEGAS). see *LAW*

NEW AFRICAN YEARBOOK. see *POLITICAL SCIENCE*

330   ZAF   ISSN 1607-2820
NEW AGENDA. Text in English. 2000. q. ZAR 100 domestic to individuals; USD 50 elsewhere to individuals; ZAR 200 domestic to institutions; USD 100 elsewhere to institutions (effective 2004).
Published by: Institute for African Alternatives, Mill St., P O Box 12491, Cape Town, 8010, South Africa. http://www.ifaasa.org/text.

NEW BOTTOM LINE. see *ENVIRONMENTAL STUDIES*

NEW BRUNSWICK. DEPARTMENT OF FINANCE. MAIN ESTIMATES. see *PUBLIC ADMINISTRATION*

330   GRC
NEW BUSINESS ADVISOR. Text in Greek. d. adv. **Document type:** *Newspaper, Trade.* **Description:** Contains the latest financial news and information on Greek and international companies in the telecommunications and information technology industries.
Related titles: Online - full text ed.
Published by: Liberis Publications S.A./Ekdoseon Lymperi A.E., Ioannou Metaxa 80, Karelas, Koropi 19400, Greece. TEL 30-1-6198000, FAX 30-1-6198608, info@netbiz.gr, info@liberis.gr, http://www.netbiz.gr, http://www.liberis.gr.

330.0711   USA
NEW HAMPSHIRE BUSINESS EDUCATION ASSOCIATION. NEWSLETTER* . Text in English. 1983. irreg. membership. back issues avail. **Document type:** *Newsletter.*
Formerly: New Hampshire Business Education Association. Journal
Published by: New Hampshire Business Education Association (NHBEA), 16 Barnesdale Rd, Nashua, NH 03062-2157. TEL 603-882-7041. Ed. Maria Matarazzo. Circ: 300.

330   USA
NEW HAMPSHIRE EDITIONS. Text in English. 1988. m. USD 20; USD 2 newsstand/cover. adv. back issues avail. **Document type:** *Consumer.* **Description:** A statewide consumer and business oriented magazine.
Related titles: Online - full text ed.
Published by: Network Publications, 150 Dow St., Manchester, NH 03101-1227. TEL 603-883-3150, FAX 603-889-5557, access@nh.com, http://www.nh.com. Ed. Richard Broussard. Pub. Patricia Gregg. Adv. contact Steve Crammes. B&W page USD 2,425, color page USD 3,075; trim 11.13 x 8.38. Circ: 22,000.

330   USA
NEW HAVEN BUSINESS DIGEST* . Text in English. 1984. m. USD 17. adv.
Published by: Vought Communications, Inc., PO Box 846, Southport, CT 06490-0846. FAX 203-787-2027. Ed. Jean McAndrews. Circ: 10,000.

330   USA
NEW HAVEN BUSINESS TIMES. Text in English. 1986. m. USD 36; USD 3 newsstand/cover (effective 2004). adv. back issues avail. **Document type:** *Newsletter.* **Description:** Local business journal featuring small to medium size business.
Former titles: Business Times (New Haven Edition); New Haven Business
Indexed: BusDate.
Published by: Choice Media, 315 Peck St, Box 580, New Haven, CT 06513-0580. TEL 203-782-1420, FAX 203-782-3793, cbtimes@ctbusinesstimes.com. Ed., Pub., R&P Joel MacClaren. Adv. contact Robert Harris. page USD 2,400; trim 13 x 10.5. Circ: 10,000.

NEW JERSEY ADMINISTRATIVE CODE. COMMERCE, ENERGY & ECONOMIC DEVELOPMENT. see *LAW*

330   USA
NEW JERSEY NOTES* ; a bimonthly news summary of grants & funding. Text in English. 1979. s-m. USD 35. **Description:** News on private and public grants and funding in the state.
Address: 165 Ward Ave, Winchester, VA 22602-2250. TEL 800-831-4497, FAX 410-778-7949. Ed. Wendy P Littman. Circ: 350.

330   USA   ISSN 0889-5937
HF3161.N6
NEW MEXICO BUSINESS, CURRENT ECONOMIC REPORT. Text in English. 1948. m. (11/yr.). USD 25 (effective 2003). charts; stat. index, cum.index. reprint service avail. from PQC. **Document type:** *Newsletter.*
Formerly (until 1980): New Mexico Business (0028-6168)
Related titles: Microfiche ed.: (from CIS); Microfilm ed.: (from PQC).
Indexed: JEL, PAIS, SRI, SSCI.
Published by: University of New Mexico, Bureau of Business and Economic Research, 1920 Lomas N E, Albuquerque, NM 87131-6021. TEL 505-277-2216, FAX 505-277-2773, bber@unm.edu, http://www.unm.edu/~bber/. Ed. Kevin Kargacin. Circ: 500.

330   USA   ISSN 0164-6796
NEW MEXICO BUSINESS JOURNAL. Text in English. 1976. m. USD 69.95 (effective 2003). bk.rev. charts; illus.; stat. back issues avail.; reprints avail. **Document type:** *Consumer.*

Related titles: Microform ed.: (from PQC); Online - full text ed.: (from EBSCO Publishing, Florida Center for Library Automation, Gale Group, Northern Light Technology, Inc., The Dialog Corporation).
Indexed: BusDate, T&II.
Published by: American City Business Journals, Inc., 420 Central S W, Ste 104, Albuquerque, NM 87102. TEL 505-243-3444, FAX 505-243-4118, albuquerque@bizjournals.com, sierrapg@ix.netcom.com, http://www.bizjournals.com/albuquerque/, http://www.nmbiz.com. Ed., Pub. Robert J Cochnar. R&P Michael Bawaya. Adv. contact Claire Garner. Circ: 22,000.

330   USA   ISSN 1524-248X
NEW MEXICO BUSINESS WEEKLY. Key Title: NM Business Weekly. Text in English. 1997. m. USD 74 (effective 2005). **Document type:** *Newspaper.*
Related titles: Online - full text ed.
—CCC.
Published by: American City Business Journals, Inc. (Albuquerque), 116 Central Ave SW Ste 202, Albuquerque, NM 87102. TEL 505-768-7008, FAX 505-768-0890, albuquerque@bizjournals.com, http://www.bizjournals.com/albuquerque/. Ed. Emily Esterson. Pub. Chuck Houser. Adv. contact Jim Hanrahan. Wire service: PR.

NEW PLANT REPORT. see *BUILDING AND CONSTRUCTION*

NEW WEST NOTES. see *POLITICAL SCIENCE*

NEW YORK BUSINESS LAW JOURNAL. see *LAW*

NEW YORK STATE BAR ASSOCIATION. ANTITRUST LAW SECTION SYMPOSIUM. see *LAW*

NEW YORK UNIVERSITY BUSINESS MAGAZINE PUBLISHING SERIES. see *PUBLISHING AND BOOK TRADE*

330   NZL   ISSN 0113-4957
HF4030.5
NEW ZEALAND BUSINESS. Abbreviated title: N Z Business. Text in English. 1938. m. (11/yr.). NZD 54.45 domestic; NZD 136.40 foreign (effective 2000). adv. bk.rev. back issues avail. **Document type:** *Trade.* **Description:** Information for business people on tax, economics, management, innovative companies and more.
Incorporates (in 2000): New Zealand Export Year Book (1172-7136); Which was formerly: Cranwell New Zealand Export Yearbook (1171-6991); (until 1986): Cranwells New Zealand Export Year Book (1170-6201); (until 1982): New Zealand Export Year Book (0549-0278); Formerly (until 1987): Better Business (0110-7100)
Related titles: Online - full text ed.: (from EBSCO Publishing, Gale Group, ProQuest Information & Learning).
Indexed: ABIX, ABIn, Emerald, INZP, Inpharma, PE&ON, Reac, WBA, WMB.
—BLDSC (6195.265000). CCC.
Published by: Profile Publishing Ltd., Wellesley St, PO Box 5544, Auckland, New Zealand. TEL 64-9-630-8940, FAX 64-9-630-1046, info@profile.co.nz, http://www.profile.co.nz/. Ed. Nick Grant. Circ: 8,397.

330   NZL   ISSN 0077-9954
HB9
➤ NEW ZEALAND ECONOMIC PAPERS. Text in English. 1966. s-a. NZD 100 domestic; NZD 120 in Australia; NZD 130 elsewhere (effective 2004). bk.rev. back issues avail. **Document type:** *Journal, Academic/Scholarly.* **Description:** Economics.
Related titles: Online - full text ed.: (from Florida Center for Library Automation, Gale Group).
Indexed: CREJ, DSA, IBSS, INZP, JEL, RRTA, WAE&RSA.
—BLDSC (6089.990000), IE, ingenta.
Published by: New Zealand Association of Economists, 111 Cuba Mall, PO Box 568, Wellington, New Zealand. TEL 64-4-8017139, FAX 64-4-8017106, economists@nzae.org.nz, http://nzae.org.nz. Ed. Tim Hazledine. Circ: 500.

➤ NEW ZEALAND GAZETTE. see *PUBLIC ADMINISTRATION*

330   NZL   ISSN 0078-0057
NEW ZEALAND INSTITUTE OF ECONOMIC RESEARCH. ANNUAL REPORT. Text in English. 1960. a. NZD 13.50 per issue (effective 2003). **Document type:** *Corporate.*
Published by: New Zealand Institute of Economic Research, PO Box 3479, Wellington 1, New Zealand. TEL 64-4-4721880, FAX 64-4-4721211, econ@nzier.org.nz, http://www.nzier.org.nz.

330   NZL   ISSN 0078-0049
HC661
NEW ZEALAND INSTITUTE OF ECONOMIC RESEARCH. DISCUSSION PAPER. Text in English. 1961. irreg. price varies. **Document type:** *Academic/Scholarly.*
Published by: New Zealand Institute of Economic Research, PO Box 3479, Wellington 1, New Zealand. TEL 64-4-4721880, FAX 64-4-4721211, econ@nzier.org.nz, http://www.nzier.org.nz.

330 NZL ISSN 0110-4470
NEW ZEALAND INSTITUTE OF ECONOMIC RESEARCH. QUARTERLY SURVEY OF BUSINESS OPINION. Text in English. 1961. q. NZD 250 (effective 2003). **Document type:** *Academic/Scholarly.* **Description:** Reports surveys of business experiences and intentions.
Published by: New Zealand Institute of Economic Research, PO Box 3479, Wellington 1, New Zealand. TEL 64-4-4721880, FAX 64-4-4721211, econ@nzier.org.nz, http://www.nzier.org.nz.

330 NZL ISSN 0113-1877
NEW ZEALAND INSTITUTE OF ECONOMIC RESEARCH. RESEARCH MONOGRAPHS. Text in English. 1961. irreg. price varies. **Document type:** *Academic/Scholarly.*
Formerly: New Zealand Institute of Economic Research. Research Paper (0078-0065)
—BLDSC (7743.124500).
Published by: New Zealand Institute of Economic Research, PO Box 3479, Wellington 1, New Zealand. TEL 64-4-4721880, FAX 64-4-4721211, econ@nzier.org.nz, http://www.nzier.org.nz.

NEW ZEALAND MANUFACTURER. see *BUSINESS AND ECONOMICS—Production Of Goods And Services*

330 FRA ISSN 1620-9419
NEWBIZ. Text in French. 2000. m. EUR 24 (effective 2002).
Published by: L'Ile des Medias, 24 Rue du Sentier, Paris, 75002, France. TEL 33-1-53001300, FAX 33-1-53001320, http://www.newbiz.fr, http://www.ile-des-medias.com.

330 USA ISSN 1059-695X
HD2771
NEWCOMEN PUBLICATION. Text in English. 1973. irreg. price varies. **Document type:** *Monographic series.*
Related titles: Online - full text ed.
Published by: The Newcomen Society of the United States, 211 Welsh Pool Rd, Ste 240, Exton, PA 19341. TEL 610-363-6600, 800-466-7604, FAX 610-363-0612, info@newcomen.org, http://www.newcomen.org.

330 GBR ISSN 1466-2264
NEWS FROM THE NEW ECONOMY. Text in English. 1987. m. GBP 20 domestic; GBP 25 foreign (effective 2000). adv. **Document type:** *Newspaper.*
Formerly (until 1999): New Economics (0951-6476)
Published by: New Economics Foundation, Cinnation House, 6 - 8 Cole St, London, SE1 4YH, United Kingdom. TEL 020-7407-7447, FAX 44-171-377-5720, info@neweconomics.org, info@neweconomics.org, http://www.neweconomics.org. Ed., R&P David Boyle. Adv. contact David Melville. Circ: 2,000.

NEWSLINE (LAWRENCE). see *SPORTS AND GAMES—Ball Games*

330 USA
NEWSWEEK BUSINESS PLUS. Text in English. 1989. w. USD 29.97 domestic; USD 64.26 in Canada & Mexico (effective 2005). adv. illus. **Document type:** *Trade.* **Description:** Reports on business and economic news and trends.
Published by: Newsweek, Inc. (Subsidiary of: Washington Post Co.), 251 W 57th St, New York, NY 10019-1894. TEL 212-445-4000, FAX 212-445-4142, customer.care@newsweek.com, http://www.newsweek.com. adv.: B&W page USD 70,745, color page USD 109,000; trim 10.75 x 8. Circ: 1,200,000 (paid).

▼ **THE NEXT AMERICAN CITY.** see *HOUSING AND URBAN PLANNING*

330 USA ISSN 1087-6278
HF5549.5.M5
NEXT STEP. Text in English. 1996. q. USD 15.95; USD 4.95 newsstand/cover. adv. bk.rev. charts; illus. index, cum.index. back issues avail. **Document type:** *Consumer.* **Description:** Advances the knowledge and understanding of diversity as it affects people and enterprises.
Related titles: Online - full text ed.
Indexed: ENW.
Published by: Next Step Enterprises, Inc., 4548 Market St, Philadelphia, PA 19139. TEL 215-387-2387, FAX 215-387-2367, normbond@nextstepmag.com, http://www.nextstepmag.com. Ed. Keith D Ellison. Pubs. Keith D Ellison, Norm Bond. R&P, Adv. contact Norm Bond. page USD 6,400; trim 11 x 8.5. Circ: 50,000. **Dist. by:** 1226 Heil Quaker Blvd, La Vergne, TN 37066-7000.

330 CAN
NIAGARA BUSINESS REPORT. Text in English. 1983. q. adv.
Formerly (until 1993): Let's Talk Business Niagara (0831-9006)
Published by: Rannie Printing and Publishing Ltd. (Subsidiary of: Burgoyne Community Newspapers Ltd.), 4309 Central Ave, Beamsville, ON L0R 1B0, Canada. TEL 905-563-1629, FAX 905-563-7977. Ed. Molly Harding. Adv. contact Jacquie Hoover. Circ: 14,500.

NICKLE'S DAILY OIL BULLETIN. see *PETROLEUM AND GAS*

330 NGA ISSN 0794-2877
HF3931
NIGERIA BUSINESS GUIDE ANNUAL; a practical guide for businessmen and foreign investors in Nigeria. Text in English. 1986. a. USD 25. adv. bk.rev. **Document type:** *Trade.*
—CCC.
Published by: Comprehensive Guide Ltd., PO Box 29262, Ibadan, Oyo, Nigeria. Ed. Joseph Ajiboye. Circ: 250,000.

338.1 NGA ISSN 0331-0361
HC517.N48
NIGERIAN ECONOMIC SOCIETY. PROCEEDINGS OF THE ANNUAL CONFERENCE. Text in English. 1973. a. included with Nigerian Journal of Economic & Social Studies. **Document type:** *Proceedings.*
Published by: Nigerian Economic Society, Department of Economics, University of Ibadan, Ibadan, Oyo, Nigeria. Ed. E Lambo. Circ: 800.

330 NGA
NIGERIAN EXPORTER. Text in English. 1985. m. **Document type:** *Trade.*
Published by: Ohida & Sons Ltd., Oshodi 41 Adewale Crescent, PO Box 742, Ikeja, Lagos, Nigeria. Ed. Cyprian Agbor.

NIGERIAN INSTITUTE OF SOCIAL AND ECONOMIC RESEARCH. ANNUAL REPORT. see *SOCIAL SCIENCES: COMPREHENSIVE WORKS*

330 NGA ISSN 0029-0092
HC517.N48
NIGERIAN JOURNAL OF ECONOMIC & SOCIAL STUDIES. Text in English. 1959. 3/yr. USD 75 Includes Proceedings of the Annual Conference. cum.index. **Document type:** *Academic/Scholarly.*
Indexed: ASD, CREJ, IBSS, ILD, JEL, PAIS, PopulInd, RASB, REE&TA, RRTA, WAE&RSA.
—CCC.
Published by: Nigerian Economic Society, Department of Economics, University of Ibadan, Ibadan, Oyo, Nigeria. Ed. E Lambo.

330 JPN ISSN 0286-1569
NIIGATA DAIGAKU KEIZAI RONSHU/JOURNAL OF ECONOMICS, NIIGATA UNIVERSITY. Text in Japanese. 1952. 3/yr.
Supersedes in part (in 1966): Niigata Daigaku Hokei Ronshu/Journal of Law and Economics, Niigata University (0468-2572); Which was formerly (1951-1952): Niigata Daigaku Shakai Kagaku Kenkyu/Social Science Review, Niigata University (0468-2580)
—BLDSC (4973.085000).
Published by: Niigata Daigaku, Keizai Gakkai/Society of Economics in Niigata University, Faculty of Economics, 8050 Ikarashi 2-no-cho, Niigata, 950-2181, Japan. http://www.econ.niigata-u.ac.jp/.

330 JPN
NIKKAN KOGYO SHIMBUN/BUSINESS & TECHNOLOGY DAILY NEWS. Text in Japanese. 1915. d. (Mon.-Fri.). JPY 4,590 per month (effective 2005). adv. **Document type:** *Newspaper, Trade.*
Indexed: B&I.
Published by: Nikkan Kogyo Shimbun, Ltd., 14-1 Nihonbashikoamicho, Chuo-ku, Tokyo, 103-8548, Japan. TEL 81-3-56447000, http://www.nikkan.co.jp/main.html. Ed. Toshio Fujiyoshi. Circ: 550,110.

330 JPN
NIKKEI. ANNUAL FOREIGN CORPORATION REPORTS. Text in Japanese. a. JPY 65,100 (effective 2005). **Document type:** *Database, Trade.* **Description:** Covers 3,700 companies from 40 countries.
Published by: Nihon Keizai Shimbun Inc., 1-9-5 Ote-Machi, Chiyoda-ku, Tokyo, 100-0004, Japan. TEL 81-3-52552825, FAX 81-3-32462861, pub_sp@nikkei.co.jp, http://www.nikkei-bookdirect.com/.

330 JPN
NIKKEI CORPORATE WHO'S WHO (YEAR). Text in Japanese. a. **Document type:** *Directory.* **Description:** Lists more than 20,000 directors and managers of 3,800 leading Japanese Corporations.
Published by: Nihon Keizai Shimbun Inc., 1-9-5 Ote-Machi, Chiyoda-ku, Tokyo, 100-0004, Japan. TEL 81-3-32700251, FAX 81-3-52552661.

NIKKEI ECOLOGY. see *ENVIRONMENTAL STUDIES*

330 JPN ISSN 0912-3881
NIKKEI REGIONAL ECONOMIC REPORT. Text in Japanese. s-m. **Document type:** *Newsletter.* **Description:** Contains regional economic and industrial information.
Published by: Nihon Keizai Shimbun Inc., Nikkei Research Institute of Industry and Markets, 1-9-5 Ote-Machi, Chiyoda-ku, Tokyo, 1000004, Japan. TEL 81-3-3270-0251, FAX 81-3-5255-2661.

330 JPN
NIKKEI VENTURE BUSINESS ALMANAC. Text in Japanese. a. **Document type:** *Trade.* **Description:** A reference work on 2,050 leading venture businesses in Japan.
Published by: Nihon Keizai Shimbun Inc., 1-9-5 Ote-Machi, Chiyoda-ku, Tokyo, 100-0004, Japan. TEL 81-3-32700251, FAX 81-3-52552661.

330 JPN ISSN 0918-5348
HC461 CODEN: JECJAU
THE NIKKEI WEEKLY. Text in English. 1962. w. JPY 21,600 domestic; USD 129 in United States; CND 195 in Canada; CND 163 in Latin America; HKD 1,300 in Hong Kong; USD 153 in China (effective 2005). adv. bk.rev. illus.; mkt.; stat. Index. reprints avail. **Document type:** *Newspaper, Trade.* **Description:** Covers Japan's business, finance, industry, stocks and technology.
Former titles (until June 1991): Japan Economic Journal (0021-4388); (until 1970): Nihon Keizai Shimbun (International weekly Edition) (0911-1999)
Related titles: Microfiche ed.; Online - full text ed.: Nikkei Net Interactive. JPY 6,000 per month to individuals (effective 2001) (from LexisNexis).
Indexed: AIA, B&I, BPIA, BrCerAb, CADCAM, CIN, ChemAb, ChemTitl, EnvAb, KES, M&MA, PROMT, RASB, RoboAb, TTI, TelAb, Telegen.
—BLDSC (6113.178420), CASDDS.
Published by: Nihon Keizai Shimbun Inc., 1-9-5 Ote-Machi, Chiyoda-ku, Tokyo, 100-0004, Japan. TEL 81-3-32700251, FAX 81-3-52552661, TELEX J22308 NIKKEI, weekly@tokyo.nikkei.co.jp, https://www.nikkei4946.com/sb/e_index/index.asp, http://www.nikkei-bookdirect.com/. Ed. Nobuo Oneda. Adv. contact Kazuo Onotera. Circ: 36,500. **Dist. by:** Nikkei America Inc., 1325 Ave. of the Americas, Ste. 2500, New York, NY 10019. TEL 212-261-6200.

330 JPN
NIKKO FORUM. Text in Japanese. 1980. m.
Published by: Nikko Forum Inc., 1-8-1 Uchikanda, Chiyoda-ku, Tokyo, 101-0047, Japan. TEL 81-3-3233-3981, FAX 81-3-3295-3968, nikko@nk-forum.co.jp, http://nk-forum.jij.co.jp/.

330 JPN
NIPPON VALQUA INDUSTRIES, LTD. ANNUAL REPORT. Text in English. a. **Document type:** *Corporate.*
Related titles: Online - full content ed.; Japanese ed.
Published by: Nihon Baruka Kougyou Kenkyuu Kaihatsu Toukatsubu/Nippon Valqua Industries, Ltd., Shinjuku Mitsui Bldg., 1-1, Nishishinjuku 2-chome, Shinjuku-ku, Tokyo, 163-0406, Japan. TEL 81-3-5325-3421, FAX 81-3-5325-3436, http://www.valqua.co.jp.

330 USA ISSN 1063-2816
THE NONPROFIT BOARD REPORT. Abbreviated title: N B R. Text in English. 1991. m. USD 249. **Document type:** *Newsletter, Trade.* **Description:** News and instructional materials for nonprofit boards.
Published by: Progressive Business Publications, 370 Technology Dr, Malvern, PA 19355-1315. TEL 610-695-8600, 800-220-5000, FAX 610-647-8089, editor@pbp.com, http://www.pbp.com. Ed. Melanie Scott. R&P Curt Brown. Circ: 41,020 (paid).

330 GBR
NORDIC BUSINESS REPORT. Text in English. irreg. **Document type:** *Trade.*
Media: Online - full content.
Published by: M2 Communications Ltd., PO Box 475, Coventry, W Mids CV1 2ZW, United Kingdom. TEL 44-1203-634700, FAX 44-1203-634144, M2PW@m2.com, http://m2.com/m2/M2Web.nsf/WebPublicationInfoView/Nordic+Business+Report?OpenDocument, http://www.m2.com.

330 SWE ISSN 1100-7559
HC341
NORDIC ECONOMIC OUTLOOK. Text in Swedish. 1974. 2/yr. SEK 500 to non-members; SEK 400 to members (effective 2000). charts; stat. **Document type:** *Journal, Trade.*
Indexed: KES.
Published by: Federation of Swedish Industries, Economic Policy Department, Fack 5501, Stockholm, 11485, Sweden. TEL 46-8-783-80-00, FAX 46-8-662-35-95, TELEX 19990, arvid.bohm@industriforbundet.se. Ed. Arvid Bohm. Circ: 1,000.

330 NOR ISSN 0805-7508
➤ **NORDIC JOURNAL OF POLITICAL ECONOMY.** Text in English. 1974. s-a. NOK 180 in Scandinavia to individuals; USD 35 elsewhere to individuals; NOK 290 in Scandinavia to institutions; USD 55 elsewhere to institutions (effective 2004). **Document type:** *Journal, Academic/Scholarly.*
Formerly (until 1995): Nordisk Tidskrift for Politisk Ekonomi (0345-8555)
Indexed: JEL.
Published by: Institutt for Samfunnsforskning, Munthes Gate 31, Oslo, 0208, Norway. TEL 47-23-086100, FAX 47-23-086101, nopec@socialresearch.no, isf@socialresearch.no, http://www.socialresearch.no/page/Tidsskrifter/Meny_Tidsskrifter/7486/7523.

▼ *new title* ➤ *refereed* ✶ *unverified* ♦ *full entry avail.*

B

320   DNK   ISSN 1399-140X
NORDISK TIDSSKRIFT FOR SELSKABSRET. Text in Danish.
1999. 4/yr. DKK 788 domestic (effective 2003). back issues
avail. **Document type:** *Journal, Academic/Scholarly.*
Description: Contains information on developments within
Scandinavian company law, new company law in Denmark,
Sweden, Norway, and Finland, and articles on current interest
within company law.
Published by: Jurist- og Oekonomforbundets Forlag, Lyngbyvej
17, PO Box 2702, Copenhagen OE, 2100, Denmark. TEL
45-39-315500, FAX 45-39-135555, fl@djoef.dk,
http://www.djoef.dk. Eds. Paul Kruger Anderson, Rolf Skog,
Tore Braathen. Circ: 1,000.

330   SWE   ISSN 0029-1838
NORRLAENDSK TIDSKRIFT. Text in Swedish. 1952. 8/yr. SEK
95, USD 7. adv. illus.
Published by: Norrlandsfoerbundet, Kyrkogatan 26, Fack 294,
Sundsvall, 85105, Sweden. Ed. Hasse Bystroem. Circ: 10,000.

330   USA   ISSN 1097-8844
THE NORTH AFRICA JOURNAL. Text in English. w. USD 150
domestic; USD 350 foreign (effective 2005). adv. **Document
type:** *Trade.* **Description:** Covers breaking economic and
political developments in Tunisia, Algeria and Morocco which
is an area known as the Maghreb.
Formerly: Maghreb Weekly Monitor (1097-8836)
Related titles: Online - full text ed.
Published by: The North Africa Journal, PO Box 1001, Concord,
MA 01742. TEL 978-371-2511, FAX 413-383-9817,
daoud@northafricajournal.com,
journal@northafricajournal.com, http://www.north-africa.com/
one.htm. Eds. Arezki Daoud, Rose Ryan. Pub. Arezki Daoud.

330   USA
**NORTH BAY BUSINESS JOURNAL (NAPA, SONOMA AND
MARIN COUNTIES).** Text in English. 1987. fortn. USD 27
(effective 2000). adv. bk.rev.; software rev. charts; stat. back
issues avail. **Document type:** *Newspaper.* **Description:**
Provides local business news for Napa, Sonoma and Marin
counties in the north San Francisco Bay, California, area.
Subscribers include executives, managers, and business
owners of local companies.
Former titles: Business Journal (Napa, Sonoma and Marin
Counties); Business Journal (Sonoma and Marin Counties)
(1057-6061); Business Journal Serving Sonoma, Marin, and
Mendocino Counties
Published by: Sloan Publications, 5964 Skylane Blvd, Ste B,
Santa Rosa, CA 95403. TEL 707-579-2900, FAX
707-579-0188, busjrnlsm@aol.com, news@busjrnl.com,
http://www.busjrnl.com. Eds. Ken Clark, Randy Sloan. Pub.
Ken Clark. R&P Debbie Ough. Adv. contact Sue Wildermuth.
page USD 2,295; trim 15 x 11. Circ: 8,000 (paid).

NORTH EAST JOURNAL OF LEGAL STUDIES. see *LAW*

330   USA
NORTHEAST OHIO WORKS. Text in English. 2002. a.
Document type: *Magazine.* **Description:** Covers information
about doing business and living in Northeast Ohio, including
the region's high-tech and manufacturing industries, quality of
life, education and healthcare systems, and financial, business
and real estate services.
Related titles: ◆ Issued with: Expansion Management. ISSN
1073-8355.
Published by: Penton Industry Media, Custom Media Group,
Penton Media Bldg, 1300 E 9th St, Cleveland, OH 44114 .
TEL 216-696-7000, FAX 216-696-1752,
information@penton.com, http://www.penton.com.
Co-sponsors: Greater Cleveland Growth Association; Ohio
Department of Development.

330   USA   ISSN 1078-5698
NORTHEAST PENNSYLVANIA BUSINESS JOURNAL. Text in
English. m. USD 29. adv. **Document type:** *Newspaper.*
Description: Provides business news and information for 10
counties in northeast Pennsylvania.
Related titles: Online - full text ed.: (from O C L C Online
Computer Library Center, Inc., ProQuest Information &
Learning).
Indexed: ABIn, BusDate.
Published by: Press - Enterprise, Inc., 3185 Lackawanna Ave,
Bloomsburg, PA 17815-3329. TEL 717-784-2121, FAX
717-784-9226, npbj@enterpe.com, http://www.enterpe.com/
npbj.html. Ed., R&P Tom Sink. Adv. contact Karen Nocerine.
Circ: 12,000.

330   GBR
NORTHERN BUSINESS AND FINANCE. Text in English. 1991.
bi-m. GBP 15; GBP 35 in Europe; GBP 75 elsewhere. adv.
bk.rev. back issues avail. **Document type:** *Trade.*
Formerly (until 1997): Finance North
Published by: Northern Business Press Ltd., 46B Bradford Rd,
Brighouse, W Yorks HD6 1RY, United Kingdom. TEL
44-1484-401484, FAX 44-1484-401114, contact@n-b-p.co.uk.
Ed., Pub. Keith J Butterick. Adv. contact Barry Denham. B&W
page GBP 1,750; 297 x 210. Circ: 17,000 (paid).

330   CAN   ISSN 0710-2755
NORTHERN ONTARIO BUSINESS. Variant title: Design North.
Northern Ontario Business Awards. Wesway Window. Text in
English. 1980. m. CND 20. adv. **Document type:** *Newspaper.*

Related titles: Microfilm ed.: (from MML); Microform ed.: (from
MML, PQC); Online - full text ed.: (from Florida Center for
Library Automation, Gale Group, Micromedia ProQuest, O C L
C Online Computer Library Center, Inc., ProQuest Information
& Learning).
Indexed: ABIn, BusDate, CBCARef, CPerl.
Published by: Laurentian Publishing Co., 158 Elgin St, Sudbury,
ON P3E 3N5, Canada. TEL 705-673-5705, FAX
705-673-9542. Ed. Patricia Mills. Circ: 10,000 (controlled).

330   USA   ISSN 1041-7869
NORTHLAND BUSINESS LEDGER. Text in English. 1987. m.
USD 12 (effective 1999). adv. **Document type:** *Newspaper.*
Published by: N P G Newspapers, Inc., 310 N.W. Englewood
Rd., Gladstone, MO 64188. TEL 816-454-3222, FAX
816-454-4236. Ed. Guy Townsend. Adv. contact Cid Prevost.
B&W page USD 800; trim 13.5 x 11.5. Circ: 5,500.

330   USA
NORTHWEST ARKANSAS BUSINESS JOURNAL. Text in
English. bi-w. USD 28.95 in state; USD 39.95 out of state;
USD 1 newsstand/cover (effective 2005). **Document type:**
Newspaper.
Published by: Arkansas Business Publishing Group, 122 E
Second St, Little Rock, AR 72203. TEL 501-372-1443, FAX
501-375-7933, bbirch@abpg.com, http://www.abpg.com. Ed.
Jeff Hankins. Circ: 944 (paid).

330   CAN
NORTHWEST BUSINESS. Text in English. 1994. 4/yr. CND 11.
Published by: Dakota Design and Advertising, Bay 114, 3907-3A
St N E, Calgary, AB T2E 6S7, Canada. TEL 403-538-0539.
Pub. Ruth Dunbar. adv.: B&W page CND 1,550, color page
CND 1,995; trim 10.75 x 8.13. Circ: 10,000.

330   USA
NORTHWEST BUSINESS JOURNAL. Text in English. fortn.
Document type: *Trade.*
Indexed: BusDate.
Published by: Arkansas Business Publishing Group, 122 E
Second St, Little Rock, AR 72203. TEL 501-372-1443.

330   ITA   ISSN 0391-0121
NOTIZIARIO ENASARCO. (Ente Nazionale Assistenza Agenti e
Rappresentanti di Commercio) Text in Italian. 1954. m.
Document type: *Bulletin, Trade.*
Published by: Ente Nazionale Agenti e Rappresentanti, Via
Antoniotto Usodimare 31, Rome, RM 00154, Italy. TEL
39-06-57931, FAX 39-06-830303, http://www.enasarco.it. Ed.
Moreno Gori. Circ: 270,000.

330   BRA   ISSN 0103-6351
HB9
➤ **NOVA ECONOMIA**; the journal of the economics department
at UFMG. Text in Portuguese. 1990. s-a. free (effective 2004).
bk.rev. **Document type:** *Academic/Scholarly.* **Description:**
Publishes articles and book reviews in all areas of economics
and related disciplines.
Related titles: Online - full text ed.: free (effective 2005).
Indexed: IBR, IBSS, IBZ, JEL, SociolAb.
Published by: (Banco de Desenvolvimento de Minas Gerais
S.A.), Universidade Federal de Minas Gerais, Faculdade de
Ciencias Economicas, Rua Curitiba, 832 - sala 701, Belo
Horizonte, MG 30170-120, Brazil. TEL 55-31-3279-9070, FAX
55-31-3279-9062, ne@face.ufmg.br, sececn@face.ufmg.br,
http://www.face.ufmg.br/novaeconomia/eng/index.html. Ed.
Joao Antonio de Paula.

330   NGA   ISSN 0331-4464
NTIEYONG BUSINESS REVIEW; magazine of the testimony of
general management. Text and summaries in English. 1999.
6/yr. NGN 20,000, USD 400 (effective 1999). adv. bk.rev. bibl.;
charts; illus.; stat. back issues avail. **Document type:**
Magazine, Academic/Scholarly. **Description:** Aims to serve
the necessity of keeping the man of business in the line, with
articles from a number of different disciplines.
Related titles: Diskette ed.
Published by: Ntieyong Hall, Plot 3 Police Headquarters Layout,
GPO Box 1588, Calabar, Nigeria. TEL 234-87-225215. Ed.
Nkanta Afanama.

330   ESP   ISSN 1577-7804
NUEVA EMPRESA.COM. Text in Spanish. 1978. w. EUR 18
domestic; EUR 21.50 foreign (effective 2005). adv. bk.rev.
illus.; stat.
Fomerly (until 2000): Nueva Empresa (Print Edition) (1131-5067)
Media: Online - full text.
Published by: Nueva Empresa, General Margallo, 20 4o. B,
Madrid, 28020, Spain. TEL 34-91-4260647, FAX
34-91-810659, http://www.nuevaempresa.com/. Ed. Jesus
Barbera. Circ: 17,000.

330   ESP   ISSN 0214-9389
NUEVO CADUCEO MAGAZINE. Text in Spanish. 1952. bi-m. adv.
bk.rev.
Formerly (until 1981): Caduceo (0409-7955)
—CINDOC.
Address: Domenico Scarlatti, 13 4o, Madrid, 28003, Spain. TEL
1-5498609, FAX 1-5498547. Ed. E Rinon Ramirez. Circ:
150,000.

330   ESP   ISSN 1133-9535
NUEVO LUNES DE LA ECONOMIA Y LA SOCIEDAD. Text in
Spanish. 1981. 48/yr.
Address: Torre de Madrid planta 7 ofc. 3, Plaza Espana, 18,
Madrid, 28008, Spain. TEL 1-24-73-101, FAX 1-248-04-06,
TELEX 41777 LUNES E. Ed. Marivi Casanneva. Circ: 25,000.

330   VEN   ISSN 0798-2003
NUMERO∗ . Text in Spanish. 1980. w. adv. bk.rev. **Document
type:** *Trade.*
Published by: Editora Triangulo s.r.l., Camonigos a San Ramon,
Edificio Parthenon, Local 1, PB, Caracas, 1010-A, Venezuela.
Circ: 20,000.

NUOVA ECONOMIA. see *BUSINESS AND ECONOMICS—
Chamber Of Commerce Publications*

330   ITA   ISSN 0029-6376
HC301.A1
NUOVO MEZZOGIORNO. Text in Italian. 1958. m. bk.rev. abstr.;
bibl.; charts; illus. index, cum.index. **Document type:**
Magazine, Consumer.
Published by: Edizioni Nuovo Mezzogiorno, Corso Vittorio
Emanuele II, 154, Rome, RM 00186, Italy. TEL
39-6-68806288, FAX 39-6-68806288. Ed. Vittorio Ciampi. Adv.
contact Maria Novelli. Circ: 15,000.

▼ **NURSING HOME & ELDER BUSINESS WEEK.** see *MEDICAL
SCIENCES—Nurses And Nursing*

NUTRITION BUSINESS JOURNAL. see *NUTRITION AND
DIETETICS*

NUTRITION INDUSTRY EXECUTIVE; the business magazine for
dietary supplement industry manufacturers. see *NUTRITION
AND DIETETICS*

O & P BUSINESS NEWS. (Orthotics & Prosthetics) see *MEDICAL
SCIENCES—Orthopedics And Traumatology*

330   FRA
O E C D ECONOMIC SURVEYS: BULGARIA. Text in English. a.
Document type: *Trade.*
Published by: Organization for Economic Cooperation and
Development, 2 Rue Andre Pascal, Paris, 75775 Cedex 16,
France. TEL 33-1-45248200, FAX 33-1-45248500,
http://www.oecd.org. **Dist. by:** O E C D Turpin North America,
PO Box 194, Downingtown, PA 19335-0194. TEL
610-524-5361, 800-456-6323, FAX 610-524-5417,
bookscustomer@turpinna.com.

330   FRA
O E C D ECONOMIC SURVEYS: KOREA. Text in English. a.
Document type: *Trade.*
Published by: Organization for Economic Cooperation and
Development, 2 Rue Andre Pascal, Paris, 75775 Cedex 16,
France. TEL 33-1-45248200, FAX 33-1-45248500,
http://www.oecd.org. **Dist. in N. America by:** O E C D Turpin
North America, PO Box 194, Downingtown, PA 19335-0194.
TEL 610-524-5361, 800-456-6323, FAX 610-524-5417,
bookscustomer@turpinna.com.

330   FRA
O E C D ECONOMIC SURVEYS: RUSSIAN FEDERATION. Text
in English. a. **Document type:** *Trade.*
Published by: Organization for Economic Cooperation and
Development, 2 Rue Andre Pascal, Paris, 75775 Cedex 16,
France. TEL 33-1-45248200, FAX 33-1-45248500,
http://www.oecd.org. **Dist. in N. America by:** O E C D Turpin
North America, PO Box 194, Downingtown, PA 19335-0194.
TEL 610-524-5361, 800-456-6323, FAX 610-524-5417,
bookscustomer@turpinna.com.

330   SVK   ISSN 1335-2008
OBCHOD. Text in Slovak. 1996. m. SKK 876 (effective 2004).
adv. **Document type:** *Magazine, Trade.*
Published by: Sanoma Magazines Slovakia s.r.o., Kopcianska 6,
Bratislava 5, 85101, Slovakia. TEL 421-2-63839900, FAX
421-2-63839914, sanomaslovakia@sanomaslovakia.sk,
http://www.sanoma.sk. adv.: page SKK 55,000; trim 230 x 297.

330   CZE   ISSN 1210-2687
OBCHODNI VESTNIK. Text in Czech. 1992. w. CZK 2,860; CZK
55 newsstand/cover (effective 2003). adv. **Document type:**
Magazine, Trade.
Published by: Economia a.s., Dobrovskeho 25, Prague 7 7, 170
55, Czech Republic. TEL 420-2-33071111, FAX
420-2-33072003, ov@economia.cz, economia@economia.cz,
http://www.economia.cz. Ed. Josef Vratislav.

330   CAN   ISSN 0826-9947
OBSERVATION. Text in English. 1974. irreg. price varies.
Document type: *Monographic series.* **Description:** Studies
on Canadian and international economics policy issues.
Formerly (until 1980): H R I Observations (0381-5250)
Related titles: Microfiche ed.: (from MML).
Indexed: CBPI, PROMT.
—CISTI.

Published by: C.D. Howe Institute, 125 Adelaide St East, Toronto, ON M5C 1L7, Canada. TEL 416-865-1904, FAX 416-865-1866, cdhowe@cdhowe.org, publicat@cdhowe.org, http://www.cdhowe.org.

330 NOR
OBSERVATOR. Text in Norwegian. 1947. m. NOK 100 to individuals; NOK 200 to institutions. bk.rev.
Formerly: Stimulator; et Fagblad for Socialoekonomer
Published by: Frederik Studentgruppa i Norske Sosialoekonomers Forening, Blindern, Postboks 1095, Blindern, Oslo, 0104, Norway. Circ: 900.

330 RUS ISSN 0207-3676
HC10
OBSHCHESTVO I EKONOMIKA. Text in Russian. 1992. m. RUR 250 for 6 mos. domestic; USD 225 in United States (effective 2004).
Related titles: Online - full text ed.: (from East View Information Services).
Indexed: IBSS, RASB, RefZh, WAE&RSA.
—East View, KNAW.
Published by: Izdatel'stvo Nauka, Profsoyuznaya ul 90, Moscow, 117864, Russian Federation. TEL 7-095-3347151, FAX 7-095-4202220, secret@naukaran.ru, http://www.naukaran.ru. **Subscr. in US to:** East View Information Services, 3020 Harbor Ln. N., Minneapolis, MN 55447. TEL 800-477-1005, FAX 800-800-3839, eastview@eastview.com, http://www.eastview.com.

320 DNK ISSN 0030-1906
HC10
OEKONOMI OG POLITIK. Text in Danish. 1927. q. DKK 375 to individuals; DKK 475 to institutions (effective 2003). adv. bk.rev. stat. index. reprint service avail. from ISI. **Document type:** *Journal, Academic/Scholarly.*
Indexed: AmH&L, HistAb, IPSA, JEL, PCI, RASB.
Published by: (Selskabet for Historie og Samfundsoekonomi), Jurist- og Oekonomforbundets Forlag, Lyngbyvej 17, PO Box 2702, Copenhagen OE, 2100, Denmark. TEL 45-39-315500, FAX 45-39-135555, fl@djoef.dk, http://www.djoef.dk/forlag/oekpol. Ed. Peter Nedergaard. Circ: 1,000.

OESTERREICHISCHES INSTITUT FUER WIRTSCHAFTSFORSCHUNG. MONATSBERICHTE. see *BUSINESS AND ECONOMICS—Economic Situation And Conditions*

330 AUT ISSN 1013-9486
OESTERREICHISCHES RECHT DER WIRTSCHAFT. Text in German. m. EUR 155; EUR 15.70 newsstand/cover (effective 2005). adv. bk.rev. 64 p./no.; **Document type:** *Magazine, Trade.*
Published by: LexisNexis Verlag ARD Orac GmbH & Co. KG (Subsidiary of: LexisNexis Europe and Africa), Marxergasse 25, Vienna, W 1030, Austria. TEL 43-1-534520, FAX 43-1-53452141, verlag@orac.at, http://www.lexisnexis.at/. Ed. Werner Doralt. Adv. contact Malgorzata Leitliner TEL 43-1-534521115. Circ: 4,300.

330 AUT
OESTERREICHS WIRTSCHAFT. Text in German. 9/yr.
Address: Eschenbachgasse 11, Vienna, W 1072, Austria. TEL 01-5873633, FAX 01-5870192. Ed. Evamaria Hawel. Circ: 4,200.

658 GBR ISSN 1472-2542
THE OFFICIAL M B A HANDBOOK (YEAR). (Masters in Business Administration) Text in English. 1990. a. GBP 29.95 domestic; GBP 34.95 in Europe; GBP 38.95 rest of world (effective 2001).
Former titles (until 1999): Association of M B As Guide to Business Schools (1369-9814); (until 1990): A M B A Guide to Business Schools
—BLDSC (6240.517000).
Published by: Association of M B As, 15 Duncan Terrace, London, N1 8BZ, United Kingdom. TEL 44-20-7837-3375, FAX 44-20-7278-3634, http://www.mba.org.uk. Pub. Mike Jones.

330 341 RUS
OFFSHORE EXPRESS. Text in Russian. 1995. m. USD 60. back issues avail. **Description:** Provides information for those who wish to form a business or establish residence overseas.
Published by: Offshore Express Corp., B Polyanka 15, kom 201, Moscow, 109108, Russian Federation. TEL 7-095-2307615, FAX 7-095-9650757. Circ: 40,000. **US dist. addr.:** East View Information Services, 3020 Harbor Ln. N., Minneapolis, MN 55447. TEL 612-550-0961.

OGGI E DOMANI. see *PUBLIC ADMINISTRATION*

OHIO & NORTHERN KENTUCKY GASOLINE DEALERS & GARAGE NEWS. see *TRANSPORTATION—Automobiles*

330 USA
▼ **OHIO ENTREPRENEUR.** Text in English. 2003. m. **Document type:** *Magazine, Trade.*
Media: Online - full content.
Address: 1422 Euclid Ave, Ste 730, Cleveland, OH 44115. TEL 877-462-4769, http://www.ohiogotogrow.com/.

330 GRC ISSN 1106-1936
OIKONOMIKOS TAHUDROMOS. Text in Greek. 1926. w. **Document type:** *Magazine, Trade.*
Published by: Lambrakis Press SA, Panepistimiou 18, Athens, 106 72, Greece. TEL 30-1-3686-452, FAX 30-1-3686-445, dolinfo@dol.gr, http://www.dol.gr.

333 JPN ISSN 0287-0916
OITA DAIGAKU KEIZAI KENKYUSHO KENKYUJCHO/OITA UNIVERSITY. RESEARCH INSTITUTE OF ECONOMICS. BULLETIN. Text in Japanese. 1967. a. per issue exchange basis. **Document type:** *Bulletin.*
Published by: Oita Daigaku, Keizai Kenkyusho/Oita University, Research Institute of Economics, 700 Dannoharu, Oita-shi, 870-1124, Japan. Ed. Fukuo Igarashi. Pub. Sunao Uchino. Circ: 550.

330 JPN ISSN 0474-0157
OITA DAIGAKU KEIZAI RONSHU/OITA UNIVERSITY ECONOMIC REVIEW. Text in Japanese. 1949. 6/yr. JPY 5,000. **Document type:** *Bulletin.*
Published by: Oita Daigaku, Keizai Gakkai/Oita University, Economic Society, Oita, Japan. Ed. Fukuo Igarashi. Pub. Katsuhiko Yoshime. Circ: 1,300.

330 CAN ISSN 1180-3975
OKANAGAN BUSINESS MAGAZINE✶. Text in English. 1989. 10/yr. CND 15. adv. bk.rev. **Document type:** *Consumer.*
Published by: Byrne Publishing Group, Inc., Ste 10, 1735 Dolphin Ave, Kelowna, BC V1Y 8A6, Canada. TEL 250-861-5399, FAX 250-868-3040. Ed. Mike Haines. Pub. Paul Byrne. Adv. contact Gerry Lee. Circ: 10,710.

330.0711 USA
OKLAHOMA COUNCIL ON ECONOMIC EDUCATION NEWSLETTER✶. Text in English. 1961. 3/yr. membership. **Document type:** *Newsletter.*
Published by: Oklahoma Council on Economic Education, University of Central Oklahoma, Economics Department, Edmond, OK 73034-0182. TEL 405-341-2980. Ed. Jean Caldwell. Circ: 3,600.

330 650 USA
OKLAHOMA STATE UNIVERSITY. COLLEGE OF BUSINESS ADMINISTRATION. WORKING PAPERS. Text in English. 1966. irreg., latest no.91-95. free.
Supersedes: Oklahoma State University. College of Business Administration. Extension Service. Business Papers (0078-4427)
Published by: Oklahoma State University, College of Business Administration, Office of Business and Economic Research, Stillwater, OK 74078-0555. TEL 405-744-5125.

▼ **ONCOLOGY BUSINESS WEEK.** see *MEDICAL SCIENCES—Oncology*

330 340 BEL ISSN 1372-357X
DE ONDERNEMER; praktisch jaarboek voor de Bedrijfsleider. Text in Dutch. 1989. a. EUR 161.50 (effective 2003); includes data diskette.
Formerly (until 1995): Succes Partner (0778-5909)
Published by: Kluwer Uitgevers (Subsidiary of: Wolters Kluwer Belgique), Ragheno Business Park, Motstraat 30, Mechelen, B-2800, Belgium. TEL 32-15-800-94571, info@kluwer.be, http://www.kluwer.be. Eds. Jack Misteli, Werner Van Minnebruggen.

330 NLD ISSN 1387-4276
ONDERNEMINGSRAAD. Text in Dutch. 1979. 10/yr. EUR 6,436 domestic; EUR 6,439 foreign (effective 2003).
Former titles (until 1997): Praktijkblad voor Medezeggenschap (0921-2442); (until 1979): O R Blad (0920-492X)
—Infotrieve.
Published by: Reed Business Information bv (Subsidiary of: Reed Business), Postbus 16500, Den Haag, 2500 BM, Netherlands. TEL 31-70-441-5237, FAX 31-70-441-5912, info@reedbusiness.nl, http://www.or-net.com, http://www.reedbusiness.nl. Ed. Joe Everaers.

ONDERNEMINGSRECHT. see *LAW*

ONLINE - CD-ROM BUSINESS SOURCEBOOK. see *BUSINESS AND ECONOMICS—Trade And Industrial Directories*

330 USA ISSN 1548-5137
▼ **ONLINE JOURNAL OF INTERNATIONAL CASE ANALYSIS.** Text in English. 2005. irreg.
Media: Online - full content.
Published by: Florida International University, Department of Management and International Business, 11200 SW 8th St. RB 345, Miami, FL 33199. TEL 305-348-2791, FAX 305-348-6146, http://cba.fiu.edu/ojica/, http://cba.fiu.edu/web/management/. Ed. J. Randall Martin.

330 658 USA
OPERATIONS UPDATE (NEW YORK). Text in English. irreg. USD 75 to non-members; USD 50 to members. **Document type:** *Trade.* **Description:** Presents developments of immediate interest to operations managers.
Published by: Securities Industry Association, 120 Broadway, 35th Fl, New York, NY 10271. TEL 212-608-1500.

330 COL
OPINION ECONOMICA✶. Text in Spanish. 1975. q.
Published by: Sociedad Antioquena de Economistas, c/o Sociedad Colombiana de Economistas, Carrera 20 36-41, Apartado Aereo 8429, Bogota, CUND, Colombia.

330 POL ISSN 1506-7637
OPTIMUM. Text in Polish. 1994. q. PLZ 25 per issue (effective 2005). **Document type:** *Journal, Academic/Scholarly.*
Formerly (until 1998): Studia Ekonomiczne (Bialystok) (1428-2763)
Published by: (Uniwersytet w Bialymstoku, Wydzial Ekonomiczny), Wydawnictwo Uniwersytetu w Bialymstoku, ul Marii Sklodowskiej-Curie 14, Bialystok, 15097, Poland. TEL 48-85-7457059, FAX 48-85-7457073, ac-dw@uwb.edu.pl.

330 AUS
OPTUS BUSINESS ADVANTAGE. Text in English. q. **Document type:** *Magazine, Trade.*
Formerly: OPTUS Advantage
Published by: A C P Custom Media, Level 7, 50 Park St, Sydney, NSW 2000, Australia. TEL 61-2-9282-8019, FAX 61-2-9267-3625, custominfo@acp.com.au, http://www.custompubs.acp.com.au/docs/customer.html. Circ: 135,000 (controlled).

B

330 USA ISSN 0279-8190
HF5001
OREGON BUSINESS MAGAZINE. Text in English. 1978. m. USD 19.95 (effective 2005). adv. bk.rev. illus. 60 p./no.; reprints avail. **Document type:** *Magazine, Consumer.* **Description:** Covers small and medium-sized businesses in Oregon.
Related titles: Microform ed.: (from PQC); Online - full text ed.: (from Florida Center for Library Automation, Gale Group, O C L C Online Computer Library Center, Inc., ProQuest Information & Learning); Supplement(s): Building Oregon; Research Oregon.
Indexed: ABIn.
Published by: MediAmerica, Inc., 610 SW Broadway, Ste 200, Portland, OR 97205. TEL 503-223-0304, FAX 503-221-6544, http://www.oregonbusiness.com. Ed. Mitchell Hartman. Pub. Gillian Floren. Adv. contact Sue Crichton. Circ: 19,200 (paid and controlled).

330 USA
OREGON BUSINESS NETWORK NEWS. Text in English. 1981. q. free. **Document type:** *Newspaper, Trade.*
Published by: Business Services Corp., PO Box 5488, Portland, OR 97228. TEL 503-244-5794, FAX 503-293-2094, oregonbusiness@usa.net. Ed. Roy Jay. Circ: 100,000 (controlled).

ORGANIC PRODUCTS RETAILER. see *FOOD AND FOOD INDUSTRIES*

330 CHE ISSN 0724-6110
ORGANISATIONSENTWICKLUNG. Text in German. 1982. q.
Indexed: ABIn, DIP, IBR, IBZ.
Published by: Organisationsentwicklung und Management, Hiltrud Schnyder, Postfach 147, Basel, 4003, Switzerland. Ed. Michael Braune-Krickau.

▼ **ORGANIZATIONAL INTERSECTIONS IN HEALTHCARE, BUSINESS AND POLICY.** see *MEDICAL SCIENCES*

ORGANIZING CORPORATE AND OTHER BUSINESS ENTERPRISES. see *LAW—Corporate Law*

ORIENTIERUNGEN ZUR GESELLSCHAFTS- UND WIRTSCHAFTSPOLITIK. see *SOCIAL SCIENCES: COMPREHENSIVE WORKS*

330 USA ISSN 8750-8656
ORLANDO BUSINESS JOURNAL. Text in English. 1984. w. (Fri.). USD 79 (effective 2005). **Document type:** *Newspaper.*
Related titles: Online - full text ed.: (from Florida Center for Library Automation, Gale Group, O C L C Online Computer Library Center, Inc., ProQuest Information & Learning).
Indexed: ABIn, BusDate, LRI.
—CCC.
Published by: American City Business Journals, Inc., 120 W Morehead St, Charlotte, NC 28202. TEL 704-973-1000, FAX 704-973-1001, orlando@bizjournals.com, info@bizjournals.com, http://www.bizjournals.com/orlando/. Ed. Ken Cogburn. Pub. Ann Sontag. Adv. contact Sue Ross. Circ: 10,500.

658 CAN ISSN 1198-8215
T177.C3
ORTECH. ANNUAL REPORT. Text in English. 1928. a. free. **Document type:** *Corporate.*
Former titles: ORTECH International. Annual Report; Ontario Research Foundation. Annual Report (0078-5083)
—CISTI.
Published by: ORTECH, Dept of Marketing, 2395 Speakman Dr, Mississauga, ON L5K 1B3, Canada. TEL 905-822-4111, FAX 905-823-1446. Ed. John Convey.

330 JPN ISSN 0914-6466
OSAKA CITY UNIVERSITY BUSINESS REVIEW. Text in English.

Published by: Osaka City University, Society of Business Research, 3-3-138, Sugimoto, Sumiyoshi-ku, Osaka, 558, Japan. http://www.bus.osaka-cu.ac.jp/.

330 CZE ISSN 1213-7405
OSOBNI FINANCE; s nami budou penize s vami. Text in Czech. 2002. m. CZK 299 (effective 2003). adv. **Document type:** *Magazine, Consumer.*
Related titles: Online - full text ed.
Published by: Computer Press a.s., Pod Vinici 23, Prague 4, 143 11, Czech Republic. TEL 420-2-225273930, FAX 420-2-225273934, webmaster@cpress.cz, http://www.osobni-finance.com, http://www.cpress.cz. Ed. Libor Kriz. Adv. contact Miroslava Doubkova.

330 USA ISSN 0197-3592
OSTARO'S MARKET NEWSLETTER. Text in English. 1980. 12/yr. USD 195. **Document type:** *Newsletter.* **Description:** World market calendar; charts gold and DJIA for the next month.
Address: 303 5th Ave, 1909, New York, NY 10016. TEL 212-686-4121. Ed. D Ostaro. Circ: 1,000.

330 DEU ISSN 0030-6460
HC244
OSTEUROPA-WIRTSCHAFT. Text in English, German. 1956. q. EUR 49; EUR 39 to students; EUR 15 newsstand/cover (effective 2004). bk.rev. stat. index. reprints avail. **Document type:** *Journal, Trade.*
Indexed: ABCPolSci, AmH&L, DIP, HistAb, IBR, IBSS, IBZ, KES, PAIS, RASB, SociolAb.
—BLDSC (6312.250000), IE, Infotrieve, ingenta. **CCC.**
Published by: (Deutsche Gesellschaft fuer Osteuropakunde), B W V - Berliner Wissenschafts Verlag GmbH, Axel-Springer-Str 54b, Berlin, 10117, Germany. TEL 49-30-8417700, FAX 49-30-84177021, bwv@bwv-verlag.de, http://www.bwv-verlag.de. Circ: 650.

OSTEUROPASTUDIEN DER HOCHSCHULEN DES LANDES HESSEN. REIHE 1. GIESSENER ABHANDLUNGEN ZUR AGRAR- UND WIRTSCHAFTSFORSCHUNG DES EUROPAEISCHEN OSTENS. see *AGRICULTURE—Agricultural Economics*

330 JPN ISSN 0475-0756
HB1
OTEMON ECONOMIC STUDIES. Text in English. 1968. a.
Indexed: IBSS.
—BLDSC (6313.270000).
Published by: Otemon Gakuin Daigaku/Otemon Gakuin University, 1-15 Nishia 2-Chome, Ibaraki, Osaka, 567-8502, Japan. TEL 81-72-641-9631, FAX 81-72-643-5651, http://www.otemon.ac.jp.

330 CAN ISSN 1207-8166
OTTAWA BUSINESS JOURNAL. Text in English. 1995. w. CND 105 domestic; CND 153 foreign (effective 2003). adv. **Document type:** *Newspaper, Trade.* **Description:** Covers local business news and events.
Related titles: Online - full content ed.
Published by: InBusiness Media Network Inc., 1686 Woodward Dr, Ottawa, ON K2C 3R8, Canada. TEL 613-230-8699, FAX 613-230-9606, obj@ottawabusinessjournal.com, http://www.ottawabusinessjournal.com/, http://www.inbusinessmedia.com.

330 USA
OUTSOURCING AND OFFSHORING NEWS. Text in English. bi-m. USD 539 (effective 2004). **Document type:** *Newsletter, Trade.* **Description:** Offers real-world intelligence on what(UNKNOWN CHARACTER)s happening in BPO in the U.S. and around the world.
Published by: Royal Media Group, 1359 Broadway, Ste 1512, New York, NY 10018. TEL 212-564-8972, FAX 212-564-8973, info@royalmedia.com, http://www.royalmedia.com/newsletter.cfm?pub=106.

▼ **OVERTIME**; the business and lifestyle guide for professional athletes. see *SPORTS AND GAMES*

310 330 GBR ISSN 0305-9049
HC10
➤ **OXFORD BULLETIN OF ECONOMICS AND STATISTICS.** Text in English. 1939. bi-m. EUR 98 combined subscription in Europe to individuals print & online eds.; USD 109 combined subscription in the Americas to individuals & Caribbean, print & online eds.; GBP 65 combined subscription elsewhere to individuals print & online eds.; GBP 349 combined subscription in Europe to institutions print & online eds.; USD 714 combined subscription in the Americas to institutions & Caribbean, print & online eds.; GBP 425 combined subscription elsewhere to institutions print & online eds. (effective 2006). adv. illus. index. reprint service avail. from PSC. **Document type:** *Journal, Academic/Scholarly.*
Former titles (until 1973): Oxford University. Institute of Economics and Statistics. Bulletin (0140-5543); (until 1963): Oxford University. Institute of Statistics. Bulletin (0030-767X)
Related titles: Online - full text ed.: ISSN 1468-0084. GBP 332 in Europe to institutions; USD 679 in the Americas to institutions & Caribbean; GBP 404 elsewhere to institutions (effective 2006) (from Blackwell Synergy, EBSCO Publishing, Gale Group, IngentaConnect, O C L C Online Computer Library Center, Inc., Swets Information Services).
Indexed: ABIn, APEL, ASCA, BPIA, CJA, CMCI, CPM, CREJ, CurCont, ESPM, FPA, FamI, ForAb, IBSS, JCQM, JEL, KES, MEA&I, MResA, NutrAb, PAA&I, PAIS, RASB, RDA, RRTA, RiskAb, SSCI, T&II, TDB, WAE&RSA, WBA.
—BLDSC (6320.640000), IDS, IE, Infotrieve, ingenta. **CCC.**
Published by: Blackwell Publishing Ltd., 9600 Garsington Rd, Oxford, OX4 2ZG, United Kingdom. TEL 44-1865-776868, FAX 44-1865-714591, customerservices@oxon.blackwellpublishing.com, http://www.blackwellpublishing.com/journals/OBES. Circ: 1,500.

330 GBR ISSN 0030-7653
HB31
➤ **OXFORD ECONOMIC PAPERS.** Text in English. 1938. q. GBP 198, USD 356, USD 297 to institutions; GBP 208, USD 374, EUR 312 combined subscription to institutions print & online eds. (effective 2006). adv. illus. index. 192 p./no.; back issues avail.; reprint service avail. from PQC,PSC. **Document type:** *Journal, Academic/Scholarly.* **Description:** Addresses theoretical and applied economics, economic history, public administration and scientific method.
Related titles: Microform ed.: (from PQC); Online - full text ed.: ISSN 1464-3812. GBP 187, USD 337, EUR 281 to institutions (effective 2006) (from bigchalk, EBSCO Publishing, Gale Group, HighWire Press, IngentaConnect, JSTOR (Web-based Journal Archive), Northern Light Technology, Inc., O C L C Online Computer Library Center, Inc., Oxford University Press Online Journals, ProQuest Information & Learning, Swets Information Services).
Indexed: ABIn, APEL, ASCA, AmH&L, BAS, CIS, CPM, CREJ, CurCont, ExcerpMed, FamI, GEOBASE, HistAb, IBR, IBSS, IBZ, JEL, KES, MEA&I, PAA&I, PAIS, PCI, RASB, RDA, RRTA, S&F, SCIMP, SSCI, SSI, WAE&RSA, WBA.
—BLDSC (6320.700000), IDS, IE, Infotrieve, ingenta. **CCC.**
Published by: Oxford University Press, Great Clarendon St, Oxford, OX2 6DP, United Kingdom. TEL 44-1865-556767, FAX 44-1865-556646, oep@economics.oxford.ac.uk, jnl.orders@oup.co.uk, http://oep.oxfordjournals.org/, http://www.oxfordjournals.org/. Eds. A. Banerjee, J Forder, S. Cowan. Pub. Martin Green. R&P Fiona Bennett. Adv. contact Helen Pearson. B&W page GBP 260, B&W page USD 440; 118 x 190. Circ: 1,900.

338 GBR ISSN 0266-903X
HC251
➤ **OXFORD REVIEW OF ECONOMIC POLICY.** Text in English. 1985. q. GBP 212, USD 379, EUR 318 to institutions; GBP 223, USD 399, EUR 335 to institutions print & online eds. (effective 2006). adv. bk.rev. charts; illus. 144 p./no.; back issues avail.; reprint service avail. from PSC. **Document type:** *Journal, Academic/Scholarly.* **Description:** Provides commentary, forecasts and articles on economic policy in the UK and the world.
Related titles: Online - full text ed.: ISSN 1460-2121. GBP 201, USD 360, EUR 302 to institutions (effective 2006) (from Chadwyck-Healey Inc., EBSCO Publishing, Gale Group, HighWire Press, IngentaConnect, O C L C Online Computer Library Center, Inc., Oxford University Press Online Journals, ProQuest Information & Learning, Swets Information Services).
Indexed: ABIn, ASCA, BrHumI, CREJ, CurCont, Emerald, GEOBASE, IBSS, JEL, PAIS, PCI, RASB, SSCI.
—BLDSC (6321.016950), CISTI, IDS, IE, Infotrieve, ingenta. **CCC.**
Published by: Oxford University Press, Great Clarendon St, Oxford, OX2 6DP, United Kingdom. TEL 44-1865-556767, FAX 44-1865-556646, econrev@herald.ox.ac.uk, jnl.orders@oup.co.uk, http://oxrep.oxfordjournals.org/, http://www.oxfordjournals.org/. Ed. T. Jenkinson. Pub. Martin Green. R&P Fiona Bennett. Adv. contact Helen Pearson. B&W page GBP 320, B&W page USD 520; 160 x 260. Circ: 1,600.

➤ **P A S MEMO.** (Planning Advisory Service) see *HOUSING AND URBAN PLANNING*

330 GBR ISSN 0963-8563
P E L OCCASIONAL PAPERS ON BUSINESS, ECONOMY AND SOCIETY. (Polytechnic of East London) Text in English. 1991. irreg., latest vol.4, 1991. GBP 10. **Document type:** *Monographic series.*
—BLDSC (6224.337000).
Published by: Polytechnic of East London, Department of Business Studies, Longbridge Rd, Dagenham, Essex RM8 2AS, United Kingdom. TEL 081-590-7722.

LES P M E AU QUEBEC. ETAT DE LA SITUATION. (Petite et Moyenne Entreprise) see *BUSINESS AND ECONOMICS—Production Of Goods And Services*

330 USA
P R NEWSWIRE. Text in English. 1954. irreg. **Document type:** *Trade.*
Media: Online - full content.
Published by: PR Newswire Association LLC, 810 Seventh Ave, 35th Fl, New York, NY 10019. TEL 212-596-1500, 800-832-5522, http://www.prnewswire.com/.

P R O; portable restroom operator. see *ENVIRONMENTAL STUDIES—Waste Management*

P S I DISCUSSION PAPERS. see *SOCIAL SCIENCES: COMPREHENSIVE WORKS*

P S I: REPORT SERIES. see *POLITICAL SCIENCE*

330 USA ISSN 0030-8552
CODEN: HOGEAF
PACIFIC BUSINESS NEWS. Text in English. 1963. w. (Fri.). USD 79.95; USD 2 per issue (effective 2005). adv. bk.rev. back issues avail. **Document type:** *Newspaper.* **Description:** News and public record information for business and professional readers in Hawaii.
Related titles: Microfilm ed.: (from PQC); Online - full text ed.: (from Florida Center for Library Automation, Gale Group, O C L C Online Computer Library Center, Inc., ProQuest Information & Learning, The Dialog Corporation).
Indexed: ABIn, BusDate, T&II.
—**CCC.**
Published by: American City Business Journals, Inc. (Honolulu), 1833 Kalakaua Ave 7th Fl, Honolulu, HI 96815-1512. TEL 808-955-8100, FAX 808-955-8078, pacific@bizjournals.com, http://www.bizjournals.com/pacific. Ed. Jim Kelly. Pub. Larry Fuller. Adv. contact Geri Cardoza. B&W page USD 4,000, color page USD 4,404. Circ: 1,400 (paid).

330 CAN
PACIFIC ECONOMIC OUTLOOK. Text in English. 1999. a.
Media: Online - full text.
Published by: Asia Pacific Foundation of Canada, 666-999 Canada Place, Vancouver, BC V6C 3E1, Canada. http://www.asiapacific.ca/analysis/pubs/outlook/index.cfm.

PAINT AND COATINGS 2000: REVIEW AND FORECAST. see *PAINTS AND PROTECTIVE COATINGS*

330.9 PAK ISSN 0253-1941
PAKISTAN AND GULF ECONOMIST. Text in English. 1962. w. PKR 1,170 (effective 1999 - 2000); PKR 30 newsstand/cover; USD 160 in Asia; USD 160 in the Middle East; USD 190 in US & Canada (effective 1999 - 2000). adv. bk.rev. charts; illus.; stat. index, cum.index. reprints avail. **Document type:** *Newspaper.* **Description:** Provides opinion, commentary and analysis on all key business, economic and financial developments in Pakistan.
Incorporating: Pakistan Economist (0030-9745); Which was formerly: Finance and Industry
Related titles: Online - full text ed.
Indexed: BAS, KES, MEA&I, RASB, RDA, RRTA, WAE&RSA.
Published by: Economist Publications (Pvt.) Limited, 3 A, Falcon Arcade, BC - 3, Block - 7, Clifton, Karachi, Pakistan. TEL 92-21-5869534, FAX 92-21-5876071, information@pak-economist.com, http://www.pak-economist.com/. Ed., R&P Suhail Abbas. Pub. Sikandar Darvesh. adv.: B&W page USD 300, color page USD 1,000. Circ: 35,000.

338.9 PAK ISSN 0030-9729
HC440.5 CODEN: JGSIAJ
PAKISTAN DEVELOPMENT REVIEW; international journal of development economics. Text in English. 1961. q. PKR 300 domestic to individuals; PKR 450 domestic to institutions; PKR 100 domestic to students; EUR 85 foreign to individuals; EUR 125 foreign to institutions; USD 100 foreign to individuals; USD 150 foreign to institutions; PKR 125 per issue domestic; EUR 35 per issue foreign (effective 2005). bk.rev. stat. back issues avail.; reprints avail. **Document type:** *Academic/Scholarly.* **Description:** Publishes empirical research on development economics with a focus on economic issues relating to Pakistan.
Indexed: AEA, APEL, ARDT, AnBrAb, BAS, BibInd, DSA, EIP, GEOBASE, HortAb, I&DA, IBSS, JEL, MaizeAb, NutrAb, PGegResA, PerIslam, PopulInd, RDA, REE&TA, RPP, RiceAb, S&F, SIA, SeedAb, TDB, TOSA, TriticAb, WAE&RSA, WeedAb.
—BLDSC (6340.680000), IE, Infotrieve, ingenta.
Published by: Pakistan Institute of Development Economics, P O Box 1091, Islamabad, 44000, Pakistan. TEL 92-51-9206610, FAX 92-51-9210886, pide@isb.paknet.com.pk, pide@appollo.net.pk, http://www.pide.org.pk. Ed. A R Kemal. Circ: 1,500.

PAKISTAN ECONOMIC AND SOCIAL REVIEW. see *BUSINESS AND ECONOMICS—International Development And Assistance*

330 PAK
PAKISTAN ECONOMIC JOURNAL. Text in English. 1973. s-a. PKR 8, USD 6. adv. bibl.
Indexed: BAS.
Published by: Pakistan Economic Association, University of the Punjab, Department of Economics, New Campus, Lahore, Pakistan. Ed. Moin Baqai.

338.9 PAK ISSN 0078-821X
PAKISTAN INSTITUTE OF DEVELOPMENT ECONOMICS. REPORT. Text in English. 1962. irreg. **Document type:** *Academic/Scholarly.*
Indexed: WAE&RSA.

Published by: Pakistan Institute of Development Economics, P O Box 1091, Islamabad, 44000, Pakistan. TEL 92-51-9206610, FAX 92-51-9210886, pide@isb.paknet.com.pk, pide@apollo.net.pk, http://www.pide.org.pk. Ed. A R Kemal. Circ: 1,000.

338.9 PAK ISSN 0078-8228
PAKISTAN INSTITUTE OF DEVELOPMENT ECONOMICS. RESEARCH REPORTS. Text in English. 1962. irreg., latest vol.183, 2001. price varies. **Document type:** Monographic series.
Media: Duplicated (not offset).
Indexed: GEOBASE, RASB, RDA.
Published by: Pakistan Institute of Development Economics, P O Box 1091, Islamabad, 44000, Pakistan. TEL 92-51-9206610, FAX 92-51-9210886, pide@isb.paknet.com.pk, pide@apollo.net.pk, http://www.pide.org.pk. Ed. A R Kemal. Circ: 500.

330 USA ISSN 1060-4952
PANEL STUDY OF INCOME DYNAMICS. Text in English. 1987. a.
Published by: Inter-University Consortium for Political and Social Research, PO Box 1248, Ann Arbor, MI 48106-1248. netmail@icpsr.umich.edu, http://www.icpsr.umich.edu.

330 ESP ISSN 1134-0584
PANORAMA ECONOMICO. Text in Spanish. 1994. m.
Indexed: PAIS.
Published by: Grupo Santander, Plaza de Canalejas no.1, Madrid, 28014, Spain.

330 ITA ISSN 1722-9383
▼ **PANORAMA ECONOMY.** Text in Italian. 2003. w. EUR 62 (effective 2004). **Document type:** Magazine, Consumer.
Published by: Arnoldo Mondadori Editore SpA, Via Mondadori 1, Segrate, 20090, Italy. TEL 39-02-66814363, FAX 39-030-3198412, http://www.mondadori.com.

330 RUS
PANORAMA PRIVATIZATSII. Text in Russian. s-m. USD 209.95 in United States.
Indexed: RASB.
Published by: Gosudarstvennyi Komitet Rossiiskoi Federatsii po Upravleniyu Gosudarstvennym Imushchestvom, Ul Arkhitektora Vlasova 51, kom 416, Moscow, 117393, Russian Federation. TEL 7-095-1289533, FAX 7-095-1289660. Ed. V G Krasnenkov. US dist. addr.: East View Information Services, 3020 Harbor Ln. N., Minneapolis, MN 55447. TEL 612-550-0961.

330 IND ISSN 0972-3811
PARADHIKRIT. Text in Hindi. 1984. a. INR 60 newsstand/cover domestic to individuals; GBP 15 newsstand/cover foreign to individuals; INR 100 newsstand/cover domestic to institutions; USD 20 newsstand/cover foreign to institutions (effective 2003).
Published by: Guru Nanak Dev University Press, Press & Publications Department, Amritsar, Punjab 143 005, India. TEL 91-183-258802, FAX 91-183-258819, dcse.gndu@yahoo.com.

330 FRA
PARTENAIRES. Text in French. s-m. **Document type:** Government. **Description:** Offers a panorama of business activity in France and Europe.
Published by: (France. Ministere du Travail, de l'Emploi et de la Formation Professionnelle), Imprimerie Nationale, BP 514, Douai, Cedex 59505, France.

330 004.678 GBR
PARTNERSHIP ONLINE. Text in English. 1998. m.
Media: Online - full content.
Published by: British Telecommunications plc., 81 Newgate St, Rm B6.G, London, EC14 7AJ, United Kingdom. http://www.partnership.bt.com.

PATHWAYS TO PROFITABILITY; a financial analysis of the decorating products centers in the U.S. see INTERIOR DESIGN AND DECORATION

330 GBR
PAY IN THE PUBLIC SERVICES (YEAR). Text in English. a., latest 2004. GBP 165 per issue (effective 2004). **Description:** Provides up-to-date details of pay and conditions throughout the public services. It includes an analysis of public sector pay bargaining, and gives detailed current pay structure for 100 staff groups. It also covers the voluntary sector.
—BLDSC (6413.109730).
Published by: Incomes Data Services Ltd., 77 Bastwick St, London, EC1V 3TT, United Kingdom. TEL 44-20-72503434, FAX 44-20-73242510, ids@incomesdata.co.uk, http://www.incomesdata.co.uk.

330 USA
PAYMENTS QUARTERLY. Text in English. q. back issues avail. **Description:** Covers news of financial services in the Eighth Federal Reserve District.
Published by: Federal Reserve Bank of St. Louis, PO Box 442, St. Louis, MO 63166. TEL 314-444-8444, http://www.stls.frb.org/publications/pq.

PAYROLL LIBRARY. Text in English. irreg. **Document type:** Trade. **Description:** Provides guidance and regular updates in every area of payroll administration and compliance, and includes hundreds of interactive forms and links to related federal, state, and local sites.
Media: Online - full content.
Published by: B N A Inc. (Subsidiary of: The Bureau of National Affairs, Inc.), 1231 25th St, NW, Washington, DC 20037. TEL 202-452-4343, FAX 202-452-4997, books@bna.com, http://www.bna.com/payroll/, http://www.bnabooks.com.

PAYROLL PRACTITIONER'S MONTHLY. see LAW

330 RUS
PECHATNYI DVOR. Text in Russian. 1996. m. USD 195 in North America (effective 2000).
Published by: Segodnya Press, Ul Pravdy 24, Moscow, 125137, Russian Federation. TEL 7-095-2575695. Ed. V V Kachurin. Dist. by: East View Information Services, 3020 Harbor Ln. N., Minneapolis, MN 55447. TEL 763-550-0961, FAX 763-559-2931.

330.948 DNK ISSN 0107-4873
PENGE & PRIVATOEKONOMI. Text in Danish. 1977. m. (11/yr.). DKK 485. adv. illus. back issues avail. **Document type:** Consumer. **Description:** News about managing personal finances: investing in bonds, shares, real estate, tax regulations, deductions, cars, housing, savings.
Formerly (until 1981): Penge og Investering (0105-4376)
Published by: Boersen Magasiner A-S, Moentergade 19, PO Box 2242, Copenhagen K, 1019, Denmark. TEL 45-33-32-44-00, FAX 45-33-11-59-06, www.penge.dk. Ed. Ole Hoy Hansen. Adv. contact Christian Samsoe. B&W page DKK 33,500, color page DKK 41,000; trim 297 x 420. Circ: 31,000.

330 USA
PENNSYLVANIA CONFERENCE OF ECONOMISTS. PROCEEDINGS OF THE ANNUAL MEETING. Text in English. 1951. a. USD 15. charts. back issues avail. **Document type:** Proceedings.
Published by: Pennsylvania Conference of Economists, c/o Alexander Garvin, Economics Dept, Indiana University of Pennsylvania, Indiana, PA 15701. TEL 412-357-2640. Ed. Joseph Horton. Circ: 500.

330 USA
➤ **PENNSYLVANIA ECONOMIC REVIEW.** Text in English. 1991. s-a. USD 25 to non-members. adv. bk.rev. back issues avail. **Document type:** Academic/Scholarly.
Published by: Pennsylvania Economic Association, Economics Dept, Millersville University, Box 1002, Millersville, PA 17551. TEL 717-872-3561, FAX 717-871-2326, margoli@marauder.millersv.edu. Ed. Marvin S Margolis. R&P, Adv. contact Marvis S Margolis. Circ: 200 (controlled).

330 HND
PENSAMIENTO ECONOMICO. Text in Spanish. 19??-1975; resumed 1979. q. adv. bibl.; charts; stat.
Indexed: PAIS.
Published by: Colegio Hondureno de Economistas, Tegucigalpa D.C., Honduras.

330 ITA ISSN 1122-8784
HB109.A2
IL PENSIERO ECONOMICO ITALIANO. Text in Italian. 1993. s-a. EUR 60 domestic to individuals; EUR 125 foreign to individuals; EUR 120 domestic to institutions print & online eds.; EUR 195 foreign to institutions print & online eds. (effective 2004). **Document type:** Academic/Scholarly. **Description:** Contains studies on economic policies relevant to Italy and other nations, with particular attention given to industialization, agriculture and demography.
Related titles: Online - full text ed.
Indexed: JEL.
Published by: (Universita degli Studi di Teramo, Dipartimento di Storia e Critica della Politica), Istituti Editoriali e Poligrafici Internazionali (Subsidiary of: Libra Web), Via Giosue' Carducci, 60, Ghezzano - La Fontina, PI 56010, Italy. TEL 39-050-878066, FAX 39-050-878732, iepi@iepi.it, http://www.iepi.it. Ed. Massimo Augello.

330 GBR ISSN 0267-9035
PENSIONS INTELLIGENCE. Text in English. 1985. m. GBP 145, USD 260. **Document type:** Newsletter. **Description:** Covers all aspects of pension-fund management, investment and regulation.
—CCC.
Published by: Longman Group UK Ltd., Law Tax and Finance Division, 21-27 Lambs Conduit St, London, WC1N 3NJ, United Kingdom. TEL 44-20-7242-2548, FAX 44-207-831-8119.

330 USA ISSN 1524-1610
PERDIDO; leadership with a conscience. Text in English. 1994. q. USD 20 domestic; USD 36 for 2 yrs. domestic; USD 50 for 3 yrs. domestic; USD 36 foreign; USD 68 for 2 yrs. foreign; USD 98 for 3 yrs. foreign (effective 2001). bk.rev. 40 p./no.; back issues avail.; reprints avail. **Document type:** Magazine, Consumer. **Description:** Its mission is to inform, educate and involve leaders and managers from various fields, both profit and non-profit. To better prepare organizations with a mission to succeed.
Published by: High Tide Press, 3650 West 183d St, Homewood, IL 60430. TEL 708-206-2054, FAX 708-206-2044, perdido@hightidepress.com, editor@hightidepress.com, http://www.perdidomagazine.com, http://www.hightidepress.com. Circ: 6,000.

PERFORMANCE CHEMICALS EUROPE. see CHEMISTRY

330 371.42 RUS
PERSONA. Text in Russian. bi-m. **Document type:** Journal.
Published by: Novyi Arbat 21, Novyi Arbat 21, Moscow, 121293, Russian Federation. TEL 7-095-2901985, persona-magazine@mail.ru, http://www.society.ru. Ed. Larisa Shamikova. Circ: 10,000.

330 USA
PERSONAL SUCCESS T M - THE NEWSLETTER; real solutions for all your problems. Text in English. 1972. m. USD 99. adv. tr.lit. **Document type:** Newsletter.
Former titles: Dax Money-Maker (0147-1112); Dacs Money Maker Newsletter
Published by: Du Vall Press Financial Publications, PO Box 14, Williamston, MI 48895-0014. FAX 517-655-5208. Ed. Dean F V Du Vall. Circ: 25,000.

330 BRA ISSN 0100-039X
PERSPECTIVA ECONOMICA. Text in Portuguese. 1966. 4/yr. USD 30. bk.rev. **Document type:** Academic/Scholarly.
Formerly: Vale do Rio dos Sinos (0042-2274)
Indexed: IBR, IBSS, IBZ, RASB.
Published by: (Universidade do Vale do Rio dos Sinos), Unisinos, Av Unisinos, 950, Sao Leopoldo, RS 93022-000, Brazil. TEL 55-51-5928239, FAX 55-51-5908238. Ed. Jaira Castumna. Circ: 1,000.

330 FRA ISSN 0304-3274
PERSPECTIVES ECONOMIQUES DE L'O E C D. Text in French. s-a. EUR 115, USD 132, GBP 75, JPY 15,500 (effective 2005).
Related titles: Online - full content ed.: ISSN 1684-3436. EUR 85, USD 97, GBP 56, JPY 11,500 (effective 2005); Online - full text ed.: (from EBSCO Publishing, Gale Group, IngentaConnect, Swets Information Services); ♦ English ed.: O E C D Economic Outlook. ISSN 0474-5574; German ed.: Wirtschafts Ausblick.
Published by: Organization for Economic Cooperation and Development, 2 Rue Andre Pascal, Paris, 75775 Cedex 16, France. TEL 33-1-45248200, FAX 33-1-45248500, http://www.oecd.org. U.S. orders to: O E C D Turpin North America, PO Box 194, Downingtown, PA 19335-0194. TEL 610-524-5361, 800-456-6323, FAX 610-524-5417, bookscustomer@turpinna.com, journalscustomer@turpinna.com.

330 BRA ISSN 0102-7603
HC186
PESQUISA E DEBATE. Text in Portuguese. 1985. s-a. USD 15 (effective 2000). **Document type:** Academic/Scholarly.
Published by: Pontificia Universidade Catolica de Sao Paulo, Programa de Estudos Pos-Graduados em Economia, Rua Ministro de Godoi, 969 - andar 4, s. 4E-20, Sao Paulo, SP 05015-000, Brazil. TEL 55-11-3670-8400, FAX 55-11-3670-8516, ecopol@pucsp.br, www.pucsp.br. Ed. Cesar Roberto Leite da Silva.

PET BUSINESS NEWS. see PETS

330 USA
PETER MONTOYA'S PERSONAL BRANDING. Text in English. 2002. q. USD 19.95 domestic; USD 26.35 in Canada (effective 2002). **Document type:** Magazine, Trade.
Published by: Peter Montoya Inc., 1921 E. Alton Ave., Ste. 200, Santa Ana, CA 92705-5834. info@petermontoya.com, http://www.petermontoya.com/pbproducts-magazine.asp.

PETROLEUM ACCOUNTING AND FINANCIAL MANAGEMENT JOURNAL. see PETROLEUM AND GAS

PFERDEMARKT; Fachblatt fuer alle Pferdefreunde. see SPORTS AND GAMES—Horses And Horsemanship

PHARMACEUTICAL BUSINESS NEWS; the executive newsletter for the pharmaceutical industry. see PHARMACY AND PHARMACOLOGY

PHARMACOECONOMICS. see PHARMACY AND PHARMACOLOGY

PHILIPPINE BUSINESS AND INDUSTRY INDEX. see BUSINESS AND ECONOMICS—Abstracting, Bibliographies, Statistics

▼ *new title* ➤ *refereed* ✴ *unverified* ◆ *full entry avail.*

330 PHL
PHILIPPINE BUSINESS REPORT. Text in English. 1990. free. **Document type:** *Newsletter, Government.* **Description:** Provides latest information on government policies, industry, investments, trade and business in the country.
Indexed: IPP.
Published by: Department of Trade and Industry, Trade & Industry Information Center, 385 Industry and Investments Bldg., Sen. Gil Puyat Ave., Makati City, 1200, Philippines. TEL 895-36-11, FAX 895-64-8787. Ed. Minerva R Fajardo. R&P Alfonso M Valenzuela.

330 PHL ISSN 0031-7500
HC451
PHILIPPINE ECONOMIC JOURNAL. Text in English. 1962. q. PHP 120, USD 20. adv. bk.rev. bibl.; charts; stat. index, cum.index.
Indexed: APEL, BAS, CREJ, IBSS, JEL, PAIS, RASB, RRTA, WAE&RSA.
Published by: Philippine Economic Society, P S S C Bldg, UP Diliman, PO Box 205, Quezon City Mm, 1128, Philippines. Ed. Ruperto P Alonzo. Circ: 1,000.

PHILIPPINE INSURANCE COMMISSION. ANNUAL REPORT. see *INSURANCE*

330 PHL
➤ **PHILIPPINE JOURNAL OF BUSINESS AND ECONOMICS.** Text in English. s-a. **Document type:** *Journal, Academic/Scholarly.* **Description:** Publishes research in the fields of accounting, business law, economics, entrepreneurship finance, law and economics, marketing, organization theory, organization analysis, and strategic management.
Indexed: JEL.
Published by: De La Salle University, College of Business and Economics, 2401 Taft Ave, Manila, 1004, Philippines. http://www.dlsu.edu.ph/academics/colleges/cbe/pjbe/default.asp. Eds. Andrea L. Santiago, Angelo A. Unite.

330 PHL ISSN 1655-1516
HC451
PHILIPPINE REVIEW OF ECONOMICS. Text in English. 1964. s-a. USD 20. adv. bk.rev. charts. index, cum.index. reprint service avail. from PQC. **Description:** Research work and articles about Philippine economic and business conditions.
Former titles (until 2000): Philippine Review of Economics and Business (0115-9011); (until 1979): Philippine Review of Business and Economics (0031-7780)
Related titles: Microfilm ed.: (from PQC).
Indexed: APEL, BAS, IPP, JEL, NutrAb, RRTA, WAE&RSA.
Published by: (School of Economics), University of the Philippines, College of Business Administration, Diliman, Quezon City Mm, 1128, Philippines. TEL 632-928-45-71, FAX 632-928-45-74, cba@nicole.upd.edu.ph. Eds. E E Patalinghug, Raul Fabella. Circ: 1,000.

PHOTO & IMAGING TRADE NEWS. see *PHOTOGRAPHY*

332.6 USA ISSN 1089-1404
R728.25
THE PHYSICIAN MEDICAL GROUP ACQUISITION REPORT. Text in English. 1996. a., latest 2000. looseleaf. USD 395 for print or online ed.; USD 545 combined subscription for print & online eds. (effective 2002). mkt.; stat. 100 p./no.; back issues avail. **Document type:** *Newsletter, Consumer.* **Description:** Includes a 20 page introduction that summarizes the acquisition market for physician groups. The majority of the report contains details on publicly announced transactions.
Published by: Irving Levin Associates, Inc., 268-1/2 Main Ave, Norwalk, CT 06851. TEL 203-846-6800, 800-248-1668, FAX 203-846-8300, general@levinassociates.com, http://www.levinassociates.com. Pub. Ms. Eleanor B Meredith. R&P Stephen M Monroe.

330 USA ISSN 1097-1394
HF3163.P6 CODEN: PBTJES
PITTSBURGH BUSINESS TIMES. Text in English. 1985. w. (Fri.). USD 98 (effective 2005). adv. **Document type:** *Newspaper, Trade.*
Formerly (until 1990): Pittsburgh Business Times - Journal (0883-7910); Which was formed by the merger of (1981-1985): Pittsburgh Business Times (0279-330X); (198?-1985): Pittsburgh Business Journal (0279-2915)
Related titles: Online - full text ed.: ISSN 1549-1927 (from Florida Center for Library Automation, Gale Group, O C L C Online Computer Library Center, Inc., ProQuest Information & Learning).
Indexed: ABIn, BusDate, LRI, T&II.
—CCC.
Address: 2313 E Carson St, Ste 200, Pittsburgh, PA 15203-2109. TEL 412-481-6397, FAX 412-481-9956, pittsburgh@bizjournals.com, http://www.bizjournals.com/pittsburgh/. Ed. Paul Furiga. Pub., Adv. contact Alan Robertson. B&W page USD 4,350. Circ: 13,396 (paid).

330 SCG ISSN 0554-2537
PLANIRANJE I ANALIZA POSLOVANJA✶. Text in Serbo-Croatian. 1958. m. YUN 1,150.
Published by: Zavod za Ekonomske Ekspertize, c/o Economical Society of Serbia, Nusiceva 6-111, P.O. Box 490, Belgrade. Ed. Sima Doncevic.

PLANNING FOR SOCIAL CHANGE. see *SOCIOLOGY*

330 RUS
POCHTOVYE VEDOMOSTI. Text in Russian. 1994. 24/yr. USD 145 in North America (effective 2000).
Address: Tverskaya ul 7 ofis 508, Moscow, 103375, Russian Federation. TEL 7-095-2016281. Ed. A N Balakin. **Dist. by:** East View Information Services, 3020 Harbor Ln. N., Minneapolis, MN 55447. TEL 763-550-0961, FAX 763-559-2931.

330 GBR ISSN 1522-6808
HA155
POCKET WORLD IN FIGURES. Text in English. 1991. a. GBP 10 per issue (effective 2004).
Published by: Economist Group, 15 Regent St, London, SW1Y 4LR, United Kingdom. TEL 44-20-7830-7000, FAX 44-20-7830-1178, http://www.economist.com, http://www.economistgroup.com/.

330 RUS
POKUPATEL'. Text in Russian. s-m. USD 145 in United States.
Published by: Informatsionnoe Agentstvo Norma, Leningradskoe shosse 58, Moscow, 125212, Russian Federation. TEL 7-095-3679425, FAX 7-095-4520976. Ed. N Patsiya. **US dist. addr.:** East View Information Services, 3020 Harbor Ln. N., Minneapolis, MN 55447. TEL 612-550-0961.

330 POL ISSN 0867-6798
POLAND; international economic report. Text in English. 1988. a. EUR 55 per vol. foreign (effective 2005). **Document type:** *Journal, Academic/Scholarly.*
Published by: Szkola Glowna Handlowa w Warszawie, Instytut Gospodarki Swiatowej/Warsaw School of Economics, World Economy Research Institute, ul Rakowiecka 24, bud A, Warsaw, 02551, Poland. weri@sgh.waw.pl, http://www.sgh.waw.pl/instytuty/igs. **Dist. by:** Ars Polona, Krakowskie Przedmiescie 7, Warsaw, Poland. TEL 48-22-9263914, FAX 48-22-9265334, arspolona@arspolona.com.pl, http://www.arspolona.com.pl.

330 POL ISSN 1643-742X
POLAND MONTHLY. Text in English. 2002. m. EUR 150 in Europe; EUR 170 elsewhere (effective 2005). **Document type:** *Magazine, Consumer.*
Published by: Poland Business Publishing, Warsaw Trade Tower, ul Chlodna 51, Warsaw, 00867, Poland. TEL 48-22-5281980, FAX 48-22-5281981, letters@polandmonthly.pl, http://www.polandmonthly.pl.

330 AUS ISSN 1032-6634
H97
➤ **POLICY**; a journal of public policy and ideas. Text in English. 1977. 4/yr. AUD 40 domestic; AUD 50 New Zealand, E. Asia & the Pacific; AUD 60 elsewhere (effective 2005). bk.rev. back issues avail. **Document type:** *Magazine, Academic/Scholarly.* **Description:** Provides regular, expert commentary on public affairs based on economic and social research.
Former titles (until 1989): C I S Policy Report (0814-9321); C I S Newsletter (0155-0144)
Related titles: Online - full text ed.: (from EBSCO Publishing, R M I T Publishing).
Indexed: AESIS, AusPAIS, JEL, PAIS, WBA, WMB.
—BLDSC (6543.320500), IE, ingenta. **CCC.**
Published by: Centre for Independent Studies, PO Box 92, St Leonards, NSW 1590, Australia. TEL 61-2-94384377, FAX 61-2-94397310, cis@cis.org.au, http://www.cis.org.au/policy/home.htm. Ed., Pub. Greg Lindsay. Circ: 2,000.

➤ **POLICY SCIENCES**; an international journal devoted to the improvement of policy making. see *POLITICAL SCIENCE*

➤ **POLICY STUDIES.** see *POLITICAL SCIENCE*

330 CAN ISSN 0832-7912
POLICY STUDY. Text in English. 1986. irreg. price varies. **Document type:** *Monographic series.* **Description:** Studies of Canadian and international economic and social policy issues.
—BLDSC (6543.329560), CISTI, IE, ingenta.
Published by: C.D. Howe Institute, 125 Adelaide St East, Toronto, ON M5C 1L7, Canada. TEL 416-865-1904, FAX 416-865-1866, cdhowe@cdhowe.org, publicat@cdhowe.org, http://www.cdhowe.org.

330 POL ISSN 0208-5666
POLITECHNIKA GDANSKA. ZESZYTY NAUKOWE. EKONOMIA. Text in English, Polish; Summaries in Russian. 1967. irreg. price varies. bibl.; charts; illus.; stat. **Document type:** *Academic/Scholarly.* **Description:** Deals with political economy and philosophy.
Published by: Politechnika Gdanska, Ul G Narutowicza 11-12, Gdansk, 80952, Poland. **Dist. by:** Osrodek Rozpowszechniania Wydawnictw Naukowych PAN, Palac Kultury i Nauki, Warsaw 00901, Poland.

330 POL
POLITECHNIKA KRAKOWSKA. ZESZYTY NAUKOWE. NAUKI SPOLECZNE I EKONOMICZNE. Text in Polish; Summaries in English, French, German, Russian. 1967. irreg. price varies. bibl.; charts; illus. **Document type:** *Monographic series, Academic/Scholarly.*
Formerly: Politechnika Krakowska. Zeszyty Naukowe. Nauki Ekonomiczne (0548-0442)
Published by: Politechnika Krakowska, Ul Warszawska 24, Krakow, 31155, Poland. TEL 48-12-6374289, FAX 48-12-6374289. Ed. Elzbieta Nachlik. Adv. contact Ewa Malochleb. Circ: 200.

POLITECHNIKA LODZKA. ZESZYTY NAUKOWE. ORGANIZACJA I ZARZADZANIE. see *SOCIAL SCIENCES: COMPREHENSIVE WORKS*

330 POL
➤ **POLITECHNIKA WARSZAWSKA. KOLEGIUM NAUK SPOLECZNYCH. ZESZYTY NAUKOWE.** Text in Polish; Summaries in English. 1972. irreg., latest vol.18, 2000. bk.rev. 160 p./no. 1 cols./p.; back issues avail. **Document type:** *Monographic series, Academic/Scholarly.*
Former titles (until 1998): Politechnika Warszawska. Osrodek Nauk Spolecznych. Zeszyty Naukowe; Politechnika Warszawska. Instytut Nauk Ekonomiczno-Spolecznych. Prace (0137-2262)
Indexed: RASB.
Published by: (Politechnika Warszawska, Kolegium Nauk Spolecznych), Oficyna Wydawnicza Politechniki Warszawskiej/Publishing House of the Warsaw University of Technology, ul Polna 50, Warsaw, 00644, Poland. http://www.wpw.pw.edu.pl. Ed., R&P Stefan Marciniak TEL 48-22-6606289. Circ: 330.

➤ **POLITICA ED ECONOMIA/POLITICS AND ECONOMICS.** see *POLITICAL SCIENCE*

330 GBR
POLITICAL ECONOMY RESEARCH CENTRE. OCCASIONAL PAPERS. Text in English. irreg.
Published by: Political Economy Research Centre (Subsidiary of: University of Sheffield), Elmfield Lodge, Elmfield, Northumberland Rd, Sheffield, S10 2TY, United Kingdom. TEL 44-114-282-6298, FAX 44-114-275-5921, PERC@Sheffield.ac.uk, http://www.shef.ac.uk/~perc.

330 GBR
POLITICAL ECONOMY RESEARCH CENTRE. POLICY PAPERS. Text in English. 1997. irreg.
Published by: Political Economy Research Centre (Subsidiary of: University of Sheffield), Elmfield Lodge, Elmfield, Northumberland Rd, Sheffield, S10 2TY, United Kingdom. TEL 44-114-282-6298, FAX 44-114-275-5921, PERC@Sheffield.ac.uk, http://www.shef.ac.uk/~perc.

330 GBR
POLITICAL ECONOMY RESEARCH CENTRE. RESEARCH PAPERS. Text in English. 1999. irreg. **Document type:** *Academic/Scholarly.*
—BLDSC (6423.137500).
Published by: Political Economy Research Centre (Subsidiary of: University of Sheffield), Elmfield Lodge, Elmfield, Northumberland Rd, Sheffield, S10 2TY, United Kingdom. TEL 44-114-282-6298, FAX 44-114-275-5921, PERC@Sheffield.ac.uk, http://www.shef.ac.uk/~perc.

330 GBR
POLITICAL ECONOMY RESEARCH CENTRE. WORKING PAPERS. Text in English. irreg.
Published by: Political Economy Research Centre (Subsidiary of: University of Sheffield), Elmfield Lodge, Elmfield, Northumberland Rd, Sheffield, S10 2TY, United Kingdom. TEL 44-114-282-6298, FAX 44-114-275-5921, PERC@Sheffield.ac.uk, http://www.shef.ac.uk/~perc.

330 CZE ISSN 0032-3233
➤ **POLITICKA EKONOMIE/JOURNAL OF POLITICAL ECONOMY**; teorie, modelovani, aplikace. Text in Czech; Summaries in English. 1953. bi-m. EUR 110 (effective 2005). adv. bk.rev. bibl. index. reprints avail. **Document type:** *Journal, Academic/Scholarly.* **Description:** Features articles on economic theory, economic policy, econometrics, modelling and comparative analyses of economic systems, as well as topical issues concerning the transformation process and recent economic literature. Also covers basic economic research documented in the Science Citation Index.
Indexed: ASCA, Acal, CurCont, HistAb, IBSS, IMFL, IPSA, JEL, PSA, RASB, SSCI, SociolAb, T&II, WAE&RSA, WBA.
—BLDSC (6543.932000), IE, Infotrieve, ingenta.
Published by: Vysoka Skola Ekonomicka, Nam W Churchilla 4, Prague, 13067, Czech Republic. TEL 42-2-24095819, FAX 42-2-24095810, papers@vse.cz, http://science.vse.cz/polek. Ed., Pub. Martin Mandel. Adv. contact Hana Rosicka. Circ: 1,000 (paid and controlled).

➤ **POLITIK EKONOMIK BULTEN GAZETESI.** see *POLITICAL SCIENCE*

330 POL ISSN 0079-3353
POLSKA AKADEMIA NAUK. ODDZIAL W KRAKOWIE. KOMISJA NAUK EKONOMICZNYCH. PRACE. Text in Polish; Summaries in English. 1960. irreg., latest vol.24, 1999. price varies. **Document type:** *Monographic series, Academic/Scholarly.*

Published by: (Polska Akademia Nauk, Oddzial w Krakowie, Komisja Nauk Ekonomicznych), Polska Akademia Nauk, Oddzial w Krakowie, ul sw Jana 28, Krakow, 31018, Poland. TEL 48-12-4224853, FAX 48-12-4222791.

330 THA
POO JAD KARN MONTHLY. Text in Thai. 1983. m. adv.
Description: Contains business , economical, political and social analysis for businessmen and executives.
Published by: Manager Co. Ltd., Chanasongkhram Phranakorn, 98-3 10 Phra A Thit Rd, Bangkok, 10200, Thailand. TEL 02-2801300, FAX 02-2810033. Ed. Permpol Bhowperrmhem. Pub. Sondhi Limthongkul. Adv. contact M Hema. B&W page THB 40,000, color page THB 52,000; trim 290 x 215.

▼ **PORK BUSINESS JOURNAL.** see *AGRICULTURE—Poultry And Livestock*

338.0029 ZAF
PORTFOLIO OF BLACK BUSINESS IN SOUTHERN AFRICA. Text in English. 1993. a. illus.; maps.
Formerly (until 1994): Portfolio of Black Business in South Africa
Published by: W R Publications, PO Box 7485, Johannesburg, 2000, South Africa.

▼ **POSITIVE MAGAZINE.** see *TRAVEL AND TOURISM*

330 HRV
POSLOVNI TJEDNIK. Text in Croatian. w. **Document type:** *Magazine, Trade.*
Address: Prilaz Gjure Dezelica 34, Zagreb, 10000, Croatia. TEL 385-1-4846048, FAX 385-1-4846053. Ed. Zoran Petrovic.

330 UKR
POSREDNIK. Text in Russian. w. USD 440 in North America (effective 2000).
Related titles: Microfiche ed.: (from EVP, IDC); Microfilm ed.: (from EVP).
Address: Ul Vyborgskaya 59-67, Kiev, Ukraine. TEL 488-38-11. **Dist. by:** East View Information Services, 3020 Harbor Ln. N., Minneapolis, MN 55447. TEL 763-550-0961, FAX 763-559-2931.

POSTCOLONIAL STUDIES; culture, politics, economy. see *HISTORY*

330 TUR ISSN 1300-8153
POWER; aylik ekonomi dergisi. Text in Turkish. 1994. m.
Document type: *Magazine, Trade.*
Published by: 1 Numara Hearst Yayincilik, Sabah Tesisleri, Tesvikiye Caddesi 123, Tesvikiye, Istanbul, 80200, Turkey. TEL 90-212-3158000, FAX 90-212-3159272, power@birnumara.com.tr, http://power.birnumara.com.tr/w/, http://www.birnumara.com.tr.

PRAEGER SERIES IN POLITICAL ECONOMY. see *POLITICAL SCIENCE*

330 CZE
PRAGUE BOOK OF LISTS (YEAR). Text in Czech. a. CZK 599, USD 29.95 (effective 1999). **Document type:** *Directory.*
Description: Contains 76 industry lists and key data on 1,500 Czech companies. Includes address, phone number, key personnel, clients, revenues and more.
Related titles: ♦ Supplement to: Prague Business Journal. ISSN 1211-3514.
Published by: New World Publishing Inc., Sokolska 22, Prague 2, 120 00, Czech Republic. TEL 42-2-2426-1360, FAX 42-2-2426-1361, hlesenarova@pbj.cz, http://www.ceebiz.com.

330 CZE ISSN 1211-3514
PRAGUE BUSINESS JOURNAL. Text in Czech. 1996. s-m. CZK 1,941; USD 195 in Europe; USD 295 elsewhere. adv.
Document type: *Consumer.*
Related titles: Online - full text ed.: (from EBSCO Publishing); ♦ Supplement(s): Prague Book of Lists (Year); ♦ Equity Central Europe. ISSN 1418-9496.
Published by: New World Publishing Inc., Sokolska 22, Prague 2, 120 00, Czech Republic. TEL 42-2-2426-1360, FAX 42-2-2426-1361, hlesenarova@pbj.cz, http://www.ceebiz.com. Ed. Vlad Jenkins. Pub. Douglas Wheeler. Adv. contact Kim Carpenter.

330 CZE ISSN 1210-0455
HB1
➤ **PRAGUE ECONOMIC PAPERS**; quarterly journal of economic theory and policy. Text in English. 1959. q. EUR 70 (effective 2005). bk.rev. bibl. **Document type:** *Journal, Academic/Scholarly.* **Description:** Provides experts abroad with information concerning the evolution of economic theory as well as actual problems of the transformation, scientific life and new economic literature published in the Czech Republic.
Formerly (until 1992): Czechoslovak Economic Papers (0590-5001)
Indexed: CREJ, IBSS, JEL, RASB.
Published by: Vysoka Skola Ekonomicka, Nam W Churchilla 4, Prague, 13067, Czech Republic. TEL 42-2-24095819, FAX 42-2-24095810, papers@vse.cz, http://science.vse.cz/pep. Ed. Martin Mandel. Circ: 500 (paid and controlled).

330 CZE ISSN 1211-314X
THE PRAGUE TRIBUNE. Text in English, Czech. 1993. m. CZK 900 in Czech Republic; USD 66 in Europe; USD 95 elsewhere. adv. **Document type:** *Magazine, Trade.*
Description: Provides information about business practices in human resources, marketing, finance, real estate and technology in the Czech Republic.
Published by: La Tribune de Prague sro, Prague, Czech Republic. TEL 42-2-548072, FAX 42-2-542289, editor@prague-tribune.cz, http://www.prague-tribune.cz/. adv.: color page CZK 125, B&W page CZK 100.

330 NOR ISSN 1501-0074
PRAKTISK OEKONOMI OG FINANS. Text in Norwegian. 1985. 4/yr. NOK 750 to individuals; NOK 950 to institutions; NOK 200 to students; NOK 175 per issue (effective 2004). adv. bk.rev. illus. index. back issues avail. **Document type:** *Monographic series, Academic/Scholarly.*
Former titles (until 1999): Praktisk Oekonomi & Ledelse (0803-4680); (until 1990): Praktisk Oekonomi (0800-8159)
Indexed: IMI.
Published by: (Norwegian Federation of Business Economists), Universitetsforlaget AS/Scandinavian University Press (Subsidiary of: Aschehoug & Co.), Sehesteds Gate 3, Postboks 508, Oslo, 0105, Norway. TEL 47-24-147500, FAX 47-24-147501, post@universitetsforlaget.no, http://www.universitetsforlaget.no/tidsskrifter/article.jhtml?articleID=12904, http://www.universitetesforlaget.no. Eds. Gunnar A. Dahl, Knut Boye.

PRAVO I EKONOMIKA. see *LAW*

PRAWO I GOSPODARKA. see *LAW*

330 POL ISSN 1230-2856
PRAWO PRZEDSIEBIORCY. Text in Polish. 1991. w. PLZ 403 (effective 2001).
Related titles: Supplement(s): Infor-Business. ISSN 1232-9436; Komputer w Firmie. ISSN 1428-4707.
Published by: Grupa Wydawnicza INFOR Sp. z o.o., Ul Okopowa 58/72, Warsaw, 01042, Poland. TEL 48-22-5304208, 48-22-5304450, bok@infor.pl. Ed. Jadwiga Sztabinska. Adv. contact Waldemar Krakowiak.

330 DEU ISSN 0341-7948
PRAXIS DES RECHNUNGSWESENS; Buchfuehrung, Bilanzierung, Betriebsabrechnung, EDV Loesungen. Text in German. 1973. bi-m. bk.rev. **Document type:** *Trade.*
Published by: Rudolf Haufe Verlag GmbH & Co. KG, Hindenburgstr 64, Freiburg Im Breisgau, 79102, Germany. TEL 49-761-3683-0, online@haufe.de.

330 DEU ISSN 0940-8428
PRAXIS HANDBUCH PERSONAL. Text in German. 1991. bi-m. looseleaf. back issues avail. **Document type:** *Bulletin, Trade.*
Published by: V N R Verlag fuer die Deutsche Wirtschaft AG, Theodor-Heuss-Str 2-4, Bonn, 53095, Germany. TEL 49-228-9550120, FAX 49-228-359710, gsc@vnr.de, http://www.vnr.de. Ed. Peter Derschka.

330 DEU ISSN 0944-2499
PRAXISHANDBUCH BUCHFUEHRUNG UND STEUERN FUER FREIBERUFLER UND KLEINUNTERNEHMER. Text in German. 1993. 8/yr. looseleaf. EUR 200 (effective 2001).
Document type: *Bulletin, Trade.* **Description:** Information on taxation for small businesses.
Published by: V N R Verlag fuer die Deutsche Wirtschaft AG, Theodor-Heuss-Str 2-4, Bonn, 53095, Germany. TEL 49-228-8205-0, FAX 49-228-359710, gsc@vnr.de, http://www.vnr.de. Ed. Dagmar Koempf.

330 USA
JC362 CODEN: PPMIEK
PRESIDENTS AND PRIME MINISTERS (CD-ROM EDITION); international perspectives from world leaders. Text in English. 1992. bi-m. USD 30 domestic; USD 60 foreign (effective 2005). adv. **Document type:** *Magazine, Consumer.*
Description: Features articles and speeches by top government officials.
Formerly: Presidents and Prime Ministers (Print Edition) (1060-5088)
Media: CD-ROM. **Related titles:** CD-ROM ed.; Microform ed.: (from PQC); Online - full text ed.: (from Florida Center for Library Automation, Gale Group, O C L C Online Computer Library Center, Inc., ProQuest Information & Learning).
Indexed: ABIn, MASUSE, MagInd, PAIS, PerIslam, TOM, WBA, WMB.
—BLDSC (6609.910000). **CCC.**
Published by: E Q E S, Inc., 799 Roosevelt Rd, Bldg 6, Ste 208, Glen Ellyn, IL 60137-5925. TEL 630-858-6161, FAX 630-858-8787, ppm@goinfo.com, http://www.goinfo.com/. Ed., Pub., R&P Newal K Agnihotri. Adv. contact Eileen Frederickson. B&W page USD 720, color page USD 1,220; trim 10.88 x 8.25. Circ: 1,200.

PRICELINE. see *PETROLEUM AND GAS*

PRINCETON ECONOMIC HISTORY OF THE WESTERN WORLD. see *HISTORY*

330 USA
➤ **PRINCETON STUDIES IN BUSINESS AND TECHNOLOGY.** Text in English. 1992. irreg., latest 2000. price varies. illus. back issues avail. **Document type:** *Monographic series, Academic/Scholarly.* **Description:** Discusses ways in which business and technology affected one another.
Published by: Princeton University Press, 41 William St, Princeton, NJ 08540-5237. TEL 609-258-4900, FAX 609-258-6305, http://www.pupress.princeton.edu/catalogs/series/psbt.html, http://pup.princeton.edu. **Subscr. addr. in US:** California - Princeton Fulfillment Services, 1445 Lower Ferry Rd, Ewing, NJ 08618. TEL 800-777-4726, FAX 800-999-1958, orders@cpfs.pupress.princeton.edu. **Dist. addr. in Canada:** University Press Group, 164 Hillsdale Ave E, Toronto, ON M4S 1T5, Canada.; **Dist. addr. in UK:** John Wiley & Sons Ltd., The Atrium, Southern Gate, Chichester, West Sussex PO19 8SQ, United Kingdom.

330 USA ISSN 0079-5291
HB139
PRINCETON UNIVERSITY. ECONOMETRIC RESEARCH PROGRAM. RESEARCH MEMORANDUM. Text in English. 1957. irreg., latest vol.372, 1995. price varies. back issues avail. **Document type:** *Academic/Scholarly.*
Related titles: Microform ed.
Published by: Princeton University, Econometric Research Program, c/o Program Secretary, Department of Economics, 203 Fisher Hall, Princeton, NJ 08544-1021. TEL 609-258-4030, FAX 609-258-5561. Ed. Gregory C Chow. Circ: 250.

PRIVATA AFFAERER. see *CONSUMER EDUCATION AND PROTECTION*

330 PHL
PRIVATE DEVELOPMENT CORPORATION OF THE PHILIPPINES. ECONOMIC PERFORMANCE AND PROSPECTS; international-domestic economy. Text in English. 1977. s-a. USD 30.
Published by: Private Development Corporation of the Philippines/Pribadong Korporasyon sa Pagpapaunlad ng Pilipinas, P.O. Box 757, Makati, Manila, 3117, Philippines. TEL 02-8100231, FAX 02-8195376, TELEX RCA-22080. Circ: 600.

330 GBR ISSN 1474-8800
PRIVATE EQUITY INTERNATIONAL. Text in English. 2001 (Oct.). 10/yr. GBP 545 domestic; EUR 895 in Europe; USD 875 elsewhere (effective 2003). **Document type:** *Trade.*
Description: Delivers relevant information and insight to institutional investors and market practitioners who have an active interest in private equity.
Published by: Investoraccess Ltd., 4 Dean's Court, St Paul's Churchyard, London, EC4V 5AA , United Kingdom. TEL 44-20-7778-0058, FAX 44-20-7778-0065, http://www.privateequityonline.com/, http://www.investoraccess.com/. Ed. Philip Borel. Adv. contact Richard O'Donohoe. Circ: 5,000.

330 GBR
PRIVATISATION & PUBLIC PRIVATE PARTNERSHIP REVIEW (YEARS). Text in English. a., latest 2005, June, 10th Ed. GBP 115, USD 195, EUR 170 per issue (effective 2005). adv.
Document type: *Yearbook, Trade.* **Description:** Provides an indispensable analysis of the global privatisation and PPP market, written by experts from investment banks, law firms, accountancy practices & consultants.
—BLDSC (6617.068694).
Published by: Euromoney Publications plc, Nestor House, Playhouse Yard, London, EC4V 5EX, United Kingdom. TEL 44-20-77798888, information@euromoneyplc.com, http://www.euromoney-yearbooks.com/default.asp?page=5&pcID=4080, http://www.euromoney.com, http://euromoney-yearbooks.com. Pub. Adrian Hornbook. Adv. contact Simon Holloway.

330 GBR ISSN 1469-0721
PRIVATISATION INTERNATIONAL YEARBOOK. Text in English. 1992. a. GBP 175, USD 300. adv. **Document type:** *Trade.*
Description: Detailed review of privatization developments in approximately 75 different countries.
Formerly (until 1997): Privatisation Yearbook (1352-3139)
—BLDSC (6617.068920), ingenta.
Published by: Privatisation International Ltd., Ste. 404, Butlers Wharf Business Centre, 45 Curlew St, London, SE1 2ND, United Kingdom. TEL 44-20-7378-1620, FAX 44-20-7403-7876, pipub@compuserve.com. Ed. Mark Baker. Adv. contact Diana Howarth.

338.242 HRV ISSN 1331-7628
PRIVATIZACIJA. Text in Croatian. m. **Document type:** *Magazine, Trade.*
Published by: Hrvatski Fond za Privatizaciju, Ivana Lucica 6, Zagreb, 10000, Croatia. TEL 385-1-4596406, FAX 385-1-4569141. Ed. Miljenko Weiss.

330 SCG ISSN 0032-8979
PRIVREDNA IZGRADNJA✶. Text mainly in Serbian; Text occasionally in English; Summaries in English. 1945. q. USD 20 (effective 1998 & 1999). adv. bk.rev. abstr.; bibl.; charts; stat. index. **Document type:** *Academic/Scholarly.*
Formerly: Privreda (Novi Sad)

B

Published by: Savez Ekonomista Vojvodine/Association of Economists of Vojvodina, c/o Savez Ekonomista Jugoslavije, Nusiceva 6-111, Postenski Fah 490, Belgrade, 21000. TEL 3381-21-24971, kosta@uns.ns.ac.yu. Ed. Branko Bijelic. Adv. contact Branko Bjelic. Circ: 700.

330 HRV ISSN 0032-8995
PRIVREDNI VJESNIK/ECONOMIC HERALD. Text in Croatian. 1954. w. index. **Document type:** *Newspaper, Consumer.*
Published by: Privredni Vjesnik Holding, Kaciceva 9, Zagreb, 41000, Croatia. TEL 385-1-4846661, FAX 385-1-4846663, info@privredni-vjesnik.hr, http://www.privredni-vjesnik.hr. Ed. Franjo Zilic. Circ: 11,200.

330 MEX ISSN 0301-7036
HC121 CODEN: PRDEFC
➤ **PROBLEMAS DEL DESARROLLO**; revista latinoamericana de economia. Variant title: Organo Oficial del Instituto de Investigaciones Economicas. Text in Spanish. 1969. q. MXP 120, USD 40 (effective 2000). adv. bk.rev. illus. cum.index. back issues avail.; reprints avail. **Document type:** *Journal, Academic/Scholarly.* **Description:** Examines economic issues and questions of political economy.
Related titles: Microfiche ed.; Microfilm ed.; Online - full text ed.
Indexed: CurCont, HAPI, IBR, ILD, JEL, PAIS, SOPODA.
—IE.
Published by: Universidad Nacional Autonoma de Mexico, Instituto de Investigaciones Economicas, Torre II de Humanidades 5o Piso, Ciudad Universitaria, Mexico City, DF 04510, Mexico. TEL 52-5-6230105, FAX 52-5-6230097, revprode@servidor.unam.mx, http://serpiente.dgsca.unam.mx/iie. Ed. Salvador Rodriguez Y Rodriguez. Circ: 2,000.

330 ALB
PROBLEME EKONOMIKE. Text in Albanian. 1953. bi-m. USD 6.16. bk.rev.
Indexed: RASB.
Published by: Academie des Sciences de la RPSA, Institut des Etudes Economiques, Tirana, Albania. TEL 042-26418. Circ: 2,000.

330 FRA ISSN 0032-9304
HC10
PROBLEMES ECONOMIQUES; selection de textes francais et etrangers. Text in French. 1948. w. EUR 68 domestic; EUR 93.40 in the European Union; EUR 87.30 DOM-TOM; EUR 111.80 elsewhere (effective 2003). index. **Document type:** *Government.*
Related titles: Microfiche ed.
Indexed: CTFA, ELLIS, ILD, KES, PAIS, PdeR, RASB, RefZh, TOSA, TriticAb, WAE&RSA, WBSS.
—BLDSC (6617.870300), IE, Infotrieve, ingenta. **CCC.**
Published by: Documentation Francaise, 29-31 quai Voltaire, Paris, Cedex 7 75344, France. FAX 33-1-40157230. Circ: 22,000.

330 USA ISSN 1061-1991
HC10
➤ **PROBLEMS OF ECONOMIC TRANSITION**; a journal of translations from Russian. Text in English. 1958. m. USD 175 domestic to individuals; USD 222 foreign to individuals; USD 1,320 combined subscription domestic to institutions print & online eds.; USD 1,452 combined subscription foreign to institutions print & online eds. (effective 2006). adv. stat.; illus. index. back issues avail.; reprints avail. **Document type:** *Journal, Academic/Scholarly.* **Description:** Scans Russian-language economic literature, from Voprosy Ekonomiki to EDO, to allow readers to follow the principal theoretical and policy issues that constitute post-Soviet economic discourse in various regions of the former USSR. Topics covered include reform policy; foreign economic relations; industrial reorganization; labor economics and social policy; and regional economic development.
Formerly: Problems in Economics (0032-9436)
Related titles: Online - full text ed.: 2001 (May) (from EBSCO Publishing, Gale Group, H.W. Wilson, O C L C Online Computer Library Center, Inc., Swets Information Services).
Indexed: ABIn, CREJ, CurCont, EIA, ESPM, EnerInd, ILD, JEL, KES, MEA&I, PAIS, PCI, RASB, RiskAb, SSCI, SSI.
—BLDSC (6617.883050), CISTI, IDS, IE, Infotrieve, ingenta. **CCC.**
Published by: M.E. Sharpe, Inc., 80 Business Park Dr, Armonk, NY 10504. TEL 914-273-1800, 800-541-6563, FAX 914-273-2106, custserv@mesharpe.com, http://www.mesharpe.com/mall/results1.asp. Ed. Ben Slay. Adv. contact Barbara Ladd TEL 914-273-1800 ext 121. page USD 300; trim 8 x 5.

➤ **PROCESO**; informativo semanal. see *POLITICAL SCIENCE*

330 USA
PRODUCTIVITY (FORT ATKINSON). Text in English. 3/yr. **Document type:** *Magazine, Trade.*
Published by: Pfingsten Publishing, L L C, 6000 Lombardo Center Dr, Ste 420, Seven Hills, OH 44131. TEL 216-328-8926, 888-772-8926, FAX 216-328-9452, info@pfpublish.com, http://www.pfpub.com.

PRODUCTS LIABILITY REPORTER. see *LAW*

330 ESP ISSN 0214-7130
PROFESIONALES Y CUADROS. Text in Spanish. 6/yr.
Formerly (until 1985): Cuadros (0214-7637)
Address: Isla de Saipan, 47, Madrid, 28035, Spain. TEL 1-373-47-50, FAX 1-316-91-77. Ed. J Menendez Zapata. Circ: 24,778.

330 346 USA
PROFESSIONAL COLLECTOR. Text in English. 1993. q. **Document type:** *Magazine, Trade.*
Published by: (Western Union International, Inc., Marketing Department), Pohly & Partners Inc., 27 Melcher St., 2nd Fl., Boston, MA 02210. TEL 617-451-1700, FAX 617-338-7767, ginnyf@pohlypartners.com, http://www.pohlypartners.com. Ed. Karen English. Circ: 135,000.

346.73 USA
PROFESSIONAL NEWSBYTES. Text in English. 1998. irreg. **Description:** Comprises the latest news and trends on business law and presents them in digestible pieces.
Related titles: Online - full text ed.
Address: 456 West Ave, Tallmadge, OH 44278. TEL 440-777-1007, profnews@aol.com, http://www.pronewsbytes.com/. Ed. C H Oster.

PROFESSIONAL SECURITY MAGAZINE. see *CRIMINOLOGY AND LAW ENFORCEMENT*

PROFESSIONAL WOMAN'S MAGAZINE; a business career and lifestyles magazine for today's woman. see *WOMEN'S INTERESTS*

330 FRA ISSN 0220-3480
PROFESSIONS DU SUD EST. Text in French. 11/yr.
Address: 16 place General de Gaulle, Marseille, Cedex 1 13231, France. TEL 91-57-71-00, FAX 91-54-86-03. Ed. T Debaille. Circ: 20,000.

330 RUS
PROFIL'. Text in Russian. w. (50/yr.). USD 319 in United States.
Published by: Kompaniya Profil', Volgogradskii pr-t 26, Moscow, 109316, Russian Federation. TEL 7-095-2707504, FAX 7-095-2709022, http://www.profil.orc.ru. Ed. D L Simonov. **US dist. addr.:** East View Information Services, 3020 Harbor Ln. N., Minneapolis, MN 55447. TEL 612-550-0961.

650 GBR
PROFINEWS. Text in English. 1995. 3/yr.
Published by: Fieldbus.com, 1 W St, Titchfield, Hants, PO14 4DH, United Kingdom. TEL 44-132-984-6166, FAX 44-132-951-2063, http://www.profibus.com. Pub. Geoff Hidgkinson. Circ: 30,000.

330 SVK ISSN 1335-387X
PROFIPREDAJ. Text in Slovak. 1998. m. adv. **Document type:** *Magazine, Trade.*
Published by: Sanoma Magazines Slovakia s.r.o., Kopcianska 6, Bratislava 5, 85101, Slovakia. sanomaslovakia@sanomaslovakia.sk, http://www.sanoma.sk.

330 DEU
PROFIRMA; Das Magazin fuer Unternehmer. Text in German. m. EUR 59 domestic; EUR 69 foreign; EUR 5 newsstand/cover (effective 2004). adv. **Document type:** *Magazine, Trade.*
Published by: Max Schimmel Verlag GmbH & Co. KG (Subsidiary of: Rudolf Haufe Verlag GmbH & Co. KG), Im Kreuz 9, Wuerzburg, 97076, Germany. TEL 49-931-2791420, FAX 49-931-2791444, info@schimmelverlag.de, http://www.profirma.de, http://www.schimmelverlag.de. Ed. Peter Steinmueller. Adv. contact Bernd Junker. B&W page EUR 6,800, color page EUR 8,500. Circ: 80,809 (paid and controlled).

338.642 CAN ISSN 1183-1324
PROFIT; the magazine for Canadian entrepreneurs. Text in English. 1982. bi-m. CND 24.95 domestic; CND 50 foreign; CND 3.50 per issue (effective 2005). adv. bk.rev. back issues avail. **Document type:** *Magazine, Trade.* **Description:** Provides hands-on management information and ideas, covers entrepreneurial successes and failures, profiles Canada's fastest-growing companies and explores political and social issues as they affect business.
Former titles (until 1990): Small Business (0833-2223); (until 1986): Magazine That's All About Small Business (0714-4210)
Related titles: Microfiche ed.: (from MML); Microform ed.: (from MML, PQC); Online - full text ed.: (from EBSCO Publishing, LexisNexis, Micromedia ProQuest, Northern Light Technology, Inc., ProQuest Information & Learning).
Indexed: ABIn, BusDate, CBCABus, CBCARef, CBPI, CPerI.
Published by: Profit: Your Guide to Business Success, One Mount Pleasant Rd, 11th Fl, Toronto, ON M4Y 2Y5, Canada. TEL 416-764-1402, FAX 416-764-1404, profit@cbmedia.ca, http://www.profitguide.com/magazine. Ed., Pub. Rick Spence. R&P Gillian Holmes. Adv. contact Richard Page. Circ: 100,000.

330 USA ISSN 1531-7455
PROFIT (REDWOOD SHORES); business to e-business. Text in English. bi-m. free to qualified personnel. **Document type:** *Consumer.*
Published by: Oracle Publishing, 500 Oracle Parkway Mailstop 10BP-1, Redwood Shores, CA 94065. FAX 650-633-2424, oracle@halldata.com, http://www.oracle.com/oramag/profit/.

330 USA ISSN 0889-9967
PROFIT-BUILDING STRATEGIES FOR BUSINESS OWNERS. Text in English. m.
Formerly (until 1986): Professional Report (0890-9288)
Related titles: Online - full text ed.: (from Florida Center for Library Automation, Gale Group, O C L C Online Computer Library Center, Inc., ProQuest Information & Learning).
Indexed: ABIn, ATI.
Published by: T P R Publishing Co., 81 Montgomery St, Scarsdale, NY 10583.

330 GBR ISSN 1476-430X
PROFIT IN STORE. U K EDITION. Text in English. 1993. q. free to qualified personnel. **Description:** Provides information to retailers on innovative new products, stocking the leading brands and merchandising to maximize sales and profits; also includes legal and financial advice.
(until 1999): Profit in Store UK (1466-9285); (until 1997): Profit in Store (1353-467X)
Published by: Highbury Business Communications (Subsidiary of: Highbury House Communications PLC), Ann Boleyn House, 9-13 Ewell Rd, Cheam, Surrey SM3 8BZ, United Kingdom. TEL 44-20-87226000, http://www.hhc.co.uk/profitinstore.

330 DEU
PROFITS. Text in German. bi-m. adv. **Document type:** *Magazine, Trade.*
Published by: Deutscher Sparkassenverlag GmbH, Am Wallgraben 115, Stuttgart, 70565, Germany. TEL 49-711-7820, FAX 49-711-7821709, webredaktion@dsv-gruppe.de, http://www.dsv-gruppe.de. adv.: B&W page EUR 4,750, color page EUR 6,100; trim 174 x 219. Circ: 125,000 (controlled).

330 ITA
PROGETTO MANAGER. Text in Italian. 10/yr. adv. **Document type:** *Magazine, Trade.*
Published by: Federazione Nazionale Dirigenti Aziende Industriali, Via Ravenna 14, I, Rome, 00161, Italy. TEL 39-06-44070100, FAX 39-06-4403376, http://www.federmanager.it. Ed. Silvano Revelli. Circ: 75,000.

▼ **PROGRESS IN INDUSTRIAL ECOLOGY**; an international journal. see *ENVIRONMENTAL STUDIES*

▼ **PROGRESS RESEARCH & DEVELOPMENT.** see *SCIENCES: COMPREHENSIVE WORKS*

380 USA ISSN 1531-7811
PROGRESSIVE DISTRIBUTOR. Text in English. bi-m. Free to qualified subscribers. adv. **Document type:** *Trade.* **Description:** Covers sales and marketing issues about industrial and construction distribution channels.
Formerly: Progressive M R O Distributor (1092-0471)
Related titles: Online - full content ed.
Published by: Pfingsten Publishing, L L C, 6000 Lombardo Center Dr, Ste 420, Seven Hills, OH 44131. TEL 216-328-8926, 888-772-8926, FAX 216-328-9452, info@pfpublish.com, http://www.progressivedistributor.com/, http://www.pfpub.com. Ed. Richard Vurva.

330 RUS ISSN 0869-7019
PROMYSHLENNOE I GRAZHDANSKOE STROITEL'STVO. Text in Russian. 1923. m. USD 142 in North America (effective 2000).
Indexed: RefZh.
—CINDOC, CISTI.
Published by: Stroiizdat, Komsomol'skii pr-t 42, Moscow, 119826, Russian Federation. TEL 7-095-9782600. Ed. A D Deminov. **Dist. by:** East View Information Services, 3020 Harbor Ln. N., Minneapolis, MN 55447. TEL 763-550-0961, FAX 763-559-2931.

PROPERTY BUSINESS. see *REAL ESTATE*

330 USA ISSN 1551-692X
▼ **PROSPER**; the business magazine. Text in English. 2004 (Oct.). m. free (effective 2005). adv. **Document type:** *Magazine.*
Published by: Prosper Publications LLC, 920 20th St Ste 125, Sacramento, CA 95814. TEL 916-233-4462, FAX 916-233-4466, prosper@prospermag.com, http://www.prospermag.com/default/. Ed. Carol Chamberlain. Adv. contact Wayne Russell.

330 FRA
PROTECTION SOCIALE INFORMATIONS. Text in French. w. FRF 4,080 (effective 1997).
Published by: Groupe Liaisons S.A. (Subsidiary of: Wolters Kluwer BV), 1 Avenue Edouard Belin, Rueil Malmaison, Cedex 92856, France. TEL 33-1-41299696, FAX 33-1-41299880.

330 USA ISSN 0887-8226
PROVIDENCE BUSINESS NEWS. Text in English. 1986. w. (Mon.). USD 89 (effective 2005). adv. bk.rev. **Document type:** *Newspaper.* **Description:** Covers local and regional business news.
Related titles: Online - full text ed.: (from Florida Center for Library Automation, Gale Group).
Indexed: BusDate.
—CCC.

Published by: Providence Business News, Inc., 300 Richmond St, Ste 202, Providence, RI 02903-4288. TEL 401-273-2201, FAX 401-274-0670, editor@pbn.com, http://www.pbn.com/. Ed. Michael Pare. Pub. Roger Bergenheim. Adv. contact Chris Santilli. Circ: 11,000.

330 POL ISSN 1428-7617
PRZEWODNIK TWOJEGO BIZNESU. Text in Polish. 1998. bi-w. PLZ 58.80 (effective 2001).
Published by: Grupa Wydawnicza INFOR Sp. z o.o., Ul Okopowa 58/72, Warsaw, 01042, Poland. TEL 48-22-5304208, 48-22-5304450, bok@infor.pl. Ed. Iwona Jaroszewska-Ignatowska. Adv. contact Waldemar Krakowiak.

330.9 USA ISSN 0048-5829
JA1
➤ **PUBLIC CHOICE.** Text in Dutch. 1966. 16/yr. EUR 1,398, USD 1,398, GBP 898 combined subscription to institutions print & online eds. (effective 2005). bk.rev. bibl.; illus. cum.index. back issues avail.; reprint service avail. from PQC,PSC. **Document type:** *Journal, Academic/Scholarly.* **Description:** Discusses issues at the intersection between economics and political science, and the application of economic methods to problems dealt with by political scientists.
Formerly (until 1968): Papers on Mon-Market Decision-Making
Related titles: Microform ed.: (from PQC); Online - full text ed.: ISSN 1573-7101 (from EBSCO Publishing, Gale Group, IngentaConnect, Kluwer Online, O C L C Online Computer Library Center, Inc., ProQuest Information & Learning, Springer LINK, Swets Information Services).
Indexed: ABCPolSci, ABIn, ASCA, AgeL, ArtHuCI, BibLing, CurCont, DIP, ESPM, HRA, IBR, IBSS, IBZ, IPSA, JEL, PAIS, PRA, PSA, RASB, RiskAb, SOPODA, SPAA, SSA, SSCI, SUSA, SociolAb.
—BLDSC (6962.900000), IDS, IE, Infotrieve, ingenta. **CCC.**
Published by: (George Mason University, Center for the Study of Public Choice), Springer-Verlag New York, Inc. (Subsidiary of: Springer Science+Business Media), 233 Spring St, New York, NY 10013. TEL 212-460-1500, FAX 212-460-1575, service@springer-ny.com, http://springerlink.metapress.com/openurl.asp?genre=journal&issn=0048-5829, http://www.springer-ny.com. Eds. Charles K Rowley, Robert D Tollison, William F Shughart II. **Subscr. to:** Journal Fulfillment, PO Box 2485, Secaucus, NJ 07096-2485. TEL 201-348-4033, FAX 201-348-4505, journals@springer-ny.com.

➤ **THE PUBLIC INTEREST.** see *SOCIAL SCIENCES: COMPREHENSIVE WORKS*

330 FRA ISSN 0297-7826
PUBLICATIONS COMMERCIALES. Text in French. 100/yr. **Description:** Provides commercial, economic, legal information covering the Bouche-du-Rhone area.
Address: 63 rue Paradis, B.P. 228, Marseille, Cedex 6 13253, France. TEL 33-91-332380, FAX 33-91-333716. Ed. Y Bertaudon. Circ: 8,000.

PUBLISHING FOR INTRANETS: MONEY MAKING STRATEGIES FOR REACHING THE CORPORATE DESKTOP. see *COMPUTERS—Computer Networks*

330 USA ISSN 8750-7757
HC108.S77
PUGET SOUND BUSINESS JOURNAL. Text in English. 1980. w. (Fri.). USD 82 (effective 2005). adv. **Document type:** *Newspaper, Trade.*
Formerly: Seattle Business Journal (0274-5453)
Related titles: Microform ed.: (from PQC); Online - full text ed.: ISSN 1549-1900 (from Florida Center for Library Automation, Gale Group, O C L C Online Computer Library Center, Inc., ProQuest Information & Learning, The Dialog Corporation).
Indexed: ABIn, BusDate, LRI, T&II.
—**CCC.**
Address: 801 2nd Ave, #210, Seattle, WA 98104. TEL 206-583-8505, FAX 206-447-8510, seattle@bizjournals.com, http://www.bizjournals.com/seattle. Ed. Mike Flynn. Circ: 20,000 (paid and controlled).

330 DEU ISSN 1439-0019
PUNCTO!. Text in German. 1997. 5/yr. adv. **Document type:** *Magazine, Consumer.*
Published by: Deutscher Sparkassenverlag GmbH, Am Wallgraben 115, Stuttgart, 70565, Germany. TEL 49-711-7820, FAX 49-711-7821709, puncto@puncto.de, webredaktion@dsv-gruppe.de, http://www.puncto.de, http://www.dsv-gruppe.de. adv.: B&W page EUR 2,400, color page EUR 3,360. Circ: 47,000 (controlled).

650 CAN
PURPLE REPORT. Text in English. 1986. w. illus.
Formerly: McGill Journal of Business (0541-6159)
Published by: McGill University, Graduate Business Students' Society, 1001 Sherbrooke St W, Montreal, PQ H3C 3G1, Canada. TEL 514-348-4311. Ed. Wendy Tassiae Chan. Circ: 200.

Q J I. (Quarterly Journal of Ideology) see *POLITICAL SCIENCE*

QANOUN WAL IQTISAD/DROIT ET ECONOMIE POLITIQUE. see *LAW*

330.05 346.066 EGY ISSN 0304-2324
AL QANUN WA-AL IQTISAD/LAW AND ECONOMICS. Text in Arabic. 1931. s-a. **Document type:** *Journal, Academic/Scholarly.*
Related titles: French ed.: Revue de Droit Economie Politique.
Published by: Cairo University, Faculty of Law, Cairo University Campus, Giza, Egypt. TEL 20-2-5688444, FAX 20-2-5688405, http://derp.sti.sci.eg/data/0030.htm.

332.645 CHN
QIHUO RIBAO/FUTURES DAILY. Text in Chinese. 1994. d. CNY 264 (effective 2004). **Document type:** *Newspaper, Trade.*
Formerly: Qihuo Daobao/The Futures Guide
Address: 69, Weilai Dadao, Weilai Dasha 1301-Shi, Zhengzhou, Henan 450008, China. TEL 86-371-5612102, jjq@qhdb.com.cn, http://www.qhrb.com.cn. **Dist. by:** China International Book Trading Corp, 35 Chegongzhuang Xilu, Haidian District, PO Box 399, Beijing 100044, China. TEL 86-10-68412045, FAX 86-10-68412023, cibtc@mail.cibtc.com.cn, http://www.cibtc.com.cn.

330 CHN ISSN 1005-443X
QIYEJIA XINXI/ENTREPRENEUR INFORMATION. Text in Chinese. 1994. m. CNY 192 (effective 2004). **Document type:** *Journal, Academic/Scholarly.*
Published by: Zhongguo Renmin Daxue, Shubao Zilio Zhongxin/Renmin University of China, Information Center for Social Server, Dongcheng-qu, 3, Zhangzizhong Lu, Beijing, 100007, China. TEL 86-10-64039458, FAX 86-10-64015080, kyes@163.net, http://www.confucius.cn.net/bkdetail.asp?fzt=X8. **Dist. in the US by:** China Publications Service, PO Box 49614, Chicago, IL 60649. TEL 312-288-3291, FAX 312-288-8570; **Dist. outside of China by:** China International Book Trading Corp, 35 Chegongzhuang Xilu, Haidian District, PO Box 399, Beijing 100044, China. TEL 86-10-68412045, FAX 86-10-68412023, cibtc@mail.cibtc.com.cn, http://www.cibtc.com.cn/.

330 DEU ISSN 0481-1224
QUAESTIONES OECONOMICAE. Text in German. 1964. irreg., latest vol.10, 1993. price varies. **Document type:** *Monographic series, Academic/Scholarly.*
Published by: Duncker und Humblot GmbH, Carl-Heinrich-Becker-Weg 9, Berlin, 12165, Germany. TEL 49-30-7900060, FAX 49-30-79000631, info@duncker-humblot.de, http://www.duncker-humblot.de.

330 FRA ISSN 0767-9432
QUALITIQUE. Text in French; Summaries in English, German, Spanish. 1988. 10/yr. EUR 139 domestic; EUR 159 in the European Union; EUR 189 elsewhere (effective 2005). adv. software rev. bibl. **Document type:** *Newspaper.* **Description:** Keeps track of evolution in all sectors of quality engineering, offers solutions to management and production problems, presents new products, technologies and strategic tools.
Published by: Groupe Qualitique, 9 rue Albert Einstein, Champs-sur-Marne, 77420, France. TEL 33-1-64682193, FAX 33-1-64687904, redaction.presse@qualitique.com. Ed. Jean Luc Laffargue. Pub. Jean-Luc Laffargue. R&P Laurence Maestri. Adv. contact Claire Pourriere. Circ: 10,000 (paid). **Subscr. to:** ATEI, 3 av. Pierre Kerautret, Romainville 93230, France.

330 CHN ISSN 1002-6584
QUANGUO QINGGONG XINXI/CHINA LIGHT INDUSTRIES NEWS. Text in Chinese. 1986. w. CNY 400 domestic; USD 100 foreign (effective 2000). **Document type:** *Bulletin, Government.*
Published by: Zhonguo Qinggongye Jingji Keji Xinxi Zhongxin/China Economic, Scientific and Technological Information Centre of Light Industry, 22 B Fuwai Dajie, Beijing, 100833, China. TEL 86-1-6839-6607, 86-1-6839-6608, FAX 86-1-6839-6607, qkxhl@clii.com.cn, qkwyy@clii.com.cn. Ed. Pang Zhenhua. Adv. contact Yanying Wang.

330 AUS
THE QUANTAS CLUB. Text in English. 1987. m. membership only. bk.rev. back issues avail.
Formerly (until Sep. 1994): Flight Deck (0819-419X)
Published by: (Australian Airlines Flight Deck Club), B R W Media, Level 2, 469 La Trobe St, Melbourne, VIC 3000, Australia. TEL 61-3-9642-8716, FAX 61-3-9642-0852. Circ: 60,000.

330 658 USA ISSN 1570-7156
HF5415.2
▼ **QUANTITATIVE MARKETING AND ECONOMICS.** Text in English. 2003. q. EUR 295, USD 295, GBP 213 combined subscription to institutions print & online eds. (effective 2005). reprint service avail. from PSC. **Document type:** *Journal, Academic/Scholarly.* **Description:** Publishes research in the intersection of marketing, economics and statistics. Focusing is on important applied problems of relevance to marketing using a quantitative approach.
Related titles: Online - full text ed.: ISSN 1573-711X (from EBSCO Publishing, Gale Group, IngentaConnect, Kluwer Online, O C L C Online Computer Library Center, Inc., Springer LINK, Swets Information Services).
Indexed: BibLing.
—BLDSC (7168.334500), IE. **CCC.**
Published by: Springer-Verlag New York, Inc. (Subsidiary of: Springer Science+Business Media), 233 Spring St, New York, NY 10013. TEL 212-460-1500, FAX 212-460-1575, service@springer-ny.com, http://springerlink.metapress.com/openurl.asp?genre=journal&issn=1570-7156, http://www.springer-ny.com. Eds. Peter Rossi, Rajiv Lal. **Subscr. to:** Journal Fulfillment, PO Box 2485, Secaucus, NJ 07096-2485. TEL 201-348-4033, FAX 201-348-4505, journals@springer-ny.com.

330 GBR ISSN 0959-6798
QUARTERLY ACCOUNT. Text in English. 1983. q. GBP 15. adv. bk.rev. **Document type:** *Trade.* **Description:** Provides personal finance-related advice and information.
Indexed: LJI.
—BLDSC (7169.890000), IE, ingenta.
Published by: Money Advice Association, 1st Fl, Gresham House, 24 Holborn Viaduct, London, EC1A 2BN, United Kingdom. TEL 44-171-236-3566. Ed. Steve Wilcox. R&P, Adv. contact Jane Guy. Circ: 500.

330 IRL ISSN 0376-7191
HC257.I6
QUARTERLY ECONOMIC COMMENTARY. Text in English. q. EUR 50.79 per issue. charts. **Document type:** *Bulletin, Corporate.*
Related titles: Online - full text ed.: (from O C L C Online Computer Library Center, Inc., ProQuest Information & Learning).
Indexed: ABIn, PAIS.
Published by: Economic and Social Research Institute, 4 Burlington Rd., Dublin, 4, Ireland. TEL 353-1-667-1525, FAX 353-1-668-6231. Ed. B J Whelan. R&P Gillian Davidson.

330 USA ISSN 0098-681X
HD9724
QUARTERLY FINANCIAL REPORT FOR MANUFACTURING, MINING AND TRADE CORPORATIONS. Text in English. 1951. q. USD 58 domestic; USD 81.20 foreign (effective 2005). **Document type:** *Government.* **Description:** Shows the financial characteristics and operating results for all United States manufacturing corporations.
Former titles (until 1974): Quarterly Financial Report for Manufacturing Corporations (0033-5509); (until 1955): Quarterly Financial Report. United States Manufacturing Corporations (0196-7479)
Related titles: Diskette ed.: USD 80; USD 50 newsstand/cover for the first disk; USD 6 newsstand/cover for each additional disc (effective 2001); Online - full text ed.: ISSN 1554-9585.
Published by: U.S. Department of Commerce, Economic and Statistics Administration, Herbert Hoover Bldg Rm 4836, 14th St & Constitution Ave, NW, Washington, DC 20230. http://www.census.gov/prod/www/abs/qfr-mm.html, http://www.esa.doc.gov/. **Subscr. to:** U.S. Government Printing Office, Superintendent of Documents, PO Box 371954, Pittsburgh, PA 15250-7954. TEL 202-512-1800, FAX 202-512-2250, orders@gpo.gov, http://www.access.gpo.gov.

330 338 USA ISSN 0747-5535
HB1
➤ **QUARTERLY JOURNAL OF BUSINESS AND ECONOMICS.** Short title: Q J B E. Text in English. 1962. q. USD 24 domestic to individuals; USD 37 foreign to individuals; USD 45 domestic to institutions; USD 55 foreign to institutions (effective 2004). charts; illus. 70 p./no.; back issues avail.; reprint service avail. from PQC. **Document type:** *Journal, Academic/Scholarly.* **Description:** Features scholarly articles that empirically test theories in the fields of finance, accounting, economics, marketing and land management.
Former titles (until 1983): N J E B: Nebraska Journal of Economics and Business (0160-6557)
Related titles: Microform ed.: (from PQC); Online - full text ed.: (from EBSCO Publishing, Florida Center for Library Automation, Gale Group, ProQuest Information & Learning).
Indexed: ABIn, APEL, ASCA, BPIA, BusI, CREJ, ESPM, HRA, JEL, MEA&I, ManagCont, PAIS, RASB, RiskAb, SSCI, T&II, WAE&RSA.
—BLDSC (7187.930000), IE, Infotrieve, ingenta. **CCC.**
Published by: University of Nebraska at Lincoln, College of Business Administration, CBA Bldg, PO Box 880407, Lincoln, NE 68588-0407. TEL 402-472-7931, FAX 402-472-5180, qjbe@unlnotes.unl.edu, myoung1@unl.edu, http://www.qjbe.unl.edu/, http://www.cba.unl.edu/. Ed. George McCabe. R&P Margo Young TEL 402-472-7931. Circ: 400 (paid).

330 650 NLD ISSN 1062-9769
HC10
THE QUARTERLY REVIEW OF ECONOMICS AND FINANCE. Text in English. 1960. 5/yr. EUR 95 in Europe to individuals; JPY 13,100 in Japan to individuals; USD 99 to individuals except Europe and Japan; EUR 422 in Europe to institutions; JPY 56,100 in Japan to institutions; USD 472 to institutions except Europe and Japan (effective 2006). adv. bk.rev. abstr.; illus. Index. back issues avail.; reprint service avail. from PQC,SCH. **Document type:** *Journal, Academic/Scholarly.* **Description:** Publishes manuscripts that cover topics in the areas of economics, financial economics and finance.
Former titles (until 1992): Quarterly Review of Economics and Business (0033-5797); Current Economic Comment

B

▼ new title ➤ refereed ✶ unverified ◆ full entry avail.

Related titles: Microform ed.: (from MIM, PQC); Online - full text ed.: (from EBSCO Publishing, Florida Center for Library Automation, Gale Group, H.W. Wilson, IngentaConnect, O C L C Online Computer Library Center, Inc., ScienceDirect, Swets Information Services).
Indexed: ABIn, APEL, ASCA, AgeL, AmH&L, BPI, BPIA, BusI, CPM, CurCont, HistAb, IBSS, JEL, MEDLINE, ManagCont, ORMS, PAIS, PCI, PMA, RASB, RRTA, SCIMP, SSCI, T&II, WAE&RSA, WorkRelAb.
—BLDSC (7206.501000), CISTI, IDS, IE, Infotrieve, ingenta. **CCC.**
Published by: (University of Illinois at Urbana-Champaign USA, Bureau of Economics and Business Research GBR), Elsevier BV, North-Holland (Subsidiary of: Elsevier Science & Technology), Sara Burgerhartstraat 25, Amsterdam, 1055 KV, Netherlands. TEL 31-20-485-3911, FAX 31-20-485-2457, nlinfo-f@elsevier.nl, http://www.elsevier.com/locate/qref, http://www.elsevier.nl. Eds. J E Finnerty, R J Arnould. Circ: 2,000. **Subscr. to:** Elsevier BV, PO Box 211, Amsterdam 1000 AE, Netherlands. TEL 31-20-485-3757, FAX 31-20-485-3432, http://www.elsevier.nl.

330 CAN ISSN 0316-5078
HB31
QUEEN'S UNIVERSITY. INSTITUTE FOR ECONOMIC RESEARCH. DISCUSSION PAPER. Text in English. 1969. irreg. CND 180; CND 210 foreign (effective 2000). bibl. **Document type:** *Academic/Scholarly.*
Indexed: RefZh.
—BLDSC (3597.590000), CISTI, ingenta.
Published by: Queen's University, Institute for Economic Research, 99 University Ave, Kingston, ON K7L 3N6, Canada. TEL 613-533-6000, FAX 613-533-6668, pachecoe@qed.econ.queensu.ca. Circ: 200.

QUIMICA LATINOAMERICANA. see *CHEMISTRY*

330 USA
QUINCY BUSINESS NEWS. Text in English. 1989. m. free. adv. bk.rev. back issues avail. **Document type:** *Newsletter.* **Description:** For residents and businesses in Quincy.
Published by: Graham Communications, 40 Oval Rd, Ste 2, Quincy, MA 02170-3813. TEL 617-328-0069, FAX 617-471-1504, rkeane@grahamcomm.com. Ed., R&P, Adv. contact Rob Keane. B&W page USD 650. Circ: 3,000.

330 DEU
QUIP. Text in German. bi-m. adv. **Document type:** *Magazine, Trade.*
Published by: V M M Wirtschaftsverlag GmbH & Co. KG, Maximilianstr 9, Augsburg, 86150, Germany. TEL 49-821-44050, FAX 49-821-4405409, info@vmm-wirtschaftsverlag.de, http://www.vmm-wirtschaftsverlag.de. Adv. contact Monika Burzler. B&W page EUR 1,980, color page EUR 3,300. Circ: 15,000 (controlled).

330 051 NLD ISSN 0920-8275
QUOTE. Text in Dutch. 1986. m. (plus 3 special issues). EUR 67; EUR 4.95 newsstand/cover (effective 2005). adv. illus. 180 p./no.; **Document type:** *Magazine, Consumer.* **Description:** Discusses careers, networking, money, and life at the top.
Related titles: Online - full text ed.: (from LexisNexis).
—IE.
Published by: Quote Media Magazines, PO Box 10209, Amsterdam, 1001 EE, Netherlands. TEL 31-20-5353600, FAX 31-20-6208149, quote@quotemedia.nl, http://www.quotemedia.nl. Ed. Jort Kelder. Pub. Maarten van den Biggelaar. Adv. contacts Niek van den Bosch TEL 31-346-584100, Renate Tromp TEL 31-346-584128. B&W page EUR 6,200; trim 185 x 250. Circ: 54,850. **Subscr. to:** PO Box 571, Haarlem 2003 RN, Netherlands.

660 JPN
R & D ACTIVITIES OF MAJOR JAPANESE CHEMICAL COMPANIES. Text in English. 1990. irreg. USD 550 per issue. **Description:** Covers business strategies of major chemical manufacturers in Japan with regard to current business operations and R & D activities.
Published by: Dodwell Marketing Consultants, Kowa no 35 Bldg, 14-14 Akasaka 1-chome, Minato-ku, Tokyo, 107-0052, Japan. TEL 03-3589-0207, FAX 03-5570-7132.

R B R R KALE MEMORIAL LECTURES. see *POLITICAL SCIENCE*

330 USA
R I C O BUSINESS DISPUTES GUIDE; business disputes and the "racketeering" laws—federal and state. (Racketeer Influenced and Corrupt Organizations) Text in English. 1985. base vol. plus m. updates. USD 730 base vol(s). (effective 2004). **Description:** Gives a comprehensive view of civil "racketeering" litigation arising from business dealings.
Related titles: CD-ROM ed.: USD 710 (effective 2004); Online - full text ed.: USD 780 (effective 2004).
Published by: C C H Inc., 2700 Lake Cook Rd, Riverwoods, IL 60015. TEL 847-267-7000, 800-449-6439, cust_serv@cch.com, http://www.cch.com. Pub. Stacey Caywood.

R T N C'S ANNUAL RESALE DIRECTORY. see *GENERAL INTEREST PERIODICALS—United States*

330 DEU ISSN 1612-3565
▼ ➤ **R W I : DISCUSSION PAPERS.** Text in English. 2003. irreg., latest vol.25, 2005. price varies. **Document type:** *Monographic series, Academic/Scholarly.* **Description:** RWI : Mitteilungen address the scientific research community, whereby a referee process ensures the quality of the articles submitted.
Published by: Rheinisch-Westfaelisches Institut fuer Wirtschaftsforschung Essen, Hohenzollernstr 1-3, Essen, 45128, Germany. TEL 49-201-81490, FAX 49-201-8149200, rwi@rwi-essen.de, http://www.rwi-essen.de.

330 DEU ISSN 0933-0089
R W I MITTEILUNGEN; Zeitschrift fuer Wirtschaftsforschung. Text in German; Summaries in English, French. 1950. q. EUR 26 per issue (effective 2006). abstr.; charts; stat. index. **Document type:** *Journal, Academic/Scholarly.*
Formerly (until 1987): Rheinisch-Westfaelisches Institut fuer Wirtschaftsforschung. Mitteilungen (0035-4465)
Indexed: IBR, IBSS, IBZ, RASB.
—CCC.
Published by: (Rheinisch-Westfaelisches Institut fuer Wirtschaftsforschung Essen), Duncker und Humblot GmbH, Carl-Heinrich-Becker-Weg 9, Berlin, 12165, Germany. TEL 49-30-7900060, FAX 49-30-79000631, info@duncker-humblot.de, http://www.rwi-essen.de/presse/publikat/index.htm, http://www.duncker-humblot.de. Circ: 600.

330 DEU ISSN 0720-7212
R W I : SCHRIFTENREIHE. Text in German. 19??. irreg., latest vol.77, 2005. price varies. **Document type:** *Monographic series, Academic/Scholarly.* **Description:** Contains articles that address various aspects of economic policy such as surveys, workshop anthologies and dissertations.
Published by: (Rheinisch-Westfaelisches Institut fuer Wirtschaftsforschung Essen), Duncker und Humblot GmbH, Carl-Heinrich-Becker-Weg 9, Berlin, 12165, Germany. TEL 49-30-7900060, FAX 49-30-79000631, info@duncker-humblot.de, http://www.duncker-humblot.de.

330 658 USA ISSN 0741-6261
HD2763.A2 CODEN: RJECEA
➤ **RAND JOURNAL OF ECONOMICS.** Text in English. 1970. q. USD 180 domestic; USD 195 foreign (effective 2003). bk.rev. illus.; abstr. Index. back issues avail.; reprint service avail. from PSC. **Document type:** *Journal, Academic/Scholarly.* **Description:** Covers microeconomics with a focus on industrial organization, regulation, and law and economics. Includes both theoretical and quantitative papers that analyze market behavior and public policy.
Former titles (until 1984): Bell Journal of Economics (0361-915X); (until 1974): Bell Journal of Economics and Management Science (0005-8556)
Related titles: Microfiche ed.; Microform ed.: (from PQC); Online - full text ed.: (from EBSCO Publishing, Florida Center for Library Automation, Gale Group, H.W. Wilson, JSTOR (Web-based Journal Archive), O C L C Online Computer Library Center, Inc., ProQuest Information & Learning).
Indexed: ABIn, AESIS, APEL, ASCA, ATI, BPI, BPIA, BusI, CPM, CREJ, CompR, CurCont, ESPM, EngInd, HRA, HRIS, IAOP, IBSS, Inspec, JEL, KES, M&MA, MEA&I, MEDLINE, ManagCont, MathR, ORMS, PAIS, PCI, PRA, RASB, RRTA, RiskAb, SPAA, SSCI, SSI, SUSA, T&II, V&AA, WAE&RSA, WorkRelAb.
—BLDSC (7254.410300), AskIEEE, IDS, IE, Infotrieve, ingenta, Linda Hall. **CCC.**
Published by: Rand Journal of Economics, 1700 Main St, Box 2138, Santa Monica, CA 90407-2138. TEL 310-393-0411, FAX 310-393-4818, TELEX 9103436878, rje@rand.org, http://www.rje.org. Ed. James R Hosek. R&P Paula Larich TEL 310-393-0411. Circ: 3,000 (paid). **Subscr. to:** Allen Press Inc., PO Box 1897, Lawrence, KS 66044. TEL 785—843-1235, FAX 784-843-1274, rej@allenpress.com.

➤ **RAND MCNALLY BUSINESS TRAVELER'S ROAD ATLAS**; and trip planner. see *TRAVEL AND TOURISM*

➤ **RANLIAO GONGYE/DYESTUFF INDUSTRY.** see *CLEANING AND DYEING*

330.0711 USA ISSN 0160-3949
RAPID READERS SERIES. Text in English. 1977. irreg., latest vol.7, 1985. price varies. **Document type:** *Monographic series.* **Description:** Provides teachers with new ideas to enliven and enrich the teaching of business subjects.
Published by: Delta Pi Epsilon Graduate Business Education Society, National Office, P O Box 4340, Little Rock, AR 72214. TEL 501-562-1233, FAX 501-562-1293.

330 ITA
RAPPORTO I R S SUL MERCATO AZIONARIO. Text in Italian. a.
Published by: Societa Editoriale Media Economici Seme SpA, Via Paolo Lomazzo, 52, Milan, MI 20154, Italy. TEL 02-331211, FAX 02-316905.

330 ITA ISSN 1120-9518
HC307.S69
RAPPORTO SULL'ECONOMIA DEL MEZZOGIORNO; rassegna annuale a cura della Svimez. Text in Italian. 1975. a. price varies. adv. back issues avail. **Document type:** *Academic/Scholarly.*
Published by: (Associazione per lo Sviluppo dell'Industria nel Mezzogiorno), Societa Editrice Il Mulino, Strada Maggiore 37, Bologna, 40125, Italy. TEL 39-051-256011, FAX 39-051-256034, riviste@mulino.it, http://www.mulino.it. Adv. contact M Luisa Vezzali. Circ: 2,000.

330 ESP
RATING. Text in Spanish. 11/yr.
Address: Torre de Madrid Planta 7 Ofc. 3, Plaza Espana, 18, Madrid, 28008, Spain. TEL 1-247-30-11, FAX 1-248-04-06. Ed. Pedro Zamarro.

330 GBR ISSN 0305-814X
➤ **READING IN POLITICAL ECONOMY.** Text in English. 1967. irreg., latest vol.39, 1993. GBP 40 (effective 2002). adv. bk.rev. **Document type:** *Academic/Scholarly.*
Formerly: Readings in Political Economy (0079-9874)
Related titles: Microfiche ed.
—BLDSC (4362.666000), IE, ingenta.
Published by: Institute of Economic Affairs, 2 Lord North St, London, SW1P 3LB, United Kingdom. TEL 44-20-77998900, FAX 44-20-77992137, iea@iea.org.uk, http://www.iea.org.uk. Ed. Colin Robinson.

➤ **REAL ESTATE EXECUTIVE.** see *REAL ESTATE*

778.53 CAN ISSN 1480-1434
REALSCREEN. Text in English. 1997. m. CND 79, USD 59; USD 99 foreign.
Related titles: Online - full text ed.: (from bigchalk, LexisNexis, Micromedia ProQuest).
Published by: Brunico Communications Inc., 366 Adelaide St W, Ste 500, Toronto, ON M5V 1R9, Canada. TEL 416-408-2300, FAX 416-408-0870, circ@brunico.com, http://www.brunico.com.

330 USA
REBUILDING WALL STREET; the restoration of America's financial marketplace. Text in English. 2001 (Sep.). bi-w. free. **Document type:** *Newsletter.* **Description:** Covers the rebuilding of Wall Street following the September 11th attacks upon the World Trade Center in New York.
Media: E-mail. **Related titles:** Online - full text ed.
Published by: Dow Jones Company, 200 Liberty St, New York, NY 10281. TEL 800-223-2274, newswires@dowjones.com, http://www.djnewswires.com/rebuilding.

330 FRA ISSN 1160-0543
RECHERCHE ET ENTREPRISES. Text in French. 1992. irreg. price varies. **Document type:** *Monographic series, Academic/Scholarly.*
Published by: (France. Centre National de la Recherche Scientifique), C N R S Editions, 15 Rue Malebranche, Paris, 75005, France. TEL 33-1-53102700, FAX 33-1-53102727, http://www.cnrseditions.fr.

330 BEL ISSN 0770-4518
HB3
➤ **RECHERCHES ECONOMIQUES DE LOUVAIN/LOUVAIN ECONOMIC STUDIES.** Text in English, French. 1929. q. EUR 150 (effective 2004). bk.rev. charts; abstr. 128 p./no.; back issues avail. **Document type:** *Monographic series, Academic/Scholarly.*
Indexed: CPM, DIP, IBR, IBSS, IBZ, JEL, NumL, PAIS, PCI.
—BLDSC (7308.400000), IE, Infotrieve, ingenta.
Published by: (Universite Catholique de Louvain, Institut des Sciences Economiques), De Boeck Universite, Fond Jean-Paques 4, Louvain-la-Neuve, 1348, Belgium. TEL 32-10-482511, FAX 32-10-482519, info@universite.deboeck.com, http://universite.deboeck.com. Ed. Michel De Vroey. Circ: 750. **Subscr. to:** Acces S.P.R.L., Fond Jean-Paques 4, Louvain-la-Neuve 1348, Belgium. TEL 32-10-482570, FAX 32-10-482519, acces+cde@deboeck.be.

➤ **DAS RECHT DER WIRTSCHAFT.** see *LAW*

➤ **RECHT UND POLITIK DES WETTBEWERBS.** see *LAW—Corporate Law*

330 DEU ISSN 1618-9442
DIE RECHTSANWALTS- UND NOTARFACHANGESTELLTEN; Zeitschrift fuer Aus- und Weiterbildung. Text in German. 1981. m. EUR 43.80; EUR 3.65 newsstand/cover (effective 2003). adv. **Document type:** *Magazine, Trade.*
Formerly (until 2002): Reno (0721-4588)
—CCC.
Published by: Friedrich Kiehl Verlag GmbH, Pfaustr 13, Ludwigshafen, 67063, Germany. TEL 49-621-635020, FAX 49-621-6350222, info@kiehl.de, http://www.kiehl.de. adv.: B&W page EUR 720, color page EUR 1,368. Circ: 5,235 (paid and controlled).

330 GBR
RECOMMENDATION FOR SURVIVAL IN BUSINESS. Text in English. 1981. irreg. GBP 4.50 (effective 1999). **Document type:** *Monographic series.*
Published by: Marcus Tobias & Co., 65 Shakespeare Dr, Shirley, Solihull, Warks B90 2AN, United Kingdom. TEL 0121-744-2912, FAX 0121-733-2902.

330 340 CAN
RECORDS RETENTION: LAW & PRACTICE. Text in English. 1975. 2/yr. looseleaf. CND 210 domestic; USD 177.96 foreign (effective 2005). index. **Document type:** *Trade.* **Description:** Provides a complete reference to the principles and practices of records retention and to the legal obligations of Canadian businesses to retain documents and files.
Published by: Carswell (Subsidiary of: Thomson Corporation), One Corporate Plaza, 2075 Kennedy Rd, Toronto, ON M1T 3V4, Canada. TEL 416-609-8000, 800-387-5164, FAX 416-298-5094, carswell.customerrelations@thomson.com, http://www.carswell.com. Ed. Ronald Anson-Cartwright.

RECOUP'S MATERIALS RECYCLING MARKETS. see *ENVIRONMENTAL STUDIES—Waste Management*

THE RED HERRING (SAN FRANCISCO); the business of technology. see *TECHNOLOGY: COMPREHENSIVE WORKS*

THE REED MCCLURE LETTER. see *LAW*

330 TUR
REFERANS. Text in Turkish. d. adv. **Document type:** *Newspaper, Trade.*
Published by: Dogan Yayin Holding, Hurriyet Medya Towers, Gunesli, Istanbul, 34212, Turkey. TEL 90-212-6770000, support@dmg.com.tr, http://www.referansgazetesi.com, http://www.dmg.com.tr.

330 BEL ISSN 0034-2971
HB3
➤ **REFLETS ET PERSPECTIVES DE LA VIE ECONOMIQUE.** Text in French. 1961. q. EUR 75 to individuals; EUR 100 to institutions (effective 2004). adv. bk.rev. abstr. index. back issues avail. **Document type:** *Monographic series, Academic/Scholarly.*
Indexed: DIP, ELLIS, ExcerpMed, IBR, IBZ, PAIS, RASB, WBSS. —BLDSC (7332.340000), IE, ingenta.
Published by: De Boeck Universite, Fond Jean-Paques 4, Louvain-la-Neuve, 1348, Belgium. TEL 32-10-482511, FAX 32-10-482519, info@universite.deboeck.com, http://universite.deboeck.com. Ed. Etienne de Callatay. Circ: 900. **Subscribe to:** Acces S.P.R.L., Fond Jean-Paques 4, Louvain-la-Neuve 1348, Belgium. TEL 32-10-482570, FAX 32-10-482519.

330 RUS
REFORMA. Text in Russian. 1995. w. USD 785 in the Americas (effective 2000).
Published by: A.K. & M., Ul Gubkina 35, Moscow, 117924, Russian Federation. TEL 7-095-1326130, FAX 7-095-1326026. **Dist. by:** East View Information Services, 3020 Harbor Ln. N., Minneapolis, MN 55447. TEL 763-550-0961, FAX 763-559-2931.

330 RUS
REFORMA - BYULLETEN' ROSSIISKOGO FONDA FEDERAL'NOGO IMUSHCHESTVA. Text in Russian. 3/m. USD 299.95 in United States.
Published by: Rossiiskii Fond Federal'nogo Imushchestva, Leninskii pr-t 9, Moscow, 117049, Russian Federation. TEL 7-095-2378564, FAX 7-095-2378564. **US dist. addr.:** East View Information Services, 3020 Harbor Ln. N., Minneapolis, MN 55447. TEL 612-550-0961.

330 RUS
REFORMA - MEZHDUNARODNYI FOND EKONOMICHESKIKH I SOTSYAL'NYKH REFORM. Text in Russian. m. USD 119.95 in United States.
Indexed: RASB.
Published by: Mezhdunarodnyi Fond Ekonomicheskikh i Sotsyal'nykh Reform, Kotel'nicheskaya nab 17, Moscow, 109240, Russian Federation. TEL 7-095-9267752, FAX 7-095-2069472. **US dist. addr.:** East View Information Services, 3020 Harbor Ln. N., Minneapolis, MN 55447. TEL 612-550-0961.

330 GBR
REGIONAL DEVELOPMENT INTERNATIONAL; the news magazine of industrial office & economic development. Text in English. 1978. m. GBP 50 (effective 1999). adv. bk.rev. back issues avail. **Description:** Reports on regional development programs, promotes inward, cross-border and indigenous investment projects. Helps overseas, mainland European and U.K. corporate investors.
Former titles: Regional Development; Industrial Planning and Development (0262-3161)
Published by: Eurocom Ltd., Princess House, 74 Princess St, Luton, Beds LU1 5AT, United Kingdom. TEL 44-1582-452911, FAX 44-1582-483841. Ed. Karen Lesley. Pub., Adv. contact Colin Robinson. R&P Pat Wauer. Circ: 28,000.

REGIONAL SCIENCE AND URBAN ECONOMICS. see *HOUSING AND URBAN PLANNING*

REGULATORY REVIEW (YEAR). see *BUSINESS AND ECONOMICS—Abstracting, Bibliographies, Statistics*

330 659.1 RUS
REKLAMA NEDELI. Text in Russian. w. USD 345 in United States (effective 2000).
Address: Ul Volzhskaya 28, Saratov, 410730, Russian Federation. TEL 8452-262350. **Dist. by:** East View Information Services, 3020 Harbor Ln. N., Minneapolis, MN 55447. TEL 763-550-0961, FAX 763-559-2931.

330 ITA ISSN 1591-9773
RENDICONTI PER GLI STUDI ECONOMICI QUANTITATIVI. Text in Italian. 1969. a.
Former titles (until 1996): Rendiconti del Comitato per gli Studi Economici (1591-9781); (until 1991): Rendiconti del Comitato per gli Studi e per la Programmazione Economica (1591-979X); (until 1979): Rendiconti del Comitato Veneto per gli Studi Economici e per la Programmazione (1591-982X); (until 1976): Rendiconti del Comitato Veneto per il Potenziamento degli Studi Economici e per la Programmazione (1591-9811); (until 1972): Rendiconti del Comitato per il Potenziamento in Venezia degli Studi Economici (1591-9803)
Indexed: MathSciNet.
Published by: Universita Ca' Foscari di Venezia, Dorsoduro 3246, Venice, 30123, Italy. TEL 39-41-2346910911, FAX 39-41-5221756, http://www.dma.unive.it/rendiconti.html, http://www.unive.it.

330 610 USA ISSN 1520-7587
REPERTOIRE MAGAZINE. Text in English. 1993. m.
Published by: Medical Distribution Solutions, Inc., 5445 Triangle Pkwy., Ste. 170, Norcross, GA 30092-2587. TEL 770-416-0071, FAX 770-416-7722. Ed. Mark Thill. Pubs. Brian Taylor, Chris Kelly.

330 GBR
THE REPORT ON BUSINESS. Text in English. m. GBP 495; GBP 595 (fax service) (effective 2000). **Document type:** *Trade.* **Description:** Provides a series of monthly economic indicators of the health of the UIC manufacturing industry.
Related titles: Fax ed.
Indexed: SRI.
Published by: (Chartered Institute of Purchasing and Supply), N T C Publications Ltd. (Subsidiary of: World Advertising Research Center Ltd.), Farm Rd, Henley-on-Thames, Oxon RG9 1EJ, United Kingdom. TEL 44-1491-411000, FAX 44-1491-571188, ntc@ntc.co.uk.

330 CAN ISSN 0827-7680
REPORT ON BUSINESS MAGAZINE. Variant title: Investment and Tax Guide. Report on Business 1000. Text in English. 1984. m. free with subscr. to the Globe and Mail (effective 1999). adv. bk.rev. illus. reprints avail. **Document type:** *Consumer.* **Description:** Provides informed journalism about business in Canada and the world.
Related titles: Online - full text ed.: Globe & Mail Report on Business Magazine; ♦ Supplement to: The Globe and Mail. ISSN 0319-0714.
Indexed: CBCARef, CBPI, CPerI. —CISTI. **CCC.**
Published by: Globe and Mail Publishing, 444 Front St W, Toronto, ON M5V 2S9, Canada. TEL 416-585-5499, FAX 416-585-5641, bbalfour@globeandmail.ca, http://www.robmagazine.com. Ed. Patricia Best. Pub. Stephen Petherbridge. Adv. contact Cheri Natale. Circ: 318,000.

330 AUS ISSN 1328-181X
REPORT ON GOVERNMENT SERVICES (YEAR). Text in English. 1995. a. (in 2 vols.), latest 2001. AUD 39.95 (effective 2001). stat. back issues avail. **Document type:** *Yearbook, Government.* **Description:** Covers benchmarks and records the performance of state governments in the follow up service areas: education, health, justice, emergency management, community services, & housing.
Related titles: CD-ROM ed.: AUD 19.95; Online - full content ed.
Published by: (Steering Committee for the Review of Commonwealth, State Service Provision), Productivity Commission, Media and Publications Section, Locked Bag 2, Collins St E., Melbourne, VIC 8003, Australia. TEL 61-3-9653-2100, FAX 61-3-9653-2199, maps@pc.gov.au, http://www.pc.gov.au. **Subscr. to:** AusInfo, GPO Box 1920, Canberra Mc, ACT 2610, Australia. TEL 61-2-6275-3442, FAX 61-2-6295-4888.

REPORTERO INDUSTRIAL; new equipment, machinery and techniques for industry. see *MACHINERY*

REPRAX; Zeitschrift zur Handelsregisterpraxis. see *PATENTS, TRADEMARKS AND COPYRIGHTS*

330 CAF
REPUBLIQUE CENTRAFRICAINE. JOURNAL OFFICIEL. Text in French. 1974. fortn. **Document type:** *Government.* **Description:** Provides economic data.
Published by: Republique Centrafricaine, BP 739, Bangui, Central African Republic. Ed. Gabriel Agba.

330.95 USA ISSN 1047-126X
HC411
RESEARCH IN ASIAN ECONOMIC STUDIES. Text in English. 1988. irreg., latest vol.10, 2002. price varies. back issues avail. **Document type:** *Monographic series, Academic/Scholarly.*
—**CCC.**
Published by: J A I Press Inc. (Subsidiary of: Elsevier Science & Technology), 360 Park Ave S, New York, NY 10010-1710. TEL 212-989-5800, FAX 212-633-3990, usinfo-f@elsevier.com, http://www.elsevier.com/wps/find/bookseriesdescription.cws_home/BS_RAES/description. Ed. M Dutta.

330 GBR ISSN 1090-9443
HC301
RESEARCH IN ECONOMICS. Text in Italian, English. 1947. 4/yr. EUR 617 in Europe to institutions; JPY 66,600 in Japan to institutions; USD 548 to institutions except Europe and Japan (effective 2006). adv. bk.rev. charts. index, cum.index. back issues avail.; reprint service avail. from PQC. **Document type:** *Academic/Scholarly.* **Description:** Publishes theoretical and empirical research in all fields of economic inquiry.
Related titles: Microform ed.: (from PQC); Online - full text ed.: ISSN 1090-9451. USD 578 (effective 2002) (from EBSCO Publishing, Gale Group, IngentaConnect, O C L C Online Computer Library Center, Inc., ScienceDirect, Swets Information Services); Italian ed.: Ricerche Economiche. ISSN 0035-5054. 1955.
Indexed: IBSS, JEL, PAIS, RRTA, WAE&RSA, ZentMath. —BLDSC (7738.925000), IE, Infotrieve, ingenta. **CCC.**
Published by: (Universita degli Studi di Venezia ITA), Academic Press (Subsidiary of: Elsevier Science & Technology), Harcourt Pl, 32 Jamestown Rd, London, NW1 7BY, United Kingdom. TEL 44-20-7424-4200, FAX 44-20-7483-2293, apsubs@acad.com, http://www.elsevier.com/locate/rie. Ed. G. Cazzavillan. R&P Catherine John. Adv. contact Nik Screen. Circ: 1,200.

330.05 346.066 USA ISSN 0193-5895
K18
RESEARCH IN LAW AND ECONOMICS. Text in English. 1979. irreg., latest vol.21, 2004. price varies. back issues avail.; reprint service avail. from WSH. **Document type:** *Monographic series, Academic/Scholarly.*
Related titles: Online - full text ed.: (from ScienceDirect); Supplement(s): Economics of Nonproprietary Organizations.
Indexed: CLI, IBSS, ILP, JEL, LRI.
—**CCC.**
Published by: J A I Press Inc. (Subsidiary of: Elsevier Science & Technology), 360 Park Ave S, New York, NY 10010-1710. TEL 212-989-5800, FAX 212-633-3990, usinfo-f@elsevier.com, http://www.elsevier.com/wps/find/bookseriesdescription.cws_home/BS_RLEC/description. Ed. Richard O Zerbe Jr.

330 USA ISSN 1094-5334
HC415.15.A1
RESEARCH IN MIDDLE EAST ECONOMICS. Text in English. 1996. irreg., latest vol.6, 2005. price varies. back issues avail. **Document type:** *Monographic series, Academic/Scholarly.*
Related titles: Online - full text ed.: (from ScienceDirect).
Published by: J A I Press Inc. (Subsidiary of: Elsevier Science & Technology), 360 Park Ave S, New York, NY 10010-1710. TEL 212-989-5800, FAX 212-633-3990, usinfo-f@elsevier.com, http://www.elsevier.com/wps/find/bookseriesdescription.cws_home/BS_RMEE/description. Ed. J Olmsted.

330 020 USA ISSN 1067-0394
HF54.52.U5
RESEARCHING MARKETS, INDUSTRIES, AND BUSINESS OPPORTUNITIES. Text in English. 1994. irreg., latest vol.5. USD 395 (effective 1999). **Document type:** *Directory, Trade.* **Description:** Helps executives, analysts, and researchers assess the performance of companies and explore new business opportunities.
Published by: Washington Researchers, Ltd., 1655 Fort Myer Dr., Ste. 800, Arlington, VA 22209-3119. TEL 703-312-2863, FAX 703-527-4586, research@researchers.com, http://www.researchers.com, http://www.washingtonresearchers.com. R&P Ellen O'Kane.

330 ITA
RESPONSABILITA E COMUNICAZIONE IMPRESA. Text in Italian. 1996. q. EUR 51.65 in the European Union; EUR 77.47 elsewhere (effective 2002). **Description:** Addresses the changing roles and responsabilities of managers. Provides articles on issues such as civic responsability and the right of communication.
Published by: Casa Editrice Dott. A. Giuffre (Subsidiary of: LexisNexis Europe and Africa), Via Busto Arsizio, 40, Milan, MI 20151, Italy. TEL 39-02-28089200, FAX 39-02-38009582, giuffre@giuffre.it, http://www.giuffre.it. Ed. Ugo Ruffolo.

330 USA
RESPONSIBILITY. Text in English. q. membership. **Document type:** *Newsletter.* **Description:** Includes information on national and district meetings, club activities, program directives, and correspondence from national officers and committee chairs.
Related titles: Online - full text ed.
Published by: National Association of Negro Business and Professional Women's Clubs, Inc., 1806 New Hampshire Ave, N W, Washington, DC 20009. TEL 202-683-4206, FAX 202-462-7253, http://www.nanbpwc.org. Ed. Joysetta Pearse. Circ: 4,000.

RESTRUCTURING TODAY. see *ENERGY*

B

▼ new title ➤ refereed ✶ unverified ♦ full entry avail.

▼ **RESURSY. TEKHNOLOGII. EKONOMIKA.** see *ENERGY*

RETAIL CONSTRUCTION; the journal for architecture, design, construction and facilities operation. see *BUILDING AND CONSTRUCTION*

330 USA
RETAIL SECTOR UPDATE. Text in English. w. **Document type:** *Newsletter, Trade.*
Media: E-mail.
Published by: 123Jump.com, 407 Lincoln Rd Ste 12D, Miami Beach, FL 33139. TEL 305-673-6339, FAX 305-673-6386, editorial@123jump.com, http://www.123jump.com/.

330 305.896073 USA ISSN 0034-6446
E185.5
➤ **THE REVIEW OF BLACK POLITICAL ECONOMY.** Text in English. 1970. q. USD 72 to individuals print or online; USD 240 to institutions print or online; USD 30 to students; USD 79 combined subscription to individuals print & online; USD 264 combined subscription to institutions print & online (effective 2004). adv. bk.rev. illus. reprint service avail. from PQC,PSC. **Document type:** *Journal, Academic/Scholarly.* **Description:** Examines issues related to the economic status of black and Third World peoples. Identifies and analyzes policy prescriptions designed to reduce racial economic inequality.
Related titles: Microform ed.: (from PQC); Online - full text ed.: (from Chadwyck-Healey Inc., EBSCO Publishing, Florida Center for Library Automation, Gale Group, O C L C Online Computer Library Center, Inc., ProQuest Information & Learning, Swets Information Services).
Indexed: ABIn, ASCA, AgeL, AmH&L, BusI, ChPerI, CurCont, ESPM, HistAb, IBSS, IIBP, JEL, LRI, PAIS, PCI, PSA, RiskAb, SPAA, SRRA, SSA, SSCI, SSI, SUSA, SociolAb, T&II, WorkRelAb.
—BLDSC (7788.700000), IDS, IE, ingenta. **CCC.**
Published by: (National Economic Association), Transaction Publishers, 390 Campus Dr, Somerset, NJ 07830. TEL 888-999-6778, FAX 732-748-9801, trans@transactionpub.com, http://www.transactionpub.com. Ed. Cecilia A Conrad TEL 909-607-2970. Pub. Mary Curtis. R&P Marlena Davidian TEL 732-445-2280 ext 100. Adv. contact Alicja Garbie. page USD 400; 5.25 x 8.5. Circ: 1,000. **Co-sponsor:** Southern Center for Studies in Public Policy of Clark College.

650 USA ISSN 0034-6454
➤ **REVIEW OF BUSINESS.** Text in English. 1964. q. free. bk.rev. charts; illus.; stat. **Document type:** *Journal, Academic/Scholarly.* **Description:** Provides information of current interest and relevance to a general business audience, especially material the business practitioner can use.
Related titles: Microform ed.: (from PQC); Online - full text ed.: (from EBSCO Publishing, Florida Center for Library Automation, Gale Group, Northern Light Technology, Inc., O C L C Online Computer Library Center, Inc., ProQuest Information & Learning).
Indexed: ABIn, BPIA, BusI, PAIS, T&II.
—BLDSC (7788.880000), IE, ingenta. **CCC.**
Published by: St. John's University, The Peter J.Tobin College of Business, Bent Hall, 8000 Utopia Pkwy, Jamaica, NY 11439. TEL 718-990-6768, FAX 718-990-1868, littlec@stjohns.edu, http://new.stjohns.edu/academics/undergraduate/tobin. Ed. Charles Little. Circ: 7,000 (controlled).

330 IND
REVIEW OF COMMERCE STUDIES. Text in English. 1972. m. INR 10, USD 2.50. back issues avail.
Related titles: ◆ Polish ed.: Przeglad Handlowy. ISSN 1231-3351.
Published by: (Department of Commerce), University of Delhi, School of Economics, New Delhi, 110 007, India. Ed. R A Sharma.

330 300 IRL
REVIEW OF E S R I RESEARCH. Text in English. a. **Document type:** *Corporate.*
—BLDSC (7790.528000).
Published by: Economic and Social Research Institute, 4 Burlington Rd., Dublin, 4, Ireland. TEL 353-1-667-1525, FAX 353-1-668-6231.

330 GBR ISSN 0034-6527
HB1
➤ **THE REVIEW OF ECONOMIC STUDIES.** Text in English. 1933. q. USD 335 combined subscription in the Americas to institutions & Caribbean (print & online eds.); GBP 181 combined subscription elsewhere to institutions print & online eds. (effective 2005). adv. illus. cum.index: vol.1-25. reprint service avail. from PSC. **Document type:** *Journal, Academic/Scholarly.*
Related titles: Online - full text ed.: ISSN 1467-937X. USD 318 to institutions in USA, Europe, Mexico, Canada, Japan, South Korea, Australia and New Zealand; GBP 172 elsewhere to institutions (effective 2005) (from Blackwell Synergy, EBSCO Publishing, Gale Group, IngentaConnect, JSTOR (Web-based Journal Archive), Northern Light Technology, Inc., O C L C Online Computer Library Center, Inc., ProQuest Information & Learning, Swets Information Services).
Indexed: ABIn, ASCA, AgeL, CCMJ, CPM, CREJ, CurCont, ESPM, FamI, GEOBASE, IBR, IBSS, IBZ, JCQM, JEL, KES, LRI, MathR, MathSciNet, PAIS, PCI, RASB, RDA, RRTA, RiskAb, SCIMP, SSCI, SSI, WAE&RSA, WBA, ZentMath.
—BLDSC (7790.200000), CISTI, IDS, IE, Infotrieve, ingenta.
Published by: Blackwell Publishing Ltd., 9600 Garsington Rd, Oxford, OX4 2ZG, United Kingdom. TEL 44-1865-776868, FAX 44-1865-714591, customerservices@oxon.blackwellpublishing.com, http://www.blackwellpublishing.com/journals/ROES.

330 519.5 USA ISSN 0034-6535
HA1 CODEN: RECSA9
➤ **THE REVIEW OF ECONOMICS AND STATISTICS.** Text in English. 1966. q. USD 58 combined subscription in US & Canada to individuals print & online eds.; USD 82 combined subscription elsewhere to individuals print & online eds.; USD 362 combined subscription in US & Canada to institutions print & online eds.; USD 386 combined subscription elsewhere to institutions print & online eds. (effective 2006). adv. charts; illus. index. back issues avail.; reprints avail. **Document type:** *Academic/Scholarly.* **Description:** Covers applied economics, emphasizing quantitative economics.
Formerly (until 1948): The Review of Economics Statistics (1553-0027)
Related titles: Microform ed.: (from PQC); Online - full content ed.: ISSN 1530-9142. USD 52 to individuals; USD 326 to institutions (effective 2006) (from Florida Center for Library Automation); Online - full text ed.: (from EBSCO Publishing, Gale Group, H.W. Wilson, IngentaConnect, JSTOR (Web-based Journal Archive), O C L C Online Computer Library Center, Inc., Swets Information Services).
Indexed: ABIn, ASCA, AgeL, Agr, AmH&L, BAS, BPI, BPIA, BusI, CIS, CJA, CPM, CREJ, CurCont, DIP, EIA, ESPM, EnerInd, ExcerpMed, FamI, HRA, HistAb, IBR, IBSS, IBZ, ILD, IPSA, JCQM, JEL, KES, LRI, MAB, MCR, MEA&I, MEDLINE, MagInd, ManagCont, PAIS, PCI, PRA, PopulInd, RILM, RRTA, RiskAb, SCIMP, SPAA, SSCI, SSI, SUSA, SWA, T&II, WAE&RSA, WBA, WBSS.
—BLDSC (7790.250000), CISTI, IDS, IE, Infotrieve, ingenta. **CCC.**
Published by: (Harvard University, Economics Department), M I T Press, 55 Hayward St, Cambridge, MA 02142-1493. TEL 617-253-5646, FAX 617-258-6779, restat@arrow.fas.harvard.edu, journals-info@mit.edu, http://mitpress.mit.edu/restat. R&P Norah Piehl. Circ: 3,500.

640 USA ISSN 1569-5239
▼ **REVIEW OF ECONOMICS OF THE HOUSEHOLD.** Text in English. 2003. q. EUR 295, USD 295, GBP 182 combined subscription to institutions print & online eds. (effective 2005). reprint service avail. from PSC. **Document type:** *Journal, Academic/Scholarly.* **Description:** Publishes empirical and theoretical research on the economic behavior of households.
Related titles: Online - full text ed.: ISSN 1573-7152 (from EBSCO Publishing, Gale Group, IngentaConnect, Kluwer Online, O C L C Online Computer Library Center, Inc., ProQuest Information & Learning, Springer LINK, Swets Information Services).
Indexed: ABIn, BibLing, FamI.
—BLDSC (7790.251000), IE, ingenta. **CCC.**
Published by: Springer-Verlag New York, Inc. (Subsidiary of: Springer Science+Business Media), 233 Spring St, New York, NY 10013. TEL 212-460-1500, FAX 212-460-1575, service@springer-ny.com, http://springerlink.metapress.com/openurl.asp?genre=journal&issn=1569-5239, http://www.springer-ny.com. Eds. Catherine Sofer, Michael Grossman, Shoshana Grossbard. **Subscr. to:** Journal Fulfillment, PO Box 2485, Secaucus, NJ 07096-2485. TEL 201-348-4033, FAX 201-348-4505, journals@springer-ny.com.

338 330 NLD ISSN 1058-3300
HF5001
➤ **REVIEW OF FINANCIAL ECONOMICS.** Text in English. 1965. 4/yr. EUR 95 in Europe to individuals; JPY 13,100 in Japan to individuals; USD 99 elsewhere to individuals; EUR 346 in Europe to institutions; JPY 46,000 in Japan to institutions; USD 387 elsewhere to institutions (effective 2006). back issues avail.; reprint service avail. from PQC,SCH. **Document type:** *Academic/Scholarly.* **Description:** Offers an academic journal for academicians and practitioners in the field of financial economics.
Former titles (until 1991): Review of Business and Economics Research (0362-7985); (until 1975): Mississippi Valley Journal of Business and Economics (0026-6418)
Related titles: Microform ed.: (from PQC); Online - full text ed.: (from Chadwyck-Healey Inc., EBSCO Publishing, Florida Center for Library Automation, Gale Group, IngentaConnect, ScienceDirect, Swets Information Services).
Indexed: ABIn, ATI, BPI, BPIA, BusI, CPM, CREJ, ESPM, JEL, ManagCont, PAIS, PCI, RiskAb, SSCI, WBA.
—BLDSC (7790.564000), IE, Infotrieve, ingenta. **CCC.**
Published by: Elsevier BV, North-Holland (Subsidiary of: Elsevier Science & Technology), Sara Burgerhartstraat 25, Amsterdam, 1055 KV, Netherlands. TEL 31-20-485-3911, FAX 31-20-485-2457, nlinfo-f@elsevier.nl, http://www.elsevier.com/locate/rfe, http://www.elsevier.nl/homepage/about/us/regional_sites.htt, http://www.elsevier.nl. Eds. Gerald Whitney, T. K. Mukherjee. Circ: 1,000. **Subscr. to:** Elsevier BV, PO Box 211, Amsterdam 1000 AE, Netherlands. TEL 31-20-485-3757, FAX 31-20-485-3432.

330 GBR ISSN 0965-7576
HF1351
➤ **REVIEW OF INTERNATIONAL ECONOMICS.** Text in English. 1992. 5/yr. EUR 84 combined subscription in Europe to individuals print & online eds.; USD 70 combined subscription in the Americas to individuals & Caribbean, print & online eds.; GBP 56 combined subscription elsewhere to individuals print & online eds.; USD 706 combined subscription in the Americas to institutions & Caribbean, print & online eds.; GBP 482 combined subscription elsewhere to institutions print & online eds. (effective 2006). back issues avail.; reprint service avail. from PSC. **Document type:** *Journal, Academic/Scholarly.* **Description:** Covers a full range of topics in international economics including both controversial and innovative ideas and detailed contributions from other directly related fields such as economic development; trade and the environment; and political economy.
Related titles: Online - full text ed.: ISSN 1467-9396. 1997. USD 671 in the Americas to institutions & Caribbean; GBP 458 elsewhere to institutions (effective 2006) (from Blackwell Synergy, EBSCO Publishing, Gale Group, IngentaConnect, O C L C Online Computer Library Center, Inc., Swets Information Services).
Indexed: ABIn, APEL, GEOBASE, IBSS, JEL.
—BLDSC (7790.905000), IE, Infotrieve, ingenta. **CCC.**
Published by: Blackwell Publishing Ltd., 9600 Garsington Rd, Oxford, OX4 2ZG, United Kingdom. TEL 44-1865-776868, FAX 44-1865-714591, customerservices@oxon.blackwellpublishing.com, http://www.blackwellpublishing.com/journal.asp?ref=0965-7576&site=1. Ed. E Kwan Choi TEL 515-294-5999.

➤ **THE REVIEW OF NETWORK ECONOMICS.** see *COMPUTERS—Computer Networks*

330 301 GBR ISSN 0034-6764
HB1
➤ **REVIEW OF SOCIAL ECONOMY.** Text in English. 1948. q. GBP 163, USD 270 combined subscription to institutions print & online eds. (effective 2006). adv. bk.rev. bibl.; charts; illus. index. back issues avail.; reprint service avail. from PQC,PSC. **Document type:** *Journal, Academic/Scholarly.* **Description:** Publishes papers on the many relationships between social values and economics.
Related titles: Microform ed.: (from PQC); Online - full text ed.: ISSN 1470-1162. GBP 155, USD 257 to institutions (effective 2006) (from EBSCO Publishing, Florida Center for Library Automation, Gale Group, IngentaConnect, Northern Light Technology, Inc., O C L C Online Computer Library Center, Inc., Swets Information Services).
Indexed: ABIn, ABS&EES, APEL, ASCA, ASSIA, AgeL, AmH&L, ArtHuCI, BAS, BPIA, BrHumI, BusI, CPL, CREJ, CurCont, DIP, FamI, HistAb, IBR, IBSS, IBZ, IPSA, JEL, PAIS, PCI, PRA, PSA, PsycInfo, PsycholAb, RASB, RDA, RRTA, SOPODA, SSA, SSCI, SociolAb, T&II, WAE&RSA.
—BLDSC (7796.910000), IDS, IE, Infotrieve, ingenta. **CCC.**
Published by: (Association for Social Economics), Routledge (Subsidiary of: Taylor & Francis Group), 4 Park Sq, Milton Park, Abingdon, Oxon OX14 4RN, United Kingdom. TEL 44-1235-828600, FAX 44-1235-829000, journals@routledge.com, http://www.tandf.co.uk/journals/titles/00346764.asp, http://www.routledge.co.uk. Eds. Deborah M Figart, Martha Starr, Robert McMaster, Wilfred Dolfsma. R&P Sally Sweet. adv.: page GBP 175; trim 180 x 110. Circ: 2,000. **Subscr. to:** Taylor & Francis Ltd, Journals Customer Service, Rankine Rd, Basingstoke, Hants RG24 8PR, United Kingdom. TEL 44-1256-813000, FAX 44-1256-330245, enquiry@tandf.co.uk.

330 DEU ISSN 1610-2878
HF1351
➤ **REVIEW OF WORLD ECONOMICS.** Text and summaries in Multiple languages. 1914. q. EUR 140 combined subscription to institutions print & online eds. (effective 2005). adv. bk.rev. bibl.; illus. index. back issues avail.; reprints avail. **Document type:** *Journal, Academic/Scholarly.* **Description:** Contains articles on international economics; emphasis on empirical research and study of national policies.
Formerly: Weltwirtschaftliches Archiv (0043-2636)
Related titles: Online - full text ed.: ISSN 1610-2886 (from EBSCO Publishing, Springer LINK).
Indexed: APEL, ASCA, BAS, BPIA, BibInd, BusI, CREJ, CurCont, DIP, IBR, IBSS, IBZ, ILD, JEL, KES, PAIS, PCI, RASB, RefZh, SCIMP, SSCI, T&II.
—BLDSC (9295.050000), IDS, IE, Infotrieve. **CCC.**
Published by: (Institut fuer Weltwirtschaft Kiel), Springer-Verlag (Subsidiary of: Springer Science+Business Media), Tiergartenstr 17, Heidelberg, 69121, Germany. TEL 49-6221-3450, FAX 49-6221-345229. Ed. Horst Siebert. Adv. contact Stephan Kroeck TEL 49-30-827875739. Circ: 1,800. **Subscr. in the Americas to:** Springer-Verlag New York, Inc., Journal Fulfillment, PO Box 2485, Secaucus, NJ 07096-2485. TEL 800-777-4643, 201-348-4033, FAX 201-348-4505, journals@springer-ny.com, http://www.springer-ny.com; **Subscr. to:** Springer GmbH Auslieferungsgesellschaft, Haberstr 7, Heidelberg 69126, Germany. TEL 49-6221-345-0, FAX 49-6221-345-4229, subscriptions@springer.de.

330 300 ARG ISSN 0328-2058
HC171
REVISTA ARGENTINA DE ECONOMIA Y CIENCIAS SOCIALES. Text in Spanish. 1994. 3/yr. **Document type:** *Academic/Scholarly.*

Published by: Universidad de Buenos Aires, Montaneses, 2958 5o A, Capital Federal, Buenos Aires 1429, Argentina.

330 BRA ISSN 0034-7140
HB9
REVISTA BRASILEIRA DE ECONOMIA. Text in Portuguese. 1947. q. USD 90 (effective 2001). adv. bk.rev. bibl.; stat. **Document type:** *Magazine, Academic/Scholarly.* **Description:** Reports on the national economic performance and the development of international economic thought.
Related titles: Online - full text ed.: free (effective 2005).
Indexed: HAPI, IBR, IBSS, ILD, JEL, PAIS, RASB, RRTA, SSCI, WAE&RSA.
—IE, Infotrieve.
Published by: (Escola de Pos-Graduacao em Economia), Fundacao Getulio Vargas, 190 Praia de Botafogo, Rio de Janeiro, RJ 22253-53-900, Brazil. TEL 55-21-2559-5544, FAX 55-21-2559-5541, assine@fgv.br, http://www.fgv.br/editora/. Ed. Joao Victor Jrisler. Adv. contact Else Flejlau. Circ: 1,500.

338 332.6 BRA ISSN 0102-9797
HG4503
REVISTA BRASILEIRA DE MERCADO DE CAPITAIS. Text in Portuguese. 1974. q. BRL 210, USD 21. adv. bk.rev. charts; illus.; stat. index.
Indexed: PAIS.
Published by: Instituto Brasileiro de Mercado de Capitais, Av Rio Branco, 108 Andar 2, Centro, Rio De Janeiro, RJ 20040-001, Brazil. TEL 242-6646. Ed. Joao Luiz Mascolo. Circ: 2,500.

330 658.5 BRA ISSN 0104-1029
HC186
REVISTA C N I. Text in Portuguese. 1968. q. free. adv. charts; illus.; pat.; stat. **Description:** Covers Brazilian industry, economics and related themes.
Former titles (until 1991): Industria e Produtividade (0019-7718); Desenvolvimento e Conjuntura
—BLDSC (3287.311540), CINDOC.
Published by: Confederacao Nacional da Industria, Av. Nilo Pecanha, 50, Gr. 2608, Rio De Janeiro, RJ 20044-900, Brazil. TEL 532-0330. Ed. Fernando Luz. Circ: 16,000.

330 PRT
REVISTA DAS EMPRESAS. Text in Portuguese. 12/yr.
Address: Rua Francisco Rodrigues Lobo, 2 r-c Dto, Lisbon, 1000, Portugal. TEL 659950, FAX 65-14-30. Ed. Jose Nunes Pereira. Circ: 18,000.

330 ESP ISSN 1138-2333
➤ **REVISTA DE ANTIGUOS ALUMNOS.** Text in Spanish, English. 4/yr. free to qualified personnel (effective 2005). adv. bk.rev. abstr.; bibl.; charts; illus.; maps. **Document type:** *Magazine, Academic/Scholarly.*
Former titles (until 1997): I E S E Revista de Antiguos (1133-4029); (until 1988): Boletin de Antiguos (1133-4037); (until 1974): I E S E Boletin de Antiguos (1133-4045)
Related titles: CD-ROM ed.; Online - full content ed.
Published by: (Universidad de Navarra, Instituto de Estudios Superiores de la Empresa), Estudios y Ediciones I E S E S.L., Juan de Alos 43, Barcelona, 08034, Spain. TEL 34-3-2534200, FAX 34-3-2534343, TELEX 50824 IESB E, http://www.ee-iese.com/, http://www.iese.edu. Ed., R&P Mercedes Castello. Adv. contact Antonio More. B&W page EUR 2,908, color page EUR 4,720; trim 275 x 185. Circ: 20,686 (controlled).

330 BRA ISSN 0556-5782
HB9
➤ **REVISTA DE ECONOMIA.** Text in Portuguese. 1960. a. **Document type:** *Academic/Scholarly.*
Published by: Universidade Federal do Parana, Faculdade de Economia e Administracao, Rua Doutor Faivre, 405, Centro, Curitiba, PR 80060-140, Brazil. TEL 55-041-3605231, FAX 55-041-2632341. Eds. Huascar Pessali, Ramon Garcia Fernandez. Circ: 500.

330 BRA ISSN 1413-8050
HC186
REVISTA DE ECONOMIA APLICADA/BRAZILIAN JOURNAL OF APPLIED ECONOMICS. Text in Portuguese. 1996. q. **Document type:** *Journal.*
Indexed: JEL.
Published by: (Universidade de Sao Paulo, Faculdade de Economia e Administracao), Fundacao Instituto de Pesquisas Economicas, Departamento de Publicacoes, Av. Prof. Luciano Gualberto, 908, FEA II, 2 andar, Cidade Universitaria, Sao Paulo, SP 05508-900, Brazil. TEL 55-11-38186071, FAX 55-11-38186073, revecap@fipe.com, http://www.fipe.com/publicacoes/Aplicada/entrada.asp. Ed. Carlos R. Azzoni.

330 ESP ISSN 1133-455X
REVISTA DE ECONOMIA APLICADA. Text in Spanish. 1993. 3/yr., latest no.25, 2001. back issues avail. **Document type:** *Academic/Scholarly.* **Description:** Contains papers on applied economics.
Indexed: JEL.
—CINDOC.
Published by: Universidad de Zaragoza, Facultad de Ciencias Economicas, Departamento de Estructura Economica y Economia Publica, Gran Via 2, Zaragoza, 50005, Spain. TEL 34-976-761841, FAX 34-976-761840, rea@posta.unizar.es, http://www.revecap.com/ingles/principal.html.

330 COL ISSN 0123-5362
HC196
➤ **REVISTA DE ECONOMIA DEL ROSARIO.** Text and summaries in Spanish, English. 1998. s-a. looseleaf. COP 20,000 domestic; USD 10 foreign (effective 2004). Index. back issues avail. **Document type:** *Journal, Academic/Scholarly.* **Description:** Publishes theoretical, empirical, applied or policy oriented papers in all fields of economics.
Related titles: Online - full text ed.
Indexed: JEL.
Published by: Universidad del Rosario, Centro Editorial Rosarista, Calle 14 6-25, Bogota, Colombia. TEL 57-1-2970200, FAX 57-1-3445763, revecono@urosario.edu.co, http://economia.urosario.edu.co/investigacion/revista/revista.htm. Ed. Jesus Otero. Pub., R&P Juan F Cordoba. Circ: 300.

330 COL ISSN 0124-5996
HB99.5
➤ **REVISTA DE ECONOMIA INSTITUCIONAL**; revista de la facultad de economia. Variant title: Economia Institucional. Text in Spanish. 1999. s-a. COP 30,000 domestic; USD 39 foreign (effective 2005). adv. bk.rev. abstr.; charts; bibl.; illus.; maps; stat. reprints avail. **Document type:** *Journal, Academic/Scholarly.* **Description:** Combines translations of foreign works with Latinamerican and Colombian articles on institutional economics. Treats topics of public economics, ethics, economic analysis of law, regulatory theory, and economic history.
Related titles: Online - full text ed.
Indexed: IBSS, JEL, PSA, SociolAb.
Published by: Universidad Externado de Colombia, Departamento de Publicaciones, Calle 12, No 0-38 Este, Apartado Aereo 034141, Santafe de Bogota, Colombia. ecoinstitucional@uexternado.edu.co, publicaciones@uexternado.edu.co, http://www.uexternado.edu.co. Ed. Alberto Supelano. Pub. Antonio Milla. R&P, Adv. contact Carolina Esguerra. Circ: 400 (paid); 600 (controlled).

330 BRA ISSN 1678-5002
▼ ➤ **REVISTA DE ECONOMIA MACKENZIE.** Contents page in Portuguese; Abstracts in English, Portuguese. 2003. s-a. free (effective 2005). **Document type:** *Journal, Academic/Scholarly.*
Published by: Universidade Presbiteriana Mackenzie (Subsidiary of: Instituto Presbiteriano Mackenzie), Rua da Consolacao 896, Pr.2, Sao Paulo-SP, SP 01302-907, Brazil. FAX 55-11-32368302, biblio.per@mackenzie.br, http://www.mackenzie.com.br. Ed., R&P Mr. Leonardo F. Cruz Basso.

330 310 ARG ISSN 0034-8066
HB9
REVISTA DE ECONOMIA Y ESTADISTICA. Text in Spanish. 1939. irreg. exchange basis. bk.rev. bibl.; charts. **Document type:** *Academic/Scholarly.*
Indexed: IBSS, JEL, PAIS.
Published by: Universidad Nacional de Cordoba, Facultad de Ciencias Economicas, Ciudad Universitaria, Ave. Valparaiso, s/n, Cordoba, 5000, Argentina.

330 PAN
REVISTA DE INVESTIGACIONES ECONOMICAS. Text in Spanish. a.?.
Published by: Universidad de Panama, Centro de Investigacion Facultad de Economia, Estafeta Universitaria, Panama City, Panama. TEL 23-0819.

REVISTA DEL DERECHO INDUSTRIAL. see *LAW*

330 VEN ISSN 1315-2467
REVISTA ECONOMIA; nueva etapa. Text in Spanish. 1961-1975; resumed 1987. a. USD 10. **Document type:** *Academic/Scholarly.* **Description:** Covers scientific articles in the field of economics; includes statistics, administration, accounting and computer science.
Formerly: Economia (0070-8399)
Related titles: Online - full text ed.
Published by: Universidad de Los Andes, Facultad de Economia IIES, Edf. B, 1r, La Hechicera, Merida 5101, Venezuela. TEL 074-401081, FAX 074-401120. Circ: 500.

330 ARG
REVISTA ECONOMICA (BUENOS AIRES); industrial, comercial y financiera. Text in Spanish. 1985. m. ARS 20 domestic; USD 100 in Europe. illus.
Formerly: Revista Economica y Politica
Published by: Prensa Argentina S.R.L., Pinchincha 364, 1o B, Buenos Aires, Argentina. TEL 54-114-9527835, FAX 54-114-9542723. Ed. Luis A Pineiro. Pub. Juan Luis Rechax.

330 ARG ISSN 0013-0419
REVISTA ECONOMICA (LA PLATA). Text in Spanish; Summaries in English, Spanish. 1954. 2/yr. ARS 30 domestic; USD 35 in South America; USD 40 in Europe. adv. bk.rev. bibl.; charts. **Document type:** *Academic/Scholarly.*
Indexed: IBR, IBSS, IBZ, IPSA, JEL.
Published by: Universidad Nacional de la Plata, Instituto de Investigaciones Administrativas, Calle 48, 555, Casilla de Correos 376, La Plata, Buenos Aires 1900, Argentina. TEL 54-221-4229383. Ed. Mario L Szychowski. Circ: 1,000 (controlled).

332 ECU ISSN 1016-7994
REVISTA ECUATORIANA DE HISTORIA ECONOMICA. Text in Spanish. 1987. s-a. USD 20. **Description:** Contains studies of economic history related to Ecuador, the Andean region and South America, as well as methodological contributions to economic history from other areas.
Published by: Banco Central del Ecuador, Avenida 10 de Agosto y Briceno, Quito, Ecuador. TEL 593-2-2580158, uweb@uio.bce.fin.ec, http://www.bce.fin.ec. Ed. Carlos Marchan Romero. Circ: 2,000.

330 ESP ISSN 0210-1025
REVISTA ESPANOLA DE ECONOMIA. Text in Spanish. 1971. s-a. bk.rev. stat. **Document type:** *Journal, Academic/Scholarly.*
Related titles: Online - full text ed.
Indexed: JEL, PCI.
—CINDOC, IE.
Published by: Instituto de Estudios Fiscales, Avda Cardenal Herrera Oria, 378, Madrid, 28035, Spain. TEL 34-91-3398800, FAX 34-91-3398964. Circ: 2,000. **Subscr. to:** Ministerio de Economia y Hacienda, Centro de Publicaciones, Pz Campillo del Mundo Nuevo, 3, Madrid 28005, Spain. TEL 91-527-1437.

REVISTA JURIDICA DE ECONOMIA PUBLICA, SOCIAL Y COOPERATIVA. see *LAW*

330 PRT
REVISTA NEGOCIOS. Text in Portuguese. m.
Address: Rua do Norte 14-1o, Lisbon, 1200, Portugal. TEL 1-3469550, FAX 3475254. Ed. J Gomes Motta. Circ: 10,000.

330 MAR ISSN 0851-0431
K13
REVUE DE DROIT ET D'ECONOMIE. Text in French. 1985. s-a.
Published by: Universite Sidi Mohamed Ben Abdellah, Dhar El Mahraz, B P 42, Fes, Morocco.

330 FRA ISSN 1145-1378
HC271
REVUE DE L'INSTITUT DE RECHERCHES ECONOMIQUES ET SOCIALES. Abbreviated title: La Revue de l'I R E S. Text in French. 1984. 3/yr.
Formerly (until 1989): Note de l'Institut de Recherches Economiques et Sociales (0762-7238)
Related titles: Online - full text ed.: (from ProQuest Information & Learning).
Indexed: ABIn.
Published by: Institut de Recherches Economiques et Sociales, 16 Boulevard du Mont d'Est, 9ieme etage, Noisy-le-Grand, France. TEL 33-1-4815-1922, info@ires-fr.org, http://www.ires-fr.org/files/publications/revue/revueires.htm, http://www.ires-fr.org/files/ires/IRES.htm.

330 FRA ISSN 1265-9576
HC271
REVUE DE L'O F C E; observations et diagnostics economiques. (Observatoire Francais des Conjonctures Economiques) Text in French; Summaries in English, French. 1982. 4/yr. EUR 54 domestic to individuals; EUR 64 foreign to individuals; EUR 82 domestic to institutions; EUR 92 foreign to institutions; EUR 42 domestic to students (effective 2005).
Formerly: Observations et Diagnostics Economiques (0751-6614)
Indexed: ELLIS, IBSS, IPSA, JEL, PAIS.
—**CCC.**
Published by: (Observatoire Francais des Conjonctures Economiques), Presses de Sciences Po, 44 rue du Four, Paris, 75006, France. TEL 33-01-44393960, FAX 33-01-45480441, info@presses.sciences-po.fr, http://www.sciences-po.fr.

330 FRA ISSN 0373-2630
REVUE D'ECONOMIE POLITIQUE. Text in French. 1887. bi-m. EUR 135 (effective 2005). bk.rev. charts. reprint service avail. from SCH. **Document type:** *Trade.*
Indexed: AmH&L, BibInd, HistAb, IBR, IBSS, ILD, JEL, KES, PAIS, PCI, RASB.
—BLDSC (7898.770000), CISTI, IE, Infotrieve, ingenta. **CCC.**
Published by: Editions Dalloz Sirey, 31-35 rue Froidevaux, Paris, Cedex 14 75685, France. TEL 33-1-40645353, FAX 33-1-40645471. Ed. Henri Guitton. Circ: 2,000.

330 FRA ISSN 0035-2764
HB3
REVUE ECONOMIQUE. Text in French; Summaries in English, French. 1950. bi-m. EUR 79 domestic to individuals; EUR 91 foreign to individuals; EUR 127 domestic to institutions; EUR 137 foreign to institutions; EUR 58 domestic to students; EUR 21 newsstand/cover (effective 2005). adv. bk.rev. bibl.; charts. index, cum.index every 10 yrs. reprint service avail. from SCH.
Indexed: AmH&L, CISA, HistAb, IBSS, ILD, IPSA, JEL, PAIS, PCI, RASB, SSCI.
—BLDSC (7898.785000), IDS, IE, Infotrieve, ingenta. **CCC.**

Published by: Presses de Sciences Po, 44 rue du Four, Paris, 75006, France. TEL 33-01-44393960, FAX 33-01-45480441, info@presses.sciences-po.fr, http://www.sciences-po.fr/edition/revues/revuec.html. Ed. Jeanne Marie Parly. Circ: 1,850.

330 FRA ISSN 0255-0830
REVUE ECONOMIQUE DE L'O C D E. Text in French. s-a. EUR 97, USD 111, GBP 63, JPY 13,100 (effective 2005).
Related titles: Online - full text ed.: ISSN 1684-3444. EUR 68, USD 78, GBP 46, JPY 9,200 (effective 2005) (from EBSCO Publishing, Gale Group, IngentaConnect, Swets Information Services); ♦ French ed.: O E C D Economic Studies. ISSN 0255-0822.
—CISTI.
Published by: Organization for Economic Cooperation and Development, 2 Rue Andre Pascal, Paris, 75775 Cedex 16, France. TEL 33-1-45248200, FAX 33-1-45248500, http://www.oecd.org.

330 300 CHE ISSN 0035-2772
HB3
REVUE ECONOMIQUE ET SOCIALE. Text in French. 1943. 4/yr. CHF 65 domestic; CHF 80 foreign (effective 2000 & 2001). adv. bk.rev. bibl.; charts. index, cum.index. back issues avail.; reprint service avail. from SCH. **Document type:** *Journal, Academic/Scholarly.*
Indexed: ELLIS, IBSS, ILD, IPSA, KES, PAIS, RASB.
—BLDSC (7898.790000), IE, Infotrieve, ingenta.
Published by: Societe d'Etudes Economiques et Sociales, B F S H 1, Dorigny, 1015, Switzerland. TEL 41-21-6915347, FAX 41-21-6923385, infosees@hec.unil.ch, http://inforge.unil.ch/sees. Ed., R&P Kaj Noschis. Adv. contact Marja Montserrat. Circ: 1,200.

330 FRA ISSN 0035-2780
REVUE ECONOMIQUE FRANCAISE. Text in French. 1878. q. bk.rev. bibl.
Indexed: PAIS, PCI, RASB.
Published by: Societe de Geographie Humaine de Paris, 8 rue Roquepine, Paris, 75008, France. Ed. Pierre Gosselin. Circ: 1,100.

REVUE INTERNATIONALE DE DROIT ECONOMIQUE; lieu de rencontre international entre juristes et economistes. see *LAW*

330 ROM ISSN 1220-5397
HC407.R8
REVUE ROUMAINE DE SCIENCES ECONOMIQUES. Text in English, French, Russian. 1956. 2/yr. bk.rev. bibl.; charts; stat. reprint service avail. from SCH.
Formerly (until 1989): Revue Roumaine des Sciences Sociales. Serie de Sciences Economiques (0035-404X); Which superseded in part (in 1964): Revue des Sciences Sociales (0484-8640)
Related titles: Online - full text ed.
Indexed: AmH&L, HistAb, IBSS, JEL, PAIS, RASB.
—KNAW.
Published by: (Academia Romana), Editura Academiei Romane/Publishing House of the Romanian Academy, Calea 13 Septembrie 13, Sector 5, Bucharest, 76117, Romania. TEL 40-21-4119008, FAX 40-21-4103983, edacad@ear.ro. Ed. N N Constantinescu. **Dist. by:** Rodipet S.A., Piata Presei Libere 1, sector 1, PO Box 33-57, Bucharest 3, Romania. TEL 40-21-2224126, 40-21-2226407, rodipet@rodipet.ro.

330 USA ISSN 0889-3357
THE RICHMOND BUSINESS JOURNAL. Text in English. 1986. w. USD 29 (effective 2003).
Related titles: Online - full text ed.: (from ProQuest Information & Learning).
Published by: Inside Business, 1901 E Franklin St, Ste 105, Richmond, VA 23223. TEL 804-343-4008, FAX 804-343-3358, http://www.richmond.com/insidebusiness.

RICHMOND JOURNAL OF GLOBAL LAW AND BUSINESS. see *LAW*

330 BEL
RIJKSUNIVERSITEIT TE GENT. FACULTEIT VAN DE ECONOMISCHE WETENSCHAPPEN. WERKEN. Text in Dutch. irreg.
Published by: Rijksuniversiteit te Gent, Faculteit van de Economische Wetenschappen, Hoveniersberg 4, Ghent, 9000, Belgium. Eds. E de Lembre, W Georges.

330 JPN
➤ **RIKKYO ECONOMIC REVIEW.** Text in Japanese. 1938. q. JPY 2,000, USD 20 (effective 2000 - 2001). bk.rev. **Document type:** *Academic/Scholarly.* **Description:** Features economic history, history of economic thought, Keynesian and Markian economics, and Japanese management.
Formerly (until 1987): St. Paul's Economic Review - Rikkyo Keizaigaku Kenkyu (0035-5356)
Indexed: AmH&L, HistAb.
—BLDSC (7971.448100).
Published by: (Rikkyo Keizaigaku Kenkyukai), Rikkyo Daigaku Keizaigaku Kenkyukai/Economic Society of Rikkyo University, Nishi-Ikebukuro, Toshima-ku, Tokyo, 171-0021, Japan. TEL 81-3-3985-2327, FAX 81-3-3985-4096, rikkyoec@rikkyo.ac.jp. Ed. Kaguhiko Kitagawa. Circ: 4,000.

669 338.476 GBR
RINGSIDER. Text in English. 3/yr. free. adv. **Document type:** *Magazine, Trade.* **Description:** Covers international metals business.
Published by: (London Metal Exchange), Highbury Customer Publications, The Publishing House, 1-3 Highbury Station Rd, London, N1 1SE, United Kingdom. TEL 44-20-226-2222, FAX 44-20-77040758, customerpublishing@hhc.co.uk, http://www.hhc.co.uk/pages/show/entry_Level/2/entry_code/HCU/single_record_flag/106. Ed. Steve Handley. Adv. contact Jim Sturrock. Circ: 10,000.

330 GBR
RISK AND REGULATION. Text in English. 2001. s-a. back issues avail. **Document type:** *Magazine, Academic/Scholarly.*
Published by: London School of Economics and Political Science, Centre for Analysis of Risk and Regulation, Houghton Street, London, WC12A 2AE, United Kingdom. TEL 44-20-79556577, FAX 44-20-79556578, risk@lse.ac.uk, http://www.lse.ac.uk/depts/carr/RiskRegulation.htm.

330 JPN ISSN 0288-0180
HB9
RITSUMEIKAN KEIZAIGAKU/RITSUMEIKAN ECONOMIC REVIEW. Text in Japanese. 1952. bi-m. JPY 500 per issue. **Document type:** *Academic/Scholarly.*
—BLDSC (7976.350000).
Published by: Ritsumeikan Daigaku, Keizai Gakkai/Ritsumeikan University, Economic Society, 1-1-1 Noji-Higashi, Kusatsu-shi, Shiga-ken 525-0058, Japan. TEL 81-77-561-3945, FAX 81-75-561-3955. Ed. Hiroshi Yamada.

330 346 ITA ISSN 0485-2281
RIVISTA DEI DOTTORI COMMERCIALISTI. Text in Italian. 1949. bi-m. EUR 98.13 in the European Union; EUR 147.19 elsewhere (effective 2002). **Description:** Contributes to the development of the study of business economics, law and finance.
Related titles: CD-ROM ed.: ISSN 1593-5817.
—IE.
Published by: (Ordine del Dottori Commercialisti di Milano), Casa Editrice Dott. A. Giuffre (Subsidiary of: LexisNexis Europe and Africa), Via Busto Arsizio, 40, Milan, MI 20151, Italy. TEL 39-02-28089200, FAX 39-02-38009582, giuffre@giuffre.it, http://www.giuffre.it. Ed. Angelo Provasoli. Circ: 6,700.

330 ITA ISSN 0035-6468
RIVISTA DI POLITICA ECONOMICA. Text in Italian. 1911. bi-m. EUR 120 domestic; EUR 145 foreign (effective 2005); includes supplement. bk.rev. charts. cum.index: 1911-1970, 1981-1990. back issues avail. **Document type:** *Journal, Academic/Scholarly.*
Related titles: ♦ Supplement(s): Rivista di Politica Economica. Selected Papers. ISSN 0391-6170.
Indexed: BAS, DIP, ELLIS, IBR, IBZ, JEL, PAIS, RRTA, WAE&RSA.
Published by: Servizio Italiano Pubblicazioni Internazionali, Viale Pasteur 6, Rome, 00144, Italy. TEL 39-06-5903601, FAX 39-06-5903339, http://www.rivistapoliticaeconomica.it. Ed. Mario Baldassarri. Circ: 1,000.

330 ITA ISSN 0391-6170
HB7
RIVISTA DI POLITICA ECONOMICA. SELECTED PAPERS. Text in Italian. 1946. bi-m. Included in Rivista di Politica Economica.. **Document type:** *Journal, Academic/Scholarly.*
Related titles: ♦ Supplement to: Rivista di Politica Economica. ISSN 0035-6468.
Indexed: IBSS, JEL, PAIS, RASB.
—BLDSC (7992.730000), IE, Infotrieve, ingenta.
Published by: Servizio Italiano Pubblicazioni Internazionali, Viale Pasteur 6, Rome, 00144, Italy. TEL 39-06-5903601, FAX 39-06-5903339, http://www.rivistapoliticaeconomica.it.

330 ITA ISSN 1120-9534
HC307.S69
RIVISTA ECONOMICA DEL MEZZOGIORNO; trimestrale della Svimez. Text in Italian. 1987. q. EUR 56 domestic to individuals; EUR 85 foreign to individuals; EUR 105 domestic to institutions print & online eds.; EUR 136 foreign to institutions print & online eds. (effective 2004). adv. index. back issues avail. **Document type:** *Academic/Scholarly.*
Related titles: Online - full text ed.
Published by: (Associazione per lo Sviluppo dell'Industria nel Mezzogiorno), Societa Editrice Il Mulino, Strada Maggiore 37, Bologna, 40125, Italy. TEL 39-051-256011, FAX 39-051-256034, riviste@mulino.it, http://www.mulino.it. Ed. Salvatore Cafiero. Adv. contact M Luisa Vezzali. Circ: 1,300.

330 380 ITA ISSN 0035-6751
H7
RIVISTA INTERNAZIONALE DI SCIENZE ECONOMICHE E COMMERCIALI. Abbreviated title: R.I.S.E.C. Text in English, French, German, Italian. 1954. 3/yr. EUR 115 domestic; EUR 175 foreign (effective 2004). adv. bk.rev. charts; illus. index. **Document type:** *Journal, Academic/Scholarly.* **Description:** Publishes original essays in doctrine, method, economic theory, finance, marketing, budgeting, politics and labor.
Indexed: BAS, CPM, CurCont, DIP, ELLIS, IBR, IBSS, IBZ, IPSA, JEL, PAIS, PCI, RASB, SSCI, WAE&RSA.
—BLDSC (7987.150000), IE, Infotrieve, ingenta.

Published by: C E D A M, Via Giuseppe Jappelli 5-6, Padua, PD 35121, Italy. TEL 39-049-8239111, FAX 39-049-8752900, info@cedam.com, http://www.cedam.com. Ed. Aldo Montesano. Circ: 1,200.

330 ITA ISSN 1593-8662
HB7
RIVISTA ITALIANA DEGLI ECONOMISTI. Text in Italian. 1996. 3/yr. EUR 55 domestic to individuals; EUR 84 foreign to individuals; EUR 99 domestic to institutions print & online eds.; EUR 135 foreign to institutions print & online eds. (effective 2004). back issues avail. **Document type:** *Academic/Scholarly.* **Description:** Publishes research and commentary of interest to economists.
Related titles: Online - full text ed.
Indexed: JEL.
Published by: Societa Editrice Il Mulino, Strada Maggiore 37, Bologna, 40125, Italy. TEL 39-051-256011, FAX 39-051-256034, riviste@mulino.it, http://www.mulino.it.

330 ITA ISSN 1593-9154
RIVISTA ITALIANA DI RAGIONERIA E DI ECONOMIA AZIENDALE. Text in Italian. 1901. m. **Description:** Provides information on accounting, economics and business economics.
Former titles (until 1971): Rivista Italiana di Ragioneria (1593-9146); (until 1908): Collegio dei Ragionieri di Roma. Rivista di Ragioneria (1593-9138)
Published by: R I R E A di Nobile Giovanna, Via Delle Isole, 30, Rome, RM 00198, Italy. TEL 39-6-8417690, FAX 39-6-8845732.

RIVISTA TRIMESTRALE DEGLI APPALTI; rivista di dottrina-legislazione-giurisprudenza. see *LAW—Corporate Law*

330 CZE ISSN 1212-4869
ROCENKA H N. (Hospodarskych Novin) Text in Czech. 1997. a. CZK 290 newsstand/cover (effective 2003). **Document type:** *Magazine, Trade.*
Published by: Economia a.s., Dobrovskeho 25, Prague 7 7, 170 55, Czech Republic. TEL 420-2-33071111, FAX 420-2-33072003, economia@economia.cz, http://www.economia.cz.

330 USA
ROCHESTER BUSINESS★. Text in English. 1984. m. USD 19.95. adv. bk.rev.
Address: 131 Eastman Est, Rochester, NY 14622-1747. TEL 716-458-8280, FAX 716-458-9831. Ed. Kristina Hutch. Pub. Joseph Julian. Circ: 11,000.

330 ROM
ROMANIA: ECONOMIC HIGHLIGHTS. Text in English. 1976 (vol.27). w. USD 205 for 6 mos.. **Document type:** *Bulletin.*
Formerly (until 1990): Romania: Articles - Features - Information (1016-250X)
Indexed: AmH&L.
Published by: Rompres the National Press Agency, Piata Presei Libere 1, Bucharest, 71341, Romania. TEL 2223233, FAX 2230089. Ed. Monica Mariana Grigorescu.

330 ROM ISSN 1223-6837
ROMANIAN BUSINESS JOURNAL. Text in English. 1994. w. ROL 120 domestic; EUR 180, USD 180 foreign (effective 2004).
Published by: Penta, Piata Presei Libere, No. 1,Corp C3, Etj. 3, cam. 317 - 321, Sector 1, OP 33, CP 32, Bucharest, Romania. TEL 40-21-2246897, http://rbj.euroweb.ro.

330 ROM
ROMANIAN BUSINESS NEWS. Text in Romanian. 1993. m. (11/yr.). ROL 100; USD 185 foreign. adv. **Document type:** *Newsletter.* **Description:** Provides an overview of the economy. Interprets current economic events, the stock exchange, general and regional news, and statistical information.
Related titles: Supplement(s): Romanian Financial and Banking News.
Published by: Cosmos Development, PO Box 22-256, Bucharest, Romania. TEL 401-6502504. Ed. Andreas Tsantis. Circ: 650 (paid). **Subscr. outside Romania to:** Cosmos Inc., P O Box 30437, Bethesda, MD 20824. TEL 301-229-5875, 301-229-5876.

330 DNK ISSN 0105-8827
ROSKILDE UNIVERSITETSCENTER. INSTITUT FOR SAMFUNDSOEKONOMI OG PLANLAEGNING. RESEARCH REPORT. Text in Danish. 1981. irreg. free.
Published by: Roskilde Universitetscenter, Institut for Samfundsoekonomi og Planlaegning, Institut VIII, Post Box 260, Roskilde, 4000, Denmark.

330 RUS ISSN 0869-5202
ROSSIISKII EKONOMICHESKII ZHURNAL. Text in Russian. 1958. m. USD 99.95 (effective 2000). adv. bk.rev. index. **Description:** Covers economic systems and theories, as well as Russian economic problems and reforms.
Formerly (until 1992): Ekonomicheskie Nauk (0130-9757)
Related titles: Microfiche ed.: (from EVP).
Indexed: IBSS, ILD, RASB, RRTA, RefZh, TriticAb, WAE&RSA, WBSS.
—East View.

Published by: Finansy i Statistika, Ryazanskii pr-t 99, Moscow, 109542, Russian Federation. TEL 7-095-3772556, FAX 7-095-3772556, rem@mail.magelan.ru, http://www.magelan.ru/~rem. Ed. A Yu. Melent'ev. Circ: 23,600. **US dist. addr.:** East View Information Services, 3020 Harbor Ln. N., Minneapolis, MN 55447. TEL 612-550-0961.

ROSSIISKII FOND FUNDAMENTAL'NYKH ISSLEDOVANII. INFORMATSIONNYI BULLETIN. see *SCIENCES: COMPREHENSIVE WORKS*

330 RUS ISSN 1605-8070
Q179.9
ROSSIISKII FOND FUNDAMENTAL'NYKH ISSLEDOVANII. VESTNIK. Text in Russian, English; Contents page in Russian. 1994. q. USD 100 (effective 2001). **Document type:** *Journal.* **Description:** Contains analytical reviews, official documents, popular scientific articels and other information in all of the natural sciences.
Indexed: RASB.
Published by: Rossiiskii Fond Fundamental'nykh Issledovanii, Leninskii pr-t 32-a, Moscow, 117334, Russian Federation. TEL 7-095-9385417, FAX 7-095-9381931, novikov@rfbr.ru, http://www.rfbr.ru. Ed. M V Alfimov. **US dist. addr.:** East View Information Services, 3020 Harbor Ln. N., Minneapolis, MN 55447. TEL 612-550-0961.

330 RUS
ROSSIISKII FONDOVYI RYNOK. Text in Russian. 2/w.
Published by: A.K. & M., Ul Gubkina 35, Moscow, 117924, Russian Federation. TEL 7-095-1326130, FAX 7-095-1326026. **US dist. addr.:** East View Information Services, 3020 Harbor Ln. N., Minneapolis, MN 55447. TEL 612-550-0961.

ROSSIYA. see *CHILDREN AND YOUTH—For*

330 RUS ISSN 0868-5789
ROSSIYA MOLODAYA. Text in Russian. m. USD 99.95 in United States.
Indexed: RASB.
—East View.
Address: Ul Noril'skaya 36, Moscow, 129336, Russian Federation. TEL 7-095-4758274. Ed. A Dmitriev. **US dist. addr.:** East View Information Services, 3020 Harbor Ln. N., Minneapolis, MN 55447. TEL 612-550-0961.

330 RUS ISSN 0869-8503
DK510.76
ROSSIYA XXI. Text in Russian. bi-m.
—East View.
Published by: Korporatsiya Eksperimental'nyi Tvorcheskii Tsentr, Sadovaya-Kudrinskaya 22, Moscow, 103001, Russian Federation. TEL 7-095-2022831, FAX 7-095-2001754. Ed. M M Gorinov. **US dist. addr.:** East View Information Services, 3020 Harbor Ln. N., Minneapolis, MN 55447. TEL 612-550-0961.

330 AUS
ROY MORGAN RETAIL MONITOR. Text in English. q. **Document type:** *Consumer.* **Description:** Provides information on the non-grocery retail market.
Published by: Roy Morgan Research, PO Box 2282 U, Melbourne, VIC 3001, Australia. TEL 61-3-96296888, FAX 61-3-96291250, http://www.roymorgan.com. Ed. Norman Woodcock.

ROY MORGAN SUPERMARKET MONITOR. see *FOOD AND FOOD INDUSTRIES—Grocery Trade*

650 AUS
ROYAL MELBOURNE INSTITUTE OF TECHNOLOGY. FACULTY OF BUSINESS. WORKING PAPER SERIES. Text in English. irreg.
Related titles: Online - full text ed.
Published by: Royal Melbourne Institute of Technology, Faculty of Business, PO Box 2476V, Melbourne, VIC 3001, Australia. TEL 61-3-9925-5555, FAX 61-3-9925-5624, http://www.bf.rmit.edu.au/RDU/staffinfo/wkg_paper.html.

RUCH PRAWNICZY, EKONOMICZNY I SOCJOLOGICZNY. see *LAW*

174.4 USA
➤ **RUFFIN SERIES IN BUSINESS ETHICS.** Text in English. biennial. USD 20 per vol. to individuals; USD 40 per vol. to institutions (effective 2004). **Document type:** *Monographic series, Academic/Scholarly.* **Description:** Contain a selection of the papers presented at the Ruffin Lectures in Business Ethics.
Related titles: Online - full text ed.
Published by: (Sociedade Brasileira de Engenharia Biomedica BRA), Philosophy Documentation Center, PO Box 7147, Charlottesville, VA 22906-7147. TEL 434-220-3300, 800-444-2419, FAX 434-220-3301, order@pdcnet.org, http://www.pdcnet.org/ruffin.html. Ed. R Edward Freeman. R&P George Leaman. **Co-sponsors:** Ruffin Foundation; University of Virginia, Olsson Center of Applied Ethics.

630.994 AUS ISSN 1039-3897
RURAL BUSINESS. Text in English. 1982. m. AUD 68.20 (effective 2001). adv. bk.rev. back issues avail. **Document type:** *Trade.* **Description:** News and information for the farm service industry.
Former titles (until 1992): Milne's Rural Business (1037-387X); (until 1991): Rural Business (1032-3872); (until 1989): Rural Business Magazine (1031-3079); (until 1988): Rural Merchant Magazine (0729-5588)
Published by: Richard Milne Pty. Ltd., PO Box 163, Drummoyne, NSW 1470, Australia. TEL 61-2-97139822, FAX 61-2-97139266, milnepublications@attglobal.net. Ed. Harry Dillon. Adv. contact Rex Holyoake. Circ: 3,221.

330 GBR
RURAL ECONOMICS SERIES. Text in English. irreg. price varies. **Document type:** *Monographic series, Academic/Scholarly.*
—BLDSC (8052.434050).
Published by: University of Cambridge, Department of Land Economy, 19 Silver St, Cambridge, Cambs CB3 9EP, United Kingdom. TEL 44-1223-337147, FAX 44-1223-337130.

RUSSIA ONLINE AND WIRELESS. see *COMMUNICATIONS—Computer Applications*

330 RUS
RUSSIAN BUSINESS MAGAZINE. Text in English. bi-m. USD 95 in United States.
Published by: Vystavochno-Ekspertno-Marketingovaya i Zakupochnaya Programma: Luchshie Tovary i Uslugina Rynkakh Rossii, Bersenevskaya nab 20-2, Moscow, 103790, Russian Federation. TEL 7-095-2386486, FAX 7-095-2301419. Ed. V Ksionzhek. **US dist. addr.:** East View Information Services, 3020 Harbor Ln. N., Minneapolis, MN 55447. TEL 612-550-0961.

330 RUS ISSN 1608-3547
RUSSIAN BUSINESS MONITOR. Text in English. 3/w. USD 695 in United States (effective 2001).
Published by: W P S Agentstvo Obzora Sredstv Massovoi Informatsii/WPS, Russian Media Monitoring Agency, a/ya 90, Moscow, 115191, Russian Federation. TEL 7-095-9552708, wpsinfo@wps.ru. **Dist. by:** W P S U.S.A., Inc, 400 Park Pl, no 1C, Fort Lee, NJ 07024. TEL 201-585-7305, FAX 201-585-7305.

330 RUS
RUSSIAN ECONOMIC NEWS. Text in English, Russian. 1997. m. free.
Media: Online - full text.
Published by: Rossiiskoe Agentstvo Mezhdunarodnoi Informatsii R I A Novosti, Zubovskii bulv 4, Moscow, 119021, Russian Federation. TEL 7-095-2012746, marketing@rian.ru, http://en.rian.ru/rian/index.cfm?prd_id=159. **Co-publisher:** Russian Federation, Ministry of the Economy.

330 RUS
RUSSKII FOKUS. Text in Russian. w. **Document type:** *Journal.*
Address: 3-ya Ul Tverskaya Yamskaya 3/5, Moscow, 125040, Russian Federation. TEL 7-095-9379069, FAX 7-095-9379060, focus@infomaker.ru, http://www.russianfocus.ru. Ed. Petr Fadeev.

330 RUS ISSN 0869-0790
RUSSKOE BOGATSTVO. Text in Russian. irreg.
Indexed: RASB.
Address: Astrakhanskii per 5, kv 86, Moscow, 129010, Russian Federation. Ed. A Zlobin. **US dist. addr.:** East View Information Services, 3020 Harbor Ln. N., Minneapolis, MN 55447. TEL 612-550-0961.

330 RUS ISSN 0869-4443
RYNOK - INFORMATSIYA - SNABZHENIE - KONKURENTSIYA. Abbreviated title: R I S K. Text in Russian. bi-m. USD 125 in United States.
Indexed: RASB, RefZh.
—East View.
Address: Ul Chernyakhovskogo 16, Moscow, 125319, Russian Federation. TEL 7-095-1521333. Ed. B V Osipov. **US dist. addr.:** East View Information Services, 3020 Harbor Ln. N., Minneapolis, MN 55447. TEL 612-550-0961.

S A S COM. see *COMPUTERS—Software*

349 USA ISSN 1051-9939
HG2150
S & L - SAVINGS BANK FINANCIAL QUARTERLY. (Savings and Loan) Text in English. q. USD 389 (effective 1997). back issues avail. **Document type:** *Trade.*
Formerly (until 1986): S and L Financial Quarterly
Published by: I D C Financial Publishing, Inc., PO Box 140, Hartland, WI 53029. TEL 800-525-5457. Ed., R&P John E Rickmeier.

340 011 USA
S C M P NEWSLETTER✶. Text in English. q. membership. **Document type:** *Newsletter.*
Published by: Society of Corporate Meeting Professionals, 2107 Del Monte Ave, Monterey, CA 93940-3711. TEL 408-649-6544, FAX 408-649-4124.

330 333.79 GBR
S E E C OCCASIONAL PAPER. Text in English. 1993. irreg., latest vol.2, 1995. GBP 25; GBP 30 foreign. **Document type:** *Monographic series.* **Description:** Promotes research and teaching in the broad area of energy economics and policy.
Published by: University of Surrey, Surrey Energy Economics Centre, School of Human Sciences, University Of Surrey, Guildford, GU2 5XH, United Kingdom. TEL 44-1483-259379, FAX 44-1483-259548, economics@surrey.ac.uk. Circ: 150.

330 333.79 GBR ISSN 0952-8490
S E E D S. (Surrey Energy Economics Discussion Paper Series) Text in English. 1980. irreg., latest vol.96, 1998. GBP 25 domestic to institutions; GBP 30 foreign to institutions; GBP 10 domestic to students; GBP 12 foreign to students. **Document type:** *Monographic series.* **Description:** Aims to promote research and teaching in the broad area of energy economics and policy.
—BLDSC (3597.970300), IE, ingenta.
Published by: University of Surrey, Surrey Energy Economics Centre, School of Human Sciences, University Of Surrey, Guildford, GU2 5XH, United Kingdom. TEL 44-1483-259379, FAX 44-1483-259548, economics@surrey.ac.uk. Ed. David Hawdon.

B

330 333.79 GBR
S E E D S TECHNICAL PAPERS. (Surrey Energy Economics Discussion Paper Series) Text in English. 1996. irreg. GBP 25; GBP 30 foreign. **Document type:** *Monographic series.*
Published by: University of Surrey, Surrey Energy Economics Centre, School of Human Sciences, University Of Surrey, Guildford, GU2 5XH, United Kingdom. TEL 44-1483-259379, FAX 44-1483-259548, economics@surrey.ac.uk.

S G B GOLF; the trade magazine. (Sports Goods Buyer) see *SPORTS AND GAMES—Ball Games*

S G B OUTDOOR. (Sports Goods Buyer) see *SPORTS AND GAMES—Outdoor Life*

S G B UK. (Sports Goods Buyer) see *SPORTS AND GAMES—Outdoor Life*

S G B UK - GUIDE TO THE TRADE. (Sports Goods Buyer) see *SPORTS AND GAMES—Outdoor Life*

338.642 PHL ISSN 0115-8341
S L U - E I S S I F NEWSLETTER. (Saint Louis University - Extension Institute for Small-Scale Industries Foundation) Text in English, Tagalog. 1981. s-a. PHP 230 domestic; USD 20 foreign (effective 2001). 4 p./no.; back issues avail. **Document type:** *Newsletter.* **Description:** Features news on small business, articles that could help small entrepreneurs, and success stories of northern Luzon entrepreneurs. Includes a directory of foundation beneficiaries.
Published by: Saint Louis University, Extension Institute for Small-Scale Industries Foundation, C-016 Center for Culture and the Arts, S L U Campus, Baguio City, Benguet 2600, Philippines. TEL 74-443-9573, FAX 74-443-9573, eissif@perfecto.slu.edu.ph. Ed. Erlinda T Manopol. Circ: 300.

S N A BOLETIN ECONOMICO. see *AGRICULTURE*

330 NOR ISSN 0803-4036
S N F - RAPPORT. (Samfunns- og Naeringslivforskning) Text in Multiple languages. 1991. irreg.
Formed by the merger of (1984-1991): Senter for Anvendt Forskning. Rapport (1502-9468); (1989-1991): Naeringsoekonomisk Institutt. Rapport (0802-7153)
Related titles: Online - full text ed.: 2000.
Indexed: ASFA, ESPM, WAE&RSA.
Published by: Samfunns- og Naeringslivsforskning A/S/Institute for Research in Economics and Business Administration, Breiviksveien 40, Bergen, 5045, Norway. TEL 47-55-95-95-00, FAX 47-55-95-94-39, http://www.snf.no/meny/indpubl.htm.

330 USA
S R C INSIGHTS. Text in English. q.
Related titles: Online - full content ed.
Published by: Federal Reserve Bank of Philadelphia, Supervision, Regulation, & Credit, 7th fl, 10 Independence Mall, Philadelphia, PA 19106-1574. cynthia.course@phil.frb.org, http://www.phil.frb.org/src/srcinsights/index.html.

330 DOM
SABADO ECONOMICO. Text in Spanish. w. USD 35.
Published by: (Fundacion Economia y Desarrollo, Inc.), Editora Taller, Apdo. 2190, Isabel la Catolica 260, Santo Domingo, Dominican Republic. TEL 809-682-9369, FAX 809-689-7259. Ed. Andres Dauhajre Jr.

330 USA ISSN 1097-7538
SACRAMENTO BUSINESS JOURNAL; serving greater Sacramento. Text in English. 1984. w. (Fri.). USD 95; USD 1.50 newsstand/cover (effective 2005). adv. **Document type:** *Newspaper.*
Formerly (until 199?): Business Journal (Sacramento, Calif.) (8756-5897)

Related titles: CD-ROM ed.: (from ProQuest Information & Learning); Microfilm ed.: (from LIB); Online - full text ed.: ISSN 1549-3210 (from CompuServe Inc., Data-Star, Florida Center for Library Automation, Gale Group, Northern Light Technology, Inc., O C L C Online Computer Library Center, Inc., ProQuest Information & Learning, The Dialog Corporation).
Indexed: ABIn, BusDate, LRI.
—CCC.
Published by: American City Business Journals, Inc. (Austin), 505 Powell St, Austin, TX 78703-5121. sacramento@bizjournals.com, http://sacramento.bcentral.com/. Ed. Lee Wessman. Pub. Dan Kennedy. adv.: B&W page USD 4,200. Circ: 16,000 (paid). **Subscr. to:** Sacramento Business Journal, 1401 21st St, Ste 200, Sacramento, CA 95818. TEL 916-447-7661, FAX 916-447-2243.

330 IDN
SADHANA. Text in Indonesian.
Published by: Komisi Pengembangan Sosial Ekonomi/ Commission for Socio-Economic Development, Gedung KWI Lt. II Jl. Cut Mutiah 10, Menteng, Tromol Pos 3044, Jakarta, 10002, Indonesia. TEL 62-21-323527, FAX 62-21-337970, hdatuslega@kawali.org, http://www.kawali.org/komisi-pse.html.

330 USA ISSN 0271-6453
HF5068.S3
ST. LOUIS BUSINESS JOURNAL. Text in English. 1980. w. (Fri.). USD 84 (effective 2005). adv. bk.rev. **Document type:** *Newspaper, Trade.*
Related titles: Microform ed.: (from PQC); Online - full text ed.: (from Florida Center for Library Automation, Gale Group, O C L C Online Computer Library Center, Inc., ProQuest Information & Learning, The Dialog Corporation).
Indexed: ABIn, BusDate, T&II.
—CCC.
Published by: St. Louis Business Journal Corp. (Subsidiary of: American City Business Journals, Inc.), 1 Metropolitan Sq., Ste. 2170, St. Louis, MO 63102-2733. TEL 314-421-6200, stlouis@bizjournals.com, http://www.bizjournals.com/stlouis/. Eds. Patricia Miller, Tom Wolf. Pub. Ellen Sherberg. Adv. contacts Barbara Richards, Glynelle Wells. Circ: 18,490.

SAINT PAUL LEGAL LEDGER. see *LAW—Corporate Law*

SALES COUNTER. see *PHOTOGRAPHY*

330 DNK ISSN 0108-3937
➤ **SAMFUNDSOEKONOMEN.** Text in Danish. 1983. 6/yr. DKK 470 (effective 2004). adv. back issues avail. **Document type:** *Academic/Scholarly.*
Related titles: Online - full text ed.
Published by: Danmarks Jurist- og Oekonomforbund, Gothersgade 133, PO Box 2126, Copenhagen K, 1015, Denmark. TEL 45-33-959700, FAX 45-33-959999, djoef@djoef.dk, http://www.djoef.dk/online/view_Folder?ID=7802&attr_folder=F. Ed. Niels Kaergaaard. adv.: B&W page DKK 5,000; trim 145 x 200.

➤ **SAMSOM ARTSENPRAKTIJK.** see *MEDICAL SCIENCES*

330 BEL ISSN 0778-127X
SAMSOM BESLOTEN VENNOOTSCHAPPEN MET BEPERKTE AANSPRAKELIJKHEID. Text in Flemish. 1986. s-m. Supplement avail. **Description:** Helps professionals to sufficiently document business activities.
Related titles: French ed.: Samsom Societe Privee a Responsabilite Limitee. ISSN 0776-1562.
Published by: C E D Samsom (Subsidiary of: Wolters Samsom Belgie n.v.), Kouterveld 14, Diegem, 1831, Belgium. TEL 32-2-7231111.

330 BEL ISSN 0776-1511
SAMSOM COOPERATIEVE VENNOOTSCHAPPEN. Text in Flemish. 1988. s-m. Supplement avail. **Description:** Disseminates information on subtle statutes and administration through fiscal questions, social problematics and economic dilemmas.
Related titles: French ed.: Samsom Societe Cooperative. ISSN 0776-152X.
Published by: C E D Samsom (Subsidiary of: Wolters Samsom Belgie n.v.), Kouterveld 14, Diegem, 1831, Belgium. TEL 32-2-7231111.

330 BEL ISSN 0778-1261
SAMSOM NAAMLOZE VENNOOTSCHAPPEN. Variant title: N V Naamloze Vennootschappen. Text in Flemish. 1985. s-m. Supplement avail. **Description:** Examines issues and concerns affecting limited liability companies.
Related titles: French ed.: Samsom Societe Anonyme. ISSN 0778-0583.
Published by: C E D Samsom (Subsidiary of: Wolters Samsom Belgie n.v.), Kouterveld 14, Diegem, 1831, Belgium. TEL 2-7231111.

382 BEL ISSN 0776-4383
SAMSOM VRIJE BEROEPEN. Text in Flemish. 1988. s-m. Supplement avail.
Related titles: French ed.: Samsom Professions Liberales. ISSN 0777-2009.
Published by: C E D Samsom (Subsidiary of: Wolters Samsom Belgie n.v.), Kouterveld 14, Diegem, 1831, Belgium. TEL 32-2-7231111.

330 USA ISSN 0895-1551
SAN ANTONIO BUSINESS JOURNAL. Text in English. 1987. w. (Fri.). USD 85 (effective 2005). adv. bk.rev. **Document type:** *Newspaper.* **Description:** Features news, statistics, and commentary about San Antonio's business community.
Related titles: Online - full text ed.: ISSN 1549-1897. 1987 (from Florida Center for Library Automation, Gale Group, O C L C Online Computer Library Center, Inc., ProQuest Information & Learning).
Indexed: ABIn, BusDate, LRI.
—CCC.
Published by: American City Business Journals, Inc. (Charlotte), 120 W Morehead St, Ste 200, Charlotte, NC 28202. TEL 704-973-1100, 800-704-3757, FAX 704-973-1102, sanantonio@bizjournals.com, http://www.bizjournals.com/sanantonio/. adv.: B&W page USD 4,400, color page USD 5,000. Circ: 9,000 (paid).

330 USA
SAN DIEGO BUSINESS✶. Text in English. 1985. m. USD 18. adv. bk.rev.
Published by: Schmidt Communications, PO Box 33166, San Diego, CA 92163-3166. TEL 619-234-7997. Ed. Don Schmidt. Circ: 12,500.

330 USA ISSN 8750-6890
SAN DIEGO BUSINESS JOURNAL. Text in English. 1980. w. (Mon.). USD 79 (effective 2005). adv. **Document type:** *Newspaper, Trade.*
Related titles: Microform ed.: (from PQC); Online - full text ed.: (from EBSCO Publishing, Florida Center for Library Automation, Gale Group, Northern Light Technology, Inc., O C L C Online Computer Library Center, Inc., ProQuest Information & Learning).
Indexed: ABIn, BusDate, LRI, T&II.
—CCC.
Published by: San Diego Business Journal, Inc., 4909 Murphy Canyon Rd, 200, San Diego, CA 92123. TEL 619-277-6359, FAX 619-571-3628, sdbj@sdbj.com, http://www.sdbj.com. Ed. John Hollon. Pub. Armon Mills. Circ: 21,500.

330 USA
SAN DIEGO METROPOLITAN MAGAZINE. Text in English. m. USD 25 in county in San Diego County; USD 35 out of county (effective 2001). adv. back issues avail. **Document type:** *Magazine, Trade.* **Description:** Covers regional business news and issues for the San Diego area.
Related titles: Online - full content ed.
Published by: Metro San Diego Communications, Inc., Ste 1200, 1250 Sixth Ave, San Diego, CA 92101. TEL 619-233-4060, FAX 619-233-4272, info@sandiegometro.com, http://www.sandiegometro.com/. Ed. Timothy McClain. Pub. Gary Shaw.

330 USA ISSN 1526-0712
SAN FERNANDO VALLEY BUSINESS JOURNAL. Text in English. 1995. fortn. USD 49.95 for 2 yrs. (effective 2002). adv. **Document type:** *Journal, Trade.*
Related titles: Online - full text ed.: (from Florida Center for Library Automation, Gale Group).
—CCC.
Address: 21300 Victory Blvd., Ste. 205, Woodland Hills, CA 91367. TEL 818-676-1750, http://www.sfvbj.com/. Ed. Jason schaff. Pub. Pegi Matsuda. Adv. contact Josh Schimmels.

330 600 VNM
SANG TAO/CREATIVITY. Text in Vietnamese. 1989. w.
Published by: Central Council of Co-operatives, 80 Hang Gai, Hanoi, Viet Nam. TEL 56122. Ed. Nguyen Huy Thong.

ST. GALLER STUDIEN ZUM PRIVAT-, HANDELS- UND WIRTSCHAFTSRECHT. see *LAW*

330 RUS
SANKT-PETERBURGSKII UNIVERSITET. VESTNIK. SERIYA: EKONOMIKA. Text in Russian; Summaries in English. 1946. q. **Document type:** *Academic/Scholarly.*
Formerly: Leningradskii Universitet. Vestnik. Seriya: Ekonomika (0233-755X); Which superseded in part (in 1985): Leningradskii Universitet. Vestnik. Seriya: Ekonomika, Filosofiya, Pravo (0024-0818)
Related titles: Microform ed.: (from EVP).
Indexed: IBSS, RASB, RefZh, SOPODA.
Published by: Izdatelstvo Sankt-Peterburgskogo Universiteta, Universitetskaya nab 7-9, St Petersburg, 199034, Russian Federation. TEL 812-2189784. **US dist. addr.:** East View Information Services, 3020 Harbor Ln. N., Minneapolis, MN 55447. TEL 612-550-0961.

658 KOR ISSN 0036-4487
SANOP KWA KYONGYONG/YONSEI BUSINESS REVIEW. Text in English, Korean. 1963. s-a. KRW 8,000, USD 12. adv. bk.rev. charts; stat.
Published by: Yonsei University, Industrial Management Research Centre, College of Business and Economics, 134 Sinchon-Dong, Sudaemoon-ku, Seoul, Korea, S. TEL 02-392-0192, FAX 02-313-5331. Ed. Hwi Suck Choo. Circ: 2,000.

330 JPN
SAPIO. Text in Japanese. 1989. bi-w. adv. **Description:** Covers business, economics and politics.
Published by: Shogakukan Inc., 3-1 Hitotsubashi 2-chome, Chiyoda-ku, Tokyo, 101-8001, Japan. TEL 81-3-3230-5367, FAX 81-3-3264-8471. Ed. Kunimasa Endo. Pub. Mitsutoshi Igarashi. Adv. contact Hajime Yokoyama. B&W page JPY 800,000, color page JPY 1,250,000; trim 285 x 210. Circ: 150,000.

330 CAN ISSN 1701-4468
SASKBUSINESS. Text in English. 1979. bi-m. CND 19.95 (effective 2004). adv. **Document type:** *Trade.* **Description:** Profiles prominent business leaders and key developments in the Saskatchewan area. Provides data on business trends and opportunities.
Formerly (until 2001): Saskatchewan Business (0709-0854)
Related titles: Microfiche ed.: (from MML); Microform ed.: (from MML); Online - full text ed.: (from bigchalk, Factiva, Gale Group, Micromedia ProQuest, Northern Light Technology, Inc., O C L C Online Computer Library Center, Inc., ProQuest Information & Learning).
Indexed: ABIn, BusDate, CBCABus, CBCARef, CBPI, CPerl, RefZh.
Published by: Sunrise Publishing Ltd., 2213 B Hanselman Ct, Saskatoon, SK S7L 6A8, Canada. TEL 306-244-5668, 800-247-5743, FAX 306-244-5679, news@sunrisepublish.com, http://www.sunrisepublish.com/sb.htm. Ed. Keith Moen. Pub., R&P, Adv. contact Twila Reddekopp. B&W page CND 2,032, color page CND 2,947. Circ: 9,000.

330 SAU
SAUDI ARABIA BUSINESS WEEK. Text in English. w.
Address: P O Box 2894, Riyadh, Saudi Arabia.

330 SAU ISSN 0252-967X
SAUDI ECONOMIC SURVEY; weekly review of Saudi Arabian economic and business activities. Text in Arabic. 1967. w. SAR 1,650 in the Middle East; USD 500 elsewhere. adv. back issues avail. **Document type:** *Newsletter, Trade.* **Description:** Covers Saudi business transactions, trade and legal changes affecting business, contracts, tenders.
Indexed: RASB.
Published by: Saudi Eco Survey, P O Box 1989, Jeddah, 21441, Saudi Arabia. TEL 966-2-651-4952. Ed. Abdelhakim Misbah Ghaith. Pub. S A Ashour. Circ: 3,000.

330 USA ISSN 1073-1741
SAVANNAH BUSINESS JOURNAL✶; the business journal of Bryan, Chatham, Effingham, and Liberty counties. Text in English. 1990. m. USD 15 (effective 1998). adv. bk.rev. **Document type:** *Newspaper.* **Description:** Features selected area businesses, general business news, newly issued licenses and special topics.
Related titles: Microform ed.: 1990 (from PQC); Online - full text ed.: 1990 (from Northern Light Technology, Inc.).
Indexed: BusDate.
Published by: DeRolf Publishing Co., 219 W Bryan St, 303, Savannah, GA 31401-2505. TEL 912-920-3086, FAX 912-925-6093. Ed. Donald R Blum. Pub., R&P, Adv. contact Shawna Derolf TEL 912-233-5711. page USD 700. Circ: 5,000.

338.948 SWE ISSN 1402-1897
SCANDINAVIA NOW. Text in English. 1996. d. free. adv. **Document type:** *Newspaper, Consumer.* **Description:** Focuses on Scandinavian trade, business and industry of interest to businesses and industries outside Scandinavia. Information on weather, economic and cultural aspects for each country is also included.
Media: Online - full text.
Published by: Elfwendahl & Co AB, PO Box 26174, Stockholm SE, 10041, Sweden. TEL 46-8-678-3230, FAX 46-8-611-23-58, mail@scandinavianow.com, http://www.scandinavianow.com. Eds. Everett M Ellestad, Nicholas Mead. Pub., R&P Tord Elfwendahl TEL 46-8-678-32-30. Adv. contact Helene Elfwendahl.

330 GBR ISSN 0347-0520
HB9
➤ **SCANDINAVIAN JOURNAL OF ECONOMICS.** Text in English. 1899. q. EUR 79 combined subscription in Europe to individuals print & online eds.; USD 76 combined subscription in the Americas to individuals & Carribean, print & online eds.; GBP 52 combined subscription elsewhere to individuals print & online eds.; GBP 217 combined subscription in Europe to institutions print & online eds.; USD 386 combined subscription in the Americas to institutions & Carribean, print & online eds.; GBP 230 combined subscription elsewhere to institutions print & online eds. (effective 2006). adv. index. reprints avail. **Document type:** *Journal, Academic/Scholarly.*
Former titles (until 1976): Swedish Journal of Economics (0039-7318); (until 1965): Ekonomisk Tidskrift
Related titles: Online - full text ed.: ISSN 1467-9442. GBP 318 in Europe to institutions; USD 366 in the Americas to institutions & Caribbean; GBP 218 elsewhere to institutions (effective 2006) (from Blackwell Synergy, EBSCO Publishing, Gale Group, IngentaConnect, O C L C Online Computer Library Center, Inc., Swets Information Services).

Indexed: ABIn, ASCA, AgeL, AmH&L, BPIA, BibInd, CREJ, CurCont, ESPM, FamI, GEOBASE, HistAb, IBSS, INIS AtomInd, JEL, KES, PAIS, PCI, RASB, RefZh, RiskAb, SSCI, ZentMath.
—BLDSC (8087.505700), IDS, IE, Infotrieve, ingenta. **CCC.**
Published by: Blackwell Publishing Ltd., 9600 Garsington Rd, Oxford, OX4 2ZG, United Kingdom. TEL 44-1865-776868, FAX 44-1865-714591, customerservices@oxon.blackwellpublishing.com, http://www.blackwellpublishing.com/journals/SJOE. Eds. Christian Schultz, Steinar Holden. Circ: 1,100.

330 UGA
SCARCITY. Text in English. 1968 (vol.2). irreg. (approx. a.).
Published by: Makerere Economics Society, PO Box 7062, Kampala, Uganda.

301 DEU ISSN 1439-121X
HB5
SCHMOLLERS JAHRBUCH; Zeitschrift fuer Wirtschafts- und Sozialwissenschaften. Text and summaries in English, German. 1871. q. EUR 88; EUR 70.40 to students; EUR 24 newsstand/cover (effective 2006). adv. bk.rev. index. Supplement avail.; reprint service avail. from SCH. **Document type:** *Journal, Academic/Scholarly.*
Former titles (until 1999): Zeitschrift fuer Wirtschafts- und Sozialwissenschaften (0342-1783); (until 1972): Schmollers Jahrbuch fuer Wirtschafts- und Sozialwissenschaften (0036-6234); (until 1968): Schmollers Jahrbuch fuer Gesetzgebung, Verwaltung und Volkswirtschaft (1619-6244); (until 1913): Jahrbuch fuer Gesetzgebung, Verwaltung und Volkswirtschaft im Deutschen Reich (1619-6260); (until 1877): Jahrbuch fuer Gesetzgebung, Verwaltung und Rechtspflege des Deutschen Reichs (1619-649X)
Indexed: ABCPolSci, BAS, DIP, ELLIS, IBR, IBSS, IBZ, IPSA, JEL, PAIS, PCI, PSA, RASB, SociolAb.
—IE. **CCC.**
Published by: (Gesellschaft fuer Wirtschafts- und Sozialwissenschaften), Duncker und Humblot GmbH, Carl-Heinrich-Becker-Weg 9, Berlin, 12165, Germany. TEL 49-30-7900060, FAX 49-30-79000631, info@duncker-humblot.de, http://www.diw.de/deutsch/publikationen/schmoller/, http://www.duncker-humblot.de. Ed. B Felderer. adv.: page EUR 550; trim 115 x 185. Circ: 750.

330 USA
SCHOOL OF BUSINESS UPDATE. Text in English. 1983. 3/yr. free to qualified personnel. back issues avail.
Published by: University of Wisconsin at Madison, School of Business, 1155 Observatory Dr, Madison, WI 53706. TEL 608-262-2401, FAX 608-263-0477. Ed. Lari Fanlund. Circ: 26,000.

334 DEU ISSN 0720-6925
SCHRIFTEN ZUM GENOSSENSCHAFTSWESEN UND ZUR OEFFENTLICHEN WIRTSCHAFT. Text in German. 1980. irreg., latest vol.36, 2000. price varies. **Document type:** *Monographic series, Academic/Scholarly.*
Published by: Duncker und Humblot GmbH, Carl-Heinrich-Becker-Weg 9, Berlin, 12165, Germany. TEL 49-30-7900060, FAX 49-30-79000631, info@duncker-humblot.de, http://www.duncker-humblot.de.

347 DEU ISSN 0582-026X
SCHRIFTEN ZUM WIRTSCHAFTSRECHT. Text in German. 1965. irreg., latest vol.162, 2003. price varies. **Document type:** *Monographic series, Academic/Scholarly.*
Published by: Duncker und Humblot GmbH, Carl-Heinrich-Becker-Weg 9, Berlin, 12165, Germany. TEL 49-30-7900060, FAX 49-30-79000631, info@duncker-humblot.de, http://www.duncker-humblot.de.

SCHRIFTEN ZUR WIRTSCHAFTSWISSENSCHAFTLICHEN ANALYSE DES RECHTS. see *LAW*

339 DEU ISSN 0720-7034
SCHRIFTENREIHE DER FORSCHUNGSSTELLE FUER DEN HANDEL. Text in German. 1929. irreg., latest vol.9, 1984. price varies. **Document type:** *Monographic series, Academic/Scholarly.*
Published by: Duncker und Humblot GmbH, Carl-Heinrich-Becker-Weg 9, Berlin, 12165, Germany. TEL 49-30-7900060, FAX 49-30-79000631, info@duncker-humblot.de, http://www.duncker-humblot.de.

170 DEU
SCHRIFTENREIHE FUER WIRTSCHAFTS- UND UNTERNEHMENSETHIK. Text in German. irreg., latest vol.13, 2005. price varies. **Document type:** *Monographic series, Academic/Scholarly.*
Published by: Rainer Hampp Verlag, Meringerzellerstr 10, Mering, 86415, Germany. TEL 49-8233-4783, FAX 49-8233-30755, Rainer_Hampp_Verlag@t-online.de, http://www.hampp-verlag.de.

330 CHE
SCHWEIZERISCHE MARKT ZEITUNG. Text in German. m.
Address: Binzmuehlestr 223, Zuerich, 8056, Switzerland. TEL 01-3715757. Ed. W E Fehr. Circ: 4,000.

330 310 CHE ISSN 0303-9692
HA1
➤ **SCHWEIZERISCHE ZEITSCHRIFT FUER VOLKSWIRTSCHAFT UND STATISTIK/REVUE SUISSE D'ECONOMIE POLITIQUE ET DE STATISTIQUE.** Text in English, French, German. 1864. q. CHF 100; CHF 30 per issue (effective 2005). adv. bk.rev. abstr.; bibl.; charts; illus. reprint service avail. from SCH. **Document type:** *Journal, Academic/Scholarly.*
Former titles (until 1944): Zeitschrift fuer Schweizerische Statistik und Volkswirtschaft (1421-2110); (until 1915): Zeitschrift fuer Schweizerische Statistik (1421-2102)
Related titles: CD-ROM ed.: (from SilverPlatter Information, Inc.); Online - full text ed.: (from The Dialog Corporation).
Indexed: CurCont, IBR, IBSS, IPSA, JEL, KES, PAIS, PCI, RASB, ST&MA.
—BLDSC (7953.362500), IE, Infotrieve, ingenta. **CCC.**
Published by: (Switzerland. Schweizerische Gesellschaft fuer Statistik und Volkswirtschaft), Verlag Peter Lang AG, Hochfeldstr. 32, Postfach 746, Bern 9, 3000, Switzerland. TEL 41-31-3061717, FAX 41-31-3061727, info@peterlang.com, http://www.peterlang.com. Ed. Mr. Peter Kugler. Circ: 1,850.

334 DEU ISSN 0486-8927
SCHWEIZERISCHES INSTITUT FUER GEWERBLICHE WIRTSCHAFT AN DER UNIVERSITAET ST. GALLEN. SCHRIFTENREIHE. Text in German. 1947. irreg., latest vol.13, 2000. price varies. **Document type:** *Monographic series, Academic/Scholarly.*
Published by: (Schweizerisches Institut fuer Gewerbliche Wirtschaft an der Universitaet St. Gallen CHE), Duncker und Humblot GmbH, Carl-Heinrich-Becker-Weg 9, Berlin, 12165, Germany. TEL 49-30-7900060, FAX 49-30-79000631, info@duncker-humblot.de, http://www.duncker-humblot.de.

330 FRA ISSN 0765-0027
SCIENCE ET VIE ECONOMIE. Text in French. 1984. 11/yr. adv.
Description: Explores the economy from all angles.
Related titles: ♦ Supplement to: Science & Vie. ISSN 0036-8369.
Published by: Emap France (Subsidiary of: Emap Media Ltd.), 150-152 Rue Gallieni, Boulogne, 92644, France. TEL 33-1-41334961, FAX 33-1-41335010, info@emapfrance.com, http://www.emapmedia.com. Circ: 115,273.

330 GBR ISSN 1467-7415
SCOTLAND IN BUSINESS. Text in English. 199?. m. GBP 30 (effective 2000). adv. **Document type:** *Magazine, Consumer.*
Description: Aims to provide independent business reports, news, reviews and profiles on all regions of Scotland.
Published by: Business Magazine Group, Adamsway, Mansfield, Notts NG18 4FP, United Kingdom. TEL 44-1623-450500, FAX 44-1623-454560, sib@bmgroup.co.uk, http://www.bmgroup.co.uk. Ed. Brett Mathews. Adv. contact Hazel Irving. B&W page GBP 1,385, color page GBP 1,840. Circ: 11,340 (paid).

SCOTTISH ECONOMIC AND SOCIAL HISTORY. see *SOCIAL SCIENCES: COMPREHENSIVE WORKS*

330 GBR ISSN 0036-9292
HB1
➤ **SCOTTISH JOURNAL OF POLITICAL ECONOMY.** Text in English. 1954. 5/yr. EUR 63 combined subscription in Europe to individuals print & online eds.; USD 71 combined subscription in the Americas to individuals & Carribean, print & online eds.; GBP 42 combined subscription elsewhere to individuals print & online eds.; GBP 178 combined subscription in Europe to institutions print & online eds.; USD 346 combined subscription in the Americas to institutions & Carribean, print & online eds.; GBP 206 combined subscription elsewhere to institutions print & online eds. (effective 2006). adv. bk.rev. illus. index. back issues avail.; reprint service avail. from PSC. **Document type:** *Journal, Academic/Scholarly.* **Description:** Dedicated to publishing research in any field of economics, without prejudice to the methodology or to the analytical techniques used.
Related titles: Online - full text ed.: ISSN 1467-9485. GBP 169 in Europe to institutions; USD 329 in the Americas to institutions & Caribbean; GBP 196 elsewhere to institutions (effective 2006) (from Blackwell Synergy, EBSCO Publishing, Gale Group, IngentaConnect, O C L C Online Computer Library Center, Inc., Swets Information Services).
Indexed: ABIn, APEL, ASCA, AmH&L, BAS, BrHumI, BusI, CPM, CREJ, CurCont, FamI, GEOBASE, HistAb, IBR, IBSS, ILD, IndVet, JEL, KES, PAIS, PCI, PSA, RRTA, SSA, SSCI, SociolAb, WAE&RSA, WBA, WorkRelAb.
—BLDSC (8210.600000), IDS, IE, Infotrieve, ingenta. **CCC.**
Published by: (Scottish Economic Society), Blackwell Publishing Ltd., 9600 Garsington Rd, Oxford, OX4 2ZG, United Kingdom. TEL 44-1865-776868, FAX 44-1865-714591, customerservices@oxon.blackwellpublishing.com, http://www.blackwellpublishing.com/journals/SJPE. Eds. Andrew Hughes Hallett, Campbell Leith, Robert A Hart. Circ: 1,500.

330 025.04 USA
THE SCOUT REPORT FOR BUSINESS & ECONOMICS. Text in English. fortn. back issues avail. **Document type:** *Bulletin.*
Description: Offers a selective collection of Internet resources covering topics in the field of business and economics.
Media: Online - full text.
Published by: University of Wisconsin at Madison, Computer Sciences Department, 5355a Computer Sciences and Statistics, 1210 West Dayton St, Madison, WI 53706. TEL 608-262-1204, FAX 608-262-9777, scout@cs.wisc.edu, http://scout.cs.wisc.edu/report/bus-econ/current/index.html, http://scout.wisc.edu/.

330 USA
SEATTLE DAILY JOURNAL OF COMMERCE. Text in English. 1893. d. (Mon.-Sat.). USD 210 (effective 2005). adv. **Document type:** *Newspaper.* **Description:** Covers construction, real estate, design, and law in the Seattle, WA, area.
Related titles: Online - full text ed.: DJC.com.
Contact: Daily Journal of Commerce, Inc., 83 Columbia St., Seattle, WA 98111. TEL 206-622-8272, FAX 206-622-8416, maude@djc.com, http://www.djc.com. Ed. Jace Krause. Pub. Phil Brown. Adv. contact Matt Brown. col. inch USD 20. Circ: 6,544 morning (paid). Wire service: AP.

330 ESP
SECTOR PUBLICO EMPRESARIAL DE LA COMUNIDAD AUTONOMA DE EUSKADI. Text in Basque, Spanish. 1989. irreg., latest 1995. **Document type:** *Government.*
Published by: (Basque Region. Ogasun eta Finantza Saila/Departamento de Hacienda y Finanzas), Eusko Jaurlaritzaren Argitalpen-Zerbitzu Nagusia/Servicio Central de Publicaciones del Gobierno Vasco, Donostia-San Sebastian, 1, Vitoria-gasteiz, Alava 01010, Spain. TEL 34-945-018561, FAX 34-945-018709, hac-sabd@ej-gv.es, http://www.ej-gv.net/publicaciones. Circ: 1,500.

▼ **SECURITY DIRECTOR NEWS.** see *CRIMINOLOGY AND LAW ENFORCEMENT—Security*

SECURITY POINT. see *CRIMINOLOGY AND LAW ENFORCEMENT—Security*

SEIJI KEIZAI SHIGAKU/JOURNAL OF HISTORICAL STUDIES. see *HISTORY*

330 JPN ISSN 0387-4753
SEIJO UNIVERSITY ECONOMIC PAPERS/SEIJO DAIGAKU KEIZAI KENKYU. Text in Japanese. 1953. q. JPY 3,000. bk.rev. **Document type:** *Academic/Scholarly.*
Indexed: IBSS.
—BLDSC (8219.655000).
Published by: Economic Institute of Seijo University/Seijo Daigaku Keizaigakkai, 1-20 Seijo 6, Setagaya-ku, Tokyo, 157-0066, Japan. Ed. Itaru Ueno. Circ: 300.

330 RUS
SEKRETARSKOE DELO. Text in Russian. q. USD 65 in United States.
Published by: Biznes Shkola Intel-Sintez, Ul Profsoyuznaya 3, Moscow, 117036, Russian Federation. TEL 7-095-1299212, FAX 7-095-1246809. Ed. T V Kuznetsova. **US dist. addr.:** East View Information Services, 3020 Harbor Ln. N., Minneapolis, MN 55447. TEL 612-550-0961.

330 USA
//SELF SERVE. Text in English. 2001 (Jul. 4th). q. USD 48 in United States; USD 72 in Canada & Mexico; USD 104 elsewhere (effective 2001). adv. **Document type:** *Trade.*
Description: Covers self-service technology, products, applications, cost & service benefits, and case studies.
Published by: (Self-Service Automation Association), VOYAGI, Inc., 3414 Taylor St NE, Minneapolis, MN 55418-1351. info@selfserv.org. Adv. contact Marty Syner TEL 248-594-8200. page USD 7,115; trim 10 x 12. Circ: 25,000.

330 USA ISSN 1046-9036
THE SELLING ADVANTAGE. Text in English. 1989. fortn. USD 94.56. bk.rev. **Document type:** *Newsletter.* **Description:** For sales professionals interested in improving performance. Includes sales strategies and techniques.
Published by: Progressive Business Publications, 370 Technology Dr, Malvern, PA 19355-1315. TEL 610-695-8600, 800-220-5000, FAX 610-647-8089, editor@pbp.com, http://www.pbp.com. Ed. Philip Ahr. Pub. Edward Satell. R&P Curt Brown. Circ: 56,415 (paid).

330 PER ISSN 0254-816X
SEMANA ECONOMICA. Text in Spanish. 1985. w. (48/yr.). USD 590 (effective 1997).
Published by: Apoyo Comunicaciones S.A., Juan De La Fuente, 625, Miraflores, Lima 18, Peru. TEL 51-14-445555, FAX 51-14-445555. Ed. Augusto Alvarez Rodrich.

330 PRT ISSN 0872-1688
SEMANARIO ECONOMICO. Text in Portuguese. 1987. w. adv. **Document type:** *Newspaper.*
Published by: Media Capital Editora Multimedia, S.A., Rua Dr. Mario Castelhano, No.40, Queluz de Baixo, 2749-502, Portugal. TEL 351-707301001, FAX 351-214347653. Circ: 20,000. **Co-publisher:** Recoletos Compania Editorial S.A.

B

▼ *new title* ➤ *refereed* ✶ *unverified* ♦ *full entry avail.*

332.6 USA ISSN 1089-1412
RA997.A1
THE SENIOR CARE ACQUISITION REPORT. Text in English. 1996. a., latest 2001. looseleaf. USD 495 for print or online; USD 645 combined subscription print & online (effective Mar. 2002). mkt.; stat.; charts. back issues avail. **Document type:** *Newsletter, Consumer.* **Description:** Contains in-depth study of the acquisition market for nursing homes, assisted living facilities and independent living (congregate) retirement communities. Includes charts, graphs and statistical analysis, and detailed transaction sheets on publicly announced senior care acquisitions for the year.
Formed by the 1996 merger of: Nursing Home Acquisition Report (1075-9115); Retirement Housing Acquisition Report (1079-2430)
Related titles: Online - full content ed.
Published by: Irving Levin Associates, Inc., 268-1/2 Main Ave, Norwalk, CT 06851. TEL 203-846-6800, 800-248-1668, FAX 203-846-8300, general@levinassociates.com, http://www.levinassociates.com. Pub. Ms. Eleanor B Meredith. R&P Stephen M Monroe.

B

332.6 USA
THE SENIORCARE INVESTOR. Text in English. 1989. m. looseleaf. USD 427 (effective 2004). mkt.; stat. back issues avail. **Document type:** *Newsletter, Consumer.* **Description:** Includes a monthly newsletter that covers skilled nursing homes, assisted living and congregate living communities. The topics include mergers and acquisitions, an analysis of factors impacting stock prices, Wall Street investment recommendations, public stock offerings, bankruptcies and alliances.
Formerly: Healthcare Investor (1075-9107)
Related titles: E-mail ed.; Online - full content ed.
Published by: Irving Levin Associates, Inc., 268-1/2 Main Ave, Norwalk, CT 06851. TEL 203-846-6800, 800-248-1668, FAX 203-846-8300, general@levinassociates.com, http://www.seniorcareinvestor.com, http://www.levinassociates.com. Pub. Ms. Eleanor B Meredith. R&P Stephen M Monroe. Adv. contact Mrs. Gail Donovan TEL 203-966-4343.

330 JPN ISSN 0386-4383
SENSHU KEIZAIGAKU RONSHU/ECONOMIC BULLETIN OF THE SENSHU UNIVERSITY. Text in Japanese. 1965. s-a. **Document type:** *Journal, Academic/Scholarly.*
—BLDSC (3652.010000).
Published by: Senshu Daigaku Keizai Gakkai/Economic Society of the Senshu University, 3-8, Kanda Jimbo-cho, Chiyoda-ku, Tokyo, 101-8425, Japan.

330 JPN ISSN 0386-5819
SENSHU SYOGAKU RONSHU/COMMERCIAL REVIEW OF SENSHU UNIVERSITY. Text in Japanese. 1965. s-a. **Document type:** *Journal, Academic/Scholarly.*
—BLDSC (3337.150000).
Published by: Senshu Daigaku Gakkai/Senshu University Research Society, 2-2-1, Higashi-mita, Tama-ku, Kawasaki-shi, Kanagawa 214-8580, Japan.

330 KOR ISSN 1226-9816
SEOUL JOURNAL OF BUSINESS. Text in English. 1995. s-a. **Document type:** *Journal, Academic/Scholarly.*
—BLDSC (8241.809600).
Published by: Seoul National University, College of Business Administration, 56-1, Shillim-Dong Kwanak-Gu, Seoul, 151-742, Korea, S. TEL 82-2-8806945, FAX 82-2-8783154, cbaadmin@plaza1.snu.ac.kr, http://cba.snu.ac.kr:10004/eng/default.asp.

330 KOR ISSN 1225-0279
SEOUL JOURNAL OF ECONOMICS. Text in English. 1988. q. USD 30 to individuals; USD 100 to institutions (effective 2000). **Document type:** *Academic/Scholarly.* **Description:** Deals with theoretical and empirical matters in all fields of economics, especially focusing on the economic development of East Asia.
Related titles: Online - full text ed.: (from Northern Light Technology, Inc., O C L C Online Computer Library Center, Inc., ProQuest Information & Learning).
Indexed: ABIn, BAS, JEL.
—BLDSC (8241.809700), IE, Infotrieve.
Published by: Seoul National University, Institute of Economic Research/Seoul Daehakkyo Kyeongje Yeonguso, Seoul, 151742, Korea, S. TEL 82-2-877-1629, FAX 82-2-888-4454. Ed. Hak K. Pyo. Circ: 300.

330 GRC ISSN 1108-2992
SERIES IN ECONOMICS, BUSINESS AND THE ENVIRONMENT. Text in English, Greek. 1998. s-a. **Description:** Publishes articles on theoretical and applied research in business, economics, and the environment.
Indexed: JEL.
Published by: East-West Press, University of Crete, Department of Economics, Gallos, Rethymno, Crete, 74100, Greece.

330 SGP
SERIES ON ECONOMIC DEVELOPMENT AND GROWTH. Text in English. irreg. price varies. **Document type:** *Journal, Academic/Scholarly.*
Published by: World Scientific Publishing Co. Pte. Ltd., 5 Toh Tuck Link, Singapore, 596224, Singapore. TEL 65-466-5775, FAX 65-467-7667, wspc@wspc.com.sg, http://www.worldscibooks.com/series/sedg_series.shtml, http://www.worldscientific.com. Ed. Linda Y Yueh. **Subscr. to:** Farrer Rd, PO Box 128, Singapore 912805, Singapore. TEL 65-382-5663, FAX 65-382-5919. **Dist. by:** World Scientific Publishing Co., Inc., 1060 Main St, River Edge, NJ 07661. TEL 201-487-9655, 800-227-7562, FAX 201-487-9656, 888-977-2665, wspc@wspc.com.

330 SGP
▼ **SERIES ON INNOVATION AND KNOWLEDGE MANAGEMENT.** Text in English. 2004. irreg., latest vol.3. price varies. **Document type:** *Monographic series, Academic/Scholarly.* **Description:** Covers issues that involves information management, knowledge acquisition, knowledge sharing, organizational culture, organizational learning, communities of practice, best practices, and learning organizations.
Published by: World Scientific Publishing Co. Pte. Ltd., 5 Toh Tuck Link, Singapore, 596224, Singapore. TEL 65-466-5775, FAX 65-467-7667, wspc@wspc.com.sg, series@wspc.com.sg, http://www.wspc.com/books/series/sikm_series.shtml, http://www.worldscientific.com. Ed. Suliman Hawamdeh. **Dist. by:** World Scientific Publishing Co., Inc., 1060 Main St, River Edge, NJ 07661. TEL 201-487-9655, 800-227-7562, FAX 201-487-9656, 888-977-2665; World Scientific Publishing Ltd., 57 Shelton St, London WC2H 9HE, United Kingdom. TEL 44-20-78360888, FAX 44-20-78362020.

SERVICE EXECUTIVE. see *TRANSPORTATION—Automobiles*

338.4 GBR ISSN 0264-2069
HD9980.1
➤ **THE SERVICE INDUSTRIES JOURNAL.** Text in English. 1981. 8/yr. GBP 535, USD 810 combined subscription to institutions print & online eds. (effective 2006). adv. bk.rev. index. back issues avail.; reprint service avail. from PSC. **Document type:** *Journal, Academic/Scholarly.* **Description:** Covers services, service industries, and management of services from an international, interdisciplinary, and academic perspective.
Related titles: Microfilm ed.: (from PQC); Online - full text ed.: ISSN 1743-9507. GBP 508, USD 795 to institutions (effective 2006) (from EBSCO Publishing, Gale Group, IngentaConnect, Northern Light Technology, Inc., O C L C Online Computer Library Center, Inc., ProQuest Information & Learning, Swets Information Services).
Indexed: ABIn, ASCA, AbHyg, BrHumI, CPM, CommAb, CurCont, DIP, Emerald, FS&TA, FamI, GEOBASE, H&TI, HRA, IBR, IBZ, M&MA, PRA, RRTA, RefZh, SSCI, SWA, WAE&RSA, WBA.
—BLDSC (8251.429000), IDS, IE, Infotrieve, ingenta. **CCC.**
Published by: Routledge (Subsidiary of: Taylor & Francis Group), 4 Park Sq, Milton Park, Abingdon, Oxon OX14 4RN, United Kingdom. TEL 44-1235-828600, FAX 44-1235-829000, journals@routledge.com, http://www.tandf.co.uk/journals/titles/02642069.asp, http://www.routledge.co.uk. Eds. Barry Howcroft, Gary Akehurst, Nicholas Alexander, Ronald Goldsmith. adv.: B&W page GBP 195, B&W page USD 285; trim 110 x 178.

650 GBR ISSN 0953-9212
SERVICE MANAGEMENT. Text in English. 1986. bi-m. free to qualified personnel (effective 2005). adv. **Document type:** *Magazine, Trade.* **Description:** Addresses the information needs of managers and directors in the high-tech service business.
Incorporates (1999-2004): Field Service Management (1469-090X)
Related titles: Online - full text ed.: (from EBSCO Publishing, ProQuest Information & Learning); ♦ Supplement(s): Service Management European Yearbook. ISSN 1461-3239.
—**CCC.**
Published by: Penton Media Europe (Subsidiary of: Penton Media, Inc.), Penton House, 288-290 Worton Rd, Isleworth, Mddx TW7 6EL, United Kingdom. TEL 44-20-8232-1600, FAX 44-20-8232-1650, information@penton.com, http://www.servicemanagement.co.uk, http://www.penton.com. Ed. Mark Turner. Adv. contact Jeremy Lord TEL 44-20-7620-0001. Circ: 14,000.

650 GBR ISSN 1461-3239
SERVICE MANAGEMENT EUROPEAN YEARBOOK. Text in English. 1990. a.
Related titles: ♦ Supplement to: Service Management. ISSN 0953-9212.
Published by: Findlay Publications Ltd., Franks Hall, Franks Ln, Horton Kirby, Kent DA4 9LL, United Kingdom. FAX 44-1322-289577, http://www.servicemanagement.com. Ed. Brain Wall.

▼ **SERVICE PROVIDER MAGAZINE.** see *COMPUTERS—Internet*

384.33 USA
SERVICE PROVIDER WEEKLY. (delivered as a PDF file; broadband Internet connection required for subscription.) Text in English. 2001 (Jan.). w. free to qualified personnel (effective 2005). adv. **Document type:** *Magazine, Trade.* **Description:** Covers the technology and news of the Internet industry.
Media: Online - full content.
Published by: Possibility Media, 10400 N.W. 33rd St., Ste. 270, Miami, FL 33172. TEL 786-206-8880, FAX 786-206-8884, info@possibilitymedia.com, http://www.spweekly.com/, http://www.possibilitymedia.com/. adv.: page USD 995.

330 ITA ISSN 1594-7637
SERVIZI; rivista di studi e ricerche. Text in Italian. 1991. s-a. **Document type:** *Magazine, Trade.*
Published by: (Confesercenti Provinciali di Pesaro e Urbino), Edizioni Quattroventi, Piazza Rinascimento 4, Urbino, PS 61029, Italy. TEL 39-072-22588, FAX 39-072-2320998, info@edizioniquattroventi.it, http://www.edizioniquattroventi.it. Ed. Giancarlo Zuccarini.

330 JPN ISSN 1340-2617
SETSUNAN UNIVERSITY. JOURNAL OF BUSINESS ADMINISTRATION AND INFORMATION/KEIEI JOHO KENKYU. Text and summaries in English, Japanese. 1994. s-a.
Published by: (Keiei Johogakubu), Setsunan Daigaku, 17-8 Ikedanaka-Machi, Neyagawa-shi, Osaka-fu 572-0074, Japan.

330 ITA
I SETTORI INDUSTRIALI. Text in Italian. 3/yr.
Related titles: ♦ Supplement to: Congiuntura Flash. ISSN 1129-6283.
Published by: Centro Studi Confindustria, Viale Pasteur 6, Rome, 00144, Italy. TEL 06-5920509, FAX 06-5924819, http://www.confindustria.it.

330 CHN ISSN 1000-971X
SHANDONG JINGJI/SHANDONG ECONOMICS. Text in Chinese. m.
Related titles: Online - full text ed.: (from East View Information Services).
Published by: Shandong Jingji Xueyuan/Shandong Institute of Economics, Jing 10 Lu, Jinan, Shandong, 250014, China. TEL 48920. Ed. Zhang Wenjie.

330 MYS ISSN 0126-9593
SHANG HAI. Text in Chinese. 1979. m. MYR 3.80 newsstand/cover (effective 2002). adv. **Document type:** *Magazine, Trade.* **Description:** Covers business related economic, social, and political topics.
Published by: Star Publications (M) Bhd., 13 Jalan 13-6, Petaling Jaya, Selangor, Selangor 46200, Malaysia. TEL 60-3-7955-4039, FAX 60-3-7955-1280. adv.: B&W page MYR 1,045, color page MYR 1,720; 187 x 265. Circ: 9,312.

330 CHN ISSN 1009-752X
SHANG-MAO JINGJI/COMMERCIAL AND TRADING ECONOMICS. Text in Chinese. 2001. m. **Document type:** *Journal, Academic/Scholarly.*
Published by: Zhongguo Renmin Daxue, Shubao Zilio Zhongxin/Renmin University of China, Information Center for Social Server, Dongcheng-qu, 3, Zhangzizhong Lu, Beijing, 100007, China. TEL 86-10-84043003, 86-10-64039458, FAX 86-10-64015080, kyes@163.net, http://www.confucius.cn.net/.

330 CHN ISSN 1000-4211
SHANGHAI JINGJI/SHANGHAI ECONOMICS. Text in Chinese. 1981. bi-m. CNY 7.20 (effective 1993).
Published by: (Bumen Jingji Yanjiusuo), Shanghai Shehui Kexueyuan/Shanghai Academy of Social Sciences, No 7 Alley 622 Huaihai Zhonglu, Shanghai, 200020, China. TEL 3271170, FAX 86-21-270004. Ed. Xu Zhihe.

330 CHN ISSN 1005-1309
HC428.S47
SHANGHAI JINGJI YANJIU/SHANGHAI ECONOMIC RESEARCH. Text in Chinese. m.
Related titles: Online - full text ed.: (from East View Information Services).
Published by: (Jingji Yanjiusuo), Shanghai Shehui Kexueyuan/Shanghai Academy of Social Sciences, No 7 Alley 622 Huaihai Zhonglu, Shanghai, 200020, China. TEL 86-21-6327-1170. Ed. Zhang Jiguang.

330 CHN ISSN 1671-3443
SHANGJIE DAOKAN/COMMERCIAL WORLD GUIDE. Text in Chinese. m. 64 p./no.; **Document type:** *Magazine, Trade.*
Published by: Zhongguo Renmin Daxue, Shubao Zilio Zhongxin/Renmin University of China, Information Center for Social Server, Dongcheng-qu, 3, Zhangzizhong Lu, Beijing, 100007, China. TEL 86-10-84043003, 86-10-64039458, FAX 86-10-64015080, kyes@163.net, http://www.confucius.cn.net/bkdetail.asp?fzt=F511. **Dist. by:** China International Book Trading Corp, 35 Chegongzhuang Xilu, Haidian District, PO Box 399, Beijing 100044, China. TEL 86-10-68412045, FAX 86-10-68412023, cibtc@mail.cibtc.com.cn, http://www.cibtc.com.cn.

330 CHN ISSN 1001-148X
SHANGYE YANJIU/COMMERCIAL RESEARCH EDITORIAL DEPARTMENT. Text in Chinese. 1958. s-m. **Document type:** *Journal, Academic/Scholarly.*
Related titles: Online - full text ed.: (from East View Information Services, WanFang Data Corp.).

Published by: Ha'erbin Shangye Daxue/Harbin University of Commerce, 138 Tongda Street, Daoli District, Ha'erbin, 150076, China. TEL 86-451-84866358, FAX 86-451-84840413, busi@chinajournal.net.cn; commrese@public.hr.hl.cn, http://syyj.periodicals.net.cn/.

320.531 CHN ISSN 1005-4294
HB97.5
SHEHUI ZHUYI JINGJI LILUN YU SHIJIAN/SOCIALIST ECONOMIC THEORY AND PRACTICE. Text in Chinese. 1978. m. CNY 180 (effective 2004). 192 p./no.; **Document type:** *Journal, Academic/Scholarly.*
Formerly (until 1994): Zhengzhi Jingjixue (Shehuizhuyi Bufen) (1001-3350)
Indexed: RASB.
Published by: Zhongguo Renmin Daxue, Shubao Zilio Zhongxin/Renmin University of China, Information Center for Social Server, Dongcheng-qu, 3, Zhangzizhong Lu, Beijing, 100007, China. TEL 86-10-64039458, FAX 86-10-64015080, kyes@163.net, http://www.confucius.cn.net/bkdetail.asp?fzt=F13. **Dist. in US by:** China Publications Service, PO Box 49614, Chicago, IL 60649. TEL 312-288-3291, FAX 312-288-8570; **Dist. by:** China International Book Trading Corp, 35 Chegongzhuang Xilu, Haidian District, PO Box 399, Beijing 100044, China. TEL 86-10-68412045, FAX 86-10-68412023, cibtc@mail.cibtc.com.cn, http://www.cibtc.com.cn.

628 CHN ISSN 1671-4407
SHENGTAI JINGJI/ECOLOGICAL ECONOMY. Text in Chinese. bi-m. 56 p./no.; **Document type:** *Magazine, Academic/Scholarly.* **Description:** Discusses theories of ecological economics. Advocates the balanced development of ecology and economics.
Indexed: RDA.
Published by: (Zhongguo Shengtai Jingji Xuehui), Yunnan Jiaoyu Chubanshe/Yunnan Education Publishing House, 3rd Floor, Yunnan Press & Publication Building, 609 West Huancheng Road, Kunming, Yunnan Province 650034, China. TEL 86-871-4138386, econtp@163.net; econtp@hotmail.com, yneph@public.km.yn.cn, http://www.yneph.com/skgc/stjingji.htm. **Dist. overseas by:** China International Book Trading Corp, 35 Chegongzhuang Xilu, Haidian District, PO Box 399, Beijing 100044, China. TEL 86-10-68412045, FAX 86-10-68412023, cibtc@mail.cibtc.com.cn, http://www.cibtc.com.cn. **Co-sponsor:** Yunnan Sheng Shengtai Jingji Xuehui.

330 CHN
SHICHANG YU XIAOFEI BAO/MARKET AND CONSUMERS. Text in Chinese. 4/w. CNY 138 (effective 2004). **Document type:** *Consumer.*
Published by: Liaoning Ribao Baoye Jituan/Liaoning Daily Newspaper Group, 339, Zhongshan Lu, Chenyang, 110001, China. TEL 86-24-22872198, FAX 86-24-22865402, http://www.scyxfb.com/. **Dist. by:** China International Book Trading Corp, 35 Chegongzhuang Xilu, Haidian District, PO Box 399, Beijing 100044, China. TEL 86-10-68412045, FAX 86-10-68412023, cibtc@mail.cibtc.com.cn, http://www.cibtc.com.cn.

330 CHN ISSN 1671-3419
SHIJIE JINGJI DAOKAN/GUIDE TO WORLD ECONOMY. Text in Chinese. m. CNY 132 (effective 2004). **Document type:** *Journal, Academic/Scholarly.*
Published by: Zhongguo Renmin Daxue, Shubao Zilio Zhongxin/Renmin University of China, Information Center for Social Server, Dongcheng-qu, 3, Zhangzizhong Lu, Beijing, 100007, China. TEL 86-10-84043003, 86-10-64039458, FAX 86-10-64015080, kyes@163.net, http://www.confucius.cn.net/bkdetail.asp?fzt=F8. **Dist. by:** China International Book Trading Corp, 35 Chegongzhuang Xilu, Haidian District, PO Box 399, Beijing 100044, China. TEL 86-10-68412045, FAX 86-10-68412023, cibtc@mail.cibtc.com.cn, http://www.cibtc.com.cn.

330 CHN
SHIJIE JINGJI YICONG/WORLD ECONOMICS TRANSLATIONS. Text in Chinese. m.
Published by: Zhongguo Shehui Kexueyuan, Shijie Jingji yu Zhengzhi Yanjiusuo/Chinese Academy of Social Sciences, Institute of World Economics and Politics, 5 Jianguomennei Dajie, Beijing, 100732, China. TEL 86-10-5137744. Ed. Gong Ronjin.

330 CHN ISSN 1007-0184
SHIJIE JINGJI YU ZHONGGUO/WORLD ECONOMY & CHINA. Text in Chinese, English. q. USD 80.
—BLDSC (9354.761200).
Published by: Zhongguo Shehui Kexueyuan, Shijie Jingji yu Zhengzhi Yanjiusuo/Chinese Academy of Social Sciences, Institute of World Economics and Politics, 5 Jianguomennei Dajie, Beijing, 100732, China. TEL 86-10-5137744. Ed. Yuanyang Gu. **Co-sponsor:** Chinese Society on World Economy.

SHKOL'NYI EKONOMICHESKII ZHURNAL. see *EDUCATION*

330 JPN ISSN 0286-2174
SHODAI RONSHU/KOBE UNIVERSITY OF COMMERCE. JOURNAL. Text in Japanese. 1949. bi-m. **Document type:** *Journal, Academic/Scholarly.*
—BLDSC (4811.200000).
Published by: Kobe Shoka Daigaku/Kobe University of Commerce, 8-2-1 Gakuen-nishimachi, Nishi-ku, Kobe, 651-2197, Japan. http://www.kobeuc.ac.jp/index.htm.

330 JPN
SHOGAKU SHUSHI✶ /NIHON UNIVERSITY JOURNAL OF BUSINESS. Text in Japanese. 1928. bi-m. bk.rev.
Supersedes in part: Keizai Shushi/Studies in Economic Science (0387-3048)
—BLDSC (5089.181000).
Published by: Nihon Daigaku, Keizaigaku Shogaku Kenkyu-kai/Nihon University, Economic and Commercial Research Society, 2-1 Kinuta 5, Setagaya-ku, Tokyo, 157-8570, Japan.

330 JPN ISSN 0474-8638
HB9
SHOGAKU TOKYU/ECONOMIC REVIEW. Text in Japanese. 1950. irreg. **Document type:** *Journal, Academic/Scholarly.*
—BLDSC (3654.739000).
Published by: Otaru Shoka Daigaku/Otaru University of Commerce, Institute of Economic Research, 3-5-21 Midori, Otaru, Hokkaido 047-8501, Japan. http://www.otaru-uc.ac.jp/dept/econ/welcome.html.

SHOPPING CENTER BUSINESS. see *REAL ESTATE*

SHUILI KEJI YU JINGJI/WATER CONSERVANCY SCIENCE AND TECHNOLOGY AND ECONOMY. see *CONSERVATION*

330 JPN
SHUKAN DAIYAMONDO/WEEKLY DIAMOND. Text in Japanese. 1913. w. JPY 16,000.
Published by: Diamond Inc., 4-2 Kasumigaseki 1-chome, Chiyoda-ku, Tokyo, 100-0013, Japan. TEL 03-3504-6519, TELEX 24461. Ed. Teiji Kajima.

330 JPN ISSN 0918-5755
HC462.7
SHUKAN TOYO KEIZAI/WEEKLY TOYO KEIZAI. Text in Japanese. 1895. w. adv.
Published by: Toyo Keizai Inc., 1-2-1 Nihonbashihongoku-cho, Chuo-ku, Tokyo, 1030021, Japan. TEL 81-3-3246-5601, FAX 81-3-3246-0679, jch@toyokeizai.co.jp, http://www.mediagalxy.co.jp/toyokeizai/. Ed. Toshiki Ohta. Adv. contact Shuji Kawase. B&W page JPY 580,000, color page JPY 820,000; trim 257 x 182. Circ: 61,024. **Subscr. to:** 380 Lexington Ave, Ste 4505, New York, NY 10168.

330 UAE
SHU'UN AL-SINA'AH. Text in Arabic. 1985. q. **Description:** Provides news and information of interest to members of the business and industry communities, and serves as a forum for discussion of concerns.
Published by: Ministry of Finance and Industry, Information Department, PO Box 398, Abu Dhabi, United Arab Emirates. TEL 726000, FAX 823901, TELEX 22937 FEDFIN EM. Ed. Rafa'at al-Mugharbel. Circ: 1,000.

330 RUS
SIBIRSKII POSAD; tyumenskii oblastnoi ekonomicheskii ezhedel'nik. Text in Russian. w. RUR 99.80 domestic (effective 2002). adv. **Document type:** *Newspaper, Consumer.*
Address: http://www.isurgut.ru/~company/sp/. adv.: page RUR 8,000.

330 DEU ISSN 1615-1364
➤ **SIGNALE.** Text in English, German. 1986. q. free. adv. illus. back issues avail. **Document type:** *Journal, Academic/Scholarly.*
Former titles (until 1999): Signale aus der Wissenschaftlichen Hochschule fuer Unternehmensfuehrung Koblenz (1433-3759); (until 1997): Signale aus der Wissenschaftlichen Hochschule fuer Unternehmensfuehrung (0943-3937); (until 1993): Hochschulnachrichten aus der Wissenschaftlichen Hochschule fuer Unternehmensfuehrung Koblenz (0933-3665)
Published by: Wissenschaftliche Hochschule fuer Unternehmensfuehrung, Otto-Beisheim-Hochschule, Burgplatz 2, Vallendar, 56179, Germany. TEL 49-261-6509600, FAX 49-261-6509509, neumann@whu.edu, whu@whu.edu, http://www.whu.edu. Ed., R&P Juergen Neumann. Adv. contact Gisbert Hoyermann. page EUR 1,660. Circ: 2,500.

910.202 BEL
SIGNATURE. Text in French. 1963. 5/yr. free to members (effective 2005). bk.rev. **Document type:** *Consumer.* **Description:** Business and lifestyle articles for Diners Club cardholders.
Related titles: Dutch ed.; Flemish ed.; English ed.
Published by: (Diners Club Benelux), Continental Publishing, Lakborslei 114, Antwerp, 2100, Belgium. TEL 32-3-360-7800, FAX 32-3-360-7801. Ed. Willy van den Bossche. Pub. Jozef Govaerts. Adv. contact Nadine Grignard. Circ: 70,000.

330 300 MAR ISSN 0851-4909
SIGNES DU PRESENT. Text in French. 1936. irreg. MAD 50. bk.rev. cum.index.
Formerly (until 1988): Bulletin Economique et Social du Maroc (0007-4586)
Related titles: Arabic ed.; English ed.
Indexed: PAIS.
Published by: Societe d'Etudes Economiques Sociales et Statistiques du Maroc, B P 535, Rabat-chellah, Morocco. TEL 792-20. Ed. Abdelkhebir Khatibi. Circ: 1,300.

330 USA
SILICON VALLEY DAILY. Text in English. d. **Document type:** *Consumer.* **Description:** Reports on business news in Silicon Valley and the San Francisco Bay area.
Media: Online - full content.
Address: svdaily@hotmail.com, http://www.svdaily.com.

330 600 CAN ISSN 1203-8601
SILICON VALLEY NORTH. Abbreviated title: S V N. Text and summaries in English. 1995. m. CND 42 domestic; CND 45 in United States (effective 2003). adv. **Document type:** *Newspaper, Trade.* **Description:** Provides local and national coverage of Canada's technology industry.
Related titles: Online - full content ed.; Regional ed(s).: Silicon Valley North Ottawa; Silicon Valley North Toronto; Silicon Valley North Alberta; Silicon Valley North British Columbia.
Published by: InBusiness Media Network Inc., 1686 Woodward Dr, Ottawa, ON K2C 3R8, Canada. TEL 613-230-8699, FAX 613-230-9606, http://www.siliconvalleynorth.com/home/, http://www.inbusinessmedia.com.

330 USA ISSN 1532-7469
SILICON VALLEY - SAN JOSE BUSINESS JOURNAL. Text in English. 1983. w. (Fri.). USD 84.95; USD 1.50 newsstand/cover (effective 2005). adv. bk.rev. 52 p./no. 4 cols./p.; **Document type:** *Newspaper.*
Former titles: The Business Journal (San Jose) (1048-8812); (until 1988): San Jose Business Journal (0886-5922); (until 1985): Business Journal (San Jose) (0737-7274)
Related titles: Online - full text ed.: (from Gale Group, O C L C Online Computer Library Center, Inc., ProQuest Information & Learning).
Indexed: ABIn, BusDate, LRI, T&II.
—**CCC.**
Published by: American City Business Journals, Inc. (Austin), 96 N. Third St, Ste 100, San Jose, CA 95112. TEL 408-295-3800, FAX 408-295-5028, sanjose@bizjournals.com, http://www.bizjournals.com/sanjose/. Ed. Delbert Schafer. Adv. contacts Matt Toledo, Jeffery Davis. Circ: 14,812 (paid); 2,800 (controlled).

330 UAE
AL-SINA'AH/INDUSTRY. Text in Arabic. 1988. m. **Description:** Covers industrial concerns, with a focus on development and the future of industry in the U.A.E.
Published by: Mu'assasat al-Aamah lil-Sina'ah, PO Box 4499, Abu Dhabi, United Arab Emirates. TEL 214900, FAX 325034, TELEX 22938 GICORP EM. Ed. Isa Abdul Rahman Atiq.

330 SGP
SINGAPORE BUSINESS REVIEW. Text in English. m. SGD 78 (effective 2005). adv. **Document type:** *Magazine, Trade.*
Published by: Charlton Media Group, 9B Stanley St, Singapore, 068728, Singapore. TEL 65-6223-7660, admin@charltonmedia.com, http://www.charltonmedia.com. Ed. Angela McFeeters. Pub. Timothy Charlton.

330 SGP ISSN 0217-5908
HB1
➤ **SINGAPORE ECONOMIC REVIEW.** Abbreviated title: S E R. Text in English. 1956. s-a. SGD 170, USD 99, EUR 87 combined subscription to institutions print & online eds. (effective 2006). adv. bk.rev. back issues avail.; reprint service avail. from SCH. **Document type:** *Journal, Academic/Scholarly.* **Description:** SER publishes scholarly work of contemporary economic interest covering policy analyses, conceptual papers, econometric investigations, and theoretical analyzes on a broad range of issues impinging on Southeast Asia and the broader Asia-Pacific region. Highlights of emerging themes that will be covered in SER include, but are not limited to, an analysis of causes, consequences, expected duration, and contagion effects of the Asian crisis, China's economic reform, the economic resurgence of India, the economics of information, the environmental crisis, ageing and health economics, Asia's business networks, the economics of innovation, technopreneurship and economic growth, the economics of globalization, analyses of productivity and dynamic competitive advantage, and economic imlpications of the knowledge-based economy.
Formerly (until 1982): Malayan Economic Review (0047-5599)
Related titles: Online - full text ed.: (from EBSCO Publishing, O C L C Online Computer Library Center, Inc., Swets Information Services).
Indexed: ABIn, APEL, ASCA, BAS, CREJ, DIP, EI, ESPM, GEOBASE, IBR, IBSS, IBZ, ILD, JEL, MEA&I, PAIS, RASB, RiceAb, RiskAb, SSCI.
—BLDSC (8285.463050), IE.

Published by: (Economic Society of Singapore), World Scientific Publishing Co. Pte. Ltd., 5 Toh Tuck Link, Singapore, 596224, Singapore. TEL 65-466-5775, FAX 65-467-7667, wspc@wspc.com.sg, http://www.worldscinet.com/ser/ser.shtml. Ed. Euston Quah. Circ: 800. **Subscr. to:** Farrer Rd, PO Box 128, Singapore 912805, Singapore. sales@wspc.com.sg. **Dist. by:** World Scientific Publishing Co., Inc., 1060 Main St, River Edge, NJ 07661. TEL 201-487-9655, 800-227-7562, FAX 201-487-9656, 888-977-2665.; World Scientific Publishing Ltd., 57 Shelton St, London WC2H 9HE, United Kingdom. TEL 44-20-78360888, FAX 44-20-78362020, sales@wspc.co.uk.

➤ **THE SINGAPORE LAW GAZETTE.** see *LAW*

330 SGP ISSN 0217-7528
HF3800.67
SINGAPORE TRADE NEWS✶. Text in English. 1984. bi-m. **Document type:** *Trade.* **Description:** Gives a general overview of Singapore and its business prospects.
Published by: Singapore Trade Development Board, Office Tower, 230 Victoria Street, 07-00 Bugis Juction, Singapore, 188024, Singapore. FAX 2740770, TELEX RS-28617-TRADEV. Ed. Jeanne Cheng. Circ: 15,000.

330 ANT
ST. MAARTEN BUSINESS JOURNAL; the authoritative independent voice of the business community. Text in English. 1985. m. USD 20. adv.
Formerly: St. Maarten Journal
Address: PO Box 372, Philipsburg, St Maarten, Netherlands Antilles. Ed. Louis N Peters. Circ: 500.

330 CHL ISSN 0716-2456
HA992
SINTESIS ESTADISTICA DE CHILE. Text in Spanish. 1978. a. USD 15. **Document type:** *Government.* **Description:** Contains general and economic statistics of Chile.
Related titles: English ed.
Published by: Banco Central de Chile, Casilla 967, Santiago, Chile. TEL 56-2-670-2000, FAX 56-2-698-4847. Circ: 2,000.

650 GBR
SIR FREDERIC HOOPER AWARD ESSAY. Text in English. 1969. a. membership.
Published by: Foundation for Business Responsibilities, 40 Doughty St, London, WC1N 2LF, United Kingdom.

338.9 GBR ISSN 0080-9780
SIR GEORGE EARLE MEMORIAL LECTURE ON INDUSTRY AND GOVERNMENT. Text in English. 1966. a. price varies. bk.rev.
Published by: Foundation for Business Responsibilities, 40 Doughty St, London, WC1N 2LF, United Kingdom.

330 ITA
SISTEMA ITALIA. Text in Italian. 1948. w.
Published by: Edizioni Sistema Italia SpA, Via Liszt, 21, Rome, RM 00144, Italy. TEL 39-6-5992442, FAX 39-6-59926702. Ed. Lorenzo Guglielmi. Circ: 35,000.

330 USA ISSN 1059-1958
SITUATIONS DIGEST✶. Text in English. 1991. q. USD 29.99. **Document type:** *Consumer.*
Published by: Publishing & Business Consultants, 4427 W Slauson Ave, Los Angeles, CA 90043-2717. TEL 213-732-3477, FAX 213-732-9123. Ed. Andeson Napoleon Atia.

SKATTEN. ERHVERV. see *BUSINESS AND ECONOMICS—Public Finance, Taxation*

330 CAN
SKEENA BUSINESS MAGAZINE. Text in English. 1993. m. CND 20; CND 30 in United States. adv.
Published by: Sterling Newspapers Limited, 413 3rd Ave E, Prince Rupert, BC V8J 1K7, Canada. TEL 604-624-2613, FAX 604-624-2680. Ed. Mike Kelly. Pub. Les Yates. adv.: B&W page CND 630; trim 10.63 x 8. Circ: 4,500.

658 HRV ISSN 1330-2833
SLOBODNO PODUZETNISTVO. Text in Croatian. 1951. m. **Document type:** *Magazine, Trade.*
Formerly (until 1993): Privredni Vjesnik - T E B (0351-806X)
Published by: TEB - Poslovno Savjetovanje, Trg Hrvatskih Velikana 15, Zagreb, 10000, Croatia. TEL 385-1-4611211, FAX 385-1-4611411. Ed. Sime Guzic.

330 SVK
SLOVENSKY PROFIT; hospodarsky a podnikatel'sky tyzdennik. Text in Slovak. w. SKK 12 newsstand/cover; USD 43 (effective 2000). charts; illus.; stat. 32 p./no. 5 cols./p.; **Document type:** *Newspaper.* **Description:** Reports business and financial news; provides information on investing.
Published by: Ringier Slovakia a. s., Prievozska 14, PO Box 46, Bratislava 24, 82004, Slovakia. TEL 42-7-2103817, FAX 42-2-2104581. Ed. Iveta Seifertova. Circ: 43,000.

SMALL-SCALE FOREST ECONOMICS, MANAGEMENT AND POLICY. see *FORESTS AND FORESTRY*

330 USA
SMART BUSINESS. Text in English. 1998. q.
Published by: Baumer Financial Publishing (Subsidiary of: Imagination Publishing, LLC), 820 W Jackson Blvd No 450, Chicago, IL 60607. TEL 312-627-1020, FAX 312-627-1105, baumerfpub@aol.com. Ed. Elizabeth Seymour. Circ: 60,000.

330 USA ISSN 1554-5962
▼ **SMART MEETINGS**; the intelligent way to plan. Text in English. 2003. m. free to qualified personnel (effective 2004). illus. **Document type:** *Magazine, Trade.* **Description:** Delivers editorial content on meeting industry trends, technologies, and meeting venues in the western region.
Related titles: Online - full text ed.
Published by: Bright Business Media, 475 Gate 5 Rd., Ste 225, Sausalito, CA 94965. TEL 415-339-9355, FAX 415-339-9361, subscriptions@smartmtgs.com, editor@smartmtgs.com, http://www.smartmtgs.com. Ed. Guy Wright. Circ: 30,000 (controlled).

330 USA
SNOHOMISH COUNTY BUSINESS JOURNAL. Text in English. 1998 (Apr.). m. free in county; USD 18 out of county (effective 2004). adv. **Document type:** *Newspaper.* **Description:** Offers news about residential and commercial real estate, people on the move and profiles of business leaders, plus helpful news for the rapidly growing small-office and home-office business sector, as well as midsize to large companies.
Formerly (until Aug.2002): The Herald Business Journal
Published by: The Daily Herald Co. (Subsidiary of: Washington Post Co.), Box 930, Everett, WA 98206. TEL 425-339-3445, FAX 425-339-3049, http://www.snohomishcountybusinessjournal.com/. Ed. John Wolcott TEL 425-339-3102. Pub. Steve Hawes TEL 425-339-3051. adv.: page USD 1,950. Circ: 14,000 (paid and free).

330 NLD
SOCIAAL-ECONOMISCHE RAAD. JAARVERSLAG/SOCIAAL-ECONOMISCHE RAAD. ANNUAL REPORT. Text in Dutch. a. free. bk.rev. **Document type:** *Corporate.* **Description:** Discusses economic and social policy issues.
Published by: Sociaal-Economische Raad, Postbus 90405, The Hague, 2509 LK, Netherlands. TEL 31-70-3499499, FAX 31-70-383-2535, http://www.ser.nl.

SOCIAL AND ECONOMIC STUDIES. see *SOCIAL SCIENCES: COMPREHENSIVE WORKS*

330 FRA ISSN 0769-055X
SOCIAL PRATIQUE. Text in French. bi-m. FRF 890 (effective 1998).
Related titles: ♦ Supplement(s): Social Pratique. Supplement. ISSN 0997-1092.
Published by: Groupe Liaisons S.A. (Subsidiary of: Wolters Kluwer BV), 1 Avenue Edouard Belin, Rueil Malmaison, Cedex 92856, France. TEL 33-1-41299696, FAX 33-1-41299880.

330 FRA ISSN 0997-1092
SOCIAL PRATIQUE. SUPPLEMENT. Text in French. 1985. m.
Related titles: ♦ Supplement to: Social Pratique. ISSN 0769-055X.
Published by: Groupe Liaisons S.A. (Subsidiary of: Wolters Kluwer BV), 1 Avenue Edouard Belin, Rueil Malmaison, Cedex 92856, France. TEL 33-1-41299696, FAX 33-1-41299880.

330 ROM
SOCIETATI LISTATE. Text in Romanian. s-a. ROL 325,000 (effective 2002). **Document type:** *Magazine, Trade.*
Published by: Ring Media, Str. Popa Tatu nr. 71, sector 1, Bucharest, Romania. TEL 40-21-3154356, FAX 40-21-3124556.

330 BEL
SOCIETE ROYALE D'ECONOMIE POLITIQUE DE BELGIQUE. SEANCES. Text in French. 1855. 8/yr.
Formerly (until 1964): Societe Royale d'Economie Politique de Belgique. Comptes Rendus des Travaux
Indexed: PAIS, RASB.
Published by: Societe Royale d'Economie Politique de Belgique, Av General Michel 1b, Charleroi, 6000, Belgium. http://www.cifop.be/srepb2.html. Circ: 900.

▼ **SOCIETY AND BUSINESS REVIEW.** see *SOCIOLOGY*

330 HUN ISSN 1588-9726
➤ **SOCIETY AND ECONOMY.** Variant title: Budapest University of Economic Sciences and Public Administration. Journal. Journal of the Budapest University of Economic Sciences and Public Administration. Text in English. 1979. 3/yr. USD 162 print & online eds. (effective 2006). **Document type:** *Journal, Academic/Scholarly.* **Description:** Covers a wide range in the field of social sciences. Publishes research papers in theoretical and applied economics, international economics, economic policy, business studies, public administration, sociology and political science. The results of scientific conferences organized by the Budapest University of Economic Sciences and Public Administration are covered in special issues.
Formerly (until 2002): Society and Economy in Central and Eastern Europe (1218-9391); Which superseded in part (in 1995): Budapesti Kozgazdasagtudomanyi Egyetem Folyoirata. Aula. Tarsadalom es Gazdasag (0866-6865); Which was formerly (until 1990): Marx Karoly Kozgazdasagtudomanyi Egyetem Folyoirata. Egyetemi Szemle (0139-4045)
Related titles: Online - full text ed.: ISSN 1588-970X (from EBSCO Publishing, Gale Group, IngentaConnect, Swets Information Services); ♦ Hungarian ed.: Tarsadalom es Gazdasag. ISSN 1588-9734.
Published by: (Budapest University of Economic Sciences and Public Administration), Akademiai Kiado Rt. (Subsidiary of: Wolters Kluwer N.V.), Prielle Kornelia U. 19, Budapest, 1117, Hungary. TEL 36-1-4648282, FAX 36-1-4648221, journals@akkrt.hu, http://www.akkrt.hu. Ed. Attila Chikan.

➤ **SOCIETY FOR BUSINESS ETHICS. NEWSLETTER.** see *PHILOSOPHY*

352.68 USA
SOCIETY OF GOVERNMENT ECONOMISTS. BULLETIN. Text in English. m. **Document type:** *Bulletin.* **Description:** Aimed at economists employed by governments or those interested in economic policy issues.
Published by: Society of Government Economists, c/o Thesia I Garner, Bicentennial Bldg, Bureau of Labor Statistics, 600 E St, N W, Rm 4103, Washington, DC 20212. TEL 202-272-2610, FAX 202-272-2610.

330 DNK ISSN 0109-2863
SOENDERJYLLANDS ERHVERVSORIENTERING: PRODUKTION, HANDEL, KONTAKT. Text in Danish. 1983. q. illus.
Published by: Langenberg Trykkeri, Falstersgade 2, Sonderborg, 6400, Denmark.

SOFT DRINK RECYCLER. see *ENVIRONMENTAL STUDIES—Waste Management*

SOFTWARE BUSINESS. see *COMPUTERS—Software*

SOGO TOSHI KENKYU/COMPREHENSIVE URBAN STUDIES. see *SOCIOLOGY*

330 GBR
THE SOLENT & SOUTH CENTRAL BUSINESS MAGAZINE. Text in English. m. GBP 35 domestic (effective 2001); Free to qualified subscribers.. adv. **Document type:** *Magazine, Trade.* **Description:** Covers business news and issues in the Solent and South Central region.
Published by: Elcot Publications (South) Ltd., 1100 Parkway, Solent Business Park, Whitely, Fareham, PO15 7AB, United Kingdom. TEL 44-1489-611631, FAX 44-1492-611732, solent@elcot.co.uk, http://www.businessmag.co.uk/index.html.

330 USA ISSN 0191-6327
SONOMA BUSINESS✶. Text in English. m.
Published by: Mariposa Press, 50 Old Courthouse Sq 105, Santa Rosa, CA 95404-4930. TEL 707-575-8282. Ed. James Dunn. Circ: 7,500.

330 USA
SONOMA COUNTY HERALD-RECORDER. Text in English. 1899. s-w. (Wed. & Fri.). USD 216.20; USD 2 per issue (effective 2005). **Document type:** *Newspaper, Trade.*
Published by: Daily Journal Corp., 1818 Fourth St, Santa Rosa, CA 95404. TEL 707-545-1166, FAX 707-545-6310, herald-recorder@dailyjournal.com. Ed., Pub. Christine Griego. Circ: 350 morning (paid). Wire service: AP.

330.1 339 TWN ISSN 0259-3769
HB9
SOOCHOW JOURNAL OF ECONOMICS AND BUSINESS. Key Title: Dongwu Jingji Shangxue Xuebao. Text in Chinese, English. 1977. a. USD 20. reprints avail. **Document type:** *Academic/Scholarly.*
Indexed: BAS.
Published by: Soochow University, Wai Shuang Hsi, Shih Lin, Taipei, Taiwan. FAX 886-2-8812317. Circ: 500.

320.531 NOR ISSN 0038-1624
SOSIALOEKONOMEN. Text in Norwegian; Text occasionally in English. 1947. 10/yr. NOK 575 to individuals; NOK 250 to students (effective 1999). adv. bk.rev. charts; illus. index. **Document type:** *Academic/Scholarly.*
Formerly (until 1958): Stimulator (0332-9488)
Indexed: RASB.
Published by: Sosialoekonomenes Forening, Youngstorget, Postboks 8872, Oslo, 0181, Norway. TEL 47-22-41-32-90, FAX 47-22-41-32-93. Ed. Torstein A Bye. adv.: B&W page NOK 4,800; trim 187 x 254. Circ: 2,500.

650 USA ISSN 1048-2970
SOUND BUSINESS. Text in English. 1978. m. USD 18. adv. charts; illus.; mkt.; stat.; tr.lit.
Formerly (until 1990): Seattle Business (0887-6630)
Related titles: Online - full text ed.: (from Gale Group, ProQuest Information & Learning, The Dialog Corporation).
Published by: Vernon Publications, 3000 Northrup Way, Ste. 200, Bellevue, WA 98004. TEL 206-827-9900. Ed. Michele Andrus Dill. Circ: 9,200.

330 CAN ISSN 0381-5471
SOUNDING BOARD. Text in English. 1935. m. (11/yr.). adv. **Document type:** *Newspaper.*
Published by: Board of Trade, World Trade Centre, Ste 400, 999 Canada Pl, Vancouver, BC V6C 3E1, Canada. TEL 604-641-1270, FAX 604-681-0437. Adv. contact Michelle Brazeau. Circ: 12,000.

SOUNDINGS (NOTRE DAME); a series of books on ethics, economics and business. see *PHILOSOPHY*

330 FRA ISSN 1729-0635
SOURCE O C D E. DEVELOPPEMENT URBAIN, RURAL ET REGIONAL. (Organisation de Cooperation et de Developpement Economiques) Text in French. irreg. EUR 425, USD 488, GBP 281, JPY 57,400 (effective 2005).
Formerly (until 2003): Source O C D E. Economie Territoriale (1683-2442)
Related titles: Online - full content ed.: ISSN 1729-0643. EUR 298, USD 342, GBP 197, JPY 40,200 (effective 2005); Online - full text ed.: (from EBSCO Publishing, Gale Group, IngentaConnect, Swets Information Services); ♦ English ed.: Source O E C D. Urban, Rural and Regional Development. ISSN 1729-0619.
Published by: Organization for Economic Cooperation and Development, 2 Rue Andre Pascal, Paris, 75775 Cedex 16, France. TEL 33-1-45248200, FAX 33-1-45248500, http://www.oecd.org. **Dist. by:** O E C D Turpin North America, PO Box 194, Downingtown, PA 19335-0194. TEL 610-524-5361, 800-456-6323, FAX 610-524-5417, bookscustomer@turpinna.com; Extenza - Turpin, Pegasus Dr, Stratton Business Park, Biggleswade, Beds SG18 8TQ, United Kingdom. TEL 44-1462-672555, FAX 44-1462-480-947, custservturpin@turpinltd.com, http://www.extenza-turpin.com.

330 300 FRA ISSN 1684-3134
SOURCE O C D E. ECONOMIE GENERALE ET ETUDES PROSPECTIVES. (Organisation de Cooperation et de Developpement Economiques) Text in French. irreg. free.
Media: Online - full content. **Related titles:** Online - full text ed.: (from Gale Group, IngentaConnect, Swets Information Services); Ed.: Source O E C D. General Economies & Future Studies. ISSN 1681-5378. 2000. free.
Published by: Organization for Economic Cooperation and Development, 2 Rue Andre Pascal, Paris, 75775 Cedex 16, France. TEL 33-1-45248200, FAX 33-1-45248500, http://www.oecd.org.

330 300 FRA ISSN 1683-2329
SOURCE O C D E. ECONOMIES EMERGENTES. (Organisation de Cooperation et de Developpement Economiques) Text in French. irreg. EUR 1,295, USD 1,489, GBP 856, JPY 174,800 (effective 2005). stat. **Document type:** *Government.*
Related titles: Online - full content ed.: ISSN 1684-2979. EUR 910, USD 1,046, GBP 600, JPY 122,900 (effective 2005); Online - full text ed.: (from EBSCO Publishing, Gale Group, IngentaConnect, Swets Information Services); ♦ English ed.: Source O E C D. Emerging Economies. ISSN 1608-0173.
Published by: Organization for Economic Cooperation and Development, 2 Rue Andre Pascal, Paris, 75775 Cedex 16, France. TEL 33-1-45248200, FAX 33-1-45248500, http://www.oecd.org. **Dist. by:** Extenza - Turpin, Pegasus Dr, Stratton Business Park, Biggleswade, Beds SG18 8TQ, United Kingdom. TEL 44-1462-687552, FAX 44-1462-480947, subscriptions@extenza-turpin.com; O E C D Turpin North America, PO Box 194, Downingtown, PA 19335-0194. TEL 610-524-5361, 800-456-6323, FAX 610-524-5417, journalscustomer@turpinna.com.

330 332 FRA ISSN 1683-2450
SOURCE O C D E. ECONOMIES EN TRANSITION. (Organisation de Cooperation et de Developpement Economiques) Text in French. irreg. EUR 1,215, USD 1,397, GBP 800, GBP 164,000 (effective 2005). **Document type:** *Government.*
Related titles: Online - full content ed.: ISSN 1684-310X. EUR 855, USD 983, GBP 564, JPY 15,400 (effective 2005); Online - full text ed.: (from EBSCO Publishing, Gale Group, IngentaConnect, Swets Information Services); ♦ English ed.: Source O E C D. Transition Economies. ISSN 1608-0157.
Published by: Organization for Economic Cooperation and Development, 2 Rue Andre Pascal, Paris, 75775 Cedex 16, France. TEL 33-1-45248200, FAX 33-1-45248500, http://www.oecd.org. **Dist. by:** Extenza - Turpin, Pegasus Dr, Stratton Business Park, Biggleswade, Beds SG18 8TQ, United Kingdom. TEL 44-1462-687552, FAX 44-1462-480947, subscriptions@extenza-turpin.com; O E C D Turpin North America, PO Box 194, Downingtown, PA 19335-0194. TEL 610-524-5361, 800-456-6323, FAX 610-524-5417, journalscustomer@turpinna.com.

330 320 FRA ISSN 1683-2388
SOURCE O C D E. GOUVERNANCE. (Organisation de Cooperation et de Developpement Economiques) Text in French. irreg. EUR 852, USD 979, GBP 562, JPY 115,000 (effective 2005).
Related titles: Online - full content ed.: ISSN 1684-3037. EUR 594, USD 683, GBP 392, JPY 80,200 (effective 2005); Online - full text ed.: (from EBSCO Publishing, Gale Group, IngentaConnect, Swets Information Services); ♦ English ed.: Source O E C D. Governance. ISSN 1608-0246.
Published by: Organization for Economic Cooperation and Development, 2 Rue Andre Pascal, Paris, 75775 Cedex 16, France. TEL 33-1-45248200, FAX 33-1-45248500, http://www.oecd.org. **Dist. by:** Extenza - Turpin, Pegasus Dr, Stratton Business Park, Biggleswade, Beds SG18 8TQ, United Kingdom. TEL 44-1462-687552, FAX 44-1462-480947, subscriptions@extenza-turpin.com; O E C D Turpin North America, PO Box 194, Downingtown, PA 19335-0194. TEL 610-524-5361, 800-456-6323, FAX 610-524-5417, journalscustomer@turpinna.com.

330 300 FRA ISSN 1608-0173
SOURCE O E C D. EMERGING ECONOMIES. Text in English. irreg. EUR 1,295, USD 1,489, GBP 856, JPY 174,800 (effective 2005). stat. **Document type:** *Government.* **Description:** Covers emerging economies with particular emphasis on Asia and Latin America.
Related titles: Online - full content ed.: ISSN 1681-5335. EUR 910, USD 1,046, GBP 600, JPY 122,900 (effective 2005); Online - full text ed.: 2000 (from EBSCO Publishing, Gale Group, IngentaConnect, Swets Information Services); ♦ French ed.: Source O C D E. Economies Emergentes. ISSN 1683-2329.
Published by: Organization for Economic Cooperation and Development, 2 Rue Andre Pascal, Paris, 75775 Cedex 16, France. TEL 33-1-45248200, FAX 33-1-45248500, http://www.oecd.org. **Dist. by:** Extenza - Turpin, Pegasus Dr, Stratton Business Park, Biggleswade, Beds SG18 8TQ, United Kingdom. TEL 44-1462-687552, FAX 44-1462-480947, subscriptions@extenza-turpin.com; O E C D Turpin North America, PO Box 194, Downingtown, PA 19335-0194. TEL 610-524-5361, 800-456-6323, FAX 610-524-5417, journalscustomer@turpinna.com.

330 300 FRA ISSN 1608-0238
SOURCE O E C D. GENERAL ECONOMICS & FUTURE STUDIES. Text in English. irreg.
Related titles: Online - full content ed.: Source O E C D. General Economies & Future Studies. ISSN 1681-5378. 2000. free; Online - full text ed.: (from Gale Group, IngentaConnect, Swets Information Services).
Published by: Organization for Economic Cooperation and Development, 2 Rue Andre Pascal, Paris, 75775 Cedex 16, France. TEL 33-1-45248200, FAX 33-1-45248500, http://www.oecd.org. **Dist. by:** Extenza - Turpin, Pegasus Dr, Stratton Business Park, Biggleswade, Beds SG18 8TQ, United Kingdom. TEL 44-1462-687552, FAX 44-1462-480947, subscriptions@extenza-turpin.com; O E C D Turpin North America, PO Box 194, Downingtown, PA 19335-0194. TEL 610-524-5361, 800-456-6323, FAX 610-524-5417, journalscustomer@turpinna.com.

330 320 FRA ISSN 1608-0246
SOURCE O E C D. GOVERNANCE. Text in English. irreg. EUR 852, USD 979, GBP 562, JPY 115,000 (effective 2005).
Related titles: Online - full content ed.: ISSN 1681-5386. 2000. EUR 594, USD 683, GBP 392, JPY 80,200 (effective 2005); Online - full text ed.: (from Gale Group, IngentaConnect, Swets Information Services); ♦ French ed.: Source O C D E. Gouvernance. ISSN 1683-2388.
Published by: Organization for Economic Cooperation and Development, 2 Rue Andre Pascal, Paris, 75775 Cedex 16, France. TEL 33-1-45248200, FAX 33-1-45248500, http://www.oecd.org. **Dist. by:** Extenza - Turpin, Pegasus Dr, Stratton Business Park, Biggleswade, Beds SG18 8TQ, United Kingdom. TEL 44-1462-687552, FAX 44-1462-480947, subscriptions@extenza-turpin.com; O E C D Turpin North America, PO Box 194, Downingtown, PA 19335-0194. TEL 610-524-5361, 800-456-6323, FAX 610-524-5417, journalscustomer@turpinna.com.

330 332 FRA ISSN 1608-0157
SOURCE O E C D. TRANSITION ECONOMIES. Text in English. irreg. EUR 1,215, USD 1,397, GBP 800, JPY 164,000 (effective 2005). stat. **Document type:** *Government.*
Related titles: Online - full content ed.: ISSN 1681-5467. EUR 855, USD 983, GBP 564, JPY 115,400 (effective 2005); Online - full text ed.: 2000 (from EBSCO Publishing, Gale Group, IngentaConnect, Swets Information Services); ♦ French ed.: Source O C D E. Economies en Transition. ISSN 1683-2450.
Published by: Organization for Economic Cooperation and Development, 2 Rue Andre Pascal, Paris, 75775 Cedex 16, France. TEL 33-1-45248200, FAX 33-1-45248500, http://www.oecd.org. **Dist. by:** Extenza - Turpin, Pegasus Dr, Stratton Business Park, Biggleswade, Beds SG18 8TQ, United Kingdom. TEL 44-1462-687552, FAX 44-1462-480947, subscriptions@extenza-turpin.com; O E C D Turpin North America, PO Box 194, Downingtown, PA 19335-0194. TEL 610-524-5361, 800-456-6323, FAX 610-524-5417, journalscustomer@turpinna.com.

330 FRA ISSN 1729-0619
SOURCE O E C D. URBAN, RURAL AND REGIONAL DEVELOPMENT. Text in English. irreg. EUR 425, USD 488, GBP 281, JPY 57,400 (effective 2005).
Formerly: Source O E C D. Territorial Economy (1608-0319)
Related titles: Online - full content ed.: ISSN 1729-0627. EUR 298, USD 342, GBP 197, JPY 40,200 (effective 2005); Online - full text ed.: 2000. USD 400 (effective 2003) (from EBSCO Publishing, Gale Group, IngentaConnect, Swets Information Services); ♦ French ed.: Source O C D E. Developpement Urbain, Rural et Regional. ISSN 1729-0635.
Published by: Organization for Economic Cooperation and Development, 2 Rue Andre Pascal, Paris, 75775 Cedex 16, France. TEL 33-1-45248200, FAX 33-1-45248500, http://www.oecd.org. **Dist. by:** Extenza - Turpin, Pegasus Dr, Stratton Business Park, Biggleswade, Beds SG18 8TQ, United Kingdom. TEL 44-1462-687552, FAX 44-1462-480947, subscriptions@extenza-turpin.com; O E C D Turpin North America, PO Box 194, Downingtown, PA 19335-0194. TEL 610-524-5361, 800-456-6323, FAX 610-524-5417, journalscustomer@turpinna.com.

330.9758231 USA
SOUTH; the business and politics of Atlanta. Text in English. 1997. m. USD 19.95; USD 2.95 newsstand/cover. adv. back issues avail. **Document type:** *Consumer.* **Description:** Aims to be "the magazine decision makers read." Content is 60% business related, 20% political, and 20% lifestyle.
Published by: Williams Communications, Inc., 2076 W Park Place, Stone Mountain, GA 30087. TEL 770-879-3700, FAX 770-498-2164. Ed. Ed Bean. Pub. Virgil Williams. Adv. contact Michael Cure. B&W page USD 2,660, color page USD 3,511. Circ: 40,000.

B

330 ZAF ISSN 1027-1724
DT763
SOUTH AFRICA SURVEY. Text in English. 1936. a.
Former titles: Race Relations Survey (0258-7246); Survey of Race Relations in South Africa (0081-9778); Race Relations Survey
Related titles: CD-ROM ed.
Indexed: HRIR.
Published by: South African Institute of Race Relations, PO Box 31044, Braamfontein, Johannesburg 2017, South Africa. TEL 27-11-403-3600, FAX 27-11-3392061, sairr@sairr.org.za, http://www.sairr.org.za/sairr. Ed. J S Kane Berman. Circ: 3,000.

330 ZAF ISSN 0038-2280
HB9
➤ **SOUTH AFRICAN JOURNAL OF ECONOMICS/SUID-AFRIKAANSE TYDSKRIF VIR EKONOMIE.** Text in English; Text occasionally in Afrikaans; Summaries in English. 1933. q. ZAR 800 (effective 2004); USD 235 combined subscription in the Americas to institutions & Caribbean, print & online eds.; USD 126, GBP 75 combined subscription in developing nations to institutions print & online eds.; GBP 145 combined subscription elsewhere to institutions print & online eds. (effective 2006). adv. bk.rev. bibl.; stat. index. back issues avail.; reprint service avail. from SCH. **Document type:** *Journal, Academic/Scholarly.* **Description:** Publishes papers on all aspects of economics and economic history from authors in South Africa and elsewhere. This journal is widely regarded as the leading economics journal in South Africa.
Related titles: CD-ROM ed.: USD 75, GBP 55 (effective 2002); Online - full text ed.: USD 223 in the Americas to institutions & Caribbean; USD 120, GBP 71 in developing nations to institutions; GBP 138 elsewhere to institutions (effective 2006) (from EBSCO Publishing, Gale Group, IngentaConnect).
Indexed: ABIn, ASCA, ASD, CREJ, CurCont, FamI, GEOBASE, IBSS, ILD, ISAP, JEL, KES, PAIS, PCI, RASB, RDA, RRTA, SSCI, WAE&RSA, WorkRelAb.
—BLDSC (8338.860000), IE, Infotrieve, ingenta. **CCC.**
Published by: (Economic Society of South Africa), Blackwell Publishing Asia (Subsidiary of: Blackwell Publishing Ltd.), 550 Swanston St, Carlton South, VIC 3053, Australia. TEL 61-383591011, FAX 61-383591120, subs@blackwellpublishingasia.com, http://www.saje.co.za, http://www.blackwellpublishing.com/. adv.: B&W page ZAR 800; trim 11.2 x 18.4. Circ: 1,800 (paid).

➤ **SOUTH AFRICAN MERCANTILE LAW JOURNAL/SUID-AFRIKAANSE TYDSKRIF VIR HANDELSREG.** see *LAW*

330 USA ISSN 1050-7698
HF3161.S6
SOUTH CAROLINA BUSINESS. Text in English. 1981. a. adv. **Document type:** *Magazine, Trade.* **Description:** Highlights contributions by the business community of South Carolina.
Related titles: Online - full text ed.: (from EBSCO Publishing).
Published by: South Carolina Chamber of Commerce, 1201 Main St, Columbia, SC 29201-3200. TEL 803-799-4601, FAX 803-779-6043, http://www.sccc.org.

330 USA ISSN 0745-4473
SOUTH CAROLINA BUSINESS JOURNAL. Text in English. 1982. m. USD 15. **Document type:** *Newspaper, Trade.* **Description:** Provides information necessary for day-to-day business decisions, including issues, court decisions, business trends and other news important to members.
Related titles: Online - full text ed.: (from bigchalk, EBSCO Publishing, O C L C Online Computer Library Center, Inc., ProQuest Information & Learning).
Indexed: ABIn, BusDate.
Published by: South Carolina Chamber of Commerce, 1201 Main St, Columbia, SC 29201-3200. TEL 803-799-4601, FAX 803-779-6043. Ed. Preston McLaurin. Pub. Deborah K Wooley. Circ: 8,300.

330 USA ISSN 1081-1257
HD2344.5.U62
SOUTH CAROLINA BUSINESS VISION. Text in English. 1994. q. USD 12 (effective 2005). adv. bk.rev. 48 p./no. 3 cols./p.; back issues avail.; reprints avail. **Document type:** *Trade.*
Description: Features information for and about African American entrepreneurs and highlights South Carolina's diversity in business , community and quality of life.
Published by: Vision Communications Group, Inc., PO Box 2084, Columbia, SC 29202-2084. TEL 803-929-0852, FAX 803-779-4352, mail@scbusinessvision.com. Eds. Cynthia Legette Davis TEL 803-865-8955, Latrice F Williams. R&P Cynthia Legette Davis TEL 803-865-8955. Adv. contact Tony D Gordon TEL 803-929-0852. Circ: 10,000 (controlled).

330 USA
SOUTH CENTRAL INDIANA'S BUSINESS JOURNAL. Short title: S C I B J. Text in English. 1991. m. USD 15; free. adv. bibl.; charts; illus.; stat.; tr.lit. back issues avail. **Document type:** *Newspaper, Consumer.* **Description:** Focuses on regional business. Direct mailed to Lawrence, Orange and contiguous counties' Chamber of Commerce members.
Published by: Times - Mail Special Products, 813 16th St, PO Box 849, Bedford, IN 47421. TEL 812-277-3470, FAX 812-277-3475. Ed. Jeff Routh. Pub. Debbie Morthland. R&P Ellen Ware TEL 812-275-3355. Adv. contact Janelle Zack. page USD 400; 14 x 11. Circ: 3,200.

B

650 USA ISSN 0038-3260
HC107.S8 CODEN: SDBRA5
SOUTH DAKOTA BUSINESS REVIEW. Text in English. 1942. q. free. charts; stat. **Document type:** *Newsletter.*
Related titles: Microfiche ed.: (from CIS); Online - full text ed.: (from bigchalk, EBSCO Publishing, Florida Center for Library Automation, Gale Group, Northern Light Technology, Inc., O C L C Online Computer Library Center, Inc., ProQuest Information & Learning).
Indexed: ABIn, BPIA, BusDate, BusI, PAIS, SRI, T&II.
Published by: (Business Research Bureau), University of South Dakota, School of Business, 414 E Clark St, Vermillion, SD 57069-2390. TEL 605-677-5287, FAX 605-677-5427, stracy@usd.edu, http://www.usd.edu/brbinfo. Ed. Steve Tracy. R&P Nancy Nelson. Circ: 1,350.

330 USA ISSN 0746-2271
SOUTH FLORIDA BUSINESS JOURNAL✶ . Text in English. 1980. w. (Fri.). USD 96 (effective 2004). adv. **Document type:** *Newspaper.*
Formerly: Miami Business Journal
Related titles: Microform ed.: 1980 (from PQC); Online - full text ed.: 1980 (from Florida Center for Library Automation, O C L C Online Computer Library Center, Inc.).
Indexed: ABIn, BusDate, T&II.
—CCC.
Published by: American City Business Journals, Inc. (Miami), 4000 Hollywood Blvd Ste 695 S, Hollywood, FL 33021-6755. FAX 305-594-1892, southflorida@bizjournals.com, http://www.bizjournals.com/southflorida/. Ed., R&P Ross Nethery. Pub. Gary Press. Adv. contact Joel Welker. Circ: 14,000. Wire service: AP.

330 USA ISSN 1067-8751
HC107.A13
SOUTHERN BUSINESS & DEVELOPMENT MAGAZINE. Text in English. 1993. q. USD 17.95 (effective 1999). adv. **Document type:** *Trade.* **Description:** Provides exclusive information on the southern states. Provides market reports, features, etc. on the South. Targeted to decision-making executives involved in corporate expansion and relocation.
Published by: E H R Publishing Inc., PO Box 380545, Birmingham, AL 35238-0545. TEL 205-733-1970, FAX 205-733-1973. Ed., Pub., Adv. contact Michael C Randle. Circ: 25,000.

330 USA
HC101
➤ **SOUTHERN BUSINESS & ECONOMIC JOURNAL.** Text in English. 1977. q. USD 25 to individuals; USD 40 to libraries (effective 1999). adv. bk.rev. **Document type:** *Academic/Scholarly.* **Description:** Emphasizes applied academic studies with a preference for data-based research with practical application.
Former titles (until 1987): Alabama Business and Economic Journal (0743-779X); (until vol.5): Alabama Business and Economic Reports (0735-2476)
Indexed: PAIS.
Published by: Auburn University at Montgomery, School of Business, PO Box 244023, Montgomery, AL 36124-4023. TEL 334-244-3561, FAX 334-244-3792, editor-sbej@monk.aum.edu. Ed., R&P Joy L Clark. Adv. contact Steven Jones. Circ: 1,500.

330 USA ISSN 0038-4038
HC107.A13 CODEN: SECJAR
➤ **SOUTHERN ECONOMIC JOURNAL.** Text in English. 1933. q. USD 115 domestic to non-members; USD 125 foreign to non-members (effective 2005). adv. bk.rev. bibl.; illus. index, cum.index vols. 1-49. reprint service avail. from PQC,PSC. **Document type:** *Journal, Academic/Scholarly.* **Description:** Presents theoretical and empirical research in economics addressed primarily to teachers, researchers, and other professionals in business, economics, and related fields.
Related titles: Microform ed.: (from MIM, PQC); Online - full text ed.: (from bigchalk, EBSCO Publishing, Florida Center for Library Automation, Gale Group, H.W. Wilson, JSTOR (Web-based Journal Archive), Northern Light Technology, Inc., O C L C Online Computer Library Center, Inc., ProQuest Information & Learning).
Indexed: ABIn, ABM, ABS&EES, AHCMS, ASCA, AgeL, AmH&L, ArtHuCI, BPI, BPIA, BusI, CJA, CMCI, CPM, CREJ, CurCont, FamI, HistAb, IBSS, ILD, JEL, KES, ManagCont, PAIS, PCI, PopulInd, RRTA, SPAA, SRRA, SSCI, SSI, SUSA, WAE&RSA, WBA, WorkRelAb.
—BLDSC (8354.020000), CISTI, IDS, IE, Infotrieve, ingenta. CCC.
Published by: Southern Economic Association, c/o Laura Razzolini, Virginia Commonwealth University, School of Business, 1015 Floyd Ave, Richmond, VA 23284. TEL 804-828-7187, FAX 804-828-2446, sej@vcu.edu, lrazzoloni@vcu.edu, http://www.okstate.edu/economics/journal/jour1.html. Circ: 4,000 (paid). **Subscr. to:** Allen Press Inc., PO Box 1897, Lawrence, KS 66044. TEL 785-843-1235, FAX 785-843-1274, orders@allenpress.com, http://www.allenpress.com.

330 IND
SOUTHERN ECONOMIC REVIEW. Text in English. 1971. q. INR 15, USD 8. bk.rev. charts; illus.; stat.
Published by: A. Ramaswami, 26 Clemens Rd., Vepery, Chennai, Tamil Nadu 600 007, India. Circ: 1,000.

330 IND ISSN 0038-4046
HC431
SOUTHERN ECONOMIST. Text in English. 1962. fortn. INR 450 domestic; USD 100 foreign (effective 2005). adv. bk.rev. 32 p./no. 3 cols./p.; **Document type:** *Newspaper.* **Description:** For policy-makers, academics, and business professionals interested in various aspects of economics. Includes topics such as: banking, development finance, monetary policy and planning, and stock market trends as well as many others.
Indexed: BAS, ILD.
Published by: Southern Economist Private Ltd., Saleh Ahmed Bldg., Saleh Ahmed Bldg., 106-108 Infantry Rd., Bangalore, Karnataka 560 001, India. TEL 91-80-25592330, southerneconomist@vsnl.net. Ed., Pub. Susheela Subrahmanya. Adv. contact H G Anandan. page INR 2,000; trim 215 x 270. Circ: 10,000.

330 USA
SOUTHFLORIDAC E O MAGAZINE. Text in English. 1998. 11/yr. USD 29.95 domestic; USD 176 foreign (effective 2005). adv. charts; illus.; maps; mkt.; stat.; tr.lit. 100 p./no.; back issues avail.; reprints avail. **Document type:** *Magazine, Trade.*
Description: Provides comprehensive and exciting coverage of the area?s economic trends, industries, markets and the people who make them happen.
Formerly: Miami Business
Address: 200 SE First St, Ste 601, Miami, FL 33131. TEL 305-379-1118, editor@southfloridaceo.com, http://www.southfloridaceo.com. Ed. J P Faber. Pub. Richard N Roffman. Circ: 2,000 (paid); 33,000 (controlled).

330 USA
SOUTHWEST FLORIDA BUSINESS. Text in English. 1997. USD 29.95 domestic; USD 34.95 in Canada; USD 125 foreign (effective 2001). **Document type:** *Magazine, Trade.*
Description: Covers regional business news and issues for local business owners and executives of Southwest Florida.
Published by: Voyager Media Inc. (Subsidiary of: Gulfshore Media, Inc.), 9051 Tamiami Trl N., Ste. 202, Naples, FL 34108-2520. TEL 239-278-4512, FAX 239-277-1773, jennifer@businessnewsnow.com, http://www.swfloridabusinessnews.com.

330 USA ISSN 8750-4294
HF5001
SOUTHWEST JOURNAL OF BUSINESS AND ECONOMICS. Text in English. 1983. s-a. USD 20. **Document type:** *Academic/Scholarly.*
Formerly (until 1975): Southwest Business and Economic Review (0195-198X)
Related titles: Online - full text ed.: (from Gale Group, O C L C Online Computer Library Center, Inc., ProQuest Information & Learning).
Indexed: ABIn, PAIS, T&II.
Published by: University of Texas at El Paso, Texas Centers, Burges Hall, Rm 410, El Paso, TX 79968-0541. Ed. James E Trumbly.

330 USA ISSN 1554-7892
➤ **SOUTHWESTERN BUSINESS ADMINISTRATION JOURNAL.** Abbreviated title: S B A J. Text in English. 2001. a. USD 25 per vol. (effective 2005). **Document type:** *Journal, Academic/Scholarly.*
Published by: Texas Southern University, Jesse H. Jones School of Business, 3100 Cleburne St, Houston, TX 77004. TEL 713-313-7215, FAX 713-313-7701, http://www.tsu.edu/academics/business/index.asp. Ed. Felix Ayadi.

➤ **SPACE NEWS (NEW YORK).** see *AERONAUTICS AND SPACE FLIGHT*

➤ **SPACEMART.** see *AERONAUTICS AND SPACE FLIGHT*

330 ESP
SPAIN. INSTITUTO NACIONAL DE INDUSTRIA. INFORME ANUAL. Text in English, Spanish. 1981. a. free. charts; stat.
Formerly: Spain. Instituto Nacional de Industria. Memoria I N I (Year)
Published by: Instituto Nacional de Industria, Plaza Marques de Salamanca 8, Madrid, 28006, Spain.

330 ESP ISSN 0214-9958
KKT925.A13
SPAIN. REGISTRO MERCANTIL. BOLETIN OFICIAL. Short title: B O R M E. Text in Spanish. 1990. d. EUR 106.38 domestic; EUR 185.71 foreign (effective 2003). stat.
Related titles: Microfiche ed.; Online - full text ed.
Indexed: RASB.
Published by: (Spain. Registro Mercantil), Boletin Oficial del Estado, Avenida Manoteras 54, Madrid, 28050, Spain. TEL 34-91-3841747, FAX 34-91-3841769, suscripciones@boe.es, http://www.boe.es.

330 GBR ISSN 1742-1772
▼ **SPATIAL ECONOMIC ANALYSIS.** Text in English. forthcoming 2006. s-a. GBP 126, USD 208 combined subscription to institutions print & online eds. (effective 2006). **Document type:** *Journal, Academic/Scholarly.*
Related titles: Online - full text ed.: ISSN 1742-1780. forthcoming 2006. GBP 120, USD 198 to institutions (effective 2006).
Published by: (Regional Science Association, British and Irish Section, Regional Studies Association), Routledge (Subsidiary of: Taylor & Francis Group), 4 Park Sq, Milton Park, Abingdon, Oxon OX14 4RN, United Kingdom. TEL 44-1235-828600, FAX 44-1235-829000, info@routledge.co.uk, http://www.tandf.co.uk/journals/titles/17421772.asp, http://www.routledge.co.uk. Ed. Bernard Fingleton.

SPECIAL LIBRARIES ASSOCIATION. BUSINESS AND FINANCE DIVISION. BULLETIN. see *LIBRARY AND INFORMATION SCIENCES*

330 346 USA
SPECIAL STUDY FOR CORPORATE COUNSEL ON USING LETTERS OF INTENT IN BUSINESS TRANSACTIONS. Text in English. 1999. irreg. USD 125 (effective 2001).
Published by: Business Laws, Inc., 11630 Chillicothe Rd, Chesterland, OH 44026. TEL 440-729-7996, FAX 440-729-0645, http://www.businesslaws.com.

330 660 USA
SPECTRUM (WALTHAM). Text in English. a. USD 500 (effective 2000). **Description:** Provides clients with expert opinion and analysis of business and technology issues affecting current global and regional markets as well as the companies participating in these markets. It publishes more than 80 reports per year. The reports are arranged by topic into five portfolios. It offers concise, insightful and informative analysis of current and prospective opportunities and challenges vital to corporate growth.
Published by: Decision Resources, Inc., Bay Colony Corporate Center, 1100 Winter St, Waltham, MA 02154-1238. TEL 781-487-3737, FAX 781-487-3735, carbone@dresources.com, http://www.dresources.com.

330 USA ISSN 1098-2485
SPORTING GOODS INTELLIGENCE ASIA. Abbreviated title: S G I Asia. Text in English. 1998. 36/yr. looseleaf. USD 395 (effective 2001). **Document type:** *Trade.* **Description:** Reports on sporting good industry in the Far East, containing news, market research, and facts & figures abut the Asian market.
Related titles: E-mail ed.: USD 395 (effective 2001); Fax ed.: USD 520 (effective 2001); ♦ Regional ed(s).: Sporting Goods Intelligence. ISSN 1060-2550; ♦ Sporting Goods Intelligence Europe. ISSN 1143-2462.
Published by: Sports Management News, Inc., 442 Featherbed Ln, Glen Mills, PA 19342. TEL 610-558-1601, 800-328-6397, FAX 610-558-1650, sginews@sginews.com, http://www.sginews.com. Ed. David Friedenrich TEL 852-2573-3078. Pub. John G Horan.

330 FRA ISSN 1143-2462
SPORTING GOODS INTELLIGENCE EUROPE. Key Title: Sporting Goods Intelligence (Bry-sur-Marne). Abbreviated title: S G I Europe. Text in English. 1990. 36/yr. **Document type:** *Trade.* **Description:** Provides financial news and analysis of sporting goods manufacturing and retail companies in the whole European sporting goods market, including all major sporting goods segments, including footwear, equipment and apparel.
Related titles: Italian ed.: ISSN 1291-6250. 1998; ♦ Regional ed(s).: Sporting Goods Intelligence. ISSN 1060-2550; ♦ Sporting Goods Intelligence Asia. ISSN 1098-2485.
Published by: E D M Publications, 32 rue de la Prairie, 94360 Bry sur, Marne, France. TEL 33-1-49838242, 33-1-49838224, edm@microking.net, http://www.sginews.com/.

▼ **SPORTOEKONOMIE IN FORSCHUNG UND PRAXIS.** see *SPORTS AND GAMES*

THE SPORTS BUSINESS DAILY. see *SPORTS AND GAMES*

SPORTSCAPE. see *SPORTS AND GAMES*

330   GRC   ISSN 1105-8919
SPOUDAI. Text in Greek. 1950. q. **Document type:** *Journal, Academic/Scholarly.*
Indexed: IBSS, JEL, PAIS.
Published by: University of Piraeus, 80 Karaoli & Dimitriou St, Piraeus, 185 34, Greece.

SPRINGERS KURZLEHRBUECHER DER WIRTSCHAFTSWISSENSCHAFTEN. see *SOCIAL SCIENCES: COMPREHENSIVE WORKS*

330   USA   ISSN 1075-2803
SPRINGFIELD BUSINESS JOURNAL. Text in English. 1980. w. USD 45.62. adv. bk.rev.; video rev. illus.; charts; maps; mkt.; stat.; tr.lit. 36 p./no. 4 cols./p.; **Document type:** *Newspaper.*
Description: Reports news concerning and of interest to locally owned businesses in the Springfield area.
Former titles (until 1994): Greater Springfield Business Journal (1058-1553); (until 1990): Springfield Business Journal (0889-8634); (until 1983): Tops Executive Journal (0745-0087)
Related titles: Microform ed.: (from PQC); Online - full text ed.: (from Northern Light Technology, Inc., ProQuest Information & Learning).
Indexed: ABIn, BusDate.
Address: 313 Park Central W, Springfield, MO 65806-1244. TEL 417-831-3238, FAX 417-831-5478, sbj@sbj.net, http://www.sbj.net. Ed. Paul Flemming. Pub., R&P Dianne Elizabeth TEL 417-831-3238. Adv. contact Steve Blalock. B&W page USD 1,736, color page USD 2,186; trim 13 x 10.13. Circ: 6,200.

330   USA
THE SPRINGFIELD HIGHLIGHTS. Text in English. irreg. (published only during the Illinois legislative session). **Document type:** *Newsletter, Trade.* **Description:** Provides information covering the General Assembly actions that effect manufacturers.
Media: Online - full content. **Related titles:** E-mail ed.; Fax ed.
Published by: The Illinois Manufacturers Association, 1301 W 22nd St., Ste. 610, Oak Brook, IL 60523. TEL 630-368-5300, 800-875-4462, FAX 630-218-7467, ima@ima-net.org, http://www.ima-net.org/. Ed. Katy Lawrence. Pub. Laurie Kaczmar TEL 630-368-5300 ext. 3122.

330 346.066   USA
ST. CHARLES BUSINESS RECORD. Text in English. d. (Mon.-Fri.). USD 66.54; USD 0.50 newsstand/cover (effective 2004). **Document type:** *Newspaper.*
Formerly: The Courier-Post.
Published by: Legal Communications Corp. (Subsidiary of: Dolan Media Corp.), PO Box 1080, St Charles, MO 63302-1080. TEL 636-949-6928, FAX 636-949-6973. Ed. Katie Brady. Circ: 1,000 morning (paid).

330   USA   ISSN 1523-6358
ST. CHARLES COUNTY BUSINESS RECORD. Text in English. w.
Fromerly (until 1983): Wentzville Union and St. Charles County Record (0199-252X)
Related titles: Online - full text ed.: (from ProQuest Information & Learning).
Published by: Legal Communications Corp. (Subsidiary of: Dolan Media Corp.), 115 1st Capitol Dr, St Charles, MO 63301. TEL 636-949-6928.

079.881   GUY   ISSN 1028-7108
STABROEK NEWS. Text in English. 1986. d. (Mon.-Sat.). GYD 13,164 domestic; GYD 35,056 in United States (effective 2002). adv. bk.rev.; dance rev.; music rev.; play rev. 24 p./no. 6 cols./p.; back issues avail. **Document type:** *Newspaper, Consumer.* **Description:** Features local and national news.
Related titles: Online - full text ed.; Alternate Frequency ed(s).: Sunday Stabroek. ISSN 1028-7116. 1986. w. GYD 4,264 domestic; GYD 11,024 in United States (effective 2002).
Published by: Guyana Publications Limited, 46-47 Robb St, Lacytown, Georgetown, Guyana. TEL 592-22-74075, FAX 592-22-54637, 592-22-59637, stabroeknews@stabroeknews.com. Ed. Anand Persaud. Adv. contact Cordelle Baird. B&W page USD 280, color page USD 420; 9 x 14. Circ: 23,000. Wire service: RN.

330   GBR
STAFFORDSHIRE UNIVERSITY. DIVISION OF ECONOMICS. WORKING PAPERS. Text in English. 1980. irreg. (approx. 10/yr.). free. **Document type:** *Academic/Scholarly.*
Description: Scholarly articles on economic theory and its application in a variety of areas.
Former titles: Staffordshire Polytechnic. Department of Economics. Discussion Papers; North Staffordshire Polytechnic. Department of Economics. Discussion Papers
Related titles: Microform ed.
Indexed: CREJ.
—BLDSC (3604.350000).
Published by: Staffordshire University, Division of Economics, Leek Rd, Stoke-on-Trent, Staffs ST4 2DF, United Kingdom. Ed. N J Adnett.

079.5125   HKG
THE STANDARD. Text in English. d. (Mon.-Fri.). HKD 1,498 domestic; CNY 3,378 in China; USD 554 in Asia; USD 577 elsewhere (effective 2003). **Document type:** *Newspaper, Trade.*

Former titles: Hong Kong iMail; The Hong Kong Standard
Published by: Sing Tao Ltd., 2/F Tower B, Sing Tao Bldg, 1 Wang Kwong Rd, Kowloon Bay, Hong Kong. TEL 852-31813668, FAX 852-27582798, http://hk-imail.singtao.com/thestandard/topstory.cfm. Ed. Karl Wilson TEL 852-27982800.

330   USA   ISSN 0196-4674
STANDARD & POOR'S CORPORATION RECORDS. CURRENT NEWS EDITION. Variant title: Standard and Poor's Daily News. Text in English. 1923. d. (5/wk.). back issues avail. **Document type:** *Trade.* **Description:** Examines mergers and acquisitions, registrations, offerings, bankruptcies, litigation, management changes, new products, capital spending, redemptions, and trading data.
Related titles: CD-ROM ed.; Online - full text ed.; ♦ Supplement(s): Standard & Poor's Corporation Records. ISSN 0277-500X.
Published by: Standard & Poor's (Subsidiary of: McGraw-Hill Companies, Inc.), 55 Water St, New York, NY 10041. TEL 212-208-8000. Ed. John Daly. Circ: 2,853.

STANFORD JOURNAL OF LAW, BUSINESS & FINANCE. see *LAW*

330   USA   ISSN 1542-7099
HD62.6
▼ **STANFORD SOCIAL INNOVATION REVIEW.** Text in English. 2003 (Spr.). q. USD 69 (effective 2004). illus.
Related titles: Online - full text ed.: (from EBSCO Publishing, ProQuest Information & Learning).
Indexed: ABIn.
Published by: Stanford University, Center for Social Innovation, Stanford Graduate School of Business, Stanford, CA 94305-5015. TEL 650-724-2219, FAX 650-723-0516, CSI_Info@gsb.stanford.edu, http://www.ssireview.com/articles/, http://www.gsb.stanford.edu/csi/index.html.

STAR TECH JOURNAL. see *BUSINESS AND ECONOMICS—Production Of Goods And Services*

330   USA
STATE CHAMBER NEWS. Text in English. 1981. 26/yr. membership only. adv.
Published by: Wilmington Chamber of Commerce, One Commerce Center, Ste 200, Wilmington, DE 19801. TEL 302-678-3616. Ed. Ruth L Mankin. Circ: 18,000.

330   RUS
STATE COMMITTEE OF THE RUSSIAN FEDERATION. CURRENT STATISTICAL SURVEY. Text in English. 1994. q. USD 275 in the Americas (effective 2000).
Published by: State Committee of the Russian Federation, Myasnitskaya ul., 39, Moscow, 103450, Russian Federation. TEL 7-095-2074492, FAX 7-095-9241582. Ed. V N Sokolin.
Dist. by: East View Information Services, 3020 Harbor Ln. N., Minneapolis, MN 55447. TEL 763-550-0961, FAX 763-559-2931.

330   BGR
STATE GAZETTE BUSINESS NEWS. Text in English. s-w.
Description: Provides information about the current official publication of all Bulgarian laws and the decrees, ordinances, etc. related to business establishment and operation. Gives short comments on the most important legal acts concerning the Bulgarian business environment.
Related titles: Online - full text ed.
Published by: Bulgarian Foreign Investment Agency, 3, Sveta Sofia Street, Sofia, 1000, Bulgaria. TEL 359-2-9800918, FAX 359-2-9801320, fia@bfia.org, http://www.bfia.org.

330   USA   ISSN 1521-8767
THE STATE JOURNAL. Text in English. m. USD 42.35; USD 1 newsstand/cover (effective 2005). **Document type:** *Newspaper.*
Related titles: Microform ed.: (from PQC); Online - full text ed.: (from O C L C Online Computer Library Center, Inc., ProQuest Information & Learning).
Indexed: ABIn, BusDate.
Published by: State Journal Corp., 13 Kanawha Blvd W., # 100, Charleston, WV 25302-2347. TEL 304-344-1630, FAX 304-345-2721, dpage@statejournal.com, http://www.statejournal.com. Ed. Dan Page. Circ: 10,000.

STATISTICS CANADA CATALOGUE. see *STATISTICS*

330   EGY   ISSN 1110-6778
STATISTICS, COMPUTER SCIENCE AND OPERATIONS RESEARCH. ANNUAL CONFERENCE. Text in English. 1965. a. **Document type:** *Proceedings, Academic/Scholarly.*
Published by: Institute of Statistical Studies and Research, Tharwat Str, Dokki, Cairo, Egypt. http://derp.sti.sci.eg/data/0350.htm.

348.489026   DNK   ISSN 0109-0798
STATUS. Text in Danish. 1983. 20/yr. DKK 150, USD 18. bk.rev. s-a. index. back issues avail.
Published by: Statens Informationstjeneste, PO Box 1103, Copenhagen K, 1009, Denmark. TEL 01-929-200. Ed. Hanne Egebjerg. Circ: 20,000. **Subscr. to:** Abonnement paa Status, Avispostkontoret, Copenhagen V 1535, Denmark.

STEM CELL BUSINESS NEWS. see *BIOLOGY—Genetics*

330 378   USA
STERN BUSINESS REPORT. Text in English. 1990. q. free.
Description: News of the School of Business.
Published by: New York University, Leonard N. Stern School of Business, 25 W Fourth St, New York, NY 10012. TEL 212-989-0962, FAX 212-995-4007. Ed. Colleen Troy. Circ: 5,000.

DER STEUERENTSCHEID; Sammlung aktueller steuerrechtlicher Entscheidungen. see *LAW*

330   SWE   ISSN 0585-3540
STOCKHOLM ECONOMIC STUDIES. PAMPHLET SERIES. Text in Multiple languages. 1959. irreg., latest vol.4, 1966. price varies. back issues avail. **Document type:** *Monographic series, Academic/Scholarly.*
Related titles: ♦ Series of: Acta Universitatis Stockholmiensis. ISSN 0346-6418.
Published by: Stockholms Universitet, Acta Universitatis Stockholmiensis, c/o Stockholms Universitetsbibliotek, Universitetsvaegen 10, Stockholm, 10691, Sweden. FAX 46-8-157776. **Dist. by:** Almqvist & Wiksell International, P O Box 7634, Stockholm 10394, Sweden. TEL 46-8-6136100, FAX 46-8-242543, info@akademibokhandeln.se, http://www.akademibokhandeln.se.

330   SWE   ISSN 0346-8305
STOCKHOLM STUDIES IN ECONOMIC HISTORY. Text in English. 1975. irreg., latest vol.40, 2004. price varies. back issues avail. **Document type:** *Monographic series, Academic/Scholarly.*
Related titles: ♦ Series of: Acta Universitatis Stockholmiensis. ISSN 0346-6418.
Published by: Stockholms Universitet, Acta Universitatis Stockholmiensis, c/o Stockholms Universitetsbibliotek, Universitetsvaegen 10, Stockholm, 10691, Sweden. FAX 46-8-157776. **Dist. by:** Almqvist & Wiksell International, P O Box 7634, Stockholm 10394, Sweden. TEL 46-8-6136100, FAX 46-8-242543, info@akademibokhandeln.se, http://www.akademibokhandeln.se.

330   MKD   ISSN 0039-1816
HB9
STOPANSKI PREGLED/ECONOMIC REVIEW; spisanie na Sojuzot na drustvata na ekonomistite od SR Makedonija. Text in Macedonian. 1950. bi-m.
Indexed: RASB.
Published by: Sojuzot na Drustvata na Ekonomistite na SR Makedonija, c/o Union of Economists of Macedonia, Ekonomiski Fakultet, K. Misirkov b. b., Skopje, 91000, Macedonia. Ed. Nikola Kljusek. Circ: 1,600.

STORAGE. see *COMPUTERS*

330   DEU   ISSN 1430-4082
STORES & SHOPS; the international trade magazine for shopfitting, furnishing and visual merchandising. Text in English, German. 1998. q. EUR 32.73 (effective 2001). adv. bk.rev. tr.lit. back issues avail. **Document type:** *Magazine, Trade.* **Description:** Reports on current developments in the international shopfitting scene, including investment trends and new products.
Published by: E H I - EuroHandelsinstitut e.V., Spichernstr 55, Cologne, 50672, Germany. TEL 49-221-57993-0, FAX 49-221-5799345, vertrieb@ehi.org, http://www.ehi.org. Eds. Dr. Bernd Hallier, Winfried Lambertz TEL 49-221-5799340. R&P Winfried Lambertz TEL 49-221-5799340. Adv. contact Claudia Husseck TEL 49-221-5799364. B&W page EUR 2,569.75, color page EUR 3,885.82. Circ: 17,000.

330   GBR   ISSN 0258-0543
HD30.28
STRATEGIC DIRECTION. Text in English. 1984. 11/yr. EUR 8,459.66 in Europe (effective 2006); USD 8,689 in North America (effective 2005); AUD 11,499 in Australasia; GBP 5,925.79 in UK & elsewhere (effective 2006). reprint service avail. from PSC. **Document type:** *Journal, Academic/Scholarly.* **Description:** Features experienced appraisal and reviews of the latest strategy publications and periodicals, related web sites, multimedia, seminar and conference events.
Incorporates: Technology Strategies
Related titles: Online - full text ed.: (from EBSCO Publishing, Emerald Group Publishing Limited, Gale Group, IngentaConnect, O C L C Online Computer Library Center, Inc., ProQuest Information & Learning, Swets Information Services).
Indexed: ABIn, Inspec.
—BLDSC (8474.031432), IE, Infotrieve, ingenta. **CCC.**
Published by: Emerald Group Publishing Limited, 60-62 Toller Ln, Bradford, W Yorks BD8 9BY, United Kingdom. TEL 44-1274-777700, FAX 44-1274-785200, infomation@emeraldinsight.com, http://www.emeraldinsight.com/sd.htm. Ed. Martin Fojt. **Subscr. addr. in N America:** Emerald Group Publishing Ltd., 44 Brattle St, 4th Fl, Cambridge, MA 02138. TEL 617-497-2175, 888-622-0075, FAX 617-354-6875.

B

330 USA
STRATEGIC TECHNOTES. Text in English. bi-m. free domestic membership (effective 2005). **Document type:** *Newsletter.*
Formerly: Ima Focus
Published by: Institute of Management Accountants, 10 Paragon Dr, Montvale, NJ 07645-1760. TEL 800-638-4427, 201-573-9000, FAX 201-474-1600, focus@imanet.org, http://www.imanet.org. Ed. Kathy Williams. Circ: 75,000 (paid).

330 SVK ISSN 1335-2016
STRATEGIE. Text in Slovak. 1994. m. SKK 1,140; SKK 804 to students (effective 2004). adv. **Document type:** *Magazine, Trade.*
Supersedes (in 1996): Strategie na Slovensku (1335-0889)
Published by: Sanoma Magazines Slovakia s.r.o., Kopcianska 6, Bratislava 5, 85101, Slovakia. TEL 421-2-63839900, FAX 421-2-63839914, sanomaslovakia@sanomaslovakia.sk, http://www.sanoma.sk. adv.: page SKK 50,000; trim 237 x 340.

330 CZE ISSN 1210-3756
STRATEGIE. Text in Czech. 1993. w. CZK 3,087 (effective 2005). adv. **Document type:** *Magazine, Trade.*
Published by: Sanoma Magazines Praha s.r.o., Lomnickeho 7, Prague 4, 12079, Czech Republic. TEL 420-2-96162111, FAX 420-2-24922995, vedrova@sanomamag-praha.cz, http://www.istrategie.cz, http://www.sanomamag-praha.cz. Ed. Vladimir Iliev. adv.: page CZK 51,500.

330 USA ISSN 1543-7760
HD30.28
▼ **STRATEGY AND INNOVATION.** Text in English. 2003 (Jul./Aug.). bi-m. USD 149 (effective 2003).
Related titles: Online - full text ed.: ISSN 1557-1300.
Published by: Harvard Business School Publishing, 60 Harvard Way, Boston, MA 02163. TEL 617-783-7500, FAX 617-783-7555, http://www.hbsp.harvard.edu.

330 USA ISSN 1083-706X
HD30.28
STRATEGY + BUSINESS. Key Title: Strategy & Business. Text in English. 1995. q. USD 38 domestic; USD 48 foreign (effective 2005). adv. bk.rev. reprints avail. **Document type:** *Trade.*
Description: Features articles that help business and professional people to manage and plan strategies for today's business challenges and opportunities.
Related titles: Online - full text ed.
Indexed: BrCerAb, C&ISA, CerAb, CorrAb, E&CAJ, EMA, IAA, LogistBibl, M&TEA, MBF, METADEX, SolStAb, WAA.
—BLDSC (8474.037500), IE, Infotrieve, ingenta, Linda Hall. **CCC.**
Published by: Booz, Allen & Hamilton, Inc., 101 Park Ave, New York, NY 10178. http://www.strategy-business.com. Ed. Randall Rothenberg. Pub. Max Henderson-Begg. R&P Trish Felix TEL 212-551-6154. Adv. contact Judith Russo TEL 212-551-6250. Circ: 105,870 (paid and controlled); 52,343 (paid). **Dist. in UK by:** Comag, Tavistock Works, Tavistock Rd, W Drayton, Middx UB7 7QX, United Kingdom. TEL 44-1895-433600, FAX 44-189-543-3606.

330 IRL
STUDENT ECONOMIC REVIEW. Text in English. 1987. irreg., latest vol.17.
Media: Online - full content.
Published by: University of Dublin, Regents House, Trinity College, House 6, Trinity College, Dublin, 2, Ireland. econrev@tcd.ie, http://econserv2.bess.tcd.ie/SER/.

330 ITA ISSN 0039-2928
HB7
STUDI ECONOMICI. Text in Italian. 1947; N.S.. 3/yr. EUR 45 domestic; EUR 73 foreign (effective 2003). bk.rev. index. 160 p./no.; reprints avail.
Indexed: DIP, IBR, IBZ, JEL, PAIS, RASB.
—BLDSC (8481.810000).
Published by: Franco Angeli Edizioni, Viale Monza 106, Milan, 20127, Italy. TEL 39-02-2837141, FAX 39-02-26144793, redazioni@francoangeli.it, http://www.francoangeli.it. Ed. Fausto Domenicantonio.

330 ITA ISSN 0391-8750
➤ **STUDI ECONOMICI E SOCIALI**; rivista di vita economica. Text in Italian. 1966. q. EUR 34 domestic; EUR 55 foreign (effective 2003). adv. bk.rev. **Document type:** *Journal, Academic/Scholarly.*
Published by: (Centro di Cultura e Studi Giuseppe Toniolo), I.P.E.M. - C.I.S.P.E., Via di Fortezza 1, Pisa, 56125, Italy. TEL 39-050-571181, FAX 39-050-571198. Ed. Romano Molesti. R&P Silvio Truceo. Adv. contact A C Cappuccilli.

330 POL
STUDIA REGIONALNE I LOKALNE. Text in Polish. 2000. q. PLZ 15 per issue (effective 2003). **Document type:** *Journal, Academic/Scholarly.*
Published by: (Uniwersytet Warszawski, Europejski Instytut Rozwoju Regionalnego i Lokalnego), Wydawnictwo Naukowe Scholar, ul Krakowskie Przedmiescie 62, Warsaw, 00322, Poland. TEL 48-22-6357404 ext 218, FAX 48-22-8289391, info@scholar.com.pl, http://www.scholar.com.pl. Ed. Grzegorz Gorzelak.

330 ROM ISSN 1224-8738
HD28
STUDIA UNIVERSITATIS "BABES-BOLYAI". NEGOTIA. Text in English, Romanian. 1996. s-a. per issue exchange basis. abstr.; charts; illus. index. **Document type:** *Academic/Scholarly.*
Published by: Universitatea "Babes-Bolyai", Biblioteca Centrala Universitara/Babes-Bolyai University, Central University Library in Cluj-Napoca, Mihail Kogalniceanu 1B, Cluj-Napoca, 3400, Romania. TEL 40-64-194315, FAX 40-64-191906, puc@hera.ubbcluj.ro, staff@staff.ubbcluj.ro. Ed. A Marga.

330 ROM ISSN 0578-5472
HB9
STUDIA UNIVERSITATIS "BABES-BOLYAI." OECONOMICA. Text in English, Romanian; Summaries in English, French, German. 1960. s-a. per issue exchange basis. abstr.; charts; illus. index. **Document type:** *Academic/Scholarly.*
Published by: Universitatea "Babes-Bolyai", Biblioteca Centrala Universitara/Babes-Bolyai University, Central University Library in Cluj-Napoca, Mihail Kogalniceanu 1B, Cluj-Napoca, 3400, Romania. TEL 40-64-194315, FAX 40-64-191906, puc@hera.ubbcluj.ro, staff@staff.ubbcluj.ro. Ed. A Marga.

330 GBR ISSN 1369-7153
➤ **STUDIES IN ASIA PACIFIC BUSINESS.** Text in English. 1996. irreg. price varies. **Document type:** *Monographic series, Academic/Scholarly.* **Description:** Covering the economic success of the Asia-Pacific region and its businesses, the series highlights the wider issues, drawing on the multidisciplinary interests of economics, management studies, sociology, culture and politics.
Published by: Routledge (Subsidiary of: Taylor & Francis Group), 2 Park Sq, Milton Park, Abingdon, Oxon OX14 4RN, United Kingdom. TEL 44-20-70176000, FAX 44-20-70176699, info@routledge.co.uk, http://www.routledge.co.uk.

650 USA ISSN 0081-7635
➤ **STUDIES IN BUSINESS AND SOCIETY.** Text in English. 1965. irreg., latest 1986. price varies. reprint service avail. from PQC,ISI. **Document type:** *Academic/Scholarly.*
—BLDSC (8489.770000).
Published by: (Graduate School of Business), University of Chicago, 5801 S Ellis Ave, Chicago, IL 60637. TEL 773-702-7899, sales@press.uchicago.edu, http://www.press.uchicago.edu.

➤ **STUDIES IN DEVELOPMENT AND PLANNING.** see *BUSINESS AND ECONOMICS—International Development And Assistance*

330 IND
STUDIES IN ECONOMIC DEVELOPMENT AND PLANNING. Text in English. 1961. irreg., latest vol.58, 1993. price varies.
Formerly: Studies in Economic Growth (0081-7848)
—BLDSC (8490.425000).
Published by: Institute of Economic Growth, University of Enclave, New Delhi, 110 007, India. TEL 2522201.

STUDIES IN ECONOMIC ETHICS AND PHILOSOPHY. see *PHILOSOPHY*

STUDIES IN INDUSTRIAL ORGANIZATION. see *BUSINESS AND ECONOMICS—Economic Systems And Theories, Economic History*

330 THA ISSN 1020-3516
STUDIES IN TRADE AND INVESTMENT. Text in English. 1995. irreg. **Document type:** *Academic/Scholarly.*
Indexed: ESPM.
Published by: Economic and Social Commission for Asia and the Pacific (Subsidiary of: United Nations), The United Nations Bldg, Rajadamnern Nok Ave, Bangkok, 10200, Thailand. TEL 66-2-288-1234, FAX 66-2-288-1000, http://www.unescap.org.

SUDEBNIK. see *LAW*

330 USA
SUMMA. Text in English. 1986. m. USD 45. adv. **Document type:** *Consumer.* **Description:** Selects and translates articles published by Forbes, The Economist, Time, the New York Times, Harvard Business Review, Sloan Management Review, and Management Review.
Published by: Carvajal International, Inc., 901, Ponce De Leon, FL 33134-3073. TEL 305-448-6875, 800-622-6657, FAX 305-448-9942. Ed. Vicky Santana. Pub. David Ashe. Circ: 124,527.

330 USA
SUN BELT JOURNAL. Text in English. 1980. bi-m. USD 75. adv. bk.rev. back issues avail. **Document type:** *Newspaper, Trade.*
Published by: Wiffden Company, 20640 N 53rd Ave, Glendale, AZ 85308-9309. Ed., Pub. Dennis Kienlen. Adv. contact Joseph Jacobs. Circ: 171,000.

330 GBR ISSN 1362-1947
SUNDAY BUSINESS. Text in English. 1996. w.
Related titles: Online - full text ed.: (from Gale Group).
Published by: Sunday Business Publishing Ltd, London, EC1N 2NP, United Kingdom. TEL 44-20-7961-0000, FAX 44-20-7961-0102.

330 AUS
SUNZINE - ABOUT QUEENSLAND AUSTRALIA. Text in English. 1995. d. **Description:** Covers travel, investment and real estate.
Media: Online - full text.
Address: PO Box 159, Peregian Beach, QLD 4573, Australia. TEL 61-7-5448-1888, FAX 61-7-5448-1686, webteam@sunzine.net, http://www.sunzine.net/. Ed. Ian Wilks.

330 FIN ISSN 1238-1683
SUOMEN PANKKI. TUTKIMUKSIA. SARJA A/BANK OF FINLAND. STUDIES. SERIES A/FINLANDS BANK. UNDERSOEKNINGAR. SERIE A. Text in English, Finnish, Swedish. 1942. irreg. free (effective 2005). **Document type:** *Monographic series.*
Former titles (until 1994): Suomen Pankki. Sarja A (0355-6034); (until 1973): Suomen Pankin Taloustieteellisen Tutkimuslaitoksen Julkaisuja. Sarja A, Taloudellisia Selvityksia (0081-9476)
Related titles: Online - full text ed.: ISSN 1456-5943. 1999.
Published by: Suomen Pankki/Bank of Finland, P O Box 160, Helsinki, 00101, Finland. TEL 358-10-8311, FAX 358-9-174872, publications@bof.fi, http://www.bof.fi. Circ: 1,600.

330 FIN ISSN 1238-1691
SUOMEN PANKKI. TUTKIMUKSIA. SARJA E/BANK OF FINLAND. STUDIES. SERIES E/FINLANDS BANK. UNDERSOEKNINGAR. SERIE E. Text in English, Finnish, Swedish. 1995. irreg. free (effective 2005). **Document type:** *Monographic series.*
Formed by the 1995 merger of: Suomen Pankki. Julkaisuja. Series B (0357-4776); Which was formerly (1943-1969): Suomen Pankki. Taloustieteellinen Tutkimuslaitos. Julkaisuja. Series B (0081-9484); Suomen Pankki. Julkaisuja. Series C (0781-4429); Which was formerly (1962-1970): Suomen Pankki. Taloustieteellinen Tutkimuslaitos. Julkaisuja. Series C (0081-9492); Suomen Pankki. Julkaisuja. Series D (0355-6042); Which was formerly (1963-1972): Suomen Pankki. Taloustieteellinen Tutkimuslaitos. Julkaisuja. Series D. Mimeographed Series (0081-9506)
Related titles: Online - full text ed.: ISSN 1456-5951. 1999.
Published by: Suomen Pankki/Bank of Finland, P O Box 160, Helsinki, 00101, Finland. TEL 358-10-8311, FAX 358-9-174872, publications@bof.fi, http://www.bof.fi. Circ: 1,500.

330 AUS
SUPPLY CHAIN REVIEW. Text in English. bi-m. AUD 52 domestic (effective 2001). adv. **Document type:** *Trade.*
Published by: Publishing Services (Australia) Pty. Ltd., 244 St Pauls Terrace, Fortitude Valley, Brisbane, QLD 4000, Australia. TEL 61-7-3854-1286, FAX 61-7-3252-4829, http://www.supplychainreview.coma.au. Ed. Gardiner Graham. adv.: B&W page AUD 3,995, color page AUD 5,710; trim 297 x 210. Circ: 8,663.

330 USA
SURPRISE!. Text in English. 2001. 11/yr. (Jul./Aug. Comb.). **Document type:** *Magazine, Trade.* **Description:** Focus on how to be organized and self-sufficient, make the right choices, communications, finance, maintain the right attitude, wellness and personal growth. Also features advice columns as well as an entertaining column that gives attention to the food and wine community.
Address: 6201 15th Ave NW, Seattle, WA 98107. TEL 206-217-0929, themag@wolfenet.com. Ed., Pub. Joan Twan. Circ: 100,000.

339 USA
SURVEYS OF APPLIED ECONOMICS. Text in English. 1973. irreg. price varies.
Published by: St. Martin's Press (Subsidiary of: Holtzbrinck Publishers), 175 Fifth Ave, New York, NY 10010.

330 GBR ISSN 0306-2201
SUSSEX BUSINESS TIMES. Text in English. 1975. m. GBP 25 domestic; GBP 50 foreign (effective 1999). adv. bk.rev. **Document type:** *Trade.*
Published by: Park View Publishing Ltd., Park View House, 19 The Ave, Eastbourne, E Sussex BN21 3YD, United Kingdom. TEL 44-1323-411601, FAX 44-1323-411654, edit@sbt.argonet.co.uk, http://www.sbt.argonet.co.uk. Ed. Kate Taylor. Pub., R&P Brian Collins. Adv. contact Dion Clements. Circ: 5,300.

330 IDN ISSN 0215-0050
SWA - SEMBRADA/BUSINESS MAGAZINE. Text in Indonesian. 1985. m. IDR 59,400, USD 28.20. adv. reprints avail. **Description:** Contains profiles of companies and successful business people.
Published by: Yayasan Sembada Swakarya, Gedung Chandra, 2nd Fl., Jl. MH Thamrin 20, Jakarta Pusat, Indonesia. TEL 062-21-3103316, FAX 062-21-3103318, TELEX 62797-IA. Ed. Geonawan Mohamad. Adv. contact Dinny Harun. B&W page USD 1,898, color page USD 2,609; trim 275 x 210. Circ: 45,195.

B

330 SWE ISSN 1400-1829
HC371
➤ **SWEDISH ECONOMIC POLICY REVIEW.** Text in English. 1989. biennial, latest vol.9, 2002. free (effective 2005). back issues avail. **Document type:** *Journal, Academic/Scholarly.*
Formerly (until 1994): Ekonomiska Raadet. Aarsbok (1100-3413)
Indexed: IBSS, JEL.
—BLDSC (8573.868000), IE, Infotrieve, ingenta.
Published by: Economic Council of Sweden, PO Box 3116, Stockholm, 103 62, Sweden. TEL 46-8-4535900, FAX 46-8-4535980, economic.council@konj.se, http://www.ekradet.konj.se/sepr/, htttp://www.ekradet.konj.se.

330 GBR
SWINDON BUSINESS NEWS. Text in English. 1982. every 6 wks. GBP 10.
Published by: County Business Publishing Ltd., The Priory, Haselton, Near Cheltenham, Glos, United Kingdom. TEL 0793-615393. Ed. L Barling. **Subscr. to:** 26 Wood St, Swindon, Wilts SN1 4AB, United Kingdom.

330 CHE
SWITZERLAND. KOMMISSION FUER KONJUNKTURFRAGEN. ALLFAELLIGE STUDIEN. Text in German. irreg., latest vol.300, 1986. **Document type:** *Government.*
Related titles: French ed.: Switzerland. Commission pour les Questions Conjoncturelles. Situation Economique. ISSN 1421-3907.
Published by: State Secretariat for Economic Affairs, Kommission fuer Konjunkturfragen, Bundesgasse 8, Bern, 3003, Switzerland. TEL 41-31-3222138, FAX 41-31-3235001.

330 RUS
SYRODELIE. Text in Russian. 1998. s-a. USD 80 in United States (effective 2000).
Indexed: RefZh.
Published by: Redaktsiya Syrodelie, Sadovaya Spasskaya 18, Moscow, 107807, Russian Federation. TEL 7-095-2072050. Ed. T A Kuznetsova. **Dist. by:** East View Information Services, 3020 Harbor Ln. N., Minneapolis, MN 55447. TEL 763-550-0961, FAX 763-559-2931.

330 THA ISSN 0857-2968
HC445.A1
T D R I QUARTERLY REVIEW. Text in English. 1985. q. THB 400 domestic; USD 29 in Asia; USD 33 in the Americas; USD 32 elsewhere (effective 2003). adv. back issues avail. **Document type:** *Academic/Scholarly.*
Indexed: APEL.
Published by: Thailand Development Research Institute, TDRI 565 Ramkhamhaeng 39 (Thepleea 1), Ramkhamhaeng Rd, Wangthonglang District, Bangkok, 10310, Thailand. TEL 662-718-5460, FAX 662-718-5461, publications@tdri.or.th, http://www.info.tdri.or.th. Ed. Farida Kapasi. R&P Poonsin Wongkoltoot TEL 66-2-7185460 ext 428.

330 639.2 USA
T S S A REPORT✶**.** Text in English. 1979. q. looseleaf. membership only. **Document type:** *Newsletter.*
Formerly: T R A I Report
Published by: American Sportfishing Association, 225 Reinehers Ln., Alexandria, VA 22314-1540. TEL 703-519-9691, FAX 703-519-1872. Ed. Nancy Lems. Circ: 400 (controlled).

346.066 USA
TACOMA DAILY INDEX. Text in English. 1890. d. (Mon.-Fri.). USD 50; USD 30 for 6 mos.; USD 0.25 newsstand/cover (effective 2005). **Document type:** *Newspaper.*
Related titles: Online - full content ed.: free (effective 2004).
Address: 1019 Pacific Ave, Ste 1216, Tacoma, WA 98402. TEL 253-627-4853, FAX 253-627-2253, editor@tacomadailyindex.com, http://www.tacomadailyindex.com. Circ: 1,000 morning (paid).

330 IRN ISSN 1010-657X
TAHQIQAT E EQTESADI (ENGLISH EDITION); quarterly journal of economic research. Text in English. 1962. q. (in 4 vols.). USD 5 (effective 1999). adv. bk.rev. bibl.; charts; stat. index. **Document type:** *Academic/Scholarly.*
Related titles: Persian, Modern ed.: Tahqiqat-i Iqtisadi (Chap-i Farsi). ISSN 0039-8969. 1962.
Indexed: JEL.
Published by: (Institute for Economic Research), University of Teheran, Faculty of Economics, P O Box 14155-6445, Tehran, Iran. Ed. Anna Enayat. Circ: 300.

TAKEOVERS AND RECONSTRUCTIONS IN AUSTRALIA. see *LAW—Corporate Law*

330 GBR
TAKEOVERS, OFFERS AND NEW ISSUES. Text in English. m. looseleaf. GBP 545. cum.index. **Document type:** *Trade.*
Description: Reports the latest capital events on UK companies quoted on the London Stock Exchange. Includes takeovers, acquisitions, new issues and rights offers.
Published by: Financial Times Information Ltd., Extel, Fitzroy House, 13-17 Epworth St, London, EC2A 4DL, United Kingdom. TEL 44-20-7825-8000, FAX 44-20-7608-2032, eic@ft.com, http://www.info.ft.com.

330 USA ISSN 1091-1006
HF5387
TAKING SIDES: CLASHING VIEWS ON CONTROVERSIAL ISSUES IN BUSINESS ETHICS AND SOCIETY. Text in English. 1990. irreg., latest 2003, 8th ed. USD 22.50 per vol. (effective 2004). illus. **Document type:** *Academic/Scholarly.*
Published by: McGraw-Hill - Dushkin (Subsidiary of: McGraw-Hill Higher Education), 2460 Kerper Blvd, Dubuque, IA 52001. TEL 800-243-6532, customer.service@mcgraw-hill.com, http://www.dushkin.com/text-data/catalog/0072917199.mhtml. Eds. Lisa H Newton, Maureen M Ford. Pub. David Dean. R&P Cheryl Greenleaf.

330 HRV
TALIJANSKA PRIVREDA DANAS; imprese e imprenditori italiani oggi. Text in Serbo-Croatian; Summaries in Italian. 1965. s-a. USD 5. adv. back issues avail. **Description:** Describes cooperation between Italy and Yugoslavia.
Published by: Informator d.d., Zelinska 3, Zagreb, 10002, Croatia. TEL 385-1-6111500. Circ: 10,000.

330 USA ISSN 1067-067X
TALKING TO THE BOSS. Text in English. 1986. 12/yr. USD 18. adv. bk.rev. **Document type:** *Newspaper.*
Address: 225 N. Michigan Ave., Ste. 1100, Chicago, IL 60601-7683. TEL 708-933-9659, FAX 708-933-9667. Ed. Myrna Petlicki. Pub., R&P David Stein. Adv. contact Michael Heimlich. Circ: 15,000 (controlled).

330 FIN ISSN 0356-5106
HC337.F5
TALOUSELAMA. Text in Finnish. 1938. w. (43/yr.). EUR 192 (effective 2005). adv. bk.rev. illus. **Document type:** *Magazine, Trade.* **Description:** Provides in-depth coverage of investment, management and marketing trends affecting Finnish business, with company profiles on major Finnish companies.
Incorporates (in 1970): Uusi Ekonomia (0358-7967); Which was formerly (1964-1969): Ekonomia (0013-2985)
Related titles: Special ed(s).: 500 Largest Companies in Finland; ♦ Supplement(s): Finns in Business. ISSN 1237-3052; ♦ Talouselaman Raportti Suuryrityksista. ISSN 0780-5969.
Indexed: P&BA.
Published by: Talentum Oyj, Malminkatu 30, PO Box 920, Helsinki, 00101, Finland. TEL 358-240-4240, FAX 358-240-424130, info@talentum.fi, http://www.talouselama.fi, http://www.talentum.fi. Ed. Pekka Seppanen TEL 358-020-4424482. Adv. contact Sanna Aravilta TEL 358-40-3424230. color page EUR 8,880; trim 273 x 200. Circ: 77,881.

330 FIN ISSN 0780-5969
TALOUSELAMAN RAPORTTI SUURYRITYKSISTA. Variant title: Report on the Largest Companies in Finland. Text in Finnish. 1982. a.
Related titles: ♦ Supplement to: Talouselama. ISSN 0356-5106.
Published by: Talentum Oyj, Malminkatu 30, PO Box 920, Helsinki, 00101, Finland. TEL 358-240-4240, FAX 358-240-424130, info@talentum.fi, http://www.talentum.fi.

330 TZA ISSN 0856-2172
TANZANIA INDUSTRIAL STUDIES AND CONSULTING ORGANISATION. ANNUAL REPORT AND ACCOUNTS. Text in English. 1978. a. free. back issues avail. **Document type:** *Corporate.*
Published by: Tanzania Industrial Studies and Consulting Organisation (TISCO), PO Box 2650, Dar Es Salaam, Tanzania. Ed. E M Ntabaye. Circ: 500.

330 HKG
TARGET DATA COMPILATION REPORT. Text in English. w. (Mondays). USD 500 (effective 2001). **Document type:** *Trade.*
Published by: Target Newspapers Ltd., 4-F, Wah Tao Bldg, 42 Wood Rd, Wanchai, Hong Kong, Hong Kong. TEL 852-2573-0379, FAX 852-2838-1597, targnews@hkstar.com, http://www.targetnewspapers.com/tnl/datacompil/index2.htm.

330 HUN ISSN 1588-9734
➤ **TARSADALOM ES GAZDASAG/SOCIETY AND ECONOMY.** Variant title: Budapest University of Economic Sciences and Public Administration. Journal. Journal of the Budapest University of Economic Sciences and Public Administration. Text in Hungarian; Summaries in English. 1994. s-a. USD 72 combined subscription print & online (effective 2006). **Document type:** *Journal, Academic/Scholarly.*
Formerly (until 2002): Tarsadalom es Gazdasag Kozep-es Kelet-Europaban (1218-9383); Which superseded in part (in 1995): Budapesti Kozgazdasagtudomanyi Egyetem Folyoirata. Aula. Tarsadalom es Gazdasag (0866-6865); Which was formerly (until 1990): Marx Karoly Kozgazdasagtudomanyi Egyetem Folyoirata. Egyetemi Szemle (0139-4045)
Related titles: Online - full text ed.: ISSN 1589-021X. 2002; ♦ English ed.: Society and Economy. ISSN 1588-9726.
Published by: (Budapest University of Economic Sciences and Public Administration), Akademiai Kiado Rt. (Subsidiary of: Wolters Kluwer N.V.), Prielle Kornelia U. 19, Budapest, 1117, Hungary. TEL 36-1-4648282, FAX 36-1-4648221, journals@akkrt.hu, http://www.akkrt.hu. Ed. Jozsef Temesi.

330 AUS
TASMANIA. DEPARTMENT OF STATE DEVELOPMENT. ANNUAL REPORT. Text in English. 1985. a. free. **Document type:** *Directory, Government.*
Formerly: Tasmanian Development Authority Annual Report (0817-6418)
Related titles: Online - full content ed.
Published by: Department of State Development, GPO Box 646, Hobart, TAS 7001, Australia. TEL 61-3-62335888, FAX 61-3-62335800, dsd@dsd.tas.gov.au, http://www.dsd.tas.gov.au. Ed., R&P Daryl Peebles TEL 61-3-62335875. Circ: 3,000.

375 330 GBR ISSN 1367-3289
HB1
TEACHING BUSINESS & ECONOMICS. Text in English. 1947. 3/yr. GBP 42 in United Kingdom to individuals; GBP 64 foreign to individuals; GBP 69 to institutions (effective 2000). adv. bk.rev. reprint service avail. from PQC. **Document type:** *Academic/Scholarly.*
Former titles: Economics and Business Education (0969-2509); (until 1992): Economics (0300-4287)
Related titles: Microform ed.: (from PQC); Online - full text ed.: (from ProQuest Information & Learning).
Indexed: BAS, BrEdI, BrHumI, CIJE, CPE, CPM, JEL, PAIS, PSI, TEA.
—BLDSC (8614.052000), IE, Infotrieve, ingenta. **CCC.**
Published by: Economics and Business Education Association, 1a Keymer Rd, Hassocks, W Sussex BN6 8AD, United Kingdom. TEL 44-1273-846033, FAX 44-1273-844646, ebeah@pavilion.co.uk, http://www.ebea.org.uk. Ed. Ian Abbot. R&P Jenny Wales. Adv. contact Sandra Halsey. Circ: 3,000.

330 USA
TECH COAST. Text in English. 2001 (Jun.). q. **Document type:** *Trade.* **Description:** Covers the southern California technology market place.
Published by: Tech Coast Alliance, 2111 Business Center Dr. Ste 211, Irvine, CA 92612. TEL 949-442-0200, http://www.techcoast.com/.

330 FRA ISSN 0184-4067
TECHNICA. Text in French. bi-m.
Published by: Association des Anciens Eleves de l'Ecole Centrale Lyonnaise, 7 rue Grolee, Lyon, 69002, France. TEL 78-37-48-05. Ed. Jean Soubiran. Circ: 4,000.

TECHNICAL REVIEW MIDDLE EAST/AL-NASHRAH AL-TIQNIYYAH AL-SHARQ AL-AWSAT. see *TECHNOLOGY: COMPREHENSIVE WORKS*

TECHNIKDIALOG. see *TECHNOLOGY: COMPREHENSIVE WORKS*

330 USA
TECHNOLOGY OPPORTUNITIES: RESEARCHING EMERGING & CRITICAL TECHNOLOGIES. Text in English. irreg., latest vol.7. USD 295 (effective 1999). **Document type:** *Directory.* **Description:** Provides managers with full contact information for organizations that monitor technology development, licensing, and commercial applications.
Published by: Washington Researchers, Ltd., 1655 Fort Myer Dr., Ste. 800, Arlington, VA 22209-3119. TEL 703-312-2863, FAX 703-527-4586, research@researchers.com, http://www.researchers.com, http://www.washingtonresearchers.com. Ed. M Newman. R&P Ellen O'Kane.

330 COL ISSN 0120-0933
HD70.C55
TECNOLOGIA ADMINISTRATIVA. Text in Spanish. 1979. 3/yr. COP 25,000 domestic; USD 15 foreign; COP 10,000 domestic to students (effective 2003). bk.rev. **Description:** Includes articles on methods and management for technology industries.
Published by: Universidad de Antioquia, Facultad de Ciencias Economicas, Apdo. Aereo 1226, Medellin, Colombia. ebarrera@epm.net.co. Circ: 500.

330 ITA
TECNORAMA. Text in Italian. 2/yr.
Published by: Pubblicita Edizioni Associati s.r.l., Via Simone D'Orsenigo, 22, Milan, MI 20135, Italy. TEL 2-551-18-42, FAX 2-551-85-263. Ed. Ugo Carutti. Circ: 6,600.

TEENPRENEUR. see *CHILDREN AND YOUTH—For*

330 ZAF
TEGNIEK. Text in Afrikaans. 1948. m. ZAR 12.
Published by: Tegniek Ltd., PO Box 51, Stellenbosch, 7600, South Africa. Ed. T J F De Villiers.

330 RUS
TEK KUR'ER. Text in Russian. 1994. 24/yr. USD 2,305 in United States (effective 2000).
Published by: Informatsionno-Analiticheskoe Agentstvo Infotek, Kitaiskii pr., 7, Moscow, 103074, Russian Federation. TEL 7-095-9273091. **Dist. by:** East View Information Services, 3020 Harbor Ln. N., Minneapolis, MN 55447. TEL 763-550-0961, FAX 763-559-2931.

B

▼ *new title* ➤ *refereed* ✶ *unverified* ♦ *full entry avail.*

TELE-SATELLITE INTERNATIONAL; Europe's satellite magazine. see *COMMUNICATIONS—Television And Cable*

TELECOM A.M. see *COMMUNICATIONS*

330 610 USA ISSN 1552-6402
▼ **TELEMEDICINE WEEK.** Text in English. 2004. w. USD 2,595 in US & Canada; USD 2,795 elsewhere; USD 2,825 in US & Canada; USD 3,055 elsewhere (effective 2005). **Document type:** *Newsletter, Academic/Scholarly.* **Description:** Reports the latest news and developments from companies marketing and manufacturing telemedicine equipment and software, including business news, new products and contracts, regulatory and legislative changes, regulatory sanctions and lawsuits.
Related titles: Online - full content ed.: ISSN 1552-6437; Online - full text ed.: (from ProQuest Information & Learning).
Published by: NewsRx, PO Box 5528, Atlanta, GA 31107-0528. TEL 800-726-4550, info@newsrx.com, http://www.newsrx.com.

330 VEN ISSN 0495-0615
TEMAS ECONOMICOS. Text in Spanish. 1951. m. stat.
Address: Conde a Pinango 22, Apdo. 2570, Caracas, Venezuela.

330 ARG
TEMAS Y PROPUESTAS. Variant title: Revistas Temas y Propuestas. Text in Spanish. 1993. q. back issues avail.
Published by: Universidad de Buenos Aires, Facultad de Ciencias Economicas, Ave. Cordoba No. 2122, Buenos Aires, 1120, Argentina. TEL 54-114-3744448, web@econ.uba.ar, http://www.econ.uba.ar/www/servicios/Secretaria_Pedagogica/temasypropuestas/principal_temasypropuestas.htm.

330 PRT
TEMPO ECONOMICO. Text in Portuguese. 26/yr.
Indexed: M&MA.
Address: Rua Duque de Palmela, 37, Lisbon, 1200, Portugal.

330 MEX
TENDENCIAS. Text in Spanish. w. USD 233 in US & Canada; USD 250 in Latin America; USD 269 in Asia. **Document type:** *Newsletter.* **Description:** For bankers, investors and business managers in Mexico.
Published by: Grupo Editorial Expansion (Subsidiary of: Capital Cities - A B C, Inc.), SALAMANCA 35, Col Roma, Mexico City, DF 06700, Mexico. servicioaclientes@expansion.com.mx.

330 340 ARG
TENDENCIAS ECONOMICAS Y FINANCIERAS. Text in Spanish. 1964. w. USD 900. adv. **Document type:** *Newsletter.* **Description:** Report for business management.
Formerly: Tendencias Economicas: Legislacion Economica Argentina (0325-5034)
Related titles: English ed.: Business Trends.
Indexed: KES.
Published by: Consejo Tecnico de Inversiones S.A., Tucuman, 834 1o, Capital Federal, Buenos Aires 1049, Argentina. FAX 54-114-3224887. Ed. Jose Luis Blanco. Pub. Daniel Sticco. Adv. contact Marta Ortega.

330 CHN ISSN 1008-3286
TEQU JINGJI YU KONGGAOTAI JINGJI/ECONOMY IN S E Z AND HONG KONG, MACAO AND TAIWAN. Text in Chinese. 1984. m. CNY 70.80 (effective 2004). 80 p./no.; **Document type:** *Journal, Academic/Scholarly.* **Description:** Covers the economic development of China's special economic zones.
Former titles (until 199?): Tequ yu Kaifaqu Jingji (1005-4308); (until 1993): Tequ yu Kaifang Chengshi Jingji (1001-3121)
Indexed: RASB.
Published by: Zhongguo Renmin Daxue, Shubao Zilio Zhongxin/Renmin University of China, Information Center for Social Server, Dongcheng-qu, 3, Zhangzizhong Lu, Beijing, 100007, China. TEL 86-10-64039458, FAX 86-10-64015080, kyes@163.net, http://www.confucius.cn.net/bkdetail.asp?fzt=F14. **Dist. in US by:** China Publications Service, PO Box 49614, Chicago, IL 60649. TEL 312-288-3291, FAX 312-288-8570; **Dist. by:** China International Book Trading Corp, 35 Chegongzhuang Xilu, Haidian District, PO Box 399, Beijing 100044, China. TEL 86-10-68412045, FAX 86-10-68412023, cibtc@mail.cibtc.com.cn, http://www.cibtc.com.cn.

330 340 FRA ISSN 1278-4249
TERRITOIRES EN MUTATION. Text in French. 1997. q.
Formed by the merger of (1979-1997): Cahiers de l'Economie Meridionale (0299-061X); (1979-1997): Espace Rural (0764-7557)
Published by: Universite de Montpellier III (Paul Valery), Centre Regional de la Productivite et des Etudes Economiques, B.P. 5043, Montpellier, Cedex 1 34032, France. Ed. R Badouin. Circ: 200.

650 USA ISSN 0040-4209
HC107.T4 CODEN: TXBRAK
TEXAS BUSINESS REVIEW. Text in English. 1926. bi-m. free. bibl.; charts; illus.; stat. index, cum.index: 1926-1961; 1975-1994. 6 p./no. 2 cols./p.; back issues avail. **Document type:** *Magazine, Trade.* **Description:** Focuses on current economic issues in Texas and competitiveness of the state's industries.
Related titles: Online - full text ed.: (from bigchalk, EBSCO Publishing, Florida Center for Library Automation, Gale Group, Northern Light Technology, Inc., O C L C Online Computer Library Center, Inc., ProQuest Information & Learning).
Indexed: ABIn, AmH&L, BAS, BPIA, PAIS, RASB, T&II.
—BLDSC (8798.680000). **CCC.**
Published by: University of Texas at Austin, Bureau of Business Research, McCombs School of Business, One University Sta, B-8500, Austin, TX 78712-0226. TEL 512-475-7813, FAX 512-471-1063, bruce.kellison@bus.utexas.edu, http://www.utexas.edu/depts/bbr/tbr/. Ed., R&P Bruce Kellison TEL 512-475-7813. Circ: 5,500 (free).

330 THA ISSN 0125-3905
THAI ECONOMIC REVIEW. Text in English, Thai. 1972. 3/yr. adv. charts; stat. **Document type:** *Academic/Scholarly.*
Indexed: BAS.
Published by: (Faculty of Economics), Chulalongkorn University, Phyathai Rd, Bangkok, 10500, Thailand. Ed. Supachai Manuspaibool.

330 MYS ISSN 0128-4134
HC59.69
➤ **THIRD WORLD ECONOMICS;** trends & analysis. Text in English. 1990. fortn. USD 55 in developing nations; USD 75 elsewhere (effective 2005). 20 p./no. 3 cols./p.; back issues avail. **Document type:** *Magazine, Academic/Scholarly.* **Description:** Provides news and analyses that reflect the grassroots interests of people in the Third World.
Indexed: PerIslam.
Published by: Third World Network, 121-S Jalan Upama, Penang, 10450, Malaysia. TEL 60-4-2266159, FAX 60-4-2264505, twnet@po.jaring.my, http://www.twnside.org.sg/twe.htm. Eds. Chakravarthi Raghavan, Martin Khor Kok Peng. R&Ps Lean Ka-Min, T. Rajamoorthy.

330 CAN ISSN 0838-7087
THIS WEEK IN BUSINESS. Text in English. 1987. 50/yr. adv.
Indexed: CBPI, CPerl.
Address: 250 St Antoine W, Montreal, PQ H2Y 3R7, Canada. TEL 514-987-2512, FAX 514-987-2638. Ed. James Ferrabee. Adv. contact Jean Sanche. Circ: 192,949.

330 ISL ISSN 1670-1968
THJODARBUSKAPURINN. Text in Icelandic. 1972. s-a. **Document type:** *Government.*
Related titles: Online - full text ed.: ISSN 1670-4347. 2002; ♦ English ed.: The Icelandic Economy. ISSN 1670-1976.
Published by: Fjarmalaraduneytid/Icelandic Ministry of Finance, Arnarhvall, Reykjavik, 150, Iceland. TEL 354-545-9200, FAX 354-562-8280, mail@fjr.stjr.is, http://www.ministryoffinance.is.

330 VNM
THOI BAO KINH TE VIETNAM. Text in Vietnamese. 2/w. adv. **Document type:** *Newspaper, Trade.* **Description:** Covers business news and items of interest to the local economy.
Related titles: ♦ Online - full text ed.: Thoi Bao Kinh Te Vietnam Online. ISSN 1563-8812.
Published by: Ringiers - Association of Vietnamese Economists, 175 Nguyen Thai Hoc, Hanoi, Viet Nam. TEL 84-4-8452411, FAX 84-4-8432755, vet@hn.vnn.vn, http://www.vneconomy.com.vn/Publications/tbktvn/. Ed. Dao Nguyen Cat. Adv. contact Le Minh Anh. Circ: 38,000 (paid and controlled).

330 VNM ISSN 1563-8812
THOI BAO KINH TE VIETNAM ONLINE. Text in Vietnamese. 199?. 2/w. **Document type:** *Trade.*
Media: Online - full text. **Related titles:** ♦ Print ed.: Thoi Bao Kinh Te Vietnam.
Published by: Ringiers - Association of Vietnamese Economists, 175 Nguyen Thai Hoc, Hanoi, Viet Nam. TEL 84-4-8452411, FAX 84-4-8432755, http://www.vneconomy.com.vn/Publications/tbktvn/.

THRIVENT. see *RELIGIONS AND THEOLOGY—Roman Catholic*

658 USA ISSN 1096-4762
HF1
➤ **THUNDERBIRD INTERNATIONAL BUSINESS REVIEW.** Text in English. 1959. bi-m. USD 525 domestic; USD 585 in Canada & Mexico; USD 636 elsewhere; USD 578 combined subscription domestic print & online eds.; USD 638 combined subscription in Canada & Mexico print & online eds.; USD 689 combined subscription elsewhere print & online eds. (effective 2006). adv. bk.rev. abstr.; bibl. back issues avail.; reprint service avail. from PQC,PSC. **Document type:** *Journal, Academic/Scholarly.* **Description:** Aims to provide a forum for scholars and practitioners in the fields of international business and politics to express their ideas and opinions. Covers international commerce and business including international marketing, finance, and international human resources issues. Addresses related political, economic, legal, and cultural issues affecting international business.
Formerly (until 1998): International Executive (0020-6652); Incorporates (1988-2001): Global Focus (1525-0369); Which was formerly (until 1999): Global Outlook (1521-0359); (until 1998): Business and the Contemporary World (1041-8482)
Related titles: Microform ed.: (from PQC); Online - full text ed.: ISSN 1520-6874. 1998. USD 525 (effective 2006) (from EBSCO Publishing, ProQuest Information & Learning, Swets Information Services, Wiley InterScience).
Indexed: ABIn, ABS&EES, BPI, ESPM, Emerald, MEA&I, PAIS, RiskAb.
—BLDSC (8820.380280), IE, Infotrieve, ingenta. **CCC.**
Published by: (Thunderbird American Graduate School of International Management), John Wiley & Sons, Inc., 111 River St, Hoboken, NJ 07030-5774. TEL 201-748-6000, FAX 201-748-5915, uscs-wis@wiley.com, http://www3.interscience.wiley.com/cgi-bin/jhome/60500187, http://www.wiley.com. Ed. Yahia H Zoubir. Adv. contact Susan Levey. B&W page USD 1,080, color page USD 2,420; trim 8.25 x 11. Circ: 1,000 (paid). **Subscr. to:** John Wiley & Sons Ltd., The Atrium, Southern Gate, Chichester, West Sussex PO19 8SQ, United Kingdom. TEL 44-1243-779777, FAX 44-1243-775878, cs-journals@wiley.co.uk.

330 TWN ISSN 1015-2784
TIANXIA/COMMONWEALTH. Text in Chinese. 1981. m. TWD 6,120 (effective 2002). **Document type:** *Magazine, Consumer.*
Related titles: Online - full content ed.: ISSN 1606-447X.
Published by: Tianxia Zazahi/Common Wealth Magazine Co., 104 Songjiang Road, no.87, 4F, Taipei, Taiwan. TEL 886-2-2662-0332, FAX 886-2-2662-6048, http://www.cw.com.tw/index.htm.

330 TUR ISSN 1301-8159
TICARET. Text in Turkish. 1942. 6/w. (Mon.-Sat.). USD 130 foreign (effective 2001). adv. back issues avail. **Document type:** *Newspaper, Trade.* **Description:** Publishes business news, current information on commodities and notices of tenders and bids.
Related titles: Online - full text ed.
Published by: Ticaret Gazetesi, 1571 Sok No.: 16, Cinarli, Izmir, 35110, Turkey. TEL 90-232-4617196, FAX 90-232-4840799, ticinfo@unimedya.net.tr, http://www.ticaretgazetesi.com. Ed. Ahmet S Tukel. Pub. Suha S Tukel. Adv. contact Kamuran Oncel. Circ: 4,700 (paid).

330 CHE
TICINO MANAGEMENT; il mensile svizzero di finanza, economia e cultura. Text in Italian. 1989. m. CHF 90, USD 55. bk.rev.; film rev.; music rev. tr.lit. **Document type:** *Consumer.*
Published by: Ticino Management SA, Centro Galleria 2, Manno, 6928, Switzerland. TEL 41-91-508800, FAX 41-91-508820. Pub. Valerio De Giorgi. Adv. contact Claus Winterhalter. B&W page CHF 3,120, color page CHF 4,400; trim 252 x 178. Circ: 20,000 (paid).

330 BEL ISSN 0772-7674
HB9
TIJDSCHRIFT VOOR ECONOMIE EN MANAGEMENT. Text in Dutch, English. 1956. q. EUR 32 to individuals; EUR 56 to institutions; EUR 16 to students; EUR 16 per issue (effective 2005). adv. bk.rev. charts. back issues avail. **Document type:** *Academic/Scholarly.*
Formerly (until 1975): Tijdschrift voor Economie (0040-7461)
Indexed: BibInd, CREJ, IBSS, JEL, KES, RASB.
—BLDSC (8839.550000), IE, ingenta.
Published by: Katholieke Universiteit Leuven, Faculteit der Economische en Toegepaste Economische Wetenschappen/Catholic University of Louvain, Faculty of Economic and Applied Economic Sciences, Naamsestraat 69, Leuven, 3000, Belgium. TEL 32-16-326688, FAX 32-16-326698, http://www.econ.kuleuven.be/tem/general_ned.htm. Ed. P Sercu. Circ: 2,000.

330 NLD ISSN 1382-5607
TIJDSCHRIFT VOOR STRATEGISCHE BEDRIJFSCOMMUNICATIE. Text in Dutch. 1995. q. EUR 128 (effective 2003).
—IE, Infotrieve.
Published by: Kluwer B.V. (Subsidiary of: Wolters Kluwer N.V.), Postbus 23, Deventer, 7400 GA, Netherlands. TEL 31-570-673449, FAX 31-570-691555, http://www.kluwer.nl.

330 USA ISSN 0898-1434
TODAY'S IMAGE. Text in English. 1988. m. free domestic to qualified personnel. 125 p./no. 3 cols./p.; back issues avail. **Document type:** *Magazine, Trade.* **Description:** Focuses on business improvements, new products, industry news and trends, marketing information, and profiles of successful entrepreneurs.
Published by: Creative Age Publications, Inc., 7628 Densmore Ave, Van Nuys, CA 91406-2042. TEL 818-782-7328, FAX 818-782-7450, todaysimage@creativeage.com, ahamaker@creativeage.com, http://www.todaysimage.com, http://www.creativeage.com. Pub. Deborah Carver. Adv. contact Jerry Lovell. Circ: 25,298 (controlled).

▼ **TODAY'S MEDICAL DEVELOPMENT**; your source for the latest in medical manufacturing. see *MEDICAL SCIENCES*

330 JPN ISSN 0493-4091
TOKYO KEIZAI UNIVERSITY. JOURNAL. Text mainly in Japanese; Text occasionally in English. 1949. 5/yr. bk.rev.
Formerly (until no.116, 1980): Tokyo College of Economics. Journal - Tokyo Keidai Gakkai-Shi
Indexed: BAS, IBSS.
—BLDSC (4908.925000), IE.
Published by: Tokyo Keizai University/Tokyo Keizai Daigaku, 34-7 Minami-cho 1-chome, Kokubunji-shi, Tokyo-to 185-0021, Japan. Circ: 2,200.

330 USA
TOLEDO BUSINESS JOURNAL. Text in English. 1984. m. USD 15. adv. **Document type:** *Newspaper.*
Related titles: Microform ed.: (from PQC); Online - full text ed.
Indexed: BusDate.
Published by: Telex Communications, Inc., 27 Broadway St, Toledo, OH 43602-1701. TEL 419-244-8200, FAX 419-244-5773. Ed. Brian Taylor. Pub. Sanford Lubin. Adv. contact Jacqueline Bruecken. Circ: 9,600.

TOLEDO JOURNAL OF GREAT LAKES' LAW, SCIENCE & POLICY. see *LAW*

TONGJI YU JINGSUAN/STATISTICS AND ACCURATE CALCULATION. see *STATISTICS*

TOP TECH NEWS. see *COMPUTERS*

TOP WOMAN. see *WOMEN'S INTERESTS*

TOPEKA METRO NEWS. see *LAW*

330 GTM ISSN 1609-8072
TOPICOS DE ACTUALIDAD. Text in Spanish. 1959. m.
Related titles: Online - full text ed.: ISSN 1609-8226. 1999.
Published by: Centro de Estudios Economico-Sociales, 6a. Calle Final, Zona 10, Campus Central Edif. Biblioteca Ludwig von Mises, Guatemala City, Guatemala. TEL 502-3387828, 502-332-2420, cees@cees.org.gt, http://www.cees.org/.

330 NLD
TORNADO-INSIDER.COM; inside Europe's new economy network. Text in English. m. USD 85 in United States; EUR 75 in Europe; USD 105 elsewhere (effective 2001).
Address: http://www.tornado-insider.com. Ed. Ives Brant.

330 CAN
HC118.T6
THE TORONTO BUSINESS AND MARKET GUIDE. Text in English. 1983. biennial. CND 65 to non-members; CND 55 to members (effective 1999). **Document type:** *Corporate.* **Description:** Statistical, economic and demographic overview of the business community and marketplace in Toronto. Includes guide to establishing a business in Toronto.
Formerly: Metropolitan Toronto Business and Market Guide (0829-2558)
Published by: Toronto Board of Trade, 1 First Canadian Place, P O Box 60, Toronto, ON M5X 1C1, Canada. TEL 416-366-6811, http://www.bot.com. Ed. Mary de Reus. Circ: 4,000.

330 CAN ISSN 1499-0601
TORONTO BUSINESS JOURNAL. Text in English. 2001. w. CND 93; free newsstand/cover (effective 2001). **Document type:** *Newspaper, Consumer.*
Published by: InBusiness Media Network Inc., 8 King Street East, Suite 710, Toronto, ON M5C 1B5, Canada. TEL 416-368-1886, 866-410-6660, FAX 416-368-1889, info@torontobusinessjournal.com, http://www.torontobusinessjournal.com. Ed. Justin Smallbridge. Pub. Bert Kleiser. Adv. contact Carol Lynne Hynes.

TOURBUS PLUS!. see *TRAVEL AND TOURISM*

TOURISM ECONOMICS; the business and finance of tourism and recreation. see *TRAVEL AND TOURISM*

TRADE & TRAVELER. see *TRAVEL AND TOURISM*

330 USA
TRADE-MARK BUSINESS NETWORK NEWS. Text in English. 1979. m. USD 15 (effective 2005). **Document type:** *Newspaper, Trade.*
Published by: Business Services Corp., PO Box 5488, Portland, OR 97228. TEL 503-244-5794, FAX 503-293-2094, oregonbusiness@usa.net. Ed., Pub. Roy Jay. Adv. contact Velma Harris. Circ: 10,000 (paid).

TRAFIKOEKONOMISKE ENHEDSPRISER. see *TRANSPORTATION—Roads And Traffic*

330 GBR
TRANSTERRA BUSINESS BRIEF. Text in English. 1972. fortn. GBP 225, USD 445 (effective 2000). adv. back issues avail. **Document type:** *Newsletter.*
Published by: Transterra Ltd., 2 Copperfields Orchard, Kemsing, Sevenoaks, Kent TN15 6QH, United Kingdom. TEL 44-1702-761687, FAX 44-1702-761687, transterra@exl.co.uk, http://www.transterra.co.uk. Ed. Mr. Richard McKeogh TEL 44-20-8325-9541. R&P S Klenke. Adv. contact S. Klenke.

TRANSVERSALES SCIENCE CULTURE. see *SOCIOLOGY*

340 CYP ISSN 1015-6585
TRAPEZIKOS/BANK EMPLOYEE. Text in Greek. 1960. every 2 wks. **Document type:** *Trade.*
Related titles: Online - full content ed.
Address: PO Box 1235, Nicosia, Cyprus. TEL 357-2-366993. Ed. L Hadjicostis. Circ: 9,500.

TRAYECTORIAS; revista de ciencias sociales de la Universidad Autonoma de Nuevo Leon. see *SOCIAL SCIENCES: COMPREHENSIVE WORKS*

330 USA
TREASURE COAST BUSINESS JOURNAL. Text in English. m. free. **Document type:** *Newspaper.*
Published by: E.W. Scripps Co., 312 Walnut St. 28th Fl., Cincinnati, OH 45202. TEL 513-977-3000, FAX 513-977-3689, classified@stuartnews.com, http://www.tcpalm.com/tcp/tc_business_journal/. Ed. Mark Tomasik. Adv. contact Margaret Brennan. Circ: 21,000 (free).

330 SVK ISSN 1335-0684
TREND; tyzdennik o hospodarstve a podnikani. Text in English, Slovak. 1991. w.
Related titles: Online - full content ed.: eTrend. ISSN 1336-2674. 2001.
Indexed: INIS AtomInd.
Published by: Trend Holding sro, PO Box 31, Bratislava, 820 07, Slovakia. TEL 421-2-43411652, redakcia@trend.sk, http://www.etrend.sk, 421-2-43331336, http://www.trend.sk/.

650 AUT ISSN 0049-4623
HC261
TREND; das oesterreichische Wirtschaftsmagazin. Text in German. 1970. m. EUR 35.97; EUR 18.53 to students (effective 2002). adv. bk.rev. charts; illus. index. **Document type:** *Magazine, Consumer.*
Related titles: Online - full text ed.: ISSN 1605-1041.
Indexed: KES.
Published by: Verlagsgruppe News Gesellschaft mbH (Subsidiary of: Gruner und Jahr AG & Co.), Lindengasse 52, Vienna, 1070, Austria. TEL 43-1-53470-0, FAX 43-1-5353250, redaktion@trend.at, http://trend.at, http://www.news.at. Eds. Christian Rainer, Thomas Martinek. Pub. Christian Rainer. Adv. contact Oswald Greil. Circ: 61,021 (paid).

330.07 DEU ISSN 0177-0780
TREND (BERLIN); Zeitschrift fuer soziale Marktwirtschaft. Text in German. 1979. q. EUR 25; EUR 7.50 newsstand/cover (effective 2005). adv. **Document type:** *Magazine, Consumer.* **Description:** Contains research and articles on various aspects and applications involving social market economics.
Published by: Information fuer die Wirtschaft GmbH, Luisenstr 44, Berlin, 10117, Germany. TEL 49-30-24087400, FAX 49-30-24087405, info@trend-zeitschrift.de, http://www.trend-zeitschrift.de. Ed. Erwin Lamberts. adv.: B&W page EUR 5,370, color page EUR 8,435; trim 180 x 248. Circ: 16,000 (paid and controlled).

330 DEU
TREND AKTUELL SURVEY DATA. Text in German. 1977. bi-m. EUR 4,300 (effective 2002). charts; stat. 38 p./no.; **Document type:** *Newsletter, Trade.* **Description:** Provides confidential information about changes of attitude and conduct in the economic, social and political fields.
Former titles: Trend Aktuell (0178-0727); (until 1985): Up to Date (0176-9731)
Published by: Trend Aktuell Verlag Klaus Peinelt, Leopoldstr 32, Munich, 80802, Germany. TEL 49-89-347514, FAX 49-89-349282, http://www.trendsaktuell.de. Ed. Klaus Peinelt. Circ: 100.

330 DEU ISSN 0935-5596
TRENDLETTER MEGATRENDS AKTUELL. Text in German. 1987. m. **Document type:** *Bulletin.*
Formed by merger of: Trendletter; Megatrends Aktuell
Published by: V N R Verlag fuer die Deutsche Wirtschaft AG, Theodor-Heuss-Str 2-4, Bonn, 53095, Germany. TEL 49-228-8205-0, FAX 49-228-364411, TELEX 17228309-TTX-D. Ed. Armin Ziegler.

330 JPN ISSN 1345-0026
TRENDS AND ISSUES IN EAST ASIA. Text in English. 1999. a.
Published by: Foundation for Advanced Studies on International Development, Keidanren Nature Conservation Fund, 22F Otemachi Financial Center, 1-5-4 Otemachi, Chiyoda-ku, Tokyo, 100, Japan. TEL 81-3-3212-8220, FAX 81-3-3212-8222, http://www.fasid.or.jp.

330 USA ISSN 1065-2094
CODEN: FOOIEF
THE TRENDS JOURNAL. Text in English. 1991. q. USD 185 domestic; USD 200 foreign (effective 2005). back issues avail. **Document type:** *Newsletter.*
Published by: Trends Research Institute, PO Box 660, Rhinebeck, NY 12572-0660. TEL 845-876-6700, gcelente@trendsresearch.com, http://www.trendsresearch.com. Ed., R&P Gerald Celente.

330 CAN
TRENDS MAGAZINE. Text in English. 1985. 12/yr. CND 22. adv.
Published by: Bowes Publishers Inc., 1383 Confederation St, Sarnia, ON N7S 5P1, Canada. TEL 519-336-1100, FAX 519-336-1833. Ed. Gayle Cooper. Adv. contact Sherry Doran. Circ: 5,000 (controlled).

330 USA ISSN 1065-6170
TRI-STATE BUSINESS TIMES. Text in English. 1991. m. free. adv. bk.rev. charts; mkt. **Document type:** *Trade.* **Description:** Covers what's happening in business, including columns on H.R., finance, real estate, and the web, plus stories on business and management trends.
Published by: (Telegraph Herald), Woodward Communications Inc., 801 Bluff St, PO Box 688, Dubuque, IA 52001-0688. TEL 319-588-3838, FAX 319-588-5745, thonline@WCInet.com. Ed. Gary Dura. Pub. Tom Yunt. R&P Brian Cooper TEL 319-588-5662. Adv. contact Dean Millius. Circ: 5,000.

330 USA
TRIANGLE BUSINESS JOURNAL (GREENSBORO). Text in English. 1998. w. USD 665 (effective 2005). adv. bk.rev. charts; illus.; stat. **Document type:** *Newspaper, Trade.* **Description:** Designed to inform decision-making executives about business growth and trends in Wake, Orange and Durham counties.
Former titles: Business Journal (Greensboro) (1525-9218)
Related titles: Online - full text ed.: (from O C L C Online Computer Library Center, Inc., ProQuest Information & Learning).
Indexed: ABIn, BusDate.
Published by: American City Business Journals, Inc. (Greensboro), 100 S Elm St, Ste 400, Greensboro, NC 27401. TEL 336-271-6539, FAX 336-574-3607, triad@bizjournals.com, triad@bizjounral.com, http://www.bizjournals.com/triad/. Ed. Kevin Bumgarner. Pub. Douglas W. Copeland Jr. Circ: 15,000.

B

330 USA ISSN 1543-5385
TRIANGLE BUSINESS JOURNAL (RALEIGH). Text in English. w. (Fri.). USD 76 (effective 2005). adv. **Document type:** *Journal, Trade.*
Former titles (until 2002): Business Journal (1527-5957); Triangle Business Journal (1060-5096); Triangle Business (0891-0022)
Related titles: Online - full text ed.: (from Gale Group, O C L C Online Computer Library Center, Inc., ProQuest Information & Learning).
Indexed: ABIn.
—CCC.
Published by: American City Business Journals, Inc. (Raleigh), 1305 Navajo Dr, Ste 100, Raleigh, NC 27609. TEL 919-878-0010, FAX 919-790-6885, triangle@bizjournals.com, info@bizjournals.com, http://triangle.bizjournals.com. Ed. Sougata Muhkerjee. Pub. Char Grunwaldt. Circ: 10,000 (paid).

330 USA ISSN 1051-7367
TRIBUNE BUSINESS WEEKLY. Text in English. 1990. w. USD 312 (effective 2005). adv. **Document type:** *Newspaper, Trade.* **Description:** Contains business news, profiles of area business people and area businesses, feature stories, and information of interest to the local business community.
Related titles: Microform ed.: (from PQC); Online - full text ed.; (from LexisNexis, Northern Light Technology, Inc., O C L C Online Computer Library Center, Inc., ProQuest Information & Learning).
Indexed: ABIn, BusDate.
Published by: South Bend Tribune, 225 W Colfax Ave, South Bend, IN 46626. TEL 574-235-6051, 574-235-6468, FAX 574-239-2646, biznews@sbtinfo.com, http://www.southbendtribune.com/business/. Ed. Phil A Vitale. Pub. Pete Baker. Adv. contact Carol Smith. Circ: 8,000 (controlled).

330 FRA ISSN 1168-6944
TRIBUNE DESFOSSES. Text in French. 1920. d. EUR 380 (effective 2005). **Document type:** *Newspaper.* **Description:** Covers the economy, stockmarket and finance.
Formed by the merger of (1920-1992): Cote Desfosses (0750-0424); (1987-1992): Tribune de l'Expansion (0989-1323)
Related titles: Online - full text ed.
Indexed: CBNB.
—CCC.
Address: 42 rue Notre Dame des Victoires, Paris, 75002, France. TEL 1-42-33-21-30, FAX 1-42-33-12-36, TELEX 680 326, http://www.latribune.fr/, http://www.edelweb.fr/Guests/LaTribune. Ed. Paul Francois Trioux. Circ: 27,344.

330 ITA
TRIESTE ECONOMICA. Text in Italian. 1970. q. free. adv. **Document type:** *Trade.*
Media: Online - full content.
Published by: Camera di Commercio Industria Artigianato e Agricoltura di Trieste, Piazza della Borsa, 14, Trieste, TS 34121, Italy. TEL 39-40-67011, FAX 39-40-6701321, http://www.ts.camcom.it/tseconrivista.htm. Ed. Arcangelo Flaminio. Circ: 1,000.

330 MEX ISSN 0041-3011
HB9
➤ **EL TRIMESTRE ECONOMICO.** Text in Spanish. 1934 (Jan.). q. MXP 225 in Mexico; USD 70 in Central America; USD 70 in the Caribbean; USD 90 in South America; USD 90 in Spain; USD 120 elsewhere (effective 2003). adv. bk.rev. bibl.; illus. index, cum.index: 1934-1983. reprints avail. **Document type:** *Academic/Scholarly.*
Related titles: Online - full text ed.: (from EBSCO Publishing).
Indexed: ASCA, HAPI, IBR, IBSS, ILD, JEL, PAIS, RASB, RRTA, SSCI, WAE&RSA.
—BLDSC (9050.650000), IDS, IE, Infotrieve, ingenta.

Published by: Fondo de Cultura Economica, Carretera PICACHO AJUSCO 227, Col Bosques del Pedregal, Mexico City, DF 14200, Mexico. TEL 52-55-52274671, FAX 52-55-54491807, trimestre@fce.com.mx. Ed. Fausto Hernandez Trillo. Circ: 1,100.

330 IRL
TRINITY ECONOMIC PAPERS. Text in English. 1999. irreg.
Description: Provides a forum for the rapid dissemination of research conducted at the Department of Economics.
Formed by the merger of (1994-1998): Trinity College. Department of Economics. Technical Papers Series; (1994-1998): Trinity College. Department of Economics. Policy Papers Series
Published by: Trinity College, Department of Economics, Dublin, 2, Ireland. TEL 353-1-608-1325, FAX 353-1-677-2503, econsec@tcd.ie, http://www.tcd.ie/Economics/economic_papers.htm. Ed. Kevin O'Rourke.

330 USA ISSN 1520-9474
TROUBLED COMPANY REPORTER. Text in English. d. (Mon.-Fri.). USD 830 for 6 mos. (effective 2002). **Document type:** *Journal, Trade.* **Description:** Covers companies in the US with assets of more than USD 10 million showing signs of financial strain or difficulty.
Media: E-mail. **Related titles:** ♦ Regional ed(s).: Troubled Company Reporter - Asia Pacific. ISSN 1520-9482; ♦ Troubled Company Reporter - Europe. ISSN 1529-2754; ♦ Troubled Company Reporter - Latin America. ISSN 1529-2746.
Published by: Beard Group, Inc, PO Box 9867, Washington, DC 20016. TEL 240-629-3300, FAX 240-629-3360, info@beard.com, http://www.beard.com. Ed. Debra Brennan. Pub., R&P Christopher Beard.

330 USA ISSN 1520-9482
TROUBLED COMPANY REPORTER - ASIA PACIFIC. Text in English. d. (Mon.-Fri.). USD 780 for 6 mos. (effective 2002). **Document type:** *Journal, Trade.* **Description:** Covers companies in Asia-Pacific region with assets of more than USD 10 million showing signs of financial strain or difficulty.
Media: E-mail. **Related titles:** ♦ Regional ed(s).: Troubled Company Reporter. ISSN 1520-9474; ♦ Troubled Company Reporter - Europe. ISSN 1529-2754; ♦ Troubled Company Reporter - Latin America. ISSN 1529-2746.
Published by: Beard Group, Inc, PO Box 9867, Washington, DC 20016. TEL 240-629-3300, FAX 240-629-3360, info@beard.com, http://www.beard.com. Ed. Lexy Mueller. Pub., R&P Christopher Beard.

330 340 USA ISSN 1529-2754
TROUBLED COMPANY REPORTER - EUROPE. Text in English. 1999. d. (Mon.-Fri.). USD 575 (effective 2005). tr.lit. Index. back issues avail. **Document type:** *Newsletter, Trade.* **Description:** Covers companies in Europe with assets of more than USD 10 million showing signs of financial strain or difficulty.
Media: E-mail. **Related titles:** ♦ Regional ed(s).: Troubled Company Reporter. ISSN 1520-9474; ♦ Troubled Company Reporter - Asia Pacific. ISSN 1520-9482; ♦ Troubled Company Reporter - Latin America. ISSN 1529-2746.
Published by: Beard Group, Inc, 502 W Patrick St, Frederick, MD 21701. TEL 240-629-3300, FAX 240-629-3360, subscriptions@beard.com, http://www.beardgroup.com. Ed. Peter Chapman. Pub. Christopher Beard.

330 USA ISSN 1529-2746
TROUBLED COMPANY REPORTER - LATIN AMERICA. Text in English. d. (Mon.-Fri.). USD 780 for 6 mos. (effective 2002). **Document type:** *Trade.* **Description:** Reports on the companies in Latin America region with assets of more than USD 10 million that shows signs of financial strain or difficulty.
Media: E-mail. **Related titles:** ♦ Regional ed(s).: Troubled Company Reporter. ISSN 1520-9474; ♦ Troubled Company Reporter - Asia Pacific. ISSN 1520-9482; ♦ Troubled Company Reporter - Europe. ISSN 1529-2754.
Published by: Beard Group, Inc, PO Box 9867, Washington, DC 20016. TEL 240-629-3300, FAX 240-629-3360, info@beard.com, http://www.beard.com.

330 RUS
TSENTR PLIUS. Text in Russian. 1995. w. USD 235 in United States (effective 2000).
Published by: Izdatel'stvo Tsentr Plius, Ul M Lubyanka 16 str 1, Moscow, 101000, Russian Federation. TEL 7-095-9218404. Ed. S A Sharakshane. **Dist. by:** East View Information Services, 3020 Harbor Ln. N., Minneapolis, MN 55447. TEL 763-550-0961, FAX 763-559-2931.

330 USA ISSN 0745-5747
TULSA BUSINESS CHRONICLE. Text in English. 1982. w. USD 30 in county; USD 60 in United States. adv. charts; stat. back issues avail. **Description:** Covers local business news, features, personal investing, real estate, and stocks for corporate individuals.
Related titles: Online - full text ed.: (from ProQuest Information & Learning).
Indexed: BusDate.
Published by: World Publishing Co. (Tulsa), PO Box 1770, Tulsa, OK 24102. TEL 918-581-8560. Ed. Bill Sansing. Circ: 2,000.

330 340 USA ISSN 1054-2493
TULSA DAILY COMMERCE & LEGAL NEWS. Text in English. 1909. d. (Mon.-Fri.). USD 0.50 newsstand/cover; USD 125.50 in county; USD 208.50 in state; USD 275.50 out of state. adv. **Document type:** *Newspaper.*
Formerly: Tulsa Daily Business Journal & Legal Record (0897-4233)
Published by: Retherford Publications, Inc., 8545 E 41st St, Tulsa, Tulsa, OK 74145-3390. TEL 918-663-1414, FAX 918-664-8161. Ed. Ralph Shaefer. Pub. Bill R. Retherford. Adv. contact Jo Brewer. col. inch USD 8. Circ: 324 (paid).

330 TUR ISSN 1300-2260
TURKEY; monthly economic newspaper. Text in English. 1982. m. adv. **Description:** Covers business and economics in Turkey.
Published by: Ihlas Magazine Group, Ihlas Holding Mrk. Binasi, 29 Ekim Cad. 23, Yenibosna - Istanbul, 34530, Turkey. TEL 90-212-4542530, bsensoz@img.com.tr, imga@img.com.tr, http://www.img.com.tr. Ed. Mehmet Soztutan. Pub. Dr. Enver Oren. R&P Muhsin Yilmaz. Adv. contact Ms. Bahar Sensoz. Circ: 2,486 (paid); 40,890 (controlled).

330 POL ISSN 1427-5112
TWOJ BIZNES. Text in Polish. 1996. w. PLZ 81.90 (effective 2001).
Published by: Grupa Wydawnicza INFOR Sp. z o.o., Ul Okopowa 58/72, Warsaw, 01042, Poland. TEL 48-22-5304208, 48-22-5304450, bok@infor.pl. Ed. Andrzej Racinski. Adv. contact Waldemar Krakowiak.

330 USA
U A M R NEWSLETTER. Text in English. 1975. m. USD 48. adv. back issues avail. **Document type:** *Newsletter.*
Published by: (United Association Manufacturers' Representatives), Keith Kittrell & Associates, Inc., P O Box 986, Dana Point, CA 92639. TEL 714-240-4966. Ed. H Keith Kittrell. Circ: 1,650.

338 650 USA ISSN 0740-851X
HC101
U C L A BUSINESS FORECAST FOR CALIFORNIA✶ . Text in English. 1960. q. USD 300 per issue. **Document type:** *Academic/Scholarly.*
Supersedes in part: U C L A Business Forecast for the Nation and California (0082-7126)
Published by: (U C L A Business Forecasting Project), University of California at Los Angeles, John E. Anderson Graduate School of Management, 110 Westwood Plaza, Ste B201, Los Angeles, CA 90095-1481. TEL 213-825-1623, FAX 213-206-9940. Ed. David G Hensley. Circ: 2,000.

330 USA
U C L A NATIONAL BUSINESS FORECAST✶ . Text in English. 1960. q. USD 300 for 1 vol.. **Document type:** *Academic/Scholarly.*
Supersedes in part: U C L A Business Forecast for the Nation and California (0082-7126)
Published by: (U C L A Business Forecasting Project), University of California at Los Angeles, John E. Anderson Graduate School of Management, 110 Westwood Plaza, Ste B201, Los Angeles, CA 90095-1481. TEL 213-825-1623, FAX 213-206-9940. Ed. David G Hensley. Circ: 2,000.

330 USA
U G I CORPORATION. ANNUAL REPORT. Text in English. a. **Document type:** *Corporate.*
Published by: U G I Corporation, Box 858, Valley Forge, PA 19482. TEL 610-337-1000, 610-337-1000, http://www.ugicorp.com, http://www.ugicorp.com/.

330 USA
U G I CORPORATION NEWS. Text in English. irreg. **Document type:** *Newsletter, Corporate.*
Published by: U G I Corporation, Box 858, Valley Forge, PA 19482. TEL 610-337-1000, 800-UGI-9453, http://www.ugicorp.com/.

330 GBR
U K ANNUAL FINANCIAL NEWS SUMMARY. Text in English. a. GBP 210; GBP 220 foreign. stat. **Document type:** *Trade.* **Description:** Aims to provide an at-a-glance picture of a company's activity during the year. Covers financial and commercial news on UK quoted companies.
Published by: Financial Times Information Ltd., Extel, Fitzroy House, 13-17 Epworth St, London, EC2A 4DL, United Kingdom. TEL 44-20-7825-8000, FAX 44-20-7608-3032, eic@ft.com, http://www.info.ft.com.

650.05 GBR ISSN 1470-3122
U K BUSINESS & PROFESSIONAL MAGAZINES DIRECTORY. Text in English. 1965. m. **Document type:** *Directory, Trade.*
Supersedes in part (in 2000): P I M S Media Directory (0261-5169); Which was formerly (until 1981): P R A D S Media List (0144-3933)
—BLDSC (6501.341000).
Published by: P I M S (UK) Ltd., PIMS House, Mildmay Ave, London, N1 4RS, United Kingdom. TEL 44-20-7354-7000, FAX 44-20-7354-7053.

330 GBR
U K RETAIL BRIEFING. Text in English. m. GBP 295, USD 475, EUR 435 per issue (effective 2003). **Document type:** *Trade.*
Media: Online - full content.
Published by: Mintel International Group Ltd., 18-19 Long Ln., London, EC1A 9PL, United Kingdom. TEL 44-20-76064533, FAX 44-20-76065932, info@mintel.com, http://www.mintel.com.

330 GBR
U K WEEKLY FINANCIAL NEWS SUMMARY. Text in English. w. looseleaf. GBP 680; GBP 755 foreign. stat. **Document type:** *Trade.*
Published by: Financial Times Information Ltd., Extel, Fitzroy House, 13-17 Epworth St, London, EC2A 4DL, United Kingdom. TEL 44-20-7608-2032, FAX 44-20-7825-8000, eic@ft.com, http://www.info.ft.com.

320 USA ISSN 0743-1694
U R P E NEWSLETTER✶ . Text in English. 1969. q. USD 15 domestic to individuals; USD 30 foreign to individuals; USD 30 to institutions. adv. bk.rev. **Document type:** *Newsletter.*
Indexed: PAIS.
Published by: Union for Radical Political Economics, 37 Howe ST, New Haven, CT 06511-4605. TEL 617-776-5888, FAX 617-628-2025, urpe@igc.apc.org. Ed. Marc Schaberg. R&P, Adv. contact Bryan Snyder. Circ: 2,000.

U S A FOR BUSINESS TRAVELERS. see *TRAVEL AND TOURISM*

U S A JOURNAL. see *TRAVEL AND TOURISM*

330 USA
U.S. BUSINESS JOURNAL. Text in English. 1998. d. USD 500 (effective 2005). adv. stat. cum.index every 5 years. back issues avail.; reprints avail. **Document type:** *Newsletter, Trade.* **Description:** Reports on both financially troubled and fast growing companies nationwide.
Media: Online - full content. **Related titles:** E-mail ed.
Published by: Bastien Financial Publications, PO Box 2170, Des Plaines, IL 60017. cred@creditnews.com, http://www.creditnews.com/. Ed. Lewis Gebhardt. Pub., Adv. contact Steve Bastien. page USD 4,500. Circ: 1,500 (paid).

330 USA ISSN 1552-6313
U S BUSINESS REVIEW. Text in English. 2000. 11/yr. free to qualified personnel (effective 2005). adv. **Document type:** *Magazine, Consumer.* **Description:** Helps companies navigate the new world of business through insightful, cross-industry articles on trends, opinions and legal issues, as well as intriguing interviews with America's most interesting and influential men and women.
Published by: Schofield Media Ltd., 303 E Wacker Dr, 23rd Fl., Chicago, IL 60601. TEL 312-236-4090, FAX 312-240-0686, http://www.usbusiness-review.com/, http://www.schofield-media.com/. adv.: B&W page USD 6,110, color page USD 7,910; trim 8.375 x 10.75. Circ: 40,000.

330
U.S. DEPARTMENT OF LABOR. SERVICE CONTRACT ACT DIRECTORY OF OCCUPATIONS. Text in English. latest 4th Edition, base vol. plus a. updates. looseleaf. USD 30 (effective 2001). **Document type:** *Government.* **Description:** Provides occupational information essential to timely development and issuance of Service Contract Act wage determinations. Includes Federal grade equivalencies for most of the occupations listed. Contains titles and descriptions for over 300 jobs.
Related titles: Online - full content ed.
Published by: U.S. Department of Labor, Employment Standards Administration, Wage Hour Division, New York City District Office, 26 Federal Plaza, Rm 3838, New York, NY 10278. http://www.dol.gov/dol/esa/public/regs/compliance/whd/wage/main.htm. **Subscr. to:** U.S. Government Printing Office, Superintendent of Documents, PO Box 371954, Pittsburgh, PA 15250-7954. TEL 202-512-1800, FAX 202-512-2250, orders@gpo.gov, http://www.access.gpo.gov.

330 USA
U.S. INTERNATIONAL TRADE COMMISSION. OFFICE OF EXTERNAL RELATIONS. NEWS. Text in English. irreg. (2-3/month). **Document type:** *Government.*
Published by: U.S. International Trade Commission, Office of External Relations, 500 E St SW, Washington, DC 20436. TEL 202-205-1819, http://www.usitc.gov.

330 USA
U.S. MARKETPLACE. Text in English. q. members only. back issues avail. **Document type:** *Newsletter, Trade.*
Related titles: Online - full content ed.
Published by: L I M R A International, Inc., 300 Day Hill Rd, Windsor, CT 06095. TEL 860-688-3358, FAX 860-298-9555, http://www.limra.com/.

330 500 LTU
UKIO. Text in Lithuanian, German, Russian, English. s-a. back issues avail. **Document type:** *Monographic series, Academic/Scholarly.*
Published by: (Vilniaus Gedimino Technikos Universitetas, Statybos Fakultetas/Vilnius Gediminas Technical University, Faculty of Civil Engineering), Lidykla Technika, Sauletekio al. 11, Vilnius, 2040, Lithuania. Ed. E K Zavadskas.

330 UKR
UKRAINA-BUSINESS. Text in Russian, Ukrainian. w. USD 235 in United States.
Address: Ul Sofievskaya 9, Kiev, Ukraine. TEL 229-26-96. **US dist. addr.:** East View Information Services, 3020 Harbor Ln. N., Minneapolis, MN 55447. TEL 612-550-0961.

330.9 USA ISSN 1080-725X
HC340.19.A1
UKRAINIAN ECONOMIC REVIEW. Text in English. irreg. USD 20 newsstand/cover (effective 2002). bk.rev. back issues avail. **Document type:** *Journal, Academic/Scholarly.*
Indexed: IBSS, JEL.
Published by: International Ukrainian Economic Association, c/o Professor I.S. Koropeckyj, Temple University, Philadelphia, PA 19122. TEL 215-517-7389, FAX 215-204-8173, iskor@nimbus.temple.edu, http://www.brama.com/ukrainecon. Ed. I S Koropeckyj.

338.09416 GBR ISSN 1363-2507
ULSTER BUSINESS. Text in English. 1987. m. GBP 27.50 domestic; GBP 37.50 in Europe (effective 2001). adv. **Document type:** *Magazine, Trade.* **Description:** Contains information and news on Northern Ireland's business to business community.
Related titles: Online - full text ed.
—CCC.
Published by: Greer Publications, 5B Edgewater Business Park, Belfast Harbour Estate, Belfast, BT3 9JQ, United Kingdom. TEL 44-28-9078-3200, FAX 44-28-9078-3210, http://www.ulsterbusiness.com, http://www.ulsterbusiness.com/greer. Ed. Russell Campbell. Adv. contact Diane Henry TEL 44-028-90-783200.

330 GBR
ULSTER BUSINESS JOURNAL. Text in English. m. GBP 1 per issue. adv. **Document type:** *Trade.*
Published by: Ulster Journals Ltd., 39 Boucher Rd, Belfast, Co Antrim, N Ireland BT12 6UT, United Kingdom. Ed. R Johnston.

650 AUS ISSN 1443-7023
➤ **ULTIBASE JOURNAL.** Text in English. 1996. m. **Document type:** *Journal, Academic/Scholarly.* **Description:** Publishes original research, personal reflections and interviews, focusing on teaching and learning in business.
Media: Online - full text.
Published by: Royal Melbourne Institute of Technology, Faculty of Education, Language and Community Services, PO Box 2476V, Melbourne, VIC 3001, Australia. TEL 61-3-9925-1702, FAX 61-3-9925-3049, manager@ultibase.rmit.edu.au, http://www.ultibase.rmit.edu.au/Journal/journal.html.

333.72 DEU ISSN 0943-3481
➤ **UMWELTWIRTSCHAFTSFORUM.** Short title: U W F. Text in German. 1990. q. EUR 168.22 to institutions (effective 2005). adv. back issues avail. **Document type:** *Journal, Academic/Scholarly.* **Description:** Provides a forum for ecological management in industry.
Formerly (until 1992): F O B - Forschungsinformationsdienst Oekologisch Orientierte Betriebswirtschaftslehre (0937-5228)
Related titles: Online - full text ed.
—IE. CCC.
Published by: (Institut fuer Umweltwirtschaftsanalysen Heidelberg e.V.), Springer-Verlag (Subsidiary of: Springer Science+Business Media), Tiergartenstr 17, Heidelberg, 69121, Germany. TEL 49-6221-3450, FAX 49-6221-345229. Ed. D G Liesegang. Adv. contact Stephan Kroeck TEL 49-30-827875739. **Subscr. in the Americas to:** Springer-Verlag New York, Inc., Journal Fulfillment, PO Box 2485, Secaucus, NJ 07096-2485. TEL 800-777-4643, 201-348-4033, FAX 201-348-4505, journals@springer-ny.com, http://www.springer-ny.com; **Subscr. to:** Springer GmbH Auslieferungsgesellschaft, Haberstr 7, Heidelberg 69126, Germany. TEL 49-6221-345-0, FAX 49-6221-345-4229, subscriptions@springer.de.

330 GBR
UNILEVER. ANNUAL ACCOUNTS. Text in English. a. **Document type:** *Corporate.*
Related titles: Dutch ed.
Published by: Unilever PLC London, P O Box 68, London, EC4P 4BQ, United Kingdom. TEL 44-20-7822-5252, FAX 44-20-7822-5951, philip.walton@unilever.com, mary.hernandez@unilever.com, http://www.unilever.com/.

330 GBR
UNILEVER. ANNUAL REVIEW. Text in English. a. **Document type:** *Corporate.*
Related titles: Dutch ed.
Published by: Unilever PLC London, P O Box 68, London, EC4P 4BQ, United Kingdom. TEL 44-20-7822-5252, FAX 44-20-7822-5951, philip.walton@unilever.com, mary.hernandez@unilever.com, http://www.unilever.com/.

330 GBR
UNILEVER. CHARTS BOOKLET. Text in English. irreg. charts. **Document type:** *Corporate.*
Published by: Unilever PLC London, P O Box 68, London, EC4P 4BQ, United Kingdom. TEL 44-20-7822-5252, FAX 44-20-7822-5951, philip.walton@unilever.com, mary.hernandez@unilever.com, http://www.unilever.com/.

330 GBR
UNILEVER. US SUPPLEMENT TO ANNUAL REVIEW. Text in English. a. **Document type:** *Corporate.*
Published by: Unilever PLC London, P O Box 68, London, EC4P 4BQ, United Kingdom. TEL 44-20-7822-5252, FAX 44-20-7822-5951, philip.walton@unilever.com, mary.hernandez@unilever.com, http://www.unilever.com/.

UNION. see *POLITICAL SCIENCE*

330 300 USA
UNITED NATIONS. ECONOMIC AND SOCIAL COUNCIL. ANNEXES. Text in English, French, Spanish. 1946. q.
Published by: (United Nations, Economic and Social Council), United Nations Publications, Rm DC2-853, United Nations Bldg, 2 United Nations Plaza, New York, NY 10017. TEL 212-963-8302, 800-253-9646, FAX 212-963-3489, publications@un.org, http://www.un.org/publications, http://www.un.org/Pubs.

330 300 USA
UNITED NATIONS. ECONOMIC AND SOCIAL COUNCIL. OFFICIAL RECORDS. SUPPLEMENTS AND SPECIAL SUPPLEMENTS. Text in English, French, Spanish. 1946. q.
Published by: (United Nations, Economic and Social Council), United Nations Publications, Rm DC2-853, United Nations Bldg, 2 United Nations Plaza, New York, NY 10017. TEL 212-963-8302, 800-253-9646, FAX 212-963-3489, publications@un.org, http://www.un.org/publications, http://www.un.org/Pubs.

330 300 USA ISSN 0251-9410
HC59
UNITED NATIONS. ECONOMIC AND SOCIAL COUNCIL. RESOLUTIONS AND DECISIONS. Text in English. 1946. q.
Related titles: Arabic ed.: ISSN 0257-1145; Chinese ed.: ISSN 0251-9380; French ed.: ISSN 0251-9429; German ed.: ISSN 0257-389X; Spanish ed.: ISSN 0251-9399.
Published by: (United Nations, Economic and Social Council), United Nations Publications, Rm DC2-853, United Nations Bldg, 2 United Nations Plaza, New York, NY 10017. TEL 212-963-8302, 800-253-9646, FAX 212-963-3489, publications@un.org, http://www.un.org/publications, http://www.un.org/Pubs.

330 300 USA
UNITED NATIONS. ECONOMIC AND SOCIAL COUNCIL. SUMMARY RECORDS OF PLENARY MEETINGS. Text in English, French, Spanish. 1946. q.
Published by: (United Nations, Economic and Social Council), United Nations Publications, Rm DC2-853, United Nations Bldg, 2 United Nations Plaza, New York, NY 10017. TEL 212-963-8302, 800-253-9646, FAX 212-963-3489.

UNITED NATIONS. TRUSTEESHIP COUNCIL. OFFICIAL RECORDS. ANNEXES - SESSIONAL FASCICLE. see *POLITICAL SCIENCE—International Relations*

UNITED NATIONS. TRUSTEESHIP COUNCIL. OFFICIAL RECORDS. RESOLUTIONS. see *POLITICAL SCIENCE—International Relations*

UNITED NATIONS. TRUSTEESHIP COUNCIL. OFFICIAL RECORDS. VERBATIM RECORDS OF PLENARY MEETINGS. see *POLITICAL SCIENCE—International Relations*

330 MEX ISSN 0041-8498
UNIVERSIDAD AUTONOMA DE NUEVO LEON. CENTRO DE INVESTIGACIONES ECONOMICAS. BOLETIN BIMESTRAL. Text in Spanish. 1963. bi-m. MXP 50, USD 20. stat. **Description:** Presents research of the institute.
Media: Duplicated (not offset).
Published by: Universidad Autonoma de Nuevo Leon, Centro de Investigaciones Economicas, LOMA REDONDA 1515-A, Col Loma Larga, Monterrey, NL 64710, Mexico. TEL 45-50-18. Ed. Jesus Ramones Saldana. Circ: 650.

330 CHL
UNIVERSIDAD DE CHILE. FACULTAD DE CIENCIAS ECONOMICAS Y ADMINISTRATIVAS. DESARROLLO. Text in Spanish. irreg.
Published by: Universidad de Chile, Facultad de Ciencias Economicas y Administrativas, Ave. Ranacagua, 257, Santiago, Chile.

330 URY ISSN 0378-9918
UNIVERSIDAD DE LA REPUBLICA. FACULTAD DE CIENCIAS ECONOMICAS Y DE ADMINISTRACION. REVISTA. Text in Spanish. 1940; N.S. 1950. irreg. bibl.; charts.
Published by: Universidad de la Republica, Facultad de Ciencias Economicas y de Administracion, Montevideo, Uruguay.

330 ESP
UNIVERSIDAD DE SEVILLA. INSTITUTO GARCIA OVIEDO. CUADERNOS. Text in Spanish. irreg. price varies. **Document type:** *Monographic series, Academic/Scholarly.*
Published by: (Universidad de Sevilla, Instituto Garcia Oviedo), Universidad de Sevilla, Secretariado de Publicaciones, Porvenir 27, Sevilla, 41013, Spain. TEL 34-95-4487444, FAX 34-95-4487443, secpub10@us.es, http://www.us.es/publius/inicio.html.

330 650 ESP
UNIVERSIDAD DE SEVILLA. SERIE: CIENCIAS ECONOMICAS Y EMPRESARIALES. Text in Spanish. 1976 (vol.2). irreg., latest vol.56, 2001. price varies. **Document type:** *Monographic series, Abstract/Index.*
Formerly (until 1967): Universidad Hispalense. Anales. Serie: Economicas y Empresariales
Published by: Universidad de Sevilla, Secretariado de Publicaciones, Porvenir 27, Sevilla, 41013, Spain. TEL 34-95-4487444, FAX 34-95-4487443, secpub10@us.es, http://www.us.es/publius/inicio.html.

330 ARG ISSN 0326-7059
UNIVERSIDAD DEL ACONCAGUA. FACULTAD DE ECONOMIA Y CIENCIAS COMERCIALES. REVISTA. Key Title: Revista de la Facultad de Economia y Ciencias Comerciales. Universidad del Aconcagua. Text in Spanish. 1980. irreg. back issues avail. **Document type:** *Academic/Scholarly.*
Published by: Universidad del Aconcagua, Facultad de Economia y Ciencias Comerciales, Catamarca 147 2o. Piso, Mendoza, 5500, Argentina. TEL 56-261-4291573, 56-261-4291573, fecc_uda@lanet.com.ar. Ed. Marta Polichenco.

330 ARG ISSN 0041-8668
UNIVERSIDAD NACIONAL DE CUYO. FACULTAD DE CIENCIAS ECONOMICAS. REVISTA. Text in Spanish. 1949. 3/yr. bk.rev. abstr.; charts; stat. index, cum.index: 1949-1966.
Indexed: RPP.
—CISTI.
Published by: Universidad Nacional de Cuyo, Facultad de Ciencias Economicas, Casilla de Correos 594, Mendoza, 5500, Argentina. Circ: 600.

330 ARG
UNIVERSIDAD NACIONAL DEL LITORAL. FACULTAD DE CIENCIAS ECONOMICAS COMERCIALES Y POLITICAS. Text in Spanish. 1926. irreg.
Published by: Universidad Nacional del Litoral, Facultad de Ciencias Economicas Comerciales y Politicas, Santa Fe, Argentina. http://www.unl.edu.ar/.

330 PER
UNIVERSIDAD NACIONAL MAYOR DE SAN MARCOS. FACULTAD DE CIENCIAS ECONOMICAS. REVISTA. Text in Spanish. 1929. irreg. bibl. **Document type:** *Bulletin.*
Formerly: Revista Economica y Financiera
Published by: Universidad Nacional Mayor de San Marcos, Facultad de Ciencias Economicas, Av German Amezaga, Lima, Peru. TEL 511-4525485, diaeco@unmsm.edu.pe, http://www.unmsm.edu.pe. Ed. Hugo Lezana Coca.

330 COL ISSN 0120-3053
HC196
UNIVERSIDAD PEDAGOGICA Y TECNOLOGICA DE COLOMBIA. CENTRO DE ESTUDIOS ECONOMICOS. APUNTES DEL C E N E S. Text in Spanish. 1991. s-a. COP 25,000, USD 12.50 (effective 2001). bk.rev. abstr. **Document type:** *Proceedings, Academic/Scholarly.* **Description:** Publishes works and research by professors and students at the university. Includes proceedings on seminars, forums, and symposiums.
Published by: Universidad Pedagogica y Tecnologica de Colombia, Centro de Estudios Economicos, Carretera Central del Norte, Apartado Aereo 1094, Tunja, BOY, Colombia. TEL 57-8-7422174, FAX 57-8-7422177 ext. 1540, cenes@donato.uptc.edu.co, http://www.uptc.edu.co. Ed., R&P, Adv. contact Luis E Vallejo Zamudio. Circ: 600 (paid).

330 PRT ISSN 0870-4252
UNIVERSIDADE DE COIMBRA. FACULDADE DE DIREITO. BOLETIM DE CIENCIAS ECONOMICAS. Text in Portuguese; Summaries in English. 1952. a. USD 10.70. bk.rev. charts; stat.
Indexed: PAIS.
Published by: (Universidade de Coimbra, Faculdade de Direito), Coimbra Editora Lda., Rua do Arnado, Apdo 101, Coimbra, 3002, Portugal. TEL 351-239-25459, FAX 351-239-37531. Circ: 500.

330 PRT ISSN 0870-1326
UNIVERSIDADE TECNICA DE LISBOA. INSTITUTO SUPERIOR DE ECONOMIA E GESTAO. ESTUDOS DE ECONOMIA. Text in Portuguese. 1980. q. EUR 19.95 to individuals in Portugal & Spain; EUR 39.90 to institutions in Portugal & Spain; USD 34 to individuals in other European countries; USD 60 to institutions in other European countries; USD 44 elsewhere to individuals; USD 70 elsewhere to institutions; EUR 14.96 to students (effective 2002).
Indexed: PAIS.
Published by: Universidade Tecnica de Lisboa, Instituto Superior de Economia e Gestao, Rua do Quelhas, 6, Lisbon, 1200-781, Portugal. TEL 351-21-392-58-75, FAX 351-21-392-58-50, pfonseca@iseg.utl.pt, http://www.iseg.utl.pt/estudos_de_economia.html.

B

▼ new title ➤ refereed ✶ unverified ◆ full entry avail.

B

330   ITA
UNIVERSITA DEGLI STUDI DI PARMA. FACOLTA DI
ECONOMIA E COMMERCIO. STUDI E RICERCHE. Text in
Italian. 1964. a.
Published by: (Universita egli Studi di Parma, Facolta di
Economia e Commercio), Universita degli Studi di Parma,
Piazzale della Pace, 7 A, Parma, PR 43100, Italy.

330   ITA
UNIVERSITA DI SASSARI. FACOLTA DI GIURISPRUDENZA.
PUBBLICAZIONI. SERIE ECONOMICA. Text in Italian. 1984.
irreg.
Published by: (Universita degli Studi di Sassari, Facolta di
Giurisprudenza), Casa Editrice Dott. A. Giuffre (Subsidiary of:
LexisNexis Europe and Africa), Via Busto Arsizio, 40, Milan,
MI 20151, Italy. TEL 39-02-28089200, FAX 39-02-38009582,
giuffre@giuffre.it, http://www.giuffre.it.

330   DEU   ISSN 0175-7261
UNIVERSITAET HAMBURG. SEMINAR FUER ALLGEMEINE
BETRIEBSWIRTSCHAFTSLEHRE. SCHRIFTENREIHE. Text
in German. 1978. irreg., latest vol.34, 1990. price varies.
Document type: Monographic series, Academic/Scholarly.
Published by: Vandenhoeck und Ruprecht, Robert-Bosch-Breite
6, Goettingen, 37079, Germany. TEL 49-551-508440, FAX
49-551-5084422, info@v-r.de, http://www.vandenhoeck-
ruprecht.de.

330   DEU
UNIVERSITAET HEIDELBERG.
WIRTSCHAFTSWISSENSCHAFTLICHE FAKULTAET.
DISKUSSIONSSCHRIFTEN. Text in German, English. 1970.
irreg., latest vol.354. Document type: Monographic series,
Academic/Scholarly.
Published by: Universitaet Heidelberg,
Wirtschaftswissenschaftliche Fakultaet, Grabengasse 14,
Heidelberg, 69117, Germany. TEL 49-6221-542915, FAX
49-6221-542914, http://www.uni-heidelberg.de/institute/fak18/
fakul/fak_publ.html.

330   DEU   ISSN 0542-1497
UNIVERSITAET MAINZ. FORSCHUNGSINSTITUT FUER
WIRTSCHAFTSPOLITIK. VEROEFFENTLICHUNGEN. Text in
German. 1954. irreg., latest vol.59, 2003. price varies.
Document type: Monographic series, Academic/Scholarly.
Published by: (Universitaet Mainz, Forschungsinstitut fuer
Wirtschaftspolitik), Duncker und Humblot GmbH,
Carl-Heinrich-Becker-Weg 9, Berlin, 12165, Germany. TEL
49-30-7900060, FAX 49-30-79000631, info@duncker-
humblot.de, http://www.duncker-humblot.de.

330   DEU   ISSN 0531-0318
UNIVERSITAET ZU KOELN. INSTITUT FUER
HANDELSFORSCHUNG. MITTEILUNGEN. SONDERHEFTE.
Text in German. 1954. irreg., latest vol.46, 2002. price varies.
Document type: Monographic series, Academic/Scholarly.
Published by: Institut fuer Handelsforschung (Subsidiary of:
Universitaet zu Koeln), Saeckinger Str. 5, Cologne, 50935,
Germany. TEL 49-221-9436070, FAX 49-221-94360799,
info@ifhkoeln.de, http://www.ifhkoeln.de.

330   COL   ISSN 0120-0941
HC59.7
UNIVERSITAS ECONOMICA. Text in Spanish. 1977. s-a. COP
7,000, USD 8 (effective 1997).
Published by: Pontificia Universidad Javeriana, Facultad de
Ciencias Economicas y Administrativas, Carrera 7 No 40-62
Piso 4o, Edificio Emilio Arango, Bogota, CUND, Colombia,
TEL 57-1-3208320, FAX 57-1-2857289, http://
www.javeriana.edu.co.

330   ROM   ISSN 0379-7864
UNIVERSITATEA "AL. I. CUZA" DIN IASI. ANALELE
STIINTICE. SECTIUNEA 3C: STIINTE ECONOMICE. Text
in English, French, Romanian. a. ROL 35. bk.rev. abstr.;
charts; illus. Description: New research in theoretical and
applied economics.
Indexed: RASB.
Published by: Universitatea "Al. I. Cuza" din Iasi/Alexandru Ioan
Cuza" University of Iasi, Carol I Boulevard, Iasi, 6600,
Romania. Ed. M Tarca. Circ: 250. Subscr. to: ILEXIM, Str. 13
Decembrie 3, PO Box 136-137, Bucharest 70116, Romania.

330   CIV
UNIVERSITE D'ABIDJAN. SERIE K. SCIENCES
ECONOMIQUES. Text in French. irreg.
Indexed: PAIS.
Published by: Universite Nationale de Cote d'Ivoire, 22 BP 535,
Abidjan 22, Ivory Coast. TEL 225-439000, FAX 225-353635.

338.9   COD
UNIVERSITE NATIONALE DU ZAIRE, KINSHASA. INSTITUT DE
RECHERCHES ECONOMIQUES ET SOCIALES. LETTRE
MENSUELLE. Text in French. 1964. m.
Published by: Universite de Kinshasa, Institut de Recherches
Economiques et Sociales, BP 257, Kinshasa, 11, Congo,
Dem. Republic.

330   NOR   ISSN 0803-0219
UNIVERSITETET I BERGEN. INSTITUTT FOR
ADMINISTRASJON OG ORGANISASJONSVITENSKAP.
RAPPORT. Text in Multiple languages. 1990. irreg. Document
type: Monographic series, Academic/Scholarly.
Indexed: ASFA.
Published by: Universitetet i Bergen, Institutt for Administrasjon
og Organisasjonsvitenskap, Christies Gt. 17, Bergen, 5007,
Norway. TEL 47-55-58-21-90, FAX 47-55-58-98-90.

330   USA
➤ UNIVERSITY AVENUE UNDERGRADUATE JOURNAL OF
ECONOMICS. Key Title: U A U J E. Text in English. 1998. a.
illus. Document type: Journal, Academic/Scholarly.
Media: Online - full content.
Published by: Illinois State University, College of Business, 328
William Hall, Normal, IL 61761. UAUJE@ilstu.edu,
http://www.econ.ilstu.edu/uauje/.

330   GBR   ISSN 1350-6722
HB1
UNIVERSITY COLLEGE LONDON. DEPARTMENT OF
ECONOMICS. DISCUSSION PAPERS IN ECONOMICS. Text
in English. irreg.
—BLDSC (3597.773800), ingenta.
Published by: University College London, Department of
Economics, Gower St, London, WC1E 6BT, United Kingdom.
TEL 44-20-76795888, http://www.ucl.ac.uk/economics/.

330   DNK   ISSN 1396-2426
HB1
UNIVERSITY OF AARHUS, DENMARK. DEPARTMENT OF
ECONOMICS. WORKING PAPER. Text in Danish. 1974. irreg.
Formerly (until 1996): Aarhus Universitet. Oekonomisk Institut.
Memo (0902-6223)
Indexed: RASB.
Published by: Aarhus Universitet, Department of Economics,
Building 350, Aarhus C, 8000, Denmark. TEL 45-89-42-11-33,
FAX 45-86-13-63-34. Eds. Niels Haldrup, Tom Engsted.

330   GBR   ISSN 0960-443X
UNIVERSITY OF ABERDEEN. DEPARTMENT OF ECONOMICS.
DISCUSSION PAPER. Text in English. 1975. irreg. GBP 3.
adv. Document type: Monographic series,
Academic/Scholarly.
Formerly (until 1986): University of Aberdeen. Department of
Economics. Occasional Paper (0143-4543)
—BLDSC (3597.662800), IE, ingenta.
Published by: University of Aberdeen, Department of Economics,
Edward Wright Bldg, Aberdeen, University Of Aberdeen,
Dunbar St, Aberdeen, AB24 3QY, United Kingdom. TEL
44-1224-272170. Ed. I Theodossiou. Adv. contact Anne
Shipley.

UNIVERSITY OF ALASKA. INSTITUTE OF SOCIAL AND
ECONOMIC RESEARCH. RESEARCH SUMMARY. see
SOCIOLOGY

330 650   NZL   ISSN 1174-9946
HF4030.5
➤ UNIVERSITY OF AUCKLAND BUSINESS REVIEW. Text and
summaries in English. 1999. s-a. NZD 25 domestic; NZD 35
foreign (effective 2002). adv. back issues avail. Document
type: Journal, Academic/Scholarly. Description: This review
aims to encourage reflection and debate on contemporary
business policy and practice and reports on new research
from academia, focusing on the implications for business
professionals.
Related titles: Online - full content ed.
Published by: University of Auckland Business School, Private
Bag 92019, Auckland, New Zealand. TEL 64-9-3737599, FAX
64-9-3082329, uabr@auckland.ac.nz, http://
www.uabr.auckland.ac.nz. Ed., Pub. Michael D. Myers. R&P
Leone Hill. Adv. contact Don Wilson. Circ: 16,500 (controlled);
300 (paid).

330   NOR   ISSN 1500-8606
UNIVERSITY OF BERGEN. DEPARTMENT OF ECONOMICS.
WORKING PAPERS IN ECONOMICS. Text in English. 1985.
irreg. Document type: Monographic series.
Formerly (until 1997): University of Bergen. Department of
Economics. Working Paper (0808-0518)
Indexed: ASFA, ESPM.
Published by: Universitetet i Bergen, Institutt for Oekonomi,
Fosswinckelsgate 6, Bergen, 5007, Norway. TEL
47-55-589200, FAX 47-55-589210, post@econ.uib.no,
http://www.econ.uib.no/workingpapers.html.

330 620   GBR
UNIVERSITY OF BRIGHTON. BUSINESS SCHOOL.
OCCASIONAL PAPERS SERIES. Text in English. irreg., latest
vol.2, 1996. price varies. Document type: Monographic
series.
Published by: University of Brighton, Business School, Centre for
Research in Innovation Management, Falmer, Brighton, E
Sussex BN1 9PH, United Kingdom.

330   GBR   ISSN 1362-3850
UNIVERSITY OF BRISTOL. DEPARTMENT OF ECONOMICS.
DISCUSSION PAPERS. Text in English. 1969. irreg.
Document type: Monographic series.
—BLDSC (3597.760000), IE, ingenta.

Published by: University of Bristol, Department of Economics,
Senate House, Tyndall Ave, Bristol, Glos BS8 1TH, United
Kingdom. http://www.bris.ac.uk.

330   CAN   ISSN 0317-0144
UNIVERSITY OF BRITISH COLUMBIA. DEPARTMENT OF
ECONOMICS. DISCUSSION PAPER. Text in English. 1968.
irreg. Document type: Academic/Scholarly.
—CISTI. CCC.
Published by: University of British Columbia, Department of
Economics, 1873 East Mall, Ste 997, University Campus,
Vancouver, BC V6T 1Y2, Canada. TEL 604-822-2876, FAX
604-822-5915, http://web.arts.ubc.ca/econ/dpintro.htm. Circ:
300.

330   IND   ISSN 0970-9657
UNIVERSITY OF CALCUTTA. BUSINESS STUDIES. Text in
English. 1975. s-a. INR 20, USD 4. bk.rev.
Published by: University of Calcutta, University College of
Business Studies, College St., Kolkata, West Bengal 700 073,
India. Ed. A K Dutta Gupta. Circ: 250.

330   GBR   ISSN 0956-862X
UNIVERSITY OF CAMBRIDGE. DEPARTMENT OF APPLIED
ECONOMICS. WORKING PAPERS. Text in English. 198?.
irreg. Document type: Monographic series.
—BLDSC (3509.880000), IE, ingenta.
Published by: University of Cambridge, Department of Applied
Economics, Austin Robinson Bldg, Sedgwick Ave, Cambridge,
CB3 9DE, United Kingdom. TEL 44-1223-335200, FAX
44-1223-335299, http://www.econ.cam.ac.uk/dae/index.htm.

330   GBR
UNIVERSITY OF CAMBRIDGE. FACULTY OF ECONOMICS
AND POLITICS. RESEARCH PAPER. Text in English. irreg.,
latest vol.45. Document type: Monographic series.
—BLDSC (7755.044800).
Published by: University of Cambridge, Faculty of Economics
and Politics, Sidgwick Ave, Cambridge, Cambs CB3 9DD,
United Kingdom.

330   NZL   ISSN 1171-0705
UNIVERSITY OF CANTERBURY. DEPARTMENT OF
ECONOMICS. DISCUSSION PAPER. Text in English. 1984.
irreg. Document type: Monographic series.
Formerly (until 1988): University of Canterbury. Department of
Economics & Operations Research. Discussion Paper
(1171-0691)
—BLDSC (3597.771530).
Published by: University of Canterbury, Department of
Economics, Private Bag 4800, Christchurch, New Zealand.
TEL 64-3-3667001, FAX 64-3-3642999, http://
www.canterbury.ac.nz.

330   DNK   ISSN 0902-6452
UNIVERSITY OF COPENHAGEN. INSTITUTE OF ECONOMICS.
DISCUSSION PAPERS. Text in English. 1987. irreg.
—BLDSC (3597.776000), ingenta.
Published by: Koebenhavns Universitet, Oekonomisk Institut
(Subsidiary of: Cykelafdelingen), Studiestraede 6,
Copenhagen K, 1455, Denmark.

330   GBR   ISSN 0956-7895
UNIVERSITY OF EAST ANGLIA. SCHOOL OF ECONOMIC AND
SOCIAL STUDIES. ECONOMICS RESEARCH CENTRE.
DISCUSSION PAPER. Text in English. 198?. irreg.
Formerly (until 198?): University of East Anglia. Discussion Paper
(0956-7887)
—BLDSC (3597.776500), IE, ingenta.
Published by: University of East Anglia, School of Economic and
Social Studies, Norwich, NR4 7TJ, United Kingdom. TEL
44-1603-456161, FAX 44-1603-458553, g.neff@uea.ac.uk,
http://www.uea.ac.uk/, http://www.uea.ac.uk/soc/econ/.

330   GBR   ISSN 0950-0464
UNIVERSITY OF ESSEX. DEPARTMENT OF ECONOMICS.
DISCUSSION PAPER SERIES. Text in English. 1981. irreg.
Document type: Monographic series.
Formerly (until 1983): Essex Economic Papers (0950-0456)
—BLDSC (3597.973000). CCC.
Published by: University of Essex, Department of Economics,
Wivenhoe Park, Colchester, CO4 3SQ, United Kingdom.
http://www.essex.ac.uk.

330   GBR
UNIVERSITY OF EXETER. DISCUSSION PAPERS IN
ECONOMICS. Text in English. irreg. Document type:
Monographic series, Academic/Scholarly.
—BLDSC (3597.929500).
Published by: University of Exeter, Department of Economics,
Amory Bldg, Rennes Dr, Exeter, EX4 4RJ, United Kingdom.
TEL 44-1392-263219, FAX 44-1392-263240, TELEX
42894-EXUNIV-G. Ed. Ben Lockwood.

UNIVERSITY OF GHANA. INSTITUTE OF STATISTICAL,
SOCIAL AND ECONOMIC RESEARCH. DISCUSSION
PAPERS. see SOCIAL SCIENCES: COMPREHENSIVE
WORKS

330   NLD
UNIVERSITY OF GRONINGEN. GRONINGEN GROWTH AND
DEVELOPMENT CENTRE. RESEARCH MEMORANDUM.
Text in English. irreg.
Published by: Rijksuniversiteit Groningen/University of Groningen,
PO Box 72, Groningen, 9700, Netherlands. TEL
31-50-3638181, FAX 31-50-3637100, ggdc@eco.rug.nl,
http://www.rug.nl.

330   GBR
UNIVERSITY OF HERTFORDSHIRE. BUSINESS SCHOOL.
WORKING PAPER SERIES. Text in English. irreg. Document
type: Monographic series, Academic/Scholarly.
—BLDSC (9350.957000).
Published by: University of Hertfordshire, Business School,
Mangrove Rd, Hertford, SG13 8AJ, United Kingdom. TEL
44-1707-285468, FAX 44-1707-285489. Ed. Al Rainnie. R&P
S M Barker.

330   USA   ISSN 1097-5438
UNIVERSITY OF ILLINOIS AT URBANA-CHAMPAIGN.
COLLEGE OF COMMERCE AND BUSINESS
ADMINISTRATION. OFFICE OF RESEARCH. RESULTS. Text
in English. 1997. s-a.
Related titles: Online - full text ed.: (from Gale Group).
Published by: University of Illinois at Urbana-Champaign, College
of Commerce and Business Administration, 350 Commerce
West Building, 1206 S Sixth St, Champaign, IL 61820. TEL
217-333-4240, http://www.cba.uiuc.edu/ba/dept/.

330   GBR   ISSN 1352-8955
UNIVERSITY OF KEELE. DEPARTMENT OF ECONOMICS.
WORKING PAPER. Text in English. 1970. irreg. Document
type: Monographic series. Description: Covers all aspects of
economic theory and application.
Formerly: University of Keele. Department of Economics and
Management Science. Working Paper (0952-1658)
—BLDSC (9350.845500).
Published by: University of Keele, Department of Economics,
University Of Keele, Keele, Staffs ST5 5BG, United Kingdom.
TEL 44-1782-583091, FAX 44-1782-717577,
ecb01@keele.ac.uk, http://www.keele.ac.uk/cwis.html. Ed.
Robin Bladen-Hovell. R&P Robin Bladen Hovell.

330   GBR   ISSN 1461-0264
UNIVERSITY OF LEEDS. LEEDS UNIVERSITY BUSINESS
SCHOOL. DISCUSSION PAPER SERIES. Text in English.
1978. irreg. GBP 5. Document type: Monographic series.
Former titles (until 1991): University of Leeds. School of
Business and Economic Studies. Discussion Paper Series
(0956-1110); (until 1989): Leeds University Business School.
Discussion Paper Series (0951-7030)
Indexed: WAE&RSA.
—BLDSC (3597.966290), ingenta.
Published by: University of Leeds, Leeds University Business
School, ESS Bldg, Leeds, W Yorks LS2 9JT, United Kingdom.
TEL 44-113-233-4466, FAX 44-113-233-4465,
eleanor@lubs.leeds.ac.uk. Ed. John Bowers. R&P Eleanor
Lynn.

330   GBR   ISSN 1363-8211
UNIVERSITY OF LEICESTER. CENTRE FOR EUROPEAN
ECONOMIC STUDIES. DISCUSSION PAPERS IN
EUROPEAN ECONOMIC STUDIES. Text in English. 1992.
irreg.
—BLDSC (3597.944400), ingenta.
Published by: University of Leicester, Centre for European
Economic Studies, University Rd, Leicester, LE1 7RH, United
Kingdom. TEL 44-116-2522522, FAX 44-116-2522200,
http://www.le.ac.uk.

330   GBR   ISSN 1367-580X
UNIVERSITY OF LONDON. PENSIONS INSTITUTE.
DISCUSSION PAPERS. Text in English. 1996. irreg. GBP 8.
Document type: Monographic series.
—BLDSC (3597.571800).
Published by: University of London, Birkbeck College, Birkbeck
College, 7-15 Gresse St, London, W1P 2LL, United Kingdom.
TEL 44-171-631-6401, FAX 44-171-631-6416,
http://www.econ.bbk.ac.uk/pi/wp.htm/. Co-sponsor: University
of London. Pensions Institute.

330   USA
UNIVERSITY OF MINNESOTA. ECONOMIC DEVELOPMENT
CENTER. BULLETIN. Text in English. irreg., latest 2002. free.
Document type: Monographic series, Academic/Scholarly.
Indexed: AEA, RDA, TriticAb, WAE&RSA.
—BLDSC (2789.797000).
Published by: University of Minnesota, Economic Development
Center, Department of Applied Economics, 231 ClaOff Bldg.,
1994 Buford Ave., St. Paul, MN 55108-6040.
wendy@umn.edu, http://www.econ.umn.edu/~econlib/
edcbu397.html, troe@apec.umn.edu.

330   AUS   ISSN 1323-8949
HB1
UNIVERSITY OF NEW SOUTH WALES. SCHOOL OF
ECONOMICS. DISCUSSION PAPER. Text in English. 1972.
irreg.
—BLDSC (3597.795000), IE, ingenta.

Published by: University of New South Wales, School of
Economics, Sydney, NSW 2052, Australia. TEL
61-2-93851000, http://www.unsw.edu.au.

330   NGA
UNIVERSITY OF NIGERIA. INAUGURAL LECTURE SERIES.
Text in English. irreg., latest vol.8. looseleaf. charts; illus. 100
p./no.; Document type: Monographic series,
Academic/Scholarly. Description: Unmasking some aversive
aspects of schools, maths & strategies for averting them.
Published by: (University of Nigeria), University of Nigeria Press,
Nsukka, Enugu State, Nigeria. misunn@aol.com. Dist.
outside Africa by: African Books Collective Ltd., The Jam
Factory, 27 Park End St, Oxford, Oxon OX1 1HU, United
Kingdom. TEL 0865-726686, FAX 0865-793298.

330   GBR
UNIVERSITY OF NOTTINGHAM BUSINESS SCHOOL.
DISCUSSION PAPERS. Text in English. irreg. GBP 2.50 per
issue (effective 2000). Document type: Academic/Scholarly.
Formerly (until 1998): School of Management and Finance.
Discussion Papers
Related titles: Online - full content ed.
—BLDSC (3597.809000), ingenta.
Published by: University of Nottingham Business School,
University Park, Nottingham, NG7 2RD, United Kingdom. TEL
0602-515251, http://www.nottingham.ac.uk/unbs/working.html.

330   NZL   ISSN 0111-1760
UNIVERSITY OF OTAGO. ECONOMICS DISCUSSION PAPERS.
Text in English. 1977. irreg. Document type: Monographic
series.
—BLDSC (3656.980000).
Published by: University of Otago, P.O. Box 56, Dunedin, New
Zealand. TEL 64-3-4791100, FAX 64-3-4741607,
university@otago.ac.nz, http://www.otago.ac.nz.

330   ROM   ISSN 1582-5949
UNIVERSITY OF PETROSANI. ECONOMICS. ANNALS. Text in
English. 2001. a. ROL 98,727 domestic; USD 5 foreign
(effective 2003).
Published by: Universitatea din Petrosani, Str. Universitatii, nr.
20, Petrosani, 2675, Romania. TEL 40-254-542994, FAX
40-254-546238. Eds. Ioan-Lucian Bolundut, Mariana Man.
Circ: 150 (paid).

330   GBR   ISSN 1366-8226
UNIVERSITY OF READING. DEPARTMENT OF ECONOMICS.
DISCUSSION PAPERS IN ECONOMICS AND
MANAGEMENT. Text in English. 1996. irreg. Document type:
Monographic series.
—BLDSC (3597.9407000).
Published by: University of Reading, Department of Economics,
Whiteknights, PO Box 218, Reading, RG6 6AA, United
Kingdom. TEL 44-118-987-5123, FAX 44-118-931-4404,
information@reading.ac.uk, http://www.reading.ac.uk.

330   GBR   ISSN 0966-4246
UNIVERSITY OF SOUTHAMPTON. DEPARTMENT OF
ECONOMICS. DISCUSSION PAPERS IN ECONOMICS AND
ECONOMETRICS. Text in English. 1990. m.
—BLDSC (3597.937000), IE, ingenta.
Published by: University of Southampton, Department of
Economics, University Rd, Highfield, Southampton, SO17 1BJ,
United Kingdom. TEL 44-23-80595000, FAX 44-23-80593939,
http://www.soton.ac.uk.

330   GBR   ISSN 1364-453X
UNIVERSITY OF ST. ANDREWS. CENTRE FOR RESEARCH
INTO INDUSTRY, ENTERPRISE, FINANCE AND THE FIRM.
DISCUSSION PAPER SERIES. Text in English. 1992. irreg.
Document type: Monographic series.
—BLDSC (3597.980880), IE, ingenta.
Published by: St. Andrews University , Centre for Research into
Industry, Enterprise, Finance and the Firm, Department of
Economics, St Salvator's College, St Andrews, Fife, Scotland
KY16 9AL, United Kingdom. TEL 44-1334-462420, FAX
44-1334-462444, cm36@st-andrews.ac.uk,
gp8@st-andrews.ac.uk, http://www.st-andrews.ac.uk/
~www_crieff/discpaps.html, http://www.st-andrews.ac.uk/
~www_crieff/CRIEFF.html.

338.9   ZAF   ISSN 0258-9338
UNIVERSITY OF STELLENBOSCH. BUREAU FOR ECONOMIC
RESEARCH. MANUFACTURING SURVEY. Text in English.
1954. q. ZAR 790 (effective Jul. 2003). Description: Covers
recent developments in South Africa's manufacturing sector,
and looks at expected performance.
Formerly: University of Stellenbosch. Bureau for Economic
Research. Opinion Survey (0561-9998)
Published by: Universiteit Stellenbosch, Bureau for Economic
Research/Stellenbosch University, University, Private Bag
5050, Stellenbosch, 7599, South Africa. TEL 27-21-8872810,
FAX 27-21-8899225, hhman@maties.sun.ac.za,
http://www.sun.ac.za/. Ed. P Laubscher. Circ: 360.

330   GBR   ISSN 0962-4090
UNIVERSITY OF STERLING. DEPARTMENT OF ECONOMICS.
DISCUSSION PAPERS IN ECONOMICS, FINANCE AND
INVESTMENT. Text in English. irreg. Document type:
Monographic series.
—BLDSC (3597.934200), ingenta.

Published by: University of Sterling, Department of Economics,
Stirling, Scotland FK9 4LA, United Kingdom. TEL
44-1786-473171, http://www.home.stir.ac.uk.

350   GBR   ISSN 0306-7866
HC257.S4
UNIVERSITY OF STRATHCLYDE. FRASER OF ALLANDER
INSTITUTE FOR RESEARCH ON THE SCOTTISH
ECONOMY. QUARTERLY ECONOMIC COMMENTARY. Text
in English. 1975. q. GBP 60 (effective 2000). adv. Document
type: Bulletin. Description: A detailed analysis of the Scottish
economy from a British-European context for the interested
lay person and professional economist alike.
Indexed: IBSS, PAIS.
Published by: University of Strathclyde, Fraser of Allander
Institute for Research on the Scottish Economy, Curran Bldg,
100 Cathedral St, Glasgow, G4 0LN, United Kingdom. TEL
44-141-548-3958, FAX 44-141-552-8347, fai@strath.ac.uk,
http://www.fraser.strath.ac.uk. Ed., R&P Brian Ashcroft. Circ:
500.

330   GBR
UNIVERSITY OF SUSSEX. SCHOOL OF SOCIAL SCIENCES.
ECONOMICS DISCUSSION PAPER. Text in English. irreg.
Document type: Monographic series.
Published by: University of Sussex, School of Social Sciences,
University Of Sussex, Falmer, Brighton, E Sussex BN1 9QN,
United Kingdom. Ed. Barry Reilly.

330   AUS   ISSN 1446-3806
UNIVERSITY OF SYDNEY. SCHOOL OF ECONOMICS AND
POLITICAL SCIENCE. WORKING PAPERS - DISCIPLINE
OF ECONOMICS. Text in English. 2000. irreg. price varies.
back issues avail. Document type: Journal,
Academic/Scholarly.
Media: Online - full content.
Published by: University of Sydney, School of Economics and
Political Sciences, Rm 384, Merewether Bldg, Corner City Rd
and Butlin Ave, Sydney, NSW 2006, Australia. TEL
61-2-9351-6625, FAX 61-2-9351-6635,
k.legge@econ.usyd.edu.au, http://www.econ.usyd.edu.au/ecop/
wp/. R&P Kerrie Legge TEL 61-2-9351-6625.

UNIVERSITY OF SYDNEY. SCHOOL OF ECONOMICS &
POLITICAL SCIENCE. WORKING PAPERS - DISCIPLINE
OF POLITICAL ECONOMY. see POLITICAL SCIENCE

330.0711   AUS   ISSN 1036-0646
UNIVERSITY OF TECHNOLOGY, SYDNEY. FACULTY OF
BUSINESS HANDBOOK. Text in English. 1990. a. AUD 16
domestic; USD 21 foreign (effective 2000). Document type:
Catalog, Academic/Scholarly. Description: Contains detailed
information about the faculty, schools, staff, courses, and
includes subject synopses.
Published by: University of Technology, Sydney, City Campus,
PO Box 123, Broadway, NSW 2007, Australia. TEL
61-2-9514-2000, FAX 61-2-9514-1551,
publications@uts.edu.au, http://www.uts.edu.au/div/
publications. Circ: 6,000.

650   USA
UNIVERSITY OF TEXAS AT AUSTIN. BUREAU OF BUSINESS
RESEARCH. RESEARCH MONOGRAPH SERIES. Text in
English. 1928. irreg., latest 1990. price varies. Document
type: Monographic series.
Former titles: University of Texas, Austin. Bureau of Business
Research. Research Report Series; University of Texas,
Austin. Bureau of Business Research. Research Monograph
(0082-3279)
Published by: University of Texas at Austin, Bureau of Business
Research, McCombs School of Business, One University Sta,
B-8500, Austin, TX 78712-0226. TEL 512-471-1616, FAX
512-471-1063, Rita.Wright@bus.utexas.edu,
danhardy@mail.utexas.edu. R&P Bruce Kellison TEL
512-475-7813.

UNIVERSITY OF THE WEST INDIES. INSTITUTE OF SOCIAL
AND ECONOMIC RESEARCH. WORKING PAPERS. see
SOCIOLOGY

330   GBR
UNIVERSITY OF THE WEST OF ENGLAND. FACULTY OF
ECONOMICS AND SOCIAL SCIENCE. SCHOOL OF
ECONOMICS. WORKING PAPERS. Text in English. irreg.
Document type: Academic/Scholarly.
Formerly: University of the West of England. Working Papers in
Economics
—BLDSC (9350.308500).
Published by: University of the West of England (Bristol), Faculty
of Economics and Social Science, Coldharbour Ln, Bristol,
BS16 1QY, United Kingdom. TEL 44-117-9763869, FAX
44-117-9763870, http://www.ess.uwe.ac.uk/faculty/economics/
econhmpg.htm. Ed. Peter Nisbet.

UNIVERSITY OF TOKUSHIMA. SOCIAL SCIENCE RESEARCH.
see SOCIAL SCIENCES: COMPREHENSIVE WORKS

301 330   CAN   ISSN 0703-6949
H67.T65
UNIVERSITY OF TORONTO. INSTITUTE FOR POLICY
ANALYSIS. ANNUAL REPORT. Text in English. 1976. irreg.
Document type: Academic/Scholarly.

Supersedes: University of Toronto. Institute for the Quantitative Analysis of Social and Economic Policy. News Letter (0082-5271)
Published by: University of Toronto, Institute for Policy Analysis, 150 St George St, Toronto, ON M5S 3G7, Canada. TEL 416-978-8623, FAX 416-978-6713. Ed. Frank Mathewson.

301 330   CAN   ISSN 0829-4909
UNIVERSITY OF TORONTO. INSTITUTE FOR POLICY ANALYSIS. WORKING PAPER SERIES. Text in English. irreg. free. **Document type:** *Academic/Scholarly.*
Formerly: University of Toronto. Institute for the Quantitative Analysis of Social and Economic Policy. Working Paper Series (0082-5301)
Media: Online - full text.
Published by: University of Toronto, Institute for Policy Analysis, 150 St George St, Toronto, ON M5S 3G7, Canada. TEL 416-978-8623, FAX 416-978-6713, ecolib@chass.utoronto.ca, http://www.chass.utoronto.ca:8080/ecipa/wpa.html. Ed. Frank Mathewson. **Co-sponsor:** Department of Economics.

330   AUS   ISSN 0811-6067
HC601
UNIVERSITY OF WESTERN AUSTRALIA. DEPARTMENT OF ECONOMICS. DISCUSSION PAPER. Text in English. 1980. irreg.
—BLDSC (3597.868000), IE, ingenta.
Published by: University of Western Australia, Business School, 35 Stirling Highway, Crawley, W.A. 6009, Australia. TEL 61-8-93803838, FAX 61-8-93801380, general.enquiries@uwa.edu.au, http://www.uwa.edu.au.

330   GBR
UNIVERSITY OF WESTMINSTER. FACULTY OF BUSINESS, MANAGEMENT AND SOCIAL STUDIES. RESEARCH WORKING PAPER SERIES. Text in English. irreg., latest vol.2. GBP 5. **Document type:** *Monographic series.*
Published by: University of Westminster, Faculty of Business, Management and Social Studies, 32-38 Wells St, London, W1P 3FG, United Kingdom. TEL 0171-911-5000, FAX 0171-911-5175. Ed. Robin Theobald.

330   CAN
UNIVERSITY OF WINDSOR. DEPARTMENT OF ECONOMICS. DISCUSSION PAPER SERIES. Text in English. irreg. **Document type:** *Monographic series.*
—BLDSC (3597.981000).
Published by: University of Windsor, Department of Economics, 401 Sunset Av, Windsor, ON N9B 3P4, Canada. TEL 519-253-3000, FAX 519-973-7050, http://cronus.uwindsor.ca.

330   GBR   ISSN 1367-3653
UNIVERSITY OF YORK. DEPARTMENT OF ECONOMICS AND RELATED STUDIES. DISCUSSION PAPERS IN ECONOMICS. Text in English. 199?. irreg.
—BLDSC (3597.934280), ingenta.
Published by: University of York, Department of Economics and Related Studies, Market Sq, Heslington, York, YO10 5NH, United Kingdom. TEL 44-1904-432222, FAX 44-1904-433433, http://www.york.ac.uk.

330   MKD
UNIVERZITET VO SKOPLJE. EKONOMSKIOT FAKULTET. GODISNIK/UNIVERSITE DE SKOPJE. FACULTE DES SCIENCES ECONOMIQUE. ANNUAIRE. Text in Macedonian; Summaries in English, French, German, Russian. 1956. a.
Published by: Univerzitet vo Skoplje, Ekonomskiot Fakultet, Bulevar Krste Misirkov bb, PO Box 576, Skopje, 91000, Macedonia. Circ: 500.

330   DEU
UNTERNEHMEN DER ZUKUNFT; FIR und IAW Zeitschrift fuer Organisation und Arbeit in Produktion und Dienstleistung. Text in German. 1968. q. adv. bk.rev. back issues avail. **Document type:** *Journal, Academic/Scholarly.*
Formerly (until 2000): F I R und I A W Mitteilungen (0934-6430)
Published by: Forschungs Institut fuer Rationalisierung und Institut fuer Arbeitswissenschaft, Pontdriesch 14-16, Aachen, 52062, Germany. TEL 49-241-47705-0, FAX 49-241-47705199, info@fir.rwth-aachen.de, http://www.fir.rwth-aachen.de. Circ: 4,000.

330   CHE
UNTERNEHMER. Text in German. m.
Address: Fliederweg 9, Trimmis, 7203, Switzerland. TEL 081-225252. Circ: 12,000.

330   DEU   ISSN 0938-3875
DIE UNTERNEHMERIN. Text in German. 1960. q. adv. bk.rev. **Document type:** *Trade.*
Published by: Verband Deutscher Unternehmerin e.V., Gustav-Heinemann-Ufer 94, Postfach 511030, Cologne, 50968, Germany. TEL 49-221-375074, FAX 49-221-343171. Ed. Irene Kuron. Circ: 4,000.

330   DEU
UNTERSUCHUNGEN ZUR ORDNUNGSTHEORIE UND ORDNUNGSPOLITIK. Text in German. 1962. irreg. price varies. **Document type:** *Monographic series.*
Formerly: Walter Eucken Institut. Wirtschaftswissenschaftliche und Wirtschaftsrechtliche Untersuchungen (0083-7113)

Published by: (Walter Eucken Institut), Mohr Siebeck, Wilhelmstr 18, Tuebingen, 72074, Germany. TEL 49-7071-923-0, FAX 49-7071-51104, info@mohr.de, http://www.mohr.de. R&P Jill Sopper.

UN'YU TO KEIZAI/TRANSPORTATION AND ECONOMY. see *TRANSPORTATION*

330   ITA   ISSN 1124-2108
UOMINI & BUSINESS. Text in Italian. 1989. 11/yr. adv. bk.rev. **Document type:** *Magazine, Consumer.* **Description:** Covers economics, politics and culture.
Published by: Uomini & Business SpA, Corso Venezia, 8, Milan, MI 20121, Italy. TEL 39-2-76009291, FAX 39-2-76009716. Ed. Giuseppe Turani. adv.: color page EUR 12,900. Circ: 13,000.

330   SWE
UPPSALA UNIVERSITET. FOERETAGSEKONOMISKA INSTITUTIONEN. OCCASIONAL PAPER. Text in Swedish, English. irreg. **Document type:** *Monographic series, Academic/Scholarly.*
Formerly (until 2000): Uppsala Universitet. Foeretagsekonomiska Institutionen. Working Paper
—BLDSC (6224.180470).
Published by: Uppsala Universitet, Foeretagsekonomiska Institutionen, Box 513, Uppsala, 75120, Sweden. TEL 46-18-4711390, FAX 46-18-4716810. Ed. Ingemund Haegg.

330   RUS
UPRAVLENIE PERSONALOM. Text in Russian. m.
Published by: Biznes Shkola Intel-Sintez, Ul Profsoyuznaya 3, Moscow, 117036, Russian Federation. TEL 7-095-1299212, FAX 7-095-1246809, http://www.top-personal.ru.

330   USA   ISSN 0092-7481
HT167
URBAN INSTITUTE. ANNUAL REPORT. Text in English. 1970. a. free. **Document type:** *Corporate.* **Description:** Reports on the Institute's activities concerning the social and economic problems confronting the nation and government policies and programs designed to alleviate them.
Formerly (until 197?): Urban Institute. Report (1042-7783)
Media: Large Type.
Indexed: MCR.
Published by: Urban Institute, 2100 M St, N W, Washington, DC 20037. TEL 202-261-5687, FAX 202-467-5775, paffairs@ui.urban.org, http://www.urban.org. Ed. Kathleen Courrier.

330   USA   ISSN 0897-7399
URBAN INSTITUTE REPORT. Text in English. 1988. irreg. price varies. **Document type:** *Monographic series, Academic/Scholarly.*
Published by: Urban Institute, 2100 M St, N W, Washington, DC 20037. TEL 202-261-5687, FAX 202-467-5775, paffairs@ui.urban.org, http://www.urban.org.

330   USA   ISSN 1091-1707
HF3161.U8
UTAH BUSINESS; the magazine for decision makers. Text in English. 1986. m. USD 29.95 domestic (effective 2001). adv. back issues avail. **Document type:** *Magazine, Trade.* **Description:** Provides information about regional business news and economic development activities in Utah.
Related titles: Online - full text ed.: (from Florida Center for Library Automation, Gale Group).
Published by: Utah Business Magazine, 1245 Brickyard Rd,, Ste. 90, Salt Lake Cty, UT 84106-2582. TEL 801-568-0114, 800-823-0038, editor@utahbusiness.com, travis@utahbusiness.com, http://www.utahbusiness.com. Ed., Pub. Martin W Lewis. Adv. contact Arkin Hill TEL 801-568-0325.

330 650   USA   ISSN 0042-1405
HC107.U8
UTAH ECONOMIC AND BUSINESS REVIEW. Text in English. 1941. 6/yr. free domestic (effective 2005). charts; illus.; stat. **Document type:** *Academic/Scholarly.*
Related titles: Microfiche ed.: (from CIS).
Indexed: PAIS, RASB, SRI.
—BLDSC (9135.160000).
Published by: University of Utah, Bureau of Economic and Business Research, 1645 E Campus Center Dr, Rm 401, Salt Lake City, UT 84112-9302. TEL 801-581-6333, FAX 801-531-3354, bureau@business.utah.edu. Ed. R Thayne Robson TEL 801-581-7274. Circ: 4,000.

330   USA
UTAH FOUNDATION. RESEARCH REPORT AND RESEARCH BRIEFS. Text in English. m. USD 95 to individuals; USD 200 to institutions. **Description:** Studies covering an agency, function, or problem of state and local government in Utah.
Published by: Utah Foundation, 10 W. Broadway., Ste. 307, Salt Lake Cty, UT 84101-2075. TEL 801-364-1837.

334.722   HUN   ISSN 1588-5909
UZLET & SIKER. Text in Hungarian. 2002. m. adv. **Document type:** *Magazine, Trade.*
Related titles: Online - full text ed.

Published by: Sanoma Budapest Kiadoi Rt. (Subsidiary of: Sanoma Magazines Finland Corporation), Bokor Utca 15-19, Budapest, 1037, Hungary. TEL 36-1-4371100, FAX 36-1-2502303, uzletessiker@sanomabp.hu, info@sanomabp.hu, http://www.uzletessiker.hu, http://www.sanoma.hu. Adv. contact Piroska Bosanszki. page HUF 650,000; trim 210 x 277. Circ: 27,312 (controlled).

330 336   FIN   ISSN 1236-0716
V A T T NYT. (Valtion Taloudellinen Tutkimuskeskus) Text in Finnish. 1992. biennial. price varies. back issues avail. **Document type:** *Journal, Government.*
Related titles: Online - full text ed.
Published by: Valtion Taloudellinen Tutkimuskeskus/Government Institute for Economic Research, Arkadiankatu 7, PO Box 1279, Helsinki, 00101, Finland. TEL 358-9-70371, FAX 358-9-7032968, http://www.vatt.fi/vattnyt/. Ed. Reino Hjerppe.

330   CHE
V H T L ZEITUNG. Text in German. 11/yr. **Document type:** *Newspaper, Trade.*
Published by: V H T L, Postfach, Zuerich, 8036, Switzerland. TEL 41-31-2423576, FAX 41-31-2429405. Ed. Daniel Stern. Circ: 13,000.

330   IND
V.T. KRISHNAMACHARI MEMORIAL LECTURE SERIES. Text in English. 1984. irreg. latest vol.6, 1990.
Published by: Institute of Economic Growth, University of Enclave, New Delhi, 110 007, India. TEL 2522201.

330   FIN   ISSN 0788-4990
VALTION TALOUDELLINEN TUTKIMUSKESKUS. V A T T - JULKAISUJA/VALTION TALOUDELLINEN TUTKIMUSKESKUS. V A T T - PUBLICATIONS. Text in Finnish. 1900. irreg., latest 2004. price varies. back issues avail. **Document type:** *Government.*
Related titles: Online - full text ed.
Published by: Valtion Taloudellinen Tutkimuskeskus/Government Institute for Economic Research, Arkadiankatu 7, PO Box 1279, Helsinki, 00101, Finland. TEL 358-9-70371, FAX 358-9-7032968, http://www.vatt.fi.

330   FIN   ISSN 0788-5016
VALTION TALOUDELLINEN TUTKIMUSKESKUS. V A T T - KESKUSTELUALOITTEITA/VALTION TALOUDELLINEN TUTKIMUSKESKUS. V A T T DISCUSSION PAPERS. Text in English, Finnish. 1990. irreg., latest vol.369, 2005. price varies. back issues avail. **Document type:** *Monographic series, Government.*
Related titles: Online - full text ed.: ISSN 1795-3359.
Published by: Valtion Taloudellinen Tutkimuskeskus/Government Institute for Economic Research, Arkadiankatu 7, PO Box 1279, Helsinki, 00101, Finland. TEL 358-9-70371, FAX 358-9-7032968, http://www.vatt.fi.

330   FIN   ISSN 0788-5008
VALTION TALOUDELLINEN TUTKIMUSKESKUS. V A T T - TUTKIMUKSIA/VALTION TALOUDELLINEN TUTKIMUSKESKUS. V A T T RESEARCH REPORTS. Text in English, Finnish. 1990. irreg., latest vol.115, 2004. price varies. back issues avail. **Document type:** *Monographic series, Government.*
Related titles: Online - full text ed.: ISSN 1795-3340.
Published by: Valtion Taloudellinen Tutkimuskeskus/Government Institute for Economic Research, Arkadiankatu 7, PO Box 1279, Helsinki, 00101, Finland. TEL 358-9-70371, FAX 358-9-7032968, http://www.vatt.fi.

VALVE MAGAZINE. see *MACHINERY*

330   USA   ISSN 1534-2956
VANCOUVER BUSINESS JOURNAL. Text in English. 1994. bi-w. USD 29 (effective 1999). adv. back issues avail. **Document type:** *Journal, Trade.* **Description:** Covers local Clark County business news.
Related titles: Online - full text ed.: (from Newsbank, Inc.).
Address: 2525 E Fourth Plain Blvd, Vancouver, WA 98661-3959. TEL 360-695-2442, FAX 360-695-3056, http://www.vbjusa.com. Ed. Jennifer Dirks. Pub., R&P David Fenton. Adv. contact Sandy Wade. B&W page USD 1,595, color page USD 1,995; trim 13.5 x 10. Circ: 10,000.

VASH PARTNER-KONSUL'TANT. see *LAW*

330   RUS
VASH VYBOR/YOUR CHOICE; nauchno-politicheskii zhurnal regionov. Text in Russian. 1992. bi-m. USD 100 in United States (effective 2000). **Description:** Covers aspects of activities in area of sociology and other humanitarian sciences. Generalizes experience in carrying-out the sociological investigations, in analysis of new political problems, etc. Describes Russian state system, problems in Russian integrity, modern economical independence of subjects of Russian Federation, local self-government in Russia.
Indexed: RASB.
Address: P.O. Box 44, Moscow, 117571, Russian Federation. TEL 7-095-2024813. **Dist. by:** East View Information Services, 3020 Harbor Ln. N., Minneapolis, MN 55447. TEL 763-550-0961, FAX 763-559-2931.

330 SWE ISSN 0506-4406
HD70.S8
VECKANS AFFAERER; den aktuella affaerstidningen. Text in Swedish. 1965. 42/yr. SEK 1,995 (effective 2004). adv. charts; illus.; stat. **Document type:** *Magazine, Trade.*
Incorporates (1983-1997): Datawaerlden (0280-6622)
Related titles: Online - full text ed.: Veckans Affarer Online. ISSN 1402-5108. 1996; Supplement(s): Maanadens Affaerer.
Indexed: CBNB, P&BA, RASB.
Published by: Bonnier Tidsskrifter AB, Sveavaegen 53, Stockholm, 10544, Sweden. TEL 46-8-7365200, FAX 46-8-7363842, red@va.se, http://www.va.se, http://www.bonnier.se. adv.: B&W page SEK 31,100, color page SEK 33,900; 190 x 265. Circ: 33,800.

330 RUS
VEDOMOSTI. Text in Russian. 1999. d. USD 770 in Europe; USD 860 in North America (effective 2005). adv. **Document type:** *Newspaper, Consumer.* **Description:** Covers economic, financial, political, and corporate news, as well as new technologies.
Related titles: Online - full content ed.: ISSN 1727-7345.
Indexed: RASB.
Published by: (Financial Times), Independent Media (Moscow), ul Vyborgskaya dom 16, str 1, Moscow, 125212, Russian Federation. TEL 7-095-2323200, FAX 7-095-2329265, vedomosti@imedia.ru, podpiska@imedia.ru, http://www.vedomosti.ru, http://www.independent-media.ru. Ed. Tatiana Lysova. Circ: 66,700. **Co-sponsor:** Dow Jones Company.

VEHICLE LEASING TODAY. see *TRANSPORTATION—Automobiles*

VENEZUELA ANALITICA. see *POLITICAL SCIENCE*

330 VEN ISSN 0798-8656
VENEZUELA. OFICINA CENTRAL DE ESTADISTICA E INFORMATICA. MEMORIA Y CUENTA. Text in Spanish. 1978. a. free. **Document type:** *Government.*
Published by: Oficina Central de Estadistica e Informatica, Apdo. de Correos 4593, Carmeliatas, Caracas, DF 1010A, Venezuela. TEL 58-2-7811380, FAX 58-2-781-13-80.

VENTUREWIRE LIFESCIENCE. see *BIOLOGY—Biotechnology*

330 338 USA
VENTUREWIRE PROFESSIONAL. Text in English. d. USD 695 (effective 2002). **Description:** Covers news and information about private capital, venture-backed companies, and the people who manage and finance them.
Media: E-mail.
Published by: Dow Jones Newsletters (Subsidiary of: Dow Jones Newswires), 1155 Av of the Americas, New York, NY 10036. TEL 212-597-5716, http://www.venturewire.com/m_professional.asp.

330 USA ISSN 0897-7925
VERMONT BUSINESS MAGAZINE. Text in English. 1972. m. USD 28 (effective 2005). adv. Supplement avail. **Document type:** *Magazine, Consumer.*
Related titles: Microform ed.: (from PQC); Online - full text ed.: (from bigchalk, Florida Center for Library Automation, Northern Light Technology, Inc., O C L C Online Computer Library Center, Inc., ProQuest Information & Learning, The Dialog Corporation).
Indexed: ABIn, BusDate, T&II.
Address: 2 Church St, Burlington, VT 05401. TEL 802-863-8038, FAX 802-863-8069, info@vtbusinessmagazine.com, http://www.vtbusinessmagazine.com. Ed. Timothy McQuiston. Pub. John Boutin. Circ: 7,500 (controlled).

384 USA ISSN 1071-2291
HE202.5
VERONIS, SUHLER & ASSOCIATES COMMUNICATIONS INDUSTRY FORECAST. Text in English. 1987. a. USD 995. **Document type:** *Trade.* **Description:** Provides an industry spending preview for 10 segments of the communications industry for the coming 5 years.
Related titles: ♦ Series: Veronis, Suhler & Associates Communications Industry Report. ISSN 1071-2283.
Published by: Veronis, Suhler & Associates Inc., 350 Park Ave, New York, NY 10022. TEL 212-935-4990, FAX 212-935-0877, madlangbay@vsacomm.com, http://www.vsacomm.com. Ed. John Suhler.

384 USA ISSN 1071-2283
P96.E252
VERONIS, SUHLER & ASSOCIATES COMMUNICATIONS INDUSTRY REPORT. Text in English. 1983. a. USD 995. **Document type:** *Trade.* **Description:** Analyzes the historical performance of every publicly reporting company in eleven segments of the communications industry over a five-year period.
Related titles: ♦ Series: Veronis, Suhler & Associates Communications Industry Forecast. ISSN 1071-2291.
Published by: Veronis, Suhler & Associates Inc., 350 Park Ave, New York, NY 10022. TEL 212-935-4990, FAX 212-935-0877, madlangbay@vacomm.com, http://www.vsacomm.com. Ed. John Suhler.

VERSLO ZINIOS. see *GENERAL INTEREST PERIODICALS—Lithuania*

330 DEU
VERTRAULICHE MITTEILUNGEN AUS POLITIK, WIRTSCHAFT UND GELDANLAGE. Text in German. 1951. w. Supplement avail. **Document type:** *Newsletter.*
Published by: Verlag Arbeit und Wirtschaft GmbH, Junkerstr 46, Buesingen, 78263, Germany. TEL 49-7734-6061, FAX 49-7734-7112. Ed. Ernst Hochheuser.

VESTED INTEREST. see *INSURANCE*

330 RUS ISSN 1609-5588
VESTNIK MOLODYCH UCHENYCH. EKONOMICHESKIYE NAUKI. Text in Russian. 1997. s-a. **Document type:** *Journal, Academic/Scholarly.*
Related titles: Online - full text ed.: ISSN 1609-5472. 2000.
Published by: Redaktsiya Zhurnala Vestnik Molodych Uchenych, 1-ya Krasnoarmeiskaya Ul., dom 1, Sankt-Peterburg, 198005, Russian Federation. maria@MC1108.spb.edu, vmu@peterlink.ru, http://www.informika.ru/text/magaz/science/vys/ECONOM/main.html. Ed. M Tsenzharik TEL 7-812-2721908. **Co-sponsors:** Ministerstvo Obrazovaniya i Nauki Rossiiskoi Federatsii/Ministry of Education and Science of the Russian Federation; Sovet Rektorov Vuzov Sankt-Peterburga; Rossiiskaya Akademiya Nauk, Sankt-Peterburgskii Nauchnyi Tsentr.

330.711 RUS ISSN 0321-0383
L51
VESTNIK VYSSHEI SHKOLY. Text in Russian. 1940. m. USD 77 (effective 1998).
Indexed: CDSP, IBSS, RASB.
Published by: Izdatel'stvo Vysshaya Shkola, Neglinnaya ul 29-14, Moscow, 127994, Russian Federation. TEL 7-095-2000456, FAX 7-095-2000301, info@v-shkola.ru, http://www.v-shkola.ru. Ed. A N Yorshenev. **Co-sponsor:** Ministerstvo Vysshego i Srednego Spetsial'nogo Obrazovaniya.

330 USA
VICTORIA BUSINESS MAGAZINE. Text in English. m. USD 19.49 domestic (effective 2001). **Document type:** *Magazine, Trade.* **Description:** Provides information about regional business news and economic development activities for Victoria and the Golden Crescent area of Texas.
Address: P O Box 4553, Victoria, TX 77903-4553. TEL 361-572-3137, FAX 361-575-4370, vbm1@viptx.net, http://www.viptx.net/vbm. Ed. Gypsy Cole. Pub., Adv. contact Peggy Cunningham.

330 PRT ISSN 0871-4320
VIDA ECONOMICA. Text in Portuguese. 1983. w. adv. bk.rev. **Document type:** *Newspaper, Trade.*
Published by: Grupo Editorial Peixoto de Sousa, Rua Goncalo Cristovao, 111, 5o, 6o e 7o, Porto, 4049-037, Portugal. TEL 351-22-2299400, FAX 351-22-2005335, vidaeco@mail.telepac.pt, http://www.centroatl.pt/ve, http://www.centroatl.pt.pt/ve. Ed. Joao Luis de Sousa. Pub. Joao Peixoto de Sousa. Adv. contact Madalena Campos. Circ: 30,000 (paid).

330 FRA ISSN 0336-142X
VIE ET SCIENCES ECONOMIQUES. Text in French, English. 1953. q. adv. bk.rev. charts; stat. **Document type:** *Academic/Scholarly.*
Indexed: PAIS.
Published by: (Association Nationale des Docteurs en Sciences Economiques), Editions de L' Andese, 2 rue Jacques Daguerre, Rueil - Malmaison, 92565, France. TEL 33-1-47143914, FAX 33-1-47143990. Ed. M de l'Andese. Circ: 1,000.

330 FRA ISSN 0766-608X
VIE FORAINE. Text in French. 11/yr.
Address: 69 bd. de Strasbourg, Paris, 75010, France. TEL 47-70-07-19, FAX 47-70-27-52. Ed. Jean Fotel. Circ: 5,000.

330 CHE
DER VIER IM SCHWEIZERISCHEN WIRTSCHAFTSLEBEN. Text in German. q. adv.
Published by: Fritz Wagner's Erben, Katzenrutistr 77, Ruemlang, 8153, Switzerland. Circ: 5,000.

330 DEU ISSN 0340-1707
VIERTELJAHRSHEFTE ZUR WIRTSCHAFTSFORSCHUNG. Variant title: Deutsches Institut fuer Wirtschaftsforschung. Vierteljahrshefte zur Wirtschaftsforschung. Text in German; Summaries in English. 1926. q. EUR 80 newsstand/cover (effective 2006). bk.rev. bibl.; charts; stat. index. **Document type:** *Journal, Academic/Scholarly.*
Formerly: Vierteljahrshefte zur Konjunkturforschung
Indexed: DIP, ELLIS, IBR, IBSS, IBZ, JEL, PAIS.
—IE, Infotrieve. **CCC.**
Published by: (Deutsches Institut fuer Wirtschaftsforschung), Duncker und Humblot GmbH, Carl-Heinrich-Becker-Weg 9, Berlin, 12165, Germany. TEL 49-30-7900060, FAX 49-30-79000631, info@duncker-humblot.de, http://www.diw.de/deutsch/produkte/publikationen/vierteljahrshefte/, http://www.duncker-humblot.de. Ed. Klaus Henkner.

330 USA ISSN 1076-0032
HF1594.5.Z4
THE VIETNAM BUSINESS JOURNAL. Text in English. 1993. bi-m. USD 30 domestic; USD 60 foreign; USD 4.95 newsstand/cover (effective 1999). adv. bk.rev. **Document type:** *Trade.* **Description:** Covers topics and business issues regarding Vietnam and Indochina.
Related titles: Online - full text ed.
Published by: Viam Communications Group Ltd., 114 E 32nd St, Ste 1010, New York, NY 10016. TEL 212-725-1717, vbj@viam.com, http://www.viam.com. Ed. Joshua Levine. Pub. Kenneth D Felberbaum. R&P Craig Stuart. Adv. contact Ahn Dang. Circ: 18,200.

330 VNM ISSN 1420-2573
HC444.A1
VIETNAM ECONOMIC TIMES. Text in English. 1994. m. VND 660,000, USD 60 domestic; USD 96 in Asia; USD 120 elsewhere; USD 5 newsstand/cover. adv. charts; maps; stat.; tr.lit. back issues avail. **Document type:** *Magazine, Trade.* **Description:** Provides for Vietnamese businessmen and foreign investors; covers investment opportunities and political developments in Vietnam.
Related titles: Online - full text ed.: ISSN 1563-8847.
Published by: Ringiers - Association of Vietnamese Economists, 175 Nguyen Thai Hoc, Hanoi, Viet Nam. TEL 84-4-8452411, FAX 84-4-8432755, vet@hn.vnn.vn, http://www.vneconomy.com.vn/Publications/vet/. Ed., Pub. Dao Nguyen Cat. Adv. contact Le Minh Anh. B&W page USD 2,500, color page USD 3,150. Circ: 28,000 (paid).

330 338.91 VNM ISSN 1021-318X
VIETNAM INVESTMENT REVIEW. Short title: V I R. Text in English. 1991. w. USD 99 domestic; USD 300 in Asia; USD 350 in Japan; USD 350 in Australia & New Zealand; USD 400 elsewhere (effective 2004).
Related titles: Online - full text ed.: (from Gale Group, O C L C Online Computer Library Center, Inc.).
Published by: Viet Nam Ministry of Planning and Investment, No 2 Hoang Van Thu St, Ha Noi, Viet Nam. TEL 84-4-8453027, FAX 84-4-8234453, http://www.vir.com.vn/Client/VIR, http://www.mpi.gov.vn/default.asp?lang=2.

330 VNM
VIETNAM RENOVATION. Text in Vietnamese, English, Chinese. 1991. q. VND 60,000; USD 12 foreign (effective 1999). adv. **Description:** Covers business and socioeconomic situations in Vietnam.
Formerly (until Apr. 1994): Business
Published by: (Vietnam. Vietnam Trade Review), Ministry of Trade, 46 Ngo Quyen, Hanoi, Viet Nam. TEL 84-4-8257558, FAX 84-4-8262311. Ed. Truong Duc Ngai. adv.: color page USD 800. Circ: 8,000.

VIEW. see *MOTION PICTURES*

330 USA ISSN 0888-1340
HC107.V8V437
VIRGINIA BUSINESS. Text in English. 1986. m. USD 30 (effective 2005). adv. **Document type:** *Magazine, Trade.* **Description:** Focuses on business, economics, and public policy, as related to the business environment in Virginia.
Related titles: Online - full text ed.
Published by: Media General, 333 E. Franklin St., Richmond, VA 23219. TEL 804-649-6999, FAX 804-649-6311, http://VirginiaBusiness.com, http://mediageneral.com/. Pub. Douglas A. Forshey. adv.: B&W page USD 5,250, color page USD 6,505. Circ: 30,000 (controlled).

330 USA ISSN 1550-3313
▼ **VIRGINIA ECONOMIC DEVELOPMENT REVIEW.** Text in English. 2003. m. USD 180; USD 227 combined subscription print & online eds. (effective 2005). **Description:** Provides comprehensive coverage of economic development news in Virginia.
Related titles: Online - full text ed.: ISSN 1550-3321.
Published by: Falls Publishing, 801 W Main St, Ste 206, Charlottesville, VA 22903. TEL 434-245-9700, FAX 434-245-9801, http://www.virginiaedreview.com/.

330 USA ISSN 1085-1046
VIRGINIA ECONOMIC JOURNAL. Text in English. 1996. a.
Indexed: JEL.
Published by: Virginia Association of Economists, Federal Reserve Bank of Richmond, Research Dept, Box 27622, Richmond, VA 23261.

330 DEU ISSN 0942-8615
VIS-A-VIS; Europa Edition. Text in French, German. 1992. bi-m. adv. **Document type:** *Bulletin.*
Published by: Verlag Haselbauer und Partner, Bergstr 18, Dattenberg, 53547, Germany. TEL 49-2644-95290, FAX 49-2644-2014, visavis@visavis.de, http://www.visavis.de. Ed. Wolfgang Haselbauer. Adv. contact Christine Schmidt. Circ: 30,000 (controlled).

VITAMIN RETAILER; the dietary supplement industry's leading magazine. see *PHARMACY AND PHARMACOLOGY*

B

▼ new title ➤ refereed ✶ unverified ♦ full entry avail.

338   BEL
DE VLAAMSE ONDERNEMER. Text in Dutch. 1989. s-m. EUR 25 (effective 2005). back issues avail. Document type: Trade. Description: Covers business and management issues of interest to companies in Flanders.
Formerly: Antwerpse Ondernemer (0777-236X)
Published by: Vlaamse Ondernemer, Pastoor Schoetersstr 10, Essen, 2910, Belgium. TEL 32-3-677-2456, FAX 32-3-677-1092, luw@dvo.be, www.dvo.be. Ed. Luc Willemijns. Adv. contact Geert Spapen TEL 32-3-3605360. Circ: 38,500.

VODOLAZNOE DELO; zhurnal dlya professionalov vodolaznogo dela. see SPORTS AND GAMES

330   DEU   ISSN 1615-1860
VOGUE BUSINESS. Text in German. 2000. 4/yr. EUR 12; EUR 3 newsstand/cover (effective 2002). adv. Document type: Magazine, Consumer.
Published by: Conde Nast Verlag GmbH, Ainmillerstr 8, Munich, 80801, Germany. TEL 49-89-38104-0, FAX 49-89-38104230, feedback@vogue-business.de, feedback@condenet.de, http://www.vogue-business.de, http://www.condenast.de. adv.: page EUR 10,700; trim 168 x 223. Circ: 100,000 (paid).

650   USA
VOICE OF WORKING WOMEN∗. Text in English. 1962. q. membership. adv. Document type: Newsletter.
Formerly (until 1985): New Jersey Business Woman (0028-5579)
Published by: New Jersey Federation of Business & Professional Women, Inc., 120 Finderne Ave, Bridgewater, NJ 08807-3670. TEL 908-233-0110. Circ: 2,000.

330   CHE   ISSN 1011-386X
DIE VOLKSWIRTSCHAFT; das Magazin fuer Wirtschaftspolitik. Text in German. 1932. m. CHF 149 domestic; CHF 169 foreign; CHF 69 to students; CHF 14.90 newsstand/cover (effective 2004). adv. bk.rev. charts; stat.; tr.lit. index. Document type: Magazine, Trade.
Incorporates (1932-1988): Bundessubventionen (1424-7054); Which superseded in part (in 1974): Bundessubventionen und Anteile der Kantone an Bundeseinnahmen (0491-8487); Which was formerly (until 1957): Bundessubventionen und Gesetzliche Anteile (1424-6910)
Related titles: French ed.: La Vie Economique. ISSN 0253-3987. 1930; ♦ Supplement(s): Switzerland. Kommission fuer Konjunkturfragen. Wirtschaftslage. ISSN 0255-9064.
Indexed: PAIS.
—IE, Infotrieve.
Published by: (Switzerland. Bundesamt fuer Wirtschaft und Arbeit), Zollikofer AG, Fuerstenlandstr 122, Postfach 2362, St. Gallen, 9001, Switzerland. TEL 41-71-2727370, FAX 41-71-2727586, leserservice@zollikofer.ch, http://www.zollikofer.ch. Circ: 5,900.

330   DEU   ISSN 0505-9372
VOLKSWIRTSCHAFTLICHE SCHRIFTEN. Text in German. 1952. irreg., latest vol.534, 2003. price varies. Document type: Monographic series, Academic/Scholarly.
Published by: Duncker und Humblot GmbH, Carl-Heinrich-Becker-Weg 9, Berlin, 12165, Germany. TEL 49-30-7900060, FAX 49-30-79000631, info@duncker-humblot.de, http://www.duncker-humblot.de.

330   RUS   ISSN 1728-8878
▼ VOPROSY EKONOMICHESKIKH NAUK. Text in Russian. 2003. bi-m. Document type: Journal, Academic/Scholarly. Description: Publishes scientific research articles written by students and applicants for graduate degrees in Economics.
Published by: Izdatel'stvo Kompaniya Sputnik+, Ryazanskii pr-kt, dom 8a, Moscow, 109428, Russian Federation. TEL 7-095-7304774, sputnikplus2000@mail.ru, http://www.sputnikplus.ru.

330   RUS   ISSN 0042-8736
HC10
VOPROSY EKONOMIKI. Text in Russian. 1929. m. USD 216 foreign (effective 2004). adv. bk.rev. stat.; abstr. Document type: Journal, Academic/Scholarly.
Related titles: Microform ed.: (from EVP).
Indexed: AmH&L, CDSP, DIP, DSA, HistAb, IBR, IBSS, IBZ, ILD, PSA, PotatoAb, RASB, RRTA, RefZh, SOPODA, SeedAb, WAE&RSA.
—East View.
Published by: (Rossiiskaya Akademiya Nauk/Russian Academy of Sciences, Institut Ekonomiki), Voprosy Ekonomiki, Nakhimovskii pr-t 32, Moscow, 117218, Russian Federation. TEL 7-095-1245228, FAX 7-095-124-5228, mail@vopreco.ru, vopreco@ofc.ru, http://www.vopreco.ru. Ed. L I Abalkin. R&P Adv. contact Sergei Popov. B&W page USD 600. Circ: 7,000.
Dist. by: M K - Periodica, ul Gilyarovskogo 39, Moscow 129110, Russian Federation. TEL 7-095-2845008, FAX 7-095-2813798, info@periodicals.ru, http://www.mkniga.ru.

320   BEL   ISSN 1370-1290
VOULOIR. Text in French. 1983. q.
Address: Victor Rousseau 28, Brussels, Belgium. Ed. Robert Steuckers.

330   RUS
VREMYA I DEN'GI. Text in Russian. 260/yr.

Address: A-ya 308, Kazan, 420503, Russian Federation. TEL 3842-32-64-50, FAX 3842-32-77-74. Ed. Yu P Alaev. US dist. addr.: East View Information Services, 3020 Harbor Ln. N., Minneapolis, MN 55447. TEL 612-550-0961.

332   IND
VYAPAR. Text in Hindi. w. INR 170 domestic; INR 1,200 foreign; INR 3 newsstand/cover (effective 1999). adv. Document type: Newspaper. Description: Covers trade, business, industries, banking, labor, and more.
Related titles: Gujarati ed.
Published by: Saurashtra Trust, Janmabhoomi Bhavan, Janmabhoomi Marg, Fort, P O Box 62, Mumbai, Maharashtra 400 001, India. TEL 91-22-2873438, FAX 91-22-2874097, bhoomi@bom3.vsnl.net.in. Ed. Rajesh Bhayani. Pub. Dhirubhai Desai. Adv. contact N G Patel. Circ: 19,274.

332   IND   ISSN 0042-9325
VYAPAR (GUJARATI EDITION). Text in Gujarati. 1949. bi-w. INR 330 domestic; INR 2,400 foreign; INR 3 newsstand/cover (effective 1999). adv. bk.rev. Document type: Newspaper. Description: Covers trade, business, industries, banking, labor, and more.
Related titles: Hindi ed.
Published by: Saurashtra Trust, Janmabhoomi Bhavan, Janmabhoomi Marg, Fort, P O Box 62, Mumbai, Maharashtra 400 001, India. TEL 91-22-2873438, bhoomi@bom3.vsnl.net.in. Ed. Rajesh Bhayani. Pub. Dhirubhai J Desai. Adv. contact N G Patel. Circ: 33,111.

330   AZE
VYSHKA. Text in Russian. w. USD 355 in United States (effective 2000).
Published by: Redaktsiya Vyshka, Pr Metbuat 529 6 etazh, Baku, 370146, Azerbaijan. TEL 994-12-394323. Dist. by: East View Information Services, 3020 Harbor Ln. N., Minneapolis, MN 55447. TEL 763-550-0961, FAX 763-559-2931.

330   USA   ISSN 1093-6580
HC101
W E F A INDUSTRIAL MONITOR. (Wharton Econometric Forecasting Associates) Text in English. 1997. a. USD 65 per issue (effective 2004).
Published by: (W E F A), John Wiley & Sons, Inc., 111 River St, Hoboken, NJ 07030-5774. TEL 201-748-6000, FAX 201-748-5915, http://www.wiley.com.

330   DEU
W I R - WIRTSCHAFT IN ROSTOCK. Text in German. m. adv. Document type: Journal, Trade.
Published by: Schmidt-Roemhild Verlag, Mengstr 16, Luebeck, 23552, Germany. TEL 49-451-7031-01, FAX 49-451-7031253, eickershoff@beleke.de, http://www.schmidt-roemhild.de. Circ: 28,000 (paid and controlled).

W I S E R. see SOCIAL SCIENCES: COMPREHENSIVE WORKS

330   DEU
W-INFO WIRTSCHAFTSMAGAZIN. Text in German. m. adv. Document type: Magazine, Trade.
Published by: Vogel IT-Medien GmbH, Gutermannstr 25, Augsburg, 86154, Germany. TEL 49-821-21770, FAX 49-821-2177150. Ed. Elmar Behringer. Adv. contact Martin Kraus.

330   USA   ISSN 0889-7956
W K KELLOGG FOUNDATION ANNUAL REPORT. Text in English. 1962. a. Document type: Corporate.
Related titles: Online - full content ed.
Published by: W K Kellogg Foundation, One Michigan Ave E, Battle Creek, MI 49017-4012. TEL 269-968-1611, FAX 269-968-0413, http://www.wkkf.org/AnnualReport/.

338   USA
W N C BUSINESS JOURNAL. (Western North Carolina) Text in English. 1987. m. USD 50 in state; USD 65 out of state; USD 4 newsstand/cover (effective 2004). adv. bk.rev. Document type: Magazine, Trade. Description: For business people throughout the 28 counties of western North Carolina.
Former titles: W N C Business Beat (1084-6352); (until 1995): Original W N C Business Journal (1065-027X); W N C Business Journal (1049-7145)
Published by: Nason & Associates, PO Box 8204, Asheville, NC 28814. TEL 828-298-1322, FAX 828-298-1312. Ed., Pub. Marilyn Nason TEL 828-298-1314. Circ: 19,000 (paid and controlled).

W S I MITTEILUNGEN. see SOCIAL SCIENCES: COMPREHENSIVE WORKS

WAGE-PRICE LAW & ECONOMICS REVIEW. see BUSINESS AND ECONOMICS—Macroeconomics

330   JPN   ISSN 1343-0637
WAKAYAMA UNIVERSITY. FACULTY OF ECONOMICS. ANNALS. Text in Japanese; Abstracts in English. 1997. a. Document type: Academic/Scholarly.
Published by: Wakayama Daigaku, Keizai Gakkai/Wakayama University, Economic Society, 930 Sakaedani, Wakayama-shi, 640-510, Japan. TEL 81-73-547-7633, FAX 81-73-457-7630, keiken@emily.eco.wakayama-u.ac.jp. Circ: 600.

330 370   USA   ISSN 1538-6732
WALL STREET JOURNAL (CLASSROOM EDITION). Text in English. 9/yr. (Sep.-May). USD 24.95 to individuals; USD 165 per academic year to institutions for 30 copies, Teacher Guide, & Wall Street Journal (effective 2003). adv. Document type: Newspaper, Academic/Scholarly. Description: Covers personal finance, economics, marketing, careers, technology, government, media and sports.
Related titles: Online - full content ed.
Published by: Dow Jones Company, PO Box 300, Princeton, NJ 08540. TEL 800-544-0522, FAX 609-520-7767, classroom.edition@wsj.com, http://www.wsjclassroomedition.com/index.html, http://www.wsj.com. Adv. contact Lawrence Cognetti. B&W page USD 12,700, color page USD 14,900; 10 x 13.25.

330   POL
WARSAW BOOK OF LISTS (YEAR). Text in Polish, English. a. USD 29.95, PLZ 59 (effective 1999). Document type: Directory. Description: Contains 76 industry lists with key data on 1500 Polish companies; includes address, phone number, key personnel, clients, revenues and more.
Related titles: ♦ Supplement to: Warsaw Business Journal. ISSN 1233-7889.
Published by: New World Publishing Inc., Ul Sloneczna 29, Warsaw, 00789, Poland. TEL 48-22-646-0575, FAX 48-22-646-0576, wbj@it.com.pl, http://www.ceebiz.com.

330   POL   ISSN 1233-7889
HF3636
WARSAW BUSINESS JOURNAL. Text in Portuguese. 1994. s-m. PLZ 199; USD 195 in Europe; USD 295 elsewhere (effective 1999). adv. Document type: Consumer.
Related titles: Online - full text ed.: (from EBSCO Publishing); ♦ Supplement(s): Warsaw Book of Lists (Year); ♦ Equity Central Europe. ISSN 1418-9496.
Indexed: B&I.
Published by: New World Publishing Inc., Ul Sloneczna 29, Warsaw, 00789, Poland. TEL 48-22-646-0575, FAX 48-22-646-0576, wbj@it.com.pl, http://www.ceebiz.com. Ed. Stephen Kirkland. Pubs. Stephen A O'Connor, Thompson B Barnhardt. Adv. contact Katarzyna M Marciniewicz.

330.9438   POL
WARSAW VOICE BUSINESS & ECONOMY YEARBOOK. Text in English. 1995. a. PLZ 55. adv. Document type: Trade. Description: Describes main facts about Poland's economy, as well as commentaries from independent experts and analysts.
Published by: Warsaw Voice S.A., Ksiecia Janusza 65, Warsaw, 01452, Poland. TEL 48-22-366377, FAX 48-22-371995, voice@warsawvoice.com.pl, http://www.warsawvoice.com.pl. Ed. Magda Sowinska. Adv. contact Dariusz Gibert. page PLZ 10,860.

650   GBR   ISSN 1363-0520
WARWICK BUSINESS SCHOOL RESEARCH PAPERS. Text in English. 1982. irreg. GBP 10 domestic; GBP 15 foreign (effective 2000). Document type: Academic/Scholarly.
Former titles (until Dec. 1990): Warwick Papers in Management (0955-4718); Warwick Papers in Industry, Business and Administration (0263-5976); Supersedes: Warwick Industrial Economic and Business Research Papers; Warwick Research Industrial and Business Studies (0083-7369)
Related titles: Online - full text ed.
—BLDSC (9261.954000), IE, ingenta.
Published by: University of Warwick, Warwick Business School, University Of Warwick, Gibbet Hill Rd, Coventry, Warks CV4 7AL, United Kingdom. TEL 44-24-7652-2089, FAX 44-24-7652-3719, http://www.wbs.warwick.ac.uk/wbsrb/. Ed. Paul Edwards. R&P Claire New. Circ: 100.

330   JPN   ISSN 0388-1008
HF41
WASEDA BUSINESS AND ECONOMIC STUDIES. Text in English. 1965. a. free. charts; illus.
Published by: Waseda University, Graduate School of Commerce, 6-1 Nishi-Waseda 1-chome, Shinjuku-ku, Tokyo, 169-50, Japan. Circ: 500.

WASEDA SEIJI KEIZAIGAKU ZASSHI/WASEDA JOURNAL OF POLITICAL SCIENCE AND ECONOMICS. see POLITICAL SCIENCE

330   USA   ISSN 0149-7618
HF125.W2
WASHINGTON (STATE). DEPARTMENT OF REVENUE. QUARTERLY BUSINESS REVIEW. Text in English. 1974. q. 64 p./no.; Document type: Government.
Published by: Department of Revenue, Research Division, PO Box 47459, Olympia, WA 98504-7459. TEL 360-570-6070, FAX 360-664-0972, http://dor.wa.gov/index.asp?/menu/stats.htm. Circ: 1,100.

330 351 USA ISSN 0083-7393
F192.5
WASHINGTON (YEAR); a comprehensive directory of the Nation's Capital, its people and institutions. Text in English. 1966. a. USD 89 (effective 2000). adv. index. **Document type:** *Directory.* **Description:** Compilation of the 5000 key public and private institutions in the Washington area and the 25,000 personnel who are responsible for directing them, broken down into 17 subject areas. Includes separate alphabetical index of organizations and individuals.
Formerly: Washington
—CISTI.
Published by: Columbia Books Inc., 1825 Connecticut Ave NW #625, Washington, DC 20009-5724. TEL 202-898-0662, 888-265-0600, FAX 202-898-0775, info@columbiabooks.com, http://www.columbiabooks.com. Ed. Buck Downs. Pub., Adv. contact Michael Goldman.

330 USA ISSN 1522-8290
HC108.W3
WASHINGTON BUSINESS FORWARD. Text in English. 1999. m. USD 30; USD 3.95 newsstand/cover domestic; USD 4.95 newsstand/cover in Canada (effective 2001). adv. **Document type:** *Magazine, Trade.* **Description:** Delivers in-depth interviews and sharp insight on the people and trends shaping the future of the Greater Washington region.
Published by: Business Forward Media, Inc., 1601 Connecticut Ave, NW, Ste 303, Washington, DC 20009. TEL 202-797-1162, editor@bizforward.com, adsales@bizforward.com, business@bixforward.com, http://www.bizforward.com. Ed. Eamon Javers. Pub. Jeremy Brosowsky. Adv. contact Kirsten Russell. B&W page USD 5,090, color page USD 5,855; bleed 8.5 x 11.125.

330 USA ISSN 0737-3147
HF3161.W18
WASHINGTON BUSINESS JOURNAL. Text in English. 1982. w. (Fri.). USD 92 (effective 2005). adv. back issues avail. **Document type:** *Newspaper.* **Description:** Covers Washington metropolitan area business news and trends.
Related titles: Online - full text ed.: (from Florida Center for Library Automation, Gale Group, O C L C Online Computer Library Center, Inc., ProQuest Information & Learning).
Indexed: ABIn, BusDate, LRI, T&II.
Published by: American City Business Journals, Inc. (Arlington), 1555 Wilson Blvd, Ste 400, Arlington, VA 22209-2405. TEL 703-875-2200, FAX 703-875-2231, washington@bizjournals.com, http://www.washington.bcentral.com. Circ: 21,000. Wire service: PR.

WASHINGTON STATE BAR ASSOCIATION. BUSINESS AND LAW SECTION. NEWSLETTER. see *LAW*

384.33 330 USA ISSN 1094-9011
WEB COMMERCE TODAY. Text in English. 1997. m. USD 49.95 (effective 2001). adv. back issues avail. **Document type:** *Newsletter, Trade.* **Description:** Covers e-commerce and business-to-business issues.
Media: Online - full content (from Florida Center for Library Automation). **Related titles:** E-mail ed.
Published by: Wilson Internet Services, P O Box 308, Rocklin, CA 95677-0308. TEL 916-652-4659, rfwilson@wilsonweb.com, http://www.wilsonweb.com/wct/. Ed., Pub. Ralph F. Wilson.

330 COL
➤ **WEBPONDO.ORG**; recursos para economistas y colombia. Text in Esperanto, English. 2001. q. **Document type:** *Journal, Academic/Scholarly.* **Description:** Contains interviews, academic and opinion articles and reviews, together with information and links about economics and Colombia.
Media: Online - full content.
Published by: Fundacion Pondo, Cra 7 No. 14-78, Piso 11, Colombia. TEL 571-3430503, FAX 571-3421804, ariascos@webpondo.org, http://www.webpondo.org/. Ed. Alvaro Jose Riascos.

➤ **WEBTRADE.** see *COMPUTERS—Internet*

330 USA
WEEKLY INSIDERS RETAIL. Text in English. w. USD 24 domestic (effective 2005). **Document type:** *Newsletter.* **Description:** Provides busy buyers and sellers with a quick snapshot of market trends and conditions in the poultry, meat, seafood, dairy, and egg industries.
Media: E-mail.
Published by: Urner Barry Publications, Inc., PO Box 389, Toms River, NJ 08754-0389. TEL 732-240-5330, FAX 732-341-0891, mail@urnerbarry.com, http://www.urnerbarry.com/frameset/retail_report_frameset.htm. Adv. contact Katie Hopkins.

330 GBR
WEEKLY REGISTRARS SERVICE. Text in English. w. GBP 305; GBP 460 foreign. **Document type:** *Trade.*
Published by: Financial Times Information Ltd., Extel, Fitzroy House, 13-17 Epworth St, London, EC2A 4DL, United Kingdom. TEL 44-20-7825-8000, FAX 44-20-7608-2032, eic@ft.com, http://www.info.ft.com.

330 CHN ISSN 1004-7778
WEISHENG JINGJI YANJIU/HEALTH ECONOMICS RESEARCH. Text in Chinese. 1984. m.
Related titles: Online - full text ed.: (from East View Information Services, WanFang Data Corp.).
Address: 91, Daxue Lu, Hangzhou, 310009, China. TEL 0571-87047596, FAX 0571-87047616, wsjjyj@mail.hz.zj.cn, http://WSJJYJ.ZJWST.GOV.CN/.

330 GBR
WELSH ENTERPRISE INSTITUTE. WORKING PAPERS SERIES. Text in English. 2000 (June). irreg. **Document type:** *Monographic series, Academic/Scholarly.*
Related titles: Online - full text ed.
—BLDSC (9288.171500).
Published by: University of Glamorgan Business School, Welsh Enterprise Institute, Pontypridd, Wales, CF37 1DL, United Kingdom. TEL 44-1443-482818, FAX 44-1443-482380, http://web.glam.ac.uk/schools/bus/Research/ResUnits/WEI/wei/index.php, http://web.glam.ac.uk/schools/bus/Research/ResUnits/WEI/wei/Publications/index.php.

330 USA
WENATCHEE BUSINESS JOURNAL. Text in English. 1987. m. USD 18; USD 2 newsstand/cover (effective 1998). adv. **Document type:** *Trade.* **Description:** Contains business news, profiles of business leaders and reports on local companies. Includes advice and management columns.
Related titles: Online - full text ed.
Published by: Wenatchee Business Journal Inc., 304 S Mission St, Wenatchee, WA 98801-3044. TEL 509-663-6730, wbjnews@nwi.net. Ed. Mike Cassidy. Pubs. Jim Corcoran, Mike Cassidy. Adv. contact Jim Corcoran. B&W page USD 940; trim 13.5 x 9.75. Circ: 4,500.

330 DEU ISSN 0723-5275
WER LEITET; das Middle Management der deutschen Wirtschaft. Text in German. 1982. a. **Document type:** *Directory.*
Published by: Hoppenstedt Bonnier Zeitschriften GmbH, Havelstr. 9, Darmstadt, 64295, Germany. TEL 49-6151-380-0, FAX 49-6151-380-360. Circ: 46,000.

330 USA
WEST CENTRAL BUSINESS JOURNAL; the business newspaper of west central Ohio. Text in English. 1992. m. free. adv. **Document type:** *Newsletter.* **Description:** Covers all business matters in 10 west central Ohio counties.
Published by: Ronald Freed, Ed. & Pub., PO Box 388, Lima, OH 45802-0388. TEL 419-991-6839, FAX 419-991-4762. R&P, Adv. contact Ronald Freed. B&W page USD 699; 12.25 x 10. Circ: 10,000 (controlled).

330 USA ISSN 0195-4644
HC107.W5
WEST VIRGINIA BUSINESS INDEX. Text in English. 1938. m. USD 60. **Document type:** *Trade.*
Published by: West Virginia Chamber of Commerce, PO Box 2789, Charleston, WV 25330. TEL 304-342-1115.

330 USA
WESTERN MASSACHUSETTS BUSINESS MAGAZINE. Text in English. 2001. 8/yr., latest no.1. USD 19.95; USD 4.95 newsstand/cover (effective 2001). adv. **Document type:** *Journal.* **Description:** Covers the people, issues and events of the Western Massachusetts economy.
Published by: Nolan Media LLC, 615 Main St, Cromwell, CT 06416. TEL 860-635-1819, FAX 860-632-7203, ctbizmag@snet.net, http://www.ctbizmag.com. Ed. John Woods. Pub., R&P Ron Nolan TEL 860-635-1819. Adv. contact Clare A Bearer. B&W page USD 1,990, color page USD 2,770; trim 8 x 10.75. Circ: 12,000 (controlled).

WETBOEK ECONOMISCH RECHT EN CONSUMENTENRECHT. see *LAW—Corporate Law*

WETTBEWERB IN RECHT UND PRAXIS. see *LAW*

WHAT IS TO BE READ. see *LITERATURE*

332 GBR ISSN 0263-8525
WHAT MORTGAGE. Text in English. 1982. m. GBP 2.50. adv. **Document type:** *Consumer.*
—CCC.
Published by: Charterhouse Communications Group Ltd., Arnold House, 36-41 Holywell Ln, London, EC2A 3ET, United Kingdom. TEL 44-20-7827-5454. Ed., R&P Nia Williams. Pub. Ivan Elliot. Adv. contact Mike Mortimore. Circ: 35,000 (paid).

WHAT'S NEW IN BUSINESS INFORMATION. see *COMMUNICATIONS*

WHICH DEGREE. SOCIAL SCIENCES, BUSINESS, EDUCATION. see *EDUCATION—Guides To Schools And Colleges*

330 USA
WHICH EXECUTIVE PROGRAMME?. Text in English. a. USD 49.99 (effective 2003). **Document type:** *Trade.* **Description:** Serves as a guide to the world's best management development courses.
Published by: Economist Intelligence Unit, 111 W 57th St, New York, NY 10019. http://store.eiu.com/index.asp?layout=product_home_page&product_id=400000240.

330 FRA
WHO'S TOP IN EUROPEAN COMMERCE AND INDUSTRY. Text in French. 1973. a. **Document type:** *Directory.*
Published by: International Herald Tribune, 6 bis, rue des Graviers, Neuilly-sur-Seine, Cedex 92521, France. TEL 33-1-41439300, FAX 33-1-41439338, ibp-berlin@t-online.de, iht@iht.com. Ed. Michael Getler. Pub. Stephan Dunbar Johnson. **Dist. by (in Europe):** I B P - Buchvertrieb Wockel & Co. GmbH, Kurfuerstendamm 92, Berlin 10709, Germany. TEL 49-30-32798040, FAX 49-30-3244589.

330 DEU
WHO'S WHO EUROPA MAGAZIN. Text in German. 1995. 4/yr. EUR 46.40 (effective 2002). adv. **Document type:** *Magazine, Trade.*
Published by: Bosse & Ortlepp Media-Projektgruppe OHG, Vorstadt 18, Oberursel, 61440, Germany. TEL 49-6171-51055, FAX 49-6171-53542, europamagazin@who-magazine.com, bosse@who-magazine.com, http://www.who-magazine.com. Ed. Wilma K. Bosse. adv.: page EUR 6,500. Circ: 50,000 (controlled).

WHO'S WHO IN EUROPEAN BUSINESS. see *BIOGRAPHY*

WHO'S WHO IN FINANCE AND INDUSTRY. see *BIOGRAPHY*

330 USA ISSN 0894-4032
WICHITA BUSINESS JOURNAL. Text in English. 1986. w. (Fri.). USD 81 (effective 2005). adv. **Document type:** *Newspaper, Consumer.* **Description:** Covers local business news.
Related titles: Online - full text ed.: ISSN 1549-2621 (from Florida Center for Library Automation, Gale Group, O C L C Online Computer Library Center, Inc., ProQuest Information & Learning).
Indexed: ABIn, BusDate.
—CCC.
Published by: American City Business Journals, Inc. (Wichita), 110 S Main St, Ste 200, Wichita, KS 67202-3745. TEL 316-267-6406, FAX 316-267-8570, wichita@bizjournals.com, http://www.bizjournals.com/wichita/. Pub. Bill Roy. Adv. contact Angela Robuck. Circ: 5,800 (paid). Wire service: PR.

330 USA ISSN 1048-3365
WICHITA JOURNAL. Text in English. 1969. w. (Thu.). USD 47.50. adv. bk.rev. tr.lit. **Document type:** *Newspaper, Consumer.* **Description:** Covers news affecting the business community.
Formerly: Record/Journal
Published by: Liberty Group Holdings Inc., PO Box 190, Derby, KS 67037. TEL 316-788-2835, FAX 316-788-0854. Ed. Renee Browning. Pub., R&P Jimmie R Stephenson. Adv. contact Eric Clutts. Circ: 750. Wire service: AP.

WIE WERKT WAAR BIJ ADVERTEERDERS (GEDRUKTE VERSIE). see *BUSINESS AND ECONOMICS—Marketing And Purchasing*

330 AUT
WIENER WIRTSCHAFT; woechentliche Information der Wirtschaftskammer Wien. Text in German. w. EUR 54 domestic; EUR 97 foreign (effective 2005). adv. **Document type:** *Newspaper, Trade.*
Published by: Oesterreichischer Wirtschaftsverlag GmbH (Subsidiary of: Sueddeutscher Verlag GmbH), Wiedner Hauptstr 120-124, Vienna, W 1051, Austria. TEL 43-1-546640, FAX 43-1-54664406, office@wirtschaftsverlag.at, http://www.wirtschaftsverlag.at. Ed. Robert Huemer. Adv. contact Erhard Witty. B&W page EUR 3,850, color page EUR 5,775; trim 194 x 250. Circ: 65,500.

330 DEU ISSN 0720-7042
WIENER WIRTSCHAFTS- UND FINANZWISSENSCHAFTLICHE UNTERSUCHUNGEN. Text in German. 1968. irreg., latest vol.10, 1977. price varies. **Document type:** *Monographic series, Academic/Scholarly.*
Published by: Duncker und Humblot GmbH, Carl-Heinrich-Becker-Weg 9, Berlin, 12165, Germany. TEL 49-30-7900060, FAX 49-30-79000631, info@duncker-humblot.de, http://www.duncker-humblot.de.

330 USA ISSN 0084-0246
WILLIAM K. MCINALLY LECTURE. Text in English. 1966. a. USD 5. reprint service avail. from PQC.
Published by: University of Michigan, Graduate School of Business Administration, Division of Research, Tappan and Monroe Sts, Ann Arbor, MI 48109. TEL 313-764-1366.

330 GBR
WINDOW ON INDUSTRY. Text in English. 1985. m. GBP 32 foreign (effective 2001); (free to qualified personnel). adv. bk.rev. tr.lit. back issues avail. **Document type:** *Trade.* **Description:** Discusses various aspects of the handling, packaging, and storage of products, as well as occupational health and safety in medium-sized firms.
Formerly (until Jan. 2001): European Window on Industry
Indexed: CEABA, CSNB, LHB.
Published by: Aydee Marketing Ltd., Nithsdale House, 159 Cambridge St, Aylesbury, Bucks HP20 1BQ, United Kingdom. TEL 44-1296-434381, FAX 44-1296-436936, info@aydee.com, http://www.aydee.com. Ed. John Quick. Pub. Richard Salmon. Adv. contact Wayne Hardy. Circ: 15,000.

WINDS OF CHANGE; American Indian education & opportunity. see *NATIVE AMERICAN STUDIES*

WINE BUSINESS INSIDER. see *BEVERAGES*

WINE BUSINESS MONTHLY; & grower and cellar news. see *BEVERAGES*

330 AUT
DIE WIRTSCHAFT; das Servicemagazin fuer Unternehmer und Manager. Text in German. 1945. m. EUR 60 domestic; EUR 81 foreign (effective 2005). adv. illus.; tr.lit. **Document type:** *Magazine, Trade.*
Former titles: Neue Wirtschaft; Wirtschaft (0043-6100)
Published by: Oesterreichischer Wirtschaftsverlag GmbH (Subsidiary of: Sueddeutscher Verlag GmbH), Wiedner Hauptstr 120-124, Vienna, W 1051, Austria. TEL 43-1-546640, FAX 43-1-54664406, wirtschaft@wirtschaftsverlag.at, office@wirtschaftsverlag.at, http://www.die-wirtschaft.at, http://www.wirtschaftsverlag.at. Ed. Harald Hornacek. Adv. contact Thomas Grojer. color page EUR 9,900; trim 190 x 255. Circ: 50,000 (paid and controlled).

B

330 AUT
WIRTSCHAFT AKTIV✶ . Text in German. q.
Published by: Landgruppe Oe Oe, Pochestrasse 3, Postfach 16, Linz, O 4010, Austria. Ed. K Kurzthaler. Circ: 42,000.

330 DEU ISSN 0936-5885
WIRTSCHAFT IM SUEDWESTEN. Text in German. 1973. m. adv. bk.rev. **Document type:** *Journal, Trade.*
Published by: (Industrie- und Handelskammern im Regierungsbezirk Freiburg), Pruefer Medienmarketing, Lichtentaler Str 33, Baden-Baden, 76530, Germany. TEL 49-7221-21190, FAX 49-7221-211915, werbeagentur@pruefer.com, http://www.pruefer.com. Ed. Ulrich Plankenhorn. adv.: B&W page EUR 4,222, color page EUR 5,501; trim 185 x 250. Circ: 89,000 (controlled).

330 DEU ISSN 0946-7378
WIRTSCHAFT IN MAINFRANKEN. Text in German. 1946. m. adv. **Document type:** *Magazine, Trade.*
Formerly: Mainfraenkische Wirtschaft
Published by: (Industrie- und Handelskammer Wuerzburg-Schweinfurt), V M M Wirtschaftsverlag GmbH & Co. KG, Maximilianstr 9, Augsburg, 86150, Germany. TEL 49-821-44050, FAX 49-821-4405409, elmar.behringer@vmm-wirtschaftsverlag.de, info@vmm-wirtschaftsverlag.de, http://www.wuerzburg.ihk.de, http://www.vmm-wirtschaftsverlag.de. adv.: B&W page EUR 1,990, color page EUR 2,560; trim 210 x 297. Circ: 20,000 (controlled).

330 DEU
WIRTSCHAFT MARKT. Text in German. 1990. m. EUR 2.50 newsstand/cover (effective 2002). adv. **Document type:** *Magazine, Trade.*
Formerly: Wirtschaft und Markt (0863-5323)
Published by: W und M Verlagsgesellschaft mbH, Neue Gruenstr 18, Berlin, 10179, Germany. TEL 49-30-2789450, FAX 49-30-27894523, wumberlin@t-online.de, http://www.wirtschaftundmarkt.de. Ed. Klaus George. Adv. contact Margit Eschment. B&W page EUR 4,500, color page EUR 6,800. Circ: 43,000.

330 DEU ISSN 0944-6249
WIRTSCHAFT REGIONAL. Text in German. m. adv. **Document type:** *Trade.*
Published by: Wirtschaft Regional Verlag GmbH, Villastr 11, Stuttgart, 70190, Germany. TEL 0711-2686131, FAX 0711-2686139. Ed. Ulrich Pfaffenberger. Adv. contact Christian Schikora. Circ: 103,000.

330 AUT ISSN 0378-5130
HC261
WIRTSCHAFT UND GESELLSCHAFT. Text in German. 1975. q. bk.rev. 136 p./no.; **Document type:** *Magazine, Trade.*
Indexed: IBR, IPSA, PAIS, RASB.
—BLDSC (9325.415550), IE, ingenta.
Published by: (Kammer fuer Arbeiter und Angestellte fuer Wien), LexisNexis Verlag ARD Orac GmbH & Co. KG (Subsidiary of: LexisNexis Europe and Africa), Marxergasse 25, Vienna, W 1030, Austria. TEL 43-1-534520, FAX 43-1-53452141, verlag@orac.at, http://www.lexisnexis.at/. Adv. contact Malgorzata Leitliner TEL 43-1-534521115. Circ: 900.

330 310 DEU ISSN 0043-6143
HC281
WIRTSCHAFT UND STATISTIK. Text in German. 1949. m. reprints avail. **Document type:** *Government.*
Indexed: ChemAb, KES, PAIS, PopulInd, RASB, RRTA, RefZh, WAE&RSA.
—CISTI, IE, Infotrieve. **CCC.**
Published by: Statistisches Bundesamt, Gustav-Stresemann-Ring 11, Wiesbaden, 65180, Germany. TEL 49-611-75-1, FAX 49-611-724000, TELEX 61186-STBA-D, http://www.statistik-bund.de.

330.07 DEU
WIRTSCHAFT UND UNTERRICHT; Informationen fuer Paedagogen in Schule und Betrieb. Text in German. 10/yr. **Published by:** Institut der Deutschen Wirtschaft, Gustav-Heinemann-Ufer 84-88, Cologne, 50968, Germany. TEL 49-221-49811, FAX 49-221-4981592.

330 DEU ISSN 0178-7209
WIRTSCHAFTS KOMPASS. Text in German. 1983. a.
Published by: Rudolf Haufe Verlag GmbH & Co. KG, Hindenburgstr 64, Freiburg Im Breisgau, 79102, Germany. TEL 49-761-3683-0, TELEX 772442-HAUFE-D, online@haufe.de. Ed. Wolfgang Bohl.

330 DEU ISSN 0170-3390
WIRTSCHAFTS-KURIER. Text in German. 11/yr. adv. **Document type:** *Consumer.*
Published by: Wirtschafts-Kurier Verlagsgesellschaft mbH, Lindwurmstr 201, Munich, 80337, Germany. TEL 089-774086, FAX 089-763938. Ed. Wilhelm Gaensler. Pub. Hans Englert. Adv. contact Anne Marie Kwak. Circ: 42,719.

330 DEU ISSN 0931-2552
WIRTSCHAFTS-NACHRICHTEN. Text in German. 1955. m. EUR 32; EUR 3 newsstand/cover (effective 2004). adv. bk.rev. stat. back issues avail. **Document type:** *Magazine, Trade.*
Formerly: Wirtschafts-Nachrichten fuer den Linken Niederrhein (0344-0249)
Published by: Stuenings Medien GmbH, Diessemer Bruch 167, Krefeld, 47805, Germany. TEL 49-2151-51000, FAX 49-2151-5100101, wirtschafts-nachrichten@stuenings.de, medien@stuenings.de, http://www.wirtschafts-nachrichten.de, http://www.stuenings.de. Ed. Bernward Franke. Adv. contact Sandra Casaretto. B&W page EUR 3,222, color page EUR 3,834; trim 210 x 280. Circ: 20,738 (paid and controlled).

330 DEU
WIRTSCHAFTS- UND SOZIALHISTORISCHE STUDIEN. Text in German. irreg., latest vol.4, 2003. price varies. **Document type:** *Monographic series, Academic/Scholarly.*
Published by: Boehlau Verlag GmbH & Cie, Ursulaplatz 1, Cologne, 50668, Germany. TEL 49-221-913900, FAX 49-221-9139011, vertrieb@boehlau.de, http://www.boehlau.de.

330 DEU ISSN 0722-3358
WIRTSCHAFTS UND STEUER HEFTE. Text in German. 1925. 24/yr. adv. **Document type:** *Newspaper, Trade.*
Related titles: CD-ROM ed.
Published by: D I E Verlag H. Schaefer GmbH, Postfach 2243, Bad Homburg, 61292, Germany. TEL 49-6172-9583-0, FAX 49-6172-71288. Ed. Erika Bressel. Pub. Peter Vollrath Kuehne. Adv. contact Peter Vollrath. Circ: 15,500.

330 DEU ISSN 0043-6275
➤ **WIRTSCHAFTSDIENST.** Text in German. 1917. m. EUR 98.13 combined subscription to institutions print & online eds. (effective 2005). bk.rev. charts; stat. index. back issues avail.; reprint service avail. from ISI. **Document type:** *Journal, Academic/Scholarly.*
Related titles: Online - full text ed.: ISSN 1613-978X (from Springer LINK, Swets Information Services).
Indexed: DIP, ELLIS, ExcerpMed, I&DA, IBR, IBSS, IBZ, ILD, KES, PAIS, RASB, RRTA, WAE&RSA.
—BLDSC (9325.550000), CISTI, IE, Infotrieve, ingenta. **CCC.**
Published by: (H W W A - Hamburgisches Welt-Wirtschafts-Archiv), Springer-Verlag (Subsidiary of: Springer Science+Business Media), Tiergartenstr 17, Heidelberg, 69121, Germany. TEL 49-6221-3450, FAX 49-6221-345229. Eds. Susanne Erbe, Dr. Klaus Kwasniewski. Adv. contact Stephan Kroeck TEL 49-30-827875739. **Subscr. in the Americas to:** Springer-Verlag New York, Inc., Journal Fulfillment, PO Box 2485, Secaucus, NJ 07096-2485. TEL 800-777-4643, 201-348-4033, FAX 201-348-4505, journals@springer-ny.com, http://www.springer-ny.com; **Subscr. to:** Springer GmbH Auslieferungsgesellschaft, Haberstr 7, Heidelberg 69126, Germany. TEL 49-6221-345-0, FAX 49-6221-345-4229, subscriptions@springer.de.

330 DEU ISSN 0722-9267
WIRTSCHAFTSECHO - HEIM UND WERK. Text in German. m. adv. **Document type:** *Trade.*
Published by: Heim und Werk GmbH, Benderstr 168A, Duesseldorf, 40625, Germany. TEL 0211-283095, FAX 0211-283827. Ed. Rolf Scheer. Adv. contact Walter Rau. Circ: 108,015.

WIRTSCHAFTSJOURNALIST; das Magazin fuer Finanz- und Wirtschaftsjournalisten, IR-Manager und Analysten. see *JOURNALISM*

330 AUT
WIRTSCHAFTSMAGAZIN. Text in German. 8/yr.
Address: Meinhardtstrasse 3, Innsbruck, T 6020, Austria. TEL 0512-52022-0. Circ: 27,500.

WIRTSCHAFTSMAGAZIN FUER DEN ALLGEMEINARZT. see *MEDICAL SCIENCES*

WIRTSCHAFTSMAGAZIN FUER DEN FRAUENARZT. see *MEDICAL SCIENCES*

WIRTSCHAFTSMAGAZIN FUER DEN HAUTARZT. see *MEDICAL SCIENCES—Dermatology And Venereology*

WIRTSCHAFTSMAGAZIN FUER DEN KINDERARZT. see *MEDICAL SCIENCES—Pediatrics*

WIRTSCHAFTSMAGAZIN FUER DEN NERVENARZT. see *MEDICAL SCIENCES—Psychiatry And Neurology*

WIRTSCHAFTSMAGAZIN FUER DEN ORTHOPAEDEN. see *MEDICAL SCIENCES—Orthopedics And Traumatology*

WIRTSCHAFTSMAGAZIN FUER DEN UROLOGEN. see *MEDICAL SCIENCES—Urology And Nephrology*

330 DEU ISSN 1437-1693
WIRTSCHAFTSPAEDAGOGISCHE STUDIEN ZUR INDIVIDUELLEN UND KOLLEKTIVEN ENTWICKLUNG. Text in German. 1999. irreg., latest vol.5, 2004. price varies. **Document type:** *Monographic series, Academic/Scholarly.*
Published by: Rainer Hampp Verlag, Meringerzellerstr 10, Mering, 86415, Germany. TEL 49-8233-4783, FAX 49-8233-30755, Rainer_Hampp_Verlag@t-online.de, http://www.hampp-verlag.de.

338 DEU ISSN 0720-6879
WIRTSCHAFTSPOLITISCHE KOLLOQUIEN DER ADOLF-WEBER-STIFTUNG. Text in German. 1977. irreg., latest vol.20, 1995. price varies. **Document type:** *Monographic series, Academic/Scholarly.*
Published by: Duncker und Humblot GmbH, Carl-Heinrich-Becker-Weg 9, Berlin, 12165, Germany. TEL 49-30-7900060, FAX 49-30-79000631, info@duncker-humblot.de, http://www.duncker-humblot.de.

WIRTSCHAFTSPSYCHOLOGISCHE SCHRIFTEN. see *PSYCHOLOGY*

340 DEU ISSN 1435-683X
WIRTSCHAFTSRECHTLICHE FORSCHUNGSERGEBNISSE.
Variant title: Studienreihe Wirtschaftsrechtliche Forschungsergebnisse. Text in German. 1991. irreg., latest vol.72, 2005. price varies. **Document type:** *Monographic series, Academic/Scholarly.*
Published by: Verlag Dr. Kovac, Arnoldstr 49, Hamburg, 22763, Germany. TEL 49-40-3988800, FAX 49-40-39888055, info@verlagdrkovac.de, http://www.verlagdrkovac.de/12-2.htm.

330 DEU
WIRTSCHAFTSREPORT SIEGEN-OLPE-WITTGENSTEIN. Text in German. m. **Document type:** *Bulletin.*
Published by: Vorlaender und Rothmaler GmbH, Obergraben 39, Siegen, 57072, Germany. TEL 0271-5941, FAX 0271-594318, TELEX 872844-SGNZT-D.

330 DEU
WIRTSCHAFTSSPIEGEL; Kurier der Industrie- und Handelskammer zu Muenster. Text in German. m. back issues avail. **Document type:** *Bulletin.*
Published by: Industrie- und Handelskammer zu Muenster, Sentmaringer Weg 61, Muenster, 48151, Germany. TEL 49-251-707-232, FAX 49-251-707-358.

WIRTSCHAFTSTRENDS ZUM JAHRESWECHSEL. see *HISTORY—History Of Europe*

330 DEU ISSN 0510-5587
WIRTSCHAFTSWISSENSCHAFTLICHE ABHANDLUNGEN. Text in German. 1952. irreg., latest vol.28, 1971. price varies. **Document type:** *Monographic series, Academic/Scholarly.*
Published by: Duncker und Humblot GmbH, Carl-Heinrich-Becker-Weg 9, Berlin, 12165, Germany. TEL 49-30-7900060, FAX 49-30-79000631, info@duncker-humblot.de, http://www.duncker-humblot.de.

330 DEU ISSN 0340-1650
WIRTSCHAFTWISSENSCHAFTLICHES STUDIUM; Zeitschrift fuer Ausbildung und Hochschulkontakt. Abbreviated title: Wi S T. Text in German. 1972. m. EUR 114 domestic; EUR 134.50 foreign; EUR 82 to students; EUR 10 newsstand/cover (effective 2005). adv. bk.rev. abstr.; bibl.; charts; stat. index. back issues avail. **Document type:** *Journal, Academic/Scholarly.*
Indexed: DIP, IBR, IBZ, PAIS, RefZh.
—BLDSC (9325.636500), IE, Infotrieve, ingenta.
Published by: Verlag C.H. Beck oHG, Wilhelmstr 9, Munich, 80801, Germany. TEL 49-89-38189338, FAX 49-89-38189398, abo.verwaltung@beck.de, http://www.beck.de. adv.: page EUR 1,480; trim 186 x 260. Circ: 3,200.

330 USA ISSN 0084-0599
WISCONSIN ECONOMY STUDIES. Text in English. 1967. irreg., latest vol.22, 1987. price varies.
Formerly: Wisconsin Commerce Studies
Published by: University of Wisconsin at Madison, Bureau of Business Research, 110 Commerce Building, 1155 Observatory Dr, Madison, WI 53706. TEL 608-262-1550.

330 DEU
WITA; Ihr Regional-Magazin zum Wirtschaftsthema. Text in German. 2000. 8/yr. **Document type:** *Magazine, Trade.*
Description: Covers a variety of business issues and themes of interest to local German companies.

Published by: Lemmens Verlags- und Mediengesellschaft mbH, Koenigswinterer Str 95, Bonn, 53227, Germany. TEL 49-228-42137-0, FAX 49-228-4213729, info@lemmens.de, http://www.lemmens.de. Ed. Markus Lemmens. Circ: 7,500 (controlled).

WIWI-PRESS. see *COLLEGE AND ALUMNI*

650 USA ISSN 0043-7441
HF5500.2
WOMEN IN BUSINESS. Text in English. 1949. 6/yr. USD 20 (effective 2004). adv. bk.rev.; software rev.; video rev. tr.lit. **Document type:** *Magazine, Corporate.* **Description:** Covers association news, business trends, women's work place issues, entrepreneurial and retirement issues.
Related titles: Microform ed.: (from PQC); Online - full text ed.: (from bigchalk, EBSCO Publishing, H.W. Wilson, Northern Light Technology, Inc., O C L C Online Computer Library Center, Inc., ProQuest Information & Learning).
Indexed: ABIn, BPI, BPIA, MASUSE, PMR, T&II, WBA, WMB.
Published by: (American Business Women's Association), A B W A Company, Inc., 9100 Ward Parkway, Box 8728, Kansas City, MO 64114-0728. TEL 816-361-6621, FAX 816-361-4991, abwa@abwahq.org, http://www.abwahq.org. Ed. Elaine Minter. Pub. Carolyn B Elman. R&P Wendy Myers. Adv. contact Wendy Mabrey. B&W page USD 2,980, color page USD 3,786; trim 10.75 x 8. Circ: 52,476 (paid).

650 USA
WOMEN IN BUSINESS & INDUSTRY. Text in English. q. **Document type:** *Magazine, Trade.*
Published by: E M Publishing Enterprises, Inc, 19456 Ventura Blvd, 200, Tarzana, CA 91356. TEL 818-654-0870, FAX 818-654-0874.

330 USA
WOMEN IN ECONOMICS; the C S W E P roster. Text in English. 1973. biennial. USD 20 (effective 2000). adv. **Document type:** *Newsletter.*
Published by: American Economic Association, Committee on the Status of Women in the Economics Profession, c/o Dr. Beth Allen, Ed., Dept of Economics, University of Minnesota, 1035 Management & Economics, 271, 19th Ave S, Minneapolis, MN 55455. TEL 612-626-8213, FAX 612-624-0209. Ed., Pub., R&P, Adv. contact Beth Allen. Circ: 6,000.

650.082 GBR ISSN 1470-8612
WOMEN'S BUSINESS. Text in English. 1998. m. GBP 21.99 domestic; GBP 40 foreign; GBP 1.80 newsstand/cover (effective 2000). **Description:** Designed for career women looking at related business issues and highlighting high profile executive females.
Formerly (until 1999): Business Woman (1464-5424)
Published by: Teallach Publications Ltd, 10 St Peters Hill, Stamford, PE9 2PE, United Kingdom. TEL 44-178-048-9111, FAX 44-178-048-9112, wib.society@virgin.net, http://www.womensbusiness.co.uk. Circ: 50,000.

330 305.4 USA
▼ **WOMEN'S BUSINESS MINNESOTA.** Text in English. 2003 (Apr.). m. **Document type:** *Magazine, Consumer.*
Published by: Decker Publications, 4601 Excelsior Blvd, Minneapolis, MN 55416. TEL 952-924-2322. Pub. Andrea Lloyd Curry. Circ: 30,000.

WOMEN'S ENTERPRISE. see *WOMEN'S INTERESTS*

WOMEN'S MONEY MAGAZINE. see *WOMEN'S INTERESTS*

330 USA ISSN 0735-9411
WOODROW WILSON SCHOOL OF PUBLIC AND INTERNATIONAL AFFAIRS. DISCUSSION PAPERS IN ECONOMICS. Text in English. 1981. irreg. **Document type:** *Monographic series.*
—BLDSC (3597.934300).
Published by: Princeton University, Woodrow Wilson School of Public and International Affairs, Robertson Hall, Princeton, NJ 08544-1013. TEL 609-258-4800, http://www.wws.princeton.edu.

330 USA
THE WORD NEWSOURCE. Text in English. 1950. m. USD 18; USD 2 newsstand/cover (effective 2005). 8 p./no.; **Document type:** *Magazine.*
Formerly: Word, The,
Published by: Electronic Service Dealers Association, 4927 W Irving Park Rd, Chicago, IL 60641. TEL 773-282-9400. Pub., Adv. contact George J. Weiss. Circ: 3,800 (controlled and free).

WORKING WOMEN. see *WOMEN'S STUDIES*

330 USA ISSN 1020-0525
WORLD BANK. POLICY RESEARCH WORKING PAPERS. Text in English. 198?. irreg., latest no.3439, 2004.
Formerly (until 1991): Policy, Research and External Affairs Working Papers (1059-7875)
Related titles: Online - full text ed.: ISSN 1564-6378.
—**CCC.**
Published by: World Bank Group, 1818 H St, NW, Washington, DC 20433. TEL 703-661-1580, 202-473-1000, FAX 703-661-1501, 202-477-6391, books@worldbank.org, http://www.worldbank.org.

WORLD CARGO ECONOMIST. see *TRANSPORTATION*

330 USA
WORLD COMMODITY FORECASTS. (Consists of two parts: Food, Feedstuffs and Beverages (1363-2604); Industrial Raw Materials (ISSN 1363-2612)) Text in English. 1989. q. USD 825 (effective 2003). **Document type:** *Trade.* **Description:** For investors, planners, analysts and businessmen; uses monitored trends to generate forecasts of spot prices for the next 18 months of 27 commodities.
Related titles: Microform ed.: (from PQC).
Indexed: FS&TA, RiceAb, SIA, TriticAb, WAE&RSA.
Published by: Economist Intelligence Unit, 111 W 57th St, New York, NY 10019. TEL 212-554-0600, 800-938-4685, FAX 212-586-1182, http://www.eiu.com.

339 USA ISSN 1092-1702
WORLD COST OF LIVING SURVEY. Text in English. 1997. biennial.
Published by: Gale Research Co. (Subsidiary of: Gale Group), 220 Book Tower, Detroit, MI 48226. TEL 800-877-4253, http://www.gale.com.

WORLD DIRECTORY OF BUSINESS INFORMATION LIBRARIES. see *LIBRARY AND INFORMATION SCIENCES*

330 615 GBR
WORLD DRUG MARKET MANUAL. COUNTRY MARKETS. (Also avail. in Lotus Notes) Text in English. a. **Document type:** *Trade.*
Related titles: CD-ROM ed.: GBP 2,000 per vol. (effective 2004); Online - full content ed.
Published by: I M S Health Inc., 7 Harewood Ave, London, NW1 6JB, United Kingdom. TEL 44-20-73935000, FAX 44-20-73935900, http://www.ims-global.com/products/studies/world.htm.

WORLD E-COMMERCE & I P REPORT. see *LAW—Corporate Law*

330 GBR ISSN 1468-1838
HF1351
WORLD ECONOMICS; the journal of current economic analysis and policy. Text in English. q. GBP 42, EUR 65, USD 299 to individuals; GBP 178, EUR 260, USD 299 to institutions (effective 2005). **Document type:** *Journal, Academic/Scholarly.*
Related titles: Online - full text ed.: (from EBSCO Publishing, Gale Group).
Indexed: ABIn, CJA.
—BLDSC (9354.575000), IE, ingenta. **CCC.**
Published by: N T C Publications Ltd. (Subsidiary of: World Advertising Research Center Ltd.), Farm Rd, Henley-on-Thames, Oxon RG9 1EJ, United Kingdom. TEL 44-1491-411000, FAX 44-1491-571188, subs@world-economics-journal.com, info@ntc.co.uk, http://www.world-economics-journal.com/.

330 382 GBR ISSN 0378-5920
HF1410
➤ **THE WORLD ECONOMY.** Text in English. 1968. 10/yr. EUR 102 combined subscription in Europe to individuals print & online eds.; GBP 32, USD 53 combined subscription in developing nations to individuals print & online eds.; USD 114 combined subscription in the Americas to individuals & Caribbean, print & online eds.; GBP 68 combined subscription elsewhere to individuals print & online eds.; GBP 908 combined subscription in Europe to institutions print & online eds.; GBP 446, USD 750 combined subscription in developing nations to institutions print & online eds.; USD 1,794 combined subscription in the Americas to institutions & Caribbean, print & online eds.; GBP 1,068 combined subscription elsewhere to institutions print & online eds. (effective 2006). adv. bk.rev. reprints avail. **Document type:** *Journal, Academic/Scholarly.* **Description:** Resource for researchers, analysts and policy-advisors interested in trade policy and other open economy issues embracing international trade and the environment, international finance, and trade and development.
Incorporates: Lectures in Commercial Diplomacy (0309-1961)
Related titles: Online - full text ed.: ISSN 1467-9701. GBP 863 in Europe to institutions; USD 1,705 in the Americas to institutions; GBP 424, USD 712 in developing nations to institutions; GBP 1,015 elsewhere to institutions (effective 2006) (from Blackwell Synergy, EBSCO Publishing, Gale Group, IngentaConnect, O C L C Online Computer Library Center, Inc., Swets Information Services).
Indexed: ABCPolSci, ABIn, APEL, BAS, BPI, BPIA, BrHumI, BusI, CurCont, ELLIS, FPA, GEOBASE, IBR, IBSS, ILD, IPSA, JEL, KES, MAB, ManagCont, PAIS, PCI, PSA, RASB, RefZh, SCIMP, SSA, SSCI, SociolAb, SoyAb, T&II, WAE&RSA, WBA, WMB.
—BLDSC (9354.760000), CISTI, IDS, IE, Infotrieve, ingenta. **CCC.**
Published by: Blackwell Publishing Ltd., 9600 Garsington Rd, Oxford, OX4 2ZG, United Kingdom. TEL 44-1865-776868, FAX 44-1865-714591, customerservices@oxon.blackwellpublishing.com, http://www.blackwellpublishing.com/journals/TWEC. Eds. David Greenaway TEL 44-1159-515469, John Whalley. Circ: 1,800.

330 GBR ISSN 0954-3074
WORLD IN (YEAR). Text in English. 1986. a. adv. **Document type:** *Trade.* **Description:** Presents information looking forward to the economic situations for the coming year.
Published by: Economist Brand Businesses, 25 St James's St, London, SW1A 1HA, United Kingdom. TEL 44-71-830-7000, FAX 44-71-839-4104, http://www.theworldin.com. Ed. Dudley Fishburn. Pub. David Hanger. Adv. contact John Dunn. Circ: 96,470 (paid).

330 TWN
WORLD INDUSTRY. Text in Chinese. 1964. m. adv.
Address: 4-7L, 59 Chung Shan N. Rd, Sec 1, Taipei, Taiwan. Ed. Evan Y C Fong. Circ: 71,000.

330 USA ISSN 1046-4778
HD1393.25
WORLD M & A NETWORK. (Merger and Acquisition) Text in English. 1988. m. USD 395; USD 425 foreign (effective 1999). adv. **Document type:** *Corporate.* **Description:** Lists privately held companies for sale and companies looking to purchase other companies: more than 2,000 merger and acquisition leads annually. Included are manufacturing, distribution and service companies with annual revenues from $1 million to $100 million.
Published by: International Executive Reports, Ltd., 717 D St, N W, Ste 300, Washington, DC 20004-2807. TEL 202-628-7767, FAX 202-628-6618, http://www.worldm-anetwork.com. Ed. John Bailey. Circ: 1,000 (paid); 15,000 (controlled).

330 USA
WORLD PRESS. Text in English. 1982. w. adv. bk.rev. **Document type:** *Newspaper.*
Address: 6872 Arlington Dr., W Bloomfield, MI 48322-2719. TEL 313-563-0360, FAX 248-669-0636. Ed. Stephen R Castor. Adv. contact Mary Neuman.

WORLD TRADE DATA. see *PAINTS AND PROTECTIVE COATINGS*

WORLDMARK YEARBOOK. see *POLITICAL SCIENCE*

WORLDWIDE. see *INSURANCE*

330 USA
▼ **WORTHWHILE.** Text in English. 2005. 6/yr. USD 15 (effective 2005). **Document type:** *Magazine.* **Description:** Offers a roadmap for business success that is more personally fulfilling and socially responsible.
Published by: Worthwhile Magazine, 1201 Peachtree St, Ste 1718, Atlanta, GA 30361. info@worthwhilemag.com, https://www.worthwhilemag.com. Circ: 90,000.

330 POL ISSN 0084-2974
WROCLAWSKI ROCZNIK EKONOMICZNY. Text in Polish. 1968. a. price varies.
Published by: (Polskie Towarzystwo Ekonomiczne), Biuro Wydawnictw i Bibliotek PAN, PO Box 24, Warsaw, 00901, Poland. Circ: 750. **Dist. by:** Ars Polona, Krakowskie Przedmiescie 7, Warsaw, Poland.

WUJIYAN GONGYE/INORGANIC CHEMICALS INDUSTRY. see *ENGINEERING—Chemical Engineering*

330 USA ISSN 1534-2557
THE WYOMING BUSINESS REPORT. Text in English. 2000. bi-m. USD 15 (effective 2000). **Document type:** *Newspaper.* **Description:** Provides breaking news anmd in-depth coverage of business and the economy in Wyoming.
Published by: Wyoming Publishing Inc, 200 W 17th St, Ste 10, Cheyenne, WY 82001. Ed. Dennis Curran. Pubs. Christopher Wood, Jeff Nuttall.

330.071 POL ISSN 0239-7951
WYZSZA SZKOLA PEDAGOGICZNA IM. KOMISJI EDUKACJI NARODOWEJ W KRAKOWIE. ROCZNIK NAUKOWO-DYDAKTYCZNY. PRACE EKONOMICZNO-SPOLECZNE. Text in Polish. 1974. irreg., latest vol.6, 1991. price varies.
Published by: (Wyzsza Szkola Pedagogiczna im. Komisji Edukacji Narodowej w Krakowie), Wydawnictwo Naukowe W S P, Ul Karmelicka 41, Krakow, 31128, Poland. TEL 33-78-20.
Co-sponsor: Ministerstwo Edukacji Narodowej.

330 CHN
XIAMEN SHANGBAO/XIAMEN ECONOMIC DAILY. Text in Chinese. 1995. d. CNY 126 (effective 2004). **Document type:** *Newspaper, Trade.*

▼ new title ➤ refereed ✶ unverified ♦ full entry avail.

Address: 78, Xinhua Lu, 14F, Xinhua Dasha, Xiamen, 361003, China. TEL 86-592-2117057, FAX 86-592-2117071, xwzhwebmaster@wisdomcomputer.com, http://www.66163.com/Fujian_w/news/xmsb/. **Dist. by:** China International Book Trading Corp, 35 Chegongzhuang Xilu, Haidian District, PO Box 399, Beijing 100044, China. TEL 86-10-68412045, FAX 86-10-68412023, cibtc@mail.cibtc.com.cn, http://www.cibtc.com.cn.

330 CHN ISSN 1001-6546
XIANDAI QIYEJIA/MODERN ENTREPRENEURS. Text in Chinese. m.
Published by: Liaoning Shehui Kexueyuan/Liaoning Academy of Social Sciences, 86, Taishan Lu, Huanggu-qu, Shenyang, Liaoning 110031, China. TEL 460511. Ed. Sun Chengci.

330 CHN ISSN 1000-355X
HC462.9
➤ **XIANDAI RIBEN JINGJI/CONTEMPORARY JAPANESE ECONOMICS.** Text in Chinese. 1982. bi-m. CNY 20 (effective 2001). adv. bk.rev. 48 p./no.; reprints avail. **Document type:** *Magazine, Academic/Scholarly.* **Description:** Introduces the development and management of all aspects of Japanese economy: industry, agriculture, transportation, finance and foreign trade.
Related titles: Online - full text ed.: (from East View Information Services).
Published by: Jilin Daxue, Xiandai Riben Jingji Bianjibu, Xiandai Riben Jingji Bianjibu, 10 Qian Wei Lu, Changchun, Jilin 130012, China. TEL 86-431-5166391, FAX 86-431-5166376, yuzhunan@public.cc.jl.cn. Ed. Bingdiao Yu. Circ: 800 (controlled). **Co-sponsor:** China Nationwide Japanese Economic Institute.

381.33 CHN
XIAOFEI XINBAO/CONSUMER'S NEWSPAPER. Text in Chinese. 1988. 2/w. CNY 100.80 (effective 2004). **Document type:** *Newspaper, Consumer.*
Address: Chenhe-qu, 118, Nanguang Lu, Chenyang, 110032, China. TEL 86-24-24111290. **Dist. by:** China International Book Trading Corp, 35 Chegongzhuang Xilu, Haidian District, PO Box 399, Beijing 100044, China. TEL 86-10-68412045, FAX 86-10-68412023, cibtc@mail.cibtc.com.cn, http://www.cibtc.com.cn.

330 CHN
XINWEN BAO/SHANGHAI NEWS, A JOURNAL OF BUSINESS & ECONOMICS. Text in Chinese. d. USD 157.40, CNY 104.40. **Document type:** *Newspaper, Consumer.*
Address: 930 Jiangning Lu, Shanghai, 200041, China. TEL 3252863. **Dist. in U.S. by:** China Books & Periodicals Inc, 360 Swift Ave., Ste. 48, S San Fran, CA 94080-6220; **Dist. by:** China International Book Trading Corp, 35 Chegongzhuang Xilu, Haidian District, PO Box 399, Beijing 100044, China.

330 CHN ISSN 1002-185X
TA479.3
➤ **XIYOU JINSHU CAILIAO YU GONGCHENG/RARE METAL MATERIALS AND ENGINEERING.** Text in Chinese. 1982. bi-m. **Document type:** *Academic/Scholarly.*
Related titles: Online - full text ed.: (from East View Information Services).
Indexed: BrCerAb, C&ISA, CerAb, CivEngAb, CorrAb, E&CAJ, EMA, EngInd, IAA, Inspec, M&TEA, MBF, METADEX, MSCI, RefZh, SolStAb, WAA.
—BLDSC (7291.826000), IE, ingenta, Linda Hall.
Published by: Xibei Youse Jinshu Yanjiuyuan/Northwest Institute of Nonferrous Metal Research, PO Box 51, Xian, Shaanxi 710016, China.

330 CHN ISSN 1000-6052
HC411
➤ **YA-TAI JINGJI/ASIAN AND PACIFIC ECONOMIC REVIEW.** Text in Chinese; Summaries in Chinese, English. 1987. bi-m. CNY 30; USD 15 foreign. adv. charts; stat. back issues avail. **Document type:** *Academic/Scholarly.* **Description:** Discusses issues in the developing Pacific Rim regional economy, including economic situations and problems, the open-door policy, management of joint ventures, and economic relationships between mainland China and Hong Kong, Taiwan, and Macao.
Related titles: Online - full text ed.: (from East View Information Services).
Published by: Fujian Sheng Shehui Kexueyuan, Yatai Jingji Yanjiusuo/Fujian Academy of Social Sciences, Institute of Economy of Asia and Pacific Rim, Linhe Rd 18, Fuzhou, Fujian 350001, China. TEL 86-591-3791405. Eds. Wong Dongling, Zhang Xuhua. R&P Li Bing Yang TEL 86-591-3730438. Adv. contact Li-bing Yang. Circ: 500 (paid); 500 (controlled). **Dist. overseas by:** Jiangsu Publications Import & Export Corp., 56 Gao Yun Ling, Nanjing, Jiangsu, China.

330 USA
YALE UNIVERSITY. ECONOMIC GROWTH CENTER. THREE YEAR REPORT. Text in English. 1961. every 3 yrs. free.
Former titles: Yale University. Economic Growth Center. Five Year Report; Yale University. Economic Growth Center. Annual Report
Published by: Yale University, Economic Growth Center, PO Box 208269, New Haven, CT 06520-8269. TEL 203-432-3610, FAX 203-432-3898. Circ: 500 (controlled).

330 TUR ISSN 1019-1232
YAPI KREDI ECONOMIC REVIEW. Text in English. 1986. s-a.
Indexed: IBSS, JEL.
Published by: Yapi ve Kredi Bankasi, Yapi ve Kredi Plaza D Blok, Levent, Istanbul, 80620, Turkey. FAX 90-212-3396130, bgurkan@ykb.com, research@ykb.com, http://www.ykb.com/english/eco_reports/eco_review.html.

330 ISR
YARHON HESHEV; prices and economic information. Text in Hebrew. m.
Published by: Cheshev Ltd., P O Box 40021, Tel Aviv, 61400, Israel.

330 CHN
YATAI JINGJI SHIBAO/ASIAN PACIFIC ECONOMIC TIMES. Text in Chinese. 1987. 2/w. CNY 216 (effective 2004). **Document type:** *Newspaper, Trade.*
Related titles: Online - full content ed.
Address: 703, Dongfeng Donglu, 14-15, Juchangyuan Wenhua Daluo, Guangzhou, 510080, China. TEL 86-20-87672656, FAX 86-20-87679523, zichuan18@163.net, http://www.ytbao.com/. **Dist. by:** China International Book Trading Corp, 35 Chegongzhuang Xilu, Haidian District, PO Box 399, Beijing 100044, China. TEL 86-10-68412045, FAX 86-10-68412023, cibtc@mail.cibtc.com.cn, http://www.cibtc.com.cn.

320.95 JPN
YEARBOOK OF ASIAN AFFAIRS/ASIA DOKO-NENPO. Text in Japanese. 1970. a. price varies. stat. **Document type:** *Academic/Scholarly.* **Description:** Provides an overview of yearly economic and political affairs in 23 Asian countries, with an outline of issues and news arranged in chronological order.
Published by: Institute of Developing Economies/Ajia Keizai Kenkyusho, 3-2-2 Wakaba, Mihana-ku, Chiba-shi, Chiba 261-8545, Japan. TEL 81-43-299-9536, FAX 84-43-299-9724, info@ide.go.jp, http://www.ide.go.jp. Circ: 1,000.

YEDA LEMEDA; journal on taxation, law and economics. see *BUSINESS AND ECONOMICS—Public Finance, Taxation*

YOUNGBIZ. see *CHILDREN AND YOUTH—For*

YOUR (YEAR) GUIDE TO SOCIAL SECURITY BENEFITS. see *SOCIAL SERVICES AND WELFARE*

330 USA
YOUR BUSINESS. Text in English. 1998. q.
Published by: Baumer Financial Publishing (Subsidiary of: Imagination Publishing, LLC), 820 W Jackson Blvd No 450, Chicago, IL 60607. TEL 312-627-1020, FAX 312-627-1105, baumerfpub@aol.com. Ed. Elizabeth Seymour. Circ: 15,000.

332.024014 AUS
YOUR LIFE, YOUR RETIREMENT. Text in English. 1989. s-a. USD 15 (effective 2004). **Document type:** *Magazine, Consumer.*
Formerly: Your Retirement (1031-6620)
Published by: Retirement Publishing Pty. Ltd., PO Box 1150N, Armadale North, VIC 3143 , Australia. TEL 613-9824-6901, FAX 613-9824-6362, publisher@yourlifechoices.com.au, http://www.yourlifechoices.com.au/.

330 346.066 NLD ISSN 1566-788X
Z E I STUDIES IN EUROPEAN ECONOMICS AND LAW. Text in English. 2000. irreg., latest vol.7, 2005. price varies. **Document type:** *Monographic series, Academic/Scholarly.*
—BLDSC (9440.248000).
Published by: (Zentrum fur Europaische Integrationsforschung/ Center for European Integration Studies DEU), Springer-Verlag Dordrecht (Subsidiary of: Springer Science+Business Media), Van Godewijckstraat 30, Dordrecht, 3311 GX, Netherlands. TEL 31-78-6576050, FAX 31-78-6576474, http://www.springeronline.com. Eds. Christian Koenig, Jurgen von Hagen.

330 DEU ISSN 1615-6781
Z E W ECONOMIC STUDIES. Text in English. 1999. irreg., latest vol.30, 2005. price varies. **Document type:** *Monographic series, Academic/Scholarly.*
—BLDSC (9512.634550).
Published by: (Zentrum fuer Europaeische Wirtschaftsforschung GmbH), Physica-Verlag GmbH und Co. (Subsidiary of: Springer-Verlag), Postfach 105280, Heidelberg, 69042, Germany. TEL 49-6221-487492, FAX 49-6221-487177, physica@springer.de, http://www.springer.de/economics. Ed. Wolfgang Franz.

330 HRV ISSN 1331-5609
ZAGREB INTERNATIONAL REVIEW OF ECONOMICS & BUSINESS. Text in English. 1998. s-a.
Indexed: JEL.
—BLDSC (9425.516900), IE.
Published by: Sveuciliste u Zagrebu, Ekonomski Fakultet/University of Zagreb, Faculty of Economics, Trg J F Kennedya 6, Zagreb, 10000, Croatia. TEL 385-1-2383333, FAX 385-1-2335633, http://www.efzg.hr/main.aspx?id=367. Ed. Soumitra Sharma.

330 DEU
ZAHLEN ZUR WIRTSCHAFTLICHEN ENTWICKLUNG DER BUNDESREPUBLIK DEUTSCHLAND. Text in German. 1962. a. **Document type:** *Bulletin, Trade.*
Published by: Deutscher Instituts Verlag GmbH, Gustav-Heinemann-Ufer 84-88, Cologne, 50968, Germany. TEL 49-221-4981510, FAX 49-221-4981533, div@iwkoeln.de, http://www.iwkoeln.de. Ed. Waltraut Peter. Circ: 100,000.

330 NLD
ZAKENREISNIEUWS. Text in Dutch. 10/yr. free.
Published by: Holland International Travel Group, Afdeling Reisbureaus, Treubstraat 16, Rijswijk (ZH), 2288 EJ, Netherlands. Circ: 12,000.

330 RUS
ZAKONODATEL'STVO I EKONOMIKA. Text in Russian. m. USD 325 in United States.
Indexed: RASB, RefZh.
Published by: Izdatel'stvo Zakonodatel'stvo i Ekonomika, Ul Yunosti, 5-1, korp 6, Moscow, 111442, Russian Federation. TEL 7-095-3747239, FAX 7-095-3745541. **US dist. addr.:** East View Information Services, 3020 Harbor Ln. N., Minneapolis, MN 55447. TEL 612-550-0961.

330 ZMB
ZAMBIA. MINISTRY OF DECENTRALISATION. DISTRICT COUNCILS REVENUE AND CAPITAL ESTIMATES. Text in English. a. **Document type:** *Government.*
Published by: (Zambia. Ministry of Decentralisation), Government Printing Department, PO Box 30316, Lusaka, Zambia. TEL 260-1-228724. Circ: 900.

330 020 ZMB
ZAMBIA. MINISTRY OF LEGAL AFFAIRS. ANNUAL REPORT. Text in English. a. **Document type:** *Government.* **Description:** Reports on the year's news at the Ministry of Legal Affairs in Zambia.
Published by: (Zambia. Ministry of Legal Affairs), Government Printing Department, PO Box 30136, Lusaka, Zambia. FAX 260-1-228724. Circ: 750.

354.4 AUT ISSN 1562-4021
ZEITSCHRIFT FUER GEMEINWIRTSCHAFT. Text in German. 1962. 6/yr. adv. bk.rev. **Document type:** *Journal, Trade.*
Formerly (until 1994): Gemeinwirtschaft (0016-6227)
Published by: Verband der oeffentlichen Wirtschaft und Gemeinwirtschaft Oesterreichs, Stadiongasse 6-8, Vienna, 1016, Austria. TEL 43-1-4082204, redaktion@voewg.at. Circ: 4,500.

330 DEU ISSN 1613-8392
HD28
➤ **ZEITSCHRIFT FUER PLANUNG UND UNTERNEHMENSSTEUERUNG/JOURNAL OF PLANNING.** Text in German. 1985. q. EUR 252.34; EUR 75.80 per issue (effective 2005). **Document type:** *Journal, Academic/Scholarly.*
Former titles (until 2004): Zeitschrift fuer Planung (0936-8787); (until 1990): Strategische Planung (0176-487X)
Related titles: Microform ed.: (from PQC); Online - full text ed.
Indexed: IAOP, IBibSS.
—IE. CCC.
Published by: Physica-Verlag GmbH und Co. (Subsidiary of: Springer-Verlag), Postfach 105280, Heidelberg, 69042, Germany. TEL 49-6221-487492, FAX 49-6221-487177, physica@springer.de. Eds. B Huch, C Freidank, J Bloech, T Guenther, U Goetze, W Berens. Adv. contact Stephan Kroeck TEL 49-30-827875739. Circ: 700. **Subscr. in the Americas to:** Springer-Verlag New York, Inc.. TEL 800-777-4643, journals@springer-ny.com, http://www.springer-ny.com; **Subscr. to:** Springer GmbH Auslieferungsgesellschaft, Haberstr 7, Heidelberg 69126, Germany. TEL 49-6221-345-0, FAX 49-6221-345-4229, subscriptions@springer.de.

170 DEU ISSN 1439-880X
➤ **ZEITSCHRIFT FUER WIRTSCHAFTS- UND UNTERNEHMENSETHIK.** Text in German; Abstracts in English. 2000. 3/yr. EUR 45 domestic; EUR 53 foreign (effective 2005). **Document type:** *Journal, Academic/Scholarly.* **Description:** Contains articles and features on economic and business ethics.
Related titles: Online - full text ed.: (from EBSCO Publishing, ProQuest Information & Learning).
Indexed: ABIn, DIP, IBR, IBSS, IBZ.
Published by: (Berliner Forum zur Wirtschafts- und Unternehmensethik), Rainer Hampp Verlag, Meringerzellerstr 10, Mering, 86415, Germany. TEL 49-8233-4783, FAX 49-8233-30755, redaktion@zfwu.de, Rainer_Hampp_Verlag@t-online.de, http://www.zfwu.de, http://www.hampp-verlag.de. **Dist. by:** Brockhaus Commission, Kreidlerstr 9, Kornwestheim 70806, Germany. TEL 49-7154-132739, FAX 49-7254-132713.

330 DEU ISSN 0721-3808
HB5 CODEN: ZEWIEZ
➤ **ZEITSCHRIFT FUER WIRTSCHAFTSPOLITIK.** Text in German. 1952. 3/yr. EUR 71 domestic; EUR 74 foreign; EUR 37 domestic to students; EUR 40 foreign to students; EUR 24 per issue (effective 2003). adv. cum.index. 120 p./no.; back issues avail.; reprint service avail. from SCH. **Document type:** *Magazine, Academic/Scholarly.*
Formerly (until 1982): Wirtschaftspolitische Chronik (0043-6305)
Related titles: Online - full text ed.: (from ProQuest Information & Learning).
Indexed: ABIn, ELLIS, IBR, IBSS, IBZ, JEL, PAIS, RASB.
—CCC.
Published by: (Institut fuer Wirtschaftspolitik an der Universitaet zu Koeln), Lucius und Lucius Verlagsgesellschaft mbH, Gerokstr 51, Stuttgart, 70184, Germany. TEL 49-711-242060, FAX 49-711-242088, lucius@luciusverlag.com, http://www.luciusverlag.com. Ed. J Donges. Pub. Wulf von Lucius. adv.: page EUR 400; 120 x 205. Circ: 600. **Dist. by:** Brockhaus Commission, Kreidlerstr 9, Kornwestheim 70806, Germany. TEL 49-7154-132737, FAX 49-7154-132713.

330 DEU ISSN 0936-8566
ZENTRALER STELLENANZEIGER MARKT UND CHANCE. Text in German. 1955. w. looseleaf. free. **Document type:** *Government.*
Formerly: Markt und Chance
Published by: Bundesagentur fuer Arbeit, Zentralstelle fuer Arbeitsvermittlung, Villemombler Str 76, Bonn, 53123, Germany. TEL 49-69-71110, http://www.arbeitsagentur.de.

330 CHN
ZHEJIANG JINGJI/ZHEJIANG ECONOMICS. Text in Chinese. m.
Published by: (Zhejiang Sheng Jihua Jingji Weiyuanhui/Zhejiang Provincial Committee of Planned Economics), China International Book Trading Corp/Zhongguo Guoji Tushu Maoyi Zonggongsi, 35 Chegongzhuang Xilu, Haidian District, PO Box 399, Beijing, 100044, China. Ed. Zhu Jialiang.

330 CHN ISSN 1009-1378
ZHENGQUAN DAOKAN/SECURITIES HERALD. Text in Chinese. 1998. w. CNY 228 (effective 2004). **Document type:** *Journal, Academic/Scholarly.*
Formerly (until 1999): Zhengquan Shichang Xinxi (1007-8339)
Related titles: Online - full text ed.: (from East View Information Services); Alternate Frequency ed(s).: q. USD 199.20 (effective 2002).
Published by: Zhongguo Renmin Daxue, Shubao Zilio Zhongxin/Renmin University of China, Information Center for Social Server, Dongcheng-qu, 3, Zhangzizhong Lu, Beijing, 100007, China. TEL 86-10-64039458, FAX 86-10-64015080, kyes@163.net, http://www.confucius.cn.net/bkdetail.asp?fzt=X6. **Dist. in the US by:** China Publications Service, PO Box 49614, Chicago, IL 60649. TEL 312-288-3191, FAX 312-288-8570; **Dist. outside of China by:** China International Book Trading Corp, 35 Chegongzhuang Xilu, Haidian District, PO Box 399, Beijing 100044, China. TEL 86-10-68412045, FAX 86-10-68412023, cibtc@mail.cibtc.com.cn, http://www.cibtc.com.cn/.

330 CHN
ZHONGGUO CAIJING BAO/CHINA FINANCIAL AND ECONOMIC NEWS. Text in Chinese. 1991. d. (Mon.-Fri.). CNY 246 (effective 2004). **Document type:** *Newspaper, Trade.*
Address: 28, Fucheng Lu Jia, 14-Ceng, Xinzhi Dasha, Beijing, 100036, China. TEL 86-10-88191433, FAX 86-10-88191489, info@fec.com.cn, http://www.fec.com.cn/fecpaper/. **Dist. by:** China International Book Trading Corp, 35 Chegongzhuang Xilu, Haidian District, PO Box 399, Beijing 100044, China. TEL 86-10-68412045, FAX 86-10-68412023, cibtc@mail.cibtc.com.cn, http://www.cibtc.com.cn.

330 CHN ISSN 1003-1014
ZHONGGUO CHENGSHI JINRONG. Abbreviated title: China Urban Finance. Text in Chinese. 1987. m. **Document type:** *Journal, Academic/Scholarly.*
Related titles: Online - full text ed.: (from East View Information Services, WanFang Data Corp.).
Published by: Zhongguo Gongshang Yinhang/Industrial and Commercial Bank of China, Haidian-qu, 15, Cuiwei Lu, Beijing, 100036, China. TEL 86-10-68217798, FAX 86-10-68217520, http://zgcsjr.periodicals.net.cn/, http://www.icbc.com.cn/index.jsp.

330 621.9 CHN ISSN 1002-977X
ZHONGGUO JIDIAN GONGYE/CHINA MACHINERY & ELECTRONICS INDUSTRY. Text in Chinese. 1989. m. **Document type:** *Journal, Academic/Scholarly.*
Related titles: Online - full text ed.: (from East View Information Services, WanFang Data Corp.).
Published by: Guojia Jiexie Gongyeju/China Machinery Electronics Industry, Xicheng-qu, 46, Sanlihe Lu, Beijing, 100823, China. TEL 86-10-68595491, FAX 86-10-68595418, jdgy2000@263.net, http://zgjdgy.periodicals.net.cn/, http://www.chinamem.com.cn/.

330 CHN
ZHONGGUO JIHUA GUANLI/CHINESE JOURNAL OF PLANNED MANAGEMENT. Text in Chinese. m.
Published by: Guojia Jihua Weiyuanhui, Zhongguo Jihua Guanli Bianjibu, Sanlihe, Beijing, 100824, China. TEL 8091803. Ed. Fang Weizhong.

ZHONGGUO SHIYOU HE HUAGONG/CHINA PETROLEUM AND CHEMICAL INDUSTRY. see *PETROLEUM AND GAS*

330 CHN ISSN 1003-398X
ZHONGGUO WUJIA/CHINA PRICE. Text in Chinese. 1988. m. **Document type:** *Journal, Academic/Scholarly.*
Related titles: Online - full text ed.: (from East View Information Services, WanFang Data Corp.).
Address: Xicheng-qu, 11, Muxidi Beilijia, Guohong Daxia B-ceng, 1213-fang, Beijing, 100038, China. TEL 86-10-63908263, FAX 86-10-63908261, ZGWJ1213@126.com, http://zgwj.periodicals.net.cn/.

330 CHN ISSN 1671-6663
ZHONGGUO WULIU YU CAIGOU/CHINA LOGISTICS AND PURCHASING. Text in Chinese. 1990. s-m. CNY 8 newsstand/cover (effective 2004).
Former titles (until 2002): Zhongguo Wuzi Liutong (1007-4139); (until 1997): Zhongguo Wuzi Jingji (1002-6657)
Related titles: Online - full text ed.: (from East View Information Services).
Address: Level 5, No. 35 Zhu He Street, Zhong Shan District, Dalian, 116001, China. pub@xin56.com.cn, http://www.jctrans.com/genzong/qikan/cg.asp. **Dist. by:** China International Book Trading Corp, 35 Chegongzhuang Xilu, Haidian District, PO Box 399, Beijing 100044, China. TEL 86-10-68412045, FAX 86-10-68412023, cibtc@mail.cibtc.com.cn, http://www.cibtc.com.cn.

330 CHN
ZHONGGUO WUZI JINGJI/CHINESE COMMODITY ECONOMICS. Text in Chinese. m.
Published by: Wuzi Bu, 25 Yuetan Beijie, Beijing, 100834, China. TEL 8392749. Ed. Liu Suinian.

330 951.104 CHN ISSN 1004-9835
ZHONGGUO XINAN/SOUTHWEST CHINA. Text in Chinese, English. bi-m. **Description:** Covers Southwest China's economy and natural resources, investment environment and policies; introduces the area's beautiful sceneries, culture and customs.
Address: Sichuan Waishi Bangongshi, 4th Fl, No. 72, Renmin Nanlu 2 Duan, Chengdu, Sichuan 610016, China. TEL 86-28-6635186, FAX 86-28-6635194, TELEX 60168 SCFAO CN. **Dist. overseas by:** China International Book Trading Corp, 35 Chegongzhuang Xilu, Haidian District, PO Box 399, Beijing 100044, China.

630 USA
ZIFF DAVIS SMART BUSINESS (ONLINE EDITION). Text in English. m. **Document type:** *Magazine, Consumer.*
Media: Online - full text (from America Online, Inc., bigchalk, EBSCO Publishing, Gale Group, ProQuest Information & Learning). **Related titles:** ♦ Print ed.: Ziff Davis Smart Business (Print Edition). ISSN 1535-9891.
Published by: Ziff Davis Media Inc., 28 E 28th St, New York, NY 10016-7930. TEL 212-503-3500, 212-503-5435, FAX 212-503-4399, info@ziffdavis.com, http://www.smartbusinessmag.com/, http://www.zdnet.com.

330 RUS
ZOLOTOI ROG. Text in Russian. 104/yr. USD 465 in United States (effective 2000).
Indexed: RASB.
Address: Pr-t Krasnogo Znameni 10, Vladivostok, 690600, Russian Federation. TEL 4232-258722. Ed. E S Barkova. **Dist. by:** East View Information Services, 3020 Harbor Ln. N., Minneapolis, MN 55447. TEL 763-550-0961, FAX 763-559-2931.

330 CHE
ZUGER GEWERBE AKTUELL. Text in German. m.
Published by: Kuendig Druck AG, Bundesplatz 10, Zug, 6304, Switzerland. TEL 042-212353. Circ: 1,500.

330 IND
▼ **360 DEGREES.** Variant title: Three-Hundred and Sixty Degrees. Text in English. 2003. bi-m. **Document type:** *Journal, Academic/Scholarly.* **Description:** Covers global economic events; regular features include a profile on Indian state, industry or service, a pen sketch of a nation, opinion columns, events calendar listing major news of past month, and a characteristic profile of well known higher learning institute, and more.
Published by: Decorum, c/o S Narasimhan, DG Vaishnav College, Department of Business Economics, Arumbakkam, Madras, 600 106, India.

330 USA
680 BUSINESS JOURNAL. Text in English. 1996. 13/yr. USD 17 (effective 2000). adv. bk.rev.; software rev. charts; stat. back issues avail. **Document type:** *Newspaper.* **Description:** Provides timely local business news from along the 680 corridor in the San Francisco Bay area. Readers include executives, managers, and business owners of local companies.
Published by: Sloan Publications, 5964 Skylane Blvd, Ste B, Santa Rosa, CA 95403. TEL 707-579-2900, FAX 707-579-0188, busjrnlsm@aol.com, news@busjrnl.com, http://www.busjrnl.com. Ed. Ken Clark. Adv. contact Paul Pastorino. page USD 2,295; trim 15 x 11. Circ: 8,000 (controlled).

▼ **1010 MAGAZINE;** a lifetime of success. see *LIFESTYLE*

BUSINESS AND ECONOMICS—Abstracting, Bibliographies, Statistics

A B C BLUE BOOK: U S AND CANADIAN BUSINESS PUBLICATIONS. see *PUBLISHING AND BOOK TRADE*

A B C BLUE BOOK: U S AND CANADIAN MAGAZINES. see *PUBLISHING AND BOOK TRADE*

016 USA ISSN 1062-5127
Z7164.C81
A B I - INFORM. (American Business Information) Text in English. 1971. m. illus. reprints avail. **Document type:** *Abstract/Index.* **Description:** Indexes and abstracts 1,300 business and management journals. Full-text articles are available from 600 journals.
Media: CD-ROM (from ProQuest Information & Learning). **Related titles:** Magnetic Tape ed.; Online - full text ed.: (from Data-Star, Questel Orbit Inc., SilverPlatter Information, Inc.).
Published by: ProQuest Information & Learning, 300 N Zeeb Rd., PO Box 1346, Ann Arbor, MI 48106-1346. TEL 734-761-4700, 800-521-0600, info@il.proquest.com, http://www.proquest.com/products/pt-product-ABI.shtml.

330.9 GBR
A B R E E S. (Abstracts Russian and East European Series) Text in English. 1970. 6/yr. USD 699 (effective 2003). abstr.; bibl. index. 80 p./no.; back issues avail.; reprints avail. **Document type:** *Abstract/Index.* **Description:** Contains economic and business information covering Eastern Europe and Russia abstracted from newspapers and periodicals.
Formerly (until 1993): A B S E E S (Abstracts Soviet and East European Series) (0044-5622); Incorporates: C R E E S Soviet Press Abstracts; Soviet Studies. Information Supplement (0584-567X)
Indexed: CurCont, PROMT, RASB.
—CCC.
Published by: A B R E E S Ltd., Flat C, St Andrews House, 77c Roupell St, London, SE1 8SS, United Kingdom. FAX 44-20-72619710, abrees@btinternet.com, http://www.abrees.org. Pub. Dan Re'em. Circ: 200.

339 USA ISSN 1070-9169
HB235.U6 CODEN: CLIIEX
A C C R A COST OF LIVING INDEX. (Association for Applied Community Research) Text in English. 1968. q. USD 130 (effective 2000). index. **Document type:** *Abstract/Index.* **Description:** Data for more than 300 urban areas. Includes a composite index, six component indexes and average prices for 59 goods or services items.
Former titles (until 1992): Cost of Living Index (1048-2830); (until 1988): A C C R A Inter-City Cost of Living Index (0740-7130); (until 1982): Inter-City Cost of Living Indicators (0734-9319); Formed by the 1981 merger of: Cost of Living Indicators: Inter-City Index Report (0734-9327); Cost of Living Indicators: Price Report (0734-9335)
Indexed: SRI.
Published by: A C C R A, 3401 N Fairfax Dr 3B1, P O Box 407, Arlington, VA 22210-0407. TEL 703-522-4980, FAX 730-522-4985, san@aacra.org, sam@accra.org, http://www.accra.org, http://www.accra.org. Ed. C A Kasdorf III. R&P Kenneth E Poole. Circ: 2,900 (paid).

331.21021 USA
A F C O M'S ANNUAL SURVEY OF DATA PROCESSING OPERATIONS SALARIES. Text in English. 1981. a. USD 195. charts; stat. **Document type:** *Trade.* **Description:** Provides statistics on current salaries and anticipated increases for data processing operation positions, as well as information on budgeting, current trends in automation, and outsourcing.
Published by: (Association for Computer Operations Management), D C M S, Inc., 742 E Chapman Ave, Orange, CA 92666. TEL 714-997-7966, FAX 714-997-9743. Ed. Len Eckhaus.

330 UAE
ABU DHABI. DA'IRAT AT-TAKHTIT. AN-NASHRAH AS-SANAWIYYAH LI-AS'AR AT-TAJZI'AH/ABU DHABI. PLANNING ADMINISTRATION. ANNUAL BULLETIN OF RETAIL PRICES. Text in Arabic, English. 1978. a.
Published by: Department of Planning, Statistical Section, P O Box 12, Abu Dhabi, United Arab Emirates. TEL 971-727200, FAX 971-727749. Circ: 500 (controlled).

330 UAE
ABU DHABI. DA'IRAT AT-TAKHTIT. AN-NASHRAH ASH-SHAHRIYYAH LI-AS'AR AT-TAJZI'AH/ABU DHABI. PLANNING ADMINISTRATION. MONTHLY BULLETIN OF RETAIL PRICES. Text in Arabic, English. 1977. m. **Description:** Provides a comprehensive overview of all consumer prices in Abu Dhabi markets.

B

Published by: Department of Planning, Statistical Section, P O Box 12, Abu Dhabi, United Arab Emirates. TEL 971-2-727200, FAX 971-2-727749. Circ: (controlled).

330 UAE
ABU DHABI. FOREIGN TRADE STATISTICS/ABU DHABI. IHSA'IYYAT AL-TIJARAH AL-KHARIJIYYAH. Text in English. 1978. m. **Description:** Comprehensive statistical information on trade between Abu Dhabi and the world, based upon customs declarations.
Published by: Government of Abu Dhabi, P O Box 255, Abu Dhabi, United Arab Emirates. TEL 720700. Circ: (controlled).

016.657 GBR
HF5635
ACCOUNTING & FINANCE ABSTRACTS. (Also avail. as a section of: Emerald Management Reviews (print & online eds.)) Text in English. 1970. bi-m. EUR 6,497.88 in Europe; USD 6,119 in North America; AUD 3,979 in Australasia; GBP 4,554.88 in the UK & rest of the world (effective 2006).
Document type: *Abstract/Index.* **Description:** Contains abstracts of articles selected from more than 400 international management journals. Covers such topics as financial accounts, software, internal and external auditing, computer management, capital investment and data transmission.
Former titles (until 2001): Anbar Accounting & Finance Abstracts (0961-2742); (until 1991): Accounting & Data Processing Abstracts (0001-4796); Which superseded in part: Anbar Management Services Abstracts (0003-2794)
Related titles: CD-ROM ed.; Online - full text ed.
Indexed: ABIn.
—CCC.
Published by: (Institute of Chartered Accountants in England and Wales), Emerald Group Publishing Limited, 60-62 Toller Ln, Bradford, W Yorks BD8 9BY, United Kingdom. TEL 44-1274-777700, FAX 44-1274-785200, infomation@emeraldinsight.com, http://www.emeraldinsight.com/. Ed. David Pollitt. **Subscr. in Australia to:** Emerald Group Publishing Ltd., PO Box 1567, Toowong, QLD 4066, Australia. TEL 61-3870-7144, FAX 61-3870-4013; **Subscr. in N America to:** Emerald Group Publishing Ltd., 44 Brattle St, 4th Fl, Cambridge, MA 02138. TEL 617-497-2175, 888-622-0075, FAX 617-354-6875.

657 USA ISSN 1063-0287
Z7164.C81
ACCOUNTING AND TAX INDEX. Text in English. 1920. q. (plus a. cumulation). illus. reprints avail. **Document type:** *Abstract/Index.*
Formerly (until 1992): Accountants' Index. Supplement (0748-7975)
Related titles: CD-ROM ed.; Microform ed.: (from PQC); Online - full text ed.
—CCC.
Published by: ProQuest Information & Learning, 300 N Zeeb Rd., PO Box 1346, Ann Arbor, MI 48106-1346. TEL 313-761-4700, 800-521-0600, FAX 800-864-0019, ., http://www.umi.com. Ed. Paula McCoy.

061.657 USA ISSN 0007-7992
ACCOUNTING ARTICLES. Text in English. 1965. base vol. plus m. updates. looseleaf. USD 780 base vol(s). (effective 2004). bk.rev. abstr.; bibl. cum.index. **Document type:** *Abstract/Index.* **Description:** Offers monthly reporting on new articles and comments appearing in accounting and business periodicals—helping you stay up-to-date on the practices, analyses, opinions, and ideas of others in the field, and providing you with possible solutions to specific accounting situations.
Formerly: C C H Accounting Articles
Published by: C C H Inc., 2700 Lake Cook Rd, Riverwoods, IL 60015. TEL 847-267-7000, 800-449-6439, FAX 800-224-8299, cust_serv@cch.com, http://www.cch.com. Pub. Kevin Robert.

016.650 658 659 USA ISSN 1538-9456
HF5410
ADVERTISING, MARKETING, AND PUBLIC RELATIONS RESOURCES; an internet miniguide. Text in English. 2002. a. USD 95 newsstand/cover (effective 2002).
Published by: InternetMiniGuides.com, P.O. Box 220, Marco Island, FL 34146. TEL 941-434-5113, zillman@internetminiguides.com, http://www.internetminiguides.com. Pub. Marcus P. Zillma.

AFFAERSBANKERNA; samtliga bankaktiebolag. see *BUSINESS AND ECONOMICS—Banking And Finance*

331.125021 USA
AFFIRMATIVE EMPLOYMENT STATISTICS. Text in English. 1976. biennial. USD 35. **Document type:** *Government.*
Formerly (until 1980): Equal Employment Opportunity Statistics (0161-245X); Supersedes: Minority Group Employment in the Federal Government (0090-3531); (1966-1975): Study of Employment of Women in the Federal Government (0097-7764)
Related titles: Microfiche ed.
Published by: U.S. Office of Personnel Management, Personnel Systems and Oversight Group, Office of Workforce Information, 1900 E St, N W, Washington, DC 20415. TEL 703-487-4650, FAX 202-606-1719. **Subscr. to:** NTIS, 5285 Port Royal Rd, Springfield, VA 22161.

338.91 332 CIV ISSN 1561-2813
HG3378.A38
AFRICAN DEVELOPMENT BANK. COMPENDIUM OF STATISTICS ON BANK GROUP OPERATIONS/BANQUE AFRICAINE DE DEVELOPPEMENT. COMPENDIUM DE STATISTIQUES SUR LES OPERATIONS DU GROUPE DE LA BANQUE. Text in English, French. a.
Published by: African Development Bank, 01 BP 1387, Abidjan, Ivory Coast. TEL 225-20-44-44, FAX 225-20-49-48.

338.91 332 CIV ISSN 1561-2805
AFRICAN DEVELOPMENT BANK. SELECTED STATISTICS ON AFRICAN COUNTRIES/BANQUE AFRICAINE DE DEVELOPPEMENT. STATISTIQUES CHOISIES SUR LES PAYS AFRICAINS. Variant title: African Development Bank. Selected Statistics on Regional Member Countries. Text in English, French. a.
Published by: African Development Bank, 01 BP 1387, Abidjan, Ivory Coast. TEL 225-20-44-44, FAX 225-20-49-48.

310 USA
ALABAMA LABOR MARKET NEWS. Text in English. 1954. m. free. **Document type:** *Government.* **Description:** Provides information on non-agricultural wage and salary employment for the State of Alabama.
Published by: Department of Industrial Relations, Labor Market Information Division, Industrial Relations Bldg, Rm 427, 649 Monroe St, Montgomery, AL 36131. TEL 334-242-8855, FAX 334-242-2543, http://www.dir.state.al.us/alalmi.htm. Circ: 3,400.

331 USA ISSN 1063-3782
HD5725.A4
ALASKA EMPLOYMENT AND EARNINGS REPORT. Text in English. 1959. a. free. stat. **Document type:** *Government.*
Formerly: Alaska Statistical Quarterly
Published by: Department of Labor, Research and Analysis Section, PO Box 25501, Juneau, AK 99802-5501. TEL 907-465-4500, FAX 907-465-2101. Circ: 600.

330 CAN ISSN 0319-4264
HC117.A6
ALBERTA ECONOMIC ACCOUNTS✶. Text in English. 1976. a. **Document type:** *Government.*
Published by: Bureau of Statistics, Alberta Treasury, 9515 107 St, Edmonton, AB T5K 2C3, Canada. TEL 403-427-3058, FAX 403-427-0409, TELEX 037-43237.

316 DZA
ALGERIA. OFFICE NATIONAL DES STATISTIQUES. INDICES DES PRIX A LA CONSOMMATION. Text in French. m. DZD 500. back issues avail. **Document type:** *Government.*
Related titles: ◆ Series: Algeria. Office National des Statistiques. Donnees Statistiques. ISSN 1111-5939.
Published by: Office National des Statistiques/Al-Diwan al-Watani lil-Ihsa'iyat, 8 & 10 rue des Moussebiline, Ferhat Boussad, B P 202, Algiers, Algeria. TEL 213-64-77-90.

332.1 016 USA ISSN 0893-2468
AMERICAN BANKER INDEX. Variant title: Index to the American Banker. Text in English. 1971. m. cum.index. **Document type:** *Abstract/Index.*
Former titles (until 1982): Bell and Howell Newspaper Index to the American Banker (0195-6426); (until 1979): Index to the American Banker (0046-8916)
Related titles: Magnetic Tape ed.; Microform ed.: (from PQC); Online - full text ed.: (from The Dialog Corporation).
Published by: ProQuest Information & Learning, 300 N Zeeb Rd., PO Box 1346, Ann Arbor, MI 48106-1346. TEL 313-761-4700, 800-521-0600, FAX 800-864-0019, http://www.umi.com.

338.0029 GBR
AMERICAN COMPANIES: GUIDE TO SOURCES OF INFORMATION/AMERICANISCHE HANDELSGESELLSCHAFTEN: HANDBUCH DER INFORMATIONSQUELLEN/SOCIETES AMERICAINES: REPERTOIRE DES SOURCES DE DOCUMENTATION. Text in English. 1997. irreg. GBP 78, USD 156 (effective 2001). **Document type:** *Directory.* **Description:** Lists and describes in detail 1,500 information sources.
Published by: C.B.D. Research Ltd., 15 Wickham Rd, Beckenham, Kent BR3 5JS, United Kingdom. TEL 44-20-86507745, FAX 44-20-86500768, cbd@cbdresearch.com, http://www.glen.co.uk/cbd/, http://www.cbdresearch.com.

331.11 USA ISSN 1055-7628
HD4973
AMERICAN SALARIES AND WAGES SURVEY. Text in English. a., latest vol.7, 2003. USD 195 (effective 2004).
Related titles: Diskette ed.; Magnetic Tape ed.
Published by: Gale Group (Subsidiary of: Thomson Corporation), 27500 Drake Rd, Farmington Hills, MI 48331-3535. TEL 248-699-8061, 800-877-4253, FAX 248-699-4253, galeord@gale.com, http://www.gale.com. Ed. Helen S Fisher.

382 CUB
ANALISIS ANUAL DEL MERCADO DEL AZUCAR. Text in Spanish. 1981. a. CUP 14. **Description:** Covers market, prices and statistics on sugar. Analyzes present and future developments.
Published by: (Cuba. Ministerio del Comercio Exterior (MINCEX)), Empresa Cubazucar, Calle 23 No. 55,, Vedado, La Habana, Cuba. TEL 70-9742.

382 316 AGO ISSN 0066-1848
ANGOLA. DIRECCAO DOS SERVICOS DE ESTATISTICA. ESTATISTICAS DO COMERCIO EXTERNO. Text in Portuguese. 1938. irreg. stat.
Published by: Direccao dos Servicos de Estatistica, Luanda, 1215, Angola. Circ: 750.

ANNOTATED BIBLIOGRAPHY OF LITERATURE ON COOPERATIVE MOVEMENTS IN SOUTH-EAST ASIA. see *BIBLIOGRAPHIES*

382 316 TGO
ANNUAIRE DES STATISTIQUES DU COMMERCE EXTERIEUR DU TOGO. Text in French. a., latest 1977. XOF 4,000.
Published by: Direction de la Statistique, BP 118, Lome, Togo.

331.1021 IRL
ANNUAL EMPLOYMENT SURVEY (YEAR). Text in English. a.
Formerly: (Year) Employment Survey
—BLDSC (1085.140500).
Published by: Forfas, Wilton Park House, Wilton Place, Dublin, 2, Ireland. TEL 353-1-6073000, FAX 353-1-6073030, info@forfas.ie, http://www.forfas.ie.

330 USA
ANNUAL SURVEY OF MANUFACTURES. GEOGRAPHIC AREA STATISTICS. Text in English. a. stat. **Document type:** *Government.*
Related titles: Online - full content ed.
Published by: U.S. Bureau of the Census (Subsidiary of: U.S. Department of Commerce), Customer Services, Washington, DC 20233. TEL 310-457-4100, http://www.census.gov/mcd/asm-as3.html.

330 USA
ANNUAL SURVEY OF MANUFACTURES. STATISTICS FOR INDUSTRY GROUPS AND INDUSTRIES. Text in English. a. **Document type:** *Government.* **Description:** Contains estimates of the value of product shipments.
Formerly: Annual Survey of Manufactures. General Statistics for Industry Groups and Industries (0095-6279)
Related titles: Online - full content ed.
Published by: U.S. Bureau of the Census (Subsidiary of: U.S. Department of Commerce), Customer Services, Washington, DC 20233. TEL 310-457-4100, http://www.census.gov/mcd/asm-as1.html.

330 USA
ANNUAL SURVEY OF MANUFACTURES. VALUE OF PRODUCT SHIPMENTS/VALUE OF PRODUCT SHIPMENTS. Text in English. a. **Document type:** *Government.*
Related titles: Online - full content ed.
Published by: U.S. Bureau of the Census (Subsidiary of: U.S. Department of Commerce), Customer Services, Washington, DC 20233. http://www.census.gov/mcd/asm-as2.html.

330 ITA
ANNUARIO GEOECONOMICO MONDIALE; commercio e produzioni. Text in Italian. a. price varies. **Document type:** *Directory, Consumer.*
Published by: De Agostini Editore, Via G da Verrazzano 15, Novara, 28100, Italy. TEL 39-0321-4241, FAX 39-0321-424305, info@deagostini.it, http://www.deagostini.it.

332 MEX ISSN 0188-3860
HG5161
ANUARIO BURSATIL. Text in Spanish. a. **Description:** Contains facts and figures, statistical data of brokerage firms, international markets, foreign investment, price trends, corporate actions, and dividends. Includes information on Mexican securities listed on foreign markets.
Related titles: English ed.: Annual Stock Exchange Statistics Report.
Published by: Bolsa Mexicana de Valores, S.A. de C.V./Mexican Stock Exchange, Paseo de la Reforma 255, Mexico City, DF 06500, Mexico. TEL 52-5-7266794, FAX 52-5-7266836, cinforma@bmv.com.mx, http://www.bmv.com.mx/suscripciones.html.

382 URY ISSN 0797-8243
ANUARIO DE IMPORTACION - EXPORTACION DEL URUGUAY. Text in Spanish. 1957. a. USD 130 (effective 2001). adv. **Document type:** *Yearbook, Trade.*
Published by: Centro de Estadisticas Nacionales y Comercio Internacional del Uruguay, Misiones, 1361, Montevideo, 11000, Uruguay. TEL 598-2-952930, FAX 598-2-954578, cenci@adinet.com.uy. Ed. C Vertesi. Circ: 2,500.

382.09 318 VEN ISSN 1013-3771
ANUARIO DEL COMERCIO EXTERIOR DE VENEZUELA. (In 2 vols.: Exportaciones and Importaciones) Text in Spanish. a. (in 2 vols.). VEB 8,000. **Description:** Covers import-export statistics, international trade and manufacturing of products.
Former titles: Estadisticas del Comercio Exterior de Venezuela. Periodicidad Anual; Estadisticas del Comercio Exterior de Venezuela. Boletin

Published by: Oficina Central de Estadistica e Informatica, Apdo. de Correos 4593, Carmeliatas, Caracas, DF 1010A, Venezuela. TEL 58-2-782-11-33, FAX 58-2-781-13-80, OCEI@platino.gov.ve, ocei@platino.gov.ve, http://www.OCEI.gov.ve, http://www.ocei.gov.ve.

382 318 GTM ISSN 0570-426X
ANUARIO ESTADISTICO CENTROAMERICANO DE COMERCIO EXTERIOR. Text in Spanish. 1964. a. USD 15.
Published by: Secretaria Permanente del Tratado General de Integracion Economica Centroamericana, 4a Avda. 10-25, ZONA, 14, PO Box 1237, Guatemala City, 01901, Guatemala. TEL 502-3682151, FAX 502-3681071, sieca@pronet.net.gt.

382 318 MEX
ANUARIO ESTADISTICO DE COMERCIO EXTERIOR DE LOS ESTADOS UNIDOS MEXICANOS. Text in Spanish. 1941-1979; resumed. a. MXP 120.
Published by: Instituto Nacional de Estadistica, Geografia e Informatica, Secretaria de Programacion y Presupuesto, Prol. Heroe de Nacozari 2301 Sur, Puerta 11, Acceso, Aguascalientes, 20270, Mexico. TEL 52-4-918-1948, FAX 52-4-918-0739. Circ: 500.

330.982021 ARG
ARGENTINA. INSTITUTO NACIONAL DE ESTADISTICA Y CENSOS. CENSO NACIONAL ECONOMICO (YEAR). AVANCE DE RESULTADOS. Text in Spanish. 1994. irreg. ARS 15, USD 25 (effective 1999). **Document type:** *Government.*
Related titles: Diskette ed.
Published by: Instituto Nacional de Estadistica y Censos, Avda. Presidente Julio A. Roca, 615 P B, Capital Federal, Buenos Aires 1067, Argentina. TEL 54-114-3499662, FAX 54-114-3499650, ces@indec.mecon.ar, http://www.indec.mecon.ar.

330.982021 ARG
ARGENTINA. INSTITUTO NACIONAL DE ESTADISTICA Y CENSOS. CENSO NACIONAL ECONOMICO (YEAR). SERIE A. RESULTADOS DEFINITIVOS. Text in Spanish. 1996. irreg. (in 7 vols.). ARS 30, USD 45 (effective 1999). **Document type:** *Government.* **Description:** Contains data on all economic aspects of the country.
Published by: Instituto Nacional de Estadistica y Censos, Avda. Presidente Julio A. Roca, 615 P B, Capital Federal, Buenos Aires 1067, Argentina. TEL 54-114-3499662, FAX 54-114-3499621, ces@indec.mecon.ar, http://www.indec.mecon.ar.

338.021 ARG
ARGENTINA. INSTITUTO NACIONAL DE ESTADISTICA Y CENSOS. ENCUESTA INDUSTRIAL ANUAL (YEAR). Text in Spanish. 1995. a. ARS 15, USD 25 (effective 1999).
Description: Presents statistical data on several Argentinean industries.
Published by: Instituto Nacional de Estadistica y Censos, Avda. Presidente Julio A. Roca, 615 P B, Capital Federal, Buenos Aires 1067, Argentina. TEL 54-114-3499662, FAX 54-114-3499650, ces@indec.mecon.ar, http://www.indec.mecon.ar.

338.528 ARG
ARGENTINA. INSTITUTO NACIONAL DE ESTADISTICA Y CENSOS. ESTADISTICA DE PRODUCTOS INDUSTRIALES. Text in Spanish. q. ARS 100, USD 140; ARS 7 newsstand/cover; USD 15 newsstand/cover in United States; includes Informa. **Document type:** *Government.* **Description:** Includes statistical data for the main products of the nation's industry.
Published by: Instituto Nacional de Estadistica y Censos, Avda. Presidente Julio A. Roca, 615 P B, Capital Federal, Buenos Aires 1067, Argentina. TEL 54-114-3499662, FAX 54-114-3499621, ces@indec.mecon.ar, http://www.indec.mecon.ar.

331.21 ARG
ARGENTINA. INSTITUTO NACIONAL DE ESTADISTICA Y CENSOS. SERIE ESTRUCTURA OCCUPACIONAL. Text in Spanish. 1997. irreg., latest vol.6, 1998. ARS 10, USD 20 (effective 1999). **Document type:** *Government.* **Description:** Presents information on occupational characteristics in the urban centers.
Published by: Instituto Nacional de Estadistica y Censos, Avda. Presidente Julio A. Roca, 615 P B, Capital Federal, Buenos Aires 1067, Argentina. TEL 54-114-3499662, FAX 54-114-3499621, ces@indec.mecon.ar, http://www.indec.mecon.ar.

338.0021 ARG
ARGENTINA. INSTITUTO NACIONAL DE ESTADISTICA Y CENSOS. SERIE NOMENCLADORES Y CORRESPONDENCIAS. Text in Spanish. 1997. irreg., latest vol.5, 1998. ARS 30, USD 45 (effective 1999). **Document type:** *Government.* **Description:** Incorporatesinto the four-digit classification system of the United Nations, the fifth national digit of the branches of industrial manufacturing.
Related titles: Diskette ed.
Published by: Instituto Nacional de Estadistica y Censos, Avda. Presidente Julio A. Roca, 615 P B, Capital Federal, Buenos Aires 1067, Argentina. TEL 54-114-3499662, FAX 54-114-3499621, ces@indec.mecon.ar, http://www.indec.mecon.ar.

330.9 USA ISSN 1045-4195
HA241
ARIZONA STATISTICAL ABSTRACT. Text in English. 1976. irreg., latest 1993. USD 27.95 domestic; USD 36 foreign (effective 2000). **Description:** Aims to develop and disseminate economic and socioeconomic data on the state of Arizona in quantitative terms over time; to permit comparison of the economic and social attainments of subareas of the state: cities, counties and metropolitan areas; and to relate Arizona's activities to those of neighboring southwestern states and to the nation as a whole.
Published by: University of Arizona, College of Business and Public Administration, Economic and Business Research Program, McClelland Hall 204, Tucson, AZ 85721. TEL 520-621-2155, FAX 520-621-2150, pmontoya@bpa.arizona.edu.

310 USA
ARKANSAS. EMPLOYMENT SECURITY DEPARTMENT. STATISTICAL REVIEW. Text in English. q. free.
Formerly: Arkansas. Department of Labor. Employment Security Division. Statistical Review
Published by: (Arkansas. Research and Information Section), Employment Security Department, PO Box 2981, Little Rock, AR 72203-2981. TEL 501-682-3119.

330 IND ISSN 0970-8162
Z7165.I6
ARTHA SUCHI. Text in English. 1983. q. INR 300 domestic; USD 30 foreign (effective Jun. 2000). index, cum.index. **Document type:** *Abstract/Index.* **Description:** A computerized index to journal articles and working papers in the field of Indian economics.
Published by: (Publication Division), National Council of Applied Economic Research, Parisila Bhawan, 11 Indraprastha Estate, New Delhi, 110 002, India. TEL 91-11-3317861, FAX 91-11-3327164. Ed. N Joseph Sebastian. Circ: 120.

338.0029 GBR ISSN 1352-3198
HF5381.A1
ASIAN AND AUSTRALASIAN COMPANIES. Text in English. 1993. irreg. GBP 87, USD 174 (effective 2001). **Document type:** *Directory.* **Description:** Compiles 2,000 sources of company information available in Asia, Australia, and Oceania.
Published by: C.B.D. Research Ltd., 15 Wickham Rd, Beckenham, Kent BR3 5JS, United Kingdom. TEL 44-20-86507745, FAX 44-20-86500768, cbd@cbdresearch.com, http://www.glen.co.uk/cbd, http://www.cbdresearch.com. **Dist. in the U.S. by:** Hoover's Inc., 6448 Hwy 290 E, Ste E 104, Austin, TX 78723.

332.1 PHL ISSN 0116-2799
HC411
ASIAN DEVELOPMENT BANK. STATISTICAL REPORT SERIES. Text in English. irreg., latest vol.15, 1991.
Published by: (Economics and Development Resource Center), Asian Development Bank, Publications Unit, P.O. Box 789, Manila, 0980, Philippines. adbpub@adb.org, http://www.adb.org.

ASIAN INSTITUTE OF TECHNOLOGY. ABSTRACTS ON MANAGEMENT OF TECHNOLOGY AND INTERNATIONAL BUSINESS. see *TECHNOLOGY: COMPREHENSIVE WORKS—Abstracting, Bibliographies, Statistics*

658 THA
ASIAN INSTITUTE OF TECHNOLOGY. M O T I C MONOGRAPHS. Text in English. 1990. irreg. price varies. **Document type:** *Monographic series, Academic/Scholarly.*
Published by: (Management of Technology Information Center), Asian Institute of Technology, School of Management, Klong Luang, PO Box 4, Pathum Thani, 12120, Thailand. TEL 66-2-524-5610, FAX 66-2-524-6132, marrof@ait.ac.th, http://www.ait.ac.th.

016.33891 AUS ISSN 0818-9935
HC411 CODEN: AELIEB
ASIAN - PACIFIC ECONOMIC LITERATURE. Text in English. 1987. s-a. GBP 78 combined subscription in Australia & New Zealand to individuals print & online eds.; USD 56 combined subscription in the Americas to individuals & Caribbean, print & online eds.; EUR 57 combined subscription in Europe to individuals print & online eds.; GBP 38 combined subscription elsewhere to individuals print & online eds.; GBP 81 combined subscription in Australia & New Zealand to institutions print & online eds.; USD 194 combined subscription in the Americas to institutions & Caribbean, print & online eds.; GBP 135 combined subscription elsewhere to institutions print & online eds. (effective 2006). bk.rev. Index. **Document type:** *Abstract/Index.* **Description:** Covers economic and related development topics in Hong Kong, Indonesia, Taiwan, mainland China, and other countries of the region.
Related titles: Online - full text ed.: ISSN 1467-8411. GBP 77 in Australia & New Zealand to institutions; USD 184 in the Americas to institutions & Caribbean; GBP 128 elsewhere to institutions (effective 2006) (from Blackwell Synergy, EBSCO Publishing, Gale Group, IngentaConnect, O C L C Online Computer Library Center, Inc., Swets Information Services).
Indexed: ABIn, BAS, GEOBASE, IBSS, JEL, RASB, SWA. —BLDSC (1742.705210), IE, Infotrieve, ingenta. **CCC.**
Published by: (Australian National University, Research School of Pacific and Asian Studies GBR, Economics Division GBR), Blackwell Publishing Asia (Subsidiary of: Blackwell Publishing Ltd.), 550 Swanston St, Carlton South, VIC 3053, Australia. TEL 61-383591011, FAX 61-383591120, subs@blackwellpublishingasia.com, http://www.blackwellpublishing.com/journals/APEL. Ed. Ron Duncan.
Subscr. to: Blackwell Publishing Ltd., Journal Customer Services, 9600 Garsington Rd, PO Box 1354, Oxford OX4 2XG, United Kingdom. TEL 44-1865-778315, FAX 44-1865-471775.

330.021 AUS
AUSTRALIA. BUREAU OF STATISTICS. A GUIDE TO THE AUSTRALIAN NATIONAL ACCOUNTS. Text in English. 1990. irreg., latest 1994. AUD 10 (effective 1998). **Document type:** *Government.* **Description:** Contains a brief outline of the most important features of the national accounts.
Published by: Australian Bureau of Statistics, PO Box 10, Belconnen, ACT 2616, Australia. TEL 61-2-6252-5249, FAX 61-2-6252-6778, http://www.abs.gov.au.

339.021 AUS
AUSTRALIA. BUREAU OF STATISTICS. A GUIDE TO THE CONSUMER INDEX. Text in English. 1978. irreg., latest 1993. AUD 10. **Document type:** *Government.*
Published by: Australian Bureau of Statistics, PO Box 10, Belconnen, ACT 2616, Australia. TEL 61-2-6252-5249, FAX 61-2-6252-6778, http://www.abs.gov.au.

339.021 AUS
AUSTRALIA. BUREAU OF STATISTICS. A GUIDE TO THE CONSUMER PRICE INDEX. Text in English. 1978. irreg., latest 2000, 14th Series. AUD 10 (effective 2003). **Document type:** *Government.*
Published by: Australian Bureau of Statistics, PO Box 10, Belconnen, ACT 2616, Australia. TEL 61-2-6252-5249, FAX 61-2-6252-6778, http://www.abs.gov.au.

310.021 AUS
AUSTRALIA. BUREAU OF STATISTICS. A PORTRAIT OF AUSTRALIAN EXPORTERS: A REPORT BASED ON THE BUSINESS LONGITUDINAL SURVEY. Text in English. 1998. irreg. AUD 25 (effective 2003). **Document type:** *Government.*
Formerly: Australia. Bureau of Statistics. Profiles of Australian Exporters
Published by: Australian Bureau of Statistics, PO Box 10, Belconnen, ACT 2616, Australia. TEL 61-2-6252-5249, FAX 61-2-6252-6778, http://www.abs.gov.au.

339.021 AUS
AUSTRALIA. BUREAU OF STATISTICS. A PROVISIONAL FRAMEWORK FOR HOUSEHOLD INCOME, CONSUMPTION, SAVING AND WEALTH. Text in English. 1995. irreg. AUD 30 (effective 1998). **Document type:** *Government.*
Published by: Australian Bureau of Statistics, PO Box 10, Belconnen, ACT 2616, Australia. TEL 61-2-6252-5249, FAX 61-2-6252-6778, http://www.abs.gov.au.

657.021 AUS
AUSTRALIA. BUREAU OF STATISTICS. ACCOUNTING SERVICES, AUSTRALIA. Text in English. 1993. irreg., latest 1995. AUD 19.50 (effective 2003). **Document type:** *Government.*
Formerly: Australia. Bureau of Statistics. Legal and Accounting Services, Australia
Published by: Australian Bureau of Statistics, PO Box 10, Belconnen, ACT 2616, Australia. TEL 61-2-6252-5249, FAX 61-2-6252-6778, http://www.abs.gov.au.

332.021 AUS
AUSTRALIA. BUREAU OF STATISTICS. ANNUAL STATISTICS ON FINANCIAL INSTITUTIONS ON HARDCOPY. Text in English. 1990. a., latest 1998. AUD 47 (effective 2003). **Document type:** *Government.*
Formerly: Australia. Bureau of Statistics. Annual Statistics on Financial Institutions
Published by: Australian Bureau of Statistics, PO Box 10, Belconnen, ACT 2616, Australia. TEL 61-2-6252-5249, FAX 61-2-6252-6778, http://www.abs.gov.au.

339.48021 AUS ISSN 1329-2056
AUSTRALIA. BUREAU OF STATISTICS. APPARENT CONSUMPTION OF FOODSTUFFS, AUSTRALIA. Text in English. 1947. a., latest 1996. AUD 20 (effective 2003). **Document type:** *Government.* **Description:** Presents a general overview of the supply and utilization of approximately 130 basic foodstuffs available for consumption in Australia.
Supersedes in part: Australia. Bureau of Statistics. Apparent Consumption of Foodstuffs and Nutrients. Australia (1031-0533)
Media: Duplicated (not offset).

Published by: Australian Bureau of Statistics, PO Box 10, Belconnen, ACT 2616, Australia. TEL 61-2-6252-5249, FAX 61-2-6252-6778, http://www.abs.gov.au. Circ: 443.

332.021 AUS
AUSTRALIA. BUREAU OF STATISTICS. ASSETS AND LIABILITIES OF FRIENDLY SOCIETIES, AUSTRALIA. Text in English. 1995. q. AUD 47 (effective 2003).
Published by: Australian Bureau of Statistics, PO Box 10, Belconnen, ACT 2616, Australia. TEL 61-2-6252-5249, FAX 61-2-6252-6778, http://www.abs.gov.au.

339.021 AUS
AUSTRALIA. BUREAU OF STATISTICS. AUSPEND. Text in English. irreg. price varies. **Document type:** *Government.* **Description:** Provides estimates of average household expenditure on 380 commodities for small geographical areas.
Published by: Australian Bureau of Statistics, PO Box 10, Belconnen, ACT 2616, Australia. TEL 61-2-6252-5249, FAX 61-2-6252-6778, http://www.abs.gov.au.

330.021 AUS
AUSTRALIA. BUREAU OF STATISTICS. AUSTRALIAN AND NEW ZEALAND STANDARD INDUSTRIAL CLASSIFICATION. Text in English. 1993. irreg., latest 1993. AUD 75 (effective 2003). **Document type:** *Government.*
Related titles: Diskette ed.
Published by: Australian Bureau of Statistics, PO Box 10, Belconnen, ACT 2616, Australia. TEL 61-2-6252-5249, FAX 61-2-6252-6778, http://www.abs.gov.au.

330.021 AUS
AUSTRALIA. BUREAU OF STATISTICS. AUSTRALIAN AND NEW ZEALAND STANDARD INDUSTRIAL CLASSIFICATION - ALPHABETIC CODING INDEX. Text in English. 1994. irreg., latest 1994. AUD 50 (effective 2003). **Document type:** *Government.*
Published by: Australian Bureau of Statistics, PO Box 10, Belconnen, ACT 2616, Australia. TEL 61-2-6252-5249, FAX 61-2-6252-6778, http://www.abs.gov.au.

330.021 AUS
AUSTRALIA. BUREAU OF STATISTICS. AUSTRALIAN AND NEW ZEALAND STANDARD INDUSTRIAL CLASSIFICATION CODER. Text in English. 1995. irreg., latest 1998. AUD 125 (effective 2003). **Document type:** *Government.*
Media: Diskette.
Published by: Australian Bureau of Statistics, PO Box 10, Belconnen, ACT 2616, Australia. TEL 61-2-6252-5249, FAX 61-2-6252-6778, http://www.abs.gov.au.

338.021 AUS
AUSTRALIA. BUREAU OF STATISTICS. AUSTRALIAN AND NEW ZEALAND STANDARD PRODUCT CLASSIFICATION - WEBSITE VERSION. Text in English. 1990. irreg., latest 2001. free. **Document type:** *Government.* **Description:** Covers all goods and services and uses the Central Product Classification as its framework.
Formerly (until 2001): Australia. Bureau of Statistics. Australian and New Zealand Standard Commodity Classification (Print)
Media: Online - full content. **Related titles:** Diskette ed.
Published by: Australian Bureau of Statistics, PO Box 10, Belconnen, ACT 2616, Australia. TEL 61-2-6252-5249, FAX 61-2-6252-6778, http://www.abs.gov.au.

330.9021 AUS
AUSTRALIA. BUREAU OF STATISTICS. AUSTRALIAN BUSINESS REGISTER, A N Z S I C INDUSTRY CLASS BY STATE. Text in English. 2000. irreg., latest 2002. price varies. **Document type:** *Government.*
Published by: Australian Bureau of Statistics, PO Box 10, Belconnen, ACT 2616, Australia. http://www.abs.gov.au.

330.021 AUS ISSN 1446-8654
AUSTRALIA. BUREAU OF STATISTICS. AUSTRALIAN CAPITAL TERRITORY STATISTICAL INDICATORS. Text in English. 1993. q. AUD 26 (effective 2003). **Document type:** *Government.* **Description:** A monthly summary of business related statistics for the Australian Capital Territory, with Australian and other State comparisons.
Formerly: Australia. Bureau of Statistics. Australian Capital Territory Business Indicators (1320-808X)
Published by: Australian Bureau of Statistics, PO Box 10, Belconnen, ACT 2616, Australia. TEL 61-2-6207-0326, FAX 61-2-6207-0282, http://www.abs.gov.au.

330.021 AUS
AUSTRALIA. BUREAU OF STATISTICS. AUSTRALIAN CONSUMER PRICE INDEX: CONCEPTS, SOURCES AND METHODS. Text in English. 1984. irreg., latest 1995. AUD 30. **Document type:** *Government.*
Published by: Australian Bureau of Statistics, PO Box 10, Belconnen, ACT 2616, Australia. TEL 61-2-6252-5249, FAX 61-2-6252-6778, http://www.abs.gov.au.

330.021 AUS ISSN 1035-865X
HC601
AUSTRALIA. BUREAU OF STATISTICS. AUSTRALIAN ECONOMIC INDICATORS. Text in English. 1991. m. AUD 36 newsstand/cover (effective 2003). **Document type:** *Government.* **Description:** Presents a statistical summary of recent developments in the Australian economy.
Incorporates (1937-1996): Monthly Summary of Statistics, Australia (0727-1689); Which was formerly: Monthly Review of Business Statistics (0027-0539)
—IE.
Published by: Australian Bureau of Statistics, PO Box 10, Belconnen, ACT 2616, Australia. TEL 61-2-6252-5249, FAX 61-2-6252-6778, http://www.abs.gov.au.

382.021 AUS
AUSTRALIA. BUREAU OF STATISTICS. AUSTRALIAN HARMONIZED EXPORT COMMODITY CLASSIFICATION. Text in English. 1988. irreg., latest 2002. AUD 117 (effective 2003). **Document type:** *Government.*
Published by: Australian Bureau of Statistics, PO Box 10, Belconnen, ACT 2616, Australia. TEL 61-2-6252-5249, FAX 61-2-6252-6778, http://www.abs.gov.au.

330.9021 AUS ISSN 1444-8637
AUSTRALIA. BUREAU OF STATISTICS. AUSTRALIAN INDUSTRY. Text in English. 1999. a. AUD 24 (effective 2003). **Document type:** *Government.*
Published by: Australian Bureau of Statistics, PO Box 10, Belconnen, ACT 2616, Australia. http://www.abs.gov.au.

331.021 AUS ISSN 1446-540X
HD5850
▼ **AUSTRALIA. BUREAU OF STATISTICS. AUSTRALIAN LABOUR MARKET STATISTICS.** Text in English. 2003 (Apr.). q. AUD 30 (effective 2003). stat. **Document type:** *Government.*
Published by: Australian Bureau of Statistics, PO Box 10, Belconnen, ACT 2616, Australia. TEL 61-2-6252-5249, FAX 61-2-6252-6778, http://www.abs.gov.au.

332.021 AUS ISSN 1038-4286
AUSTRALIA. BUREAU OF STATISTICS. AUSTRALIAN NATIONAL ACCOUNTS: FINANCIAL ACCOUNTS. Text in English. q. AUD 27 newsstand/cover (effective 2003). **Document type:** *Government.* **Description:** Contains information about the level (stock) of financial assets and liabilities of each sector of the economy, as well as information about financial transactions between the sectors.
Supersedes (in 1989): Information Paper: Australian National Accounts: Flow of Funds, Developmental Estimates (1034-0475)
Published by: Australian Bureau of Statistics, PO Box 10, Belconnen, ACT 2616, Australia. TEL 61-2-6252-5249, FAX 61-2-6252-6778, http://www.abs.gov.au.

330.021 AUS ISSN 0727-9434
AUSTRALIA. BUREAU OF STATISTICS. AUSTRALIAN NATIONAL ACCOUNTS: INPUT-OUTPUT TABLES. Text in English. 1958. a. AUD 29 (effective 2003). **Document type:** *Government.* **Description:** Provides input by industry and output by commodity group, industry by industry flow matrices, direct and total requirement coefficient matrices.
Formerly (until 1989): Australian National Accounts: Input-Output Multipliers
Published by: Australian Bureau of Statistics, PO Box 10, Belconnen, ACT 2616, Australia. TEL 61-2-6252-5249, FAX 61-2-6252-6778, http://www.abs.gov.au.

330.021 AUS ISSN 0727-1476
AUSTRALIA. BUREAU OF STATISTICS. AUSTRALIAN NATIONAL ACCOUNTS: INPUT-OUTPUT TABLES (PRODUCT DETAILS). Text in English. 1968. a. AUD 25 (effective 2003). **Document type:** *Government.* **Description:** Provides detailed information about the input-output commodity classification, value of Australian production, and imports and exports for over 1,000 commodities.
Published by: Australian Bureau of Statistics, PO Box 10, Belconnen, ACT 2616, Australia. TEL 61-2-6252-5249, FAX 61-2-6252-6778, http://www.abs.gov.au.

339.021 AUS ISSN 1322-2902
AUSTRALIA. BUREAU OF STATISTICS. AUSTRALIAN NATIONAL ACCOUNTS: NATIONAL INCOME, EXPENDITURE AND PRODUCT. Text in English. 1960. q. AUD 30 newsstand/cover (effective 2003). charts. **Document type:** *Government.* **Description:** Presents detailed quarterly national accounts at both current prices and average prices in both original and seasonally adjusted terms.
Incorporates (1988-1992): Australian National Accounts: Gross Product, Employment and Hours Worked (1030-9047); Former titles: Australian National Accounts: National Income and Expenditure (Quarterly) (1031-5128); Quarterly Estimates of National Income and Expenditure, Australia (1030-0988); National Income and Expenditure, Quarterly Estimates (0004-8577)
Media: Duplicated (not offset).
Published by: Australian Bureau of Statistics, PO Box 10, Belconnen, ACT 2616, Australia. TEL 61-2-6252-5249, FAX 61-2-6252-6778, http://www.abs.gov.au. Circ: 786.

332.021 AUS
AUSTRALIA. BUREAU OF STATISTICS. AUSTRALIAN NATIONAL ACCOUNTS: NON-PROFIT INSTITUTIONS SATELLITE ACCOUNT. Text in English. 2000. irreg. AUD 23 (effective 2003). stat. **Document type:** *Government.*
Published by: Australian Bureau of Statistics, PO Box 10, Belconnen, ACT 2616, Australia. TEL 61-2-6252-5249, FAX 61-2-6252-6778, http://www.abs.gov.au.

330.021 310 AUS ISSN 0819-7423
AUSTRALIA. BUREAU OF STATISTICS. AUSTRALIAN NATIONAL ACCOUNTS: STATE ACCOUNTS (ANNUAL). Text in English. 1985. a. AUD 26 (effective 2003). **Document type:** *Government.* **Description:** Contains dissections for the last 12 years of various national accounting aggregates by state and territory, including household income, private consumption expenditure, farm income, prices, wages and gross operating surplus by industry.
Published by: Australian Bureau of Statistics, PO Box 10, Belconnen, ACT 2616, Australia. TEL 61-2-6252-5249, FAX 61-2-6252-6778, http://www.abs.gov.au.

332.021 AUS
AUSTRALIA. BUREAU OF STATISTICS. AUSTRALIAN STANDARD RESEARCH CLASSIFICATION. Text in English. 1992. irreg., latest 1998. AUD 46 (effective 2003). **Document type:** *Government.*
Published by: Australian Bureau of Statistics, PO Box 10, Belconnen, ACT 2616, Australia. TEL 61-2-6252-5249, FAX 61-2-6252-6778, http://www.abs.gov.au.

339.021 AUS ISSN 1441-1075
HC601.A1
AUSTRALIA. BUREAU OF STATISTICS. AUSTRALIAN SYSTEM OF NATIONAL ACCOUNTS. Text in English. 1948. a. AUD 33 (effective 2003). illus. **Document type:** *Government.* **Description:** Presents detailed information about Australian national accounts, including income components of gross domestic product, corporate trading enterprises, and financial enterprises.
Former titles: Australia. Bureau of Statistics. Australian National Accounts: National Income, Expenditure and Products (1322-5006); Australia. Bureau of Statistics. Australian National Accounts: National Income and Expenditure (Annual) (0067-1983)
Published by: Australian Bureau of Statistics, PO Box 10, Belconnen, ACT 2616, Australia. TEL 61-2-6252-5249, FAX 61-2-6252-6778, http://www.abs.gov.au. Circ: 676.

339.021 AUS
AUSTRALIA. BUREAU OF STATISTICS. AUSTRALIAN SYSTEM OF NATIONAL ACCOUNTS: CONCEPTS, SOURCES AND METHODS. Text in English. 1981. irreg., latest 2000. AUD 75 (effective 2003).
Formerly: Australia. Bureau of Statistics. Australian National Accounts: Concepts, Sources and Methods
Published by: Australian Bureau of Statistics, PO Box 10, Belconnen, ACT 2616, Australia. TEL 61-2-6252-5249, FAX 61-2-6252-6778, http://www.abs.gov.au.

332.021 AUS ISSN 0812-5546
AUSTRALIA. BUREAU OF STATISTICS. AVERAGE RETAIL PRICES OF SELECTED ITEMS, EIGHT CAPITAL CITIES. Text in English. 1962. q. AUD 18.50 newsstand/cover (effective 2003). **Document type:** *Government.* **Description:** Contains average retail prices of selected items for each of the six state capitals, and Canberra and Darwin.
Published by: Australian Bureau of Statistics, PO Box 10, Belconnen, ACT 2616, Australia. TEL 61-2-6252-5249, FAX 61-2-6252-6778, http://www.abs.gov.au.

331.21021 AUS ISSN 1444-903X
AUSTRALIA. BUREAU OF STATISTICS. AVERAGE WEEKLY EARNINGS, AUSTRALIA. Text in English. 1967. q. AUD 22 per issue (effective 2003). **Document type:** *Government.*
Former titles: Australia. Bureau of Statistics. Average Weekly Earnings, States and Australia; Average Weekly Earnings, Australia
Published by: Australian Bureau of Statistics, PO Box 10, Belconnen, ACT 2616, Australia. TEL 61-2-6252-5249, FAX 61-2-6252-6778, http://www.abs.gov.au.

331.21021 AUS ISSN 1031-0584
AUSTRALIA. BUREAU OF STATISTICS. AVERAGE WEEKLY EARNINGS, AUSTRALIA, PRELIMINARY. Text in English. 1977. q. AUD 17 per issue (effective 2001). **Document type:** *Government.* **Description:** Contains preliminary estimates for Australia of average weekly ordinary time earnings and average weekly total earnings for full-time adult employees and average weekly total earnings for all employees.
Formerly: Average Weekly Earnings, Preliminary
Published by: Australian Bureau of Statistics, PO Box 10, Belconnen, ACT 2616, Australia. TEL 61-2-6252-5249, FAX 61-2-6252-6778, http://www.abs.gov.au.

336.021 AUS ISSN 1329-508X
HG5891
AUSTRALIA. BUREAU OF STATISTICS. BALANCE OF PAYMENTS AND INTERNATIONAL INVESTMENT POSITION, AUSTRALIA (QUARTERLY). Text in English. 1997. q. AUD 26 newsstand/cover (effective 2003). **Document type:** *Government.* **Description:** Provides detailed quarterly balance of payments tables on current and capital transactions.
Formed by the merger of (1961-1997): Australia. Bureau of Statistics. Balance of Payments, Australia (Quarterly) (0819-114X); (1976-1997): Australia. Bureau of Statistics. International Investment Position, Australia (Quarterly) (1037-8774); Which was formerly: Foreign Investment, Australia (0819-0925); Incorporated (1976-1991): Foreign Investment, Australia. Preliminary (0819-5900)
Related titles: Diskette ed.
Published by: Australian Bureau of Statistics, PO Box 10, Belconnen, ACT 2616, Australia. TEL 61-2-6252-5249, FAX 61-2-6252-6778, http://www.abs.gov.au.

336.021 AUS
AUSTRALIA. BUREAU OF STATISTICS. BALANCE OF PAYMENTS AND INTERNATIONAL INVESTMENT POSITION, AUSTRALIA - CONCEPTS, SOURCES AND METHODS. Text in English. 1981. irreg., latest 1998. AUD 40 (effective 2002). **Document type:** *Government.* **Description:** Provides a comprehensive description of the concepts and structure of the Australian balance of payments and of the data sources and methods used to compile the statistics contained in Australian balance of payments publications.
Published by: Australian Bureau of Statistics, PO Box 10, Belconnen, ACT 2616, Australia. TEL 61-2-6252-5249, FAX 61-2-6252-6778, http://www.abs.gov.au.

339.021 AUS
AUSTRALIA. BUREAU OF STATISTICS. BALANCE OF PAYMENTS, AUSTRALIA - QUARTERLY FORWARD SEASONAL FACTORS SERVICE. Text in English. irreg. AUD 111 (effective 2002). **Document type:** *Government.*
Published by: Australian Bureau of Statistics, PO Box 10, Belconnen, ACT 2616, Australia. TEL 61-2-6252-5249, FAX 61-2-6252-6778, http://www.abs.gov.au.

339.021 AUS
AUSTRALIA. BUREAU OF STATISTICS. BALANCE OF PAYMENTS, AUSTRALIA - REGIONAL SERIES. Text in English. irreg. price varies. **Document type:** *Government.*
Published by: Australian Bureau of Statistics, PO Box 10, Belconnen, ACT 2616, Australia. TEL 61-2-6252-5249, FAX 61-2-6252-6778, http://www.abs.gov.au.

331.021 AUS
AUSTRALIA. BUREAU OF STATISTICS. BUSINESS EVENTS VENUES INDUSTRY, AUSTRALIA. Text in English. 2002. irreg. AUD 19.50 (effective 2003). **Document type:** *Government.*
Published by: Australian Bureau of Statistics, PO Box 10, Belconnen, ACT 2616, Australia. http://www.abs.gov.au.

330.021 AUS
AUSTRALIA. BUREAU OF STATISTICS. BUSINESS EXITS, AUSTRALIA. Text in English. 1995. irreg., latest 1996. AUD 16 (effective 2001). **Document type:** *Government.* **Description:** Classified by type of exit, industry, size, age, type of legal organisation and state of head office.
Formerly: Australia. Bureau of Statistics. Occasional Paper: Business Exits, Australia
Published by: Australian Bureau of Statistics, PO Box 10, Belconnen, ACT 2616, Australia. TEL 61-2-6252-5249, FAX 61-2-6252-6778, http://www.abs.gov.au.

332.021 AUS ISSN 1445-3762
HC601
AUSTRALIA. BUREAU OF STATISTICS. BUSINESS INDICATORS, AUSTRALIA. Text in English. 2001. q. AUD 22 (effective 2003). **Document type:** *Government.*
Published by: Australian Bureau of Statistics, PO Box 10, Belconnen, ACT 2616, Australia. http://www.abs.gov.au.

330.021 AUS ISSN 1036-272X
HD2930.A1
AUSTRALIA. BUREAU OF STATISTICS. BUSINESS OPERATIONS AND INDUSTRY PERFORMANCE, AUSTRALIA. Text in English. 1990. a. AUD 24 (effective 2003). **Document type:** *Government.* **Description:** Economic statistics, including aggregates and ratios, based on profit and loss and balance sheet accounts of businesses in most industries of the Australian economy.
Published by: Australian Bureau of Statistics, PO Box 10, Belconnen, ACT 2616, Australia. TEL 61-2-6252-5249, FAX 61-2-6252-6778, http://www.abs.gov.au.

330.9021 AUS ISSN 1328-2190
AUSTRALIA. BUREAU OF STATISTICS. BUSINESS OPERATIONS AND INDUSTRY PERFORMANCE, AUSTRALIA, PRELIMINARY. Text in English. 1998. a. AUD 20 (effective 2003). **Document type:** *Government.*
Published by: Australian Bureau of Statistics, PO Box 10, Belconnen, ACT 2616, Australia. TEL 61-2-6252-5249, FAX 61-2-6252-6778, http://www.abs.gov.au.

330.9021 AUS
AUSTRALIA. BUREAU OF STATISTICS. BUSINESS REGISTER CONSULTANCY - LOCATIONS. Text in English. irreg. price varies. **Document type:** *Government.*
Published by: Australian Bureau of Statistics, PO Box 10, Belconnen, ACT 2616, Australia. TEL 61-2-6252-5249, FAX 61-2-6252-6778, http://www.abs.gov.au.

330.9021 AUS
AUSTRALIA. BUREAU OF STATISTICS. BUSINESS REGISTER CONSULTANCY - MANAGEMENT UNITS. Text in English. q. price varies. **Document type:** *Government.*
Published by: Australian Bureau of Statistics, PO Box 10, Belconnen, ACT 2616, Australia. TEL 61-2-6252-5249, FAX 61-2-6252-6778, http://www.abs.gov.au.

330.021 AUS
AUSTRALIA. BUREAU OF STATISTICS. BUSINESS SPONSORSHIP, AUSTRALIA. Text in English. 1998. irreg. AUD 15 (effective 2003). **Document type:** *Government.* **Description:** Provides the amount of sponsorship and types of activities sponsored by businesses.
Published by: Australian Bureau of Statistics, PO Box 10, Belconnen, ACT 2616, Australia. TEL 61-2-6252-5249, FAX 61-2-6252-6778, http://www.abs.gov.au.

330.021 AUS
AUSTRALIA. BUREAU OF STATISTICS. CASH MANAGEMENT TRUSTS, AUSTRALIA: DATA REPORT. Text in English. 1995. m. AUD 47 (effective 2003). **Document type:** *Government.*
Published by: Australian Bureau of Statistics, PO Box 10, Belconnen, ACT 2616, Australia. TEL 61-2-6252-5249, FAX 61-2-6252-6778, http://www.abs.gov.au.

338.021 AUS ISSN 1327-3949
AUSTRALIA. BUREAU OF STATISTICS. CHARACTERISTICS OF SMALL BUSINESS, AUSTRALIA. Text in English. 1995. biennial. AUD 32 (effective 2003). **Document type:** *Government.*
Published by: Australian Bureau of Statistics, PO Box 10, Belconnen, ACT 2616, Australia. TEL 61-2-6252-5249, FAX 61-2-6252-6778, http://www.abs.gov.au.

332.021 AUS
AUSTRALIA. BUREAU OF STATISTICS. COMMON FUNDS, AUSTRALIA. Text in English. 1996. q. AUD 47 (effective 2003).
Published by: Australian Bureau of Statistics, PO Box 10, Belconnen, ACT 2616, Australia. TEL 61-2-6252-5249, FAX 61-2-6252-6778, http://www.abs.gov.au.

330.021 AUS ISSN 0818-9986
HC610.P7
AUSTRALIA. BUREAU OF STATISTICS. COMPANY PROFITS, AUSTRALIA. Text in English. 1986. q. AUD 17.50 newsstand/cover (effective 2002). **Document type:** *Government.* **Description:** Contains preliminary estimates derived from a sample survey of incorporated business enterprises of company profits, depreciation and net interest paid.
Published by: Australian Bureau of Statistics, PO Box 10, Belconnen, ACT 2616, Australia. TEL 61-2-6252-5249, FAX 61-2-6252-6778, http://www.abs.gov.au.

338.021 AUS ISSN 1034-4748
AUSTRALIA. BUREAU OF STATISTICS. CONSTANT PRICE ESTIMATES OF MANUFACTURING PRODUCTION, AUSTRALIA. Text in English. 1968. a. AUD 10.50. **Document type:** *Government.* **Description:** Contains constant price estimates of manufacturing gross product.
Published by: Australian Bureau of Statistics, PO Box 10, Belconnen, ACT 2616, Australia. TEL 61-2-6252-5249, FAX 61-2-6252-6778, http://www.abs.gov.au.

330.021 AUS ISSN 1442-3987
AUSTRALIA. BUREAU OF STATISTICS. CONSUMER PRICE INDEX, AUSTRALIA. Text in English. 1960. q. AUD 21 (effective 2003). **Document type:** *Government.* **Description:** Measures movements in retail prices of goods and services commonly purchased by metropolitan wage and salary earner households.
Formerly: Australia. Bureau of Statistics. Consumer Price Index (1031-0207)
Published by: Australian Bureau of Statistics, PO Box 10, Belconnen, ACT 2616, Australia. TEL 61-2-6252-5249, FAX 61-2-6252-6778, http://www.abs.gov.au.

339.021 AUS
AUSTRALIA. BUREAU OF STATISTICS. CONSUMER PRICE INDEX: CONCORDANCE WITH HOUSEHOLD EXPENDITURE CLASSIFICATION, AUSTRALIA. Text in English. 2000. irreg. free. **Document type:** *Government.*
Media: Online - full text.
Published by: Australian Bureau of Statistics, PO Box 10, Belconnen, ACT 2616, Australia. http://www.abs.gov.au.

339.021 AUS
AUSTRALIA. BUREAU OF STATISTICS. CONSUMER PRICE INDEX STANDARD DATA REPORT: CAPITAL CITIES INDEX NUMBERS BY EXPENDITURE CLASS. Text in English. 1998. q. AUD 47 (effective 2003).
Published by: Australian Bureau of Statistics, PO Box 10, Belconnen, ACT 2616, Australia. TEL 61-2-6252-5249, FAX 61-2-6252-6778, http://www.abs.gov.au.

330.021 AUS
AUSTRALIA. BUREAU OF STATISTICS. CULTURAL INDUSTRIES, AUSTRALIA, PRELIMINARY. Text in English. 1998. irreg. AUD 16 (effective 1998). **Document type:** *Government.* **Description:** Offers information on libraries, museums and arts industries.
Published by: Australian Bureau of Statistics, PO Box 10, Belconnen, ACT 2616, Australia. TEL 61-2-6252-5249, FAX 61-2-6252-6778, http://www.abs.gov.au.

330.021 AUS
AUSTRALIA. BUREAU OF STATISTICS. DETAILED INDUSTRY PERFORMANCE, INCORPORATING BUSINESS INCOME TAX DATA, AUSTRALIA. Text in English. 1998. a. AUD 21 (effective 2001). **Document type:** *Government.*
Published by: Australian Bureau of Statistics, PO Box 10, Belconnen, ACT 2616, Australia. TEL 61-2-6252-5249, FAX 61-2-6252-6778, http://www.abs.gov.au.

332.021 AUS
AUSTRALIA. BUREAU OF STATISTICS. DIRECTORY OF CAPITAL EXPENDITURE DATA SOURCES AND RELATED STATISTICS. Text in English. 1997. irreg., latest 1996. AUD 24 (effective 2001). **Document type:** *Government.*
Published by: Australian Bureau of Statistics, PO Box 10, Belconnen, ACT 2616, Australia. TEL 61-2-6252-5249, FAX 61-2-6252-6778, http://www.abs.gov.au.

331.021 AUS
AUSTRALIA. BUREAU OF STATISTICS. DIRECTORY OF INDUSTRIAL RELATIONS STATISTICS. Text in English. 1992. irreg., latest 1996. AUD 17.50 (effective 2003). **Document type:** *Directory, Government.* **Description:** Brief overview of the types of ABS data that are available relating to industrial relations issues and an understanding of the wide range of statistics available, and how they can be used.
Published by: Australian Bureau of Statistics, PO Box 10, Belconnen, ACT 2616, Australia. TEL 61-2-6252-5249, FAX 61-2-6252-6778, http://www.abs.gov.au.

331.021 AUS
AUSTRALIA. BUREAU OF STATISTICS. DIRECTORY OF LABOUR MARKET AND SOCIAL SURVEY DATA. Text in English. 1994. irreg. AUD 10 (effective 1998). **Document type:** *Directory, Government.* **Description:** Provides descriptive information on recent labor market and social household surveys conducted by the ABS.
Published by: Australian Bureau of Statistics, PO Box 10, Belconnen, ACT 2616, Australia. TEL 61-2-6252-5249, FAX 61-2-6252-6778, http://www.abs.gov.au.

331.12021 362.6021 AUS
AUSTRALIA. BUREAU OF STATISTICS. DIRECTORY OF SUPERANNUATION RELATED STATISTICS. Text in English. 1991. irreg., latest 1997. AUD 27 (effective 2001). **Document type:** *Government.* **Description:** Contains information relating to superannuation and retirement collected from 19 data collection organizations.
Published by: Australian Bureau of Statistics, PO Box 10, Belconnen, ACT 2616, Australia. TEL 61-2-6252-5249, FAX 61-2-6252-6778, http://www.abs.gov.au.

331.259021 AUS
AUSTRALIA. BUREAU OF STATISTICS. EDUCATION AND TRAINING EXPERIENCE, AUSTRALIA. Text in English. 1989. irreg., latest 2001. AUD 27 (effective 2003). **Document type:** *Government.* **Description:** Provides details of the training and education experiences of persons who had worked as wage and salary earners in the last twelve months, as well as those who are employers, self-employed, unemployed or marginally attached to the labour force.
Former titles: Australia. Bureau of Statistics. Training and Education Experience, Australia; How Workers Get Their Training, Australia
Published by: Australian Bureau of Statistics, PO Box 10, Belconnen, ACT 2616, Australia. TEL 61-2-6252-5249, FAX 61-2-6252-6778, http://www.abs.gov.au.

331.2021 AUS ISSN 1325-7854
HD5100.A1
AUSTRALIA. BUREAU OF STATISTICS. EMPLOYEE EARNINGS AND HOURS, AUSTRALIA. Text in English. biennial. AUD 26 (effective 2003). **Document type:** *Government.* **Description:** Contains survey results about the distribution and composition of average weekly earnings and hours of employees, classified by sex, adult-junior, industry, occupation, type of employment, and composition of earnings and hours.
Former titles: Australia. Bureau of Statistics. Distribution and Composition of Employee Earnings and Hours, Australia (1031-024X); (until 1985): Earnings and Hours of Employees, Distribution and Composition, Australia
Published by: Australian Bureau of Statistics, PO Box 10, Belconnen, ACT 2616, Australia. TEL 61-2-6252-5249, FAX 61-2-6252-6778, http://www.abs.gov.au. Circ: 349.

331.2021 AUS ISSN 1325-7773
AUSTRALIA. BUREAU OF STATISTICS. EMPLOYEE EARNINGS AND HOURS, AUSTRALIA, PRELIMINARY. Text in English. 1974. biennial. AUD 21 (effective 2003).
Document type: *Government.* **Description:** Contains information about the distribution of average weekly earnings of employees classified by sex.
Former titles: Australia. Bureau of Statistics. Distribution and Composition of Employee Earnings and Hours, Australia, Preliminary (1031-0231); (until 1985): Earnings and Hours of Employees, Distribution and Composition, Preliminary (Canberra) (0312-4460)
Published by: Australian Bureau of Statistics, PO Box 10, Belconnen, ACT 2616, Australia. TEL 61-2-6252-5249, FAX 61-2-6252-6778, http://www.abs.gov.au.

331.21021 AUS
AUSTRALIA. BUREAU OF STATISTICS. EMPLOYEE EARNINGS AND HOURS, STATES AND AUSTRALIA - DATA SERVICE. Text in English. 1983. a. price varies.
Document type: *Government.*
Formerly: Australia. Bureau of Statistics. Distribution and Composition of Employee Earnings and Hours, States and Australia - Data Service
Related titles: Diskette ed.
Published by: Australian Bureau of Statistics, PO Box 10, Belconnen, ACT 2616, Australia. TEL 61-2-6252-5249, FAX 61-2-6252-6778, http://www.abs.gov.au.

331.2 AUS ISSN 1442-0171
AUSTRALIA. BUREAU OF STATISTICS. EMPLOYEE EARNINGS, BENEFITS AND TRADE UNION MEMBERSHIP, AUSTRALIA. Text in English. 1972. a. AUD 26 (effective 2003). **Document type:** *Government.*
Former titles: Australia. Bureau of Statistics. Weekly Earnings of Employees, Australia; Australia. Bureau of Statistics. Average Weekly Earnings of Employees, Australia (1038-0604); Australia. Bureau of Statistics. Average Earnings and Hours of Employees, Australia (0815-9912)
Published by: Australian Bureau of Statistics, PO Box 10, Belconnen, ACT 2616, Australia. http://www.abs.gov.au.

331.259021 AUS
AUSTRALIA. BUREAU OF STATISTICS. EMPLOYER TRAINING EXPENDITURE AND PRACTICES, AUSTRALIA. Text in English. 1989. irreg., latest 2003. AUD 23 (effective 2003). stat. **Document type:** *Government.* **Description:** Provides comprehensive information on employer training expenditure in Australia. Australia. Bureau of Statistics. Employer Training Expenditure, Australia
Published by: Australian Bureau of Statistics, PO Box 10, Belconnen, ACT 2616, Australia. TEL 61-2-6252-5249, FAX 61-2-6252-6778, http://www.abs.gov.au.

331.259021 AUS
AUSTRALIA. BUREAU OF STATISTICS. EMPLOYMENT ARRANGEMENTS AND SUPERANNUATION, AUSTRALIA. Text in English. 2000. irreg. AUD 24 (effective 2003).
Document type: *Government.*
Published by: Australian Bureau of Statistics, PO Box 10, Belconnen, ACT 2616, Australia. TEL 61-2-6252-5249, FAX 61-2-6252-6778, http://www.abs.gov.au.

331.11021 AUS
AUSTRALIA. BUREAU OF STATISTICS. EMPLOYMENT IN SELECTED CULTURE-LEISURE OCCUPATIONS, AUSTRALIA. Text in English. 1991. irreg., latest 1996. AUD 22 (effective 2003). **Document type:** *Government.*
Published by: Australian Bureau of Statistics, PO Box 10, Belconnen, ACT 2616, Australia. TEL 61-2-6252-5249, FAX 61-2-6252-6778, http://www.abs.gov.au.

331.11021 790.1021 AUS
AUSTRALIA. BUREAU OF STATISTICS. EMPLOYMENT IN SELECTED SPORT AND RECREATION OCCUPATIONS, AUSTRALIA. Text in English. 1998. every 5 yrs. AUD 16 (effective 1998). **Document type:** *Government.*
Published by: Australian Bureau of Statistics, PO Box 10, Belconnen, ACT 2616, Australia. TEL 61-2-6252-5249, FAX 61-2-6252-6778, http://www.abs.gov.au.

331.021 AUS
AUSTRALIA. BUREAU OF STATISTICS. EMPLOYMENT SERVICES, AUSTRALIA. Text in English. 2000. irreg., latest 2003. AUD 21 (effective 2003).
Published by: Australian Bureau of Statistics, PO Box 10, Belconnen, ACT 2616, Australia. TEL 61-2-6252-5249, FAX 61-2-6252-6778, http://www.abs.gov.au.

330.9021 AUS ISSN 1446-1714
AUSTRALIA. BUREAU OF STATISTICS. EXPERIMENTAL ESTIMATES, AUSTRALIAN INDUSTRY, A STATE PERSPECTIVE. Text in English. 1999. a. AUD 21 (effective 2002). **Document type:** *Government.*
Published by: Australian Bureau of Statistics, PO Box 10, Belconnen, ACT 2616, Australia. http://www.abs.gov.au.

331.021 AUS
AUSTRALIA. BUREAU OF STATISTICS. EXPERIMENTAL ESTIMATES, REGIONAL SMALL BUSINESS STATISTICS, AUSTRALIA. Text in English. 1998. irreg. AUD 22 (effective 2003). stat. **Document type:** *Government.*
Published by: Australian Bureau of Statistics, PO Box 10, Belconnen, ACT 2616, Australia. TEL 61-2-6252-5249, FAX 61-2-6252-6778, http://www.abs.gov.au.

331.021 AUS
AUSTRALIA. BUREAU OF STATISTICS. EXPERIMENTAL ESTIMATES, REGIONAL WAGE AND SALARY EARNER STATISTICS, AUSTRALIA. Text in English. 1997. irreg. AUD 10 (effective 2003). stat. **Document type:** *Government.*
Published by: Australian Bureau of Statistics, PO Box 10, Belconnen, ACT 2616, Australia. TEL 61-2-6252-5249, FAX 61-2-6252-6778, http://www.abs.gov.au.

332.021 AUS
AUSTRALIA. BUREAU OF STATISTICS. FINANCIAL ESTIMATES OF COMMONWEALTH PUBLIC TRADING ENTERPRISES, AUSTRALIA. Text in English. 1993. irreg. AUD 13 (effective 1998). **Document type:** *Government.*
Description: Shows current and capital outlays, revenue and financing transactions for the last five years.
Published by: Australian Bureau of Statistics, PO Box 10, Belconnen, ACT 2616, Australia. TEL 61-2-6252-5249, FAX 61-2-6252-6778, http://www.abs.gov.au.

331.021 AUS
AUSTRALIA. BUREAU OF STATISTICS. FORMS OF EMPLOYMENT, AUSTRALIA. Text in English. 1998. irreg., latest 2002. AUD 23 (effective 2003). **Document type:** *Government.*
Published by: Australian Bureau of Statistics, PO Box 10, Belconnen, ACT 2616, Australia. TEL 61-2-6252-5249, FAX 61-2-6252-6778, http://www.abs.gov.au.

330.021 AUS
AUSTRALIA. BUREAU OF STATISTICS. GENEROSITY OF AUSTRALIAN BUSINESSES. Text in English. 2001. irreg. AUD 18.50 (effective 2003). stat. **Document type:** *Government.*
Published by: Australian Bureau of Statistics, PO Box 10, Belconnen, ACT 2616, Australia. TEL 61-2-6252-5249, FAX 61-2-6252-6778, http://www.abs.gov.au.

339.021 AUS
AUSTRALIA. BUREAU OF STATISTICS. GOVERNMENT BENEFITS, TAXES AND HOUSEHOLD INCOME, AUSTRALIA. Text in English. 1984. quinquennial. AUD 24 (effective 2003). **Document type:** *Government.*
Formerly: Australia. Bureau of Statistics. Household Expenditure Survey, Australia: the Effects of Government Benefits and Taxes on Household Income
Published by: Australian Bureau of Statistics, PO Box 10, Belconnen, ACT 2616, Australia. TEL 61-2-6252-5249, FAX 61-2-6252-6778, http://www.abs.gov.au.

336.021 AUS ISSN 1031-7104
HJ90
AUSTRALIA. BUREAU OF STATISTICS. GOVERNMENT FINANCE STATISTICS, AUSTRALIA. Text in English. 1989. a. AUD 24 (effective 2003). **Document type:** *Government.*
Description: Provides details of the consolidated financial transactions of non-financial public enterprises of all levels of government compiled in accordance with national accounting concepts.
Formed by the merger of (1961-1989): Commonwealth Government Finance, Australia (0725-3427); (1971-1989): State and Local Government Finance, Australia (0158-9946); Which was formerly: Government Finance Statistics; Public Authority Finance. State and Local Authorities.
Related titles: Diskette ed.
Published by: Australian Bureau of Statistics, PO Box 10, Belconnen, ACT 2616, Australia. TEL 61-2-6252-5249, FAX 61-2-6252-6778, http://www.abs.gov.au. Circ: 362.

332.021 AUS
AUSTRALIA. BUREAU OF STATISTICS. GOVERNMENT FINANCE STATISTICS - CONCEPTS, SOURCES AND METHODS. Text in English. 1994. irreg. AUD 40 (effective 1998). **Document type:** *Government.*
Published by: Australian Bureau of Statistics, PO Box 10, Belconnen, ACT 2616, Australia. TEL 61-2-6252-5249, FAX 61-2-6252-6778, http://www.abs.gov.au.

332.021 AUS
AUSTRALIA. BUREAU OF STATISTICS. GOVERNMENT FINANCE STATISTICS, EDUCATION, AUSTRALIA, DATA REPORT. Text in English. a. AUD 43 (effective 2001).
Document type: *Government.*
Media: Online - full content.
Published by: Australian Bureau of Statistics, PO Box 10, Belconnen, ACT 2616, Australia. TEL 61-2-6252-5249, FAX 61-2-6252-6778, http://www.abs.gov.au.

332.1021 AUS
▼ **AUSTRALIA. BUREAU OF STATISTICS. GOVERNMENT FINANCIAL ESTIMATES, AUSTRALIAN CAPITAL TERRITORY, ELECTRONIC DELIVERY.** Text in English. 2003. a. price varies. stat. **Document type:** *Government.*
Published by: Australian Bureau of Statistics, PO Box 10, Belconnen, ACT 2616, Australia. TEL 61-2-6252-5249, FAX 61-2-6252-6778, http://www.abs.gov.au.

331.1021 AUS
AUSTRALIA. BUREAU OF STATISTICS. HEALTH AND COMMUNITY SERVICES LABOUR FORCE. Text in English. 1996. quinquennial. AUD 21.50 (effective 2003). **Document type:** *Government.*
Published by: Australian Bureau of Statistics, PO Box 10, Belconnen, ACT 2616, Australia. http://www.abs.gov.au.

331.021 AUS
AUSTRALIA. BUREAU OF STATISTICS. HIRE INDUSTRIES, AUSTRALIA. Text in English. 2001. irreg. AUD 18.50 (effective 2003). **Document type:** *Government.*
Published by: Australian Bureau of Statistics, PO Box 10, Belconnen, ACT 2616, Australia. TEL 61-2-6252-5249, FAX 61-2-6252-6778, http://www.abs.gov.au.

331.021 AUS
AUSTRALIA. BUREAU OF STATISTICS. HIRE INDUSTRIES, AUSTRALIA, PRELIMINARY. Text in English. 2000. irreg. AUD 17 (effective 2003). **Document type:** *Government.*
Published by: Australian Bureau of Statistics, PO Box 10, Belconnen, ACT 2616, Australia. http://www.abs.gov.au.

330.021 AUS
AUSTRALIA. BUREAU OF STATISTICS. HOSPITALITY INDUSTRIES, AUSTRALIA. Text in English. 1992. irreg. AUD 25 (effective 1998). **Document type:** *Government.*
Description: Includes cafes and restaurants, pubs, taverns and bars, accommodations, licensed clubs, and casinos.
Published by: Australian Bureau of Statistics, PO Box 10, Belconnen, ACT 2616, Australia. TEL 61-2-6252-5249, FAX 61-2-6252-6778, http://www.abs.gov.au.

339.021 AUS
AUSTRALIA. BUREAU OF STATISTICS. HOUSEHOLD EXPENDITURE SURVEY, AUSTRALIA: CONFIDENTIALISED UNIT RECORD FILE ON CD-ROM. Text in English. 1994. quinquennial. AUD 8,000 (effective 2003). **Document type:** *Government.*
Media: CD-ROM.
Published by: Australian Bureau of Statistics, PO Box 10, Belconnen, ACT 2616, Australia. TEL 61-2-6252-5249, FAX 61-2-6252-6778, http://www.abs.gov.au.

339.021 AUS
AUSTRALIA. BUREAU OF STATISTICS. HOUSEHOLD EXPENDITURE SURVEY, AUSTRALIA: CONFIDENTIALISED UNIT RECORD FILE ON FLOPPY DISK. Text in English. 1994. irreg. AUD 8,000 (effective 2002). **Document type:** *Government.*
Media: Diskette. **Related titles:** Magnetic Tape ed.
Published by: Australian Bureau of Statistics, PO Box 10, Belconnen, ACT 2616, Australia. TEL 61-2-6252-5249, FAX 61-2-6252-6778, http://www.abs.gov.au.

339.021 AUS
AUSTRALIA. BUREAU OF STATISTICS. HOUSEHOLD EXPENDITURE SURVEY, AUSTRALIA: DETAILED EXPENDITURE ITEMS. Text in English. 1984. quinquennial. AUD 24 (effective 2001). **Document type:** *Government.*
Related titles: Diskette ed.
Published by: Australian Bureau of Statistics, PO Box 10, Belconnen, ACT 2616, Australia. TEL 61-2-6252-5249, FAX 61-2-6252-6778, http://www.abs.gov.au.

339.021 AUS
AUSTRALIA. BUREAU OF STATISTICS. HOUSEHOLD EXPENDITURE SURVEY, AUSTRALIA: HOUSEHOLD CHARACTERISTICS. Text in English. 1984. irreg., latest 1994. AUD 24 (effective 2003). **Document type:** *Government.*
Related titles: Diskette ed.
Published by: Australian Bureau of Statistics, PO Box 10, Belconnen, ACT 2616, Australia. TEL 61-2-6252-5249, FAX 61-2-6252-6778, http://www.abs.gov.au.

339.021 AUS
AUSTRALIA. BUREAU OF STATISTICS. HOUSEHOLD EXPENDITURE SURVEY, AUSTRALIA: SUMMARY OF RESULTS. Text in English. 1984. irreg., latest 1994. AUD 20 (effective 2003). **Document type:** *Government.*
Related titles: Diskette ed.
Published by: Australian Bureau of Statistics, PO Box 10, Belconnen, ACT 2616, Australia. TEL 61-2-6252-5249, FAX 61-2-6252-6778, http://www.abs.gov.au.

339.021 AUS
AUSTRALIA. BUREAU OF STATISTICS. HOUSEHOLD EXPENDITURE SURVEY, AUSTRALIA: USER GUIDE. Text in English. 1984. irreg., latest 1994. AUD 30 (effective 2003). **Document type:** *Government.*
Published by: Australian Bureau of Statistics, PO Box 10, Belconnen, ACT 2616, Australia. TEL 61-2-6252-5249, FAX 61-2-6252-6778, http://www.abs.gov.au.

332.6021 AUS
AUSTRALIA. BUREAU OF STATISTICS. HOUSEHOLD INVESTORS IN RENTAL DWELLINGS, AUSTRALIA. Text in English. 1993. irreg., latest 1997. AUD 19.50 (effective 2002). **Document type:** *Government.*
Formerly: Australia. Bureau of Statistics. Investors in Rental Dwellings, Australia
Related titles: Diskette ed.; Magnetic Tape ed.

Published by: Australian Bureau of Statistics, PO Box 10, Belconnen, ACT 2616, Australia. TEL 61-2-6252-5249, FAX 61-2-6252-6778, http://www.abs.gov.au.

332.021   AUS   ISSN 1031-0320
AUSTRALIA. BUREAU OF STATISTICS. HOUSING FINANCE FOR OWNER OCCUPATION, AUSTRALIA. Text in English. 1975. m. AUD 19.50 newsstand/cover (effective 2003). **Document type:** *Government.* **Description:** Contains secured finance commitments to individuals for construction of dwellings, purchase of new and established dwellings by savings and trading banks, permanent building societies and other lenders.
Published by: Australian Bureau of Statistics, PO Box 10, Belconnen, ACT 2616, Australia. TEL 61-2-6252-5249, FAX 61-2-6252-6778, http://www.abs.gov.au.

331.021   AUS
AUSTRALIA. BUREAU OF STATISTICS. HUMAN RESOURCES IN SCIENCE AND TECHNOLOGY (HRST), AUSTRALIA. Text in English. 1996. irreg., latest 2003. AUD 22 (effective 2003). **Document type:** *Government.*
Published by: Australian Bureau of Statistics, PO Box 10, Belconnen, ACT 2616, Australia. TEL 61-2-6252-5249, FAX 61-2-6252-6778, http://www.abs.gov.au.

339.021   AUS
AUSTRALIA. BUREAU OF STATISTICS. INCOME AND HOUSING COSTS SURVEY, AUSTRALIA: CONFIDENTIALISED UNIT RECORD FILE ON CD-ROM. Text in English. 1997. a. AUD 8,000 (effective 2001). **Media:** CD-ROM.
Published by: Australian Bureau of Statistics, PO Box 10, Belconnen, ACT 2616, Australia. TEL 61-2-6252-5249, FAX 61-2-6252-6778, http://www.abs.gov.au.

330.021   AUS   ISSN 1322-9788
HC610.I5
AUSTRALIA. BUREAU OF STATISTICS. INCOME DISTRIBUTION, AUSTRALIA. Text in English. 1978. a. AUD 25 (effective 2003). **Document type:** *Government.*
Description: Presents details on the distribution of income in Australia, and on the various characteristics of income units, their compositions, and the principal source of income.
Formerly: Survey of Income and Housing Costs and Amenities: Income Distribution: Income Units, Australia
Published by: Australian Bureau of Statistics, PO Box 10, Belconnen, ACT 2616, Australia. TEL 61-2-6252-5249, FAX 61-2-6252-6778, http://www.abs.gov.au.

331.021   AUS   ISSN 1031-0347
AUSTRALIA. BUREAU OF STATISTICS. INDUSTRIAL DISPUTES, AUSTRALIA (MONTHLY). Text in English. 1970. m. AUD 19 newsstand/cover (effective 2003). **Document type:** *Government.* **Description:** Provides information on the number of labor disputes, workers involved, working days lost in disputes involving work stoppages lasting ten working days or more.
Published by: Australian Bureau of Statistics, PO Box 10, Belconnen, ACT 2616, Australia. TEL 61-2-6252-5249, FAX 61-2-6252-6778, http://www.abs.gov.au.

336.2021   AUS
AUSTRALIA. BUREAU OF STATISTICS. INFORMATION PAPER: A.B.S. STATISTICS AND THE NEW TAX SYSTEM. Text in English. 2000. irreg. AUD 10 (effective 2003).
Published by: Australian Bureau of Statistics, PO Box 10, Belconnen, ACT 2616, Australia. TEL 61-2-6252-5249, FAX 61-2-6252-6778, http://www.abs.gov.au.

332.021   AUS
AUSTRALIA. BUREAU OF STATISTICS. INFORMATION PAPER: ACCRUALS-BASED GOVERNMENT FINANCE STATISTICS. Text in English. 2000. irreg. AUD 10 (effective 2003).
Published by: Australian Bureau of Statistics, PO Box 10, Belconnen, ACT 2616, Australia. TEL 61-2-6252-5249, FAX 61-2-6252-6778, http://www.abs.go.au.

339.021   AUS
AUSTRALIA. BUREAU OF STATISTICS. INFORMATION PAPER: AUSTRALIAN CONSUMER PRICE INDEX 13TH SERIES REVIEW. Text in English. 1998. irreg. AUD 10 (effective 1998). **Document type:** *Government.*
Published by: Australian Bureau of Statistics, PO Box 10, Belconnen, ACT 2616, Australia. TEL 61-2-6252-5249, FAX 61-2-6252-6778, http://www.abs.gov.au.

339.021   AUS
AUSTRALIA. BUREAU OF STATISTICS. INFORMATION PAPER: AUSTRALIAN NATIONAL ACCOUNTS, INTRODUCTION OF CHAIN VOLUME AND PRICE INDEXES. Text in English. 1997. irreg. AUD 10 (effective 2002). **Document type:** *Government.*
Published by: Australian Bureau of Statistics, PO Box 10, Belconnen, ACT 2616, Australia. TEL 61-2-6252-5249, FAX 61-2-6252-6778, http://www.abs.gov.au.

339.021   AUS
AUSTRALIA. BUREAU OF STATISTICS. INFORMATION PAPER: AUSTRALIAN NATIONAL ACCOUNTS: INTRODUCTION TO INPUT - OUTPUT MULTIPLIERS. Text in English. 1990. irreg. AUD 19.50 (effective 1998). **Document type:** *Government.*
Published by: Australian Bureau of Statistics, PO Box 10, Belconnen, ACT 2616, Australia. TEL 61-2-6252-5249, FAX 61-2-6252-6778, http://www.abs.gov.au.

338.021   AUS
AUSTRALIA. BUREAU OF STATISTICS. INFORMATION PAPER: AVAILABILITY OF STATISTICS RELATED TO MANUFACTURING. Text in English. 1996. irreg. AUD 10 (effective 2002).
Published by: Australian Bureau of Statistics, PO Box 10, Belconnen, ACT 2616, Australia. TEL 61-2-6252-5249, FAX 61-2-6252-6778, http://www.abs.gov.au.

331.021   AUS
AUSTRALIA. BUREAU OF STATISTICS. INFORMATION PAPER: CHANGES TO LABOUR FORCE STATISTICS PRODUCTS. Text in English. 2002. irreg. AUD 10 (effective 2003). stat. **Document type:** *Government.*
Published by: Australian Bureau of Statistics, PO Box 10, Belconnen, ACT 2616, Australia. TEL 61-2-6252-5249, FAX 61-2-6252-6778, http://www.abs.gov.au.

332.021   AUS
AUSTRALIA. BUREAU OF STATISTICS. INFORMATION PAPER: DEVELOPMENTS IN GOVERNMENT FINANCE STATISTICS. Text in English. 1997. irreg. AUD 10 (effective 2001). **Document type:** *Government.*
Published by: Australian Bureau of Statistics, PO Box 10, Belconnen, ACT 2616, Australia. TEL 61-2-6252-5249, FAX 61-2-6252-6778, http://www.abs.gov.au.

336.021   AUS
AUSTRALIA. BUREAU OF STATISTICS. INFORMATION PAPER: EXPANDED USE OF BUSINESS INCOME TAX DATA IN A.B.S. ECONOMIC STATISTICS - EXPERIMENTAL ESTIMATES FOR SELECTED INDUSTRIES. Text in English. 1995. irreg. AUD 10 (effective 2003).
Published by: Australian Bureau of Statistics, PO Box 10, Belconnen, ACT 2616, Australia. TEL 61-2-6252-5249, FAX 61-2-6252-6778, http://www.abs.gov.au.

339.021   AUS
AUSTRALIA. BUREAU OF STATISTICS. INFORMATION PAPER: IMPACT OF REVISED INTERNATIONAL STANDARDS ON THE AUSTRALIAN NATIONAL ACCOUNTS. Text in English. 1998. irreg. AUD 10 (effective 1998). **Document type:** *Government.*
Published by: Australian Bureau of Statistics, PO Box 10, Belconnen, ACT 2616, Australia. TEL 61-2-6252-5249, FAX 61-2-6252-6778, http://www.abs.gov.au.

339.021   AUS
AUSTRALIA. BUREAU OF STATISTICS. INFORMATION PAPER: IMPLEMENTATION OF REVISED INTERNATIONAL STANDARDS IN THE AUSTRALIAN NATIONAL ACCOUNTS. Text in English. 1997. irreg. AUD 10 (effective 2001). **Document type:** *Government.*
Published by: Australian Bureau of Statistics, PO Box 10, Belconnen, ACT 2616, Australia. TEL 61-2-6252-5249, FAX 61-2-6252-6778, http://www.abs.gov.au.

330.021   AUS
AUSTRALIA. BUREAU OF STATISTICS. INFORMATION PAPER: IMPLEMENTING NEW INTERNATIONAL STATISTICAL STANDARDS IN A.B.S. INTERNATIONAL ACCOUNTS STATISTICS. Text in English. 1997. irreg. AUD 10 (effective 2001). **Document type:** *Government.*
Published by: Australian Bureau of Statistics, PO Box 10, Belconnen, ACT 2616, Australia. TEL 61-2-6252-5249, FAX 61-2-6252-6778, http://www.abs.gov.au.

331.021   AUS
AUSTRALIA. BUREAU OF STATISTICS. INFORMATION PAPER: IMPLEMENTING THE REDESIGNED LABOUR FORCE SURVEY QUESTIONNAIRE. Text in English. 2001. irreg. AUD 10 (effective 2003). **Document type:** *Government.*
Published by: Australian Bureau of Statistics, PO Box 10, Belconnen, ACT 2616, Australia. TEL 61-2-6252-5249, FAX 61-2-6252-6778, http://www.abs.gov.au.

382.021   AUS
AUSTRALIA. BUREAU OF STATISTICS. INFORMATION PAPER: INTERNATIONAL MERCHANDISE TRADE AND SHIPPING STATISTICS, AUSTRALIA: DATA CONFIDENTIALITY. Text in English. 1994. irreg. AUD 10 (effective 2001). **Document type:** *Government.*
Published by: Australian Bureau of Statistics, PO Box 10, Belconnen, ACT 2616, Australia. TEL 61-2-6252-5249, FAX 61-2-6252-6778, http://www.abs.gov.au.

382.021   AUS
AUSTRALIA. BUREAU OF STATISTICS. INFORMATION PAPER: INTERNATIONAL MERCHANDISE TRADE STATISTICS, AUSTRALIA: DATA CONFIDENTIALITY. Text in English. 1994. irreg., latest 1999. AUD 10 (effective 2003). **Document type:** *Government.*

Formerly: Australia. Bureau of Statistics. Information Paper: International Merchandise Trade Statistics: (Year) Revision of Commodity Classifications
Published by: Australian Bureau of Statistics, PO Box 10, Belconnen, ACT 2616, Australia. TEL 61-2-6252-5249, FAX 61-2-6252-6778, http://www.abs.gov.au.

658.021   AUS
AUSTRALIA. BUREAU OF STATISTICS. INFORMATION PAPER: INTRODUCTION OF CONCURRENT SEASONAL ADJUSTMENT INTO THE RETAIL TRADE SERIES. Text in English. 1999. irreg. AUD 10 (effective 2003). **Document type:** *Government.*
Published by: Australian Bureau of Statistics, PO Box 10, Belconnen, ACT 2616, Australia. TEL 61-2-6252-5249, FAX 61-2-6252-6778, http://www.abs.gov.au.

339.021   AUS
AUSTRALIA. BUREAU OF STATISTICS. INFORMATION PAPER: INTRODUCTION OF THE 13TH SERIES AUSTRALIAN CONSUMER PRICE INDEX. Text in English. 1998. irreg., latest 14th Series. AUD 10 (effective 2002). **Document type:** *Government.*
Published by: Australian Bureau of Statistics, PO Box 10, Belconnen, ACT 2616, Australia. TEL 61-2-6252-5249, FAX 61-2-6252-6778, http://www.abs.gov.au.

339.021   AUS
AUSTRALIA. BUREAU OF STATISTICS. INFORMATION PAPER: ISSUES TO BE CONSIDERED DURING THE 13TH SERIES AUSTRALIAN CONSUMER PRICE INDEX REVIEW. Text in English. 1997. irreg., latest 1997. AUD 10 (effective 2002). **Document type:** *Government.*
Related titles: Online - full text ed.
Published by: Australian Bureau of Statistics, PO Box 10, Belconnen, ACT 2616, Australia. TEL 61-2-6252-5249, FAX 61-2-6252-6778, http://www.abs.gov.au.

331.021   AUS
AUSTRALIA. BUREAU OF STATISTICS. INFORMATION PAPER: LABOUR FORCE SURVEY, AUSTRALIA: REVISIONS TO HISTORICAL ANZSIC INDUSTRY DATA. Text in English. 1994. irreg., latest 1996. AUD 10 (effective 2000).
Published by: Australian Bureau of Statistics, PO Box 10, Belconnen, ACT 2616, Australia. TEL 61-2-6252-5249, FAX 61-2-6252-6778, http://www.abs.gov.au.

331.021   AUS   ISSN 1442-7133
AUSTRALIA. BUREAU OF STATISTICS. INFORMATION PAPER: LABOUR FORCE SURVEY QUESTIONNAIRE REDESIGN. Text in English. 2000. irreg. AUD 10 (effective 2002). **Document type:** *Government.*
Published by: Australian Bureau of Statistics, PO Box 10, Belconnen, ACT 2616, Australia. TEL 61-2-6252-5249, FAX 61-2-6252-6778, http://www.abs.gov.au.

331.11021   AUS
AUSTRALIA. BUREAU OF STATISTICS. INFORMATION PAPER: LABOUR FORCE SURVEY SAMPLE DESIGN. Text in English. 1987. irreg., latest 1997. AUD 10 (effective 2003). **Document type:** *Government.*
Published by: Australian Bureau of Statistics, PO Box 10, Belconnen, ACT 2616, Australia. TEL 61-2-6252-5249, FAX 61-2-6252-6778, http://www.abs.gov.au.

331.021   AUS
▼ **AUSTRALIA. BUREAU OF STATISTICS. INFORMATION PAPER: LABOUR FORCE SURVEY STANDARD ERRORS.** Text in English. 2003. 5/yr. AUD 10 (effective 2003). stat. **Document type:** *Government.*
Published by: Australian Bureau of Statistics, PO Box 10, Belconnen, ACT 2616, Australia. TEL 61-2-6252-5249, FAX 61-2-6252-6778, http://www.abs.gov.au.

331.125021   AUS
AUSTRALIA. BUREAU OF STATISTICS. INFORMATION PAPER: MEASURING EMPLOYMENT AND UNEMPLOYMENT. Text in English. 1991. irreg., latest 1999. AUD 10 (effective 2002). **Document type:** *Government.*
Description: Provides information about the Monthly Labour Fource Survey and discusses the Australian labor force framework.
Published by: Australian Bureau of Statistics, PO Box 10, Belconnen, ACT 2616, Australia. TEL 61-2-6252-5249, FAX 61-2-6252-6778, http://www.abs.gov.au.

382.021   AUS
AUSTRALIA. BUREAU OF STATISTICS. INFORMATION PAPER: MEASURING REGION OF ORIGIN MERCHANDISE EXPORTS. Text in English. 2000. irreg. AUD 10 (effective 2001). **Document type:** *Government.*
Published by: Australian Bureau of Statistics, PO Box 10, Belconnen, ACT 2616, Australia. TEL 61-2-6252-5249, FAX 61-2-6252-6778, http://www.abs.gov.au.

339.021   AUS
AUSTRALIA. BUREAU OF STATISTICS. INFORMATION PAPER: OUTCOME OF THE 13TH SERIES AUSTRALIAN CONSUMER PRICE INDEX REVIEW. Text in English. 1997. irreg., latest 1997. AUD 10 (effective 2001). **Document type:** *Government.*

Related titles: Online - full text ed.
Published by: Australian Bureau of Statistics, PO Box 10, Belconnen, ACT 2616, Australia. TEL 61-2-6252-5249, FAX 61-2-6252-6778, http://www.abs.gov.au.

339.021 AUS
AUSTRALIA. BUREAU OF STATISTICS. INFORMATION PAPER: PRICE INDEXES AND THE NEW TAX SYSTEM. Text in English. 2000. irreg. AUD 10 (effective 2003). **Document type:** *Government.*
Published by: Australian Bureau of Statistics, PO Box 10, Belconnen, ACT 2616, Australia. TEL 61-2-6252-5249, FAX 61-2-6252-6778, http://www.abs.gov.au.

339.021 AUS
AUSTRALIA. BUREAU OF STATISTICS. INFORMATION PAPER: PRODUCER PRICE INDEX DEVELOPMENTS. Text in English. 1999. irreg. AUD 10 (effective 2003).
Published by: Australian Bureau of Statistics, PO Box 10, Belconnen, ACT 2616, Australia. TEL 61-2-6252-5249, FAX 61-2-6252-6778, http://www.abs.gov.au.

339.021 AUS
AUSTRALIA. BUREAU OF STATISTICS. INFORMATION PAPER: QUALITY OF AUSTRALIAN BALANCE OF PAYMENTS STATISTICS. Text in English. 1996. irreg. AUD 10 (effective 1998). **Document type:** *Government.*
Published by: Australian Bureau of Statistics, PO Box 10, Belconnen, ACT 2616, Australia. TEL 61-2-6252-5249, FAX 61-2-6252-6778, http://www.abs.gov.au.

331.021 AUS
AUSTRALIA. BUREAU OF STATISTICS. INFORMATION PAPER: QUESTIONNAIRES IN THE LABOUR FORCE. Text in English. 1978. irreg. AUD 10 (effective 2003). **Document type:** *Government.*
Published by: Australian Bureau of Statistics, PO Box 10, Belconnen, ACT 2616, Australia. http://www.abs.gov.au.

331.11021 AUS
AUSTRALIA. BUREAU OF STATISTICS. INFORMATION PAPER: REGIONAL LABOUR FORCE STATISTICS. Text in English. 1985. irreg., latest 1997. AUD 10 (effective 2001). **Document type:** *Government.*
Published by: Australian Bureau of Statistics, PO Box 10, Belconnen, ACT 2616, Australia. TEL 61-2-6252-5249, FAX 61-2-6252-6778, http://www.abs.gov.au.

339.021 AUS
AUSTRALIA. BUREAU OF STATISTICS. INFORMATION PAPER: REVIEW OF THE IMPORT PRICE INDEX AND EXPORT PRICE INDEX, AUSTRALIA. Text in English. 1999. irreg. AUD 10 (effective 2003). **Document type:** *Government.*
Published by: Australian Bureau of Statistics, PO Box 10, Belconnen, ACT 2616, Australia. TEL 61-2-6252-5249, FAX 61-2-6252-6778, http://www.abs.gov.au.

658.021 AUS
AUSTRALIA. BUREAU OF STATISTICS. INFORMATION PAPER: SEASONAL INFLUENCES ON RETAIL TRADE. Text in English. 1998. irreg. AUD 10 (effective 2003). **Document type:** *Government.*
Published by: Australian Bureau of Statistics, PO Box 10, Belconnen, ACT 2616, Australia. TEL 61-2-6252-5249, FAX 61-2-6252-6778, http://www.abs.gov.au.

336.021 AUS
AUSTRALIA. BUREAU OF STATISTICS. INFORMATION PAPER: THE USE OF INDIVIDUAL TAXPAYER DATA FOR A.B.S. REGIONAL STATISTICS - WAGE AND SALARY INDICATORS FOR SMALL AREAS. Text in English. 1995. irreg., latest 1996. AUD 10 (effective 2000).
Published by: Australian Bureau of Statistics, PO Box 10, Belconnen, ACT 2616, Australia. TEL 61-2-6252-5249, FAX 61-2-6252-6778, http://www.abs.gov.au.

339.021 AUS
AUSTRALIA. BUREAU OF STATISTICS. INFORMATION PAPER: UPGRADED AUSTRALIAN NATIONAL ACCOUNTS. Text in English. 1998. irreg. AUD 10 (effective 2002).
Published by: Australian Bureau of Statistics, PO Box 10, Belconnen, ACT 2616, Australia. TEL 61-2-6252-5249, FAX 61-2-6252-6778, http://www.abs.gov.au.

339.021 AUS
AUSTRALIA. BUREAU OF STATISTICS. INFORMATION PAPER: UPGRADED AUSTRALIAN NATIONAL ACCOUNTS: FINANCIAL ACCOUNTS. Text in English. 1998. irreg. AUD 23 (effective 2002).
Published by: Australian Bureau of Statistics, PO Box 10, Belconnen, ACT 2616, Australia. TEL 61-2-6252-5249, FAX 61-2-6252-6778, http://www.abs.gov.au.

332.6021 AUS
AUSTRALIA. BUREAU OF STATISTICS. INFORMATION PAPER: UPGRADED BALANCE OF PAYMENTS AND INTERNATIONAL INVESTMENT POSITION STATISTICS. Text in English. 1997. irreg. AUD 10; free by email (effective 2003). **Document type:** *Government.*
Published by: Australian Bureau of Statistics, PO Box 10, Belconnen, ACT 2616, Australia. TEL 61-2-6252-5249, FAX 61-2-6252-6778, http://www.abs.gov.au.

331.021 AUS
AUSTRALIA. BUREAU OF STATISTICS. INFORMATION PAPER: USING THE A S G C REMOTENESS STRUCTURE TO ANALYSE CHARACTERISTICS OF WAGE AND SALARY EARNERS OF AUSTRALIA. Text in English. 2000. irreg. AUD 10 (effective 2003). stat. **Document type:** *Government.*
Published by: Australian Bureau of Statistics, PO Box 10, Belconnen, ACT 2616, Australia. TEL 61-2-6252-5249, FAX 61-2-6252-6778, http://www.abs.gov.au.

331.021 AUS
AUSTRALIA. BUREAU OF STATISTICS. INFORMATION PAPER: WAGE COST INDEX, AUSTRALIA. Text in English. 1998. irreg., latest 2000. AUD 10 (effective 2003). **Document type:** *Government.*
Published by: Australian Bureau of Statistics, PO Box 10, Belconnen, ACT 2616, Australia. TEL 61-2-6252-5249, FAX 61-2-6252-6778, http://www.abs.gov.au.

338.021 AUS
AUSTRALIA. BUREAU OF STATISTICS. INNOVATION IN MANUFACTURING, AUSTRALIA. Text in English. 1994. irreg., latest 1996. AUD 17 (effective 2002). **Document type:** *Government.*
Published by: Australian Bureau of Statistics, PO Box 10, Belconnen, ACT 2616, Australia. TEL 61-2-6252-5249, FAX 61-2-6252-6778, http://www.abs.gov.au.

330.021 AUS
AUSTRALIA. BUREAU OF STATISTICS. INNOVATION IN SELECTED INDUSTRIES, AUSTRALIA. Text in English. 1994. irreg., latest 1998. AUD 22 (effective 1998). **Document type:** *Government.*
Published by: Australian Bureau of Statistics, PO Box 10, Belconnen, ACT 2616, Australia. TEL 61-2-6252-5249, FAX 61-2-6252-6778, http://www.abs.gov.au.

332.65021 AUS
AUSTRALIA. BUREAU OF STATISTICS. INTERNATIONAL INVESTMENT POSITION. AUSTRALIA: AUSTRALIAN SECURITIES HELD BY NOMINEES ON BEHALF OF NON-RESIDENTS. Text in English. 1987. a. AUD 100. **Document type:** *Government.* **Description:** Provides information on the value of Australian securities held by nominees on behalf of non-residents classified by type of security, institutional sector of the issuing enterprise and country of the non-resident investor.
Formerly: Foreign Investment, Australia: Australian Securities Held by Nominees on Behalf of Non-residents
Published by: Australian Bureau of Statistics, PO Box 10, Belconnen, ACT 2616, Australia. TEL 61-2-6252-5249, FAX 61-2-6252-6778, http://www.abs.gov.au.

332.6021 AUS
AUSTRALIA. BUREAU OF STATISTICS. INTERNATIONAL INVESTMENT POSITION, AUSTRALIA: SUPPLEMENTARY COUNTRY STATISTICS. Text in English. 1988. a. price varies. **Document type:** *Government.* **Description:** Contains details on country and industry of investment, level of investment, investment flows and associated income.
Formerly: Foreign Investment, Australia: Supplementary Country and Industry Statistics (1030-8997)
Related titles: ♦ Supplement(s): Australia. Bureau of Statistics. International Trade in Services, Australia. ISSN 1324-2601.
Published by: Australian Bureau of Statistics, PO Box 10, Belconnen, ACT 2616, Australia. TEL 61-2-6252-5249, FAX 61-2-6252-6778, http://www.abs.gov.au.

382.021 AUS
AUSTRALIA. BUREAU OF STATISTICS. INTERNATIONAL MERCHANDISE EXPORTS, AUSTRALIA - ELECTRONIC DELIVERY. Text in English. 2000. m. price varies.
Published by: Australian Bureau of Statistics, PO Box 10, Belconnen, ACT 2616, Australia. TEL 61-2-6252-5249, FAX 61-2-6252-6778, http://www.abs.gov.au.

332.6021.310 AUS ISSN 1328-2980
AUSTRALIA. BUREAU OF STATISTICS. INTERNATIONAL MERCHANDISE IMPORTS, AUSTRALIA. Text in English. 1994. m. AUD 18.50 newsstand/cover (effective 2003). **Document type:** *Government.* **Description:** Presents the total imports for the reference month only.
Supersedes in part (in 1997): Australia. Bureau of Statistics. Merchandise Imports, Australia: Balance of Payments Basis (1321-8271)
Published by: Australian Bureau of Statistics, PO Box 10, Belconnen, ACT 2616, Australia. TEL 61-2-6252-5249, FAX 61-2-6252-6778, http://www.abs.gov.au.

332.6021 AUS ISSN 1321-3512
HF3941
AUSTRALIA. BUREAU OF STATISTICS. INTERNATIONAL MERCHANDISE TRADE, AUSTRALIA. Text in English. 1978. q. AUD 27 newsstand/cover (effective 2003). **Document type:** *Government.*
Former titles: Foreign Trade, Australia: Merchandise Exports and Imports by Country (1037-9061); Exports and Imports, Australia: Trade with Selected Countries and Major Country Groups (1031-0304)
Published by: Australian Bureau of Statistics, PO Box 10, Belconnen, ACT 2616, Australia. TEL 61-2-6252-5249, FAX 61-2-6252-6778, http://www.abs.gov.au.

382.021 AUS
AUSTRALIA. BUREAU OF STATISTICS. INTERNATIONAL MERCHANDISE TRADE, AUSTRALIA: CONCEPTS, SOURCES AND METHODS. Text in English. 2001. irreg. AUD 35 (effective 2003).
Published by: Australian Bureau of Statistics, PO Box 10, Belconnen, ACT 2616, Australia. TEL 61-2-6252-5249, FAX 61-2-6252-6778, http://www.abs.gov.au.

382.021 AUS
AUSTRALIA. BUREAU OF STATISTICS. INTERNATIONAL TRADE, AUSTRALIA - INFORMATION CONSULTANCY AD HOC SERVICE. Text in English. irreg. price varies. **Document type:** *Government.* **Description:** Includes the full range of reported export and import data items.
Published by: Australian Bureau of Statistics, PO Box 10, Belconnen, ACT 2616, Australia. TEL 61-2-6252-5249, FAX 61-2-6252-6778, http://www.abs.gov.au.

332.6021 AUS ISSN 1328-2778
HF3941
AUSTRALIA. BUREAU OF STATISTICS. INTERNATIONAL TRADE IN GOODS AND SERVICES, AUSTRALIA. Text in English. 1997. m. AUD 19.50 newsstand/cover (effective 2003). **Document type:** *Government.* **Description:** Provides estimates for 15 months of the major aggregates for, and the balance on, international trade in goods and services.
Formed by the merger of (1976-1997): Australia. Bureau of Statistics. Balance of Payments, Australia (Canberra, 1976) (0313-2773); part of (1994-1997): Australia. Bureau of Statistics. Merchandise Imports, Australia: Balance of Payments Basis (1321-8271)
Published by: Australian Bureau of Statistics, PO Box 10, Belconnen, ACT 2616, Australia. TEL 61-2-6252-5249, FAX 61-2-6252-6778, http://www.abs.gov.au.

332.6021 AUS
AUSTRALIA. BUREAU OF STATISTICS. INTERNATIONAL TRADE IN GOODS AND SERVICES, AUSTRALIA: MONTHLY FORWARD SEASONAL FACTORS. Text in English. 1998. a. AUD 130 (effective 2003). **Document type:** *Government.*
Published by: Australian Bureau of Statistics, PO Box 10, Belconnen, ACT 2616, Australia. http://www.abs.gov.au.

382.021 AUS
AUSTRALIA. BUREAU OF STATISTICS. INTERNATIONAL TRADE IN GOODS AND SERVICES, MONTHLY FORWARD SEASONAL FACTORS SERVICE, AUSTRALIA. Text in English. 1998. a. price varies. **Document type:** *Government.*
Published by: Australian Bureau of Statistics, PO Box 10, Belconnen, ACT 2616, Australia. TEL 61-2-6252-5249, FAX 61-2-6252-6778, http://www.abs.gov.au.

332.6021 AUS ISSN 1324-2601
HG5150
AUSTRALIA. BUREAU OF STATISTICS. INTERNATIONAL TRADE IN SERVICES, AUSTRALIA. Text in English. 1993. a. AUD 29 per issue (effective 2001). **Document type:** *Government.* **Description:** Presents detailed tables on balance of payments accounts and international investment position for the latest six years.
Formed by the merger of (1987-1993): Australia. Bureau of Statistics. International Trade in Services, Australia (1034-0505); (1946-1993): Australia. Bureau of Statistics. Balance of Payments, Australia (Annual) (0045-0111); (1955-1993): Australia. Bureau of Statistics. International Investment Position, Australia (Annual) (1037-8782); Which was formerly: Foreign Investment, Australia (1031-2609)
Related titles: ♦ Supplement to: Australia. Bureau of Statistics. International Investment Position, Australia: Supplementary Country Statistics.
Published by: Australian Bureau of Statistics, PO Box 10, Belconnen, ACT 2616, Australia. TEL 61-2-6252-5249, FAX 61-2-6252-6778, http://www.abs.gov.au.

339.021 AUS ISSN 1445-2588
HF3941
AUSTRALIA. BUREAU OF STATISTICS. INTERNATIONAL TRADE PRICE INDEXES, AUSTRALIA. Text in English. 2001. q. AUD 19.50 (effective 2003). **Document type:** *Government.*
Published by: Australian Bureau of Statistics, PO Box 10, Belconnen, ACT 2616, Australia. http://www.abs.gov.au.

331.021 AUS
AUSTRALIA. BUREAU OF STATISTICS. INVOLVEMENT IN ORGANIZED SPORT AND PHYSICAL ACTIVITY, AUSTRALIA. Text in English. 1993. irreg., latest 2001. AUD 22 (effective 2003). **Document type:** *Government.*
Published by: Australian Bureau of Statistics, PO Box 10, Belconnen, ACT 2616, Australia. http://www.abs.gov.au.

331.11021 790.1021 AUS
AUSTRALIA. BUREAU OF STATISTICS. INVOLVEMENT IN SPORT, AUSTRALIA. Text in English. 1993. irreg., latest 2001. AUD 19 (effective 2001). **Document type:** *Government.*

B

Published by: Australian Bureau of Statistics, PO Box 10, Belconnen, ACT 2616, Australia. TEL 61-2-6252-5249, FAX 61-2-6252-6778, http://www.abs.gov.au.

331.021 AUS ISSN 0815-9971
AUSTRALIA. BUREAU OF STATISTICS. JOB SEARCH EXPERIENCE, AUSTRALIA. Text in English. 1976. a. AUD 23 (effective 2003). **Document type:** *Government.*
Published by: Australian Bureau of Statistics, PO Box 10, Belconnen, ACT 2616, Australia. TEL 61-2-6252-5249, FAX 61-2-6252-6778, http://www.abs.gov.au.

331.021 AUS ISSN 1038-6637
AUSTRALIA. BUREAU OF STATISTICS. LABOUR COSTS, AUSTRALIA. Text in English. 1985. quinquennial. AUD 18 (effective 2002). **Document type:** *Government.* **Description:** Contains estimates of major labor costs for the private and public sectors, including employee earnings, employee payments for superannuation, workers' compensation, payroll tax and fringe benefits tax paid.
Former titles: Major Labour Costs, Australia (1030-9020); Major Labour Costs, Private Sector, Australia (0819-5080)
Published by: Australian Bureau of Statistics, PO Box 10, Belconnen, ACT 2616, Australia. TEL 61-2-6252-5249, FAX 61-2-6252-6778, http://www.abs.gov.au.

331.021 AUS ISSN 1030-0996
HD5850
AUSTRALIA. BUREAU OF STATISTICS. LABOUR FORCE, AUSTRALIA. Text in English. 1966. m. AUD 27 (effective 2003). **Document type:** *Government.* **Description:** Provides information on the civilian population aged 15 and over, classified by sex, labor force status, age, marital status, education, birthplace, occupation and hours worked.
Incorporates (1979-1994): Weekly Earnings of Employees (Distribution), Australia (1031-0819)
Published by: Australian Bureau of Statistics, PO Box 10, Belconnen, ACT 2616, Australia. TEL 61-2-6252-5249, FAX 61-2-6252-6778, http://www.abs.gov.au.

331.021 AUS ISSN 1031-038X
AUSTRALIA. BUREAU OF STATISTICS. LABOUR FORCE, AUSTRALIA, PRELIMINARY. Text in English. 1972. m. AUD 22 newsstand/cover (effective 2003). **Document type:** *Government.* **Description:** Provides information on the civilian population aged 15 and over, classified by sex, labor force status, and full-time and part-time status and other items.
Related titles: Diskette ed.: Australia. Bureau of Statistics. Labour Force, Australia - Preliminary Data on Floppy Disk. ISSN 1033-3940. AUD 47 (effective 2003).
Published by: Australian Bureau of Statistics, PO Box 10, Belconnen, ACT 2616, Australia. TEL 61-2-6252-5249, FAX 61-2-6252-6778, http://www.abs.gov.au.

331.021 AUS ISSN 1443-0045
AUSTRALIA. BUREAU OF STATISTICS. LABOUR FORCE, AUSTRALIA - SEASONAL FACTORS. Text in English. 2000. a. price varies. **Document type:** *Government.*
Published by: Australian Bureau of Statistics, PO Box 10, Belconnen, ACT 2616, Australia. TEL 61-2-6252-5249, FAX 61-2-6252-6778, http://www.abs.gov.au.

331.11021 AUS
AUSTRALIA. BUREAU OF STATISTICS. LABOUR FORCE, AUSTRALIA - STANDARD TABLES ON MICROFICHE. Text in English. irreg. price varies. **Document type:** *Government.*
Media: Microfiche.
Published by: Australian Bureau of Statistics, PO Box 10, Belconnen, ACT 2616, Australia. TEL 61-2-6252-5249, FAX 61-2-6252-6778, http://www.abs.gov.au.

331.021 AUS ISSN 1031-0398
AUSTRALIA. BUREAU OF STATISTICS. LABOUR FORCE EXPERIENCE, AUSTRALIA. Text in English. 1969. biennial. AUD 22 (effective 2003).
Published by: Australian Bureau of Statistics, PO Box 10, Belconnen, ACT 2616, Australia. TEL 61-2-6252-5249, FAX 61-2-6252-6778, http://www.abs.gov.au.

331.11021 AUS
AUSTRALIA. BUREAU OF STATISTICS. LABOUR FORCE PROJECTIONS, AUSTRALIA. Text in English. 1992. irreg., latest 1999. AUD 18.50 (effective 2003). **Document type:** *Government.*
Published by: Australian Bureau of Statistics, PO Box 10, Belconnen, ACT 2616, Australia. TEL 61-2-6252-5249, FAX 61-2-6252-6778, http://www.abs.gov.au.

331.021 AUS
AUSTRALIA. BUREAU OF STATISTICS. LABOUR FORCE, SELECTED SUMMARY TABLES, AUSTRALIA. Text in English. 1998. m. AUD 47 (effective 2003). **Document type:** *Government.*
Published by: Australian Bureau of Statistics, PO Box 10, Belconnen, ACT 2616, Australia. TEL 61-2-6252-5249, FAX 61-2-6252-6778, http://www.abs.gov.au.

331.021 AUS ISSN 1031-0401
AUSTRALIA. BUREAU OF STATISTICS. LABOUR FORCE STATUS AND OTHER CHARACTERISTICS OF FAMILIES, AUSTRALIA. Text in English. 1979. a. AUD 20 (effective 2003). **Document type:** *Government.*
Published by: Australian Bureau of Statistics, PO Box 10, Belconnen, ACT 2616, Australia. TEL 61-2-6252-5249, FAX 61-2-6252-6778, http://www.abs.gov.au.

331.11021 AUS ISSN 1326-9380
AUSTRALIA. BUREAU OF STATISTICS. LABOUR FORCE STATUS AND OTHER CHARACTERISTICS OF MIGRANTS, AUSTRALIA. Text in English. 1984. triennial. AUD 19.50 (effective 2003). **Document type:** *Government.*
Published by: Australian Bureau of Statistics, PO Box 10, Belconnen, ACT 2616, Australia. TEL 61-2-6252-5249, FAX 61-2-6252-6778, http://www.abs.gov.au.

331.021 AUS ISSN 0729-364X
AUSTRALIA. BUREAU OF STATISTICS. LABOUR MOBILITY, AUSTRALIA. Text in English. 1972. biennial. AUD 22 (effective 2003).
Published by: Australian Bureau of Statistics, PO Box 10, Belconnen, ACT 2616, Australia. TEL 61-2-6252-5249, FAX 61-2-6252-6778, http://www.abs.gov.au.

331.021 AUS
AUSTRALIA. BUREAU OF STATISTICS. LABOUR STATISTICS: CONCEPTS, SOURCES AND METHODS. Text in English. 1986. irreg., latest 2001. AUD 62 (effective 2003).
Published by: Australian Bureau of Statistics, PO Box 10, Belconnen, ACT 2616, Australia. TEL 61-2-6252-5249, FAX 61-2-6252-6778, http://www.abs.gov.au.

331.021 AUS ISSN 1031-041X
AUSTRALIA. BUREAU OF STATISTICS. LABOUR STATISTICS IN BRIEF, AUSTRALIA. Text in English. 1986. a. free (effective 2003). **Document type:** *Government.* **Description:** Presents a range of summary statistics with an emphasis on simple tabular and graphical presentations.
Published by: Australian Bureau of Statistics, PO Box 10, Belconnen, ACT 2616, Australia. TEL 61-2-6252-5249, FAX 61-2-6252-6778, http://www.abs.gov.au.

332.021 AUS ISSN 1327-4376
AUSTRALIA. BUREAU OF STATISTICS. LENDING FINANCE, AUSTRALIA. Text in English. 1997. m. AUD 19 newsstand/cover (effective 2003). **Document type:** *Government.* **Description:** Contains time series data on the value of monthly commitments for secured housing finance, other personal finance, commercial and lease finance.
Published by: Australian Bureau of Statistics, PO Box 10, Belconnen, ACT 2616, Australia. TEL 61-2-6252-5249, FAX 61-2-6252-6778, http://www.abs.gov.au.

371.3021 AUS ISSN 1442-8598
AUSTRALIA. BUREAU OF STATISTICS. LOCATIONS OF WORK, AUSTRALIA. Text in English. 1989. triennial. AUD 20 (effective 2003). **Document type:** *Government.*
Formerly (until 2001): Australia. Bureau of Statistics. Persons Employed at Home, Australia (1039-1088)
Published by: Australian Bureau of Statistics, PO Box 10, Belconnen, ACT 2616, Australia. TEL 61-2-6252-5249, FAX 61-2-6252-6778, http://www.abs.gov.au.

332.021 AUS ISSN 1037-7786
HG5894.5
AUSTRALIA. BUREAU OF STATISTICS. MANAGED FUNDS, AUSTRALIA. Text in English. 1992. q. AUD 20 newsstand/cover (effective 2003). **Document type:** *Government.* **Description:** Provides information about money pooled for investment purposes on a consolidated basis for a range of institutions, classified according to type of fund and type of asset.
Incorporates (1989-1993): Assets and Liabilities of Friendly Societies, Australia (1036-8299); (1989-1993): Common Funds, Australia (1037-2857); (1985-1993): Public Unit Trusts, Australia (0818-9722); (1983-1994): Cash Management Trusts, Australia (0813-1139)
Published by: Australian Bureau of Statistics, PO Box 10, Belconnen, ACT 2616, Australia. TEL 61-2-6252-5249, FAX 61-2-6252-6778, http://www.abs.gov.au.

338.0021 AUS ISSN 1329-4741
AUSTRALIA. BUREAU OF STATISTICS. MANUFACTURING, AUSTRALIA. Text in English. 1997. a. AUD 37 (effective 2003). **Document type:** *Government.* **Description:** Includes industry performance, employment and output levels, export activity, cost structures and profits.
Published by: Australian Bureau of Statistics, PO Box 10, Belconnen, ACT 2616, Australia. TEL 61-2-6252-5249, FAX 61-2-6252-6778, http://www.abs.gov.au.

330.021 AUS ISSN 1036-2738
HD9738.A8 CODEN: MAAWFZ
AUSTRALIA. BUREAU OF STATISTICS. MANUFACTURING INDUSTRY, AUSTRALIA. Text in English. 1968. a. AUD 24 (effective 2003). **Document type:** *Government.* **Description:** Presents final results from the manufacturing census, including the number of establishments, employment, and wages and salaries.
Formerly (until 1989): Manufacturing Industry: Details of Operations, Australia (0312-1607)
Published by: Australian Bureau of Statistics, PO Box 10, Belconnen, ACT 2616, Australia. TEL 61-2-6252-5249, FAX 61-2-6252-6778, http://www.abs.gov.au.

330.021 AUS ISSN 1033-4033
AUSTRALIA. BUREAU OF STATISTICS. MANUFACTURING INDUSTRY, AUSTRALIA, PRELIMINARY. Text in English. 1968. a. AUD 18.50 (effective 2003). **Document type:** *Government.* **Description:** Contains statistics on the Australian manufacturing sector, including number of establishments, employment, wages and salaries, and turnover.
Formerly: Census of Manufacturing Establishments, Australia, Preliminary
Published by: Australian Bureau of Statistics, PO Box 10, Belconnen, ACT 2616, Australia. TEL 61-2-6252-5249, FAX 61-2-6252-6778, http://www.abs.gov.au.

338.021 AUS ISSN 1323-3645
HD9738.A8
AUSTRALIA. BUREAU OF STATISTICS. MANUFACTURING PRODUCTION, AUSTRALIA. Text in English. 1961. q. AUD 18.50 per issue (effective 2003). **Document type:** *Government.* **Description:** Contains estimates of production for 28 major indicators, including metals and textiles.
Formerly: Australia. Bureau of Statistics. Manufacturing Production, Australia, Preliminary (1035-9311); Supersedes in part (1989-1994): Manufacturing Production, Australia: Metal Products (1035-9184); Which was formerly: Production of Metal Products, Australia
Published by: Australian Bureau of Statistics, PO Box 10, Belconnen, ACT 2616, Australia. TEL 61-2-6252-5249, FAX 61-2-6252-6778, http://www.abs.gov.au.

B

658.021 AUS
AUSTRALIA. BUREAU OF STATISTICS. MARKET RESEARCH SERVICES, AUSTRALIA. Text in English. 2000. irreg., latest 2003. AUD 21 (effective 2003). **Document type:** *Government.*
Published by: Australian Bureau of Statistics, PO Box 10, Belconnen, ACT 2616, Australia. TEL 61-2-6252-5249, FAX 61-2-6252-6778, http://www.abs.gov.au.

330.9021 AUS ISSN 1039-1444
AUSTRALIA. BUREAU OF STATISTICS. MEASURING AUSTRALIA'S ECONOMY. Text in English. 1993. biennial. AUD 46 (effective 2003). **Document type:** *Government.*
Published by: Australian Bureau of Statistics, PO Box 10, Belconnen, ACT 2616, Australia. TEL 61-2-6252-5249, FAX 61-2-6252-6778, http://www.abs.gov.au.

330.9021 AUS ISSN 1445-7121
AUSTRALIA. BUREAU OF STATISTICS. MEASURING AUSTRALIA'S PROGRESS. Text in English. 2002. a. AUD 39 (effective 2003). **Document type:** *Government.*
Published by: Australian Bureau of Statistics, PO Box 10, Belconnen, ACT 2616, Australia. http://www.abs.gov.au.

330.9021 AUS
AUSTRALIA. BUREAU OF STATISTICS. MODELLERS' DATABASE. Text in English. 1995. q. AUD 172 (effective 2003).
Media: Diskette.
Published by: Australian Bureau of Statistics, PO Box 10, Belconnen, ACT 2616, Australia. TEL 61-2-6252-5249, FAX 61-2-6252-6778, http://www.abs.gov.au.

331.021 AUS
AUSTRALIA. BUREAU OF STATISTICS. MULTIPLE JOBHOLDING, AUSTRALIA. Text in English. 1965. irreg. AUD 18 (effective 2002).
Published by: Australian Bureau of Statistics, PO Box 10, Belconnen, ACT 2616, Australia. TEL 61-2-6252-5249, FAX 61-2-6252-6778, http://www.abs.gov.au.

339.021 AUS ISSN 1031-2641
AUSTRALIA. BUREAU OF STATISTICS. N I F - 10S MODEL DATA BASE MANUAL. (National Income Forecasting) Text in English. 1989. q. AUD 40. **Document type:** *Government.* **Description:** Provides over 300 time series forming the data base for the National Income Forecasting Model of the Australian economy.
Related titles: Diskette ed.; Magnetic Tape ed.; Microfiche ed.
Published by: Australian Bureau of Statistics, PO Box 10, Belconnen, ACT 2616, Australia. TEL 61-2-6252-5249, FAX 61-2-6252-6778, http://www.abs.gov.au.

332.1021 AUS
▼ **AUSTRALIA. BUREAU OF STATISTICS. NEW SOUTH WALES OFFICE. GOVERNMENT FINANCIAL ESTIMATES, NEW SOUTH WALES, ELECTRONIC DELIVERY.** Text in English. 2003. a. price varies. stat. **Document type:** *Government.*
Media: Online - full text.
Published by: Australian Bureau of Statistics, New South Wales Office, St. Andrews House, 5th Fl., Sydney Square George St., Sydney, NSW 2000, Australia. TEL 61-2-9268-4620, FAX 61-2-9268-4668, http://www.abs.gov.au.

338.021 AUS ISSN 1326-9836
AUSTRALIA. BUREAU OF STATISTICS. NEW SOUTH WALES OFFICE. MANUFACTURING INDUSTRY, NEW SOUTH WALES AND AUSTRALIAN CAPITAL TERRITORY. Text in English. 1990. a. AUD 21 (effective 2003). **Document type:** *Government.*

▼ *new title* ➤ *refereed* ✶ *unverified* ♦ *full entry avail.*

Published by: Australian Bureau of Statistics, New South Wales Office, St. Andrews House, 5th Fl., Sydney Square George St., Sydney, NSW 2000, Australia. TEL 61-2-9268-4620, FAX 61-2-9268-4668, http://www.abs.gov.au.

658.021   AUS
AUSTRALIA. BUREAU OF STATISTICS. NEW SOUTH WALES OFFICE. RETAILING IN NEW SOUTH WALES. Text in English. 1968. irreg., latest 1991. AUD 15. **Document type:** *Government.* **Description:** Contains details by industry group and statistical local area of number of retail locations, employment, wages and salaries, turnover and floorspace.
Formerly: Retail Industry, Small Area Statistics, New South Wales
Published by: Australian Bureau of Statistics, New South Wales Office, St. Andrews House, 5th Fl., Sydney Square George St., Sydney, NSW 2000, Australia. http://www.abs.gov.au.

▼ 332.1021   AUS
AUSTRALIA. BUREAU OF STATISTICS. NORTHERN TERRITORY OFFICE. GOVERNMENT FINANCIAL ESTIMATES, NORTHERN TERRITORY, ELECTRONIC DELIVERY. Text in English. 2003. a. price varies. stat. **Document type:** *Government.*
Media: Online - full text.
Published by: Australian Bureau of Statistics, Northern Territory Office, 5th Fl., 81 Smith St, Darwin, N.T. 0800, Australia. TEL 61-8-8943-2110, FAX 61-8-8981-1218, http://www.abs.gov.au.

331.021   AUS
AUSTRALIA. BUREAU OF STATISTICS. OCCASIONAL PAPER: A RISK INDEX APPROACH TO UNEMPLOYMENT - AN APPLICATION USING THE SURVEY OF EMPLOYMENT AND UNEMPLOYMENT PATTERNS. Text in English. 1998. irreg. AUD 24 (effective 2003). **Document type:** *Government.*
Published by: Australian Bureau of Statistics, PO Box 10, Belconnen, ACT 2616, Australia. TEL 61-2-6252-5249, FAX 61-2-6252-6778, http://www.abs.gov.au.

330.9021   AUS
AUSTRALIA. BUREAU OF STATISTICS. OCCASIONAL PAPER: AUSTRALIAN BUSINESS REGISTER - A SNAPSHOT. Text in English. 2000. irreg. AUD 19.50 (effective 2003). **Document type:** *Government.*
Published by: Australian Bureau of Statistics, PO Box 10, Belconnen, ACT 2616, Australia. http://www.abs.gov.au.

331.021   AUS
AUSTRALIA. BUREAU OF STATISTICS. OCCASIONAL PAPER: DYNAMICS OF EARNED INCOME - AN APPLICATION USING THE SURVEY OF EMPLOYMENT AND UNEMPLOYMENT PATTERNS. Text in English. 2000. irreg. AUD 22 (effective 2001). **Document type:** *Government.*
Published by: Australian Bureau of Statistics, PO Box 10, Belconnen, ACT 2616, Australia. TEL 61-2-6252-5249, FAX 61-2-6252-6778, http://www.abs.gov.au.

331.021   AUS
AUSTRALIA. BUREAU OF STATISTICS. OCCASIONAL PAPER: JOB QUALITY AND CHURNING OF THE POOL OF THE UNEMPLOYED. Text in English. 1997. irreg. AUD 33 (effective 2003). **Document type:** *Government.*
Published by: Australian Bureau of Statistics, PO Box 10, Belconnen, ACT 2616, Australia. TEL 61-2-6252-5249, FAX 61-2-6252-6778, http://www.abs.gov.au.

331.11021   AUS
AUSTRALIA. BUREAU OF STATISTICS. OCCASIONAL PAPER: LABOUR FORCE CHARACTERISTICS, INDIGENOUS AUSTRALIANS. Text in English. 1998. every 5 yrs. AUD 18.50 (effective 1998). **Document type:** *Government.*
Published by: Australian Bureau of Statistics, PO Box 10, Belconnen, ACT 2616, Australia. TEL 61-2-6252-5249, FAX 61-2-6252-6778, http://www.abs.gov.au.

331.021   AUS
AUSTRALIA. BUREAU OF STATISTICS. OCCASIONAL PAPER: LABOUR MARKET DYNAMICS IN AUSTRALIA - AN APPLICATION USING THE SURVEY OF EMPLOYMENT AND UNEMPLOYMENT PATTERNS. Text in English. 2000. irreg. AUD 23 (effective 2003). **Document type:** *Government.*
Published by: Australian Bureau of Statistics, PO Box 10, Belconnen, ACT 2616, Australia. TEL 61-2-6252-5249, FAX 61-2-6252-6778, http://www.abs.gov.au.

331.021   AUS
AUSTRALIA. BUREAU OF STATISTICS. OCCASIONAL PAPER: LABOUR MARKET OUTCOMES OF LOW PAID ADULT WORKERS. Text in English. 1997. irreg. AUD 22 (effective 2003). **Document type:** *Government.*
Published by: Australian Bureau of Statistics, PO Box 10, Belconnen, ACT 2616, Australia. TEL 61-2-6252-5249, FAX 61-2-6252-6778, http://www.abs.gov.au.

331.021   AUS
AUSTRALIA. BUREAU OF STATISTICS. OCCASIONAL PAPER: LABOUR MARKET PROGRAMS, UNEMPLOYMENT AND EMPLOYMENT HAZARDS. Text in English. 1997. irreg. AUD 21 (effective 2003). **Document type:** *Government.*
Published by: Australian Bureau of Statistics, PO Box 10, Belconnen, ACT 2616, Australia. TEL 61-2-6252-5249, FAX 61-2-6252-6778, http://www.abs.gov.au.

331.021   AUS
AUSTRALIA. BUREAU OF STATISTICS. OCCASIONAL PAPER: THE DYNAMICS OF WELFARE RECEIPT AND LABOUR MARKET STATUS. Text in English. 1997. irreg. AUD 25 (effective 2000).
Published by: Australian Bureau of Statistics, PO Box 10, Belconnen, ACT 2616, Australia. TEL 61-2-6252-5249, FAX 61-2-6252-6778, http://www.abs.gov.au.

331.021   AUS   ISSN 0819-9914
AUSTRALIA. BUREAU OF STATISTICS. PERSONS NOT IN THE LABOUR FORCE, AUSTRALIA. Text in English. 1979. a. AUD 23 (effective 2003).
Published by: Australian Bureau of Statistics, PO Box 10, Belconnen, ACT 2616, Australia. TEL 61-2-6252-5249, FAX 61-2-6252-6778, http://www.abs.gov.au.

332.021   AUS   ISSN 1323-2568
AUSTRALIA. BUREAU OF STATISTICS. PRIVATE NEW CAPITAL EXPENDITURE AND EXPECTED EXPENDITURE, AUSTRALIA. Text in English. 1947. q. AUD 20 newsstand/cover (effective 2003). **Document type:** *Government.* **Description:** Contains estimates of actual and expected new capital expenditure by type of asset and by selected Australian and New Zealand Standard Industrial Classification subdivisions.
Incorporates (1963-1994): Private New Capital Expenditure, Australia, Actual and Expected Expenditure (0819-002X); **Formerly:** Private New Capital Expenditure, Australia. Actual and Expected Expenditure, Preliminary (1033-5048)
Published by: Australian Bureau of Statistics, PO Box 10, Belconnen, ACT 2616, Australia. TEL 61-2-6252-5249, FAX 61-2-6252-6778, http://www.abs.gov.au.

339.021   AUS   ISSN 1445-2618
AUSTRALIA. BUREAU OF STATISTICS. PRODUCER PRICE INDEXES, AUSTRALIA. Text in English. 2001. q. AUD 24 (effective 2003). **Document type:** *Government.*
Published by: Australian Bureau of Statistics, PO Box 10, Belconnen, ACT 2616, Australia. http://www.abs.gov.au.

330.021   AUS   ISSN 1036-3785
AUSTRALIA. BUREAU OF STATISTICS. PROFILES OF AUSTRALIAN BUSINESS. Text in English. 1992. irreg., latest 1995. AUD 23. **Document type:** *Government.* **Description:** Contains statistical information extracted from the ABS Business Register.
Published by: Australian Bureau of Statistics, PO Box 10, Belconnen, ACT 2616, Australia. TEL 61-2-6252-5249, FAX 61-2-6252-6778, http://www.abs.gov.au.

332.021   AUS
AUSTRALIA. BUREAU OF STATISTICS. PUBLIC UNIT TRUSTS, AUSTRALIA. Text in English. 1993. q. AUD 47 (effective 2003).
Published by: Australian Bureau of Statistics, PO Box 10, Belconnen, ACT 2616, Australia. TEL 61-2-6252-5249, FAX 61-2-6252-6778, http://www.abs.gov.au.

▼ 332.1021   AUS
AUSTRALIA. BUREAU OF STATISTICS. QUEENSLAND OFFICE. GOVERNMENT FINANCIAL ESTIMATES, QUEENSLAND, ELECTRONIC DELIVERY. Text in English. 2003. a. price varies. stat. **Document type:** *Government.*
Media: Online - full text.
Published by: Australian Bureau of Statistics, Queensland Office, 313 Adelaide St, Brisbane, QLD 4000, Australia. TEL 61-7-3222-6350, FAX 61-7-3222-6283, http://www.abs.gov.au.

330.021   AUS   ISSN 1036-2762
AUSTRALIA. BUREAU OF STATISTICS. QUEENSLAND OFFICE. MANUFACTURING INDUSTRY, QUEENSLAND. Text in English. 1968. a. AUD 21 (effective 2003). **Document type:** *Government.* **Description:** Presents final detailed results from the manufacturing census for structural variables: number of establishments, employment, wages and salaries, turnover, stocks, purchases and more, value added and fixed capital expenditure by industry group.
Formerly (until 1990): Manufacturing Establishments: Details of Operations, Queensland (0818-7185)
Published by: Australian Bureau of Statistics, Queensland Office, 313 Adelaide St, Brisbane, QLD 4000, Australia. TEL 61-7-3222-6350, FAX 61-7-3222-6283, http://www.abs.gov.au.

330.021   AUS
AUSTRALIA. BUREAU OF STATISTICS. QUEENSLAND OFFICE. RETAIL INDUSTRY: SMALL AREA STATISTICS, QUEENSLAND. Text in English. 1969. every 5 yrs. AUD 10.50. **Description:** Presents retail establishments: number of establishments, employment, trading hours, turnover and total floor space by statistical retail areas, statistical divisions and industry class; establishments, employment, wages and salaries, turnover and total floor space by statistical local areas, statistical divisions and statistical districts.
Formerly: Census of Retail Establishments and Selected Service Establishments: Industry Details for Statistical Retail Areas
Related titles: Diskette ed.
Published by: Australian Bureau of Statistics, Queensland Office, 313 Adelaide St, Brisbane, QLD 4000, Australia. TEL 61-7-3222-6350, FAX 61-7-3222-6283, http://www.abs.gov.au.

331.021   AUS
AUSTRALIA. BUREAU OF STATISTICS. QUEENSLAND OFFICE. WORKING HOURS OF WAGE AND SALARY EARNERS, QUEENSLAND. Text in English. 1999. irreg. AUD 15.50 (effective 2003). **Document type:** *Government.*
Published by: Australian Bureau of Statistics, Queensland Office, 313 Adelaide St, Brisbane, QLD 4000, Australia. TEL 61-7-3222-6350, FAX 61-7-3222-6283, http://www.abs.gov.au.

330.021   AUS   ISSN 0819-9876
AUSTRALIA. BUREAU OF STATISTICS. RESEARCH AND EXPERIMENTAL DEVELOPMENT, ALL SECTOR SUMMARY (INTER-YEAR SURVEY), AUSTRALIA. Text in English. 1985. biennial. AUD 10 per issue. **Document type:** *Government.* **Description:** Contains estimates of the level of distribution of expenditure and human resources devoted to research and experimental development carried out by business enterprises, government, higher education and private non-profit sectors in Australia.
Published by: Australian Bureau of Statistics, PO Box 10, Belconnen, ACT 2616, Australia. TEL 61-2-6252-5249, FAX 61-2-6252-6778, http://www.abs.gov.au.

330.021   AUS   ISSN 0159-1584
AUSTRALIA. BUREAU OF STATISTICS. RESEARCH AND EXPERIMENTAL DEVELOPMENT, BUSINESS ENTERPRISES, AUSTRALIA, PRELIMINARY. Text in English. 1978. biennial. **Document type:** *Government.* **Description:** Covers expenditure and human resources devoted to research and experimental development carried out in Australia by business enterprises, classified by broad industry group.
Published by: Australian Bureau of Statistics, PO Box 10, Belconnen, ACT 2616, Australia. TEL 61-2-6252-5249, FAX 61-2-6252-6778, http://www.abs.gov.au.

330.021   AUS   ISSN 1442-5440
AUSTRALIA. BUREAU OF STATISTICS. RESEARCH AND EXPERIMENTAL DEVELOPMENT, BUSINESSES, AUSTRALIA. Text in English. 1976. a. AUD 21 (effective 2003). **Document type:** *Government.* **Description:** Covers expenditure and human resources devoted to research and experimental development carried out by business enterprises in Australia.
Formerly: Australia. Bureau of Statistics. Research and Experimental Development, Business Enterprises, Australia (0728-5140); Which incorporates (1983-1994): Research and Experimental Development, Business Enterprises (Inter-year Survey), Australia
Published by: Australian Bureau of Statistics, PO Box 10, Belconnen, ACT 2616, Australia. TEL 61-2-6252-5249, FAX 61-2-6252-6778, http://www.abs.gov.au.

330.021   AUS   ISSN 1444-2663
AUSTRALIA. BUREAU OF STATISTICS. RESEARCH AND EXPERIMENTAL DEVELOPMENT, GOVERNMENT AND PRIVATE NON-PROFIT ORGANISATIONS, AUSTRALIA. Text in English. 1978. biennial. AUD 22 (effective 2003). **Document type:** *Government.* **Description:** Provides statistics on expenditure and human resources devoted to research and experimental development carried out by general government organizations.
Former titles (until 2000): Australia. Bureau of Statistics. Research and Experimental Development, General Government and Private Non-Profit Organisations, Australia (1032-6219); (until 1985): Research and Experimental Development. General Government Organisations, Australia (0729-5014)
Published by: Australian Bureau of Statistics, PO Box 10, Belconnen, ACT 2616, Australia. TEL 61-2-6252-5249, FAX 61-2-6252-6778, http://www.abs.gov.au.

658.021   AUS
AUSTRALIA. BUREAU OF STATISTICS. RETAIL INDUSTRY, AUSTRALIA. Text in English. 1968. irreg., latest 1998. AUD 21 (effective 2003). **Document type:** *Government.* **Description:** Contains details by industry of number of business units, employment, wages and salaries, income and expenditure, operating profit, gross product and selected performance measures.
Formerly: Retail Industry: Details of Operations, Australia
Published by: Australian Bureau of Statistics, PO Box 10, Belconnen, ACT 2616, Australia. TEL 61-2-6252-5249, FAX 61-2-6252-6778, http://www.abs.gov.au.

658.8021   AUS
AUSTRALIA. BUREAU OF STATISTICS. RETAIL INDUSTRY, AUSTRALIA: COMMODITY SALES. Text in English. 1992. irreg., latest 1998. AUD 21 (effective 2003). **Document type:** *Government.*
Published by: Australian Bureau of Statistics, PO Box 10, Belconnen, ACT 2616, Australia. TEL 61-2-6252-5249, FAX 61-2-6252-6778, http://www.abs.gov.au.

658.0021   AUS
AUSTRALIA. BUREAU OF STATISTICS. RETAIL INDUSTRY, STATE AND TERRITORY SUMMARY. Text in English. 1992. irreg. AUD 30 (effective 1998). **Document type:** *Government.*
Published by: Australian Bureau of Statistics, PO Box 10, Belconnen, ACT 2616, Australia. TEL 61-2-6252-5249, FAX 61-2-6252-6778, http://www.abs.gov.au.

330.021 AUS ISSN 1032-3651
HF5429.6.A8
AUSTRALIA. BUREAU OF STATISTICS. RETAIL TRADE, AUSTRALIA. Text in English. 1961. m. AUD 20 (effective 2003). **Document type:** *Government.* **Description:** Contains monthly estimates of turnover for retail and selected service establishments.
Published by: Australian Bureau of Statistics, PO Box 10, Belconnen, ACT 2616, Australia. TEL 61-2-6252-5249, FAX 61-2-6252-6778, http://www.abs.gov.au.

658.021 AUS ISSN 1031-8046
AUSTRALIA. BUREAU OF STATISTICS. RETAIL TRADE, AUSTRALIA: COMMODITY DETAILS. Text in English. 1988. irreg. AUD 18. **Document type:** *Government.* **Description:** Annual sales for major commodity groups for Australia, each State and Territory.
Published by: Australian Bureau of Statistics, PO Box 10, Belconnen, ACT 2616, Australia. TEL 61-2-6252-5249, FAX 61-2-6252-6778, http://www.abs.gov.au.

658.021 AUS
AUSTRALIA. BUREAU OF STATISTICS. RETAIL TRADE SPECIAL DATA SERVICE: CUSTOMISED REPORTS - DATA REPORT. Text in English. irreg. price varies. **Document type:** *Government.*
Published by: Australian Bureau of Statistics, PO Box 10, Belconnen, ACT 2616, Australia. TEL 61-2-6252-5249, FAX 61-2-6252-6778, http://www.abs.gov.au.

658.021 AUS
AUSTRALIA. BUREAU OF STATISTICS. RETAIL TRADE SPECIAL DATA SERVICES: PERFORMANCE REPORTS - DATA REPORT. Text in English. irreg. price varies.
Published by: Australian Bureau of Statistics, PO Box 10, Belconnen, ACT 2616, Australia. TEL 61-2-6252-5249, FAX 61-2-6252-6778, http://www.abs.gov.au.

658.021 AUS
AUSTRALIA. BUREAU OF STATISTICS. RETAIL TRADE SPECIAL DATA SERVICES: SELF COMPARISON REPORTS - DATA REPORT. Text in English. irreg. price varies. **Document type:** *Government.*
Published by: Australian Bureau of Statistics, PO Box 10, Belconnen, ACT 2616, Australia. TEL 61-2-6252-5249, FAX 61-2-6252-6778, http://www.abs.gov.au.

658.021 AUS
AUSTRALIA. BUREAU OF STATISTICS. RETAILING IN AUSTRALIA. Text in English. 1979. irreg., latest 1992. **Document type:** *Government.* **Description:** Presents results from the retail industry location census.
Published by: Australian Bureau of Statistics, PO Box 10, Belconnen, ACT 2616, Australia. TEL 61-2-6252-5249, FAX 61-2-6252-6778, http://www.abs.gov.au.

331.021 AUS ISSN 0819-2855
AUSTRALIA. BUREAU OF STATISTICS. RETIREMENT AND RETIREMENT INTENTIONS, AUSTRALIA. Text in English. 1980. triennial. AUD 21 (effective 2002). **Document type:** *Government.*
Published by: Australian Bureau of Statistics, PO Box 10, Belconnen, ACT 2616, Australia. TEL 61-2-6252-5249, FAX 61-2-6252-6778, http://www.abs.gov.au.

331.11021 AUS
AUSTRALIA. BUREAU OF STATISTICS. RETRENCHMENT AND REDUNDANCY, AUSTRALIA. Text in English. 1998. irreg., latest 2002. AUD 22 (effective 2003). **Document type:** *Government.* **Description:** Provides information on aspects of structural change in the Australian economy relating to employment.
Published by: Australian Bureau of Statistics, PO Box 10, Belconnen, ACT 2616, Australia. TEL 61-2-6252-5249, FAX 61-2-6252-6778, http://www.abs.gov.au.

659.021 AUS
AUSTRALIA. BUREAU OF STATISTICS. SELECTED BUSINESS SERVICES, AUSTRALIA. Text in English. 1993. irreg. AUD 20 (effective 1998). **Document type:** *Government.* **Description:** Includes industry analysis, selected performance ratios, income and expenditure, employment and state information.
Published by: Australian Bureau of Statistics, PO Box 10, Belconnen, ACT 2616, Australia. TEL 61-2-6252-5249, FAX 61-2-6252-6778, http://www.abs.gov.au.

338.021 AUS ISSN 1326-8643
AUSTRALIA. BUREAU OF STATISTICS. SMALL BUSINESS IN AUSTRALIA. Text in English. 1983. biennial. AUD 37 (effective 2003). **Document type:** *Government.* **Description:** Contains statistics on the number and employment of small businesses on a national, state and industry basis. Also contains statistics on bankruptcy, earnings, labour costs and research and development for small businesses and compares these with other businesses.
Published by: Australian Bureau of Statistics, PO Box 10, Belconnen, ACT 2616, Australia. TEL 61-2-6252-5249, FAX 61-2-6252-6778, http://www.abs.gov.au.

332.1021 AUS
▼ **AUSTRALIA. BUREAU OF STATISTICS. SOUTH AUSTRALIAN OFFICE. GOVERNMENT FINANCIAL ESTIMATES, SOUTH AUSTRALIA, ELECTRONIC DELIVERY.** Text in English. 2003. a. price varies. stat. **Document type:** *Government.*
Media: Online - full text.
Published by: Australian Bureau of Statistics, South Australian Office, GPO Box 2272, Adelaide, SA 5001, Australia. TEL 61-8-82377582, FAX 61-8-8237-7566, http://www.abs.gov.au.

338.021 AUS ISSN 1036-2770
AUSTRALIA. BUREAU OF STATISTICS. SOUTH AUSTRALIAN OFFICE. MANUFACTURING INDUSTRY, SOUTH AUSTRALIA. Text in English. 1987. a. AUD 21 (effective 2003). **Document type:** *Government.* **Description:** Contains statistics on employment, wages and salaries paid and turnover.
Formerly (until 1989): Manufacturing, South Australia (1034-4004)
Published by: Australian Bureau of Statistics, South Australian Office, GPO Box 2272, Adelaide, SA 5001, Australia. TEL 61-8-82377582, FAX 61-8-8237-7566, http://www.abs.gov.au.

338.021 AUS
AUSTRALIA. BUREAU OF STATISTICS. SOUTH AUSTRALIAN OFFICE. SALES OF GOODS AND SERVICES BY BUSINESSES INVOLVED IN WATER RELATED ACTIVITY IN SOUTH AUSTRALIA. Text in English. 1993. irreg., latest 1994. AUD 10 (effective 1998). **Document type:** *Government.*
Published by: Australian Bureau of Statistics, South Australian Office, GPO Box 2272, Adelaide, SA 5001, Australia. TEL 61-8-82377582, FAX 61-8-8237-7566, http://www.abs.gov.au.

330.021 AUS ISSN 1039-8880
AUSTRALIA. BUREAU OF STATISTICS. SOUTH AUSTRALIAN OFFICE. SOUTH AUSTRALIAN ECONOMIC INDICATORS. Text in English. 1993. m. AUD 21 (effective 2003). **Document type:** *Government.* **Description:** Provides an up-to-date overview of the South Australian economy.
Published by: Australian Bureau of Statistics, South Australian Office, GPO Box 2272, Adelaide, SA 5001, Australia. TEL 61-8-82377582, FAX 61-8-8237-7566, http://www.abs.gov.au.

AUSTRALIA. BUREAU OF STATISTICS. STANDARD AUSTRALIAN CLASSIFICATION OF COUNTRIES. see *POPULATION STUDIES—Abstracting, Bibliographies, Statistics*

330.021 AUS
AUSTRALIA. BUREAU OF STATISTICS. STANDARD ECONOMIC SECTOR CLASSIFICATIONS OF AUSTRALIA. Text in English. 1987. irreg., latest 2002. AUD 28 (effective 2003). **Document type:** *Government.* **Description:** Includes public-private, level of government, State of jurisdiction, resident and non-resident classifications.
Published by: Australian Bureau of Statistics, PO Box 10, Belconnen, ACT 2616, Australia. TEL 61-2-6252-5249, FAX 61-2-6252-6778, http://www.abs.gov.au.

AUSTRALIA. BUREAU OF STATISTICS. STANDARDS FOR CASH INCOME STATISTICS. see *STATISTICS*

331.021 AUS
AUSTRALIA. BUREAU OF STATISTICS. STANDARDS FOR LABOUR FORCE STATISTICS. Text in English. 1996. irreg., latest 1996. AUD 17.50 (effective 2002). **Document type:** *Government.*
Published by: Australian Bureau of Statistics, PO Box 10, Belconnen, ACT 2616, Australia. TEL 61-2-6252-5249, FAX 61-2-6252-6778, http://www.abs.gov.au.

331.021 AUS ISSN 0818-9978
AUSTRALIA. BUREAU OF STATISTICS. SUCCESSFUL AND UNSUCCESSFUL JOB SEARCH EXPERIENCE, AUSTRALIA. Text in English. 1982. biennial. AUD 19.50 (effective 2003). **Document type:** *Government.*
Published by: Australian Bureau of Statistics, PO Box 10, Belconnen, ACT 2616, Australia. TEL 61-2-6252-5249, FAX 61-2-6252-6778, http://www.abs.gov.au.

331.259021 AUS
AUSTRALIA. BUREAU OF STATISTICS. SUPERANNUATION: COVERAGE AND FINANCIAL CHARACTERISTICS, AUSTRALIA. Text in English. 2000. irreg. AUD 23 (effective 2003). **Document type:** *Government.*
Published by: Australian Bureau of Statistics, PO Box 10, Belconnen, ACT 2616, Australia. TEL 61-2-6252-5249, FAX 61-2-6252-6778, http://www.abs.gov.au.

339.021 AUS
AUSTRALIA. BUREAU OF STATISTICS. SURVEY OF INCOME AND HOUSING COSTS, AUSTRALIA: USER GUIDE. Text in English. 1997. irreg., latest 1997. AUD 20 (effective 2001). **Document type:** *Government.*
Published by: Australian Bureau of Statistics, PO Box 10, Belconnen, ACT 2616, Australia. TEL 61-2-6252-5249, FAX 61-2-6252-6778, http://www.abs.gov.au.

331.021 AUS
AUSTRALIA. BUREAU OF STATISTICS. TASMANIAN OFFICE. BALANCING WORK AND CARING RESPONSIBILITIES, TASMANIA. Text in English. 2000. irreg. AUD 15 (effective 2003). **Document type:** *Government.*
Published by: Australian Bureau of Statistics, Tasmanian Office, GPO Box 66 A, Hobart, TAS 7001, Australia. TEL 61-3-6222-5800, FAX 61-3-6222-5995, http://www.abs.gov.au.

330.021 AUS ISSN 1036-2797
AUSTRALIA. BUREAU OF STATISTICS. TASMANIAN OFFICE. MANUFACTURING INDUSTRY, TASMANIA. Text in English. 1981. a. AUD 20 (effective 2003). **Document type:** *Government.* **Description:** Presents final results for Tasmania from the manufacturing census.
Formerly (until 1988): Census of Manufacturing Establishments: Summary of Operations by Industry Class, Tasmania (0811-9848)
Published by: Australian Bureau of Statistics, Tasmanian Office, GPO Box 66 A, Hobart, TAS 7001, Australia. TEL 61-3-6222-5800, FAX 61-3-6222-5995, http://www.abs.gov.au.

336.021 AUS ISSN 0819-9361
HJ90
AUSTRALIA. BUREAU OF STATISTICS. TAXATION REVENUE, AUSTRALIA. Text in English. 1969. a. AUD 20 (effective 2003). **Document type:** *Government.* **Description:** Details the revenue from taxation of Commonwealth, state and local authorities in Australia.
Published by: Australian Bureau of Statistics, PO Box 10, Belconnen, ACT 2616, Australia. TEL 61-2-6252-5249, FAX 61-2-62526788, http://www.abs.gov.au.

330.9021 AUS
AUSTRALIA. BUREAU OF STATISTICS. TREASURY MODEL OF THE AUSTRALIAN ECONOMY - DOCUMENTATION. Text in English. 1997. irreg., latest 2002. AUD 41 (effective 2002). **Document type:** *Government.* **Description:** Designed to assist in policy analysis and forecasting at the macro-economic level.
Published by: Australian Bureau of Statistics, PO Box 10, Belconnen, ACT 2616, Australia. TEL 61-2-6252-5249, FAX 61-2-6252-6778, http://www.abs.gov.au.

330.9021 AUS
AUSTRALIA. BUREAU OF STATISTICS. TREASURY MODEL OF THE AUSTRALIAN ECONOMY - TSP VERSION. Text in English. 1995. q. AUD 1,055 (effective 2003).
Media: Diskette.
Published by: Australian Bureau of Statistics, PO Box 10, Belconnen, ACT 2616, Australia. TEL 61-2-6252-5249, FAX 61-2-6252-6778, http://www.abs.gov.au.

331.021 AUS ISSN 1032-4941
AUSTRALIA. BUREAU OF STATISTICS. UNDEREMPLOYED WORKERS, AUSTRALIA. Text in English. 1985. a. AUD 22 (effective 2003). **Document type:** *Government.*
Published by: Australian Bureau of Statistics, PO Box 10, Belconnen, ACT 2616, Australia. TEL 61-2-6252-5249, FAX 61-2-6252-6778, http://www.abs.gov.au.

388.021 AUS ISSN 1036-2754
AUSTRALIA. BUREAU OF STATISTICS. VICTORIAN OFFICE. MANUFACTURING INDUSTRY, VICTORIA. Text in English. 1986. a. AUD 21 (effective 2003). **Document type:** *Government.* **Description:** Contains statistics on the number of establishments, employment, wages and salaries, and turnover.
Supersedes (in 1989): Manufacturing, Victoria (1033-7784)
Published by: Australian Bureau of Statistics, Victorian Office, GPO Box 2796 Y, Melbourne, VIC 3001, Australia. TEL 61-3-96157000, FAX 61-3-96157926, http://www.abs.gov.au.

330.021 AUS ISSN 1032-4429
AUSTRALIA. BUREAU OF STATISTICS. VICTORIAN OFFICE. RETAIL INDUSTRY: DETAILS OF OPERATIONS, VICTORIA. Text in English. 1968. irreg., latest 1986. AUD 15 per issue. **Document type:** *Government.* **Description:** Contains number of establishments, employment, wages, turnover, stocks, purchases and expenses for Victoria.
Formerly: Census of Retail Establishments and Selected Service Establishments: Details of Operations by Industry Class, Victoria
Published by: Australian Bureau of Statistics, Victorian Office, GPO Box 2796 Y, Melbourne, VIC 3001, Australia. TEL 61-3-96157000, FAX 61-3-96157926, http://www.abs.gov.au.

331.021 AUS
AUSTRALIA. BUREAU OF STATISTICS. VIDEO HIRE INDUSTRY, AUSTRALIA. Text in English. 2000. irreg. AUD 18 (effective 2003). **Document type:** *Government.*
Published by: Australian Bureau of Statistics, PO Box 10, Belconnen, ACT 2616, Australia. http://www.abs.gov.au.

331.2021 AUS
AUSTRALIA. BUREAU OF STATISTICS. WAGE AND SALARY EARNERS, AUSTRALIA. Text in English. 1983. q. AUD 20 (effective 2003). **Document type:** *Government.* **Description:** Contains estimates of gross earnings classified by industry and sector for Australia, states and territories.
Formerly: Australia. Bureau of Statistics. Employed Wage and Salary Earners, Australia (0814-6195)

B

▼ new title ➤ refereed ✱ unverified ♦ full entry avail.

Published by: Australian Bureau of Statistics, PO Box 10, Belconnen, ACT 2616, Australia. TEL 61-2-6252-5249, FAX 61-2-6252-6778, http://www.abs.gov.au.

331.2021 AUS ISSN 1327-5356
AUSTRALIA. BUREAU OF STATISTICS. WAGE COST INDEX, AUSTRALIA. Text in English. 1982. q. AUD 20 per issue (effective 2003). stat. **Document type:** *Government.* **Description:** Measures changes in the cost of ordinary time payments and overtime payments.
Supersedes (in 1997): Australia. Bureau of Statistics. Award Rates of Pay Indexes, Australia (0812-0137); Formed by the merger of (1979-1982): Wage Rates, Indexes, Australia, Preliminary (0812-0145); Which was formerly (until 1979): Wage Rates Indexes, Preliminary (0812-0382); (1979-1982): Wage Rates, Australia (0812-0153); Which was formerly (until 1979): Wage Rates
Media: Duplicated (not offset).
Published by: Australian Bureau of Statistics, PO Box 10, Belconnen, ACT 2616, Australia. TEL 61-2-6252-5249, FAX 61-2-6252-6778, http://www.abs.gov.au. Circ: 977.

332.1021 AUS
▼ **AUSTRALIA. BUREAU OF STATISTICS. WESTERN AUSTRALIAN OFFICE. GOVERNMENT FINANCIAL ESTIMATES, WESTERN AUSTRALIA, ELECTRONIC DELIVERY.** Text in English. 2003. a. price varies. stat. **Document type:** *Government.*
Media: Online - full text.
Published by: Australian Bureau of Statistics, Western Australian Office, PO Box K 881, Perth, W.A. 6001, Australia. TEL 61-8-9360-5307, FAX 61-8-9360-5955, http://www.abs.gov.au.

330.021 AUS ISSN 1036-2789
AUSTRALIA. BUREAU OF STATISTICS. WESTERN AUSTRALIAN OFFICE. MANUFACTURING INDUSTRY, WESTERN AUSTRALIA. Text in English. 1988. a. AUD 21 (effective 2003). **Document type:** *Government.* **Description:** Presents final results for Western Australia from the manufacturing census.
Formerly (until 1989): Manufacturing, Western Australia (1036-5753)
Published by: Australian Bureau of Statistics, Western Australian Office, PO Box K 881, Perth, W.A. 6001, Australia. TEL 61-8-9360-5307, FAX 61-8-9360-5955, http://www.abs.gov.au.

658.021 AUS
AUSTRALIA. BUREAU OF STATISTICS. WHOLESALE INDUSTRY, AUSTRALIA. Text in English. 1981. irreg., latest 1998. AUD 21 (effective 2003). **Document type:** *Government.* **Description:** Estimates of the number of wholesale business units; employment; wages and salaries; turnover; profit; gross product and selected operating ratios - classified by industry.
Published by: Australian Bureau of Statistics, PO Box 10, Belconnen, ACT 2616, Australia. TEL 61-2-6252-5249, FAX 61-2-6252-6778, http://www.abs.gov.au.

331.11021 AUS
AUSTRALIA. BUREAU OF STATISTICS. WORK IN SELECTED CULTURE AND LEISURE ACTIVITIES, AUSTRALIA. Text in English. 1993. irreg., latest 2001. AUD 21 (effective 2003). **Document type:** *Government.*
Published by: Australian Bureau of Statistics, PO Box 10, Belconnen, ACT 2616, Australia. TEL 61-2-6252-5249, FAX 61-2-6252-6778, http://www.abs.gov.au.

331.11021 AUS
AUSTRALIA. BUREAU OF STATISTICS. WORK-RELATED INJURIES, AUSTRALIA. Text in English. 2000. irreg. AUD 19.50 (effective 2003). **Document type:** *Government.*
Published by: Australian Bureau of Statistics, PO Box 10, Belconnen, ACT 2616, Australia. http://www.abs.gov.au.

331.11021 AUS ISSN 1326-9054
AUSTRALIA. BUREAU OF STATISTICS. WORKING ARRANGEMENTS, AUSTRALIA. Text in English. 1993. triennial. AUD 22 (effective 2003). **Document type:** *Government.*
Published by: Australian Bureau of Statistics, PO Box 10, Belconnen, ACT 2616, Australia. TEL 61-2-6252-5249, FAX 61-2-6252-6778, http://www.abs.gov.au.

330.021 310 AUS ISSN 1320-5099
AUSTRALIA. BUREAU OF STATISTICS. WORKING PAPERS IN ECONOMETRICS AND APPLIED STATISTICS. Text in English. 1993. irreg., latest 2003. AUD 22 (effective 2003). **Document type:** *Government.* **Description:** Contains working papers drawn from ABS research in the fields of econometrics, time series and statistics.
Published by: Australian Bureau of Statistics, PO Box 10, Belconnen, ACT 2616, Australia. TEL 61-2-6252-5249, FAX 61-2-6252-6778, http://www.abs.gov.au.

330.9 AUS ISSN 1031-8968
AUSTRALIA. DEPARTMENT OF THE TREASURY. ECONOMIC ROUND-UP. Text in English. q. AUD 40 (effective 1999). charts. **Document type:** *Government.* **Description:** Contains an overview of recent economic conditions, which ties together the statistics on the economy.
Former titles (until 1988): Australia. Department of the Treasury. Round-Up (0815-1881); (until 1985): Australia. Department of the Treasury. Round-Up of Economic Statistics (0310-4230)
Related titles: Online - full text ed.
Indexed: RASB.
Published by: (Australia. Department of the Treasury), AusInfo, GPO Box 1920, Canberra Mc, ACT 2610, Australia. TEL 61-2-6295-4512, FAX 61-2-6295-4455, http://www.treasury.gov.au. **Subscr. to:** NMM-The Treasury, National Mailing and Marketing Pty. Ltd., PO Box 7077, Canberra Mail Centre, ACT 2610, Australia. TEL 61-2-6263-2111, FAX 61-2-6273-2614.

330.9 AUS
AUSTRALIA. DEPARTMENT OF THE TREASURY. MID - YEAR ECONOMIC FISCAL OUTLOOK. Text in English. 1998. a. back issues avail. **Document type:** *Government.* **Description:** Provides updated information to allow for the assessment of the fiscal performance of the Government of the Commonwealth of Australia vis-a-vis its strategic projections, as required under the Charter of Budget Honesty Act of 1998.
Related titles: Online - full text ed.
Published by: (Australia. Department of the Treasury), AusInfo, GPO Box 1920, Canberra Mc, ACT 2610, Australia. TEL 61-2-6295-4512, FAX 61-2-6295-4455, http://www.treasury.bov.au. **Subscr. to:** NMM-The Treasury, National Mailing and Marketing Pty. Ltd., PO Box 7077, Canberra Mail Centre, ACT 2610, Australia. TEL 61-2-6263-2111, FAX 61-2-6273-2614.

330.9 AUS
AUSTRALIA. DEPARTMENT OF THE TREASURY. NATIONAL FISCAL OUTLOOK. Abbreviated title: N F O. Text in English. a. charts. back issues avail. **Document type:** *Government.* **Description:** Presents medium-term financial projections for the Australian Commonwealth, State, and Territory general government sectors.
Related titles: Online - full text ed.
Published by: (Australia. Department of the Treasury), AusInfo, GPO Box 1920, Canberra Mc, ACT 2610, Australia. TEL 61-8-6295-4512, FAX 61-2-6295-4455, http://www.treasury.gov.au. **Orders to:** AusInfo Mail Order Sales, GPO Box 84, Canberra, ACT 2601, Australia. FAX 61-2-6295-4888.

330.9 AUS
AUSTRALIA. DEPARTMENT OF THE TREASURY. PRE-ELECTION ECONOMIC AND FISCAL OUTLOOK. Abbreviated title: P E F O. Text in English. 1998. irreg. price varies. charts. back issues avail. **Document type:** *Government.* **Description:** Releases financial and economic predictions when a general election is called for, as required under the Charter of Budget Honesty Act of 1998.
Related titles: Online - full text ed.
Published by: (Australia. Department of the Treasury), AusInfo, GPO Box 1920, Canberra Mc, ACT 2610, Australia. TEL 61-2-6295-4512, TELEX AA62013, http://www.treasury.gov.au. **Subscr. to:** NMM-The Treasury, National Mailing and Marketing Pty. Ltd., PO Box 7077, Canberra Mail Centre, ACT 2610, Australia. TEL 61-2-6263-2111, FAX 61-2-6273-2614.

332 310 AUS ISSN 1034-9685
AUSTRALIAN BANKING STATISTICS. Text in English. 1990. m. AUD 29.50 (effective 1999). **Document type:** *Bulletin.* **Description:** Presents selected liabilities and assets recorded on Banks' Australian Books as at close of business on Wednesdays.
Related titles: Diskette ed.
Published by: Australian Prudential Regulation Authority, 400 George St, Sydney, NSW 2000, Australia. TEL 61-2-92103286, FAX 61-2-92103311, http://www.apra.gov.au/abs. Circ: 300.

330.021 AUS ISSN 1325-8109
HF1040.9.A9
AUSTRALIAN BUREAU OF AGRICULTURAL AND RESOURCE ECONOMICS. AUSTRALIAN COMMODITY STATISTICS (YEAR). Text in English. 1986. a. AUD 129 paper copy; AUD 65 online edition (effective 2003). index. **Document type:** *Bulletin, Government.* **Description:** Covers all aspects of Australian economics: agriculture, minerals, energy, forestry and fishing industries.
Formerly (until 1995): Australian Bureau of Agricultural and Resource Economics. Commodity Statistical Bulletin (Year) (0817-685X); Which was formed by the merger of (1949-1986): Wool Situation and Outlook (0311-8797); (1972-1986): Meat Situation and Outlook (0311-0885); (1953-1986): Dairy Products Situation and Outlook (0311-8843); (1951-1986): Wheat Situation and Outlook (0310-9917); (1955-1986): Eggs Situation and Outlook (0311-1415); (1974-1986): Coarse Grains Situation and Outlook (0311-0788); (1974-1986): Oilseeds Situation and Outlook (0311-8789)
Related titles: Online - full content ed.
Indexed: ASFA, ESPM, FPA, ForAb, HortAb, PN&I, PoultAb, RiceAb, SIA, TTI, TriticAb, WAE&RSA.
—CISTI. **CCC.**
Published by: Australian Bureau of Agricultural and Resource Economics, GPO Box 1563, Canberra, ACT 2601, Australia. TEL 61-2-62722000, FAX 61-2-62722001, sales@abare.gov.au, http://www.abareconomics.com. Ed., R&P Andrew Wright TEL 61-2-62722290.

330 310 028.5 AUS ISSN 1035-6142
AUSTRALIA'S ECONOMIC STATISTICS; a student guide to recent Australian experience. Text in English. 1989. a. AUD 14.25 (effective 2002). charts. back issues avail. **Document type:** *Academic/Scholarly.* **Description:** Presents economic statistics relating to the Australian economy of the past year for 12 grade students.
Published by: Warringal Publications, 116 Argyle St, Fitzroy, VIC 3065, Australia. TEL 61-3-94160200, FAX 61-3-94160402, mareeprince@edassist.com.au, http://www.edassist.com.au. Ed. Ted Kramer. Pub. Maree Prince. Circ: 2,000.

330.9 DEU ISSN 0005-0598
HG1505
AUSZUEGE AUS PRESSEARTIKELN. Text in German. 1948. s-w. looseleaf. free. **Document type:** *Abstract/Index.* **Description:** Includes excerpts from published articles and press releases of the Bundesbank.
Indexed: ELLIS.
—**CCC.**
Published by: Deutsche Bundesbank, Postfach 100602, Frankfurt Am Main, 60006, Germany. TEL 49-69-9566-1, FAX 49-69-5601071, http://www.bundesbank.de. Circ: 16,800.

338.476292021 CAN ISSN 1706-8568
AUTOMOTIVE TRADE. Text in English. 1983. a.
Former titles (until 2001): Statistical Review of the Canadian Automotive Industry (0842-6732); (until 1987): Report on the Canadian Automotive Industry (0827-4320)
Published by: (Industry Canada, Aerospace and Automotive Branch), Industry Canada/Industrie Canada, Distribution Services, Communications & Marketing Branch, Rm 268D, West Tower, C.D. Howe Bldg, 235 Queen St, Ottawa, ON K1A 0H5, Canada. TEL 613-947-7466, FAX 613-954-6436, publications@ic.gc.ca, http://strategis.ic.gc.ca/epic/internet/inauto-auto.nsf/en/h_am01671e.html, http://www.ic.gc.ca.

382 MEX ISSN 0187-4942
HF3231
AVANCE DE INFORMACION ECONOMICA. BALANZA COMERCIAL. Text in Spanish. 1986. m. MXP 77, USD 35.
Published by: Instituto Nacional de Estadistica, Geografia e Informatica, Secretaria de Programacion y Presupuesto, Prol. Heroe de Nacozari 2301 Sur, Puerta 11, Acceso, Aguascalientes, 20270, Mexico. TEL 52-4-918-1948, FAX 52-4-918-0739, http://www.inegi.gob.mx. Circ: 950.

331.021 MEX ISSN 0187-4969
HD5731
AVANCE DE INFORMACION ECONOMICA. EMPLEO. Text in Spanish. 1986. m. MXP 77, USD 26.
Published by: Instituto Nacional de Estadistica, Geografia e Informatica, Secretaria de Programacion y Presupuesto, Prol. Heroe de Nacozari 2301 Sur, Puerta 11, Acceso, Aguascalientes, 20270, Mexico. TEL 52-4-918-1948, FAX 52-4-918-0739, http://www.inegi.gob.mx. Circ: 900.

381 MEX
AVANCE DE INFORMACION ECONOMICA. ENCUESTA SOBRE ESTABLECIMIENTOS COMERCIALES. CIUDADES DE: MEXICO, GUADALAJARA Y MONTERREY. Text in Spanish. 1986. m. MXP 420, USD 140.
Formed by the 1991 merger of: Avance de Informacion Economica. Encuesta sobre Establecimientos Comerciales. Cuidad de Mexico (0187-4985); Avance de Informacion Economica. Encuesta sobre Establecimientos Comerciales. Cuidad de Guadalajara (0187-6708); Avance de Informacion Economica. Encuesta sobre Establecimientos Comerciales. Ciudad de Monterrey (0187-5000)
Published by: Instituto Nacional de Estadistica, Geografia e Informatica, Secretaria de Programacion y Presupuesto, Prol. Heroe de Nacozari 2301 Sur, Puerta 11, Acceso, Aguascalientes, 20270, Mexico. TEL 52-4-918-1948, FAX 52-4-918-0739, http://www.inegi.gob.mx. Circ: 800.

338 MEX
AVANCE DE INFORMACION ECONOMICA. INDICADORES DE LA ACTIVIDAD INDUSTRIAL. Text in Spanish. 1986. m. MXP 77, USD 26.
Published by: Instituto Nacional de Estadistica, Geografia e Informatica, Secretaria de Programacion y Presupuesto, Prol. Heroe de Nacozari 2301 Sur, Puerta 11, Acceso, Aguascalientes, 20270, Mexico. TEL 52-4-918-1948, FAX 52-4-918-0739, http://www.inegi.gob.mx. Circ: 1,050.

338 MEX ISSN 0187-4977
AVANCE DE INFORMACION ECONOMICA. INDICADORES DEL SECTOR MANUFACTURERO; 145 clases de actividad. Text in Spanish. 1986. m. MXP 77, USD 26.
Published by: Instituto Nacional de Estadistica, Geografia e Informatica, Secretaria de Programacion y Presupuesto, Prol. Heroe de Nacozari 2301 Sur, Puerta 11, Acceso, Aguascalientes, 20270, Mexico. TEL 52-4-918-1948, FAX 52-4-918-0739, http://www.inegi.gob.mx. Circ: 900.

382 MEX ISSN 0187-5019
AVANCE DE INFORMACION ECONOMICA. INDUSTRIA MAQUILADORA DE EXPORTACION. Text in Spanish. 1986. m. MXP 77, USD 26.

Published by: Instituto Nacional de Estadistica, Geografia e Informatica, Secretaria de Programacion y Presupuesto, Prol. Heroe de Nacozari 2301 Sur, Puerta 11, Acceso, Aguascalientes, 20270, Mexico. TEL 52-4-918-1948, FAX 52-4-918-0739, http://www.inegi.gob.mx. Circ: 800.

330.9 MEX
AVANCE DE INFORMACION ECONOMICA. PRODUCTO INTERNO BRUTO TRIMESTRAL. Text in Spanish. 1986. q. MXP 48, USD 16.
Published by: Instituto Nacional de Estadistica, Geografia e Informatica, Secretaria de Programacion y Presupuesto, Prol. Heroe de Nacozari 2301 Sur, Puerta 11, Acceso, Aguascalientes, 20270, Mexico. TEL 52-4-918-1948, FAX 52-4-918-0739, http://www.inegi.gob.mx. Circ: 800.

331.21021 USA
AVERAGE ANNUAL PAY BY STATE AND INDUSTRY. Text in English. a. **Document type:** *Government.*
Related titles: ◆ Series of: U.S. Bureau of Labor Statistics. National Office News Releases.
Published by: U.S. Department of Labor, Bureau of Labor Statistics, Postal Square Bldg., 2 Massachusetts Ave, NE, Washington, DC 20212-0001 . TEL 202-655-4000. **Subscr. to:** U.S. Government Printing Office, Superintendent of Documents.

316.3 330.9 ETH
AVERAGE RETAIL PRICES OF GOODS AND SERVICES BY RURAL AREAS. Text in English. q. ETB 92, USD 13. back issues avail. **Document type:** *Government.* **Description:** Presents average retail prices of food items milled and unmilled, fruits and vegetables, stimulants, beverages, tobacco and cigarettes, ready-made clothes and shoes, household equipment, medical care, recreation, personal care items, livestock and more.
Related titles: CD-ROM ed.; Diskette ed.
Published by: Central Statistical Authority, PO Box 1143, Addis Ababa, Ethiopia. TEL 251-1-115470, FAX 251-1-550334.

650 016 USA ISSN 0005-318X
B I T S. (Business Industry Technology Service) Text in English. 1954. m. (except July & Aug.). free. bk.rev. **Description:** Previews of new books in the business and technology fields.
Media: Duplicated (not offset).
Published by: Dayton & Montgomery County Public Library, 215 E Third St, Dayton, OH 45402. TEL 513-227-9500. Ed. Rita White. Circ: 1,500.

331.021 USA ISSN 1047-0352
HC101
B L S UPDATE. Text in English. q. free. bibl.; stat. back issues avail. **Document type:** *Catalog, Newsletter, Government.* **Description:** Lists publications issued by B.L.S. and provides news of the bureau.
Formerly (until 1988): New from B L S (0898-1965)
Related titles: Online - full text ed.
Published by: (Department of Labor), U.S. Department of Labor, Bureau of Labor Statistics, Postal Square Bldg., 2 Massachusetts Ave, NE, Washington, DC 20212-0001 . TEL 202-691-5200, http://www.bls.gov. **Subscr. to:** Bureau of Labor Statistics Publications Sales Center.

310.3309 ITA
HC301
B N L BASIC STATISTICS ON THE ITALIAN ECONOMY. Text in English, German. 1959. m. EUR 52 (effective 2003). charts; stat.
Former titles: B N L Trends; (until 1988): Italian Trends (0021-3004)
Published by: B N L Edizioni SpA (Subsidiary of: Gruppo BNL), Via San Basilio 48, Rome, 00187, Italy. TEL 39-06-42012918, FAX 39-06-42012921, sliberati@bnledizioni.com. Ed. Bruno Brovedani. Circ: 5,600.

330.021 318.021 BRA ISSN 0103-8117
HA988.B3
BAHIA ANALISE & DADOS. Text in Portuguese. 1991. q. **Description:** Covers socio-economic topics, statistics, natural resources and other matters pertaining to the Brazilian State of Bahia.
Published by: Superintendencia de Estudos Economicos e Sociais da Bahia, Ave Luiz Vianna Filho s/n, Salvador, Bahia 41 750-300, Brazil. TEL 55-71-3704847, FAX 55-71-371853, http://www.sei.ba.gov.br.

336 BHR
BAHRAIN. MONETARY AGENCY. QUARTERLY STATISTICAL BULLETIN. Text in English. 1975. q. charts; stat. **Document type:** *Bulletin, Government.*
Formerly: Bahrain. Monetary Agency. Quarterly Statement of Affairs and Statistical Bulletin
Published by: Monetary Agency, PO Box 27, Manama, Bahrain. TEL 535535, FAX 533342, TELEX BN9191.

336 382 TTO ISSN 0067-3005
BALANCE OF PAYMENTS OF TRINIDAD AND TOBAGO. Text in English. a. TTD 15, USD 7.50 (effective 2000). **Document type:** *Government.*
Published by: Central Statistical Office, 35-41 Queen St, PO Box 98, Port-of-Spain, Trinidad, Trinidad & Tobago. TEL 868-623-6495, FAX 868-625-3802.

332.1 315 PAK
BALANCE SHEET ANALYSIS OF JOINT STOCK COMPANIES. Text in English. a. PKR 250, USD 20 (effective 2000). **Document type:** *Government.*
Published by: State Bank of Pakistan, Central Directorate, Public Relations Department, I.I. Chundrigar Rd, PO Box 4456, Karachi, Pakistan. TEL 92-21-9212400, FAX 92-21-9212436, TELEX 21774 SBPK PK.

330 314 GRC ISSN 1105-2511
BALANCE SHEETS. Text in Greek. 1987. a. adv. stat. **Description:** Analyzes the finances of private, public, industrial, and service sectors of Greece with particular attention to banking and insurance companies.
Related titles: ◆ Supplement to: Epilogi. ISSN 1105-2503.
Published by: Electra Press, 4 Stadiou St, Athens, 105 64, Greece. TEL 30-1-323-3203, FAX 30-1-323-5160. Ed. Christos Papaioannou. Circ: 11,000.

332 BOL
BANCO CENTRAL DE BOLIVIA. BOLETIN DEL SECTOR EXTERNO. Text in Spanish. 1989. s-a. BOB 22 domestic; USD 15 foreign (effective 2004). **Document type:** *Bulletin.*
Related titles: CD-ROM ed.; Diskette ed.
Published by: Banco Central de Bolivia, Casilla de Correo 3118, La Paz, Bolivia. TEL 591-2-2409090, FAX 591-2-2406614, bcb@bcb.gov.bo, http://www.bcb.gov.bo. Ed. Luis Alberto Arce Catacora.

332 BOL ISSN 0522-0939
HG185.B6
BANCO CENTRAL DE BOLIVIA. BOLETIN ESTADISTICO. Text in Spanish. 1967. q. BOB 44 domestic; USD 31 foreign (effective 2004). charts; stat. **Document type:** *Bulletin.*
Related titles: CD-ROM ed.; Diskette ed.
Indexed: PAIS.
Published by: Banco Central de Bolivia, Casilla de Correo 3118, La Paz, Bolivia. TEL 591-2-2409090, FAX 591-2-2406614, bcb@bcb.gov.bo, http://www.bcb.gov.bo. Ed. Luis Alberto Arce Catacora.

332 BOL
BANCO CENTRAL DE BOLIVIA. BOLETIN MENSUAL. Text in Spanish. m. BOB 131 domestic; USD 92 foreign (effective 2004).
Related titles: CD-ROM ed.; Diskette ed.
Published by: Banco Central de Bolivia, Casilla de Correo 3118, La Paz, Bolivia. TEL 591-2-2409090, FAX 591-2-2406614, bcb@bcb.gov.bo, http://www.bcb.gov.bo.

332 BOL ISSN 1023-361X
BANCO CENTRAL DE BOLIVIA. MEMORIA. Text in Spanish. 1929. a. BOB 16 domestic; USD 8 foreign (effective 2004). **Document type:** *Corporate.*
Related titles: CD-ROM ed.; Diskette ed.
Published by: Banco Central de Bolivia, Casilla de Correo 3118, La Paz, Bolivia. TEL 591-2-2409090, FAX 591-2-2406614, bcb@bcb.gov.bo, http://www.bcb.gov.bo. Ed. Luis Alberto Arce Catacora.

330.9 318 HND ISSN 1012-9510
BANCO CENTRAL DE HONDURAS. DEPARTAMENTO DE ESTUDIOS ECONOMICOS. BOLETIN ESTADISTICO MENSUAL. Text in Spanish. 1950. m. charts; stat. **Description:** Provides statistics on banking and the economy in Honduras, with emphasis on the Central Bank of Honduras.
Formerly: Banco Central de Honduras. Departamento de Estudios Economicos. Boletin Estadistico (0252-9033)
Indexed: PAIS.
Published by: Banco Central de Honduras, Departamento de Estudios Economicos, 6a y 7a Avda., 1a Calle, Tegucigalpa D C, Honduras. TEL 22-2270.

332 318 ARG ISSN 0005-4674
HA943
BANCO CENTRAL DE LA REPUBLICA ARGENTINA. BOLETIN ESTADISTICO. Text in Spanish. 1958. m. free.
Indexed: PAIS.
Published by: Banco Central de la Republica Argentina, Centro de Estudios Monetarios y Bancarios, Department de Tramite General, Reconquista, 266, Buenos Aires, 1003, Argentina.

332 VEN ISSN 0798-295X
BANCO CENTRAL DE VENEZUELA. ANUARIO DE BALANZA DE PAGOS. Text in Spanish. a. USD 10 (effective 2000).
Published by: Banco Central de Venezuela, Av Urdaneta Esq Las Carmelitas, Caracas, 1010, Venezuela. FAX 582-8611646, info@bcv.org.ve, http://www.bcv.org.ve.

332 VEN
BANCO CENTRAL DE VENEZUELA. ANUARIO DE CUENTAS NACIONALES. Text in Spanish. a. USD 12 (effective 2000).
Published by: Banco Central de Venezuela, Av Urdaneta Esq Las Carmelitas, Caracas, 1010, Venezuela. FAX 582-8611646, info@bcv.org.ve, http://www.bcv.org.ve.

332.1 VEN
BANCO CENTRAL DE VENEZUELA. ANUARIO DE ESTADISTICAS INTERNACIONALES. Text in Spanish. a. USD 3 (effective 2000).
Published by: Banco Central de Venezuela, Av Urdaneta Esq Las Carmelitas, Caracas, 1010, Venezuela. FAX 582-8611646, info@bcv.org.ve, http://www.bcv.org.ve.

330 VEN ISSN 1316-0664
BANCO CENTRAL DE VENEZUELA. ANUARIO DE ESTADISTICAS: PRECIOS Y MERCADO LABORAL. Text in Spanish. a. USD 12 (effective 2000).
Published by: Banco Central de Venezuela, Av Urdaneta Esq Las Carmelitas, Caracas, 1010, Venezuela. FAX 582-8611646, info@bcv.org.ve, http://www.bcv.org.ve.

332 VEN
BANCO CENTRAL DE VENEZUELA. ANUARIO DE ESTADISTICAS: SECTOR FINANCIERO. Text in Spanish. a. USD 3 (effective 2000).
Published by: Banco Central de Venezuela, Av Urdaneta Esq Las Carmelitas, Caracas, 1010, Venezuela. FAX 582-8611646, info@bcv.org.ve, http://www.bcv.org.ve.

332 VEN
BANCO CENTRAL DE VENEZUELA. BOLETIN DE INDICADORES SEMANALES. Text in Spanish. 1981. w. USD 189; USD 2 newsstand/cover (effective 2000).
Published by: Banco Central de Venezuela, Av Urdaneta Esq Las Carmelitas, Caracas, 1010, Venezuela. FAX 582-8611646, info@bcv.org.ve, http://www.bcv.org.ve.

332 VEN ISSN 0252-8991
HG2966
BANCO CENTRAL DE VENEZUELA. BOLETIN MENSUAL. Text in Spanish. 1944. m. USD 120; USD 5 newsstand/cover (effective 2000).
Indexed: PAIS.
Published by: Banco Central de Venezuela, Av Urdaneta Esq Las Carmelitas, Caracas, 1010, Venezuela. FAX 582-8611646, info@bcv.org.ve, http://www.bcv.org.ve.

332.1 330 ECU
BANCO CENTRAL DEL ECUADOR. BALANZA DE PAGOS. Text in English, Spanish. a. free.
Published by: Banco Central del Ecuador, Avenida 10 de Agosto y Briceno, Quito, Ecuador. TEL 593-2-2580158, uweb@uio.bce.fin.ec, http://www.bce.fin.ec. Circ: 15,000.

332 011 ECU
BANCO CENTRAL DEL ECUADOR. INFORMACION ESTADISTICA MENSUAL. Text in Spanish. m. charts; stat.
Former titles: Banco Central del Ecuador. Informacion Estadistica Quincenal; Banco Central del Ecuador. Informacion Estadistica Mensual; Banco Central del Ecuador. Informacion Estadistica
Published by: Banco Central del Ecuador, Avenida 10 de Agosto y Briceno, Quito, Ecuador. TEL 593-2-2580158, uweb@uio.bce.fin.ec, http://www.bce.fin.ec. Circ: 6,000.

318.92 PRY
BANCO CENTRAL DEL PARAGUAY. GERENCIA DE ESTUDIOS ECONOMICOS. ESTADISTICAS ECONOMICAS. Text in Spanish. q.
Published by: (Gerencia de Estudios Economicos), Banco Central del Paraguay, Avda. Pablo VI y Avda. Sgt. Marecos, Asuncion, Paraguay. TEL 595-21-608011, FAX 595-21-6192637.

310 URY ISSN 0797-0684
BANCO CENTRAL DEL URUGUAY. BOLETIN ESTADISTICO. Text in Spanish. 1967. q. back issues avail.
Related titles: Online - full text ed.: ISSN 1688-0684. 1999.
Published by: Banco Central del Uruguay, Diagonal Fabini 777, Montevideo, Uruguay. info@bcu.gub.uy, http://www.bcu.gub.uy/autoriza/sgoioi/publica.html.

330.9 URY
BANCO CENTRAL DEL URUGUAY. DEPARTAMENTO DE ESTADISTICAS ECONOMICAS. BOLETIN ESTADISTICO. Text in Spanish. 1942. m. free. charts; stat.
Former titles: Banco Central del Uruguay. Departamento de Investigaciones Economicas. Boletin Estadistico.; Banco Central del Uruguay. Boletin Estadistico Mensual (0005-4747); Supersedes: Banco de la Republica Oriental del Uruguay. Revista
Related titles: Supplement(s): Endeudamiento Externo del Uruguay.
Indexed: PAIS.
Published by: Banco Central del Uruguay, Departamento de Estadisticas Economicas, Casilla 1467, Paysando y Florida, Montevideo, Uruguay. FAX 598-2-921782, TELEX 26939 BACENUR UY.

BANCO DE ESPANA. BOLETIN ESTADISTICO. see *BUSINESS AND ECONOMICS—Banking And Finance*

BANCO DE GUATEMALA. BOLETIN ESTADISTICO. see *BUSINESS AND ECONOMICS—Banking And Finance*

332.6 MEX
BANCO DE MEXICO. INDICADORES DEL SECTOR EXTERNO. Text in Spanish. m. MXP 800; USD 240 in United States; USD 300 in Europe; USD 360 elsewhere.

B

Published by: Banco de Mexico, Subdireccion de Investigacion Economica y Bancaria, 06059 Mexico, Mexico, Ave. JUAREZ 90, Centro Urbano Benito Juarez, Del. Cuauhtemoc, Ciudad De Mexico, DF 06059, Mexico. TEL 525-761-8588.

330 MEX
BANCO DE MEXICO. INDICE DE PRECIOS. Text in Spanish. m. MXP 800; USD 240 in United States; USD 300 in Europe; USD 360 elsewhere.
Published by: Banco de Mexico, Subdireccion de Investigacion Economica y Bancaria, 06059 Mexico, Mexico, Ave. JUAREZ 90, Centro Urbano Benito Juarez, Del. Cuauhtemoc, Ciudad De Mexico, DF 06059, Mexico. TEL 525-761-8588.

330 318 PRT
BANCO DE PORTUGAL. ESTATISTICA E ESTUDOS ECONOMICOS. Text in Portuguese. m.
Published by: Banco de Portugal, Rua do Ouro 27, Lisbon, 1100-150, Portugal. TEL 351-21-3213200, FAX 351-21-3464843, http://www.bportugal.pt.

330.9 318 URY
BANCO HIPOTECARIO DEL URUGUAY. BOLETIN ESTADISTICO. Text in Spanish. s-a. charts; illus.; stat.
Published by: (Departamento de Planificacion y Metodos), Banco Hipotecario del Uruguay, Montevideo, Uruguay.

BANCOS CENTRALES DE LOS PAISES DEL ACUERDO DE CARTAGENA. BOLETIN ESTADISTICO. see *BUSINESS AND ECONOMICS—Banking And Finance*

332 310 BGD
BANGLADESH BANK. STATISTICS DEPARTMENT. ANNUAL BALANCE OF PAYMENTS. Text in English. 1974. a. stat.
Published by: (Department of Public Relations and Publications), Bangladesh Bank, Motijheel Commercial Area, Dhaka, 2, Bangladesh.

382 316 BGD
BANGLADESH BANK. STATISTICS DEPARTMENT. ANNUAL IMPORT PAYMENTS. Text in English. 1973. a. stat.
Published by: (Department of Public Relations and Publications), Bangladesh Bank, Motijheel Commercial Area, Dhaka, 2, Bangladesh.

332 336 BGD
BANGLADESH BANK. STATISTICS DEPARTMENT. BALANCE OF PAYMENTS. Text in English. 1974. q.
Published by: (Department of Public Relations and Publications), Bangladesh Bank, Motijheel Commercial Area, Dhaka, 2, Bangladesh.

332.1 316 BGD
BANGLADESH BANK. STATISTICS DEPARTMENT. QUARTERLY SCHEDULED BANKS STATISTICS. Text in English. 1977. q.
Published by: (Department of Public Relations and Publications), Bangladesh Bank, Motijheel Commercial Area, Dhaka, 2, Bangladesh.

332.021 CHE
BANK FOR INTERNATIONAL SETTLEMENTS. CONSOLIDATED INTERNATIONAL BANKING STATISTICS. Text in English. q.
Published by: Bank for International Settlements, Centralbahnplatz 2, Basel, 4002, Switzerland. http://www.bis.org.

332.021 CHE
BANK FOR INTERNATIONAL SETTLEMENTS. STATISTICS ON PAYMENT AND SETTLEMENT SYSTEMS IN SELECTED COUNTRIES. Text in English. 1994. a.
Formerly: Bank for International Settlements. Statistics on Payment Systems in the Group of Ten Countries (1024-3380)
Published by: Bank for International Settlements, Centralbahnplatz 2, Basel, 4002, Switzerland. TEL 41-61-2808080, FAX 41-61-2809100, 41-61-2808100, publications@bis.org, http://www.bis.org/cpss/cpsspubl.htm.

330.9 MYS
BANK NEGARA MALAYSIA. STATISTICAL BULLETIN. Text in English, Malay. m. USD 80 in Asia; USD 99 in Europe; USD 108 in Africa. charts; stat. back issues avail. **Document type:** *Bulletin.* **Description:** Reports the monetary, banking, liquidity, capital market and macroeconomic situations.
Published by: Bank Negara Malaysia/Central Bank of Malaysia, Jalan Dato'Onn, PO Box 10922, Kuala Lumpur, 50480, Malaysia. TEL 2988044, FAX 2912990. Circ: (controlled).

332 317 CAN ISSN 0005-5158
BANK OF CANADA. WEEKLY FINANCIAL STATISTICS/ BANQUE DU CANADA. BULLETIN HEBDOMADAIRE DE STATISTIQUES FINANCIERES. Text in English. 1954. w. CND 55 domestic; CND 70 in United States; CND 110 elsewhere (effective 2004). 19 p./no.; **Document type:** *Bulletin, Government.* **Description:** Shows banking statistics and economic indicators in Canada.
Media: Duplicated (not offset).
Published by: Bank of Canada, Publications Distribution, Communications Services, 234 Wellington St, Ottawa, ON K1A 0G9, Canada. TEL 613-782-8248, FAX 613-782-8874, publications@bank-banque-canada.ca, http://www.bank-banque-canada.ca, http://www.bankofcanada.ca. Circ: 1,600.

332 314 GRC ISSN 1105-0519
HG3066
BANK OF GREECE. MONTHLY STATISTICAL BULLETIN. Text in English, Greek. 1932. m. USD 30 domestic; USD 55 foreign (effective 2000). charts; mkt.; stat. **Document type:** *Bulletin.*
Published by: Bank of Greece, Economic Research Division, 21 Panepistimiou St, Athens, 102 50, Greece. FAX 30-1-3233025, TELEX 30-1-215102. Circ: 2,500.

332.1021 ISR ISSN 0793-2081
HG3260
BANK OF ISRAEL. ANNUAL INFORMATION ON THE BANKING CORPORATIONS/MEDA' SHNATI 'AL HATTA'AGIDIM HABBANQA'IYYIM. Text in Hebrew, English. 1978. a. ILS 54 (effective 2000).
Formerly (until 1993): Bank of Israel. Annual Statistics of the Banking System (0334-4541)
Published by: Bank of Israel, Kiryath Ben Gurion, P O Box 780, Jerusalem, 91007, Israel. http://www.bankisrael.gov.il.

332.1 ISR
BANK OF ISRAEL. CURRENT INFORMATION ON BANKS. Text in English, Hebrew. m. ILS 182 (effective 2000).
Former titles: Bank of Israel. Current Banking Statistics; Bank of Israel. Banking Statistics (0039-0607)
Media: Duplicated (not offset).
Published by: (Publications Unit), Bank of Israel, Kiryath Ben Gurion, P O Box 780, Jerusalem, 91007, Israel.

332 ISR
BANK OF ISRAEL. EXCHANGE RATES. Text in English, Hebrew. w. ILS 48 (effective 2000).
Formerly: Bank of Israel. Exchange Rates (Print)
Media: Online - full text. **Related titles:** Diskette ed.; Fax ed.: ILS 223 (effective 2001).
Published by: (Publications Unit), Bank of Israel, Kiryath Ben Gurion, P O Box 780, Jerusalem, 91007, Israel.

332 ISR
BANK OF ISRAEL. MAIN ISRAELI ECONOMIC DATA. Text in English, Hebrew. s-m. ILS 182 (effective 2000).
Published by: (Publications Unit), Bank of Israel, Kiryath Ben Gurion, P O Box 780, Jerusalem, 91007, Israel. http://www.bankisrael.gov.il/.

330.9 315 JAM ISSN 1018-9084
HC154.A1
BANK OF JAMAICA. ECONOMIC STATISTICS. Text in English. 1991. m. free. illus.; stat.
Published by: (Research & Economic Programming Division), Bank of Jamaica, Nethersole Place, P O Box 621, Kingston, Jamaica. TEL 809-922-0750, FAX 809-967-4265. Circ: 1,200 (controlled).

330 JPN
BANK OF JAPAN. COMMODITY GROUPS, WEIGHTS, ITEMS OF COMMODITY GROUPS AND LINKED INDEXES OF (YEAR) BASE INPUT - OUTPUT PRICE INDEXES OF MANUFACTURING INDUSTRY BY SECTOR. Text in English, Japanese. every 5 yrs. JPY 1,733 (effective 1998). 180 p./no.;
Formerly: Bank of Japan. Commodity Groups, Weights, Items of Commodity Groups and Linked Indexes
Published by: (Research and Statistics Department), Bank of Japan/Nippon Ginko, c/o Public Relations Department, 2-1-1 Hongoku-cho-Nihonbashi, Chuo-ku, Tokyo, 1030000, Japan. TEL 81-3-3279-1111, FAX 81-3-3510-1374, http://www.boj.or.jp/en.index.htm. **Dist. by:** Tokiwa Sohgoh Service Co. Ltd., Publication and Research Department, Kyodo Bldg, 2-4 Hongokucho, Nihonbashi 3-chome, Chuo-ku, Tokyo 103-0027, Japan. TEL 81-3-3270-5713, FAX 81-3-3270-5710; **Dist. overseas by:** Japan Publications Trading Co., Ltd., Book Export II Dept, PO Box 5030, Tokyo International, Tokyo 101-3191, Japan. TEL 81-3-32923753, FAX 81-3-32920410, infoserials@jptco.co.jp, http://www.jptco.co.jp.

310 JPN
BANK OF JAPAN. ECONOMIC AND FINANCIAL DATA ON CD-ROM. Text in English, Japanese. 1997. a. JPY 1,300 (effective 1998). **Description:** Contains data from "Economic Statistics Monthly," "Economic Statistics Annual," "Tankan - Short-Term Economic Survey of Enterprises in Japan," "Charts - Main Economic Indicators of Japan," and price data.
Media: CD-ROM.
Published by: (Research and Statistics Department), Bank of Japan/Nippon Ginko, c/o Public Relations Department, 2-1-1 Hongoku-cho-Nihonbashi, Chuo-ku, Tokyo, 1030000, Japan. TEL 81-3-3279-1111, FAX 81-3-3510-1374, http://www.boj.or.jp/en.index.htm. **Dist. by:** Tokiwa Sohgoh Service Co. Ltd., Publication and Research Department, Kyodo Bldg, 2-4 Hongokucho, Nihonbashi 3-chome, Chuo-ku, Tokyo 103-0027, Japan. TEL 81-3-3270-5713, FAX 81-3-3270-5710; **Dist. overseas by:** Japan Publications Trading Co., Ltd., Book Export II Dept, PO Box 5030, Tokyo International, Tokyo 101-3191, Japan. TEL 81-3-32923753, FAX 81-3-32920410, infoserials@jptco.co.jp, http://www.jptco.co.jp.

330.9 315 JPN ISSN 0005-5247
HG41
BANK OF JAPAN. ECONOMIC STATISTICS MONTHLY. Text in English, Japanese. 1946. m. JPY 1,050 per issue. charts; mkt.; stat. 250 p./no.; **Description:** Contains statistics covering the overall monetary and economic activities of Japan.
Indexed: RASB.
Published by: (Research and Statistics Department), Bank of Japan/Nippon Ginko, c/o Public Relations Department, 2-1-1 Hongoku-cho-Nihonbashi, Chuo-ku, Tokyo, 1030000, Japan. TEL 81-3-3279-1111, FAX 81-3-3510-1374, http://www.boj.or.jp/en.index.htm. **Dist. by:** Tokiwa Sohgoh Service Co. Ltd., Publication and Research Department, Kyodo Bldg, 2-4 Hongokucho, Nihonbashi 3-chome, Chuo-ku, Tokyo 103-0027, Japan. TEL 81-3-3270-5713, FAX 81-3-3270-5710; **Dist. oveseas by:** Japan Publications Trading Co., Ltd., Book Export II Dept, PO Box 5030, Tokyo International, Tokyo 101-3191, Japan. TEL 81-3-32923753, FAX 81-3-32920410, infoserials@jptco.co.jp, http://www.jptco.co.jp.

382 JPN ISSN 1342-4521
BANK OF JAPAN. PRICE INDEXES ANNUAL/BUKKA SHISU NENPO. Text in English, Japanese. a. JPY 3,700 (effective 1998). 700 p./no.; **Description:** Contains statistics on prices useful in reviewing Japanese price levels, supply and demand conditions of commodities, and developments in the economy.
Published by: (Research and Statistics Department), Bank of Japan/Nippon Ginko, c/o Public Relations Department, 2-1-1 Hongoku-cho-Nihonbashi, Chuo-ku, Tokyo, 1030000, Japan. TEL 81-3-3279-1111, FAX 81-3-3292-0410, http://www.boj.or.jp/en.index.htm. **Dist. by:** Tokiwa Sohgoh Service Co. Ltd., Publication and Research Department, Kyodo Bldg, 2-4 Hongokucho, Nihonbashi 3-chome, Chuo-ku, Tokyo 103-0027, Japan. TEL 81-3-3270-5713, FAX 81-3-3270-5710; **Overseas dist. by:** Japan Publications Trading Co., Ltd., Book Export II Dept, PO Box 5030, Tokyo International, Tokyo 101-3191, Japan. TEL 81-3-32923753, FAX 81-3-32920410, infoserials@jptco.co.jp, http://www.jptco.co.jp.

330.9 315 KOR ISSN 1013-0055
BANK OF KOREA. MONTHLY STATISTICAL BULLETIN. Text in English. 1983 (vol.37). m. illus.; stat.
Former titles: Bank of Korea. Monthly Bulletin; Bank of Korea. Monthly Economic Statistics; Bank of Korea. Monthly Statistical Review (0005-5263)
Related titles: Korean ed.
Indexed: PAIS.
Published by: Bank of Korea, Research Department, 110 3 Ka Namdaemun Ro, Chung-Ku, Seoul, 100794, Korea, S. TEL 82-2759-4172, FAX 82-2-752-0946, TELEX KOREABK K24711, K24712, bokdrar@bok.or.kr, http://www.bok.or.kr. Ed. Seong Tae Lee.

382 316 SDN ISSN 0522-246X
HF273.S8
BANK OF SUDAN. FOREIGN TRADE STATISTICAL DIGEST. Text in English. 1968. q. **Description:** Documents the foreign trade statistics and balance of payments covering all exports and imports through Port Sudan.
Published by: (Statistics Department), Bank of Sudan, P O Box 313, Khartoum, Sudan. TEL 78064.

332 USA ISSN 1075-282X
Z7164.F5
BANKING INFORMATION INDEX. Text in English. 1982. m. (plus a. cumulation). illus. back issues avail.; reprints avail. **Document type:** *Abstract/Index.* **Description:** Information tracking system for new developments in the banking and financial services industry. Provides subject access to more than 185 journals, magazines, newspapers, and newsletters.
Formerly (until 1994): Banking Literature Index (0736-5659)
Published by: ProQuest Information & Learning, 300 N Zeeb Rd., PO Box 1346, Ann Arbor, MI 48106-1346. TEL 734-761-4700, 800-521-0600, info@proquest.com, http://www.aba.com/, http://www.latimes.com/. Circ: 450 (paid).

330.9 316 COD
BANQUE CENTRALE DU CONGO. BULLETIN MENSUEL DE LA STATISTIQUE. Text in French. m. **Document type:** *Bulletin.*
Formerly: Banque du Zaire. Bulletin Mensuel de la Statistique
Indexed: RASB.
Published by: Banque Centrale du Congo, BP 269, Kinshasa, Gombe, Congo, Dem. Republic. TEL 243-20704, FAX 243-8805152, http://www.bcc.cd.

332.1 FRA
BANQUE DE FRANCE. CAHIER DES TITRES DE CREANCES NEGOCIABLES. Text in French. m. EUR 381 (effective 2003). **Description:** Covers certificates of deposit and treasury bills.

B

Published by: Banque de France, Service Relations avec le Public, 48 rue Croix-des-Petits-Champs, Paris, 75049, France. TEL 33-1-42923908, FAX 33-1-42923940, http://www.banque-france.fr.

332 CMR ISSN 0014-2069
HG3409.E65
BANQUE DES ETATS DE L'AFRIQUE CENTRALE. ETUDES ET STATISTIQUES; bulletin mensuel. Text in French. 1956. 10/yr. stat. **Document type:** *Bulletin.*
Indexed: ASD, PAIS.
Published by: Banque des Etats de l'Afrique Centrale, Direction des Etudes et de la Documentation, Services Centraux, BP 1917, Yaounde, Cameroon. TEL 22-25-05, FAX 23-33-29, TELEX 8343. Circ: 1,500.

332.021 BEL
BANQUE NATIONALE DE BELGIQUE. BELGOSTAT (YEAR). Text in French, Dutch. quadrennial. EUR 60; EUR 25 newsstand/cover (effective 2003). **Document type:** *Government.*
Media: CD-ROM.
Published by: Banque Nationale de Belgique/Nationale Bank van Belgie, Service Documentation, Bd de Berlaimont 14, Brussels, 1000, Belgium.

332.021 BEL
BANQUE NATIONALE DE BELGIQUE. INDICATEURS ECONOMIQUES POUR LA BELGIQUE. Text in French, Dutch, English. m. free. **Document type:** *Government.*
Published by: Banque Nationale de Belgique/Nationale Bank van Belgie, Service Documentation, Bd de Berlaimont 14, Brussels, 1000, Belgium.

332.021 BEL ISSN 1372-7877
HC320.I5
BANQUE NATIONALE DE BELGIQUE. INSTITUT DES COMPTES NATIONAUX. AGREGATS ANNUELS. Text in French, Dutch. a. EUR 12.39 newsstand/cover (effective 2003). **Document type:** *Government.*
Published by: Banque Nationale de Belgique, Institut des Comptes Nationaux/Nationale Bank van Belgie, Instituut voor de Nationale Rekeningen, Service Documentation, Bd de Berlaimont 14, Brussels, 1000, Belgium.

332.021 BEL ISSN 1373-9441
BANQUE NATIONALE DE BELGIQUE. INSTITUT DES COMPTES NATIONAUX. COMPTES NATIONAUX: AGREGATS TRIMESTRIELS. Text in French, Dutch. q. EUR 19.83; EUR 6.20 newsstand/cover (effective 2003). **Document type:** *Government.*
Published by: Banque Nationale de Belgique, Institut des Comptes Nationaux/Nationale Bank van Belgie, Instituut voor de Nationale Rekeningen, Service Documentation, Bd de Berlaimont 14, Brussels, 1000, Belgium.

332.021 BEL
BANQUE NATIONALE DE BELGIQUE. INSTITUT DES COMPTES NATIONAUX. COMPTES REGIONAUX. Text in French, Dutch. a. EUR 19.83 newsstand/cover (effective 2003). **Document type:** *Government.*
Published by: Banque Nationale de Belgique, Institut des Comptes Nationaux/Nationale Bank van Belgie, Instituut voor de Nationale Rekeningen, Service Documentation, Bd de Berlaimont 14, Brussels, 1000, Belgium.

382.021 BEL
BANQUE NATIONALE DE BELGIQUE. INSTITUT DES COMPTES NATIONAUX. STATISTIQUES DES EXPORTATIONS BELGES: RESULTATS REGIONAUX. Text in French, Dutch. q. EUR 81.79; EUR 26.03 newsstand/cover (effective 2003). **Document type:** *Government.*
Published by: Banque Nationale de Belgique, Institut des Comptes Nationaux/Nationale Bank van Belgie, Instituut voor de Nationale Rekeningen, Service Documentation, Bd de Berlaimont 14, Brussels, 1000, Belgium.

332.1 BEL
BANQUE NATIONALE DE BELGIQUE. INSTITUT DES COMPTES NATIONAUX. STATISTIQUES DU COMMERCE EXTERIEUR. Text in French, Dutch. m. (or quarterly). EUR 81.79; EUR 7.43 newsstand/cover (effective 2003). **Document type:** *Government.*
Published by: Banque Nationale de Belgique, Institut des Comptes Nationaux/Nationale Bank van Belgie, Instituut voor de Nationale Rekeningen, Service Documentation, Bd de Berlaimont 14, Brussels, 1000, Belgium.

332.1 BEL
BANQUE NATIONALE DE BELGIQUE. INSTITUT DES COMPTES NATIONAUX. STATISTIQUES DU COMMERCE EXTERIEUR. ANNUAIRE. Text in French, Dutch. a. EUR 54.52 newsstand/cover (effective 2003). **Document type:** *Government.*
Published by: Banque Nationale de Belgique, Institut des Comptes Nationaux/Nationale Bank van Belgie, Instituut voor de Nationale Rekeningen, Service Documentation, Bd de Berlaimont 14, Brussels, 1000, Belgium.

332.1021 BEL
BANQUE NATIONALE DE BELGIQUE. LA CENTRALE DES BILANS. STATISTIQUES. Text in French, Dutch. a. EUR 25 (effective 2003). **Document type:** *Government.*
Media: CD-ROM.
Published by: Banque Nationale de Belgique/Nationale Bank van Belgie, Service Documentation, Bd de Berlaimont 14, Brussels, 1000, Belgium.

332.021 BEL
BANQUE NATIONALE DE BELGIQUE. LA CENTRALE DES CREDITS AUX PARTICULIERS. Text in French, Dutch. q. free. **Document type:** *Government.*
Published by: Banque Nationale de Belgique/Nationale Bank van Belgie, Service Documentation, Bd de Berlaimont 14, Brussels, 1000, Belgium.

310 BRB
BARBADOS. STATISTICAL SERVICE. BULLETIN. OVERSEAS TRADE. Text in English. 1983. m. free. stat. **Document type:** *Government.* **Description:** Detailed figures on imports and exports of CARICOM countries.
Published by: Statistical Service, National Insurance Bldg. 3rd Fl., Fairchild St., Bridgetown, Barbados. Circ: 200.

011 USA ISSN 0360-8379
HG1
BARRON'S INDEX. Text in English. irreg. **Document type:** *Abstract/Index.*
Related titles: ♦ Issued with: The Wall Street Journal Index. ISSN 1042-9840.
Indexed: HlthInd.
Published by: ProQuest Information & Learning, 300 N Zeeb Rd., PO Box 1346, Ann Arbor, MI 48106-1346. TEL 313-761-4700, 800-521-0600, FAX 800-864-0019.

330.9021 BEL ISSN 0779-4312
BELGIUM. COMMUNAUTE FRANCAISE DE BELGIQUE. INSTITUT NATIONAL DE STATISTIQUE. ANNUAIRE STATISTIQUE. Text in French. 1965. a. charts. back issues avail. **Document type:** *Government.*
Formerly (until 1991): Belgium. Institut National de Statistique. Annuaire Statistique de Poche (0067-5431)
Related titles: ♦ Dutch ed.: Belgium. Nationaal Instituut voor de Statistiek. Statistisch Zakjaarboek. ISSN 1370-1754.
Published by: Institut National de Statistique/Nationaal Instituut voor de Statistiek (Subsidiary of: Ministere des Affaires Economiques), Rue de Louvain 44, Brussels, 1000, Belgium. TEL 32-2-548-6211, FAX 32-2-548-6367, http://www.statbel.fgov.be.

314.93021 BEL ISSN 0770-0369
HA1393
BELGIUM. INSTITUT NATIONAL DE STATISTIQUE. ANNUAIRE DE STATISTIQUES REGIONALES. Key Title: Annuaire de Statistiques Regionales. Text in French. 1976. a. EUR 16 foreign (effective 2001). charts. back issues avail. **Document type:** *Government.*
Related titles: ♦ Dutch ed.: Belgium. Nationaal Instituut voor de Statistiek. Regionaal Statistisch Jaarboek. ISSN 0770-772X.
Indexed: RASB.
Published by: Institut National de Statistique/Nationaal Instituut voor de Statistiek (Subsidiary of: Ministere des Affaires Economiques), Rue de Louvain 44, Brussels, 1000, Belgium. TEL 32-2-548-6211, FAX 32-2-548-6367, http://www.statbel.fgov.be.

330.9021 BEL ISSN 0045-1703
HA1393
BELGIUM. INSTITUT NATIONAL DE STATISTIQUE. BULLETIN DE STATISTIQUE. Text in French. 1915. m. (9/yr). EUR 50; EUR 5 per issue (effective 2002). charts. back issues avail. **Document type:** *Government.*
Related titles: ♦ Dutch ed.: Belgium. Nationaal Instituut voor de Statistiek. Statistisch Tijdschrift. ISSN 0778-8789.
Indexed: PAIS, RASB.
Published by: Institut National de Statistique/Nationaal Instituut voor de Statistiek (Subsidiary of: Ministere des Affaires Economiques), Rue de Louvain 44, Brussels, 1000, Belgium. TEL 32-2-548-6211, FAX 32-2-548-6367, http://www.statbel.fgov.be.

330.9021 BEL ISSN 0772-6341
BELGIUM. INSTITUT NATIONAL DE STATISTIQUE. COMMUNIQUE HEBDOMADAIRE. Text in French. 1945. w. EUR 50 (effective 2002). charts. **Document type:** *Government.*
Supersedes in part (in 1982): Institut National de Statistique. Communique Hebdomadaire (Edition Bilingue) (0771-0364)
Related titles: ♦ Dutch ed.: Belgium. Nationaal Instituut voor de Statistiek. Weekbericht. ISSN 0771-0410.
Published by: Institut National de Statistique/Nationaal Instituut voor de Statistiek (Subsidiary of: Ministere des Affaires Economiques), Rue de Louvain 44, Brussels, 1000, Belgium. TEL 32-2-548-6211, FAX 32-2-548-6367, http://www.statbel.fgov.be.

330.9021 BEL ISSN 1379-3845
HD5786
BELGIUM. INSTITUT NATIONAL DE STATISTIQUE. EMPLOI ET CHOMAGE. ENQUETE SUR LES FORCES DE TRAVAIL (YEAR). Key Title: Emploi et Chomage. Enquete sur les Forces de Travail. Text in French. 1991. a. charts. back issues avail. **Document type:** *Government.*
Formerly (until 2000): Belgium. Institut National de Statistique. Enquete sur les Forces de Travail (1373-9913)
Related titles: ♦ Dutch ed.: Belgium. Nationaal Instituut voor de Statistiek. Werkgelegenheid en Werkloosheid. Enquete naar de Arbeidskrachten (Year). ISSN 1379-3853.
Published by: Institut National de Statistique/Nationaal Instituut voor de Statistiek (Subsidiary of: Ministere des Affaires Economiques), Rue de Louvain 44, Brussels, 1000, Belgium. TEL 32-2-548-6211, FAX 32-2-548-6367, http://www.statbel.fgov.be.

330.9021 BEL
BELGIUM. INSTITUT NATIONAL DE STATISTIQUE. ENQUETE SUR LES BUDGETS DES MENAGES. Key Title: Enquete sur les Budgets des Menages - Institut National de Statistique. Text in French. a. EUR 50 (effective 2001); price varies. charts. back issues avail. **Document type:** *Government.*
Published by: Institut National de Statistique/Nationaal Instituut voor de Statistiek (Subsidiary of: Ministere des Affaires Economiques), Rue de Louvain 44, Brussels, 1000, Belgium. TEL 32-2-548-6211, FAX 32-2-548-6367, http://www.statbel.fgov.be.

314.93021 BEL ISSN 1377-137X
HC311
BELGIUM. INSTITUT NATIONAL DE STATISTIQUE. INDUSTRIE ET CONSTRUCTION. Key Title: Statistiques Industrielles (Brussels). Text in French. 1967. m. (11/yr). BEF 2,300 foreign (effective 2000). charts. back issues avail. **Document type:** *Government.* **Description:** Provides a statistical overview of industrial trends and the current state of Belgian industry.
Formerly (until 2001): Belgium. Institut National de Statistique. Statistiques Industrielles (0772-7704)
Related titles: ♦ Dutch ed.: Belgium. Nationaal Instituut voor de Statistiek. Industrie en Bouwnijverheid. ISSN 1377-1361.
Indexed: PAIS, RASB.
Published by: Institut National de Statistique/Nationaal Instituut voor de Statistiek (Subsidiary of: Ministere des Affaires Economiques), Rue de Louvain 44, Brussels, 1000, Belgium. TEL 32-2-548-6211, FAX 32-2-548-6367, http://www.statbel.fgov.be.

BELGIUM. INSTITUT NATIONAL DE STATISTIQUE. INDUSTRIE ET CONSTRUCTION. CONSTRUCTION ET LOGEMENT. see *HOUSING AND URBAN PLANNING—Abstracting, Bibliographies, Statistics*

330.9021 BEL ISSN 1379-4027
BELGIUM. INSTITUT NATIONAL DE STATISTIQUE. MEDIA. NOMBRE DE LICENCES D'APPAREILS DE RADIO SUR VEHICULE ET DE TELEVISION. Key Title: Nombre de Licences d'Appareils de Radio sur Vehicule et de Television au 31 Decembre. Text in French. 1964. a. charts. back issues avail. **Document type:** *Government.*
Former titles (until 2000): Belgium. Institut National de Statistique. Statistiques sur les Medias et l'Audiovisuel. Nombre de Licences d'Appareils de Radio sur Vehicule et de Television (1379-4000); (until 1999): Belgium. Institut National de Statistique. Nombre de Licences d'Appareils de Radio sur Vehicule et de Television au 31 Decembre (1372-634X); (until 1996): Belgium. Institut National de Statistique. Nombre de Detenteurs d'Autoradios et de Televiseurs au 31 Decembre; (until 1986): Belgium. Institut National de Statistique. Nombre de Detenteurs d'Appareils de Radio et Television au 31 Decembre (0772-2230)
Related titles: ♦ Dutch ed.: Belgium. Nationaal Instituut voor de Statistiek. Media. Aantal Vergunningen voor Autoradio's en Televisietoestellen. ISSN 1379-4035.
Published by: Institut National de Statistique/Nationaal Instituut voor de Statistiek (Subsidiary of: Ministere des Affaires Economiques), Rue de Louvain 44, Brussels, 1000, Belgium. TEL 32-2-548-6211, FAX 32-2-548-6367, http://www.statbel.fgov.be.

330.9021 BEL ISSN 1371-6271
BELGIUM. INSTITUT NATIONAL DE STATISTIQUE. NOUVELLES ECONOMIQUES. Key Title: Nouvelles Economiques - Institut National de Statistique. Text in French. 1996. w. (50/yr). charts. back issues avail. **Document type:** *Government.*
Related titles: ♦ Dutch ed.: Belgium. Nationaal Instituut voor de Statistiek. Economische Nieuws. ISSN 1371-7111.
Published by: Institut National de Statistique/Nationaal Instituut voor de Statistiek (Subsidiary of: Ministere des Affaires Economiques), Rue de Louvain 44, Brussels, 1000, Belgium. TEL 32-2-548-6211, FAX 32-2-548-6367, http://www.statbel.fgov.be.

330.9021 BEL ISSN 1371-7111
BELGIUM. NATIONAAL INSTITUUT VOOR DE STATISTIEK. ECONOMISCHE NIEUWS. Key Title: Economische Nieuws - Nationaal Instituut voor de Statistiek. Text in Dutch. 1996. w. (50/yr). charts. back issues avail. **Document type:** *Government.*

B

Related titles: ♦ French ed.: Belgium. Institut National de Statistique. Nouvelles Economiques. ISSN 1371-6271.
Published by: Institut National de Statistique/Nationaal Instituut voor de Statistiek (Subsidiary of: Ministere des Affaires Economiques), Rue de Louvain 44, Brussels, 1000, Belgium. TEL 32-2-548-6211, FAX 32-2-548-6367, http://www.statbel.fgov.be.

314.93021 BEL ISSN 1377-1361
BELGIUM. NATIONAAL INSTITUUT VOOR DE STATISTIEK. INDUSTRIE EN BOUWNIJVERHEID. Key Title: Industrie en Bouwnijverheid. Text in Dutch. 1967. m. charts. **Document type:** *Government.* **Description:** Examines industrial trends and conditions in Belgium.
Formerly (until 2001): Belgium. Nationaal Instituut voor de Statistiek. Industriele Statistieken (0772-7690)
Related titles: ♦ French ed.: Belgium. Institut National de Statistique. Industrie et Construction. ISSN 1377-137X.
Published by: Institut National de Statistique/Nationaal Instituut voor de Statistiek (Subsidiary of: Ministere des Affaires Economiques), Rue de Louvain 44, Brussels, 1000, Belgium. TEL 32-2-548-6211, FAX 32-2-548-6367, http://www.statbel.fgov.be.

BELGIUM. NATIONAAL INSTITUUT VOOR DE STATISTIEK. INDUSTRIE EN BOUWNIJVERHEID. BOUWNIJVERHEID EN HUISVESTING. see *HOUSING AND URBAN PLANNING—Abstracting, Bibliographies, Statistics*

330.9021 BEL ISSN 1379-4035
BELGIUM. NATIONAAL INSTITUUT VOOR DE STATISTIEK. MEDIA. AANTAL VERGUNNINGEN VOOR AUTORADIO'S EN TELEVISIETOESTELLEN. Key Title: Aantal Vergunningen voor Autoradio's en Televisietoestellen - Nationaal Instituut voor de Statistiek. Text in Dutch. 1964. a. back issues avail. **Document type:** *Government.*
Former titles (until 2000): Belgium. Nationaal Instituut voor de Statistiek. Statistieken over communicatiemedia. Aantal Vergunningen voor Autoradio's en Televisietoestellen (1379-4019); (until 1999): Belgium. Nationaal Instituut voor de Statistiek. Aantal Vergunningen voor Autoradio's en Televisietoestellen (1372-6366); (until 1996): Nationaal Instituut voor de Statistiek. Aantal Houders van Autoradio- en Televisietoestellen; (until 1986): Belgium. Nationaal Instituut voor de Statistiek. Aantal Houders van Radio en Televisietoestellen (0773-4514)
Related titles: ♦ French ed.: Belgium. Institut National de Statistique. Media. Nombre de Licences d'Appareils de Radio sur Vehicule et de Television. ISSN 1379-4027.
Published by: Institut National de Statistique/Nationaal Instituut voor de Statistiek (Subsidiary of: Ministere des Affaires Economiques), Rue de Louvain 44, Brussels, 1000, Belgium. TEL 32-2-548-6211, FAX 32-2-548-6367, http://www.statbel.fgov.be.

330.9021 BEL ISSN 0770-772X
BELGIUM. NATIONAAL INSTITUUT VOOR DE STATISTIEK. REGIONAAL STATISTISCH JAARBOEK. Key Title: Regionaal Statistisch Jaarboek. Text in Dutch. 1976. a. charts. back issues avail. **Document type:** *Government.*
Related titles: ♦ French ed.: Belgium. Institut National de Statistique. Annuaire de Statistiques Regionales. ISSN 0770-0369.
Published by: Institut National de Statistique/Nationaal Instituut voor de Statistiek (Subsidiary of: Ministere des Affaires Economiques), Rue de Louvain 44, Brussels, 1000, Belgium. TEL 32-2-548-6211, FAX 32-2-548-6367, http://www.statbel.fgov.be.

330.9021 BEL ISSN 0778-8789
BELGIUM. NATIONAAL INSTITUUT VOOR DE STATISTIEK. STATISTISCH TIJDSCHRIFT. Key Title: Statistisch Tijdschrift - Nationaal Instituut voor de Statistiek. Text in Dutch. m. charts. **Document type:** *Government.*
Related titles: ♦ French ed.: Belgium. Institut National de Statistique. Bulletin de Statistique. ISSN 0045-1703.
Published by: Institut National de Statistique/Nationaal Instituut voor de Statistiek (Subsidiary of: Ministere des Affaires Economiques), Rue de Louvain 44, Brussels, 1000, Belgium. TEL 32-2-548-6211, FAX 32-2-548-6367, http://www.statbel.fgov.be.

330.9021 BEL ISSN 1370-1754
BELGIUM. NATIONAAL INSTITUUT VOOR DE STATISTIEK. STATISTISCH ZAKJAARBOEK. Key Title: Statistisch Zakjaarboek - Nationaal Instituut voor de Statistiek. Text in Dutch. 1996. a.
Related titles: ♦ French ed.: Belgium. Communaute Francaise de Belgique. Institut National de Statistique. Annuaire Statistique. ISSN 0779-4312.
Published by: Institut National de Statistique/Nationaal Instituut voor de Statistiek (Subsidiary of: Ministere des Affaires Economiques), Rue de Louvain 44, Brussels, 1000, Belgium. TEL 32-2-548-6211, FAX 32-2-548-6367, http://www.statbel.fgov.be.

330.9021 BEL ISSN 0771-0410
HA1393
BELGIUM. NATIONAAL INSTITUUT VOOR DE STATISTIEK. WEEKBERICHT. Text in Dutch. 1945. w. charts. back issues avail. **Document type:** *Government.*
Supersedes in part (in 1982): Communique Hebdomadaire - Institut National de Statistique (Bilingual Edition) (0771-0364)
Related titles: ♦ French ed.: Belgium. Institut National de Statistique. Communique Hebdomadaire. ISSN 0772-6341.
Published by: Institut National de Statistique/Nationaal Instituut voor de Statistiek (Subsidiary of: Ministere des Affaires Economiques), Rue de Louvain 44, Brussels, 1000, Belgium. TEL 32-2-548-6211, FAX 32-2-548-6367, http://www.statbel.fgov.be.

330.9021 BEL ISSN 1379-3853
BELGIUM. NATIONAAL INSTITUUT VOOR DE STATISTIEK. WERKGELEGENHEID EN WERKLOOSHEID. ENQUETE NAAR DE ARBEIDSKRACHTEN (YEAR). Key Title: Werkgelegenheid en Werkloosheid. Enquete naar de Arbeidskrachten. Text in Dutch. 1991. a. charts. **Document type:** *Government.*
Former titles (until 2000): Belgium. Nationaal Instituut voor de Statistiek. Sociale Statistieken. Enquete naar de Arbeidskrachten (1379-3837); (until 1999): Belgium. Nationaal Instituut voor de Statistiek. Sociale Statistieken: Enquete naar de Beroepsbevolking (1373-9921)
Related titles: ♦ French ed.: Belgium. Institut National de Statistique. Emploi et Chomage. Enquete sur les Forces de Travail (Year). ISSN 1379-3845.
Published by: Institut National de Statistique/Nationaal Instituut voor de Statistiek (Subsidiary of: Ministere des Affaires Economiques), Rue de Louvain 44, Brussels, 1000, Belgium. TEL 32-2-548-6211, FAX 32-2-548-6367, http://www.statbel.fgov.be.

331.11021 BLZ
(YEAR) BELIZE LABOUR FORCE INDICATORS. Text in English. a.
Published by: Ministry of Finance, Central Statistical Office, Belmopan, Belize. TEL 501-8-22352, FAX 501-8-23206, csogob@btl.net.

658.3 MEX
BENEFITS SURVEY. Text in English, Spanish. a. USD 150 (effective 2003). **Document type:** *Corporate.* **Description:** Provides information on fringe benefits received by executives, other high-level personnel and salespeople by company size, location and industrial sector within Mexico.
Published by: American Chamber of Commerce of Mexico A.C., Lucerna 78, Col. Juarez, Mexico City, D F 06600, Mexico. TEL 52-55-51413800, FAX 52-55-57032911, amchamm@amcham.com.mx, http://www.amcham.com.mx/. Ed. Jose Antonio Hernandez. R&P Diana H de Hernandez. Adv. contact Rommy Strevel.

016.331 BRA ISSN 0103-2038
Z7165.B7
BIBLIOGRAFIA DE POLITICA INDUSTRIAL. Text in Portuguese. 1987. a.
Published by: Confederacao Nacional da Industria, Av. Nilo Pecanha, 50, Gr. 2608, Rio De Janeiro, RJ 20044-900, Brazil.

330 POL
BIBLIOGRAFIA PUBLIKACJI PRACOWNIKOW NAUKOWYCH AKADEMII EKONOMICZNEJ W KRAKOWIE (ONLINE EDITION). Text in Polish. 1984. a., latest 1998. free. index. **Document type:** *Directory, Bibliography.* **Description:** Lists publications of the academic staff of the Cracow University of Economics.
Formerly (until 2001): Bibliografia Publikacji Pracownikow Naukowych Akademii Ekonomicznej w Krakowie (Print Edition)
Media: Online - full text.
Published by: Akademia Ekonomiczna w Krakowie, Biblioteka Glowna/Main Library of the Cracow University of Economics, ul Rakowicka 27, Krakow, 31510, Poland. TEL 48-12-2935009, FAX 48-12-2935010, agogut@bibl.ae.krakow.pl, http://kangur.ae.krakow.pl.

330 015 MEX ISSN 0188-6673
Z7165.M45
BIBLIOGRAFIA SOBRE LA ECONOMIA MEXICANA. LIBROS. Text in Spanish. 1955. irreg., latest 1990-1992 ed. MXP 70; USD 20 in the Americas; USD 25 in Europe. bibl. **Description:** Covers publications from Mexico and about Mexico.
Formerly (until 1981): Bibliografia Economica de Mexico (0006-100X)
Published by: Banco de Mexico, Subdireccion de Investigacion Economica y Bancaria, 06059 Mexico, Mexico, Ave. JUAREZ 90, Centro Urbano Benito Juarez, Del. Cuauhtemoc, Ciudad De Mexico, DF 06059, Mexico. TEL 525-761-8588. Circ: 200.

330 USA ISSN 0360-2702
Z7164.C81
BIBLIOGRAPHIC GUIDE TO BUSINESS AND ECONOMICS. Text in English. 1974. a. USD 935 (effective 2005). **Document type:** *Abstract/Index.* **Description:** Covers books, reports, conference papers and miscellaneous publications in the New York Public Library, with additional entries covering all aspects of business and economics: theory, history, population, demography, land-agriculture, industry, labor, transportation, communication, commerce, business administration, finance, foreign exchange, insurance, taxation, statistics.
Published by: G.K. Hall & Co. (Subsidiary of: Gale Group), 12 Lunar Dr, Woodbridge, CT 06525. TEL 203-397-2600, 800-444-0799, FAX 203-397-8296, http://www.galegroup.com/gkhall. **Subscr. to:** Simon & Schuster, PO Box 7500, Riverside, NJ 08075-8075. TEL 800-223-2336.

330 016 DEU ISSN 0006-1417
Z7164.E2
BIBLIOGRAPHIE DER WIRTSCHAFTSPRESSE. Text in German. 1949. m. reprint service avail. from ISI. **Document type:** *Bibliography.*
Indexed: KES, PAIS, RASB.
—CCC.
Published by: H W W A - Institut fuer Wirtschaftsforschung Hamburg, Informationszentrum, Neuer Jungfernstieg 21, Hamburg, 20347, Germany. TEL 49-40-428340, FAX 49-40-42834451, hwwa@hwwa.de, http://www.hwwa.de.

016.331 DEU ISSN 0343-4117
Z7164.L1
BIBLIOGRAPHIE ZUR GESCHICHTE DER DEUTSCHEN ARBEITERBEWEGUNG. Text in English, French, German. 1976. a. reprints avail. **Document type:** *Bibliography.*
Indexed: PAIS, RASB.
—CCC.
Published by: Verlag J.H.W. Dietz Nachf. GmbH, In der Raste 2, Bonn, 53129, Germany. TEL 49-228-238083, FAX 49-228-234104, info@dietz-verlag.de. Ed. Wolfgang Budde Roth.

016.33 USA ISSN 0749-1786
BIBLIOGRAPHIES AND INDEXES IN ECONOMICS AND ECONOMIC HISTORY. Text in English. 1984. irreg. price varies. **Document type:** *Bibliography.*
Published by: Greenwood Publishing Group Inc. (Subsidiary of: Harcourt International), 88 Post Rd W, PO Box 5007, Westport, CT 06881. TEL 203-226-3571, FAX 203-226-1502, bookinfo@greenwood.com, http://www.greenwood.com.

016.658 LKA
BIBLIOGRAPHY OF ECONOMIC AND SOCIAL DEVELOPMENT SRI LANKA. Text in English. 1982. irreg. LKR 200, USD 25. back issues avail. **Document type:** *Bibliography.* **Description:** Provides bibliographical data on development information related to Sri Lanka from various government, non-governmental, private, and international agencies.
Published by: (Sri Lanka. Centre for Development Information), Ministry of Policy Planning & Implementation, National Planning Dept., Treasury Bldg., Columbo 01, Sri Lanka. FAX 549823, TELEX 21409-FINMIN-CE. Circ: 250.

016.33 TZA
BIBLIOGRAPHY OF ECONOMIC AND STATISTICAL PUBLICATIONS ON TANZANIA. Text in English. 1967. irreg. stat. **Document type:** *Bibliography.*
Published by: National Bureau of Statistics, PO Box 796, Dar Es Salaam, Tanzania. **Orders to:** Government Publications Agency, PO Box 1801, Dar Es Salaam, Tanzania.

016.33 IND
BIBLIOGRAPHY OF PUBLICATIONS FROM ECONOMIC RESEARCH CENTRES IN INDIA. Text in English. 1973. irreg., latest 1988. INR 250, USD 75. adv. Supplement avail. **Document type:** *Bibliography.*
Published by: Information Research Academy, 37 Syed Amir Ali Ave, Flat #9, Kolkata, West Bengal 700 019, India. Ed. Partha Subir Guha. Circ: 1,900.

016.332 USA ISSN 1063-3197
BIO-BIBLIOGRAPHIES IN ECONOMICS. Text in English. 1992. irreg. price varies. **Document type:** *Monographic series, Bibliography.*
Published by: Greenwood Publishing Group Inc. (Subsidiary of: Harcourt International), 88 Post Rd W, PO Box 5007, Westport, CT 06881. TEL 203-226-3571, FAX 203-226-1502, bookinfo@greenwood.com, http://www.greenwood.com.

330.9 BRA ISSN 0104-5458
BOLETIM CONJUNTURAL DO NORDESTE DO BRASIL. Text in Portuguese. 1993. irreg. **Document type:** *Government.*
Published by: Superintendencia do Desenvolvimento do Nordeste, Praca Ministro J. Goncalves de Souza, Edf. Sudene, Cidade Universitaria, Recife, PE 50670900, Brazil. TEL 55-81-4162222, FAX 55-81-4531277.

330.9 332 GTM
BOLETIN DE ESTADISTICAS BANCARIAS. Text in Spanish. 1951. q. free. charts; illus.; stat. index. back issues avail. **Document type:** *Bulletin.* **Description:** Statistics on the 60 institutions under the supervision of Superintendencia de Bancos.
Published by: (Guatemala. Seccion de Estadistica), Superintendencia de Bancos, Departamento Tecnico, Edificio Bco. de Guatemala, 10 Nivel, 7a. Av. 22-01, Guatemala City Zona, Guatemala. TEL 53-42-43.

331 ESP ISSN 0212-7180
HD8581
BOLETIN DE ESTADISTICAS LABORALES. Text in Spanish. m. **Document type:** *Government.*

Published by: Ministerio de Trabajo y Asuntos Sociales, Centro de Publicaciones, Agustin de Bethencourt, 11, Madrid, 28003, Spain. TEL 34-1-5543400, FAX 34-1-915333847, libreria@mundiprensa.es, http://www.mtas.es/. **Subscr. to:** Mundi-Prensa Libros, S.A., Castello, 37, Madrid 28001, Spain. TEL 34-1-4313222, FAX 34-1-5753998.

332 HND
BOLETIN MENSUAL DE ESTADISTICAS DEL SISTEMA FINANCIERO. Text in Spanish. 1996. m. free. **Document type:** *Bulletin.*
Published by: Comision Nacional de Bancos y Seguros, Seccion de Estadisticas y Control de Riesgos, Comayaguela, M D C, Honduras. TEL 504-220-0111, FAX 504-237-6232.

310 382 BOL
BOLIVIA. INSTITUTO NACIONAL DE ESTADISTICA. ANUARIO DE COMERCIO EXTERIOR. Text in Spanish. 1910. a. USD 12.
Published by: Instituto Nacional de Estadistica, Casilla de Correos 6129, La Paz, Bolivia.

310 338 BOL
BOLIVIA. INSTITUTO NACIONAL DE ESTADISTICA. ANUARIO DE ESTADISTICAS INDUSTRIALES. Text in Spanish. 1939. a. USD 15.
Published by: Instituto Nacional de Estadistica, Casilla de Correos 6129, La Paz, Bolivia.

339 318 BOL
BOLIVIA. INSTITUTO NACIONAL DE ESTADISTICA. INDICE DE PRECIOS AL CONSUMIDOR. Text in Spanish. 1974. m. USD 43.
Related titles: Cumulative ed(s).: Resumen Anual.
Published by: Instituto Nacional de Estadistica, Casilla de Correos 6129, La Paz, Bolivia.

332.64 ECU
BOLSA DE VALORES DE QUITO. BOLETIN DE OPERACIONES. Text in Spanish. d. (& w.). ECS 690,000.
Description: Contains information on the ECU-index, volumes, most active securities traded, and other current market information.
Published by: Bolsa de Valores de Quito, Amazonas 540 y Carrion, Apartado 17-01-3772, Quito, Ecuador. TEL 593-2-526805, FAX 593-2-500942, information@ccbvq.com, http://www.ccbvq.com.

332 MEX ISSN 0188-3879
HC131
BOLSA MEXICANA DE VALORES. ANUARIO FINANCIERO (YEAR). Text in Spanish. a. **Description:** Contains individual and sectorial financial data of companies listed on the Mexican Stock Exchange. Includes 4 years historical information, Board of Directors' report, general company information and basic data.
Related titles: English ed.: Mexican Stock Exchange. Annual Financial Facts and Figures (Year).
Published by: Bolsa Mexicana de Valores, S.A. de C.V./Mexican Stock Exchange, Paseo de la Reforma 255, Mexico City, DF 06500, Mexico. TEL 52-5-726+6794, FAX 52-5-7266836, cinforma@bmv.com.mx, http://www.bmv.com.mx/suscripciones.html.

332 MEX ISSN 0188-3925
HG5161
BOLSA MEXICANA DE VALORES. INDICADORES FINANCIEROS/MEXICAN STOCK EXCHANGE. FINANCIAL FACTS AND FIGURES. Text in Spanish. q. MXP 780 (effective 1999). **Description:** Contains balance sheets, income statements and financial ratios, by sector and by issuer.
Incorporates: Bolsa Mexicana de Valores. Financial Studies
Published by: Bolsa Mexicana de Valores, S.A. de C.V./Mexican Stock Exchange, Paseo de la Reforma 255, Mexico City, DF 06500, Mexico. TEL 52-5-7266794, FAX 52-5-7266836, cinforma@bmv.com.mx, http://www.bmv.com.mx/suscripciones.html.

332.6 MEX ISSN 1405-230X
HG5161
BOLSA MEXICANA DE VALORES. RESUMEN BURSATIL/MEXICAN STOCK EXCHANGE. STATISTICS SUMMARY. Text in Spanish. m. USD 35. **Description:** Summarizes securities market activity.
Published by: Bolsa Mexicana de Valores, S.A. de C.V./Mexican Stock Exchange, Paseo de la Reforma 255, Mexico City, DF 06500, Mexico. TEL 525-726-67-91, FAX 525-591-0534.

338.528 BWA
BOTSWANA. CENTRAL STATISTICS OFFICE. CONSUMER PRICE STATISTICS. Text and summaries in English. m. charts. back issues avail. **Document type:** *Government.*
Description: Provides figures on the rate of inflation and the cost-of-living index.
Related titles: E-mail ed.; Fax ed.
Published by: Central Statistics Office, c/o Government Statistician, Private Bag 0024, Gaborone, Botswana. TEL 267-31-352200, FAX 267-31-352201, csobots@gov.bw, csobots@gov.bw. Ed. G M Charumbira. **Subscr. to:** Government Printer, Private Bag 0081, Gaborone, Botswana. TEL 267-353202, FAX 267-312001, http://www.gov.bw.

330.1 BWA
BOTSWANA. CENTRAL STATISTICS OFFICE. DEMOGRAPHIC AND HEALTH SURVEY. Text in English. a., latest 1996. charts. back issues avail. **Document type:** *Government.*
Description: Provides demographic profiles of family planning, pregnancy, infant and childhood mortality, and child care.
Related titles: E-mail ed.; Fax ed.
Published by: Central Statistics Office, c/o Government Statistician, Private Bag 0024, Gaborone, Botswana. TEL 267-31-352200, FAX 267-31-352201, csobots@gov.bw. Ed. G M Charumbira. Pub. J G Segwe. **Subscr. to:** Government Printer, Private Bag 0081, Gaborone, Botswana. TEL 267-353202, FAX 267-312001, http://www.gov.bw.

330.9021 332.6021 BWA ISSN 1013-5707
HF3906
BOTSWANA. CENTRAL STATISTICS OFFICE. EXTERNAL TRADE STATISTICS. Text in English. a. BWP 20. charts. back issues avail. **Document type:** *Government.* **Description:** Compiles data on foreign trade to and from Botswana.
Related titles: E-mail ed.; Fax ed.
Published by: Central Statistics Office, c/o Government Statistician, Private Bag 0024, Gaborone, Botswana. TEL 267-31-352200, FAX 267-31-352201, csobots@gov.bw. Ed. G M Charumbira. Pub. J G Segwe. **Subscr. to:** Government Printer, Private Bag 0081, Gaborone, Botswana. TEL 267-353202, FAX 267-312001, http://www.gov.bw.

330.021 BWA
BOTSWANA. CENTRAL STATISTICS OFFICE. HOUSEHOLD INCOME AND EXPENDITURE SURVEY. Text in English. irreg., latest 1993. BWP 10 per vol.. charts. back issues avail. **Document type:** *Government.* **Description:** Analyzes household income and expenditure data for Botswana.
Related titles: E-mail ed.; Fax ed.
Published by: Central Statistics Office, c/o Government Statistician, Private Bag 0024, Gaborone, Botswana. TEL 267-31-352200, FAX 267-31-352201, csobots@gov.bw. Ed. G M Charumbira. Pub. J G Segwe. **Subscr. to:** Government Printer, Private Bag 0081, Gaborone, Botswana. TEL 267-353202, FAX 267-312001, http://www.gov.bw.

338.0921 BWA
BOTSWANA. CENTRAL STATISTICS OFFICE. INDUSTRIAL STATISTICS. Text and summaries in English. 1998. a. BWP 5, USD 1 (effective 2000). charts. back issues avail. **Document type:** *Government.* **Description:** Provides data on characteristic output of manufacturing by quarter, year and industry. Includes data on public utilities.
Related titles: E-mail ed.; Fax ed.
Published by: Central Statistics Office, c/o Government Statistician, Private Bag 0024, Gaborone, Botswana. TEL 267-31-352200, FAX 267-31-352201, csobots@gov.bw. Ed. G M Charumbira. Circ: 200. **Subscr. to:** Government Printer, Private Bag 0081, Gaborone, Botswana. TEL 267-353202, FAX 267-312001, http://www.gov.bw.

331.1109417 BWA
BOTSWANA. CENTRAL STATISTICS OFFICE. LABOUR FORCE SURVEY. Text and summaries in English. irreg., latest 1996. charts. back issues avail. **Document type:** *Government.*
Related titles: E-mail ed.; Fax ed.
Published by: Central Statistics Office, c/o Government Statistician, Private Bag 0024, Gaborone, Botswana. TEL 267-31-352200, FAX 267-31-352201, csobots@gov.bw. Ed. G M Charumbira. **Subscr. to:** Government Printer, Private Bag 0081, Gaborone, Botswana. TEL 267-353202, FAX 267-312001, http://www.gov.bw.

331.021 BWA
BOTSWANA. CENTRAL STATISTICS OFFICE. LABOUR STATISTICS. Text in English. a. BWP 5. charts. back issues avail. **Document type:** *Government.* **Description:** Provides information on number of persons employed and their earnings broken down by industry.
Formerly: Botswana. Central Statistics Office. Employment Survey
Related titles: E-mail ed.; Fax ed.
Published by: Central Statistics Office, c/o Government Statistician, Private Bag 0024, Gaborone, Botswana. TEL 267-31-352200, FAX 267-31-352201, csobots@gov.bw. Ed. G M Charumbira. Pub. J G Segwe. **Subscr. to:** Government Printer, Private Bag 0081, Gaborone, Botswana. TEL 267-353202, FAX 267-312001, http://www.gov.bw.

316.8021 BWA ISSN 1013-5693
BOTSWANA. CENTRAL STATISTICS OFFICE. STATISTICAL BULLETIN. Text in English. 1975. q. BWP 5. charts; illus. back issues avail. **Document type:** *Government.* **Description:** Compiles economic and social statistics.
Formerly: Botswana. Central Statistical Office. Statistical Newsletter
Related titles: E-mail ed.; Fax ed.
Published by: Central Statistics Office, c/o Government Statistician, Private Bag 0024, Gaborone, Botswana. TEL 267-31-352200, FAX 267-31-352201, csobots@gov.bw. Ed. G M Charumbira. Pub. J G Segwe. **Subscr. to:** Government Printer, Private Bag 0081, Gaborone, Botswana. TEL 267-353202, FAX 267-312001, http://www.gov.bw.

BOTSWANA. MINISTRY OF AGRICULTURE. FARM MANAGEMENT SURVEY RESULTS. see *AGRICULTURE—Agricultural Economics*

330 CAN ISSN 1184-9207
BRITISH COLUMBIA BUSINESS INDICATORS. Text in English. 1991. m. CND 60 (effective 1997). **Document type:** *Government.* **Description:** Provides a range of up-to-date economic and financial data, including production and shipments for British Columbia's major industries.
Published by: Ministry of Finance and Corporate Relations, B C Stats, Sta Prov Govt, P O Box 9410, Victoria, BC V8W 9V1, Canada. TEL 250-387-0359, FAX 250-387-0380, bcstats@fincc04.fin.gov.bc.ca, http://www.bcstats.gov.bc.ca.

382 CAN ISSN 1186-2920
BRITISH COLUMBIA ORIGIN EXPORTS. Text in English. 12/yr. CND 60 (effective 1997). **Document type:** *Government.*
Description: Reports on the latest British Columbia exports to major trading partners and blocs. Contains commodity detail.
Published by: Ministry of Finance and Corporate Relations, B C Stats, Sta Prov Govt, P O Box 9410, Victoria, BC V8W 9V1, Canada. TEL 250-387-1502, FAX 250-387-0329, bcstats@fincc04.fin.gov.bc.ca, http://www.bcstats.gov.bc.ca.

330.9 CAN
BRITISH COLUMBIA REGIONAL INDEX. Text in English. irreg. CND 40 (effective 1997). **Document type:** *Government.*
Description: Provides detailed demographic and economic data by eight development regions and 73 sub-areas in B.C.
Published by: Ministry of Finance and Corporate Relations, B C Stats, Sta Prov Govt, P O Box 9410, Victoria, BC V8W 9V1, Canada. TEL 250-387-1502, FAX 250-387-0329, bcstats@fincc04.fin.gov.bc.ca, http://www.bcstats.gov.bc.ca.

319 VGB
BRITISH VIRGIN ISLANDS. STATISTICS OFFICE. BALANCE OF PAYMENTS. Text in English. irreg.
Published by: Statistics Office, Finance Department, Road Town, Tortola, Virgin Isl., UK.

319 VGB
BRITISH VIRGIN ISLANDS. STATISTICS OFFICE. NATIONAL INCOME AND EXPENDITURE. Text in English. irreg. USD 3.50.
Published by: Statistics Office, Finance Department, Road Town, Tortola, Virgin Isl., UK.

331 CHE ISSN 0007-4950
HD4826
BULLETIN OF LABOUR STATISTICS; supplementing the annual data presented in the Year Book of Labour Statistics. Text in English, French, Spanish. 1965. 4/yr. CHF 105, USD 84. stat.; illus. Index. reprints avail. **Document type:** *Bulletin.*
Description: Contains articles on methodology and special topics. Includes trilingual tables of current statistics on employment, unemployment, wages, hours of work and consumer prices.
Related titles: ♦ Supplement(s): Supplement du Bulletin des Statistiques du Travail. ISSN 0378-5505; Statistics on Occupational Wages and Hours of Work and on Food Prices. ISSN 1020-0134.
Indexed: IIS, PAIS, RASB.
—CCC.
Published by: (International Labour Office), I L O Publications, PO Box 6, Geneva 22, 1211, Switzerland. TEL 41-22-799-6111, FAX 41-22-798-6358, TELEX 415-647-ILOCH, PRESSE@ilo.org, http://US.ilo.org/. **Dist. in US by:** I L O Publications Center, 9 Jay Gould Court, Ste. CT, PO Box 753, Waldorf, MD 20604. TEL 301-638-3152, FAX 301-843-0159, ilopubs@tasco1.com.

330.9 316 BFA
BURKINA FASO. INSTITUT NATIONAL DE LA STATISTIQUE ET DE LA DEMOGRAPHIE. BULLETIN D'INFORMATION STATISTIQUE ET ECONOMIQUE. Text in French. 1975 (no.16). a. **Document type:** *Bulletin.*
Former titles: Burkina Faso. Institut National de la Statistique et de la Demographie. Bulletin Annuaire d'Information Statistique et Economique; Upper Volta. Institut National de la Statistique et de la Demographie. Bulletin Annuaire d'Information Statistique et Economique; Supersedes: Upper Volta. Direction de la Statistique et de la Mecanographie. Bulletin Mensuel d'Information Statistique et Economique; Upper Volta. Directions de la Statistique et de la Mecanographie. Bulletin Annuaire Statistique et Economique
Published by: Institut National de la Statistique et de la Demographie, Ouagadougou, Burkina Faso.

381 BDI
BURUNDI. INSTITUT DE STATISTIQUES ET D'ETUDES ECONOMIQUES. COMPTES ECONOMIQUES. Text in French. a. USD 30. **Document type:** *Monographic series.*
Published by: Institut de Statistiques et d'Etudes Economiques, BP 1156, Bujumbura, Burundi.

016.05 USA
BUSINESS AND COMPANY PROFILES A S A P. Text in English. d. price varies. **Document type:** *Trade.* **Description:** Provides indexing, abstracts and full text for business, finance, management and industry periodicals.
Media: Online - full content.

B

Published by: Gale Group (Subsidiary of: Thomson Corporation), 27500 Drake Rd, Farmington Hills, MI 48331-3535. TEL 248-699-4253, 800-347-4253, FAX 248-699-8035, gale.galeord@thomson.com, http://www.galegroup.com.

016.33 USA
BUSINESS AND INDUSTRY (BEACHWOOD). Text in English. 1994. d. **Document type:** *Abstract/Index.*
Media: Online - full content. **Related titles:** CD-ROM ed.: ISSN 1548-9310.
Published by: Responsive Database Services (Subsidiary of: Gale Group), 23611 Chagrin Blvd Ste 320, Beachwood, OH 44122. http://www.rdsinc.com.

016.33 USA
BUSINESS DATELINE. Text in English. 1985. w. **Document type:** *Abstract/Index.* **Description:** Contains bibliographic information, indexing, and full-text articles from 450 city business journals, newspapers, and news services.
Media: Online - full content. **Related titles:** CD-ROM ed.
Published by: ProQuest Information & Learning, 300 N Zeeb Rd., PO Box 1346, Ann Arbor, MI 48106-1346. TEL 734-761-4700, 800-521-0600, info@il.proquest.com, http://www.latimes.com/.

B

332 GBR
BUSINESS MONITOR: ASSETS AND LIABILITIES OF FINANCE HOUSES AND OTHER CONSUMER CREDIT COMPANIES. Text in English. q. charts. back issues avail. **Document type:** *Consumer.*
Related titles: Series of: Service and Distributive Monitors Series.
Published by: Office for National Statistics, Government Buildings, Cardiff Rd, Newport, Gwent NP9 1XG, United Kingdom. TEL 44-1633-812973, FAX 44-1633-812599, library@ons.gov.uk. **Subscr. to:** Stationery Office, PO Box 276, London SW8 5DT, United Kingdom. TEL 44-20-7873-9090, FAX 44-207-873-8200.

BUSINESS MONITOR: CATERING AND ALLIED TRADES. see *HOTELS AND RESTAURANTS—Abstracting, Bibliographies, Statistics*

332 GBR
BUSINESS MONITOR: COMPANY FINANCE. Text in English. a. charts. back issues avail. **Document type:** *Government.*
Formerly: Business Monitor: Miscellaneous Series. M3 Company Finance (0068-4457)
Related titles: Series of: Miscellaneous Monitors Series.
Indexed: IPackAb, P&BA.
Published by: Office for National Statistics, Office For National Statistics, Government Buildings, 551 Cardiff Rd, Newport, NP9 1XG, United Kingdom. TEL 44-1633-812973, FAX 44-1633-812599, TELEX 497121 ALBBSONPT G, library@ons.gov.uk. **Subscr. to:** Stationery Office, PO Box 276, London SW8 5DT, United Kingdom. TEL 44-20-7873-9090, FAX 44-207-873-8200.

BUSINESS MONITOR: COMPUTER SERVICES. see *COMPUTERS—Computer Industry*

332 GBR ISSN 0957-2813
BUSINESS MONITOR: CREDIT BUSINESS. Text in English. 198?. m. charts; stat. back issues avail. **Document type:** *Government.*
Related titles: Series of: Service and Distributive Monitors Series.
Published by: Office for National Statistics, Government Buildings, Cardiff Rd, Newport, Gwent NP9 1XG, United Kingdom. TEL 44-1633-812973, FAX 44-1633-812599, library@ons.gov.uk. **Subscr. to:** Stationery Office, PO Box 276, London SW8 5DT, United Kingdom. TEL 44-20-7873-9090, FAX 44-207-873-8200.

332.6 GBR ISSN 0958-4838
BUSINESS MONITOR: GUIDE TO THE CLASSIFICATION OF OVERSEAS TRADE STATISTICS. Text in English. 1989. a. charts; stat. back issues avail. **Document type:** *Government.*
Formerly (until 1989): Guide to the Classification of Overseas Trade Statistics (0533-9669)
Related titles: Series of: Miscellaneous Monitors Series.
—BLDSC.
Published by: Office for National Statistics, Government Buildings, Cardiff Rd, Newport, Gwent NP9 1XG, United Kingdom. TEL 44-1633-812973, FAX 44-1633-812599, library@ons.govk. **Subscr. to:** Stationery Office, PO Box 276, London SW8 5DT, United Kingdom. TEL 44-20-7873-9090, FAX 44-207-873-8200.

BUSINESS MONITOR: MOTOR TRADES. see *TRANSPORTATION—Abstracting, Bibliographies, Statistics*

382 GBR
BUSINESS MONITOR: OVERSEAS DIRECT INVESTMENT. Text in English. a. GBP 23.95. back issues avail. **Document type:** *Government.*
Formerly (until 1992): Business Monitor: Overseas Transactions (0068-4465)
Related titles: Series of: Miscellaneous Monitors Series.
Indexed: P&BA.
—BLDSC (2934.324750).

Published by: Office for National Statistics, Office For National Statistics, Government Buildings, 551 Cardiff Rd, Newport, NP9 1XG, United Kingdom. TEL 44-1633-812973, FAX 44-1633-512599, libraryons@gov.uk, library@ons.gov.uk. **Subscr. to:** Stationery Office, PO Box 276, London SW8 5DT, United Kingdom. TEL 44-20-7873-9090, FAX 44-207-873-8200.

332.6 GBR ISSN 1353-0208
BUSINESS MONITOR: OVERSEAS TRADE STATISTICS OF THE UNITED KINGDOM (QUARTERLY REVISION). Text in English. 1993. q. charts; stat. back issues avail. **Document type:** *Government.* **Description:** Provides statistical information on U.K. manufacturing and other economic activity.
Related titles: Microfiche ed.: (from PQC); Series of: Miscellaneous Monitors Series.
Published by: Office for National Statistics, Government Buildings, Cardiff Rd, Newport, Gwent NP9 1XG, United Kingdom. TEL 44-1633-512973, FAX 44-1633-812599, TELEX 497121 ALB BSONPT G, library@ons.gov.uk. **Dist. by:** Stationery Office, PO Box 276, London SW8 5DT, United Kingdom. TEL 44-20-7873-9090, FAX 44-207-873-8200.

BUSINESS MONITOR: OVERSEAS TRAVEL AND TOURISM. see *TRAVEL AND TOURISM—Abstracting, Bibliographies, Statistics*

330.9 GBR
BUSINESS MONITOR. RETAIL PRICES INDEX. Text in English. m. GBP 70 (effective 1993). charts; stat. **Document type:** *Government.*
Related titles: Series of: Miscellaneous Monitors Series.
Published by: Office for National Statistics, Government Buildings, Cardiff Rd, Newport, Gwent NP9 1XG, United Kingdom. TEL 44-1633-812973, FAX 44-1633-812599, TELEX 497121 ALBBSONPT G, library@ons.gov.uk. **Subscr. to:** Stationery Office, PO Box 276, London SW8 5DT, United Kingdom. TEL 44-20-7873-9090, FAX 44-207-873-8200.

658 GBR
BUSINESS MONITOR: RETAILING. Text in English. a. charts; stat. back issues avail. **Document type:** *Government.*
Related titles: Series of: Service and Distributive Monitors Series.
Published by: Office for National Statistics, Government Buildings, Cardiff Rd, Newport, Gwent NP9 1XG, United Kingdom. TEL 44-1633-812973, FAX 44-1633-812599. **Subscr. to:** Stationery Office, PO Box 276, London SW8 5DT, United Kingdom. TEL 44-20-7873-9090, FAX 44-207-873-8200.

338 GBR ISSN 0957-5758
BUSINESS MONITOR: SERVICE TRADES. Text in English. a. charts; stat. back issues avail. **Document type:** *Government.*
Related titles: Series of: Service and Distributive Monitors Series.
Published by: Office for National Statistics, Government Buildings, Cardiff Rd, Newport, Gwent NP9 1XG, United Kingdom. TEL 44-1633-812973, FAX 44-1633-812599, library@ons.gov.uk. **Subscr. to:** Stationery Office, PO Box 276, London SW8 5DT, United Kingdom. TEL 44-20-7873-9090, FAX 44-207-873-8200.

658 GBR
BUSINESS MONITOR: WHOLESALING. Text in English. a. charts; stat. back issues avail. **Document type:** *Government.*
Related titles: Series of: Service and Distributive Monitors Series.
Published by: Office for National Statistics, Government Buildings, Cardiff Rd, Newport, Gwent NP9 1XG, United Kingdom. TEL 44-1633-812973, FAX 44-1633-812599, library@ons.gov.uk. **Subscr. to:** Stationery Office, PO Box 276, London SW8 5DT, United Kingdom. TEL 44-20-7873-9090, FAX 44-207-873-8200.

016.33 USA ISSN 0007-6961
BUSINESS PERIODICALS INDEX. Text in English. 1958. m. (except Aug., plus q. & a. cumulations). USD 540 in US & Canada (effective 2006). **Document type:** *Abstract/Index.* **Description:** Cumulative subject index to English-language periodicals in the fields of accounting, advertising and public relations, automation, banking, communications, economics, finance and investments, insurance, labor, management and specific businesses and trades. Indexes the Wall Street Journal and the business section of the New York Times.
Supersedes in part: Industrial Arts Index (0275-1682)
Related titles: CD-ROM ed.: ISSN 1076-7053 (from H.W. Wilson, SilverPlatter Information, Inc.); Magnetic Tape ed.; Online - full text ed.: USD 2,310 in US & Canada (effective 2006).
Indexed: RASB.
—BLDSC (2934.555000), Linda Hall.
Published by: H.W. Wilson Co., 950 University Ave, Bronx, NY 10452-4224. TEL 718-588-8400, 800-367-6770, FAX 718-590-1617, 800-590-1617, custserv@hwwilson.com, http://www.hwwilson.com/Databases/business.htm. Ed. Hiyol Yang.

330 USA ISSN 1043-7908
HG4050
BUSINESS RANKINGS ANNUAL. Text in English. a., latest 2005. USD 370 (effective 2003). **Document type:** *Trade.*

Published by: (Brooklyn Public Library, Business Library), Gale Group (Subsidiary of: Thomson Corporation), 27500 Drake Rd, Farmington Hills, MI 48331-3535. TEL 248-699-8061, 800-877-4253, FAX 248-699-4253, galeord@gale.com, http://www.gale.com.

016.33 USA ISSN 1538-5604
BUSINESS RESOURCES; an internet miniguide. Text in English. 2002. a. USD 125 newsstand/cover (effective 2002).
Published by: InternetMiniGuides.com, P.O. Box 220, Marco Island, FL 34146. TEL 941-434-5113, zillman@internetminiguides.com, http://www.internetminiguides.com. Pub. Marcus P. Zillma.

C S A COMPOSITES INDUSTRY ABSTRACTS. see *PLASTICS—Abstracting, Bibliographies, Statistics*

657 CHN
CAIKUAI WENZHAI KA/FINANCE AND ACCOUNTING ABSTRACTS ON CARDS. Text in Chinese. bi-m. CNY 30 (effective 2004). 80 p./no.; **Document type:** *Journal, Abstract/Index.*
Media: Cards.
Published by: Zhongguo Renmin Daxue, Shubao Zilio Zhongxin/Renmin University of China, Information Center for Social Server, Dongcheng-qu, 3, Zhangzizhong Lu, Beijing, 100007, China. TEL 86-10-64039458, FAX 86-10-64015080, kyes@163.net, http://www.confucius.cn.net/bkdetail.asp?fzt=WF101. **Dist. in the US by:** China Publications Service, PO Box 49614, Chicago, IL 60649. TEL 312-288-3291, FAX 312-288-8570; **Dist. outside of China by:** China International Book Trading Corp, 35 Chegongzhuang Xilu, Haidian District, PO Box 399, Beijing 100044, China. TEL 86-10-68412045, FAX 86-10-68412023, cibtc@mail.cibtc.com.cn, http://www.cibtc.com.cn.

368.4 FRA
CAISSES CENTRALES DE MUTUALITE SOCIALE AGRICOLE. STATISTIQUES. (In two parts: Resultats d'Ensemble; Resultats Detailles) Text in French. 1969. a. stat.
Published by: Union des Caisses Centrales de la Mutualite Agricole, 8-10 rue d' Astorg, Paris, Cedex 8 75380, France.

310 USA ISSN 1050-303X
HC107.C23
CALIFORNIA COUNTY PROJECTIONS (YEAR). Text in English. 1987. a. USD 250 per issue worldwide (effective 2004). charts; stat. 200 p./no. 1 cols./p.; back issues avail. **Document type:** *Government.* **Description:** Projects the population, households, per capita income, average household income, total personal income, taxable retail sales, and total taxable salesfor each of California's 58 counties. Includes recent historical data and projections to 2010.
Published by: Center for Continuing Study of the California Economy, 610 University Ave, Palo Alto, CA 94301. TEL 650-321-8550, FAX 650-321-5451, info@ccsce.com, nlevy@ccsce.com, http://www.ccsce.com. Ed., R&P Nancy Levy.

310 USA ISSN 1053-7252
HC107.C23
CALIFORNIA ECONOMIC GROWTH (YEAR). Text in English. 1988. a. USD 250 per issue (effective 2004). charts; stat. 300 p./no. 1 cols./p.; back issues avail. **Document type:** *Academic/Scholarly.* **Description:** Explores economic growth in 5 California regions projected to 2010, focusing on jobs, construction trends, income, and spending. Analyzes and discusses the main economic trends and issues in California.
Published by: Center for Continuing Study of the California Economy, 610 University Ave, Palo Alto, CA 94301. TEL 650-321-8550, FAX 650-321-5451, info@ccsce.com, nlevy@ccsce.com, http://www.ccsce.com. Ed. Nancy Levy.

CALIFORNIA STATISTICAL ABSTRACTS. see *BUSINESS AND ECONOMICS—Banking And Finance*

330.1 ITA ISSN 1125-8292
CAMERA DI COMMERCIO, INDUSTRIA, E AGRICOLTURA DI GENOVA. SEGNALAZIONI BIBLIOGRAFICHE. Text in Italian. 1948. q.
Supersedes in part (until 1978): Bollettino Emerografico di Economia Internazionale (0006-680X)
Published by: (Camera di Commercio, Industria, e Agricoltura di Genova), Istituto di Economia Internazionale, Via Garibaldi, 4, Genoa, GE 16124, Italy. TEL 39-10-2704202, FAX 39-10-2704300.

316.7 CMR
CAMEROON. DIRECTION DE LA STATISTIQUE ET DE LA COMPTABILITE NATIONALE. NOTE ANNUELLE DE STATISTIQUE. Text in French. 1974. a. XAF 4,000. stat.
Related titles: Microfiche ed.: (from PQC).
Published by: Direction de la Statistique et de la Comptabilite Nationale/Department of Statistics and National Accounts, BP 660, Yaounde, Cameroon.

336.71021 CAN ISSN 1208-4484
HC111
CANADA. DEPARTMENT OF FINANCE. FISCAL REFERENCE TABLES. Text in English. 1992. a. **Document type:** *Government.* **Description:** Provides information on federal public finances and fiscal indicators at provincial and international levels.
Supersedes in part (in 1994): Canada. Department of Finance. Economic and Fiscal Reference Tables (1200-4324); Which was formerly (until 1993): Canada. Department of Finance. Economic Reference Tables (1200-4316)
Related titles: Online - full content ed.: ISSN 1489-5005.
Published by: Canada. Department of Finance, Distribution Centre, West Tower, Rm P-135, 300 Laurier Ave W, Ottawa, ON K1A 0G5, Canada. TEL 613-995-2855, FAX 613-996-0518, services-distribution@fin.gc.ca, http://www.fin.gc.ca/purl/frt-e.html.

016 CAN
▼ **CANADA INFO DESK**; Canada's most comprehensive online directory database. Text in English. 2004. m. CND 2,000 to libraries (effective 2005). **Document type:** *Directory.* **Description:** Integrates the content of 6 directories into a single online Canadian resource. Provides access to over 100,000 Canadian organizations, contacts, facts and figures in one easy-to-use online resource.
Media: Online - full content.
Published by: Micromedia ProQuest (Subsidiary of: ProQuest Information & Learning), 20 Victoria St, Toronto, ON M5C 2N8, Canada. TEL 416-362-5211, 800-387-2689, FAX 416-362-6161, info@micromedia.ca, http://www.micromedia.ca/Directories/Canada_Info_Desk.htm.

336.242021 CAN ISSN 1489-4483
CANADA REVENUE AGENCY. INCOME STATISTICS. Text in English, French. a.
Former titles (until 1998): Canada. Revenue Canada. Tax Statistics on Individuals (1209-1103); (until 1995): Canada. Revenue Canada. Taxation Statistics (0700-1665)
—CISTI.
Published by: Canada Revenue Agency/Agence du Revenu du Canada, International Tax Services Office, 2204 Walkley Rd, Ottawa, ON K1A 1A8, Canada. TEL 613-952-3741, 800-959-2221, FAX 613-941-2505, SD-Client_Services@ccra-adrc.gc.ca, http://www.cra-arc.gc.ca/agency/stats/menu-e.html.

338.76021 CAN ISSN 0838-2182
CANADA. STATISTICS CANADA. BUSINESS SERVICES/CANADA. STATISTIQUE CANADA. SERVICES AUX ENTREPRISES. Text in English, French. 1984. a. **Description:** Includes revenue and expense breakdowns, employment and client base at the Canadian level, and total revenue at the provincial level.
Supersedes in part (in 1986): Canada. Statistics Canada. Selected Service Industries in Canada (0835-5401)
Published by: Statistics Canada, Publications Sales and Services, Ottawa, ON K1A 0T6, Canada. TEL 613-951-8116, infostats@statcan.ca, http://www.statcan.ca.

382.17021 CAN ISSN 0847-074X
CANADA. STATISTICS CANADA. CANADA'S BALANCE OF INTERNATIONAL PAYMENTS/CANADA. STATISTIQUE CANADA. BALANCE DES PAIEMENTS INTERNATIONAUX DU CANADA. Text in English, French. 1980. q. CND 133 (effective 2004).
Formerly (until 1989): Canada. Statistics Canada. Quarterly Estimates of the Canadian Balance of International Payments (Preliminary Edition) (0225-3763)
—CISTI.
Published by: Statistics Canada, Publications Sales and Services, Ottawa, ON K1A 0T6, Canada. TEL 613-951-8116, infostats@statcan.ca, http://www.statcan.ca/english/IPS/Data/67-001-XPB.htm.

382.17021 CAN ISSN 0848-5216
CANADA. STATISTICS CANADA. CANADA'S BALANCE OF INTERNATIONAL PAYMENTS (FINAL EDITION). Text in English, French. 1953. q.
Formerly (until 1989): Canada. Statistics Canada. Quarterly Estimates of the Canadian Balance of International Payments (0410-5788)
Related titles: Online - full content ed.: ISSN 1209-1286. CND 100.
—CISTI.
Published by: Statistics Canada, Publications Sales and Services, Ottawa, ON K1A 0T6, Canada. TEL 613-951-8116, infostats@statcan.ca, http://www.statcan.ca.

332.64 CAN ISSN 1183-4315
CANADA. STATISTICS CANADA. CANADA'S INTERNATIONAL TRANSACTIONS IN SECURITIES/OPERATIONS INTERNATIONALES DU CANADA EN VALEURS MOBILIERES. Text in English, French. 1935. m. CND 176; USD 176 foreign (effective 1999). **Document type:** *Government.* **Description:** Presents trading in Canadian and foreign bonds and stocks with non-residents.
Formerly: Canada. Statistics Canada. Security Transactions with Non-Residents (0702-6587)
Related titles: Microform ed.: (from MML).
Published by: Statistics Canada, Operations and Integration Division, Circulation Management, Jean Talon Bldg, 2 C12, Tunney's Pasture, Ottawa, ON K1A 0T6, Canada. TEL 613-951-7277, 800-267-6677, FAX 613-951-1584, http://www.statcan.ca.

330.9 CAN ISSN 0835-9148
HC111
CANADA. STATISTICS CANADA. CANADIAN ECONOMIC OBSERVER/OBSERVATEUR ECONOMIQUE CANADIEN. Text in English, French. 1926. m. CND 227 domestic; USD 227 foreign (effective 1999). **Document type:** *Government.* **Description:** Offers a monthly summary of the economy, major economic and statistical events, a feature article and a technical note.
Supersedes (in 1988): Canadian Statistical Review (0008-509X); Canada. Statistics Canada. Current Economic Indicators (0828-0851); Canada. Statistics Canada. Quarterly Economic Summary (0828-086X); Canada. Statistics Canada. Quarterly Economic Summary. Statistical Supplement (0828-0878)
Related titles: Microfiche ed.: (from MML); Microform ed.: (from MML); Online - full text ed.: (from EBSCO Publishing, Micromedia ProQuest); Supplement(s): Canada. Statistics Canada. Canadian Economic Observer. Historical Statistical Supplement. ISSN 0838-0236.
Indexed: CBCABus, CBCARef, CBPI, CPerl, PAIS, RASB.
—CISTI, IE, Infotrieve.
Published by: Statistics Canada, Operations and Integration Division, Circulation Management, Jean Talon Bldg, 2 C12, Tunney's Pasture, Ottawa, ON K1A 0T6, Canada. TEL 613-951-7277, 800-267-6677, FAX 613-951-1584, http://www.statcan.ca.

332.6 317 CAN ISSN 0833-0042
CANADA. STATISTICS CANADA. CAPITAL AND REPAIR EXPENDITURES, MANUFACTURING SUB-INDUSTRIES, INTENTIONS. (Catalogue 61-007) Text in English, French. 1975. irreg. CND 280.
Former titles (until 1986): Canada. Statistics Canada. Investment Statistics. Manufacturing Sub-Industries and Selected Energy Related Industries, Intentions (0830-1980); (until 1983): Canada. Statistics Canada. Investment Statistics. Manufacturing Sub-Industries and Selected Energy Related Industries, Outlook (0229-7361); (until 1980): Canada. Statistics Canada. Capital and Repair Expenditures, Manufacturing Sub-Industries, Canada (0708-4196); (until 1980): Canada. Statistics Canada. Investment Statistics (0380-7053)
Published by: Statistics Canada, Communications Division, 3rd Fl, R H Coats Bldg, Ottawa, ON K1A 0A6, Canada.

330.21 CAN ISSN 1195-9983
CANADA. STATISTICS CANADA. CORPORATIONS, ASPECTS OF BUSINESS ORGANIZATION. Text in English. 1993. a.
—CISTI.
Published by: Statistics Canada, Corporations Section, Statistical Reference Center, Rm 1500, Main Building, Holland Avenue, Ottawa, ON K1A 0T6, Canada.

330.21 CAN ISSN 1195-9991
CANADA. STATISTICS CANADA. CORPORATIONS, ASPECTS OF FOREIGN CONTROL. Text in English. a.
—CISTI.
Published by: Statistics Canada, Corporations Section, Statistical Reference Center, Rm 1500, Main Building, Holland Avenue, Ottawa, ON K1A 0T6, Canada.

658.8 317 CAN ISSN 0590-5702
HF5429.6.C3
CANADA. STATISTICS CANADA. DIRECT SELLING IN CANADA/CANADA. STATISTIQUE CANADA. VENTE DIRECTE AU CANADA. Text in English, French. 1966. a. CND 25 domestic; USD 25 foreign. **Document type:** *Government.* **Description:** Presents non-store retail sales for Canada, giving data on commodities sold and breakdowns by methods of distribution.
Related titles: Microform ed.: (from MML).
Published by: Statistics Canada, Operations and Integration Division, Circulation Management, Jean Talon Bldg, 2 C12, Tunney's Pasture, Ottawa, ON K1A 0T6, Canada. TEL 613-951-7277, 800-267-6677, FAX 613-951-1584, http://www.statcan.ca.

331.2 317 CAN ISSN 0380-6936
CANADA. STATISTICS CANADA. EMPLOYMENT, EARNINGS AND HOURS/CANADA. STATISTIQUE CANADA. EMPLOI, GAINS ET DUREE DU TRAVAIL. Text in English, French. 1922. m. CND 320; USD 320 foreign (effective 1999). **Document type:** *Government.* **Description:** Provides detailed industrial and geographical data on employment, average weekly earnings, hours and hourly earnings by types of employees for firms of all sizes and take-all firms.
Related titles: Microform ed.: (from MML).
Published by: Statistics Canada, Operations and Integration Division, Circulation Management, Jean Talon Bldg, 2 C12, Tunney's Pasture, Ottawa, ON K1A 0T6, Canada. TEL 613-951-7277, 800-267-6677, FAX 613-951-1584, http://www.statcan.ca.

382 CAN ISSN 1181-6732
CANADA. STATISTICS CANADA. EXPORTS BY COMMODITY/CANADA. STATISTIQUE CANADA. EXPORTATIONS PAR MARCHANDISES. Text in English, French. 1944. m. CND 773 domestic (effective 1999); USD 773 foreign. **Document type:** *Government.* **Description:** Presents detailed export trade data, quantity and value by commodity and country according to the harmonized system at the six digit level and summarized data by country, section and province of origin.
Related titles: Microform ed.: (from MML).
—CISTI.
Published by: Statistics Canada, Operations and Integration Division, Circulation Management, Jean Talon Bldg, 2 C12, Tunney's Pasture, Ottawa, ON K1A 0T6, Canada. TEL 613-651-7277, 800-267-6677, FAX 613-951-1584, http://www.statcan.ca.

382 CAN ISSN 0317-5375
CANADA. STATISTICS CANADA. EXPORTS, MERCHANDISE TRADE/CANADA. STATISTIQUE CANADA. EXPORTATIONS, COMMERCE DE MARCHANDISES. Text in English, French. 1939. a. CND 258 domestic; USD 258 foreign (effective 1999). **Document type:** *Government.* **Description:** Provides detailed annual export data for the current year (quantity and value) by commodity and country according to the Harmonized System at the six-digit level.
Related titles: Microform ed.: (from MML).
—CISTI.
Published by: Statistics Canada, Operations and Integration Division, Circulation Management, Jean Talon Bldg, 2 C12, Tunney's Pasture, Ottawa, ON K1A 0T6, Canada. TEL 613-951-7277, 800-267-6677, FAX 613-951-1584, http://www.statcan.ca.

331.12021 CAN ISSN 1704-6939
CANADA. STATISTICS CANADA. HELP-WANTED INDEX/CANADA. STATISTIQUE CANADA. INDICE DE L'OFFRE D'EMPLOI. Text in English, French. 1985. irreg. free (effective 2004).
Formerly (until 1998): Canada. Statistics Canada. Help-Wanted Index (Print Edition) (0828-1300)
Media: Online - full content.
Published by: (Statistics Canada, Labour Division), Statistics Canada, Publications Sales and Services, Ottawa, ON K1A 0T6, Canada. TEL 613-951-8116, infostats@statcan.ca, http://www.statcan.ca:80/english/freepub/71-540-XIB/free.htm.

331.11 317 CAN ISSN 1181-957X
CANADA. STATISTICS CANADA. HISTORICAL LABOUR FORCE STATISTICS/CANADA. STATISTIQUE CANDA. STATISTIQUES CHRONOLOGIQUES SUR LA POPULATION ACTIVE. Text in English, French. 1953. a. CND 114 domestic; USD 114 foreign (effective 1999). **Document type:** *Government.* **Description:** Presents historical labor force statistics and related seasonal adjustment information. Contains time series from the monthly Labour Force Survey.
Formerly: Canada. Statistics Canada. Historical Labour Force Statistics, Actual Data, Seasonal Factors, Seasonally Adjusted Data (0703-2684)
Related titles: Microform ed.: (from MML).
—CISTI.
Published by: Statistics Canada, Operations and Integration Division, Circulation Management, Jean Talon Bldg, 2 C12, Tunney's Pasture, Ottawa, ON K1A 0T6, Canada. TEL 613-951-7277, 800-267-6677, FAX 613-951-1584, http://www.statcan.ca.

382 CAN ISSN 0380-1349
CANADA. STATISTICS CANADA. IMPORTS, MERCHANDISE TRADE/CANADA. STATISTIQUE CANADA. IMPORTATIONS, COMMERCE DE MARCHANDISES. Text in English, French. 1939. a. CND 258 domestic; USD 258 foreign (effective 1999). **Document type:** *Government.* **Description:** Provides detailed annual import data for the current year, showing values only by commodity and country according to the Harmonized System at the six-digit level.
Related titles: Microform ed.: (from MML).
Published by: Statistics Canada, Operations and Integration Division, Circulation Management, Jean Talon Bldg, 2 C12, Tunney's Pasture, Ottawa, ON K1A 0T6, Canada. TEL 613-951-7277, 800-267-6677, FAX 613-951-1584, http://www.statcan.ca.

CANADA. STATISTICS CANADA. INCOME IN CANADA. see *BUSINESS AND ECONOMICS—Labor And Industrial Relations*

339.22021 CAN ISSN 1492-1545
CANADA. STATISTICS CANADA. INCOME TRENDS IN CANADA/CANADA. STATISTIQUE CANADA. TENDANCES DU REVENU AU CANADA. Text in English, French. 1996. a. CND 195 (effective 2004).
Formerly (until 1997): Canada. Statistics Canada. Income Historical Review (1480-8641)
Media: CD-ROM. **Related titles:** Online - full text ed.: CND 209.
Published by: Statistics Canada, Publications Sales and Services, Ottawa, ON K1A 0T6, Canada. TEL 613-951-8116, infostats@statcan.ca, http://www.statcan.ca:8096/bsolc/english/bsolc?catno=13F0022X.

331.1 317 CAN ISSN 0708-3157
CANADA. STATISTICS CANADA. LABOUR FORCE INFORMATION/CANADA. STATISTIQUE CANADA. INFORMATION POPULATION ACTIVE. Text in English, French. 1945. m. CND 103; USD 103 foreign (effective 1999). **Document type:** *Government.* **Description:** Presents seasonally adjusted and unadjusted estimates of labour force, employment and unemployment, with unemployment and participation rates analyzed by selected geographic, demographic and occupational variables.
Formerly: Canada. Statistics Canada. The Labour Force (0380-6804)
Related titles: Microform ed.: (from MML).
—CISTI.
Published by: Statistics Canada, Operations and Integration Division, Circulation Management, Jean Talon Bldg, 2 C12, Tunney's Pasture, Ottawa, ON K1A 0T6, Canada. TEL 613-651-7277, 800-267-6677, FAX 613-951-1584, http://www.statcan.ca.

658 CAN ISSN 0590-9325
CANADA. STATISTICS CANADA. MARKET RESEARCH HANDBOOK/CANADA. STATISTIQUE CANADA. MANUEL STATISTIQUE POUR ETUDES DE MARCHE. Text in English, French. 1975. a. CND 114 domestic; USD 114 foreign (effective 1999). **Description:** Source of socio-economic statistics for market researchers, strategists, product planners and sales leaders.
Related titles: Microform ed.: (from MML).
—CISTI.
Published by: Statistics Canada, Operations and Integration Division, Circulation Management, Jean Talon Bldg, 2 C12, Tunney's Pasture, Ottawa, ON K1A 0T6, Canada. TEL 613-951-7277, 800-267-6677, FAX 613-951-1584, http://www.statcan.ca.

339 317 CAN ISSN 1488-576X
CANADA. STATISTICS CANADA. NATIONAL INCOME AND EXPENDITURE ACCOUNTS, QUARTERLY ESTIMATES/CANADA. STATISTIQUE CANADA. COMPTES ECONOMIQUES ET FINANCIERS NATIONAUX, ESTIMATIONS TRIMESTRIELLES. Text in English, French. 1995. q. CND 145; USD 145 foreign (effective 1999). **Document type:** *Government.* **Description:** Gives a comprehensive statistical picture of Canadian economic developments.
Formerly (until 1999): Canada. Statistics Canada. National Economic and Financial Accounts, Quarterly Estimates (1201-6772); Which was formed by the merger of (1971-1995): Canada. Statistics Canada. Financial Flow Accounts (0380-0938); Which incorporated (198?-1983): Canada. Statistics Canada. Comptes des Flux Financiers. Donnees Preliminaires (0828-3060); (194?-1995): Canada. Statistics Canada. National Income and Expenditure Accounts - Comptes Nationaux des Revenus et des Depenses (0318-708X); Which was formerly (until 1968): Canada. Bureau of Statistics. National Accounts. Income and Expenditure (0575-9196)
Related titles: Diskette ed.; Microform ed.: (from MML).
—CISTI.
Published by: Statistics Canada, Operations and Integration Division, Circulation Management, Jean Talon Bldg, 2 C12, Tunney's Pasture, Ottawa, ON K1A 0T6, Canada. TEL 613-951-7277, 800-267-6677, FAX 613-951-1584, http://www.statcan.ca.

338 CAN ISSN 0835-0191
HD9734.C2
CANADA. STATISTICS CANADA. OTHER MANUFACTURING INDUSTRIES/CANADA. STATISTIQUE CANADA. AUTRES INDUSTRIES MANUFACTURIERES. Text in English, French. 1930. a. CND 40 domestic; USD 40 foreign (effective 1999). **Document type:** *Government.*
Former titles: Canada. Statistics Canada. Miscellaneous Manufacturing Industries (0575-9021); Sporting Goods and Toy Industries (0575-979X); Scientific and Professional Equipment Industries (0384-4242); Jewellery and Precious Metal Industries (0828-9832)
Related titles: Microform ed.: (from MML).
—CISTI.
Published by: Statistics Canada, Operations and Integration Division, Circulation Management, Jean Talon Bldg, 2 C12, Tunney's Pasture, Ottawa, ON K1A 0T6, Canada. TEL 613-951-7277, 800-267-6677, FAX 613-951-1584, http://www.statcan.ca.

338.4766557102 CAN ISSN 1488-7754
CANADA. STATISTICS CANADA. PIPELINE TRANSPORTATION OF CRUDE OIL AND REFINED PETROLEUM PRODUCTS (ONLINE EDITION). Text in English, French. 1952. a. CND 19 (effective 2004). **Description:** Presents information from companies primarily engaged in the gathering and transportation of crude oil and liquefied petroleum gases to refineries and for export.
Former titles (until 1999): Canada. Statistics Canada. Pipeline Transportation of Crude Oil and Refined Petroleum Products (Print Edition) (1481-4226); (until 1997): Canada. Statistics Canada. Oil Pipe Line Transport (Annual Edition) (0410-5591); (until 1958): Canada. Dominion Bureau of Statistics. Public Finance and Transportation Division. Transportation Section. Pipe Lines (Oil) Statistics (0225-6940)
Media: Online - full content.
Published by: (Statistics Canada, Manufacturing, Construction and Energy Division), Statistics Canada, Publications Sales and Services, Ottawa, ON K1A 0T6, Canada. TEL 613-951-8116, infostats@statcan.ca, http://www.statcan.ca/english/IPS/Data/55-201-XIB.htm.

339 317 CAN ISSN 0823-065X
CANADA. STATISTICS CANADA. PRIVATE AND PUBLIC INVESTMENT IN CANADA. INTENTIONS/CANADA. STATISTIQUE CANADA. INVESTISSEMENTS PRIVES ET PUBLICS AU CANADA. PERSPECTIVE. Text in English, French. 1946. a. CND 47 domestic; USD 47 foreign (effective 1999). **Document type:** *Government.* **Description:** Presents capital and repair expenditures on construction and machinery and equipment for all sectors of the Canadian economy and by province for selected industry groups.
Formerly: Canada. Statistics Canada. Private and Public Investment in Canada. Outlook (0318-2274)
Related titles: Microform ed.: (from MML); Online - full text ed.
Indexed: RASB.
—CISTI.
Published by: Statistics Canada, Operations and Integration Division, Circulation Management, Jean Talon Bldg, 2 C12, Tunney's Pasture, Ottawa, ON K1A 0T6, Canada. TEL 613-951-7277, 800-267-6677, FAX 613-951-1584, http://www.statcan.ca.

339 317 CAN ISSN 0823-0668
CANADA. STATISTICS CANADA. PRIVATE AND PUBLIC INVESTMENT IN CANADA. REVISED INTENTIONS/CANADA. STATISTIQUE CANADA. INVESTISSEMENTS PRIVES ET PUBLICS AU CANADA, PERSPECTIVE REVISEE. Text in English, French. 1968. a. CND 33 domestic; USD 33 foreign (effective 1999). **Document type:** *Government.* **Description:** Presents capital and repair expenditures on construction and machinery and equipment for all sectors of the Canadian economy and by province for selected industry groups.
Formerly: Canada. Statistics Canada. Private and Public Investment in Canada, Mid-Year Review (0707-9559)
Related titles: Microform ed.: (from MML); Online - full text ed.
—CISTI.
Published by: Statistics Canada, Operations and Integration Division, Circulation Management, Jean Talon Bldg, 2 C12, Tunney's Pasture, Ottawa, ON K1A 0T6, Canada. TEL 613-951-7277, 800-267-6677, FAX 613-951-1584, http://www.statcan.ca.

CANADA. STATISTICS CANADA. PRODUCTION AND DISPOSITION OF TOBACCO PRODUCTS/CANADA. STATISTIQUE CANDA. PRODUCTION ET DISPOSITION DES PRODUITS DU TABAC. see *TOBACCO—Abstracting, Bibliographies, Statistics*

338 317 CAN ISSN 1492-8612
CANADA. STATISTICS CANADA. PRODUCTIVITY GROWTH IN CANADA. Text in English. 1946. a. CND 46 domestic; USD 46 foreign (effective 2004). **Document type:** *Government.* **Description:** Shows output per person employed and per person-hour, and unit labor costs for all commercial industries as well as industry groupings. Provides corresponding US official measures where available.
Former titles (until 2001): Canada. Statistics Canada. Aggregate Productivity Measures (0317-7882); (until 1972): Canada. Statistics Canada. Aggregate Productivity Trends (0068-7073); (until 1966): Indexes of Output per Person Employed and per Man-Hour in Canada, Commercial Industries (0073-6082)
Related titles: Microform ed.: (from MML); Online - full text ed.: ISSN 1496-4732. CND 35 (effective 2004); French ed.
—CISTI.
Published by: (Statistics Canada, Micro-Economic Studies and Analysis Division), Statistics Canada, Publications Sales and Services, Ottawa, ON K1A 0T6, Canada. TEL 613-951-8116, infostats@statcan.ca, http://www.statcan.ca/english/IPS/Data/15-204-XPE.htm.

338.4 317 CAN ISSN 0575-9455
CANADA. STATISTICS CANADA. PRODUCTS SHIPPED BY CANADIAN MANUFACTURERS/CANADA. STATISTIQUE CANADA. PRODUITS LIVRES PAR LES FABRICANTS CANADIENS. Text in English, French. 1961. a. CND 67 domestic; USD 67 foreign (effective 1999). **Document type:** *Government.* **Description:** Presents value and quantity of products shipped by manufacturers, classified by commodity according to the Industrial Commodity Classification for Canada and the provinces.
Related titles: CD-ROM ed.: ISSN 1480-6363; Microform ed.: (from MML).
—CISTI.
Published by: Statistics Canada, Operations and Integration Division, Circulation Management, Jean Talon Bldg, 2 C12, Tunney's Pasture, Ottawa, ON K1A 0T6, Canada. TEL 613-951-7277, 800-267-6677, FAX 613-951-1584, http://www.statcan.ca.

330.9 CAN ISSN 1494-6815
CANADA. STATISTICS CANADA. PROVINCIAL ECONOMIC ACCOUNTS. ANNUAL ESTIMATES, TABLES AND ANALYTICAL DOCUMENT/CANADA. STATISTIQUE CANADA. COMPTES ECONOMIQUES PROVINCIAUX ESTIMATIONS ANNUELLES. Text in English. 1961. a. CND 80; USD 80 foreign. **Document type:** *Government.* **Description:** Provides a regional perspective on Canadian economic developments. Includes separate sets of statistical tables for each of the twelve provinces and territories.
Former titles (until 1996): Canada. Statistics Canada. Provincial Economic Accounts Annual Estimates (0847-0359); (until 1987): Canada. Statistics Canada. Provincial Economic Accounts. Experimental Data (0706-3083)
—CISTI.
Published by: Statistics Canada, Operations and Integration Division, Circulation Management, Jean Talon Bldg, 2 C12, Tunney's Pasture, Ottawa, ON K1A 0T6, Canada. TEL 800-267-6677, http://www.statcan.ca.

331.125 CAN ISSN 1494-5797
JL106
CANADA. STATISTICS CANADA. PUBLIC SECTOR STATISTICS. Text in English, French. 2000. a. CND 44; USD 44 foreign. **Document type:** *Government.* **Description:** Presents employment and remuneration data for federal, provincial and territorial, and local governments, as well as data for federal, provincial and territorial, and local government business enterprises.
Formed by the merger of (1995-2000): Canada. Statistics Canada. Public Sector Finance (1201-6284); (1993-2000): Canada. Statistics Canada. Public Sector Employment and Wages and Salaries (1201-8481); Which was formerly (until 1993): Canada. Statistics Canada. Public Sector Employment and Renumeration (Year) (1188-0619); Which was formed by the merger of (1970-1991): Canada. Statistics Canada. Local Government Employment (0703-7392); Which was formerly (1967-1970): Canada. Dominion Bureau of Statistics. Municipal Government Employment (0575-9145); (1984-1991): Canada. Statistics Canada. Provincial and Territorial Government Employment (0825-9224); Which was formerly (1959-1984): Canada. Statistics Canada. Provincial Government Employment (0527-608X); (1954-1991): Canada. Statistics Canada. Federal Government Employment (0575-8491); Which was formerly (until 1954): Canada. Dominion Bureau of Statistics. Federal Government Employment and Payrolls (0318-5079); (until 1953): Canada. Dominion Bureau of Statistics. Government of Canada Employment and Payrolls (0837-8452); (until 1952): Canada. Dominion Bureau of Statistics. Federal Civil Service Employment and Payrolls (0318-5087); (until 1950): Canada. Dominion Bureau of Statistics. Summary Statistics, Federal Civil Service Employment and Payrolls (0837-8444); (until 1949): Canada. Dominion Bureau of Statistics. Summary Statistics of the Civil Service of Canada (0318-5095); (until 1942): Canada. Bureau of Statistics. Statistics of the Civil Service of Canada (0318-5109); (until 1925): Canada. Bureau of Statistics. Statement of Civil Service Personnel and Salaries
Related titles: Microform ed.: (from MML).
Published by: Statistics Canada, Operations and Integration Division, Circulation Management, Jean Talon Bldg, 2 C12, Tunney's Pasture, Ottawa, ON K1A 0T6, Canada. TEL 613-951-7277, 800-267-6677, FAX 613-951-1584, http://www.statcan.ca.

331 317 CAN ISSN 0700-205X
CANADA. STATISTICS CANADA. QUARTERLY ESTIMATES OF TRUSTEED PENSION FUNDS/CANADA. STATISTIQUE CANADA. ESTIMATIONS TRIMESTRIELLES SUR LES REGIMES DE PENSIONS EN FIDUCIE. Text in English, French. 1973. q. CND 62; USD 62 foreign (effective 1999). **Document type:** *Government.* **Description:** Provides estimates for Canada of the income, expenditures and asset portfolios of trusteed pension funds, as well as advance estimates of the annual survey of Trusteed Pension Funds.
Related titles: Microform ed.: (from MML).
Published by: Statistics Canada, Operations and Integration Division, Circulation Management, Jean Talon Bldg, 2 C12, Tunney's Pasture, Ottawa, ON K1A 0T6, Canada. TEL 613-951-7277, 800-267-6677, FAX 613-951-1584, http://www.statcan.ca.

658.8 317 CAN ISSN 0227-017X
CANADA. STATISTICS CANADA. RETAIL CHAIN AND DEPARTMENT STORES/CANADA. STATISTIQUE CANADA. MAGASINS DE DETAIL A SUCCURSALES ET LES GRANDES MAGASINS. Text in English, French. 1933. a. CND 39 domestic; USD 39 foreign (effective 1999). **Document type:** *Government.* **Description:** Presents retail sales of chain and department store organizations by kind of business, province, selected localities, number of stores operated and by annual sales volume.
Formerly: Canada. Statistics Canada. Retail Chain Stores (0380-7878)
Related titles: Microform ed.: (from MML); Online - full text ed.
—CISTI.
Published by: Statistics Canada, Operations and Integration Division, Circulation Management, Jean Talon Bldg, 2 C12, Tunney's Pasture, Ottawa, ON K1A 0T6, Canada. TEL 613-951-7277, 800-267-6677, FAX 613-951-1584, http://www.statcan.ca.

B

658　　　　CAN　　　　ISSN 0380-6146
CANADA. STATISTICS CANADA. RETAIL TRADE/CANADA. STATISTIQUE CANADA. COMMERCE DE DETAIL. Text in English, French. 1929. m. CND 206 domestic (effective 1999); USD 206 foreign. **Document type:** *Government.* **Description:** Presents data on retail sales, for chain and independent stores; seasonally adjusted sales. Includes data analysis, definitions, methodology, data reliability and bibliography.
Related titles: Microform ed.: (from MML); Online - full text ed. —CISTI.
Published by: Statistics Canada, Operations and Integration Division, Circulation Management, Jean Talon Bldg, 2 C12, Tunney's Pasture, Ottawa, ON K1A 0T6, Canada. TEL 613-951-7277, 800-267-6677, FAX 613-951-1584, http://www.statcan.ca.

330.1　　　　CAN　　　　ISSN 1188-6293
CANADA. STATISTICS CANADA. SERVICE INDUSTRIES IN THE CANADIAN INPUT - OUTPUT ACCOUNTS: CURRENT PRICES, SOURCES OF DATA AND METHODS OF ESTIMATION/CANADA. STATISTIQUE CANADA. INDUSTRIES DE SERVICES DANS LES COMPTES D'ENTREES - SORTIES DU CANADA: EN PRIX COURANTS, SOURCES DE DONNEES ET METHODES D'ESTIMATION. Text in English, French. irreg. CND 45; USD 45 foreign. **Document type:** *Government.* **Description:** Outlines the conceptual and statistical framework of the services sector in the Canadian input-output accounts.
Related titles: Microform ed.: (from MML); Series of: Input-Output Accounts Sources and Methods.
Published by: Statistics Canada, Operations and Integration Division, Circulation Management, Jean Talon Bldg, 2 C12, Tunney's Pasture, Ottawa, ON K1A 0T6, Canada. TEL 613-951-7277, 800-267-6677, FAX 613-951-1584, http://www.statcan.ca.

330.021　　　　CAN　　　　ISSN 1488-0261
CANADA. STATISTICS CANADA. SERVICES PRICE INDEXES. Text in English. 1999. irreg.
Published by: Statistics Canada, Communications Division, 3rd Fl, R H Coats Bldg, Ottawa, ON K1A 0A6, Canada. TEL 613-951-7276, FAX 613-951-1582.

338.642021　　　　CAN　　　　ISSN 0835-2801
CANADA. STATISTICS CANADA. SMALL BUSINESS PROFILES, ALBERTA. Text in English. 1984. biennial. **Description:** Presents selected revenue, expense, profit and balance sheet items, financial ratios, and employment data.
Published by: (Statistics Canada, Small Business and Special Surveys Division), Statistics Canada, Publications Sales and Services, Ottawa, ON K1A 0T6, Canada. TEL 613-951-8116, infostats@statcan.ca, http://www.statcan.ca.

338.642021　　　　CAN　　　　ISSN 0835-2828
CANADA. STATISTICS CANADA. SMALL BUSINESS PROFILES, BRITISH COLUMBIA. Text in English. 1984. biennial. **Description:** Presents selected revenue, expense, profit and balance sheet items, financial ratios, and employment data.
Published by: (Statistics Canada, Small Business and Special Surveys Division), Statistics Canada, Publications Sales and Services, Ottawa, ON K1A 0T6, Canada. TEL 613-951-8116, infostats@statcan.ca, http://www.statcan.ca.

338.642021　　　　CAN　　　　ISSN 0835-2623
CANADA. STATISTICS CANADA. SMALL BUSINESS PROFILES, CANADA. Text in English. 1984. biennial. **Description:** Presents revenue, expense, profit and balance sheet items, as well as financial ratios and employment data on small business in Canada.
—CISTI.
Published by: (Statistics Canada, Small Business and Special Surveys Division), Statistics Canada, Publications Sales and Services, Ottawa, ON K1A 0T6, Canada. TEL 613-951-8116, infostats@statcan.ca, http://www.statcan.ca/english/dssd/5028.htm.

338.642021　　　　CAN　　　　ISSN 0835-2763
CANADA. STATISTICS CANADA. SMALL BUSINESS PROFILES, MANITOBA. Text in English. biennial. **Description:** Presents selected revenue, expense, profit and balance sheet items, financial ratios, and employment data.
Published by: (Statistics Canada, Small Business and Special Surveys Division), Statistics Canada, Publications Sales and Services, Ottawa, ON K1A 0T6, Canada. TEL 613-951-8116, infostats@statcan.ca, http://www.statcan.ca.

338.642021　　　　CAN　　　　ISSN 0835-2704
CANADA. STATISTICS CANADA. SMALL BUSINESS PROFILES, NEW BRUNSWICK. Text in English. 1984. biennial. **Description:** Presents selected revenue, expense, profit and balance sheet items, financial ratios, and employment data.
Published by: (Statistics Canada, Small Business and Special Surveys Division), Statistics Canada, Publications Sales and Services, Ottawa, ON K1A 0T6, Canada. TEL 613-951-8116, infostats@statcan.ca, http://www.statcan.ca.

338.642021　　　　CAN　　　　ISSN 0835-264X
CANADA. STATISTICS CANADA. SMALL BUSINESS PROFILES, NEWFOUNDLAND. Text in English. 1984. biennial. **Description:** Presents selected revenue, expense, profit and balance sheet items, financial ratios, and employment data.
Published by: (Statistics Canada, Small Business and Special Surveys Division), Statistics Canada, Publications Sales and Services, Ottawa, ON K1A 0T6, Canada. TEL 613-951-8116, infostats@statcan.ca, http://www.statcan.ca.

338.642021　　　　CAN　　　　ISSN 0835-2860
CANADA. STATISTICS CANADA. SMALL BUSINESS PROFILES, NORTHWEST TERRITORIES. Text in English. 1984. biennial. **Description:** Presents selected revenue, expense, profit and balance sheet items, financial ratios, and employment data.
Published by: (Statistics Canada, Small Business and Special Surveys Division), Statistics Canada, Publications Sales and Services, Ottawa, ON K1A 0T6, Canada. TEL 613-951-8116, infostats@statcan.ca, http://www.statcan.ca.

338.642021　　　　CAN　　　　ISSN 0835-2682
CANADA. STATISTICS CANADA. SMALL BUSINESS PROFILES, NOVA SCOTIA. Text in English. 1984. biennial. **Description:** Presents selected revenue, expense, profit and balance sheet items, financial ratios, and employment data.
Published by: (Statistics Canada, Small Business and Special Surveys Division), Statistics Canada, Publications Sales and Services, Ottawa, ON K1A 0T6, Canada. TEL 613-951-8116, infostats@statcan.ca, http://www.statcan.ca.

338.642021　　　　CAN　　　　ISSN 0835-2747
CANADA. STATISTICS CANADA. SMALL BUSINESS PROFILES, ONTARIO. Text in English. 1984. biennial. **Description:** Presents selected revenue, expense, profit and balance sheet items, financial ratios, and employment data.
Published by: (Statistics Canada, Small Business and Special Surveys Division), Statistics Canada, Publications Sales and Services, Ottawa, ON K1A 0T6, Canada. TEL 613-951-8116, infostats@statcan.ca, http://www.statcan.ca.

338.642021　　　　CAN　　　　ISSN 0835-2666
CANADA. STATISTICS CANADA. SMALL BUSINESS PROFILES, PRINCE EDWARD ISLAND. Text in English. 1984. biennial. **Description:** Presents selected revenue, expense, profit and balance sheet items, financial ratios, and employment data.
Published by: (Statistics Canada, Small Business and Special Surveys Division), Statistics Canada, Publications Sales and Services, Ottawa, ON K1A 0T6, Canada. TEL 613-951-8116, infostats@statcan.ca, http://www.statcan.ca.

338.642021　　　　CAN　　　　ISSN 0835-2720
CANADA. STATISTICS CANADA. SMALL BUSINESS PROFILES, QUEBEC. Text in English. 1984. biennial. **Description:** Presents selected revenue, expense, profit and balance sheet items, financial ratios, and employment data.
Published by: (Statistics Canada, Small Business and Special Surveys Division), Statistics Canada, Publications Sales and Services, Ottawa, ON K1A 0T6, Canada. TEL 613-951-8116, infostats@statcan.ca, http://www.statcan.ca.

338.642021　　　　CAN　　　　ISSN 0835-278X
CANADA. STATISTICS CANADA. SMALL BUSINESS PROFILES, SASKATCHEWAN. Text in English. 1984. biennial. **Description:** Presents selected revenue, expense, profit and balance sheet items, financial ratios, and employment data.
Published by: (Statistics Canada, Small Business and Special Surveys Division), Statistics Canada, Publications Sales and Services, Ottawa, ON K1A 0T6, Canada. TEL 613-951-8116, infostats@statcan.ca, http://www.statcan.ca.

338.642021　　　　CAN　　　　ISSN 0835-2844
CANADA. STATISTICS CANADA. SMALL BUSINESS PROFILES, YUKON. Text in English. 1984. biennial. **Description:** Presents selected revenue, expense, profit and balance sheet items, financial ratios, and employment data.
Published by: (Statistics Canada, Small Business and Special Surveys Division), Statistics Canada, Publications Sales and Services, Ottawa, ON K1A 0T6, Canada. TEL 613-951-8116, infostats@statcan.ca, http://www.statcan.ca.

339.47021　　　　CAN　　　　ISSN 1488-3406
CANADA. STATISTICS CANADA. SPENDING PATTERNS IN CANADA. Text in English, French. 1997. a. CND 45 (effective 2004). **Description:** Publishes statistical data about expenditures by households and families in Canada on a variety of goods and services, as well as dwelling characteristics and possession of household equipment.
Related titles: Online - full text ed.: ISSN 1488-447X. CND 34.
Published by: (Statistics Canada, Expenditure Surveys Section), Statistics Canada, Publications Sales and Services, Ottawa, ON K1A 0T6, Canada. TEL 613-951-8116, infostats@statcan.ca, http://www.statcan.ca:8096/bsolc/english/bsolc?catno=62-202-XPE.

336.021　　　　CAN　　　　ISSN 1709-4585
CANADA. STATISTICS CANADA. STATISTIQUES SUR LE SECTEUR PUBLIC. Text in French, English. 199?. a. **Document type:** *Government.*

Supersedes in part (in 2002): Canada. Statistics Canada. Public Sector Statistics (1494-5797); Which was formed by the merger of (1995-2000): Canada. Statistics Canada. Public Sector Finance (1201-6284); (1993-2000): Canada. Statistics Canada. Public Sector Employment and Wages and Salaries (1201-8481); Which was formerly (until 1993): Canada. Statistics Canada. Public Sector Employment and Remuneration (Year) (1188-0619); Which was formed by the merger of (1970-1991): Canada. Statistics Canada. Local Government Employment (0703-7392); Which was formerly (1967-1970): Canada. Dominion Bureau of Statistics. Municipal Government Employment (0575-9145); (1984-1991): Canada. Statistics Canada. Provincial and Territorial Government Employment (0825-9224); Which was formerly (1959-1984): Canada. Statistics Canada. Provincial Government Employment (0527-608X); (1954-1991): Canada. Statistics Canada. Federal Government Employment (0575-8491); Which was formerly (until 1954): Canada. Dominion Bureau of Statistics. Federal Government Employment and Payrolls (0318-5079); (until 1953): Canada. Dominion Bureau of Statistics. Government of Canada Employment and Payrolls (0837-8452); (until 1952): Canada. Dominion Bureau of Statistics. Federal Civil Service Employment and Payrolls (0318-5087); (until 1950): Canada. Dominion Bureau of Statistics. Summary Statistics, Federal Civil Service Employment and Payrolls (0837-8444); (until 1948): Canada. Dominion Bureau of Statistics. Summary Statistics of the Civil Service of Canada (0318-5095); (until 1942): Canada. Bureau of Statistics. Statistics of the Civil Service of Canada (0318-5109); (until 1925): Canada. Bureau of Statistics. Statement of Civil Service Personnel and Salaries
Published by: Statistics Canada, Public Institutions Division, Rm 1500, Main Building, Ottawa, ON K1A 0T6, Canada.

332.6 317　　　　CAN
CANADA. STATISTICS CANADA. SYSTEM OF NATIONAL ACCOUNTS, CANADA'S INTERNATIONAL INVESTMENT POSITION/CANADA. STATISTIQUE CANADA. BILAN DES INVESTISSEMENTS INTERNATIONAUX DU CANADA. Text in English, French. 1926. a. CND 52 domestic; USD 52 foreign (effective 1999). **Document type:** *Government.* **Description:** Presents the external financial position of Canada in terms of foreign investments in Canada and Canadian investments abroad at year end.
Formerly: Canada's International Investment Position (0318-8868)
Related titles: Microform ed.: (from MML).
Indexed: RASB.
—CISTI.
Published by: Statistics Canada, Operations and Integration Division, Circulation Management, Jean Talon Bldg, 2 C12, Tunney's Pasture, Ottawa, ON K1A 0T6, Canada. TEL 613-951-7277, 800-267-6677, FAX 613-951-1584, http://www.statcan.ca.

331 317　　　　CAN　　　　ISSN 0835-4634
CANADA. STATISTICS CANADA. TRUSTEED PENSION FUNDS - FINANCIAL STATISTICS/CANADA. STATISTIQUE CANADA. CAISSES DE RETRAITE EN FIDUCIE, STATISTIQUES FINANCIERES. Text in English, French. 1957. biennial. CND 42 domestic; USD 51 foreign (effective 1999). **Document type:** *Government.* **Description:** Presents information on the income, expenditure and assets of all trusteed pension funds in both the public and private sectors at the national level.
Formerly (until 1984): Canada. Statistics Canada. Trusteed Pension Plans - Financial Statistics (0575-9978); Which incorporates: Canada. Statistics Canada. Regimes de Pensions en Fiducie - Statistiques Financieres (0825-3781)
Related titles: Microform ed.: (from MML).
Published by: Statistics Canada, Operations and Integration Division, Circulation Management, Jean Talon Bldg, 2 C12, Tunney's Pasture, Ottawa, ON K1A 0T6, Canada. TEL 613-951-7277, 800-267-6677, FAX 613-951-1584, http://www.statcan.ca.

380 317　　　　CAN　　　　ISSN 0380-7894
CANADA. STATISTICS CANADA. WHOLESALE TRADE/CANADA. STATISTIQUE CANADA. COMMERCE DE GROS. Text in English, French. 1935. m. CND 186; CND 186 foreign (effective 1999). **Document type:** *Government.* **Description:** Presents data on wholesale trade: percentage changes for sales and inventors and stocks-sales ratios of wholesale merchants.
Related titles: Microform ed.: (from MML); Online - full text ed.: ISSN 1480-7467.
Published by: Statistics Canada, Operations and Integration Division, Circulation Management, Jean Talon Bldg, 2 C12, Tunney's Pasture, Ottawa, ON K1A 0T6, Canada. TEL 613-951-7277, 800-267-6677, FAX 613-951-1584, http://www.statcan.ca.

B

▼ *new title*　　➤ *refereed*　　✳ *unverified*　　◆ *full entry avail.*

016.33 CAN ISSN 1484-6497
CANADIAN BUSINESS AND CURRENT AFFAIRS BUSINESS; Canada's premier periodical database. Key Title: C B C A Fulltext Business. Abbreviated title: C B C A. Text in English. 1992. m. CND 2,100 to libraries (effective 2005). **Description:** Provides in depth access to a broad range of Canadian business periodicals. It satisfies the information needs of business professionals, journalists, students, and teachers interested in business issues in Canada. Over 400 journals make up the collection, with file depth back to the early 1980s. Trade journals, general business publications, academic journals, topical journals, and professional publications are all included.
Supersedes in part (in 1998): C B C A Fulltext (1484-6470); Which was formerly (until 1997): Canadian Business and Current Affairs Fulltext (CD-ROM) (1206-1816)
Media: Online - full content.
Published by: Micromedia ProQuest (Subsidiary of: ProQuest Information & Learning), 20 Victoria St, Toronto, ON M5C 2N8, Canada. TEL 416-593-5211, 800-387-2689, FAX 416-362-6161, info@micromedia.ca, http://www.micromedia.ca/Products_Services/CBCABUS.htm. Adv. contact Mr. Peter Asselstine.

016.330 016.0013 CAN
CANADIAN BUSINESS AND CURRENT AFFAIRS CURRENT EVENTS. Text in English. 1986. m. CND 2,000 to libraries (effective 2005). **Document type:** *Abstract/Index.* **Description:** Includes Canadian titles focusing on current events.
Media: Online - full content.
Published by: Micromedia ProQuest (Subsidiary of: ProQuest Information & Learning), 20 Victoria St, Toronto, ON M5C 2N8, Canada. TEL 416-362-5211, 800-387-2689, FAX 416-362-6161, info@micromedia.ca, http://www.micromedia.ca/Products_Services/CBCACEv.htm. Ed. Mr. Tom McGreevy.

336 340 CAN
CANADIAN INCOME TAX RESEARCH INDEX. Text in English. q. looseleaf. CND 638 (effective 2005). **Document type:** *Trade.* **Description:** Indexes of interpretive articles, court decisions and other references relating to federal income tax.
Related titles: CD-ROM ed.: CND 593 (effective 2005); Online - full text ed.: CND 582 (effective 2005).
Published by: C C H Canadian Ltd., 90 Sheppard Ave E, Ste 300, North York, ON M2N 6X1, Canada. TEL 416-224-2248, 800-268-4522, FAX 416-224-2243, cservice@cch.ca, http://www.cch.ca.

382 CAN ISSN 1198-7391
HF3221
CANADIAN INTERNATIONAL MERCHANDISE TRADE/LE COMMERCE INTERNATIONAL DE MARCHANDISE DU CANADA. Text in English, French. 1947. m. CND 188 domestic (effective 1999); USD 188 foreign. charts. **Document type:** *Government.* **Description:** Contains a series of summary tables and charts showing monthly, quarterly and annual trade data.
Formerly (until 1994): Summary of Canadian International Trade (0828-1556); Incorporates in part (in 1994): Preliminary Statement of Canadian International Trade (0828-1998); Which was previously (until 1985): Canada. Statistics Canada. Summary of External Trade (0318-2347); Which was formed by the 1975 merger of: Canada. Statistics Canada. Summary of Foreign Trade (0575-9951); Which was formerly (until 1962): Canada. Statistics Canada. Monthly Summary of Foreign Trade (0318-2355); (1935-1947): Canada. Statistics Canada. Trade of Canada by Months (0840-3414); And: Canada. Statistics Canada. Summary of Imports (0527-6330); Which, in turn, was formed by the merger of (1934-1947): Canada. Statistics Canada. Imports into Canada for Consumption by Countries (0844-6539); And: Canada. Statistics Canada. Summary of Canada's Imports for Consumption (0840-3430); Which was previously (1931-1945): Canada. Statistics Canada. Summary of Canada's Imports (0840-3422)
Related titles: Diskette ed.; Microform ed.: (from MML); Online - full text ed.
Indexed: RASB.
—CISTI.
Published by: Statistics Canada, Operations and Integration Division, Circulation Management, Jean Talon Bldg, 2 C12, Tunney's Pasture, Ottawa, ON K1A 0T6, Canada. TEL 613-951-7277, 800-267-6677, FAX 613-951-1584, http://statcan.ca:80/cgi-bin/downpub/downpub.cgi.

330 COL ISSN 0120-4564
Z7165.C64
CATALOGO COLECTIVO DE LIBROS Y MONOGRAFIAS ECONOMICAS. Text in English, French, Portuguese, Spanish. 1979. 3/yr. **Document type:** *Catalog.*
Published by: Camara de Comercio de Bogota, Carrera 26 68D-35, Bogota, Colombia. TEL 57-1-3830300, FAX 57-1-3830330, http://www.ccb.org.co/. Eds. Fabiola de Briceno, Rubby Angel Giraldo. Circ: 300.

331 CHE ISSN 1011-0569
CATALOGUE OF I L O PUBLICATIONS IN PRINT. Text in English. a. **Document type:** *Catalog.*
Related titles: French ed.: Catalogue des Publications du B I T. ISSN 0259-3726.
Published by: (International Labour Office), I L O Publications, 4 route des Morillons, Geneva 22, 1211, Switzerland. TEL 41-22-799-6111, FAX 41-22-798-6358.

310 338.9 JPN ISSN 0301-9837
Z7164.U5
CATALOGUE OF STATISTICAL MATERIALS OF DEVELOPING COUNTRIES. Text in English, Japanese. 1969. irreg., latest 1999. price varies. **Document type:** *Catalog.*
Published by: Institute of Developing Economies/Ajia Keizai Kenkyusho, 3-2-2 Wakaba, Mihana-ku, Chiba-shi, Chiba 261-8545, Japan. TEL 81-43-299-9536, FAX 84-43-299-9724, info@ide.go.jp, http://www.ide.go.jp.

330 BRA ISSN 0103-5312
CENSO COMERCIAL. Text in Portuguese. 1940. quinquennial. USD 30 (effective 1998). **Document type:** *Government.*
Media: Diskette.
Published by: Fundacao Instituto Brasileiro de Geografia e Estatistica, Centro de Documentacao e Disseminacao de Informacoes, Rua General Canabarro, 706 Andar 2, Maracana, Rio de Janeiro, RJ 20271-201, Brazil. TEL 55-21-264-5424, FAX 55-21-2841959, http://www.ibge.gov.br.

338 BRA ISSN 0103-5320
CENSO DOS SERVICOS. Text in Portuguese. 1940. quinquennial. USD 40 (effective 1998). **Document type:** *Government.* **Description:** Contains data on number of service establishments, employed persons, salaries and wages, receipts and more.
Published by: Fundacao Instituto Brasileiro de Geografia e Estatistica, Centro de Documentacao e Disseminacao de Informacoes, Rua General Canabarro, 706 Andar 2, Maracana, Rio de Janeiro, RJ 20271-201, Brazil. TEL 55-21-264-5424, FAX 55-21-2841959, http://www.ibge.gov.br.

338 BRA ISSN 0103-6165
CENSO INDUSTRIAL. Text in Portuguese. 1940. quinquennial. USD 30. **Document type:** *Government.* **Description:** Presents data on the establishments, employed persons, salaries and wages, gross value of industrial production, industrial operation costs etc.
Related titles: Diskette ed.
Published by: Fundacao Instituto Brasileiro de Geografia e Estatistica, Centro de Documentacao e Disseminacao de Informacoes, Rua General Canabarro, 706 Andar 2, Maracana, Rio de Janeiro, RJ 20271-201, Brazil. TEL 55-21-264-5424, FAX 55-21-2841959, http://www.ibge.gov.br.

338 316 ZMB ISSN 0069-1429
CENSUS OF INDUSTRIAL PRODUCTION IN ZAMBIA. Text in English. 1962. a., latest 1980. ZMK 3.
Published by: Central Statistical Office, PO Box 31908, Lusaka, Zambia. TEL 211-231.

310 FJI
CENSUS OF PRIVATE NON-PROFIT MAKING INSTITUTIONS IN FIJI. A REPORT. Text in English. irreg., latest 1990. USD 5 per issue (effective 2000). **Document type:** *Government.*
Published by: Bureau of Statistics, c/o Librarian, Govt. Bldg. 5, PO Box 2221, Suva, Fiji. TEL 679-315-822, FAX 679-303-656.

330.9 USA
CENSUS OF SERVICE INDUSTRIES: FINAL REPORTS. (Issued in 3 series: Geographic Area Series, Industry Series, and Subject Series) Text in English. 1933. quinquennial. **Document type:** *Government.*
Supersedes in part: U.S. Bureau of the Census. Census of Retail Trade, Wholesale Trade and Selected Service Industries; Which was formerly: U.S. Bureau of the Census. Census of Business (0082-9323)
Related titles: CD-ROM ed.; Online - full content ed.
Published by: U.S. Bureau of the Census (Subsidiary of: U.S. Department of Commerce), Customer Services, Washington, DC 20233. TEL 301-457-4100, FAX 301-457-4714, http://www.census.gov/.

319 BRB ISSN 0255-8432
HG3883.B35
CENTRAL BANK OF BARBADOS. BALANCE OF PAYMENTS. Variant title: Balance of Payments of Barbados. Text in English. 1976. a. free. **Document type:** *Corporate.* **Description:** The BOP contains data on the country's current account, capital flows, trade, travel, transfer payments, banks and international reserves. Also included is an analysis of the BOP, summary of the BOP survey and Notes and Definitions.
Published by: Central Bank of Barbados, Research Department, Spry St., PO Box 1016, Bridgetown, Barbados. TEL 246-4366870, FAX 246-4271431, TELEX CENBANK 2251, cbb.libr@caribsurf.com, http://www.centralbank.org.bb. R&P Neville Pollard. Circ: 2,000 (controlled).

CENTRAL BANK OF BARBADOS. ECONOMIC AND FINANCIAL STATISTICS. see *BUSINESS AND ECONOMICS—Banking And Finance*

336 BLZ ISSN 1025-1642
CENTRAL BANK OF BELIZE. ANNUAL STATISTICAL DIGEST. Text in English. 1982. a. free.
Formerly (until 1982): Monetary Authority of Belize. Statistical Digest
Published by: Central Bank of Belize, Library, PO Box 852, Belize City, Belize. TEL 501-2-36194, FAX 501-2-36226, cenbank@btl.net.

310 ISL ISSN 1607-6680
HC360.5.A1
CENTRAL BANK OF ICELAND. MONETARY BULLETIN. Text in English. 1980. q. free. **Document type:** *Bulletin, Government.* **Description:** Contains an abbreviated version of the Icelandic economy information found in Hagtoelur Manadarins published monthly by the Central Bank.
Supersedes (in 1999): Central Bank of Iceland. Economic Statistics (0256-193X)
Related titles: ♦ Icelandic ed.: Peningamal. ISSN 1605-9468.
—BLDSC (5908.335320).
Published by: (Hagfraedideild), Sedlabanki Islands/Central Bank of Iceland, Kalkofnsvegur 1, Reykjavik, 150, Iceland. TEL 354-569-9600, FAX 354-569-9608, sedlabanki@sedlabanki.is, http://www.sedlabanki.is. Ed. Birgir Isl Gunnarsson. Circ: 1,500.

332 IRL ISSN 0332-2696
CENTRAL BANK OF IRELAND. IRISH ECONOMIC STATISTICS. Text in English. 1973. a. free. stat. 6 p./no.; back issues avail. **Document type:** *Corporate.* **Description:** Pocket-sized compendium of Irish economic statistics.
Related titles: Online - full text ed.
Published by: Central Bank of Ireland, Dame St., PO Box 559, Dublin, 2, Ireland. TEL 353-1-6716666, FAX 353-1-6716561, erp@centralbank.ie, enquiries@centralbank.ie, http://www.centralbank.ie. Circ: 5,000.

330.9 JOR
CENTRAL BANK OF JORDAN. MONTHLY STATISTICAL BULLETIN. Text in Arabic, English. 1965. m. free. stat. **Document type:** *Bulletin, Government.* **Description:** Statistical tables and graphic charts covering all aspects of money and banking activities, public finance, external trade and balance of payments, production and price indexes of the Central Bank of Jordan.
Formerly: Central Bank of Jordan. Quarterly Bulletin (0008-9265)
Indexed: BAS.
Published by: (Department of Research and Studies), Central Bank of Jordan, P O Box 37, Amman, 11118, Jordan. TEL 4630301, FAX 4638889, redp@cbj.gov.jo, http://www.cbj.gov.jo.

330.9 KEN
CENTRAL BANK OF KENYA. STATISTICAL BULLETIN. Text in English. m. charts; stat. **Document type:** *Government.* **Description:** Takes a statistical look at various economic indicators for Kenya, including bank assets, deposits and debt ratios, international trade, central government finance, and general economic indicators (including gross domestic product).
Published by: Central Bank of Kenya, Research Department, PO Box 60000, Nairobi, Kenya. cbk-resd@africaonline.co.ke, http://www.africaonline.co.ke/cbk.

332 330.9 KWT ISSN 1029-4562
CENTRAL BANK OF KUWAIT. MONTHLY MONETARY STATISTICS. Text in Arabic, English. 1979. m. free. charts; stat. **Document type:** *Government.* **Description:** Covers monthly financial and monetary indicators and statistics for the State of Kuwait.
Former titles: Central Bank of Kuwait. Monthly Monetary Review; Central Bank of Kuwait. Monthly Monetary Tables
Related titles: Online - full content ed.
Published by: Central Bank of Kuwait, Economic Research Department/Bank al-Kuwayt al-Markazi, Idarat al-Buhuth al-ektisadia, P O Box 526, Safat, 13006, Kuwait. TEL 965-2449200, FAX 965-2440887, cbk@cbk.gov.kw, http://www.cbk.gov.kw. R&P Sami H Al-Anbaee TEL 965-2403257.

332 330.9 KWT ISSN 1012-4209
CENTRAL BANK OF KUWAIT. QUARTERLY STATISTICAL BULLETIN/BANK AL-KUWAYT AL-MARKAZI. AL-NASHRAH AL-IHSA'IYYAH AL-FASLIYYAH. Text in Arabic, English. 1974. q. free. charts; stat. **Document type:** *Government.*
Related titles: Online - full content ed.
Published by: Central Bank of Kuwait, Economic Research Department/Bank al-Kuwayt al-Markazi, Idarat al-Buhuth al-ektisadia, P O Box 526, Safat, 13006, Kuwait. TEL 965-2449200, FAX 965-2440887, TELEX 22101, cbk@cbk.gov.kw, http://ww.cbk.gov.kw. R&P Sami H Al-Anbaee TEL 965-2403257. Circ: 900.

330 LKA ISSN 1391-3557
HC424
CENTRAL BANK OF SRI LANKA. SOCIO ECONOMIC DATA. Text in English. 1979. irreg., latest 1997. LKR 70, USD 3.
Published by: Central Bank of Sri Lanka, Janadhipathi Mawatha, P O Box 590, Colombo, 1, Sri Lanka. TEL 94-1-346278, FAX 94-1-346266.

332.1 BHS
CENTRAL BANK OF THE BAHAMAS. QUARTERLY STATISTICAL DIGEST. Text in English. 1992. q. free. charts. back issues avail. **Document type:** *Government.*

Published by: Central Bank of the Bahamas, Research Department, PO Box N 4868, Nassau, Bahamas. TEL 242-302-2639, FAX 242-356-4324, TELEX 20-115, research@centralbankbahamas.com. Ed. Wendy Craigg. Circ: 1,300.

330 TTO
CENTRAL BANK OF TRINIDAD AND TOBAGO. ECONOMIC BULLETIN. Text in English. 1970. 3/yr. USD 35 (effective 2001). **Document type:** *Bulletin, Corporate.*
Former titles (until 1999): Central Bank of Trinidad and Tobago. Quarterly Economic Bulletin; (until 1976): Central Bank of Trinidad and Tobago. Economic Bulletin (1011-6346)
Media: Duplicated (not offset).
Indexed: PAIS, WBA.
Published by: Central Bank of Trinidad and Tobago, Eric Williams Plaza, Independence Sq, PO Box 1250, Port-of-Spain, Trinidad, Trinidad & Tobago. TEL 868-625-4835, FAX 868-627-4696, library@central-bank.org.tt, http://www.central-bank.org.tt. Circ: 750.

332.1 TTO ISSN 1011-6362
CENTRAL BANK OF TRINIDAD AND TOBAGO. QUARTERLY STATISTICAL DIGEST. Text in English. q. USD 55 (effective 2001); includes Annual Economic Survey, Quarterly Economic Bulletin, and Quarterly Statistical Digest. stat. back issues avail. **Document type:** *Bulletin, Corporate.*
Supersedes in part: Central Bank of Trinidad and Tobago. Statistical Digest
Published by: Central Bank of Trinidad and Tobago, Eric Williams Plaza, Independence Sq, PO Box 1250, Port-of-Spain, Trinidad, Trinidad & Tobago. TEL 868-625-4835, FAX 868-627-4696, library@central-bank.org.tt, http://www.central-bank.org.tt. Circ: 850.

380.1029 GBR ISSN 0958-7322
CENTRE RANKINGS. Text in English. 1990. a. GBP 195.
Description: An authoritative guide to shopping centre retailing in the UK.
Published by: Chas E. Goad Ltd., 8-12 Salisbury Sq, Old Hatfield, Herts AL9 5BJ, United Kingdom. TEL 0707-271171, FAX 0707-274641, TELEX 83147 TEMCOL. Eds. Jonathan Reynolds, Trevor Wood.

CENTRES, BUREAUX & RESEARCH INSTITUTES; the directory of UK concentrations of effort, information, and expertise. see *BUSINESS AND ECONOMICS—Trade And Industrial Directories*

381 TCD
CHAD. BULLETIN MENSUEL DE STATISTIQUES. Text in French. m. **Document type:** *Bulletin.*
Published by: Commission for Trade and Industry, BP 453, N'djamena, Chad.

330 GBR ISSN 0955-1034
CD1040
CHARTERED INSTITUTE OF PUBLIC FINANCE AND ACCOUNTANCY. ARCHIVES STATISTICS. ESTIMATES. Text in English. 1988. a. GBP 55. back issues avail. **Document type:** *Bulletin.*
—CCC.
Published by: (Statistical Information Service), Chartered Institute of Public Finance and Accountancy, 3 Robert St, London, WC2N 6RL, United Kingdom. TEL 44-20-7543-5800, FAX 44-20-7543-5700, http://www.cipfa.org.uk.

310 330 GBR ISSN 0263-2985
HJ9431
CHARTERED INSTITUTE OF PUBLIC FINANCE AND ACCOUNTANCY. CAPITAL EXPENDITURE AND DEBT FINANCING STATISTICS. ACTUALS. Text in English. 1946. a. GBP 105. stat. back issues avail. **Description:** Analyzes local authority debt in England, Wales, Scotland, and Northern Ireland.
Formerly: Return of Outstanding Debt (0143-103X)
—CCC.
Published by: (Statistical Information Service), Chartered Institute of Public Finance and Accountancy, 3 Robert St, London, WC2N 6RL, United Kingdom. TEL 44-20-7543-5800, FAX 44-20-7543-5700, http://www.cipfa.org.uk.

336.2 GBR
CHARTERED INSTITUTE OF PUBLIC FINANCE AND ACCOUNTANCY. COUNCIL TAX STATISTICS. ESTIMATES. Text in English. a. GBP 55. back issues avail.
Published by: (Statistical Information Service), Chartered Institute of Public Finance and Accountancy, 3 Robert St, London, WC2N 6RL, United Kingdom. TEL 44-20-7543-5800, FAX 44-20-7543-5700, http://www.cipfa.org.uk.

332 310 GBR
CHARTERED INSTITUTE OF PUBLIC FINANCE AND ACCOUNTANCY. FINANCE AND GENERAL STATISTICS. ESTIMATES. Text in English. 1978. a. GBP 105. back issues avail.
Former titles: Chartered Institute of Public Finance and Accountancy. Financial General and Rating Statistics; Chartered Institute of Public Finance and Accountancy. Return of Rates (0263-2276)
—CCC.
Published by: (Statistical Information Service), Chartered Institute of Public Finance and Accountancy, 3 Robert St, London, WC2N 6RL, United Kingdom. TEL 44-20-7543-5800, FAX 44-20-7543-5700, http://www.cipfa.org.uk.

CHARTERED INSTITUTE OF PUBLIC FINANCE AND ACCOUNTANCY. LEISURE CHARGES STATISTICS. ACTUALS. see *SPORTS AND GAMES—Abstracting, Bibliographies, Statistics*

336 GBR
CHARTERED INSTITUTE OF PUBLIC FINANCE AND ACCOUNTANCY. RATING REVIEW (SCOTLAND) STATISTICS. ACTUALS. Text in English. a. GBP 8. back issues avail.
Published by: (Statistical Information Service), Chartered Institute of Public Finance and Accountancy, 3 Robert St, London, WC2N 6RL, United Kingdom. TEL 44-20-7543-5800, FAX 44-20-7543-5700, http://www.cipfa.org.uk.

336 GBR
CHARTERED INSTITUTE OF PUBLIC FINANCE AND ACCOUNTANCY. RATING REVIEW (SCOTLAND) STATISTICS. ESTIMATES. Text in English. a. GBP 8. back issues avail.
Published by: (Statistical Information Service), Chartered Institute of Public Finance and Accountancy, 3 Robert St, London, WC2N 6RL, United Kingdom. TEL 44-20-7543-5800, FAX 44-20-7543-5700, http://www.cipfa.org.uk.

336.2 310 GBR ISSN 0260-5546
CHARTERED INSTITUTE OF PUBLIC FINANCE AND ACCOUNTANCY. REVENUE COLLECTION STATISTICS. ACTUALS. Text in English. 1945. a. GBP 80. back issues avail.
—BLDSC (7785.818420).
Published by: (Statistical Information Service), Chartered Institute of Public Finance and Accountancy, 3 Robert St, London, WC2N 6RL, United Kingdom. TEL 44-20-7543-5800, FAX 44-20-7543-5700, http://www.cipfa.org.uk.

330.9 GBR
CHARTERED INSTITUTE OF PUBLIC FINANCE AND ACCOUNTANCY. TRADING STANDARDS STATISTICS. ACTUALS & ESTIMATES. Text in English. 1994. a. GBP 55.
Formed by the merger of (1984-1994): Chartered Institute of Public Finance and Accountancy. Trading Standards Statistics. Estimates (0954-1853); (1984-1994): Chartered Institute of Public Finance and Accountancy. Trading Standards Statistics. Actuals (0954-1780)
Published by: (Statistical Information Service), Chartered Institute of Public Finance and Accountancy, 3 Robert St, London, WC2N 6RL, United Kingdom. TEL 44-20-7543-5800, FAX 44-20-7543-5700, http://www.cipfa.org.uk. Circ: 1,500.

381 CHL
CHILE. INSTITUTO NACIONAL DE ESTADISTICAS. ANUARIO DE COMERCIO INTERIOR Y SERVICIOS. Text in Spanish. 1970. a. CLP 2,000; USD 13.50 in United States; USD 15.90 elsewhere.
Related titles: Diskette ed.
Published by: Instituto Nacional de Estadisticas, Casilla 498, Correo 3, Ave. Bulnes, 418, Santiago, Chile. TEL 56-2-6991441, FAX 56-2-6712169.

381 CHL
CHILE. INSTITUTO NACIONAL DE ESTADISTICAS. ANUARIO DE PRECIOS. Text in Spanish. 1983. a. CLP 2,000; USD 13.50 in United States; USD 15.90 elsewhere.
Published by: Instituto Nacional de Estadisticas, Casilla 498, Correo 3, Ave. Bulnes, 418, Santiago, Chile. TEL 56-2-6991441, FAX 56-2-6712169.

330 318 CHL
CHILE. INSTITUTO NACIONAL DE ESTADISTICAS. ENCUESTA NACIONAL DEL EMPLEO. Text in Spanish. m. CLP 3,010.
Media: Duplicated (not offset). **Related titles:** Diskette ed.
Published by: Instituto Nacional de Estadisticas, Casilla 498, Correo 3, Ave. Bulnes, 418, Santiago, Chile. TEL 56-2-6991441, FAX 56-2-6712169.

331.2 318 CHL
CHILE. INSTITUTO NACIONAL DE ESTADISTICAS. ESTADISTICAS E INDICE DE REMUNERACIONES. Text in Spanish. 1959. m. CLP 1,550; USD 12.30 foreign (effective 1999).
Formerly (until 1983): Chile. Instituto Nacional de Estadisticas. Indice de Sueldos y Salarios
Published by: Instituto Nacional de Estadisticas, Casilla 498, Correo 3, Ave. Bulnes, 418, Santiago, Chile. TEL 56-2-6991441, FAX 56-2-6712169.

332 CHL
CHILE. INSTITUTO NACIONAL DE ESTADISTICAS. FINANZAS. Text in Spanish. 1912. a. CLP 1,200 domestic; USD 8.20 in US & Canada; USD 9.40 elsewhere (effective 1999). stat.
Formerly (until 1958): Finanzas, Bancos y Cajas Sociales
Media: Duplicated (not offset).
Published by: Instituto Nacional de Estadisticas, Casilla 498, Correo 3, Ave. Bulnes, 418, Santiago, Chile. TEL 56-2-6991441, FAX 56-2-6712169. Circ: (controlled).

330 CHL
CHILE. INSTITUTO NACIONAL DE ESTADISTICAS. INDICADORES DE EMPLEO, POR SEXO Y GRUPOS DE EDAD, TOTAL NACIONAL. Text in Spanish. 1985. a. CLP 1,200; USD 8.20 in North America; USD 9.40 elsewhere.
Related titles: Diskette ed.
Published by: Instituto Nacional de Estadisticas, Casilla 498, Correo 3, Ave. Bulnes, 418, Santiago, Chile. TEL 56-2-6991441, FAX 56-2-6712169.

339 318 CHL
CHILE. INSTITUTO NACIONAL DE ESTADISTICAS. INDICE DE PRECIOS AL CONSUMIDOR. Text in Spanish. 1928. m. CLP 1,790 (effective 1999).
Related titles: Diskette ed.: CLP 12,490 (effective 1999).
Published by: Instituto Nacional de Estadisticas, Casilla 498, Correo 3, Ave. Bulnes, 418, Santiago, Chile. TEL 56-2-6991441, FAX 56-2-6712169.

330 318 CHL
CHILE. INSTITUTO NACIONAL DE ESTADISTICAS. INDICE DE PRECIOS AL POR MAYOR. (With 2 subseries: Series, Informe) Text in Spanish. 1974. m. **Document type:** *Government.*
Related titles: Diskette ed.
Published by: Instituto Nacional de Estadisticas, Casilla 498, Correo 3, Ave. Bulnes, 418, Santiago, Chile.

338 CHL
CHILE. INSTITUTO NACIONAL DE ESTADISTICAS. INDICE DE PRODUCCION Y VENTA FISICA DE INDUSTRIAS MANUFACTURERAS. Text in Spanish. 1983. q. CLP 2,250; USD 14.90 in United States; USD 17.90 elsewhere.
Document type: *Government.*
Published by: Instituto Nacional de Estadisticas, Casilla 498, Correo 3, Ave. Bulnes, 418, Santiago, Chile. TEL 56-2-6991441, FAX 56-2-6712169.

658.3 CHL
CHILE. INSTITUTO NACIONAL DE ESTADISTICAS. INDICE DE REMUNERACIONES. Text in Spanish. 1983. m. **Document type:** *Government.*
Media: Duplicated (not offset).
Published by: Instituto Nacional de Estadisticas, Casilla 498, Correo 3, Ave. Bulnes, 418, Santiago, Chile.

338 CHL ISSN 0716-842X
CHILE. INSTITUTO NACIONAL DE ESTADISTICAS. INDUSTRIAS MANUFACTURERAS. Text in Spanish. 1960. a. CLP 2,700; USD 18.60 in United States; USD 23.60 elsewhere.
Published by: Instituto Nacional de Estadisticas, Casilla 498, Correo 3, Ave. Bulnes, 418, Santiago, Chile. TEL 56-2-6991441, FAX 56-2-6712169.

332 658 CHL
CHILE MARKETING AND FINANCIAL STATISTICS. Text in Spanish. 1990. a.
Published by: Time - America Economia, Casilla 113, Correo 35, Galvarino Gallardo, 1576, Santiago, Chile. TEL 02-2237913, FAX 02-223-1903.

330 CHN
CHINA CHEMICAL FERTILIZER STATISTICS. Text in Chinese. 1980. a. USD 3,000 (effective 2004). stat. **Document type:** *Trade.*
Published by: C N C I C Chemdata Co., Ltd, 53, Xiaoguanjie, Anwai, Beijing, 100029, China. TEL 86-10-64444102, FAX 86-10-64437116, sinofi@cheminfo.gov.cn, chemdata@cheminfo.gov.cn, http://www.chemdata.com.cn/.

339 310 CHN
CHINA MONTHLY STATISTICS. Text in English. m. CNY 2,040, USD 240. **Description:** Contains statistics on China's social and economic situations.
Published by: China Statistical Information and Consultancy Service Center, 38 Yuetan Nanjie, Sanlihe, Beijing, 100826, China. TEL 86-10-8515076, FAX 86-10-8515078. Ed. Zhang Shu. **Co-sponsor:** International Centre for the Advancement of Science and Technology Ltd.

381 338.91 HKG ISSN 0258-3046
CHINA'S CUSTOMS STATISTICS. Text in English. 1982. m. HKD 648, USD 135. back issues avail.
Published by: Economic Information & Agency, 342 Hennessy Rd 10th Fl, 10 th Fl, Wanchai, Hong Kong. TEL 852-573-8217, FAX 852-838-8304.

355.6 USA ISSN 0882-8857
UA23.2
CIVILIAN MANPOWER STATISTICS. Text in English. 1980. q. USD 12; USD 15 foreign. back issues avail. **Document type:** *Government.* **Description:** Comprises tables containing official summary data on Department of Defense civilian employment levels. Includes selected data on trends on civilian employment and accession and separation rates.
Indexed: AmStI.
Published by: U.S. Department of Defense, Washington Headquarters Services, Directorate for Information, Operations and Reports, The Pentagon, Washington, DC 20301-1155.
Subscr. to: U.S. Government Printing Office, Superintendent of Documents.

B

▼ new title ➤ refereed ✶ unverified ♦ full entry avail.

B

016.331   USA
KF3362.7
CLASSIFIED INDEX OF N.L.R.B. AND RELATED COURT DECISIONS. Text in English. bi-m. price varies. reprints avail. **Document type:** *Government.*
Former titles: Classified Index of National Labor Relations Board Decisions and Related Court Decisions (0092-4962); U.S. National Labor Relations Board. Digest of Decisions of the National Labor Relations Board (0012-2734)
Related titles: Microfiche ed.: (from BHP).
Published by: U.S. National Labor Relations Board, 1099 14th St, N W, Washington, DC 20570-0001. TEL 202-273-1991, FAX 202-273-1789, http://www.nlrb.gov. **Subscr. to:** U.S. Government Printing Office, Superintendent of Documents, PO Box 371954, Pittsburgh, PA 15250-7954. TEL 202-512-1800, FAX 202-512-2250, orders@gpo.gov, http://www.access.gpo.gov.

651   AUS
CLERICAL SALARY REVIEW. Text in English. 1970. s-a. looseleaf. AUD 1,650. charts; stat. **Document type:** *Trade.* **Description:** Provides salary data on clerical positions in Australia.
Published by: Cullen Egan Dell, Level 8, 50 Bridge St, Sydney, NSW 2000, Australia. TEL 61-2-9375-9800, FAX 61-2-9233-6800. Ed. Matt Darian. Circ: 125.

CLINICAL TRIALS INSIGHT CLASSICS. PHARMACOECONOMICS. see *PHARMACY AND PHARMACOLOGY—Abstracting, Bibliographies, Statistics*

COLOMBIA. DEPARTAMENTO ADMINISTRATIVO NACIONAL DE ESTADISTICA. ANUARIO DE COMERCIO EXTERIOR. see *BUSINESS AND ECONOMICS—International Commerce*

338   COL
COLOMBIA. DEPARTAMENTO ADMINISTRATIVO NACIONAL DE ESTADISTICA. ANUARIO DE INDUSTRIA MANUFACTURERA. Text in Spanish. 1972. a. USD 75.
Formerly: Colombia. Departamento Administrativo Nacional de Estadistica. Anuario de Estadisticas Industriales; Which superseded: Colombia. Departamento Administrativo Nacional de Estadistica. Industria Manufacturera Nacional
Published by: Departamento Administrativo Nacional de Estadistica, Banco Nacional de Datos, Centro Administrativo Nacional (CAN), Avenida Eldorado, Apartado Aereo 80043, Bogota, CUND, Colombia.

330   COL
COLOMBIA. SUPERINTENDENCIA BANCARIA. INFORMACION ESTADISTICA POR CIUDADES. Text in Spanish. 1976. q. free.
Published by: Superintendencia Bancaria, Apartado Aereo 3460, Bogota, CUND, Colombia. TEL 57-1-2804060, FAX 57-1-2800864. Circ: 500.

310 330   MEX   ISSN 0186-0496
COMERCIO EXTERIOR DE MEXICO. INFORMACION PRELIMINAR. Text in Spanish. 1977. m. MXP 2,200, USD 150. **Document type:** *Government.*
Published by: Instituto Nacional de Estadistica, Geografia e Informatica, Secretaria de Programacion y Presupuesto, Prol. Heroe de Nacozari 2301 Sur, Puerta 11, Acceso, Aguascalientes, 20270, Mexico. TEL 52-4-918-19488, FAX 52-4-918-0739, http://www.inegi.gob.mx. Circ: 900.

310 382   PRT   ISSN 0873-092X
COMERCIO EXTRACOMUNITARIO. Text in French, Portuguese. 1975. m. stat. index. back issues avail. **Document type:** *Bulletin, Government.*
Former titles (until 1995): Indicadores do Comercio Externo (0871-9179); (until 1990): Boletim Mensal das Estatisticas do Comercio Externo (0377-2160)
Related titles: Microfiche ed.: 1975.
Indexed: RASB.
Published by: Instituto Nacional de Estatistica, Ave. Antonio Jose de Almeida 2, Lisbon, 1000-043, Portugal. TEL 351-21-8426100, FAX 351-21-8426380, ine@ine.pt, http://www.ine.pt/. Circ: 1,000.

382   ROM   ISSN 1223-5636
HF3741
COMERTUL EXTERIOR AL ROMANIEI/FOREIGN TRADE OF ROMANIA. Text in English, Romanian. biennial. ROL 150,000; USD 50 foreign. **Document type:** *Government.* **Description:** Presents data regarding Rumania's exports and imports structured by sections and chapters, according to the harmonized system of products classification by origin and destination countries.
Published by: Comisia Nationala pentru Statistica/National Commission for Statistics, Bd. Libertatii 16, Sector 5, Bucharest, 70542, Romania. TEL 40-1-3363370, FAX 40-1-3124873.

382 314   GRC   ISSN 0071-738X
HF197
COMMERCE EXTERIEUR DE LA GRECE/EXOTERIKON EMPORION TES ELLADOS. Text in French, Greek. 1866. a., latest 1992. USD 60. back issues avail. **Document type:** *Government.*
Formerly (until 1965): Foreign Trade of Greece

Published by: National Statistical Service of Greece, Statistical Information and Publications Division/Ethniki Statistiki Yperesia tes Ellados, 14-16 Lykourgou St, Athens, 101 66, Greece. TEL 30-1-3289-397, FAX 30-1-3221-102.

338 315   TWN   ISSN 0257-5728
COMMODITY PRICE STATISTICS MONTHLY IN TAIWAN AREA. Key Title: Wujia Tongji Yuebao. Text in Chinese, English; Summaries in Chinese. 1971. m. TWD 100 (effective 2000). index, cum.index. **Description:** Provides statistics on recent changing conditions of commodity prices in the Taiwan area of the Republic of China. Includes export and import price indices.
Media: Microfilm.
Published by: Executive Yuan, Directorate-General of Budget, Accounting & Statistics, 2 Kwangchow St, Taipei, Taiwan. TEL 886-2-2371-1521, FAX 886-2-2381-8246, http://www.dgbasey.gov.tw/, http://www.stat.gov.tw/main.htm/. Circ: 1,300. **Subscr. to:** Chen Chung Book Co., 3F, 20 Heng-Yang Rd, Taipei, Taiwan. TEL 886-2-2382-1394, FAX 886-2-2382-2805.

339 310   USA   ISSN 0010-3233
HF1
COMMODITY TRADE STATISTICS; according to the Standard International Trade Classification. Text in English. 1950. 28/yr. USD 225. **Description:** Analyzes more than 150 groups of commodities exported or imported by the world's principal trading nations.
Related titles: Microfiche ed.: (from CIS).
Indexed: IIS.
Published by: United Nations Publications, Subscription Office, P O Box 361, Birmingham, AL 35201-0361.

331.1 339 318   BHS
THE COMMONWEALTH OF THE BAHAMAS ANNUAL LABOUR FORCE AND HOUSEHOLD INCOME REPORT. Text in English. 1973. irreg., latest 1999. USD 7. illus. **Document type:** *Consumer.*
Formerly (until 1999): Bahamas. Department of Statistics. Household Income Report; Incorporates (in 1975): Bahamas. Department of Statistics. Labour Force and Income Distribution
Related titles: Diskette ed.; E-mail ed.; Fax ed.
Published by: Department of Statistics, PO Box N 3904, Nassau, Bahamas. TEL 242-502-1251, FAX 242-325-5149, dpsdp@batelnet.bs. Ed. Cypreanna Winter.

330   BHS
COMMONWEALTH OF THE BAHAMAS CONSUMER PRICE INDEX MONTHLY REPORT & ANNUAL REVIE OF PRICES. Text in English. 1974. a., latest 2000. USD 6 (effective 2001). stat. **Document type:** *Consumer.*
Formerly (unitl 1995): Bahamas. Department of Statistics. Annual Review of Prices: Report
Related titles: Diskette ed.; E-mail ed.; Fax ed.
Published by: Department of Statistics, PO Box N 3904, Nassau, Bahamas. TEL 242-502-1171, FAX 242-325-5149, dpsdp@batelnet.bs. Ed. Brendalee Adderley.

318 382   BHS
COMMONWEALTH OF THE BAHAMAS FOREIGN TRADE STATISTICS ANNUAL REPORT. Text in English. a. USD 20 (effective 2001). stat. 316 p./no.; reprints avail. **Document type:** *Trade.*
Formerly (until 1997): Bahamas. Department of Statistics. External Trade
Related titles: CD-ROM ed.; E-mail ed.
Published by: Department of Statistics, PO Box N 3904, Nassau, Bahamas. TEL 242-502-1062, FAX 242-325-5149, dpsdp@batelnet.bs. Ed. Dawson Ferguson.

318 382   BHS
THE COMMONWEALTH OF THE BAHAMAS. VITAL STATISTICS REPORT ANNUAL. Text in English. 1967. q., latest 1999. USD 5 (effective 2001). stat.
Formerly: Bahamas. Department of Statistics. Summary of External Trade Statistics
Related titles: Diskette ed.; E-mail ed.; Fax ed.
Published by: Department of Statistics, PO Box N 3904, Nassau, Bahamas.

016.381   NZL
COMPANIES REGISTERED IN NEW ZEALAND - ADDRESS INDEX. Text in English. irreg. NZD 90 (effective 2001). **Document type:** *Trade.* **Description:** Covers incorporated societies, industrial and provident societies, and charitable trusts, in addition to companies. Includes name, file number and address of each registered office.
Media: Microfiche.
Published by: GP Legislation Services, P.O. Box 12418, Thorndon, Wellington, New Zealand. TEL 64-4-496-5655, FAX 64-4-496-5698, http://www.gplegislation.co.nz.

016.381   NZL
COMPANIES REGISTERED IN NEW ZEALAND - NOMINAL INDEX. Text in English. irreg. NZD 45 (effective 2001). **Document type:** *Trade.* **Description:** Includes the name and file number of incorporated societies, industrial and provident societies and charitable trusts, in addition to companies.

Published by: GP Legislation Services, P.O. Box 12418, Thorndon, Wellington, New Zealand. TEL 64-4-496-5655, FAX 64-4-496-5698, http://www.gplegislation.co.nz.

330.9   JPN   ISSN 0918-7057
COMPARATIVE ECONOMIC AND FINANCIAL STATISTICS - JAPAN AND OTHER MAJOR COUNTRIES. Key Title: Nihon Keizai o Chushin Tosuru Kokusai Hikaku Tokei. Text in English, Japanese. 1964. a. JPY 1,800 (effective 1998). 350 p./no.; **Description:** Contains key economic indicators of the Group of Seven countries as well as other countries. Aims to facilitate comparison.
Formerly: International Comparative Statistics Centering on the Japanese Economy
Published by: (International Department), Bank of Japan/Nippon Ginko, c/o Public Relations Department, 2-1-1 Hongoku-cho-Nihonbashi, Chuo-ku, Tokyo, 1030000, Japan. TEL 81-3-3279-1111, FAX 81-3-3510-1374, http://www.boj.or.jp/en.index.htm. **Dist. by:** Tokiwa Sohgoh Service Co. Ltd., Publication and Research Department, Kyodo Bldg, 2-4 Hongokucho, Nihonbashi 3-chome, Chuo-ku, Tokyo 103-0027, Japan. TEL 81-3-3270-5713, FAX 81-3-3270-5710; **Overseas dist. by:** Japan Publications Trading Co., Ltd., Book Export II Dept, PO Box 5030, Tokyo International, Tokyo 101-3191, Japan. TEL 81-3-32923753, FAX 81-3-32920410.

330   COG
LES COMPTES DE LA NATION. Text in French. 1970. a. XAF 8,000 per issue.
Published by: Centre National de la Statistique et des Etudes Economiques, BP 2031, Brazzaville, Congo, Republic. TEL 242-83-43-24.

330   GLP
COMPTES ECONOMIQUES DE LA GUADELOUPE. Text in French. 1968. a. stat.
Published by: Institut National de la Statistique et des Etudes Economiques, Service Regional Guadeloupe, Ave. Paul Lacave, BP 96, Basse-Terre, Cedex 97102, Guadeloupe. Circ: 530.

330 318   MTQ   ISSN 0532-4785
COMPTES ECONOMIQUES DE LA MARTINIQUE. Text in French. 1968. irreg., latest 1987. price varies. adv. **Document type:** *Government.*
Published by: Institut National de la Statistique et des Etudes Economiques, Pointe de Jaham, Cedex, Martinique, BP 7212, Schoelcher, Cedex 97233, Martinique. TEL 61-60-88, FAX 61-27-22, TELEX 912394 MR. Circ: 600.

330   NER
COMPTES ECONOMIQUES DE LA NATION. Text in French. s-a. stat.
Published by: Direction de la Statistique et de l'Informatique, BP 862, Niamey, Niger. TEL 227-72-34-44. Circ: 200.

381   RWA   ISSN 1013-6118
COMPTES ECONOMIQUES NATIONAUX DU RWANDA. Text in English. 1976. a. USD 17. **Document type:** *Government.*
Published by: Direction Generale de la Statistique, BP 46, Kigali, Rwanda.

CONFERENCE BOARD OF CANADA. INDEX OF BUSINESS CONFIDENCE. see *BUSINESS AND ECONOMICS—Investments*

CONFERENCE BOARD OF CANADA. INDEX OF CONSUMER ATTITUDES. see *BUSINESS AND ECONOMICS—Marketing And Purchasing*

330.9021   COG
CONGO. CENTRE NATIONAL DE LA STATISTIQUE ET DES ETUDES ECONOMIQUES. ANNUAIRE STATISTIQUE. Text in French. 1959. a. XAF 12,000 per issue.
Published by: Centre National de la Statistique et des Etudes Economiques, BP 2031, Brazzaville, Congo, Republic. TEL 242-83-43-24.

330.9021   COG
CONGO. CENTRE NATIONAL DE LA STATISTIQUE ET DES ETUDES ECONOMIQUES. BULLETIN DE STATISTIQUE. Text in French. 1977. q.
Published by: Centre National de la Statistique et des Etudes Economiques, BP 2031, Brazzaville, Congo, Republic. TEL 242-83-43-24. Ed. Marcel Mouelle.

330.9021   COG
CONGO. CENTRE NATIONAL DE LA STATISTIQUE ET DES ETUDES ECONOMIQUES. BULLETIN TRIMESTRIEL DE LA CONJONCTURE. Text in French. q. XAF 12,500.
Published by: Centre National de la Statistique et des Etudes Economiques, BP 2031, Brazzaville, Congo, Republic. TEL 242-83-43-24.

330   COG
CONGO. CENTRE NATIONAL DE LA STATISTIQUE ET DES ETUDES ECONOMIQUES. CADRE COMPTABLE NATIONAL. Text in French. 1977. a. XAF 5,000.

Published by: Centre National de la Statistique et des Etudes Economiques, BP 2031, Brazzaville, Congo, Republic. TEL 242-83-43-24.

330 COG
CONGO. CENTRE NATIONAL DE LA STATISTIQUE ET DES ETUDES ECONOMIQUES. CADRE MACRO-ECONOMIQUE. Text in French. 1983. a. XAF 8,000.
Published by: Centre National de la Statistique et des Etudes Economiques, BP 2031, Brazzaville, Congo, Republic. TEL 242-83-43-24.

CONSUMER GOODS INTELLIGENCE. see *BUSINESS AND ECONOMICS—Production Of Goods And Services*

330.9 BLZ
CONSUMER PRICE INDEX OF BELIZE. Text in English. 1980. q. free. **Document type:** *Bulletin, Government.* **Description:** Measures inflation in the 7 geographic districts of Belize. Includes 7 index tables.
Published by: Ministry of Finance, Central Statistical Office, New Administration Bldg., Belmopan, Belize. TEL 501-8-22352, FAX 501-8-23206, csogob@btl.net.

316.3 330.9 ETH
CONSUMER PRICE INDICES OF ETHIOPIA AT COUNTRY, RURAL AND URBAN LEVELS. Text in English. 1995. m. ETB 3 newsstand/cover; USD 0.40 newsstand/cover in United States. back issues avail. **Document type:** *Government.* **Description:** Presents country-level general consumer price indices; food price index, rural consumer price index, and urban consumer price index.
Related titles: CD-ROM ed.; Diskette ed.
Published by: Central Statistical Authority, PO Box 1143, Addis Ababa, Ethiopia. TEL 251-1-115470, FAX 251-1-550334.

CONTAS NACIONAIS TRIMESTRAIS. see *BUSINESS AND ECONOMICS—Macroeconomics*

339.021 ITA ISSN 0390-6574
HC301
CONTI DEGLI ITALIANI. Text in Italian. 1967. a. **Document type:** *Government.*
Published by: Istituto Nazionale di Statistica, Via Cesare Balbo 16, Rome, 00184, Italy. FAX 39-06-46735198.

330 ITA
CONTI ECONOMICI TRIMESTRALI. Text in Italian. q. **Document type:** *Government.*
Published by: Istituto Nazionale di Statistica, Via Cesare Balbo 16, Rome, 00184, Italy. FAX 39-06-46735198.

339 331.12 GBR ISSN 0957-8919
COST OF LIVING REPORT. REGIONAL COMPARISONS. Text in English. 1982. s-a.
Formerly (until 1986): Cost of Living (0954-819X)
—BLDSC (3477.241420).
Published by: Croner Reward, Reward House, Diamond Way, Stone Business Park, Stone, Staffordshire ST15 0SD, United Kingdom. http://www.reward-group.co.uk.

318 331.11 CRI ISSN 1409-0198
HD5734
COSTA RICA. DIRECCION GENERAL DE ESTADISTICA Y CENSOS. ENCUESTA DE HOGARES DE PROPOSITOS MULTIPLES MODULO DE EMPLEO. Text in Spanish. 1976. a. **Description:** Presents national statistics on homes and their residents, especially workforce data.
Published by: Ministerio de Economia Industria y Comercio, Direccion General de Estadistica y Censos, Apdo 10163, San Jose, 1000, Costa Rica. Circ: 1,000.

382 314 CRI
COSTA RICA. ESTADISTICAS DE COMERCIO EXTERIOR. Text in Spanish. 1996. a. free. charts; stat. **Document type:** *Government.* **Description:** Reports on imports and exports, broken down by trading partner and category of goods. Charts totals by month over the previous year.
Published by: Ministerio de Economia Industria y Comercio, Area de Estadistica y Censos, Apto. 10163, San Jose, 1000, Costa Rica.

650 USA ISSN 1064-539X
HC101
COUNTY BUSINESS PATTERNS. (Consists of 1 report per state and a U.S. summary) Text in English. 1946. a., latest 1996. USD 249 domestic for complete set; USD 311.25 foreign; USD 8 for United States Summary (effective 2000); reports of individual states price varies. **Document type:** *Government.*
Related titles: CD-ROM ed.; Online - full text ed.
Published by: U.S. Bureau of the Census (Subsidiary of: U.S. Department of Commerce), Customer Services, Washington, DC 20233. TEL 301-457-4100, FAX 301-457-4714, http://www.census.gov/. **Subscr. to:** U.S. Government Printing Office, Superintendent of Documents.

330.9 310 CUB
CUBA EN CIFRAS. Text in Spanish. a. charts; stat.
Indexed: RASB.
Published by: Comite Estatal de Estadisticas, Centro de Informacion Cientifico-Tecnica, Almendares No. 156, esq. a Desague, Gaveta Postal 6016, Havana, Cuba.

310 CUB ISSN 0138-7766
HC152.5.A1
CUBA QUARTERLY ECONOMIC REPORT. Text in English. q.
Indexed: RASB.
Published by: Banco Nacional de Cuba, Comite Estatal de Estadisticas, Almendares No. 156, esq. a Desague, Gaveta Postal 6016, Havana, Cuba.

016.33 PHL
CURRENT AWARENESS BULLETIN. Text in English. 1988. m. free. **Document type:** *Bulletin, Abstract/Index.* **Description:** Provides a list of current acquisitions of TIIC and their abstracts.
Published by: Department of Trade and Industry, Trade & Industry Information Center, 385 Industry and Investments Bldg., Sen. Gil Puyat Ave., Makati City, 1200, Philippines. FAX 63-2-8956487, RemediosAbing@dti.dti.gov.ph, http://www.dti.gov.ph/contentment/7/150/929.jsp. Circ: 800.

658 016 JPN ISSN 0011-3328
CURRENT BIBLIOGRAPHY ON SCIENCE AND TECHNOLOGY: MANAGEMENT SCIENCE AND SYSTEMS ENGINEERING/KAGAKU GIJUTSU BUNKEN SOKUHO. KANRI SHISUTEMU GIJUTSU-HEN. Text in Japanese. 1963. m. USD 1,090. index. **Document type:** *Bibliography.*
Related titles: CD-ROM ed.; Online - full text ed.: (from JICST).
Published by: Japan Science and Technology Corporation, Information Center for Science and Technology/Kagaku Gijutsu Shinko Jigyodan, 5-3 Yonban-cho, Chiyoda-ku, Tokyo, 102-0081, Japan. TEL 81-3-5214-8413, FAX 81-3-5214-8410. Circ: 500.

330 USA
CURRENT BUSINESS REPORTS. ANNUAL BENCHMARK REPORT FOR WHOLESALE TRADE. Text in English. 1992. a.
Formerly (until 1996): Current Business Reports. Combined Annual and Revised Monthly Wholesale Trade (1073-0079); Which was formed by the merger of (1978-1992): Current Business Reports. Wholesale Trade, Annual Sales and Year-End Inventories, Purchases, and Gross Margin Estimates of Merchant Wholesalers (0272-1244); (19??-1992): Current Business Reports. Revised Monthly Wholesale Trade, Sales and Inventories (0741-7268)
Related titles: Online - full content ed.
Published by: U.S. Bureau of the Census (Subsidiary of: U.S. Department of Commerce), c/o John Trimble, Service Sector Statistics Division, 4700 Silver Hill Rd., Washington, DC 20233. TEL 301-763-2703, johntrimble@census.gov, http://www.census.gov/prod/www/abs/bw_month.html.

016 658 330 KOR
CURRENT CONTENTS OF FOREIGN JOURNALS: MANAGEMENT & ECONOMICS. Text in Multiple languages. 1972. m. USD 62. reprint service avail. from PQC. **Document type:** *Abstract/Index.*
Formerly: Current Contents of Journals in Managerial Sciences
Published by: Korea Institute for Economics and Technology, 206-9 Cheongryangri-Dong, Dongdaimun-Ku, P.O. Box 205, Seoul, Korea, S. Ed. Moon Shin Hong. Circ: 300.

331.1 USA ISSN 0091-9209
HD8011.A1
CURRENT GOVERNMENTS REPORTS: CITY EMPLOYMENT. Key Title: City Employment. Text in English. 1948. a. price varies. **Document type:** *Government.*
Media: Online - full text (from CompuServe Inc., The Dialog Corporation). **Related titles:** Microfiche ed.
Published by: U.S. Bureau of the Census (Subsidiary of: U.S. Department of Commerce), c/o Donna Hirsch, Governments Division, 4700 Silver Hill Rd., Washington, DC 20233. TEL 800-242-2184, http://www.census.gov/.

336.73 317 USA ISSN 0090-5895
HJ275
CURRENT GOVERNMENTS REPORTS: STATE GOVERNMENT FINANCES. Key Title: State Government Finances. Text in English. a. **Document type:** *Government.*
Formerly: U.S. Bureau of the Census. State Finances
Media: Online - full text. **Related titles:** Microfiche ed.
Published by: U.S. Bureau of the Census (Subsidiary of: U.S. Department of Commerce), c/o Donna Hirsch, Governments Division, 4700 Silver Hill Rd., Washington, DC 20233. TEL 800-242-2184, http://www.census.gov/.

658 016 IND ISSN 0376-7604
Z7164.07
CURRENT MANAGEMENT LITERATURE. Text in English. m. INR 60, USD 20. **Document type:** *Abstract/Index.*
Published by: Administrative Staff College of India, Bella Vista, Raj Bhavan Road, Khairatabad, P O Box 4, Hyderabad, Andhra Pradesh 500 082, India. Ed. P R K Murthy.

310 CYP
CYPRUS. DEPARTMENT OF STATISTICS AND RESEARCH. CENSUS OF COTTAGE INDUSTRY. Text in English, Greek. 1967. irreg. CYP 5 (effective 1999). **Document type:** *Government.* **Description:** Compiles data on establishments, employment, output, investments, structure and regional distribution of cottage industry.
Published by: Ministry of Finance, Department of Statistics and Research, 13 Andreas Araouzos St, Nicosia, 1444, Cyprus. TEL 357-2-309318, FAX 357-2-374830, cydsr@cytanet.com.cy, http://www.pio.gov.cy/dsr.

310 CYP
CYPRUS. DEPARTMENT OF STATISTICS AND RESEARCH. CENSUS OF INDUSTRIAL PRODUCTION. Text in English. 1955. irreg. CYP 0.75 (effective 1999). **Document type:** *Government.* **Description:** Compiles data on the number of enterprises, employment, labor costs and other expenses, output, sales, stocks, fixed assets and capacity of mining and quarrying, manufacturing, electricity, gas and water.
Published by: Ministry of Finance, Department of Statistics and Research, 13 Andreas Araouzos St, Nicosia, 1444, Cyprus. TEL 357-2-309318, FAX 357-2-374830, cydsr@cytanet.com.cy, http://www.pio.gov.cy/dsr.

B

381 CYP
CYPRUS. DEPARTMENT OF STATISTICS AND RESEARCH. CENSUS OF WHOLESALE AND RETAIL TRADE. Text in English. 1981. irreg. CYP 5 (effective 1999). **Document type:** *Government.* **Description:** Enumeration of trade establishments, with data on the number of establishments by size of employment, persons engaged, sales, stocks, costs and gross margins.
Formerly: Census of Distribution
Published by: Ministry of Finance, Department of Statistics and Research, 13 Andreas Araouzos St, Nicosia, 1444, Cyprus. TEL 357-2-309301, FAX 357-2-374830, cydsr@cytanet.com.cy, http://www.pio.gov.cy/dsr.

330 314 CYP ISSN 0070-2412
HC415.2.A1
CYPRUS. DEPARTMENT OF STATISTICS AND RESEARCH. ECONOMIC REPORT. Text in English, Greek. 1954. a. CYP 6 (effective 1999). **Document type:** *Government.* **Description:** Provides comprehensive information on the Cypriot economy.
Published by: Ministry of Finance, Department of Statistics and Research, 13 Andreas Araouzos St, Nicosia, 1444, Cyprus. TEL 357-2-309318, FAX 357-2-374830, cydsr@cytanet.com.cy, http://www.pio.gov.cy/dsr.

310 CYP
CYPRUS. DEPARTMENT OF STATISTICS AND RESEARCH. HOUSEHOLD INCOME AND EXPENDITURE SURVEY. Text in English. 1971. irreg. CYP 10 (effective 1999). **Document type:** *Government.* **Description:** Covers both urban and rural households residing in the government-controlled area.
Formerly: Cyprus. Department of Statistics and Research. Household Consumption Expenditure Survey
Published by: Ministry of Finance, Department of Statistics and Research, 13 Andreas Araouzos St, Nicosia, 1444, Cyprus. TEL 357-2-309301, FAX 357-2-374830, cydsr@cytanet.com.cy, http://www.pio.gov.cy/dsr.

382 314 CYP ISSN 0253-858X
HF259.C9
CYPRUS. DEPARTMENT OF STATISTICS AND RESEARCH. IMPORTS AND EXPORTS STATISTICS. Text in English. q. CYP 3 (effective 1999). **Document type:** *Government.* **Description:** Supplies detailed statistics of imports and exports by commodity.
Media: Duplicated (not offset).
Published by: Ministry of Finance, Department of Statistics and Research, 13 Andreas Araouzos St, Nicosia, 1444, Cyprus. TEL 357-2-309318, FAX 357-2-374830, cydsr@cytanet.com.cy, http://www.pio.gov.cy/dsr.

331 CYP ISSN 1010-1160
HC497.C9
CYPRUS. DEPARTMENT OF STATISTICS AND RESEARCH. INDUSTRIAL STATISTICS. Text in English, Greek. a. CYP 7 per issue (effective 1999). **Document type:** *Government.* **Description:** Provides a broad account of industrial statistics in Cyprus.
Incorporates (1976-1984): Employment, Output and Capital Formation in the Industrial Sector; Industrial Production Survey; Sales of Vine Products; Price Index for the Manufacturing Sector
Published by: Ministry of Finance, Department of Statistics and Research, 13 Andreas Araouzos St, Nicosia, 1444, Cyprus. TEL 357-2-309318, FAX 357-2-374830, cydsr@cytanet.com.cy, http://www.pio.gov.cy/dsr.

331 CYP
CYPRUS. DEPARTMENT OF STATISTICS AND RESEARCH. LABOUR STATISTICS. Text in English, Greek. a. CYP 47 (effective 1999). **Document type:** *Government.* **Description:** Presents annual statistics on employment, unemployment, vacancies and government labor force.
Formerly: Labour Statistics Report (0255-8386); Which supersedes: Annual Report on Unemployment

▼ new title ➤ refereed ✶ unverified ◆ full entry avail.

Published by: Ministry of Finance, Department of Statistics and Research, 13 Andreas Araouzos St, Nicosia, 1444, Cyprus. TEL 357-2-309318, FAX 357-2-374830, cydsr@cytanet.com.cy, http://www.pio.gov.cy/dsr.

382 310   CYP   ISSN 0070-2420
HF3757
CYPRUS. DEPARTMENT OF STATISTICS AND RESEARCH. STATISTICS OF IMPORTS AND EXPORTS. Text in English. 1927. a. CYP 20 (effective 1999). **Document type:** *Government.* **Description:** Presents detailed statistics of imports and exports by commodity and by country.
Published by: Ministry of Finance, Department of Statistics and Research, 13 Andreas Araouzos St, Nicosia, 1444, Cyprus. TEL 357-2-309318, FAX 357-2-374830, cydsr@cytanet.com.cy, http://www.pio.gov.cy/dsr.

CYPRUS. PUBLIC LOANS FUND. ACCOUNTS AND STATISTICS FOR THE YEAR. see *BUSINESS AND ECONOMICS—Public Finance, Taxation*

330 947   CZE   ISSN 1211-4812
CZECH REPUBLIC. CESKY STATISTICKY URAD. STATISTICKA ROCENKA CESKE REPUBLIKY/CZECH REPUBLIC. CZECH STATISTICAL OFFICE. STATISTICAL YEARBOOK. Text in Czech, English. 1957. a. **Description:** Presents an aggregative statistical survey of all branches of the national economy.
Former titles (until 1992): Statisticka Rocenka Ceske a Slovenske Federalni Republiky (0862-7843); (until 1990): Statisticka Rocenka Ceskoslovenske Socialisticke Republiki (0139-6196)
Related titles: Microfiche ed.: (from PQC).
Indexed: RASB.
Published by: Cesky Statisticky Urad, Sokolovska 142, Prague, 18604, Czech Republic. TEL 420-2-74052451, FAX 420-2-66310429, infoservis@gw.czso.cz, http://www.czso.cz. Circ: 13,300. **Subscr. to:** Scientia, Pedagogicke Nakladatelstvo s.r.o., Obchodni Oddileni, Radimova 37-50, Boevnov, Prague 169 00, Czech Republic.

330   CZE
CZECH REPUBLIC. CESKY STATISTICKY URAD. STATISTICKY BULLETIN/CZECH REPUBLIC. CZECH STATISTICAL OFFICE. STATISTICAL BULLETIN. Text in Czech, English. q. USD 108 foreign (effective 2001). **Description:** Contains reports on the development of the national economy. Jointly issued by the central statistical bodies of the Czech Republic, Slovakia, Hungary.
Published by: Cesky Statisticky Urad, Sokolovska 142, Prague, 18604, Czech Republic. TEL 420-2-74052451, FAX 420-2-66310429, infoservis@gw.czso.cz, http://www.czso.cz.

314.37 330   CZE   ISSN 0322-788X
CZECH REPUBLIC. CESKY STATISTICKY URAD. STATISTIKA/CZECH REPUBLIC. CZECH STATISTICAL OFFICE. STATISTICS; ekonomicko-statisticky casopis - journal of Economics and Statistics. Text in Czech; Summaries in English. 1962. m. USD 276 (effective 2001). bk.rev. charts; stat. index. **Description:** Presents statistical theory, methodology as well as statistical experience and practice.
Supersedes in part: Statistika a Demografie
Indexed: CurCont, RASB, ST&MA.
Published by: Cesky Statisticky Urad, Sokolovska 142, Prague, 18604, Czech Republic. TEL 420-2-74052451, FAX 420-2-66310429, infoservis@gw.czso.cz, http://www.czso.cz. Ed. J Jilek. Circ: 4,000.

330   CZE
CZECH REPUBLIC. CZECH STATISTICAL OFFICE. BULLETIN. Text in English. q. USD 104 (effective 2001). **Description:** Jointly issued by the central statistical bodies of the Czech Republic, Slovakia, Hungary and Poland. Intended for experts and the general public, both in the CR and abroad.
Published by: Cesky Statisticky Urad, Sokolovska 142, Prague, 18604, Czech Republic. TEL 420-2-74052451, FAX 420-2-66310429, infoservis@gw.czso.cz, http://www.czso.cz.

330.021   CZE
CZECH REPUBLIC. CZECH STATISTICAL OFFICE. INDICATORS OF SOCIAL AND ECONOMIC DEVELOPMENT IN THE CZECH REPUBLIC/CZECH REPUBLIC. CESKY STATISTICKY URAD. UKAZATELE SOCIALNIHO A HOSPODARSKEHO VYVOJE CESKE REPUBLIKY. Text in English. q. USD 48 (effective 2001). **Description:** Contains the annual time series from 1985, or 1991, and the quarterly series from 1994. The time series includes selected indicators of industry, construction, agriculture, transport, trade, consumer prices, external trade, demography, organization statistics, and the state budget of the Czech Republic. Also includes figures on unemployment and the GDP.
Formed by the merger of: Ciselne Zrcadlo Ceske Ekonomiky; Prahled Ukazatelu Ekonomickeho a Socialniho Rozvoje Ceske Republiky
Published by: Cesky Statisticky Urad, Sokolovska 142, Prague, 18604, Czech Republic. TEL 420-2-74052451, FAX 420-2-66310429, infoservis@gw.czso.cz, http://www.czso.cz.

330   CZE
CZECH REPUBLIC. CZECH STATISTICAL OFFICE. QUARTERLY STATISTICAL BULLETIN/BULLETIN STATISTIQUE TRIMESTRIEL. Text in English, French. q. USD 56 (effective 2001). **Description:** Provides statistical analysis and tabulation covering the development of the Czech economy and its gradual shift to a free market system.
Published by: Cesky Statisticky Urad, Sokolovska 142, Prague, 18604, Czech Republic. TEL 420-2-74052451, FAX 420-2-66310429, infoservis@gw.czso.cz, http://www.czso.cz.

330.021   CAN
DAILY-FROM STATS CAN. Text in English. 1993. d.
Media: Online - full content.
Published by: Statistics Canada, Communications Division, 3rd Fl, R H Coats Bldg, Ottawa, ON K1A 0A6, Canada. http://www.statcan.ca/start.html.

382.094 314   DNK   ISSN 1398-0777
HF3641
DANMARKS VAREIMPORT OG- EKSPORT/EXTERNAL TRADE OF DENMARK. Text in Danish; Notes in English. 1883. a. DKK 434 (effective 2002). **Document type:** *Government.* **Description:** Danish foreign trade statistics.
Formerly (until 1998): Danmarks Vareindfoersel og Udfoersel (0070-2781)
Indexed: RASB.
Published by: Danmarks Statistik, Sejroegade 11, Copenhagen Oe, 2100, Denmark. TEL 45-39-173917, FAX 45-39-173939.

331.21 314.21   DNK   ISSN 0909-0347
HD5049
DANSK ARBEJDSGIVERFORENING. D A LOENSTATISTIK. Text in Danish. 1993. q. charts. **Document type:** *Trade.*
Formed by the merger of (1978-1993): Dansk Arbejdsgiverforening. Statistikken. Funktionaerloen (0107-086X); (1978-1993): Dansk Arbejdsgiverforening. Statistikken. Arbejderloen (0107-0851); Which superseded in part (1953-1978): Dansk Arbejdsgiverforening. Statistikken (0011-619X)
Related titles: ◆ Series: Strukturstatistik. ISSN 1601-717X.
Published by: Dansk Arbejdsgiverforening/Danish Employers Confederation, Vester Voldgade 113, Copenhagen V, 1790, Denmark. TEL 45-33-389000, FAX 45-33-122976, da@da.dk, http://www.da.dk. Ed. Ulla Stroeger.

330   MEX   ISSN 0187-6163
DATOS BASICOS SOBRE LA ECONOMIA DE MEXICO. Text in Spanish. irreg., latest 1988.
Published by: Instituto Nacional de Estadistica, Geografia e Informatica, Secretaria de Programacion y Presupuesto, Prol. Heroe de Nacozari 2301 Sur, Puerta 11, Acceso, Aguascalientes, 20270, Mexico. TEL 52-4-918-1948, FAX 52-4-918-0739, http://www.inegi.gob.mx.

331.1379489   DNK   ISSN 0108-5514
HD5799
DENMARK. DANMARKS STATISTIK. ARBEJDSMARKED. Text in Danish. 1983. a. price varies. **Document type:** *Government.*
Supersedes in part (1976-1983): Statistiske Efterretninger A (0105-306X); (1976-1983): Statistiske Efterretninger B (0105-3078); Which both superseded in part (1909-1976): Statistiske Efterretninger (0039-0674)
Related titles: ◆ Series of: Denmark. Danmarks Statistik. Statistiske Efterretninger. Indhold. ISSN 1396-8173.
Published by: Danmarks Statistik, Sejroegade 11, Copenhagen Oe, 2100, Denmark. TEL 45-39-173917, FAX 45-39-173939.

330.9489   DNK   ISSN 0108-5573
DENMARK. DANMARKS STATISTIK. GENEREL ERHVERVSSTATISTIK OG HANDEL. Text in Danish. 1983. price varies. **Document type:** *Government.*
Supersedes in part (1976-1983): Statistiske Efterretninger A (0105-306X); (1976-1983): Statistiske Efterretninger B (0105-3078); Which both superseded in part (1909-1976): Statistiske Efterretninger (0039-0674)
Related titles: ◆ Series of: Denmark. Danmarks Statistik. Statistiske Efterretninger. Indhold. ISSN 1396-8173.
Published by: Danmarks Statistik, Sejroegade 11, Copenhagen Oe, 2100, Denmark. TEL 45-39-173917, FAX 45-39-173939.

330.9489   DNK   ISSN 0108-5565
HC360.I5
DENMARK. DANMARKS STATISTIK. INDKOMST, FORBRUG OG PRISER. Text in Danish. 1983. price varies. **Document type:** *Government.*
Supersedes in part (1976-1983): Statistiske Efterretninger A (0105-306X); (1976-1983): Statistiske Efterretninger B (0105-3078); Which both superseded in part (1909-1976): Statistiske Efterretninger (0039-0674)
Related titles: ◆ Series of: Denmark. Danmarks Statistik. Statistiske Efterretninger. Indhold. ISSN 1396-8173.
Published by: Danmarks Statistik, Sejroegade 11, Copenhagen Oe, 2100, Denmark. TEL 45-39-173917, FAX 45-39-173939.

339.2209489   DNK   ISSN 0107-105X
HC360.I5
DENMARK. DANMARKS STATISTIK. INDKOMSTER OG FORMUER. Text in Danish; Notes in English. 1975. a. DKK 212 (effective 2000). **Document type:** *Government.*

Supersedes: Denmark. Danmarks Statistik. Indkomster og Formuer Ved Slutligningen; Denmark. Danmarks Statistik. Indkomstansaettelser til Staten (0070-3524)
Published by: Danmarks Statistik, Sejroegade 11, Copenhagen Oe, 2100, Denmark. TEL 45-39-17-39-17, FAX 45-31-18-48-01.

338.09489   DNK   ISSN 0108-5468
DENMARK. DANMARKS STATISTIK. INDUSTRI OG ENERGI. Text in Danish. 1983. irreg. price varies. **Document type:** *Government.*
Supersedes in part (1976-1983): Statistiske Efterretninger A (0105-306X); (1976-1983): Statistiske Efterretninger B (0105-3078); Which both superseded in part (1909-1976): Statistiske Efterretninger (0039-0674)
Related titles: ◆ Series of: Denmark. Danmarks Statistik. Statistiske Efterretninger. Indhold. ISSN 1396-8173.
Published by: Danmarks Statistik, Sejroegade 11, Copenhagen Oe, 2100, Denmark. TEL 45-39-173917, FAX 45-39-173939.

314.89   DNK
HC10
DENMARK. DANMARKS STATISTIK. KONJUNKTURSTATISTIK. Text in Danish; Summaries in English. 1983. m. **Document type:** *Government.*
Former titles (until 1998): Denmark. Danmarks Statistik. Konjunkturtendenser i Udvalgte Lande (0109-1271); Denmark. Danmarks Statistik. Statistisk Maanedsoversigt (0108-5603)
Related titles: Online - full content ed.
Published by: Danmarks Statistik, Sejroegade 11, Copenhagen Oe, 2100, Denmark. TEL 45-39-173917, FAX 45-39-173939.

339.3489   DNK   ISSN 0107-8771
HD5049
DENMARK. DANMARKS STATISTIK. LOEN- OG INDKOMSTATISTIK/STATISTICS OF EARNINGS AND INCOMES. Text in Danish. 1982. irreg. (4-6/yr.). DKK 256; DKK 23.20 newsstand/cover pp.4-22; DKK 119.20 newsstand/cover pp.76-88 (effective 2000). **Document type:** *Government.* **Description:** Contains detailed statistics of indexes of hourly wage costs and monthly salary costs.
Published by: Danmarks Statistik, Sejroegade 11, Copenhagen Oe, 2100, Denmark. TEL 45-39-17-39-17, FAX 45-31-18-48-01.

331.09489   DNK   ISSN 0105-1083
HD5049
DENMARK. DANMARKS STATISTIK. MAANEDLIG BESKAEFTIGELSES- OG LOENSTATISTIK FOR INDUSTRI/MONTHLY STATISTICS OF INDUSTRIAL EMPLOYMENT AND LABOUR COSTS. Text in Danish; Notes in English. m. DKK 216.39 (effective 2000). **Document type:** *Government.*
Published by: Danmarks Statistik, Sejroegade 11, Copenhagen Oe, 2100, Denmark. TEL 45-39-17-39-17, FAX 45-31-18-48-01, TELEX 16236.

338.09489   DNK   ISSN 0105-0877
DENMARK. DANMARKS STATISTIK. MAANEDLIG ORDRE- OG OMSAETNINGSSTATISTIK FOR INDUSTRI/MONTHLY STATISTICS OF INDUSTRIAL SALES AND ORDER BOOKS. Text in Danish; Notes in English. m. DKK 340; DKK 54.40 newsstand/cover (effective 2000). **Document type:** *Government.*
Published by: Danmarks Statistik, Sejroegade 11, Copenhagen Oe, 2100, Denmark. TEL 45-39-17-39-17, FAX 45-31-18-48-01.

336.489 354.489007231   DNK   ISSN 0108-545X
DENMARK. DANMARKS STATISTIK. NATIONALREGNSKAB, OFFENTLIGE FINANSER, BETALINGSBALANCE. Text in Danish. 1983. irreg. price varies. **Document type:** *Government.*
Supersedes in part (1976-1983): Statistiske Efterretninger A (0105-306X); (1976-1983): Statistiske Efterretninger B (0105-3078); Which both superseded in part (1909-1976): Statistiske Efterretninger (0039-0674)
Related titles: ◆ Series of: Denmark. Danmarks Statistik. Statistiske Efterretninger. Indhold. ISSN 1396-8173.
Published by: Danmarks Statistik, Sejroegade 11, Copenhagen Oe, 2100, Denmark. TEL 45-39-173917, FAX 45-39-173939.

330.9021   DNK   ISSN 0108-8173
HC360.I5
DENMARK. DANMARKS STATISTIK. NATIONALREGNSKABSSTATISTIK/NATIONAL ACCOUNTS STATISTICS. Text in Danish, English. 1983. a. DKK 212 (effective 2000). **Document type:** *Government.*
Indexed: RASB.
Published by: Danmarks Statistik, Sejroegade 11, Copenhagen Oe, 2100, Denmark. TEL 45-39-17-39-17, FAX 45-31-18-48-01.

332.09489   DNK   ISSN 0108-5476
HG27
DENMARK. DANMARKS STATISTIK. PENGE- OG KAPITALMARKED/MONEY AND CAPITAL MARKET. Text in Danish. 1983. irreg. price varies. **Document type:** *Government.* **Description:** Liquidity, bank balances, mortgage registrations, bond issues, insolvencies. Insurance, pension funds and fires damages.

Formerly (until 1983): Denmark. Danmarks Statistik. Kreditmarkedsstatistik. (0107-3095); Which superseded in part (1976-1983): Statistiske Efterretninger A (0105-306X); (1976-1983): Statistiske Efterretninger B (0105-3078); Which both superseded in part (1909-1976): Statistiske Efterretninger (0039-0674)
Related titles: ♦ Series of: Denmark. Danmarks Statistik. Statistiske Efterretninger. Indhold. ISSN 1396-8173.
Published by: Danmarks Statistik, Sejroegade 11, Copenhagen Oe, 2100, Denmark. TEL 45-39-173917, FAX 45-39-173939.

338.528 DNK ISSN 0106-6684
HB235.D4
DENMARK. DANMARKS STATISTIK. PRISSTATISTIK. Text in Danish; Notes in English. 1980. m. price varies. **Document type:** *Government.*
Published by: Danmarks Statistik, Sejroegade 11, Copenhagen Oe, 2100, Denmark. TEL 45-39-173917, FAX 45-39-173939, TELEX 16238.

338.09489 DNK ISSN 0108-738X
HC360.F55
DENMARK. DANMARKS STATISTIK. REGNSKABSSTATISTIK FOR INDUSTRI/DENMARK. DANMARKS STATISTIK. INDUSTRIAL ACCOUNTS STATISTICS. Text in Danish, English. 1981. a. DKK 136.80 (effective 2000). **Document type:** *Government.*
Formerly (until 1981): Denmark. Danmarks Statistik. Driftsregnskabsstatistik for Industrien
Published by: Danmarks Statistik, Sejroegade 11, Copenhagen Oe, 2100, Denmark. TEL 45-39-17-39-17, FAX 45-31-18-48-01.

366.2009489 DNK ISSN 0105-1164
HJ4369
DENMARK. DANMARKS STATISTIK. SKATTER OG AFGIFTER. OVERSIGT (YEAR)/TAXES AND DUTIES. Text in Danish; Notes in English. a. DKK 236 (effective 2000). **Document type:** *Government.*
Supersedes in part: Denmark. Danmarks Statistik. Ejendoms- og Selskabsbeskatningen i Skatteaaret
Indexed: RASB.
Published by: Danmarks Statistik, Sejroegade 11, Copenhagen Oe, 2100, Denmark. TEL 45-39-17-39-17, FAX 45-31-18-48-01.

382.09489 DNK ISSN 0108-5506
HF3641
DENMARK. DANMARKS STATISTIK. UDENRIGSHANDEL/ DENMARK. DANMARKS STATISTIK. EXTERNAL TRADE. Text in Danish; Notes in English. 1980. a. price varies. **Document type:** *Government.* **Description:** Imports, exports, current-value indexes, quantity indexes, the terms of trade, distributions by countries, by commodity groups and by modes of transport. EU export subsidies and external trade of Greenland.
Formerly: Denmark. Danmarks Statistik. Handelsstatistiske Meddelelser. Maanedsstatistik over Udenrigshandelen (0017-7342)
Related titles: ♦ Series of: Denmark. Danmarks Statistik. Statistiske Efterretninger. Indhold. ISSN 1396-8173.
Published by: Danmarks Statistik, Sejroegade 11, Copenhagen Oe, 2100, Denmark. TEL 45-39-173917, FAX 45-39-173939, TELEX 16236.

338.476 DNK ISSN 0107-0967
DENMARK. DANMARKS STATISTIK. VARESTATISTIK FOR INDUSTRI. SERIES A. Text in Danish. 1970. q. DKK 136.80; DKK 37.60 newsstand/cover (effective 2000). **Document type:** *Government.*
Supersedes in part (in 1980): Denmark. Danmarks Statistik. Kvartalsstatistik for Industrien
Published by: Danmarks Statistik, Sejroegade 11, Copenhagen Oe, 2100, Denmark. TEL 45-39-17-39-17, FAX 45-31-18-48-01.

338.476 DNK ISSN 0107-0975
DENMARK. DANMARKS STATISTIK. VARESTATISTIK FOR INDUSTRI. SERIES B. Text in Danish. 1970. q. DKK 176; DKK 48 newsstand/cover (effective 2000). **Document type:** *Government.*
Supersedes in part (in 1980): Denmark. Danmarks Statistik. Kvartalsstatistik for Industrien
Published by: Danmarks Statistik, Sejroegade 11, Copenhagen Oe, 2100, Denmark. TEL 45-39-17-39-17, FAX 45-31-18-48-01.

338.476 DNK ISSN 0107-0983
DENMARK. DANMARKS STATISTIK. VARESTATISTIK FOR INDUSTRI. SERIES C. Text in Danish. 1970. q. DKK 113.60; DKK 32 newsstand/cover (effective 2000). **Document type:** *Government.*
Supersedes in part (in 1980): Denmark. Danmarks Statistik. Kvartalsstatistik for Industrien
Published by: Danmarks Statistik, Sejroegade 11, Copenhagen Oe, 2100, Denmark. TEL 45-39-17-39-17, FAX 45-31-18-48-01.

338.476 DNK ISSN 0107-0991
DENMARK. DANMARKS STATISTIK. VARESTATISTIK FOR INDUSTRI. SERIES D. Text in Danish. 1970. q. DKK 202.40; DKK 56 newsstand/cover (effective 2000). **Document type:** *Government.*
Supersedes in part (in 1980): Denmark. Danmarks Statistik. Kvartalsstatistik for Industrien
Published by: Danmarks Statistik, Sejroegade 11, Copenhagen Oe, 2100, Denmark. TEL 45-39-17-39-17, FAX 45-31-18-48-01.

658 CAN ISSN 0380-7045
DEPARTMENT STORE SALES & STOCKS. Text in English. 1938. m. CND 144, USD 173 domestic; USD 202 foreign. **Description:** Presents data on department stores: sales, stocks and number of outlets. Includes data analysis, definitions, methodology, data reliability, list of department store organizations and bibliography.
Published by: Statistics Canada, Operations and Integration Division, Circulation Management, Jean Talon Bldg, 2 C12, Tunney's Pasture, Ottawa, ON K1A 0T6, Canada. TEL 613-951-7277, 800-267-6677, FAX 613-951-1584, http://www.statcan.ca.

338 CHE
DETAILHANDELSUMSAETZE/CHIFFRES D'AFFAIRES DU COMMERCE DE DETAIL. Text in French, German. 1988. m. CHF 32 (effective 2001). **Document type:** *Government.*
Published by: Bundesamt fuer Statistik, Espace de l'Europe 10, Neuchatel, 2010, Switzerland. TEL 41-32-7136011, FAX 41-32-7136012, information@bfs.admin.ch, http://www.admin.ch/bfs.

322.1 DEU ISSN 0943-8750
HG3051
DEUTSCHE BUNDESBANK. BANKENSTATISTIK. Text in German; Summaries in English. 1969. m. **Document type:** *Bulletin.*
Formerly (until 1993): Deutsche Bundesbank. Monatsberichte. Statistische Beihefte. Reihe 1: Bankenstatistik nach Bankengruppen (0419-9014)
Published by: Deutsche Bundesbank, Postfach 100602, Frankfurt Am Main, 60006, Germany. TEL 49-69-9566-1, FAX 49-69-5601071, http://www.bundesbank.de.

332.4 DEU ISSN 0943-8793
DEUTSCHE BUNDESBANK. DEVISENKURSSTATISTIK. Text in German; Summaries in English. 1968. q. **Document type:** *Bulletin.*
Former titles (until 1993): Deutsche Bundesbank. Monatsberichte. Statistische Beihefte. Reihe 5: Devisenkursstatistik (0341-8928); (until 1974): Deutsche Bundesbank. Monatsberichte. Statistische Beihefte. Reihe 5: Waehrungen der Welt (0341-9029)
Indexed: RASB.
Published by: Deutsche Bundesbank, Postfach 100602, Frankfurt Am Main, 60006, Germany. TEL 49-69-9566-1, FAX 49-69-5601071, http://www.bundesbank.de.

332.1 DEU ISSN 0943-8769
HG5491
DEUTSCHE BUNDESBANK. MONATSBERICHTE. STATISTISCHE BEIHEFTE. REIHE 2: KAPITALMARKTSTATISTIK. Text in German; Summaries in English. 1968. m. **Document type:** *Bulletin.*
Formerly (until 1993): Deutsche Bundesbank. Monatsberichte. Statistische Beihefte. Reihe 2: Wertpapierstatistik (0418-8314)
Indexed: RASB.
Published by: Deutsche Bundesbank, Postfach 100602, Frankfurt Am Main, 60006, Germany. TEL 49-69-9566-1, FAX 49-69-5601071, http://www.bundesbank.de.

332.1 DEU ISSN 0943-8785
HC290.5.I5
DEUTSCHE BUNDESBANK. SAISONBEREINIGTE WIRTSCHAFTSZAHLEN. Text in German; Summaries in English. m. **Document type:** *Bulletin.*
Formerly (until 1993): Deutsche Bundesbank. Monatsberichte. Statistische Beihefte. Reihe 4: Saisonbereinigte Wirtschaftszahlen (0418-8330)
Published by: Deutsche Bundesbank, Postfach 100602, Frankfurt Am Main, 60006, Germany. TEL 49-69-9566-1, FAX 49-69-5601071, http://www.bundesbank.de.

332.1 DEU ISSN 0943-8777
HG3883.G3
DEUTSCHE BUNDESBANK. ZAHLUNGSBILANZSTATISTIK. Text in German; Summaries in English. 1968. m. **Document type:** *Bulletin.*
Formerly (until 1993): Deutsche Bundesbank. Monatsberichte. Statistische Beihefte. Reihe 3: Zahlungsbilanzstatistik (0418-8322)
Indexed: RASB.
Published by: Deutsche Bundesbank, Postfach 100602, Frankfurt Am Main, 60006, Germany. TEL 49-69-9566-1, FAX 49-69-5601071, http://www.bundesbank.de.

334 310 DEU ISSN 1434-3525
DIE DEUTSCHEN GENOSSENSCHAFTEN. STATISTIK✶. Text in German. 1977. biennial. stat. **Document type:** *Journal, Trade.* **Description:** Statistical changes in the German cooperative system.
Formerly (until 1995): Genossenschaften in der Bundesrepublik Deutschland. Statistik (1434-3517)
Published by: Deutsche Zentral-Genossenschaftsbank, Am Platz der Republik, Frankfurt Am Main, 60265, Germany. TEL 49-69-744701, FAX 49-69-74471685, mail@dzbank.de, http://www.dzbank.de. Circ: 2,000.

THE DIRECTORY OF BUSINESS INFORMATION RESOURCES. see *BUSINESS AND ECONOMICS—Trade And Industrial Directories*

DIRECTORY OF EUROPEAN MEDICAL ORGANISATIONS. see *MEDICAL SCIENCES—Abstracting, Bibliographies, Statistics*

DIRECTORY OF EUROPEAN SPORTS ORGANISATIONS. see *SPORTS AND GAMES—Abstracting, Bibliographies, Statistics*

336 CHE
DIREKTE BUNDESSTEUER, STEUERERTRAEGE UND KOPFQUOTEN, NACH GEMEINDEN DER VERANLAGUNGSPERIODE/IMPOT FEDERAL DIRECT, RENDEMENTS DE L'IMPOT ET COTES PAR TETE, PAR COMMUNE DE LA PERIODE DE TAXATION. Text in French, German. 1983. biennial. CHF 10 (effective 2001). **Document type:** *Government.*
Published by: Bundesamt fuer Statistik, Espace de l'Europe 10, Neuchatel, 2010, Switzerland. TEL 41-32-7136011, FAX 41-32-7136012, information@bfs.admin.ch, http://www.admin.ch/bfs.

B

331 USA
DISPLACED WORKERS. Text in English. irreg. **Document type:** *Government.* **Description:** Provides information on workers who lost their jobs to cutbacks or plant closings.
Related titles: ♦ Series of: U.S. Bureau of Labor Statistics. Bulletin. ISSN 0082-9021.
Published by: U.S. Department of Labor, Bureau of Labor Statistics, Postal Square Bldg., 2 Massachusetts Ave, NE, Washington, DC 20212-0001 . TEL 202-691-5200, http://www.bls.gov. **Subscr. to:** U.S. Government Printing Office, Superintendent of Documents.

336.2 382 316 CAF
DIVISION D'AIDE ET DE COOPERATION FRANCAISE. BULLETIN TRIMESTRIEL DE STATISTIQUE. Text in French. 1963. q. XAF 21,660, USD 81. charts. **Document type:** *Bulletin.*
Former titles: Union Douaniere et Economique de l'Afrique Centrale. Bulletin des Statistiques Generales (0041-6851); Union Douaniere Equatoriale. Bulletin des Statistiques Generales
Published by: Division d'Aide et de Cooperation Francaise, BP 1418, Bangui, Central African Republic. TEL 614574. **Subscr. to:** Division des Statistiques et des Etudes Economiques, BP 1418, Bangui, Central African Republic.

330.021 RUS
DOKHODY, RASKHODY I POTREBLENIE DOMASHNIKH KHOZYAISTV/INCOMES, EXPENDITURES AND CONSUMPTION OF HOUSEHOLDS. Text in Russian. q. RUR 880 (effective 2005). **Document type:** *Bulletin, Government.* **Description:** Contains statistical data on urban and rural household budgets in Russia.
Published by: Gosudarstvennyi Komitet Rossiiskoi Federatsii po Statistike/Federal State Statistics Office, ul Myasnitskaya 39, Moscow, 107450, Russian Federation. TEL 7-095-2074902, FAX 7-095-2074087, stat@gks.ru, http://www.gks.ru.

382 DMA ISSN 0417-9382
DOMINICA. MINISTRY OF FINANCE. CENTRAL STATISTICAL OFFICE. ANNUAL OVERSEAS TRADE REPORT. Text in English. a. USD 9.30. **Document type:** *Government.*
Formerly: Dominica. Ministry of Finance and Development. Annual Overseas Trade Report
Published by: Ministry of Finance, Central Statistical Office, Kennedy Ave., Roseau, Dominica. Ed. Michael Murphy.

330 DMA
DOMINICA. MINISTRY OF FINANCE. CENTRAL STATISTICAL OFFICE. CONSUMER PRICE INDICES. Text in English. a. USD 13.50. **Document type:** *Government.*
Published by: Ministry of Finance, Central Statistical Office, Kennedy Ave., Roseau, Dominica. Ed. Michael Murphy.

330 DMA
DOMINICA. MINISTRY OF FINANCE. CENTRAL STATISTICAL OFFICE. NATIONAL ACCOUNTS AND BALANCE OF PAYMENTS. Text in English. a. USD 13.50. **Document type:** *Government.*
Published by: Ministry of Finance, Central Statistical Office, Kennedy Ave., Roseau, Dominica. Ed. Michael Murphy.

330 DMA
DOMINICA. MINISTRY OF FINANCE. CENTRAL STATISTICAL OFFICE. QUARTERLY ECONOMIC INDICATORS. Text in English. q. free. **Document type:** *Government.*
Published by: Ministry of Finance, Central Statistical Office, Kennedy Ave:, Roseau, Dominica. Ed. Michael Murphy.

▼ new title ➤ refereed ✶ unverified ♦ full entry avail.

DOMINICAN REPUBLIC. CENTRO DOMINICANO DE PROMOCION DE EXPORTACIONES. BOLETIN ESTADISTICO. see *BUSINESS AND ECONOMICS—International Commerce*

339 314 SCG ISSN 0300-2527
DRUSTVENI PROIZVOD I NARODNI DOHODAK. Text in Serbo-Croatian. 1969. a. YUN 30, USD 1.67. stat.
Related titles: ♦ Series of: Srbija i Crna Gora. Zavod za Statistiku. Statisticki Bilten.
Published by: Srbija i Crna Gora Zavod za Statistiku/Serbia and Montenegro Statistical Office, Kneza Milosa 20, Postanski Fah 203, Belgrade, 11000. TEL 381-11-3617273.

330 UAE
DUBAI EXTERNAL TRADE STATISTICS/IHSA'IYYAT DUBAI LIL-TIJARAH AL-KHARIJIYYAH. Text in English. 1979. a. **Description:** Covers imports, exports and re-exports, with statistics for fuel supplied to ships and aircraft, and Free Zone Port Rashid activity reports.
Published by: Central Accounting Administration, Statistics Section/Idarat al-Hisabat al-Markazi, Qism al-Ihsa', PO Box 516, Dubai, United Arab Emirates. TEL 531074, FAX 531959, TELEX 47470 HISAB EM. Circ: 500 (controlled).

332.6 LUX
E C U - E U R O EUROBOND MARKET. (European Currency Unit) Text in English, French. 1983. a. free. **Description:** Contains statistical information on the bond market in ECU regarding listings, trading volumes.
Supersedes: Marche des Emprunts Obligataires en E C U - Bond Market in E C U; Which superseded in part: Bond Market in Luxembourg Francs and E C U; Which was formed by the merger of: Marche des Emprunts Obligataires; Marche National des Emprunts Obligataires
Published by: Societe de la Bourse de Luxembourg/Luxembourg Stock Exchange, 11 av. de la Porte Neuve, BP 165, Luxembourg, L-2011, Luxembourg. TEL 352-4779361, FAX 352-473298, info@bourse.lu, http://www.bourse.lu. Circ: 600.

330 016 SWE ISSN 0348-968X
E F I - NYTT/E F I - NEWS. Text in Swedish; Summaries in English. 1968. irreg. free. bk.rev. **Document type:** *Newsletter.*
Indexed: ABIPC, EngInd.
Published by: Handelshoegskolan i Stockholm, Ekonomiska Forskningsinstitutet/Economic Research Institute at the Stockholm School of Economics, Fack 6501, Stockholm, 11383, Sweden. Ed. Rune Castenaes. Circ: 4,000.

331 CAN
EARNINGS AND EMPLOYMENT TRENDS. Text in English. 12/yr. CND 60 (effective 1997). **Document type:** *Directory.* **Description:** Provides sectoral analysis of the B.C. labor force and its wage structure.
Published by: Ministry of Finance and Corporate Relations, B C Stats, Sta Prov Govt, P O Box 9410, Victoria, BC V8W 9V1, Canada. TEL 250-387-1502, FAX 250-387-0329, bcstats@fincc04.fin.gov.bc.ca, http://www.bcstats.gov.bc.ca. Ed. Anne Kittredge.

314 LUX ISSN 0259-0492
HD5014.5
EARNINGS - INDUSTRY AND SERVICES. Text in English, French, German, Italian, Spanish. s-a. USD 71.
Related titles: Microfiche ed.: (from CIS).
Indexed: IIS.
Published by: European Commission, Statistical Office of the European Communities, Rue Alcide de Gasperi, Luxembourg, 2920, Luxembourg. **Dist. in the U.S. by:** Unipub, 4611-F Assembly Drive, Lanham, MD 20706-4391. TEL 800-274-4888.

316 316 KEN ISSN 0012-9992
EAST AFRICAN COMMUNITY. ECONOMIC AND STATISTICAL REVIEW. Text in English. 1948. q. KES 10. bibl.; charts.
Formerly: East African Quarterly Economic and Statistical Bulletin
Indexed: PAIS.
Published by: East African Community, Statistical Department, PO Box 30462, Nairobi, Kenya. Circ: 1,000.

330 011 GBR
EAST ASIA BIBLIOGRAPHY; a review of new publications on China & the Far East. Text in English. 1979. irreg. GBP 8. adv. bk.rev. **Document type:** *Bibliography.*
Published by: East Asia Co., 103 Camden High St, London, NW1 7JN, United Kingdom. Circ: 2,000.

330 639.2 DNK
EASTFISH COMMODITY UPDATES. Text in English. a. EUR 150 (effective 2002). **Description:** Contains information on prices, imports, exports and landings by commodity.
Published by: Eurofish International Organisation, UN Centre, Midermolen 3, Copenhagen, DK-2100, Denmark. TEL 45-35-467136, FAX 45-35-467181, john.ryder@eastfish.org, http://www.eurofish.dk/.

381 CAN ISSN 0229-1665
HC117.B8
ECONOMIC ACCOUNTS. Text in English. a. CND 20 (effective 1997). charts. **Document type:** *Government.* **Description:** Presents the principal estimates of aggregate economic activity in the province.
Published by: Ministry of Finance and Corporate Relations, B C Stats, Sta Prov Govt, P O Box 9410, Victoria, BC V8W 9V1, Canada. TEL 250-387-0359, FAX 250-387-0380, bcstats@fincc04.fin.gov.bc.ca, http://www.bcstats.gov.bc.ca.

302.015195 LKA ISSN 1391-3611
ECONOMIC AND SOCIAL STATISTICS OF SRI LANKA. Text in English. 1978. a. LKR 100, USD 12. **Document type:** *Academic/Scholarly.* **Description:** Provides statistical information on population, labor force, employment, national accounts, agriculture, industry, trade, finance and transportation in Sri Lanka.
Published by: Central Bank of Sri Lanka, Janadhipathi Mawatha, P O Box 590, Colombo, 1, Sri Lanka. TEL 94-1-346278, FAX 94-1-712486. Circ: 1,500.

330 USA
ECONOMIC CENSUS CD-ROM SERIES. Text in English. q. (in 3 vols.). USD 200 domestic for vol.1 & vol.2; USD 400 foreign for vol.1 & vol.2 (effective 2000); USD 65 per year (for vol.3) (Effective Spring 2001). stat. **Document type:** *Government.*
Media: CD-ROM. **Related titles:** Online - full text ed.; ♦ Print ed.: U.S. Bureau of the Census. (Year) Economic Census. Census of Retail Trade; ♦ U.S. Bureau of the Census. (Year) Economic Census. Manufacturing; ♦ U.S. Bureau of the Census. (Year) Economic Census. Transportation and Warehousing; ♦ U.S. Bureau of the Census. (Year) Economic Census. Utilities; ♦ U.S. Bureau of the Census. (Year) Economic Census. Information; ♦ U.S. Bureau of the Census. (Year) Economic Census. Census of Wholesale Trade; ♦ U.S. Bureau of the Census. (Year) Economic Census. Mining; ♦ U.S. Bureau of the Census. (Year) Economic Census. Construction.
Published by: U.S. Bureau of the Census (Subsidiary of: U.S. Department of Commerce), Customer Services, Washington, DC 20233. TEL 310-457-4100, FAX 301-457-4714, http://www.census.gov.

352.7 GBR
ECONOMIC DEVELOPMENT TODAY. Text in English. 1984. m. GBP 140 to non-members; GBP 130 to members (effective 2000). adv. **Document type:** *Bulletin, Abstract/Index.* **Description:** Abstracts of literature, news, and features on local and regional economic development, and news of initiatives.
Incorporates (in 1998): Local Eonomic Development Initiatives; Which was formerly: Local Economic Development Information Service; Former titles (until 1996): Economic Development Digest (0266-4194); L E D I S (Local Economic Development Initiatives)
—CCC.
Published by: Planning Exchange, Tontine House, 8 Gordon St, Glasgow, G1 3PL, United Kingdom. TEL 44-141-248-8541, FAX 44-141-248-8277, publications@planex.co.uk, info@planex.co.uk, http://www.planex.co.uk. Ed. Malcolm Patterson. R&P Connie Young. Adv. contact Michelle Buchan.

339 PHL
ECONOMIC INDICATORS. Text in English. m. USD 279 in Asia; USD 345 in Australia & New Zealand; USD 399 in US & Canada; USD 447 in Europe; USD 555 elsewhere. **Document type:** *Government.* **Description:** Presents statistical indicators of the levels and trends of economic activities and performance. Covers production and consumption, transportation and tourism, external sector, employment, prices, money and banking, and public finance.
Former titles: N E D A Philippine Economic Indicators; N E D A Economic Indicators
Published by: National Statistical Coordination Board, c/o National Statistical Information Center, Midland-Buendia Bldg, 403 Sen. Gil Puyat Ave., Makati City, Philippines. TEL 63-2-890-9405, FAX 63-2-890-9408, nscb_nsic@mozcom.com.

330 USA ISSN 1075-3834
HC101
ECONOMIC INDICATORS HANDBOOK; time series, conversions, documentation. Text in English. 1992. biennial, latest vol.6, 2002. USD 225 per vol. (effective 2004). **Document type:** *Directory, Trade.* **Description:** Provides aggregate national economic indicators in 175 different statistical series.
Published by: Gale Group (Subsidiary of: Thomson Corporation), 27500 Drake Rd, Farmington Hills, MI 48331-3535. TEL 248-699-8061, 800-877-4253, FAX 248-699-4253, galeord@gale.com, http://www.gale.com.

ECONOMIST. ANNUAL INDEX. see *BUSINESS AND ECONOMICS—Economic Situation And Conditions*

330 ECU
ECUADOR. DEPARTAMENTO DE ESTADISTICAS FISCALES. ESTADISTICAS FISCALES. Text in Spanish. irreg.
Published by: Departamento de Estadisticas Fiscales, Subsecretaria de Presupuesto y Credito Publico, Quito, Pichincha, Ecuador.

381 ECU
ECUADOR. INSTITUTO NACIONAL DE ESTADISTICA Y CENSOS. ENCUESTA ANUAL DE COMERCIO INTERNO. Text in Spanish. a. USD 9.58 newsstand/cover (effective 2001). **Document type:** *Government.*
Related titles: Diskette ed.
Published by: Instituto Nacional de Estadistica y Censos, Juan Larrea N15-36 y Jose Riofrio, Quito, Ecuador. TEL 593-2-529858, FAX 593-2-509836, inec1@ecnet.ec, http://www.inec.gov.ec.

338 318 ECU ISSN 0302-5233
ECUADOR. INSTITUTO NACIONAL DE ESTADISTICA Y CENSOS. ENCUESTA ANUAL DE MANUFACTURA Y MINERIA. Text in Spanish. a. USD 16.56 newsstand/cover (effective 2001). charts; stat.
Related titles: Diskette ed.
Published by: Instituto Nacional de Estadistica y Censos, Juan Larrea N15-36 y Jose Riofrio, Quito, Ecuador. TEL 593-2-529858, FAX 593-2-509836, inec1@ecnet.ec, http://www.inec.gov.ec.

331.11 318 ECU ISSN 0070-8917
ECUADOR. INSTITUTO NACIONAL DE ESTADISTICA Y CENSOS. ESTADISTICA DEL TRABAJO; INDICE DE EMPLEO Y REMUNERACIONES. Text in Spanish. 198?. q. USD 11.
Published by: Instituto Nacional de Estadistica y Censos, Juan Larrea N15-36 y Jose Riofrio, Quito, Ecuador. TEL 593-2-529858, FAX 593-2-509836, inec1@ecnet.ec, http://www.inec.gov.ec.

339 318 ECU ISSN 0019-7025
ECUADOR. INSTITUTO NACIONAL DE ESTADISTICA Y CENSOS. INDICE DE PRECIOS AL CONSUMIDOR; area urbana. Text in Spanish. 1953. m. ECS 140, USD 8 per issue. charts. index.
Media: Duplicated (not offset).
Published by: Instituto Nacional de Estadistica y Censos, Ave. 10 DE AGOSTO, 229, Quito, Pichincha, Ecuador. TEL 519320, FAX 513557. Circ: 1,000.

330.021 ECU
ECUADOR. INSTITUTO NACIONAL DE ESTADISTICAS Y CENSOS. SISTEMA ARMONIZADO DE NOMENCLATURAS DE CARACTER ECONOMICO. Text in Spanish. irreg. **Document type:** *Government.*
Related titles: Diskette ed.
Published by: Instituto Nacional de Estadistica y Censos, Juan Larrea N15-36 y Jose Riofrio, Quito, Ecuador. TEL 593-2-529858, FAX 593-2-509836, inec1@ecnet.ec, http://www.inec.gov.ec.

382 316 EGY ISSN 0027-0237
EGYPT. CENTRAL AGENCY FOR PUBLIC MOBILISATION AND STATISTICS. MONTHLY BULLETIN OF FOREIGN TRADE. Text in Arabic, English. 1964. m. EGP 60. stat. **Document type:** *Bulletin.*
Published by: Central Agency for Public Mobilisation & Statistics, Nasr City, P O Box 2086, Cairo, Egypt.

016.33 POL ISSN 1641-750X
EKONOMIA ON-LINE. Text in English, Polish. 1999. q. free. 241 p./no. 1 cols./p.; **Document type:** *Academic/Scholarly.* **Description:** Guide to economics resources on the Internet. Provides academic staff, students, and business people with current information in the field of economics.
Formerly (until 2000): Przewodnik po Ekonomicznych Zasobach w Internecie
Media: Online - full content.
Published by: Akademia Ekonomiczna w Krakowie, Biblioteka Glowna/Main Library of the Cracow University of Economics, ul Rakowicka 27, Krakow, 31510, Poland. TEL 48-12-2935009, FAX 48-12-2935010, agogut@bibl.ae.krakow.pl, http://kangur.ae.krakow.pl/Biblioteka/Ekonomia/. Ed. Anna Sokolowka-Gogut. Circ: 520.

330.021 RUS
EKONOMICHESKIE POKAZATELI RAZVITIYA RAYONOV KRAINEGO SEVERA I PRIRAVNENNYKH K NIM MESTNOSTEI/ECONOMIC INDICATORS OF THE DEVELOPMENT OF THE FAR NORTH AND OTHER SIMILAR AREAS. Text in Russian. q. RUR 484 (effective 2005). **Document type:** *Bulletin, Government.* **Description:** Contains statistical data on employment, average salary, as well as agriculture, investments, transportation, consumer market, finances, and economy of the regions of the Far North of Russia.
Published by: Gosudarstvennyi Komitet Rossiiskoi Federatsii po Statistike/Federal State Statistics Office, ul Myasnitskaya 39, Moscow, 107450, Russian Federation. TEL 7-095-2074902, FAX 7-095-2074087, stat@gks.ru, http://www.gks.ru.

330.021 360.021 RUS
EKONOMICHESKOE I SOTSIAL'NOE RAZVITIE KORENNYKH MALOCHISLENNYKH NARODOV SEVERA/ECONOMIC AND SOCIAL DEVELOPMENT OF INDIGENOUS SMALL NATIONALITIES OF THE FAR NORTH. Text in Russian. a. **Document type:** *Bulletin, Government.* **Description:** Provides a list of areas of indigenous small-size nationalities of the Far North. Contains data on the size of population, its age and sex structure and vital statistics, the breakdown of the employees number by origins and industries of economy.
Published by: Gosudarstvennyi Komitet Rossiiskoi Federatsii po Statistike/Federal State Statistics Office, ul Myasnitskaya 39, Moscow, 107450, Russian Federation. TEL 7-095-2074902, FAX 7-095-2074087, stat@gks.ru, http://www.gks.ru.

016.33   UKR
EKONOMIKA. EKONOMICHNI NAUKY. Text in Ukrainian. 1998. m. USD 207 foreign (effective 2005). **Document type:** *Bibliography.* **Description:** Bibliography of books and articles on economics published in Ukraine.
Related titles: Online - full text ed.
Published by: Knyzhkova Palata Ukrainy/Book Chamber of Ukraine, Pr Gagarina 27, Kyiv, 02094, Ukraine. TEL 380-44-5520134, ukrbook@ukr.net, http://www.ukrbook.net.
Dist. by: East View Information Services, 3020 Harbor Ln. N., Minneapolis, MN 55447. TEL 800-477-1005, FAX 800-800-3839, eastview@eastview.com, http://www.eastview.com.

330.016   RUS
EKONOMIKA SIBIRI I DAL'NEGO VOSTOKA; tekushchii ukazatel' literatury. Text in Russian. 1967. a. USD 55 foreign. **Document type:** *Bibliography.* **Description:** Covers books, articles, summaries, and reports on conferences and symposia on economics, industrial planning, natural resources, sociology and foreign economic relations of Siberia and the Far East.
Formerly: Narodnoe Khozyaistvo Sibiri i Dal'nego Vostoka (0130-6987)
Indexed: RASB.
Published by: Rossiiskaya Akademiya Nauk, Sibirskoe Otdelenie, Gosudarstvennaya Publichnaya Nauchno-Tekhnicheskaya Biblioteka/State Public Scientific and Technical Library of the Siberian Branch of the Russian Academy of Sciences, Ul Voskhod 15, Novosibirsk, 630200, Russian Federation. TEL 7-3832-661367, FAX 7-3832-663365, root@libr.nsk.su, onb@spsl.nsc.ru. Ed. L A Sergeeva.

382   SLV
EL SALVADOR. MINISTERIO DE COMERCIO EXTERIOR. ESTADISTICAS. Text in Spanish. a.
Published by: Ministerio de Comercio Exterior/Ministry of Foreign Trade of El Salvador, Alameda Juan Pablo II y Calle Guadalupe, Edificio C1-C2, San Salvador, El Salvador. TEL 503-281-1122, FAX 503-221-5446.

331.11 318   SLV
EL SALVADOR. MINISTERIO DE TRABAJO Y PREVISION SOCIAL. ESTADISTICAS DEL TRABAJO. Text in Spanish. a.
Published by: Ministerio de Trabajo y Prevision Social, Avda. Norte 428, Edif. 2A, San Salvador, El Salvador. TEL 77-1250.

016.658   GBR
EMERALD FULLTEXT. Text in English. 1995. base vol. plus m. updates. EUR 27,482.08 in Europe; USD 27,049 in North America; AUD 34,049 in Australasia; GBP 19,245.33 in UK & elsewhere (effective 2006). **Document type:** *Database, Abstract/Index.* **Description:** Delivers full access to a large variety of management articles and journals.
Former titles: Emerald Intelligence & Fulltext (1468-4616); (until 1999): Emerald
Media: Online - full content.
Published by: Emerald Group Publishing Limited, 60-62 Toller Ln, Bradford, W Yorks BD8 9BY, United Kingdom. TEL 44-1274-777700, FAX 44-1274-785200, infomation@emeraldinsight.com, http://www.emeraldinsight.com/fulltext/. **Subscr. addr. in Australia:** Emerald Group Publishing Ltd., PO Box 1567, Toowong, QLD 4066, Australia. TEL 61-3870-7144, FAX 61-3870-4013; **Subscr. addr. in N America:** Emerald Group Publishing Ltd., 44 Brattle St, 4th Fl, Cambridge, MA 02138. TEL 617-497-2175, 888-622-0075, FAX 617-354-6875.

658 016   GBR
EMERALD MANAGEMENT REVIEWS (ONLINE EDITION). Text in English. m. EUR 8,035.83 in Europe; USD 7,999 in North America; AUD 12,429 in Australasia; GBP 5,627.08 in the UK and rest of the world (effective 2006). **Document type:** *Abstract/Index.* **Description:** Fully searchable, independent abstracts of business and management articles from the top 400 professional and academic journals on all areas of management. Abstracts are assessed, keyworded and indexed.
Former titles (until 2002): Emerald Reviews (Online Edition); (until 2001): Anbar International Management Database (1463-6891); (until 1999): Anbar Management Intelligence (CD-ROM Edition) (1362-9352)
Media: Online - full text (from ProQuest Information & Learning).
Related titles: ♦ Print ed.: Emerald Management Reviews (Print Edition). ISSN 1474-6085.
—CCC.
Published by: Emerald Group Publishing Limited, 60-62 Toller Ln, Bradford, W Yorks BD8 9BY, United Kingdom. TEL 44-1274-777700, FAX 44-1274-785200, infomation@emeraldinsight.com, http://www.emeraldinsight.com/. Eds. David Pollitt, Deborah Spurgeon. **Subscr. in Australasia to:** Emerald Group Publishing Ltd., PO Box 1567, Toowong, QLD 4066, Australia. TEL 61-3870-7144, FAX 61-3870-4013; **Subscr. in N. America to:** Emerald Group Publishing Ltd., 44 Brattle St, 4th Fl, Cambridge, MA 02138. TEL 617-497-2175, 888-622-0075, FAX 617-354-6875.

658 016   GBR   ISSN 1474-6085
EMERALD MANAGEMENT REVIEWS (PRINT EDITION). (Consists of: 7 subject libraries sections: Accounting & Finance Abstracts; Human Resource Management Abstracts; Information Management & Technology Reviews; Management of Quality Abstracts; Marketing & Logistics Abstracts; Operations & Production Management Abstracts and Top Management Abstracts. Each section is also avail. separately in print & online.) Text in English. bi-m. EUR 2,179 in Europe; USD 2,499 in North America; AUD 3,159 in Australasia; GBP 1,529 in the UK & rest of the world; EUR 14,057.72 combined subscription in Europe print & online; USD 12,629 combined subscription in North America print & online; AUD 17,619 combined subscription in Australasia print & online; GBP 9,847.88 combined subscription in the UK & rest of the world, print & online (effective 2006). reprint service avail. from PSC. **Description:** Provides rapid access to significant information from around the world enabling you to keep abreast of the latest developments.
Former titles (until 2002): Emerald Reviews (Print Edition) (1472-9334); (until 2000): Anbar Management Abstracts (1465-2897); (until 1999): Anbar Management Intelligence (Print Edition) (1464-326X); Which incorporated (1989-1998): Management Bibliographies & Reviews (0309-0582)
Related titles: ♦ Online - full text ed.: Emerald Management Reviews (Online Edition).
Indexed: ABIn.
Published by: Emerald Group Publishing Limited, 60-62 Toller Ln, Bradford, W Yorks BD8 9BY, United Kingdom. TEL 44-1274-777700, FAX 44-1274-785200, infomation@emeraldinsight.com, http://www.emeraldinsight.com/.

331.21021   USA
EMPLOYER COSTS FOR EMPLOYEE COMPENSATION. Text in English. m. **Document type:** *Government.*
Related titles: ♦ Series of: U.S. Bureau of Labor Statistics. National Office News Releases.
Published by: U.S. Department of Labor, Bureau of Labor Statistics, Postal Square Bldg., 2 Massachusetts Ave, NE, Washington, DC 20212-0001 . **Subscr. to:** U.S. Government Printing Office, Superintendent of Documents.

352.47021   USA
EMPLOYMENT AND PAYROLLS IN WASHINGTON STATE BY COUNTY AND INDUSTRY; industries covered by the Employment Security Act and federal employment covered by Title 5, U.S.C. 85. Text in English. q. (plus a. summary). USD 20. charts. back issues avail. **Document type:** *Government.* **Description:** Contains employment and wage data for businesses and organizations subject to the Washington State Employment Security Act.
Related titles: Diskette ed.: USD 25.
Published by: Employment Security Department, PO Box 9046, Olympia, WA 98507-9046.

331.21021   USA   ISSN 0748-5336
HD5723
EMPLOYMENT AND WAGES ANNUAL AVERAGES. Text in English. a. USD 48 (effective 2000). **Document type:** *Bulletin, Government.* **Description:** Provides a complete count of employment and wages for workers covered by state unemployment programs; national employment and wage totals are given for specific industries.
Related titles: ♦ Series of: U.S. Bureau of Labor Statistics. Bulletin. ISSN 0082-9021.
Published by: U.S. Department of Labor, Bureau of Labor Statistics, Postal Square Bldg., 2 Massachusetts Ave, NE, Washington, DC 20212-0001 . TEL 202-691-5200, http://www.bls.gov. **Subscr. to:** U.S. Government Printing Office, Superintendent of Documents.

331.11   USA
EMPLOYMENT IN PERSPECTIVE: MINORITY WORKERS. Text in English. q. **Document type:** *Government.* **Description:** Examines the extent of nonagricultural self-employment among minority workers.
Related titles: ♦ Series of: U.S. Bureau of Labor Statistics. Reports.
Published by: U.S. Department of Labor, Bureau of Labor Statistics, Postal Square Bldg., 2 Massachusetts Ave, NE, Washington, DC 20212-0001 . TEL 202-691-5200, http://www.bls.gov. **Subscr. to:** U.S. Government Printing Office, Superintendent of Documents, PO Box 371954, Pittsburgh, PA 15250-7954. TEL 202-512-1800, FAX 202-512-2250, orders@gpo.gov, http://www.access.gpo.gov.

330   VEN   ISSN 0798-8648
ENCUESTA CUANTITATIVA DE COMERCIO AL DETAL∗ . Text in Spanish. 1985. a. VEB 500. **Document type:** *Government.*
Published by: Oficina Central de Estadistica e Informatica, Apdo. de Correos 4593, Carmeliatas, Caracas, DF 1010A, Venezuela. TEL 58-2-782-11-33, FAX 58-2-781-13-80, OCEI@platino.gov.ve, ocei@platino.gov.ve, http://www.OCEI.gov.ve, http://www.ocei.gov.ve.

338 318   VEN   ISSN 0259-515X
ENCUESTA INDUSTRIAL: RESULTADOS NACIONALES. Text in Spanish. 1974. a. VEB 250. stat. **Description:** Covers accounting and labor issues.
Formerly: Encuesta Industrial de Venezuela

Published by: Oficina Central de Estadistica e Informatica, Apdo. de Correos 4593, Carmeliatas, Caracas, DF 1010A, Venezuela. TEL 58-2-782-11-33, FAX 58-2-781-13-80.

330.021   URY   ISSN 0797-3209
ENCUESTA INDUSTRIAL TRIMESTRAL. Text in Spanish. 1985. q. back issues avail.
Related titles: Online - full text ed.: Encuesta Industrial Annual.
Published by: Instituto Nacional de Estadistica, Rio Negro 1520, Montevideo, 11100, Uruguay. TEL 598-2-9027303, http://www.ine.gub.uy/biblioteca/publicaciones.htm#SERIE%20PUBLICACIONES%20PERIODICAS.

331.125021   CHL
ENCUESTA NACIONAL DEL EMPLEO TOTAL PAIS. Text in Spanish. 1966. irreg., latest 1986-91. USD 9.
Published by: Instituto Nacional de Estadisticas, Casilla 498, Correo 3, Ave. Bulnes, 418, Santiago, Chile. Circ: 700.

338.91 610 551   DEU   ISSN 0722-0111
Z7164.U5
ENTWICKLUNGSLAENDER-STUDIEN; Bibliographie entwicklungslaenderbezogener Forschungsarbeiten. Text in German. 1966. a. index. back issues avail. **Document type:** *Bibliography.*
Indexed: RDA, WAE&RSA.
—BLDSC (3791.040000).
Published by: Deutsche Stiftung fuer Internationale Entwicklung, Zentrale Dokumentation/German Foundation for International Development, Hans-Boeckler-Str 5, Bonn, 53225, Germany. TEL 49-228-4001-0, FAX 49-228-4001-111. Ed. Herbert H Henselek.

338   PRI
ESTABLECIMIENTOS MANUFACTURERAS EN PUERTO RICO. Text in Spanish. a. free. index. **Document type:** *Government.*
Published by: Department of Labor, Bureau of Labor Statistics, 505 Munoz Rivera Ave., Hato Rey, 00918, Puerto Rico. TEL 787-754-5348. Ed. Myrta Olmos Quinones. Circ: 775.

382   MEX   ISSN 0187-4845
HD9734.M4
ESTADISTICA DE LA INDUSTRIA MAQUILADORA DE EXPORTACION. Text in Spanish. 1981. a. MXP 20 (effective 1999).
Published by: Instituto Nacional de Estadistica, Geografia e Informatica, Secretaria de Programacion y Presupuesto, Prol. Heroe de Nacozari 2301 Sur, Puerta 11, Acceso, Aguascalientes, 20270, Mexico. TEL 52-4-918-1948, FAX 52-4-918-0739, http://www.inegi.gob.mx.

330.9   PAN   ISSN 1023-3318
ESTADISTICA PANAMENA. INDICADORES ECONOMICOS. SECCION 011. Text in Spanish. 1965. s-a. PAB 1 domestic (effective 2000). **Document type:** *Bulletin, Government.* **Description:** Presents information on the economic situation of the country.
Supersedes in part (in 1994): Estadistica Panamena. Indicadores Economicos y Sociales. Section 011 (0378-4940)
Published by: Direccion de Estadistica y Censo, Contraloria General, Apdo. 5213, Panama City, 5, Panama. FAX 507-210-4801. Circ: 700.

ESTADISTICA PANAMENA. INDICADORES SOCIALES. SECCION 012. see *SOCIAL SERVICES AND WELFARE—Abstracting, Bibliographies, Statistics*

ESTADISTICA PANAMENA. SITUACION DEMOGRAFICA. SECCION 231. MOVIMIENTO INTERNACIONAL DE PASAJEROS. see *POPULATION STUDIES—Abstracting, Bibliographies, Statistics*

318 338   PAN   ISSN 0378-2557
HC147
ESTADISTICA PANAMENA. SITUACION ECONOMICA. SECCION 314, 323, 324, 325, 353. INDUSTRIA. Text in Spanish. 1958. s-a. PAB 3.75 domestic (effective 2000). **Document type:** *Bulletin, Government.* **Description:** Offers data on fishing, manufacturing, construction, and energy, gas, and water usage and production on a national level.
Published by: Direccion de Estadistica y Censo, Contraloria General, Apdo. 5213, Panama City, 5, Panama. FAX 507-210-4801. Circ: 800.

330 318   PAN
ESTADISTICA PANAMENA. SITUACION ECONOMICA. SECCION 321. INDUSTRIA MANUFACTURERA. Text in Spanish. 1957. a. PAB 1.50 domestic (effective 2000). **Document type:** *Bulletin, Government.* **Description:** Presents information on establishments dedicated to the manufacturing industry.
Former titles: Estadistica Panamena. Situacion Economica. Seccion 321. Industria Encuesta (0379-4245); Panama. Direccion de Estadistica y Censo. Estadistica Panamena. Serie F. Industrias Encuestas (0078-8937)
Published by: Direccion de Estadistica y Censo, Contraloria General, Apdo. 5213, Panama City, 5, Panama. FAX 507-210-4801. Circ: 800.

B

338 310   PAN
ESTADISTICA PANAMENA. SITUACION ECONOMICA. SECCION 323. INDICE DE LA PRODUCCION DE LA INDUSTRIA MANUFACTURERA. Text in Spanish. 1968. a. PAB 1.50 (effective 2000). **Document type:** *Bulletin, Government.*
Former titles (until 1998): Estadistica Panamena. Situacion Economica. Seccion 323. Indice de la Produccion Fisica de la Industria Manufacturera; Estadistica Panamena. Situacion Economica. Seccion 323. Indice de Volumen Fisico de la Produccion Industrial; Estadistica Panamena. Situacion Economica. Seccion 323. Produccion Manufacturera (0379-0754)
Published by: Direccion de Estadistica y Censo, Contraloria General, Apdo. 5213, Panama City, 5, Panama. FAX 507-69-7294. Circ: 700.

318   PAN   ISSN 0378-4983
HF142
ESTADISTICA PANAMENA. SITUACION ECONOMICA. SECCION 331. COMERCIO. ANUARIO DE COMERCIO EXTERIOR. Text in Spanish. 1953. a. (in 4 vols.). PAB 12 domestic (effective 2000). charts. **Document type:** *Bulletin, Government.* **Description:** Presents information on the movement of commercial goods.
Formerly: Estadistica Panamena. Situacion Economica. Seccion 331. Comercio. Comercio Exterior. (Anual)
Published by: Direccion de Estadistica y Censo, Contraloria General, Apdo. 5213, Panama City, 5, Panama. FAX 507-69-7294. Circ: 800.

ESTADISTICA PANAMENA. SITUACION ECONOMICA. SECCION 333. TRANSPORTE. see *TRANSPORTATION*

382   PAN   ISSN 0378-7397
HG3883.P25
ESTADISTICA PANAMENA. SITUACION ECONOMICA. SECCION 341. BALANZA DE PAGOS. Text in Spanish. 1954. a. PAB 3 domestic (effective 2000). **Document type:** *Bulletin, Government.* **Description:** Presents statistics on goods, services, rents, and other exchanges.
Published by: Direccion de Estadistica y Censo, Contraloria General, Apdo. 5213, Panama City, 5, Panama. FAX 507-210-4801. Circ: 900.

338.97287   PAN   ISSN 0378-2603
HC147.Z9
ESTADISTICA PANAMENA. SITUACION ECONOMICA. SECCION 342. CUENTAS NACIONALES. Text in Spanish. 1950. a. PAB 2.50 domestic (effective 2000). **Document type:** *Bulletin, Government.* **Description:** Offers information on the various macroeconomic aggregates, such as national revenue, per-capita revenue, gross national product, and their means of calculation.
Published by: Direccion de Estadistica y Censo, Contraloria General, Apdo. 5213, Panama City, 5, Panama. FAX 507-210-4801. Circ: 1,000.

318   PAN   ISSN 1017-4273
HJ21
ESTADISTICA PANAMENA. SITUACION ECONOMICA. SECCION 343. HACIENDA PUBLICA. Text in Spanish. 1958. a. PAB 3 (effective 2000). **Document type:** *Bulletin, Government.* **Description:** Presents information on budgets, revenues, expenditures, and debts of the public sector.
Supersedes in part (in 1988): Estadistica Panamena. Situacion Economica. Seccion 343-344. Hacienda Publica y Finanzas (0378-6730)
Published by: Direccion de Estadistica y Censo, Contraloria General, Apdo. 5213, Panama City, 5, Panama. FAX 507-210-4801. Circ: 750.

332   PAN   ISSN 1017-4281
HG2771
ESTADISTICA PANAMENA. SITUACION ECONOMICA. SECCION 344. FINANZAS. Text in Spanish. 1958. a. PAB 1.50 domestic (effective 2000). **Document type:** *Bulletin, Government.* **Description:** Contains statistics on the banking system and the International Bank of Panama. Presents information on credit institutions, savings and loan associations, and cooperatives.
Supersedes in part (in 1988): Estadistica Panamena. Situacion Economica. Seccion 343-344. Hacienda Publica y Finanzas (0378-6730)
Published by: Direccion de Estadistica y Censo, Contraloria General, Apdo. 5213, Panama City, 5, Panama. FAX 507-210-4801. Circ: 700.

318   PAN   ISSN 0378-2522
HB235.P35
ESTADISTICA PANAMENA. SITUACION ECONOMICA. SECCION 351. INDICE DE PRECIOS AL POR MAYOR Y AL CONSUMIDOR. Text in Spanish. 1957. q. PAB 3 domestic (effective 2000). **Document type:** *Bulletin, Government.* **Description:** Presents indexes of prices from the import, industrial, and agricultural sectors.
Published by: Direccion de Estadistica y Censo, Contraloria General, Apdo. 5213, Panama City, 5, Panama. FAX 507-210-4801. Circ: 900.

338 318   PAN
ESTADISTICA PANAMENA. SITUACION SOCIAL. SECCION 441. ESTADISTICAS DEL TRABAJO. Text in Spanish. 1963. a. (in 2 vols.). PAB 13.50 domestic (effective 2000). **Document type:** *Bulletin, Government.* **Description:** Presents data from the census of housing and employment.
Formerly: Estadistica Panamena. Situacion Social. Seccion 441 - Trabajo y Salarios. Estadisticas del Trabajo (0379-072X); **Supersedes:** Estadistica Panamena. Serie M. Empleo
Published by: Direccion de Estadistica y Censo, Contraloria General, Apdo. 5213, Panama City, 5, Panama. FAX 507-210-4801. Circ: 750.

332.021   CHL
ESTADISTICAS BANCA INTERNET. Text in Spanish. 2000. s-a. back issues avail.
Media: Online - full text. **Related titles:** E-mail ed.
Published by: Superintendencia de Bancos e Instituciones Financieras, Moneda 1123, Santiago, Chile. TEL 56-2-4426200, http://www.sbif.cl/cgi-bin/publicaciones.pl.

339   GTM
ESTADISTICAS MACROECONOMICAS DE CENTROAMERICA. Text in Spanish. a. USD 10.
Published by: Secretaria Permanente del Tratado General de Integracion Economica Centroamericana, 4a Avda. 10-25, ZONA, 14, PO Box 1237, Guatemala City, 01901, Guatemala. TEL 502-3682151, FAX 502-3681071, sieca@pronet.net.gt.

332.021   CHL
ESTADOS FINANCIEROS ANUALES DE SOCIEDADES FILIALES. Text in Spanish. a. back issues avail.
Related titles: Online - full text ed.
Published by: Superintendencia de Bancos e Instituciones Financieras, Moneda 1123, Santiago, Chile. TEL 56-2-4426200, http://www.sbif.cl/.

330   PRT   ISSN 0872-9298
HC391
ESTATISTICAS DA PRODUCAO INDUSTRIAL/PORTUGAL. STATISTIQUES INDUSTRIELLES: CONTINENT, ACORES ET MADERE. VOLUME 2: INDUSTRIES MANUFACTURIERES. Text in Portuguese. 1971. a. **Document type:** *Government.*
Supersedes in part (in 1990): Estatisticas Industriais (0079-418X)
Published by: Instituto Nacional de Estatistica, Ave. Antonio Jose de Almeida 2, Lisbon, 1000-043, Portugal. TEL 351-21-8426100, FAX 351-21-8426380, ine@ine.pt, http://www.ine.pt/

330   PRT   ISSN 0872-8879
ESTATISTICAS DAS EMPRESAS. INDUSTRIA. Text in Portuguese. 1971. a. **Document type:** *Government.*
Supersedes in part (in 1990): Estatisticas Industriais (0079-418X)
Published by: Instituto Nacional de Estatistica, Ave. Antonio Jose de Almeida 2, Lisbon, 1000-043, Portugal. TEL 351-21-8426100, FAX 351-21-8426380, ine@ine.pt, http://www.ine.pt/.

336.2 314   PRT   ISSN 0873-6324
HJ2856
ESTATISTICAS DAS RECEITAS FISCAIS. Text in Portuguese. 1967. a. EUR 16.96 (effective 2005). **Document type:** *Government.* **Description:** Provides statistical data on income tax, liquidation and taxes in general for the mainland and autonomous regions.
Formerly (until 1989): Portugal. Instituto Nacional de Estatistica. Estatisticas das Contribuicoes e Impostos (0079-4120)
Published by: Instituto Nacional de Estatistica, Ave. Antonio Jose de Almeida 2, Lisbon, 1000-043, Portugal. TEL 351-21-8426100, FAX 351-21-8426380, ine@ine.pt, http://www.ine.pt/.

382 314   PRT   ISSN 0873-0687
HF221
ESTATISTICAS DO COMERCIO INTERNACIONAL. Text in Portuguese. 1930. a. EUR 27.50 (effective 2005). **Document type:** *Government.* **Description:** Provides statistical data on imports and exports divided by goods and countries.
Formerly (until 1993): Portugal. Instituto Nacional de Estatistica. Estatisticas do Comercio Externo (0079-4147)
Published by: Instituto Nacional de Estatistica, Ave. Antonio Jose de Almeida 2, Lisbon, 1000-043, Portugal. TEL 351-21-8426100, FAX 351-21-8426380, ine@ine.pt, http://www.ine.pt/. Ed. C Correa Gago. Circ: 650.

ESTATISTICAS DO EMPREGO. see *BUSINESS AND ECONOMICS—Small Business*

338 314   PRT   ISSN 0377-2314
HC391
ESTATISTICAS INDUSTRAIS. SUPLEMENTO/PORTUGAL. STATISTIQUES INDUSTRIELLES: CONTINENT, ACORES ET MADERE. VOLUME 1: INDUSTRIES EXTRACTIVES, ELECTRICITE, GAZ, EAU. Text in French, Portuguese. 1974. a. **Document type:** *Government.*
Published by: Instituto Nacional de Estatistica, Ave. Antonio Jose de Almeida 2, Lisbon, 1000-043, Portugal. TEL 351-21-8426100, FAX 351-21-8426380, ine@ine.pt, http://www.ine.pt/.

ESTATISTICAS MONETARIAS E FINANCIERAS. see *BUSINESS AND ECONOMICS—Banking And Finance*

387   CAN
ESTIMATES OF REVENUE AND EXPENDITURE. Text in English. a. CND 16.70. Supplement avail. **Description:** Outlines the revenue and expenditure intentions of the government for the next fiscal year.
Published by: Ministry of Finance and Corporate Relations, Sta Prov Govt, P O Box 9410, Victoria, BC V8W 9V1, Canada. TEL 604-387-1502, FAX 604-387-0329. **Subscr. to:** Crown Publications Inc., 521 Fort St, Victoria, BC BC V8W 1E7, Canada. TEL 604-386-4636.

382 316   ETH   ISSN 0425-4309
ETHIOPIA. CUSTOMS HEAD OFFICE. EXTERNAL TRADE STATISTICS. Text in English. 1946. a. USD 21. charts.
Published by: Customs Head Office, PO Box 3248, Addis Ababa, Ethiopia. TELEX 21177.

338.0029   GBR   ISSN 0071-2582
EUROPEAN COMPANIES; guide to sources of information. Text in English. 1962. irreg., latest vol.4, 1992. GBP 80, USD 160 (effective 2001). adv. **Document type:** *Directory.* **Description:** Compiles 1,400 sources of company information available in all European countries.
Published by: C.B.D. Research Ltd., 15 Wickham Rd, Beckenham, Kent BR3 5JS, United Kingdom. TEL 44-20-86507745, FAX 44-20-86500768, cbd@cbdresearch.com, http://www.cbdresearch.com. Ed. R Rickson. Circ: 2,000. **Dist. in the U.S. by:** Hoover's Inc., 6448 Hwy 290 E, Ste E 104, Austin, TX 78723.

384   GBR   ISSN 0966-7458
THE EUROPEAN JOURNAL OF TELEWORKING. Text in English. 1993. q. GBP 50 to individuals; GBP 99 to institutions (effective 2000). adv. **Document type:** *Journal.* **Description:** Covers research on all aspects of teleworking from academic, industrial, and commercial sources. Aimed at policymakers and practitioners interested in cutting-edge developments in the field.
—IE.
Published by: (National Association of Teleworkers), Addico Cornix Ltd., 70 Causewayhead, Penzance, Cornwall TR18 2SR, United Kingdom. TEL 44-1736-332736, FAX 44-1736-334702, srs@cornix.co.uk. Ed. Stephen Simmons. R&P Suze White. Adv. contact Niki Grover.

658.8   GBR   ISSN 0071-2930
HC79.C6
EUROPEAN MARKETING DATA AND STATISTICS (YEAR). Text in English. 1962. a. GBP 325 domestic; EUR 530 in Europe; USD 530 elsewhere (effective 2003). **Document type:** *Directory, Trade.* **Description:** Contains more than 100,000 statistics on a wide range of business, economic, and social topics covering the European countries.
—CISTI.
Published by: Euromonitor, 60-61 Britton St, London, EC1 5UX, United Kingdom. TEL 44-20-7251-8024, FAX 44-20-7608-3149, info@euromonitor.com, http://www.euromonitor.com.

016.658   GBR
EUROPEAN MARKETING FORECASTS. Text in English. 1997. biennial. GBP 775 domestic; EUR 1,290 in Europe; USD 1,290 elsewhere (effective 2003). **Description:** Presents statistical forecasts for 24 European countries for consumer products and socio-economic parameters.
Published by: Euromonitor, 60-61 Britton St, London, EC1 5UX, United Kingdom. TEL 44-20-7251-8024, FAX 44-20-7608-3149, info@euromonitor.com, http://www.euromonitor.com.

EUROSTAT GAS PRICES. see *ENERGY—Abstracting, Bibliographies, Statistics*

332.021   LUX   ISSN 1562-3041
HG930.5
EUROSTAT GELD, FINANZEN UND DER EURO: STATISTIKEN. Text in English, French, German. 1984. m. **Document type:** *Bulletin, Government.* **Description:** Collection of various statistics relating to the European Communities, Japan and the United States. A detailed methodological introduction presents the numerical data, which are in three sections: structural indicators, European monetary system, and current statistics.
Formerly (until 1999): Eurostat. Money and Finance (0255-6510)
Related titles: CD-ROM ed.: ISSN 1562-5311; Microfiche ed.: (from CIS).
Indexed: IIS.
Published by: European Commission, Statistical Office of the European Communities, Rue Alcide de Gasperi, Luxembourg, 2920, Luxembourg. TEL 352-4301-34526, FAX 352-4301-34415, eurostat-infodesk@cec.eu.int, http://www.europa.eu.int/comm/eurostat. **Dist. in the U.S. by:** Unipub, 4611-F Assembly Drive, Lanham, MD 20706-4391. TEL 800-274-4888.

330.9 LUX ISSN 1024-4298
HC241.2.A1
EUROSTAT STATISTICS IN FOCUS. ECONOMY AND FINANCE. Text in English. m. charts. **Document type:** *Bulletin, Government.*
Formerly (until 1994): Eurostat. Rapid Reports. Economy and Finance (1016-0213)
Related titles: ♦ French ed.: Eurostat Statistiques en Bref. Economie et Finances. ISSN 1024-4301; ♦ German ed.: Eurostat Statistik Kurz Gefasst. Wirtschaft und Finanzen. ISSN 1024-431X.
Indexed: IIS.
—BLDSC (8453.536750).
Published by: European Commission, Statistical Office of the European Communities, Rue Alcide de Gasperi, Luxembourg, 2920, Luxembourg. TEL 352-4301-34526, FAX 352-4301-33415, eurostat-infodesk@cec.eu.int, http://www.europa.eu.int/comm/eurostat. **Dist. in the U.S. by:** Unipub, 4611-F Assembly Drive, Lanham, MD 20706-4391. TEL 800-274-4888.

332.6 LUX ISSN 1024-6878
HF1371
EUROSTAT STATISTICS IN FOCUS. EXTERNAL TRADE. Text in English. 1991. m. charts. **Document type:** *Government.*
Formerly (until 1995): Eurostat. Rapid Reports. Foreign Trade (1017-5792)
Related titles: French ed.: Eurostat Statistiques Rapides. Commerce Exterieur. ISSN 1016-5762; German ed.: Eurostat Schnellberichte. Aussenhandel. ISSN 1017-5806.
Indexed: IIS.
—BLDSC (8453.536765).
Published by: European Commission, Statistical Office of the European Communities, Rue Alcide de Gasperi, Luxembourg, 2920, Luxembourg. TEL 352-4301-34526, FAX 352-4301-33415, eurostat-infodesk@cec.eu.int, http://www.europa.eu.int/comm/eurostat. **Dist. in the U.S. by:** Bernan Associates, Bernan, 4611-F Assembly Dr., Lanham, MD 20706-4391. TEL 301-459-0056, 800-274-4888.

330.9 LUX ISSN 1561-4875
HA1107.5.A1
EUROSTAT STATISTICS IN FOCUS. GENERAL STATISTICS. Text in English. m. charts. **Document type:** *Bulletin, Government.*
Former titles (until 1999): Eurostat. Statistics in Focus. Regions (1024-6886); (until 1995): Eurostat. Rapid Reports. Regions (1013-0535)
Related titles: French ed.: Eurostat Statistiques en Bref. Statistiques Generales. ISSN 1561-4883; German ed.: Eurostat Statistik Kurz Gefasst. Allgemeine Statistik. ISSN 1561-4867.
Indexed: IIS.
—BLDSC (8453.536780).
Published by: European Commission, Statistical Office of the European Communities, Rue Alcide de Gasperi, Luxembourg, 2920, Luxembourg. TEL 352-4301-34526, FAX 352-4301-33415, eurostat-infodesk@cec.eu.int, http://www.europa.eu.int/comm/eurostat. **Dist. in the U.S. by:** Unipub, 4611-F Assembly Drive, Lanham, MD 20706-4391. TEL 800-274-4888.

330.9 333.79 LUX ISSN 1561-4840
HD9502.E85
EUROSTAT STATISTICS IN FOCUS. INDUSTRY, TRADE AND SERVICES. Text in English. 1987. m. charts. **Document type:** *Government.*
Former titles: Eurostat. Statistics in Focus. Energy and Industry (1024-4328); (until 1994): Eurostat. Rapid Reports. Energy and Industry (1016-0191); Eurostat. Rapid Reports. Energy (1013-0403)
Related titles: ♦ French ed.: Eurostat Statistiques en Bref. Industrie, Commerce et Services. ISSN 1561-4859; ♦ German ed.: Eurostat Statistik Kurz Gefasst. Industrie, Handel und Dienstleistungen. ISSN 1561-4832.
Indexed: IIS.
—BLDSC (8453.536760).
Published by: European Commission, Statistical Office of the European Communities, Rue Alcide de Gasperi, Luxembourg, 2920, Luxembourg. TEL 352-4301-34526, FAX 352-4301-33415, eurostat-infodesk@cec.eu.int, http://www.europa.eu.int/comm/eurostat. **Dist. in the U.S. by:** Unipub, 4611-F Assembly Drive, Lanham, MD 20706-4391. TEL 800-274-4888, FAX 800-865-3450.

330.9 LUX ISSN 1024-4352
HB3581
EUROSTAT STATISTICS IN FOCUS. POPULATION AND SOCIAL CONDITIONS. Text in English. m. charts. **Document type:** *Government.*
Formerly (until 1994): Eurostat. Rapid Reports. Population and Social Conditions (1016-0205)
Related titles: ♦ French ed.: Eurostat Statistiques en Bref. Population et Conditions Sociales. ISSN 1024-4360; ♦ German ed.: Eurostat Statistik Kurz Gefasst. Bevoelkerung und Soziale Bedingungen. ISSN 1024-4379.
Indexed: IIS.
—BLDSC (8453.536770).
Published by: European Commission, Statistical Office of the European Communities, Rue Alcide de Gasperi, Luxembourg, 2920, Luxembourg. TEL 352-4301-32526, FAX 352-4301-33415, eurostat-infodesk@cec.eu.int, http://www.europa.eu.int/comm/eurostat. **Dist. in the U.S. by:** Unipub, 4611-F Assembly Drive, Lanham, MD 20706-4391. TEL 800-274-4888.

330 LUX ISSN 1609-5995
HD77.5.E86
EUROSTAT STATISTICS IN FOCUS. SCIENCE AND TECHNOLOGY. Text in English. 1995. m. charts. **Document type:** *Government.*
Formerly (until 2001): Eurostat. Statistics in Focus. Research and Development (1024-7971)
Related titles: ♦ French ed.: Eurostat Statistiques en Bref. Science et Technologie. ISSN 1609-5987; ♦ German ed.: Eurostat Statistik Kurz Gefasst. Wissenschaft und Technologie. ISSN 1609-6002.
Indexed: IIS.
—BLDSC (8453.536778).
Published by: European Commission, Statistical Office of the European Communities, Rue Alcide de Gasperi, Luxembourg, 2920, Luxembourg. TEL 352-4301-34526, FAX 352-4301-33415, eurostat-infodesk@cec.eu.int, http://www.europa.eu.int/comm/eurostat. **Dist. in the U.S. by:** Unipub, 4611-F Assembly Drive, Lanham, MD 20706-4391. TEL 800-274-4888.

330.9 LUX ISSN 1024-4379
EUROSTAT STATISTIK KURZ GEFASST. BEVOELKERUNG UND SOZIALE BEDINGUNGEN. Text in German. m. charts. **Document type:** *Government.*
Formerly (until 1994): Eurostat. Schnellberichte. Bevoelkerung und Soziale Bedingungen (1017-5865)
Related titles: ♦ English ed.: Eurostat Statistics in Focus. Population and Social Conditions. ISSN 1024-4352; ♦ French ed.: Eurostat Statistiques en Bref. Population et Conditions Sociales. ISSN 1024-4360.
Published by: European Commission, Statistical Office of the European Communities, Rue Alcide de Gasperi, Luxembourg, 2920, Luxembourg. TEL 352-4301-34526, FAX 352-4301-34415, eurostat-infodesk@cec.eu.int, http://www.europa.eu.int/comm/eurostat. **Dist. in the U.S. by:** Unipub, 4611-F Assembly Drive, Lanham, MD 20706-4391. TEL 800-274-4888.

330.9 333.79 LUX ISSN 1561-4832
EUROSTAT STATISTIK KURZ GEFASST. INDUSTRIE, HANDEL UND DIENSTLEISTUNGEN. Text in German. m. charts. **Document type:** *Government.*
Former titles (until 1999): Eurostat. Statistik Kurzgefasst. Energie und Industrie (1024-4344); (until 1994): Eurostat. Schnellberichte. Energie und Industrie (1017-5822)
Related titles: ♦ English ed.: Eurostat Statistics in Focus. Industry, Trade and Services. ISSN 1561-4840; ♦ French ed.: Eurostat Statistiques en Bref. Industrie, Commerce et Services. ISSN 1561-4859.
Published by: European Commission, Statistical Office of the European Communities, Rue Alcide de Gasperi, Luxembourg, 2920, Luxembourg. TEL 352-4301-34526, FAX 352-4301-34415, eurostat-infodesk@cec.eu.int, http://www.europa.eu.int/comm/eurostat. **Dist. in the U.S. by:** Unipub, 4611-F Assembly Drive, Lanham, MD 20706-4391. TEL 800-274-4888.

330.9 LUX ISSN 1024-431X
EUROSTAT STATISTIK KURZ GEFASST. WIRTSCHAFT UND FINANZEN. Text in German. m. charts. **Document type:** *Government.*
Formerly (until 1994): Eurostat. Schnellberichte. Wirtschaft und Finanzen (1017-5814)
Related titles: ♦ English ed.: Eurostat Statistics in Focus. Economy and Finance. ISSN 1024-4298; ♦ French ed.: Eurostat Statistiques en Bref. Economie et Finances. ISSN 1024-4301.
Published by: European Commission, Statistical Office of the European Communities, Rue Alcide de Gasperi, Luxembourg, 2920, Luxembourg. TEL 352-4301-34526, FAX 352-4301-33415, eurostat-infodesk@cec.eu.int, http://www.europa.eu.int/comm/eurostat. **Dist. in the U.S. by:** Unipub, 4611-F Assembly Drive, Lanham, MD 20706-4391. TEL 800-274-4888.

330 LUX ISSN 1609-6002
EUROSTAT STATISTIK KURZ GEFASST. WISSENSCHAFT UND TECHNOLOGIE. Text in German. 1995. m. charts. **Document type:** *Government.*
Formerly (until 2001): Eurostat. Statistik Kurzgefasst. Forschung und Entwicklung (1024-798X)
Related titles: ♦ English ed.: Eurostat Statistics in Focus. Science and Technology. ISSN 1609-5995; ♦ French ed.: Eurostat Statistiques en Bref. Science et Technologie. ISSN 1609-5987.
Published by: European Commission, Statistical Office of the European Communities, Rue Alcide de Gasperi, Luxembourg, 2920, Luxembourg. TEL 352-4301-34526, FAX 352-4301-34415. **Dist. in the U.S by:** Unipub, 4611-F Assembly Drive, Lanham, MD 20706-4391. TEL 800-274-4888.

330.9 LUX ISSN 1024-4301
EUROSTAT STATISTIQUES EN BREF. ECONOMIE ET FINANCES. Text in French. m. charts. **Document type:** *Bulletin, Government.*
Formerly (until 1994): Eurostat. Statistiques Rapides. Economie et Finances (1015-8944)
Related titles: ♦ English ed.: Eurostat Statistics in Focus. Economy and Finance. ISSN 1024-4298; ♦ German ed.: Eurostat Statistik Kurz Gefasst. Wirtschaft und Finanzen. ISSN 1024-431X.
Published by: European Commission, Statistical Office of the European Communities, Rue Alcide de Gasperi, Luxembourg, 2920, Luxembourg. TEL 352-4301-34526, FAX 352-4301-33415, eurostat-infodesk@cec.eu.int, http://www.europa.eu.int/comm/eurostat. **Dist. in the U.S. by:** Unipub, 4611-F Assembly Drive, Lanham, MD 20706-4391. TEL 800-274-4888.

330.9 333.79 LUX ISSN 1561-4859
EUROSTAT STATISTIQUES EN BREF. INDUSTRIE, COMMERCE ET SERVICES. Text in French. m. charts. **Document type:** *Government.*
Former titles: Eurostat. Statistiques en Bref. Energie et Industrie (1024-4336); (until 1994): Eurostat. Statistiques Rapides. Energie et Industrie (1015-891X)
Related titles: ♦ English ed.: Eurostat Statistics in Focus. Industry, Trade and Services. ISSN 1561-4840; ♦ German ed.: Eurostat Statistik Kurz Gefasst. Industrie, Handel und Dienstleistungen. ISSN 1561-4832.
Published by: European Commission, Statistical Office of the European Communities, Rue Alcide de Gasperi, Luxembourg, 2920, Luxembourg. TEL 352-4301-34526, FAX 352-4301-33415, eurostat-infodesk@cec.eu.int, http://www.europa.eu.int/comm/eurostat. **Dist. in the U.S. by:** Unipub, 4611-F Assembly Drive, Lanham, MD 20706-4391. TEL 800-274-4888.

330.9 LUX ISSN 1024-4360
EUROSTAT STATISTIQUES EN BREF. POPULATION ET CONDITIONS SOCIALES. Text in French. m. charts. **Document type:** *Government.*
Formerly (until 1994): Eurostat. Statistiques Rapides. Population et Conditions Sociales (1015-3306)
Related titles: ♦ English ed.: Eurostat Statistics in Focus. Population and Social Conditions. ISSN 1024-4352; ♦ German ed.: Eurostat Statistik Kurz Gefasst. Bevoelkerung und Soziale Bedingungen. ISSN 1024-4379.
Published by: European Commission, Statistical Office of the European Communities, Rue Alcide de Gasperi, Luxembourg, 2920, Luxembourg. TEL 352-4301-34526, FAX 352-4301-34415, eurostat-infodesk@cec.eu.int, http://www.europa.eu.int/comm/eurostat. **Dist. in the U.S. by:** Unipub, 4611-F Assembly Drive, Lanham, MD 20706-4391. TEL 800-274-4888.

330 LUX ISSN 1609-5987
EUROSTAT STATISTIQUES EN BREF. SCIENCE ET TECHNOLOGIE. Text in French. 1995. m. charts. **Document type:** *Government.*
Formerly (until 2001): Eurostat. Statistiques en Bref. Recherche et Developpement (1024-7963)
Related titles: ♦ English ed.: Eurostat Statistics in Focus. Science and Technology. ISSN 1609-5995; ♦ German ed.: Eurostat Statistik Kurz Gefasst. Wissenschaft und Technologie. ISSN 1609-6002.
Published by: European Commission, Statistical Office of the European Communities, Rue Alcide de Gasperi, Luxembourg, 2920, Luxembourg. TEL 352-4301-34526, FAX 352-4301-33415. **Dist. in the U.S. by:** Unipub, 4611-F Assembly Drive, Lanham, MD 20706-4391. TEL 800-274-4888.

330 LUX ISSN 0252-8266
HC241.2.A1
EUROSTATISTICS DATA FOR SHORT TERM ECONOMIC ANALYSIS. Text in English. m. USD 180 (effective 2005).
Description: Enables the reader to keep a close watch on general economic and social trends in the European Community.
Formerly: Eurostatistics
Related titles: Microfiche ed.: (from CIS); Online - full text ed.
Indexed: IIS.
—BLDSC (3830.445000).
Published by: (European Commission, Statistical Office of the European Communities), European Commission, Office for Official Publications of the European Union, 2 Rue Mercier, Luxembourg, L-2985, Luxembourg. **Subscr. in U.S. to:** Bernan Associates, Bernan, 4611-F Assembly Dr., Lanham, MD 20706-4391. TEL 301-459-0056.

EXPORT STATISTICAL SCHEDULE OF JAPAN (YEAR). see *BUSINESS AND ECONOMICS—International Commerce*

332.6021 CAN ISSN 1181-6724
EXPORTS BY COUNTRIES. Text in English. q.
—CISTI.
Published by: Statistics Canada, External Trade Division, Statistical Reference Centre, Rm 1500, Main Building, Holland Avenue, Ottawa, ON K1A 0T6, Canada. TEL 613-951-8116.

▼ new title ➤ refereed ✶ unverified ♦ full entry avail.

382 GMB ISSN 0303-9277
CODEN: CRSYD2
EXTERNAL TRADE STATISTICS OF GAMBIA. Variant title: Gambia. Central Statistics Department. Annual Report of External Trade Statistics. Text in English. 1973. a. GMD 25.
Published by: Central Statistics Department, Wellington St., Banjul, Gambia.

332.6 GHA ISSN 0435-8805
HF266.G6
EXTERNAL TRADE STATISTICS OF GHANA (ANNUAL). Text in English. 1951. a. USD 60. **Document type:** *Government.*
Published by: Statistical Service, Information Section, PO Box 1098, Accra, Ghana. TEL 233-21-663758, FAX 233-21-667069, TELEX 2205 MIFAEP GH.

332.6 GHA
EXTERNAL TRADE STATISTICS OF GHANA (HALF-YEARLY). Text in English. s-a. USD 30. **Document type:** *Government.*
Published by: Statistical Service, Information Section, PO Box 1098, Accra, Ghana. TEL 233-21-663758, FAX 233-21-667069.

382 GHA ISSN 0855-1049
HF266.G6
EXTERNAL TRADE STATISTICS OF GHANA (QUARTERLY). Text in English. 1993. q. USD 30. **Document type:** *Government.*
Published by: Statistical Service, Information Section, PO Box 1098, Accra, Ghana. TEL 233-21-663758, FAX 233-21-667069.

EXTRACTION SYSTEM OF AGRICULTURAL STATISTICS/SYSTEME D'EXTRACTION DES STATISTIQUES AGRICOLES. see *AGRICULTURE—Abstracting, Bibliographies, Statistics*

016.3380973 USA ISSN 1076-4941
F & S INDEX. UNITED STATES (ANNUAL). Text in English. 1964. a. USD 1,625 (effective 2005). **Description:** Provides information on corporate acquisitions and mergers, new products, technological developments, and social and political factors affecting business.
Former titles (until 1993): Predicasts F & S Index. United States (Annual) (0277-9676); (until 1979): F & S Index of Corporations and Industries (0014-567X)
—CISTI. **CCC.**
Published by: Gale Group (Subsidiary of: Thomson Corporation), 27500 Drake Rd, Farmington Hills, MI 48331-3535. TEL 248-699-4253, 800-877-4253, FAX 800-414-5043, gale.galeord@thomson.com, http://www.gale.com.

332 USA
F D I C STATISTICS ON BANKING. Text in English. q. free. **Document type:** *Government.*
Media: Online - full content.
Published by: U.S. Federal Deposit Insurance Corp., 550 17th St, N W, Washington, DC 20429. TEL 202-416-6940, 800-276-6003, FAX 202-416-2076, publicinfo@fdic.gov, http://www2.fdic.gov/SDI/SOB/, http://www.fdic.gov.

338 016 NGA
F I I R O INDUSTRIAL ABSTRACTS. Text in English. 1976. q. **Document type:** *Government.*
Published by: Federal Institute of Industrial Research Oshodi, PMB 21023, Ikeja, Lagos, Nigeria. Circ: 200.

330 DEU
FACHBUCHVERZEICHNIS WIRTSCHAFTSWISSENSCHAFTEN. Text in German. a. **Document type:** *Bibliography.*
Published by: Rossipaul Kommunikation GmbH, Menzinger Str 37, Munich, 80638, Germany. TEL 49-89-179106-0, FAX 49-89-17910622. Ed. Angela Sendlinger. Circ: 25,000 (controlled).

330 CAN ISSN 0838-3715
FAMILY EXPENDITURE IN CANADA. Text in English. 1971. irreg. CND 38 domestic; USD 46 foreign. **Description:** Offers a comprehensive look at the budgets of families and unattached individuals belonging to variety of demographic and economic groups.
Former titles (until 1978): Urban Family Expenditure (0837-9297); (until 1972): Urban Family Expenditure on Shelter and Household Durables (0837-5399); Which was formed by the merger of (1953-1971): Family Expenditure in Canada (0837-5372); Which was formerly (until 1969): Urban Family Expenditure (0576-0038); (until 1959): City Family Expenditure (0821-0861); (1969-1971): Depenses des Familles au Canada (0837-5380)
—CISTI.
Published by: Statistics Canada, Operations and Integration Division, Circulation Management, Jean Talon Bldg, 2 C12, Tunney's Pasture, Ottawa, ON K1A 0T6, Canada. TEL 613-951-7277, 800-267-6677, FAX 613-951-1584, http://www.statcan.ca.

330 CAN ISSN 0838-3898
FAMILY FOOD EXPENDITURE IN CANADA. Text in English. 1982. biennial. CND 28 domestic; USD 28 foreign. **Description:** Offers a comprehensive look at food expenditure detail of families and unattached individuals living in both urban and rural areas of Canada classified by a variety of demographic and economic groups.
—CISTI.
Published by: Statistics Canada, Operations and Integration Division, Circulation Management, Jean Talon Bldg, 2 C12, Tunney's Pasture, Ottawa, ON K1A 0T6, Canada. TEL 613-951-7277, 800-267-6677, FAX 613-951-1584, http://www.statcan.ca.

332 USA
Z7164.F5
FED IN PRINT (ONLINE EDITION); economics and banking topics. Text in English. 1969. s-a. free (effective 2005). **Document type:** *Database, Abstract/Index.*
Formerly: Fed in Print (Print Edition) (0891-2769)
Media: Online - full text.
Published by: Federal Reserve Bank of San Francisco, PO Box 7702, San Francisco, CA 94120. TEL 415-974-2163, 888-339-3506, http://www.frbsf.org/publications/fedinprint/index.html. Circ: 2,400.

352.63 USA
FEDERAL CIVILIAN WORKFORCE STATISTICS. AFFIRMATIVE EMPLOYMENT STATISTICS. Text in English. 1965. biennial. **Document type:** *Government.*
Former titles: Federal Civilian Workforce Statistics. Equal Employment Opportunity Statistics; Federal Civilian Work Force Statistics. Minority Group Employment in the Federal Government; Federal Civilian Manpower Statistics. Minority Group Employment in the Federal Government; Minority Group Employment in the Federal Government; Study of Minority Group Employment in the Federal Government
Related titles: Microfiche ed.
Indexed: CISI.
Published by: U.S. Office of Personnel Management, Personnel Systems and Oversight Group, Statistical Analysis and Services Division, Washington, DC 20415. TEL 202-655-4000. Circ: 2,000. **Dist. by:** U.S. Government Printing Office, Superintendent of Documents, PO Box 371954, Pittsburgh, PA 15250-7954. TEL 202-512-1800, FAX 202-512-2250, orders@gpo.gov, http://www.access.gpo.gov.

351.1 317 USA ISSN 1058-0859
JK671
FEDERAL CIVILIAN WORKFORCE STATISTICS. EMPLOYMENT AND TRENDS. Text in English. 1969. bi-m. USD 11; USD 13.75 foreign. back issues avail.; reprint service avail. from CIS. **Document type:** *Government.* **Description:** Presents employment information on civilians working for the federal government on the basis of reports received from each department and agency.
Former titles: Federal Civilian Workforce Statistics. Monthly Release (0163-8270); (until 1976): Federal Civilian Manpower Statistics. Monthly Release (0090-7227)
Related titles: Microfiche ed.: (from CIS).
Indexed: AmStI, CISI.
Published by: U.S. Office of Personnel Management, Personnel Systems and Oversight Group, Office of Workforce Information, 1900 E St, N W, Washington, DC 20415. TEL 202-606-1178. Circ: 950 (controlled). **Subscr. to:** U.S. Government Printing Office, Superintendent of Documents, PO Box 371954, Pittsburgh, PA 15250-7954. TEL 202-512-1800, FAX 202-512-2250.

352.63 USA
FEDERAL CIVILIAN WORKFORCE STATISTICS. PAY STRUCTURE OF THE FEDERAL CIVIL SERVICE. Text in English. 1947. a. USD 15.95. charts. **Document type:** *Government.*
Former titles: Federal Civilian Manpower Statistics. Pay Structure of the Federal Civil Service; Pay Structure of the Federal Civil Service
Related titles: Microfiche ed.
Indexed: CISI.
Published by: U.S. Office of Personnel Management, Personnel Systems and Oversight Group, Statistical Analysis and Services Division, Washington, DC 20415. TEL 703-487-4650, FAX 202-606-1719. Circ: 900 (controlled). **Subscr. to:** National Technical Information Service, Government Research Center, 5285 Port Royal Rd, Springfield, VA 22161.

352.36021 USA ISSN 0277-3325
JK776
FEDERAL CIVILIAN WORKFORCE STATISTICS. WORK YEARS AND PERSONNEL COSTS. EXECUTIVE BRANCH, UNITED STATES GOVERNMENT. Text in English. 1970. a. USD 17. charts. **Document type:** *Government.*
Former titles: Work-Years and Personnel Costs. Executive Branch of the United States Government; Work-Years and Personnel Costs. Executive Branch, U.S. Government; Man-Years and Personnel Costs. Executive Branch, U.S. Government
Related titles: Microfiche ed.
Published by: U.S. Office of Personnel Management, Personnel Systems and Oversight Group, Office of Workforce Information, 1900 E St, N W, Washington, DC 20415. TEL 703-487-4650. Circ: 400 (controlled). **Subscr. to:** National Technical Information Service, Government Research Center, 5285 Port Royal Rd, Springfield, VA 22161. TEL 703-605-6060, 800-363-2068, http://www.ntis.gov.

338.973021 USA ISSN 0747-5616
FEDERAL R & D FUNDING BY BUDGET FUNCTION. Text in English. 1972. a.
Formerly (until 1980): An Analysis of Federal R & D Funding by Function (0145-4625)
—Linda Hall.
Published by: U.S. National Science Foundation, Division of Science Resources Statistics, 4201 Wilson Blvd., Suite 965, Arlington, VA 22230. TEL 703-292-8774, FAX 703-292-9092, srsweb@nsf.gov, http://www.nsf.gov/sbe/srs/frdfbf/.

338 319 FJI ISSN 0259-6024
FIJI. BUREAU OF STATISTICS. CENSUS OF DISTRIBUTION AND SERVICES. Text in English. 1971. irreg. USD 5 per issue (effective 2000). **Document type:** *Government.*
Published by: Bureau of Statistics, c/o Librarian, Govt. Bldg. 5, PO Box 2221, Suva, Fiji. TEL 679-315-822, FAX 679-303-656.

338 FJI
FIJI. BUREAU OF STATISTICS. CENSUS OF INDUSTRIES. Text in English. 1968. a., latest 1993. USD 5 (effective 2000). **Document type:** *Government.*
Formerly: Fiji. Bureau of Statistics. Census of Industrial Production (0259-6032)
Published by: Bureau of Statistics, c/o Librarian, Govt. Bldg. 5, PO Box 2221, Suva, Fiji. TEL 679-315-822, FAX 679-303-656.

330 319 FJI ISSN 0015-0894
FIJI. BUREAU OF STATISTICS. CURRENT ECONOMIC STATISTICS. Text in English. 1969. q. USD 5 per issue (effective 2000). charts. **Document type:** *Government.*
Supersedes: Fiji. Bureau of Statistics. Quarterly Statistical Summary
Media: Duplicated (not offset).
Published by: Bureau of Statistics, c/o Librarian, Govt. Bldg. 5, PO Box 2221, Suva, Fiji. TEL 679-315-822, FAX 679-303-656. Circ: 580.

336 FJI
FIJI. BUREAU OF STATISTICS. ECONOMIC AND FUNCTIONAL CLASSIFICATION OF GOVERNMENT ACCOUNTS. Text in English. 1968. irreg., latest 1986. USD 5 per issue (effective 2001). **Document type:** *Government.*
Published by: Bureau of Statistics, c/o Librarian, Govt. Bldg. 5, PO Box 2221, Suva, Fiji. TEL 679-315-822, FAX 679-303-656, statsfiji@govt.fj.

331.021 FJI
FIJI. BUREAU OF STATISTICS. EMPLOYMENT SURVEY OF FIJI. Text in English. 1969. a., latest 1996. USD 5 (effective 2000). **Document type:** *Government.*
Published by: Bureau of Statistics, c/o Librarian, Govt. Bldg. 5, PO Box 2221, Suva, Fiji. TEL 679-315-822, FAX 679-303-656.

315 339 FJI
FIJI. BUREAU OF STATISTICS. FIJI HOUSEHOLD INCOME AND EXPENDITURE SURVEY. Text in English. 1973. irreg., latest 1977. USD 5 (effective 2000). stat. **Document type:** *Government.*
Published by: Bureau of Statistics, c/o Librarian, Govt. Bldg. 5, PO Box 2221, Suva, Fiji. TEL 679-315-822, FAX 679-303-656.

331.137 FJI
FIJI. BUREAU OF STATISTICS. NATIONWIDE UNEMPLOYMENT SURVEY. Text in English. 1973. irreg. USD 5 per issue (effective 2000). **Document type:** *Government.*
Published by: Bureau of Statistics, c/o Librarian, Govt. Bldg. 5, PO Box 2221, Suva, Fiji. TEL 679-315-822, FAX 679-303-656.

382.021 FJI
FIJI. BUREAU OF STATISTICS. OVERSEAS TRADE (YEAR). Text in English. irreg. stat. **Document type:** *Government.*
Published by: Burea of Statistics, PO Box 98, Suva, Fiji. TEL 679-385999, FAX 679-370203.

380 FJI
FIJI. BUREAU OF STATISTICS. SURVEY OF DISTRIBUTIVE TRADE. Text in English. irreg., latest 1994. USD 5 (effective 2000 - 2001). **Document type:** *Government.*
Published by: Bureau of Statistics, c/o Librarian, Govt. Bldg. 5, PO Box 2221, Suva, Fiji. TEL 679-315-822, FAX 679-303-656.

382 FJI
FIJI. BUREAU OF STATISTICS. TRADE REPORT. Text in English. 1939. a., latest 1988. USD 15 (effective 2000). **Document type:** *Government.*
Published by: Bureau of Statistics, c/o Librarian, Govt. Bldg. 5, PO Box 2221, Suva, Fiji. TEL 679-315-822, FAX 679-303-656.

B

330.9 FJI
FIJI. BUREAU OF STATISTICS. VITAL STATISTICS. Text in English. 1976. irreg., latest 1988. USD 5 (effective 2000). **Document type:** *Government.* **Description:** Includes statistics on births, marriages and deaths.
Published by: Bureau of Statistics, c/o Librarian, Govt. Bldg. 5, PO Box 2221, Suva, Fiji. TEL 679-315-822, FAX 679-303-656.

330 FJI
FIJI FACTS AND FIGURES. Text in English. 1975. a., latest 1997. free. **Document type:** *Government.*
Published by: Bureau of Statistics, c/o Librarian, Govt. Bldg. 5, PO Box 2221, Suva, Fiji. TEL 679-315-822, FAX 679-303-656.

332.1 USA ISSN 1066-7350
HG181
FINANCE, INSURANCE AND REAL ESTATE U S A. Text in English. 1993. biennial, latest 1998, Edition 4. USD 235 (effective 2003). **Document type:** *Trade.* **Description:** Contains statistics in these areas of the American economy.
Published by: Gale Group (Subsidiary of: Thomson Corporation), 27500 Drake Rd, Farmington Hills, MI 48331-3535. TEL 248-699-8061, 800-877-4253, FAX 248-699-4253, galeord@gale.com, http://www.gale.com. Ed. Arsen J Darnay.

330 CAN ISSN 0380-075X
HG185.C2
FINANCIAL INSTITUTIONS, FINANCIAL STATISTICS. Text in English. 1963. q. CND 176, USD 211 domestic; USD 246 foreign. **Description:** Focuses on the financial position and operations of financial institutions, financial intermediaries and investment funds operating in Canada.
—CISTI.
Published by: Statistics Canada, Operations and Integration Division, Circulation Management, Jean Talon Bldg, 2 C12, Tunney's Pasture, Ottawa, ON K1A 0T6, Canada. TEL 613-951-7277, 800-267-6677, FAX 613-951-1584, http://www.statcan.ca.

332 GBR
FINANCIAL JOURNALS INDEX. Text in English. 1995. m. adv. cum.index. back issues avail. **Document type:** *Abstract/Index.*
Formed by the merger of (1992-1995): Pensions Journals Index (0966-825X); (1992-1995): Insurance Journals Index (0966-8241); (1993-1995): Banking Journals Index
Related titles: CD-ROM ed.; Online - full text ed.
Published by: Sweet & Maxwell Ltd., The Hatchery, Hall Bank Ln, Mytholmroyd, Hebden Bridge, W Yorks HX7 5HQ, United Kingdom. TEL 44-1422-888000, FAX 44-1422-888001, julie.lord@itps.co.uk, customer.services@sweetandmaxwell.co.uk, http://www.sweetandmaxwell.co.uk. Ed. Nigel Smith.

336.52 JPN ISSN 0289-1522
HG41
FINANCIAL STATISTICS OF JAPAN. Text in Japanese. 1952. a. free. **Document type:** *Government.*
Formerly (until 1983): Japan. Finance Department. Quarterly Bulletin of Financial Statistics (0447-4740)
Published by: Ministry of Finance, Institute of Fiscal and Monetary Policy/Okura-sho, 3-1-1 Kasumigaseki, Chiyoda-ku, Tokyo, 100-0013, Japan.

016.72 GBR ISSN 1369-9938
FINANCIAL TIMES INDEX (ANNUAL). Key Title: Official Index to the Financial Times. Text in English. a. USD 1,181.90 (effective 1996). **Document type:** *Abstract/Index.*
Formerly (until 1997): Annual Index to the Financial Times (0263-6891)
Related titles: CD-ROM ed.; Microform ed.; ◆ Cumulative ed. of: Financial Times Index (Monthly). ISSN 0265-4237.
Published by: Primary Source Microfilm (Subsidiary of: Gale Group), High Holborn House, 50/51 Bedford Row, London, WC1R 4LR, United Kingdom. TEL 44-20-70672663, FAX 44-20-70672600, psmcs@gale.com, http://www.galegroup.com/psm/. Pub. Mark Holland.

330 011 GBR ISSN 0265-4237
FINANCIAL TIMES INDEX (MONTHLY). Key Title: Monthly Index to The Financial Times. Text in English. 1981. m. Contact pubblisher for pricing.. back issues avail. **Document type:** *Abstract/Index.* **Description:** Contains concise, informative abstracts with complete with page, date and column references that direct users to the relevant articles in the full-image microfilm edition of the newspaper.
Related titles: CD-ROM ed.; Microform ed.: 1981; Online - full text ed.: 1981 (from The Dialog Corporation); ◆ Cumulative ed(s).: Financial Times Index (Annual). ISSN 1369-9938.
Published by: Primary Source Microfilm (Subsidiary of: Gale Group), High Holborn House, 50/51 Bedford Row, London, WC1R 4LR, United Kingdom. TEL 44-20-70672663, FAX 44-20-70672600, psmcs@gale.com, http://www.galegroup.com/psm/. Pub. Mark Holland.

336 MEX ISSN 0187-4853
HJ15
FINANZAS PUBLICAS ESTATALES Y MUNICIPALES DE MEXICO. Text in Spanish. 1984. irreg. price varies.
Published by: Instituto Nacional de Estadistica, Geografia e Informatica, Secretaria de Programacion y Presupuesto, Prol. Heroe de Nacozari 2301 Sur, Puerta 11, Acceso, Aguascalientes, 20270, Mexico. TEL 52-4-918-1948, FAX 52-4-918-0739, http://www.inegi.gob.mx. Circ: 1,500.

331.2 FIN ISSN 0784-8218
FINLAND. TILASTOKESKUS. ANSIOTASOINDEKSI/FINLAND. STATISTICS FINLAND. INDEX OF WAGE AND SALARY EARNINGS. Text in Finnish, Swedish. 1979. q. EUR 37; EUR 13 per issue (effective 2005). **Document type:** *Government.*
Formerly (until 1988): Finland. Tilastokeskus. Indeksitiedotus AT. Palkansaajien Ansiotasoindeksi (0357-7201)
Related titles: Online - full content ed.: ISSN 0789-7294. FIM 800 (effective 2000).
Indexed: RASB.
Published by: Tilastokeskus/Statistics Finland, Tyopajakatu 13, Statistics Finland, Helsinki, 00022, Finland. TEL 358-9-17341, FAX 358-9-17342750, http://www.stat.fi/.

331.021 FIN ISSN 0789-2462
HB235.F56
FINLAND. TILASTOKESKUS. HINTA- JA PALKKATIEDOTE. Text in Finnish. 1991. 5/yr. EUR 32; EUR 10 per issue (effective 2005). **Document type:** *Government.*
Related titles: ◆ English ed.: Finland. Tilastokeskus. Prices and Wages Review. ISSN 1239-2847; ◆ Series of: Finland. Tilastokeskus. Palkat. ISSN 0784-8374.
Published by: Tilastokeskus/Statistics Finland, Tyopajakatu 13, Statistics Finland, Helsinki, 00022, Finland. TEL 358-9-17341, FAX 358-9-17342750, http://www.stat.fi/.

FINLAND. TILASTOKESKUS. HYVINVOINTIKATSAUS. see *SOCIAL SERVICES AND WELFARE—Abstracting, Bibliographies, Statistics*

330 FIN ISSN 1459-1219
FINLAND. TILASTOKESKUS. I B S WORLD NEWSLETTER. Text in Multiple languages. 1994. m. EUR 499 (effective 2005). **Document type:** *Newsletter, Government.*
Formerly (until 2002): Finland. Tilastokeskus. International Business Statistics (1236-7540)
Published by: Tilastokeskus/Statistics Finland, Tyopajakatu 13, Statistics Finland, Helsinki, 00022, Finland. TEL 358-9-17341, FAX 358-9-17342750, http://www.stat.fi/.

332.021 FIN ISSN 0784-9788
FINLAND. TILASTOKESKUS. JOUKKOVELKAKIRJAT/FINLAND. STATISTKCENTRALEN. MASSKULDEBREV. Text in Finnish, Swedish. 1971. a. EUR 16.82 (effective 2001). **Document type:** *Government.*
Formerly (until 1987): Finland. Tilastokeskus. Tilastotiedotus - Tilastokeskus. RT, Rahoitus (0355-2322)
Related titles: ◆ Series of: Finland. Tilastokeskus. Rahoitus. ISSN 0784-8382.
Published by: Tilastokeskus/Statistics Finland, Tyopajakatu 13, Statistics Finland, Helsinki, 00022, Finland. TEL 358-9-17341, FAX 358-9-17342750, http://www.stat.fi/.

330 FIN ISSN 0784-8323
FINLAND. TILASTOKESKUS. JULKINEN TALOUS. Text in Finnish. 1982. 6/yr. EUR 111 (effective 2005). **Document type:** *Government.*
Supersedes in part (in 1986): Finland. Tilastokeskus. Tilastotiedotus - Tilastokeskus. JT, Julkisyhteisot (0359-081X)
Related titles: ◆ Series: Finland. Tilastokeskus. Kuntayhtymien Talous. ISSN 1238-4909; ◆ Finland. Tilastokeskus. Kuntayhtymien Talousarviot. ISSN 1236-6595; ◆ Finland. Tilastokeskus. Kuntien Talous ja Toiminta. ISSN 1239-1980; ◆ Finland. Tilastokeskus. Julkisyhteisojen Alijaama ja Bruttovelka EMU-Kriteerien Mukaisina. ISSN 1238-6111.
Published by: Tilastokeskus/Statistics Finland, Tyopajakatu 13, Statistics Finland, Helsinki, 00022, Finland. TEL 358-9-17341, FAX 358-9-17342750, http://www.stat.fi/.

330.021 FIN ISSN 1238-6111
FINLAND. TILASTOKESKUS. JULKISYHTEISOJEN ALIJAAMA JA BRUTTOVELKA EMU-KRITEERIEN MUKAISINA. Text in Finnish. 1995. a. EUR 9 (effective 2005). **Document type:** *Government.*
Related titles: ◆ Series of: Finland. Tilastokeskus. Julkinen Talous. ISSN 0784-8323.
Published by: Tilastokeskus/Statistics Finland, Tyopajakatu 13, Statistics Finland, Helsinki, 00022, Finland. TEL 358-9-17341, FAX 358-9-17342750, http://www.stat.fi/.

330 FIN ISSN 1235-3981
FINLAND. TILASTOKESKUS. KANSANTALOUDEN TILINPITO. Text in Finnish. q.
Media: Diskette. **Related titles:** Alternate Frequency ed(s).: ISSN 0789-5089. s-a.
Published by: Tilastokeskus/Statistics Finland, Tyopajakatu 13, Statistics Finland, Helsinki, 00022, Finland. TEL 358-9-17341.

330.021 FIN ISSN 0784-9613
HC340.2.Z9
FINLAND. TILASTOKESKUS. KANSANTALOUDEN TILINPITO. TAULUKOT/FINLAND. STATISTICS FINLAND. NATIONAL ACCOUNTS. TABLES/FINLAND. STATISTIKCENTRALEN. NATIONALRAEKENSKAPERNA. TABELLER. Text and summaries in English, Finnish, Swedish. 1968. a. EUR 55 (effective 2005). **Document type:** *Government.*
Supersedes in part (in 1987): Finland. Tilastokeskus. KT, Kansantalouden Tilinpito (0355-2276)
Related titles: ◆ Series of: Finland. Tilastokeskus. Kansantalous. ISSN 0784-8331.
—CISTI.
Published by: Tilastokeskus/Statistics Finland, Tyopajakatu 13, Statistics Finland, Helsinki, 00022, Finland. TEL 358-9-17341, FAX 358-9-17342750, http://www.stat.fi/.

330 FIN ISSN 0784-834X
FINLAND. TILASTOKESKUS. KAUPPA/FINLAND TILASTOKESKUS. TRADE. Text in Finnish, English, Swedish. 1968. m. EUR 70 (effective 2005). **Document type:** *Government.*
Formerly (until 1988): Finland. Tilastokeskus. KA, Kauppa (0355-225X)
Published by: Tilastokeskus/Statistics Finland, Tyopajakatu 13, Statistics Finland, Helsinki, 00022, Finland. TEL 358-9-17341, FAX 358-9-17342750, http://www.stat.fi/.

FINLAND. TILASTOKESKUS. KIINTEISTON YLLAPIDON KUSTANNUSINDEKSI. see *HOUSING AND URBAN PLANNING—Abstracting, Bibliographies, Statistics*

330 FIN ISSN 0784-820X
FINLAND. TILASTOKESKUS. KULUTTAJAHINTAINDEKSI. Text in Finnish. m. EUR 63; EUR 9 per issue (effective 2005). stat. **Document type:** *Government.*
Published by: Tilastokeskus/Statistics Finland, Tyopajakatu 13, Statistics Finland, Helsinki, 00022, Finland. TEL 358-9-17341.

331.021 FIN ISSN 1459-6369
JS6294.A35
FINLAND. TILASTOKESKUS. KUNTASEKTORIN PALKAT/FINLAND. STATISTIKCENTRALEN. MAANADSLOENER FOER KOMMUNALANSTAELLDA. Text in Finnish, Swedish. 1988. a., latest 2004. EUR 33 (effective 2005). **Document type:** *Government.*
Formerly (until 2003): Finland. Tilastokeskus. Kuntasektorin Kuukausipalkat (0784-9370)
Related titles: ◆ Series of: Finland. Tilastokeskus. Palkat. ISSN 0784-8374.
Published by: Tilastokeskus/Statistics Finland, Tyopajakatu 13, Statistics Finland, Helsinki, 00022, Finland. TEL 358-9-17341, FAX 358-9-17342750.

331.021 FIN ISSN 1459-6377
FINLAND. TILASTOKESKUS. KUNTASEKTORIN PALKAT AMMATEITTAIN. Text in Finnish, Swedish. 1989. a., latest 2004. EUR 20 (effective 2005). **Document type:** *Government.*
Former titles (until 2003): Finland. Tilastokeskus. Kuntien Kuukausipalkat Ammateittain (1239-8179); (until 1995): Finland. Tilastokeskus. Kunnallinen Virkaluettelo (0786-3624)
Related titles: ◆ Series of: Finland. Tilastokeskus. Palkat. ISSN 0784-8374.
Published by: Tilastokeskus/Statistics Finland, Tyopajakatu 13, Statistics Finland, Helsinki, 00022, Finland. TEL 358-9-17341, FAX 358-9-17342750, http://www.stat.fi/.

331.021 FIN ISSN 1457-5590
FINLAND. TILASTOKESKUS. KUNTASEKTORIN TUNTIPALKAT/FINLAND. STATISTIKCENTRALEN. TIMLOENER I KOMMUNERNA. Text in Finnish, Swedish. 1992. a. EUR 11.77 (effective 2001). **Document type:** *Government.*
Former titles (until 2000): Finland. Tilastokeskus. Kuntien Tuntipalkat (1455-3775); (until 1997): Finland. Tilastokeskus. Julkisen Sektorin Tuntipalkat (1235-7154); Which was formed by the merger of (1988-1991): Finland. Tilastokeskus. Kuntasektorin Tuntipalkat (0784-9397); (1988-1991): Finland. Tilastokeskus. Valtion Tuntipalkat (0784-9524)
Related titles: ◆ Series of: Finland. Tilastokeskus. Palkat. ISSN 0784-8374.
Published by: Tilastokeskus/Statistics Finland, Tyopajakatu 13, Statistics Finland, Helsinki, 00022, Finland. TEL 358-9-17341, FAX 358-9-17342750, http://www.stat.fi/.

330.021 FIN ISSN 1238-4909
FINLAND. TILASTOKESKUS. KUNTAYHTYMIEN TALOUS/FINLAND. STATISTIKCENTRALEN. SAMKOMMUNERNAS EKONOMI. Text in Finnish, Swedish. 1972. a., latest 2003. EUR 18 (effective 2005). **Document type:** *Government.*
Formerly (until 1994): Finland. Tilastokeskus. Kuntainliittojen Talous (0784-9699); Which superseded in part (1982-1986): Tilastotiedotus - Tilastokeskus. J T, Julkisyhteisot (0359-081X)
Related titles: ◆ Series of: Finland. Tilastokeskus. Julkinen Talous. ISSN 0784-8323.
Published by: Tilastokeskus/Statistics Finland, Tyopajakatu 13, Statistics Finland, Helsinki, 00022, Finland. TEL 358-9-17341, FAX 358-9-17342750, http://www.stat.fi/.

330.021 FIN ISSN 1236-6595
FINLAND. TILASTOKESKUS. KUNTAYHTYMIEN TALOUSARVIOT/FINLAND. STATISTIKCENTRALEN. SAMKOMMUNERNAS BUDGETER. Text in Finnish, Swedish. 1982. a., latest 2005. EUR 13 (effective 2005).
Formerly (until 1993): Finland. Tilastokeskus. Kuntainliittojen Talousarviot (0784-9702); Which superseded in part (in 1986): Finland. Tilastokeskus. JT. Julkisyhteisot (0359-081X)
Related titles: ◆ Series of: Finland. Tilastokeskus. Julkinen Talous. ISSN 0784-8323.

B

Published by: Tilastokeskus/Statistics Finland, Tyopajakatu 13, Statistics Finland, Helsinki, 00022, Finland. TEL 358-9-17341, FAX 358-9-17342750, http://www.stat.fi/.

330.021   FIN   ISSN 1239-1980
FINLAND. TILASTOKESKUS. KUNTIEN TALOUS JA TOIMINTA/FINLAND. STATISTIKCENTRALEN. KOMMUNERNAS EKONOMI OCH VERKSAMHET. Text in Finnish, Swedish. 1956. a., latest 2004. EUR 27 (effective 2005). **Document type:** *Government.*
Former titles (until 1995): Finland. Tilastokeskus. Kuntien Talous (0784-9710); (until 1989): Suomen Virallinen Tilasto. 31. Kuntien Finanssitilastoa. (0430-5566); Which was formed by the merger of (1935-1955: Suomen Virallinen Tilasto. 31. Kuntien Finanssitilastoa. A. Kaupunkien ja Kauppalain Finanssit (1239-6362); (1934-1955): Suomen Virallinen Tilasto. 31. Kuntien Finanssitilastoa. B. Kauppalain ja maalaiskuntien Finanssit (1239-6370)
Related titles: ◆ Series of: Finland. Tilastokeskus. Julkinen Talous. ISSN 0784-8323.
Published by: Tilastokeskus/Statistics Finland, Tyopajakatu 13, Statistics Finland, Helsinki, 00022, Finland. TEL 358-9-17341, FAX 358-9-17342750, http://www.stat.fi/.

330.021   FIN   ISSN 1456-4408
FINLAND. TILASTOKESKUS. KUNTIEN TALOUS JA TOIMINTA. KUNNITTAISIA TIETOJA/FINLAND. STATISTIKCENTRALEN. KOMMUNERNAS EKONOMI OCH VERKSAMHET - KOMMUNVISA UPPGIFTER. Text in Finnish, Swedish. 1988. a., latest 2004. EUR 45 (effective 2005). **Document type:** *Government.*
Formerly (until 1998): Finland. Tilastokeskus. Kuntien Talous. Kunnittaisia Tietoja (0784-9729)
Related titles: ◆ Series of: Finland. Tilastokeskus. Rahoitus. ISSN 0784-8382.
Published by: Tilastokeskus/Statistics Finland, Tyopajakatu 13, Statistics Finland, Helsinki, 00022, Finland. TEL 358-9-17341, FAX 358-9-17342750, http://www.stat.fi/.

330.021 314   FIN   ISSN 0784-9737
HJ55.3
FINLAND. TILASTOKESKUS. KUNTIEN TALOUSARVIOT/ FINLAND. STATISTIKCENTRALEN. KOMMUNERNAS BUDGETER/FINLAND.STATISTICS FINLAND. MUNICIPAL FINANCES. (Section XXXI of Official Statistics of Finland) Text in Finnish, Swedish; Summaries in English. 1968. a., latest 2005. EUR 18 (effective 2005). **Document type:** *Government.*
Former titles (until 1988): Finland. Tilastokeskus. Tilastotiedotus - Tilastokeskus. JT, Julkisyhteisot (0359-081X); (until 1982): Finland. Tilastokeskus. Kuntien Finanssitilasto (0430-5566)
Indexed: RASB.
Published by: Tilastokeskus/Statistics Finland, Tyopajakatu 13, Statistics Finland, Helsinki, 00022, Finland. TEL 358-9-17341, FAX 358-9-17342750, http://www.stat.fi/.

FINLAND. TILASTOKESKUS. KUORMA-AUTOLIIKENTEEN KUSTANNUSINDEKSI. see *TRANSPORTATION—Abstracting, Bibliographies, Statistics*

330   FIN   ISSN 0788-723X
FINLAND. TILASTOKESKUS. L Y - TUNNUSKIRJA. Text in Finnish. 1993. s-a. stat. **Document type:** *Government.*
Published by: Tilastokeskus/Statistics Finland, Tyopajakatu 13, Statistics Finland, Helsinki, 00022, Finland. TEL 358-9-17341, FAX 358-9-17342750, http://www.stat.fi/.

336.021   FIN   ISSN 1459-5451
FINLAND. TILASTOKESKUS. LUOTTOKANTA/FINLAND. STATISTIKCENTRALEN. DET REGIONALE KREDITBESTAANDET. Text in Finnish, Swedish. 1981. a., latest 2004. EUR 30 (effective 2005). **Document type:** *Government.*
Former titles (until 2003): Finland. Tilastokeskus. Alueellinen Luottokanta (0784-9761); (until 1989): Finland. Tilastokeskus. Tilastotiedotus - Tilastokeskus. RT, Rahoitus (0355-2322)
Related titles: ◆ Series of: Finland. Tilastokeskus. Rahoitus. ISSN 0784-8382.
Published by: Tilastokeskus/Statistics Finland, Tyopajakatu 13, Statistics Finland, Helsinki, 00022, Finland. TEL 358-9-17341, FAX 358-9-17342750, http://www.stat.fi/.

336.021   FIN   ISSN 0785-7934
FINLAND. TILASTOKESKUS. LUOTTOKORTIT. Text in Finnish. 1989. a. EUR 18.50 (effective 2001). **Document type:** *Government.*
Related titles: ◆ Series of: Finland. Tilastokeskus. Rahoitus. ISSN 0784-8382.
Published by: Tilastokeskus/Statistics Finland, Tyopajakatu 13, Statistics Finland, Helsinki, 00022, Finland. TEL 358-9-17341, FAX 358-9-17342750, http://www.stat.fi/.

FINLAND. TILASTOKESKUS. MAARAKENNUSKUSTANNUSINDEKSI. see *BUILDING AND CONSTRUCTION—Abstracting, Bibliographies, Statistics*

310 314 330   FIN   ISSN 0784-8374
HD5047.3
FINLAND. TILASTOKESKUS. PALKAT/FINLAND. STATISTICS FINLAND. WAGES AND SALARIES. Text in English, Finnish, Swedish. 1968. m. EUR 179 (effective 2005). stat. **Document type:** *Government.*

Formerly (until 1988): Finland. Tilastokeskus. Tilastotiedotus P A. Palkat (0355-2306)
Related titles: ◆ Series: Finland. Tilastokeskus. Kuntasektorin Tuntipalkat. ISSN 1457-5590; ◆ Finland. Tilastokeskus. Kuntasektorin Palkat. ISSN 1459-6369; ◆ Finland. Tilastokeskus. Hinta- ja Palkkatiedote. ISSN 0789-2462; ◆ Finland. Tilastokeskus. Prices and Wages Review. ISSN 1239-2847; ◆ Finland. Tilastokeskus. Valtion Kuukausipalkat. ISSN 0785-8884; ◆ Finland. Tilastokeskus. Yksityisen Sektorin Kuukausipalkat. ISSN 1455-1454; ◆ Finland. Tilastokeskus. Kuntasektorin Palkat Ammateittain. ISSN 1459-6377; ◆ Finland. Tilastokeskus. Palkkarakenne. ISSN 1457-5973; ◆ Finland. Tilastokeskus. Tyotunnin Kustannus. Tyovoimakustannusindeksi. ISSN 1457-084X.
Indexed: RASB.
Published by: Tilastokeskus/Statistics Finland, Tyopajakatu 13, Statistics Finland, Helsinki, 00022, Finland. TEL 358-9-17341, FAX 358-9-17342750, http://www.stat.fi/.

331.021   FIN   ISSN 1457-5973
FINLAND. TILASTOKESKUS. PALKKARAKENNE. Text in Finnish. 1998. a., latest 2003. EUR 27 (effective 2005).
Document type: *Government.*
Formerly (until 1999): Palkkatilasto (0784-8056)
Related titles: ◆ Series of: Finland. Tilastokeskus. Palkat. ISSN 0784-8374.
Published by: Tilastokeskus/Statistics Finland, Tyopajakatu 13, Statistics Finland, Helsinki, 00022, Finland. TEL 358-9-17341, FAX 358-9-17342750, http://www.stat.fi/.

331.021   FIN   ISSN 1239-2847
FINLAND. TILASTOKESKUS. PRICES AND WAGES REVIEW. Text in English. 1995. a. EUR 11.77 (effective 2001). **Document type:** *Government.*
Related titles: ◆ Finnish ed.: Finland. Tilastokeskus. Hinta- ja Palkkatiedote. ISSN 0789-2462; ◆ Series of: Finland. Tilastokeskus. Palkat. ISSN 0784-8374.
Published by: Tilastokeskus/Statistics Finland, Tyopajakatu 13, Statistics Finland, Helsinki, 00022, Finland. TEL 358-9-17341, FAX 358-9-17342750, http://www.stat.fi/.

336.0021   FIN   ISSN 1795-2050
HG3729.F49
FINLAND. TILASTOKESKUS. RAHALAITOKSET. Text in English, Finnish, Swedish. 1911. 3/yr. EUR 57; EUR 22 per issue (effective 2005). **Document type:** *Government.*
Former titles (until 2004): Finland. Tilastokeskus. Pankit: Vuositilasto (0784-9842); (until 1987): Finland. Tilastokeskus. Suomen Virallinen Tilasto. 7 C, Pankit (0355-2454)
Related titles: ◆ Series of: Finland. Tilastokeskus. Rahoitus. ISSN 0784-8382.
Published by: Tilastokeskus/Statistics Finland, Tyopajakatu 13, Statistics Finland, Helsinki, 00022, Finland. TEL 358-9-17341, FAX 358-9-17342750, http://www.stat.fi/.

332   FIN   ISSN 0784-8382
HG3729.F49
FINLAND. TILASTOKESKUS. RAHOITUS/FINLAND. STATISTICS FINLAND. FINANCING/FINLAND. STATISTIKCENTRALEN. FINANSIERING. Text in English, Finnish, Swedish. 1971. 25/yr. EUR 445 (effective 2005). stat. **Document type:** *Government.*
Formerly (until 1988): Finland. Tilastokeskus. R T. Rahoitus (0355-2322)
Related titles: ◆ Series: Finland. Tilastokeskus. Kuntien Talous ja Toiminta. Kunnittaisia Tietoja. ISSN 1456-4408; ◆ Finland. Tilastokeskus. Rahalaitokset. ISSN 1795-2050; ◆ Finland. Tilastokeskus. Sijoituspalveluyrittykset. ISSN 1457-148X; ◆ Finland. Tilastokeskus. Sijoitusrahastot. ISSN 0784-994X; ◆ Finland. Tilastokeskus. Joukkovelkakirjat. ISSN 0784-9788; ◆ Finland. Tilastokeskus. Luottokortit. ISSN 0785-7934; ◆ Finland. Tilastokeskus. Rahoitusleasing. ISSN 1237-024X; ◆ Finland. Tilastokeskus. Luottokanta. ISSN 1459-5451.
Published by: Tilastokeskus/Statistics Finland, Tyopajakatu 13, Statistics Finland, Helsinki, 00022, Finland. TEL 358-9-17341, FAX 358-9-17342750, http://www.stat.fi/.

336.021   FIN   ISSN 1237-024X
FINLAND. TILASTOKESKUS. RAHOITUSLEASING/FINLAND. STATISTIKCENTRALEN. FINANSIELL LEASING. Text mainly in Finnish, Swedish. 1971. a. EUR 16.82 (effective 2001). **Document type:** *Government.*
Supersedes in part (in 1993): Finland. Tilastokeskus. Rahoitusyhtiot (0784-9923); Which superseded in part (in 1987): Finland. Tilastokeskus. R T. Rahoiyus (0355-2322); Incorporates (1988-1988): Finland. Tilastokeskus. Rahoitusleasing (1988) (0784-9885)
Related titles: ◆ Series of: Finland. Tilastokeskus. Rahoitus. ISSN 0784-8382.
Published by: Tilastokeskus/Statistics Finland, Tyopajakatu 13, Statistics Finland, Helsinki, 00022, Finland. TEL 358-9-17341, FAX 358-9-17342750, http://www.stat.fi/.

330.021   FIN   ISSN 0784-9672
FINLAND. TILASTOKESKUS. RAHOITUSTILINPITO/FINLAND. STATISTICS FINLAND. FLOW-OF-FUNDS-ACCOUNTS/ FINLAND. STATISTIKCENTRALEN. FINANSRAEKENSKAPER. Text in English, Finnish, Swedish. 1971. a. EUR 36 (effective 2005). **Document type:** *Government.*

Supersedes in part (in 1988): Finland. Tilastokeskus. R T. Rahoitus (0355-2322); Incorporates (1988-1996): Finland. Tilastokeskus. Rahoitusmarkkinatilasto (0784-9893)
Related titles: ◆ Online - full text ed.: ISSN 1795-4886. 2004; ◆ Series of: Finland. Tilastokeskus. Kansantalous. ISSN 0784-8331.
Published by: Tilastokeskus/Statistics Finland, Tyopajakatu 13, Statistics Finland, Helsinki, 00022, Finland. TEL 358-9-17341, FAX 358-9-17342750, http://www.stat.fi/til/rtp/.

FINLAND. TILASTOKESKUS. RAKENNUSKUSTANNUSINDEKSI. (VUOSITILASTO)/ STATISTICS FINLAND. BUILDING COST INDEX. see *BUILDING AND CONSTRUCTION—Abstracting, Bibliographies, Statistics*

332.021   FIN   ISSN 1457-148X
FINLAND. TILASTOKESKUS. SIJOITUSPALVELUYRITTYKSET/ FINLAND. STATISTICS FINLAND. INVESTMENT FIRMS/FINLAND. STATISTIKCENTRALEN. VAERDEPAPPERSFOERETAG. Text in English, Finnish, Swedish. 1999. a. EUR 20.18 (effective 2001). **Document type:** *Government.*
Related titles: ◆ Series of: Finland. Tilastokeskus. Rahoitus. ISSN 0784-8382.
Published by: Tilastokeskus/Statistics Finland, Tyopajakatu 13, Statistics Finland, Helsinki, 00022, Finland. TEL 358-9-17341, FAX 358-9-17342750, http://www.stat.fi/.

332.6021   FIN   ISSN 0784-994X
FINLAND. TILASTOKESKUS. SIJOITUSRAHASTOT/FINLAND. STATISTICS FINLAND. MUTUAL FUNDS/FINLAND. STATISTIKCENTRALEN. INVESTERINGSFONDER. Text in Finnish, Swedish. 1989. a. EUR 20.18 (effective 2001). **Document type:** *Government.*
Related titles: ◆ Series of: Finland. Tilastokeskus. Rahoitus. ISSN 0784-8382.
Published by: Tilastokeskus/Statistics Finland, Tyopajakatu 13, Statistics Finland, Helsinki, 00022, Finland. TEL 358-9-17341, FAX 358-9-17342750, http://www.stat.fi/.

338.021   FIN   ISSN 0788-1738
HD2877.3.A1
FINLAND. TILASTOKESKUS. SUOMEN YRITYKSET/FINLAND. STATISTICS FINLAND. CORPORATE ENTERPRISES AND PERSONAL BUSINESSES IN FINLAND/FINLAND. STATISTIKCENTRALEN. FINLANDS FOERETAG. Text in English, Finnish, Swedish. 1988. a., latest 2003. EUR 37 (effective 2005). **Document type:** *Government.*
Formerly (until 1990): Finland. Tilastokeskus. Yritys- ja Toimipaikkarekisteri (0785-143X)
Related titles: ◆ Series of: Finland. Tilastokeskus. Yritykset. ISSN 0784-8463.
Published by: Tilastokeskus/Statistics Finland, Tyopajakatu 13, Statistics Finland, Helsinki, 00022, Finland. TEL 358-9-17341, FAX 358-9-17342750, http://www.stat.fi/.

330.021   FIN   ISSN 0785-6016
FINLAND. TILASTOKESKUS. TULO- JA VARALLISUUSTILASTO/FINLAND. STATISTICS FINLAND. STATISTICS OF INCOME AND PROPERTY/FINLAND. STATISTIKCENTRALEN. INKOMST- OCH FOERMOEGENHETSTATISTIK. (Section IV B of Official Statistics of Finland) Text in English, Finnish, Swedish. 1926. a., latest 2003. EUR 29 (effective 2005). **Document type:** *Government.*
Former titles (until 1987): Finland. Tilastokeskus. Suomen Virallinen Tilasto. 4 B, Tulo- ja Varallisuustilasto (0780-9352); (until 1977): Finland. Tilastokeskus. Suomen Virallinen Tilasto. 4 B, Varallisuustilastoa (0355-211X)
Related titles: ◆ Series of: Finland. Tilastokeskus. Tulot ja Kulutus. ISSN 0784-8420.
Published by: Tilastokeskus/Statistics Finland, Tyopajakatu 13, Statistics Finland, Helsinki, 00022, Finland. TEL 358-9-17341, FAX 358-9-17342750, http://www.stat.fi/.

330.021   FIN   ISSN 0785-9880
FINLAND. TILASTOKESKUS. TULONJAKOTILASTO/FINLAND. STATISTICS FINLAND. INCOME DISTRIBUTION STATISTICS/FINLAND. STATISTIKCENTRALEN. INKOMSTFOERDELINGSSTATISTIK. Text in English, Finnish, Swedish. 1980. a., latest 2003. EUR 29 (effective 2005). **Document type:** *Government.*
Formerly (until 1980): Suomen Virallen Tilasto. 41. Tulonjakotilasto (0358-2825)
Related titles: ◆ Series of: Finland. Tilastokeskus. Tulot ja Kulutus. ISSN 0784-8420.
Published by: Tilastokeskus/Statistics Finland, Tyopajakatu 13, Statistics Finland, Helsinki, 00022, Finland. TEL 358-9-17341, FAX 358-9-17342750, http://www.stat.fi/.

331   FIN   ISSN 0784-8420
HC340.2.Z9
FINLAND. TILASTOKESKUS. TULOT JA KULUTUS/FINLAND. STATISTICS FINLAND. INCOME AND CONSUMPTION. Text in English, Finnish, Swedish. 1972. 31/yr. EUR 497 (effective 2005). stat. **Document type:** *Government.*
Formerly (until 1988): Tilastokeskus. Tilastotiedotus. TU, Tulot (0355-2349)
Related titles: ◆ Series: Finland. Tilastokeskus. Tulo- ja Varallisuustilasto. ISSN 0785-6016; ◆ Finland. Tilastokeskus. Tulonjakotilasto. ISSN 0785-9880.

Published by: Tilastokeskus/Statistics Finland, Tyopajakatu 13, Statistics Finland, Helsinki, 00022, Finland. TEL 358-9-17341, FAX 358-9-17342750, http://www.stat.fi/.

330.9 338 FIN ISSN 0784-817X
FINLAND. TILASTOKESKUS. TUOTTAJAHINTAINDEKSIT/ STATISTICS FINLAND. PRODUCER PRICE INDICES. Text in Finnish. 1968. m. EUR 63; EUR 9 per issue (effective 2005). stat. **Document type:** *Government.*
Formerly (until 1988): Finland Tilastokeskus. Indeksitiedotus (0355-2403)
Related titles: Series: Finland. Tilastokeskus. Tyotaistelut (Neljannesvuositilasto). ISSN 0785-0204.
Published by: Tilastokeskus/Statistics Finland, Tyopajakatu 13, Statistics Finland, Helsinki, 00022, Finland. TEL 358-9-17341, FAX 358-9-17342750, http://www.stat.fi/.

330.021 FIN ISSN 1239-3975
FINLAND. TILASTOKESKUS. TUOTTAVUUSKATSAUS. Text in Finnish. 1996. a., latest 2005. EUR 30 (effective 2005). **Document type:** *Government.*
Related titles: ♦ Series of: Finland. Tilastokeskus. Kansantalous. ISSN 0784-8331.
Published by: Tilastokeskus/Statistics Finland, Tyopajakatu 13, Statistics Finland, Helsinki, 00022, Finland. TEL 358-9-17341, FAX 358-9-17342750, http://www.stat.fi/.

331 FIN ISSN 0785-0107
FINLAND. TILASTOKESKUS. TYOEMARKINNAT/FINLAND. STATISTICS FINLAND. LABOUR MARKET. Text in English, Finnish, Swedish. 1969. 21/yr. EUR 230 (effective 2005). stat. **Document type:** *Government.*
Supersedes in part (in 1988): Finland. Tilastikeskus. Tilastotiedotus. T Y, Tyovoima (0355-2357)
Related titles: ♦ Series: Finland. Tilastokeskus. Tyovoimatilasto. ISSN 0785-0050; ♦ Finland. Tilastokeskus. Tyotapaturmat. ISSN 0789-1180.
Published by: Tilastokeskus/Statistics Finland, Tyopajakatu 13, Statistics Finland, Helsinki, 00022, Finland. TEL 358-9-17341, FAX 358-9-17342750, http://www.stat.fi/.

331.021 FIN ISSN 0785-8221
HD5797.3
FINLAND. TILASTOKESKUS. TYOSSAKAYNTITILASTO/ FINAND. STATISTICS FINLAND. EMPLOYMENT STATISTICS/FINLAND. STATISTICENTRALEN. SYSSELSAETTNINGSSTATISTIK. Text in Finnish, Swedish, English. 1989. a. EUR 31.96 (effective 2001). **Document type:** *Government.*
Related titles: ♦ Series of: Finland. Tilastokeskus. Vaestoe. ISSN 0784-8447.
Published by: Tilastokeskus/Statistics Finland, Tyopajakatu 13, Statistics Finland, Helsinki, 00022, Finland. TEL 358-9-17341, FAX 358-9-17342750, http://www.stat.fi/.

331.021 FIN ISSN 0789-1180
FINLAND. TILASTOKESKUS. TYOTAPATURMAT/FINLAND. STATISTICS FINLAND. INDUSTRIAL ACCIDENTS. Text in Finnish, Swedish, English. 1898. a., latest 2003. EUR 27 (effective 2005). **Document type:** *Government.*
Former titles (until 1987): Finland. Tilastokeskus. Suomenvirallinen Tilasto. 26, Tyotapaturmat (0781-3732); (until 1979): Finland. Tilastokeskus. Suomenvirallinen Tilasto. 26 A. Tyotapaturmat (0356-2069)
Related titles: ♦ Series of: Finland. Tilastokeskus. Tyoemarkinnat. ISSN 0785-0107.
Published by: Tilastokeskus/Statistics Finland, Tyopajakatu 13, Statistics Finland, Helsinki, 00022, Finland. TEL 358-9-17341, FAX 358-9-17342750, http://www.stat.fi/.

331.021 FIN ISSN 1457-084X
FINLAND. TILASTOKESKUS. TYOTUNNIN KUSTANNUS. TYOVOIMAKUSTANNUSINDEKSI/FINLAND. STATISTICS FINLAND. COST OF HOUR WORKED. LABOUR COST INDEX. Variant title: Finland. Statistics Finland. Labour Cost Index. Finland. Tilastokeskus. Tyovoimakustannusindeksi. Text in English, Finnish. 1999. a. EUR 27 (effective 2005). **Document type:** *Government.*
Related titles: ♦ Series of: Finland. Tilastokeskus. Palkat. ISSN 0784-8374.
Published by: Tilastokeskus/Statistics Finland, Tyopajakatu 13, Statistics Finland, Helsinki, 00022, Finland. TEL 358-9-17341, FAX 358-9-17342750, http://www.stat.fi/.

331.11 FIN ISSN 0785-0050
HD5797.3
FINLAND. TILASTOKESKUS. TYOVOIMATILASTO/FINLAND. STATISTICS FINLAND. LABOUR FORCE STATISTICS/FINLAND. STATISTIKCENTRALEN. ARBETSKRAFTSSTATISTIK. (Section XL of Official Statistics of Finland) Text in English, Finnish, Swedish. 1969. a., latest 2004. EUR 33 (effective 2005). **Document type:** *Government.*
Formerly (until 1988): Tilastokeskus. Tilastotiedotus. TY, Tyovoima (0355-2357)
Related titles: ♦ Series of: Finland. Tilastokeskus. Tyoemarkinnat. ISSN 0785-0107.
Published by: Tilastokeskus/Statistics Finland, Tyopajakatu 13, Statistics Finland, Helsinki, 00022, Finland. TEL 358-9-17341, FAX 358-9-17342750, http://www.stat.fi/.

331.021 FIN ISSN 0785-8884
JN7396.Z2
FINLAND. TILASTOKESKUS. VALTION KUUKAUSIPALKAT/ FINLAND. STATISTIKCENTRALEN. LOENER FOER STATSANSTAELLDA MAANADSAVLOENADE. Text in Finnish, Swedish, English. 1989. a., latest 2004. EUR 27 (effective 2005). **Document type:** *Government.*
Formed by the merger of (1988-1989): Finland. Tilastokeskus. Valtion Kuukausiplakat. Tyosuhteiset (0784-9540); (1988-1989): Finland. Tilastokeskus. Valtion Kuukausipalkat. Virkamiehet (0784-9532)
Related titles: ♦ Series of: Finland. Tilastokeskus. Palkat. ISSN 0784-8374.
Published by: Tilastokeskus/Statistics Finland, Tyopajakatu 13, Statistics Finland, Helsinki, 00022, Finland. TEL 358-9-17341, FAX 358-9-17342750, http://www.stat.fi/.

331.021 FIN ISSN 1455-1454
FINLAND. TILASTOKESKUS. YKSITYISEN SEKTORIN KUUKAUSIPALKAT/FINLAND. STATISTIKCENTRALEN. MAANADSLOENER FOER ANSTAELLDA INOM DEN PRIVATA SEKTORN. Text in Finnish, Swedish. 1997. a., latest 2004. EUR 29 (effective 2005). **Document type:** *Corporate.*
Formed by the merger of (1991-1997): Finland. Tilastokeskus. Palvelualan Palkat: Elokuu (0789-6646); (1989-1997): Finland. Tilastokeskus. Teollisuuden Toimihenkiloiden Palkat: Vuositilasto (0784-9494)
Related titles: ♦ Series of: Finland. Tilastokeskus. Palkat. ISSN 0784-8374.
Published by: Tilastokeskus/Statistics Finland, Tyopajakatu 13, Statistics Finland, Helsinki, 00022, Finland. TEL 358-9-17341, FAX 358-9-17342750, http://www.stat.fi/.

310 330 FIN ISSN 0784-8463
HE255.3.A15
FINLAND. TILASTOKESKUS. YRITYKSET/FINLAND. STATISTICS FINLAND. ENTERPRISES. Text in English, Finnish, Swedish. 1972. 5/yr. EUR 138 (effective 2005). **Document type:** *Government.*
Formerly (until 1988): Finland. Tilastokeskus. Tilastotiedotus YR. Yritykset (0355-2373)
Related titles: ♦ Series: Finland. Tilastokeskus. Yritystoiminnan Talous ja Tasset. ISSN 1459-3785; ♦ Finland. Tilastokeskus. Suomen Yritykset. ISSN 0788-1738.
Indexed: RASB.
Published by: Tilastokeskus/Statistics Finland, Tyopajakatu 13, Statistics Finland, Helsinki, 00022, Finland. TEL 358-9-17341, FAX 358-9-17342750, http://www.stat.fi/.

338.021 FIN ISSN 1459-3785
HC340.2.A1
FINLAND. TILASTOKESKUS. YRITYSTOIMINNAN TALOUS JA TASSET/FINLAND. STATISTICS FINLAND. FINANCIAL STATEMENTS STATISTICS/FINLAND. STATISTIKCENTRALEN. BOKSLUTSSTATISTIK. Text in English, Finnish, Swedish. 1992. a., latest 2003. EUR 50 (effective 2005). **Document type:** *Government.*
Formerly (until 2003): Finland. Tilastokeskus. Tilinpaatostilasto (1235-1342)
Related titles: ♦ Series of: Finland. Tilastokeskus. Yritykset. ISSN 0784-8463.
Published by: Tilastokeskus/Statistics Finland, Tyopajakatu 13, Statistics Finland, Helsinki, 00022, Finland. TEL 358-9-17341, FAX 358-9-17342750, http://www.stat.fi/.

382 314 FIN ISSN 0789-743X
FINLAND. TULLIHALLITUS. ULKOMAANKAUPPA/FINLAND. NATIONAL BOARD OF CUSTOMS. FOREIGN TRADE/FINLAND. TULLSTYRELSEN. UTRIKESHANDEL. Text in English, Finnish, Swedish. 1904. m. charts. **Document type:** *Government.*
Formerly (until 1989): Finland. Tullihallituksen Tilastotoimisto. Ulkomaankauppa-Kuukausijulkaisu - Foreign Trade Monthly Bulletin (0041-6177)
Published by: Tullihallitus/National Board of Customs, PO Box 512, Helsinki, 00101, Finland. TEL 358-9-6141, FAX 358-20-4922852, tullitil@tulli.fi, http://www.tulli.fi. Ed. Tuula Eriksson. Circ: 1,170. **Dist. by:** Edita Ltd., Annankatu 44, Helsinki 00100, Finland.

318 USA
FLORIDA LONG-TERM ECONOMIC FORECAST. Text in English. a. (in 2 vol.). USD 49. **Document type:** *Government.* **Description:** Provides a long-range economic forecast for the state of Florida, its metropolitan statistical areas, and counties.
Related titles: Diskette ed.: USD 39.
Published by: (Bureau of Economic and Business Research), University of Florida, PO Box 117145, Gainesville, FL 32611-7145. TEL 352-392-0171, FAX 352-392-4739. Ed. David Lenze. **Co-sponsor:** College of Business Administration.

318.021 USA ISSN 0071-6022
HA311
FLORIDA STATISTICAL ABSTRACT. Variant title: Florida Statistical Abstracts Annual. Text in English. 1967. a. USD 39.95 (effective 1999). charts; maps; stat. back issues avail. **Document type:** *Government.* **Description:** Contains more than 800 pages of current and historical information about the economy and demography of Florida, its counties, and metropolitan areas.
Related titles: Diskette ed.: USD 75.
Indexed: SRI.
Published by: (Bureau of Economic and Business Research), University of Florida, PO Box 117145, Gainesville, FL 32611-7145. TEL 352-392-0171, FAX 352-392-4739, jgalvez@ufl.edu, http://www.bebr.ufl.edu. Ed. Susan Floyd. Circ: 3,700. **Co-sponsor:** College of Business Administration.

382 316 ETH ISSN 0071-7398
FOREIGN TRADE STATISTICS OF AFRICA. SERIES A: DIRECTION OF TRADE. Text in English, French. 1962. irreg., latest vol.25, 1977. price varies. charts. **Document type:** *Newsletter.* **Description:** Presents statistical data for northern, southern, central, western, and eastern Africa.
Related titles: Microfiche ed.: (from CIS).
Indexed: IIS, RASB.
—CISTI.
Published by: United Nations, Economic Commission for Africa/Commission Economique pour l'Afrique, PO Box 3001, Addis Ababa, Ethiopia. Ed. Joanne Cabrera. **Subscr. to:** United Nations Publications, Distribution and Sales Section, Palais des Nations, Rm C-116, 8-14 av de la Paix, Geneva 1211, Switzerland. **Dist. by:** United Nations Publications, Distribution and Sales Section, Palais des Nations, Rm C-116, 8-14 av de la Paix, Geneva 1211, Switzerland.; Bernan Associates, Bernan, 4611-F Assembly Dr., Lanham, MD 20706-4391.

B

382 ETH ISSN 0252-2012
FOREIGN TRADE STATISTICS OF AFRICA. SERIES C: SUMMARY TABLES/STATISTIQUES AFRICAINES DU COMMERCE EXTERIEUR. SERIE C: TABLEAUX RECAPITULATIFS. Text in English. 1977. irreg., latest vol.3, 1980. **Document type:** *Newsletter.* **Description:** Presents statistical summaries for foreign trades for northern, southern, central, western, and eastern Africa.
Related titles: Microfiche ed.: (from CIS).
Indexed: IIS, RASB.
Published by: United Nations, Economic Commission for Africa/Commission Economique pour l'Afrique, PO Box 3001, Addis Ababa, Ethiopia. TELEX 21029. Ed. Joanne Cabrera. **Dist. by:** United Nations Sales Section, Palais des Nations, Geneva 10 1211, Switzerland; Bernan Associates, Bernan, 4611-F Assembly Dr., Lanham, MD 20706-4391.

382 315 THA ISSN 1011-4858
HF3751
FOREIGN TRADE STATISTICS OF ASIA AND THE PACIFIC. Text in English, French. N.S. 1987. a., latest 2001-2002 ed. USD 45 (effective 2005). stat. back issues avail.; reprint service avail. from PSC. **Document type:** *Government.* **Description:** Provides data, in time-series form and in country sequence, on imports and exports of ESCAP reporting countries or areas by country of provenance and destination.
Formed by the 1987 merger of: Foreign Trade Statistics of Asia and the Pacific. Series A (0252-4538); Which was formerly (until 1969): Foreign Trade Statistics of Asia and the Far East. Series A (0532-1409); Foreign Trade Statistics of Asia and the Pacific. Series B (0252-4546); Which was formerly: Foreign Trade Statistics of Asia and the Far East. Series B (0532-1417); Both of which superseded: Foreign Trade Statistics of Asia and the Far East (0256-3444)
Related titles: Microfiche ed.: (from CIS).
Indexed: IIS.
Published by: United Nations Economic and Social Commission for Asia and the Pacific, United Nations Bldg., Rajadamnern Ave., Bangkok, 10200, Thailand. TEL 662-2881174, FAX 662-2883022, unescap@unescap.org, http://www.unescap.org. **Subscr. to:** United Nations Publications, Distribution and Sales Section, Palais des Nations, Rm C-116, 8-14 av de la Paix, Geneva 1211, Switzerland; United Nations Publications, Rm DC2-853, United Nations Bldg, 2 United Nations Plaza, New York, NY 10017. **Dist. by:** United Nations Publications, Distribution and Sales Section, Palais des Nations, Rm C-116, 8-14 av de la Paix, Geneva 1211, Switzerland.; Conference Services Unit, Conference Services Unit, ESCAP, Bangkok 10200, Thailand.; United Nations Publications, Rm DC2-853, United Nations Bldg, 2 United Nations Plaza, New York, NY 10017.

315 BGD
FOREIGN TRADE STATISTICS OF BANGLADESH. Text in English. 1961. a. BDT 400, USD 60. **Description:** Articles and data on export, import and balance of trade in Bangladesh.
Formerly: Annual Foreign Trade Statistics of Bangladesh (0071-7371)
Published by: Bureau of Statistics, Secretariat, Dhaka, 2, Bangladesh.

382 315 IRN
FOREIGN TRADE STATISTICS OF IRAN/AMAR-E BAZARGANI-YE KHAREJI-YE IRAN. Text in Persian, Modern, English. 1900. q. IRR 100 per issue.
Published by: Ministry of Finance and Economic Affairs, Naser Khosrow Ave, Teheran, Iran.

382 315 IRN ISSN 0075-0492
FOREIGN TRADE STATISTICS OF IRAN. YEARBOOK✶. Text in Arabic, English. a.
Published by: Ministry of Finance and Economic Affairs, Naser Khosrow Ave, Teheran, Iran.

382 315   PHL   ISSN 0116-1822
FOREIGN TRADE STATISTICS OF THE PHILIPPINES. Text in English. a. USD 110. Supplement avail. **Description:** Focuses on the quality and value of Philippine trade with other countries for the calendar year.
Related titles: Diskette ed.
Published by: National Statistics Office, Ramon Magsaysay Blvd, PO Box 779, Manila, Philippines. TEL 63-2-606-909, FAX 63-2-716-0247. Circ: 250.

382 315   YEM   ISSN 0376-5695
HF235
FOREIGN TRADE STATISTICS OF YEMEN ARAB REPUBLIC. Text in English. a.
Published by: (Research Department), Central Bank of Yemen, P O Box 59, Sana, Yemen.

330 310   FRA   ISSN 1263-1973
FRANCE. DIRECTION DE L'ANIMATION DE LA RECHERCHE, DES ETUDES ET DES STATISTIQUES. DOSSIERS. Short title: Les Dossiers de la D A R E S. Text in French. 6/yr. EUR 105 domestic (effective 2003). **Document type:** Government.
Formerly (until 1995): Premieres Informations. Dossiers Statistiques (1268-6484)
Published by: (France. Direction de l'Animation, de la Recherche, des Etudes et des Statistiques), Documentation Francaise, 29-31 quai Voltaire, Paris, Cedex 7 75344, France. FAX 33-1-40157230.

382 314   FRA   ISSN 0071-8688
FRANCE. DIRECTION GENERALE DES DOUANES ET DROITS INDIRECTS. STATISTIQUES DU COMMERCE EXTERIEUR: IMPORTATIONS - EXPORTATIONS. NOMENCLATURE: N.G.P. (NOMENCLATURE GENERALE DES PRODUITS). Text in French. a. **Description:** Presents total of imports and exports by principal country of origin and destination.
Published by: (France. Direction Generale des Douanes et Droits Indirects), Imprimerie Nationale, BP 514, Douai, Cedex 59505, France. TEL 37-93-70-70, FAX 27-93-70-96.

330 310   FRA   ISSN 0769-489X
HB139
FRANCE. INSTITUT NATIONAL DE LA STATISTIQUE ET DES ETUDES ECONOMIQUES. ANNALES D'ECONOMIE ET DE STATISTIQUE. Text in French; Summaries in English, Spanish. 1986. q. **Description:** Original theoretical or applied research in economics, econometrics and statistics.
Formed by the merger of (1969-1986): France. Institut National de la Statistique et des Etudes Economiques. Annales (0019-0209); (1951-1986): France. Institut National de la Statistique et des Etudes Economiques. Cahiers du Seminaire d'Econometrie (0071-8343)
Indexed: CCMJ, CIS, IBSS, JEL, PAIS, RefZh.
—BLDSC (0971.835000), CISTI, IE, Infotrieve, ingenta. **CCC.**
Published by: (France. Association pour le Developpement de la Recherche en Economie et en Statistique), Institut National de la Statistique et des Etudes Economiques, 1 rue Vincent Auriol, Amiens, Cedex 1 80027, France. TEL 33-3-22927322, FAX 33-3-22979295, inseeactualites@insee.fr. Circ: 9,900.

330.9   FRA   ISSN 1152-9776
FRANCE. INSTITUT NATIONAL DE LA STATISTIQUE ET DES ETUDES ECONOMIQUES. CONJONCTURE IN FRANCE; a bi-annual short term economic report by INSEE. Text in English. 1990. 2/yr. charts. back issues avail.
Published by: Institut National de la Statistique et des Etudes Economiques, 1 rue Vincent Auriol, Amiens, Cedex 1 80027, France. TEL 33-3-22927322, FAX 33-3-22979295, inseeactualites@insee.fr.

330 314   FRA   ISSN 0336-1454
HC271
FRANCE. INSTITUT NATIONAL DE LA STATISTIQUE ET DES ETUDES ECONOMIQUES. ECONOMIE ET STATISTIQUE. Text in French. 1953. 10/yr. **Description:** Analyzes social and economic news.
Supersedes in part (in 1969): Institut National de la Statistique et des Etudes Economiques. Etudes et Conjoncture (0423-5681); Which was formed by the merger of (1945-1953): Etudes et Conjoncture. Serie Bleue (1149-3755); Which was formerly (until 1946): La Conjoncture (1149-3747); (until 1946): Revue de la Situation Economique a l'Etranger (1149-3739); (1944-1953): Etudes et Conjoncture. Serie Rouge (1149-3720); Which was formerly (until 1946): Point Economique (1149-3712)
Related titles: Microfiche ed.
Indexed: IBSS, ILD, KES, PAIS, PopulInd, RefZh.
—BLDSC (3657.850000), CISTI, IE, Infotrieve, ingenta.
Published by: Institut National de la Statistique et des Etudes Economiques, 1 rue Vincent Auriol, Amiens, Cedex 1 80027, France. TEL 33-3-22927322, FAX 33-3-22979295, inseeactualites@insee.fr, http://www.insee.fr. Ed. Pierre Morin. Pub. Paul Champsaur.

330 314   FRA   ISSN 0151-1475
FRANCE. INSTITUT NATIONAL DE LA STATISTIQUE ET DES ETUDES ECONOMIQUES. INFORMATIONS RAPIDES. Text in French. 1974. 350/yr. charts.
Published by: Institut National de la Statistique et des Etudes Economiques, 1 rue Vincent Auriol, Amiens, Cedex 1 80027, France. TEL 33-3-22927322, FAX 33-3-22979295, inseeactualites@insee.fr. Circ: 340.

331.1 314   FRA   ISSN 1161-8205
FRANCE. MINISTERE DE L'EMPLOI ET DE LA SOLIDARITE. BULLETIN MENSUEL DES STATISTIQUES DU TRAVAIL. Short title: B M S T. Text in French. m. EUR 98.33 domestic; EUR 100.62 in the European Union; EUR 99.09 DOM-TOM; EUR 99.85 elsewhere (effective 2003). adv. Supplement avail. **Document type:** Government.
Former titles: France. Ministere du Travail. Statistiques du Travail (0338-4284); France. Ministere du Travail. Bulletin Mensuel des Statistiques du Travail (0338-4276)
Related titles: Microfiche ed.
Indexed: PAIS.
Published by: (France. Ministere de l'Emploi et de la Solidarite), Documentation Francaise, 29-31 quai Voltaire, Paris, Cedex 7 75344, France. FAX 33-1-40157230. Circ: 3,800.

338 314   FRA
FRANCE. SERVICE D'ETUDE DES STRATEGIES ET DES STATISTIQUES INDUSTRIELLES. ANNUAIRE DE STATISTIQUE INDUSTRIELLE. Text in French. 1947. a. **Description:** Statistics on industry: production and sales figures.
Former titles: France. Service du Traitement de l'Information et des Statistiques Industrielles. Annuaire de Statistique Industrielle (0071-8211); France. Bureau Centrale de Statistique Industrielle. Annuaire de Statistique Industrielle
Published by: Service d'Etude des Strategies et des Statistiques Industrielles (SESSI), 85 bd. du Montparnasse, Paris, Cedex 6 75270, France. TEL 45-56-42-34, FAX 45-56-40-71.

381   FRA
FRANCE. SERVICE D'ETUDE DES STRATEGIES ET DES STATISTIQUES INDUSTRIELLES. LA DISPERSION DES PERFORMANCES DES ENTREPRISES. Text in French. a. **Description:** Analyzes performance in 300 industrial categories.
Related titles: Diskette ed.
Published by: Service d'Etude des Strategies et des Statistiques Industrielles (SESSI), 85 bd. du Montparnasse, Paris, Cedex 6 75270, France. TEL 45-56-42-34, FAX 45-56-40-71.

338 310   FRA   ISSN 0998-4208
FRANCE. SERVICE D'ETUDE DES STRATEGIES ET DES STATISTIQUES INDUSTRIELLES. LA SITUATION DE L'INDUSTRIE: PREMIERS RESULTATS. Text in French. 1968. a.
Supersedes in part: France. Ministere de l'Industrie, des P & T et du Tourisme. Enquete Annuelle d'Entreprise; Which was formerly: France. Ministere de Redeploiement Industriel et du Commerce Exterieur. Enquete Annuelle
Published by: Service d'Etude des Strategies et des Statistiques Industrielles (SESSI), 85 bd. du Montparnasse, Paris, Cedex 6 75270, France. TEL 45-56-42-34, FAX 45-56-40-71.

330.9 381   FRA
FRANCE. SERVICE D'ETUDE DES STRATEGIES ET DES STATISTIQUES INDUSTRIELLES. LA SITUATION DE L'INDUSTRIE: RESULTATS AGREGES. Text in French. a. **Description:** Analyzes recent growth, net results, employment, investments and exports in 40 sectors of industry. Data presented by size of business.
Supersedes in part: France. Ministere de l'Industrie, des P & T et du Tourisme. Enquete Annuelle d'Entreprise; Which was formerly: France. Ministere de Redeploiement Industriel et du Commerce Exterieur. Enquete Annuelle
Published by: Service d'Etude des Strategies et des Statistiques Industrielles (SESSI), 85 bd. du Montparnasse, Paris, Cedex 6 75270, France. TEL 45-56-42-34, FAX 45-56-40-71.

330.9 381   FRA
FRANCE. SERVICE D'ETUDE DES STRATEGIES ET DES STATISTIQUES INDUSTRIELLES. LA SITUATION DE L'INDUSTRIE: RESULTATS DETAILLES. Text in French. a. **Description:** Complete analysis of 250 industrial sectors. Data by branch, size and region.
Supersedes in part: France. Ministere de l'Industrie, des P & T et du Tourisme. Enquete Annuelle d'Entreprise; Which was formerly: France. Ministere de Redeploiement Industriel et du Commerce Exterieur. Enquete Annuelle
Published by: Service d'Etude des Strategies et des Statistiques Industrielles (SESSI), 85 bd. du Montparnasse, Paris, Cedex 6 75270, France. TEL 45-56-42-34, FAX 45-56-40-71.

381   FRA   ISSN 1240-747X
FRANCE. SERVICE D'ETUDE DES STRATEGIES ET DES STATISTIQUES INDUSTRIELLES. LES CHIFFRES CLES DE L'INDUSTRIE. Text in French. a. bibl.; charts. **Description:** Presents essential statistics on 85 industrial activities.
Published by: Service d'Etude des Strategies et des Statistiques Industrielles (SESSI), 85 bd. du Montparnasse, Paris, Cedex 6 75270, France. TEL 45-56-42-34, FAX 45-56-40-71.

381   FRA
FRANCE. SERVICE D'ETUDE DES STRATEGIES ET DES STATISTIQUES INDUSTRIELLES. LES CHIFFRES CLES DE L'INDUSTRIE DANS LES REGIONS. Text in French. a. charts. **Description:** Permits regional comparison of principal industrial characteristics.
Published by: Service d'Etude des Strategies et des Statistiques Industrielles (SESSI), 85 bd. du Montparnasse, Paris, Cedex 6 75270, France. TEL 45-56-42-34, FAX 45-56-40-71.

381 338   FRA
FRANCE. SERVICE D'ETUDE DES STRATEGIES ET DES STATISTIQUES INDUSTRIELLES. L'IMPLANTATION ETRANGERE DANS L'INDUSTRIE. Text in French. a. **Description:** Covers foreign-controlled industrial activity in France. Lists by sector, origin of investment, and location in France.
Published by: Service d'Etude des Strategies et des Statistiques Industrielles (SESSI), 85 bd. du Montparnasse, Paris, Cedex 6 75270, France. TEL 45-56-42-34, FAX 45-56-40-71.

FRITZ-HUESER-INSTITUT FUER DEUTSCHE UND AUSLAENDISCHE ARBEITERLITERATUR. INFORMATIONEN. see LITERATURE—Abstracting, Bibliographies, Statistics

330.9   USA   ISSN 1079-929X
HA154
GALE COUNTRY AND WORLD RANKINGS REPORTER. Text in English. 1995. biennial. latest 1997. USD 180 (effective 2004). charts. **Document type:** Directory. **Description:** Provides statistical information on population, health and welfare, education, law and justice, defense, agriculture, and the arts, travel, and entertainment.
Published by: Gale Group (Subsidiary of: Thomson Corporation), 27500 Drake Rd, Farmington Hills, MI 48331-3535. TEL 248-699-8061, 800-877-4253, FAX 248-699-4253, galeord@gale.com, http://www.gale.com. Ed. Arsen Darney.

330.9   USA   ISSN 1074-8792
GALE STATE RANKINGS REPORTER. Text in English. irreg. latest vol.2, 1996. USD 145 (effective 2004). charts. **Description:** Ranks US states in such categories as housing, education, income levels, environmental conditions, and the arts.
Published by: Gale Group (Subsidiary of: Thomson Corporation), 27500 Drake Rd, Farmington Hills, MI 48331-3535. FAX 248-699-4253, galeord@gale.com, http://www.gale.com.

316 916.6   GMB
GAMBIA. CENTRAL STATISTICS DEPARTMENT. CONSUMER PRICE INDEX. Text in English. m. GMD 12. **Document type:** Government.
Published by: Central Statistics Department, Wellington St., Banjul, Gambia.

382   GMB
GAMBIA. CENTRAL STATISTICS DEPARTMENT. MONTHLY SUMMARY OF EXTERNAL TRADE STATISTICS. Text in English. m. **Document type:** Government.
Published by: Central Statistics Department, Wellington St., Banjul, Gambia.

331.21021   GMB
GAMBIA. CENTRAL STATISTICS DEPARTMENT. QUARTERLY SURVEY OF EMPLOYMENT AND EARNINGS. Text in English. q. GMD 7.50.
Published by: Central Statistics Department, Wellington St., Banjul, Gambia.

330.9   GHA
GAZETTEER; alphabetical list of localities with statistics on population, number of houses and main source of water supply. Text in English. irreg. (in 2 vols.). latest 1984. USD 35 for both vols.. **Document type:** Government.
Related titles: Microform ed.: (from PQC).
Published by: Statistical Service, Information Section, PO Box 1098, Accra, Ghana. TEL 233-21-336758, FAX 233-21-667069.

317   USA   ISSN 0085-1043
HA321
GEORGIA STATISTICAL ABSTRACT. Text in English. 1951. biennial. USD 50 (effective 2000); includes CD-ROM. **Document type:** Academic/Scholarly.
Related titles: CD-ROM ed.: ISSN 1551-3513; Microfiche ed.: (from BHP).
Published by: (Selig Center for Economic Growth), University of Georgia, Terry College of Business, 535 Brooks Hall, Athens, GA 30602. TEL 706-542-4085, FAX 706-542-3858, http://www.selig.uga.edu. Ed. Lorena Akioka. Circ: 1,000.

331.11 314   DEU   ISSN 0071-1101
GERMANY. BUNDESANSTALT FUER ARBEIT. BERUFSBERATUNG. Text in German. 1953. a. index. **Document type:** Government.
Formerly (until 1969): Germany. Bundesanstalt fuer Arbeit. Berufsberatung. Ergebnisse der Berufsberatungsstatistik (0521-761X)
Published by: Bundesanstalt fuer Arbeit, Regensburger Str 104, Nuernberg, 90478, Germany. TEL 49-911-1790, FAX 49-911-1792123, zentrale@arbeitsagentur.de, http://www.arbeitsagentur.de.

382 310   DEU   ISSN 0072-1638
GERMANY. STATISTISCHES BUNDESAMT. ALPHABETISCHES LAENDERVERZEICHNIS FUER DIE AUSSENHANDELSSTATISTIK. Text in German. irreg. **Document type:** Government.
Published by: Statistisches Bundesamt, Gustav-Stresemann-Ring 11, Wiesbaden, 65180, Germany. TEL 49-611-75-1, FAX 49-611-724000, http://www.statistik-bund.de.

331 314 DEU ISSN 0072-1832
GERMANY. STATISTISCHES BUNDESAMT. FACHSERIE 1, BEVOELKERUNG UND ERWERBSTAETIGKEIT, REIHE 4: ERWERBSTAETIGKEIT. Text in German. irreg. Price varies. **Document type:** *Government.*
Published by: Statistisches Bundesamt, Gustav-Stresemann-Ring 11, Wiesbaden, 65180, Germany. TEL 49-611-75-1, FAX 49-611-724000, http://www.statistik-bund.de.

336 314 DEU
GERMANY. STATISTISCHES BUNDESAMT. FACHSERIE 14: FINANZEN UND STEUERN. (Consists of several subseries) Text in German. 1959. irreg. Price varies. **Document type:** *Government.*
Published by: Statistisches Bundesamt, Gustav-Stresemann-Ring 11, Wiesbaden, 65180, Germany. TEL 49-611-75-1, FAX 49-611-724000, http://www.statistik-bund.de.

339.42 314 DEU ISSN 0176-9405
GERMANY. STATISTISCHES BUNDESAMT. FACHSERIE 15, WIRTSCHAFTSRECHNUNGEN, REIHE 1: EINNAHMEN UND AUSGABEN AUSGEWAEHLTER PRIVATER HAUSHALTE. Text in German. 1954. q. **Document type:** *Government.*
Supersedes: Germany (Federal Republic, 1949-) Statistisches Bundesamt. Fachserie 15, Reihe 1: Wirtschaftsrechnungen (0072-386X)
Published by: Statistisches Bundesamt, Gustav-Stresemann-Ring 11, Wiesbaden, 65180, Germany. TEL 49-611-75-1, FAX 49-611-724000, http://www.statistik-bund.de.

331.2 314 DEU ISSN 0177-2473
GERMANY. STATISTISCHES BUNDESAMT. FACHSERIE 16, LOEHNE UND GEHAELTER, REIHE 2.1: ARBEITERVERDIENSTE IN DER INDUSTRIE. Text in German. q. **Document type:** *Government.*
Formerly: Germany (Federal Republic, 1949-) Statistisches Bundesamt. Fachserie 16, Reihe 2: Angestelltenverdienste in Industrie und Handel (0072-3789)
Published by: Statistisches Bundesamt, Gustav-Stresemann-Ring 11, Wiesbaden, 65180, Germany. TEL 49-611-75-1, FAX 49-611-724000, http://www.statistik-bund.de.

331.2 DEU
GERMANY. STATISTISCHES BUNDESAMT. FACHSERIE 16, LOEHNE UND GEHAELTER, REIHE 2.2: ANGESTELLTENVERDIENST IN INDUSTRIE UND HANDEL. Text in German. 1959. q. price varies. adv. **Document type:** *Government.*
Indexed: RASB.
Published by: (Germany. Statistisches Bundesamt), Servicecenter Fachverlage GmbH, Holzwiesenstr 2, Kusterdingen, 72127, Germany. TEL 49-7071-93530, FAX 49-7071-33653.

331.2 314 DEU ISSN 0072-3797
GERMANY. STATISTISCHES BUNDESAMT. FACHSERIE 16, LOEHNE UND GEHAELTER, REIHE 3: ARBEITERVERDIENSTE IM HANDWERK. Text in German. 1957. a. **Document type:** *Government.*
Indexed: RASB.
Published by: Statistisches Bundesamt, Gustav-Stresemann-Ring 11, Wiesbaden, 65180, Germany. TEL 49-611-75-1, FAX 49-611-724000, http://www.statistik-bund.de.

336 314 DEU ISSN 0072-3843
GERMANY. STATISTISCHES BUNDESAMT. FACHSERIE 16, LOEHNE UND GEHAELTER, REIHE 4: TARIFLOEHNE UND TARIFGEHAELTER. Text in German. irreg. price varies. **Document type:** *Government.*
Published by: Statistisches Bundesamt, Gustav-Stresemann-Ring 11, Wiesbaden, 65180, Germany. TEL 49-611-75-1, FAX 49-611-724000, http://www.statistik-bund.de.

331.2 310 DEU ISSN 0941-3685
GERMANY. STATISTISCHES BUNDESAMT. FACHSERIE 16, LOEHNE UND GEHAELTER, REIHE 5: LOEHNE, GEHAELTER UND ARBEITSKOSTEN IM AUSLAND. Text in German. 1950. a. **Document type:** *Government.*
Formerly: Germany (Federal Republic, 1949-). Statistisches Bundesamt. Fachserie 16, Loehne und Gehaelter, Reihe 5.2: Tarifloehne und Gehaelter des Auslandes
Published by: Statistisches Bundesamt, Gustav-Stresemann-Ring 11, Wiesbaden, 65180, Germany. TEL 49-611-75-1, FAX 49-611-724000, http://www.statistik-bund.de.

339 310 DEU ISSN 0072-3827
GERMANY. STATISTISCHES BUNDESAMT. FACHSERIE 17, PREISE, REIHE 10: INTERNATIONALER VERGLEICH DER PREISE FUER DIE LEBENSHALTUNG. Text in German. 1960. m. **Document type:** *Government.*
Indexed: RASB.
Published by: Statistisches Bundesamt, Gustav-Stresemann-Ring 11, Wiesbaden, 65180, Germany. TEL 49-611-75-1, FAX 49-611-724000, http://www.statistik-bund.de.

382 310 DEU ISSN 0072-3940
GERMANY. STATISTISCHES BUNDESAMT. FACHSERIE 17, PREISE, REIHE 11: PREISE UND PREISINDIZES IM AUSLAND. Text in German. m. **Document type:** *Government.*
Indexed: RASB.
Published by: Statistisches Bundesamt, Gustav-Stresemann-Ring 11, Wiesbaden, 65180, Germany. TEL 49-611-75-1, FAX 49-611-724000, http://www.statistik-bund.de.

338.5 314 DEU ISSN 0721-121X
HB235.G3
GERMANY. STATISTISCHES BUNDESAMT. FACHSERIE 17, PREISE, REIHE 2: PREISE UND PREISINDIZES FUER GEWERBLICHE PRODUKTE. ERZEUGERPREISE. Text in German. m. **Document type:** *Government.*
Formerly: Germany (Federal Republic, 1949-) Statistisches Bundesamt. Fachserie 17, Reihe 2: Preise und Preisindizes fuer Industrielle Produkte. Erzeugerpreise (0072-3886)
Indexed: RASB.
Published by: Statistisches Bundesamt, Gustav-Stresemann-Ring 11, Wiesbaden, 65180, Germany. TEL 49-611-75-1, FAX 49-611-724000, http://www.statistik-bund.de.

338.5 314 DEU ISSN 0940-3949
GERMANY. STATISTISCHES BUNDESAMT. FACHSERIE 17, PREISE, REIHE 3: PREISINDEX FUER DEN WARENEINGANG DES PRODUZIERENDEN GEWERBES. Text in German. 1955. m. **Document type:** *Government.*
Formerly: Germany (Federal Republic, 1949-). Statistisches Bundesamt. Fachserie 17, Preise, Reihe 3: Index der Grundstoffpreise (0072-3878)
Published by: Statistisches Bundesamt, Gustav-Stresemann-Ring 11, Wiesbaden, 65180, Germany. TEL 49-611-75-1, FAX 49-611-724000, http://www.statistik-bund.de.

380 314 DEU ISSN 0720-4221
GERMANY. STATISTISCHES BUNDESAMT. FACHSERIE 17, PREISE, REIHE 4: MESSZAHLEN FUER BAULEISTUNGSPREISE UND PREISINDIZES FUER BAUWERKE. Text in German. q. **Document type:** *Government.*
Indexed: RASB.
Published by: Statistisches Bundesamt, Gustav-Stresemann-Ring 11, Wiesbaden, 65180, Germany. TEL 49-611-75-1, FAX 49-611-724000, http://www.statistik-bund.de.

339 314 DEU
GERMANY. STATISTISCHES BUNDESAMT. FACHSERIE 17, PREISE, REIHE 7: PREISINDICES FUER DIE LEBENSHALTUNG. Text in German. m. **Document type:** *Government.*
Formerly: Germany. Statistisches Bundesamt. Fachserie 17, Preise, Reihe 7: Preise und Preisindizes fuer die Lebenshaltung (0072-3916)
Indexed: RASB.
Published by: Statistisches Bundesamt, Gustav-Stresemann-Ring 11, Wiesbaden, 65180, Germany. TEL 49-611-75-1, FAX 49-611-724000, http://www.statistik-bund.de.

382 314 DEU
GERMANY. STATISTISCHES BUNDESAMT. FACHSERIE 17, PREISE, REIHE 8: PREISINDIZES FUER DIE EIN- UND AUSFUHR. Text in German. 1955. m. **Document type:** *Government.*
Formerly: Germany. Statistisches Bundesamt. Fachserie 17, Preise, Reihe 8: Preise und Preisindizes fuer die Ein- und Ausfuhr (0177-1787)
Indexed: RASB.
Published by: Statistisches Bundesamt, Gustav-Stresemann-Ring 11, Wiesbaden, 65180, Germany. TEL 49-611-75-1, FAX 49-611-724000, http://www.statistik-bund.de.

330 314 DEU ISSN 0072-4009
GERMANY. STATISTISCHES BUNDESAMT. FACHSERIE 18, VOLKSWIRTSCHAFTLICHE GESAMTRECHNUNGEN, REIHE 1: KONTEN UND STANDARDTABELLEN. Text in German. a. price varies. **Document type:** *Government.*
Published by: Statistisches Bundesamt, Gustav-Stresemann-Ring 11, Wiesbaden, 65180, Germany. TEL 49-611-75-1, FAX 49-611-724000, http://www.statistik-bund.de.

338 314 DEU
GERMANY. STATISTISCHES BUNDESAMT. FACHSERIE 2, UNTERNEHMEN UND ARBEITSSTAETTEN, REIHE 3: ABSCHLUESSE DER OEFFENTLICHEN VERSORGUNGS-, ENTSORGUNGS- UND VERKEHRSUNTERNEHMEN. Text in German. 1959. a. **Document type:** *Government.*
Formerly: Germany (Federal Republic, 1949-). Statistisches Bundesamt. Fachserie 2, Unternehmen und Arbeitsstaetten, Reihe 3: Abschluesse der Oeffentlichen Versorgungs- und Verkehrsunternehmen
Published by: Statistisches Bundesamt, Gustav-Stresemann-Ring 11, Wiesbaden, 65180, Germany. TEL 49-611-75-1, FAX 49-611-724000, http://www.statistik-bund.de.

332.1 314 DEU
GERMANY. STATISTISCHES BUNDESAMT. FACHSERIE 2, UNTERNEHMEN UND ARBEITSSTAETTEN, REIHE 4.1: INSOLVENZVERFAHREN. (Consists of two subseries) Text in German. m. **Document type:** *Government.*
Formerly: Germany. Statistisches Bundesamt. Fachserie 2, Unternehmen und Arbeitsstaetten, Reihe 4: Zahlungsschwierigkeiten (0072-2030)
Published by: Statistisches Bundesamt, Gustav-Stresemann-Ring 11, Wiesbaden, 65180, Germany. TEL 49-611-75-1, FAX 49-611-724000, http://www.statistik-bund.de.

338 314 DEU
GERMANY. STATISTISCHES BUNDESAMT. FACHSERIE 4, PRODUZIERENDES GEWERBE, REIHE 2.1: INDIZES DER PRODUKTION UND PRODUKTION AUSGEWAEHLTER ERZEUGNISSE IM PRODUZIERENDEN GEWERBE. (Consists of several subseries) Text in German. 1951. m. **Document type:** *Government.*
Formerly: Germany. Statistisches Bundesamt. Fachserie 4, Produzierendes Gewerbe, Reihe 2: Indices fuer das Produzierende Gewerbe
Published by: Statistisches Bundesamt, Gustav-Stresemann-Ring 11, Wiesbaden, 65180, Germany. TEL 49-611-75-1, FAX 49-611-724000, http://www.statistik-bund.de.

338 314 DEU
GERMANY. STATISTISCHES BUNDESAMT. FACHSERIE 4, PRODUZIERENDES GEWERBE, REIHE 2.2: AUFTRAGSEINGANG UND UMSATZ IM VERARBEITENDEN GEWERBE, AUFTRAGSEINGANG UND AUFTRAGSBESTAND IM BAUHAUPTGEWERBE. INDICES. Text in German. m. **Document type:** *Government.*
Formerly: Germany (Federal Republic, 1949-). Statistisches Bundesamt. Fachserie 4, Produzierendes Gewerbe, Reihe 2.2: Indices des Auftragseingangs, des Umsatzes und des Auftragsbestands fuer das Verarbeitende Gewerbe und fuer das Bauhaupt Gewerbe; Which superseded: Germany (Federal Republic, 1949-) Statistisches Bundesamt. Fachserie 4, Reihe 2: Indices des Auftragseingangs in Ausgewaehlten Industriezweigen und im Bauhauptgewerbe (0072-209X)
Published by: Statistisches Bundesamt, Gustav-Stresemann-Ring 11, Wiesbaden, 65180, Germany. TEL 49-611-75-1, FAX 49-611-724000, http://www.statistik-bund.de.

338 314 DEU
GERMANY. STATISTISCHES BUNDESAMT. FACHSERIE 4, PRODUZIERENDES GEWERBE, REIHE 3.1: PRODUKTION IM PRODUZIERENDEN GEWERBE. (Consists of several subseries) Text in German. 1951. q. (plus a.). **Document type:** *Government.*
Formerly (until 1991): Germany (Federal Republic, 1949-). Statistisches Bundesamt. Fachserie 4, Produzierendes Gewerbe, Reihe 3.1: Produktion Gewerbe des In- und Auslandes
Published by: Statistisches Bundesamt, Gustav-Stresemann-Ring 11, Wiesbaden, 65180, Germany. TEL 49-611-75-1, FAX 49-611-724000, http://www.statistik-bund.de.

338 314 DEU
GERMANY. STATISTISCHES BUNDESAMT. FACHSERIE 4, PRODUZIERENDES GEWERBE, REIHE 7.1: HANDWERK. BESCHAEFTIGTE UND UMSATZ IM HANDWERK. Text in German. q. **Document type:** *Government.*
Formerly: Germany (Federal Republic, 1949-). Statistisches Bundesamt. Fachserie 4, Produzierende Gastgewerbe, Reihe 7.1: Handwerk. Beschaeftigte um Umsatz im Handwerk (0072-2103)
Published by: Statistisches Bundesamt, Gustav-Stresemann-Ring 11, Wiesbaden, 65180, Germany. TEL 49-611-75-1, FAX 49-611-724000, http://www.statistik-bund.de.

380 314 DEU
GERMANY. STATISTISCHES BUNDESAMT. FACHSERIE 6, BINNENHANDEL, GASTGEWERBE, TOURISMUS; REIHE 1: GROSSHANDEL. Text in German. irreg. price varies. **Document type:** *Government.*
Formerly: Germany. Statistisches Bundesamt. Fachserie 6, Handel, Gastgewerbe, Reiseverkehr; Reihe 1: Grosshandel (0072-1964)
Published by: Statistisches Bundesamt, Gustav-Stresemann-Ring 11, Wiesbaden, 65180, Germany. TEL 49-611-75-1, FAX 49-611-724000, http://www.statistik-bund.de.

380 314 DEU
GERMANY. STATISTISCHES BUNDESAMT. FACHSERIE 6, BINNENHANDEL, GASTGEWERBE, TOURISMUS; REIHE 3: EINZELHANDEL. (Consists of several subseries) Text in German. irreg. Price varies. **Document type:** *Government.*
Formerly: Germany. Statistisches Bundesamt. Fachserie 6, Handel, Gastgewerbe, Reiseverkehr; Reihe 3: Einzelhandel (0072-1972)
Published by: Statistisches Bundesamt, Gustav-Stresemann-Ring 11, Wiesbaden, 65180, Germany. TEL 49-611-75-1, FAX 49-611-724000, http://www.statistik-bund.de.

382 314 DEU ISSN 0072-1646
GERMANY. STATISTISCHES BUNDESAMT. FACHSERIE 7, AUSSENHANDEL, REIHE 1: ZUSAMMENFASSENDE UEBERSICHTEN FUER DEN AUSSENHANDEL. Text in German. m. **Document type:** *Government.*
Indexed: RASB.
Published by: Statistisches Bundesamt, Gustav-Stresemann-Ring 11, Wiesbaden, 65180, Germany. TEL 49-611-75-1, FAX 49-611-724000, http://www.statistik-bund.de.

382 314 DEU ISSN 0072-1654
GERMANY. STATISTISCHES BUNDESAMT. FACHSERIE 7, AUSSENHANDEL, REIHE 2: AUSSENHANDEL NACH WAREN UND LAENDERN (SPEZIALHANDEL). Text in German. m. (plus a. cumulation). **Document type:** *Government.*
Indexed: RASB.

B

Published by: Statistisches Bundesamt, Gustav-Stresemann-Ring 11, Wiesbaden, 65180, Germany. TEL 49-611-75-1, FAX 49-611-724000, http://www.statistik-bund.de.

382 314 DEU ISSN 0072-1662
GERMANY. STATISTISCHES BUNDESAMT. FACHSERIE 7, AUSSENHANDEL, REIHE 3: AUSSENHANDEL NACH LAENDERN UND WARENGRUPPEN (SPEZIALHANDEL). Text in German. s-a. **Document type:** *Government.*
Indexed: RASB.
Published by: Statistisches Bundesamt, Gustav-Stresemann-Ring 11, Wiesbaden, 65180, Germany. TEL 49-611-75-1, FAX 49-611-724000, http://www.statistik-bund.de.

382 314 DEU
GERMANY. STATISTISCHES BUNDESAMT. FACHSERIE 7, AUSSENHANDEL, REIHE 4. AUSSENHANDEL MIT AUSGEWAEHLTEN WAREN; Reihe 4.1: Ein- und Ausfuhr von Mineraloel (Generalhandel). Text in German. m. (plus a. cumulation). **Document type:** *Government.*
Indexed: RASB.
Published by: Statistisches Bundesamt, Gustav-Stresemann-Ring 11, Wiesbaden, 65180, Germany. TEL 49-611-75-1, FAX 49-611-724000, http://www.statistik-bund.de.

382 314 DEU
GERMANY. STATISTISCHES BUNDESAMT. FACHSERIE 7, AUSSENHANDEL, REIHE 7: AUSSENHANDEL NACH LAENDERN UND GUETERGRUPPEN DER PRODUKTIONSSTATISTIKEN (SPEZIALHANDEL). Text in German. a. **Document type:** *Government.*
Formerly: Germany (Federal Republic, 1949-). Statistiches Bundesamt. Fachserie 7, Aussenhandel, Reihe 7: Sonderbeitraege (0072-1700)
Indexed: RASB.
Published by: Statistisches Bundesamt, Gustav-Stresemann-Ring 11, Wiesbaden, 65180, Germany. TEL 49-611-75-1, FAX 49-611-724000, http://www.statistik-bund.de.

382 314 DEU
GERMANY. STATISTISCHES BUNDESAMT. FREMDSPRACHIGE VEROEFFENTLICHUNGEN NR. 6370010: FOREIGN TRADE ACCORDING TO STANDARD INTERNATIONAL TRADE CLASSIFICATION (SITC) - SPECIAL TRADE. Text in German. a. **Document type:** *Government.*
Indexed: RASB.
Published by: Statistisches Bundesamt, Gustav-Stresemann-Ring 11, Wiesbaden, 65180, Germany. TEL 49-611-75-1, FAX 49-611-724000, http://www.statistik-bund.de.

314 DEU ISSN 0072-4106
GERMANY. STATISTISCHES BUNDESAMT. WARENVERZEICHNIS FUER DIE AUSSENHANDELSSTATISTIK. Text in German. a. **Document type:** *Government.*
Published by: Statistisches Bundesamt, Gustav-Stresemann-Ring 11, Wiesbaden, 65180, Germany. TEL 49-611-75-1, FAX 49-611-724000, http://www.statistik-bund.de.

338 CHE
GESCHAEFTSGANG IM SEKUNDEN SEKTOR/EVOLUTION DE LA SITUATION DANS LE SECTUER SECONDAIRE. Text in French, German. 1987. a. CHF 20 (effective 2001). **Document type:** *Government.*
Former titles (until 1995): Geschaeftsgang in der Schweizer Industrie. Produktions-, Auftrags-, Umsatz- und Lagerindizes; Auftrags-, Produktions-, Umsatz- und Lagerverhaeltnisse in der Industrie und im Bauhauptgewerbe
Published by: Bundesamt fuer Statistik, Espace de l'Europe 10, Neuchatel, 2010, Switzerland. TEL 41-32-7136011, FAX 41-32-7136012, information@bfs.admin.ch, http://www.admin.ch/bfs.

330.9 GHA
GHANA INDUSTRIAL CENSUS. DIRECTORY OF INDUSTRIAL ESTABLISHMENTS. Text in English. irreg., latest 1988. USD 15. **Document type:** *Directory, Government.*
Published by: Statistical Service, Information Section, PO Box 1098, Accra, Ghana. TEL 233-21-663578, FAX 233-21-667069.

330.9 GHA
GHANA INDUSTRIAL CENSUS. PHASE II REPORT. Text in English. irreg., latest 1987. USD 9. **Document type:** *Government.*
Published by: Statistical Service, Information Section, PO Box 1098, Accra, Ghana. TEL 233-21-663578, FAX 233-21-337069.

330.9 304.6 GHA
GHANA LIVING STANDARDS SURVEY. ROUND REPORT. Text in English. 1988. irreg., latest vol.3, 1992. USD 30; includes all Round Reports and Rural Communities in Ghana. **Document type:** *Government.*
Published by: Statistical Service, Information Section, PO Box 1098, Accra, Ghana. TEL 233-21-663578, FAX 223-21-667069.

330.9 304.6 GHA
GHANA LIVING STANDARDS SURVEY. RURAL COMMUNITIES IN GHANA. Text in English. irreg. USD 9. **Document type:** *Government.*
Published by: Statistical Service, Information Section, PO Box 1098, Accra, Ghana. TEL 233-21-663578, FAX 233-21-667069.

330.9 GHA
GHANA. STATISTICAL SERVICE. CONSUMER PRICE INDEX NUMBERS. Text in English. m. USD 24. **Document type:** *Government.*
Formerly: Ghana. Central Bureau of Statistics. Consumer Price Index
Published by: Statistical Service, Information Section, PO Box 1098, Accra, Ghana. TEL 233-21-663578, FAX 233-21-667069.

330.9 316 GHA ISSN 0855-0247
GHANA. STATISTICAL SERVICE. ECONOMIC SURVEY. Text in English. 1951. irreg., latest 1982. USD 20. **Document type:** *Government.*
Formerly: Ghana. Central Bureau of Statistics. Economic Survey (0072-4335)
Published by: Statistical Service, Information Section, PO Box 1098, Accra, Ghana. TEL 233-21-663578, FAX 233-21-667069.

657 USA ISSN 1055-3940
GLOBAL COMMUNIQUE. Text in English. 6/yr. membership. **Document type:** *Newsletter.*
Formerly (until 1990): E D P Auditor Update (0885-9450)
—CCC.
Published by: Information Systems Audit & Control Association, 3701 Algonquin Rd, Ste 1010, Rolling Meadows, IL 60008. TEL 847-253-1545, FAX 847-253-1443, jperry@isaca.org, http://www.isaca.org. R&P Janet K Perry. Circ: 18,160.

330.021 MAC
GOBERNO DA REGIAO ADMINISTRATIVA ESPECIAL DE MACAU. DIRECCAO DOS SERVICOS DE ESTATISTICA E CENSOS. CONTAS DO SECTOR PUBLICO/GOVERNMENT OF MACAO SPECIAL ADMINISTRATIVE REGION. STATISTICS AND CENSUS SERVICE. PUBLIC SECTOR ACCOUNTS. Text in Chinese, Portuguese. 1982. a. free. **Document type:** *Government.*
Formerly: Macao. Direccao dos Servicos de Estatistica e Censos. Contas Economicas do Sector Publico nao Empresarial
Published by: Direccao dos Servicos de Estatistica e Censos, Rua Inacio Baptista, No. 4-6, P.O. Box 3022, Macau. TEL 853-3995311, FAX 853-307825, info@dsec.gov.mo, http://www.dsec.gov.mo/.

382 314 NLD ISSN 1383-5777
GOEDERENNAALIJST. Text in Dutch. 1969. a. **Document type:** *Government.*
Formerly (until 1993): Netherlands. Central Bureau voor de Statistiek. Naamlijsten voor de Statistieken van de Buitenlandse Handel (0168-4094)
Published by: Centraal Bureau voor de Statistiek, Prinses Beatrixlaan 428, PO Box 4000, Voorburg, 2270 JM, Netherlands. TEL 31-70-3373800, FAX 31-70-3877429, infoservice@cbs.nl, http://www.cbs.nl. **Subscr. to:** Sdu Uitgevers bv, Christoffel Plantijnstraat, The Hague 2515 TZ, Netherlands.

382.021 MAC
GOVERNO DA REGIAO ADMINISTRATIVA ESPECIAL DE MACAU. DIRECCAO DOS SERVICOS DE ESTATISTICA E CENSOS. ESTATISTICAS DO COMERCIO EXTERNO/GOVERNMENT OF MACAO SPECIAL ADMINISTRATIVE REGION. STATISTICS AND CENSUS SERVICE EXTERNAL TRADE STATISTICS. Text in Portuguese, Chinese, English. 1955. a. free. **Document type:** *Government.*
Formerly: Macao. Direccao dos Servicos de Estatistica e Censos. Anuario Estatistico do Comercio Externo
Published by: Direccao dos Servicos de Estatistica e Censos, Rua Inacio Baptista, No. 4-6, P.O. Box 3022, Macau. TEL 853-3995311, FAX 853-307825, info@dsec.gov.mo, http://www.dsec.gov.mo/.

332.621 MAC
GOVERNO DA REGIAO ADMINISTRATIVA ESPECIAL DE MACAU. DIRECCAO DOS SERVICOS DE ESTATISTICA E CENSOS. INQUERITO AOS ORCAMENTOS FAMILIARES/GOVERNMENT OF MACAO SPECIAL ADMINISTRATIVE REGION. STATISTICS AND CENSUS SERVICE. HOUSEHOULD BUDGET SURVEY. Text in Chinese, Portuguese. 1981. quinquennial. free. **Document type:** *Government.* **Description:** Analyzes household structure expenditure and receipt data for the computation of the Consumer Price Index.
Formerly: Macao. Direccao dos Servicos de Estatistica e Censos. Inquerito as Despesas Familiares (0870-5674)
Published by: Direccao dos Servicos de Estatistica e Censos, Rua Inacio Baptista, No. 4-6, P.O. Box 3022, Macau. TEL 853-3995311, FAX 853-307825, info@dsec.gov.mo, http://www.dsec.gov.mo/.

381.021 MAC
GOVERNO DA REGIAO ADMINISTRATIVA ESPECIAL DE MACAU. DIRECCAO DOS SERVICOS DE ESTATISTICA E CENSOS. REVISAO DO PERIODO BASE DO INDICE DE PRECOS NO CONSUMIDOR/GOVERNMENT OF MACAO SPACIAL ADMINISTRATIVE REGION. STATISTICS AND CENSUS SERVICE. REBASING OF CONSUMER PRICE INDEX. Text in Chinese, Portuguese, English. 1984. irreg. free. **Document type:** *Government.*
Formerly: Macao. Direccao dos Servicos de Estatistica e Censos. Metodologia do Indice de Precos no Consumidor
Published by: Direccao dos Servicos de Estatistica e Censos, Rua Inacio Baptista, No. 4-6, P.O. Box 3022, Macau. TEL 853-3995311, FAX 853-307825, info@dsec.gov.mo, http://www.dsec.gov.mo/.

338 314 GBR
GREAT BRITAIN. CENTRAL STATISTICAL OFFICE. ANNUAL CENSUS OF PRODUCTION REPORTS. Text in English. 1970. a. price varies. stat. **Document type:** *Government.* **Description:** Compiles statistical information on UK manufacturing and other economic activities.
Former titles: Great Britain. Department of Trade and Industry. Business Statistics Office Report on the Census of Production; Great Britain. Department of Industry. Business Statistics Office Report on the Census of Production; Great Britain. Department of Trade and Industry. Business Statistics Office. Report on the Census of Production
Related titles: Series of: Business Monitor Series.
Published by: Office for National Statistics, Government Buildings, Cardiff Rd, Newport, Gwent NP9 1XG, United Kingdom. TEL 44-1633-812973, FAX 44-1633-812599, TELEX 497121 BSO NPT G, library@ons.gov.uk. **Orders to:** Stationery Office, PO Box 276, London SW8 5DT, United Kingdom. TEL 44-20-7873-9090, FAX 44-207-873-8200.

GREAT BRITAIN. CENTRAL STATISTICAL OFFICE. KEY DATA. see *STATISTICS*

330.9 314 GBR
GREAT BRITAIN. CENTRAL STATISTICAL OFFICE. STANDARD INDUSTRIAL CLASSIFICATION OF ECONOMIC ACTIVITIES (YEAR). Text in English. a. GBP 18. stat. index. **Document type:** *Government.* **Description:** Classifies U.K. industries and cross-indexes them with the E.U. system.
Published by: Office for National Statistics, Government Buildings, Cardiff Rd, Newport, Gwent NP9 1XG, United Kingdom. TEL 44-1633-812973, FAX 44-1633-812599. **Orders to:** Stationery Office, PO Box 276, London SW8 5DT, United Kingdom. TEL 44-20-7873-9090, FAX 44-207-873-8200.

332.152 GBR ISSN 0950-7558
HF3501
GREAT BRITAIN. CENTRAL STATISTICAL OFFICE. UNITED KINGDOM BALANCE OF PAYMENTS. Variant title: Pink Book. Text in English. 1948. a. GBP 13.25. stat. back issues avail. **Document type:** *Government.* **Description:** Gives detailed balance-of-payments data for a range of areas, including foreign trade.
—BLDSC (9093.500000).
Published by: Office for National Statistics, Government Buildings, Cardiff Rd, Newport, Gwent NP9 1XG, United Kingdom. TEL 44-1633-812973, FAX 44-1633-812599, library@ons.gov.uk. **Orders to:** Stationery Office, PO Box 276, London SW8 5DT, United Kingdom. TEL 44-20-7873-9090, FAX 44-207-873-8200.

339.341 GBR ISSN 0267-8691
HC260.I5
GREAT BRITAIN. CENTRAL STATISTICAL OFFICE. UNITED KINGDOM NATIONAL ACCOUNTS. Variant title: Blue Book. Text in English. 1984. a. GBP 15.50. stat. back issues avail. **Document type:** *Government.* **Description:** Examines all aspects of the UK economy.
—BLDSC (9096.463000).
Published by: Office for National Statistics, Government Buildings, Cardiff Rd, Newport, Gwent NP9 1XG, United Kingdom. TEL 44-1633-812973, FAX 44-1633-812599, library@ons.gov.uk. **Orders to:** Stationery Office, PO Box 276, London SW8 5DT, United Kingdom. TEL 44-20-7873-9090, FAX 44-207-873-8200.

332 314 GBR
HG186.G7
GREAT BRITAIN. OFFICE FOR NATIONAL STATISTICS. FINANCIAL STATISTICS. Text in English. 1962. m. GBP 260 includes annual Explanatory Handbook (effective 2000). stat. reprint service avail. from SCH. **Document type:** *Government.* **Description:** Provides data on topics including financial accounts for sectors of the economy, government income and expenditure, public sector borrowing, banking statistics, money supply, institutional investment, company finance and liquidity, security prices and exchange rates.
Formerly (until Apr. 1996): Great Britain. Central Statistical Office. Financial Statistics (0015-203X)
Related titles: Online - full text ed.: (from ProQuest Information & Learning).
Indexed: ABIn, BLI, RASB.
—CCC.

Published by: Office for National Statistics, c/o Phil Lewin, Room B110, Pimlico, London, SW1V 2QQ, United Kingdom. TEL 44-20-7533-6165, FAX 44-20-7533-6185, library@ons.gov.uk, http://www.statistics.gov.uk. **Subscr. to:** Stationery Office Publications Centre, PO Box 267, London SW8 5DT, United Kingdom. TEL 44-20-7873-9090, FAX 44-20-7873-8200.

338 314   GRC   ISSN 0072-7393
HC291
GREECE. NATIONAL STATISTICAL SERVICE. ANNUAL INDUSTRIAL SURVEY. Text in English, Greek. 1958. a., latest 1992. USD 16. back issues avail. **Document type:** *Government.*
Formerly (until 1963): Greece. National Statistical Service. Results of the Annual Industrial Survey
Published by: National Statistical Service of Greece, Statistical Information and Publications Division/Ethniki Statistiki Yperesia tes Ellados, 14-16 Lykourgou St, Athens, 101 66, Greece. TEL 30-1-3289-397, FAX 30-1-3241-102.

330.9   GRC   ISSN 1012-2397
GREECE. NATIONAL STATISTICAL SERVICE. HOUSEHOLD EXPENDITURE SURVEY. Text in English, Greek. 1957. irreg., latest 1987-88. USD 12. back issues avail. **Document type:** *Government.*
Published by: National Statistical Service of Greece, Statistical Information and Publications Division/Ethniki Statistiki Yperesia tes Ellados, 14-16 Lykourgou St, Athens, 101 66, Greece. TEL 30-1-3289-397, FAX 30-1-3241-102.

331.1   GRC   ISSN 0256-3576
HB2722.5.A3
GREECE. NATIONAL STATISTICAL SERVICE. LABOUR FORCE SURVEY. Text in Greek. 1974. a., latest 1993. back issues avail. **Document type:** *Government.*
Formerly (until 1980): Greece. National Statistical Service. Employment Survey Conducted in Urban and Semi-Urban Areas (0256-8004)
Published by: National Statistical Service of Greece, Statistical Information and Publications Division/Ethniki Statistiki Yperesia tes Ellados, 14-16 Lykourgou St, Athens, 101 66, Greece. TEL 30-1-3289-397, FAX 30-1-3241-102, http://www.statistics.gr, http://www.statistics.gr/Main_eng.asp.

338   GRC
GREECE. NATIONAL STATISTICAL SERVICE. PRODUCTION OF MANUFACTURED ITEMS. Text in Greek. 1987. triennial. USD 5. **Document type:** *Government.*
Published by: National Statistical Service of Greece, Statistical Information and Publications Division/Ethniki Statistiki Yperesia tes Ellados, 14-16 Lykourgou St, Athens, 101 66, Greece. TEL 30-1-3289-397, FAX 30-1-3241-102, TELEX 216 ESYE GR.

236   GRC   ISSN 0259-997X
GREECE. NATIONAL STATISTICAL SERVICE. PROVISIONAL NATIONAL ACCOUNTS OF GREECE. Key Title: Prosorinoi Ethnikoi Logariasmoi tes Ellados. Text in English, Greek. 1980. a., latest 1995. back issues avail. **Document type:** *Government.*
Published by: National Statistical Service of Greece, Statistical Information and Publications Division/Ethniki Statistiki Yperesia tes Ellados, 14-16 Lykourgou St, Athens, 101 66, Greece. TEL 30-1-3289-397, FAX 30-1-3241-102, http://www.statistics.gr, http://www.statistics.gr/Main_eng.asp.

336 314   GRC   ISSN 0256-3568
HJ50
GREECE. NATIONAL STATISTICAL SERVICE. PUBLIC FINANCE STATISTICS. Text in English, Greek. 1973. a., latest 1995. back issues avail. **Document type:** *Government.*
Formerly (until 1974): Greece. National Statistical Service. Statistical Yearbook of Public Finance (0072-7431)
Indexed: CPE.
Published by: National Statistical Service of Greece, Statistical Information and Publications Division/Ethniki Statistiki Yperesia tes Ellados, 14-16 Lykourgou St, Athens, 101 66, Greece. TEL 30-1-3289-397, FAX 30-1-3241-102, http://www.statistics.gr, http://www.statistics.gr/Main_eng.asp.

336   GRC   ISSN 1105-2147
GREECE. NATIONAL STATISTICAL SERVICE. QUARTERLY NATIONAL ACCOUNTS OF GREECE. Text in Greek, English. 1984. q. USD 3 per issue. back issues avail. **Document type:** *Government.*
Published by: National Statistical Service of Greece, Statistical Information and Publications Division/Ethniki Statistiki Yperesia tes Ellados, 14-16 Lykourgou St, Athens, 101 66, Greece. TEL 30-1-3289-397, FAX 30-1-3241-102.

338   GRC
GREECE. NATIONAL STATISTICAL SERVICE. REVISED CONSUMER PRICE INDEX. Text in English, Greek. 1960. irreg., latest 1998. back issues avail. **Document type:** *Government.*
Published by: National Statistical Service of Greece, Statistical Information and Publications Division/Ethniki Statistiki Yperesia tes Ellados, 14-16 Lykourgou St, Athens, 101 66, Greece. TEL 30-1-3289-397, FAX 30-1-3241-102, http://www.statistics.gr, http://www.statistics.gr/Main_eng.asp.

381   GRC
GREECE. NATIONAL STATISTICAL SERVICE. STANDARD CLASSIFICATION OF THE BRANCHES OF ECONOMIC ACTIVITY. Variant title: Greece. National Statistical Service. Greek Industrial Classification. Text in Greek. 1975. irreg., latest 1991. USD 4. **Document type:** *Government.*
Published by: National Statistical Service of Greece, Statistical Information and Publications Division/Ethniki Statistiki Yperesia tes Ellados, 14-16 Lykourgou St, Athens, 101 66, Greece. TEL 30-1-3289-397, FAX 30-1-3241-102.

336 314   GRC   ISSN 0256-3592
HJ50
GREECE. NATIONAL STATISTICAL SERVICE. STATISTICAL BULLETIN OF PUBLIC FINANCE. Text in English, Greek. q. back issues avail. **Document type:** *Bulletin, Government.*
Formerly (until 1973): Greece. National Statistical Service. Monthly Statistical Bulletin of Public Finance (0028-0259)
Published by: National Statistical Service of Greece, Statistical Information and Publications Division/Ethniki Statistiki Yperesia tes Ellados, 14-16 Lykourgou St, Athens, 101 66, Greece. TEL 30-1-3289-397, FAX 30-1-3241-102, TELEX 216734 ESYE GR, http://www.statistics.gr, http://www.statistics.gr/Main_eng.asp.

336   GRC   ISSN 0302-1416
GREECE. NATIONAL STATISTICAL SERVICE. STATISTICS OF THE DECLARED INCOME OF LEGAL ENTITIES AND ITS TAXATION. Text in Greek. 1959. a. USD 4. back issues avail. **Document type:** *Government.*
Published by: National Statistical Service of Greece, Statistical Information and Publications Division/Ethniki Statistiki Yperesia tes Ellados, 14-16 Lykourgou St, Athens, 101 66, Greece. TEL 30-1-3289-397, FAX 30-1-3241-102.

336   GRC   ISSN 0302-1114
GREECE. NATIONAL STATISTICAL SERVICE. STATISTICS ON THE DECLARED INCOME OF PHYSICAL PERSONS AND ITS TAXATION. Text in Greek. 1960. a., latest 1997. back issues avail. **Document type:** *Government.*
Published by: National Statistical Service of Greece, Statistical Information and Publications Division/Ethniki Statistiki Yperesia tes Ellados, 14-16 Lykourgou St, Athens, 101 66, Greece. TEL 30-1-3289-397, FAX 30-1-3241-102, http://www.statistics.gr, http://www.statistics.gr/Main_eng.asp.

331.1   GRC   ISSN 1106-1502
GREECE. NATIONAL STATISTICAL SERVICE. STATISTIQUES DU TRAVAIL. Key Title: Statistikes Ergasias - Ethnike Statistike Upersia tes Ellados. Text in Greek. 1967. q. **Document type:** *Bulletin, Government.*
Published by: National Statistical Service of Greece, Statistical Information and Publications Division/Ethniki Statistiki Yperesia tes Ellados, 14-16 Lykourgou St, Athens, 101 66, Greece. TEL 30-1-3289-397, FAX 30-1-3241-102, http://www.statistics.gr, http://www.statistics.gr/Main_eng.asp.

330 314   GRC   ISSN 0257-7240
GREEK ECONOMY IN FIGURES (YEAR). Text in English, Greek. 1980. a. USD 180. adv. stat. **Description:** Statistical guide to Greece concerning information about Greece and other EEC economies, demographics, national accounts, industrial production and capacity, public finance, money and credit prices. Provides comparative tables and diagrams with commentary about data and trends of the Greek, major OECD, EC and neighboring economies.
Published by: Electra Press, 4 Stadiou St, Athens, 105 64, Greece. TEL 01-32-33-203, FAX 01-32-35-160. Ed. Christos Papaioannou. Circ: 6,000.

651.2   GBR   ISSN 1476-3842
Z265   CODEN: MMPLEO
THE GREEN SHEET. Text in English. 2002 (Jan.). 6/yr. GBP 130 domestic; EUR 198 in Europe; USD 198 in US & Canada (effective 2005). adv. bk.rev. back issues avail. **Document type:** *Trade.* **Description:** Includes new products, trade news, letters, application studies and relevant articles.
Formed by the merger of (1986-2002): Micrographics Market Place (0953-3737); (1969-2002): Micrographics and Hybrid Imaging Systems Newsletter; Which was formerly (until 1998): Micrographics Newsletter (0883-9808); (until 1975): Microfilm Newsletter (0026-2749)
Related titles: Online - full text ed.: (from Gale Group).
Indexed: Inspec.
—IE.
Published by: Micrographics Marketing Ltd., 65 Winchester Dr, Burbage, Hinckley, Leics LE10 2BA, United Kingdom. TEL 44-24-76382328, FAX 44-24-76382319, gsinfo@green-sheet.net, http://www.green-sheet.net/. Eds. Mitch Badler, Tim Nixon. Pub. Tim Nixon. adv.: color page GBP 650; 190 x 275. Circ: 3,500.

330.9982   GRL   ISSN 0906-3315
HG3769.G83
GREENLAND. GROENLANDS STATISTIK. KONJUNKTURSTATISTIK. Text in Danish. 1991. irreg. **Document type:** *Government.*
Published by: Groenlands Statistik (GL)/Kalaallit Nunaanni Naatsorsueqqissaartarfik, PO Box 1025, Nuuk, 3900, Greenland. TEL 299-345000, FAX 299-322954.

330.9982   GRL   ISSN 1395-6159
GREENLAND. GROENLANDS STATISTIK. NATIONALREGNSKAB. Text in Danish. 1994. a. **Document type:** *Government.*
Published by: Groenlands Statistik (GL)/Kalaallit Nunaanni Naatsorsueqqissaartarfik, PO Box 1025, Nuuk, 3900, Greenland. TEL 299-345000, FAX 299-322954.

330.9982   GRL   ISSN 1397-2405
GREENLAND. GROENLANDS STATISTIK. OFFENTLIGE FINANSER. Text in Danish. 1996. a. **Document type:** *Government.*
Published by: Groenlands Statistik (GL)/Kalaallit Nunaanni Naatsorsueqqissaartarfik, PO Box 1025, Nuuk, 3900, Greenland. TEL 299-345000, FAX 299-322954.

330.1   USA
GROSS REPORT∗; a summary of key economic statistics. Text in English. 1992. m. USD 225. stat.; illus. **Document type:** *Newsletter, Consumer.* **Description:** Provides a quick overview of the economy structured in a unique and easy to read format.
Formerly: Economy at a Glance (1063-1208)
Published by: John E. Gross, Ed. & Pub., PO Box 460, Huntington, NY 11743-0569.

330   HKG
GUANGDONG SOCIOECONOMIC STATISTICS MONTHLY. Text in Chinese, English. m. HKD 1,200, USD 185.
Published by: Economic Information & Agency, 342 Hennessy Rd 10th Fl, 10 th Fl, Wanchai, Hong Kong. TEL 852-573-8217, FAX 852-838-8304.

658   CHN   ISSN 1009-7309
GUANLIXUE WENZHAI KA/SCIENCE OF MANAGEMENT ABSTRACTS ON CARDS. Text in Chinese. bi-m. (q. until 2002). CNY 30 (effective 2004). **Document type:** *Abstract/Index.*
Media: Cards.
Published by: Zhongguo Renmin Daxue, Shubao Zilio Zhongxin/Renmin University of China, Information Center for Social Server, Dongcheng-qu, 3, Zhangzizhong Lu, Beijing, 100007, China. TEL 86-10-64039458, FAX 86-10-64015080, kyes@163.net, http://www.confucius.cn.net/bkdetail.asp?fzt=WC3. **Dist. in the US by:** China Publications Service, PO Box 49614, Chicago, IL 60649. TEL 312-288-3291, FAX 312-288-8570; **Dist. outside of China by:** China International Book Trading Corp, 35 Chegongzhuang Xilu, Haidian District, PO Box 399, Beijing 100044, China. TEL 86-10-68412045, FAX 86-10-68412023, cibtc@mail.cibtc.com.cn, http://www.cibtc.com.cn/.

338 318   GTM
GUATEMALA. INSTITUTO NACIONAL DE ESTADISTICA. DIRECTORIO NACIONAL DE ESTABLECIMIENTOS INDUSTRIALES. Text in Spanish. a. USD 15; (effective 1993 ed.). **Document type:** *Directory.*
Published by: Instituto Nacional de Estadistica, Ministerio de Economia, 8A Calle no. 9-55, Guatemala City Zona, Guatemala. TEL 502-26136.

382   USA   ISSN 0565-0933
HF105
GUIDE TO FOREIGN TRADE STATISTICS. Text in English. irreg. price varies. stat. **Document type:** *Government.*
Related titles: Microfiche ed.
Published by: (Foreign Trade Division), U.S. Bureau of the Census (Subsidiary of: U.S. Department of Commerce), 4700 Silver Hill Rd., Washington, DC 20233. TEL 301-457-3041.

382 339 016   CHE   ISSN 0255-9358
Z7164.E17
GUIDE TO U N C T A D PUBLICATIONS. Text in English, French, Spanish, Arabic. 1968. a. free. abstr. back issues avail. **Document type:** *Catalog, Bibliography.*
Formerly: U N C T A D Guide to Publications (0041-5227)
Published by: United Nations Conference on Trade and Development, Palais des Nations, 8-14 Av de la Paix, Geneva 10, 1211, Switzerland. TEL 41-22-907-1234, FAX 41-22-9070046, info@unctad.org, http://www.unctad.org/en/pub/. **Subscr. to:** United Nations Publications, Distribution and Sales Section, Palais des Nations, Geneva CH-1211, Switzerland. TEL 41-22-907-2612.

336   GUY   ISSN 0301-7168
GUYANA. AUDITOR GENERAL. REPORT ON THE PUBLIC ACCOUNTS. Key Title: Public Accounts of the Government of Guyana. Text in English. a.
Published by: Auditor General, PO Box 10002, Georgetown, Guyana. Ed. Anand Goolsarran.

382   GUY   ISSN 0533-991X
HF172.G88
GUYANA. STATISTICAL BUREAU. ANNUAL ACCOUNT RELATING TO EXTERNAL TRADE. Text in English. 1954. a. USD 3.
Published by: Statistical Bureau, Georgetown, Guyana.

H I A'S NATIONWIDE CRAFT & HOBBY INDUSTRY CONSUMER SURVEY (YEAR). see *HOBBIES—Abstracting, Bibliographies, Statistics*

330.021 USA ISSN 0017-7199
HC101
HANDBOOK OF BASIC ECONOMIC STATISTICS✱; a manual of basic economic data on industry, commerce, labor and agriculture in the United States. Text in English. 1947. m. USD 132. mkt. index.
Indexed: RASB.
Published by: Economic Statistics Bureau of Washington, D.C., 4550 N Park Ave, Apt T106, Chevy Chase, MD 20815-7233. TEL 202-393-5070. Ed. Charles L Franklin.

331 317 USA
HANDBOOK OF OKLAHOMA EMPLOYMENT STATISTICS. Text in English. 1952. a. (in 2 vols.). free. charts; stat. **Document type:** *Government.*
Published by: Employment Security Commission, Research Department, Will Rogers Bldg, 2401 N Lincoln Blvd, Oklahoma City, OK 73105. Ed. Brenda Beed. Circ: 750.

549.021 CHE
HANDBOOK OF WORLD MINERAL STATISTICS. Text in English. a. USD 50 (effective 2001). back issues avail. **Document type:** *Yearbook, Trade.* **Description:** Contains statistics on the international trade of major non-fuel minerals and metals from primary to semi-processed forms at world, regional and country levels.
Published by: United Nations Conference on Trade and Development, 8-14 Avenue de la Paix, Geneva 10, 1211, Switzerland. TEL 41-22-9174924, FAX 41-22-9070195, info@unctad.org, http://www.unctad.org.

B

330 USA
HARVARD BUSINESS REVIEW CATALOG (YEAR). Text in English. a. USD 10 to individuals; USD 5 to institutions (effective 2000). index, cum.index. **Document type:** *Journal, Academic/Scholarly.* **Description:** Includes indexes of all Harvard Business Review articles published between 1985 and 1990 and best-selling articles published between 1952 and 1985.
Published by: (Harvard University, Harvard University, Graduate School of Business Administration), Harvard Business School Publishing, Soldier's Field Rd, Boston, MA 02163. TEL 617-495-6192, FAX 617-495-6985.

330 317 USA
HAWAII. DEPARTMENT OF BUSINESS, ECONOMIC DEVELOPMENT & TOURISM. QUARTERLY STATISTICAL & ECONOMIC REPORT. Text in English. q. USD 16 (effective 2000). **Description:** Presents recent economic trends and outlook.
Media: Online - full text.
Published by: Department of Business, Economic Development & Tourism, Communications & Publications, P O Box 2359, Honolulu, HI 96804. TEL 808-586-2423, FAX 808-586-2427, virion@dbedt.hawaii.gov, http://www.hawaii.gov/dbedt/qser.html.

330 016.33 FIN ISSN 0356-8164
HELSINGIN KAUPPAKORKEAKOULU. JULKAISUSARJA D. Text in English, Finnish. 1975. irreg. price varies. bibl.
Indexed: RASB.
—BLDSC (4286.718100).
Published by: Helsingin Kauppakorkeakoulu/Helsinki School of Economics, Runeberginkatu 22-24, Helsinki, 00100, Finland. Circ: 300.

352.14 DEU ISSN 1437-7365
HERNE IN ZAHLEN. JAHRBUCH (YEAR). Text in German. 1956. a. EUR 17.90 (effective 2000). stat. **Document type:** *Government.*
Formerly: Herne in Zahlen. Jahresheft (Year)
Published by: Stadt Herne, Amt fuer Informationsverarbeitung und Stadtforschung, Friedrich-Ebert-Platz 2, Postfach 101820, Herne, 44621, Germany. TEL 49-2323-16-0, FAX 49-2323-162311. Circ: 300.

352.14 DEU
HERNE IN ZAHLEN. MONATSBERICHT. Text in German. 1992. m. **Document type:** *Government.*
Published by: Stadt Herne, Amt fuer Informationsverarbeitung und Stadtforschung, Friedrich-Ebert-Platz 2, Postfach 101820, Herne, 44621, Germany. TEL 49-2323-16-0, FAX 49-2323-162311. Circ: 280.

352.14 DEU ISSN 1437-7357
HERNE IN ZAHLEN. VIERTELJAHRESBERICHTE. Text in German. 1956. q. EUR 2.56 (effective 2000). **Document type:** *Government.*
Published by: Stadt Herne, Amt fuer Informationsverarbeitung und Stadtforschung, Friedrich-Ebert-Platz 2, Postfach 101820, Herne, 44621, Germany. TEL 49-2323-16-0, FAX 49-2323-162311. Circ: 270.

HONG KONG ANNUAL DIGEST OF STATISTICS. see *POPULATION STUDIES—Abstracting, Bibliographies, Statistics*

332.1 HKG
HONG KONG. COMMISSIONER OF BANKING. ANNUAL REPORT. Text in English. a. HKD 20. **Document type:** *Government.*
Related titles: Chinese ed.
Published by: (Hong Kong. Commissioner of Banking), Government Publications Centre, G.P.O. Bldg, Ground Fl, Connaught Pl, Hong Kong, Hong Kong. TEL 852-842-8801. **Subscr. to:** Director of Information Services, Information Services Dept., 1 Battery Path G-F, Central, Hong Kong, Hong Kong.

330 315 HKG
HONG KONG ECONOMIC TRENDS. Text in Chinese, English. 1977. s-m. HKD 240; HKD 10 newsstand/cover (effective 2002). charts. back issues avail. **Document type:** *Government.* **Description:** Presents up-to-date monthly and quarterly data of major economic indicators which help readers grasp the pulse of Hong Kong's economy before more detailed statistics become available.
Former titles: Hong Kong Economic Trends and Indexes; Hong Kong Economic Indicators
Related titles: Online - full text ed.
Published by: Census and Statistics Department/Zhengfu Tongjichu, General Statistics Section 1(B), 19/F Wanchai Tower, 12 Harbour Rd, Wan Chai, Hong Kong. TEL 852-2582-4068, FAX 852-2827-1708, genenq@censtatd.gov.hk, http://www.info.gov.hk/censtatd, http://www.statisticalbookstore.gov.hk. Circ: 500. **Subscr. to:** Information Services Department, Publications Sales Section, 4/F, Murray Bldg, Garden Rd, Hong Kong, Hong Kong. TEL 852-2842-8844, FAX 852-2598-7482, puborder@isd.gcn.gov.hk, http://www.info.gov.hk/isd/book_e.htm. **Dist. by:** Government Publications Centre, Low Block, Ground Fl, Queensway Government Offices, 66 Queensway, Hong Kong, Hong Kong. TEL 852-2537-1910, FAX 852-2523-7195.

330 HKG
HONG KONG SHIPPING STATISTICS (CD-ROM EDITION). Text in Chinese, English. base vol. plus q. updates. HKD 2,800 (effective 2002). stat. back issues avail. **Document type:** *Government.*
Media: CD-ROM. **Related titles:** Online - full content ed.; ◆ Print ed.: Hong Kong Special Administrative Region of China. Census and Statistics Department. Hong Kong Shipping Statistics.
Published by: (Hong Kong Special Administrative Region of China. Census and Statistics Department/Zhengfu Tongjichu), Smartal Solutions Ltd, Unit 201, Kodak House II, 321 Java Rd, North Point, Hong Kong. TEL 852-2811 0079, FAX 852-2811-8103, enquiry@smartalsolutions.com, http://www.smartalsolutions.com/details/hka117.htm, http://www.smartalsolutions.com/hongkong.htm.

HONG KONG SPECIAL ADMINISTRATIVE REGION OF CHINA. CENSUS AND STATISTICS DEPARTMENT. ANNUAL REPORT ON THE CONSUMER PRICE INDEX. see *STATISTICS*

330 HKG
HONG KONG SPECIAL ADMINISTRATIVE REGION OF CHINA. CENSUS AND STATISTICS DEPARTMENT. ANNUAL REVIEW OF HONG KONG EXTERNAL TRADE. Text in Chinese, English. 1965. a. USD 46 (effective 2002). charts; stat. **Document type:** *Government.* **Description:** Provides a concise annual review of Hong Kong's external trade performance in a year and is useful for medium-term analysis of Hong Kong's trade performance. It contains a brief text, graphs and some 50 tables, giving a concise review of Hong Kong's external trade in the latest year compared with earlier years and bringing together annual statistics (in value terms) and index numbers for Hong Kong's external trade.
Formerly (until 1992): Hong Kong Review of Overseas Trade
Related titles: Online - full content ed.
Published by: Census and Statistics Department/Zhengfu Tongjichu, Trade Statistics Dissemination Section, 19/F Wanchai Tower, 12 Harbour Rd, Wan Chai, Hong Kong. TEL 852-2582-5041, FAX 852-2802-1101, tradenq@censtatd.gov.hk, http://www.info.gov.hk/censtatd, http://www.statisticalbookstore.gov.hk. **Subscr. to:** Information Services Department, Publications Sales Section, 4/F, Murray Bldg, Garden Rd, Hong Kong, Hong Kong. TEL 852-2842-8844, FAX 852-2598-7482, puborder@isd.gcn.gov.hk, http://www.info.gov.hk/isd/book_e.htm. **Dist. by:** Government Publications Centre, Low Block, Ground Fl, Queensway Government Offices, 66 Queensway, Hong Kong, Hong Kong. TEL 852-2537-1910, FAX 852-2523-7195.

382 HKG
HONG KONG SPECIAL ADMINISTRATIVE REGION OF CHINA. CENSUS AND STATISTICS DEPARTMENT. ANNUAL SURVEY OF WHOLESALE, RETAIL AND IMPORT AND EXPORT TRADES, RESTAURANTS AND HOTELS. Text in Chinese, English. 1979. a., latest 1999. USD 44 newsstand/cover (effective 2001). stat. **Document type:** *Government.* **Description:** Contains the statistics on the structure and operating characteristics of the wholesale, retail and import and export trades, restaurants and hotel industries.
Related titles: Online - full text ed.
Published by: Census and Statistics Department/Zhengfu Tongjichu, Distribution and Services Statistics Section 1(A), 19/F Chuang's Hung Hom Plaza, 83 Wuhu St, Hung Hom, Kowloon, Hong Kong. TEL 852-2802-1264, FAX 852-2827-0551, asw@censtatd.gov.hk, http://www.info.gov.hk/censtatd, http://www.statisticalbookstore.gov.hk. **Subscr. to:** Information Services Department, Publications Sales Section, 4/F, Murray Bldg, Garden Rd, Hong Kong, Hong Kong. TEL 852-2842-8844, FAX 852-2598-7482, puborder@isd.gcn.gov.hk, http://www.info.gov.hk/isd/book_e.htm. **Dist. by:** Government Publications Centre, Low Block, Ground Fl, Queensway Government Offices, 66 Queensway, Hong Kong, Hong Kong. TEL 852-2537-1910, FAX 852-2523-7195.

330 HKG
HONG KONG SPECIAL ADMINISTRATIVE REGION OF CHINA. CENSUS AND STATISTICS DEPARTMENT. AVERAGE DAILY WAGES OF WORKERS ENGAGED IN GOVERNMENT BUILDING AND CONSTRUCTION PROJECTS. Text in Chinese, English. 1970. m. looseleaf. free (effective 2001). stat. **Document type:** *Government.* **Description:** Covers the average daily wages for common occupations in government building and construction sites.
Related titles: Online - full content ed.
Published by: Census and Statistics Department/Zhengfu Tongjichu, Wage and Labour Costs Statistics Section, 20/F Wanchai Tower, 12 Harbour Rd, Wan Chai, Hong Kong. TEL 852-2582-4641, FAX 852-2827-2296, w1_1@censtatd.gov.hk, http://www.info.gov.hk/censtatd, http://www.statisticalbookstore.gov.hk. **Subscr. to:** Information Services Department, Publications Sales Section, 4/F, Murray Bldg, Garden Rd, Hong Kong, Hong Kong. TEL 852-2842-8844, FAX 852-2598-7482, puborder@isd.gcn.gov.hk, http://www.info.gov.hk/isd/book_e.htm. **Dist. by:** Government Publications Centre, Low Block, Ground Fl, Queensway Government Offices, 66 Queensway, Hong Kong, Hong Kong. TEL 852-2537-1910, FAX 852-2523-7195.

330 HKG
HONG KONG SPECIAL ADMINISTRATIVE REGION OF CHINA. CENSUS AND STATISTICS DEPARTMENT. BALANCE OF PAYMENTS STATISTICS OF HONG KONG. Text in Chinese, English. 2000. q. HKD 56; HKD 14 newsstand/cover (effective 2001). stat. **Document type:** *Government.* **Description:** Contains the latest Balance of Payments (BoP) statistics, including interpretation of Hong Kong's BoP account and more detailed information on BoP account of Hong Kong.
Published by: Census and Statistics Department/Zhengfu Tongjichu, Balance of Payments Branch (1), Units 602-606, 6/F Stelux House, 698 Prince Edward Rd East, San Po Kong, Kowloon, Hong Kong. TEL 852-2116-8660, FAX 852-2116-0278, bop11_1@censtatd.gov.hk, http://www.info.gov.hk/censtatd, http://www.statisticalbookstore.gov.hk. **Subscr. to:** Information Services Department, Publications Sales Section, 4/F, Murray Bldg, Garden Rd, Hong Kong, Hong Kong. TEL 852-2842-8844, FAX 852-2598-7482, puborder@isd.gcn.gov.hk, http://www.info.gov.hk/isd/book_e.htm. **Dist. by:** Government Publications Centre, Low Block, Ground Fl, Queensway Government Offices, 66 Queensway, Hong Kong, Hong Kong. TEL 852-2537-1910, FAX 852-2523-7195.

330 HKG
HONG KONG SPECIAL ADMINISTRATIVE REGION OF CHINA. CENSUS AND STATISTICS DEPARTMENT. BALANCE OF PAYMENTS STATISTICS OF HONG KONG (CUMULATIVE EDITION). Text in Chinese, English. 2000. irreg., latest 1997-1999. HKD 14 newsstand/cover (effective 2001). stat. **Document type:** *Government.* **Description:** Provides a dedicated publication on Balance of Payments (BoP) statistics of Hong Kong. It contains conceptual framework of BoP account, detailed description on the methodology and data sources of compiling the BoP statistics, as well as interpretation of Hong Kong's BoP account.
Published by: Census and Statistics Department/Zhengfu Tongjichu, Balance of Payments Branch (1), Units 602-606, 6/F Stelux House, 698 Prince Edward Rd East, San Po Kong, Kowloon, Hong Kong. TEL 852-2116-8660, FAX 852-2116-0278, bop11_1@censtatd.gov.hk, http://www.info.gov.hk/censtatd, http://www.statisticalbookstore.gov.hk. **Subscr. to:** Information Services Department, Publications Sales Section, 4/F, Murray Bldg, Garden Rd, Hong Kong, Hong Kong. TEL 852-2842-8844, FAX 852-2598-7482, puborder@isd.gcn.gov.hk, http://www.info.gov.hk/isd/book_e.htm. **Dist. by:** Government Publications Centre, Low Block, Ground Fl, Queensway Government Offices, 66 Queensway, Hong Kong, Hong Kong. TEL 852-2537-1910, FAX 852-2523-7195.

330 HKG
HONG KONG SPECIAL ADMINISTRATIVE REGION OF CHINA. CENSUS AND STATISTICS DEPARTMENT. CONSUMER PRICE INDEX. Text in Chinese, English. 1986. irreg., latest 1999. looseleaf. **Document type:** *Government.* **Description:** Provides information on uses of the Consumer Price Index (CPI), definitions and coverage of the different CPI series, and data sources and methods used in the compilation of the CPI. It also discusses proper methods of interpretation of the CPI and common misconceptions.
Published by: Census and Statistics Department/Zhengfu Tongjichu, Consumer Price Index Section, 22/F Chuang's Hung Hom Plaza, 83 Wuhu St, Hung Hom, Wowloon, Hong Kong. TEL 852-2805-6403, FAX 852-2577-6253, cpi_1@censtatd.gov.hk, http://www.info.gov.hk/censtatd/eng/statliteracy/edu_booklet/cpi/cpi_index.html, http://www.statisticalbookstore.gov.hk.

330 HKG
HONG KONG SPECIAL ADMINISTRATIVE REGION OF CHINA. CENSUS AND STATISTICS DEPARTMENT. DOMESTIC EXPORTS OF MANUFACTURED GOODS CLASSIFIED BY INDUSTRIAL ORIGIN. Text in Chinese, English. 1988. q. free. stat. **Document type:** *Government.* **Description:** Contains statistics on domestic exports analyzed by industrial origin are derived by regrouping merchandise exports items originally grouped under the external trade classification system according to industries in which these merchandise items are normally produced.
Published by: Census and Statistics Department/Zhengfu Tongjichu, Industrial Production Statistics Section, 16/F Chuang's Hung Hom Plaza, 83 Wuhu St, Hung Hom, Kowloon, Hong Kong. TEL 852-2805-6167, FAX 852-2805-6105, ips_2@censtatd.gov.hk, http://www.info.gov.hk/censtatd, http://www.statisticalbookstore.gov.hk. **Subscr. to:** Information Services Department, Publications Sales Section, 4/F, Murray Bldg, Garden Rd, Hong Kong, Hong Kong. TEL 852-2842-8844, FAX 852-2598-7482, puborder@isd.gcn.gov.hk, http://www.info.gov.hk/isd/book_e.htm. **Dist. by:** Government Publications Centre, Low Block, Ground Fl, Queensway Government Offices, 66 Queensway, Hong Kong, Hong Kong. TEL 852-2537-1910, FAX 852-2523-7195.

HONG KONG SPECIAL ADMINISTRATIVE REGION OF CHINA. CENSUS AND STATISTICS DEPARTMENT. EMPLOYMENT AND VACANCIES STATISTICS (DETAILED TABLES) SERIES B. WHOLESALE AND RETAIL TRADES, RESTAURANTS AND HOTELS. see *OCCUPATIONS AND CAREERS—Abstracting, Bibliographies, Statistics*

330.9 HKG
HONG KONG SPECIAL ADMINISTRATIVE REGION OF CHINA. CENSUS AND STATISTICS DEPARTMENT. EMPLOYMENT AND VACANCIES STATISTICS (DETAILED TABLES) SERIES C. INDUSTRIAL SECTORS. Text in Chinese, English. 1980. a., latest 2001. USD 72 (effective 2002). stat. **Document type:** *Bulletin, Government.* **Description:** Contains detailed employment and vacancies statistics in respect of the industrial sectors, viz. the mining and quarrying sector; the manufacturing sector; and the electricity and gas sector. The statistics are analyzed by District Council district and size of establishment.
Formerly: Employment and Vacancy Statistics: Manufacturing, Mining and Quarrying, Electricity and Gas
Related titles: Online - full text ed.
Published by: Census and Statistics Department/Zhengfu Tongjichu, Employment Statistics Section, 20/F Wanchai Tower, 12 Harbour Rd, Wan Chai, Hong Kong. TEL 852-2582-5076, FAX 852-2827-2296, es_2@censtatd.gov.hk, http://www.info.gov.hk/censtatd/eng/public/pub_list/ES/sev_c_index.html, http://www.statisticalbookstore.gov.hk. **Subscr. to:** Information Services Department, Publications Sales Section, 4/F, Murray Bldg, Garden Rd, Hong Kong, Hong Kong. TEL 852-2842-8844, FAX 852-2598-7482, puborder@isd.gcn.gov.hk, http://www.info.gov.hk/isd/book_e.htm. **Dist. by:** Government Publications Centre, Low Block, Ground Fl, Queensway Government Offices, 66 Queensway, Hong Kong, Hong Kong. TEL 852-2537-1910, FAX 852-2523-7195.

332.6 HKG
HONG KONG SPECIAL ADMINISTRATIVE REGION OF CHINA. CENSUS AND STATISTICS DEPARTMENT. EXTERNAL DIRECT INVESTMENT STATISTICS OF HONG KONG (YEAR). Text in Chinese, English. 1998. a. HKD 22 newsstand/cover (effective 2001). stat. **Document type:** *Government.* **Description:** Compasses both the stock and flow of inward and outward direct investments.
Formerly (until 1999): Hong Kong Special Administrative Region of China. Census and Statistics Department. External Investment in Hong Kong's Non-manufacturing Sectors
Related titles: Online - full content ed.
Published by: Census and Statistics Department/Zhengfu Tongjichu, Balance of Payments Branch (2), 10/F Stelux House, 698 Prince Edward Rd East, San Po Kong, Kowloon, Hong Kong. TEL 852-2116-5150, FAX 852-2116-0370, bop21_2@censtatd.gov.hk, http://www.info.gov.hk/censtatd/eng/public/pub_list/BoP/edis_index.html, http://www.statisticalbookstore.gov.hk. **Subscr. to:** Information Services Department, Publications Sales Section, 4/F, Murray Bldg, Garden Rd, Hong Kong, Hong Kong. TEL 852-2842-8844, FAX 852-2598-7482, puborder@isd.gcn.gov.hk, http://www.info.gov.hk/isd/book_e.htm. **Dist. by:** Government Publications Centre, Low Block, Ground Fl, Queensway Government Offices, 66 Queensway, Hong Kong, Hong Kong. TEL 852-2537-1910, FAX 852-2523-7195.

330 HKG
HONG KONG SPECIAL ADMINISTRATIVE REGION OF CHINA. CENSUS AND STATISTICS DEPARTMENT. EXTERNAL TRADE FIGURES. Text in Chinese, English. m. free. stat. back issues avail. **Document type:** *Government.* **Description:** Contains the most up-to-date aggregate values of imports, domestic exports and re-exports, as well as comparisons with figures for the same period in the preceding year.
Related titles: Online - full content ed.
Published by: Census and Statistics Department/Zhengfu Tongjichu, Trade Statistics Dissemination Section, 19/F Wanchai Tower, 12 Harbour Rd, Wan Chai, Hong Kong. TEL 852-2582-5041, FAX 852-2802-1101, tradenq@censtatd.gov.hk, http://www.info.gov.hk/censtatd, http://www.statisticalbookstore.gov.hk. **Subscr. to:** Information Services Department, Publications Sales Section, 4/F, Murray Bldg, Garden Rd, Hong Kong, Hong Kong. TEL 852-2842-8844, FAX 852-2598-7482, puborder@isd.gcn.gov.hk, http://www.info.gov.hk/isd/book_e.htm. **Dist. by:** Government Publications Centre, Low Block, Ground Fl, Queensway Government Offices, 66 Queensway, Hong Kong, Hong Kong. TEL 852-2537-1910, FAX 852-2523-7195.

330 HKG
HONG KONG SPECIAL ADMINISTRATIVE REGION OF CHINA. CENSUS AND STATISTICS DEPARTMENT. GROSS DOMESTIC PRODUCT (ANNUAL EDITION). Text in Chinese, English. 1973. a., latest 2001. HKD 84 newsstand/cover (effective 2001). stat. **Document type:** *Government.* **Description:** Contains quarterly series of GDP from the first quarter 1973 and annual series of GDP from 1961. It also gives a detailed description on the concepts, definitions, data sources and compilation methods for the GDP. Figures of GNP are also included.
Related titles: ♦ Alternate Frequency ed(s).: Hong Kong Special Administrative Region of China. Census and Statistics Department. Gross Domestic Product (Quarterly Edition). q.
Published by: Census and Statistics Department/Zhengfu Tongjichu, National Income Branch (1), 22/F Wanchai Tower, 12 Harbour Rd, Wan Chai, Hong Kong. TEL 852-2582-5077, FAX 852-2157-9295, ni11_1@censtatd.gov.hk, http://www.info.gov.hk/censtatd/eng/public/pub_list/NI11/agdp_index.html, http://www.statisticalbookstore.gov.hk. **Subscr. to:** Information Services Department, Publications Sales Section, 4/F, Murray Bldg, Garden Rd, Hong Kong, Hong Kong. TEL 852-2842-8844, FAX 852-2598-7482, puborder@isd.gcn.gov.hk, http://www.info.gov.hk/isd/book_e.htm. **Dist. by:** Government Publications Centre, Low Block, Ground Fl, Queensway Government Offices, 66 Queensway, Hong Kong, Hong Kong. TEL 852-2537-1910, FAX 852-2523-7195.

339 315 HKG
HONG KONG SPECIAL ADMINISTRATIVE REGION OF CHINA. CENSUS AND STATISTICS DEPARTMENT. GROSS DOMESTIC PRODUCT (QUARTERLY EDITION). Text in Chinese, English. 1991. q. HKD 88; HKD 22 newsstand/cover (effective 2002). stat. **Document type:** *Government.* **Description:** Contains the latest figures of Gross Domestic Product (GDP). Figures of Gross National Product (GNP) are also included.
Related titles: Online - full text ed.; ♦ Alternate Frequency ed(s).: Hong Kong Special Administrative Region of China. Census and Statistics Department. Gross Domestic Product (Annual Edition). a.
Published by: Census and Statistics Department/Zhengfu Tongjichu, National Income Branch (1), 22/F Wanchai Tower, 12 Harbour Rd, Wan Chai, Hong Kong. TEL 852-2582-5077, FAX 852-2157-9295, ni11_1@censtatd.gov.hk, http://www.info.gov.hk/censtatd/eng/public/pub_list/NI11/qgdp_index.html, http://www.statisticalbookstore.gov.hk. **Subscr. to:** Information Services Department, Publications Sales Section, 4/F, Murray Bldg, Garden Rd, Hong Kong, Hong Kong. TEL 852-2842-8844, FAX 852-2598-7482, puborder@isd.gcn.gov.hk, http://www.info.gov.hk/isd/book_e.htm. **Dist. by:** Government Publications Centre, Low Block, Ground Fl, Queensway Government Offices, 66 Queensway, Hong Kong, Hong Kong. TEL 852-2537-1910, FAX 852-2523-7195.

382 HKG
HONG KONG SPECIAL ADMINISTRATIVE REGION OF CHINA. CENSUS AND STATISTICS DEPARTMENT. HONG KONG EXTERNAL TRADE. Text in Chinese, English. 1968. m. HKD 78 newsstand/cover (effective 2001). charts; stat. back issues avail. **Document type:** *Government.* **Description:** Contains summary tables on external trade performance, information on important changes in direction and content of trade, trade statistics analyzed by principal products and main markets, and statistics on airborne and seaborne trade.
Incorporates (1968-1989): Hong Kong Trade Statistics. Summary
Related titles: CD-ROM ed.: Hong Kong External Trade (CD-ROM Edition). HKD 6,600, USD 850 newsstand/cover per vol. for vol.5; HKD 3,100, USD 405 updates per issue (effective 2001); Online - full text ed.
Published by: Census and Statistics Department/Zhengfu Tongjichu, Trade Statistics Dissemination Section, 19/F Wanchai Tower, 12 Harbour Rd, Wan Chai, Hong Kong. TEL 852-2582-5041, FAX 852-2802-1101, tradenq@censtatd.gov.hk, http://www.info.gov.hk/censtatd/eng/public/pub_list/TSD/etr_index.html, http://www.statisticalbookstore.gov.hk. Circ: 700 (controlled). **Subscr. to:** Information Services Department, Publications Sales Section, 4/F, Murray Bldg, Garden Rd, Hong Kong, Hong Kong. TEL 852-2842-8844, FAX 852-2598-7482, puborder@isd.gcn.gov.hk, http://www.info.gov.hk/isd/book_e.htm. **Dist. by:** Government Publications Centre, Low Block, Ground Fl, Queensway Government Offices, 66 Queensway, Hong Kong, Hong Kong. TEL 852-2537-1910, FAX 852-2523-7195.

330 HKG
HONG KONG SPECIAL ADMINISTRATIVE REGION OF CHINA. CENSUS AND STATISTICS DEPARTMENT. HONG KONG HARMONIZED COMMODITY DESCRIPTION AND CODING SYSTEM HANDBOOK. Text in Chinese, English. 1991. irreg., latest 1992. HKD 10 newsstand/cover (effective 2002). stat. back issues avail. **Document type:** *Government.* **Description:** Gives a comprehensive account of the HS and discusses the General Interpretative Rules, Section Notes, Chapter Notes and Subheading Notes with some illustrative examples. In addition, it describes the steps to locate correct HKHS code systematically for a commodity. A number of useful exercises for readers to familiarize with the classification system are also included.
Related titles: Online - full content ed.
Published by: Census and Statistics Department/Zhengfu Tongjichu, Trade Classification Section, 17/F Wanchai Tower, 12 Harbour Rd, Wanchai, Hong Kong. TEL 852-2582-4250, FAX 852-2824-2782, tc_1@censtatd.gov.hk, http://www.info.gov.hk/censtatd/eng/public/pub_list/TC/hshb_index.html, http://www.statisticalbookstore.gov.hk. **Subscr. to:** Information Services Department, Publications Sales Section, 4/F, Murray Bldg, Garden Rd, Hong Kong, Hong Kong. TEL 852-2842-8844, FAX 852-2598-7482, puborder@isd.gcn.gov.hk, http://www.info.gov.hk/isd/book_e.htm. **Dist. by:** Government Publications Centre, Low Block, Ground Fl, Queensway Government Offices, 66 Queensway, Hong Kong, Hong Kong. TEL 852-2537-1910, FAX 852-2523-7195.

330 HKG
HONG KONG SPECIAL ADMINISTRATIVE REGION OF CHINA. CENSUS AND STATISTICS DEPARTMENT. HONG KONG SHIPPING STATISTICS. Text in Chinese, English. 1983. q. HKD 168; HKD 42 newsstand/cover (effective 2002). stat. back issues avail. **Document type:** *Government.* **Description:** Contains vessel arrival statistics, port cargo and laden container throughputs, and detailed statistics on port cargo and laden containers analyzed by seaborne/river, shipment type, major port and principal commodity. Supplementary statistics on cargo throughput by mode of transport and container throughput of leading container ports are also shown.
Related titles: ♦ CD-ROM ed.: Hong Kong Shipping Statistics (CD-ROM Edition); Online - full content ed.
Published by: Census and Statistics Department/Zhengfu Tongjichu, Shipping and Cargo Statistics Section, 22/F Wanchai Tower, 12 Harbour Rd, Wan Chai, Hong Kong. TEL 852-2582-4891, shipping@censtatd.gov.hk, shipping@censtatd.gov.hk, http://www.info.gov.hk/censtatd/eng/public/pub_list/SHIPPING/ship_index.html, http://www.statisticalbookstore.gov.hk. **Subscr. to:** Information Services Department, Publications Sales Section, 4/F, Murray Bldg, Garden Rd, Hong Kong, Hong Kong. TEL 852-2842-8844, FAX 852-2598-7482, puborder@isd.gcn.gov.hk, http://www.info.gov.hk/isd/book_e.htm. **Dist. by:** Government Publications Centre, Low Block, Ground Fl, Queensway Government Offices, 66 Queensway, Hong Kong, Hong Kong. TEL 852-2537-1910, FAX 852-2523-7195.

330 HKG
HONG KONG SPECIAL ADMINISTRATIVE REGION OF CHINA. CENSUS AND STATISTICS DEPARTMENT. HONG KONG STANDARD INDUSTRIAL CLASSIFICATION. VOLUME ONE. Text in English. 1991. irreg., latest 1996. HKD 135 newsstand/cover (effective 2002). stat. **Document type:** *Government.* **Description:** A manual which gives a full list of industry codes, titles and descriptions of various economic activities under the Hong Kong Standard Industrial Classification.
Related titles: Online - full content ed.; Chinese ed.: Zhonghua Renmin Gongheguo Hongkong Tebei Xingzhengqu. Zhengfu Tongjichu. Hong Kong Baiozhun Xingye Fenlei. Diyece. 1996.
Published by: Census and Statistics Department/Zhengfu Tongjichu, Central Register of Establishments Section, 20/F Wanchai Tower, 12 Harbour Rd, Wan Chai, Hong Kong. TEL 852-2582-4767, FAX 852-2827-2296, genenq@censtatd.gov.hk, cre_1@censtatd.gov.hki, http://www.info.gov.hk/censtatd/eng/public/pub_list/CRE/cre_I_index.html, http://www.statisticalbookstore.gov.hk. **Subscr. to:** Information Services Department, Publications Sales Section, 4/F, Murray Bldg, Garden Rd, Hong Kong, Hong Kong. TEL 852-2842-8844, FAX 852-2598-7482, puborder@isd.gcn.gov.hk, http://www.info.gov.hk/isd/book_e.htm. **Dist. by:** Government Publications Centre, Low Block, Ground Fl, Queensway Government Offices, 66 Queensway, Hong Kong, Hong Kong. TEL 852-2537-1910, FAX 852-2523-7195.

382 HKG
HONG KONG SPECIAL ADMINISTRATIVE REGION OF CHINA. CENSUS AND STATISTICS DEPARTMENT. HONG KONG TRADE INDEX NUMBERS. Text in Chinese, English. 1977. m. HKD 132; HKD 11 newsstand/cover (effective 2002). stat. back issues avail. **Document type:** *Government.* **Description:** Contains trade index numbers for Hong Kong's external trade. Trade index numbers include value index, unit value index and quantum index which measure changes in the value, price and volume of external trade respectively.
Related titles: Online - full text ed.

B

▼ new title ➤ refereed ✶ unverified ♦ full entry avail.

Published by: Census and Statistics Department/Zhengfu Tongjichu, Trade Analysis Section, 19/F Wanchai Tower, 12 Harbour Rd, Wan Chai, Hong Kong. TEL 852-2582-4918, FAX 852-2802-1101, tradenq@censtatd.gov.hk, http://www.info.gov.hk/censtatd/eng/public/pub_list/TA/hktin_index.html, http://www.statisticalbookstore.gov.hk. **Subscr. to:** Information Services Department, Publications Sales Section, 4/F, Murray Bldg, Garden Rd, Hong Kong, Hong Kong. TEL 852-2842-8844, FAX 852-2598-7482, puborder@isd.gcn.gov.hk, http://www.info.gov.hk/isd/book_e.htm. **Dist. by:** Government Publications Centre, Low Block, Ground Fl, Queensway Government Offices, 66 Queensway, Hong Kong, Hong Kong. TEL 852-2537-1910, FAX 852-2523-7195.

330 HKG

HONG KONG SPECIAL ADMINISTRATIVE REGION OF CHINA. CENSUS AND STATISTICS DEPARTMENT. HONG KONG TRADE STATISTICS CLASSIFICATION. Text in Chinese, English. 1992. irreg., latest 1992. HKD 84 newsstand/cover (effective 2002). stat. back issues avail. **Document type:** *Government.* **Description:** Contains the commodity descriptions and codes which have been used in trade statistics reports published by the Census & Statistics Department since January 1992. The classification follows the Standard International Trade Classification Revision 3 (SITC Rev.3) which is recommended by the United Nations for Classifying trade statistics for economic analysis.

Related titles: Online - full content ed.

Published by: Census and Statistics Department/Zhengfu Tongjichu, Trade Statistics Dissemination Section, 19/F Wanchai Tower, 12 Harbour Rd, Wan Chai, Hong Kong. TEL 852-2582-5041, FAX 852-2802-1101, tradenq@censtatd.gov.hk, http://www.info.gov.hk/censtatd/eng/public/pub_list/TC/sitc_index.html, http://www.statisticalbookstore.gov.hk. **Subscr. to:** Information Services Department, Publications Sales Section, 4/F, Murray Bldg, Garden Rd, Hong Kong, Hong Kong. TEL 852-2842-8844, FAX 852-2598-7482, puborder@isd.gcn.gov.hk, http://www.info.gov.hk/isd/book_e.htm. **Dist. by:** Government Publications Centre, Low Block, Ground Fl, Queensway Government Offices, 66 Queensway, Hong Kong, Hong Kong. TEL 852-2537-1910, FAX 852-2523-7195.

330 HKG

HONG KONG SPECIAL ADMINISTRATIVE REGION OF CHINA. CENSUS AND STATISTICS DEPARTMENT. HONG KONG TRADE STATISTICS. DOMESTIC EXPORTS AND RE-EXPORTS. Text in Chinese, English. 1952. m. HKD 204 newsstand/cover (effective 2002). **Document type:** *Government.* **Description:** Contains a detailed breakdown of monthly and year-to-date figures by commodity item and of each commodity item by country/territory.

Related titles: ♦ Supplement(s): Hong Kong Special Administrative Region of China. Census and Statistics Department. Hong Kong Trade Statistics. Domestic Exports and Re-Exports: Annual Supplement. Country by Commodity.

Published by: Census and Statistics Department/Zhengfu Tongjichu, Trade Statistics Dissemination Section, 19/F Wanchai Tower, 12 Harbour Rd, Wan Chai, Hong Kong. TEL 852-2582-5041, FAX 852-2802-1101, tradenq@censtatd.gov.hk, http://www.info.gov.hk/censtatd/eng/public/pub_list/TSD/hkts_exp_index.html, http://www.statisticalbookstore.gov.hk. **Subscr. to:** Information Services Department, Publications Sales Section, 4/F, Murray Bldg, Garden Rd, Hong Kong, Hong Kong. TEL 852-2842-8844, FAX 852-2598-7482, puborder@isd.gcn.gov.hk, http://www.info.gov.hk/isd/book_e.htm. **Dist. by:** Government Publications Centre, Low Block, Ground Fl, Queensway Government Offices, 66 Queensway, Hong Kong, Hong Kong. TEL 852-2537-1910, FAX 852-2523-7195.

330 HKG

HONG KONG SPECIAL ADMINISTRATIVE REGION OF CHINA. CENSUS AND STATISTICS DEPARTMENT. HONG KONG TRADE STATISTICS. DOMESTIC EXPORTS AND RE-EXPORTS: ANNUAL SUPPLEMENT. COUNTRY BY COMMODITY. Text in Chinese, English. 1964. a. HKD 170 newsstand/cover (effective 2002). stat. **Document type:** *Government.* **Description:** Contains a detailed breakdown of the annual figures of the latest year and the preceding year analysed by country/territory and of each country/territory by commodity item.

Related titles: ♦ Supplement to: Hong Kong Special Administrative Region of China. Census and Statistics Department. Hong Kong Trade Statistics. Domestic Exports and Re-Exports.

Published by: Census and Statistics Department/Zhengfu Tongjichu, Trade Statistics Dissemination Section, 19/F Wanchai Tower, 12 Harbour Rd, Wan Chai, Hong Kong. TEL 852-2582-5041, FAX 852-2802-1101, tradenq@censtatd.gov.hk, http://www.info.gov.hk/censtatd/eng/public/pub_list/TSD/hktsas_exp_index.html, http://www.statisticalbookstore.gov.hk. **Subscr. to:** Information Services Department, Publications Sales Section, 4/F, Murray Bldg, Garden Rd, Hong Kong, Hong Kong. TEL 852-2842-8844, FAX 852-2598-7482, puborder@isd.gcn.gov.hk, http://www.info.gov.hk/isd/book_e.htm. **Dist. by:** Government Publications Centre, Low Block, Ground Fl, Queensway Government Offices, 66 Queensway, Hong Kong, Hong Kong. TEL 852-2537-1910, FAX 852-2523-7195.

382 315 HKG

HONG KONG SPECIAL ADMINISTRATIVE REGION OF CHINA. CENSUS AND STATISTICS DEPARTMENT. HONG KONG TRADE STATISTICS. IMPORTS. Text in Chinese, English. 1952. m. HKD 204 newsstand/cover (effective 2002). stat. **Document type:** *Government.* **Description:** Contains a detailed breakdown of monthly and year-to-date figures by commodity item and of each commodity item by country/territory.

Related titles: Online - full text ed.; ♦ Supplement to: Hong Kong Special Administrative Region of China. Census and Statistics Department. Hong Kong Trade Statistics. Imports: Annual Supplement. Country by Commodity.

Published by: Census and Statistics Department/Zhengfu Tongjichu, Trade Statistics Dissemination Section, 19/F Wanchai Tower, 12 Harbour Rd, Wan Chai, Hong Kong. TEL 852-2582-5041, FAX 852-2802-1101, tradenq@censtatd.gov.hk, http://www.info.gov.hk/censtatd/eng/public/pub_list/TSD/hkts_im_index.html, http://www.statisticalbookstore.gov.hk. Circ: 900. **Subscr. to:** Information Services Department, Publications Sales Section, 4/F, Murray Bldg, Garden Rd, Hong Kong, Hong Kong. TEL 852-2842-8844, FAX 852-2598-7482, puborder@isd.gcn.gov.hk, http://www.info.gov.hk/isd/book_e.htm. **Dist. by:** Government Publications Centre, Low Block, Ground Fl, Queensway Government Offices, 66 Queensway, Hong Kong, Hong Kong. TEL 852-2537-1910, FAX 852-2523-7195.

330 HKG

HONG KONG SPECIAL ADMINISTRATIVE REGION OF CHINA. CENSUS AND STATISTICS DEPARTMENT. HONG KONG TRADE STATISTICS. IMPORTS: ANNUAL SUPPLEMENT. COUNTRY BY COMMODITY. Text in Chinese, English. a., latest 2000. HKD 170 newsstand/cover (effective 2001). stat. **Document type:** *Government.* **Description:** Contains a detailed breakdown of the annual figures of the latest year and the preceding year analysed by country/territory and of each country/territory by commodity item.

Related titles: ♦ Supplement(s): Hong Kong Special Administrative Region of China. Census and Statistics Department. Hong Kong Trade Statistics. Imports.

Published by: Census and Statistics Department/Zhengfu Tongjichu, Trade Statistics Dissemination Section, 19/F Wanchai Tower, 12 Harbour Rd, Wan Chai, Hong Kong. TEL 852-2582-5041, FAX 852-2802-1101, tradenq@censtatd.gov.hk, http://www.info.gov.hk/censtatd/eng/public/pub_list/TSD/hktsas_im_index.html, http://www.statisticalbookstore.gov.hk. **Subscr. to:** Information Services Department, Publications Sales Section, 4/F, Murray Bldg, Garden Rd, Hong Kong, Hong Kong. TEL 852-2842-8844, FAX 852-2598-7482, puborder@isd.gcn.gov.hk, http://www.info.gov.hk/isd/book_e.htm. **Dist. by:** Government Publications Centre, Low Block, Ground Fl, Queensway Government Offices, 66 Queensway, Hong Kong, Hong Kong. TEL 852-2537-1910, FAX 852-2523-7195.

330 HKG

HONG KONG SPECIAL ADMINISTRATIVE REGION OF CHINA. CENSUS AND STATISTICS DEPARTMENT. HOUSEHOLD EXPENDITURE SURVEY AND THE REBASING OF THE CONSUMER PRICE INDICES. Text in Chinese, English. irreg. HKD 28 newsstand/cover (effective 2001). stat. back issues avail. **Document type:** *Government.* **Description:** Presents the results and methodology of the latest round of Household Expenditure Survey (HES) conducted in the survey year. It also describes the main features of the rebased Consumer Price Indices (CPIs).

Published by: Census and Statistics Department/Zhengfu Tongjichu, Price Statistics Branch, 22/F Chuang's Hung Hom Plaza, Hung Hom, Kowloon, Hong Kong. TEL 852-2805-6404, FAX 852-2577-6253, cpi_1@censtatd.gov.hk, http://www.info.gov.hk/censtatd/eng/public/pub_list/PRICE/hes_index.html, http://www.statisticalbookstore.gov.hk. **Subscr. to:** Information Services Department, Publications Sales Section, 4/F, Murray Bldg, Garden Rd, Hong Kong, Hong Kong. TEL 852-2842-8844, FAX 852-2598-7482, puborder@isd.gcn.gov.hk, http://www.info.gov.hk/isd/book_e.htm. **Dist. by:** Government Publications Centre, Low Block, Ground Fl, Queensway Government Offices, 66 Queensway, Hong Kong, Hong Kong. TEL 852-2537-1910, FAX 852-2523-7195.

330 HKG

HONG KONG SPECIAL ADMINISTRATIVE REGION OF CHINA. CENSUS AND STATISTICS DEPARTMENT. INDEX NUMBERS OF THE COSTS OF LABOUR AND MATERIALS USED IN PUBLIC SECTOR CONSTRUCTION PROJECTS. Text in Chinese, English. 1995. m. free (effective 2001). stat. **Document type:** *Government.* **Description:** Shows the changes in the costs of labor and selected building materials.

Related titles: Online - full content ed.

Published by: Census and Statistics Department/Zhengfu Tongjichu, Price Statistics Branch, 22/F Chuang's Hung Hom Plaza, Hung Hom, Kowloon, Hong Kong. TEL 852-2805-6404, FAX 852-2577-6253, cpi_1@censtatd.gov.hk, http://www.info.gov.hk/censtatd/eng/public/index2.html, http://www.statisticalbookstore.gov.hk. **Subscr. to:** Government Publications Centre; Information Services Department, Publications Sales Section, 4/F, Murray Bldg, Garden Rd, Hong Kong, Hong Kong. TEL 852-2842-8844, FAX 852-2598-7482, puborder@isd.gcn.gov.hk, http://www.info.gov.hk/isd/book_e.htm.

HONG KONG SPECIAL ADMINISTRATIVE REGION OF CHINA. CENSUS AND STATISTICS DEPARTMENT. MONTHLY REPORT ON THE CONSUMER PRICE INDEX. see *STATISTICS*

330 HKG

HONG KONG SPECIAL ADMINISTRATIVE REGION OF CHINA. CENSUS AND STATISTICS DEPARTMENT. MONTHLY SURVEY OF ORDERS-ON-HAND. Text in English, Chinese. 1993. m. HKD 6 newsstand/cover (effective 2002). stat. **Document type:** *Government.* **Description:** Provides the statistics on manufacturing firms as short-term economic indicators.

Related titles: Online - full content ed.

Published by: Census and Statistics Department/Zhengfu Tongjichu, Industrial Production Statistics Section, 16/F Chuang's Hung Hom Plaza, 83 Wuhu St, Hung Hom, Kowloon, Hong Kong. TEL 852-2805-6167, FAX 852-2805-6105, ips_1@censtatd.gov.hk, http://www.info.gov.hk/censtatd/eng/public/pub_list/IPS/msoh_index.html, http://www.statisticalbookstore.gov.hk. **Subscr. to:** Government Publications Centre; Information Services Department, Publications Sales Section, 4/F, Murray Bldg, Garden Rd, Hong Kong, Hong Kong. TEL 852-2842-8844, FAX 852-2598-7482, puborder@isd.gcn.gov.hk, http://www.info.gov.hk/isd/book_e.htm.

330 HKG

HONG KONG SPECIAL ADMINISTRATIVE REGION OF CHINA. CENSUS AND STATISTICS DEPARTMENT. QUARTERLY BUSINESS RECEIPTS INDICES FOR SERVICE INDUSTRIES. Text in Chinese, English. 1994. q. HKD 28; HKD 7 newsstand/cover (effective 2001). stat. **Document type:** *Government.* **Description:** Shows short-term changes of business receipts of various types of services industries.

Published by: Census and Statistics Department/Zhengfu Tongjichu, Distribution and Services Statistics Section 2(A), 21/F Chuang's Hung Hom Plaza, 83 Wuhu St, Hung Hom, Kowloon, Hong Kong. TEL 852-2802-1269, FAX 852-2123-1048, ds2a_1@censtatd.gov.hk, http://www.info.gov.hk/censtatd/eng/public/pub_list/DS2A/qbri_index.html, http://www.statisticalbookstore.gov.hk. **Subscr. to:** Information Services Department, Publications Sales Section, 4/F, Murray Bldg, Garden Rd, Hong Kong, Hong Kong. TEL 852-2842-8844, FAX 852-2598-7482, puborder@isd.gcn.gov.hk, http://www.info.gov.hk/isd/book_e.htm. **Dist. by:** Government Publications Centre, Low Block, Ground Fl, Queensway Government Offices, 66 Queensway, Hong Kong, Hong Kong. TEL 852-2537-1910, FAX 852-2523-7195.

HONG KONG SPECIAL ADMINISTRATIVE REGION OF CHINA. CENSUS AND STATISTICS DEPARTMENT. QUARTERLY INDEX OF INDUSTRIAL PRODUCTION. see *BUSINESS AND ECONOMICS—Production Of Goods And Services*

330 HKG

HONG KONG SPECIAL ADMINISTRATIVE REGION OF CHINA. CENSUS AND STATISTICS DEPARTMENT. QUARTERLY PRODUCER PRICE INDICES FOR MANUFACTURING INDUSTRIES. Text in Chinese, English. 1997. q. HKD 32; HKD 8 newsstand/cover (effective 2002). stat. back issues avail. **Document type:** *Government.* **Description:** Shows the up-to-date trends of producer prices in various manufacturing industries.

Published by: Census and Statistics Department/Zhengfu Tongjichu, Industrial Production Statistics Section, 16/F Chuang's Hung Hom Plaza, 83 Wuhu St, Hung Hom, Kowloon, Hong Kong. TEL 852-2805-6167, FAX 852-2805-6105, ips_1@censtatd.gov.hk, http://www.info.gov.hk/censtatd/eng/public/pub_list/IPS/ppi_index.html, http://www.statisticalbookstore.gov.hk. **Subscr. to:** Information Services Department, Publications Sales Section, 4/F, Murray Bldg, Garden Rd, Hong Kong, Hong Kong. TEL 852-2842-8844, FAX 852-2598-7482, puborder@isd.gcn.gov.hk, http://www.info.gov.hk/isd/book_e.htm. **Dist. by:** Government Publications Centre, Low Block, Ground Fl, Queensway Government Offices, 66 Queensway, Hong Kong, Hong Kong. TEL 852-2537-1910, FAX 852-2523-7195.

330 HKG
HONG KONG SPECIAL ADMINISTRATIVE REGION OF CHINA. CENSUS AND STATISTICS DEPARTMENT. QUARTERLY REPORT OF EMPLOYMENT AND VACANCIES STATISTICS. Text in Chinese, English. 1980. q. HKD 104; HKD 26 newsstand/cover (effective 2002). stat. **Document type:** *Government.* **Description:** Contains up-to-date statistics on number of establishments, persons, engaged and vacancies analysed by industry class. These statistics indicated the short -term changes on labor demand.
Published by: Census and Statistics Department/Zhengfu Tongjichu, Employment Statistics Section, 20/F Wanchai Tower, 12 Harbour Rd, Wan Chai, Hong Kong. TEL 852-2582-5076, FAX 852-2827-2296, es_2@censtatd.gov.hk, http://www.info.gov.hk/censtatd/eng/public/pub_list/ES/qsev_index.html, http://www.statisticalbookstore.gov.hk. **Subscr. to:** Information Services Department, Publications Sales Section, 4/F, Murray Bldg, Garden Rd, Hong Kong, Hong Kong. TEL 852-2842-8844, FAX 852-2598-7482, puborder@isd.gcn.gov.hk, http://www.info.gov.hk/isd/book_e.htm. **Dist. by:** Government Publications Centre, Low Block, Ground Fl, Queensway Government Offices, 66 Queensway, Hong Kong, Hong Kong. TEL 852-2537-1910, FAX 852-2523-7195.

330 HKG
HONG KONG SPECIAL ADMINISTRATIVE REGION OF CHINA. CENSUS AND STATISTICS DEPARTMENT. QUARTERLY REPORT OF WAGE AND PAYROLL STATISTICS. Text in Chinese, English. 1982. q. HKD 104; HKD 26 newsstand/cover (effective 2001). stat. **Document type:** *Government.* **Description:** Presents summary statistics on wage rates and payroll compiled from the findings of the Labour Earnings Survey (LES) conducted by the Census and Statistics Department. Breakdowns of wage and payroll statistics by major industry sectors and industries are also presented.
Formerly (until 1997): Hong Kong Special Administrative Region of China. Census and Statistics Department. Half-yearly Report of Wage Statistics
Related titles: Online - full content ed.
Published by: Census and Statistics Department/Zhengfu Tongjichu, Wage and Labour Costs Statistics Section, 20/F Wanchai Tower, 12 Harbour Rd, Wan Chai, Hong Kong. TEL 852-2582-4641, FAX 852-2827-2296, w1_1@censtatd.gov.hk, http://www.info.gov.hk/censtatd/eng/public/pub_list/WL/w-e-cat_index.html, http://www.statisticalbookstore.gov.hk. **Subscr. to:** Information Services Department, Publications Sales Section, 4/F, Murray Bldg, Garden Rd, Hong Kong, Hong Kong. TEL 852-2842-8844, FAX 852-2598-7482, puborder@isd.gcn.gov.hk, http://www.info.gov.hk/isd/book_e.htm. **Dist. by:** Government Publications Centre, Low Block, Ground Fl, Queensway Government Offices, 66 Queensway, Hong Kong, Hong Kong. TEL 852-2537-1910, FAX 852-2523-7195.

331 HKG
HONG KONG SPECIAL ADMINISTRATIVE REGION OF CHINA. CENSUS AND STATISTICS DEPARTMENT. QUARTERLY REPORT ON GENERAL HOUSEHOLD SURVEY. Text in Chinese, English. 1982. q. HKD 30 (effective 2001). stat. **Document type:** *Government.* **Description:** Contains the analysis of labor force participation, unemployment and under-employment, with tables and charts showing the characteristics of the labor force.
Former titles: Hong Kong. Census and Statistics Department. General Household Survey Labour Force Characteristics; (until 1981): Hong Kong. Census and Statistics Department. Labour Force Survey Report
Related titles: Online - full text ed.
Published by: Census and Statistics Department/Zhengfu Tongjichu, General Household Survey Section (2), 5/F Fortress Tower, 250 King's Rd, North Point, Hong Kong. TEL 852-2887-5508, FAX 852-2508-1501, ghs2_1@censtatd.gov.hk, http://www.info.gov.hk/censtatd/eng/public/pub_list/GHS2/ghs_index.html, http://www.statisticalbookstore.gov.hk. **Subscr. to:** Information Services Department, Publications Sales Section, 4/F, Murray Bldg, Garden Rd, Hong Kong, Hong Kong. TEL 852-2842-8844, FAX 852-2598-7482, puborder@isd.gcn.gov.hk, http://www.info.gov.hk/isd/book_e.htm. **Dist. by:** Government Publications Centre, Low Block, Ground Fl, Queensway Government Offices, 66 Queensway, Hong Kong, Hong Kong. TEL 852-2537-1910, FAX 852-2523-7195.

330 HKG
HONG KONG SPECIAL ADMINISTRATIVE REGION OF CHINA. CENSUS AND STATISTICS DEPARTMENT. QUARTERLY SUPPLEMENT TO STATISTICAL DIGEST OF THE SERVICES SECTOR. Text in Chinese, English. 1998. q. HKD 180; HKD 60 newsstand/cover (effective 2001). stat. back issues avail. **Document type:** *Government.* **Description:** Provides some up-to-date quarterly statistics on the 14 major service industries/domains of Hong Kong presented in the Statistical Digest of the Services Sector. Apart from providing quarterly statistics on the services sector, the publication also contains feature articles that analyse statistics of interest and present methodological materials of relevance to the service industries/domains.
Related titles: Online - full content ed.; ♦ Supplement to: Hong Kong Special Administrative Region of China. Census and Statistics Department. Statistical Digest of the Services Sector.
Published by: Census and Statistics Department/Zhengfu Tongjichu, Distribution and Services Statistics Section 2(B), 20/F Chuang's Hung Hom Plaza, 83 Wuhu St, Hung Hom, Kowloon, Hong Kong. TEL 852-2802-1273, FAX 852-2123-1048, ds2b_1@censtatd.gov.hk, http://www.info.gov.hk/censtatd/eng/public/pub_list/DS2B/qssdss_index.html, http://www.statisticalbookstore.gov.hk. **Subscr. to:** Information Services Department, Publications Sales Section, 4/F, Murray Bldg, Garden Rd, Hong Kong, Hong Kong. TEL 852-2842-8844, FAX 852-2598-7482, puborder@isd.gcn.gov.hk, http://www.info.gov.hk/isd/book_e.htm. **Dist. by:** Government Publications Centre, Low Block, Ground Fl, Queensway Government Offices, 66 Queensway, Hong Kong, Hong Kong. TEL 852-2537-1910, FAX 852-2523-7195.

331 HKG
HONG KONG SPECIAL ADMINISTRATIVE REGION OF CHINA. CENSUS AND STATISTICS DEPARTMENT. REPORT OF SALARIES AND EMPLOYEE BENEFITS STATISTICS MANAGERIAL AND PROFESSIONAL EMPLOYEES (EXCLUDING TOP MANAGEMENT). Text in Chinese, English. 1984. a., latest 2000. HKD 22 newsstand/cover (effective 2001). stat. **Document type:** *Government.*
Related titles: Online - full text ed.
Published by: Census and Statistics Department/Zhengfu Tongjichu, Wage and Labour Costs Statistics Section, 20/F Wanchai Tower, 12 Harbour Rd, Wan Chai, Hong Kong. TEL 852-2582-4641, FAX 852-2827-2296, w1_1@censtatd.gov.hk, http://www.info.gov.hk/censtatd/eng/public/pub_list/WL/m-e-cat_index.html, http://www.statisticalbookstore.gov.hk. **Subscr. to:** Information Services Department, Publications Sales Section, 4/F, Murray Bldg, Garden Rd, Hong Kong, Hong Kong. TEL 852-2842-8844, FAX 852-2598-7482, puborder@isd.gcn.gov.hk, http://www.info.gov.hk/isd/book_e.htm. **Dist. by:** Government Publications Centre, Low Block, Ground Fl, Queensway Government Offices, 66 Queensway, Hong Kong, Hong Kong. TEL 852-2537-1910, FAX 852-2523-7195.

330 HKG
HONG KONG SPECIAL ADMINISTRATIVE REGION OF CHINA. CENSUS AND STATISTICS DEPARTMENT. REPORT ON (YEAR) ESTABLISHMENT SURVEY ON MANPOWER TRAINING AND JOB SKILLS REQUIREMENTS. Text in Chinese, English. 2000. a., latest 2000. HKD 50 newsstand/cover (effective 2001). stat. **Document type:** *Government.* **Description:** Covers employers' view on business prospects over the medium to longer term, future manpower requirements and occupational mix, possible impacts of Hong Kong's economic restructuring on business turnover and employment, aspirations towards China's accession to World Trade Organization, and training requirements for their employees.
Published by: Census and Statistics Department/Zhengfu Tongjichu, Economic Surveys Development Section (1), 23/F Chuang's Hung Hom Plaza, 83 Wuhu St, Hung Hom, Kowloon, Hong Kong. TEL 852-2805-6102, FAX 852-2123-1053, esd_1@censtatd.gov.hk, http://www.info.gov.hk/censtatd/eng/public/pub_list/ESD1/esmtjsr_index.html, http://www.statisticalbookstore.gov.hk. **Subscr. to:** Information Services Department, Publications Sales Section, 4/F, Murray Bldg, Garden Rd, Hong Kong, Hong Kong. TEL 852-2842-8844, FAX 852-2598-7482, puborder@isd.gcn.gov.hk, http://www.info.gov.hk/isd/book_e.htm. **Dist. by:** Government Publications Centre, Low Block, Ground Fl, Queensway Government Offices, 66 Queensway, Hong Kong, Hong Kong. TEL 852-2537-1910, FAX 852-2523-7195.

330 HKG
HONG KONG SPECIAL ADMINISTRATIVE REGION OF CHINA. CENSUS AND STATISTICS DEPARTMENT. REPORT ON ANNUAL SURVEY OF INDUSTRIAL PRODUCTION. Text in Chinese, English. 1973. a., latest 1999. HKD 44 newsstand/cover (effective 2001). stat. **Document type:** *Government.* **Description:** Contains statistics on the structure and operating characteristics of the manufacturing industries.
Published by: Census and Statistics Department/Zhengfu Tongjichu, Industrial Production Statistics Section, 16/F Chuang's Hung Hom Plaza, 83 Wuhu St, Hung Hom, Kowloon, Hong Kong. TEL 852-2805-6167, FAX 852-2805-6105, ips_1@censtatd.gov.hk, http://www.info.gov.hk/censtatd/, http://www.statisticalbookstore.gov.hk. **Subscr. to:** Information Services Department, Publications Sales Section, 4/F, Murray Bldg, Garden Rd, Hong Kong, Hong Kong. TEL 852-2842-8844, FAX 852-2598-7482, puborder@isd.gcn.gov.hk, http://www.info.gov.hk/isd/book_e.htm. **Dist. by:** Government Publications Centre, Low Block, Ground Fl, Queensway Government Offices, 66 Queensway, Hong Kong, Hong Kong. TEL 852-2537-1910, FAX 852-2523-7195.

330 HKG
HONG KONG SPECIAL ADMINISTRATIVE REGION OF CHINA. CENSUS AND STATISTICS DEPARTMENT. REPORT ON ANNUAL SURVEY OF REGIONAL OFFICES REPRESENTING OVERSEAS COMPANIES IN HONG KONG. Text in Chinese, English. 1991. a., latest 2001. HKD 22 newsstand/cover (effective 2002). **Description:** Provides summary statistics on the economic character of the regional headquarters/offices and local offices, as well as their views on Hong Kong as a location for regional representation.
Published by: Census and Statistics Department/Zhengfu Tongjichu, Economic Surveys Development Section (3), 23/F Chuang's Hung Hom Plaza, 83 Wuhu St, Hung Hom, Kowloon, Hong Kong. TEL 852-2882-4558, FAX 852-2123-1053, esd3_1@censtatd.gov.hk, http://www.info.gov.hk/censtatd/eng/public/pub_list/ESD3/roroc_index.html, http://www.statisticalbookstore.gov.hk. **Subscr. to:** Information Services Department, Publications Sales Section, 4/F, Murray Bldg, Garden Rd, Hong Kong, Hong Kong. TEL 852-2842-8844, FAX 852-2598-7482, puborder@isd.gcn.gov.hk, http://www.info.gov.hk/isd/book_e.htm. **Dist. by:** Government Publications Centre, Low Block, Ground Fl, Queensway Government Offices, 66 Queensway, Hong Kong, Hong Kong. TEL 852-2537-1910, FAX 852-2523-7195.

330 HKG
HONG KONG SPECIAL ADMINISTRATIVE REGION OF CHINA. CENSUS AND STATISTICS DEPARTMENT. REPORT ON ANNUAL SURVEY OF STORAGE, COMMUNICATION, FINANCING, INSURANCE AND BUSINESS SERVICES. Text in Chinese, English. 1980. a., latest 1999. HKD 39 newsstand/cover (effective 2002). **Document type:** *Government.* **Description:** Contains statistics on the structure and operating characteristics of the storage, communications, financing, insurance and business service industries.
Related titles: Online - full content ed.
Published by: Census and Statistics Department/Zhengfu Tongjichu, Distribution and Services Statistics Section 2(A), 21/F Chuang's Hung Hom Plaza, 83 Wuhu St, Hung Hom, Kowloon, Hong Kong. TEL 852-2802-1269, FAX 852-2123-1048, ds2a_1@censtatd.gov.hk, http://www.info.gov.hk/censtatd/eng/public/pub_list/DS2A/asscsib_index.html, http://www.statisticalbookstore.gov.hk. **Subscr. to:** Information Services Department, Publications Sales Section, 4/F, Murray Bldg, Garden Rd, Hong Kong, Hong Kong. TEL 852-2842-8844, FAX 852-2598-7482, puborder@isd.gcn.gov.hk, http://www.info.gov.hk/isd/book_e.htm. **Dist. by:** Government Publications Centre, Low Block, Ground Fl, Queensway Government Offices, 66 Queensway, Hong Kong, Hong Kong. TEL 852-2537-1910, FAX 852-2523-7195.

330 HKG
HONG KONG SPECIAL ADMINISTRATIVE REGION OF CHINA. CENSUS AND STATISTICS DEPARTMENT. REPORT ON ANNUAL SURVEY ON INFORMATION TECHNOLOGY USAGE AND PENETRATION IN THE BUSINESS SECTOR. Text in Chinese, English. a. HKD 56 newsstand/cover (effective 2002). stat. back issues avail. **Document type:** *Government.* **Description:** Presents findings of the Annual Survey on Information Technology Usage and Penetration in the Business Sector conducted during survey year, showing the usage and penetration of information technology in different industry sectors in Hong Kong.
Related titles: Online - full content ed.
Published by: Census and Statistics Department/Zhengfu Tongjichu, Economic Surveys Development Section (2), 23/F Chuang's Hung Hom Plaza, 83 Wuhu St, Hung Hom, Kowloon, Hong Kong. TEL 852-2805-6112, FAX 852-2123-1053, esd2_1@censtatd.gov.hk, http://www.info.gov.hk/censtatd/eng/public/pub_list/ESD2/itup_index.html, http://www.statisticalbookstore.gov.hk. **Subscr. to:** Information Services Department, Publications Sales Section, 4/F, Murray Bldg, Garden Rd, Hong Kong, Hong Kong. TEL 852-2842-8844, FAX 852-2598-7482, puborder@isd.gcn.gov.hk, http://www.info.gov.hk/isd/book_e.htm. **Dist. by:** Government Publications Centre, Low Block, Ground Fl, Queensway Government Offices, 66 Queensway, Hong Kong, Hong Kong. TEL 852-2537-1910, FAX 852-2523-7195.

382 HKG
HONG KONG SPECIAL ADMINISTRATIVE REGION OF CHINA. CENSUS AND STATISTICS DEPARTMENT. REPORT ON HALF-YEARLY BUSINESS PROSPECTS SURVEY. Text in English, Chinese. s-a. HKD 9 newsstand/cover (effective 2002). stat. back issues avail. **Document type:** *Government.* **Description:** Presents the finds of the Half-yearly Business Prospects Survey (BPS) and provides the expectations of business in the immediate future.
Published by: Census and Statistics Department/Zhengfu Tongjichu, Economic Surveys Development Section (3), 23/F Chuang's Hung Hom Plaza, 83 Wuhu St, Hung Hom, Kowloon, Hong Kong. TEL 852-2882-4558, FAX 852-2123-1053, esd3_1@censtatd.gov.hk, http://www.info.gov.hk/censtatd/eng/public/pub_list/ESD3/rhbps_index.html, http://www.statisticalbookstore.gov.hk. **Subscr. to:** Information Services Department, Publications Sales Section, 4/F, Murray Bldg, Garden Rd, Hong Kong, Hong Kong. TEL 852-2842-8844, FAX 852-2598-7482, puborder@isd.gcn.gov.hk, http://www.info.gov.hk/isd/book_e.htm. **Dist. by:** Government Publications Centre, Low Block, Ground Fl, Queensway Government Offices, 66 Queensway, Hong Kong, Hong Kong. TEL 852-2537-1910, FAX 852-2523-7195.

HONG KONG SPECIAL ADMINISTRATIVE REGION OF CHINA. CENSUS AND STATISTICS DEPARTMENT. REPORT ON MONTHLY SURVEY OF RETAIL SALES. see *STATISTICS*

B

330 HKG
HONG KONG SPECIAL ADMINISTRATIVE REGION OF CHINA. CENSUS AND STATISTICS DEPARTMENT. STATISTICAL DIGEST OF THE SERVICES SECTOR. Text in Chinese, English. 1998. a. HKD 76 newsstand/cover (effective 2001). stat. back issues avail. **Document type:** *Government.* **Description:** Brings together in one volume some of the important statistical series, including number of establishments and persons engaged, business receipts index, gross output, value added and other industry/domain specific statistics on the fourteen major service industries/domains of Hong Kong.
Related titles: Online - full content ed.; ♦ Supplement(s): Hong Kong Special Administrative Region of China. Census and Statistics Department. Quarterly Supplement to Statistical Digest of the Services Sector.
Published by: Census and Statistics Department/Zhengfu Tongjichu, Distribution and Services Statistics Section 2(B), 20/F Chuang's Hung Hom Plaza, 83 Wuhu St, Hung Hom, Kowloon, Hong Kong. TEL 852-2802-1273, FAX 852-2123-1048, ds2b_1@censtatd.gov.hk, http://www.info.gov.hk/censtatd/eng/public/pub_list/DS2B/sdss_index.html, http://www.statisticalbookstore.gov.hk. **Subscr. to:** Information Services Department, Publications Sales Section, 4/F, Murray Bldg, Garden Rd, Hong Kong, Hong Kong. TEL 852-2842-8844, FAX 852-2598-7482, puborder@isd.gcn.gov.hk, http://www.info.gov.hk/isd/book_e.htm. **Dist. by:** Government Publications Centre, Low Block, Ground Fl, Queensway Government Offices, 66 Queensway, Hong Kong, Hong Kong. TEL 852-2537-1910, FAX 852-2523-7195.

330 HKG
HONG KONG SPECIAL ADMINISTRATIVE REGION OF CHINA. CENSUS AND STATISTICS DEPARTMENT. THE HONG KONG IMPORTS AND EXPORTS CLASSIFICATION LIST (HARMONIZED SYSTEM). VOLUME ONE. Text in Chinese, English. 1995. irreg., latest 2002. HKD 24 newsstand/cover (effective 2002). stat. back issues avail. **Document type:** *Government.* **Description:** Volume 1 contains commodity codes classified under Hong Kong Harmonized System (HKHS). The HKHS uses an 8-digit classification system, with the first 6-digit adopting the Harmonized System designed by the World Customs Organization and the 7th and 8th digits representing a further breakdown in commodity classification to meet the needs of Hong Kong.
Supersedes in part (until 2002): Hong Kong Special Administrative Region of China. Census and Statistics Department. The Hong Kong Imports and Exports Classification List (Harmonized System)
Related titles: Online - full content ed.; ♦ Series: Hong Kong Special Administrative Region of China. Census and Statistics Department. The Hong Kong Imports and Exports Classification List (Harmonized System). Volume Two; ♦ Hong Kong Special Administrative Region of China. Census and Statistics Department. The Hong Kong Imports and Exports Classification List (Harmonized System). Volume Three.
Published by: Census and Statistics Department/Zhengfu Tongjichu, Trade Classification Section, 17/F Wanchai Tower, 12 Harbour Rd, Wanchai, Hong Kong. TEL 852-2582-4250, FAX 852-2824-2782, tc_1@censtatd.gov.hk, http://www.info.gov.hk/censtatd/eng/public/pub_list/TC/hkiecl1.htm, http://www.statisticalbookstore.gov.hk. **Subscr. to:** Information Services Department, Publications Sales Section, 4/F, Murray Bldg, Garden Rd, Hong Kong, Hong Kong. TEL 852-2842-8844, FAX 852-2598-7482, puborder@isd.gcn.gov.hk, http://www.info.gov.hk/isd/book_e.htm. **Dist. by:** Government Publications Centre, Low Block, Ground Fl, Queensway Government Offices, 66 Queensway, Hong Kong, Hong Kong. TEL 852-2537-1910, FAX 852-2523-7195.

330 HKG
HONG KONG SPECIAL ADMINISTRATIVE REGION OF CHINA. CENSUS AND STATISTICS DEPARTMENT. THE HONG KONG IMPORTS AND EXPORTS CLASSIFICATION LIST (HARMONIZED SYSTEM). VOLUME THREE. Text in Chinese, English. irreg. HKD 28 newsstand/cover (effective 2002). stat. **Document type:** *Government.* **Description:** Contains an alphabetical index of commodities with the appropriate HKHS codes (Hong Kong Harmonized System) and a summary of changes between the editions of the HKHS.
Supersedes in part (in 2002): Hong Kong Special Administrative Region of China. Census and Statistics Department. The Hong Kong Imports and Exports Classification List (Harmonized System)
Related titles: ♦ Series: Hong Kong Special Administrative Region of China. Census and Statistics Department. The Hong Kong Imports and Exports Classification LIst (Harmonized System). Volume One; ♦ Hong Kong Special Administrative Region of China. Census and Statistics Department. The Hong Kong Imports and Exports Classification List (Harmonized System). Volume Two.
Published by: Census and Statistics Department/Zhengfu Tongjichu, Trade Classification Section, 17/F Wanchai Tower, 12 Harbour Rd, Wanchai, Hong Kong. TEL 852-2582-4250, FAX 852-2824-2782, genenq@censtatd.gov.hk, tc_1@censtatd.gov.hk, http://www.info.gov.hk/censtatd/eng/public/pub_list/TC/hkiecl3.htm, http://www.statisticalbookstore.gov.hk. **Subscr. to:** Information Services Department, Publications Sales Section, 4/F, Murray Bldg, Garden Rd, Hong Kong, Hong Kong. TEL 852-2842-8844, FAX 852-2598-7482, puborder@isd.gcn.gov.hk, http://www.info.gov.hk/isd/book_e.htm. **Dist. by:** Government Publications Centre, Low Block, Ground Fl, Queensway Government Offices, 66 Queensway, Hong Kong, Hong Kong. TEL 852-2537-1910, FAX 852-2523-7195.

330 HKG
HONG KONG SPECIAL ADMINISTRATIVE REGION OF CHINA. CENSUS AND STATISTICS DEPARTMENT. THE HONG KONG IMPORTS AND EXPORTS CLASSIFICATION LIST (HARMONIZED SYSTEM). VOLUME TWO. Text in Chinese, English. irreg. HKD 26 newsstand/cover (effective 2002). **Document type:** *Government.*
Supersedes in part (in 2002): Hong Kong Special Administrative Region of China. Census and Statistics Department. The Hong Kong Imports and Exports Classification List (Harmonized System)
Related titles: ♦ Series: Hong Kong Special Administrative Region of China. Census and Statistics Department. The Hong Kong Imports and Exports Classification LIst (Harmonized System). Volume One; ♦ Hong Kong Special Administrative Region of China. Census and Statistics Department. The Hong Kong Imports and Exports Classification List (Harmonized System). Volume Three.
Published by: Census and Statistics Department/Zhengfu Tongjichu, Trade Classification Section, 17/F Wanchai Tower, 12 Harbour Rd, Wanchai, Hong Kong. TEL 852-2582-4250, FAX 852-2824-2782, genenq@censtatd.gov.hk, tc_1@censtatd.gov.hk, http://www.info.gov.hk/censtatd/eng/public/pub_list/TC/hkiecl2.htm, http://www.statisticalbookstore.gov.hk. **Subscr. to:** Information Services Department, Publications Sales Section, 4/F, Murray Bldg, Garden Rd, Hong Kong, Hong Kong. TEL 852-2842-8844, FAX 852-2598-7482, puborder@isd.gcn.gov.hk, http://www.info.gov.hk/isd/book_e.htm. **Dist. by:** Government Publications Centre, Low Block, Ground Fl, Queensway Government Offices, 66 Queensway, Hong Kong, Hong Kong. TEL 852-2537-1910, FAX 852-2523-7195.

016.33 USA ISSN 1097-7864
HG4057
HOOVER'S HANDBOOKS INDEX. Text in English. 1997. a., latest 2001. USD 39.95 per issue (effective 2002). **Document type:** *Directory, Trade.* **Description:** Combined index to the Hoover's Handbooks series.
Published by: Hoover's Inc., 5800 Airport Blvd, Austin, TX 78752-3824. TEL 512-374-4500, FAX 512-374-4501, orders@hoovers.com, http://www.hoovers.com. R&P Dana Smith TEL 512-374-4528.

658.3 016 GBR ISSN 1462-5881
HF5549.A2
HUMAN RESOURCE MANAGEMENT ABSTRACTS. (Also avail. as a section of: Emerald Management Reviews (print & online eds.)) Text in English. 1971. bi-m. EUR 6,497.88 in Europe; USD 6,119 in North America; AUD 3,979 in Australasia; GBP 4,554.88 in the UK & elsewhere (effective 2006). **Document type:** *Abstract/Index.* **Description:** Contains fully searchable and independent abstracts of articles from top 400 international management journals. Abstracts are keyworded, indexed and assessed. Covers such topics as health and safety, management development, industrial relations, training techniques, and equal opportunities.
Formerly (until 1999): Personnel & Training Abstracts (0305-067X); Supersedes in part: Anbar Management Services Abstracts (0003-2794)
Related titles: CD-ROM ed.; Online - full text ed.
—CCC.
Published by: (Institute of Personnel and Management), Emerald Group Publishing Limited, 60-62 Toller Ln, Bradford, W Yorks BD8 9BY, United Kingdom. TEL 44-1274-777700, FAX 44-1274-785200, infomation@emeraldinsight.com, http://www.emeraldinsight.com/. Ed. David Pollitt. **Subscr. in Australasia to:** Emerald Group Publishing Ltd., PO Box 1567, Toowong, QLD 4066, Australia. TEL 61-3870-7144, FAX 61-3870-4013; **Subscr. in N. America to:** Emerald Group Publishing Ltd., 44 Brattle St, 4th Fl, Cambridge, MA 02138. TEL 617-497-2175, 888-622-0075, FAX 617-354-6875.

016.6583 USA ISSN 0099-2453
Z7165.U5
HUMAN RESOURCES ABSTRACTS; an international information service. Text in English. 1966. q. USD 1,034, GBP 667 to institutions (effective 2006). adv. illus. index. back issues avail.; reprint service avail. from PQC. **Document type:** *Journal, Abstract/Index.* **Description:** Abstracts the most important literature for persons interested in human resources development and related social and governmental policy questions.
Former titles (until 1975): Poverty and Human Resources Abstracts (0094-4394); (until 1971): Poverty and Human Resources (0032-5864); (until 1970): Poverty and Human Resources Abstracts (0092-6396)
Related titles: Microfilm ed.: (from PQC); Online - full text ed.
—IE, Infotrieve. **CCC.**
Published by: Sage Publications, Inc., 2455 Teller Rd, Thousand Oaks, CA 91320. TEL 805-499-0721, FAX 805-499-8096, info@sagepub.com, http://www.sagepub.com/journal.aspx?pid=104. Pub. Sara Miller McCune. Adv. contact Kirsten Beaulieu TEL 805-499-0721 ext 7160. page USD 350. Circ: 800 (paid). **Subscr. overseas to:** Sage Publications Ltd., 1 Oliver's Yard, 55 City Rd, London EC1 1SP, United Kingdom. TEL 44-20-73740645, FAX 44-20-73748741, subscription@sagepub.co.uk.

381 314 HUN ISSN 0866-1146
HF192.H8
HUNGARY. KOZPONTI STATISZTIKAI HIVATAL. BELKERESKEDELM. Text in Hungarian. a. HUF 321. **Document type:** *Government.*
Formed by the 1989 merger of: Hungary. Kozponti Statisztikai Hivatal. A Kiskereskedem es a Fogyasztasi Szolgalt (0865-0926); Hungary. Kozponti Statisztikai Hivatal. Belkereskedelmi Statisztikai Evkonyv (0238-9916); Which was formerly: Hungary. Kozponti Statisztikai Hivatal. Belkereskedelmi Evkonyv (0134-1138)
Published by: Kozponti Statisztikai Hivatal, Marketing Oszta'ly, Keleti Karoly utca 5-7, Budapest, 1024, Hungary. TEL 36-1-345-6000, FAX 36-1-345-6699, http://www.ksh.hu. Circ: 1,200.

331.2 314 HUN ISSN 0133-543X
HD5022.H8
HUNGARY. KOZPONTI STATISZTIKAI HIVATAL. FOGLALKOZTATOTTSAG ES KERESETI ARANYOK. Text in Hungarian. a. stat. **Document type:** *Government.*
Published by: Kozponti Statisztikai Hivatal, Marketing Oszta'ly, Keleti Karoly utca 5-7, Budapest, 1024, Hungary. TEL 36-1-345-6000, FAX 36-1-345-6699, http://www.ksh.hu. Circ: 900.

338 690 314 HUN ISSN 0239-1589
HC300.2
HUNGARY. KOZPONTI STATISZTIKAI HIVATAL. GAZDASAG ES STATISZTIKA. Text in Hungarian; Contents page in English, German, Russian. 1949. bi-m. HUF 480, USD 14.30. bk.rev. charts; stat. **Document type:** *Government.*
Formerly: Hungary. Kozponti Statisztikai Hivatal. Ipari es Epitoipari Statisztikai Ertesito (0018-7801)
Indexed: RASB.
Published by: Kozponti Statisztikai Hivatal, Marketing Oszta'ly, Keleti Karoly utca 5-7, Budapest, 1024, Hungary. TEL 36-1-345-6000, FAX 36-1-345-6699, http://www.ksh.hu. Ed. Albert Kiss. Circ: 1,000.

338 314 HUN ISSN 0209-4002
HC300.2
HUNGARY. KOZPONTI STATISZTIKAI HIVATAL. IPARSTATISZTIKAI EVKONYV. Text in Hungarian. a. HUF 348. stat. **Document type:** *Government.*
Published by: (Hungary. Kozponti Statisztikai Hivatal), Statisztikai Kiado Vallalat, Kaszas utca 10-12, PO Box 99, Budapest 3, 1300, Hungary. TEL 36-1-180-3311, FAX 36-1-168-8635. Circ: 1,200. **Subscr. to:** Kultura, PO Box 149, Budapest 1389, Hungary.

382 314 HUN ISSN 0139-3634
HF192.5
HUNGARY. KOZPONTI STATISZTIKAI HIVATAL. KULKERESKEDELMI STATISZTIKAI EVKONYV. Text in Hungarian. 1971. a. HUF 411. stat. **Document type:** *Government.*
Published by: Kozponti Statisztikai Hivatal, Marketing Oszta'ly, Keleti Karoly utca 5-7, Budapest, 1024, Hungary. TEL 36-1-345-6000, FAX 36-1-345-6699, http://www.ksh.hu. Circ: 1,200.

330 HUN ISSN 1217-5269
HC267.A23
HUNGARY. KOZPONTI STATISZTIKAI HIVATAL. LAKOSSAG FOGYASZTASA. Text in Hungarian. 1960. irreg. stat. **Document type:** *Government.*
Former titles (until 1993): Hungary. Kozponti Statisztikai Hivatal. Lakossag Jovedelme es Fogyasztasa (0455-1923); (until 1965): Lakossag Fogyasztasa (0200-7037)
Published by: Kozponti Statisztikai Hivatal, Marketing Oszta'ly, Keleti Karoly utca 5-7, Budapest, 1024, Hungary. TEL 36-1-345-6000, FAX 36-1-345-6699, http://www.ksh.hu.

330.9 AUS ISSN 1030-0856
HUNTER REGION ECONOMIC INDICATORS. Text in English. 1980. q. charts. back issues avail.
Formerly: Hunter Region Quarterly Economic Indicators (0725-6809)
Published by: Hunter Valley Research Foundation, PO Box 323, Hamilton DC, NSW 2303, Australia. TEL 61-49-69-4566, FAX 61-49-614981, oukhvrf@cc.newcastle.edu.au, info@hvrf.com.au, http://www.hvrf.com.au. Circ: 600.

B

330 IND ISSN 0250-9695
I C S S R JOURNAL OF ABSTRACTS AND REVIEWS: ECONOMICS. (Abstracts of selected articals from Indian Economic periodicals and Reviews of selected books published in English in India.) Text in English. 1971. s-a. INR 250 domestic to individuals; USD 120 elsewhere to individuals; INR 250 domestic to institutions; USD 120 elsewhere to institutions; GBP 80 in Europe to individuals; GBP 80 in Europe to institutions (effective 2001). adv. bk.rev. abstr. author index. back issues avail. **Document type:** *Journal, Abstract/Index.* **Description:** Abstracts of articles in Indian economics periodicals.
Published by: Indian Council of Social Science Research, 35 Ferozshah Rd., New Delhi, 110 001, India. FAX 91-11-6179836, info@icssr.org, http://www.icssr.org. Ed. Amitabh Kundu. Circ: 550. **Co-sponsor:** Giri Institute of Development Studies.

310 338.91 JPN
I D E STATISTICAL DATA SERIES. Text in Japanese, English. 1971. irreg. price varies.
Published by: Institute of Developing Economies/Ajia Keizai Kenkyusho, 3-2-2 Wakaba, Mihana-ku, Chiba-shi, Chiba 261-8545, Japan. TEL 81-43-299-9536, FAX 84-43-299-9724, info@ide.go.jp, http://www.ide.go.jp. Circ: 200.

330 FRA
I N S E E BULLETIN MENSUEL STATISTIQUE. Text in French. m.
Indexed: PAIS.
Published by: Institut National de la Statistique et des Etudes Economiques, 18 bd. Adolphe Pinard, Paris, Cedex 14 75675, France.

330 FRA
I N S E E ILE-DE-FRANCE A LA PAGE. Text in French. 1987. m. adv. bk.rev. **Description:** Statistics and economic articles about l'Ile-de-France.
Formerly (until 1996): Ile-de-France a la Page (0984-4724)
Published by: Institut National de la Statistique et des Etudes Economiques (INSEE), Direction Regionale d'Ile-de-France, 7 rue Stephenson, Saint-quentin-en-yvelines, Cedex 78188, France. TEL 33-1-30969000, FAX 33-1-30969001. Ed. Annie Etienne. Adv. contact Francoise Charbonnier. Circ: 800.

330 FRA ISSN 1142-3080
I N S E E METHODES. Text in French. 1989. 10/yr.
Published by: Institut National de la Statistique et des Etudes Economiques, 1 rue Vincent Auriol, Amiens, Cedex 1 80027, France. TEL 33-3-22927322, FAX 33-3-22979295, inseeactualites@insee.fr.

330.9 310 FRA ISSN 1249-4399
I N S E E PICARDIE DOSSIERS. Text in French. 1994. 4/yr. **Document type:** *Newsletter.*
Published by: Institut National de la Statistique et des Etudes Economiques, Observatoire Regional de Picardie, 1 rue Vincent Auriol, Amiens, Cedex 1 80040 , France. TEL 33-3-22973210, FAX 33-3-22973204. Ed. Victor-Pierre Morales. Pub. Christian Gabet.

330.9 310 FRA ISSN 1261-3797
I N S E E PICARDIE PREMIERE. Text in French. 1995. m. (11/yr.). **Document type:** *Newsletter.*
Published by: Institut National de la Statistique et des Etudes Economiques, Observatoire Regional de Picardie, 1 rue Vincent Auriol, Amiens, Cedex 1 80040 , France. TEL 33-3-22973210, FAX 33-3-22973204. Ed. Victor-Pierre Morales. Pub. Christian Gabet.

330.9 310 FRA ISSN 0396-3128
I N S E E PICARDIE RELAIS. Key Title: Relais. Text in French. 1977. m. (11/yr.). EUR 38 domestic; EUR 47 elsewhere. back issues avail. **Document type:** *Newsletter.*
Published by: (France. Direction Regionale de Picardie), Institut National de la Statistique et des Etudes Economiques, 1 rue Vincent Auriol, Amiens, Cedex 1 80027, France. TEL 33-3-22927322, FAX 33-3-22979295, inseeactualites@insee.fr, http://www.insee.fr. Ed. Victor Pierre Morales. Pub. Claude Arquembourg.

330 FRA ISSN 0997-3192
HC276.3
I N S E E PREMIERE. Text in French. 1989. 60/yr.
Published by: Institut National de la Statistique et des Etudes Economiques, 1 rue Vincent Auriol, Amiens, Cedex 1 80027, France. TEL 33-3-22927322, FAX 33-3-22979295, inseeactualites@insee.fr.

330 FRA ISSN 1629-5560
I N S E E RESULTATS. Text in French. 1989. 70/yr.
Related titles: ♦ Series: I N S E E Resultats: Economie Generale. ISSN 0998-4712; ♦ I N S E E Resultats: Systeme Productif. ISSN 0998-4895; I N S E E Resultats: Societe. ISSN 1630-862X. 2002.
Indexed: WAE&RSA.
Published by: Institut National de la Statistique et des Etudes Economiques, 1 rue Vincent Auriol, Amiens, Cedex 1 80027, France. TEL 33-3-22927322, FAX 33-3-22979295, inseeactualites@insee.fr.

330 FRA ISSN 0998-4712
HC271
I N S E E RESULTATS: ECONOMIE GENERALE. Text in French. 1989. 20/yr.
Formerly: I N S E E Cadrage. Economie Generale (0998-4828)
Related titles: ♦ Series of: I N S E E Resultats. ISSN 1629-5560.
Published by: Institut National de la Statistique et des Etudes Economiques, 1 rue Vincent Auriol, Amiens, Cedex 1 80027, France. TEL 33-3-22973210, FAX 33-3-22973204.

330 FRA ISSN 0998-4895
HD2346.F8
I N S E E RESULTATS: SYSTEME PRODUCTIF. Text in French. 1989. 15/yr.
Formerly: I N S E E Cadrage. Systeme Productif (0998-4836)
Related titles: ♦ Series of: I N S E E Resultats. ISSN 1629-5560.
Published by: Institut National de la Statistique et des Etudes Economiques, 1 rue Vincent Auriol, Amiens, Cedex 1 80027, France. TEL 33-3-22927322, FAX 33-3-22979295, inseeactualites@insee.fr.

330 FRA
I N S E E STATISTIQUES ET ETUDES: MIDI-PYRENEES. Text in French. irreg.
Indexed: PAIS.
Published by: Institut National de la Statistique et des Etudes Economiques, 18 bd. Adolphe Pinard, Paris, Cedex 14 75675, France.

336 USA
ILLINOIS PROPERTY TAX STATISTICS. Text in English. 1940. a., latest 1998. free. stat. back issues avail. **Document type:** *Government.*
Published by: Department of Revenue, Office of Local Government Services, 101 W Jefferson St, Mail Code 3 520, Springfield, IL 62702. FAX 217-524-0526. Ed. Bill Aoe. Circ: 1,500.

332.6021 CAN ISSN 1181-6759
IMPORTS BY COMMODITIES. Text in English. m.
Published by: Statistics Canada, External Trade Division, Statistical Reference Centre, Rm 1500, Main Building, Holland Avenue, Ottawa, ON K1A 0T6, Canada. TEL 613-951-8116.

332.6021 CAN ISSN 1181-6740
IMPORTS BY COUNTRIES. Text in English. 1962. q.
Published by: Statistics Canada, External Trade Division, Statistical Reference Centre, Rm 1500, Main Building, Holland Avenue, Ottawa, ON K1A 0T6, Canada. TEL 613-951-8116.

330 016 USA ISSN 0536-647X
Z7164.E2
INDEX OF ECONOMIC ARTICLES IN JOURNALS AND COLLECTIVE VOLUMES. Text in English. 1961. irreg., latest 1995. USD 160 (effective 2000). illus. back issues avail.; reprints avail. **Document type:** *Abstract/Index.* **Description:** Lists by subject category and by author, articles in economic journals and in collective volumes published during a specific year.
Related titles: Online - full text ed.
Published by: American Economic Association, 2014 Broadway, Ste 305, Nashville, TN 37203. TEL 615-322-2595, FAX 615-343-7590, http://www.vanderbilt.edu/aea/. **Subscr. to:** JEL, 2403 Sidney St., Ste. 260, Pittsburgh, PA 15203-5118.

353 016 USA ISSN 0149-6166
INDEX TO FEDERAL TAX ARTICLES (SUPPLEMENT). Text in English. base vol. plus q. updates. USD 695 (effective 1999). **Document type:** *Abstract/Index.* **Description:** Lists every significant article on federal income, estate, and gift taxation since 1913, including information by professionals about various tax issues.
Published by: W G & L Financial Reporting & Management Research (Subsidiary of: R I A), 90 Fifth Ave, New York, NY 10011. TEL 212-645-4800, FAX 212-337-4280.

330 016 IND ISSN 0019-4026
Z7164.E2
INDEX TO INDIAN ECONOMIC JOURNALS. Text in English. 1966. m. INR 5,000, USD 450 (effective 2005). adv. bk.rev. cum.index. **Document type:** *Abstract/Index.* **Description:** Indexes all economic and allied periodicals published in India.
Related titles: CD-ROM ed.: INR 5,000, USD 450 (effective 2005).
Indexed: RASB.
Published by: Information Research Academy, 37 Syed Amir Ali Ave, Flat #9, Kolkata, West Bengal 700 019, India. TEL 91-33-22402681, info@irakol.net, http://www.irakol.net. Ed., Adv. contact Partha Subir Guha. Circ: 2,100.

016.33 IND
▼ **INDEX TO SOUTH ASIAN ECONOMIC JOURNALS.** Text in English. 2003. q. INR 7,500, USD 700 (effective 2005). adv. bk.rev. Index. back issues avail. **Document type:** *Abstract/Index.* **Description:** Indexes approximately 400 economic and allied periodicals published in South Asia.
Related titles: CD-ROM ed.: INR 7,500, USD 700 (effective 2005).
Published by: Information Research Academy, 37 Syed Amir Ali Ave, Flat #9, Kolkata, West Bengal 700 019, India. info@irakol.net, http://www.irakol.net. Ed. Partha Subir Guha.

016.33 IND
▼ **INDEX TO SOUTH ASIAN MANAGEMENT JOURNALS.** Text in English. 2003. q. INR 6,500, USD 600 (effective 2005). adv. bk.rev. Index. back issues avail. **Document type:** *Abstract/Index.* **Description:** Indexes all major management and allied English language periodicals published in South Asia.
Related titles: CD-ROM ed.: INR 6,500, USD 600 (effective 2005).
Published by: Information Research Academy, 37 Syed Amir Ali Ave, Flat #9, Kolkata, West Bengal 700 019, India. info@irakol.net, http://www.irakol.net. Ed. Partha Subir Guha.

330 IND
INDIA. CENTRAL STATISTICAL ORGANIZATION. NATIONAL ACCOUNTS STATISTICS: SOURCES AND METHODS. Text in English. 1980. irreg. INR 16.50, USD 5.94. **Document type:** *Government.*
Published by: Central Statistical Organization, Sardar Patel Bhavan, Sansad Marg, New Delhi, 110 001, India.

331 315 IND
INDIA. LABOUR BUREAU. POCKET BOOK OF LABOUR STATISTICS. Text in English. 1959. a. INR 15, USD 5.40. **Document type:** *Government.*
Published by: Labour Bureau, Simla, Himachal Pradesh 171 004, India. Circ: 2,700. **Subscr. to:** Controller of Publications, Civil Lines, New Delhi 110 006, India.

331 016 IND
INDIA. MINISTRY OF LABOUR. BULLETIN OF CURRENT AWARENESS. Text in English. **Document type:** *Government.*
Formerly: Labour Bulletin of Current Awareness; Which superseded: India. Department of Labour and Employment. Library. Documentation of Labour
Media: Duplicated (not offset).
Published by: Ministry of Labour, Library, Sharam Shakti Bhavan, Rafi Marg, New Delhi, 110 001, India.

330.971021 CAN ISSN 1498-6132
INDIAN AND NORTHERN AFFAIRS CANADA. NORTHERN INDICATORS. Variant title: Affaires Indiennes et du Nord Canada. Indicateurs du Nord. Text in English, French. 1987. a.
Related titles: Online - full text ed.: ISSN 1498-3141. 2000.
Published by: (Canada. First Nations and Northern Statistics), Indian and Northern Affairs Canada/Affaires Indiennes et du Nord Canada, Terrasses de la Chaudiere, 10 Wellington, North Tower, Hull, PQ K1A 0H4, Canada. TEL 800-567-9604, infopubs@ainc-inac.gc.ca, http://www.ainc-inac.gc.ca/pr/sts/nia_e.html.

016.33 IND
INDIAN ECONOMIC ABSTRACTS. Text in English. 1990. q. INR 7,500, USD 700 (effective 2005). adv. bk.rev. Index. back issues avail. **Document type:** *Abstract/Index.* **Description:** Abstracts articles from all economic and allied English language periodicals published in India.
Related titles: CD-ROM ed.: INR 7,500, USD 700 (effective 2005).
Published by: Information Research Academy, 37 Syed Amir Ali Ave, Flat #9, Kolkata, West Bengal 700 019, India. info@irakol.net, http://www.irakol.net. Ed. Partha Subir Guha.

INDIAN GRANITE EXPORTERS' PERFORMANCE MONITOR. see *MINES AND MINING INDUSTRY—Abstracting, Bibliographies, Statistics*

658 016 IND ISSN 0019-5820
INDIAN MANAGEMENT ABSTRACTS. Text in English. 1972. q. INR 5,500, USD 500 (effective 2005). adv. bk.rev. cum.index. **Document type:** *Abstract/Index.* **Description:** Abstracts articles on management and allied topics published in India.
Incorporates (1972-1989): Management Abstracts (0377-1172)
Related titles: CD-ROM ed.: INR 5,500, USD 500 (effective 2005).
Published by: Information Research Academy, 37 Syed Amir Ali Ave, Flat #9, Kolkata, West Bengal 700 019, India. TEL 91-33-22402681, info@irakol.net, http://www.irakol.net. Ed. Partha Subir Guha. Circ: 2,050.

INDIAN RICE EXPORTERS' PERFORMANCE MONITOR. see *FOOD AND FOOD INDUSTRIES—Abstracting, Bibliographies, Statistics*

INDIAN SPICES EXPORTERS' PERFORMANCE MONITOR. see *FOOD AND FOOD INDUSTRIES—Abstracting, Bibliographies, Statistics*

INDIAN TEA EXPORTERS' PERFORMANCE MONITOR. see *FOOD AND FOOD INDUSTRIES—Abstracting, Bibliographies, Statistics*

332 MEX ISSN 0188-3909
HG5161
INDICADORES BURSATILES. Text in Spanish. m. MXP 2,750 (effective 1999). **Description:** Contains information on the securities market, trading by issue and series, foreign investment in stocks, trading summary by brokerage firm, methodological notes and member directory.
Related titles: English ed.: Mexican Stock Exchange. Facts and Figures.
Published by: Bolsa Mexicana de Valores, S.A. de C.V./Mexican Stock Exchange, Paseo de la Reforma 255, Mexico City, DF 06500, Mexico. TEL 52-5-7266794, FAX 52-5-7266836, cinforma#bmv.com.mx, http://www.bmv.com.mx/bmv/suscripciones.html.

330.021 URY ISSN 1688-1079
INDICADORES DE ACTIVIDAD. INDUSTRIA MANUFACTURERA. Text in English. 2000. bi-m.
Media: Online - full text.
Published by: Instituto Nacional de Estadistica, Rio Negro 1520, Montevideo, 11100, Uruguay. TEL 598-2-9027303, http://www.ine.gub.uy/biblioteca/publicaciones.htm#SERIE%20PUBLICACIONES%20PERIODICAS.

331.11 VEN ISSN 0798-8796
INDICADORES DE LA FUERZA DE TRABAJO✱; total nacional y por regiones. Text in Spanish. 1967. s-a. VEB 4,000. **Document type:** *Government.*
Formerly (until 1983): Encuesta de Hogares por Muestreo
Published by: Oficina Central de Estadistica e Informatica, Apdo. de Correos 4593, Carmeliatas, Caracas, DF 1010A, Venezuela. TEL 58-2-782-11-33, FAX 58-2-781-13-80, OCEI@platino.gov.ve, ocei@platino.gov.ve, http://www.OCEI.gov.ve, http://www.ocei.gov.ve.

332.021 MEX
INDICADORES DEL MERCADO DE PRODUCTOS DERIVADOS. Text in Spanish. d. MXP 3,990 (effective 1999).
Published by: Bolsa Mexicana de Valores, S.A. de C.V./Mexican Stock Exchange, Paseo de la Reforma 255, Mexico City, DF 06500, Mexico. TEL 52-5-7266794, FAX 52-5-7266836, cinforma@bmv.com.mx, http://www.bmv.com.mx/bmv/suscripciones.html.

317.2 PAN ISSN 0250-4332
INDICADORES ECONOMICOS Y SOCIALES DE PANAMA. Text in Spanish. a. free. **Document type:** *Bulletin, Government.* **Description:** Presents a brief statistical extract of demographic, economic and social data.
Published by: Direccion de Estadistica y Censo, Contraloria General, Apdo. 5213, Panama City, 5, Panama. FAX 507-210-4801.

339 318 SLV
INDICE DE PRECIOS AL CONSUMIDOR. Text in Spanish. 1954. m. free or exchange basis. stat. **Document type:** *Government.*
Formerly (until 1979): Indice de Precios al Consumidor para San Salvador, Mejicanos y Villa Delgado (0019-7009)
Published by: Direccion General de Estadistica y Censos, 1 Calle Poniente y 43 Avenida Sur, San Salvador, El Salvador.

330 318 BRA
INDICE DE PRECO AO CONSUMIDOR. Text in Portuguese. 1977. m.
Published by: Superintendencia de Estudos Economicos e Sociais da Bahia, Ave Luiz Vianna Filho s/n, Salvador, Bahia 41 750-300, Brazil. TEL 55-71-3704847, FAX 55-71-371853, http://www.sei.ba.gov.br.

INDICE DE PRECOS NO CONSUMIDOR. see *BUSINESS AND ECONOMICS—Domestic Commerce*

INDICE DO COMERCIO EXTERNO. see *BUSINESS AND ECONOMICS—International Commerce*

INDICES DA PRODUCAO INDUSTRIAL. see *MINES AND MINING INDUSTRY*

339 IDN ISSN 0126-2319
HC448.Y63
INDONESIA. CENTRAL BUREAU OF STATISTICS. ECONOMIC INDICATOR BULLETIN. Text in English, Indonesian. 1970. m. IDR 12,000, USD 5.25. charts; illus. **Document type:** *Bulletin, Government.*
Published by: Central Bureau of Statistics/Biro Pusat Statistik, Jalan Dr. Sutomo No. 8, PO Box 3, Jakarta Pusat, Indonesia. TEL 62-21-372808. Circ: 900.

315.98 IDN ISSN 0376-9984
HA1815
INDONESIA STATISTICS✱. Text in English. a.
Published by: First National City Bank, c/o Ministry of Information, Jalan Merdeka Barat 9, Jakarta Pusat, Indonesia.

331 016 USA ISSN 0070-0142
INDUSTRIAL AND LABOR RELATIONS BIBLIOGRAPHY SERIES. Text in English. 1952. irreg., latest vol.17, 1994. price varies. adv. **Document type:** *Monographic series.*
Indexed: CurCont, EI.
Published by: (New York State School of Industrial and Labor Relations), I L R Press, Cornell University Press, 512 E State St, Ithaca, NY 14850. TEL 607-277-2338, 800-666-2211. Ed. Frances Benson. R&P Tonya Cook. Adv. contact Elizabeth Larsen.

330 310 USA
HC59
INDUSTRIAL COMMODITY STATISTICS YEARBOOK. Text in English. 1950. a. USD 110 (effective 1997).
Former titles (until 1992): Industrial Statistics Yearbook (0257-7208); (until 1981): Yearbook of Industrial Statistics (0250-9873); (until 1973): Growth of World Industry
Related titles: Microfiche ed.: (from CIS).
Indexed: IIS, RASB.
Published by: (United Nations, Department of Economic and Social Affairs), United Nations Publications, Rm DC2-853, United Nations Bldg, 2 United Nations Plaza, New York, NY 10017. TEL 212-963-8300, 800-253-9646, FAX 212-963-3489, publications@un.org, http://www.un.org/publications, http://www.un.org/Pubs.

016.33 USA
INDUSTRIAL LITERATURE REVIEW; presents catalogs and brochures to buyers and specifiers in the US industrial marketplace. Text in English. 1976. q. free with subscr. to I E N: Industrial Equipment News. adv. bibl. **Document type:** *Catalog, Trade.* **Description:** Distributes product information to buying team members across all of the industry. Manufacturers offer their catalogs or product literature to buyers and specifiers.
Related titles: ◆ Supplement to: I E N: Industrial Equipment News. ISSN 0019-8285.
Published by: Thomas Publishing Company, Five Penn Plaza, New York, NY 10001. TEL 212-629-1546, FAX 212-629-1542, info@thomasimg.com, http://www.thomaspublishing.com. Circ: 205,000.

338.021 CAN ISSN 1201-7582
INDUSTRIAL MONITOR ON CD-ROM/HORIZON INDUSTRIEL SUR CD-ROM. Text in English, French. 1995. m.
Media: CD-ROM.
Published by: Statistics Canada, Publications Sales and Services, Ottawa, ON K1A 0T6, Canada. TEL 613-951-8116, infostats@statcan.ca, http://www.statcan.ca.

314 LUX ISSN 0258-1922
HC241.2
INDUSTRIAL TRENDS. Text in English. m. USD 140. **Description:** Information on industrial activity in the European Community.
Related titles: Microfiche ed.: (from CIS).
Indexed: IIS, RASB.
Published by: (European Commission, Statistical Office of the European Communities), European Commission, Office for Official Publications of the European Union, 2 Rue Mercier, Luxembourg, L-2985, Luxembourg. **Dist. in U.S. by:** Bernan Associates, Bernan, 4611-F Assembly Dr., Lanham, MD 20706-4391. TEL 301-459-0056, 800-274-4447.

943 310 DEU ISSN 0949-2917
INDUSTRIE- UND HANDELSKAMMER ZU DORTMUND. STATISTISCHES JAHRBUCH. Text in German. 1954. a. back issues avail. **Document type:** *Journal, Trade.*
Formerly (until 1994): Nordrhein-Westfaelischen Industrie- und Handelskammer. Statistisches Jahrbuch (0490-8937)
Published by: Industrie- und Handelskammer zu Dortmund, Maerkische Str 120, Dortmund, 44141, Germany. TEL 49-231-54170, FAX 49-231-5417109, info@dortmund.ihk.de, http://www.dortmund.ihk24.de. Circ: 1,000.

338 314 SCG
INDUSTRIJSKI PROIZVODI. Text in Serbo-Croatian. a. **Document type:** *Government.*
Related titles: ◆ Series of: Srbija i Crna Gora. Zavod za Statistiku. Statisticki Bilten.
Published by: Srbija i Crna Gora Zavod za Statistiku/Serbia and Montenegro Statistical Office, Kneza Milosa 20, Postanski Fah 203, Belgrade, 11000. TEL 381-11-3617273. Circ: 1,000.

330.021 CAN ISSN 1206-2588
INDUSTRY CANADA. MICRO-ECONOMIC POLICY ANALYSIS BRANCH. MONTHLY ECONOMIC INDICATORS. Text in English. 1999. m.
Published by: Industry Canada, Micro-Economic Policy Analysis Branch, C D Howe Bldg, 235 Queen St, Ottawa, ON K1A 0H5, Canada. TEL 613-952-3466, FAX 613-952-6927.

330 CAN ISSN 0700-2033
INDUSTRY PRICE INDEXES. Text in English. 1971. m. CND 182, USD 218 domestic; USD 255 foreign. **Document type:** *Government.* **Description:** Indexes of industry selling prices for manufacturing industries, with commodity detail.
Published by: Statistics Canada, Operations and Integration Division, Circulation Management, Jean Talon Bldg, 2 C12, Tunney's Pasture, Ottawa, ON K1A 0T6, Canada. TEL 613-951-7277, 800-267-6677, FAX 613-951-1584, http://www.statcan.ca.

016.33 USA
INFO - A S E A N & PACIFIC RIM. Text in English. q. **Document type:** *Trade.* **Description:** Enables researchers to quickly locate professional and academic literature on emerging business trends and technologies in Southeast Asia and the Pacific Rim.
Media: CD-ROM (from National Information Services Corp. (N I S C)). **Related titles:** Online - full text ed.: (from National Information Services Corp. (N I S C)).
Published by: National Information Services Corp. (N I S C), Ste 6, Wyman Towers, 3100 St Paul St, Baltimore, MD 21218. TEL 410-243-0797, FAX 410-243-0982, sales@nisc.com, http://www.nisc.com.

016.33 USA
INFO - C I S. (Commonwealth of Independent States) Text in English. q. **Document type:** *Abstract/Index.* **Description:** Enables researchers to quickly locate professional and academic literature on emerging business trends and technologies in the Commonwealth of Independent States.
Media: CD-ROM (from National Information Services Corp. (N I S C)). **Related titles:** Online - full text ed.: (from National Information Services Corp. (N I S C)).
Published by: National Information Services Corp. (N I S C), Ste 6, Wyman Towers, 3100 St Paul St, Baltimore, MD 21218. TEL 410-243-0797, FAX 410-243-0982, sales@nisc.com, http://www.nisc.com.

016.33 USA
INFO - LATINOAMERICA. Text in English. w. **Document type:** *Abstract/Index.* **Description:** Enables researchers to quickly locate professional and academic literature on emerging business trends and technologies throughout Central and South America.
Media: Online - full text (from National Information Services Corp. (N I S C)).
Published by: National Information Services Corp. (N I S C), Ste 6, Wyman Towers, 3100 St Paul St, Baltimore, MD 21218. TEL 410-243-0797, FAX 410-243-0982, sales@nisc.com, http://www.nisc.com.

016.33 USA
INFO - S A A R C. (South Asian Association of Regional Cooperation) q. **Document type:** *Trade.* **Description:** Enables researchers to quickly locate professional and academic literature on emerging business trends and technologies in southern Asia and the Indian Ocean islands.
Media: CD-ROM (from National Information Services Corp. (N I S C)). **Related titles:** Online - full text ed.
Published by: National Information Services Corp. (N I S C), Ste 6, Wyman Towers, 3100 St Paul St, Baltimore, MD 21218. TEL 410-243-0797, FAX 410-243-0982, sales@nisc.com, http://www.nisc.com.

382 ESP
INFORMACION COMERCIAL ESPANOLA. SECTOR EXTERIOR (YEAR). Text in Spanish. 1986. a. **Document type:** *Government.*
Published by: Ministerio de Comercio y Turismo, Paseo Castellana, 162, pl. 16, Madrid, 28046, Spain. TEL 34-1-349-36-47, FAX 34-1-349-36-34. Circ: 1,500.

THE INFORMATION REPORT. see *BIBLIOGRAPHIES*

016.330 DEU
INFORMATIONSDIENST F I Z TECHNIK. LOGISTIK AKTUELL. Variant title: Logistik Aktuell. Text in German. 1990. bi-m. EUR 183 (effective 2003). **Document type:** *Journal, Abstract/Index.*
Formerly: Informationsdienst V D I. Logistik Aktuell (0937-2253)
Published by: Fachinformationszentrum Technik e.V., Ostbahnhofstr 13-15, Frankfurt Am Main, 60314, Germany. TEL 49-69-4308213, kundenberatung@fiz-technik.de, http://www.fiz-technik.de.

INFORMATIONSDIENST F I Z TECHNIK. QUALITAETSMANAGEMENT. see *ENGINEERING—Abstracting, Bibliographies, Statistics*

016.33 RUS
INFORMATSIONNYI BYULLETEN'. EKONOMIKA I UPRAVLENIE V ZARUBEZHNYKH STRANAKH. Text in Russian. 1960. m. USD 90 foreign (effective 2006). **Document type:** *Journal, Abstract/Index.*
Published by: Vserossiiskii Institut Nauchnoi i Tekhnicheskoi Informatsii (VINITI), Ul Usievicha 20, Moscow, 125190, Russian Federation. TEL 7-095-1526441, FAX 7-095-9430060, dir@viniti.ru, http://www.viniti.ru. **Dist. by:** Informnauka Ltd., Ul Usievicha 20, Moscow 125190, Russian Federation. alfimov@viniti.ru.

016.33 RUS ISSN 1609-1442
HC340.12.A1
INFORMATSIONNYI SBORNIK. EKONOMICHESKAYA NAUKA SOVREMENNOI ROSSII. Text in Russian. 1998. q. USD 54 foreign (effective 2006). **Document type:** *Journal, Abstract/Index.*
Indexed: RefZh.

Published by: Vserossiiskii Institut Nauchnoi i Tekhnicheskoi Informatsii (VINITI), Ul Usievicha 20, Moscow, 125190, Russian Federation. TEL 7-095-1526441, FAX 7-095-9430060, dir@viniti.ru, http://www.viniti.ru. **Dist. by:** Informnauka Ltd., Ul Usievicha 20, Moscow 125190, Russian Federation. alfimov@viniti.ru.

016.33 RUS
INFORMATSIONNYI SBORNIK. FEDERAL'NYE I REGIONAL'NYE PROGRAMMY ROSSII. Text in Russian. 1997. q. USD 43 foreign (effective 2006). **Document type:** *Journal, Abstract/Index.*
Published by: Vserossiiskii Institut Nauchnoi i Tekhnicheskoi Informatsii (VINITI), Ul Usievicha 20, Moscow, 125190, Russian Federation. TEL 7-095-1526441, FAX 7-095-9430060, dir@viniti.ru, http://www.viniti.ru. **Dist. by:** Informnauka Ltd., Ul Usievicha 20, Moscow 125190, Russian Federation. alfimov@viniti.ru.

330.021 302.045195 RUS
INFORMATSIYA O SOTSIAL'NO-EKONOMICHESKOM POLOZHENII ROSSII/INFORMATION ON SOCIAL AND ECONOMIC SITUATION OF RUSSIA. Text in Russian. 2001. m. USD 314 foreign (effective 2005). charts; stat. **Document type:** *Journal, Government.* **Description:** Reports on Russia's socioeconomic situation, separate industries and sectors for the last month of the current year.
Related titles: E-mail ed.: RUR 1,840 (effective 2005).
Published by: Gosudarstvennyi Komitet Rossiiskoi Federatsii po Statistike/Federal State Statistics Office, ul Myasnitskaya 39, Moscow, 107450, Russian Federation. TEL 7-095-2074902, FAX 7-095-2074087, stat@gks.ru, http://www.gks.ru. **Dist. by:** East View Information Services, 3020 Harbor Ln. N., Minneapolis, MN 55447. TEL 800-477-1005, FAX 800-800-3839, eastview@eastview.com, http://www.eastview.com.

016.330 RUS
INOSTRANNAYA PECHAT' OB EKONOMICHESKOM, NAUCHNO-TEKHNICHESKOM I VOENNOM POTENTSIALE GOSUDARSTV-UCHASTNIKOV SNG I TEKHNICHESKIKH SREDSTVAKH EGO VYIAVLENIYA. SERIYA: EKONOMICHESKII I NAUCHNO-TEKHNICHESKII POTENTSIAL. Text in Russian. 1996. m. USD 90 foreign (effective 2006). **Document type:** *Journal, Abstract/Index.*
Indexed: RASB.
Published by: Vserossiiskii Institut Nauchnoi i Tekhnicheskoi Informatsii (VINITI), Ul Usievicha 20, Moscow, 125190, Russian Federation. TEL 7-095-1526441, FAX 7-095-9430060, dir@viniti.ru, http://www.viniti.ru. **Dist. by:** Informnauka Ltd., Ul Usievicha 20, Moscow 125190, Russian Federation. alfimov@viniti.ru.

016.330 RUS
INOSTRANNAYA PECHAT' OB EKONOMICHESKOM, NAUCHNO-TEKHNICHESKOM I VOENNOM POTENTSIALE GOSUDARSTV-UCHASTNIKOV SNG I TEKHNICHESKIKH SREDSTVAKH EGO VYIAVLENIYA. SERIYA: TEKHNICHESKIE SREDSTVA RAZVEDYVATELNYKH SLUZHB ZARUBEZHNYKH GOSUDARSTV. Text in Russian. 1996. m. USD 90 foreign (effective 2006). **Document type:** *Journal, Abstract/Index.*
Formerly: Tekhnicheskie Sredstva Razvedyvatelnykh Sluzhb Kapitalisticheskikh Gosudarstv
Indexed: RASB.
Published by: Vserossiiskii Institut Nauchnoi i Tekhnicheskoi Informatsii (VINITI), Ul Usievicha 20, Moscow, 125190, Russian Federation. TEL 7-095-1526441, FAX 7-095-9430060, dir@viniti.ru, http://www.viniti.ru. **Dist. by:** Informnauka Ltd., Ul Usievicha 20, Moscow 125190, Russian Federation. alfimov@viniti.ru.

016.330 RUS
INOSTRANNAYA PECHAT' OB EKONOMICHESKOM, NAUCHNO-TEKHNICHESKOM I VOENNOM POTENTSIALE GOSUDARSTV-UCHASTNIKOV SNG I TEKHNICHESKIKH SREDSTVAKH EGO VYIAVLENIYA. SERIYA: VOORUZHENNYE SILY I VOENNO-PROMYSHLENNYI POTENTSIAL. Text in Russian. 1996. m. USD 90 foreign (effective 2006). **Document type:** *Journal, Abstract/Index.*
Indexed: RASB.
Published by: Vserossiiskii Institut Nauchnoi i Tekhnicheskoi Informatsii (VINITI), Ul Usievicha 20, Moscow, 125190, Russian Federation. TEL 7-095-1526441, FAX 7-095-9430060, dir@viniti.ru, http://www.viniti.ru. **Dist. by:** Informnauka Ltd., Ul Usievicha 20, Moscow 125190, Russian Federation. alfimov@viniti.ru.

INQUERITO DE CONJUNTURA AO INVESTIMENTO. see *BUSINESS AND ECONOMICS—Investments*

330.021 CAN ISSN 1201-6292
INSIGHTS ON. Text in English. 1996. q.
Published by: Statistics Canada, Business and Trade Statistics Field, Ste 1500 Main Bldg, Holland Ave, Ottawa, ON K1A 0T6, Canada. TEL 613-951-8116.

338.9 GBR ISSN 0955-0569
HC59.69
INSTITUTE OF DEVELOPMENT STUDIES. DEVELOPMENT BIBLIOGRAPHY SERIES. Text in English. 1988. irreg. (1-3/yr.). price varies. **Document type:** *Bibliography.* **Description:** Contains bibliographies devoted to a key theme in development studies.
Indexed: RDA.
—BLDSC (3579.011500).
Published by: Institute of Development Studies, University Of Sussex, Brighton, BN1 9RE, United Kingdom. TEL 44-1273-606261, FAX 44-1273-678420. Ed. Katherine Henry. Circ: 500.

658.3 016 USA ISSN 1542-8397
HF5549
INTERNATIONAL ABSTRACTS OF HUMAN RESOURCES. Text in English. 1955. q. USD 210 domestic; USD 500 print & online (effective 2003); includes a. cumulation. adv. bk.rev. abstr.; illus. index, cum.index. reprint service avail. from PQC. **Document type:** *Abstract/Index.*
Formerly (until 2003): Personnel Management Abstracts (0031-577X)
Related titles: Microform ed.: (from PQC); Online - full text ed.: ISSN 1542-8400. USD 100 (effective 2003).
Published by: Personnel Management Abstracts, 704 Island Lake Rd, Chelsea, MI 48118. TEL 313-475-1979, http://www.hrabstracts.com. Ed., Pub. Gloria Reo. Circ: 850.

330 016 GBR ISSN 0085-204X
Z7164.E2
INTERNATIONAL BIBLIOGRAPHY OF THE SOCIAL SCIENCES. ECONOMICS/BIBLIOGRAPHIE INTERNATIONALE DE SCIENCES ECONOMIQUES. Added title page title: International Bibliography of Economics. Text in English; Prefatory materials in French. 1952. a., latest vol.51, 2002. GBP 215, USD 300 per vol. (effective Oct. 2003). adv. back issues avail.; reprints avail. **Document type:** *Bibliography.* **Description:** Indexes monographs and the contents of more than 2,000 journals in the social sciences from a selective bibliography by subject, geographical terms, and author.
Related titles: ♦ CD-ROM ed.: I B S S CD-ROM. ISSN 1544-9289; ♦ Online - full text ed.: International Bibliography of the Social Sciences.
—BLDSC (4537.111000).
Published by: (British Library of Political and Economic Science), Routledge (Subsidiary of: Taylor & Francis Group), 4 Park Square, Milton Park, Abingdon, Oxon OX14 4RN, United Kingdom. TEL 44-1235-828600, FAX 44-1235-829000, aileen.harvey@tandf.co.uk, info@routledge.co.uk, http://www.lse.ac.uk/collections/IBSS/access/access_print.htm, http://www.tandf.co.uk. Circ: 2,000.

INTERNATIONAL DEVELOPMENT ABSTRACTS. see *GEOGRAPHY—Abstracting, Bibliographies, Statistics*

332 310 USA ISSN 0020-6725
HG3881
INTERNATIONAL FINANCIAL STATISTICS. Text in English. 1948. m. USD 495; USD 65 newsstand/cover (effective 2004 & 2005). mkt.; charts. reprint service avail. from PQC. **Document type:** *Journal, Government.* **Description:** Covers all aspects of international and domestic finance.
Related titles: CD-ROM ed.; Magnetic Tape ed.; Microfiche ed.: (from CIS); Microfilm ed.: (from BHP, PMC, PQC); Online - full text ed.; French ed.: Statistiques Financieres Internationales. ISSN 0252-2977; Spanish ed.: Estadisticas Financieras Internacionales. ISSN 0252-3078. 1948.
Indexed: Cadscan, IIS, IMI, KES, LeadAb, MEA&I, PAIS, PROMT, RASB, RefZh, Zincscan.
—CISTI. **CCC.**
Published by: International Monetary Fund, Publication Services, 700 19th St, N W, Ste 12-607, Washington, DC 20431. TEL 202-623-7430, FAX 202-623-7201, publications@imf.org, http://www.imf.org. Ed. Carol Carson. Circ: 12,500.

332 USA ISSN 0250-7463
HG61
INTERNATIONAL FINANCIAL STATISTICS YEARBOOK. Text in English. 1976. a. USD 95 (effective 2004 & 2005). reprint service avail. from PQC. **Description:** Cumulates over 35 years of annual data, by country, from the monthly issues of IFS including some additional time series in country tables and some additional tables of area and world aggregates.
Related titles: Microfiche ed.: (from CIS); French ed.: Statistiques Financieres Internationales Annuaire. ISSN 0252-029X; Spanish ed.: Estadisticas Financieras Internacionales Anuario. ISSN 0252-3043.
Indexed: IIS, RASB.
—BLDSC (4540.201200), CISTI. **CCC.**
Published by: International Monetary Fund, Publication Services, 700 19th St, N W, Ste 12-607, Washington, DC 20431. TEL 202-623-7430, FAX 202-623-7201, publications@imf.org, http://www.imf.org.

INTERNATIONAL INSTITUTE FOR LABOUR STUDIES. BIBLIOGRAPHY SERIES. see *SOCIOLOGY*

310 658.8 GBR ISSN 0308-2938
HA42
INTERNATIONAL MARKETING DATA AND STATISTICS (YEAR). Text in English. 1975. a. GBP 325 per issue domestic; EUR 530 per issue in Europe; USD 530 per issue elsewhere (effective 2003). **Document type:** *Directory.* **Description:** Provides business and marketing statistical information from non-European countries around the globe.
Related titles: CD-ROM ed.: GBP 695, USD 1,390.
—CISTI.
Published by: Euromonitor, 60-61 Britton St, London, EC1 5UX, United Kingdom. TEL 44-20-7251-8024, FAX 44-20-7608-3149, info@euromonitor.com, http://www.euromonitor.com.

016.658 GBR
INTERNATIONAL MARKETING FORECASTS. Text in English. 1997. a., latest 2003, 6th Edition. GBP 795 per vol. domestic; EUR 1,290 per vol. in Europe; USD 1,290 per vol. elsewhere (effective 2003). **Description:** Provides statistical forecasts to 2005 for consumer products and predictions to 2013 in demographics, economics and lifestyle.
Published by: Euromonitor, 60-61 Britton St, London, EC1 5UX, United Kingdom. TEL 44-20-7251-8024, FAX 44-20-7608-3149, info@euromonitor.com, http://www.euromonitor.com.

332 USA ISSN 0252-3035
HG3882
INTERNATIONAL MONETARY FUND. BALANCE OF PAYMENTS STATISTICS YEARBOOK. Text in English. 1949. a. USD 98 (effective 2004). reprint service avail. from PQC. **Document type:** *Yearbook, Government.* **Description:** Covers balance of payments statistics for most of the world, compiled in accordance with the IMF(UNKNOWN CHARACTER)s Balance of Payments Manual.
Supersedes (in 1981): Balance of Payments Yearbook (0378-2662)
Related titles: Magnetic Tape ed.; Microfiche ed.: (from CIS); Microfilm ed.: (from BHP); Microform ed.: (from CIS); Online - full text ed.
Indexed: IIS.
—**CCC.**
Published by: International Monetary Fund, Publication Services, 700 19th St, N W, Ste 12-607, Washington, DC 20431. TEL 202-623-7430, FAX 202-623-7201, publications@imf.org, http://www.imf.org. Circ: 4,000.

382 310 USA ISSN 0252-306X
HF1016
INTERNATIONAL MONETARY FUND. DIRECTION OF TRADE STATISTICS. Text in English. 1958. q. USD 155; USD 25 newsstand/cover (effective 2004 & 2005). charts; mkt. reprint service avail. from PQC. **Document type:** *Journal, Government.* **Description:** Provides data on the country and area distribution of countries' exports and imports as reported by themselves or by their partners.
Formerly (until 1980): Direction of Trade (0012-3226); (until 1963): Direction of International Trade. Series T. Statistical Papers (0417-5344)
Related titles: Magnetic Tape ed.; Microfiche ed.: (from CIS); Microfilm ed.: (from PQC); Online - full text ed.: ISSN 1017-2734; Special ed(s).: International Monetary Fund. Direction of Trade Statistics. Yearbook. ISSN 0252-3019. 1962. USD 70 per issue (effective 2004 & 2005).
Indexed: IIS, RASB, RefZh.
—CISTI. **CCC.**
Published by: International Monetary Fund, Publication Services, 700 19th St, N W, Ste 12-607, Washington, DC 20431. TEL 202-623-7430, FAX 202-623-7201, publications@imf.org, http://www.imf.org. Circ: 6,000.

332.1 USA ISSN 0250-7374
HJ101 CODEN: GFSYEV
INTERNATIONAL MONETARY FUND. GOVERNMENT FINANCE STATISTICS YEARBOOK. Text in English. 1977. a. USD 80 per issue (effective 2004). charts. back issues avail. **Document type:** *Yearbook, Government.* **Description:** Provides information on the various units of government, government accounts, the enterprises and financial institutions that governments own and control, and the national sources of data on government operations.
Related titles: Microform ed.: (from CIS, PQC).
Indexed: IIS, WBA.
—**CCC.**
Published by: International Monetary Fund, Publication Services, 700 19th St, N W, Ste 12-607, Washington, DC 20431. TEL 202-623-7430, FAX 202-623-7201, publications@imf.org, http://www.imf.org. Circ: 3,000.

332 016 USA ISSN 0047-083X
HG3881
INTERNATIONAL MONETARY FUND SURVEY. Text in English. 22/yr. USD 109 (effective 2004 & 2005). abstr. Index. reprint service avail. from PQC. **Document type:** *Government.* **Description:** Covers all IMF activities (including all press releases, communiques and major speeches, and SDR valuation) presented in the broader context of developments in the world economy, economic research and policy, national economies, and international finance.
Supersedes: International Financial News Survey (0020-6717)

B

▼ new title ➤ refereed ✶ unverified ♦ full entry avail.

Related titles: Microfilm ed.: (from CIS, PQC); French ed.: Bulletin du F M I. ISSN 0250-7412; Spanish ed.: Boletin del F M I. ISSN 0250-7420.
Indexed: IIS, IPARL, KES, PROMT, RASB, WBA.
—CISTI. **CCC.**
Published by: International Monetary Fund, Publication Services, 700 19th St, N W, Ste 12-607, Washington, DC 20431. TEL 202-623-7430, FAX 202-623-7201, publications@imf.org, http://www.imf.org. Circ: 22,000.

INTERNATIONAL PETROLEUM MONTHLY. see *STATISTICS*

016.382   USA   ISSN 1538-8875
HF54.56
INTERNATIONAL TRADE RESOURCES; an internet miniguide. Text in English. 2002. a. USD 95 newsstand/cover (effective 2002).
Published by: InternetMiniGuides.com, P.O. Box 220, Marco Island, FL 34146. TEL 941-434-5113, zillman@internetminiguides.com, http://www.internetminiguides.com. Pub. Marcus P. Zillma.

330.021 310.021   GBR
INTERNATIONAL YEARBOOK OF INDUSTRIAL STATISTICS (YEAR). Text in English. a. GBP 145 per vol. in Europe; USD 215 per vol. in the Americas (effective 2001). charts. 728 p./no.; back issues avail. **Document type:** *Yearbook, Trade.*
Description: Presents up-to-date internationally comparable statistics for more than 120 countries at different levels of detail in industry-product specification.
Supersedes (1982-1995): Handbook of Industrial Statistics (1014-4641); Incorporates (in 1995): Industrial Statistics Yearbook, Volume 1. General Industrial Statistics; Which was formerly (until 1981): Yearbook of Industrial Statistics (0250-9873); (until 1973): Growth of World Industry
Indexed: RASB.
—BLDSC (4552.333000).
Published by: (United Nations Industrial Development Organization AUT), Edward Elgar Publishing Ltd, Glensanda House, Montpellier Parade, Cheltenham, Glos GL50 1UA, United Kingdom. TEL 44-1242-226934, FAX 44-1242-262111, info@e-elgar.co.uk, http://www.e-elgar.co.uk. Circ: 5,000.

330   DEU
INTERNATIONALE WIRTSCHAFTSZAHLEN/INTERNATIONAL ECONOMIC INDICATORS. Text in English, German. 1980. a. **Document type:** *Journal, Trade.*
Published by: (Institut der Deutschen Wirtschaft), Deutscher Instituts Verlag GmbH, Gustav-Heinemann-Ufer 84-88, Cologne, 50968, Germany. TEL 49-221-4981510, FAX 49-221-4981533, div@iwkoeln.de, http://www.iwkoeln.de. Ed. Joerg Beyfuss. Circ: 5,000.

332.67 314   SCG   ISSN 0351-4129
INVESTICIJE. Text in Serbo-Croatian. 1966. a. YUN 100, USD 3.24. **Document type:** *Government.*
Related titles: ♦ Series of: Srbija i Crna Gora. Zavod za Statistiku. Statisticki Bilten.
Published by: Srbija i Crna Gora Zavod za Statistiku/Serbia and Montenegro Statistical Office, Kneza Milosa 20, Postanski Fah 203, Belgrade, 11000. TEL 381-11-3617273. Circ: 1,000.

332.021   RUS
INVESTITSIONNAYA DEYATEL'NOST' V ROSSII: USLOVIYA, FAKTORY, TENDENTSII (YEAR)/INVESTMENT ACTIVITY IN RUSSIA: CONDITIONS, FACTORS AND TENDENCIES. Text in Russian. a. RUR 220 per issue (effective 2005). **Document type:** *Bulletin, Government.* **Description:** Contains information on the conditions of investment, macroeconomic conjuncture, investment potential and activity; structure of investment formation, financial depositions of enterprises and organizations.
Published by: Gosudarstvennyi Komitet Rossiiskoi Federatsii po Statistike/Federal State Statistics Office, ul Myasnitskaya 39, Moscow, 107450, Russian Federation. TEL 7-095-2074902, FAX 7-095-2074087, stat@gks.ru, http://www.gks.ru.

INVESTMENT AND OPERATING COST IN THE PHILIPPINES. see *BUSINESS AND ECONOMICS—Investments*

330 315   IRN
IRAN. MINISTRY OF ECONOMY. BUREAU OF STATISTICS. SERIES. Text in Persian, Modern. 1969 (no.49). irreg. charts. **Document type:** *Government.*
Published by: (Bureau of Statistics), Ministry of Finance and Economic Affairs, Teheran, Iran. Ed. A Sh Shaheen.

381 315   IRN
IRAN. MINISTRY OF ECONOMY. INTERNAL WHOLESALE TRADE STATISTICS∗ . Text in English. a. free. **Document type:** *Government.*
Related titles: Record ed.
Published by: (Bureau of Statistics), Ministry of Finance and Economic Affairs, Teheran, Iran. Circ: (controlled).

382 315   IRN
IRAN. MINISTRY OF ECONOMY. INTERNATIONAL TRADE STATISTICS∗ . Text in English. irreg. (approx. 1/yr.). free. **Document type:** *Government.*
Related titles: Record ed.
Published by: (Bureau of Statistics), Ministry of Finance and Economic Affairs, Teheran, Iran. Circ: (controlled).

338 315   IRN   ISSN 0075-0506
IRANIAN INDUSTRIAL STATISTICS. Text in English, Persian, Modern. 1962. a. free. **Document type:** *Government.*
Published by: (Bureau of Statistics), Ministry of Finance and Economic Affairs, Teheran, Iran.

330   IRL   ISSN 1393-0583
HD9986.I73
IRELAND. CENTRAL STATISTICS OFFICE. ANNUAL SERVICES INQUIRY. Text in English. 1994. a. EUR 15 (effective 2005). charts; stat. **Document type:** *Government.* **Description:** Provides estimates of accounting and employment variables based on a sample survey of services firms.
Related titles: Online - full text ed.
Published by: Central Statistics Office/Eire, An Phriomh-Oifig Staidrimh, Skehard Rd., Cork, Ireland. TEL 353-21-4535000, FAX 353-21-4535555, information@cso.ie, http://www.cso.ie/releasespublications/pr_services.htm.

336.021   IRL   ISSN 0791-3370
IRELAND. CENTRAL STATISTICS OFFICE. BALANCE OF INTERNATIONAL PAYMENTS. Text in English. 1985. q. charts; stat. **Document type:** *Government.* **Description:** Produces estimates of the balance of international payments on current and capital accounts.
Media: Duplicated (not offset). **Related titles:** Online - full text ed.
Published by: Central Statistics Office/Eire, An Phriomh-Oifig Staidrimh, Skehard Rd.., Cork, Ireland. TEL 353-21-4535000, FAX 353-21-4535555, information@cso.ie, http://www.cso.ie/releasespublications/pr_bop.htm.

330.9021   IRL   ISSN 0791-3168
IRELAND. CENTRAL STATISTICS OFFICE. BANKING, INSURANCE AND BUILDING SOCIETIES. EMPLOYMENT AND EARNINGS. Text in English. 1990. q. **Document type:** *Government.* **Description:** Monitors employment levels and earnings trends in banks, insurance companies and building societies.
Formerly (until 1990): Ireland. Central Statistics Office. Banking, Insurance and Building Societies. New Quarterly Series on Employment and Earnings (0791-3699)
Related titles: Online - full text ed.
Published by: Central Statistics Office/Eire, An Phriomh-Oifig Staidrimh, Skehard Rd., Cork, Ireland. TEL 353-21-4535000, FAX 353-21-4535555, information@cso.ie, http://www.cso.ie/releasespublications/pr_services.htm.

IRELAND. CENTRAL STATISTICS OFFICE. BUILDING AND CONSTRUCTION PLANNING PERMISSIONS. see *HOUSING AND URBAN PLANNING—Abstracting, Bibliographies, Statistics*

332.64021   IRL   ISSN 1393-5755
IRELAND. CENTRAL STATISTICS OFFICE. CAPITAL ASSETS IN INDUSTRY. Text in English. 1998. q. charts; stat. **Document type:** *Government.*
Related titles: Online - full text ed.
Published by: Central Statistics Office/Eire, An Phriomh-Oifig Staidrimh, Skehard Rd., Cork, Ireland. TEL 353-21-4535000, FAX 353-21-4535555, information@cso.ie, http://www.cso.ie/releasespublications/pr_ind.htm.

330.9021   IRL   ISSN 0790-6080
HC257.I6
IRELAND. CENTRAL STATISTICS OFFICE. CENSUS OF INDUSTRIAL PRODUCTION. Text in English. 1984. a. EUR 20 (effective 2005). charts; stat. **Document type:** *Government.* **Description:** Compiles detailed information on the structure and production activity of the Irish industrial sector.
Related titles: Online - full text ed.
Published by: Central Statistics Office/Eire, An Phriomh-Oifig Staidrimh, Skehard Rd., Cork, Ireland. TEL 353-21-4535000, FAX 353-21-4535555, information@cso.ie, http://www.cso.ie/releasespublications/pr_ind.htm.

330.9021   IRL   ISSN 1393-6913
IRELAND. CENTRAL STATISTICS OFFICE. CENSUS OF INDUSTRIAL PRODUCTION. PROVISIONAL RESULTS. Text in English. 1996. a. charts; stat. **Document type:** *Government.* **Description:** Focuses on the trading dimensions of industrial production in Ireland, covering the turnover, purchases, and labor costs of firms.
Formerly (until 1998): Ireland. Central Statistics Office. Census of Industrial Production. Provisional Overall Results for Industrial Enterprises and Industrial Local Units (1393-3523); Which was formed by the merger of (1995-1996): Ireland. Central Statistics Office. Census of Industrial Production. Provisional Overall Results for Industrial Enterprises (1393-2578); Which was formerly (1989-1993): Ireland. Central Statistics Office. Census of Industrial Production. Overall Results for Industrial Enterprises (0791-2897); (1995-1996): Ireland. Central Statistics Office. Census of Industrial Production. Overall Results for Industrial Local Units (1393-2535); Which was formerly: Ireland. Central Statistics Office. Census of Industrial Production. Provisional Overall Results for Industrial Establishments (1393-2586); (until 1990): Ireland. Central Statistics Office. Census of Industrial Production. Overall Results for Industrial Establishments (1393-2594); Which superseded (1975-1985): Ireland. Central Statistics Office. Census of Industrial Production. Initial Summary Results for Industrial Establishments

Related titles: Online - full text ed.
Published by: Central Statistics Office/Eire, An Phriomh-Oifig Staidrimh, Skehard Rd., Cork, Ireland. TEL 353-21-4535000, FAX 353-21-4535555, information@cso.ie, http://www.cso.ie/releasespublications/pr_ind.htm.

330.9021   IRL   ISSN 0791-3303
IRELAND. CENTRAL STATISTICS OFFICE. CONSUMER PRICE INDEX. Text in English. 196?. m. charts; stat. **Document type:** *Government.* **Description:** Measures the change in the average level of prices paid for consumer goods and services purchased by Irish households.
Related titles: Online - full text ed.
Published by: Central Statistics Office/Eire, An Phriomh-Oifig Staidrimh, Skehard Rd., Cork, Ireland. TEL 353-21-4535000, FAX 353-21-4535555, information@cso.ie, http://www.cso.ie/releasespublications/pr_prices.htm.

330.9021   IRL   ISSN 1649-1866
IRELAND. CENTRAL STATISTICS OFFICE. COUNTY INCOMES AND REGIONAL GDP. Text in English. 1996. a. **Document type:** *Government.* **Description:** Contains accounts that have been complied showing gross value added (GVA) at basis prices, market prices and factor costs for the regional authority areas.
Former titles (until 2002): Ireland. Central Statistics Office. Regional Accounts. GDP by Region (1393-4791); (until 1997): Ireland. Central Statistics Office. Regional Accounts (1393-3868)
Related titles: Online - full text ed.
Published by: Central Statistics Office/Eire, An Phriomh-Oifig Staidrimh, Skehard Rd., Cork, Ireland. TEL 353-21-4535000, FAX 353-21-4535555, information@cso.ie, http://www.cso.ie.

IRELAND. CENTRAL STATISTICS OFFICE. EARNINGS OF AGRICULTURAL WORKERS. see *AGRICULTURE—Abstracting, Bibliographies, Statistics*

382.021   IRL   ISSN 1393-5364
IRELAND. CENTRAL STATISTICS OFFICE. EXTERNAL TRADE. Text in English. m. charts; stat. **Document type:** *Government.*
Formerly (until 1997): Ireland. Central Statistics Office. Total External Trade - Provisional Estimates (0791-8984); Which superseded in part (in 1993): Ireland. Central Statistics Office. External Trade - Provisional Figures (0791-3478); Which incorporated (1987-1989): Ireland. Central Statistics Office. External Trade - Provisional Figures, Further Details (0791-3486)
Related titles: Online - full text ed.
Published by: Central Statistics Office/Eire, An Phriomh-Oifig Staidrimh, Skehard Rd., Cork, Ireland. TEL 353-21-4535000, FAX 353-21-4535555, information@cso.ie, http://www.cso.ie/releasespublications/pr_extrade.htm.

331.021   IRL   ISSN 0791-329X
                                    CODEN: PJESE2
IRELAND. CENTRAL STATISTICS OFFICE. INDUSTRIAL DISPUTES. Text in English. q. charts; stat. **Document type:** *Government.*
Formerly: Ireland. Central Statistics Office. Strikes or Lock-Outs Reported During the Quarter
Related titles: Online - full text ed.
Published by: Central Statistics Office/Eire, An Phriomh-Oifig Staidrimh, Skehard Rd., Cork, Ireland. TEL 353-21-4535000, FAX 353-21-4535555, information@cso.ie, http://www.cso.ie/releasespublications/pr_labfor.htm.

330.9021   IRL   ISSN 0791-2900
IRELAND. CENTRAL STATISTICS OFFICE. INDUSTRIAL EARNINGS AND HOURS WORKED. Text in English. 1981. q. charts; stat. **Document type:** *Government.*
Supersedes in part (in 1987): Ireland. Central Statistics Office. Industrial Employment Earnings and Hours Worked (0790-0996); Which was formerly (until 1981): Ireland. Central Statistics Office. Employment Earnings and Hours Worked (0790-1011)
Related titles: Online - full text ed.
Published by: Central Statistics Office/Eire, An Phriomh-Oifig Staidrimh, Skehard Rd., Cork, Ireland. TEL 353-21-4535000, FAX 353-21-4535555, information@cso.ie, http://www.cso.ie/releasespublications/pr_earns.htm.

330.9021   IRL   ISSN 0791-2919
IRELAND. CENTRAL STATISTICS OFFICE. INDUSTRIAL EMPLOYMENT. Text in English. q. charts; stat. **Document type:** *Government.*
Supersedes in part (1981-1987): Ireland. Central Statistics Office. Industrial Employment Earnings and Hours Worked (0790-0996); Which was formerly: Ireland. Central Statistics Office. Employment Earnings and Hours Worked (0790-1011)
Related titles: Online - full text ed.
Published by: Central Statistics Office/Eire, An Phriomh-Oifig Staidrimh, Skehard Rd., Cork, Ireland. TEL 353-21-4535000, FAX 353-21-4535555, information@cso.ie, http://www.cso.ie/releasespublications/pr_ind.htm.

330.9021   IRL   ISSN 1649-2773
IRELAND. CENTRAL STATISTICS OFFICE. INDUSTRIAL PRODUCTION AND TURNOVER. Text in English. 2002. m. charts; stat. **Document type:** *Government.* **Description:** Monitors trends in the volume of production of industrial establishments with three or more persons engaged.

Formed by the merger of (1975-2002): Ireland. Central Statistics Office. Industrial Production Index (0790-5130); (1984-2002): Ireland. Central Statistics Office. Industrial Turnover Index (0791-2889)
Media: Duplicated (not offset). **Related titles:** Online - full text ed.
Published by: Central Statistics Office/Eire, An Phriomh-Oifig Staidrimh, Skehard Rd., Cork, Ireland. TEL 353-21-4535000, FAX 353-21-4535555, information@cso.ie, http://www.cso.ie/releasespublications/pr_ind.htm.

332.64021 IRL ISSN 1393-5747
IRELAND. CENTRAL STATISTICS OFFICE. INDUSTRIAL STOCKS. Text in English. 1998. q. charts; stat. **Document type:** *Government.*
Related titles: Online - full text ed.
Published by: Central Statistics Office/Eire, An Phriomh-Oifig Staidrimh, Skehard Rd., Cork, Ireland. TEL 353-21-4535000, FAX 353-21-4535555, information@cso.ie, http://www.cso.ie/releasespublications/pr_ind.htm.

331.021 IRL ISSN 0790-9160
HD5018
IRELAND. CENTRAL STATISTICS OFFICE. LABOUR COSTS SURVEY - IN INDUSTRY, DISTRIBUTION, CREDIT AND INSURANCE. Text in English. 1982. irreg. (every 3-4 yrs.), latest 1992. EUR 7 (effective 2005). charts; stat. **Document type:** *Government.* **Description:** Projects, in detail, labor costs of enterprises, classified by activity and size, including wages and salaries, social security payments, training costs, and severance packages, among others.
Published by: Central Statistics Office/Eire, An Phriomh-Oifig Staidrimh, Skehard Rd., Cork, Ireland. TEL 353-21-4535000, FAX 353-21-4535555, information@cso.ie, http://www.cso.ie.

330.9021 IRL ISSN 1649-2544
IRELAND. CENTRAL STATISTICS OFFICE. LIVE REGISTER ANALYSIS. Text in English. 2002. m. charts; stat. **Document type:** *Government.* **Description:** Information on flows on or off the live register.
Formed by the merger of (1997-2002): Ireland. Central Statistics Office. Live Register Flow Analysis (1393-5550); Which was formerly (until 1997): Ireland. Central Statistics Office. Live Register - Monthly Flow Analysis (0791-3192); Which superseded in part (1987-1989): Ireland. Central Statistics Office. Live Register - Industrial Analysis (0791-3281); (1997-2002): Ireland. Central Statistics Office. Live Register Area Analysis (1393-5542); Which was formerly (until 1997): Ireland. Central Statistics Office. Live Register - Monthly Arrea Analysis (0791-3206); (until 1989): Ireland. Central Statistics Office. Live Register - Quarterly Area of Residence Analysis (0791-3214); (until 1987): Ireland. Central Statistics Office. Analysis of the Live Register According to Area of Residence; (1989-2002): Ireland. Central Statistics Office. Live Register Statement (0791-3222); Which was formerly (until 1989): Ireland. Central Statistics Office. Live Register, Monthly Statement (0791-3230); (1983-1987): Ireland. Central Statistics Office. Monthly Live Register Statement (0791-3249)
Related titles: Online - full text ed.
Published by: Central Statistics Office/Eire, An Phriomh-Oifig Staidrimh, Skehard Rd., Cork, Ireland. TEL 353-21-4535000, FAX 353-21-4535555, information@cso.ie, http://www.cso.ie/releasespublications/pr_labfor.htm.

336.021 IRL ISSN 0075-0603
IRELAND. CENTRAL STATISTICS OFFICE. NATIONAL INCOME AND EXPENDITURE. Text in English. 1958. a. EUR 12 (effective 2005). charts; stat. **Document type:** *Government.* **Description:** Provides detailed analyses of GNP, private and public expenditures, classification by purpose of public authorities' public expenditure, gross national disposable income and its uses, savings and capital formation, and balance of international payments. Shows receipts of expenditure on public welfare programs.
Supersedes in part (1949-1960): Irish Statistical Survey (0790-5971)
Related titles: Online - full text ed.
Published by: Central Statistics Office/Eire, An Phriomh-Oifig Staidrimh, Skehard Rd., Cork, Ireland. TEL 353-21-4535000, FAX 353-21-4535555, information@cso.ie, http://www.cso.ie/releasespublications/pr_natacc.htm. Circ: 2,000. **Subscr. to:** Government Supplies Agency, 4-5 Harcourt Rd., Dublin 2, Ireland.

330.9021 IRL ISSN 1393-2047
IRELAND. CENTRAL STATISTICS OFFICE. NATIONAL INCOME AND EXPENDITURE. FIRST RESULTS. Text in English. 1994. a. **Document type:** *Government.* **Description:** Contains estimates of national income and expenditure.
Published by: Central Statistics Office/Eire, An Phriomh-Oifig Staidrimh, Skehard Rd., Cork, Ireland. TEL 353-21-4535000, FAX 353-21-4535555, information@cso.ie, http://www.cso.ie.

IRELAND. CENTRAL STATISTICS OFFICE. OUTPUT, INPUT AND INCOME IN AGRICULTURE. see *AGRICULTURE—Abstracting, Bibliographies, Statistics*

330.9 IRL ISSN 1649-1793
IRELAND. CENTRAL STATISTICS OFFICE. PRODCOM PRODUCT SALES. Text in English. 1997. a. EUR 20 (effective 2005). charts; stat. **Document type:** *Government.* **Description:** Surveys and examines the value and volume of some 2,100 products manufactured in Ireland.
Related titles: Online - full text ed.
Published by: Central Statistics Office/Eire, An Phriomh-Oifig Staidrimh, Skehard Rd., Cork, Ireland. TEL 353-21-4535000, FAX 353-21-4535555, information@cso.ie, http://www.cso.ie/releasespublications/pr_ind.htm.

330.9021 IRL ISSN 1393-9505
HD5018.I7
IRELAND. CENTRAL STATISTICS OFFICE. PUBLIC SECTOR EMPLOYMENT EARNINGS. Text in English. 2000. q. charts; stat. **Document type:** *Government.*
Formed by the merger of (1996-2000): Ireland. Central Statistics Office. Public Sector Average Earnings Index (1393-3876); (1993-2000): Ireland. Central Statistics Office. Public Sector Employment (1393-2896)
Related titles: Online - full text ed.
Published by: Central Statistics Office/Eire, An Phriomh-Oifig Staidrimh, Skehard Rd., Cork, Ireland. TEL 353-21-4535000, FAX 353-21-4535555, information@cso.ie, http://www.cso.ie.

331.021 IRL ISSN 1393-6875
IRELAND. CENTRAL STATISTICS OFFICE. QUARTERLY NATIONAL HOUSEHOLD SURVEY. Text in English. q. charts; stat. **Document type:** *Government.* **Description:** Provides quarterly statistics on employment and unemployment. Deals with a range of important social topics.
Former titles (until May 1998): Ireland. Central Statistics Office. Labour Force Survey (0791-0533); (until 1988): Ireland. Central Statistics Office. Labour Force Survey. First Results (0790-5866)
Related titles: Online - full text ed.
Published by: Central Statistics Office/Eire, An Phriomh-Oifig Staidrimh, Skehard Rd., Cork, Ireland. TEL 353-21-4535000, FAX 353-21-4535555, information@cso.ie, http://www.cso.ie/releasespublications/pr_labfor.htm.

330.9021 339.021 IRL ISSN 0791-315X
IRELAND. CENTRAL STATISTICS OFFICE. RETAIL SALES INDEX. Text in English. 197?. m. charts; stat. **Document type:** *Government.* **Description:** Measures changes in both the value and volume levels of retail sales.
Media: Duplicated (not offset).
Published by: Central Statistics Office/Eire, An Phriomh-Oifig Staidrimh, Skehard Rd., Cork, Ireland. TEL 353-21-4535000, FAX 353-21-4535555, information@cso.ie, http://www.cso.ie/releasespublications/pr_services.htm.

330 IRL ISSN 0790-9934
IRELAND. CENTRAL STATISTICS OFFICE. ROAD FREIGHT TRANSPORT SURVEY. Text in English. 1983. a. EUR 15 (effective 2005). charts; stat. **Document type:** *Government.* **Description:** Contains the results of the National Road Freight Transport Survey.
Related titles: Online - full text ed.
Published by: Central Statistics Office/Eire, An Phriomh-Oifig Staidrimh, Skehard Rd., Cork, Ireland. TEL 353-21-4535000, FAX 353-21-4535555, information@cso.ie, http://www.cso.ie/releasespublications/pr_transport.htm. **Subscr. to:** Government Supplies Agency, 4-5 Harcourt Rd., Dublin 2, Ireland.

330.9 IRL ISSN 0790-8334
HF189
IRELAND. CENTRAL STATISTICS OFFICE. STATISTICAL BULLETIN/FEASCHAN STAIDRIMH. Text in English. 1925. q. EUR 12.70 newsstand/cover (effective 2005). charts; mkt.; stat. **Document type:** *Government.* **Description:** Presents detailed results of all short-term economic series with retrospection. Periodic articles on annual inquiries and methodology are also included.
Former titles (until 1987): Ireland. Central Statistics Office. Irish Statistical Bulletin (0021-1370); (until 1964): Ireland. Department of Industry and Commerce. Irish Trade Journal and Statistical Bulletin (0790-1038); (until 1937): Ireland. Department of Industry and Commerce. Irish Trade Journal (0790-102X)
Indexed: CLFP, PAIS, PROMT, RASB, RehabLit.
—CISTI.
Published by: Central Statistics Office/Eire, An Phriomh-Oifig Staidrimh, Skehard Rd., Cork, Ireland. TEL 353-21-4535000, FAX 353-21-4535555, information@cso.ie, http://www.cso.ie/releasespublications/periodicals.htm. **Subscr. to:** Government Supplies Agency, 4-5 Harcourt Rd., Dublin 2, Ireland.

IRELAND. CENTRAL STATISTICS OFFICE. STATISTICS OF PORT TRAFFIC. see *TRANSPORTATION—Abstracting, Bibliographies, Statistics*

336.021 IRL ISSN 1649-5918
IRELAND. CENTRAL STATISTICS OFFICE. SUPPLY AND USE AND INPUT-OUTPUT TABLES. Text in English. 1970. irreg., latest 1998. EUR 12 (effective 2005). charts; stat. **Document type:** *Government.* **Description:** Provides a statistical description of the inputs and outputs of the various branches of the Irish economy and their inter-relationships.
Formerly: Ireland. Central Statistics Office. Input - Output Tables (1393-4104)
Related titles: Online - full text ed.
Published by: Central Statistics Office/Eire, An Phriomh-Oifig Staidrimh, Skehard Rd., Cork, Ireland. TEL 353-21-4535000, FAX 353-21-4535555, information@cso.ie, http://www.cso.ie/releasespublications/pr_natacc.htm.

382 314 IRL ISSN 0790-9381
IRELAND. CENTRAL STATISTICS OFFICE. TRADE STATISTICS. Text in English. 1924. m. EUR 157 (effective 2005). charts; stat. **Document type:** *Government.* **Description:** Compiles detailed information on imports and exports by country and commodities for the reference months, with year-to-date totals.
Former titles (until 1987): Ireland. Central Statistics Office. Trade Statistics of Ireland (0790-5122); (until 1949): Irish Free State. Department of Industry and Commerce. Trade Statistics (0790-5114); (until 1933): Trade Statistics of the Irish Free State (0790-5106); (until 1930): Irish Free State. Ministry of Industry and Commerce. Trade and Shipping Statistics (0790-5092); (until 1925): Trade and Shipping Statistics of the Irish Free State (0790-5084)
Published by: Central Statistics Office/Eire, An Phriomh-Oifig Staidrimh, Skehard Rd., Cork, Ireland. TEL 353-21-4535000, FAX 353-21-4535555, information@cso.ie, http://www.cso.ie. Circ: 600.

330 IRL ISSN 1393-5585
IRELAND. CENTRAL STATISTICS OFFICE. TRADE WITH NON - E U COUNTRIES. Text in English. 1993. m. charts; stat. **Document type:** *Government.*
Former titles (until 1997): Ireland. Central Statistics Office. Trade with Non - E U Countries. Provisional Figures (0791-8976); (until 1994): Ireland. Central Statistics Office. Trade with Non E C - Countries - Provisional Figures (1393-5380); Which superseded in part (in 1993): Ireland. Central Statistics Office. External Trade - Provisional Figures (0791-3478); Which incorporated (1987-1989): Ireland. Central Statistics Office. External Trade - Provisional Figures, Further Details (0791-3486)
Related titles: Online - full text ed.
Published by: Central Statistics Office/Eire, An Phriomh-Oifig Staidrimh, Skehard Rd., Cork, Ireland. TEL 353-21-4535000, FAX 353-21-4535555, information@cso.ie, http://www.cso.ie/releasespublications/pr_extrade.htm.

381.021 330.9021 IRL ISSN 1393-5305
IRELAND. CENTRAL STATISTICS OFFICE. VEHICLES LICENSED FOR THE FIRST TIME (MONTH). Text in English. m. charts; stat. **Document type:** *Government.* **Description:** Presents final detailed data on motor registrations.
Formed by the 1997 merger of: Ireland. Central Statistics Office. Particulars of Vehicles Licensed for the First Time in Each County and County Borough for the Month (0791-8682); Which was formerly (1976-1993): Ireland. Central Statistics Office. Particulars of Vehicles Registered and Licensed for the First Time in Each County and County Borough During the Month (0791-3427); Ireland. Central Statistics Office. Vehicle Licensing - Provisional Results (0791-8453); Which was formerly (1973-1993): Ireland. Central Statistics Office. Motor Registrations - Provisional Results (0791-3435)
Related titles: Online - full text ed.
Published by: Central Statistics Office/Eire, An Phriomh-Oifig Staidrimh, Skehard Rd., Cork, Ireland. TEL 353-21-4535000, FAX 353-21-4535555, information@cso.ie, http://www.cso.ie/releasespublications/pr_transport.htm.

330.9021 IRL ISSN 0791-3311
IRELAND. CENTRAL STATISTICS OFFICE. WHOLESALE PRICE INDEX. Text in English. 1978. m. charts; stat. **Document type:** *Government.*
Related titles: Online - full text ed.
Published by: Central Statistics Office/Eire, An Phriomh-Oifig Staidrimh, Skehard Rd., Cork, Ireland. TEL 353-21-4535000, FAX 353-21-4535555, information@cso.ie, http://www.cso.ie/releasespublications/pr_prices.htm.

382 315 ISR ISSN 0333-8436
ISRAEL. CENTRAL BUREAU OF STATISTICS. FOREIGN TRADE STATISTICS (ANNUAL) - EXPORTS. Text in English, Hebrew. 1951. a. ILS 190; price varies. **Document type:** *Government.*
Related titles: Diskette ed.
Published by: Central Bureau of Statistics, PO Box 13015, Jerusalem, 91130, Israel. TEL 972-2-6553364, FAX 972-2-6521340.

382 315 ISR ISSN 0333-8487
ISRAEL. CENTRAL BUREAU OF STATISTICS. FOREIGN TRADE STATISTICS (ANNUAL) - IMPORTS. Text in English, Hebrew. 1974. a. ILS 270. **Document type:** *Government.*
Related titles: Diskette ed.
Indexed: RASB.
—CCC.
Published by: Central Bureau of Statistics, PO Box 13015, Jerusalem, 91130, Israel. TEL 972-2-6553364, FAX 972-2-6521340.

382 315 ISR ISSN 0334-2972
ISRAEL. CENTRAL BUREAU OF STATISTICS. FOREIGN TRADE STATISTICS QUARTERLY. Text in English, Hebrew. 1980. q. USD 30. **Document type:** *Government.*

▼ new title ➤ refereed ✶ unverified ♦ full entry avail.

Supersedes: Israel's Foreign Trade (0075-1421); Israel. Central Bureau of Statistics. Foreign Trade Statistics Quarterly (0021-1990); Israel. Central Bureau of Statistics. Monthly Foreign Trade Statistics
Published by: Central Bureau of Statistics, PO Box 13015, Jerusalem, 91130, Israel. TEL 972-2-6553364, FAX 972-2-6521340.

338.642   ISR   ISSN 0578-8420
ISRAEL. CENTRAL BUREAU OF STATISTICS. INDUSTRY AND CRAFTS SURVEY. Text in English, Hebrew. irreg., latest 1995. ILS 36. **Document type:** *Government.*
Published by: Central Bureau of Statistics, PO Box 13015, Jerusalem, 91130, Israel. TEL 972-2-6553364, FAX 972-2-6521340.

331 315   ISR   ISSN 0075-1049
ISRAEL. CENTRAL BUREAU OF STATISTICS. LABOUR FORCE SURVEYS. Text in English, Hebrew. 1954. irreg., latest 1997. ILS 36. **Document type:** *Government.*
Related titles: Diskette ed.
Published by: Central Bureau of Statistics, PO Box 13015, Jerusalem, 91130, Israel. TEL 972-2-6553364, FAX 972-2-6521340.

331   ISR
ISRAEL. CENTRAL BUREAU OF STATISTICS. LABOUR MOBILITY SURVEY. Text in English, Hebrew. 1977. irreg. **Document type:** *Government.*
Formerly: Israel. Central Bureau of Statistics. Labour Force Mobility Survey (0333-9599)
Published by: Central Bureau of Statistics, PO Box 13015, Jerusalem, 91130, Israel. TEL 972-2-6553364, FAX 972-2-6521340.

336   ISR   ISSN 0333-886X
ISRAEL. CENTRAL BUREAU OF STATISTICS. LOCAL AUTHORITIES IN ISRAEL: FINANCIAL DATA. Text in Hebrew. irreg., latest 1995. ILS 121. **Document type:** *Government.*
Related titles: Diskette ed.
Published by: Central Bureau of Statistics, PO Box 13015, Jerusalem, 91130, Israel. TEL 972-2-6553364, FAX 972-2-6521340.

338 315   ISR   ISSN 0021-2008
ISRAEL. CENTRAL BUREAU OF STATISTICS. MONTHLY PRICE STATISTICS. Text in Hebrew. 1949. m. USD 120. **Document type:** *Government.*
Related titles: Diskette ed.
Published by: Central Bureau of Statistics, PO Box 13015, Jerusalem, 91130, Israel. TEL 972-2-6553364, FAX 972-2-6521340.

332   ISR   ISSN 0793-2235
HA1931
ISRAEL. CENTRAL BUREAU OF STATISTICS. NATIONAL ACCOUNTS OF ISRAEL. Text in English, Hebrew. 1994. irreg., latest covers 1950-1995. ILS 121. **Document type:** *Government.*
Related titles: Diskette ed.
Published by: Central Bureau of Statistics, PO Box 13015, Jerusalem, 91130, Israel. TEL 972-2-6553364, FAX 972-2-6521340.

332   ISR   ISSN 0333-9440
HB141.5
ISRAEL. CENTRAL BUREAU OF STATISTICS. NATIONAL ACCOUNTS OF JUDEA, SAMARIA, AND THE GAZA AREA. Text in English, Hebrew. 1979. irreg., latest covers 1968-1993. ILS 121. **Document type:** *Government.*
Related titles: Diskette ed.
Published by: Central Bureau of Statistics, PO Box 13015, Jerusalem, 91130, Israel. TEL 972-2-6553364, FAX 972-2-6521340.

330   ISR   ISSN 0333-9793
HA1931
ISRAEL. CENTRAL BUREAU OF STATISTICS. SURVEY ON RESEARCH AND DEVELOPMENT IN INDUSTRY. Text in English, Hebrew. irreg. ILS 35. **Document type:** *Government.*
Published by: Central Bureau of Statistics, PO Box 13015, Jerusalem, 91130, Israel. TEL 972-2-6553364, FAX 972-2-6521340.

382 314   ITA
ITALY. ISTITUTO NAZIONALE DI STATISTICA. NOTIZIARIO. Short title: Notiziari I S T A T. Text in Italian. 1970 (vol.22). m. charts. **Document type:** *Government.*
Formerly: Italy. Istituto Centrale di Statistica. Notiziario (0029-4381)
Related titles: Series: Demografiche e Sociali; Attivita produttive; Lavoro Retribuzione, Prezzi; Argomenti Vari.
Published by: Istituto Nazionale di Statistica, Via Cesare Balbo 16, Rome, 00184, Italy. FAX 39-06-46735198.

382 314   ITA
ITALY. ISTITUTO NAZIONALE DI STATISTICA. STATISTICA ANNUALE DEL COMMERCIO CON L'ESTERO. TOMO 2: MERCI PER PAESI. Text in Italian. 1953. a. **Document type:** *Government.*

Supersedes in part (in 1963): Italy. Istituto Centrale di Statistica. Statistica Annuale del Commercio con l'Estero (0075-1871)
Media: CD-ROM.
Published by: Istituto Nazionale di Statistica, Via Cesare Balbo 16, Rome, 00184, Italy. FAX 39-06-46735198. Circ: 1,100.

381 314   ITA
ITALY. ISTITUTO NAZIONALE DI STATISTICA. STATISTICHE DEL COMMERCIO INTERNO. Text in Italian. 1957. a. **Document type:** *Government.*
Supersedes in part: Italy. Istituto Centrale di Statistica. Annuario Statistico del Commercio Interno e del Turismo; Which was formerly: Italy. Istituto Centrale di Statistica. Annuario Statistico del Commercio Interno (0075-1782)
Indexed: RASB.
Published by: Istituto Nazionale di Statistica, Via Cesare Balbo 16, Rome, 00184, Italy. FAX 39-06-46735198. Circ: 1,200.

330 314   ITA
HC301
ITALY. ISTITUTO NAZIONALE DI STATISTICA. STATISTICHE INDUSTRIALI. Text in Italian. 1956. a. charts; illus. **Document type:** *Government.*
Formerly: Italy. Istituto Centrale di Statistica. Annuario di Statistiche Industriali (0075-1723)
Indexed: RASB.
Published by: Istituto Nazionale di Statistica, Via Cesare Balbo 16, Rome, 00184, Italy. TEL 39-06-46732380, FAX 39-06-46735198. Circ: 1,500.

330.9021   CIV   ISSN 0444-9746
IVORY COAST. DIRECTION DE LA STATISTIQUE. BULLETIN MENSUEL DE STATISTIQUES. Text in French. 1948. m.
Indexed: PAIS.
Published by: Direction de la Statistique, 01 BP V55, Abidjan, Ivory Coast. TEL 21-15-38.

300 016   DEU   ISSN 0948-5139
H9
➤ **JAHRBUCH FUER WIRTSCHAFTSWISSENSCHAFTEN**; review of economics. Text in English, German. 1950. 3/yr. EUR 96; EUR 39 newsstand/cover (effective 2005). adv. index. reprints avail. **Document type:** *Journal, Academic/Scholarly.*
Formerly (until 1995): Jahrbuch fuer Sozialwissenschaft (0075-2770)
Related titles: Online - full text ed.: (from ProQuest Information & Learning).
Indexed: ABIn, ASCA, BAS, CurCont, ELLIS, IBR, IBSS, IBZ, IPSA, KES, PAIS, SSCI.
—IDS, IE, Infotrieve. **CCC.**
Published by: Vandenhoeck und Ruprecht, Robert-Bosch-Breite 6, Goettingen, 37079, Germany. TEL 49-551-508440, FAX 49-551-5084422, info@v-r.de, http://www.vandenhoeck-ruprecht.de. adv.: page EUR 460; trim 117 x 190. Circ: 500 (paid and controlled).

330 314   DEU   ISSN 0021-4027
HB5   CODEN: JNSTE3
➤ **JAHRBUECHER FUER NATIONALOEKONOMIE UND STATISTIK**; journal of economics and statistics. Text and summaries in German, English. 1863. bi-m. EUR 307 domestic; EUR 311 foreign; EUR 58 newsstand/cover (effective 2003). adv. bk.rev. charts. index, cum.index. 130 p./no.; back issues avail.; reprint service avail. from SCH. **Document type:** *Journal, Academic/Scholarly.*
Related titles: Online - full text ed.: (from ProQuest Information & Learning).
Indexed: ABIn, ASCA, ArtHuCI, CIS, DIP, IBR, IBSS, IBZ, JEL, KES, PAIS, RASB, RefZh, SSCI.
—BLDSC (4631.780000), IDS, IE, Infotrieve, ingenta. **CCC.**
Published by: Lucius und Lucius Verlagsgesellschaft mbH, Gerokstr 51, Stuttgart, 70184, Germany. TEL 49-711-242060, FAX 49-711-242088, lucius@luciusverlag.com, http://www.luciusverlag.com. Eds. A Wagner, H Strecker. Pub. Wulf von Lucius. Adv. contact Bettina Schmidt. page EUR 400; 117 x 187. Circ: 600. **Dist. by:** Brockhaus Commission, Kreidlerstr 9, Kornwestheim 70806, Germany. TEL 49-7154-132737, FAX 49-7154-132713.

330   IND   ISSN 0303-9234
HA1728.K35
JAMMU AND KASHMIR. DIRECTORATE OF ECONOMICS AND STATISTICS. DIGEST OF STATISTICS. Text in English. 1955. q. adv. stat. **Document type:** *Government.*
Published by: Directorate of Economics and Statistics, Planning and Development Department, Jammu, Jammu & Kashmir, India. Ed. G R Malik. adv.: B&W page INR 250, color page INR 300. Circ: 450 (paid and controlled).

332.6   JPN   ISSN 0910-3007
HF251
JAPAN EXPORTS & IMPORTS: COMMODITY BY COUNTRY. Text in Japanese, English. m. USD 27,184. **Document type:** *Government.*
Published by: Japan Tariff Association, c/o Jibiki Daini Bldg, 4-7-8 Koji-Machi, Chiyoda-ku, Tokyo, 102-0083, Japan. **Dist. by:** International Marketing Corp., I.P.O. Box 5056, Tokyo 100-30, Japan. TEL 81-3-3661-7458, FAX 81-3-3667-9646.

331 315   JPN
JAPAN. MINISTRY OF LABOUR. YEARBOOK OF LABOUR STATISTICS. Text in English, Japanese. 1948. a. JPY 8,000. charts. **Document type:** *Government.*
Published by: (Japan. Statistics and Information Department), Ministry of Labour/Nihon Rodosho, Minister's Secretariat, Tokyo, 100, Japan. Circ: 800.

331.021   JPN   ISSN 0289-1344
JAPAN. STATISTICS BUREAU. MANAGEMENT AND COORDINATION AGENCY. ANNUAL REPORT ON THE LABOUR FORCE SURVEY/NIHON TOKEI KYOKAI. RODORYOKU CHOSA NENPO. Text in English, Japanese. 1965. a. JPY 3,885. **Document type:** *Government.*
Formerly (until 1976): Office of the Prime Minister. Bureau of Statistics. Annual Report on the Labour Force Survey (0289-128X)
Published by: Somucho. Tokeikyoko/Statistics Bureau. Management and Coordination Agency, 19-1 Wakamatsu-cho, Shinjyuku-ku, Tokyo, 162-8668, Japan. TEL 81-3-5273-1116, FAX 81-3-5273-1180, jsatokai@t3.rim.or.jp, http://www.jstat.or.jp. Ed. Akihiko Ito.

331   JPN   ISSN 0289-1301
JAPAN. STATISTICS BUREAU. MANAGEMENT AND COORDINATION AGENCY. ANNUAL REPORT ON THE RETAIL PRICE SURVEY/NIHON TOKEI KYOKAI. KOURI BUKKA TOKEI CHOSA NENPO. Text in English, Japanese. 1956. a. JPY 7,245 (effective 2000). **Document type:** *Government.*
Formerly (until 1962): Report on the Retail Price Survey. Price Data Edition - Kouri Bukka Tokei Chosa Kekka Hokoku. Kakaku Shiryo-hen (0289-1298)
Published by: Somucho. Tokeikyoko/Statistics Bureau. Management and Coordination Agency, 19-1 Wakamatsu-cho, Shinjyuku-ku, Tokyo, 162-8668, Japan. TEL 81-3-5273-1116, FAX 81-3-5273-1180, jsatokai@t3.rim.or.jp, http://www.jstat.or.jp. Ed. Akihiko Ito.

331   JPN   ISSN 0448-7141
HD2346.J3
JAPAN. STATISTICS BUREAU. MANAGEMENT AND COORDINATION AGENCY. ANNUAL REPORT ON THE UNINCORPORATED ENTERPRISE SURVEY (YEAR)/NIHON TOKEI KYOKAI. KOJIN KIGYO KEIZAI CHOSA NENPO. Text in English, Japanese. 1952. a. JPY 3,150 (effective 2000). **Document type:** *Government.*
Formerly (until 1960): Annual Report on the Unincorporated Commercial and Manufacturing Enterprise Survey - Kojin Shokogyo Keizai Chosa Nenpo (0448-7168)
Published by: Somucho. Tokeikyoko/Statistics Bureau. Management and Coordination Agency, 19-1 Wakamatsu-cho, Shinjyuku-ku, Tokyo, 162-8668, Japan. TEL 81-3-5273-1116, FAX 81-3-5273-1180, jsatokai@t3.rim.or.jp, http://www.jstat.or.jp. Ed. Akihiko Ito.

331.11 315   JPN
JAPAN. STATISTICS BUREAU. MANAGEMENT AND COORDINATION AGENCY. EMPLOYMENT STATUS SURVEY (YEAR). Text in Japanese. 1956. 5/yr. price varies. **Document type:** *Government.*
Published by: Somucho. Tokeikyoko/Statistics Bureau. Management and Coordination Agency, 19-1 Wakamatsu-cho, Shinjyuku-ku, Tokyo, 162-8668, Japan. TEL 81-3-5273-1116, FAX 81-3-5273-1180.

330 310   JPN   ISSN 0448-7109
HD7057   CODEN: NMFRE3
JAPAN. STATISTICS BUREAU. MANAGEMENT AND COORDINATION AGENCY. FAMILY SAVINGS SURVEY (YEAR)/NIHON TOKEI KYOKAI. CHOCHIKU DOKO CHOSA HOKOKU. Text in Japanese. 1958. a. JPY 3,885 (effective 2000). **Document type:** *Government.*
Published by: Somucho. Tokeikyoko/Statistics Bureau. Management and Coordination Agency, 19-1 Wakamatsu-cho, Shinjyuku-ku, Tokyo, 162-8668, Japan. TEL 81-3-5273-1116, FAX 81-3-5273-1180, jsatokai@t3.rim.or.jp, http://www.jstat.or.jp. R&P Akihiko Ito.

658 310   JPN   ISSN 0448-7176
JAPAN. STATISTICS BUREAU. MANAGEMENT AND COORDINATION AGENCY. MONTHLY REPORT OF RETAIL PRICES SURVEY/NIHON TOKEI KYOKAI. KOURI BUKKA TOKEI CHOSA HOKOKU. Text in English, Japanese. 1951. m. JPY 650 per issue (effective 2000). **Document type:** *Government.*
Published by: Somucho. Tokeikyoko/Statistics Bureau. Management and Coordination Agency, 19-1 Wakamatsu-cho, Shinjyuku-ku, Tokyo, 162-8668, Japan. TEL 81-3-5273-1116, FAX 81-3-5273-1180, jsatokai@t3.rim.or.jp, http://www.jstat.or.jp. R&P Akihiko Ito.

339 310   JPN
JAPAN. STATISTICS BUREAU. MANAGEMENT AND COORDINATION AGENCY. MONTHLY REPORT ON THE FAMILY INCOME AND EXPENDITURE SURVEY/NIHON TOKEI KYOKAI. KAKEI CHOSA HOKOKU. Text in English, Japanese. m. JPY 870 per issue (effective 2000). **Document type:** *Government.*

Former titles (until 1953): Family Income and Expenditure - Shohi Jittai Chosa Hokoku (0289-1042); (until 1951): City Worker's Family Income Survey - Shohisha Kakaku Chosa Hokoku (0446-5830)
Published by: Somucho. Tokeikyoko/Statistics Bureau. Management and Coordination Agency, 19-1 Wakamatsu-cho, Shinjyuku-ku, Tokyo, 162-8668, Japan. TEL 81-3-5332-3151, FAX 81-3-5389-0691, jsatokai@t3.rim.or.jp, http://www.jstat.or.jp. R&P Akihiko Ito.

331.11021   JPN
JAPAN. STATISTICS BUREAU. MANAGEMENT AND COORDINATION AGENCY. MONTHLY REPORT ON THE LABOUR FORCE SURVEY. Text in English, Japanese. m. JPY 550 per issue (effective 1999). **Document type:** *Government.*
Published by: Somucho. Tokeikyoko/Statistics Bureau. Management and Coordination Agency, 19-1 Wakamatsu-cho, Shinjyuku-ku, Tokyo, 162-8668, Japan. TEL 81-3-5273-1116, FAX 81-3-5273-1180, jsatokai@t3.rim.or.jp, http://www.jstat.or.jp. R&P Akihiko Ito.

331   JPN   ISSN 0448-715X
HG4245
JAPAN. STATISTICS BUREAU. MANAGEMENT AND COORDINATION AGENCY. QUARTERLY REPORT ON THE UNINCORPORATED ENTERPRISE SURVEY/NIHON TOKEI KYOKAI. KOJIN KIGYO KEIZAI CHOSA KIHO. Text in Japanese. 1963. q. **Document type:** *Government.*
Published by: Somucho. Tokeikyoko/Statistics Bureau. Management and Coordination Agency, 19-1 Wakamatsu-cho, Shinjyuku-ku, Tokyo, 162-8668, Japan. TEL 81-3-5273-1116, FAX 81-3-5273-1180, jsatokai@t3.rim.or.jp, http://www.jstat.or.jp.

331.11   JPN   ISSN 0448-7214
HD5827
JAPAN. STATISTICS BUREAU. MANAGEMENT AND COORDINATION AGENCY. REPORT ON THE SPECIAL SURVEY OF THE LABOUR FORCE SURVEY (YEAR)/NIHON TOKEI KYOKAI. RODORYOKU CHOSA TOKUBETSU CHOSA HOKOKU. Text in Japanese. irreg., latest 1998. JPY 5,040 (effective 2000). **Document type:** *Government.*
Formerly: (until 1961): Rodoryoku Chosa Rinji Chosa Hokoku - Report on the Special Survey of the Labor Force Survey (0448-7206)
Published by: Somucho. Tokeikyoko/Statistics Bureau. Management and Coordination Agency, 19-1 Wakamatsu-cho, Shinjyuku-ku, Tokyo, 162-8668, Japan. TEL 81-3-5273-1116, FAX 81-3-5273-1180, http://www.jstat.or.jp.

330   CHN   ISSN 1009-7341
JINGJIXUE WENZHAI KA/ECONOMICS ABSTRACTS ON CARDS. Text in Chinese. q. CNY 20 (effective 2004). **Document type:** *Abstract/Index.*
Formerly: Jingjixue Wenzhai
Media: Cards.
Published by: Zhongguo Renmin Daxue, Shubao Zilio Zhongxin/Renmin University of China, Information Center for Social Server, Dongcheng-qu, 3, Zhangzizhong Lu, Beijing, 100007, China. TEL 86-10-64039458, FAX 86-10-64015080, kyes@163.net, http://www.confucius.cn.net/bkdetail.asp?fzt=WF1. **Dist. in the US by:** China Publications Service; **Dist. outside of China by:** China International Book Trading Corp, 35 Chegongzhuang Xilu, Haidian District, PO Box 399, Beijing 100044, China. TEL 86-10-68412045, FAX 86-10-68412023, cibtc@mail.cibtc.com.cn, http://www.cibtc.com.cn/.

331.11021   JOR
JORDAN. DEPARTMENT OF STATISTICS. EMPLOYMENT SURVEY FOR ESTABLISHMENTS ENGAGING FIVE PERSONS OR MORE. Text in Arabic, English. 1967. a. USD 15 (effective 2000). **Document type:** *Government.*
Published by: Department of Statistics, P O Box 2015, Amman, Jordan. TEL 962-6-842171, FAX 962-6-833518, TELEX 24117 STATIS JO.

310   JOR
JORDAN. DEPARTMENT OF STATISTICS. EMPLOYMENT, UNEMPLOYMENT AND INCOME SURVEY. Text in Arabic, English. 1988. a. USD 25 (effective 2000). **Document type:** *Government.*
Formerly: Jordan. Department of Statistics. Services Survey
Published by: Department of Statistics, P O Box 2105, Amman, Jordan. TEL 962-6-842171, FAX 962-6-833518, TELEX 24117 STATIS JO.

382 315   JOR   ISSN 0075-4021
HF259.J6
JORDAN. DEPARTMENT OF STATISTICS. EXTERNAL TRADE STATISTICS. Text in Arabic. 1965. a. USD 105 (effective 2000). **Document type:** *Government.*
Published by: Department of Statistics, P O Box 2015, Amman, Jordan. TEL 962-6-842171, FAX 962-6-833518.

330   JOR
JORDAN. DEPARTMENT OF STATISTICS. INDUSTRIAL SURVEY. Text in Arabic, English. 1965. a. USD 15 (effective 2000). **Document type:** *Government.*
Published by: Department of Statistics, P O Box 2015, Amman, Jordan. TEL 962-6-842171, FAX 962-6-833518.

381   JOR
JORDAN. DEPARTMENT OF STATISTICS. WHOLESALE & RETAIL TRADE SURVEY. Text in Arabic, English. 1985. a. USD 15 (effective 2000). **Document type:** *Government.*
Formerly: Jordan. Department of Statistics. Internal Trade Survey
Published by: Department of Statistics, P O Box 2015, Amman, Jordan. TEL 962-6-842171, FAX 962-6-833518.

330.9 310   USA   ISSN 0735-0015
HB137
➤ **JOURNAL OF BUSINESS AND ECONOMIC STATISTICS.** Text in English. 1983. q. USD 115 to libraries; USD 56 combined subscription to members print & online eds; USD 135 combined subscription to non-members print & online eds; USD 14 combined subscription to students print & online eds; USD 135 combined subscription to institutions print & online eds (effective 2005). illus. reprints avail. **Document type:** *Journal, Academic/Scholarly.*
Related titles: Online - full text ed.: ISSN 1537-2707 (from EBSCO Publishing, Gale Group, IngentaConnect, JSTOR (Web-based Journal Archive), ProQuest Information & Learning).
Indexed: ABIn, ASCA, BPI, CCMJ, CIS, CMCI, CPM, CurCont, FamI, IBSS, Inspec, JCQM, JEL, MathR, MathSciNet, ORMS, PCI, QC&AS, RASB, SSCI, ST&MA, TriticAb, WAE&RSA.
—BLDSC (4954.661000), IDS, IE, Infotrieve, ingenta. **CCC.**
Published by: American Statistical Association, 1429 Duke St, Alexandria, VA 22314-3415. TEL 703-684-1221, 888-231-3473, FAX 703-684-2037, asainfo@amstat.org, http://www.amstat.org/publications/jbes/index.cfm?fuseaction=main, http://www.amstat.org/publications/index.html. R&P Jim Dicky. **Subscr. to:** Department 79081, Baltimore, MD 21279-0081.

➤ **JOURNAL OF ECONOMIC AND SOCIAL MEASUREMENT.**
see *STATISTICS*

330 016   USA   ISSN 0022-0515
HB1   CODEN: JECLB3
➤ **JOURNAL OF ECONOMIC LITERATURE.** Text in English. 1963. q. free to members (effective 2005). adv. bk.rev. illus. index. back issues avail.; reprint service avail. from PQC,WSH. **Document type:** *Magazine, Abstract/Index.*
Description: Designed to provide economists with a guide to ongoing research and publications. Includes index of articles on economic subjects in English-language journals. Focuses on academic and research topics rather than on popular literature.
Formerly: (until 1968): Journal of Economic Abstracts (0364-281X)
Related titles: CD-ROM ed.: (from SilverPlatter Information, Inc.); Microform ed.: (from PQC); Online - full text ed.: (from EBSCO Publishing, Gale Group, IngentaConnect, JSTOR (Web-based Journal Archive), ProQuest Information & Learning).
Indexed: ABIn, ABS&EES, AgeL, AmH&L, BRD, BRI, CBRI, CIS, CurCont, FamI, HistAb, IBSS, PAIS, PCI, PopulInd, RASB, SSCI, SSI.
—BLDSC (4973.053000), CISTI, IDS, IE, Infotrieve, ingenta, Linda Hall. **CCC.**
Published by: American Economic Association, 2014 Broadway, Ste 305, Nashville, TN 37203. TEL 615-322-2595, FAX 615-343-7590, info@econlit.org, http://www.aeaweb.org/journal.html, http://www.vanderbilt.edu/AEA/. Ed. Roger Gordon. R&P Edda B Leithner. Circ: 17,267 (paid).

330.9   NGA
KANO (STATE). LOCAL GOVERNMENT SURVEY OF TOWNS, VILLAGES AND HAMLETS. Text in English. 1993. quinquennial. USD 30 (effective 1996). **Document type:** *Government.*
Published by: Budget & Economic Planning Directorate, Ministry of Finance, Audu Bako Secretariat, PMB 3291, Kano, Kano State, Nigeria.

331.11   NGA
KANO (STATE) MANPOWER STATISTICS. Text in English. 1984. biennial. USD 30 (effective 1996). stat. **Document type:** *Government.*
Published by: (Kano (State). Department of Manpower Statistics), Budget & Economic Planning Directorate, Ministry of Finance, Audu Bako Secretariat, PMB 3291, Kano, Kano State, Nigeria.

330.9   NGA
KANO (STATE). PRICES OF SELECTED COMMODITIES IN SOME TOWNS IN KANO STATE. Text in English. 1981. q. stat. **Document type:** *Government.*
Published by: Budget & Economic Planning Directorate, Ministry of Finance, Audu Bako Secretariat, PMB 3291, Kano, Kano State, Nigeria.

336   NGA
KANO (STATE). PUBLIC FINANCE STATISTICS OF KANO STATE & LOCAL GOVERNMENT COUNCILS. Text in English. 1991. biennial. USD 30 (effective 1996). stat. **Document type:** *Government.*
Published by: Budget & Economic Planning Directorate, Ministry of Finance, Audu Bako Secretariat, PMB 3291, Kano, Kano State, Nigeria.

316.69 330.9   NGA
KANO (STATE). STATISTICAL YEAR - BOOK. Text in English. 1970. biennial. USD 30 (effective 1996). bk.rev. **Document type:** *Government.*
Supersedes: Northern Nigeria. Ministry of Economic Planning. Statistical Year Book
Published by: Budget & Economic Planning Directorate, Ministry of Finance, Audu Bako Secretariat, PMB 3291, Kano, Kano State, Nigeria.

016 330   MAR   ISSN 1113-531X
KATAB: INDEX ANALYTIQUE BIBLIOGRAPHIQUE. Text in French. 1972. irreg. (4-6/yr.). MAD 120 per issue. adv. bk.rev. **Document type:** *Bibliography.* **Description:** Multi-disciplinary periodical bibliography which includes documents published about Morocco, whether inside the country or abroad.
Former titles: Index Analytique Signaletique Bibliographique; (until 1994, no.48): I D E S T (Index Documentation - Economie - Science - Technique) (0851-0016)
Related titles: Microfiche ed.; Online - full text ed.
Published by: Ministere de la Prevision Economique et du Plan, Centre National de Documentation, Avenue Ahmed Cherkaoui - C.P. 10100, C.P. 10004 Agdal, B P 826, Rabat, 10004, Morocco. TEL 212-7-774944, FAX 212-7-773134, maghridoc@mpep.gov, http://www.mpep.gov.ma. Ed. Battiwa Lekbir. Circ: 1,000.

338.9   KEN
KENYA. CENTRAL BUREAU OF STATISTICS. DEVELOPMENT ESTIMATES. Text in English. a. stat. **Document type:** *Government.*
Formerly: Kenya. Ministry of Economic Planning and Development. Statistics Division. Development Estimates (0075-5818)
Published by: Ministry of Finance and Planning, Central Bureau of Statistics, PO Box 30266, Nairobi, Kenya. **Subscr. to:** Government Press, Haile Selaissie Ave., PO Box 30128, Nairobi, Kenya. TEL 254-2-334075.

316 331   KEN   ISSN 0376-8864
HD5841.K4
KENYA. CENTRAL BUREAU OF STATISTICS. EMPLOYMENT AND EARNINGS IN THE MODERN SECTOR. Key Title: Employment and Earnings in the Modern Sector. Text in English. 1971. irreg., latest 1981. KES 50. stat. **Document type:** *Government.*
Published by: Ministry of Finance and Planning, Central Bureau of Statistics, PO Box 30266, Nairobi, Kenya. **Subscr. to:** Government Press, Haile Selaissie Ave., PO Box 30128, Nairobi, Kenya. TEL 254-2-334075.

338.9   KEN   ISSN 0075-5834
KENYA. CENTRAL BUREAU OF STATISTICS. ESTIMATES OF RECURRENT EXPENDITURES. Text in English. 1959. a. stat. **Document type:** *Government.*
Published by: Ministry of Finance and Planning, Central Bureau of Statistics, PO Box 30266, Nairobi, Kenya. **Subscr. to:** Government Press, Haile Selaissie Ave., PO Box 30128, Nairobi, Kenya. TEL 254-2-334075.

338.9   KEN
KENYA. CENTRAL BUREAU OF STATISTICS. ESTIMATES OF REVENUE EXPENDITURES. Text in English. 1959. a. stat. **Document type:** *Government.*
Formerly: Kenya. Ministry of Economic Planning and Development. Estimates of Revenue Expenditures (0075-5826)
Published by: Ministry of Finance and Planning, Central Bureau of Statistics, PO Box 30266, Nairobi, Kenya. **Subscr. to:** Government Press, Haile Selaissie Ave., PO Box 30128, Nairobi, Kenya. TEL 254-2-334075.

338 316   KEN
KENYA. CENTRAL BUREAU OF STATISTICS. REGISTER OF MANUFACTURING FIRMS. Text in English. 1970. irreg. stat. **Document type:** *Government.*
Formerly: Kenya. Ministry of Finance and Economic Planning. Statistics Division. Register of Manufacturing Firms
Published by: Ministry of Finance and Planning, Central Bureau of Statistics, PO Box 30266, Nairobi, Kenya. **Subscr. to:** Government Press, Haile Selaissie Ave., PO Box 30128, Nairobi, Kenya. TEL 254-2-334075.

338   KEN
KENYA. CENTRAL BUREAU OF STATISTICS. SURVEYS OF INDUSTRIAL PRODUCTION. Text in English. irreg. **Document type:** *Government.*
Published by: Ministry of Finance and Planning, Central Bureau of Statistics, PO Box 30266, Nairobi, Kenya. **Subscr. to:** Government Press, Haile Selaissie Ave., PO Box 30128, Nairobi, Kenya. TEL 254-2-334075.

330.9   THA
KEY STATISTICS OF THAILAND (YEAR). Text in English, Thai. 1982. a. price varies. **Document type:** *Government.* **Description:** Contains data on population and labor statistics, agricultural statistics, industrial statistics, price statistics, transport statistics, money and banking statistics, government statistics, national income statistics, household income and expenditure statistics.

B

Published by: (Thailand. Statistical Data Bank and Information Dissemination Division), National Statistical Office, Larn Luang Rd, Bangkok, 10100, Thailand. TEL 66-2-282-1535, FAX 66-2-281-3814, binfodsm@nso.go.th, http://www.nso.go.th/. Circ: 1,000.

330   DEU   ISSN 1433-8688
KIELER BIBLIOGRAPHIEN ZU AKTUELLEN
OEKONOMISCHEN THEMEN. Text in German. irreg., latest vol.18, 1999. **Document type:** *Monographic series, Bibliography.*
Formerly: Kieler Schnellbibliographien zu Aktuellen Wirtschaftsthemen
Published by: Institut fuer Weltwirtschaft, Duesternbrooker Weg 120, Kiel, 24105, Germany. TEL 49-431-8814305, FAX 49-431-85853, info@ifw.uni-kiel.de, http://www.uni-kiel.de/ifw. Ed. Horst Siebert. R&P Dr. Harmen Lehment.

330.9   ITA
KOMPASS ITALIA - ANNUARIO GENERALE DELL'ECONOMIA
ITALIANA. Variant title: Annuario Generale dell'Economia Italiana. Text in Italian. 1961. a. (in 3 vols.). price varies. adv. charts. **Document type:** *Directory, Trade.* **Description:** Gives information on the activity, products, and structure of 50,000 Italian companies that are leaders in their areas.
Formerly: Annuario Kompass Repertorio Generale dell'Economia Italiana
Related titles: CD-ROM ed.
Published by: Kompass Italia SpA, Strada del Lionetto 6, Turin, TO 10146, Italy. TEL 39-011-4353536, FAX 39-011-4353535, kompass.to@seat.it, http://www.kompassitalia.com. Circ: 15,000.

338.9 315   KOR
KOREA (REPUBLIC). NATIONAL STATISTICAL OFFICE.
ANNUAL REPORT ON CONSUMER PRICE INDEX/MULGA
YONBO. Text in English, Korean. 1967. a. KRW 8,000, USD 12 (effective 1999). **Document type:** *Government.*
Former titles: Korea (Republic). National Statistical Office. Annual Report on the Price Survey; Korea (Republic). National Bureau of Statistics. Annual Report on the Price Survey (0075-6830)
Published by: National Statistical Office, Government Complex III no.920, Dusan-Dong So-Gu, Taejon, 302701, Korea, S. TEL 82-42-472-2615, FAX 82-42-481-2465, http://www.nso.go.kr. **Subscr. to:** Korean Statistical Association, Rm. 103, Seoul Statistical Branch Office Bldg. 71, Nonhyun-Dong, Kangnam-Ku, Seoul, Korea, S.. TEL 82-2-3443-7954, FAX 82-2-3443-7957.

338.9   KOR
KOREA (REPUBLIC). NATIONAL STATISTICAL OFFICE.
ANNUAL REPORT ON MONTHLY INDUSTRIAL
PRODUCTION STATISTICS. Text in English, Korean. 1970. a. KRW 28,000, USD 27 (effective 1999). **Document type:** *Government.*
Former titles: Korea (Republic). National Statistical Office. Annual Report on Current Industrial Production Survey; Korea (Republic). Economic Planning Board. Annual Report on Current Industrial Production Survey
Published by: National Statistical Office, Government Complex III no.920, Dusan-Dong So-Gu, Taejon, 302701, Korea, S. TEL 83-42-472-2615, FAX 82-42-481-2465, http://www.nso.go.kr. **Subscr. to:** The Korean Statistical Association, Rm. 103, Seoul Statistical Branch Office Bldg. 71, Nonhyun-Dong, Kangnam-Ku, Seoul 135701, Korea, S.. TEL 82-2-3443-7954, FAX 83-2-3443-7957.

331.021   KOR
KOREA (REPUBLIC). NATIONAL STATISTICAL OFFICE.
ANNUAL REPORT ON THE ECONOMICALLY ACTIVE
POPULATION SURVEY. Text in English, Korean. 1963. a. KRW 6,000, USD 9 (effective 1999). **Document type:** *Government.*
Formerly: Korea (Republic). Economic Planning Board. Annual Report on the Economically Active Population Survey (0454-7543)
Published by: National Statistical Office, Government Complex III no.920, Dusan-Dong So-Gu, Taejon, 302701, Korea, S. TEL 82-42-472-2615, FAX 82-42-481-2465, http://www.nso.go.kr. **Subscr. to:** The Korean Statistical Association, Rm. 103, Seoul Statistical Branch Office Bldg. 71, Nonhyun-Dong, Kangnam-Ku, Seoul 135701, Korea, S.. TEL 82-2-3443-7954, FAX 82-2-3443-7957.

339 315   KOR   ISSN 1011-6222
KOREA (REPUBLIC). NATIONAL STATISTICAL OFFICE.
ANNUAL REPORT ON THE FAMILY INCOME AND
EXPENDITURE SURVEY. Text in English, Korean. 1963. a. KRW 8,000, USD 12 (effective 1999). **Document type:** *Government.*
Formerly: Korea (Republic). National Bureau of Statistics. Annual Report on the Family Income and Expenditure Survey (0075-6822)
Published by: National Statistical Office, Government Complex III no.920, Dusan-Dong So-Gu, Taejon, 302701, Korea, S. TEL 82-2-472-2615, FAX 82-42-481-2465, http://www.nso.go.kr. **Subscr. to:** The Korean Statistical Association, Rm. 103, Seoul Statistical Branch Office Bldg. 71, Nonhyun-Dong, Kangnam-Ku, Seoul 135701, Korea, S.. TEL 82-2-3443-7954, FAX 82-2-3443-7957.

KOREA (REPUBLIC). NATIONAL STATISTICAL OFFICE.
REPORT ON MINING AND MANUFACTURING SURVEY. see
MINES AND MINING INDUSTRY—Abstracting, Bibliographies, Statistics

330.021   RUS
KRATKOSROCHNYE EKONOMICHESKIE POKAZATELI
ROSSIISKOI FEDERATSII/SHORT-TERM INDICATORS OF
THE RUSSIA'S ECONOMY. Text in Russian. m. RUR 7,080 (effective 2005). charts; stat. **Document type:** *Journal, Government.* **Description:** Contains economic indicators of Russia: GDP and its structure, volume of industrial output, agricultural output, transport freight turnover, fixed capital investments, foreign trade turnover, deficit of consolidated budget, retail and catering turnover, consumer price indices, value of minimal basket of foodstuffs.
Media: Online - full content.
Published by: Gosudarstvennyi Komitet Rossiiskoi Federatsii po Statistike/Federal State Statistics Office, ul Myasnitskaya 39, Moscow, 107450, Russian Federation. TEL 7-095-2074902, FAX 7-095-2074087, stat@gks.ru, http://www.gks.ru.

332.6   KWT
KUWAIT. CENTRAL STATISTICAL OFFICE. ANNUAL BULLETIN
OF FOREIGN TRADE STATISTICS/KUWAIT. AL-IDARAH
AL-MARKAZIYYAH LIL-IHSA'. AL-NASHRAH
AL-SANAWIYYAH LI-IHSA'AT AL-TIJARAH
AL-KHARIJIYYAH. Text in Arabic, English. 1964. a., latest 1996. KWD 1. **Document type:** *Government.* **Description:** Provides statistics on commodity imports and exports and commercial exchanges between Kuwait and foreign countries.
Published by: Central Statistical Office/Al-Idarah al-Markaziyyah lil-Ihsa', P O Box 26188, Safat, 13122, Kuwait. TEL 965-2428200, FAX 965-2430464.

338   KWT
KUWAIT. CENTRAL STATISTICAL OFFICE. ANNUAL SURVEY
OF ESTABLISHMENTS - INDUSTRIAL/KUWAIT. AL-IDARAH
AL-MARKAZIYYAH LIL-IHSA'. AL-BAHTH AL-SANAWI
LIL-MANSHAAT - AL-SINA'AH. Text in Arabic, English. 1983. a., latest 1995. **Document type:** *Government.*
Published by: Central Statistical Office/Al-Idarah al-Markaziyyah lil-Ihsa', P O Box 26188, Safat, 13122, Kuwait. TEL 965-2428200, FAX 965-2430464.

338   KWT
KUWAIT. CENTRAL STATISTICAL OFFICE. ANNUAL SURVEY
OF ESTABLISHMENTS - SERVICES/KUWAIT. AL-IDARAH
AL-MARKAZIYYAH LIL-IHSA'. AL-BAHTH AL-SANAWI
LIL-MANSHAAT - AL-KHADAMAT. Text in Arabic, English. 1982. a., latest 1995. **Document type:** *Government.*
Published by: Central Statistical Office/Al-Idarah al-Markaziyyah lil-Ihsa', P O Box 26188, Safat, 13122, Kuwait. TEL 965-2428200, FAX 965-2430464.

338   KWT
KUWAIT. CENTRAL STATISTICAL OFFICE. ANNUAL SURVEY
OF ESTABLISHMENTS - WHOLESALE & RETAIL
TRADE/KUWAIT. AL-IDARAH AL-MARKAZIYYAH LIL-IHSA'.
AL-BAHTH AL-SANAWI LIL-MANSHAAT - TIJARAH
AL-JUMLAH WAL-TAJZI'AH. Text in Arabic, English. 1983. a., latest 1994. **Document type:** *Government.*
Published by: Central Statistical Office/Al-Idarah al-Markaziyyah lil-Ihsa', P O Box 26188, Safat, 13122, Kuwait. TEL 965-2428200, FAX 965-2430464.

330   KWT
KUWAIT. CENTRAL STATISTICAL OFFICE. BUILDINGS AND
DWELLINGS CENSUS/KUWAIT. AL-IDARAH
AL-MARKAZIYYAH LIL-IHSA'. TA'DAD AL-MABANI
WAL-MASAKIN. Text in Arabic. 1957. irreg., latest vol.7, 1985. **Document type:** *Government.*
Published by: Central Statistical Office/Al-Idarah al-Markaziyyah lil-Ihsa', P O Box 26188, Safat, 13122, Kuwait. TEL 965-2428200, FAX 965-2430464.

330   KWT
KUWAIT. CENTRAL STATISTICAL OFFICE. ESTABLISHMENT
CENSUS/KUWAIT. AL-IDARAH AL-MARKAZIYYAH
LIL-IHSA'. TA'DAD AL-MUNSHAAT. Text in Arabic. 1957. irreg., latest vol.7, 1985. **Document type:** *Government.*
Published by: Central Statistical Office/Al-Idarah al-Markaziyyah lil-Ihsa', P O Box 26188, Safat, 13122, Kuwait. TEL 965-2428200, FAX 965-2430464.

330   KWT
KUWAIT. CENTRAL STATISTICAL OFFICE. FAMILY BUDGET
SURVEY - FINAL RESULTS/KUWAIT. AL-IDARAH
AL-MARKAZIYYAH LIL-IHSA'. MIZANIYYAT AL-USRAH -
AL-NATA'IJ AL-TAJMI'IYYAH AL-NIHA'IYYAH. Text in Arabic, English. 1973. irreg., latest 1987. **Document type:** *Government.*
Published by: Central Statistical Office/Al-Idarah al-Markaziyyah lil-Ihsa', P O Box 26188, Safat, 13122, Kuwait. TEL 965-2428200, FAX 965-2430464.

330   KWT
KUWAIT. CENTRAL STATISTICAL OFFICE. FINANCIAL
STATISTICS/KUWAIT. AL-IDARAH AL-MARKAZIYYAH
LIL-IHSA'. AL-IHSA'AT AL-MAALIYYAH. Text in Arabic, English. 1975. a., latest 1996. **Document type:** *Government.* **Description:** Provides statistics relating to banking and monetary activities, the insurance sector, shareholding companies, and development assistance from the Kuwait Fund for Arab Economic Development.
Published by: Central Statistical Office/Al-Idarah al-Markaziyyah lil-Ihsa', P O Box 26188, Safat, 13122, Kuwait. TEL 965-2428200, FAX 965-2430464.

336   KWT
KUWAIT. CENTRAL STATISTICAL OFFICE. GOVERNMENT
FINANCIAL STATISTICS/KUWAIT. AL-IDARAH
AL-MARKAZIYYAH LIL-IHSA'. AL-IHSA'AT AL-MAALIYYAH
LIL-HUKUMAH. Text in Arabic, English. 1975. a., latest covers 1995-1996. **Document type:** *Government.*
Supersedes in part (in 1981): Kuwait. Al-Idarah al-Markaziyyah lil-Ihsa'. Al-Ihsa'at al-Maaliyyah
Published by: Central Statistical Office/Al-Idarah al-Markaziyyah lil-Ihsa', P O Box 26188, Safat, 13122, Kuwait. TEL 965-2428200, FAX 965-2430464.

332.6   KWT   ISSN 0454-7063
KUWAIT. CENTRAL STATISTICAL OFFICE. MONTHLY
BULLETIN OF FOREIGN TRADE STATISTICS/KUWAIT.
AL-IDARAH AL-MARKAZIYYAH LIL-IHSA'. AL-NASHRAH
AL-SHAHRIYYAH LI-IHSA'AT AL-TIJARAH
AL-KHARIJIYYAH. Text in Arabic, English. 1964. m. **Document type:** *Government.* **Description:** Provides summary statistical tables on monthly imports and exports during the preceding three years, information on imports and exports by major commodity group and country of origin or destination.
Published by: Central Statistical Office/Al-Idarah al-Markaziyyah lil-Ihsa', P O Box 26188, Safat, 13122, Kuwait. TEL 965-2428200, FAX 965-2430464.

339   KWT
KUWAIT. CENTRAL STATISTICAL OFFICE. MONTHLY
CONSUMER PRICE INDEX NUMBERS. Text in Arabic, English. 1973. m. KWD 0.50. **Document type:** *Government.*
Formerly: Kuwait. Al-Idarah al-Markaziyyah lil-Ihsa'. Al-Nashrah al-Shahriyyah lil-Arqam al-Qiyasiyyah li-As'ar al-Mustahlak; **Supersedes in part:** Kuwait. Central Statistical Office. Annual Bulletin for Prices and Index Numbers
Published by: Central Statistical Office/Al-Idarah al-Markaziyyah lil-Ihsa', P O Box 26188, Safat, 13122, Kuwait. TEL 965-2428200, FAX 965-2430464.

336   KWT
KUWAIT. CENTRAL STATISTICAL OFFICE. NATIONAL
ACCOUNTS STATISTICS/KUWAIT. AL-IDARAH
AL-MARKAZIYYAH LIL-IHSA'. IHSA'AT AL-HISABAT
AL-QAWMIYYAH. Text in Arabic, English. 1975. a., latest covers 1978-1994. **Document type:** *Government.*
Supersedes in part (in 1981): Kuwait. Al-Idarah al-Markaziyyah lil-Ihsa'. Al-Ihsa'at al-Maaliyyah
Published by: Central Statistical Office/Al-Idarah al-Markaziyyah lil-Ihsa', P O Box 26188, Safat, 13122, Kuwait. TEL 965-2428200, FAX 965-2430464.

330   KWT
KUWAIT. CENTRAL STATISTICAL OFFICE. PRELIMINARY
RESULTS OF LABOUR FORCE BY SAMPLE. Text in Arabic. 1973. irreg., latest 1990. **Document type:** *Government.*
Supersedes: Kuwait. Central Statistical Office. Labour Force by Sample Survey
Published by: Central Statistical Office/Al-Idarah al-Markaziyyah lil-Ihsa', P O Box 26188, Safat, 13122, Kuwait. TEL 965-2428200, FAX 965-2430464.

336   KWT
KUWAIT. CENTRAL STATISTICAL OFFICE. PROVISIONAL
ESTIMATES - NATIONAL ACCOUNTS. Text in Arabic, English. 1976. a., latest covers 1994-1996. **Document type:** *Government.*
Supersedes (in 1983): Kuwait. Al-Idarah al-Markaziyyah lil-Ihsa'. Al-Hisabat al-Qawmiyyah wa-Jadawal al-Mudkhalat wal-Mukharajat
Published by: Central Statistical Office/Al-Idarah al-Markaziyyah lil-Ihsa', P O Box 26188, Safat, 13122, Kuwait. TEL 965-2428200, FAX 965-2430464.

330   KWT
KUWAIT. CENTRAL STATISTICAL OFFICE. QUARTERLY
BULLETIN FOR RETAIL PRICES. Text in Arabic, English. q. KWD 0.50 per issue (effective 1998). **Document type:** *Government.*
Published by: Central Statistical Office/Al-Idarah al-Markaziyyah lil-Ihsa', P O Box 26188, Safat, 13122, Kuwait. TEL 965-2428200, FAX 965-2430464.

330   KWT
KUWAIT. CENTRAL STATISTICAL OFFICE. QUARTERLY
BULLETIN FOR WHOLESALE PRICES. Text in Arabic, English. q. KWD 0.50 per issue (effective 1998). **Document type:** *Government.*

Published by: Central Statistical Office/Al-Idarah al-Markaziyyah lil-Ihsa', P O Box 26188, Safat, 13122, Kuwait. TEL 965-2428200, FAX 965-2430464.

330   KWT
KUWAIT. CENTRAL STATISTICAL OFFICE. WHOLESALE PRICE INDEX NUMBERS/KUWAIT. AL-IDARAH AL-MARKAZIYYAH LIL-IHSA'. AL-ARQAM AL-QIYASIYYAH LI-AS'AR AL-JUMLAH. Variant title: Price Index Numbers - Wholesale. Text in Arabic, English. 1973. m. **Document type:** *Government.*
Published by: Central Statistical Office/Al-Idarah al-Markaziyyah lil-Ihsa', P O Box 26188, Safat, 13122, Kuwait. TEL 965-2428200, FAX 965-2430464.

332.6   KWT
KUWAIT. CENTRAL STATISTICAL OFFICE. YEARLY BULLETIN OF TRANSIT STATISTICS/KUWAIT. AL-IDARAH AL-MARKAZIYYAH LIL-IHSA'. NASHRAH IHSA'AT AL-TRANSIT. Text in Arabic, English. 1981. a. latest 1989. **Document type:** *Government.* **Description:** Provides statistics on transit movement through Kuwait, listed by major commodity group, country of origin and destination.
Published by: Central Statistical Office/Al-Idarah al-Markaziyyah lil-Ihsa', P O Box 26188, Safat, 13122, Kuwait. TEL 965-2428200, FAX 965-2430464.

314 381   NLD   ISSN 1570-1719
KWARTAALBERICHT DETAILHANDEL. Text in Dutch. 1953. m. EUR 20 newsstand/cover (effective 2005). stat. index. **Document type:** *Government.*
Former titles (until 2002): Netherlands. Centraal Bureau voor de Statistiek. Maandstatistiek Detailhandel (1385-0105); (until 1996): Netherlands. Centraal Bureau voor de Statistiek. Maandstatistiek van de Binnenlandse Handel en Dienstverlening (0166-9281); (until 1976): Netherlands. Centraal Bureau voor de Statistiek. Maandstatistiek van de Binnenlandse Handel (0024-872X)
Published by: Hoofbedrijfschap Detailhandel, Postbus 90703, The Hague, 2509 LS, Netherlands. TEL 31-70-3385666, FAX 31-70-3385711, info@hbd.nl, http://www.hbd.nl. Circ: 935.
Co-publisher: Centraal Bureau voor de Statistiek.

331.11   USA
LABOR FORCE AND EMPLOYMENT IN WASHINGTON STATE. Text in English. m. (plus a. reports). USD 5. charts. **Document type:** *Government.* **Description:** Presents current and historical labor force and employment data for the state of Washington and each of its 12 Metropolitan Statistical Areas.
Published by: Employment Security Department, Labor Market and Economic Analysis Branch, PO Box 9046, Olympia, WA 98507-9046. Ed. Gary Bodeutsch.

331.11   USA
LABOR FORCE AND NONAGRICULTURAL EMPLOYMENT ESTIMATES. Text in English. 1970. a. free. **Document type:** *Government.*
Formerly: Tennessee Annual Average Labor Force Estimates; Which was formed by the merger of: Tennessee Civilian Work Force Estimates (0085-7165); Tennessee Annual Average Work Force Estimates
Published by: (Tennessee. Research and Statistics Division), Department of Employment Security, 500 James Robertson Pkwy, 11th Fl, Nashville, TN 37245-1040. TEL 615-741-1729. Circ: (controlled).

331.88   IDN
LABOUR FORCE SITUATION IN INDONESIA: PRELIMINARY FIGURES/KEADAAN ANGAKATAN KERJA DE INDONESIA: ANGKA SEMENTARA. Text in English, Indonesian. 1964. a. IDR 27,500, USD 11.97. **Document type:** *Government.*
Published by: Central Bureau of Statistics/Biro Pusat Statistik, Jalan Dr. Sutomo No. 8, PO Box 3, Jakarta Pusat, Indonesia. TEL 62-21-372808. Circ: 500.

331.11   CAN
LABOUR FORCE SURVEY. Text in English. 12/yr. CND 60 (effective 1997). **Document type:** *Government.* **Description:** Shows employment and unemployment by age, sex, occupation and industry, with regional breakdowns.
Published by: Ministry of Finance and Corporate Relations, B C Stats, Sta Prov Govt, P O Box 9410, Victoria, BC V8W 9V1, Canada. TEL 250-387-1502, FAX 250-387-0329, bcstats@fincc04.fin.gov.bc.ca, http://www.bcstats.gov.bc.ca.

331.11021   BLZ
LABOUR FORCE SURVEY. Text in English. 1993. a. free. **Document type:** *Government.* **Description:** Contains in-depth analysis of Belize labor force.
Published by: Ministry of Finance, Central Statistical Office, Belmopan, Belize. TEL 501-8-22352, FAX 501-8-23206, csogob@btl.net.

330.9   GBR   ISSN 1351-4504
LABOUR MARKET BULLETIN. Text in English. 1991. m. GBP 68 domestic; GBP 83 foreign (effective 2002). **Document type:** *Abstract/Index.* **Description:** Covers the employment and economic development.
Indexed: INZP.

Published by: London Research Centre, Research Library, 81 Black Prince Rd, London, SE1 7SZ, United Kingdom. TEL 020-7983-4672, FAX 020-7983-4674, sue.williams@london.gov.uk. Adv. contact Sue Williams.

331.021   PHL   ISSN 0118-8747
LABSTAT UPDATES. Text in English. 1997. irreg., latest vol.3, no.7. looseleaf. free. **Document type:** *Bulletin.* **Description:** Provides information on varying topics on labor and employment which aim to simplify the understanding of available labor and employment statistics and concepts.
Published by: Department of Labor and Employment, Bureau of Labor and Employment Statistics, 31 F Dole Bldg, Intramuros, Manila, 1002, Philippines. TEL 63-2-5273577, FAX 63-2-5273579, tsd@manila-online.net, http://www.manila-online.net/bles. Circ: 250.

658   CHE
LANDESINDEX DER KONSUMENTENPREISE/INDICE SUISSE DES PRIX A LA CONSOMMATION. Text in French, German. 1988. m. CHF 44 (effective 2001). **Document type:** *Government.*
Published by: Bundesamt fuer Statistik, Espace de l'Europe 10, Neuchatel, 2010, Switzerland. TEL 41-32-7136011, FAX 41-32-7136012, information@bfs.admin.ch, http://www.admin.ch/bfs.

338.021 333.79021   ETH
LARGE AND MEDIUM SCALE MANUFACTURING AND ELECTRICITY INDUSTRY SURVEY. Text in English. a. ETB 13, USD 1.75 (effective 1999). back issues avail. **Document type:** *Government.* **Description:** Presents data on number of persons engaged by industrial group, employees by industrial group, ratio of major indicators, ratio of imported to total raw materials, percentage distribution of value added by industry, energy consumed and more.
Related titles: CD-ROM ed.; Diskette ed.
Published by: Central Statistical Authority, PO Box 1143, Addis Ababa, Ethiopia. TEL 251-1-115470, FAX 251-1-550334.

330   COL   ISSN 0120-2596
HC196
LECTURAS DE ECONOMIA. Text in Spanish. 1980. s-a. COP 30,000 domestic; USD 130 foreign (effective 2003). adv. bk.rev. back issues avail. **Document type:** *Journal, Academic/Scholarly.* **Description:** Presents some articles on national economic issues.
Formerly (until no.2, 1980): Revista Temas Economicos (0120-1794)
Indexed: IBR, IBZ, JEL, PAIS, PCI.
Published by: Universidad de Antioquia, Centro de Investigaciones Economicas, Apdo Aereo 1226, Medellin, Colombia. TEL 57-4-210-5842, FAX 57-4-233-1249, lecturas@caribe.udea.edu.co, http://caribe.udea.edu.co/~lecturas. Ed. Gonzalo Betancur. R&P Juan Enrique Hernandez. Adv. contact Ricardo Arango. Circ: 1,000.

330 314   ITA   ISSN 0024-1326
LETTERE D'AFFARI. Text in Italian. 1946. m. bibl.; charts; mkt. **Document type:** *Monographic series.*
Published by: Centro per la Statistica Aziendale, Via Augusto Baldesi, 18, Florence, FI 50131, Italy. TEL 39-55-576041, FAX 39-55-576265. Ed. Massimo Livi Bacci.

382   LBY
LIBYA. CENSUS AND STATISTICS DEPARTMENT. EXTERNAL TRADE INDEX. Text in Arabic, English. irreg. free. **Document type:** *Government.*
Published by: Secretariat of Planning, Census and Statistics Department, P O Box 600, Tripoli, Libya.

382 316   LBY   ISSN 0075-9228
LIBYA. CENSUS AND STATISTICS DEPARTMENT. EXTERNAL TRADE STATISTICS. Text in Arabic, English. 1954. a. free. **Document type:** *Government.*
Published by: Secretariat of Planning, Census and Statistics Department, P O Box 600, Tripoli, Libya.

338 316   LBY   ISSN 0075-9244
LIBYA. CENSUS AND STATISTICS DEPARTMENT. INDUSTRIAL CENSUS. Text in Arabic, English. 1964. decennial. free. **Document type:** *Government.*
Published by: Secretariat of Planning, Census and Statistics Department, P O Box 600, Tripoli, Libya.

338 316   LBY   ISSN 0075-9252
LIBYA. CENSUS AND STATISTICS DEPARTMENT. REPORT OF THE ANNUAL SURVEY OF LARGE MANUFACTURING ESTABLISHMENTS. Text in Arabic, English. 1965. a. free. **Document type:** *Government.*
Published by: Secretariat of Planning, Census and Statistics Department, P O Box 600, Tripoli, Libya.

330   LBY
LIBYA. CENSUS AND STATISTICS DEPARTMENT. STATISTICAL HANDBOOK OF THE LIBYAN ARAB JAMAHIRIYA. Text in Arabic, English. 1980. a. free. **Document type:** *Government.*
Published by: Secretariat of Planning, Census and Statistics Department, P O Box 600, Tripoli, Libya.

382 316   LBY
LIBYA. CENSUS AND STATISTICS DEPARTMENT. TRENDS OF EXTERNAL TRADE. Text in Arabic, English. 1958. m. free. **Document type:** *Government.*
Formerly: Libya. Census and Statistics Department. Summary of External Trade Statistics (0023-1622)
Published by: Secretariat of Planning, Census and Statistics Department, P O Box 600, Tripoli, Libya.

330   LBY   ISSN 1013-736X
LIBYA. CENSUS AND STATISTICS DEPARTMENT. VITAL STATISTICS OF THE SOCIALIST PEOPLE'S LIBYAN ARAB JAMAHIRIYA. Key Title: Al-Ihsa'iyyat al-Hayawiyyat. Text in Arabic, English. 1972. a. free. **Document type:** *Government.*
Published by: Secretariat of Planning, Census and Statistics Department, P O Box 600, Tripoli, Libya.

338 316   LBY   ISSN 0075-9295
LIBYA. CENSUS AND STATISTICS DEPARTMENT. WHOLESALE PRICES IN TRIPOLI TOWN. Text in Arabic, English. 1967. q. free. **Document type:** *Government.*
Published by: Secretariat of Planning, Census and Statistics Department, P O Box 600, Tripoli, Libya.

331.2 314   SCG   ISSN 0300-2535
HA1631
LICNI DOHOCI. Text in Serbo-Croatian. a. YUN 30, USD 1.67. stat. **Document type:** *Government.*
Related titles: ◆ Series of: Srbija i Crna Gora. Zavod za Statistiku. Statisticki Bilten.
Published by: Srbija i Crna Gora Zavod za Statistiku/Serbia and Montenegro Statistical Office, Kneza Milosa 20, Postanski Fah 203, Belgrade, 11000. TEL 381-11-3617273. Circ: 1,000.

LIFESTYLE CHARACTERISTICS OF SPORTING GOODS CONSUMERS. see *SPORTS AND GAMES—Abstracting, Bibliographies, Statistics*

382   ITA
LISTINO QUINDICINALE PREZZI. Text in Italian. fortn. EUR 140 (effective 2005). **Document type:** *Directory, Consumer.*
Published by: Camera di Commercio Industria Artigianato e Agricoltura di Torino, Via carlo Alberto 16, Turin, TO 10123, Italy. TEL 39-011-57161, FAX 39-011-5716516, info@to.camcom.it, http://www.to.camcom.it.

331 016   DEU   ISSN 0935-4743
LITERATURDOKUMENTATION ZUR ARBEITSMARKT- UND BERUFSFORSCHUNG. Text in German. 1972. 2/yr. **Document type:** *Bibliography.* **Description:** List of journals, monographs, and conference papers on labor market and occupational research.
Indexed: ILD.
Published by: Bundesanstalt fuer Arbeit, Institut fuer Arbeitsmarkt- und Berufsforschung, Regensburger Str 104, Nuernberg, 90478, Germany. TEL 49-911-1790, FAX 49-911-1793258, iab.anfragen@iab.de, http://iab.de. Circ: 3,000.

016.331   USA
LITERATURE OF AMERICAN LABOR SERIES. Text in English. 1989. irreg. price varies. adv. **Document type:** *Academic/Scholarly.*
Published by: (New York State School of Industrial and Labor Relations), I L R Press, Cornell University Press, 512 E State St, Ithaca, NY 14850. TEL 607-277-2338, 800-666-2211. Ed. Frances Benson. R&P Clare Wellnitz. Adv. contact Heidi Marschner.

330   GBR
LONDON RESEARCH CENTRE. LONDON (YEAR). Text in English. 1966. a. **Document type:** *Abstract/Index.*
Formerly: Annual Abstract of Greater London Statistics (0960-9741)
Published by: London Research Centre, 81 Black Prince Rd, London, SE1 7SZ, United Kingdom. TEL 44-171-735-4250, FAX 44-171-627-9606.

314 330   LUX   ISSN 0076-1575
HA1411
LUXEMBOURG. SERVICE CENTRAL DE LA STATISTIQUE ET DES ETUDES ECONOMIQUES. ANNUAIRE STATISTIQUE. Text in French. 1955. a. adv. **Document type:** *Government.* **Description:** Reports economic and social statistical data for Luxembourg.
Formerly (until 1962): Luxembourg. Office de la Statistique Generale. Annuaire Statistique
Related titles: Diskette ed.
Published by: Service Central de la Statistique et des Etudes Economiques, 13, rue Erasme, Luxembourg, L-1468, Luxembourg. TEL 352-478-4233, FAX 352-464-289, statec.post@statec.etat.lu, http://www.statec.public.lu. Ed. Robert Weides. Pub. Guy Zacharias. Adv. contact Eliane Schreurs. Circ: 1,300.

▼ *new title*   ➤ *refereed*   ✳ *unverified*   ◆ *full entry avail.*

330 314 LUX ISSN 0076-1583
HC330
LUXEMBOURG. SERVICE CENTRAL DE LA STATISTIQUE ET DES ETUDES ECONOMIQUES. BULLETIN DU STATEC. Text in French. 1955. 8/yr. EUR 22 (effective 2005). **Document type:** *Bulletin, Government.* **Description:** Contains commentaries on specific statistical surveys and studies on economic problems of Luxembourg.
Indexed: PAIS, RASB.
Published by: Service Central de la Statistique et des Etudes Economiques, 13, rue Erasme, Luxembourg, L-1468, Luxembourg. TEL 352-478-4233, FAX 352-464-289, statec.post@statec.etat.lu, http://www.statec.public.lu. Circ: 900.

332.6 LUX ISSN 0076-1605
LUXEMBOURG. SERVICE CENTRAL DE LA STATISTIQUE ET DES ETUDES ECONOMIQUES. CAHIERS ECONOMIQUES. Text in French. 1951. irreg., latest vol.89, 1997. price varies. **Document type:** *Monographic series, Government.* **Description:** Comprises various statistical studies of the economic condition of Luxembourg.
Published by: Service Central de la Statistique et des Etudes Economiques, 13, rue Erasme, Luxembourg, L-1468, Luxembourg. TEL 352-478-4268, FAX 352-464289, statec.post@statec.etat.lu, http://statec.lu, http://www.statec.public.lu.

332.6 LUX
LUXEMBOURG. SERVICE CENTRAL DE LA STATISTIQUE ET DES ETUDES ECONOMIQUES. CONJONCTURE ACTUELLE. Text in French, German. m. free. **Document type:** *Government.* **Description:** Provides a quick statistical reference to the Saar-Lor-Lux-Treves Palatinat occidental border region.
Published by: Service Central de la Statistique et des Etudes Economiques, 13, rue Erasme, Luxembourg, L-1468, Luxembourg. TEL 352-478-4268, FAX 352-464289, statec.post@statec.etat.lu, http://statec.lu, http://www.statec.public.lu.

330 LUX ISSN 1012-6619
LUXEMBOURG. SERVICE CENTRAL DE LA STATISTIQUE ET DES ETUDES ECONOMIQUES. INDICATEURS RAPIDES. SERIE A1: INDICES DES PRIX A LA COMSOMMATION. Text in French. 1979. m. looseleaf. **Document type:** *Government.*
Published by: Service Central de la Statistique et des Etudes Economiques, 13, rue Erasme, Luxembourg, L-1468, Luxembourg. TEL 352-478-4233, FAX 352-464-289, statec.post@statec.etat.lu, http://www.statec.public.lu.

330 LUX ISSN 1012-6589
LUXEMBOURG. SERVICE CENTRAL DE LA STATISTIQUE ET DES ETUDES ECONOMIQUES. INDICATEURS RAPIDES. SERIE A3: INDICES DES PRIX A LA PRODUCTION DES PRODUITS INDUSTRIELS. Text in French. m. looseleaf. **Document type:** *Government.*
Published by: Service Central de la Statistique et des Etudes Economiques, 13, rue Erasme, Luxembourg, L-1468, Luxembourg. TEL 352-478-4233, FAX 352-464-289, statec.post@statec.etat.lu, http://www.statec.public.lu.

330 314 LUX ISSN 0019-6916
LUXEMBOURG. SERVICE CENTRAL DE LA STATISTIQUE ET DES ETUDES ECONOMIQUES. INDICATEURS RAPIDES. SERIE B1: INDICES DE L'ACTIVITE INDUSTRIELLE. Text in French. 1963. m. looseleaf. charts. **Document type:** *Government.*
Published by: Service Central de la Statistique et des Etudes Economiques, 13, rue Erasme, Luxembourg, L-1468, Luxembourg. TEL 352-478-4268, FAX 352-464289, statec.post@statec.etat.lu, http://www.statec.public.lu. Circ: 400.

330 LUX ISSN 1012-6627
LUXEMBOURG. SERVICE CENTRAL DE LA STATISTIQUE ET DES ETUDES ECONOMIQUES. INDICATEURS RAPIDES. SERIE C: EMPLOI ET CHOMAGE - SIDERURGIE - FINANCES- TRANSPORT ET COMMERCE. Text in French. m. looseleaf. **Document type:** *Government.*
Published by: Service Central de la Statistique et des Etudes Economiques, 13, rue Erasme, Luxembourg, L-1468, Luxembourg. TEL 352-478-4233, FAX 352-464-289, statec.post@statec.etat.lu, http://www.statec.public.lu.

LUXEMBOURG. SERVICE CENTRAL DE LA STATISTIQUE ET DES ETUDES ECONOMIQUES. INDICATEURS RAPIDES. SERIE D. IMMATRICULATIONS DE VEHICULES AUTOMOTEURS. see *TRANSPORTATION—Abstracting, Bibliographies, Statistics*

332.6 LUX ISSN 1012-6678
LUXEMBOURG. SERVICE CENTRAL DE LA STATISTIQUE ET DES ETUDES ECONOMIQUES. INDICATEURS RAPIDES. SERIE H: COMMERCE EXTERIEUR DU LUXEMBOURG. Text in French. 3/yr. looseleaf. **Document type:** *Government.*
Published by: Service Central de la Statistique et des Etudes Economiques, 13, rue Erasme, Luxembourg, L-1468, Luxembourg. TEL 352-478-4233, FAX 352-464-289, statec.post@statec.etat.lu, http://www.statec.public.lu.

330.9 LUX ISSN 1019-6463
HC380
LUXEMBOURG. SERVICE CENTRAL DE LA STATISTIQUE ET DES ETUDES ECONOMIQUES. NOTE DE CONJONCTURE. Text in French. 1972. q. **Document type:** *Government.* **Description:** Analyzes the current situation and short-term perspective for the economy and the international environment.
Formerly: Luxembourg. Service Central de la Statistique et des Etudes Economiques. Notes Trimestrielles de Conjoncture (0256-1913)
Published by: Service Central de la Statistique et des Etudes Economiques, 13, rue Erasme, Luxembourg, L-1468, Luxembourg. TEL 352-478-4233, FAX 352-464-289, statec.post@statec.etat.lu, http://www.statec.public.lu. Circ: 1,000.

330.021 LUX
LUXEMBOURG. SERVICE CENTRAL DE LA STATISTIQUE ET DES ETUDES ECONOMIQUES. STATISTIQUES HISTORIQUES. Text in French. 1960. irreg., latest 1990. bibl. **Document type:** *Government.* **Description:** Contains historical statistical data covering the 150 years of Luxembourg's independence.
Formerly: Luxembourg. Service Central de la Statistique et des Etudes Economiques. Statistiques Retrospectif
Published by: Service Central de la Statistique et des Etudes Economiques, 13, rue Erasme, Luxembourg, L-1468, Luxembourg. TEL 352-478-4268, FAX 352-164289, statec.post@statec.etat.lu, http://www.statec.public.lu.

330.016 GBR
M I R A AUTOMOTIVE BUSINESS NEWS. Text in English. 1979. fortn. GBP 340 (effective 2000). **Document type:** *Trade.* **Description:** Contains items from the business and technical press on commercial aspects of the motor industry.
Former titles: M I R A Automotive Business Index; Business News Index (0260-194X); Business Information for the Motor Industry
Related titles: Online - full text ed.
Published by: M I R A Ltd., Watling St, Nuneaton, Warks CV10 0TU, United Kingdom. TEL 44-24-76355000, FAX 44-24-76355355, enquiries@mira.co.uk, http://www.mira.co.uk. Ed. Dennis McVey.

016.658 DEU ISSN 1434-7490
HD28
M@BS. Variant title: M@+abs. Text in German. 1998. bi-m. free. bk.rev. back issues avail. **Document type:** *Abstract/Index.* **Description:** Contains abstracts on management that cover personnel issues, industrial relations, transformation processes, leadership and organizational development.
Formerly (until 1998): Management Abstract (0944-3347)
Media: Online - full text. **Related titles:** E-mail ed.
Published by: Rainer Hampp Verlag, Meringerzellerstr 10, Mering, 86415, Germany. TEL 49-8233-4783, FAX 49-8233-30755, Rainer_Hampp_Verlag@t-online.de, http://www.hampp-verlag.de/hampp_mabs.htm.

381 MAC
MACAO. DIRECCAO DOS SERVICOS DE ESTATISTICA E CENSOS. C A M CLASSIFICACAO DAS ACTIVIDADES ECONOMICAS DE MACAU/MACAO. CENSUS AND STATISTICS DEPARTMENT. C A M CLASSIFICATION OF ECONOMIC ACTIVITIES OF MACAO. Text in Chinese, Portuguese. 1986. irreg. free. **Document type:** *Government.*
Published by: Direccao dos Servicos de Estatistica e Censos, Rua Inacio Baptista, No. 4-6, P.O. Box 3022, Macau. TEL 853-3995311, FAX 853-307825, info@dsec.gov.mo, http://www.dsec.gov.mo/.

382 310 MAC
MACAO. DIRECCAO DOS SERVICOS DE ESTATISTICA E CENSOS. ESTATISTICAS DO COMERCIO EXTERNO/MACAO. CENSUS AND STATISTICS DEPARTMENT. STATISTICS ON EXTERNAL TRADE. Text in Chinese, Portuguese. 1977. q. **Document type:** *Government.* **Description:** Contains a series of summary tables showing monthly and annual trade data by principal trading countries and selected commodity groupings.
Formerly: Macao. Direccao dos Servicos de Estatistica e Censos. Boletim Mensual do Comercio Exterior (0872-4628)
Published by: Direccao dos Servicos de Estatistica e Censos, Rua Inacio Baptista, No. 4-6, P.O. Box 3022, Macau. TEL 853-3995311, FAX 853-307825, info@dsec.gov.mo, http://www.dsec.gov.mo/.

382 MAC
MACAO. DIRECCAO DOS SERVICOS DE ESTATISTICA E CENSOS. ESTATISTICAS DO COMERCIO EXTERNO/MACAO. CENSUS AND STATISTICS DEPARTMENT. EXTERNAL TRADE INDICATORS. Text in Chinese, Portuguese. 1992. m. **Document type:** *Government.*
Formerly (until 1998): Macao. Direccao dos Servicos de Estatistica e Censos. Indicadores do Comercio Externo
Published by: Direccao dos Servicos de Estatistica e Censos, Rua Inacio Baptista, No. 4-6, P.O. Box 3022, Macau. TEL 853-3995311, FAX 853-307825, info@dsec.gov.mo, http://www.dsec.gov.mo/.

330 MAC
MACAO. DIRECCAO DOS SERVICOS DE ESTATISTICA E CENSOS. ESTIMATIVAS DO PRODUTO INTERNO BRUTO/MACAO. CENSUS AND STATISTICS DEPARTMENT. GROSS DOMESTIC PRODUCT ESTIMATES. Text in Chinese, English, Portuguese. 1982. a. free. **Document type:** *Government.* **Description:** Estimates the GDP in Macao by using the expenditure approach that covers private consumption expenditure, government consumption expenditure, gross domestic fixed capital formation, and increase in stock, exports and imports.
Published by: Direccao dos Servicos de Estatistica e Censos, Rua Inacio Baptista, No. 4-6, P.O. Box 3022, Macau. TEL 853-3995269, FAX 853-307825, info@dsec.gov.mo, http://www.dsec.gov.mo/.

381 MAC ISSN 0870-5577
MACAO. DIRECCAO DOS SERVICOS DE ESTATISTICA E CENSOS. INDICE DE PRECOS NO CONSUMIDOR/MACAO. CENSUS AND STATISTICS DEPARTMENT. CONSUMER PRICE INDEX. Text in Chinese, Portuguese. 1984. m. free. Supplement avail. **Document type:** *Government.* **Description:** Presents statistics on price movement of representative consumer goods and services.
Published by: Direccao dos Servicos de Estatistica e Censos, Rua Inacio Baptista, No. 4-6, P.O. Box 3022, Macau. FAX 853-307825, info@dsec.gov.mo, info@dsec.gov.mo, http://www.dsec.gov.mo/.

381 MAC ISSN 0870-5631
MACAO. DIRECCAO DOS SERVICOS DE ESTATISTICA E CENSOS. INDICE DE PRECOS NO CONSUMIDOR (RELATORIO ANUAL)/MACAO. CENSUS AND STATISTICS DEPARTMENT. CONSUMER PRICE INDEX (ANNUAL REPORT). Text in Chinese, Portuguese. 1984. a. free. **Document type:** *Government.* **Description:** Presents statistics on price movement of representative consumer goods and services in annual base.
Published by: Direccao dos Servicos de Estatistica e Censos, Rua Inacio Baptista, No. 4-6, P.O. Box 3022, Macau. TEL 853-3995311, FAX 853-307825, info@dsec.gov.mo, http://www.dsec.gov.mo/.

331.021 MAC
MACAO. DIRECCAO DOS SERVICOS DE ESTATISTICA E CENSOS. INDICES E SALARIOS NA CONSTRUCAO CIVIL/MACAO. CENSUS AND STATISTICS DEPARTMENT. INDEXES AND WAGES IN CIVIL CONTRUCTION. Text in Chinese, Portuguese. 1985. q. free. **Document type:** *Government.* **Description:** Presents the salaries of construction workers engaged in private and public sectors.
Formerly: Macao. Direccao dos Servicos de Estatistica e Censos. Inquerito ao Emprego e Salarios na Construcao Civil - Survey of Employment and Wages in the Construction Industry (0870-5607)
Published by: Direccao dos Servicos de Estatistica e Censos, Rua Inacio Baptista, No. 4-6, P.O. Box 3022, Macau. TEL 853-3995311, FAX 853-307825, info@dsec.gov.mo, http://www.dsec.gov.mo/.

331.11 MAC
MACAO. DIRECCAO DOS SERVICOS DE ESTATISTICA E CENSOS. INQUERITO AO EMPREGO/MACAO. CENSUS AND STATISTICS DEPARTMENT. EMPLOYMENT SURVEY. Text in Chinese, Portuguese. m. (and q.). free. **Document type:** *Government.*
Published by: Direccao dos Servicos de Estatistica e Censos, Rua Inacio Baptista, No. 4-6, P.O. Box 3022, Macau. TEL 853-3995311, FAX 853-307825, info@dsec.gov.mo, http://www.dsec.gov.mo/.

330 MAC
MACAO. DIRECCAO DOS SERVICOS DE ESTATISTICA E CENSOS. INQUERITO INDUSTRIAL/MACAO. CENSUS AND STATISTICS DEPARTMENT. INDUSTRIAL SURVEY. Text in Chinese, Portuguese. 1979. a. free. **Document type:** *Government.*
Formerly: Macao Direccao dos Servicos de Estatistica e Censos. Recesamento Industrial; Macao. Direccao dos Servicos de Estatistica e Censos. Inquerito Industrial (0870-5666)
Published by: Direccao dos Servicos de Estatistica e Censos, Rua Inacio Baptista, No. 4-6, P.O. Box 3022, Macau. TEL 853-3995311, FAX 853-307825, info@dsec.gov.mo, http://www.dsec.gov.mo/.

330 MAC
MACAO. DIRECCAO DOS SERVICOS DE ESTATISTICA E CENSOS. INQUERITOS AS NECESSIDADES DE MAO-DE-OBRA E AS REMUNERACOES/MACAO. CENSUS AND STATISTICS DEPARTMENT. MANPOWER NEEDS AND WAGES SURVEY. Text in Chinese, Portuguese. q. free. **Document type:** *Government.*
Formerly: Macao. Direccao dos Servicos de Estatistica e Censos. Avaliacao das Necessidades de Mao-de-Obra
Published by: Direccao dos Servicos de Estatistica e Censos, Rua Inacio Baptista, No. 4-6, P.O. Box 3022, Macau. TEL 853-3995311, FAX 853-307825, info@dsec.gov.mo, http://www.dsec.gov.mo/.

381 MDG
MADAGASCAR. DIRECTION GENERALE DE L'INSTITUT NATIONAL DE LA STATISTIQUE. BULLETIN DE STATISTIQUE MENSUELLE. Text in French. s-a. MGF 13,200. **Document type:** *Bulletin, Government.*
Formerly: Malagasy Republic. Direction Generale de la Banque des Donnees de l'Etat. Bulletin Mensuel de Statistique
Published by: (Madagascar. Ministere des Finances et de l' Economie), Direction Generale de l'Institut National de la Statistique, BP 485, Antananarivo, 101, Madagascar. TEL 261-2-200-70, FAX 261-2-200-80.

330 315 IND ISSN 0025-0481
MAHARASHTRA QUARTERLY BULLETIN OF ECONOMICS AND STATISTICS. Text in English. 1960. q. INR 200. charts; mkt.; stat. **Document type:** *Bulletin, Government.*
Formerly: Quarterly Bulletin of Economics and Statistics
Indexed: RDA.
Published by: Directorate of Economics and Statistics, MHADA Bldg., Kalanagar Bandra (E), Mumbai, Maharashtra 400 051, India. TEL 91-22-6438781, FAX 91-22-6438781. **Subscr. to:** Government Printing and Stationery, Charni Rd. Gardens, Mumbai, Maharashtra 400 004, India.

MAJOR U K COMPANIES HANDBOOK. see *BUSINESS AND ECONOMICS—Investments*

382 316 MWI ISSN 0076-325X
MALAWI. NATIONAL STATISTICAL OFFICE. ANNUAL STATEMENT OF EXTERNAL TRADE. Text in English. 1964. a. MWK 300. **Document type:** *Government.*
Published by: (Malawi. Commissioner for Census and Statistics), National Statistical Office, PO Box 333, Zomba, Malawi. TEL 265-50-522377, FAX 265-50-523130.

330 316 MWI ISSN 0076-3241
MALAWI. NATIONAL STATISTICAL OFFICE. ANNUAL SURVEY OF ECONOMIC ACTIVITIES. (Issued in 1966 as: Census of Industrial Production) Text in English. 1966. a. MWK 100. **Document type:** *Government.*
Published by: (Malawi. Commissioner for Census and Statistics), National Statistical Office, PO Box 333, Zomba, Malawi. TEL 265-50-522377, FAX 265-50-523130.

336 382 MWI ISSN 0085-3003
MALAWI. NATIONAL STATISTICAL OFFICE. BALANCE OF PAYMENTS. Text in English. 1964. a. MWK 200. **Document type:** *Government.*
Published by: (Malawi. Commissioner for Census and Statistics), National Statistical Office, PO Box 333, Zomba, Malawi. TEL 265-50-522377, FAX 265-50-523130.

331 316 MWI
MALAWI. NATIONAL STATISTICAL OFFICE. EMPLOYMENT AND EARNINGS: ANNUAL REPORT. Text in English. a. MWK 150. **Document type:** *Government.*
Formerly: Malawi. National Statistical Office. Reported Employment and Earnings: Annual Report
Published by: (Malawi. Commissioner for Census and Statistics), National Statistical Office, PO Box 333, Zomba, Malawi. TEL 265-50-522377, FAX 265-50-523130.

310 MYS ISSN 1394-4924
HD9736.M3
MALAYSIA. DEPARTMENT OF STATISTICS. ANNUAL STATISTICS OF MANUFACTURING INDUSTRIES, MALAYSIA - PART A/MALAYSIA. JABATAN PERANGKAAN. PERANGKAAN TAHUNAN INDUSTRI PEMBUSATAN, MALAYSIA - BAHAGIAN A. Text in English, Malay. 1995. a. MYR 22. **Document type:** *Government.*
Published by: Department of Statistics/Jabatan Perangkaan, Jalan Cenderasari, Kuala Lumpur, 50514, Malaysia. TEL 60-3-294-4264, FAX 60-3-291-4535, jpmeto@po.jaring.my, http://www.statistics.gov.my/.

310 MYS ISSN 1394-6048
HD9736.M3
MALAYSIA. DEPARTMENT OF STATISTICS. ANNUAL STATISTICS OF MANUFACTURING INDUSTRIES, MALAYSIA - PART B/MALAYSIA. JABATAN PERANGKAAN. PERANGKAAN TAHUNAN INDUSTRI PEMBUATAN, MALAYSIA - BAHAGIAN B. Text in English, Malay. **Document type:** *Government.*
Published by: Department of Statistics/Jabatan Perangkaan, Jalan Cenderasari, Kuala Lumpur, 50514, Malaysia. TEL 60-3-294-4264, FAX 60-3-291-4535, jpmeto@po.jaring.my, http://www.statistics.gov.my/.

338 310 MYS ISSN 0128-973X
HC445.5.A1
MALAYSIA. DEPARTMENT OF STATISTICS. ANNUAL SURVEY OF MANUFACTURING INDUSTRIES, MALAYSIA/ MALAYSIA. JABATAN PERGANGKAAN. PENYIASATAN TAHUNAN INDUSTRI PEMBUATAN, MALAYSIA. Text in English, Malay. a. MYR 22 per issue (effective 1999). **Document type:** *Government.*
Published by: Department of Statistics/Jabatan Perangkaan, Jalan Cenderasari, Kuala Lumpur, 50514, Malaysia. TEL 60-3-294-4264, FAX 60-3-291-4535, jpmeto@po.jaring.my, http://www.statistics.gov.my.

330.9 330 MYS ISSN 0127-8541
MALAYSIA. DEPARTMENT OF STATISTICS. BALANCE OF PAYMENTS REPORT, MALAYSIA/MALAYSIA. JABATAN PERANGKAAN. LAPORAN IMBANGAN PEMBAYARAN, MALAYSIA. Text in English, Malay. 1981. irreg., latest 1993-1995. MYR 13. **Document type:** *Government.*
Published by: Department of Statistics/Jabatan Perangkaan, Jalan Cenderasari, Kuala Lumpur, 50514, Malaysia. TEL 60-3-294-4264, FAX 60-3-291-4535, jpmeto@po.jaring.my, http://www.statistics.gov.my.

330 MYS ISSN 0126-6837
HD8038.M4
MALAYSIA. DEPARTMENT OF STATISTICS. CENSUS OF PROFESSIONAL AND INSTITUTIONAL ESTABLISHMENTS - PRIVATE SECTOR/MALAYSIA. JABATAN PERANGKAAN. BANCI PERTUBUHAN PROFESIONAL DAN INSTITUSI - SEKTOR SWASTA. Text in English, Malay. 1981. a. MYR 20. **Document type:** *Government.*
Published by: Department of Statistics/Jabatan Perangkaan, Jalan Cenderasari, Kuala Lumpur, 50514, Malaysia. TEL 60-3-294-4264, FAX 30-3-291-4535, jpmeto@po.jaring.my, http://www.statistics.gov.my/.

310 MYS ISSN 0127-8363
HD9987.M3
MALAYSIA. DEPARTMENT OF STATISTICS. CENSUS OF SELECTED SERVICE INDUSTRIES, MALAYSIA/MALAYSIA. JABATAN PERANGKAAN. PERANGKAAN AKAUN NEGARA, MALAYSIA. Text in English, Malay. 1971. a. MYR 25 (effective 1999). **Document type:** *Government.*
Description: Contains statistics on shipping, real estate, transportation, tourism, advertising, banking and financial service industries.
Published by: Department of Statistics/Jabatan Perangkaan, Jalan Cenderasari, Kuala Lumpur, 50514, Malaysia. TEL 60-3-294-4264, FAX 60-3-291-4535, jpmeto@po.jaring.my, http://www.statistics.gov.my.

382 315 MYS ISSN 0127-8533
HF3800.6
MALAYSIA. DEPARTMENT OF STATISTICS. EXTERNAL TRADE STATISTICS, MALAYSIA/MALAYSIA. JABATAN PERANGKAAN. PERANGKAAN PERDAGANGAN LUAR NEGERI, MALAYSIA. Text in English, Malay. 1962. a. (in 2 vols.). price varies. **Document type:** *Government.*
Formerly (until 1981): West Malaysia Annual Statistics of External Trade (0085-8080)
Published by: Department of Statistics/Jabatan Perangkaan, Jalan Cenderasari, Kuala Lumpur, 50514, Malaysia. TEL 60-3-294-4264, FAX 60-3-291-4535, pmeto@po.jaring.my, http://www.statistics.gov.my/. Circ: 1,400.

382 MYS
MALAYSIA. DEPARTMENT OF STATISTICS. EXTERNAL TRADE STATISTICS, SABAH/MALAYSIA. JABATAN PERANGKAAN. PERANGKAAN PERDANGANGAN LUAR NEGERI. SABAH. Text in English, Malay. irreg. price varies. **Document type:** *Government.*
Published by: Department of Statistics/Jabatan Perangkaan, Jalan Cenderasari, Kuala Lumpur, 50514, Malaysia. TEL 60-3-294-4264, FAX 60-3-291-4535, jpmeto@po.jaring.my, http://www.statistics.gov.my.

382 MYS ISSN 0127-9637
MALAYSIA. DEPARTMENT OF STATISTICS. EXTERNAL TRADE SUMMARY MALAYSIA. Text in English. m. MYR 10 per issue. **Document type:** *Government.*
Published by: Department of Statistics/Jabatan Perangkaan, Jalan Cenderasari, Kuala Lumpur, 50514, Malaysia. TEL 60-3-2922133, FAX 60-3-2937018.

338.021 MYS
MALAYSIA. DEPARTMENT OF STATISTICS. INDEX OF INDUSTRIAL PRODUCTION, MALAYSIA/MALAYSIA. JABATAN PERANGKAAN. INDEKS PENGELUARAN PERIDUSTRIAN, MALAYSIA. Text in English, Malay. m. MYR 5 per issue (effective 1999). **Document type:** *Government.*
Published by: Department of Statistics/Jabatan Perangkaan, Jalan Cenderasari, Kuala Lumpur, 50514, Malaysia. TEL 60-3-294-4264, FAX 60-3-291-4535, jpmeto@po.jaring.my, http://www.statistics.gov.my.

338 MYS ISSN 0126-6993
MALAYSIA. DEPARTMENT OF STATISTICS. INDUSTRIAL SURVEYS, MALAYSIA/MALAYSIA. JABATAN PERANGKAAN. PENYIASATAN - PENYIASATAN PERINDUSTRIAN, MALAYSIA. Text in English, Malay. 1981. a. USD 25. **Document type:** *Government.*
Formerly: Penyiasatan Perusahaan Semenanjung Malaysia
Published by: Department of Statistics/Jabatan Perangkaan, Jalan Cenderasari, Kuala Lumpur, 50514, Malaysia. TEL 60-3-294-4264, FAX 60-3-291-4535, jpmeto@po.jaring.my, http://www.statistics.gov.my/.

330 MYS ISSN 1394-0546
MALAYSIA. DEPARTMENT OF STATISTICS. MALAYSIAN ECONOMY IN BRIEF/MALAYSIA. JABATAN PERANGKAAN. EKONOMI MALAYSIA SEPINTAS LALU. Text in English. 1994. m. MYR 5 per issue. **Document type:** *Government.*
Published by: Department of Statistics/Jabatan Perangkaan, Jalan Cenderasari, Kuala Lumpur, 50514, Malaysia. TEL 60-3-294-4264, FAX 60-3-291-4535, jpmeto@po.jaring.my, http://www.statistics.gov.my/.

382.021 MYS
MALAYSIA. DEPARTMENT OF STATISTICS. MONTHLY EXTERNAL TRADE STATISTICS, MALAYSIA/MALAYSIA. JABATAN PERANGKANN. PERANGKAAN PERDAGANGAN LUAR NEGERI BULANAN, MALAYSIA. Text in English, Malay. m. MYR 10 per issue (effective 1999). **Document type:** *Government.*
Published by: Department of Statistics/Jabatan Perangkaan, Jalan Cenderasari, Kuala Lumpur, 50514, Malaysia. TEL 60-3-294-4264, FAX 60-3-291-4535, jpmeto@po.jaring.my, http://www.statistics.gov.my.

338 MYS ISSN 0128-3499
HC447.5
MALAYSIA. DEPARTMENT OF STATISTICS. MONTHLY MANUFACTURING STATISTICS, MALAYSIA. Text in English. 1989. m. MYR 7 per issue. **Document type:** *Government.*
Published by: Department of Statistics/Jabatan Perangkaan, Jalan Cenderasari, Kuala Lumpur, 50514, Malaysia. TEL 60-3-2922133, FAX 60-3-2937018.

MALAYSIA. DEPARTMENT OF STATISTICS. MONTHLY RUBBER STATISTICS, MALAYSIA/MALAYSIA. JABATAN PERANGKAAN. PERANGKAAN GETAH BULANAN, MALAYSIA. see *RUBBER—Abstracting, Bibliographies, Statistics*

382.1721 MYS
MALAYSIA. DEPARTMENT OF STATISTICS. QUARTERLY BALANCE OF PAYMENTS REPORT, MALAYSIA/MALAYSIA. JABATAN PERANGKAAN. LAPORAN IMBANGAN PEMBAYARAN SUKU TAHUNAN, MALAYSIA. Text in English, Malay. 1981. q. MYR 10 per issue (effective 1999). **Document type:** *Government.*
Published by: Department of Statistics/Jabatan Perangkaan, Jalan Cenderasari, Kuala Lumpur, 50514, Malaysia. TEL 60-3-294-4264, FAX 60-3-291-4535, jpmeto@po.jaring.my, http://www.statistics.gov.my.

382 MYS
MALAYSIA. DEPARTMENT OF STATISTICS. REPORT OF THE FINANCIAL SURVEY OF LIMITED COMPANIES, MALAYSIA/MALAYSIA. JABATAN PERANGKAAN. LAPORAN PENYIASATAN KEWANGAN SYARIKAT - SYARIKAT BHD., MALAYSIA. Text in English, Malay. a. **Document type:** *Government.*
Published by: Department of Statistics/Jabatan Perangkaan, Jalan Cenderasari, Kuala Lumpur, 50514, Malaysia. TEL 60-3-294-4264, FAX 30-3-291-4535, jpmeto@po.jaring.my, http://www.statistics.gov.my.

MALAYSIA. DEPARTMENT OF STATISTICS. SPECIAL RELEASE 2 - FOR BUILDING WORKS, PENINSULAR MALAYSIA/MALAYSIA. JABATAN PERANGKAAN. SIARAN KHAS 2 - UNTUK KERJA-KERJA PEMBINAAN, SEM. MALAYSIA. see *BUILDING AND CONSTRUCTION—Abstracting, Bibliographies, Statistics*

MALAYSIA. DEPARTMENT OF STATISTICS. SPECIAL RELEASE 2 - FOR BUILDING WORKS, SABAH/MALAYSIA. JABATAN PERANGKAAN. SIARAN KHAS 2 - UNTUK KERJA-KERJA PEMBINAAN, SABAH. see *BUILDING AND CONSTRUCTION—Abstracting, Bibliographies, Statistics*

332 MYS
MALAYSIA. DEPARTMENT OF STATISTICS. STATE - DISTRICT DATA BANK, MALAYSIA/MALAYSIA. JABATAN PERANGKAAN. BANK DATA NEGERI - DAERAH, MALAYSIA. Text in English, Malay. a. MYR 20. **Document type:** *Government.*
Published by: Department of Statistics/Jabatan Perangkaan, Jalan Cenderasari, Kuala Lumpur, 50514, Malaysia. TEL 60-3-294-4264, FAX 30-3-291-4535, jpmeto@po.jaring.my, http://www.statistics.gov.my/.

382 315 MYS ISSN 0127-0451
HF3800.6.Z8
MALAYSIA. DEPARTMENT OF STATISTICS. STATISTICS OF EXTERNAL TRADE. SARAWAK/MALAYSIA. JABATAN PERANGKAAN. PERANGKAAN PERDAGANGAN LUAR NEGERI. SARAWAK. Text in English. 1954. a. MYR 60. **Document type:** *Government.*
Formerly: Sarawak External Trade Statistics (0080-6455)
Published by: Department of Statistics/Jabatan Perangkaan, Jalan Cenderasari, Kuala Lumpur, 50514, Malaysia. TEL 60-3-294-4264, FAX 60-3-291-4535, jpmeto@po.jaring.my, http://www.statistics.gov.my.

315 MYS
MALAYSIA. DEPARTMENT OF STATISTICS. YEARBOOK OF STATISTICS, SABAH/MALAYSIA. JABATAN PERANGKAAN. BUKU TAHUNAN PERANGKAAN, SABAH. Text in English, Malay. 1964. a. MYR 25. **Document type:** *Government.*
Former titles: Siaran Perangkaan Tahunan - Sabah; (until 1969): Malaysia Department of Statistics. Annual Bulletin of Statistics Sabah (0080-5203)

B

Published by: Department of Statistics/Jabatan Perangkaan, Jalan Cenderasari, Kuala Lumpur, 50514, Malaysia. TEL 60-3-294-4264, FAX 60-3-291-4535, jpmeto@po.jaring.my, http://www.statistics.gov.my. Circ: 465.

310 MYS
HA4600.6.Z9
MALAYSIA. DEPARTMENT OF STATISTICS. YEARBOOK OF STATISTICS, SARAWAK/MALAYSIA. JABATAN PERANGKAAN. BUKU TAHUNAN PERANGKAAN, SARAWAK. Text in English. 1964. a. MYR 8. **Document type:** *Government.*
Former titles: Malaysia. Department of Statistics. Annual Statistical Bulletin Sarawak (0127-4732); (until 1971): Malaysia. Department of Statistics. Annual Bulletin of Statistics. State of Sarawak (0080-6439)
Published by: Department of Statistics/Jabatan Perangkaan, Jalan Cenderasari, Kuala Lumpur, 50514, Malaysia. TEL 60-3-294-4264, FAX 60-3-291-4535, http:// www.statistics.gov.my. **Dist. by:** Malaysia (Sarawak Branch), 5th Fl, Bangunan Tun Datuk, Patinggi Tuanku Hj. Bujang, Kuching, Sazawak 93514, Malaysia.

330 316 MLI
MALI. DIRECTION NATIONALE DE LA STATISTIQUE ET DE L'INFORMATIQUE. ANNUAIRE STATISTIQUE*. Text in English. 1962. a. price varies. index. **Document type:** *Government.*
Former titles: Mali. Service de la Statistique Generale, de la Comptabilite Nationale et de la Mecanographie. Annuaire Statistique (0076-3411); Supersedes (in 1962): Chambre de Commerce, d'Agriculture et d'Industrie de Bamako, Mali. Annuaire Statistique (0069-2522)
Related titles: Microfiche ed.: 1962 (from PQC).
Published by: Direction Nationale de la Statistique et de l'Informatique, BP 12, Bamako, Mali.

336 316 MLI
MALI. SERVICE DE LA STATISTIQUE GENERALE, DE LA COMPTABILITE NATIONALE ET DE LA MECANOGRAPHIE. STATISTIQUES DOUANIERES DU COMMERCE EXTERIEUR*. Text in French. irreg. **Document type:** *Government.*
Published by: Direction Nationale de la Statistique et de l'Informatique, BP 12, Bamako, Mali.

338.642021 RUS
MALOE PREDPRINIMATEL'STVO V ROSSII (YEAR). Text in Russian. a. RUR 165 per issue (effective 2005). **Document type:** *Yearbook, Government.*
Related titles: Online - full text ed.: RUR 177 (effective 2005).
Published by: Gosudarstvennyi Komitet Rossiiskoi Federatsii po Statistike/Federal State Statistics Office, ul Myasnitskaya 39, Moscow, 107450, Russian Federation. TEL 7-095-2074902, FAX 7-095-2074087, stat@gks.ru, http://www.gks.ru.

338 314 MLT ISSN 1027-4960
MALTA. CENTRAL OFFICE OF STATISTICS. INDUSTRY STATISTICS. Text in English. a. MTL 8. **Document type:** *Government.*
Former titles (until 1993): Malta. Central Office of Statistics. Industrial Statistics (1027-393X); Malta. Central Office of Statistics. Census of Industrial Production Report (0076-3462); Incorporates: Malta. Central Office of Statistics. Census of Industrial Production Summary Report; Malta. Central Office of Statistics. Census of Production Report
Published by: Central Office of Statistics, Auberge d'Italie, Merchants' St., Valletta, Malta. FAX 356-248483, cos@magnet.mt. **Subscr. to:** Publications Bookshop, Castille Place, Valletta, Malta.

330 MLT
MALTA'S ECONOMIC INDICATORS. Text in English. 1955. a. free. **Document type:** *Government.*
Formerly: Malta. Central Office of Statistics. Economic Trends
Published by: Central Office of Statistics, Auberge d'Italie, Merchants' St., Valletta, Malta. FAX 356-248483, cos@magnet.mt.

658.8 016 GBR ISSN 0308-2172
HD28
MANAGEMENT AND MARKETING ABSTRACTS. Text in English. 1972. m. GBP 699 in Europe; EUR 1,120, USD 1,050 elsewhere (effective 2005). bk.rev. abstr. index. back issues avail. **Document type:** *Journal, Abstract/Index.*
Formerly (until 1976): Marketing Abstracts (0307-0794)
Related titles: CD-ROM ed.: (from The Dialog Corporation); Online - full text ed.: (from Data-Star, G B I).
—BLDSC (5359.008800). **CCC.**
Published by: Pira International, Cleeve Rd, Leatherhead, Surrey KT22 7RU, United Kingdom. TEL 44-1372-802080, FAX 44-1372-802238, publications@pira.co.uk, http:// www.piranet.com/pira/p.asp?page=b.htm&ProductID=143. Pub., R&P Diana Deavin TEL 44-1372-802058.

016.658 GBR ISSN 1462-5873
HD28
MANAGEMENT BOOKS AND RESOURCES. Text in English. 1961. bi-m. EUR 11,221.38 in Europe; USD 11,229 in North America; AUD 13,479 in Australasia; GBP 7,860.22 in the UK & elsewhere (effective 2006). **Document type:** *Abstract/Index.* **Description:** Provides short evaluative reviews on management books and resources, searchable by ISBN, author, title, keywords, and subject classification.
Former titles (until 1998): Management Bibliographies and Reviews (0309-0582); (until 1988): Anbar Management Bibliography (0953-5713); (until 1987): Anbar Management Publications Bibliography (0261-0108); (until 1979): Anbar Maganement Services Bibliography (0003-2808); Incorporates: Business Education (0144-2813)
—CISTI. **CCC.**
Published by: Emerald Group Publishing Limited, 60-62 Toller Ln, Bradford, W Yorks BD8 9BY, United Kingdom. TEL 44-1274-777700, FAX 44-1274-785200, infomation@emeraldinsight.com, http:// www.emeraldinsight.com/. Ed. David Pollitt. **Subscr. in Australasia to:** Emerald Group Publishing Ltd., PO Box 1567, Toowong, QLD 4066, Australia. TEL 61-3870-7144, FAX 61-3870-4013; **Subscr. in N America to:** Emerald Group Publishing Ltd., 44 Brattle St, 4th Fl, Cambridge, MA 02138. TEL 617-497-2175, 888-622-0075, FAX 617-354-6875.

011.658 USA ISSN 1046-9524
MANAGEMENT CONSULTING*; annotated bibliography of selected references. Text in English. biennial. USD 45. **Document type:** *Bibliography.* **Description:** Disseminates information on where to find current published information covering the scope of management consulting.
Published by: Association of Management Consulting Firms, 380 Lexington Ave No.1699, New York, NY 10168-0002. TEL 212-697-9693.

330 GBR
MANAGEMENT OF QUALITY ABSTRACTS. (Also avail. as a section of: Emerald Management Reviews (print & online eds.)) Text in English. 1994. bi-m. EUR 2,198.72 in Europe; USD 1,909 in North America; AUD 2,409 in Australasia; GBP 1,539.88 in the UK & elsewhere (effective 2006). **Document type:** *Abstract/Index.* **Description:** Contains fully searchable independent abstracts of articles from top 400 international management journals on all aspects of quality. Abstracts are assessed, keyworded and indexed.
Formerly (until 2001): Anbar Management of Quality Abstracts (1351-3044)
Related titles: CD-ROM ed.; Online - full text ed.
—**CCC.**
Published by: Emerald Group Publishing Limited, 60-62 Toller Ln, Bradford, W Yorks BD8 9BY, United Kingdom. TEL 44-1274-777700, FAX 44-1274-785200, infomation@emeraldinsight.com, http:// www.emeraldinsight.com/. Ed. David Pollitt. **Subscr. in Australasia to:** Emerald Group Publishing Ltd., PO Box 1567, Toowong, QLD 4066, Australia. TEL 61-3870-7144, FAX 61-3870-4013; **Subscr. in N. America to:** Emerald Group Publishing Ltd., 44 Brattle St, 4th Fl, Cambridge, MA 02138. TEL 617-497-2175, 888-622-0075, FAX 617-354-6875.

658 DEU ISSN 0935-9915
➤ **MANAGEMENT REVUE**; the international review of management studies. Text in English. 1990. q. EUR 60 domestic; EUR 68 foreign (effective 2005). **Document type:** *Journal, Bibliography.*
Related titles: Online - full text ed.: (from EBSCO Publishing, ProQuest Information & Learning).
Indexed: ABIn, DIP, IBR, IBZ.
Published by: Rainer Hampp Verlag, Meringerzellerstr 10, Mering, 86415, Germany. TEL 49-8233-4783, FAX 49-8233-30755, Rainer_Hampp_Verlag@t-online.de, http://www.hampp-verlag.de/hampp_ZS03.htm. Eds. Richard Croucher, Rita Kellerman, Ruediger Kabst, Wenzel Matiaske. Pub. Rainer Hampp. **Dist. by:** Brockhaus Commission, Kreidlerstr 9, Kornwestheim 70806, Germany. TEL 49-7154-132739, FAX 49-7154-132713.

332.6 LUX
LE MARCHE DES EMPRUNTS OBLIGATAIRES EN FRANCS LUXEMBOURGEOIS/BOND MARKET IN LUXEMBOURG FRANCS. Text in English, French. 1984. a. free. **Description:** Contains statistical information on the bond market in LUF regarding listings, trading volume.
Supersedes in part: Bond Market in Luxembourg Francs and in E C U; Formed by the merger of: Marche des Emprunts Internationaux en E C U; Marche National des Emprunts Obligataires
Published by: Societe de la Bourse de Luxembourg/Luxembourg Stock Exchange, 11 av. de la Porte Neuve, BP 165, Luxembourg, L-2011, Luxembourg. TEL 352-4779361, FAX 352-473298, info@bourse.lu, http://www.bourse.lu. Circ: 600.

332.6 LUX
LE MARCHE EURO-OBLIGATAIRE EN E C U - STATISTIQUES MENSUELLES/EUROBOND MARKET IN E C U - MONTHLY STATISTICS. (European Currency Unit) Text in English, French. 1991. m. free. **Description:** Tracks the main trends of the E C U Eurobond market.
Formerly: E C U
Published by: Societe de la Bourse de Luxembourg/Luxembourg Stock Exchange, 11 av. de la Porte Neuve, BP 165, Luxembourg, L-2011, Luxembourg. TEL 352-4779361, FAX 352-473298, info@bourse.lu, http://www.bourse.lu. Circ: 250.

658.8 016 GBR
HF5415.2
MARKET RESEARCH ABSTRACTS (ONLINE EDITION). Text in English. 1963. a. price varies. reprints avail. **Document type:** *Abstract/Index.* **Description:** Covers all fields of marketing and advertising research, as well as relevant papers in statistics, psychology, economics, sociology and other fields relevant to market researchers.
Formerly (until 2000): Market Research Abstracts (Print) (0025-3596)
Related titles: Microfilm ed.: (from PQC).
—**CCC.**
Published by: Market Research Society, 15 Northburgh St, London, EC1V 0JR, United Kingdom. TEL 44-20-74904911, FAX 44-20-74900608, info@marketresearch.org.uk, http://www.warc.com, http://www.marketresearch.org.uk.

330 USA ISSN 1052-9578
HF5410
MARKET SHARE REPORTER; an annual compilation of reported market share data on companies, products, and services. Text in English. a., latest 2003. USD 475 (effective 2005). reprints avail.
Published by: Gale Group (Subsidiary of: Thomson Corporation), 27500 Drake Rd, Farmington Hills, MI 48331-3535. TEL 248-699-8061, 800-877-4253, FAX 248-699-4253, galeord@gale.com, http://www.gale.com. Ed. Arsen J Darnay.

016.6588 GBR ISSN 1462-5865
HF5415
MARKETING & LOGISTICS ABSTRACTS. (Also avail. as a section of: Emerald Management Reviews (print & online eds.)) Text in English. 1971. bi-m. EUR 6,497.88 in Europe; USD 6,119 in North America; AUD 3,979 in Australasia; GBP 4,554.88 in the UK & elsewhere (effective 2006). **Document type:** *Abstract/Index.* **Description:** Contains fully searchable, independent abstracts of articles from top 400 international management journals. Abstracts are keyworded, indexed and assessed.
Formerly (until 1999): Marketing & Distribution Abstracts (0305-0661)
Related titles: CD-ROM ed.; Online - full text ed.
—**CCC.**
Published by: (Chartered Institute of Marketing), Emerald Group Publishing Limited, 60-62 Toller Ln, Bradford, W Yorks BD8 9BY, United Kingdom. TEL 44-1274-777700, FAX 44-1274-785200, infomation@emeraldinsight.com, http://www.emeraldinsight.com/. Ed. David Pollitt. **Subscr. in Australasia to:** Emerald Group Publishing Ltd., PO Box 1567, Toowong, QLD 4066, Australia. TEL 61-3870-7144, FAX 61-3870-4013; **Subscr. in N America to:** Emerald Group Publishing Ltd., 44 Brattle St, 4th Fl, Cambridge, MA 02138. TEL 617-497-2175, 888-622-0075, FAX 617-354-6875.

658.8 GBR ISSN 0952-2581
MARKETSEARCH. Text in English. 1976. a. (plus q. updates). GBP 189 domestic; GBP 310 foreign (effective 2001). 700 p./no.; **Document type:** *Directory.* **Description:** Lists 25,000 published market research studies. Each listing includes title, a brief summary, countries covered, page count, price, date of publication, and author reference. Other sections include a publishers directory and a directory of report titles by author.
Formerly: International Directory of Published Market Research
Related titles: CD-ROM ed.: USD 310 (effective 2001); Online - full text ed.: USD 310 (effective 2001).
—BLDSC (5381.698600).
Published by: Arlington Management Publications Ltd., 1 Hay Hill, Berkeley Sq, London, WIJ 6DH, United Kingdom. TEL 44-20-7495-1940, FAX 44-20-7409-2557, marketsearch@execuplace.co.uk. Ed. Sara Peacock.

331.125 USA
MASSACHUSETTS. DEPARTMENT OF EMPLOYMENT AND TRAINING. EMPLOYMENT AND WAGES STATE SUMMARY. Text in English. 1970. a. free. **Document type:** *Government.*
Former titles: Massachusetts. Division of Employment Security. Employment and Wages in Establishments Subject to the Massachusetts Employment Security Law. State Summary (0076-4922); Massachusetts. Division of Employment Security. Employment and Wages in the Establishments Subject to the Massachusetts Employment Security Law. (0360-8301); Massachusetts. Division of Employment Security. Employment and Wages for the Year
Published by: Department of Employment and Training, Charles F Hurley Bldg, Government Center, Boston, MA 02114. TEL 617-727-6360. Circ: 700.

MATERIALS BUSINESS FILE. see *METALLURGY—Abstracting, Bibliographies, Statistics*

330.9 MUS ISSN 1013-6061
HA2305
MAURITIUS. CENTRAL STATISTICAL OFFICE. ANNUAL DIGEST OF STATISTICS. Text in English. 1966. a. MUR 100 per vol. (effective 2001). stat. **Document type:** *Government.* **Description:** Offers a summary of census statistics.

Former titles (until 1984): Mauritius. Central Statistical Office. Bi-Annual Digest of Statistics; Mauritius. Central Statistical Office. Quarterly Digest of Statistics; Mauritius. Central Statistical Office. Bi-Annual Digest of Statistics; Mauritius. Central Statistical Office. Quarterly Digest of Statistics (0025-6056)

Published by: Mauritius. Central Statistical Office, L.I.C. Centre, President John Kennedy St, Port Louis, Mauritius. TEL 230-212-2316, FAX 230-212-4150, cso@intnet.mu, http://statsmauritius.gov.mu. **Subscr. to:** Mauritius. Government Printing Office, Ramtoolah Bldg, Sir S Ramgoolam St, Port Louis, Mauritius. TEL 230-234-5294, 230-242-0234, FAX 230-234-5322.

330.9   MUS
MAURITIUS. CENTRAL STATISTICAL OFFICE. BUSINESS ACTIVITY STATISTICS. Text in English. 1997. a., latest 1997. MUR 50 per issue (effective 2001). charts. **Document type:** Government. **Description:** Provides a statistical economic review of business activities in Mauritius.

Published by: Mauritius. Central Statistical Office, L.I.C. Centre, President John Kennedy St, Port Louis, Mauritius. TEL 230-212-2316, FAX 230-212-4150, cso@intnet.mu, http://statsmauritius.gov.mu. **Subscr. to:** Mauritius. Government Printing Office, Ramtoolah Bldg, Sir S Ramgoolam St, Port Louis, Mauritius. TEL 230-234-5294, 230-242-0234, FAX 230-234-5322.

382   MUS
MAURITIUS. CENTRAL STATISTICAL OFFICE. DIGEST OF EXTERNAL TRADE STATISTICS. Text in English. 1977. a., latest 1999. MUR 100 per issue (effective 2001). charts. **Document type:** Government. **Description:** Provides a statistical overview of Mauritius's foreign trade.

Former titles (until 1998): Mauritius. Central Statistical Office. External Trade Statistics; (until 1989): Mauritius. Central Statistical Office. External Trade Statistics (Annual); (until 1986): Mauritius. Central Statistical Office. Quarterly External Trade Statistics; (until 1985): Mauritius. Central Statistical Office. External Trade Statistics

Published by: Mauritius. Central Statistical Office, L.I.C. Centre, President John Kennedy St, Port Louis, Mauritius. TEL 230-212-2316, FAX 230-212-4150, cso@intnet.mu, http://statsmauritius.gov.mu. **Subscr. to:** Mauritius. Government Printing Office, Ramtoolah Bldg, Sir S Ramgoolam St, Port Louis, Mauritius. TEL 230-234-5294, 230-242-0234, FAX 230-234-5322.

330.9   MUS
MAURITIUS. CENTRAL STATISTICAL OFFICE. DIGEST OF INDUSTRIAL STATISTICS. Text in English. 1984. a., latest 1997. MUR 75 per issue (effective 2001). charts. **Document type:** Government. **Description:** Contains latest available statistical information on the industrial sector. Topics covered include quarrying, manufacturing, electricity, gas and water, and construction.

Published by: Mauritius. Central Statistical Office, L.I.C. Centre, President John Kennedy St, Port Louis, Mauritius. TEL 230-212-2316, FAX 230-212-4150, cso@intnet.mu, http://statsmauritius.gov.mu. **Subscr. to:** Mauritius. Government Printing Office, Ramtoolah Bldg, Sir S Ramgoolam St, Port Louis, Mauritius. TEL 230-234-5294, 230-242-0234, FAX 230-234-5322.

331.021   MUS
MAURITIUS. CENTRAL STATISTICAL OFFICE. DIGEST OF LABOUR STATISTICS. Text in English. 1966. a., latest 2000. MUR 100 per issue (effective 2001). charts. **Document type:** Government.

Formerly (until 1992): Mauritius. Central Statistical Office. Bi-annual Survey of Employment and Earnings (1013-6053)

Published by: Mauritius. Central Statistical Office, L.I.C. Centre, President John Kennedy St, Port Louis, Mauritius. TEL 230-212-2316, FAX 230-212-4150, cso@intnet.mu, http://statsmauritius.gov.mu. **Subscr. to:** Mauritius. Government Printing Office, Ramtoolah Bldg, Sir S Ramgoolam St, Port Louis, Mauritius. TEL 230-234-5294, 230-242-0234, FAX 230-234-5322.

330.9   MUS
MAURITIUS. CENTRAL STATISTICAL OFFICE. DIGEST OF PRODUCTIVITY AND COMPETITIVENESS STATISTICS. Text in English. 1997. a., latest 1999. MUR 100 per issue (effective 2001). charts. **Document type:** Government. **Description:** Offers a statistical overview of the economic productivity and business competitiveness of the economy and industry of Mauritius for the past 15 years.

Formerly (until 1997): Mauritius. Central Statistical Office. Productivity and Competitiveness Indicators

Published by: Mauritius. Central Statistical Office, L.I.C. Centre, President John Kennedy St, Port Louis, Mauritius. TEL 230-212-2316, FAX 230-212-4150, cso@intnet.mu, http://statsmauritius.gov.mu. **Subscr. to:** Mauritius. Government Printing Office, Ramtoolah Bldg, Sir S Ramgoolam St, Port Louis, Mauritius. TEL 230-234-5294, 230-242-0234, FAX 230-234-5322.

336   MUS
MAURITIUS. CENTRAL STATISTICAL OFFICE. DIGEST OF PUBLIC FINANCE STATISTICS. Text in English. 1988. a., latest 2000. MUR 50 per issue (effective 2001). charts. **Document type:** Government. **Description:** Provides an overview of all aspects of public finance in Mauritius.

Published by: Mauritius. Central Statistical Office, L.I.C. Centre, President John Kennedy St, Port Louis, Mauritius. TEL 230-212-2316, FAX 230-212-4150, cso@intnet.mu, http://statsmauritius.gov.mu. **Subscr. to:** Mauritius. Government Printing Office, Ramtoolah Bldg, Sir S Ramgoolam St, Port Louis, Mauritius. TEL 230-234-5294, 230-242-0234, FAX 230-234-5322.

330.9   MUS
MAURITIUS. CENTRAL STATISTICAL OFFICE. HOUSING AND POPULATION CENSUS. CENSUS OF ECONOMIC ACTIVITIES (YEAR). Text in English. decennial. MUR 100 per vol. (effective 2001). charts. **Document type:** Government. **Description:** Assesses the economic activity of Mauritius.

Related titles: Series: Mauritius. Central Statistical Office. Housing and Population Census. Census of Economic Activities. Vol 1: Small Establishments and Itinerant Units. MUR 100 per issue (effective 2001); Mauritius. Central Statistical Office. Housing and Population Census. Census of Economic Activities. Vol 2: Large Establishments. MUR 100 per issue (effective 2001).

Published by: Mauritius. Central Statistical Office, L.I.C. Centre, President John Kennedy St, Port Louis, Mauritius. TEL 230-212-2316, FAX 230-212-4150, cso@intnet.mu, http://statsmauritius.gov.mu. **Subscr. to:** Mauritius. Government Printing Office, Ramtoolah Bldg, Sir S Ramgoolam St, Port Louis, Mauritius. TEL 230-234-5294, 230-242-0234, FAX 230-234-5322.

381   MUS
MAURITIUS. CENTRAL STATISTICAL OFFICE. NATIONAL ACCOUNTS OF MAURITIUS. Text in English. 1983. a., latest 2000. MUR 100 per issue (effective 2001). charts. **Document type:** Government. **Description:** Provides a statistical overview of the public finances of the government of Mauritius.

Published by: Mauritius. Central Statistical Office, L.I.C. Centre, President John Kennedy St, Port Louis, Mauritius. TEL 230-212-2316, FAX 230-212-4150, cso@intnet.mu, http://statsmauritius.gov.mu. **Subscr. to:** Mauritius. Government Printing Office, Ramtoolah Bldg, Sir S Ramgoolam St, Port Louis, Mauritius. TEL 230-234-5294, 230-242-0234, FAX 230-234-5322.

330.9   MUS
MAURITIUS. CENTRAL STATISTICAL OFFICE. STATISTICS ON RODRIGUES. Text in English. 1994. a., latest 2000. MUR 30 per issue (effective 2001). charts. **Document type:** Government. **Description:** Provides a statistical overview of the economic situation for the island of Rodrigues.

Formerly: Mauritius. Central Statistical Office. Abstract of Statistical Data on Rodrigues

Published by: Mauritius. Central Statistical Office, L.I.C. Centre, President John Kennedy St, Port Louis, Mauritius. TEL 230-212-2316, FAX 230-212-4150, cso@intnet.mu, http://statsmauritius.gov.mu. **Subscr. to:** Mauritius. Government Printing Office, Ramtoolah Bldg, Sir S Ramgoolam St, Port Louis, Mauritius. TEL 230-234-5294, 230-242-0234, FAX 230-208-5322.

657   USA
MEMBER FIRM CONFIDENTIAL STATISTICS REPORT✶ . Text in English. irreg. **Document type:** Bulletin.

Published by: American Group of C P A Firms, 17W662 Butterfield Rd., Ste. 303, Oakbrook Terrace, IL 60181-4006. TEL 708-916-0300.

330   BRA   ISSN 1021-7398
HC161
MERCOSUL: SINOPSE ESTATISTICA/MERCOSUR: SINOPSIS ESTADISTICA. Text in Portuguese. 1993. biennial. price varies. back issues avail. **Document type:** Government. **Description:** Provides information on the main characteristics of the population, housing, labor force, and economic affairs. Provides analysis of Latin American integration.

Published by: Fundacao Instituto Brasileiro de Geografia e Estatistica, Rua General Canabarro 666, Bloco B, Maracana, Rio de Janeiro, RJ 20271201, Brazil. TEL 55-21-2645424, FAX 55-21-2841959, http://www.ibge.gov.br.

330.98   ARG
MERCOSUR; sinopsis estadistica. Text in Portuguese, Spanish. 1993. irreg., latest vol.2, 1996. ARS 55, USD 70. **Document type:** Government. **Description:** Covers economics, demography, foreign trade and related issues.

Related titles: CD-ROM ed.

Published by: Instituto Nacional de Estadistica y Censos, Avda. Presidente Julio A. Roca, 615 P B, Capital Federal, Buenos Aires 1067, Argentina. TEL 54-114-3499662, FAX 54-114-3499621, ces@indec.mecon.ar, http://www.indec.mecon.ar.

310 332.6   USA   ISSN 1527-4683
HG4961
MERGENT'S INDUSTRY REVIEW. Text in English. 1978. s-a. USD 675 (effective 1999). stat. **Description:** Covers comparative statistics and rankings of 3,000 leading corporations in 137 industry groups.

Former titles (until 1999): Moody's Industry Review (1047-3114); (until 1989): Moody's Investors Industry Review (1062-7685); (until 1984): Moody's Investors Fact Sheet: Industry Review —CCC.

Published by: Mergent, 5250 77 Center Dr, Ste 150, Charlotte, NC 28217. customerservice@mergent.com, http://www.mergent.com.

MEXICO. COMISION NACIONAL BANCARIA. BOLETIN ESTADISTICO. see BUSINESS AND ECONOMICS—Banking And Finance

330   MEX
MEXICO DATA BANK/MEXICO BANCO DE DATOS. Text in English, Spanish. 1982. a. USD 298 in North America; USD 330 elsewhere. **Document type:** Trade. **Description:** Yearbook on Mexican economy and finances for business and research purposes.

Published by: Inversionista Mexicano S.A. de C.V., FELIX CUEVAS 301-204, Col Del Valle, Deleg. Benito Juarez, Mexico City, DF 03100, Mexico. TEL 52-5-524-3131, FAX 52-5-5243794. Ed., R&P Hugo Ortiz Dietz. Pub. Ruben Sanchez Crespo. Circ: 1,200 (paid).

338 318   MEX   ISSN 0186-0488
HC131
MEXICO. INSTITUTO NACIONAL DE ESTADISTICA, GEOGRAFIA E INFORMATICA. ENCUESTA INDUSTRIAL MENSUAL; 129 clases de actividad. Text in Spanish. 1964. m. MXP 45 (effective 1999). charts. **Document type:** Government.

Formerly (until 1978): Mexico. Direccion General de Estadistica. Estadistica Industrial Mensual

Published by: Instituto Nacional de Estadistica, Geografia e Informatica, Secretaria de Programacion y Presupuesto, Prol. Heroe de Nacozari 2301 Sur, Puerta 11, Acceso, Aguascalientes, 20270, Mexico. TEL 52-4-918-1948, FAX 52-4-918-0739, http://www.inegi.gob.mx.

MEXICO. INSTITUTO NACIONAL DE ESTADISTICA, GEOGRAFIA E INFORMATICA. ENCUESTA NACIONAL DE EDUCACION CAPACITACION Y EMPLEO. see EDUCATION—Abstracting, Bibliographies, Statistics

330.9   ANT
MODUS STATISTISCH MAGAZINE. Text and summaries in Dutch. 1979; N.S. 1995. q. ANG 25. **Document type:** Government.

Formerly (until 1995): Economisch Profiel Nederlandse Antillen

Published by: Central Bureau of Statistics, Fort Amsterdam z/n, Willemstad, Curacao, Netherlands Antilles. TEL 599-9-4611031, FAX 599-9-4611696, cbscur@ibm.net. Ed. F Vierbergen. Pub., R&P Harely Martina. Circ: 450.

382.7   CHE   ISSN 0251-6438
MONTHLY COMMODITY PRICE BULLETIN. Text in English. 1970. a. **Document type:** Bulletin, Trade. **Description:** Covers monthly and annual average price data on forty six commodities, encompassing food, tropical beverages, vegetable oilseeds and oils, agricultural raw materials, minerals, ores and metals.

Published by: United Nations Conference on Trade and Development, 8-14 Avenue de la Paix, Geneva 10, 1211, Switzerland. TEL 41-22-9174924, FAX 41-22-9070195, info@unctad.org, http://www.unctad.org.

315 330.9   BGD
MONTHLY INDICATORS OF CURRENT ECONOMIC SITUATION OF BANGLADESH. Text in English. 1974. m. BDT 480, USD 120. **Document type:** Government. **Description:** Economic trends, such as money and banking, foreign aid and trade protocols, agriculture and the food situation in Bangladesh.

Formed by the merger of: Monthly Economic Situation of Bangladesh; Monthly Economic Indicators of Bangladesh; Which was formerly: Economic Indicators of Bangladesh; Quarterly Economic Indicators of Bangladesh

Published by: Bureau of Statistics, Secretariat, Dhaka, 2, Bangladesh. Circ: 250.

382 315   IND   ISSN 0027-0547
MONTHLY STATISTICS OF FOREIGN TRADE OF INDIA. Text in English. 1957. m. (in 2 vols). INR 1,160, USD 417.60. stat. **Document type:** Government.

Published by: Government of India, Department of Publications, Civil Lines, New Delhi, 110 054, India. Circ: 6,181.

382   FRA   ISSN 1607-0623
MONTHLY STATISTICS OF INTERNATIONAL TRADE/STATISTIQUES MENSUELLES DU COMMERCE INTERNATIONAL. Text in English, French. 1974. m. EUR 297, USD 341, GBP 195, JPY 40,100 (effective 2005). **Description:** Shows the trade of individual OECD member countries and main country groupings with most of their partner countries.

▼ *new title*   ➤ *refereed*   ✶ *unverified*   ◆ *full entry avail.*

Former titles (until 1999): O E C D Monthly Statistics of Foreign Trade Series A (0256-1743); (until 1982): Statistics of Foreign Trade. Series A (0474-5388)
Related titles: Online - full content ed.: ISSN 1609-7343. EUR 208, USD 239, GBP 136, JPY 28,100 (effective 2005); Online - full text ed.: (from EBSCO Publishing, Gale Group, IngentaConnect, O C L C Online Computer Library Center, Inc., Swets Information Services).
Indexed: IIS, RASB.
—CISTI, IE.
Published by: Organization for Economic Cooperation and Development, 2 Rue Andre Pascal, Paris, 75775 Cedex 16, France. TEL 33-1-45248200, FAX 33-1-45248500, http://www.oecd.org/std/its. **Subscr. in N. America to:** O E C D Turpin North America, PO Box 194, Downingtown, PA 19335-0194. TEL 610-524-5361, 800-456-6323, FAX 610-524-5417, journalscustomer@turpinna.com.

382 MSR
MONTSERRAT. STATISTICS OFFICE. DIGEST OF STATISTICS. Text in English. 1975 (no.2). a. USD 10. **Document type:** *Government.*
Formerly: Montserrat. Statistics Office. Digest of Overseas Trade Statistics
Published by: Statistics Office, Government Headquarters, Plymouth, Montserrat.

338 MAR ISSN 0851-0954
MOROCCO. DIRECTION DE LA STATISTIQUE. INDICE DES PRIX A LA PRODUCTION INDUSTRIELLE, ENERGETIQUE ET MINIERE. Text in Arabic, French. q. MAD 165 for all 3 Indices (effective 2000). **Document type:** *Government.*
Published by: Morocco. Direction de la Statistique, B P 178, Rabat, Morocco. TEL 212-7-77-36-06, FAX 212-7-77-32-17.

338 MAR ISSN 0851-0970
HB235.M68
MOROCCO. DIRECTION DE LA STATISTIQUE. INDICE DES PRIX DE GROS. Text in Arabic, French. m. MAD 165 for all 3 Indices (effective 2000). **Document type:** *Government.*
Published by: Morocco. Direction de la Statistique, B P 178, Rabat, Morocco. TEL 212-7-77-36-06, FAX 212-7-77-32-17.

338 MAR ISSN 1113-2175
MOROCCO. DIRECTION DE LA STATISTIQUE. INDICE DU COUT DE LA VIE. Text in Arabic, French. m. MAD 165 (effective 2000). **Document type:** *Government.*
Related titles: Microfiche ed.
Published by: Morocco. Direction de la Statistique, B P 178, Rabat, Morocco. TEL 212-7-77-36-06, FAX 212-7-77-32-17.

382 MOZ
MOZAMBIQUE. INSTITUTO NACIONAL DE ESTATISTICA. ESTATISTICAS DO COMERCIO EXTERNO. Text in Portuguese. a.
Published by: Instituto Nacional de Estatistica, Av Ahmed Sekou Toure 21, Maputo, Mozambique. TEL 258-1-491054, FAX 258-1-493547, info@ine.gov.mz, http://www.ine.gov.mz.

338 MOZ
MOZAMBIQUE. INSTITUTO NACIONAL DE ESTATISTICA. ESTATISTICAS INDUSTRIAIS. Text in Portuguese. a.
Published by: Instituto Nacional de Estatistica, Av Ahmed Sekou Toure 21, Maputo, Mozambique. TEL 258-1-491054, FAX 258-1-493547, info@ine.gov.mz, http://www.ine.gov.mz.

330 MOZ
MOZAMBIQUE. INSTITUTO NACIONAL DE ESTATISTICA. INDICE DE PREPRECOS AO CONSUMIDOR. Text in Portuguese. m.
Published by: Instituto Nacional de Estatistica, Av Ahmed Sekou Toure 21, Maputo, Mozambique. TEL 258-1-491054, FAX 258-1-493547, info@ine.gov.mz, http://www.ine.gov.mz.

330 016 620 HUN ISSN 0238-9878
MUSZAKI-GAZDASAGI MAGAZIN/TECHNICAL ECONOMIC DIGEST. Text in Hungarian; Contents page in English, Russian, German. 1960. m. HUF 6,000, USD 100. adv. bk.rev. charts; illus.; mkt. index.
Formerly (until 1989): Muszaki-Gazdasagi Tajekoztato (0027-4933)
Indexed: RASB.
Published by: Orszagos Muszaki Informacios Kozpont es Konyvtar/National Technical Information Centre and Library, Muzeum utca 17, PO Box 12, Budapest, 1428, Hungary. Ed. Schonviszkyne Anna Galdi. Circ: 1,400. **Subscr. to:** Kultura, PO Box 149, Budapest 1389, Hungary.

N A B E INDUSTRY SURVEY. see *BUSINESS AND ECONOMICS—Economic Situation And Conditions*

N A B E OUTLOOK & POLICY SURVEY. see *BUSINESS AND ECONOMICS—Economic Situation And Conditions*

650 330 016 USA ISSN 1074-1674
N T I S ALERTS: BUSINESS & ECONOMICS. Text in English. s-m. USD 241.50 in North America; USD 316.25 elsewhere (effective 2005). index. back issues avail. **Document type:** *Newsletter, Bibliography.* **Description:** Contains summaries of the latest Governement sponsored projects and their findings. Covers banking and finance, consumer affairs, domestic commerce, marketing, and economics.
Former titles: Abstract Newsletter: Business and Economics; Weekly Abstract Newsletter: Business and Economics; Weekly Government Abstracts. Business and Economics (0364-7978)
Related titles: Microform ed.: (from NTI).
Published by: U.S. Department of Commerce, National Technical Information Service, 5285 Port Royal Rd, Springfield, VA 22161. TEL 703-605-6000, info@ntis.gov, http://www.ntis.gov.

330 322 FRA ISSN 0256-758X
HC79.I5
NATIONAL ACCOUNTS OF O E C D COUNTRIES. VOLUME 1 MAIN AGGREGATES/COMPTES NATIONAUX DES PAYS DE L'O C D E. VOLUME I. Key Title: National Accounts. Main Aggregates. O E C D Department of Economics and Statistics. Text in French. 1969. a. price varies. **Document type:** *Monographic series.* **Description:** Covers expenditure-based GDP, output-based GDP, income-based GDP, disposable income, saving and net lending, population and employment. It also includes comparative tables based on exchange rates and purchasing power parities.
Supersedes in part (in 1976): National Accounts of O E C D Countries (0304-3401)
Related titles: CD-ROM ed.; Online - full content ed.; ♦ Series of: National Accounts of O E C D Countries.
Indexed: IIS.
Published by: Organization for Economic Cooperation and Development, 2 Rue Andre Pascal, Paris, 75775 Cedex 16, France. TEL 33-1-45248200, FAX 33-1-45248500, http://www.oecd.org. **Dist. in N. America by:** O E C D Turpin North America, PO Box 194, Downingtown, PA 19335-0194. TEL 610-524-5361, 800-456-6323, FAX 610-524-5417, bookscustomer@turpinna.com.

330 322 FRA ISSN 0256-7571
HC79.I5
NATIONAL ACCOUNTS OF O E C D COUNTRIES. VOLUME 2 DETAILED TABLES. Key Title: National Accounts. Detailed Tables. O E C D Department of Economics and Statistics. Text in French. 1969. a. price varies. **Document type:** *Monographic series.*
Supersedes in part (in 1976): National Accounts of O E C D Countries (0304-3401)
Related titles: CD-ROM ed.; Online - full content ed.; ♦ Series of: National Accounts of O E C D Countries.
Indexed: IIS.
Published by: Organization for Economic Cooperation and Development, 2 Rue Andre Pascal, Paris, 75775 Cedex 16, France. TEL 33-1-45248200, FAX 33-1-45248500, http://www.oecd.org. **Dist. in N. America by:** O E C D Turpin North America, PO Box 194, Downingtown, PA 19335-0194. TEL 610-524-5361, 800-456-6323, FAX 610-524-5417, bookscustomer@turpinna.com.

336 MLT ISSN 0077-295X
NATIONAL ACCOUNTS OF THE MALTESE ISLANDS. Text in English. 1957. a. MTL 4.50. **Document type:** *Government.*
Published by: Central Office of Statistics, Auberge d'Italie, Merchants' St., Valletta, Malta. FAX 356-248483, cos@magent.mt. **Subscr. to:** Publications Bookshop, Castille Place, Valletta, Malta.

657.75 331.252 GBR ISSN 0269-011X
NATIONAL ASSOCIATION OF PENSION FUNDS. ANNUAL SURVEY OF OCCUPATIONAL PENSION SCHEMES. Text in English. 1975. a. GBP 125 to non-members; GBP 75 to members (effective 2000). **Document type:** *Bulletin.* **Description:** Provides a source of statistics on occupational pension plans in the UK including contributions, benefits, investments and other topical issues.
Formerly (until 1981): National Association of Pension Funds. Annual Survey (0309-0078)
—BLDSC (1534.918000), IE, ingenta.
Published by: National Association of Pension Funds, NIOC House, 4 Victoria St, London, SW1H 0NE, United Kingdom. TEL 020 7808 1300, FAX 020 7222 7585, http://www.napf.co.uk. Ed. Mike Brown.

657.75 331.252 GBR ISSN 0144-2589
NATIONAL ASSOCIATION OF PENSION FUNDS. YEAR BOOK. Text in English. 1979. a. GBP 65 to non-members; GBP 35 to members (effective 2000). **Document type:** *Directory.* **Description:** Provides information on the NAPF and its members including a breakdown of the largest UK funds.
Related titles: Online - full text ed.: (may not contain a full list of members).
Published by: National Association of Pension Funds, NIOC House, 4 Victoria St, London, SW1H 0NE, United Kingdom. TEL 44-171-730-0585, FAX 44-171-730-2595, http://www.napf.co.uk. Ed. Sheila Longley. Circ: 4,000.

330.9021 CAN ISSN 0825-9216
NATIONAL BALANCE SHEET ACCOUNTS. Text in Multiple languages. 1984. a.
Related titles: Diskette ed.: ISSN 1498-8437. 1994.
—CISTI.
Published by: (Statistics Canada, National Accounts and Environment Division), Statistics Canada, Publications Sales and Services, Ottawa, ON K1A 0T6, Canada. TEL 613-951-8116, 800-267-6677, infostats@statcan.ca, http://www.statcan.ca.

338.4 USA
NATIONAL HOUSEWARES MANUFACTURERS ASSOCIATION. STATE OF THE INDUSTRY REPORT. Text in English. a. USD 200 (effective 1995).
Supersedes: Marketing Research Study of the Housewares Industry
Published by: National Housewares Manufacturers Association, 6400 Shafer Ct., Ste. 650, Rosemont, IL 60018-4914. TEL 847-292-4200, FAX 847-292-4211, http://www.housewares.org. Pub. Philip Brandle. R&P Debora Teschele TEL 847-692-0110.

339 315 THA
NATIONAL INCOME OF THAILAND. Text in English, Thai. 1964. a. free. charts. **Document type:** *Government.*
Formerly: National Income Statistics of Thailand (0077-4723)
Published by: National Economic and Social Development Board, National Accounts Division, Office of the Prime Minister, Bangkok, 10100, Thailand. TEL 662-2829156, FAX 662-2810946.

330.9021 RUS
NATSIONAL'NYE SCHETA ROSSII. Text in Russian. a. RUR 330 per issue (effective 2005). **Document type:** *Yearbook, Government.*
Related titles: Online - full text ed.: RUR 354 (effective 2005).
Published by: Gosudarstvennyi Komitet Rossiiskoi Federatsii po Statistike/Federal State Statistics Office, ul Myasnitskaya 39, Moscow, 107450, Russian Federation. TEL 7-095-2074902, FAX 7-095-2074087, stat@gks.ru, http://www.gks.ru.

330 NPL
NEPAL BANK LIMITED. TATHYANK BIBARAN. Text in Nepali. s-a.
Published by: Nepal Bank Limited, Dharma Path, Kathmandu, Nepal.

016 338.9 NPL
NEPAL DOCUMENTATION; occasional bibliography. Text in English, Nepali. 1972. irreg. NPR 10, USD 4. index. back issues avail. **Document type:** *Bibliography.*
Published by: Centre for Economic Development and Administration, Publications and Information Services Division, Kirtipur Campus, P O Box 797, Kathmandu, Nepal.

338.9 315 NPL ISSN 0077-6564
NEPAL INDUSTRIAL DEVELOPMENT CORPORATION. STATISTICAL ABSTRACTS. Text in English. irreg.
Published by: Nepal Industrial Development Corporation, N.I.D.C. Bldg., Durbar Marg, P O Box 10, Kathmandu, Nepal.

330.021 NLD ISSN 1385-2434
HD2870
NETHERLANDS. CENTRAAL BUREAU VOOR DE STATISTIEK. BEDRIJVEN IN NEDERLAND (YEAR). Key Title: Bedrijven in Nederland. Text in Dutch. 1996. a. EUR 11.35 per vol. (effective 2000). **Description:** Affords a comprehensive statistical picture of Dutch corporate life and management.
Formed by the merger of (1992-1995): Netherlands. Centraal Bureau voor de Statistiek. Bedrijfstelling. Bedrijven tot 10 Werkzame Personen (0928-4818); (1988-1995): Netherlands. Centraal Bureau voor de Statistiek. Sector Waarnemingsmethodologie (0924-3372); Which superseded (1985-1988): Netherlands. Centraal Bureau voor de Statistiek. Statistiek van het Ondernemingen- en Vestingenbestand (0169-1619)
Published by: Centraal Bureau voor de Statistiek, Prinses Beatrixlaan 428, PO Box 4000, Voorburg, 2270 JM, Netherlands. TEL 31-70-3373800, FAX 31-70-3877429, infoservice@cbs.nl, http://www.cbs.nl.

330.121 304.621 339.2221 NLD ISSN 0168-3985
NETHERLANDS. CENTRAAL BUREAU VOOR DE STATISTIEK. BUDGETONDERZOEK. KERNCIJFERS (YEAR). Key Title: Budgetonderzoek. Kerncijfers (Year). Text in Dutch. 1978. a. charts. **Document type:** *Government.* **Description:** Conducts statistical reserach on household budgets.
Related titles: ♦ Supplement(s): Netherlands. Centraal Bureau voor de Statistiek. Gebruikershandboek Budgetonderzoek, Methodologie: Enquetedocumenten. ISSN 1385-9528.
—KNAW.
Published by: Centraal Bureau voor de Statistiek, Prinses Beatrixlaan 428, PO Box 4000, Voorburg, 2270 JM, Netherlands. TEL 31-70-3373800, FAX 31-70-3877429, infoservice@cbs.nl, http://www.cbs.nl.

330.121 304.621 339.2221 NLD ISSN 1385-9528
NETHERLANDS. CENTRAAL BUREAU VOOR DE STATISTIEK. GEBRUIKERSHANDBOEK BUDGETONDERZOEK, METHODOLOGIE: ENQUETEDOCUMENTEN. Key Title: Gebruikershandboek Budgetonderzoek. Text in Dutch. 1992. a. charts. **Document type:** *Government.* **Description:** Outlines the methodology the Netherlands Central Bureau for Statistics used to compile data for research on household budgets - income and expenditures.

Related titles: ♦ Supplement to: Netherlands. Centraal Bureau voor de Statistiek. Budgetonderzoek. Kerncijfers (Year). ISSN 0168-3985.
—KNAW.
Published by: Centraal Bureau voor de Statistiek, Prinses Beatrixlaan 428, PO Box 4000, Voorburg, 2270 JM, Netherlands. TEL 31-70-3373800, FAX 31-70-3877429, infoservice@cbs.nl, http://www.cbs.nl.

NETHERLANDS. CENTRAAL BUREAU VOOR DE STATISTIEK. INDEX, FEITEN EN CIJFERS OVER ONZE SAMENLEVING. see *POPULATION STUDIES—Abstracting, Bibliographies, Statistics*

330.921 NLD ISSN 1386-8136
NETHERLANDS. CENTRAAL BUREAU VOOR DE STATISTIEK. JAARBOEK WELVAARTSVERDELING. Key Title: Jaarboek Welvaartsverdeling. Text in Dutch. 1990. a. EUR 30.18 (effective 1999). charts. **Document type:** *Government.* **Description:** Offers accessibly presented fundamentals of the incomes and expenditures of Dutch households with one or two wage earners.
Formerly (until 1997): Netherlands. Centraal Bureau voor de Statistiek. Jaarboek Inkomen en Consumptie (0925-2681)
Published by: Centraal Bureau voor de Statistiek, Prinses Beatrixlaan 428, PO Box 4000, Voorburg, 2270 JM, Netherlands. TEL 31-70-3373800, FAX 31-70-3877429, infoservice@cbs.nl, http://www.cbs.nl.

NETHERLANDS. CENTRAAL BUREAU VOOR DE STATISTIEK. JEUGD: FEITEN EN CIJFERS. see *POPULATION STUDIES—Abstracting, Bibliographies, Statistics*

336 NLD ISSN 0168-3489
HG186.N4
NETHERLANDS. CENTRAAL BUREAU VOOR DE STATISTIEK. NATIONALE REKENINGEN/NETHERLANDS. CENTRAL BUREAU OF STATISTICS. NATIONAL ACCOUNTS. Text in Dutch, English. 1948. a. **Document type:** *Government.*
Published by: Centraal Bureau voor de Statistiek, Prinses Beatrixlaan 428, PO Box 4000, Voorburg, 2270 JM, Netherlands. TEL 31-70-3373800, FAX 31-70-3877429, infoservice@cbs.nl, http://www.cbs.nl. **Orders to:** Sdu Uitgevers bv, Christoffel Plantijnstraat 2, The Hague 2500 EA, Netherlands.

NETHERLANDS. CENTRAAL BUREAU VOOR DE STATISTIEK. SOCIAAL-ECONOMISCHE TRENDS. see *SOCIAL SERVICES AND WELFARE—Abstracting, Bibliographies, Statistics*

332.021 NLD ISSN 0921-5999
NETHERLANDS. CENTRAAL BUREAU VOOR DE STATISTIEK. STATISTIEK FINANCIEN VAN ONDERNEMINGEN. Key Title: Statistiek Financien van Ondernemingen. Text in Dutch. 1988. a. EUR 15.88 per vol. (effective 2000). charts. **Document type:** *Government.* **Description:** Gives a fairly detailed insight into the financial structure and profitability of a range of Dutch enterprises.
Formed by the merger of (1980-1987): Netherlands. Centraal Bureau voor de Statistiek. Statistiek Financien van Ondernemingen Nijverheid (0168-5147); (1986-1987): Netherlands. Centraal Bureau voor de Statistiek. Statistiek Financien van Ondernemingen, Handel, Transport en Dienstverlening (0169-8583); Which superseded (1984-1986): Netherlands. Centraal Bureau voor de Statistiek. Statistiek Financien van Ondernemingen Handel (0168-8405)
Published by: Centraal Bureau voor de Statistiek, Prinses Beatrixlaan 428, PO Box 4000, Voorburg, 2270 JM, Netherlands. TEL 31-70-3373800, FAX 31-70-3877429, infoservice@cbs.nl, http://www.cbs.nl.

304.021 NLD ISSN 0166-9680
HA1381
NETHERLANDS. CENTRAAL BUREAU VOOR DE STATISTIEK. STATISTISCH BULLETIN. Text in Dutch. 1976. w. charts. **Document type:** *Government.* **Description:** Presents the most recently available information from Statistics Netherlands, displayed in tables, graphs, and text.
Related titles: ♦ Supplement(s): Jaar in Cijfers (Year). ISSN 0927-4634.
—IE, Infotrieve.
Published by: Centraal Bureau voor de Statistiek, Prinses Beatrixlaan 428, PO Box 4000, Voorburg, 2270 JM, Netherlands. TEL 31-70-3373800, FAX 31-70-3877429, infoserv@cbs.nl, http://www.cbs.nl. Circ: 3,500.

330 310 NCL
HC684.5.A1
NEW CALEDONIA. INSTITUT DE LA STATISTIQUE ET DES ETUDES ECONOMIQUES. POINT ECONOMIQUE. Text in French. 1983. q. abstr.; charts; stat. 4 p./no.; **Document type:** *Directory, Government.*
Formerly (until 1992): New Caledonia. Institut Territorial de la Statistique et des Etudes Economiques. Bulletin de Conjoncture (0757-9888)
Published by: Institut de la Statistique et des Etudes Economiques, BP 823, Noumea, 98845, New Caledonia. TEL 687-283156, FAX 687-288148, dp@itsee.nc, http://www.isee.nc/. Ed. Gerard Baudchon.

330 310 NCL ISSN 1623-1945
HC684.5.Z9
NEW CALEDONIA. INSTITUT DE LA STATISTIQUE ET DES ETUDES ECONOMIQUES. TABLEAUX DE L'ECONOMIE CALEDONIENNE. Short title: T E C. Text in French. 3/yr. price varies. abstr.; charts; illus.; bibl.; maps; stat. 256 p./no.; **Document type:** *Directory, Government.*
Incorporates: New Caledonia. Institut Territorial de la Statistique et des Etudes Economiques. Annuaires Statistiques
Related titles: English ed.
Published by: Institut de la Statistique et des Etudes Economiques, BP 823, Noumea, 98845, New Caledonia, TEL 687-283156, FAX 687-288148. Ed. Gerard Baudchon.

330 310 NCL ISSN 0988-3215
HD9715.N36
NEW CALEDONIA. INSTITUT TERRITORIAL DE LA STATISTIQUE ET DES ETUDES ECONOMIQUES. INDICES DES PRIX A LA CONSOMMATION. Short title: I P C. Text in French. 1982. m. charts; illus. 22 p./no.; **Document type:** *Directory, Government.*
Formerly (until 1989): New Caledonia. Institut Territorial de la Statistique et des Etudes Economiques. Indice Mensuel des Prix de Detail a la Consommation des Menages (0758-0339)
Published by: Institut de la Statistique et des Etudes Economiques, BP 823, Noumea, 98845, New Caledonia. TEL 687-283156, FAX 687-288148, dp@itsee.nc, http://www.isee.nc/. Ed. Gerard Baudochon.

331.21 GBR ISSN 0262-0510
NEW EARNINGS SURVEY. PART B: ANALYSES BY AGREEMENT. Text in English. 1970. a. **Document type:** *Government.*
Supersedes in part (in 1975): Great Britain. Department of Employment. New Earnings Survey (0308-1419)
Published by: Office for National Statistics, Government Offices, Rm 65c-3, Great George St, London, SW1P 3AQ, United Kingdom. TEL 44-171-270-6081, FAX 44-171-270-6019. **Dist. by:** Her Majesty's Stationery Office Publications Centre. TEL 44-171-873-9090, FAX 44-171-873-8200.

331.21 GBR ISSN 0262-0537
NEW EARNINGS SURVEY. PART D: ANALYSES BY OCCUPATION. Text in English. 1970. a. **Document type:** *Government.*
Supersedes in part (in 1975): Great Britain. Department of Employment. New Earnings Survey (0308-1419)
Published by: Office for National Statistics, Government Offices, Rm 65c-3, Great George St, London, SW1P 3AQ, United Kingdom. TEL 44-171-270-6081, FAX 44-171-270-6019. **Dist. by:** Her Majesty's Stationery Office Publications Centre. TEL 44-171-873-9090, FAX 44-171-873-8200.

331.21 GBR ISSN 0262-0545
NEW EARNINGS SURVEY. PART E: ANALYSES BY REGION AND AGE GROUP. Text in English. 1970. a. **Document type:** *Government.*
Supersedes in part (in 1975): Great Britain. Department of Employment. New Earnings Survey (0308-1419)
Published by: Office for National Statistics, Government Offices, Rm 65c-3, Great George St, London, SW1P 3AQ, United Kingdom. TEL 44-171-270-6081, FAX 44-171-270-6019. **Dist. by:** Her Majesty's Stationery Office Publications Centre. TEL 44-171-873-9090, FAX 44-171-873-8200.

331.21 GBR ISSN 0262-0553
HD5015
NEW EARNINGS SURVEY. PART F: HOURS, EARNINGS AND HOURS OF PART-TIME WOMEN WORKERS. Text in English. a. **Document type:** *Government.*
Supersedes in part (1970-1975): Great Britain. Department of Employment. New Earnings Survey (0308-1419)
—BLDSC (6083.642000).
Published by: Office for National Statistics, Government Offices, Rm 65c-3, Great George St, London, SW1P 3AQ, United Kingdom. TEL 44-171-270-6081, FAX 44-171-270-6019. **Dist. by:** Her Majesty's Stationery Office Publications Centre. TEL 44-171-873-9090, FAX 44-171-873-8200.

330 NZL
NEW ZEALAND. STATISTICS NEW ZEALAND. ANNUAL ENTERPRISE SURVEY. Text in English. a. **Document type:** *Government.*
Published by: Statistics New Zealand/Te Tari Tatau, PO Box 2922, Wellington, New Zealand. TEL 64-4-495-4600, FAX 64-4-473-2626, info@stats.govt.nz, http://www.stats.govt.nz.

330 NZL
NEW ZEALAND. STATISTICS NEW ZEALAND. BALANCE OF PAYMENTS. Text in English. q. stat. **Document type:** *Government.* **Description:** Contains records of the value of New Zealand's transactions in goods, services, income and transfers with the rest of the world, and the changes in New Zealand's financial claims on (assets), and liabilities to, the rest of the world.
Published by: Statistics New Zealand/Te Tari Tatau, PO Box 2922, Wellington, New Zealand. TEL 64-4-495-4600, FAX 64-4-473-2626, info@stats.govt.nz, http://www.stats.govt.nz.

330 NZL
NEW ZEALAND. STATISTICS NEW ZEALAND. BUSINESS ACTIVITY (GST) INDICATOR. (Goods and Services Tax) Text in English. q. stat. **Document type:** *Government.* **Description:** Provides information derived from Goods and Services Tax (GST) data designed to provide a set of indicators of business activity by industry.
Published by: Statistics New Zealand/Te Tari Tatau, PO Box 2922, Wellington, New Zealand. TEL 64-4-495-4600, FAX 64-4-473-2626, info@stats.govt.nz, http://www.stats.govt.nz.

330 NZL
NEW ZEALAND. STATISTICS NEW ZEALAND. BUSINESS ACTIVITY STATISTICS (YEAR) - REFERENCE REPORTS. Text in English. a., latest 1998. NZD 35 (effective 2000). stat. **Document type:** *Government.* **Description:** Brings together structural and financial information on the business sector of New Zealand. This year, an expanded range of economic data is included for the retail, wholesale and manufacturing sectors.
Related titles: Online - full content ed.
Published by: Statistics New Zealand/Te Tari Tatau, PO Box 2922, Wellington, New Zealand. TEL 64-4-495-4600, FAX 64-4-473-2626, info@stats.govt.nz, http://www.stats.govt.nz.

330 NZL
NEW ZEALAND. STATISTICS NEW ZEALAND. BUSINESS PRICE INDEX REVISIONS. Text in English. q. stat. **Document type:** *Government.*
Published by: Statistics New Zealand/Te Tari Tatau, PO Box 2922, Wellington, New Zealand. TEL 64-4-495-4600, FAX 64-4-473-2626, info@stats.govt.nz, http://www.stats.govt.nz.

330 NZL
NEW ZEALAND. STATISTICS NEW ZEALAND. CAPITAL GOODS PRICE INDEX. Text in English. q. stat. **Document type:** *Government.* **Description:** Provides a measure of the change in the general level of fixed capital assets.
Published by: Statistics New Zealand/Te Tari Tatau, PO Box 2922, Wellington, New Zealand. TEL 64-4-495-4600, FAX 64-4-473-2626, info@stats.govt.nz, http://www.stats.govt.nz.

NEW ZEALAND. STATISTICS NEW ZEALAND. CENSUS REPORTS. UNPAID WORK. see *POPULATION STUDIES—Abstracting, Bibliographies, Statistics*

319 339 NZL ISSN 1170-747X
HD7707.5
NEW ZEALAND. STATISTICS NEW ZEALAND. CONSUMER EXPENDITURE. Text in English. 1974. every 3 yrs. NZD 35 (effective 2000). **Document type:** *Government.*
Formerly: New Zealand. Department of Statistics. Consumer Expenditure; Supersedes in part (in 1991): New Zealand Household Expenditure and Income Survey (0112-6601); Which was formerly (until 1985): New Zealand Household Survey Report (0110-392X); New Zealand. Department of Statistics. Household Sample Survey
Related titles: Online - full content ed.
—CISTI.
Published by: Statistics New Zealand/Te Tari Tatau, PO Box 2922, Wellington, New Zealand. TEL 64-4-495-4600, FAX 64-4-473-2626.

338.528 NZL
NEW ZEALAND. STATISTICS NEW ZEALAND. CONSUMERS PRICE INDEX (QUARTERLY). Text in English. q. stat. **Document type:** *Government.* **Description:** Provides a measure of the price change of goods and services purchased by private New Zealand households.
Published by: Statistics New Zealand/Te Tari Tatau, PO Box 2922, Wellington, New Zealand. TEL 64-4-495-4600, FAX 64-4-473-2626, info@stats.govt.nz, http://www.stats.govt.nz.

330 NZL
NEW ZEALAND. STATISTICS NEW ZEALAND. CROWN ACCOUNTS ANALYSIS. Text in English. stat. **Document type:** *Government.*
Published by: Statistics New Zealand/Te Tari Tatau, PO Box 2922, Wellington, New Zealand. TEL 64-4-495-4600, FAX 64-4-473-2626, info@stats.govt.nz, http://www.stats.govt.nz.

330 NZL
NEW ZEALAND. STATISTICS NEW ZEALAND. CROWN RESEARCH INSTITUTE STATISTICS. Text in English. stat. **Document type:** *Government.*
Published by: Statistics New Zealand/Te Tari Tatau, PO Box 2922, Wellington, New Zealand. TEL 64-4-495-4600, FAX 64-4-473-2626, info@stats.govt.nz, http://www.stats.govt.nz.

330 NZL
NEW ZEALAND. STATISTICS NEW ZEALAND. ENTERPRISE SURVEY. Text in English. a. stat. **Document type:** *Government.*
Published by: Statistics New Zealand/Te Tari Tatau, PO Box 2922, Wellington, New Zealand. TEL 64-4-495-4600, FAX 64-4-473-2626, info@stats.govt.nz, http://www.stats.govt.nz.

B

▼ new title ➤ refereed ✶ unverified ♦ full entry avail.

B

330   NZL
NEW ZEALAND. STATISTICS NEW ZEALAND. GROSS DOMESTIC PRODUCT. Text in English. q. stat. **Document type:** *Government.* **Description:** Provides a three-month snapshot of the performance of the economy measured in prices for production and in prices for expenditure on production.
Published by: Statistics New Zealand/Te Tari Tatau, PO Box 2922, Wellington, New Zealand. TEL 64-4-495-4600, FAX 64-4-473-2626, info@stats.govt.nz, http://www.stats.govt.nz.

330   NZL
NEW ZEALAND. STATISTICS NEW ZEALAND. HOUSEHOLD ECONOMIC SURVEY. Text in English. q. stat. **Document type:** *Government.*
Published by: Statistics New Zealand/Te Tari Tatau, PO Box 2922, Wellington, New Zealand. TEL 64-4-495-4600, FAX 64-4-473-2626, info@stats.govt.nz, http://www.stats.govt.nz.

330   NZL
NEW ZEALAND. STATISTICS NEW ZEALAND. INCOMES OF PERSONS (PROVISIONAL). Text in English. a. stat. **Document type:** *Government.* **Description:** Provides provisional information on the taxable income and tax paid of personal taxpayers in New Zealand.
Published by: Statistics New Zealand/Te Tari Tatau, PO Box 2922, Wellington, New Zealand. TEL 64-4-495-4600, FAX 64-4-473-2626, info@stats.govt.nz, http://www.stats.govt.nz.

319   NZL
HA3032
NEW ZEALAND. STATISTICS NEW ZEALAND. KEY STATISTICS. Text in English. 1914. m. (except Jan.). NZD 288 domestic; NZD 324 in Australia & S. Pacific; NZD 354 in N. America & Asia; NZD 375 elsewhere (effective 2001). adv. charts; mkt.; stat. **Document type:** *Government.* **Description:** Contains over 100 selected tables summaries the most important economic and social indicators released in the previous four weeks. Each edition features and article on specific topics such as life expectancy, overseas trade and environmental accounts. A highlights page gives an at-a-glance picture of the latest trends.
Former titles: New Zealand. Statistics New Zealand. Incomes: Monthly Abstract of Statistics; New Zealand. Department of Statistics. Key Statistics (0114-2119); (until 1989): New Zealand. Department of Statistics. Monthly Abstract of Statistics (0027-0180).
Related titles: Online - full content ed.
Indexed: RASB.
—CCC.
Published by: Statistics New Zealand/Te Tari Tatau, PO Box 2922, Wellington, New Zealand. TEL 64-4-495-4600, FAX 64-4-473-2626, info@stats.govt.nz, http://www.stats.govt.nz. Ed. Diane Ramsey. Adv. contact Anne Hannah. Circ: 2,400.
Subscr. to: GP Legislation Services, P.O. Box 12418, Thorndon, Wellington, New Zealand. TEL 64-4-496-5655, FAX 64-4-496-5698, http://www.gplegislation.co.nz, legislationservices@gp.co.nz.

330   NZL
NEW ZEALAND. STATISTICS NEW ZEALAND. NEW ZEALAND BUSINESS DEMOGRAPHIC STATISTICS. Text in English. a. stat. **Document type:** *Government.*
Published by: Statistics New Zealand/Te Tari Tatau, PO Box 2922, Wellington, New Zealand. TEL 64-4-495-4600, FAX 64-4-473-2626, info@stats.govt.nz, http://www.stats.govt.nz.

330 310   NZL
NEW ZEALAND. STATISTICS NEW ZEALAND. NEW ZEALAND INCOME SURVEY. Text in English. q. stat. **Document type:** *Government.*
Published by: Statistics New Zealand/Te Tari Tatau, PO Box 2922, Wellington, New Zealand. TEL 64-4-495-4600, FAX 64-4-473-2626, info@stats.govt.nz, http://www.stats.govt.nz.

330 310   NZL
NEW ZEALAND. STATISTICS NEW ZEALAND. PRODUCERS PRICE INDEX. Text in English. q. stat. **Document type:** *Government.* **Description:** Provide a measure of the change in the general level of prices for the productive sector of New Zealand.
Published by: Statistics New Zealand/Te Tari Tatau, PO Box 2922, Wellington, New Zealand. TEL 64-4-495-4600, FAX 64-4-473-2626, info@stats.govt.nz, http://www.stats.govt.nz.

330 310   NZL
NEW ZEALAND. STATISTICS NEW ZEALAND. PROVISIONAL NATIONAL ACCOUNTS. Text in English. a. stat. **Document type:** *Government.*
Published by: Statistics New Zealand/Te Tari Tatau, PO Box 2922, Wellington, New Zealand. TEL 64-4-495-4600, FAX 64-4-473-2626, info@stats.govt.nz, http://www.stats.govt.nz.

330 310   NZL
NEW ZEALAND. STATISTICS NEW ZEALAND. QUARTERLY EMPLOYMENT SURVEY. Text in English. q. stat. **Document type:** *Government.*
Published by: Statistics New Zealand/Te Tari Tatau, PO Box 2922, Wellington, New Zealand. TEL 64-4-495-4600, FAX 64-4-473-2626, info@stats.govt.nz, http://www.stats.govt.nz.

330   NZL
NEW ZEALAND. STATISTICS NEW ZEALAND. REPORT OF THE CONSUMERS PRICE INDEX REVISION ADVISORY COMMITTEE. Text in English. every 5 yrs., latest 1997. free. stat. **Document type:** *Government.*
Related titles: Online - full content ed.
Published by: Statistics New Zealand/Te Tari Tatau, PO Box 2922, Wellington, New Zealand. TEL 64-4-495-4600, FAX 64-4-473-2626, info@stats.govt.nz, http://www.stats.govt.nz.

330 310   NZL
NEW ZEALAND. STATISTICS NEW ZEALAND. RETAIL TRADE SURVEY. Text in English. m. stat. **Document type:** *Government.*
Published by: Statistics New Zealand/Te Tari Tatau, PO Box 2922, Wellington, New Zealand. TEL 64-4-495-4600, FAX 64-4-473-2626, info@stats.govt.nz, http://www.stats.govt.nz.

330 310   NZL
NEW ZEALAND. STATISTICS NEW ZEALAND. WHOLESALE TRADE SURVEY. Text in English. q. stat. **Document type:** *Government.* **Description:** Provides information on the state of the New Zealand wholesaling sector.
Published by: Statistics New Zealand/Te Tari Tatau, PO Box 2922, Wellington, New Zealand. TEL 64-4-495-4600, FAX 64-4-473-2626, info@stats.govt.nz, http://www.stats.govt.nz.

330 310   NZL
NEW ZEALAND. STATISTICS NEW ZEALAND. WORK STOPPAGES. Text in English. q. stat. **Document type:** *Government.* **Description:** Shows the number of person-days of work lost, the amount of salaries & wages lost & the number of employees involved.
Indexed: RASB.
Published by: Statistics New Zealand/Te Tari Tatau, PO Box 2922, Wellington, New Zealand. TEL 64-4-495-4600, FAX 64-4-473-2626, info@stats.govt.nz, http://www.stats.govt.nz.

332.6   USA   ISSN 0733-432X
NEWSLETTER DIGEST. Text in English. 1979. s-m. looseleaf. USD 75. bk.rev. charts. back issues avail. **Document type:** *Abstract/Index.* **Description:** Selected abstracts from reviewed investment newsletters worldwide, with editorial commentary.
Address: 2201 Big Cove Rd, Huntsville, AL 35801. TEL 205-534-1535, FAX 205-533-4871. Ed. Al Owen. Circ: 1,500.

338   NIC
NICARAGUA. INSTITUTO NACIONAL DE ESTADISTICAS Y CENSOS. ENCUESTA ANUAL INDUSTRIA MANUFACTURERA. Text in Spanish. a. **Document type:** *Government.*
Published by: Instituto Nacional de Estadisticas y Censos, Apartado Postal 4031, Managua, Nicaragua.

331.021   NGA
NIGERIA. FEDERAL MINISTRY OF LABOUR AND PRODUCTIVITY. QUARTERLY BULLETIN OF LABOUR STATISTICS. Text in English. 1981. q. free. **Document type:** *Government.*
Media: Duplicated (not offset).
Published by: (Nigeria. Federal Secretariat, Phase I), Federal Ministry of Labour and Productivity, Planning, Research and Statistics Department, PMB 12576, Lagos, Ikoyi, Nigeria. Circ: 500.

316 382   NGA   ISSN 0078-0634
HF3931.A45
NIGERIA. FEDERAL OFFICE OF STATISTICS. REVIEW OF EXTERNAL TRADE. Text in English. 1964. a. NGN 5. **Document type:** *Government.*
Published by: Federal Office of Statistics, Dissemination Division, c/o Mrs. M.T. Osita, 36-38 Broad St, PMB 12528, Lagos, Nigeria.

338 310   NGA   ISSN 0331-1570
NIGERIA. NATIONAL INTEGRATED SURVEY OF HOUSEHOLDS. INDUSTRIAL SURVEY. Key Title: Industrial Survey of Nigeria. Text in English. a. **Document type:** *Government.*
Supersedes: Nigeria. Federal Office of Statistics. Industrial Survey
Published by: (Nigeria. National Integrated Survey of Households), Federal Office of Statistics, Dissemination Division, c/o Mrs. M.T. Osita, 36-38 Broad St, PMB 12528, Lagos, Nigeria. TEL 234-1-2601710-4.

658 310   NGA
NIGERIA. NATIONAL INTEGRATED SURVEY OF HOUSEHOLDS. REPORT ON GENERAL CONSUMER SURVEY. Text in English. a. NGN 2. **Document type:** *Government.*
Supersedes: Nigeria. Federal Office of Statistics. Report on General Consumer Survey; Which incorporated in part: Nigeria. Federal Office of Statistics. Report on Rural Household Survey; Nigeria. Federal Office of Statistics. Report on Rural Economic Survey; Nigeria. Federal Office of Statistics. Report on Rural Consumer Survey; Nigeria. Federal Office of Statistics. Report on Consumer Survey; Nigeria. Federal Office of Statistics. Report on Urban Household Survey

Published by: (Nigeria. National Integrated Survey of Households), Federal Office of Statistics, Dissemination Division, c/o Mrs. M.T. Osita, 36-38 Broad St, PMB 12528, Lagos, Nigeria. TEL 234-1-2601710-4.

330.9 310   NGA
NIGERIA. NATIONAL INTEGRATED SURVEY OF HOUSEHOLDS. REPORT ON GENERAL HOUSEHOLD. Text in English. a. **Document type:** *Government.*
Supersedes: Nigeria. Federal Office of Statistics. Report on General Household; Which incorporated in part: Nigeria. Federal Office of Statistics. Report on Rural Household Survey; Nigeria. Federal Office of Statistics. Report on Rural Economic Survey; Nigeria. Federal Office of Statistics. Report on Rural Consumer Survey; Nigeria. Federal Office of Statistics. Report on Consumer Survey; Nigeria. Federal Office of Statistics. Report on Urban Household Survey
Published by: (Nigeria. National Integrated Survey of Households), Federal Office of Statistics, Dissemination Division, c/o Mrs. M.T. Osita, 36-38 Broad St, PMB 12528, Lagos, Nigeria. TEL 234-1-2601710-4.

658 310   NGA   ISSN 0189-336X
HA4731
NIGERIA. NATIONAL INTEGRATED SURVEY OF HOUSEHOLDS. REPORT ON NATIONAL CONSUMER SURVEY. Key Title: Report on National Consumer Survey. Text in English. a. NGN 10, USD 10. **Document type:** *Government.*
Supersedes: Nigeria. Federal Office of Statistics. Report on National Consumer Survey; Which incorporated in part: Nigeria. Federal Office of Statistics. Report on Rural Household Survey; Nigeria. Federal Office of Statistics. Report on Rural Economic Survey; Nigeria. Federal Office of Statistics. Report on Rural Consumer Survey; Nigeria. Federal Office of Statistics. Report on Consumer Survey; Nigeria. Federal Office of Statistics. Report on Urban Household Survey
Published by: (Nigeria. National Integrated Survey of Households), Federal Office of Statistics, Dissemination Division, c/o Mrs. M.T. Osita, 36-38 Broad St, PMB 12528, Lagos, Nigeria. TEL 234-1-2601710-4.

330   JPN   ISSN 0389-5602
HA1
NIHON TOKEI GAKKAISHI (TOKYO, 1971)/JAPAN STATISTICAL SOCIETY. JOURNAL. Text in English, Japanese. 1971. s-a. JPY 8,000, USD 50. adv. bk.rev. back issues avail. **Document type:** *Academic/Scholarly.*
Related titles: Online - full text ed.: ISSN 1348-6365. free (effective 2005) (from J-Stage).
Indexed: CCMJ, CIS, CurCont, MathR, MathSciNet, ST&MA, ZentMath.
—CCC.
Published by: Nihon Tokei Gakkai/Japan Statistical Society, c/o Institute of Statistical Mathematics, 4-6-7 Minami-azabu Minato-ku, Tokyo, 106-8569, Japan. TEL 81-3-3442-5801, FAX 81-3-3442-5924, jimu@jss.grjp, http://www.jstage.jst.go.jp/browse/jjss, http://www.jss.gr.jp/. Eds. Satoru Kanoh, Tatsuya Kubokawa. Circ: 1,500.

NIPPERDEY PLUS ARBEITSRECHT. see *LAW—Abstracting, Bibliographies, Statistics*

331.1021   NOR   ISSN 0300-5585
NORGES OFFISIELLE STATISTIKK/OFFICIAL STATISTICS OF NORWAY. Text in Norwegian. irreg.
Related titles: ◆ Series: Norway. Statistisk Sentralbyraa. Arbeidsundersoekelsen. ISSN 1503-4712; ◆ Norway. Statistisk Sentralbyraa. Overnattingsstatistikk. ISSN 1503-4119; ◆ Norway. Statistisk Sentralbyraa. Nasjonalregnskapsstatistikk. Institusjonelt Sektorregnskap. ISSN 0809-201X; ◆ Norway. Statistisk Sentralbyraa. Industristatistikk. Naeringstall. ISSN 0807-4763; ◆ Norway. Statistisk Sentralbyraa. Jordbruksstatistikk. ISSN 0078-1894; ◆ Norway. Statistisk Sentralbyraa. Loennsstatistikk. ISSN 0078-1916; ◆ Norway. Statistisk Sentralbyraa. Statistisk Aarbok. ISSN 0377-8908; ◆ Norway. Statistisk Sentralbyraa. Utenrikshandel. ISSN 0802-9571; ◆ Norway. Statistisk Sentralbyraa. Varehandelsstatistikk. ISSN 0078-1959; ◆ Norway. Statistisk Sentralbyraa. Stortingsvalget. ISSN 0802-9067; ◆ Norway. Statistisk Sentralbyraa. Kriminalstatistikk. ISSN 0809-0742; ◆ Norway. Statistisk Sentralbyraa. Helsestatistikk. ISSN 0332-7906; ◆ Norway. Statistisk Sentralbyraa. Kommunestyrevalget. ISSN 0332-8023; ◆ Norway. Statistisk Sentralbyraa. Strukturstatistikk for Samfersel og Reiseliv. ISSN 1503-4364; ◆ Norway. Statistisk Sentralbyraa. Elektrisitesstatistikk. ISSN 0333-3779; ◆ Norway. Statistisk Sentralbyraa. Framskriving av Folkemengden. ISSN 0332-8015; ◆ Norway. Statistisk Sentralbyraa. Skogstatistikk. ISSN 0468-8155; ◆ Norway. Statistisk Sentralbyraa. Befolkningsstatistikk. Hefte II. ISSN 0801-6690; ◆ Norway. Statistisk Sentralbyraa. Fiskeristatistikk. ISSN 0333-3728; ◆ Norway. Statistisk Sentralbyraa. Befolkningsstatistikk. Hefte I. ISSN 0801-6682; ◆ Norway. Statistisk Sentralbyraa. Levekaarsundersoekelsen. ISSN 0800-7233; ◆ Norway. Statistisk Sentralbyraa. Pasientstatistikk. ISSN 0806-0711; ◆ Norway. Statistisk Sentralbyraa. Olje- og Gassvirksomhet. ISSN 0802-0477; ◆ Norway. Statistisk Sentralbyraa. Sosialhjelp, Barnevern og Familievern; ◆ Norway. Statistisk Sentralbyraa.

Byggearealstatistikk. ISSN 0550-7162; ♦ Fiskeopdrett. ISSN 0809-4527; ♦ Jaktstatistikk (Year). ISSN 0550-0400; ♦ Norway. Statistisk Sentralbyraa. Statistikk over Eiendomsdrift, Forretningsmessig Tjenesteyting og Utleiervirksomhet. ISSN 0808-2159; ♦ Kulturstatistikk. ISSN 0800-2959; ♦ Norway. Statistisk Sentralbyraa. Innenlandske Transportytelser. ISSN 1503-4445.
Published by: Statistisk Sentralbyraa/Statistics Norway, Kongensgate 6, Postboks 8131, Dep, Oslo, 0033, Norway. TEL 47-21-090000, FAX 47-21-094973, ssb@ssb.no, http://www.ssb.no.

382.21 CAN ISSN 0225-9907
HA747.N6
NORTHWEST TERRITORIES. BUREAU OF STATISTICS. STATISTICS QUARTERLY. Text in English. q.
Published by: Bureau of Statistics, Northwest Territories, Box 1320, Yellowknife, NT X1A 2L9, Canada. TEL 867-873-7147, FAX 867-873-0275, info@stats.gov.nt.ca.

331.1021 NOR ISSN 1503-4712
HA1501
NORWAY. STATISTISK SENTRALBYRAA. ARBEIDSUNDERSOEKELSEN. Text in Norwegian Bokmal; Text occasionally in English. 1968. a. **Document type:** *Government.*
Formerly (until 2003): Norway. Statistisk Sentralbyraa. Arbeidsmarkedstatistikk. Hefte I: Hovedtall (0804-8894); Which superseded in part (in 1993): Norway. Statistisk Sentralbyraa. Arbeidsmarkedstatistikk - Labor Market Statistics (0078-1878)
Related titles: Online - full text ed.; ♦ Series of: Norges Offisielle Statistikk. ISSN 0300-5585.
Published by: Statistisk Sentralbyraa/Statistics Norway, Kongensgate 6, Postboks 8131, Dep, Oslo, 0033, Norway. TEL 47-21-090000, FAX 47-21-094973, ssb@ssb.no, http://www.ssb.no/emner/06/01/aku/.

332.1021 NOR ISSN 0333-1504
HG3161
NORWAY. STATISTISK SENTRALBYRAA. BANK- OG KREDITTSTATISTIKK. AKTUELLE TALL. Text in Norwegian. 1976. irreg. (11/yr.). back issues avail. **Document type:** *Government.*
Formerly (until 1981): Kvartalshefte for Private og Offentlige Banker (0333-0788)
Related titles: Online - full text ed.
Published by: Statistisk Sentralbyraa/Statistics Norway, Kongensgate 6, Postboks 8131, Dep, Oslo, 0033, Norway. TEL 47-21-090000, FAX 47-21-094973, ssb@ssb.no, http://www.ssb.no/emner/10/13/bk/.

339 314 NOR ISSN 0807-4763
HA1501 subser.
NORWAY. STATISTISK SENTRALBYRAA. INDUSTRISTATISTIKK. NAERINGSTALL/STATISTICS NORWAY. MANUFACTURING STATISTICS. INDUSTRIAL FIGURES. Text in English, Norwegian. 1961. a. **Document type:** *Government.*
Formerly (until 1992): Norway. Statistisk Sentralbyraa. Industrialstatistikk. Hefte 1: Naeringstall (0800-580X); Supersedes in part (in 1982): Norway. Statistisk Sentralbyraa. Industristatistikk (0078-1886)
Related titles: Online - full text ed.; ♦ Series of: Norges Offisielle Statistikk. ISSN 0300-5585.
Published by: Statistisk Sentralbyraa/Statistics Norway, Kongensgate 6, Postboks 8131, Dep, Oslo, 0033, Norway. TEL 47-21-090000, FAX 47-21-094973, ssb@ssb.no, http://www.ssb.no/emner/10/07/nos_industri/. Ed. Morten Qvenild TEL 47-21-094764.

331.2 314 NOR ISSN 0078-1916
HA1501
NORWAY. STATISTISK SENTRALBYRAA. LOENNSSTATISTIKK/ STATISTICS NORWAY. WAGE STATISTICS. Text in English, Norwegian. 1930. a. back issues avail. **Document type:** *Government.*
Formerly (until 1950): Arbeidsloenninger
Related titles: Online - full text ed.; ♦ Series of: Norges Offisielle Statistikk. ISSN 0300-5585.
Indexed: RASB.
Published by: Statistisk Sentralbyraa/Statistics Norway, Kongensgate 6, Postboks 8131, Dep, Oslo, 0033, Norway. TEL 47-21-090000, FAX 47-21-094973, ssb@ssb.no, http://www.ssb.no/emner/06/05/nos_lonn/. Ed. Harald Lunde TEL 47-62-885552.

339.3 NOR ISSN 0809-201X
HA1501
NORWAY. STATISTISK SENTRALBYRAA. NASJONALREGNSKAPSSTATISTIKK. INSTITUSJONELT SEKTORREGNSKAP/NATIONAL ACCOUNTS STATISTICS. Text in Norwegian. 1953. a. **Document type:** *Government.*
Supersedes in part (in 1996): Norway. Statistisk Sentralbyraa. Nasjonalregnskapsstatistikk (0808-5277); Which was formerly (until 1989): Norway. Statistisk Sentralbyraa. Nasjonalregnskap - National Accounts Statistics (0550-0494)
Related titles: Online - full text ed.; English ed.: ISSN 0809-2028; ♦ Series of: Norges Offisielle Statistikk. ISSN 0300-5585.
Published by: Statistisk Sentralbyraa/Statistics Norway, Kongensgate 6, Postboks 8131, Dep, Oslo, 0033, Norway. TEL 47-21-090000, FAX 47-21-094973, ssb@ssb.no, http://www.ssb.no/emner/09/01/nos_nasjonal_inst/.

382.09481 NOR ISSN 0802-9571
NORWAY. STATISTISK SENTRALBYRAA. UTENRIKSHANDEL/ STATISTICS NORWAY. EXTERNAL TRADE. Text in English, Norwegian. 1961. a. NOK 170 (effective 1998). **Document type:** *Government.*
Related titles: ♦ Series of: Norges Offisielle Statistikk. ISSN 0300-5585.
Indexed: RASB.
Published by: Statistisk Sentralbyraa/Statistics Norway, Kongensgate 6, Postboks 8131, Dep, Oslo, 0033, Norway. TEL 47-22-86-45-00, FAX 47-22-86-49-73. Circ: 1,300.

381.021 314 NOR ISSN 0078-1959
HA1501
NORWAY. STATISTISK SENTRALBYRAA. VAREHANDELSSTATISTIKK/STATISTICS NORWAY. WHOLESALE AND RETAIL TRADE STATISTICS. Text in English, Norwegian. 1966. a. **Document type:** *Government.*
Related titles: Online - full text ed.; ♦ Series of: Norges Offisielle Statistikk. ISSN 0300-5585.
Published by: Statistisk Sentralbyraa/Statistics Norway, Kongensgate 6, Postboks 8131, Dep, Oslo, 0033, Norway. TEL 47-21-090000, FAX 47-21-094973, ssb@ssb.no, http://www.ssb.no/emner/10/10/10/nos_varehandel/. Circ: 900.

330 011 RUS
NOVAYA LITERATURA PO SOTSIAL'NYM I GUMANITARNYM NAUKAM. EKONOMIKA; bibliograficheskii ukazatel'. Text in Russian. 1992. m. USD 450 in United States (effective 2004). **Document type:** *Bibliography.* **Description:** Contains information about Russian and foreign books on economics acquired by the INION library.
Formed by the merger of (1951-1992): Novaya Inostrannaya Literatura po Obshchestvennym Naukam. Ekonomika (0134-2835); (1934-1992): Novaya Sovetskaya Literatura po Obshchestvennym Naukam. Ekonomika (0134-272X)
Indexed: RASB.
Published by: Rossiiskaya Akademiya Nauk, Institut Nauchnoi Informatsii po Obshchestvennym Naukam, Nakhimovskii pr-t 51/21, Moscow, 117997, Russian Federation. TEL 7-095-1288930, FAX 7-095-4202261, info@inion.ru, http://www.inion.ru. Ed. V A Arkhangel'skaya. **US dist. addr.:** East View Information Services, 3020 Harbor Ln. N., Minneapolis, MN 55447. TEL 800-477-1005, FAX 800-800-3839, eastview@eastview.com, http://www.eastview.com.

336 FRA ISSN 1015-4159
HJ8899
O E C D EXTERNAL DEBT STATISTICS. Text in English. 1987. a. price varies.
Related titles: French ed.: O C D E Statistiques de la Dette Exterieure. ISSN 1018-7049.
Indexed: IIS.
Published by: Organization for Economic Cooperation and Development, 2 Rue Andre Pascal, Paris, 75775 Cedex 16, France. TEL 33-1-45248200, FAX 33-1-45248500, http://www.oecd.org. **Dist. in N. America by:** O E C D Turpin North America, PO Box 194, Downingtown, PA 19335-0194. TEL 610-524-5361, 800-456-6323, FAX 610-524-5417, bookscustomer@turpinna.com.

330 011 FRA
O E C D HISTORICAL STATISTICS. Text in English, French. 1982. irreg., latest 2001. price varies.
Former titles: Historical Statistics (1026-1877); (until 1992): O E C D Economic Outlook Historical Statistics (0256-9531)
Related titles: CD-ROM ed.; Online - full content ed.
Published by: Organization for Economic Cooperation and Development, 2 Rue Andre Pascal, Paris, 75775 Cedex 16, France. TEL 33-1-45248200, FAX 33-1-45248500, http://www.oecd.org. **Dist. in N. America by:** O E C D Turpin North America, PO Box 194, Downingtown, PA 19335-0194. TEL 610-524-5361, 800-456-6323, FAX 610-524-5417, bookscustomer@turpinna.com.

382 FRA
O E C D INTERNATIONAL TRADE BY COMMODITIES STATISTICS/O E C D STATISTIQUES DU COMMERCE INTERNATIONAL PAR PRODUITS. Text in English, French. 1975. 5/yr. EUR 697, USD 801, GBP 461, JPY 94,100 (effective 2005). stat. **Document type:** *Government.* **Description:** Matrix tables show trade between OECD countries and partner countries for commodity groups defined at 1 and 2-digit levels of the standard international trade classification.
Former titles (until 2000): O E C D Foreign Trade by Commodities. Series C / O E C D Commerce Exterieur par Produits. Serie C (1028-8376); (until 1983): O E C D Statistics of Foreign Trade. Series C: Trade by Commodities, Market Summaries: Exports (0474-540X)
Related titles: Online - full text ed.: ISSN 1609-7297 (from EBSCO Publishing, Gale Group, IngentaConnect, O C L C Online Computer Library Center, Inc., Swets Information Services).
Indexed: IIS, RASB.
Published by: Organization for Economic Cooperation and Development, 2 Rue Andre Pascal, Paris, 75775 Cedex 16, France. TEL 33-1-45248200, FAX 33-1-45248500, http://www.oecd.org. **U.S. orders to:** O E C D Turpin North America, PO Box 194, Downingtown, PA 19335-0194. TEL 610-524-5361, 800-456-6323, FAX 610-524-5417, journalscustomer@turpinna.com.

331.11021 FRA ISSN 0474-5515
HD5764.A6
O E C D LABOUR FORCE STATISTICS/O C D E STATISTIQUES DE LA POPULATION ACTIVE. Text in English, French. 1968. a., latest 2004. price varies. stat. **Document type:** *Government.*
Related titles: Magnetic Tape ed.
Indexed: IIS.
—CISTI.
Published by: Organization for Economic Cooperation and Development, 2 Rue Andre Pascal, Paris, 75775 Cedex 16, France. TEL 33-1-45248200, FAX 33-1-45248500, http://www.oecd.org. **U.S. orders to:** O E C D Turpin North America, PO Box 194, Downingtown, PA 19335-0194. TEL 610-524-5361, 800-456-6323, FAX 610-524-5417, bookscustomer@turpinna.com.

310 330.9 ATG ISSN 1021-7320
O E C S DIGEST OF EXTERNAL TRADE STATISTICS. Text in English. 1984. irreg. XEC 160, USD 60. stat. **Document type:** *Trade.* **Description:** Provides a statistical picture of trade relations of the OECS countries locally and internationally.
Formerly: O E C S Trade Digest
Published by: Organisation of Eastern Caribbean States, Economic Affairs Secretariat, PO Box 822, St John's, Antigua. TEL 809-462-3500, FAX 809-462-1537, economico@candw.ag.

B

331.12021 RUS
OBSLEDOVANIE NASELENIYA PO PROBLEMAM ZANYATOSTI/SURVEY ON EMPLOYMENT OF POPULATION. Text in Russian. 1992. q. RUR 1,452 (effective 2005). **Document type:** *Bulletin, Government.* **Description:** Contains statistical information on the current employment situation in Russia.
Related titles: Online - full content ed.: RUR 1,557 (effective 2005).
Published by: Gosudarstvennyi Komitet Rossiiskoi Federatsii po Statistike/Federal State Statistics Office, ul Myasnitskaya 39, Moscow, 107450, Russian Federation. TEL 7-095-2074902, FAX 7-095-2074087, stat@gks.ru, http://www.gks.ru.

331.21 USA
OCCUPATIONAL COMPENSATION SUMMARIES. Text in English. a. **Document type:** *Government.* **Description:** Summarizes B L S findings on occupations and wages for selected regions.
Published by: U.S. Department of Labor, Bureau of Labor Statistics, Postal Square Bldg., 2 Massachusetts Ave, NE, Washington, DC 20212-0001 . TEL 202-691-5200, http://www.bls.gov. **Subscr. to:** U.S. Government Printing Office, Superintendent of Documents.

OCCUPATIONAL OUTLOOK HANDBOOK. see *OCCUPATIONS AND CAREERS—Abstracting, Bibliographies, Statistics*

OCCUPATIONAL OUTLOOK QUARTERLY. see *OCCUPATIONS AND CAREERS—Abstracting, Bibliographies, Statistics*

016.338 AUT
OESTERREICHISCHE FORSCHUNGSSTIFTUNG FUER ENTWICKLUNGSHILFE. ANNOTIERTE BIBLIOGRAPHIE; ausgewaehlte neue Literatur zur Entwicklungspolitik. Text in German. 1993. 3/yr. **Document type:** *Bibliography.* **Description:** Compiles literature on topics of development politics.
Media: Online - full text.
Published by: Oesterreichische Forschungsstiftung fuer Entwicklungshilfe/Austrian Foundation for Development Research, Berggasse 7, Vienna, W 1090, Austria. TEL 43-1-317-4010, FAX 43-1-317-4015, office@oefse.at, http://www.oefse.at.

339 314 AUT ISSN 0085-4433
OESTERREICHS VOLKSEINKOMMEN. Text in German. 1952. a. EUR 14.53. **Document type:** *Government.* **Description:** Data on national accounts, gross domestic production and national income.
Published by: Statistik Austria, Guglgasse 13, Vienna, W 1110, Austria. TEL 43-1-711280, FAX 43-1-711287728, info@statistik.gv.at, http://www.statistik.at.

382 665.5 USA
OIL IMPORTS INTO THE UNITED STATES AND PUERTO RICO (E I A 814). Text in English. m. USD 240 in North America; USD 480 elsewhere (effective 1999). **Description:** Surveys firms importing crude oil, unfinished oil, and finished petroleum products in the United States and Puerto Rico. Collects data on port of entry, country of origin, location of refinery, quantity of crude or products in barrels, and sulfur content.
Media: Magnetic Tape.
Published by: (U.S. Department of Energy, Energy Information Administration), U.S. Department of Commerce, National Technical Information Service, 5285 Port Royal Rd, Springfield, VA 22161. TEL 703-605-6000, info@ntis.gov, http://www.ntis.gov.

650 USA ISSN 0030-1671
HC107.O5
OKLAHOMA BUSINESS BULLETIN. Text in English. 1928. q. USD 10 (effective 2000). charts; mkt. back issues avail.; reprint service avail. from PQC. **Document type:** *Bulletin.*

Related titles: Microfiche ed.: (from CIS); Microform ed.: (from PQC); Online - full text ed.: (from O C L C Online Computer Library Center, Inc., ProQuest Information & Learning).
Indexed: ABIn, SRI.
Published by: University of Oklahoma, Center for Economic and Management Research, Michael F Price, College of Business, 307 W Brooks St, Rm 4, Norman, OK 73019. TEL 405-325-2931, FAX 405-325-7688. Ed. John McCraw. Circ: 600.

331 USA
OKLAHOMA. EMPLOYMENT SECURITY COMMISSION. RESEARCH DIVISION. COUNTY EMPLOYMENT AND WAGE DATA. Text in English. 1952. a. free. stat. **Document type:** *Government.*
Formerly: Oklahoma. Employment Security Commission. Research and Planning Division. County Employment and Wage Data
Published by: Employment Security Commission, Research Department, Will Rogers Bldg, 2401 N Lincoln Blvd, Oklahoma City, OK 73105. Ed. Connie Field. Circ: 600.

B

016.6588 USA
ONLINE LOGISTICS BIBLIOGRAPHY. Short title: Logistics Bibliography. Text in English. 1967. w. free (effective 2003). **Document type:** *Abstract/Index.* **Description:** Provides abstracts on logistics-related articles from periodicals and journal from 1993 to the present.
Formerly: Bibliography of Logistics Management. Supplement (Print)
Media: Online - full text.
Published by: Council of Supply Chain Management Professionals, 2805 Butterfield Rd., Ste. 200, Oak Brook, IL 60523. TEL 630-574-0985, FAX 630-574-0989, CSCMPpublications@cscmp.org, http://www.clm1.org/bibliography, http://www.cscmp.org/.

016.658 658 GBR ISSN 1353-5498
TS155.A1
OPERATIONS & PRODUCTION MANAGEMENT ABSTRACTS. (Also avail. as a section of: Emerald Management Reviews (print & online eds.)) Text in English. 1973. bi-m. EUR 1,953.05 in Europe; USD 1,779 in North America; AUD 2,139 in Australasia; GBP 1,372.38 in the UK & elsewhere (effective 2006). **Document type:** *Abstract/Index.* **Description:** Contains fully searchable and independent abstracts of articles from top 400 international management journals. Abstracts are keyworded, indexed and assessed. Covers topics such as: productivity, logistics, work measurement, operational research, safety, production methods.
Former titles (until 1994): Management Services & Production Abstracts (0952-4614); Work Study and O and M Abstracts (0305-0653); Which superseded in part: Anbar Management Services Abstracts (0003-2794)
Related titles: CD-ROM ed.; Online - full text ed.
—CCC.
Published by: Emerald Group Publishing Limited, 60-62 Toller Ln, Bradford, W Yorks BD8 9BY, United Kingdom. TEL 44-1274-777700, FAX 44-1274-785200, infomation@emeraldinsight.com, http://www.emeraldinsight.com/. Ed. David Pollit. **Subscr. in Australasia to:** Emerald Group Publishing Ltd., PO Box 1567, Toowong, QLD 4066, Australia. TEL 61-3870-7144, FAX 61-3870-4013; **Subscr. in N America to:** Emerald Group Publishing Ltd., 44 Brattle St, 4th Fl, Cambridge, MA 02138.

658.4 016 USA ISSN 0030-3658
OPERATIONS RESEARCH - MANAGEMENT SCIENCE; international literature digest service. Text in English. 1961. bi-m. USD 36 domestic to individuals; USD 57 foreign to individuals; USD 56 domestic to institutions; USD 77 foreign to institutions (effective 2005). abstr.; charts; illus.; stat.; bibl. index. 128 p./no.; back issues avail. **Document type:** *Abstract/Index.*
Indexed: RASB.
—IE, Infotrieve.
Published by: Executive Sciences Institute, 1005 Mississippi Ave, Davenport, IA 52803. TEL 319-324-4463, FAX 319-327-3725, greta.lane@usa.net. Ed., R&P Bruce Brocka.

003 658.4 USA ISSN 0473-0496
HD20
OPERATIONS RESEARCH - MANAGEMENT SCIENCE YEARBOOK. Text in English. 1961. a., latest vol.40. USD 295 (effective 2001). bk.rev. abstr.; charts; illus.; stat. 768 p./no.; back issues avail. **Document type:** *Yearbook, Abstract/Index.*
Published by: Executive Sciences Institute, 1005 Mississippi Ave, Davenport, IA 52803. TEL 319-324-4463, FAX 319-327-3725, greta.lane@usa.net. Ed., R&P Bruce Brocka.

336.2 USA
OREGON PERSONAL INCOME TAX STATISTICS. Text in English. 1969. a. USD 5. **Document type:** *Government.* **Description:** Statistical breakdown of Oregon personal income tax data by income levels, filer types, counties and other measures.
Former titles: Analysis of Oregon Personal Income; Personal Income Tax Analysis (0092-6655); Analysis of Oregon's Personal Income Tax Returns
Published by: Department of Revenue, Revenue Bldg, Salem, OR 97310. TEL 503-945-8636, FAX 503-945-8672.

336.2 USA ISSN 0145-4269
HJ4121.O7
OREGON PROPERTY TAX STATISTICS. Text in English. 1970. a. USD 5. **Document type:** *Government.* **Description:** Contains tables of property values and tax levies for counties and cities in Oregon.
Formerly: Oregon. Department of Revenue. Summary of Levies and Statistics
Published by: Department of Revenue, Revenue Bldg, Salem, OR 97310. TEL 503-945-8636, FAX 503-945-8672.

332.6021 690.021 RUS
OSNOVNYE POKAZATELI INVESTITSIONNOI I STROITEL'NOI DEYATEL'NOSTI V ROSSIISKOI FEDERATSII/MAIN INDICATORS OF CONSTRUCTION AND INVESTMENT ACTIVITIES IN THE RUSSIAN FEDERATION. Text in Russian. q. RUR 528 (effective 2005). **Document type:** *Bulletin, Government.* **Description:** Presents statistical data on changes and structure of investments in the fixed capital by sources of financing, types of property, by branches of the economy and industry.
Published by: Gosudarstvennyi Komitet Rossiiskoi Federatsii po Statistike/Federal State Statistics Office, ul Myasnitskaya 39, Moscow, 107450, Russian Federation. TEL 7-095-2074902, FAX 7-095-2074087, stat@gks.ru, http://www.gks.ru.

332.6 314 GBR ISSN 1465-671X
HF3501
OVERSEAS TRADE STATISTICS. UNITED KINGDOM TRADE WITH THE EUROPEAN COMMUNITY AND THE WORLD. Text in English. 1970. a. GBP 350 (effective 2000). charts; stat. back issues avail. **Document type:** *Government.* **Description:** Provides statistical information on U.K. manufacturing and other economic activity.
Formerly (until 1999): Business Monitor: Overseas Trade Statistics of the United Kingdom with the World (1465-4857); Supersedes in part (in 1993): Business Monitor: Overseas Trade Statistics of the United Kingdom (Annual Revision) (0436-3574)
Related titles: Microfiche ed.: (from PQC); Series of: Miscellaneous Monitors Series.
Indexed: RASB.
—BLDSC (6317.606000).
Published by: Office for National Statistics, Government Buildings, Cardiff Rd, Newport, Gwent NP9 1XG, United Kingdom. TEL 44-1633-812973, FAX 44-1633-812599, TELEX 497121 ALBBSONPT G613, library@ons.gov.uk. Circ: 1,375. **Orders to:** Stationery Office, PO Box 276, London SW8 5DT, United Kingdom. TEL 44-20-7873-9090, FAX 44-207-873-8200.

OXFORD BULLETIN OF ECONOMICS AND STATISTICS. see *BUSINESS AND ECONOMICS*

336 PAK
PAKISTAN. FINANCE DIVISION. PUBLIC FINANCE STATISTICS. Text in English. 1975. a. **Document type:** *Government.*
Published by: Finance Division, Islamabad, Pakistan.

338.9 315 PAK
PAKISTAN INSTITUTE OF DEVELOPMENT ECONOMICS. STATISTICAL PAPERS SERIES. Text in English. 1980. irreg. price varies. stat. **Document type:** *Monographic series.*
Published by: Pakistan Institute of Development Economics, P O Box 1091, Islamabad, 44000, Pakistan. TEL 92-51-9206610, FAX 92-51-9210886, pide@isb.paknet.com.pk, pide@appollo.net.pk, http://www.pide.org.pk. Circ: 1,000.

318 PAN ISSN 0078-8996
HA851
PANAMA EN CIFRAS. Text in Spanish. 1953. a. PAB 3 domestic (effective 2000). **Document type:** *Government.* **Description:** Contains demographic, economic and social statistical information.
Related titles: Microfiche ed.: (from PQC).
Published by: Direccion de Estadistica y Censo, Contraloria General, Apdo. 5213, Panama City, 5, Panama. FAX 507-210-4801. Circ: 7,000.

330 310 AUS
PAPUA NEW GUINEA HANDBOOK. Text in English. 1954. irreg. (plus a. updates). AUD 500 (effective 2000). adv. index. **Document type:** *Academic/Scholarly.* **Description:** A comprehensive survey of the Papua New Guinea economy.
Formerly (until 1990): Handbook of Papua and New Guinea (0072-9868)
Published by: Australian National University, National Centre for Development Studies, Canberra, ACT 0200, Australia. TEL 61-2-6249-4705, FAX 61-2-6257-2886. **Subscr. to:** Landmark Educational Supplies, PO Box 130, Drovin, VIC 3818, Australia.

338 315 PNG ISSN 1023-6481
PAPUA NEW GUINEA. NATIONAL STATISTICAL OFFICE. ANNUAL BUSINESS CENSUS. Text in English. 1994. a. PGK 3 domestic; PGK 6 foreign (effective 2005). 8 p./no.; **Document type:** *Government.* **Description:** Contains employment and financial information from all business units listed on the business register maintained by the NSO.
Formed by the 1994 merger of: Rural Industries (0078-7701); Agriculture Largeholdings (Preliminary) (0078-9321); Secondary Industries (0078-933X); Secondary Industries (Preliminary) (0078-9313); Capital Expenditure by Private Businesses (0078-9259); Census of Retail Sales and Selected Services (1017-6470); Census of Employment (1017-6489)
Published by: National Statistical Office, Waigani, National Capital District, PO Box 337, Port Moresby, Papua New Guinea. TEL 675-3011226, FAX 675-3251869, TELEX FINANCE 22312. Ed. Francis K Kasau.

339 PNG ISSN 1017-6403
PAPUA NEW GUINEA. NATIONAL STATISTICAL OFFICE. DOMESTIC FACTOR INCOMES, BY REGION AND PROVINCE. Text in English. a. PGK 1.50. **Document type:** *Government.* **Description:** Contains estimates of domestic factor incomes for each of the four regions and 20 provinces, including the National Capital District.
Published by: National Statistical Office, Waigani, National Capital District, PO Box 337, Port Moresby, Papua New Guinea. TEL 675-3011226, FAX 675-3251869. Ed. Francis K Kasau.

382 PNG ISSN 1017-6527
PAPUA NEW GUINEA. NATIONAL STATISTICAL OFFICE. EXPORT PRICE INDEXES. Text in English. q. PGK 12; PGK 20 foreign (effective 1999). **Document type:** *Government.* **Description:** Covers price indices of all major domestic exports.
Published by: National Statistical Office, Waigani, National Capital District, PO Box 337, Port Moresby, Papua New Guinea. TEL 675-3011226, FAX 675-3251869. Ed. Francis K Kasau.

339 PNG ISSN 1017-6411
PAPUA NEW GUINEA. NATIONAL STATISTICAL OFFICE. GOVERNMENT FINANCE STATISTICS. Text in English. a. PGK 3; PGK 6 foreign (effective 1999). **Document type:** *Government.*
Published by: National Statistical Office, Waigani, National Capital District, PO Box 337, Port Moresby, Papua New Guinea. TEL 675-3011226, FAX 675-3251869. Ed. Francis K Kasau.

319 330 PNG ISSN 1017-639X
HC683.5.Z9
PAPUA NEW GUINEA. NATIONAL STATISTICAL OFFICE. GROSS DOMESTIC PRODUCT AND EXPENDITURE. Text in English. a. PGK 3; PGK 6 foreign (effective 1999). **Document type:** *Government.* **Description:** Provides a summary of all economic activity in Papua New Guinea.
Formed by the merger of: Papua New Guinea. Bureau of Statistics. Gross Domestic Product and Domestic Factor Incomes by Kind of Economic Activity; Papua New Guinea. Bureau of Statistics. Consolidated National Economic Accounts; Papua New Guinea. Bureau of Statistics. Gross Domestic Product at Constant Prices; Which was formerly: Papua New Guinea. Bureau of Statistics. National Accounts Statistics: Expenditure of Gross Domestic Product at Constant Purchasers' Values
Published by: National Statistical Office, Waigani, National Capital District, PO Box 337, Port Moresby, Papua New Guinea. TEL 675-3011226, FAX 675-3251869. Ed. Francis K Kasau.

382 PNG ISSN 1017-6543
PAPUA NEW GUINEA. NATIONAL STATISTICAL OFFICE. IMPORT PRICE INDEXES. Text in English. a. PGK 1.50. **Document type:** *Government.* **Description:** Contains price indexes for imports in each of Sections 0-8 of the Standard International Trade Classification.
Published by: National Statistical Office, Waigani, National Capital District, PO Box 337, Port Moresby, Papua New Guinea. TEL 675-3011226, FAX 675-3251869. Ed. Francis K Kasau.

382 PNG ISSN 1017-6519
PAPUA NEW GUINEA. NATIONAL STATISTICAL OFFICE. INTERNATIONAL TRADE - EXPORTS. Text in English. q. PGK 3; PGK 6 foreign (effective 1999). **Document type:** *Government.* **Description:** Includes summaries of export values classified by port of shipment and country of destination, along with quantities and values of major exports, classified by country of destination and commodity.
Published by: National Statistical Office, Waigani, National Capital District, PO Box 337, Port Moresby, Papua New Guinea. TEL 675-3011226, FAX 675-3251869. Ed. Francis K Kasau.

382 PNG ISSN 1017-6535
HF4032
PAPUA NEW GUINEA. NATIONAL STATISTICAL OFFICE. INTERNATIONAL TRADE - IMPORTS. Text in English. q. PGK 12; PGK 20 foreign (effective 1999). **Document type:** *Government.* **Description:** Summarizes values of imports, by statistical section and group, port of entry, country of origin, and broad economic category.
Published by: National Statistical Office, Waigani, National Capital District, PO Box 337, Port Moresby, Papua New Guinea. TEL 675-3011226, FAX 675-325869. Ed. Francis K Kasau.

338 318 PRY ISSN 0085-4743
PARAGUAY. MINISTERIO DE INDUSTRIA Y COMERCIO. DIVISION DE REGISTRO Y ESTADISTICA INDUSTRIAL. ENCUESTA INDUSTRIAL. Text in Spanish. irreg. free. stat.
Media: Duplicated (not offset).
Published by: Ministerio de Industria y Comercio, C.C. 1772, Ave. ESPANA, 374, Asuncion, Paraguay.

330.9 318 BRA
PARANA, BRAZIL. SECRETARIA DE ESTADO DA FAZENDA. ESTATISTICA ECONOMICO-FINANCEIRA. Text in Portuguese. 1972. irreg., latest 1989. free. illus. **Document type:** *Government.*
Published by: Secretaria de Estado da Fazenda, Rua Vicente Machado, 445, 10o, PA, Centro, Curitiba, PR 80420-010, Brazil. TEL 041-223-2216, FAX 041-222-3505, TELEX 41-6007 SFIN. Ed. Everlindo Henklein. Circ: 1,000.

330.021 ISL ISSN 1605-9468
PENINGAMAL. Text in Icelandic. 1999. q. **Document type:** *Government.* **Description:** Contains economic statistics in tables, short articles on the latest economic developments, an overview of various aspects of the Icelandic economy, and announcements from the Central Bank of Iceland.
Supersedes (in 1999): Hagtoelur Manadarins (0256-7288)
Related titles: ♦ English ed.: Central Bank of Iceland. Monetary Bulletin. ISSN 1607-6680.
Published by: (Hagfraedideild), Sedlabanki Islands/Central Bank of Iceland, Kalkofnsvegur 1, Reykjavik, 150, Iceland. TEL 354-569-9600, FAX 354-569-9608, sedlabanki@sedlabanki.is, http://www.sedlabanki.is. Ed. Mar Gudmundsson.

331.2 CAN ISSN 0840-8750
CODEN: PLAIEY
PERSPECTIVES ON LABOUR AND INCOME. Text in English. 1989. q. CND 63 (effective 2005). index. **Document type:** *Government.* **Description:** Brings together and analyzes a wide range of data.
Related titles: Online - full text ed.: (from Micromedia ProQuest); French ed.: L'Emploi et le Revenu en Perspective. ISSN 0843-4565.
Indexed: CBCABus, CBCARef, CBPI, CPerI, JEL, PAIS, SOPODA, SSA, SociolAb.
—CISTI. **CCC.**
Published by: Statistics Canada, Operations and Integration Division, Circulation Management, Jean Talon Bldg, 2 C12, Tunney's Pasture, Ottawa, ON K1A 0T6, Canada. TEL 613-951-7277, 800-267-6677, FAX 613-951-1584, http://www.statcan.ca.

339 PER
PERU. INSTITUTO NACIONAL DE ESTADISTICA. BOLETIN ANUAL. Text in Spanish. 1983. irreg.
Published by: Instituto Nacional de Estadistica y Informatica, Oficina Regional de Estadistica del Cusco (Subsidiary of: Instituto Nacional de Estadistica), Direccion General de Indicadores Economicos y Sociales, Av. 28 de Julio 1056, Lima, Peru. Ed. Eduardo Diaz Zarate. Pub. Jorge Maza. R&P Marleni Orrillo Huaman. Adv. contact Dr. Boris Lopez Acuna. Circ: 500.

338 BRA ISSN 0100-5138
HC186
PESQUISA INDUSTRIAL. Text in Portuguese. 1952. a. USD 40 per vol.. **Document type:** *Government.*
Formerly (until 1972): Producao Industrial (0525-3969)
Published by: Fundacao Instituto Brasileiro de Geografia e Estatistica, Centro de Documentacao e Disseminacao de Informacoes, Rua General Canabarro, 706 Andar 2, Maracana, Rio de Janeiro, RJ 20271-201, Brazil. TEL 55-21-264-5424, FAX 55-21-2841959, http://www.ibge.gov.br.

PHARMACOECONOMICS AND OUTCOMES NEWS; rapid alerts to world pharmacoeconomic news, views and practical application. see *PHARMACY AND PHARMACOLOGY—Abstracting, Bibliographies, Statistics*

016.33 PHL ISSN 0115-4192
PHILIPPINE BUSINESS AND INDUSTRY INDEX. Text in English. 1980. a. USD 200. bk.rev. **Document type:** *Abstract/Index.*
Published by: Library Integrated Services Cooperative, U.P. Campus, P.O. Box 192, Quezon City, 1101, Philippines. TEL 921-9231. Ed. Vidal E Santos. Circ: 500.

330 310 PHL
PHILIPPINE STATISTICAL DEVELOPMENT PROGRAM. Text in English. every 5 yrs., latest 1993. USD 56 in Asia; USD 64 in Australia & New Zealand; USD 75 in US & Canada; USD 88 in Latin America; USD 108 elsewhere. **Document type:** *Government.* **Description:** Analyzes the major developments in the Philippine Statistical System during the preceding planning period; sets objectives, strategies and statistical programs for the next six years.
Published by: National Statistical Coordination Board, c/o National Statistical Information Center, Midland-Buendia Bldg, 403 Sen. Gil Puyat Ave., Makati City, Philippines. TEL 63-2-890-9405, FAX 63-2-890-9408, nscb_nsic@mozcom.com.

315 336 PHL
PHILIPPINE STATISTICAL YEARBOOK. Text in English. 1974. a. USD 142 in Asia; USD 153 in Australia & New Zealand; USD 163 in US & Canada; USD 165 in Europe; USD 185 in Latin America; USD 213 elsewhere. **Document type:** *Government.* **Description:** Contains a comprehensive compilation of major economic and social statistical information about the Philippines, its people and environment, and selected countries of the world produced by various government agencies, and international organization.
Formerly: N E D A Statistical Yearbook of the Philippines
Published by: National Statistical Coordination Board, c/o National Statistical Information Center, Midland-Buendia Bldg, 403 Sen. Gil Puyat Ave., Makati City, Philippines. TEL 63-2-890-9405, FAX 63-2-890-9408, nscb_nsic@mozcom.com.

331.021 PHL
PHILIPPINES. BUREAU OF LABOR AND EMPLOYMENT STATISTICS. CURRENT LABOR STATISTICS. Text in English. 1980. m. PHP 400 (effective 1999). stat. **Document type:** *Government.* **Description:** Statistical compendium; data presented in monthly and quarterly breakdown for current year.
Published by: Bureau of Labor and Employment Statistics, Department of Labor and Employment, 3-F Dole Bldg, Intramuros, Manila, 1002, Philippines. TEL 63-2-5273577, FAX 63-2-5273579, tsd@manila-online.net, http://www.manila-online.net. Circ: 350.

331.021 PHL
PHILIPPINES. BUREAU OF LABOR AND EMPLOYMENT STATISTICS. LABOR AND EMPLOYMENT STATISTICAL REPORT. Text in English. 1989. q. PHP 128. charts; stat. **Document type:** *Government.* **Description:** Descriptive analysis of quarterly labor and employment statistics compared to previous year.
Published by: Bureau of Labor and Employment Statistics, Department of Labor and Employment, 3-F Dole Bldg, Intramuros, Manila, 1002, Philippines. TEL 63-2-5273577, FAX 63-2-5273579, tsd@manila-online.net, http://www.manila-online.net. Circ: 300.

331.21021 PHL
PHILIPPINES. BUREAU OF LABOR AND EMPLOYMENT STATISTICS. OCCUPATIONAL WAGES SURVEY. Text in English. 1990. a. free. **Document type:** *Government.*
Published by: Bureau of Labor and Employment Statistics, Department of Labor and Employment, 3-F Dole Bldg, Intramuros, Manila, 1002, Philippines. TEL 63-2-5273577, FAX 63-2-5273579, tsd@manila-online.net, http://www.manila-online.net. Circ: 500.

331.1 315 PHL
HD8713
PHILIPPINES. BUREAU OF LABOR AND EMPLOYMENT STATISTICS. YEARBOOK OF LABOR STATISTICS. Text in English. 1973. a. PHP 300. stat. **Document type:** *Government.* **Description:** Statistical compendium containing some historical data series.
Formerly: Philippines. Labor Statistics Service. Yearbook of Labor Statistics (0115-1851)
Published by: Bureau of Labor and Employment Statistics, Department of Labor and Employment, 3-F Dole Bldg, Intramuros, Manila, 1002, Philippines. TEL 63-2-5273577, FAX 63-2-5273579, tsd@manila-online.net, http://www.manila-online.net/bles. Circ: 350.

330 310 PHL
PHILIPPINES. NATIONAL STATISTICAL COORDINATION BOARD. ECONOMIC AND SOCIAL INDICATORS. Text in English. a. USD 127 in Asia; USD 138 in Australia & New Zealand; USD 148 in US & Canada; USD 150 in Europe; USD 170 in Latin America; USD 198 elsewhere. **Document type:** *Government.* **Description:** Contains about 100 indicators grouped into 13 developmental goal areas and subareas: production, finance, foreign trade, natural and energy resources, employment, household income, expenditures and prices, population, health and nutrition, housing, education, social welfare and community development, public order, safety and justice.
Published by: National Statistical Coordination Board, c/o National Statistical Information Center, Midland-Buendia Bldg, 403 Sen. Gil Puyat Ave., Makati City, Philippines. TEL 63-2-890-9405, FAX 63-2-890-9408, nscb_nsic@mozcom.com.

330 310 PHL
PHILIPPINES. NATIONAL STATISTICAL COORDINATION BOARD. REGIONAL SOCIAL AND ECONOMIC TRENDS SERIES. (Separate regional issues avail.) Text in English. 1993. a. USD 102 in Asia; USD 113 in Australia & New Zealand; USD 123 in US & Canada; USD 125 in Europe; USD 145 in Latin America; USD 173 elsewhere. **Document type:** *Government.* **Description:** Presents major social and economic developments at the regional and subregional levels in data series with textual analysis and graphical illustration.
Published by: National Statistical Coordination Board, c/o National Statistical Information Center, Midland-Buendia Bldg, 403 Sen. Gil Puyat Ave., Makati City, Philippines. TEL 63-2-890-9405, FAX 63-2-890-9408, nscb_nsic@mozcom.com.

381 PHL ISSN 0116-2659
LA1290
PHILIPPINES. NATIONAL STATISTICS OFFICE. ANNUAL SURVEY OF ESTABLISHMENTS. Text in English. 1973. a., latest 1992. USD 50. Supplement avail. **Document type:** *Government.* **Description:** Presents the final results of the survey on the structure, trends, and levels of economic activity in the country.
Formerly: Philippines. National Census and Statistics Office. Annual Survey of Establishments
Related titles: Diskette ed.
Published by: National Statistics Office, Ramon Magsaysay Blvd, PO Box 779, Manila, Philippines. FAX 63-2-610794.

330 310 PHL
PHILIPPINES. NATIONAL STATISTICS OFFICE. CENSUS OF ESTABLISHMENTS. Text in English. every 5 yrs. (in 11 vols.). **Document type:** *Government.* **Description:** A nationwide comprehensive collection and compilation of statistical information pertaining to business operations of establishments at any time or the whole year.
Related titles: Diskette ed.
Published by: National Statistics Office, Ramon Magsaysay Blvd, PO Box 779, Manila, Philippines. FAX 63-2-610794.

B

330 310 PHL ISSN 0117-9772
HB235.P46
PHILIPPINES. NATIONAL STATISTICS OFFICE. CONSUMER PRICE INDEX IN THE PHILIPPINES. Text in English. a. illus. **Document type:** *Government.* **Description:** Presents changes in the price level of goods and services that most people buy for day-to-day consumption. Also reports inflation rates and the purchasing power of the peso, and includes a textual analysis.
Related titles: Diskette ed.
Published by: National Statistics Office, Ramon Magsaysay Blvd, PO Box 779, Manila, Philippines. FAX 63-2-610794.

330 310 PHL
PHILIPPINES. NATIONAL STATISTICS OFFICE. DIRECTORY OF LARGE ESTABLISHMENTS. Text in English. irreg., latest 1983. USD 90. **Document type:** *Directory, Government.*
Published by: National Statistics Office, Ramon Magsaysay Blvd, PO Box 779, Manila, Philippines. FAX 63-2-610794.

330 USA
PLAYBOY ENTERPRISES. ANNUAL REPORT. Text in English. a. **Document type:** *Corporate.*
Published by: Playboy Enterprises, Inc., 680 N Lake Shore Dr, Chicago, IL 60611. TEL 312-751-8000, FAX 312-751-2818.

331 314 POL ISSN 1506-7904
HD5701
POLAND. GLOWNY URZAD STATYSTYCZNY. PRACUJACY W GOSPODARCE NARODOWEJ. Text in Polish. 1969. a. PLZ 24. **Document type:** *Government.*
Formerly (until 1996): Poland. Glowny Urzad Statystyczny. Zatrudnienie w Gospodarce Narodowej (0079-2896)
Published by: (Poland. Glowny Urzad Statystyczny), Zaklad Wydawnictw Statystycznych, Al Niepodleglosci 208, Warsaw, 00925, Poland. TEL 48 22 25-03-45.

382 314 POL ISSN 1643-7721
HF3636
POLAND. GLOWNY URZAD STATYSTYCZNY. ROCZNIK STATYSTYCZNY HANDLU ZAGRANICZNEGO/YEARBOOK OF FOREIGN TRADE STATISTICS. Text in Polish. 1965. irreg. PLZ 56. **Document type:** *Government.*
Former titles (until 1993): Poland. Glowny Urzad Statystyczny. Handel Zagraniczny (0867-3004); (until 1990): Poland. Glowny Urzad Statystyczny. Rocznik Statystyczny Handlu Zagranicznego (0079-2691)
Related titles: CD-ROM ed.: ISSN 1642-4204. 2001.
Published by: (Poland. Glowny Urzad Statystyczny), Zaklad Wydawnictw Statystycznych, Al Niepodleglosci 208, Warsaw, 00925, Poland. TEL 48 22 25-03-45.

PORTUGAL. INSTITUTO NACIONAL DE ESTATISTICA. CONTAS NACIONAIS. see *BUSINESS AND ECONOMICS—Macroeconomics*

336 314 PRT
PORTUGAL. INSTITUTO NACIONAL DE ESTATISTICA. ESTATISTICAS DAS FINANCAS PUBLICAS. CONTINENTE, ACORES E MADEIRA. Text in French, Portuguese. 1968. a. **Document type:** *Government.* **Description:** Provides information on public sector divided into three categories: Central Government, Local Government and Social Security.
Formerly: Portugal. Instituto Nacional de Estatistica. Estatisticas das Financas Publicas (0377-2276)
Published by: Instituto Nacional de Estatistica, Ave. Antonio Jose de Almeida 2, Lisbon, 1000-043, Portugal. TEL 351-21-8426100, FAX 351-21-8426380, ine@ine.pt, http://www.ine.pt/.

331.11 314 PRT
PORTUGAL. MINISTERIO DO TRABALHO. SERVICO DE ESTATISTICAS. ESTATISTICAS DO TRABALHO. Text in Portuguese; Summaries in English, French. 1975. irreg. **Document type:** *Government.*

▼ new title ➤ refereed ✶ unverified ♦ full entry avail.

Published by: (Portugal. Servico de Informacao Cientifica e Tecnica), Ministerio do Trabalho, Praca de Londres, 2 - 16o, Lisbon, 1049-056, Portugal. TEL 351-21-8424100, FAX 351-21-8424108, gmtss@mtss.gov.pt, http://www.mtss.gov.pt/.

330 332.1 JPN ISSN 0386-6297
PRICE INDEXES MONTHLY. Text in English, Japanese. m. JPY 920 per issue (effective 1998). 130 p./no.; **Description:** Contains wholesale price indexes, export and import price indexes, corporate service price index, input-output price indexes of manufacturing industry by sector, and monthly percentage change for all commodities.
Indexed: RASB.
Published by: (Research and Statistics Department), Bank of Japan/Nippon Ginko, c/o Public Relations Department, 2-1-1 Hongoku-cho-Nihonbashi, Chuo-ku, Tokyo, 1030000, Japan. TEL 81-3-3279-1111, FAX 81-3-3510-1374, http://www.boj.or.jp/en.index.htm. **Dist. by:** Tokiwa Sohgoh Service Co. Ltd., Publication and Research Department, Kyodo Bldg, 2-4 Hongokucho, Nihonbashi 3-chome, Chuo-ku, Tokyo 103-0027, Japan. TEL 81-3-3270-5713, FAX 81-3-3270-5710; **Overseas dist. by:** Japan Publications Trading Co., Ltd., Book Export II Dept, PO Box 5030, Tokyo International, Tokyo 101-3191, Japan. TEL 81-3-32923753, FAX 81-3-32920410.

B

331 016 USA ISSN 0037-1351
Z7164.L1
PRINCETON UNIVERSITY. INDUSTRIAL RELATIONS SECTION. SELECTED REFERENCES. Text in English. 1969. 5/yr. **Document type:** *Academic/Scholarly.*
Indexed: PAIS.
Published by: Princeton University, Industrial Relations Section, Firestone Library, Princeton, NJ 08544. TEL 609-258-4040. Circ: 1,500.

330 DEU ISSN 0342-0922
Z7164.L1
PROARBEIT; Informationssystem zu Arbeit, Beruf, Berufsbildung und Arbeitswissenschaft. Text in German. 2/yr. **Document type:** *Bibliography.*
Related titles: CD-ROM ed.; Online - full text ed.
Published by: Bundesanstalt fuer Arbeit, Institut fuer Arbeitsmarkt- und Berufsforschung, Regensburger Str 104, Nuernberg, 90478, Germany. TEL 49-911-1790, FAX 49-911-1793258, iab.anfragen@iab.de, http://iab.de.

338.528 USA ISSN 1099-2863
HB235.U6
PRODUCER PRICE INDEXES. Text in English. 1956. m. USD 56 domestic includes supplement; USD 70 foreign includes supplement. Supplement avail.; back issues avail.; reprint service avail. from CIS. **Document type:** *Government.* **Description:** Reports on price movements at the primary market level, arranged by stage of processing and by commodity.
Former titles (until 1997): P P I Detailed Report (1099-2855); (until 1996): Producer Price Indexes (0882-5270); (until 1985): Producer Prices and Price Indexes (0161-7311); (until 1978): Wholesale Prices and Price Indexes (0498-7667)
Related titles: ♦ Abridged ed.: U.S. Bureau of Labor Statistics. P P I Detailed Report. ISSN 1543-3145.
Indexed: AmStI, PAIS, PROMT, RASB.
Published by: U.S. Department of Labor, Bureau of Labor Statistics, Postal Square Bldg., 2 Massachusetts Ave, NE, Washington, DC 20212-0001. TEL 202-691-5200, http://www.bls.gov. **Subscr. to:** U.S. Government Printing Office, Superintendent of Documents.

338 310 JPN ISSN 1342-338X
HC415.L3
PRODUCTIVITY STATISTICS; productivity indexes and levels in APO member countries. Text in Japanese. 1984. a. free.
Published by: Asian Productivity Organization, 1-2-10Hirakawa-cho, Chiyoda-ku, Tokyo, 102-0093, Japan. FAX 81-3-5226-3950, apo@gol.com, http://www.apo-tokyo.com. Circ: 800.

330.9 CHE
PRODUKTIONS- UND WERTSCHOEPFUNGSSTATISTIK. BUCHHALTUNGSERGEBNISSE SCHWEIZERISCHER UNTERNEHMUNGEN/STATISTIQUE DE LA PRODUCTION ET DE LA VALEUR AJOUTEE. LES RESULTATS COMPTABLES DES ENTREPRISES SUISSES. Text in French, German. 1980. a. CHF 16 (effective 2001). **Document type:** *Government.*
Formerly: Buchhaltungsergebnisse Schweizerische Unternehmungen
Published by: Bundesamt fuer Statistik, Espace de l'Europe 10, Neuchatel, 2010, Switzerland. TEL 41-32-7136011, FAX 41-32-7136012, information@bfs.admin.ch, http://www.admin.ch/bfs.

380 CHE
PRODUZENTEN- UND IMPORTPREISINDEX/INDICE DES PRIX A LA PRODUCTION ET A L'IMPORTATION. Text in French, German. 1988. m. CHF 44 (effective 2001). **Document type:** *Government.*
Formerly: Grosshandelspreisinde
Published by: Bundesamt fuer Statistik, Espace de l'Europe 10, Neuchatel, 2010, Switzerland. TEL 41-32-7136011, FAX 41-32-7136012, information@bfs.admin.ch, http://www.admin.ch/bfs.

314 CYP
PROFILES OF EARNINGS IN CYPRUS: BY EDUCATION, OCCUPATION, EXPERIENCE, AGE, SEX AND SECTOR. Text in English. 1979. irreg. CYP 0.50 (effective 1999). **Document type:** *Government.* **Description:** Analyzes earnings by education, occupational experience, age, sex, and sector.
Published by: Ministry of Finance, Department of Statistics and Research, 13 Andreas Araouzos St, Nicosia, 1444, Cyprus. TEL 357-2-309318, FAX 357-2-374830, cydsr@cytanet.com.cy, http://www.pio.gov.cy/dsr.

322 GBR
PROJECT FINANCE BOOK OF LISTS (YEARS). Text in English. a. GBP 100, USD 160 (effective 1998). **Document type:** *Trade.* **Description:** Consists of league tables of project financing globally, by region, country and sector, ranking top arrangers, providers, sponsors, contractors, advisers and lawyers. Includes contact listing.
Related titles: ♦ Supplement to: Project Finance. ISSN 1462-0014.
Published by: Euromoney Publications plc, Nestor House, Playhouse Yard, London, EC4V 5EX, United Kingdom. TEL 44-207-7798673, FAX 44-20-77798541.

PUBLIC RELATIONS REVIEW. see *ADVERTISING AND PUBLIC RELATIONS*

330.9 LUX ISSN 1606-4879
PUBLICATIONS ET BASES DE DONNEES. Variant title: Mini-Guide Pratique. Text in French. 1996. a. **Document type:** *Government.*
Related titles: English ed.: Eurostat Publications and Databases. ISSN 1606-4941; German ed.: Eurostat Veroeffentlichungen und Datenbanken. ISSN 1606-4933.
Published by: European Commission, Statistical Office of the European Communities, Rue Alcide de Gasperi, Luxembourg, 2920, Luxembourg. TEL 352-4301-34526, FAX 352-4301-34415, eurostat-infodesk@cec.eu.int, http://www.europa.eu.int/comm/eurostat.

331 317 PRI
PUERTO RICO. DEPARTMENT OF LABOR. EMPLEO, ASALARIADO NO AGRICOLA EN PUERTO RICO. Text in English, Spanish. m. **Document type:** *Government.*
Former titles: Puerto Rico. Department of Labor. Empleo, Horas y Salarios en las Industrias Manufactureras - Employment, Hours and Earnings in the Manufacturing Industries; Puerto Rico. Bureau of Labor Statistics. Salarios, Horas Semanales Trabajadas y Otras Condiciones de Trabajo
Published by: Department of Labor, Bureau of Labor Statistics, 505 Munoz Rivera Ave., Hato Rey, 00918, Puerto Rico. TEL 787-754-5351. Ed. Antonio Padilla Torres.

330.9 PRI
PUERTO RICO ECONOMIC INDICATORS. Text in English. q. charts; stat. **Description:** Compiles basic economic and statistical information from various sources.
Published by: Government Development Bank for Puerto Rico, PO Box 42001, Minillas Sta, San Juan, 00940-2001, Puerto Rico. TEL 787-728-9200, FAX 787-268-5496.

332.1 ITA
QUADRO DI SINTESI DEL BOLLETTINO STATISTICO; dati territoriali sul credito, la finanza e i tassi di interesse bancari. Text in Italian. 1998. q. free to institutions. back issues avail. **Document type:** *Bulletin.*
Published by: Banca d'Italia, Via Nazionale 187, Rome, 00184, Italy. TEL 39-06-47922333, FAX 39-06-47922059, http://www.bancaditalia.it. Ed. Claudio Conegliani.

310 330 IND ISSN 0079-9564
HA1728.R3
RAJASTHAN, INDIA. DIRECTORATE OF ECONOMICS AND STATISTICS. BASIC STATISTICS. Text in English. 1956. a. INR 50. **Document type:** *Government.*
Published by: Directorate of Economics and Statistics, Tilak Marg, Jaipur, Rajasthan, India.

330 COG
RAPPORT D'ACTIVITES DES ENTREPRISES DU SECTEUR MODERNE. Text in French. 1974. a. XAF 5,000. **Document type:** *Government.*
Indexed: RASB.
Published by: Centre National de la Statistique et des Etudes Economiques, BP 2031, Brazzaville, Congo, Republic. TEL 242-83-36-94.

016.658 RUS ISSN 0235-8883
REFERATIVNYI ZHURNAL. EKONOMICHESKIE ASPEKTY ORGANIZATSII I TEKHNIKI SISTEM UPRAVLENIYA. Text in Russian. 1970. m. USD 113 foreign (effective 2006). **Document type:** *Journal, Abstract/Index.*
Related titles: CD-ROM ed.; Online - full text ed.
Published by: Vserossiiskii Institut Nauchnoi i Tekhnicheskoi Informatsii (VINITI), Ul Usievicha 20, Moscow, 125190, Russian Federation. TEL 7-095-1526441, FAX 7-095-9430060, dir@viniti.ru, http://www.viniti.ru. **Dist. by:** Informnauka Ltd., Ul Usievicha 20, Moscow 125190, Russian Federation. alfimov@viniti.ru.

016.33 RUS
REFERATIVNYI ZHURNAL. EKONOMIKA NEPROIZVODSTVENNOI SFERY. Text in Russian. 1960. m. USD 103 foreign (effective 2006). **Document type:** *Journal, Abstract/Index.*
Related titles: CD-ROM ed.; Online - full text ed.
Published by: Vserossiiskii Institut Nauchnoi i Tekhnicheskoi Informatsii (VINITI), Ul Usievicha 20, Moscow, 125190, Russian Federation. TEL 7-095-1526441, FAX 7-095-9430060, dir@viniti.ru, http://www.viniti.ru. **Dist. by:** Informnauka Ltd., Ul Usievicha 20, Moscow 125190, Russian Federation. alfimov@viniti.ru.

016.33 RUS ISSN 0135-9797
REFERATIVNYI ZHURNAL. EKONOMIKA OTRASLEI KHIMIKO-LESNOGO KOMPLEKSA. Text in Russian. 1960. m. USD 113 foreign (effective 2006). **Document type:** *Journal, Abstract/Index.*
Related titles: CD-ROM ed.; Online - full text ed.
Published by: Vserossiiskii Institut Nauchnoi i Tekhnicheskoi Informatsii (VINITI), Ul Usievicha 20, Moscow, 125190, Russian Federation. TEL 7-095-1526441, FAX 7-095-9430060, dir@viniti.ru, http://www.viniti.ru. **Dist. by:** Informnauka Ltd., Ul Usievicha 20, Moscow 125190, Russian Federation. alfimov@viniti.ru.

016.33 RUS ISSN 0135-9800
REFERATIVNYI ZHURNAL. EKONOMIKA OTRASLEI LEGKOI PROMYSHLENNOSTI. Text in Russian. 1960. m. USD 96 foreign (effective 2006). **Document type:** *Journal, Abstract/Index.*
Related titles: CD-ROM ed.; Online - full text ed.
Published by: Vserossiiskii Institut Nauchnoi i Tekhnicheskoi Informatsii (VINITI), Ul Usievicha 20, Moscow, 125190, Russian Federation. TEL 7-095-1526441, FAX 7-095-9430060, dir@viniti.ru, http://www.viniti.ru. **Dist. by:** Informnauka Ltd., Ul Usievicha 20, Moscow 125190, Russian Federation. alfimov@viniti.ru.

016.33 016.669 RUS ISSN 0204-3793
REFERATIVNYI ZHURNAL. EKONOMIKA OTRASLEI METALLURGICHESKOGO I MASHINOSTROITELNOGO KOMPLEKSOV. Text in Russian. 1960. m. USD 103 foreign (effective 2006). **Document type:** *Journal, Abstract/Index.*
Related titles: CD-ROM ed.; Online - full text ed.
Published by: Vserossiiskii Institut Nauchnoi i Tekhnicheskoi Informatsii (VINITI), Ul Usievicha 20, Moscow, 125190, Russian Federation. TEL 7-095-1526441, FAX 7-095-9430060, dir@viniti.ru, http://www.viniti.ru. **Dist. by:** Informnauka Ltd., Ul Usievicha 20, Moscow 125190, Russian Federation. alfimov@viniti.ru.

016.33 016.664 RUS ISSN 0204-3777
REFERATIVNYI ZHURNAL. EKONOMIKA OTRASLEI PISHCHEVOI PROMYSHLENNOSTI. Text in Russian. 1960. m. USD 110 foreign (effective 2006). **Document type:** *Journal, Abstract/Index.*
Related titles: CD-ROM ed.; Online - full text ed.
Published by: Vserossiiskii Institut Nauchnoi i Tekhnicheskoi Informatsii (VINITI), Ul Usievicha 20, Moscow, 125190, Russian Federation. TEL 7-095-1526441, FAX 7-095-9430060, dir@viniti.ru, http://www.viniti.ru. **Dist. by:** Informnauka Ltd., Ul Usievicha 20, Moscow 125190, Russian Federation. alfimov@viniti.ru.

016.33 RUS ISSN 0204-3785
REFERATIVNYI ZHURNAL. EKONOMIKA OTRASLEI TOPLIVNO - ENERGETICHESKOGO KOMPLEKSA. Text in Russian. 1960. m. USD 113 foreign (effective 2006). **Document type:** *Journal, Abstract/Index.*
Related titles: CD-ROM ed.; Online - full text ed.
Published by: Vserossiiskii Institut Nauchnoi i Tekhnicheskoi Informatsii (VINITI), Ul Usievicha 20, Moscow, 125190, Russian Federation. TEL 7-095-1526441, FAX 7-095-9430060, dir@viniti.ru, http://www.viniti.ru. **Dist. by:** Informnauka Ltd., Ul Usievicha 20, Moscow 125190, Russian Federation. alfimov@viniti.ru.

016.33 RUS ISSN 0203-6223
HC10
REFERATIVNYI ZHURNAL. EKONOMIKA PROMYSHLENNOSTI. Text in Russian. 1960. m. USD 1,121 foreign (effective 2006). **Document type:** *Journal, Abstract/Index.*
Related titles: CD-ROM ed.; Online - full text ed.
—Linda Hall.
Published by: Vserossiiskii Institut Nauchnoi i Tekhnicheskoi Informatsii (VINITI), Ul Usievicha 20, Moscow, 125190, Russian Federation. TEL 7-095-1526441, FAX 7-095-9430060, dir@viniti.ru, http://www.viniti.ru. **Dist. by:** Informnauka Ltd., Ul Usievicha 20, Moscow 125190, Russian Federation. alfimov@viniti.ru.

016.33 016.691 RUS
REFERATIVNYI ZHURNAL. EKONOMIKA STROITEL'STVA. Text in Russian. 1960. m. USD 103 foreign (effective 2006). **Document type:** *Journal, Abstract/Index.*
Related titles: CD-ROM ed.; Online - full text ed.
Published by: Vserossiiskii Institut Nauchnoi i Tekhnicheskoi Informatsii (VINITI), Ul Usievicha 20, Moscow, 125190, Russian Federation. TEL 7-095-1526441, FAX 7-095-9430060, dir@viniti.ru, http://www.viniti.ru. **Dist. by:** Informnauka Ltd., Ul Usievicha 20, Moscow 125190, Russian Federation. alfimov@viniti.ru.

016.33 016.388 016.385 RUS
REFERATIVNYI ZHURNAL. EKONOMIKA TRANSPORTA, SVIAZI I TELEKOMMUNIKATSII. Text in Russian. 1960. m. USD 103 foreign (effective 2006). **Document type:** *Journal, Abstract/Index.*
Related titles: CD-ROM ed.; Online - full text ed.
Published by: Vserossiiskii Institut Nauchnoi i Tekhnicheskoi Informatsii (VINITI), Ul Usievicha 20, Moscow, 125190, Russian Federation. TEL 7-095-1526441, FAX 7-095-9430060, dir@viniti.ru, http://www.viniti.ru. **Dist. by:** Informnauka Ltd., Ul Usievicha 20, Moscow 125190, Russian Federation. alfimov@viniti.ru.

016.6583 RUS ISSN 0235-8832
REFERATIVNYI ZHURNAL. KADRY, EKONOMIKA OBRAZOVANIYA. Text in Russian. 1960. m. USD 147 foreign (effective 2006). **Document type:** *Journal, Abstract/Index.*
Related titles: CD-ROM ed.; Online - full text ed.
—East View.
Published by: Vserossiiskii Institut Nauchnoi i Tekhnicheskoi Informatsii (VINITI), Ul Usievicha 20, Moscow, 125190, Russian Federation. TEL 7-095-1526441, FAX 7-095-9430060, dir@viniti.ru, http://www.viniti.ru. **Dist. by:** Informnauka Ltd., Ul Usievicha 20, Moscow 125190, Russian Federation. alfimov@viniti.ru.

016.677 RUS ISSN 0034-2432
TS1300 CODEN: RZRAA7
REFERATIVNYI ZHURNAL. LEGKAYA PROMYSHLENNOST'. TEKHNOLOGIYA I OBORUDOVANIYE. Text in Russian. 1956. m. USD 399 foreign (effective 2006). **Document type:** *Journal, Abstract/Index.*
Related titles: CD-ROM ed.; Online - full text ed.
Indexed: ChemAb.
—East View, Linda Hall.
Published by: Vserossiiskii Institut Nauchnoi i Tekhnicheskoi Informatsii (VINITI), Ul Usievicha 20, Moscow, 125190, Russian Federation. TEL 7-095-1526441, FAX 7-095-9430060, dir@viniti.ru, http://www.viniti.ru. Ed. Yurii Arskii. **Dist. by:** Informnauka Ltd., Ul Usievicha 20, Moscow 125190, Russian Federation. alfimov@viniti.ru.

016.33 RUS ISSN 0235-8891
REFERATIVNYI ZHURNAL. METODY UPRAVLENIYA EKONOMIKOI. Text in Russian. 1970. m. USD 180 foreign (effective 2006). **Document type:** *Journal, Abstract/Index.*
Related titles: CD-ROM ed.; Online - full text ed.
Published by: Vserossiiskii Institut Nauchnoi i Tekhnicheskoi Informatsii (VINITI), Ul Usievicha 20, Moscow, 125190, Russian Federation. TEL 7-095-1526441, FAX 7-095-9430060, dir@viniti.ru, http://www.viniti.ru. **Dist. by:** Informnauka Ltd., Ul Usievicha 20, Moscow 125190, Russian Federation. alfimov@viniti.ru.

016.33 RUS ISSN 0204-3807
REFERATIVNYI ZHURNAL. MIROVAYA EKONOMIKA. SOTSYAL'NO-EKONOMICHESKOE RAZVITIE STRAN MIRA. Text in Russian. 1960. m. USD 178 foreign (effective 2006). **Document type:** *Journal, Abstract/Index.*
Related titles: CD-ROM ed.; Online - full text ed.
—East View.
Published by: Vserossiiskii Institut Nauchnoi i Tekhnicheskoi Informatsii (VINITI), Ul Usievicha 20, Moscow, 125190, Russian Federation. TEL 7-095-1526441, FAX 7-095-9430060, dir@viniti.ru, http://www.viniti.ru. **Dist. by:** Informnauka Ltd., Ul Usievicha 20, Moscow 125190, Russian Federation. alfimov@viniti.ru.

016.33 RUS ISSN 0135-9789
REFERATIVNYI ZHURNAL. OBSHCHEOTRASLEVYE VOPROSY SOVERSHENSTVOVANIYA KHOZYAISTVENNOGO MEKHANIZMA. Text in Russian. 1960. m. USD 112 foreign (effective 2006). **Document type:** *Journal, Abstract/Index.*
Related titles: CD-ROM ed.; Online - full text ed.
Published by: Vserossiiskii Institut Nauchnoi i Tekhnicheskoi Informatsii (VINITI), Ul Usievicha 20, Moscow, 125190, Russian Federation. TEL 7-095-1526441, FAX 7-095-9430060, dir@viniti.ru, http://www.viniti.ru. **Dist. by:** Informnauka Ltd., Ul Usievicha 20, Moscow 125190, Russian Federation. alfimov@viniti.ru.

016.658 RUS ISSN 0132-5639
HD28 CODEN: RZOUEM
REFERATIVNYI ZHURNAL. ORGANIZATSIYA UPRAVLENIYA. Text in Russian. 1965. m. USD 224 foreign (effective 2006). **Document type:** *Journal, Abstract/Index.*
Formerly: Referativnyi Zhurnal. Organizatsiya Upravleniya Promyshlennost'yu (0034-253X)
Related titles: CD-ROM ed.; Online - full text ed.
Indexed: RASB.
—Linda Hall.
Published by: Vserossiiskii Institut Nauchnoi i Tekhnicheskoi Informatsii (VINITI), Ul Usievicha 20, Moscow, 125190, Russian Federation. TEL 7-095-1526441, FAX 7-095-9430060, dir@viniti.ru, http://www.viniti.ru. Ed. Gavriil Popov. **Dist. by:** Informnauka Ltd., Ul Usievicha 20, Moscow 125190, Russian Federation. alfimov@viniti.ru.

016.51 016.33 RUS ISSN 0868-4685
REFERATIVNYI ZHURNAL. PRIMENENIE MATEMATICHESKIKH METODOV V EKONOMICHESKIKH ISSLEDOVANIYAKH I PLANIROVANII. Text in Russian. 1960. m. USD 117 foreign (effective 2006). **Document type:** *Journal, Abstract/Index.*
Related titles: CD-ROM ed.; Online - full text ed.
—East View.
Published by: Vserossiiskii Institut Nauchnoi i Tekhnicheskoi Informatsii (VINITI), Ul Usievicha 20, Moscow, 125190, Russian Federation. TEL 7-095-1526441, FAX 7-095-9430060, dir@viniti.ru, http://www.viniti.ru. **Dist. by:** Informnauka Ltd., Ul Usievicha 20, Moscow 125190, Russian Federation. alfimov@viniti.ru.

016.33 RUS
REFERATIVNYI ZHURNAL. PROBLEMY FUNKTSIONIROVANIYA RYNOCHNOGO KHOZIAISTVA. Text in Russian. 1960. m. USD 110 foreign (effective 2006). **Document type:** *Journal, Abstract/Index.*
Related titles: CD-ROM ed.; Online - full text ed.
Published by: Vserossiiskii Institut Nauchnoi i Tekhnicheskoi Informatsii (VINITI), Ul Usievicha 20, Moscow, 125190, Russian Federation. TEL 7-095-1526441, FAX 7-095-9430060, dir@viniti.ru, http://www.viniti.ru. **Dist. by:** Informnauka Ltd., Ul Usievicha 20, Moscow 125190, Russian Federation. alfimov@viniti.ru.

330.021 302.045195 RUS
REGIONY ROSSII. SOTSIAL'NO-EKONOMICHESKIE POKAZATELI (YEAR). Text in Russian. a., latest 2005. RUR 704 per issue (effective 2005). **Document type:** *Yearbook, Government.*
Published by: Gosudarstvennyi Komitet Rossiiskoi Federatsii po Statistike/Federal State Statistics Office, ul Myasnitskaya 39, Moscow, 107450, Russian Federation. TEL 7-095-2074902, FAX 7-095-2074087, stat@gks.ru, http://www.gks.ru.

338.0021 GBR
REGULATORY REVIEW (YEAR). Text in English. 1993. a. GBP 15 to non-members; price varies. **Document type:** *Trade.* **Description:** Reviews the year's important issues concerning the regulation of industries in the U.K.
Published by: Centre for the Study of Regulated Industries, School of Management, University of Bath, Bath, BA2 7AY, United Kingdom. TEL 44-1225-386742, FAX 44-1225-386743, recep@management.bath.ac.uk, http://www.bath.ac.uk/management/cri/home.htm. Ed. Peter Vass.

330.9 338 THA
REPORT OF THE (YEAR) BUSINESS TRADE AND SERVICES SURVEY. Text in English, Thai. 1969. a. (in 2 vols.). price varies. **Document type:** *Government.* **Description:** Contains data on number of establishments, persons engaged, employees and their compensation, expenditures and receipts, and value of fixed assets of business establishments.
Published by: (Thailand. Statistical Data Bank and Information Dissemination Division), National Statistical Office, Larn Luang Rd, Bangkok, 10100, Thailand. TEL 66-2-282-1535, FAX 66-2-281-3814, binfodsm@nso.go.th, http://www.nso.go.th/. Circ: 600.

330.9 338 THA
REPORT OF THE (YEAR) INDUSTRIAL CENSUS. Text in English, Thai. 1964. every 10 yrs. (in 7 vols.). price varies. **Document type:** *Government.* **Description:** Contains data on number, type and size of manufacturing establishments, number of persons engaged and remuneration, cost of production and various expenses, value of gross output, receipts and fixed assets of establishment.
Published by: (Thailand. Statistical Data Bank and Information Dissemination Division), National Statistical Office, Larn Luang Rd, Bangkok, 10100, Thailand. TEL 66-2-282-1535, FAX 66-2-281-3814, binfodsm@nso.go.th, http://www.nso.go.th/. Circ: 2,300.

304.6 330.9 THA
REPORT OF THE (YEAR) SURVEY OF FERTILITY IN THAILAND. Text in Thai. 1975. every 10 yrs. price varies. **Document type:** *Government.* **Description:** Contains a summary of statistics on age at first marriage, duration of marriage, age at first birth, number of children ever born, living children, children desired, prenatal care, delivering and breast feeding, rearing children and type of abortion if any.
Published by: (Thailand. Statistical Data Bank and Information Dissemination Division), National Statistical Office, Larn Luang Rd, Bangkok, 10100, Thailand. TEL 66-2-282-1535, FAX 66-2-281-3814, binfodsm@nso.go.th, http://www.nso.go.th/. Circ: 500.

330.9 331.12 THA
REPORT OF THE LABOR FORCE SURVEY, WHOLE KINGDOM, ROUND FOUR (YEAR). Text in Thai, English. 1963. q. (in 2 vols.). price varies. **Document type:** *Government.* **Description:** Contains information on the number and characteristics of the labor supply in Thailand.
Published by: (Thailand. Statistical Data Bank and Information Dissemination Division), National Statistical Office, Larn Luang Rd, Bangkok, 10100, Thailand. TEL 66-2-282-1535, FAX 66-2-281-3814, binfodsm@nso.go.th, http://www.nso.go.th/. Circ: 500.

338.021 ETH
REPORT ON SMALL SCALE MANUFACTURING INDUSTRIES SURVEY. Text in English. a. ETB 16, USD 2.20 (effective 1999). back issues avail. **Document type:** *Government.* **Description:** Presents data on total persons engaged, value and percentage contribution, gross value of production, value added by industrial group, fixed assets, investments, operations, employees, labor cost, sales revenue, establishments and more.
Related titles: CD-ROM ed.; Diskette ed.
Published by: Central Statistical Authority, PO Box 1143, Addis Ababa, Ethiopia. TEL 251-1-115470, FAX 251-1-550334.

332.1 319 330.9 AUS ISSN 0725-0320
HG189
RESERVE BANK OF AUSTRALIA. BULLETIN. Text in English. 1937. m. AUD 25 (effective 2003). charts; stat. cum.index. **Document type:** *Bulletin, Trade.*
Formerly (until Jul. 1981): Reserve Bank of Australia. Statistical Bulletin (0034-5504)
Related titles: Diskette ed.
Indexed: AusPAIS, KES, PAIS.
Published by: Reserve Bank of Australia, 65 Martin Place, PO Box 3947, Sydney, NSW 2001, Australia. TEL 61-2-9551-8111, FAX 61-2-9551-8000, rbainfo@rba.gov.au, http://www.rba.gov.au/. Circ: 2,000.

310 314 ROM ISSN 1454-4482
RESULTS AND PERFORMANCES OF CONSTRUCTION, TRADE AND SERVICES ENTERPRISES. Text in English, Romanian; Summaries in English, Romanian. 1999. a. ROL 75,000; USD 12 foreign. stat. **Document type:** *Government.* **Description:** Characterizes productive enterprises and commercial sectors in Rumania.
Published by: Comisia Nationala pentru Statistica/National Commission for Statistics, Bd. Libertatii 16, Sector 5, Bucharest, 70542, Romania. TEL 40-1-3363370, FAX 40-1-3124873, ciu@cus.kappa.ro. R&P Ivan Ungureanu Clementina.

RESULTS AND PERFORMANCES OF INDUSTRIAL ENTERPRISES (YEAR). see *STATISTICS*

382 ESP
RESUMENES ESTADISTICOS DE IMPORTACION. Text in Spanish. 1991. a. **Document type:** *Government.*
Related titles: Diskette ed.
Published by: Ministerio de Comercio y Turismo, Paseo Castellana, 162, pl. 16, Madrid, 28046, Spain. TEL 34-1-349-39-65, FAX 34-1-349-36-34. Circ: 1,000.

658.8021 GBR ISSN 1369-0469
RETAIL SALES. Cover title: U K Service Sector. SDM 28, Retail Sales. Text in English. 1980. m. charts; stat. back issues avail. **Document type:** *Government.*
Formerly (until 1996): Business Monitor: Retail Sales (0264-3979)
Related titles: Series of: Service and Distributive Monitors Series.
—BLDSC (7785.504392).
Published by: Office for National Statistics, Zone DG/18, 1 Drummond Gate, London, SW1V 2QQ, United Kingdom. TEL 44-20-7533-5888, FAX 44-1633-652747, info@statistics.gov.uk, http://www.statistics.gov.uk/products/p1478.asp. Ed. David Parker TEL 44-1633-812509. **Subscr. to:** Stationery Office, PO Box 276, London SW8 5DT, United Kingdom. TEL 44-20-7873-9090, FAX 44-207-873-8200.

336.2 FRA ISSN 1560-3660
REVENUE STATISTICS/STATISTIQUES DES RECETTES PUBLIQUES. Text in English, French. 1965. a. price varies.
Formerly: Revenue Statistics of O E C D Member Countries (0259-5249)
Related titles: Online - full content ed.: USD 145 (effective 1999).
Indexed: IIS.
—BLDSC (7785.819700).
Published by: Organization for Economic Cooperation and Development, 2 Rue Andre Pascal, Paris, 75775 Cedex 16, France. TEL 33-1-45248200, FAX 33-1-45248500, http://www.oecd.org. **Subscr. in N. America to:** O E C D Turpin North America, PO Box 194, Downingtown, PA 19335-0194. TEL 610-524-5361, 800-456-6323, FAX 610-524-5417, bookscustomer@turpinna.com.

330 016 ARG ISSN 0034-7825
REVISTA DE COMPENDIOS DE ARTICULOS DE ECONOMIA. Text in Spanish. 1964. irreg. exchange basis. **Document type:** *Academic/Scholarly.* **Description:** Covers brief summaries of articles on economics.

B

Published by: (Instituto de Economia y Finanzas), Universidad Nacional de Cordoba, Facultad de Ciencias Economicas, Ciudad Universitaria, Ave. Valparaiso, s/n, Cordoba, 5000, Argentina. TELEX BUCOR - AR 51822. Circ: 500.

REVISTA DE ECONOMIA Y ESTADISTICA. see *BUSINESS AND ECONOMICS*

RIVISTA ITALIANA DI ECONOMIA DEMOGRAFIA E STATISTICA. see *POPULATION STUDIES—Abstracting, Bibliographies, Statistics*

330.021 302.045195 RUS
ROSSIISKII STATISTICHESKII YEZHEGODNIK/RUSSIAN STATISTICAL YEARBOOK. Text in Russian. a., latest 2005. RUR 792 per issue (effective 2005). **Document type:** *Yearbook, Government.*
Related titles: CD-ROM ed.: RUR 1,475 per issue (effective 2005).
Published by: Gosudarstvennyi Komitet Rossiiskoi Federatsii po Statistike/Federal State Statistics Office, ul Myasnitskaya 39, Moscow, 107450, Russian Federation. TEL 7-095-2074902, FAX 7-095-2074087, stat@gks.ru, http://www.gks.ru.

330.021 RUS
ROSSIYA (YEAR). Text in Russian. a., latest 2005. RUR 38.50 per issue (effective 2005). **Document type:** *Government.* **Description:** Contains statistical data on main macro socio-economic indicators of different sectors of the economy.
Related titles: ♦ English Translation: Russia (Year).
Published by: Gosudarstvennyi Komitet Rossiiskoi Federatsii po Statistike/Federal State Statistics Office, ul Myasnitskaya 39, Moscow, 107450, Russian Federation. TEL 7-095-2074902, FAX 7-095-2074087, stat@gks.ru, http://www.gks.ru.

382.021 RUS
ROSSIYA I STRANY MIRA/RUSSIA AND COUNTRIES OF THE WORLD. Text in Russian. a. **Document type:** *Government.*
Published by: Gosudarstvennyi Komitet Rossiiskoi Federatsii po Statistike/Federal State Statistics Office, ul Myasnitskaya 39, Moscow, 107450, Russian Federation. TEL 7-095-2074902, FAX 7-095-2074087, stat@gks.ru, http://www.gks.ru.

330.021 RUS
ROSSIYA I STRANY S N G/RUSSIA AND C I S COUNTRIES. (Sodruzhestvo Nezavisimykh Gosudarstv) Text in Russian. q. RUR 484 (effective 2005). charts; stat. **Document type:** *Bulletin, Government.* **Description:** Contains main social and economic indicators of situation in Russia and the CIS countries. Publishes data on external economic relations and migration, official rates of exchange of national currencies of the CIS countries.
Published by: Gosudarstvennyi Komitet Rossiiskoi Federatsii po Statistike/Federal State Statistics Office, ul Myasnitskaya 39, Moscow, 107450, Russian Federation. TEL 7-095-2074902, FAX 7-095-2074087, stat@gks.ru, http://www.gks.ru.

330.021 302.045195 RUS
ROSSIYA V TSIFRAKH (YEAR); kratkii statisticheskii zbornik. Text in Russian. 1995. a., latest 2005. RUR 275 per issue (effective 2005). **Description:** Presented Information pertains to the social sphere, inflationary processes, financial performance of enterprises and organizations, investment activities, prices and tariffs.
Related titles: CD-ROM ed.: RUR 649 per issue (effective 2005); ♦ English Translation: Russia in Figures (Year).
Published by: Gosudarstvennyi Komitet Rossiiskoi Federatsii po Statistike/Federal State Statistics Office, ul Myasnitskaya 39, Moscow, 107450, Russian Federation. TEL 7-095-2074902, FAX 7-095-2074087, stat@gks.ru, http://www.gks.ru.

382 ROM ISSN 1223-0510
RUMANIA. COMISIA NATIONALA PENTRU STATISTICA. BULETIN STATISTIC DE COMERT EXTERIOR/RUMANIA. NATIONAL COMMISSION FOR STATISTICS. FOREIGN TRADE STATISTICS. Text in English, Romanian. m. ROL 330,000; USD 110 foreign. **Document type:** *Government.* **Description:** Presents data on foreign trade by exports, imports, trade balance, and destination and origin countries.
Published by: Comisia Nationala pentru Statistica/National Commission for Statistics, Bd. Libertatii 16, Sector 5, Bucharest, 70542, Romania. TEL 40-1-3363370, FAX 40-1-3124873.

330 ROM ISSN 1221-7050
HB235.R8
RUMANIA. COMISIA NATIONALA PENTRU STATISTICA. BULETIN STATISTIC DE PRETURI/RUMANIA. NATIONAL COMMISSION FOR STATISTICS. PRICES STATISTICAL BULLETIN. Text in English, Romanian. m. ROL 275,000; USD 110 foreign. **Document type:** *Government.* **Description:** Presents consumer price indices of the population by total, grouped by goods and services, industrial output, prices indices per total, sections and branches.
Published by: Comisia Nationala pentru Statistica/National Commission for Statistics, Bd. Libertatii 16, Sector 5, Bucharest, 70542, Romania. TEL 40-1-3363370, FAX 40-1-3124873.

338 ROM ISSN 1223-0502
HC405.A1
RUMANIA. COMISIA NATIONALA PENTRU STATISTICA. BULETIN STATISTIC INDUSTRIE/RUMANIA. NATIONAL COMMISSION FOR STATISTICS. STATISTICAL BULLETIN - INDUSTRY. Text in English, Romanian. m. ROL 220,000; USD 88 foreign. **Document type:** *Government.* **Description:** Presents data and comments referring to the level and evolution of industrial production, per total and by branches, the power resources from own production and import.
Published by: Comisia Nationala pentru Statistica/National Commission for Statistics, Bd. Libertatii 16, Sector 5, Bucharest, 70542, Romania. TEL 40-1-3363370, FAX 40-1-3124873.

330 ROM ISSN 1224-290X
RUMANIA. NATIONAL COMMISSION FOR STATISTICS. NATIONAL ACCOUNTS. Text in English. a. ROL 60,000; USD 15 foreign. **Document type:** *Government.* **Description:** Analyzes the evolution of main macroeconomic aggregates and their structure by sectors and branches. Covers the tables system data specific to national accounts.
Published by: Comisia Nationala pentru Statistica/National Commission for Statistics, Bd. Libertatii 16, Sector 5, Bucharest, 70542, Romania. TEL 40-1-3363370, FAX 40-1-3124873.

330.021 RUS
RUSSIA (YEAR). Text in English. a., latest 2005. RUR 55 per issue (effective 2005). **Document type:** *Government.* **Description:** Contains statistical data on main macro socio-economic indicators of different sectors of the economy.
Related titles: ♦ Translation of: Rossiya (Year).
Published by: Gosudarstvennyi Komitet Rossiiskoi Federatsii po Statistike/Federal State Statistics Office, ul Myasnitskaya 39, Moscow, 107450, Russian Federation. TEL 7-095-2074902, FAX 7-095-2074087, stat@gks.ru, http://www.gks.ru.

330.021 302.045195 RUS
RUSSIA IN FIGURES (YEAR). Text in English. a., latest 2005. RUR 374 per issue (effective 2005). **Document type:** *Yearbook, Government.* **Description:** Contains data supplied by ministries, agencies of the Russian Federation and materials of international organizations. Presented Information pertains to the social sphere, inflationary processes, financial performance of enterprises and organizations, investment activities, prices and tariffs, demographic processes, employment situation, incomes of households.
Related titles: CD-ROM ed.: RUR 649 per issue (effective 2005); ♦ Translation of: Rossiya v Tsifrakh (Year).
Published by: Gosudarstvennyi Komitet Rossiiskoi Federatsii po Statistike/Federal State Statistics Office, ul Myasnitskaya 39, Moscow, 107450, Russian Federation. TEL 7-095-2074902, FAX 7-095-2074087, stat@gks.ru, http://www.gks.ru.

330.021 RUS
S N G V (YEAR). (Sodruzhestvo Nezavisimykh Gosudarst) Text in Russian. a. RUR 460 per issue (effective 2005). **Document type:** *Government.*
Published by: Gosudarstvennyi Komitet Rossiiskoi Federatsii po Statistike/Federal State Statistics Office, ul Myasnitskaya 39, Moscow, 107450, Russian Federation. TEL 7-095-2074902, FAX 7-095-2074087, stat@gks.ru, http://www.gks.ru.

658 USA ISSN 1067-182X
HF5415.33.U6
S R D S LIFESTYLE MARKET ANALYST. Text in English. 1989. a. USD 460 per issue (effective 2005). **Document type:** *Directory, Trade.* **Description:** Covers national, regional, and local markets. Offers detailed demographic data, including age, income, occupation, education, and home ownership.
Published by: S R D S, 1700 Higgins Rd, Des Plaines, IL 60018-5605. TEL 847-375-5000, FAX 847-375-5001, jlevy@srds.com, http://www.srds.com. Ed. June Levy.

S R D S TECHNOLOGY MEDIA SOURCE. see *ADVERTISING AND PUBLIC RELATIONS—Abstracting, Bibliographies, Statistics*

S R D S THE BULLET; the latest in list activity. (Standard Rate and Data Service) see *ADVERTISING AND PUBLIC RELATIONS—Abstracting, Bibliographies, Statistics*

382 LCA
ST. LUCIA. STATISTICAL DEPARTMENT. ANNUAL OVERSEAS TRADE REPORT: PART 2. Text in English. 1960. a. XEC 20. **Document type:** *Government.*
Published by: Statistical Department, New Government Bldg, Block C, 2nd Fl, Conway, Castries, St. Lucia. TEL 758-45-22697, FAX 758-45-31648, TELEX 6394 FORAFF. Ed. Bryan Boxill.

382 LCA
ST. LUCIA. STATISTICAL DEPARTMENT. QUARTERLY OVERSEAS TRADE REPORTS. Text in English. 1960. q. XEC 20. **Document type:** *Government.*
Published by: Statistical Department, New Government Bldg, Block C, 2nd Fl, Conway, Castries, St. Lucia. TEL 758-45-22697, FAX 758-45-31648, TELEX 6394 FORAFF. Ed. Brian Bixill.

658.8 310 USA ISSN 0361-1329
SALES & MARKETING MANAGEMENT SURVEY OF BUYING POWER. Text in English. 1995. a. USD 99 combined subscription domestic for Sales and Marketing Management & Sales & Marketing Management Survey of Buying Pow; USD 120 combined subscription in Canada for Sales and Marketing Management & Sales & Marketing Management Survey of Buying Pow; USD 199 combined subscription elsewhere for Sales and Marketing Management & Sales & Marketing Management Survey of Buying Pow (effective 1999). adv. charts; stat. reprint service avail. from PQC. **Document type:** *Journal, Trade.* **Description:** Metro market county and city data on population income and retail sales.
Formed by the merger of (1929-1995): Sales Management Survey of Buying Power (Part I); (1973-1995): Sales Management Survey of Buying Power (Part II)
Published by: V N U Business Publications (Subsidiary of: V N U Business Media), 770 Broadway, New York, NY 10003-9595. bmcomm@vnuinc.com, http://www.vnubusinessmedia.com/. Circ: 65,000.

338 310 CAN ISSN 0837-8649
HA747.S3
SASKATCHEWAN. BUREAU OF STATISTICS. MONTHLY STATISTICAL REVIEW. Text in English. 1975. m. free. charts; stat. **Document type:** *Government.*
Former titles (until 1975): Saskatchewan. Bureau of Statistics. Monthly Statistical Review (0706-7836); (until 1977): Saskatchewan Monthly Statistical Review (0837-8630)
Related titles: Online - full text ed.
Indexed: CSI.
—CISTI.
Published by: Bureau of Statistics, 5th Fl, 2350 Albert St, Regina, SK S4P 4A6, Canada. TEL 306-787-6327, FAX 306-787-6311, http://www.gov.sk.ca/bureau.stats. Ed. Yvonne Small.

382 319 SAU
SAUDI ARABIA. CENTRAL DEPARTMENT OF STATISTICS. FOREIGN TRADE STATISTICS. Text in Arabic, English. a. **Document type:** *Government.*
Published by: Central Department of Statistics, P O Box 3735, Riyadh, 11118, Saudi Arabia.

382 319 SAU
SAUDI ARABIA. CENTRAL DEPARTMENT OF STATISTICS. QUARTERLY DIGEST OF FOREIGN TRADE STATISTICS. Text in Arabic, English. q. **Document type:** *Government.*
Published by: Central Department of Statistics, P O Box 3735, Riyadh, 11118, Saudi Arabia.

330 315.6 SAU
SAUDI ARABIA. CENTRAL DEPARTMENT OF STATISTICS. STATISTICAL INDICATOR. Text in Arabic, English. 1976. a. free. charts; stat. **Document type:** *Government.*
Published by: Central Department of Statistics, P O Box 3735, Riyadh, 11118, Saudi Arabia.

SAUDI ARABIAN MONETARY AGENCY. STATISTICAL SUMMARY. see *BUSINESS AND ECONOMICS—Banking And Finance*

658 CHE
SCHLATTER GESCHAEFTSBERICHT (YEAR). Text in German. a. **Document type:** *Corporate.*
Published by: H.A. Schlatter AG, Brandstr 24, Schlieren, 8952, Switzerland. TEL 41-1-7327111, FAX 41-1-7309476, TELEX 827790-HAS-CH.

355.6021 USA ISSN 0501-9427
SELECTED MANPOWER STATISTICS. Text in English. a.
Published by: U.S. Department of Defense, Washington Headquarters Services, The Pentagon, Washington, DC 20301-1155. TEL 703-545-6700, http://www.dior.whs.mil/MMID/PUBS.HTM.

330.21 SEN
SENEGAL. MINISTERE DE L'ECONOMIE, DES FINANCES ET DU PLAN. BANQUE DE DONNEES ECONOMIQUES ET FINANCIERES. Text in French. a. XOF 20,000; XOF 30,000 foreign (effective 1998). **Document type:** *Government.*
Published by: Ministere de l'Economie des Finances et du Plan, Direction de la Prevision et de la Statistique, BP 116, Dakar, Senegal. TEL 221-21-03-01. Pub. Ibrahima Sarr.

316.63 SEN
SENEGAL. MINISTERE DE L'ECONOMIE, DES FINANCES ET DU PLAN. BULLETIN ECONOMIQUE ET STATISTIQUE. Text in French. bi-m. XOF 2,000; XOF 4,000 foreign (effective 1998). charts; mkt. **Document type:** *Government.*
Former titles: Senegal. Ministere de l'Economie et des Finances. Bulletin Statistique et Economique; Senegal. Ministere de l'Economie et des Finances. Bulletin Statistique Mensuel; Senegal. Ministere de l'Economie et des Finances. Bulletin Statistique et Economique Mensuel (0037-2153)
Indexed: PAIS.
Published by: Ministere de l'Economie des Finances et du Plan, Direction de la Prevision et de la Statistique, BP 116, Dakar, Senegal. TEL 221-21-03-01. Pub. Ibrahima Sarr.

SENEGAL. MINISTERE DE L'ECONOMIE, DES FINANCES ET DU PLAN. COMPTES ECONOMIQUES. see *BUSINESS AND ECONOMICS—Economic Situation And Conditions*

330.21   SEN
SENEGAL. MINISTERE DE L'ECONOMIE, DES FINANCES ET DU PLAN. DOSSIERS DOCUMENTAIRES. Text in French. irreg. XOF 7,000 per issue. **Document type:** *Government.*
Published by: Ministere de l'Economie des Finances et du Plan, Direction de la Prevision et de la Statistique, BP 116, Dakar, Senegal. TEL 221-21-03-01. Ed. Jean N'Dong. Pub. Ibrahima Sarr.

338.21   SEN   ISSN 0850-1203
SENEGAL. MINISTERE DE L'ECONOMIE, DES FINANCES ET DU PLAN. INDICE DE LA PRODUCTION INDUSTRIELLE. Text in French. 1969. q. XOF 2,000; XOF 4,000 foreign (effective 1998). **Document type:** *Government.*
Published by: Ministere de l'Economie des Finances et du Plan, Direction de la Prevision et de la Statistique, BP 116, Dakar, Senegal. TEL 221-21-03-01. Pub. Ibrahima Sarr.

338.21   SEN
SENEGAL. MINISTERE DE L'ECONOMIE, DES FINANCES ET DU PLAN. INDICE DES PRIX A LA CONSOMMATION. Text in French. m. XOF 500; XOF 1,000 foreign (effective 1998). **Document type:** *Government.*
Formerly: Senegal. Ministere de l'Economie et des Finances. Indice des Prix
Published by: Ministere de l'Economie des Finances et du Plan, Direction de la Prevision et de la Statistique, BP 116, Dakar, Senegal. TEL 221-21-03-01. Pub. Ibrahima Sarr.

382.21   SEN
SENEGAL. MINISTERE DE L'ECONOMIE, DES FINANCES ET DU PLAN. NOTE D'ANALYSE DU COMMERCE EXTERIEUR. Text in French. 1975. a. XOF 4,000; XOF 6,000 foreign (effective 1998). **Document type:** *Government.*
Former titles: Senegal. Ministere de l'Economie et des Finances. Analyse du Commerce Exterieur; (until 1982): Commerce Exterieur du Senegal
Published by: Ministere de l'Economie des Finances et du Plan, Direction de la Prevision et de la Statistique, BP 116, Dakar, Senegal. TEL 221-21-03-01. Pub. Ibrahima Sarr.

330.21   SEN
SENEGAL. MINISTERE DE L'ECONOMIE, DES FINANCES ET DU PLAN. NOTE DE CONJONCTURE. Text in French. 1971. q. XOF 3,000; XOF 5,000 foreign (effective 1998). **Document type:** *Government.*
Formerly: Senegal. Ministere de l'Economie et des Finances. Evolution Conjoncturelle (0850-1300)
Published by: Ministere de l'Economie des Finances et du Plan, Direction de la Prevision et de la Statistique, BP 116, Dakar, Senegal. TEL 221-21-03-01. Pub. Ibrahima Sarr.

330.21   SEN
SENEGAL. MINISTERE DE L'ECONOMIE, DES FINANCES ET DU PLAN. RAPPORT SUR LES PERSPECTIVES ECONOMIQUES. Text in French. biennial. XOF 5,000; XOF 7,000 foreign (effective 1998). **Document type:** *Government.*
Published by: Ministere de l'Economie des Finances et du Plan, Direction de la Prevision et de la Statistique, BP 116, Dakar, Senegal. TEL 221-21-03-01. Pub. Ibrahima Sarr.

330.21   SEN
SENEGAL. MINISTERE DE L'ECONOMIE, DES FINANCES ET DU PLAN. SITUATION ECONOMIQUE REGIONALE. Text in French. irreg. XOF 5,000; XOF 7,000 foreign (effective 1998). **Document type:** *Government.*
Published by: Ministere de l'Economie des Finances et du Plan, Direction de la Prevision et de la Statistique, BP 116, Dakar, Senegal. TEL 221-21-03-01. Pub. Ibrahima Sarr.

330.21   SEN
SENEGAL. MINISTERE DE L'ECONOMIE, DES FINANCES ET DU PLAN. TABLEAU DE BORD DE L'ECONOMIE SENEGALAISE. Text in French. m. XOF 1,000; XOF 2,000 foreign (effective 1998). **Document type:** *Government.*
Published by: Ministere de l'Economie des Finances et du Plan, Direction de la Prevision et de la Statistique, BP 116, Dakar, Senegal. TEL 221-21-03-01. Pub. Ibrahima Sarr.

330   GTM
SERIES ESTADISTICAS SELECCIONADAS DE CENTROAMERICA Y PANAMA. Text in Spanish. a. USD 10. **Document type:** *Government.*
Published by: Secretaria Permanente del Tratado General de Integracion Economica Centroamericana, 4a Avda. 10-25, ZONA, 14, PO Box 1237, Guatemala City, 01901, Guatemala. TEL 502-3682151, FAX 502-3681071, sieca@pronet.net.gt.

658   GBR
SERVICE SECTOR RETAIL SALES. Text in English. m. **Document type:** *Government.*
Formerly (until 1996): U K Service Sector Retail Sales
Published by: Office for National Statistics, Government Offices, Rm 65c-3, Great George St, London, SW1P 3AQ, United Kingdom. TEL 44-171-396-2828, FAX 44-171-270-6019.

SERVICES INDICATORS (ONLINE)/INDICATEURS DES SERVICES. see *BUSINESS AND ECONOMICS—Domestic Commerce*

330 319   SYC
SEYCHELLES. DEPARTMENT OF FINANCE. ECONOMIC INDICATORS. Text in English. q. SCR 1.50. **Document type:** *Government.*
Published by: Department of Finance, Statistics Division, PO Box 206, Victoria, Mahe, Seychelles.

339.021   SYC
SEYCHELLES. DEPARTMENT OF FINANCE. NATIONAL ACCOUNTS. Text in English. a. SCR 5.
Published by: Department of Finance, Statistics Division, PO Box 206, Victoria, Mahe, Seychelles.

330.9 310   SYC
SEYCHELLES. PRESIDENT'S OFFICE. STATISTICS DIVISION. EMPLOYMENT & EARNINGS. Text in English. 1982. q. SCR 5. **Document type:** *Government.*
Published by: (Seychelles. Statistics Division), President's Office, Department of Finance, Box 206, Victoria, Mahe, Seychelles.

382 310   SYC
SEYCHELLES. PRESIDENT'S OFFICE. STATISTICS DIVISION. EXTERNAL TRADE. Text in English. 1982. q. SCR 5. **Document type:** *Government.*
Published by: (Seychelles. Statistics Division), President's Office, Department of Finance, Box 206, Victoria, Mahe, Seychelles.

310   SYC
SEYCHELLES. PRESIDENT'S OFFICE. STATISTICS DIVISION. HOUSEHOLD EXPENDITURE SURVEY. Text in English. irreg., latest 1984. SCR 45. stat. **Document type:** *Government.*
Published by: President's Office, Statistics Division, PO Box 206, Victoria, Mahe, Seychelles.

338 310   SYC
SEYCHELLES. PRESIDENT'S OFFICE. STATISTICS DIVISION. PRODUCTION INDICATORS. Text in English. 1982. q. SCR 2.50. **Document type:** *Government.*
Published by: (Seychelles. Statistics Division), President's Office, Department of Finance, Box 206, Victoria, Mahe, Seychelles.

658 310   SYC
SEYCHELLES. PRESIDENT'S OFFICE. STATISTICS DIVISION. RETAIL PRICES. Text in English. 1982. m. SCR 2.50. **Document type:** *Government.*
Published by: (Seychelles. Statistics Division), President's Office, Department of Finance, Box 206, Victoria, Mahe, Seychelles.

316   SYC
SEYCHELLES. PRESIDENT'S OFFICE. STATISTICS DIVISION. STATISTICAL ABSTRACT. Text in English. a. SCR 60. **Document type:** *Government.*
Published by: President's Office, Statistics Division, PO Box 206, Victoria, Mahe, Seychelles.

SEYCHELLES. STATISTICS DIVISION. STATISTICAL BULLETIN. VISITOR SURVEY. see *TRAVEL AND TOURISM—Abstracting, Bibliographies, Statistics*

330   HKG
SHANTOU SPECIAL ECONOMIC ZONE YEARBOOK (YEAR). Text in Chinese. 1992. a. HKD 240, USD 55.
Published by: Economic Information & Agency, 342 Hennessy Rd 10th Fl, 10 th Fl, Wanchai, Hong Kong. TEL 852-573-8217, FAX 852-838-8304.

330   HKG
SHENZHEN TONGJI NIANJIAN (YEAR)/SHENZHEN STATISTICAL YEARBOOK. Text in Chinese. 1992. a. HKD 200, USD 45.
Published by: Economic Information & Agency, 342 Hennessy Rd 10th Fl, 10 th Fl, Wanchai, Hong Kong. TEL 852-573-8217, FAX 852-838-8304.

330   SGP
SINGAPORE. DEPARTMENT OF STATISTICS. RETAIL SALES & CATERING TRADE INDICES. Text in English. m. stat. **Document type:** *Government.* **Description:** Analyzes the changes in the receipts at current prices in the retail sales and catering trades.
Published by: Department of Statistics, 100 High St #05-01, The Treasury, Singapore, 179434, Singapore. TEL 65-3327686, FAX 65-3327689, info@singstat.gov.sg, http://www.singstat.gov.sg/.

338 315   SGP   ISSN 0080-9675
HC445.8.A1
SINGAPORE. ECONOMIC DEVELOPMENT BOARD. REPORT ON THE CENSUS OF INDUSTRIAL PRODUCTION. Text in English. a. SGD 16.
Published by: Economic Development Board, 250 N. Bridge Rd, 24-00 Raffles City Tower, Singapore, 0617, Singapore.

381   SGP   ISSN 0129-7414
HF3800.67 .A242
SINGAPORE MONTHLY TRADE STATISTICS: IMPORTS & EXPORTS∗ . Text in English. m. SGD 95 domestic; SGD 100 in Asia; SGD 105 elsewhere. **Description:** Provides detailed information on the imports and exports of Singapore, classified by commodity, country of origin and country of destination.
Related titles: CD-ROM ed.
Published by: Trade Statistics, c/o SNP Corporation Ltd., Publication Division, 97 Ubi Ave 4, Singapore, 408754, Singapore. TEL 65-740-4584. **U.S. subscr. to:** I.S.B.S. Inc., 5602 N E Hassalo St, Portland, OR 97213. TEL 800-547-7734, 503-284-8858.

330 016   ARG   ISSN 0080-9772
SINTESIS BIBLIOGRAFICA. Text in Spanish. 1964. irreg., latest vol.9, 1972. free.
Formerly: Boletin Hemerografico
Published by: Universidad Nacional de la Plata, Facultad de Ciencias Economicas, Biblioteca, 6 Esq. 47, La Plata, Buenos Aires 1900, Argentina.

330   CHL   ISSN 0716-2480
HG185.C5
SINTESIS MONETARIA Y FINANCIERA, EN SALDOS Y PROMEDIOS. Text in Spanish. 1980. a. CLP 20,000, USD 58 newsstand/cover.
Published by: Banco Central de Chile, Casilla 967, Santiago, Chile. TEL 56-2-670-2000, FAX 56-2-698-4847. Circ: 200.

330.9   SEN
SITUATION ECONOMIQUE ET SOCIALE DU SENEGAL. Text in French. 1962. a. XOF 25,000; XOF 30,000 foreign. **Document type:** *Government.*
Formerly: Situation Economique du Senegal (0080-9853)
Related titles: Microfiche ed.: (from PQC).
Published by: Ministere de l'Economie des Finances et du Plan, Direction de la Prevision et de la Statistique, BP 116, Dakar, Senegal. TEL 221-21-03-01. Pub. Ibrahima Sarr.

SIZE OF THE CRAFT - HOBBY INDUSTRY SURVEY. see *HOBBIES—Abstracting, Bibliographies, Statistics*

338.64   USA   ISSN 0502-5133
SMALL BUSINESS BIBLIOGRAPHY. Text in English. irreg.
Formerly (until 1962): Small Business Bulletin (0081-010X)
Published by: U.S. Small Business Administration, 409 Third St, S W, MC 3114, Washington, DC 20416. TEL 800-827-5722, http://www.sba.gov.

016.33   AUS
SMARTBIX. Text in English. d. (updated twice daily). AUD 5,003 single user (effective 2005). **Document type:** *Database, Abstract/Index.*
Media: Online - full text.
Published by: Business Intelligence International Pty. Ltd., Level 2, 627 Chapel St, South Yarra, VIC 3141, Australia. TEL 61-3-98563900, FAX 61-3-98563999, abix@abix.com.au, http://www.smartbix.com.au/pro, http://www.abix.com.au. R&P Jane Sunderland TEL 61-3-98563908.

332.6   LUX
SOCIETE DE LA BOURSE DE LUXEMBOURG. FAITS ET CHIFFRES/LUXEMBOURG STOCK EXCHANGE. FACTS AND FIGURES. Text in English, French. 1983. s-a. free. **Description:** Contains general statistical and organizational information.
Published by: Societe de la Bourse de Luxembourg/Luxembourg Stock Exchange, 11 av. de la Porte Neuve, BP 165, Luxembourg, L-2011, Luxembourg. TEL 352-4779361, FAX 352-473298, info@bourse.lu, http://www.bourse.lu. Circ: 4,500.

332.64021   MAR
SOCIETE DE LA BOURSE DES VALEURS DE CASABLANCA. STATISTIQUES MENSUELLES. Text in French. 1976. m. MAD 330. **Document type:** *Bulletin.*
Formerly: Bourse des Valeurs de Casablanca. Bulletin Mensuel d'Information
Published by: Societe de la Bourse des Valeurs de Casablanca, Avenue de l'Armee Royale, Casablanca, Morocco. TEL 212-2-452626, FAX 212-2-452612.

330.021 304.6021   RUS
SOTSIAL'NO-EKONOMICHESKOE POLOZHENIE DAL'NEVOSTOCHNOGO FEDERAL'NOGO OKRUGA/SOCIO-ECONOMIC SITUATION OF THE FAR EASTERN FEDERAL REGION. Text in Russian. 2000. q. USD 182 foreign (effective 2005). **Document type:** *Journal, Government.* **Description:** Contains statistics of the socioeconomic situation in the Far Eastern District of the Russian Federation and its components. Demographic situation, living standards, prices, finance, and investments.
Published by: Gosudarstvennyi Komitet Rossiiskoi Federatsii po Statistike/Federal State Statistics Office, ul Myasnitskaya 39, Moscow, 107450, Russian Federation. TEL 7-095-2074902, FAX 7-095-2074087, stat@gks.ru, http://www.gks.ru. **Dist. by:** East View Information Services, 3020 Harbor Ln. N., Minneapolis, MN 55447. TEL 800-477-1005, FAX 800-800-3839, eastview@eastview.com, http://www.eastview.com.

▼ *new title*   ➤ *refereed*   ∗ *unverified*   ◆ *full entry avail.*

330.021 304.6021 RUS
SOTSIAL'NO-EKONOMICHESKOE POLOZHENIE PRIVOLZHSKOGO FEDERAL'NOGO OKRUGA/SOCIO-ECONOMIC SITUATION OF THE VOLGA FEDERAL REGION. Text in Russian. 2000. q. USD 182 foreign (effective 2005). **Document type:** *Journal, Government.* **Description:** Contains statistics of the socioeconomic situation in the Volga District of the Russian Federation and its components. Demographic situation, living standards, prices, finance, and investments.
Published by: Gosudarstvennyi Komitet Rossiiskoi Federatsii po Statistike/Federal State Statistics Office, ul Myasnitskaya 39, Moscow, 107450, Russian Federation. TEL 7-095-2074902, FAX 7-095-2074087, stat@gks.ru, http://www.gks.ru. **Dist. by:** East View Information Services, 3020 Harbor Ln. N., Minneapolis, MN 55447. TEL 800-477-1005, FAX 800-800-3839, eastview@eastview.com, http://www.eastview.com.

330.021 304.6021 RUS
SOTSIAL'NO-EKONOMICHESKOE POLOZHENIE ROSSII/SOCIAL AND ECONOMIC SITUATION IN RUSSIA; ekonomicheskii obzor. Text in Russian. 1992. m. USD 944 foreign (effective 2005). charts; stat. **Document type:** *Journal, Government.* **Description:** Provides broad information on major production branches, transport and communication, external economic relations, wholesale and consumer markets, prices, finances, labour market, standard of living, demographic situation.
Related titles: Online - full content ed.: RUR 7,080 (effective 2005).
Published by: Gosudarstvennyi Komitet Rossiiskoi Federatsii po Statistike/Federal State Statistics Office, ul Myasnitskaya 39, Moscow, 107450, Russian Federation. TEL 7-095-2074902, FAX 7-095-2074087, stat@gks.ru, http://www.gks.ru. **Dist. by:** East View Information Services, 3020 Harbor Ln. N., Minneapolis, MN 55447. TEL 800-477-1005, FAX 800-800-3839, eastview@eastview.com, http://www.eastview.com.

330.021 304.6021 RUS
SOTSIAL'NO-EKONOMICHESKOE POLOZHENIE SEVERO-ZAPADNOGO FEDERAL'NOGO OKRUGA/SOCIO-ECONOMIC SITUATION OF THE NORTH-WESTERN FEDERAL REGION. Text in Russian. 2000. q. USD 182 foreign (effective 2005). **Document type:** *Journal, Government.* **Description:** Contains information on the socioeconomic situation in the Northwestern District of the Russian Federation and its components. Demographic situation, living standard, prices, finance, and investments.
Published by: Gosudarstvennyi Komitet Rossiiskoi Federatsii po Statistike/Federal State Statistics Office, ul Myasnitskaya 39, Moscow, 107450, Russian Federation. TEL 7-095-2074902, FAX 7-095-2074087, stat@gks.ru, http://www.gks.ru. **Dist. by:** East View Information Services, 3020 Harbor Ln. N., Minneapolis, MN 55447. TEL 800-477-1005, FAX 800-800-3839, eastview@eastview.com, http://www.eastview.com.

330.021 304.6021 RUS
SOTSIAL'NO-EKONOMICHESKOE POLOZHENIE SIBIRSKOGO FEDERAL'NOGO OKRUGA/SOCIO-ECONOMIC SITUATION OF THE SIBERIAN FEDERAL REGION. Text in Russian. 2000. q. USD 182 foreign (effective 2005). **Document type:** *Journal, Government.* **Description:** Contains statistics of the socioeconomic situation in the Siberian District of the Russian Federation and its components. Demographic situation, living standards, prices, finance, and investments.
Published by: Gosudarstvennyi Komitet Rossiiskoi Federatsii po Statistike/Federal State Statistics Office, ul Myasnitskaya 39, Moscow, 107450, Russian Federation. TEL 7-095-2074902, FAX 7-095-2074087, stat@gks.ru, http://www.gks.ru. **Dist. by:** East View Information Services, 3020 Harbor Ln. N., Minneapolis, MN 55447. TEL 800-477-1005, FAX 800-800-3839, eastview@eastview.com, http://www.eastview.com.

330.021 304.6021 RUS
SOTSIAL'NO-EKONOMICHESKOE POLOZHENIE TSENTRAL'NOGO FEDERAL'NOGO OKRUGA/SOCIO-ECONOMIC SITUATION OF THE CENTRAL FEDERAL REGION. Text in Russian. 2000. q. **Document type:** *Journal, Government.* **Description:** Contains information on the socioeconomic situation in the Central Federal District of the Russian Federation and its components. The key statistics reflect the position quarter by quarter of the previous and current year. Demographic situation, living standards, prices, finance, and investments.
Published by: Gosudarstvennyi Komitet Rossiiskoi Federatsii po Statistike/Federal State Statistics Office, ul Myasnitskaya 39, Moscow, 107450, Russian Federation. TEL 7-095-2074902, FAX 7-095-2074087, stat@gks.ru, http://www.gks.ru.

330.021 304.6021 RUS
SOTSIAL'NO-EKONOMICHESKOE POLOZHENIE URAL'SKOGO FEDERAL'NOGO OKRUGA/SOCIO-ECONOMIC SITUATION OF THE URAL FEDERAL REGION. Text in Russian. 2000. q. USD 182 foreign (effective 2005). **Document type:** *Journal, Government.* **Description:** Information on the socioeconomic situation in the Urals Federal District of the Russian Federation and its components. Demographic situation, living standard, prices, finance, and investments.
Published by: Gosudarstvennyi Komitet Rossiiskoi Federatsii po Statistike/Federal State Statistics Office, ul Myasnitskaya 39, Moscow, 107450, Russian Federation. TEL 7-095-2074902, FAX 7-095-2074087, stat@gks.ru, http://www.gks.ru. **Dist. by:** East View Information Services, 3020 Harbor Ln. N., Minneapolis, MN 55447. TEL 800-477-1005, FAX 800-800-3839, eastview@eastview.com, http://www.eastview.com.

330.021 304.6021 RUS
SOTSIAL'NO-EKONOMICHESKOE POLOZHENIE YUZHNOGO FEDERAL'NOGO OKRUGA/SOCIO-ECONOMIC SITUATION OF THE SOUTHERN FEDERAL REGION. Text in Russian. 2000. q. USD 182 foreign (effective 2005). **Document type:** *Journal, Government.* **Description:** Contains statistics of the socioeconomic situation in the Southern Federal District of the Russian Federation and its components. Demographic situation, living standards, prices, finance, and investments.
Published by: Gosudarstvennyi Komitet Rossiiskoi Federatsii po Statistike/Federal State Statistics Office, ul Myasnitskaya 39, Moscow, 107450, Russian Federation. TEL 7-095-2074902, FAX 7-095-2074087, stat@gks.ru, http://www.gks.ru. **Dist. by:** East View Information Services, 3020 Harbor Ln. N., Minneapolis, MN 55447. TEL 800-477-1005, FAX 800-800-3839, eastview@eastview.com, http://www.eastview.com.

016.33 RUS
SOTSIAL'NYE I GUMANITARNYE NAUKI. OTECHESTVENNAYA I ZARUBEZHNAYA LITERATURA. EKONOMIKA; referativnyi zhurnal. Text in Russian. 1992. q. USD 165 in United States (effective 2004). **Document type:** *Abstract/Index.* **Description:** Contains abstracts of foreign and Russian books devoted to economics acquired lately by INION.
Formed by the merger of (1973-1992): Obshchestvennye Nauki v S.S.S.R. Ekonomika (0202-2044); (1972-1992): Obshchestvennye Nauki za Rubezhom. Ekonomika (0132-7372)
Indexed: RASB.
—East View.
Published by: Rossiiskaya Akademiya Nauk, Institut Nauchnoi Informatsii po Obshchestvennym Naukam, Nakhimovskii pr-t 51/21, Moscow, 117997, Russian Federation. TEL 7-095-1288930, FAX 7-095-4202261, info@inion.ru, http://www.inion.ru. Ed. I M Osadchaya. **Subscr. in US to:** East View Information Services, 3020 Harbor Ln. N., Minneapolis, MN 55447. TEL 800-477-1005, FAX 800-800-3839, eastview@eastview.com, http://www.eastview.com.

330 FRA ISSN 1683-2477
SOURCE O C D E. COMPTES NATIONAUX ET STATISTIQUES RETROSPECTIVES. (Organisation de Cooperation et de Developpement Economiques) Text in French. irreg. EUR 646, USD 708, GBP 407, JPY 83,200 combined subscription print & online eds. (effective 2005). stat.
Related titles: Online - full content ed.: ISSN 1684-3126. EUR 431, USD 495, GBP 284, JPY 58,200 (effective 2005); Online - full text ed.: (from EBSCO Publishing, Gale Group, IngentaConnect, Swets Information Services); ◆ English ed.: Source O E C D. National Accounts & Historical Statistics. ISSN 1681-2018.
Published by: Organization for Economic Cooperation and Development, 2 Rue Andre Pascal, Paris, 75775 Cedex 16, France. TEL 33-1-45248200, FAX 33-1-45248500, http://www.oecd.org. **Dist. by:** Extenza - Turpin, Pegasus Dr, Stratton Business Park, Biggleswade, Beds SG18 8TQ, United Kingdom. TEL 44-1462-687552, FAX 44-1462-480947, subscriptions@extenza-turpin.com; O E C D Turpin North America, PO Box 194, Downingtown, PA 19335-0194. TEL 610-524-5361, 800-456-6323, FAX 610-524-5417, journalscustomer@turpinna.com.

332.1 336 FRA ISSN 1608-1064
SOURCE O E C D. BANK PROFITABILITY STATISTICS/ SOURCE O C D E RENTABILITE DES BANQUES. Text in English. 2000. irreg. EUR 135, USD 155, GBP 88, JPY 18,200 (effective 2005). **Description:** Provides information on financial statements of banks in all member countries.
Media: Online - full text (from Gale Group, IngentaConnect).
Published by: Organization for Economic Cooperation and Development, 2 Rue Andre Pascal, Paris, 75775 Cedex 16, France. TEL 33-1-45248200, FAX 33-1-45248500, http://www.oecd.org.

330 FRA ISSN 1608-1153
SOURCE O E C D. ECONOMIC OUTLOOK STATISTICS/ SOURCE O C D E STATISTIQUES DES PERSPECTIVES ECONOMIQUES DE L'O C D E. Text in English. 2000. irreg. EUR 354, USD 407, GBP 235, JPY 47,800 (effective 2005). **Description:** Provides projections for output, employment, prices, and current balances over the coming two years.
Media: Online - full text (from Gale Group, IngentaConnect).
Published by: Organization for Economic Cooperation and Development, 2 Rue Andre Pascal, Paris, 75775 Cedex 16, France. TEL 33-1-45248200, FAX 33-1-45248500, http://www.oecd.org.

331.12 FRA ISSN 1608-1161
SOURCE O E C D. EMPLOYMENT STATISTICS. Text in English. 2000. irreg. EUR 194, USD 223, GBP 130, JPY 28,200 (effective 2005). stat. **Description:** Publishes annual, quarterly, and monthly indicators including employment, unemployment, labor compensation, vacancies, and labor disputes.
Incorporates: Quarterly Labour Force Statistics; O E C D Non-Members Labour Market Database
Media: Online - full text (from Gale Group, IngentaConnect).
Published by: Organization for Economic Cooperation and Development, 2 Rue Andre Pascal, Paris, 75775 Cedex 16, France. TEL 33-1-45248200, FAX 33-1-45248500, http://www.oecd.org.

382 FRA ISSN 1608-1218
SOURCE O E C D. I T C S. Variant title: Source O E C D. International Trade by Commodities Statistics. Text in English. 2000. irreg. EUR 446, USD 513, GBP 294, JPY 60,200 (effective 2005). **Description:** Provides yearly statistical data on imports and exports in OECD and non-OECD member countries.
Media: Online - full content. **Related titles:** Online - full text ed.: (from Gale Group, IngentaConnect).
Published by: Organization for Economic Cooperation and Development, 2 Rue Andre Pascal, Paris, 75775 Cedex 16, France. TEL 33-1-45248200, FAX 33-1-45248500, http://www.oecd.org.

332.6 FRA ISSN 1608-1072
SOURCE O E C D. INSTITUTIONAL INVESTORS STATISTICS. Text in English, French. 2000. irreg. EUR 135, USD 155, GBP 88, JPY 18,200 (effective 2005). **Description:** Provides cross-country comparisons on the financial assets of each category of investor.
Media: Online - full content. **Related titles:** Online - full text ed.: (from Gale Group, IngentaConnect).
Published by: Organization for Economic Cooperation and Development, 2 Rue Andre Pascal, Paris, 75775 Cedex 16, France. TEL 33-1-45248200, FAX 33-1-45248500, http://www.oecd.org.

338.91 FRA ISSN 1608-1110
SOURCE O E C D. INTERNATIONAL DEVELOPMENT STATISTICS. Text in English. 2000. irreg. EUR 135, USD 155, GBP 88, JPY 18,200 (effective 2005).
Incorporates: External Debt Statistics; Geographical Distribution of Financial Flows to Aid Recipients
Media: Online - full content. **Related titles:** Online - full text ed.: (from Gale Group, IngentaConnect).
Published by: Organization for Economic Cooperation and Development, 2 Rue Andre Pascal, Paris, 75775 Cedex 16, France. TEL 33-1-45248200, FAX 33-1-45248500, http://www.oecd.org. **Dist. by:** Extenza - Turpin, Pegasus Dr, Stratton Business Park, Biggleswade, Beds SG18 8TQ, United Kingdom. TEL 44-1462-687552, FAX 44-1462-480947, subscriptions@extenza-turpin.com; O E C D Turpin North America, PO Box 194, Downingtown, PA 19335-0194. TEL 610-524-5361, 800-456-6323, FAX 610-524-5417, journalscustomer@turpinna.com.

332.6 FRA ISSN 1608-1080
SOURCE O E C D. INTERNATIONAL DIRECT INVESTMENT STATISTICS. Text in English. 2000. irreg. EUR 135, USD 155, GBP 88, JPY 18,200 (effective 2005). stat. **Description:** Provides detailed historical statistics on international direct investment to and from the OECD area.
Media: Online - full content. **Related titles:** Online - full text ed.: (from Gale Group, IngentaConnect).
Published by: Organization for Economic Cooperation and Development, 2 Rue Andre Pascal, Paris, 75775 Cedex 16, France. TEL 33-1-45248200, FAX 33-1-45248500, http://www.oecd.org.

331 304.6 FRA ISSN 1608-1269
SOURCE O E C D. INTERNATIONAL MIGRATION STATISTICS/SOURCE O C D E STATISTIQUES DES MIGRATIONS INTERNATIONALES. Text in English. 2000. irreg. EUR 135, USD 155, GBP 88, JPY 18,200 (effective 2005). **Description:** Provides information on foreign and immigrant populations, migration flows, foreign workers, and naturalizations.
Media: Online - full content. **Related titles:** Online - full text ed.: (from Gale Group, IngentaConnect).
Published by: Organization for Economic Cooperation and Development, 2 Rue Andre Pascal, Paris, 75775 Cedex 16, France. TEL 33-1-45248200, FAX 33-1-45248500, http://www.oecd.org.

382 FRA ISSN 1608-1145
SOURCE O E C D. INTERNATIONAL TRADE AND COMPETITIVENESS STATISTICS/SOURCE O C D E INDICATEURS DU COMMERCE INTERNATIONAL ET DE LA COMPETITIVITE. Text in English. 2000. irreg. EUR 185, USD 212, GBP 124, JPY 25,000 (effective 2005). **Description:** Covers foreign trade, export performance and market growth, and international competitiveness.
Media: Online - full content. **Related titles:** Online - full text ed.: (from Gale Group, IngentaConnect).

Published by: Organization for Economic Cooperation and Development, 2 Rue Andre Pascal, Paris, 75775 Cedex 16, France. TEL 33-1-45248200, FAX 33-1-45248500, http://www.oecd.org.

330 FRA ISSN 1608-1234
SOURCE O E C D. MAIN ECONOMIC INDICATORS. Text in English, French. 2000. m. EUR 624, USD 718, GBP 411, JPY 83,400 (effective 2005). **Description:** Publishes comparative statistics of the most recent changes in OECD countries and many non-member countries.
Media: Online - full content. **Related titles:** Online - full text ed.: (from Gale Group, IngentaConnect).
Published by: Organization for Economic Cooperation and Development, 2 Rue Andre Pascal, Paris, 75775 Cedex 16, France. TEL 33-1-45248200, FAX 33-1-45248500, http://www.oecd.org.

330 FRA ISSN 1608-1293
SOURCE O E C D. MEASURING GLOBALISATION STATISTICS. Text in English, French. 2000. irreg. EUR 135, USD 155, GBP 88, JPY 18,200 (effective 2005). **Description:** Provides detailed statistical data for assessing and analyzing the role played by multinationals in the industrial sectors of sixteen OECD countries.
Media: Online - full content. **Related titles:** Online - full text ed.: (from Gale Group, IngentaConnect).
Published by: Organization for Economic Cooperation and Development, 2 Rue Andre Pascal, Paris, 75775 Cedex 16, France. TEL 33-1-45248200, FAX 33-1-45248500, http://www.oecd.org.

382 FRA ISSN 1608-1226
SOURCE O E C D. MONTHLY INTERNATIONAL TRADE AGGREGATES/SOURCE O C D E STATISTIQUES MENSUELLES DU COMMERCE INTERNATIONAL. Text in English, French. 2000. m. EUR 135, USD 155, GBP 88, JPY 18,200 (effective 2005). **Description:** Provides international statistics on international trade of OECD countries.
Media: Online - full content. **Related titles:** Online - full text ed.: (from Gale Group, IngentaConnect).
Published by: Organization for Economic Cooperation and Development, 2 Rue Andre Pascal, Paris, 75775 Cedex 16, France. TEL 33-1-45248200, FAX 33-1-45248500, http://www.oecd.org.

330 FRA ISSN 1681-2018
SOURCE O E C D. NATIONAL ACCOUNTS & HISTORICAL STATISTICS. Text in English. 2000. irreg. EUR 616, USD 708, GBP 407, JPY 83,200 (effective 2005).
Related titles: Online - full content ed.: ISSN 1681-5394. EUR 431, USD 495, GBP 284, JPY 58,200 (effective 2005); Online - full text ed.: 2000 (from EBSCO Publishing, Gale Group, IngentaConnect, Swets Information Services); ♦ French ed.: Source O C D E. Comptes Nationaux et Statistiques Retrospectives. ISSN 1683-2477.
Published by: Organization for Economic Cooperation and Development, 2 Rue Andre Pascal, Paris, 75775 Cedex 16, France. TEL 33-1-45248200, FAX 33-1-45248500, http://www.oecd.org. **Dist. by:** Extenza - Turpin, Pegasus Dr, Stratton Business Park, Biggleswade, Beds SG18 8TQ, United Kingdom. TEL 44-1462-687552, FAX 44-1462-480947, subscriptions@extenza-turpin.com; O E C D Turpin North America, PO Box 194, Downingtown, PA 19335-0194. TEL 610-524-5361, 800-456-6323, FAX 610-524-5417, journalscustomer@turpinna.com.

336.2 FRA ISSN 1608-1099
SOURCE O E C D. REVENUE STATISTICS OF O E C D MEMBER COUNTRIES. Text in English, French. 2000. irreg. EUR 135, USD 155, GBP 88, JPY 18,200 (effective 2005). **Description:** Defines which goverment receipts should be regarded as taxes and classifies the different types of taxes.
Media: Online - full content. **Related titles:** Online - full text ed.: (from Gale Group, IngentaConnect).
Published by: Organization for Economic Cooperation and Development, 2 Rue Andre Pascal, Paris, 75775 Cedex 16, France. TEL 33-1-45248200, FAX 33-1-45248500, http://www.oecd.org.

330 FRA ISSN 1608-1307
SOURCE O E C D. S T A N INDUSTRY ANALYSIS DATABASE. Text in English, French. 2000. irreg. USD 246, USD 283, GBP 163, JPY 33,300 (effective 2005). **Description:** Combines industrial surveys and national accounts data, which permits the construction of a wide range of industry and aggregate level indicators of industrial structure and the evolution of performance.
Formerly: Structural Analysis Industrial Database
Media: Online - full content. **Related titles:** Online - full text ed.: (from Gale Group, IngentaConnect).
Published by: Organization for Economic Cooperation and Development, 2 Rue Andre Pascal, Paris, 75775 Cedex 16, France. TEL 33-1-45248200, FAX 33-1-45248500, http://www.oecd.org.

382 FRA ISSN 1608-1277
SOURCE O E C D. SERVICES STATISTICS/SOURCE O C D E STATISTIQUES DES SERVICES. Text in English, French. 2000. irreg. EUR 135, USD 155, GBP 88, JPY 18,200 (effective 2005). **Description:** Publishes annual national account statistics on output and employment in service activities, coupled with statistics on international trade in services.
Incorporates: Services: Statistics on Value Added and Employment; Statistics on International Trade in Services
Media: Online - full content. **Related titles:** Online - full text ed.: (from Gale Group, IngentaConnect).
Published by: Organization for Economic Cooperation and Development, 2 Rue Andre Pascal, Paris, 75775 Cedex 16, France. TEL 33-1-45248200, FAX 33-1-45248500, http://www.oecd.org.

336 FRA ISSN 1608-117X
SOURCE O E C D. SOCIAL EXPENDITURE DATABASE/ SOURCE O C D E BASE DE DONNEES DE L'O C D E SUR LES DEPENSES SOCIALES. Text in English. 2000. irreg. EUR 135, USD 155, GBP 88, JPY 182,000 (effective 2005). **Description:** Provides comparable statistics on public and private social expenditure, which can be used to monitor trends in aggregate social expenditure and analyze changes in its composition.
Media: Online - full content. **Related titles:** Online - full text ed.: (from Gale Group, IngentaConnect).
Published by: Organization for Economic Cooperation and Development, 2 Rue Andre Pascal, Paris, 75775 Cedex 16, France. TEL 33-1-45248200, FAX 33-1-45248500, http://www.oecd.org.

338 FRA ISSN 1608-120X
HC10
SOURCE O E C D. STRUCTURAL STATISTICS FOR INDUSTRY AND SERVICES. Text in English. 2000. irreg. USD 135 (effective 2003). **Description:** Provides annual data for detailed industry and services sectors, covering a number of variables describing the structure of the economy.
Media: Online - full text (from Gale Group, IngentaConnect). **Related titles:** ♦ Print ed.: Structural Statistics for Industry and Services. ISSN 1727-2327.
—CISTI.
Published by: Organization for Economic Cooperation and Development, 2 Rue Andre Pascal, Paris, 75775 Cedex 16, France. TEL 33-1-45248200, FAX 33-1-45248500, http://www.sourceoecd.org/content/html/index.htm, http://www.oecd.org. **Dist. by:** Extenza - Turpin, Pegasus Dr, Stratton Business Park, Biggleswade, Beds SG18 8TQ, United Kingdom. TEL 44-1462-687552, FAX 44-1462-480947, subscriptions@extenza-turpin.com; O E C D Turpin North America, PO Box 194, Downingtown, PA 19335-0194. TEL 610-524-5361, 800-456-6323, FAX 610-524-5417, journalscustomer@turpinna.com.

336.2 FRA ISSN 1608-1102
SOURCE O E C D. TAXING WAGES STATISTICS/SOURCE O C D E STATISTIQUES DES IMPOTS SUR LES SALAIRES. Text in English. 2000. irreg. EUR 135, USD 155, GBP 88, JPY 18,200 (effective 2005). stat. **Description:** Publishes information on income tax and social security contributions from employees and their employers in all OECD countries.
Media: Online - full content. **Related titles:** Online - full text ed.: (from Gale Group, IngentaConnect).
Published by: Organization for Economic Cooperation and Development, 2 Rue Andre Pascal, Paris, 75775 Cedex 16, France. TEL 33-1-45248200, FAX 33-1-45248500, http://www.oecd.org.

331 310 CHE ISSN 1014-9856
HD7262
SOURCES AND METHODS. LABOUR STATISTICS. Text in English, French, Spanish. 1992. a. **Document type:** *Bulletin.*
Related titles: ♦ Supplement(s): Year Book of Labour Statistics. ISSN 0084-3857.
—BLDSC (8330.592000).
Published by: (International Labour Office), I L O Publications, PO Box 6, Geneva 22, 1211, Switzerland. TEL 41-22-799-6111, FAX 41-22-798-6358. **Dist. in US by:** I L O Publications Center, 9 Jay Gould Court, Ste. CT, PO Box 753, Waldorf, MD 20604. TEL 301-638-3152, FAX 301-843-0159, ilopubs@tasco1.com.

382 316 ZAF
SOUTH AFRICA. COMMISSIONER FOR CUSTOMS AND EXCISE. FOREIGN TRADE STATISTICS. Text in English. a. price varies. charts. **Document type:** *Government.*
Formerly: South Africa. Department of Customs and Excise. Foreign Trade Statistics (0081-2196)
Published by: Commissioner for Customs and Excise, Private Bag X47, Pretoria, 0001, South Africa. Ed. J M Heyns. **Subscr. to:** Government Printing Works.

382 ZAF
SOUTH AFRICA. COMMISSIONER FOR CUSTOMS AND EXCISE. MONTHLY ABSTRACT OF TRADE STATISTICS. Text in English. m. ZAR 100 (effective 2000). charts. **Document type:** *Government.*
Formerly: South Africa. Department of Customs and Excise. Monthly Abstract of Trade Statistics
Published by: Commissioner for Customs and Excise, Private Bag X47, Pretoria, 0001, South Africa. Ed. J M Heyns. **Subscr. to:** Government Printing Works.

338.4 316.8 ZAF
SOUTH AFRICA. STATISTICS SOUTH AFRICA. CENSUS OF MANUFACTURING - (YEAR) PRINCIPAL STATISTICS ON A REGIONAL BASIS. Text in English. triennial. ZAR 50 per issue domestic; ZAR 55 per issue foreign (effective 2000). **Document type:** *Government.*
Formerly (until Aug. 1998): South Africa. Central Statistical Service. Census of Manufacturing - Principal Statistics on a Regional Basis; Supersedes in part: South Africa. Department of Statistics. Census of Manufacturing (0259-5303)
Published by: Statistics South Africa/Statistieke Suid-Afrika, Private Bag X44, Pretoria, 0001, South Africa. TEL 27-12-310-8911, FAX 27-12-310-8500, info@statssa.pwv.gov.za, http://www.statssa.gov.za.

B

330 ZAF
SOUTH AFRICA. STATISTICS SOUTH AFRICA. CENSUS OF MANUFACTURING (YEAR). PRINCIPAL STATISTICS ON A REGIONAL BASIS (PART 1) WESTERN CAPE. Text in English. irreg. ZAR 20 (effective 2000). stat. **Document type:** *Government.*
Published by: Statistics South Africa/Statistieke Suid-Afrika, Private Bag X44, Pretoria, 0001, South Africa. TEL 27-12-310-8911, FAX 27-12-310-8500, info@statssa.pwv.gov.za, http://www.statssa.gov.za.

330 ZAF
SOUTH AFRICA. STATISTICS SOUTH AFRICA. CENSUS OF MANUFACTURING (YEAR). PRINCIPAL STATISTICS ON A REGIONAL BASIS (PART 3) NORTHERN CAPE. Text in English. irreg., latest 1993. stat. **Document type:** *Government.*
Published by: Statistics South Africa/Statistieke Suid-Afrika, Private Bag X44, Pretoria, 0001, South Africa. TEL 27-12-310-8911, FAX 27-12-310-8500, info@statssa.pwv.gov.za, http://www.statssa.gov.za.

330 ZAF
SOUTH AFRICA. STATISTICS SOUTH AFRICA. CENSUS OF MANUFACTURING (YEAR). PRINCIPAL STATISTICS ON A REGIONAL BASIS (PART 4) FREE-STATE. Text in English. irreg. ZAR 20 (effective 2000). stat. **Document type:** *Government.*
Published by: Statistics South Africa/Statistieke Suid-Afrika, Private Bag X44, Pretoria, 0001, South Africa. TEL 27-12-310-8911, FAX 27-12-310-8500, info@statssa.pwv.gov.za, http://www.statssa.gov.za.

330 ZAF
SOUTH AFRICA. STATISTICS SOUTH AFRICA. CENSUS OF MANUFACTURING (YEAR). PRINCIPAL STATISTICS ON A REGIONAL BASIS (PART 5) KWA-CULA-NATAL. Text in English. irreg. ZAR 30 (effective 2000). stat. **Document type:** *Government.*
Published by: Statistics South Africa/Statistieke Suid-Afrika, Private Bag X44, Pretoria, 0001, South Africa. TEL 27-12-310-8911, FAX 27-12-310-8500, info@statssa.pwv.gov.za, http://www.statssa.gov.za.

330 ZAF
SOUTH AFRICA. STATISTICS SOUTH AFRICA. CENSUS OF MANUFACTURING (YEAR). PRINCIPAL STATISTICS ON A REGIONAL BASIS (PART 6) NORTHWEST. Text in English. irreg. ZAR 20 (effective 2000). stat. **Document type:** *Government.*
Published by: Statistics South Africa/Statistieke Suid-Afrika, Private Bag X44, Pretoria, 0001, South Africa. TEL 27-12-310-8911, FAX 27-12-310-8500, info@statssa.pwv.gov.za, http://www.statssa.gov.za.

330 ZAF
SOUTH AFRICA. STATISTICS SOUTH AFRICA. CENSUS OF MANUFACTURING (YEAR). PRINCIPAL STATISTICS ON A REGIONAL BASIS (PART 7) GAUTENG. Text in English. irreg. ZAR 30 (effective 2000). stat. **Document type:** *Government.*
Published by: Statistics South Africa/Statistieke Suid-Afrika, Private Bag X44, Pretoria, 0001, South Africa. TEL 27-12-310-8911, FAX 27-12-310-8500, info@statssa.pwv.gov.za, http://www.statssa.gov.za.

330 ZAF
SOUTH AFRICA. STATISTICS SOUTH AFRICA. CENSUS OF MANUFACTURING (YEAR). PRINCIPAL STATISTICS ON A REGIONAL BASIS (PART 8) MPUMALANGA. Text in English. irreg. ZAR 20 per issue (effective 2000). stat. **Document type:** *Government.*
Published by: Statistics South Africa/Statistieke Suid-Afrika, Private Bag X44, Pretoria, 0001, South Africa. TEL 27-12-310-8911, FAX 27-12-310-8500, info@statssa.pwv.gov.za, http://www.statssa.gov.za.

330 ZAF
SOUTH AFRICA. STATISTICS SOUTH AFRICA. CENSUS OF MANUFACTURING (YEAR). PRINCIPAL STATISTICS ON A REGIONAL BASIS (PART 9) NORTHERN PROVINCE. Text in English. irreg. ZAR 20 (effective 2000). stat. **Document type:** *Government.*

Published by: Statistics South Africa/Statistieke Suid-Afrika, Private Bag X44, Pretoria, 0001, South Africa. TEL 27-12-310-8911, FAX 27-12-310-8500, info@statssa.pwv.gov.za, http://www.statssa.gov.za.

330 ZAF
SOUTH AFRICA. STATISTICS SOUTH AFRICA. CENSUS OF MANUFACTURING (YEAR). REGISTER OF MANUFACTURERS ACCORDING TO PRODUCTS MANUFACTURED IN SOUTH AFRICA. EASTERN CAPE. Text in English. irreg. ZAR 10 (effective 2000). stat.
Document type: *Government.*
Published by: Statistics South Africa/Statistieke Suid-Afrika, Private Bag X44, Pretoria, 0001, South Africa. TEL 27-12-310-8911, FAX 27-12-310-8500, info@statssa.pwv.gov.za, http://www.statssa.gov.za.

300 ZAF
SOUTH AFRICA. STATISTICS SOUTH AFRICA. CENSUS OF MANUFACTURING (YEAR). REGISTER OF MANUFACTURERS ACCORDING TO PRODUCTS MANUFACTURED IN SOUTH AFRICA. FREE STATE. Text in English. irreg. ZAR 10 per issue (effective 2000). stat.
Document type: *Academic/Scholarly.*
Published by: Statistics South Africa/Statistieke Suid-Afrika, Private Bag X44, Pretoria, 0001, South Africa. TEL 27-12-310-8911, FAX 27-12-310-8500, info@statssa.pwv.gov.za, http://www.statssa.gov.za.

330 ZAF
SOUTH AFRICA. STATISTICS SOUTH AFRICA. CENSUS OF MANUFACTURING (YEAR). REGISTER OF MANUFACTURERS ACCORDING TO PRODUCTS MANUFACTURED IN SOUTH AFRICA. GAUTERY. Text in English. irreg. ZAR 10 per issue (effective 2000). stat.
Document type: *Government.*
Published by: Statistics South Africa/Statistieke Suid-Afrika, Private Bag X44, Pretoria, 0001, South Africa. TEL 27-12-310-8911, FAX 27-12-310-8500, info@statssa.pwv.gov.za, http://www.statssa.gov.za.

330 ZAF
SOUTH AFRICA. STATISTICS SOUTH AFRICA. CENSUS OF MANUFACTURING (YEAR). REGISTER OF MANUFACTURERS ACCORDING TO PRODUCTS MANUFACTURED IN SOUTH AFRICA. KWAZULU-NATAL. Text in English. irreg. ZAR 10 per issue (effective 2000). stat.
Document type: *Government.*
Published by: Statistics South Africa/Statistieke Suid-Afrika, Private Bag X44, Pretoria, 0001, South Africa. TEL 27-12-310-8911, FAX 27-12-310-8500, info@statssa.pwv.gov.za, http://www.statssa.gov.za.

330 ZAF
SOUTH AFRICA. STATISTICS SOUTH AFRICA. CENSUS OF MANUFACTURING (YEAR). REGISTER OF MANUFACTURERS ACCORDING TO PRODUCTS MANUFACTURED IN SOUTH AFRICA. MPUMALANGA. Text in English. irreg., latest 1999. ZAR 10 (effective 2000). stat.
Document type: *Government.*
Published by: Statistics South Africa/Statistieke Suid-Afrika, Private Bag X44, Pretoria, 0001, South Africa. TEL 27-12-310-8911, FAX 27-12-310-8500, info@statssa.pwv.gov.za, http://www.statssa.gov.za.

330 ZAF
SOUTH AFRICA. STATISTICS SOUTH AFRICA. CENSUS OF MANUFACTURING (YEAR). REGISTER OF MANUFACTURERS ACCORDING TO PRODUCTS MANUFACTURED IN SOUTH AFRICA. NORTHERN CAPE. Text in English. irreg. ZAR 10 per issue (effective 2000). stat.
Document type: *Government.*
Published by: Statistics South Africa/Statistieke Suid-Afrika, Private Bag X44, Pretoria, 0001, South Africa. TEL 27-12-310-8911, FAX 27-12-310-8500, info@statssa.pwv.gov.za, http://www.statssa.gov.za.

330 ZAF
SOUTH AFRICA. STATISTICS SOUTH AFRICA. CENSUS OF MANUFACTURING (YEAR). REGISTER OF MANUFACTURERS ACCORDING TO PRODUCTS MANUFACTURED IN SOUTH AFRICA. NORTHERN PROVINCE. Text in English. irreg., latest 1999. ZAR 10 (effective 2000). stat. **Document type:** *Government.*
Published by: Statistics South Africa/Statistieke Suid-Afrika, Private Bag X44, Pretoria, 0001, South Africa. TEL 27-12-310-8911, FAX 27-12-310-8500, info@statssa.pwv.gov.za, http://www.statssa.gov.za.

330 ZAF
SOUTH AFRICA. STATISTICS SOUTH AFRICA. CENSUS OF MANUFACTURING (YEAR). REGISTER OF MANUFACTURERS ACCORDING TO PRODUCTS MANUFACTURED IN SOUTH AFRICA. NORTHWEST. Text in English. irreg. ZAR 10 per issue (effective 2000). stat.
Document type: *Government.*
Published by: Statistics South Africa/Statistieke Suid-Afrika, Private Bag X44, Pretoria, 0001, South Africa. TEL 27-12-310-8911, FAX 27-12-310-8500, info@statssa.pwv.gov.za, http://www.statssa.gov.za.

330 ZAF
SOUTH AFRICA. STATISTICS SOUTH AFRICA. CENSUS OF MANUFACTURING (YEAR). REGISTER OF MANUFACTURERS ACCORDING TO PRODUCTS MANUFACTURED IN SOUTH AFRICA. WESTERN CAPE. Text in English. irreg. ZAR 10 per issue (effective 2000). stat.
Document type: *Government.*
Published by: Statistics South Africa/Statistieke Suid-Afrika, Private Bag X44, Pretoria, 0001, South Africa. TEL 27-12-310-8911, FAX 27-12-310-8500, info@statssa.pwv.gov.za, http://www.statssa.gov.za.

338.4 316.8 ZAF
SOUTH AFRICA. STATISTICS SOUTH AFRICA. CENSUS OF MANUFACTURING - MATERIALS PURCHASED AND MANUFACTURES SOLD. Text in English. triennial. ZAR 30 domestic; ZAR 33 foreign (effective 2000). **Document type:** *Government.*
Former titles (until Aug 1998): South Africa. Central Statistical Service. Census of Manufacturing - Materials Purchased and Manufactures Sold; Supersedes in part: South Africa. Department of Statistics. Census of Manufacturing (0259-5303)
Published by: Statistics South Africa/Statistieke Suid-Afrika, Private Bag X44, Pretoria, 0001, South Africa. TEL 27-12-310-8911, FAX 27-12-310-8500, info@statssa.pwv.gov.za, http://www.statssa.gov.za.

338.4 ZAF
SOUTH AFRICA. STATISTICS SOUTH AFRICA. CENSUS OF MANUFACTURING - PRINCIPAL STATISTICS ON A REGIONAL BASIS PART-I. Text in English. triennial. ZAR 30 domestic; ZAR 33 foreign (effective 2000). **Document type:** *Government.*
Former titles (until Aug. 1998): South Africa. Central Statistical Service. Census of Manufacturing - Register of Manufactures According to Products Manufactured in South Africa; South Africa. Central Statistical Service. Register of Products Manufactured in South Africa
Published by: Statistics South Africa/Statistieke Suid-Afrika, Private Bag X44, Pretoria, 0001, South Africa. TEL 27-12-310-8911, FAX 27-12-310-8500, info@statssa.pwv.gov.za, http://www.statssa.gov.za.

338.4 316.8 ZAF
SOUTH AFRICA. STATISTICS SOUTH AFRICA. CENSUS OF MANUFACTURING - STATISTICS ACCORDING TO MAJOR GROUPS AND SUBGROUPS. Text in English. triennial. ZAR 30 domestic; ZAR 30 foreign (effective 2000). **Document type:** *Government.*
Former titles (until Aug. 1998): South Africa. Central Statistical Service. Census of Manufacturing - Statistics According to Major Groups and Subgroups; Supersedes in part: South Africa. Department of Statistics. Census of Manufacturing (0259-5303)
Published by: Statistics South Africa/Statistieke Suid-Afrika, Private Bag X44, Pretoria, 0001, South Africa. TEL 27-12-310-8911, FAX 27-12-310-8500, info@statssa.pwv.gov.za, http://www.statssa.gov.za.

381 316.8 ZAF
SOUTH AFRICA. STATISTICS SOUTH AFRICA. CENSUS OF MOTOR TRADE AND REPAIR SERVICES. Text in English. irreg., latest 1983. ZAR 10 (effective 2000). **Document type:** *Government.*
Formerly (until Aug. 1998): South Africa. Central Statistical Service. Census of Motor Trade and Repair Services
Published by: Statistics South Africa/Statistieke Suid-Afrika, Private Bag X44, Pretoria, 0001, South Africa. TEL 27-12-310-8911, FAX 27-12-310-8500, info@statssa.pwv.gov.za, http://www.statssa.gov.za.

338.4 316.8 ZAF
SOUTH AFRICA. STATISTICS SOUTH AFRICA. CENSUS OF PROFESSIONAL AND BUSINESS SERVICES - ACCOUNTING, AUDITING AND BOOK-KEEPING SERVICES. Text in English. irreg., latest 1987. ZAR 10 (effective 2000). **Document type:** *Government.*
Former titles: South Africa. Statistics South Africa. Census of Business Services - Accounting, Auditing and Book-keeping Services; (until Aug. 1998): South Africa. Central Statistical Service. Census of Business Services - Accounting, Auditing and Book-keeping Services
Published by: Statistics South Africa/Statistieke Suid-Afrika, Private Bag X44, Pretoria, 0001, South Africa. TEL 27-12-310-8911, FAX 27-12-310-8500, info@statssa.pwv.gov.za, http://www.statssa.gov.za.

338.4 316.8 ZAF
SOUTH AFRICA. STATISTICS SOUTH AFRICA. CENSUS OF PROFESSIONAL AND BUSINESS SERVICES - CONSULTING ENGINEERS. Text in English. irreg., latest 1993. ZAR 10 (effective 2000). **Document type:** *Government.*
Former titles: South Africa. Statistics South Africa. Census of Business Services - Consulting Engineers; (until Aug. 1998): South Africa. Central Statistical Service. Census of Business Services - Consulting Engineers
Published by: Statistics South Africa/Statistieke Suid-Afrika, Private Bag X44, Pretoria, 0001, South Africa. TEL 27-12-310-8911, FAX 27-12-310-8500, info@statssa.pwv.gov.za, http://www.statssa.gov.za.

004.021 ZAF
SOUTH AFRICA. STATISTICS SOUTH AFRICA. CENSUS OF PROFESSIONAL AND BUSINESS SERVICES - DATA PROCESSING SERVICES. Text in English. irreg., latest 1993. ZAR 10 (effective 2000). **Document type:** *Government.*
Former titles: South Africa. Statistics South Africa. Census of Business Services - Data Processing Services; (until Aug. 1998): South Africa. Central Statistical Service. Census of Business Services - Data Processing Services
Published by: Statistics South Africa/Statistieke Suid-Afrika, Private Bag X44, Pretoria, 0001, South Africa. TEL 27-12-310-8911, FAX 27-12-310-8500, info@statssa.pwv.gov.za, http://www.statssa.gov.za.

338.4 316.8 ZAF
SOUTH AFRICA. STATISTICS SOUTH AFRICA. CENSUS OF PROFESSIONAL AND BUSINESS SERVICES - EMPLOYMENT PLACEMENT AGENCIES, RECRUITING ORGANISATIONS AND LABOUR BROKERS SERVICES. Text in English. irreg., latest 1997. ZAR 10 (effective 2000).
Document type: *Government.*
Former titles: South Africa. Statistics South Africa. Census of Business Services - Employment Placement Agencies, Recruiting Organisations and Labour Brokers Services; (until Aug. 1998): South Africa. Central Statistical Service. Census of Business Services - Employment Placement Agencies, Recruiting Organisations and Labour Brokers Services
Published by: Statistics South Africa/Statistieke Suid-Afrika, Private Bag X44, Pretoria, 0001, South Africa. TEL 27-12-310-8911, FAX 27-12-310-8500, info@statssa.pwv.gov.za, http://www.statssa.gov.za.

338.4 316.8 ZAF
SOUTH AFRICA. STATISTICS SOUTH AFRICA. CENSUS OF PROFESSIONAL AND BUSINESS SERVICES - LEGAL SERVICES. Text in English. irreg., latest 1993. ZAR 10 (effective 2000). **Document type:** *Government.*
Former titles: South Africa. Statistics South Africa. Census of Business Services - Legal Services; (until Aug. 1998): South Africa. Central Statistical Service. Census of Business Services - Legal Services
Published by: Statistics South Africa/Statistieke Suid-Afrika, Private Bag X44, Pretoria, 0001, South Africa. TEL 27-12-310-8911, FAX 27-12-310-8500, info@statssa.pwa.gov.za, info@statssa.pwv.gov.za, http://www.statssa.gov.za.

330 ZAF
SOUTH AFRICA. STATISTICS SOUTH AFRICA. EARNING AND SPENDING IN SOUTH AFRICA; selected findings of the (Year) (Month) household survey. Text in English. irreg.
Document type: *Government.*
Published by: Statistics South Africa/Statistieke Suid-Afrika, Private Bag X44, Pretoria, 0001, South Africa. TEL 27-12-310-8911, FAX 27-12-310-8500, info@statssa.pwv.gov.za, http://www.statssa.gov.za.

351.7 316.8 ZAF
SOUTH AFRICA. STATISTICS SOUTH AFRICA. INPUT OUTPUT TABLES. Key Title: Inset-Uitset-Tabelle. Text in Afrikaans, English. irreg., latest 1989. ZAR 20 domestic; ZAR 25 foreign (effective 2000). **Document type:** *Government.*
Formerly (until Aug.1998): South Africa. Central Statistical Service. Input Output Tables (0259-6075)
Related titles: Diskette ed.: ZAR 15 domestic; ZAR 18.75 foreign (effective 1999).
Published by: Statistics South Africa/Statistieke Suid-Afrika, Private Bag X44, Pretoria, 0001, South Africa. TEL 27-12-310-8911, FAX 27-12-310-8500, info@statssa.pwv.gov.za, http://www.statssa.gov.za.

330 ZAF
SOUTH AFRICA. STATISTICS SOUTH AFRICA. LABOUR STATISTICS. SURVEY OF TOTAL EMPLOYMENT AND EARNINGS. Text in English. irreg. **Document type:** *Government.*
Published by: Statistics South Africa/Statistieke Suid-Afrika, Private Bag X44, Pretoria, 0001, South Africa. TEL 27-12-310-8911, FAX 27-12-310-8500, info@statssa.pwv.gov.za, http://www.statssa.gov.za.

331 316.8 ZAF
SOUTH AFRICA. STATISTICS SOUTH AFRICA. MANPOWER SURVEY (OCCUPATIONAL INFORMATION). Key Title: Mannekragopname Beroepsgegewens. Text in Afrikaans, English. a., latest 1994. ZAR 10 domestic; ZAR 11 foreign (effective 2000). **Document type:** *Government.*
Formerly (until Aug.1998): South Africa. Central Statistical Service. Manpower Survey (Occupational Information) (1018-2306)
Published by: Statistics South Africa/Statistieke Suid-Afrika, Private Bag X44, Pretoria, 0001, South Africa. TEL 27-12-310-8911, FAX 27-12-310-8500, info@statssa.pwv.gov.za, http://www.statssa.gov.za.

330 ZAF
SOUTH AFRICA. STATISTICS SOUTH AFRICA. RURAL SURVEY (YEAR). Text in English. irreg. ZAR 40 per issue (effective 2000). **Document type:** *Government.*

B

Published by: Statistics South Africa/Statistieke Suid-Afrika, Private Bag X44, Pretoria, 0001, South Africa. TEL 27-12-310-8911, FAX 27-12-310-8500, info@statssa.pwv.gov.za, http://www.statssa.gov.za.

336 316.8 ZAF
SOUTH AFRICA. STATISTICS SOUTH AFRICA. STATISTICAL RELEASE. ACTUAL AND ANTICIPATED CAPITAL EXPENDITURE OF THE PUBLIC SECTOR. Text in English. a. free. **Document type:** *Government.*
Formerly (until Aug.1998): South Africa. Central Statistical Service. Statistical Release. Actual and Anticipated Capital Expenditure of the Public Sector
Published by: Statistics South Africa/Statistieke Suid-Afrika, Private Bag X44, Pretoria, 0001, South Africa. TEL 27-12-310-8911, FAX 27-12-310-8500, info@statssa.pwv.gov.za, http://www.statssa.gov.za.

336 316.8 ZAF
SOUTH AFRICA. STATISTICS SOUTH AFRICA. STATISTICAL RELEASE. ACTUAL AND ANTICIPATED CONSTRUCTION EXPENDITURE OF THE PUBLIC SECTOR BY REGION. Text in English. a. free. **Document type:** *Government.*
Formerly (until Aug. 1998): South Africa. Central Statistical Service. Statistical Release. Actual and Anticipated Construction Expenditure of the Public Sector by Region
Published by: Statistics South Africa/Statistieke Suid-Afrika, Private Bag X44, Pretoria, 0001, South Africa. TEL 27-12-310-8911, FAX 27-12-310-8500, info@statssa.pwv.gov.za, http://www.statssa.gov.za.

338.4 316.8 ZAF
SOUTH AFRICA. STATISTICS SOUTH AFRICA. STATISTICAL RELEASE. CENSUS OF MANUFACTURING. Text in English. irreg. **Document type:** *Government.*
Formerly (until Aug. 1998): South Africa. Central Statistical Service. Statistical Release. Census of Manufacturing
Published by: Statistics South Africa/Statistieke Suid-Afrika, Private Bag X44, Pretoria, 0001, South Africa. TEL 27-12-310-8911, FAX 27-12-310-8500, info@statssa.pwv.gov.za, http://www.statssa.gov.za.

339 316.8 ZAF
SOUTH AFRICA. STATISTICS SOUTH AFRICA. STATISTICAL RELEASE. CONSUMER PRICE INDEX. Text in English. m. free. **Document type:** *Government.*
Formerly (until Aug. 1998): South Africa. Central Statistical Service. Statistical Release. Consumer Price Index
Published by: Statistics South Africa/Statistieke Suid-Afrika, Private Bag X44, Pretoria, 0001, South Africa. TEL 27-12-310-8911, FAX 27-12-310-8500, info@statssa.pwv.gov.za, http://www.statssa.gov.za.

339 316.8 ZAF
SOUTH AFRICA. STATISTICS SOUTH AFRICA. STATISTICAL RELEASE. CONSUMER PRICE INDEX BASE. Text in English. irreg., latest 1996. **Document type:** *Government.* **Description:** Cumulative information, with conversion factors.
Formerly (until Aug. 1998): South Africa. Central Statistical Service. Statistical Release. Consumer Price Index Base
Published by: Statistics South Africa/Statistieke Suid-Afrika, Private Bag X44, Pretoria, 0001, South Africa. TEL 27-12-310-8911, FAX 27-12-310-8500, info@statssa.pwv.gov.za, http://www.statssa.gov.za.

339 316.8 ZAF
SOUTH AFRICA. STATISTICS SOUTH AFRICA. STATISTICAL RELEASE. CONSUMER PRICE INDEX WEIGHTS. Text in English. irreg., latest 1996. **Document type:** *Government.*
Formerly (until Aug. 1998): South Africa. Central Statistical Service. Statistical Release. Consumer Price Index Weights
Published by: Statistics South Africa/Statistieke Suid-Afrika, Private Bag X44, Pretoria, 0001, South Africa. TEL 27-12-310-8911, FAX 27-12-310-8500, info@statssa.pwv.gov.za, http://www.statssa.gov.za.

332 316.8 ZAF
SOUTH AFRICA. STATISTICS SOUTH AFRICA. STATISTICAL RELEASE. FINANCIAL STATISTICS OF COMPANIES. Text in Afrikaans, English. irreg. **Document type:** *Government.*
Formerly (until Aug. 1998): South Africa. Central Statistical Service. Statistical Release. Financial Statistics of Companies
Published by: Statistics South Africa/Statistieke Suid-Afrika, Private Bag X44, Pretoria, 0001, South Africa. TEL 27-12-310-8911, FAX 27-12-310-8500, info@statssa.pwv.gov.za, http://www.statssa.gov.za.

336 316.8 ZAF
SOUTH AFRICA. STATISTICS SOUTH AFRICA. STATISTICAL RELEASE. FINANCIAL STATISTICS OF EXTRABUDGETARY ACCOUNTS AND FUNDS. Text in English. a. **Document type:** *Government.*
Formerly (until Aug. 1998): South Africa. Central Statistical Service. Statistical Release. Financial Statistics of Extrabudgetary Accounts and Funds
Published by: Statistics South Africa/Statistieke Suid-Afrika, Private Bag X44, Pretoria, 0001, South Africa. TEL 27-12-310-8911, FAX 27-12-310-8500, info@statssa.pwv.gov.za, http://www.statssa.gov.za.

339 316.8 ZAF
SOUTH AFRICA. STATISTICS SOUTH AFRICA. STATISTICAL RELEASE. GROSS DOMESTIC PRODUCT AT CONSTANT PRICES. Text in English. q. **Document type:** *Government.*
Formerly (until Aug. 1998): South Africa. Central Statistical Service. Statistical Release. Gross Domestic Product at Constant Prices
Published by: Statistics South Africa/Statistieke Suid-Afrika, Private Bag X44, Pretoria, 0001, South Africa. TEL 27-12-310-8911, FAX 27-12-310-8500, info@statssa.pwv.gov.za, http://www.statssa.gov.za.

339 316.8 ZAF
SOUTH AFRICA. STATISTICS SOUTH AFRICA. STATISTICAL RELEASE. GROSS GEOGRAPHIC PRODUCT AT FACTOR INCOMES. Text in English. irreg., latest 1988. **Document type:** *Government.*
Formerly (until Aug. 1998): South Africa. Central Statistical Service. Statistical Release. Gross Geographic Product at Factor Incomes
Published by: Statistics South Africa/Statistieke Suid-Afrika, Private Bag X44, Pretoria, 0001, South Africa. TEL 27-12-310-8911, FAX 27-12-310-8500, info@statssa.pwv.gov.za, http://www.statssa.gov.za.

339 316.8 ZAF
SOUTH AFRICA. STATISTICS SOUTH AFRICA. STATISTICAL RELEASE. HOUSEHOLD EXPENDITURE. Text in English. irreg., latest 1995. **Document type:** *Government.* **Description:** Income and expenditure data for households.
Formerly (until Aug. 1998): South Africa. Central Statistical Service. Statistical Release. Household Expenditure
Published by: Statistics South Africa/Statistieke Suid-Afrika, Private Bag X44, Pretoria, 0001, South Africa. TEL 27-12-310-8911, FAX 27-12-310-8500, info@statssa.pwv.gov.za, http://www.statssa.gov.za.

338.4021 ZAF
SOUTH AFRICA. STATISTICS SOUTH AFRICA. STATISTICAL RELEASE. MANUFACTURING - CAPITAL EXPENDITURE ON NEW ASSETS. Text in English. irreg., latest covers 1991-1999. **Document type:** *Government.*
Formerly (until Aug. 1998): South Africa. Central Statistical Service. Statistical Release. Manufacturing - Capital Expenditure on New Assets
Published by: Statistics South Africa/Statistieke Suid-Afrika, Private Bag X44, Pretoria, 0001, South Africa. TEL 27-12-310-8911, FAX 27-12-310-8500, info@statssa.pwv.gov.za, http://www.statssa.gov.za.

338.4 316.8 ZAF
SOUTH AFRICA. STATISTICS SOUTH AFRICA. STATISTICAL RELEASE. MANUFACTURING - FINANCIAL STATISTICS. Text in English. irreg. **Document type:** *Government.*
Formerly (until Aug. 1998): South Africa. Central Statistical Service. Statistical Release. Manufacturing - Financial Statistics
Published by: Statistics South Africa/Statistieke Suid-Afrika, Private Bag X44, Pretoria, 0001, South Africa. TEL 27-12-310-8911, FAX 27-12-310-8500, info@statssa.pwv.gov.za, http://www.statssa.gov.za.

338.4 316.8 ZAF
SOUTH AFRICA. STATISTICS SOUTH AFRICA. STATISTICAL RELEASE. MANUFACTURING - FINANCIAL STATISTICS (QUARTERLY). Text in English. q. **Document type:** *Government.*
Formerly (until Aug. 1998): South Africa. Central Statistical Service. Statistical Release. Manufacturing - Financial Statistics (Quarterly)
Published by: Statistics South Africa/Statistieke Suid-Afrika, Private Bag X44, Pretoria, 0001, South Africa. TEL 27-12-310-8911, FAX 27-12-310-8500, info@statssa.pwv.gov.za, http://www.statssa.gov.za.

338.4 316.8 ZAF
SOUTH AFRICA. STATISTICS SOUTH AFRICA. STATISTICAL RELEASE. MANUFACTURING PRODUCTION. Text in English. irreg. **Document type:** *Government.* **Description:** Historical data of production indices and value of sales and unfilled orders by subgroup of Standard Industrial Classification.
Formerly (until Aug. 1998): South Africa. Central Statistical Service. Statistical Release. Manufacturing Production
Published by: Statistics South Africa/Statistieke Suid-Afrika, Private Bag X44, Pretoria, 0001, South Africa. TEL 27-12-310-8911, FAX 27-12-310-8500, info@statssa.pwv.gov.za, http://www.statssa.gov.za.

338.4 316.8 ZAF
SOUTH AFRICA. STATISTICS SOUTH AFRICA. STATISTICAL RELEASE. MANUFACTURING - PRODUCTION AND SALES. Text in English. m. **Document type:** *Government.*
Formerly (until Aug. 1998): South Africa. Central Statistical Service. Statistical Release. Manufacturing - Production and Sales
Published by: Statistics South Africa/Statistieke Suid-Afrika, Private Bag X44, Pretoria, 0001, South Africa. TEL 27-12-310-8911, FAX 27-12-310-8500, info@statssa.pwv.gov.za, http://www.statssa.gov.za.

338.4 316.8 ZAF
SOUTH AFRICA. STATISTICS SOUTH AFRICA. STATISTICAL RELEASE. MANUFACTURING STATISTICS: BASIC METAL AND FABRICATED METAL PRODUCTS, MACHINERY AND EQUIPMENT, MOTOR VEHICLES AND PARTS AND MISCELLANEOUS PRODUCTS. Text in English. bi-m. **Document type:** *Government.*
Formerly (until Aug. 1998): South Africa. Central Statistical Service. Statistical Release. Manfacturing Statistics: Basic Metal and Fabricated Metal Products, Machinery and Equipment, Mortor Vehicles and Parts and Miscellaneous Products
Published by: Statistics South Africa/Statistieke Suid-Afrika, Private Bag X44, Pretoria, 0001, South Africa. TEL 27-12-310-8911, FAX 27-12-310-8500, info@statssa.pwv.gov.za, http://www.statssa.gov.za.

338.4 316.8 ZAF
SOUTH AFRICA. STATISTICS SOUTH AFRICA. STATISTICAL RELEASE. MANUFACTURING STATISTICS: CHEMICAL, RUBBER, PLASTIC, GLASS AND NON-METALLIC MINERAL PRODUCTS. Text in English. bi-m. **Document type:** *Government.*
Formerly (until Aug. 1998): South Africa. Central Statistical Service. Statistical Release. Manufacturing Statistics: Chemical, Rubber, Plastic, Glass and Non-metallic Mineral Products
Published by: Statistics South Africa/Statistieke Suid-Afrika, Private Bag X44, Pretoria, 0001, South Africa. TEL 27-12-310-8911, FAX 27-12-310-8500, info@statssa.pwv.gov.za, http://www.statssa.gov.za.

B

338.4 316.8 ZAF
SOUTH AFRICA. STATISTICS SOUTH AFRICA. STATISTICAL RELEASE. MANUFACTURING STATISTICS: PRODUCTS MANUFACTURED: FOODS, BEVERAGES AND TOBACCO PRODUCTS. Text in English. bi-m. free. **Document type:** *Government.*
Formerly (until Aug. 1998): South Africa. Central Statistical Service. Statistical Release. Manufacturing Statistics: Products Manufactured: Foods, Beverages and Tobacco Products
Published by: Statistics South Africa/Statistieke Suid-Afrika, Private Bag X44, Pretoria, 0001, South Africa. TEL 27-12-310-8911, FAX 27-12-310-8500, info@statssa.pwv.gov.za, http://www.statssa.gov.za.

338.4 316.8 ZAF
SOUTH AFRICA. STATISTICS SOUTH AFRICA. STATISTICAL RELEASE. MANUFACTURING STATISTICS: PRODUCTS MANUFACTURED: TEXTILES, CLOTHING, LEATHER AND LEATHER PRODUCTS, WOOD AND WOOD PRODUCTS, PAPER AND PAPER PRODUCTS AND PRINTING. Text in English. bi-m. **Document type:** *Government.*
Formerly (until Aug.1998): South Africa. Central Statistical Service. Statistical Release. Manufacturing Statistics: Products Manufactured: Textiles, Clothing, Leather and Leather Products, Wood and Wood Products, Paper and Paper Products and Printing
Published by: Statistics South Africa/Statistieke Suid-Afrika, Private Bag X44, Pretoria, 0001, South Africa. TEL 27-12-310-8911, FAX 27-12-310-8500, info@statssa.pwv.gov.za, http://www.statssa.gov.za.

380.1 316.8 ZAF
SOUTH AFRICA. STATISTICS SOUTH AFRICA. STATISTICAL RELEASE. MOTOR TRADE - FINANCIAL STATISTICS. Text in English. q. **Document type:** *Government.*
Formerly (until Aug. 1998): South Africa. Central Statistical Service. Statistical Release. Motor Trade - Financial Statistics
Published by: Statistics South Africa/Statistieke Suid-Afrika, Private Bag X44, Pretoria, 0001, South Africa. TEL 27-12-310-8911, FAX 27-12-310-8500, info@statssa.pwv.gov.za, http://www.statssa.gov.za.

339 316.8 ZAF
SOUTH AFRICA. STATISTICS SOUTH AFRICA. STATISTICAL RELEASE. PRODUCTION PRICE INDEX. Text in English. m. **Document type:** *Government.* **Description:** Price indices of commodities for South African consumption, of output of South Africa industry groups and of selected materials.
Formerly (until Aug. 1998): South Africa. Central Statistical Service. Statistical Release. Production Price Index
Published by: Statistics South Africa/Statistieke Suid-Afrika, Private Bag X44, Pretoria, 0001, South Africa. TEL 27-12-310-8911, FAX 27-12-310-8500, info@statssa.pwv.gov.za, http://www.statssa.gov.za.

339 316.8 ZAF
SOUTH AFRICA. STATISTICS SOUTH AFRICA. STATISTICAL RELEASE. PRODUCTION PRICE INDEX BASE (YEAR). Text in English. irreg., latest covers 1971-1995. **Document type:** *Government.* **Description:** Price indices of commodities for South African consumption, of output of South African industry groups and of certain selected materials. 1990 is used as the base year.
Formerly (until Aug. 1998): South Africa. Central Statistical Service. Statistical Release. Production Price Index Base (Year)
Published by: Statistics South Africa/Statistieke Suid-Afrika, Private Bag X44, Pretoria, 0001, South Africa. TEL 27-12-310-8911, FAX 27-12-310-8500, info@statssa.pwv.gov.za, http://www.statssa.gov.za.

▼ *new title* ➤ *refereed* ✶ *unverified* ◆ *full entry avail.*

380.1 316.8 ZAF
SOUTH AFRICA. STATISTICS SOUTH AFRICA. STATISTICAL RELEASE. RETAIL TRADE - FINANCIAL STATISTICS. Text in English. q. **Document type:** *Government.*
Formerly: South Africa. Central Statistical Service. Statistical Release. Retail Trade - Financial Statistics
Published by: Statistics South Africa/Statistieke Suid-Afrika, Private Bag X44, Pretoria, 0001, South Africa. TEL 27-12-310-8911, FAX 27-12-310-8500, info@statssa.pwv.gov.za, http://www.statssa.gov.za.

380.1 316.8 ZAF
SOUTH AFRICA. STATISTICS SOUTH AFRICA. STATISTICAL RELEASE. RETAIL TRADE IN MOTOR VEHICLES AND ACCESSORIES - TRADING REVENUE (FINAL). Text in English. m. **Document type:** *Government.*
Formerly (until Aug. 1998): South Africa. Central Statistical Service. Statistical Release. Retail Trade in Motor Vehicles and Accessories - Trading Revenue (Final)
Published by: Statistics South Africa/Statistieke Suid-Afrika, Private Bag X44, Pretoria, 0001, South Africa. TEL 27-12-310-8911, FAX 27-12-310-8500, info@statssa.pwv.gov.za, http://www.statssa.gov.za.

B

380.1 316.8 ZAF
SOUTH AFRICA. STATISTICS SOUTH AFRICA. STATISTICAL RELEASE. RETAIL TRADE SALES. Text in English. irreg., latest covers 1990-1996. **Document type:** *Government.* **Description:** Cumulative statistics on retail trade sales by kind of business, economic regions, kind of merchandise, and kind of sales, at national and provincial level.
Formerly (until Aug. 1998): South Africa. Central Statistical Service. Statistical Release. Retail Trade Sales
Published by: Statistics South Africa/Statistieke Suid-Afrika, Private Bag X44, Pretoria, 0001, South Africa. TEL 27-12-310-8911, FAX 27-12-310-8500, info@statssa.pwv.gov.za, http://www.statssa.gov.za.

380.1 316.8 ZAF
SOUTH AFRICA. STATISTICS SOUTH AFRICA. STATISTICAL RELEASE. RETAIL TRADE SALES (FINAL). Text in English. m. **Document type:** *Government.*
Formerly (until Aug. 1998): South Africa. Central Statistical Service. Statistical Release. Retail Trade Sales (Final)
Published by: Statistics South Africa/Statistieke Suid-Afrika, Private Bag X44, Pretoria, 0001, South Africa. TEL 27-12-310-8911, FAX 27-12-310-8500, info@statssa.pwv.gov.za, http://www.statssa.gov.za.

380.1 316.8 ZAF
SOUTH AFRICA. STATISTICS SOUTH AFRICA. STATISTICAL RELEASE. RETAIL TRADE SALES - PRELIMINARY. Text in English. m. **Document type:** *Government.*
Formerly (until Aug. 1998): South Africa. Central Statistical Service. Statistical Release. Retail Trade Sales - Preliminary
Published by: Statistics South Africa/Statistieke Suid-Afrika, Private Bag X44, Pretoria, 0001, South Africa. TEL 27-12-310-8911, FAX 27-12-310-8500, info@statssa.pwv.gov.za, http://www.statssa.gov.za.

380.1 316.8 ZAF
SOUTH AFRICA. STATISTICS SOUTH AFRICA. STATISTICAL RELEASE. TOTAL VALUE OF WHOLESALE TRADE SALES - EXPECTED SALES. Text in English. m. **Document type:** *Government.*
Formerly (until Aug. 1998): South Africa. Central Statistical Service. Statistical Release. Total Value of Wholesale Trade Sales - Expected Sales
Published by: Statistics South Africa/Statistieke Suid-Afrika, Private Bag X44, Pretoria, 0001, South Africa. TEL 27-12-310-8911, FAX 27-12-310-8500, info@statssa.pwv.gov.za, http://www.statssa.gov.za.

338.4 316.8 ZAF
SOUTH AFRICA. STATISTICS SOUTH AFRICA. STATISTICAL RELEASE. UTILIZATION OF PRODUCTION CAPACITY. Text in English. q. **Document type:** *Government.* **Description:** Indicates percentage utilization and reasons for under-utilization by major group of Standard Industrial Classification.
Formerly (until 1998): South Africa. Central Statistical Service. Statistical Release. Utilization of Production Capacity
Published by: Statistics South Africa/Statistieke Suid-Afrika, Private Bag X44, Pretoria, 0001, South Africa. TEL 27-12-310-8911, FAX 27-12-310-8500, info@statssa.pwv.gov.za, http://www.statssa.gov.za.

380.1 316.8 ZAF
SOUTH AFRICA. STATISTICS SOUTH AFRICA. STATISTICAL RELEASE. WHOLESALE TRADE SALES. Text in English. m. **Document type:** *Government.*
Formerly (until Aug. 1998): South Africa. Central Statistical Service. Statistical Release.
Published by: Statistics South Africa/Statistieke Suid-Afrika, Private Bag X44, Pretoria, 0001, South Africa. TEL 27-12-310-8911, FAX 27-12-310-8500, info@statssa.pwv.gov.za, http://www.statssa.gov.za.

331 316.8 ZAF
SOUTH AFRICAN LABOUR STATISTICS. Text in English. a., latest 1994. ZAR 60 domestic; ZAR 64.50 foreign (effective 2000). **Document type:** *Government.*
Published by: Statistics South Africa/Statistieke Suid-Afrika, Private Bag X44, Pretoria, 0001, South Africa. TEL 27-12-310-8911, FAX 27-12-310-8500, info@statssa.pwv.gov.za, http://www.statssa.gov.za.

332 316 ZAF
SOUTH AFRICAN RESERVE BANK. MONTHLY RELEASE OF SELECTED DATA/SUID-AFRIKAANSE RESERWEBANK. MAANDELIKSE VRYSTELLING VAN UITGESOEKTE GEGEWENS. Text in Afrikaans, English. 1966. m. free. **Document type:** *Bulletin.*
Formerly: South African Reserve Bank. Monthly Release of Money and Banking Statistics (0584-3073)
Published by: South African Reserve Bank/Suid-Afrikaanse Reserwebank, PO Box 427, Pretoria, 0001, South Africa. TEL 27-12-313-3911, FAX 27-12-313-3197, info@gwisel.resbank.co.za, http://www.resbank.co.za. Ed. B L de Jager. R&P B P Pretorius TEL 27-12-3133690. Circ: 750.

SOUTH AFRICAN RESERVE BANK. QUARTERLY BULLETIN/SUID-AFRIKAANSE RESERWEBANK. KWARTAALBLAD. see *BUSINESS AND ECONOMICS—Banking And Finance*

016.33 IND
▼ **SOUTH ASIAN ECONOMIC ABSTRACTS.** Text in English. 2003. q. INR 9,000 domestic; USD 900 foreign (effective 2005). adv. bk.rev. Index. **Document type:** *Abstract/Index.* **Description:** Abstracts articles from approximately 400 economic and allied English language periodicals published in South Asia.
Related titles: CD-ROM ed.: INR 10,000, USD 1,000 (effective 2005).
Published by: Information Research Academy, 37 Syed Amir Ali Ave, Flat #9, Kolkata, West Bengal 700 019, India. info@irakol.net, http://www.irakol.net. Ed. Partha Subir Guha.

016.33 IND
▼ **SOUTH ASIAN MANAGEMENT ABSTRACTS.** Text in English. 2003. q. INR 8,500 domestic; USD 800 foreign (effective 2005). adv. bk.rev. Index. back issues avail. **Document type:** *Abstract/Index.* **Description:** Abstracts articles from all major management and allied English language periodicals published in South Asia.
Related titles: CD-ROM ed.: INR 9,500, USD 900 (effective 2005).
Published by: Information Research Academy, 37 Syed Amir Ali Ave, Flat #9, Kolkata, West Bengal 700 019, India. info@irakol.net, http://www.irakol.net. Ed. Partha Subir Guha.

336.2 317 USA ISSN 0085-6460
HJ11
SOUTH DAKOTA. DEPARTMENT OF REVENUE. ANNUAL STATISTICAL REPORT. Text in English. 1952. a. charts. **Document type:** *Government.*
Formerly: South Dakota. Department of Revenue. Annual Report
Related titles: Microfiche ed.: (from CIS).
Indexed: SRI.
Published by: Department of Revenue, Administrative Services, 445 E Capitol Ave, Pierre, SD 57501-3185. TEL 605-773-5137, FAX 605-773-5129. Ed. Laurie Bonrud. Circ: 450.

330 310 NCL ISSN 1018-0958
SOUTH PACIFIC ECONOMIES: STATISTICAL SUMMARY. Text in English, French. 1978. a.
Related titles: Microfiche ed.: (from CIS).
Indexed: IIS.
Published by: Secretariat of the Pacific Community, PO Box D5, Noumea, Cedex 98848, New Caledonia. TEL 687-262000, FAX 687-263818, spc@spc.int, http://www.spc.int.

331 314 ESP ISSN 0212-6532
SPAIN. INSTITUTO NACIONAL DE ESTADISTICA. ENCUESTA DE POBLACION ACTIVA. PRINCIPALES RESULTADOS. Text in Spanish. q. **Document type:** *Government.*
Former titles: Spain. Instituto Nacional de Estadistica. Encuesta de la Poblacion Activa; Spain. Instituto Nacional de Estadistica. Poblacion Activa (0081-3389)
Indexed: PAIS.
Published by: Instituto Nacional de Estadistica, P. de la Castellana, 183, Madrid, 28071, Spain.

331 ESP ISSN 0212-6990
SPAIN. INSTITUTO NACIONAL DE ESTADISTICA. ENCUESTA DE POBLACION ACTIVA. RESULTADOS DETALLADOS. Text in Spanish. q. **Document type:** *Government.*
Indexed: PAIS.
Published by: Instituto Nacional de Estadistica, P. de la Castellana, 183, Madrid, 28071, Spain.

338 314 ESP
SPAIN. INSTITUTO NACIONAL DE ESTADISTICA. ENCUESTA INDUSTRIAL. Text in Spanish. a. **Document type:** *Government.*
Formerly (until 1978): Spain. Instituto Nacional de Estadistica. Estadistica Industrial (0081-3354)
Published by: Instituto Nacional de Estadistica, P. de la Castellana, 183, Madrid, 28071, Spain.

336 314 ESP
SPAIN. MINISTERIO DE ECONOMIA Y HACIENDA. ESTADISTICAS PRESUPUESTARIAS Y FISCALES. Text in Spanish. a. **Document type:** *Government.*
Former titles (until 1973): Spain. Ministerio de Economia y Hacienda. Informacion Estadistica; Spain. Ministerio de Hacienda. Informacion Estadistica (0081-3435)
Published by: (Centro de Publicaciones), Ministerio de Economia y Hacienda, Secretaria General Tecnica, Pz Campillo del Mundo Nuevo, 3, Madrid, 28005, Spain. TEL 34-1-5271437.

SPORT CLOTHING EXPENDITURES IN (YEAR). see *SPORTS AND GAMES—Abstracting, Bibliographies, Statistics*

SPORTING GOODS MARKET. see *SPORTS AND GAMES—Abstracting, Bibliographies, Statistics*

SPORTS EQUIPMENT EXPENDITURES. see *SPORTS AND GAMES—Abstracting, Bibliographies, Statistics*

SPORTS PARTICIPATION IN (YEAR): LIFECYCLE DEMOGRAPHICS. see *SPORTS AND GAMES—Abstracting, Bibliographies, Statistics*

SPORTS PARTICIPATION IN (YEAR): SERIES II. see *SPORTS AND GAMES—Abstracting, Bibliographies, Statistics*

SPORTS PARTICIPATION IN (YEAR): STATE BY STATE. see *SPORTS AND GAMES—Abstracting, Bibliographies, Statistics*

339.4 314 SCG
SRBIJA I CRNA GORA ZAVOD ZA STATISTIKU. ANKETA O PORODICNIM BUDZETIMA RADNICKIH DOMACINSTAVA. Text in Serbian. irreg. **Document type:** *Government.*
Formerly: Yugoslavia. Savezni Zavod za Statistiku. Anketa o Porodicnim Budzetima Radnickih Domacinstava
Related titles: English ed.; ♦ Series of: Srbija i Crna Gora. Zavod za Statistiku. Statisticki Bilten.
Published by: Srbija i Crna Gora Zavod za Statistiku/Serbia and Montenegro Statistical Office, Kneza Milosa 20, Postanski Fah 203, Belgrade, 11000. http://www.szs.sv.gov.yu.

314 338 SCG
SRBIJA I CRNA GORA ZAVOD ZA STATISTIKU. INDUSTRIJSKE ORGANIZACIJE. Text in Serbo-Croatian. irreg. stat. **Document type:** *Government.*
Formerly: Yugoslavia. Savezni Zavod za Statistiku. Industrijske Organizacije
Related titles: ♦ Series of: Srbija i Crna Gora. Zavod za Statistiku. Statisticki Bilten.
Published by: Srbija i Crna Gora Zavod za Statistiku/Serbia and Montenegro Statistical Office, Kneza Milosa 20, Postanski Fah 203, Belgrade, 11000. TEL 381-11-3617273.

331 314 SCG
SRBIJA I CRNA GORA ZAVOD ZA STATISTIKU. SAMOUPRAVLJANJE U PRIVREDI. Text in Serbo-Croatian. irreg. **Document type:** *Government.*
Formerly: Yugoslavia. Savezni Zavod za Statistiku. Samoupravljanje u Privredi
Related titles: ♦ Series of: Srbija i Crna Gora. Zavod za Statistiku. Statisticki Bilten.
Published by: Srbija i Crna Gora Zavod za Statistiku/Serbia and Montenegro Statistical Office, Kneza Milosa 20, Postanski Fah 203, Belgrade, 11000. TEL 381-11-3617273. Circ: 1,000.

658 331 314 SCG
SRBIJA I CRNA GORA ZAVOD ZA STATISTIKU. SAMOUPRAVLJANJE U USTANOVAMA DRUSTVENIH SLUZBI. Text in Serbo-Croatian. irreg. **Document type:** *Government.*
Formerly: Yugoslavia. Savezni Zavod za Statistiku. Samoupravljanje u Ustanovama Drustvenih Sluzbi
Related titles: ♦ Series of: Srbija i Crna Gora. Zavod za Statistiku. Statisticki Bilten.
Published by: Srbija i Crna Gora Zavod za Statistiku/Serbia and Montenegro Statistical Office, Kneza Milosa 20, Postanski Fah 203, Belgrade, 11000. TEL 381-11-3617273.

331.11 314 SCG
SRBIJA I CRNA GORA ZAVOD ZA STATISTIKU. ZAPOSLENOST. Text in Serbo-Croatian. 1956. s-a. **Document type:** *Government.*
Formerly (until 2003): Yugoslavia. Savezni Zavod za Statistiku. Zaposlenost (0513-0891)
Related titles: ♦ Series of: Srbija i Crna Gora. Zavod za Statistiku. Statisticki Bilten.
Published by: Srbija i Crna Gora Zavod za Statistiku/Serbia and Montenegro Statistical Office, Kneza Milosa 20, Postanski Fah 203, Belgrade, 11000. TEL 381-11-3617273.

330.9 LKA ISSN 0256-808X
DS488
SRI LANKA YEARBOOK. Text in English, Tamil, Singhalese. 1948. irreg., latest 1982. LKR 21. **Document type:** *Government.*
Formerly: Ceylon Yearbook
Published by: Department of Census and Statistics, 15-12 Maitland Crescent, P O Box 563, Colombo, 07, Sri Lanka. TEL 94-1-695291, FAX 94-1-695291. Circ: 4,640. **Subscr. to:** Superintendent.

330 011 DEU
STAEDTE- UND KREISSTATISTIK RUHRGEBIET. Text in German. 1976. a. **Document type:** *Trade.*
Published by: Kommunalverband Ruhrgebiet, Kronprinzenstr 35, Essen, 45128, Germany. TEL 49-201-2069-0, FAX 49-201-2069-500. Circ: 1,000.

332 USA ISSN 1054-7282
HG1501
STANDARD & POOR'S FINANCIAL INSTITUTIONS RATINGS (QUARTERLY EDITION). Text in English. q. **Document type:** *Trade.*
Published by: Standard & Poor's (Subsidiary of: McGraw-Hill Companies, Inc.), 55 Water St, New York, NY 10041. TEL 212-208-8000.

332.1 315 PAK
STATE BANK OF PAKISTAN. EQUITY YIELDS ON ORDINARY SHARES. Text in English. a. PKR 30, USD 6 (effective 2000). **Document type:** *Government.*
Published by: State Bank of Pakistan, Central Directorate, Public Relations Department, I.I. Chundrigar Rd, PO Box 4456, Karachi, Pakistan. TEL 92-21-9212400, FAX 92-21-9212436, TELEX 21774 SBPK PK.

332.6 PAK ISSN 0081-4466
STATE BANK OF PAKISTAN. INDEX NUMBERS OF STOCK EXCHANGE SECURITIES. Text in English. 1963. a. PKR 50, USD 8 (effective 2000). **Document type:** *Government.* **Description:** Includes an index of share prices.
Published by: State Bank of Pakistan, Central Directorate, Public Relations Department, I.I. Chundrigar Rd, PO Box 4456, Karachi, Pakistan. TEL 92-21-9212400, FAX 92-21-9212436, TELEX 21774 SBPK PK.

334.2 315 PAK ISSN 0039-0569
STATE BANK OF PAKISTAN. STATISTICS ON CO-OPERATIVE BANKS. Text in English. 1965-1976; resumed. q. PKR 40, USD 22 (effective 2000). **Document type:** *Government.*
Published by: State Bank of Pakistan, Central Directorate, Public Relations Department, I.I. Chundrigar Rd, PO Box 4456, Karachi, Pakistan. TEL 92-21-9212400, FAX 92-21-9212436, TELEX 21774 SBPK PK.

332.1 315 PAK ISSN 0039-0577
STATE BANK OF PAKISTAN. STATISTICS ON SCHEDULED BANKS. Text in English. 1961. q. PKR 100, USD 36 (effective 2000). **Document type:** *Government.* **Description:** Includes information on deposits.
Published by: State Bank of Pakistan, Central Directorate, Public Relations Department, I.I. Chundrigar Rd, PO Box 4456, Karachi, Pakistan. TEL 92-21-9212400, FAX 92-21-9212436, TELEX 21774 SBPK PK.

350 336 IND
STATE DOMESTIC PRODUCT OF HIMACHAL PRADESH. Text in English. 1963. a. **Document type:** *Government.*
Supersedes: State Income of Himachal Pradesh
Published by: Directorate of Economics and Statistics, Simla, Himachal Pradesh, India. Circ: 700.

338.9 317 USA ISSN 0073-1080
HA329.1
STATE OF HAWAII DATA BOOK, A STATISTICAL ABSTRACT. Text in English. 1962. biennial. USD 22 (effective 2000). stat. **Document type:** *Government.*
Formerly: Statistical Abstract of Hawaii
Related titles: Microfiche ed.: (from CIS).
Indexed: SRI.
Published by: Department of Business, Economic Development & Tourism, Communications & Publications, P O Box 2359, Honolulu, HI 96804. TEL 808-586-2423, FAX 808-586-2427, http://www.hawaii.gov/dbedt/. Ed. Glenn Ifuku. Circ: 1,200.

338.91 FRA ISSN 0224-098X
HA37.A33
STATECO. Text in French. 1972. q. free. **Document type:** *Government.* **Description:** Methodological presentation of the work of statisticians and economists working in transition and developing countries.
Published by: Institut National de la Statistique et des Etudes Economiques, Division Etudes et Methodes Statistiques pour le Developpement, Timbre D340, 18 bd. A. Pinard, Paris, Cedex 14 75675, France. TEL 33-1-41175313, FAX 33-1-41176652, inseeactualites@insee.fr.

317 650 USA ISSN 0191-0310
HA581
STATISTICAL ABSTRACT OF OKLAHOMA. Text in English. 1956. a. USD 22 (effective 2000). illus. **Document type:** *Academic/Scholarly.*
Indexed: SRI.
Published by: University of Oklahoma, Center for Economic and Management Research, Michael F Price, College of Business, 307 W Brooks St, Rm 4, Norman, OK 73019. TEL 405-325-2931, FAX 405-325-7688. Eds. John McCraw, Patricia Wickham. Circ: 1,000.

332.1 315 THA
STATISTICAL DATA ON COMMERCIAL BANKS IN THAILAND. Text in English. 1964. a. free. illus.
Published by: Bangkok Bank Ltd., Economic Research Division, 9 Suapa Rd, Bangkok, Thailand.

315 THA ISSN 0252-4457
HC411
STATISTICAL INDICATORS FOR ASIA AND THE PACIFIC. Text in English. 1971. q. USD 20 (effective 2003). back issues avail.
Former titles (until 1977): Statistical Indicators in E S C A P Countries (1010-5131); (until 1974): Statistical Indicators in E C A F E Countries (1010-5123)
Related titles: Microfiche ed.: (from CIS).
Indexed: IIS, RASB.
—CISTI.
Published by: United Nations Economic and Social Commission for Asia and the Pacific, United Nations Bldg., Rajadamnern Ave., Bangkok, 10200, Thailand. TEL 662-2881174, FAX 662-2883022, unescap@unescap.org, http://www.unescap.org. **Dist. by:** United Nations Publications, Distribution and Sales Section, Palais des Nations, Rm C-116, 8-14 av de la Paix, Geneva 1211, Switzerland; United Nations Publications, Rm DC2-853, United Nations Bldg, 2 United Nations Plaza, New York, NY 10017; Conference Services Unit, Conference Services Unit, ESCAP, Bangkok 10200, Thailand.

339 318 JAM
STATISTICAL INSTITUTE OF JAMAICA. CONSUMER PRICE INDICES BULLETIN. Text in English. 1957. m. USD 42. stat. **Document type:** *Bulletin.*
Former titles (until 1976): Statistical Institute of Jamaica. Consumer Price Indices; Jamaica. Department of Statistics. Consumer Price Indices (0302-9336); Jamaica. Department of Statistics. Rural Retail Price Index (0021-4108)
Media: Duplicated (not offset).
Published by: Statistical Institute of Jamaica, 9 Swallowfield Rd, Kingston, 5, Jamaica. FAX 809-92-64859. Circ: 709.

318 382 JAM
STATISTICAL INSTITUTE OF JAMAICA. EXTERNAL TRADE. Text in English. q. USD 15.50 per issue.
Formerly: Jamaica. Department of Statistics. External Trade
Published by: Statistical Institute of Jamaica, 9 Swallowfield Rd, Kingston, 5, Jamaica. FAX 809-92-64859. Circ: 11.

382 318 JAM
STATISTICAL INSTITUTE OF JAMAICA. EXTERNAL TRADE ANNUAL REVIEW. Text in English. 1936. a. USD 47.50. stat.
Formerly (until 1969): Jamaica. Department of Statistics. External Trade Annual Review
Published by: Statistical Institute of Jamaica, 9 Swallowfield Rd, Kingston, 5, Jamaica. FAX 809-92-64859. Circ: 150.

382 JAM
STATISTICAL INSTITUTE OF JAMAICA. EXTERNAL TRADE MONTHLY BULLETIN. Text in English. 1949. m. USD 42. stat.
Former titles (until 1975): Statistical Institute of Jamaica. External Trade Summary Tables; (until 1968): Jamaica. Department of Statistics. External Trade Summary Tables; Jamaica. Department of Statistics. Monthly Trade Bulletin (0027-0628)
Media: Duplicated (not offset).
Published by: Statistical Institute of Jamaica, 9 Swallowfield Rd, Kingston, 5, Jamaica. FAX 809-92-64859. Circ: 303.

318 330 JAM
STATISTICAL INSTITUTE OF JAMAICA. NATIONAL INCOME AND PRODUCT. Text in English. 1950. a. USD 41.
Formerly (until 1975): Jamaica. Department of Statistics. National Income and Product
Published by: Statistical Institute of Jamaica, 9 Swallowfield Rd, Kingston, 5, Jamaica. FAX 809-92-64859.

339 314 LUX ISSN 0081-4911
STATISTICAL OFFICE OF THE EUROPEAN COMMUNITIES. NATIONAL ACCOUNTS YEARBOOK. Text in Dutch, English, French, German, Italian. a. price varies.
Published by: European Commission, Statistical Office of the European Communities, Rue Alcide de Gasperi, Luxembourg, 2920, Luxembourg. **Dist. in the U.S. by:** Bernan Associates, Bernan, 4611-F Assembly Dr., Lanham, MD 20706-4391. TEL 301-459-0056, 800-274-4888.

657 LUX ISSN 1010-1764
STATISTICAL OFFICE OF THE EUROPEAN COMMUNITIES. QUARTERLY NATIONAL ACCOUNTS. Text in English, French, German. q.
Related titles: Microfiche ed.: (from CIS).
Indexed: IIS.
Published by: European Commission, Statistical Office of the European Communities, Rue Alcide de Gasperi, Luxembourg, 2920, Luxembourg. **Dist. in the U.S. by:** Bernan Associates, Bernan, 4611-F Assembly Dr., Lanham, MD 20706-4391. TEL 301-459-0056, 800-274-4888.

338 314 LUX
STATISTICAL OFFICE OF THE EUROPEAN COMMUNITIES. STATISTICAL STUDIES AND SURVEYS. Text in English. 4/yr. USD 120.
Published by: European Commission, Statistical Office of the European Communities, Rue Alcide de Gasperi, Luxembourg, 2920, Luxembourg. **Dist. in the U.S. by:** Bernan Associates, Bernan, 4611-F Assembly Dr., Lanham, MD 20706-4391. TEL 301-459-0056, 800-274-4888.

330.921 THA
STATISTICAL REPORT OF REGION. Text in English, Thai. a. (in 5 vols.). price varies. **Document type:** *Monographic series, Government.* **Description:** Contains data on population, education, public health, agriculture, production and business, establishment, communication and transport, banking and finance, as well as information on the climate conditions of all the regions, by changwat level.
Formerly: Statistical Report of Thailand
Published by: (Thailand. Statistical Data Bank and Information Dissemination Division), National Statistical Office, Larn Luang Rd, Bangkok, 10100, Thailand. TEL 66-2-282-1535, FAX 66-2-281-3814, binfodsm@nso.go.th, http://www.nso.go.th/. Circ: 5,000.

331 CHE ISSN 0255-3465
STATISTICAL SOURCES AND METHODS. Text in English. 1984. bi-m.
Published by: International Labour Office, Publications Sales Service, 4, route des Morillons, Geneva, 1211, Switzerland. FAX 41-22-7996938, pubvente@ilo.org, http://www.ilo.org.

338.9 316 KEN ISSN 0377-5712
STATISTICAL SURVEY OF THE EAST AFRICAN COMMUNITY INSTITUTIONS. Text in English. 1973. a.
Published by: East African Community, Statistical Department, PO Box 30462, Nairobi, Kenya.

330 CHL ISSN 0716-2464
HA992
STATISTICAL SYNTHESIS OF CHILE. Text in Spanish. 1978. a. CLP 1,500. **Document type:** *Government.* **Description:** Contains general and economic statistics of Chile.
Published by: Banco Central de Chile, Casilla 967, Santiago, Chile. TEL 56-2-670-2000, FAX 56-2-698-4847, TELEX 405 69 CENBC. Circ: 2,000.

300.8 THA ISSN 0252-3655
HA1665
STATISTICAL YEARBOOK FOR ASIA AND THE PACIFIC/ANNUAIRE STATISTIQUE POUR L'ASIE ET LE PACIFIQUE. Text in English, French. 1968. a., latest 2000. reprint service avail. from PSC.
Formerly (until 1973): Statistical Yearbook for Asia and the Far East (0085-6711)
Related titles: Microfiche ed.: (from CIS).
Indexed: IIS, RASB.
Published by: United Nations Economic and Social Commission for Asia and the Pacific, United Nations Bldg., Rajadamnern Ave., Bangkok, 10200, Thailand. TEL 662-2881174, FAX 662-2883022, unescap@unescap.org, http://www.unescap.org. **Dist. by:** United Nations Publications, Distribution and Sales Section; United Nations Publications, Rm DC2-853, United Nations Bldg, 2 United Nations Plaza, New York, NY 10017; United Nations, Conference Services Unit, ESCAP, Bangkok, Thailand.

330 HKG
STATISTICAL YEARBOOK OF GUANGDONG (YEAR). Text in Chinese. 1992. a. HKD 300, USD 58.
Published by: Economic Information & Agency, 342 Hennessy Rd 10th Fl, 10 th Fl, Wanchai, Hong Kong. TEL 852-573-8217, FAX 852-838-8304.

336 315 TWN ISSN 0256-7857
HA1710.5
STATISTICAL YEARBOOK OF THE REPUBLIC OF CHINA. Text in English. 1975. a. TWD 350 (effective 2000). stat. **Document type:** *Government.*
Published by: Executive Yuan, Directorate-General of Budget, Accounting & Statistics, 2 Kwangchow St, Taipei, Taiwan. TEL 886-2-2381-4910, http://www.dgbasey.gov.tw/, http://www.stat.gov.tw/main.htm/. **Subscr. to:** Chen Chung Book Co., 3F, 20 Heng-Yang Rd, Taipei, Taiwan. TEL 886-2-2382-1394, FAX 886-2-2382-2805, http://www.ccbc.com.tw.

330.021 RUS
STATISTICHESKII BULLETEN'. Text in Russian. 1998. 10/yr. USD 252 foreign (effective 2005). charts; stat. **Document type:** *Bulletin, Government.* **Description:** Contains information and analysis of various aspects of the Russian economy and social affairs: dynamics of retail prices, results of quarterly studies of the economic situation, and business activities in construction and retail trade, etc.
Published by: Gosudarstvennyi Komitet Rossiiskoi Federatsii po Statistike/Federal State Statistics Office, ul Myasnitskaya 39, Moscow, 107450, Russian Federation. TEL 7-095-2074902, FAX 7-095-2074087, stat@gks.ru, http://www.gks.ru. **Dist. by:** East View Information Services, 3020 Harbor Ln. N., Minneapolis, MN 55447. TEL 800-477-1005, FAX 800-800-3839, eastview@eastview.com, http://www.eastview.com.

330.021 RUS
STATISTICHESKOE OBOZRENIE/CURRENT STATISTICAL SURVEY. Text in Russian, English. 1994. q. USD 242 foreign (effective 2005). **Document type:** *Journal, Government.*
Description: Presents various tables and color diagrams of macroeconomic situation in Russia during the current year. Most tables feature monthly economic figures.
Related titles: Online - full content ed.: RUR 1,062 (effective 2005).
Published by: Gosudarstvennyi Komitet Rossiiskoi Federatsii po Statistike/Federal State Statistics Office, ul Myasnitskaya 39, Moscow, 107450, Russian Federation. TEL 7-095-2074902, FAX 7-095-2074087, stat@gks.ru, http://www.gks.ru. **Dist. by:** East View Information Services, 3020 Harbor Ln. N., Minneapolis, MN 55447. TEL 800-477-1005, FAX 800-800-3839, eastview@eastview.com, http://www.eastview.com.

314 GBR ISSN 0081-5101
STATISTICS - EUROPE; sources for market research. Text in English. 1968. irreg., latest vol.6, 1997. GBP 97.50, USD 195 (effective 2001). stat. index. **Document type:** *Directory.*
Description: Contains 1,250 sources for social, economic, and market research in each European country.
Published by: C.B.D. Research Ltd., 15 Wickham Rd, Beckenham, Kent BR3 5JS, United Kingdom. TEL 44-20-86507745, FAX 44-20-86500768, cbd@cbdresearch.com, http://www.cbdresearch.com. Ed. Joan M Harvey. Circ: 2,000.

382 315 SYR ISSN 0081-5136
STATISTICS OF FOREIGN TRADE OF SYRIA; classified according to United Nations standard international trade classification revised. Text in Arabic, English. 1964. a., latest 1999. USD 50 in the Middle East; USD 75 elsewhere (effective 2002). **Document type:** *Government.*
Published by: Central Bureau of Statistics, Damascus, Syria. TEL 963-11-3335830, FAX 963-11-3322292, TELEX STC 411093 SY.

382 679 IND ISSN 0971-3204
STATISTICS OF MARINE PRODUCTS EXPORTS. Text in English. 1973. a. USD 5. charts; illus.; stat. **Document type:** *Trade.*
Formerly: Marine Products Export Review
Indexed: ASFA.
Published by: Marine Products Export Development Authority, MPEDA House, Panampilly Avenue Rd., Cochin, Kerala 682 036, India. TEL 311979.

338.91 314 GBR
HC60
STATISTICS ON INTERNATIONAL DEVELOPMENT; statistics of U.K. economic assistance to developing countries and countries of transition. Text in English. 1966. a. GBP 12 (effective 2000). **Document type:** *Government.*
Formerly (until 1998): British Aid Statistics (0068-1210)
—CCC.
Published by: Department for International Development, Publications Section, Abercrombie House, Eaglesham Rd, East Kilbride, Glasgow, G75 8EA, United Kingdom. TEL 44-1355-843246, FAX 44-1355-843632. Ed., Pub., R&P Elizabeth Robin.

330.9 310 MEX
STATISTICS ON THE MEXICAN ECONOMY/ECONOMIA MEXICANA EN CIFRAS. Text in Spanish. 1977. biennial. MXP 90. **Document type:** *Government.*
Published by: Nacional Financiera S.N.C., Subdireccion de Informacion Tecnica y Publicaciones, INSURGENTES SUR 1971, Nivel Fuente, Col Guadalupe Inn, Mexico City, DF 01020, Mexico. TEL 52-5-3256047.

382 314 AUT ISSN 0572-1822
STATISTIK AUSTRIA. AUSSENHANDEL OESTERREICHS. SERIE 1A. Text in German. 1947. q. EUR 101; EUR 32 per issue (effective 2005); series 1 and 2. adv. bk.rev. stat. back issues avail. **Document type:** *Government.* **Description:** Export and import data, classification in goods and countries.
Former titles: Austria. Statistisches Zentralamt. Aussenhandel Oesterreichs; Statistik des Aussenhandels Oesterreichs (0004-816X)
Published by: Statistik Austria, Guglgasse 13, Vienna, W 1110, Austria. TEL 43-1-711280, FAX 43-1-711287728, info@statistik.gv.at, http://www.statistik.at.

382 314 AUT ISSN 0572-1849
STATISTIK AUSTRIA. AUSSENHANDEL OESTERREICHS. SERIE 2. Text in German. s-a. EUR 30; EUR 19 per issue (effective 2005). **Document type:** *Government.*
Published by: Statistik Austria, Guglgasse 13, Vienna, W 1110, Austria. TEL 43-1-711280, FAX 43-1-711287728, info@statistik.gv.at, http://www.statistik.at.

314.3 331.7 AUT
STATISTIK AUSTRIA. LAND- UND FORSTWIRTSCHAFTLICHE ARBEITSKRAEFTE. Text in German. irreg. price varies. **Document type:** *Government.* **Description:** Census of agricultural and forestry laborers.
Former titles: Oesterreichisches Statistisches Zentralamt. Land- und Forstwirtschaftliche Arbeitskraefte; Austria. Statistisches Zentralamt. Erhebung der Land und Forstwirtschaftlichen Arbeitskraefte
Published by: Statistik Austria, Guglgasse 13, Vienna, W 1110, Austria. TEL 43-1-711280, FAX 43-1-711287728, info@statistik.gv.at, http://www.statistik.at.

338.7 314 AUT
STATISTIK AUSTRIA. STATISTIK DER AKTIENGESELLSCHAFTEN IN OESTERREICH. Text in German. 1961. a. EUR 18.17. **Document type:** *Government.*
Formerly: Austria. Statistisches Zentralamt. Statistik der Aktiengesellschaften in Oesterreich (0081-5233)
Published by: Statistik Austria, Guglgasse 13, Vienna, W 1110, Austria. TEL 43-1-711280, FAX 43-1-711287728, info@statistik.gv.at, http://www.statistik.at.

332 315 IDN ISSN 0126-3846
HG187.I7
STATISTIK EKONOMI-KEUANGAN INDONESIA/INDONESIAN FINANCIAL STATISTICS. Text in English, Indonesian. 1968-1975; resumed 1976. m. USD 84. bk.rev. stat.
Indexed: PAIS.
Published by: (Urusan Ekonomi dan Statistik), Bank Indonesia/Bank Indonesia, Economics & Statistics Department, Kantor Pusat, Jl. Kebon Sirih No. 82-84, Teromol Pos 422, Jakarta, Indonesia. Circ: 1,000.

382 316 TUN ISSN 0330-163X
STATISTIQUES DU COMMERCE EXTERIEUR. Text in French. a. TND 15,000 (effective 2000). **Document type:** *Trade.*
Formerly (until 1975): Statistiques du Commerce Exterieur de la Tunisie (0081-5292)
Published by: Institut National de la Statistique, 70 Rue Ech-Cham, B P 260, Tunis, Tunisia. TEL 216-1-891002, FAX 216-1-792559.

382 316 DZA
STATISTIQUES DU COMMERCE EXTERIEUR DE L'ALGERIE. Text in French. 1963. m. (plus q. & a. cumulations). price varies. **Document type:** *Government.*
Published by: Direction des Douanes, 19, rue du Docteur Saadane, Algiers, Algeria. **Dist. in US by:** African & Caribbean Imprint Library Services, PO Box 2780, South Portland, ME 04116-2780. TEL 207-767-5333, FAX 207-767-5335, ailscils@msn.com, http://www.africanbooks.com/.

STATS - MONTHLY STATISTICAL AND MARKETING DIGEST. see *STATISTICS*

016.6583 USA ISSN 1521-9011
HD30.37
STERN'S CYBERSPACE SOURCEFINDER; HR and business management Internet directory. Text in English. 1998. q. USD 69.95 (effective 2001). **Document type:** *Directory, Abstract/Index.* **Description:** Describes and indexes 1,717 non-commercial Web sites and newsgroups of interest to human resources management professionals.
Published by: (Stern & Associates), Michael Daniels, Publishers, PO Box 3233, Culver City, CA 90231-3233. TEL 310-838-4437, 800-773-0029, FAX 310-838-2344, stern@hrconsultant.com, http://www.hrconsultant.com. Eds. Gerry Stern, Yvette Borcia. Pub. Michael Daniels. Circ: 2,000 (paid).

016.6583 USA ISSN 1052-4819
Z7164.C81
STERN'S SOURCEFINDER; the master directory to human resources and business management information and resources. Text in English. 1991. biennial. USD 239.95 (effective 2001). bk.rev. back issues avail. **Document type:** *Directory.* **Description:** Covers information sources for every aspect of strategy, organization, leadership and human resource management, including organization design, development and change, compensation, benefits, motivation, communication, law, health, and safety, general management and labor relations.
Published by: (Stern & Associates), Michael Daniels, Publishers, PO Box 3233, Culver City, CA 90231-3233. TEL 310-838-4437, 800-773-0029, FAX 310-838-2344, stern@hrconsultant.com, http://www.hrconsultant.com. Eds. Gerry Stern, Yvette Borcia. Pub. Michael Daniels. Circ: 2,000 (paid).

336.2 016 AUT ISSN 1025-806X
STEUER UND WIRTSCHAFT INTERNATIONAL. Text in German. 1991. m. EUR 159.50 (effective 2005). back issues avail. **Document type:** *Magazine, Trade.*
Published by: Linde Verlag Wien GmbH, Scheydgasse 24, Vienna, W 1211, Austria. TEL 43-1-246300, FAX 43-1-2463023, office@lindeverlag.at, http://www.swionline.at, http://www.lindeverlag.at. R&P Susanne Haslinger. Circ: 5,000 (paid).

336.2 016 AUT ISSN 1025-8078
KJJ3541.2
STEUER- UND WIRTSCHAFTSKARTEI. Text in German. 1925. 3/m. EUR 240.90 (effective 2005). **Document type:** *Magazine, Consumer.*
Formerly (until 1983): Oesterreichische Steuer und Wirtschaftskarei (0029-9510)
Published by: Linde Verlag Wien GmbH, Scheydgasse 24, Vienna, W 1211, Austria. TEL 43-1-246300, FAX 43-1-2463023, office@lindeverlag.at, http://www.swk.at, http://www.lindeverlag.at. R&P Susanne Haslinger. Circ: 19,000 (paid).

336 CHE ISSN 1423-4696
STEUERBELASTUNG IN DER SCHWEIZ - NATUERLICHE PERSONEN NACH GEMEINDEN/CHARGE FISCALE EN SUISSE - PERSONNES PHYSIQUES PAR COMMUNES. Text in French, German. 1931. a. CHF 8 (effective 2001). **Document type:** *Government.*
Formerly (until 1986): Steuerbelastung in der Schweiz (0259-6105)
Published by: Bundesamt fuer Statistik, Espace de l'Europe 10, Neuchatel, 2010, Switzerland. TEL 41-32-7136011, FAX 41-32-7136012, information@bfs.admin.ch, http://www.admin.ch/bfs.

330 310 FRA ISSN 1727-2327
STRUCTURAL STATISTICS FOR INDUSTRY AND SERVICES. Text in French. 1984. a. price varies.
Formerly (until 1999): O E C D Industrial Structure Statistics (0256-3142)
Related titles: CD-ROM ed.; ♦ Online - full text ed.: Source O E C D. Structural Statistics for Industry and Services. ISSN 1608-120X.
Indexed: IIS.
Published by: Organization for Economic Cooperation and Development, 2 Rue Andre Pascal, Paris, 75775 Cedex 16, France. TEL 33-1-45248200, FAX 33-1-45248500, http://www.oecd.org.

STRUKTURSTATISTIK. see *BUSINESS AND ECONOMICS—Labor And Industrial Relations*

382 310 SDN ISSN 0585-8488
SUDAN. DEPARTMENT OF STATISTICS. FOREIGN TRADE STATISTICS. Text in Arabic, English. q. **Document type:** *Government.*
Indexed: RASB.
Published by: Department of Statistics, P O Box 700, Khartoum, Sudan.

310 381 SDN ISSN 0377-0125
HF273.S8
SUDAN. DEPARTMENT OF STATISTICS. INTERNAL TRADE AND OTHER STATISTICS. Text in English. a. **Document type:** *Government.*
Published by: Department of Statistics, P O Box 700, Khartoum, Sudan.

330 370 SDN
SUDAN. NATIONAL COUNCIL FOR RESEARCH. ECONOMIC AND SOCIAL RESEARCH COUNCIL. BIBLIOGRAPHIES. Text in Arabic, English. 1974. irreg., latest vol.10, 1985. **Document type:** *Bibliography.*
Published by: National Council for Research, Economic and Social Research Council, P O Box 1166, Khartoum, Sudan. TEL 78805.

336 FIN ISSN 1456-5811
HG5581
SUOMEN PANKKI. TILASTOKATSAUS. RAHOITUSMARKKINAT (EURO VERSION)/BANK OF FINLAND. STATISTICAL REVIEW. FINANCIAL MARKETS/FINLANDS BANK. STATISTISK OEVERSIKT. FINANSMARKNADEN. Text in English, Finnish, Swedish. 1987. m. EUR 33; EUR 3 per issue (effective 2002). **Document type:** *Trade.* **Description:** Includes daily, weekly, monthly, quarterly and annual series covering key interest rates, money market liquidity, lending, monetary aggregates and deposits, exchange rates and bank forex transactions, balance of payments, Bank of Finland balance sheets, and bonds.
Former titles (until 2002): Suomen Pankki. Tilastokatsaus. Rahoitusmarkkinat (Finnish Mark version) (0789-9955); (until 1992): Suomen Pankki. Tiedote. Raha- ja Valuuttamarkkinatilastoja (0784-0462)
Related titles: Online - full text ed.: ISSN 1456-582X. 1992.
Indexed: RASB.
Published by: (Julkaisut), Suomen Pankki/Bank of Finland, P O Box 160, Helsinki, 00101, Finland. TEL 358-9-183-2566, FAX 358-9-174-872, publications@bof.fi, http://www.bof.fi/env/rhinden.htm.

331 CHE ISSN 0378-5505
SUPPLEMENT DU BULLETIN DES STATISTIQUES DU TRAVAIL. Text in English, French. 1965. q.
Related titles: ♦ Supplement to: Bulletin of Labour Statistics. ISSN 0007-4950.
Indexed: RASB.
Published by: I L O Publications, PO Box 6, Geneva 22, 1211, Switzerland. TEL 41-22-799-6111, FAX 41-22-798-6350, http://www.ilo.org/publns. Ed. Ivan M C S Elsmark.

318.8 388 SUR ISSN 0585-9913
HA1037.S8
SURINAM. ALGEMEEN BUREAU VOOR DE STATISTIEK. KWARTAAL STATISTIEK VAN DE INDUSTRIELE PRODUKTIE. Text in Dutch. 1979 (Jul.). irreg. **Document type:** *Government.* **Description:** Contains collected statistics of industrial production.
Published by: Algemeen Bureau voor de Statistiek/General Bureau of Statistics, PO Box 244, Paramaribo, Suriname.

658.3 MEX
SURVEY OF SALARIES. Text in English, Spanish. a. USD 350 (effective 2003). **Document type:** *Trade.* **Description:** Lists salary rates of executives and other high-level personnel by company size, location and industrial sector within Mexico.
Formerly: Salary Survey
Published by: American Chamber of Commerce of Mexico A.C., Lucerna 78, Col. Juarez, Mexico City, D F 06600, Mexico. TEL 52-55-51413800, FAX 52-55-57032911, amchamm@amcham.com.mx, http://www.amcham.com.mx/. Ed. Jose Antonio Hernandez. R&P Diana H de Hernandez. Adv. contact Rommy Strevel.

352.1 ISL ISSN 1017-6357
SVEITARSJODAREIKNINGAR/LOCAL GOVERNMENT FINANCE. Text in Icelandic. 1959. a. USD 25 (effective 2001). back issues avail. **Document type:** *Government.*
Published by: Hagstofa Islands/Statistics Iceland, Borgartuni 12 A, Reykjavik, 150, Iceland. TEL 354-1-560-9800, FAX 354-1-562-3312, information@statice.is, hagstofa@hag.stjr.is, http://www.statice.is, http://www.statice.is/stat/e-mail.htm. Ed. Gudni Baldursson.

338 316 SWZ
SWAZILAND. CENTRAL STATISTICAL OFFICE. CENSUS OF INDUSTRIES. Text in English. 1967. a. free. **Document type:** *Government.*
Formerly: Swaziland. Central Statistical Office. Census of Industrial Production
Published by: Central Statistical Office, PO Box 456, Mbabane, Swaziland. TEL 268-43765. Circ: 500.

331.21 SWZ ISSN 0303-3953
SWAZILAND. CENTRAL STATISTICAL OFFICE. EMPLOYMENT AND WAGES. Text in English. 1969. a. free. **Document type:** *Government.*
Published by: Central Statistical Office, PO Box 456, Mbabane, Swaziland. TEL 268-43765. Circ: 500.

382 314 SWE ISSN 0281-0050
HF3671
SWEDEN. STATISTISKA CENTRALBYRAAN. FOREIGN TRADE: IMPORT-EXPORT. DISTRIBUTION BY COUNTRY - COMMODITY ACCORDING TO THE S I T C. Text in Swedish; Summaries in English. 1964. a. SEK 280. **Document type:** *Government.*
Supersedes: Sweden. Statistika Centralbyraan. Utrikeshandel - Foreign Trade (0082-0369)
Published by: Statistiska Centralbyraan/Statistics Sweden, Publishing Unit, Orebro, 70189, Sweden. Circ: 1,500.

338 314 SWE
SWEDEN. STATISTISKA CENTRALBYRAAN. INDUSTRI. Text in Swedish; Summaries in English. 1911. a. SEK 560. **Document type:** *Government.*
Supersedes (in 1970): Industri (0082-0172)
—CISTI.
Published by: Statistiska Centralbyraan/Statistics Sweden, Publishing Unit, Orebro, 70189, Sweden. Circ: 1,500.

658.3 314 SWE
SWEDEN. STATISTISKA CENTRALBYRAAN. LOENER OCH SYSSELSATTNING INOM OFFENTLIG SEKTOR. (In 2 parts: Part 1: Statsaellda (ISSN 0283-8141); Part 2: Kommunal Personal (ISSN 0283-815X)) Text in Swedish. 1968. a. SEK 320. **Document type:** *Government.*
Published by: Statistiska Centralbyraan/Statistics Sweden, Publishing Unit, Orebro, 70189, Sweden. Circ: 600.

314 331 SWE ISSN 0082-0237
HD5801
SWEDEN. STATISTISKA CENTRALBYRAAN. STATISTISKA MEDDELANDEN. SERIE AM, ARBETSMARKNAD. Text in Swedish; Summaries in English. N.S. 1964. irreg. SEK 2,400. **Document type:** *Government.*
Published by: Statistiska Centralbyraan/Statistics Sweden, Publishing Unit, Orebro, 70189, Sweden. Circ: 1,250.

338 314 SWE ISSN 1100-1038
HC371
SWEDEN. STATISTISKA CENTRALBYRAAN. STATISTISKA MEDDELANDEN. SERIE I, INDUSTRI. Text in Swedish; Summaries in English. N.S. 1963. irreg. SEK 300. **Document type:** *Government.*
Published by: Statistiska Centralbyraan/Statistics Sweden, Publishing Unit, Orebro, 70189, Sweden. Circ: 1,300.

338 334 SWE ISSN 0346-6078
SWEDEN. STATISTISKA CENTRALBYRAAN. STATISTISKA MEDDELANDEN. SERIE K, KREDITMARKNAD. Text in Swedish; Summaries in English. 1976. irreg. SEK 1,160 (effective 1992). **Document type:** *Government.*
Published by: Statistiska Centralbyraan, Publishing Unit, Orebro, 70189, Sweden.

336 314 SWE ISSN 0282-3489
HC380.I5
SWEDEN. STATISTISKA CENTRALBYRAAN. STATISTISKA MEDDELANDEN. SERIE N, NATIONALRAEKENSKAPERNA. Text in Swedish; Summaries in English. 1963. irreg. SEK 500 (effective 1991). **Document type:** *Government.*
Supersedes in part (in 1986): Sweden. Statiska Centralybraan. Statiska Meddelanden. Serie N, Nationalraekenskaper och Offentliga Finanser
Published by: Statistiska Centralbyraan/Statistics Sweden, Publishing Unit, Orebro, 70189, Sweden. Circ: 1,500.

336 SWE ISSN 0282-3497
HJ59
SWEDEN. STATISTISKA CENTRALBYRAAN. STATISTISKA MEDDELANDEN. SERIE O, OFFTENTLIGA FINANSER. Text in Swedish; Summaries in English. 1985. irreg. SEK 300 (effective 1992). **Document type:** *Government.*
Published by: Statistiska Centralbyraan, Publishing Unit, Orebro, 70189, Sweden.

330 314 SWE ISSN 0082-030X
SWEDEN. STATISTISKA CENTRALBYRAAN. STATISTISKA MEDDELANDEN. SERIE P, PRISER OCH KONSUMTION. Text in Swedish; Summaries in English. N.S. 1963. irreg. SEK 1,550. **Document type:** *Government.*
Incorporates (in 1976): Sweden. Statistiska Centralbyraan. Statistiska Meddelanden. Serie Pa, Konsumentprisindex
Published by: Statistiska Centralbyraan/Statistics Sweden, Publishing Unit, Orebro, 70189, Sweden. Circ: 2,150.

380.1 338 314 SWE ISSN 1100-9373
HF31
SWEDEN. STATISTISKA CENTRALBYRAAN. STATISTISKA MEDDELANDEN. SERIE SE, SERVICENAERINGAR. Text in Swedish; Summaries in English. N.S. 1963. 28/yr. SEK 500 (effective 1991). **Document type:** *Government.*
Supersedes in part (in 1990): Sweden. Statistiska Centralbyraan. Statistiska Meddelanden. Serie H, Handel (0082-0261)
Published by: Statistiska Centralbyraan/Statistics Sweden, Publishing Unit, Orebro, 70189, Sweden. Circ: 2,000.

381 SWE ISSN 1100-9381
SWEDEN. STATISTISKA CENTRALBYRAAN. STATISTISKA MEDDELANDEN. SERIE UH, UTRIKESHANDEL. Text in Swedish; Summaries in English. N.S. 1963. 14/yr. SEK 1,900 (effective 1991). **Document type:** *Government.*
Supersedes in part (in 1990): Sweden. Statistiska Centralbyraan. Statistiska Meddelanden. Serie H, Handel (0082-0261)
Published by: Statistiska Centralbyraan/Statistics Sweden, Publishing Unit, Orebro, 70189, Sweden.

338 314 SWE ISSN 0346-606X
HC371
SWEDEN. STATISTISKA CENTRALBYRAAN. STATISTISKA MEDDELANDEN. SUBGROUP F (ENTREPRISES). Text in Swedish; Summaries in English. 1976. irreg. SEK 400 (effective 1992). **Document type:** *Government.*
Published by: Statistiska Centralbyraan, Publishing Unit, Orebro, 70189, Sweden.

336 CHE
SWITZERLAND. BUNDESAMT FUER STATISTIK. DIREKTE BUNDESSTEUER. EINSCHAETZUNGSERGEBNISSE DER NATUERLICHEN UND JURISTISCHEN PERSONEN. VERANLAGUNGSPERIODE/IMPOT FEDERAL DIRECT. RESULTATS DE LA TAXATION DES PERSONNES PHYSIQUES ET MORALES. PERIODE DE TAXATION. Text in French, German. 1983. biennial. CHF 9 (effective 2001). **Document type:** *Government.*
Formerly (until 1994): Switzerland. Bundesamt fuer Statistik. Direkte Bundessteuer - Statistik der Veranlagungsperiode (Year)
Published by: Bundesamt fuer Statistik, Espace de l'Europe 10, Neuchatel, 2010, Switzerland. TEL 41-32-7136011, FAX 41-32-7136012, information@bfs.admin.ch, http://www.admin.ch/bfs.

382 314 CHE ISSN 1421-9468
SWITZERLAND. DIRECTORATE GENERAL OF CUSTOMS. ANNUAL REPORT. Text in French, German. a. CHF 29.60; CHF 34 foreign (effective 2000). **Document type:** *Government.*
Published by: Directorate General of Customs, Section Statistics, Monbijoustr 40, Bern, 3003, Switzerland. TEL 41-31-3226610, FAX 41-31-3233927.

382 314 CHE ISSN 1422-7339
SWITZERLAND. DIRECTORATE GENERAL OF CUSTOMS. QUARTERLY STATISTICS. Text in French, German. 1885. q. CHF 180; CHF 200 foreign (effective 2000). stat. **Document type:** *Government.*
Formerly (until 1998): Switzerland. Directorate General of Customs. Monthly Statistics (0049-2183)
Published by: Directorate General of Customs, Section Statistics, Monbijoustr 40, Bern, 3003, Switzerland. TEL 41-31-3226610, FAX 41-31-3233927, TELEX 911100-OZD-CH.

382 314 CHE ISSN 1421-9352
SWITZERLAND. DIRECTORATE GENERAL OF CUSTOMS. SCHWEIZERISCHE AUSSENHANDELSSTATISTIK. JAHRESSTATISTIK. Text in French, German. 1885. a. (2 vols.). CHF 70.40 per vol.; CHF 80 foreign (effective 2000). **Document type:** *Government.*
Former titles (until 1989): Switzerland. Directorate General of Customs. Jahresstatistik des Aussenhandels der Schweiz (0081-525X); (until 1939): Jahresstatistik des Auswaertigen Handels der Schweiz (1421-9379)
Published by: Directorate General of Customs, Section Statistics, Monbijoustr 40, Bern, 3003, Switzerland. TEL 41-31-3226610, FAX 41-31-3233927.

382 315 SYR
SYRIA. CENTRAL BUREAU OF STATISTICS. SUMMARY OF FOREIGN TRADE. Text in Arabic, English. 1958. q. USD 40 per vol. in the Middle East; USD 75 per vol. elsewhere (effective 2002). mkt.; stat. **Document type:** *Government.* **Description:** Includes tables of imports and exports by sections and chapters, lists important items and main countries by item of import, export, and transit under the code of unified Arab classification.
Former titles: Syria. Central Bureau of Statistics. Monthly Summary of Foreign Trade; Syria. Central Bureau of Statistics. Summary of Foreign Trade Statistics (0039-7954)
Published by: Central Bureau of Statistics, Damascus, Syria. TEL 963-11-3335830, FAX 963-11-3322292, TELEX STC 411093 SY.

330 PYF ISSN 0765-1104
HC688.A1
TABLEAUX DE L'ECONOMIE POLYNESIENNE. Text in French. 1985. a. XPF 2,000 domestic; XPF 4,000 foreign.
Published by: Institut Territorial de la Statistique, BP 395, Papeete, Tahiti Cedex 98713, French Polynesia. TEL 689-54-32-32, FAX 689-42-72-52, TELEX 537 FP. Ed. Daniel Huart.

330 FRA ISSN 0291-8692
TABLEAUX ECONOMIQUES DE MIDI-PYRENEES. Text in French. 1981. biennial. **Description:** Offers important statistical information concerning the Midi-Pyrenees region.
Published by: Institut National de la Statistique et des Etudes Economiques (INSEE - Midi-Pyrenees), 36 rue des 36 Ponts, Toulouse, Cedex 4 31054, France. TEL 33-61366136, FAX 33-61366200.

330 GLP ISSN 0999-1271
TABLEAUX ECONOMIQUES REGIONAUX: GUADELOUPE (YEAR). Text in French. 1988. q. **Document type:** *Government.*
Published by: Institut National de la Statistique et des Etudes Economiques, Service Regional Guadeloupe, Ave. Paul Lacave, BP 96, Basse-Terre, Cedex 97102, Guadeloupe. TEL 590-81-42-50.

330 GUF ISSN 0999-128X
TABLEAUX ECONOMIQUES REGIONAUX: GUYANE (YEAR). Text in French. 1988. irreg., latest 1997. GNF 70, EUR 10.67 (effective 2000). back issues avail.
Published by: Institut National de la Statistique et des Etudes Economiques, Service Regional Guyane, BP 6017, Cayenne, Cedex 97306, French Guiana. TEL 594-297300, FAX 594-297301, http://www.insee.fr.

330 MTQ ISSN 0999-1409
TABLEAUX ECONOMIQUES REGIONAUX: MARTINIQUE (YEAR). Text in French. 1988. a. **Document type:** *Government.*
Published by: (Martinique. Service Regional de Martinique FRA), Institut National de la Statistique et des Etudes Economiques, Pointe de Jaham, Cedex, Martinique, BP 7212, Schoelcher, Cedex 97233, Martinique. TEL 590-915980, FAX 590-838925.

338 TWN ISSN 0257-5671
TAIWAN, REPUBLIC OF CHINA. EXECUTIVE YUAN. DIRECTORATE-GENERAL OF BUDGET, ACCOUNTING & STATISTICS. NATIONAL INCOME IN TAIWAN AREA, R.O.C. Key Title: National Income in Taiwan Area, Republic of China. Text in Chinese, English. 1969. a. TWD 500 (effective 2000).
Description: Provides information about GNP, economic growth, and the main statistical data on Taiwan's economy.
Published by: Executive Yuan, Directorate-General of Budget, Accounting & Statistics, 2 Kwangchow St, Taipei, Taiwan. TEL 886-2-2381-4910, http://www.dgbasey.gov.tw/dgbaso3/english/pubcat/catalog.htm, http://www.stat.gov.tw/main.htm/. Circ: 350.
Subscr. to: Chen Chung Book Co., 3F, 20 Heng-Yang Rd, Taipei, Taiwan. TEL 886-2-2382-1394, FAX 886-2-2382-2805, http://www.ccbc.com.tw.

382 315 TWN
TAIWAN, REPUBLIC OF CHINA. MINISTRY OF FINANCE. DEPARTMENT OF STATISTICS. MONTHLY STATISTICS OF EXPORTS AND IMPORTS/CHIN CH'U K'OU MAO I T'UNG CHI YUEH PAO. Text in Chinese, English. 1965. m. charts; stat. **Description:** Covers goods exported to and imported from foreign countries.
Published by: Ministry of Finance, Department of Statistics, 5F, no.2, Kwang Chow St, Taipei, 100, Taiwan.

B

▼ new title ➤ refereed ∗ unverified ◆ full entry avail.

336.2 315 TWN
TAIWAN, REPUBLIC OF CHINA. MINISTRY OF FINANCE. DEPARTMENT OF STATISTICS. YEARBOOK OF TAX STATISTICS. Text in Chinese, English. 1974. a.
Published by: Ministry of Finance, Department of Statistics, 5F, no.2, Kwang Chow St, Taipei, 100, Taiwan.

336.021 RUS
TAMOZHENNAYA STATISTIKA VNESHNEI TORGOVLI ROSSIISKOI FEDERATSII. Text in Russian. q. USD 229.95 in United States.
Indexed: RASB.
Published by: Gosudarstvennyi Tamozhennyi Komitet Rossiiskoi Federatsii, Komsomol'skaya pl 1-a, Moscow, 141411, Russian Federation. TEL 7-095-9751183. **US dist. addr.:** East View Information Services, 3020 Harbor Ln. N., Minneapolis, MN 55447. TEL 612-550-0961.

331.021 TZA
TANZANIA. NATIONAL BUREAU OF STATISTICS. SURVEY OF EMPLOYMENT. Text in English. 1961. irreg. (approx. a.). **Document type:** *Government.*
Formerly: Tanzania. Bureau of Statistics. Employment and Earnings (0049-2973)
Published by: National Bureau of Statistics, PO Box 796, Dar Es Salaam, Tanzania. **Subscr. to:** Government Publications Agency, PO Box 1801, Dar Es Salaam, Tanzania.

338 316 TZA
TANZANIA. NATIONAL BUREAU OF STATISTICS. SURVEY OF INDUSTRIAL PRODUCTION. Text in English. 1965. a. **Document type:** *Government.*
Formerly: Tanzania. Central Statistical Bureau. Survey of Industrial Production (0564-6545)
Published by: National Bureau of Statistics, PO Box 796, Dar Es Salaam, Tanzania. **Subscr. to:** Government Publications Agency, PO Box 1801, Dar Es Salaam, Tanzania.

TENNESSEE. LABOR MARKET INFORMATION DIRECTORY. see *BUSINESS AND ECONOMICS—Labor And Industrial Relations*

TENNESSEE. THE LABOR MARKET REPORT. see *BUSINESS AND ECONOMICS—Labor And Industrial Relations*

310 THA
THAILAND. NATIONAL OFFICE OF STATISTICS. REPORT OF BUSINESS TRADE AND SURVEY (YEAR). Text in English, Thai. 1966. a. price varies. **Document type:** *Government.* **Description:** Contains data on number of business establishments, number of employees and their compensation, expenditure and receipts, and value of fixed assets.
Published by: (Thailand. Statistical Data Bank and Information Dissemination Division), National Statistical Office, Larn Luang Rd, Bangkok, 10100, Thailand. TEL 66-2-282-1535, FAX 66-2-281-3814. Circ: 300.

310 THA
THAILAND. NATIONAL STATISTICAL OFFICE. REPORT OF HOUSEHOLD SOCIO - ECONOMIC SURVEY (YEAR). Text in English, Thai. 1957. biennial (in 6 vols.). price varies. **Document type:** *Newspaper.* **Description:** Contains news on household income, consumption expenditures, changes in assets and liabilities, housing, and ownership of some durable goods.
Published by: (Thailand. Statistical Data Bank and Information Dissemination Division), National Statistical Office, Larn Luang Rd, Bangkok, 10100, Thailand. TEL 66-2-282-1535, FAX 66-2-281-3814, binfodsm@nso.go.th, http://www.nso.go.th/. Circ: 2,500.

310 THA
THAILAND. NATIONAL STATISTICAL OFFICE. REPORT OF INDUSTRIAL SURVEY (YEAR). Text in English, Thai. 1968. a. (in 2 vols.). price varies. **Document type:** *Government.* **Description:** Constitutes an industrial survey. Contains information on number of establishments, persons engaged, employees, compensations, value of raw materials, parts and components purchased, sales value of goods produced and purchased for resale, inventory and value of fixed assets.
Published by: (Thailand. Statistical Data Bank and Information Dissemination Division), National Statistical Office, Larn Luang Rd, Bangkok, 10100, Thailand. TEL 66-2-282-1535, FAX 66-2-281-3814, binfodsm@nso.go.th, http://www.nso.go.th/. Circ: 600.

331.021 THA ISSN 0858-0200
THAILAND. NATIONAL STATISTICAL OFFICE. REPORT OF THE LABOR FORCE SURVEY, WHOLE KINGDOM (YEAR). Text in English, Thai. 1963. 3/yr. **Document type:** *Government.* **Description:** Contains statistics on the number and characteristics of the labor supply in the country.
Published by: (Thailand. Statistical Data Bank and Information Dissemination Division), National Statistical Office, Larn Luang Rd, Bangkok, 10100, Thailand. TEL 66-2-282-1535, FAX 66-2-281-3814. Circ: 750.

382 THA
THAILAND'S FOREIGN TRADE STATISTICS. Text mainly in Thai, English; Text occasionally in Chinese. irreg. THB 250.
Published by: Interstate Publications, Pathumwan, P.O. Box 5-85, Bangkok 5, Thailand.

330.9 310 TGO
TOGO. MINISTRY OF ECONOMY AND FINANCE. BULLETIN DE STATISTIQUES. Text in French. m. **Document type:** *Bulletin, Government.*
Published by: Ministry of Economy and Finance, Service de la Statistique Generale, BP 118, Lome, Togo.

658 016 GBR ISSN 0049-4100
HD28
TOP MANAGEMENT ABSTRACTS. (Also avail. as a section of: Emerald Management Reviews (print & online eds.)) Text in English. 1971. bi-m. EUR 6,497.88 in Europe; USD 6,119 in North America; AUD 3,979 in Australasia; GBP 4,554.88 in UK & elsewhere (effective 2006). **Document type:** *Abstract/Index.* **Description:** Contains fully searchable, independent abstracts of articles from top 400 international management journals, on topics of interest to senior management. Abstracts are assessed, keyworded and indexed.
Supersedes in part: Anbar Management Services Abstracts (0003-2794)
Related titles: CD-ROM ed.; Online - full text ed.
—CCC.
Published by: Emerald Group Publishing Limited, 60-62 Toller Ln, Bradford, W Yorks BD8 9BY, United Kingdom. TEL 44-1274-777700, FAX 44-1274-785200, infomation@emeraldinsight.com, http://www.emeraldinsight.com/. Ed. David Pollitt. **Subscr. in N America to:** Emerald Group Publishing Ltd., 44 Brattle St, 4th Fl, Cambridge, MA 02138. TEL 617-497-2175, 888-622-0075, FAX 617-354-6875.

TOPICATOR; classified guide to articles in the advertising/communications/marketing periodical press. see *ADVERTISING AND PUBLIC RELATIONS—Abstracting, Bibliographies, Statistics*

381.021 RUS
TORGOVLYA V ROSSII (YEAR). Text in Russian. a., latest 2005. RUR 275 per issue (effective 2005). **Document type:** *Government.*
Published by: Gosudarstvennyi Komitet Rossiiskoi Federatsii po Statistike/Federal State Statistics Office, ul Myasnitskaya 39, Moscow, 107450, Russian Federation. TEL 7-095-2074902, FAX 7-095-2074087, stat@gks.ru, http://www.gks.ru.

330 JPN
TOUKEI BINRAN/BANK OF JAPAN. STATISTICS HANDBOOK. Text in Japanese. m. JPY 830 per issue. 160 p./no.; **Description:** Contains key economic indicators.
Published by: (Research and Statistics Department), Bank of Japan/Nippon Ginko, c/o Public Relations Department, 2-1-1 Hongoku-cho-Nihonbashi, Chuo-ku, Tokyo, 1030000, Japan. TEL 81-3-3279-1111, FAX 81-3-3510-1374, http://www.boj.or.jp/en.index.htm. **Dist. by:** Tokiwa Sohgoh Service Co. Ltd., Publication and Research Department, Kyodo Bldg, 2-4 Hongokucho, Nihonbashi 3-chome, Chuo-ku, Tokyo 103-0027, Japan. TEL 81-3-3270-5713, FAX 81-3-3270-5710; **Overseas dist. by:** Japan Publications Trading Co., Ltd., Book Export II Dept, PO Box 5030, Tokyo International, Tokyo 101-3191, Japan. TEL 81-3-32923753, FAX 81-3-32920410.

330 658.3 USA ISSN 1049-3875
HF5549.5.T7
TRAINING AND DEVELOPMENT YEARBOOK✶. Text in English. 1990. a. USD 79.95. **Description:** Consists of reprint articles and abstracts from training literature of the previous year. Case studies and research summaries are highlighted.
Published by: (Advanced Personnel Systems), Prentice Hall, 405 Murray Hill Pkwy., E Rutherford, NJ 07073-2136. Ed. Richard B Frantzreb.

330.9 ITA
TRIBUNA ECONOMICA. Text in Italian. 1972. m. free. **Description:** Covers economics, statistics and information on business.
Published by: Camera di Commercio Industria Artigianato e Agricoltura di Livorno, Piazza Del Municipio, 48, Livorno, LI 57123, Italy. TEL 30-586-231111, FAX 39-586-886689, TELEX 500486 CCIA LI. Circ: 10,000.

318 330.9 TTO
TRINIDAD AND TOBAGO. CENTRAL STATISTICAL OFFICE. BUSINESS SURVEYS. Text in English. irreg., latest 1990. TTD 4 (effective 2000). **Document type:** *Government.*
Published by: Central Statistical Office, 35-41 Queen St, PO Box 98, Port-of-Spain, Trinidad, Trinidad & Tobago. TEL 868-623-6495, FAX 868-625-3802.

330.9 318 TTO
TRINIDAD AND TOBAGO. CENTRAL STATISTICAL OFFICE. ECONOMIC INDICATORS. Text in English. 1974. biennial. TTD 15 (effective 2000). **Document type:** *Government.*
Published by: Central Statistical Office, 35-41 Queen St, PO Box 98, Port-of-Spain, Trinidad, Trinidad & Tobago. TEL 868-623-6495, FAX 868-625-3802.

317.29 331.1 TTO
TRINIDAD AND TOBAGO. CENTRAL STATISTICAL OFFICE. LABOUR FORCE BY SEX. Text in English. q. TTD 3 (effective 2000). illus.; stat. **Document type:** *Government.*
Related titles: ♦ Series of: Trinidad and Tobago. Central Statistical Office. Continuous Sample Survey of Population. ISSN 0564-2612.
Published by: Central Statistical Office, 35-41 Queen St, PO Box 98, Port-of-Spain, Trinidad, Trinidad & Tobago. TEL 868-623-6495, FAX 868-625-3802.

382 318 TTO ISSN 0082-6545
TRINIDAD AND TOBAGO. CENTRAL STATISTICAL OFFICE. OVERSEAS TRADE. ANNUAL REPORT. Text in English. 1951. a. (in 3 vols.). USD 40 for Part A; USD 10 for Part B; USD 20 for Part C (effective 2000). **Document type:** *Government.*
Published by: Central Statistical Office, 35-41 Queen St, PO Box 98, Port-of-Spain, Trinidad, Trinidad & Tobago. TEL 868-623-6495, FAX 868-625-3802.

382 318 TTO ISSN 0030-7505
TRINIDAD AND TOBAGO. CENTRAL STATISTICAL OFFICE. OVERSEAS TRADE. BI-MONTHLY REPORT. Text in English. 1951. m. TTD 24 (effective 2000). mkt.; stat. **Document type:** *Government.*
Formerly: Trinidad and Tobago. Statistical Office. Overseas Trade Report
Published by: Central Statistical Office, 35-41 Queen St, PO Box 98, Port-of-Spain, Trinidad, Trinidad & Tobago. TEL 868-623-6495, FAX 868-625-3802. Circ: 650.

330 TTO ISSN 0041-3046
HC157.T8
TRINIDAD AND TOBAGO. CENTRAL STATISTICAL OFFICE. QUARTERLY ECONOMIC REPORT. Text in English. 1950. biennial. TTD 15, USD 7.50 (effective 2000). charts; stat. **Document type:** *Government.*
Published by: Central Statistical Office, 35-41 Queen St, PO Box 98, Port-of-Spain, Trinidad, Trinidad & Tobago. TEL 868-623-6495, FAX 868-625-3802. Circ: 700.

331.021 RUS
TRUD I ZANYATOST' V ROSSII (YEAR). Text in Russian. a., latest 2005. RUR 440 per issue (effective 2005). **Document type:** *Government.*
Published by: Gosudarstvennyi Komitet Rossiiskoi Federatsii po Statistike/Federal State Statistics Office, ul Myasnitskaya 39, Moscow, 107450, Russian Federation. TEL 7-095-2074902, FAX 7-095-2074087, stat@gks.ru, http://www.gks.ru.

339 317 RUS
TSENA DAIDZHEST. Text in Russian. q.
Published by: Tsena Inform, Vorotnikovskii per 11, str 3, Moscow, 103006, Russian Federation. TEL 7-095-1431388, FAX 7-095-1431388. Ed. V A Podymov. **US dist. addr.:** East View Information Services, 3020 Harbor Ln. N., Minneapolis, MN 55447. TEL 612-550-0961.

338.5 314 BGR ISSN 1311-2457
TSENI, INDEKSI NA TSENITE I INFLATSIA. Text in Bulgarian, English. 1969. m. USD 58 foreign (effective 2002). stat. **Document type:** *Journal.* **Description:** Covers consumer price index, average prices of goods and services, price indices by major groups of consumer goods and services.
Published by: Natsionalen Statisticheski Institut/National Statistical Institute, ul P Volov, # 2, Sofia, 1038, Bulgaria. FAX 359-2-9803319, publikacii@nsi.bg, http://www.nsi.bg. Circ: 280.

315.61 TUR ISSN 1300-0802
HF3756.5
TURKEY. DEVLET ISTATISTIK ENSTITUSU. AYLIK DIS TICARET OZETI/TURKEY. STATE INSTITUTE OF STATISTICS. MONTHLY SUMMARY OF FOREIGN TRADE. Key Title: Aylik Dis Ticaret Ozeti. Text in English, Turkish. 1964. m. USD 20. **Document type:** *Government.*
Related titles: Diskette ed.
Published by: Devlet Istatistik Enstitusu/State Institute of Statistics, Necatibey Caddesi 114, Ankara, 06100, Turkey. TEL 90-312-4185027, FAX 90-312-4170432. Circ: 2,100.

315.61 TUR
TURKEY. DEVLET ISTATISTIK ENSTITUSU. AYLIK EKONOMIK GOSTERGELER/TURKEY. STATE INSTITUTE OF STATISTICS. MONTHLY ECONOMIC INDICATORS. Text in English, Turkish. 1980. m. USD 8.80. **Document type:** *Government.*
Published by: Devlet Istatistik Enstitusu/State Institute of Statistics, Necatibey Caddesi 114, Ankara, 06100, Turkey. TEL 90-312-4185027, FAX 90-312-4170432. Circ: 2,000.

315.61 TUR ISSN 0259-5338
TURKEY. DEVLET ISTATISTIK ENSTITUSU. DIS TICARET ISTATISTIKLERI/TURKEY. STATE INSTITUTE OF STATISTICS. FOREIGN TRADE STATISTICS. Key Title: Dis Ticaret Istatistikleri. Text in English, Turkish. 1926. a. USD 65 (effective 1998). **Document type:** *Government.*
Formerly: Turkey. Devlet Istatistik Enstitusu. Dis Ticaret Yillik Istatistik - Annual Foreign Trade Statistics (0082-6901)
Related titles: Diskette ed.
—BLDSC (3987.437000).
Published by: Devlet Istatistik Enstitusu/State Institute of Statistics, Necatibey Caddesi 114, Ankara, 06100, Turkey. TEL 90-312-4185027, FAX 90-312-4170432, yayin@die.gov.tr, http://www.die.gov.tr. Circ: 800.

315.61 TUR ISSN 1300-090X
HD9736.T9
TURKEY. DEVLET ISTATISTIK ENSTITUSU. DONEMLER ITIBARIYLE IMALAT SANAYII: ISTIHDAM - ODEMELER - URETIM EGILIM (GECICI SONUCLAR)/TURKEY. STATE INSTITUTE OF STATISTICS. MANUFACTURING INDUSTRY (QUARTERLY) EMPLOYMENT - PAYMENTS - PRODUCTION - EXPECTATIONS (PROVISIONAL RESULTS). Text in English, Turkish. q. USD 60 (effective 1998). **Document type:** *Government.*
Related titles: Diskette ed.
Published by: Devlet Istatistik Enstitusu/State Institute of Statistics, Necatibey Caddesi 114, Ankara, 06100, Turkey. TEL 90-312-4185027, FAX 90-312-4170432, yayin@die.gov.tr, http://www.die.gov.tr.

315.61 TUR
TURKEY. DEVLET ISTATISTIK ENSTITUSU. GAYRI SAFI MILLI HASILA, HABER BULTENI/TURKEY. STATE INSTITUTE OF STATISTICS. GROSS NATIONAL PRODUCT RESULTS, NEWS BULLETIN. Text in English, Turkish. 1947. q. (plus a. cumulation). **Document type:** *Bulletin, Government.*
Published by: Devlet Istatistik Enstitusu/State Institute of Statistics, Necatibey Caddesi 114, Ankara, 06100, Turkey. TEL 90-312-4185027, FAX 90-312-4170432.

338.528 TUR ISSN 1300-1035
TURKEY. DEVLET ISTATISTIK ENSTITUSU. PERAKENDE FIYAT ISTATISTIKLERI/TURKEY. STATE INSTITUTE OF STATISTICS. RETAIL PRICE STATISTICS. Key Title: Perakende Fiyat Istatistikleri. Text in English, Turkish. 1972. a., latest covers 1993-1995. USD 60 (effective 1998). **Document type:** *Government.*
Related titles: Diskette ed.
Published by: Devlet Istatistik Enstitusu/State Institute of Statistics, Necatibey Caddesi 114, Ankara, 06100, Turkey. TEL 90-312-4185027, FAX 90-312-4170432, yayin@die.gov.tr, http://www.die.gov.tr.

315.61 TUR
TURKEY. DEVLET ISTATISTIK ENSTITUSU. SANAYI URETIM INDEKSI (DONEMLER ITIBARIYLE)/TURKEY. STATE INSTITUTE OF STATISTICS. INDUSTRIAL PRODUCTION INDEXES (QUARTERLY). Text in English, Turkish. 1984. q. USD 45. **Document type:** *Government.*
Related titles: Diskette ed.
Published by: Devlet Istatistik Enstitusu/State Institute of Statistics, Necatibey Caddesi 114, Ankara, 06100, Turkey. TEL 90-312-4185027, FAX 90-312-4170432. Circ: 1,242.

338.7021 TUR ISSN 1300-1124
HA1911
TURKEY. DEVLET ISTATISTIK ENSTITUSU. SIRKETLER KOOPERATIFLER VE FIRMA ISTATISTIKLERI/TURKEY. STATE INSTITUTE OF STATISTICS. COMPANIES, COOPERATIVES AND FIRMS STATISTICS. Key Title: Sirketler Kooperatifler ve Firma Istatistikleri. Text in English, Turkish. 1967. a., latest 1995. USD 45 (effective 1998). **Document type:** *Government.*
Published by: Devlet Istatistik Enstitusu/State Institute of Statistics, Necatibey Caddesi 114, Ankara, 06100, Turkey. TEL 90-312-4085027, FAX 90-312-4170432, yayin@die.gov.tr, http://www.die.gov.tr. Circ: 1,200.

381 TUR ISSN 1300-3992
HF3756.5
TURKEY. DEVLET ISTATISTIK ENSTITUSU. TASIMACELIK ACISINDAN TURKIYE'NIN DIS TICAETI/TURKEY. STATE INSTITUTE OF STATISTICS. FOREIGN TRADE BY TRANSPORT SYSTEM. Text in English, Turkish. 1994. a. USD 45 (effective 1998). **Document type:** *Newspaper.*
Published by: Devlet Istatistik Enstitusu/State Institute of Statistics, Necatibey Caddesi 114, Ankara, 06100, Turkey. TEL 90-312-4185027, FAX 90-312-4170432, yayin@die.gov.tr, http://www.die.gov.tr.

315.61 TUR ISSN 1012-6376
TURKEY. DEVLET ISTATISTIK ENSTITUSU. TOPTAN ESYA VE TUKETICI FIYATLARI AYLIK INDEKS BULTENI/TURKEY. STATE INSTITUTE OF STATISTICS. WHOLESALE AND CONSUMER PRICE INDEXES MONTHLY BULLETIN. Key Title: Toptan Esya ve Tuketici Fiyatlari Aylik Indeks Bulteni. Text in English, Turkish. 1963. m. USD 25. **Document type:** *Government.*
Related titles: Diskette ed.
Published by: Devlet Istatistik Enstitusu/State Institute of Statistics, Necatibey Caddesi 114, Ankara, 06100, Turkey. TEL 90-312-4185027, FAX 90-312-4170432. Circ: 2,000.

315.61 TUR ISSN 1300-1140
TURKEY. DEVLET ISTATISTIK ENSTITUSU. TOPTAN FIYAT ISTATISTIKLERI/TURKEY. STATE INSTITUTE OF STATISTICS. WHOLESALE PRICE STATISTICS. Key Title: Toptan Fiyat Istatistikleri. Text in English, Turkish. 1974. a., latest covers 1991-1995. USD 45 (effective 1998). index, cum.index. **Document type:** *Government.*
Related titles: Diskette ed.
Published by: Devlet Istatistik Enstitusu/State Institute of Statistics, Necatibey Caddesi 114, Ankara, 06100, Turkey. TEL 90-312-4185027, FAX 90-312-4170432, yayin@die.gov.tr, http://www.die.gov.tr. Circ: 500 (controlled).

315.61 TUR ISSN 1300-1264
HC491
TURKEY. DEVLET ISTATISTIK ENSTITUSU. TURKIYE EKONOMISI ISTATISTIK VE YORUMLAR/TURKEY. STATE INSTITUTE OF STATISTICS. TURKISH ECONOMY STATISTICS AND EVALUATIONS. Text in Turkish. 1990. m. USD 80 (effective 1998). **Document type:** *Government.* **Description:** Provides statistical information on price fluctuations, GNP, household income and consumption, foreign trade, labor force and industry, mining, construction, agriculture, as well as the environment, education, social and economic characteristics of the population.
Related titles: Diskette ed.
Published by: Devlet Istatistik Enstitusu/State Institute of Statistics, Necatibey Caddesi 114, Ankara, 06100, Turkey. TEL 90-312-4185027, FAX 90-312-4170432, yayin@die.gov.tr, http://www.die.gov.tr.

315.61 TUR
TURKEY. DEVLET ISTATISTIK ENSTITUSU. YAYINLAY VE ELEKTRONIK HIZMETLER KATALOGU/PUBLICATIONS AND ELECTRONIC SERVICES CATALOGUE. Text in Turkish. 1994. irreg. free. illus. **Document type:** *Catalog, Government.* **Description:** Presents information on available statistical publications covering social and economic conditions in Turkey.
Related titles: English ed.: Turkey. State Institute of Statistics. Publications and Electronic Services Catalogue.
Published by: Devlet Istatistik Enstitusu/State Institute of Statistics, Necatibey Caddesi 114, Ankara, 06100, Turkey. TEL 90-312-4185027, FAX 90-312-4170432, yayin@die.gov.tr, http://www.die.gov.tr.

315.61 TUR ISSN 0259-5141
HA1911
TURKEY. DEVLET ISTATISTIK ENSTITUSU. YILLIK IMALAT SANAYI ISTATISTIKLERI/TURKEY. STATE INSTITUTE OF STATISTICS. ANNUAL MANUFACTURING INDUSTRY STATISTICS. Key Title: Yillik Imalat Sanayi Istatistikleri. Text in English, Turkish. 1974. a., latest 1991. USD 65 (effective 1998). **Document type:** *Government.* **Description:** Provides detailed information about all aspects of the Turkish manufacturing sector.
Related titles: Diskette ed.
Published by: Devlet Istatistik Enstitusu/State Institute of Statistics, Necatibey Caddesi 114, Ankara, 06100, Turkey. TEL 90-312-4185027, FAX 90-312-4170432, yayin@die.gov.tr, http://www.die.gov.tr. Circ: 1,100.

315.61 TUR ISSN 1300-7173
TURKEY. STATE INSTITUTE OF STATISTICS. CENSUS OF INDUSTRY AND BUSINESS ESTABLISHMENTS - 1ST STAGE RESULTS. Text in English, Turkish. 1974. irreg., latest 1992. USD 60 (effective 1998). **Document type:** *Government.*
Published by: Devlet Istatistik Enstitusu/State Institute of Statistics, Necatibey Caddesi 114, Ankara, 06100, Turkey. TEL 90-4-4176440, FAX 90-4-4253387, yayin@die.gov.tr, http://www.die.gov.tr. Circ: 550.

315.61 TUR
TURKEY. STATE INSTITUTE OF STATISTICS. CENSUS OF INDUSTRY AND BUSINESS ESTABLISHMENTS - 2ND STAGE RESULTS, LARGE SCALE MANUFACTURING INDUSTRIES. Text in English, Turkish. 1976. irreg., latest 1985. **Document type:** *Government.*
Published by: Devlet Istatistik Enstitusu/State Institute of Statistics, Necatibey Caddesi 114, Ankara, 06100, Turkey. TEL 90-4-4176440, FAX 90-4-4253387. Circ: 1,350.

315.61 TUR
TURKEY. STATE INSTITUTE OF STATISTICS. CENSUS OF INDUSTRY AND BUSINESS ESTABLISHMENTS - 2ND STAGE RESULTS, SERVICE, HOTEL, RESTAURANT, GUEST HOUSE, CAFE. Text in English, Turkish. 1974. irreg., latest 1985. **Document type:** *Government.*
Published by: Devlet Istatistik Enstitusu/State Institute of Statistics, Necatibey Caddesi 114, Ankara, 06100, Turkey. TEL 90-4-4176440, FAX 90-4-4253387.

315.61 TUR
TURKEY. STATE INSTITUTE OF STATISTICS. CENSUS OF INDUSTRY AND BUSINESS ESTABLISHMENTS - 2ND STAGE RESULTS, SMALL-SCALE MANUFACTURING INDUSTRIES. Text in English, Turkish. 1975. irreg., latest 1985. **Document type:** *Government.*
Published by: Devlet Istatistik Enstitusu/State Institute of Statistics, Necatibey Caddesi 114, Ankara, 06100, Turkey. TEL 90-4-4176440, FAX 90-4-4253387. Circ: 1,350.

315.61 TUR
TURKEY. STATE INSTITUTE OF STATISTICS. CENSUS OF INDUSTRY AND BUSINESS ESTABLISHMENTS - 2ND STAGE RESULTS, TRADE. Text in English, Turkish. 1974. irreg., latest 1985. **Document type:** *Government.*
Published by: Devlet Istatistik Enstitusu/State Institute of Statistics, Necatibey Caddesi 114, Ankara, 06100, Turkey. TEL 90-4-4176440, FAX 90-4-4253387. Circ: 1,350.

315.61 TUR
TURKEY. STATE INSTITUTE OF STATISTICS. CONSUMPTION EXPENDITURES. Text in English, Turkish. 1979. a., latest 1987. **Document type:** *Government.*
Published by: Devlet Istatistik Enstitusu/State Institute of Statistics, Necatibey Caddesi 114, Ankara, 06100, Turkey. TEL 90-4-4176440, FAX 90-4-4253387. Circ: 1,350.

315.61 TUR ISSN 0259-5036
TURKEY. STATE INSTITUTE OF STATISTICS. HOUSEHOLD LABOR FORCE SURVEY RESULTS. Text in English, Turkish. 1968. irreg., latest 1996. USD 60 (effective 1998). **Document type:** *Government.*
Published by: Devlet Istatistik Enstitusu/State Institute of Statistics, Necatibey Caddesi 114, Ankara, 06100, Turkey. TEL 90-4-4176440, FAX 90-4-4253387, yayin@die.gov.tr, http://www.die.gov.tr. Circ: 1,150.

315.61 TUR
TURKEY. STATE INSTITUTE OF STATISTICS. INCOME DISTRIBUTION. Text in English, Turkish. a., latest 1987. **Document type:** *Government.*
Published by: Devlet Istatistik Enstitusu/State Institute of Statistics, Necatibey Caddesi 114, Ankara, 06100, Turkey. TEL 90-4-4176440, FAX 90-4-4253387.

315.61 TUR
TURKEY. STATE INSTITUTE OF STATISTICS. METHODOLOGY EXPLANATION OF TRADE PRICE AND QUANTITY INDEXES. Text in English. 1992. irreg. free. **Document type:** *Government.*
Published by: Devlet Istatistik Enstitusu/State Institute of Statistics, Necatibey Caddesi 114, Ankara, 06100, Turkey. TEL 90-4-4176440, FAX 90-4-4253387.

330 ITA ISSN 1122-5009
TUTTOINDICI. Text in Italian. 1994. m. EUR 82 (effective 2005). **Document type:** *Magazine, Trade.* **Description:** Contains financial indexes.
Published by: De Lillo Editore s.r.l., Via Mecenate 76/3, Milan, 20138, Italy. TEL 39-02-58013112, FAX 39-02-58012450, http://www.delillo.it. Ed. Pietro de Lillo. Circ: 11,000.

330 310 USA ISSN 1012-0793
HF1040
U N C T A D COMMODITY YEARBOOK. Text in English. 1984. a. USD 52.
Formerly (until 1987): Yearbook of International Commodity Statistics (0257-1870)
Related titles: Microfiche ed.: (from CIS).
Indexed: IIS.
Published by: (United Nations, Conference on Trade and Development), United Nations Publications, Rm DC2-853, United Nations Bldg, 2 United Nations Plaza, New York, NY 10017. TEL 212-963-8302, 800-253-9646, FAX 212-963-3489, publications@un.org, http://www.un.org/publications, http://www.un.org/Pubs.

382 CHE ISSN 1020-7988
HF1016
U N C T A D HANDBOOK OF STATISTICS/MANUEL DE STATISTIQUES DE LA C N U C E D. (United Nations Conference on Trade and Development) Text in English, French. 2000. a. USD 150 (effective 2001). **Document type:** *Bulletin, Trade.* **Description:** Provides a comprehensive collection of statistical data relevant to the analysis of world trade, investment and development.
Media: CD-ROM.
—CISTI.
Published by: United Nations Conference on Trade and Development, Palais des Nations, 8-14 Av de la Paix, Geneva 10, 1211, Switzerland. TEL 41-22-907-1234, FAX 41-22-9070195, publications@un.org, http://www.unctad.org. **Subscr. to:** United Nations Publications, Distribution and Sales Section, Palais des Nations, Geneva CH-1211, Switzerland. TEL 41-22-907-2612, unpubli@unog.ch.

332.6 USA ISSN 1059-4418
HA4551
U S AND ASIA STATISTICAL HANDBOOK. Text in English. 19??. a. USD 9.50 (effective 2004). **Document type:** *Journal, Academic/Scholarly.* **Description:** Contains information on political, military, economic and social conditions in 34 countries and territories in Asia.
Published by: Heritage Foundation, 214 Massachusetts Ave, N E, Washington, DC 20002. TEL 202-546-4400, FAX 202-546-8328, info@heritage.org, http://www.heritage.org. Ed. Paolo Pasicolan.

331.021 USA ISSN 0082-9021
HD8051
U.S. BUREAU OF LABOR STATISTICS. BULLETIN. Variant title: B L S Bulletins. Text in English. 1913. irreg. price varies. back issues avail. **Document type:** *Bulletin, Government.*
Related titles: ◆ Series: Employment, Hours, and Earnings: States and Areas; ◆ Industry Wage Surveys. Corrugated and Solid Fiber Boxes. ISSN 0148-9208; ◆ Occupational Outlook Handbook. ISSN 0082-9072; ◆ Census of Maine Manufactures. ISSN 0090-7111; ◆ Consumer Expenditure Survey; ◆ Employment and Wages Annual Averages. ISSN 0748-5336; ◆ Employment Cost Indexes and Levels; ◆ Displaced Workers; ◆ Geographic Profile of Employment and Unemployment. ISSN 0145-7330; ◆ Occupational Compensation Surveys.
Indexed: PAIS.
—CISTI.

B

Published by: U.S. Department of Labor, Bureau of Labor Statistics, Postal Square Bldg., 2 Massachusetts Ave, NE, Washington, DC 20212-0001 . TEL 202-691-5200, http://www.bls.gov. **Subscr. to:** U.S. Government Printing Office, Superintendent of Documents, PO Box 371954, Pittsburgh, PA 15250-7954. TEL 202-512-1800, FAX 202-512-2250.

331.021 USA
U.S. BUREAU OF LABOR STATISTICS. NATIONAL COMPENSATION SURVEY. Text in English. irreg. USD 300 (effective 2001). stat. **Document type:** *Government.* **Description:** Reports on earnings in 70 major metropolitan areas for occupations common to a wide variety of establishments. Coverage includes office clerical, professional and technical, maintenance, custodial, and material movement occupations. Information on employee benefits is provided for about one-third of the areas each year.
Formerly: U.S. Bureau of Labor Statistics. Area Wage Surveys
Published by: U.S. Department of Labor, Bureau of Labor Statistics, Postal Square Bldg., 2 Massachusetts Ave, NE, Washington, DC 20212-0001 . TEL 202-691-5200, http://stats.bls.gov/compub.htm, http://www.bls.gov. **Subscr. to:** U.S. Government Printing Office, Superintendent of Documents, PO Box 371954, Pittsburgh, PA 15250-7954. TEL 202-512-1800, FAX 202-512-2250, orders@gpo.gov, http://www.access.gpo.gov.

331.021 USA
U.S. BUREAU OF LABOR STATISTICS. NATIONAL OFFICE NEWS RELEASES. Text in English. irreg. free. **Document type:** *Government.*
Related titles: Online - full text ed.; ♦ Series: The Employment Situation. ISSN 0364-491X; ♦ Department Store Inventories; ♦ Major Collective Bargaining Settlements in Private Industry; ♦ B L S Releases: Demographic Data Book for States and Large Metropolitan Areas; ♦ Consumer Expenditures in (Year); ♦ Average Annual Pay Levels in Metropolitan Areas (Year); ♦ Employment and Earnings: Characteristics of Families; ♦ News, Productivity and Costs. ISSN 0738-2650; ♦ Productivity by Industry (Year); ♦ Real Earnings; ♦ Retail Food Price Index: Washington, D.C.; ♦ State and Metropolitan Area Employment and Unemployment; ♦ Unemployment in States; ♦ U.S. Import and Export Price Indexes; ♦ Usual Weekly Earnings of Wage and Salary Workers; ♦ Average Annual Pay by State and Industry; ♦ Employer Costs for Employee Compensation; ♦ International Comparisons of Manufacturing Productivity and Unit Labor Cost Trends (Year); ♦ Major Collective Bargaining Settlements in State and Local Government.
Published by: U.S. Department of Labor, Bureau of Labor Statistics, Postal Square Bldg., 2 Massachusetts Ave, NE, Washington, DC 20212-0001 . TEL 202-691-5200, http://www.bls.gov. **Subscr. to:** U.S. Government Printing Office, Superintendent of Documents.

331.021 USA
U.S. BUREAU OF LABOR STATISTICS. REPORTS. Variant title: B L S Reports. Text in English. irreg. price varies. back issues avail. **Document type:** *Government.*
Related titles: ♦ Series: Consumer Expenditure Survey: Quarterly Data from the Interview Survey; ♦ Employment in Perspective: Minority Workers; ♦ Employment in Perspective: Women in the Labor Force; ♦ B L S Reports on Employee Benefits in the United States.
Published by: U.S. Department of Labor, Bureau of Labor Statistics, Postal Square Bldg., 2 Massachusetts Ave, NE, Washington, DC 20212-0001 . TEL 202-691-5200, http://www.bls.gov. **Subscr. to:** U.S. Government Printing Office, Superintendent of Documents, PO Box 371954, Pittsburgh, PA 15250-7954. TEL 202-512-1800, FAX 202-512-2250.

331.021 USA
U.S. BUREAU OF LABOR STATISTICS. REPRINT SERIES. Text in English. irreg. **Document type:** *Government.* **Description:** Reissues key articles from Monthly Labor Review and other B.L.S. publications.
Published by: U.S. Department of Labor, Bureau of Labor Statistics, Postal Square Bldg., 2 Massachusetts Ave, NE, Washington, DC 20212-0001 . TEL 202-691-5200, http://www.bls.gov. **Subscr. to:** U.S. Government Printing Office, Superintendent of Documents, PO Box 371954, Pittsburgh, PA 15250-7954. TEL 202-512-1800, FAX 202-512-2250.

330.9 USA
U.S. BUREAU OF LABOR STATISTICS. SOUTHWEST STATISTICAL SUMMARY. Text in English. m. free. reprint service avail. from CIS. **Document type:** *Government.*
Formerly (until 1985): U.S. Bureau of Labor Statistics. Southwest Employment and Earnings
Related titles: Microfiche ed.: (from CIS).
Indexed: AmStI.
Published by: U.S. Bureau of Labor Statistics, Southwest Regional Office, 525 Griffin St, Rm 221, Dallas, TX 75202. TEL 214-767-6970. Ed. Bill Luker Jr. Circ: 10,000.

650.021 USA
U.S. BUREAU OF THE CENSUS. (YEAR) ECONOMIC CENSUS. CENSUS OF RETAIL TRADE. (Issued in 3 series: Geographic Area Series, Industry Series, and Subject Series) Text in English. 1929. quinquennial. USD 253 domestic; USD 316.25 foreign (effective 2000); for Geographic Area Series. **Document type:** *Government.*
Formerly: Census of Retail Trade: Final Reports; Supersedes in part: U.S. Bureau of the Census. Census of Retail Trade, Wholesale Trade and Selected Service Industries; Which was formerly: U.S. Bureau of the Census. Census of Business (0082-9323)
Related titles: ♦ CD-ROM ed.: Economic Census CD-ROM Series; Online - full content ed.
Published by: U.S. Bureau of the Census (Subsidiary of: U.S. Department of Commerce), Customer Services, Washington, DC 20233. TEL 301-457-4100, FAX 301-457-4714, http://www.census.gov.

330.021 USA
U.S. BUREAU OF THE CENSUS. (YEAR) ECONOMIC CENSUS. CENSUS OF WHOLESALE TRADE. (Issued in 3 series: Geographic Area Series, Industry Series, and Subject Series.) Text in English. quinquennial. price varies. **Document type:** *Government.* **Description:** Provides statistical information on establishments engaged in wholesaling merchandise, generally without transformation, and rendering services incidental to the sale of merchandise.
Formerly: Census of Wholesale Trade: Final Reports; Supersedes in part: U.S. Bureau of the Census. Census of Retail Trade, Wholesale Trade and Service Industries; Which was formerly: U.S. Bureau of the Census. Census of Business (0082-9323)
Related titles: ♦ CD-ROM ed.: Economic Census CD-ROM Series; Online - full content ed.
Published by: U.S. Bureau of the Census (Subsidiary of: U.S. Department of Commerce), Customer Services, Washington, DC 20233. TEL 301-457-4100, FAX 301-457-4714.

338.0021 USA
U.S. BUREAU OF THE CENSUS. (YEAR) ECONOMIC CENSUS. MANUFACTURING. (Issued in 3 series: Geographic Area Series, Industry Series, and Subject Series) Text in English. 1810. quinquennial. **Document type:** *Government.*
Formerly: Census of Manufactures: Final Reports (0082-9374)
Related titles: ♦ CD-ROM ed.: Economic Census CD-ROM Series; Online - full content ed.
Published by: U.S. Bureau of the Census (Subsidiary of: U.S. Department of Commerce), Customer Services, Washington, DC 20233. TEL 301-457-4100, FAX 301-457-4714, http://www.census.gov.

330.9 USA
U.S. BUREAU OF THE CENSUS. ANNUAL CAPITAL EXPENDITURES. Text in English. a., latest 2002. charts. **Document type:** *Government.*
Published by: U.S. Bureau of the Census (Subsidiary of: U.S. Department of Commerce), c/o Victor Souphom, 4700 Silver Hill Rd., Washington, DC 20233. TEL 301-763-3334, csd@census.gov, http://www.census.gov/csd/ace/ace-pdf.html.

330 USA
U.S. BUREAU OF THE CENSUS. GOVERNMENTS DIVISION. LOCAL GOVERNMENT EMPLOYMENT AND PAYROLL DATA. Text in English. irreg. stat. **Document type:** *Government.*
Media: Online - full content.
Published by: U.S. Bureau of the Census, Governments Division TEL 800-642-4901, govs.employ@census.gov, http://www.census.gov/govs/www/apesloc.html, http://www.census.gov/govs/www/index.html.

U.S. DEPARTMENT OF AGRICULTURE. NATIONAL AGRICULTURAL STATISTICS SERVICE. FARM LABOR. see *AGRICULTURE—Abstracting, Bibliographies, Statistics*

331.021 USA ISSN 1058-0018
JK774
U.S. DEPARTMENT OF STATE INDEXES OF LIVING COSTS ABROAD, QUARTERS ALLOWANCES, AND HARDSHIP DIFFERENTIALS. Text in English. 1982. q.
Published by: U.S. Department of State, Office of Allowances, Rm H426 SA-1, Bureau of Administration, Washington, DC 20522-0104. TEL 202-663-1121, FAX 202-261-8707.

U.S. FEDERAL RESERVE SYSTEM. ANNUAL STATISTICAL DIGEST. see *BUSINESS AND ECONOMICS—Banking And Finance*

336.2 USA ISSN 0730-0743
HJ4653.S7
U.S. INTERNAL REVENUE SERVICE. STATISTICS OF INCOME BULLETIN. Key Title: Statistics of Income. S O I Bulletin. Text in English. 1981. q. USD 35 (effective 2001). **Description:** Provides information and statistics on income, assets, and expenses of individuals and businesses, as compiled from Federal tax returns.
Incorporates (1977-19??): Statistics of Income. Partnership Returns (0734-1709); (197?-19??): Statistics of Income. Sole Proprietorship Returns (0744-0030)
Related titles: Online - full text ed.: (from Florida Center for Library Automation, Gale Group, ProQuest Information & Learning).
Indexed: PAIS.
Published by: U.S. Internal Revenue Service, 1111 Constitution Ave, N W, Washington, DC 20224. TEL 800-829-1040. **Subscr. to:** U.S. Government Printing Office, Superintendent of Documents, PO Box 371954, Pittsburgh, PA 15250-7954. TEL 202-512-1800, FAX 202-512-2250, orders@gpo.gov, http://www.access.gpo.gov.

U.S. NATIONAL SCIENCE FOUNDATION. RESEARCH AND DEVELOPMENT IN INDUSTRY. see *TECHNOLOGY: COMPREHENSIVE WORKS—Abstracting, Bibliographies, Statistics*

352.63021 USA ISSN 0739-1404
JK671
U.S. OFFICE OF PERSONNEL MANAGEMENT. PERSONNEL SYSTEMS AND OVERSIGHT GROUP. FEDERAL CIVILIAN WORKFORCE STATISTICS. OCCUPATIONS OF FEDERAL WHITE-COLLAR AND BLUE-COLLAR WORKERS. Text in English. 1956. biennial. USD 29. **Document type:** *Government.*
Formed by the 1981 merger of: Occupations of Federal White-Collar Workers (0146-4906); Which was formerly: Federal White-Collar Workers. Their Occupations and Salaries; (1957-1980): Occupations of Federal Blue-Collar Workers (0146-2490)
Related titles: Microfiche ed.
Indexed: CISI.
Published by: U.S. Office of Personnel Management, Personnel Systems and Oversight Group, Office of Workforce Information, 1900 E St, N W, Washington, DC 20415. TEL 703-487-4650, http://www.opm.gov/feddata/html/occ.asp. **Subscr. to:** National Technical Information Service, Government Research Center, 5285 Port Royal Rd, Springfield, VA 22161. TEL 703-605-6060, 800-363-2068, http://www.ntis.gov.

331.21021 USA
HD7116.R118
U.S. RAILROAD RETIREMENT BOARD. QUARTERLY BENEFIT STATISTICS. Text in English. 1968. q. free. reprint service avail. from CIS. **Document type:** *Government.*
Formerly (until 1997): U.S. Railroad Retirement Board. Monthly Benefit Statistics (0364-7129)
Related titles: Microfiche ed.: (from CIS).
Indexed: AmStI.
Published by: U.S. Railroad Retirement Board, 844 N Rush St, Chicago, IL 60611. TEL 312-751-4776. Ed. W Poulos. Circ: 1,500.

382.09489 DNK ISSN 0109-5420
HF211
UDENRIGSHANDELEN FORDELT PAA VARER OG LANDE/EXTERNAL TRADE BY COMMODITIES AND COUNTRIES. Text in Danish; Notes in English. 1969. q. DKK 2,060; DKK 604.80 newsstand/cover (effective 2000). back issues avail. **Document type:** *Government.* **Description:** Contains detailed statistics of imports and exports by Working Tariff items and countries.
Formerly (until 1984): Denmark. Danmarks Statistik. Kvartalsstatistik over Udenrigshandelen (0106-9780)
Published by: Danmarks Statistik, Sejroegade 11, Copenhagen Oe, 2100, Denmark. TEL 45-39-17-39-17, FAX 45-31-18-48-01.

UNEMPLOYMENT INSURANCE STATISTICS. see *BUSINESS AND ECONOMICS—Labor And Industrial Relations*

UNESCO STATISTICS ON SCIENCE AND TECHNOLOGY/ ESTADISTICAS RELATIVAS A LA CIENCIA Y A LA TECNOLOGIA/STATISTIQUES RELATIVES AUX SCIENCE ET A LA TECHNOLOGIE. see *SCIENCES: COMPREHENSIVE WORKS—Abstracting, Bibliographies, Statistics*

UNIFORM COMMERCIAL CODE LAW JOURNAL. see *LAW—Abstracting, Bibliographies, Statistics*

336 330 CAF
UNITE - DIGNITE - TRAVAIL: PROGRAMME TRIENNAL D'INVESTISSEMENT DE L'ETAT. Text in French. 1988. a. USD 80. **Document type:** *Government.*
Published by: Ministry of Economics, Division of Programs and Projects, BP 696, Bangui, Central African Republic. FAX 236-61-09-92, TELEX 5208 RC. Ed. Alexis Ngomba.

330 UAE
UNITED ARAB EMIRATES. AL-MASRAF AL-MARKAZI. AL-MULHIQ AL-IHSA'I/UNITED ARAB EMIRATES. CENTRAL BANK. STATISTICAL SUPPLEMENT. Text in Arabic, English. 1979. q. **Document type:** *Government.* **Description:** Statistical information on Central Bank activities, the petroleum industries, and external trade of the U.A.E.
Published by: Central Bank, P O Box 854, Abu Dhabi, United Arab Emirates. TEL 652220, FAX 668483. Circ: 500 (controlled).

330.021 GBR ISSN 1475-7354
UNITED KINGDOM INPUT - OUTPUT ANALYSES. Text in English. 1999. a.
Formerly (until 2001): United Kingdom Input - Output Supply and Use Tables (1468-0718)

—BLDSC (9096.348500).

Published by: (National Statistics), Stationery Office (Norwich), St Crispins House, Duke St, PO Box 29, Norwich, NR3 1PD, United Kingdom. TEL 44-870-600-5522, FAX 44-870-600-5533, customer.services@theso.co.uk, http://www.thestationeryoffice.com/.

330.021 941   GBR
UNITED KINGDOM. OFFICE FOR NATIONAL STATISTICS. UNITED KINGDOM ECONOMIC ACCOUNTS. Text in English. 1993. q.
Formerly (until 2000): United Kingdom. Office for National Statistics. U K Economic Accounts (1350-4401)
Related titles: ♦ Supplement to: Economic Trends. ISSN 0013-0400.
—BLDSC (9094.700000).
Published by: Office for National Statistics, Zone DG/18, 1 Drummond Gate, London, SW1V 2QQ, United Kingdom. TEL 44-20-7533-5888, FAX 44-1633-652747, info@statistics.gov.uk, http://www.statistics.gov.uk. Ed. Jon Beadle TEL 44-20-7533-5938. **Subscr. to:** Stationery Office (Norwich), St Crispins House, Duke St, PO Box 29, Norwich NR3 1PD, United Kingdom. TEL 44-870-600-5522, FAX 44-870-600-5533.

310   THA   ISSN 0252-3647
HA37
UNITED NATIONS ECONOMIC AND SOCIAL COMMISSION FOR ASIA AND THE PACIFIC. STATISTICAL NEWSLETTER. Text in English. 1971. q., latest 2002. stat.
Related titles: Microfiche ed.: (from CIS).
Indexed: IIS.
Published by: United Nations Economic and Social Commission for Asia and the Pacific, Statistics Division, United Nations Bldg., Rajdamnern Nok Ave, Bangkok, 10200, Thailand. stat.unescap@un.org.

316   ETH
UNITED NATIONS ECONOMIC COMMISSION FOR AFRICA. STATISTICAL NEWSLETTER. Text in Arabic, English, French. a.
Related titles: Microfiche ed.: (from CIS).
Indexed: IIS.
Published by: (Documents & Publishing Services Unit), United Nations, Economic Commission for Africa/Commission Economique pour l'Afrique, PO Box 3001, Addis Ababa, Ethiopia.

382 310   USA   ISSN 1010-447X
UNITED NATIONS. INTERNATIONAL TRADE STATISTICS YEARBOOK. Text in English, French. 1950. a. (in 2 vols..), latest 2003. USD 150 (effective 2004). back issues avail.; reprints avail. **Document type:** Yearbook. **Description:** Covers commodity trade, international trade, trade statistics.
Formerly (until 1983): United Nations. Yearbook of International Trade Statistics (0084-3822)
Related titles: Microfiche ed.: (from CIS).
Indexed: IIS, RASB.
Published by: (United Nations Statistical Office), United Nations Publications, Rm DC2-853, United Nations Bldg, 2 United Nations Plaza, New York, NY 10017. TEL 212-963-8302, 800-253-9646, FAX 212-963-3489, publications@un.org, http://www.un.org/Pubs.

339   USA   ISSN 0259-3017
UNITED NATIONS. NATIONAL ACCOUNTS STATISTICS. ANALYSIS OF MAIN AGGREGATES. Text in English. 1958. a. USD 125. reprint service avail. from PSC.
Supersedes in part (in 1985): Yearbook of National Account Statistics (0084-3881)
Related titles: Microfiche ed.: (from CIS).
Indexed: IIS, RASB.
—CISTI.
Published by: United Nations Publications, Rm DC2-853, United Nations Bldg, 2 United Nations Plaza, New York, NY 10017. TEL 212-963-8302, 800-253-9646, FAX 212-963-3489, publications@un.org, http://www.un.org/publications, http://www.un.org/Pubs.

339   USA   ISSN 0259-3009
UNITED NATIONS. NATIONAL ACCOUNTS STATISTICS. GOVERNMENT ACCOUNTS AND TABLES. Text in English. 1958. a. reprint service avail. from PSC.
Supersedes in part (in 1985): Yearbook of National Account Statistics (0084-3881)
—CISTI.
Published by: United Nations Publications, Rm DC2-853, United Nations Bldg, 2 United Nations Plaza, New York, NY 10017. TEL 212-963-8302, 800-253-9646, FAX 212-963-3489, publications@un.org, http://www.un.org/publications, http://www.un.org/Pubs.

339   USA   ISSN 0259-3025
UNITED NATIONS. NATIONAL ACCOUNTS STATISTICS. MAIN AGGREGATES AND DETAILED TABLES. Text in English. 1958. a. reprint service avail. from PSC.
Supersedes in part (in 1985): Yearbook of National Account Statistics (0084-3881)
Related titles: Microfiche ed.: (from CIS); Online - full text ed.
Indexed: IIS.
—CISTI.

Published by: United Nations Publications, Rm DC2-853, United Nations Bldg, 2 United Nations Plaza, New York, NY 10017. TEL 212-963-8302, 800-253-9646, FAX 212-963-3489, publications@un.org, http://www.un.org/publications, http://www.un.org/Pubs.

330 016   CHL
UNIVERSIDAD DE CHILE. FACULTAD DE CIENCIAS ECONOMICAS Y ADMINISTRATIVAS. BIBLIOTECA. LISTA DE MEMORIAS Y LIBROS SELECCIONADOS; libros y folletos recibidos, articulos seleccionados. Text in English, French, Spanish. 1964. bi-m.
Supersedes (since 1978): Universidad de Chile. Instituto de Economia. Biblioteca. Boletin (0041-8366)
Published by: Universidad de Chile, Facultad de Ciencias Economicas y Administrativas, Ave. Ranacagua, 257, Santiago, Chile. Ed. Mariela Morales Piderit. Circ: 300.

330 310   GHA
UNIVERSITY OF GHANA. INSTITUTE OF STATISTICAL, SOCIAL AND ECONOMIC RESEARCH. TECHNICAL PUBLICATION SERIES. Text in English. 1966. irreg., latest vol.57, 1993. **Document type:** Monographic series. **Description:** Addresses social structure and poverty in selected rural communities in Ghana.
Formerly: University of Ghana. Institute of Statistical, Social and Economic Research. Technical Research Monographs (0072-4416)
Published by: University of Ghana, Institute of Statistical, Social and Economic Research, PO Box 74, Legon, Ghana.

318   URY   ISSN 0797-258X
URUGUAY. DIRECCION GENERAL DE ESTADISTICA Y CENSOS. INDICE MEDIO DE SALARIOS. Text in Spanish. q. **Document type:** Government.
Published by: Direccion General de Estadistica y Censos, Montevideo, Uruguay.

382   ISL   ISSN 1024-7467
UTANRIKISVERSLUN EFTIR TOLLSKRARNUMERUM/ EXTERNAL TRADE BY HS-NUMBERS. Text in Icelandic. 1995. a. USD 40 (effective 2001). back issues avail. **Document type:** Government.
Published by: Hagstofa Islands/Statistics Iceland, Borgartuni 12 A, Reykjavik, 150, Iceland. TEL 354-560-9800, FAX 354-562-3312, information@statice.is, hagstofa@hag.stjr.is, http://www.statice.is, http://www.statice.is/stat/e-mail.htm. Ed. Audur Svararsdottir.

330   HUN   ISSN 1219-7793
HG4149.5
VALLALATOK PENZUGYI ADATAI/FINANCIAL DATA OF NON-FINANCIAL CORPORATIONS. Text in Hungarian. irreg. USD 28. **Document type:** Government.
Supersedes in part (in 1992): Gazdasagstatisztikai Evkonyv (1215-6728)
Published by: Kozponti Statisztikai Hivatal, Marketing Oszta'ly, Keleti Karoly utca 5-7, Budapest, 1024, Hungary. TEL 36-1-345-6000, FAX 36-1-345-6699, http://www.ksh.hu.

658 016   HUN   ISSN 0231-0759
Z7164.O7
VALLALATSZERVEZESI ES IPARGAZDASAGI SZAKIRODALMI TAJEKOZTATO/INDUSTRIAL MANAGEMENT ABSTRACTS. Text in Hungarian. 1950. m. HUF 9,900.
Supersedes (in 1982): Muszaki Lapszemle. Uzemszervezes, Ipargazdasag - Technical Abstracts. Business Organization, Industrial Economics (0027-4941)
Indexed: Inspec, RASB.
Published by: Orszagos Muszaki Informacios Kozpont es Konyvtar/National Technical Information Centre and Library, Muzeum utca 17, PO Box 12, Budapest, 1428, Hungary. Ed. Ernone Huszar. Circ: 750. **Subscr. to:** Kultura, PO Box 149, Budapest 1389, Hungary.

382   VUT
VANUATU. STATISTICS OFFICE. ANNUAL SUMMARY OF OVERSEAS TRADE. Text in English, French. 1971. a. VUV 500, USD 5 (effective 1996). adv. **Document type:** Government.
Former titles: Vanuatu. Statistics Office. Overseas Trade (1013-6088); Vanuatu. National Planning and Statistics Office. Overseas Trade; Vanuatu. Bureau of Statistics. Overseas Trade
Published by: Statistics Office, PMB 19, Port Vila, Vanuatu. TEL 678-22110, FAX 678-24583. Ed. Jacob Isaiah. Adv. contact Tali Saurei. Circ: 400.

331.11   VUT
VANUATU. STATISTICS OFFICE. MANPOWER AND EMPLOYMENT SURVEYS. Text in English, French. 1973. irreg. USD 19. adv. stat. **Document type:** Government.
Former titles: Vanuatu. National Planning and Statistics Office. Manpower and Employment Survey. Final Results; (until 1984): Vanuatu. Bureau of Statistics. Manpower and Employment Survey. Final Results
Published by: Statistics Office, PMB 19, Port Vila, Vanuatu. TEL 678-22110, FAX 678-24583. Ed. Jacob Isaiah. Adv. contact Tali Saurei. Circ: 500.

332   VUT
VANUATU. STATISTICS OFFICE. MONETARY AND BANKING STATISTICS. Text in English, French. 1982. q. VUV 100, USD 10 (effective 1996). adv. **Document type:** Bulletin, Government. **Description:** Provides the latest statistics on major monetary indicators, money supply, foreign currency liquidity, bank assets, and bank loans.
Formerly: Vanuatu. National Planning and Statistics Office. Monetary and Banking Statistics
Published by: Statistics Office, PMB 19, Port Vila, Vanuatu. TEL 678-22110, FAX 678-24583. Ed. Jacob Isaiah. Adv. contact Tali Saurei. Circ: 300.

657   VUT
VANUATU. STATISTICS OFFICE. NATIONAL ACCOUNTS OF VANUATU. Text in Multiple languages. irreg., latest 1985-1989 ed. VUV 500, USD 5 (effective 1996). adv. **Document type:** Government. **Description:** Highlights the Vanuatu economy, including data on the gross domestic product and expenditure, national disposable income and its appropriation, household income and outlay account and more.
Published by: Statistics Office, PMB 19, Port Vila, Vanuatu. TEL 678-22110, FAX 678-24583. Ed. Jacob Isaiah. Adv. contact Tali Saurei. Circ: 300.

330   VUT
VANUATU. STATISTICS OFFICE. SECOND NATIONAL DEVELOPMENT PLAN. Text in English. every 5 yrs. (in 2 vols.). USD 40. adv. **Document type:** Government.
Published by: Statistics Office, PMB 19, Port Vila, Vanuatu. TEL 678-22110, FAX 678-24583. Ed. Jacob Isaiah. Adv. contact Tali Saurei.

330.9   VUT
VANUATU. STATISTICS OFFICE. STATISTICAL INDICATORS. Text in English, French. 1976. q. VUV 300, USD 13 (effective 1996). adv. charts; stat. **Document type:** Government. **Description:** Provides statistics on overseas trade, consumer prices, migration, tourism, monetary and banking, transport, energy consumption, construction and employment.
Former titles: Vanuatu. National Planning and Statistics Office. Statistical Indicators; Vanuatu. Bureau of Statistics. Statistical Indicators
Published by: Statistics Office, PMB 19, Port Vila, Vanuatu. TEL 678-22110, FAX 678-24583. Ed. Jacob Isaiah. Adv. contact Tali Saurei. Circ: 350.

330 318   VEN   ISSN 0798-1546
VENEZUELA. OFICINA CENTRAL DE ESTADISTICA E INFORMATICA. COYUNTURA ECONOMICA. Text in Spanish. 1975 (no.2). q. VEB 270. **Document type:** Government.
Former titles: Boletin de Indicadores de Coyuntura; Indicadores Socioeconomicos y de Coyuntura
Related titles: Diskette ed.
Indexed: PAIS.
Published by: Oficina Central de Estadistica e Informatica, Apdo. de Correos 4593, Carmeliatas, Caracas, DF 1010A, Venezuela. TEL 58-2-782-11-33, FAX 58-2-781-13-80, TELEX 21241. Circ: 1,000.

330   VEN   ISSN 0798-8761
VENEZUELA. OFICINA CENTRAL DE ESTADISTICA E INFORMATICA. ENCUESTA CUALITATIVA* . Text in Spanish. 1984. a. VEB 400. **Document type:** Government.
Published by: Oficina Central de Estadistica e Informatica, Apdo. de Correos 4593, Carmeliatas, Caracas, DF 1010A, Venezuela. TEL 58-2-782-11-33, FAX 58-2-781-13-80. Circ: (controlled).

658   CHE
VERBRAUCHSERHEBUNG. AUSGABEN UND EINNAHMEN DER PRIVATEN HAUSHALTE/ENQUETE SUR LA CONSOMMATION LES DEPENSES ET LES REVENUS DES MENAGES PRIVES. Text in German. 1987. quinquennial. CHF 10 per vol.. **Document type:** Government.
Formerly: Verbrauchserhebung. Ausgaben und Einnahmen
Related titles: French ed.
Published by: Bundesamt fuer Statistik, Espace de l'Europe 10, Neuchatel, 2010, Switzerland. TEL 41-32-7136011, FAX 41-32-7136012, information@bfs.admin.ch, http://www.admin.ch/bfs.

331   USA
VERMONT. DEPARTMENT OF EMPLOYMENT & TRAINING. LABOR MARKET BULLETIN. Text in English. q. **Document type:** Bulletin, Government.
Published by: Department of Employment & Training, PO Box 488, Montpelier, VT 05601-0488. TEL 802-828-4000. Ed. Susan Auld.

382   ISL   ISSN 1017-6365
HA1491
VERSLUNARSKYRSLUR/EXTERNAL TRADE. Text in Icelandic. 1914. a. USD 40 (effective 2001). back issues avail. **Document type:** Government. **Description:** Presents external trade statistics of Iceland.
Published by: Hagstofa Islands/Statistics Iceland, Borgartuni 12 A, Reykjavik, 150, Iceland. TEL 354-560-9800, FAX 354-562-3312, information@statice.is, hagstofa@hag.stjr.is, http://www.statice.is, http://www.statice.is/stat/e-mail.htm. Ed. Audur Svararsdottir.

▼ *new title*   ➤ *refereed*   * *unverified*   ♦ *full entry avail.*

331.11021 ISL ISSN 1024-0020
HF3651
VINNUMARKADUR/LABOR MARKET STATISTICS. Text in Icelandic. 1994. irreg. (irregular starting 1998). USD 20 (effective 2001). back issues avail.
Published by: Hagstofa Islands/Statistics Iceland, Borgartuni 12 A, Reykjavik, 150, Iceland. TEL 354-560-9800, FAX 354-562-3312, information@statice.is, http://www.statice.is, http://www.statice.is/e-mail.htm. Ed. Omar Hardason.

331.021 VIR ISSN 8756-1638
HD5744.3
VIRGIN ISLANDS (U.S.). DEPARTMENT OF LABOR. BUREAU OF LABOR STATISTICS. LABOR MARKET REVIEW. Key Title: Virgin Islands Labor Market Review. Text in English. 1978. m. **Document type:** Government. **Description:** Provides an update on labor market changes, on nonagricultural wage and slary employment and average hours and earnings for production workers in selected industries.
Published by: Department of Labor, Bureau of Labor Statistics, P O Box 3359, Charlotte Amalie, St Thomas, 00803, Virgin Isl., US. TEL 809-776-3700, FAX 809-774-5908. Circ: 900 (controlled).

310 USA ISSN 0081-475X
VIRGINIA STATISTICAL ABSTRACT (YEAR)∗. Text in English. 1966. a.
Related titles: Microfiche ed.: 1966 (from BHP).
Published by: University of Virginia, Center for Public Service, 918 Emmet St N Ste 300, Charlottesville, VA 22903-4832. TEL 804-924-4871, FAX 804-924-4538.

330.021 RUS
HA1431
VOPROSY STATISTIKI/STATISTICAL STUDIES. Text in Russian. 1949. m. USD 199 foreign (effective 2005). index. reprints avail. **Document type:** Journal, Government. **Description:** Reflects domestic and world practice of statistical services. Statistical and analytical materials highlighting social and economic economic situation, business activity in Russia, main indicators of CIS and foreign states.
Formerly (until 1993): Vestnik Statistiki (0320-8168)
Related titles: Online - full content ed.: RUR 2,124 (effective 2005) (from EVP).
Indexed: CDSP, PopulInd, RASB, RRTA, RefZh, WAE&RSA.
Published by: Gosudarstvennyi Komitet Rossiiskoi Federatsii po Statistike/Federal State Statistics Office, ul Myasnitskaya 39, Moscow, 107450, Russian Federation. TEL 7-095-2074902, FAX 7-095-2074087, stat@gks.ru, http://www.gks.ru. Circ: 35,000. **Dist. by:** East View Information Services, 3020 Harbor Ln. N., Minneapolis, MN 55447. TEL 800-477-1005, FAX 800-800-3839, eastview@eastview.com, http://www.eastview.com.

336.2 USA
WASHINGTON (STATE). DEPARTMENT OF REVENUE. RESEARCH DIVISION. PROPERTY TAX STATISTICS. Text in English. 1970. a. stat. 70 p./no.; **Document type:** Government.
Former titles: Washington (State). Department of Revenue. Research Section. Property Tax Levy and Collection Statistics; Washington (State). Department of Revenue. Research and Information Division. Property Tax Levy and Collection Statistics.
Published by: Department of Revenue, Research Division, PO Box 47459, Olympia, WA 98504-7459. TEL 360-570-6070, FAX 360-664-0972, http://dor.wa.gov/index.asp?/menu/stats.htm.

336.2 USA
WASHINGTON (STATE). DEPARTMENT OF REVENUE. RESEARCH DIVISION. TAX STATISTICS. Text in English. 1973. a. 58 p./no.; **Document type:** Government.
Indexed: SRI.
Published by: Department of Revenue, Research Division, PO Box 47459, Olympia, WA 98504-7459. TEL 360-570-6070, FAX 360-664-0972, http://dor.wa.gov/index.asp?/menu/stats.htm. Circ: 1,000.

331.133021 USA
WASHINGTON (STATE). EMPLOYMENT SECURITY DEPARTMENT. AFFIRMATIVE ACTION INFORMATION. Text in English. biennial. USD 1 per region. charts; stat. **Document type:** Government. **Description:** Provides statistics and other information regarding the hiring of minority applicants to implement affirmative action programs.
Related titles: Regional ed(s).: Affirmative Action Information. Pasco and Franklin Counties. ISSN 0742-2970; Affirmative Action Information. Yakima County. ISSN 0742-2962.
Published by: Employment Security Department, PO Box 9046, Olympia, WA 98507-9046.

WASHINGTON (STATE). EMPLOYMENT SECURITY DEPARTMENT. MONTHLY JOB SERVICE STATISTICS. see OCCUPATIONS AND CAREERS—Abstracting, Bibliographies, Statistics

WASHINGTON (STATE). EMPLOYMENT SECURITY DEPARTMENT. OCCUPATIONAL PROFILES. see OCCUPATIONS AND CAREERS—Abstracting, Bibliographies, Statistics

WASHINGTON (STATE). EMPLOYMENT SECURITY DEPARTMENT. WEEKLY INSURED UNEMPLOYMENT REPORT. see INSURANCE—Abstracting, Bibliographies, Statistics

331.11 USA
WASHINGTON LABOR MARKET. Text in English. 1942. m. free. charts. back issues avail. **Document type:** Newsletter, Government. **Description:** Provides a broad picture of economic conditions in Washington State and individual counties and regions. Contains nonagricultural wage and salary employment data by industry, employment and unemployment data by state and county, figures on hours worked and wages earned among nonsupervisory workers in various nonmanufacturing industries, and economic information such as consumer price index and per capita income.
Former titles (until 1974): Washington (State). Employment Security Department. Labor Area Summary Reports; Washington (State) Employment Security Department. Local Labor Market Developments
Related titles: Microfiche ed.: (from CIS).
Indexed: SRI.
Published by: Employment Security Department, Labor Market and Economic Analysis Branch, PO Box 9046, Olympia, WA 98507-9046. TEL 360-438-4820, FAX 360-438-4846. Circ: 1,700.

338 GBR ISSN 0262-8309
WELSH ECONOMIC TRENDS. Text in English. 1974. a. GBP 10 (effective 2000). **Document type:** Government. **Description:** Contains specifics on industrial activity, earnings, working population, capital and public expenditure, employment, unemployment and regional income.
—CCC.
Published by: (Great Britain. Publication Unit), National Assembly of Wales, Statistical Directorate, Cathays Park, Cardiff, CF10 3NQ, United Kingdom. TEL 44-2920-825054, FAX 44-2920-825350, stats.pubs@wales.gsi.gov.uk.

331.021 NLD ISSN 1386-7903
WERKGELEGENHEID IN DE NEDERLANDSE ZEEHAVENS∗. Text in Dutch. 1989-1993; resumed 1994. a. free. **Document type:** Government. **Description:** Provides statistical data relating to employment in Dutch seaports, covering the period from 1985 to the present.
Formerly (until 1990): Werkgelegenheidsstatistiek Nederlandse Zeehavens
Published by: Nationale Havenraad, Uitgeverij Noordhoek, Postbus 85189, Utrecht, 3508 AD, Netherlands. TEL 31-70-3517615, FAX 31-70-3517600.

336 310 IND
WEST BENGAL. ANNUAL FINANCIAL STATEMENT (BUDGET). Text in English. a. **Document type:** Government.
Published by: Government Press, Publication Branch, 38 Gopal Nagar Rd., Alipore, Kolkata, West Bengal 700 027, India.

315.4 330 IND ISSN 0511-5493
WEST BENGAL. BUREAU OF APPLIED ECONOMICS AND STATISTICS. STATISTICAL HANDBOOK. Text in English. 1960. a., latest 1999. INR 60 domestic (effective 2001); price varies. bk.rev. charts; illus.; maps; stat. 300 p./no.; back issues avail. **Document type:** Yearbook, Government.
Published by: Bureau of Applied Economics and Statistics, 1 Kiron Sankar Roy Rd., Kolkata, West Bengal 700 001, India. TEL 033-248-3032, FAX 033-248-3032, appecon@wl.nic.in. Circ: 200 (paid); 150 (controlled).

WHAT'S NEW IN ADVERTISING AND MARKETING. see ADVERTISING AND PUBLIC RELATIONS—Abstracting, Bibliographies, Statistics

339 IRN
WHOLESALE PRICE INDEX IN IRAN. Text in Persian, Modern. m.
Published by: (Iran. Economic Statistics Department), Bank Markazi Jomhouri Islami Iran/Central Bank of the Islamic Republic of Iran, P O Box 11365-8531, Tehran, Iran. FAX 982-21-390323.

330.9 310 AUT ISSN 1028-074X
WIEN IN ZAHLEN; Ausgabe (Year). Text in German, English, French. 1987. a. free. stat. back issues avail. **Document type:** Yearbook, Government. **Description:** Presents a brief overview of population, economy, education, political structure of Vienna with statistical tables.
Related titles: Diskette ed.; E-mail ed.; Fax ed.; Online - full text ed.; English ed.: Vienna in Figures. ISSN 1028-0723; French ed.: Vienne en Chiffres. ISSN 1028-0731; Italian ed.: Vienna in Cifre. ISSN 1028-0715; Czech ed.: Viden v Cislech. ISSN 1028-0707; Hungarian ed.: Becs Szamokbau. ISSN 1028-0693.
Published by: Statistisches Amt der Stadt Wien, Volksgartenstrasse 3, Vienna, 1010, Austria. TEL 43-1-4000-88629, FAX 43-1-4000-7166, post@m66.magwien.gv.at, http://www.statistik.wien.at. Ed. Peter Pokay. Circ: 10,000.

016.33 USA ISSN 1057-6533
WILSON BUSINESS ABSTRACTS. Text in English. 1991. w. **Document type:** Abstract/Index. **Description:** Contains article abstracts and indexing for business periodicals.
Related titles: CD-ROM ed.: (from H.W. Wilson, SilverPlatter Information, Inc.); ♦ Online - full text ed.: Wilson Business Full Text. ISSN 1529-9945.
Published by: H.W. Wilson Co., 950 University Ave, Bronx, NY 10452-4224. TEL 718-588-8400, 800-367-6770, FAX 718-590-1617, 800-590-1617, custserv@hwwilson.com, http://www.hwwilson.com/Databases/business.htm.

016.33 USA ISSN 1529-9945
WILSON BUSINESS FULL TEXT. Text in English. 2000. d. USD 3,870 in US & Canada (effective 2006). **Document type:** Abstract/Index. **Description:** Contains article abstracts and full-text articles relating to business.
Media: Online - full text. **Related titles:** CD-ROM ed.: ISSN 1092-8685 (from H.W. Wilson, SilverPlatter Information, Inc.); ♦ Print ed.: Wilson Business Abstracts. ISSN 1057-6533.
Published by: H.W. Wilson Co., 950 University Ave, Bronx, NY 10452-4224. TEL 718-588-8400, 800-367-6770, FAX 718-590-1617, 800-590-1617, custserv@hwwilson.com, http://www.hwwilson.com/Databases/business.htm.

016.658 USA ISSN 0149-8703
WORK IN AMERICA INSTITUTE: HIGHLIGHTS OF THE LITERATURE. Text in English. 1978. 6/yr. USD 180.
Related titles: Microform ed.; ♦ Series of: Work in America Institute Studies in Productivity. ISSN 0149-869X.
—CCC.
Published by: Work in America Institute, Inc., 700 White Plains Rd, Scarsdale, NY 10583. TEL 914-472-9600. Ed. Jerome M Rosow.

016.658 USA ISSN 0149-869X
WORK IN AMERICA INSTITUTE STUDIES IN PRODUCTIVITY. Text in English. 1978. irreg.
Related titles: ♦ Series: Work in America Institute: Highlights of the Literature. ISSN 0149-8703.
Published by: Work in America Institute, Inc., 700 White Plains Rd, Scarsdale, NY 10583. TEL 914-472-9600, FAX 914-472-9606.

338.9 USA ISSN 0258-3143
HC60
WORLD BANK RESEARCH PROGRAM. Text in English. 1974. a. **Document type:** Abstract/Index.
Former titles (until 1986): World Bank. Abstracts of Current Studies (0253-9535); (until 1981): World Bank Research Program (1010-3023)
—CCC.
Published by: World Bank Group, PO Box 960, Herndon, VA 20172-0960. TEL 703-661-1580, FAX 703-661-1501, books@worldbank.org.

WORLD BANKING ABSTRACTS; the international journal of the financial services industry. see BUSINESS AND ECONOMICS—Banking And Finance

WORLD COUNCIL OF CREDIT UNIONS. ANNUAL AND STATISTICAL REPORT. see BUSINESS AND ECONOMICS—Banking And Finance

016.338 GBR
WORLD DATABASE OF BUSINESS INFORMATION SOURCES. Variant title: World Database of Business Information Sources on the Internet. Text in English. 1996. m. GBP 3,900, USD 5,985, EUR 5,985 (effective 2003). **Document type:** Trade. **Description:** Provides information on approximately 35,000 sources of business information. Includes details on trade associations, business libraries, and publications.
Media: Online - full text. **Related titles:** CD-ROM ed.
Published by: Euromonitor, 60-61 Britton St, London, EC1 5UX, United Kingdom. TEL 44-20-7251-8024, FAX 44-20-7608-3149, info@euromonitor.com, http://www.euromonitor.com.

382.029 GBR
WORLD DIRECTORY OF NON-OFFICIAL STATISTICAL SOURCES. Text in English. 1993. irreg. latest 2002, May. GBP 395, EUR 650, USD 650 per issue (effective 2004). **Document type:** Directory, Trade. **Description:** Contains descriptions of more than 3,000 important business periodicals, trade association publications, economic research journals, statistical database newsletters, and other current reference sources spanning a broad range of products. Entries provide complete bibliographical details.
Formed by the merger of (1990-1993): International Directory of Non-Official Statistics Sources (0959-5139); (1988-1993): European Directory of Non-Official Statistical Sources (0953-0258)
Published by: Euromonitor, 60-61 Britton St, London, EC1 5UX, United Kingdom. TEL 44-20-7251-8024, FAX 44-20-7608-3149, info@euromonitor.com, http://www.euromonitor.com/World_Directory_of_Non-Official_Statistical_Sources. R&P T J Remmetter.

330 GBR
WORLD ECONOMIC FACTBOOK. Text in English. 1993. a., latest 2002/2003. GBP 325 per vol. domestic; EUR 530 per vol. in Europe; USD 530 per vol. elsewhere (effective Oct. 2002). stat. **Document type:** *Trade.* **Description:** Supplies demographic, economic, and political reference data on 205 countries worldwide.
Published by: Euromonitor, 87-88 Turnmill St, London, EC1M 5QU, United Kingdom. info@euromonitor.com, http://www.euromonitor.com. **Dist. by:** Current Pacific Ltd., PO Box 36-536, Northcote, Auckland, New Zealand. TEL 64-9-480-1388, FAX 64-9-480-1387, info@cplnz.com, http://www.cplnz.com.

330 USA ISSN 1078-6783
HD2757.15
WORLD MARKET SHARE REPORTER. Text in English. 1996. biennial, latest 2001, 5th ed. USD 350 (effective 2004).
Published by: Gale Group (Subsidiary of: Thomson Corporation), 27500 Drake Rd, Farmington Hills, MI 48331-3535. TEL 248-699-8061, 800-877-4253, FAX 248-699-4253, galeord@gale.com, http://www.gale.com. Eds. Marlita A Reddy, Robert Lazich.

382 USA ISSN 0512-3739
HF53
WORLD TRADE ANNUAL. Text in English. 1963. a. price varies. reprints avail. **Document type:** *Directory.* **Description:** Provides complete statistical data on world trade.
Published by: (United Nations Statistical Office), Walker & Co., 435 Hudson St, New York, NY 10014-3941. TEL 212-727-8300, FAX 212-727-0984. Ed. United Nations.

382 USA ISSN 0512-3747
WORLD TRADE ANNUAL SUPPLEMENT. Text in English. 1964. a. price varies. **Document type:** *Directory.* **Description:** Provides comprehensive statistical data on world trade.
Published by: (United Nations Statistical Office), Walker & Co., 435 Hudson St, New York, NY 10014-3941. TEL 212-727-8300, FAX 212-727-0984. Ed. United Nations.

331 310 CHE ISSN 0084-3857
HD4826
YEAR BOOK OF LABOUR STATISTICS/ANNUAIRE DES STATISTIQUES DU TRAVAIL/ANUARIO DE ESTADISTICAS DEL TRABAJO. Text in English, French, Spanish. 1935. a. CHF 210, USD 168. stat. reprints avail. **Document type:** *Bulletin.* **Description:** Contains essential statistical information for following the evolution of labor and of living and working conditions throughout the world.
Related titles: Microfiche ed.: (from ILO); ♦ Supplement to: Sources and Methods. Labour Statistics. ISSN 1014-9856.
Indexed: IIS, RASB.
—BLDSC (9414.300000). **CCC.**
Published by: (International Labour Office), I L O Publications, PO Box 6, Geneva 22, 1211, Switzerland. TEL 41-22-799-6111, FAX 41-22-798-6358. Circ: 5,600. **Dist. in US by:** I L O Publications Center, 9 Jay Gould Court, Ste. CT, PO Box 753, Waldorf, MD 20604. TEL 301-638-3152, FAX 301-843-0159, ilopubs@tasco1.com.

382 387 ISR ISSN 0084-3830
YEARBOOK OF ISRAEL PORTS STATISTICS/SHENATON STATISTI: LE NEMLEI ISRAEL. Text in English, Hebrew. 1963. a.
Published by: Israel Ports Authority, P O Box 20121, Tel-aviv, Israel.

382 316 ZMB ISSN 0084-4489
HF3903
ZAMBIA. CENTRAL STATISTICAL OFFICE. ANNUAL STATEMENT OF EXTERNAL TRADE. Text in English. 1964. a. (in 2 vols.). USD 5. **Document type:** *Government.*
Published by: Central Statistical Office, PO Box 31908, Lusaka, Zambia. TEL 260-1-211231.

382.1 336 ZMB
ZAMBIA. CENTRAL STATISTICAL OFFICE. BALANCE OF PAYMENTS STATISTICS. Text in English. a. USD 3. **Document type:** *Government.*
Published by: Central Statistical Office, PO Box 31908, Lusaka, Zambia. TEL 260-1-211231.

658 ZMB
ZAMBIA. CENTRAL STATISTICAL OFFICE. CONSUMER PRICE STATISTICS. Text in English. 1980. q. USD 4. **Document type:** *Government.*
Published by: Central Statistical Office, PO Box 31908, Lusaka, Zambia. TEL 260-1-211231.

316 331 ZMB ISSN 0084-4500
ZAMBIA. CENTRAL STATISTICAL OFFICE. EMPLOYMENT AND EARNINGS. Text in English. 1969. irreg., latest 1980. ZMK 3. **Document type:** *Government.*
Published by: Central Statistical Office, PO Box 31908, Lusaka, Zambia. TEL 260-1-211231.

316 650 ZMB ISSN 0084-4519
ZAMBIA. CENTRAL STATISTICAL OFFICE. FINANCIAL STATISTICS OF PUBLIC CORPORATIONS. Text in English. 1965. a. USD 2.50. **Document type:** *Government.*
Published by: Central Statistical Office, PO Box 31908, Lusaka, Zambia. TEL 260-1-211231.

330 ZMB
ZAMBIA. CENTRAL STATISTICAL OFFICE. INDUSTRY MONOGRAPHS. Text in English. irreg. ZMK 4. **Document type:** *Monographic series, Government.*
Published by: Central Statistical Office, PO Box 31908, Lusaka, Zambia. TEL 260-1-211231.

331.11 ZMB
ZAMBIA. CENTRAL STATISTICAL OFFICE. MANPOWER SURVEY. Text in English. 1975. a. USD 3. **Document type:** *Government.*
Published by: Central Statistical Office, PO Box 31908, Lusaka, Zambia. TEL 260-1-211231.

330 CHN
ZHONGGUO GONGYE JINGJI TONGJI NIANJIAN/STATISTICAL YEARBOOK OF CHINA'S INDUSTRIAL ECONOMY. Text in Chinese. 1998 (Nov.). a. CNY 63 per issue (effective 2003). stat. **Document type:** *Yearbook, Government.*
—BLDSC (9512.734230).
Published by: Zhonghua Renmin Gongheguo Guojia Tongjiju/National Bureau of Statistics of China, Xicheng-qu, Yuetan Nan Jie, Beijing, 100826, China. FAX 86-10-68580964, info@stats.gov.cn, http://www.stats.gov.cn/.

332 315 TWN ISSN 1017-9593
ZHONGHUA MINGUO TAIWAN DIQU. JINRONG TONGJI YUEBAO/FINANCIAL STATISTICS MONTHLY, TAIWAN DISTRICT, REPUBLIC OF CHINA. Text in Chinese, English. 1951. m. USD 40.
Formerly: Taiwan Financial Statistics Monthly (0496-7046)
Published by: Central Bank of China, 2 Roosevelt Rd, Sec 1, Taipei, 107, Taiwan. TEL 886-2-23936161. Circ: 2,250.

330 HKG
ZHUHAI TONGJI NIANJIAN (YEAR)/ZHUHAI STATISTICAL YEARBOOK. Text in Chinese. 1992. a. HKD 220, USD 50.
Published by: Economic Information & Agency, 342 Hennessy Rd 10th Fl, 10 th Fl, Wanchai, Hong Kong. TEL 852-573-8217, FAX 852-838-8304.

338 330 ZWE
ZIMBABWE. CENTRAL STATISTICAL OFFICE. CENSUS OF PRODUCTION. Text in English. 1962. a. ZWD 188.50 in Africa; ZWD 245.20 in Europe; ZWD 292.50 elsewhere. **Document type:** *Government.*
Published by: Central Statistical Office, Causeway, PO Box 8063, Harare, Zimbabwe. TEL 263-4-706681, FAX 263-4-728529. Circ: 220.

339.021 ZWE
ZIMBABWE. CENTRAL STATISTICAL OFFICE. FACTS AND FIGURES. Text in English. a. ZWD 39.50 in Africa; ZWD 50 in Europe; ZWD 61.50 elsewhere (effective 2000). **Document type:** *Government.*
Published by: Central Statistical Office, Causeway, PO Box 8063, Harare, Zimbabwe. TEL 263-4-706681, FAX 263-4-728529.

332 ZWE
ZIMBABWE. CENTRAL STATISTICAL OFFICE. FINANCIAL STATISTICS REPORT. Text in English. a. ZWD 185.80 in Africa; ZWD 245.20 in Europe; ZWD 294.70 elsewhere (effective 2000). **Document type:** *Government.*
Published by: Central Statistical Office, Causeway, PO Box 8063, Harare, Zimbabwe. TEL 263-4-706681, FAX 263-4-728529.

339.021 ZWE
ZIMBABWE. CENTRAL STATISTICAL OFFICE. NATIONAL ACCOUNTS. Text in English. a. ZWD 248 in Africa; ZWD 315.30 in Europe; ZWD 388.20 elsewhere (effective 2000). **Document type:** *Government.*
Published by: Central Statistical Office, Causeway, PO Box 8063, Harare, Zimbabwe. TEL 263-4-706681, FAX 263-4-728529.

339.021 ZWE
ZIMBABWE. CENTRAL STATISTICAL OFFICE. STATISTICAL YEARBOOK. Text in English. a. ZWD 480.10 in Africa; ZWD 630.60 in Europe; ZWD 736.90 elsewhere (effective 2000). **Document type:** *Government.*
Published by: Central Statistical Office, Causeway, PO Box 8063, Harare, Zimbabwe. TEL 263-4-706681, FAX 263-4-728529.

BUSINESS AND ECONOMICS—Accounting

657 USA
A A C P A NEWSLETTER✶. Text in English. bi-m. **Document type:** *Newsletter.* **Description:** Covers activities and events. Includes membership list.
Published by: Asian American Certified Public Accountants, 225 Bush St, Ste 780, San Francisco, CA 94104. TEL 415-393-4300.

A A S B ACCOUNTING STANDARDS. (Australian Accounting Standards Board) see *LAW—Corporate Law*

657 GBR
A C C A FOCUS - AUSTRALIA NEWSLETTER. Text in English. s-a. **Document type:** *Trade.*
Related titles: Online - full text ed.
—ingenta.
Published by: Association of Chartered Certified Accountants, 64 Finnieston Square, Glasgow, G3 8DT, United Kingdom. TEL 44-171-396-5734, FAX 44-171-396-5959, http://www.accaglobal.com/publications/australia/.

657 GBR
A C C A FOCUS - CANADA NEWSLETTER. Text in English. 2000. q. **Document type:** *Trade.*
Related titles: Online - full text ed.
—ingenta.
Published by: Association of Chartered Certified Accountants, 64 Finnieston Square, Glasgow, G3 8DT, United Kingdom. TEL 44-171-396-5734, FAX 44-171-396-5959, http://www.accaglobal.com/publications/canada/.

657 GBR
A C C A FOCUS - MALAYSIA NEWSLETTER. Text in English. 2000. s-a. **Document type:** *Trade.*
Related titles: Online - full text ed.
—ingenta.
Published by: Association of Chartered Certified Accountants, 64 Finnieston Square, Glasgow, G3 8DT, United Kingdom. TEL 44-171-396-5734, FAX 44-171-396-5959, http://www.accaglobal.com/publications/malaysia/.

657 GBR
A C C A FOCUS - PAKISTAN NEWSLETTER. Text in English. 2002. q.
Related titles: Online - full text ed.
—ingenta.
Published by: Association of Chartered Certified Accountants, 64 Finnieston Square, Glasgow, G3 8DT, United Kingdom. TEL 44-171-396-5734, FAX 44-171-396-5959, http://www.accaglobal.com/publications/pakistan/.

657 GBR
A C C A FOCUS - SINGAPORE NEWSLETTER. Text in English. 2000. q. **Document type:** *Trade.*
Related titles: Online - full text ed.
—ingenta.
Published by: Association of Chartered Certified Accountants, 64 Finnieston Square, Glasgow, G3 8DT, United Kingdom. TEL 44-171-396-5734, FAX 44-171-396-5959, http://www.accaglobal.com/publications/singapore/.

657 GBR
A C C A FOCUS - U S A NEWSLETTER. Text in English. 2002. q. **Document type:** *Trade.*
Related titles: Online - full text ed.
—ingenta.
Published by: Association of Chartered Certified Accountants, 64 Finnieston Square, Glasgow, G3 8DT, United Kingdom. TEL 44-171-396-5734, FAX 44-171-396-5959, http://www.accaglobal.com/publications/usa/.

657 GBR
A C C A RESEARCH REPORT. (Association of Chartered Certified Accountants) Text in English. irreg. **Document type:** *Trade.*
Related titles: Online - full text ed.
—ingenta.
Published by: Association of Chartered Certified Accountants, 64 Finnieston Square, Glasgow, G3 8DT, United Kingdom. TEL 44-20-7396-5800, FAX 44-171-396-5959, http://www.accaglobal.com/publications/research_reports/.

657 GBR
A C C A RESEARCH T & R. OCCASIONAL RESEARCH PAPER. Text in English. irreg.
Formerly (until no.15): Chartered Association of Certified Accountants. Technical and Research Committee. Occasional Research Paper
Published by: Association of Chartered Certified Accountants, 64 Finnieston Square, Glasgow, G3 8DT, United Kingdom. TEL 44-171-396-59806, mary.oliver@acca.co.uk.

150 332 AUS ISSN 0728-4969
A F M EXPLANATORY SERIES (NO.). Text in English. irreg., latest vol.2. **Document type:** *Academic/Scholarly.*
Published by: (University Of New England, Department of Accounting and Financial Management), University of New England, Armidale, NSW 2351, Australia. TEL 61-67-732201, FAX 61-67-711778. R&P J J Staunton TEL 61-67-733276.

657 AUS ISSN 0155-1221
A F M EXPLORATORY SERIES. Text in English. 1975. irreg., latest vol.4. **Document type:** *Academic/Scholarly.*
Published by: (University Of New England, Department of Accounting and Financial Management), University of New England, Armidale, NSW 2351, Australia. TEL 61-67-733333, FAX 61-67-733122. R&P J J Staunton TEL 61-67-733276. Circ: 500.

B

657 USA ISSN 1058-9198
HF5601
A I C P A VEST-POCKET ACCOUNTING AND AUDITING REFERENCE. Text in English. 1991. a. **Document type:** *Directory.*
Indexed: ATI.
Published by: American Institute of Certified Public Accountants, Harborside Financial Ctr., 201 Plaza Three, 3rd Fl, Jersey City, NJ 07311-9801. TEL 888-777-7077, FAX 800-302-5766, journal@aicpa.org, http://www.aicpa.org.

657 USA ISSN 1047-5079
THE A I C P A'S UNIFORM C P A EXAM. (American Institute of Certified Public Accountants) Text in English. 1988. a.
—**CCC.**
Published by: American Institute of Certified Public Accountants, Harborside Financial Ctr., 201 Plaza Three, 3rd Fl, Jersey City, NJ 07311-9801. TEL 888-777-7077, FAX 800-302-5766, journal@aicpa.org, http://www.aicpa.org.

657 USA ISSN 0883-2102
A P I ACCOUNT. Text in English. 1974. q. USD 40 membership (effective 2001). adv. **Document type:** *Newsletter, Consumer.* **Description:** Includes reports on national and affiliate volunteer activities, and on issues relating to volunteer accounting.
Related titles: Online - full text ed.: (from ProQuest Information & Learning).
Indexed: ATI.
Published by: Accountants for the Public Interest, University of Baltimore, Thummel Business Center Rm 519, 1420 N Charles St., Baltimore, MD 21201-5720. TEL 410-837-6533, FAX 410-837-6532. Ed. T L Woods. Circ: 3,500.

657 USA
A P I AFFILIATE NEWSBRIEF. Text in English. 3/yr. **Document type:** *Bulletin.*
Published by: Accountants for the Public Interest, University of Baltimore, Thummel Business Center Rm 519, 1420 N Charles St., Baltimore, MD 21201-5720. TEL 410-837-6533, FAX 410-837-6532, http://www.accountingnet.com. Ed. T L Woods.

657 USA
A W S C P A NEWSLETTER. Text in English. q. membership. **Document type:** *Newsletter.*
Published by: American Women's Society of Certified Public Accountants, 136 S Keowee St, Dayton, OH 45402. TEL 800-297-2721, info@awscpa.org, http://www.awscpa.org. Ed. Kim Santaci. Circ: 5,000 (controlled).

657 USA
A W T A O ANNUAL REPORT. Text in English. a. **Document type:** *Corporate.*
Published by: Association of Water Transportation Accounting Officers, PO BOX 53, BOWLING GREEN STA, New York, NY 10004. TEL 212-264-1384.

657 USA
A W T A O BULLETIN. Text in English. bi-m. **Document type:** *Bulletin.*
Published by: Association of Water Transportation Accounting Officers, PO BOX 53, BOWLING GREEN STA, New York, NY 10004. TEL 212-264-1384.

657 AUS ISSN 0001-3072
HF5601 CODEN: ABACAF
➤ **ABACUS;** a journal of accounting, finance and business studies. Text in English. 1964. 3/yr. AUD 112 combined subscription in Australia & New Zealand to individuals print & online eds.; EUR 120 combined subscription in Europe to individuals print & online eds.; GBP 80 combined subscription rest of world to individuals print & online eds.; USD 114 combined subscription to individuals in the Americas & the Caribbean for print & online eds.; AUD 148 combined subscription in Australia & New Zealand to institutions print & online eds.; GBP 247 combined subscription in Europe to institutions print & online eds.; USD 393 combined subscription to institutions in the Americas & the Caribbean for print & online eds.; GBP 274 combined subscription rest of world to institutions print & online eds. (effective 2006). adv. bk.rev. illus. cum.index every 4 yrs. back issues avail.; reprint service avail. from PQC. **Document type:** *Journal, Academic/Scholarly.* **Description:** Provides a vehicle for the expression of independent and critical thought on matters of current academic and professional interest in accounting, finance and business.
Related titles: Microfilm ed.; Online - full text ed.: ISSN 1467-6281. AUD 140 in Australia & New Zealand to institutions; GBP 235 in Europe to institutions; USD 373 in the Americas to institutions & the Caribbean; GBP 260 rest of world to institutions (effective 2006) (from Blackwell Synergy, EBSCO Publishing, Gale Group, IngentaConnect, O C L C Online Computer Library Center, Inc., Swets Information Services).
Indexed: AAR, ABIn, ADPA, ATI, AusPAIS, BPIA, BusI, CPM, CurCont, Emerald, IBSS, M&MA, ManagCont, PAIS, SSCI, WBA.
—BLDSC (0537.724000), IE, Infotrieve, ingenta. **CCC.**
Published by: (Accounting and Finance Foundation AUT), Blackwell Publishing Asia (Subsidiary of: Blackwell Publishing Ltd.), 550 Swanston St, Carlton South, VIC 3053, Australia. TEL 61-383591011, FAX 61-383591120, subs@blackwellpublishingasia.com, http://www.blackwellpublishing.com/journals/ABACUS. Ed. G W Dean. Circ: 1,200.

657.6 332.1 GBR
ABERDEEN PAPERS IN ACCOUNTANCY AND FINANCE. Text in English. 1991. irreg. GBP 5. **Document type:** *Monographic series.* **Description:** Stimulates debate on financial and accounting issues.
Formerly: Aberdeen Papers in Accountancy, Finance and Management (0962-4627)
Published by: University of Aberdeen, Department of Accountancy, Edward Wright Bldg, Aberdeen, University Of Aberdeen, Dunbar St, Aberdeen, AB24 3QY, United Kingdom. TEL 44-1224-272205, FAX 44-1224-272214. Ed., R&P Patricia Fraser. Circ: 200 (controlled). **Co-sponsor:** University of Aberdeen, Department of Economics.

657 DEU ISSN 0948-0633
ABRECHNUNG AKTUELL. Text in German. 1988. m. EUR 150 (effective 2004). **Document type:** *Journal, Trade.*
Published by: (Institut fuer Wirtschaftspublizistik), Vogel Verlag und Druck GmbH & Co. KG, Max-Planck-Str 7-9, Wuerzburg, 97064, Germany. TEL 49-931-4180, FAX 49-931-4182100, marliese_bernhardt@vogel-medien.de, http://www.vogel-medien.de. **Subscr. to:** DataM-Services GmbH, Fichtestr 9, Wuerzburg 97074, Germany. TEL 49-931-417001, FAX 49-931-4170499, swestenberger@datam-services.de, http://www.datam-services.de.

657 USA ISSN 1096-3685
➤ **ACADEMY OF ACCOUNTING AND FINANCIAL STUDIES JOURNAL.** Text in English. 1997. s-a. **Document type:** *Journal, Academic/Scholarly.*
Related titles: Online - full text ed.: ISSN 1528-2635.
Published by: (Academy of Accounting Studies), Allied Academies, 145 Travis Rd., P. O. Box 2689, Cullowhee, NC 28723. http://www.alliedacademies.org/accounting/index.html. Ed. Janet Dye.

657 NLD ISSN 0924-4182
ACCOUNT. Text in Dutch. 1988. 8/yr. adv. illus. **Document type:** *Journal, Trade.*
Published by: Reed Business Information bv (Subsidiary of: Reed Business), Van de Sande, Bakhuyzenstraat 4, Amsterdam, 1061 AG, Netherlands. TEL 31-20-515-9222, FAX 31-20-515-9990, info@reedbusiness.nl, http://www.reedbusiness.nl. Circ: 52,000.

657 GBR ISSN 1742-7703
▼ **ACCOUNTABILITY FORUM;** a quarterly journal on social and ethical accounting, auditing and reporting. Text in English. 2004 (Mar.). q. GBP 52.50, USD 87.50 to individuals; GBP 105, USD 175 to institutions (effective 2004). **Description:** Provides information on the practice and theory of social and ethical accounting, auditing and reporting worldwide. Essential resource for businesses, NGOs, government and academia to learn about the most recent and important developments in accountability for sustainable development.
Published by: Greenleaf Publishing, Aizlewood Business Centre, Aizlewoods Mill, Nursery St, Sheffield, S3 8GG, United Kingdom. TEL 44-144-2823475, FAX 44-144-2823476, info@greenleaf-publishing.com, http://www.greenleaf-publishing.com/af/afframe.htm.

657 GBR ISSN 0001-4664
HF5601 CODEN: ACTYAD
ACCOUNTANCY. Text in English. 1889. m. USD 100 in United States; GBP 5.10 newsstand/cover domestic; USD 10 newsstand/cover foreign (effective 2000). adv. bk.rev. charts; illus. index. reprints avail. **Document type:** *Trade.* **Description:** Covers both the technical and business aspects of the profession, along with international issues. UK edition concentrates on UK developments. International edition includes both UK and international events.
Related titles: CD-ROM ed.: GBP 60; GBP 63 foreign (effective 1999); Microform ed.: (from PQC); Online - full text ed.: (from EBSCO Publishing, Factiva, Northern Light Technology, Inc., O C L C Online Computer Library Center, Inc., ProQuest Information & Learning).
Indexed: AAR, ABIn, ADPA, ASEANManA, ATI, BPI, BPIA, BusI, CPM, ELJI, Emerald, ExcerpMed, HECAB, Inspec, LJI, M&MA, ManagCont, PROMT, PSI, RICS, SCIMP, T&II, WBA.
—BLDSC (0573.540000), AskIEEE, IE, ingenta. **CCC.**
Published by: Institute of Chartered Accountants in England and Wales, Chartered Accountants' Hall, PO Box 433, London, EC2P 2BJ, United Kingdom. TEL 44-20-78333291, FAX 44-20-78332085, magazine_customerservices@croner.co.uk, http://www.accountancymagazine.com/, http://www.accountancymag.co.uk. Ed. Brian Singleton Green. Adv. contact Karen Glaseby. Circ: 70,000. **Subscr. to:** 40 Bernard St, London WC1N 1LD, United Kingdom. **Dist. by:** Seymour Distribution Ltd, 86 Newman St, London W1T 3EX, United Kingdom. enquiries@seymour.co.uk, http://www.seymour.co.uk.; **Dist. outside the UK by:** BTB Mailflight Ltd., Wolseley Rd, Woburn Rd Industrial Estate, Kempston, Beds MK42 7HA, United Kingdom.

657 GBR ISSN 0001-4672
ACCOUNTANCY AGE. Text in English. 1969. w. GBP 100; GBP 2 newsstand/cover (effective 1999). adv. bk.rev. charts; illus.; stat. **Document type:** *Newspaper, Trade.* **Description:** Keeps members of the main accountancy institutes informed of all the important developments that could affect them in their professional lives.
Related titles: Microform ed.: (from PQC); Online - full text ed.: (from Gale Group, LexisNexis).
Indexed: ADPA, ATI, Emerald.
—BLDSC (0573.545000). **CCC.**
Published by: V N U Business Publications Ltd., VNU House, 32-34 Broadwick St, London, W1A 2HG, United Kingdom. TEL 44-20-7316-9000, FAX 44-20-7316-9160, http://www.accountancyage.vnu.co.uk. Ed. Douglas Broom. Pub. Melanie Williams. Adv. contact Chris Willis. Circ: 77,381 (controlled).

657 EGY ISSN 0001-4680
ACCOUNTANCY, BUSINESS & INSURANCE REVIEW. Text in Arabic, English, French. 1961. s-a. bk.rev. charts. **Document type:** *Trade.*
Published by: University of Cairo, Faculty of Commerce, Cairo, Egypt. Circ: 500.

657 IRL ISSN 0001-4699
ACCOUNTANCY IRELAND. Text in English. 1969. bi-m. EUR 40 in Europe; EUR 85 elsewhere (effective 2005). adv. bk.rev.; Website rev. bibl.; charts; illus. **Document type:** *Magazine, Trade.* **Description:** Focuses mainly on accountancy matters, its content also deals with business and management subjects, taxation, information technology, general news, leisure and lifestyles, etc.
Related titles: Online - full text ed.: (from EBSCO Publishing, Florida Center for Library Automation, Gale Group, ProQuest Information & Learning).
Indexed: ABIn, ADPA, ATI, Emerald, IMI, RILM.
—BLDSC (0573.547000), IE, ingenta.
Published by: Institute of Chartered Accountants in Ireland, CA House, 87-89 Pembroke Rd, Ballsbridge, Dublin, 4, Ireland. TEL 353-1-6377240, 353-1-6377241, FAX 353-1-6685685, editor@accountancyireland.ie, ca@icai.ie, subscribe@accountancyireland.ie, http://www.icai.ie/publications.lp-curntissue.cfm. R&P Daisy Downes TEL 353-1-6377240. Adv. contact Mairead Walsh TEL 353-1-6377241. Circ: 20,484.

657 ZAF ISSN 0258-7254
HF5601
➤ **ACCOUNTANCY S A/REKENINGKUNDE S A.** Text in Multiple languages. 1914. m. (11/yr.). ZAR 235 domestic; ZAR 277 in Southern Africa; ZAR 700 elsewhere (effective 2003). adv. index. back issues avail.; reprint service avail. from PQC. **Document type:** *Journal, Academic/Scholarly.* **Description:** Publishes articles and features of a broad accounting-financial-business nature.
Formerly (until 1983): South African Chartered Accountant - Suid-Afrikaanse Geoktrooieerde Rekenmeester (0038-206X)
Related titles: Microform ed.: (from PQC); Online - full text ed.: free (from ProQuest Information & Learning); Supplement(s): Employment Supplement.
Indexed: ATI, Emerald, ISAP.
—BLDSC (0573.549000), IE, ingenta.
Published by: South African Institute of Chartered Accountants, PO Box 59875, Kengray, Johannesburg 2100, South Africa. TEL 27-11-9149900, FAX 27-11-6223321, journal@saica.co.za, http://www.accountancysa.org.za. Ed., R&P Tersia Booyzer. Adv. contact Eleanor Bowden. B&W page ZAR 13,980, color page ZAR 14,480; trim 210 x 297.

657 GBR ISSN 0001-4710
HF5601
THE ACCOUNTANT. Text in English. 1874. m. GBP 867, EUR 1,207, USD 1,447 (effective 2005). bk.rev. illus. Index. reprint service avail. from PSC. **Document type:** *Trade.* **Description:** Provides professional intelligence for accountants.
Related titles: Online - full text ed.: IEP 450, USD 750 (effective 1999) (from Factiva, Florida Center for Library Automation, Gale Group, LexisNexis, Northern Light Technology, Inc., O C L C Online Computer Library Center, Inc., ProQuest Information & Learning).
Indexed: AAR, ADPA, ATI, B&I, BPIA, Emerald, IMI, Inspec, KES, LRI.
—BLDSC (0573.560000), IE, ingenta. **CCC.**
Published by: Lafferty Publications Ltd., The Colonnades, 82 Bishops Bridge Rd, London, W2 6BB, United Kingdom. TEL 44-20-75635700, FAX 44-20-75635701, cuserv@lafferty.com, http://www.lafferty.com/newsletter_publication.php?id=9. Ed. Marc Barber.

657 KEN ISSN 1010-4135
CODEN: ENBUDZ
➤ **THE ACCOUNTANT.** Text in English. 1983. q. KES 600 domestic; USD 15 foreign (effective 2002). adv. bk.rev. back issues avail. **Document type:** *Journal, Academic/Scholarly.*
Related titles: Online - full text ed.: (from Northern Light Technology, Inc.).
Indexed: ATI.

Published by: Institute of Certified Public Accountants of Kenya, PO Box 59963, Nairobi, Kenya. TEL 80-2635-606-745, 254-02-860930, FAX 80-2635-62206, 254-02-862206, icpak@icpak.com, icpak@form-net.com. Ed. J K Njiraini. adv.: B&W page KES 50,000, color page KES 60,000. Circ: 18,000 (controlled).

657 NLD ISSN 0001-4729
DE ACCOUNTANT. Text in Dutch. 1895. 11/yr. adv. bk.rev. charts. index. **Document type:** *Journal, Academic/Scholarly.*
Related titles: Online - full text ed.: (from Northern Light Technology, Inc.).
Indexed: ABIn, ADPA, BusI, ELLIS, KES.
—IE.
Published by: Koninklijk Nederlands Instituut van Registeraccountants, Postbus 7984, Amsterdam, 1008 AD, Netherlands. TEL 31-20-3010301, FAX 31-20-3010302, nivra@nivra.nl, http://www.nivra.nl. Ed. H Mik. Adv. contact J ter Laak. Circ: 18,000.

657 NLD ISSN 0165-2729
ACCOUNTANT ADVISEUR. Key Title: A A. Accountant Adviseur. Text in Dutch. 1966. 10/yr. EUR 113.91 (effective 2005). adv. bk.rev. stat. index. **Document type:** *Trade.*
—IE, Infotrieve.
Published by: (Nederlandse Orde van Accountants-Administratieconsulenten), Reed Business Information bv (Subsidiary of: Reed Business), Postbus 152, Amsterdam, 1000 AD, Netherlands. TEL 31-20-5159222, FAX 31-20-5159990, accountantadviseur@novaa.nl, info@reedbusiness.nl, http://www.reedbusiness.nl. Circ: 8,595.

657 GBR ISSN 0307-0336
ACCOUNTANT'S DIGEST. Text in English. 1973. 18/yr. GBP 270; GBP 310.50 foreign (effective 2000). **Document type:** *Trade.*
—BLDSC (0573.564000), IE, ingenta.
Published by: (Institute of Chartered Accountants in England and Wales), A B G Professional Information (Subsidiary of: Croner.C C H Group Ltd.), 145 London Rd, Kingston upon Thames, KT2 6SR, United Kingdom. TEL 44-20-85473333, FAX 44-20-85472637, lovellv@croner.cch.co.uk, http://www.abgweb.com/.

657.6 658.3 USA
ACCOUNTANT'S GUIDE TO EMPLOYEE BENEFIT PLANS. Text in English. base vol. plus a. updates. looseleaf. USD 205; USD 283.55 foreign (effective 1998). **Document type:** *Trade.* **Description:** Guides personnel managers through the complex array of laws and accounting and auditing standards.
Former titles: Accounting and Auditing for Employee Benefits; Accounting and Auditing for Employee Benefit Plans
Indexed: ATI.
Published by: W G & L Financial Reporting & Management Research (Subsidiary of: R I A), 395 Hudson St, New York, NY 10014. TEL 212-367-6300, FAX 212-367-6718. Ed. Paul Rosenfield. **Subscr. to:** The Park Square Bldg., 31 St James Ave, Boston, MA 02116-4112. TEL 800-950-1207.

346.73033 347.30633 USA ISSN 8756-4262
KF2920.3.Z9
ACCOUNTANT'S LIABILITY. Text in English. base vol. plus a. updates. looseleaf. USD 125 (effective 1996).
Related titles: Online - full text ed.: (from LexisNexis).
Indexed: ATI.
Published by: Practising Law Institute, 810 Seventh Ave, New York, NY 10019. TEL 212-824-5700, 800-260-4754, FAX 800-321-0093, info@pli.edu, http://www.pli.edu. Eds. Dan L Goldwasser, Thomas Arnold.

657 332.6 USA
ACCOUNTANTS S E C PRACTICE MANUAL. Text in English. 1976. 2 base vols. plus bi-m. updates. looseleaf. USD 780 base vol(s). (effective 2004). **Document type:** *Trade.* **Description:** Offers guidance for preparing and filing financial statements with the SEC, including regulations, forms and helpful summaries and checklists.
Related titles: CD-ROM ed.: USD 850 (effective 2004); Online - full text ed.: USD 850 (effective 2004).
Published by: C C H Inc., 2700 Lake Cook Rd, Riverwoods, IL 60015. TEL 847-267-7000, 800-449-6439, cust_serv@cch.com, http://www.cch.com. Pub. Stacey Caywood.

657 AUS ISSN 1445-954X
➤ **ACCOUNTING, ACCOUNTABILITY & PERFORMANCE.** Text in English. 1995. s-a. AUD 50 domestic to individuals; AUD 60 foreign to individuals; AUD 80 domestic to libraries; AUD 90 foreign to libraries (effective 2004). charts; stat. 100 p./no.; back issues avail.; reprints avail. **Document type:** *Journal, Academic/Scholarly.* **Description:** Covers public sector performance and accountability, accounting, banking, finance and capital markets, managerial accounting, accounting research.
Formerly (until 1998): Accountability and Performance (1323-711X)
Published by: Griffith University, Department of Accounting, Finance & Economics, Griffith Business School, PMB 50, Gold Coast Mail Centre, QLD 9726, Australia. TEL 61-7-55528314, FAX 61-7-55528068, http://www.griffith.edu.au/text/school/gbs/afe/journal/home.html, http://www.griffith.edu.au/school/gbs/. Ed. Dr. Chris Guilding. R&P Melinda John. Circ: 300.

657.6 USA ISSN 0737-3325
HF5658
THE ACCOUNTING & AUDITING DISCLOSURE MANUAL. Text in English. a. USD 155; USD 221.45 foreign. **Document type:** *Trade.* **Description:** Compiles all relevant G.A.A.P. and G.A.A.S. requirements.
Indexed: ATI.
—CCC.
Published by: W G & L Financial Reporting & Management Research (Subsidiary of: R I A), 395 Hudson St, New York, NY 10014. TEL 212-367-6300, FAX 212-367-6718. Eds. Allan B Afterman, Rowan H Jones. **Subscr. to:** The Park Square Bldg., 31 St James Ave, Boston, MA 02116-4112. TEL 800-950-1207.

657 USA ISSN 1045-1447
ACCOUNTING AND AUDITING UPDATE SERVICE. Text in English. 1984. 27/yr. USD 315; USD 409.50 foreign (effective 1998). **Document type:** *Newsletter.* **Description:** Analyzes and interprets all F.A.S.B. and A.I.C.P.A. pronouncements as they are issued.
—CCC.
Published by: W G & L Financial Reporting & Management Research (Subsidiary of: R I A), 395 Hudson St, New York, NY 10014. TEL 212-367-6360, FAX 212-367-6718, http://www.wglcorpfinance.com. Eds. Allan B Afterman, Dorothy Cummings. **Subscr. to:** The Park Square Bldg., 31 St James Ave, Boston, MA 02116-4112. TEL 800-950-1207.

657 GBR ISSN 1460-406X
HF5601
ACCOUNTING & BUSINESS. Text in English. 1905. m. GBP 42 to individuals; GBP 85 to institutions; GBP 25 to students; USD 3.50 newsstand/cover. adv. bk.rev. illus.; stat. index. reprints avail. **Document type:** *Trade.* **Description:** Covers news, features and developments of interest to certified accounts in the UK and elsewhere, as well as association news.
Former titles (until 1998): Certified Accountant (0306-2406); (until 1972): Certified Accountants Journal (0009-0417)
Related titles: Microform ed.: 1905; Supplement(s): Accounting & Business Members Supplement.
Indexed: ADPA, ASEANManA, ATI, BPIA, Emerald, WBA.
—BLDSC (0573.587500), IE, Infotrieve, ingenta.
Published by: Association of Chartered Certified Accountants, 64 Finnieston Square, Glasgow, G3 8DT, United Kingdom. TEL 44-20-7396-5800, FAX 44-20-7396-5858, http://www.accaglobal.com/publications/accountingandbusiness/. Ed., R&P John Prosser. Adv. contact Philip Northcolt. Circ: 59,450.

657 SGP
ACCOUNTING AND BUSINESS IN ASIA. Text in English. 1997. irreg., latest vol.2. price varies. **Document type:** *Monographic series, Trade.*
Published by: World Scientific Publishing Co. Pte. Ltd., 5 Toh Tuck Link, Singapore, 596224, Singapore. TEL 65-466-5775, FAX 65-467-7667, wspc@wspc.com.sg, series@wspc.com.sg, http://www.wspc.com.sg/books/series/aba_series.shtml, http://www.worldscientific.com. Eds. Amy Lau, Benjamin Tai, Ronald Ma. **Dist. by:** World Scientific Publishing Co., Inc., 1060 Main St, River Edge, NJ 07661. TEL 201-487-9655, FAX 201-487-9656, 888-977-2665, wspc@wspc.com; World Scientific Publishing Ltd., 57 Shelton St, London WC2H 9HE, United Kingdom. TEL 44-20-78360888, FAX 44-20-78362020, sales@wspc.co.uk.

657 GBR ISSN 0001-4788
➤ **ACCOUNTING AND BUSINESS RESEARCH.** Text in English. 1970. q. bk.rev. illus. index. back issues avail.; reprint service avail. from SCH. **Document type:** *Journal, Academic/Scholarly.* **Description:** Academic articles on issues affecting the profession.
Formerly (until 1970): Accounting Research
Related titles: Microfilm ed.: (from WMP); Microform ed.: (from PQC); Online - full text ed.: (from EBSCO Publishing, O C L C Online Computer Library Center, Inc.).
Indexed: ABIn, ADPA, ATI, BPI, BPIA, BusI, CPM, CREJ, Emerald, ExcerpMed, HECAB, IBSS, Inspec, M&MA, ManagCont, PAIS, PCI, SCIMP, T&II, WBA.
—BLDSC (0573.588000), IE, Infotrieve, ingenta. **CCC.**
Published by: Institute of Chartered Accountants in England and Wales, Chartered Accountants' Hall, PO Box 433, London, EC2P 2BJ, United Kingdom. TEL 44-20-79208100, FAX 44-20-79200547, http://www.icaew.co.uk/. Ed. J A Darnill. Adv. contact Karen Glaseby. Circ: 1,500.

657.0711 AUS ISSN 0810-5391
HF5601
➤ **ACCOUNTING AND FINANCE.** Text in English. 1960. q. GBP 130 combined subscription in Australia & New Zealand to institutions print & online eds.; USD 361 combined subscription in the Americas to institutions & the Caribbean (print & online eds.); GBP 250 combined subscription elsewhere to institutions print & online eds. (effective 2006). adv. bk.rev. back issues avail.; reprints avail. **Document type:** *Journal, Academic/Scholarly.* **Description:** Using a wide range of research methods including statistical analysis, analytical work, case studies, field research and historical analysis, the journal applies economic, organizational and other theories to accounting and finance phenomena.
Former titles: Accounting Education; Australasian Association of University Teachers of Accounting. New Bulletin
Related titles: Microform ed.: (from PQC); Online - full text ed.: ISSN 1467-629X. GBP 123 in Australia & New Zealand to institutions; USD 343 in the Americas to institutions & Caribbean; GBP 238 elsewhere to institutions (effective 2006) (from Blackwell Synergy, EBSCO Publishing, Gale Group, IngentaConnect, O C L C Online Computer Library Center, Inc., Swets Information Services).
Indexed: AAR, ABIn, ATI, BPIA, BusI, ManagCont, RHEA, T&II.
—BLDSC (0573.589300), IE, Infotrieve, ingenta. **CCC.**
Published by: (Accounting Association of Australia and New Zealand), Blackwell Publishing Asia (Subsidiary of: Blackwell Publishing Ltd.), 550 Swanston St, Carlton South, VIC 3053, Australia. TEL 61-383591011, FAX 61-383591120, subs@blackwellpublishingasia.com, http://www.blackwellpublishing.com/journals/ACFI. Ed. Robert Faff. Circ: 900. **Subscr. to:** Blackwell Publishing Ltd., Journal Customer Services, 9600 Garsington Rd, PO Box 1354, Oxford OX4 2XG, United Kingdom. TEL 44-1865-778315, FAX 44-1865-471775, customerservices@oxon.blackwellpublishing.com.

➤ **ACCOUNTING & FINANCE ABSTRACTS.** see *BUSINESS AND ECONOMICS—Abstracting, Bibliographies, Statistics*

657 346.066 USA
ACCOUNTING AND FINANCIAL PLANNING FOR LAW FIRMS. Text in English. m. USD 275 combined subscription print & online eds. (effective 2003). **Document type:** *Newsletter, Trade.*
Related titles: Online - full content ed.: USD 225 (effective 2003).
Published by: Law Journal Newsletters (Subsidiary of: A L M), 1617 JFK Blvd, Ste 1750, Philadelphia, PA 19103. TEL 800-888-8300, lawcatalog@amlaw.com, http://www.ljnonline.com/pub/ljn_accounting/.

657 GBR
ACCOUNTING AND SUSTAINABILITY E-NEWSLETTER. Text in English. m. **Document type:** *Trade.*
Media: Online - full content.
—ingenta.
Published by: Association of Chartered Certified Accountants, 64 Finnieston Square, Glasgow, G3 8DT, United Kingdom. TEL 44-171-396-5734, FAX 44-171-396-5959, http://www.accaglobal.com/publications/as_index/.

657 USA ISSN 1530-9320
ACCOUNTING AND THE PUBLIC INTEREST. Text in English. 2001. m. USD 125 (effective 2003). back issues avail.
Media: Online - full text.
Published by: American Accounting Association, 5717 Bessie Dr, Sarasota, FL 34233-2399. TEL 941-921-7747, FAX 941-923-4093, office@aaahq.org, http://aaahq.org/ic/browse.htm.

657 GBR ISSN 1368-0668
➤ **ACCOUNTING AUDITING AND ACCOUNTABILITY JOURNAL.** Text in English. 1987. 6/yr. EUR 5,327.66, USD 4,779, AUD 4,779, GBP 3,729.04 (effective 2006). illus. Index. reprint service avail. from PSC. **Document type:** *Journal, Academic/Scholarly.* **Description:** Provides a forum for the publication of high quality manuscripts concerning the interaction between accounting/auditing and their socio-economic and political environments.
Formerly (until 1989): Accounting Auditing and Accountability (0951-3574)
Related titles: Online - full text ed.: (from EBSCO Publishing, Emerald Group Publishing Limited, Gale Group, IngentaConnect, O C L C Online Computer Library Center, Inc., ProQuest Information & Learning, Swets Information Services).
Indexed: ABIn, ATI, CPM, EmerIntel, Emerald, IBSS, SCIMP.
—BLDSC (0573.590900), IE, ingenta. **CCC.**
Published by: Emerald Group Publishing Limited, 60-62 Toller Ln, Bradford, W Yorks BD8 9BY, United Kingdom. TEL 44-1274-777700, FAX 44-1274-785200, infomation@emeraldinsight.com, http://www.emeraldinsight.com/aaaj.htm. Eds. James E Guthrie TEL 612-9850-9030, Lee D Parker TEL 61-8-8303-4236. **Subscr. in Australia to:** Emerald Group Publishing Ltd., PO Box 1567, Toowong, QLD 4066, Australia. TEL 61-3-3870-7144, FAX 61-3870-4013; **Subscr. in N America to:** Emerald Group Publishing Ltd., 44 Brattle St, 4th Fl, Cambridge, MA 02138. TEL 617-497-2175, 888-622-0075, FAX 617-354-6875.

657.0993 NZL ISSN 1174-6157
ACCOUNTING, CORPORATE AND TAX ALERT. Text in English. w.
Published by: Brooker's Limited, Level 1 - Telecom Networks House, 68-86 Jervois Quay, Wellington, New Zealand. TEL 64-4-4998178, FAX 64-4-4998173, publishing@brookers.co.nz.

657 USA ISSN 1541-115X
ACCOUNTING DEPARTMENT MANAGEMENT REPORT. Text in English. 1988. m. looseleaf. USD 268.95 in US & Canada print & online eds.; USD 283 elsewhere print & online eds. (effective 2005). index. back issues avail. **Document type:** *Newsletter, Trade.* **Description:** Covers how to manage corporate accounting departments more effectively, boost staff productivity, reduce operating costs and adopt new systems and technology.
Formerly: Accounting Department Management & Administration Report (1042-928X)

Related titles: Diskette ed.; E-mail ed.; Online - full content ed.; Online - full text ed.: (from EBSCO Publishing, Florida Center for Library Automation, Gale Group, LexisNexis, O C L C Online Computer Library Center, Inc., ProQuest Information & Learning).
Indexed: ATI.
—CCC.
Published by: Institute of Management & Administration, Inc., 3 Park Ave, New York, NY 10016-5902. TEL 212-244-0360, FAX 212-564-0465, subserve@ioma.com, http://www.ioma.com. Ed. Timothy Harris. Pub. Perry Patterson. R&P Sofie Kourkoutakis.

657.0711 GBR ISSN 0963-9284
HF5630
➤ **ACCOUNTING EDUCATION.** Text in English. 1992. q. GBP 475, USD 774 combined subscription to institutions print & online eds. (effective 2006). bk.rev. illus. Index. back issues avail.; reprint service avail. from PSC. **Document type:** *Academic/Scholarly.* **Description:** Covers research and key issues of accounting education and training.
Related titles: Online - full text ed.: ISSN 1468-4489. GBP 451, USD 735 to institutions (effective 2006) (from EBSCO Publishing, Gale Group, IngentaConnect, O C L C Online Computer Library Center, Inc., Swets Information Services).
Indexed: ATI, BrEdI, CPE, CPM, DIP, ERA, ETA, Emerald, MEA, RHEA, SEA, SENA, SOMA, SWA, TEA.
—BLDSC (0573.593000), IE, Infotrieve, ingenta. **CCC.**
Published by: Routledge (Subsidiary of: Taylor & Francis Group), 4 Park Sq, Milton Park, Abingdon, Oxon OX14 4RN, United Kingdom. TEL 44-1235-828600, FAX 44-1235-829000, info@routledge.co.uk, http://www.tandf.co.uk/journals/routledge/09639284.html, http://www.routledge.co.uk. Ed. Richard M S Wilson. **Subscr. in N. America to:** Taylor & Francis Inc., Customer Services Dept, 325 Chestnut St, 8th Fl, Philadelphia, PA 19106. TEL 800-354-1420, FAX 215-625-8914; **Subscr. to:** Taylor & Francis Ltd, Journals Customer Service, Rankine Rd, Basingstoke, Hants RG24 8PR, United Kingdom. TEL 44-1256-813000, FAX 44-1256-330245, enquiry@tandf.co.uk.

657.07 USA ISSN 0882-956X
ACCOUNTING EDUCATION NEWS. Text in English. 1973. q. USD 145 membership; USD 165 combined subscription membership print & online eds. (effective 2005). adv. **Document type:** *Newsletter, Academic/Scholarly.*
Related titles: Online - full text ed.: (from bigchalk, EBSCO Publishing, Northern Light Technology, Inc., ProQuest Information & Learning).
Indexed: ABIn, ATI.
—CCC.
Published by: American Accounting Association, 5717 Bessie Dr, Sarasota, FL 34233-2399. TEL 941-921-7747, FAX 941-923-4093. Eds. Craig E Polhemus, Michael A Diamond. R&P Mary Cole. Adv. contact Judy Cothern.

657 USA ISSN 1041-0392
ACCOUNTING EDUCATORS' JOURNAL. Text in English. 1988. s-a.
Indexed: ATI.
—BLDSC (0573.594000), IE.
Published by: (American Accounting Association), University of Nevada, Las Vegas, 4505 Maryland Pkw., Las Vegas, NV 89154. TEL 702-895-3011, http://www.unlv.edu.

657 332 USA
ACCOUNTING FOR BANKS. Text in English. 1982. base vol. plus s-a. updates. looseleaf. USD 237 (effective 2003). Supplement avail. **Description:** Discusses accounting principles applicable to banks within the framework of their operations.
Published by: Matthew Bender & Co., Inc. (Subsidiary of: LexisNexis North America), 1275 Broadway, Albany, NY 12204. international@bender.com, http://www.bender.com, http://bender.lexisnexis.com. Ed. James M Koltveit.

ACCOUNTING FOR GOVERNMENT CONTRACTS: COST ACCOUNTING STANDARDS. see *PUBLIC ADMINISTRATION*

ACCOUNTING FOR GOVERNMENT CONTRACTS: FEDERAL ACQUISITION REGULATION. see *PUBLIC ADMINISTRATION*

657 USA ISSN 0898-8102
KF320.A2
ACCOUNTING FOR LAW FIRMS. Text in English. 1988. m. looseleaf. USD 225 (effective 2004). index. **Document type:** *Newsletter.* **Description:** Provides analyses of new and pending statutes, regulations and cases, as well as practical strategies for increasing firms' profitability to law firm partners, chief financial officers, administrators, accountants and financial planners.
Related titles: Online - full text ed.
—CCC.
Published by: A L M, 345 Park Ave., S, New York, NY 10010. TEL 212-313-9000, 800-888-8300, FAX 212-481-8255, mhopkins@amlaw.com, apress@amlaw.com, http://www.ljx.com, http://www.alm.com. Ed. Joe Danowsky. Pub., R&P Stuart M Wise TEL 917-256-2001.

657.834 USA ISSN 0730-7721
HF5601
ACCOUNTING FOR LAWYERS. Text in English. a. USD 99 (effective 1996).
Published by: Practising Law Institute, 810 Seventh Ave, New York, NY 10019. TEL 212-824-5700, 800-260-4754, FAX 800-321-0093, info@pli.edu, http://www.pli.edu.

657 USA
ACCOUNTING FOR PUBLIC UTILITIES. Text in English. 1983. base vol. plus a. updates. looseleaf. USD 299 base vol(s). (effective 2005). **Description:** Provides analysis of public utility accounting for anyone involved in rate-making and utility accounting.
Published by: Matthew Bender & Co., Inc. (Subsidiary of: LexisNexis North America), 1275 Broadway, Albany, NY 12204. TEL 518-487-3575, 800-252-9257, FAX 518-462-3788, international@bender.com, http://bender.lexisnexis.com. Eds. Gregory Aliff, Robert Hanne.

657 338.642 GBR ISSN 0155-9982
HF5616.A8
➤ **ACCOUNTING FORUM.** Text in English. 1978. 4/yr. EUR 63 in Europe to individuals; JPY 6,300 in Japan to individuals; USD 61 elsewhere to individuals; EUR 283 in Europe to institutions; JPY 28,200 in Japan to institutions; USD 274 elsewhere to institutions (effective 2006). adv. bk.rev. cum.index. back issues avail. **Document type:** *Journal, Academic/Scholarly.* **Description:** Covers accounting education and practice with regard to accounting theory, practice and policy.
Related titles: Online - full text ed.: ISSN 1467-6303. GBP 134 in Europe to institutions; USD 194 in the Americas to institutions; AUD 209 in Australia & New Zealand to institutions; GBP 134 elsewhere to institutions (effective 2003) (from Blackwell Synergy, EBSCO Publishing, Gale Group, IngentaConnect, O C L C Online Computer Library Center, Inc., ScienceDirect, Swets Information Services).
Indexed: AusPAIS, Emerald.
—BLDSC (0573.594500), IE, Infotrieve, ingenta. **CCC.**
Published by: Elsevier Ltd. (Subsidiary of: Elsevier Science & Technology), The Boulevard, Langford Ln, Kidlington, Oxford, OX5 1GB, United Kingdom. TEL 44-1865-843000, FAX 44-1865-843010, nlinfo-f@elsevier.nl, http://www.elsevier.com/locate/accfor. Eds. Glen Lehman, Tony Tinker.

657 AUS ISSN 1031-3109
ACCOUNTING GUIDANCE RELEASE. Text in English. 1985. irreg. AUD 6 per issue. **Document type:** *Newsletter.*
Published by: Australian Accounting Research Foundation, 211 Hawthorn Rd, Caulfield, VIC 3162, Australia. TEL 61-3-95243600, FAX 61-3-95235499, standard@aarf.asn.au. Circ: 1,400. **Co-sponsors:** Institute of Chartered Accountants in Australia; Australian Society of Certified Practising Accountants.

657 USA ISSN 0148-4184
HF5601
➤ **ACCOUNTING HISTORIANS JOURNAL.** Text in English. 1974. s-a. USD 45 to individuals; USD 55 to institutions (effective 2004). bk.rev. bibl.; illus. index. back issues avail.; reprints avail. **Document type:** *Journal, Academic/Scholarly.* **Description:** Features articles on accounting history.
Formerly (until 1977): Accounting Historian
Related titles: Online - full text ed.: (from Florida Center for Library Automation, Northern Light Technology, Inc., ProQuest Information & Learning).
Indexed: AAR, ATI, AmH&L, HistAb.
—BLDSC (0573.595200), IE, Infotrieve, ingenta.
Published by: Academy of Accounting Historians, c/o Culverhouse School of Accountancy, University of Alabama, Tuscaloosa, AL 35487. TEL 205-348-9784, FAX 205-348-8453, WalkerS2@cardiff.ac.uk, krice510@comcast.net, http://accounting.rutgers.edu/raw/aah/. Ed., R&P Stephen P Walker TEL 44-1222-20875130. Circ: 900.

657 USA ISSN 1075-1416
HF5601
ACCOUNTING HISTORIANS NOTEBOOK. Text in English. s-a. membership. back issues avail. **Document type:** *Newsletter, Academic/Scholarly.* **Description:** Contains short articles and observations on accounting history.
Published by: Academy of Accounting Historians, c/o Culverhouse School of Accountancy, University of Alabama, Tuscaloosa, AL 35487. FAX 205-348-8453, krice510@comcast.net. Ed. Joann Cross.

657 GBR ISSN 1032-3732
➤ **ACCOUNTING HISTORY**; journal of the accounting history special interest group of the accounting association of Australia and New Zealand. Text in English. 1996. q. GBP 189, USD 330 to institutions; GBP 196, USD 343 combined subscription to institutions print & online eds. (effective 2005). bk.rev. bibl.; charts; illus.; stat. index. back issues avail. **Document type:** *Journal, Academic/Scholarly.* **Description:** Publishes papers concerned with exploring the advent and development of accounting bodies, conventions, ideas, practices and rules.
Related titles: Online - full text ed.: GBP 187, USD 326 to institutions (effective 2006) (from Northern Light Technology, Inc., ProQuest Information & Learning).
Indexed: ATI, Emerald.
—BLDSC (0573.595310). **CCC.**
Published by: (Accounting & Finance Association of Australia and New Zealand AUS), Sage Publications Ltd. (Subsidiary of: Sage Publications, Inc.), 1 Oliver's Yard, 55 City Rd, London, EC1 1SP, United Kingdom. TEL 44-20-73248500, FAX 44-20-73248600, info@sagepub.co.uk, http://www.sagepub.co.uk/journal.aspx?pid=107297. Ed. Garry Carnegie. Circ: 170 (paid). **Subscr. to:** Sage Publications, Inc., 2455 Teller Rd, Thousand Oaks, CA 91320. TEL 805-499-0721, FAX 805-499-0871, journals@sagepub.com. **Co-publisher:** Accounting & Finance Association of Australia and New Zealand.

657 USA ISSN 0888-7993
HF5616.U5
➤ **ACCOUNTING HORIZONS.** Text in English. 1987. q. USD 225 (effective 2005). adv. abstr.; illus. Index. reprint service avail. from PSC. **Document type:** *Academic/Scholarly.*
Related titles: Online - full text ed.: (from EBSCO Publishing, Florida Center for Library Automation, Gale Group, H.W. Wilson, Northern Light Technology, Inc., O C L C Online Computer Library Center, Inc., ProQuest Information & Learning).
Indexed: ABIn, ATI, BPI, Emerald, IBSS.
—BLDSC (0573.595400), IE, Infotrieve, ingenta. **CCC.**
Published by: American Accounting Association, 5717 Bessie Dr, Sarasota, FL 34233-2399. TEL 941-921-7747, FAX 941-923-4093, http://www.rutgers.edu/Accounting/raw/aaa/pubs/horizons.htm, http://aaahq.org. Ed. Eugene Imhoff. R&P Mary Cole.

657 MYS ISSN 0126-625X
HF5601
ACCOUNTING JOURNAL. Text in English. 1971. a. MYR 4. adv. bibl.; charts.
Published by: (University of Malaya, Faculty of Economics & Administration), University of Malaya/Perpustakaan Universiti Malaya, Lembah Pantai, Kuala Lumpur, 59100, Malaysia. http://www.um.edu.my. Circ: 750.

658 USA ISSN 0749-2928
ACCOUNTING OFFICE MANAGEMENT & ADMINISTRATION REPORT. Abbreviated title: A O M A R. Text in English. 1983. m. looseleaf. USD 291.95 combined subscription in US & Canada print & online eds.; USD 303 combined subscription elsewhere print & online eds. (effective 2006). index. 16 p./no.; back issues avail. **Document type:** *Newsletter, Trade.* **Description:** Presents strategies for increasing accounting office efficiency and profitability. Offers practical guidance on fees and billing rates, compensation levels and benefits for CPAs and staff, firm performance, benchmarks.
Related titles: Diskette ed.; E-mail ed.; Online - full content ed.; Online - full text ed.: (from EBSCO Publishing, LexisNexis, ProQuest Information & Learning).
Indexed: ABIn, ATI.
—CCC.
Published by: Institute of Management & Administration, Inc., 3 Park Ave, New York, NY 10016-5902. TEL 212-244-0360, FAX 212-564-0465, subserve@ioma.com, http://www.ioma.com/products/prod_detail.php?prodid=29. Ed. Sue Sandler. Pub. Lee Rath.

657 GBR ISSN 0361-3682
➤ **ACCOUNTING, ORGANIZATIONS AND SOCIETY.** Text in English. 1976. 8/yr. EUR 288 in Europe to individuals; JPY 38,300 in Japan to individuals; USD 321 elsewhere to individuals; EUR 1,618 in Europe to institutions; JPY 214,800 in Japan to institutions; USD 1,809 elsewhere to institutions; EUR 63 in Europe to students; JPY 8,400 in Japan to students; USD 73 elsewhere to students (effective 2006). adv. abstr.; charts; illus. index. back issues avail.; reprints avail. **Document type:** *Journal, Academic/Scholarly.* **Description:** Concerned with all aspects of the relationship between accounting and human behavior, organizational structures and processes and the changing social and political environment of the enterprise.
Related titles: Microform ed.: (from PQC); Online - full text ed.: (from EBSCO Publishing, Gale Group, IngentaConnect, ScienceDirect, Swets Information Services).
Indexed: ABIn, ADPA, ASCA, ATI, AgeL, ArtHuCI, BPIA, BusI, CPM, CurCont, Emerald, IBSS, ILD, Inspec, MEA&I, ManagCont, RI-1, RI-2, RefZh, SCIMP, SSCI, WBA.
—BLDSC (0573.598000), IDS, IE, Infotrieve, ingenta. **CCC.**
Published by: Pergamon (Subsidiary of: Elsevier Science & Technology), The Boulevard, Langford Ln, East Park, Kidlington, Oxford OX5 1GB, United Kingdom. TEL 44-1865-843000, FAX 44-1865-843010, http://www.elsevier.com/locate/aos. Ed. Anthony G. Hopwood. adv.: B&W page USD 550, color page USD 1,350; trim 9.75 x 7.25. **Subscr. to:** Elsevier BV, PO Box 211, Amsterdam 1000 AE, Netherlands. nlinfo-f@elsevier.nl.

637 USA
ACCOUNTING PROFESSIONALS PRODUCT NEWS. Text in English. 1992. bi-m. free. adv. bk.rev. **Document type:** *Trade.* **Description:** Devoted to presenting the new high technology products for the accounting industry in the form of articles and editorial comment on new trends and late breaking areas of interest.

Published by: Accounting Professional Product News, Inc., 4210 W. Vickery Blvd., Ft. Worth, TX 76107. TEL 817-738-3122, FAX 817-731-9704, hawk@cpanews.com, http://www.cpanews.com. Ed., R&P. Adv. contact Hawk Chud. B&W page USD 2,200, color page USD 2,650; trim 10.75 x 8.63. Circ: 40,000 (controlled).

657 332   AUS   ISSN 1030-9616
➤ **ACCOUNTING RESEARCH JOURNAL.** Text in English. 1988. s-a. AUD 30 domestic; AUD 35 foreign (effective 2001). adv. bk.rev. cum.index. **Document type:** *Academic/Scholarly.* **Description:** Covers research and practice of accounting, finance, auditing, commercial law and cognate disciplines.
Indexed: AusPAIS.
Published by: Royal Melbourne Institute of Technology, Department of Economics and Finance, GPO Box 2476 V, Melbourne, VIC 3001, Australia. robert.faff@tmit.edu.au, http://www.bf.rmit.edu.au/Ecofin.arj.html. Ed., R&P. Adv. contact Robert Faff. Circ: 250.

657   USA   ISSN 0001-4826
HF5601   CODEN: ACRVAS
➤ **ACCOUNTING REVIEW.** Text in English. 1926. q. USD 275 to non-members; USD 300 combined subscription to non-members print & online eds. (effective 2005). adv. bk.rev. charts; abstr.; illus. index. back issues avail.; reprint service avail. from PSC. **Document type:** *Journal, Academic/Scholarly.* **Description:** Publishes articles reporting the results of accounting research and explaining and illustrating related research methodology.
Related titles: Microform ed.: (from PQC); Online - full text ed.: (from Chadwyck-Healey Inc., EBSCO Publishing, Gale Group, H.W. Wilson, JSTOR (Web-based Journal Archive), O C L C Online Computer Library Center, Inc., ProQuest Information & Learning).
Indexed: AAR, ABIn, ADPA, ASCA, ASEANManA, ATI, BPI, BPIA, BRI, BusI, CBRI, CIS, CPM, CREJ, CompAb, CurCont, Emerald, HECAB, IBR, IBSS, IBZ, IMI, IPARL, JEL, M&MA, MEA&I, ManagCont, PCI, PROMT, RASB, SCIMP, SSCI, WBA.
—BLDSC (0573.700000), IE, Infotrieve, ingenta. **CCC.**
Published by: American Accounting Association, 5717 Bessie Dr, Sarasota, FL 34233-2399. TEL 941-921-7747, FAX 941-923-4093, accounting-review@terry.uga.edu, office@aaahq.org, http://aaahq.org/ic/browse.htm. R&P Mary Cole. Adv. contact Judy Cothern. Circ: 18,000 (paid).

657   USA   ISSN 0745-886X
ACCOUNTING STANDARDS. CURRENT TEXT. Text in English. 1982. a. looseleaf. USD 415 (effective 2005).
Published by: Financial Accounting Standards Board (Subsidiary of: Financial Accounting Foundation), 401 Merritt 7, Box 5116, Norwalk, CT 06856-5116. TEL 203-847-0700, 800-748-0659, FAX 203-849-9714, http://www.fasb.org.

657   USA   ISSN 1043-7940
HF5616.U5
ACCOUNTING STANDARDS. STATEMENTS OF FINANCIAL ACCOUNTING CONCEPTS. Text in English. a. price varies. **Document type:** *Monographic series, Trade.*
Indexed: ATI.
Published by: Financial Accounting Standards Board (Subsidiary of: Financial Accounting Foundation), 401 Merritt 7, Box 5116, Norwalk, CT 06856-5116. TEL 203-847-0700, 800-748-0659, FAX 203-849-9714, http://www.fasb.org.

657 340   USA
ACCOUNTING SYSTEMS FOR LAW OFFICES. Text in English. 1978. irreg. (in 1 vol.). looseleaf. Supplement avail.
Description: Provides details on financial and accounting systems for law offices.
Published by: Matthew Bender & Co., Inc. (Subsidiary of: LexisNexis North America), 1275 Broadway, Albany, NY 12204. international@bender.com, http://bender.lexisnexis.com. Eds. Carl Bradbury, William Burke.

657   USA   ISSN 1049-5401
HF5601
THE ACCOUNTING SYSTEMS JOURNAL. Text in English. 1989. s-a.
Indexed: ATI.
Published by: Memphis State University, Fogelman College of Business and Economics, School of Accountancy, Memphis, TN 38152.

657   USA   ISSN 1068-6452
HF5679   CODEN: ACCTEJ
ACCOUNTING TECHNOLOGY. Text in English. 1984. 11/yr. USD 89 domestic; USD 99 foreign (effective 2005). adv. illus. back issues avail.; reprints avail. **Document type:** *Magazine, Trade.* **Description:** Covers technology issues for the accounting profession, including hardware, software and office equipment.
Formerly (until 1993): Computers in Accounting (0883-1866)
Related titles: Online - full text ed.: (from EBSCO Publishing, Factiva, Florida Center for Library Automation, Gale Group, LexisNexis, Northern Light Technology, Inc., O C L C Online Computer Library Center, Inc., ProQuest Information & Learning); Supplement(s): C P A Wealth Provider. 2001. free with subscr. to any financial planning publication by Source Media, Inc.
Indexed: ABIn, ATI, B&I, CompD, CompLI, Inspec, SoftBase.

—BLDSC (0573.702500), AskIEEE, IE, ingenta. **CCC.**
Published by: Source Media, Inc., One State St Plaza, 27th Fl, New York, NY 10004. TEL 212-803-6077, 800-221-1809, FAX 212-747-1154, custserv@sourcemedia.com, http://www.sourcemedia.com. Ed. Robert W Scott. adv.: B&W page USD 4,435, color page USD 6,585. Circ: 30,000 (paid and controlled).

657   AUS   ISSN 0818-9412
ACCOUNTING THEORY MONOGRAPH. Text in English. 1982. irreg., latest vol.10, 1998. price varies. **Document type:** *Monographic series.*
Published by: Australian Accounting Research Foundation, 211 Hawthorn Rd, Caulfield, VIC 3162, Australia. TEL 61-3-95243600, FAX 61-3-95235499, standard@aarf.asn.au. Circ: 1,400. **Co-sponsors:** Institute of Chartered Accountants in Australia; Australian Society of Certified Practising Accountants.

657   PHL   ISSN 0028-9418
ACCOUNTING TIMES. Text in English. 1950. m. USD 21 in Asia; USD 23 in the Middle East; USD 25 elsewhere (effective 2000). adv. charts; illus. **Description:** Covers news and activities of PICPA, technical advisory on cooperatives and other inquiries related to accountancy.
Formerly (until 1981): Newsette
Published by: Philippine Institute of Certified Public Accountants, PICPA House, 700 Shaw Blvd, Mandaluyong City, Metro-manila, Philippines. TEL 63-2-701166, FAX 63-2-796787. Eds. Aphat C Martinez, Erwin G Alcala. R&P Beth Paguio TEL 632-723-5467. Circ: 27,500.

657   USA   ISSN 1044-5714
HF5601
ACCOUNTING TODAY; the business newspaper for the tax and accounting community. Text in English. 1987. bi-w. (except Apr., Aug.). USD 99 domestic; USD 113 foreign (effective 2005). adv. bk.rev. illus.; tr.lit. back issues avail.; reprints avail. **Document type:** *Newspaper, Trade.* **Description:** Reports the news of the profession, emphasizing the people, organizations, technology, emerging issues and competitive strategies that influence the field's direction.
Related titles: Online - full text ed.: (from bigchalk, EBSCO Publishing, Factiva, Florida Center for Library Automation, Gale Group, LexisNexis, Northern Light Technology, Inc., O C L C Online Computer Library Center, Inc., ProQuest Information & Learning); Supplement(s): C P A Wealth Provider. 2001. free with subscr. to any financial planning publication by Source Media, Inc.
Indexed: ATI, LRI, SoftBase.
—**CCC.**
Published by: Source Media, Inc., One State St Plaza, 27th Fl, New York, NY 10004. TEL 212-803-6077, 800-221-1809, FAX 212-747-1154, custserv@sourcemedia.com, http://www.sourcemedia.com. Ed. Bill Carlino. Circ: 32,000.

657   USA   ISSN 1531-4340
HF5681.B2
ACCOUNTING TRENDS & TECHNIQUES. Text in English. 1962. a. reprint service avail. from PSC.
—BLDSC (0573.704000).
Published by: American Institute of Certified Public Accountants, Harborside Financial Ctr., 201 Plaza Three, 3rd Fl, Jersey City, NJ 07311-9801. TEL 888-777-7077, FAX 800-302-5766, journal@aicpa.org, http://www.aicpa.org.

657   USA
ACCREDITATION COUNCIL FOR ACCOUNTANCY AND TAXATION. ACTION LETTER. Text in English. q. membership. **Document type:** *Newsletter.*
Formerly: Accreditation Council for Accountancy. Action Letter
Published by: Accreditation Council for Accountancy and Taxation, 1010 N Fairfax St, Alexandria, VA 22314-1574. TEL 703-549-6400, FAX 703-549-2984. Circ: 6,000 (controlled).

ACTUARIAL UPDATE. see *INSURANCE*

ADMINISTRATIE EN BEHEER. see *RELIGIONS AND THEOLOGY—Protestant*

657   USA   ISSN 0882-6110
HF5601
ADVANCES IN ACCOUNTING. Text in English. 1984. a., latest vol.21, 2005. price varies. 192 p./no.; back issues avail. **Document type:** *Monographic series, Academic/Scholarly.* **Description:** Provides a forum for discourse among and between academic and practicing accountants on issues of significance to the future of the discipline.
Related titles: Online - full text ed.: (from ScienceDirect); ◆ Supplement(s): Advances in Accounting. Supplement. ISSN 1046-5715.
Indexed: ATI.
—BLDSC (0697.220000). **CCC.**
Published by: J A I Press Inc. (Subsidiary of: Elsevier Science & Technology), 360 Park Ave S, New York, NY 10010-1710. TEL 212-989-5800, FAX 212-633-3990, usinfo-f@elsevier.com, http://www.elsevier.com/wps/find/bookseriesdescription.cws_home/BS_AA/description. Ed. Philip Reckers.

657   GBR   ISSN 1475-1488
HF5630
ADVANCES IN ACCOUNTING BEHAVIORAL RESEARCH. Text in English. 1998. a., latest vol.6, 2003. price varies. **Document type:** *Monographic series, Academic/Scholarly.* **Description:** Publishes articles encompassing all areas of accounting that incorporate theory from and contribute new knowledge and understanding to the fields of applied psychology, sociology, management science, and economics.
Related titles: Online - full text ed.: (from ScienceDirect).
—BLDSC (0967.221500).
Published by: Elsevier Ltd. (Subsidiary of: Elsevier Science & Technology), The Boulevard, Langford Ln, Kidlington, Oxford, OX5 1GB, United Kingdom. TEL 44-1865-843000, FAX 44-1865-843010, nlinfo-f@elsevier.nl, http://www.sciencedirect.com/science/bookseries/14751488, http://www.elsevier.com. Ed. James E Hunton.

657.0711   USA   ISSN 1527-893X
HF5630
➤ **ADVANCES IN ACCOUNTING EDUCATION**; teaching and curriculum innovations. Text in English. 1996. a., latest vol.6, 2005. price varies. illus. back issues avail.; reprints avail. **Document type:** *Academic/Scholarly.* **Description:** Meets the needs of individuals interested in the education process in the field of accounting.
Formerly (until 1998): Accounting Education (1085-4622)
Related titles: Online - full text ed.: (from EBSCO Publishing).
Indexed: ABIn.
—**CCC.**
Published by: J A I Press Inc. (Subsidiary of: Elsevier Science & Technology), 360 Park Ave S, New York, NY 10010-1710. TEL 212-989-5800, 800-325-4177, FAX 212-633-3990, usinfo-f@elsevier.com, http://www.elsevier.com/wps/find/bookseriesdescription.cws_home/BS_AAE/description. Eds. B N Schwartz, J Edward Ketz.

657   USA
HF5679
ADVANCES IN ACCOUNTING INFORMATION SYSTEMS. Text in English. 1992. irreg., latest vol.6, 1998. price varies. back issues avail. **Document type:** *Monographic series, Academic/Scholarly.*
Indexed: ATI, Inspec.
—BLDSC (0697.222000).
Published by: J A I Press Inc. (Subsidiary of: Elsevier Science & Technology), 360 Park Ave S, New York, NY 10010-1710. TEL 212-989-5800, FAX 212-633-3990, usinfo-f@elsevier.com, http://www.elsevier.com/inca/tree/?key=B1AAIS. Eds. K W Harmon, S G Sutton, V Arnold.

657   USA   ISSN 1046-5715
HF5601
ADVANCES IN ACCOUNTING. SUPPLEMENT. Text in English. 1989. irreg. price varies. **Document type:** *Monographic series, Trade.*
Related titles: ◆ Supplement to: Advances in Accounting. ISSN 0882-6110.
Published by: J A I Press Inc. (Subsidiary of: Elsevier Science & Technology), 360 Park Ave S, New York, NY 10010-1710. TEL 212-989-5800, FAX 212-633-3990, usinfo-f@elsevier.com, http://www.elsevier.com.

657   USA   ISSN 0897-3660
HF5601
➤ **ADVANCES IN INTERNATIONAL ACCOUNTING.** Text in English. 1987. a. price varies. back issues avail. **Document type:** *Monographic series, Academic/Scholarly.* **Description:** Examines how the advancements in the development of accounting and its related disciplines affect the financial reporting and disclosure practices, taxation, management accounting practices, and auditing of multinational corporations, as well as their effect on the education of professional accountants worldwide.
Related titles: Online - full text ed.: (from ScienceDirect); Supplement(s): ISSN 1543-6551.
Indexed: ABIn, ATI.
—BLDSC (0709.253250), IE, ingenta. **CCC.**
Published by: (University of Cincinnati, Department of Accounting and Information Systems), J A I Press Inc. (Subsidiary of: Elsevier Science & Technology), 360 Park Ave S, New York, NY 10010-1710. TEL 212-989-5800, FAX 212-633-3990, usinfo-f@elsevier.com, http://www.elsevier.com/wps/find/bookdescription.cws_home/BS_AIA/description#description.

657   USA   ISSN 1474-7871
ADVANCES IN MANAGEMENT ACCOUNTING. Text in English. 1992. irreg., latest vol.13, 2004. price varies. back issues avail. **Document type:** *Monographic series, Academic/Scholarly.* **Description:** Publishes articles on a variety of current topics in management accounting that are relevant to both practitioners and academicians.
Related titles: Online - full text ed.: (from ScienceDirect).
Indexed: ATI.
—BLDSC (0709.336000), ingenta.
Published by: J A I Press Inc. (Subsidiary of: Elsevier Science & Technology), 360 Park Ave S, New York, NY 10010-1710. TEL 212-989-5800, FAX 212-633-3990, usinfo-f@elsevier.com, http://www.elsevier.com/wps/find/bookseriesdescription.cws_home/BS_ADVMA/description. Eds. J Y Lee, M J Epstein.

▼ *new title*   ➤ *refereed*   ✱ *unverified*   ◆ *full entry avail.*

657 USA ISSN 1041-7060
HD60
ADVANCES IN PUBLIC INTEREST ACCOUNTING. Text in English. 1986. irreg., latest vol.11, 2005. price varies. back issues avail. **Document type:** *Monographic series, Academic/Scholarly.*
Related titles: Online - full text ed.: (from ScienceDirect).
Indexed: ATI.
—BLDSC (0711.120000). **CCC.**
Published by: J A I Press Inc. (Subsidiary of: Elsevier Science & Technology), 360 Park Ave S, New York, NY 10010-1710. TEL 212-989-5800, FAX 212-633-3990, usinfo-f@elsevier.com, http://www.elsevier.com/wps/find/bookdescription.cws_home/BS_APIA/description#description. Ed. C Lehman.

657 332 SGP ISSN 1061-8910
HG174
ADVANCES IN QUANTITATIVE ANALYSIS OF FINANCE AND ACCOUNTING. Text in English. 1991; N.S. 2004. a., latest vol.2. price varies. **Document type:** *Monographic series, Academic/Scholarly.*
Indexed: ATI.
—BLDSC (0711.140000). **CCC.**
Published by: World Scientific Publishing Co. Pte. Ltd., 5 Toh Tuck Link, Singapore, 596224, Singapore. TEL 65-466-5775, FAX 65-467-7667, series@wspc.com.sg, http://www.wspc.com/books/series/aqafa_series.shtml, http://www.worldscientific.com. Ed. Cheng-Few Lee. **Subscr. to:** Farrer Rd, PO Box 128, Singapore 912805, Singapore. TEL 65-382-5663, FAX 65-382-5919. **Dist. by:** World Scientific Publishing Ltd., 57 Shelton St, London WC2H 9HE, United Kingdom. TEL 44-20-78360888, FAX 44-20-78362020, sales@wspc.co.uk.; World Scientific Publishing Co., Inc., 1060 Main St, River Edge, NJ 07661. TEL 201-487-9655, 800-227-7562, FAX 201-487-9656, 888-977-2665, wspc@wspc.com.

657 IDN ISSN 0002-3892
HF5601
AKUNTANSI & ADMINISTRASI✶; Indonesian journal of accountancy. Text in English, Indonesian. 1962. m. IDR 3,000. adv.
Media: Duplicated (not offset).
Published by: Ikatan Akuntan Indonesia, Jalan Tosari 26, Jakarta, Indonesia. Ed. B Soenasto. Circ: 2,000.

657 336 BEL ISSN 0772-6465
ALGEMEEN FISKAAL TIJDSCHRIFT; informatie voor de belastingkundige en de administratieve en financiele managers. Short title: A F T. Text in Flemish. 1949. m. (except Jul. & Aug.). index. Supplement avail. **Description:** Details trends in national and local taxation.
Related titles: Ed.: Revue Generale de Fiscalite. ISSN 0772-6473. 1970. BEF 8,586.
Published by: C E D Samsom (Subsidiary of: Wolters Samsom Belgie n.v.), Kouterveld 14, Diegem, 1831, Belgium. TEL 32-2-7231111. Ed. A Tiberghein.

657 USA ISSN 0732-6815
AMERICAN ACCOUNTING ASSOCIATION. COLLECTED ABSTRACTS OF THE ANNUAL MEETING. Text in English. 1975. a. illus.
Formerly (until 1980): American Accounting Association. Collected Papers of the Annual Meeting (0270-6059)
Indexed: ATI.
—CCC.
Published by: American Accounting Association, 5717 Bessie Dr, Sarasota, FL 34233-2399. TEL 941-921-7747, FAX 941-923-4093. R&P Mary Cole.

657 USA
AMERICAN GROUP DIRECTORY OF SPECIALIZED KNOWLEDGE✶. Text in English. irreg. **Document type:** *Directory.*
Published by: American Group of C P A Firms, 17W662 Butterfield Rd., Ste. 303, Oakbrook Terrace, IL 60181-4006. TEL 708-916-0300.

657 USA
AMERICAN GROUP OF C P A FIRMS. CHRONICLE✶. (Certified Public Accountant) Text in English. irreg. **Document type:** *Trade.*
Published by: American Group of C P A Firms, 17W662 Butterfield Rd., Ste. 303, Oakbrook Terrace, IL 60181-4006. TEL 708-916-0300.

657.029 USA ISSN 0743-3948
HF5616.U5
AMERICAN INSTITUTE OF CERTIFIED PUBLIC ACCOUNTANTS. DIRECTORY OF MEMBER FIRMS. Text in English. a. **Document type:** *Directory.*
Published by: American Institute of Certified Public Accountants, Harborside Financial Ctr., 201 Plaza Three, 3rd Fl, Jersey City, NJ 07311-9801. TEL 888-777-7077, FAX 800-302-5766, journal@aicpa.org, http://www.aicpa.org.

657.84 USA
AMERICAN INSTITUTE OF CERTIFIED PUBLIC ACCOUNTANTS. PUBLIC OVERSIGHT BOARD. ANNUAL REPORT. Text in English. 1979. a. **Document type:** *Corporate.*
Indexed: ATI.
Published by: American Institute of Certified Public Accountants, Harborside Financial Ctr., 201 Plaza Three, 3rd Fl, Jersey City, NJ 07311-9801. TEL 888-777-7077, FAX 800-302-5766, journal@aicpa.org, http://www.aicpa.org. Circ: 8,000.

657 USA ISSN 1096-4282
ANNUAL EDITIONS: ACCOUNTING. Text in English. 1998. a., latest 1998, 2nd ed. USD 20.31 per vol. (effective 2004). illus. **Document type:** *Academic/Scholarly.*
Published by: McGraw-Hill - Dushkin (Subsidiary of: McGraw-Hill Higher Education), 2460 Kerper Blvd, Dubuque, IA 52001. TEL 800-243-6532, customer.service@mcgraw-hill.com, http://www.dushkin.com/text-data/catalog/0070305781.mhtml. Ed. Aileen Ormiston.

ANSWER BOOK, INCOME TAX LAW PRINCIPLES, INCOME TAX LAW APPLICATIONS. see *BUSINESS AND ECONOMICS—Public Finance, Taxation*

657 GBR ISSN 1368-2318
APPLIED ACCOUNTING RESEARCH SERIES. Text in English. 1996. irreg. **Document type:** *Monographic series.*
—BLDSC (1571.394000).
Published by: University of the West of England, Bristol Business School, Frenchay Campus, Coldharbour Lane, Bristol, BS16 1QY, United Kingdom. http://www.uwe.ac.uk/bbs.

657 GBR ISSN 1368-2288
HF5681.B2
APPLYING G A A P. Text in English. 1992. a.
—BLDSC (1580.113600).
Published by: Institute of Chartered Accountants in England and Wales, Chartered Accountants' Hall, PO Box 433, London, EC2P 2BJ, United Kingdom. TEL 44-20-78333291, FAX 44-20-78332085.

657 USA
APPLYING G A A P AND G A A S. (Generally Accepted Accounting Principles and Generally Accepted Accounting Standards) Text in English. 1985. irreg. (in 2 vols.). looseleaf. USD 358 (effective 2002). **Description:** Provides information on how to handle all aspects of financial reporting, including debt, equity, operations, income taxes, investments, pensions and leases. Covers the interrelationship of accounting and auditing.
Related titles: CD-ROM ed.: USD 385 (effective 2002).
Published by: Matthew Bender & Co., Inc. (Subsidiary of: LexisNexis North America), 1275 Broadway, Albany, NY 12204. international@bender.com, http://bender.lexisnexis.com. Ed. Paul Munter.

657 USA
APPLYING GOVERNMENT ACCOUNTING PRINCIPLES. Text in English. 1990. base vol. plus a. updates. looseleaf. USD 241 base vol(s). (effective 2005). **Description:** covers virtually every aspect of accounting and financial reporting for state and local governments, as well as federal government programs.
Published by: Matthew Bender & Co., Inc. (Subsidiary of: LexisNexis North America), 1275 Broadway, Albany, NY 12204. TEL 518-487-3575, 800-252-9257, FAX 518-462-3788, international@bender.com, http://bender.lexisnexis.com. Ed. Mortimer Dittenhofer.

657.6 USA
APPLYING GOVERNMENT AUDITING STANDARDS. Text in English. 1990. base vol. plus a. updates. looseleaf. USD 204 base vol(s). (effective 2005). **Description:** includes the single audit act and its amendments, assessing risk, reviewing internal controls, gathering evidence, independence, quality control, detecting fraud and analyzing financial statements.
Published by: Matthew Bender & Co., Inc. (Subsidiary of: LexisNexis North America), 1275 Broadway, Albany, NY 12204. TEL 518-487-3575, 800-252-9257, FAX 518-462-3788, international@bender.com, http://bender.lexisnexis.com. Ed. Mortimer Dittenhofer.

657.0711 GBR ISSN 0263-1768
APPROVED COURSES FOR ACCOUNTANCY EDUCATION. Text in English. 1981. a. free.
Formerly: Degree Studies and the Accountancy Profession
Published by: Board of Accreditation of Educational Courses, Central Milton Keynes, P.O. Box 686, London, MK9 2PB, United Kingdom. Circ: 10,000.

ART LAW & ACCOUNTING REPORTER. see *LAW*

657 HKG ISSN 1608-1625
ASIA - PACIFIC JOURNAL OF ACCOUNTING & ECONOMICS. Text in English. 1993. s-a. USD 35 to individuals; USD 50 to institutions (effective 2001). **Document type:** *Journal, Academic/Scholarly.* **Description:** Publishes high quality original research that rigorously applies economic or legal theory to accounting issues and problems, with an emphasis on empirical research.
Formerly (until 2000): Asia - Pacific Journal of Accounting (1029-3574)
—BLDSC (1742.260678), IE, ingenta.
Published by: City University of Hong Kong, Dept. of Accountancy, c/o Kate Walsh, 83 Tat Chee Ave, Kowloon, Hong Kong. ackate@cityu.edu.hk, http://fbweb.cityu.edu.hk/ac/. Eds. Dan A Simunic, Ferdinand A Gul.

657 AUS ISSN 1321-7348
ASIAN REVIEW OF ACCOUNTING. Text in English. 1992. s-a. AUD 55 to individuals; AUD 88 to institutions (effective 2001).
Related titles: Online - full text ed.
Published by: Curtin University of Technology, School of Accounting, GPO U 1987, Perth, W.A. 6845, Australia. TEL 61-8-9266-7906, FAX 61-8-9266-7196, wardb@cbs.curtin.edu.au, http://www.cbs.curtin.edu.au/acc/ANSA/ARA.HTM. Ed. Dennis Taylor.

657 USA ISSN 0883-7384
ASSET. Text in English. 1952. m. adv. **Document type:** *Newsletter.* **Description:** Covers news of the accounting profession in Missouri, educational seminars and technical information.
Related titles: Online - full text ed.
Indexed: ATI.
Published by: Missouri Society of Certified Public Accountants, 275 N. Lindbergh Blvd., Ste. 10, St. Louis, MO 63141. TEL 314-997-7966, FAX 314-997-2592, http://www.MOCP.org. Ed., Adv. contact Kristen Templin. Circ: 7,250.

657 333.33 USA ISSN 1094-3528
ASSISTED HOUSING FINANCIAL MANAGEMENT INSIDER. Text in English. bi-m. USD 229; USD 379 combined subscription print & online (effective 2004). **Document type:** *Newsletter.* **Description:** Explains how to comply with HUD regulatory requirements for accounting and auditing for federally assisted housing.
Formerly: Assisted Housing Accounts and Audits Insider
Published by: Brownstone Publishers, Inc., 149 Fifth Ave, 16th Fl, New York, NY 10010-6801. TEL 212-473-8200, FAX 212-473-8786, custserv@brownstone.com, http://www.brownstone.com. Ed. Carolyn Zezima. Circ: 1,100 (paid).

657 USA
ASSOCIATION OF INSOLVENCY & RESTRUCTURING ADVISORS NEWSLETTER. Text in English. bi-m. membership. adv. bk.rev. **Document type:** *Newsletter.*
Formerly: Association of Insolvency Accountants Newsletter
Published by: Association of Insolvency & Restructuring Advisors, 221 W. Stewart Ave., Ste. 207, Medford, OR 97501-3647. TEL 541-858-1665, FAX 541-858-9187, aira@airacira.org, http://www.airacira.org. Ed., R&P Grant Newton. Circ: 1,100 (paid).

647 UKR
ATLANTA - NALOGI I BUKHGALTERSKII UCHET. Text in Ukrainian. w. USD 445 in United States.
Published by: Korporatsiya Atlanta, A-ya 19, Kharkov, 310052, Ukraine. TEL 380-57-24474. **US dist. addr.:** East View Information Services, 3020 Harbor Ln. N., Minneapolis, MN 55447. TEL 612-550-0961.

ATTORNEY - C P A. see *LAW—Corporate Law*

ATTORNEY'S HANDBOOK OF ACCOUNTING, AUDITING AND FINANCIAL REPORTING. see *LAW—Corporate Law*

657 USA
ATTORNEY'S REPORT. Text in English. q. membership only. **Document type:** *Newsletter.*
Published by: Associated Regional Accounting Firms, 3700 Crestwood Pky N W, Duluth, GA 30136-5599. TEL 770-279-4560.

657 FRA ISSN 1624-6969
AUDIT; revue francaise de l'Audit Interne. Text in French. 1971. 5/yr. EUR 76.22 (effective 2001). adv. bk.rev. **Document type:** *Bulletin.*
Formerly (until 1999): Revue Francaise de l'Audit Interne (0762-4301)
Published by: Institut de l'Audit Interne, 40 av. Hoche, Paris, 75008, France. TEL 33-1-53535900, FAX 33-1-45624089, institut@ifaci.com, http://www.ifaci.com. Ed., Adv. contact Pascale du Mesnildot. Pub. Xavier de Phily. Circ: 4,500.

657 AUS ISSN 0816-4746
AUDIT GUIDE. Text in English. 1985. irreg., latest vol.5, 1999. price varies. **Document type:** *Monographic series.*
Published by: Australian Accounting Research Foundation, 211 Hawthorn Rd, Caulfield, VIC 3162, Australia. TEL 61-3-95243600, FAX 61-3-95235499, standard@aarf.asn.au. Circ: 1,000. **Co-sponsors:** Institute of Chartered Accountants in Australia; Australian Society of Certified Practising Accountants.

657.6 332.1 RUS
➤ **AUDIT I FINANSOVYI ANALIZ/AUDIT AND FINANCIAL ANALYSIS.** Text in Russian, English. 1995. q. RUR 8,920 domestic; USD 285 foreign (effective 2003). bk.rev. 500 p./no.; **Document type:** *Magazine, Trade.* **Description:** Analyzes the Russian financial situation and presents alternatives for ending the crisis. Provides an overview of general and bank audits; training materials on internal and external audits, as well as financial and economic analysis; national and international accounting and audit standards. Also makes recommendations on how to develop and optimize business plans.
Formerly: Audit i Finansovyi Analiz, Problemy Vosstanovleniya Ucheta
Related titles: CD-ROM ed.; E-mail ed.

Indexed: RASB, RefZh.
Published by: Izdatel'stvo Komp'yuternyi Audit/Publishing House Computer Audit, Graivoronovskaya ul 8-2, kom 45, Moscow, 109518, Russian Federation. TEL 7-095-1731822, http://www.optim.ru/fin. Ed. Vladimir V Chistiakov TEL 7-095-9324709. **Subscr. in US to:** East View Information Services, 3020 Harbor Ln. N., Minneapolis, MN 55447. TEL 763-550-0961, FAX 763-559-2931, eastview@eastview.com, http://www.eastview.com. **Co-publisher:** Optim.Ru.

657 RUS ISSN 0234-6745
AUDIT I NALOGOOBLOZHENIE. Text in Russian. 1993. m. USD 109.95 in United States. 48 p./no.; **Document type:** *Magazine.*
Indexed: RASB, RefZh.
Published by: Mezhdunarodnyi Konsul'tativno-pravovoi Tsentr po Nalogooblozheniyu, Prechistenka 10, str 1, k 49, Moscow, 119034, Russian Federation. TEL 7-095-2022198, FAX 7-095-2024221, ain@mkpcn.ru, mkpcn@mkpcn.ru, http://www.auditpress.ru, http://www.mkpcn.ru. Ed. A I Zaichenko. Circ: 3,500.

657 AUS ISSN 1034-3423
AUDIT MONOGRAPH. Text in English. 1990. irreg. price varies. **Document type:** *Monographic series.*
Published by: Australian Accounting Research Foundation, 211 Hawthorn Rd, Caulfield, VIC 3162, Australia. TEL 61-3-95243600, FAX 61-3-95235499, standard@aarf.asn.au. Circ: 1,000. **Co-sponsors:** Institute of Chartered Accountants in Australia; Australian Society of Certified Practising Accountants.

657.6 USA ISSN 0278-0380
HF5667
AUDITING; a journal of practice and theory. Text in English. 1981. s-a. USD 120 (effective 2005). adv. illus. reprint service avail. from PSC. **Description:** Contains technical articles as well as news and reports on current activities of the association.
Related titles: Online - full text ed.: (from EBSCO Publishing, Florida Center for Library Automation, Gale Group, O C L C Online Computer Library Center, Inc., ProQuest Information & Learning).
Indexed: ABIn, ASCA, ATI, CurCont, Emerald, SSCI.
—BLDSC (1789.680000), IDS, IE, Infotrieve, ingenta. **CCC.**
Published by: American Accounting Association, 5717 Bessie Dr, Sarasota, FL 34233-2399. TEL 941-921-7747, FAX 941-923-4093, http://www.indiana.edu/~audsec/newjc.html, http://aaahq.org. Ed. William L Felix Jr. Adv. contact Mary Cole. Circ: 2,000.

657 AUS ISSN 0818-8122
AUDITING DISCUSSION PAPER. Text in English. 1986. irreg. price varies. **Document type:** *Monographic series.*
Published by: Australian Accounting Research Foundation, 211 Hawthorn Rd, Caulfield, VIC 3162, Australia. TEL 61-3-95243600, FAX 61-3-95235499, standard@aarf.asn.au. Circ: 1,000. **Co-sponsors:** Institute of Chartered Accountants in Australia; Australian Society of Certified Practising Accountants.

657 AUS
AUDITING GUIDANCE STATEMENTS. Text in English. 1985. irreg. AUD 6 per issue.
Formerly: Auditing Guidance Release (1031-3117)
Published by: Australian Accounting Research Foundation, 211 Hawthorn Rd, Caulfield, VIC 3162, Australia. TEL 61-3-95243600, FAX 61-3-95235499, standard@aarf.asn.au. Circ: 1,000. **Co-sponsors:** Institute of Chartered Accountants in Australia; Australian Society of Certified Practising Accountants.

657 RUS
AUDITOR. Text in Russian. 1995. m. USD 230 in the Americas (effective 2000).
Indexed: RefZh.
Published by: Izdatel'skii Dom Auditor, Kronshtadskii b-r., 12b, A-ya 133, Moscow, 125212, Russian Federation. TEL 7-095-4521918, FAX 7-095-4521918. Ed. N P Korobochkin.
Dist. by: East View Information Services, 3020 Harbor Ln. N., Minneapolis, MN 55447. TEL 763-550-0961, FAX 763-559-2931.

657 IRN
AUDITOR. Text in Persian, Modern. q.
Address: 77 Ferdowsi Ave., N., Teheran, Iran.

657.6 ESP ISSN 1137-3911
AUDITORIA INTERNA. Text in Spanish. 1985. q.
—CINDOC.
Published by: Instituto de Auditores Internos de Espana, Francisco de Rojas, 5a. Pl., Madrid, 28010, Spain. TEL 34-91-5932345, FAX 34-91-5712354.

657.6 RUS ISSN 1727-8058
AUDITORSKIE VEDOMOSTI. Text in Russian. 1997. m. **Document type:** *Magazine, Trade.*
Published by: Redaktsiya Mezhdunarodnogo Ezhenedel'nika Finansovaya Gazeta, A-ya 598, Glavpochtamt, Moscow, 101000, Russian Federation. fingazeta@fingazeta.ru, http://www.fingazeta.ru/stranic/buklet/av.htm. **Co-sponsors:** Auditorskaya Palata Rossii; Tsentral'nyi Bank Rossiiskoi Federatsii.

657 USA ISSN 1083-9380
AUDITS OF FINANCE COMPANIES; including independent and captive financing activities of other copanies. Text in English. 1988. a.
Published by: American Institute of Certified Public Accountants, Harborside Financial Ctr., 201 Plaza Three, 3rd Fl, Jersey City, NJ 07311-9801. journal@aicpa.org, http://www.aicpa.org.

657.6 USA
AUDITWIRE. Text in English. 1980. bi-m. USD 60 in US & Canada; USD 84 elsewhere; free to members (effective 2005). adv. charts; illus.; stat.; tr.lit. back issues avail. **Document type:** *Newsletter, Trade.* **Description:** Covers IIA members' news and perspectives on current and emerging issues and delivers news about The IIA and the people, events, and issues that shape the profession.
Formerly (until Jan. 1999): I I A Today (0744-1223); Which superseded (in 1981): Internos (0199-9249)
Published by: Institute of Internal Auditors, Inc., 247 Maitland Ave, Altamonte Springs, FL 32701-4201. TEL 407-830-7600, 407-937-1100, FAX 407-831-5171, 407-937-1101, http://www.theiia.org/iia/index.cfm?doc_id=757. R&P Gretchen Gorfine. Adv. contact Paula Short. B&W page USD 1,794, color page USD 3,247. Circ: 40,000.

AUSTRALIA. BUREAU OF STATISTICS. ACCOUNTING SERVICES, AUSTRALIA. see *BUSINESS AND ECONOMICS—Abstracting, Bibliographies, Statistics*

657 305 AUS ISSN 1321-4462
AUSTRALIAN ACCOUNTING LAW JOURNAL. Text in English. 1994. q. AUD 99. bk.rev. back issues avail. **Document type:** *Academic/Scholarly.* **Description:** Provides analysis of the law relating to accounting for scholars, professionals and consumers.
Published by: Australian Law Publishers Pty. Ltd., 254 Hawken Dr, St Lucia, QLD 4067, Australia. TEL 61-7-38709111, FAX 61-7-38702222, la510737@student.uq.edu.au. Ed. Russell Mathews. Circ: 200.

657 AUS ISSN 1037-5570
AUSTRALIAN ACCOUNTING RESEARCH FOUNDATION. ACCOUNTING RESEARCH STUDY. Text in English. 1970. irreg. price varies. **Document type:** *Monographic series, Academic/Scholarly.*
Formerly: Accountancy Research Foundation, Melbourne. Accounting and Auditing Research Committee. Research Studies (0084-5884)
Published by: Australian Accounting Research Foundation, 211 Hawthorn Rd, Caulfield, VIC 3162, Australia. TEL 61-3-95243600, FAX 61-3-95235499, standard@aarf.asn.au. Circ: 1,000. **Co-sponsors:** Institute of Chartered Accountants in Australia; Australian Society of Certified Practising Accountants.

657 AUS ISSN 0818-9404
AUSTRALIAN ACCOUNTING RESEARCH FOUNDATION. DISCUSSION PAPER (ACCOUNTING). Text in English. 1979. irreg. price varies. **Document type:** *Monographic series.*
Published by: Australian Accounting Research Foundation, 211 Hawthorn Rd, Caulfield, VIC 3162, Australia. TEL 61-3-95243600, FAX 61-3-95235499, standard@aarf.asn.au. Circ: 1,000. **Co-sponsors:** Institute of Chartered Accountants in Australia; Australian Society of Certified Practising Accountants.

657 AUS ISSN 1035-6908
HF5601
➤ **AUSTRALIAN ACCOUNTING REVIEW.** Abbreviated title: A A R. Text in English. 1991. 3/yr. AUD 50 to non-members; AUD 60 to institutions. adv. **Document type:** *Academic/Scholarly.* **Description:** Resource for academics, students and all those accountants interested in the theoretical side of their profession.
Related titles: Online - full text ed.: (from bigchalk, Northern Light Technology, Inc., ProQuest Information & Learning).
Indexed: ABIX, ATI, Emerald.
—BLDSC (1796.711000).
Published by: Australian Society of Certified Practising Accountants, Level 28, 385 Bourke St, Melbourne, VIC 3000, Australia. cpaonline@cpaaustralia.com.au, http://www.cpaaustralia.com.au. Ed. Linda M English. Adv. contact Jan Fraser. Circ: 2,400.

657 AUS ISSN 1034-3717
AUSTRALIAN ACCOUNTING STANDARD. Text in English. 1989. irreg. AUD 6 per issue.
Published by: Australian Accounting Research Foundation, 211 Hawthorn Rd, Caulfield, VIC 3162, Australia. TEL 61-3-95243600, FAX 61-3-95235499, standard@aarf.asn.au. Circ: 1,400. **Co-sponsors:** Institute of Chartered Accountants in Australia; Australian Society of Certified Practising Accountants.

657 AUS
AUSTRALIAN SOCIETY OF CERTIFIED PRACTISING ACCOUNTANTS. ANNUAL REPORT. Text in English. a. members only. **Document type:** *Corporate.*
Formerly: Australian Society of Accountants. Annual Report
Related titles: ♦ Supplement to: Intheblack. ISSN 1832-0899.
Published by: Australian Society of Certified Practising Accountants, Level 28, 385 Bourke St, Melbourne, VIC 3000, Australia. cpaonline@cpaaustralia.com.au, http://www.cpaaustralia.com.au.

657 SWE ISSN 1103-5765
B F N INFORMERAR. Text in Swedish. 1987. irreg. (2-5/yr.). **Document type:** *Government.* **Description:** Publishes information on new accounting standards.
Published by: (Bokfoereningsnaemnden), Fritzes Offentliga Publikationer (Subsidiary of: Norstedts Juridik AB), c/o Norstedts Juridik AB, Stockholm, 10647, Sweden. TEL 46-8-690-9090, FAX 46-8-690-9091.

657 SWE ISSN 0346-8208
➤ **BALANS.** Text in Swedish. 1975. m. SEK 555; SEK 222 to students (effective 2005). adv. **Document type:** *Magazine, Trade.*
Published by: Foereningen Autoriserade Revisorer (FAR), PO Box 6417, Stockholm, 11382, Sweden. TEL 46-8-50611243, FAX 46-8-50611244, balans@far.se, sekr@far.se, http://www.far.se/balans. Ed. Aasa Ehlin. Adv. contact Haakan Hansson TEL 46-8-4060510. B&W page SEK 15,500, color page SEK 21,800; trim 186 x 254. Circ: 15,000.

B

657 BEL ISSN 0772-4853
BALANS; nieuwsbrief voor accountancy en financieel management. Text in Dutch. 1982. 22/yr. EUR 237 (effective 2005). index. back issues avail. **Document type:** *Newsletter.*
Related titles: Microfiche ed.; ♦ French ed.: Bilan. ISSN 0772-4861.
Published by: Biblo N.V., Brasschaatsteenweg 308, Kalmthout, 2920, Belgium. TEL 32-3-620-0280, FAX 32-3-620-0363, http://www.fiscologue.be/balans/default.asp. Ed. Jan Van Dijck.

657 332 USA ISSN 0894-3958
HG1707
BANK ACCOUNTING & FINANCE. Text in English. 1987. bi-m. USD 345 (effective 2005). adv. illus. Index. 48 p./no.; reprints avail. **Document type:** *Newsletter, Trade.* **Description:** Provides information for senior-level banking professionals on accounting rules, banking and securities regulation, investment portfolios and asset/liability management.
Related titles: Online - full text ed.: (from EBSCO Publishing, Florida Center for Library Automation, Gale Group, O C L C Online Computer Library Center, Inc., ProQuest Information & Learning).
Indexed: ATI, BLI.
—BLDSC (1861.753500), IE, Infotrieve, ingenta. **CCC.**
Published by: C C H Tax and Accounting (Subsidiary of: Wolters Kluwer N.V.), 2700 Lake Cook Rd, Riverwoods, IL 60015. TEL 847-267-7000, 888-224-7377, FAX 773-866-3895, clairegreene@verizon.net, http://www.bankaccountingandfinance.com, http://tax.cchgroup.com. Ed. Claire Greene. Pub. Mark Fried. adv.: B&W page USD 1,900, color page USD 2,500. Circ: 800 (paid).

BANK AUDITING & ACCOUNTING REPORT. see *BUSINESS AND ECONOMICS—Banking And Finance*

BANK INTERNAL AUDIT: A WORKING GUIDE TO REGULATORY COMPLIANCE. see *BUSINESS AND ECONOMICS—Banking And Finance*

657 150 USA ISSN 1050-4753
HF5601
BEHAVIORAL RESEARCH IN ACCOUNTING. Text in English. 1989. a. USD 20 (effective 2005). back issues avail.; reprint service avail. from PSC. **Description:** Publishes original research related to accounting and how it affects and is affected by individuals and organizations.
Related titles: Microform ed.: (from PQC); Online - full text ed.: (from EBSCO Publishing, Florida Center for Library Automation, Gale Group, O C L C Online Computer Library Center, Inc., ProQuest Information & Learning).
Indexed: ABIn, ATI, JEL, e-psyche.
—BLDSC (1877.780000), IE, Infotrieve, ingenta. **CCC.**
Published by: American Accounting Association, 5717 Bessie Dr, Sarasota, FL 34233-2399. TEL 941-921-7747, FAX 941-923-4093, http://www.hsb.baylor.edu/html/davisc/abo/bria/briahome.htm, http://aaahq.org. Ed. Don W Finn. R&P Mary Cole.

657 CHN
BEIJING CAIKUAI/BEIJING ACCOUNTING. Text in Chinese. bi-m.
Published by: Beijing Caizheng Xuehui, 6 Chegongzhuang Dajie, Xicheng-qu, Beijing, 100044, China. TEL 8314043. Ed. Gao Xuezeng.

BENEFITS COORDINATOR. see *BUSINESS AND ECONOMICS—Personnel Management*

BESTUUR EN BELEID V Z W. see *BUSINESS AND ECONOMICS*

▼ new title ➤ refereed ✶ unverified ♦ full entry avail.

657 DEU ISSN 0930-0597
BILANZ- UND BUCHHALTUNG; Zeitschrift fuer Rechnungswesen und Steuern. Text in German. 1955. 11/yr. EUR 149; EUR 14.60 newsstand/cover (effective 2004). adv. bk.rev. abstr.; stat. index. reprint service avail. from SCH. **Document type:** *Magazine, Trade.*
Formerly (until 1986): Bilanz- und Buchhaltungspraxis (0006-2359)
—CCC.
Published by: Verlag Praktisches Wissen GmbH (Subsidiary of: Wolters Kluwer Deutschland GmbH), Marlener Str 2, Offenburg, 77656, Germany. TEL 49-781-605300, FAX 49-781-59825, W.Strecker@wortpower.de, info@praktisches-wissen.de, http://www.steuern-online.de/gratis-info/biball/?code=&l=0, http://www.praktisches-wissen.de. adv.: B&W page EUR 1,480, color page EUR 2,220. Circ: 3,681 (paid and controlled).

657 DEU ISSN 1432-699X
BILANZBUCHHALTER UND CONTROLLER; Zeitschrift fuer Fuehrungskraefte im Finanz- und Rechnungswesen und Controlling. Text in German. 1977. m. EUR 105 domestic; EUR 125.50 foreign; EUR 72 to students; EUR 9.80 newsstand/cover (effective 2005). adv. bk.rev. back issues avail.; reprint service avail. from SCH. **Document type:** *Journal, Trade.* **Description:** Covers management of financial and accounting affairs.
Formerly: Bilanzbuchhalter (0940-8851)
Indexed: IBR, IBZ.
Published by: (Bundesverband der Bilanzbuchhalter e.V.), Verlag C.H. Beck oHG, Wilhelmstr 9, Munich, 80801, Germany. TEL 49-89-38189338, FAX 49-89-38189398, abo.service@beck.de, http://www.bc-online.de, http://www.beck.de. adv.: B&W page EUR 1,900, color page EUR 3,287.50; trim 186 x 260. Circ: 8,216 (paid and controlled).

657.6 DEU ISSN 1612-1546
BILANZIERUNG PLUS. Text in German. q. EUR 149 (effective 2004). **Document type:** *Journal, Trade.*
Published by: Verlag Praktisches Wissen GmbH (Subsidiary of: Wolters Kluwer Deutschland GmbH), Marlener Str 2, Offenburg, 77656, Germany. TEL 49-781-605300, FAX 49-781-59825, info@praktisches-wissen.de, http://www.praktisches-wissen.de.

BILANZIERUNGS-RICHTLINIEN SPECIAL; Das Special-Wissen fuer alle Bilanzierungsfaelle. see *BUSINESS AND ECONOMICS—Public Finance, Taxation*

657 384.6 GBR ISSN 1467-2782
BILLING & CUSTOMER CARE REVIEW. Text in English. 1995. m.
Formerly (until 1998): Billing Systems Review (1360-922X)
Published by: Phillips Tarifica Ltd (Subsidiary of: Access Intelligence, LLC), 40/41 Furnival St, London, EC4A 1JQ, United Kingdom. TEL 44 171 440 6500, FAX 44 171 831 8552, consult@tarifica.com, http://www.tarifica.com.

657 USA
BOLETIN INTERAMERICANO DE CONTABILIDAD/INTERAMERICAN BULLETIN. Text in English. 1968. bi-m. USD 50; includes Revista Interamericana. **Document type:** *Bulletin.*
Published by: Asociacion Interamericana de Contabilidad/Interamerican Accounting Association, c/o Victor Abreu Paez, Exec Dir, Fontainebleau Exec Center, 275 Fountainebleau Blvd, Ste 245, Miami, FL 33172. TEL 305-225-1991, FAX 305-225-2011. Circ: 2,000 (paid).

657 IND
BOMBAY CHARTERED ACCOUNTANT JOURNAL. Text in English. 1958. m. INR 750 (effective 2003). adv. bk.rev. index. Supplement avail. **Document type:** *Journal, Trade.*
Published by: Bombay Chartered Accountants' Society, Churchgate Mansion 1st Fl., A Rd., Churchgate, Mumbai, Maharashtra 400 020, India. TEL 91-22-22870173, FAX 91-22-22826457, bcas@vsnl.com, http://www.bcasonline.org. Ed. Ashok Dhere. Pub. Narayan Verma. Adv. contact R Mehta. Circ: 13,000.

657.2 USA
BOOKKEEPER'S TAX LETTER. Text in English. 1991. m. USD 143.40. **Document type:** *Newsletter.*
Published by: ProPub Inc., PO Box 102, Wyckoff, NJ 07481-0102. TEL 201-447-6485, FAX 201-447-9356. Pub. Randy Cochran.

657 USA ISSN 0279-1889
CODEN: DNASDD
THE BOTTOMLINE. Text in English. 1974. bi-m. free to members (effective 2005). adv. bk.rev. Index. **Document type:** *Magazine, Trade.* **Description:** Provides information to accountants, controllers and financial officers on hospitality accounting, management, technology, law and more.
Related titles: Online - full text ed.: (from ProQuest Information & Learning).
Indexed: ATI, RRTA.
—BLDSC (2264.027000), IE, ingenta.
Published by: Hospitality Financial and Technology Professionals, 11709 Boulder Ln, Ste 110, Austin, TX 78726-1832. TEL 512-249-5333, FAX 512-249-1533, the bottomline@hftp.org, http://www.hftp.org/publications. adv.: B&W page USD 800, color page USD 1,480. Circ: 4,337 (paid and free).

657 GBR ISSN 0890-8389
HF5601
THE BRITISH ACCOUNTING REVIEW. Text in English. 4/yr. EUR 69 in Europe to individuals; JPY 7,500 in Japan to individuals; USD 60 elsewhere to individuals; EUR 602 in Europe to institutions; JPY 65,000 in Japan to institutions; USD 536 elsewhere to institutions (effective 2006). adv. bk.rev. reprint service avail. from SCH. **Document type:** *Journal, Academic/Scholarly.* **Description:** Provides a forum for communication throughout the world between members of the academic and professional communities concerned with the research and teaching, at degree level and above, of accounting, finance, and cognate disciplines.
Related titles: Online - full text ed.: ISSN 1095-8347. USD 565 (effective 2002) (from EBSCO Publishing, Gale Group, IngentaConnect, O C L C Online Computer Library Center, Inc., ScienceDirect, Swets Information Services).
Indexed: ABIn, ATI, CPM, ERA, ETA, Emerald, IBSS, MEA, RHEA, SEA, SENA, SOMA, TEA.
—BLDSC (2286.864000), IE, Infotrieve, ingenta. **CCC.**
Published by: (British Accounting Association), Academic Press (Subsidiary of: Elsevier Science & Technology), 24-28 Oval Rd, London, NW1 7DX, United Kingdom. TEL 44-20-72674466, FAX 44-20-74822293, apsubs@acad.com, http://www.elsevier.com/locate/bar. Eds. C. Emmanuel, V. Beattie.

657 GBR ISSN 1368-0293
BRITISH INSTITUTE OF INTERNATIONAL AND COMPARATIVE LAW. DIRECTOR'S REPORT. Text in English. 1962. a.
Former titles (until 198?): British Institute of International and Comparative Law. Report (0953-3516); British Institute of International and Comparative Law. Report by the Director on the Activities of the Institute (0524-6180)
—BLDSC (3590.610000).
Published by: British Institute of International and Comparative Law, Charles Clore House, 17 Russell Sq, London, WC1B 5DR, United Kingdom. TEL 44-20-7862-5151, FAX 44-20-7862-5152, info@biicl.org, http://www.biicl.org/.

657.6 DEU
BUCHEN, BILANZIEREN UND STEUERN SPAREN VON A-Z. Text in German. base vol. plus updates 13/yr. EUR 99.70 (effective 2004). **Document type:** *Directory, Trade.*
Published by: Verlag Praktisches Wissen GmbH (Subsidiary of: Wolters Kluwer Deutschland GmbH), Marlener Str 2, Offenburg, 77656, Germany. TEL 49-781-605300, FAX 49-781-59825, info@praktisches-wissen.de, http://www.praktisches-wissen.de.

BUILDING SOCIETY ANNUAL ACCOUNTS MANUAL. see *BUILDING AND CONSTRUCTION*

647 UKR
BUKHGALTERIYA. NALOGI. BIZNES. Text in Russian, Ukrainian. 1995. w. USD 315 in the Americas (effective 2000).
Published by: Asotsyatsiya Rozrobky Ekonomika, A-ya 30, Kiev, 254123, Ukraine. TEL 442-92-22. **Dist. by:** East View Information Services, 3020 Harbor Ln. N., Minneapolis, MN 55447. TEL 763-550-0961, FAX 763-559-2931.

657 RUS
BUKHGALTERSKAYA GAZETA. Text in Russian. s-m. RUR 10 newsstand/cover (effective 2002). **Document type:** *Newspaper, Consumer.*
Published by: Biznes Praktika, Ul Sovetskaya 30, Novosibirsk, 630099, Russian Federation. business@online.nsk.su.

657 RUS
BUKHGALTERSKIE KONSUL'TATSII. Text in Russian. irreg. RUR 912 domestic (effective 2002). **Document type:** *Monographic series.*
Published by: Berator-Press, Ul Khalturinskaya 2, str 2, Moscow, 107392, Russian Federation. TEL 7-095-3639542, http://www.berator.ru.

647 RUS
BUKHGALTERSKII BYULLETEN'. Text in Russian. m.
Address: Profsoyuznaya ul 3, A-ya 10, Moscow, 117036, Russian Federation. TEL 7-095-1299236, FAX 7-095-1246809. Ed. L P Khabarova. **US dist. addr.:** East View Information Services, 3020 Harbor Ln. N., Minneapolis, MN 55447. TEL 612-550-0961.

657 RUS ISSN 0321-0154
BUKHGALTERSKII UCHET. Text in Russian. 1937. m. USD 159.95. index.
Indexed: AEA, RASB, RefZh, WAE&RSA.
—East View.
Published by: Ministerstvo Finansov Rossiiskoi Federatsii, Sadovaya-Triumfal'naya ul 4-10, Moscow, 103006, Russian Federation. TEL 7-095-2992012, FAX 7-095-2998670. Ed. N D Vrublevskii. **US dist. addr.:** East View Information Services, 3020 Harbor Ln. N., Minneapolis, MN 55447. TEL 612-550-0961, FAX 612-559-2931.

647 UKR
BUKHGALTERSKII UCHET I AUDIT. Text in Russian. 1994. m. USD 173 foreign (effective 2005). **Document type:** *Magazine, Trade.* **Description:** Publishes groundwork done by leading scientists in accounting, auditing, taxation, law, foreign economic activities. Full texts of all regulatory documents with regard to accounting and auditing, commentaries.
Published by: Tovarystvo Ekaunting, PO Box 45, Kyiv, 04071, Ukraine. **US dist. addr.:** East View Information Services, 3020 Harbor Ln. N., Minneapolis, MN 55447. TEL 800-477-1005, FAX 800-800-3839, eastview@eastview.com, http://www.eastview.com.

647 RUS
BUKHGALTERSKII UCHET I NALOGI. Text in Russian. bi-m.
Indexed: RASB.
Published by: Izdatel'stvo Delo i Servis, A-ya 530, Moscow, 121096, Russian Federation. TEL 7-095-1489562, FAX 7-095-1617091. Ed. A I Kochetkov. **US dist. addr.:** East View Information Services, 3020 Harbor Ln. N., Minneapolis, MN 55447. TEL 612-550-0961.

657.2 RUS
BUKHGALTERSKII UCHET V TORGOVLE. Text in Russian. 1995. q. **Document type:** *Magazine, Trade.*
Published by: Optim.Ru, ul Amundsena, 15/ 1-7, Moscow, 129343, Russian Federation. TEL 7-095-1800201, audit@optim.ru, http://www.optim.ru/trade. Ed. V Yu Chistyakov TEL 7-095-9324709. Circ: 3,000.

657 RUS
BUKHGALTERSKOYE PRILOZHENIYE. Text in Russian. w.
Related titles: ♦ Supplement to: Ekonomika i Zhizn'. ISSN 1607-0615.
Published by: Izdatel'skii Dom Ekonomicheskaya Gazeta, Bumazhnyi proezd 14, Moscow, 101462, Russian Federation. TEL 7-095-2573153, FAX 7-095-2002297, akdi@akdi.ru, http://www.akdi.ru.

657 658.1511 IDN
BULETIN AKUNTAN MANAJEMEN/MANAGEMENT ACCOUNTANTS COMPARTMENT OF THE INDONESIAN INSTITUTE OF ACCOUNTANTS BULLETIN. Text in Indonesian. 1999. q. free to members. adv. 8 p./no.; back issues avail.
Published by: Ikakan Akantan Indonesia, Kompartemen Akuntan Managemen/Indonesian Institute of Accountant, Management Accountants Compartment, Jl. Sisingamangaraja 59, Jakarta, 12120, Indonesia. TEL 62-21-722-2989, FAX 62-21-724-5078, iai-info@akuntan-iai.or.id. Ed. Eddie M Gunadi. adv.: page IDR 50,000; 3 x 5. Circ: 1,000.

657 IDN
BULETIN ANTARA KITA/PUBLIC ACCOUNTANTS COMPARTMENT OF THE INDONESIAN INSTITUTE OF ACCOUNTANTS BULLETIN. Text in Indonesian. 1992. q. IDR 2,000 (effective 2000).
Published by: The Indonesian Institute of Accountants, Public Accountants Compartment, Jl Sisingamangaraja 59, Jakarta, 12120, Indonesia. TEL 62-21-722-2989, iai-kap@akuntan-iai.or.id. Ed. Firdaus Asikin. Circ: 1,000.

657 FRA ISSN 0220-2352
BULLETIN COMPTABLE & FINANCIER. Text in French. 1978. m. EUR 140 combined subscription print & online eds. (effective 2005). **Document type:** *Bulletin, Trade.*
Related titles: Online - full text ed.
Published by: Editions Francis Lefebvre, 42 rue de Villiers, Levallois-Perret, 92300, France. TEL 33-1-41052222, http://www.efl.fr.

657 FRA ISSN 0984-9114
HJ9925.F8
BULLETIN OFFICIEL DE LA COMPTABILITE PUBLIQUE. Text in French. 1981. m.
Published by: Imprimerie Nationale, BP 514, Douai, Cedex 59505, France. TEL 27-93-70-70, FAX 27-93-70-96.

657 346 USA ISSN 0885-1034
KF1357.A15
BUSINESS ACCOUNTING FOR LAWYERS NEWSLETTER; summary, analysis, and application of current accounting concepts in the practice of law. Text in English. 1984. 8/yr. USD 110. reprint service avail. from PQC. **Document type:** *Newsletter.*
Published by: Practising Law Institute, 810 Seventh Ave, New York, NY 10019. TEL 212-824-5700, 800-260-4754, FAX 800-321-0093, info@pli.edu, http://www.pli.edu. Ed. Samuel P Gunther.

657 USA
BUSINESS ADVISORY CLIENT NEWSLETTER. Text in English. q. **Description:** Promotes role of members as consultants to business.
Published by: C P A Associates International, Inc., Meadows Office Complex, 201 Rte 17 N, Rutherford, NJ 07070-2574. TEL 212-804-8686.

BUSINESS FINANCE. see *BUSINESS AND ECONOMICS—Management*

BUSINESS MONEY. see *BUSINESS AND ECONOMICS—Banking And Finance*

346.063 GBR
BUTTERWORTHS ACCOUNTANTS' LEGAL SERVICE. Text in English. 1993. base vol. plus q. updates. looseleaf. GBP 175 (effective 2000). **Document type:** *Trade.* **Description:** Provides non-specialist accountants with the background legal knowledge that is essential to their work.
Published by: Butterworths Tolley (Subsidiary of: LexisNexis UK (Scottish Office)), Halsbury House, 35 Chancery Ln, London, Mddx WC2A 1EL, United Kingdom. TEL 44-20-74002500, FAX 44-20-7400-2842, order.line@butterworths.co.uk, http://www.butterworths.co.uk, http://www.butterworths.co.uk/. Ed. Denis Keenan.

346.063 GBR
BUTTERWORTHS SOLICITORS ACCOUNTS AND FINANCIAL MANAGEMENT. Text in English. 1999. a. looseleaf. GBP 55. **Description:** Offers all the technical information necessary for advising on compliance work and on financial management projects aimed at improving practice profitability.
Published by: Butterworths Tolley (Subsidiary of: LexisNexis UK (Scottish Office)), Halsbury House, 35 Chancery Ln, London, Mddx WC2A 1EL, United Kingdom. TEL 44-20-74002500, FAX 44-20-7400-2842, order.line@butterworths.co.uk, http://www.butterworths.co.uk, http://www.butterworths.co.uk/.

657 CAN ISSN 0317-6878
CODEN: CAMADJ
C A MAGAZINE. (Chartered Accountant) Text in English. 1911. 10/yr. adv. bk.rev. charts; illus. index. back issues avail.; reprint service avail. from PQC. **Document type:** *Journal, Trade.* **Description:** Covers developments in areas of accounting, auditing, financial management, tax legislation and EDP.
Incorporates (1969-1996): C I C A Dialogue (0045-4982); Former titles (until 1974): C A. Chartered Accountant (0703-685X); (until 1971): Canadian Chartered Accountant (0008-316X)
Related titles: Microform ed.: (from PQC); Online - full text ed.: (from EBSCO Publishing, Factiva, Gale Group, H.W. Wilson, Micromedia ProQuest, O C L C Online Computer Library Center, Inc., ProQuest Information & Learning); French ed.: ISSN 0832-9117. 1911.
Indexed: AAR, ABIn, AHCMS, ATI, BPI, BPIA, BusI, CBCARef, CBPI, CPerI, DPD, Emerald, ICLPL, Inspec, LRI, ManagCont, PAIS, PSI, RefZh, T&II, WBA.
—BLDSC (2943.183000), AskIEEE, CISTI, IE, Infotrieve, ingenta. **CCC.**
Published by: Canadian Institute of Chartered Accountants, 277 Wellington St W, Toronto, ON M5V 3H2, Canada. TEL 416-977-3222, FAX 416-977-8585, camagazine@cica.ca, http://www.camagazine.com/index.cfm/ci_id/13941/la_id/1.htm, http://www.cica.ca/new/index.htm. Ed. Christian Bellavance. Pub. Cairine M Wilson. Adv. contact Landon Anderson TEL 416-204-3255. B&W page CND 4,445, color page CND 5,940; trim 10.88 x 8.13. Circ: 76,635 (paid).

657 GBR ISSN 1352-9021
HF5601
C A MAGAZINE. (Chartered Accountant) Text in English. 1897. m. GBP 45 domestic; GBP 65 foreign; GBP 3.75 newsstand/cover (effective 2003). adv. illus. index. back issues avail. **Document type:** *Journal, Trade.* **Description:** Contains features on technology, personal finance, management, legal developments, and accountancy.
Incorporates (in 1997): C A News; Formerly (until 1993): Accountants Magazine (0001-4761)
Related titles: Microform ed.: (from PQC); ♦ Supplement(s): C A News.
Indexed: AAR, ADPA, ATI, BPIA, BusI, CPM, CPerI, ExcerpMed, IMI, Inspec, ManagCont, T&II.
—BLDSC (2943.182000), AskIEEE, IE, Infotrieve, ingenta. **CCC.**
Published by: Institute of Chartered Accountants of Scotland, CA House, 21 Haymarket Yards, Edinburgh, Scotland EH12 5BH, United Kingdom. TEL 44-131-3437500, FAX 44-131-3437505, publisher@icas.org.uk, http://www.icas.org.uk. Ed., R&P Robert Outram. Pub. David McMurray. Adv. contact Jennifer Whyte. B&W page GBP 1,939, color page GBP 2,723; trim 210 x 297. Circ: 21,984.

657 GBR
➤ **C A S S L NEWSPAPER.** (Chartered Accountant Students' Society of London) Text in English. 1974. bi-m. free to members. adv. bk.rev. **Document type:** *Newsletter, Academic/Scholarly.*
Formerly (until 2000): Libra
Published by: Chartered Accountant Students' Society of London, 15 Basinghall St, London, EC2V 5BR, United Kingdom. TEL 44-20-7776-6934, FAX 44-20-7776-6930, christine@cassl.org.uk, http://www.cassl.org.uk. Ed., Pub. Christine Stocker Gibson. R&P, Adv. contact Christine S Gibson. Circ: 7,000 (controlled).

657 USA ISSN 1081-9525
C F O & CONTROLLER ALERT. (Chief Financial Officer) Text in English. 1995. s-m. USD 299. charts; mkt. **Document type:** *Newsletter.* **Description:** Current information on how financial professionals can increase cash flow and control costs.
Published by: Progressive Business Publications, 370 Technology Dr, Malvern, PA 19355-1315. TEL 610-695-8600, 800-220-5000, FAX 610-647-8089, editor@pbp.com, http://www.pbp.com. Ed. Ron McRae. R&P Curt Brown. Circ: 16,917 (paid).

657 382 CAN
C G A - CANADA RESEARCH FOUNDATION. STUDY PAPERS. (Certified General Accountants) Text in English, French. 1981. irreg. price varies. back issues avail. **Document type:** *Monographic series, Academic/Scholarly.*
Formerly: Canadian Certified General Accountants' Research Foundation. Study Papers
Published by: Certified General Accountants Association of Canada, 1188 W Georgia St, Ste 700, Vancouver, BC V6E 4A2, Canada. TEL 604-669-3555, FAX 604-689-5845. Circ: 700.

657 CAN ISSN 0318-742X
C G A MAGAZINE. Text in English. 1967. 10/yr. CND 30 domestic; CND 45 foreign (effective 2000). adv. bk.rev. illus. **Document type:** *Trade.* **Description:** Covers accounting, auditing, taxation, computers and law for Canadian professional accountants and financial executives.
Former titles: Certified General Accountant (0009-0425); Canadian Certified Accountant (0008-3151)
Related titles: Microfiche ed.: (from MML); Microfilm ed.: (from MML); Microform ed.: (from MML); Online - full text ed.
Indexed: ABIn, ATI, CBCARef, CBPI, CPerI, RefZh.
—BLDSC (3128.541000), IE, Infotrieve, ingenta.
Published by: Certified General Accountants Association of Canada, 1188 W Georgia St, Ste 700, Vancouver, BC V6E 4A2, Canada. TEL 604-669-3555, FAX 604-689-5845, http://www.cga-canada.org. Ed., R&P Alison Arnot. Pub. Lesley Wood. Adv. contact Linda Davies. B&W page CND 2,720, color page CND 3,580; trim 10.88 x 8.38. Circ: 60,000 (paid).

657 CAN ISSN 0068-8983
C I C A HANDBOOK. Text in English. 1968. irreg. looseleaf. CND 95 base vol.; CND 74 supplements (effective 2000). **Document type:** *Trade.*
Related titles: French ed.
Published by: Canadian Institute of Chartered Accountants, 277 Wellington St W, Toronto, ON M5V 3H2, Canada. TEL 416-977-3222, FAX 416-977-8585. Circ: 84,000.

657 GBR
➤ **C I M A QUESTIONS AND SUGGESTED ANSWERS.** Text in English. 1987. s-a. (in 4 vols.). GBP 7.50 per vol.. adv. back issues avail. **Document type:** *Academic/Scholarly.* **Description:** Offers assistance to students studying for their accounting certification exams.
Published by: Chartered Institute of Management Accountants, 63 Portland Pl, London, W1N 4AB, United Kingdom. TEL 44-20-7917-9229, FAX 44-20-7323-1487, pubs@cima.org.uk. R&P R Hawkins. Adv. contact T Walter.

657 658 CAN ISSN 1490-4225
HF5601 CODEN: CMAAEA
C M A MANAGEMENT; for strategic business ideas. Text in English, French. 1926. 10/yr. CND 15 (effective 2005). adv. bk.rev. charts; illus. index. reprint service avail. from PQC. **Document type:** *Magazine, Trade.* **Description:** Information for practitioners of accounting and management.
Former titles: Management for Strategic Business Ideas; (until 1999): C M A Magazine (1207-5183); (until 1995): C M A. Certified Management Accountant (0831-3881); (until 1985): Cost and Management (0010-9592)
Related titles: Microfiche ed.: (from MML); Microfilm ed.: (from PQC); Microform ed.: (from MML); Online - full text ed.: (from EBSCO Publishing, Gale Group, Micromedia ProQuest, O C L C Online Computer Library Center, Inc., ProQuest Information & Learning).
Indexed: ABIn, ADPA, ASEANManA, ATI, BPIA, CBCARef, CBPI, CPerI, DPD, Emerald, Inspec, KES, ManagCont, PMA, PROMT, SSCI, T&II, WorkRelAb.
—BLDSC (3287.175000), AskIEEE, IE, ingenta. **CCC.**
Published by: Society of Management Accountants of Canada, Mississauga Executive Centre, One Robert Speck Pkwy, Ste 1400, Mississauga, ON L4Z 3M3, Canada. TEL 905-949-4200, 800-263-7622, rcolman@managementmag.com, info@cma-canada.org, http://www.managementmag.com, http://www.cma-canada.org/cmacan/. Ed. Rob Colman TEL 905-949-3109. Adv. contact Beth Kukkonen. B&W page CND 4,710, color page CND 6,210; trim 10.88 x 8.13. Circ: 72,336.

657 USA
C P A ASSOCIATES. UPDATE. (Certified Public Accountant) Text in English. bi-m. membership. **Description:** Updates professional staff of members on relevant association changes and developments.
Published by: C P A Associates International, Inc., Meadows Office Complex, 201 Rte 17 N, Rutherford, NJ 07070-2574. TEL 212-804-8686. Circ: 1,600.

336 338 USA
C P A CLIENT BULLETIN. Text in English. 1976. m. USD 195 (effective 2005). **Document type:** *Bulletin, Trade.* **Description:** Covers the range of topics a CPA would discuss with small business and tax clients.
Related titles: Diskette ed.; Online - full text ed.
Indexed: ATI.
Published by: American Institute of Certified Public Accountants, Harborside Financial Ctr., 201 Plaza Three, 3rd Fl, Jersey City, NJ 07311-9801. TEL 201-938-3000, FAX 201-938-3329, journal@aicpa.org, http://www.aicpa.org. Ed. Maria Albanese. Circ: 390,000 (controlled).

C P A CLIENT TAX LETTER. (Certified Public Accountant) see *BUSINESS AND ECONOMICS—Public Finance, Taxation*

657 USA
C P A CONSULTANT. (Certified Public Accountant) Text in English. 1986. bi-m. **Document type:** *Newsletter, Trade.*
Related titles: Online - full text ed.
Indexed: ATI.
Published by: American Institute of Certified Public Accountants, Harborside Financial Ctr., 201 Plaza Three, 3rd Fl, Jersey City, NJ 07311-9801. TEL 201-938-3000, FAX 201-938-3329, http://www.aicpa.org. Ed. William Moran. Pub. Coleen Katz. Circ: 5,500 (controlled).

657 USA ISSN 0743-815X
HF5661
C P A EXAMINATION REVIEW. (Certified Public Accountant) Cover title: Wiley C P A Examination Review. Text in English. 1974. a.
Formerly (until 1974): C P A Examination Review Outlines and Study Guides (0743-8567)
Published by: Professional Publications, Inc., 1250 Fifth Ave, Belmont, CA 94002. TEL 612-332-1022, FAX 612-332-1511, marketing@ppi2pass.com, http://www.ppi2pass.com.

657 USA
C P A EXPERT. Text in English. 1995. q. USD 72 (effective 1999). **Document type:** *Newsletter.* **Description:** Articles on business valuation, damages for personal injury, wrongful termination, and death for providers of business valuation and litigation services.
Published by: (Certified Public Accountant), American Institute of Certified Public Accountants, Harborside Financial Ctr., 201 Plaza Three, 3rd Fl, Jersey City, NJ 07311-9801. TEL 888-777-7077, FAX 800-302-5766, journal@aicpa.org, http://www.aicpa.org. Eds. James R. Rigby, Michael Wagner. Pub. Coleen Katy. Circ: 1,800 (paid); 200 (controlled).

657 USA ISSN 1052-7362
HF5681.B2
C P A FIRM PRACTICE MANUAL (YEAR). (Certified Public Accountant) Text in English. a. USD 139.95; USD 237.95 foreign. **Document type:** *Trade.*
Published by: W G & L Financial Reporting & Management Research (Subsidiary of: R I A), 395 Hudson St, New York, NY 10014. TEL 212-367-6300, FAX 212-367-6718. **Subscr. to:** The Park Square Bldg., 31 St James Ave, Boston, MA 02116-4112. TEL 800-950-1207.

657 USA ISSN 1069-7403
C P A GOVERNMENT AND NONPROFIT REPORT; the CPA's advisory service on government and nonprofit accounting and auditing. Text in English. m. USD 312 (effective 2004). **Document type:** *Newsletter.* **Description:** Gives advice on governmental and nonprofit accounting, auditing nonprofits, coverage of government reporting issues, overviews of FASB,GASB,GAO,AICPA projects, and more.
Related titles: Online - full text ed.: (from Florida Center for Library Automation, Gale Group).
Indexed: ATI.
—**CCC.**
Published by: Aspen Publishers, Inc. (Subsidiary of: Wolters Kluwer N.V.), 5301 Buckeystown Pike, Ste. 400, Frederick, MD 21704-8319. customer.service@aspenpubl.com, http://www.aspenpublishers.com. Ed. Rhett D Harrell.

657 USA ISSN 0732-8435
HF5601 CODEN: CPAABS
THE C P A JOURNAL. (Certified Public Accountants) Text in English. 1930. m. USD 42 domestic; USD 21 domestic to students; USD 54 foreign (effective 2005). adv. bk.rev. illus. reprint service avail. from PQC. **Document type:** *Magazine, Trade.* **Description:** Studies accounting, auditing, personal financial planning and estate planning.
Former titles (until 1975): The C P A (0732-8443); (until 1975): C P A Journal (0094-2049); (until 1972): Certified Public Accountant (0886-3253); New York Certified Public Accountant: C P A (0028-7148)
Related titles: Online - full text ed.: 1930 (from EBSCO Publishing, Florida Center for Library Automation, Gale Group, H.W. Wilson, O C L C Online Computer Library Center, Inc., ProQuest Information & Learning, The Dialog Corporation).
Indexed: AAR, ABIn, ADPA, ATI, BPI, BPIA, Emerald, ManagCont, PSI, T&II.
—BLDSC (3486.170000), IE, Infotrieve, ingenta.
Published by: New York State Society of Certified Public Accountants, 530 Fifth Ave, 5th Fl, New York, NY 10036-5101. TEL 212-719-8300, 800-697-7272, FAX 410-893-8004, http://www.nysscpa.org. Eds. Louis Grumet, Robert Colson. Pub. Louis Grumet. adv.: B&W page USD 2,966, color page USD 5,278. Circ: 40,000 (paid).

657 IRL
C P A JOURNAL OF ACCOUNTANCY. Text in English. 1941. q. adv. bk.rev. **Document type:** *Journal, Trade.* **Description:** Features include legislation, finance and banking, insurance, taxation, education, computing, business and management.
Formerly: C P A Newsletter
Published by: Institute of Certified Public Accountants in Ireland, 9 Ely Pl., Dublin, 2, Ireland. TEL 353-1-6767353, FAX 353-1-6612367. Ed., Adv. contact Deirdre McDonnell. Circ: 2,900.

657 USA ISSN 0094-792X
HF5601
THE C P A LETTER; a news report to members. Text in English. 1920. s-m. (except July-Aug. & Feb.-Mar. combined). free to members; USD 40 to non-members (effective 2005). bk.rev. bibl. back issues avail. **Document type:** *Newsletter, Trade.*
Related titles: Online - full text ed.: (from EBSCO Publishing, Florida Center for Library Automation, Gale Group, LexisNexis, ProQuest Information & Learning).
Indexed: ATI.
—CCC.
Published by: American Institute of Certified Public Accountants, Harborside Financial Ctr., 201 Plaza Three, 3rd Fl, Jersey City, NJ 07311-9801. TEL 888-777-7077, FAX 800-302-5766, journal@aicpa.org, http://www.aicpa.org/pubs/cpaltr/index.htm. Ed. Ellen J Goldstein. Circ: 330,000.

657 USA
C P A MAGAZINE. (Certified Public Accountant) Text in English. 2002. bi-m. USD 99; USD 25 per issue (effective 2005). adv. **Document type:** *Magazine, Trade.*
Published by: Magazine Publishing Group, 400 Ginger Ct, Southlake, TX 76092. TEL 817-442-1166, FAX 817-442-1177, cpa@cpamag.com. Pub. T Allen Rose TEL 817-442-1166. Adv. contact Jason Pickett. B&W page USD 4,200. Circ: 24,323.

657 658 USA ISSN 0894-1815
CODEN: PFBLA2
C P A MANAGING PARTNER REPORT; management news for accounting executives. Text in English. 1984. m. looseleaf. USD 396 (effective 2004). back issues avail. **Document type:** *Newsletter.* **Description:** Provides partners with problem-solving tactics and management methods that can help the firm maintain stability and enhance profitability as it strives to achieve short-term and long-range goals.
Related titles: Online - full text ed.: (from EBSCO Publishing).
Indexed: ATI.
—CCC.
Published by: Aspen Publishers, Inc. (Subsidiary of: Wolters Kluwer N.V.), 111Eighth Ave., 7th Fl, New York, NY 10011. TEL 212-771-0600, FAX 212-771-0885, custserv@aspenpub.com, customer.service@aspenpubl.com, http://www.aspenpub.com, http://www.aspenpublishers.com.

C P A MARKETING REPORT. see *BUSINESS AND ECONOMICS—Marketing And Purchasing*

C P A PERSONNEL REPORT. see *BUSINESS AND ECONOMICS—Personnel Management*

657 USA ISSN 1541-1532
HF5733.F6
▼ **C P A 'S GUIDE TO MANAGEMENT LETTER COMMENTS.** (Certified Public Accountant) Text in English. 2003. a. USD 179 newsstand/cover (effective 2003).
Published by: Aspen Publishers, Inc. (Subsidiary of: Wolters Kluwer N.V.), 111Eighth Ave., 7th Fl, New York, NY 10011. TEL 212-771-0600, FAX 212-771-0885, http:// www.aspenpublishers.com.

THE C P A TECHNOLOGY ADVISOR. (Certified Public Accountant) see *BUSINESS AND ECONOMICS—Computer Applications*

C R I OCCASIONAL PAPERS. see *PUBLIC ADMINISTRATION*

C R I PROCEEDINGS SERIES. see *PUBLIC ADMINISTRATION*

657 USA
C S A SENTINEL. (Control Self-Assessment) Text in English. 1996. 3/yr. USD 40 (effective 2001). adv. tr.lit.; charts; illus. back issues avail. **Document type:** *Newsletter, Trade.* **Description:** Covers all aspects of control self-assessment (CSA), offering a forum for CSA practicioners to exchange ideas and experiences with other professionals worldwide.
Related titles: E-mail ed.
Published by: Institute of Internal Auditors, Inc., 247 Maitland Ave, Altamonte Springs, FL 32701-4201. TEL 407-830-7600, FAX 407-830-4832, http://www.theiia.org. Ed. Joanne Hodges. R&P Gretchen Gorfine. Adv. contact Paula Short. color page USD 3,000; trim 11 x 8.25. Circ: 850 (paid).

657 346 USA ISSN 0884-7282
C S C P A NEWSLETTER✶ . (Connecticut Society of Certified Public Accountants) Text in English. 1961. 10/yr. looseleaf. membership. adv. **Document type:** *Newsletter.* **Description:** Provides members with news of events of interest to the profession of accountancy in Connecticut. Covers legislation, ethics, regulations, firm news; and profiles members in public service.
Published by: Connecticut Society of Certified Public Accountants, 845 Brook St, Bldg 2, Rocky Hill, CT 06067-3405. TEL 860-549-3596, FAX 860-525-1153, http://www.cs-cpa.org. Ed., R&P Mark Zampino. Adv. contact Lisa Trescot.

657 CHN ISSN 1009-7546
CAIWU YU KUAIJI DAOKAN/FINANCE AND ACCOUNTING. Text in Chinese. 1978. m. CNY 96 (effective 2004). 80 p./no.; **Document type:** *Journal, Academic/Scholarly.*
Formerly (until 2000): Caiwu yu Kuaiji (1001-3172)
Related titles: Alternate Frequency ed(s).: a. USD 52.70 newsstand/cover (effective 2001).
Published by: Zhongguo Renmin Daxue, Shubao Zilio Zhongxin/Renmin University of China, Information Center for Social Server, Dongcheng-qu, 3, Zhangzizhong Lu, Beijing, 100007, China. TEL 86-10-64039458, FAX 86-10-64015080, kyes@163.net, http://www.confucius.cn.net/bkdetail.asp?fzt=F101. **Dist. in the US by:** China Publications Service, PO Box 49614, Chicago, IL 60649. TEL 312-288-3291, FAX 312-288-8570; **Dist. outside of China by:** China International Book Trading Corp, 35 Chegongzhuang Xilu, Haidian District, PO Box 399, Beijing 100044, China. TEL 86-10-68412045, FAX 86-10-68412023, cibtc@mail.cibtc.com.cn, http://www.cibtc.com.cn/.

657 USA
CALIFORNIA ACCOUNTANCY ACT WITH RULES AND REGULATIONS. Text in English. 1901. quadrennial. USD 5 (effective 1999). **Document type:** *Government.*
Published by: Department of Consumer Affairs, Board of Accountancy, 2000 Evergreen St, Ste 250, Sacramento, CA 95815-3832. TEL 916-263-3680, FAX 916-263-3675, http://www.dcs.ca.gov/cba. Ed., Pub. Carol Sigmann. Circ: 65,000 (controlled).

657 USA ISSN 1530-4035
HF5601
CALIFORNIA C P A. (Certified Public Accountants) Text in English. 1925. 10/yr. USD 75 domestic to non-members; USD 110 foreign to non-members (effective 2005). adv. reprint service avail. from PQC. **Document type:** *Magazine, Trade.*
Former titles (until July 2000): Outlook (Redwood City) (0273-835X); (until 1980): California C P A Quarterly (0008-0934); California Certified Public Accountant
Related titles: Microform ed.: (from PQC); Online - full text ed.: (from bigchalk, EBSCO Publishing, Florida Center for Library Automation, Gale Group, ProQuest Information & Learning); Supplement(s): Techonology Resource Guide. ISSN 1534-2654. 2001.
Indexed: AAR, ATI, BPIA, BusI, Emerald, T&II.
—BLDSC (3012.150000).
Published by: California Society of Certified Public Accountants, 1235 Radio Rd, Redwood City, CA 94065-1217. TEL 650-802-2600, FAX 650-802-2300, clar.rosso@calcpa.org, http://www.calcpa.org/californiacpa. Eds. Aldo Maragoni, Clar Rosso TEL 650-802-2428. R&P Clar Rosso TEL 650-802-2428. Adv. contact Bobbi Petrov. B&W page USD 2,300, color page USD 3,650. Circ: 31,339 (paid and controlled).

657 CAN ISSN 1499-8653
CANADIAN ACCOUNTING PERSPECTIVES/PERSPECTIVES COMPTABLES CANADIENNES. Text in English, French. 2001. s-a. CND 40 to individuals; CND 65 to institutions (effective 2003). **Document type:** *Journal, Academic/Scholarly.* **Description:** Publishes original research, analysis, and commentary of interest to academics, practitioners, financial analysts, financial executives, regulators, and accounting policy makers.
Related titles: Online - full content ed.; Online - full text ed.: (from EBSCO Publishing, Micromedia ProQuest, ProQuest Information & Learning, Swets Information Services).
Indexed: ABIn.
—CCC.
Published by: Canadian Academic Accounting Association/Association Canadienne des Professeurs de Comptabilite, 3997 Chesswood Dr, Toronto, ON M3J 2R8, Canada. TEL 416-486-5361, FAX 416-486-6158, admin@caaa.ca, http://www.caaa.ca/publications/cap.html. Ed. Alan J Richardson.

657 CAN ISSN 0713-357X
HF5616.C2
CANADIAN INSTITUTE OF CHARTERED ACCOUNTANTS. UNIFORM FINAL EXAMINATION REPORT. Text in English. 1979. a. price varies. **Document type:** *Trade.* **Description:** Contains UFE questions and approaches to answering the uniform final examination, as well as the report of the Board of Governors to the Provincial Institutes of Chartered Accountants.
Formerly (until 1980): Canadian Institute of Chartered Accountants. Uniform Final Examination Handbook (0226-0247); Which was formed by the merger of (19??-1979): Approaches to Answering the Uniform Final Examinations plus Examiners' Comments (0318-1081); Which was formerly (until 1969): Institutes of Chartered Accountants in Canada. Solutions. Intermediate and Final Examinations. (0318-109X); (19??-1979): Institutes and Order of Chartered Accountants in Canada. Uniform Final Examination (0703-6981); Which was formerly (until 1977): Institutes of Chartered Accountants in Canada. Final Examinations (0384-8612); (until 1969): Institutes of Chartered Accountants in Canada. Intermediate and Final Examinations (0384-8604)
Related titles: ◆ French ed.: Ordres des Comptables Agrees du Canada et des Bermudes. Annales de l'Examen Final Uniforme. ISSN 0820-0386.
Published by: Canadian Institute of Chartered Accountants, 277 Wellington St W, Toronto, ON M5V 3H2, Canada. TEL 416-977-3222, FAX 416-977-8585. Circ: 10,000.

657 NZL
THE CAPITAL EXPENDITURE. Text in English. a. (Oct.). NZD 350 (effective 2001).
Published by: Liberty Holdings, PO Box 1881, Auckland 1, New Zealand. TEL 64-9-307-1287, 800-658-765, FAX 64-9-373-2634.

657 USA ISSN 1544-158X
HF5601 CODEN: OCPAA7
CATALYST (DUBLIN); the leading edge of Ohio business. Text in English. 1941. bi-m. USD 39.95; USD 10 newsstand/cover (effective 2005). adv. bk.rev. charts; stat. Index. back issues avail.; reprint service avail. from PQC. **Document type:** *Magazine, Trade.* **Description:** Contains articles that are of interest to the practicing certified public accountant. Subject matter dealing with public accounting, auditing, taxes, management services, business issues, technology, and consulting.
Former titles (until 2002): The Ohio C P A Journal (0749-8284); (until 1979): Ohio C P A (0737-7371); (until 1958): Ohio Certified Public Accountant
Related titles: Microform ed.: (from PQC); Online - full text ed.: (from EBSCO Publishing, Gale Group, O C L C Online Computer Library Center, Inc., ProQuest Information & Learning).
Indexed: ABIn, ADPA, ATI, BPIA, Emerald, Inspec, ManagCont, T&II.
—BLDSC (6245.582000), AskIEEE, IE.
Published by: Ohio Society of Certified Public Accountants, 535 Metro Place S, PO Box 1810, Dublin, OH 43017. TEL 614-764-2727, 800-686-2727, FAX 614-764-5880, catalyst@ohio-cpa.com, http://www.ohioscpa.com/. Ed. Sandy Spieker. adv.: color page USD 2,380, B&W page USD 1,667. Circ: 23,000 (controlled).

657 CAN
CERTIFIED MANAGEMENT ACCOUNTANTS SOCIETY OF BRITISH COLUMBIA. UPDATE. Text in English. bi-m. free. adv. back issues avail. **Document type:** *Newsletter.* **Description:** For certified management accountants in British Columbia.
Formerly: Society of Management Accountants of British Columbia. Update
Published by: Certified Management Accountants of British Columbia, 1575 650 W Georgia St, P O Box 11548, Vancouver, BC V6B 4W7, Canada. TEL 604-687-5891, 800-663-9646, FAX 604-687-6688, cmabc@cmabc.com, http://www.cmabc.com. Ed., Pub., R&P, Adv. contact Heather Treleaven.

657 AUS ISSN 1037-6267
CHARTAC ACCOUNTANCY NEWS. Text in English. 1976. fortn. AUD 450 domestic; AUD 409.09 foreign (effective 2004). back issues avail. **Document type:** *Newsletter.* **Description:** Covers the latest news, advice to improve your accounting, management and leadership skills. Contains updates on rule changes, new guidelines and working risks and responsibilities.
Formerly (until 1991): Chartac Accounting Report (0814-8074)
Related titles: Online - full content ed.
Published by: Crown Content, Level 1, 141 Capel St, Nth Melbourne, VIC 3051, Australia. TEL 6-13-93299800, FAX 6-13-93299698, rex@crowncontent.com.au, scott@crowncontent.com.au, http://www.crowncontent.com.au/prod/newsletters/chartac.htm. Ed. Rex Pannell.

657 AUS
CHARTAC TAX PLANNING NEWS. Text in English. 1982. m. looseleaf. AUD 397. back issues avail. **Document type:** *Newsletter.*
Former titles: Chartac Tax Practice Ideas; Chartac Tax Planning News (1037-6275); Chartac Taxation Report (0814-8120); Tax Action Report
Published by: Professional Information Pty. Ltd., 196 Drummond St, Carlton, VIC 3053, Australia. TEL 61-3-662-2822, FAX 61-3-662-3191. Ed. Ashley Gordon McKeon.

657 AUS
HF5601
CHARTER. Text in English. 1930. 11/yr. AUD 85 domestic to non-members; AUD 99 foreign to non-members; free to members (effective 2005). adv. bk.rev. tr.lit. Index. back issues avail. **Document type:** *Magazine, Trade.* **Description:** Provides topical, in-depth coverage on areas of concern to the business professional.
Former titles (until 2003): C A Charter (1446-4543); (until 2002): Charter (1035-0748); (until 1990): Chartered Accountant (1033-1549); (until 1989): Chartered Accountant in Australia (0009-1898)

Related titles: Online - full text ed.
Indexed: AAR, ADPA, ATI, AusPAIS, CompR, Emerald.
—BLDSC (2943.180170), IE, ingenta.
Published by: Institute of Chartered Accountants in Australia, GPO Box 3921, Sydney, NSW 2001, Australia. TEL 61-2-92901344, FAX 61-2-92621512, charter@icaa.org.au, http://www.icaa.org.au/services/index.cfm?menu=311&id=A105934260. Ed. Maureen Jordan. Circ: 38,567.

657 IND ISSN 0009-188X
HF5601
CHARTERED ACCOUNTANT. Text and summaries in English. 1952. m. INR 400; USD 75 foreign. adv. bk.rev. index. **Document type:** *Trade.* **Description:** Provides information on corporate finance, corporate practices, economy, and news of interest to accounting, finance professionals.
Indexed: ATI, BAS.
—BLDSC (3129.973000), IE, ingenta.
Published by: Institute of Chartered Accountants of India, Indraprastha Marg, P O Box 7100, New Delhi, 110 002, India. TEL 91-11-3312055, TELEX 031-62236 CICA IN. Ed. K M Agarwal. Circ: 28,000 (paid); 75,000 (controlled).

657 LKA
CHARTERED ACCOUNTANTS. Text in English, Singhalese, Tamil. 1966. s-a. LKR 85. adv. bk.rev.
Former titles (until 1987): Institute of Chartered Accountants of Sri Lanka. Journal (1015-0005); (until 1977): Accountant; (until 1973): Accountant Journal (0001-4702)
Indexed: ATI.
Published by: Institute of Chartered Accountants of Sri Lanka, 30 A Malalasekera Mawatha, Colombo, 7, Sri Lanka. Circ: 1,000.

657 NZL ISSN 1172-9929
HF5601
CHARTERED ACCOUNTANTS' JOURNAL OF NEW ZEALAND. Text in English. 1922. m. NZD 122 domestic to non-members; NZD 175.50 to non-members in Australia & S. Pacific; NZD 214 to non-members in Asia & N. America; NZD 243 elsewhere to non-members; NZD 98 domestic to members; NZD 157.50 to members in Australia & S. Pacific; NZD 196.88 to members in Asia & N. America; NZD 225 elsewhere to members (effective 2005). adv. bk.rev. bibl.; charts; illus. Index. **Document type:** *Journal, Trade.*
Formerly: Accountants' Journal (0001-4745)
Related titles: Online - full text ed.: (from EBSCO Publishing).
Indexed: ABIn, ADPA, ATI, BPI, Emerald, INZP.
—BLDSC (3129.976950), IE, ingenta. **CCC.**
Published by: Institute of Chartered Accountants, Level 2, Cigna House, 40 Mercer St, PO Box 11 342, Wellington, 6034, New Zealand. TEL 64-4-4747840, FAX 64-4-4736303, registry@icanz.co.nz, http://www.icanz.co.nz/StaticContent/Services/CA_Journal.cfm. Ed. Jean Cryer. R&P Angus McLeod TEL 64-4-474-7842. Adv. contact Maureen McCort.

657 GBR
CHARTERED INSTITUTE OF MANAGEMENT ACCOUNTANTS. ADVANCED MANAGEMENT ACCOUNTING & FINANCE SERIES. Text in English. irreg. price varies. back issues avail. **Document type:** *Monographic series, Trade.* **Description:** Treats a specific area of management accounting in depth and aims to assist undergraduate and postgraduate students in their courses and certification.
Published by: (Chartered Institute of Management Accountants), Academic Press (Subsidiary of: Elsevier Science & Technology), 24-28 Oval Rd, London, NW1 7DX, United Kingdom. TEL 44-20-72674466, FAX 44-20-74822293, apsubs@acad.com, http://www.elsevier.com/. Ed. David Otley. **Orders to:** C.I.M.A., Publishing Sales Department, 63 Portland Pl, London W1N 4AB, United Kingdom. TEL 44-171-917-9229, FAX 44-171-631-5309.

657 GBR
CHARTERED INSTITUTE OF MANAGEMENT ACCOUNTANTS. FINANCIAL SKILLS SERIES. Text in English. 1994. irreg. price varies. **Document type:** *Monographic series.* **Description:** Provides up-to-the minute advice on a variety of specific occupational skills.
Published by: (Chartered Institute of Management Accountants), Kogan Page Ltd., 120 Pentonville Rd, London, N1 9JN, United Kingdom. FAX 44-20-7837-6348. R&P Linda Bathan. **Orders to:** C.I.M.A., Publishing Sales Department, 63 Portland Pl, London W1N 4AB, United Kingdom. TEL 44-171-917-9229, FAX 44-171-631-5309.

657 GBR
CHARTERED INSTITUTE OF MANAGEMENT ACCOUNTANTS. FRAMEWORK SERIES IN ACCOUNTING. Text in English. 1983. irreg. price varies. back issues avail. **Document type:** *Monographic series.* **Description:** Contains news of accounting from various industries and commercial sectors.
Formerly: Institute of Cost and Management Accountants. Framework Series in Accounting
Published by: Chartered Institute of Management Accountants, 63 Portland Pl, London, W1N 4AB, United Kingdom. TEL 44-20-7917-9229, FAX 44-20-7323-1487.

657 GBR
CHARTERED INSTITUTE OF MANAGEMENT ACCOUNTANTS. OCCASIONAL PAPERS SERIES. Text in English. irreg. price varies. back issues avail. **Document type:** *Monographic series.* **Description:** Findings of research carried out under the auspices of the Chartered Institute of Management Accountants Research and Technical Committee.
Formerly: Institute of Cost and Management Accountants. Occasional Papers Series
Published by: Chartered Institute of Management Accountants, 63 Portland Pl, London, W1N 4AB, United Kingdom. TEL 44-20-7637-2311, FAX 44-20-7495-6098, http://www.aicpa.org.uk, http://www.cima.org.uk.

657 GBR
CHARTERED INSTITUTE OF MANAGEMENT ACCOUNTANTS. PROFESSIONAL HANDBOOK SERIES. Text in English. irreg., latest 2002. price varies. back issues avail. **Document type:** *Monographic series, Trade.* **Description:** Helps management accountants keep abreast of key developments in the profession.
Published by: (Chartered Institute of Management Accountants), Butterworth - Heinemann (Subsidiary of: Elsevier Ltd., Books Division), Linacre House, Jordan Hill, Oxford, OX2 8DP, United Kingdom. TEL 44-1865-310366, FAX 44-1865-310898. **Orders in N. America to:** Elsevier Inc., 6277 Sea Harbor Dr., Orlando, FL 32887-4800. TEL 407-345-4000, FAX 407-363-9661, 800-225-6030; **Orders to:** C.I.M.A., Publishing Sales Department, 63 Portland Pl, London W1N 4AB, United Kingdom. TEL 44-171-917-9229, FAX 44-171-631-5309.

657 GBR
CHARTERED INSTITUTE OF MANAGEMENT ACCOUNTANTS. RESEARCH STUDIES. Text in English. irreg. price varies. **Document type:** *Monographic series.*
Published by: Chartered Institute of Management Accountants, 63 Portland Pl, London, W1N 4AB, United Kingdom. TEL 44-20-7917-9229, FAX 44-20-7323-1487.

657 GBR
CHARTERED INSTITUTE OF PUBLIC FINANCE AND ACCOUNTANCY. CONFERENCE HANDBOOK. Text in English. 1890. a. membership.
Published by: Chartered Institute of Public Finance and Accountancy, 3 Robert St, London, WC2N 6RL, United Kingdom. TEL 44-20-7543-5800, FAX 44-20-7543-5700. Circ: (controlled).

657 GBR
CHARTERED INSTITUTE OF PUBLIC FINANCE AND ACCOUNTANCY. MEMBERS' YEARBOOK (YEAR). Text in English. a. membership.
Published by: Chartered Institute of Public Finance and Accountancy, 3 Robert St, London, WC2N 6RL, United Kingdom. TEL 44-20-7543-5800, FAX 44-20-7543-5793, http://www.cipfa.org.uk.

657 USA ISSN 1056-134X
HF5686.O5
CHECKLIST FOR DEFINED BENEFIT PENSION PLANS AND ILLUSTRATIVE FINANCIAL STATEMENTS. Text in English. 1990. a. USD 29.50 to non-members; USD 27 to members. **Document type:** *Trade.*
Published by: American Institute of Certified Public Accountants, Harborside Financial Ctr., 201 Plaza Three, 3rd Fl, Jersey City, NJ 07311-9801. TEL 888-777-7077, FAX 800-302-5766, journal@aicpa.org, http://www.aicpa.org.

657 692.8 USA ISSN 1056-1331
HF5686.B7
CHECKLIST SUPPLEMENT AND ILLUSTRATIVE FINANCIAL STATEMENTS FOR CONSTRUCTION CONTRACTORS. Text in English. 1990. a. USD 29.50 to non-members; USD 27 to members. **Document type:** *Bulletin.*
Published by: American Institute of Certified Public Accountants, Harborside Financial Ctr., 201 Plaza Three, 3rd Fl, Jersey City, NJ 07311-9801. TEL 888-777-7077, FAX 800-302-5766, journal@aicpa.org, http://www.aicpa.org.

657 332 USA ISSN 1056-5183
HG1708
CHECKLISTS AND ILLUSTRATIVE FINANCIAL STATEMENTS FOR BANKS. Text in English. 1989. a. USD 29.50 to non-members; USD 27 to members. **Document type:** *Trade.*
Formerly (until 1989): Disclosure Checklists and Illustrative Financial Statements for Banks (1046-428X)
Published by: American Institute of Certified Public Accountants, Harborside Financial Ctr., 201 Plaza Three, 3rd Fl, Jersey City, NJ 07311-9801. TEL 888-777-7077, FAX 800-302-5766, journal@aicpa.org, http://www.aicpa.org.

657 USA ISSN 1055-9558
HF5686.C7
CHECKLISTS AND ILLUSTRATIVE FINANCIAL STATEMENTS FOR CORPORATIONS. Text in English. 1990. a. USD 29.50 to non-members; USD 27 to members. **Document type:** *Trade.*
Published by: American Institute of Certified Public Accountants, Harborside Financial Ctr., 201 Plaza Three, 3rd Fl, Jersey City, NJ 07311-9801. TEL 888-777-7077, FAX 800-302-5766, journal@aicpa.org, http://www.aicpa.org.

657 334 USA ISSN 1056-0572
HF5686.C92
CHECKLISTS AND ILLUSTRATIVE FINANCIAL STATEMENTS FOR CREDIT UNIONS. Text in English. 1990. a. USD 29.50 to non-members; USD 27 to members. **Document type:** *Trade.*
Published by: American Institute of Certified Public Accountants, Harborside Financial Ctr., 201 Plaza Three, 3rd Fl, Jersey City, NJ 07311-9801. TEL 888-777-7077, FAX 800-302-5766, journal@aicpa.org, http://www.aicpa.org.

657 332 USA ISSN 1056-0580
HF5686.C495
CHECKLISTS AND ILLUSTRATIVE FINANCIAL STATEMENTS FOR FINANCE COMPANIES. Text in English. 1990. a. **Document type:** *Trade.*
Published by: American Institute of Certified Public Accountants, Harborside Financial Ctr., 201 Plaza Three, 3rd Fl, Jersey City, NJ 07311-9801. TEL 888-777-7077, FAX 800-302-5766, journal@aicpa.org, http://www.aicpa.org.

657.3 360 USA ISSN 1059-2679
HF5686.N56
CHECKLISTS AND ILLUSTRATIVE FINANCIAL STATEMENTS FOR NONPROFIT ORGANIZATIONS. Text in English. 1989. irreg. USD 29.50 to non-members; USD 27 to members. **Document type:** *Trade.*
Formerly (until 1990): Disclosure Checklists and Illustrative Financial Statements for Nonprofit Organizations (1046-4271)
Published by: American Institute of Certified Public Accountants, Harborside Financial Ctr., 201 Plaza Three, 3rd Fl, Jersey City, NJ 07311-9801. TEL 888-777-7077, FAX 800-302-5766, journal@aicpa.org, http://www.aicpa.org.

657 USA ISSN 0732-2038
THE CHRONICLE (CHICAGO). Text in English. 1941. m. **Document type:** *Journal, Trade.*
Formerly (until 1977): Arthur Andersen Chronicle (0731-6062)
Indexed: ABIn.
Published by: Arthur Andersen LLP, 33 W Monroe, Chicago, IL 60603.

657.41 IND
CIRCULATION AUDITING AROUND THE WORLD; memorandum report by the secretary-general. Text in English. 1962. a. free. **Document type:** *Monographic series.*
Published by: International Federation of Audit Bureau of Circulations, c/o A.B.C. Wakefield House, Sprott Rd., Ballard Estate, Mumbai, Maharashtra 400 038, India. Ed. Charles S Karnik.

657 USA
CLIENT ADVISORY. Text in English. m. **Document type:** *Newsletter.* **Description:** Serves as a practice development tool for accountants. Covers a broad range of topics, including tax planning, record retention, employee benefits, and computers.
Published by: W P I Communications Inc., 55 Morris Ave, Springfield, NJ 07081. TEL 973-467-8700, 800-323-4995, FAX 973-467-0368, http://www.wpicomm.com. Ed. Ken Berry. Pub. Steven H Klinghoffer.

657 USA
CLIENT INFORMATION BULLETIN. Text in English. m. **Description:** Aims to serve as a practice development tool for accountants. Devoted exclusively to current tax topics.
Related titles: Diskette ed.
Published by: W P I Communications Inc., 55 Morris Ave, Springfield, NJ 07081. TEL 973-467-8700, 800-323-4995, FAX 973-467-0368, http://www.wpicomm.com. Ed. Ken Berry. Pub. Steven H Klinghoffer.

657 336 USA
CLIENT TAX NEWSLETTER✶. Text in English. s-a. **Document type:** *Newsletter.*
Published by: American Group of C P A Firms, 17W662 Butterfield Rd., Ste. 303, Oakbrook Terrace, IL 60181-4006. TEL 708-916-0300.

336.2 658.153 USA
CLIENT'S MONTHLY ALERT; monthly roundup of significant business & tax developments. Text in English. 1971. m. **Document type:** *Trade.* **Description:** For small practices to major accounting firms to help them build and strengthen their accounting practice.
Published by: Practitioners Publishing Co., PO Box 966, Fort Worth, TX 76101-0966. Circ: 400.

657.6 USA ISSN 0147-0469
HF5667
CODIFICATION OF STATEMENTS ON AUDITING STANDARDS. Text in English. a., latest 2004. USD 84 per issue to members; USD 105 per issue to non-members (effective 2004). **Description:** Codified with all amendments and conforming changes as of January 2004, it gives the most up-to-date guidance.
—**CCC.**
Published by: American Institute of Certified Public Accountants, Harborside Financial Ctr., 201 Plaza Three, 3rd Fl, Jersey City, NJ 07311-9801. TEL 888-777-7077, FAX 800-302-5766, journal@aicpa.org, http://www.aicpa.org.

B

▼ new title ➤ refereed ✶ unverified ♦ full entry avail.

THE COLLEGE OF LAW PRACTICE PAPERS. VOLUME 3. see *LAW—Corporate Law*

657 GBR ISSN 1468-117X
COMPANY ACCOUNTANT. Text in English. 1928. bi-m. EUR 24 in United Kingdom; EUR 26 in Europe (effective 2002). adv. bk.rev. **Document type:** *Trade.*
Incorporates: Accountants Record (0954-8106)
Indexed: ATI, Emerald.
—BLDSC (3363.734000), IE, ingenta.
Published by: The Institute of Company Accountants, 40 Tyndalls Park Rd, Bristol, Glos BS8 1PL, United Kingdom. TEL 44-117-973-8261, FAX 44-117-923-8292. Ed., R&P B T Banks. Adv. contact J S Slade. Circ: 6,000.

COMPLIANCE WEEK. see *LAW—Corporate Law*

657 FRA
COMPTABILITE ET MECANOGRAPHIE. Text in French. 11/yr. Supplement avail.
Address: 14 rue de la Somme, Cachan, 94230, France. Ed. Jean Deit.

COMPUTER ACCOUNTING LETTER. see *BUSINESS AND ECONOMICS—Computer Applications*

657.450285 USA ISSN 0738-4270
COMPUTER AUDIT NEWS AND DEVELOPMENTS. Text in English. 1983. 6/yr. USD 70 domestic; USD 85 foreign (effective 2000). **Document type:** *Trade.* **Description:** Analysis of developments in information technologies and its impact on auditing and control procedures for audit managers, auditors, EDP auditors, security and computer control experts. Also of use to information security and systems managers who must review and secure their computer systems.
Published by: Management Advisory Publications, 57 Greylock Rd, Wellesley, MA 02481. TEL 617-235-2895, http://www.masp.com. Ed. J F Kuong. Adv. contact N Lagos.

COMPUTER DIGEST AND DATA PROCESSING. see *COMPUTERS—Electronic Data Processing*

657 USA
CONSTRUCTION CLIENT NEWSLETTER. Text in English. q. **Document type:** *Newsletter.* **Description:** Focuses on services for members' clients.
Published by: C P A Associates International, Inc., Meadows Office Complex, 201 Rte 17 N, Rutherford, NJ 07070-2574. TEL 212-804-8686.

657 336 USA
CONSTRUCTION CONTROLLER'S MANUAL. Text in English. base vol. plus s-a. updates. looseleaf. USD 172; USD 240.80 foreign (effective 1998). **Document type:** *Trade.* **Description:** Provides accounting professionals in the construction industry with accounting, auditing, tax, and financial guidance.
Formerly: Construction Accounting Manual
Indexed: ATI.
Published by: W G & L Financial Reporting & Management Research (Subsidiary of: R I A), 395 Hudson St, New York, NY 10014. TEL 212-367-6300, FAX 212-367-6718. Eds. Hugh L Rice, John L Callan. **Subscr. to:** The Park Square Bldg., 31 St James Ave, Boston, MA 02116-4112. TEL 800-950-1207.

657 CHL
CONTABILIDAD, TEORIA Y PRACTICA. Text in Spanish. 1986. q. CLP 4,000.
Published by: Universidad de Chile, Facultad de Ciencias Economicas y Administrativas, Ave. Ranacagua, 257, Santiago, Chile. TEL 56-2-2220704, FAX 56-2-2220309. Ed. Jorge Nino.

657 COL ISSN 0120-4203
HF5616.C7
CONTADURIA UNIVERSIDAD DE ANTIOQUIA. Text in Spanish; Summaries in English, Spanish. 1992. s-a. COP 40,000 domestic; USD 60 foreign; COP 30,000 domestic to students (effective 2003). abstr. **Document type:** *Journal, Academic/Scholarly.* **Description:** Provides short articles and research papers on accounting.
Published by: Universidad de Antioquia, Departamento de Contaduria, Apartado Postal 1226, Medellin, Colombia. TEL 57-4-210-5810, FAX 57-4-212-4812, revconta@caribe.udea.edu.co, http://caribe.udea.edu.co/~revconta. Ed. Miguel Angel Zapata Monsalve.

657 MEX ISSN 0186-1042
CONTADURIA Y ADMINISTRACION. Text in Spanish. 1957. q. MXP 80 (effective 2000). charts; stat. back issues avail. **Description:** Publishes original articles about accounting, management and computer applications on those fields.
Formerly (until 1972): Contabilidad Administracion (0010-7212)
Indexed: PAIS.
Published by: Universidad Nacional Autonoma de Mexico, Facultad de Contaduria y Administracion, Edificio de la Direccion, 2o. Piso, Cub. 21, Circuito Exterior, Ciudad Universitaria, Apartado Postal 70-287, Mexico City, DF 04510, Mexico. TEL 52-5-6228396, FAX 52-5-6161355, publica@server.contad.unam.mx, http://server.contad.unam.mx/. Ed. Arturo Diaz Alonso.

657 CAN ISSN 0823-9150
➤ **CONTEMPORARY ACCOUNTING RESEARCH/RECHERCHE COMPTABLE CONTEMPORAINE.** Text in English; Abstracts in French. 1984. q. USD 110 to individuals; USD 225 to institutions (effective 2004). adv. bk.rev. illus. back issues avail.; reprints avail. **Document type:** *Academic/Scholarly.* **Description:** Presents scholarly and practical research in the field of accounting.
Related titles: Microform ed.: 1984 (from PQC); Online - full text ed.: (from EBSCO Publishing, Micromedia ProQuest, Northern Light Technology, Inc., O C L C Online Computer Library Center, Inc., ProQuest Information & Learning, Swets Information Services).
Indexed: ABIn, ATI, CurCont, Emerald, IBSS, JEL, RefZh, SSCI.
—BLDSC (3425.168950), IE, ingenta. **CCC.**
Published by: Canadian Academic Accounting Association/Association Canadienne des Professeurs de Comptabilite, 3997 Chesswood Dr, Toronto, ON M3J 2R8, Canada. TEL 416-486-5361, FAX 416-486-6158, admin@caaa.ca, http://www.caaa.ca/publications/car.html. Ed. Dr. Gordon Richardson. Pub., R&P, Adv. contact Paul Granatstein. Circ: 1,400 (paid).

657 694 USA ISSN 1058-9260
CONTRACTOR'S BUSINESS MANAGEMENT REPORT. Text in English. 1991. m. looseleaf. USD 278.95 combined subscription in US & Canada print & online eds.; USD 293 combined subscription elsewhere print & online eds. (effective 2006). index. back issues avail. **Document type:** *Newsletter, Trade.* **Description:** Shows how to increase profitability, as well as find new projects in soft markets. Offers practical guidance on salary levels for management staff, construction bonds, and purchasing equipment.
Related titles: Diskette ed.; E-mail ed.; Online - full text ed.: (from EBSCO Publishing, Northern Light Technology, Inc., ProQuest Information & Learning).
Indexed: ABIn.
—**CCC.**
Published by: Institute of Management & Administration, Inc., 3 Park Ave, New York, NY 10016-5902. TEL 212-244-0360, FAX 212-564-0465, subserve@ioma.com, http://www.ioma.com/products/prod_detail.php?prodid=35. Ed. Donis Ford. Pub. Lee Rath.

657 USA
CONTROLLER'S BUSINESS ADVISOR. Text in English. a. USD 116.45; USD 175.45 foreign. **Document type:** *Trade.*
Indexed: ATI.
Published by: W G & L Financial Reporting & Management Research (Subsidiary of: R I A), 395 Hudson St, New York, NY 10014. TEL 212-971-5000. **Subscr. to:** The Park Square Bldg., 31 St James Ave, Boston, MA 02116-4112. TEL 800-950-1207.

657 332 NLD ISSN 0926-7158
CONTROLLERS MAGAZINE. Text in Dutch. 1987. bi-m. illus. **Document type:** *Journal, Trade.*
—IE, Infotrieve.
Published by: Reed Business Information bv (Subsidiary of: Reed Business), Van de Sande, Bakhuyzenstraat 4, Amsterdam, 1061 AG, Netherlands. TEL 31-20-515-9222, FAX 31-20-515-9990, info@reedbusiness.nl, http://www.reedbusiness.nl.

657 USA ISSN 0895-2787
THE CONTROLLER'S REPORT. Text in English. 1986. m. looseleaf. USD 278.95 in US & Canada print & online eds.; USD 293 elsewhere print & online eds. (effective 2006). index. back issues avail. **Document type:** *Newsletter, Trade.* **Description:** Shows corporate controllers how to monitor costs and eliminate waste. Includes cost benchmarks broken down by industry, region and company size. Exclusive surveys describe cost-cutting measures for workers' compensation, 401(k) plans. Also features a profile of a different top controller each month.
Incorporates: Building Corporate Cash
Related titles: Diskette ed.; E-mail ed.; Online - full text ed.: (from EBSCO Publishing, Florida Center for Library Automation, Gale Group, LexisNexis, Northern Light Technology, Inc., O C L C Online Computer Library Center, Inc., ProQuest Information & Learning); ◆ Cumulative ed(s).: Controller's Report Yearbook. ISSN 1528-2090.
Indexed: ABIn, ATI.
—**CCC.**
Published by: Institute of Management & Administration, Inc., 3 Park Ave, New York, NY 10016-5902. TEL 212-244-0360, FAX 212-564-0465, subserve@ioma.com, http://www.ioma.com/products/prod_detail.php?prodid=11. Ed. Timothy Harris. Pub. Perry Patterson.

657 USA ISSN 1528-2090
HG4001
CONTROLLER'S REPORT YEARBOOK. Text in English. 2000. a. USD 224.95 print & online eds. (effective 2003). **Description:** Covers financial leadership, Internet and IT costs, supply chain metrics, and benefits and compensation costs.
Related titles: Online - full text ed.: USD 219 (effective 2003); ◆ Cumulative ed. of: The Controller's Report. ISSN 0895-2787.
Published by: Institute of Management & Administration, Inc., 3 Park Ave, New York, NY 10016-5902. TEL 212-244-0360, FAX 212-564-0465, subserve@ioma.com, http://www.ioma.com. Ed. Timothy Harris.

CONTROLLER'S TAX LETTER. see *LAW*

657 USA ISSN 8756-5676
CONTROLLERS UPDATE. Text in English. 1985. m. USD 75 (effective 2000). bk.rev. tr.lit. back issues avail. **Document type:** *Trade.* **Description:** Provides information for controllers and other financial management executives.
Related titles: Online - full text ed.: (from Northern Light Technology, Inc., ProQuest Information & Learning).
Indexed: ATI.
—**CCC.**
Published by: Institute of Management Accountants, 10 Paragon Dr, Montvale, NJ 07645-1760. TEL 201-573-9000, FAX 201-573-8185. Ed. Karen Sanders. Circ: 2,400.

657 NLD ISSN 1380-3344
CONTROLLERSVIZIER. Text in Dutch. 1989. 4/yr. **Document type:** *Trade.*
Published by: (Vereniging van Registercontrollers), Wolters Kluwer N.V., Leewunburg 101, Deventer, 7411 TH, Netherlands. TEL 31-5700-48999, FAX 31-5700-11504. **Subscr. to:** Intermedia bv, Postbus 4, Alphen aan den Rijn 2400 MA, Netherlands. TEL 31-172-466321, FAX 31-172-435527.

657 POL ISSN 1428-8117
CONTROLLING I RACHUNKOWOSC ZARZADCZA W FIRMIE. Text in Polish. 1999. m. PLZ 84 (effective 2001).
Published by: Grupa Wydawnicza INFOR Sp. z o.o., Ul Okopowa 58/72, Warsaw, 01042, Poland. TEL 48-22-5304208, 48-22-5304450, bok@infor.pl. Ed. Stanislaw Wozniak. Adv. contact Waldemar Krakowiak.

CONTROLLING & MANAGEMENT; Zeitschrift fuer Controlling & Management. see *BUSINESS AND ECONOMICS—Management*

657 340 ITA
IL CONTROLLO LEGALE DEI CONTI. Text in Italian. 1997. bi-m. EUR 82.63 in the European Union; EUR 123.95 elsewhere (effective 2002). **Description:** Addresses problems in the accounting field through legal, technical, professional and cultural perspectives.
Related titles: CD-ROM ed.
Published by: (Fondazione dei Dottori Commercialisti di Milano), Casa Editrice Dott. A. Giuffre (Subsidiary of: LexisNexis Europe and Africa), Via Busto Arsizio, 40, Milan, MI 20151, Italy. TEL 39-02-28089200, FAX 39-02-38009582, giuffre@giuffre.it, http://www.giuffre.it. Ed. Claudio Badalotti.

657 334 USA ISSN 0010-8391
HF5686.C67
THE COOPERATIVE ACCOUNTANT. Text in English. 1947. q. USD 60 domestic; USD 70 foreign. index. **Description:** For accountants, auditors, bankers, attorneys and others actively involved in the financial planning and management of cooperative businesses.
Related titles: Online - full text ed.
Indexed: AAR, ATI.
—CISTI.
Published by: National Society of Accountants for Cooperatives (NSAC), 136 S. Keowee St., Dayton, OH 45402-2241. TEL 937-222-6707, FAX 937-222-5794 937-222-5794, info@nsacoop.org, http://www.nsacoop.org/publications.php#tac. Ed. James L Evans. Circ: 2,000.

CORPORATE MONEY; the newsletter of corporate financings and transactions. see *BUSINESS AND ECONOMICS—Banking And Finance*

657 343.06 USA ISSN 1078-3342
K4544.A13
CORPORATE TAXES WORLDWIDE SUMMARIES. Text in English. a. USD 119 per issue (effective 2004).
Incorporates in part (1982-1998): International Tax Summaries (8755-1551); Former titles (until 1980): Corporate Taxes in 80 Countries (0733-6187); (until 1970): Corporate Taxes in 70 Countries
Published by: PricewaterhouseCoopers, 1177 Ave of the Americas, New York, NY 10036. TEL 646-471-4000, FAX 646-471-3188, http://www.pwcglobal.com.

657 USA ISSN 0162-1165
COST ACCOUNTING STANDARDS GUIDE. Text in English. 1972. base vol. plus m. updates. USD 455 base vol(s). (effective 2004). **Description:** Ensures the contract complies with federally mandated standards; Equitably compare proposals with actual costs; Get the full text of Cost Accounting Standards Board Regulations with prefaces; Research any subject, topic, case, or document related to cost accounting standards quickly and easily.
Related titles: CD-ROM ed.: USD 490 (effective 2004); Online - full text ed.: USD 475 (effective 2004).
Indexed: ATI.
—**CCC.**
Published by: C C H Inc., 2700 Lake Cook Rd, Riverwoods, IL 60015. TEL 847-267-7000, 800-449-6439, cust_serv@cch.com, http://www.cch.com. Pub. Stacey Caywood.

COST ENGINEERS' NOTEBOOK. see *ENGINEERING*

336 USA
HD30.28
COST MANAGEMENT UPDATE. Text in English. 1985. m. USD 75 (effective 2000). bk.rev. back issues avail. **Document type:** *Trade.* **Description:** Information for cost management executives.
Formerly (until 1991): Business and Tax Planning Quarterly (0898-1841)
Related titles: Online - full text ed.
Indexed: ATI.
—CCC.
Published by: Institute of Management Accountants, 10 Paragon Dr, Montvale, NJ 07645-1760. TEL 201-573-9000. Ed. Karen Sanders. Circ: 1,600.

352.43 AUS ISSN 1323-6164
COSTS WATCH. Text in English. 1995. q. (4-6 issues/yr.). AUD 110 (effective 2004). **Document type:** *Newsletter.* **Description:** Provides concise and convenient information relating to developments, trends and news in the costs arena.
Published by: Lawbook Co. (Subsidiary of: Thomson Legal & Regulatory Ltd.), PO Box 3502, Rozelle, NSW 2039, Australia. LRA.Service@thomson.com, http://onlineecom01.thomson.com.au/thomson/Catalog.asp?EES_CMD=SI&EES_ID=100321, http://www.lawbookco.com.au/. Eds. Maurice Polkinghorne, Michelle Castle.

657 332 GBR ISSN 0143-5329
CREDIT CONTROL. Variant title: Credit Control Journal. Text in English. 1979. m. GBP 350 domestic; GBP 395 foreign (effective 2005). **Document type:** *Journal, Trade.*
Incorporates: Financial Risk Review
Related titles: CD-ROM ed.; Microfiche ed.; Online - full text ed.: (from EBSCO Publishing, O C L C Online Computer Library Center, Inc., ProQuest Information & Learning).
Indexed: ATI.
—BLDSC (3487.282000), IE, ingenta. **CCC.**
Published by: House of Words Ltd., 7 Greding Walk, Hutton, Brentwood, Essex CM13 2UF, United Kingdom. TEL 44-1277-225402, info@creditcontrol.co.uk, http://www.creditcontrol.co.uk. Ed., R&P, Adv. contact Carol Baker. Pub. Gareth Price.

657 USA ISSN 1540-4501
CREDIT UNION ACCOUNTANT (ARLINGTON). Text in English. 1987. bi-w. (excpt. Aug. & Dec.). USD 455 (effective 2005). **Document type:** *Newsletter.*
Published by: A.S. Pratt & Sons, Inc., 1911 Fort Myer Dr, Arlington, VA 22209. TEL 703-528-0145, 800-572-2797, FAX 703-528-1736, http://www.aspratt.com. Eds. Alan Rice, Nena Groskind.

657 USA
CREDIT UNION AUDITOR. Text in English. q. membership only. **Document type:** *Newsletter.*
Published by: Associated Regional Accounting Firms, 3700 Crestwood Pky N W, Duluth, GA 30136-5599. TEL 770-279-4560.

657 GBR ISSN 1045-2354
HF5601
➤ **CRITICAL PERSPECTIVES ON ACCOUNTING.** Text in English. 1990. 8/yr. EUR 146 in Europe to individuals; JPY 15,800 in Japan to individuals; USD 131 elsewhere to individuals; EUR 657 in Europe to institutions; JPY 71,000 in Japan to institutions; USD 585 elsewhere to institutions (effective 2006). adv. illus. reprints avail. **Document type:** *Journal, Academic/Scholarly.* **Description:** Provides a forum for the growing number of accounting researchers and practitioners who realize that conventional theory and practice is ill suited to the challenges of the modern environment, and that accounting practices and corporate behavior are inextricably connected with many allocative, distributive, social, and ecological problems of our era.
Related titles: Online - full text ed.: ISSN 1095-9955. USD 617 (effective 2002) (from EBSCO Publishing, Gale Group, IngentaConnect, O C L C Online Computer Library Center, Inc., ScienceDirect, Swets Information Services).
Indexed: ABIn, ATI, Emerald, IBSS.
—BLDSC (3487.457100), IE, Infotrieve, ingenta. **CCC.**
Published by: Academic Press (Subsidiary of: Elsevier Science & Technology), Harcourt Pl, 32 Jamestown Rd, London, NW1 7BY, United Kingdom. TEL 44-20-7424-4200, FAX 44-20-7483-2293, apsubs@acad.com, http://www.elsevier.com/locate/cpa. Eds. C. Carter, David Cooper, Tony Tinker. **Subscr. to:** Harcourt Publishers Ltd., Foots Cray High St, Sidcup, Kent DA14 5HP, United Kingdom. TEL 44-208-3085700, FAX 44-20-8309-0807.

657 086 USA
LA CUENTA. Text in English. q. membership. **Document type:** *Newsletter.*
Published by: American Association of Hispanic C P A's, 19726 E Colima Rd, Ste 270, Rowland Heights, CA 91748. Ed. John Hernandez.

657 ESP ISSN 1579-346X
CUENTAS PATRIMONIALES DEL SECTOR DE SOCIEDADES NO FINANCIERAS DE LA COMUNIDAD DE MADRID. Text in Spanish. 2001. a. free (effective 2003).
Related titles: CD-ROM ed.: ISSN 1579-3478.
Published by: Comunidad de Madrid, Consejeria de Economia e Innovacion Tecnologica. Instituto de Estadistica, Principe de Vargara, 108, Madrid, 28002, Spain. TEL 34-91-5802540, jestadis@madrid.org, http://www.madrid.org/iestadis/index.htm.

657 332.1 USA
CURRENT ISSUES IN THE FINANCIAL SERVICES INDUSTRIES. Text in English. 1983. a. free. stat. back issues avail. **Description:** Review of accounting and regulatory issues influencing the industry.
Former titles: Current Issues in the Financial Securities Industry; Current Issues in Banks and Thrift Institutions; Current Issues in Banking; Supersedes: Current Issues in Savings Institutions
Published by: Ernst & Young, 5 Times Sq., New York, NY 10036-6530. TEL 212-773-6000. Ed. Richard Brezover. Circ: 55,000.

657 USA
HF5601.A1D36
DELOITTE & TOUCHE REVIEW. Text in English. s-m. free. **Document type:** *Newsletter.*
Formerly: Week in Review
Published by: Deloitte & Touche, 10 Westport Rd, C 2 N, Box 820, Wilton, CT 06897. TEL 203-761-3202, FAX 203-761-3327. Ed. R Eugene Marion. Circ: 85,000.

657 658 BGR ISSN 0861-6272
DELOVA SEDMITSA/BUSINESS WEEKLY. Text in Bulgarian. w. USD 430 foreign (effective 2002). **Document type:** *Newspaper, Trade.*
Published by: Delova Sedmitsa, J.S.Co., Liulin Planina St 33, Sofia, 1606, Bulgaria. TEL 359-2-543007, FAX 359-2-541055, sbd@bol.bg, http://www.yellowpages-bg.com/club/firmi/sbd.htm. **Dist. by:** Sofia Books, ul Silivria 16, Sofia 1404, Bulgaria. TEL 359-2-9586257, info@sofiabooks-bg.com, http://www.sofiabooks-bg.com.

DEUTSCHE BILANZIERUNGS-RICHTLINIEN. see *BUSINESS AND ECONOMICS—Public Finance, Taxation*

657 346.07 FRA ISSN 1631-0675
DICTIONNAIRE PERMANENT: RECOUVREMENT DES CREANCES ET PROCEDURES D'EXECUTION. Text in French. 1999. 2 base vols. plus m. updates. looseleaf. EUR 288 base vol(s). (effective 2004).
Related titles: CD-ROM ed.; Online - full text ed.
Published by: Editions Legislatives, 80 Avenue de la Marne, Montrouge, Cedex 92546, France. TEL 33-1-40923636, FAX 33-1-40923663, infocom@editions-legislatives.fr, http://www.editions-legislatives.fr. Ed. Hubert Tubiana. Pub. Michel Vaillant.

657 USA ISSN 0161-4290
KF2920.Z95
DIGEST OF STATE ACCOUNTANCY LAWS AND STATE BOARD REGULATIONS. Text in English. a. USD 40 per issue to non-members; USD 32 per issue to members (effective 2004).
—CCC.
Published by: (American Institute of Certified Public Accountants), National Association of State Boards of Accountancy, 150 4th Ave N Ste 700, Nashville, TN 37219-2417. TEL 615-880-4200, FAX 615-880-4290, http://www.nasba.org.

657.029 CAN ISSN 0527-9275
DIRECTORY OF CANADIAN CHARTERED ACCOUNTANTS. Text in English. a. CND 175 to non-members; CND 55 to members (effective 2000). **Document type:** *Directory.* **Description:** Contains a list of all CICA members (with addresses, year of graduation, and province), as well as a list of all Canadian Chartered Accountancy Firms (with addresses, telephone numbers and partners).
Indexed: ATI.
Published by: Canadian Institute of Chartered Accountants, 277 Wellington St W, Toronto, ON M5V 3H2, Canada. TEL 416-977-3222, FAX 416-977-8585. Circ: 4,000.

657 343.034 IDN
DIRECTORY OF PUBLIC ACCOUNTING FIRM. Text in Indonesian. 1980. a. IDR 60,000 (effective 2000).
Published by: The Indonesian Institute of Accountants, Public Accountants Compartment, Jl Sisingamangaraja 59, Jakarta, 12120, Indonesia. TEL 62-21-722-2989, iai-kap@akuntan-iai.or.id. Ed. Agung Adiasa. Circ: 2,000.

657.05 USA
HF5601
DISCLOSURES. Text in English. 1988. m. free to members (effective 2005). adv. **Document type:** *Magazine, Trade.* **Description:** Contains editorials, limited technical and feature articles, updates on changes in the accounting profession, announcements of member involvement, highlights of member benefits and services.
Supersedes (1947-1988): Virginia Accountant (0042-644X)
Published by: Virginia Society of Certified Public Accountants, PO Box 4620, Glen Allen, VA 23058-4620. TEL 804-270-5344, FAX 804-273-1741, vscpa@vscpa.com, http://www.vscpa.com/Resources/Publications/Disclosures/. Eds. Jill Edmonds, Marlene A Childs. Pub. Alika Rosser. Circ: 8,000 (paid and controlled).

657 RUS
DOS'E BUKHGALTERA. Text in Russian. 24/yr.
Published by: Izdatel'skii Dom Infra M, Dmitrovskoe shosse 107, Moscow, 127214, Russian Federation. TEL 7-095-4855779, FAX 7-095-4855318. Ed. V M Prudnikov. **US dist. addr.:** East View Information Services, 3020 Harbor Ln. N., Minneapolis, MN 55447. TEL 612-550-0961.

657 USA ISSN 1055-3746
HF5616.U5
E I T F ABSTRACTS. (Emerging Issues Task Force) Text in English. 1984. a. USD 54 (effective 2004).
Published by: Financial Accounting Standards Board (Subsidiary of: Financial Accounting Foundation), 401 Merritt 7, Box 5116, Norwalk, CT 06856-5116. TEL 203-847-0700, FAX 203-849-9714, http://www.fasb.org.

657 336.2 RUS
E Z - VOPROS - OTVET. (Ekonomika i Zhizn') Text in Russian. 2000. m.
Related titles: ◆ Supplement to: Ekonomika i Zhizn'. ISSN 1607-0615.
Published by: Izdatel'skii Dom Ekonomicheskaya Gazeta, Bumazhnyi proezd 14, Moscow, 101462, Russian Federation. TEL 7-095-2573153, FAX 7-095-2002297, buhgalt@akdi.ru, akdi@akdi.ru, http://www.akdi.ru.

657 ITA
ECONOMIA D'AZIENDA E BILANCI. Text in Italian. 1989. irreg., latest vol.3, 1999. price varies. adv. **Document type:** *Monographic series.*
Published by: Liguori Editore srl, Via Posillipo 394, Naples, 80123, Italy. TEL 39-81-7206111, FAX 39-81-7206244, http://www.liguori.it. Pub. Guido Liguori. Adv. contact Maria Liguori.

657 USA ISSN 1095-080X
THE EDGE. Text in English. 1953. bi-m. free to members; USD 35 to non-members (effective 2005). adv. bk.rev. 24 p./no.; back issues avail. **Document type:** *Magazine, Consumer.*
Former titles (until 1997): Coordinator (Chicago) (0744-8937); American Society of Women Accountants Coordinator (0279-6163); American Society of Women Accountants Newsletter (0199-204X)
Published by: American Society of Women Accountants, 8405 Greensboro Dr., Ste. 800, McLean, VA 22102. TEL 703-506-3265, FAX 703-506-3266, aswa@aswa.org, http://www.aswa.org. adv.: B&W page USD 935; bleed. Circ: 5,000 (paid).

657 RUS
EKONOMIKA I UCHET TRUDA. Text in Russian. 1997. m. USD 165 in the Americas (effective 2000).
Published by: Izdatel'stvo Uchet, Ul. B. Androp'evskaya, 5-11, Moscow, 109544, Russian Federation. TEL 7-095-2780067, FAX 7-095-2594435.

EMERSON'S DIRECTORY OF LEADING U.S. ACCOUNTING FIRMS. see *BUSINESS AND ECONOMICS—Trade And Industrial Directories*

EMPLOYEE BENEFITS COMPLIANCE COORDINATOR. see *BUSINESS AND ECONOMICS—Personnel Management*

ENROLLED ACTUARIES REPORT. see *INSURANCE*

ENVIRONMENTAL ACCOUNTING AND AUDITING REPORTER. see *ENVIRONMENTAL STUDIES*

ENVIRONMENTAL TAXATION AND ACCOUNTING. see *BUSINESS AND ECONOMICS—Public Finance, Taxation*

657 ESP ISSN 1138-9540
KKT3541.2
ESTUDIOS FINANCIEROS. REVISTA DE CONTABILIDAD Y TRIBUTACION. COMENTARIOS, CASOS PRACTICOS. Text in Spanish. 1995. m.
Supersedes in part (1988-1995): Estudios Financieros. Revista de Contabilidad y Tributacion (1138-9575); Which superseded in part (1981-1988): Estudios Financieros (1138-9524)
Published by: Centro de Estudios Financieros, C. Viriato, 52 5o., Madrid, 28010, Spain. TEL 34-91-4444920, FAX 34-91-5938861, director@cef.es, http://www.cef.es/.

657 GBR ISSN 0955-4882
EUROPEAN ACCOUNTING FOCUS. Text in English. 1989. 10/yr. GBP 375, USD 638 (effective 2000). adv. stat. back issues avail. **Document type:** *Newsletter.* **Description:** Profiles accounting firms in the U.K. and abroad, covers accounting trends and legislation in various countries around the world, and reports news in the field.
—CCC.
Published by: Informa Law (Subsidiary of: Informa Publishing), Informa House, 30-32 Mortimer St, London, W1W 7RE, United Kingdom. TEL 44-207-5531000, FAX 44-207-5531593. Ed. Hannah Doran. Pub. Frania Weaver. Adv. contact Harry Fisher.

B

▼ new title ➤ refereed ✶ unverified ◆ full entry avail.

657 GBR ISSN 0963-8180
HF5616.E8
➤ **THE EUROPEAN ACCOUNTING REVIEW.** Text in English. 1992. q. GBP 280, USD 461 combined subscription to institutions print & online eds. (effective 2006). adv. back issues avail.; reprint service avail. from PSC. **Document type:** *Journal, Academic/Scholarly.* **Description:** Provides a European forum for the reporting of accounting research and developments, including analytical, empirical and policy-oriented scholarship.
Supersedes (1989-1992): European Accounting Association. Newsletter (1015-5686)
Related titles: Online - full text ed.: ISSN 1468-4497. GBP 266, USD 461 to institutions (effective 2006) (from EBSCO Publishing, Gale Group, IngentaConnect, O C L C Online Computer Library Center, Inc., Swets Information Services).
Indexed: ATI, DIP, Emerald, IBR, IBSS, IBZ.
—BLDSC (3829.482940), IE, Infotrieve, ingenta. **CCC.**
Published by: (European Accounting Association), Routledge (Subsidiary of: Taylor & Francis Group), 4 Park Square, Milton Park, Abingdon, Oxon OX14 4RN, United Kingdom. TEL 44-1235-828600, FAX 44-1235-829000, info@routledge.co.uk, http://www.tandf.co.uk/journals/titles/09638180.asp, http://www.routledge.co.uk. Ed. Kari Lukka. R&P Sally Sweet. Adv. contact Gemma Heiser. **Subscr. in US & Canada to:** Taylor & Francis Inc., Customer Services Dept, 325 Chestnut St, 8th Fl, Philadelphia, PA 19106. TEL 215-625-8900, 800-354-1420, FAX 215-625-8914; **Subscr. to:** Taylor & Francis Ltd, Journals Customer Service, Rankine Rd, Basingstoke, Hants RG24 8PR, United Kingdom. TEL 44-1256-813000, FAX 44-1256-330245, enquiry@tandf.co.uk.

B

657 CAN ISSN 1493-390X
EXAMINATIONS, SUGGESTED SOLUTIONS - EXAMINERS' COMMENTS. Text in English. 1999. a.
Media: CD-ROM.
Published by: Certified General Accountants Association of Canada, 1188 W Georgia St, Ste 700, Vancouver, BC V6E 4A2, Canada. TEL 604-669-3555, FAX 604-689-5845, http://www.cga-canada.org.

657.6 USA ISSN 0190-2733
➤ **THE EXAMINER (RALEIGH).** Text in English. 1980 (vol.5). q. USD 65 to non-members (effective 1999). **Document type:** *Academic/Scholarly.* **Description:** Includes articles about the regulation of insurance companies, financial institutions and credit unions.
Published by: Society of Financial Examiners, PO Box 163209, Altamonte Spg, FL 32716-3209. safe@olsonmgmt.com, http://www.sofe.org. Ed., R&P Holly Marquardt. Circ: 2,400.

657 GBR
EXECUTIVE ACCOUNTANT. Text in English. 1974. q. GBP 15. adv. bk.rev.
Related titles: Online - full text ed.
Indexed: ATI.
Published by: Institute of Cost and Executive Accountants Educational Trust, 139 Fonthill Rd, London, N4 3HF, United Kingdom. TEL 44-171-272-3925, FAX 44-171-281-5723. Ed., Adv. contact Kyriacos Tsiouparas. R&P Sushil Das Gupta. Circ: 5,000.

657 FRA
EXPERT COMPTABLE DE DEMAIN. Text in French. 6/yr.
Published by: National Association of Probationary Chartered Accountants, 92 rue de Rivoli, Paris, 75004, France. TEL 42-72-73-72, FAX 42-78-20-26. Ed. Valerie Hervouet. Circ: 7,000.

657 AUS ISSN 1030-5882
EXPOSURE DRAFT (ACCOUNTING STANDARDS). Text in English. 1990. irreg. AUD 6 per issue.
Formed by the merger of (1989-1990): Invitation to Comment (1032-660X); (1989-1990): Proposed Approved Accounting Standard and Proposed Australian Accounting Standard (1033-9191); (1989-1990): Proposed Australian Accounting Standard (1034-3415); Which was formerly (1971-1989): Proposed Statement of Accounting Standards
Published by: Australian Accounting Research Foundation, 211 Hawthorn Rd, Caulfield, VIC 3162, Australia. TEL 61-3-95243600, FAX 61-3-95235499, standard@aarf.asn.au. Circ: 1,000. **Co-sponsors:** Institute of Chartered Accountants in Australia; Australian Society of Certified Practising Accountants.

657 AUS ISSN 1030-603X
EXPOSURE DRAFT (AUDITING PRACTICE). Text in English. 1990. irreg. AUD 6 per issue.
Formed by the merger of (1989-1990): Proposed Statement on Applicability; (1980-1990): Proposed Statement of Auditing Practice
Published by: Australian Accounting Research Foundation, 211 Hawthorn Rd, Caulfield, VIC 3162, Australia. TEL 61-3-95243600, FAX 61-3-95235499, standard@aarf.asn.au. Circ: 1,000. **Co-sponsors:** Institute of Chartered Accountants in Australia; Australian Society of Certified Practising Accountants.

EXTEL DIVIDEND & INTEREST RECORD. see *BUSINESS AND ECONOMICS—Banking And Finance*

351 USA
F A R FASTSEARCH. (Federal Acquisition Regulations) Text in English. 1990. q. (plus m. updates). USD 399.
Published by: FastSearch Corporation, PO Box 12427, Scottsdale, AZ 85267-2427. TEL 800-232-4590, FAX 612-595-0229. Ed. Alan Rosenauer. Circ: 3,750.

657 USA ISSN 0193-7855
F A S B INTERPRETATION. (Financial Accounting Standards Board) Text in English. 1974. irreg. USD 175 (effective 2004). **Document type:** *Monographic series.*
Related titles: Series of: Financial Accounting Series. ISSN 0885-9051. 1985.
Published by: Financial Accounting Standards Board (Subsidiary of: Financial Accounting Foundation), 401 Merritt 7, Box 5116, Norwalk, CT 06856-5116. TEL 203-847-0700, 800-748-0659, FAX 203-849-9714, http://www.fasb.org.

657 USA ISSN 0886-4535
F A S B TECHNICAL BULLETIN. (Financial Accounting Standards Board) Text in English. 1979. irreg. USD 8.50 per issue (effective 2004).
Related titles: Series of: Financial Accounting Series. ISSN 0885-9051. 1985.
Published by: Financial Accounting Standards Board (Subsidiary of: Financial Accounting Foundation), 401 Merritt 7, Box 5116, Norwalk, CT 06856-5116. TEL 203-847-0700, 800-748-0659, FAX 203-849-9714, http://www.fasb.org, http://www.fasb.org/public.

657 GBR
FARM BUSINESS ACCOUNTS. SUMMARY OF RESULTS (YEAR). Text in English. a. GBP 250 per issue (effective 2002). **Document type:** *Trade.* **Description:** Covers average dairy farm results and the range in performance between the top and bottom 25%. Additionally, it shows interpretation of the results and likely future prospects.
Formerly (until 1999): Axient Farm Business Accounts. Summary of Results (Year)
—BLDSC (3871.912500).
Published by: Promar International, Northcroft House, Newbury, Berks RG14 1HD, United Kingdom. TEL 44-1635-46112, FAX 44-1635-43945, research@promar-international.com, http://www.farm-and-rural.co.uk/fbainfo1.asp, http://www.promar-international.com.

657.6 USA
FEDERAL AUDIT GUIDES. Text in English. 4 base vols. plus irreg. updates. USD 825 base vol(s). (effective 2004). **Description:** Designed to aid state and local government auditors and independent public accountants in understanding the special requirements for the external audit coverage of these program recipients.
Published by: C C H Inc., 2700 Lake Cook Rd, Riverwoods, IL 60015. TEL 847-267-7000, 800-449-6439, cust_serv@cch.com, http://www.cch.com. Pub. Stacey Caywood.

FINANCE INDIA; the quarterly journal of finance. see *BUSINESS AND ECONOMICS—Banking And Finance*

657 GBR
HF5616.G7
FINANCIAL ACCOUNTANT. Text in English. 1920. 6/yr. GBP 18; free to members & students (effective 2002). adv. bk.rev. reprint service avail. from PQC. **Document type:** *Trade.*
Former titles: Accounting World (0953-2579); Administrative Accountant; Administrative Accounting (0143-9359); Book-Keepers Journal (0006-7253)
Related titles: Microfilm ed.: 1920 (from PQC).
Published by: Institute of Financial Accountants, Burford House, 44 London Rd, Sevenoaks, Kent TN13 1AS, United Kingdom. TEL 44-1732-458080, FAX 44-1732-455848, mail@ifa.org.uk, http://www.accountingweb.co.uk/ifa/journal/. Ed., R&P Garry Carter. Circ: 13,000.

657 USA ISSN 0196-9692
FINANCIAL ACCOUNTING FOUNDATION. ANNUAL REPORT. Text in English. a.
Published by: Financial Accounting Foundation, 401 Merritt 7, Box 5116, Norwalk, CT 06856-5116.

657 USA ISSN 0888-7896
FINANCIAL ACCOUNTING STANDARDS BOARD. ORIGINAL PRONOUNCEMENTS. Text in English. 8 base vols. plus irreg. updates. looseleaf. USD 595 (effective 2004).
Formerly (until 1982): Financial Accounting Standards. Original Pronouncements
Published by: Financial Accounting Standards Board (Subsidiary of: Financial Accounting Foundation), 401 Merritt 7, Box 5116, Norwalk, CT 06856-5116. TEL 203-847-0700, 800-748-0659, FAX 203-849-9714, http://www.fasb.org.

657 USA
FINANCIAL INFORMATION SYSTEMS MANUAL. Text in English. base vol. plus a. updates. looseleaf. USD 205; USD 287 foreign (effective 1998). Supplement avail. **Document type:** *Trade.* **Description:** Focuses on how technology can be used to obtain important financial information.
Indexed: ATI.
Published by: W G & L Financial Reporting & Management Research (Subsidiary of: R I A), 395 Hudson St, New York, NY 10014. TEL 212-367-6300, FAX 212-367-6718. Ed. S W Barcus. **Subscr. to:** The Park Square Bldg., 31 St James Ave, Boston, MA 02116-4112. TEL 800-950-1207.

657 USA
FINANCIAL LENDING NOTES. Text in English. q. membership only. **Document type:** *Newsletter.*
Published by: Associated Regional Accounting Firms, 3700 Crestwood Pky N W, Duluth, GA 30136-5599. TEL 770-279-4560.

657 GBR ISSN 1471-9185
HF5686.C8 CODEN: FMLUBJ
FINANCIAL MANAGEMENT. Text in English. 1921. m. GBP 40 (effective Sep. 2000); GBP 3 newsstand/cover (effective 2000). adv. bk.rev. charts; illus.; stat. index. reprint service avail. from SCH. **Document type:** *Trade.*
Former titles: Management Accounting (0025-1682); (until 1965): Cost Accountant
Related titles: Online - full text ed.: (from EBSCO Publishing, Florida Center for Library Automation, Gale Group, O C L C Online Computer Library Center, Inc., ProQuest Information & Learning).
Indexed: ABIn, ASEANManA, ATI, BMT, BPIA, BldManAb, BusI, CPM, DPD, Emerald, IMI, Inspec, JEL, KES, M&MA, ManagCont, SCIMP, T&II, WBA.
—BLDSC (3926.960000), AskIEEE, IE, Infotrieve. **CCC.**
Published by: Chartered Institute of Management Accountants, 63 Portland Pl, London, W1N 4AB, United Kingdom. TEL 44-20-7637-2311, FAX 44-20-7495-6098, journal@cima.org.uk, http://www.cima.org.uk. Ed. Gemma Townley. Circ: 55,000.

657 690 USA
FINANCIAL MANAGEMENT AND ACCOUNTING FOR THE CONSTRUCTION INDUSTRY. Text in English. 1988. a. (in 2 vols.). looseleaf. USD 193 (effective 2002). **Description:** Exclusively for the construction industry. Covers such vital topics as how to recognize income and expenses, plan for income taxation, and prepare bids and estimates.
Published by: (Construction Financial Management Association), Matthew Bender & Co., Inc. (Subsidiary of: LexisNexis North America), 1275 Broadway, Albany, NY 12204. international@bender.com, http://bender.lexisnexis.com.

657.305 GBR ISSN 0969-1545
FINANCIAL REPORTING & AUDITING NEWSLETTER. Text in English. 1993. m. GBP 90. **Document type:** *Newsletter.* **Description:** Provides commentary on current events and new regulations affecting the accounting and auditing professions.
Published by: Butterworth & Co. Ltd. (Subsidiary of: LexisNexis UK (Scottish Office)), Halsbury House, 35 Chancery Ln, London, WC2A 1EL, United Kingdom. TEL 44-171-400-2500, FAX 44-171-400-2842. Ed. Richard Derwent.

657 CAN ISSN 0071-5115
HF5681.B2
FINANCIAL REPORTING IN CANADA. Text in English. 1953. biennial. price varies. **Document type:** *Trade.* **Description:** Studies 300 Canadian companies with annual sales revenues of Can.$1 million to Can.$1 billion. Covers the preparation of their financial statements, the terminology, and the techniques.
Related titles: French ed.
Indexed: ATI.
Published by: Canadian Institute of Chartered Accountants, 277 Wellington St W, Toronto, ON M5V 3H2, Canada. TEL 416-977-3222, FAX 416-977-8585. Circ: 3,500.

657 GBR
FINANCIAL SERVICES SOCIETY NEWSLETTER. Text in English. bi-m. bk.rev. back issues avail. **Document type:** *Newsletter.* **Description:** Covers issues of concern to members in the financial services sector.
Published by: Association of Chartered Certified Accountants, 64 Finnieston Square, Glasgow, G3 8DT, United Kingdom. TEL 44-20-7396-5800, FAX 44-171-396-5959. Ed. Liz Treadway. Circ: 3,000.

657 340 BGR
FINANSI I PRAVO. Text in Bulgarian. m. BGL 88.80 domestic; USD 120 foreign (effective 2002). **Description:** Covers financial rulings, accounting practices, duties, law, stocks, and insurance policies.
Related titles: CD-ROM ed.
Published by: Izdatelski Kompleks Trud i Pravo/Labour and Law Publishing House, Pl. Makedonia 1, Fl. 7, Sofia, 1040, Bulgaria. TEL 359-2-9875110, FAX 359-2-9870612, office@trudipravo.bg, http://www.trudipravo.bg. **Dist. by:** Sofia Books, ul Silivria 16, Sofia 1404, Bulgaria. TEL 359-2-9586257, info@sofiabooks-bg.com, http://www.sofiabooks-bg.com.

FINANSOVAYA GAZETA; mezhdunarodnyi finansovyi ezhenedel'nik. see *BUSINESS AND ECONOMICS—Banking And Finance*

FINANSOVAYA GAZETA. EKSPO. see *BUSINESS AND ECONOMICS—Public Finance, Taxation*

FINANSOVAYA GAZETA. REGIONAL'NYI VYPUSK. see *BUSINESS AND ECONOMICS—Banking And Finance*

657 POL ISSN 0867-3748
FISCUS. Text in Polish. 1991. bi-w. PLZ 133 (effective 2001).
Published by: Grupa Wydawnicza INFOR Sp. z o.o., Ul Okopowa 58/72, Warsaw, 01042, Poland. TEL 48-22-5304208, 48-22-5304450, bok@infor.pl. Ed. Grazyna Gonciarska. Adv. contact Waldemar Krakowiak.

332 AUS ISSN 1441-3906
FLINDERS UNIVERSITY OF SOUTH AUSTRALIA. SCHOOL OF COMMERCE. RESEARCH PAPER SERIES. Text in English. 1998. irreg. (9 issues in 2002; 11 issues in 2003, 7 issues in 2004). back issues avail. **Document type:** *Academic/Scholarly.* **Description:** Addresses current issues in professional accounting, finance and management.
Related titles: Online - full content ed.
—CCC.
Published by: Flinders University of South Australia, School of Commerce, PO Box 2100, Adelaide, SA 1001, Australia. TEL 61-8-82012226, FAX 61-8-82012644, bet.roffey@flinders.edu.au, commerce@flinders.edu.au, http://www.ssn.flinders.edu.au/commerce/researchpapers/.

657 USA
FLORIDA C P A TODAY. (Certified Public Accountant) Text in English. adv. back issues avail. **Document type:** *Magazine, Trade.* **Description:** Covers the latest news and events shaping the accounting profession.
Related titles: Online - full text ed.
Published by: Florida Institute of Certified Public Accountants, 325 W College Ave, Tallahassee, FL 32301. TEL 850-224-2727, 800-342-2727, FAX 850-222-8190, cpatoday@ficpa.org, webmaster@ficpa.org, http://www.ficpa.org/communication/fct/index.html. adv.: B&W page USD 1,715, color page USD 2,419.

657 USA
FLORIDA INDEPENDENT ACCOUNTANT. Text in English. 1986. q. adv. **Document type:** *Trade.* **Description:** Covers association activities and legislative concerns.
Published by: Florida Association of Independent Accountants, PO Box 13089, Tallahassee, FL 32317. TEL 904-878-3134, FAX 904-878-1291. Circ: 900 (controlled).

657 USA
FOCUS (MONTVALE). Text in English. q. adv. **Document type:** *Newsletter.* **Description:** Focuses on improving communication between members and the national office. Includes calendar of events and conference information.
Former titles: Leader (Montvale); Association Leader (Montvale) (0896-2847)
Published by: Institute of Management Accountants, 10 Paragon Dr, Montvale, NJ 07645-1760. TEL 201-573-9000, 800-638-4427, FAX 201-573-8601. Ed. Marie Gartshore. R&P Robert F Randall. Adv. contact Jim Hart. Circ: 60,000.

657 USA
FOOTNOTE. Text in English. m. USD 25 to non-members; free to members (effective 2005). adv. **Document type:** *Newsletter.*
Published by: Minnesota Society of Certified Public Accountants, 1650 W 82nd St, Ste 6, Bloomington, MN 55431. TEL 952-831-2707, 800-331-4288, FAX 952-831-7875, advertising@mncpa.org, http://www.mncpa.org. adv.: page USD 875. Circ: 9,500 (paid and controlled).

657 USA
FOOTNOTE. Text in English. m. free to members. **Document type:** *Newsletter, Trade.* **Description:** Contains the latest accounting industry news, Virginia Board of Accountancy updates and regulatory information, in addition to VSCPA announcements and upcoming CPE opportunities.
Media: E-mail. **Related titles:** Online - full content ed.: free (effective 2005).
Published by: Virginia Society of Certified Public Accountants, PO Box 4620, Glen Allen, VA 23058-4620. TEL 804-270-5344, 800-733-8272, FAX 804-273-1741, vscpa@vscpa.com, http://www.vscpa.com/Resources/Publications/Footnote/. Ed. Jill Edmonds.

657.6 USA ISSN 1548-5110
▼ **FORENSIC ACCOUNTING.** Text in English. forthcoming 2006. q. free (effective 2005).
Media: Online - full content.
Published by: Florida Atlantic University, 111 E. Las Olas Blvd., Ft. Lauderdale, FL 33301. TEL 561-297-3000, http://masters-in-forensic-accounting.com/journal, http://www.fau.edu. Ed. Somnath Bhattacharya.

FORENSIC ACCOUNTING REVIEW. see *BUSINESS AND ECONOMICS*

657 USA
FORESIGHT. Text in English. q. membership only. **Document type:** *Newsletter.*
Formerly: Foresight Client Newsletter
Published by: Associated Regional Accounting Firms, 3700 Crestwood Pky N W, Duluth, GA 30136-5599. TEL 770-279-4560. Ed. Missy Patrick.

657 USA ISSN 1554-0642
▼ ➤ **FOUNDATIONS AND TRENDS IN ACCOUNTANCY.** Text in English. forthcoming 2006. q. USD 300 in North America; EUR 300 elsewhere; USD 340 combined subscription in North America print & online eds.; EUR 340 combined subscription elsewhere print & online eds. (effective 2006). **Document type:** *Journal, Academic/Scholarly.* **Description:** Publishes high-quality survey and tutorial monographs related to the field of accounting.
Related titles: Online - full text ed.: ISSN 1554-0650. forthcoming 2006. USD 300 in North America; EUR 300 elsewhere (effective 2006).
Published by: Now Publishers Inc., PO Box 1024, Hanover, MA 02339. TEL 781-871-0245, FAX 781-871-6172, sales@nowpublishers.com, http://www.nowpublishers.com/acc. Ed. Stefan Reichelstein. Pub., R&P Zac Rolnik.

➤ **FRAUD MAGAZINE.** see *CRIMINOLOGY AND LAW ENFORCEMENT—Security*

657 USA ISSN 1529-0751
HF5626
G A A P HANDBOOK OF POLICIES AND PROCEDURES. (generally accepted accounting principles) Text in English. 1999. a.
Published by: Aspen Publishers, Inc. (Subsidiary of: Wolters Kluwer N.V.), 111Eighth Ave., 7th Fl, New York, NY 10011. TEL 212-771-0600, FAX 212-771-0885, http://www.aspenpub.com.

657 ZAF
GENERALLY ACCEPTED ACCOUNTING PRACTICE. A SOUTH AFRICAN VIEWPOINT (STUDENT EDITION). Text in English. irreg. ZAR 250 (effective 2001). **Document type:** *Academic/Scholarly.*
Published by: Juta & Company Ltd., Law and Professional Publishing Division, PO Box 14373, Kenwyn, 7790, South Africa. TEL 27-21-7975101, FAX 27-21-7970121, cserv@juta.co.za, http://www.juta.co.za.

657 ESP ISSN 1139-5974
GESTION DE ACTIVOS INDUSTRIALES. Variant title: Ingenieria y Gestion de Mantenimiento. Text in Spanish. 1998. bi-m. EUR 62 domestic; EUR 90 in Europe; USD 133 elsewhere (effective 2003).
Related titles: Online - full text ed.
—CINDOC.
Published by: Editorial Alcion Ingenieria Quimica, S.A., Medea, 4, Madrid, 28037, Spain. TEL 34-91-4402920, FAX 34-91-4402931, info@alcion.es, http://www.alcion.es.

657 346 BEL ISSN 1373-3346
GIDS VOOR ACCOUNTANTS & BEDRIFSREVISOREN. Text in Dutch. 1989. a. EUR 406.45 (effective 2003). **Document type:** *Trade.*
Formerly (until 1997): Gids voor Accountants (0776-9148)
Published by: Kluwer Uitgevers (Subsidiary of: Wolters Kluwer Belgique), Ragheno Business Park, Motstraat 30, Mechelen, B-2800, Belgium. TEL 32-15-800-94571, info@kluwer.be, http://www.kluwer.be. Eds. Andre Chiau, Jo Van den Bossche.

GILBERT LAW SUMMARIES. ACCOUNTING AND FINANCE FOR LAWYERS. see *LAW—Corporate Law*

657 BGR
GLAVEN SCHETOVODITEL. Text in Bulgarian. bi-w. BGL 35.76 (effective 2002).
Published by: Izdatel Koman, Pl Raiko Daskalov 1, vkh B, Sofia, 1000, Bulgaria. TEL 359-2-9803561, FAX 359-2-9818651, office@zakonnik.net, http://www.zakonnik.net. Ed. Liubov Vinarova.

GLOBAL COMMUNIQUE. see *BUSINESS AND ECONOMICS—Abstracting, Bibliographies, Statistics*

657 RUS
GORYACHAYA LINIYA BUKHGALTERA. Text in Russian. m.
Published by: Biznes Shkola Intel-Sintez, Ul Profsoyuznaya 3, Moscow, 117036, Russian Federation. TEL 7-095-1299212, FAX 7-095-1246809, http://www.top-personal.ru.

354.8 USA
GOVERNMENT ACCOUNTING AND FINANCIAL REPORTING MANUAL. Text in English. base vol. plus a. updates. looseleaf. USD 205; USD 287 foreign (effective 1998). Supplement avail. **Document type:** *Trade.* **Description:** Guides in all areas of government accounting and financial reporting.
Published by: W G & L Financial Reporting & Management Research (Subsidiary of: R I A), 395 Hudson St, New York, NY 10014. TEL 212-367-6300, FAX 212-367-6718. Ed. William J Raftery. **Subscr. to:** The Park Square Bldg., 31 St James Ave, Boston, MA 02116-4112. TEL 800-950-1207.

657 USA ISSN 0886-2982
HJ9701
GOVERNMENTAL ACCOUNTING STANDARDS BOARD. ACTION REPORT. Text in English. 1984. m. **Document type:** *Newsletter, Government.*
Published by: Governmental Accounting Standards Board, 401 Merritt 7, P O Box 5116, Norwalk, CT 06856-5116. TEL 203-847-0700, FAX 203-849-9714. Ed. Deborah Harrington. Circ: 10,125.

657 FRA ISSN 1144-5777
GUIDE DES DECLARATIONS FISCALES. Text in French. 1989. 2 base vols. plus updates 5/yr. looseleaf. EUR 492.69 print & CD-ROM eds. (effective 2004). Supplement avail. **Document type:** *Trade.* **Description:** Provides instructions to aid in filling out fiscal forms.
Published by: Lamy S.A. (Subsidiary of: Wolters Kluwer France), 21/23 rue des Ardennes, Paris, 75935 Cedex 19, France. TEL 33-1-825080800, FAX 33-1-44721388, lamy@lamy.fr, http://www.lamy.fr.

657 FRA ISSN 1290-3728
GUIDE DU RESPONSABLE COMPTABLE ET FINANCIER. Text in French. 1998. base vol. plus q. updates. EUR 283.80 print & CD-ROM eds. (effective 2004). 1000 p./no.;
Related titles: CD-ROM ed.; Online - full text ed.: EUR 83 (effective 2003).
Published by: Lamy S.A. (Subsidiary of: Wolters Kluwer France), 21/23 rue des Ardennes, Paris, 75935 Cedex 19, France. TEL 33-1-825080800, FAX 33-1-44721388, lamy@lamy.fr, http://www.lamy.fr.

B

657 USA ISSN 1099-453X
HF5686.N56
GUIDE TO NONPROFIT G A A P. (generally accepted accounting principles) Text in English. 1997. a. USD 119 newsstand/cover (effective 2003).
Published by: Practitioners Publishing Co., PO Box 966, Fort Worth, TX 76101-0966. TEL 817-332-3709, 800-323-8724, FAX 817-877-3694, http://www.ppcnet.com.

657 USA
HANDBOOK FOR INTERNAL AUDITORS. Text in English. 1985. irreg. looseleaf. USD 384 (effective 2002). **Description:** Provides guidance on every aspect of internal auditing - from establishing an internal auditing function within a company, to managing an internal auditing department, to performing audit fieldwork.
Published by: Matthew Bender & Co., Inc. (Subsidiary of: LexisNexis North America), 1275 Broadway, Albany, NY 12204. FAX 518-462-3788, international@bender.com, http://bender.lexisnexis.com. Eds. Stanley Chang, William E Perry.

657 658 USA ISSN 1079-8455
HANDBOOK OF COST MANAGEMENT. Text in English. 1992. base vol. plus a. updates. USD 270 (effective 2005). Supplement avail. **Document type:** *Trade.* **Description:** Enables managers to implement and improve cost-management programs for every phase of their operations.
Related titles: Online - full text ed.: USD 325 (effective 2005).
Indexed: ATI.
—CCC.
Published by: W G & L Financial Reporting & Management Research (Subsidiary of: R I A), 395 Hudson St, New York, NY 10014. TEL 212-367-6300, 800-431-9025, ria.customerservices@thomson.com, http://ria.thomson.com/estore/detail.asp?ID=HBM. **Subscr. to:** The Park Square Bldg., 31 St James Ave, Boston, MA 02116-4112. TEL 800-950-1207.

657 332 USA
HF5686.C7
HANDBOOK OF S E C ACCOUNTING AND DISCLOSURE MANUAL. (Securities and Exchange Commission) Text in English. 1988. a. USD 205; USD 287 foreign. **Document type:** *Trade.* **Description:** Guides public accountants in all steps of preparing disclosure statements for the Securities and Exchange Commission.
Formerly: Handbook of S E C Accounting and Disclosure (1046-3534)
Indexed: ATI.
—CCC.
Published by: W G & L Financial Reporting & Management Research (Subsidiary of: R I A), 395 Hudson St, New York, NY 10014. TEL 212-367-6300, FAX 212-367-6718. Ed. Allan B Afterman. **Subscr. to:** The Park Square Bldg., 31 St James Ave, Boston, MA 02116-4112. TEL 800-950-1207.

657.6 USA ISSN 1543-7264
HEALTH CARE AUDITING STRATEGIES. Text in English. 2002 (Dec.). m. USD 299 (effective 2004). **Document type:** *Newsletter.*
—CCC.
Published by: H C Pro, Inc., 200 Hoods Ln, Marblehead, MA 01945. TEL 781-639-1872, 800-650-6787, 877-727-1728, FAX 781-639-7857, hcprocustomerservice@hcpro.com, http://www.hcpro.com. Pub. Suzanne Perney.

657 USA ISSN 1521-7612
HEALTH NICHE ADVISOR. Text in English. 1988. m. USD 289 to individuals (effective 2003). back issues avail. **Document type:** *Newsletter.* **Description:** Delivers successful practice management techniques, niche-building strategies, billable engagement ideas youn can apply right away, plus the latest accounting, auditing, and tax developments.

Formerly (until 1998): C P A Health Niche Advisor (1047-580X)
Related titles: Online - full text ed.: (from Florida Center for Library Automation, Gale Group).
Indexed: ATI.
Published by: Aspen Publishers, Inc. (Subsidiary of: Wolters Kluwer N.V.), 111Eighth Ave., 7th Fl, New York, NY 10011. TEL 212-771-0600, FAX 212-771-0885, customer.service@aspenpubl.com, http://www.aspenpublishers.com/Product.asp?catalog%5Fname=Aspen&category%5Fname=&product%5Fid=SS1047580X&Mode=SEARCH&ProductType=L. **Subscr. to:** Customer Care, 7201 McKinney Circle, Frederick, MD 21704. TEL 800-234-1660, FAX 800-901-9075.

657 CHN ISSN 1003-0131
HEBEI CAIKUAI/HEBEI FINANCE AND ACCOUNTING. Text in Chinese. m.
Published by: Hebei Sheng Caizheng Ting, Fu 9, Kangle Jie, Shijiazhuang, Hebei 050051, China. TEL 744621. Ed. Lu Baorui. Circ: (controlled).

HONG KONG SPECIAL ADMINISTRATIVE REGION OF CHINA. AUDIT COMMISSION. DIRECTOR OF AUDIT'S REPORTS. see *STATISTICS*

HORSE OWNERS AND BREEDERS TAX HANDBOOK. see *SPORTS AND GAMES—Horses And Horsemanship*

THE HOSPITAL ACCOUNTS RECEIVABLE ANALYSIS. see *HEALTH FACILITIES AND ADMINISTRATION*

657 GBR ISSN 1474-2675
HF5626
I A S B UPDATE. Text in English. 1991. m.
Formerly (until 2001): I A S C Update (0966-5773)
Published by: International Accounting Standards Board, 30 Cannon St, London, EC4M 6XH, United Kingdom. TEL 44-20-72466410, 44-20-73322730, FAX 44-20-72466411, 44-20-73322749, iasb@iasb.org.uk, publications@iasb.org, http://www.iasb.org/meetings/iasb_decisionsummaries.asp, http://www.iasb.org.uk.

657 DEU ISSN 0937-4019
I D W FACHNACHRICHTEN. Text in German. 1947. m. bk.rev. back issues avail. **Document type:** *Trade.*
Published by: Institut der Wirtschaftspruefer in Deutschland e.V., Tersteegenstr 14, Duesseldorf, 40474, Germany. TEL 49-211-4561, FAX 49-211-4541097. Ed. Horst Kaminski. Circ: 16,500.

657 CHE
I F A ANNUAL REPORT✶. Text in English. a.
Published by: International Federation of Accountants, PO Box 395, Geneva 12, 1211, Switzerland.

I F A C INTERNATIONAL PUBLIC SECTOR GUIDELINE (NO.). see *BUSINESS AND ECONOMICS—Public Finance, Taxation*

657 CHE
I F A NEWSLETTER✶. Text in English. q.
Published by: International Federation of Accountants, PO Box 395, Geneva 12, 1211, Switzerland.

I I F NEWSLETTER. see *BUSINESS AND ECONOMICS—Banking And Finance*

657 USA ISSN 1090-2244
I O M A'S PAYROLL MANAGER'S REPORT. Variant title: Payroll Manager's Report. Text in English. 1996. m. USD 261.95 combined subscription in US & Canada print & online eds.; USD 273 combined subscription elsewhere print & online eds. (effective 2006). back issues avail. **Document type:** *Newsletter, Trade.* **Description:** Shows payroll executives how to improve the accuracy and efficiency of their department and reduce paperwork. Includes information on software and new technologies, products.
Related titles: Online - full text ed.: (from EBSCO Publishing, Florida Center for Library Automation, Gale Group, ProQuest Information & Learning); ◆ Cumulative ed(s).: Payroll Manager's Report Yearbook.
Indexed: ABIn.
—CCC.
Published by: Institute of Management & Administration, Inc., 3 Park Ave, New York, NY 10016-5902. TEL 212-244-0360, FAX 212-564-0465, subserve@ioma.com, http://www.ioma.com/products/prod_detail.php?prodid=21. Ed. Donis Ford. R&P Sofie Kourkoutakis.

657 USA ISSN 1555-3604
I O M A'S REPORT ON MANAGING ACCOUNTS PAYABLE. Variant title: Managing Accounts Payable. Text in English. 1995. m. USD 281.95 combined subscription in US & Canada print & online eds.; USD 293 combined subscription elsewhere print & online eds. (effective 2006). back issues avail. **Document type:** *Newsletter, Trade.* **Description:** Covers policies and techniques related to payables. Includes international payments, exceptions, pay on receipts, procurement card programs, and avoiding double payments. Also looks at the latest payment systems.
Former titles (until 2002): I O M A's Report on Managing T & E (1525-7789); (until 1999): I O M A's Report on Managing Accounts Payable (1080-5753)
Related titles: Diskette ed.; E-mail ed.; Online - full content ed.; Online - full text ed.: (from EBSCO Publishing, Gale Group, LexisNexis, O C L C Online Computer Library Center, Inc.); ◆ Cumulative ed(s).: Managing Accounts Payable Yearbook.
—CCC.
Published by: Institute of Management & Administration, Inc., 3 Park Ave, New York, NY 10016-5902. TEL 212-244-0360, FAX 212-564-0465, subserve@ioma.com, http://www.ioma.com/products/prod_detail.php?prodid=15. Ed. Mary Schaeffer. Pub. Lee Rath. R&P Sofie Kourkoutakis.

I R S LETTER RULINGS REPORTER. (Internal Revenue Service) see *BUSINESS AND ECONOMICS—Public Finance, Taxation*

657 USA
INCOME AND FEES OF ACCOUNTANTS IN PUBLIC PRACTICE. Text in English. triennial. USD 50 to non-members (effective 2000); USD 35 to members. **Document type:** *Trade.*
Indexed: ATI, SRI.
Published by: National Society of Accountants, 1010 N Fairfax St, Alexandria, VA 22314. TEL 703-549-6400. Ed., R&P, Adv. contact Jody Felski TEL 703-549-6400 ext 1310. Circ: 23,000.

657 USA
INDEPENDENT ACCOUNTANTS INTERNATIONAL. UPDATE. Text in English. 1979. m. looseleaf. membership. adv. bk.rev.; software rev.; Website rev. abstr. back issues avail. **Document type:** *Newsletter, Trade.*
Formerly: International Affiliation of Independent Accounting Firms. Update
Related titles: E-mail ed.
Published by: Independent Accountants International, 9200 S Dadeland Blvd, Ste 510, Miami, FL 33156-2703. TEL 305-670-0580, FAX 305-670-3818, info@accountants.org, http://iai.org/, http://accountants.org/. Ed., R&P Art Goessel. Circ: 700.

657 IDN
THE INDONESIAN INSTITUTE OF ACCOUNTANTS NEWSLETTER. Text in Indonesian. 1999. m. IDR 2,000 (effective 2000). **Document type:** *Newsletter.*
Published by: Indonesian Institute of Accountants, Jl. Sisingamangaraja 59, Jakarta, 12120, Indonesia. TEL 62-21-722-2989, iai-info@akuntan-iai.or.id. Ed. Ladiman Djaiz. Circ: 2,000.

657 GBR ISSN 1471-7727
HF5679 CODEN: IONRAW
➤ **INFORMATION AND ORGANIZATION.** Text in English. 1991. 4/yr. EUR 616 in Europe to institutions; JPY 81,700 in Japan to institutions; USD 689 elsewhere to institutions (effective 2006). index. back issues avail. **Document type:** *Journal, Academic/Scholarly.* **Description:** Offers a forum for research on the interrelations of information technologies with accounting and control systems and with management practices and policies.
Formerly (until Jan. 2001): Accounting, Management and Information Technologies (0959-8022)
Related titles: Microform ed.: (from PQC); Online - full text ed.: (from EBSCO Publishing, Gale Group, IngentaConnect, ScienceDirect, Swets Information Services).
Indexed: CompLI, InfoSAb, Inspec.
—BLDSC (4481.840500), IE, Infotrieve, ingenta. **CCC.**
Published by: Pergamon (Subsidiary of: Elsevier Science & Technology), The Boulevard, Langford Ln, East Park, Kidlington, Oxford OX5 1GB, United Kingdom. TEL 44-1865-843000, FAX 44-1865-843010, http://www.elsevier.com/locate/infoandorg. Ed. Dr. Daniel Robey. **Subscr. to:** Elsevier BV, PO Box 211, Amsterdam 1000 AE, Netherlands. TEL 31-20-485-3757, FAX 31-20-485-3432, nlinfo-f@elsevier.nl, http://www.elsevier.nl.

657 USA ISSN 1552-7239
HF5616.U5
INSIDE PUBLIC ACCOUNTING; the competitive advantage for accounting firm leaders since 1987. Text in English. 1987. m. looseleaf. USD 345 domestic; USD 420 foreign (effective 2005). bk.rev.; software rev. charts; stat. back issues avail.; reprints avail. **Document type:** *Newsletter, Trade.* **Description:** News, analysis and commentary of events, trends, strategies, and politics in the accounting profession, analysis of fiscal performance and ranking of 100 largest US firms and Big Five firms.
Formerly (until Apr 2004): Bowman's Accounting Report (0897-3482)
Related titles: Microform ed.: (from PQC); Online - full text ed.: (from Northern Light Technology, Inc., ProQuest Information & Learning).
Indexed: ATI.
Published by: Hudson Sawyer Professional Services Marketing, Inc., 3340 Peachtree Rd NE, Ste. 2600, Atlanta, GA 30326-1089. TEL 404-264-9977, FAX 404-264-9968, awbowman@hs-bowmans.com. Ed. Julie Lindy.

637 USA ISSN 1053-8542
INSIGHT MAGAZINE (CHICAGO). Text in English. 1947. 8/yr. USD 30 domestic; USD 40 in Canada & Mexico; USD 42 rest of world (effective 2000). adv. bk.rev. **Document type:** *Trade.* **Description:** Contains analyses of issues that affect the working lives of high level business and finance professionals.
Formerly (until 1990): Newsjournal (1043-7215)
Related titles: Microfilm ed.
Published by: Illinois C P A Society, 550 W. Jackson Blvd., Ste. 900, Chicago, IL 60661-5741. TEL 312-993-0393, FAX 312-993-7713, giannetto-adamsj@icpas.org, http://www.icpas.org. Ed., R&P Judy Giannetto-Adams. Pub. Marty Rosenberg. Adv. contact Ilene Zurla. B&W page USD 1,360, color page USD 1,890; trim 10.88 x 8.38. Circ: 28,000 (controlled).

657 AUS
INSTITUTE OF CHARTERED ACCOUNTANTS IN AUSTRALIA. ANNUAL REPORT AND ACCOUNTS. Text in English. a. **Document type:** *Corporate.*
Published by: Institute of Chartered Accountants in Australia, GPO Box 3921, Sydney, NSW 2001, Australia. TEL 61-2-92901344, FAX 61-2-92623953. R&P Deborah Leake.

657 GBR
INSTITUTE OF CHARTERED ACCOUNTANTS IN ENGLAND AND WALES. ACCOUNTING STANDARDS BOARD. PAPERS. Text in English. irreg. price varies. back issues avail. **Document type:** *Monographic series.*
Former titles: Institute of Chartered Accountants in England and Wales. Exposure Drafts and Statements of Standard Accounting Practice; Institute of Chartered Accountants in England and Wales. Practice Administration Series, Exposure Drafts and Statements of Standard Accounting Practice (0073-9049)
Related titles: Series of: Financial Reporting Standars, Exposure Drafts.
Published by: Institute of Chartered Accountants in England and Wales, Central Milton Keynes, 620, London, MK9 2JX, United Kingdom.

657 GBR
INSTITUTE OF CHARTERED ACCOUNTANTS IN ENGLAND AND WALES. ADDING VALUE: FOR THE GENERAL PRACTITIONER SUPPORTING SMALL BUSINESS. Variant title: Adding Value: For the General Practitioner Supporting Small Business. Text in English. 1997. q. GBP 60; GBP 69 foreign (effective 2000). **Document type:** *Trade.*
Published by: (Institute of Chartered Accountants in England and Wales), A B G Professional Information (Subsidiary of: Croner.C C H Group Ltd.), 145 London Rd, Kingston upon Thames, KT2 6SR, United Kingdom. TEL 44-20-85473333, FAX 44-20-85472637, lovellv@croner.cch.co.uk, http://www.abgweb.com/.

657 GBR
INSTITUTE OF CHARTERED ACCOUNTANTS IN ENGLAND AND WALES. BUSINESS DIGEST. Variant title: Business Digest. Text in English. 1997. m. GBP 130; GBP 149.50 foreign (effective 2000). **Document type:** *Trade.*
Published by: (Institute of Chartered Accountants in England and Wales), A B G Professional Information (Subsidiary of: Croner.C C H Group Ltd.), 145 London Rd, Kingston upon Thames, KT2 6SR, United Kingdom. TEL 44-20-85473333, FAX 44-20-85472637, lovellv@croner.cch.co.uk, http://www.abgweb.com/.

657 GBR
INSTITUTE OF CHARTERED ACCOUNTANTS IN ENGLAND AND WALES. INTERNAL CONTROL NEWSLETTER. Variant title: Internal Control Newsletter. Text in English. 1997. 10/yr. GBP 199; GBP 288.85 foreign (effective 2000). **Document type:** *Trade.*
Published by: (Institute of Chartered Accountants in England and Wales), A B G Professional Information (Subsidiary of: Croner.C C H Group Ltd.), 145 London Rd, Kingston upon Thames, KT2 6SR, United Kingdom. TEL 44-20-85473333, FAX 44-20-85472637, lovellv@croner.cch.co.uk, http://www.abgweb.com/.

657 GBR
INSTITUTE OF CHARTERED ACCOUNTANTS IN ENGLAND AND WALES. INTERNATIONAL ACCOUNTING STANDARDS COMMITTEE. PAPERS. Text in English. 1975. irreg., latest 1993, Jan. USD 5 (effective 1999). **Document type:** *Monographic series.*
Published by: Institute of Chartered Accountants in England and Wales, Central Milton Keynes, 620, London, MK9 2JX, United Kingdom.

INSTITUTE OF CHARTERED ACCOUNTANTS IN ENGLAND AND WALES. TAX DIGEST. see *BUSINESS AND ECONOMICS—Public Finance, Taxation*

657 GBR ISSN 0266-7053
INSTITUTE OF CHARTERED ACCOUNTANTS IN ENGLAND AND WALES. UPDATE. Text in English. 1979. m. GBP 85; GBP 97.75 foreign (effective 2000). **Document type:** *Trade.*
Formerly (until 1984): Institute of Chartered Accountants in England and Wales. Technical Bulletin (0143-9758)

Published by: (Institute of Chartered Accountants in England and Wales), A B G Professional Information (Subsidiary of: Croner.C C H Group Ltd.), 145 London Rd, Kingston upon Thames, KT2 6SR, United Kingdom. TEL 44-20-85473333, FAX 44-20-85472637, TELEX 827502, lovellv@croner.cch.co.uk, http://www.abgweb.com/.

657 CAN
INSTITUTE OF CHARTERED ACCOUNTANTS OF ALBERTA. C A MONTHLY STATEMENT. Text in English. 1968. m. membership. adv. bk.rev. **Document type:** *Newsletter.*
Formerly: Institute of Chartered Accountants of Alberta. Monthly Statement (0316-6546)
Related titles: Online - full text ed.
Published by: Institute of Chartered Accountants of Alberta, 580 Manulife Pl, 10180 101 St, Edmonton, AB T5J 4R2, Canada. TEL 780-424-7391, FAX 780-425-8766, general.delivery@icaa.ab.ca, http://www.icaa.ab.ca. Ed., R&P, Adv. contact Karin Holmgren. Circ: 8,000.

657 CAN ISSN 1208-5499
INSTITUTE OF CHARTERED ACCOUNTANTS OF BRITISH COLUMBIA. BEYOND NUMBERS. Text in English. 1945. 10/yr. CND 25 to members (effective 1998). adv. bk.rev. **Document type:** *Trade.* **Description:** Information for chartered accountants in British Columbia.
Former titles (until 1996): Institute of Chartered Accountants of British Columbia. Communication (0834-0188); (until 1986): Institute of Chartered Accountants of British Columbia. News and Views (0380-4011)
Related titles: Online - full text ed.
Published by: Institute of Chartered Accountants of British Columbia, 1133 Melville St, 6th Fl, Vancouver, BC V6E 4E5, Canada. TEL 604-681-3264, FAX 604-681-1523. Ed., R&P Craig Fitzsimmons. Pub. Douglas McClelland. Adv. contact Mark Bologna. B&W page CND 1,180, color page CND 2,280. Circ: 8,000.

657.029 GBR ISSN 0073-9057
INSTITUTE OF CHARTERED ACCOUNTANTS OF SCOTLAND. OFFICIAL DIRECTORY. Text in English. 1896. a. GBP 47 (effective 2000). adv. **Document type:** *Directory.*
Published by: Institute of Chartered Accountants of Scotland, CA House, 21 Haymarket Yards, Edinburgh, Scotland EH12 5BH, United Kingdom. TEL 44-131-225-5673, FAX 44-131-225-3813. Ed. David Brew. Pub. David McMurray. R&P Robert Outram. Adv. contact Laura Lynch. Circ: 700.

INSTITUTE OF FINANCE MANAGEMENT. PROSPECTUS. see *BUSINESS AND ECONOMICS—Banking And Finance*

657 ESP
INSTITUTO DE CENSORES JURADOS DE CUENTAS DE ESPAGNA. REVISTA TECHNICA. Text in Spanish. fortn. —CINDOC.
Published by: Instituto de Censores Jurados de Cuentas de Espagna, c/o General Arrando 9, Madrid, 28010, Spain. TEL 91-445-03-54.

INTELLIGENT SYSTEMS IN ACCOUNTING, FINANCE & MANAGEMENT. see *BUSINESS AND ECONOMICS—Computer Applications*

657 USA ISSN 0897-0378
HF5668
INTERNAL AUDITING. Text in English. 1986. bi-m. USD 220 (effective 2005). adv. 48 p./no.; back issues avail.; reprints avail. **Document type:** *Magazine, Trade.* **Description:** Provides timely information and ideas that show the practitioner how to devise an overall internal auditing approach and develop strategic plans.
Related titles: Online - full text ed.: (from ProQuest Information & Learning).
Indexed: ABIn, ATI.
—BLDSC (4534.678070), IE, ingenta. **CCC.**
Published by: W G & L Financial Reporting & Management Research (Subsidiary of: R I A), 395 Hudson St, New York, NY 10014. TEL 212-367-6623, FAX 212-367-6314, http://www.riag.com/estore/detail.asp?ID=INTA, http://www.wglcorpfinance.com. Ed. Andrea Kingston. adv.: B&W page USD 1,070, color page USD 1,640. Circ: 3,500 (paid).

657.6 USA ISSN 0744-2947
INTERNAL AUDITING ALERT. Text in English. 1981. m. USD 172; USD 240.80 foreign (effective 1998). illus. reprints avail. **Document type:** *Newsletter.* **Description:** Focuses on the means of monitoring and controlling the accounting system used by any enterprise or organization.
—**CCC.**
Published by: W G & L Financial Reporting & Management Research (Subsidiary of: R I A), 395 Hudson St, New York, NY 10014. TEL 212-367-6300, FAX 212-367-6718, http://www.wgl.com. **Subscr. to:** The Park Square Bldg., 31 St James Ave, Boston, MA 02116-4112. TEL 800-950-1207.

657 GBR
INTERNAL AUDITING & BUSINESS RISK. Text in English. 1978. m. EUR 120 (effective 2001). adv. bk.rev. illus. 48 p./no.; reprints avail. **Document type:** *Magazine, Corporate.*
Formerly: Internal Auditing (0140-2676)
Indexed: Emerald.
—BLDSC (4534.679600), ingenta. **CCC.**
Published by: Institute of Internal Auditors (UK and Ireland), 13 Abbeville Mews, 88 Clapham Park Rd, London, SW4 7BX, United Kingdom. TEL 44-20-7498-0101, FAX 44-20-7978-2492, info@iia.org.uk, http://www.iia.org.uk/. Ed. Neil Baker. adv.: page EUR 1,500, color page EUR 1,950. Circ: 6,000 (paid).

657 USA ISSN 0020-5745
CODEN: ITAUA
INTERNAL AUDITOR. Text in English. 1944. bi-m. USD 60 in North America; USD 84 elsewhere (effective 2005). adv. bk.rev. illus. Index. back issues avail.; reprint service avail. from SCH. **Document type:** *Magazine, Trade.* **Description:** For internal auditors, mid- to high-level corporate executives and board members.
Formerly: I I A Research Reports
Related titles: Microform ed.: (from PQC); Online - full text ed.: (from EBSCO Publishing, Florida Center for Library Automation, Gale Group, H.W. Wilson, Northern Light Technology, Inc., O C L C Online Computer Library Center, Inc., ProQuest Information & Learning).
Indexed: ABIn, ADPA, ATI, BPI, BPIA, BusI, Emerald, ExcerpMed, IMI, Inspec, ManagCont, T&II.
—BLDSC (4534.680000), AskIEEE, IE, Infotrieve, ingenta. **CCC.**
Published by: Institute of Internal Auditors, Inc., 247 Maitland Ave, Altamonte Springs, FL 32701-4201. TEL 407-937-1100, FAX 407-937-1101, custserv@theiia.org, http://www.theiia.org/iia/index.cfm?doc_id=540. adv.: B&W page USD 2,718, color page USD 4,919; trim 10.88 x 8. Circ: 49,500.

657.6 USA ISSN 1553-8222
▼ **INTERNAL AUDITOR ALERT.** Text in English. 2004 (Mar). m. USD 475 (effective 2005). **Document type:** *Newsletter.*
Published by: AlexInformation, 807 Las Cimas Pkwy Ste 300, Austin, TX 78746. TEL 512-652-4400, FAX 512-652-4499, inforeply@alexinformation.com, http://www.alexinformation.com.

657 GBR ISSN 1465-5144
HF5601
INTERNATIONAL ACCOUNTANT. Text in English. 1928. q. GBP 16 (effective 2003). adv. bk.rev. charts. index. 40 p./no.; back issues avail. **Document type:** *Journal, Trade.* **Description:** Serves as offcial journal for the association. Covers subjects of particular interest to qualified accountants as well as students. Includes articles on such topics as accounting and auditing standards, accounting in developing countries, passing exams, etc.
Supersedes: Student Accounting Review (1353-5609); Former titles (until 1993): Association of International Accountants. Newsreview (0969-4935); (until 1992): Association of International Accountants. Newsletter (0969-4897); (until 1990): International Accountant (0020-5826); (until 1967): International Accountants' Journal
Related titles: E-mail ed.
Indexed: ATI.
Published by: Association of International Accountants, South Bank Bldg, Kingsway, Team Valley, Newcastle upon Tyne, Tyne & Wear NE11 0JS, United Kingdom. TEL 44-191-4824409, FAX 44-191-4825578, aia@aia.org.uk, http://www.aia.org.uk. Ed. Nicola Hind. R&P Mrs. Nicola Perry. Adv. contact Mrs. Rachel Perry.

657 USA ISSN 1058-272X
HF5601
INTERNATIONAL ACCOUNTING AND AUDITING TRENDS✶. Text in English. 1991. a.
Indexed: ATI.
Published by: C I F A R Publications, Inc., PO Box 3228, Princeton, NJ 08543-3228. TEL 609-520-9333, FAX 609-520-0905. Ed. Vinod Bavishi.

657 USA ISSN 1014-4633
INTERNATIONAL ACCOUNTING AND REPORTING ISSUES. Text in English. 1984. a.
Indexed: ATI, IIS.
Published by: United Nations Publications, Rm DC2-853, United Nations Bldg, 2 United Nations Plaza, New York, NY 10017. FAX 212-963-4116.

657 GBR ISSN 0265-0223
INTERNATIONAL ACCOUNTING BULLETIN. Text in English. 1983. 20/yr. GBP 1,297, EUR 2,097, USD 2,197 (effective 2005). back issues avail. **Document type:** *Bulletin.* **Description:** Provides news, analysis and reports in the world accounting market.
Related titles: Online - full text ed.: GBP 800 (effective 1999) (from EBSCO Publishing, Florida Center for Library Automation, Gale Group, LexisNexis, O C L C Online Computer Library Center, Inc., ProQuest Information & Learning).
Indexed: ATI, B&I.
—IE, Infotrieve.
Published by: Lafferty Publications Ltd., The Colonnades, 82 Bishops Bridge Rd, London, W2 6BB, United Kingdom. TEL 44-20-75635700, FAX 44-20-75635701, cuserv@lafferty.com, http://www.lafferty.com/newsletter_publication.php?id=8. Ed. Marc Barber.

657 GBR
INTERNATIONAL FINANCIAL REPORTING STANDARDS. Text in English. 1981. a.
Formerly (until 2003): International Accounting Standards (0261-3913)
—BLDSC (4540.195000).
Published by: (International Accounting Standards Board), Institute of Chartered Accountants in England and Wales, Chartered Accountants' Hall, PO Box 433, London, EC2P 2BJ, United Kingdom. TEL 44-20-79208899, FAX 44-20-78332085, http://www.icaew.co.uk/. **Orders to:** I A S C F Publications Department, 30 Cannon St, London EC4M 6XH, United Kingdom. TEL 44-20-72466410, FAX 44-20-73327249, publications@iasb.org.uk.

657.0711 GBR ISSN 1094-4060
HF5601
➤ **THE INTERNATIONAL JOURNAL OF ACCOUNTING.** Text in English. 1965. 4/yr. EUR 128 in Europe to individuals; JPY 16,800 in Japan to individuals; USD 141 to individuals except Europe and Japan; EUR 337 in Europe to institutions; JPY 44,700 in Japan to institutions; USD 378 to institutions except Europe and Japan (effective 2006). bk.rev. illus. cum.index every 2 yrs. back issues avail.; reprints avail. **Document type:** *Journal, Academic/Scholarly.* **Description:** Advances the academic and professional understanding of accounting theory and practice from an international perspective and viewpoint.
Formerly (until 1989): The International Journal of Accounting Education and Research (0020-7063)
Related titles: Online - full text ed.: (from EBSCO Publishing, Gale Group, IngentaConnect, ScienceDirect, Swets Information Services).
Indexed: ABIn, APEL, ATI, CPM, Emerald, IBSS, Inspec, MEA&I, PAIS, SCIMP, WBA.
—BLDSC (4541.525000), IE, Infotrieve, ingenta. **CCC.**
Published by: Pergamon (Subsidiary of: Elsevier Science & Technology), The Boulevard, Langford Ln, East Park, Kidlington, Oxford OX5 1GB, United Kingdom. TEL 44-1865-843000, FAX 44-1865-843010, http://www.elsevier.com/locate/intacc. Ed. A. R. Abdel-Khalik. **Subscr. to:** Elsevier BV, PO Box 211, Amsterdam 1000 AE, Netherlands. TEL 31-20-485-3757, FAX 31-20-485-3432, nlinfo-f@elsevier.nl, http://www.elsevier.nl.

657 GBR ISSN 1740-8008
▼ ➤ **INTERNATIONAL JOURNAL OF ACCOUNTING, AUDITING AND PERFORMANCE EVALUATION.** Text in English. 2004. q. USD 450 to institutions; EUR 545 combined subscription to institutions print & online eds. (effective 2005). **Document type:** *Journal, Academic/Scholarly.* **Description:** Provides a forum for the exchange of knowledge, information, insights and evidences in the changing field of accounting, auditing and performance evaluation from both developed and developing countries.
Related titles: Online - full text ed.: ISSN 1740-8016. USD 450 to institutions (effective 2005) (from EBSCO Publishing).
Indexed: BrCerAb, C&ISA, CerAb, CorrAb, E&CAJ, EMA, IAA, Inspec, M&TEA, MBF, METADEX, WAA.
—BLDSC (4541.527500), IE. **CCC.**
Published by: Inderscience Publishers, IEL Editorial Office, PO Box 735, Olney, Bucks MK46 5WB, United Kingdom. TEL 44-1234-240519, FAX 44-1234-240515, ijaape@inderscience.com, info@inderscience.com, http://www.inderscience.com/ijaape. Ed. Prem Lal Joshi. **Subscr. to:** World Trade Centre Bldg, 29 route de Pre-Bois, Case Postale 896, Geneva 15 1215, Switzerland. FAX 41-22-7910885, subs@inderscience.com.

657 330 GBR ISSN 1467-0895
HF5679 CODEN: IJAIA7
INTERNATIONAL JOURNAL OF ACCOUNTING INFORMATION SYSTEMS. Text in English. 2000. 4/yr. EUR 76 in Europe to individuals; JPY 10,200 in Japan to individuals; USD 102 to individuals except Europe and Japan; EUR 323 in Europe to institutions; JPY 42,800 in Japan to institutions; USD 361 to institutions except Europe and Japan (effective 2006). **Document type:** *Journal, Academic/Scholarly.* **Description:** Publishes articles that examine the rapidly evolving relationship between accounting and information technology.
Related titles: Online - full text ed.: (from EBSCO Publishing, Gale Group, IngentaConnect, ScienceDirect, Swets Information Services).
Indexed: CompLI, Inspec, RefZh.
—BLDSC (4541.531000), IE, ingenta. **CCC.**
Published by: Pergamon (Subsidiary of: Elsevier Science & Technology), The Boulevard, Langford Ln, East Park, Kidlington, OX5 1GB, United Kingdom. TEL 44-1865-843000, FAX 44-1865-843010, http://www.elsevier.com/locate/accinf. Ed. S. G. Sutton. **Subscr. to:** Elsevier BV, PO Box 211, Amsterdam 1000 AE, Netherlands. TEL 31-20-485-3757, FAX 31-20-485-3432, nlinfo-f@elsevier.nl, http://www.elsevier.nl.

B

657 GBR ISSN 1090-6738
HF5667 CODEN: IJAUFE
➤ **INTERNATIONAL JOURNAL OF AUDITING.** Text in English. 1997. 3/yr. GBP 59 combined subscription in Europe to individuals print & online eds.; USD 66 combined subscription in the Americas to individuals & Caribbean (print & online eds.); GBP 39 combined subscription elsewhere to individuals print & online eds.; USD 595 combined subscription in the Americas to institutions & Caribbean (print & online eds.); GBP 354 combined subscription elsewhere to institutions print & online eds. (effective 2006). abstr. a.index. 100 p./no. 2 cols./p.; back issues avail.; reprint service avail. from PSC. **Document type:** *Journal, Academic/Scholarly.* **Description:** Provides an international forum for academics, professionals and policy makers with research interests in new ideas, techniques and approaches within all aspects of auditing.
Related titles: Online - full text ed.: ISSN 1099-1123. 1997. USD 564 in the Americas to institutions & Caribbean; GBP 336 elsewhere to institutions (effective 2006) (from Blackwell Synergy, EBSCO Publishing, Gale Group, IngentaConnect, O C L C Online Computer Library Center, Inc., Swets Information Services, Wiley InterScience).
Indexed: ABIn, IBSS.
—BLDSC (4542.120000), IE, ingenta. **CCC.**
Published by: Blackwell Publishing Ltd., 9600 Garsington Rd, Oxford, OX4 2ZG, United Kingdom. TEL 44-1865-776868, FAX 44-1865-714591, customerservices@oxon.blackwellpublishing.com, http://www.blackwellpublishing.com/journals/IJAU. Ed. Anthony Chambers.

B

▼ ➤ **INTERNATIONAL JOURNAL OF BUSINESS RESEARCH.** see *BUSINESS AND ECONOMICS—Management*

657 003 ESP ISSN 1577-8517
THE INTERNATIONAL JOURNAL OF DIGITAL ACCOUNTING RESEARCH. Text in English. 2001. s-a. **Document type:** *Journal, Trade.*
Related titles: Online - full text ed.: (from ProQuest Information & Learning).
Indexed: ABIn.
—BLDSC (4542.185370).
Published by: (Rutgers, the State University of New Jersey USA), Universidad de Huelva, Servicio de Publicaciones, Campus el Carmen, Ave. de las Fuerzas Armadas, s-n, Huelva, Andalucia 21071, Spain. TEL 34-95-9018000, publica@uhu.es, http://www.uhu.es/publicaciones/index.html.

INTERNATIONAL JOURNAL OF MANAGEMENT. see *BUSINESS AND ECONOMICS—Management*

657 510 USA
INTERNATIONAL SOCIETY OF PARAMETRIC ANALYSTS. CONFERENCE PROCEEDINGS. Text in English. 1983. a. price varies. adv. **Document type:** *Proceedings.*
—BLDSC (3409.770612).
Published by: International Society of Parametric Analysts, Inc. (ISPA), PO Box 3185, Chandler, AZ 85244. TEL 480-917-4747, FAX 480-792-6930, ispaoffice@earthlink.net, http://www.ispa-cost.org/conf.htm. Circ: 400.

657 USA
▼ ➤ **THE INTERNET JOURNAL OF ACCOUNTING.** Text in English. 2004. irreg. free to individuals; USD 500 to institutions (effective 2004). **Document type:** *Journal, Academic/Scholarly.*
Published by: Internet Scientific Publications, L.L.C., 23 Rippling Creek Dr, Sugar Land, TX 77479. TEL 832-443-1193, FAX 281-240-1533, wenker@ispub.com, http://www.ispub.com.

➤ **INTERNET TAX ADVISOR.** see *BUSINESS AND ECONOMICS—Banking And Finance—Computer Applications*

657 USA ISSN 1099-5765
HF5626
INTERPRETATION AND APPLICATION OF INTERNATIONAL ACCOUNTING STANDARDS. Text in English. 1997. a.
Published by: John Wiley & Sons, Inc., 111 River St, Hoboken, NJ 07030-5774.

THE INTERPRETER (DURHAM). see *INSURANCE*

657 AUS ISSN 1832-0899
HF5601 CODEN: AUACAC
INTHEBLACK. Text in English. 1936. m. (except Jan.). AUD 115.50 domestic to individuals; AUD 135 foreign to individuals; AUD 160 domestic libraries & institutions; AUD 180 foreign libraries & institutions (effective 2005). adv. bk.rev. Index. back issues avail.; reprints avail. **Document type:** *Magazine, Trade.* **Description:** Deals with contemporary business, finance, accounting and management issues.
Former titles (until 2004): Australian C P A (1440-8880); (until 1998): Australian Accountant (0004-8631); Which incorporated: Financial Forum
Related titles: Online - full text ed.: (from O C L C Online Computer Library Center, Inc., ProQuest Information & Learning); ◆ Supplement(s): Australian Society of Certified Practising Accountants. Annual Report.
Indexed: AAR, ABIX, ABIn, ADPA, AESIS, ATI, AusPAIS, Emerald, PCI, WBA, WMB.
—BLDSC (1798.262350), IE, ingenta. **CCC.**
Published by: (Australian Society of Certified Practising Accountants), Hardie Grant Magazines, 85 High St, Prahran, VIC 3181, Australia. TEL 61-3-85206444, FAX 61-3-85206422, jackieblondell@hardiegrant.com.au, info@hardiegrant.com.au, http://www.hardiegrant.com.au. Ed. Jackie Blondell. Circ: 94,727.

657 GBR ISSN 0791-9638
HF5601
IRISH ACCOUNTING REVIEW. Text in English. 1994. a. **Description:** Publishes papers in the areas of accounting, finance, and their related disciplines.
Related titles: Online - full text ed.: (from O C L C Online Computer Library Center, Inc., ProQuest Information & Learning).
Indexed: ABIn.
—BLDSC (4567.955000). **CCC.**
Published by: Irish Accounting and Finance Association, c/o Tony Wall, School of Accounting, University of Ulster, Shore Rd, Newtownabbey, Co. Antrim BT37 0QB, United Kingdom. TEL 44-28-90366024, FAX 44-28-90368502, ap.wall@ulster.ac.uk, http://www.iafa.ie/irish_accounting_review/. Eds. Keith Warnock, Noel Hyndman.

657 GBR ISSN 1350-6242
IRISH COMPANY REPORTING. Text in English. 1993. irreg. GBP 30 (effective 2000). **Document type:** *Monographic series.*
Published by: University of Ulster, School of Management, Newtownabbey, Antrim BT37 0QB, United Kingdom. TEL 44-1232-365131, FAX 44-1232-366805, rj.kirk@ulst.ac.uk. Ed., R&P Robert Kirk. Circ: 100 (controlled).

657.07 USA ISSN 0739-3172
HF5630
➤ **ISSUES IN ACCOUNTING EDUCATION.** Text in English. 1983. s-a. USD 225 (effective 2005). adv. bk.rev. illus. reprint service avail. from PSC. **Document type:** *Journal, Academic/Scholarly.* **Description:** Contains research articles for accounting faculty that describe or discuss aspects of accounting education.
Related titles: Online - full text ed.: (from bigchalk, EBSCO Publishing, Florida Center for Library Automation, Gale Group, Northern Light Technology, Inc., O C L C Online Computer Library Center, Inc., ProQuest Information & Learning).
Indexed: ABIn, ATI, Emerald.
—BLDSC (4584.065000), IE, Infotrieve, ingenta. **CCC.**
Published by: American Accounting Association, 5717 Bessie Dr, Sarasota, FL 34233-2399. TEL 941-921-7747, FAX 941-923-4093, http://www.rutgers.edu/Accounting/raw/aaa/pubs.htm, http://aaahq.org. Ed. David E Stout. R&P Mary Cole. Adv. contact Judy Cothern.

657 POL ISSN 1428-8184
JAK PROWADZIC KSIEGE PRZYCHODOW I ROZCHODOW?. Text in Polish. 1997. bi-w. PLZ 126 (effective 2001).
Published by: Grupa Wydawnicza INFOR Sp. z o.o., Ul Okopowa 58/72, Warsaw, 01042, Poland. TEL 48-22-5304208, 48-22-5304450, bok@infor.pl. Ed. Grazyna Gonciarska. Adv. contact Waldemar Krakowiak.

657 ISR
JERUSALEM CONFERENCE ON ACCOUNTANCY. Text in English. 1971. triennial. price varies.
Published by: Institute of Certified Public Accountants in Israel, 1 Montefiore St., P O Box 29281, Tel Aviv, Israel. TEL 972-3-5161114, FAX 972-3-5103105.

657 PRT ISSN 0870-8789
JORNAL DE CONTABILIDADE. Text in Portuguese. 1977. m. EUR 45 (effective 2005). adv. bk.rev. index. 6 p./no.; back issues avail. **Document type:** *Journal, Trade.* **Description:** For accountants and business managers.
Published by: Associacao Portuguesa de Tecnicos de Contabilidade, Rua Rodrigues Sampaio, 50-3o Esq, Lisbon, 1169 029, Portugal. TEL 351-21-3552900, FAX 351-21-3552909, apotec@mail.telepac.pt, http://www.apotec.pt. Ed. Dr. Severo Praxedes Soares. Adv. contact Antonio Lopes Reis. Circ: 9,000.

657 332 USA
THE JOURNAL OF 21ST CENTURY ACCOUNTING. Text in English. q. free (effective 2004). **Document type:** *Journal, Academic/Scholarly.* **Description:** Dedicated to providing a forum for the accounting academic, practitioner and student. The purpose of the Journal is to provide an outlet for topics that are interesting and useful to all segments of the accounting community. Submissions are welcome from faculty and students.
Media: Online - full text.
Published by: Nova Southeastern University, 3100 S W 9th St, Fort Lauderdale, FL 33315. walter@huizenga.nova.edu, ron@nsu.nova.edu, http://www.theaccountingjournal.org/. Ed. Dr. Walter B Moore.

657 USA ISSN 0021-8448
CODEN: JACYAD
JOURNAL OF ACCOUNTANCY. Text in English. 1905. m. USD 69 to non-members (effective 2005). adv. bk.rev. bibl.; charts; illus. s-a. index. reprint service avail. from PQC. **Document type:** *Magazine, Trade.* **Description:** Reports on developments, trends, management advisory services, taxation, education, professional subjects.
Related titles: Microform ed.: (from MIM, PQC); Online - full text ed.: Journal of Accountancy Online (from bigchalk, EBSCO Publishing, Florida Center for Library Automation, Gale Group, H.W. Wilson, LexisNexis, Northern Light Technology, Inc., O C L C Online Computer Library Center, Inc., ProQuest Information & Learning).
Indexed: ABIn, ABRCLP, ATI, AgeL, BPI, BPIA, BRI, BusEdI, BusI, CBRI, CLI, CPM, CurCont, DPD, Emerald, FamI, HECAB, IMI, Inspec, LOIS, LRI, M&MA, ManagCont, ORMS, PAIS, PROMT, PSI, SCIMP, SSCI, SoftBase, T&II, WBA.
—BLDSC (4918.860000), CASDDS, IDS, IE, Infotrieve, ingenta. **CCC.**
Published by: American Institute of Certified Public Accountants, Harborside Financial Ctr., 201 Plaza Three, 3rd Fl, Jersey City, NJ 07311-9801. TEL 201-938-3000, 888-777-7077, FAX 201-938-3329, 800-302-5766, journal@aicpa.org, http://www.aicpa.org/pubs/jofa/joahome.htm. Ed., Pub. Colleen Katz. R&P Marie Bareille. Adv. contacts Richard Flynn, Thomas Greve. B&W page USD 12,350, color page USD 16,315. Circ: 376,691 (paid).

657 330.9 NLD ISSN 0165-4101
HF5601 CODEN: JAECDS
➤ **JOURNAL OF ACCOUNTING AND ECONOMICS.** Text in English. 1979. 6/yr. EUR 73 in Europe to individuals; JPY 9,600 in Japan to individuals; USD 76 elsewhere to individuals; EUR 999 in Europe to institutions; JPY 132,800 in Japan to institutions; USD 1,119 elsewhere to institutions; EUR 44 in Europe to students; JPY 5,700 in Japan to students; USD 49 elsewhere to students (effective 2006). adv. bibl.; illus. Index. back issues avail.; reprints avail. **Document type:** *Journal, Academic/Scholarly.* **Description:** Provides a forum for the publication of economic analyses of accounting problems.
Related titles: Microform ed.: (from PQC); Online - full text ed.: (from EBSCO Publishing, Gale Group, IngentaConnect, ScienceDirect, Swets Information Services).
Indexed: ABIn, ASCA, ATI, BPIA, BusI, CREJ, CurCont, ESPM, Emerald, IBSS, JCQM, JEL, ManagCont, RiskAb, SSCI, T&II, WBA.
—BLDSC (4918.866000), IDS, IE, Infotrieve, ingenta. **CCC.**
Published by: Elsevier BV, North-Holland (Subsidiary of: Elsevier Science & Technology), Sara Burgerhartstraat 25, Amsterdam, 1055 KV, Netherlands. TEL 31-20-485-3911, FAX 31-20-485-2457, nlinfo-f@elsevier.nl, http://www.elsevier.com/locate/jae, http://www.elsevier.nl. Eds. Jerold L Zimmerman, Ross L Watts, S. P. Kothari. **Subscr. to:** Elsevier BV, PO Box 211, Amsterdam 1000 AE, Netherlands. TEL 31-20-485-3757, FAX 31-20-485-3432, http://www.elsevier.nl.

657 332 USA ISSN 1093-5770
JOURNAL OF ACCOUNTING AND FINANCE RESEARCH. Text in English. 1994. q.
Related titles: Online - full text ed.: (from EBSCO Publishing, ProQuest Information & Learning).
Indexed: BLI.
Published by: American Academy of Accounting and Finance, PO Box 1399, Clinton, MS 39056-9643. TEL 601-924-5514, FAX 601-877-2326, info@aaafonline.org, http://www.aaafonline.org. Ed. Roger Calcode.

657 GBR ISSN 1832-5912
▼ ➤ **JOURNAL OF ACCOUNTING AND ORGANISATIONAL CHANGE.** Text in English. 2005. 3/yr. AUD 449 combined subscription print & online eds. (effective 2006). **Document type:** *Journal, Academic/Scholarly.* **Description:** Provides a platform for researchers and practitioners from multiple disciplines to disseminate information on organizational and accounting systems change.
Related titles: Online - full text ed.
Published by: Emerald Group Publishing Limited, 60-62 Toller Ln, Bradford, W Yorks BD8 9BY, United Kingdom. TEL 44-1274-777700, FAX 44-1274-785200, infomation@emeraldinsight.com, www.emeraldinsight.com/jaoc.htm, http://www.emeraldinsight.com/. R&P Ms. Anne-Marie Thorslund.

657 USA ISSN 0278-4254
H97 CODEN: JACPDN
➤ **JOURNAL OF ACCOUNTING AND PUBLIC POLICY.** Text in English. 1982. 6/yr. EUR 97 in Europe to individuals; JPY 12,900 in Japan to individuals; USD 108 to individuals except Europe and Japan; EUR 578 in Europe to institutions; JPY 76,700 in Japan to institutions; USD 647 to institutions except Europe and Japan (effective 2006). adv. bibl.; illus. Index. reprints avail. **Document type:** *Journal, Academic/Scholarly.* **Description:** Publishes articles exploring the interaction of accounting with a wide range of disciplines including economics, public administration, political science, social psychology, policy science, and the law.
Related titles: Microform ed.: (from PQC); Online - full text ed.: (from EBSCO Publishing, Gale Group, IngentaConnect, ScienceDirect, Swets Information Services).
Indexed: ABIn, ASCA, ATI, AgeL, BPIA, CPM, CurCont, EAA, ESPM, Emerald, IBSS, PAIS, RiskAb, SPAA, SSCI, WBA.
—BLDSC (4918.868000), IDS, IE, Infotrieve, ingenta. **CCC.**
Published by: Elsevier Inc. (Subsidiary of: Elsevier Science & Technology), 360 Park Ave. S, New York, NY 10010-1710. TEL 212-989-5800, 888-437-4636, FAX 212-633-3990, a.gaskin@elsevier.com, usinfo-f@elsevier.com, http://www.elsevier.com/locate/jaccpubpol. Ed. Lawrence A Gordon. adv.: B&W page USD 855, color page USD 2,030.

657 USA ISSN 0148-558X
HF5601

➤ **JOURNAL OF ACCOUNTING, AUDITING & FINANCE.** Text in English. 1977-1985; N.S. 1986. q. USD 90 domestic to individuals; USD 105 foreign to individuals; USD 225 domestic to institutions; USD 260 foreign to institutions; USD 60 newsstand/cover (effective 2006). illus. reprint service avail. from WSH. **Document type:** *Journal, Academic/Scholarly.* **Description:** Publishes papers on a wide variety of papers in the field of accounting research.
Indexed: ABIn, ATI, BLI, BPI, BPIA, BusI, CLI, CPM, Emerald, ILP, JEL, LII, ManagCont.
—BLDSC (4918.870000), IE, Infotrieve, ingenta. **CCC.**
Published by: (New York University, Vincent C. Ross Institute of Accounting Research), Greenwood Publishing Group Inc. (Subsidiary of: Harcourt International), 88 Post Rd W, PO Box 5007, Westport, CT 06881. TEL 203-226-3571, 800-225-5800, FAX 203-222-1502, webmaster@greenwood.com, http://w4.stern.nyu.edu/ross/research.cfm?doc_id=1746, http://www.greenwood.com/. Ed. Kashi Balachandran. Circ: 1,000.

657.0711 GBR ISSN 0748-5751
HF5630

➤ **JOURNAL OF ACCOUNTING EDUCATION.** Text in English. 1982. 4/yr. EUR 109 in Europe to individuals; JPY 14,400 in Japan to individuals; USD 121 to individuals except Europe and Japan; EUR 555 in Europe to institutions; JPY 73,600 in Japan to institutions; USD 620 to institutions except Europe and Japan (effective 2006). adv. illus. Index. back issues avail.; reprints avail. **Document type:** *Journal, Academic/Scholarly.* **Description:** Provides a forum for the exchange of ideas, opinion and research results among accounting educators around the world.
Related titles: Microfilm ed.: (from PQC); Online - full text ed.: (from EBSCO Publishing, Gale Group, IngentaConnect, ScienceDirect, Swets Information Services).
Indexed: ABIn, ATI, CPE, ERA, ETA, Emerald, TEA.
—BLDSC (4918.875000), IE, Infotrieve, ingenta. **CCC.**
Published by: (James Madison University USA), Pergamon (Subsidiary of: Elsevier Science & Technology), The Boulevard, Langford Ln, East Park, Kidlington, Oxford OX5 1GB, United Kingdom. TEL 44-1865-843000, FAX 44-1865-843010, http://www.elsevier.com/locate/jaccedu. Ed. James E Rebele. Circ: 1,500. **Subscr. to:** Elsevier BV, PO Box 211, Amsterdam 1000 AE, Netherlands. TEL 31-20-485-3757, FAX 31-20-485-3432, nlinfo-f@elsevier.nl, http://www.elsevier.nl.

657 USA ISSN 1089-652X
HF5625.15

JOURNAL OF ACCOUNTING, ETHICS & PUBLIC POLICY. Text in English. 199?. q. **Document type:** *Academic/Scholarly.* **Description:** Publishes articles in the interdisciplinary areas of accounting, ethics, & public policy.
Published by: The Dumont Institute for Public Policy Research, 71 South Orange Ave, PMB 260, South Orange, NJ 07079. info@dumontinst.com, http://www.dumontinst.com. Ed. Robert W McGee. **Dist. by:** Book Masters, Inc., PO Box 388, Ashland, OH 44805. TEL 800-247-6553, FAX 419-281-6883, order@bookmaster.com.

657 USA ISSN 0737-4607
HF5601

➤ **JOURNAL OF ACCOUNTING LITERATURE.** Text in English. 1982. a. USD 25 to individuals; USD 29 to institutions; USD 15 to students (effective 2004). illus. back issues avail.; reprint service avail. from PSC. **Document type:** *Academic/Scholarly.* **Description:** Provides in-depth review articles on accounting topics, as well as research on accounting and auditing standards.
Related titles: Online - full text ed.: (from Northern Light Technology, Inc., ProQuest Information & Learning).
Indexed: ABIn, ATI.
—BLDSC (4918.877000), IE, Infotrieve, ingenta. **CCC.**
Published by: University of Florida, Fisher School of Accounting, College of Business Administration, PO Box 117166, Gainesville, FL 32611-7166. TEL 352-273-0229, FAX 352-392-7962, kathy.murphy@cba.ufl.edu, http://www.cba.ufl.edu/fsoa/JAL/jal.html. Eds. Bipin B Ajinkya, Stephen Kwaka Asare.

657 USA ISSN 0021-8456
HF5601 CODEN: JACRBR

➤ **JOURNAL OF ACCOUNTING RESEARCH.** Text in English. 1963. 5/yr. USD 114 combined subscription in the Americas to individuals & Caribbean, print & online eds.; EUR 119 combined subscription in Europe to individuals print & online eds.; GBP 79 combined subscription elsewhere to individuals print & online eds.; USD 595 combined subscription in the Americas to institutions & Caribbean, print & online eds.; GBP 412 combined subscription elsewhere to institutions print & online eds.; USD 44 combined subscription in the Americas to students & Caribbea, print & online eds.; EUR 50 combined subscription in Europe to students print & online eds.; GBP 33 combined subscription elsewhere to students print & online eds. (effective 2006). charts; stat.; illus. index. Supplement avail.; reprint service avail. from PQC. **Document type:** *Journal, Academic/Scholarly.* **Description:** Unpublished original research in the fields of empirical, analytic and experimental accounting.
Related titles: Microform ed.: (from MIM, PQC); Online - full text ed.: ISSN 1475-679X. USD 565 in the Americas to institutions & Caribbean; GBP 391 elsewhere to institutions (effective 2006) (from Blackwell Synergy, EBSCO Publishing, Gale Group, IngentaConnect, JSTOR (Web-based Journal Archive), Northern Light Technology, Inc., O C L C Online Computer Library Center, Inc., Swets Information Services).
Indexed: ABIn, ADPA, ASCA, ATI, BPI, BPIA, BusI, CIS, CPM, CREJ, CurCont, Emerald, IBR, IBSS, IBZ, ISAP, Inspec, JCQM, JEL, ManagCont, ORMS, SCIMP, SSCI, T&II, WBA.
—BLDSC (4918.880000), IE, Infotrieve, ingenta. **CCC.**
Published by: (Institute of Professional Accounting), Blackwell Publishing, Inc. (Subsidiary of: Blackwell Publishing Ltd.), Commerce Place, 350 Main St, Malden, MA 02148. TEL 781-388-8206, FAX 781-388-8232, jar@gsb.uchicago.edu, subscrip@blackwellpub.com, http://www.blackwellpublishing.com/journals/JAR. Eds. Abbie Smith, Ray Ball, Richard Leftwich. Circ: 2,800 (paid).

➤ **JOURNAL OF ACTUARIAL PRACTICE.** see *INSURANCE*

657.072 GBR ISSN 0967-5426
JOURNAL OF APPLIED ACCOUNTING RESEARCH. Text in English. 1992. 3/yr. **Document type:** *Academic/Scholarly.*
Indexed: ABIn.
—BLDSC (4939.870000).
Published by: (Department of Accounting & Finance), De Montfort University, Leicester Business School, The Gateway, Leicester, LE1 9BH, United Kingdom. TEL 44-116-2511551, FAX 44-116-2517548. Ed. Leigh Holland.

657 338 GBR ISSN 0306-686X
HG11

➤ **JOURNAL OF BUSINESS FINANCE & ACCOUNTING.** Text in English. 1974. 5/yr. GBP 97, EUR 146 combined subscription in Europe to individuals print & online eds.; USD 200 combined subscription in the Americas to individuals & Caribbean (print & online eds.); GBP 119 combined subscription elsewhere to individuals print & online eds.; GBP 701 combined subscription in Europe to institutions print & online eds.; USD 1,337 combined subscription in the Americas to institutions & Caribbean (print & online eds.); GBP 796 combined subscription elsewhere to institutions print & online eds. (effective 2006). adv. illus. Index. reprint service avail. from PSC,PQC. **Document type:** *Journal, Academic/Scholarly.* **Description:** Advances both the academic understanding and the professional practice of effective financial management, control, and accountability.
Related titles: Online - full text ed.: ISSN 1468-5957. GBP 666 in Europe to institutions; USD 1,270 in the Americas to institutions & Caribbean; GBP 756 elsewhere to institutions (effective 2006) (from Blackwell Synergy, EBSCO Publishing, Gale Group, IngentaConnect, O C L C Online Computer Library Center, Inc., Swets Information Services).
Indexed: ABIn, ADPA, ATI, BPIA, BusI, CPM, CREJ, ESPM, Emerald, IBSS, JCQM, M&MA, ManagCont, RiskAb, SCIMP, T&II, WBA.
—BLDSC (4954.693000), IE, Infotrieve, ingenta. **CCC.**
Published by: Blackwell Publishing Ltd., 9600 Garsington Rd, Oxford, OX4 2ZG, United Kingdom. TEL 44-1865-776868, FAX 44-1865-714591, customerservices@oxon.blackwellpublishing.com, http://www.blackwellpublishing.com/journals/JBFA. Eds. A W Stark, M Walker, P F Pope. Circ: 1,350.

657 336 USA ISSN 1054-3007
HF5686.B7

JOURNAL OF CONSTRUCTION ACCOUNTING AND TAXATION. Text in English. 1991. 6/yr. USD 230 (effective 2004). reprints avail. **Document type:** *Journal, Trade.* **Description:** Provides in-depth coverage of accounting, tax, and financial problems encountered in the construction industry.
Related titles: Online - full text ed.: (from ProQuest Information & Learning).
Indexed: ABIn, ATI.
—CCC.
Published by: W G & L Financial Reporting & Management Research (Subsidiary of: R I A), 395 Hudson St, New York, NY 10014. TEL 212-367-6300, FAX 212-367-6718, ria@thomson.com. Ed. John Metz.

657 USA ISSN 1044-8136
HF5686.C7 CODEN: JCAFFX

JOURNAL OF CORPORATE ACCOUNTING AND FINANCE. Text in English. 1979. bi-m. USD 570 in North America; USD 606 elsewhere; USD 627 combined subscription in North America print & online eds.; USD 663 combined subscription elsewhere print & online eds. (effective 2006). adv. bk.rev. 96 p./no. 3 cols./p.; reprint service avail. from WSH,PSC. **Document type:** *Magazine, Trade.* **Description:** Provides advice on dealing with current issues. Examines corporate accounting practices and policies and analyzes existing and proposed professional regulatory and tax law developments.
Former titles (until 1989): Financial Accounting Reporter (0890-3484); (until 1986): Corporate Accounting Reporter (0199-0683); Financial Regulation Report
Related titles: Microfiche ed.: (from WSH); Online - full text ed.: ISSN 1097-0053. USD 570 (effective 2006) (from EBSCO Publishing, ProQuest Information & Learning, Swets Information Services, Wiley InterScience).
Indexed: ATI, BPI, BPIA.
—BLDSC (4965.333000), IE, Infotrieve, ingenta. **CCC.**
Published by: John Wiley & Sons, Inc., 111 River St, Hoboken, NJ 07030-5774. TEL 201-748-6000, 800-825-7550, FAX 201-748-5915, uscs-wis@wiley.com, http://www.wiley.com/WileyCDA/WileyTitle/productCd-JCAF.html. Eds. Edward J Stone, Paul Munter. adv.: B&W page GBP 640, color page GBP 1,515; trim 210 x 279. **Subscr. to:** John Wiley & Sons Ltd., The Atrium, Southern Gate, Chichester, West Sussex PO19 8SQ, United Kingdom. TEL 44-1243-779777, FAX 44-1243-775878, cs-journals@wiley.co.uk.

657 USA ISSN 0882-3871
HF5686.C8

➤ **JOURNAL OF COST ANALYSIS AND MANAGEMENT.** Text in English. 1984. a. USD 55 (effective 2005). abstr.; bibl.; illus. **Document type:** *Academic/Scholarly.*
Indexed: ATI.
Published by: Society of Cost Estimating and Analysis, 101 S Whiting St, Ste 201, Alexandria, VA 22304. TEL 703-751-8069, scea@sceaonline.net, http://www.sceaonline.net. Ed. David S Christensen. Circ: 2,500.

B

657 SGP

▼ ➤ **JOURNAL OF DERIVATIVES ACCOUNTING.** Text in English. 2004 (Mar). q. SGD 141, USD 80, EUR 79 to individuals; SGD 493, USD 280, EUR 277 combined subscription to institutions print & online eds. (effective 2004). back issues avail. **Document type:** *Journal, Academic/Scholarly.* **Description:** Covers the issues of financial innovations such as derivatives and their implications to accounting, finance, tax, standards setting, and corporate practices.
Related titles: Online - full content ed.
—BLDSC (4968.759000).
Published by: World Scientific Publishing Co. Pte. Ltd., 5 Toh Tuck Link, Singapore, 596224, Singapore. TEL 65-466-5775, wspc@wspc.com.sg, series@wspc.com.sg, http://www.worldscientific.com. Ed. Mamouda Mbemap. **Dist. by:** World Scientific Publishing Co., Inc., 1060 Main St, River Edge, NJ 07661. TEL 201-487-9655, FAX 201-487-9656, 888-977-2665; World Scientific Publishing Ltd., 57 Shelton St, London WC2H 9HE, United Kingdom. FAX 44-20-78362020, sales@wspc.co.uk.

657 USA ISSN 1554-1908
HF5601

▼ **JOURNAL OF EMERGING TECHNOLOGIES IN ACCOUNTING.** Text in English. 2004. a. USD 100 per issue (effective 2005).
Related titles: Online - full text ed.: (from EBSCO Publishing).
Published by: American Accounting Association, 5717 Bessie Dr, Sarasota, FL 34233-2399. TEL 941-921-7747, FAX 941-923-4093, office@aaahq.org, http://aaahq.org.

657 GBR ISSN 1475-1283
JOURNAL OF FINANCE AND MANAGEMENT IN PUBLIC SERVICES. Text in English. 2001. s-a. GBP 15 (effective 2002). **Document type:** *Journal, Academic/Scholarly.* **Description:** Aims to disseminate research regarding public accounting practices, management, policy and governance.
—BLDSC (4984.228000), IE.
Published by: (A C I P F A L), Earlybrave Publications Ltd., Springfield Lyons House, Chelmsford Business Park, Chelmsford, Essex CM2 5TH, United Kingdom. TEL 44-1245-236584, FAX 44-1245-236611, information@earlybrave.com, http://www.earlybrave.com.

JOURNAL OF FINANCIAL PLANNING. see *BUSINESS AND ECONOMICS—Investments*

657.2 364.4 346.06 657.6 USA ISSN 1524-5586
HV8079.W47

➤ **JOURNAL OF FORENSIC ACCOUNTING**; auditing, fraud, and taxation. Abbreviated title: J F A. Text in English. 2000. s-a. USD 119 to individuals; USD 239 to institutions; USD 49 to students; USD 125 per issue (effective 2005). adv. bk.rev.; Website rev. Index. 130 p./no.; back issues avail.; reprints avail. **Document type:** *Journal, Academic/Scholarly.* **Description:** Contains papers on fraud auditing, bankruptcy studies, GAAP violation, internal auditing and the underground economy. Includes techniques, technologies and preventative controls. Audience: Researchers and educators specializing in forensic accounting, as well as auditors, process security specialists and legal, tax and insurance personnel.
Published by: (Louisiana State University, E J Ourso College of Business Administration), R. T. Edwards, Inc., P.O. Box 27388, Philadelphia, PA 19118. TEL 215-233-5046, FAX 215-233-2421, info@edwardspub.com, http://www.rtedwards.com/journals/JFA. Eds. Mark S Beasley, Todd DeZoort, D Larry Crumbley. R&P, Adv. contact Chris Wade. page USD 190; trim 9.25 x 7.5. Circ: 325 (paid); 50 (controlled); 125 (free).

657 USA ISSN 1533-1385
HJ9801

➤ **THE JOURNAL OF GOVERNMENT FINANCIAL MANAGEMENT.** Text in English. 1950. q. USD 95 domestic; USD 115 foreign (effective 2005). bk.rev. charts; illus. cum.index. back issues avail.; reprint service avail. from PQC. **Document type:** *Journal, Academic/Scholarly.*
Former titles: Government Accountants Journal (0883-1483); (until vol.25, 1976): Federal Accountant (0014-9004)

▼ *new title* ➤ *refereed* ✶ *unverified* ◆ *full entry avail.*

Related titles: Microform ed.: (from PQC); Online - full text ed.: (from Northern Light Technology, Inc., O C L C Online Computer Library Center, Inc., ProQuest Information & Learning).
Indexed: ABIn, ADPA, ATI, BPIA, BusI, ManagCont, PAIS, PersLit.
—BLDSC (4996.422500), IE, ingenta.
Published by: Association of Government Accountants, 2208 Mount Vernon Ave, Alexandria, VA 22301-1314. TEL 703-684-6931, FAX 703-548-9367, mforce@agacgfm.org, JCurtin@agacgfm.org, http://www.agacgfm.org/publications/journal. Ed., R&P, Adv. contact Marie S. Force. Circ: 18,000 (paid).

➤ **JOURNAL OF I T FINANCIAL MANAGEMENT.** see *COMPUTERS—Electronic Data Processing*

➤ **THE JOURNAL OF INFORMATION SYSTEMS.** see *COMPUTERS—Information Science And Information Theory*

657 336   GBR   ISSN 1061-9518
HF5601
➤ **JOURNAL OF INTERNATIONAL ACCOUNTING, AUDITING AND TAXATION.** Text in English. 1992. 2/yr. EUR 103 in Europe to individuals; JPY 13,600 in Japan to individuals; USD 114 to individuals except Europe and Japan; EUR 312 in Europe to institutions; JPY 41,400 in Japan to institutions; USD 349 to institutions except Europe and Japan (effective 2006). illus. Index. back issues avail.; reprints avail.
Document type: *Journal, Academic/Scholarly.* **Description:** Publishes articles which deal with all areas of international accounting including auditing, taxation and management advisory services.
Related titles: Microform ed.: (from PQC); Online - full text ed.: (from EBSCO Publishing, Gale Group, IngentaConnect, ScienceDirect, Swets Information Services).
Indexed: ABIn, ATI, IBSS.
—BLDSC (5007.548900), IE, Infotrieve, ingenta. **CCC.**
Published by: Pergamon (Subsidiary of: Elsevier Science & Technology), The Boulevard, Langford Ln, East Park, Kidlington, Oxford OX5 1GB, United Kingdom. TEL 44-1865-843000, FAX 44-1865-843010, http://www.elsevier.com/locate/intaat. Eds. H. J. Dykxhoorn, Kathleen E. Sinning. **Subscr. to:** Elsevier BV, PO Box 211, Amsterdam 1000 AE, Netherlands. TEL 31-20-485-3757, FAX 31-20-485-3432, nlinfo-f@elsevier.nl, http://www.elsevier.nl.

657   USA   ISSN 1542-6297
HF5601
JOURNAL OF INTERNATIONAL ACCOUNTING RESEARCH. Text in English. 2002 (Dec.). a.
Related titles: Online - full text ed.: (from EBSCO Publishing, Gale Group, O C L C Online Computer Library Center, Inc., ProQuest Information & Learning).
Indexed: ABIn.
Published by: American Accounting Association, 5717 Bessie Dr, Sarasota, FL 34233-2399. TEL 941-921-7747, FAX 941-923-4093, office@aaahq.org, http://aaahq.org. Ed. R.S. Olusegun Wallace.

JOURNAL OF INTERNATIONAL FINANCIAL MANAGEMENT AND ACCOUNTING. see *BUSINESS AND ECONOMICS—Banking And Finance*

657 658   USA   ISSN 1049-2127
HF5657.4
➤ **JOURNAL OF MANAGEMENT ACCOUNTING RESEARCH.** Text in English. 1989. a. USD 15 (effective 2005). illus. reprint service avail. from PSC. **Document type:** *Academic/Scholarly.*
Related titles: Online - full text ed.: (from EBSCO Publishing, Florida Center for Library Automation, Gale Group, Northern Light Technology, Inc., O C L C Online Computer Library Center, Inc., ProQuest Information & Learning).
Indexed: ABIn, ATI, Emerald, JEL.
—BLDSC (5011.130000), IE, Infotrieve, ingenta. **CCC.**
Published by: American Accounting Association, 5717 Bessie Dr, Sarasota, FL 34233-2399. TEL 941-921-7747, FAX 941-923-4093, http://accounting.rutgers.edu/raw/aaa/aaamas/JMAR/jmarhome.htm, http://aaahq.org. Ed. Anthony A Atkinson. R&P Mary Cole.

➤ **JOURNAL OF MANAGERIAL ISSUES.** see *BUSINESS AND ECONOMICS—Management*

657 510   USA   ISSN 1015-7891
JOURNAL OF PARAMETRICS. Text in English. 1981. s-a. USD 55 membership (effective 2004). adv. **Document type:** *Journal, Trade.* **Description:** Covers cost estimating and analysis.
Indexed: CIS.
—BLDSC (5028.650000).
Published by: International Society of Parametric Analysts, Inc. (ISPA), PO Box 3185, Chandler, AZ 85244. TEL 480-917-4747, FAX 480-792-6930, ispaoffice@earthlink.net, http://www.ispa-cost.org/journal.htm. Ed. Steve Book TEL 310-640-0003. Circ: 400.

JOURNAL OF PASSTHROUGH ENTITIES. see *LAW—Corporate Law*

JOURNAL OF PERFORMANCE MANAGEMENT. see *BUSINESS AND ECONOMICS—Banking And Finance*

657   GBR   ISSN 1476-6930
HG4028.C45
JOURNAL OF REVENUE AND PRICING MANAGEMENT. Text in English. 2002. q. GBP 100 in Europe to individuals based at universities or other educational establishment; USD 170 in US & Canada to individuals based at universities or other educational establishment; GBP 115 elsewhere to individuals based at universities or other educational establishment; GBP 200 in Europe to institutions; USD 350 in US & Canada to institutions; GBP 215 elsewhere to institutions (effective 2005).
Document type: *Journal, Academic/Scholarly.* **Description:** Publishes the highest quality articles and briefings on the major developments, new strategic thinking and applied research in the fields of Revenue Management and Pricing.
Related titles: Online - full text ed.: ISSN 1477-657X (from EBSCO Publishing, Gale Group, IngentaConnect, O C L C Online Computer Library Center, Inc., ProQuest Information & Learning, Swets Information Services).
Indexed: ABIn.
—BLDSC (5052.046000), IE. **CCC.**
Published by: Palgrave Macmillan Ltd. (Subsidiary of: Macmillan Publishers Ltd.), Houndmills, Basingstoke, Hants RG21 6XS, United Kingdom. TEL 44-1256-329242, FAX 44-1256-810526, journal-info@palgrave.com, http://www.palgrave-journals.com/. Ed. Ian Yeoman.

657   IDN   ISSN 1410-6817
HF5601
➤ **JURNAL RISET AKUNTANSI INDONESIA/JOURNAL OF THE EDUCATIONAL COMPARTMENT OF ACCOUNTANTS OF THE INDONESIAN INSTITUTE OF ACCOUNTANTS.** Abstracts and contents page in Indonesian, English. 1998. 3/yr. IDR 65,000 domestic; USD 15 foreign; IDR 30,000 newsstand/cover (effective 2001). adv. abstr. 130 p./no.; back issues avail. **Document type:** *Journal, Academic/Scholarly.* **Description:** Contains articles on financial and management accounting, capital market, public sector accounting, information system and taxation.
Published by: Indonesian Institute of Accountants, Educational Compartment of Accountants, Gd FE UGM-B-112 Bulaksumur, Yogyakarta, 55281, Indonesia. TEL 62-274-901-239, FAX 62-274-563-212, jrai@economics-gmu.com. Ed. Dr. Zaki Baridwan. adv.: page USD 2,500; 180 x 255. Circ: 2,000.

657   ISL
K P M G FRETTIR/K P M G NEWS. Text in Icelandic. 1995. irreg. free to qualified personnel. illus. **Document type:** *Newsletter, Trade.* **Description:** Contains news and other material of interest to public accountants and their clients in Iceland and elsewhere.
Published by: Klynveld Peat Marwick Goerdeler Endurskodun hf., Vegmuli 3, Reykjavik, 108, Iceland. TEL 354-533-5555, FAX 354-533-5550. Ed. Saemundur Valdimarsson. Pub. Olafur Nilsson. Circ: 2,000.

657   IDN
KATALOG PENDIDIKAN PROFESIONAL BERKELANJUTAN/INDONESIAN INSTITUTE OF ACCOUNTANTS CATALOG. Text in Indonesian. 1997. a. IDR 7,500 (effective 2000).
Published by: Indonesian Institute of Accountants, Training and Education Division, Jl. Sisingamangaraja 59, Jakarta, 12120, Indonesia. TEL 62-21-722-2989, iai-info@akuntan-iai.or.id. Ed. Hanief Arie. Circ: 5,000.

657   USA   ISSN 1098-0202
KEEP UP TO DATE ON ACCOUNTS PAYABLE. Abbreviated title: K A P. Text in English. 1998. s-m. USD 299. software rev. charts. **Document type:** *Newsletter.* **Description:** Information on how leading companies are managing cash and payments.
Published by: Progressive Business Publications, 370 Technology Dr, Malvern, PA 19355-1315. TEL 610-695-8600, 800-220-5000, FAX 610-647-8089, editor@pbp.com, http://www.pbp.com. Ed. Jennifer Azara. R&P Curt Brown. Circ: 3,000 (paid).

657   USA   ISSN 1076-3309
KEEP UP TO DATE ON PAYROLL. Abbreviated title: K U D P. Text in English. 1994. s-m. USD 230. charts. **Document type:** *Newsletter.* **Description:** Information on how payroll professionals can avoid legal and procedural pitfalls.
Published by: Progressive Business Publications, 370 Technology Dr, Malvern, PA 19355-1315. TEL 610-695-8600, 800-220-5000, FAX 610-647-8089, editor@pbp.com, http://www.pbp.com. Ed. Jenny Weiss. R&P Curt Brown, Circ: 16,334 (paid).

657   GBR
KEY NOTE MARKET REPORT: ACCOUNTANCY. Variant title: Accountancy. Text in English. 1995. irreg., latest 2001, July. GBP 340 per issue (effective 2002). **Document type:** *Trade.* **Description:** Provides an overview of a specific UK market segment and includes executive summary, market definition, market size, industry background, competitor analysis, current issues, forecasts, company profiles, and more.
Formerly: Key Note Report: Accountancy
Related titles: CD-ROM ed.; Online - full text ed.
Published by: Key Note Ltd., Field House, 72 Oldfield Rd, Hampton, Mddx TW12 2HQ, United Kingdom. TEL 44-20-8481-8750, FAX 44-20-8783-0049, info@keynote.co.uk, http://www.keynote.co.uk. Ed. Jenny Baxter.

657   RUS
KOMMENTARII K DOKUMENTAM DLYA BUKHGALTERA. Text in Russian. m. **Document type:** *Journal.* **Description:** Contains further interpretaion on changes to Russian tax laws, emphasizing concrete examples.
Published by: Berator-Press, Ul Khalturinskaya 2, str 2, Moscow, 107392, Russian Federation. TEL 7-095-3639542, http://www.berator.ru.

657   RUS
KOMMENTARII K NOVYM DOKUMENTAM. Text in Russian. m. RUR 1,800 elsewhere to individuals; RUR 2,400 domestic to institutions (effective 2002). **Document type:** *Journal.* **Description:** Includes full texts of new Russian federal and Moscow municipal tax documentation.
Published by: Berator-Press, Ul Khalturinskaya 2, str 2, Moscow, 107392, Russian Federation. TEL 7-095-3639542, http://www.berator.ru.

KOMP'YUTER V BUKHGALTERSKOM UCHETE I AUDITE. see *BUSINESS AND ECONOMICS—Computer Applications*

KONSUL'TANT/CONSULTANT; informatsionno-spravochnyi zhurnal dlia bukhgalterov i rukovoditelii predpriyatii. see *BUSINESS AND ECONOMICS—Public Finance, Taxation*

KONSUL'TANT BUKHGALTERA. see *BUSINESS AND ECONOMICS—Public Finance, Taxation*

KONSUL'TANT DIREKTORA. see *BUSINESS AND ECONOMICS—Public Finance, Taxation*

KOSZTY. see *BUSINESS AND ECONOMICS*

LAMY OPTIMISATION FISCALE DE L'ENTREPRISE. see *LAW—Corporate Law*

LAWYERS' AND ACCOUNTANTS' GUIDE TO PURCHASE - SALE OF SMALL BUSINESS. see *LAW*

LEDGER QUARTERLY. see *BUSINESS AND ECONOMICS— Banking And Finance*

LEGAL ABACUS. see *LAW*

LEGISLATIVE POLICY DISCUSSION PAPER. see *LAW—Corporate Law*

657   USA   ISSN 1042-0231
LOCAL GOVERNMENTAL ACCOUNTING TRENDS AND TECHNIQUES. Text in English. 1988. a.
Published by: American Institute of Certified Public Accountants, Harborside Financial Ctr., 201 Plaza Three, 3rd Fl, Jersey City, NJ 07311-9801. TEL 888-777-7077, FAX 800-302-5766, journal@aicpa.org, http://www.aicpa.org.

657   GBR
LONDON ACCOUNTANT. Text in English. 1995. 10/yr. GBP 60 in Europe; GBP 64 elsewhere. back issues avail. **Document type:** *Trade.* **Description:** Official publication of the society. Features a wide range of topics from IT to factoring & discounting, and tax to education.
Published by: London Society of Chartered Accountants, 75 Cannon St, London, EC4N 5BN, United Kingdom. TEL 44-20-75567053, FAX 44-20-75567520, LSCA@icaew.co.uk, http://www.lcsa.co.uk. Circ: 21,041 (controlled).

651 658 368   EGY   ISSN 1110-628X
MAGALLAT AL-MUHASABT WA-AL-IDARAT WA-AL-TA'MIN LIL-BUHUTH AL-'ILMIYYAT/ACCOUNTING, MANAGEMENT AND INSURANCE REVIEW. Text in Arabic. 1962. irreg. EGP 10 newsstand/cover (effective 2004). **Document type:** *Academic/Scholarly.*
Published by: Cairo University, Faculty of Commerce, Gamiat El-Qahira Str, Giza, Egypt. TEL 20-2-5671885, 20-2-5705258, http://derp.sti.sci.eg/data/0153.htm. Ed. Dr. Kamel Aly Metwalli Aumran.

657   IND   ISSN 0025-1674
HF5686.C8
THE MANAGEMENT ACCOUNTANT. Text in English. 1955. m. INR 300, USD 150 (effective 2001). adv. bk.rev. charts; illus.; stat. index. **Document type:** *Academic/Scholarly.*
Supersedes: Cost and Works Accountant
Related titles: Microfiche ed.: (from PQC).
Indexed: ATI, IMI, PAA&I.
—BLDSC (5359.003000), IE, ingenta.
Published by: The Institute of Cost and Works Accountants of India, 12 Sudder St., Kolkata, West Bengal 700 016, India. TEL 91-33-244-1031, FAX 91-33-244-0993, TELEX 215503 ICWA IN, icwai@giasc101.vsnl.net.in, ssicwai@vsnl.net, http://www.icwai.org. Ed. Siddhartha Sen. Pub. D C Bajaj. adv.: B&W page INR 12,000, B&W page USD 1,200; 200 x 260. Circ: 20,000.

657 PAK
HD47
MANAGEMENT ACCOUNTANT. Text in English. 1962; N.S. 1992. q. PKR 60; USD 5 foreign (effective 1999). adv. bk.rev. charts; illus. reprint service avail. from PQC. **Document type:** *Academic/Scholarly.* **Description:** Covers professional management accountancy, information technology, etc., to keep students and members updated.
Formerly (until 1992): Industrial Accountant (0019-7793)
Related titles: Microform ed.: N.S. (from PQC).
Indexed: ATI.
Published by: Institute of Cost and Management Accountants of Pakistan, ST-18 C, Block 6, Gulshan-e-Iqbal, Karachi, 75300, Pakistan. TEL 92-21-4983251, FAX 92-21-4983390, ed@icmap.khi.sdnpk.undp.org, http://www.brain.net.pk/~icmalhr. Ed. Badruddin Fakhri. Pub. Ghazala Younus. Circ: 10,000.

657 CAN ISSN 1182-8951
MANAGEMENT ACCOUNTER✶ . Text in English. q. free to members. adv. bk.rev. **Document type:** *Newsletter.*
Formerly: Accounter (0702-5300)
Published by: Society of Management Accountants of Alberta, 300 706 7th Ave, S W, Calgary, AB T2P 0Z1, Canada. TEL 403-269-5341, FAX 403-262-5477, socmanaa@ccinet.ab.ca. Ed. Barbara Warburton. Adv. contact Joan Bedard. Circ: 7,000 (controlled).

657 USA
➤ **MANAGEMENT ACCOUNTING QUARTERLY (ONLINE).** Text in English. 2002. q. free. **Document type:** *Journal, Trade.* **Description:** Contains articles by and for academics and practitioners of corporate accounting and financial management; including subjects such as cost/management accounting techniques, ABC/ABM, statistical process controls, target costing, theory of constraints, methods of calculating stock options, techniques to improve accounting and finance education, new theories in finance and accounting, and more.
Media: Online - full content. **Related titles:** Online - full text ed.: (from EBSCO Publishing, Gale Group, O C L C Online Computer Library Center, Inc., ProQuest Information & Learning).
Published by: Institute of Management Accountants, 10 Paragon Dr, Montvale, NJ 07645-1760. ma@imanet.org, http://www.imanet.org/ima/sec.asp?TRACKID=&cid=860&did=1167, http://www.strategicfinancemag.com. Ed. Kathy Williams.

657 GBR ISSN 1044-5005
HF5657.4
➤ **MANAGEMENT ACCOUNTING RESEARCH.** Short title: M A R. Text in English. 1983. 4/yr. EUR 146 in Europe to individuals; JPY 15,800 in Japan to individuals; USD 131 to individuals except Europe and Japan; EUR 404 in Europe to institutions; JPY 43,800 in Japan to institutions; USD 360 to institutions except Europe and Japan (effective 2006). adv. illus. reprints avail. **Document type:** *Academic/Scholarly.* **Description:** Aims to encourage scholarship and empirical research in management accounting by providing a vehicle for publishing original research in the field.
Supersedes: I C M A Abstracts Bulletin
Related titles: Online - full text ed.: ISSN 1096-1224. USD 380 (effective 2002) (from EBSCO Publishing, Gale Group, IngentaConnect, O C L C Online Computer Library Center, Inc., ScienceDirect, Swets Information Services).
Indexed: ABIn, ATI, CPM, Emerald, IBSS, Inspec.
—BLDSC (5359.006370), IE, Infotrieve, ingenta. **CCC.**
Published by: (Chartered Institute of Management Accountants), Academic Press (Subsidiary of: Elsevier Science & Technology), 24-28 Oval Rd, London, NW1 7DX, United Kingdom. apsubs@acad.com, http://www.elsevier.com/locate/mar. Eds. M Bromwich, R W Scapens. R&P Catherine John. Adv. contact Nik Screen. Circ: 400.

657 USA
MANAGING ACCOUNTS PAYABLE YEARBOOK. Text in English. a. USD 224.95 print & online eds. (effective 2003). **Description:** Covers electronic invoicing, fraud, technology, staff management, and travel and expenditures.
Related titles: CD-ROM ed.: USD 224.95; Online - full text ed.: USD 219 (effective 2003); ◆ Cumulative ed. of: I O M A's Report on Managing Accounts Payable. ISSN 1555-3604.
Published by: Institute of Management & Administration, Inc., 3 Park Ave, New York, NY 10016-5902. TEL 212-244-0360, FAX 212-564-0465, subserve@ioma.com, http://www.ioma.com. Ed. Mary Schaeffer.

657.04 ZAF
MANEO. Text in Afrikaans, English. 1993. bi-m. membership. illus. **Document type:** *Newsletter.*
Published by: Public Accountants' and Auditors' Board/Openbare Rekenmeesters- en Ouditeursraad, P O Box 751595, Garden View, Johannesburg 2047, South Africa. TEL 011-622-8533, FAX 011-622-4029, 011-622-1536, board@paab.co.za, http://www.paab.co.za/paabwebsite.html.

657 346.065 NZL ISSN 1175-2874
HF5601
MASSEY UNIVERSITY. SCHOOL OF ACCOUNTANCY. DISCUSSION PAPER SERIES. Text in English. 1972. irreg., latest vol.216, 2003. NZD 15 per issue (effective 2003). bk.rev. back issues avail. **Document type:** *Monographic series, Academic/Scholarly.* **Description:** Intends to provide staff and postgraduate students working in the School of Accountancy with a means of communication for new and partly developed ideas in order to facilitate academic debate.
Former titles: Massey University. Department of Accountancy and Business Law. Discussion Paper Series (1174-6491); (until 1997): Massey University. Department of Accountancy. Discussion Paper Series (1172-1065); (until 1990): Massey University. Division of Accountancy. Discussion Paper Series (1170-6902); Massey University. Department of Accountancy. Discussion Paper Series (0114-5932); Massey University. Department of Accounting and Finance. Discussion Paper Series (0111-7874); (until 1981): Massey University. Faculty of Business Studies. Occasional Paper Series
—**CCC.**
Published by: Massey University, School of Accountancy, Private Bag 11222, Palmerston North, New Zealand. TEL 64-9-4439700, FAX 64-9-4418133, c.van-staden@massey.ac.nz, accountancy@massey.ac.nz, http://www-accountancy.massey.ac.nz/publications.htm. Ed., R&P Chris van Staden. Circ: 100.

657 IDN ISSN 1410-0886
MEDIA AKUNTANSI; Indonesian magazine of accountancy. Text in Indonesian. 1992. m. IDR 10,000 (effective 2000).
Published by: Indonesian Institute of Accountants, Jl. Sisingamangaraja 59, Jakarta, 12120, Indonesia. TEL 62-21-722-2989, iai-info@akuntan-iai.or.id. Ed. Sri Yanto. Circ: 5,000.

657 USA
MEDICAL CLIENT NEWSLETTER. Text in English. q. **Description:** Information on members' services to clients.
Published by: C P A Associates International, Inc., Meadows Office Complex, 201 Rte 17 N, Rutherford, NJ 07070-2574. TEL 212-804-8686.

657 ZAF ISSN 1022-2529
MEDITARI. Text in Afrikaans, English. 1993. a. ZAR 80. **Document type:** *Academic/Scholarly.*
Indexed: ISAP.
Published by: (University of Pretoria/Universiteit van Pretoria), LexisNexis Butterworths South Africa (Subsidiary of: LexisNexis Europe and Africa), PO Box 792, Durban, KwaZulu-Natal 4000, South Africa. FAX 27-31-2683110, cdeville@hakuna.up.ac.za. Ed. Charl de Villiers. Pub. Christa de Beer. Circ: 500.

657 USA ISSN 1539-6959
MERGENT COMPANY ARCHIVES MANUAL. Text in English. 2001. irreg. **Description:** Contains business descriptions, histories, and financial analyses of companies that ceased to exist under the names listed until 2000.
Related titles: Supplement(s):.
Published by: Mergent, 5250 77 Center Dr, Ste 150, Charlotte, NC 28217. TEL 704-559-7601, 800-342-5647, FAX 704-559-6945, customerservice@mergent.com, http://www.mergent.com/publish/product60.asp.

MICHAEL GRAY CPA'S BOTTOM LINE. see *BUSINESS AND ECONOMICS—Public Finance, Taxation*

657 USA ISSN 0026-2064
MICHIGAN C P A✶ . Text in English. 1901. 10/yr. USD 20 (effective 1999). adv. **Document type:** *Newsletter.*
Related titles: Online - full text ed.: (from Florida Center for Library Automation, Gale Group, ProQuest Information & Learning).
Indexed: ATI.
Published by: Michigan Association of CPAs, 5480 Corporate Dr No.200, Troy, MI 48098-2642. TEL 248-855-2288, FAX 248-855-9122, muanness@ix.netcom.com, http://www.michacpa.org. Eds. Gwen McRae, Marla Janness. R&P Gwen McRae. Adv. contact Tracey Kersnaw. B&W page USD 1,220; trim 8.25 x 11. Circ: 15,000.

657 USA ISSN 1540-3610
HF5681.F54
MILLER FINANCIAL INSTRUMENTS. Text in English. 2002. a. USD 249 newsstand/cover (effective 2003).
Published by: Aspen Publishers, Inc. (Subsidiary of: Wolters Kluwer N.V.), 111Eighth Ave., 7th Fl, New York, NY 10011. TEL 212-771-0600, FAX 212-771-0885, http://www.aspenpublishers.com.

657 USA ISSN 1077-8489
HF5616.U5
MILLER G A A P GUIDE (YEAR); a comprehensive restatement of all current promulgated generally accepted accounting principles. Text in English. 1980. a. (plus m. Update Service). USD 129 level A (2 vols.); USD 149 level B, C & D (2 vols.) (effective 2005). **Document type:** *Trade.* **Description:** Restates accounting pronouncements in clear, easy-to-understand language along with examples, illustrations and expert analyses.
Former titles (until 1994): H B J Miller Comprehensive G A A P Guide (1077-8470); (until 1992): Miller's Comprehensive G A A P Guide (0734-8355)
Related titles: CD-ROM ed.: USD 139 (effective 2003); Online - full text ed.: (from LexisNexis).
Indexed: ATI.
Published by: C C H Inc., 2700 Lake Cook Rd, Riverwoods, IL 60015. TEL 847-267-7000, 800-248-3248, 800-449-6439, http://www.aspenpublishers.com/Product.asp?catalog%5Fname=Aspen&category%5Fname=&product%5Fid=0735532605&Mode=SEARCH&ProductType=M, http://www.cch.com. Ed. Jennifer Crane.

657 USA ISSN 1541-1567
HF5616.U5
MILLER G A A P PRACTICE MANUAL. (Generally Accepted Accounting Principles) Text in English. 1999. a. USD 139 (effective 2004). **Document type:** *Monographic series, Trade.* **Description:** Contains FASB Technical Bulletins, AICPA AcSEC Practice Bulletins, FASB Implementation Guides, AICPA Statements of Position, and AICPA Accounting Interpretations.
Formerly (until 2000): Miller G A A P Implementation Manual; Incorporates: Miller G A A P Implementation Manual. E I T F (1536-9404); Which was formerly (until 1999): Miller G A A P from the Emerging Issues Task Force
Published by: Aspen Publishers, Inc. (Subsidiary of: Wolters Kluwer N.V.), 5301 Buckeystown Pike, Ste. 400, Frederick, MD 21704-8319. customer.service@aspenpubl.com, http://www.aspenpub.com.

657.6 USA ISSN 1088-9159
HF5667
MILLER G A A S GUIDE; a comprehensive restatement of standards for auditing, attestation, compilation and review and the code of professional conduct. (Generally Accepted Auditing Standards) Variant title: G A A S Guide. Generally Accepted Auditing Standards Guide. Text in English. 1982. a. (plus m. update service). USD 225 per vol. (effective 2004). **Document type:** *Trade.* **Description:** Contains comprehensive analysis of all auditing standards. Also includes sections on auditing in a microcomputer environment, compliance auditing, new guidance on completing the audit and litigation support service.
Former titles (until 1993): H B J Miller Comprehensive G A A S Guide; (until 1991): Miller's Comprehensive G A A S guide (0736-8526)
Related titles: CD-ROM ed.: USD 82.
Published by: Aspen Publishers, Inc. (Subsidiary of: Wolters Kluwer N.V.), 111Eighth Ave., 7th Fl, New York, NY 10011. TEL 212-771-0600, FAX 212-771-0885, customer.service@aspenpubl.com, http://www.aspenpublishers.com/Product.asp?catalog%5Fname=Aspen&category%5Fname=&product%5Fid=0735532710&Mode=SEARCH&ProductType=M. Ed. Dr. Larry P. Bailey. **Subscr. to:** Customer Care, 7201 McKinney Circle, Frederick, MD 21704. TEL 800-234-1660, FAX 800-901-9075.

657.2 USA ISSN 1543-1312
MILLER GOVERNMENTAL G A A P GUIDE; a comprehensive interpretation of current promulgated governmental generally accepted accounting principles for state and local governments. Text in English. a. (plus m. update service). USD 225 per vol. (effective 2004). **Document type:** *Trade.*
Indexed: ATI.
Published by: Aspen Publishers, Inc. (Subsidiary of: Wolters Kluwer N.V.), 111Eighth Ave., 7th Fl, New York, NY 10011. TEL 212-771-0600, FAX 212-771-0885, customer.service@aspenpubl.com, http://www.aspenpublishers.com/Product.asp?catalog%5Fname=Aspen&category%5Fname=&product%5Fid=0735532729&Mode=SEARCH&ProductType=M. Ed. Dr. Larry P. Bailey. **Subscr. to:** Customer Care, 7201 McKinney Circle, Frederick, MD 21704. TEL 800-234-1660, FAX 800-901-9075.

657 USA ISSN 1541-9177
HJ10.2
MILLER GOVERNMENTAL G A A P PRACTICE MANUAL. Text in English. 2002. a. USD 109 newsstand/cover (effective 2002).
Published by: Aspen Law & Business (Subsidiary of: Wolters Kluwer N.V.), 1185 Ave of the Americas, 37th Fl, New York, NY 10036. TEL 212-597-0210, 800-638-8437, FAX 212-597-0336, customer.service@aspenpubl.com, http://www.aspenpub.com.

657 USA ISSN 1537-8373
HF5686.N56
MILLER NOT-FOR-PROFIT REPORTING. Text in English. 1999. a. USD 139 (effective 2003). **Document type:** *Monographic series, Trade.*
Formerly (until 1999): Miller G A A P for Non-Profit Organizations (1098-0393)
Published by: Aspen Publishers, Inc. (Subsidiary of: Wolters Kluwer N.V.), 111Eighth Ave., 7th Fl, New York, NY 10011. TEL 212-771-0600, FAX 212-771-0885, customer.service@aspenpubl.com, http://www.aspenpublishers.com.

B

▼ new title ➤ refereed ✶ unverified ◆ full entry avail.

657 USA ISSN 1542-0159
HF5681.R5
▼ **MILLER REVENUE RECOGNITION GUIDE.** Text in English. 2003. a. USD 225 newsstand/cover (effective 2002).
Published by: Aspen Publishers, Inc. (Subsidiary of: Wolters Kluwer N.V.), 111Eighth Ave., 7th Fl, New York, NY 10011. TEL 212-597-0213, FAX 212-771-0885, http://www.aspenpublishers.com.

657 NLD
MINAS ACCOUNTANCY. Text occasionally in English; Text mainly in Dutch. 1924. 10/yr. adv. bk.rev. abstr.; charts; stat. index. **Document type:** *Journal, Trade.* **Description:** Forum for practical and scholarly debate of issues of interest to the accounting profession.
Former titles: M A B - Maandblad voor Accountancy en Bedrijfseconomie (0924-6304); (until 1989): Maandblad voor Accountancy en Bedrijfshuishoudkunde (0024-8622)
Indexed: KES.
—IE.
Published by: Reed Business Information bv (Subsidiary of: Reed Business), Postbus 16400, Den Haag, 2500 BK, Netherlands. TEL 31-70-313-1500, FAX 31-70-313-1506. Circ: 5,000.

657 USA ISSN 1076-660X
KF1357
MODERN ACCOUNTING AND AUDITING CHECKLISTS. Text in English. 2 base vols. plus s-a. updates. looseleaf. USD 197; USD 275.80 foreign (effective 1998). **Document type:** *Trade.*
Indexed: ATI.
Published by: W G & L Financial Reporting & Management Research (Subsidiary of: R I A), 395 Hudson St, New York, NY 10014. TEL 212-367-6300, FAX 212-367-6718. **Subscr. to:** The Park Square Bldg., 31 St James Ave, Boston, MA 02116-4112. TEL 800-950-1207.

657 USA
MOORE STEPHENS NORTH AMERICA NEWSLETTER. Text in English. 1969. s-a. membership. **Document type:** *Newsletter.* **Description:** Provides a summary of the association's meetings, plans for the future, and updates on members and the profession.
Formerly (until 1998): Associated Accounting Firms International Newsletter
Published by: Moore Stephens North America, Inc., 1000 Connecticut Ave, N W, Ste 1006, Washington, DC 20036-5302. TEL 202-463-7900, FAX 202-296-0741, msna@msnainc.com, http://www.msnainc.com. Ed., R&P Gregory Hickman. Circ: 3,500 (controlled).

657 RUS
MOSKOVSKII BUKHGALTER. Text in Russian. 2001. m. RUR 540 for 6 mos. domestic to individuals; RUR 780 for 6 mos. domestic to institutions (effective 2002). **Document type:** *Journal.*
Published by: Berator-Press, Ul Khalturinskaya 2, str 2, Moscow, 107392, Russian Federation. TEL 7-095-3639542, mosbuh@berator.ru, http://www.berator.ru/mb. Ed. Yulia Vitkina. Circ: 18,000. **Subscr. to:** Rospechat', Pr-t Marshala Zhukova 4, Moscow 123995, Russian Federation.

657 USA
N O S A UPDATE. Text in English. 1982. m. USD 76 to non-members. **Document type:** *Newsletter, Trade.*
Formerly: National One-Write Systems Association Newsletter
Published by: National Office Systems Association, PO Box 8187, Silver Spring, MD 20907-8187. TEL 301-589-8125, FAX 301-589-0564.

657 USA
HF5601 CODEN: NPACAI
N P A. (National Public Accountant) Text in English. 1949. 6/yr. USD 25 domestic to non-members; USD 50 foreign to non-members (effective 2005). adv. bk.rev. illus. index. back issues avail.; reprint service avail. from PQC. **Document type:** *Magazine, Trade.* **Description:** For accounting and tax practitioners.
Formerly (until 2005): National Public Accountant (0027-9978)
Related titles: Microfilm ed.: (from PQC); Online - full text ed.: (from EBSCO Publishing, Florida Center for Library Automation, Gale Group, H.W. Wilson, O C L C Online Computer Library Center, Inc., ProQuest Information & Learning).
Indexed: ABIn, ATI, BPI, BPIA, BusI, ManagCont, PAIS, PSI, T&II.
—BLDSC (6029.900000), IE, Infotrieve, ingenta.
Published by: National Society of Accountants, 1010 N Fairfax St, Alexandria, VA 22314. TEL 703-549-6400, 800-966-6679, FAX 703-549-2984, http://www.nsacct.org/npa_issues.asp?id=532. Ed. Arleen Richman. Circ: 20,000 (paid).

657 USA ISSN 1091-1596
THE N S A PRACTITIONER. Text in English. 19??. s-m. free domestic to members (effective 2005). 16 p./no.; **Document type:** *Newsletter, Trade.* **Description:** Updates on accounting and tax related issues for practitioners.
Published by: National Society of Accountants, 1010 N. Fairfax St., Alexandria, VA 22314-1574. TEL 800-966-6679, http://www.nsacct.org. Ed. Arleen Richman. Circ: 22,000 (controlled).

657 USA ISSN 0469-3922
N S P A WASHINGTON REPORTER. Text in English. 1947. m. membership. **Description:** Newsletter featuring updates on the activities of NSPA, Congress and the IRS.
Published by: National Society of Accountants, 1010 N Fairfax St, Alexandria, VA 22314. TEL 703-549-6400. Ed. Susan Cappitelli. Circ: 22,000.

657 RUS
NALOGOVYI I BUKHGALTERSKII UCHET. Text in Russian. d.
Media: Online - full content.
Published by: Biznes Praktika, Ul Sovetskaya 30, Novosibirsk, 630099, Russian Federation. business@online.nsk.su, http://www.nsk.su/~practica/.

657 336 AUS ISSN 1039-608X
NATIONAL ACCOUNTANT. Text in English. 1985. bi-m. AUD 55 (effective 2004). adv. bk.rev.; software rev. back issues avail. **Document type:** *Journal, Trade.* **Description:** Contains technical accounting, management and taxation articles.
Formerly (until 1993): Counting House (0816-5599)
Published by: (National Institute of Accountants), Niche Media Pty Ltd (Subsidiary of: Waivcom Worldwide Ltd.), 165 Fitzroy St, St Kilda, VIC 3182, Australia. TEL 61-3-95255566, 800-804-160, FAX 61-3-95255628, subscription@niche.com.au, http://www.nia.com.au/nationalAccountantJournal.asp, http://www.niche.com.au. Ed. Ros O'Sullivan. Adv. contact Gusto Simandjuntak. page AUD 2,850; trim 206 x 275. Circ: 14,701. **Subscr. to:** National Institute of Accountants, Reply Paid 18204, Collins St E, PO Box 18204, Melbourne, VIC 8003, Australia. TEL 61-3-86653100, FAX 61-3-86653130.

657 305.896073 USA
NATIONAL ASSOCIATION OF BLACK ACCOUNTANTS. CHAPTER TO CHAPTER. Text in English. 3/yr. **Document type:** *Newsletter.*
Formerly: National Association of Black Accountants. Student News Plus
Published by: National Association of Black Accountants, 7249A Hanover Pkwy, Greenbelt, MD 20770-3653. TEL 301-474-6222. Circ: 2,500.

657 305.896073 USA
NATIONAL ASSOCIATION OF BLACK ACCOUNTANTS. NEWS PLUS. Text in English. q. USD 15. **Document type:** *Newsletter.*
Published by: National Association of Black Accountants, 7249A Hanover Pkwy, Greenbelt, MD 20770-3653. TEL 301-474-6222. Circ: 3,000.

657 USA ISSN 0889-3500
NATIONAL ASSOCIATION OF STATE BOARDS OF ACCOUNTANCY. STATE BOARD REPORT. Text in English. 1992 (vol.21). m. USD 65. index. back issues avail. **Description:** Represents a digest of current developments affecting state accountancy regulations.
Published by: National Association of State Boards of Accountancy, 150 4th Ave N Ste 700, Nashville, TN 37219-2417. Ed., R&P Louise Dratler Haberman TEL 212-644-6469. Circ: 1,400.

657 USA
NATIONAL C P A GROUP. NEWSLETTER✶. (Certified Public Accountant) Text in English. bi-m.
Published by: National C P A Group, c/o BKR Int'l, 40 Exchange Pl 1100, New York, NY 10005-2701. TEL 212-766-4260.

657 NLD
NEDERLANDSE ORDE VAN ACCOUNTANTS - ADMINISTRATIECONSULTENTEN. LEDEN - INFO. Text in Dutch. bi-m.
Published by: Nederlandse Orde van Accountants - Administratieconsultenten, Nieuwe Parklaan 25, The Hague, 2597 LA, Netherlands. TEL 31-70-3383600, FAX 31-70-3512836.

657.6 DEU
DAS NEUE BILANZ-HANDBUCH. Text in German. base vol. plus updates 9/yr. EUR 129 (effective 2004). **Document type:** *Directory, Trade.*
Published by: Verlag Praktisches Wissen GmbH (Subsidiary of: Wolters Kluwer Deutschland GmbH), Marlener Str 2, Offenburg, 77656, Germany. TEL 49-781-605300, FAX 49-781-59825, info@praktisches-wissen.de, http://www.praktisches-wissen.de.

657.6 DEU
DAS NEUE KONTIERUNGS-PRAXIS-ABC. Text in German. 2 base vols. plus updates 11/yr. EUR 99.70 (effective 2004). **Document type:** *Directory, Trade.*
Published by: Verlag Praktisches Wissen GmbH (Subsidiary of: Wolters Kluwer Deutschland GmbH), Marlener Str 2, Offenburg, 77656, Germany. TEL 49-781-605300, FAX 49-781-59825, info@praktisches-wissen.de, http://www.praktisches-wissen.de.

657 USA ISSN 0882-8067
NEW ACCOUNTANT. Text in English. 1985. 8/yr. (m. Sep.-Apr.). USD 85 to individuals; USD 25 to libraries (effective 2001). adv. bk.rev. stat. index. back issues avail. **Document type:** *Magazine, Trade.* **Description:** Covers business news with special focus on careers, issues, and developments in accounting and finance.
Related titles: Online - full text ed.: 1985 (from Northern Light Technology, Inc., ProQuest Information & Learning).
Indexed: ATI.
—BLDSC (6081.671000), IE, ingenta.
Published by: Real Estate News Corp, 3550 W Peterson Ave, Ste 100, Chicago, IL 60659. TEL 773-866-9900, FAX 773-866-9881, rencpublishing@earthlink.net, inquiries@renpublishing.com, http://www.newaccountantusa.com. Ed. John R Connolly Jr. Circ: 64,632 (controlled).

657 CAN
NEW BRUNSWICK INSTITUTE OF CHARTERED ACCOUNTANTS. NEWSLETTER. Text in English. q.
Published by: New Brunswick Institute of Chartered Accountants/Institut des Comptables Agrees du Nouveau-Brunswick, 93 Prince William St, 4th Fl, Saint John, NB E2L 2B2, Canada. TEL 506-634-1558.

150 332 AUS ISSN 0155-123X
NEW ENGLAND ACCOUNTING RESEARCH STUDIES (NO.). Text in English. irreg., latest vol.13.
Published by: (University Of New England, Department of Accounting and Financial Management), University of New England, Armidale, NSW 2351, Australia. TEL 61-67-73221, FAX 61-67-711778. R&P J J Staunton TEL 61-67-733276.

657 USA
NEW WORKS IN ACCOUNTING HISTORY✶. Text in English. irreg. reprints avail. **Document type:** *Monographic series.*
Formerly: Academy of Accounting Historians. Monograph Series
Indexed: ATI.
Published by: Garland Publishing, Inc., 325 Chestnut St #8, Philadelphia, PA 19106-2614. TEL 212-269-0400, 800-821-8312, FAX 215-269-0363, info@garland.com. Ed. Richard P Brief.

657 USA
NEWS & VIEWS (LAKE SUCCESS). Text in English. m. USD 25 to non-members (effective 1999). adv. **Document type:** *Newsletter.*
Formerly: National Conference of C P A Practitioners. Newsletter
Published by: National Conference of C P A Practitioners, 3000 Marcus Ave., Lake Success, NY 11042. TEL 516-488-5400, FAX 516-488-5549, exdir@nccpap.org, http://www.nccpap.org. Ed., R&P Brenda Mahler. Adv. contact Holly Coscetta. Circ: 1,200.

657 CHN ISSN 1002-5588
NONGCUN CAIWU KUAIJI/RURAL FINANCE AND ACCOUNTING. Text in Chinese. m. CNY 12. adv.
Related titles: Online - full text ed.: (from East View Information Services).
Published by: Nongye Bu, Hezuo Jingji Jingying Guanli Zongzhan, 11 Nongzhanguan Nanli, Beijing, 100026, China. TEL 86-1-5005773, FAX 86-1-5002448, TELEX 22233 MAGR CN. Ed. Gaorang Shi. Pub. Jianfeng Hu. Adv. contact Jun Dai.

657 USA
NONPROFIT ACCOUNTING AND AUDITING DISCLOSURE MANUAL. Text in English. base vol. plus a. updates. looseleaf. USD 160; USD 224 foreign. Supplement avail. **Document type:** *Trade.* **Description:** Outlines all G.A.A.P. and G.A.A.S. disclosure requirements for nonprofit organizations.
Indexed: ATI.
Published by: W G & L Financial Reporting & Management Research (Subsidiary of: R I A), 395 Hudson St, New York, NY 10014. TEL 212-367-6300, FAX 212-367-6718. Eds. Allan B Afterman, Rowan H Jones. **Subscr. to:** The Park Square Bldg., 31 St James Ave, Boston, MA 02116-4112. TEL 800-950-1207.

657 USA ISSN 1056-5094
HF5686.N56
THE NONPROFIT REPORT; accounting, taxation & management. Text in English. 1991. m. USD 210 (effective 2004). **Document type:** *Newsletter.* **Description:** Offers certified public accountants working with nonprofit organizations insight into key financial and tax legislation.
—CCC.
Published by: W G & L Financial Reporting & Management Research (Subsidiary of: R I A), 395 Hudson St, New York, NY 10014. TEL 212-367-6419, http://www.riahome.com. Ed. Murray Dropkin.

657 ESP ISSN 1138-8846
NORMATIVA CONTABLE. Text in Spanish. 1989. biennial.
Related titles: ◆ Supplement to: Estudios Financieros. Revista de Contabilidad y Tributacion. Legislacion, Consultas, Jurisprudencia. ISSN 1138-9613.
Published by: Centro de Estudios Financieros, C. Viriato, 52 5o., Madrid, 28010, Spain. TEL 34-91-4444920, FAX 34-91-5938861, director@cef.es, http://www.cef.es/.

657   RUS   ISSN 1028-7442
NOVOE V BUKHGALTERSKOM UCHETE I OTCHETNOSTI V
ROSSIISKOI FEDERATSII. Text in Russian. 1992. m. USD
195 foreign (effective 2001). adv.
Indexed: RASB.
Published by: ID FBK-PRESS, Myasnitskaya ul 44-1, Moscow,
101000, Russian Federation. TEL 7-095-7375353, fbk@fbk.ru.
Ed. S M Shapigoozov. R&P, Adv. contact Elena Biriukova.
Circ: 4,500. US dist. addr.: East View Information Services,
3020 Harbor Ln. N., Minneapolis, MN 55447. TEL
612-550-0961.

657   SWE   ISSN 1104-2982
NYTT FRAAN REVISORN. Text in Swedish. 1977. 9/yr. SEK 375
(effective 2001). adv. bk.rev. Document type: Magazine,
Trade.
Supersedes (in 1994): Revisorn Informerar (0349-5361)
Related titles: Online - full text ed.
Published by: FAR Foerlag AB, Box 6417, Stockholm, 11382,
Sweden. TEL 46-8-506-112-00, FAX 46-8-34-14-61,
http://www.farforlag.se. Ed. Lars Waldengren. Pub. Margareta
Damberg. Adv. contact Inger Weman. B&W page SEK 35,000;
trim 166 x 260.

657   AUT
OESTERREICHISCHE ZEITSCHRIFT FUER RECHT UND
RECHNUNGSWESEN. Text in German. m. EUR 155; EUR
15.70 newsstand/cover (effective 2005). adv. bk.rev. 36 p./no.;
Document type: Magazine, Trade.
Formerly: Oesterreichische Zeitschrift fuer Rechnungswesen
(1018-3779)
Published by: LexisNexis Verlag ARD Orac GmbH & Co. KG
(Subsidiary of: LexisNexis Europe and Africa), Marxergasse
25, Vienna, W 1030, Austria. TEL 43-1-534520, FAX
43-1-53452141, verlag@orac.at, http://www.lexisnexis.at/. Adv.
contact Malgorzata Leitliner TEL 43-1-534521115. Circ: 2,300.

657   USA
THE OHIO E-C P A WEEKLY. Text in English. w. Document
type: Bulletin, Trade.
Media: E-mail.
Published by: Ohio Society of Certified Public Accountants, 535
Metro Place S, PO Box 1810, Dublin, OH 43017. TEL
614-764-2727, FAX 614-764-5880.

657   USA
HJ9701
ON BALANCE. Text in English. 1952. 6/yr. free membership. adv.
bk.rev. illus. Document type: Magazine, Trade.
Former titles (until Jan. 2005): The Wisconsin C P A
(0043-6402); Wisconsin Society of Certified Public
Accountants. Newsletter
Indexed: ATI.
Published by: Wisconsin Institute of Certified Public Accountants,
235 N Executive Dr, Brookfield, WI 53008-1010. TEL
262-785-0445, 800-772-6939, FAX 262-785-0838,
http://www.wicpa.org/Multimedia/onbalance.htm. Ed. Amy
Gaeth. Adv. contact Tressa Lindner. page USD 1,500. Circ:
8,300 (controlled and free). Subscr. to: PO Box 1010,
Brookfield, WI 53008-1010.

657   CAN
ORDRE DES COMPTABLES AGREES DU QUEBEC. BILAN.
Text in English, French. 1953. 6/yr. CND 21.85 to individuals;
CND 12 to students. adv. bk.rev. illus. Document type:
Newsletter. Description: Includes articles on accounting,
business, economy, taxation and new technology.
Former titles: Ordre des Comptables Agrees du Quebec. Bilans
(0828-6833); (until Mar. 1983): Ordre des Comptables Agrees
du Quebec. Journal (0711-3560); Order of Chartered
Accountants of Quebec. Newsletter
Published by: Editions de l' O C A Q, Inc., 680 Sherbrooke St W,
7th Fl, Montreal, PQ H3A 2S3, Canada. TEL 514-982-4620,
FAX 514-843-8375, pm.adam@ocaq.qc.ca,
http://www.ocaq.qc.ca. Ed. Francois de Falkensteen. R&P,
Adv. contact Paul-Marcel Adam. B&W page CND 1,220, color
page CND 2,545; trim 11 x 8.25. Circ: 19,000.

657.076   CAN   ISSN 0820-0386
ORDRES DES COMPTABLES AGREES DU CANADA ET DES
BERMUDES. ANNALES DE L'EXAMEN FINAL UNIFORME.
Text in French. 1981. a.
Related titles: ◆ English ed.: Canadian Institute of Chartered
Accountants. Uniform Final Examination Report. ISSN
0713-357X.
Published by: Canadian Institute of Chartered Accountants, 277
Wellington St W, Toronto, ON M5V 3H2, Canada.

OVERHEIDSMANAGEMENT; vakblad voor financien
automatisering en personeel & organisatie. see BUSINESS
AND ECONOMICS—Banking And Finance

657   GBR   ISSN 1352-8645
P A S S; the first choice for Rart Qualified Accountants.
(Professional Accountancy Student Service) Text in English.
1984. m. GBP 35 domestic (effective 2000). adv. bk.rev. bibl.;
charts; illus.; stat. back issues avail. Document type: Trade.
Description: Journal for part-qualified accountants.

Published by: Reed Business Information Ltd. (Subsidiary of:
Reed Business), Quadrant House, The Quadrant, Brighton
Rd, Sutton, Surrey SM2 5AS, United Kingdom. TEL
44-208-652-3500, FAX 44-208-652-8977,
rbi.subscriptions@qss-uk.com, http://www.reedbusiness.co.uk/.
Ed. Graham Hambly TEL 44-20-8652-4720. Pub. Giles Grant.
Adv. contact Katherine Bellamy. Circ: 25,000. Subscr. to:
Quadrant Subscription Services, PO Box 302, Haywards
Heath, W Sussex RH16 3YY, United Kingdom. TEL
44-1444-445566, FAX 44-1444-445447.

657   USA   ISSN 1553-4839
HF5681.R33
▼ P P C'S GUIDE TO RELATED PARTIES (INCLUDING
VARIABLE INTEREST ENTITIES). (Practitioners Publishing
Company) Text in English. 2004. a. USD 210 per issue
(effective 2005).
Published by: Practitioners Publishing Co., PO Box 966, Fort
Worth, TX 76101-0966. TEL 817-332-3709, 800-323-8724,
FAX 817-877-3694, http://www.ppcnet.com.

657.6   USA   ISSN 1549-0416
HF5686.B7
▼ P P C'S GUIDE TO RISK-BASED AUDITS OF
CONSTRUCTION CONTRACTORS. (Practitioners Publishing
Company) Text in English. 2003. a. USD 170 base vol(s).
(effective 2004).
Published by: Practitioners Publishing Co., PO Box 966, Fort
Worth, TX 76101-0966. TEL 817-332-3709, 800-323-8724,
FAX 817-877-3694, http://www.ppcnet.com.

657.6   USA   ISSN 1549-0408
HD7288.78.U5
▼ P P C'S GUIDE TO RISK-BASED AUDITS OF H U D
PROJECTS; and other affordable housing. (Practitioners
Publishing Company) Text in English. 2003. a. USD 199 base
vol(s). (effective 2004).
Published by: Practitioners Publishing Co., PO Box 966, Fort
Worth, TX 76101-0966. TEL 817-332-3709, 800-323-8724,
FAX 817-877-3694, http://www.ppcnet.com.

657   USA   ISSN 1550-1167
KF6606.A15
▼ P P C'S GUIDE TO SALES AND USE TAX SAVINGS FOR
MANUFACTURERS. (Practitioners Publishing Company) Text
in English. 2003. a. USD 395 base vol(s). (effective 2004).
Published by: Practitioners Publishing Co., PO Box 966, Fort
Worth, TX 76101-0966. TEL 817-332-3709, 800-323-8724,
FAX 817-877-3694, http://www.ppcnet.com.

657 510   USA   ISSN 1072-3803
PARAMETRIC WORLD. Text in English. 1981. q. USD 55
domestic; USD 50 foreign (effective 2000). adv. charts; illus.;
stat.; tr.lit. back issues avail. Document type: Trade.
Description: Discusses parametrics, with emphasis on cost
estimating.
Published by: International Society of Parametric Analysts Inc.
(ISPA), PO Box 6402, Chesterfield, MO 63006-6402. TEL
636-527-2955, FAX 636-256-8358, clydeperry@aol.com. Eds.
Clyde Perry, Karen Davies. adv.: B&W page USD 500. Circ:
500.

657   ESP   ISSN 1133-7869
PARTIDA DOBLE. Text in Spanish. 1990. 11/yr. EUR 218
combined subscription Print & online eds. (effective 2005).
adv. Document type: Magazine, Consumer.
Related titles: Online - full text ed.
—CINDOC.
Published by: Grupo Especial Directivos (Subsidiary of: Wolters
Kluwer BV), Orense 16, Madrid, 28020, Spain. TEL
34-902-250520, FAX 34-902-250502,
clientes@edirectivos.com, http://www.partidadoble.es,
http://www.e-directivos.com. Ed. Francisco Serrano. Adv.
contact Ricardo Zavala. Circ: 7,500.

657   USA   ISSN 1097-5527
PARTNER-TO-PARTNER ADVISORY. Text in English. 1997. m.
USD 255 to individuals (effective 2003). Document type:
Newsletter.
Incorporates (in 1999): C P A Profitability Monthly (1080-5745);
Which was formerly (until 1995): C P A Quality Client Service
(1080-7101); (1988-1993): Quality Client Service (1047-5842)
Related titles: Online - full text ed.: (from Florida Center for
Library Automation, Gale Group).
Indexed: ATI.
Published by: Aspen Publishers, Inc. (Subsidiary of: Wolters
Kluwer N.V.), 111 Eighth Ave., 7th Fl, New York, NY 10011.
TEL 212-771-0600, FAX 212-771-0885,
customer.service@aspenpubl.com, http://
www.aspenpublishers.com/Product.asp?catalog%5Fname=
Aspen&category%5Fname=&product%5Fid=
SS10975527&Mode=SEARCH&ProductType=L. Ed. Dr. August
Aquila. Subscr. to: Customer Care, 7201 McKinney Circle,
Frederick, MD 21704. TEL 800-234-1660, FAX 800-901-9075.

657   USA   ISSN 1043-7428
PARTNER'S REPORT (NEW YORK, 1989); the monthly update
for C P A firm owners. Text in English. 1989. m. looseleaf.
USD 291.95 combined subscription in US & Canada print &
online eds.; USD 303 combined subscription elsewhere print &
online eds. (effective 2006). index. back issues avail.
Document type: Newsletter, Trade. Description: Offers
management advice for owners of CPA firms to help them
improve partner distributions, increase firm margins, and
improve their stewardship of the firm. Includes guidance on
partner and staff compensation and benefits, retirement plan
alternatives, professional liability coverage, "rainmaking." etc.
Related titles: Diskette ed.; E-mail ed.; Online - full content ed.;
Online - full text ed.: (from LexisNexis, ProQuest Information
& Learning).
Indexed: ABIn.
—CCC.
Published by: Institute of Management & Administration, Inc., 3
Park Ave, New York, NY 10016-5902. TEL 212-244-0360, FAX
212-564-0465, subserve@ioma.com, http://www.ioma.com/
products/prod_detail.php?prodid=30. Ed. Sue Sandler. Pub.
Lee Rath.

PAYMENTS SYSTEM REPORT. see BUSINESS AND
ECONOMICS—Banking And Finance—Computer Applications

657   USA
PAYROLL MANAGER'S REPORT YEARBOOK. Text in English.
a. USD 224.95 print & online eds. (effective 2003).
Description: Provides federal and state legislative changes,
cost-cutting strategies, surveys on the effectiveness of payroll
software and other technology, and case studies with payroll
professionals.
Related titles: Online - full text ed.: USD 219 (effective 2003); ◆
Cumulative ed. of: I O M A's Payroll Manager's Report. ISSN
1090-2244.
Published by: Institute of Management & Administration, Inc., 3
Park Ave, New York, NY 10016-5902. TEL 212-244-0360, FAX
212-564-0465, subserve@ioma.com, http://www.ioma.com. Ed.
Donis Ford.

657 336   USA   ISSN 1063-3200
KF6436
PAYROLL PRACTITIONER'S COMPLIANCE HANDBOOK;
year-end and quarterly reporting. Text in English. base vol.
plus a. updates. looseleaf. USD 160 (effective 1998). charts.
Document type: Trade. Description: Training manual that
includes all payroll essentials with clear explanations of laws
and accounting procedures.
Published by: W G & L Financial Reporting & Management
Research (Subsidiary of: R I A), 395 Hudson St, New York,
NY 10014. TEL 212-367-6300, FAX 212-367-6718,
http://www.InsideHR.com. Ed. Debera J Salam. Subscr. to:
The Park Square Bldg., 31 St James Ave, Boston, MA
02116-4112. TEL 800-950-1207.

657   USA   ISSN 0746-1062
PENNSYLVANIA C P A JOURNAL. Text in English. 1931. q. USD
8 to non-members; USD 4 to members (effective 2005). adv.
index. back issues avail. Document type: Magazine, Trade.
Description: Focuses on information and developments that
affect the day-to-day operations of CPAs in Pennsylvania.
Formerly (until 1983): Pennsylvania C P A Spokesman
(0031-4390)
Related titles: Online - full text ed.: (from EBSCO Publishing, O
C L C Online Computer Library Center, Inc., ProQuest
Information & Learning).
Indexed: ABIn, ATI.
—BLDSC (6421.704000).
Published by: Pennsylvania Institute of Certified Public
Accountants, 1650 Arch St, 17th Fl, Philadelphia, PA
19103-2099. TEL 215-496-9272, 888-272-2001, FAX
215-496-9212, journal@picpa.org, info@picpa.org,
http://www.picpa.org/journal/index.asp. Ed. Bill Hayes. Pub.
Albert Trexler. Adv. contact Jennifer Melchiorre. B&W page
USD 1,220, color page USD 1,930; trim 8.125 x 10.875. Circ:
21,000 (controlled).

PENSION COORDINATOR. see BUSINESS AND
ECONOMICS—Personnel Management

657   USA
PERSONAL FINANCE PLANNING QUARTERLY∗. Text in
English. q.
Published by: National C P A Group, c/o BKR Int'l, 40 Exchange
Pl 1100, New York, NY 10005-2701. TEL 212-766-4260.

PEYRON TAX ACCOUNTANT'S COMMUNIQUE. see BUSINESS
AND ECONOMICS—Public Finance, Taxation

657 658   USA   ISSN 0895-3570
KF6296.A15
PLANNER. Text in English. 1986. bi-m. Document type:
Newsletter. Description: Provides personal financial planning
service for CPA providers.
Related titles: Online - full text ed.: (from ProQuest Information &
Learning).
Indexed: ATI.

B

Published by: American Institute of Certified Public Accountants, Harborside Financial Ctr., 201 Plaza Three, 3rd Fl, Jersey City, NJ 07311-9801. TEL 888-777-7077, FAX 800-302-5766, journal@aicpa.org, http://www.aicpa.org. Ed. William Moran. Pub. Coleen Katz. Circ: 8,000 (controlled).

DER PLATOW BRIEF. see *BUSINESS AND ECONOMICS—Economic Situation And Conditions*

PONTIFICIA UNIVERSIDADE CATOLICA DE CAMPINAS. FACULDADE DE CIENCIAS ECONOMICAS CONTABEIS E ADMINISTRATIVAS. CADERNOS. see *BUSINESS AND ECONOMICS—Economic Systems And Theories, Economic History*

657 336.2 USA ISSN 0032-6321
HF5601 CODEN: PACNBD
PRACTICAL ACCOUNTANT; providing the competitive edge. Text in English. 1967. m. USD 89 domestic; USD 109 foreign (effective 2005). adv. bk.rev. charts; illus.; stat. index. 48 p./no. 3 cols./p.; back issues avail.; reprint service avail. from PQC. **Document type:** *Magazine, Trade.* **Description:** Forum covering every facet of accounting and taxes.
Formerly: Practical Accounting
Related titles: Microform ed.: (from PQC); Online - full text ed.: (from EBSCO Publishing, Factiva, Florida Center for Library Automation, Gale Group, H.W. Wilson, LexisNexis, Northern Light Technology, Inc., O C L C Online Computer Library Center, Inc., ProQuest Information & Learning); Supplement(s): C P A Wealth Provider. 2001. free with subscr. to any financial planning publication by Source Media, Inc.
Indexed: ABIn, ATI, AgeL, BPI, BPIA, BusI, LOIS, LegCont, ManagCont, PROMT, PSI, SoftBase, T&II.
—BLDSC (6593.870000), CISTI, IE, Infotrieve, ingenta. **CCC.**
Published by: Source Media, Inc., One State St Plaza, 27th Fl, New York, NY 10004. TEL 212-803-6077, 800-221-1809, FAX 212-747-1154, custserv@sourcemedia.com, http://www.sourcemedia.com. adv.: B&W page USD 4,700, color page USD 6,715. Circ: 40,000 (paid and controlled).

PRACTICAL TAX STRATEGIES. see *BUSINESS AND ECONOMICS—Public Finance, Taxation*

657 USA ISSN 0885-6931
THE PRACTICING C P A. Text in English. 1991. m. membership. adv. index. back issues avail. **Document type:** *Newsletter.* **Description:** Offers professional accountants in private companies practice advice and commentary.
Related titles: Online - full text ed.: (from Florida Center for Library Automation, Gale Group, ProQuest Information & Learning).
Indexed: ATI.
—CCC.
Published by: American Institute of Certified Public Accountants, Harborside Financial Ctr., 201 Plaza Three, 3rd Fl, Jersey City, NJ 07311-9801. TEL 888-777-7077, FAX 800-302-5766, journal@aicpa.org, http://www.aicpa.org. Ed. John von Brachel. R&P Jessica Cedar TEL 201-938-3297. Adv. contact Michael Guglielmo. Circ: (controlled).

657 POL ISSN 1640-9930
PRACTYCZNY PORADNIK KSIEGOWEGO. Text in Polish. s-m. PLZ 90 (effective 2001).
Published by: Grupa Wydawnicza INFOR Sp. z o.o., Ul Okopowa 58/72, Warsaw, 01042, Poland. TEL 48-22-5304208, 48-22-5304450, bok@infor.pl. Ed. Ewa Slawinska. Adv. contact Waldemar Krakowiak.

657 RUS
PRAKTICHESKAYA BUKHGALTERIYA. Text in Russian. m. RUR 1,920 domestic to individuals; RUR 2,640 domestic to institutions (effective 2002). **Document type:** *Journal.* **Description:** Contains practical information on accounting practices.
Published by: Berator-Press, Ul Khalturinskaya 2, str 2, Moscow, 107392, Russian Federation. TEL 7-095-3639542, http://www.berator.ru.

657 NLD ISSN 1380-0256
PRAKTIJK REGISTER ACCOUNTANTS (YEAR). Variant title: N I V R A Gids. Text in Dutch. a. **Document type:** *Directory.* **Description:** Discusses significant developments in the accounting profession, and provides current information on practicing accountants in the Netherlands, as well as information on accounting divisions of government agencies at a national, regional and local level.
Indexed: ATI.
Published by: Reed Business Information bv (Subsidiary of: Reed Business), Postbus 16400, Den Haag, 2500 BK, Netherlands. TEL 31-70-3624800, FAX 31-70-3605606.

PRAKTIJKBOEK VOOR VENNOOTSCHAPPEN; juridisch, boekhoudkundig, fiscaal. see *LAW—Corporate Law*

PRINCIPLES OF PAYROLL ADMINISTRATION; the complete learning and reference guide. see *BUSINESS AND ECONOMICS—Management*

657 IDN
PROCEEDING OF I A I CONGRESS. Text in Indonesian. 1980. s-a. IDR 100,000 (effective 2000).
Published by: Indonesian Institute of Accountants, Jl. Sisingamangaraja 59, Jakarta, 12120, Indonesia. TEL 62-21-722-2989, iai-info@akuntan-iai.or.id. Ed. Sri Yanto. Circ: 4,000.

657 IDN
PROCEEDING OF I A I CONVENTION. Text in Indonesian. 1990. s-a. IDR 100,000 (effective 2000).
Published by: Indonesian Institute of Accountants, Jl. Sisingamangaraja 59, Jakarta, 12120, Indonesia. TEL 62-21-722-2989, iai-info@akuntan-iai.or.id. Ed. Sri Yanto. Circ: 4,000.

657 AUS ISSN 1030-5890
PROPOSED STATEMENT OF ACCOUNTING CONCEPTS. Text in English. 1987. irreg. AUD 6 per issue.
Published by: Australian Accounting Research Foundation, 211 Hawthorn Rd, Caulfield, VIC 3162, Australia. TEL 61-3-95243600, FAX 61-3-95235499, standard@aarf.asn.au. Circ: 1,400. **Co-sponsors:** Institute of Chartered Accountants in Australia; Australian Society of Certified Practising Accountants.

657 USA ISSN 0161-309X
CODEN: NRATBG
PUBLIC ACCOUNTING REPORT; competitive intelligence for accounting firms. Text in English. 1978. bi-w. looseleaf. USD 360 (effective 2005). back issues avail. **Document type:** *Newsletter.* **Description:** Provides firms with authoritative news and analysis of developments in the profession today, as well as trends.
Incorporates (2000-2004): C P A Financial Services Advisor (1528-171X)
Related titles: Online - full text ed.: (from EBSCO Publishing).
Indexed: ATI.
—CCC.
Published by: C C H Tax and Accounting (Subsidiary of: Wolters Kluwer N.V.), 2700 Lake Cook Rd, Riverwoods, IL 60015. TEL 847-267-7000, FAX 779-866-3895, http://tax.cchgroup.com/Store/Products/Product%20Detail.htm?cs_id=CCE-CCH-2628(CCE)&cs_catalog=TADS.

PUBLIC MONEY. see *BUSINESS AND ECONOMICS—Public Finance, Taxation*

657 658 GBR ISSN 1176-6093
▼ **QUALITATIVE RESEARCH IN ACCOUNTING AND MANAGEMENT.** Variant title: Q R A M. Text in English. 2004. 3/yr. AUD 199 combined subscription print & online eds. (effective 2005). **Document type:** *Journal, Academic/Scholarly.* **Description:** Publishes qualitative research on topics relevant to management, organization studies, financial and management accounting, management and accounting education, social and environmental issues, and critical and historical approaches.
Related titles: Online - full text ed.
—BLDSC (7163.820000).
Published by: Emerald Group Publishing Limited, 60-62 Toller Ln, Bradford, W Yorks BD8 9BY, United Kingdom. TEL 44-1274-777700, FAX 44-1274-785200, infomation@emeraldinsight.com, http://www.emeraldinsight.com/qram.htm. R&P Ms. Anne-Marie Thorslund.

005.5 USA ISSN 1055-0208
QUANTUM P C REPORT FOR C P AS. Text in English. 19??. m. USD 235 domestic; USD 270 foreign (effective 2001). bk.rev.; software rev. abstr.; charts; illus.; mkt. back issues avail. **Document type:** *Newsletter.* **Description:** Articles by CPAs to help CPAs become more proficient with PCs.
Related titles: Online - full text ed.
Indexed: SoftBase.
Published by: QNet, 5350 S. Roslyn St., Ste. 4000, Englewood, CO 80111. info@quantum.org, http://www.quantum.org. Ed., Pub. Jack C McClure. R&P Rob Hecker. Circ: 1,300 (paid).

QUESTION BOOK, INCOME TAX LAW PRINCIPLES, INCOME TAX LAW APPLICATIONS. see *BUSINESS AND ECONOMICS—Public Finance, Taxation*

358.1554 AUS
QUICK ON COSTS. Text in English. 2 base vols. plus q. updates. AUD 1,628 (effective 2004). Supplement avail. **Document type:** *Trade.* **Description:** Covers the law of costs, contemporary issues impacting on traditional costs law and provides a comparative evolution of costs law in Supreme Courts of the States and Territories, the Federal, Family and High Courts of Australia, the High Court of New Zealand and the English High Court.
Related titles: Online - full content ed.: AUD 825 for practices with up to 20 practitioners (effective 2003).
Published by: Lawbook Co. (Subsidiary of: Thomson Legal & Regulatory Ltd.), PO Box 3502, Rozelle, NSW 2039, Australia. LRA.Service@thomson.com, http://onlineecom01.thomson.com.au/thomson/Catalog.asp?EES_CMD=SI&EES_ID=100323, http://www.lawbookco.com.au/. Eds. David Garnsworthy, Roger Quick.

657 336 POL ISSN 0481-5475
RACHUNKOWOSC. Text in Polish. 1949. m. PLZ 19 (effective 1999). adv. bk.rev. bibl. index. **Document type:** *Trade.* **Description:** Covers accounting matters, taxation, finance, financial analysis, auditing.
Published by: (Stowarzyszenie Ksiegowych w Polsce), Rachunkowosc Sp. z o.o., Ul Tamka 18 m 29, Warsaw, 00349, Poland. TEL 48-22-8265621, FAX 48-22-8265621, redakcja@rachunkowosc.com.pl, http://www.rachunkowosc.com.pl. Ed. Zdzislaw Fedak. R&P Roza Sokolowska. Adv. contact Grzegorz Sioch. Circ: 32,000. **Dist. by:** Centrala Kolportazy "Ruch", Towarowa 28, Warsaw 00958, Poland.

657 POL ISSN 1428-8176
RACHUNKOWOSC BUDZETOWA. Text in Polish. 1999. s-m. PLZ 78 (effective 2001).
Published by: Grupa Wydawnicza INFOR Sp. z o.o., Ul Okopowa 58/72, Warsaw, 01042, Poland. TEL 48-22-5304208, 48-22-5304450, bok@infor.pl. Ed. Agata Eichler. Adv. contact Waldemar Krakowiak.

657.2 336.2 POL ISSN 1508-0560
RACHUNKOWOSC. PORADNIK PRAKTYCZNY. Text in Polish. 1999. m. PLZ 275 (effective 2003).
Published by: Wydawnictwo Prawnicze LexisNexis Sp. z o.o. (Subsidiary of: LexisNexis Europe and Africa), ul Gen K Sosnkowskiego 1, Warsaw, 02-495, Poland. TEL 48-22-6677543, FAX 48-22-7230739, biuro@LexisNexis.pl, http://sklep.lexpolonica.pl.

657 POL ISSN 1429-3056
RACHUNKOWOSC Z KOMENTARZEM. Text in Polish. 1997. m. PLZ 78 (effective 2001).
Published by: Grupa Wydawnicza INFOR Sp. z o.o., Ul Okopowa 58/72, Warsaw, 01042, Poland. TEL 48-22-5304208, 48-22-5304450, bok@infor.pl. Ed. Ryszard Perlejewski. Adv. contact Waldemar Krakowiak.

657 HRV ISSN 0350-4506
HF5616.C77
RACUNOVODSTVO I FINANCIJE. Text in Croatian. 1955. m. HRK 950 (effective 2002). adv. **Document type:** *Magazine, Trade.*
Formerly (until 1972): Knjigovoda (1330-2086)
Published by: Hrvatska Zajednica Racunovoda i Financijskih Djelatnika, Jakova Gotovca 1/II, p.p. 732, Zagreb, 10000, Croatia. TEL 385-1-4664105, FAX 385-1-4664370, rif@rif.hr, http://www.rif.hr. Ed. Ferdo Spajic. adv.: page HRK 2,000; trim 170 x 255.

RAILWAY ACCOUNTING RULES. see *TRANSPORTATION—Railroads*

657 RUS
RASCHET. Text in Russian. m. RUR 2,400 domestic to individuals; RUR 3,240 domestic to institutions (effective 2002). **Document type:** *Journal.* **Description:** Covers all aspects of Russian taxation and includes commentary from leading accounting experts.
Published by: Berator-Press, Ul Khalturinskaya 2, str 2, Moscow, 107392, Russian Federation. TEL 7-095-3639542.

658 USA ISSN 1060-0418
THE RECEIVABLES REPORT; the monthly newsletter for America's health care financial manager. Text in English. 1986. m. USD 365 (effective 2004). **Document type:** *Newsletter, Trade.* **Description:** Includes actual profit-improvement examples from facilities nationwide, secrets for successfully challenging denials, tips for using automation to increase cash flow, and strategies that are currently being used to prepare for health care reform.
Related titles: Online - full text ed.: (from EBSCO Publishing).
—CCC.
Published by: Aspen Publishers, Inc. (Subsidiary of: Wolters Kluwer N.V.), 5301 Buckeystown Pike, Ste. 400, Frederick, MD 21704-8319. TEL 800-638-8437, customer.service@aspenpubl.com, http://www.aspenpub.com. Ed. Joann Petaschnick. **Dist. by:** Distribution Center, 7201 McKinney Circle, Frederick, MD 21701. TEL 301-698-7100, FAX 301-417-7550.

657 GBR
RECOMMENDATION FOR ACCOUNTANTS AND AUDITORS. Text in English. 1980. irreg. GBP 4.50 (effective 1999). **Document type:** *Monographic series.*
Published by: Marcus Tobias & Co., 65 Shakespeare Dr, Shirley, Solihull, Warks B90 2AN, United Kingdom. TEL 0121-744-2912, FAX 0121-733-2902.

657 USA ISSN 1052-0457
K18
➤ **RESEARCH IN ACCOUNTING REGULATION.** Text in English. 1987. irreg., latest vol.17, 2004. price varies. back issues avail. **Document type:** *Monographic series, Academic/Scholarly.* **Description:** Seeks to publish high quality manuscripts, which address regulatory issues and policy affecting the practice of accountancy, broadly defined.
Indexed: ATI.
—BLDSC (7714.305000), IE, ingenta. **CCC.**

Published by: J A I Press Inc. (Subsidiary of: Elsevier Science & Technology), 360 Park Ave S, New York, NY 10010-1710. TEL 212-989-5800, FAX 212-633-3990, usinfo-f@elsevier.com, http://www.elsevier.com/wps/find/bookdescription.cws_home/BS_RAR/description#description. Ed. Gary Previts.

657 USA ISSN 0884-0741
HJ9701
RESEARCH IN GOVERNMENTAL AND NON-PROFIT ACCOUNTING. Text in English. 1985. irreg., latest vol.11, 2004. price varies. **Document type:** *Monographic series.*
Indexed: ATI.
—BLDSC (7741.146000), IE, ingenta. **CCC.**
Published by: J A I Press Inc. (Subsidiary of: Elsevier Science & Technology), 360 Park Ave S, New York, NY 10010-1710. TEL 212-989-5800, FAX 212-633-3990, usinfo-f@elsevier.com, http://www.elsevier.com/wps/find/bookseriesdescription.cws_home/BS_RGNA/description. Ed. Paul Copley.

657 USA
RESEARCH INSTITUTE OF AMERICA. SPECIAL STUDIES. Text in English. m. USD 125. **Document type:** *Academic/Scholarly.* **Description:** Provides in-depth discussions of key tax developments.
Published by: R I A (Subsidiary of: Thomson Corporation), 395 Hudson St, New York, NY 10014. TEL 212-367-6300, RIA.CustomerServices@Thomson.com, http://ria.thomson.com/.

657 170 USA ISSN 1574-0765
HF5657
RESEARCH ON PROFESSIONAL RESPONSIBILITY AND ETHICS IN ACCOUNTING. Text in English. 1995. a., latest vol.10, 2005. price varies. back issues avail. **Document type:** *Monographic series, Academic/Scholarly.* **Description:** Seeks to publish high-quality research and cases that focus on the professional responsibilities of accountants and how they deal with the ethical issues they face.
Formerly (until vol.9, 2003): Research on Accounting Ethics (1529-207X)
—BLDSC (7755.083500).
Published by: J A I Press Inc. (Subsidiary of: Elsevier Science & Technology), 360 Park Ave S, New York, NY 10010-1710. TEL 212-989-5800, FAX 212-633-3990, usinfo-f@elsevier.com, http://www.elsevier.com/wps/find/bookseriesdescription.cws_home/BS_RPREA/description. Eds. B N Schwartz, Cynthia Jeffrey.

REVENUE ACCOUNTING MANUAL. see *TRANSPORTATION—Air Transport*

REVENUE-CYCLE STRATEGIST; insights and actions for successful results. see *HEALTH FACILITIES AND ADMINISTRATION*

657 GBR ISSN 1475-7702
REVIEW OF ACCOUNTING & FINANCE. Text in English. 2001. q. EUR 519 in Europe; USD 519 in North America; GBP 349 in the UK & elsewhere (effective 2005). reprint service avail. from PSC. **Document type:** *Journal, Academic/Scholarly.*
Related titles: Online - full text ed.: (from ProQuest Information & Learning).
Indexed: ABIn.
—BLDSC (7786.740100), IE.
Published by: Emerald Group Publishing Limited, 60-62 Toller Ln, Bradford, W Yorks BD8 9BY, United Kingdom. TEL 44-1274-777700, FAX 44-1274-785200, infomation@emeraldinsight.com, http://www.emeraldinsight.com/.

657 USA ISSN 1380-6653
HF5601 CODEN: RASTFZ
➤ **REVIEW OF ACCOUNTING STUDIES.** Text in English. 1996. q. EUR 418, USD 428, GBP 265 combined subscription to institutions print & online eds. (effective 2005). adv. illus. reprint service avail. from PSC. **Document type:** *Journal, Academic/Scholarly.* **Description:** Provides an outlet for significant academic research in accounting, including theoretical, empirical, and experimental work.
Related titles: Online - full text ed.: ISSN 1573-7136 (from EBSCO Publishing, Gale Group, IngentaConnect, Kluwer Online, O C L C Online Computer Library Center, Inc., ProQuest Information & Learning, Springer LINK, Swets Information Services).
Indexed: ABIn, BibLing, CurCont, ESPM, JEL, RiskAb, SSCI.
—BLDSC (7786.740500), IE, Infotrieve, ingenta. **CCC.**
Published by: Springer-Verlag New York, Inc. (Subsidiary of: Springer Science+Business Media), 233 Spring St, New York, NY 10013. TEL 212-460-1500, FAX 212-460-1575, service@springer-ny.com, http://springerlink.metapress.com/openurl.asp?genre=journal&issn=1380-6653, http://www.springer-ny.com. **Subscr. to:** Journal Fulfillment, PO Box 2485, Secaucus, NJ 07096-2485. TEL 201-348-4033, FAX 201-348-4505, journals@springer-ny.com.

657 330 USA ISSN 1534-665X
HF5679
➤ **REVIEW OF BUSINESS INFORMATION SYSTEMS.** Text in English. 1997. q. USD 275 domestic to institutions; USD 315 foreign to institutions (effective 2003). bk.rev.; software rev. abstr. 120 p./no. 1 cols./p.; back issues avail.; reprints avail. **Document type:** *Journal, Academic/Scholarly.* **Description:** Aims to provide a forum for the discusion of how computers, the Internet, and electronic commerce are impacting on Business. Articles cover all aspects of systems research, approaches to teaching accounting systems, and reviews of Information, textbooks and software.
Formerly (until 2001): Review of Accounting Information Systems (1089-8670)
—BLDSC (7788.907500). **CCC.**
Published by: Western Academic Press, PO Box 620760, Littleton, CO 80162. TEL 303-904-4750, FAX 303-978-0413, cluter@wapress.com, http://www.wapress.com/RBISMain.htm. Ed. Ronald C Clute. Circ: 600.

330 USA ISSN 0924-865X
HG173 CODEN: RQFAEO
➤ **REVIEW OF QUANTITATIVE FINANCE AND ACCOUNTING.** Text in English. 1991. 8/yr. EUR 798, USD 808, GBP 498 combined subscription to institutions print & online eds. (effective 2005). adv. illus. back issues avail.; reprint service avail. from PSC. **Document type:** *Academic/Scholarly.* **Description:** Deals with research involving the interaction of finance with accounting, economics and quantitative methods. Publishes theoretical and methodological research, as well as empirical applications.
Related titles: Microform ed.: (from PQC); Online - full text ed.: ISSN 1573-7179 (from EBSCO Publishing, Gale Group, IngentaConnect, Kluwer Online, O C L C Online Computer Library Center, Inc., ProQuest Information & Learning, Springer LINK, Swets Information Services).
Indexed: ABIn, BLI, BibLing, ESPM, IBR, IBSS, IBZ, JEL, RiskAb.
—BLDSC (7794.183500), IE, Infotrieve, ingenta. **CCC.**
Published by: Springer-Verlag New York, Inc. (Subsidiary of: Springer Science+Business Media), 233 Spring St, New York, NY 10013. TEL 212-460-1500, FAX 212-460-1575, service@springer-ny.com, http://springerlink.metapress.com/openurl.asp?genre=journal&issn=0924-865X, http://www.springer-ny.com. Ed. Cheng-few Lee. **Subscr. to:** Journal Fulfillment, PO Box 2485, Secaucus, NJ 07096-2485. TEL 201-348-4033, FAX 201-348-4505, journals@springer-ny.com.

657.45 DNK ISSN 0034-6918
REVISION & REGNSKABSVAESEN; tidsskrift for erhvervsoekonomi og skatteforhold. Text in Danish. 1932. m. DKK 915 (effective 2004). adv. bk.rev. charts; illus. index. **Document type:** *Trade.*
Formerly (until 1934): Foreningen af Statsautoriserede Revisorer. Meddelelser (0909-4075)
Published by: (Foreningen af Statsautoriserede Revisorer/Institute of State Authorized Public Accountants in Denmark), Forlaget Thomson S/A, Nytorv 5, Copenhagen K, 1450, Denmark. TEL 45-33-740700, FAX 45-33-121636, thomson@thomson.dk, http://www.thomson.dk/pls/pdb/katpage.support1?p_side_id=6, http://www/thomson.dk. Ed. Henrik Hansen. Adv. contact Per Christensen TEL 45-33-778875. color page DKK 17,700; 185 x 268. Circ: 6,500.

657 NOR ISSN 0332-7795
REVISJON OG REGNSKAP. Text in Norwegian. 1931. 8/yr. NOK 680 domestic; NOK 820 foreign (effective 2001). adv. **Document type:** *Academic/Scholarly.*
Formerly: Tidsskrift for Revisjon og Regnskapsvesen (0040-7151)
Published by: Den Norske Revisorforening, Pilestredet 75 D, Postboks 5864, Majorstua, Oslo, 0308, Norway. TEL 47-23-36-52-00, FAX 47-22-69-05-55, rrred@revisornett.no. Ed. Dag Bredal. Adv. contact Else Marie Lindeman. Circ: 8,400.

REVISOR POSTEN. see *BUSINESS AND ECONOMICS—Public Finance, Taxation*

657 DNK ISSN 0106-5203
REVISORBLADET. Text in Danish. 1940. 8/yr. DKK 470 (effective 1999). adv. bk.rev. reprints avail. **Document type:** *Trade.*
Published by: Foreningen Registrerede Revisorer, Aamarksvej 1, Hvidovre, 2650, Denmark. FAX 45-36-34-44-44. Ed. Per Hastrup Andersen. Circ: 4,500.

657 DNK ISSN 1399-5995
REVISORHAANDBOGEN, REGNSKAB. Text in Danish. 1982. a. price varies.
Supersedes in part (in 1998): Revisorhaandbogen (0108-3716)
Related titles: CD-ROM ed.: Revisorhaandbogen. ISSN 1600-7700.
Published by: (Foreningen af Statsautoriserede Revisorer/Institute of State Authorized Public Accountants in Denmark), Forlaget Thomson S/A, Nytorv 5, Copenhagen K, 1450, Denmark. TEL 45-33-740700, FAX 45-33-121636, thomson@thomson.dk, http://www/thomson.dk.

657.45 DNK ISSN 1399-5987
REVISORHAANDBOGEN, REVISION. Text in Danish. 1998. a. (in 2 vols.). price varies. **Document type:** *Trade.*
Supersedes in part (1982-1998): Revisorhaandbogen (0108-3716)
Related titles: CD-ROM ed.: Revisorhaandbogen. ISSN 1600-7700.
Published by: (Foreningen af Statsautoriserede Revisorer/Institute of State Authorized Public Accountants in Denmark), Forlaget Thomson S/A, Nytorv 5, Copenhagen K, 1450, Denmark. TEL 45-33-740700, FAX 45-33-121636, thomson@thomson.dk, http://www/thomson.dk.

657 332.1 ARG
REVISTA DE CIENCIAS ECONOMICAS. Text in Spanish. 1987. bi-m. free. back issues avail. **Description:** Covers accounting, banking, domestic commerce and economic situation.
Indexed: PAIS.
Published by: Consejo Profesional de Ciencias Economicas de la Provincia de Santa Fe, Camara 1, C, Colegio de Graduados en Ciencias Economicas de Santa Fe, San Lorenzo, 1849, Camara 1, Santa Fe, 3000, Argentina. TEL 042-31924.

657 ESP ISSN 1138-4891
REVISTA DE CONTABILIDAD. Text in Spanish. 1997. q. EUR 36 domestic; USD 70 foreign (effective 2002). abstr. back issues avail.
Related titles: Online - full text ed.
—CINDOC.
Published by: Asociacion Espanola de Profesores Universitarios de Contabilidad, Ave. de los Castros, s-n, Santander, Cantabria 39005, Spain. TEL 34-942-201647, FAX 34-942-201890, revconta@ccaix3.unican.es, http://asepuc.unizar.es/.

657 ARG ISSN 0327-022X
REVISTA DE INVESTIGACION CONTABLE (TEUKEN). Abstracts in English, French, Portuguese, Spanish. 1987. q. USD 120. bk.rev. bibl.; charts. **Document type:** *Academic/Scholarly.*
Related titles: CD-ROM ed.
Published by: Universidad Nacional de la Patagonia San Juan Bosca, Facultad de Ciencias Economicas, Sarmiento, 553, Casilla de Correos 172, Comodoro Rivadavia, Chubut 9000, Argentina. TEL 0967-24463, FAX 54-96724463, TELEX 86022 UNPCR, http://www.unp.edu.ar/. Ed. Jorge Manuel Gil. Circ: 700.

657 USA
REVISTA INTERAMERICANA/INTER-AMERICAN NEWSLETTER. Text in English. 1980. q. USD 50; includes Boletin Interamericano. **Document type:** *Newsletter.*
Indexed: HistAb.
Published by: Asociacion Interamericana de Contabilidad/Interamerican Accounting Association, c/o Victor Abreu Paez, Exec Dir, Fontainebleau Exec Center, 275 Fountainebleau Blvd, Ste 245, Miami, FL 33172. TEL 305-225-1991, FAX 305-225-2011. Ed. Victor Abreu Paez. Circ: 1,500 (paid).

657 336 FRA ISSN 0035-2713
LA REVUE DU TRESOR; organe d'etudes et d'informations professionnelles. Text in French. 1921. m. (except Mar.-Apr. and Aug.-Sep. combined). bk.rev. bibl.; charts; illus. index.
Indexed: PAIS, RASB.
—BLDSC (7956.620000), IE, ingenta.
Published by: Les Editions du Tresor, 26 rue de Lille, Paris, 75007, France. TEL 33-1-45489919, FAX 33-1-40497011.

657 FRA ISSN 0484-8764
HF5601
REVUE FRANCAISE DE COMPTABILITE. Text in French; Summaries in English, German, Spanish. 1955. m. adv. bk.rev. index. reprint service avail. from SCH. **Description:** Covers accounting, tax and business law, management, tax control and more.
Related titles: Online - full text ed.: (from ProQuest Information & Learning).
Indexed: ABIn, SCIMP.
—BLDSC (7902.800000), IE, Infotrieve, ingenta.
Published by: (Societe d'Edition de l'Ordre des Experts Comptables, Conseil Superieur), Editions Comptables Malesherbes, 88 rue de Courcelles, Paris, 75008, France. TEL 44-15-95-95, FAX 44-15-90-76, TELEX 640 994 ORDREXP. Ed. G Nicol. Adv. contact Georges Gelly. Circ: 17,000.

657 AUS
RISK - IT. Text in English. 1982. q. membership. adv. bk.rev. **Document type:** *Newsletter.*
Formerly (until 1998): Password (1037-7093)
Published by: Information Systems Audit and Control Association, Melbourne Chapter, GPO Box 451 C, Melbourne, VIC 3001, Australia. TEL 61-3-9288-8979, FAX 61-3-9654-6162, john.fleh@ernstyang.cern.au. Ed. J Fleh. Circ: 900.

RISK MEASUREMENT SERVICE. see *BUSINESS AND ECONOMICS—Banking And Finance*

657 ISR ISSN 0035-7790
HF5616.I75
ROEH HACHESHBON. Text in Hebrew. 1950. bi-m. adv. bk.rev. abstr.; bibl.; charts; illus. index. **Document type:** *Bulletin.*
Indexed: IHP.

B

Published by: Institute of Certified Public Accountants in Israel, 1 Montefiore St., P O Box 29281, Tel Aviv, Israel. TEL 972-3-5161114, FAX 972-3-5103105. Ed. Yoram Eden. Circ: 8,500 (controlled).

ROSTOCKER BEITRAEGE ZU CONTROLLING UND RECHNUNGSWESEN. see *BUSINESS AND ECONOMICS—Management*

657   GBR
ROYAL SOCIETY FOR THE PREVENTION OF CRUELTY TO ANIMALS. TRUSTEES' REPORT AND ACCOUNTS. Variant title: Trustee's Reports and Accounts. Text in English. a. Members. **Document type:** *Corporate.* **Description:** Contains full accounts for the RSPCA.
Published by: Royal Society for the Prevention of Cruelty to Animals, Wilberforce Way, Oakhurst Business Park, Southwater, Horsham, W Sussex RH13 7WN, United Kingdom. TEL 44-707-5335-999, 0870-010-1181, FAX 0870-753-0048, publications@rspca.org.uk, http://www.rspca.org.uk.

657   USA
S E C ACCOUNTING AND AUDITING UPDATE SERVICE. Text in English. 1984. 27/yr. USD 400; USD 560 foreign (effective 1998). **Document type:** *Newsletter.* **Description:** Reports on S.E.C. pronouncements within three weeks, including detailed analysis and practical examples.
Formerly: S E C Accounting and Reporting Update Service (1045-1439)
—CCC.
Published by: (U.S. Securities and Exchange Commission), W G & L Financial Reporting & Management Research (Subsidiary of: R I A), 395 Hudson St, New York, NY 10014. TEL 212-367-6300, FAX 212-367-6718. Eds. Allan B Afterman, Charles Maurer, Dorothy Cummings. **Subscr. to:** The Park Square Bldg., 31 St James Ave, Boston, MA 02116-4112. TEL 800-950-1207.

657   USA   ISSN 0146-485X
KF1446.A15
S E C ACCOUNTING REPORT. (Securities and Exchange Commission) Text in English. 1974. m. USD 550 (effective 2005). illus. index. reprints avail. **Document type:** *Newsletter, Trade.* **Description:** Covers S.E.C., F.A.S.B., and related financial reporting matters. Offers up-to-date information on new S.E.C. developments and federal regulations.
Related titles: Online - full text ed.: (from ProQuest Information & Learning).
Indexed: ATI.
—CCC.
Published by: W G & L Financial Reporting & Management Research (Subsidiary of: R I A), 395 Hudson St, New York, NY 10014. TEL 212-367-6300, FAX 212-367-6718, http://www.riahome.com. Ed. Paul J Wendell. **Subscr. to:** The Park Square Bldg., 31 St James Ave, Boston, MA 02116-4112. TEL 800-950-1207.

S E C ACCOUNTING RULES. (Securities and Exchange Commission) see *BUSINESS AND ECONOMICS— Investments*

S E C FINANCIAL REPORTING: ANNUAL REPORTS TO SHAREHOLDERS, FORM 10-K, QUARTERLY FINANCIAL REPORTING. see *BUSINESS AND ECONOMICS— Investments*

657   USA   ISSN 0745-2667
KF1444.A15
S E C TODAY. (Securities Exchange Commission) Text in English. 1982. 250/yr. adv. back issues avail. **Document type:** *Newsletter.*
—CCC.
Published by: Washington Service Bureau, Inc., 655 15th St, N W, Washington, DC 20005. TEL 202-508-0600, FAX 202-659-3655, http://secnet.cch.com/, http://www.wsb.com/ sectoday. Ed. Jacquelyn Lumb. Pub. Lawrence Hamm. R&P Jaquelyn Lumb. Adv. contact John Stricklett.

657   FRA
S I C. Text in French. 1983. m. (11/yr.). **Document type:** *Bulletin.* **Description:** Covers the French accountancy profession.
Published by: Ordre des Experts Comptables, 153 rue de Courcelles, Paris, 75017, France. TEL 33-1-45156000, FAX 33-1-45159005. Ed. Rene Ricol. R&P G Gelly. Circ: 20,500.

657 336   BEL   ISSN 0776-0590
SAMSOM ACTUALITE COMPTABLE; lettre bimensuelle a l'usage des experts-comptables, reviseurs d'enterprises, directeurs financiers et administratifs. Text in French. 1984. s-m. index. Supplement avail. **Description:** Articles on all aspects of accountancy, including financial analysis.
Related titles: Dutch ed.: Samsom Accountancy Actualiteit. ISSN 0773-2155.
Published by: C E D Samsom (Subsidiary of: Wolters Samsom Belgie n.v.), Kouterveld 14, Diegem, 1831, Belgium. TEL 32-2-7231111.

657.6   BEL   ISSN 0773-8625
SAMSOM AUDIT & REVISORAAT. Text in Flemish. s-m. Supplement avail. **Description:** Consists of professional information on internal audits, controls, enterprise laws.

Published by: (Instituut der Interne Auditors), C E D Samsom (Subsidiary of: Wolters Samsom Belgie n.v.), Kouterveld 14, Diegem, 1831, Belgium. TEL 32-2-7231111.

SAMSOM BESLOTEN VENNOOTSCHAPPEN MET BEPERKTE AANSPRAKELIJKHEID. see *BUSINESS AND ECONOMICS*

SAMSOM COOPERATIEVE VENNOOTSCHAPPEN. see *BUSINESS AND ECONOMICS*

SAMSOM GELD EN ONDERNEMING. see *BUSINESS AND ECONOMICS—Banking And Finance*

657   RUS
SCHETNAYA PALATA ROSSIISKOI FEDERATSII. BYULLETEN'. Text in Russian. 1997. m. USD 205 in the Americas (effective 2000).
Published by: Schetnaya Palata Rossiiskoi Federatsii, Ul. Gilyarovskogo, 31, Moscow, 129090, Russian Federation. TEL 7-095-2848080. **Dist. by:** East View Information Services, 3020 Harbor Ln. N., Minneapolis, MN 55447. TEL 763-550-0961, FAX 763-559-2931.

SCHRIFTEN ZUM BETRIEBLICHEN RECHNUNGSWESEN UND CONTROLLING. see *BUSINESS AND ECONOMICS— Management*

657   CHE   ISSN 0036-746X
DER SCHWEIZER TREUHAENDER/EXPERT-COMPTABLE SUISSE. Text in French, German. 1926. 10/yr. CHF 145 Includes CD-ROM (effective 1999). adv. bk.rev. **Document type:** *Trade.*
Related titles: CD-ROM ed.
Published by: Treuhand-Kammer/Chambre Fiduciaire, Postfach 892, Zuerich, 8025, Switzerland. TEL 41-1-2677575, FAX 41-1-2677555. Ed. Kurt Schuele. Circ: 10,814 (controlled).

657 332   BGR   ISSN 1310-9901
KJM911.2
SEDMICHEN ZAKONNIK. Text in Bulgarian. w. BGL 116.40 (effective 2002). **Description:** Covers accounting, legislation, banking, customs practice, insurance.
Published by: Izdatel Koman, Pl Raiko Daskalov 1, vkh B, Sofia, 1000, Bulgaria. TEL 359-2-9803561, FAX 359-2-9818651, office@zakonnik.net, http://www.zakonnik.net. Ed. Liubov Vinarova.

657   POL   ISSN 1232-6003
SERWIS FINANSOWO-KSIEGOWY. Text in Polish. 1994. w. PLZ 208 (effective 2001).
Published by: Grupa Wydawnicza INFOR Sp. z o.o., Ul Okopowa 58/72, Warsaw, 01042, Poland. TEL 48-22-5304208, 48-22-5304450, bok@infor.pl. Ed. Marzena Nikiel. Adv. contact Waldemar Krakowiak.

657   CHN   ISSN 1007-5135
SHANGHAI KUAIJI/SHANGHAI ACCOUNTING. Text in Chinese. 1979. m. CNY 69.60 (effective 2001). adv. **Document type:** *Academic/Scholarly.* **Description:** Provides information on the financial policies and laws in China and introduces advanced accounting knowledge to accountants, accounting faculty and students.
Related titles: Online - full text ed.: (from East View Information Services).
Published by: Shanghai Kuaiji Xuehui/Shanghai Accounting Association, 2230 Zhongshan Xilu, Room 1415, Shanghai, 200233, China. TEL 86-21-6438-0914, shhkj@126.com. Ed., R&P Zhonghua Ouyang. Adv. contact Yizhong Wang. Circ: 57,000.

657.6   CHN   ISSN 1002-3739
➤ **SHENJI LILUN YU SHIJIAN/AUDITING THEORY AND PRACTICE.** Text in Chinese. 1986. m. CNY 42; CNY 3.50 newsstand/cover. bk.rev. **Document type:** *Academic/Scholarly.* **Description:** Covers basic auditing theories, methods, practice, experience, case analysis, professional auditing and directory of laws and regulations.
Related titles: Online - full text ed.: (from East View Information Services).
Published by: Beijing Shenji Yanjiusuo, 69 Xibianmennei Dajie, Beijing, 100053, China. TEL 86-10-67619220. Ed., R&P Daxian Liu. Circ: 40,000 (paid).

657.6   CHN   ISSN 1008-3243
SHENJI WENZHAI/AUDITOR'S DIGEST. Text in Chinese. 1999. m. CNY 72 (effective 2004). **Document type:** *Journal, Academic/Scholarly.*
Published by: Zhongguo Renmin Daxue, Shubao Zilio Zhongxin/Renmin University of China, Information Center for Social Server, Dongcheng-qu, 3, Zhangzizhong Lu, Beijing, 100007, China. TEL 86-10-64039458, FAX 86-10-64015080, kyes@163.net, http://www.confucius.cn.net/bkdetail.asp?fzt= V3. **Dist. by:** China International Book Trading Corp, 35 Chegongzhuang Xilu, Haidian District, PO Box 399, Beijing 100044, China. TEL 86-10-68412045, FAX 86-10-68412023, cibtc@mail.cibtc.com.cn, http://www.cibtc.com.cn; China Publications Service, PO Box 49614, Chicago, IL 60649. TEL 312-288-3291, FAX 312-288-8570.

657   CHN   ISSN 1002-4239
SHENJI YANJIU/AUDITING STUDIES. Text in Chinese. 1985. bi-m. CNY 15; USD 10 foreign. **Document type:** *Academic/Scholarly.*
Related titles: Online - full text ed.: (from East View Information Services).
Published by: Zhongguo Shenji Xuehui/Chinese Auditing Society, A-4 Baishiqiao Lu, Beijing, 100086, China. TEL 2170223. Ed. Yang Shuzi. **Co-sponsor:** Chinese Internal Auditing Society.

657   CHN   ISSN 1003-2452
SICHUAN KUAIJI/SICHUAN ACCOUNTANTS. Text in Chinese. 1981. m. CNY 21 (effective 1994). adv. **Document type:** *Academic/Scholarly.*
Related titles: Online - full text ed.: (from East View Information Services).
Published by: Sichuan Kuaiji Xuehui/Sichuan Accountants Association, 37 Nanxin Jie, Chengdu, Sichuan 610016, China. TEL 665220. Ed. Tao Sipu. Adv. contact Benqian Zhang. Circ: 30,000. **Dist. overseas by:** China National Publishing Industry Trading Corporation, PO Box 782, Beijing 100011, China. TEL 86-1-64215031 ext 3130, 86-1-64266648. **Co-sponsor:** Sichuan Caiwu Chengben Yanjiuhui.

657 340   SGP   ISSN 0217-4456
SINGAPORE ACCOUNTANT. Text in English. 1984. bi-m. SGD 86. adv. bk.rev. **Description:** Covers accounting, legal, management and computer information services with reports on case law, new legislation and other local and international developments.
Indexed: ABIn, ATI.
—BLDSC (8285.430000), IE, ingenta.
Published by: Longman Singapore Publishers (Pte) Ltd., 25 First Lok Yang Rd, Singapore, 629734, Singapore. TEL 2682666, FAX 2641740, TELEX LMS-RS-24268. Ed. June Oei. Circ: 8,000.

657.835045   USA   ISSN 8756-3886
SINGLE AUDIT INFORMATION SERVICE. Text in English. 1985. m. USD 274. **Document type:** *Trade.* **Description:** Publishes audit requirements for federal grantees (local and state governments, universities, and nonprofit organizations).
Published by: Thompson Publishing Group, 1725 K St, N W, Ste 700, Washington, DC 20006. TEL 202-739-9698, FAX 202-739-9686. Ed. Denise Lamoreaux.

657   MKD   ISSN 0351-9643
SMETKOVODSTVENO FINANSISKA REVIJA; spisanie za smetkovodstveno-finansiska i organizaciona problematika na rabotnite organizacii. Text in Macedonian. 1958. bi-m. adv. bk.rev.
Formerly (until 1981): Sovremeno Pretprijatie (0038-5964)
Published by: Zdruzenie na Smetkovodstveno-Finansiskite Rabotnici na Makedonija, PO Box 267, Skopje, Macedonia. Ed. Boris Stojmenov. Circ: 1,000.

657   PRT
SOCIEDADE PORTUGUESA DE CONTABILIDADE. BOLETIM. Text in Portuguese. 4/yr. **Document type:** *Bulletin.*
Published by: Sociedade Portuguesa de Contabilidade, Rua Barata Salgueiro, 1-2o, Lisbon, 1100, Portugal. TEL 57-18-44.

657.6   USA   ISSN 1067-8689
HF5681.D5
➤ **SOCIETY OF DEPRECIATION PROFESSIONALS. JOURNAL.** Text in English. 1989. a. USD 15 (effective 2000). adv. back issues avail. **Document type:** *Monographic series, Academic/Scholarly.* **Description:** Promotes professional developments and ethics, recognizes the field of depreciation, and collects and exchanges information.
Published by: Society of Depreciation Professionals, 5505 Connecticut Ave N W, 280, Washington, DC 20015-2601. TEL 202-362-0680, FAX 202-866-2283, http://www.depr.org. Ed., Pub., R&P Rod Daniel. Adv. contact Jerry Houck. Circ: 400 (controlled).

657 658   CAN
SOCIETY OF MANAGEMENT ACCOUNTANTS OF CANADA. ANNUAL REPORT. Text in English. a. **Document type:** *Corporate.*
Published by: Society of Management Accountants of Canada, Mississauga Executive Centre, One Robert Speck Pkwy, Ste 1400, Mississauga, ON L4Z 3M3, Canada. TEL 905-949-4200, 800-263-7622, info@cma-canada.org, http://www.cma-canada.org/cmacan/.

657 305.896073   USA   ISSN 1099-7814
➤ **SPECTRUM (GREENBELT).** Text in English. 1972. a. USD 20. **Document type:** *Proceedings, Academic/Scholarly.* **Description:** Educational and technical information for minorities in the accounting profession.
Indexed: ATI.
Published by: National Association of Black Accountants, 7249A Hanover Pkwy, Greenbelt, MD 20770-3653. TEL 301-474-6222. Circ: 3,000.

657   AUS
THE STANDARD (CAULFIELD). Text in English. 1989. irreg. price varies. **Document type:** *Monographic series.*
Supersedes (in 1966): A A R F Report (1034-2060)

Published by: Australian Accounting Research Foundation, 211 Hawthorn Rd, Caulfield, VIC 3162, Australia. TEL 61-3-95243600, FAX 61-3-95235499, standard@aarf.asn.au. Circ: 1,400. **Co-sponsors:** Institute of Chartered Accountants in Australia; Australian Society of Certified Practising Accountants.

657 USA
STATE TAX ACTION COORDINATOR. Text in English. 6 base vols. plus irreg. updates. looseleaf. USD 725.
Published by: R I A (Subsidiary of: Thomson Corporation), 395 Hudson St, New York, NY 10014. TEL 212-367-6300, RIA.CustomerServices@Thomson.com, http://ria.thomson.com/.

657 AUS ISSN 1035-3631
STATEMENT OF ACCOUNTING CONCEPTS. Text in English. 1990. irreg. AUD 6 per issue. **Document type:** *Academic/Scholarly.*
Published by: Australian Accounting Research Foundation, 211 Hawthorn Rd, Caulfield, VIC 3162, Australia. TEL 61-3-95243600, FAX 61-3-95235499, standard@aarf.asn.au. Circ: 1,400. **Co-sponsors:** Institute of Chartered Accountants in Australia; Australian Society of Certified Practising Accountants.

657 AUS ISSN 1034-859X
STATEMENT OF AUDITING PRACTICE. Text in English. 1990. irreg. AUD 6 per issue. **Document type:** *Trade.*
Published by: Australian Accounting Research Foundation, 211 Hawthorn Rd, Caulfield, VIC 3162, Australia. TEL 61-3-95243600, FAX 61-3-95235499, standard@aarf.asn.au. Circ: 1,000. **Co-sponsors:** Institute of Chartered Accountants in Australia; Australian Society of Certified Practising Accountants.

657 AUS
STATEMENT OF AUDITING PRACTICE - RELATED SERVICES. Text in English. 1990. irreg. AUD 6 per issue. **Document type:** *Trade.*
Formerly (until 1992): Statement of Auditing Standards (1034-8603)
Published by: Australian Accounting Research Foundation, 211 Hawthorn Rd, Caulfield, VIC 3162, Australia. TEL 61-3-95243600, FAX 61-3-95235499, standard@aarf.asn.au. Circ: 1,000. **Co-sponsors:** Institute of Chartered Accountants in Australia; Australian Society of Certified Practising Accountants.

657.6 USA ISSN 0746-7486
STATEMENT OF FINANCIAL ACCOUNTING STANDARDS. Text in English. 1973. q. USD 185 (effective 2005); Includes Statements, Interpretations, and The FASB Report Newsletter.. **Document type:** *Trade.*
Published by: Financial Accounting Standards Board (Subsidiary of: Financial Accounting Foundation), 401 Merritt 7, Box 5116, Norwalk, CT 06856-5116. TEL 203-847-0700, 800-748-0659, FAX 203-849-9714, http://www.fasb.org/st/index.shtml, http://www.fasb.org/public.

657 USA ISSN 1524-833X
HF5686.C8
➤ **STRATEGIC FINANCE.** Text in English. 1919. m. USD 175 to institutions; USD 88 to libraries (effective 2005). adv. bk.rev. charts; illus. cum.index: 1920-1990, 1990-1995. back issues avail.; reprint service avail. from PQC,SCH. **Document type:** *Journal, Academic/Scholarly.* **Description:** It publishes articles on corporate finanaical management, cost accounting, cash management, controllership, strategic planning, budgeting, corporate and personal taxes, information systems/computers, employee benefits and profiles of companies and their financial executives.
Former titles (until 1999): Management Accounting Quarterly (0025-1690); N A A Bulletin - Management Accounting
Related titles: Microform ed.: (from PQC); Online - full text ed.: (from EBSCO Publishing, Florida Center for Library Automation, Gale Group, H.W. Wilson, O C L C Online Computer Library Center, Inc., ProQuest Information & Learning).
Indexed: ABIn, ASEANManA, ATI, AgeL, BPI, BPIA, BusI, CIS, CPM, DPD, Emerald, EngInd, IMI, Inspec, JEL, KES, ManagCont, PAIS, PSI, RASB, SCIMP, SoftBase, T&II.
—BLDSC (8474.031443), AskIEEE, CISTI, IE, Infotrieve, ingenta. **CCC.**
Published by: Institute of Management Accountants, 10 Paragon Dr, Montvale, NJ 07645-1760. TEL 201-573-9000, 800-638-4427, FAX 201-474-1603, sfmag@imanet.org, ma@imanet.org, http://www.strategicfinancemag.com, http://www.imanet.org. Ed. Kathy Williams. Adv. contact Alice Schulman. B&W page USD 7,350, color page USD 9,421. Circ: 68,000. **Subscr. to:** Allen Press Inc., PO Box 1897, Lawrence, KS 66044.

657 GBR ISSN 1473-0979
STUDENT ACCOUNTANT. Text in English. 2000. m. GBP 22 domestic; GBP 28 foreign (effective 2004). adv. back issues avail. **Document type:** *Newsletter, Trade.*
Formed by the merger of (1997-2000): A C C A Technician Bulletin (1460-1435); (1976-2000): A C C A Students' Newsletter (0955-5013); Which was formerly (until 1988): Students' Newsletter (0268-1706); (until 1984): Certified Accountant Students' Newsletter (0308-1303)
Published by: (Certified Accountant Educational Trust), Association of Chartered Certified Accountants, 64 Finnieston Square, Glasgow, G3 8DT, United Kingdom. TEL 44-141-582-2000, FAX 44-141-582-2222, info@accaglobal.com, http://www.accaglobal.com/publications/studentaccountant. adv.: page GBP 2,122. Circ: 150,000.

657 USA ISSN 0586-5050
HF5601
STUDIES IN ACCOUNTING RESEARCH. Text in English. 1969. irreg., latest vol.31, 1990. price varies. reprint service avail. from PSC. **Document type:** *Academic/Scholarly.*
Published by: American Accounting Association, 5717 Bessie Dr, Sarasota, FL 34233-2399. TEL 941-921-7747, FAX 941-923-4093. R&P Mary Cole.

657 USA ISSN 1078-0106
HF5616.U62
THE SUCCESSFUL CALIFORNIA ACCOUNTANT. Text in English. 1946. q. (plus m. updates). USD 30 to non-members (effective 2004). adv. back issues avail. **Document type:** *Trade.* **Description:** Examines various accounting subjects, the upgrading of computer systems, spreadsheet formats for accountants, and continuing education seminars.
Formerly (until 1994): California Accountant (0744-9895)
Published by: Society of California Accountants, 9099, Santa Rosa, CA 95405-1099. TEL 916-443-2057, FAX 916-443-0486, http://www.gosca.com. Adv. contact Diana Granger. Circ: 1,550.

657.0711 USA
SUM NEWS; the newsletter of the Massachusetts Society of CPAs. Text in English. 1990. bi-m. membership. adv. 32 p./no.; back issues avail. **Document type:** *Newsletter, Trade.*
Formerly: Sum Monthly News
Related titles: Microform ed.: (from PQC).
Published by: Massachusetts Society of Certified Public Accountants, Inc., 105 Chauncy St, 10th Fl, Boston, MA 02111-1742. TEL 617-556-4000, FAX 617-556-4126, mscpa@mscpaonline.org, http://www.mscpaonline.org. Ed., R&P Lisa A Murphy. Pub. Theodore J Flynn. Adv. contact Heather Fuessley. page USD 1,080; trim 10.5 x 8. Circ: 8,400.

657 ITA
SUMMA (ROME)✶ . Text in Italian. 6/yr.
Published by: National Association of Accountants and Commercial Experts, Via Giovanni Paisiello, 24, Rome, RM 00198, Italy. TEL 824761.

657 AUS ISSN 1034-8298
SUPPLEMENTARY STATEMENT TO STATEMENT OF AUDITING PRACTICE. Text in English. 1990. irreg. AUD 6 per issue. **Document type:** *Academic/Scholarly.*
Published by: Australian Accounting Research Foundation, 211 Hawthorn Rd, Caulfield, VIC 3162, Australia. TEL 61-3-95243600, FAX 61-3-95235499, standard@aarf.asn.au. Circ: 1,000. **Co-sponsors:** Institute of Chartered Accountants in Australia; Australian Society of Certified Practising Accountants.

657 CHE
SWISCO MAGAZINE; revue professionnelle suisse d'economie d'entreprise. Text in French. q. CHF 75 (effective 2001). adv. **Document type:** *Magazine, Trade.*
Formerly (until 1993): Courrier du Comptable
Published by: Association Suisse des Comptables Controleurs de Gestion Diplomes, Rue de Neuchatel 1, Yverdon-les-Bains, 1400, Switzerland. TEL 41-24-4252172, FAX 41-24-4252171, info@swisco.ch, http://www.swisco.ch. Ed. Rosmarie Kohli TEL 41-21-9228155. adv.: page CHF 1,300; trim 175 x 265. Circ: 2,100.

657 336 USA
TAX ACCOUNTING. Text in English. 1982. a. (in 2 vols.). looseleaf. USD 439 (effective 2002). Supplement avail. **Description:** Provides a comprehensive analysis of the accounting methods and periods available for tax purposes, with explanation of their tax advantages and disadvantages. Details the requirements for electing, using, or changing a method to ensure effective tax planning.
Published by: Matthew Bender & Co., Inc. (Subsidiary of: LexisNexis North America), 1275 Broadway, Albany, NY 12204. international@bender.com, http://bender.lexisnexis.com. Ed. Steven Rice.

657 336 USA
TAX & BUSINESS ADVISER. Text in English. 1982. bi-m. free. **Document type:** *Newsletter.*
Formerly (until Jan. 1990): Tax Planner - Scan; Incorporates: Tax Planner and Business Scan
Address: 800 One Prudential Plaza, Chicago, IL 60601. TEL 312-856-0001, FAX 312-861-1340. Eds. Lee O'Connor, Mary Jaspers. Circ: 60,000.

TAX AND BUSINESS PLANNING OF LIMITED LIABILITY COMPANIES. see *BUSINESS AND ECONOMICS—Public Finance, Taxation*

657 336 GBR
TAX FILE. Text in English. 1980. w. looseleaf. GBP 245. adv. bk.rev. index. back issues avail. **Document type:** *Trade.* **Description:** Offers tax information and advice for businessmen and their advisers.
Published by: TaxFile 2000 Ltd., Briar House, Spinfield Ln, Marlow, Bucks SL7 2JT, United Kingdom. TEL 44-1622-757032, FAX 44-1622-690802. Ed., R&P, Adv. contact Joe Watson. Circ: 2,000.

657 USA
TAX OUTLOOK. Text in English. q. membership. **Description:** Concerned with the federal tax law changes, from both individual and corporate perspectives.
Published by: C P A Associates International, Inc., Meadows Office Complex, 201 Rte 17 N, Rutherford, NJ 07070-2574. TEL 212-804-8686. Circ: 20,000.

346.066 336.2 USA
TAXATION OF EXECUTIVE COMPENSATION: PLANNING AND PRACTICE. Text in English. 1983. base vol. plus s-a. updates. looseleaf. USD 210 (effective 1999). **Description:** Updated to reflect all the newest legislation (including thorough analysis of the new statutory limitations on the deductibility of executive compensation), this essential publication covers all the vital issues and creative planning opportunities of the field.
Formerly: Tax Planning for Executive Companies: Planning and Practice
Published by: Matthew Bender & Co., Inc. (Subsidiary of: LexisNexis North America), 1275 Broadway, Albany, NY 12204. international@bender.com, http://bender.lexisnexis.com. Ed. Harvey L Frutkin.

657 ESP ISSN 0210-2129
TECNICA CONTABLE. Text in Spanish. 1949. m.
—CINDOC.
Published by: Instituto de Contabilidad Madrid, Glorieta de Quevedo, 7, Madrid, 28015, Spain. TEL 34-91-4466236. Ed. Jeronimo Grande Villazan.

657 332 NLD ISSN 1389-7713
TIJDSCHRIFT CONTROLLING. Text in Dutch. 1986. 10/yr. EUR 139; EUR 49 to students (effective 2005). adv. **Document type:** *Trade.* **Description:** Provides practical information for controllers and administrators.
Formerly (until 1998): T A C (0920-0428)
—IE, Infotrieve.
Published by: (N G A Vereniging van Financieel-Administratieve Managers), Wolters Kluwer N.V., Postbus 23, Deventer, 7400 GA, Netherlands. TEL 31-570-648872, info@kluwer.nl, http://www.tijdschriftcontrolling.nl/. Ed. Marjorie Berghuis. Adv. contact Edwin Benning. Circ: 6,353.

TIJDSCHRIFT VOOR BEDRIJFSADMINISTRATIE. see *BUSINESS AND ECONOMICS—Management*

657 USA ISSN 0889-4337
TODAY'S C P A. Text in English. 1927. bi-m. USD 28 (effective 2005). charts; illus.; stat.; tr.lit. index. back issues avail. **Document type:** *Magazine, Trade.*
Formerly (until 1986): C P A (0164-5099)
Related titles: Online - full text ed.
Indexed: ATI.
Published by: Texas Society of C P A's, 14860 Montfort Dr, Ste 150, Dallas, TX 75240-6718. TEL 800-428-0272, FAX 972-687-8646, bgaither@tscpa.net, http://www.tscpa.org. Ed. DeLynn Beakins. Circ: 31,000 (paid).

TODAY'S LAWYER. see *LAW*

657 388 GBR ISSN 1367-1871
TOLLEY'S PRACTICAL AUDIT & ACCOUNTING. Text in English. 1989. m. GBP 115 (effective 2000). bk.rev. **Document type:** *Trade.* **Description:** Covers topics such as financial reporting standards and accounting practice, changes in audit regulations, the latest developments in audit exemption and company law and ethics.
Formerly (until 1996): Audit Briefing (0958-367X)
Published by: Butterworths Tolley (Subsidiary of: LexisNexis UK (Scottish Office)), 2 Addiscombe Rd, Croydon, Surrey CR9 5AF, United Kingdom. TEL 44-20-8686-9141, FAX 44-20-8686-3155, paa@tolley.co.uk, http://www.tolley.co.uk. Ed. Sylvia Courtnage.

657.07 USA
THE TRUSTED PROFESSIONAL. Text in English. 1998. m. adv. **Document type:** *Newspaper.*
Formed by the 1998 merger of: F A E Update; Member's Quarterly; CPA Candidates Newsletter; Government Relations Alert; Tax, Accounting, and Regulatory Bulletin
Published by: New York State Society of Certified Public Accountants, 530 Fifth Ave, 5th Fl, New York, NY 10036-5101. TEL 212-719-8300, 212-719-8300, trustedprofessional@nysscpa.org, http://www.nysscpa.org. Adv. contact Cristina Carmenata.

UGESKRIFT FOR RETSVAESEN (U F R). see *LAW*

B

657.6 GBR
UNITED KINGDOM. AUDIT COMMISSION. EXECUTIVE BRIEFING. Text in English. irreg.
Indexed: ABIn.
Published by: Audit Commission for Local Authorities and the National Health Service in England and Wales, 1 Vincent Sq, London, SW1P 2PN, United Kingdom.

UNITED STATES GOVERNMENT ACCOUNTABILITY OFFICE. TODAY'S REPORTS. see *PUBLIC ADMINISTRATION*

657 GBR ISSN 1368-8286
UNIVERSITY OF ESSEX. DEPARTMENT OF ACCOUNTING AND FINANCIAL MANAGEMENT. WORKING PAPER SERIES. Text in English. irreg., latest 1997, no.97-06. **Document type:** *Academic/Scholarly.*
—BLDSC (9350.949200).
Published by: University of Essex, Department of Accounting and Financial Management, Wivenhoe Park, Colchester, CO4 3SQ, United Kingdom. TEL 44-1206-872546, FAX 44-1206-873429, afm@essex.ac.uk, http://www.essex.ac.uk/.

657 USA ISSN 0071-6065
UNIVERSITY OF FLORIDA. DEPARTMENT OF ACCOUNTING. ACCOUNTING SERIES. Text in English. 1963. irreg., latest vol.12, 1982. price varies. **Document type:** *Monographic series.*
Published by: (University of Florida, Department of Accounting), University Press of Florida, 15 NW 15th St, Gainesville, FL 32611. TEL 352-392-1351, 800-226-3822, FAX 352-392-7302, http://www.upf.com. Ed. A Rashad Abdel Khalik.

657 USA ISSN 0073-5191
UNIVERSITY OF ILLINOIS AT URBANA-CHAMPAIGN. CENTER FOR INTERNATIONAL EDUCATION AND RESEARCH IN ACCOUNTING. MONOGRAPHS. Text in English. 1964. irreg. price varies. adv. **Document type:** *Monographic series, Academic/Scholarly.*
Published by: University of Illinois at Urbana-Champaign, Center for International Education and Research in Accounting, 320 Commerce West Bldg, 1206 S Sixth St, Champaign, IL 61820-6271. TEL 217-333-4545, FAX 217-244-6565, TELEX 5106015276 COL COMM UI, gllinam@uiuc.edu, http://www.cba.uiuc.edu/clera/. Ed. Young Kwon. Circ: 700.

UNIVERSITY OF LEICESTER. QUALITY AUDIT REPORT. see *EDUCATION—Higher Education*

657 332 AUS ISSN 0814-9372
UNIVERSITY OF NEW ENGLAND. DEPARTMENT OF ACCOUNTING & FINANCIAL MANAGEMENT. WORKING PAPERS. Text in English. 1985. irreg. free. back issues avail. **Document type:** *Academic/Scholarly.*
Published by: (Department of Accounting & Financial Management), University of New England, Armidale, NSW 2351, Australia. TEL 61-67-732178, FAX 61-67-733122, TELEX 166050. Ed. Jim Psaros. R&P J J Staunton TEL 61-67-733276. Circ: 150.

657 NLD ISSN 1389-1065
VAKBLAD VOOR DE M K B - ADVISEUR. Text in Dutch. 1992. 10/yr. adv. back issues avail. **Document type:** *Trade.*
Formerly (until 1999): Advies (0928-0685)
Published by: Kluwer B.V. (Subsidiary of: Wolters Kluwer N.V.), Postbus 23, Deventer, 7400 GA, Netherlands. TEL 31-570-673449, FAX 31-570-691555, juridisch@kluwer.nl, http://www.kluwer.nl. Ed. L G M Stevens. Circ: 1,600.

THE VALUE EXAMINER; a professional development journal for the consulting disciplines. see *BUSINESS AND ECONOMICS—Management*

VANUATU. STATISTICS OFFICE. NATIONAL ACCOUNTS OF VANUATU. see *BUSINESS AND ECONOMICS—Abstracting, Bibliographies, Statistics*

657 CHE
DIE VOLKSWIRTSCHAFTLICHE GESAMTRECHNUNG DER SCHWEIZ. Text in French, German. 1984. a. CHF 9 (effective 2001). **Document type:** *Government.*
Formerly (until 1993): Die Nationale Buchhaltung der Schweiz
Published by: Bundesamt fuer Statistik, Espace de l'Europe 10, Neuchatel, 2010, Switzerland. TEL 41-32-7136011, FAX 41-32-7136012, information@bfs.admin.ch, http://www.admin.ch/bfs.

657 RUS
VSE DLYA BUKHGALTERA. Text in Russian. m. USD 279 in United States.
Published by: Finnova, A-ya 10, Moscow, 111401, Russian Federation. TEL 7-095-3034676, FAX 7-095-3034676. Ed. V A Gorokhova. **US dist. addr.:** East View Information Services, 3020 Harbor Ln. N., Minneapolis, MN 55447. TEL 612-550-0961.

657 USA ISSN 0043-3217
WEST VIRGINIA C.P.A. Text in English. 1970 (vol.15). bi-m. membership. adv. illus. **Document type:** *Newsletter.*
Published by: West Virginia Society of Certified Public Accountants, Drawer 1673, Charleston, WV 25326. FAX 304-344-4636. Ed. Patricia M Moyers. Adv. contact Patricia A Moyers. Circ: 3,500.

WHAT'S WORKING IN CREDIT & COLLECTION. see *LAW—Corporate Law*

657 USA ISSN 1549-0041
HF5667
WILEY C P A EXAMINATION REVIEW. AUDITING AND ATTESTATION. Text in English. a. USD 49.95 per vol. (effective 2004).
Former titles (until 2004): Wiley C P A Examination Review. Auditing (1541-4949); (until 1996): C P A Examination Review. Auditing (0749-9485)
Published by: John Wiley & Sons, Inc., 111 River St, Hoboken, NJ 07030-5774. TEL 201-748-6000, FAX 201-748-5915, uscs-wis@wiley.com, http://www.wiley.com.

657.2 USA ISSN 1538-6880
WILEY G A A P. (Generally Accepted Accounting Principles) Text in English. 1985. a. USD 77 (effective 2004). **Description:** Presents the most recent developments and analysis of all generally accepted accounting principles.
Formerly (until 1998): G A A P (0883-4245)
Related titles: CD-ROM ed.: USD 89.
Published by: John Wiley & Sons, Inc., 111 River St, Hoboken, NJ 07030-5774. TEL 201-748-6000, FAX 201-748-5915, http://www.wiley.com.

657 DEU ISSN 0936-5117
WIRTSCHAFTSPRUEFERKAMMER. MITTEILUNGEN; Zeitschrift fuer Berufspolitik, Berufsrecht und berufliche Praxis. Text in German. 1961. q. EUR 17 newsstand/cover (effective 2005). adv. index. reprints avail. **Document type:** *Bulletin, Trade.*
Published by: Verlag Dr. Otto Schmidt KG, Gustav-Heinemann-Ufer 58, Cologne, 50968, Germany. TEL 49-221-93738460, FAX 49-221-93738943, info@otto-schmidt.de, http://www.otto-schmidt.de. adv.: B&W page EUR 2,275, color page EUR 3,981.25. Circ: 21,293 (paid and controlled).

657 AUT ISSN 0043-6321
DER WIRTSCHAFTSTREUHAENDER. Text in German. 1949. 6/yr. adv. bk.rev. **Document type:** *Journal, Trade.*
Published by: Vereinigung Oesterreichischer Wirtschaftstreuhaender, Falkestr 3, Vienna, 1010, Austria. TEL 43-1-5122069, FAX 43-1-512206920, vwt@vwt.at, http://www.vwt.at/der_wirtschafts_treuhaender/. Ed. Walter Holiczki. adv.: color page EUR 2,450; trim 210 x 297. Circ: 4,100.

657 346 USA
WORLD ACCOUNTING. Text in English. 1986. 3 base vols. plus s-a. updates. looseleaf. USD 679 base vol(s). (effective 2002). **Description:** Practical guide to accounting standards of the thirty most important trading partners of the U.S. Coverage includes for each jurisdiction financial statement requirements, standard setting bodies, chart of accounts, differences in treatment for financial statements and tax purposes.
Published by: Matthew Bender & Co., Inc. (Subsidiary of: LexisNexis North America), 1275 Broadway, Albany, NY 12204. international@bender.com, http://bender.lexisnexis.com.

657 GBR ISSN 1469-2716
HF5601
WORLD ACCOUNTING REPORT. Abbreviated title: W A R. Text in English. 1976. m. GBP 335 domestic; GBP 350 foreign (effective 1999). **Document type:** *Newsletter.* **Description:** Provides coverage and analysis of accounting developments worldwide. Activities of the national and international accounting committees and regulatory bodies, new accounting laws, regulations and auditing standards, and in-depth surveys on the accounting profession in individual countries.
Former titles (until 1999): F T World Accounting Report (1468-7208); (until 1997): Financial Times World Accounting Report (0308-4965)
Related titles: Microform ed.: (from PQC); Online - full text ed.: (from Data-Star, ProQuest Information & Learning).
Indexed: ATI.
—BLDSC (9352.370000), IE.
Published by: F T Financial Publishing, Newsletters (Subsidiary of: Pearson Professional Ltd.), Maple House, 149 Tottenham Court Rd, London, W1P 9LL, United Kingdom. TEL 44-171-896-2222, FAX 44-171-896-2319, Ftwar@cairns.co.uk. Ed. David Cairns. Pub. John McLachlan.

657 DEU ISSN 0340-9031
WPG - DIE WIRTSCHAFTSPRUEFUNG. Text in German. 1948. s-m. EUR 208; EUR 12.80 newsstand/cover (effective 2003). adv. bk.rev. charts; tr.lit. index. back issues avail.; reprints avail. **Document type:** *Magazine, Academic/Scholarly.*
Formerly (until 1970): Die Wirtschaftspruefung (0043-6313)
Indexed: ABIn, ADPA, DIP, ELLIS, IBR, IBZ.
—IE, Infotrieve. **CCC.**
Published by: (German Institute of Accountants), I D W Verlag GmbH, Tersteegenstr 14, Duesseldorf, 40474, Germany. TEL 49-211-4561-0, FAX 49-211-4561206, post@idw-verlag.com, http://www.idw-verlag.com. Ed. Guenter Siepe. Circ: 12,500.

657 340 POL ISSN 1641-0777
WSKAZNIKI, STAWKI, DOKUMENTY. Text in Polish. 2000. m. PLZ 60 (effective 2001).
Published by: Grupa Wydawnicza INFOR Sp. z o.o., Ul Okopowa 58/72, Warsaw, 01042, Poland. TEL 48-22-5304208, 48-22-5304450, bok@infor.pl. Ed. Grazyna Gonciarska. Adv. contact Waldemar Krakowiak.

657 USA
YEAR-END TAX PLANNING GUIDE. Text in English. a. membership. **Description:** Examines legislative and financial developments. Provides tax information for planning.
Published by: C P A Associates International, Inc., Meadows Office Complex, 201 Rte 17 N, Rutherford, NJ 07070-2574. TEL 212-804-8686. Circ: 30,000.

ZEITSCHRIFT FUER DAS GESAMTE INSOLVENZRECHT. see *LAW—Corporate Law*

657 DEU ISSN 0044-3816
HF5667 CODEN: ZIREAM
ZEITSCHRIFT INTERNE REVISION; Fachzeitschrift fuer Wissenschaft und Praxis. Text in German. 1966. 6/yr. EUR 60; EUR 12.50 newsstand/cover (effective 2006). adv. bk.rev. charts; stat.; tr.lit. index. **Document type:** *Journal, Academic/Scholarly.*
Indexed: ABIn, ADPA, DIP, IBR, IBZ, SCIMP.
—IE, Infotrieve. **CCC.**
Published by: (Institut fuer Interne Revision e.V.), Erich Schmidt Verlag GmbH & Co. (Berlin), Genthiner Str 30G, Berlin, 10785, Germany. TEL 49-30-2500850, FAX 49-30-250085305, esv@esvmedien.de, http://www.erich-schmidt-verlag.de. Ed. W. Hohloch. Adv. contact Winfried Plochl. page EUR 1,400; trim 185 x 254.

657.6 CHN ISSN 1002-5049
ZHONGGUO SHENJI/AUDITING IN CHINA. Text in Chinese. 1983. m. adv. bk.rev. 70 p./no.; **Document type:** *Magazine, Government.*
Related titles: Online - full text ed.: (from East View Information Services).
Published by: Zhonghua Renmin Gongheguo Xianfa/National Audit Office of the People's Republic of China, Xicheng-qu, Zhanlan Lu, 1, Beiluyuan, Beijing, 100830, China. TEL 86-10-68301671, master@audit.gov.cn, http://www.audit.gov.cn/cysite/chpage/c178/.

657 ZWE
ZIMBABWE CHARTERED ACCOUNTANT. Text in English. 1987. bi-m. ZWD 268.80; ZWD 299.40 foreign (effective 1999). **Document type:** *Trade.*
Formerly: Zimbabwe Quarterly; Supersedes: Zimbabwe Commercial and Legal Quarterly
Indexed: PLESA.
Published by: (Institute of Chartered Accountants of Zimbabwe), Thomson Publications Zimbabwe (Pvt) Ltd., Thomson House, PO Box 1683, Harare, Zimbabwe. TEL 263-4-736835, FAX 263-4-752390.

BUSINESS AND ECONOMICS—Banking And Finance

see also BUSINESS AND ECONOMICS—Economic Situation And Conditions ; BUSINESS AND ECONOMICS—Investments ; INSURANCE

332 USA ISSN 1555-9416
HG1643
A B A BANK CARD SURVEY REPORT. Text in English. biennial. USD 500 per vol. to non-members; USD 250 per vol. to members (effective 2005). charts. **Description:** Contains current data on every aspect of bank card operations and marketing.
Former titles (until 2001?): Bank Card Industry Survey Report (1087-3252); (until 1995?): Bank Card Industry Report (1075-7449); (until 1992): Bank Card Credit Report (1043-9196); Which supersedes in part (in 1987): Retail Bank Credit Report (0276-9093)
Published by: American Bankers Association, Retail Service Center, 1120 Connecticut Ave, N W, Washington, DC 20036. TEL 202-663-5430, FAX 301-843-8405. **Subscr. to:** Order Processing Department, PO Box 630544, Baltimore, MD 21263-0544. TEL 800-338-0626.

332.1 346 USA ISSN 0887-0187
KF967
A B A BANK COMPLIANCE. Text in English. 1980. m. USD 450 domestic to non-members; USD 300 domestic to members; USD 562.50 foreign (effective 2005). adv. back issues avail. **Document type:** *Trade.* **Description:** Provides information on legislative and regulatory changes, what they mean for your bank, and how to satisfy new requirements.
Formerly: Bank Compliance (0276-4253)
Related titles: Microform ed.: (from PQC); Online - full text ed.: (from O C L C Online Computer Library Center, Inc., ProQuest Information & Learning); ♦ Supplement(s): Legislative and Regulatory Update; Regulatory & Legislative Update.
Indexed: ABIn, ATI, BLI.

Published by: American Bankers Association, 1120 Connecticut Ave NW, Washington, DC 20036-3971. TEL 202-663-5268, 800-338-0626, FAX 202-828-4540, custserv@aba.com, http://www.aba.com. Ed. Kelly Saxton. Adv. contact Laurence Price TEL 202-663-5378. Circ: 3,500. **Subscr. to:** ABA Customer Service Center, PO Box 79064, Baltimore, MD 21279-0064. TEL 800-226-5377, FAX 202-663-7543.

332.1 658.8 USA ISSN 1539-7890
HG1501 CODEN: BAMAFA
A B A BANK MARKETING. Text in English. 1915. m. (combined Jan.-Feb & July-Aug issues). USD 120 domestic to non-members; USD 80 domestic to members; USD 160 foreign (effective 2005). illus. 56 p./no.; reprints avail. **Document type:** *Journal, Trade.* **Description:** Explores all aspects of retail and corporate bank marketing. Feature articles include informative how-tos, banker-written case histories, and updates on "hot topics" in bank marketing.
Former titles (until 2001): Bank Marketing (0888-3149); (until 1972): Bank Marketing Management (0572-595X)
Related titles: Microfilm ed.: (from PQC); Online - full text ed.: (from EBSCO Publishing, Gale Group, H.W. Wilson, Northern Light Technology, Inc., O C L C Online Computer Library Center, Inc., ProQuest Information & Learning).
Indexed: ABIn, BLI, BPI, BPIA, BusI, CurCont, Inspec, ManagCont, T&II, WBA.
—BLDSC (1861.818000), AskIEEE, IDS, IE, ingenta.
Published by: American Bankers Association, 1120 Connecticut Ave NW, Washington, DC 20036-3971. TEL 202-663-5268, 800-338-0626, FAX 202-828-4540, walbro@aba.com, custserv@aba.com, http://www.aba.com/bankmarketing. Ed. Walt Albro. Pub., Adv. contact Laurence Price TEL 202-663-5378. R&P Carole McGuinn TEL 202-663-5032. Circ: 4,015 (paid). **Subscr. to:** ABA Customer Service Center, PO Box 79064, Baltimore, MD 21279-0064. TEL 800-226-5377, FAX 202-663-7543.

332.1 USA ISSN 1530-1125
A B A BANKERS NEWS. Text in English. 1981. bi-w. USD 96 to non-members; USD 48 to members. adv. **Document type:** *Newspaper, Trade.* **Description:** Covers current legislative and regulatory information, association stance and news for CEOs of most U.S. banks.
Former titles (until 2000): Bankers News (1069-5907); (until 1993): A B A Bankers Weekly (0889-7662); Which incorporated: Agricultural Banker; (until 1986): A B A Bankers News Weekly (0746-3367); (until 1983): Bankers News Weekly (0744-2688); Superseded (in Feb. 1982): Capital (0195-444X)
Related titles: Online - full text ed.: (from Northern Light Technology, Inc., ProQuest Information & Learning).
Indexed: ABIn, BLI.
Published by: American Bankers Association, Member Communications, 1120 Connecticut Ave, N W, Washington, DC 20036. TEL 202-663-5445, FAX 202-296-9258. Ed. Teresa Dean. Circ: 22,000.

332.1 USA ISSN 0194-5947
CODEN: ABAJD5
A B A BANKING JOURNAL. Text in English. 1908. m. free domestic to qualified personnel; USD 35 domestic financial institutions; USD 40 domestic to institutions; USD 265 foreign (effective 2005). adv. bk.rev. charts; illus.; stat. index. back issues avail.; reprints avail. **Document type:** *Magazine, Trade.* **Description:** Provides current look at trends, products, and developments in financial services.
Incorporates: Banking Buying Guide; Former titles (until 1979): Banking (0005-5492); American Bankers Association. Journal
Related titles: Microform ed.: (from PQC); Online - full text ed.: (from EBSCO Publishing, Factiva, Florida Center for Library Automation, Gale Group, H.W. Wilson, LexisNexis, O C L C Online Computer Library Center, Inc., ProQuest Information & Learning).
Indexed: ABIn, ATI, BLI, BPI, BPIA, ChPerI, DPD, ESPM, Inspec, LRI, MEA&I, ManagCont, PAIS, PCI, RASB, RI-1, RI-2, RiskAb, T&DA, T&II, WBA.
—BLDSC (0537.721000), AskIEEE, IE, Infotrieve. **CCC.**
Published by: (American Bankers Association, Member Communications), Simmons-Boardman Publishing Corp., 345 Hudson St, 12th Fl, New York, NY 10014-4502. TEL 212-620-7200, FAX 212-633-1165, ababj@sbpub.com, http://www.ababj.com. Eds. Steven Cocheo, William W Streeter. Pub. Gus Blumberg TEL 212-620-7224. R&P Linda Liebowitz TEL 212-221-9595 ext. 322. Adv. contacts Gus Blumberg TEL 212-620-7224, Russell Selover. Circ: 31,500 (paid).

332.1 346 USA
A B A COMPLIANCE SOURCEBOOK; a manual for implementing and managing the compliance program. Text in English. irreg., latest vol.3, 1996. looseleaf. USD 245 to non-members; USD 165 to members. **Document type:** *Trade.* **Description:** Defines the qualifications and responsibilities of a compliance officer, offers advice on building and managing a compliance program, and provides tips on training and managing staff.
Published by: American Bankers Association, Compliance Division, c/o Chris Kelly, 1120 Connecticut Ave, N W, Washington, DC 20036. TEL 202-663-5497, 800-338-0626, FAX 202-663-7543, http://www.aba.org. Ed. Jennifer K McCollough.

332.1 640.73 USA
A B A CONSUMER BANKING DIGEST. Text in English. 1982. 6/yr. USD 115 to non-members; USD 75 to members. **Description:** Features articles on treatment of key consumer banking issues including industry trends, innovative programs, organizational issues, and changing market conditions.
Related titles: Microform ed.: (from PQC).
Published by: American Bankers Association, Retail Service Center, 1120 Connecticut Ave, N W, Washington, DC 20036. TEL 202-663-5094, FAX 202-828-4544. Ed. Craig Sablosky. Circ: 800.

332 USA ISSN 1537-1697
HG1642.U5
A B A INSTALLMENT CREDIT SURVEY REPORT. Text in English. a. USD 325 to non-members; USD 225 to members. charts; stat. **Document type:** *Trade.* **Description:** Provides comprehensive data on installment loans, ordered by bank size. Covers variable-rate loans, loan delinquencies and losses, and expense elements.
Former titles (until 1998): Installment Credit Survey Report (1537-1700); (until 1995): Installment Credit Report (1041-6390); Which superseded in part (in 1987): Retail Bank Credit Report (0276-9093)
Published by: American Bankers Association, Retail Service Center, 1120 Connecticut Ave, N W, Washington, DC 20036. TEL 202-663-5430, 800-338-0626, FAX 202-663-7543, http://www.aba.org. **Subscr. to:** Order Processing Department, 10 Jay Gould Court, Waldorf, MD 20602-2725. TEL 800-338-0626.

332.1 USA ISSN 1059-7190
A B A TRUST & INVESTMENTS. Text in English. 1997. bi-m. USD 120 domestic to non-members; USD 80 domestic to members; USD 160 foreign (effective 2005). **Document type:** *Trade.* **Description:** Compendium of articles written by industry leaders, academicians, and management consultants, providing information on management issues, industry trends, and reports on innovative bank programs in trust and private banking.
Formerly: Trust & Investments (1098-3759); Which was formed by the merger of: A B A Management Update of Personal Trust and Private Banking; (1989-1997): Employee Benefits Quarterly; (1987-1997): Trends (Washington, 1997); (199?-1997): Trust and Financial Advisor (1081-9843)
Related titles: Microform ed.: (from PQC); Online - full text ed.: (from ProQuest Information & Learning).
Indexed: BLI.
Published by: American Bankers Association, 1120 Connecticut Ave NW, Washington, DC 20036-3971. TEL 202-663-5268, 800-338-0626, FAX 202-828-4540, custserv@aba.com, http://www.aba.com/ti. Circ: 4,500. **Subscr. to:** ABA Customer Service Center, PO Box 79064, Baltimore, MD 21279-0064. TEL 800-226-5377, FAX 202-663-7543.

346.092 USA ISSN 1524-4210
A B A TRUST LETTER. Text in English. 1976 (no.97). m. USD 270 domestic to non-members; USD 180 domestic to members; USD 331.50 foreign (effective 2005). index. **Document type:** *Newsletter.* **Description:** Provides current information on national legislation and regulation that affect trust and investment businesses.
Related titles: Microform ed.: (from PQC); Online - full text ed.
Published by: American Bankers Association, 1120 Connecticut Ave NW, Washington, DC 20036-3971. TEL 202-663-5268, 800-338-0626, FAX 202-828-4540, custserv@aba.com, http://www.aba.com/trustletter/default.htm. Pub. Laurence Price TEL 202-663-5378. R&P Carole McGuinn TEL 202-663-5032. **Subscr. to:** ABA Customer Service Center, PO Box 79064, Baltimore, MD 21279-0064. TEL 800-226-5377, FAX 202-663-7543.

332 346 USA
KF1507.A24
A B I JOURNAL. Text in English. 1983. 10/yr. membership. adv. bk.rev. reprints avail. **Document type:** *Journal, Trade.*
Formerly: A B I Newsletter
Published by: American Bankruptcy Institute, 44 Canal Center Plz, Ste 404, Alexandria, VA 22314-1592. TEL 703-739-0800, FAX 703-739-1060, http://www.abiworld.org. Ed. Samuel J Gerdano. Adv. contact Sharisa Sloan. Circ: 21,000.

332.1 LBN
A B L MONTHLY BULLETIN. Text in Arabic. m. **Document type:** *Bulletin.* **Description:** Provides insights into the local economy with emphasis on the banking sector.
Published by: Association of Banks in Lebanon, DORA Centre Moucarri, P O Box 80536, Beirut, Lebanon.

332 KEN
A C C O S C A NEWSLETTER. Text in English, French. q. free. **Document type:** *Newsletter.*
Formerly: A C C O S C A News
Published by: African Confederation of Savings and Credit Cooperatives, PO Box 43278, Nairobi, Kenya. TEL 254-2-721944, FAX 254-2-721274, TELEX 23176 ACCOSCA NAIROBI KE.

332.2 KEN
A C O S C A NEWS. Text in English, French. 1980. q. KES 5 per issue. **Document type:** *Newsletter.*
Formerly (until 1982): A C O S C A Eastern Regional Newsletter
Published by: Africa Cooperative Savings and Credit Association, PO Box 43278, Nairobi, Kenya. FAX 254-2-721274, TELEX 23176-ACCOSCA-N. Ed. Mr. Gicheri Kimaru. Circ: 1,000.

332.1 CIV
A D B NEWS. Text in French. m. **Document type:** *Newsletter.*
Published by: (Information and Public Relations Division), African Development Bank, 01 BP 1387, Abidjan, Ivory Coast.

332.1 URY ISSN 0001-1010
A E B U✶. Text in Spanish. 1967 (vol.20). m. adv. charts; stat.
Published by: Asociacion de Bancos del Uruguay, Rincon, 468 2o, Montevideo, 11007, Uruguay. TEL 2-965051. Ed. Felix Duarte.

A F M EXPLANATORY SERIES (NO.). see *BUSINESS AND ECONOMICS—Accounting*

332 USA ISSN 1528-4077
HG4028.C45
A F P EXCHANGE. Text in English. 1981. bi-m. USD 90 domestic to individuals (effective 2005); USD 100 in Canada & Mexico to individuals; USD 120 elsewhere to individual members (effective 2003). adv. bk.rev. illus.; charts. Index. reprints avail. **Document type:** *Magazine, Trade.* **Description:** Publishes in-depth articles on the latest developments in the treasury field. Includes columns on banking, international trends and short-term investments and the industry's most comprehensive calendar of events.
Former titles (until 1999): T M A Journal (Treasury Management Association) (1080-1162); (until Jan. 1994): Journal of Cash Management (0731-1281)
Related titles: Online - full text ed.: (from O C L C Online Computer Library Center, Inc., ProQuest Information & Learning).
Indexed: ABIn, ATI, BLI, BPI, ESPM, RiskAb.
—BLDSC (0732.073300), IE, Infotrieve, ingenta. **CCC.**
Published by: Association for Financial Professionals, 7315 Wisconsin Ave, Ste 600 W, Bethesda, MD 20814. TEL 301-907-2862, FAX 301-907-2864, Exchange@AFPonline.org, AFP@AFPonline.org, http://www.afponline.org/pub/res/ex/2004_24_1.html, http://www.AFPonline.org. Eds. Christy Kincade, John T Hiatt. adv.: B&W page USD 2,500; trim 11 x 8.5. Circ: 15,000.

332 LUX ISSN 1561-8366
A G E F I LUXEMBOURG. (Agence Economique et Financiere) Text in French. 1988. m. EUR 800 (effective 2005). back issues avail. **Document type:** *Newspaper.* **Description:** Covers a wide range of business-oriented subjects, including finance, economy, computers, business travel, and corporate reports.
Related titles: CD-ROM ed.; E-mail ed.; Fax ed.: EUR 800 (effective 2005); Online - full text ed.
Published by: A G E F I Luxembourg S.A., Route d'Arlon 111 b, Capellen, 8311, Luxembourg. TEL 32-30-575721, 32-30-575723, agefi.luxembourg@sl.lu, http://www.agefi.lu. Ed. Olivier Minguet. Pub. Alfred Sluse. Adv. contact B Pirenne. Circ: 15,000.

332 IRL
A I B REVIEW. Text in English. m. **Document type:** *Bulletin.*
Published by: Allied Irish Banks Ltd., Bankcentre, Ballsbridge, Dublin, Dublin 4, Ireland. TEL 353-1-600311, FAX 353-1-609508.

332 USA ISSN 1539-5634
A I M R EXCHANGE. Text in English. q. USD 25 (effective 2000). **Description:** Provides updates on the activities of the association and its members. Includes information about programs, publications, and candidate activities, as well as the AIMR Board of Trustees and AIMR policy decisions.
Former titles: A I M R Newsletter; C F A Newsletter
Published by: Association for Investment Management and Research, 560 Ray C Hunt Drive, Charlottesville, VA 22903. TEL 804-951-5499, FAX 804-951-5262, http://www.aimr.org.

332 DEU
A LA CARD EURO-NEWS. Text in English, German. 1991. m. adv. **Document type:** *Trade.* **Description:** Provides the latest news on card applications, card-based payment systems and international card management.
Published by: Steinau Verlag GmbH, Am Kurgarten 1, Moelln, 23879, Germany. TEL 49-4542-8461-0, FAX 49-4542-846111, 100637.610@compuserve.com, http://www.alacard.de. Ed. Meike Wolff. Adv. contact Sabine Pohlmeyer. Circ: 4,000 (paid).

A M E INFO MIDDLE EAST BUSINESS INFORMATION. see *BUSINESS AND ECONOMICS—Economic Situation And Conditions*

332 ITA
A S E F I. Text in Italian. 1984. a. EUR 110 domestic; USD 250 foreign (effective 2004). **Document type:** *Directory, Trade.*
Published by: Annuario Servizi Finanziari, Via San Simpliciano, 2, Milan, MI 20121, Italy. TEL 39-2-86463056, FAX 39-2-804179, http://www.asefi.it/Asefi/annuario.htm. Ed. Gianfranco Monti. Adv. contact Donatella Joan.

B

▼ new title ➤ refereed ✶ unverified ♦ full entry avail.

332 USA
A T M & DEBIT NEWS. (Automated Teller Machine) Text in English. w. USD 525 (effective 2005). **Document type:** *Newsletter, Trade.* **Description:** Informs about the latest industry trends, competitive strategies, emerging markets and market opportunities.
Media: E-mail.
Published by: Source Media, Inc., One State St Plaza, 27th Fl, New York, NY 10004. TEL 212-803-6077, 800-221-1809, FAX 212-747-1154, custserv@sourcemedia.com, http://www.cardforum.com, http://www.sourcemedia.com.

332 USA
A T M MAGAZINE. (Automated Telled Machine) Text in English. w. adv. **Description:** Covers the automated teller industry.
Media: Online - full text.
Indexed: B&I.
Published by: NetWorld Alliance LLC, 13100 Eastpoint Park Blvd., Louisville, KY 40223-3157. http://www.atmmagazine.com. Ed. Ann All.

ABBEYVIEW. see *GENERAL INTEREST PERIODICALS—Great Britain*

ABERDEEN PAPERS IN ACCOUNTANCY AND FINANCE. see *BUSINESS AND ECONOMICS—Accounting*

332 USA
ACCESS (FRANKLIN). Text in English. 1945. q. membership only. adv. **Document type:** *Trade.*
Formerly: National News
Published by: American Safe Deposit Association, PO Box 519, Franklin, IN 46131-0519. TEL 317-738-4432, FAX 317-738-5267, jmclin@aol.com. Ed., Pub., R&P, Adv. contact Joyce A McLin TEL 317-738-4432. Circ: 3,900.

ACCOUNTING, ACCOUNTABILITY & PERFORMANCE. see *BUSINESS AND ECONOMICS—Accounting*

ACCOUNTING FOR BANKS. see *BUSINESS AND ECONOMICS—Accounting*

ACCOUNTING RESEARCH JOURNAL. see *BUSINESS AND ECONOMICS—Accounting*

332 USA
THE ACKER LETTER. Text in English. m. (10-14/yr.). USD 160 subscr - mailed domestic; USD 190 domestic faxed; USD 170 subscr - mailed elsewhere (effective 2005). **Document type:** *Newsletter, Trade.*
Published by: The Acker Letter, 2718 E. 63rd St., Brooklyn, NY 11234-6814. TEL 718-531-8981, FAX 718-531-2814. Ed. Bob Acker.

332 USA
ACTIONS OF THE BOARD: APPLICATIONS AND REPORTS RECEIVED. Text in English. w. USD 55. **Document type:** *Government.*
Published by: U.S. Federal Reserve System, Board of Governors, Publications Services, Rm MS 138, Washington, DC 20551. TEL 202-452-3244, FAX 202-728-5886.

AD IDEAS. see *ADVERTISING AND PUBLIC RELATIONS*

332 SGP ISSN 1793-0944
▼ **ADVANCED RESEARCH IN ASIAN ECONOMIC STUDIES.** Text in English. 2004. irreg. price varies. **Document type:** *Magazine, Academic/Scholarly.*
Published by: World Scientific Publishing Co. Pte. Ltd., 5 Toh Tuck Link, Singapore, 596224, Singapore. TEL 65-466-5775, FAX 65-467-7667, wspc@wspc.com.sg, http://www.wspc.com/books/series/araes_series.shtml, http://www.worldscientific.com. Ed. Manoranjan Dutta. **Subscr. to:** Farrer Rd, PO Box 128, Singapore 912805, Singapore. TEL 65-382-5663, FAX 65-382-5919. **Dist. in Europe by:** World Scientific Publishing Ltd., 57 Shelton St, London WC2H 9HE, United Kingdom. TEL 44-20-78360888, FAX 44-20-78362020, sales@wspc.co.uk.; **Dist. in the US by:** World Scientific Publishing Co., Inc., 1060 Main St, River Edge, NJ 07661. TEL 201-487-9655, 800-227-7562, FAX 201-487-9656, 888-977-2665, wspc@wspc.com.

ADVANCES IN FINANCE, INVESTMENT AND BANKING. see *BUSINESS AND ECONOMICS—Investments*

332 USA
ADVANCES IN FINANCIAL PLANNING AND FORECASTING. Text in English. 1985. irreg., latest vol.11, 2003. price varies. back issues avail. **Document type:** *Monographic series, Academic/Scholarly.*
Published by: J A I Press Inc. (Subsidiary of: Elsevier Science & Technology), 360 Park Ave S, New York, NY 10010-1710. TEL 212-989-5800, FAX 212-633-3990, usinfo-f@elsevier.com, http://www.elsevier.com/wps/find/bookseriesdescription.cws_home/BS_AFPF/description. Ed. Cheng-Few Lee.

ADVANCES IN FINANCIAL PLANNING AND FORECASTING. SUPPLEMENT. see *BUSINESS AND ECONOMICS—Management*

332 USA ISSN 1529-2371
HG187.A2
ADVANCES IN PACIFIC BASIN FINANCIAL MARKETS. Text in English. 1995. irreg., latest vol.6, 2000. price varies. back issues avail. **Document type:** *Monographic series, Academic/Scholarly.*
—BLDSC (0709.574200).
Published by: J A I Press Inc. (Subsidiary of: Elsevier Science & Technology), 360 Park Ave S, New York, NY 10010-1710. TEL 212-989-5800, FAX 212-633-3990, usinfo-f@elsevier.com, http://www.elsevier.com/wps/find/bookseriesdescription.cws_home/BS_APBFM/description. Ed. T A Fetherston.

ADVANCES IN QUANTITATIVE ANALYSIS OF FINANCE AND ACCOUNTING. see *BUSINESS AND ECONOMICS—Accounting*

332.1 SWE ISSN 0281-787X
AFFAERSBANKERNA; samtliga bankaktiebolag. Text in Swedish. 1912. m. SEK 400 (effective 1990).
Former titles (until 1984): Bankerna; (until 1954): Statistiska Meddelanden. Ser. E, Uppgifter om Bankerna
Published by: Statistiska Centralbyraan, Bankinspektionen, Orebro, 70189, Sweden.

332 CAN ISSN 0229-3404
LES AFFAIRES. Text in English. 1928. w. CND 59.95 domestic; CND 230 in United States (effective 2003). adv.
Former titles (until 1979): Journal les Affaires (0705-1859); (until 1978): Affaires (0044-6459)
Related titles: Online - full text ed.: (from F P Infomart Ltd.).
Indexed: CBCARef, CBPI, CPerI, PdeR.
—CISTI.
Published by: Transcontinental Media, Inc. (Subsidiary of: Transcontinental, Inc.), 1100 Blvd Rene Levesque W, 24th Fl, Montreal, PQ H3B 4X9, Canada. TEL 514-392-9000, FAX 514-392-1489, info@transcontinental.ca, http://www.lesaffaires.com, http://www.transcontinental-gtc.com/en/home.html. Pub. Jean Paul Gagne. Adv. contact Joanne Proulx. Circ: 90,780 (paid).

AFFAIRES ET GENS D'AFFAIRES. see *HISTORY—History Of Europe*

AFRICA ANALYSIS; fortnightly bulletin on financial and political trends. see *BUSINESS AND ECONOMICS—Economic Situation And Conditions*

332 332.6 GBR ISSN 1355-1884
AFRICA FINANCING REVIEW. Text in English. 1994. m. GBP 200, USD 350; GBP 20, USD 30 per issue (effective 2005). adv. bk.rev. back issues avail. **Document type:** *Magazine, Trade.*
Related titles: Online - full content ed.
Published by: Africa International Ltd, 438 Ley St, Ilford, Essex 1G2 7BS, United Kingdom. afreview@iafrica.com, http://www.africafinancereview.com/. Ed. Francis Daniels. Pub., R&P Judith Aidoo. adv.: B&W page GBP 1,000, color page GBP 1,500. Circ: 200 (paid). **Subscr. addr. in the US:** World Publication Services, 1 Maple St, Unit 8A, E Rutherford, NJ 07073. TEL 201-531-0760, FAX 201-531-0827.

332 KEN
AFRICAN CONFEDERATION OF SAVINGS AND CREDIT COOPERATIVES. ANNUAL REPORT. Text in English, French. a. **Document type:** *Corporate.*
Formerly: Africa Cooperative Savings and Credit Association. Annual Report
Published by: African Confederation of Savings and Credit Cooperatives, PO Box 43278, Nairobi, Kenya.

AFRICAN DEVELOPMENT BANK. COMPENDIUM OF STATISTICS ON BANK GROUP OPERATIONS/BANQUE AFRICAINE DE DEVELOPPEMENT. COMPENDIUM DE STATISTIQUES SUR LES OPERATIONS DU GROUPE DE LA BANQUE. see *BUSINESS AND ECONOMICS—Abstracting, Bibliographies, Statistics*

AFRICAN DEVELOPMENT BANK. SELECTED STATISTICS ON AFRICAN COUNTRIES/BANQUE AFRICAINE DE DEVELOPPEMENT. STATISTIQUES CHOISIES SUR LES PAYS AFRICAINS. see *BUSINESS AND ECONOMICS—Abstracting, Bibliographies, Statistics*

AFRICAN DEVELOPMENT REPORT (YEAR)/RAPPORT SUR LE DEVELOPPEMENT EN AFRIQUE; rural development and poverty reduction in Africa. see *BUSINESS AND ECONOMICS—International Development And Assistance*

AFRICAN DEVELOPMENT REVIEW/REVUE AFRICAINE DE DEVELOPPEMENT. see *BUSINESS AND ECONOMICS—International Development And Assistance*

332 ZAF ISSN 1605-9786
THE AFRICAN FINANCE JOURNAL. Text in English. 1999. q. USD 35 in Africa to individuals; USD 50 elsewhere to individuals; USD 90 in Africa to institutions; USD 150 elsewhere to institutions; USD 15 in Africa to students; USD 20 elsewhere to students (effective 2004). **Document type:** *Journal.* **Description:** Devoted to the study and promotion of knowledge about finance relevant to development in Africa.
Related titles: Online - full text ed.
Indexed: IBSS, JEL.
—BLDSC (0732.446000).
Published by: African Finance Association, Graduate School of Business, University of Stellenbosch, PO Box 610, Bellville, 7535, South Africa. TEL 27-21-9184469, FAX 27-21-9184262, dinap@acia.sun.ac.za, http://www.acia.sun.ac.za/projects/afa/afjt.htm.

332 ITA ISSN 1124-3163
AFRICAN REVIEW OF MONEY FINANCE AND BANKING. Text in English. 1987. a. abstr.; bibl.; charts; stat. 130 p./no.; back issues avail. **Document type:** *Academic/Scholarly.*
Related titles: ◆ Supplement to: Savings and Development. ISSN 0393-4551.
Indexed: ASD.
—BLDSC (0732.926200).
Published by: Giordano dell'Amore Foundation, Via San Vigilio, 10, Milan, MI 20142, Italy. TEL 39-02-8135341, FAX 39-02-8137481, publications@fgda.org, http://www.fgda.org. Ed. Arnaldo Mauri. Pub. Felice Tambussi. R&P Cinzia Raimondi.

380.141 332.3 USA ISSN 1532-8902
HG2051.U5
AG LENDER. Text in English. 1998. m. USD 159 in US & Canada; USD 229 elsewhere (effective 2005). adv. bk.rev. charts; illus.; stat. index. 16 p./no.; back issues avail.; reprints avail. **Document type:** *Magazine, Trade.* **Description:** Reaches key agricultural financial leaders with editorial material geared to their business success.
Formerly (until Aug. 1998): Agri Finance (0002-1164)
Related titles: Microform ed.: (from PQC); Online - full text ed.
Indexed: BLI, F&GI.
—CISTI.
Published by: Doane Agricultural Service Co., 11701 Borman Dr, Ste 300, St. Louis, MO 63146-4199. TEL 314-569-2700, FAX 314-569-1083, AgLender@doane.com, http://www.doane.com. Eds. Dan Manternach, Lynn Henderson. Pub. Lynn Henderson. adv.: color page USD 1,725. Circ: 2,000 (paid).

332.1 FRA ISSN 0755-1940
L'AGENCE ECONOMIQUE ET FINANCIERE. Short title: L'A G E F I. Text in French. 1911. d. (5/w.). adv. back issues avail. **Document type:** *Newspaper.* **Description:** Solely dedicated to finance.
Related titles: ◆ Supplement(s): Cahiers de l'AGEFI. ISSN 1167-4326.
Published by: Agence Economique et Financiere, 48 rue Notre Dame des Victoires, Paris, 75002, France. TEL 44884646, FAX 448847253. Ed. Eric Dadier. Pub. Philippe Micouleau. R&P Marc Ladefroux. Adv. contact Jerome Gacoin.

AGENDA; a journal of policy analysis and reform. see *BUSINESS AND ECONOMICS—Public Finance, Taxation*

332 USA ISSN 0749-9035
AGGREGATE RESERVES OF DEPOSITORY INSTITUTIONS AND THE MONETARY BASE. Text in English. w. USD 15. **Document type:** *Government.*
Published by: U.S. Federal Reserve System, Board of Governors, Publications Services, Rm MS 138, Washington, DC 20551. TEL 202-452-3244, FAX 202-728-5886.

332 USA
AGGREGATE SUMMARIES OF ANNUAL SURVEYS OF SECURITIES CREDIT EXTENSION. Text in English. a. USD 5. **Document type:** *Government.*
Related titles: Diskette ed.
Published by: U.S. Federal Reserve System, Board of Governors, Publications Services, Rm MS 138, Washington, DC 20551. TEL 202-452-3244, FAX 202-728-5886.

332.3 DEU
AGRARFINANZ. Text in German. 1952. m. adv. **Document type:** *Magazine, Trade.*
Published by: Deutscher Sparkassenverlag GmbH, Am Wallgraben 115, Stuttgart, 70565, Germany. TEL 49-711-7820, FAX 49-711-7821709, webredaktion@dsv-gruppe.de, http://www.dsv-gruppe.de. adv.: B&W page EUR 3,000, color page EUR 4,230. Circ: 14,648 (controlled).

AGRICULTURAL CREDIT. see *AGRICULTURE—Agricultural Economics*

332 USA ISSN 1070-6755
AGRICULTURAL FINANCE DATABOOK. Text in English. q. USD 5. **Document type:** *Government.*
Formerly (until 1989): Agricultural Finance Databook. Quarterly Series
Indexed: AmStI.
Published by: U.S. Federal Reserve System, Board of Governors, Publications Services, Rm MS 138, Washington, DC 20551. TEL 202-452-3244, FAX 202-728-5886.

B

332 ESP
AGRUPACION SINDICAL NACIONAL DE EMPRESAS DE FINANCIACION. CENSO✶. Text in Spanish. irreg.
Published by: Agrupacion Sindical Nacional de Empresa de Financiacion, Paseo del Prado 18 y 20, Madrid, Spain.

AIRCRAFT VALUE JOURNAL. see *AERONAUTICS AND SPACE FLIGHT*

332.6 387.7 GBR ISSN 0266-2132
HD9711.A1
AIRFINANCE ANNUAL; reference book on the aircraft financing markets. Variant title: Air Finance Annual (Years). Text in English. 1984. a., latest 2001/2001. adv. back issues avail. **Document type:** *Yearbook, Trade.* **Description:** Includes articles on all aspects of aircraft financing techniques. Includes a directory of over 1,600 companies active in the marketplace.
—CCC.
Published by: Euromoney Institutional Investor Plc., Nestor House, Playhouse Yard, London, EC4V 5EX, United Kingdom. TEL 44-20-7779-8673, FAX 44-20-7779-8541, http://www.euromoney.com. **Dist. in US by:** American Educational Systems, PO Box 246, New York, NY 10024-0246. TEL 800-431-1579, aesbooks@aol.com; **Orders to:** Plymbridge Distributors Ltd, Plymbridge House, Estover Rd, Plymouth, Devon PL6 7PY, United Kingdom. TEL 44-1752-202300, FAX 44-1752-202330, enquiries@plymbridge.com, http://www.plymbridge.com.

AIRFINANCE JOURNAL. see *TRANSPORTATION—Air Transport*

ALABAMA BUSINESS CREDIT DIRECTORY. see *BUSINESS AND ECONOMICS—Trade And Industrial Directories*

332 KWT
ALAHLI BANK OF KUWAIT K.S.C. ANNUAL REPORT AND BALANCE SHEET. Text in English. a. charts; illus.; stat. **Document type:** *Corporate.*
Published by: Alahli Bank of Kuwait K.S.C., Mubarak Al-Kabir Street, P O Box 1387, Safat, Kuwait.

332 CAN
ALBERTA FINANCE MINISTRY. QUARTER FISCAL UPDATE. Text in English. 1994. q. **Document type:** *Government.*
Formerly: Alberta. Alberta Treasury. Quarterly Budget Report (1207-8182)
Related titles: Online - full content ed.
Published by: Alberta Finance Ministry, Rm 426, Terrace Bldg, 9515 - 107 St., Edmonton, AB T5K 2C3, Canada. TEL 780-427-3035, FAX 780-427-1147, http://www.finance.gov.ab.ca/publications/budget/index.html.

336 ESP ISSN 0214-6770
ALCABALA. Text in Spanish. 1988. q.
—CINDOC.
Published by: Junta de Andalucia, Consejeria de Economia y Hacienda. Direccion General de Tributos e Inspection Tributaria, Torretriana, Isla de la Cartuja, Sevilla, 41092, Spain. TEL 34-955-064722, FAX 34-955-065000.

332 AUT
ALLGEMEINE SPARKASSE. KURZ NOTIERT. Text in German. 1960. m. free. bk.rev. **Document type:** *Bulletin.*
Formerly: Allgemeine Sparkasse Linz. Kurz Notiert (0002-5933)
Published by: Allgemeine Sparkasse, Promenade 11-13, Linz, O 4041, Austria. FAX 0732-23912802. Ed. Kurt Mueller. Circ: 8,000.

332.1 IRL ISSN 0332-320X
ALLIED IRISH BANK REVIEW. Text in English. 1973. q. free. **Document type:** *Bulletin.*
Indexed: PAIS, WBA.
Published by: Allied Irish Banks Ltd., Bankcentre, Ballsbridge, Dublin, Dublin 4, Ireland. TEL 353-1-6600311, FAX 353-1-6604715. Ed. John Beggs. Circ: 7,000.

332 USA ISSN 0747-9107
HF5681.R25
ALMANAC OF BUSINESS AND INDUSTRIAL FINANCIAL RATIOS. Text in English. 1971. a. USD 149 per issue (effective 2005); includes CD-ROM. charts; stat. Index. **Document type:** *Trade.* **Description:** Provides performance data for 50 operating and financial factors in 192 industries derived from the latest available IRS data.
Indexed: SRI.
Published by: C C H Inc., 2700 Lake Cook Rd, Riverwoods, IL 60015. TEL 800-248-3248, cust_serv@cch.com, http://www.cch.com. Ed. Leo Troy. Circ: 5,000.

332 LBN
ALMANACH DES BANQUES AU LIBAN. Text in English. 1980. biennial. USD 25 (effective 1999). **Document type:** *Directory.* **Description:** Provides information on addresses, branches, and management of all banks operating in Lebanon.
Published by: Association of Banks in Lebanon, DORA Centre Moucarri, P O Box 80536, Beirut, Lebanon. TELEX ASSOBLE 43069 LE. Circ: 1,000.

330 USA ISSN 1522-9823
ALTERNATIVE CURRENTS. Text in English. 1982. q. free. back issues avail. **Document type:** *Newsletter.* **Description:** Provides information on a credit union's role in providing financial services for low income people and in community development.
Related titles: Online - full text ed.
Published by: Alternatives Federal Credit Union, 301 W State St, Ithaca, NY 14850-5431. TEL 607-273-4666, FAX 607-277-6391, afcu@alternatives.org, http://www.alternatives.org. Ed. Leni Hochman.

AM SONNENPLATZ. see *LIFESTYLE*

332.1 USA ISSN 0569-292X
HG2441
AMERICAN BANK DIRECTORY. Text in English. a. USD 255. adv. **Document type:** *Directory.*
Published by: Thomson Financial Services Company, 4709 W Golf Rd, Skokie, IL 60076-1256. TEL 847-676-9600, 800-321-3373, FAX 847-933-8101. Ed. Beth Swann. Circ: 57,773.

332.1 USA ISSN 0002-7561
HG1501
AMERICAN BANKER. Text in English. 1836. d. (5/wk.). USD 895 combined subscription domestic for print & online eds.; USD 950 combined subscription in Canada for print & online eds.; USD 1,195 combined subscription elsewhere for print & online eds. (effective 2005). adv. bk.rev. mkt.; stat.; illus. cum.index. back issues avail.; reprint service avail. from PQC. **Document type:** *Newspaper, Trade.* **Description:** Provides an unparallelled package of news, data and analysis. Includes large and small financial institutions, investment products and insurance, technology and electronic commerce, mortgages and cards, regulators and government, markets and commentary.
Incorporates (1999-2002): Financial Services Marketing (1523-0775)
Related titles: CD-ROM ed.: USD 3,895 Cum. ed. (effective 2000) (from The Dialog Corporation); Microform ed.: (from PQC); Online - full text ed.: USD 595 (effective 2000) (from Data-Star, EBSCO Publishing, Florida Center for Library Automation, Gale Group, Northern Light Technology, Inc., O C L C Online Computer Library Center, Inc., ProQuest Information & Learning); ♦ Supplement(s): Managing Technology. ISSN 1062-1709.
Indexed: ATI, AgeL, B&I, BLI, BusI, LRI, NewsAb, PROMT, SRI, T&II, WBA.
—CCC.
Published by: Source Media, Inc., One State St Plaza, 27th Fl, New York, NY 10004. TEL 212-803-6077, FAX 212-747-1154, custserv@americanbanker.com, custserv@sourcemedia.com, http://www.americanbanker.com, http://www.sourcemedia.com. Ed. David Longobardi. Adv. contact Robert A Raidt Jr. B&W page USD 10,480, color page USD 13,430. Circ: 40,000.

332.1 USA ISSN 1064-5349
HG2441
AMERICAN BANKERS ASSOCIATION KEY TO ROUTING NUMBERS. Text in English. 1911. a. USD 169 (effective 2001). adv. **Document type:** *Directory.* **Description:** Is the official registry of the A.B.A. routing and transit number system. Includes all routing numbers, both active and retired, assigned to banks, institutions and credit unions. Listings are cross-referenced by city, state and federal district.
Related titles: Magnetic Tape ed.
Published by: (American Bankers Association), Thomson Financial Services Company, 4709 W Golf Rd, Skokie, IL 60076-1256. TEL 847-676-9600, 800-321-3373, customerservice@tfp.com, http://www.tfp.com/.

332 USA ISSN 1524-0886
HG181
AMERICAN BANKER'S FINANCIAL MODERNIZATION REPORT. Text in English. 1999. w.
Formerly (until 1999): Regulatory Compliance Watch (1086-0789)
Related titles: Online - full text ed.: (from Gale Group, O C L C Online Computer Library Center, Inc., ProQuest Information & Learning).
Indexed: BLI.
Published by: Thomson Financial Media, One State St Plaza, 27th Fl, New York, NY 10004-1549. TEL 212-803-8200, FAX 212-843-9600, http://www.americanbanker.com.

332.7 346 USA ISSN 1068-0861
K1
AMERICAN BANKRUPTCY INSTITUTE LAW REVIEW. Text in English. 1993. s-a. USD 169 (effective 2005). back issues avail. **Document type:** *Journal, Academic/Scholarly.* **Description:** Covers a current, significant bankruptcy topic written by nationally recognized experts in the field.
Related titles: Online - full text ed.: (from LexisNexis, Northern Light Technology, Inc.).
Indexed: CLI, ILP, LRI.
—CCC.
Published by: Thomson West (Subsidiary of: Thomson Corporation, The), 610 Opperman Dr, Eagan, MN 55123-1396. TEL 651-687-7000, 800-328-9352, 800-328-4880, FAX 651-687-7302, customer.service@westgroup.com, http://west.thomson.com/product/15317606/product.asp.

AMERICAN BANKRUPTCY LAW JOURNAL. see *LAW*

332 USA ISSN 1548-8845
AMERICAN CASH FLOW JOURNAL. Text in English. 1993. m. free to members (effective 2004). adv.
Published by: American Cash Flow Association, P O Box 2668, Orlando, FL 32802. TEL 800-253-1294, http://www.americancashflowjournal.com, http://www.americancashflow.com. Pub. Fred Rewey. Adv. contact Nicole Cole.

332.6029 USA ISSN 1047-9759
HG2441
AMERICAN FINANCIAL DIRECTORY. Variant title: McFadden American Financial Directory. Text in English. s-a. USD 523 (effective 2005). **Document type:** *Directory, Trade.* **Description:** Lists financial information on banks, savings and loans, bank holding companies and major credit unions in North America.
—CCC.
Published by: Source Media, Inc., 195 Broadway, New York, NY 10007. TEL 646-822-2000, 800-321-3373, customerservice@tfp.com, http://www.tfp.com/.

B

332.6029 USA
AMERICAN RECOVERY ASSOCIATION. NEWS AND VIEWS. Short title: A R A. Text in English. 1962. q. free. **Description:** News for banks, credit unions, finance companies and leasing companies dealing with repossessions.
Published by: American Recovery Association, Inc., 231565, New Orleans, LA 70183-1565. TEL 504-392-0672, FAX 504-367-6412, ara@repo.org, http://www.repo.org. Ed. Cathy Rodi. Circ: 32,000. **Subscr. to:** PO Box 231565, New Orleans, LA 70183-1565.

332.2 USA
AMERICAN SAVINGS DIRECTORY. Text in English. 1981. a. USD 169. adv. **Document type:** *Directory.*
Published by: Thomson Financial Services Company, 4709 W Golf Rd, Skokie, IL 60076-1256. TEL 847-676-9600, 800-321-3373, FAX 847-933-8101. Ed. Beth Swann. Circ: 5,200.

332 USA
AMERICAN STOCK EXCHANGE GUIDE. Text in English. 1960. 2 base vols. plus m. updates. looseleaf. USD 595 base vol(s). (effective 2004). **Description:** It is the official publication of the Directory, Constitution, Rules and policies of the Exchange and the American Stock Exchange Clearing Corporation.
Related titles: CD-ROM ed.: USD 589 (effective 2004); Online - full content ed.: USD 589 (effective 2004).
Published by: C C H Inc., 2700 Lake Cook Rd, Riverwoods, IL 60015. TEL 847-267-7000, 800-449-6439, cust_serv@cch.com, http://www.cch.com. Pub. Stacey Caywood.

332.2 USA
AMERICA'S COMMUNITY BANKERS. REGULATORY REPORT. Text in English. m. USD 605 to non-members; USD 365 to members (effective 1999). back issues avail. **Document type:** *Newsletter.* **Description:** Provides in-depth information on regulations affecting the operations of savings and community banking institutions.
Former titles: Savings & Community Bankers of America. Regulatory Report; National Council of Savings Institutions. Regulatory Update
Published by: America's Community Bankers, 900 19th St, N W, Ste 400, Washington, DC 20006. TEL 202-857-3100, FAX 202-296-8716. Ed. Michael Carrier. R&P Brian Nixon TEL 202-857-3142. Circ: 3,000.

AMERICA'S CORPORATE FINANCE DIRECTORY. see *BUSINESS AND ECONOMICS—Trade And Industrial Directories*

332 ITA
AMMINISTRAZIONE E FINANZA. Text in Italian. 1986. s-m. EUR 194 (effective 2005). **Document type:** *Magazine, Consumer.*
Published by: IPSOA Editore (Subsidiary of: Wolters Kluwer Italia Srl), Strada 1, Palazzo F6, Milanofiori, Assago, MI 20090, Italy. TEL 39-02-82476888, FAX 39-02-82476436, http://www.ipsoa.it. Ed. Massimiliano Galioni. Circ: 20,500.

332 ITA ISSN 1121-2438
AMMINISTRAZIONE E FINANZA ORO. Text in Italian. 1990. 6/yr. EUR 112 (effective 2005). adv. **Document type:** *Magazine, Consumer.*
Related titles: Online - full text ed.: (from EBSCO Publishing).
Published by: IPSOA Editore (Subsidiary of: Wolters Kluwer Italia Srl), Strada 1, Palazzo F6, Milanofiori, Assago, MI 20090, Italy. TEL 39-02-82476888, FAX 39-02-82476436, http://www.ipsoa.it. Ed. Massimiliano Galioni. Circ: 8,815.

332 341 NLD
AMSTERDAM FINANCIAL SERIES. FINANCIAL SERVICES AND E E C LAW: MATERIALS AND CASES. Text in English. 1991. 2 base vols. plus s-a. updates. looseleaf. EUR 180, USD 180 (effective 2003). **Description:** Provides comprehensive and practical coverage of EEC legislation, case law and decisions of the European Commission relating to capital movements, banking, securities and stock exchanges.

Published by: Kluwer Law International (Subsidiary of: Aspen Publishers, Inc.), Laan van Meerdervoort 70, PO Box 85889, The Hague, 2508 CN, Netherlands. TEL 31-70-3081500, FAX 31-70-3081515, sales@kluwerlaw.com, http://www.kluwerlaw.com. Ed. Martijn van Empel. **Dist. by:** Libresso Distribution Centre, PO Box 23, Deventer 7400 GA, Netherlands. TEL 31-570-633155, FAX 31-570-633834.

332.1 NLD ISSN 0066-1309
AMSTERDAM-ROTTERDAM BANK. ANNUAL REPORT. Text in Dutch. 1964. a. **Document type:** *Corporate.*
Published by: (Amsterdam-Rotterdam Bank N.V.), A B N Amro Bank N.V., PO Box 283, Amsterdam, 1000 EA, Netherlands.

332.1 658 USA
ANALYSIS OF BANK MARKETING EXPENDITURES. Text in English. a. USD 180 to non-members; USD 165 to members (effective 2000). charts; stat. **Document type:** *Journal, Trade.* **Description:** Compares bank marketing budgets and expenditures among US banks. Presents statistics on advertising, public relations, sales promotion, research and training.
Published by: American Bankers Association, 1120 Connecticut Ave NW, Washington, DC 20036-3971. TEL 202-663-5268, 800-338-0626, FAX 202-828-4540, jyao@aba.com, custserv@aba.com, http://www.aba.com.

ANDREWS LITIGATION REPORTER: ANTITRUST. see *LAW—Corporate Law*

332.75 USA ISSN 1556-9969
KF1519
ANDREWS LITIGATION REPORTER: BANKRUPTCY. Text in English. 1974. base vol. plus bi-w. updates. looseleaf. USD 850 (effective 2005). adv. back issues avail. **Document type:** *Newsletter, Trade.*
Formerly: National Bankruptcy Reporter (0275-0252)
Related titles: Online - full text ed.
—CCC.
Published by: Andrews Publications (Subsidiary of: Thomson West), 175 Strafford Ave, Ste 140, Wayne, PA 19087. TEL 610-225-0510, 800-345-1101, FAX 610-225-0501, http://www.andrewsonline.com. Ed. Kristine Whimpenny. Pub., R&P Robert Maroldo. Adv. contact Sofia Pables.

ANGEL ADVISOR; the magazine for early stage investing. see *BUSINESS AND ECONOMICS—Investments*

332 DEU ISSN 1614-2446
▼ **ANNALS OF FINANCE.** Text in English. 2005. q. EUR 198 (effective 2005). **Document type:** *Journal, Academic/Scholarly.* **Description:** Publishes research in all areas of finance and its applications to other disciplines having a clear and substantive link to the general theme of finance.
Related titles: Online - full text ed.: ISSN 1614-2454 (from EBSCO Publishing, Springer LINK, Swets Information Services).
—BLDSC (1040.570000), IE. **CCC.**
Published by: Springer-Verlag (Subsidiary of: Springer Science+Business Media), Tiergartenstr 17, Heidelberg, 69121, Germany. TEL 49-6221-3450, FAX 49-6221-345229, subscriptions@springer.de, http://www.springer.de. Ed. Charalambos D Aliprantis. Adv. contact Stephan Kroeck TEL 49-30-827875739.

332 FRA
ANNUAIRE DES PRODUITS D'ASSURANCE (YEAR). Text in French. 1999. a. EUR 670 domestic; EUR 693 foreign (effective 2000). **Document type:** *Directory.* **Description:** Covers over 200 products launched by French insurers in 1998 and 1999. It gives you, in condensed form, the technical and commercial description of those products, including their characteristics, launches, and availability.
Published by: Publi-News, 47 rue Aristide Briand, Levallois-Perret, 92300, France. TEL 33-1-41499360, FAX 33-1-47573725, publi.news@wanadoo.fr. Ed. Ange Galula.

ANNUAL INSTITUTE ON MUNICIPAL FINANCE. see *LAW—Corporate Law*

332 334 USA ISSN 0195-5756
KF1440
ANNUAL INSTITUTE ON SECURITIES REGULATION. Text in English. 1969. a. back issues avail.; reprint service avail. from PQC.
Related titles: Online - full text ed.
Indexed: CLI, ILP, LRI.
Published by: Practising Law Institute, 810 Seventh Ave, New York, NY 10019. TEL 212-824-5700, 800-260-4754, FAX 800-321-0093, info@pli.edu, http://www.pli.edu.

ANNUAL REPORT ON THE ENVIRONMENT AND NATURAL RESOURCES. see *ENVIRONMENTAL STUDIES*

346.082 USA ISSN 1544-4627
K1
ANNUAL REVIEW OF BANKING AND FINANCIAL LAW. Text in English. 1982. a., latest vol.21, 2002. USD 166 (effective 2005). reprint service avail. from WSH. **Document type:** *Journal, Academic/Scholarly.* **Description:** Covers emerging issues and legal developments in the banking and financial services field with analysis and commentary.
Formerly (until 2003): Annual Review of Banking Law (0739-2451)
Related titles: Microfiche ed.: (from WSH); Microform ed.: (from WSH); Online - full text ed.
Indexed: CLI, ILP, LRI.
—CCC.
Published by: (Morin Center for Banking Law Studies), Michie Company (Subsidiary of: LexisNexis North America), PO Box 7587, Charlottesville, VA 22906-7587. TEL 434-972-7266, 800-542-0957, FAX 434-972-7666, custserv@michie.com, http://www.bu.edu/law/jd/journals/banking/, http://www.michie.com. Ed. P. Gifford Carter. **Co-sponsor:** Boston University, School of Law.

332.1 ESP
ANNUARIO ESTADISTICO DE LA BANCA PRIVADA. Text in Spanish. 1974. a.
Published by: Consejo Superior Bancario, Jose Abascal, 57, Madrid, 28003, Spain. TEL 91-441-06-11, FAX 91-441-27-20. Circ: 1,500.

332.09 CHL
ANTECEDENTES REGIONALES. Text in Spanish. m. back issues avail.
Related titles: Online - full text ed.
Published by: Superintendencia de Bancos e Instituciones Financieras, Moneda 1123, Santiago, Chile. TEL 56-2-4426200, http://www.sbif.cl/.

332 USA ISSN 1554-2858
▼ **ANTI-MONEY LAUNDERING UPDATE.** Text in English. 2004 (Oct.). m. USD 425 (effective 2005). **Document type:** *Newsletter.*
Formerly (until Nov.2004): Anti-Money Laundering Alert
Published by: A.S. Pratt & Sons, Inc., 1911 Fort Myer Dr, Arlington, VA 22209. TEL 703-528-0145, 800-572-2797, FAX 703-528-1736, http://www.aspratt.com/. Ed. Alan Rice.

332 ATG
ANTIGUA COMMERCIAL BANK. ANNUAL REPORT. Text in English. a. **Document type:** *Corporate.*
Published by: Antigua Commercial Bank, Thames and St. Mary Sts., PO Box 95, St John's, Antigua. TEL 809-462-1217, FAX 809-462-1220.

ANUARIO BURSATIL. see *BUSINESS AND ECONOMICS—Abstracting, Bibliographies, Statistics*

APPLIED ECONOMETRICS AND INTERNATIONAL DEVELOPMENT. see *POLITICAL SCIENCE*

APPLIED FINANCIAL ECONOMICS. see *BUSINESS AND ECONOMICS—Economic Situation And Conditions*

APPLIED MATHEMATICAL FINANCE. see *MATHEMATICS*

338.91 330 SDN
ARAB BANK FOR ECONOMIC DEVELOPMENT IN AFRICA. ANNUAL REPORT. Text in English. 1975. a. charts; illus.; stat. **Document type:** *Corporate.*
Published by: Arab Bank for Economic Development in Africa, Abdulrahman el-Mahdi St., P O Box 2640, Khartoum, 1111, Sudan. TEL 249-11-773709, FAX 249-11-770498, TELEX 22739 BADEA SD.

332.1 BHR
ARAB BANKING AND FINANCE. Abbreviated title: A B F. Text in English. 1983. a. BHD 20 domestic; USD 79 foreign (effective 2001). adv. stat. **Document type:** *Directory, Trade.* **Description:** Covers banks in the Arab countries, and Arab banks in non-Arab countries with market profiles, and information on the principal banks, insurance and investment companies, central banks, and more.
Former titles: Arab Banking and Finance Directory; Arab Banking and Finance Handbook
Published by: Tele-Gulf Directory Publications W L L, Bahrain Tower 3rd Fl., PO Box 2738, Manama, Bahrain. TEL 973-213301, FAX 973-210503, abfdir@batelco.com.bh. Ed., Adv. contact Manuel Fernandes. B&W page USD 2,444, color page USD 3,056; trim 240 x 170. Circ: 10,000.

332 USA ISSN 1089-1080
HG4523
THE ARBITRAGEUR. Text in English. 1998. 2/yr. USD 25; USD 65 foreign. adv. **Document type:** *Trade.* **Description:** Composes solutions to specific problems and questions relevant to the supply and demand sides of capital markets.
Related titles: E-mail ed.; Fax ed.; Online - full text ed.: (from Florida Center for Library Automation, Gale Group).
—CCC.
Published by: Financier, Inc., 220 Locust St, Apt 3 E, Philadelphia, PA 19106-3928. TEL 215-829-1354, FAX 215-829-1376, zfinance@interserv.com, http://www.the-financier.com, http://www.asset-backed.com. Ed. Charles Stone. Adv. contact Anne Zissu.

ARIZONA BUSINESS CREDIT DIRECTORY. see *BUSINESS AND ECONOMICS—Trade And Industrial Directories*

332.1 USA ISSN 0004-1726
ARKANSAS BANKER. Text in English. 1917. m. USD 27.95 (effective 2005). adv. bk.rev. illus. **Document type:** *Magazine, Trade.*
Related titles: Online - full text ed.
Indexed: BLI.
Published by: Arkansas Bankers Association, 1220 W 3rd St, Little Rock, AR 72201-1904. TEL 501-376-3741, FAX 501-376-9243, donna.lemmons@arkbankers.org, http://www.arkbankers.org. Adv. contact Donna Lemmons. Circ: 2,400.

332.1 340 GBR
ARMOUR ON VALUATION. Text in English. 1985. base vol. plus a. updates. looseleaf. GBP 355 (effective 2006). **Document type:** *Journal, Trade.*
Published by: Sweet & Maxwell Ltd., 100 Avenue Road, London, NW3 3PF, United Kingdom. TEL 44-20-74491111, FAX 44-20-74491144, customer.services@sweetandmaxwell.co.uk, http://www.sweetandmaxwell.co.uk. **Subscr. to:** Cheriton House, North Way, Andover, Hants SP10 5BE, United Kingdom.

ARREARS MANAGEMENT MANUAL. see *REAL ESTATE*

332 IND
ARTHIK JAGAT. Text in Hindi. 1956. w. INR 60; INR 1.50 newsstand/cover.
Published by: Arvind Vajpeyi Ed. & Pub., 4-2 B Leonard Rd., Hastings, Kolkata, West Bengal 700 022, India. TEL 2420651. adv.: page INR 2,500; trim 200 x 250. Circ: 11,248.

332.1 JPN
ASAHI BANK. ANNUAL REPORT. Text in English. a. **Document type:** *Bulletin, Corporate.* **Description:** Contains details on the financial statements and strategies of the Asahi Bank.
Published by: Asahi Bank, Ltd., 1-2, Otemachi 1-chome, Chiyoda-ku, Tokyo, 100-8106, Japan. TEL 81-3-3287-2111, FAX 81-3-3212-3484, http://www.asahibank.co.jp.

332 SGP ISSN 0219-1466
HG187.A2
➤ **ASIA PACIFIC JOURNAL OF FINANCE.** Text in English. 1998. s-a. adv. bk.rev. abstr.; bibl.; charts; illus.; stat. **Document type:** *Journal, Academic/Scholarly.* **Description:** Publishes original manuscripts that analyze issues regarding financial markets for scholars and practitioners. Preference is given to empirical research work focusing on the unique characteristics of Asia Pacific markets.
Incorporates (1997-1999): Review of Financial Markets (0218-9283)
Related titles: Online - full text ed.
—BLDSC (1742.260689), IE.
Published by: Centre for Business & Research Development, Faculty of Business Administration, The National University of Singapore, 10 Kent Ridge Crescent, Singapore, 119260, Singapore. fbacbrd@nus.edu.sg, http://www.fba.nus.edu.sg/qm/journals/apjf.htm.

332.7 332.6 GBR ISSN 1464-1011
ASIA RISK. Text in English. 1995. bi-m. GBP 220, USD 396, EUR 330 (effective 2005). adv. back issues avail. **Document type:** *Journal, Trade.* **Description:** Provides a complete overview of risk management in Asia, including Japan and Austrailia. Covering vital topics such as new products, alternative risk management tools and the latest methods of risk mitigation, and is an essential read for all finance professionals involving managing risk.
—BLDSC (1742.267800), IE. **CCC.**
Published by: Risk Waters Group (Subsidiary of: Incisive Media Plc.), Haymarket House, 28-29 Haymarket, London, SW1Y 4RX, United Kingdom. TEL 44-20-74849700, FAX 44-20-79302238, http://www.asiarisk.com.hk, http://www.incisivemedia.com. Ed. James Ockenden. Adv. contact Nat Knight. B&W page GBP 8,295, color page GBP 9,645.

332 JPN
ASIABANKING✶. Text in Chinese. 1980. m. adv. bk.rev.
Former titles (until 1984): Asian Banking and Corporate Finance (0250-9717); (until 1983): Asian Banking
Indexed: RASB, WBA.
Address: c/o Intercontinental Marketing Corp, I.P.O. Box 5056, Tokyo, 100-30, Japan. Ed. Steven Thompson. Circ: 10,000.

332 HKG
ASIAMONEY. Text in English. 1989. 10/yr. HKD 3,550 combined subscription domestic print & online eds.; USD 455 combined subscription foreign print & online eds. (effective 2005). adv. bk.rev. illus. reprints avail. **Document type:** *Trade.* **Description:** Covers financial market and investment developments in Asia and the Pacific Rim.

Former titles: Asia Money and Finance; (until Nov. 1991): Asiamoney (0958-9309); Which incorporated: Billion and Asian Finance

Related titles: Online - full text ed.: ISSN 1607-0526. 1989 (from EBSCO Publishing, Factiva, Gale Group, H.W. Wilson, O C L C Online Computer Library Center, Inc., ProQuest Information & Learning).

Indexed: ABIn, BPI, HongKongiana.

—BLDSC (1742.269750), IE, ingenta. **CCC.**

Published by: Asia Law & Practice Ltd. (Subsidiary of: Euromoney Institutional Investor Plc.), 5/F Printing House, 6 Duddell St, Central Hong Kong, Hong Kong. TEL 852-2842-6910, FAX 852-2543-7617, http://www.asiamoney.com/, http://www.asialaw.com/. Pub. Philip Owens TEL 852-2111-6022. Circ: 25,000. **Subscr. to:** Euromoney Institutional Investor Plc., Quadrant Subscription Services, PO Box 18083, London EC4V 5JS, United Kingdom. TEL 44-20-7779-8610, 44-1444-445523.

---

332   SGP
ASIAN BANKER JOURNAL. Text in English. 1996. bi-m. USD 160 to individuals; USD 240 to corporations (effective 2001). adv. back issues avail. **Document type:** *Magazine, Trade.* **Description:** Provides news and analysis of the banking and financial services industry in the Asia-Pacific region.

Published by: T A B International Pte. Ltd., 7500A Beach Rd, #06-301 The Plaza, Singapore, 199591, Singapore. TEL 65-2957300, 65-2957314, FAX 65-2954600, editor@asianbanker.com.sg, adm@asianbanker.com.sg, http://www.theasianbanker.com. Ed. Emmanuel David TEL 65-2957301. Adv. contacts Dominic Daud TEL 65-2957307, John Barrios TEL 210-531-0760.

---

332   SGP
ASIAN BANKER MONITOR. Text in English. w. back issues avail. **Document type:** *Newsletter, Trade.* **Description:** Provides recent news and press releases about financial institutions and their partner organizations in the Asia-Pacific region.

Related titles: Online - full text ed.

Published by: T A B International Pte. Ltd., 7500A Beach Rd, #06-301 The Plaza, Singapore, 199591, Singapore. TEL 65-2957300, 65-2957314, FAX 65-2954600, editor@asianbanker.com.sg, adm@asianbanker.com.sg, http://www.theasianbanker.com. Ed. Emmanuel David TEL 65-2957301. Adv. contacts Dominic Daud TEL 65-2957307, John Barrios TEL 210-531-0760.

332.1   SGP
ASIAN BANKING & FINANCE. Text in English. m. USD 360 (effective 2005). **Document type:** *Magazine, Trade.* **Description:** Focuses on commercial and retail banking and on securities markets from a banking perspective.

Published by: Charlton Media Group, 9B Stanley St, Singapore, 068728, Singapore. TEL 65-6223-7660, admin@charltonmedia.com, http://www.charltonmedia.com.

332.1 338.9   PHL   ISSN 0116-1164
HG4517
ASIAN DEVELOPMENT BANK. ANNUAL REPORT. Text in English. 1967. a. free; shipping fee of USD 10 per issue.

Related titles: Online - full text ed.

Indexed: IIS, RDA.

—BLDSC (1109.527500).

Published by: Asian Development Bank, Publications Unit, P.O. Box 789, Manila, 0980, Philippines. adbpub@adb.org, http://www.adb.org.

ASIAN DEVELOPMENT BANK. BOARD OF GOVERNORS. SUMMARY OF PROCEEDINGS. see *BUSINESS AND ECONOMICS—International Development And Assistance*

---

332   PHL
ASIAN DEVELOPMENT BANK. ECONOMIC STAFF PAPER (NUMBER). Text in English. irreg. USD 5 newsstand/cover (effective 2001); free with the purchase of another publication.. **Document type:** *Government.*

Indexed: RDA.

—BLDSC (1742.407720).

Published by: Asian Development Bank, Publications Unit, P.O. Box 789, Manila, 0980, Philippines. adbpub@adb.org, http://www.adb.org.

332.1 338.9   PHL   ISSN 0116-3000
HC411
ASIAN DEVELOPMENT BANK. KEY INDICATORS OF DEVELOPING ASIAN AND PACIFIC COUNTRIES. Text in English. 1969. a. USD 38 newsstand/cover (effective 2001). stat. **Description:** Presents the latest statistical data and socioeconomic indicators from the ADB member countries.

Formerly: Asian Development Bank. Key Indicators of Developing Member Countries of A D B

Indexed: IIS.

—CISTI.

Published by: (Economics and Development Resource Center), Asian Development Bank, Publications Unit, P.O. Box 789, Manila, 0980, Philippines. adbpub@adb.org, http://www.adb.org.

ASIAN DEVELOPMENT BANK. STATISTICAL REPORT SERIES. see *BUSINESS AND ECONOMICS—Abstracting, Bibliographies, Statistics*

---

332 004.678   SGP
ASIAN E-BANKER. Text in English. m. USD 380 (effective 2001). adv. back issues avail. **Document type:** *Newsletter, Trade.* **Description:** Covers the business and technology behind the development of electronic banking in the Asia-Pacific region.

Related titles: Online - full content ed.: USD 320 (effective 2001).

Published by: T A B International Pte. Ltd., 7500A Beach Rd, #06-301 The Plaza, Singapore, 199591, Singapore. TEL 65-2957300, 65-2957314, FAX 65-2954600, editor@asianbanker.com.sg, adm@asianbanker.com.sg, http://www.theasianbanker.com. Ed. Emmanuel David TEL 65-2957301. Adv. contacts Dominic Daud TEL 65-2957307, John Barrios TEL 210-531-0760.

---

332   HKG   ISSN 0377-9920
                                     CODEN: AWSJD4
THE ASIAN WALL STREET JOURNAL. Text in English. 1976. d. (Mon.-Fri.). HKD 2,550 in Hong Kong; AUD 960 in Australia; BND 715 in Brunei Darussalam; USD 685 in China; INR 10,500 in India; IDR 1,650,000 in Indonesia; JPY 94,500 in Japan; KRW 295,000 in Korea, S.; MYR 680 in Malaysia; USD 650 in New Zealand; TWD 8,900 in Taiwan; PKR 1,200 in Pakistan; PHP 6,500 in Philippines; SGD 498 in Singapore; LKR 22,800 in Sri Lanka; THB 7,900 in Thailand; USD 610 in Viet Nam; USD 640 elsewhere in Asia; USD 970 rest of world (effective 2004). adv. **Document type:** *Newspaper.* **Description:** Regional business and financial daily newspaper.

Related titles: Microfilm ed.: (from PQC); Online - full text ed.: (from ProQuest Information & Learning).

Indexed: CIN, ChemAb, ChemTitl.

—CASDDS. **CCC.**

Published by: Dow Jones Publishing Company (Asia) Inc., 25F Central Plaza, 18 Harbour Rd, Wanchai, Hong Kong, Hong Kong. TEL 852-2573-7121, FAX 852-2834-5291, TELEX 83828 AWSJ HX, http://www.awsj.com, http://www.wsj.com. Circ: 81,947.

---

332   AUS
ASSET. Text in English. 2000. 11/yr. AUD 79 (effective 2002). **Document type:** *Magazine, Trade.* **Description:** Provides information about financial planning and investments for finance professionals.

Published by: Fairfax Business Media (Subsidiary of: John Fairfax Holdings Ltd.), 469 La Trobe St, Melbourne 3000, NSW 3000, Australia. TEL 61-3-9603-3888, FAX 61-3-9670-4328, http://www.assetmag.com/, http://www.fxj.com.au/. Ed. Bruce Madden.

332.1 340   GBR
ASSET & PROJECT FINANCE LAW & PRACTICE. Text in English. 1997. 2 base vols. plus updates 2/yr. looseleaf. GBP 674 base vol(s).; GBP 345, EUR 519 updates in Europe; GBP 355, USD 645 updates elsewhere (effective 2006). **Document type:** *Journal, Trade.*

Published by: Sweet & Maxwell Ltd., 100 Avenue Road, London, NW3 3PF, United Kingdom. TEL 44-20-74491111, FAX 44-20-74491144, customer.services@sweetandmaxwell.co.uk, http://www.sweetandmaxwell.co.uk. **Subscr. to:** Cheriton House, North Way, Andover, Hants SP10 5BE, United Kingdom.

---

332 340   USA
ASSET BASED FINANCING: A TRANSACTIONAL GUIDE. Text in English. 1985. s-a. looseleaf. USD 628 (effective 2005). Supplement avail. **Description:** For commercial banks, commercial finance companies, thrift institutions, and attorneys representing corporations engaged in asset based borrowing. Provides how-to information on structuring the loan transaction, monitoring the security underlying the loan, and proceeding in case of default.

Published by: Matthew Bender & Co., Inc. (Subsidiary of: LexisNexis North America), 1275 Broadway, Albany, NY 12204. TEL 518-487-3575, 800-252-9257, FAX 518-462-3788, international@bender.com, http://bender.lexisnexis.com. Ed. Howard Ruda.

---

332   USA
ASSETS AND LIABILITIES OF INSURED DOMESTICALLY CHARTERED AND FOREIGN RELATED BANKING INSTITUTIONS. Text in English. w. USD 30. **Document type:** *Government.*

Published by: U.S. Federal Reserve System, Board of Governors, Publications Services, Rm MS 138, Washington, DC 20551. TEL 202-452-3244, FAX 202-728-5886.

---

332   USA
ASSOCIATION FOR INVESTMENT MANAGEMENT AND RESEARCH. SEMINAR PROCEEDINGS. Text in English. irreg. (approx. 5/yr.). USD 100 (effective 2000). **Document type:** *Proceedings.*

Formerly: Institute of Chartered Financial Analysts. Seminar Proceedings

Published by: Association for Investment Management and Research, 560 Ray C Hunt Drive, Charlottesville, VA 22903. TEL 804-951-5499, FAX 804-951-5262, http://www.aimr.org.

ASSOCIATION OF WINE SUPPLIERS. BANKRUPTCY UPDATE. see *BEVERAGES*

---

332   RUS
ASSOTSYATSIYA ROSSIISKIKH BANKOV. VESTNIK. Text in Russian. w.

Published by: Assotsiatsiya Rossiiskikh Bankov, B Sadovaya 4, str 2, Moscow, 103001, Russian Federation. TEL 7-095-2091037, FAX 7-095-2097664. **US dist. addr.:** East View Information Services, 3020 Harbor Ln. N., Minneapolis, MN 55447. TEL 612-550-0961.

---

332   KWT   ISSN 1029-4589
AT-TAQRIR AS-SANAWI. BANK AL-KUWAYT AL-MARKAZI. Text in English. 1970. a. free. stat. **Document type:** *Government.* **Description:** Covers the financial and monetary developments of the State of Kuwait in a fiscal year. Data such as interest rates, exchange prices, credit policy, etc. as well as Central Bank activities as related to the implementation of monetary policy are available.

Related titles: ♦ English ed.: Central Bank of Kuwait. Annual Report. ISSN 1029-4546.

Published by: Central Bank of Kuwait, Economic Research Department/Bank al-Kuwayt al-Markazi, Idarat al-Buhuth al-ektisadia, P O Box 526, Safat, 13006, Kuwait. TEL 965-2449200, FAX 965-2440887, cbk@cbk.gov.kw, http://www.cbk.gov.kw. R&P Sami H Al-Anbaee TEL 965-2403257.

AUDIT I FINANSOVYI ANALIZ/AUDIT AND FINANCIAL ANALYSIS. see *BUSINESS AND ECONOMICS—Accounting*

AUSTRALIA. BUREAU OF STATISTICS. ANNUAL STATISTICS ON FINANCIAL INSTITUTIONS ON HARDCOPY. see *BUSINESS AND ECONOMICS—Abstracting, Bibliographies, Statistics*

AUSTRALIA. BUREAU OF STATISTICS. ASSETS AND LIABILITIES OF FRIENDLY SOCIETIES, AUSTRALIA. see *BUSINESS AND ECONOMICS—Abstracting, Bibliographies, Statistics*

AUSTRALIA. BUREAU OF STATISTICS. AUSTRALIAN NATIONAL ACCOUNTS: FINANCIAL ACCOUNTS. see *BUSINESS AND ECONOMICS—Abstracting, Bibliographies, Statistics*

AUSTRALIA. BUREAU OF STATISTICS. AUSTRALIAN NATIONAL ACCOUNTS: NON-PROFIT INSTITUTIONS SATELLITE ACCOUNT. see *BUSINESS AND ECONOMICS—Abstracting, Bibliographies, Statistics*

AUSTRALIA. BUREAU OF STATISTICS. AUSTRALIAN STANDARD RESEARCH CLASSIFICATION. see *BUSINESS AND ECONOMICS—Abstracting, Bibliographies, Statistics*

AUSTRALIA. BUREAU OF STATISTICS. BUSINESS INDICATORS, AUSTRALIA. see *BUSINESS AND ECONOMICS—Abstracting, Bibliographies, Statistics*

AUSTRALIA. BUREAU OF STATISTICS. COMMON FUNDS, AUSTRALIA. see *BUSINESS AND ECONOMICS—Abstracting, Bibliographies, Statistics*

AUSTRALIA. BUREAU OF STATISTICS. DIRECTORY OF CAPITAL EXPENDITURE DATA SOURCES AND RELATED STATISTICS. see *BUSINESS AND ECONOMICS—Abstracting, Bibliographies, Statistics*

AUSTRALIA. BUREAU OF STATISTICS. FINANCIAL ESTIMATES OF COMMONWEALTH PUBLIC TRADING ENTERPRISES, AUSTRALIA. see *BUSINESS AND ECONOMICS—Abstracting, Bibliographies, Statistics*

AUSTRALIA. BUREAU OF STATISTICS. GOVERNMENT FINANCE STATISTICS - CONCEPTS, SOURCES AND METHODS. see *BUSINESS AND ECONOMICS—Abstracting, Bibliographies, Statistics*

AUSTRALIA. BUREAU OF STATISTICS. GOVERNMENT FINANCE STATISTICS, EDUCATION, AUSTRALIA, DATA REPORT. see *BUSINESS AND ECONOMICS—Abstracting, Bibliographies, Statistics*

▼ **AUSTRALIA. BUREAU OF STATISTICS. GOVERNMENT FINANCIAL ESTIMATES, AUSTRALIAN CAPITAL TERRITORY, ELECTRONIC DELIVERY.** see *BUSINESS AND ECONOMICS—Abstracting, Bibliographies, Statistics*

AUSTRALIA. BUREAU OF STATISTICS. HOUSING FINANCE FOR OWNER OCCUPATION, AUSTRALIA. see *BUSINESS AND ECONOMICS—Abstracting, Bibliographies, Statistics*

AUSTRALIA. BUREAU OF STATISTICS. INFORMATION PAPER: ACCRUALS-BASED GOVERNMENT FINANCE STATISTICS. see *BUSINESS AND ECONOMICS—Abstracting, Bibliographies, Statistics*

AUSTRALIA. BUREAU OF STATISTICS. INFORMATION PAPER: DEVELOPMENTS IN GOVERNMENT FINANCE STATISTICS. see *BUSINESS AND ECONOMICS—Abstracting, Bibliographies, Statistics*

B

AUSTRALIA. BUREAU OF STATISTICS. LENDING FINANCE, AUSTRALIA. see *BUSINESS AND ECONOMICS—Abstracting, Bibliographies, Statistics*

AUSTRALIA. BUREAU OF STATISTICS. MANAGED FUNDS, AUSTRALIA. see *BUSINESS AND ECONOMICS—Abstracting, Bibliographies, Statistics*

▼ **AUSTRALIA. BUREAU OF STATISTICS. NEW SOUTH WALES OFFICE. GOVERNMENT FINANCIAL ESTIMATES, NEW SOUTH WALES, ELECTRONIC DELIVERY.** see *BUSINESS AND ECONOMICS—Abstracting, Bibliographies, Statistics*

▼ **AUSTRALIA. BUREAU OF STATISTICS. NORTHERN TERRITORY OFFICE. GOVERNMENT FINANCIAL ESTIMATES, NORTHERN TERRITORY, ELECTRONIC DELIVERY.** see *BUSINESS AND ECONOMICS—Abstracting, Bibliographies, Statistics*

AUSTRALIA. BUREAU OF STATISTICS. PRIVATE NEW CAPITAL EXPENDITURE AND EXPECTED EXPENDITURE, AUSTRALIA. see *BUSINESS AND ECONOMICS—Abstracting, Bibliographies, Statistics*

AUSTRALIA. BUREAU OF STATISTICS. PUBLIC UNIT TRUSTS, AUSTRALIA. see *BUSINESS AND ECONOMICS—Abstracting, Bibliographies, Statistics*

▼ **AUSTRALIA. BUREAU OF STATISTICS. QUEENSLAND OFFICE. GOVERNMENT FINANCIAL ESTIMATES, QUEENSLAND, ELECTRONIC DELIVERY.** see *BUSINESS AND ECONOMICS—Abstracting, Bibliographies, Statistics*

▼ **AUSTRALIA. BUREAU OF STATISTICS. SOUTH AUSTRALIAN OFFICE. GOVERNMENT FINANCIAL ESTIMATES, SOUTH AUSTRALIA, ELECTRONIC DELIVERY.** see *BUSINESS AND ECONOMICS—Abstracting, Bibliographies, Statistics*

▼ **AUSTRALIA. BUREAU OF STATISTICS. WESTERN AUSTRALIAN OFFICE. GOVERNMENT FINANCIAL ESTIMATES, WESTERN AUSTRALIA, ELECTRONIC DELIVERY.** see *BUSINESS AND ECONOMICS—Abstracting, Bibliographies, Statistics*

332 AUS ISSN 1325-1228
AUSTRALIAN BANKING AND FINANCE. Text in English. 1992. s-m. AUD 122.10 domestic; AUD 203.50 foreign (effective 2004). **Document type:** *Magazine, Trade.* **Description:** Reports on the issues in the Australian Financial Services and Banking Sectors.
Related titles: Online - full text ed.: (from Gale Group).
Published by: First Charlton Communications, Level 9, Tenix House, 100 Arthur St, North Sydney, NSW 2060, Australia. TEL 61-2-99553622, FAX 61-2-99571512, pctc@charlton.com.au, http://www.charlton.com.au/. Ed. Phil Ayling. Adv. contact Tony May TEL 61-2-99579809.

332 346 AUS ISSN 1321-4454
AUSTRALIAN BANKING LAW JOURNAL. Text in English. 1994. q. looseleaf. AUD 99. bk.rev. back issues avail. **Document type:** *Academic/Scholarly.* **Description:** Provides analysis of the law as it relates to banking for scholars, professionals and consumers.
Published by: Australian Law Publishers Pty. Ltd., 254 Hawken Dr, St Lucia, QLD 4067, Australia. TEL 61-7-38709111, FAX 61-7-38702222, lal510737@student.uq.edu.au. Ed. Russell Mathews. Circ: 200.

AUSTRALIAN BANKING STATISTICS. see *BUSINESS AND ECONOMICS—Abstracting, Bibliographies, Statistics*

AUSTRALIAN CONSUMER CREDIT LAW. see *LAW*

332.7 AUS ISSN 0725-0665
AUSTRALIAN CREDIT UNIONS MAGAZINE. Text in English. 1980. bi-m. AUD 55 (effective 2000). adv. bk.rev. **Document type:** *Trade.* **Description:** Contains information on the management of individual credit unions with each credit union being totally autonomous for all buying decisions. This audience represents a vast potential for advertising products and services intrinsic to effective financial and general office management.
Published by: (Credit Union Services Corporation (Australia) Ltd.), Australian Credit Unions Magazine, Level 6, 51 Druitt St, Sydney, NSW 2000, Australia. TEL 61-2-9333-7539, 61-2-9333-7777, FAX 61-2-9333-7762. Ed., Pub., Adv. contact Lisa Lintern TEL 61-2-9333-7753. page AUD 1,030; trim 297 x 210. Circ: 2,100 (paid).

332 AUS ISSN 0404-2018
AUSTRALIAN FINANCIAL REVIEW. Text in English. 1951. d. (Mon.-Fri.). adv. **Document type:** *Newspaper.* **Description:** National economic newspaper with financial and business articles.
Related titles: Microfilm ed.: (from PQC); Online - full text ed.: ISSN 1444-9900. 1995; Alternate Frequency ed(s).: Australian Financial Review Quarterly on CD-ROM. ISSN 1322-0683. 1994. q.; Weekend Australian Financial Review. w. (Saturdays); Cumulative ed(s).: Australian Financial Review Archive CD. ISSN 1326-4753; ♦ Includes: Australian Financial Review Magazine; ♦ Financial Review Boss.
Indexed: ABIX, B&I.
Published by: Fairfax Business Media (Subsidiary of: John Fairfax Holdings Ltd.), 201 Sussex St, Sydney, NSW 2000, Australia. TEL 61-2-9282-3137, http://afr.com/, http://www.fxj.com.au/. Ed. Colleen Ryan. Circ: 90,000.

332.7 346 AUS
AUSTRALIAN INSOLVENCY JOURNAL. Text in English. 1933. q. AUD 160 (effective 1999). adv. bk.rev. **Document type:** *Academic/Scholarly.*
Former titles (until 1998): Australian Insolvency Bulletin (1033-9345); (until 1989): Australian Bankruptcy Bulletin (0045-0286)
Related titles: Microfilm ed.: (from PQC).
Published by: Insolvency Practitioners Association of Australia, GPO Box 3921, Sydney, NSW 2001, Australia. TEL 61-2-92905700, FAX 61-2-92902820. Ed., R&P Hugh Parsons. Adv. contact Fidelma Warner. Circ: 860 (paid).

332 USA ISSN 1098-8335
AUTO FINANCE NEWS. Text in English. bi-m. USD 525 (effective 2004). **Document type:** *Magazine, Trade.* **Description:** Covers auto lending and leasing.
Published by: Royal Media Group, 1359 Broadway, Ste 1512, New York, NY 10018. TEL 212-564-8972, 800-320-4418, FAX 212-564-8973, info@royalmedia.com, http://www.royalmedia.com/newsletter.cfm?pub=101.

AUTOMOTIVE FINANCE. see *TRANSPORTATION—Automobiles*

AVIATION STRATEGY. see *TRANSPORTATION—Air Transport*

332 330.9 FRA ISSN 1283-8691
AVIS ET DECISIONS DU CONSEIL DE LA CONCURRENCE. Key Title: Avis de la Commission de la Concurrence et de la Commission Technique des Ententes et des Positions Dominantes. Text in French. 1986. base vol. plus s-a. updates. looseleaf. EUR 559.15 (effective 2004). index. **Description:** A guide to the decisions, actions, and economic and financial sanctions of the council.
Published by: Lamy S.A. (Subsidiary of: Wolters Kluwer France), 21/23 rue des Ardennes, Paris, 75935 Cedex 19, France. TEL 33-1-825080800, FAX 33-1-44721388, lamy@lamy.fr, http://www.lamy.fr. Ed. Pierre Storrer.

332.1 CHE ISSN 1683-0121
B I S QUARTERLY REVIEW. Text in English. q. **Document type:** *Journal, Trade.* **Description:** Contains information and statistics on international banking and financial market developments.
Former titles (until 1998): International Banking and Financial Market Developments (1012-9979); (until 1986): International Banking Developments
Indexed: JEL.
—BLDSC (2094.099092).
Published by: Bank for International Settlements, Centralbahnplatz 2, Basel, 4002, Switzerland. TEL 41-61-2808080, FAX 41-61-2809100, 41-61-2808100, publications@bis.org, http://www.bis.org.

332 336.066 USA ISSN 1522-5984
B N A'S BANKING REPORT (ONLINE EDITION). Text in English. 1996 (Feb.). w. USD 2,028 (effective 2005 - 2006).
Media: Online - full text (from The Bureau of National Affairs, Inc.). **Related titles:** ♦ Print ed.: B N A's Banking Report (Print Edition). ISSN 0891-0634.
Published by: The Bureau of National Affairs, Inc., 1231 25th St., NW, Washington, DC 20037. TEL 800-372-1033, http://pubs.bna.com/ip/BNA/BAR.NSF/highlights/highlights?OpenDocument, http://www.bna.com. **Subscr. to:** 9435 Key West Ave, Rockville, MD 20850.

332 ITA
B P M. Text in Italian. bi-m.
Published by: Banco Popolare di Milano, Piazza Filippo Meda, 4, Milan, MI 20121, Italy. Ed. Enrico Falcetti.

332 HTI ISSN 1012-3326
CODEN: NAAMEF
B R H MAGAZINE. Text in French. q. HTG 80, USD 20.
Indexed: PAIS.
Published by: Banque de la Republique d'Haiti, Direction Administrative, B.P. 1570, Port-au-Prince, Haiti. TEL 23-1944, FAX 22-2607, TELEX BRH DGA 2030537.

B S A DIRECTORY OF MEMBERS. see *REAL ESTATE*

332 DEU
B V - EUROLETTER; E G-Binnenmarkt: Tips, Trends, Termine. (Bayerische Vereinsbank) Text in German. 1989. m. free. back issues avail. **Description:** News and trends in the European Common Market.
Published by: Bayerische Vereinsbank AG, Zentralbereich Kommunikation und Volkwirtschaft, Kardinal-Faulhaber-Str 1, Munich, 80333, Germany. TEL 49-89-2132-5530, FAX 49-89-2132-5699. Circ: 24,000.

332 GBR ISSN 1355-7793
BACK OFFICE FOCUS. Text in English. 1994. m. GBP 455, USD 775 (effective 2001). adv. back issues avail. **Document type:** *Newsletter.* **Description:** Covers global issues relating to post-trade activity in the securities industry, for heads of IT, electronic settlements and operations, and fund managers in brokerage houses and banks.
Published by: Informa U K Limited (Subsidiary of: T & F Informa plc), Customer Service Dept, Sheepen Pl, Colchester, Essex CO3 3LP, United Kingdom. TEL 44-1206-772223, FAX 44-1206-772771, hdoran@llplimited.com, enquiries@informa.com, http://www.informa.com. **Subscr. addr. in the US:** L L P Inc, Customer Service, PO Box 1017, Westborough, MA 01581-6017. TEL 1-800-493-4080, FAX 508-231-0856, enquiries.usa@informa.com.

BALANCE SHEET ANALYSIS OF JOINT STOCK COMPANIES. see *BUSINESS AND ECONOMICS—Abstracting, Bibliographies, Statistics*

332 USA
BALANCE SHEETS FOR THE U.S. ECONOMY. Text in English. s-a. USD 5. **Document type:** *Government.*
Published by: U.S. Federal Reserve System, Board of Governors, Publications Services, Rm MS 138, Washington, DC 20551. TEL 202-452-3244, FAX 202-728-5886.

332.1 ESP
BALANCES Y ESTADISTICAS DE LA BANCA EN ESPANA. Text in Spanish. 1924. m. back issues avail.
Formerly: Balances y Estadisticas de la Banca Privada
Related titles: Diskette ed.; Magnetic Tape ed.
Published by: Consejo Superior Bancario, Jose Abascal, 57, Madrid, 28003, Spain. TEL 91-441-06-11, FAX 91-441-27-20. Circ: 1,500.

332 USA
BALANCING ACT; life is a balancing act between frugality, creativity, efficiency and conservation. Text in English. 1997. bi-m. USD 6. **Document type:** *Newsletter.* **Description:** Offers consumers advice on simplifying their finances and their lives.
Address: PO Box 309, Ghent, NY 12075-0309. Ed. Betsy Giese Sullivan. R&P Betsy Giese Sullivan TEL 518-392-7729.

332 ESP ISSN 1135-0652
BANCA & FINANZAS. Text in Spanish. 1995. m.
—CINDOC.
Published by: Instituto Superior de Tecnicas y Practicas Bancarias, Via de los Poblados, 17, Nave 3-9, Madrid, 28033, Spain. TEL 34-91-3821214, FAX 34-91-3837751, ist@banca-finanzas.es, http://www.iberfinanzas.com/.

332 340.5 ITA ISSN 0390-9522
KKH940.A15
BANCA BORSA E TITOLI DI CREDITO; rivista di dottrina e giurisprudenza. Text in Italian. 1934. bi-m. EUR 113.62 in the European Union; EUR 170.43 elsewhere (effective 2002). adv. **Description:** Discusses problems in banking, the stock exchange and titles of credit, all from a legal perspective.
Related titles: CD-ROM ed.: ISSN 1591-8009.
Indexed: IBR, IBZ.
Published by: Casa Editrice Dott. A. Giuffre (Subsidiary of: LexisNexis Europe and Africa), Via Busto Arsizio, 40, Milan, MI 20151, Italy. TEL 39-02-28089200, FAX 39-02-38009582, giuffre@giuffre.it, http://www.giuffre.it. Ed. Federico Martorano. Circ: 3,900.

332 DEU ISSN 1561-0276
BANCA CENTRALE EUROPEA. BOLLETTINO MENSILE. Text in Italian. 1999. m.
Related titles: ♦ English ed.: European Central Bank. Monthly Bulletin. ISSN 1561-0136; ♦ Spanish ed.: Banco Central Europeo. Boletin Mensual. ISSN 1561-0268; ♦ Portuguese ed.: Banco Central Europeu. Boletin Mensal. ISSN 1561-0284; ♦ German ed.: Europaische Zentralbank. Monatsbericht. ISSN 1561-0292; ♦ Dutch ed.: Europese Centrale Bank. Maandbericht. ISSN 1561-0314; ♦ Spanish ed.: Euroopan Keskuspankki. Kuukausikatsaus. ISSN 1561-0322; ♦ Greek ed.: Europaike Kentrike Trapeza. Meniaio Deltio. ISSN 1561-025X; ♦ Swedish ed.: Europeiska Centralbanken. Manadsrapport. ISSN 1561-0144; ♦ Danish ed.: Europaeiske Centralbank. Manedsoversigt. ISSN 1561-0241; ♦ French ed.: Banque Central Europeenne. Bulletin Mensuel. ISSN 1561-0306.
Published by: European Central Bank, Postfach 16 03 19, Frankfurt am Main, 60066, Germany. TEL 49-69-1344-0, FAX 49-69-1344-6000, http://www.ecb.int.

332.1 ITA ISSN 0391-4712
BANCA D'ITALIA. ASSEMBLEA GENERALE ORDINARIA DEI PARTECIPANTI. Text in Italian. 1894. a. free. back issues avail. **Document type:** *Proceedings.*
Related titles: English ed.: Banca d'Italia. Ordinary General Meetings of Shareholders.

Published by: Banca d'Italia, Via Nazionale 187, Rome, 00184, Italy. TEL 39-06-47922333, FAX 39-06-47922059, http://www.bancaditalia.it. Circ: 14,000.

332 ITA
BANCA D'ITALIA. BOLLETTINO DI VIGILANZA. Text in Italian. 1962. m. free. **Document type:** *Bulletin.*
Formerly (until 1994): Banca d'Italia. Bollettino - Vigilanza delle Aziende di Credito (0005-4593); Supersedes (1936-1943): Ispettorato per la Difesa del Risparmio e per l'Esercizio del Credito. Bollettino
Published by: (Servizio Normativa e Affari Generali di Vigilanza), Banca d'Italia, Via Nazionale 187, Rome, 00184, Italy. TEL 39-06-47922333, FAX 39-06-47922059, http://www.bancaditalia.it. Ed. Giovanni Castaldi. Circ: 3,000.

332 ITA
HG3084
BANCA D'ITALIA. BOLLETTINO STATISTICO. STATISTICHE ANALITICHE MONETARIE E FINANZIARIE. NUOVA SERIE. Text in Italian. 1945-1988; N.S. 1991. q. free. charts; mkt.; stat. index. back issues avail. **Document type:** *Bulletin.*
Former titles (until 1988): Banca d'Italia. Bollettino Statistico - Servizio Studi (0393-604X); (until 1983): Banca d'Italia. Bollettino - Servizio Studi (0393-6090); (until 1978): Banca d'Italia. Bollettino (0392-467X); (until 1950): Banca d'Italia. Bollettino del Servizio Studi Economici (0391-4720); (until 1947): Bollettino Mensile del Servizio Studi Economici
Related titles: CD-ROM ed.: N.S.
Indexed: PAIS.
Published by: Banca d'Italia, Via Nazionale 187, Rome, 00184, Italy. TEL 39-06-47922333, FAX 39-06-47922059, http://www.bancaditalia.it. Ed. Claudio Conigliani. Circ: 6,200.

332 ITA
BANCA D'ITALIA. SERVIZIO STUDI. TEMI DI DISCUSSIONE. Text in Italian. 1979. irreg. free. back issues avail. **Document type:** *Monographic series.*
—BLDSC (8789.770000).
Published by: Banca d'Italia, Via Nazionale 187, Rome, 00184, Italy. TEL 39-06-47922333, FAX 39-06-47922059, http://www.bancaditalia.it. Circ: 5,000.

332 ESP ISSN 0210-1688
BANCA ESPANOLA. Text in Spanish. 1970. m. USD 45 foreign. adv.
—CINDOC.
Published by: Justo de la Mota Ed. & Pub., Avda Alfonso XIII, 15 bajo B, Madrid, 28002, Spain. TEL 34-91-5191800, FAX 34-91-5191795. Circ: 6,500.

332.1 ITA ISSN 1120-9453
HG3071
BANCA IMPRESA SOCIETA. Text in Italian. 1983. 3/yr. EUR 54 domestic to individuals; EUR 84 foreign to individuals; EUR 99 domestic to institutions print & online eds.; EUR 135 foreign to institutions print & online eds (effective 2004). adv. index. back issues avail. **Document type:** *Academic/Scholarly.*
Related titles: Online - full text ed.
Published by: Societa Editrice Il Mulino, Strada Maggiore 37, Bologna, 40125, Italy. TEL 39-051-256011, FAX 39-051-256034, riviste@mulino.it, http://www.mulino.it. Adv. contact M Luisa Vezzali. Circ: 3,500.

332.1 ITA
BANCA NAZIONALE DEL LAVORO. QUADERNI DI RICERCA. Text in Italian. a. EUR 20 (effective 2003). back issues avail. **Document type:** *Academic/Scholarly.* **Description:** Reports on savings institutions.
Related titles: ♦ English ed.: Banca Nazionale del Lavoro. Quarterly Review. ISSN 0005-4607.
Published by: B N L Edizioni SpA (Subsidiary of: Gruppo BNL), Via San Basilio 48, Rome, 00187, Italy. TEL 39-06-42012918, FAX 39-06-42012921, sliberati@bnledizioni.com.

330 ITA ISSN 0005-4607
HC301
BANCA NAZIONALE DEL LAVORO. QUARTERLY REVIEW. Text in English. 1947. q. EUR 62 domestic to individuals; EUR 68 foreign to individuals; EUR 41 domestic to students; EUR 45 foreign to students (effective 2003). adv. index. back issues avail.; reprint service avail. from PQC,SCH. **Document type:** *Academic/Scholarly.* **Description:** Publishes articles by leading economists on macroeconomic theory and policy, international trade and finance, the evolution of national monetary and financial institutions and allied topics.
Related titles: Online - full text ed.: (from Northern Light Technology, Inc., ProQuest Information & Learning); ♦ Italian ed.: Banca Nazionale del Lavoro. Quaderni di Ricerca.
Indexed: BAS, BPIA, BusI, CREJ, ELLIS, IBSS, JEL, KES, PAIS, RASB, T&II, WBA.
—BLDSC (7203.525000), IE, Infotrieve, ingenta.
Published by: (Banca Nazionale del Lavoro), B N L Edizioni SpA (Subsidiary of: Gruppo BNL), Via San Basilio 48, Rome, 00187, Italy. TEL 39-06-42012918, FAX 39-06-42012921, sliberati@bnledizioni.com. Ed. Alessandro Roncaglia. Adv. contact Filippo Cucuccio. Circ: 3,500.

332.1 MEX ISSN 0005-4615
BANCA Y COMERCIO. Text in Spanish. 1936. q. MXP 3,750, USD 8. adv. bk.rev.
Published by: Escuela Bancaria y Comercial, Paseo de la Reforma 202, Mexico City, DF 06600, Mexico. FAX 905-546-0326. Ed. Carlos Prieto Sierra. Circ: 6,500 (controlled).

332 COL ISSN 0120-7040
HG185.C6
BANCA Y FINANZAS. Text in Spanish. 1976. q. USD 70 (effective 1998). **Description:** Provides articles on economic theory and policy, and comprehensive financial analyses.
Published by: Asociacion Bancaria y de Entidades Financieras, Apartado Aereo 13994, Bogota, CUND, Colombia. TEL 57-1-2114811, FAX 57-1-2119915, info@asobancaria.com, http://www.asobancaria.com.

331 ITA ISSN 0393-7062
BANCAMATICA; mensile di elettronica informatica e sicurezza nella banca e nella finanza. Text in Italian. 1985. m. EUR 100 domestic; EUR 120 in Europe; EUR 135 elsewhere (effective 2005). adv. charts; illus. **Document type:** *Magazine, Trade.*
Published by: Insic, Via dell' Acqua Traversa 189, Rome, 00135, Italy. TEL 39-06-3313000, FAX 39-06-33111043, info@insic.it, http://www.insic.it. Ed. Adalberto Biasiotti. Pub. Pier Roberto Pais. Adv. contact Roberto Barberini. Circ: 7,500.

332.1 ITA ISSN 0005-4623
HG19
BANCARIA. Text in Italian. 1945. m. EUR 80 domestic; EUR 100 foreign (effective 2005). adv. bk.rev. abstr.; bibl.; charts; stat. index, cum.index. **Document type:** *Magazine, Trade.*
Formerly (until 1948): Associazione Bancaria Italiana. Rassegna (1128-9171)
Indexed: DIP, IBR, IBSS, IBZ, JEL, KES, PAIS, RASB.
Published by: Bancaria Editrice (Subsidiary of: Associazione Bancaria Italiana), Via della Cordonata 7, Rome, 00186, Italy. TEL 39-06-67671, FAX 39-06-6767457, abi@abi.it, http://www.bancariaeditrice.it/portal/ssm/page.do?pageId=3418.

BANCASSURANCE REPORT. see *INSURANCE*

332 ITA ISSN 0390-1378
BANCHE E BANCHIERI. Text in Italian. 1974. bi-m. EUR 60 domestic; EUR 80 foreign (effective 2005). adv. bk.rev. **Document type:** *Magazine, Trade.* **Description:** Covers research articles on areas related to the institutional aspects of credit systems and their management technique.
Indexed: PAIS.
Published by: Associazione Nazionale Banche Private, Via Cosimo del Fante 7, Milan, 20122, Italy. TEL 39-02-582126, FAX 39-02-582126, assbank@assbank.it, http://www.assbank.it/pubblicazioni/default.asp. Ed. Laura Pirovano. Circ: 2,500.

332.1 SVN ISSN 0005-4631
HG3234.S5
BANCNI VESTNIK/BANKING NEWSLETTER; revija za denarnistvo in bancnistvo. Text in Slovenian; Summaries in English. 1951. m. SIT 12,900 (effective 2001). adv. bk.rev. stat. 48 p./no. 3 cols./p.; **Document type:** *Newsletter.* **Description:** Covers money and banking in Slovenia and throughout the European Union. Includes financial markets and banks, investment banking, international standards, banks and legal practice, system reforms, and banking news.
Related titles: CD-ROM ed.: ISSN 1408-2799.
Published by: Zdruzenje Bank Slovenije/Bank Association of Slovenia, Subiceva 2, Ljubljana, 1001, Slovenia. TEL 386-61-4252432, FAX 386-61-4255440, bancni.vestnik@zbs-giz.si, http://www.zbs-giz.si. Ed., R&P Emil Lah. Circ: 1,100.

332 BOL
BANCO CENTRAL DE BOLIVIA. REVISTA DE ANALISIS. Text in Spanish. s-a. BOB 32 domestic; USD 17 foreign (effective 2004).
Published by: Banco Central de Bolivia, Casilla de Correo 3118, La Paz, Bolivia. TEL 591-2-2409090, FAX 591-2-2406614, bcb@bcb.gov.bo, http://www.bcb.gov.bo.

332.1 CHL ISSN 0716-2901
HG2896
BANCO CENTRAL DE CHILE. ANNUAL REPORT. Text in English. 1983. a. free. **Document type:** *Corporate.* **Description:** Contains balance sheet and financial statements, with summary of Chilean economic development during the year.
Published by: Banco Central de Chile, Casilla 967, Santiago, Chile. TEL 56-2-670-2000, FAX 56-2-698-4847. Circ: 600.

332 330.9 CHL ISSN 0716-2367
HG2900.S3
BANCO CENTRAL DE CHILE. BOLETIN MENSUAL. Text in Spanish. 1928. m. CLP 65,000, USD 250 (effective 1999). illus.; mkt.; stat. index, cum.index: 1928-1992. **Document type:** *Bulletin.* **Description:** Presents statistical charts of all economic and external sectors with articles on Chilean economic policy.
Indexed: PAIS.
Published by: Banco Central de Chile, Casilla 967, Santiago, Chile. TEL 56-2-670-2000, FAX 56-2-698-4847, TELEX 405 69 CENBC CL. Circ: 1,350.

332.1 330.9 CHL ISSN 0716-2448
HG2900.S3
BANCO CENTRAL DE CHILE. MEMORIA ANUAL. Text in Spanish. 1926. a. free. **Document type:** *Corporate.* **Description:** Contains balance sheet and financial statement, with summary of Chilean economic development during the year.
Related titles: English ed.
Published by: Banco Central de Chile, Casilla 967, Santiago, Chile. TEL 56-2-670-2000, FAX 56-2-698-4847, TELEX 40569 CENBC CL. Circ: 800.

332 DOM
BANCO CENTRAL DE LA REPUBLICA DOMINICANA. BOLETIN TRIMESTRAL. Text in Spanish. 1947. q. USD 48. charts; stat. **Document type:** *Bulletin.*
Formerly: Banco Central de la Republica Dominicana. Boletin Mensual (0005-4682)
Indexed: PAIS.
Published by: (Departamento de Estudios Economicos), Banco Central de la Republica Dominicana, Apdo Postal 1347, Santo Domingo, Dominican Republic. Circ: 1,000.

332 DOM
BANCO CENTRAL DE LA REPUBLICA DOMINICANA. MEMORIA. Text in Spanish. a.
Published by: Banco Central de la Republica Dominicana, Apdo Postal 1347, Santo Domingo, Dominican Republic.

332 DOM
BANCO CENTRAL DE LA REPUBLICA DOMINICANA. PRINCIPALES INDICADORES ECONOMICOS. Text in Spanish. 1992. m.
Published by: Banco Central de la Republica Dominicana, Apdo Postal 1347, Santo Domingo, Dominican Republic.

332 NIC
BANCO CENTRAL DE NICARAGUA. BIBLIOTECA Y SERVICIOS DE INFORMACION. BARRICADA INDICE TEMATICO Y ONOMASTICO✶. Text in Spanish. a.
Published by: Ministerio de Comercio Exterior (MICE), Apdo 2412, Managua, Nicaragua.

332 NIC
BANCO CENTRAL DE NICARAGUA. BOLETIN ANUAL✶. Text in Spanish. 1936. a. free. bk.rev. charts; stat.
Former titles: Banco Central de Nicaragua. Boletin Semestral; Banco Central de Nicaragua. Boletin Trimestral (0005-4690)
Published by: Ministerio de Comercio Exterior (MICE), Apdo 2412, Managua, Nicaragua. Ed. Ramon Cabrales. Circ: 2,500.

332.1 330.9 NIC
BANCO CENTRAL DE NICARAGUA. CARTA QUINCENAL✶. Text in Spanish. 1978 (Nov., no.79). fortn.
Published by: Ministerio de Comercio Exterior (MICE), Apdo 2412, Managua, Nicaragua.

332.1 NIC ISSN 0067-3226
HG2766
BANCO CENTRAL DE NICARAGUA. INFORME ANUAL✶. Text in Spanish. 1961. a.
Published by: Ministerio de Comercio Exterior (MICE), Apdo 2412, Managua, Nicaragua. Ed. Noel Lacayo Baretto.

332 SLV
BANCO CENTRAL DE RESERVA DE EL SALVADOR. BOLETIN ECONOMICO. Text in Spanish. 1988. m. free. stat. **Document type:** *Bulletin.* **Description:** Articles and analysis on money and banking, trade, public finance, commerce and production.
Published by: (Gerencia de Estudios y Politica Economica), Banco Central de Reserva de El Salvador, Alameda Juan Pablo II y 17 Ave. Norte, Apdo. Postal (06) 106, San Salvador, El Salvador. TEL 503-281-8000. Circ: 2,000.

332.1 SLV
BANCO CENTRAL DE RESERVA DE EL SALVADOR. MEMORIA DE LABORES. Text in Spanish. 1934. a. stat. **Document type:** *Corporate.* **Description:** Compares current economic and financial performance to the previous year. Covers the GNP, inflation, balance of payments, fiscal and monetary sectors, exchange rate, and monetary and credit policies and measures.
Formerly (until 1993): Banco Central de Reserva de El Salvador. Memoria
—BLDSC (5670.538500).
Published by: (Gerencia de Estudios y Politica Economica), Banco Central de Reserva de El Salvador, Alameda Juan Pablo II y 17 Ave. Norte, Apdo. Postal (06) 106, San Salvador, El Salvador. TEL 503-281-8000. Circ: 3,100.

332 SLV
HF6
BANCO CENTRAL DE RESERVA DE EL SALVADOR. REVISTA TRIMESTRAL. Text in Spanish. 1934. q. donation. stat. **Document type:** *Bulletin.* **Description:** Covers the statistics of money and banking, balance of payments, public finance, and prices and production of goods and services.
Formerly: Banco Central de Reserva de El Salvador. Revista Mensual (0005-4704)
Indexed: PAIS, PROMT.

B

▼ *new title* ➤ *refereed* ✶ *unverified* ♦ *full entry avail.*

Published by: (Gerencia de Estudios y Politica), Banco Central de Reserva de El Salvador, Alameda Juan Pablo II y 17 Ave. Norte, Apdo. Postal (06) 106, San Salvador, El Salvador. TEL 503-281-8000, FAX 503-281-8199. Ed. Rafael Barraza. Circ: 3,100.

332 PER ISSN 0005-4712
HG2946
BANCO CENTRAL DE RESERVA DEL PERU. BOLETIN. Text in Spanish. 1931. m. free. charts; mkt.; stat.
Indexed: PAIS, RASB.
Published by: Banco Central de Reserva del Peru, Seccion Publicaciones, Apdo. 1958, Lima, Peru. Circ: 4,200.

332 PER
BANCO CENTRAL DE RESERVA DEL PERU. MEMORIA. Text in Spanish. 1922. a. charts; stat.
Published by: Banco Central de Reserva del Peru, Seccion Publicaciones, Apdo. 1958, Lima, Peru.

BANCO CENTRAL DE VENEZUELA. ANUARIO DE BALANZA DE PAGOS. see *BUSINESS AND ECONOMICS—Abstracting, Bibliographies, Statistics*

BANCO CENTRAL DE VENEZUELA. ANUARIO DE CUENTAS NACIONALES. see *BUSINESS AND ECONOMICS—Abstracting, Bibliographies, Statistics*

BANCO CENTRAL DE VENEZUELA. ANUARIO DE ESTADISTICAS: PRECIOS Y MERCADO LABORAL. see *BUSINESS AND ECONOMICS—Abstracting, Bibliographies, Statistics*

BANCO CENTRAL DE VENEZUELA. ANUARIO DE ESTADISTICAS: SECTOR FINANCIERO. see *BUSINESS AND ECONOMICS—Abstracting, Bibliographies, Statistics*

BANCO CENTRAL DE VENEZUELA. BOLETIN DE INDICADORES SEMANALES. see *BUSINESS AND ECONOMICS—Abstracting, Bibliographies, Statistics*

BANCO CENTRAL DE VENEZUELA. BOLETIN MENSUAL. see *BUSINESS AND ECONOMICS—Abstracting, Bibliographies, Statistics*

332.1 VEN ISSN 1316-0680
HG2966
BANCO CENTRAL DE VENEZUELA. INFORME SEMESTRAL. Text in Spanish. 1940. q. free.
Formerly: Banco Central de Venezuela. Memoria (0067-3269)
Published by: Banco Central de Venezuela, Av Urdaneta Esq Las Carmelitas, Caracas, 1010, Venezuela. TEL 58-2-8015111. Circ: 2,000.

332 VEN ISSN 0005-4720
HG1505
BANCO CENTRAL DE VENEZUELA. REVISTA. Text in Spanish. 1941-1975 (no.370); resumed 1986. s-a. USD 20 (effective 2000). charts; mkt.; stat.
Related titles: ◆ English ed.: Central Bank of Venezuela. Report.
Indexed: PAIS.
Published by: Banco Central de Venezuela, Av Urdaneta Esq Las Carmelitas, Caracas, 1010, Venezuela. TEL 58-212-8015111, FAX 58-212-8611649, info@bcv.org.ve, http://www.bcv.org.ve. Circ: 4,500.

BANCO CENTRAL DEL ECUADOR. BALANZA DE PAGOS. see *BUSINESS AND ECONOMICS—Abstracting, Bibliographies, Statistics*

332 ECU ISSN 0005-4739
HG2916
BANCO CENTRAL DEL ECUADOR. BOLETIN. Text in Spanish. 1927. s-a. free. charts; stat. cum.index: 1927-1976.
Description: Provides statistics on public and private banking in Ecuador.
Indexed: PAIS, RASB.
Published by: Banco Central del Ecuador, Avenida 10 de Agosto y Briceno, Quito, Ecuador. TEL 593-2-2580158, uweb@uio.bce.fin.ec, http://www.bce.fin.ec. Circ: 6,000.

332 PRY ISSN 0408-330X
BANCO CENTRAL DEL PARAGUAY. BOLETIN ESTADISTICO. Text in Esperanto. 1953. m. **Document type:** *Bulletin, Government.*
Published by: Banco Central del Paraguay, Avda. Pablo VI y Avda. Sgt. Marecos, Asuncion, Paraguay. TEL 595-21-608011, FAX 595-21-6192637, vmaidana@bcp.gov.py, http://www.bcp.gov.py/bcpweb/.

332.1 PRY ISSN 0067-3285
BANCO CENTRAL DEL PARAGUAY. MEMORIA. Text in Spanish. 1952. a. free.
Published by: Banco Central del Paraguay, Avda. Pablo VI y Avda. Sgt. Marecos, Asuncion, Paraguay. TEL 595-21-608011, FAX 595-21-6192637.

332.1 URY
BANCO CENTRAL DEL URUGUAY. RESENA DE LA ACTIVIDAD ECONOMICO-FINANCIERA. Text in Spanish. irreg. stat.
Published by: Banco Central del Uruguay, Departamento de Estadisticas Economicas, Casilla 1467, Paysando y Florida, Montevideo, Uruguay.

332 BRA ISSN 0101-4668
HG2886
BANCO CENTRAL DO BRASIL. BOLETIM. Text in Portuguese. 1965. m. (plus 1 a. report). BRL 258 domestic; BRL 801.11 foreign (effective 1999). stat. **Document type:** *Bulletin.*
Related titles: Supplement(s): Banco Central do Brasil. Relatorio Anual.
Published by: Banco Central do Brasil/Central Bank of Brazil, Departamento Economico, Ed. Sede, 10 Andar, Brasilia, DF 70074900, Brazil. TEL 55-61-414-1764. Circ: 1,350. **Subscr. to:** DEMAP - DISUP, SIG - Quadra 8 - Lote 2025, Brasilia, DF 70610400, Brazil. TEL 55-61-344-1554, FAX 55-61-344-2982.

332 DEU ISSN 1561-0268
BANCO CENTRAL EUROPEO. BOLETIN MENSUAL. Text in Spanish. 1999. m.
Related titles: Online - full text ed.; ◆ English ed.: European Central Bank. Monthly Bulletin. ISSN 1561-0136; ◆ Italian ed.: Banca Centrale Europea. Bollettino Mensile. ISSN 1561-0276; ◆ Portuguese ed.: Banco Central Europeu. Boletim Mensal. ISSN 1561-0284; ◆ German ed.: Europaische Zentralbank. Monatsbericht. ISSN 1561-0292; ◆ Dutch ed.: Europese Centrale Bank. Maandbericht. ISSN 1561-0314; ◆ Spanish ed.: Euroopan Keskuspankki. Kuukausikatsaus. ISSN 1561-0322; ◆ Greek ed.: Europaike Kentrike Trapeza. Meniaio Deltio. ISSN 1561-025X; ◆ Swedish ed.: Europeiska Centralbanken. Manadsrapport. ISSN 1561-0144; ◆ Danish ed.: Europaeiske Centralbank. Manedsoversigt. ISSN 1561-0241; ◆ French ed.: Banque Central Europeenne. Bulletin Mensuel. ISSN 1561-0306.
—CINDOC.
Published by: European Central Bank, Postfach 16 03 19, Frankfurt am Main, 60066, Germany. TEL 49-69-1344-0, FAX 49-69-1344-6000, http://www.bde.es/informes/bce/bolemen.htm, http://www.ecb.int.

332 DEU ISSN 1561-0284
BANCO CENTRAL EUROPEU. BOLETIM MENSAL. Text in Portuguese. 1999. m.
Related titles: ◆ English ed.: European Central Bank. Monthly Bulletin. ISSN 1561-0136; ◆ Spanish ed.: Banco Central Europeo. Boletin Mensual. ISSN 1561-0268; ◆ Italian ed.: Banca Centrale Europea. Bollettino Mensile. ISSN 1561-0276; ◆ German ed.: Europaische Zentralbank. Monatsbericht. ISSN 1561-0292; ◆ Dutch ed.: Europese Centrale Bank. Maandbericht. ISSN 1561-0314; ◆ Spanish ed.: Euroopan Keskuspankki. Kuukausikatsaus. ISSN 1561-0322; ◆ Greek ed.: Europaike Kentrike Trapeza. Meniaio Deltio. ISSN 1561-025X; ◆ Swedish ed.: Europeiska Centralbanken. Manadsrapport. ISSN 1561-0144; ◆ Danish ed.: Europaeiske Centralbank. Manedsoversigt. ISSN 1561-0241; ◆ French ed.: Banque Central Europeenne. Bulletin Mensuel. ISSN 1561-0306.
Published by: European Central Bank, Postfach 16 03 19, Frankfurt am Main, 60066, Germany. TEL 49-69-1344-0, FAX 49-69-1344-6000, http://www.ecb.int.

332.1 HND
BANCO CENTROAMERICANO DE INTEGRACION ECONOMICA. MEMORIA ANUAL. Text in English, Spanish. 1962. a. index. back issues avail. **Document type:** *Corporate.*
Published by: Banco Centroamericano de Integracion Economica, Apdo. Postal 772, Tegucigalpa D.C, Honduras. TEL 504-222230. Ed. Carlos Guillermo Herrera. Circ: 1,200.

332.1 ESP
BANCO DE BILBAO. AGENDA FINANCIERA. Text in Spanish. 1975 (vol.14). a.
Published by: (Servicio de Estudios), Banco de Bilbao, Gran via, 12, Bilbao, Spain.

332 ESP
BANCO DE BILBAO. INFORME - MEMORIA. Text in Spanish. a. charts; illus.; stat.
Formerly: Banco de Bilbao. Memoria
Published by: (Servicio de Estudios), Banco de Bilbao, Gran via, 12, Bilbao, Spain.

332 ESP ISSN 0005-4798
HG3186
BANCO DE ESPANA. BOLETIN ESTADISTICO. Text in Spanish. 1960. m. bk.rev.
Related titles: Magnetic Tape ed.; ◆ Supplement to: Banco de Espana. Boletin Economico. ISSN 0210-3737.
Indexed: PAIS.
—CCC.
Published by: Banco de Espana, Alcala 50, Madrid, 28014, Spain. TEL 34-91-3385180, FAX 34-91-3385320, http://www.bde.es.

332 ESP
BANCO DE ESPANA. DOCUMENTO DE TRABAJO. Text mainly in Spanish; Text occasionally in English. irreg., latest 1995.
Published by: Banco de Espana, Alcala 50, Madrid, 28014, Spain. TEL 34-91-3385180, FAX 34-91-3385320, http://www.bde.es.

332.1 ESP ISSN 0067-3315
HC381
BANCO DE ESPANA. INFORME ANUAL. Text in Spanish. 1962. a. charts; stat. **Description:** Provides information on economic and financial institutions; includes a separate statistical appendix.
Related titles: English ed.
Published by: Banco de Espana, Alcala 50, Madrid, 28014, Spain. TEL 34-91-3385180, FAX 34-91-3385320, http://www.bde.es.

332 GTM ISSN 0005-481X
HG2746
BANCO DE GUATEMALA. BOLETIN ESTADISTICO. Text in Spanish. 1947. q. free. charts; stat. **Description:** Statistics from the National Bank on money and banking, public finance, commerce, and tourism.
Indexed: PAIS.
Published by: Banco de Guatemala, 7a Av. 22-01, ZONA, 1, Guatemala, 01001, Guatemala. TEL 53-4053.

332 GTM
BANCO DE GUATEMALA. ESTUDIO ECONOMICO Y MEMORIA DE LABORES. Text in Spanish. 1945. a.
Formerly (until 1967): Banco de Guatemala. Memoria
Published by: (Departamento de Relaciones Publicas), Banco de Guatemala, 7a Av. 22-01, ZONA, 1, Guatemala, 01001, Guatemala. TEL 535932.

332 GTM
BANCO DE GUATEMALA. NOTAS MONETARIAS. Text and summaries in Spanish. m. free. charts; illus.; stat. **Document type:** *Bulletin.* **Description:** Covers financial and economic news.
Formerly (until 1999): Banco de Guatemala. Boletin Informativo
Related titles: E-mail ed.
Published by: Banco de Guatemala, 7a Av. 22-01, ZONA, 1, Guatemala, 01001, Guatemala. TEL 502-230-6222, FAX 502-253-4035, TELEX 5231 45461, webmaster@banquat.gob.gt, sahr@banquat.gob.gt, http://www.banquet.gob.gt. Ed. Francisco Albizurez Palma. Pub. Mario Garcia Lara. Circ: 800.

332 330.9 COL ISSN 0005-4828
HG2906
BANCO DE LA REPUBLICA. REVISTA. Text in Spanish. 1927. m. COP 15,000, USD 60. bk.rev. charts; mkt.; stat. index, cum.index: 1927-1991. **Description:** Includes articles on economics and related topics.
Indexed: IBSS, KES, PAIS, RASB.
Published by: Banco de la Republica, Biblioteca Luis Angel Arango, Barrio de la Candelaria, Calle 11, 4-14, Bogota, CUND, Colombia. Circ: 4,500.

332.1 330.9 MEX ISSN 0067-3374
HG2720.M44
BANCO DE MEXICO. INFORME ANUAL. Text in Spanish. a. MXP 80 domestic; USD 20 in the Americas; USD 25 in Europe; USD 30 elsewhere. charts.
Related titles: Microfiche ed.
Published by: Banco de Mexico, Subdireccion de Investigacion Economica y Bancaria, 06059 Mexico, Mexico, Ave. JUAREZ 90, Centro Urbano Benito Juarez, Del. Cuauhtemoc, Ciudad De Mexico, DF 06059, Mexico. TEL 525-761-8588.

332.1 MEX
BANCO DE MEXICO. SERIE DOCUMENTOS DE INVESTIGACION. Text in Spanish. 1978-1991; N.S. 1995. irreg., latest 1996. MXP 70 domestic; USD 20 in North America; USD 25 in Europe.
Published by: Banco de Mexico, Subdireccion de Investigacion Economica y Bancaria, 06059 Mexico, Mexico, Ave. JUAREZ 90, Centro Urbano Benito Juarez, Del. Cuauhtemoc, Ciudad De Mexico, DF 06059, Mexico. TEL 525-761-8588.

BANCO DE PORTUGAL. ESTATISTICA E ESTUDOS ECONOMICOS. see *BUSINESS AND ECONOMICS—Abstracting, Bibliographies, Statistics*

332 PRT ISSN 0870-0060
BANCO DE PORTUGAL. REPORT OF THE DIRECTORS AND ECONOMIC AND FINANCIAL SURVEY. Key Title: Banco de Portugal. Relatorio do Conselho de Administracao. Text in Portuguese. 1862. a.
Related titles: Online - full content ed.
Published by: Banco de Portugal, Rua do Ouro 27, Lisbon, 1100-150, Portugal. TEL 351-21-3213200, FAX 351-21-3464843, http://www.bportugal.pt.

332 VEN
BANCO DE VENEZUELA. INFORME SEMESTRAL. Text in Spanish. 1974. s-a. charts; illus.; stat.
Published by: Banco Central de Venezuela, Av Urdaneta Esq Las Carmelitas, Caracas, 1010, Venezuela. TEL 58-212-8015111, FAX 58-212-8611649, info@bcv.org.ve, http://www.bcv.org.ve.

332.1 BRA ISSN 0101-0646
HG2886
BANCO DO BRASIL. ANNUAL REPORT. Text in English. a. free. charts; illus.; stat. **Document type:** *Corporate.*

B

Published by: Banco do Brasil S.A., Setor Bancario Sul, Quadra 4, Bloco C, Lote 32, Brasilia, DF 70089900, Brazil. TEL 55-61-3103774, FAX 55-61-3103735, http://www.bbnet.com.br.

332.1 BRA
BANCO DO BRASIL. BOLETIM DE INFORMACAO AO PESSOAL✶. Text in Portuguese. 1978. fortn. free to qualified personnel. charts; illus.; stat. **Description:** Internal organization of bank.
Published by: Banco do Brasil S.A., Departamento Geral de Selecao e Desenvolvimento do Pessoal, Setor Bancario Sul, LOTE, 23, Bloco C, A Sul (P Piloto), Caixa Postal 562, Brasilia, DF 70359-970, Brazil. Circ: 100,000 (controlled).

332.1 BRA
BANCO DO ESTADO DE PERNAMBUCO. BANDEPE RELATORIO. Summaries in English. 1969. a. free. illus.; stat.
Published by: Banco do Estado de Pernambuco, Cais do Apolo, 222, Recife, PE 50030-230, Brazil. Circ: 3,000.

332 BOL
BANCO MINERO DE BOLIVIA. MEMORIA. Text in Spanish. a.
Published by: Banco Minero de Bolivia, Casilla 1410, La Paz, Bolivia.

332 MEX
BANCO NACIONAL DE COMERCIO EXTERIOR, MEXICO. ANNUAL REPORT. Text in English. 1938. a. free. illus.; stat.
Related titles: ♦ Spanish ed.: Banco Nacional de Comercio Exterior, Mexico. Informe Anual. ISSN 0188-2783.
Indexed: KES.
Published by: Banco Nacional de Comercio Exterior S.A., Gerencia de Publicaciones, PERIFERICO SUR 4333, 4o Pte., Mexico, Jardines En la Montana, Mexico City, DF 14210, Mexico.

332 MEX ISSN 0188-2783
BANCO NACIONAL DE COMERCIO EXTERIOR, MEXICO. INFORME ANUAL. Text in Spanish. 1950. a.
Related titles: ♦ English ed.: Banco Nacional de Comercio Exterior, Mexico. Annual Report.
Published by: Banco Nacional de Comercio Exterior S.A., Gerencia de Publicaciones, PERIFERICO SUR 4333, 4o Pte., Mexico, Jardines En la Montana, Mexico City, DF 14210, Mexico.

332.1 HND
BANCO NACIONAL DE DESARROLLO AGRICOLA. MEMORIA ANUAL. Text in Spanish. 1950. a. free. charts; illus.; stat. **Document type:** *Corporate.* **Description:** Covers all areas of agriculture as it relates to banking and the economy of Honduras.
Formerly (until 1979): Banco Nacional de Fomento, Tegucigalpa. Memoria Anual (0067-3390)
Published by: Banco National de Desarrollo Agricola, Unidad de Estudios Economicos, Tegucigalpa DC, Honduras. FAX 37-5187. Ed. Cesar Marini. Circ: 2,000.

332 ECU
BANCO NACIONAL DE FOMENTO. BOLETIN. Text in Spanish. 1975. bi-m. free. illus.
Published by: (Departamento de Divulgacion Tecnica), Banco Nacional de Fomento, Apdo 685, Quito, Pichincha, Ecuador.

332 PAN
BANCO NACIONAL DE PANAMA. INFORME DEL GERENTE GENERAL. Text in Spanish. 1904. a.
Published by: Banco Nacional de Panama, Via Espana-Torre B.N.P., PO Box 5220, Panama City, 5, Panama.

332.1 PAN
BANCO NACIONAL DE PANAMA. MEMORIA ANUAL. Text in Spanish. 1904. a. free.
Formerly: Banco Nacional de Panama. Asesoria Economica. Memoria Anual
Published by: (Gerencia de Mercadotecnia y Comunicacion Social), Banco Nacional de Panama, Gerencia de Mercadotecnia y Comunicacion Social, Apdo 5220, Panama City, 5, Panama. TEL 507-69-2529. Circ: 1,500.

332.1 COL
BANCOS CENTRALES DE LOS PAISES DEL ACUERDO DE CARTAGENA. BOLETIN ESTADISTICO. Text in Spanish. N.S. 1984. q. free. charts; stat. **Document type:** *Bulletin.*
Published by: Latin American Reserve Fund/Fondo Latinoamericano de Reservas, Apartado Aereo 241523, Bogota, CUND, Colombia. FAX 57-1-288-1117, TELEX 45586. Circ: 1,200.

332 COL ISSN 0120-5226
HG1505
BANCOS Y BANCARIOS DE COLOMBIA. Text in Spanish. 1957. q. COP 15,000; USD 35 foreign (effective 1999). adv. bk.rev. charts; illus.; stat. **Document type:** *Trade.* **Description:** Covers economics, banking, business administration and people who work in the financial sector.
Address: Edificio Lerner, Oficina 1003, Ave. Jimenez, 4-03, PO Box 9418, Bogota, CUND, Colombia. TEL 57-911-2831262, FAX 57-911-342-9453, revbyb@colomsat.net.co. Ed. Arcesio Ramirez Jaramillo. adv.: B&W page COP 1,300,000, color page COP 2,000,000; trim 165 x 240. Circ: 19,700 (paid).

330.9 PHL
HC451
BANGKO SENTRAL REVIEW. Text in English. 1949. m. USD 20. charts; mkt.; stat.
Former titles (until Jul. 1993): C B Review (0115-1401); Which incorporated (in 1986): Countryside Banking (0115-0693); Central Bank News Digest (0008-9214)
Indexed: IPP, KES, PAIS, PROMT, WBA.
Published by: Central Bank of the Philippines, A. Mabini corner Vito Cruz Streets, Manila, Philippines. FAX 632-523-5735. Ed. Diwa C Guinigundo. Circ: 5,500.

332 THA ISSN 0125-0302
BANGKOK BANK. MONTHLY REVIEW. Text in English. 1962. m. free. charts; stat. index.
Indexed: APEL, BAS, CTFA, KES, MaizeAb, PAIS, PN&I, PoultAb, RRTA, RiceAb, WAE&RSA.
Published by: Bangkok Bank Ltd., Research Office, 333 Silom Rd, Bangkok, Thailand. Ed. Viraphong Vachratit. Circ: 5,500.

332.1 BGD
BANGLADESH BANK. ANNUAL REPORT. Text in English. a.
Published by: (Department of Public Relations and Publications), Bangladesh Bank, Motijheel Commercial Area, Dhaka, 2, Bangladesh.

BANGLADESH BANK. STATISTICS DEPARTMENT. ANNUAL BALANCE OF PAYMENTS. see *BUSINESS AND ECONOMICS—Abstracting, Bibliographies, Statistics*

BANGLADESH BANK. STATISTICS DEPARTMENT. BALANCE OF PAYMENTS. see *BUSINESS AND ECONOMICS—Abstracting, Bibliographies, Statistics*

332.1 DEU ISSN 0342-3182
DIE BANK; Zeitschrift fuer Bankpolitik und Bankpraxis. Text in German. 1900. m. EUR 67.41; EUR 8 newsstand/cover (effective 2004). adv. bk.rev. bibl.; charts. reprint service avail. from SCH. **Document type:** *Magazine, Trade.*
Formerly (until 1976): Bank-Betrieb (0005-5034)
Related titles: CD-ROM ed.: EUR 101.75 (effective 2001); Online - full text ed.: (from LexisNexis).
Indexed: DIP, IBR, IBZ, PAIS, RefZh.
—IE, Infotrieve.
Published by: (Bundesverband Deutscher Banken e.V.), Bank-Verlag Koeln GmbH, Wendelinstr 42, Cologne, 50933, Germany. TEL 49-221-5490153, FAX 49-221-5490315, die-bank@bdb.de, medien@bank-verlag.de, http://www.die-bank.de, http://www.bank-verlag.de. Eds. Werner Karsch, Wilhelm Buerklin. Adv. contact Renate Franken. B&W page EUR 1,900, color page EUR 3,400; trim 164 x 250. Circ: 8,720 (paid and controlled).

BANK ACCOUNTING & FINANCE. see *BUSINESS AND ECONOMICS—Accounting*

332 346 CAN
BANK ACT: LEGISLATION AND COMMENTARY. Text in English. 1998. 3/yr. looseleaf. CND 185 (effective 2001). **Document type:** *Academic/Scholarly.* **Description:** Provides expert analysis of federal rules governing banks.
Published by: LexisNexis Butterworths Canada Inc. (Subsidiary of: LexisNexis North America), 123 Commerce Valley Dr E, Ste 700, Markham, ON L3T 7W8, Canada. TEL 800-660-6481, FAX 905-479-6266.

332 659.1 USA ISSN 0274-7111
HG1616.M3
BANK ADVERTISING NEWS; the independent national newspaper of financial marketing. Text in English. bi-w. USD 398 (effective 1999 & 2000). **Document type:** *Trade.* **Description:** Provides coverage of bank, thrift and credit union promotions, marketing efforts and advertising campaigns in the nation's top 100 markets, as well as financial marketing related conferences.
Related titles: Online - full text ed.: (from EBSCO Publishing, Florida Center for Library Automation, Gale Group, LexisNexis, Northern Light Technology, Inc., O C L C Online Computer Library Center, Inc., ProQuest Information & Learning).
Indexed: ABIn, B&I, BLI.
—CCC.
Published by: Thomson Financial Media, One State St Plaza, 27th Fl, New York, NY 10004-1549. TEL 212-803-8200, 800-733-4571, FAX 212-843-9600, http://www.bankrate.com. Ed. Bonnie McGeer. Pub. Mario Diubaldi. Circ: 500 (paid).

332.1 MAR
BANK AL-MAGHRIB. RAPPORT ANNUEL. Text in French. 1959. a. free.
Formerly: Banque du Maroc. Rapport Annuel (0067-396X)
Published by: Bank Al-Maghrib, 277 Ave. Mohammed V, Rabat, Morocco.

332 AUT ISSN 1015-1516
BANK ARCHIV; Zeitschrift fuer das gesamte Bank- und Boersenwesen. Text in German. m. EUR 132 to institutions (effective 2005). adv. bk.rev. 68 p./no.; reprint service avail. from SCH. **Document type:** *Journal, Trade.*
Formerly: Oesterreichisches Bank-Archiv (0029-9839)
Indexed: DIP, IBR, IBZ, PAIS, RefZh.
—IE. **CCC.**
Published by: (Oesterreichische Bankwissenschaftliche Gesellschaft), Springer-Verlag Wien (Subsidiary of: Springer Science+Business Media) journals@springer.at, http://www.springer.at. Ed. Otto Lucius. adv.: B&W page EUR 1,060, color page EUR 1,908; trim 17.053 x 253. Circ: 3,500 (paid and controlled).

332.1 657 USA ISSN 0522-2478
BANK AUDITING & ACCOUNTING REPORT. Text in English. 1967. m. USD 290 (effective 2004). adv. **Document type:** *Newsletter.* **Description:** Covers developments in regard to government regulations, practices and techniques in bank accounting, and financial controls surrounding the industry.
Related titles: Online - full text ed.: (from ProQuest Information & Learning).
Indexed: BLI.
—CCC.
Published by: W G & L Financial Reporting & Management Research (Subsidiary of: R I A), 395 Hudson St, New York, NY 10014. TEL 212-367-6300, FAX 212-367-6718, http://www.riahome.com. **Subscr. to:** The Park Square Bldg., 31 St James Ave, Boston, MA 02116-4112. TEL 800-950-1207.

B

332.1 USA ISSN 0005-5042
BANK BOARD LETTER. Text in English. 1969. m. USD 68 (effective 2005). **Document type:** *Newsletter, Trade.* **Description:** Edited exclusively for directors of financial institutions and their holding companies.
Published by: Bank News, Inc., PO Box 29156, Shawnee Mission, KS 66201-9156. TEL 913-261-7000, 800-336-1120, FAX 913-261-7010, info@banknews.com, http://www.banknews.com. Ed. R W Poquette. Circ: 4,000 (paid).

BANK CONTROLLERS REPORT. see *BUSINESS AND ECONOMICS—Economic Situation And Conditions*

332 USA
BANK DIGEST. Text in English. 1988. d. USD 650. back issues avail. **Document type:** *Newsletter.*
Published by: Washington Service Bureau, Inc., 655 15th St, N W, Washington, DC 20005. TEL 202-508-0600, FAX 202-508-0694, http://www.wsb.com/sectoday.

332 USA ISSN 1070-7611
HG1615
BANK DIRECTOR. Text in English. 1991. q. USD 115; USD 30 per issue (effective 2005). adv. bk.rev. charts; illus.; maps; stat. 70 p./no. 2 cols./p.; back issues avail. **Document type:** *Magazine, Trade.* **Description:** For directors of financial institutions. Addresses concerns of bank boards, including issues of banking leadership, corporate governance and personal liability.
Related titles: Online - full text ed.: (from ProQuest Information & Learning).
Indexed: BLI.
Published by: Board Member Inc., 5110 Maryland Way, Ste 250, Brentwood, TN 37027. TEL 615-309-3200, FAX 615-371-0899, bankdirector@boardmember.com, http://www.bankdirector.com. Ed. Deborah Scally. Pub. L William Seidman. R&P Melissa E Musgrove TEL 615-309-3247. Adv. contact Mika Moser. color page USD 7,990. Circ: 35,000 (paid and controlled). **Subscr. to:** 2 Maryland Farms, Ste 123, Brentwood, TN 37027.

332 USA ISSN 1523-4134
BANK DIRECTOR'S BRIEFING. Text in English. 1979. m. USD 44 (effective 2003). **Document type:** *Newsletter.* **Description:** Provides a concise and readable summary of events in banking for outside directors of community banks.
Related titles: Online - full text ed.: (from ProQuest Information & Learning).
Indexed: BLI.
Published by: (Member Communications), Simmons-Boardman Publishing Corp., 345 Hudson St, 12th Fl, New York, NY 10014-4502. TEL 212-620-7200, FAX 212-633-1165. Ed. Steven Cocheo. Pub. Russell S Selover.

330.9 IDN ISSN 0302-6795
HG3310.J34
BANK EKSPORT IMPORT INDONESIA. ANNUAL REPORT. Text in English, Indonesian. a. illus.; stat.
Published by: Bank Eksport Import Indonesia, Jl. Lapagan Setasium 1, PO Box 32, Jakarta, Indonesia.

332.1 NLD ISSN 0005-5018
BANK- EN EFFECTENBEDRIJF. Text in Dutch. 1952. 10/yr. EUR 138 domestic; EUR 150 foreign (effective 2005). adv. bk.rev. abstr.; stat. index. **Document type:** *Bulletin.*
—IE, Infotrieve, KNAW.
Published by: Nederlands Instituut voor het Bank-, Verzekerings- en Effectenbedrijf - Stichting Vakontwikkeling Verzekeringsbedrijf, Postbus 2285, Amsterdam, 1000 CG, Netherlands. TEL 31-20-5208520, FAX 31-20-6229446, info@nibesvv.nl, http://www.nibesvv.nl. Circ: 4,500.

332 USA
BANK FINANCIAL QUARTERLY (HARTLAND). Text in English. q. USD 398 (effective 1998). back issues avail. **Document type:** *Trade.*
Published by: I D C Financial Publishing, Inc., PO Box 140, Hartland, WI 53029. TEL 414-367-7231, 800-525-5457. Ed., Pub., R&P John E Rickmeier.

▼ new title ➤ refereed ✶ unverified ♦ full entry avail.

332.1 USA
BANK FINANCIAL QUARTERLY (ROCKVILLE). Text in English. 1986. 4/yr. USD 349. **Description:** Gives 30 key financial indicators on most of the commercial banks in the U.S.. Also rates safety and soundness.
Published by: United Communications Group, 11300 Rockville Pike Ste 1100, Rockville, MD 20852-3030. TEL 301-816-8950, FAX 301-816-8945. Ed. Daniel Brown.

332.1 CHE ISSN 1021-2477
HG1997.I6
BANK FOR INTERNATIONAL SETTLEMENTS. ANNUAL REPORT. Text in English, French, German, Italian. 1931. a. avail. to limited qualified personnel only.. charts; stat. index. reprints avail. **Document type:** *Corporate.*
Related titles: Online - full text ed.; French ed.: Banque des Reglements Internationaux. Rapport Annuel. ISSN 1021-2493; German ed.: Bank fuer Internationalen Zahlungsausgleich. Jahresbericht. ISSN 1021-2485; Italian ed.: Banca dei Regolamenti Internazionali. Relazione Annuale. ISSN 1021-2507; Spanish ed.: Banco de Pagos Internacionales. Informe Anual. ISSN 1560-3024.
—BLDSC (1113.115000), CISTI.
Published by: Bank for International Settlements, Centralbahnplatz 2, Basel, 4002, Switzerland. TEL 41-61-2808080, FAX 41-61-2809100, 41-61-2808100. R&P Margaret Critchlow. Circ: (controlled).

BANK FOR INTERNATIONAL SETTLEMENTS. CONSOLIDATED INTERNATIONAL BANKING STATISTICS. see *BUSINESS AND ECONOMICS—Abstracting, Bibliographies, Statistics*

332.1 CHE ISSN 1609-0381
BANK FOR INTERNATIONAL SETTLEMENTS. PAPERS. Text in English. irreg.
Published by: Bank for International Settlements, Centralbahnplatz 2, Basel, 4002, Switzerland. http://www.bis.org.

332.1 CHE
BANK FOR INTERNATIONAL SETTLEMENTS. WORKING PAPERS. Text in English. irreg.
Published by: Bank for International Settlements, Centralbahnplatz 2, Basel, 4002, Switzerland. http://www.bis.org.

332 USA ISSN 1065-8165
BANK FRAUD. Text in English. 1986. m. USD 225 domestic; USD 250 foreign (effective 2000). **Document type:** *Newsletter.* **Description:** Covers fraud and risk management, including typical fraud cases, telling what happened, how it was handled, the final outcome, and preventative measures.
Formerly: Bank Fraud Alert
—CCC.
Published by: Bank Administration Institute Foundation, 1 N Franklin St, Chicago, IL 60606. TEL 312-683-2248, FAX 312-683-2373. Ed. Richard G Kemmer. R&P Alison Estnada TEL 312-683-2452.

▼ **BANK FRAUD AND I T SECURITY REPORT.** (Information Technology) see *COMPUTERS—Computer Security*

332.1 USA
BANK HOLDING COMPANY (Y-9). Text in English. q. USD 1,816 in North America; USD 3,632 elsewhere (effective 2001).
Related titles: Magnetic Tape ed.
Published by: (Federal Reserve System), U.S. Department of Commerce, National Technical Information Service, 5285 Port Royal Rd, Springfield, VA 22161. TEL 703-605-6000, info@ntis.gov, http://www.ntis.gov.

BANK HOLDING COMPANY COMPLIANCE MANUAL. see *LAW*

332 POL ISSN 0137-5520
➤ **BANK I KREDYT.** Text in Polish; Summaries in English. 1945. m. EUR 104 foreign (effective 2005). abstr.; charts. 88 p./no. 2 cols./p.; back issues avail. **Document type:** *Bulletin.* **Description:** Presents basic trends of theoretical thought in the field of finance and banking, reflecting changes in the Polish banking system and also indicating the foreign approaches.
Formerly (until 1970): Narodowy Bank Polski. Wiadomosci
Indexed: AgrLib, RASB.
Published by: Narodowy Bank Polski, ul Swietokrzyska 11-21, Warsaw, 00919, Poland. TEL 48-22-6531000, FAX 48-22-6208518, nbp@nbp.pl, http://www.nbp.pl. Ed. Boguslaw Pietrzak. R&P Iwona Stefaniak TEL 48-22-6532571. Circ: 2,000 (paid). **Dist. by:** Ars Polona, Krakowskie Przedmiescie 7, Warsaw, Poland. TEL 48-22-9263914, FAX 48-22-9265334, arspolona@arspolona.com.pl, http://www.arspolona.com.pl.

332.1 336 USA ISSN 0734-8037
KF6495.B2
THE BANK INCOME TAX RETURN MANUAL. Text in English. 1983. a. USD 215 (effective 1999). **Document type:** *Trade.* **Description:** Enables bank tax professionals to prepare bank income tax return schedules accurately, reducing the possibility of an I.R.S. audit.
Published by: W G & L Financial Reporting & Management Research (Subsidiary of: R I A), 90 Fifth Ave, New York, NY 10011. TEL 212-645-4800, FAX 212-337-4280, http://www.riag.com. Eds. Charles W Wheeler, Jack B Wilson Jr.

330 DEU ISSN 0941-0163
BANK-INFORMATION UND GENOSSENSCHAFTSFORUM. Text in German. 1990. m. EUR 98; EUR 9.40 newsstand/cover (effective 2004). adv. **Document type:** *Magazine, Trade.*
Formed by the merger of (1974-1990): Bank-Information (0721-5517); Which was formerly (until 1981): Bank-Information fuer Volksbanken und Raiffeisenbanken (0342-9725); Which was formed by the merger of (196?-1974): Bankbetriebliche Information (0342-9717); (19??-1974): Der Volksbank-Betrieb (0342-9660); (1974-1990): Genossenschaftsforum (0343-2424); Which was formed by the merger of (1949-1974): Raiffeisen-Rundschau (0343-2408); (1951-1974): Blaetter fuer Genossenschaftswesen (0006-4432)
Indexed: DIP, IBR, IBZ.
Published by: Deutscher Genossenschafts-Verlag eG, Leipziger Str 35, Wiesbaden, 65191, Germany. TEL 49-611-50660, FAX 49-611-50661500, direct@dgverlag.de, http://www.bankinformation.de/www/php_fe/index.php, http://www.dgverlag.de. adv.: B&W page EUR 2,100, color page EUR 3,990. Circ: 12,000 (paid and controlled).

BANK INSURANCE AND RISK MANAGEMENT. see *INSURANCE*

BANK INSURANCE SURVEY REPORT. see *INSURANCE*

332 657.2 USA
BANK INTERNAL AUDIT: A WORKING GUIDE TO REGULATORY COMPLIANCE. Text in English. 1991. 3 base vols. plus s-a. updates. looseleaf. USD 395; USD 235 renewals (effective 2004). **Document type:** *Directory, Trade.* **Description:** Enables bank audit personnel to implement and run effective audit programs.
Related titles: ◆ Series of: Compliance Officer's Management Manual.
Indexed: ATI.
Published by: Sheshunoff Information Services Inc., 807 Las Cimas Pkwy, Ste 300, Austin, TX 78746. TEL 512-472-2244, 800-456-2340, FAX 512-305-6575, customercare.sis@sheshunoff.com, http://www.sheshunoff.com/store/498.html.

332 USA ISSN 1095-3698
HG1723
BANK INVESTOR. Text in English. 1987. m. USD 499 (effective 1998). adv. charts; mkt.; stat. back issues avail. **Document type:** *Trade.* **Description:** Provides investors with the most current financial, market and merger information available on the publicly traded banks.
Formerly: Bank Securities Monthly (1074-6552)
Media: Online - full content.
Published by: S N L Financial LC, 212 7th St NE, Charlottesvle, VA 22902-5307. TEL 434-977-1600, FAX 434-293-0407, http://www.snl.com. Eds. Joe Maloney, Mark Saunders. Pub. Alan Zimmerman. Adv. contact Mark Outlaw.

BANK KARAMCHARI. see *LABOR UNIONS*

332.1 USA ISSN 1099-3398
BANK LOAN REPORT. Text in English. 1986. w. USD 3,600 (effective 2005). adv. reprints avail. **Document type:** *Newsletter, Trade.* **Description:** Contains information available on the $1 trillion US loan marketplace.
Related titles: Online - full text ed.: (from bigchalk, EBSCO Publishing, Florida Center for Library Automation, Gale Group, O C L C Online Computer Library Center, Inc.).
Indexed: ATI, B&I.
Published by: Source Media, Inc., One State St Plaza, 27th Fl, New York, NY 10004. TEL 212-803-6077, 800-221-1809, FAX 212-747-1154, custserv@sourcemedia.com, http://www.bankloanreport.com, http://www.sourcemedia.com. Ed. Sarah Husband. Adv. contact James MacDonald TEL 212-803-8749. B&W page USD 2,315, color page USD 4,465; trim 8.5 x 11. Circ: 108.

332.1 DEU ISSN 0944-3223
BANK MAGAZIN; die Zeitschrift fuer Bankmanagement, Finanzvertrieb und e-business. Text in German. 1952. m. EUR 96 domestic; EUR 60 to students; EUR 8.50 newsstand/cover (effective 2004). adv. bk.rev. abstr.; tr.lit. **Document type:** *Magazine, Trade.*
Formerly (until 1993): Bankkaufmann (0005-5085)
Indexed: RASB.
—CCC.
Published by: Betriebswirtschaftlicher Verlag Dr. Th. Gabler GmbH (Subsidiary of: Springer Science+Business Media), Abraham-Lincoln-Str 46, Wiesbaden, 65189, Germany. FAX 49-611-7878450, bankmagazin@bertelsmann.de, gabler.service@gwv-fachverlage.de, http://www.bankmagazin.de, http://www.gabler.de. Ed. Margaretha Hamm. Adv. contact Tanja Pfisterer. B&W page EUR 3,890, color page EUR 5,990. Circ: 13,200 (paid and controlled).

332 330.9 IRN ISSN 0256-5323
HC471
BANK MARKAZI JOMHOURI ISLAMI IRAN. BULLETIN. Key Title: Bulletin - Bank Markazi Islamic Republic of Iran. Text in Persian, Modern. 1962. q. free. charts; stat. index. **Document type:** *Bulletin.*
Formerly (until 1983): Bank Markazi Iran Bulletin (0005-5093)
Indexed: KES, PROMT.
—BLDSC (2435.160000).
Published by: (Iran. Economic Research Department), Bank Markazi Jomhouri Islami Iran/Central Bank of the Islamic Republic of Iran, P O Box 11365-8531, Tehran, Iran. FAX 98-21-390323, TELEX 216219. Circ: 1,800.

332.1 USA ISSN 1540-4315
BANK MARKETING AND COMPLIANCE ALERT. Text in English. m. USD 345 (effective 2002).
Published by: A.S. Pratt & Sons, Inc., 1911 Fort Myer Dr, Arlington, VA 22209. TEL 703-528-0145, 800-572-2797, FAX 703-528-1736, pratt.info@thomsonmedia.com, http://www.aspratt.com/.

332 GBR ISSN 0791-2765
BANK MARKETING INTERNATIONAL. Text in English. 1990. m. GBP 997, EUR 1,597, USD 1,697 (effective 2005). **Document type:** *Trade.* **Description:** Market intelligence for the financial services industry.
Related titles: Online - full text ed.: (from Gale Group, LexisNexis, Northern Light Technology, Inc., O C L C Online Computer Library Center, Inc., ProQuest Information & Learning).
Indexed: B&I, BLI.
Published by: Lafferty Publications Ltd., The Colonnades, 82 Bishops Bridge Rd, London, W2 6BB, United Kingdom. TEL 44-20-75635700, FAX 44-20-75635701, cuserv@lafferty.com, http://www.lafferty.com/newsletter_publication.php?id=1. Ed. John Evans.

332 USA ISSN 1074-6706
HG1722
BANK MERGERS & ACQUISITIONS. Text in English. 1986. m. USD 795 (effective 2002). adv. back issues avail. **Document type:** *Newsletter.*
Related titles: Diskette ed.; Supplement(s): Bank Mergers & Acquisitions Scoreboard.
Published by: S N L Financial LC, 212 7th St NE, Charlottesvle, VA 22902-5307. TEL 434-977-1600, FAX 804-977-4466, subscriptions@snlnet.com, http://www.snlnet.com. Ed. Jack Milligan. Pub. Reid Nagle. Adv. contact Mark Outlaw.

BANK MERGERS & ACQUISITIONS WEEKLY. see *BUSINESS AND ECONOMICS—Investments*

332 MYS
BANK NEGARA MALAYSIA. DIRECTOR GENERAL OF INSURANCE ANNUAL REPORT. Text in English, Malay. a.
Published by: Bank Negara Malaysia/Central Bank of Malaysia, Jalan Dato'Onn, PO Box 10922, Kuala Lumpur, 50480, Malaysia. TEL 03-2988044, FAX 03-2912990.

332 MYS
BANK NEGARA MALAYSIA. DISCUSSION PAPERS. Text in English. 1986. irreg., latest vol.33. **Description:** Contains papers prepared by Bank Negara staff on various topics.
Published by: Bank Negara Malaysia/Central Bank of Malaysia, Jalan Dato'Onn, PO Box 10922, Kuala Lumpur, 50480, Malaysia. TEL 03-2988044, FAX 03-2912990.

332 MYS
BANK NEGARA MALAYSIA. OCCASIONAL PAPERS. Text in English. 1984. irreg., latest vol.4. **Description:** Contains studies on a variety of economic and financial subjects by Bank Negara staff.
Published by: Bank Negara Malaysia/Central Bank of Malaysia, Jalan Dato'Onn, PO Box 10922, Kuala Lumpur, 50480, Malaysia. TEL 03-2988044, FAX 03-2912990.

BANK NEGARA MALAYSIA. STATISTICAL BULLETIN. see *BUSINESS AND ECONOMICS—Abstracting, Bibliographies, Statistics*

332.1 USA ISSN 0005-5123
HG1501
BANK NEWS. Text in English. 1901. m. USD 79 (effective 2005). adv. bk.rev. charts; illus.; stat.; tr.lit. back issues avail.; reprints avail. **Document type:** *Magazine, Trade.*
Incorporates (1919-1984): Mountain States Banker (0027-2590); (1983-1986): Mid-Continent Banker. Southern Edition (0749-7911); Which superseded (1918-1982): Mid-Continent Banker (0026-296X); Which incorporated (1926-1982): Mid-Western Banker (0026-3060)
Related titles: Microform ed.: (from PQC); Online - full text ed.: (from Northern Light Technology, Inc., ProQuest Information & Learning).
Indexed: ABIn, BLI, PAIS.
Published by: Bank News, Inc., 5115 Roe Blvd., Ste 200, Shawnee Mission, KS 66205. TEL 913-261-7000, FAX 913-261-7010, info@banknews.com, http://www.banknews.com. Ed. R W Poquette. Pub. Pam Baker. Circ: 7,200 (paid and controlled).

330 332 BWA
BANK OF BOTSWANA. BULLETIN. Text in English. 1983. q. USD 2. back issues avail. **Document type:** *Bulletin.*
Indexed: IBSS.
Published by: Bank of Botswana, PO Box 712, Gaborone, Botswana. Circ: 600.

332.1 CAN ISSN 0067-3587
HG2706
BANK OF CANADA. ANNUAL REPORT. Text in English, French. 1935. a. free. **Document type:** *Corporate.*
—CISTI.
Published by: Bank of Canada, Publications Distribution, Communications Services, 234 Wellington St, Ottawa, ON K1A 0G9, Canada. TEL 613-782-8248, FAX 613-782-8874, publications@bank-banque-canada.ca, http://www.bank-banque-canada.ca, http://www.bankofcanada.ca. R&P Monique Longtin.

332 CAN ISSN 1488-4186
HC111
BANK OF CANADA BANKING AND FINANCIAL STATISTICS. Text in English, French. 1999. m.
—CISTI.
Published by: Bank of Canada, Publications Distribution, Communications Services, 234 Wellington St, Ottawa, ON K1A 0G9, Canada. TEL 613-782-8248, FAX 613-782-8874, publications@bank-banque-canada.ca, http://www.bankofcanada.ca.

332.1 CAN ISSN 0045-1460
BANK OF CANADA. REVIEW/BANQUE DU CANADA. REVUE. Text in English, French. 1971. q. CND 25 domestic; CND 25 in United States; CND 50 elsewhere; CND 7.50 per issue (effective 2004). index. back issues avail. **Document type:** *Corporate.* **Description:** Contains economic commentary and feature articles.
Supersedes: Bank of Canada Statistical Summary (0005-514X)
Related titles: Microform ed.: (from PQC); Online - full text ed.: (from EBSCO Publishing, Micromedia ProQuest, O C L C Online Computer Library Center, Inc., ProQuest Information & Learning).
Indexed: ABIn, BLI, CBCARef, CBPI, CPerI, PAIS, PdeR.
—CISTI. **CCC.**
Published by: Bank of Canada, Publications Distribution, Communications Services, 234 Wellington St, Ottawa, ON K1A 0G9, Canada. TEL 613-782-8248, FAX 613-782-8874, publications@bank-banque-canada.ca, http://www.bank-banque-canada.ca, http://www.bankofcanada.ca. Circ: 4,600.

332.1 CAN ISSN 0713-7931
HC111
BANK OF CANADA. TECHNICAL REPORTS. Text in English. 1969. irreg. free. **Document type:** *Corporate.*
Formerly (until 1973): Bank of Canada. Staff Research Studies (0067-3595)
—BLDSC (8711.940000), CISTI.
Published by: Bank of Canada, Publications Distribution, Communications Services, 234 Wellington St, Ottawa, ON K1A 0G9, Canada. TEL 613-782-8248, FAX 613-782-8874, publications@bank-banque-canada.ca, http://www.bank-banque-canada.ca, http://www.bankofcanada.ca.

332 CAN ISSN 1192-5434
HC111
BANK OF CANADA. WORKING PAPERS/BANQUE DU CANADA. DOCUMENT DE TRAVAIL. Text in English. irreg. free.
Formerly (until 1975): Bank of Canada. Staff Research Studies
Published by: Bank of Canada, Publications Distribution, Communications Services, 234 Wellington St, Ottawa, ON K1A 0G9, Canada. TEL 613-782-8248, FAX 613-782-8874, publications@bank-banque-canada.ca, http://www.bank-banque-canada.ca, http://www.bankofcanada.ca.

330.9 LKA
BANK OF CEYLON. ANNUAL REPORT AND ACCOUNTS. Text in English. 1939. a. free to institutions. illus.
Formerly (until 1965): Bank of Ceylon. Annual Report
Published by: Bank of Ceylon, 4 Bank of Ceylon Mawatha, Colombo, 1, Sri Lanka. TEL 348878, FAX 445798. Circ: 3,500.

332.1 GBR ISSN 1467-016X
HG2994
BANK OF ENGLAND. ANNUAL REPORT. Text in English. a. free. reprint service avail. from PQC. **Document type:** *Corporate.* **Description:** Contains the annual report of the bank on the exercise of functions conferred on it by the Banking Act of 1979.
Former titles: Bank of England. Report and Accounts (0308-5279); Bank of England. Report (0067-3625)
Indexed: RASB.
—BLDSC (1113.114806).
Published by: Bank of England, Press Office, Bank Of England, London, EC2R 8AH, United Kingdom. TEL 44-20-7601-3904, FAX 44-20-7601-5460.

332 GBR ISSN 1365-7690
HG2994
BANK OF ENGLAND. MONETARY AND FINANCIAL STATISTICS. Variant title: Bankstats. Text in English. 1997. q. GBP 60 domestic; GBP 85 in Europe Rest of Europe incl. Republic of Ireland; GBP 115 in Asia & the Pacific; GBP 105 rest of world; GBP 40 domestic to Academics (UK only); GBP 17 newsstand/cover domestic; GBP 22 newsstand/cover in Europe; GBP 29 newsstand/cover in Asia & the Pacific; GBP 27 newsstand/cover rest of world; GBP 12 newsstand/cover domestic to Academics (UK only) (effective 2003); available free on the internet.. stat. back issues avail. **Document type:** *Bulletin, Academic/Scholarly.*
Related titles: Online - full text ed.
Published by: Bank of England, Publications Group, Threadneedle St, London, EC2R 8AH, United Kingdom. TEL 44-20-76014030, FAX 44-20-76013298, mapublications@bankofengland.co.uk, http://www.bankofengland.co.uk/mfsd/ms/001129/index.htm.

332.46 GBR ISSN 1473-4249
HC251
BANK OF ENGLAND. MONETARY POLICY COMMITTEE. MINUTES AND PRESS NOTICES. Text in English. 1993. q.
Supersedes in part (in 2001): Bank of England. Inflation Report (1353-6737)
Published by: Bank of England, Publications Group, Threadneedle St, London, EC2R 8AH, United Kingdom. TEL 44-20-76014030, FAX 44-20-76013298, http://www.bankofengland.co.uk/.

332.1 GBR
BANK OF ENGLAND. OVERVIEW. Text in English. q. free (effective 2003). 1 p./no.; **Document type:** *Bulletin.* **Description:** Provides a digest of the Bank of England Inflation Report.
Formerly (May 2001): Bank of England. Bank Briefing
Related titles: Online - full text ed.
Published by: (Public Enquiries), Bank of England, Publications Group, Threadneedle St, London, EC2R 8AH, United Kingdom. TEL 44-20-76014030, FAX 44-20-76013298, mapublications@bankofengland.co.uk, http://www.bankofengland.co.uk/. Circ: 16,000.

332 GBR
➤ **BANK OF ENGLAND. WORKING PAPER SERIES.** Text in English. 1991. irreg. free (effective 2003). back issues avail.; reprint service avail. from PQC. **Document type:** *Monographic series, Academic/Scholarly.* **Description:** Working papers written by the bank on topics of general interest.
Formed by the merger of (1978-1991): Bank of England. Discussion Papers (0142-6753); (1982-1991): Bank of England. Technical Series
Related titles: Online - full text ed.
—BLDSC (9350.830800), ingenta.
Published by: Bank of England, Publications Group, Threadneedle St, London, EC2R 8AH, United Kingdom. TEL 44-20-76014030, FAX 44-20-76013298, mapublications@bankofengland.co.uk, http://www.bankofengland.co.uk/.

332 FIN ISSN 1239-9345
HG3133
BANK OF FINLAND. ANNUAL REPORT. Text in English. 1914. a. free. **Document type:** *Trade.* **Description:** Covers economic developments, monetary policy, payment systems and maintenance of currency supply, international relations, balance sheet, charts, tables and more.
Formerly (until 1995): Bank of Finland Year Book (0081-9468); Incorporates (1866-1987): Bank of Finland. Annual Statement (0081-945X)
Related titles: Online - full text ed.: ISSN 1456-579X. 1998; ♦ Finnish ed.: Suomen Pankki. Vuosikertomus. ISSN 1239-9329; ♦ Swedish ed.: Finlands Bank. Aarsberaettelse. ISSN 1239-9337.
Indexed: RASB.
Published by: Suomen Pankki/Bank of Finland, P O Box 160, Helsinki, 00101, Finland. TEL 358-9-183-2566, FAX 358-9-174-872, publications@bof.fi, http://www.bof.fi/env/rhinden.htm. Circ: 8,000.

332 FIN ISSN 0784-6509
HC337.F5
BANK OF FINLAND. BULLETIN. Text in English. 1921. q. free (effective 2005). charts; mkt.; stat. index, cum.index. back issues avail.; reprint service avail. from PQC. **Document type:** *Bulletin, Consumer.* **Description:** Covers topics relating to the banking industry, including monetary policy and financial market analysis providing foreign experts with current information on the Finnish economy.
Formerly (in 1921-1939 and 1946-1987): Bank of Finland. Monthly Bulletin (0005-5174)
Related titles: Online - full text ed.: ISSN 1456-5870. 1998.
Indexed: IBSS, KES, PAIS, RASB, WBA.
—BLDSC (2409.683500).
Published by: Suomen Pankki/Bank of Finland, P O Box 160, Helsinki, 00101, Finland. TEL 358-10-8311, FAX 358-9-174872, publications@bof.fi, publications@bof.fi., http://www.bof.fi/env/rhinden.htm. Ed. Matti Vanhala. Circ: 5,600.

332 FIN ISSN 0785-3572
HG37.F5
BANK OF FINLAND. DISCUSSIONS PAPERS. Text in English, Finnish, Swedish. 1988. irreg. free. reprints avail. **Document type:** *Monographic series, Trade.*
Related titles: Online - full text ed.: ISSN 1456-6184. 1996.
—BLDSC (1861.797000), IE, ingenta.
Published by: Suomen Pankki/Bank of Finland, P O Box 160, Helsinki, 00101, Finland. TEL 358-9-183-2566, FAX 358-9-174-872, publications@bof.fi., http://www.bof.fi/env/rhinden.htm. Circ: 500.

332 FIN
BANK OF FINLAND. STATEMENT; the balance sheet. Text in Finnish. w. free.
Published by: Bank of Finland Accounting Department, PL 160, Helsinki, 00101, Finland. TEL 358-9-1832566, FAX 358-9-174872, publications@bof.fi.

332 GRC ISSN 1107-5287
BANK OF GREECE. BULLETIN OF CONJUNCTURAL INDICATORS. Text in Greek. 1997. m. free. charts; stat. **Document type:** *Bulletin.*
Published by: Bank of Greece, Economic Research Division, 21 Panepistimiou St, Athens, 102 50, Greece. FAX 30-1-3233025, boglibr@ath.forthnet.gr.

332 GRC ISSN 1105-9729
HC295
BANK OF GREECE. ECONOMIC BULLETIN. Text in Greek. 1993. s-a. free. charts; stat. **Document type:** *Bulletin.*
Published by: Bank of Greece, Economic Research Division, 21 Panepistimiou St, Athens, 102 50, Greece. FAX 30-1-3233025, boglibr@ath.forthnet.gr.

BANK OF GREECE. MONTHLY STATISTICAL BULLETIN. see *BUSINESS AND ECONOMICS—Abstracting, Bibliographies, Statistics*

332 GRC ISSN 1105-0527
HG3250.5
BANK OF GREECE. REPORT OF THE GOVERNOR. Text in English, Greek. 1928. a. free. charts; stat. **Document type:** *Corporate.*
Published by: Bank of Greece, Economic Research Division, 21 Panepistimiou St, Athens, 102 50, Greece. FAX 30-1-3233025, TELEX 215102, boglibr@ath.forthnet.gr.

BANK OF INDIA. BULLETIN. see *BUSINESS AND ECONOMICS—Economic Situation And Conditions*

BANK OF ISRAEL. ANNUAL INFORMATION ON THE BANKING CORPORATIONS/MEDA' SHNATI 'AL HATTA'AGIDIM HABBANQA'IYYIM. see *BUSINESS AND ECONOMICS—Abstracting, Bibliographies, Statistics*

332.1 ISR ISSN 0067-365X
HG3361.P22
BANK OF ISRAEL. ANNUAL REPORT. Text in English. a. ILS 88 (effective 2000). **Document type:** *Government.* **Description:** Deals with Israel's economy.
Related titles: Hebrew ed.
Published by: Bank of Israel, Kiryath Ben Gurion, P O Box 780, Jerusalem, 91007, Israel. http://www.bankisrael.gov.il/publeng/publeng.htm.

BANK OF ISRAEL. CURRENT INFORMATION ON BANKS. see *BUSINESS AND ECONOMICS—Abstracting, Bibliographies, Statistics*

BANK OF ISRAEL. ECONOMIC REVIEW. see *BUSINESS AND ECONOMICS—Economic Situation And Conditions*

BANK OF JAMAICA. ECONOMIC STATISTICS. see *BUSINESS AND ECONOMICS—Abstracting, Bibliographies, Statistics*

332 JAM ISSN 0799-1037
BANK OF JAMAICA QUARTERLY MONETARY POLICY REPORT. Text in English. q.
Formerly (until 2000): Economic Bulletin
Published by: Bank of Jamaica, Nethersole Place, P O Box 621, Kingston, Jamaica. TEL 876-922-0750, FAX 876-922-0854, info@boj.org.jm, http://www.boj.org.jm/qmpr.asp.

332 JAM ISSN 0067-3668
HG2826
BANK OF JAMAICA. REPORT AND STATEMENT OF ACCOUNTS. Text in English. a. free.
Published by: Bank of Jamaica, Nethersole Place, P O Box 621, Kingston, Jamaica. TEL 809-922-0750, FAX 809-967-4265, TELEX 2165. Circ: 1,200.

332 JAM ISSN 0572-5968
HG2824
BANK OF JAMAICA. STATISTICAL DIGEST. Text in English. 1969. m. free. stat.
Published by: Bank of Jamaica, Nethersole Place, P O Box 621, Kingston, Jamaica. TEL 809-922-0750, FAX 809-967-4265. Circ: 990.

332 JPN
BANK OF JAPAN. ANNUAL REVIEW. Text in English. a. free. 180 p./no.; **Document type:** *Corporate.* **Description:** Contains a review of monetary and economic developments of the previous fiscal year, an outline of the Bank's policy measures and financial statements, a chronological listing of events, an introduction to the bank's organization, and other materials.
—BLDSC (1515.925400).
Published by: Bank of Japan/Nippon Ginko, c/o Public Relations Department, 2-1-1 Hongoku-cho-Nihonbashi, Chuo-ku, Tokyo, 1030000, Japan. TEL 81-3-3279-1111, FAX 81-3-3510-1374, http://www.boj.or.jp/en.index.htm.

332 JPN ISSN 0919-1380
HC461
BANK OF JAPAN QUARTERLY BULLETIN. Text in English. q. JPY 550 per issue. stat. 130 p./no.; **Description:** Contains research papers on finance and the economy of Japan, various statistics, and a chronology of financial events in Japan. Includes "Minutes of the Monetary Policy Meeting," "Monthly Report of Recent Economic and Financial Developments," and the Governor's speeches.
—BLDSC (7171.421000).
Published by: Bank of Japan/Nippon Ginko, c/o Public Relations Department, 2-1-1 Hongoku-cho-Nihonbashi, Chuo-ku, Tokyo, 1030000, Japan. TEL 81-3-3279-1111, FAX 81-3-5210-1374, http://www.boj.or.jp/en.index.htm. **Dist. by:** Overseas Courier Service Co. Ltd., Tokyo, Japan. TEL 81-3-5476-8130, FAX 81-3-3453-9338.

332.1 KOR ISSN 0067-3706
BANK OF KOREA. ANNUAL REPORT. Key Title: Annual Report - Bank of Korea. Text in English. a.
Published by: Bank of Korea, Research Department, 110 3 Ka Namdaemun Ro, Chung-Ku, Seoul, 100794, Korea, S. TEL 82-2759-4172, FAX 82-2-752-0946, bokdrar@bok.or.kr, http://www.bok.or.kr. Ed. Seong Tae Lee.

BANK OF KOREA. MONTHLY STATISTICAL BULLETIN. see *BUSINESS AND ECONOMICS—Abstracting, Bibliographies, Statistics*

332.1 KOR ISSN 1226-7589
HG187.K62
BANK OF KOREA. RESEARCH DEPARTMENT. ECONOMIC PAPERS. Text in Korean. 1998. s-a. **Document type:** *Academic/Scholarly.*
Indexed: IBSS, JEL.
—BLDSC (3653.946000).
Published by: Bank of Korea, Research Department, 110 3 Ka Namdaemun Ro, Chung-Ku, Seoul, 100794, Korea, S. TEL 82-2759-4172, FAX 82-2-752-0946, bokdrar@bok.or.kr, http://www.bok.or.kr.

332.1 MUS ISSN 0067-3722
BANK OF MAURITIUS. ANNUAL REPORT. Text in English. 1968. a. free. charts; stat. **Document type:** *Corporate.*
Published by: Bank of Mauritius, Sir William Newton St, PO Box 29, Port Louis, Mauritius. TEL 230-208-4164, FAX 230-208-9204. Circ: 1,000.

332 MUS ISSN 0005-5301
HC517.M5
BANK OF MAURITIUS. MONTHLY BULLETIN. Text in English. 1968. m. free. charts; stat. **Document type:** *Trade.*
Formerly (until 1996): Bank of Mauritius. Quarterly Review
Related titles: Online - full text ed.
Indexed: WBA.
Published by: Bank of Mauritius, Sir William Newton St, PO Box 29, Port Louis, Mauritius. TEL 230-208-4164, FAX 230-208-9204, TELEX 4253 MAUBNK IW, bomrd@bow.intnet.mu, http://bom.intnet.mu. Circ: 1,000.

332.1 MUS
BANK OF MAURITIUS. THE BULLION. Text in English. m. free to qualified personnel. charts; stat.
Published by: Bank of Mauritius, Sir William Newton St, PO Box 29, Port Louis, Mauritius. TEL 230-208-4164, FAX 230-208-9204.

332.1 PNG
BANK OF PAPUA NEW GUINEA. QUARTERLY ECONOMIC BULLETIN. Text in English. q. free; PGK 30 postage fee (effective 2000). **Document type:** *Bulletin.* **Description:** Reviews economic conditions for the past quarter and contains a comprehensive set of updated statistical tables. The bank staff also includes special articles related to current economic policy.
Indexed: KES, PAIS.
Published by: Bank of Papua New Guinea, Economics Department, PO Box 121, Port Moresby, Papua New Guinea. TEL 675-22-7200, FAX 675-21-1617, TELEX NE 22128. Ed. Sali David. Pub., R&P, Adv. contact Marie Uvillio TEL 675-3227326.

332.1 PNG
BANK OF PAPUA NEW GUINEA. REPORT AND FINANCIAL STATEMENTS. Text in English. 1974. a. free. illus.; stat.
Published by: Bank of Papua New Guinea, Economics Department, PO Box 121, Port Moresby, Papua New Guinea. TEL 675-22-7200, FAX 675-21-1617. Circ: 2,000.

332 KOR
BANK OF SEOUL AND TRUST COMPANY. ECONOMIC REVIEW✶. Text in Korean. 1977 (no.5). irreg.
Published by: Bank of Seoul and Trust Company, 2-10-1, Nandaemun-ro, Jung-gu, Seoul, Korea, S. TEL 82-2-7716000, FAX 82-2-7740428.

332.1 SDN ISSN 0067-3749
HG3387.A7
BANK OF SUDAN. REPORT. Text in English. a. free.
Description: Provides annual coverage for all economic and financial developments, starting with the world economic situation, agricultural and industrial production and ending with the accounts of the bank.
Published by: Bank of Sudan, P O Box 313, Khartoum, Sudan.

BANK OF TAIWAN QUARTERLY. see *BUSINESS AND ECONOMICS—Economic Situation And Conditions*

BANK OF TANZANIA. ECONOMIC AND OPERATIONS REPORT (YEAR). see *BUSINESS AND ECONOMICS—Economic Situation And Conditions*

332 JPN
BANK OF TOKYO - MITSUBISHI. ANNUAL REPORT. Text in Japanese. 1978. a. charts. cum.index every 2 yrs.
Former titles: Bank of Tokyo. Annual Report; Bank of Tokyo. Semiannual Report (0005-5360)
Published by: Bank of Tokyo - Mitsubishi Ltd., Research Office, 7-1 Marunouchi 2-chome, Chiyoda-ku, Tokyo, Japan. TEL 81-3-32401111, TELEX J22358, http://www.btm.co.jp/. Circ: 12,000.

332.1 TON
BANK OF TONGA. ANNUAL REPORT. Text in English. a.
Published by: Bank of Tonga, Head Office, PO Box 924, Nuku' alofa, Tonga.

332 ZMB
BANK OF ZAMBIA. QUARTERLY FINANCIAL AND STATISTICAL REVIEW. Text in English. 1971. 3/yr. free. charts.
Formerly: Bank of Zambia. Quarterly Statistical Review
Indexed: WBA.
Published by: Bank of Zambia, c/o Librarian, PO Box 30080, Lusaka, 10101, Zambia. Circ: 1,500.

332.1 ZMB
BANK OF ZAMBIA. REPORT AND STATEMENT OF ACCOUNTS. Text in English. a.
Published by: Bank of Zambia, c/o Librarian, PO Box 30080, Lusaka, 10101, Zambia.

332 USA
BANK OPERATIONS AND TECHNOLOGY ALERT. Text in English. m. USD 425 (effective 2005). **Document type:** *Newsletter, Trade.*
Formerly (until 2005): Sheshunoff Bank Ownership News
Published by: Sheshunoff Information Services Inc., 807 Las Cimas Pkwy, Ste 300, Austin, TX 78746. TEL 512-472-2244, 800-456-2340, FAX 512-305-6575, sheshunoff.info@tfn.com, customercare.sis@sheshunoff.com, http://www.sheshunoff.com. Ed. Ruth Razook.

332.1 USA ISSN 1540-3947
BANK OPERATIONS & TECHNOLOGY ALERT. Text in English. 1997. m. USD 375 (effective 2004). **Document type:** *Newsletter, Trade.* **Description:** Provides the latest information, ideas, and techniques for managing every area of bank operations, including fast-changing technology issues.
Published by: Sheshunoff Information Services Inc., 807 Las Cimas Pkwy, Ste 300, Austin, TX 78746. TEL 512-472-2244, 800-456-2340, FAX 512-305-6575, customercare.sis@sheshunoff.com, http://www.sheshunoff.com/store/815.html. Ed. David W. Harrop.

332 IDN ISSN 0408-4632
HG3308.P4
BANK PEMBANGUNAN INDONESIA. ANNUAL REPORT. Text in English. 1960. a. free. charts; illus.; stat.
Published by: Bank Pembangunan Indonesia/Development Bank of Indonesia, 2-4 Jalan Gondangdia Lama, P.O. Box 140, Jakarta, Indonesia.

332.1 IDN ISSN 0045-1495
BANK PEMBANGUNAN INDONESIA. NEWSLETTER. Text in English, Indonesian. q. free. charts; stat. **Document type:** *Newsletter.*
Published by: Bank Pembangunan Indonesia/Development Bank of Indonesia, 2-4 Jalan Gondangdia Lama, P.O. Box 140, Jakarta, Indonesia.

332 IDN
BANK PEMBANGUNAN INDONESIA. OPERATIONS OF BAPINDO. Text in English. s-a.
Published by: Bank Pembangunan Indonesia/Development Bank of Indonesia, 2-4 Jalan Gondangdia Lama, P.O. Box 140, Jakarta, Indonesia.

332 USA
BANK RATE MONITOR✶; the weekly financial rate reporter. Text in English. 1982. w. looseleaf. USD 895 (effective 2000); includes online edition and m. supplement. charts; mkt.; stat. back issues avail. **Document type:** *Trade.* **Description:** Covers deposit and loan rates set by banks and thrifts as well as special surveys listing rates, fees, and balance requirements on products of the week. Audiences include financial institutions, consulting firms, and government agencies.
Related titles: E-mail ed.; Fax ed.; Online - full text ed.: Bank Rate Motor Online.
Published by: Bankrate Inc., 11811 US Hwy 1, North Palm Beach, FL 33408. TEL 561-630-2400, webmaster@bankrate.com, http://www.bankrate.com. Circ: 260 (paid); 40 (controlled).

332 USA ISSN 1540-3858
BANK REGULATORY COMPLIANCE ALERT. Text in English. m. USD 375 (effective 2004). **Document type:** *Newsletter, Trade.* **Description:** Provides practical advice on complying with new and current requirements.
Related titles: CD-ROM ed.: ISSN 1540-384X.
Published by: Sheshunoff Information Services Inc., 807 Las Cimas Pkwy, Ste 300, Austin, TX 78746. TEL 512-472-2244, 800-456-2340, FAX 512-305-6575, customercare.sis@sheshunoff.com, http://www.sheshunoff.com/store/802.html.

332 USA
BANK SECURITY NEWS. Text in English. m. USD 419 (effective 2004). **Document type:** *Newsletter, Trade.* **Description:** Provides the most compelling insights on protecting and securing your financial systems and operations. Every issue will give you actionable security ideas and tips, as well as must-know compliance strategies.
Published by: Royal Media Group, 1359 Broadway, Ste 1512, New York, NY 10018. TEL 212-564-8972, FAX 212-564-8973, info@royalmedia.com, http://www.royalmedia.com/newsletter.cfm?pub=102.

332.1 USA
BANK STRUCTURE FILE TAPE. Text in English. q. USD 1,816 in North America; USD 3,632 elsewhere (effective 2001).
Media: Magnetic Tape.
Published by: (Federal Reserve System), U.S. Department of Commerce, National Technical Information Service, 5285 Port Royal Rd, Springfield, VA 22161. TEL 703-605-6000, info@ntis.gov, http://www.ntis.gov.

332.1 USA ISSN 1045-9472
CODEN: BSYTEE
BANK SYSTEMS & TECHNOLOGY; for senior-level executives in perations and technology management. Text in English. 1964. 13/yr. USD 65 domestic; USD 67 in Canada; USD 100 elsewhere; free in US & Canada to qualified personnel (effective 2005). adv. bk.rev. illus.; tr.lit. index. back issues avail. **Document type:** *Magazine, Trade.* **Description:** For senior-level banking executives interested in emerging technologies and products that reshaping the future of banking.
Former titles (until 1989): Bank Systems and Equipment; Bank Equipment News (0146-0900)
Related titles: Microform ed.: (from PQC); Online - full text ed.: (from Factiva, Florida Center for Library Automation, Gale Group, H.W. Wilson, LexisNexis, Northern Light Technology, Inc., O C L C Online Computer Library Center, Inc., ProQuest Information & Learning).
Indexed: ABIn, BLI, BPI, BPIA, ChPerI, CompD, DPD, Inspec, ResCtrInd, SoftBase.
—BLDSC (1861.833100), AskIEEE, IE, ingenta. **CCC.**
Published by: C M P Media LLC (Subsidiary of: United News & Media), 3 Park Ave., New York, NY 10016-5902. http://www.banktech.com/. Ed. Katherine Burger. adv.: B&W page USD 8,175, color page USD 10,660. Circ: 24,000 (controlled).

332 USA ISSN 1060-3506
BANK TECHNOLOGY NEWS. Text in English. 1987. m. USD 99 domestic; USD 121 foreign (effective 2005). adv. **Document type:** *Magazine, Trade.* **Description:** Provides in-depth analysis of the latest technologies and strategies in the rapidly changing banking industry.
Formerly (until 1991): Bank New Product News (0895-9293)
Related titles: Microform ed.: (from PQC); Online - full text ed.: (from EBSCO Publishing, Florida Center for Library Automation, Gale Group, Northern Light Technology, Inc., O C L C Online Computer Library Center, Inc., ProQuest Information & Learning).
Indexed: ABIn, B&I, BLI.
—**CCC.**
Published by: Source Media, Inc., One State St Plaza, 27th Fl, New York, NY 10004. TEL 212-803-6077, FAX 212-747-1154, custserv@sourcemedia.com, http://www.banktechnews.com, http://www.sourcemedia.com. adv.: B&W page USD 8,570; trim 10.25 x 14. Circ: 25,000.

332.1 USA ISSN 0162-7473
BANK TELLER'S REPORT. Text in English. 1969. m. USD 425 (effective 2005). **Document type:** *Newsletter, Trade.* **Description:** Provides bank tellers with practical advice on all phases of banking: cross-selling, security, operations, money-handling techniques, and customer relations.
Incorporates (in Sep. 1975): Teller's Marketing Bulletin
Related titles: Microform ed.: (from PQC); Online - full text ed.
Indexed: BLI.
—CCC.
Published by: Sheshunoff Information Services Inc., 807 Las Cimas Pkwy, Ste 300, Austin, TX 78746. TEL 512-472-2244, 800-456-2340, FAX 512-305-6575, customercare.sis@sheshunoff.com, http://www.sheshunoff.com/store/896.html. Ed. Marge Simmons.

332.1 CHE ISSN 1420-7583
➤ **BANK- UND FINANZWIRTSCHAFTLICHE FORSCHUNGEN.** Text in German, English. 1969. irreg., latest vol.344, 2003. price varies. **Document type:** *Monographic series, Academic/Scholarly.*
Formerly (until 1991): Bankwirtschaftliche Forschungen (0067-382X)
—CCC.
Published by: (Universitaet Zuerich, Institut fuer Schweizerisches Bankwesen), Paul Haupt AG, Falkenplatz 14, Bern, 3001, Switzerland. TEL 41-31-3012425, FAX 41-31-3014669, verlag@haupt.ch, http://www.haupt.ch. **Co-sponsor:** Hochschule St. Gallen fuer Wirtschafts- und Sozialwissenschaften, Institut fuer Bankwirtschaft.

332 658.8 DEU ISSN 1433-5204
BANK UND MARKT; Zeitschrift fuer Management, Marketing, Technik, E-Commerce und Organisation. Text in German. 1972. m. EUR 250.08; EUR 17.90 newsstand/cover (effective 2004). adv. bk.rev. illus. index. reprint service avail. from SCH. **Document type:** *Magazine, Trade.*
Former titles (until 1992): Bank und Markt und Technik (0933-3770); (until 1986): Bank und Markt (0341-3667); Which incorporated (1968-1984): Zeitschrift fuer das Gesamte Kreditwesen. Ausgabe Technik (0341-6194)
Related titles: ♦ Supplement(s): Karten. ISSN 0937-597X.
Indexed: DIP, IBR, IBZ.
—BLDSC (1861.837000), IE, Infotrieve. **CCC.**
Published by: Fritz Knapp Verlag GmbH, Postfach 111151, Frankfurt Am Main, 60046, Germany. TEL 49-69-9708330, FAX 49-69-7078400, verlagsleitung@kreditwesen.de, http://www.kreditwesen.de. Ed. Swantje Benkelberg. Adv. contact Werner Scholz. B&W page EUR 4,120, color page EUR 6,220. Circ: 2,895 (paid and controlled).

336.71 HRV ISSN 0353-6335
HG3238
BANKA. Text in Croatian. 1989. m. HRK 396 domestic; HRK 280 to students (effective 2001). adv. **Document type:** *Magazine, Trade.*
Related titles: Online - full text ed.
Published by: Marketing Zagrebacke Banke d.o.o., Savska 28, Zagreb, 10000, Croatia. TEL 385-1-4843855, FAX 385-1-4843083, http://www.bankamagazine.hr. adv.: B&W page HRK 7,000, color page HRK 9,400; trim 205 x 280.

BANKA VE TICARET HUKUKU DERGISI. see *LAW*

332 SCG ISSN 1451-4354
BANKARSTVO. Text in Serbo-Croatian. 1972. bi-m. bk.rev. **Document type:** *Magazine, Trade.*
Formerly (until 2003): Jugoslovensko Bankarstvo (0350-4077)
Indexed: RASB.
Published by: Udruzenje Banaka Srbije, Bulevar Kralja Aleksandra 86, Belgrade, 11000. TEL 381-11-3020760, FAX 381-11-3370179, ubs@finnet.co.yu, http://www.finnet.co.yu/ubj/ubj.htm. Ed. Dr. Milovan Milutinovic. Circ: 2,100.

332 640.73 USA
BANKCARD BAROMETER. Text in English. 1989. m. USD 995 (effective 1999). adv. **Document type:** *Trade.* **Description:** Provides broad proprietary data on approximately 500 U.S. card portfolios. Covers all aspects of the bank credit card industry: card base, cardmix, accounts receivables, interest rates, transaction volume, outstandings, attrition, yields, delinquency, charge-offs and market share.
Former titles: R A M Research Bank Card Barometer (1040-6905); (until 1990): R A M Research Bank Credit Card Issuers Yearbook
Published by: Ram Research, PO Box 1700, Frederick, MD 21702. TEL 301-695-4660, FAX 301-695-0160. Ed., Pub. Robert B McKinley. R&P, Adv. contact Harriet Haxton TEL 301-631-9100 Ext 112. Circ: 1,000.

332.1 USA
BANKCARD CONSUMER NEWS✶. Text in English. 1986. bi-m. USD 24. bk.rev. **Document type:** *Consumer.*
Published by: Bankcard Holders of America, 333 Maple Ave E, Vienna, VA 22180-4717. TEL 703-389-5445, FAX 703-481-6037. Ed. Ruth Susswein. Circ: 100,000.

332 640.73 USA
BANKCARD UPDATE. Text in English. 1987. m. USD 995 (effective 1999). adv. **Document type:** *Newsletter, Trade.* **Description:** Covers pricing, management benchmarks, marketing trends and data on bank credit card industry.
Former titles: R A M Research Bankcard Update (1040-8959); R A M Bankcard Update (0894-2390)
Published by: Ram Research, PO Box 1700, Frederick, MD 21702. TEL 301-695-4660, FAX 301-695-0160. Ed., Pub. Robert B McKinley. R&P, Adv. contact Harriet Haxton TEL 301-631-9100 Ext 112. Circ: 1,000.

332.1 CHE ISSN 1422-3902
DIE BANKEN IN DER SCHWEIZ. Text in German. 1910. a. stat. **Document type:** *Bulletin, Government.*
Formerly (until 1997): Schweizerische Bankwesen (1420-1860)
Related titles: French ed.: Les Banques Suisses. ISSN 1420-1887.
Published by: Schweizerische Nationalbank/Banque Nationale Suisse, Boersenstr. 15, Postfach, Zurich, 8022, Switzerland. TEL 41-1-6313111, FAX 41-1-6313911, snb@snb.ch, http://www.snb.ch.

332 DEU ISSN 0722-2424
BANKEN-JAHRBUCH. Text in German. 1982. a. EUR 350.23 (effective 1999). **Document type:** *Trade.*
Published by: Hoppenstedt Bonnier Zeitschriften GmbH, Havelstr. 9, Darmstadt, 64295, Germany. TEL 49-6151-380-0, FAX 49-6151-380-360.

332 DEU ISSN 1615-3723
BANKEN UND SPARKASSEN. Text in German. 1993. bi-m. EUR 10 newsstand/cover (effective 2004). adv. **Document type:** *Magazine, Trade.*
Formerly (until 1998): Banken und Versicherungen (0949-4634)
Published by: BAUVE AG i.G., Kirchdorfer Str 87, Bad Woerishofen, 86825, Germany. TEL 49-82473800, FAX 49-8247-380100, information@bauve.de, http://www.bauve.de. adv.: B&W page EUR 3,502, color page EUR 4,882. Circ: 7,459 (paid and controlled).

332 BGR
BANKER. Text in Bulgarian. 1993. w. BGL 40 (effective 2002). **Document type:** *Newspaper.*
Published by: Finansova Informatsionna Agentsia/Financial Information Agency, Lozenets, ul. Nikolai Liliev 14A, Sofia, 1000, Bulgaria. TEL 359-2-662362, http://www.banker.bg/subscr.asp. Ed. Bistra Georgieva.

332 IND ISSN 0522-2931
THE BANKER. Text in English. 1954. m. USD 50 (effective 2000). adv. bk.rev. reprints avail. **Description:** Information about the public, private and co-operative sectors of banking, as well as economy, business and finance.
Indexed: RASB, T&II.
Published by: Rajesh Suneja Ed. & Pub., 24/90 Connaught Circus, New Delhi, 110 001, India. TEL 91-11-3345501, FAX 91-11-3345501, TELEX 31-61184 GNS IN, thebanker@pacific.net.in. Adv. contact Rajesh Suneja. B&W page INR 7,400, color page INR 11,900; trim 27.3 x 19.1. Circ: 4,736.

332.1 GBR ISSN 0005-5395
CODEN: BNKRB2
THE BANKER. Text in English. 1926. m. GBP 245, EUR 361, USD 441 (effective 2005). adv. bk.rev. stat.; illus. index. Supplement avail.; back issues avail.; reprint service avail. from SCH. **Document type:** *Magazine, Trade.* **Description:** Includes articles and editorials covering key aspects of banking, capital markets, country economical situations, trade finance, risk analysis, and interviews.
Related titles: Microfilm ed.: (from PQC); Online - full text ed.: (from Florida Center for Library Automation, Gale Group, LexisNexis, O C L C Online Computer Library Center, Inc.); Supplement(s): Eurofile.
Indexed: ABIn, B&I, BLI, BPI, BPIA, BrHumI, BusI, C&CSA, CPM, CREJ, ELLIS, Emerald, IndBusRep, KES, M&MA, PAIS, PCI, RASB, RRTA, RefZh, SCIMP, T&II, WAE&RSA, WBA.
—BLDSC (1861.850000), IE, Infotrieve.
Published by: Financial Times Business Information, Magazines (Subsidiary of: Financial Times Group), Tabernacle Court, 16-28 Tabernacle St, London, EC2A 4DD, United Kingdom. TEL 44-20-73828000, FAX 44-20-73828099, thebanker.ed@ft.com, http://www.thebanker.com. Eds. Brian Caplen TEL 44-20-73828504, Stephen Timewell TEL 44-20-73828507. Circ: 12,500. **Subscr. to:** 126 Jermyn St, London SW1Y 4UJ, United Kingdom.

BANKER & TRADESMAN. see *REAL ESTATE*

332 UAE
BANKER MIDDLE EAST. Text in English. m. USD 150 (effective 2002). **Document type:** *Magazine, Trade.*
Published by: Corporate Publishing International, PO Box 13700, Dubai, United Arab Emirates. TEL 971-4-351-5316, FAX 971-4-359-8486, cpi@emirates.net.ae, http://www.cpilive.net.

332.1 GBR ISSN 1462-4125
HG2984
BANKERS' ALMANAC. Text in English. 1866. s-a. (in 6 vols.). GBP 2,020 (effective 2005). adv. **Document type:** *Directory, Trade.* **Description:** Covers more than 27,000 financial institutions that have the legal status of banks in their country of registration.
Formerly (until 1993): Bankers' Almanac and Year Book (0067-379X)
Related titles: CD-ROM ed.; Online - full text ed.
—CCC.
Published by: Reed Business Information Ltd. (Subsidiary of: Reed Business), Windsor Ct., East Grinstead, W Sussex RH19 1XA, United Kingdom. TEL 44-1342-326972, FAX 44-1342-335860, rbi.subscriptions@qss-uk.com, http://www.bankersalmanac.com/, http://www.reedbusiness.co.uk/. Ed. R Phelps. Circ: 20,000.

321.1 GBR
BANKERS' ALMANAC WORLD RANKING. Text in English. a., latest 2003. GBP 350 (effective 2003). **Document type:** *Directory.* **Description:** Covers the world's leading 3,000 international banks, providing reference to the standing of a bank both internationally and within its own country.
Published by: Reed Business Information Ltd. (Subsidiary of: Reed Business), Windsor Ct., East Grinstead, W Sussex RH19 1XA, United Kingdom. TEL 44-1342-326972, FAX 44-1342-335860, rbi.subscriptions@qss-uk.com, http://www.reedbusiness.co.uk/rb2_products/rb2_products_bankers_almanac_world.htm. Ed. R Phelps.

332.1 USA ISSN 0005-5425
BANKERS DIGEST; a weekly news magazine devoted to Southwest bank news. Text in English. 1942. w. USD 29 (effective 2005). adv. bk.rev. tr.lit. 16 p./no. 3 cols./p.; back issues avail.; reprints avail. **Document type:** *Magazine, Trade.* **Description:** Covers news and people in the southwest banking industry, public relations programs and band activities.
Address: 9550 Forest Ln, Ste 125, Dallas, TX 75243-5964. TEL 214-221-4544, FAX 214-221-4546, bankersdigest@bankersdigest.com, http://www.bankersdigest.com. Ed., Pub. Bonnie Jamison Blackman. Adv. contact Glenn Garrett. Circ: 3,100 (paid and controlled).

332.1 USA ISSN 1540-3920
BANKER'S ECONOMIC & INVESTMENT ALERT. Text in English. 1993. m. USD 395 (effective 2004). **Document type:** *Newsletter, Trade.* **Description:** Contains up-to-date information on the latest changes in all the key areas of funds management.
Published by: Sheshunoff Information Services Inc., 807 Las Cimas Pkwy, Ste 300, Austin, TX 78746. TEL 512-472-2244, 800-456-2340, FAX 512-305-6575, customercare.sis@sheshunoff.com, http://www.sheshunoff.com/store/804.html. Ed. Edmund A. Mennis.

332 HKG ISSN 1012-9952
BANKERS HANDBOOK FOR ASIA✶. Text in Chinese. 1976. a. USD 140. adv. charts; illus.
Published by: Dataline Asia - Pacific Ltd., 3rd Fl Hollywood Centre, 233 Hollywood Rd, Hong Kong, Hong Kong. TEL 8155221, FAX 8542794. Ed. Amitabha Chowdhury. Circ: 10,000.

332.1 340 USA ISSN 0005-5433
KF967
BANKER'S LETTER OF THE LAW. Text in English. 1967. m. looseleaf. USD 315 (effective 2004). **Document type:** *Newsletter.* **Description:** Alerts bank attorneys to the latest rulings involving federal and state banking issues. Cites specific cases and translates "legalese" into everyday language.
Related titles: Microform ed.: (from PQC); Online - full text ed.
Indexed: BLI.
—CCC.
Published by: A.S. Pratt & Sons, Inc., 1911 Fort Myer Dr, Arlington, VA 22209. TEL 703-528-0145, 800-572-2797, FAX 703-528-1736, pratt.info@tfn.com, pratt.info@thomsonmedia.com, http://www.sheshunoff.com/store/849.html, http://www.aspratt.com/. Ed. Robert Volk. Circ: 1,200 (paid).

332.1 DEU ISSN 0341-6208
BANKHISTORISCHES ARCHIV; Zeitschrift zur Banken- und Finanzgeschichte. Text in German. 1975. s-a. EUR 58.60; EUR 37 newsstand/cover (effective 2006). adv. bk.rev. reprint service avail. from SCH. **Document type:** *Journal, Academic/Scholarly.* **Description:** Covers banking history.
Indexed: AmH&L, HistAb, IBR, IBZ.
—IE. **CCC.**
Published by: Franz Steiner Verlag Stuttgart GmbH, Birkenwaldstr 44, Stuttgart, 70191, Germany. TEL 49-711-25820, FAX 49-711-2582290, service@steiner-verlag.de, http://www.steiner-verlag.de.

332 GEO
BANKI PLUS. Text in Georgian. 1994. w. adv. **Description:** Special features focus on banking and finance.
Published by: National Bank of Georgia, Ul Leonidze 3-5, Tbilisi, 380018, Georgia. TEL 995-32-936449, FAX 995-32-987794, bankiplus@caucasus.net, http://members.tripod.com/bankiplus/index.htm. Ed. David Bagituria. R&P George Khantadze. Adv. contact Zurab Zhuzhunashvili. **US dist. addr.:** East View Information Services, 3020 Harbor Ln. N., Minneapolis, MN 55447. TEL 612-550-0961.

332.1 362.5 USA
BANKING AND COMMUNITY PERSPECTIVES. Text in English. 1992. s-a. free. **Document type:** *Newsletter.* **Description:** Examines issues related to community development, community reinvestment, fair lending, and affordable housing.

B

Related titles: Online - full text ed.: E-perspectives.
Published by: Federal Reserve Bank of Texas, PO Box 655906, Dallas, TX 75265-5906. TEL 214-922-5254, FAX 214-922-5268, Kay.Champagne@dal.frb.org, http://www.dallasfed.org. Ed., R&P Kay Champagne. Circ: 6,000.

332 NGA ISSN 0795-932X
BANKING & FINANCE DIGEST. Text in English. 1989. q. NGN 560. back issues avail. **Document type:** *Trade.*
Published by: Research & Data Services Ltd., Marina, 54-55 Taiwo St off Abibu Oki St, PO Box 2720, Lagos, Nigeria. TEL 234-2-664639, FAX 234-2-660926. Ed. Chike Uchime.

332.1 340 CAN ISSN 0832-8722
K2
BANKING AND FINANCE LAW REVIEW/REVUE DE DROIT BANCAIRE ET DE FINANCE. Text and summaries in English, French. 1986. 3/yr. (plus 1 bound vol.) CND 238 domestic; USD 201.69 foreign (effective 2005). adv. bk.rev. **Document type:** *Journal.* **Description:** Provides discussion and insight into issues and problems which confront both the legal and financial communities in Canada. Information is arranged in four sections: articles, commentaries on recent developments in banking in Canada and internationally, case notes and book reviews.
Related titles: Online - full text ed.
Indexed: CLI, ICLPL, ILP, LRI.
—BLDSC (1861.924300), IE, ingenta. **CCC.**
Published by: Carswell (Subsidiary of: Thomson Corporation), One Corporate Plaza, 2075 Kennedy Rd, Toronto, ON M1T 3V4, Canada. TEL 416-609-8000, 800-387-5164, FAX 416-298-5094, carswell.customerrelations@thomson.com, http://www.carswell.com. Ed. Benjamin Geva.

332 ZAF
BANKING & FINANCE WERKS. Text in English. 1992. irreg. illus.
Published by: Werksmans, PO Box 927, Johannesburg, 2000, South Africa.

332.1 AUS ISSN 1445-4351
HG1503
BANKING AND FINANCIAL SERVICES. Key Title: B & F S. Text in English. 1895. bi-m. AUD 110 domestic; AUD 130 foreign (effective 2002). adv. bk.rev. index. **Document type:** *Academic/Scholarly.* **Description:** Strives to improve the individual and finance practitioner and thus to maintain and improve the safety, integrity, trust and global competence of the Australian and New Zealand financial system.
Former titles (until 2000): Journal of Banking and Financial Services (1443-6035); (until 1999): Australian Banker (0814-2912); (until 1983): Bankers' Magazine (0811-6423); (until 1982): Bankers' Magazine of Australasia (0005-5468)
Related titles: Online - full content ed.; Online - full text ed.: (from EBSCO Publishing, Gale Group).
Indexed: AusPAIS, PAIS, WBA.
—BLDSC (1854.130000), IE, ingenta.
Published by: Australasian Institute of Banking and Finance, Level 19, 385 Bourke St, Melbourne, VIC 3000, Australia. TEL 61-3-9602-5811, FAX 61-3-9602-3923, info@aibf.com.au, journal@aibf.com.au, http://www.aibf.com.au. Ed., R&P Carmel Lococo TEL 61-3-9602-5811. Adv. contacts Barry Telfer, Carmel Lococo TEL 61-3-9602-5811. B&W page AUD 2,750, color page AUD 3,850; trim 210 x 270. Circ: 12,099 (paid and controlled).

332.1 USA ISSN 1530-499X
KF967
BANKING & FINANCIAL SERVICES POLICY REPORT; a journal on trends in regulation and supervision. Text in English. 1982. m. looseleaf. USD 510 (effective 2004). index. **Document type:** *Newsletter, Trade.* **Description:** Provides clear analysis on legislative, regulatory, and legal developments dealing with new financial products and services and geographic diversification.
Former titles (until 2000): Banking Policy Report (1059-1257); (until 1991): Banking Expansion Reporter (0730-689X)
Related titles: Online - full text ed.: (from EBSCO Publishing, Florida Center for Library Automation, Gale Group, ProQuest Information & Learning).
Indexed: BLI.
—CCC.
Published by: Aspen Publishers, Inc. (Subsidiary of: Wolters Kluwer N.V.), 111Eighth Ave., 7th Fl, New York, NY 10011. TEL 212-771-0600, FAX 212-771-0885, customer.service@aspenpubl.com, http://www.aspenpublishers.com. Ed. Shulte Roth. Circ: 2,000. **Subscr. to:** Customer Care, 7201 McKinney Circle, Frederick, MD 21704. TEL 800-234-1660, FAX 800-901-9075.

332.0715 GBR ISSN 0265-7988
BANKING & FINANCIAL TRAINING. Text in English. 1985. 10/yr. GBP 245, USD 385 (effective 2000). adv. bk.rev.; film rev. back issues avail. **Document type:** *Trade.* **Description:** Provides information about training products and techniques in banking and finance.
Indexed: CPE.
Published by: Informa Law (Subsidiary of: Informa Publishing), Informa House, 30-32 Mortimer St, London, W1W 7RE, United Kingdom. TEL 44-207-5531000, FAX 44-207-5531593, dave.mckensie@informa.com. Ed. Hannah Doran. Pub. Frania Weaver. Adv. contact Harry Fisher. Circ: 2,100.

332 GBR ISSN 1351-5543
BANKING AUTOMATION BULLETIN FOR EUROPE. Text in English. 1991. m.
Related titles: Online - full text ed.
Published by: Retail Banking Research Ltd., 304 Sandycombe Rd, Kew Gardens, Richmond, Surrey TW9 3NG, United Kingdom.

332 346.006 USA ISSN 1526-5013
BANKING DAILY. Text in English. 1999 (Jan.). d. USD 2,155 (effective 2005 - 2006). back issues avail. **Document type:** *Trade.* **Description:** Covers latest news and analysis of U.S. banking legislation, regulatory policy, litigation, and investment at state and federal levels.
Media: Online - full text (from The Bureau of National Affairs, Inc., Thomson West).
—CCC.
Published by: The Bureau of National Affairs, Inc., 1231 25th St., NW, Washington, DC 20037. TEL 800-372-1033, 800-452-7773, FAX 800-253-0332, customercare@bna.com, http://www.bna.com/products/corplaw/bnkd.htm. **Subscr. to:** 9435 Key West Ave, Rockville, MD 20850.

332.1 USA
BANKING GUIDES - ASIA, AUSTRALIA, NEW ZEALAND WITH PRINCIPAL HOTELS AND BANK HOLIDAYS✶ . Cover title: Asian Banking Guide. Text in English. a.
Published by: Manufacturers Hanover Trust Co., International Division, 270 Park Ave, New York, NY 10022.

332 GBR
BANKING IN THE E C; structures and sources of finance. (European Community) Text in English. irreg., latest 1991, Apr. GBP 175, USD 315. **Document type:** *Trade.* **Description:** Explains the operation, supervision, and regulation of the national financial systems of each E.C. member state.
Formerly: Banking Structures and Sources of Finance in the European Community
Published by: Financial Times Business Information, Management Reports (Subsidiary of: Financial Times Group), 102-108 Clerkenwell Rd, London, EC1M 5SA, United Kingdom. TEL 44-171-251-9321, FAX 44-171-251-4686. **Orders to:** F T B I, 126 Jermyn St, London, Mddx SW1Y 4UJ, United Kingdom. TEL 44-1209-612193, FAX 44-1209-612811.

332.1 GBR
BANKING IN THE E U AND SWITZERLAND (YEAR). Text in English. 198?. a. GBP 250, USD 416; GBP 260 foreign. charts. **Document type:** *Trade.* **Description:** Covers important banking developments in the nations of the European Union.
Published by: Financial Times Business Information, Management Reports (Subsidiary of: Financial Times Group), 102-108 Clerkenwell Rd, London, EC1M 5SA, United Kingdom. TEL 44-171-814-9770, FAX 44-171-814-9778. **Orders to:** F T B I, 126 Jermyn St, London, Mddx SW1Y 4UJ, United Kingdom. TEL 44-1209-612493, FAX 44-1209-612811.

332 GBR
BANKING IN THE FAR EAST. Text in English. 1986. irreg., latest 1993. GBP 186, USD 333. **Document type:** *Trade.* **Description:** Covers the operation, supervision, and regulation of the financial systems of 12 major Pacific Rim nations.
Formerly (until 1986): Banking Structures and Sources of Finance in the Far East
Published by: Financial Times Business Information, Management Reports (Subsidiary of: Financial Times Group), 102-108 Clerkenwell Rd, London, EC1M 5SA, United Kingdom. TEL 44-171-251-9321, FAX 44-171-251-4686. **Subscr. to:** F T B I, 126 Jermyn St, London, Mddx SW1Y 4UJ, United Kingdom. TEL 44-1209-612493, FAX 44-1209-612811.

332.1 IRL ISSN 0791-1386
BANKING IRELAND. Text in English. 1898. q. adv. bk.rev. index. **Document type:** *Magazine, Trade.*
Supersedes: Institute of Bankers in Ireland. Journal (0020-272X)
Indexed: PAIS, WBA.
—BLDSC (1861.926600).
Published by: (Institute of Bankers in Ireland), Ashville Media Group, Apollo House, Tara St., Dublin, 2, Ireland. TEL 353-1-4322200, FAX 353-1-6727100, info@ashville.com, http://www.ashville.com. adv.: B&W page EUR 2,223, color page EUR 2,477. Circ: 19,300 (controlled).

332.1 USA
BANKING ISSUES AND INNOVATIONS IN PRODUCTS, MARKETING AND TECHNOLOGY✶ . Text in English. m. USD 120.
Former titles: Issues and Innovations; Ideas and Innovations in Banking; Banking Issues and Innovations
Indexed: BLI.
Published by: (Bank Administration Institute), Probus & Bankers Publishing, 1333 Burr Ridge Pkwy., Burr Ridge, IL 60521-6489. TEL 312-868-1100. Ed. Phyllis L van Holland.

332 USA
BANKING: LATIN AMERICAN INDUSTRIAL REPORT✶ . (Avail. for each of 22 Latin American countries) Text in English. 1985. a. USD 435; per country report.
Published by: Aquino Productions, P O Box 15760, Stamford, CT 06901-0760. Ed. Andres C Aquino.

BANKING LAW. see *LAW*

345.026 USA
BANKING LAW IN THE UNITED STATES. Text in English. 1992. 2 base vols. plus a. updates. looseleaf. USD 185.
Published by: LexisNexis (Subsidiary of: LexisNexis North America), PO Box 7587, Charlottesville, VA 22906-7587. TEL 804-972-7600, 800-562-1197, FAX 804-972-7666, llp.customer.support@lexis-nexis.com, http://www.lexislawpublishing.com.

332.1 340 USA ISSN 0005-5506
➤ **BANKING LAW JOURNAL.** Text in English. 1889. 10/yr. USD 325 (effective 2005). bk.rev. illus. Index. reprint service avail. from WSH,SCH. **Document type:** *Journal, Academic/Scholarly.* **Description:** Covers every area of major interest to bankers and bank attorneys, with practical material for bank counsel use.
Incorporates (1895-1943): Bankers Magazine (0730-4080); Which was formerly (until 1896): Rhodes' Journal of Banking and the Bankers' Magazine Consolidated (0730-4110)
Related titles: Online - full text ed.
Indexed: ABIn, ASCA, ATI, BLI, BPIA, BusI, CLI, CurCont, ESPM, FamI, ILP, LRI, LegCont, PAIS, RASB, RiskAb, SSCI, WBA.
—BLDSC (1861.930000), IE, ingenta. **CCC.**
Published by: Sheshunoff Information Services Inc., 807 Las Cimas Pkwy, Ste 300, Austin, TX 78746. TEL 512-472-2244, 800-456-2340, FAX 512-305-6575, leeann.mcintosh@sheshunoff.com, customercare.sis@sheshunoff.com, http://www.sheshunoff.com/store/819.html. Ed. Steven A Meyerowitz. Circ: 4,000 (paid).

332.1 340 USA ISSN 0271-6909
KF971.3
BANKING LAW JOURNAL DIGEST. Text in English. 1924. a. USD 375 (effective 2004). **Document type:** *Yearbook, Trade.* **Description:** Summarizes leading federal court decisions in the law of banking, commercial paper, trusts and estates, bankruptcy, and other subjects of practical interest to bankers and attorneys with a banking practice.
Published by: Sheshunoff Information Services Inc., 807 Las Cimas Pkwy, Ste 300, Austin, TX 78746. TEL 512-472-2244, 800-456-2340, FAX 512-305-6575, customercare.sis@sheshunoff.com, http://www.sheshunoff.com/store/828.html. Ed. James Pannabecker.

BANKING LAW MANUAL: LEGAL GUIDE TO COMMERCIAL BANKS, THRIFT INSTITUTIONS AND CREDIT UNIONS. see *LAW*

346 341.7 GBR ISSN 0961-7256
K2
BANKING LAW REPORTS. Text in English. 1991. 10/yr. (plus a. cumulation). GBP 248, USD 422 (effective 2001); includes cumulation. **Document type:** *Academic/Scholarly.*
—CCC.
Published by: Informa U K Limited (Subsidiary of: T & F Informa plc), Customer Service Dept, Sheepen Pl, Colchester, Essex CO3 3LP, United Kingdom. TEL 44-207-553-1000, 44-1206-772223, FAX 44-1206-772771, enquiries@informa.com, http://www.llplimited.com. **Subscr. addr. in the US:** L L P Inc, Customer Service, PO Box 1017, Westborough, MA 01581-6017. TEL 1-800-493-4080, FAX 508-231-0856, enquiries.usa@informa.com.

332 BGR
BANKING LAWS AND REGULATIONS. Text in English. a. USD 48 foreign (effective 2002). **Document type:** *Trade.*
Published by: Bulgarska Narodna Banka/Bulgarian National Bank, 1 Alexander Batterberg Sq, Sofia, 1000, Bulgaria. TEL 359-2-91459, FAX 359-2-9802425, press_office@bnbank.org, http://www.bnb.bg. **Dist. by:** Sofia Books, ul Silivria 16, Sofia 1404, Bulgaria. TEL 359-2-9586257, info@sofiabooks-bg.com, http://www.sofiabooks-bg.com.

332.1 USA
BANKING NEWS. Text in English. w. **Document type:** *Newsletter, Consumer.* **Description:** Delivers information and current rates on all bank and credit union products.
Media: E-mail.
Published by: Bankrate Inc., 11811 US Hwy 1, North Palm Beach, FL 33408. TEL 561-630-2400, FAX 561-625-4540, webmaster@bankrate.com, http://bankrate.process9.com/bankrate/subscribe.html, http://www.bankrate.com.

332 GBR
BANKING NEWSLETTER. Text in English. q. **Document type:** *Newsletter.*
Published by: Lovell White Durrant, 65 Holburn Viaduct, London, EC1A 2DY, United Kingdom. TEL 44-20-7236-0066, FAX 44-20-7248-4212, publications@lovellwhitedurrant.com, http://www.lovellwhitedurrant.com.

332.1   PAK   ISSN 0067-3811
BANKING STATISTICS OF PAKISTAN. Text in English. 1948. a. PKR 200, USD 18 (effective 2000). **Document type:** *Government.* **Description:** Includes scheduled advances of the bank.
Published by: State Bank of Pakistan, Central Directorate, Public Relations Department, I.I. Chundrigar Rd, PO Box 4456, Karachi, Pakistan. TEL 92-21-9212400, FAX 92-21-9212436, TELEX 21774 SBPK PK. Circ: 470.

332.1   USA   ISSN 1091-6385
HG1501   CODEN: BASTFT
BANKING STRATEGIES. Text in English. 1925. bi-m. USD 66.50 domestic; USD 101.50 foreign; free to qualified personnel (effective 2005). adv. illus.; tr.lit. index. back issues avail.; reprint service avail. from PQC. **Document type:** *Magazine, Trade.* **Description:** Deals exclusively with the strategic planning and thinking of upper management in financial institutions worldwide.
Former titles (until 1996): Bank Management (1049-1775); (until 1990): Bank Administration (1046-1264); (until 1986): Magazine of Bank Administration (0024-9823); Auditgram; Incorporated (in 1993): Bankers Monthly (0005-5476)
Related titles: Microform ed.: (from PQC); Online - full text ed.: (from Gale Group, O C L C Online Computer Library Center, Inc.).
Indexed: AAR, ABIn, ATI, BLI, BPI, BPIA, BusI, Emerald, Inspec, ManagCont, PAIS, SPPI, WBA.
—BLDSC (1861.930505), AskIEEE, IE, Infotrieve, ingenta. **CCC.**
Published by: Bank Administration Institute, One N Franklin, Ste. 1000, Chicago, IL 60606-3421. TEL 312-683-2464, 800-224-9889, FAX 312-683-2373, 800-375-5543, info@bai.org, http://www.bai.org/bankingstrategies. Ed. Ken Cline. Adv. contact John Wagner TEL 312-683-2393. B&W page USD 7,300, color page USD 9,150; trim 8 x 10.5. Circ: 48,000 (paid and controlled).

332   GBR   ISSN 0266-0865
CODEN: BATEEM
BANKING TECHNOLOGY; the authority on financial systems worldwide. Text in English. 1984. 10/yr. GBP 385, EUR 597, USD 732, SGD 1,232, AUD 1,009 (effective 2005). adv. bk.rev. back issues avail. **Document type:** *Magazine, Trade.* **Description:** Provides senior executives in the financial sector with important information on financial technology products and services.
Related titles: Microform ed.: (from PQC); Online - full text ed.: (from ProQuest Information & Learning).
Indexed: B&I, BLI, C&CSA, CPM, Emerald, Inspec, RASB.
—BLDSC (1861.930550), AskIEEE, IE, Infotrieve, ingenta. **CCC.**
Published by: Informa Professional (Subsidiary of: T & F Informa plc), Informa House, 30-32 Mortimer St, London, W1W 7RE, United Kingdom. TEL 44-20-70175532, FAX 44-20-70174135, professional.enquiries@informa.com, http://www.bankingtech.com. Ed. David Bannister. Adv. contact Zoe Bishop. Circ: 12,654.

332 340   ZAF
BANKING UPDATE. Text in English. irreg. free.
Related titles: Online - full text ed.
Published by: Deneys Reitz Attorneys, PO Box 61334, Marshalltown, Johannesburg 2107, South Africa. TEL 27-11-8335600, FAX 27-11-8387444, jhb@deneysreitz.co.za, http://www.deneysreitz.co.za. Ed. Patrick Bracher. R&P Jacqui Hampton.

332.1   MDG
BANKIN'NY INDOSTRIA. RAPPORT ANNUEL. Text in French. 1964. a. free.
Formerly (until 1977): Banque Nationale Malagasy de Developpement. Rapport d'Activite (0067-401X)
Published by: Bankin'Ny Indostria/Bank Nationale pour le Developpement Industriel, BP 174, Antananarivo, 101, Madagascar. TEL 239-51, FAX 33749, TELEX 22205 BNI MG. Circ: 1,500.

368   PAK   ISSN 0005-5522
BANKINSURANCE NEWS. Text in English. 1971. w. PKR 150, USD 35. adv. bk.rev.
Published by: Tareen & Tareen Ltd., 4 Amil St. off Robson Rd., Karachi 1, Pakistan. Ed. Naushad Shamimul Haq. Circ: 9,000.

332   KGZ
BANKIR. Text in Russian. w. **Document type:** *Newspaper, Consumer.*
Published by: Bankovskii Vestnik, Chui 262, Bishkek, Kyrgyzstan. FAX 996-312-243875, http://homepage.kg/~Vestnik/ Gazeta.htm.

332   UKR
BANKIVS'KA SPRAVA. Text in Ukrainian. bi-m. USD 135 in United States.
Published by: Tovarystvo Znannya, Ul Strylets'ka 28, Kiev, Ukraine. TEL 380-212-4291. **US dist. addr.:** East View Information Services, 3020 Harbor Ln. N., Minneapolis, MN 55447. TEL 612-550-0961.

332.1   USA
BANKNEWS DIRECTORY OF KANSAS BANKS. Text in English. s-a. USD 56 domestic (effective 2002).
Published by: Bank News, Inc., PO Box 29156, Shawnee Mission, KS 66201-9156. TEL 800-336-1120.

332.1   USA
BANKNEWS DIRECTORY OF MISSOURI BANKS. Text in English. s-a. USD 56 domestic (effective 2002). **Document type:** *Directory.*
Published by: Bank News, Inc., PO Box 29156, Shawnee Mission, KS 66201-9156. TEL 800-336-1120.

332.1   USA
BANKNEWS DIRECTORY OF NEBRASKA BANKS. Text in English. a. USD 28 domestic (effective 2002). **Document type:** *Directory.*
Published by: Bank News, Inc., PO Box 29156, Shawnee Mission, KS 66201-9156. TEL 800-336-1120.

332.1   USA
BANKNEWS DIRECTORY OF OKLAHOMA BANKS. Text in English. a. USD 28 domestic (effective 2002). **Document type:** *Directory.*
Published by: Bank News, Inc., PO Box 29156, Shawnee Mission, KS 66201-9156. TEL 800-336-1120.

332.1   USA
BANKNEWS MOUNTAIN STATES BANK DIRECTORY. Text in English. a. USD 32 domestic (effective 2002). **Document type:** *Directory.*
Published by: Bank News, Inc., PO Box 29156, Shawnee Mission, KS 66201-9156. TEL 800-336-1120.

336.71   CZE   ISSN 1212-4273
BANKOVNICTVI. Text in Czech. 1999. m. CZK 990; CZK 90 newsstand/cover (effective 2003). adv. **Document type:** *Magazine, Trade.*
Published by: Economia a.s., Dobrovskeho 25, Prague 7 7, 170 55, Czech Republic. TEL 420-2-33071111, FAX 420-2-33072003, bankovnictvi@economia.cz, economia@economia.cz, http://www.economia.cz. Ed. Jana Chuchvalcova. Adv. contact Lukas Polak. B&W page CZK 39,000, color page CZK 49; trim 143 x 216.

332   RUS
BANKOVSKIE USLUGI. Text in Russian. m. USD 145 in United States.
Published by: Finansovaya Gruppa Nika, Ul Narvskaya 23, k 306, 113, Moscow, 125493, Russian Federation. TEL 7-095-1557135, FAX 7-095-4521720, vikiniki@aha.ru. Ed. V N Volodina. **US dist. addr.:** East View Information Services, 3020 Harbor Ln. N., Minneapolis, MN 55447. TEL 612-550-0961.

332   KGZ
BANKOVSKII VESTNIK. Text in Russian. w. **Document type:** *Newspaper, Consumer.*
Address: Chui 262, Bishkek, Kyrgyzstan. FAX 996-312-243875, vestnik@infotel.kg, http://homepage.kg/~Vestnik.

332   RUS
BANKOVSKOE DELO. Text in Russian. 1994. m. USD 159 foreign (effective 2004). **Document type:** *Magazine, Trade.* **Description:** Covers monetary policy, analysis, forecasting, auditing, regulation, supervision, banking technology, etc.
Indexed: RASB, RefZh.
Published by: Informbank - Informatsionnoe Agentstvo, Ul T Frunze 8-5, k 35-36, Moscow, 119021, Russian Federation. Ed. V F Nesterenko. **US dist. addr.:** East View Information Services, 3020 Harbor Ln. N., Minneapolis, MN 55447. TEL 800-477-1005, FAX 800-800-3839, eastview@eastview.com, http://www.eastview.com.

332   RUS
BANKOVSKOE DELO V MOSKVE. Text in Russian. m. USD 229 in United States.
Indexed: RASB, RefZh.
Published by: Izdatel'stvo Rossiiskii Salon, Ul Balchug 22, A-ya 46, Moscow, 113035, Russian Federation. TEL 7-095-9726260, FAX 7-095-2310395. Ed. V L Kovalenko. **US dist. addr.:** East View Information Services, 3020 Harbor Ln. N., Minneapolis, MN 55447. TEL 612-550-0961.

332.1   USA
BANKRATE DAILY. Text in English. d. **Document type:** *Newsletter, Consumer.* **Description:** Contains up-to-date financial news and rate information.
Media: E-mail.
Published by: Bankrate Inc., 11811 US Hwy 1, North Palm Beach, FL 33408. TEL 561-630-2400, FAX 561-625-4540, webmaster@bankrate.com, http://bankrate.process9.com/bankrate/subscribe.html, http://www.bankrate.com.

BANKRUPTCY: A PRACTICE SYSTEMS LIBRARY MANUAL. see *LAW*

BANKRUPTCY COURT DECISIONS. see *LAW—Corporate Law*

BANKRUPTCY DESK GUIDE. see *LAW*

BANKRUPTCY EVIDENCE MANUAL. see *LAW*

BANKRUPTCY EXEMPTION MANUAL. see *LAW*

BANKRUPTCY IN AUSTRALIA: A GUIDEBOOK. see *LAW*

332.7   USA
▼ **BANKRUPTCY INSIDER**; an absolute priority for bankruptcy profesionals. Text in English. 2004 (Apr.). 44/yr. **Document type:** *Newsletter, Trade.* **Description:** Contains breakdowns and analysis on bankruptcy trends, providing unique contexts and perspectives.
Published by: The Deal, LLC (Subsidiary of: A L M), 105 Madison Ave, 5th Fl, New York, NY 10016. TEL 212-313-9238, 888-667-3325, FAX 212-313-9293, dmarcus@thedeal.com, http://www.thedeal.com/.

BANKRUPTCY LAW DIGEST. see *LAW*

BANKRUPTCY LAW FUNDAMENTALS. see *LAW*

332   USA   ISSN 0744-7671
KF1507
BANKRUPTCY LAW LETTER. Text in English. 1981. m. USD 156.25 domestic; USD 218.65 overseas. back issues avail. **Document type:** *Trade.* **Description:** Covers recent developments in bankruptcy law; includes involuntary position, adequate positions, automatic stay, use, sale, and lease of property.
Related titles: Microform ed.: (from PQC).
Published by: W G & L Financial Reporting & Management Research (Subsidiary of: R I A), 395 Hudson St, New York, NY 10014. TEL 212-367-6300, FAX 212-367-6718. Ed. Charles J Tabb. **Subscr. to:** The Park Square Bldg., 31 St James Ave, Boston, MA 02116-4112. TEL 800-950-1207.

BANKRUPTCY LAW MANUAL. see *LAW*

BANKRUPTCY LEGISLATION. see *LAW*

BANKRUPTCY LIBRARY (PREMISE CD-ROM EDITION). see *LAW*

332.7   USA
▼ **BANKRUPTCY LITIGATION REPORTER.** Text in English. 2004. 24/yr. USD 850 (effective 2005). **Document type:** *Newsletter, Trade.* **Description:** Provides timely and unbiased information about the constantly evolving area of bankruptcy law.
Published by: Andrews Publications (Subsidiary of: Thomson West), 175 Strafford Ave, Ste 140, Wayne, PA 19087. TEL 610-225-0510, FAX 610-225-0501, http://www.andrewsonline.com.

BANKRUPTCY PRACTICE FOR GENERAL PRACTITIONER. see *LAW*

BANKRUPTCY PRACTICE HANDBOOK. see *LAW*

BANKRUPTCY PROCEDURE MANUAL. see *LAW*

332   USA   ISSN 0747-8917
KF1507
BANKRUPTCY STRATEGIST. Text in English. 1983. m. USD 349; USD 399 combined subscription print & online eds. (effective 2005). bk.rev. **Document type:** *Newsletter.* **Description:** Devoted to practical tips and viable solutions for practitioners of bankruptcy law. Reports on legislative developments, fee awards, procedural techniques and judicial rulings.
Formerly: Leader'S Bankruptcy Strategis
Related titles: Online - full text ed.: USD 349 (effective 2004). —CCC.
Published by: Law Journal Newsletters (Subsidiary of: A L M), 1617 JFK Blvd, Ste 1750, Philadelphia, PA 19103. TEL 215-557-2300, 800-888-8300, FAX 215-557-2301, lawcatalog@amlaw.com, http://www.ljnonline.com/. Pub. Marjorie A Weiner.

332   USA   ISSN 1054-9463
KF1507.5
BANKRUPTCY YEARBOOK AND ALMANAC. Text in English. 1991. a. **Document type:** *Trade.*
Published by: New Generation Research, Inc., 225 Friend St, Ste 801, Boston, MA 02114. TEL 617-573-9550. Ed., R&P Christopher McHugh. Pub. George Putnam III.

332   RUS
BANKS AND EXCHANGES WEEKLY. Text in English. w. USD 1,150 in United States. **Document type:** *Trade.*
Published by: Agentstsvo Obzora SMI WPS, A-ya 90, Moscow, 113191, Russian Federation. TEL 7-095-9552950, FAX 7-095-9552927, wpsreg@sovam.com. **US dist. addr.:** East View Information Services, 3020 Harbor Ln. N., Minneapolis, MN 55447. TEL 612-550-0961.

332 340   USA
BANKS AND THRIFTS: ENFORCEMENT AND RECEIVERSHIP LAW. Text in English. 1991. base vol. plus a. updates. looseleaf. USD 201 base vol(s). (effective 2005). **Description:** covers evalute claims, choose the best course of conduct in each case, protect banks against regulat violations, proceed knowledgeably through informal enforcement proceedings, defend ot litigate with confidence, guide financial institutions through the seizure process and represent debtors and creditors.

Published by: Matthew Bender & Co., Inc. (Subsidiary of: LexisNexis North America), 1275 Broadway, Albany, NY 12204. TEL 518-487-3575, 800-252-9257, FAX 518-462-3788, international@bender.com, http://bender.lexisnexis.com. Ed. Barry Zisman.

332.1 GRC
BANKS, INVESTMENT & STOCKMARKET. Text in Greek. 1990. a. adv. **Document type:** *Trade.*
Formerly: Banking Sector
Related titles: ♦ Supplement to: Epilogi. ISSN 1105-2503.
Published by: Electra Press, 4 Stadiou St, Athens, 105 64, Greece. TEL 30-1-323-3203, FAX 30-1-323-5160. Ed. Christos Papaioannou. Circ: 11,000.

BANQUE ASSURANCE. see *INSURANCE*

332 DEU ISSN 1561-0306
BANQUE CENTRAL EUROPEENNE. BULLETIN MENSUEL. Text in French. 1999. m.
Related titles: ♦ English ed.: European Central Bank. Monthly Bulletin. ISSN 1561-0136; ♦ Spanish ed.: Banco Central Europeo. Boletin Mensual. ISSN 1561-0268; ♦ Italian ed.: Banca Centrale Europea. Bollettino Mensile. ISSN 1561-0276; ♦ Portuguese ed.: Banco Central Europeu. Boletin Mensal. ISSN 1561-0284; ♦ German ed.: Europaische Zentralbank. Monatsbericht. ISSN 1561-0292; ♦ Dutch ed.: Europese Centrale Bank. Maandbericht. ISSN 1561-0314; ♦ Spanish ed.: Euroopan Keskuspankiki. Kuukausikatsaus. ISSN 1561-0322; ♦ Greek ed.: Europaike Kentrike Trapeza. Meniaio Deltio. ISSN 1561-025X; ♦ Swedish ed.: Europeiska Centralbanken. Manadsrapport. ISSN 1561-0144; ♦ Danish ed.: Europaeiske Centralbank. Manedsoversigt. ISSN 1561-0241.
Published by: European Central Bank, Postfach 16 03 19, Frankfurt am Main, 60066, Germany. TEL 49-69-1344-0, FAX 49-69-1344-6000, http://www.ecb.int.

332.1 TUN ISSN 0067-3854
BANQUE CENTRALE DE TUNISIE. BULLETIN. Text in French. 1959-1971 (no.43); resumed 1986. q. **Document type:** *Bulletin.*
Published by: Banque Centrale de Tunisie, Rue Hedi Nouira, B P 777, Tunis, 1080, Tunisia. TEL 216-1-340588, FAX 216-1-354214, TELEX 14865, bact@bact.gov.tn.

332.1 TUN ISSN 0067-3862
BANQUE CENTRALE DE TUNISIE. RAPPORT D'ACTIVITE. Text in English. 1959. a. TND 5 domestic; TND 10 foreign.
Published by: Banque Centrale de Tunisie, Rue Hedi Nouira, B P 777, Tunis, 1080, Tunisia. TEL 216-1-340588, FAX 216-1-354214, bact@bact.gov.tn.

332 TUN
BANQUE CENTRALE DE TUNISIE. STATISTIQUES FINANCIERES. Text in French. 1972. q. charts; stat.
Indexed: PAIS.
Published by: Banque Centrale de Tunisie, Rue de la Monnaie, Tunis, 1001, Tunisia.

332 SEN ISSN 0005-559X
HC547.W5
BANQUE CENTRALE DES ETATS DE L'AFRIQUE DE L'OUEST. NOTES D'INFORMATION ET STATISTIQUES. Text in French. 1956. m. looseleaf. XOF 12,000, USD 40 (effective 1998). bk.rev. bibl.; charts; illus.; stat. index. **Document type:** *Bulletin, Government.*
Indexed: ASD, KES, PAIS, RASB.
Published by: Banque Centrale des Etats de l'Afrique de l'Ouest-Siege, Av Abdoulaye Fadiga, BP 3108, Dakar, Senegal. TEL 839-05-00, TELEX BCEAO 21.530. Ed. Amadou Sadickh. Circ: 600.

332 SEN ISSN 0067-3889
BANQUE CENTRALE DES ETATS DE L'AFRIQUE DE L'OUEST. RAPPORT ANNUEL. Text in French. 1955. a. XOF 12,000, USD 40 (effective 1998). **Document type:** *Directory, Corporate.*
Indexed: PAIS.
Published by: Banque Centrale des Etats de l'Afrique de l'Ouest-Siege, Av Abdoulaye Fadiga, BP 3108, Dakar, Senegal. TEL 839-05-00. Ed. Amadou Sadickh. Circ: 2,000.

332.1 SEN ISSN 0067-3897
HG3421.A7
BANQUE CENTRALE DES ETATS DE L'AFRIQUE DE L'OUEST. RAPPORT D'ACTIVITE. Text in French. 1955. a.
Indexed: RASB.
Published by: Banque Centrale des Etats de l'Afrique de l'Ouest-Siege, Av Abdoulaye Fadiga, BP 3108, Dakar, Senegal. TEL 839-05-00.

332.1 COD
BANQUE CENTRALE DU CONGO. RAPPORT ANNUEL. Text in French. a. **Document type:** *Bulletin, Corporate.*
Former titles: Banque du Zaire. Rapport Annuel (0300-1172); Banque Nationale du Congo. Rapport Annuel (0067-4001)
Published by: Banque Centrale du Congo, BP 269, Kinshasa, Gombe, Congo, Dem. Republic. TEL 243-20704, FAX 243-8805152, http://www.bcc.cd.

332.1 COD
BANQUE COMMERCIALE ZAIROISE. RAPPORTS ET BILANS ANNUELS/BANQUE COMMERCIALE ZAIROISE. REPORTS AND BALANCE SHEETS. Text in French. a.
Published by: Banque Commerciale Zairoise, BP 2798, Kinshasa, Congo, Dem. Republic. Ed. Kitoko Pene Kiyayo.

332.1 FRA ISSN 1167-5128
BANQUE DE FRANCE. ANALYSES COMPARATIVES. Text in French. 1988. a. (in 2 vols.). EUR 38 (effective 2003).
Former titles (until 1991): France. Commission Bancaire. Etudes et Analyses Comparatives; (until 1989): France. Commission Bancaire. Resultats des Etablissements de Credit et des Maisons de Titres (0992-5635)
Published by: Banque de France, Service Relations avec le Public, 48 rue Croix-des-Petits-Champs, Paris, 75049, France. http://www.banque-france.fr.

332.1 330.9 FRA ISSN 1250-5765
HG3021
BANQUE DE FRANCE. BULLETIN. Text in French. 1971. m. free. stat. back issues avail.; reprint service avail. from SCH. **Document type:** *Bulletin.* **Description:** Analyzes monetary developments and their economic environment in France and abroad.
Formed by the merger of (1967-1994): Banque de France. Situation Economique a l'Etranger (0242-5904); (1990-1994): Banque de France. Bulletin Mensuel (1145-5535); (1971-1994): Banque de France. Bulletin Trimestriel (0150-7583); Banque de France. Statistiques Monetaires et Financieres (1161-2967); Which was (1984-1991): Banque de France. Statistiques Monetaires Definitives (0999-1085)
Related titles: ♦ Supplement(s): Banque de France. Bulletin Digest. ISSN 1250-5862; ♦ Banque de France. Bulletin. Supplement Statistiques. ISSN 1250-5846.
Indexed: ELLIS, KES, PAIS.
—CCC.
Published by: Banque de France, Service Relations avec le Public, 48 rue Croix-des-Petits-Champs, Paris, 75049, France. TEL 33-1-42923908, FAX 33-1-42923940, http://www.banque-france.fr. Circ: 7,200.

332.1 FRA ISSN 1250-5862
HG3021
BANQUE DE FRANCE. BULLETIN DIGEST. Text in English. 1994. 4/yr. **Description:** Reference work on economic, monetary, and financial issues.
Related titles: ♦ Supplement to: Banque de France. Bulletin. ISSN 1250-5765.
Published by: Banque de France, Service Relations avec le Public, 48 rue Croix-des-Petits-Champs, Paris, 75049, France. TEL 33-1-42923908, FAX 33-1-42923940, http://www.banque-france.fr.

332.1 FRA ISSN 1250-5846
HG3021 CODEN: EJCRF5
BANQUE DE FRANCE. BULLETIN. SUPPLEMENT STATISTIQUES. Text in French. 1994. q.
Related titles: ♦ Supplement to: Banque de France. Bulletin. ISSN 1250-5765.
Published by: Banque de France, Service Relations avec le Public, 48 rue Croix-des-Petits-Champs, Paris, 75049, France. FAX 33-1-42922954, cdoc@banque-france.fr.

BANQUE DE FRANCE. CAHIER DES TITRES DE CREANCES NEGOCIABLES. see *BUSINESS AND ECONOMICS—Abstracting, Bibliographies, Statistics*

332.1 FRA
BANQUE DE FRANCE. CENTRALE DE BILANS: FASCICULES DE RESULTATS SECTORIELS. Text in French. a. EUR 381 per sector; EUR 15 per issue per sector (effective 2003).
Description: Allows businesses to compare their professional results with data from the sample taken by the Centrale de Bilans.
Related titles: Diskette ed.
Published by: Banque de France, Service Relations avec le Public, 48 rue Croix-des-Petits-Champs, Paris, 75049, France. TEL 33-1-42923908, FAX 33-1-42923940, http://www.banque-france.fr.

332.1 FRA
BANQUE DE FRANCE. CENTRALE DE BILANS. METHODE D'ANALYSE FINANCIERE. Text in French. a. EUR 38.11 (effective 2003).
Formerly: Banque de France. Centrale de Bilans. Selection d'Indicateurs
Published by: Banque de France, Service Relations avec le Public, 48 rue Croix-des-Petits-Champs, Paris, 75049, France. TEL 33-1-42923908, FAX 33-1-42923940, http://www.banque-france.fr.

332 FRA ISSN 1169-8489
BANQUE DE FRANCE. COMITE CONSULTATIF. RAPPORT. Text in French. 1987. a. free. **Description:** Studies the problems in the relationship between credit institutions and their clientele.
Published by: Banque de France, Service Relations avec le Public, 48 rue Croix-des-Petits-Champs, Paris, 75049, France. TEL 33-1-42922710, FAX 33-1-42923940, http://www.banque-france.fr. **Co-sponsor:** Conseil National du Credit et du Titre.

332 FRA
BANQUE DE FRANCE. COMITE DE LA REGLEMENTATION BANCAIRE ET FINANCIERE. RAPPORT. Text in French. 1989. a. EUR 38 (effective 2003).
Formerly: Banque de France. Comite de la Reglementation Bancaire. Rapport (1169-8462)
Published by: Banque de France, Service Relations avec le Public, 48 rue Croix-des-Petits-Champs, Paris, 75049, France. TEL 33-1-42922972, 33-1-42923908, FAX 33-1-42923940, http://www.banque-france.fr.

332.7 FRA
BANQUE DE FRANCE. COMITE DES ETABLISSEMENTS DE CREDIT ET DES ENTREPRISES D'INVESTISSEMENTS. RAPPORT. Text in French. a. EUR 38 (effective 2003).
Formerly: Banque de France. Comite des Etablissements de Credit. Rapport (1153-2785)
Published by: Banque de France, Service Relations avec le Public, 48 rue Croix-des-Petits-Champs, Paris, 75049, France. TEL 33-1-42923908, FAX 33-1-42923940, http://www.banque-france.fr.

332.1 FRA ISSN 1142-2858
BANQUE DE FRANCE. COMMISSION BANCAIRE. BULLETIN. Text in French. 1989. s-a. EUR 38 (effective 2003).
Description: Examines the role of the commission and the decisions it makes.
Published by: Banque de France, Service Relations avec le Public, 48 rue Croix-des-Petits-Champs, Paris, 75049, France. TEL 33-1-42923908, FAX 33-1-42923940, http://www.banque-france.fr. **Co-sponsor:** Commission Bancaire.

332.1 FRA ISSN 0984-5585
BANQUE DE FRANCE. COMMISSION BANCAIRE. RAPPORT (YEAR). Text in French. a. EUR 38 (effective 2003).
Description: Provides a summary of the activities of the commission as well as reviews legislation and new rules governing credit institutions.
Formerly: Commission de Controle des Banques. Rapport Annuel (0984-5631)
Related titles: ♦ English ed.: Banque de France. Commission Bancaire. Report (Year). ISSN 1142-3110.
Published by: Banque de France, Service Relations avec le Public, 48 rue Croix-des-Petits-Champs, Paris, 75049, France. TEL 33-1-42923908, FAX 33-1-42923940, http://www.banque-france.fr. **Co-sponsor:** Commission Bancaire.

332.1 FRA
BANQUE DE FRANCE. COMMISSION BANCAIRE. RECUEIL B A F I. Text in French. 1994. a. EUR 182.94 (effective 2003).
Published by: Banque de France, Service Relations avec le Public, 48 rue Croix-des-Petits-Champs, Paris, 75049, France. TEL 33-1-42923908, FAX 33-1-42923940, http://www.banque-france.fr.

332.1 FRA ISSN 1142-3110
BANQUE DE FRANCE. COMMISSION BANCAIRE. REPORT (YEAR). Text in English. a. EUR 38 (effective 2003).
Description: Reference book about French banking system.
Related titles: ♦ French ed.: Banque de France. Commission Bancaire. Rapport (Year). ISSN 0984-5585.
Published by: Banque de France, Service Relations avec le Public, 48 rue Croix-des-Petits-Champs, Paris, 75049, France. TEL 33-1-42923908, FAX 33-1-42923940, http://www.banque-france.fr.

332.1 FRA ISSN 0767-9505
BANQUE DE FRANCE. COMPTES ANNUELS DES ETABLISSEMENTS DE CREDIT. Text in French. 1949. a. EUR 76 in two volumes (effective 2003).
Formerly (until 1987): France. Commission Bancaire. Bilans des Banques
Related titles: Diskette ed.: EUR 91 2 volumes (effective 2002).
Published by: Banque de France, Service Relations avec le Public, 48 rue Croix-des-Petits-Champs, Paris, 75049, France. TEL 33-1-42923908, FAX 33-1-42923940, http://www.banque-france.fr.

332.7 FRA
BANQUE DE FRANCE. CONSEIL NATIONAL DU CREDIT ET DU TITRE. RAPPORT. Text in French. 1986. a. free. back issues avail. **Description:** Covers developments affecting the financial system.
Formerly: Banque de France. Conseil National du Credit. Rapports des Groupes de Travail
Related titles: English ed.
Published by: Banque de France, Service Relations avec le Public, 48 rue Croix-des-Petits-Champs, Paris, 75049, France. TEL 33-1-42923908, FAX 33-1-42923940, http://www.banque-france.fr.

332.7 FRA
BANQUE DE FRANCE. CONSEIL NATIONAL DU CREDIT ET DU TITRE. RAPPORTS DES GROUPES DE TRAVAIL. Text in French. irreg. EUR 38.11 (effective 2003).
Related titles: ♦ English ed.: Banque de France. Conseil National du Credit et du Titre. Reports of the Working Groups.
Published by: Banque de France, Service Relations avec le Public, 48 rue Croix-des-Petits-Champs, Paris, 75049, France. TEL 33-1-42922710, 33-1-42923908, FAX 33-1-42923940, http://www.banque-france.fr. **Co-sponsor:** Comite Consultatif.

332.7   FRA
BANQUE DE FRANCE. CONSEIL NATIONAL DU CREDIT ET DU TITRE. REPORTS OF THE WORKING GROUPS. Text in English. irreg. back issues avail. **Description:** Covers developments affecting the financial system.
Formerly: Banque de France. Conseil National du Credit. Reports of the Working Groups
Related titles: ◆ French ed.: Banque de France. Conseil National du Credit et du Titre. Rapports des Groupes de Travail.
Published by: Banque de France, Service Relations avec le Public, 48 rue Croix-des-Petits-Champs, Paris, 75049, France. TEL 33-1-42923908, FAX 33-1-42923940, http://www.banque-france.fr.

332.1   FRA
BANQUE DE FRANCE. ETUDES PAR SECTEURS; contexte, resultats, perspectives. Text in French. a. EUR 91 per issue (effective 2003).
Former titles: Banque de France. Etudes Sectorielles; Banque de France. Centrale de Bilans. Etudes
Published by: Banque de France, Service Relations avec le Public, 48 rue Croix-des-Petits-Champs, Paris, 75049, France. TEL 33-1-42923908, FAX 33-1-42923940, http://www.banque-france.fr.

332.1   FRA   ISSN 0242-5866
BANQUE DE FRANCE. LA MONNAIE EN... Variant title: La Monnaie en (Year). Text in French. 1970. a. free. charts; stat. **Description:** Summarizes main data relating to monetary policy as well as developments in money, credit and financial investment.
Published by: Banque de France, Service Relations avec le Public, 48 rue Croix-des-Petits-Champs, Paris, 75049, France. TEL 33-1-42923908, FAX 33-1-42923940, http://www.banque-france.fr.

332   FRA
BANQUE DE FRANCE. LA SITUATION DES ENTREPRISES INDUSTRIELLES. Text in French. a. EUR 38 per issue (effective 2003).
Published by: Banque de France, Service Relations avec le Public, 48 rue Croix-des-Petits-Champs, Paris, 75049, France. TEL 33-1-42923908, cdoc@banque-france.fr, http://www.banque-france.fr.

332.1   FRA
BANQUE DE FRANCE. NOTES D'INFORMATION. Text in French. 1971. irreg. free.
Published by: Banque de France, Service Relations avec le Public, 48 rue Croix-des-Petits-Champs, Paris, 75049, France. TEL 33-1-42923908, FAX 33-1-42923940, http://www.banque-france.fr.

332.1   FRA   ISSN 1250-5242
BANQUE DE FRANCE. RAPPORT. Text in French. a. free. **Description:** Describes the bank's activities, its balance sheet and income statements and presents the Governor's comments on the economic and monetary situation.
Former titles (until 1994): Banque de France. Compte Rendu (0242-5890); (until 1973): Banque de France. Compte Rendu des Operations (0067-3927)
Related titles: ◆ English ed.: Banque de France. Report. ISSN 1240-6813.
Published by: Banque de France, Service Relations avec le Public, 48 rue Croix-des-Petits-Champs, Paris, 75049, France. TEL 33-1-42923908, FAX 33-1-42923940, http://www.banque-france.fr.

332.1   FRA
BANQUE DE FRANCE. RECUEIL DES TEXTES RELATIFS A L'EXERCICE DES ACTIVITES BANCAIRES ET FINANCIERES. Text in French. a. EUR 76 (effective 2003).
Formerly: Banque de France. Recueil des Textes Applicables a l'Exercice des Activites Bancaires
Related titles: ◆ English ed.: Banque de France. Selected French Banking and Financial Regulations. ISSN 1240-6694.
Published by: Banque de France, Service Relations avec le Public, 48 rue Croix-des-Petits-Champs, Paris, 75049, France. TEL 33-1-42923908, FAX 33-1-42923940, http://www.banque-france.fr.

332.1   FRA   ISSN 1240-6813
BANQUE DE FRANCE. REPORT. Text in English. 1992. a. free. **Description:** Describes the bank's activities, its balance sheet and income statements and presents the Governor's comments on the economic and monetary situation.
Related titles: ◆ French ed.: Banque de France. Rapport. ISSN 1250-5242.
Published by: Banque de France, Service Relations avec le Public, 48 rue Croix-des-Petits-Champs, Paris, 75049, France. TEL 33-1-42923908, FAX 33-1-42922954, http://www.banque-france.fr.

332.3   FRA   ISSN 1240-6694
BANQUE DE FRANCE. SELECTED FRENCH BANKING AND FINANCIAL REGULATIONS. Text in English. 1992. a. EUR 76 (effective 2003). **Description:** Contains the Banking Act, together with the main legal, accounting, prudential and monetary provisions applicable to credit institutions doing business in France.

Related titles: ◆ French ed.: Banque de France. Recueil des Textes Relatifs a l'Exercice des Activites Bancaires et Financieres.
Published by: Banque de France, Service Relations avec le Public, 48 rue Croix-des-Petits-Champs, Paris, 75049, France. TEL 33-1-42923908, FAX 33-1-42923940, http://www.banque-france.fr.

332.1   FRA
BANQUE DE FRANCE. SERVICE DE L'INFORMATION. COLLECTION NOTES D'INFORMATION. Text in French. 1992. irreg. free.
Formerly (until 2001): Collection Documentation et Information (1152-538X)
Related titles: CD-ROM ed.; Online - full text ed.; ◆ Series: Les Principales Procedures de Financement - Entreprises et Menages.
Published by: Banque de France, Service Relations avec le Public, 48 rue Croix-des-Petits-Champs, Paris, 75049, France. http://www.banque-france.fr.

332   FRA
BANQUE DE FRANCE. T E O R B E. (Texte, outils, references bancaires et economiques) Text in French. q. EUR 548; EUR 274 to institutions schools (effective 2002).
Media: CD-ROM.
Published by: Banque de France, Service Relations avec le Public, 48 rue Croix-des-Petits-Champs, Paris, 75049, France. TEL 33-1-42923908, http://www.banque-france.fr.

332   HTI   ISSN 0257-4349
HG2813
BANQUE DE LA REPUBLIQUE D'HAITI. BULLETIN. Text in French. s-a. HTG 50, USD 12.
Published by: Banque de la Republique d'Haiti, Direction Administrative, B.P. 1570, Port-au-Prince, Haiti. TEL 23-1944, FAX 22-2607.

332.1   HTI   ISSN 0257-4357
BANQUE DE LA REPUBLIQUE D'HAITI. RAPPORT ANNUEL. Text in French. a. HTG 25, USD 6.
Formerly: Banque Nationale de la Republique d'Haiti. Rapport du Departement Fiscal
Published by: Banque de la Republique d'Haiti, Direction Administrative, B.P. 1570, Port-au-Prince, Haiti.

332.1   BDI   ISSN 1013-5332
HC880.A1
BANQUE DE LA REPUBLIQUE DU BURUNDI. BULLETIN MENSUEL. Text in French. 1978. m. BIF 10,000; USD 60 to individuals Africa; EUR 70 to individuals Europe; USD 80 to individuals,elsewhere (effective 1999). charts; stat. **Document type:** Bulletin. **Description:** Covers industrial production statistics on the monetary situation.
Indexed: PAIS.
Published by: Banque de la Republique du Burundi, Service des Etudes, BP 705, Bujumbura, Burundi. TEL 257-222745, FAX 257-224206. Ed. B Sota.

332.1   BDI   ISSN 1013-5359
BANQUE DE LA REPUBLIQUE DU BURUNDI. RAPPORT ANNUEL. Text in French. 1964. a. USD 20 in Africa; USD 25 in Europe; USD 30 elsewhere (effective 1999). charts; stat. **Document type:** Corporate. **Description:** Discusses numerous sectors in the economy such as major import-exported products, employment conditions, the budget, political events influencing the economy, balance sheet and other financial documents.
Published by: Banque de la Republique du Burundi, Service des Etudes, BP 705, Bujumbura, Burundi. TEL 257-222745, FAX 257-8224206. Circ: 400.

BANQUE DES ETATS DE L'AFRIQUE CENTRALE. ETUDES ET STATISTIQUES; bulletin mensuel. see BUSINESS AND ECONOMICS—Abstracting, Bibliographies, Statistics

332.1   CMR   ISSN 0067-3900
BANQUE DES ETATS DE L'AFRIQUE CENTRALE. RAPPORT D'ACTIVITE. Text in French. 1973. a. free.
Indexed: PAIS.
Published by: Banque des Etats de l'Afrique Centrale, Direction des Etudes et de la Documentation, Services Centraux, BP 1917, Yaounde, Cameroon. Circ: 1,500.

332   LBN
BANQUE DU LIBAN. ANNUAL REPORT. Text in English. a.
Published by: Banque du Liban, P.O. Box 11-5544, Beirut, Lebanon.

332   LBN
BANQUE DU LIBAN. MONTHLY BULLETIN. Text in English. m.
Indexed: PAIS.
Published by: Banque du Liban, P.O. Box 11-5544, Beirut, Lebanon.

332   LBN
BANQUE DU LIBAN. QUARTERLY BULLETIN. Text in English. q.
Indexed: PAIS.
Published by: Banque du Liban, P.O. Box 11-5544, Beirut, Lebanon.

332.1   LUX
BANQUE ET CAISSE D'EPARGNE DE L'ETAT, LUXEMBOURG. ANNUAL REPORT. Text in English. a.
Related titles: Ed.: Banque et Caisse d'Epargne de l'Etat, Luxembourg. Rapports et Bilan. 1901. free.
Published by: Banque et Caisse d'Epargne de l'Etat Luxembourg, 1 Place de Metz, Luxembourg, L-2954, Luxembourg.

332   CHE
BANQUE & FINANCE. Text in French. 3/yr. **Document type:** Consumer.
Published by: Promoedition SA, 35 rue des Bain, Case Postale 5615, Geneva 11, 1211, Switzerland. TEL 41-22-8099460, FAX 41-22-7811414. Ed. Thierry Oppikofer. Circ: 15,000.

332   LUX   ISSN 0257-7755
HC240.A1
BANQUE EUROPEENNE D'INVESTISSEMENT. CAHIERS/EUROPEAN INVESTMENT BANK. PAPERS. Key Title: BEI. Cahiers. Text in Multiple languages. 1986. irreg.
Indexed: JEL.
—BLDSC (3664.771000).
Published by: European Investment Bank/Banque Europeenne d'Investissement, 100 bd. Konrad Adenauer, Luxembourg, L-2950, Luxembourg. TEL 352-4379-3122, FAX 352-4379-3189, http://www.eib.org.

332.1   MAR
BANQUE MAROCAINE DU COMMERCE EXTERIEUR. ANNUAL REPORT. Text in French. 1961. a. **Document type:** Corporate.
Related titles: Arabic ed.; English ed.
Indexed: PAIS.
Published by: Banque Marocaine du Commerce Exterieur, 140 Ave Hassan II, Casablanca, Morocco. TEL 21-22-200496, FAX 21-22-200512, http://www.e-bmcebank.ma. Circ: 6,000.

332   MAR   ISSN 0851-0202
BANQUE MAROCAINE DU COMMERCE EXTERIEUR. INFORMATION REVIEW. Text in English. 1972. bi-m. free. adv. bk.rev.
Formerly: B M C E. Monthly Information Review; Formed by the (1976) merger of: Banque Marocaine du Commerce Exterieur. Revue Bimensuelle; Banque Marocaine du Commerce Exterieur. Monthly Bulletin of Information (0522-327X)
Related titles: ◆ French ed.: Banque Marocaine du Commerce Exterieur. Revue d'Informations. ISSN 0251-3013.
Indexed: ELLIS, PAIS.
—BLDSC (4494.215500).
Published by: Banque Marocaine du Commerce Exterieur, 140 Ave Hassan II, Casablanca, Morocco. TEL 21-22-200496, FAX 21-22-200512, http://www.e-bmcebank.ma.

332   MAR   ISSN 0251-3013
BANQUE MAROCAINE DU COMMERCE EXTERIEUR. REVUE D'INFORMATIONS. Text in French. bi-m.
Related titles: ◆ English ed.: Banque Marocaine du Commerce Exterieur. Information Review. ISSN 0851-0202.
Indexed: PAIS.
Published by: Banque Marocaine du Commerce Exterieur, 140 Ave Hassan II, Casablanca, Morocco. TEL 21-22-200496, FAX 21-22-200512, http://www.e-bmcebank.ma.

BANQUE NATIONALE DE BELGIQUE. BELGOSTAT (YEAR). see BUSINESS AND ECONOMICS—Abstracting, Bibliographies, Statistics

332 330.9   BEL   ISSN 1372-7893
HC311
BANQUE NATIONALE DE BELGIQUE. BULLETIN STATISTIQUE. Text in French, Dutch, Bilingual. 1926. q. EUR 94.19 (effective 2002). bibl.; charts; stat. Supplement avail. **Document type:** Bulletin, Government.
Related titles: Online - full text ed.; Flemish ed.: Nationale Bank van Belgie. Statistisch Tijdschrift. ISSN 1372-7885. 1971.
Indexed: PAIS.
Published by: Banque Nationale de Belgique/Nationale Bank van Belgie, Service Documentation, Bd de Berlaimont 14, Brussels, 1000, Belgium. TEL 32-2-2212033, FAX 32-2-2213163, documentation@nbb.be, http://www.nbb.be.

BANQUE NATIONALE DE BELGIQUE. INDICATEURS ECONOMIQUES POUR LA BELGIQUE. see BUSINESS AND ECONOMICS—Abstracting, Bibliographies, Statistics

BANQUE NATIONALE DE BELGIQUE. INSTITUT DES COMPTES NATIONAUX. AGREGATS ANNUELS. see BUSINESS AND ECONOMICS—Abstracting, Bibliographies, Statistics

BANQUE NATIONALE DE BELGIQUE. INSTITUT DES COMPTES NATIONAUX. COMPTES NATIONAUX: AGREGATS TRIMESTRIELS. see BUSINESS AND ECONOMICS—Abstracting, Bibliographies, Statistics

BANQUE NATIONALE DE BELGIQUE. INSTITUT DES COMPTES NATIONAUX. COMPTES REGIONAUX. see BUSINESS AND ECONOMICS—Abstracting, Bibliographies, Statistics

B

BANQUE NATIONALE DE BELGIQUE. INSTITUT DES COMPTES NATIONAUX. STATISTIQUES DU COMMERCE EXTERIEUR. see *BUSINESS AND ECONOMICS— Abstracting, Bibliographies, Statistics*

BANQUE NATIONALE DE BELGIQUE. INSTITUT DES COMPTES NATIONAUX. STATISTIQUES DU COMMERCE EXTERIEUR. ANNUAIRE. see *BUSINESS AND ECONOMICS—Abstracting, Bibliographies, Statistics*

332.1   BEL
BANQUE NATIONALE DE BELGIQUE. LA CENTRALE DES BILANS. COMPTES ANNUELS DES ENTREPRISES BELGES. Text in French, Dutch. 5/yr. EUR 284.94 (effective 2003). **Document type:** *Government.*
Media: CD-ROM.
Published by: Banque Nationale de Belgique/Nationale Bank van Belgie, Service Documentation, Bd de Berlaimont 14, Brussels, 1000, Belgium.

332.1   BEL
BANQUE NATIONALE DE BELGIQUE. LA CENTRALE DES BILANS. IMAGES DES COMPTES ANNUELS DEPOSES. Text in French, Dutch. a. EUR 1,500 (effective 2003). **Document type:** *Government.*
Media: CD-ROM.
Published by: Banque Nationale de Belgique/Nationale Bank van Belgie, Service Documentation, Bd de Berlaimont 14, Brussels, 1000, Belgium.

BANQUE NATIONALE DE BELGIQUE. LA CENTRALE DES BILANS. STATISTIQUES. see *BUSINESS AND ECONOMICS—Abstracting, Bibliographies, Statistics*

BANQUE NATIONALE DE BELGIQUE. LA CENTRALE DES CREDITS AUX PARTICULIERS. see *BUSINESS AND ECONOMICS—Abstracting, Bibliographies, Statistics*

332.1   BEL
BANQUE NATIONALE DE BELGIQUE. RAPPORT ANNUEL. ACTIVITE ET COMPTES ANNUELS. Text in French. 1852. a. free. **Document type:** *Government.*
Supersedes in part (in 2000): Banque Nationale de Belgique. Rapport sur les Operations
Related titles: Online - full text ed.; Dutch ed.; English ed.
Published by: Banque Nationale de Belgique/Nationale Bank van Belgie, Service Documentation, Bd de Berlaimont 14, Brussels, 1000, Belgium. TEL 32-2-2212033, FAX 32-2-2213163, documentation@nbb.be, http://www.nbb.be.

332.1   BEL
BANQUE NATIONALE DE BELGIQUE. RAPPORT ANNUEL. EVOLUTION ECONOMIQUE ET FINANCIERE. Text in French. 1852. a. free. **Document type:** *Government.*
Description: Information on the Belgian economy and business outlook.
Supersedes in part (in 2000): Banque Nationale de Belgique. Rapport sur les Operations
Related titles: Online - full text ed.; Dutch ed.; English ed.
Published by: Banque Nationale de Belgique/Nationale Bank van Belgie, Service Documentation, Bd de Berlaimont 14, Brussels, 1000, Belgium. TEL 32-2-2212033, FAX 32-2-2213163, documentation@nbb.be, http://www.nbb.be.

332.1   BEL   ISSN 1372-3162
BANQUE NATIONALE DE BELGIQUE. REVUE ECONOMIQUE. Text in French, Dutch. q. free. **Document type:** *Government.*
Formerly (until 1996): Banque Nationale de Belgique. Bulletin (0005-5611)
Indexed: PAIS.
Published by: Banque Nationale de Belgique/Nationale Bank van Belgie, Service Documentation, Bd de Berlaimont 14, Brussels, 1000, Belgium.

332.1   BEL
BANQUE NATIONALE DE BELGIQUE. WORKING PAPERS. Text in English, French, Dutch. irreg. free. **Document type:** *Government.*
Published by: Banque Nationale de Belgique/Nationale Bank van Belgie, Service Documentation, Bd de Berlaimont 14, Brussels, 1000, Belgium.

332.1   RWA
BANQUE NATIONALE DU RWANDA. BULLETIN. Text in French. s-a. RWF 1,500, USD 60. **Document type:** *Bulletin.*
Formerly: Banque Nationale du Rwanda. Bulletin Trimestriel
Indexed: PAIS, RASB.
Published by: Banque Nationale du Rwanda, BP 531, Kigali, Rwanda. FAX 250-72551, TELEX 508-589.

332.1   RWA
BANQUE NATIONALE DU RWANDA. RAPPORT SUR L'EVOLUTION ECONOMIQUE ET MONETAIRE DU RWANDA. Text in English. a. USD 35 foreign. stat.
Former titles: Banque Nationale du Rwanda. Rapport d'Activites; (until 1986): Banque Nationale du Rwanda. Rapport Annuel
Published by: Banque Nationale du Rwanda, BP 531, Kigali, Rwanda.

332.1   MDG
BANQUE NATIONALE POUR LE DEVELOPPEMENT RURAL. RAPPORT ANNUEL. Text in French. a. free.
Published by: Banque Nationale pour le Developpement Rural, BP 183, Antananarivo, Madagascar. FAX 21398, TELEX 22208 BTM MG.

332   CHE   ISSN 1423-3797
HC395
BANQUE NATIONALE SUISSE. BULLETIN TRIMESTRIEL. Text in French. 1983. q. **Document type:** *Bulletin, Government.*
Supersedes in part (in 1997): Geld, Wahrung und Konjunktur (0257-4616)
Indexed: RefZh.
Published by: Schweizerische Nationalbank/Banque Nationale Suisse, Boersenstr. 15, Postfach, Zurich, 8022, Switzerland. TEL 41-1-6313111, FAX 41-1-6313911, snb@snb.ch, http://www.snb.ch.

332   CHE   ISSN 0005-4240
BANQUE POPULAIRE SUISSE. BALANCE SHEET PROSPECTUS. Text in English. s-a. free.
Related titles: French ed.; German ed.; Italian ed.
Published by: Banque Populaire Suisse, Weltpostr 5, Case Postale 2620, Bern, 3001, Switzerland. Circ: 30,000.

332.1   CHE   ISSN 0067-4028
BANQUE POPULAIRE SUISSE. INFORMATION. Text in French. 3/yr. free.
Related titles: English ed.; German ed.
Published by: Banque Populaire Suisse, Weltpostr 5, Case Postale 2620, Bern, 3001, Switzerland. Circ: 80,000.

332   CHE
BANQUE POPULAIRE SUISSE. JOURNAL. Text in French. 4/yr. free.
Supersedes (1962-1977): Fragments (0015-9336)
Related titles: German ed.; Italian ed.
Published by: Banque Populaire Suisse, Weltpostr 5, Case Postale 2620, Bern, 3001, Switzerland.

332.1   RWA
BANQUE RWANDAISE DE DEVELOPPEMENT. RAPPORT ANNUEL. Text in French. 1985. a., latest 1997. free. charts; stat. **Description:** The purpose of the report is to give an overview of the bank's activities during the year.
Published by: Banque Rwandaise de Developpement, BP 1341, Kigali, Rwanda. TEL 75079, FAX 73569, TELEX 22 563 DEVELBANK RW, jbrd@rwandatel.1.com.

332.1   TGO
BANQUE TOGOLAISE DE DEVELOPPEMENT. RAPPORT D'ACTIVITES. Text in French. a. **Description:** Consists of reports concerning financial operations, deposits and external relations.
Formerly: Banque Togolaise de Developpement. Rapport Annuel (0067-4036)
Published by: Banque Togolaise de Developpement, BP 65; Lome, Togo.

332   FRA   ISSN 1168-0377
BANQUES DES ENTREPRISES. Text in French. 1992. m. EUR 541 domestic; EUR 569 foreign (effective 2000). **Document type:** *Newsletter.*
Published by: Publi-News, 47 rue Aristide Briand, Levallois-Perret, 92300, France. TEL 33-1-41499360, FAX 33-1-47573725, publi.news@wanadoo.fr. Ed. Ange Galula.

332   FRA   ISSN 1163-7773
BANQUES DES PARTICULIERS. Text in French. 1992. m. (14/yr.). EUR 579 domestic; EUR 595 foreign (effective 2000). **Document type:** *Newsletter.*
Published by: Publi-News, 47 rue Aristide Briand, Levallois-Perret, 92300, France. TEL 33-1-41499360, FAX 33-1-47573725, publi.news@wanadoo.fr. Ed. Ange Galula.

332 338.642   FRA   ISSN 1148-1978
BANQUES DES PROFESSIONNELS. Text in French. 1991. m. EUR 514 domestic; EUR 569 foreign (effective 2000). **Document type:** *Newsletter.* **Description:** Covers banks' strategies for small sized companies, shops, newly created companies, shopkeepers as well as doctors and lawyers.
Published by: Publi-News, 47 rue Aristide Briand, Levallois-Perret, 92300, France. TEL 33-1-41499360, FAX 33-1-47573725, publi.news@wanadoo.fr. Ed. Ange Galula.

332 330   MAR   ISSN 0851-2167
BANQUES ET ENTREPRISES AU MAROC. Text in French. 1985. q.
Published by: Revue Banques et Entreprises au Maroc, 8 rue 4 Guise, Roches Noires, Casablanca 05, Morocco. Ed. Ibnou Zahir Abdelwahab.

332 658.3   FRA   ISSN 1162-1516
BANQUES RESSOURCES HUMAINES. Text in French. 1991. m. EUR 508 domestic; EUR 541 foreign (effective 2000). **Document type:** *Newsletter.* **Description:** Covers training, human resources management, motivation, recruiting and more.
Published by: Publi-News, 47 rue Aristide Briand, Levallois-Perret, 92300, France. TEL 33-1-41499360, FAX 33-1-47573725, publi.news@wanadoo.fr. Ed. Ange Galula.

332.1   CAN   ISSN 0822-6849
LE BANQUIER. Text in French. 1893. bi-m. CND 35 domestic; USD 60 foreign (effective 1999). adv. bk.rev. index.
Description: Offers an analytical forum for information about banking, including developments in financial services and the economy, technology and management, policy, legislative and ethical issues.
Related titles: Microfilm ed.; Online - full content ed.; ♦ English ed.: Canadian Banker (Print Edition). ISSN 0822-6830.
Indexed: CPerI, PdeR.
Published by: Canadian Bankers Association (Montreal), Tour Scotia, 1002 rue Sherbrooke Ouest Bur 900, Montreal, PQ H3A 3M5, Canada. TEL 514-840-8747, 416-362-6093 ext.337, FAX 514-282-7551, smaclennan@cba.ca, http://www.cba.ca. Ed. Jacques Hebert. Adv. contact Bob Dumouchel. Circ: 33,915; 32,800 (paid).

332.1   BRB
BARBADOS NATIONAL BANK. ANNUAL REPORT & STATEMENT OF ACCOUNTS. Text in English. a.
Published by: Barbados National Bank, James St., Bridgetown, Barbados.

BASE INFORMATIVA PUBBLICA. see *STATISTICS*

DER BAYERISCHE STEUERZAHLER. see *BUSINESS AND ECONOMICS—Public Finance, Taxation*

332   DEU   ISSN 0720-6801
BEIHEFTE ZU KREDIT UND KAPITAL. Text in German, English. 1972. irreg., latest vol.15, 2000. price varies. **Document type:** *Monographic series, Academic/Scholarly.*
Related titles: ♦ Supplement to: Kredit und Kapital. ISSN 0023-4591.
Indexed: PCI.
Published by: Duncker und Humblot GmbH, Carl-Heinrich-Becker-Weg 9, Berlin, 12165, Germany. TEL 49-30-7900060, FAX 49-30-79000361, info@duncker-humblot.de, http://www.duncker-humblot.de. Ed. G Besier.

332.6   DEU   ISSN 0172-0236
BERLINER BANK. BOERSENBRIEF. Key Title: Boersenbrief. Text in German. 1950. fortn. free. **Document type:** *Bulletin, Trade.*
Published by: Berliner Bank Aktiengesellschaft, Hardenbergstr 32, Berlin, 10623, Germany. TEL 49-30-31090, FAX 49-30-31092165, kundendienste@berliner-bank.de, http://www.berliner-bank.de. Circ: 12,500.

332   BMU
BERMUDA MONETARY AUTHORITY. REPORTS & ACCOUNTS. Text in English. 1969. a. free.
Published by: Bermuda Monetary Authority, Burnaby House, 26 Burnaby St, PO Box HM 2447, Hamilton, HM11, Bermuda. TEL 441-295-5278, FAX 441-292-7471, info@bma.bm, http://www.bma.bm. Circ: 1,000.

BETRIEBSWIRTSCHAFTLICHE BLAETTER. see *BUSINESS AND ECONOMICS—Management*

332   SCG   ISSN 0354-3242
BILTEN - SLUZBENA OBJASNJENJA I STRUCNA MISLJENJA ZA PRIMENU FINANSIJSKIH PROPISA. Text in Serbo-Croatian. 1961. m.
Former titles: Bilten Objasnjenja za Primenu Propisa iz Oblasti Finansija i Strucna Misljenja (0354-2688); (until 1992): Bilten Objasnjenja za Primenu Propisa iz Oblasti Finansija (0523-6126)
Related titles: ♦ Supplement to: Finansije. ISSN 0015-2145.
Published by: (Poslovni Sistem "Grmec" YUG), Privredni Pregled, Marsala Birjuzova 3-5, Belgrade, 11000. Ed. Viden Pancic.

BIOTECH FINANCIAL REPORTS. see *BIOLOGY—Biotechnology*

BIOWORLD FINANCIAL WATCH. see *BIOLOGY*

332.1   ITA
BIREL NEWSLETTER. Text in English, Italian. 1996. irreg. free. **Description:** Addresses managers who are responsible for treasury and organizational matters as well as marketing and credit managers.
Published by: Banca d'Italia, Via Nazionale 187, Rome, 00184, Italy. TEL 39-06-47922333, FAX 39-06-47922059, http://www.bancaditalia.it. Circ: 6,000.

332   BGR
BIUDZHET. Text in Bulgarian. m. USD 96 foreign (effective 2002). **Document type:** *Journal, Trade.*
Published by: Ministerstvo na Finansite, 102 Rakovski ul, Sofia, 1000, Bulgaria. **Dist. by:** Sofia Books, ul Silivria 16, Sofia 1404, Bulgaria. TEL 359-2-9586257, info@sofiabooks-bg.com, http://www.sofiabooks-bg.com.

332   RUS   ISSN 1560-0521
BIZNES I BANKI. Text in Russian. 1990. w. USD 100 (effective 2000). adv. **Document type:** *Newspaper.* **Description:** Covers all aspects of banking.
Related titles: Microfiche ed.; (from EVP).
Indexed: RASB.

B

Published by: Biznes i Banki Gazeta Ltd., Ul Dekabristov 10, korp 1, ofis 71, Moscow, 127562, Russian Federation. TEL 7-095-9078201, FAX 7-095-9078210, bbanks@online.ru, bbanks@glasnet.ru. Ed., Pub. S I Korepanov. Adv. contact Olga Barnicheva. page USD 500. Circ: 7,000. **US dist. addr.:** East View Information Services, 3020 Harbor Ln. N., Minneapolis, MN 55447. TEL 612-550-0961.

BLAY'S COMMERCIAL MORTGAGEMATCH. see *REAL ESTATE*

BOERSE ONLINE; das Anlegermagazin. see *BUSINESS AND ECONOMICS—Investments*

332 DNK
BOERSEN. Text in Danish. 1896. d. DKK 2,445 domestic; DKK 2,772 in Europe; DKK 4,032 in US & Canada; DKK 4,914 rest of world (effective 2001). adv. **Document type:** *Newspaper, Consumer.*
Related titles: Microfilm ed.: (from PQC); Online - full text ed.; ♦ Supplement(s): Borsen Informatik. ISSN 0906-8317.
Indexed: B&I.
Published by: Dagbladet Boersen A-S, Moentergade 19, Copenhagen K, 1140, Denmark. TEL 45-33-32-01-02, FAX 45-33-12-24-45, redaktionen@borsen.dk, http://www.borsen.dk. Eds. Bent Soerensen, Leif Beck Fallesen. Circ: 43,455.

BOLETIN DE ESTADISTICAS BANCARIAS. see *BUSINESS AND ECONOMICS—Abstracting, Bibliographies, Statistics*

332 COL ISSN 0121-0629
KHH1142
BOLETIN JURIDICO Y FINANCIERO. Text in Spanish. 1988. w. USD 170 (effective 1998). **Description:** Compiles all legislation pertaining to the financial sector and the country's monetary, credit and foreign exchange policies.
Published by: Asociacion Bancaria y de Entidades Financieras, Apartado Aereo 13994, Bogota, CUND, Colombia. TEL 57-1-2114811, FAX 57-1-2119915, info@asobancaria.com, http://www.asobancaria.com.

BOLETIN MENSUAL DE ESTADISTICAS DEL SISTEMA FINANCIERO. see *BUSINESS AND ECONOMICS—Abstracting, Bibliographies, Statistics*

332 URY
BOLSA DE VALORES DE MONTEVIDEO. ESTUDIOS ESTADISTICOS. Text in Spanish. 1976. q.
Published by: Bolsa de Valores de Montevideo, Misiones, 1400, Montevideo, 11006, Uruguay.

BOLSA MEXICANA DE VALORES. ANUARIO FINANCIERO (YEAR). see *BUSINESS AND ECONOMICS—Abstracting, Bibliographies, Statistics*

BOLSA MEXICANA DE VALORES. INDICADORES FINANCIEROS/MEXICAN STOCK EXCHANGE. FINANCIAL FACTS AND FIGURES. see *BUSINESS AND ECONOMICS—Abstracting, Bibliographies, Statistics*

332 DNK ISSN 0906-8317
BORSEN INFORMATIK. Text in Danish. 1991.
Related titles: Online - full text ed.: (from O C L C Online Computer Library Center, Inc.); ♦ Supplement to: Boersen.
Published by: Dagbladet Boersen A-S, Moentergade 19, Copenhagen K, 1140, Denmark. TEL 45-33-32-01-02, FAX 45-33-12-24-45.

332 FRA ISSN 1161-9430
BOTTIN DE LA FINANCE. Text in French. a. **Document type:** *Directory.*
Related titles: Diskette ed.; Magnetic Tape ed.
Published by: Bottin S A, 4 rue Andre Boulle, Cretil, Cedex 9 94961, France. TEL 49-81-56-56, FAX 49-81-56-76.

BOWNE DIGEST FOR CORPORATE & SECURITIES LAWYERS; abstracts of current articles from more than 280 legal periodicals. see *LAW—Abstracting, Bibliographies, Statistics*

332 USA
BOWNE REVIEW FOR C F OS AND INVESTMENT BANKERS (ONLINE EDITION). Text in English. 1989. m. looseleaf. free (effective 2005). back issues avail. **Document type:** *Newsletter, Trade.*
Formerly: Bowne Review for C F Os and Investment Bankers (Print Edition) (1047-6172)
Media: Online - full content.
Published by: Brumberg Publications, Inc., 124 Harvard St, Brookline, MA 02146. TEL 617-734-1979, FAX 617-734-1989, brumberg@compuserve.com, http://www.bowne.com. Ed. Susan Koffman. Pub. Bruce Brumberg. Circ: 5,000 (free).

332 USA
BRANCH OPERATIONS MANAGEMENT SERVICE. Text in English. 3 base vols. plus s-a. updates. looseleaf. USD 425 (effective 2004). **Document type:** *Directory, Trade.*
Related titles: Series: Financial Management Series.
Published by: Sheshunoff Information Services Inc., 807 Las Cimas Pkwy, Ste 300, Austin, TX 78746. TEL 512-472-2244, 800-456-2340, FAX 512-305-6575, customercare.sis@sheshunoff.com, http://www.sheshunoff.com.

332 USA
BRANCHES OF NEW YORK. Text in English. m. charts; stat. **Document type:** *Newsletter, Trade.* **Description:** Contains competitive analyses of New York banks by county and city, along with a historical growth overview and information on bank holding companies and their subsidiaries.
Published by: Sheshunoff Information Services Inc., 807 Las Cimas Pkwy, Ste 300, Austin, TX 78746. TEL 512-472-2244, 800-456-2340, FAX 512-305-6575, customercare.sis@sheshunoff.com, http://www.sheshunoff.com.

BRIEFINGS IN REAL ESTATE FINANCE. see *REAL ESTATE*

BRITISH ACTUARIAL JOURNAL. see *INSURANCE*

332 CAN
BRITISH COLUMBIA MAJOR PROJECTS INVENTORY. Text in English. q. CND 75 (effective 1997). **Document type:** *Government.* **Description:** Covers major capital projects. For developers, suppliers of goods and services, retailers, transportation providers, planners and other government officials.
Published by: Ministry of Finance and Corporate Relations, B C Stats, Sta Prov Govt, P O Box 9410, Victoria, BC V8W 9V1, Canada. TEL 250-387-1502, FAX 250-387-0329, bcstats@fincc04.fin.gov.bc.ca, http://www.bcstats.gov.bc.ca. Circ: 500.

BROADCAST BANKER/BROKER. see *COMMUNICATIONS*

332.4 USA ISSN 1527-7046
BROKER. Text in English. 1999. bi-m. USD 48 domestic; USD 58 in Canada; USD 78 elsewhere (effective 2005). adv. **Document type:** *Magazine, Trade.* **Description:** Contains practical information on the cutting-edge techniques and technologies used by mortgage brokers.
Published by: Source Media, Inc., One State St Plaza, 27th Fl, New York, NY 10004. TEL 212-803-6077, 800-221-1809, FAX 212-747-1154, custserv@sourcemedia.com, http://www.brokermagazine.com, http://www.sourcemedia.com. adv.: B&W page USD 2,495, color page USD 3,545; trim 10 x 7.

332 USA ISSN 1098-3651
HG181
BROOKINGS-WHARTON PAPERS ON FINANCIAL SERVICES. Text in English. 1998. a.
Related titles: Online - full text ed.: ISSN 1533-4430. 2000 (from EBSCO Publishing, O C L C Online Computer Library Center, Inc., Project MUSE, Swets Information Services).
Indexed: JEL.
—BLDSC (2350.085000). **CCC.**
Published by: (Wharton School, Financial Institutions Center), Brookings Institution Press, 1775 Massachusetts Ave, NW, Washington, DC 20036-2188. TEL 202-797-6004, FAX 202-797-6195, http://www.brookings.edu/press/books/brookingswhartonpapersonfinancialservices2004.htm.

332 HUN ISSN 1418-8937
BUDAPEST BUSINESS JOURNAL'S WHO'S WHO IN FINANCE/KI KICSODA A PENZUGYI ELETBEN. Text in Hungarian. 1998. irreg. **Document type:** *Directory.*
Related titles: ♦ Supplement to: Budapest Business Journal. ISSN 1216-7304.
Published by: New World Publishing Inc., Szent Istvan Korut 11, III emelet, Budapest, 1055, Hungary. TEL 36-1-374-3344, FAX 361-374-3345, editor@bbj.hu, http://www.ceebiz.com.

BUDGET OF THE UNITED STATES GOVERNMENT. HISTORICAL TABLES. see *PUBLIC ADMINISTRATION*

332 GBR ISSN 0963-6528
BUILDING SOCIETIES. YEAR BOOK✶. Text in English. 1927. a. GBP 63. adv. **Document type:** *Trade.*
Published by: (Building Societies), Franey and Co. Ltd., 100 Avenue Rd, London, N14 4EA, United Kingdom.

BUILDING SOCIETIES YEARBOOK. see *REAL ESTATE*

BUILDING SOCIETY ANNUAL ACCOUNTS DATA. see *REAL ESTATE*

BUILDING SOCIETY LEAGUE TABLES (FINANCIAL). see *REAL ESTATE*

332 GBR
BUILDING SOCIETY MORTGAGE ARREARS AND LOSSES REPORT. Text in English. a. GBP 195 to non-members; GBP 136 to members. **Document type:** *Trade.* **Description:** Contains a detailed analysis of arrears, provisions, and losses for each U.K. building society, along with commentary and accounting policy statements as reported by each society in its annual report.
Published by: Building Societies Association, 3 Savile Row, London, W1X 1AF, United Kingdom. TEL 44-20-7437-0655, FAX 44-20-7287-0109. **Co-sponsor:** Council of Mortgage Lenders.

BUILDING SOCIETY PEER GROUPS (FINANCIAL). see *REAL ESTATE*

332 BGR
BULGARIAN BANKING SYSTEM. Text in English. a. USD 46 foreign (effective 2002).
Published by: Bulgarska Narodna Banka/Bulgarian National Bank, 1 Alexander Batterberg Sq, Sofia, 1000, Bulgaria. TEL 359-2-91459, FAX 359-2-9802425, press_office@bnbank.org, http://www.bnb.bg. **Dist. by:** Sofia Books, ul Silivria 16, Sofia 1404, Bulgaria. TEL 359-2-9586257, info@sofiabooks-bg.com, http://www.sofiabooks-bg.com.

332 339 BGR
BULGARIAN ECONOMIC REVIEW (ONLINE EDITION). Text in English. 1992. fortn. BGL 150 (effective 2005). Index. back issues avail. **Document type:** *Newspaper, Trade.* **Description:** Covers news, anlaysis and commentary on daily events in the economy, financial sector and industry.
Formerly (until Jul. 1996): Bulgarian Economic Review (Print Edition) (0861-5640)
Media: Online - full content. **Related titles:** CD-ROM ed.; E-mail ed.; ♦ Bulgarian ed.: Pari. ISSN 0861-5608.
Published by: Roubicon ITK PARI AD, 47A Tsarigradsko Shaussee Blvd, Sofia, 1504, Bulgaria. TEL 359-2-9433646, 359-2-9433147, FAX 359-2-9433646, kiril@pari.bg, vpan@mail.pari.bg, http://www.news.pari.bg/cgi-bin/ber.home.cgi, http://www.pari.bg. Ed. Vladimir Sabev. Pub. Valentin Panayotov. Adv. contact Elka Kamenova. Circ: 6,000 (paid).

332 BGR ISSN 1310-3067
HG3221
BULGARIAN NATIONAL BANK. MONTHLY BULLETIN. Text in English. m. USD 96 foreign (effective 2002). **Document type:** *Bulletin, Trade.* **Description:** Covers official reports, analyses, and statistics of BNB along with themes on the whole economy. Includes resolutions of the BNB Board.
Published by: Bulgarska Narodna Banka/Bulgarian National Bank, 1 Alexander Batterberg Sq, Sofia, 1000, Bulgaria. TEL 359-2-91459, FAX 359-2-9802425, press_office@bnbank.org, http://www.bnb.bg. **Dist. by:** Sofia Books, ul Silivria 16, Sofia 1404, Bulgaria. TEL 359-2-9586257, info@sofiabooks-bg.com, http://www.sofiabooks-bg.com.

332.1 330 COL
BULLETIN L A R F. Text in English. 1982. q. free. **Document type:** *Bulletin.* **Description:** Covers quarterly economic summaries of the member countries: Bolivia, Colombia, Ecuador, Peru and Venezuela.
Former titles: Bulletin A R F; Andean Reserve Fund. Bulletin
Related titles: Spanish ed.
Published by: Latin American Reserve Fund/Fondo Latinoamericano de Reservas, Apartado Aereo 241523, Bogota, CUND, Colombia. FAX 57-1-288-1117.

330.9 KWT
BURGAN BANK S.A.K. ANNUAL REPORT. Text in English. 1977. a. **Document type:** *Corporate.*
Published by: Burgan Bank S.A.K., Ahmed Al-Jaber St., P O Box 5389, Safat, 13054, Kuwait. TEL 965-2439000, FAX 965-2433276, mainbr@burgan.com.kw, http://www.burgan.com.

339.13 ROM ISSN 1220-7586
BURSA. Text in Romanian. 1990. d. ROL 924,000 (effective 2002). adv. **Document type:** *Newspaper, Consumer.*
Published by: Ring Media, Str. Popa Tatu nr. 71, sector 1, Bucharest, Romania. TEL 40-21-3154356, FAX 40-21-3124556, marketing@bursa.ro, http://www.bursa.ro.

336 ROM ISSN 1454-9948
BURSA - ANUL FINANCIAR. Text in Romanian. 1997. s-a. ROL 97,500 (effective 2002). adv. **Document type:** *Magazine, Trade.*
Published by: Ring Media, Str. Popa Tatu nr. 71, sector 1, Bucharest, Romania. TEL 40-21-3154356, FAX 40-21-3124556.

330 ROM
BURSA CADOURI DE CRACIUN. Text in Romanian. a. ROL 25,000 (effective 2002). **Document type:** *Magazine, Trade.*
Published by: Ring Media, Str. Popa Tatu nr. 71, sector 1, Bucharest, Romania. TEL 40-21-3154356, FAX 40-21-3124556.

BURSA CONSTRUCTIILOR. see *BUILDING AND CONSTRUCTION*

332 330 USA
BUSINESS ADVICE AND FINANCIAL PLANNING. Text in English. 1987. q. USD 68; USD 38 to non-profit organizations (effective 2006). **Document type:** *Newsletter, Trade.*
Published by: Illinois State Bar Association, Illinois Bar Center, 424 S Second St, Springfield, IL 62701. TEL 217-525-1760, 800-252-8908, sanderson@isba.org, http://www.isba.org. Ed. Malcolm L Morris.

332 USA ISSN 1527-6864
BUSINESS ADVISOR. Text in English. 2000. q. free (effective 2005). **Document type:** *Magazine, Consumer.*
Related titles: Online - full content ed.

Published by: (Wells Fargo Bank), Imagination Publishing, 2222 N. Elston Ave., 2nd Fl., Chicago, IL 60614. FAX 773-252-3290, rbaumer@imaginepub.com, http://www.imaginepub.com. Circ: 300,000 (controlled).

332 USA ISSN 0738-7253
BUSINESS & ACQUISITION NEWSLETTER. Text in English. 1966. m. USD 300 (effective 2001). bk.rev. **Document type:** *Newsletter.* **Description:** Covers acquisitions and merger opportunities.
Former titles: Acquisition Newsletter International; Acquisition Newsletter
Published by: Newsletters International, Inc., 7710 T Cherry Park Dr #421, Houston, TX 77095. TEL 888-972-4662, 888-972-4662. Ed., Pub., R&P Len Fox.

B

650 332 IRL ISSN 0007-6473
HF5001
BUSINESS AND FINANCE. Text in English. 1964. fortn. adv. illus. **Document type:** *Newspaper, Trade.*
Related titles: Online - full text ed.: (from LexisNexis).
Indexed: ELLIS, KES, PAIS, PROMT, WBA.
Published by: Moranna Ltd., 1-4 Swift's Alley, Dublin, 8, Ireland. TEL 353-1-4167800, FAX 353-1-4167899. Ed. Gabi Thesing. Pub. Ian Hyland. Adv. contact Brenda McPadden. B&W page EUR 2,260, color page EUR 3,429; trim 210 x 297. Circ: 9,827.

332.7 658 USA ISSN 0897-0181
HF5565
BUSINESS CREDIT. Text in English. 1898. 10/yr. USD 54 (effective 2005). adv. charts; illus.; stat. index. back issues avail.; reprint service avail. from PQC. **Document type:** *Magazine, Trade.* **Description:** For corporate credit and financial professionals.
Formerly: Credit and Financial Management (0011-0973)
Related titles: Microform ed.: (from PQC); Online - full text ed.: (from EBSCO Publishing, Florida Center for Library Automation, Gale Group, H.W. Wilson, Northern Light Technology, Inc., O C L C Online Computer Library Center, Inc., ProQuest Information & Learning).
Indexed: AAR, ABIn, ATI, BLI, BPI, BPIA, BusI, DPD, IMI, LRI, ManagCont, PROMT, T&II.
—BLDSC (2933.419200), IE, Infotrieve, ingenta. **CCC.**
Published by: National Association of Credit Management, 8840 Columbia 100 Parkway, Columbia, MD 21045. TEL 410-740-5560, FAX 410-740-5574, http://www.nacm.org/bcmag/bcm_index.html. Ed. Norma Heim. adv.: B&W page USD 3,885, color page USD 4,860. Circ: 30,000 (controlled).

332.1 CAN ISSN 1209-5400
HG2708.F4
BUSINESS DEVELOPMENT BANK OF CANADA. ANNUAL REPORT. Variant title: New Times and New Horizons. Text in English. 1970. a.
Former titles (until 1996): Federal Business Development Bank. Annual Report (0703-0347); (until 1977): Federal Business Development Bank. Financial Report (0708-6512); (until 1976): Industrial Development Bank. Annual Report (0382-1552)
Related titles: Online - full text ed.: ISSN 1495-6721.
—CISTI.
Published by: Business Development Bank of Canada, 5 Place Ville Marie, Ste 400, Montreal, PQ H3B 5E7, Canada. TEL 877-232-2269, FAX 877-329-9232, http://www.bdc.ca/en/about/events_publications/default.htm.

332 346 GBR ISSN 1350-1038
BUSINESS MONEY. Text in English. 1993. 10/yr. GBP 119 domestic; GBP 138 in Europe; USD 189 elsewhere (effective 2003). adv. back issues avail. **Document type:** *Magazine, Trade.* **Description:** Serves as the trade magazine for the UK business funding industry. Aimed at accountants, lawyers, bankers, financial advisers, and brokers.
—CCC.
Published by: Business Money Ltd., Unit 6, Bowdens Business Centre, Hambridge, Curry Rivel, Somerset, TA10 0BP, United Kingdom. TEL 44-1458-253536, FAX 44-1458-253538, editor@business-money.com, http://www.business-money.com. Ed., Pub., R&P Robert Lefroy. Adv. contact Caroline Grimster. B&W page GBP 1,750, color page GBP 1,950; 297 x 210. Circ: 5,896 (paid); 5,438 (controlled). **Subscr. to:** Wigglesworth House, Wigglesworth House, 69 Southwark Bridge Rd, London SE1 0NG, United Kingdom. TEL 44-20-7403-9393.

BUSINESS MONITOR: ASSETS AND LIABILITIES OF FINANCE HOUSES AND OTHER CONSUMER CREDIT COMPANIES. see *BUSINESS AND ECONOMICS—Abstracting, Bibliographies, Statistics*

BUSINESS MONITOR: COMPANY FINANCE. see *BUSINESS AND ECONOMICS—Abstracting, Bibliographies, Statistics*

BUSINESS MONITOR: CREDIT BUSINESS. see *BUSINESS AND ECONOMICS—Abstracting, Bibliographies, Statistics*

332 CHL
BUSINESS NEWS AMERICAS. Text in English, Portuguese, Spanish. d. **Description:** Includes news that covers the most important original news stories in 10 different business sectors throughout Latin America and the Caribbean.
Media: Online - full content. **Related titles:** E-mail ed.
Address: Carmencita No. 106, Los Condes, Santiago de Chile, Chile. TEL 56-2-2320302, FAX 56-2-2329376, info@bnamericas.com, http://www.bnamericas.com/.

BUSINESS NEWS FROM POLAND. see *BUSINESS AND ECONOMICS*

THE BUSINESS OWNER. see *BUSINESS AND ECONOMICS—Small Business*

333.33 USA ISSN 0897-1781
BUSINESS VALUATION REVIEW. Text in English. 1982. q. USD 50 to members; USD 60 to non-members. cum.index. **Document type:** *Trade.* **Description:** Provides up-to-date information for all persons who have an interest in the valuation of businesses, professional practices, corporate stock, and tangible and intangible assests.
Formerly (until 1987): Business Valuation News (0882-2875)
—CCC.
Published by: American Society of Appraisers, Business Valuation Committee, 555 Herndon Parkway, Ste 125, Herndon, VA 20170. TEL 703-478-2228, FAX 703-742-8471, asainfo@appraisers.org, http://www.bvappraisers.org/bv_review/, http://www.appraisers.org/. Ed. James H Schilt. Pub. John E Bakker. R&P Shelly Chamberlain. Circ: 2,500.

BUTTERWORTHS JOURNAL OF INTERNATIONAL BANKING AND FINANCIAL LAW. see *LAW*

BUTTERWORTHS MONEY LAUNDERING LAW. see *CRIMINOLOGY AND LAW ENFORCEMENT*

332.1 GBR
BUTTERWORTHS P F I MANUAL; law, practice and procedure relating to the private finance initiative and public - private partnerships. Text in English. 3/yr. (plus irreg. bulletin). looseleaf. GBP 550 (effective 1999). back issues avail. **Document type:** *Trade.* **Description:** Addresses all aspects of law and practice of private finance. Includes relevant UK and EU primary source material.
Published by: Butterworths Tolley (Subsidiary of: LexisNexis UK (Scottish Office)), Halsbury House, 35 Chancery Ln, London, Mddx WC2A 1EL, United Kingdom. TEL 44-20-74002500, FAX 44-20-74002583, http://www.butterworths.co.uk/. Ed. Garth Lindrup.

332 658 GBR
C C A NEWS. Text in English. 1980. q. GBP 30 to non-members. adv. back issues avail. **Description:** In-house magazine for members of the largest U.K. Trade Association for the unsecured lending industry.
Published by: (Consumer Credit Association), C C A (U.K.) Advisory Services Ltd., Queens House, Queens Rd, Chester, CH1 3BQ, United Kingdom. TEL 44-1244-312044, FAX 44-1244-318035. Ed. Bill Williams. R&P, Adv. contact Steve Yong TEL 44-1244-505906. Circ: 1,400.

332 USA ISSN 0273-7302
C C H FINANCIAL AND ESTATE PLANNING. (Commerce Clearing House) Text in English. 1980. 4 base vols. plus m. updates. looseleaf. USD 1,132 base vol(s). (effective 2004). **Description:** Covers all stages of the estate plan—from development to administration. Includes detailed explanations, strategies and planning aids that target these major areas: income, estate and gift tax planning, general investment planning, insurance planning, pension, and retirement planning and estate administration.
Related titles: CD-ROM ed.: USD 1,131 (effective 2004); Online - full text ed.
Indexed: ATI.
Published by: C C H Inc., 2700 Lake Cook Rd, Riverwoods, IL 60015. TEL 847-267-7000, 800-449-6439, FAX 800-224-8299, cust_serv@cch.com, http://www.cch.com. Pub. Kevin Robert.

C C I A NEWSLETTER. see *INSURANCE*

332 BRB ISSN 0257-6090
HG2794.C38
C D B NEWS. Text in English. 1983. q. free. bk.rev. reprints avail. **Document type:** *Newsletter.* **Description:** Gives general information about the Bank's activities and serves as an aid in project design & equipment selection by potential investors.
Published by: Caribbean Development Bank, Wildey, PO Box 408, St Michael, Barbados. TEL 246-431-1600, FAX 246-426-7269, marshsh@caribank.com. Ed. Sharon H Marshall. Circ: 5,000.

332 USA
THE C E O REPORT. Text in English. w. (48/yr.). USD 389 (effective 2005). back issues avail. **Document type:** *Trade.*
Published by: (National Center for Credit Unions), Argosy Group (Subsidiary of: United Communications Group), 11300 Rockville Pike, Ste 1100, Rockville, MD 20852. TEL 888-287-2223, FAX 301-816-8945, ceocustomer@ucg.com, http://www.cuceo.com/, http://www.ucg.com/argosy.html. Ed. Timothy Maier TEL 301-287-2491. Pub. Dennis Sullivan TEL 301-287-2211.

332 USA ISSN 0046-9777
HG4501
C F A DIGEST. (Chartered Financial Analyst) Text in English. 1971. q. USD 50 to members; USD 75 to non-members (effective 2005). illus. reprints avail.
Published by: Association for Investment Management and Research, 560 Ray C Hunt Drive, Charlottesville, VA 22903. TEL 804-951-5499, FAX 804-951-5262, http://www.aimrpubs.org/cfa/home.html., http://www.aimr.org. Circ: 30,000 (controlled).

C F M A BUILDING PROFITS. see *BUILDING AND CONSTRUCTION*

C F O & CONTROLLER ALERT. (Chief Financial Officer) see *BUSINESS AND ECONOMICS—Accounting*

C F O ASIA. (Chief Financial Officer) see *BUSINESS AND ECONOMICS—Management*

C F O EUROPE. (Chief Financial Officer) see *BUSINESS AND ECONOMICS—Management*

332.1 GBR ISSN 1360-4678
C I B NEWS. (Chartered Institute of Bankers) Text in English. 1995. 10/yr. GBP 50 (effective 2000). **Document type:** *Newsletter.*
Published by: Chartered Institute of Bankers, Emmanuel House, 4-9 Burgate Ln, Canterbury, Kent CT1 2XJ, United Kingdom. TEL 44-12-2781-8653, FAX 44-12-2747-9641, tbancroft@cib.org.uk, http://www.cib.org.uk/. Ed. Lucia Dore. Adv. contact Lee Mann. Circ: 65,490.

332.6 USA ISSN 1546-3664
HG4655
C M B S WORLD. (Commerical Mortgage Backed Securities) Text in English. 1999 (Spr.). q. USD 100 (effective 2004). adv.
Published by: Commercial Mortgage Securities Association, 30 Broad St. 28th Fl., New York, NY 10004-2304. TEL 212-509-1844, FAX 212-509-1895, info@cmbs.org, http://www.cmbs.org. Ed. Jun Han. Adv. contact Elizabeth Hanes.

C M L ANNUAL REPORT. see *REAL ESTATE*

C M L LIBRARY BULLETIN. see *REAL ESTATE*

C M L MARKET BRIEFING. see *REAL ESTATE*

C M L PARLIAMENTARY CUTTING SERVICE. see *REAL ESTATE*

332 USA ISSN 0734-0486
C M R E MONOGRAPHS. Text in English. 1971. irreg., latest vol.53. USD 5 per issue. **Document type:** *Monographic series.*
Former titles: C M R E Monetary Tracts; C M R E Money Tracts
Published by: Committee for Monetary Research and Education, Inc., 10004 Greenwood Ct, Charlotte, NC 28215-9621. TEL 704-598-3717, FAX 704-599-7036. Circ: 3,000.

332.1 ECU
C O F I E C. INFORME ANUAL. Text in Spanish. a. illus.; stat.
Published by: Compania Financiera Ecuatoriana de Desarrollo, Apdo 411, Quito, Pichincha, Ecuador. FAX 564224, TELEX 22131. Circ: 3,000.

C P A G'S INCOME - RELATED BENEFITS: THE LEGISLATION. see *SOCIAL SERVICES AND WELFARE*

332 340 USA
C S B S EXAMINER. Text in English. 1969. w. membership. **Document type:** *Newsletter, Trade.*
Formerly: Capitol Comments
Published by: Conference of State Bank Supervisors, 1155 Connecticut Ave, NW, 5th Fl, Washington, DC 20036. TEL 202-296-2840, FAX 202-296-1928, http://www.csbs.org.

334.2 USA ISSN 1087-108X
C U E S - FOR YOUR INFORMATION. Abbreviated title: C U E S - F Y I. Text in English. m. USD 456 membership. **Document type:** *Newsletter.*
Formerly: F Y I Management Memo
Published by: Credit Union Executives Society, PO Box 14167, Madison, WI 53708-0167. TEL 608-271-2664, FAX 608-271-2303, cues@cues.org. Circ: 3,500.

334.2 USA
C U I S. (Credit Union Information Service) Text in English. 1973. bi-w. USD 277. **Description:** Gives the latest innovations in credit union management, asseses investment options, and provides industry news.
Related titles: ◆ Supplement(s): C U I S Special Reports.
Published by: United Communications Group, 11300 Rockville Pike Ste 1100, Rockville, MD 20852-3030. TEL 301-816-8950, FAX 301-816-8945. Ed. Jonathan Stern.

CABLE PROGRAM INVESTOR. see *COMMUNICATIONS—Television And Cable*

CABLE T V FINANCE; newsletter on bank, insurance, commercial loans to cable operators. see *COMMUNICATIONS—Television And Cable*

332.1 FRA ISSN 1167-4326
CAHIERS DE L'AGEFI. (Agence Economique et Financiere) Text in French. 1992. w.
Related titles: ♦ Supplement to: L' Agence Economique et Financiere. ISSN 0755-1940.
Published by: Agence Economique et Financiere, 48 rue Notre Dame des Victoires, Paris, 75002, France. TEL 44884646, FAX 448847253.

332 CHN ISSN 1000-8306
HB9
CAIJING KEXUE/FINANCE AND ECONOMICS. Text in Chinese. 1957. bi-m. USD 18.50. adv. **Document type:** *Academic/Scholarly.*
Related titles: Online - full text ed.: (from East View Information Services).
Indexed: RASB.
Published by: Xinan Caijing Daxue/Southwestern University of Finance and Economics, 55 Guanghua Cun, Xijiao, Chengdu, Sichuan 610074, China. Ed. Lei Qiquan. Adv. contact Fu Xianqing. **Dist. in US by:** China Books & Periodicals Inc, 360 Swift Ave., Ste. 48, S San Fran, CA 94080-6220. TEL 415-282-2994.

332 CHN ISSN 1000-176X
HB9
CAIJING WENTI YANJIU/RESEARCH ON FINANCIAL AND ECONOMIC PROBLEMS. Text in Chinese. 1979. m. CNY 66. **Document type:** *Academic/Scholarly.*
Related titles: Online - full text ed.: (from East View Information Services).
Published by: Dongbei Caijing Daxue/Northeast University of Finance and Economics, Dalian, Liaoning 116025, China. TEL 467-1101. Ed., R&P Jian He.

332 CHN ISSN 1001-9952
CAIJING YANJIU/STUDY OF FINANCE & ECONOMICS. Text in Chinese. 1956. m. CNY 6.50 newsstand/cover (effective 2004). 80 p./no.; back issues avail. **Document type:** *Journal, Academic/Scholarly.*
Related titles: Online - full text ed.: (from East View Information Services).
Indexed: RASB.
Published by: Shanghai Caijing Daxue/Shanghai University of Finance and Economics, 321, Wudong Lu Yi 7-Luo, Shanghai, 200434, China. cjyj@mail.shufe.edu.cn, http://www.shufe.edu.cn/xsqk/cja.html. Circ: 6,000. **Dist. in US by:** China Books & Periodicals Inc, 360 Swift Ave., Ste. 48, S San Fran, CA 94080-6220. TEL 415-282-2994; **Dist. by:** China International Book Trading Corp, 35 Chegongzhuang Xilu, Haidian District, PO Box 399, Beijing 100044, China. TEL 86-10-68412045, FAX 86-10-68412023, cibtc@mail.cibtc.com.cn, http://www.cibtc.com.cn.

332 CHN ISSN 1004-0994
CAIKUAI YUEKAN/MONTHLY OF FINANCE AND ACCOUNTING. Text in Chinese. 1980. s-m. CNY 78 domestic; USD 50 foreign (effective 2000). adv. bk.rev. abstr. **Document type:** *Trade.* **Description:** Contains 2 parts: "Treasure" which covers wealth and success, and "Accounting" which covers finance and accounting, tax and auditing, as well as economic and financial policies.
Formerly (until 1991): Hubei Caikua
Related titles: Fax ed.
Published by: Wuhan Shi Caizheng Ju/Wuhan Finance Bureau, No 19, Wansongyuan Rd, Wuhan, Hubei 430022, China. TEL 86-27-85792958, FAX 86-27-85792844. Ed., Adv. contact Xingbang Liu. B&W page CNY 7,000, color page CNY 12,000. Circ: 200,000.

332 382 CHN ISSN 1002-8102
CAIMAO JINGJI/FINANCE AND TRADE ECONOMICS. Text in Chinese; Contents page in English. 1980. m. CNY 18, USD 48.60. adv. **Document type:** *Journal, Academic/Scholarly.*
Related titles: Online - full content ed.: (from WanFang Data Corp.); Online - full text ed.: (from East View Information Services).
Indexed: RASB.
Published by: (Zhongguo Shehui Kexueyuan/Chinese Academy of Social Sciences, Caimao Wuzi Jingji Yanjiusuo/Finance Economics Institute), Caimao Jingji Zazhishe, 2 Yuetan Beixiaojie, Fuwai, Beijing, 100836, China. TEL 86-10-68034659, cmjj2003@yahoo.com.cn, http://cmjj.periodicals.net.cn/. Ed. Zhang Zhuoyuan. **Dist. in US by:** China Books & Periodicals Inc, 360 Swift Ave., Ste. 48, S San Fran, CA 94080-6220; **Dist. outside China by:** China International Book Trading Corp, 35 Chegongzhuang Xilu, Haidian District, PO Box 399, Beijing 100044, China.

332 640.73 CAN ISSN 0225-4700
MA CAISSE; revue d'information des caisses populaires et des caisses d'economie Desjardins. Text in English. 1963. bi-m. (plus special issue). CND 6.50. adv. back issues avail. **Document type:** *Consumer.*
Indexed: PdeR.
Published by: Confederation des Caisses Populaires et d'Economie Desjardins du Quebec, 100 Ave. des Commandeurs, Levis, PQ G6V 7N5, Canada. TEL 800-463-4810, FAX 418-833-5873. Ed. Micheline Piche. Circ: 130,000.

332 TWN
CAIWU JINRONG XUEKAN/JOURNAL OF FINANCIAL STUDIES. Text in Chinese. 1993. s-a. (Jan. & July). TWD 800 domestic to individuals; USD 60 foreign to individuals; TWD 2,000 domestic to institutions; USD 120 foreign to institutions (effective 2004). **Document type:** *Journal, Academic/Scholarly.*
Formerly: Zhongguo Caiwu Xuekan (1022-2898)
Published by: Zhongguo Caiwu Xuehui/Chinese Finance Association, c/o Dr. Simon H. Yen, Department of Finance, College of Commerce, National Chengchi University, Taipei, 11623, Taiwan. TEL 886-7-5252000 ext 4806. Ed. Ma Tai. Pub. Victor W Liu.

332 CHN
CAIZHENG JINRONG WENZHAI KA/FINANCE AND BANKING ABSTRACTS ON CARDS. Text in English. 2001. bi-m. CNY 30 (effective 2004). abstr. 80 p./no.; **Document type:** *Journal, Abstract/Index.*
Media: Cards.
Published by: Zhongguo Renmin Daxue, Shubao Zilio Zhongxin/Renmin University of China, Information Center for Social Server, Dongcheng-qu, 3, Zhangzizhong Lu, Beijing, 100007, China. TEL 86-10-64039458, FAX 86-10-64015080, kyes@163.net, http://www.confucius.cn.net/bkdetail.asp?fzt=WF6. **Dist. by:** China Publications Service, PO Box 49614, Chicago, IL 60649. TEL 312-288-3291, FAX 312-288-8570; China International Book Trading Corp, 35 Chegongzhuang Xilu, Haidian District, PO Box 399, Beijing 100044, China. TEL 86-10-68412045, FAX 86-10-68412023, cibtc@mail.cibtc.com.cn, http://www.cibtc.com.cn/.

332 CHN ISSN 1003-2878
HJ77.6
CAIZHENG YANJIU/PUBLIC FINANCE RESEARCH. Text in Chinese. 1980. m. USD 85. adv. **Document type:** *Academic/Scholarly.*
Related titles: Online - full text ed.: (from East View Information Services).
Published by: Caizheng-bu, Caizheng Kexue Yanjiusuo/Ministry of Finance, Financial Science Institute, Sanlihe, Beijing, 100820, China. TEL 86-10-6818-1225, FAX 86-10-6818-9001, ckswcs@public3.bta.net.cn. Ed., Adv. contact Kang Jia. R&P King Jia.

332.1 USA
CALIFORNIA BANKER. Text in English. q. adv. **Document type:** *Magazine.*
Published by: (California Bank Association), Bank News, Inc., PO Box 29156, Shawnee Mission, KS 66201-9156. TEL 800-336-1120, www.banknews.com/california.htm. Adv. contact Laura Baldwin. B&W page USD 1,729, color page USD 2,229; bleed 8.5 x 11.125.

CALIFORNIA BUSINESS CREDIT DIRECTORY. see *BUSINESS AND ECONOMICS—Trade And Industrial Directories*

332.72 346.043 USA
CALIFORNIA REAL ESTATE FINANCE AND CONSTRUCTION LAW. Text in English. 1995. 2 base vols. plus irreg. updates. looseleaf. USD 180.
Published by: LexisNexis (Subsidiary of: LexisNexis North America), PO Box 7587, Charlottesville, VA 22906-7587. TEL 804-972-7600, 800-562-1197, FAX 804-972-7666, llp.customer.support@lexis-nexis.com, http://www.lexislawpublishing.com. Eds. D Steven Blake, Jerome J Curtis Jr.

332.2021 USA ISSN 0575-6200
CALIFORNIA STATISTICAL ABSTRACTS. Text in English. a.
Published by: California Department of Finance, 915 L St, Sacramento, CA 95814. TEL 916-445-3878, ficpalad@dof.ca.gov, http://www.dof.ca.gov/.

332 USA ISSN 1522-0745
CALLAHAN'S CREDIT UNION REPORT. Text in English. 1985. m. USD 149 (effective 2000). adv. **Document type:** *Newsletter.*
Published by: Challahan & Associates, 1001 Connecticut Ave, N W, Ste 1001, Washington, DC 20036. TEL 202-223-3920, FAX 202-223-1311, callahan@creditunions.com, http://www.callahan.com/publications/calreport.htm. Ed. Brooke Stoddard. R&P Becky Horst. Adv. contact Tanya Baker. Circ: 1,000.

CAMPO; boletin de informacion agraria. see *AGRICULTURE*

332 CAN ISSN 1189-8895
CANADA. DEPARTMENT OF FINANCE. BUDGET PLAN. Text in English. 1994. a.
Published by: Canada. Department of Finance, Distribution Centre, West Tower, Rm P-135, 300 Laurier Ave W, Ottawa, ON K1A 0G5, Canada. TEL 613-995-2855, FAX 613-996-0518, http://www.fin.gc.ca/.

CANADA. DEPARTMENT OF FINANCE. FISCAL REFERENCE TABLES. see *BUSINESS AND ECONOMICS—Abstracting, Bibliographies, Statistics*

CANADA. DEPARTMENT OF INSURANCE. REPORT. CO-OPERATIVE CREDIT ASSOCIATIONS. see *INSURANCE*

CANADA. DEPARTMENT OF INSURANCE. REPORT. SMALL LOANS COMPANIES AND MONEY-LENDERS. see *INSURANCE*

CANADA. DEPARTMENT OF INSURANCE. REPORT. TRUST AND LOAN COMPANIES. see *INSURANCE*

332 CAN
CANADA NEWSWIRE. Text in English, French. d. **Description:** Aims to deliver news releases to professionals in the media and financial community.
Media: Online - full text. **Related titles:** E-mail ed.; Fax ed.
Published by: Canada Newswire, Ltd cnw@newswire.ca, http://www.newswire.ca, http://www.newswire.ca/.

332 CAN
CANADA. TREASURY BOARD. ACCESS REGISTER. Text in English. a. CND 10.
Supersedes in part: Canada. Treasury Board. Index of Federal Information Banks
Related titles: French ed.
Published by: (Canada. Treasury Board), Supply and Services Canada, Printing and Publishing, 270 Albert St, Ottawa, ON K1A 0S9, Canada. TEL 613-997-2560.

332 CAN
CANADA. TREASURY BOARD. INDEX TO PERSONAL INFORMATION. Text in English. a. CND 10. **Document type:** *Government.*
Supersedes in part: Canada. Treasury Board. Index of Federal Information Banks
Related titles: French ed.
Published by: (Canada. Treasury Board), Supply and Services Canada, Printing and Publishing, 270 Albert St, Ottawa, ON K1A 0S9, Canada. TEL 613-997-2560.

332.1 CAN ISSN 1486-4983
CANADIAN BANK FACTS. Text in English. 1968. a. free. **Document type:** *Trade.*
Former titles (until 1998): Bank Facts (0711-6497); (until 1981): Chartered Banks of Canada. Factbook (0317-4751)
Related titles: French ed.: Activites Bancaires Canadiennes. ISSN 1490-8522.
Published by: Canadian Bankers Association, Commerce Ct W, Ste 3000, 30th fl, P O Box 348, Toronto, ON M5L 1G2, Canada. TEL 416-362-6092. R&P Ralph Frustaglio. Circ: 64,000 (paid).

332 CAN
CANADIAN BANKER (ONLINE EDITION). Text in English. q. bk.rev. illus.; abstr. index. back issues avail.; reprints avail. **Document type:** *Trade.*
Media: Online - full content (from Florida Center for Library Automation, Northern Light Technology, Inc.). **Related titles:** Online - full text ed.: (from EBSCO Publishing, Gale Group, H.W. Wilson, O C L C Online Computer Library Center, Inc.); ♦ Print ed.: Canadian Banker (Print Edition). ISSN 0822-6830; French ed.
Indexed: ABIn, BLI, BPIA, BusI, CBCABus, CBCARef, CBPI, CPerI, ICLPL, LRI, ManagCont, PAIS, RASB, T&II, WBA.
Published by: Canadian Bankers Association, Commerce Ct W, Ste 3000, 30th fl, P O Box 348, Toronto, ON M5L 1G2, Canada. TEL 416-362-6092, FAX 416-362-5658, inform@cba.ca, http://www.canadian-banker.com, http://www.cba.ca. Circ: 33,915; 32,800 (paid).

332 CAN ISSN 0822-6830
CANADIAN BANKER (PRINT EDITION); the magazine for Canada's banking professionals. Text in English. 1973. q. bk.rev. illus.; abstr. back issues avail.; reprint service avail. from PQC. **Document type:** *Magazine, Trade.* **Description:** Provides a forum for the presentation of authoritative and stimulating information about banking and other subjects pertinent to the industry.
Formerly (until 1983): Canadian Banker and I C B Review (0315-6230); Which was formed by the merger of (1936-1973): Canadian Banker (0008-297X); Which was formerly (1893-1936): Canadian Bankers' Association. Journal (0315-6222); (1971-1973): I C B Review (0315-6257); Which was formerly (1967-1970): I C B Bulletin (0315-6249)
Related titles: Microform ed.: (from MML, PQC); ♦ Online - full content ed.: Canadian Banker (Online Edition); Online - full text ed.: (from EBSCO Publishing, Gale Group, H.W. Wilson, O C L C Online Computer Library Center, Inc.); ♦ French ed.: Le Banquier. ISSN 0822-6849.
Indexed: BPI, CPerI, PAIS.
—CCC.
Published by: Canadian Bankers Association, Commerce Ct W, Ste 3000, 30th fl, P O Box 348, Toronto, ON M5L 1G2, Canada. TEL 416-362-6092, 800-263-0231, FAX 416-362-7705, inform@cba.ca, http://www.cba.ca/en/magazine/. Ed. Simon Hally. R&P, Adv. contact Sharon MacLennan. Circ: 33,915; 32,800 (paid).

332.1 CAN ISSN 0068-8347
CANADIAN BANKRUPTCY REPORTS (4TH SERIES). Text in English. 1921; N.S. 1960. 8/yr. CND 248 per vol. domestic; USD 210.17 per vol. foreign (effective 2005). adv. cum.index.
Description: Includes all important bankruptcy decisions across Canada, as well as extensive notes, commentaries and annotations.
Indexed: CLI, ICLPL, LRI.
—CCC.
Published by: Carswell (Subsidiary of: Thomson Corporation), One Corporate Plaza, 2075 Kennedy Rd, Toronto, ON M1T 3V4, Canada. TEL 416-609-8000, 800-387-5164, FAX 416-298-5094, carswell.customerrelations@thomson.com, http://www.carswell.com. Ed. Geoffrey B Morawetz. Adv. contact Mariam Lalani TEL 416-298-5050.

332.1 CAN
CANADIAN FORMS & PRECEDENTS. BANKING AND FINANCE. Text in English. 2/yr. looseleaf. CND 700 (effective 2001). back issues avail. **Document type:** *Trade.*
Related titles: CD-ROM ed.: CND 420.
Published by: LexisNexis Butterworths Canada Inc. (Subsidiary of: LexisNexis North America), 123 Commerce Valley Dr E, Ste 700, Markham, ON L3T 7W8, Canada. TEL 905-479-2665, FAX 905-479-2826, info@lexisnexis.ca, http://www.lexisnexis.ca. Ed. J S Johnson.

B

332.1 CAN
CANADIAN FORMS & PRECEDENTS. DEBTOR-CREDITOR. Text in English. 3/yr. looseleaf. CND 275 (effective 2001). **Document type:** *Trade.*
Related titles: CD-ROM ed.: CND 225.
Published by: LexisNexis Butterworths Canada Inc. (Subsidiary of: LexisNexis North America), 123 Commerce Valley Dr E, Ste 700, Markham, ON L3T 7W8, Canada. TEL 905-479-2665, FAX 905-479-2826, info@lexisnexis.ca, http://www.lexisnexis.ca.

332.1 CAN
CANADIAN PAYMENTS DIRECTORIES. Text in English. 1981. a. (in 3 vols.). CND 105.60 domestic; CND 127.94 in United States; CND 146.39 elsewhere. **Document type:** *Directory.*
Formerly: Bank Directory of Canada (0045-1436)
Published by: (Canadian Payments Association), Bowne of Canada, Ltd., 60 Gervais Dr, Toronto, ON M3C 1Z3, Canada. TEL 416-449-6400, FAX 416-449-7114. Circ: 9,000.

332 CAN ISSN 0845-7328
CANADIAN TREASURER. Text in English. 1985. 6/yr. CND 45. adv. bk.rev. **Document type:** *Trade.*
Former titles: T M A C Journal (1041-9020); (until 1988): Cash Management Association of Canada. Journal (0888-6474)
Indexed: CBCARef, CBPI.
—CCC.
Published by: Treasury Management Association of Canada, 8 King St E, Ste 1010, Toronto, ON M5C 1B5, Canada. FAX 416-367-3240, brucer@home.com, http://www.tmac.ca. Ed., R&P Bruce McDougall TEL 416-920-2668. Adv. contact Peter Stamp. Circ: 4,500.

332 CAN ISSN 0829-4003
CANADIAN TREASURY MANAGEMENT REVIEW. Text in English. 1980. bi-m. CND 75. **Description:** Provides news about cash and treasury management for corporate treasurers.
Related titles: Microform ed.: (from PQC); Online - full text ed.: (from Micromedia ProQuest, ProQuest Information & Learning); ♦ French ed.: Revue Canadienne de Gestion de Tresorerie. ISSN 0829-4011.
Indexed: BLI.
Published by: Royal Bank of Canada, S Tower, 9th Fl, Royal Bank Plaza, Toronto, ON M5J 2J5, Canada. TEL 416-974-2274, FAX 416-974-0365. Ed. Colleen Killeavy. Circ: 4,000.

CAPITAL GROWTH INTERACTIVE. see *BUSINESS AND ECONOMICS—Investments*

332 IND
CAPITAL MARKET★. Text in English. 1986. fortn. INR 14 newsstand/cover. adv.
Indexed: B&I.
Published by: Investwel Publishers Pvt. Ltd., c/o S. Anatharaman Pub. & Ed., 401 Swastic Chambers, Sion-Trombay Rd., Chembur, Mumbai, Maharashtra 400 071, India. TEL 2043430, TELEX 011-6890 FICS IN. Adv. contact Ruby Anand. B&W page INR 17,500, color page INR 42,000.

332 GBR
CAPITAL MARKET STRATEGIES. Text in English. 1987. q. GBP 295, USD 443. **Document type:** *Trade.* **Description:** Discusses finance and investment strategies.
Formerly (until Jul. 1994): Journal of International Securities Markets (0952-7486)
Indexed: ELLIS.
—CCC.
Published by: I F R Publishing (Subsidiary of: Thomson Financial Services Ltd.), 11 New Fetter Ln, London, EC4A 1JN, United Kingdom. TEL 44-207-815-3800, FAX 44-207-315-3850. Ed. Julie Davis. Pub. Anne O'Brien.

332.7029 USA ISSN 1051-6778
HG3756.U54
CARD INDUSTRY DIRECTORY. Text in English. 1989. a., latest 16th ed. USD 495 per issue (effective 2005). 500 p./no.; **Document type:** *Directory.* **Description:** Contains revised rankings of the top 250 credit cards and the top 300 debit card issuers.
Related titles: Online - full text ed.: Card Source One (from Gale Group, Northern Light Technology, Inc., O C L C Online Computer Library Center, Inc.); ♦ Supplement to: Debit Card Directory. ISSN 1094-5350.
Indexed: B&I.
—CCC.
Published by: Source Media, Inc., One State St Plaza, 27th Fl, New York, NY 10004. TEL 212-803-6077, 800-221-1809, FAX 212-747-1154, custserv@sourcemedia.com, http://www.cardforum.com, http://www.sourcemedia.com. Ed. Jim Daly TEL 312-983-6120. Pub. Andrew Rowe. Adv. contacts Hope Lerman TEL 312-983-6102, Robert Mitchell TEL 312-983-6147.

332.1 USA ISSN 0894-0797
CARD NEWS. Text in English. bi-w. USD 995 domestic; USD 1,044 foreign (effective 2005). **Document type:** *Newsletter, Trade.* **Description:** Provides information on developments affecting credit card issuers and manufacturers of equipment for credit card transactions and management.
Incorporates (1990-2000): Credit Risk Management (1054-5069); (1992-2000): Credit Card Insider
Related titles: Online - full text ed.: (from Data-Star, Gale Group, LexisNexis, The Dialog Corporation).
Indexed: ABIn, BLI.
—CCC.
Published by: Access Intelligence, LLC (Subsidiary of: Veronis, Suhler & Associates Inc.), 1201 Seven Locks Rd, Ste 300, Potomac, MD 20854. TEL 301-354-2000, 800-777-5006, FAX 301-340-1451, clientservices@accessintel.com, http://www.pbimedia.com. Ed. Susan Aluise.

332.7 GBR ISSN 0954-8564
CARD WORLD; international journal for the plastic card, financial and retail services industries. Text in English. 1988. m. GBP 395, USD 665 (effective 1999). back issues avail. **Document type:** *Newsletter.*
—CCC.
Published by: C & M Publications Ltd., 3 A Market Pl, Uppingham, Leics LE15 9QH, United Kingdom. publisher@cm-media.net, http://www.cm-media.net/. Ed., R&P Annich McIntosh. Adv. contact Marie Sinclair. Circ: 5,000.

332.7 GBR ISSN 0967-8026
CARD WORLD USER GUIDE. Text in English. 1990. a. GBP 50 per issue (effective 2005). adv. back issues avail. **Document type:** *Directory, Trade.* **Description:** Review of the plastic card, financial, and retail services industries.
Published by: C & M Publications Ltd., 3 A Market Pl, Uppingham, Leics LE15 9QH, United Kingdom. TEL 44-1572-820088, FAX 44-1572-820099, publisher@cm-media.net, http://www.cm-media.net/. Ed. Annich McIntosh. Adv. contact Marie Sinclair. color page GBP 3,350. Circ: 10,000.

332 640.73 USA
CARDDIRECTORY. Text in English. 1989. a. USD 50 (effective 2001). **Description:** Guide to cards available to U.S. consumers. Provides comprehensive data on over 400 bank credit card issuers, including roundup of industry developments directly affecting consumers.
Former titles: Cardsearch; R A M Research Cardsearch (1040-6662); (until 1990): R A M Research Consumer Credit Card Yearbook
Published by: Cardweb.com, Inc., PO Box 1700, Frederick, MD 21702. TEL 301-631-9100, FAX 301-631-9112, cardmail@cardweb.com, http://www.cardweb.com. Ed. Robert B McKinley. Adv. contact Harriet Haxton TEL 301-631-9100 Ext 112. Circ: 100,000.

332.1 GBR ISSN 0966-6656
CARDIFF BUSINESS SCHOOL. DISCUSSION PAPER SERIES IN FINANCIAL AND BANKING ECONOMICS. Text in English. 1992. q. **Document type:** *Monographic series.* **Description:** Publishes research papers, short articles, notes, and commentary on financial economics and banking and monetary economics, with emphasis on practical aspects and applied topics.
—BLDSC (3597.983300).
Published by: Cardiff Business School, Cardiff University, Aberconway Bldg, Colum Drive, Cardiff, Wales CF10 3EU, United Kingdom. TEL 44-29-20874000, FAX 44-29-20874419, http://www.cf.ac.uk. Ed. Victor Murinde.

332 USA
CARDLINE. Text in English. d. USD 945 (effective 2005). **Document type:** *Newsletter, Trade.* **Description:** Reports late-breaking credit and debit news.
Media: E-mail.
Published by: Source Media, Inc., One State St Plaza, 27th Fl, New York, NY 10004. TEL 212-803-6077, 800-221-1809, FAX 212-747-1154, custserv@sourcemedia.com, http://www.sourcemedia.com.

332 USA
▼ **CARDLINE EUROPE.** Text in English. 2005. d. USD 945 (effective 2005). **Document type:** *Newsletter.* **Description:** Reports late-breaking credit and debit news of the European market.
Media: E-mail.
Published by: Source Media, Inc., One State St Plaza, 27th Fl, New York, NY 10004. TEL 212-803-6077, 800-221-1809, FAX 212-747-1154, custserv@sourcemedia.com, http://www.sourcemedia.com.

332 USA ISSN 1557-0762
CARDS & PAYMENTS; credit, debit and beyond. Text in English. 1988. m. USD 98 in US & Canada; USD 128 elsewhere (effective 2006). **Document type:** *Journal, Trade.* **Description:** Delivers targeted intelligence on the products, strategies, tools and techniques favored by today's credit, debit, and electronic transactions pacesetters.
Formerly (until June 2005): Credit Card Management (0896-9329)
Related titles: Online - full text ed.: (from EBSCO Publishing, Gale Group, LexisNexis, O C L C Online Computer Library Center, Inc., ProQuest Information & Learning).
Indexed: ABIn, ATI, BLI.
—BLDSC (3487.280300), IE. CCC.
Published by: Source Media, Inc., One State St Plaza, 27th Fl, New York, NY 10004. TEL 212-803-6077, 800-221-1809, FAX 212-747-1154, custserv@sourcemedia.com, http://www.cardforum.com, http://www.sourcemedia.com.

332 640.73 USA
CARDTRAK. Text in English. 1991. m. USD 100 to individuals (effective 2005). **Document type:** *Newsletter, Consumer.* **Description:** Covers developments affecting credit card users. Monthly 14 page report on the best credit card deals available to U.S. consumers. Each issue covers the latest details on hundreds of credit cards including low rate, no fee, gold, platinum, secured and business, student and reward cards.
Formerly: R A M Research Cardtrak (1053-9719)
Published by: Cardweb.com, Inc., PO Box 1700, Frederick, MD 21702. TEL 301-631-9100, FAX 301-631-9112, http://www.cardweb.com/cardtrak/. Ed., Pub. Robert B McKinley. Adv. contact Harriet Haxton TEL 301-631-9100 Ext 112. Circ: 500,000.

332 BRB ISSN 0257-6120
CARIBBEAN DEVELOPMENT BANK. ANNUAL REPORT. Text in English. a. charts; stat. reprints avail. **Document type:** *Corporate.* **Description:** Provides a detailed summary of economic developments, policies, and financial statements for the preceding year.
Related titles: Microfiche ed.: (from CIS).
Indexed: IIS.
Published by: Caribbean Development Bank, Wildey, PO Box 408, St Michael, Barbados. TEL 246-431-1600, FAX 246-426-7269, marshsh@caribank.com. Ed. Sharon H Marshall. Circ: 2,750.

332.1 BRB
CARIBBEAN DEVELOPMENT BANK. BOARD OF GOVERNORS. ANNUAL MEETING OF THE BOARD OF GOVERNORS: SUMMARY OF PROCEEDINGS. Text in English. 1971. a. reprints avail. **Document type:** *Proceedings.*
—BLDSC (1087.632000).
Published by: (Board of Governors), Caribbean Development Bank, Wildey, PO Box 408, St Michael, Barbados. TEL 246-431-1600, FAX 246-426-7269, TELEX WB 2287, marshsh@caribank.com. Ed., R&P Sharon H Marshall. Circ: 300.

385.1 332 USA ISSN 0008-6924
CARRIER REPORTS★. Text in English. 1960. a. USD 50 (effective 1999). adv. stat. **Document type:** *Trade.*
Address: 30 School St, Tilton, NH 03276-5750. TEL 207-733-2856, rhoner@hotmail.com. Pub. Richard W Honer.

332 CHE
CASH; die Wirtschaftszeitung der Schweiz. Text in German. 1989. w. CHF 184; CHF 4.50 newsstand/cover (effective 2000). adv. bibl.; charts; illus.; stat. back issues avail. **Document type:** *Newspaper, Trade.* **Description:** Reports on economic and financial subjects.
Published by: Ringier AG, Dufourstr 47, Zuerich, 8008, Switzerland. TEL 41-1-2596483, FAX 41-1-2596996, cash@ringier.ch, http://www.cash.ch. Ed. Markus Gisler. Adv. contact Daniela Thuring. B&W page CHF 12,920, color page CHF 17,000; trim 260 x 365. Circ: 70,311 (paid).

332 BRB ISSN 0255-8440
HG185.B35
CENTRAL BANK OF BARBADOS. ANNUAL STATISTICAL DIGEST. Text in English. 1975. a. free. charts; stat. **Document type:** *Bulletin, Corporate.* **Description:** This document provides statistical time series information. The tables contain annual and quarterly data on such indicators as Central Bank and commercial bank assets and liabilities, consumer installment credit, money supply, interest rates, government operations, foreign exchange rates, general statistics on GDP, sugar production, energy consumption, employment; CARICOM data on the national debt, BOP, GDP production and consumer prices. The tables are accompanied by comprehensive notes.

Published by: Central Bank of Barbados, Research Department, Spry St., PO Box 1016, Bridgetown, Barbados. TEL 246-4366870, FAX 246-4271431, cbb.libr@caribsurf.com, http://www.centralbank.org.bb. R&P Neville Pollard. Circ: 1,200.

332   BRB   ISSN 0378-178X
HC157.B35
CENTRAL BANK OF BARBADOS. ECONOMIC AND FINANCIAL STATISTICS. Text in English. 1973. m. free. **Document type:** *Bulletin, Corporate.* **Description:** This document provides mainly quarterly and monthly time series information from 1974 to the present and annual data from 1971. Tables provide information on the same topics as the Annual Statistical Digest. Comprehensive notes accompany the tables.
Published by: Central Bank of Barbados, Research Department, Spry St., PO Box 1016, Bridgetown, Barbados. TEL 246-4366870, FAX 246-4271431, cbb.libr@caribsurf.com, http://www.centralbank.org.bb. R&P Neville Pollard. Circ: 500.

332   BRB   ISSN 0255-7460
HC157.B35
CENTRAL BANK OF BARBADOS. ECONOMIC REVIEW. Text in English. 1975. 3/yr. free. adv. bk.rev. bibl.; charts; stat. **Document type:** *Bulletin, Corporate.* **Description:** This is a report on the economic activity during the year - with tables and charts on selected economic indicators; the Bank's operations and administration, along with its financial statement.
Formerly (until 1981): Central Bank of Barbados. Quarterly Report (0378-1771)
Indexed: KES, PAIS, WBA.
Published by: Central Bank of Barbados, Research Department, Spry St., PO Box 1016, Bridgetown, Barbados. TEL 246-4366870, FAX 246-4271431, cbb.libr@caribsurf.com, http://www.centralbank.org.bb. R&P, Adv. contact Neville Pollard. Circ: 600.

332.1   TWN   ISSN 1017-9674
HG3280.5.A7
CENTRAL BANK OF CHINA. ANNUAL REPORT. Text in English. 1962. a. **Document type:** *Corporate.*
Related titles: Online - full content ed.; Chinese ed.: Zhongyang Yinhang Nianbao. ISSN 0069-150X. 1962.
Published by: Central Bank of China, 2 Roosevelt Rd, Sec 1, Taipei, 107, Taiwan. TEL 886-2-23936161, FAX 886-2-23571974, adminrol@mail.cbc.gov.tw, http://www.cbc.gov.tw/EngHome/Eeconomic/Publications/annual.asp. Circ: 2,000.

332.1   TWN
CENTRAL BANK OF CHINA. QUARTERLY. Text in Chinese. 1979. q. USD 20.
Published by: Central Bank of China, 2 Roosevelt Rd, Sec 1, Taipei, 107, Taiwan. TEL 886-2-23936161. Circ: 2,500.

332.1   CYP   ISSN 0069-1518
HG3361.C93
CENTRAL BANK OF CYPRUS. ANNUAL REPORT. Text in English. 1965. a. free. back issues avail. **Document type:** *Corporate.*
Published by: Central Bank of Cyprus, PO Box 25529, Nicosia, Cyprus. TEL 357-2-714100, FAX 357-2-378153, erdep@centralbak.gov.cy, http://www.centralbank.gov.cy. Circ: 940.

332.1   CYP
HG3361.C93
CENTRAL BANK OF CYPRUS. QUARTERLY ECONOMIC REVIEW. Text in English. 1964. q. free. **Document type:** *Bulletin.*
Formerly: Central Bank of Cyprus. Bulletin
Indexed: KES, WBA.
Published by: Central Bank of Cyprus, PO Box 5529, Nicosia, Cyprus.

332.1   EGY   ISSN 0258-8706
CENTRAL BANK OF EGYPT. ANNUAL REPORT. Text in English. 1961. a. free. **Document type:** *Corporate.*
Former titles: Central Bank of Egypt. Report of the Board of Directors for the Year (1012-5604); Central Bank of Egypt. Board of Directors. Report (0069-1526)
Related titles: Arabic ed.
—BLDSC (1141.240000).
Published by: Central Bank of Egypt, Research Department, 31 Sharia Kasr-el Nil, Cairo, Egypt. Eds. Mahasen Abdel Rehim, Mohamed Saad Badr. Circ: 2,500.

332   IRQ   ISSN 0069-1534
CENTRAL BANK OF IRAQ, BAGHDAD. REPORT∗. Text in Arabic, English. 1951. a. free.
Published by: (Statistics and Research Department), Central Bank of Iraq, Rashid St, Baghdad, Iraq. Circ: 2,000.

332 330.9   IRQ   ISSN 0008-9257
CENTRAL BANK OF IRAQ. QUARTERLY BULLETIN∗. Text in Arabic, English. 1952. q. (and monthly statement of accounts). free. charts; stat. **Document type:** *Bulletin.*
Published by: (Statistics and Research Department), Central Bank of Iraq, Rashid St, Baghdad, Iraq. Circ: 2,000.

332.1   IRL   ISSN 0069-1542
HG37.I75
CENTRAL BANK OF IRELAND. ANNUAL REPORT. Text in English. 1943. a., latest 2000. free. 200 p./no. 1 cols./p.; **Document type:** *Yearbook, Corporate.* **Description:** Review of Irish economy, monetary developments in Ireland and international developments. Articles on current financial and economic topics.
Related titles: Online - full text ed.
Indexed: PAIS.
Published by: Central Bank of Ireland, Dame St., PO Box 559, Dublin, 2, Ireland. TEL 353-1-6716666, FAX 353-1-6716561, erp@centralbank.ie, enquiries@centralbank.ie, http://www.centralbank.ie. Circ: 4,000.

332   IRL
CENTRAL BANK OF IRELAND. BULLETIN. Text in English. 1943. q. stat. 200 p./no. 1 cols./p.; back issues avail. **Document type:** *Bulletin, Corporate.* **Description:** Review of Irish economy, monetary developments in Ireland, international developments and articles on current financial and economic topics. Statistical appendix.
Former titles: Central Bank of Ireland. Quarterly Bulletin (0332-2645); (until 1962): Central Bank of Ireland. Quarterly Statistical Bulletin (0332-2599); (until 1943): Currency Commission. Quarterly Statistical Bulletin (0332-2823)
Related titles: Online - full text ed.
Indexed: CPM, CREJ, ELLIS, IBSS, KES, PAIS, WBA.
Published by: Central Bank of Ireland, Dame St., PO Box 559, Dublin, 2, Ireland. TEL 353-1-6716666, FAX 353-1-6716561, 353-1-6706871, erp@centralbank.ie, enquiries@centralbank.ie, http://www.centralbank.ie. Circ: 3,000.

CENTRAL BANK OF IRELAND. IRISH ECONOMIC STATISTICS. see *BUSINESS AND ECONOMICS—Abstracting, Bibliographies, Statistics*

332   IRL   ISSN 0791-1785
CENTRAL BANK OF IRELAND. MONTHLY STATISTICS. Text in English. 1965. m. free. stat. **Document type:** *Bulletin.*
Former titles (until Mar. 1989): Central Bank of Ireland. Statistical Supplement (0790-3979); (until 1983): Central Bank of Ireland. Statistical Supplement to the Quarterly Bulletin (0332-2742); (Until 1968): Central Bank of Ireland. Statistical Tables of the Quarterly Bulletin (0332-2793)
Related titles: Online - full text ed.
Published by: Central Bank of Ireland, Dame St., PO Box 559, Dublin, 2, Ireland. TEL 353-1-6716666, FAX 353-1-6716561, mps@centralbank.ie, enquiries@centralbank.ie, http://www.centralbank.ie. Circ: 300.

332   JOR   ISSN 0069-1550
CENTRAL BANK OF JORDAN. ANNUAL REPORT/BANK AL-MARKAZI AL-URDUNI. ANNUAL REPORT. Text in English. a. free. charts; stat. **Document type:** *Government.* **Description:** Analysing the economic developments of money and banking activities, public finance, external and internal public debt, external sector, production prices and companies.
Related titles: Arabic ed.
Published by: (Department of Research and Studies), Central Bank of Jordan, P O Box 37, Amman, 11118, Jordan. TEL 4630301, FAX 4638889, redp@cbj.gov.jo.

332.1   KEN
CENTRAL BANK OF KENYA. ANNUAL ECONOMIC REPORT. Text in English. 1966. a. **Document type:** *Corporate.*
Formerly: Central Bank of Kenya. Annual Report (0069-1569)
Published by: Central Bank of Kenya, Research Department, PO Box 60000, Nairobi, Kenya. cbk@africaonline.co.ke, http://www.africaonline.co.ke/cbk.

332   KWT   ISSN 1029-4546
HG3361.K83
CENTRAL BANK OF KUWAIT. ANNUAL REPORT. Text in English. 1970. a. free. stat. **Document type:** *Government.* **Description:** Covers the financial and monetary developments of the State of Kuwait in a fiscal year. Data such as interest rates, exchange prices, credit policy, etc. as well as Central Bank activities are related to the implementation of monetary policy are available.
Related titles: ♦ English ed.: At-Taqrir as-Sanawi. Bank al-Kuwayt al-Markazi. ISSN 1029-4589.
Published by: Central Bank of Kuwait, Economic Research Department/Bank al-Kuwayt al-Markazi, Idarat al-Buhuth al-ektisadia, P O Box 526, Safat, 13006, Kuwait. TEL 965-2449200, FAX 965-2440887, cbk@cbk.gov.kw, http://www.cbk.gov.kw. R&P Sami H Al-Anbaee TEL 965-2403257. Circ: 2,000.

332   MLT   ISSN 0577-0653
HG3090.5.A7
CENTRAL BANK OF MALTA. ANNUAL REPORT. Text in English. 1968. a. free. **Document type:** *Corporate.*
Published by: Central Bank of Malta, Economics and Research Department, Castille Pl, Valletta, CMR 01, Malta. TEL 356-247480, FAX 356-243051, info@centralbankmalta.com, http://www.centralbankmalta.com. Ed. Anton Caruana Galizia. Circ: 2,200.

332   MLT   ISSN 0008-9273
HG3090.5.A7
CENTRAL BANK OF MALTA. QUARTERLY REVIEW. Text in English. 1968. q., latest no.1. free. charts; stat. **Document type:** *Corporate.*
Indexed: IBR, IBZ, KES, PAIS, WBA.
—BLDSC (7203.545000).
Published by: Central Bank of Malta, Economics and Research Department, Castille Pl, Valletta, CMR 01, Malta. TEL 356-247480, FAX 356-243051, info@centralbankmalta.com, http://www.centralbankmalta.com. Ed. Anton Caruana Galizia. Circ: 2,000.

332.1   NGA   ISSN 0069-1577
HG3399.N5
CENTRAL BANK OF NIGERIA. ANNUAL REPORT AND STATEMENT OF ACCOUNTS. Text in English. 1960. a. **Document type:** *Corporate.*
Indexed: RASB.
—BLDSC (1505.500000).
Published by: Central Bank of Nigeria, Tinubu Sq., PMB 12194, Lagos, Nigeria. Circ: 4,000.

332   NGA   ISSN 0008-929X
CENTRAL BANK OF NIGERIA. MONTHLY REPORT. Text in English. m. charts; stat.
Media: Duplicated (not offset).
Indexed: WBA.
Published by: Central Bank of Nigeria, Tinubu Sq., PMB 12194, Lagos, Nigeria. Circ: 2,000.

332.1   LKA   ISSN 1391-3581
HG1220.8
CENTRAL BANK OF SRI LANKA. ANNUAL REPORT. Text in English, Singhalese, Tamil. 1950. a. LKR 100, USD 20 (effective 1999). **Document type:** *Corporate.*
Formerly (until 1972): Central Bank of Ceylon. Annual Report (0069-1496)
Published by: Central Bank of Sri Lanka, Janadhipathi Mawatha, P O Box 590, Colombo, 1, Sri Lanka. TEL 94-1-346275, FAX 94-1-346289.

332   LKA
CENTRAL BANK OF SRI LANKA. NEWS SURVEY. Text in English. m. LKR 50; USD 12 foreign.
Published by: Central Bank of Sri Lanka, Janadhipathi Mawatha, P O Box 590, Colombo, 1, Sri Lanka. TEL 94-1-847243, FAX 94-1-867353.

332   LKA
CENTRAL BANK OF SRI LANKA. SURVEY REPORTS. Text in English. irreg. price varies.
Published by: Central Bank of Sri Lanka, Janadhipathi Mawatha, P O Box 590, Colombo, 1, Sri Lanka. TEL 94-1-346278, FAX 94-1-712486.

CENTRAL BANK OF SYRIA. QUARTERLY BULLETIN. see *BUSINESS AND ECONOMICS—Economic Situation And Conditions*

354   BHS
CENTRAL BANK OF THE BAHAMAS. ANNUAL REPORT AND STATEMENT OF ACCOUNTS. Text in English. 1974. a. free. illus.; stat. back issues avail. **Document type:** *Government.*
Published by: Central Bank of the Bahamas, Research Department, PO Box N 4868, Nassau, Bahamas. TEL 242-302-2639, FAX 242-356-4324, TELEX 20-115, research@centralbankbahamas.com. Ed. Wendy Craigg. Circ: 1,400.

332   BHS
CENTRAL BANK OF THE BAHAMAS. ECONOMIC REVIEW. Text in English. 1974. q. free. charts; stat. back issues avail. **Document type:** *Government.*
Supersedes (in 1992): Central Bank of the Bahamas. Quarterly Review
Indexed: KES, WBA.
Published by: Central Bank of the Bahamas, Research Department, PO Box N 4868, Nassau, Bahamas. TEL 242-302-2639, FAX 242-356-4324, TELEX CENTRALBANK 20115, research@centralbankbahamas.com. Ed. Wendy Craigg. Circ: 1,300.

CENTRAL BANK OF THE BAHAMAS. QUARTERLY STATISTICAL DIGEST. see *BUSINESS AND ECONOMICS—Abstracting, Bibliographies, Statistics*

332.1   GMB   ISSN 0796-1049
CENTRAL BANK OF THE GAMBIA. ANNUAL REPORT. Text in English. 1971. a. free. **Document type:** *Bulletin.*
Indexed: RASB.
Published by: Central Bank of the Gambia, Economic Research Department, 1-2 Buckle St, Banjul, Gambia. TEL 228103, FAX 226969. Ed. Buah Saidy. Circ: 200.

B

▼ *new title*   ➤ *refereed*   ∗ *unverified*   ◆ *full entry avail.*

332 TUR ISSN 1013-6193
CENTRAL BANK OF THE REPUBLIC OF TURKEY. ANNUAL REPORT. Key Title: Annual Report - Central Bank of the Republic of Turkey. Text in English. 1931. a. stat. **Document type:** *Government.* **Description:** Covers the results of the Central Bank's accounting year. Contains a detailed study of those international economic developments which relate to similar economic developments at home.
Published by: Central Bank of the Republic of Turkey, General Directorate of Planning and Research, Directorate of Documentation, Ankara, Turkey. FAX 90-312-3116685. Circ: 2,000.

332 TUR
CENTRAL BANK OF THE REPUBLIC OF TURKEY. MONTHLY STATISTICAL AND EVALUATION BULLETIN. Text in Turkish. 1986. m. free. **Document type:** *Bulletin.* **Description:** Publishes the data used by the research staff of the Central Bank.
Published by: Central Bank of the Republic of Turkey, General Directorate of Planning and Research, Directorate of Documentation, Ankara, Turkey. FAX 90-324-2303. Circ: 2,000.

B

332 TTO ISSN 1011-6311
HC157.A1
CENTRAL BANK OF TRINIDAD AND TOBAGO. ANNUAL ECONOMIC SURVEY. Text in English. 1986. a. USD 12 (effective 2000). stat. back issues avail. **Document type:** *Bulletin, Corporate.*
Indexed: AgBio, AgrForAb, AnBrAb, BioCN&I, CPA, DSA, FCA, ForAb, HerbAb, HortAb, I&DA, IndVet, MaizeAb, NemAb, NutrAb, OrnHort, PBA, PGegResA, PGrRegA, PHN&I, PN&I, PoultAb, RA&MP, RDA, RPP, S&F, SeedAb, TDB, TriticAb, VetBull, WAE&RSA, WeedAb.
Published by: Central Bank of Trinidad and Tobago, Eric Williams Plaza, Independence Sq, PO Box 1250, Port-of-Spain, Trinidad, Trinidad & Tobago. TEL 868-625-4835, FAX 868-627-4696, library@central-bank.org.tt, http://www.central-bank.org.tt.

332.1 TTO ISSN 0069-1593
HC157.T8
CENTRAL BANK OF TRINIDAD AND TOBAGO. ANNUAL REPORT. Text in English. 1965. a. free. back issues avail. **Document type:** *Bulletin, Corporate.*
Published by: Central Bank of Trinidad and Tobago, Eric Williams Plaza, Independence Sq, PO Box 1250, Port-of-Spain, Trinidad, Trinidad & Tobago. TEL 868-625-4835, FAX 868-627-4696, library@central-bank.org.tt, http://www.central-bank.org.tt. Circ: 1,000.

332.1 TTO ISSN 1011-6338
HG185.T74
CENTRAL BANK OF TRINIDAD AND TOBAGO. MONTHLY STATISTICAL DIGEST. Text in English. 1974 (vol.7). m. USD 40 (effective 2000). stat. back issues avail. **Document type:** *Bulletin, Corporate.*
Supersedes in part: Central Bank of Trinidad and Tobago. Statistical Digest
Media: Duplicated (not offset).
Published by: Central Bank of Trinidad and Tobago, Eric Williams Plaza, Independence Sq, PO Box 1250, Port-of-Spain, Trinidad, Trinidad & Tobago. TEL 868-625-4835, FAX 868-627-4696, TELEX 386-270, library@central-bank.org.tt, http://www.central-bank.org.tt. Circ: 350.

CENTRAL BANK OF TRINIDAD AND TOBAGO. QUARTERLY STATISTICAL DIGEST. see *BUSINESS AND ECONOMICS—Abstracting, Bibliographies, Statistics*

332 VEN
CENTRAL BANK OF VENEZUELA. REPORT. Text in English. s-a.
Related titles: ◆ Spanish ed.: Banco Central de Venezuela. Revista. ISSN 0005-4720.
Published by: Banco Central de Venezuela, Av Urdaneta Esq Las Carmelitas, Caracas, 1010, Venezuela.

332 YEM ISSN 0301-6625
CENTRAL BANK OF YEMEN. ANNUAL REPORT. Text in Arabic, English. 1971. a. free.
Published by: Central Bank of Yemen, P O Box 59, Sana, Yemen.

332 USA
CENTRAL BANKER. Text in English. q. **Description:** Contains news of the Eighth Federal Reserve Distrsct. Includes a Feditorial, regional review, and facts of the federal reserve.
Published by: Federal Reserve Bank of St. Louis, PO Box 442, St. Louis, MO 63166. http://www.stls.frb.org/publications/cb. R&P Alice Dames TEL 314-444-8593.

332 GBR ISSN 0960-6319
HG1811
CENTRAL BANKING; policy, markets, supervision. Text in English. 1990. q. GBP 295 domestic; USD 502 in United States; EUR 472 elsewhere (effective 2005). bk.rev. charts; illus.; stat. index. back issues avail. **Document type:** *Journal, Trade.* **Description:** Provides a news, analysis, and commentary on the activities and policies of the world's centeral banks.
Indexed: IBSS, PAIS.
—BLDSC (3105.982000), IE, ingenta.
Published by: Central Banking Publications Ltd., Fifth Fl, Tavistock House, Tavistock Sq, London, WC1H 9JZ, United Kingdom. TEL 44-20-73880006, FAX 44-20-73889040, info@centralbanking.co.uk, http://www.centralbanking.co.uk/publications/journals/cbj.htm. Ed. Robert Pringle.

332 ANT ISSN 0920-9905
HG2847.5.A7
CENTRALE BANK VAN ARUBA. QUARTERLY BULLETIN. Text in English. 1987. q. **Document type:** *Bulletin.*
Published by: Centrale Bank van Aruba, Economic Policy Dept, Havenstraat 2, Oranjestad, Netherlands Antilles. TEL 297-822509, FAX 297-832251, cbaua@setarnet.org, http://www.cbaruba.org.

332 BEL ISSN 0772-7798
CENTRE D'ESTUDES FINANCIERES. NEWSLETTER. Text in French. bi-m. **Document type:** *Newsletter.*
Related titles: ◆ Supplement to: Financieel Forum. Bank - en Financiewezen. ISSN 1376-7720; ◆ Supplement to: Financieel Forum. Bank - en Finacieel Recht. ISSN 1377-8013.
Published by: Forum Financier Belge/Belgisch Financeel Forum, Ravensteinstraat 36 B-5, Brussels, 1000, Belgium. FAX 32-2-5125861, jv@abb-bvb.be.

332 BEL
CENTRE FOR EUROPEAN POLICY STUDIES. FINANCIAL MARKETS UNIT. RESEARCH REPORT. Text in English. 1989. irreg., latest vol.20, 1996. EUR 40 per issue (effective 2005). back issues avail. **Document type:** *Monographic series.*
Related titles: Online - full content ed.: EUR 30 per issue (effective 2005).
Published by: Centre for European Policy Studies, Pl du Congres 1, Brussels, 1000, Belgium. TEL 32-2-229-3911, FAX 32-2-219-4151, info@ceps.be, http://www.ceps.be/Default.php. R&P Dominic Gilmore.

332 GBR ISSN 1472-362X
CENTRE FOR MONETARY AND FINANCIAL ECONOMICS. DISCUSSION PAPERS. Text in English. 2000. irreg.
—BLDSC (3597.951227).
Published by: South Bank University, Centre for Monetary and Financial Economics (CEMFE), Business School, 103 Borough Rd, London, SE1 0AA, United Kingdom. TEL 44-20-7815-7078, FAX 44-20-7815-8226, cipolla@sbu.ac.uk. Ed. Guglielmo Maria Caporale.

CENTRES, BUREAUX & RESEARCH INSTITUTES; the directory of UK concentrations of effort, information, and expertise. see *BUSINESS AND ECONOMICS—Trade And Industrial Directories*

332.4 MEX ISSN 0186-7229
HG6
CENTRO DE ESTUDIOS MONETARIOS LATINOAMERICANOS. BOLETIN BIMENSUAL. Variant title: C E M L A Boletin Bimensual. Text in Spanish. 1955. 7/yr. USD 70. adv. charts. index. **Document type:** *Bulletin.*
Formerly: Centro de Estudios Monetarios Latinoamericanos. Boletin Mensual (0008-9958)
Related titles: Online - full text ed.: (from EBSCO Publishing).
Indexed: IBSS, JEL, PAIS, RASB.
Published by: Centro de Estudios Monetarios Latinoamericanos, A.C., Durango 54, Mexico City, DF 06700, Mexico. TEL 915-533030, FAX 525-4432. Ed., Pub. Juan Manuel Rodriguez. R&P Luis A Giorgio Burzilla TEL 525-514-3165. Adv. contact Claudio Antonovich. Circ: 700.

332.1 MEX ISSN 0577-2451
CENTRO DE ESTUDIOS MONETARIOS LATINOAMERICANOS. ENSAYOS. Text in Spanish. 1963. irreg. price varies. adv. **Document type:** *Monographic series.*
Published by: Centro de Estudios Monetarios Latinoamericanos, A.C., Durango 54, Mexico City, DF 06700, Mexico. TEL 915-5330300, FAX 525-4432. Pub. Juan Manuel Rodriguez. R&P Luis A Giorgio Burzilla TEL 525-514-3165. Adv. contact Claudio Antonovich. Circ: 1,000.

CHAPTER 11 REORGANIZATIONS. see *LAW*

CHAPTER 13: PRACTICE & PROCEDURE. see *LAW*

332 332.6 FRA ISSN 1162-9614
CHART'S; la lettre des previsions boursieres. Text in French. 1991. w. adv. **Document type:** *Newsletter.* **Description:** Forecasts on Paris stock exchange (Bourse de Paris).
Address: 22 rue Fallempin, Paris, 75015, France. TEL 33-1-45774707, FAX 33-1-40598467, http://www.charts.fr. Ed. David Bunan. Pub., R&P, Adv. contact Laurent Thiaville. Circ: 5,000.

CHECKLISTS AND ILLUSTRATIVE FINANCIAL STATEMENTS FOR BANKS. see *BUSINESS AND ECONOMICS—Accounting*

CHECKLISTS AND ILLUSTRATIVE FINANCIAL STATEMENTS FOR FINANCE COMPANIES. see *BUSINESS AND ECONOMICS—Accounting*

CHECKS, DRAFTS AND NOTES. see *LAW*

332.1 USA ISSN 1066-3029
HG1704
CHEKLIST. Text in English. 1989. q. USD 25; USD 10 newsstand/cover (effective 2005). adv. 56 p./no. 3 cols./p.; back issues avail. **Document type:** *Magazine, Trade.* **Description:** Helps executives in the check-cashing industry manage their business for continued growth. Includes general news, feature articles, legislative updates, reports on trends, marketing tips, product information and news of state and national association activities.
Related titles: Supplement(s): Special N a C C A Convention Issue.
Published by: B K B Publications Inc, 98 Greenwich Ave, 1st Fl, New York, NY 10011-7743. TEL 212-807-0148, FAX 212-807-1821, bkbpub1@ix.netcom.com. Ed. Charlene Komar Storey. Pub., R&P, Adv. contact Brian K Burkart TEL 212-807-7933. B&W page USD 1,525, color page USD 2,565; trim 8.25 x 10.75. Circ: 8,500 (paid and controlled).

332 CHN ISSN 1007-0346
➤ **CHENGSHI JINRONG LUNTAN/URBAN FINANCE FORUM.** Text in Chinese. 1996. CNY 84; HKD 120 in Hong Kong; USD 72 elsewhere. **Document type:** *Academic/Scholarly.* **Description:** Covers all aspects of Chinese urban finance, including theory, research, administration, macroeconomy analysis, financial market, and much more.
Published by: (Industrial and Commercial Bank of China), Chengshi Jinrong Luntan Bianjibu, 15 Cuiwei Rd, Haidian, Beijing, 100036, China. TEL 86-10-8185253, FAX 86-10-8217853, TELEX 22770 LCBHO CN. Ed. Dazhi Xun. Pub. Jingen Pan. R&P Xiangyang Zhan. Adv. contact Biao Liu. Circ: 25,000. **Co-sponsors:** Urban Finance Research Institute of China; Urban Finance Association of China.

332 TWN
CHIAO TUNG BANK. ANNUAL REPORT. Text in English. 1961. a. free. **Document type:** *Corporate.*
Formerly (until Mar. 1992): Bank of Communications. Annual Report
Published by: Chiao Tung Bank, 91 Hengyang Rd, Taipei, 100, Taiwan. TEL 886-2-3613000, FAX 886-2-3612046, TELEX 11341 CHIAOTUNG. Ed. H L Huang.

332 CAN ISSN 1492-7888
CHIEF ELECTION OFFICER OF ONTARIO UNDER THE ELECTION FINANCES ACT. ANNUAL REPORT. Text in English. 1975. a.
Former titles (until 1998): Commission on Election Finances. Annual Report (0835-1872); (until 1975): Commission on Election Contributions and Expenses Administering the Election Finances Reform Act. Annual Report (0704-3414); (until 1975): Commission on Election Contributions and Expenses Administering the Election Finances Reform Act. Report (0700-3757)
Published by: Election Finances Officer, 51 Rolark Dr, Toronto, ON M1R 3B1, Canada. TEL 416-325-9401, FAX 416-325-9466, electfin@electionsontario.on.ca, http://www.electionsontario.on.ca.

CHIEF ELECTORAL OFFICER. ANNUAL REPORT. see *PUBLIC ADMINISTRATION*

CHILE. INSTITUTO NACIONAL DE ESTADISTICAS. FINANZAS. see *BUSINESS AND ECONOMICS—Abstracting, Bibliographies, Statistics*

CHILE MARKETING AND FINANCIAL STATISTICS. see *BUSINESS AND ECONOMICS—Abstracting, Bibliographies, Statistics*

332 318 CHL ISSN 0716-2820
HG185.C5
CHILE. SUPERINTENDENCIA DE BANCOS E INSTITUCIONES FINANCIERAS. INFORMACION FINANCIERA✱. Text in Spanish. 1975. m. USD 20.
Formed by the 1978 merger of: Chile. Superintendencia de Bancos. Boletin Estadistico; Estadistica Bancaria
Indexed: PAIS.
Published by: Superintendencia de Bancos e Instituciones Financieras, Moneda 1123, Santiago, Chile. TEL 56-2-4426200, 56-2-4426200. Ed. Arturo Tagle. Circ: 1,200.

332.1 GBR ISSN 1369-1260
THE CITY MAGAZINE. Text in English. 1997. q. GBP 29.95 (effective 2000). **Description:** Contains a business section written by writers whose interests lie in the activities of the 'Square Mile' and are well=known within their fields on subjects ranging from financial information, stockbroking, etc.
Published by: Roxby Media Ltd, Roxby House, 5-6 Roxby Pl, London, SW6 1RU, United Kingdom. TEL 44-20-7903-8333, FAX 44-20-7381-8890, http://www.thecitymagazine.com. Circ: 29,000.

332 GBR
CITY UNIVERSITY BUSINESS SCHOOL. DEPARTMENT OF BANKING & FINANCE. FINANCE WORKING PAPER. Text in English. irreg.
Published by: City University Business School, Department of Banking & Finance, c/o Mrs. Debra Durston, Sec., Room F-1344, Frobisher Crescent, Barbican Centre, London, EC2Y 8HB, United Kingdom. TEL 44-171-477-8741, FAX 44-171-477-8881, bd593@city.ac.uk.

332.6029 GBR ISSN 1362-3672
CITYFILE. Text in English. 1985. 6/yr. GBP 230 (effective 1997). **Document type:** *Directory.* **Description:** Provides details on key U.K. based financial media and stockbroking houses and their analysts.
Former titles (until 1996): Pims Business, Investor and Government Relations Directory (0963-6978); Pims Financial Directory (0268-2117)
Published by: P I M S (UK) Ltd., PIMS House, Mildmay Ave, London, N1 4RS, United Kingdom. TEL 44-20-7226-1000, FAX 44-20-7354-7053. **Co-publisher:** Edinburgh Financial Publishing.

332 USA ISSN 1063-2220
CLARK'S BANK DEPOSITS AND PAYMENTS MONTHLY. Text in English. 1992. m. USD 365 (effective 2004). **Document type:** *Newsletter, Trade.* **Description:** Reports on legal developments affecting bank deposits, collections, and credit cards.
Related titles: Microform ed.: (from PQC).
Indexed: BLI.
—CCC.
Published by: Sheshunoff Information Services Inc., 807 Las Cimas Pkwy, Ste 300, Austin, TX 78746. TEL 512-472-2244, 800-456-2340, FAX 512-305-6575, customercare.sis@sheshunoff.com, http://www.sheshunoff.com/store/003.html. Eds. Barbara Clark, Barkley Clark.

362 USA ISSN 1540-3734
CLARK'S SECURED LENDING WEB REPORT. Text in English. 2000. m. USD 345 (effective 2004). **Document type:** *Newsletter, Trade.* **Description:** Covers all aspects of secured transactions, including documentation, bankruptcy, and regulation.
Media: Online - full content.
Published by: Sheshunoff Information Services Inc., 807 Las Cimas Pkwy, Ste 300, Austin, TX 78746. TEL 512-472-2244, 800-456-2340, FAX 512-305-6575, customercare.sis@sheshunoff.com, http://www.sheshunoff.com/store/B03.html. Eds. Barbara Clark, Barkley Clark.

332 USA ISSN 1063-5289
CLARK'S SECURED TRANSACTIONS MONTHLY. Text in English. 1984. m. USD 425 (effective 2005). back issues avail. **Document type:** *Newsletter, Trade.* **Description:** Provides "how-to" guidance on drafting air-tight lending agreements.
Formerly (until 1992): Secured Lending Alert (0895-5492)
—CCC.
Published by: Sheshunoff Information Services Inc., 807 Las Cimas Pkwy, Ste 300, Austin, TX 78746. TEL 512-472-2244, 800-456-2340, FAX 512-305-6575, customercare.sis@sheshunoff.com, http://www.sheshunoff.com/store/885.html. Eds. Barbara Clark, Barkley Clark.

332 CHL
CLASIFICACION DE INSTRUMENTOS DE OFERTA PUBLICA. Text in Spanish. 2000. m. back issues avail.
Media: Online - full text. **Related titles:** E-mail ed.
Published by: Superintendencia de Bancos e Instituciones Financieras, Moneda 1123, Santiago, Chile. TEL 56-2-4426200, http://www.sbif.cl/cgi-bin/publicaciones.pl.

332.1 KEN
CO-OPERATIVE BANK OF KENYA. ANNUAL REPORT & ACCOUNTS. Text in English. 1969. a. free. **Document type:** *Corporate.*
Formerly: Co-operative Bank of Kenya. Annual Report and Statement of Accounts
Published by: Co-operative Bank of Kenya Ltd., PO Box 48231, Nairobi, Kenya. TEL 254-2-228453, FAX 254-2-336073, TELEX 22938. Ed. L.C. Karissa. R&P L C Karissa. Circ: 3,000.

332 USA ISSN 1052-4029
COLLECTION AGENCY REPORT. Text in English. 1990. m. USD 420 (effective 2000). bk.rev. abstr.; charts; mkt. index. 8 p./no. 1 cols./p.; back issues avail. **Document type:** *Newsletter, Trade.* **Description:** News and advisory service for collection agency executives and major credit grantors.
Published by: First Detroit Corp., PO Box 5025, Warren, MI 48090-5025. TEL 810-573-0045, FAX 810-573-9219, info@firstdetroit.com, http://www.firstdetroit.com. Ed., Pub., R&P, Adv. contact Albert W Scace.

332 USA
COLLECTION TECHNOLOGY NEWS. Text in English. m. USD 325 (effective 2004). **Document type:** *Newsletter, Trade.* **Description:** Covers the latest trends in repossessions, foreclosure, and bankruptcy.
Published by: Royal Media Group, 1359 Broadway, Ste 1512, New York, NY 10018. TEL 212-564-8972, FAX 212-564-8973, info@royalmedia.com, http://www.royalmedia.com/newsletter.cfm?pub=103.

332.7 USA ISSN 1093-1260
HG3752.7.U6
COLLECTIONS AND CREDIT RISK; the monthly magazine for collections and credit policy professionals. Text in English. 1996. m. USD 98 domestic; USD 128 in Canada; USD 148 elsewhere (effective 2005). illus. **Document type:** *Magazine, Trade.* **Description:** Delivers reports on operational, technological, market, and legal developments that are changing the face of the credit and collections field.
Related titles: Online - full text ed.: (from Factiva, Florida Center for Library Automation, Gale Group, LexisNexis, O C L C Online Computer Library Center, Inc., ProQuest Information & Learning).
Indexed: ABIn, B&I, BLI.
—CCC.
Published by: Source Media, Inc., One State St Plaza, 27th Fl, New York, NY 10004. TEL 212-803-6077, 800-221-1809, FAX 212-747-1154, custserv@sourcemedia.com, http://www.creditcollectionsworld.com, http://www.sourcemedia.com.

332.7 USA ISSN 0010-082X
COLLECTOR. Text in English. 1939. m. USD 70 to non-members; USD 35 to members (effective 2005). adv. bk.rev. charts; illus. index. **Document type:** *Magazine, Trade.* **Description:** Covers collection techniques, legislation and management issues in the customer debt collection industry.
Published by: American Collectors Association, Inc., 4040 W 70th St, PO Box 390106, Minneapolis, MN 55435. TEL 952-926-6547, FAX 952-926-1624, comm@collector.com, http://www.collector.com. Ed., R&P Timothy Dressen. Circ: 6,000.

332 USA ISSN 0099-1848
KF1515.A2
COLLIER BANKRUPTCY CASES. Text in English. 1979. 7 base vols. plus bi-w. updates. looseleaf. USD 1,773 (effective 2005). back issues avail. **Description:** Includes concise summaries of significant ban issues in virtually all current bankruptcy cases decided by the federal courts.
—CCC.
Published by: Matthew Bender & Co., Inc. (Subsidiary of: LexisNexis North America), 1275 Broadway, Albany, NY 12204. international@bender.com, http://bender.lexisnexis.com. Eds. Lawrence King, Roy Babiit.

332 340 USA
COLLIER BANKRUPTCY COMPENSATION GUIDE. Text in English. 1988. irreg. (in 1 vol.). looseleaf. Supplement avail. **Description:** Examines the Bankruptcy Code's provisions, case law, and current practice trends relevant to the compensation of attorneys, trustees and other professionals involved in bankruptcy cases. Contains substantive analysis as well as strategic and practical guidance.
Related titles: CD-ROM ed.
Published by: Matthew Bender & Co., Inc. (Subsidiary of: LexisNexis North America), 1275 Broadway, Albany, NY 12204. international@bender.com, http://bender.lexisnexis.com.

332 340 USA
COLLIER BANKRUPTCY MANUAL. Text in English. 1979. irreg. (in 3 vols.); latest 3 rd ed. looseleaf. USD 545 (effective 2003). Supplement avail. **Document type:** *Trade.* **Description:** Provides substantive analysis necessary for handling a case under the Bankruptcy Code, keyed to the section numbers of the 1978 Code.
Related titles: CD-ROM ed.
Published by: Matthew Bender & Co., Inc. (Subsidiary of: LexisNexis North America), 1275 Broadway, Albany, NY 12204. international@bender.com, http://bender.lexisnexis.com. Ed. Henry J Sommer.

332 340 USA
COLLIER BANKRUPTCY PRACTICE GUIDE. Text in English. 1981. 6 base vols. plus irreg. updates. looseleaf. USD 1,327 base vol(s). (effective 2003). Supplement avail. **Description:** Each chapter within a section begins with Scope and Use for a brief overview of the subject, explaining what issues are involved and what practical problems may arise. Practice aids and practice discussions provide time-saving features, strategies and tactics.
Related titles: CD-ROM ed.
Published by: Matthew Bender & Co., Inc. (Subsidiary of: LexisNexis North America), 1275 Broadway, Albany, NY 12204. international@bender.com, http://bookstore.lexis.com/bookstore/catalog?action=product&prod_id=10112, http://bender.lexisnexis.com. Eds. Alan N Resnick, Henry J Sommer.

332 USA ISSN 1044-0917
KF1544
COLLIER HANDBOOK FOR CREDITORS' COMMITTEES. Text in English. 1988. base vol. plus irreg. updates. looseleaf. USD 131 (effective 2002). Supplement avail. **Description:** Covers the role of Chapter 11 creditors' committees, fiduciary responsibilities and Chapter 11 plan negotiations.
Related titles: CD-ROM ed.
Published by: Matthew Bender & Co., Inc. (Subsidiary of: LexisNexis North America), 1275 Broadway, Albany, NY 12204. international@bender.com, http://bender.lexisnexis.com. Ed. Lawrence P King.

332 340 USA
COLLIER LENDING INSTITUTIONS AND THE BANKRUPTCY CODE. Text in English. 1986. irreg. (in 1 vol.). looseleaf. USD 258 (effective 2003). Supplement avail. **Description:** Practice-oriented guide to the impact of bankruptcy on lending transactions.
Related titles: CD-ROM ed.
Published by: Matthew Bender & Co., Inc. (Subsidiary of: LexisNexis North America), 1275 Broadway, Albany, NY 12204. international@bender.com, http://bender.lexisnexis.com. Eds. Alan N Resnick, Henry J Sommer.

332 340 USA
COLLIER ON BANKRUPTCY. Text in English. 1979. irreg. (in 23 vols.). looseleaf. USD 2,820 (effective 2003). Supplement avail.; reprint service avail. from WSH. **Description:** Provides detailed discussion, by the leading bankruptcy authorities, of the Bankruptcy Code as amended. Includes coverage of the bankruptcy judges, United States trustees, and Family Farmer Bankruptcy Act of 1986.
Related titles: CD-ROM ed.: USD 2,054 (effective 2002); Microfiche ed.: (from WSH).
Published by: Matthew Bender & Co., Inc. (Subsidiary of: LexisNexis North America), 1275 Broadway, Albany, NY 12204. international@bender.com, http://bender.lexisnexis.com. Eds. Alan N Resnick, Henry J Sommer.

332 333.33 USA
COLLIER REAL ESTATE TRANSACTIONS AND THE BANKRUPTCY CODE. Text in English. 1984. irreg. (in 1 vol.). looseleaf. USD 259 (effective 2003). Supplement avail. **Description:** Practice-oriented guide to the impact of bankruptcy on real estate transactions, for both the general practitioner and the real estate specialist.
Related titles: CD-ROM ed.
Published by: Matthew Bender & Co., Inc. (Subsidiary of: LexisNexis North America), 1275 Broadway, Albany, NY 12204. international@bender.com, http://bender.lexisnexis.com. Eds. Alan N Resnick, Henry J Sommer.

332 COL
COLOMBIA. SUPERINTENDENCIA BANCARIA. INFORME DE LABORES. Text in Spanish. 1924. a. free.
Published by: Superintendencia Bancaria, Apartado Aereo 3460, Bogota, CUND, Colombia. TEL 57-1-2804060, FAX 57-1-2800864. Circ: 1,400.

332 COL ISSN 0120-4017
HG2901
COLOMBIA. SUPERINTENDENCIA BANCARIA. REVISTA. Text in Spanish. 1935. q. free.
Published by: Superintendencia Bancaria, Apartado Aereo 3460, Bogota, CUND, Colombia. TEL 57-1-2804060, FAX 57-1-2800864. Circ: 1,600.

COLORADO BUSINESS CREDIT DIRECTORY. see *BUSINESS AND ECONOMICS—Trade And Industrial Directories*

COLORADO. GENERAL SUPPORT SERVICES. DIVISION OF ACCOUNTS & CONTROL. COMPREHENSIVE ANNUAL FINANCIAL REPORT. see *PUBLIC ADMINISTRATION*

COLORADO REGISTER. see *PUBLIC ADMINISTRATION*

332 CAN
COMMENTAIRES DE LA C I B C. (Canadian Imperial Bank of Commerce) Text in French. m.
Related titles: Supplement(s): C I B C Observations. ISSN 1204-931X.
Published by: Canadian Imperial Bank of Commerce, Commerce Court, 25 King St W, Toronto, ON M5L 1A2, Canada. TEL 416-980-2211, customer.care@cibc.com, http://www.cibc.com.

332 USA
COMMERCE FOLIO. Text in English. 1995. bi-m. free domestic to members print ed.; free domestic online ed.. **Document type:** *Newsletter, Consumer.*
Published by: Oklahoma Department of Commerce, 900 N. Stiles, Oklahoma City, OK 73126. TEL 405-815-6552, 800-879-6552, FAX 405-815-5281. Circ: 7,400 morning (free).

332 ETH ISSN 0588-6694
COMMERCIAL BANK OF ETHIOPIA. ANNUAL REPORT. Text in English. a. free charts; illus.; stat. **Document type:** *Corporate.*
Published by: Commercial Bank of Ethiopia, PO Box 255, Addis Ababa, Ethiopia. TEL 251-1-515000, TELEX 21037A.

B

▼ new title ➤ refereed ✶ unverified ◆ full entry avail.

332 ETH ISSN 0045-7574
COMMERCIAL BANK OF ETHIOPIA. MARKET REPORT. Text in English. 1964. 6/yr. adv.
Published by: (Market Research Department), Commercial Bank of Ethiopia, PO Box 255, Addis Ababa, Ethiopia. Ed. Leikun Berhanu. Circ: 1,000.

332.1 GRC ISSN 0424-9402
COMMERCIAL BANK OF GREECE. ANNUAL REPORT BY THE CHAIRMAN OF THE BOARD OF DIRECTORS. Text in English, Greek. 1954. a. free. illus.; stat.; charts. **Document type:** *Corporate.*
Former titles (until 1962): Commercial Bank of Greece. Annual Report; (until 1960): Commercial Bank of Greece. Report of the Directors and Statement of Accounts
Published by: (Public Relations Department), Commercial Bank of Greece, Sofokleous 11, Athens, 105 56, Greece.

332 GRC ISSN 1106-6571
COMMERCIAL BANK OF GREECE. ECONOMIC REVIEW/EMPORIKE TRAPEZA TES ELLADOS. OIKONOMIKE EPITHEORESE. Text in Greek. 1995. q.
Published by: (Economic Research Division, Economics Sector), Commercial Bank of Greece, Sofokleous 11, Athens, 105 56, Greece. Ed. Pavlos Dermenakis.

332 KWT
COMMERCIAL BANK OF KUWAIT. ANNUAL REPORT. Text in English. a. free. **Document type:** *Corporate.*
Formerly: Commercial Bank of Kuwait. Annual Report and Accounts (0257-4454); Supersedes: Commercial Bank of Kuwait. Annual Report of the Board of Directors and Accounts
Published by: Commercial Bank of Kuwait S.A.K., Mubarak al-Kabir St., P O Box 2861, Safat, 13029, Kuwait. TEL 965-2411001, FAX 965-2450150, TELEX 22004 CBK KT.

332.1 USA ISSN 1090-2538
KF974
THE COMMERCIAL BANKING REGULATORY HANDBOOK. Text in English. 1993. a. price varies. **Document type:** *Trade.*
Formerly (until 1997): Safety and Soundness Compliance Handbook (1084-5062)
Related titles: ◆ Series of: PricewaterhouseCoopers Regulatory Handbook Series. ISSN 1522-1334.
Published by: (PricewaterhouseCoopers), M.E. Sharpe, Inc., 80 Business Park Dr, Armonk, NY 10504. TEL 914-273-1800, 800-541-6563, FAX 914-273-2106, mesinfo@usa.net, custserv@mesharpe.com, http://www.mesharpe.com.

COMMERCIAL BANKRUPTCY LITIGATION. see *LAW—Corporate Law*

332 BGR ISSN 1311-4824
HG3221
COMMERCIAL BANKS IN BULGARIA. Text in English. q. USD 56 foreign (effective 2002). **Document type:** *Bulletin, Trade.* **Description:** Provides information about banking system as a whole and of each individual bank.
Published by: Bulgarska Narodna Banka/Bulgarian National Bank, 1 Alexander Batterberg Sq, Sofia, 1000, Bulgaria. TEL 359-2-91459, FAX 359-2-9802425, press_office@bnbank.org, http://www.bnb.bg. **Dist. by:** Sofia Books, ul Silivria 16, Sofia 1404, Bulgaria. TEL 359-2-9586257, info@sofiabooks-bg.com, http://www.sofiabooks-bg.com.

332 340 USA
COMMERCIAL FINANCE GUIDE. Text in English. 1990. 2 base vols. plus irreg. updates. looseleaf. USD 288 base vol(s). (effective 2005). **Description:** provides exterm coverage of commercial financing devices from basic secured loans to more sophisticated complex structures.
Published by: Matthew Bender & Co., Inc. (Subsidiary of: LexisNexis North America), 1275 Broadway, Albany, NY 12204. TEL 518-487-3575, 800-252-9257, FAX 518-462-3788, international@bender.com, http://bender.lexisnexis.com. Ed. Joseph North.

332 346.066 USA
KF967
COMMERCIAL LENDING LITIGATION NEWS. Text in English. 1989. bi-w. USD 597 (effective 2006). **Document type:** *Newsletter, Trade.* **Description:** Offers a Washington-based lawyer-written newsletter on failed bank and thrift liquidation issues. Includes in-depth analysis of the latest cases in the transactional, professional liability, enforcement and other areas of failed bank law.
Formerly (until 2005): Bank Bailout Litigation News (1047-5133); Incorporates: Bank - Thrift Litigation and Enforcement News (1047-1502)
Related titles: Online - full text ed.: (from LexisNexis).
—CCC.
Published by: L R P Publications, 747 Dresher Rd, PO Box 980, Horsham, PA 19044. TEL 800-341-7874, FAX 215-784-9639, custserve@lrp.com, http://www.shoplrp.com/product/p-40005.LLN.html, http://www.lrp.com.

332 USA ISSN 0886-8204
HG1641
COMMERCIAL LENDING REVIEW. Text in English. 1985. bi-m. USD 350 (effective 2005). adv. bk.rev. reprints avail. **Document type:** *Newsletter, Trade.* **Description:** Covers all aspects of lending for commercial banks, community and regional banks and other financial institutions.
Related titles: Online - full text ed.: (from EBSCO Publishing, Florida Center for Library Automation, Gale Group, LexisNexis, O C L C Online Computer Library Center, Inc., ProQuest Information & Learning).
Indexed: ABIn, ATI, BLI.
—BLDSC (3336.969800), IE, ingenta. **CCC.**
Published by: (American Bankers Association), C C H Tax and Accounting (Subsidiary of: Wolters Kluwer N.V.), 2700 Lake Cook Rd, Riverwoods, IL 60015. TEL 847-267-7000, 888-224-7377, 800-449-8114, FAX 773-866-3895, clairegreene@verizon.net, http://www.commerciallendingreview.com, http://tax.cchgroup.com. Ed. Claire Greene. Pub. Mark Fried. adv.: B&W page USD 1,000. Circ: 1,000 (paid).

332.1 USA
COMMERCIAL LOAN DOCUMENTATION GUIDE. Text in English. 1988. irreg. (in 2 vols.) looseleaf. USD 239 (effective 2003). Supplement avail. **Description:** Covers the full spectrum of loan documentation; includes forms, checklists and useful hints for both borrowers and lenders.
Published by: Matthew Bender & Co., Inc. (Subsidiary of: LexisNexis North America), 1275 Broadway, Albany, NY 12204. international@bender.com, http://bender.lexisnexis.com. Ed. Michael A Leichtling.

332 USA
THE COMMERCIAL RECORD (BOSTON). Text in English. 1882. w. (Fri.). USD 127 domestic; USD 219 foreign (effective 2005). **Document type:** *Newsletter, Consumer.*
Contact Owner: Warren Publishing Corp., 280 Summer St., Boston, MA 02210. TEL 617-428-5100, FAX 617-428-5120, http://www.thewarrengroup.com. Circ: 3,500 (paid).

COMMERSANT WEEKLY. see *BUSINESS AND ECONOMICS—Economic Situation And Conditions*

332 DEU ISSN 1433-6081
COMMERZBANK JOURNAL; Geld- und Finanzthemen im Fokus. Text in German. 1989. q. EUR 4.10 newsstand/cover (effective 2003). adv. bk.rev. back issues avail. **Document type:** *Magazine, Trade.*
Published by: (Commerzbank AG), Publikom Z Verlagsgesellschaft mbH, Frankfurter Str 168, Kassel, 34121, Germany. TEL 49-561-2031742, andrea_lepold@commerzbank.com, publikom_z@dierichs.de, http://www.commerzbank.de/journal/index.htm, http://www.publikom-z.de. Ed. Armin Noll. adv.: B&W page EUR 8,000, color page EUR 12,235; trim 210 x 280. Circ: 268,621 (controlled).

384 USA ISSN 1079-994X
COMMUNICATIONS, BUSINESS AND FINANCE. Text in English. 1994. bi-w.
Published by: B R P Publications, Inc., 1333 H St N W, 11th Floor-West, Ste 220-W, Washington, DC 20005. TEL 202-842-0520, FAX 202-842-1875.

COMMUNICATIONS FINANCE. see *COMMUNICATIONS*

332.7 USA
COMMUNICATOR (WASHINGTON, 1953). Text in English. 1953. m. USD 65 to non-members (effective 2005). adv. illus. **Document type:** *Newsletter, Trade.* **Description:** Keeps owners and managers of credit bureaus, collection agencies, mortgage reporting employment screening, tenant screening, check services companies and related services throughout the US, Canada, and Mexico abreast of the latest developments affecting the credit reporting industry.
Formerly: Communicator (Print Edition)
Media: Online - full text.
Published by: Consumer Data Industry Association, 1090 Vermont Ave, N W, Ste 200, Washington, DC 20005-4905. TEL 202-408-7408, FAX 202-371-0134, http://www.cdiaonline.org. Ed. Kitson Flynn. Circ: 3,000.

332 USA ISSN 0276-0908
THE COMMUNITY BANK PRESIDENT. Text in English. 1980. m. USD 329 (effective 2001). index. back issues avail. **Document type:** *Newsletter.* **Description:** Offers profit-making ideas for community banks.
Related titles: Online - full text ed.
Published by: Siefer Consultants, Inc., 525 Cayuga St, Storm Lake, IA 50588. TEL 712-732-7340, FAX 712-732-7906, info@siefer.com, http://www.siefer.com. Ed. Joe Sheller. Pub. Dan R Siefer. Circ: 1,200 (paid).

332 USA ISSN 1540-4307
COMMUNITY BANK TAX REPORT. Variant title: Pratt's Community Bank Tax Report. Text in English. 1996 (May). m. USD 355 (effective 2004). **Document type:** *Newsletter.*
Published by: A.S. Pratt & Sons, Inc., 1911 Fort Myer Dr, Arlington, VA 22209. TEL 703-528-0145, 800-572-2797, FAX 703-528-1736, http://www.sheshunoff.com. Ed. Stanley I Langbein.

332.2 USA ISSN 1529-1332
HG1921
COMMUNITY BANKER. Text in English. 1880. m. USD 75 to members; USD 95 domestic to non-members; USD 95 in Canada & Mexico to non-members; USD 105 elsewhere to non-members (effective 2005). adv. charts; illus. index. back issues avail. **Document type:** *Newsletter, Trade.* **Description:** Provides analysis of the latest legislative and regulatory developments, in-depth coverage of economic trends and guidance for meeting managerial concerns and challenges.
Former titles (until 2000): America's Community Bankers (1082-7919); (until 1995): Savings and Community Banker (1067-1757); Which was formed by the merger of (1952-1993): Savings Institution Magazine (0746-1321); Which was formerly (until 1983): Savings and Loan News (0036-5114); (1983-1993): Bottomline (Washington) (0740-5464); Which was formed by the merger of (1921-1983): Savings Bank Journal (0036-5130); (1974-1983): National Savings and Community League Journal; Incorporates: National League Journal of Insured Savings Associations (0027-9617)
Related titles: Microform ed.: (from PQC); Online - full text ed.: (from EBSCO Publishing, Gale Group, H.W. Wilson, O C L C Online Computer Library Center, Inc., ProQuest Information & Learning).
Indexed: ABIn, BLI, BPI, H&TI, PAIS.
—BLDSC (3363.591400). **CCC.**
Published by: America's Community Bankers, 900 19th St, N W, Ste 400, Washington, DC 20006. TEL 202-857-3100, FAX 202-296-8716, dcope@acbankers.org, http://www.americascommunitybankers.org. Ed., Pub. Debra Cope. adv.: B&W page USD 2,830, color page USD 4,065; trim 8.5 x 10.88. Circ: 10,000 (controlled).

COMMUNITY INVESTMENT AND AFFORDABLE HOUSING. see *BUSINESS AND ECONOMICS—Investments*

332 USA ISSN 1058-5931
COMMUNITY REINVESTMENT ACT BULLETIN. Text in English. 1991. m. looseleaf. USD 172.25; USD 239.45 foreign. back issues avail. **Document type:** *Bulletin, Newsletter.* **Description:** Covers developments related to the Community Reinvestment Act and discusses compliance issues.
Related titles: Online - full text ed.
—CCC.
Published by: W G & L Financial Reporting & Management Research (Subsidiary of: R I A), 395 Hudson St, New York, NY 10014. TEL 212-367-6300, FAX 212-367-6718. Eds. Jerome D, Nina Groskind. **Subscr. to:** The Park Square Bldg., 31 St James Ave, Boston, MA 02116-4112. TEL 800-950-1207.

COMPANY LAW INSTITUTE OF INDIA. REPORTS OF COMPANY CASES INCLUDING BANKING & INSURANCE. see *LAW—Corporate Law*

332 GBR ISSN 1356-255X
COMPANY R E F S (MONTHLY). (Really Essential Financial Statistics) Text in English. 1994. m. GBP 675 in United Kingdom; GBP 750 in Europe; GBP 795 elsewhere (effective 2001). charts; mkt. back issues avail. **Document type:** *Directory, Consumer.*
Related titles: CD-ROM ed.: Company R E F S (Monthly CD-ROM). GBP 675.63 in the European Union; GBP 575 elsewhere (effective 2001); Company R E F S (Quarterly CD-ROM). GBP 293.75 in the European Union; GBP 250 elsewhere (effective 2001); Online - full text ed.; Alternate Frequency ed(s).: Company R E F S (Quarterly). q.
—CCC.
Published by: H S Financial Publishing Ltd., City Innovation Centre, 26-31 Whiskins St, London, EC1R 0JD, United Kingdom. TEL 44-20-7278-7769, FAX 44-20-7278-9808, http://www.companyrefs.co.uk, http://www.hsfinancial.com. Pub., R&P James Ranft. Adv. contact Ray Witter TEL 44-20-7278-7769.

332 USA
COMPLIANCE ALERT. Text in English. 1988. 26/yr. USD 385 domestic; USD 420 foreign (effective 2000). **Document type:** *Newsletter.* **Description:** Provides immediate and specific analyses of federal laws and rules complete with impact statements, and exploration of long-term implications.
Published by: Bank Administration Institute Foundation, 1 N Franklin St, Chicago, IL 60606. TEL 312-683-2248, 800-323-8552, FAX 312-683-2273. Ed. Mollie Sudaoff. R&P Alison Estnada TEL 312-683-2452.

COMPLIANCE EXAMINATIONS UPDATE. see *LAW*

332.1 USA ISSN 1522-0664
KF975
COMPLIANCE LINK; the PricewaterhouseCoopers Regulatory Handbook cross-index. Text in English. 1996. irreg. price varies. **Document type:** *Trade.*
Related titles: ◆ Series of: PricewaterhouseCoopers Regulatory Handbook Series. ISSN 1522-1334.
Published by: (PricewaterhouseCoopers), M.E. Sharpe, Inc., 80 Business Park Dr, Armonk, NY 10504. TEL 914-273-1800, 800-541-6563, FAX 914-273-2106, mesinfo@usa.net, custserv@mesharpe.com, http://www.mesharpe.com.

332.1 346 657 USA
COMPLIANCE OFFICER'S MANAGEMENT MANUAL. Text in English. 2 base vols. plus s-a. updates. looseleaf. USD 445 (effective 2004). **Document type:** *Directory, Trade.*
Description: Enables bank managers to develop, implement, and maintain effective compliance audit and training programs.
Related titles: CD-ROM ed.; Diskette ed.; ♦ Series: Bank Internal Audit: A Working Guide to Regulatory Compliance; ♦ Bank Data Processing Policies and Procedures; Compliance and Law Series.
Published by: Sheshunoff Information Services Inc., 807 Las Cimas Pkwy, Ste 300, Austin, TX 78746. TEL 512-472-2244, 800-456-2340, FAX 512-305-6575, customercare.sis@sheshunoff.com, http://www.sheshunoff.com/store/985.html.

332 USA ISSN 1529-5699
KF1066.A3
COMPLIANCE REPORTER. Text in English. 1994. bi-w. USD 2,430 combined subscription domestic print & online eds.; USD 2,505 combined subscription foreign print & online eds. (effective 2005). **Document type:** *Newsletter, Trade.*
Description: Presents information for brokers, dealers and investment advisors.
Related titles: Online - full text ed.: (from EBSCO Publishing, Florida Center for Library Automation, ProQuest Information & Learning).
Indexed: BLI.
—CCC.
Published by: Institutional Investor News (Subsidiary of: Euromoney Institutional Investor Plc.), 225 Park Ave S, 7th Fl, New York, NY 10003-1605. TEL 800-715-9195, info@iiplatinum.com, http://www.compliancereporter.com, http://www.iinews.com. Pub. Aaron Finkel TEL 212-224-3268.

COMPTROLLER'S HANDBOOK. see *BUSINESS AND ECONOMICS—Public Finance, Taxation*

332.1 USA
COMPUTER FINANCE. Text in English. 1995. m.
Related titles: Online - full text ed.
Published by: Computerwire Inc, 770 Broadway, # 229, New York, NY 10003-9522. info@computerwire.com, http://www.computerwire.com. Ed. Lynn Haber.

334 USA
CONCLUSIONSONLINE. Text in English. m. USD 175 domestic to institutions small institutions; USD 225 domestic to institutions large institutions (effective 2001). back issues avail. **Document type:** *Magazine, Trade.* **Description:** Covers compliance issues affecting financial institutions and professionals, including regulation changes, legislative updates, and Federal Reserve Bank initiatives.
Media: Online - full text.
Address: editor@conclusionsonline.com, mailroom@conclusionsonline.com, http://www.conclusionsonline.com.

332.1 USA ISSN 0084-9154
CONFERENCE ON BANK STRUCTURE AND COMPETITION. PROCEEDINGS. Text in English. 1964. a. USD 12 (effective 2001). **Document type:** *Proceedings, Academic/Scholarly.*
Published by: (Research Dept.), Federal Reserve Bank of Chicago, Public Information Center, PO Box 834, Chicago, IL 60690. TEL 312-322-5111.

332 USA
CONNECTICUT BANKING. Text in English. q. free domestic to qualified personnel. **Document type:** *Magazine, Trade.*
Published by: Warren Publishing Corp., 280 Summer St., Boston, MA 02210. TEL 617-428-5100, FAX 617-428-5120, http://www.thewarrengroup.com/wp/ctb/home.asp. Ed. Terance Egan. Pub. Timothy M Warren Jr. Circ: 3,300 (free).

CONSEILLER DES ASSURANCES ET DE LA FINANCE. see *INSURANCE*

CONSTRUCTION INDUSTRY ANNUAL FINANCIAL SURVEY. see *BUILDING AND CONSTRUCTION*

332.1 USA ISSN 1090-2546
KF975
THE CONSUMER BANKING REGULATORY HANDBOOK. Text in English. 1993. a. price varies. **Document type:** *Trade.*
Formerly (until 1996): Consumer Compliance Handbook (1084-7812)
Related titles: ♦ Series of: PricewaterhouseCoopers Regulatory Handbook Series. ISSN 1522-1334.
Published by: (PricewaterhouseCoopers), M.E. Sharpe, Inc., 80 Business Park Dr, Armonk, NY 10504. TEL 914-273-1800, 800-541-6563, FAX 914-273-2106, custserv@mesharpe.com, http://www.mesharpe.com.

332.7 GBR
CONSUMER CREDIT. Text in English. 1947. bi-m. GBP 30; GBP 36 overseas. adv. bk.rev. **Document type:** *Trade.*
Description: Covers news of relevance to credit grantors' and consumers' rights, business trends and innovations, and related topics.
Indexed: AmStl.
Published by: Consumer Credit Trade Association, 1st Fl, Tennyson House 159-165, 159-163 Great Portland St, London, W1N 5FD, United Kingdom. TEL 44-171-636-7564, FAX 44-171-323-0096. Ed. P J Patrick. R&P P.J. Patrick. Adv. contact N Squire. Circ: 1,300.

CONSUMER CREDIT & TRUTH IN LENDING COMPLIANCE REPORT. see *LAW*

332.1 USA ISSN 1058-8841
CONSUMER CREDIT DELINQUENCY BULLETIN. Text in English. q. USD 260 domestic to non-members; USD 135 domestic to members; USD 260 foreign (effective 2005). charts; stat. **Document type:** *Bulletin, Trade.* **Description:** For the consumer credit manager; features tables and graphs reporting delinquency rates and repossession ratios.
Formerly (until 1984): Consumer Credit Delinquency Rates
Related titles: Microform ed.: (from PQC); Online - full text ed.: (from ProQuest Information & Learning).
Indexed: ABIn, BLI, SRI.
Published by: (Retail Services Center), American Bankers Association, 1120 Connecticut Ave NW, Washington, DC 20036-3971. TEL 202-663-5268, 800-338-0626, FAX 202-828-4540, custserv@aba.com, http://www.aba.com.
Subscr. to: ABA Customer Service Center, PO Box 79064, Baltimore, MD 21279-0064. TEL 800-226-5377, FAX 202-663-7543.

332.7 340 USA
CONSUMER CREDIT: LAW TRANSACTIONS AND FORMS. Text in English. 1984. 6 base vols. plus irreg. updates. looseleaf. USD 770 base vol(s). (effective 2002). **Description:** Detailed treatment of the law with practical, step-by-step guidance for every stage of a consumer credit transaction. Covers the 13 major consumer credit laws.
Published by: Matthew Bender & Co., Inc. (Subsidiary of: LexisNexis North America), 1275 Broadway, Albany, NY 12204. international@bender.com, http://bender.lexisnexis.com. Ed. Kenneth Lapine.

332 640.73 USA
CONSUMER FINANCE BULLETIN. Text in English. 1947. m. looseleaf. USD 126 (effective 1998). s-a. index.
Published by: American Financial Services Association, 919 18th St, N W, 3rd Fl, Washington, DC 20006. TEL 202-296-5544, FAX 202-223-0321. Eds. Melissa Ward, Robert E McKew. Circ: 500.

332 USA ISSN 0364-2844
CONSUMER INSTALLMENT CREDIT. Text in English. m. USD 5. **Document type:** *Government.*
Formerly: Consumer Credit (0196-5379)
Related titles: Diskette ed.
Published by: U.S. Federal Reserve System, Board of Governors, Publications Services, Rm MS 138, Washington, DC 20551. TEL 202-452-3244, FAX 202-728-5886.

332 USA ISSN 1077-0445
CONSUMER LENDING NEWS. Text in English. 1993. m. USD 329 (effective 2001). index. back issues avail. **Document type:** *Newsletter.* **Description:** Case studies of how financial institutions increase consumer loans or improve consumer loan quality. Covers auto loans, home equity loans, lines of credit, credit cards, collections and underwriting.
Published by: Siefer Consultants, Inc., 525 Cayuga St, Storm Lake, IA 50588. TEL 712-732-7340, FAX 712-732-7906, info@siefer.com, http://www.siefer.com. Ed. Shere Siefer. Circ: 1,500 (paid).

CONTEMPORARY STUDIES IN ECONOMIC AND FINANCIAL ANALYSIS; an international series of monographs. see *BUSINESS AND ECONOMICS*

CONTROLLERS MAGAZINE. see *BUSINESS AND ECONOMICS—Accounting*

332 COL
CONVENCION BANCARIA Y DE ENTIDADES FINANCIERAS. MEMORIA. Text in Spanish. a. USD 8 (effective 1991).
Published by: Asociacion Bancaria de Colombia, Carrera 7 No. 17-01 Piso 3, Bogota, DE, Colombia. TEL 57-1-281-3501, FAX 57-1-281-3017.

332.1 TZA
COOPERATIVE AND RURAL DEVELOPMENT BANK. ANNUAL REPORT AND ACCOUNTS. Text in English, Swahili. 1972. a. free. **Document type:** *Corporate.*
Formerly: Tanzania Rural Development Bank. Annual Report and Accounts
Published by: Cooperative and Rural Development Bank, PO Box 268, Dar Es Salaam, Tanzania. TEL 255-51-26511, TELEX 41643 TARDEB TZ.

332.1 TWN
COOPERATIVE BANK OF TAIWAN. ANNUAL REPORT/TAI-WAN SHENG HO-TSO CHIN-K'U. ANNUAL REPORT. Text in Chinese. 1957. a. free. illus.; stat.
Published by: Cooperative Bank of Taiwan, 75-1 Kuan Chien Rd, Taipei, Taiwan.

CORPORATE ACQUISITIONS & MERGERS. see *LAW*

CORPORATE DEALMAKER. see *BUSINESS AND ECONOMICS—Investments*

CORPORATE EXAMINER. see *BUSINESS AND ECONOMICS*

332 GBR ISSN 0958-2053
HG3810
CORPORATE FINANCE. Text in English. 1984. 11/yr. GBP 326 combined subscription domestic; EUR 520 combined subscription in Europe; USD 579 combined subscription elsewhere (effective 2005). adv. illus. Index. 44 p./no. 3 cols./p.; reprints avail. **Document type:** *Magazine, Trade.*
Description: Provides information and analysis of mergers and acquisitions, risk management and derivatives, debt offerings and county capital.
Formerly: Euromoney Corporate Finance (0266-7002)
Related titles: Online - full text ed.: (from EBSCO Publishing, Factiva, Florida Center for Library Automation, Gale Group, H.W. Wilson, O C L C Online Computer Library Center, Inc., ProQuest Information & Learning); ♦ Supplement(s): Global M & A Handbook (Year).
Indexed: ABIn, B&I, BLI, BPI.
—BLDSC (3472.062500), IE, Infotrieve, ingenta. **CCC.**
Published by: Euromoney Institutional Investor Plc., Nestor House, Playhouse Yard, London, EC4V 5EX, United Kingdom. TEL 44-20-7779-8673, FAX 44-20-7779-8541, http://www.corporatefinancemag.com, http://www.euromoney.com. Ed. Tabitha Neville TEL 44-20-77798075. Adv. contact Jonathan Wright TEL 44-20-77798372. Circ: 11,200. **Subscr. to:** Quadrant Subscription Services, Rockwood House, 9-17 Perrymount Rd, Haywards Heath, W. Sussex RH16 3DH, United Kingdom. TEL 44-20-8652-3500, FAX 44-20-8652-8932. **Dist. in US by:** American Educational Systems, PO Box 246, New York, NY 10024-0246. TEL 800-431-1579.

332 330 USA ISSN 1089-327X
HG4001
➤ **CORPORATE FINANCE REVIEW.** Text in English. 1997. bi-m. USD 230 (effective 2004). adv. bk.rev.; software rev.; Website rev. charts; illus.; stat.; tr.lit. 48 p./no. 3 cols./p.; **Document type:** *Journal, Academic/Scholarly.* **Description:** Covers accounting, finance, and business topics for corporate finance professionals and scholarly researchers.
Related titles: Online - full content ed.
—CCC.
Published by: W G & L Financial Reporting & Management Research (Subsidiary of: R I A), 395 Hudson St, New York, NY 10014. TEL 212-367-6300, FAX 212-367-6314, http://www.riahome.com/. Eds. Katherine Laughran, Morgen Witzel. Pub. Bruce Safford. Adv. contact Terry Storholm TEL 800-322-3192. Circ: 1,000 (paid).

332 USA ISSN 1064-1912
HG4050
CORPORATE FINANCING WEEK; the newsweekly of corporate finance, investment banking and M & A. Text in English. 1975. w. (51x/yr). USD 2,395 combined subscription domestic print & online eds.; USD 2,625 combined subscription elsewhere print & online eds. (effective 2005). adv. **Document type:** *Newsletter, Trade.* **Description:** Informs finance executives at corporations about innovations, trends, and ways to save money on new debt and equity issues, private placements, mergers and acquisitions, leveraged buyouts, venture capital and tax and accounting issues.
Supersedes: Corporation Finance and New Issue Weekly (0090-919X)
Related titles: CD-ROM ed.; Microfiche ed.; Online - full text ed.: (from Florida Center for Library Automation, Gale Group, Northern Light Technology, Inc., O C L C Online Computer Library Center, Inc.).
Indexed: ATI, BusI.
—CCC.
Published by: Institutional Investor, Inc. (Subsidiary of: Euromoney Institutional Investor Plc.), 488 Madison Ave., 12th Fl., New York, NY 10022. TEL 212-224-3300, FAX 212-224-3294, http://www.corporatefinancingweek.com. Pub. Elayne Glick. Circ: 7,500 (paid).

332 USA
(YEAR) CORPORATE LOAN MARKET DIRECTORY. Text in English. 1998. a. USD 95 (effective 1998).
Published by: Institutional Investor News (Subsidiary of: Euromoney Institutional Investor Plc.), 225 Park Ave S, 7th Fl, New York, NY 10003-1605. TEL 212-224-3800, FAX 212-224-3491.

332 657 GBR ISSN 0951-3639
CORPORATE MONEY; the newsletter of corporate financings and transactions. Text in English. 1987. bi-w. adv. back issues avail. **Document type:** *Newsletter.* **Description:** Contains news and features on corporate deals and financings.
Related titles: Diskette ed.; Online - full text ed.: (from Gale Group, H.W. Wilson, LexisNexis, O C L C Online Computer Library Center, Inc.).
Indexed: BPI, WTA.
Published by: Centaur Publishing, St Giles House, 50 Poland St, London, W1V 4AX, United Kingdom. TEL 44—20-7970-4000, FAX 44-20-7970-4009. Ed. Jonathan Isaacs. Adv. contact Phil Dwyer.

332 CAN
CORPORATE RETRIEVER. Text in English. 2000. m. CND 1,500 to libraries (effective 2005). **Document type:** *Trade.*
Description: Online access to Canadian coporate information and financials.
Media: Online - full content.
Published by: Micromedia ProQuest (Subsidiary of: ProQuest Information & Learning), 20 Victoria St, Toronto, ON M5C 2N8, Canada. TEL 416-362-5211, 800-387-2689, FAX 416-362-6161, info@micromedia.ca, http://www.micromedia.ca/products_services/CorpRet.htm. Ed. Mr. Tom McGreevy.

332 IND
CORPORATE RUPEE. Text in English. 1988. fortn. INR 90; INR 4 newsstand/cover. adv. 8 p./no. 8 cols./p.
Published by: Promilla Kapoor Ed. & Pub., 252-E Sant Nagar, East of Kailash, New Delhi, 110 065, India. TEL 6431256. Adv. contact Mohan Sontakay.

CORPORATION, BANKING & BUSINESS LAW NEWSLETTER.
see *LAW—Corporate Law*

332.1 USA
CORRESPONDENT (TOPEKA). Text in English. 1991. q. free.
Description: Contains member and industry news and information about bank products and services.
Former titles (until 1996): Banking News; (until 1993): Correspondent (Topeka)
Published by: Federal Home Loan Bank of Topeka, 2 Townsite Plaza, Box 176, Topeka, KS 66601-0176. FAX 785-234-1700. Ed. Laura Lutz.

332.1 USA ISSN 0091-3855
HG1628
COST OF PERSONAL BORROWING IN THE UNITED STATES✶. Text in English. 1971. a. USD 175 (effective 1998). charts.
Published by: Financial Publishing Company, 6 Becon St Ste 225, Boston, MA 02108. TEL 617-262-4040, FAX 617-247-0136. Ed. Jeff Buysse. Circ: 625.

332 USA ISSN 1067-4349
HG2040.5.U5
THE COST STUDY; income & cost for origination & servicing of 1-4 unit residential loans. Text in English. 1977. a. USD 150 to members; USD 300 to non-members (effective 2000). adv. back issues avail.
Published by: (Economics Department), Mortgage Bankers Association, 1919 Pennsylvania Ave NW, Washington, DC 20006-3438. TEL 202-557-2827, FAX 202-721-0245, http://www.mbaa.org. Ed. Douglas Duncan. Adv. contact Tiffany Rowan.

332.1 AUS ISSN 1443-6345
COUNCIL OF FINANCIAL REGULATORS. ANNUAL REPORT. Text in English. 1993. a.
Formerly (until 1998): Council of Financial Supervisors. Annual Report (1321-0041)
Published by: Reserve Bank of Australia, 65 Martin Place, PO Box 3947, Sydney, NSW 2001, Australia. TEL 61-2-9551-8111, FAX 61-2-9551-8000, ecpubs@rbs.gov.au.

332.1 333.33 GBR
COUNCIL OF MORTGAGE LENDERS. RESEARCH PAPERS. Text in English. 1995. irreg., latest vol.4. GBP 20 per issue. back issues avail. **Document type:** *Monographic series.*
Description: Covers topics in housing and housing finance issues. Helps agencies involved in providing housing and housing finance focus on and make informed decisions across a range of subjects.
Published by: Council of Mortgage Lenders, 3 Savile Row, London, W1X 1AF, United Kingdom. TEL 44-20-74370075, FAX 44-20-7434-3791.

332 USA
COUNTRY EXPOSURE LENDING SURVEY. Text in English. q. USD 5. **Document type:** *Government.*
Indexed: AmStI.
Published by: U.S. Federal Reserve System, Board of Governors, Publications Services, Rm MS 138, Washington, DC 20551. TEL 202-452-3244, FAX 202-728-5886.

332 USA
COUNTRY FINANCE. AFRICA. Text in English. base vol. plus s-a. updates. USD 445 print or online (effective 2004).
Former titles: Financing Operations. Africa; (until 1997): Financing Foreign Operations. Middle East - Africa; Financing Foreign Operations. Europe - Middle East - Africa
Related titles: Online - full text ed.: (from The Dialog Corporation).
Published by: Economist Intelligence Unit, 111 W 57th St, New York, NY 10019. TEL 212-554-0600, 800-938-4685, FAX 212-586-1181, http://www.eiu.com.

332 USA ISSN 1548-2472
HG185.A7
COUNTRY FINANCE. ARGENTINA. Text in English. base vol. plus q. updates. looseleaf. USD 445 print or online (effective 2004). **Description:** Provides details on critical areas such as exchange controls, sources of funding, financial markets, cash management and trade credit facilities for Argentina.
Former titles (until 1999): Financing Operations. Argentina; (until 1997): Financing Foreign Operations. Argentina (1353-596X)
Related titles: Online - full text ed.: (from The Dialog Corporation).
Published by: Economist Intelligence Unit, 111 W 57th St, New York, NY 10019. TEL 212-554-0600, 800-938-4685, FAX 212-586-1181, http://www.eiu.com.

332 USA
COUNTRY FINANCE. AUSTRALIA. Text in English. base vol. plus s-a. updates. looseleaf. USD 445 print or online (effective 2004). **Description:** Provides details on critical areas such as exchange controls, sources of funding, financial markets, cash management and trade credit facilities for Australia.
Former titles: Financing Operations. Australia; (until 1997): Financing Foreign Operations. Australia (1353-5986)
Related titles: Online - full text ed.: (from The Dialog Corporation).
Published by: Economist Intelligence Unit, 111 W 57th St, New York, NY 10019. TEL 212-554-0600, 800-938-4685, FAX 212-586-1181, http://www.eiu.com.

332 USA
COUNTRY FINANCE. BELGIUM. Text in English. base vol. plus s-a. updates. looseleaf. USD 445 print or online (effective 2004). **Description:** Provides details on critical areas such as exchange controls, sources of funding, financial markets, cash management and trade credit facilities for Belgium.
Former titles: Financing Operations. Belgium; (until 1997): Financing Foreign Operations. Belgium (1352-5875)
Related titles: Online - full text ed.: (from The Dialog Corporation).
Published by: Economist Intelligence Unit, 111 W 57th St, New York, NY 10019. TEL 212-554-0600, 800-938-4685, FAX 212-586-1181, http://www.eiu.com.

332 USA ISSN 1552-9932
HG185.B7
COUNTRY FINANCE. BRAZIL. Text in English. base vol. plus q. updates. looseleaf. USD 445 (effective 2004). **Description:** Provides details on critical areas such as exchange controls, sources of funding, financial markets, cash management and trade credit facilities for Brazil.
Former titles (until 2000): Financing Operations. Brazil; (until 1997): Financing Foreign Operations. Brazil (1352-5883)
Related titles: Online - full text ed.: (from The Dialog Corporation).
Published by: Economist Intelligence Unit, 111 W 57th St, New York, NY 10019. TEL 212-554-0600, 800-938-4685, FAX 212-586-1181, http://www.eiu.com.

332 USA
COUNTRY FINANCE. CANADA. Text in English. base vol. plus s-a. updates. looseleaf. USD 445 print or online (effective 2004). **Description:** Provides details on critical areas such as exchange controls, sources of funding, financial markets, cash management and trade credit facilities for Canada.
Former titles: Financing Operations. Canada; (until 1997): Financing Foreign Operations. Canada (1353-5951)
Related titles: Online - full text ed.: (from The Dialog Corporation).
Published by: Economist Intelligence Unit, 111 W 57th St, New York, NY 10019. TEL 212-554-0600, 800-938-4685, FAX 212-586-1181, http://www.eiu.com.

332 USA
COUNTRY FINANCE. CENTRAL AMERICA. Text in English. base vol. plus s-a. updates. looseleaf. USD 445 print or online (effective 2004).
Published by: Economist Intelligence Unit, 111 W 57th St, New York, NY 10019. http://www.eiu.com.

332 USA
COUNTRY FINANCE. CHILE. Text in English. base vol. plus s-a. updates. looseleaf. USD 445 print or online (effective 2004).
Description: Provides details on critical areas such as exchange controls, sources of funding, financial markets, cash management and trade credit facilities for Chile.
Former titles: Financing Operations. Chile; (until 1997): Financing Foreign Operations. Chile
Related titles: Online - full text ed.: (from The Dialog Corporation).
Published by: Economist Intelligence Unit, 111 W 57th St, New York, NY 10019. TEL 212-554-0600, 800-938-4685, FAX 212-586-1181.

332 USA ISSN 1547-934X
HG187.C6
COUNTRY FINANCE. CHINA. Text in English. 1993. base vol. plus q. updates. USD 445 (effective 2004). **Document type:** *Trade.* **Description:** Provides details on such critical areas as exchange controls, sources of funding, financial markets, cash management and trade credit facilities for China.
Former titles (until 2000): Financing Operations. China; (until 1997): Financing Foreign Operations. China (1353-5943)
Published by: Economist Intelligence Unit, 111 W 57th St, New York, NY 10019. TEL 212-554-0600, 800-938-4685, FAX 212-586-1181, http://www.eiu.com.

332 USA
COUNTRY FINANCE. COLOMBIA. Text in English. base vol. plus s-a. updates. looseleaf. USD 445 (effective 2004).
Description: Provides details on critical areas such as exchange controls, sources of funding, financial markets, cash management and trade credit facilities for Colombia.
Former titles: Financing Operations. Colombia; (until 1997): Financing Foreign Operations. Colombia (1352-5905)
Related titles: Online - full text ed.: (from The Dialog Corporation).
Published by: Economist Intelligence Unit, 111 W 57th St, New York, NY 10019. TEL 212-554-0600, 800-938-4685, FAX 212-586-1181, http://www.eiu.com.

332 USA ISSN 1548-2480
HG186.C95
COUNTRY FINANCE. CZECH REPUBLIC. Text in English. base vol. plus q. updates. looseleaf. USD 45 print or online (effective 2004). **Description:** Provides details on critical areas such as exchange controls, sources of funding, financial markets, cash management and trade credit facilities for the Czech Republic and Slovakia.
Former titles (until 1999): Financing Operations. Czech Republic; (until 1997): Financing Foreign Operations. Czech Republic; (until Apr. 1995): Financing Foreign Operations. Czech Republic and Slovakia; Financing Foreign Operations. Czechoslovakia (1352-5735)
Related titles: Online - full text ed.: (from The Dialog Corporation).
Published by: Economist Intelligence Unit, 111 W 57th St, New York, NY 10019. TEL 212-554-0600, 800-938-4685, FAX 212-586-1181, http://www.eiu.com.

332 USA ISSN 1548-2405
HG186.F8
COUNTRY FINANCE. FRANCE. Text in English. base vol. plus s-a. updates. looseleaf. USD 445 print or online (effective 2004). **Description:** Provides details on critical areas such as exchange controls, sources of funding, financial markets, cash management and trade credit facilities for France.
Former titles (until 1999): Financing Operations. France; (until 1997): Financing Foreign Operations. France (1353-6311)
Related titles: Online - full text ed.: (from The Dialog Corporation).
Published by: Economist Intelligence Unit, 111 W 57th St, New York, NY 10019. TEL 212-554-0600, 800-938-4685, FAX 212-586-1181, http://www.eiu.com.

332 USA ISSN 1547-9242
HG186.G3
COUNTRY FINANCE. GERMANY. Text in English. base vol. plus s-a. updates. looseleaf. USD 445 (effective 2004).
Description: Provides details on critical areas such as exchange controls, sources of funding, financial markets, cash management and trade credit facilities for Germany.
Former titles (until 2000): Financing Operations. Germany; (until 1997): Financing Foreign Operations. Germany (1352-5743)
Related titles: Online - full text ed.: (from The Dialog Corporation).
Published by: Economist Intelligence Unit, 111 W 57th St, New York, NY 10019. TEL 800-938-4685, FAX 212-586-1181, http://www.eiu.com.

332 USA
COUNTRY FINANCE. GREECE. Text in English. base vol. plus s-a. updates. looseleaf. USD 445 print or online (effective 2004). **Description:** Provides details on critical areas such as exchange controls, sources of funding, financial markets, cash management and trade credit facilities for Greece.
Former titles: Financing Operations. Greece; (until 1997): Financing Foreign Operations. Greece (1366-3070)
Related titles: Online - full text ed.: (from The Dialog Corporation).
Published by: Economist Intelligence Unit, 111 W 57th St, New York, NY 10019. TEL 212-554-0600, 800-938-4685, FAX 212-586-1181, http://www.eiu.com.

332 USA ISSN 1548-2375
HG187.H85
COUNTRY FINANCE. HONG KONG. Text in English. base vol. plus s-a. updates. looseleaf. USD 445 print or online (effective 2004). **Description:** Provides details on critical areas such as exchange controls, sources of funding, financial markets, cash management and trade credit facilities for Hong Kong.
Former titles (until 2000): Financing Operations. Hong Kong; (until 1997): Financing Foreign Operations. Hong Kong (1352-5751)
Related titles: Online - full text ed.: (from The Dialog Corporation).
Published by: Economist Intelligence Unit, 111 W 57th St, New York, NY 10019. TEL 212-554-0600, 800-938-4685, FAX 212-586-1181, http://www.eiu.com.

332 USA ISSN 1550-3771
HG186.H8
COUNTRY FINANCE. HUNGARY. Text in English. base vol. plus q. updates. looseleaf. USD 445 (effective 2004). **Description:** Provides details on critical areas such as exchange controls, sources of funding, financial markets, cash management and trade credit facilities for Hungary.
Former titles: Financing Operations. Hungary; (until 1997): Financing Foreing Foreign Operations. Hungary (1366-0225)

Related titles: Online - full text ed.: (from The Dialog Corporation).
Published by: Economist Intelligence Unit, 111 W 57th St, New York, NY 10019. TEL 212-554-0600, 800-938-4685, FAX 212-586-1181, http://www.eiu.com.

332 USA ISSN 1548-2383
HG187.I4
COUNTRY FINANCE. INDIA. Text in English. base vol. plus q. updates. looseleaf. USD 445 print or online (effective 2004).
Description: Provides details on critical areas such as exchange controls, sources of funding, financial markets, cash management and trade credit facilities for India.
Former titles (until 1999): Financing Operations. India; (until 1997): Financing Foreign Operations. India (1366-364X)
Related titles: Online - full text ed.: (from The Dialog Corporation).
Published by: Economist Intelligence Unit, 111 W 57th St, New York, NY 10019. TEL 800-938-4685, FAX 212-586-1181, http://www.eiu.com.

332 USA ISSN 1548-2367
HG187.I7
COUNTRY FINANCE. INDONESIA. Text in English. 1993. base vol. plus s-a. updates. USD 445 print or online (effective 2004). **Document type:** *Trade.* **Description:** Provides details on such critical areas as exchange controls, sources of funding, financial markets, cash management and trade credit facilities for Indonesia.
Former titles (until 1999): Financing Operations. Indonesia; (until 1997): Financing Foreign Operations. Indonesia (1352-576X)
Published by: Economist Intelligence Unit, 111 W 57th St, New York, NY 10019. TEL 212-554-0600, 800-938-4685, FAX 212-586-1181, http://www.eiu.com.

332 USA
COUNTRY FINANCE. ITALY. Text in English. base vol. plus s-a. updates. looseleaf. USD 445 print or online (effective 2004).
Description: Provides details on critical areas such as exchange controls, sources of funding, financial markets, cash management and trade credit facilities for Italy.
Former titles: Financing Operations. Italy; (until 1997): Financing Foreign Operations. Italy (1366-3054)
Related titles: Online - full text ed.: (from The Dialog Corporation).
Published by: Economist Intelligence Unit, 111 W 57th St, New York, NY 10019. TEL 212-554-0600, 800-938-4685, FAX 212-586-1181, http://www.eiu.com.

332 USA ISSN 1551-8183
HG187.J3
COUNTRY FINANCE. JAPAN. Text in English. base vol. plus s-a. updates. looseleaf. USD 445 print or online (effective 2004).
Description: Provides details on critical areas such as exchange controls, sources of funding, financial markets, cash management and trade credit facilities for Japan.
Former titles (until 1999): Financing Operations. Japan; (until 1997): Financing Foreign Operations. Japan (1353-632X)
Related titles: Online - full text ed.: (from The Dialog Corporation).
Published by: Economist Intelligence Unit, 111 W 57th St, New York, NY 10019. TEL 212-554-0600, 800-938-4685, FAX 212-586-1182, http://www.eiu.com.

332 USA ISSN 1545-4061
HG187.M4
COUNTRY FINANCE. MALAYSIA. Text in English. base vol. plus q. updates. looseleaf. USD 445 print or online (effective 2004). **Description:** Provides details on critical areas such as exchange controls, sources of funding, financial markets, cash management and trade credit facilities for Malaysia.
Former titles (until 2000): Financing Operations. Malaysia; (until 1997): Financing Foreign Operations. Malaysia (1352-5778)
Related titles: Online - full text ed.: (from The Dialog Corporation).
Published by: Economist Intelligence Unit, 111 W 57th St, New York, NY 10019. TEL 212-554-0600, 800-938-4685, FAX 212-586-1181, http://www.eiu.com.

332 USA ISSN 1551-8159
HG5161
COUNTRY FINANCE. MEXICO. Text in English. base vol. plus q. updates. looseleaf. USD 445 print or online (effective 2004).
Description: Provides details on critical areas such as exchange controls, sources of funding, financial markets, cash management and trade credit facilities for Mexico.
Former titles (until 2000): Financing Operations. Mexico; (until 1997): Financing Foreign Operations. Mexico (1352-5786)
Related titles: Online - full text ed.: (from The Dialog Corporation).
Published by: Economist Intelligence Unit, 111 W 57th St, New York, NY 10019. TEL 212-554-0600, 800-938-4685, FAX 212-586-1181, http://www.eiu.com.

332 USA
COUNTRY FINANCE. NETHERLANDS. Text in English. base vol. plus s-a. updates. USD 445 print or online (effective 2004). **Description:** Provides details on critical areas such as exchange controls, sources of funding, financial markets, cash management and trade credit facilities for the Netherlands.
Former titles: Financing Operations. Netherlands; (until 1997): Financing Foreign Operations. Netherlands (1353-5846)

Related titles: Online - full text ed.: (from The Dialog Corporation).
Published by: Economist Intelligence Unit, 111 W 57th St, New York, NY 10019. TEL 212-554-0600, 800-938-4685, FAX 212-586-1181, http://www.eiu.com.

382.0993 USA ISSN 1547-9226
HG189.5
COUNTRY FINANCE. NEW ZEALAND. Text in English. 1993. base vol. plus s-a. updates. USD 445 print or online (effective 2004). **Document type:** *Trade.* **Description:** Provides details on such critical areas as exchange controls, sources of funding, financial markets, cash management and trade credit facilities for New Zealand.
Former titles (until 1999): Financing Operations. New Zealand; (until 1997): Financing Foreign Operations. New Zealand (1352-5794)
Published by: Economist Intelligence Unit, 111 W 57th St, New York, NY 10019. TEL 212-554-0600, 800-938-4685, FAX 212-586-1181, http://www.eiu.com.

332 USA
COUNTRY FINANCE. NIGERIA. Text in English. base vol. plus s-a. updates. looseleaf. USD 445 print or online (effective 2004). **Description:** Details areas such as exchange control, source of funding, financial markets, cash management and trade credit facilities.
Former titles: Financing Operations. Nigeria; (until 1997): Financing Foreign Operations. Nigeria (1353-582X)
Related titles: Online - full text ed.: (from The Dialog Corporation).
Published by: Economist Intelligence Unit, 111 W 57th St, New York, NY 10019. TEL 212-554-0600, 800-938-4685, FAX 212-586-1181, http://www.eiu.com.

332 USA
COUNTRY FINANCE. NORWAY. Text in English. base vol. plus s-a. updates. looseleaf. USD 445 print or online (effective 2004). **Description:** Provides details on critical areas such as exchange controls, sources of funding, financial markets, cash management and trade credit facilities for Norway.
Former titles: Financing Operations. Norway; (until 1997): Financing Foreign Operations. Norway (1352-5808)
Related titles: Online - full text ed.: (from The Dialog Corporation).
Published by: Economist Intelligence Unit, 111 W 57th St, New York, NY 10019. TEL 212-554-0600, 800-938-4685, FAX 212-586-1181, http://www.eiu.com.

332 USA
COUNTRY FINANCE. PANAMA. Text in English. base vol. plus s-a. updates. looseleaf. USD 445 print or online (effective 2004). **Description:** Provides details on critical areas such as exchange controls, sources of funding, financial markets, cash management and trade credit facilities for Panama.
Former titles: Financing Operations. Panama; (until 1997): Financing Foreign Operations. Panama (1366-3097)
Related titles: Online - full text ed.: (from The Dialog Corporation).
Published by: Economist Intelligence Unit, 111 W 57th St, New York, NY 10019. TEL 212-554-0600, 800-938-4685, FAX 212-586-1181, http://www.eiu.com.

332 USA ISSN 1548-2499
HG187.P6
COUNTRY FINANCE. PHILIPPINES. Text in English. base vol. plus s-a. updates. looseleaf. USD 445 print or online (effective 2004). **Description:** Provides details on critical areas such as exchange controls, sources of funding, financial markets, cash management and trade credit facilities for the Philippines.
Former titles (until 1999): Financing Operations. Philippines; (until 1997): Financing Foreign Operations. Philippines
Related titles: Online - full text ed.: (from The Dialog Corporation).
Published by: Economist Intelligence Unit, 111 W 57th St, New York, NY 10019. TEL 212-554-0600, 800-938-4685, FAX 212-586-1181, http://www.eiu.com.

332 USA ISSN 1548-2391
HG186.P7
COUNTRY FINANCE. POLAND. Text in English. base vol. plus q. updates. looseleaf. USD 445 print or online (effective 2004).
Description: Provides details on critical areas such as exchange controls, sources of funding, financial markets, cash management and trade credit facilities for Poland.
Former titles (until 1999): Financing Operations. Poland; (until 1997): Financing Foreign Operations. Poland (1352-5816)
Related titles: Online - full text ed.: (from The Dialog Corporation).
Published by: Economist Intelligence Unit, 111 W 57th St, New York, NY 10019. TEL 212-554-0600, 800-938-4685, FAX 212-586-1181, http://www.eiu.com.

332.6 382 USA
COUNTRY FINANCE. PORTUGAL. Text in English. base vol. plus s-a. updates. USD 445 print or online (effective 2004).
Description: Provides details on critical areas such as exchange controls, sources of funding, financial markets, cash management and trade credit facilities for Portugal.
Former titles: Financing Operations. Portugal; (until 1997): Financing Foreign Operations. Portugal (1353-5811)

Published by: Economist Intelligence Unit, 111 W 57th St, New York, NY 10019. TEL 212-554-0600, 800-938-4685, FAX 212-586-1181, http://www.eiu.com.

332 USA
COUNTRY FINANCE. RUSSIA. Text in English. base vol. plus q. updates. looseleaf. USD 445 print or online (effective 2004).
Description: Provides details on critical areas such as exchange controls, sources of funding, financial markets, cash management and trade credit facilities for Russia.
Former titles: Financing Operations. Russia (1352-5824); (until 1993): Financing Foreign Operations. Commonwealth of Independent States
Related titles: Online - full text ed.: (from The Dialog Corporation).
Published by: Economist Intelligence Unit, 111 W 57th St, New York, NY 10019. TEL 212-554-0600, 800-938-4685, FAX 212-586-1181, http://www.eiu.com.

332 USA ISSN 1548-3541
HG187.S33
COUNTRY FINANCE. SAUDI ARABIA. Text in English. base vol. plus s-a. updates. looseleaf. USD 445 print or online (effective 2004). **Description:** Provides details on critical areas such as exchange controls, sources of funding, financial markets, cash management and trade credit facilities for Saudi Arabia.
Former titles (until 2000): Financing Operations. Saudi Arabia; (until 1997): Financing Foreign Operations. Saudi Arabia
Related titles: Online - full text ed.: (from The Dialog Corporation).
Published by: Economist Intelligence Unit, 111 W 57th St, New York, NY 10019. TEL 212-554-0600, 800-938-4685, FAX 212-586-1181, http://www.eiu.com.

332 USA ISSN 1548-3312
HG5750.67.A2
COUNTRY FINANCE. SINGAPORE. Text in English. base vol. plus s-a. updates. looseleaf. USD 445 print or online (effective 2004). **Description:** Provides details on critical areas such as exchange controls, sources of funding, financial markets, cash management and trade credit facilities for Singapore.
Former titles (until 1999): Financing Operations. Singapore; (until 1997): Financing Foreign Operations. Singapore (1353-5862)
Related titles: Online - full text ed.: (from The Dialog Corporation).
Published by: Economist Intelligence Unit, 111 W 57th St, New York, NY 10019. TEL 212-554-0600, 800-938-4685, FAX 212-586-1181, http://www.eiu.com.

332 USA ISSN 1548-3371
HG187.5.S6
COUNTRY FINANCE. SOUTH AFRICA. Text in English. base vol. plus s-a. updates. looseleaf. USD 445 print or online (effective 2004). **Description:** Provides details on critical areas such as exchange controls, sources of funding, financial markets, cash management and trade credit facilities for South Africa.
Former titles (until 1999): Financing Operations. South Africa; (until 1997): Financing Foreign Operations. South Africa (1353-5854)
Related titles: Online - full text ed.: (from The Dialog Corporation).
Published by: Economist Intelligence Unit, 111 W 57th St, New York, NY 10019. TEL 212-554-0600, 800-938-4685, FAX 212-586-1181, http://www.eiu.com.

332 USA ISSN 1550-3755
HG186.K5
COUNTRY FINANCE. SOUTH KOREA. Text in English. base vol. plus s-a. updates. looseleaf. USD 445 print or online (effective 2004). **Description:** Provides details on critical areas such as exchange controls, sources of funding, financial markets, cash management and trade credit facilities for Korea.
Former titles: Financing Operations. South Korea (1365-9634); Financing Foreign Operations. Korea
Related titles: Online - full text ed.: (from The Dialog Corporation).
Published by: Economist Intelligence Unit, 111 W 57th St, New York, NY 10019. TEL 212-554-0600, 800-938-4685, FAX 212-586-1181, http://www.eiu.com.

332 USA ISSN 1548-3525
HG186.S6
COUNTRY FINANCE. SPAIN. Text in English. base vol. plus s-a. updates. looseleaf. USD 445 print or online (effective 2004).
Description: Provides details on critical areas such as exchange controls, sources of funding, financial markets, cash management and trade credit facilities for Spain.
Former titles (until 1999): Financing Operations. Spain; (until 1997): Financing Foreign Operations. Spain (1352-5859)
Related titles: Online - full text ed.: (from The Dialog Corporation).
Published by: Economist Intelligence Unit, 111 W 57th St, New York, NY 10019. TEL 212-554-0600, 800-938-4685, FAX 212-586-1181, http://www.eiu.com.

332 USA ISSN 1548-4548
HG186.S85
COUNTRY FINANCE. SWEDEN. Text in English. base vol. plus s-a. updates. looseleaf. USD 445 print or online (effective 2004). **Description:** Provides details on critical areas such as funding, financial markets, cash management and trade credit facilities for Sweden.

▼ new title ➤ refereed ✶ unverified ♦ full entry avail.

B

Former titles (until 1999): Financing Operations. Sweden; (until 1997): Financing Foreign Operations. Sweden
Related titles: Online - full text ed.: (from The Dialog Corporation).
Published by: Economist Intelligence Unit, 111 W 57th St, New York, NY 10019. TEL 212-554-0600, 800-938-4685, FAX 212-586-1181, http://www.eiu.com.

332   USA   ISSN 1548-4521
HG186.S9
COUNTRY FINANCE. SWITZERLAND. Text in English. base vol. plus s-a. updates. looseleaf. USD 445 print or online (effective 2004). **Description:** Provides details on critical areas such as exchange controls, sources of funding, financial markets, cash management and trade credit facilities for Switzerland.
Former titles (until 1999): Financing Operations. Switzerland; (until 1997): Financing Foreign Operations. Switzerland
Related titles: Online - full text ed.: (from The Dialog Corporation).
Published by: Economist Intelligence Unit, 111 W 57th St, New York, NY 10019. TEL 212-554-0600, 800-938-4685, FAX 212-586-1181, http://www.eiu.com.

332   USA   ISSN 1548-4653
HG5796
COUNTRY FINANCE. TAIWAN. Text in English. base vol. plus s-a. updates. looseleaf. USD 445 print or online (effective 2004). **Description:** Provides details on critical areas such as exchange controls, sources of funding, financial markets, cash management and trade credit facilities for Taiwan.
Former titles (until 1999): Financing Operations. Taiwan; (until 1997): Financing Foreign Operations. Taiwan
Related titles: Online - full text ed.: (from The Dialog Corporation).
Published by: Economist Intelligence Unit, 111 W 57th St, New York, NY 10019. TEL 212-554-0600, 800-938-4685, FAX 212-586-1181, http://www.eiu.com.

332   USA   ISSN 1548-453X
HG187.T5
COUNTRY FINANCE. THAILAND. Text in English. base vol. plus q. updates. looseleaf. USD 445 print or online (effective 2004). **Description:** Provides details on critical areas such as exchange controls, sources of funding, financial markets, cash management and trade credit facilities for Thailand.
Former titles (until 2000): Financing Operations. Thailand; (until 1997): Financing Foreign Operations. Thailand (1353-5900)
Related titles: Online - full text ed.: (from The Dialog Corporation).
Published by: Economist Intelligence Unit, 111 W 57th St, New York, NY 10019. TEL 212-554-0600, 800-938-4685, FAX 212-586-1181, http://www.eiu.com.

332.67   USA   ISSN 1548-4823
HG187.T9
COUNTRY FINANCE. TURKEY. Text in English. 1993. base vol. plus s-a. updates. USD 445 print or online (effective 2004). **Document type:** *Trade.* **Description:** Provides details on such critical areas as exchange controls, sources of funding, financial markets, cash management and trade credit facilities for Turkey.
Former titles (until 2000): Financing Operations. Turkey; (until 1997): Financing Foreign Operations. Turkey (1352-5840)
Published by: Economist Intelligence Unit, 111 W 57th St, New York, NY 10019. TEL 212-554-0600, 800-938-4685, FAX 212-586-1181, http://www.eiu.com.

332   USA   ISSN 1548-3304
HG186.G7
COUNTRY FINANCE. UNITED KINGDOM. Text in English. base vol. plus s-a. updates. looseleaf. USD 445 print or online (effective 2004). **Description:** Provides details on critical areas such as exchange controls, sources of funding, financial markets, cash management and trade credit facilities for the United Kingdom.
Former titles (until 1999): Financing Operations. United Kingdom; (until 1997): Financing Foreign Operations. United Kingdom
Related titles: Online - full text ed.: (from The Dialog Corporation).
Published by: Economist Intelligence Unit, 111 W 57th St, New York, NY 10019. TEL 212-554-0600, 800-938-4685, FAX 212-586-1181, http://www.eiu.com.

332   USA   ISSN 1548-3126
HG181
COUNTRY FINANCE. UNITED STATES OF AMERICA. Text in English. base vol. plus s-a. updates. looseleaf. USD 445 print or online (effective 2004). **Description:** Provides details on critical areas such as exchange controls, sources of funding, financial markets, cash management and trade credit facilities for the US.
Former titles (until 2000): Financing Operations. United States of America; (until 1997): Financing Foreign Operations. United States of America (1352-5867)
Related titles: Online - full text ed.: (from The Dialog Corporation).
—CCC.
Published by: Economist Intelligence Unit, 111 W 57th St, New York, NY 10019. TEL 212-554-0600, 800-938-4685, FAX 212-586-1181, http://www.eiu.com.

332   USA   ISSN 1548-3274
HG185.V4
COUNTRY FINANCE. VENEZUELA. Text in English. base vol. plus q. updates. looseleaf. USD 445 print or online (effective 2004). **Description:** Provides details on critical areas such as exchange controls, sources of funding, financial markets, cash management and trade credit facilities for Venezuela.
Former titles (until 1999): Financing Operations. Venezuela; (until 1997): Financing Foreign Operations. Venezuela (1353-5897)
Related titles: Online - full text ed.: (from The Dialog Corporation).
Published by: Economist Intelligence Unit, 111 W 57th St, New York, NY 10019. TEL 212-554-0600, 800-938-4685, FAX 212-586-1181, http://www.eiu.com.

COUNTRY FORECASTS (SYRACUSE). see *BUSINESS AND ECONOMICS*

COUNTRY RISK SERVICE. see *BUSINESS AND ECONOMICS—Economic Situation And Conditions*

COUNTRY RISK SERVICE. ALGERIA. see *BUSINESS AND ECONOMICS—Economic Situation And Conditions*

COUNTRY RISK SERVICE. ANGOLA. see *BUSINESS AND ECONOMICS—Economic Situation And Conditions*

COUNTRY RISK SERVICE. ARGENTINA. see *BUSINESS AND ECONOMICS—Economic Situation And Conditions*

COUNTRY RISK SERVICE. AUSTRALIA. see *BUSINESS AND ECONOMICS—Economic Situation And Conditions*

COUNTRY RISK SERVICE. BAHRAIN. see *BUSINESS AND ECONOMICS—Economic Situation And Conditions*

COUNTRY RISK SERVICE. BANGLADESH. see *BUSINESS AND ECONOMICS—Economic Situation And Conditions*

COUNTRY RISK SERVICE. BOLIVIA. see *BUSINESS AND ECONOMICS—Economic Situation And Conditions*

COUNTRY RISK SERVICE. BOTSWANA. see *BUSINESS AND ECONOMICS—Economic Situation And Conditions*

COUNTRY RISK SERVICE. BRAZIL. see *BUSINESS AND ECONOMICS—Economic Situation And Conditions*

COUNTRY RISK SERVICE. BULGARIA. see *BUSINESS AND ECONOMICS—Economic Situation And Conditions*

COUNTRY RISK SERVICE. CAMEROON. see *BUSINESS AND ECONOMICS—Economic Situation And Conditions*

COUNTRY RISK SERVICE. CHILE. see *BUSINESS AND ECONOMICS—Economic Situation And Conditions*

COUNTRY RISK SERVICE. CHINA. see *BUSINESS AND ECONOMICS—Economic Situation And Conditions*

COUNTRY RISK SERVICE. COLOMBIA. see *BUSINESS AND ECONOMICS—Economic Situation And Conditions*

COUNTRY RISK SERVICE. CONGO. see *BUSINESS AND ECONOMICS—Economic Situation And Conditions*

COUNTRY RISK SERVICE. COSTA RICA. see *BUSINESS AND ECONOMICS—Economic Situation And Conditions*

COUNTRY RISK SERVICE. COTE D'IVOIRE. see *BUSINESS AND ECONOMICS—Economic Situation And Conditions*

COUNTRY RISK SERVICE. CUBA. see *BUSINESS AND ECONOMICS—Economic Situation And Conditions*

COUNTRY RISK SERVICE. CYPRUS. see *BUSINESS AND ECONOMICS—Economic Situation And Conditions*

COUNTRY RISK SERVICE. CZECH REPUBLIC. see *BUSINESS AND ECONOMICS—Economic Situation And Conditions*

COUNTRY RISK SERVICE. DOMINICAN REPUBLIC. see *BUSINESS AND ECONOMICS—Economic Situation And Conditions*

COUNTRY RISK SERVICE. ECUADOR. see *BUSINESS AND ECONOMICS—Economic Situation And Conditions*

COUNTRY RISK SERVICE. EGYPT. see *BUSINESS AND ECONOMICS—Economic Situation And Conditions*

COUNTRY RISK SERVICE. EL SALVADOR. see *BUSINESS AND ECONOMICS—Economic Situation And Conditions*

COUNTRY RISK SERVICE. ESTONIA. see *BUSINESS AND ECONOMICS—Economic Situation And Conditions*

COUNTRY RISK SERVICE. GABON. see *BUSINESS AND ECONOMICS—Economic Situation And Conditions*

COUNTRY RISK SERVICE. GHANA. see *BUSINESS AND ECONOMICS—Economic Situation And Conditions*

COUNTRY RISK SERVICE. GREECE. see *BUSINESS AND ECONOMICS—Economic Situation And Conditions*

COUNTRY RISK SERVICE. GUATEMALA. see *BUSINESS AND ECONOMICS—Economic Situation And Conditions*

COUNTRY RISK SERVICE. HONDURAS. see *BUSINESS AND ECONOMICS—Economic Situation And Conditions*

COUNTRY RISK SERVICE. HONG KONG. see *BUSINESS AND ECONOMICS—Economic Situation And Conditions*

COUNTRY RISK SERVICE. HUNGARY. see *BUSINESS AND ECONOMICS—Economic Situation And Conditions*

COUNTRY RISK SERVICE. INDIA. see *BUSINESS AND ECONOMICS—Economic Situation And Conditions*

COUNTRY RISK SERVICE. INDONESIA. see *BUSINESS AND ECONOMICS—Economic Situation And Conditions*

COUNTRY RISK SERVICE. IRAN. see *BUSINESS AND ECONOMICS—Economic Situation And Conditions*

COUNTRY RISK SERVICE. IRAQ. see *BUSINESS AND ECONOMICS—Economic Situation And Conditions*

COUNTRY RISK SERVICE. ISRAEL. see *BUSINESS AND ECONOMICS—Economic Situation And Conditions*

COUNTRY RISK SERVICE. JAMAICA. see *BUSINESS AND ECONOMICS—Economic Situation And Conditions*

COUNTRY RISK SERVICE. JORDAN. see *BUSINESS AND ECONOMICS—Economic Situation And Conditions*

COUNTRY RISK SERVICE. KAZAKHSTAN. see *BUSINESS AND ECONOMICS—Economic Situation And Conditions*

COUNTRY RISK SERVICE. KENYA. see *BUSINESS AND ECONOMICS—Economic Situation And Conditions*

COUNTRY RISK SERVICE. KUWAIT. see *BUSINESS AND ECONOMICS—Economic Situation And Conditions*

COUNTRY RISK SERVICE. LATVIA. see *BUSINESS AND ECONOMICS—Economic Situation And Conditions*

COUNTRY RISK SERVICE. LIBYA. see *BUSINESS AND ECONOMICS—Economic Situation And Conditions*

COUNTRY RISK SERVICE. LITHUANIA. see *BUSINESS AND ECONOMICS—Economic Situation And Conditions*

COUNTRY RISK SERVICE. MACEDONIA. see *BUSINESS AND ECONOMICS—Economic Situation And Conditions*

COUNTRY RISK SERVICE. MALAWI. see *BUSINESS AND ECONOMICS—Economic Situation And Conditions*

COUNTRY RISK SERVICE. MALAYSIA. see *BUSINESS AND ECONOMICS—Economic Situation And Conditions*

COUNTRY RISK SERVICE. MAURITIUS. see *BUSINESS AND ECONOMICS—Economic Situation And Conditions*

COUNTRY RISK SERVICE. MEXICO. see *BUSINESS AND ECONOMICS—Economic Situation And Conditions*

COUNTRY RISK SERVICE. MOLDOVA. see *BUSINESS AND ECONOMICS—Economic Situation And Conditions*

COUNTRY RISK SERVICE. MOROCCO. see *BUSINESS AND ECONOMICS—Economic Situation And Conditions*

COUNTRY RISK SERVICE. NAMIBIA. see *BUSINESS AND ECONOMICS—Economic Situation And Conditions*

COUNTRY RISK SERVICE. NEW ZEALAND. see *BUSINESS AND ECONOMICS—Economic Situation And Conditions*

COUNTRY RISK SERVICE. NICARAGUA. see *BUSINESS AND ECONOMICS—Economic Situation And Conditions*

COUNTRY RISK SERVICE. NIGERIA. see *BUSINESS AND ECONOMICS—Economic Situation And Conditions*

COUNTRY RISK SERVICE. OMAN. see *BUSINESS AND ECONOMICS—Economic Situation And Conditions*

COUNTRY RISK SERVICE. PAKISTAN. see *BUSINESS AND ECONOMICS—Economic Situation And Conditions*

COUNTRY RISK SERVICE. PANAMA. see *BUSINESS AND ECONOMICS—Economic Situation And Conditions*

COUNTRY RISK SERVICE. PAPUA NEW GUINEA. see *BUSINESS AND ECONOMICS—Economic Situation And Conditions*

COUNTRY RISK SERVICE. PARAGUAY. see *BUSINESS AND ECONOMICS—Economic Situation And Conditions*

COUNTRY RISK SERVICE. PERU. see *BUSINESS AND ECONOMICS—Economic Situation And Conditions*

COUNTRY RISK SERVICE. PHILIPPINES. see *BUSINESS AND ECONOMICS—Economic Situation And Conditions*

COUNTRY RISK SERVICE. POLAND. see *BUSINESS AND ECONOMICS—Economic Situation And Conditions*

COUNTRY RISK SERVICE. PORTUGAL. see *BUSINESS AND ECONOMICS—Economic Situation And Conditions*

COUNTRY RISK SERVICE. QATAR. see *BUSINESS AND ECONOMICS—Economic Situation And Conditions*

COUNTRY RISK SERVICE. ROMANIA. see *BUSINESS AND ECONOMICS—Economic Situation And Conditions*

COUNTRY RISK SERVICE. RUSSIA. see *BUSINESS AND ECONOMICS—Economic Situation And Conditions*

COUNTRY RISK SERVICE. SAUDI ARABIA. see *BUSINESS AND ECONOMICS—Economic Situation And Conditions*

COUNTRY RISK SERVICE. SENEGAL. see *BUSINESS AND ECONOMICS—Economic Situation And Conditions*

COUNTRY RISK SERVICE. SINGAPORE. see *BUSINESS AND ECONOMICS—Economic Situation And Conditions*

COUNTRY RISK SERVICE. SLOVAKIA. see *BUSINESS AND ECONOMICS—Economic Situation And Conditions*

COUNTRY RISK SERVICE. SLOVENIA. see *BUSINESS AND ECONOMICS—Economic Situation And Conditions*

COUNTRY RISK SERVICE. SOUTH AFRICA. see *BUSINESS AND ECONOMICS—Economic Situation And Conditions*

COUNTRY RISK SERVICE. SOUTH KOREA. see *BUSINESS AND ECONOMICS—Economic Situation And Conditions*

COUNTRY RISK SERVICE. SPAIN. see *BUSINESS AND ECONOMICS—Economic Situation And Conditions*

COUNTRY RISK SERVICE. SRI LANKA. see *BUSINESS AND ECONOMICS—Economic Situation And Conditions*

COUNTRY RISK SERVICE. SUDAN. see *BUSINESS AND ECONOMICS—Economic Situation And Conditions*

COUNTRY RISK SERVICE. SYRIA. see *BUSINESS AND ECONOMICS—Economic Situation And Conditions*

COUNTRY RISK SERVICE. TAIWAN. see *BUSINESS AND ECONOMICS—Economic Situation And Conditions*

COUNTRY RISK SERVICE. TAJIKISTAN. see *BUSINESS AND ECONOMICS—Economic Situation And Conditions*

COUNTRY RISK SERVICE. THAILAND. see *BUSINESS AND ECONOMICS—Economic Situation And Conditions*

COUNTRY RISK SERVICE. TRINIDAD AND TOBAGO. see *BUSINESS AND ECONOMICS—Economic Situation And Conditions*

COUNTRY RISK SERVICE. TUNISIA. see *BUSINESS AND ECONOMICS—Economic Situation And Conditions*

COUNTRY RISK SERVICE. TURKEY. see *BUSINESS AND ECONOMICS—Economic Situation And Conditions*

COUNTRY RISK SERVICE. UKRAINE. see *BUSINESS AND ECONOMICS—Economic Situation And Conditions*

COUNTRY RISK SERVICE. UNITED ARAB EMIRATES. see *BUSINESS AND ECONOMICS—Economic Situation And Conditions*

COUNTRY RISK SERVICE. URUGUAY. see *BUSINESS AND ECONOMICS—Economic Situation And Conditions*

COUNTRY RISK SERVICE. UZBEKISTAN. see *BUSINESS AND ECONOMICS—Economic Situation And Conditions*

COUNTRY RISK SERVICE. VENEZUELA. see *BUSINESS AND ECONOMICS—Economic Situation And Conditions*

COUNTRY RISK SERVICE. VIETNAM. see *BUSINESS AND ECONOMICS—Economic Situation And Conditions*

COUNTRY RISK SERVICE. YEMEN. see *BUSINESS AND ECONOMICS—Economic Situation And Conditions*

COUNTRY RISK SERVICE. YUGOSLAVIA (SERBIA-MONTENEGRO). see *BUSINESS AND ECONOMICS—Economic Situation And Conditions*

COUNTRY RISK SERVICE. ZAIRE. see *BUSINESS AND ECONOMICS—Economic Situation And Conditions*

COUNTRY RISK SERVICE. ZAMBIA. see *BUSINESS AND ECONOMICS—Economic Situation And Conditions*

COUNTRY RISK SERVICE. ZIMBABWE. see *BUSINESS AND ECONOMICS—Economic Situation And Conditions*

307.76029 GBR ISSN 0953-8089
CRAWFORD'S DIRECTORY OF CITY CONNECTIONS. Text in English. 1973. a. (plus updates 5/yr.). GBP 325 domestic (effective 2001). adv. stat. **Document type:** *Directory, Trade.* **Description:** Lists U.K. companies and their advisers, with full contact details, names, addresses, and telephone numbers of senior directors, major shareholders, and corporate advisers.
Related titles: CD-ROM ed.; Diskette ed.
—BLDSC (3593.285000).
Published by: A P Information Services, Marlborough House, 298 Regents Park Rd, London, N3 2UU, United Kingdom. TEL 44-20-83499988, FAX 44-20-83499797, info@apinfo.co.uk, http://www.crawfordsonline.co.uk, http://www.ap-info.co.uk. Ed. Robyn Andrews. Pub. Alan Philipp. Adv. contact Jacinta Tobin.

332.3 336 USA
CRED-ALERT. Text in English. 1972. m. USD 36 to non-members; USD 18 to members. back issues avail. **Document type:** *Newsletter, Trade.* **Description:** Covers state and federal legislation that affects credit and the collection industry.
Published by: American Collectors Association, Inc., 4040 W 70th St, PO Box 390106, Minneapolis, MN 55435. TEL 612-926-6547, FAX 612-926-1624. Circ: 3,600 (paid).

332.7 332.6 GBR
CREDIT. Text in English. 2000 (Feb). m. GBP 695, EUR 1,040, USD 1,145 (effective 2000). adv. **Document type:** *Journal, Trade.* **Description:** Offers a mix of news, profiles, features, sector reports, data and tehnical articles. Credit provides unique, independent, dedicated content which is highly respected by your clients, your peers and by your competitors.
Indexed: AgeL.
Published by: Risk Waters Group (Subsidiary of: Incisive Media Plc.), Haymarket House, 28-29 Haymarket, London, SW1Y 4RX, United Kingdom. TEL 44-20-74849700, FAX 44-20-79302238, credit@riskwaters.com, http://www.creditmag.com/, http://www.incisivemedia.com. Ed. Clive Howood TEL 44-20-7484-9852. Adv. contact Rupert Gibbs TEL 44-20-7484-9920.

332 658 USA ISSN 1060-2739
CREDIT & COLLECTION MANAGER'S LETTER. Text in English. 1967. s-m. USD 230 to individuals (effective 2004). index. **Document type:** *Newsletter.* **Description:** Provides business and consumer lenders and creditors with up-to-date information on credit procedures, collection practices, legal problems, financial analyses and bankruptcy proceedings.
Formerly (until 199?): Credit and Collection Management Bulletin (1048-275X); Which was formed by the merger of: Commercial Credit and Collection Management (0273-9623); Consumer Credit and Collection Management (0746-1232)
Related titles: Online - full text ed.: (from Florida Center for Library Automation, Gale Group).
—CCC.
Published by: Bureau of Business Practice (Subsidiary of: Aspen Publishers, Inc.), 1185 Avenue of the Americas, 37th Fl, New York, NY 10036. TEL 860-442-4365, 800-243-0876, FAX 860-437-3555, rebecca_armitage@prenhall.com, http://www.bbpnews.com. Ed. Wayne Muller. Pub. Peter Garabedian. R&P Kathryn Mennone.

332.7 USA
CREDIT CARD NEWS (NORTH PALM BEACH). Text in English. w. **Document type:** *Newsletter, Consumer.* **Description:** Contains current news on credit card deals, teaser rates, platinum perks, frequent-flier miles, balance transfers, and other credit card features.
Media: E-mail.
Published by: Bankrate Inc., 11811 US Hwy 1, North Palm Beach, FL 33408. TEL 561-630-2400, FAX 561-625-4540, webmaster@bankrate.com, http://bankrate.process9.com/bankrate/subscribe.html, http://www.bankrate.com.

332 BEL ISSN 0011-099X
CREDIT COMMUNAL DE BELGIQUE. BULLETIN TRIMESTRIEL. Text in French. 1947. q. free. bk.rev. charts; illus. **Document type:** *Bulletin.*
Related titles: Dutch ed.: Gemeentekrediet van Belgie. Driemaandelijks Tijdschrift. ISSN 0773-9273. 1947.
Indexed: PAIS.
Published by: Credit Communal de Belgique/Gemeentekrediet van Belgie, Bd Pacheco 44, Brussels, 1000, Belgium. TEL 32-2-2224597, FAX 32-2-2225674. Ed. G Helbig. Circ: 8,000.

CREDIT CONTROL. see *BUSINESS AND ECONOMICS—Accounting*

346.066 AUS ISSN 1326-5520
CREDIT LAW ALERT✶ ; compliance and practice. Text in English. 199?. 8/yr. AUD 445. Supplement avail. **Document type:** *Trade.*
Contact Corp. Auth.: Australian Institute of Banking and Finance, Level 19, 385 Bourke St, Melbourne, VIC 3000, Australia. TEL 61-3-9602-5811, FAX 61-3-9602-3923, jlsydney@mpx.com.au, info@aibf.com.au, http://www.aibf.com.au/main/homepage.htm.

332 USA ISSN 1078-0149
CREDIT LINE; concise advise for the credit & collection staff. Text in English. 1994. m. USD 85 (effective 1999). **Document type:** *Newsletter.* **Description:** Covers a variety of topics of interest to credit and collection staffers including credit checks, telephone collections, where to turn for in-depth credit information, UCC law, collection tips, dealing with angry customers, dealing with stress, and teamwork.
Published by: Bureau of Business Practice (Subsidiary of: Aspen Publishers, Inc.), 1185 Avenue of the Americas, 37th Fl, New York, NY 10036. TEL 860-442-4365, 800-243-0876, FAX 860-437-3555, rebecca_armitage@prenhall.com, http://www.bbpnews.com. Ed. Brendan Johnston. Pub. Peter Garabedian. R&P Kathryn Mennone.

332.7 330.9 CHE ISSN 0011-1023
CREDIT SUISSE. BULLETIN. Text in English. 1895. 6/yr. free. adv. charts; mkt.; stat. index. **Document type:** *Bulletin.*
Related titles: French ed.; German ed.
Indexed: PAIS, WBA.
—BLDSC (2463.100000).
Published by: Credit Suisse, Postfach 100, Zurich, 8070, Switzerland. TEL 41-1-3337394, FAX 41-1-3336404, bulletin@credit-suisse.ch, http://www.credit-suisse.ch/bulletin. Ed. Christian Pfister. Circ: 140,000.

332.1 USA ISSN 1540-3939
CREDIT UNION ASSET/LIABILITY MANAGEMENT REPORT. Variant title: Sheshunoff Credit Union Asset/Liability Management Report. Text in English. 1998. m. USD 375 (effective 2004). **Document type:** *Newsletter, Trade.*
Published by: Sheshunoff Information Services Inc., 807 Las Cimas Pkwy, Ste 300, Austin, TX 78746. TEL 512-472-2244, 800-456-2340, FAX 512-305-6575, customercare.sis@sheshunoff.com, http://www.sheshunoff.com/store/044.html. Ed. Belinda B Early.

332 USA ISSN 0892-1075
CREDIT UNION DIGEST. Text in English. m. USD 250 domestic to non-members; free domestic to members (effective 2005). **Document type:** *Magazine, Trade.*
Published by: California Credit Union League, 9500 Cleveland Ave. #200, Rancho Cucamong a, CA 91730-5908. TEL 909-980-8890, FAX 909-581-3377, http://www.ccul.org/information/cudigest.cfm. Ed. Carol Payne. Circ: 5,000 (paid).

332.3 USA ISSN 1058-1561
CODEN: JNTOER
CREDIT UNION DIRECTORS NEWSLETTER. Text in English. 1976. m. USD 78 (effective 2005). adv. 4 p./no. 2 cols./p.; **Document type:** *Newsletter, Trade.* **Description:** Policy issues for credit union boards of directors.
Former titles: Credit Union Board C E O Newsletter; Credit Union President Newsletter
Related titles: Online - full text ed.: (from EBSCO Publishing).
—CCC.
Published by: Credit Union National Association, Inc., 5710 Mineral Point Rd, Madison, WI 53701. TEL 608-231-4082, 800-356-9655, FAX 608-231-4263, srodgers@cuna.com, http://www.cuna.org, http://www.cumanagement.org. Ed. Kathryn Kuehn TEL 800-356-9655 Ext 4075. Circ: 8,179 (paid and controlled).

332.3 USA
CREDIT UNION EXECUTIVE NEWSLETTER. Text in English. 1975. 21/yr. USD 198 (effective 2005). adv. 4 p./no.; **Document type:** *Newsletter.*
Formerly: Credit Union Manager Newsletter (1068-2120)
Related titles: Online - full text ed.: (from EBSCO Publishing).
—CCC.
Published by: Credit Union National Association, Inc., 5710 Mineral Point Rd, Madison, WI 53701. TEL 608-231-4082, 800-356-9655, FAX 608-231-4263, kkuehn@cuna.com, askem@cuna.com, http://www.cuna.org, http://www.cuna.org/. Ed. Kathryn Kuehn. Pub. Jim Hanson. Adv. contact Rick Sheridan. Circ: 1,746 (paid and controlled).

332 USA ISSN 1043-1888
HG2037
CREDIT UNION FINANCIAL PROFILES. Text in English. q. (s-a). USD 398. charts; illus.; stat. back issues avail. **Document type:** *Trade.* **Description:** Covers the world of banking and finance with special attention to credit and credit unions.
Published by: I D C Financial Publishing, Inc., PO Box 140, Hartland, WI 53029. TEL 414-367-7231, 800-525-5457. Ed., Pub., R&P John E Rickmeier.

B

332.7 USA ISSN 1521-5105
CREDIT UNION JOURNAL. Text in English. 1981. s-m. USD 119 (effective 2005). adv. bk.rev. **Document type:** *Newspaper, Trade.* **Description:** Provides management of credit unions with timely reports of regulatory and technical matters. Contains news of conventions, government activities, personnel changes.
Formerly (until 1998): Credit Union News (0199-9311)
Related titles: Online - full text ed.: (from EBSCO Publishing, Florida Center for Library Automation, Gale Group, Northern Light Technology, Inc., O C L C Online Computer Library Center, Inc., ProQuest Information & Learning).
Indexed: BLI.
—CCC.
Published by: Source Media, Inc., One State St Plaza, 27th Fl, New York, NY 10004. TEL 212-803-6077, FAX 212-747-1154, custserv@sourcemedia.com, http://www.cujournal.com, http://www.sourcemedia.com. Circ: 7,000. **Co-publisher:** Deutsche Bank.

334.2 USA ISSN 0011-1066
HG2033
CREDIT UNION MAGAZINE; for credit union elected officials, managers and employees. Text in English. 1924. m. USD 50 (effective 2005). adv. charts; illus.; tr.lit. index. 100 p./no. 3 cols./p.; back issues avail.; reprint service avail. from PQC. **Document type:** *Trade.*
Formerly: Credit Union Bridge
Related titles: Microform ed.: (from PQC); Online - full text ed.: (from EBSCO Publishing, Northern Light Technology, Inc., O C L C Online Computer Library Center, Inc., ProQuest Information & Learning).
Indexed: ABIn, BLI, BPIA, PAIS, WBA.
—BLDSC (3487.290000), CISTI, IE, ingenta. **CCC.**
Published by: (Publications Department), Credit Union National Association, Inc., PO Box 431, Madison, WI 53701. TEL 608-231-4079, FAX 608-231-4370, http://www.creditunionmagazine.com, http://www.cuna.org/. Ed. Kathryn Kuehn. Pub. Roger Napiwocki. Adv. contact Rich Sheridan TEL 800-356-9655 Ext 4434. Circ: 30,983.

332 USA ISSN 0273-9267
HG2032
CREDIT UNION MANAGEMENT. Text in English. 1978. m. USD 99 to non-members; USD 60 to members; USD 6 newsstand/cover (effective 2005). adv. bk.rev. charts; illus. index. 64 p./no. 3 cols./p.; back issues avail.; reprints avail. **Document type:** *Magazine, Trade.* **Description:** Feature articles, departments, classifieds, regular sections devoted to general management, operations, marketing, and human resources issues.
Incorporates (1983-199?): Credit Union Director Magazine (1040-9246); Incorporates (1986-1990): Financial Operations; (1979-1990): Credit Union Marketing (0884-2469)
Related titles: Microfiche ed.; Online - full text ed.: (from EBSCO Publishing, Northern Light Technology, Inc., O C L C Online Computer Library Center, Inc., ProQuest Information & Learning); Supplement(s): Credit Union Management Buyer's Guide.
Indexed: ABIn, BLI, PAIS.
—BLDSC (3487.290500), IE, ingenta. **CCC.**
Published by: Credit Union Executives Society, PO Box 14167, Madison, WI 53708-0167. editors@cues.org, cues@cues.org, http://www.cues.org/pls/enetrixcues/!cues1.main?section_id_in=3069489, http://www.cumanagement.org. Eds. Lisa Hochgraf, Mary Auestad Arnold, Mary Arnold, Theresa Sweeney. adv.: B&W page USD 2,589, color page USD 3,589. Circ: 7,134 (paid).

332.3 334 IRL ISSN 1649-377X
CREDIT UNION NEWS. Text in English. 1980. bi-m. adv. bk.rev. illus. **Document type:** *Trade.* **Description:** Contains general and financial information relevant to credit unions and their members, including policy articles and reports from credit union events around the country.
Former titles (until 2003): Irish League of Credit Unions. Review (0790-505X); (until 1984): Credit Union Review (0790-5041)
Published by: Irish League of Credit Unions, 33-41 Lower Mount St., Dublin, 2, Ireland. TEL 353-1-6146700, FAX 353-1-6146701, info@creditunion.ie, http://www.creditunion.ie. Ed. Richard Good. R&P, Adv. contact Roger Cole. Circ: 11,000.

332 USA ISSN 0889-5597
CREDIT UNION NEWSWATCH. Text in English. 1981. w. looseleaf. USD 125 (effective 2000). back issues avail. **Document type:** *Newsletter.*
Supersedes (1972-1981): Credit Union Leadership Letter
Related titles: Online - full text ed.: (from ProQuest Information & Learning).
Indexed: ABIn.
—CCC.
Published by: Credit Union National Association, Inc., 5710 Mineral Point Rd, Madison, WI 53701. TEL 608-231-4042, FAX 608-231-4858. Ed. Steve Bosack. Pub. Mark Wolff. Circ: 17,000.

332 USA ISSN 1540-4528
CREDIT UNION REGULATORY INSIDER. Variant title: Pratt's Credit Union Regulatory Insider. Text in English. 1985. w. (excpt. Aug. & Dec.). USD 455 (effective 2005). **Document type:** *Newsletter, Trade.*
Formerly: Ncua Watch
Related titles: Online - full text ed.
Published by: A.S. Pratt & Sons, Inc., 1911 Fort Myer Dr, Arlington, VA 22209. TEL 703-528-0145, 800-572-2797, FAX 703-528-1736, prattinfo@tfn.com, http://www.sheshunoff.com. Ed. Alan Rice.

310 USA ISSN 0894-752X
HG2037
CREDIT UNION REPORT. Text in English. a. USD 25 (effective 2000). back issues avail. **Document type:** *Monographic series.*
Indexed: SRI.
Published by: Credit Union National Association, Inc., 5710 Mineral Point Rd, Madison, WI 53701. TEL 608-231-4043, FAX 608-231-4858. Ed. Marc Shafroth. Circ: 9,000.

332.3 334 USA ISSN 1548-6176
▼ **CREDIT UNION TELLER/M S R REPORT.** (Member Service Representative) Text in English. 2004 (Jan.). m. USD 295 (effective 2004). **Document type:** *Newsletter, Trade.* **Description:** Aims to provide tellers and MSRs with crucial information and continuing training.
Published by: Sheshunoff Information Services Inc., 807 Las Cimas Pkwy, Ste 300, Austin, TX 78746. TEL 512-472-2244, 800-456-2340, FAX 512-305-6575, customercare.sis@sheshunoff.com, http://www.sheshunoff.com/store/H32.html. Eds. Robyn Sandoval, Marge Simmons.

332 USA ISSN 1058-7764
HG2037
CREDIT UNION TIMES. Text in English. 1990. w. USD 120 domestic; USD 169 foreign (effective 2005). adv. **Document type:** *Trade.*
Related titles: Online - full text ed.
Indexed: BLI.
Published by: Credit Union Times, Inc., 560 Village Blvd, Ste 325, West Palm Beach, FL 33409-1962. TEL 561-683-8515, FAX 561-683-8514, http://www.cutimes.com/. Ed. Paul Gentile. Pub. Mike Welch. Circ: 9,500 (paid).

332 334 CAN ISSN 0829-2175
CREDIT UNION WAY. Text in English. 1948. m. (10/yr.). CND 35, USD 35 domestic; CND 43 foreign. adv. bk.rev. index. back issues avail. **Document type:** *Trade.* **Description:** For directors, employees and members of Canadian credit unions and co-operatives.
Related titles: Microfiche ed.: (from MML); Microform ed.: (from MML).
Indexed: CBPI.
Published by: Credit Union Central of Saskatchewan, 2055 Albert St, P O Box 3030, Regina, SK S4P 3G8, Canada. TEL 306-566-1360, FAX 306-566-1847. Ed. James Duggleby. Pub. Eric Eggertson. Adv. contact Kelly Lee. Circ: 5,600.

332.3 AUT ISSN 0304-6915
HG3020.V54
CREDITANSTALT-BANKVEREIN. ANNUAL REPORT. Text in English. a.
Formerly: Creditanstalt-Bankverein. Report
Published by: Creditanstalt-Bankverein, Schottengasse 6, Vienna, W 1010, Austria.

332.7 NOR ISSN 0802-4138
CREDITINFORM. Text in Norwegian. 1914. s-m. NOK 890. adv. stat.
Former titles (until 1989): Creditreform (0011-1104); (until 1926): Kredittidende (0801-1567)
—CCC.
Published by: Creditinform a-s, Postboks 5275, Majorstua, Oslo, 0303, Norway. FAX 47-22-46-53-90, TELEX 11093 CINFO N. Ed. Bjoern Oestgaard. Circ: 7,000.

332.7 ITA ISSN 0011-1090
CREDITO POPOLARE∗. Text in Italian. 1899. bi-m. free to qualified personnel. bk.rev.
Indexed: PAIS.
Published by: Associazione Nazionale "L. Luzzati" fra le Banche Popolari, Piazza Venezia II, Rome, RM 00187, Italy.

332.7 DEU ISSN 0343-3854
CREDITREFORM; das Unternehmermagazin aus der Verlagsgruppe Handelsblatt. Text in German. 1885. m. EUR 50; EUR 4.55 newsstand/cover (effective 2003). adv. **Document type:** *Magazine, Trade.*
Related titles: Online - full text ed.
Published by: Verlagsgruppe Handelsblatt GmbH, Kasernenstr 67, Duesseldorf, 40213, Germany. TEL 49-211-8870, FAX 49-211-371792, fachverlag@vhb.de, http://www.creditreform-magazin.de, http://www.vhb.de. Ed. Klaus-Werner Ernst. Adv. contact Marlies Piotrowicz. B&W page EUR 6,512, color page EUR 9,512. Circ: 129,659 (paid and controlled).

CRITTENDEN REPORT REAL ESTATE FINANCING. see *REAL ESTATE*

332 USA ISSN 1066-6419
CROSS SALES REPORT. Text in English. 1992. m. USD 329 (effective 2001). index. back issues avail. **Document type:** *Newsletter.* **Description:** Case studies on how financial institutions increase market share and retain customers, especially by selling additional services to existing client.
Related titles: Online - full text ed.
Indexed: BLI.
Published by: Siefer Consultants, Inc., 525 Cayuga St, Storm Lake, IA 50588. TEL 712-732-7340, FAX 712-732-7906, info@siefer.com, http://www.siefer.com. Ed. Marty Gallagher. Circ: 2,100 (paid).

332 CHL ISSN 0716-2383
CUENTAS NACIONALES DE CHILE. Text in English, Spanish. 1981. a. CLP 4,000, USD 20 (effective 1999). **Description:** Presents definitions and basic concepts of the national accounts and general methodology aspects.
Published by: Banco Central de Chile, Casilla 967, Santiago, Chile. TEL 56-2-670-2000, FAX 56-2-698-4847. Circ: 700 (paid).

330.9 ECU ISSN 0252-8673
HC201
CUESTIONES ECONOMICAS. Text in Spanish. 1979. 3/yr.
Indexed: PAIS, RASB.
Published by: Banco Central del Ecuador, Avenida 10 de Agosto y Briceno, Quito, Ecuador. TEL 593-2-2580158, uweb@uio.bce.fin.ec, http://www.bce.fin.ec. Circ: 2,000.

332 ECU ISSN 0252-8657
F3710
CULTURA (QUITO). Text in Spanish. 1978. 3/yr. USD 14.
Published by: Banco Central del Ecuador, Avenida 10 de Agosto y Briceno, Quito, Ecuador. TEL 593-2-2580158, uweb@uio.bce.fin.ec, http://www.bce.fin.ec.

CURIERUL NATIONAL. see *BUSINESS AND ECONOMICS—Economic Situation And Conditions*

332 GBR ISSN 0955-6656
CURRENCY AND INTEREST RATE OUTLOOK. Text in English. 1987. m. GBP 428 worldwide (effective 2001). **Document type:** *Newsletter.* **Description:** Provides forecasting details on currency and interest rate movements for the next six months, with analysis and summaries based on economic and other fundamentals and market factors.
Related titles: E-mail ed.
Published by: Chilton Magazine Services, 2a Altons House Office Park, Gatehouse Way, Aylesbury, HP10 3XU, United Kingdom. http://www.biz-lib.com/ZCRCI.html.

332 GBR ISSN 0143-0769
CURRENCY PROFILES∗. Text in English. 1977. m. GBP 850. illus. **Description:** Short- and medium-range analysis of prospects for international currencies against the pound and the dollar.
Incorporates: Forecasts of Exchange Rate Movements (0305-9944); Former titles: Forecasts of Exchange Rate Movements (Dollar Edition) (0140-9247); Forecasts of Exchange Rate Movements (Overseas Edition) (0140-9255)
Published by: Henley Centre for Forecasting Ltd., 9 Bridewell Pl, London, EC4Y 6AY, United Kingdom. Ed. Filippo Dell'Osso.

CURRENT ISSUES IN ECONOMICS AND FINANCE. see *BUSINESS AND ECONOMICS*

CURRENT ISSUES IN REAL ESTATE FINANCE & ECONOMICS. see *REAL ESTATE*

CURRENT ISSUES IN THE FINANCIAL SERVICES INDUSTRIES. see *BUSINESS AND ECONOMICS—Accounting*

332.1 GBR ISSN 1464-9454
CUSTOMER RELATIONSHIP TECHNOLOGY IN FINANCE; for customer centric banking and insurance. Text in English. 1998. 10/yr. GBP 400, USD 680 (effective 1999). **Document type:** *Trade.* **Description:** Looks at developments in the selection and the development of customer relationship technology in the financial services industry.
Published by: Informa Professional (Subsidiary of: T & F Informa plc), Informa House, 30-32 Mortimer St, London, W1W 7RE, United Kingdom. TEL 44-171-553-1000, FAX 44-171-553-1593, http://www.bankingtech.com.

332.1 340 DEU ISSN 1681-9616
K1081
➤ **CYBERBANKING & LAW.** Text in English. 1999. irreg. **Document type:** *Academic/Scholarly.*
Media: Online - full content.
Published by: Universitaet des Saarlandes, Institut fuer Rechtsinformatik, Gebaeude 15, Im Stadtwald, Saarbruecken, 66123, Germany. http://rechtsinformatik.jura.uni-sb.de/cbl/cbl-journal.php. Ed. James Graham.

332 USA ISSN 1055-1700
CYCLE PROJECTIONS. Text in English. 1990. m. USD 125. **Document type:** *Newsletter.* **Description:** Offers timely projections in a variety of markets. Covers short, intermediate and long term cycles.
Indexed: RefZh.
Published by: Cycles Research Institute, 214 Carnegie Ctr, Ste 204, Princeton, NJ 08540-6237. TEL 610-995-2120, FAX 610-995-2130, cycles@cycles.org, http://www.cycles.org/~cycles, http://www.cyclesresearchinstitute.org. Ed. Chester Joy.

B

332 CYP
CYPRUS DEVELOPMENT BANK. ANNUAL REPORT. Text in English. 1963. a. free. **Document type:** *Corporate.*
Published by: Cyprus Development Bank, Nicosia, Cyprus. TEL 357-2-846500, FAX 357-2-846603, TELEX 2797 DEBANK CY, info@cdb.com.cy. Circ: 1,100.

332 DEU
CZERWENSKY INTERN. Text in German. 1988. 2/w. **Document type:** *Newsletter, Consumer.*
Published by: Kronberger Verlags GmbH, Eschersheimer Landstr 9, Frankfurt Am Main, 60322, Germany. TEL 49-69-550002, FAX 49-69-550006. Ed. Gerhard Czerwensky. Pub., R&P Cornelia Czerwensky.

384.5 332 USA ISSN 1054-0814
THE D B S REPORT. (Direct Broadcast Satellite) Text in English. 1990. m. USD 1,045; USD 1,440 combined subscription print & e-mail eds. (effective 2005). adv. **Document type:** *Newsletter, Trade.* **Description:** Analyzes direct broadcast satellite ventures. Projects future scenarios, costs, values. Quarterly subscriber stats and financials for key operators. Detailed data on new technology, consumer demand and programming lineups.
Related titles: E-mail ed.: USD 945 (effective 2005); Fax ed.: USD 945 (effective 2001).
Published by: Kagan Research, LLC, One Lower Ragsdale Dr, Bldg One, Ste 130, Monterey, CA 93940. TEL 831-624-1536, FAX 831-625-3225, info@kagan.com, http://research.kagan.com/keo/subscriptionsDetailPage.aspx?SubscriptionID=13, http://www.kagan.com. adv.: color page USD 3,400.

332 USA ISSN 1554-3110
D C PLAN NEWS & ANALYSIS. (Defined Contribution) Text in English. 1989. s-m. looseleaf. USD 1,218.90 in US & Canada print & online eds.; USD 1,247 elsewhere print & online eds. (effective 2005). index. back issues avail. **Document type:** *Newsletter, Trade.* **Description:** Ratings of money managers and bundled service providers, with risk-return benchmarks. Current asset allocation trends for participants in the DC plan marketplace. Also includes GIC yields.
Former titles (until 2005): I O M A's D C Plan Investing (1554-3129); (until 1997): I O M A's Report on Defined Contribution Plan Investing; (until 1992): I O M A's G I C - B I C Yields and Market Report (Guaranteed Investment Contracts - Bank Investment Contracts) (1047-9244)
Related titles: Diskette ed.; E-mail ed.; Online - full content ed.; Online - full text ed.: (from Factiva, Gale Group, O C L C Online Computer Library Center, Inc.).
—CCC.
Published by: Institute of Management & Administration, Inc., 3 Park Ave, New York, NY 10016-5902. TEL 212-244-0360, FAX 212-564-0465, subserve@ioma.com, http://www.ioma.com/products/prod_detail.php?prodid=12. Ed. Sean Hanna. Pub. Perry Patterson. R&P Sofie Kourkoutakis.

332 DNK ISSN 0109-7644
DAGENS DANMARK. Text in Danish. 1984. q. membership. illus.
Published by: Kreditforeningen Danmark, Jarmers Plads 2, Copenhagen V, 1590, Denmark.

332 ZAF ISSN 0258-8986
DAILY TENDER BULLETIN. Text in English. 1938. d.
Formerly (until 1976): Daily Bulletin
Published by: Trade Information Services (Subsidiary of: Times Media Ltd.), PO Box 56311, Pinegowrie, Transvaal 2123, South Africa. TEL 27-11-886-3166.

332 IND
DALAL STREET JOURNAL. Text in English. 1986. fortn. INR 330; INR 20 newsstand/cover. adv.
Related titles: Online - full text ed.
Indexed: B&I.
Published by: Dalal Street Communications Pvt. Ltd., 31-A Noble Chambers, 4th Fl., Janmabhoomi Marg, Mumbai, Maharashtra 400 001, India. TEL 2870287, FAX 2872779, TELEX 011-81130, dsj@hotmail.com, http://www.cyberindia.net/DSJ/home.htm. Ed. Pratap V Padode. Adv. contact T N Streekrishna. B&W page INR 48,000, color page INR 62,000; trim 180 x 240. Circ: 74,302.

332.1109489 DNK ISSN 1397-4017
DANMARKS NATIONALBANK. BERETNING OG REGNSKAB. Text in Danish. 1819. a. free. illus.
Former titles (until 1997): Danmarks Nationalbank. Beretning og Regnskab (Dansk Udgave) (0108-6979); (until 1937): Nationalbankens Regnskab
Related titles: Online - full content ed.: ISSN 1398-3830; ◆ English ed.: Danmarks Nationalbank. Report and Accounts for the Year. ISSN 1397-520X.
Published by: Danmarks Nationalbank, Havnegade 5, Copenhagen K, 1093, Denmark. TEL 45-33-636363, FAX 45-33-637103, info@nationalbanken.dk, http://www.nationalbanken.dk.

354.88 DNK ISSN 1399-2023
DANMARKS NATIONALBANK. DANISH GOVERNMENT BORROWING AND DEBT. Text in English. 1999. a. free.
Formed by the merger of (1994-1999): Danish Government Securities (0909-0487); (1988-1999): Data on Danish Public Foreign Borrowing (0906-6993); Which was formerly (until 1991): Danish Data on the Public Foreign Borrowing and the Economy Etc. (0905-1473)
Related titles: Online - full content ed.: ISSN 1399-3941; ◆ Danish ed.: Danmarks Nationalbank. Statens Laantagning og Gaeld. ISSN 0902-6681.
Published by: Danmarks Nationalbank, Havnegade 5, Copenhagen K, 1093, Denmark. TEL 45-33-636363, FAX 45-33-637103, info@nationalbanken.dk, http://www.nationalbanken.dk.

330 DNK ISSN 1602-057X
HG186.D4
DANMARKS NATIONALBANK. FINANCIAL STABILITY. Text in English. 1963. a.
Supersedes in part (in 2002): Danmarks Nationalbank. Monetary Review (0011-6149)
Related titles: Online - full content ed.: ISSN 1602-0588; ◆ Danish ed.: Danmarks Nationalbank. Finansiel Stabilitet. ISSN 1602-0553.
Published by: Danmarks Nationalbank, Havnegade 5, Copenhagen K, 1093, Denmark. TEL 45-33-636363, FAX 45-33-637103, info@nationalbanken.dk, http://www.nationalbanken.dk.

330 DNK ISSN 1602-0553
DANMARKS NATIONALBANK. FINANSIEL STABILITET. Text in Danish. 1972. a.
Supersedes in part (in 2002): Danmarks Nationalbank. Kvartalsoversigt (0107-1289)
Related titles: Online - full content ed.: ISSN 1602-0561; ◆ English ed.: Danmarks Nationalbank. Financial Stability. ISSN 1602-057X.
Published by: Danmarks Nationalbank, Havnegade 5, Copenhagen K, 1093, Denmark. TEL 45-33-636363, FAX 45-33-637103, info@nationalbanken.dk, http://www.nationalbanken.dk.

330.9489 DNK ISSN 0107-1289
DANMARKS NATIONALBANK. KVARTALSOVERSIGT. Text in Danish. 1972. q. free (effective 2004).
Related titles: Online - full content ed.: ISSN 1398-3857; ◆ English ed.: Danmarks Nationalbank. Monetary Review. ISSN 0011-6149.
Published by: Danmarks Nationalbank, Havnegade 5, Copenhagen K, 1093, Denmark. TEL 45-33-636363, FAX 45-33-637103, info@nationalbanken.dk, http://www.nationalbanken.dk.

330.9489 DNK ISSN 0011-6149
HC351
DANMARKS NATIONALBANK. MONETARY REVIEW. Text in English. 1962. q. free. charts; stat. reprints avail. **Description:** Descriptions and comments on external finances and domestic credit. Includes press releases and speeches by the Board of Governors.
Related titles: Online - full content ed.: ISSN 1398-3865. 1998; ◆ Danish ed.: Danmarks Nationalbank. Kvartalsoversigt. ISSN 0107-1289.
Indexed: ELLIS, WBA.
Published by: Danmarks Nationalbank, Havnegade 5, Copenhagen K, 1093, Denmark. TEL 45-33-636363, FAX 45-33-637103, info@nationalbanken.dk, http://www.nationalbanken.dk.

332.1109489 DNK ISSN 1397-520X
DANMARKS NATIONALBANK. REPORT AND ACCOUNTS FOR THE YEAR. Text in English. 1946. a.
Formerly (until 1997): Danmarks Nationalbank. Report and Accounts for the Year (English edition) (0108-6995)
Related titles: Online - full content ed.: ISSN 1398-3849; ◆ Danish ed.: Danmarks Nationalbank. Beretning og Regnskab. ISSN 1397-4017.
Published by: Danmarks Nationalbank, Havnegade 5, Copenhagen K, 1093, Denmark. TEL 45-33-636363, FAX 45-33-637103, info@nationalbanken.dk, http://www.nationalbanken.dk.

332.1 DNK
DEN DANSKE BANK AKTIESELSKAB. REPORT AND ACCOUNTS. Text in Danish. s-a. free to qualified personnel. charts; stat.
Formerly (until 1990): Copenhagen HandelsBank. Report and Accounts
Related titles: English ed.
Published by: Danske Bank Aktieselskab, Communications, Holmens Kanal 2-12, Copenhagen K, 1092, Denmark. TEL 45-33-44-00-00, FAX 45-39-18-58-73, http://www.danskebank.dk.

332.1 DNK
DEN DANSKE BANK. ANNUAL REPORT. Text in English. 1871. a. illus.
Former titles: Danske Bank af 1871. Annual Report; (until 1976): Danske Landmandsbank. Annual Report (0070-2838)
Published by: Danske Bank, c/o Library, Holmens Kanal 12, Copenhagen K, 1092, Denmark. TEL 45-33-15-65-00, FAX 45-33-44-37-78, TELEX 27000.

332 658 USA ISSN 1094-5350
DEBIT CARD DIRECTORY. Variant title: Credit Card Management. Text in English. 1988. m. USD 98 in North America; USD 113 elsewhere (effective 2001). **Document type:** *Trade.* **Description:** Shows new ideas, products and strategies from successful credit card programs. Covers all aspects of the business from finance to marketing to new technology.
Incorporates (in 1991): Journal of Consumer Lending
Related titles: Online - full text ed.: (from Northern Light Technology, Inc.); ◆ Supplement(s): Card Industry Directory. ISSN 1051-6778.
Indexed: ABIn, ATI, B&I.
—BLDSC (3487.280300), ingenta.
Published by: Faulkner & Gray, Inc., PO Box 87271, Chicago, IL 60680. TEL 312-913-1334, 800-535-8403, faulknerygray@msn.com. Ed. James L Daly. Pub. John Stewart.

332 USA
DEBIT CARD NEWS; newsletter for retail electronic payments. (Includes 3 special issues.) Text in English. 1984. m. USD 245. index. back issues avail. **Document type:** *Newsletter.* **Description:** Covers developments affecting debit card marketing, economics and pricing issues, technology and operations and new POS applications.
Formerly: P O S News (Point of Sale)
Related titles: Online - full text ed.
Indexed: ATI, B&I.
Published by: Faulkner & Gray, Inc., PO Box 87271, Chicago, IL 60680. TEL 312-913-1334. Ed. Don Davies.

332 USA ISSN 0731-0536
DEBITS AND DEPOSIT TURNOVER AT COMMERCIAL BANKS. Text in English. m. USD 5. **Document type:** *Government.*
Formerly (until 1977): Bank Debits, Deposits, and Deposit Turnover (0730-4900)
Published by: U.S. Federal Reserve System, Board of Governors, Publications Services, Rm MS 138, Washington, DC 20551. TEL 202-452-3244, FAX 202-728-5886.

DEBT ADVICE HANDBOOK. see *SOCIAL SERVICES AND WELFARE*

332 USA ISSN 1076-9676
DEBT-FREE AND PROSPEROUS LIVING. Text in English. 1992. m. looseleaf. USD 69 (effective 1999). **Document type:** *Newsletter, Consumer.* **Description:** Helps middle class baby boomers get debt-free and reclaim their incomes instead of transfering their lives' wealth to credit companies.
Formerly: Personal Financial Success
Published by: Debt Free & Prosperous Living, Inc., 310 Second St, Boscobel, WI 53805-1164. TEL 608-375-2900, FAX 608-375-2901, john@getdebtfree.com, sales@getdebtfree.com, http://www.getdebtfree.com. Ed. John M Cummuta. R&P John Cummuta. Circ: 3,000 (paid).

DEBT SURVIVAL NEWSLETTER; get out and stay out of debt. see *HOME ECONOMICS*

332 340 USA
DEBTOR - CREDITOR LAW. Text in English. 1982. 10 base vols. plus irreg. updates. looseleaf. USD 1,979 base vol(s). (effective 2003). **Description:** Covers all aspects of the creation and enforcement of the debtor-creditor relationship, including: Federal consumer credit legislation; UCC Articles 2 (Sales), 3 (Commercial Paper), 6 (Bulk Transfers), 7 (Documents of Title), and 9 (Secured Transactions); A comprehensive treatment of usury; The rights and obligations of third parties with respect to Guaranty, Suretyship, Subrogation, Community Property, Escrowees and Fraudulent Conveyances; The methods of satisfying obligations by non-judicial remedies and possessory proceedings; Extensive analysis of judicial remedies, including Insolvency, Enforcement of Judgments and Federal Tax Liens; Foreign insolvency.
Related titles: CD-ROM ed.: USD 1,819 (effective 2002).
Published by: Matthew Bender & Co., Inc. (Subsidiary of: LexisNexis North America), 1275 Broadway, Albany, NY 12204. TEL 518-487-3575, 800-252-9257, FAX 518-462-3788, international@bender.com, http://bender.lexisnexis.com. Ed. Theodore Eisenberg.

332 USA
DEBTZAPPER. Text in English. m. free. **Document type:** *Newsletter.* **Description:** Designed to inform and educate the average individual in the art of financial management.
Media: Online - full text.
Address: pbalweirz@earthlink.net, http://www.gen.com/debtzapper/tour/2044.

332.1 MEX
DECISION FINANCIERA OPORTUNA; diario de opinion e information financiera para toma de mejores decisiones de inversion. Text in Spanish. 1998. d. MXP 3,000 (effective 1999). back issues avail. **Document type:** *Newspaper.* **Description:** Covers Mexican banking and financial information.
Media: Online - full text.
Published by: Decision Oportuna, S.A. de C.V., Mexico. FAX 52-3-110-1112, webmaster@decisionfinanciera.com, http://www.decisionfinanciera.com/. Ed. Andres Fernandez.

▼ new title ➤ refereed ✶ unverified ◆ full entry avail.

346.08 USA
DELAWARE FINANCIAL INSTITUTIONAL LAW. Text in English. a., latest 2000. USD 65 w/ CD-ROM (effective 2003). 30 p./no.;
Formerly (until 1997): State of Delaware. Laws Relating to Financial Institutions
Published by: Michie Company (Subsidiary of: LexisNexis North America), PO Box 7587, Charlottesville, VA 22906-7587. TEL 434-972-7266, 800-542-0957, FAX 434-972-7666, custserv@michie.com, http://bookstore.lexis.com/bookstore/catalog?action=product&prod_id=12917&cat_id=T&pcat_id=107&pub_id=2, http://www.michie.com. Ed. George Harley.

DELAWARE GOVERNMENT REGISTER. see *PUBLIC ADMINISTRATION*

332 USA
DELUXE; ideas for the business of living. Text in English. 1985. q.
Published by: (Deluxe Check Printers, Inc.), Maxwell Custom Publishing, 1999 Shepard Rd., St. Paul, MN 55666. TEL 612-690-7200, FAX 612-690-7357. Ed. George Ashfield. Circ: (controlled).

332 RUS ISSN 0130-3090
DEN'GI I KREDIT. Text in Russian. 1932. m. USD 78 foreign (effective 2003). bk.rev. charts; illus.; stat. index.
Indexed: IBSS, RASB, RRTA, RefZh, WAE&RSA.
—BLDSC (0052.700000), East View.
Address: Neglinnaya ul 12, Moscow, 103016, Russian Federation. TEL 7-095-9254503. Ed. Y G Dmitriev. Circ: 30,000. **Dist. by:** M K - Periodica, ul Gilyarovskogo 39, Moscow 129110, Russian Federation. TEL 7-095-2845008, FAX 7-095-2813798, info@periodicals.ru, http://www.mkniga.ru; **Dist. in U.S. by:** Victor Kamkin Inc., 220 Girard St, Ste 1, Gaithersburg, MD 20877. TEL 301-881-1637, kamkin@kamkin.com.

332 DNK ISSN 0905-0965
HG8655
DENMARK. FINANSTILSYNET. BERETNING. Text in Danish. 1989. a. DKK 50 (effective 1996).
Formed by the merger of (1975-1989): Denmark. Finanstilsynet. Banker og Sparekasser (0108-9129); (1988-1989): Denmark. Finanstilsynet. Fondsboersen og Boersmaeglerselskaber (0904-437X); (1984-1989): Denmark. Finanstilsynet. Investeringsforeninger (0109-9426); (1988-1989): Denmark. Finanstilsynet. Forsikringsselskaber og Pensionskasser m.v. (0904-4361); Which was formerly (1982-1988): Denmark. Forsikringstilsynet. Beretning (0108-7304); Incorporated (1983-1989): Denmark. Tilsynet med Realkreditinstitutter. Beretning (0108-819X)
Published by: Finanstilsynet, Gl Kongevej 74 A, Frederiksberg C, 1850, Denmark. TEL 45-33-55-82-82, FAX 45-33-55-82-00. **Dist. by:** D B K Bogdistribution, Siljangade 2-8, Copenhagen S 2300, Denmark.

332 DNK ISSN 0907-3744
HG5594.3
DENMARK. FINANSTILSYNET. STATISTISK MATERIALE: BOERSOMRAADET. Text in Danish. 1989. a. DKK 25.
Formerly (until 1991): Denmark. Finanstilsynet. Beretning. Bilag 4: Boersomraadet
Published by: Finanstilsynet, Gl Kongevej 74 A, Frederiksberg C, 1850, Denmark. TEL 45-33-55-82-82, FAX 45-33-55-82-00. **Dist. by:** D B K Bogdistribution, Siljangade 2-8, Copenhagen S 2300, Denmark.

332 DNK ISSN 0907-3736
HG8655
DENMARK. FINANSTILSYNET. STATISTISK MATERIALE: SKADESFORSIKRINGSSELSKABER M.V. Text in Danish. 1989. a. DKK 50.
Formerly (until 1991): Denmark. Finanstilsynet. Beretning. Bilag 3: Skadesforsikringsselskaber
Published by: Finanstilsynet, Gl Kongevej 74 A, Frederiksberg C, 1850, Denmark. TEL 45-33-55-82-82, FAX 45-33-52-82-00. Circ: 3,500. **Dist. by:** D B K Bogdistribution, Siljangade 2-8, Copenhagen S 2300, Denmark.

332.3 DNK ISSN 0906-5563
DENMARK. FINANSTILSYNET. TILSYNET MED REALKREDITINSTITUTTER. BERETNING. Text in Danish, English, French. 1983. a. DKK 45. **Document type:** *Government.*
Formerly (until 1991): Denmark. Boligstyrelsen. Finanstilsynet. Tilsynet med Realkreditinstitutter. Beretning (0108-819X)
Published by: Finanstilsynet, Gl Kongevej 74 A, Frederiksberg C, 1850, Denmark. TEL 45-33-55-82-82, FAX 45-33-55-82-00. **Dist. by:** D B K Bogdistribution, Siljangade 2-8, Copenhagen S 2300, Denmark.

THE DENTAL PRACTICE ACQUISITION REPORT. see *MEDICAL SCIENCES—Dentistry*

332 USA ISSN 1082-8605
DEPOSIT GROWTH STRATEGIES. Text in English. 1994. m. USD 329 (effective 2001). back issues avail. **Document type:** *Newsletter.* **Description:** Discusses strategies for financial institutions to increase profits with deposits.
Related titles: Online - full text ed.
Published by: Siefer Consultants, Inc., 525 Cayuga St, Storm Lake, IA 50588. TEL 712-732-7340, FAX 712-732-7906, jsheller@siefer.com, siefer@ncn.net, http://www.siefer.com. Eds. Joe Sheller, Shere Siefer. Circ: 2,000 (paid).

DEUDA EXTERNA DE CHILE. see *BUSINESS AND ECONOMICS*

332 DEU ISSN 0722-3250
DEUTSCHE BANK BULLETIN; current economic and monetary issues. Text in English. 1982. q. **Document type:** *Bulletin, Trade.* **Description:** Analyses of German and international business activity, financial markets, monetary policy, and industries reports.
Published by: Deutsche Bank, Taunusanlage 12, Frankfurt Am Main, 60325, Germany. TEL 49-69-910-43800, FAX 49-69-910-33422, db.presse@db.com, http://www.deutsche-bank.de. Ed. Dieter Brauninger.

DEUTSCHE BUNDESBANK. BANKENSTATISTIK. see *BUSINESS AND ECONOMICS—Abstracting, Bibliographies, Statistics*

DEUTSCHE BUNDESBANK. DEVISENKURSSTATISTIK. see *BUSINESS AND ECONOMICS—Abstracting, Bibliographies, Statistics*

332.1 DEU ISSN 0070-394X
HG3054
DEUTSCHE BUNDESBANK. GESCHAEFTSBERICHT. Text in German. 1948. a. charts; stat. **Document type:** *Corporate.* **Description:** Covers economic developments and bank policy, international monetary developments and policy, annual accounts.
Related titles: English ed.: Deutsche Bundesbank. Report. ISSN 0418-8306.
Published by: Deutsche Bundesbank, Postfach 100602, Frankfurt Am Main, 60006, Germany. TEL 49-69-9566-1, FAX 49-69-5601071, http://www.bundesbank.de. Circ: 63,000.

332 DEU ISSN 0011-9997
DEUTSCHE BUNDESBANK. MITTEILUNGEN. Text in German. 1966. w. **Document type:** *Bulletin, Trade.*
Published by: Deutsche Bundesbank, Postfach 100602, Frankfurt Am Main, 60006, Germany. TEL 49-69-95661, FAX 49-69-95663077, presse-information@bundesbank.de, http://www.bundesbank.de.

332 DEU ISSN 0012-0006
HC281
DEUTSCHE BUNDESBANK. MONATSBERICHTE. Text in German. 1948. m. free. charts; mkt.; stat. index. reprints avail. **Document type:** *Bulletin.* **Description:** Covers economic and financial situation in Germany.
Related titles: English ed.: Deutsche Bundesbank. Monthly Report. ISSN 0418-8292.
Indexed: ELLIS, IBSS, KES, PAIS, RASB, WBA.
Published by: Deutsche Bundesbank, Postfach 100602, Frankfurt Am Main, 60006, Germany. TEL 49-69-9566-1, FAX 49-69-5601071, http://www.bundesbank.de. Circ: 52,500 (controlled).

DEUTSCHE BUNDESBANK. MONATSBERICHTE. STATISTISCHE BEIHEFTE. REIHE 2: KAPITALMARKTSTATISTIK. see *BUSINESS AND ECONOMICS—Abstracting, Bibliographies, Statistics*

DEUTSCHE BUNDESBANK. SAISONBEREINIGTE WIRTSCHAFTSZAHLEN. see *BUSINESS AND ECONOMICS—Abstracting, Bibliographies, Statistics*

DEUTSCHE BUNDESBANK. ZAHLUNGSBILANZSTATISTIK. see *BUSINESS AND ECONOMICS—Abstracting, Bibliographies, Statistics*

332 DEU
DEUTSCHE GELD- UND KREDITINSTITUTE. BANKEN-ORTSLEXIKON. Text in German. 1950. base vol. plus m. updates. looseleaf. **Document type:** *Directory.*
Related titles: CD-ROM ed.
Published by: Hoppenstedt Bonnier Zeitschriften GmbH, Havelstr. 9, Darmstadt, 64295, Germany. TEL 49-6151-380-0, FAX 49-6151-380-360.

332 DEU
DEUTSCHE POSTBANK AG GESCHAEFTSBERICHT. Text in German. 1990. a. **Document type:** *Corporate.*
Published by: Deutsche Postbank AG, Kaiserplatz 5-9, Postfach 4000, Bonn, 53105, Germany. TEL 49-228-920-1101, FAX 49-228-920-1810, http://www.postbank.de.

332.1 DEU ISSN 1611-4396
HD3500.A1
DEUTSCHE ZENTRAL-GENOSSENSCHAFTSBANK. GESCHAEFTSBERICHT. Text in German. 2002. a. charts; stat. **Document type:** *Journal, Corporate.*
Formed by the merger of (2001-2002): G Z Bank. Geschaeftsbericht (1611-4388); (1951-2002): D G Deutsche Genossenschaftsbank. Geschaeftsbericht (0947-6768); Which was formerly (until 1993): D G Bank Deutsche Genossenschaftsbank. Bericht ueber das Geschaeftsjahr (0722-5334); (until 1976): Deutsche Genossenschaftsbank. Bericht (0417-1888)
Related titles: English ed.: Annual report - D G-Bank. ISSN 0936-7810; French ed.: Rapport d'Exercice - D G-Bank. ISSN 0936-7829.
Published by: Deutsche Zentral-Genossenschaftsbank, Am Platz der Republik, Frankfurt Am Main, 60265, Germany. TEL 49-69-744701, FAX 49-69-74471685, mail@dzbank.de, http://www.dgbank.de, http://www.dzbank.de.

332 331.8 DEU
DEUTSCHES BANKEN-HANDBUCH. Text in German. 3/yr. looseleaf. adv. bk.rev. **Document type:** *Trade.*
Formerly: Bankangestellte (0067-3781)
Published by: Walhalla Fachverlag, Haus an der Eisernen Bruecke, Regensburg, 93042, Germany. TEL 49-941-5684-0, FAX 49-941-5684111, walhalla@walhalla.de, http://www.walhalla.de. Circ: 5,500.

332 DEU
DEUTSCHES SPARKASSEN HANDBUCH. Text in German. 3/yr. looseleaf. adv. **Document type:** *Trade.*
Published by: Walhalla Fachverlag, Haus an der Eisernen Bruecke, Regensburg, 93042, Germany. TEL 49-941-5684-0, FAX 49-941-5684111, walhalla@walhalla.de, http://www.walhalla.de. Circ: 5,800.

332.1 MUS
DEVELOPMENT BANK OF MAURITIUS. REPORT AND ACCOUNTS. Text in English. 1965. a.
Published by: Development Bank of Mauritius, PO Box 157, Port Louis, Mauritius.

DEVELOPMENT BANK OF SOUTHERN AFRICA. DEVELOPMENT PAPERS. see *BUSINESS AND ECONOMICS—International Development And Assistance*

332.1 ZMB
DEVELOPMENT BANK OF ZAMBIA. ANNUAL REPORT✶. Text in English. a. **Document type:** *Corporate.*
Published by: Development Bank of Zambia, Katondo St., Lusaka, Zambia. TEL 260-1-228576, FAX 260-1-222426, TELEX ZA 45040.

332 KEN
DEVELOPMENT FINANCE COMPANY OF KENYA. ANNUAL REPORT AND STATEMENT OF ACCOUNTS. Text in English. a. **Document type:** *Corporate.*
Published by: Development Finance Company of Kenya Ltd., Finance House, Loitta St., PO Box 30483, Nairobi, Kenya.

332 FRA ISSN 0758-7325
DICTIONNAIRE PERMANENT: EPARGNE ET PRODUITS FINANCIERS. Text in French. 2 base vols. plus m. updates. looseleaf. EUR 314 base vol(s). (effective 2004). **Description:** Examines financial, legal and fiscal problems pertaining to savings and investments.
Related titles: CD-ROM ed.; Online - full text ed.
Published by: Editions Legislatives, 80 Avenue de la Marne, Montrouge, Cedex 92546, France. TEL 33-1-40923636, FAX 33-1-40923663, infocom@editions-legislatives.fr, http://www.editions-legislatives.fr. Ed. Sylviane Mambrini. Pub. Michel Vaillant.

332.3 USA
DIMENSIONS (MADISON). Text in English. 1974. bi-m. free to qualified personnel (effective 2004). **Document type:** *Trade.* **Description:** Business magazine for the credit union marketplace.
Published by: C U N A Mutual Insurance Group, 5910 Mineral Point Rd, Madison, WI 53705. TEL 608-238-5851, FAX 608-236-7272, tom.burton@cunamutual.com, http://www.cunamutual.com/. Ed. Glenn Deutsch. Circ: 16,000 (controlled).

332 COL
DIRECTORIO DE INSTITUCIONES FINANCIERAS. Text in Spanish. a. COP 3,000, USD 10.
Published by: Corporacion Editorial Interamericana, Ave. Jimenez, 403, Of 907, PO Box 14965, Bogota, CUND 1, Colombia.

DIRECTORIO DEL SECTOR FINANCIERO. see *BUSINESS AND ECONOMICS—Trade And Industrial Directories*

332.2 USA ISSN 1068-6460
HG2150
DIRECTORS & TRUSTEES DIGEST. Text in English. 198?. m. USD 80 to non-members; USD 40 to members (effective 1999). back issues avail. **Document type:** *Newsletter.* **Description:** Provides the latest details on board-management relations, legislation and regulations and corporate governance challenges facing savings and community bankers.
Formed by the 1992 merger of: Directors Digest; Trustees and Directors Letter

Related titles: Online - full text ed.: (from Northern Light Technology, Inc., ProQuest Information & Learning).
Indexed: ABIn, BLI.
Published by: America's Community Bankers, 900 19th St, N W, Ste 400, Washington, DC 20006. TEL 202-857-3100, FAX 202-296-8716, http://www.acbankers.org, http://www.americascommunitybankers.org. Ed. William Marshall. R&P Brian Nixon TEL 202-857-3142. Circ: 8,000.

332 GBR
DIRECTORY OF FINANCIAL REGULATORY AGENCIES. Text in English. 1996. irreg. GBP 110; GBP 119 foreign. **Document type:** *Directory.* **Description:** Identifies agencies responsible for regulating banking, insurance and securities in 85 different countries. Covers 185 institutions, including central banks. Contains contact information, names of senior staff, and a summary of the functions and responsibilities of each agency.
Published by: Central Banking Publications Ltd., Fifth Fl, Tavistock House, Tavistock Sq, London, WC1H 9JZ, United Kingdom. TEL 44-20-73880006, FAX 44-20-73889040, info@centralbanking.co.uk, http://centralbanking.co.uk, http://www.centralbanking.co.uk/. Ed. Robert Pringle.

332.1 USA ISSN 0093-951X
HG4347.A1
DIRECTORY OF TRUST INSTITUTIONS. Text in English. 1962. a. USD 79.95 domestic; USD 94.95 foreign (effective 2001). adv. illus. **Document type:** *Directory, Trade.*
Formerly: Directory of Trust Institutions of United States and Canada
Published by: Primedia Business Magazines & Media, Inc. (Subsidiary of: Primedia, Inc.), 249 W 17th St, New York, NY 10011. TEL 212-462-3600, FAX 212-206-3622, inquiries@primediabusiness.com, http://www.primediabusiness.com. Circ: 12,583.

332 ITA ISSN 1722-8360
DIRITTO DELLA BANCA E DEL MERCATO FINANZIARIO. Text in Italian. 1987. q. EUR 95 domestic; EUR 130 foreign (effective 2004). **Document type:** *Journal, Academic/Scholarly.*
Published by: (Centro Studi di Diritto e Legislazione Bancaria), C E D A M, Via Giuseppe Jappelli 5-6, Padua, PD 35121, Italy. TEL 39-049-8239111, FAX 39-049-8752900, info@cedam.com, http://www.cedam.com. Ed. Alessandro Nigro. Circ: 1,000.

332 382 FRA ISSN 1024-008X
DOCUMENTARY CREDITS INSIGHT. Text in English. 1995. q. back issues avail. **Document type:** *Newsletter.* **Description:** Contains expert commentary.
Published by: (International Chamber of Commerce), I C C Publishing, 38 Cours Albert 1er, Paris, 75008, France. TEL 33-1-49532956, FAX 33-1-49532902, pub@iccwbo.org. Ed. Ron Katz.

332.024 USA ISSN 1527-2974
THE DOLLAR STRETCHER. Text in English. 1996. w. free (effective 2003). adv. 20 p./no. 2 cols./p.; **Document type:** *Newsletter.* **Description:** Covers personal financial management. Includes time and money saving articles and ideas.
Media: Online - full text. **Related titles:** E-mail ed.; Print ed.
Published by: Dollar Stretcher, Inc., PO Box 14160, Bradenton, FL 34280-4160. TEL 941-752-6693, FAX 941-752-1628, gary@stretcher.com, http://www.stretcher.com. Eds. Gary Foreman, Larry Wilson. Pub. Gary Foreman. Adv. contact Mary Foreman. Circ: 94,000.

DOLLARS & CENTS. see *BUSINESS AND ECONOMICS—Management*

332.1 DOM ISSN 0302-5241
DOMINICAN REPUBLIC. SUPERINTENDENCIA DE BANCOS. ANUARIO ESTADISTICO. Text in Spanish. 1971. a. **Document type:** *Government.*
Published by: Superintendencia de Bancos, Avda. Mexico esq. L. Navarro, Apdo. 1326, Santo Domingo, Dominican Republic.

332 DOM
DOMINICAN REPUBLIC. SUPERINTENDENCIA DE BANCOS. INFORME ESTADISTICO TRIMESTRAL. Text in Spanish. q. **Document type:** *Government.*
Published by: Superintendencia de Bancos, Avda. Mexico esq. L. Navarro, Apdo. 1326, Santo Domingo, Dominican Republic.

334.2 CAN ISSN 0012-6934
DUCA POST. Text in English. 1960. 8/yr. membership. adv. bk.rev. **Document type:** *Newsletter.*
Published by: Duca Community Credit Union Ltd., P O Box 1100, Willowdale, ON M2N 5W5, Canada. TEL 416-223-8502, FAX 416-223-2575, duca.into@duca.com, http://www.duca.com. Ed., R&P, Adv. contact Jack Vanderkooy. Circ: 11,000 (controlled).

332.024 USA
DUMMIES DAILY QUICKEN NEWSLETTER. Text in English. 1999. d. **Document type:** *Newsletter.*
Media: Online - full text.
Published by: I D G Books Worldwide, Inc., 919 E. Hillsdale Blvd., Ste. 400, Foster City, CA 94404. david@mkpr.com, http://www.dummiesdaily.com/. Ed. David Hafner.

332 GBR
E BANKER. Text in English. 1998. m.
—BLDSC (3637.709000).
Published by: Financial Times Financial Publishing (Subsidiary of: Financial Times Group), Maple House, 149 Tottenham Court Rd, London, W1P 9LL, United Kingdom. TEL 44-171-896-2314, FAX 44-171-896-2319.

332 USA
E F T DATA BOOK. (Electronic Funds Transfer) Text in English. a. USD 195 per issue (effective 2003). **Document type:** *Trade.*
Published by: Thomson Financial Media, One State St Plaza, 27th Fl, New York, NY 10004-1549. TEL 212-803-8200, FAX 212-292-5216, 800-235-5552, custserv@thomsonmedia.com, http://www.thomsonmedia.com.

E I U COUNTRY RISK SERVICE ON DISC: EUROPE. (Economist Intelligence Unit) see *BUSINESS AND ECONOMICS—Economic Situation And Conditions*

E I U COUNTRY RISK SERVICE ON DISC: LATIN AMERICA. (Economist Intelligence Unit) see *BUSINESS AND ECONOMICS—Economic Situation And Conditions*

E I U COUNTRY RISK SERVICE ON DISC: MIDDLE EAST-NORTH AFRICA. (Economist Intelligence Unit) see *BUSINESS AND ECONOMICS—Economic Situation And Conditions*

E I U COUNTRY RISK SERVICE ON DISC: SUB-SAHARAN AFRICA. (Economist Intelligence Unit) see *BUSINESS AND ECONOMICS—Economic Situation And Conditions*

332 GBR
EARNINGS GUIDE; weekly analysis of profits and earnings estimates. (Also avail. direct via modem) Text in English. 1978. m. GBP 270. adv. back issues avail. **Document type:** *Trade.*
Address: Box 1, Horsham, W Sussex RH12 3YY, United Kingdom. TEL 0403-791155, FAX 0403-701152. Ed. R Finch Hatton.

332.1 UGA ISSN 1015-0676
HG3729.E37
EAST AFRICAN DEVELOPMENT BANK. ANNUAL REPORT. Text in English. 1968. a.
Published by: East African Development Bank, PO Box 7128, Kampala, Uganda.

332 KNA
EASTERN CARIBBEAN CENTRAL BANK. QUARTERLY COMMERCIAL BANKING STATISTICS. Text in English. q. free. **Document type:** *Bulletin.*
Published by: Eastern Caribbean Central Bank, Research Department, P O Box 89, Basseterre, St Kitts, St. Kitts & Nevis. TEL 869-465-2537, FAX 869-465-5614.

332 BEL
ECHO DES TIRAGES. Text in French. m. adv.
Published by: Agefi Luxembourg, Rue de Birmingham 131, Brussels, 1070, Belgium. Circ: 18,000.

332 MAR ISSN 0851-1470
LES ECHOS AFRICAINS; mensuel marocain d'informations economiques et financieres. Text in French. 1972. m. MAD 150 (effective 2004). adv. **Document type:** *Newspaper.* **Description:** Covers international and domestic business and government news affecting Morocco.
Published by: Echos Africains, Immeuble SONIR, Rue d'Anjou angle rue Mohamed Smiha, B P 13140, Casablanca, Morocco. TEL 21-22-307271, FAX 21-22-319680, Echosafricains@usa.net. Ed. Mohamed Chouffani El Fassi. Circ: 5,000.

332 658 SGP
ECONOMETRICS IN THE INFORMATION AGE; theory and practice of measurement. Text in English. 1997. irreg., latest vol.3. price varies. **Document type:** *Monographic series, Academic/Scholarly.* **Description:** Focuses on fresh econometric methods and application to substantive problems that are subject to econometric explanation. The working of global financial markets, the modelling of economic development, and the management of large microeconomic data files for new insights into behavior are typical issues that will fit in this series.
Published by: World Scientific Publishing Co. Pte. Ltd., 5 Toh Tuck Link, Singapore, 596224, Singapore. TEL 65-466-5775, FAX 65-467-7667, wspc@wspc.com.sg, series@wspc.com.sg, http://www.wspc.com/books/series/eia_series.shtml, http://www.worldscientific.com. Eds. K Marwah, L R Klein. **Dist. by:** World Scientific Publishing Co., Inc., 1060 Main St, River Edge, NJ 07661. TEL 201-487-9655, 800-227-7562, FAX 201-487-9656, 888-977-2665; World Scientific Publishing Ltd., 57 Shelton St, London WC2H 9HE, United Kingdom. TEL 44-20-78360888, FAX 44-20-78362020, sales@wspc.co.uk.

ECONOMIC & FINANCIAL QUARTERLY. see *BUSINESS AND ECONOMICS—Economic Situation And Conditions*

332.1 CHL ISSN 0716-2421
ECONOMIC AND FINANCIAL REPORT. Text in English. 1982. m. CLP 30,000, USD 200 (effective 1999). charts; stat. **Document type:** *Government.* **Description:** Contains Chilean economic survey with 54 statistical tables.
Published by: Banco Central de Chile, Casilla 967, Santiago, Chile. TEL 56-2-670-2000, FAX 56-2-698-4847. Circ: 320.

332 USA ISSN 1526-3940
HC101
ECONOMIC AND FINANCIAL REVIEW (DALLAS). Text in English. 1999. q. free. **Document type:** *Journal, Academic/Scholarly.* **Description:** Looks at policies regarding economic, banking and financial issues.
Formed by the merger of (19??-1999): Financial Industry Studies (1526-4076); (1982-1999): Economic Review (Dallas) (0732-1414)
Related titles: Online - full text ed.: (from EBSCO Publishing, Florida Center for Library Automation, Gale Group, O C L C Online Computer Library Center, Inc., ProQuest Information & Learning).
Indexed: ABIn, BLI, JEL.
—BLDSC (3651.451700), IE.
Published by: Federal Reserve Bank of Dallas, PO Box 655906, Dallas, TX 75265-5906. TEL 214-922-5254, 214-922-5366, Kay.Champagne@dal.frb.org, http://www.dallasfed.org. Eds. Mark Wynne, Steven P A Brown.

ECONOMIC COMMENTARY. see *BUSINESS AND ECONOMICS*

ECONOMIC OUTLOOK. see *BUSINESS AND ECONOMICS—Economic Situation And Conditions*

332.2 USA
ECONOMIC OUTLOOK; a newsletter on economic issues for financial institutions. Text in English. 1991. m. USD 212 to non-members; USD 106 to members. charts. back issues avail. **Document type:** *Newsletter.* **Description:** Tracks the changes in interest rates, the housing market and the U.S. economy.
Formerly (until 1993): Economic Insight
Published by: American Community Bankers, 900 19th St, N W, Ste 400, Washington, DC 20006. TEL 202-857-3160, FAX 202-296-8716. Ed. Paul Taylor. Circ: 4,500.

ECONOMIC PORTRAIT OF THE EUROPEAN UNION. see *BUSINESS AND ECONOMICS—Cooperatives*

332 USA ISSN 0013-0281
HC107.O3 CODEN: ERFCBR
ECONOMIC REVIEW. Text in English. 1919. q. free. charts; stat. back issues avail.; reprint service avail. from CIS. **Document type:** *Journal, Academic/Scholarly.*
Supersedes: Monthly Business Review
Related titles: Microfiche ed.: (from CIS); Online - full text ed.: (from EBSCO Publishing, Florida Center for Library Automation, Gale Group, O C L C Online Computer Library Center, Inc., ProQuest Information & Learning).
Indexed: ABIn, AmStI, BLI, CREJ, Emerald, FiP, JEL, PAIS, PROMT.
—BLDSC (3654.930000), IE, ingenta.
Published by: Federal Reserve Bank of Cleveland, PO Box 6387, Cleveland, OH 44101. TEL 216-579-3079, FAX 216-579-2477. Eds. Michele Lachman, Monica Crabtree-Reuser. R&P Lee Faulhaber TEL 216-579-2961. Circ: 12,100.

330 IND ISSN 0013-0389
HC424.A1
ECONOMIC TIMES. Text in English. 1961. d. USD 200. adv. bk.rev. charts; illus.; stat. reprints avail. **Document type:** *Newspaper.*
Related titles: Microfiche ed.; Microfilm ed.; Online - full text ed.: (from Gale Group, Newsbank, Inc., O C L C Online Computer Library Center, Inc.).
Indexed: RASB.
Published by: Bennett Coleman & Co. Ltd., 7, Bahadurshah Zafar Marg, Dr. D.N. Rd., New Delhi, 110 002, India. TEL 91-11-23302000, servicedesk@timesgroup.com, http://www.economictimes.com. Ed. Hannan Ezekiel. Circ: 45,300. **Subscr. in US to:** M-s. Kalpana, 42 75 Main St, Flushing, NY 11355.

332 LKA
ECONOMIC TIMES. Text in English. 1970. fortn. USD 16 (effective 2001). adv. bk.rev. tr.lit.; stat. 12 p./no. 6 cols./p.; **Document type:** *Newspaper, Trade.*
Indexed: RASB, SLSI.
Published by: Albion Publications, 51-1 Sri Dharmarama Rd., Colombo, 9, Sri Lanka. TEL 94-686337, FAX 94-670887. Ed., R&P Thimsy Fahim. Adv. contact Al Haj M A C M Fahim. page USD 286. Circ: 10,000.

332 USA
ECONOMIC TOPICS* . Text in English. m. USD 100 to non-members. **Description:** Contains analysis and forecasting of major market trends to determine their impact on the savings institution business.
Formerly: Economic Topics for Savings and Loan Management
Published by: United States League of Savings Institutions, 900 19th St, N W, 900, Washington, DC 20006-2105. TEL 312-644-3100, FAX 312-644-9358. Ed. James Christian. Circ: 11,000.

332 PHL ISSN 0117-0511
HC411
ECONOMICS AND DEVELOPMENT RESOURCE CENTER. REPORT SERIES. Text in English. irreg., latest vol.55, 1991.
Published by: (Economics and Development Resource Center), Asian Development Bank, Publications Unit, P.O. Box 789, Manila, 0980, Philippines. adbpub@adb.org, http://www.adb.org.

ECONOMICS MONITOR. see *BUSINESS AND ECONOMICS—Economic Situation And Conditions*

330 ARG ISSN 0013-0648
ECONOMISTA; semanario economico-financiero. Text in Spanish. 1951. w. ARS 5,800. adv. bk.rev. stat.; tr.lit. **Document type:** *Newspaper.*
Published by: Empresa Editorial el Economista s.r.l., Avda. Cordoba, 632 2o, Capital Federal, Buenos Aires 1054, Argentina. TEL 54-114-3223308, FAX 54-114-3228157, TELEX 23542. Ed. D Radonjic. Circ: 37,800.

B

332 ECU
ECUADOR. SUPERINTENDENCIA DE BANCOS. BOLETIN ESTADISTICO. Text in Spanish. 1938. a. ECS 2,000. charts; stat. **Document type:** *Bulletin, Government.*
Formerly: Ecuador. Superintendencia de Bancos. Boletin
Published by: Superintendencia de Bancos, Apdo. de Correos 17-17-770, Ave. 12 DE OCTUBRE, 1561, Quito, Pichincha, Ecuador. FAX 563-652, TELEX 21102 SUPBAN ED.

332 ECU
ECUADOR. SUPERINTENDENCIA DE BANCOS. MEMORIA. Text in Spanish. a. ECS 18,000. charts; stat.
Published by: Superintendencia de Bancos, Apdo. de Correos 17-17-770, Ave. 12 DE OCTUBRE, 1561, Quito, Pichincha, Ecuador. FAX 563-652.

336 EST ISSN 1406-1392
EESTI PANK. BULLETIN/BANK OF ESTONIA. BULLETIN. Text in Estonian. 1994. bi-m. **Document type:** *Bulletin, Trade.*
Related titles: Online - full text ed.
Published by: Eesti Pank/Bank of Estonia, Estonia bld 13, Tallinn, 15095, Estonia. TEL 372-631-0951, FAX 372-631-0954, info@epbe.ee, http://www.ee/epbe/.

336 EST
EESTI PANK. NEWSLETTER/BANK OF ESTONIA. NEWSLETTER. Text in Estonian. 2/yr. **Document type:** *Trade.*
Published by: Eesti Pank/Bank of Estonia, Estonia bld 13, Tallinn, 15095, Estonia. TEL 372-631-0951, FAX 372-631-0954, info@epbe.ee, http://www.ee/epbe/.

332 UKR
EKONOMIKA, FINANSY, PRAVO. Text in Ukrainian. m. USD 160 in United States.
Address: Ul Goloseevskaya 7, Kiev, Ukraine. TEL 380-44-264-9885, FAX 380-44-265-8462. **US dist. addr.:** East View Information Services, 3020 Harbor Ln. N., Minneapolis, MN 55447. TEL 612-550-0961.

332 332.6 RUS
EKSPERT. Text in Russian. 48/yr.
Address: Ul Krzhizhanovskogo 24-35, Moscow, 117218, Russian Federation. TEL 7-095-1246390, FAX 7-095-1295015, ask@expert.ru, http://www.expert.ru. Ed. N V Kirichenko. **US dist. addr.:** East View Information Services, 3020 Harbor Ln. N., Minneapolis, MN 55447. TEL 612-550-0961.

305.26 USA
ELDERCARE FORUM. Text in English. 1994. q. USD 14. **Document type:** *Trade.* **Description:** Educates and informs caregivers about issues related to aging and taking care of an aging parent. Focuses on personal financial management, health and medical issues, housing, government programs, and resources for caregivers.
Related titles: Online - full text ed.
Published by: ElderCare Financial Management, Inc., 170 Elaine Dr, Roswell, GA 30075. TEL 770-518-2767, hwlj87a@prodigy.com, http://www.mindspung.com/~eldercare/elderweb.htm. Ed., R&P Laura Beller. Circ: 15,000 (paid).

332 FRA ISSN 1630-9553
ELECTRONIC BANKING NEWS. Text in English. 1998. m. (11/yr). EUR 793 domestic; EUR 960 foreign (effective 2000). **Document type:** *Newsletter.* **Description:** Keeps readers informed on strategic moves of other banks and financial institutions, and covers all aspects of electronic banking in both retail and corporate sectors.
Published by: Publi-News, 47 rue Aristide Briand, Levallois-Perret, 92300, France. TEL 33-1-41499360, FAX 33-1-47573725, publi.news@wanadoo.fr. Ed. Ange Galula.

ELECTRONIC COMMERCE ADVISOR. see *BUSINESS AND ECONOMICS—Banking And Finance—Computer Applications*

ELSEVIER V P B ALMANAK. see *BUSINESS AND ECONOMICS—Public Finance, Taxation*

332 NLD ISSN 1566-0141
HG5993
➤ **EMERGING MARKETS REVIEW.** Text in English. 2000. 4/yr. EUR 52 in Europe to individuals; JPY 7,000 in Japan to individuals; USD 54 elsewhere to individuals; EUR 196 in Europe to institutions; JPY 25,900 in Japan to institutions; USD 219 elsewhere to institutions (effective 2006). back issues avail.; reprints avail. **Document type:** *Journal, Academic/Scholarly.* **Description:** Addresses the many challenges the emerging markets pose.
Related titles: Online - full text ed.: (from EBSCO Publishing, Gale Group, IngentaConnect, ScienceDirect, Swets Information Services).
Indexed: CJA, ESPM, JEL, RiskAb.
—BLDSC (3733.426947), IE, Infotrieve, ingenta. **CCC.**
Published by: Elsevier BV, North-Holland (Subsidiary of: Elsevier Science & Technology), Sara Burgerhartstraat 25, Amsterdam, 1055 KV, Netherlands. TEL 31-20-485-3911, FAX 31-20-485-2457, nlinfo-f@elsevier.nl, http://www.elsevier.com/locate/emr, http://www.elsevier.nl. Ed. J. Estrada. **Subscr. to:** Elsevier BV, PO Box 211, Amsterdam 1000 AE, Netherlands. TEL 31-20-485-3757, FAX 31-20-485-3432, http://www.elsevier.nl.

332 658.3 USA
EMPLOYEE MOTIVATION & INCENTIVE STRATEGIES FOR FINANCIAL INSTITUTIONS. Text in English. 1993. m. USD 279 (effective 2004). **Document type:** *Newsletter.*
Published by: Siefer Consultants, Inc., 525 Cayuga St, Storm Lake, IA 50588. TEL 712-732-7340, FAX 712-732-7906, info@siefer.com, http://www.siefer.com. Ed. Ed Gallagher. Circ: 1,500 (paid).

EMPLOYMENT LAW SERIES. QUALIFIED RETIREMENT PLANS. see *BUSINESS AND ECONOMICS—Personnel Management*

332 PRT
EMPRESAS NA BOLSA✶. Text in Portuguese. a.
Published by: (Ascor Dealer Sociedade Financeira de Corretagem), Texto Editora Lda., Alto de Bela Vista Casal de Vale Mourao, Cacem, 2735, Portugal. TEL 1-9180208. Eds. Alvaro Mendonca, Ana Paula Saude.

ENCYCLOPEDIA OF BANKING LAW. see *LAW*

332.7 340 GBR ISSN 0142-2820
ENCYCLOPEDIA OF COMPULSORY PURCHASE AND COMPENSATION. Text in English. 1968. 2 base vols. plus updates 3/yr. looseleaf. GBP 555 base vol(s).; GBP 398, EUR 599 updates in Europe; GBP 415, USD 754 updates elsewhere (effective 2006). **Document type:** *Trade.*
Published by: Sweet & Maxwell Ltd., 100 Avenue Road, London, NW3 3PF, United Kingdom. TEL 44-20-74491111, FAX 44-20-74491144, customer.services@sweetandmaxwell.co.uk, http://www.sweetandmaxwell.co.uk. **Subscr. to:** Cheriton House, North Way, Andover, Hants SP10 5BE, United Kingdom.

332.7 340 GBR ISSN 0142-2812
ENCYCLOPEDIA OF CONSUMER CREDIT LAW. Text in English. 1975. 3 base vols. plus updates 3/yr. looseleaf. GBP 712 base vol(s).; GBP 470, EUR 707 updates in Europe; GBP 485, USD 881 updates elsewhere (effective 2006). **Document type:** *Trade.*
Published by: Sweet & Maxwell Ltd., 100 Avenue Road, London, NW3 3PF, United Kingdom. TEL 44-20-74491111, FAX 44-20-74491144, customer.services@sweetandmaxwell.co.uk, http://www.sweetandmaxwell.co.uk. **Subscr. to:** Cheriton House, North Way, Andover, Hants SP10 5BE, United Kingdom.

332 340 GBR
ENCYCLOPEDIA OF FINANCIAL SERVICES LAW. Text in English. 1987. 5 base vols. plus updates 4/yr. looseleaf. GBP 1,035 base vol(s).; GBP 995, EUR 1,480 updates in Europe; GBP 1,015, USD 1,852 updates elsewhere; GBP 498, EUR 740 updates in Europe to students; GBP 508, USD 926 updates elsewhere to students (effective 2005).
Published by: Sweet & Maxwell Ltd., 100 Avenue Road, London, NW3 3PF, United Kingdom. TEL 44-20-74491111, FAX 44-20-74491144, http://www.sweetandmaxwell.co.uk. **Subscr. to:** Cheriton House, North Way, Andover, Hants SP10 5BE, United Kingdom.

332.1 334 USA
END POINT EXPRESS; exclusive report for bank operations professionals. Text in English. 1984. fortn. USD 247. bk.rev. **Description:** Covers changing technologies, new approaches and cost-saving ideas.
Former titles: Back-Office Bulletin; Executive Automation Report for the Community Banker
Published by: United Communications Group, 11300 Rockville Pike Ste 1100, Rockville, MD 20852-3030. TEL 301-816-8950, FAX 301-816-8945. Ed. Martin Zook.

332 333.79 GBR ISSN 1742-4305
ENERGY RISK. Text in English. 1994. 10/yr. GBP 344, EUR 540, USD 575 to individuals (effective 2004). adv. back issues avail. **Document type:** *Trade.* **Description:** Delivers comprehensive, cutting-edge analysis of financial risk management in the world's energy and power markets.
Former titles (until 2003): Energy & Power Risk Management (1362-5403); (until 1996): Energy Risk (1352-0768)
—IE. **CCC.**
Published by: Risk Waters Group (Subsidiary of: Incisive Media Plc.), Haymarket House, 28-29 Haymarket, London, SW1Y 4RX, United Kingdom. TEL 44-20-74849700, FAX 44-20-79302238, http://db.riskwaters.com/public/showPage.html?page=erisk_index, http://www.incisivemedia.com. Adv. contacts Adam Jordan, Trevor Wilkins. B&W page GBP 2,250, color page GBP 2,670; trim 210 x 297. Circ: 4,000. **Affiliate:** Risk Waters Group.

332 CAN
ENTERPRISE (VANCOUVER). Text in English. bi-m.
Published by: Credit Union Central of British Columbia, 1441 Creekside Dr, Vancouver, BC V6J 4S7, Canada. TEL 604-734-2511, FAX 604-730-6434. Ed. Roberta Staley. Circ: 2,500.

332 DEU ISSN 0421-2991
ENTSCHEIDUNGEN DER FINANZGERICHTE. Text in German. 1953. s-m. EUR 271.80; EUR 13.30 newsstand/cover (effective 2005). adv. back issues avail. **Document type:** *Bulletin, Trade.*
—**CCC.**
Published by: Stollfuss Verlag GmbH & Co. KG, Dechenstr 7, Bonn, 53115, Germany. TEL 49-228-7240, FAX 49-228-72491181, info@stollfuss.de, http://www.stollfuss.de/programm/products/0400030.htm. Ed. Eckart Ranft. adv.: B&W page EUR 1,435, color page EUR 2,585. Circ: 9,000 (paid and controlled).

ENVIRONMENTAL OBLIGATIONS IN BANKRUPTCY. see *LAW*

332.1 FRA ISSN 1157-6472
EPARGNE ET FINANCE; le magazine de l'actualite et des mutations bancaires. Text in French. 1882. bi-m. bk.rev. charts; illus.; stat. **Description:** For bank managers, financiers and economists.
Formerly (until 1992): Journal des Caisses d'Epargne (0047-2182)
Indexed: ELLIS, PAIS, RASB.
Published by: Journal des Caisses d'Epargne SARL, 29 rue de la Tombe-Issoire, Paris, Cedex 14 75673, France. TEL 40-78-41-01, FAX 40-78-40-10, TELEX 200 668. Ed. Nicolas de Bourgies. Circ: 15,000.

332 GRC ISSN 1105-2503
HC291
EPILOGI/CHOICE; oikonomiki epitheorisi. Text in Greek; Summaries in English. 1963. m. USD 150. adv. bk.rev. stat. **Description:** Economic reviews of banking, the financial markets, management, and international and domestic business. Examines the impact of current domestic and international developments.
Related titles: ◆ Supplement(s): Banks, Investment & Stockmarket; ◆ Economic Review of the Year - The Greek Economy. ISSN 1105-252X; ◆ Economy and the Foreign Policy; ◆ Regional Development - The Regions of Greece; ◆ Capital Markets; ◆ Business in Greece; ◆ Balance Sheets. ISSN 1105-2511; ◆ Shipping and Tourism; ◆ Northern Greece - Thessaloniki International Trade Fair (Year); ◆ Defence and the Economy.
Indexed: LibLit.
Published by: Electra Press, 4 Stadiou St, Athens, 105 64, Greece. TEL 30-1-323-3203, FAX 323-5160, TELEX 210564. Ed. Christos Papaioannou. Circ: 9,000.

332.1 AUT
ERSTE BANK. QUARTALSBERICHT. Text in German. q. **Document type:** *Bulletin, Trade.*
Published by: Erste Bank, Graben 21, Vienna, W 1010, Austria. TEL 43-1-531001511, FAX 43-1-531003112, service.center@erstebank.at, investor.relations@erstebank.at, http://www.erstebank.at.

ESTADISTICA PANAMENA. SITUACION ECONOMICA. SECCION 344. FINANZAS. see *BUSINESS AND ECONOMICS—Abstracting, Bibliographies, Statistics*

ESTADISTICAS BANCA INTERNET. see *BUSINESS AND ECONOMICS—Abstracting, Bibliographies, Statistics*

332 CHL
ESTADOS FINANCIEROS ANUALES BANCOS Y SOCIEDADES FINANCIERAS. Text in Spanish. 2000. a.
Media: Online - full content. **Related titles:** E-mail ed.
Published by: Superintendencia de Bancos e Instituciones Financieras, Moneda 1123, Santiago, Chile. TEL 56-2-4426200, http://www.sbif.cl/cgi-bin/publicaciones.pl.

ESTADOS FINANCIEROS ANUALES DE SOCIEDADES FILIALES. see *BUSINESS AND ECONOMICS—Abstracting, Bibliographies, Statistics*

ESTATE AND PERSONAL FINANCIAL PLANNING. see *REAL ESTATE*

332.1021 PRT ISSN 0377-2322
HG186.P8
ESTATISTICAS MONETARIAS E FINANCEIRAS. Text in Portuguese. 1968. a. EUR 5 (effective 2005). **Document type:** *Government.* **Description:** Provides statistical data on banking, financial institutions, insurance companies and mutual aid societies.
Related titles: CD-ROM ed.
Published by: Instituto Nacional de Estatistica, Ave. Antonio Jose de Almeida 2, Lisbon, 1000-043, Portugal. TEL 351-21-8426100, FAX 351-21-8426380, ine@ine.pt, http://www.ine.pt/.

332 CHL ISSN 0716-1255
ESTRATEGIA. Text in Spanish. 1978. d. (5/w.). CLP 89,900 domestic; USD 700 foreign. adv. charts; mkt.; stat.
Related titles: Online - full text ed.
Indexed: B&I.
Published by: Editorial Gestion Ltda., Casilla 16485 Correo 9, Rafael Canas, 114, Santiago, Chile. TEL 56-2-2361313, FAX 56-2-2361114, estrategia@edgestion.cl, http://www.estrategia.cl/. Ed. Victor Manuel Ojeda. Adv. contact Rodrigo Sepulveda. Circ: 42,000.

332 ESP ISSN 1130-8753
ESTRATEGIA FINANCIERA. Text in Spanish. 1987. 11/yr. EUR 216 combined subscription Print & online eds. (effective 2005). adv. **Document type:** *Magazine, Consumer.*
Published by: Grupo Especial Directivos (Subsidiary of: Wolters Kluwer BV), Orense 16, Madrid, 28020, Spain. TEL 34-902-250520, FAX 34-902-250502, clientes@edirectivos.com, http://www.estrategiafinanciera.es/, http://www.e-directivos.com. Ed. Juan Jose Gonzalez Ortiz. Adv. contact Ricardo Zavala. Circ: 8,000 (controlled).

332.1 ESP
ESTUDIA Y AHORRA. Text in Spanish. 1966. q. free. bk.rev.
Published by: Caja de Ahorros de Ronda, VIRGEN DE LA PAZ, 18, Ronda, Malaga 29400, Spain.

332 BEL ISSN 1780-7611
➤ **EUREDIA - REVUE EUROPEENE DE DROIT BANCAIRE ET FINANCIER/EUREDIA - EUROPEAN BANKING & FINANCIAL LAW REVIEW.** Text in French, English. 1999. q. EUR 200 (effective 2004). bk.rev. **Document type:** *Journal, Academic/Scholarly.* **Description:** Reviews developments and cases in banking and financial law.
Published by: Euredia, c/o AEDBF, 54 Rue De Boeck, Bruxelles, B-1140, Belgium. info@euredia.be, http://www.euredia.be.

332 GBR
THE EURO. Text in English. 1998. bi-m. **Document type:** *Trade.* **Description:** Devoted to coverage of the "euro-zone." Looks at the implications for commercial banking, investment banking and underwriting, bank capital raising, and government and corporate funding, as well as more technical issues.
Published by: Euromoney Institutional Investor Plc., Nestor House, Playhouse Yard, London, EC4V 5EX, United Kingdom. TEL 44-20-7779-8673, FAX 44-20-7779-8541.

332.6 DEU
EURO AM SONNTAG. Text in German. 1999. w. (Sun.). EUR 2.50 newsstand/cover (effective 2003). adv. **Document type:** *Newspaper, Consumer.* **Description:** Covers all aspects of the business and finance industries.
Related titles: Online - full text ed.
Published by: Finanzen Verlagsgesellschaft mbH (Subsidiary of: Axel Springer Verlag AG), Isabellastr 32, Munich, 80796, Germany. TEL 49-89-272640, FAX 49-89-27264199, redaktion@eurams.de, http://www.eurams.de. Ed. Frank Bernhard Werner. R&P Bernd Engelke TEL 49-89-27264291. Adv. contact Nikos Koloutsos. B&W page EUR 8,200, color page EUR 12,240; trim 235 x 340. Circ: 125,207 (paid).

EUROMARKET DECISIONS. see *BUSINESS AND ECONOMICS—Investments*

332.1 338 USA ISSN 1083-8880
EUROMEDIA ACQUISITIONS & FINANCE. Text in English. 1992. m. adv. **Document type:** *Newsletter, Trade.* **Description:** Contains comprehensive analyses of single-country and cross-border media financing throughout Europe. Gain access to information on financing activity, sources of capital, capital markets, financing structures and company growth projections.
Formed by the merger of: Euromedia Acquisitions (1061-2874); Euromedia Finance (1070-3233)
Related titles: E-mail ed.: USD 845 (effective 2001); Fax ed.: USD 845 (effective 2001).
Published by: Kagan Research, LLC, 1 Lower Ragsdale Dr., Ste. 130, Monterey, CA 93940-5741. TEL 831-624-1536, FAX 831-625-3225, info@kagan.com, http://www.kagan.com/cgi-bin/pkcat/eaf.html. Pub. Paul Kagan.

332.4 382 GBR ISSN 0014-2433
HG3881
EUROMONEY; the monthly journal of international money and capital markets. Text in English. 1969. m. GBP 349 combined subscription domestic print & online eds.; EUR 515 combined subscription in Europe print & online eds.; USD 539 combined subscription elsewhere print & online eds. (effective 2005). bk.rev. illus. index. reprint service avail. from PQC. **Document type:** *Magazine, Trade.* **Description:** Covers the world of international finance.
Related titles: CD-ROM ed.; Microform ed.: (from PQC); Online - full text ed.: Euromoney Online. GBP 40; USD 60 elsewhere (effective Aug. 2001) (from EBSCO Publishing, Florida Center for Library Automation, Gale Group, H.W. Wilson, O C L C Online Computer Library Center, Inc., ProQuest Information & Learning, The Dialog Corporation).
Indexed: ABIn, B&I, BLI, BPI, BPIA, BusI, CREJ, ELJI, ELLIS, IBSS, IPARL, IndBusRep, KES, LJI, MEA&I, ManagCont, PAIS, PROMT, RefZh, SCIMP, T&II, WBA, WMB.
—BLDSC (3829.286000), IE, Infotrieve, ingenta. **CCC.**
Published by: Euromoney Institutional Investor Plc., Nestor House, Playhouse Yard, London, EC4V 5EX, United Kingdom. TEL 44-20-7779-8673, FAX 44-20-7779-8541, information@euromoneyplc.com, gevans@pobox.com, http://www.euromoney.com. Ed. Peter Lee. Pub. Neil Osborn. Circ: 20,674. **Subscr. to:** Eclipse, The In-house Fulfillment Bureau, PO Box 18083, London EC4V 5JS, United Kingdom. TEL 44-20-7779-8610, FAX 44-20-7779-8602, CustomerService@euromoneyplc.com. **Dist. in US by:** American Educational Systems, PO Box 246, New York, NY 10024-0246. TEL 800-431-1579, aesbooks@aol.com.

332 GBR
EUROMONEY BANK REGISTER (YEAR). Text in English. 1983. a. GBP 180, USD 335 (effective 1998). **Document type:** *Directory.* **Description:** Provides contact information and details on more than 12,000 commercial banks, investment banks, central banks, brokers, exchanges, finance companies, private equity firms and investment managers.
Published by: Euromoney Publications plc, Nestor House, Playhouse Yard, London, EC4V 5EX, United Kingdom. TEL 44-20-77798673, FAX 44-20-77798541.

332.4 GBR
EUROMONEY CAPITAL MARKETS GUIDE; the complete data service on syndicated loans and Eurobonds. Text in English. 1980. q. GBP 2,300 domestic; USD 3,700 foreign (effective 2002). **Document type:** *Journal, Trade.*
Formerly: Euromoney Syndication Guide (0260-6747)
Published by: Euromoney Institutional Investor Plc., Nestor House, Playhouse Yard, London, EC4V 5EX, United Kingdom. TEL 44-20-7779-8673, FAX 44-20-7779-8541, http://www.euromoneyplc.com. Ed. Nick Evans. **Subscr. to:** Quadrant Subscription Services, Rockwood House, 9-17 Perrymount Rd, Haywards Heath, W. Sussex RH16 3DH, United Kingdom. TEL 44-20-8652-3500, FAX 44-20-8652-8932. **Dist. in US by:** American Educational Systems, PO Box 246, New York, NY 10024-0246. TEL 800-431-1579, aesbooks@aol.com.

332 GBR
THE EUROMONEY FOREIGN EXCHANGE HANDBOOK (YEAR). Text in English. a. GBP 135, USD 245 (effective 1998). **Description:** Provides information and contact details for managers and dealers in foreign exchange throughout the world.
Published by: Euromoney Publications plc, Nestor House, Playhouse Yard, London, EC4V 5EX, United Kingdom. TEL 44-207-7798673, FAX 44-20-77798541.

332 GBR ISSN 0264-6706
EUROMONEY TRADE FINANCE REPORT. Text in English. 1985. m.
Indexed: PAIS.
—IE.
Published by: Euromoney Publications plc, Nestor House, Playhouse Yard, London, EC4V 5EX, United Kingdom.

332 DEU ISSN 1561-0322
EUROOPAN KESKUSPANKIKI. KUUKAUSIKATSAUS. Text in Spanish. 1999. m.
Related titles: ♦ English ed.: European Central Bank. Monthly Bulletin. ISSN 1561-0136; ♦ Spanish ed.: Banco Central Europeo. Boletin Mensual. ISSN 1561-0268; ♦ Italian ed.: Banca Centrale Europea. Bollettino Mensile. ISSN 1561-0276; ♦ Portuguese ed.: Banco Central Europeu. Boletin Mensal. ISSN 1561-0284; ♦ German ed.: Europaische Zentralbank. Monatsbericht. ISSN 1561-0292; ♦ Dutch ed.: Europese Centrale Bank. Maandbericht. ISSN 1561-0314; ♦ Greek ed.: Europaike Kentrike Trapeza. Meniaio Deltio. ISSN 1561-025X; ♦ Swedish ed.: Europeiska Centralbanken. Manadsrapport. ISSN 1561-0144; ♦ Danish ed.: Europaeiske Centralbank. Manedsoversigt. ISSN 1561-0241; ♦ French ed.: Banque Central Europeenne. Bulletin Mensuel. ISSN 1561-0306.
Published by: European Central Bank, Postfach 16 03 19, Frankfurt am Main, 60066, Germany. TEL 49-69-1344-0, FAX 49-69-1344-6000, http://www.ecb.int.

332 DEU ISSN 1561-0241
EUROPAEISKE CENTRALBANK. MANEDSOVERSIGT. Text in Danish. 1999. m.
Related titles: ♦ English ed.: European Central Bank. Monthly Bulletin. ISSN 1561-0136; ♦ Spanish ed.: Banco Central Europeo. Boletin Mensual. ISSN 1561-0268; ♦ Italian ed.: Banca Centrale Europea. Bollettino Mensile. ISSN 1561-0276; ♦ Portuguese ed.: Banco Central Europeu. Boletin Mensal. ISSN 1561-0284; ♦ German ed.: Europaische Zentralbank. Monatsbericht. ISSN 1561-0292; ♦ Dutch ed.: Europese Centrale Bank. Maandbericht. ISSN 1561-0314; ♦ Spanish ed.: Euroopan Keskuspankiki. Kuukausikatsaus. ISSN 1561-0322; ♦ Greek ed.: Europaike Kentrike Trapeza. Meniaio Deltio. ISSN 1561-025X; ♦ Swedish ed.: Europeiska Centralbanken. Manadsrapport. ISSN 1561-0144; ♦ French ed.: Banque Central Europeenne. Bulletin Mensuel. ISSN 1561-0306.
Published by: European Central Bank, Postfach 16 03 19, Frankfurt am Main, 60066, Germany. TEL 49-69-1344-0, FAX 49-69-1344-6000, http://www.ecb.int.

332 DEU ISSN 1561-025X
EUROPAIKE KENTRIKE TRAPEZA. MENIAIO DELTIO. Text in Greek. 1999. m.
Related titles: ♦ English ed.: European Central Bank. Monthly Bulletin. ISSN 1561-0136; ♦ Spanish ed.: Banco Central Europeo. Boletin Mensual. ISSN 1561-0268; ♦ Italian ed.: Banca Centrale Europea. Bollettino Mensile. ISSN 1561-0276; ♦ Portuguese ed.: Banco Central Europeu. Boletin Mensal. ISSN 1561-0284; ♦ German ed.: Europaische Zentralbank. Monatsbericht. ISSN 1561-0292; ♦ Dutch ed.: Europese Centrale Bank. Maandbericht. ISSN 1561-0314; ♦ Spanish ed.: Euroopan Keskuspankiki. Kuukausikatsaus. ISSN 1561-0322; ♦ Swedish ed.: Europeiska Centralbanken. Manadsrapport. ISSN 1561-0144; ♦ Danish ed.: Europaeiske Centralbank. Manedsoversigt. ISSN 1561-0241; ♦ French ed.: Banque Central Europeenne. Bulletin Mensuel. ISSN 1561-0306.
Published by: European Central Bank, Postfach 16 03 19, Frankfurt am Main, 60066, Germany. TEL 49-69-1344-0, FAX 49-69-1344-6000, http://www.ecb.int.

332 DEU ISSN 1561-0292
EUROPAISCHE ZENTRALBANK. MONATSBERICHT. Text in German. 1999. m.
Related titles: ♦ English ed.: European Central Bank. Monthly Bulletin. ISSN 1561-0136; ♦ Spanish ed.: Banco Central Europeo. Boletin Mensual. ISSN 1561-0268; ♦ Italian ed.: Banca Centrale Europea. Bollettino Mensile. ISSN 1561-0276; ♦ Portuguese ed.: Banco Central Europeu. Boletin Mensal. ISSN 1561-0284; ♦ Dutch ed.: Europese Centrale Bank. Maandbericht. ISSN 1561-0314; ♦ Spanish ed.: Euroopan Keskuspankiki. Kuukausikatsaus. ISSN 1561-0322; ♦ Greek ed.: Europaike Kentrike Trapeza. Meniaio Deltio. ISSN 1561-025X; ♦ Swedish ed.: Europeiska Centralbanken. Manadsrapport. ISSN 1561-0144; ♦ Danish ed.: Europaeiske Centralbank. Manedsoversigt. ISSN 1561-0241; ♦ French ed.: Banque Central Europeenne. Bulletin Mensuel. ISSN 1561-0306.
Published by: European Central Bank, Postfach 16 03 19, Frankfurt am Main, 60066, Germany. TEL 49-69-1344-0, FAX 49-69-1344-6000, http://www.ecb.int.

332 GBR ISSN 0953-8399
EUROPEAN BANKER. Text in English. 1989. m. GBP 997, EUR 1,597, USD 1,597 (effective 2005). **Document type:** *Newsletter.* **Description:** Gives news and market intelligence on national and cross-border developments in European banking, insurance and finance.
Related titles: Online - full text ed.: (from Gale Group, LexisNexis, Northern Light Technology, Inc., O C L C Online Computer Library Center, Inc., ProQuest Information & Learning).
Indexed: ABIn.
—IE.
Published by: Lafferty Publications Ltd., The Colonnades, 82 Bishops Bridge Rd, London, W2 6BB, United Kingdom. TEL 44-20-75635700, FAX 44-20-75635701, cuserv@lafferty.com, http://www.lafferty.com/newsletter_publication.php?id=2. Ed. Diane Sim.

332.1 GBR
THE EUROPEAN BANKING REVIEW. Text in English. a. adv. **Document type:** *Trade.*
Published by: P P F Publications Ltd., Roman House, 296 Golders Green Rd, London, NW11 9PY, United Kingdom. TEL 44-181-455-1166, FAX 44-171-573-7819. Ed. Paul Davidson. Adv. contact Sharon Hand.

332 DEU ISSN 1561-4573
HG2976
EUROPEAN CENTRAL BANK. ANNUAL REPORT. Text in English. 1992. a. **Document type:** *Yearbook, Trade.*
Former titles (until 1998): European Monetary Institute. Annual Report (1024-560X); (until 1994): Committee of Governors of the Central Banks of the Member States of the European Economic Community. Annual Report (1021-3384)
Related titles: Danish ed.: Europaeiske Centralbank. Arsberetning. ISSN 1561-4506; Greek ed.: Europaike Kentrike Trapeza. Etesia Ekthese. ISSN 1561-4514; Spanish ed.: Banco Central Europeo. Informe Anual. ISSN 1561-4522; Italian ed.: Banca Centrale Europea. Rapporto Annuale. ISSN 1561-4530; Portuguese ed.: Banco Central Europeu. Relatorio Anual. ISSN 1561-4549; Swedish ed.: Europeiska

Centralbanken. Arsrapport. ISSN 1561-4557; German ed.: Europaische Zentralbank. Jahresbericht. ISSN 1561-4565; French ed.: Banque Centrale Europeenne. Rapport Annuel. ISSN 1561-4581; Dutch ed.: Europese Centrale Bank. Jaarverslag. ISSN 1561-459X; Finnish ed.: Euroopan Keskuspankki. Vuosikertomous. ISSN 1561-4603.
Published by: European Central Bank, Postfach 16 03 19, Frankfurt am Main, 60066, Germany. TEL 49-69-1344-0, FAX 49-69-1344-6000, TELEX 411 144 ECB D, http://www.ecb.int.

332 DEU
EUROPEAN CENTRAL BANK. COMPENDIUM. Text in English. bi-m. free. **Document type:** *Government.*
Published by: European Central Bank, Postfach 16 03 19, Frankfurt am Main, 60066, Germany. http://www.ecb.int.

332 DEU
EUROPEAN CENTRAL BANK. CONVERGENCE REPORT. Text in English. irreg.
Related titles: Online - full text ed.
Published by: European Central Bank, Postfach 16 03 19, Frankfurt am Main, 60066, Germany. http://www.ecb.int/.

332 DEU ISSN 1561-0136
HG2976
EUROPEAN CENTRAL BANK. MONTHLY BULLETIN/BANQUE CENTRALE EUROPEENNE. BULLETIN MENSUEL. Text in English. 1999. m. **Document type:** *Bulletin.* **Description:** Attempts to explain to the public, through a comprehensive economic analysis, the monetary policy decisions taken by the Governing Council of the ECB.
Related titles: ♦ Spanish ed.: Banco Central Europeo. Boletin Mensual. ISSN 1561-0268; ♦ Italian ed.: Banca Centrale Europea. Bollettino Mensile. ISSN 1561-0276; ♦ Portuguese ed.: Banco Central Europeu. Boletin Mensal. ISSN 1561-0284; ♦ German ed.: Europaische Zentralbank. Monatsbericht. ISSN 1561-0292; ♦ Dutch ed.: Europese Centrale Bank. Maandbericht. ISSN 1561-0314; ♦ Spanish ed.: Euroopan Keskuspankiki. Kuukausikatsaus. ISSN 1561-0322; ♦ Greek ed.: Europaike Kentrike Trapeza. Meniaio Deltio. ISSN 1561-025X; ♦ Swedish ed.: Europeiska Centralbanken. Manadsrapport. ISSN 1561-0144; ♦ Danish ed.: Europaeiske Centralbank. Manedsoversigt. ISSN 1561-0241; ♦ French ed.: Banque Central Europeenne. Bulletin Mensuel. ISSN 1561-0306.
Indexed: PAIS.
—BLDSC (5931.375000).
Published by: European Central Bank, Postfach 16 03 19, Frankfurt am Main, 60066, Germany. TEL 49-69-1344-0, FAX 49-69-1344-6000, TELEX 411 144 ECB D, http://www.ecb.int.

332 DEU
EUROPEAN CENTRAL BANK. OCCASIONAL PAPERS. Text in English. irreg. free. **Document type:** *Government.*
Published by: European Central Bank, Postfach 16 03 19, Frankfurt am Main, 60066, Germany. http://www.ecb.int.

332 DEU
EUROPEAN CENTRAL BANK. PAYMENT SYSTEMS IN THE EUROPEAN UNION. Text in English. a. free. **Document type:** *Government.*
Published by: European Central Bank, Postfach 16 03 19, Frankfurt am Main, 60066, Germany. http://www.ecb.int.

332 DEU
EUROPEAN CENTRAL BANK. WORKING PAPERS. Text in English. irreg. free. **Document type:** *Government.*
Published by: European Central Bank, Postfach 16 03 19, Frankfurt am Main, 60066, Germany. http://www.ecb.int.

332.1 BEL ISSN 0071-2787
EUROPEAN FEDERATION OF FINANCE HOUSE ASSOCIATIONS. ANNUAL REPORT. Short title: Eurofinas. Annual Report. Text in English, French, German. 1963. a. free.
Published by: European Federation of Finance House Associations, Av de Tervuren 267, Brussels, 1150, Belgium. FAX 32-2-7780579. Ed. M Baert. Circ: (controlled).

332 BEL ISSN 0300-4252
EUROPEAN FEDERATION OF FINANCE HOUSE ASSOCIATIONS. NEWSLETTER. Short title: Eurofinas. Newsletter. Text in English, French, German. 1961. 6/yr. free. **Document type:** *Newsletter.*
Published by: European Federation of Finance House Associations, Av de Tervuren 267, Brussels, 1150, Belgium. FAX 32-2-7780579. Ed. M Baert. Circ: (controlled).

332 GBR ISSN 0955-4033
EUROPEAN FINANCE DIRECTOR. Text in English. 1987. q. GBP 38. back issues avail. **Description:** Contains articles of interest to political leaders, civil servants, financial company senior management, attorneys, and accountants.
Published by: Harrington Kilbride plc., Harrington Kilbride Plc, 3 Highbury Station Rd, Islington, London, N1 1SE, United Kingdom. TEL 071-226-2222, FAX 071-226-1255, TELEX 263174 HKP G. Ed. Alan Spence.

332 GBR ISSN 1369-0086
EUROPEAN FINANCIAL INSTITUTIONS AND MARKETS SERIES✶ . Text in English. 1993. irreg. **Document type:** *Monographic series.*
Published by: Routledge (Subsidiary of: Taylor & Francis Group), 4 Park Square, Milton Park, Abingdon, Oxon OX14 4RN, United Kingdom. TEL 44-1235-828600, FAX 44-1235-829000, info@routledge.co.uk, http://www.routledge.co.uk. Eds. Jack Revell, Richard Harrington.

332 GBR ISSN 1354-7798
HG186.A2
➤ **EUROPEAN FINANCIAL MANAGEMENT.** Text in English. 1995. 5/yr. USD 1,131 combined subscription in the Americas to institutions & Caribbean (print & online eds.); GBP 673 combined subscription elsewhere to institutions print & online eds.; EUR 60 combined subscription in Europe to students print & online eds.; USD 67 combined subscription in the Americas to students & Caribbean (print & online eds.); GBP 40 combined subscription elsewhere to students print & online eds. (effective 2006). reprint service avail. from PSC. **Document type:** *Journal, Academic/Scholarly.* **Description:** Discusses issues in financial management.
Related titles: Online - full text ed.: ISSN 1468-036X. USD 1,074 in the Americas to institutions & Caribbean; GBP 639 elsewhere to institutions (effective 2006) (from Blackwell Synergy, EBSCO Publishing, Gale Group, IngentaConnect, O C L C Online Computer Library Center, Inc., Swets Information Services).
Indexed: ABIn, IBSS, JEL.
—BLDSC (3829.711530), IE, Infotrieve, ingenta. **CCC.**
Published by: (European Financial Management Association), Blackwell Publishing Ltd., 9600 Garsington Rd, Oxford, OX4 2ZG, United Kingdom. TEL 44-1865-776868, FAX 44-1865-714591, customerservices@oxon.blackwellpublishing.com, http://www.blackwellpublishing.com/journals/EUFM. Ed. Bernard Dumas.

332.6 LUX ISSN 0071-2868
HG3881
EUROPEAN INVESTMENT BANK. ANNUAL REPORT. Text in English. 1958. a. free. charts; illus.; stat. **Document type:** *Corporate.* **Description:** Reviews the European Investment Bank's borrowing and lending during the calendar year.
Related titles: CD-ROM ed.; Danish ed.; Dutch ed.; Finnish ed.; French ed.; German ed.; Greek ed.; Italian ed.; Portuguese ed.; Spanish ed.; Swedish ed.
Indexed: IIS.
—BLDSC (1245.465000).
Published by: European Investment Bank/Banque Europeenne d'Investissement, 100 bd. Konrad Adenauer, Luxembourg, L-2950, Luxembourg. TEL 352-4379-3122, FAX 352-4379-3189, TELEX 3530 BNKEU LU, http://www.eib.org. **Dist. in U.S. by:** European Community Information Service, 2100 M St, NW Ste 707, Washington, DC 20037.

332.6 LUX
EUROPEAN INVESTMENT BANK IN (YEAR). Text in Danish, Dutch, English, French, Finnish, German, Greek, Italian, Portuguese, Spanish, Swedish. 1987. a. free. **Document type:** *Corporate.* **Description:** Presents a general description and key figures of the bank for the previous year.
Indexed: IIS.
Published by: European Investment Bank/Banque Europeenne d'Investissement, 100 bd. Konrad Adenauer, Luxembourg, L-2950, Luxembourg. TEL 352-4379-3122, FAX 352-4379-3189, http://www.eib.org. **Dist. in U.S. by:** European Community Information Service, 2100 M St, NW Ste 707, Washington, DC 20037.

332 GBR ISSN 1351-847X
HG11
➤ **THE EUROPEAN JOURNAL OF FINANCE.** Text in English. 1995. 8/yr. GBP 1,002, USD 1,652 combined subscription to institutions print & online eds. (effective 2006). adv. reprint service avail. from PSC. **Document type:** *Journal, Academic/Scholarly.* **Description:** Devoted to theoretical, practical, and empirical issues in finance.
Related titles: Online - full text ed.: ISSN 1466-4364. GBP 952, USD 1,569 to institutions (effective 2006) (from EBSCO Publishing, Gale Group, IngentaConnect, O C L C Online Computer Library Center, Inc., Swets Information Services).
Indexed: ABIn, CPM, DIP, IBR, IBSS, IBZ, JEL.
—BLDSC (3829.728960), IE, Infotrieve, ingenta. **CCC.**
Published by: Routledge (Subsidiary of: Taylor & Francis Group), 4 Park Sq, Milton Park, Abingdon, Oxon OX14 4RN, United Kingdom. TEL 44-1235-828600, FAX 44-1235-829000, info@routledge.co.uk, http://www.tandf.co.uk/journals/titles/1351847X.asp, http://www.routledge.co.uk. Ed. Christopher Adcock. R&P Sally Sweet. **Subscr. in US & Canada to:** Taylor & Francis Inc., Customer Services Dept, 325 Chestnut St, 8th Fl, Philadelphia, PA 19106. TEL 800-354-1420, FAX 215-625-8914; **Subscr. to:** Taylor & Francis Ltd, Journals Customer Service, Rankine Rd, Basingstoke, Hants RG24 8PR, United Kingdom. TEL 44-1256-813000, FAX 44-1256-330245, enquiry@tandf.co.uk.

320 BEL ISSN 1021-4267
EUROPEAN REPORT. Text in English. s-w. (94/yr.). EUR 1,375; EUR 200 for the index (effective 2000). q. index. **Document type:** *Bulletin.* **Description:** Covers developments in European legislative and related regulatory issues.
Related titles: CD-ROM ed.; Online - full text ed.: (from bigchalk, Gale Group, LexisNexis, Northern Light Technology, Inc., O C L C Online Computer Library Center, Inc.); ♦ French ed.: Europolitique (Bruxelles). ISSN 1021-4275.
—BLDSC (3829.910000).
Published by: Europe Information Service SA, Av Adolphe Lacomble 66-68, Brussels, 1030, Belgium. TEL 32-2-242-6020, FAX 32-2-242-9410, eis@eis.be, http://www.eis.be. Pub. Eric Damiens.

332.2 BEL
EUROPEAN SAVINGS BANK. ACTIVITY REPORT. Text in English. 1966. a.
Related titles: French ed.; German ed.
Published by: European Savings Banks Group/Groupement Europeen des Caisses d'Epargne, Av Marie Therese 11, Brussels, 1000, Belgium. TEL 32-2-2111111, FAX 32-2-2111199. Ed. C De Noose. Circ: 3,000.

EUROPEAN SECURITIES TRADING. see *BUSINESS AND ECONOMICS—Investments*

332 GBR ISSN 1461-9326
EUROPEAN SINGLE FINANCIAL MARKET (YEARS). Text in English. 1998. a. GBP 95, USD 170 (effective 1998).
Published by: Euromoney Publications plc, Nestor House, Playhouse Yard, London, EC4V 5EX, United Kingdom. TEL 44-207-7798673, FAX 44-20-77798541.

332 DEU ISSN 1561-0144
EUROPEISKA CENTRALBANKEN. MANADSRAPPORT. Text in Swedish. 1999. m.
Related titles: ♦ English ed.: European Central Bank. Monthly Bulletin. ISSN 1561-0136; ♦ Spanish ed.: Banco Central Europeo. Boletin Mensual. ISSN 1561-0268; ♦ Italian ed.: Banca Centrale Europea. Bollettino Mensile. ISSN 1561-0276; ♦ Portuguese ed.: Banco Central Europeu. Boletin Mensal. ISSN 1561-0284; ♦ German ed.: Europaische Zentralbank. Monatsbericht. ISSN 1561-0292; ♦ Dutch ed.: Europese Centrale Bank. Maandbericht. ISSN 1561-0314; ♦ Spanish ed.: Euroopan Keskuspankiki. Kuukausikatsaus. ISSN 1561-0322; ♦ Greek ed.: Europaike Kentrike Trapeza. Meniaio Deltio. ISSN 1561-025X; ♦ Danish ed.: Europaeiske Centralbank. Manedsoversigt. ISSN 1561-0241; ♦ French ed.: Banque Central Europeenne. Bulletin Mensuel. ISSN 1561-0306.
Published by: European Central Bank, Postfach 16 03 19, Frankfurt am Main, 60066, Germany. TEL 49-69-1344-0, FAX 49-69-1344-6000, http://www.ecb.int.

332 DEU ISSN 1561-0314
EUROPESE CENTRALE BANK. MAANDBERICHT. Text in Dutch. 1999. m.
Related titles: ♦ English ed.: European Central Bank. Monthly Bulletin. ISSN 1561-0136; ♦ Spanish ed.: Banco Central Europeo. Boletin Mensual. ISSN 1561-0268; ♦ Italian ed.: Banca Centrale Europea. Bollettino Mensile. ISSN 1561-0276; ♦ Portuguese ed.: Banco Central Europeu. Boletin Mensal. ISSN 1561-0284; ♦ German ed.: Europaische Zentralbank. Monatsbericht. ISSN 1561-0292; ♦ Spanish ed.: Euroopan Keskuspankiki. Kuukausikatsaus. ISSN 1561-0322; ♦ Greek ed.: Europaike Kentrike Trapeza. Meniaio Deltio. ISSN 1561-025X; ♦ Swedish ed.: Europeiska Centralbanken. Manadsrapport. ISSN 1561-0144; ♦ Danish ed.: Europaeiske Centralbank. Manedsoversigt. ISSN 1561-0241; ♦ French ed.: Banque Central Europeenne. Bulletin Mensuel. ISSN 1561-0306.
Published by: European Central Bank, Postfach 16 03 19, Frankfurt am Main, 60066, Germany. TEL 49-69-1344-0, FAX 49-69-1344-6000, http://www.ecb.int.

332 LUX ISSN 1024-4239
EUROSTAT ECU-EMS INFORMATION AND CENTRAL BANK INTEREST RATES. Text in English. m.
Formerly (until 1994): Eurostat. ECU-EMS Information (1011-0844)
Related titles: German ed.: Eurostat ECU-EWS Information und Zinssatze der Zentralbanken. ISSN 1024-4255. 1994.
—BLDSC (3659.641010).
Published by: European Commission, Office for Official Publications of the European Union, 2 Rue Mercier, Luxembourg, L-2985, Luxembourg. FAX 352-2929-1, http://publications.eu.int.

EUROSTAT GELD, FINANZEN UND DER EURO: STATISTIKEN. see *BUSINESS AND ECONOMICS—Abstracting, Bibliographies, Statistics*

EUROSTAT STATISTICS IN FOCUS. ECONOMY AND FINANCE. see *BUSINESS AND ECONOMICS—Abstracting, Bibliographies, Statistics*

EUROSTAT STATISTIK KURZ GEFASST. WIRTSCHAFT UND FINANZEN. see *BUSINESS AND ECONOMICS—Abstracting, Bibliographies, Statistics*

EUROSTAT STATISTIQUES EN BREF. ECONOMIE ET FINANCES. see *BUSINESS AND ECONOMICS—Abstracting, Bibliographies, Statistics*

332 GBR ISSN 0952-7036
HG3879
EUROWEEK. Text in English. 1987. w. (50x/yr). GBP 3,095 combined subscription domestic print & online eds.; EUR 4,720 combined subscription in Europe print & online eds.; USD 5,095 combined subscription elsewhere print & online eds. (effective 2005). **Document type:** *Newspaper, Trade.* **Description:** Compiles financial market news, Forex forecasts, data on deals, and league tables.
Incorporates (1996-2002): M T N Week (1472-2925)
Related titles: Online - full text ed.: (from bigchalk, EBSCO Publishing, Florida Center for Library Automation, Gale Group, O C L C Online Computer Library Center, Inc., ProQuest Information & Learning).
Indexed: ABIn, B&I.
—CCC.
Published by: Euromoney Institutional Investor Plc., Nestor House, Playhouse Yard, London, EC4V 5EX, United Kingdom. TEL 44-20-7779-8673, FAX 44-20-7779-8541, meuer@euromoneyplc.com, http://www.euroweek.com, http://www.euromoney.com. Ed. Nigel Pavay. **Subscr. to:** Quadrant Subscription Services, PO Box 18083, London EC4V 5JS, United Kingdom. TEL 44-20-7779-8610, FAX 44-20-7779-8602. **Dist. in US by:** American Educational Systems, PO Box 246, New York, NY 10024-0246. TEL 800-431-1579.

332 CHL
EVOLUCION BANCARIA. Text in Spanish. 2000. q.
Media: Online - full text. **Related titles:** E-mail ed.
Published by: Superintendencia de Bancos e Instituciones Financieras, Moneda 1123, Santiago, Chile. TEL 56-2-4426200, http://www.sbif.cl/cgi-bin/publicaciones.pl.

332 USA ISSN 0094-5609
EXAMINATION OF FINANCIAL STATEMENTS INTER-AMERICAN FOUNDATION. Text in English. irreg. **Document type:** *Government.*
Published by: United States Government Accountability Office, 441 G St, NW, Washington, DC 20548-0001. TEL 202-512-4800, webmaster@gao.gov, http://www.gao.gov.

332 658 GBR
EXECUTIVE GRAPEVINE, VOLUME 8: GRAPEVINE INDEX OF FINANCE EXECUTIVES. Text in English. 1997. a. GBP 135 (effective 2000). **Document type:** *Directory.* **Description:** For financial professionals. Includes profiles of over 1500 Finance Directors in the UK.
Formerly: Executive Grapevine, Volume 8: Grapevine Index of Finance Directors
Published by: Executive Grapevine International Ltd., New Barnes Mill, Cottonmill Ln, St Albans, Herts AL1 2HA, United Kingdom. TEL 44-1727-844355, FAX 44-1727-844779, sales@executive-grapevine.co.uk, info@executive-grapevine.co.uk, http://www.executive-grapevine.co.uk, http://www.executive-grapevine.co.uk/.

332 GBR ISSN 0954-2760
EXPAT INVESTOR. Text in English. 1991. 10/yr. free to qualified personnel (effective 2005). adv. back issues avail. **Document type:** *Magazine, Consumer.*
Related titles: Online - full text ed.
Published by: Livewire Media Services Ltd., PO Box 503, Taunton, TA4 1YA, United Kingdom. TEL 44-1823-401000, FAX 44-1823-400711, livewirems@aol.com, http://www.expatinvestor.com/. Ed. Hannah Beecham TEL 44-1273-777463. Pub. Melanie Walker. Adv. contact Rosemary Nolte. page GBP 3,000; trim 272 x 383. Circ: 25,000 (controlled).

EXPORT - IMPORT BANK OF JAPAN. ANNUAL REPORT. see *BUSINESS AND ECONOMICS—International Commerce*

332.1 USA ISSN 0270-5109
HG3754.U5
EXPORT-IMPORT BANK OF THE UNITED STATES. ANNUAL REPORT. Text in English. 1945. a. free. **Document type:** *Corporate.*
Former titles: Export-Import Bank of the United States. Statement of Condition (0270-5087); Export-Import Bank of the United States. Summary of Operations (0071-3511); Export-Import Bank of the United States. Report to Congress
Published by: Export-Import Bank of the United States, 811 Vermont Ave, N W, Washington, DC 20571. TEL 202-566-8990, FAX 202-566-7524. Circ: 10,000.

332.1 USA ISSN 1077-6729
EXPORT-IMPORT BANK OF THE UNITED STATES. REPORT TO CONGRESS ON EXPORT CREDIT COMPETITION AND THE EXPORT-IMPORT BANK OF THE UNITED STATES. Text in English. 1972. a. free. **Document type:** *Corporate.*
Formerly: Export-Import Bank of the United States. Semiannual Report to Congress on Export Credit Competition and the Export-Import Bank of the United States
Published by: Export-Import Bank of the United States, 811 Vermont Ave, N W, Washington, DC 20571. TEL 202-566-8861, FAX 202-566-7524, TELEX (TRT) 197681 EXIMUT. Circ: 1,250.

332 FRA ISSN 0014-5289
EXPRESS DOCUMENTS; juridique fiscal & social. Text in French. 1967 (vol.27). 45/yr. adv. charts; illus.
Published by: Groupe Revenu Francais, 1 bis av. de la Republique, Paris, 75011, France. TEL 33-1-49293000, FAX 33-1-43559141. Ed. Robert Monteux. Circ: 15,000. **Subscr. to:** B.P. 522, Sainte Genevieve Cedex 60732, France.

332 336 GBR ISSN 1362-007X
EXTEL DIVIDEND & INTEREST RECORD. (Consists of: UK Dividend and Interest Record and International Dividend and Interest Record) Text in English. 1967. a. GBP 175 per vol.; GBP 220 per vol. with supplements. Supplement avail. **Description:** Covers dividend and fixed payments made by UK equities and unit trusts.
Formerly (until 1995): UK Dividend and Interest Record (0959-5775); Which was formed by the 1982 merger of: Extel Dividend Record (0141-8327); Extel Fixed Interest Record (0141-8653)
Published by: Financial Times Information Ltd., Fitzroy House, 13-17 Epworth St, London, EC2A 4DL, United Kingdom. TEL 44-20-7825-8000, FAX 44-20-7608-2032, TELEX 884319, justine.dye@ft.com, http://www.ft.com.

F & A ACTUEEL. (Financieel en Administratief) see *BUSINESS AND ECONOMICS—Management*

332 ZAF ISSN 1024-7408
F & T WEEKLY. (Finansies en Tegniek) Text in English. 1984. w. (Fri.). ZAR 260 (effective 1998). adv. **Description:** Covers business, financial and related issues.
Formerly (until 1995): Finansies en Tegniek (0256-470X)
Indexed: ISAP.
Published by: Nasionale Media, PO Box 786466, Sandton, Transvaal 2146, South Africa. TEL 27-11-8847676, FAX 27-11-8840851. Ed. Lucas de Lange. Pub. G.L. Marais. R&P G L Marais. Adv. contact Tony Glencross. Circ: 12,595 (paid).

F C I B COUNTRY REPORT. see *BUSINESS AND ECONOMICS—International Commerce*

F C I B INTERNATIONAL BULLETIN. see *BUSINESS AND ECONOMICS—International Commerce*

F C I B MINUTES OF ROUND TABLE CONFERENCE. (Finance, Credit and International Business) see *BUSINESS AND ECONOMICS—International Commerce*

332 368.4 USA ISSN 1041-939X
HG1662.U5
F D I C BANKING REVIEW. Text in English. 1986. q. back issues avail. **Document type:** *Government.* **Description:** Provides original research on issues related to banking and deposit insurance; also contains a summary both of actions taken by the various bank regulatory agencies and of state and federal legislation that affects the financial services industry.
Formerly (until 1988): Banking and Economic Review (1040-5127)
Related titles: Online - full content ed.; Online - full text ed.: (from ProQuest Information & Learning).
Indexed: BLI, JEL.
—BLDSC (3901.344800), IE, ingenta.
Published by: U.S. Federal Deposit Insurance Corp., Public Information Center, 801 17th St., N.W., Washington, DC 20434-0001t. TEL 202-416-6940, 877-275-3342, FAX 202-416-2076, publicinfo@fdic.gov, http://www.fdic.gov/bank/analytical/banking/.

THE F D I C QUARTERLY BANKING PROFILE. see *INSURANCE*

332.1 USA
F D I C. SUMMARY OF DEPOSITS. BANK & THRIFT BRANCH OFFICE DATA BOOK. CENTRAL REGION; Illinois, Indiana, Kentucky, Michigan, Ohio, Wisconsin. Spine title: Bank & Thrift Branch Office Data Book. Central Region. Text in English. a. free. **Document type:** *Government.*
Formerly: Operating Banks and Branches. Data Book 3: Illinois, Indiana, Kentucky, Michigan, Ohio, Wisconsin
Related titles: Online - full content ed.: U.S. Federal Deposit Insurance Corp. Summary of Deposits (Online). 2001.
Published by: U.S. Federal Deposit Insurance Corp., Division of Insurance and Research, Reports Analysis and Quality Control Section, 550 17th Street, N.W., Washington, DC 20429. http://www2.fdic.gov/sod/sodPublications.asp?barItem=5.

332.1 USA
F D I C. SUMMARY OF DEPOSITS. BANK & THRIFT BRANCH OFFICE DATA BOOK. MIDWEST REGION; Iowa, Kansas, Minnesota, Missouri, Nebraska, North Dakota, South Dakota. Spine title: Bank & Thrift Branch Office Data Book. Midwest Region. Text in English. a. free. **Document type:** *Government.*
Formerly: Operating Banks and Branches. Data Book 4: Alabama, Arkansas, Louisiana, Mississippi, Oklahoma, Tennessee, Texas
Related titles: Online - full content ed.: U.S. Federal Deposit Insurance Corp. Summary of Deposits (Online). 2001.
Published by: U.S. Federal Deposit Insurance Corp., Division of Insurance and Research, Reports Analysis and Quality Control Section, 550 17th Street, N.W., Washington, DC 20429. http://www2.fdic.gov/sod/sodPublications.asp?barItem=5.

332.1 USA
F D I C. SUMMARY OF DEPOSITS. BANK & THRIFT BRANCH OFFICE DATA BOOK. NATIONAL; United States (states, counties, and other areas). Text in English. a., latest 2004. free.
Formerly: Operating Banks and Branches. Data Book: United States, States, Counties, Other Areas
Related titles: Online - full content ed.: U.S. Federal Deposit Insurance Corp. Summary of Deposits (Online). 2001.
Published by: U.S. Federal Deposit Insurance Corp., Division of Insurance and Research, Reports Analysis and Quality Control Section, 550 17th Street, N.W., Washington, DC 20429. http://www2.fdic.gov/sod/sodPublications.asp?barItem=5.

332.1 USA
F D I C. SUMMARY OF DEPOSITS. BANK & THRIFT BRANCH OFFICE DATA BOOK. NORTHEAST REGION; Connecticut, Delaware, District of Columbia, Maine, Maryland, Massachusetts, New Hampshire, New Jersey, New York, Pennsylvania, Puerto Rico, Rhode Island, Vermont, U.S. Virgin Islands. Spine title: Bank & Thrift Branch Office Data Book. Northeast Region. Text in English. a. free. **Document type:** *Government.*
Formerly: Operating Banks and Branches. Data Book 1: Connecticut, Maine, Massachusetts, New Hampshire, New Jersey, New York, Pennsylvania, Rhode Island, Vermont, Puerto Rico, Virgin Islands
Related titles: Online - full content ed.: U.S. Federal Deposit Insurance Corp. Summary of Deposits (Online). 2001.
Published by: U.S. Federal Deposit Insurance Corp., Division of Insurance and Research, Reports Analysis and Quality Control Section, 550 17th Street, N.W., Washington, DC 20429. http://www2.fdic.gov/sod/sodPublications.asp?barItem=5.

B

332.1 USA
F D I C. SUMMARY OF DEPOSITS. BANK & THRIFT BRANCH OFFICE DATA BOOK. SOUTHEAST REGION; Alabama, Florida, Georgia, Mississippi, North Carolina, South Carolina, Tennessee, Virginia, West Virginia. Text in English. a. free. **Document type:** *Government.*
Formerly: Operating Banks and Branches. Data Book 2: Delaware, District of Columbia, Florida, Georgia, Maryland, North Carolina, South Carolina, Virginia, West Virginia
Related titles: Online - full content ed.: U.S. Federal Deposit Insurance Corp. Summary of Deposits (Online). 2001.
Published by: U.S. Federal Deposit Insurance Corp., Division of Insurance and Research, Reports Analysis and Quality Control Section, 550 17th Street, N.W., Washington, DC 20429. http://www2.fdic.gov/sod/sodPublications.asp?barItem=5.

332.1 USA
F D I C. SUMMARY OF DEPOSITS. BANK & THRIFT BRANCH OFFICE DATA BOOK. SOUTHWEST REGION; Arkansas, Louisiana, New Mexico, Oklahoma, Texas. Text in English. a. free.
Formerly: Operating Banks and Branches. Data Book 6: Alaska, Arizona, California, Colorado, Hawaii, Idaho, Montana, Nevada, New Mexico, Oregon, Utah, Washington, Wyoming, Pacific Islands
Related titles: Online - full content ed.: U.S. Federal Deposit Insurance Corp. Summary of Deposits (Online). 2001.
Published by: U.S. Federal Deposit Insurance Corp., Division of Insurance and Research, Reports Analysis and Quality Control Section, 550 17th Street, N.W., Washington, DC 20429. http://www2.fdic.gov/sod/sodPublications.asp?barItem=5.

332 NLD ISSN 1570-5196
F E M BUSINESS. (Financieel Economisch Magazine) Text in Dutch. 2002. w. (50 issues). EUR 125 (effective 2003). adv. bk.rev. illus. **Document type:** *Journal, Trade.*
Formed by the merger of (1970-2002): F E M - De Week (1388-4514); (1970-2002): NeXT! (1388-4522); Both of which superseded in part (in 1998): Financieel-Economisch Magazine (0165-5655); Which incorporated (1970-1985): F E M Trends (0165-5604)
Related titles: Online - full content ed.: F E M De Week; Supplement(s): The Executive.nl. ISSN 1568-5756. 2000.
Indexed: ELLIS, KES.
—IE.
Published by: Reed Business Information bv (Subsidiary of: Reed Business), Hanzestraat 1, Doetinchem, 7006 RH, Netherlands. TEL 31-314-349911, FAX 31-314-343839, info@reedbusiness.nl, http://www.femdeweek.nl, http://www.reedbusiness.nl. Circ: 13,000.

332.1 USA
THE F E R C REPORT. (Financial Enforcement Regulation Compliance) Text in English. 1980. bi-w. USD 276. **Description:** Offers news and guidance on financial enforcement, regulation and compliance for CEO's and compliance officers in banks, thrifts and credit unions.
Former titles: Bank President's Letter; Community Banker
—BLDSC (3363.588200).
Published by: United Communications Group, 11300 Rockville Pike Ste 1100, Rockville, MD 20852-3030. TEL 301-816-8950. Ed. Jason Huffman.

658 USA
F R M WEEKLY. (Fund Raising Management) Text in English. w. USD 115; USD 165 foreign (effective 1996). adv. back issues avail. **Document type:** *Newsletter.*

Published by: Hoke Communications, 224 Seventh St, Garden City, NY 11530. TEL 516-746-6700. Ed. Bill Olcott. Pub. Henry R Hoke III. Circ: 300.

332 GBR ISSN 1351-5195
F X & M M. (Foreign Exchange & Money Markets) Text in English. 1994. bi-m. GBP 95 (effective 2003). adv. 64 p./no.; back issues avail. **Document type:** *Magazine, Trade.*
Description: Trends and developments in foreign exchange and money markets.
Published by: Russell Publishing Ltd., Court Lodge, Hogtrough Hill, Brasted, Kent TN16 1NU, United Kingdom. TEL 44-1959-563311, FAX 44-1959-563123, mailto:s.coldicot@russellpublishing.com, admin@russellpublishing.com, http://www.russellpublishing.com/pages/fxmm/fxmm1.html. Eds. Steve Westcott, Steven Coldicott. R&P, Adv. contact Steven Coldicott. color page GBP 4,277. Circ: 478 (paid); 15,051 (controlled).

B

332 332.1 PHL
FACTBOOK ON THE PHILIPPINE FINANCIAL SYSTEM. Text and summaries in English. 1976. a. PHP 600, USD 50. back issues avail.
Published by: Central Bank of the Philippines, A. Mabini corner Vito Cruz Streets, Manila, Philippines. Circ: 500.

332 USA ISSN 8755-1624
FACTORS AFFECTING RESERVES OF DEPOSITORY INSTITUTIONS AND CONDITION STATEMENT OF FEDERAL RESERVE BANKS. Text in English. w. USD 20. **Document type:** *Government.*
Published by: U.S. Federal Reserve System, Board of Governors, Publications Services, Rm MS 138, Washington, DC 20551. TEL 202-452-3244, FAX 202-728-5886.

332 CAN ISSN 1704-6203
FARM CREDIT CANADA ANNUAL REPORT. Text in English. 1960. a. free. **Document type:** *Corporate.*
Former titles (until 2002): Farm Credit Corporation Canada. Annual Report (1704-6181); (until 1981): Farm Credit Corporation. Annual Report (0382-1501); (until 1967): Farm Credit Corporation. Annual Report and Financial Statements (0837-8533); (until 1963): Farm Credit Corporation. Report (0071-3864)
Published by: Farm Credit Corporation Canada, 1800 Hamilton St, P O Box 4320, Regina, SK S4P 4L3, Canada. TEL 306-780-8100, FAX 306-780-5456.

332 USA
FED RATE WATCH. Text in English. w. **Document type:** *Newsletter, Consumer.* **Description:** Provides current information on economic trends and Federal Reserve Board interest rate moves.
Media: E-mail.
Published by: Bankrate Inc., 11811 US Hwy 1, North Palm Beach, FL 33408. TEL 561-630-2400, FAX 561-625-4540, webmaster@bankrate.com, http://bankrate.process9.com/bankrate/subscribe.html, http://www.bankrate.com.

FEDERAL ADVERTISING AND MARKETING LAW GUIDE. see *LAW*

332 340 USA ISSN 0162-1157
FEDERAL BANKING LAW REPORTER. Text in English. 1914. 8 base vols. plus w. updates. looseleaf. USD 1,895 base vol(s). (effective 2004). **Description:** Provides full text of all federal banking statutes and regulations as well as analysis and explanation. Also includes full text of relevant court decisions.
Related titles: CD-ROM ed.: USD 1,860 (effective 2004); Online - full text ed.: USD 2,050 (effective 2004).
—CCC.
Published by: C C H Inc., 2700 Lake Cook Rd, Riverwoods, IL 60015. TEL 847-267-7000, 800-449-6439, cust_serv@cch.com, http://www.cch.com. Pub. Stacey Caywood.

332 USA ISSN 1043-7789
HG2037
FEDERAL CREDIT UNION. Text in English. 1976. bi-m. USD 100 (effective 2005). adv. **Document type:** *Magazine, Trade.*
Description: Written and edited to inform credit union professionals and volunteers about the issues, trends, and developments affecting or expected to affect their operations.
Published by: National Association of Federal Credit Unions, 3138 N Tenth St, Arlington, VA 22201. TEL 703-522-4770, 800-336-4644, FAX 703-524-1082, nafcu@nafcunet.org, http://www.nafcunet.org. Ed., Pub. Robin Johnston. Adv. contact Sally Lyon. Circ: 8,000 (paid and controlled).

332 USA ISSN 0195-5330
FEDERAL ELECTION CAMPAIGN FINANCING GUIDE. Text in English. 1976. base vol. plus m. updates. USD 675 base vol(s). (effective 2004). **Description:** Provides a comprehensive view of the restrictions and limitations governing campaign contributions under this Act.
—CCC.
Published by: C C H Inc., 2700 Lake Cook Rd, Riverwoods, IL 60015. TEL 847-267-7000, 800-449-6439, cust_serv@cch.com, http://www.cch.com. Pub. Stacey Caywood.

332.1 333.33 USA
FEDERAL HOME LOAN BANK OF ATLANTA. ANNUAL REPORT. Text in English. a. free. adv. illus.; stat. **Document type:** *Bulletin, Corporate.*
Published by: Federal Home Loan Bank of Atlanta, 1475 Peachtree St, Atlanta, GA 30309. TEL 404-888-8000, 800-536-9650, jmunro@fhlbatl.com, http://www.fhlbatl.com. Ed. James McDougall. Adv. contact Avis McGhee.

332.1 USA
FEDERAL HOME LOAN BANK OF CHICAGO. ANNUAL REPORT. Text in English. 1933. a. adv. **Document type:** *Corporate.*
Published by: Federal Home Loan Bank of Chicago, 111 E Wacker Dr, Chicago, IL 60601. Ed. Michael O'Malley. Adv. contact Charles Huston. Circ: 2,000.

332.1 USA
FEDERAL HOME LOAN BANK OF DALLAS. ANNUAL REPORT. Text in English. 1932. a. **Document type:** *Bulletin, Corporate.*
Published by: Federal Home Loan Bank of Dallas, Marketing Office, PO Box 619026, Dallas, TX 75261-9026. TEL 214-441-8500, FAX 214-441-8552, fhlb@fhlb.com, http://www.fhlb.com. Ed. Libby A York.

332.1 USA
FEDERAL HOME LOAN BANK OF DES MOINES. ANNUAL REPORT. Text in English. a. free. **Document type:** *Corporate.*
Published by: Federal Home Loan Bank of Des Moines, 907 Walnut St, Des Moines, IA 50309. TEL 515-281-1101, FAX 515-281-1022. Ed. Nichola Schissel. Circ: 2,000.

332.1 USA
FEDERAL HOME LOAN BANK OF DES MOINES. WEEKLY FINANCIAL BULLETIN. Text in English. w. free. **Document type:** *Bulletin.*
Published by: Federal Home Loan Bank of Des Moines, 907 Walnut St, Des Moines, IA 50309. TEL 515-281-1101, FAX 515-281-1022.

332.1 USA
FEDERAL HOME LOAN BANK OF INDIANAPOLIS. ANNUAL REPORT. Text in English. 1934. a. free. **Document type:** *Corporate.*
Published by: Federal Home Loan Bank of Indianapolis, Library, PO Box 60, Indianapolis, IN 46206-0060. Ed. Mike Barker.

332.3 USA ISSN 0098-2830
HG2626.S3
FEDERAL HOME LOAN BANK OF SAN FRANCISCO. ANNUAL REPORT. Key Title: Annual Report - Federal Home Loan Bank of San Francisco. Text in English. a. free. illus. **Document type:** *Corporate.*
Published by: Federal Home Loan Bank of San Francisco, PO Box 7948, San Francisco, CA 94120. TEL 415-616-2610.

332.1 USA
FEDERAL HOME LOAN BANK OF SEATTLE. ANNUAL REPORT. Text in English. a. free. **Document type:** *Corporate.*
Published by: Federal Home Loan Bank of Seattle, 1501 Fourth Ave, Ste 1900, Seattle, WA 98101-1693. TEL 206-340-2300, FAX 206-340-2485. Ed. Mary Grace Helsper.

332.1 USA
FEDERAL HOME LOAN BANK OF TOPEKA. ANNUAL REPORT. Text in English. a. free. **Document type:** *Corporate.*
Description: Contains member and industry news and information about bank products and services.
Published by: Federal Home Loan Bank of Topeka, 2 Townsite Plaza, Box 176, Topeka, KS 66601-0176. FAX 785-234-1700. Ed. Laura Lutz.

332.1 USA ISSN 0094-7156
HG2040.5.U5
FEDERAL HOME LOAN MORTGAGE CORPORATION. REPORT. Key Title: Report of the Federal Home Loan Mortgage Corporation. Variant title: Federal Home Loan Mortgage Corporation. Annual Report. Text in English. a. illus.; stat. **Document type:** *Corporate.*
Published by: Federal Home Loan Mortgage Corporation, 8200 Jones Branch Dr., Mclean, VA 22102-3107. TEL 703-903-2000, FAX 703-759-8069.

FEDERAL INCOME TAXATION OF BANKS AND FINANCIAL INSTITUTIONS (SUPPLEMENT). see *BUSINESS AND ECONOMICS—Public Finance, Taxation*

332 USA ISSN 0899-6563
FEDERAL RESERVE BANK OF ATLANTA. FINANCIAL UPDATE. Text in English. 1988. q. free. **Document type:** *Newsletter.*
Related titles: Online - full text ed.: ISSN 1545-911X (from EBSCO Publishing, Florida Center for Library Automation, Gale Group, ProQuest Information & Learning).
Indexed: BLI.
Published by: Federal Reserve Bank of Atlanta, 1000 Peachtree St NE, Atlanta, GA 30309-3904. TEL 404-521-8020, FAX 404-521-8050, http://www.frbatlanta.org. Ed. Pierce Nelson. Circ: 7,500.

330 USA
FEDERAL RESERVE BANK OF ATLANTA. WORKING PAPER SERIES. Text in English. 1976. irreg. free. back issues avail. **Document type:** *Academic/Scholarly.*
Related titles: Online - full text ed.
Indexed: FiP.
Published by: Federal Reserve Bank of Atlanta, 1000 Peachtree St NE, Atlanta, GA 30309-3904. TEL 404-521-8020, http://www.frbatlanta.org. Circ: 3,400.

332.1 USA
FEDERAL RESERVE BANK OF BOSTON. WORKING PAPER SERIES. Text in English. irreg. free (effective 2003). **Document type:** *Monographic series, Government.*
Published by: Federal Reserve Bank of Boston, Research Department, 55882, Boston, MA 02205-5882. TEL 617-973-3397, FAX 617-973-4221, http://www.bos.frb.org/economic/wp/index.htm.

332 USA ISSN 0361-798X
FEDERAL RESERVE BANK OF CLEVELAND. ANNUAL REPORT. Text in English. a. **Document type:** *Corporate.*
—BLDSC (1250.790000).
Published by: Federal Reserve Bank of Cleveland, PO Box 6387, Cleveland, OH 44101. TEL 216-579-2052, Publications@clev.frb.org, http://www.clevelandfed.org/.

332 USA
FEDERAL RESERVE BANK OF CLEVELAND. WORKING PAPER. Text in English. 1976. irreg. (approx. 12/yr.). **Document type:** *Academic/Scholarly.*
Media: Online - full text.
Indexed: FiP.
Published by: (Research Department), Federal Reserve Bank of Cleveland, PO Box 6387, Cleveland, OH 44101. TEL 216-579-2380, FAX 216-579-2477. Ed. Michele Lachman. R&P Lee Faulhaber TEL 216-579-2961. Circ: 233.

332.1 USA
FEDERAL RESERVE BANK OF DALLAS SOUTHWEST ECONOMY. Text in English. 1982. bi-m. free. charts; maps; illus.; stat. back issues avail. **Document type:** *Newsletter, Trade.* **Description:** Covers economic conditions and business developments in the Eleventh Federal Reserve District, nation and world. Includes coverage of agriculture, banking, energy, high technology, manufacturing and international trade.
Incorporates (1991-1999): Financial Industry Issues; Formerly (until 1988): Roundup (Dallas)
Related titles: Online - full text ed.
Indexed: HistAb.
Published by: Federal Reserve Bank of Dallas, PO Box 655906, Dallas, TX 75265-5906. Kay.Champagne@dal.frb.org, http://www.dallasfed.org/research/swe/index.html. Eds. Evan F Koenig, Steven P A Brown, William C. Gruben. R&P Kay Champagne. Circ: 10,000 (controlled).

332.1 USA ISSN 1072-0049
HG2613.K34
FEDERAL RESERVE BANK OF KANSAS CITY. FINANCIAL INDUSTRY PERSPECTIVES. Text in English. 1983. a. free. **Document type:** *Academic/Scholarly.* **Description:** Provides index of bank control share prices, financial facts and structure statistics.
Former titles (until 199?): Federal Reserve Bank of Kansas City. Financial Industry Trends and Perspectives; (until 1991): Federal Reserve Bank of Kansas City. Banking Studies (0743-6351)
Related titles: Online - full text ed.: (from Factiva, ProQuest Information & Learning).
Indexed: BLI, WBA.
Published by: (Division of Bank Supervision and Structure), Federal Reserve Bank of Kansas City, 925 Grand Blvd, Kansas City, MO 64198-0001. TEL 816-881-2934. Ed. John Yorke. Circ: 5,500.

332.1 USA ISSN 0091-5947
FEDERAL RESERVE BANK OF MINNEAPOLIS. NINTH DISTRICT EXPONENT. Text in English. irreg. **Document type:** *Monographic series.*
Indexed: PAIS.
Published by: Federal Reserve Bank of Minneapolis, 90 Hennepin Ave, Minneapolis, MN 55401. TEL 612-204-5000, http://minneapolisfed.org.

332.1 USA ISSN 0361-7998
HG2613.N54
FEDERAL RESERVE BANK OF NEW YORK. ANNUAL REPORT. Text in English. 1942. a. charts; stat. back issues avail.; reprints avail. **Document type:** *Corporate.*
—BLDSC (1250.800000).
Published by: Federal Reserve Bank of New York, Public Information, 33 Liberty St, New York, NY 10045-0001. TEL 212-720-6150. Circ: 38,000.

332 330.9 USA
FEDERAL RESERVE BANK OF NEW YORK. CURRENT ISSUES IN ECONOMICS AND FINANCE. Text in English. m. free. **Document type:** *Newsletter, Consumer.*
Indexed: AmStI, PAIS.

Published by: Federal Reserve Bank of New York, Research and Market Analysis Group, 33 Liberty St, New York, NY 10045-0001. TEL 212-720-6134, http://www.ny.frb.org/rmaghome/curr_iss/1999.htm. Ed. Dorothy Meadow Sobol.

332.1 USA
FEDERAL RESERVE BANK OF NEW YORK. STAFF REPORTS. Text in English. irreg. **Document type:** *Newsletter.*
Media: Online - full text.
Indexed: ABIn.
Published by: Federal Reserve Bank of New York, Public Information, 33 Liberty St, New York, NY 10045-0001.

FEDERAL RESERVE BANK OF PHILADELPHIA. BUSINESS REVIEW. see *BUSINESS AND ECONOMICS—Economic Situation And Conditions*

332 USA ISSN 0164-0798
HG2613.R54
FEDERAL RESERVE BANK OF RICHMOND. ANNUAL REPORT. Text in English. 1916. a. **Document type:** *Government.*
Published by: Federal Reserve Bank of Richmond, Research Department, 701 E Byrd St, Richmond, VA 23219. TEL 804-697-8785, FAX 804-697-8287, eg@rich.frb.org, http://www.rick.frb.org. R&P Elaine Mandaleris TEL 804-697-8144. **Subscr. to:** Public Affairs, PO Box 27622, Richmond, VA 23261. TEL 804-697-8111.

332.1 USA ISSN 0190-2814
FEDERAL RESERVE BANK OF SAN FRANCISCO. ANNUAL REPORT. Text in English. 1916. a.
Published by: Federal Reserve Bank of San Francisco, PO Box 7702, San Francisco, CA 94120. TEL 415-974-2163, 888-339-3506, http://www.frbsf.org/publications/federalreserve/annual/index.html.

332 USA ISSN 0014-9209
HG2401 CODEN: FDRBAU
FEDERAL RESERVE BULLETIN. Text in English. 1915. q. USD 10 domestic; USD 15 foreign (effective 2005). charts; mkt.; stat. index. reprint service avail. from CIS,PQC,WSH. **Document type:** *Bulletin, Government.*
Related titles: Microfiche ed.: (from CIS); Microform ed.: (from MIM, PMC, PQC); Online - full text ed.: (from bigchalk, EBSCO Publishing, Florida Center for Library Automation, Gale Group, H.W. Wilson, Northern Light Technology, Inc., O C L C Online Computer Library Center, Inc., ProQuest Information & Learning, The Dialog Corporation).
Indexed: ABIn, AcaI, AgeL, AmStI, BLI, BPI, BPIA, BusI, CLI, CREJ, FiP, IBSS, ILP, IUSGP, JEL, KES, MEA&I, ManagCont, PAIS, PROMT, RASB, RefZh, T&II, WAE&RSA, WBA.
—BLDSC (3901.935000), CISTI, IE, Infotrieve, ingenta.
Published by: U.S. Federal Reserve System, Board of Governors, Publications Services, Rm MS 138, Washington, DC 20551. TEL 202-452-3000, 202-452-3245, http://www.federalreserve.gov/pubs/bulletin/default.htm. Circ: 26,000.

332 USA
FEDERAL RESERVE FORMS AND INSTRUCTIONS. Text in English. a. (March). **Document type:** *Government.*
Formed by the merger of: Federal Reserve Forms; Federal Reserve Instructions
Published by: U.S. Department of Commerce, National Technical Information Service, 5285 Port Royal Rd, Springfield, VA 22161. TEL 703-605-6000, info@ntis.gov, http://www.ntis.gov.

332.1 USA
FEDERAL RESERVE REGULATORY SERVICE. (Includes 4 handbooks updated at least monthly: Consumer and Community Affairs; Monetary Policy and Reserve Requirements; Securities Credit Transactions; Payment System) Text in English. 4 base vols. plus irreg. updates. looseleaf. USD 75 domestic per handbook; USD 90 foreign per handbook; USD 200 domestic per set; USD 250 foreign per set. **Document type:** *Government.*
Related titles: Diskette ed.
Published by: Federal Reserve System, Board of Governors, Publications Services, Rm MS 127, 20th and Constitution Ave, N W, Washington, DC 20551. TEL 202-452-3244, FAX 202-728-5886.

FEDERAL RESERVE SYSTEM. BOARD OF GOVERNORS. ANNUAL REPORT. see *BUSINESS AND ECONOMICS—Economic Situation And Conditions*

332 FRA ISSN 0071-4380
FEDERATION NATIONALE DU CREDIT AGRICOLE. ANNUAIRE DU CREDIT AGRICOLE MUTUEL✶. Text in French. 1960. a., latest vol.3.
Published by: Federation Nationale du Credit Agricole, 48 rue la Boetie, Paris, 75008, France.

FIELD GUIDE TO ESTATE PLANNING, BUSINESS PLANNING & EMPLOYEE BENEFITS. see *INSURANCE*

332 USA
FIERCEFINANCE; the financial services daily monitor. Text in English. d. free. **Document type:** *Newsletter, Trade.* **Description:** Covers the financial services industry for investment bankers, venture capitalists, and fund managers.
Media: E-mail.
Published by: FierceMarkets, Inc., 1319 F St, NW, Ste 604, Washington, DC 20004. TEL 202-628-8778, info@fiercemarkets.com, http://www.fiercefinance.com, http://www.fiercemarkets.com. Eds. Jim Kim, Scott Gordon.

332 IRL ISSN 0790-8628
FINANCE. Text in English. 1987. m. EUR 225 (effective 2005). adv. **Document type:** *Trade.* **Description:** Examines Ireland's money and capital markets.
Published by: Fintel Publications Ltd., Fintel House, 6 The Mall, Beacon Court, Sandyford, Dublin, 18, Ireland. TEL 353-1-2930566, FAX 353-1-2930560, subs@finance-magazine.com, editorial@finance-magazine.com, mb@finance-magazine.com, http://www.finance-magazine.com/. Ed. Ken O'Brien. Circ: 2,800.

332 FRA ISSN 0752-6180
FINANCE. Text in French. 1980. s-a. EUR 90 domestic; EUR 110 foreign (effective 2004). **Document type:** *Journal, Academic/Scholarly.* **Description:** Covers management, market equilibrium, taxes, investments, the balance of payments, and exchange rates.
Formerly (until 1982): Association Francaise de Finance. Revue (0248-0107)
Related titles: Online - full text ed.: (from ProQuest Information & Learning).
Indexed: ABIn, BLI, JEL.
—BLDSC (3926.853000), IE, ingenta. **CCC.**
Published by: Association Francaise de Finance, c/o CERAG, UMMF, BP 47, Grenoble, 38040, France. TEL 33-047-6635363, FAX 33-047-6546068, secretariat@affi.asso.fr, http://www.affi.asso.fr.

332 JPN ISSN 0448-6072
FINANCE✶ /FAINANSU. Text in Japanese. 1965. m. JPY 5,400. adv. bk.rev.
Published by: Ministry of Finance, General Coordination Division/Okura-sho, Minister's Secretariat, 3-1-1 Kasumigaseki, Chiyoda-ku, Tokyo, 100-0013, Japan. Ed. Toshiyuki Tsukazaki. Circ: 13,000.

330 CZE ISSN 0015-1920
FINANCE A UVER; Czech journal of economics and finance. Text in Czech, Slovak, English; Summaries in English. 1950. bi-m. EUR 95 in Europe; USD 145 elsewhere (effective 2005). bk.rev. bibl.; illus. index. **Document type:** *Journal, Academic/Scholarly.* **Description:** Publishes articles dealing with public finance, monetary and fiscal theory and policy problems, capital markets, corporate finance and restructuring, as well as general economic issues.
Indexed: ABIn, CurCont, JEL, RASB, SSCI.
Published by: (Universita Karlova), Datakonekt s.r.o., Libice 10, Dobris, 263 01, Czech Republic. FAX 420-3-18520489, redakce@financeauver.org, subscription@financeauver.org, http://www.financeauver.org. Ed. Jan Frait.

FINANCE AND ACCOUNTING JOBS REPORT. see *OCCUPATIONS AND CAREERS*

332 USA ISSN 8750-6149
KFM5831
FINANCE AND COMMERCE. Text in English. 1896. d. (M-F). USD 175 (effective 2005). adv. back issues avail. **Document type:** *Newspaper.* **Description:** Covers business and legal matters in the city of Minneapolis and Hennepin County.
Published by: Finance and Commerce, Inc., 730 2nd Ave, S 100, Minneapolis, MN 55402-3400. TEL 612-333-4244, FAX 612-333-4243, info@finance-commerce.com, http://www.finance-commerce.com. Ed. Monte Hanson. Pub. Debra Quaal. Adv. contact Kris Kurtzahn. Circ: 4,500 (paid).

332 658 NLD ISSN 1567-553X
FINANCE & CONTROL. Text in Dutch. 2002. bi-m. EUR 185 print & online eds. (effective 2005). adv. **Document type:** *Magazine, Trade.*
Formed by the merger of (1991-2001): Financieel Management Select (0926-1753); (1981-2001): Tijdschrift Financieel Management (0167-0581)
—IE, Infotrieve.
Published by: Wolters Kluwer N.V., Postbus 23, Deventer, 7400 GA, Netherlands. TEL 31-570-673358, FAX 31-570-691555, info@kluwer.nl. Circ: 1,747.

FINANCE & CREDIT LAW. see *LAW*

332 USA ISSN 1564-5142
FINANCE & DEVELOPMENT (ONLINE EDITION). Text in English. 1996. q.
Media: Online - full text. **Related titles:** Microform ed.: (from CIS, PQC); ♦ Print ed.: Finance and Development (Print Edition). ISSN 0145-1707; Spanish ed.: Finanzas y Desarrollo (Online Edition). ISSN 1607-9531; French ed.: Finances et Developpement (Online Edition). ISSN 1607-9523.
—**CCC.**
Published by: International Monetary Fund, 700 19th St, N W, Washington, DC 20431. publications@imf.org, http://www.imf.org/external/pubs/ft/fandd/2002/09/index.htm.

332.1 338.9 USA ISSN 0145-1707
HG3881 CODEN: FNDVAM
FINANCE AND DEVELOPMENT (PRINT EDITION). Text in English. 1964. q. free. adv. bk.rev. charts; illus. Index. reprint service avail. from PQC. **Document type:** *Journal.* **Description:** Publishes articles of an informative or analytical character on the policies and activities of the institutions, emphasizing new aspects of approaches as they arise, as well as general pieces on financial and development issues.
Formerly (until 1967): Fund and Bank Review (1020-4601)
Related titles: Microform ed.: (from CIS, PQC); ♦ Online - full text ed.: Finance & Development (Online Edition). ISSN 1564-5142; ♦ French ed.: Finances et Developpement (Print Edition). ISSN 0430-473X; Arabic ed.: Tamwil wa-al-tanmiyat. ISSN 0250-7455; German ed.: Finanzierung und Entwicklung. ISSN 0250-7439; Portuguese ed.: Financas e Desenvolvimento. ISSN 0255-7622; Spanish ed.: Finanzas y Desarrollo (Print Edition). ISSN 0250-7447; Chinese ed.: Jinrong yu Fazhan. ISSN 0256-2561; Russian ed.: Rinansy i Razvitie. ISSN 1020-8151.
Indexed: ABIn, AESIS, APEL, ASFA, ATI, AmH&L, BAS, BPIA, BusI, EI, EIP, Emerald, GEOBASE, HistAb, IBR, IBSS, IBZ, IFP, IIS, IPARL, JEL, KES, MEA&I, ManagCont, PAIS, PROMT, PSI, PerIslam, RASB, RDA, REE&TA, SPAA, SSI, T&II, WAE&RSA.
—BLDSC (3926.864000), CISTI, Infotrieve, ingenta. **CCC.**
Published by: International Monetary Fund, Publication Services, 700 19th St, N W, Ste 12-607, Washington, DC 20431. TEL 202-623-7430, FAX 202-623-7201, fandd@imf.org, http://www.imf.org/external/pubs/ft/fandd/2002/09/index.htm. Circ: 121,000.

332.3 KWT
FINANCE AND INDUSTRY. JOURNAL. Text in English, Arabic. 1980. free.
Published by: Industrial Bank of Kuwait/Bank al-Kuwayt al-Sinai, P O Box 3146, Safat, Kuwait. TEL 965-2457661, FAX 965-2462057, IBK@ncc.moc.kw, http://ncc.moc.kw.users/I.B.K. Ed. Amro Mohie Al-din. Circ: 1,500.

332 TUR
FINANCE & INVESTMENT. Text in Turkish. w. adv. **Document type:** *Magazine, Trade.*
Published by: D B R - Dogan Burda Rizzoli Dergi Yayyncylyk ve Pazarlama A.S., Hurriyet Medya Towers, Gunesli - Istanbul, 34212, Turkey. TEL 90-212-4103111, FAX 90-212-4103112, abone@dbr.com.tr, http://www.dbr.com.tr.

332 510 DEU ISSN 0949-2984
HG174
➤ **FINANCE AND STOCHASTICS.** Text in English. q. EUR 368 combined subscription to institutions print & online eds. (effective 2005). adv. back issues avail.; reprint service avail. from PSC. **Document type:** *Journal, Academic/Scholarly.* **Description:** Provides a forum for research in all areas of finance based on stochastic methods and on specific topics in mathematics motivated by the analysis of problems in finance.
Related titles: Online - full text ed.: ISSN 1432-1122 (from EBSCO Publishing, ProQuest Information & Learning, Springer LINK, Swets Information Services).
Indexed: ABIn, CCMJ, CMCI, CurCont, IBSS, JEL, MathR, MathSciNet, SSCI, ST&MA, ZentMath.
—BLDSC (3926.910000), IE, Infotrieve, ingenta. **CCC.**
Published by: Springer-Verlag (Subsidiary of: Springer Science+Business Media), Tiergartenstr 17, Heidelberg, 69121, Germany. TEL 49-6221-3450, FAX 49-6221-345229, http://link.springer.de/link/service/journals/00780/index.htm. Ed. Dieter Sondermann TEL 49-228-739263. Adv. contact Stephan Kroeck TEL 49-30-827875739. **Subscr. in the Americas to:** Springer-Verlag New York, Inc., Journal Fulfillment, PO Box 2485, Secaucus, NJ 07096-2485. TEL 800-777-4643, 201-348-4033, FAX 201-348-4505, journals@springer-ny.com, http://www.springer-ny.com; **Subscr. to:** Springer GmbH Auslieferungsgesellschaft, Haberstr 7, Heidelberg 69126, Germany. TEL 49-6221-345-0, FAX 49-6221-345-4229, subscriptions@springer.de.

332 USA ISSN 1523-2670
HG201
FINANCE AND TREASURY'S INTERNATIONAL REPORTS. Text in English. 1947. w. stat. **Document type:** *Newsletter, Trade.* **Description:** Provides insights on world financial markets and economies as well as analysis of the trends and events that matter to the international financial community.
Formerly (until 1997): International Reports (0020-8507)
Indexed: PerIslam.
—**CCC.**
Published by: WorldTrade Executive, Inc., 2250 Main St, Ste 100, PO Box 761, Concord, MA 01742. TEL 978-287-0301, FAX 978-287-0302, info@wtexec.com, http://www.wtexec.com.

332 USA ISSN 0364-0132
FINANCE COMPANIES. Text in English. m. USD 5. **Document type:** *Government.*
Published by: U.S. Federal Reserve System, Board of Governors, Publications Services, Rm MS 138, Washington, DC 20551. TEL 202-452-3244, FAX 202-728-5886.

B

332 GBR ISSN 0262-5695
FINANCE CONFIDENTIAL✶. Text in English. 1981. m. GBP 134.
—CCC.
Published by: Fleet Street Publications Ltd., 271 Regent St, London, WIR 7PAU, United Kingdom. TEL 44-20-7447-4040, FAX 44-20-7447-4041. Ed. Malcolm Craig.

658.1505 GBR ISSN 1462-866X
FINANCE DIRECTOR EUROPE. Text in English. 1992. s-a. GBP 5.95 per issue; free to qualified personnel (effective 2005). adv. reprints avail. **Document type:** *Journal, Trade.* **Description:** Examines, by means of privileged case histories and expert analysis, all the crucial issues, trends, financial techniques and economic factors which influence corporate activity, from mergers and acquisitions to insurance, pension and corporate relocation, finance, leasing, information technology, and international investment opportunities.
Formerly (until 1996): Corporate Finance Europe (1350-4525)
Published by: S P G Media Ltd. (Subsidiary of: Sterling Publishing Group Plc.), Brunel House, 55-57 North Wharf Rd, London, W2 1LA, United Kingdom. TEL 44-20-79159600, FAX 44-20-77242089, info@spgmedia.com, info@sterlingpublications.com, http://www.financedirectoreurope.com/, http://www.spgmedia.com/. Ed. Mr. Dougal Thomson. Pub. Mr. William Crocker. R&P Mr. Derek Deschamps. Adv. contact Mr. Patrick Agyeman TEL 44-20-79159738. B&W page GBP 6,400, color page GBP 7,920. Circ: 15,400 (controlled).

332 GBR ISSN 0260-1176
FINANCE DIRECTOR'S REVIEW. Text in English. 1980. m. GBP 180 in United Kingdom; GBP 220 overseas (effective 2000). **Document type:** *Trade.*
Published by: Butterworths Tolley (Subsidiary of: LexisNexis UK (Scottish Office)), 2 Addiscombe Rd, Croydon, Surrey CR9 5AF, United Kingdom. TEL 44-20-8686-9141, FAX 44-20-8686-3155, http://www.tolley.co.uk. Ed. Claire Melvin. Circ: 650.

332 GBR
THE FINANCE DIRECTOR'S YEARBOOK. Abbreviated title: FDY. Text in English. 2000. a. GBP 75 per issue (effective 2001). **Document type:** *Directory, Trade.* **Description:** Contains details for finance directors and senior contacts in over 6000 major UK companies, also listing over 2,500 advisers to corporate finance directors, including accountants, bankers and insurance brokers.
Published by: A P Information Services, Marlborough House, 298 Regents Park Rd, London, N3 2UU, United Kingdom. TEL 44-20-83499988, FAX 44-20-83499797, info@apinfo.co.uk, http://www.ap-info.co.uk. Ed. Annick Ireland. Pub. Alan Philipp.

332 657 IND ISSN 0970-3772
HG41
➤ **FINANCE INDIA;** the quarterly journal of finance. Text in English. 1987. q. INR 800 domestic to individuals; USD 80 foreign to individuals; INR 1,000 domestic to institutions; USD 100 foreign to institutions (effective 2003). adv. bk.rev. abstr.; bibl.; stat. 450 p./no.; back issues avail.; reprints avail. **Document type:** *Journal, Academic/Scholarly.* **Description:** Provides a forum for intradisciplinary study of finance, accounting and related areas.
Related titles: Online - full text ed.: (from O C L C Online Computer Library Center, Inc., ProQuest Information & Learning).
Indexed: ABIn, BLI, IBSS, JEL, RDA, RiceAb, WAE&RSA.
—BLDSC (3926.924685), IE, ingenta.
Published by: Indian Institute of Finance, 4, Community Center II, Ashok Vihar II, P O Box 8486, New Delhi, 110 052, India. TEL 91-11-27136257, FAX 91-11-27454128, aa@iif.edu, aa@finance.india.org, http://www.financeindia.org. Ed. J D Agarwal. R&P, Adv. contact J.D. Agarwal TEL 91-11-7136257. page INR 10,000, page USD 500; trim 4.5 x 8. Circ: 1,200 (paid).

➤ **FINANCE, INSURANCE AND REAL ESTATE U S A.** see *BUSINESS AND ECONOMICS—Abstracting, Bibliographies, Statistics*

332 USA
FINANCE: LATIN AMERICAN INDUSTRIAL REPORT✶. (Avail. for each of 20 Latin American countries) Text in English. 1985. a. USD 235; per country report.
Published by: Aquino Productions, P O Box 15760, Stamford, CT 06901-0760. Ed. Andres C Aquino.

332 USA
HG1
▼ **FINANCE RESEARCH LETTERS.** Text in English. 2004 (Jan.). 4/yr. EUR 68 in Europe to individuals; JPY 7,400 in Japan to individuals; USD 54 elsewhere to individuals; EUR 387 in Europe to institutions; JPY 42,100 in Japan to institutions; USD 416 elsewhere to institutions (effective 2006). **Document type:** *Journal, Academic/Scholarly.* **Description:** Covers all areas of finance.
Formerly (until 2005): Finance Letters (1544-6123)
Related titles: Online - full text ed.: ISSN 1544-6131 (from EBSCO Publishing, ScienceDirect, Swets Information Services).
—IE. **CCC.**
Published by: Elsevier Inc. (Subsidiary of: Elsevier Science & Technology), 525 B St. Ste. 1900, San Diego, CA 92101-4495. TEL 619-231-6616, FAX 619-699-6422, FRL@elsevier.com, usinfo-f@elsevier.com, http://www.elsevier.com/locate/frl. Ed. R Gencay.

332 ZAF ISSN 0256-0321
HG46
FINANCE WEEK. Text in English. 1979. w. ZAR 195. adv. bk.rev. **Document type:** *Trade.*
Related titles: Online - full text ed.: (from EBSCO Publishing, O C L C Online Computer Library Center, Inc.); ♦ Afrikaans ed.: Finansies & Tegniek.
Indexed: ABIn, ISAP.
—BLDSC (3926.924880).
Published by: National Magazines (Subsidiary of: National Media Ltd.), PO Box 1802, Cape Town, 8000, South Africa. TEL 27-21-406-3678, FAX 27-21-406-3289, http://www.natmags.com. Ed. Gert Marais. adv.: B&W page ZAR 11,500, color page ZAR 14,800. Circ: 18,000 (paid).

332 FRA
FINANCEMENTS DES PARTICULIERS. Text in French. 1993. m. EUR 524 domestic; EUR 564 foreign (effective 2000). **Document type:** *Newsletter.* **Description:** Covers mortgage loans, revolving credit, consumer financing, and auto financing.
Published by: Publi-News, 47 rue Aristide Briand, Levallois-Perret, 92300, France. TEL 33-1-41499360, FAX 33-1-47573725, publi.news@wanadoo.fr. Ed. Ange Galula.

332 338.9 USA ISSN 0430-473X
FINANCES ET DEVELOPPEMENT (PRINT EDITION). Text in French. 1968. q. free (effective 2005).
Related titles: Online - full content ed.: Finances et Developpement (Online Edition). ISSN 1607-9523; ♦ English ed.: Finance and Development (Print Edition). ISSN 0145-1707; Arabic ed.: Tamwil wa-al-tanmiyat. ISSN 0250-7455; German ed.: Finanzierung und Entwicklung. ISSN 0250-7439; Portuguese ed.: Financas e Desenvolvimento. ISSN 0255-7622; Spanish ed.: Finanzas y Desarrollo (Print Edition). ISSN 0250-7447; Chinese ed.: Jinrong yu Fazhan. ISSN 0256-2561; Russian ed.: Rinansy i Razvitie. ISSN 1020-8151.
Indexed: JEL.
—CCC.
Published by: International Monetary Fund, Publication Services, 700 19th St, N W, Ste 12-607, Washington, DC 20431. TEL 202-623-8300, 202-623-7430, FAX 202-623-6149, 202-623-7201, publications@imf.org, http://www.imf.org. Ed. Laura Wallace.

FINANCIAL ADVERTISING REVIEW; the monthly report on advertising by banks, savings & loans, and credit unions. see *ADVERTISING AND PUBLIC RELATIONS*

FINANCIAL ADVICE & COMMUNITY. see *BUSINESS AND ECONOMICS—Investments*

332 IND
FINANCIAL ANALYSIS. Text in English. 1991. m. INR 7 per issue.
Published by: Quick Data Organization Pvt. Ltd., 306 Jyoti Bhawan, Commercial Complex, Dr. Mukherjee Nagar, New Delhi, 110 009, India. Ed. J R Gupta.

FINANCIAL AND ESTATE PLANNING FOR THE MATURE CLIENT IN ONTARIO. see *LAW—Estate Planning*

336.74 NLD ISSN 0921-8580
FINANCIAL AND MONETARY POLICY STUDIES. Text in Dutch. 1974. irreg., latest vol.35, 2001. price varies. back issues avail. **Document type:** *Monographic series, Academic/Scholarly.* **Description:** In depth analysis and discussion of European and international issues relating to fiscal, taxation and monetary policy, financial integration, financial institutions. Certain volumes constitute lectures presented at SUERF Colloquia.
Formerly: Financial and Monetary Studies
—BLDSC (3926.946400), ingenta.
Published by: (Societe Universitaire Europeenne de Recherches Financieres), Springer-Verlag Dordrecht (Subsidiary of: Springer Science+Business Media), Van Godewijckstraat 30, Dordrecht, 3311 GX, Netherlands. TEL 31-78-6576050, FAX 31-78-6576474, http://www.springeronline.com.

FINANCIAL CONDITION OF COLORADO MUNICIPALITIES. see *PUBLIC ADMINISTRATION—Municipal Government*

332.024 USA ISSN 1052-3073
HG179
➤ **FINANCIAL COUNSELING AND PLANNING.** Text in English. 1990. s-a. USD 80 to individuals membership; USD 80 to libraries membership; USD 30 to students membership; free to members (effective 2005). back issues avail. **Document type:** *Journal, Academic/Scholarly.* **Description:** Disseminates scholarly research related to financial counseling and planning education.
Indexed: BusEdI.
—BLDSC (3926.952160).
Published by: Association for Financial Counseling and Planning Education, 2112 Arlington Ave, Ste H, Upper Arlington, OH 43221-4339. TEL 614-485-9650, FAX 614-485-9621, fcp@oregonstate.edu, http://www.afcpe.org. Ed. Dr. Sandra Helmick.

658 USA ISSN 1531-0965
HV6768
FINANCIAL CRIME REVIEW. Text in English. 2000. q. **Document type:** *Journal, Trade.* **Description:** Contains advice on the detection and prevention of money laundering and fraud covering the securities, banking and insurance sectors.
—CCC.
Published by: Institutional Investor, Journals (Subsidiary of: Euromoney Institutional Investor Plc.), 225 Park Ave S, 7th Fl., New York, NY 10003-1605. TEL 212-224-3800, FAX 212-224-3491, info@iijournals.com, http://www.iijournals.com.

332 GBR ISSN 0961-2556
FINANCIAL DIRECTOR. Text in English. 1984. m. GBP 68 (effective 1999). **Document type:** *Trade.* **Description:** Provides authoritative, high quality editorial to senior financial decision-makers focusing on their need for information on topics such as corporate finance, information technology, economic forecasts, corporate governance, and shareholder value.
Formerly (until 1989): Financial Decisions (0267-4785)
Related titles: Online - full text ed.: (from Gale Group, LexisNexis, O C L C Online Computer Library Center, Inc.).
Indexed: Inspec.
—BLDSC (3926.952280), AskIEEE, IE, ingenta. **CCC.**
Published by: V N U Business Publications Ltd., VNU House, 32-34 Broadwick St, London, W1A 2HG, United Kingdom. TEL 44-20-7316-9000, FAX 44-20-7316-9160, http://www.financialdirector.co.uk. Circ: 20,281 (controlled).

332 IND ISSN 0015-2005
FINANCIAL EXPRESS. Text in English. 1961. d. INR 145. bk.rev. stat.; tr.lit. **Document type:** *Newspaper.*
Related titles: Online - full text ed.: (from Newsbank, Inc.); Regional ed(s).: Financial Express (Bangalore Edition); Financial Express (Bombay Edition); Financial Express (Calcutta Edition); Financial Express (Madras Edition); Financial Express (New Delhi Edition).
Indexed: B&I.
Published by: Indian Express Newspapers (Mumbai) Pvt. Ltd., Express Towers, Nariman Point, P O Box 867, Mumbai, Maharashtra 400 021, India. TEL 91-22-2022627, FAX 91-22-2022139, TELEX 011-82585 INEX IN. Ed. A M Khusro. Circ: 20,000.

332 USA
FINANCIAL FAX. Text in English. w.
Formerly: Comments on Money and Credit
Related titles: Fax ed.; Online - full text ed.
Published by: D R I - McGraw-Hill, 24 Hartwell Ave, Lexington, MA 02173. TEL 617-863-5100, FAX 617-860-6332. Ed. Cynthia Latta.

346 345.0263 USA ISSN 1093-9717
FINANCIAL FRAUD. Text in English. 1997. 6/yr. USD 96 domestic; USD 108 in Canada; USD 128 elsewhere (effective 2005). **Document type:** *Newsletter, Trade.* **Description:** Covers fraud in financial reporting and in financial services and products. How investors, investment managers, and fiduciaries should conduct financial and legal due diligence.
Published by: Assets Protection Publishing, 5029 Sheboygan Ave #201, Madison, WI 53705. Ed. Charles H Calhoun.

FINANCIAL HANDBOOK FOR BANKRUPTCY PROFESSIONALS. see *LAW*

332 973 USA ISSN 1520-4723
HG4633
➤ **FINANCIAL HISTORY.** Text in English. 1978. q. USD 40 membership (effective 2000). adv. bk.rev. bibl.; illus. 40 p./no.; back issues avail. **Document type:** *Magazine, Academic/Scholarly.* **Description:** Covers the history of commerce and the development of the American capital markets.
Formerly: Friends of Financial History (0278-8861)
Related titles: Online - full text ed.
Indexed: AmH&L, HistAb.
Published by: Museum of American Financial History, 26 Broadway, New York, NY 10004-1763. TEL 212-908-4695, 212-908-4519, FAX 212-908-4601, kaguilera@financialhistory.org, http://www.financialhistory.org. Ed., R&P, Adv. contact Kristin Aguilera. Pub. Brian Thompson. B&W page USD 640, color page USD 1,350; trim 10.88 x 8.38. Circ: 5,000 (paid).

332 GBR ISSN 0968-5650
HG171
➤ **FINANCIAL HISTORY REVIEW.** Text in English. 1994. s-a. GBP 81 to institutions; USD 138 in North America to institutions; GBP 85 combined subscription to institutions print & online eds.; USD 143 combined subscription in North America to institutions print & online eds. (effective 2006). adv. bk.rev. illus. back issues avail.; reprint service avail. from ISI. **Document type:** *Journal, Academic/Scholarly.* **Description:** Provides an international forum for scholars interested in the development of banking, finance and other monetary matters.

Related titles: Online - full text ed.: ISSN 1474-0052. GBP 75 to institutions; USD 127 in North America to institutions (effective 2006) (from EBSCO Publishing, O C L C Online Computer Library Center, Inc., Swets Information Services).
Indexed: AmH&L, BAS, HistAb, IBSS, JEL, RASB.
—BLDSC (3926.956230), IE, Infotrieve, ingenta. **CCC.**
Published by: (European Association for Banking History), Cambridge University Press, The Edinburgh Bldg, Shaftesbury Rd, Cambridge, CB2 2RU, United Kingdom. TEL 44-1223-312393, FAX 44-1223-315052, journals@cambridge.org, http://uk.cambridge.org/journals/fhr. Eds. David Weiman, Duncan M Ross, Youssef Cassis. R&P Linda Nicol TEL 44-1223-325757. Adv. contact Rebecca Curtis TEL 44-1223-325757. **Subscr. to:** Cambridge University Press, 100 Brook Hill Dr, West Nyack, NY 10994. TEL 845-353-7500, FAX 845-353-4141, journals_subscriptions@cup.org

332.1 USA ISSN 0362-1405
HG4512
FINANCIAL INDUSTRY NUMBER STANDARD DIRECTORY. Text in English. 1976. irreg. **Document type:** *Directory.*
Published by: Depository Trust Company, 55 Water St, New York, NY 10041. TEL 212-558-8000.

332 USA
FINANCIAL INDUSTRY STUDIES WORKING PAPERS. Text in English. irreg. free. charts. back issues avail. **Document type:** *Academic/Scholarly.*
Related titles: Online - full text ed.
Published by: Federal Reserve Bank of Dallas, PO Box 655906, Dallas, TX 75265-5906. TEL 214-922-5906, FAX 214-922-5268. Circ: 1,100.

332 USA
FINANCIAL INSTITUTIONS DIRECTORY OF NEW ENGLAND. Text in English. 1913. a. USD 32. **Document type:** *Directory.*
Formerly: Bank Directory of New England
Published by: Shawmut Bank, N.A., Correspondent Banking Group, One Federal St, Boston, MA 02211. TEL 617-292-3823, FAX 617-292-4417. Circ: (controlled). **Dist. by:** R.L. Polk Co., PO Box 305100, Nashville, TN 37230-5100. TEL 800-788-2230.

332 ZAF ISSN 0015-2013
HG46
FINANCIAL MAIL. Text in English. 1959. w. (Wed.). ZAR 292 (effective 1999). adv. bk.rev. charts; illus.; stat. index. **Document type:** *Newspaper.* **Description:** Covers the economy and financial markets, companies and investment, business and current affairs in South Africa and the world, providing a broad spectrum of news, information and comment.
Related titles: Microfilm ed.; Online - full text ed.: Financial Mail Interactive (from EBSCO Publishing, Florida Center for Library Automation, LexisNexis); ◆ Supplement(s): Top Companies. ISSN 0563-8895.
Indexed: ISAP, KES, PAIS, PROMT, RASB.
Published by: Times Media Limited, PO Box 1746, Saxonwold, Johannesburg 2133, South Africa. TEL 27-11-280-3000, FAX 27-11-280-3773, fmmail@tml.co.za, http://www.fm.co.za. Ed. Peter Bruce. Circ: 32,500 (paid). **Subscr. to:** Circulation Manager, PO Box 10493, Johannesburg 2000, South Africa. TEL 27-860-131313, FAX 27-860-562613.

THE FINANCIAL MANAGER. see *COMMUNICATIONS—Television And Cable*

332 USA
FINANCIAL MANAGERS SOCIETY. Text in English. bi-w. USD 395 to members (effective 2005). adv. **Document type:** *Newsletter, Trade.* **Description:** Covers the latest accounting and regulatory information related to financial institutions, as well as trends relating to financial management practice.
Former titles (until 1994): F M S Update; Update Newsletter; Printout (8755-5751)
Published by: Financial Managers Society, Inc., 100 W Monroe, Ste 810, Chicago, IL 60603. TEL 312-578-1300, 800-275-4367, FAX 312-578-1308, info@fmsinc.org, http://www.fmsinc.org. Ed. Thomas Lannig. adv.: B&W page USD 700; trim 10 x 7.5. Circ: 1,450 (paid and controlled).

332 FRA ISSN 0378-651X
HG136 CODEN: FMTRDI
FINANCIAL MARKET TRENDS. Text in English. 1977. s-a. EUR 68, USD 78, GBP 46, JPY 9,200 (effective 2005). illus. Index. back issues avail.; reprints avail. **Document type:** *Government.* **Description:** Provides an assessment of trends and prospects in the international and major domestic financial markets of the OECD area.
Related titles: Online - full content ed.: ISSN 1609-6886. USD 68 (effective 2004) (from Florida Center for Library Automation, Northern Light Technology, Inc.); Online - full text ed.: (from EBSCO Publishing, Gale Group, IngentaConnect, O C L C Online Computer Library Center, Inc., ProQuest Information & Learning, Swets Information Services); French ed.: ISSN 0378-6528.
Indexed: ABIn, BLI, BPIA, IIS, KES, PAIS, RASB, T&II.
—CISTI, IE, Infotrieve. **CCC.**
Published by: Organization for Economic Cooperation and Development, 2 Rue Andre Pascal, Paris, 75775 Cedex 16, France. TEL 33-1-45248200, FAX 33-1-45248500, http://www.oecd.org. **Subscr. in N. America to:** O E C D Turpin North America, PO Box 194, Downingtown, PA 19335-0194. TEL 610-524-5361, 800-456-6323, FAX 610-524-5417, journalscustomer@turpinna.com.

FINANCIAL MARKETING (LONDON). see *BUSINESS AND ECONOMICS—Investments*

332 USA ISSN 0963-8008
HG1
➤ **FINANCIAL MARKETS, INSTITUTIONS AND INSTRUMENTS.** Text in English. 1928; N.S. 1975. 5/yr. USD 128 combined subscription in the Americas to individuals & Caribbean, print & online eds.; EUR 162 combined subscription in Europe to individuals print & online eds.; GBP 108 combined subscription elsewhere to individuals print & online eds.; USD 400 combined subscription in the Americas to institutions & Caribbean, print & online eds.; GBP 299 combined subscription elsewhere to institutions print & online eds. (effective 2006). adv. illus. reprint service avail. from PSC. **Document type:** *Journal, Academic/Scholarly.* **Description:** Provides in-depth coverage of topics of current interest in the areas of financial markets, institutions and instruments.
Former titles (until 1992): Monograph Series in Finance and Economics (0276-2021); (until 1990): Salomon Brothers Center for the Study of Financial Institutions. Monograph Series; New York University Institute of Finance. Bulletin
Related titles: Online - full text ed.: ISSN 1468-0416. N.S. USD 380 in the Americas to institutions & Caribbean; GBP 284 elsewhere to institutions (effective 2006) (from Blackwell Synergy, EBSCO Publishing, Gale Group, IngentaConnect, O C L C Online Computer Library Center, Inc., Swets Information Services).
Indexed: BLI, IBSS, JEL.
—BLDSC (3926.962550), IE, Infotrieve, ingenta. **CCC.**
Published by: (New York University, Salomon Center), Blackwell Publishing, Inc. (Subsidiary of: Blackwell Publishing Ltd.), Commerce Place, 350 Main St, Malden, MA 02148. TEL 781-388-8206, FAX 781-388-8232, subscrip@blackwellpub.com, http://www.blackwellpublishing.com/journals/FMII. Ed. Anthony Saunders.

332 USA
FINANCIAL NEWS & DAILY RECORD. Text in English. 1912. d. (Mon.-Fri.). USD 89; USD 0.35 newsstand/cover (effective 2005). **Document type:** *Newspaper, Trade.*
Published by: Bailey Publishing & Communications Inc., 10 N Newnan St, Jacksonville, FL 32202. TEL 904-356-2466, FAX 904-353-2628, jbailey@baileypub.com, http://www.jaxdailyrecord.com. Ed. Fred Seeley. Pub. James F Bailey Jr. Circ: 5,500 morning (paid).

332 SGP ISSN 0218-6756
FINANCIAL PLANNER. Text in English. 1993. bi-m. SGD 48. **Document type:** *Magazine, Consumer.* **Description:** Covers issues and trends related to personal finance.
Indexed: PAIS.
Published by: Arima Research & Consultancy Pte Ltd., No 6, #10-07 Battery Rd, Singapore, 049909, Singapore. TEL 65-2240121, FAX 65-2241651, subscription@financial-planner.com.sg, http://www.financial-planner.com.sg/. Ed. Maurice Chia.

332 AUS ISSN 1033-0046
FINANCIAL PLANNING. Text in English. 1985. bi-m. free to members. adv. **Document type:** *Trade.* **Description:** Represents the interests of all professional financial and investment advisors in Australia.
Formerly (until 1988): I A F P News (1033-0038)
Published by: (Financial Planning Association), Reed Business Information Pty Ltd (Subsidiary of: Reed Business Information International), Locked Bag 2999, Chatswood, NSW 2067, Australia. customerservice@reedbusiness.com.au, http://www.reedbusiness.com.au. Ed. Julie Bennett. Pub. Jeremy Knibbs TEL 61-2-9422-2930. Adv. contact Brad Lawson. Circ: 9,700.

FINANCIAL PLANNING. see *BUSINESS AND ECONOMICS—Management*

332.1 332.6 CAN ISSN 1489-7563
FINANCIAL POST DIVIDENDS, ANNUAL RECORD & 10 YEAR PRICE RANGE. Text in English. a. CND 59.95. **Description:** A 10 year "snapshot" of price history for all securities listed on the Toronto, Montreal, Vancouver and Alberta stock exchanges.
Formerly (until 1998): Annual Dividend Record - Ten Year Price Range (1198-1180); which was formed by the merger of: Financial Post Annual Dividend Record (1204-329X); Financial Post Ten Year Price Range (0844-1774); which was formerly: Financial Post Eight Year Price Range (0828-153X); (until 1978): Financial Post Six Year Price Range
Published by: Financial Post Datagroup, 300-1450 Don Mills Rd, Don Mills, ON M3B 3R5, Canada. TEL 416-350-6507, 800-661-7678, FAX 416-350-6501, fpdg@fpdata.finpost.com. Ed. Joanne Bryant.

332 USA ISSN 1540-4463
FINANCIAL PRIVACY ALERT. Text in English. 1998. m. USD 335 (effective 2005). **Document type:** *Newsletter.*
Formerly: Pratt'S Financial Privacy Report
Published by: A.S. Pratt & Sons, Inc., 1911 Fort Myer Dr, Arlington, VA 22209. TEL 703-528-0145, 800-572-2797, FAX 703-528-1736, pratt.info@thomsonmedia.com, http://www.aspratt.com/. Eds. Alan Rice, David Stemler, Sarah Snell.

332.024 323.4 USA ISSN 1059-0013
FINANCIAL PRIVACY REPORT. Text in English. 1991. m. USD 144; USD 164 foreign (effective 1997). bk.rev. back issues avail. **Document type:** *Newsletter.* **Description:** How to protect your personal and financial privacy.
Address: 12254 Nicollet Ave, Burnsville, MN 55337. TEL 612-895-8757, FAX 612-895-5526. Ed. Michael Ketcher. Pub. Daniel Rosenthal. Circ: 7,000 (paid).

332 GBR ISSN 1364-8128
FINANCIAL PRODUCTS. Text in English. 1993. w. GBP 870 in United Kingdom; USD 1,665 in Europe, US & Canada; USD 1,745 rest of world (effective 2001). **Description:** Includes practical applications of financial instruments to manage risk.
Formerly (until 1995): I F R Swaps (0968-4816)
—CCC.
Published by: Metal Bulletin plc, Park House, 3 Park Terr, Worcester Park, Surrey KT4 7HY, United Kingdom. TEL 44-20-78279977, FAX 44-20-78275290, subscriptions@metalbulletin.plc.uk, http://www.metalbulletin.com. Ed. Abed Kamed. Adv. contact Michael Popay. Circ: 1,350.

B

332 GBR ISSN 1473-3323
KF1428.A15
FINANCIAL REGULATION INTERNATIONAL. Text in English. 1986. 10/yr. GBP 697, USD 1,184, EUR 11,150 (effective 2003); effective 1993. **Document type:** *Journal, Trade.* **Description:** Provides a service on regulatory developments and their market implications in the global financial industry.
Formerly (until 2000): Financial Regulation Report (0952-0953)
Related titles: Microform ed.: (from PQC); Online - full text ed.: (from Data-Star).
Indexed: ABIn.
—IE.
Published by: Informa U K Limited (Subsidiary of: T & F Informa plc), 30-32 Mortimer St, London, W1W 7RE, United Kingdom. TEL 44-20-70174600, FAX 44-20-75531109, http://www.informa.com. Ed. Geoff Whitehouse.

332 GBR ISSN 1362-7511
K1066.A15
THE FINANCIAL REGULATOR; policy journal of international financial regulation. Text in English. 1996. q. EUR 240; EUR 250 foreign (effective 2002). adv. bk.rev. charts; illus.; stat. back issues avail. **Description:** Aims to serve as the policy journal of international financial regulation. Reports and analyses new regulations issued by agencies and central banks in the major capital markets.
Published by: Central Banking Publications Ltd., Fifth Fl, Tavistock House, Tavistock Sq, London, WC1H 9JZ, United Kingdom. TEL 44-20-73880006, FAX 44-20-73889040, centralbank@easynet.co.uk, info@centralbanking.co.uk, http://www.centralbanking.co.uk/. Ed., Pub. Robert Pringle. Adv. contact Jean Somerville.

332 GBR ISSN 0968-2651
FINANCIAL REGULATORY BRIEFING; the monthly digest of official pronouncements. Text in English. 1992. m. GBP 135 domestic; GBP 139 foreign (effective 2005). back issues avail. **Document type:** *Journal, Trade.* **Description:** Aimed for those interested in financial regulation.
Address: 2 Clifton Villas, London, W9 2PH, United Kingdom. TEL 44-20-72899784, FAX 44-20-72661991, frb@synopsis.co.uk, http://www.frb.co.uk. Ed. Lance Poynter. Circ: 1,500.

332 USA ISSN 0732-8516
HG181
➤ **THE FINANCIAL REVIEW (STATESBORO).** Text in English. 1966. q. USD 266 combined subscription in the Americas to institutions & Caribbean (print & online eds.); GBP 192 combined subscription elsewhere to institutions print & online eds. (effective 2006). adv. bk.rev. illus. index. back issues avail.; reprints avail. **Document type:** *Journal, Academic/Scholarly.* **Description:** Publishes empirical, theoretical and methodological articles on topics of micro- and macrofinance.
Incorporates: Eastern Finance Association. Proceedings of the Annual Meeting (0163-6855)
Related titles: Microform ed.: (from PQC); Online - full text ed.: ISSN 1540-6288. USD 253 in the Americas to institutions & Caribbean; GBP 182 elsewhere to institutions (effective 2006) (from Blackwell Synergy, EBSCO Publishing, Gale Group, IngentaConnect, O C L C Online Computer Library Center, Inc., ProQuest Information & Learning, Swets Information Services).
Indexed: ABIn, ATI, BLI, BPI, BPIA, JEL, PAIS, PROMT.
—BLDSC (3926.979800), IE, Infotrieve, ingenta.

▼ new title ➤ refereed ✶ unverified ◆ full entry avail.

Published by: (Eastern Finance Association), Blackwell Publishing, Inc. (Subsidiary of: Blackwell Publishing Ltd.), Commerce Place, 350 Main St, Malden, MA 02148. TEL 781-388-8206, FAX 781-388-8232, subscrip@blackwellpub.com, http://www.blackwellpublishing.com/journals/FR. Eds. Arnold R Cowan, Cynthia J Campbell. Circ: 2,000.

332 GBR
FINANCIAL RISK NEWSLETTER. Text in English. bi-m.
Document type: *Newsletter.*
Published by: Lovell White Durrant, 65 Holburn Viaduct, London, EC1A 2DY, United Kingdom. TEL 44-20-7236-0066, FAX 44-20-7248-4212, publications@lovellwhitedurrant.com, http://www.lovellwhitedurrant.com.

FINANCIAL SECTOR TECHNOLOGY. see *BUSINESS AND ECONOMICS—Banking And Finance—Computer Applications*

332 USA
FINANCIAL SERVICES ALERT. Text in English. 1986. w. USD 5.25. back issues avail. **Document type:** *Newsletter.*
Formerly: Bankalert
Published by: ISD Shaw, 900 17th St NW, Ste 506, Washington, DC 20006. TEL 202-296-5240, FAX 202-452-6816, isdninfo@isdshaw.com, http://www.isdshaw.com. Ed. Karen Shaw Petrou. Circ: 250.

332 CAN ISSN 1484-2408
FINANCIAL SERVICES CANADA; Canada's definitive financial services industry reference directory. Text in English. 1998. a. CND 325 per issue to libraries (effective 2005); for foreign subscr. prices, please contact publisher.. **Document type:** *Directory.* **Description:** Lists key players in the Canadian financial services sector.
Related titles: CD-ROM ed.; Online - full content ed.
Published by: Micromedia ProQuest (Subsidiary of: ProQuest Information & Learning), 20 Victoria St, Toronto, ON M5C 2N8, Canada. TEL 416-362-5211, 800-387-2689, FAX 416-362-6161, info@micromedia.ca, http://www.micromedia.ca/Directories/FinancialServices.htm. Ed. Mrs. Janet Hawtin.

FINANCIAL SERVICES DOCUMENT WATCH - PUBLIC FINANCE EDITION. see *BUSINESS AND ECONOMICS—Public Finance, Taxation*

332 GBR ISSN 1363-9005
FINANCIAL SERVICES IN LEEDS; a survey of the financial services industry. Text in English. 1996. a. **Document type:** *Trade.*
Published by: Yorkshire and Humberside Regional Research Observatory, University of Leeds, School of Geography, Leeds, W Yorks LS2 9JT, United Kingdom. TEL 44-113-233-3336, FAX 44-113-233-3308, chris@goeg.leeds.ac.uk. Ed. J C H Stillwell.

FINANCIAL SERVICES - LAW & PRACTICE. see *LAW*

332 USA
FINANCIAL SERVICES REGULATION AND LEGISLATION✶ . Text in English. 1986. 26/yr. USD 1,250. s-a. index.
Document type: *Newsletter.*
Formerly: Bank Regulation and Legislation Review
Published by: Financial Executive Institute, 900 17th St, NW, Ste 506, Washington, DC 20006. TEL 202-296-5240, FAX 202-452-6816. Ed. Theodore B Dolmatch. Circ: 200.

332 USA ISSN 1057-0810
HG179
➤ **FINANCIAL SERVICES REVIEW;** the journal of individual financial management. Abbreviated title: F S R. Text in English. 1991. q. USD 65 to individuals; USD 100 domestic to institutions; USD 150 foreign to institutions (effective 2005). adv. abstr. 1 cols./p.; back issues avail. **Document type:** *Journal, Academic/Scholarly.* **Description:** Encourages rigorous empirical research that examines individual behavior in terms of financial planning and services.
Related titles: Microform ed.: (from PQC); Online - full text ed.: (from EBSCO Publishing, Gale Group, IngentaConnect, O C L C Online Computer Library Center, Inc., ProQuest Information & Learning, ScienceDirect, Swets Information Services).
Indexed: ABIn, BLI.
—BLDSC (3926.986030), IE, Infotrieve, ingenta. **CCC.**
Published by: Academy of Financial Services, c/o Conrad Ciccotello, Ed., Dept. of Risk Management, Robinson College of Business, Georgia State University, PO Box 4036, Atlanta, GA 30302-4036. TEL 404-651-1711, FAX 404-651-4219, cciccotello@gsu.edu, http://www.rmi.gsu.edu/FSR/FSRhome.htm, http://www.academyfinancial.org. R&P, Adv. contact Conrad Ciccotello TEL 404-651-1711. page USD 100; 8 x 11. Circ: 500 (paid).

332 SWE ISSN 1404-2207
HG3729.S849
FINANCIAL STABILITY REPORT. Text in English. 2/yr.
Formerly (until 1999): Sveriges Riksbank. Financial Market Report (1403-0004)
Related titles: Online - full text ed.; ♦ Swedish ed.: Finansiell Stabilitet. ISSN 1404-2193.
Published by: Sveriges Riksbank, Brunkebergstorg 11, Stockholm, 10337, Sweden. TEL 46-8-7870000, FAX 46-8-210531, registratorn@riksbank.se, http://www.riksbank.se.

332 GBR
FINANCIAL STABILITY REVIEW. Text in English. 1997. irreg. GBP 10. **Description:** Aims to promote the latest thinking on risk, regulation and financial markets, to facilitate discussion of issues that might affect risks in the UK financial system, and to provide a forum for debate among practitioners, policy makers, and academics.
Published by: Bank of England, HO-3, Threadneedle St, London, EC2R 8AH, United Kingdom. TEL 44-20-7601-5191, FAX 44-20-7601-3217.

332 ISR ISSN 0334-2492
FINANCIAL STATEMENTS FOR THE YEAR. Text in English. 1978. a. ILS 24 per issue (effective 2005).
Published by: Bank of Israel, Kiryath Ben Gurion, P O Box 780, Jerusalem, 91007, Israel. TEL 972-2-655-2211, FAX 972-2-652-8805, http://www.bankisrael.gov.il/firsteng.htm.

332 USA ISSN 1018-2276
FINANCIAL STATEMENTS OF THE INTERNATIONAL MONETARY FUND. Text in English. q. **Document type:** *Trade.*
Formerly (until 1990): Financial Statements of the General Department and the S D R Department and Accounts Administered by the International Monetary Fund (1013-9273)
Published by: International Monetary Fund, Publication Services, 700 19th St, N W, Ste 12-607, Washington, DC 20431. TEL 202-623-8300, FAX 202-623-6149, publications@imf.org, http://www.imf.org/external/pubs/ft/quart/.

332.1 USA ISSN 0363-8987
HD2346.U5
FINANCIAL STUDIES OF THE SMALL BUSINESS. Text in English. 1976. a., latest 2003, 29th ed. looseleaf. USD 104; USD 178 combined subscription with CD-ROM (effective 2003). stat. **Document type:** *Directory, Academic/Scholarly.* **Description:** Presents financial ratios and statistics for small businesses capitalized $1 million and under. Includes five-year trends.
Related titles: CD-ROM ed.: USD 136 (effective 2000).
Indexed: ATI.
Published by: Financial Research Associates, 203 Avenue A NW, # 202, Winter Haven, FL 33881-4503. TEL 863-299-3969, FAX 863-299-2131, http://www.frafssb.com. Ed., Pub. Karen Goodman. R&P Grant Lacerte. Circ: 6,000.

FINANCIAL SURVEY. COMMODITY BROKERS. ENGLAND AND WALES; company data for success. see *BUSINESS AND ECONOMICS—Trade And Industrial Directories*

FINANCIAL SURVEY. INSTALLMENT, CREDIT, AND FINANCE; company data for success. see *BUSINESS AND ECONOMICS—Trade And Industrial Directories*

332 CAN ISSN 1705-1290
HG2701
FINANCIAL SYSTEM REVIEW/REVUE DU SYSTEME FINANCIER. Text in English, French. 2002. s-a. free (effective 2004). **Description:** Publishes a review of developments in the financial system and an analysis of policy directions in the financial sector.
Published by: Bank of Canada, Publications Distribution, Communications Services, 234 Wellington St, Ottawa, ON K1A 0G9, Canada. TEL 613-782-8248, FAX 613-782-8874, publications@bank-banque-canada.ca, http://www.bankofcanada.ca/en/frsr/.

FINANCIAL TECHNOLOGY BULLETIN; the international review of IT in the banking industry. see *BUSINESS AND ECONOMICS—Banking And Finance—Computer Applications*

330 DEU ISSN 0174-7363
CODEN: FITIBT
FINANCIAL TIMES (FRANKFURT EDITION). Text in English. 1888. d. adv. **Document type:** *Newspaper, Trade.*
Related titles: CD-ROM ed.: (from Chadwyck-Healey Inc.); ♦ Regional ed(s).: Financial Times (London, 1888). ISSN 0307-1766; ♦ Financial Times (North American Edition). ISSN 0884-6782.
Indexed: RAPRA.
—CASDDS. **CCC.**
Published by: Financial Times (Europe) GmbH, Nibelungenplatz 3, Frankfurt Am Main, 60318, Germany. TEL 49-69-156850, FAX 49-69-5964481. Circ: 70,000.

332 GBR ISSN 0307-1766
FINANCIAL TIMES (LONDON, 1888). Text in English. 1888. d. (Mon.-Sat.). GBP 167.40, EUR 270, USD 270 (effective 2005). adv. bk.rev. m. index. **Document type:** *Newspaper, Trade.*
Related titles: CD-ROM ed.: (from Chadwyck-Healey Inc.); Microfilm ed.: (from RPI); Online - full text ed.: (from Florida Center for Library Automation, Gale Group, LexisNexis, O C L C Online Computer Library Center, Inc., ProQuest Information & Learning); German ed.; ♦ Regional ed(s).: Financial Times (North American Edition). ISSN 0884-6782; ♦ Financial Times (Frankfurt Edition). ISSN 0174-7363.
Indexed: B&I, BNI, BrHumI, BrTechI, Emerald, IMMAb, IPackAb, IndBusRep, M&MA, P&BA, PROMT, RAPRA, RASB, RILM, WSCA.
—BLDSC (3926.994000). **CCC.**
Published by: Primary Source Microfilm (Subsidiary of: Gale Group), High Holborn House, 50/51 Bedford Row, London, WC1R 4LR, United Kingdom. TEL 44-20-70672663, FAX 44-20-70672600, psmcs@gale.com, http://www.ft.com, http://www.galegroup.com/psm/. Pub. Mark Holland. adv.: B&W page GBP 34,500, color page GBP 52,500; trim 345 x 560. Circ: 440,036. **Subscr. to:** Johnson's International Media Services, 43 Millharbour, London E14 9TR, United Kingdom. TEL 44-20-7538-8288, FAX 44-20-7537-3594.

320 USA ISSN 0884-6782
CODEN: FITIEW
FINANCIAL TIMES (NORTH AMERICAN EDITION). Text in English. 1985. d. (Mon.-Sat.). USD 298 domestic; CND 498 in Canada (effective 2005). adv. illus. cum.index. reprints avail.
Document type: *Newspaper, Trade.*
Related titles: CD-ROM ed.: (from Chadwyck-Healey Inc.); Microform ed.: (from RPI); Online - full text ed.: FT.com (from Gale Group, O C L C Online Computer Library Center, Inc.); ♦ Regional ed(s).: Financial Times (London, 1888). ISSN 0307-1766; ♦ Financial Times (Frankfurt Edition). ISSN 0174-7363.
Indexed: B&I, CIN, ChemAb, ChemTitl, M&MA.
—CASDDS. **CCC.**
Published by: The Financial Times Inc., 1330 Ave of the Americas, New York, NY 10019. TEL 212-641-6500, 800-628-8088, FAX 212-753-4814, circulation@financialtimes.com, http://news.ft.com/home/us, http://www.ft.com. adv.: B&W page USD 85,120, color page USD 123,000. Circ: 107,973.

330 DEU
FINANCIAL TIMES DEUTSCHLAND. Text in German. 2000. d. EUR 324 domestic; EUR 372 foreign; EUR 162 to students (effective 2002). adv. **Document type:** *Newspaper, Consumer.* **Description:** Provides the latest information on all aspects of trade and business in Germany.
Published by: Financial Times Deutschland GmbH & Co. KG, Stubbenhuk 3, Hamburg, 20459, Germany. TEL 49-40-31990-0, FAX 49-40-31990310, abo@ftd.de, http://ftd.de. adv.: page EUR 20,760; trim 314 x 445. Circ: 95,652 (paid and controlled).

332 GBR ISSN 1473-0413
HF5549.5.E45
FINANCIAL TIMES EXPAT. Key Title: F T Expat. Text in English. 2001. m.
Related titles: Online - full text ed.: (from Gale Group).
Published by: Financial Times Business Ltd. (Subsidiary of: Financial Times Group), Maple House, 149 Tottenham Court Rd, London, W1P 9LL, United Kingdom. TEL 44-20-7896-2525, FAX 44-20-7896-2054, http://www.ft.com.

332 LKA
FINANCIAL TIMES OF CEYLON. Text in English. 1961. q. adv.
Published by: Union Co. Ltd., 323 Union Place, P O Box 330, Colombo, 2, Sri Lanka. Ed. Cyril Gardiner. Circ: 2,800.

332 USA
FINANCIAL TIMES ON CD-ROM. Text in English. 1990. q. USD 1,600 (effective 1999). **Document type:** *Newspaper.*
Media: CD-ROM (from Chadwyck-Healey Inc.).
Published by: (Financial Times Information), ProQuest Information & Learning, 300 N Zeeb Rd., PO Box 1346, Ann Arbor, MI 48106-1346. TEL 703-683-7589, info@il.proquest.com, http://www.chadwyck.com.

332 IND
FINANCIAL WIZARD. Text in English. 1990. w. INR 5 newsstand/cover.
Published by: Digital Finance & Investment Consultancy Pvt. Ltd., 24-B Rajabahadur Compound, Ambalal Doshi Marg, Mumbai, Maharashtra 400 023, India. Ed. Ravi Shankar. Circ: 42,135.

332.1 USA ISSN 1059-3950
HG181
FINANCIAL WOMAN TODAY. Text in English. 1985. 4/yr. USD 24 to non-members (effective 2005). adv. bk.rev. illus. **Document type:** *Newsletter, Trade.* **Description:** Empowers women in the financial services industry to attain professional, economic, and personal goals, and to influence the future shape of the industry.
Formerly (until 1990): Executive Financial Women (0886-540X); Which supersedes (1924-1985): N A B W Journal (0885-5080)
Indexed: ABIn, BLI, BPIA.
Published by: Financial Women International, 1027 Roselawn Ave W., Saint Paul, MN 55113-6406. TEL 651-487-7632, FAX 651-489-1322, publications@fwi.org, http://www.fwi.org. Ed. Judi Marden. Adv. contact Kathleen Robeson. page USD 1,000. Circ: 10,000.

332 USA
FINANCIAL WOMEN'S ASSOCIATION OF NEW YORK NEWSLETTER. Text in English. 1956. m. USD 90 (effective 1999). adv. **Document type:** *Newsletter.* **Description:** Provides information on the organization, its programs and members.
Published by: Financial Women's Association of New York, 215 Park Ave S Ste 1713, New York, NY 10003. TEL 212-533-2141, FAX 212-982-3008, http://www.fwa.org. Ed. Nancy Sellar. Circ: 1,500 (paid).

332 GBR ISSN 1465-6078
FINANCIAL WORLD. Text in English. 1995. m. GBP 75 domestic to non-members; GBP 145 foreign to non-members; free to members (effective 2003). **Document type:** *Trade.*
Description: Reports on how new technologies are affecting relationships between customers and financial services providers as well as features and articles by financial journalists and senior practitioners from banks, building societies and insurance companies.
Formerly (until vol.4, no.10, 1998): Chartered Banker (1360-4295)
Related titles: Online - full text ed.: (from Northern Light Technology, Inc.).
Indexed: CPM, Emerald, Inspec.
—BLDSC (3927.120000), IE, ingenta.
Published by: Institute of Financial Services, IFS House, 4-9 Burgate Ln, Canterbury, CT1 2XJte, United Kingdom. TEL 44-1227-818608, FAX 44-1227-479641, cwraight@ifslearning.com, http://www.financialworld.co.uk/magazine/index.htm. Ed. Denise Smith. Circ: 34,307 (controlled).

332 NLD ISSN 0005-8343
FINANCIEEL ECONOMISCH WEEKBLAD BELEGGERS BELANGEN. Key Title: Beleggers Belangen. Text in Dutch. 1956. w. adv. bk.rev. illus. **Document type:** *Journal, Trade.*
Incorporates (1980-1992): Geldactief (1380-4626)
Related titles: Online - full content ed.: Beleggers Belangen Internet.
Indexed: KES.
Published by: Reed Business Information bv (Subsidiary of: Reed Business), Van de Sande, Bakhuyzenstraat 4, Amsterdam, 1061 AG, Netherlands. TEL 31-20-515-9222, FAX 31-20-515-9990, info@reedbusiness.nl, http://www.belbel.nl, http://www.reedbusiness.nl. Circ: 10,800.

332 341 BEL ISSN 1377-8013
FINANCIEEL FORUM. BANK - EN FINACIEEL RECHT/FORUM FINANCIER. DROIT BANCAIRE ET FINANCIER. Text in English, French, Dutch. 1936. 4/yr. **Document type:** *Journal, Trade.*
Formerly (until 2001): Revue de la Banque (0772-778X)
Related titles: ♦ Supplement(s): Revue de la Banque. Cahier. ISSN 0772-7801; ♦ Centre d'Estudes Financieres. Newsletter. ISSN 0772-7798.
—BLDSC (4024.086042), ingenta.
Published by: Larcier, Fond Jean-Paques 4, Louvain-la-Neuve, 1348, Belgium. TEL 32-10-482500, FAX 32-10-482519, lawbooks@larcier.be, http://www.editions.larcier.com/revues.

332 BEL ISSN 1376-7720
FINANCIEEL FORUM. BANK - EN FINANCIEWEZEN/FORUM FINANCIER. REVUE BANCAIRE ET FINANCIERE. Text in Dutch, English, French. 1936. 8/yr. adv. bk.rev. **Document type:** *Bulletin.*
Supersedes in part (in 2001): Revue de la Banque (0772-778X)
Related titles: ♦ Supplement(s): Revue de la Banque. Cahier. ISSN 0772-7801; ♦ Centre d'Estudes Financieres. Newsletter. ISSN 0772-7798.
Indexed: ELLIS, KES, NumL, PdeR, WBA.
—BLDSC (4024.086042), IE.
Published by: Larcier, Fond Jean-Paques 4, Louvain-la-Neuve, 1348, Belgium. TEL 32-10-482500, FAX 32-10-482519, lawbooks@larcier.be, http://www.editions.larcier.com/revues. Circ: 4,000.

332 NLD ISSN 1383-7656
FINANCIELE & MONETAIRE STUDIES. Text in Dutch. 1982. q. **Document type:** *Academic/Scholarly.*
Formerly (until 1996): Rotterdamse Monetaire Studies (1381-0650)
Published by: Wolters-Noordhoff Groningen (Subsidiary of: Wolters Kluwer N.V.), Postbus 58, Groningen, 9700 MB, Netherlands. TEL 31-50-5226524, FAX 31-50-5264866. Ed. Mrs. C H Zwansweg.

332 MEX
EL FINANCIERO INTERNATIONAL EDITION. Text in English. 1995. w. USD 180. adv. bk.rev. mkt.; stat. **Document type:** *Newspaper, Trade.* **Description:** Contains in-depth news and analysis of Mexican business, trade and politics.
Related titles: CD-ROM ed.; Online - full text ed.: ISSN 1563-7441; ♦ Spanish ed.: El Financiero.
Published by: El Financiero International Inc., Lago Bolsena 176, Col Anahuac, Mexico City, DF 11320, Mexico. TEL 525-227-7600, FAX 525-227-7634, http://www.elfinanciero.com.mx, http://www.elfinaciero.com.mx. Ed. Alejandro Ramos. Pub. Rogelio Cardenas. R&P Jane Johnson. Adv. contact Laura Knapp.

336 HRV ISSN 1330-8122
FINANCIJE. Text in Croatian. 1995. m. **Document type:** *Magazine, Trade.*
Published by: P B F d.o.o., Barciceva 12, Zagreb, 10000, Croatia. TEL 385-1-4551455, FAX 385-1-4551450.

FINANCIJSKA TEORIJA I PRAKSA. see *BUSINESS AND ECONOMICS—Macroeconomics*

FINANCING AGRICULTURE. see *AGRICULTURE*

332.1 USA
FINANCING AND INSURING EXPORTS: A USER'S GUIDE TO EXIMBANK AND F.C.I.A. PROGRAMS. Text in English. 1985. a. USD 55.
Published by: Export-Import Bank of the United States, 811 Vermont Ave, N W, Washington, DC 20571. TEL 202-566-8990, FAX 202-566-7524. Circ: 2,100.

332 USA
THE FINANCING NEWS. Text in English. irreg. **Document type:** *Trade.* **Description:** Offers how-to advice for seekers of venture capital, small-business loans, and private placement funding.
Media: Online - full text.
Published by: Datamerge, Inc. TEL 303-757-6298, 800-580-1188, FAX 303-757-3149, news@datamerge.com, http://www.datamerge.com/financingnews/index.html.

332 CZE ISSN 0322-9653
FINANCNI ZPRAVODAJ. Text in Czech. 1956. irreg. (approx. 12/yr.). CZK 60. charts; illus. index.
Formerly: Federalni Ministerstvo Financi. Vestnik (0042-4641)
Published by: Ministerstvo Financi Ceske Republiky, Letenska 15, Prague, 11810, Czech Republic. Ed. Alena Sauerova.

331.881 DNK ISSN 0907-0192
FINANS. Text in Danish. 1992. m. DKK 400 (effective 2003). adv.
Formed by the merger of (1942-1992): Sparekassestanden (0108-612X); (1938-1992): Bankstanden (0901-3385)
Related titles: Online - full text ed.
Published by: Finansforbundet, Langebrogade 5, PO Box 1960, Copenhagen K, 1411, Denmark. TEL 46-32-964600, FAX 46-32-961225, post@finansforbundet.dk, http://www.finansforbundet.dk/default.asp?p=456. Ed. Carsten Rasmussen TEL 46-32-651484. adv.: color page DKK 21,500; 297 x 230. Circ: 50,000.

332 RUS ISSN 1727-6349
FINANS. Text in Russian. 1996. w. RUR 127.60 per month domestic (effective 2004). **Document type:** *Magazine, Trade.*
Formerly (until 2003): Finansovaya Rossiya (1029-4503)
Related titles: Online - full content ed.: ISSN 1727-7574.
Published by: Redaktsiya Zhurnala Finans., B Sukharevskii per 19, str 1, Moscow, 103051, Russian Federation. TEL 7-095-2075755, 7-095-2075761, fr@fr.ru, http://www.finansmag.ru. Ed. Oleg Anisimov. Circ: 99,016. **US dist. addr.:** East View Information Services, 3020 Harbor Ln. N., Minneapolis, MN 55447. TEL 763-550-0961, FAX 763-559-2931, eastview@eastview.com, http://www.eastview.com.

332.1 NOR ISSN 1502-0053
FINANSFOKUS. Text in Norwegian. 2000. m. adv.
Incorporated (in 2000): Assurandoeren (0806-2412); Formed by the 2000 merger of (1992-2000): Din Forsikring (0803-7620); (1993-2000): Finansforum (0804-5755); Which was formerly (until 1993): Norske Bankfunksjonaerers Forbund. Bank (0332-9100); (until 1933): Tidsskrift for Norske Bankfunksjonaerer
Published by: Finansforbundet/Finance Sector Union of Norway, PO Box 9234, Groenland, Oslo, 0134, Norway. TEL 47-22-05-63-00, FAX 47-22-17-06-90. Ed. Bjoerg Buvik TEL 47-22-05-63-90. Adv. contact Anne Greve TEL 47-22-05-63-04.

332 UKR
FINANSI UKRAINY. Text in Ukrainian. m. USD 145 in United States.
Address: Ul Degtyarevskaya 38-44, Kiev, Ukraine. TEL 211-04-41, FAX 211-03-90. **US dist. addr.:** East View Information Services, 3020 Harbor Ln. N., Minneapolis, MN 55447. TEL 612-550-0961.

332.7 SWE ISSN 1404-2193
➤ **FINANSIELL STABILITET.** Text in Swedish. 1997. 2/yr. free. charts. back issues avail. **Document type:** *Bulletin, Government.* **Description:** Presents appraisals of tendencies in the Swedish financial system and their implications for stability.
Formerly (until 1999): Sveriges Riksbank. Finansmarknadsrapport (1403-0012)
Related titles: E-mail ed.; Fax ed.; Online - full text ed.; ♦ English ed.: Financial Stability Report. ISSN 1404-2207.
Published by: Sveriges Riksbank, Brunkebergstorg 11, Stockholm, 10337, Sweden. TEL 46-8-7870000, FAX 46-8-210531, registratorn@riksbank.se, http://www.riksbank.se/templates/YearList.aspx?id=10536. Circ: 1,000 (controlled).

332 SCG ISSN 0015-2145
FINANSIJE; casopis za teoriju i praksu iz oblasti finansija. Text in Serbo-Croatian. 1946. bi-m. **Description:** Covers the theory and practice from the field of finance.
Related titles: ♦ Supplement(s): Bilten - Sluzbena Objasnjenja i Strucna Misljenja za Primenu Finansijskih Propisa. ISSN 0354-3242.
Indexed: RASB.
Published by: Privredni Pregled, Marsala Birjuzova 3-5, Belgrade, 11000. Ed. Vuk Ognjanovicevic.

332 RUS
FINANSIST; nformarmatsionno-analiticheskoe izdanie o problemakh finansovogo rynka. Text in Russian. 1994. w. USD 619 in North America; USD 619 in Europe; USD 644 elsewhere (effective 2000).
Published by: Biznes za Rubezhom, Georgievskii per 1, Moscow, 103009, Russian Federation. TEL 7-095-9242585, FAX 7-095-9211759, periodicals@eastview.com, http://home.eastview.com. Ed. F A Shmaiger. **US dist. addr.:** East View Information Services, 3020 Harbor Ln. N., Minneapolis, MN 55447. TEL 612-550-0961.

332.7 658.8 SWE ISSN 1104-7348
FINANSMARKNADET. Text in Swedish. 1985. a. free.
Formerly (until 1994): Kredit- och Valutamarknaden (0282-8111)
Related titles: English ed.: Swedish Financial Market. ISSN 1104-7356.
Published by: Sveriges Riksbank, Financial Statistics Department/Swedish Central Bank, Stockholm, 10337, Sweden.

332 ARM
FINANSNER EV BANKNER. Text in Armenian. 104/yr. USD 259 in United States.
Address: Ul Grigora Lusavoricha 15, Erevan, 375015, Armenia. TEL 3742-56-29-56. **US dist. addr.:** East View Information Services, 3020 Harbor Ln. N., Minneapolis, MN 55447. TEL 612-550-0961.

332.1 BGR
FINANSOV ALMANAKH. Text in Bulgarian. a. USD 40 foreign (effective 2002). **Document type:** *Yearbook.*
Published by: Asotsiatsiia na Turgovskite Banki v Bulgaria/Association of Trade Banks in Bulgaria, 36 Vitosha Blvd., Sofia, 1000, Bulgaria. TEL 359-2-9816493, FAX 359-2-9814391, atb@intech.bg, http://www.acb.bg. **Dist. by:** Sofia Books, ul Silivria 16, Sofia 1404, Bulgaria. TEL 359-2-9586257, info@sofiabooks-bg.com, http://www.sofiabooks-bg.com.

332 657 RUS ISSN 1727-7981
FINANSOVAYA GAZETA; mezhdunarodnyi finansovyi ezhenedel'nik. Text in Russian. 1991. w. USD 190 in United States (effective 2004). **Document type:** *Newspaper, Trade.*
Related titles: CD-ROM ed.: ISSN 1727-8082. 1997; Online - full content ed.: ISSN 1607-4947; Supplement(s): Uchet, Nalogi, Pravo.
Published by: Redaktsiya Mezhdunarodnogo Ezhenedel'nika Finansovaya Gazeta, A-ya 598, Glavpochtamt, Moscow, 101000, Russian Federation. fingazeta@fingazeta.ru, http://www.fingazeta.ru. Ed. V M Silin. Circ: 84,000. **US dist. addr.:** East View Information Services, 3020 Harbor Ln. N., Minneapolis, MN 55447. TEL 763-550-0961, FAX 763-559-2931, eastview@eastview.com, http://www.eastview.com.

332 657 RUS ISSN 1727-8015
FINANSOVAYA GAZETA. REGIONAL'NYI VYPUSK. Text in Russian. 1995. w. USD 326 in United States (effective 2004). **Document type:** *Newspaper, Trade.* **Description:** Presents information of interest to accountants, auditors and financial managers.
Published by: Redaktsiya Mezhdunarodnogo Ezhenedel'nika Finansovaya Gazeta, A-ya 598, Glavpochtamt, Moscow, 101000, Russian Federation. fingazeta@fingazeta.ru, http://www.fingazeta.ru/stranic/buklet/rv.htm. Ed. V M Silin. **US dist. addr.:** East View Information Services, 3020 Harbor Ln. N., Minneapolis, MN 55447. TEL 763-550-0961, FAX 763-559-2931, eastview@eastview.com, http://www.eastview.com.

332 UKR
FINANSOVAYA TEMA. Text in Ukrainian. m. USD 165 in United States.
Address: Pr Pobedy 65, Kiev, Ukraine. TEL 442-9106, FAX 442-9222. **US dist. addr.:** East View Information Services, 3020 Harbor Ln. N., Minneapolis, MN 55447. TEL 612-550-0961.

332 336 RUS ISSN 0869-7264
FINANSOVYE I BUKHGALTERSKIE KONSUL'TATSII. Text in Russian. 1993. m. USD 135 in United States (effective 2001). adv. index. back issues avail.
Related titles: Online - full text ed.
Indexed: RASB.
—East View.
Published by: ID FBK-PRESS, Myasnitskaya ul 44-1, Moscow, 101000, Russian Federation. TEL 7-095-7375353, FAX 7-095-73753, fbk@fbk.ru. Ed. S M Shapigoozov. R&P, Adv. contact Elena Biriukova. Circ: 9,000. **Dist. by:** M K - Periodica, ul Gilyarovskogo 39, Moscow 129110, Russian Federation. TEL 7-095-2845008, FAX 7-095-2813798, info@periodicals.ru, http://www.mkniga.ru; **US dist. addr.:** East View Information Services, 3020 Harbor Ln. N., Minneapolis, MN 55447. TEL 612-550-0961.

332 RUS ISSN 1560-098X
FINANSOVYE IZVESTIYA. Text in Russian. 1992. 96/yr. **Document type:** *Newspaper, Consumer.*
Related titles: Online - full content ed.: ISSN 1684-8020. 2001.

B

▼ new title ➤ refereed ✶ unverified ♦ full entry avail.

Address: ul Tverskaya 18, korpus 1, Moscow, 127994, Russian Federation. TEL 7-095-2090581, subscribe@izvestia.ru, info@izvestia.ru, http://www.finiz.ru. Ed. Raf Shakirov.

332 RUS
FINANSOVYE NOVOSTI. Text in Russian. 360/yr. USD 1,200 in United States.
Address: Khvostov per 11-a, Moscow, 109180, Russian Federation. TEL 7-095-2361011. **US dist. addr.:** East View Information Services, 3020 Harbor Ln. N., Minneapolis, MN 55447. TEL 612-550-0961.

332 RUS
FINANSOVYE RYNKI/FINANCIAL MARKETS OUTLOOK. Text in English, Russian. m. USD 485 in United States.
Indexed: RASB.
Address: B Spasskaya 25, Moscow, 129010, Russian Federation. TEL 7-095-9741901. **US dist. addr.:** East View Information Services, 3020 Harbor Ln. N., Minneapolis, MN 55447. TEL 612-550-0961.

332 RUS
FINANSOVYI BIZNES. Text in Russian. m. USD 179.95 in United States.
Indexed: RASB, RefZh.
Published by: Firma Ankil, Elizavetinskii pr-d 6-1, ofis 23, Moscow, 107005, Russian Federation. TEL 7-095-2653718, FAX 7-095-2653718. Ed. Yu I Fedinskii. **US dist. addr.:** East View Information Services, 3020 Harbor Ln. N., Minneapolis, MN 55447. TEL 612-550-0961.

332.1 331.8 SWE
FINANSVAERLDEN. Text in Swedish. 1911. 12/yr. SEK 250 (effective 2001). adv. bk.rev. abstr.; charts; illus.; stat. index. **Document type:** *Magazine, Trade.* **Description:** Deals with matters of interest to bank employees at all levels.
Former titles: Bankvaerlden (0005-5549); (until 1920): Svenska Bankmannafoereningens Tidskrift
Related titles: Audio cassette/tape ed.
Published by: Finansfoerbundet/Union of Financial Sector Employees, Box 38151, Stockholm, 10064, Sweden. TEL 46-8-614-03-00, FAX 46-8-678-67-13, finansvarlden@finansforbundet.se, http://www.finansforbundet.se/finansvarlden. Ed., Pub. Stefan Ahlqvist. adv.: B&W page SEK 18,300, color page SEK 21,900; trim 180 x 257. Circ: 45,200 (controlled).

332 RUS ISSN 0869-446X
HJ109.R8
FINANSY. Text in Russian. 1954. m. USD 162 foreign (effective 2004). bk.rev. bibl.; stat.; tr.lit. index. **Description:** Covers theory and information on finances; compiling and execution of the state budget, insurance, lending, taxation etc.
Former titles: Finansy S.S.S.R. (0130-576X); Sovetskie Finansy
Indexed: CDSP, DSA, HistAb, IBSS, RASB, RRTA, RefZh, WAE&RSA.
—East View.
Address: Tverskaya ul 22-b, Moscow, 103009, Russian Federation. TEL 7-095-2994427, FAX 7-095-2999616. Ed. Yu M Artemov. Circ: 50,000. **Dist. by:** M K - Periodica, ul Gilyarovskogo 39, Moscow 129110, Russian Federation. TEL 7-095-2845008, FAX 7-095-2813798, info@periodicals.ru, http://www.mkniga.ru.

332.7 RUS
FINANSY I KREDIT. Text in Russian. m. USD 229.95 in United States.
Indexed: RASB, RefZh.
Published by: Firma Fininnova, A-ya 10, Moscow, 111401, Russian Federation. TEL 7-095-3745785, FAX 7-095-3034676. Ed. V A Gorokhova. **US dist. addr.:** East View Information Services, 3020 Harbor Ln. N., Minneapolis, MN 55447. TEL 612-550-0961.

332 KAZ
FINANSY KAZAKHSTANA - KARZHY - KARAZHAT. Text in Russian, Kazakh. m. USD 139 in United States.
Published by: Ministry of Finances, Ul Shevchenko 67, Almaty, 480091, Kazakstan. TEL 3272-63-03-66. Ed. M E Talabueva. **US dist. addr.:** East View Information Services, 3020 Harbor Ln. N., Minneapolis, MN 55447. TEL 612-550-0961.

332 DEU ISSN 1437-8981
FINANZ BETRIEB; Zeitschrift fuer Unternehmensfinanzierung und Finanzmanagement. Text in German. m. adv. **Document type:** *Magazine, Trade.* **Description:** Covers the latest news, developments and trends in the worldwide financial markets.
Indexed: DIP, IBR, IBZ.
Published by: Verlagsgruppe Handelsblatt GmbH, Kasernenstr 67, Duesseldorf, 40213, Germany. TEL 49-211-8870, FAX 49-211-371792, leser-service@vhb.de, http://www.vhb.de.

332 AUT
FINANZ-COMPASS. Text in German. a. adv. **Document type:** *Directory, Trade.* **Description:** Information on banks, savings banks, credit associations, insurance institutes.
Indexed: RASB.
Published by: Compass Verlag, Matznergasse 17, Vienna, W 1141, Austria. TEL 43-1-98116-0, FAX 43-1-98116148, office@compass.at, http://www.compass.at. Ed. Werner Futter. R&P Christine Buzzi. Adv. contact Michael Bayer TEL 43-1-98116160.

332 AUT ISSN 1017-5695
K6
FINANZ JOURNAL; die umfassende Fachinformation fuer Steuerrechtsthemen. Text in German. 1961. m. EUR 160; EUR 14 newsstand/cover (effective 2005). adv. bk.rev. **Document type:** *Journal, Trade.*
Indexed: PAIS.
Published by: Grenz Verlag, Flossgasse 6, Vienna, W 1025, Austria. TEL 43-1-2141715, FAX 43-1-214171530, office@grenzverlag.at, http://www.finanzjournal.at, http://www.grenzverlag.at. Ed. Stefan Steiger. R&P Martin Baumgartner TEL 43-1-214171541. Adv. contact Gertrude Hauder.

332 DEU
DER FINANZBERATER. Text in English, German. 1984. q. index. **Document type:** *Journal, Academic/Scholarly.*
Published by: Akademie fuer Finanz-Marketing, Postfach 102143, Langenfeld, 40764, Germany. TEL 49-2173-23047, FAX 49-2173-23575, http://www.finplan.de. Ed. Harold Kraemer. Circ: 18,000 (controlled).

332 DEU
FINANZBUSINESS. Text in German. q. adv. **Document type:** *Magazine, Trade.*
Published by: Betriebswirtschaftlicher Verlag Dr. Th. Gabler GmbH (Subsidiary of: Springer Science+Business Media), Abraham-Lincoln-Str 46, Wiesbaden, 65189, Germany. TEL 49-611-78780, FAX 49-611-7878400, gabler.service@gwv-fachverlage.de, http://www.gabler.de. adv.: B&W page EUR 3,890, color page EUR 5,990. Circ: 14,077 (paid and controlled).

332 DEU ISSN 0944-0968
FINANZEN; Boerse & Wirtschaft fuer Anleger. Text in German. 1990. m. EUR 59.40; EUR 40.80 to students; EUR 5.50 newsstand/cover (effective 2003). adv. index. back issues avail. **Document type:** *Magazine, Consumer.* **Description:** Provides news and information on the stock markets and economy for investors.
Published by: Finanzen Verlagsgesellschaft mbH (Subsidiary of: Axel Springer Verlag AG), Isabellastr 32, Munich, 80796, Germany. TEL 49-89-272640, FAX 49-89-27264199, redaktion@finanzen.net, http://www.finanzen.net. Ed. Holger Wiedemann. Pub. Frank Bernhard Werner. R&P Bernd Engelke TEL 49-89-27264291. Adv. contact Belinda Lohse. B&W page EUR 8,385, color page EUR 11,739; trim 213 x 275. Circ: 117,941 (paid).

332 DEU ISSN 0939-7825
FINANZIERUNGS BERATER. Text in German. 1991. q. looseleaf. **Document type:** *Bulletin.*
Published by: V N R Verlag fuer die Deutsche Wirtschaft AG, Theodor-Heuss-Str 2-4, Bonn, 53095, Germany. TEL 49-228-8205-0, FAX 49-228-364411. Ed. Hans Joachim Oberhettinger.

332.1 DEU ISSN 1439-5266
FINANZMANAGEMENT. Text in German. 2000. irreg., latest vol.26, 2005. price varies. **Document type:** *Monographic series, Academic/Scholarly.*
Published by: Verlag Dr. Kovac, Arnoldstr 49, Hamburg, 22763, Germany. TEL 49-40-3988800, FAX 49-40-39888055, info@verlagdrkovac.de, http://www.verlagdrkovac.de/3-11.htm.

332 DEU
FINANZWIRTSCHAFT (MUNICH). Text in German. m. **Document type:** *Magazine, Trade.*
Published by: Verlagsgruppe Huethig Jehle Rehm GmbH (Subsidiary of: Sueddeutscher Verlag GmbH), Emmy-Noether-Str 2, Munich, 80992, Germany. FAX 49-89-4706998, info@hjr-verlag.de. Ed. Wolfgang Bergs.

FINCAREER EUROMONEY CAPITAL MARKETS DIRECTORY (YEAR). see *BUSINESS AND ECONOMICS—Trade And Industrial Directories*

332 FIN ISSN 1239-9337
FINLANDS BANK. AARSBERAETTELSE. Text in Swedish. 1914. a. free. charts. **Description:** Covers economic developments, monetary policy, payment systems and maintenance of currency supply, international relations, balance sheet, charts, tables and more.
Formerly (until 1997): Finlands Bank. Aersbok (0355-5933)
Related titles: Online - full text ed.: ISSN 1456-5781. 1997; ♦ English ed.: Bank of Finland. Annual Report. ISSN 1239-9345; ♦ Finnish ed.: Suomen Pankki. Vuosikertomus. ISSN 1239-9329.
Published by: Suomen Pankki/Bank of Finland, P O Box 160, Helsinki, 00101, Finland. TEL 358-9-183-2566, FAX 358-9-174-872, publications@bof.fi, http://www.bof.fi/env/rhinden.htm.

330 ITA ISSN 0391-6405
FIORINO; quotidiano del mattino di finanza economia e attualita. Text in Italian. 1969. d. **Document type:** *Newspaper, Consumer.*
Published by: Societa Editrice Esedra s.r.l., Via Parigi, 11, Rome, RM 00185, Italy. TEL 06-474901, FAX 06-4883435. Ed. Luigi d'Amato. Circ: 30,000.

332.1 USA
FIRST EMPIRE STATE CORPORATION. ANNUAL REPORT. Text in English. a. **Document type:** *Corporate.*
Published by: First Empire State Corporation, One M & T Plaza, Buffalo, NY 14240. TEL 716-842-5138, FAX 716-842-5021.

332.1 USA
FIRST EMPIRE STATE CORPORATION. INTERIM REPORT. Text in English. q.
Published by: First Empire State Corporation, One M & T Plaza, Buffalo, NY 14240. TEL 716-842-5138, FAX 716-842-5021.

332.1 LBR
FIRST NATIONAL CITY BANK, LIBERIA. ANNUAL REPORT✶. Text in English. a. illus.; stat.
Published by: First National City Bank, P O Box 280, Monrovia, Liberia.

332 BEL
FISCALITEIT. MONOGRAFIEEN. Text in Flemish. irreg. price varies. **Document type:** *Monographic series.*
Published by: C E D Samsom (Subsidiary of: Wolters Samsom Belgie n.v.), Kouterveld 14, Diegem, 1831, Belgium. TEL 32-2-7231111.

332 ISL ISSN 0015-3346
HC360.5
➤ **FJARMALATIDINDI;** timarit um efnahagsmal. Text in Icelandic; Summaries in English. 1954. s-a. ISK 1,500 (effective 2002). charts; stat. index. **Document type:** *Bulletin, Academic/Scholarly.* **Description:** Covers economics in general and Icelandic economy in particular.
—BLDSC (3949.680000).
Published by: Sedlabanki Islands/Central Bank of Iceland, Kalkofnsvegur 1, Reykjavik, 150, Iceland. TEL 354-569-9600, FAX 354-569-9608, publish@sedlabanki.is, sedlabanki@sedlabanki.is, http://www.sedlabanki.is. Ed. Birgir Isl Gunnarsson. Circ: 1,600 (controlled).

332 USA
FLASHWIRE WEEKLY. Text in English. 1974. w. looseleaf. USD 599 domestic (effective 2005). adv. bk.rev. index. back issues avail. **Document type:** *Newsletter, Trade.* **Description:** Presents a middle market M & A newsletter.
Former titles: Corporate Acquisitions; National Review of Corporate Acquisitions (0097-6202)
Related titles: E-mail ed.
Published by: Factset Mergerstat, 2150 Colorado Ave, Ste 150, Santa Monica, CA 90404. TEL 800-455-8871, 310-315-3100, FAX 310-829-4855, info@factset.com, http://www.mergerstat.com. Ed. Chris Murray. Pub. Kurt Kunert.

FLINDERS UNIVERSITY OF SOUTH AUSTRALIA. SCHOOL OF COMMERCE. RESEARCH PAPER SERIES. see *BUSINESS AND ECONOMICS—Accounting*

332.1 USA ISSN 1064-0673
FLORIDA BANKING; for Florida banking industry. Text in English. 1974. bi-m. USD 25 (effective 2005). adv. bk.rev. illus. back issues avail.; reprints avail. **Document type:** *Magazine, Trade.*
Former titles (until 1987): Banking Today (1052-0562); (until 1984): Florida Banker (0147-1961)
Related titles: Online - full text ed.
Indexed: BLI, WBA.
—BLDSC (3955.291000).
Published by: Florida Bankers Association, 1001 Thomasville Rd., Ste. 201, Tallahassee, FL 32303. TEL 850-224-2265, FAX 850-224-2423, info@floridabankers.com, http://www.floridabankers.com. Ed. Pam Ricco. Circ: 6,500 (controlled).

FLORIDA BUSINESS CREDIT DIRECTORY. see *BUSINESS AND ECONOMICS—Trade And Industrial Directories*

332.7 USA
FLORIDA MORTGAGE BROKER. Text in English. 1965. q. membership. adv. **Document type:** *Trade.* **Description:** Covers legislative concerns and association activities.
Published by: Florida Association of Mortgage Brokers, PO Box 6477, Tallahassee, FL 32314-6477. TEL 904-942-6411, FAX 904-942-4654. Ed., R&P, Adv. contact Carolyn Devonshire. Circ: 2,000.

332 USA
FLOW OF FUNDS ACCOUNTS: SEASONALLY ADJUSTED AND UNADJUSTED. Text in English. q. USD 25. **Document type:** *Government.*
Related titles: Diskette ed.
Published by: U.S. Federal Reserve System, Board of Governors, Publications Services, Rm MS 138, Washington, DC 20551. TEL 202-452-3244, FAX 202-728-5886.

332.1 TWN ISSN 1017-9658
HF5681.B2
FLOW OF FUNDS IN TAIWAN DISTRICT, REPUBLIC OF CHINA. Text in Chinese, English. 1968. a. USD 5.
Published by: Central Bank of China, 2 Roosevelt Rd, Sec 1, Taipei, 107, Taiwan. TEL 886-2-23936161. Circ: 1,200.

332 USA
FLOW OF FUNDS SUMMARY STATISTICS. Text in English. q. USD 5. **Document type:** *Government.*
Published by: U.S. Federal Reserve System, Board of Governors, Publications Services, Rm MS 138, Washington, DC 20551. TEL 202-452-3244, FAX 202-728-5886.

332 AUT
FOCUS ON TRANSITION. Text in German. 1996. s-a. free. **Document type:** *Bulletin.* **Description:** Covers economic developments in Central and Eastern Europe.
Published by: Oesterreichische National Bank, Otto-Wagner-Platz 3, Vienna, W 1090, Austria. TEL 43-1-404206666, FAX 43-1-404206696, http://www.oenb.co.at, http://www.oenb.at.

332 ECU
FOMENTO Y PRODUCCION. Text in Spanish. 1983. s-a.
Published by: Banco Nacional de Fomento, Apdo 685, Quito, Pichincha, Ecuador. Ed. Hernan Luna Ponce.

332 USA ISSN 0252-2993
FONDO MONETARIO INTERNACIONAL. SERIE DE FOLLETOS. Text in Spanish. 1964. irreg.
Related titles: ♦ English ed.: International Monetary Fund. Pamphlet Series. ISSN 0538-8759; ♦ French ed.: Fonds Monetaire International. Serie des Brochures. ISSN 0252-2985.
Published by: International Monetary Fund, Publication Services, 700 19th St, N W, Ste 12-607, Washington, DC 20431.

FONDOV PAZAR/STOCK MARKET; sedmichen obzor za investitsii i finansi. see *BUSINESS AND ECONOMICS—Investments*

332 BEL ISSN 0779-9411
FONDS ET SICAV. Text in French. 1993. m. (11/yr.). **Document type:** *Consumer.*
Related titles: Dutch ed.: Fondsen en Sicav. ISSN 0779-942X.
Published by: Association des Consommateurs/Verbruikersunie, Rue de Hollande 13, Bruxelles, 1060, Belgium. TEL 32-2-5423211, FAX 32-2-5423250, http://www.test-achats.be/map/show/70651/src/271981.htm.

332.1 338.9 USA ISSN 1020-5101
FONDS MONETAIRE INTERNATIONAL. ETUDES ECONOMIQUES ET FINANCIERES. Text in French. 1986. s-a.
Related titles: ♦ English ed.: International Monetary Fund. World Economic and Financial Surveys. ISSN 0258-7440.
Indexed: PAIS.
Published by: International Monetary Fund, Publication Services, 700 19th St, N W, Ste 12-607, Washington, DC 20431. TEL 202-623-8300, FAX 202-623-6149.

332 USA ISSN 0252-2985
FONDS MONETAIRE INTERNATIONAL. SERIE DES BROCHURES. Text in French. 1964. irreg.
Related titles: ♦ English ed.: International Monetary Fund. Pamphlet Series. ISSN 0538-8759; ♦ Spanish ed.: Fondo Monetario Internacional. Serie de Folletos. ISSN 0252-2993.
Published by: International Monetary Fund, Publication Services, 700 19th St, N W, Ste 12-607, Washington, DC 20431.

332 GBR
FORCES NEWS. Text in English. 1976. bi-m. free. adv. bk.rev. **Document type:** *Newsletter.*
Formerly: Forces Financial News
Published by: Mandrake Associates Ltd., 6 North Brink, Wisbech, Cambs PE13 1JR, United Kingdom. TEL 01945-65177, FAX 01945-64712. Ed. Douglas Nicholson. Circ: 35,000 (controlled).

332.4 USA ISSN 1089-4462
FOREIGN CURRENCIES HELD BY THE U.S. GOVERNMENT. Text in English. s-a. stat. **Document type:** *Government.*
Former titles (until 1991): U.S. Department of the Treasury. Bureau of Government Financial Operations. Report on Foreign Currencies Held by the U.S. Government (0098-3896); U.S. Department of the Treasury. Bureau of Accounts. Report on Foreign Currencies in the Custody of the United States
Published by: U.S. Department of the Treasury, Bureau of Government Financial Operations, Washington, DC 20226. TEL 202-566-4531. **Orders to:** U.S. Government Printing Office, Superintendent of Documents.

332 GBR ISSN 1351-0983
FOREIGN EXCHANGE CONSENSUS FORECASTS. Text in English. 1995. m. GBP 448, USD 698 (effective 2003). 36 p./no.; back issues avail. **Document type:** *Journal, Academic/Scholarly.* **Description:** Provides currency exchange rate projections for over 100 currencies. Includes individual and consensus forecasts, cross rates, the European Monetary System and analysis of the countries' inflation and interest rates, balance of payments and political policy and environment.
Related titles: Diskette ed.; E-mail ed.
—IE.
Published by: Consensus Economics Inc., 53 Upper Brook St, London, W1K 2LT, United Kingdom. TEL 44-20-7491-3211, FAX 44-20-7409-2331, editors@consensuseconomics.com, http://www.consensuseconomics.com. Ed. Che-wing Pang. Pub. Philip M Hubbard.

346.082 AUS
FOREIGN EXCHANGE IN PRACTICE. Text in English. irreg., latest 1997, 2nd ed. AUD 95 per issue (effective 2004). **Document type:** *Academic/Scholarly.*
Published by: Lawbook Co. (Subsidiary of: Thomson Legal & Regulatory Ltd.), PO Box 3502, Rozelle, NSW 2039, Australia. LRA.Service@thomson.com, http://onlineecom01.thomson.com.au/thomson/Catalog.asp?EES_CMD=SI&EES_ID=100215, http://www.lawbookco.com.au/. Ed. Steve Anthony.

332 USA ISSN 0364-1341
FOREIGN EXCHANGE RATES. Text in English. w. (& m.). USD 20 for w. release; USD 5 for m. release. **Document type:** *Government.*
Published by: U.S. Federal Reserve System, Board of Governors, Publications Services, Rm MS 138, Washington, DC 20551. TEL 202-452-3244, FAX 202-728-5886.

332 GBR
FOREIGN EXCHANGE RATES RECORD. Text in English. m. GBP 205; GBP 215 foreign.
Published by: Financial Times Information Ltd., Extel, Fitzroy House, 13-17 Epworth St, London, EC2A 4DL, United Kingdom. TEL 44-20-7825-8000, FAX 44-20-7608-2032, eic@ft.com, http://www.info.ft.com.

FORTUNE. see *BUSINESS AND ECONOMICS—Management*

332.7 DEU
FORUM (HEIDELBERG). Text in German. 1996. 4/yr. EUR 2.50 newsstand/cover (effective 2003). adv. **Document type:** *Magazine, Consumer.*
Published by: M L P AG, Forum 7, Heidelberg, 69126, Germany. TEL 49-6221-3080, FAX 49-6221-3088701, info@mlp-ag.com, http://www.mlp.de. adv.: B&W page EUR 9,200, color page EUR 10,900. Circ: 402,906 (paid and controlled).

332 USA ISSN 1567-2395
▼ ➤ **FOUNDATIONS AND TRENDS IN FINANCE.** Text in English. 2005. 8/yr. USD 450, EUR 450; USD 495, EUR 495 combined subscription print & online eds. (effective 2006). **Document type:** *Journal, Academic/Scholarly.*
Related titles: Online - full text ed.: ISSN 1567-2409. 2005. USD 450, EUR 450 (effective 2005).
Published by: Now Publishers Inc., PO Box 1024, Hanover, MA 02339. TEL 781-871-0245, FAX 781-871-6172, sales@nowpublishers.com, http://www.nowpublishers.com/fin. Ed. George Constantinides. Pub. Zac Rolnik. R&P Mike Casey.

332.31 FRA ISSN 0071-8254
FRANCE. CAISSE NATIONALE DU CREDIT AGRICOLE. RAPPORT SUR LE CREDIT AGRICOLE MUTUEL. Text in French. 1975. a. free.
Related titles: English ed.: Credit Agricole Annual Report.
Published by: Caisse Nationale du Credit Agricole, 91-93 bd. Pasteur, Paris, 75015, France. Circ: 4,000.

332.7 FRA
FRANCE. CONSEIL NATIONAL DU CREDIT ET DU TITRE. RAPPORT ANNUEL. Text in French. a. EUR 38 (effective 2002).
Formerly: France. Conseil National du Credit. Rapport Annuel (0980-0107)
Related titles: English ed.: France. Conseil National du Credit. Annual Report. ISSN 1249-528X.
Published by: Banque de France, Service Relations avec le Public, 48 rue Croix-des-Petits-Champs, Paris, 75049, France. TEL 33-1-42923908, FAX 33-1-42923940, http://www.banque-france.fr.

332.1 DEU
FRANKFURTER FINANZMARKT BERICHT. Text in German. 1990. bi-m.
Published by: (Hauptverwaltung der Deutschen Bundesbank), Landeszentralbank in Hessen, Taunusanlage 5, Frankfurt Am Main, 60329, Germany. TEL 069-2388-0, FAX 069-2388-2130.

364.163 GBR ISSN 1360-4740
FRAUD REPORT. Text in English. m. GBP 480; GBP 495 foreign. tr.lit. **Document type:** *Newsletter.* **Description:** Presents news and features on financial sector fraud, its detection and prevention, and legal cases. Includes regulation, money laundering, and international law enforcement.
Published by: Financial Times Business Ltd. (Subsidiary of: Financial Times Group), Maple House, 149 Tottenham Court Rd, London, W1P 9LL, United Kingdom. TEL 44-20-7896-2525, FAX 44-20-7896-2587, philip.neville@ftfinance.com. Ed. Philip Neville. Pub. Alex Chisholm.

332 364.1 GBR ISSN 0966-7334
FRAUD WATCH. Text in English. 1992. bi-m. GBP 195, EUR 340, USD 340 (effective 2005). adv. back issues avail. **Document type:** *Newsletter, Trade.* **Description:** Covers all aspects of financial fraud, including legislation and regulatory changes, card fraud, money laundering, counterfeiting, anti-terrorism, whistleblowing and internal fraud. Brings together information, resources and expertise from crime fighting organizations, financial institutions and government bodies worldwide.
Related titles: Online - full content ed.
Indexed: C&CSA.
—CCC.
Published by: C & M Publications Ltd., 3 A Market Pl, Uppingham, Leics LE15 9QH, United Kingdom. TEL 44-1572-820088, FAX 44-1572-820099, publisher@fraudwatchonline.com, publisher@cm-media.net, http://www.fraudwatchonline.com/, http://www.cm-media.net/. Ed., R&P Annich McIntosh. Adv. contact Marie Sinclair. Circ: 5,000.

FREIRAUM. see *INTERIOR DESIGN AND DECORATION*

▼ **FRONTIERS OF REAL ESTATE FINANCE.** see *REAL ESTATE*

332.7 DEU
FUCHS-DEVISEN. Text in German. w. adv. **Document type:** *Newsletter, Trade.* **Description:** Provides up-to-date information on interest and exchange rates and trends in Germany.
Related titles: E-mail ed.
Published by: Verlag Fuchsbriefe (Subsidiary of: Springer Science+Business Media), Albrechtstr 22, Berlin, 10117, Germany. TEL 49-30-28881720, FAX 49-30-28045576, http://www.fuchsbriefe.de. Ed., Pub. Ralf Vielhaber.

FUEL RIGHTS HANDBOOK. see *SOCIAL SERVICES AND WELFARE*

332 CHN ISSN 1002-2740
FUJIAN JINRONG/FUJIAN FINANCE. Text in Chinese. 1986. m. CNY 12. **Description:** Provides information on the flexible financial policies applicable in the special economic zones of Fujian Province.
Related titles: Online - full text ed.: (from East View Information Services).
Published by: Fujian Jingrong Zazhishe, No21, Guping Lu, Fuzhou, Fujian 350003, China. TEL 557778. Ed. Wang Liangyuan. **Dist. overseas by:** Jiangsu Publications Import & Export Corp., 56 Gao Yun Ling, Nanjing, Jiangsu, China.

332 USA ISSN 1054-5956
HG4930
FUND ACTION. Text in English. 1989. w. (51X/yr). USD 2,525 combined subscription domestic print & online eds.; USD 2,600 combined subscription foreign print & online eds. (effective 2005). adv. **Document type:** *Newsletter, Trade.* **Description:** Covers important news and trends in the U.S. mutual fund industry.
Related titles: Online - full text ed.: (from Florida Center for Library Automation, Gale Group, ProQuest Information & Learning).
Indexed: ABIn, BLI.
—CCC.
Published by: Institutional Investor News (Subsidiary of: Euromoney Institutional Investor Plc.), 225 Park Ave S, 7th Fl, New York, NY 10003-1605. TEL 212-224-3800, FAX 212-224-3491, info@iiplatinum.com, http://www.fundaction.com, http://www.iinews.com. Pub. Nanzeen Kanga TEL 212-224-3005. **Subscr. to:** New Orders, PO Box 5063, Brentwood, TN 37024. TEL 615-377-3322, 800-945-2034, 800-715-9197, FAX 615-337-0525, vlockridge@sunbeltfs.com.

332 USA ISSN 1529-2363
FUND MARKETING ALERT. Text in English. 1996. w. (51X/yr). USD 2,145 combined subscription domestic print & online eds.; USD 2,220 combined subscription foreign print & online eds. (effective 2005). adv. back issues avail. **Document type:** *Newsletter, Trade.* **Description:** Deals exclusively with mutual fund marketing, sales and distribution strategies.
Related titles: Online - full text ed.: (from Florida Center for Library Automation, Gale Group, O C L C Online Computer Library Center, Inc.).
Indexed: B&I.
—CCC.
Published by: Institutional Investor News (Subsidiary of: Euromoney Institutional Investor Plc.), 225 Park Ave S, 7th Fl, New York, NY 10003-1605. TEL 212-224-3800, FAX 212-224-3491, info@iiplatinum.com, http://www.fundmarketing.com, http://www.iinews.com. Pub. Nanzeen Kanga TEL 212-224-3005. **Subscr. to:** New Orders, PO Box 5063, Brentwood, TN 37024. TEL 615-377-3322, 800-945-2034, 800-715-9197, FAX 615-337-0525, vlockridge@sunbeltfs.com.

B

658 USA ISSN 0016-268X
HV41
FUND RAISING MANAGEMENT. Text in English. 1969. m. USD 58 (effective 2005). adv. bk.rev. illus. **Document type:** *Magazine, Trade.* **Description:** Features articles on fund raising and related activities among academic religious, health, civic and cultural groups.
Related titles: Microform ed.: suspended (from PQC); Online - full text ed.: suspended (from EBSCO Publishing, Florida Center for Library Automation, Gale Group, Northern Light Technology, Inc., O C L C Online Computer Library Center, Inc., ProQuest Information & Learning, The Dialog Corporation).
Indexed: ABIn, BLI, BPIA, BusI, LRI, MEDLINE, PAIS, PSI, T&II.
—BLDSC (4055.955000), IE, Infotrieve, ingenta. **CCC.**
Published by: Hoke Communications, 224 Seventh St, Garden City, NY 11530. TEL 516-746-6700, 800-229-6700, FAX 516-294-8141. Ed. George R Reis. Pub. Henry R Hoke III. adv.: B&W page USD 1,295, color page USD 2,045; trim 8.25 x 10.88. Circ: 10,000 (paid).

FUNDING YOUR EDUCATION. see *EDUCATION*

332 DEU ISSN 1432-265X
FUNDRAISING MAGAZIN; magazin fuer fundraising, sponsoring, marketing. Text in German. 1996. bi-m. EUR 30; EUR 6 newsstand/cover (effective 2002). adv. bk.rev.; Website rev. 56 p./no. 3 cols./p.; back issues avail. **Document type:** *Magazine, Trade.*
Related titles: CD-ROM ed.; Online - full text ed.
Published by: Non Profit Verlag, Zollernstr 4, Konstanz, 78462, Germany. TEL 49-7531-282141, FAX 49-7531-282179, verlag@nonprofit.de, http://www.nonprofit.de. Eds. Hans-Willy Brockes, Wolfgang Happes. Adv. contact Christel Willig TEL 49-9087-90055. B&W page EUR 525, color page EUR 1,065; trim 185 x 265. Circ: 5,500.

332 GBR ISSN 1393-0486
FUNDS INTERNATIONAL. Text in English. 1994. 14/yr. GBP 997, EUR 1,597, USD 1,597 (effective 2005). **Document type:** *Trade.* **Description:** Gives news, information and advice on the fund management industry worldwide.
Related titles: Online - full text ed.: (from Gale Group, LexisNexis, Northern Light Technology, Inc., O C L C Online Computer Library Center, Inc., ProQuest Information & Learning).
Indexed: ABIn, BLI.
Published by: Lafferty Publications Ltd., The Colonnades, 82 Bishops Bridge Rd, London, W2 6BB, United Kingdom. TEL 44-20-75635700, FAX 44-20-75635701, cuserv@lafferty.com, http://www.lafferty.com/newsletter_publication.php?id=10. Ed. Martin Owens.

FUTURES AND OPTIONS. see *BUSINESS AND ECONOMICS—Investments*

332.3 CHE
G-24 DISCUSSION PAPER SERIES. Text in English. 2000. irreg., latest vol.10, 2001. back issues avail. **Document type:** *Monographic series, Academic/Scholarly.* **Description:** Aims to enhance the understanding of policy makers in developing countries of the complex issues in the international monetary and financial system, and to raise the awareness outside of developing countries of the need to introduce a development dimension into the discussion of international financial and institutional reform.
Published by: United Nations Conference on Trade and Development, 8-14 Avenue de la Paix, Geneva 10, 1211, Switzerland. TEL 41-22-9174924, FAX 41-22-9070195, info@unctad.org, http://www.unctad.org.

G A M A INTERNATIONAL JOURNAL. (General Agents and Managers Association) see *INSURANCE*

332 POL ISSN 0860-7613
HG3136
GAZETA BANKOWA. Text in Polish. 1988. w. PLZ 234 domestic to individuals; PLZ 328 domestic to institutions academic; PLZ 468 domestic to institutions; EUR 227 foreign (effective 2005). adv. **Document type:** *Newspaper, Consumer.* **Description:** Covers economy and finance.
Related titles: Microfilm ed.: 1988 (from PQC).
Address: ul Okrzei 1A, Warsaw, 03715, Poland. TEL 48-22-3338887, FAX 48-22-3338899, redakcja@wtrendy.pl, http://gazetabankowa.pl. Ed. Andrzej Wroblewski. Adv. contact Nina Tyszkiewicz. Circ: 45,000. **Dist. by:** Ars Polona, Krakowskie Przedmiescie 7, Warsaw, Poland. TEL 48-22-9263914, FAX 48-22-9265334, arspolona@arspolona.com.pl, http://www.arspolona.com.pl.

GELD. see *CONSUMER EDUCATION AND PROTECTION*

332.1 DEU ISSN 1616-0185
HG2980.7
GELD UND KAPITAL. Text in German. 1997. a. EUR 31; EUR 36 per issue (effective 2006). **Document type:** *Journal, Academic/Scholarly.* **Description:** Contains academic and scholarly articles on the history of banking.
Published by: Franz Steiner Verlag Stuttgart GmbH, Birkenwaldstr 44, Stuttgart, 70191, Germany. TEL 49-711-25820, FAX 49-711-2582290, service@steiner-verlag.de, http://www.steiner-verlag.de. Ed. Alois Mosser.

332 DEU
GELDIDEE. Text in German. 1998. fortn. EUR 48; EUR 2.30 newsstand/cover (effective 2003). adv. **Document type:** *Magazine, Consumer.* **Description:** Provides information on finance and investing.
Published by: Heinrich Bauer Verlag, Burchardstr 11, Hamburg, 20077, Germany. TEL 49-40-30193040, FAX 49-40-30193046, leser@geldidee.de, kommunikation@hbv.de, http://www.geldidee.de, http://www.bauerverlag.de. Ed. Gerhard Kromschroeder. Adv. contact Karl Keller. page EUR 13,000. Circ: 164,837 (paid). **Dist. in UK by:** Powers International Ltd., 100 Rochester Row, London SW1P 1JP, United Kingdom. TEL 44-20-7630-9966, FAX 44-20-7630-9922.

332.1 DEU ISSN 0343-8740
GELDINSTITUTE. Text in German. 1969. 8/yr. EUR 96 domestic; EUR 107.70 foreign (effective 2002). adv. **Document type:** *Magazine, Consumer.*
Indexed: RefZh.
Published by: Hans Holzmann Verlag GmbH, Gewerbestr 2, Bad Woerishofen, 86825, Germany. TEL 49-8247-35401, FAX 49-8247-354170, redgivb@holzmannverlag.de, http://www.geldinstitute.de/index.html, http://www.holzmannverlag.de. Ed. Erwin Stroebele. Adv. contact Susanne Erhart. Circ: 6,062.

332 BEL
GENERALE BANK. BULLETIN. Text in Dutch, French. 1963. m. **Document type:** *Bulletin.*
Formerly: Societe Generale de Banque. Bulletin
Indexed: BAS, ELLIS.
Published by: Generale Bank, Montagne du Parc 3, Brussels, 1000, Belgium. TEL 32-2-5162266, FAX 32-2-5163283. Ed. Anne Vleminckx.

332.1 BEL
GENERALE BANK. REPORT. Text in Dutch, English, French, German. a.
Formerly: Societe Generale de Banque. Rapport
Published by: Generale Bank, Montagne du Parc 3, Brussels, 1000, Belgium. TEL 32-2-565111, FAX 32-2-5654222, TELEX 21283 GEBA B. Ed. Anne Vleminckx.

332 USA
GEOGRAPHICAL DISTRIBUTION OF ASSETS AND LIABILITIES OF MAJOR FOREIGN BRANCHES OF U.S. BANKS. Text in English. q. USD 5. **Document type:** *Government.*
Indexed: AmStI.
Published by: U.S. Federal Reserve System, Board of Governors, Publications Services, Rm MS 138, Washington, DC 20551. TEL 202-452-3244, FAX 202-728-5886.

GEORGIA BUSINESS CREDIT DIRECTORY. see *BUSINESS AND ECONOMICS—Trade And Industrial Directories*

332 346.06 USA
GEORGIA COMMERCIAL FINANCING FORMS. Text in English. 1991. 2-3 updates/yr), 2 base vols. plus irreg. updates. looseleaf. USD 234. **Description:** Used to evidence, secure and guarantee commercial financing transactions.
Related titles: Diskette ed.
Published by: Michie Company (Subsidiary of: LexisNexis North America), 701 E Water St, Charlottesville, VA 22902-5389. TEL 434-972-7600, 800-446-3410, FAX 434-972-7677, custserv@michie.com, http://www.michie.com.

332 USA ISSN 0882-5971
HC107.G4
GEORGIA TREND; magazine of Georgia business & finance. Text in English. 1985. m. USD 24 (effective 2005). adv. illus. **Document type:** *Magazine, Trade.* **Description:** Covers issues relating to Georgia business and finance.
Incorporates: Business Atlanta (0192-0855); Which was formerly: Real Estate and Business Atlanta; Real Estate Atlanta
Related titles: Online - full text ed.: (from bigchalk, EBSCO Publishing, Gale Group, O C L C Online Computer Library Center, Inc., ProQuest Information & Learning).
Indexed: ABIn, BusDate.
Address: 5880 Live Oak Pkwy, Ste 280, Norcross, GA 30093. TEL 770-931-9410, FAX 770-931-9505, info@georgiatrend.com, http://www.georgiatrend.com. Ed. Susan Percy. Adv. contact Amanda Patterson. B&W page USD 4,218, color page USD 5,507. Circ: 39,400 (controlled).

GERMAN FINANCIAL MARKETS YEARBOOK (YEAR). see *BUSINESS AND ECONOMICS—Investments*

338.0029 332.1 DEU
GERMANY'S TOP 500; a handbook of Germany's largest corporations. Text in English. 1991. a. EUR 100. back issues avail. **Document type:** *Directory, Trade.* **Description:** Provides detailed information on Germany's leading companies, insurers and banks.
Formerly: Germany's Top 300
Related titles: Diskette ed.; E-mail ed.; Fax ed.; Online - full text ed.
Published by: Frankfurter Allgemeine Zeitung GmbH, Postfach 200163, Frankfurt Am Main, 60605, Germany. TEL 49-69-75911888, FAX 49-69-75911843, info@faz-institut.de, http://www.faz-institut.de. Ed. Geraldine Deegan. Adv. contact Karin Gangl.

332 CHL ISSN 0716-1239
GESTION. Text in Spanish. 1975. m. CLP 37,524 domestic; USD 260 foreign. adv.
Indexed: PdeR.
Published by: Editorial Gestion Ltda., Casilla 16485 Correo 9, Rafael Canas, 114, Santiago, Chile. TEL 56-2-2361313, FAX 56-2-2361114, estrategia@edgestion.cl. Ed. Victor Manuel Ojeda. Adv. contact Rodrigo Sepulveda. Circ: 38,000.

332 332.6 FRA ISSN 1163-720X
GESTION DE FORTUNE; le journal de la gestion de patrimoine. Text in French. 1992. m. EUR 60 (effective 2005). bk.rev. back issues avail. **Description:** For individual financial advisers and private investors.
Related titles: Online - full text ed.
Published by: Editions de Verneuil, 35 rue de Liege, Paris, 75008, France. TEL 33-1-44706666, FAX 33-1-44706669, gef@imaginet.fr, http://www.gestiondefortune.com. Ed. Eric Bengel. Pub. Jean Luc Bengel. Adv. contact Eliane De Vaulx. Circ: 16,000 (paid).

GIURISPRUDENZA COMMERCIALE. see *LAW—Corporate Law*

GLOBAL ASSET ALLOCATION. see *BUSINESS AND ECONOMICS—Investments*

332 GBR ISSN 1364-9159
HG3879
GLOBAL BANKING & FINANCIAL POLICY REVIEW (YEARS). Text in English. 199?. a. GBP 145, USD 240. **Document type:** *Trade.* **Description:** Features exclusive policy statements from over 100 of the world's finance ministers and Central Bank Governors.
—BLDSC (4195.351300).
Published by: Euromoney Publications plc, Nestor House, Playhouse Yard, London, EC4V 5EX, United Kingdom. TEL 44-207-7798673, FAX 44-20-77798541.

GLOBAL BUSINESS & FINANCE REVIEW. see *BUSINESS AND ECONOMICS—International Commerce*

GLOBAL COMPANY HANDBOOK. see *BUSINESS AND ECONOMICS—International Commerce*

GLOBAL ECONOMIC FORECASTS. see *BUSINESS AND ECONOMICS—Economic Situation And Conditions*

GLOBAL ECONOMICS PROSPECTS AND THE DEVELOPING COUNTRIES. see *BUSINESS AND ECONOMICS—International Development And Assistance*

332.1 382 USA ISSN 0896-4181
HG4027.5
GLOBAL FINANCE. Text in English. 1987. m. USD 350 (effective 2005). adv. illus. reprints avail. **Document type:** *Magazine, Trade.* **Description:** Aimed at corporate executives and institutional investors. Covers current issues and major trends in international finance.
Related titles: Online - full text ed.: (from bigchalk, EBSCO Publishing, Northern Light Technology, Inc., ProQuest Information & Learning).
Indexed: ABIn, BLI, PAIS.
—BLDSC (4195.397800), IE, ingenta. **CCC.**
Published by: Global Finance Media, Inc., 411 Fifth Ave., 7th Fl, New York, NY 10016. TEL 212-447-7900, FAX 212-447-7750, srodriguez@gfmag.com, http://www.gfmag.com. Pub. Joseph Giarraputo. adv.: page USD 20,500, color page USD 28,000. Circ: 50,000 (controlled).

332 NLD ISSN 1044-0283
HG3879
➤ **GLOBAL FINANCE JOURNAL.** Text in English. 1989. 3/yr. EUR 95 in Europe to individuals; JPY 13,100 in Japan to individuals; USD 99 to individuals except Europe and Japan; EUR 359 in Europe to institutions; JPY 47,700 in Japan to institutions; USD 402 to institutions except Europe and Japan (effective 2006). bk.rev. abstr.; illus. Index. back issues avail.; reprints avail. **Document type:** *Journal, Academic/Scholarly.* **Description:** Provides a forum for the exchange of ideas and techniques among academicians and practitioners in order to advance applied research in global financial management.
Related titles: Microform ed.: (from PQC); Online - full text ed.: (from EBSCO Publishing, Gale Group, IngentaConnect, ScienceDirect, Swets Information Services).
Indexed: ABIn, BAS, ESPM, JEL, RiskAb.
—BLDSC (4195.398000), IE, Infotrieve, ingenta. **CCC.**
Published by: Elsevier BV, North-Holland (Subsidiary of: Elsevier Science & Technology), Sara Burgerhartstraat 25, Amsterdam, 1055 KV, Netherlands. TEL 31-20-485-3911, FAX 31-20-485-2457, nlinfo-f@elsevier.nl, http://www.elsevier.com/locate/gfj, http://www.elsevier.nl. Ed. M. Shahrokhi. **Subscr. to:** Elsevier BV, PO Box 211, Amsterdam 1000 AE, Netherlands. TEL 31-20-485-3757, FAX 31-20-485-3432, http://www.elsevier.nl.

B

➤ **GLOBAL GUARANTY'S CREDIT ENHANCEMENT AND FINANCIAL GUARANTY DIRECTORY.** see *BUSINESS AND ECONOMICS*

332 USA ISSN 1058-3920
GLOBAL INVESTMENT TECHNOLOGY. Text in English. 1991. bi-w. USD 695 domestic; USD 785 foreign (effective 2004). adv. 27 p./no.; back issues avail.; reprints avail. **Document type:** *Magazine, Trade.* **Description:** Addresses strategic business issues affecting US and non-US investment institutions and pension plan sponsors. Examines systems solutions to current business needs, including reports on innovative financial technologies.
Related titles: Online - full text ed.
Published by: Investment Media, Inc., 820 Second Ave, 4th Fl, New York, NY 10017. TEL 212-370-3700, FAX 212-370-4606, info@globalinv.com, http://www.globalinv.com. Circ: 3,560 (paid).

332 330.9 GBR ISSN 0951-3604
HG4502
GLOBAL INVESTOR. Text in English, Japanese. 1987. 10/yr. GBP 350 combined subscription domestic print & online eds.; EUR 535 combined subscription in Europe print & online eds.; USD 595 combined subscription elsewhere print & online eds. (effective 2005). **Document type:** *Magazine, Trade.*
Incorporates (1996-1998): International Bond Investor (1352-0431)
Related titles: Online - full text ed.: (from EBSCO Publishing, Factiva, Florida Center for Library Automation, Gale Group, H.W. Wilson, O C L C Online Computer Library Center, Inc., ProQuest Information & Learning).
Indexed: ABIn, BPI.
—BLDSC (4195.447000), IE, ingenta. **CCC.**
Published by: Euromoney Institutional Investor Plc., Nestor House, Playhouse Yard, London, EC4V 5EX, United Kingdom. TEL 44-20-77798888, FAX 44-20-7779-8595, erodd@euromoneyplc.com, fkeane@euromoneyplc.com, http://www.globalinvestormagazine.com, http://www.euromoneyplc.com. Ed. Claire Milhench TEL 44-20-77798390. Pub. Will Goodhart TEL 44-20-77798989. Adv. contact Elliot Jacobs TEL 44-20-7779-8432. Circ: 10,000. **Subscr. to:** Quadrant Subscription Services, PO Box 18083, London EC4V 5JS, United Kingdom. TEL 44-20-7779-8610, FAX 44-20-7779-8602. **Dist. in US by:** American Educational Systems, PO Box 246, New York, NY 10024-0246. TEL 800-431-1579.

332 GBR
GLOBAL M & A HANDBOOK (YEAR). Text in English. a. GBP 95 in United Kingdom; USD 170 elsewhere (effective 2001). **Document type:** *Yearbook, Trade.* **Description:** Aims to provide a greater understanding of the major developments within the global mergers and acquisitions market. Includes a directory section organised on a country-by-country basis.
Formerly: Global M and A and Corporate Strategy (1355-7866)
Related titles: ♦ Supplement to: Corporate Finance. ISSN 0958-2053.
Published by: Euromoney Institutional Investor Plc., Nestor House, Playhouse Yard, London, EC4V 5EX, United Kingdom. TEL 44-20-7779-8673, FAX 44-20-7779-8541, http://www.euromoney.com. **Dist. in US by:** American Educational Systems, PO Box 246, New York, NY 10024-0246. TEL 800-431-1579, aesbooks@aol.com.

332 USA ISSN 1534-8822
GLOBAL PROXY WATCH. Text in English. 1996. w. USD 1,750 (effective 2005). **Document type:** *Newsletter.*
Media: E-mail.
Published by: Davis Global Advisors, 57 Hancock Street, Newton, MA 02466 2308. TEL 617-630-8792, FAX 617-630-0398, dga@davisglobal.com, http://www.davisglobal.com/publications/gpw/index.html.

332 GBR ISSN 1368-4906
GLOBAL UTILITIES FINANCE REPORT (YEAR). Text in English. 1997. a., latest 2002. GBP 115, USD 195 per issue (effective 2002). **Document type:** *Yearbook, Trade.* **Description:** Serves as a guide for the new global utilities market, providing information on the developments in private funding and regulation.
Published by: Euromoney Institutional Investor Plc., Nestor House, Playhouse Yard, London, EC4V 5EX, United Kingdom. TEL 44-20-7779-8888, information@euromoneyplc.com, http://www.euromoneyplc.com/. **Dist. addr:** Portica, Portica House, 2 Lady Lane Industrial Estate, Hadleigh, Ipswich, Suffolk IP7 6BQ, United Kingdom; **Dist. addr. in the USA:** Institutional Investor, Inc., 225 Park Ave. S., 7th Fl., New York, NY 10003-1605. TEL 212-224-3800, FAX 212-224-3974.

332 333.91 GBR ISSN 1471-3322
GLOBAL WATER INTELLIGENCE. Text in English. 2000. m. GBP 695 (effective 2005). adv. mkt.; stat. a.index. back issues avail. **Document type:** *Newsletter, Trade.* **Description:** Contains market leading analysis of private water projects and finance.
Related titles: E-mail ed.
Published by: Media Analytics, PO Box 458, Oxford, OX2 0ZX, United Kingdom. TEL 44-1865-437403, FAX 44-1865-437421, subscriptions@globalwaterintel.com, http://www.globalwaterintel.com. Ed. Peter Allison. Pub., R&P Christopher Gasson. Adv. contact Alison Ireland. B&W page GBP 1,950, color page GBP 2,950; trim 260 x 385. Circ: 1,000 (paid).

GLOS. see *ETHNIC INTERESTS*

332.6029 USA
GOLDEN STATES FINANCIAL DIRECTORY. Text in English. s-a. USD 124 (effective 2001). **Document type:** *Directory, Trade.* **Description:** Lists financial information for banks, bank holding companies, thrifts and major credit union institutions for the following states: Alaska, Arizona, California, Colorado, Hawaii, Idaho, Montana, Nevada, New Mexico, Oregon, Utah, Washington, and Wyoming.
Published by: Thomson Financial Services Company, 4709 W Golf Rd, Skokie, IL 60076-1256. TEL 847-676-9600, 800-321-3373, FAX 847-933-8101, prodinfo@tfp.com, customerservice@tfp.com, http://www.tfp.com/banks.

332.1 GBR ISSN 1353-6923
GOLDMAN SACHS FOREIGN EXCHANGE HANDBOOK (YEAR). Text in English. 1992. a. (in 2 vols.). GBP 135, USD 250. **Document type:** *Trade.* **Description:** Lists more than 2,500 institutions and 35,000 personnel in foreign exchange.
Published by: Euromoney Publications plc, Nestor House, Playhouse Yard, London, EC4V 5EX, United Kingdom. TEL 44-207-7798673, FAX 44-20-77798541. **Orders to:** Plymbridge Distributors Ltd, Plymbridge House, Estover Rd, Plymouth, Devon PL6 7PY, United Kingdom. TEL 44-1752-202300, FAX 44-1752-202330.

332 PRI ISSN 0093-7479
HG2838
GOVERNMENT DEVELOPMENT BANK FOR PUERTO RICO. ANNUAL REPORT. Key Title: Banco Gubernamental de Fomento para Puerto Rico Informe Anual. Text in English, Spanish. 1978. a. charts; illus.; stat. **Document type:** *Corporate.*
Formerly: Government Development Bank for Puerto Rico. Report of Activities
Published by: Government Development Bank for Puerto Rico, PO Box 42001, Minillas Sta, San Juan, 00940-2001, Puerto Rico. TEL 787-728-9200, FAX 787-268-5496. Ed. Mariluz Frontera. Circ: 7,500.

332 USA ISSN 1540-3955
GOVERNMENT FINANCIAL MANAGEMENT REPORT. Text in English. m. USD 425 (effective 2005). **Document type:** *Newsletter.*
Published by: A.S. Pratt & Sons, Inc., 1911 Fort Myer Dr, Arlington, VA 22209. TEL 703-528-0145, 800-572-2797, FAX 703-528-1736. Eds. Nancy Webman, Rhett Harrell.

GRANT'S INTEREST RATE OBSERVER. see *BUSINESS AND ECONOMICS—Investments*

332 GBR
GREAT BRITAIN. DEPARTMENT OF TRADE AND INDUSTRY. INSOLVENCY: GENERAL ANNUAL REPORT. Text in English. a. reprint service avail. from PQC. **Document type:** *Government.*
Former titles: Great Britain. Department of Trade. Insolvency: General Annual Report; Great Britain. Department of Trade. Bankruptcy: General Annual Report (0072-5633)
Published by: (Great Britain. Department of Trade and Industry), Stationery Office, 51 Nine Elms Ln, London, SW8 5DA, United Kingdom. TEL 44-20-7873-0011, FAX 44-20-7873-8247, book.orders@theso.co.uk, http://www.national-publishing.co.uk.

332 USA
GREEN MONEY JOURNAL. Text in English. 1992. q. USD 35 (effective 1996). bk.rev. back issues avail. **Document type:** *Newsletter, Consumer.* **Description:** Covers ethical spending, investing, and business practices.
Related titles: Online - full text ed.
Address: PO Box 67, Santa Fe, NM 87504-0067. TEL 509-328-1741, http://www.greenmoney.com. Ed. Tom Kliewer. Pub. Cliff Feigerbaum. adv.: page USD 1,500. Circ: 7,000.

322 DEU ISSN 0340-9392
GRUNDLAGEN UND PRAXIS DES BANK- UND BOERSENWESENS. Text in German. 1976. irreg., latest vol.40, 2000. price varies. **Document type:** *Monographic series, Academic/Scholarly.*
Published by: Erich Schmidt Verlag GmbH & Co. (Bielefeld), Viktoriastr 44A, Bielefeld, 33602, Germany. TEL 49-521-58308-0, esv@esvmedien.de, http://www.erich-schmidt-verlag.de.

332 ESP
GRUPO SANTANDER. BOLETIN FINANCIERO. Text in Spanish. q.
Published by: Grupo Santander, Plaza de Canalejas no.1, Madrid, 28014, Spain. http://www.gruposantander.com/pagina/indice/0,,427_1_2,00.html.

332 ESP
GRUPO SANTANDER. BOLETIN LA ACCION. Text in Spanish. q.
Published by: Grupo Santander, Plaza de Canalejas no.1, Madrid, 28014, Spain. http://www.gruposantander.com/pagina/indice/0,,427_1_2,00.html.

332 ESP
GRUPO SANTANDER. INFORME ANUAL (YEAR). Text in Spanish. a.
Published by: Grupo Santander, Plaza de Canalejas no.1, Madrid, 28014, Spain.

332 SWE ISSN 1650-4704
GRUS & GULD. Text in Swedish. 1969. 5/yr. SEK 150 to non-members; SEK 30 per issue to non-members (effective 2002).
Former titles (until 1999): Raentefri (1104-3938); (until 1993): J A K-info (1103-8780); (until 1991): Raentefri Ekonomi (0284-4761); (until 1987): J A K Bladet (0281-4595); (until 1981): J A K Information
Published by: J A K Medlemsbank, Vasagatan 14, Skoevde, 54150, Sweden. TEL 46-500-46-45-00, FAX 46-500-46-45-61, http://www.grusoguld. Ed. Maria Loevfors TEL 46-08-429 95 25.

332 CHN
GUANGDONG JINRONG/GUANGDONG FINANCE. Text in Chinese. m.
Published by: Guangdong Sheng Jinrong Xuehui, No 137 Changti, Guangzhou, Guangdong 510120, China. TEL 884316. Ed. Li Dan'er.

332 ECU
GUIA DEL SECTOR FINANCIERO ECUATORIANO. Text in Spanish. 1991. a.
Published by: Dinediciones S.A., Av. Gonzalez Suarez 335 y San Ignacio, Quito, Ecuador. TEL 565-477.

332 URY ISSN 0797-1176
GUIA FINANCIERA. Key Title: Guia Financiera Magui. Text in Spanish. 1977. w.
Published by: Miguel Malis Pub., Nicaragua, 1579, Montevideo, 11813, Uruguay. TEL 202689. Ed. Romeo Guida. Circ: 5,000.

332 USA
GUIDE TO BANK AND THRIFTS. Text in English. q. USD 438. Website rev. charts; stat. 440 p./no.; back issues avail. **Document type:** *Directory, Consumer.* **Description:** Offers a guide to the financial strength of US banks and savings and loans, including their safety ratings.
Former titles: Weiss Ratings' Guide to Bank and Thrifts; (until 1998, no.31): Weiss Bank Safety Directory (1049-5673)
Published by: Weiss Ratings, Inc., 4176 Burns Rd, Palm Beach, FL 33410. TEL 561-627-3300, FAX 561-625-6685, wr@weissinc.com, http://www.weissratings.com. Pub. Martin Weiss. R&P Shelley Klovsky.

GUIDE TO PRICE REVIEWS AT THE M M C. (Monopolies and Mergers Commission) see *ENERGY*

GUIDE TO THE CANADIAN FINANCIAL SERVICES INDUSTRY. see *BUSINESS AND ECONOMICS—Trade And Industrial Directories*

332 USA ISSN 1539-6002
GUIDE TO WEALTH PROTECTION STRATEGIES. Text in English. 2001. a.
Published by: Practitioners Publishing Co., PO Box 966, Fort Worth, TX 76101-0966. TEL 817-332-3709, 800-323-8724, FAX 817-877-3694, http://www.ppcnet.com.

H K EX CASH AND DERIVATIVES MARKETS QUARTERLY REPORT. (Hong Kong Exchange) see *BUSINESS AND ECONOMICS—Investments*

H K EX FACT BOOK (YEAR). (Hong Kong Exchange) see *BUSINESS AND ECONOMICS—Investments*

658.3 332.1 USA
H R BANKER. Text in English. m. USD 150 to non-members; USD 100 to members. **Document type:** *Journal, Trade.* **Description:** Reports on developments in banking, private industry, and the Equal Employment Opportunity Commission, National Labor Relations Board, Congress, the federal courts, and other government agencies.
Formerly (until Sep. 1997): Bank Personnel News (0272-3271)
Related titles: Microform ed.: (from PQC); Online - full text ed.
Published by: Cover to Cover, 2906 Bidle Rd, Middletown, MD 21769. TEL 301-371-9656, 800-371-5686, FAX 301-371-7820, adeptusab@aol.com. Ed. Allie Buzzell.

H R BANKER (AUSTIN); for hr professionals in financial institutions. (Human Resources) see *BUSINESS AND ECONOMICS—Personnel Management*

332 AUS
H W W RATE CHECK BOOK: AT CALL DEPOSITS. Text in English. 1988. d. (w., m.). AUD 2,000 (effective 2000). **Document type:** *Trade.*

B

B

Formerly: Retail Banking Products Survey: At Call Deposits (1032-870X); Which superseded in part (in 1989): H W W Retail Banking Products Survey (1031-4148)
Published by: H W W Limited, PO Box 996, Darlinghurst, NSW 2010, Australia. TEL 61-2-8268-8268, FAX 61-2-8268-8267, http://www.hww.com.au.

332   AUS
H W W RATE CHECK BOOK: CREDIT CARDS. Text in English. 1988. m. AUD 2,000 (effective 2000). Document type: Trade.
Formerly: Retail Banking Products Survey: Credit Cards (1032-8742); Which superseded in part (in 1989): H W W Retail Banking Products Survey (1031-4148)
Published by: H W W Limited, PO Box 996, Darlinghurst, NSW 2010, Australia. TEL 61-2-8268-8268, FAX 61-2-8268-8267, http://www.hww.com.au.

332   AUS
H W W RATE CHECK BOOK: TERM DEPOSITS. Text in English. 1988. d. (w., m.). AUD 2,000 (effective 2000). Document type: Trade.
Formerly: Retail Banking Products Survey: Term Deposits (1032-8718); Which superseded in part (in 1989): H W W Retail Banking Products Survey (1031-4148)
Published by: H W W Limited, PO Box 996, Darlinghurst, NSW 2010, Australia. TEL 61-2-8268-8268, FAX 61-2-8268-8267, http://www.hww.com.au.

332   AUS
H W W RATE CHECK BOOK: TERM LOANS. Text in English. 1988. d. (w., m.). AUD 2,000 (effective 2000). Document type: Trade.
Formerly: Retail Banking Products Survey: Term Loans (1032-8734); Which superseded in part (in 1989): H W W Retail Banking Products Survey (1031-4148)
Published by: H W W Limited, PO Box 996, Darlinghurst, NSW 2010, Australia. TEL 61-2-8268-8268, FAX 61-2-8268-8267, http://www.hww.com.au.

332   CHN
HAINAN JINRONG/HAINAN FINANCE. Text in Chinese. m.
Published by: Hainan Sheng Jinrong Xuehui/Hainan Society of Finance, Sheng Renmin Yinhang, Binhai Dadao, Haikou, Hainan 570005, China. TEL 74205. Ed. Wu Qiping.

HALLO SPAREFROH; Freund der Sparjugend. see CHILDREN AND YOUTH—For

HAMBROS DEALERS DIRECTORY (YEAR); foreign exchange treasury and bullion. see BUSINESS AND ECONOMICS—Trade And Industrial Directories

HANDBOOK OF S E C ACCOUNTING AND DISCLOSURE MANUAL. (Securities and Exchange Commission) see BUSINESS AND ECONOMICS—Accounting

332   USA
(YEAR) HANDBOOK OF WORLD STOCK AND COMMODITY EXCHANGES* . Text in English. a. USD 265. Description: Provides a comprehensive guide to stock, futures, and options exchanges worldwide.
Published by: Basil Blackwell Inc., 350 Main St, Malden, MA 02148. TEL 617-547-7110, 800-488-2665, FAX 617-547-0789.

332   DNK   ISSN 1398-6163
HANDELSHOEJSKOLEN I AARHUS. CENTRE FOR ANALYTICAL FINANCE. WORKING PAPERS SERIES. Variant title: C A F Working Papers. Text in English. 199?. irreg. back issues avail. Document type: Monographic series, Academic/Scholarly.
Related titles: Online - full text ed.: ISSN 1399-6789.
Published by: Handelshoejskolen i Aarhus, Centre for Analytical Finance., Building 322, Aarhus Universitet, Aarhus C, 8000, Denmark. TEL 45-89-421580, FAX 45-86-136334, caf@cls.dk, http://www.caf.dk/.

332   DNK   ISSN 0105-4058
HANDELSHOEJSKOLEN I AARHUS. INSTITUT FOR FINANSIERING OG KREDITVAESEN. KOMPENDIUM D. Text in Danish. 1981 (no.8). irreg. illus.
Published by: Handelshoejskolen i Aarhus, Institut for Finansiering og Kreditvaesen, Aarhus, Denmark.

HARVARD BUSINESS SCHOOL GUIDE TO CAREERS IN FINANCE. see OCCUPATIONS AND CAREERS

HARVARD COLLEGE ECONOMIST. see BUSINESS AND ECONOMICS—Macroeconomics

332.1   AUT
HAUPTVERBAND DER OESTERREICHISCHEN SPARKASSEN. JAHRESBERICHT. Text in German; Summaries in English, French, German. 1912. a. free. charts; stat. Document type: Corporate.
Published by: Hauptverband der Oesterreichischen Sparkassen, Postfach 256, Vienna, W 1011, Austria. TEL 0222-71169, FAX 0222-7138926. Circ. 4,000.

THE HEALTH CARE M & A MONTHLY. see BUSINESS AND ECONOMICS

THE HEALTH CARE SERVICES ACQUISITION REPORT. see BUSINESS AND ECONOMICS

HEALTH CITY SUN. see LAW

HEALTHCARE CORPORATE FINANCE NEWS; market intelligence on healthcare venture capital, M&A and IPOs. see HEALTH FACILITIES AND ADMINISTRATION

332   CHN   ISSN 1003-3793
HEBEI CAIJING XUEYUAN XUEBAO/HEBEI INSTITUTE OF FINANCE AND ECONOMICS. JOURNAL. Text in Chinese. 1978. m. USD 18. adv. Document type: Academic/Scholarly. Description: Covers theories, policies and practices in the field of finance and economics.
Published by: Hebei Caijing Xueyuan, Xuebao Bianjibu, 106 Hongqi Dajie, Shijiazhuang, Hebei 050091, China. TEL 0311-333427, FAX 0311-614039. Ed. Chen Jinlung. Adv. contact Liu Wenming. page USD 100.

HEDGE FUND ALERT. see BUSINESS AND ECONOMICS—Investments

332   CHN   ISSN 1001-0432
HEILONGJIANG JINGRONG/HEILONGJIANG FINANCE. Text in Chinese. 1981. m. CNY 1.50 per issue. Document type: Academic/Scholarly.
Related titles: Online - full text ed.: (from East View Information Services).
Published by: Heilongjiang Jinrong Yanjiusuo/Heilongjiang Institute of Finance, 75, Zhongshan Lu, Xiangfang-qu, Harbin, Heilongjiang 150036, China. TEL 0451-2623247, FAX 0451-2623247. Ed. Li Qingshan. Circ. 12,000.

332   GBR   ISSN 1465-8658
THE HEMSCOTT COMPANY GUIDE; a detailed guide to U.K. stockmarket companies. Text in English. 1978. q. GBP 155 (effective 2000). Document type: Directory. Description: Provides financial details for all UK listed companies.
Formerly (until Aug. 1998): Hambro Company Guide (0144-2015)
—CCC.
Published by: Hemmington Scott Publishing Ltd., City Innovation Centre, 26-31 Whiskin St, London, EC1R 0JD, United Kingdom. TEL 44-20-7278-7769, FAX 44-20-7278-9808, http://www.hemscott.net. Ed., Pub. James Ranft. R&P Tricia Beney TEL 44-20-7287-7769.

HERZOG'S BANKRUPTCY FORMS AND PRACTICE. see LAW

332.6327   USA
HI-GROWTH JOURNAL NEWSLETTER* ; The Hi-Growth Journal Newsletter. Text in English. bi-m. free. adv. Document type: Newsletter.
Related titles: Online - full text ed.
Published by: Hawke Group, Inc., 50 NE 26th Ave Ste 201, Pompano Beach, FL 33062-5226. TEL 954-564-7114, 888-429-5347, FAX 954-564-9848, mluppino@hawkegroup.com, http://www.higrowth.com/. Ed. Mary Anne Luppino. Circ. 50,000.

332   USA   ISSN 1540-3963
HIGH PERFORMANCE BANKING. Text in English. 198?. m. USD 425 (effective 2004). Document type: Newsletter, Trade. Description: Contains information on new ways to manage and solve problems in such important areas as banking services, cost control, technology, investing, sales and marketing, product pricing, service quality, compliance, and more.
Published by: Sheshunoff Information Services Inc., 807 Las Cimas Pkwy, Ste 300, Austin, TX 78746. TEL 512-472-2244, 800-456-2340, FAX 512-305-6575, customercare.sis@sheshunoff.com, http://www.sheshunoff.com/store/851.html.

332   USA   ISSN 1094-8945
HIGH YIELD REPORT. Text in English. 1992. w. USD 1,295 domestic; USD 1,395 foreign (effective 2005). adv. Document type: Newsletter. Description: Reports on high-yield bond market, workouts, bankruptcies and distressed securities. Includes pricing information for both primary and secondary markets, and analysis of the high-yield sector.
Formed by the merger of: Junk Bond Reporter; Distressed Debt Report
Related titles: Online - full text ed.: (from EBSCO Publishing, Florida Center for Library Automation, Gale Group, O C L C Online Computer Library Center, Inc., The Dialog Corporation)
Indexed: B&I.
—CCC.
Published by: Source Media, Inc., One State St Plaza, 27th Fl, New York, NY 10004. TEL 212-803-6077, 800-221-1809, FAX 212-747-1154, custserv@sourcemedia.com, http://www.highyieldreport.com, http://www.sourcemedia.com. Pub. John Toth TEL 212-803-6565.

332   IND   ISSN 0971-7528
HINDU BUSINESS LINE. Text in English. 1994. d. USD 1,603; USD 186 Sunday ed. (effective 2005). adv. 6 cols./p.; . Document type: Newspaper, Consumer.
Related titles: Microfilm ed.; Online - full text ed.: (from Gale Group, O C L C Online Computer Library Center, Inc.).

Published by: Kasturi & Sons Ltd., Kasturi Bldgs., 859-860 Anna Salai, Chennai, Tamil Nadu 600 002, India. TEL 9144-28589060, FAX 9144-28545703, thehindu@vsnl.com, subs@thehindu.co.in, http://www.thehindu.com. Ed. N Ram. Pub. S Rangarajan. Adv. contact K V Balasubramaniam. color page INR 200,000. Circ. 24,823.

320.711   GBR   ISSN 0266-402X
HOBSONS FINANCE CASEBOOK. Text in English. 1981. a. GBP 9.99 per issue (effective 2002). Description: Recent graduates discuss their finance careers.
Published by: (Careers Research and Advisory Centre), Hobsons PLC, Challenger House, 42 Adler St, London, E1 1EE, United Kingdom. TEL 44-1223-460366, FAX 44-1223-301506. Dist. by: Biblios Publishers' Distribution Services Ltd., Star Rd, Partridge Green, W Sussex RH13 8LD, United Kingdom. TEL 44-1403-710851, FAX 44-1403-711143.

334.2   USA   ISSN 1090-042X
HOME & FAMILY FINANCE; a guide to family finance and consumer action. Text in English. 1961. q. avail. only to credit unions, bulk price varies. bk.rev.; software rev.; video rev.; Website rev. charts. 24 p./no. 2 cols./p.; back issues avail.; reprint service avail. from PQC. Document type: Magazine, Trade.
Formerly (until 1996): Everybody's Money (0423-8710)
Indexed: Consl.
—CCC.
Published by: Credit Union National Association, Inc., 5710 Mineral Point Rd, Madison, WI 53701. TEL 608-231-4082, 800-356-9655, FAX 608-231-4263, askem@cuna.com, http://www.cuna.org/. Ed. Susan Tiffany. Circ. 300,000 (paid).

332.7   USA   ISSN 1051-4902
HG2040.45
HOME EQUITY LINES OF CREDIT REPORT. Text in English. a. USD 90 to non-members; USD 60 to members.
Formerly (until 1989): Home Equity Credit Report (1043-6499); Which supersedes in part (in 1987): Retail Bank Credit Report (0276-9093)
Published by: American Bankers Association, Retail Service Center, 1120 Connecticut Ave, N W, Washington, DC 20036. TEL 202-663-5430, FAX 301-843-8405.

332.63   USA   ISSN 1085-0902
HOME EQUITY NEWS. Text in English. 1995. bi-m. USD 545 (effective 2004). back issues avail. Document type: Magazine, Trade. Description: Source for profit-making, insider tips and info on today's cut-throat world of second mortgage finance and lending to borrowers with damaged credit.
Published by: Royal Media Group, 1359 Broadway, Ste 1512, New York, NY 10018. TEL 212-564-8972, 800-320-4418, FAX 212-564-8973, info@royalmedia.com, http://www.royalmedia.com/newsletter.cfm?pub=104.

THE HOME HEALTH CARE ACQUISITION REPORT. see MEDICAL SCIENCES—Nurses And Nursing

HONG KONG. COMMISSIONER OF BANKING. ANNUAL REPORT. see BUSINESS AND ECONOMICS—Abstracting, Bibliographies, Statistics

332.6   HKG
HONG KONG EXCHANGES AND CLEARING LTD. MONTHLY MARKET DATA (MAIN BOARD AND STOCK OPTIONS MARKET). Text in English. m. HKD 100 (effective 2001). Document type: Trade.
Formerly (until Feb. 2001): S E H K Monthly Bulletin
Published by: Hong Kong Exchanges and Clearing Ltd., Corporate Communications, 12/F, One International Finance Centre, 1 Harbour View St, Hong Kong, Hong Kong. TEL 852-2522-1122, FAX 852-2845-3554, info@sehk.com.hk, info@hkex.com.hk, http://www.sehk.com.hk, http://www.hkex.com.hk.

HONG KONG EXCHANGES AND CLEARING LTD. MONTHLY MARKET STATISTICS. see BUSINESS AND ECONOMICS—Investments

HONG KONG EXCHANGES AND CLEARING LTD. WEEKLY QUOTATIONS. see BUSINESS AND ECONOMICS—Investments

332.7   HKG
HONG KONG EXPORT CREDIT INSURANCE CORPORATION. ANNUAL REPORT. Text in Chinese. a.
Published by: Hong Kong Export Credit Insurance Corporation, South Seas Centre Tower 1-2nd Fl, Tsimshatsui East, 75 Mody Rd, Kowloon, Hong Kong.

332   HKG
HONG KONG FINANCIAL SERVICES. Text in English. a. Document type: Trade.
Published by: Hong Kong Trade Development Council, 38th Fl Office Tower, Convention Plaza, 1 Harbour Rd, Wanchai, Hong Kong. TEL 852-2584-4333, publications@tdc.org.hk, hktdc@tdc.org.hk, http://www.tdc.org.hk, http://www.tdc.org.hk/. Ed. Mary Wong.

HONG KONG SPECIAL ADMINISTRATIVE REGION OF CHINA. CENSUS AND STATISTICS DEPARTMENT. REPORT ON ANNUAL SURVEY OF STORAGE, COMMUNICATION, FINANCING, INSURANCE AND BUSINESS SERVICES. see *BUSINESS AND ECONOMICS—Abstracting, Bibliographies, Statistics*

332.1 USA ISSN 0018-473X
HOOSIER BANKER. Text in English. 1916. m. USD 35 to non-members; free to members (effective 2005). adv. bk.rev. illus. 56 p./no.; back issues avail.; reprints avail. **Document type:** *Magazine, Trade.* **Description:** Covers information on Indiana Banker's Association events, career posting section, timely general banking news including legislative and regulatory updates, and the charters, branches and changes column, tracking Indiana banking trends.
Indexed: ABIn, BLI.
Published by: Indiana Bankers Association, 3135 N Meridian St, Indianapolis, IN 46208-4717. TEL 317-921-3135, FAX 317-921-3131, http://www.inbankers.org. Ed., R&P Laura Wilson TEL 317-921-3135. Pub. James H. Cousins. adv.: page USD 650. Circ: 4,000 (paid).

332 DEU ISSN 0171-5658
HOPPENSTEDT BOERSENFUEHRER. Text in German; Summaries in English. q. EUR 193.78 (effective 1999). adv. **Document type:** *Trade.*
Published by: Hoppenstedt Bonnier Zeitschriften GmbH, Havelstr. 9, Darmstadt, 64295, Germany. TEL 49-6151-380-0, FAX 49-6151-380-360. Ed. Friederike Mueller. R&P, Adv. contact Judith Kuehnert TEL 49-6151-380290. Circ: 3,000 (controlled).

332 332.65 DEU
HOPPENSTEDT CHARTS. Text in German. 1970. w. price varies. adv. **Document type:** *Bulletin.*
Published by: Hoppenstedt Bonnier Zeitschriften GmbH, Havelstr. 9, Darmstadt, 64295, Germany. TEL 49-6151-380-0, FAX 49-6151-380-360. Ed. Thomas Thelen. R&P, Adv. contact Fabian Engler TEL 49-6151-380-313.

332.3 USA
HOTLINE (LOS ANGELES)* . Text in English. 1927. s-m. looseleaf. USD 40 to non-members. bk.rev. **Document type:** *Newsletter.* **Description:** General membership newsletter covering industry trends, federal and state legislation, and activities in California.
Former titles: California Hotline; California Savings and Loan Hotline; (until 1981): California Savings and Loan Journal (0886-3245); California S & L Journal (0886-3318)
Indexed: PAIS.
Published by: Western League of Savings Institutions, 9841 Airport Blvd, Ste 418, Los Angeles, CA 90045. TEL 310-414-8300, FAX 310-414-8399. Ed. Kathleen Wedeking. Circ: 3,600.

HOUSING FINANCE. see *REAL ESTATE*

HOUSING FINANCE COMPANY OF KENYA. ANNUAL REPORT AND ACCOUNTS. see *HOUSING AND URBAN PLANNING*

332 GBR ISSN 0269-8978
HOUSING FINANCE INTERNATIONAL. Text in English. 1986. q. GBP 88; GBP 25 newsstand/cover (effective 2003). **Document type:** *Journal, Trade.* **Description:** Items of interest to both the developed, as well as the developing world with emphasis on thematic content.
Related titles: Online - full text ed.: (from EBSCO Publishing).
Indexed: ABIn.
—BLDSC (4335.098840), IE, ingenta.
Published by: International Union for Housing Finance, 3 Savile Row, London, W1S 3PB, United Kingdom. TEL 44-20-7494-2995, FAX 44-20-7734-6426, info.iuhf@housingfinance.org, http://www.housingfinance.org.

HOUSING LEGISLATION MANUAL. see *PUBLIC ADMINISTRATION*

HOW TO AVOID FINANCIAL TANGLES. see *BUSINESS AND ECONOMICS—Management*

332 USA ISSN 1052-2654
HG4061
HOW TO FIND FINANCIAL INFORMATION ABOUT COMPANIES. Text in English. 1990. irreg. **Document type:** *Directory.*
Published by: Washington Researchers, Ltd., 1655 Fort Myer Dr., Ste. 800, Arlington, VA 22209-3119. TEL 703-312-2863, FAX 703-527-4586, research@researchers.com, http://www.researchers.com, http://www.washingtonresearchers.com. Ed. M Newman. R&P Ellen O'Kane.

332 GBR
HYPOVEREINSBANK VALUES. Abbreviated title: H V B Values. Text in English. every 3 mos. free to qualified personnel. **Document type:** *Magazine, Consumer.* **Description:** Covers wealth management, real estate and retirement planning.
Formed by the merger of: Anleger; Immobilien
Published by: (HypoVereinsbank DEU), Highbury Customer Publications, The Publishing House, 1-3 Highbury Station Rd, London, N1 1SE, United Kingdom. TEL 44-20-226-2222, FAX 44-20-77040758, customerpublishing@hhc.co.uk, http://www.hhc.co.uk/pages/show/entry_Level/2/entry_code/HCU/single_record_flag/90. Ed. Thomas Schmitz TEL 49-4042-31300. Circ: 150,000.

332 JPN
I B J ANNUAL REPORT. Text in English. a., latest 2000. **Document type:** *Trade.*
Related titles: Online - full content ed.; Japanese ed.
Published by: Industrial Bank of Japan/Nippon Kogyo Ginko, 3-3, Marunouchi 1-chome, Chiyoda-ku, Tokyo, 100-8210, Japan. TEL 81-3-3214-1111, FAX 81-3-3201-7643, http://www.ibjbank.co.jp/English/ar.html.

332.3 KWT
THE I B K PAPERS. Text in English, Arabic. 1980. free.
Published by: Industrial Bank of Kuwait/Bank al-Kuwayt al-Sinai, P O Box 3146, Safat, Kuwait. TEL 965-2457661, FAX 965-2462057, IBK@ncc.moc.kw, http://ncc.moc.kw.users/I.B.K. Ed. Amro Mohie Al-din. Circ: 1,500.

332.1 GBR ISSN 1355-8447
I C B NEWSLETTER. (International Correspondent Banker) Text in English. m. GBP 435 in Europe; USD 795 elsewhere (effective 2001). **Document type:** *Newsletter.* **Description:** Dedicated to covering banks' transaction processing-related business.
—CCC.
Published by: Euromoney Institutional Investor Plc., Nestor House, Playhouse Yard, London, EC4V 5EX, United Kingdom. TEL 44-20-7779-8673, FAX 44-20-7779-8541, meuer@euromoneyplc.com, http://www.euromoney.com. **Dist. in US by:** American Educational Systems, PO Box 246, New York, NY 10024-0246. TEL 800-431-1579, aesbooks@aol.com.

332 338.9 USA
I D B AMERICA. Text in English. 1974. m. free. illus.; stat. **Document type:** *Newsletter.* **Description:** Reports on economic and social trends in Latin America and the Caribbean and on the activities of the Bank.
Formerly: I D B
Related titles: Microfiche ed.: (from CIS); Spanish ed.; Supplement(s): I D B Extra.
Indexed: IIS, WBA.
Published by: Inter-American Development Bank/Banco Interamericano de Desarrollo, 1300 New York Ave, N W, Washington, DC 20577. TEL 202-623-1709, FAX 202-623-1753, http://iadb.org/exr/pub/engcatalog/Pages/brochures.htm. Ed. Barbara Rierveld TEL 202-623-1154.

332.2 USA ISSN 1076-8424
HG3881.5.I44
I D B PROJECTS. Text in English. 1994. 10/yr. USD 590 to institutions; USD 550 to institutions online; USD 795 combined subscription to institutions print & online (effective 2005). **Document type:** *Newsletter.* **Description:** Deals with the various projects of the Inter-American Development Bank.
Indexed: IIS.
Published by: Inter-American Development Bank/Banco Interamericano de Desarrollo, 1300 New York Ave, N W, Washington, DC 20577. TEL 202-623-1709, FAX 202-623-1753, jlorder@jhupress.jlu.edu, http://www.press.jhu.edu/press/journals/idb/idb.html, http://www.iadb.org/exr/pub/encatalog/Pages/brochures.htm. Ed. Suzanne Gallagher. Adv. contact Tamara Barnes TEL 410-516-6984. **Subscr. to:** The Johns Hopkins University Press, Journals Publishing Division, PO Box 19966, Baltimore, MD 21211. TEL 410-516-6987, 800-548-1784, FAX 410-516-6968, jlorder@jhunix.hcf.jhu.edu.

332 USA
I DNEWSWIRE. Text in English. bi-w. **Document type:** *Newsletter.* **Description:** Designed to provide news and analysis on developments and trends in advanced personal identification technologies.
Media: E-mail.
Published by: Source Media, Inc., One State St Plaza, 27th Fl, New York, NY 10004. TEL 212-803-6077, 800-221-1809, FAX 212-747-1154, custserv@sourcemedia.com, http://www.sourcemedia.com.

332.1 GBR
I F A ONLINE. (Independent Financial Advisers) Text in English. 1997. d. free to qualified personnel (effective 2005). adv. **Document type:** *Magazine, Trade.* **Description:** Combines editorial coverage and features with product research, quotations, fund comparison data, portfolios, event listings and directories.
Media: Online - full text.
Published by: Incisive Media Plc., Haymarket House, 28-29 Haymarket, London, SW1Y 4RX, United Kingdom. TEL 44-20-74849700, FAX 44-20-79302238, info@ifaonline.co.uk, customerservices@incisivemedia.com, http://www.ifaonline.co.uk/, http://www.incisivemedia.com/. Ed. Julie Henderson TEL 44-20-79684571. Pub. Mike Jones TEL 44-20-79684530. Adv. contact Mark Jennings TEL 44-20-79684530.

332 GBR ISSN 1356-4773
I F A REVIEW. (International Fiscal Association) Text in English. 1995. 10/yr. GBP 19 (effective 1999). adv. back issues avail. **Document type:** *Trade.* **Description:** Covers company technology, financial advisors, pensions, and mortgages.
Published by: Mitre House Publishing Ltd., 154 Graham Rd, Wimbledon, London, SW19 3SJ, United Kingdom. http://www.mitrehousepublishing.co.uk/. Ed., Pub. Richard Blausten. Adv. contact Christopher Lukey.

332 DEU ISSN 0081-7279
I F O STUDIEN ZUR FINANZPOLITIK. Text in German. 1964. irreg., latest vol.69, 1999. price varies. **Document type:** *Monographic series.*
Published by: I F O Institut fuer Wirtschaftsforschung, Poschingerstr 5, Munich, 81679, Germany. TEL 49-89-9224-0, FAX 49-89-985369, ifo@ifo.de, http://www.ifo.de. Circ: 400.

332.2 USA
I I C ANNUAL REPORT. Text in English. a. free. charts; illus.; stat. **Document type:** *Corporate.* **Description:** Reports on efforts of the IIC to fund private enterprise in Latin America.
Related titles: French ed.; Portuguese ed.; Spanish ed.
Published by: (Inter-American Investment Corporation), Inter-American Development Bank/Banco Interamericano de Desarrollo, 1300 New York Ave, N W, Washington, DC 20577. TEL 202-623-1709, FAX 202-623-1753, http://www.iadb.org/exr/pub/engcatalog/Pages/anpubs.htm.

332 657 IND ISSN 0970-3780
➤ **I I F NEWSLETTER.** Text in English. 1987. m. bk.rev. abstr.; tr.lit. 4 p./no.; back issues avail. **Document type:** *Newsletter, Academic/Scholarly.* **Description:** Provides a forum for interdisciplinary knowledge on finance and economics. Highlights news items, articles on economic trends and financial industry. It also brings forth the activities of the institutes, its research progress and documents abstracts of seminars organized by the institute in the month.
Related titles: E-mail ed.; Online - full text ed.
Published by: Indian Institute of Finance, 4, Community Center II, Ashok Vihar II, P O Box 8486, New Delhi, 110 052, India. TEL 91-11-27136257, FAX 91-11-27454128, nl@iif.edu, aa@finance.india.org, http://www.iif.edu, http://www.financeindia.org. R&P J D Agarwal. Adv. contact Aman Agarwal. Circ: 20,000.

332 USA ISSN 1020-1637
I M F COMMITTEE ON BALANCE OF PAYMENTS STATISTICS. ANNUAL REPORT. (International Monetary Fund) Text in English. 1994. a., latest 2002.
Published by: International Monetary Fund, 700 19th St, N W, Washington, DC 20431. TEL 202-623-7430, FAX 202-623-7201, publications@imf.org, http://www.imf.org.

I O M A'S REPORT ON MANAGING 401K PLANS. see *BUSINESS AND ECONOMICS—Personnel Management*

332 USA ISSN 1074-8903
I O M A'S REPORT ON MANAGING CREDIT, RECEIVABLES AND COLLECTIONS. Variant title: Managing Credit, Receivables and Collections. Text in English. 1994. m. looseleaf. USD 281.95 in US & Canada print & online eds.; USD 293 elsewhere print & online eds. (effective 2006). index. back issues avail. **Document type:** *Newsletter, Trade.* **Description:** Helps credit and receivables managers set credit policies and accelerate receivables. Examines related technologies and techniques.
Related titles: Diskette ed.; E-mail ed.; Online - full content ed.; Online - full text ed.: (from EBSCO Publishing, Florida Center for Library Automation, Gale Group, LexisNexis, O C L C Online Computer Library Center, Inc., ProQuest Information & Learning); ♦ Cumulative ed(s).: Managing Credit, Receivables & Collections Yearbook.
Indexed: ATI, BLI.
—CCC.
Published by: Institute of Management & Administration, Inc., 3 Park Ave, New York, NY 10016-5902. TEL 212-244-0360, FAX 212-564-0465, subserve@ioma.com, http://www.ioma.com/products/prod_detail.php?prodid=16. Ed. Mary Schaeffer. Pub. Perry Patterson. R&P Sofie Kourkoutakis.

332 TUR ISSN 1301-1642
HG5706.5.I88
I S E REVIEW. Text in English. q.
Indexed: JEL.
Published by: Istanbul Stock Exchange, Resitpasa Mah. Tuncay ARTUN Cd., Emirgan, Istanbul 34467, Turkey. TEL 90-212-2982100, FAX 90-212-2982500, info@ise.org, http://www.ise.org.

332.1 USA
▼ **I S O & AGENT.** Text in English. 2004. 26/yr. free to qualified personnel. **Document type:** *Newsletter, Trade.* **Description:** Contains trade news and information for resellers of payment terminals and ATMs.
Media: Online - full content.
Published by: Source Media, Inc., One State St Plaza, 27th Fl, New York, NY 10004. TEL 212-803-6077, 800-221-1809, FAX 212-747-1154, custserv@sourcemedia.com, http://www.cardforum.com/emailform-iso.html, http://www.sourcemedia.com.

▼ new title ➤ refereed ✶ unverified ♦ full entry avail.

332.1 GBR ISSN 1369-9601
I T NOTES ON BANKING. Text in English. 1997. q. GBP 50, USD 85 (effective 1999). **Document type:** *Trade.*
Indexed: Inspec.
Published by: I B C Business Publishing Ltd., 69-77 Paul St, London, EC2A 4LQ, United Kingdom. TEL 44-20-7553-1567, FAX 44-20-7553-1593.

332 BGR ISSN 0204-711X
HC403.A1
IKONOMIKA. Text in Bulgarian; Summaries in English. m. USD 120 foreign (effective 2002). bibl.; charts; stat. **Document type:** *Journal.*
Formerly: Finansi i Kredit
Indexed: BSLEcon, RASB.
Published by: Ministerstvo na Finansite, 102 Rakovski ul, Sofia, 1000, Bulgaria. Circ: 5,000. **Dist. by:** Hemus, 6 Rouski Blvd., Sofia 1000, Bulgaria; **Dist. by:** Sofia Books, ul Silivria 16, Sofia 1404, Bulgaria. TEL 359-2-9586257, info@sofiabooks-bg.com, http://www.sofiabooks-bg.com. **Co-sponsor:** Bulgarska Narodna Banka/Bulgarian National Bank.

B

332.1 USA ISSN 0019-185X
ILLINOIS BANKER. Text in English. 1916. m. USD 85 to non-members; USD 42.50 to members (effective 2005). adv. bk.rev. **Document type:** *Magazine, Trade.*
Related titles: Online - full text ed.: (from EBSCO Publishing).
Indexed: BLI, BPIA, WBA.
Published by: Illinois Bankers Association, 133 S 4th St, Ste 300, Springfield, IL 62701. TEL 217-789-9340, FAX 217-789-5410, djemison@ilbanker.com, http://www.ilbanker.com. Eds. Debbie Jemison, Kathleen C Gill. Pub. William J Hocter. Adv. contact Rich Galloway. B&W page USD 915, color page USD 1,590; trim 8.38 x 10.88. Circ: 2,200 (paid).

332 USA
KFI1365.A29
ILLINOIS BANKING ACT AND RELATED LAWS. Text in English. irreg., latest 2001. USD 39 (effective 2003). 792 p./no.; **Description:** Features the full-text of Chapter 205.
Related titles: CD-ROM ed.: ISSN 1551-0719.
Published by: Michie Company (Subsidiary of: LexisNexis North America), 701 E Water St, Charlottesville, VA 22902-5389. TEL 434-972-7600, 800-446-3410, FAX 434-972-7677, http://www.michie.com.

332 USA
ILLINOIS BANKNEWS✶. Text in English. fortn. USD 70 to non-members; USD 35 to members. adv. back issues avail. **Document type:** *Newsletter, Trade.*
Published by: Illinois Bankers Association, 133 S 4th St, Ste 300, Springfield, IL 62701. TEL 217-789-9340, FAX 217-789-5410. Ed. Kathleen C Grill. Adv. contact Cind L Altman. B&W page USD 650, color page USD 1,000; 10.56 x 7.06. Circ: 2,200.

ILLINOIS BUSINESS CREDIT DIRECTORY. see *BUSINESS AND ECONOMICS—Trade And Industrial Directories*

332 USA
ILLINOIS COMMERCIAL FINANCING FORMS WITH PRACTICE COMMENTARY. Text in English. 1993. 2 base vols. plus a. updates. looseleaf. USD 179. Supplement avail. **Description:** Covers preliminary documentation, credit agreements, promissory notes, security instruments, subordination contracts, and more.
Published by: LexisNexis (Subsidiary of: LexisNexis North America), PO Box 7587, Charlottesville, VA 22906-7587. TEL 804-972-7666, 800-562-1197, FAX 804-972-7666, llp.customer.support@lexis-nexis.com, http://www.lexislawpublishing.com. Eds. Mary C Gontaine, Ronald B Given.

332 USA
ILLINOIS REPORTER. Text in English. bi-m. free domestic membership; USD 15 domestic to non-members (effective 2005). **Document type:** *Magazine, Trade.*
Published by: Illinois League of Financial Institutions, 133 S Fourth St, Ste 206, Springfield, IL 62701. TEL 217-522-5575, FAX 217-789-9115, http://www.ilfi.org. Ed., Pub. Jay R Stevenson. Circ: 1,000.

332 DEU ISSN 1618-7741
IMMOBILIEN UND FINANZIERUNG. Text in German. 1950. fortn. EUR 290.40; EUR 17.90 newsstand/cover (effective 2004). adv. bk.rev. charts; stat. reprints avail. **Document type:** *Magazine, Trade.*
Formerly (until 2002): Der Langfristige Kredit (0342-0930)
Indexed: RefZh.
—CCC.
Published by: Helmut Richardi Verlag GmbH, Postfach 111151, Frankfurt Am Main, 60046, Germany. TEL 49-69-970833-0, FAX 49-69-7078400, verlagsleitung@kreditwesen.de, http://www.kreditwesen.de. Ed. Klaus Friedrich Otto. Adv. contact Anne Guckes. B&W page EUR 3,120, color page EUR 4,620; trim 185 x 265. Circ: 1,719 (paid and controlled).

332.1 USA ISSN 0019-3674
INDEPENDENT BANKER. Text in English. 1950. m. USD 50 to non-members; USD 35 to members (effective 2005). adv. illus. back issues avail.; reprints avail. **Document type:** *Magazine, Trade.* **Description:** Focuses on the nation's independent banks, mostly the small to medium-size commercial banks.
Related titles: Microfiche ed.: (from PQC); Online - full text ed.: (from Northern Light Technology, Inc., ProQuest Information & Learning).
Indexed: ABIn, BLI, BPIA, PAIS.
Published by: Independent Community Bankers of America, One Thomas Circle, N W, Ste 400, Washington, DC 20005-5802. TEL 800-422-8439, FAX 202-659-9216, info@icba.org, http://www.icba.org. Eds. Nicole Swann, Tim Cook. Adv. contact Richard Solomon. Circ: 12,000 (paid).

332 IND ISSN 0019-4204
INDIA. MINISTRY OF FINANCE. FINANCE LIBRARY. WEEKLY BULLETIN. Text in English. 1954. w. free. **Document type:** *Bulletin, Government.*
Media: Duplicated (not offset).
Published by: Ministry of Finance, Finance Library, North Block, New Delhi, 110 001, India. TEL 3013852. Ed. H S Pooji. Circ: (controlled).

332 IND
INDIAN BANK TODAY AND TOMORROW. Text in English. 1976. m. INR 116.
Published by: S.R. Suneja Ed. & Pub., B4/29 Safdarjang Enclave, New Delhi, 110 029, India.

332.1 IND ISSN 0019-4921
HG1505
INDIAN INSTITUTE OF BANKERS. JOURNAL. Text in English. 1929. q. **Document type:** *Journal, Academic/Scholarly.*
Indexed: BAS, PAA&I, WBA.
Published by: Indian Institute of Bankers, The Arcade, 2nd Fl, World Trade Centre, Cuffe Parade, Mumbai, Maharashtra 400 005, India. TEL 91-22-22187003, FAX 91-22-22185147, iibedu@bom5.vsnl.net.in, http://isidev.nic.in/jrnls/j56.html, http://www.iib-online.org. Ed. R H Sarma. Circ: 300,000.

332 IND ISSN 0971-0566
HG4001
➤ **INDIAN JOURNAL OF FINANCE AND RESEARCH.** Text in English. 1991. s-a. USD 30 (effective 1995). adv. bk.rev. **Document type:** *Academic/Scholarly.* **Description:** Publishes research articles on finance, especially corporate finance, to bridge the gap between theory and practice.
Published by: Indian Financial Management Association, 116-D Pocket IV, Mayur Vihar, New Delhi, Bihar 110 091, India. TEL 2250164. Ed. Mohinder N Kaura. Adv. contact D Jagananthan. Circ: 500.

➤ **INDIANA BUSINESS CREDIT DIRECTORY.** see *BUSINESS AND ECONOMICS—Trade And Industrial Directories*

➤ **INDICADORES BURSATILES.** see *BUSINESS AND ECONOMICS—Abstracting, Bibliographies, Statistics*

332.1 KOR
INDUSTRIAL BANK OF KOREA. ANNUAL REPORT. Text in English. 1962. a. free. charts; stat.; illus. **Description:** Covers the financial and economic performance of the Industrial Bank of Korea, as well as its management and organization.
Former titles: Small and Medium Industry Bank, Seoul. Annual Report; Medium Industry Bank, Seoul. Report (0076-6143)
Published by: Industrial Bank of Korea, 50 Ulchiro 2-ga, Chung-gu, Seoul, Korea, S. TEL 02-729-6114, FAX 02-729-7095, TELEX K-23932. Ed. Jhoh Dong Hweh. Circ: 4,000.

332.3 KWT
INDUSTRIAL BANK OF KUWAIT. ANNUAL REPORT. Text in English, Arabic. 1975. a. free.
Published by: Industrial Bank of Kuwait/Bank al-Kuwayt al-Sinai, P O Box 3146, Safat, Kuwait. TEL 965-2457661, FAX 965-2462057, IBK@ncc.moc.kw, http://ncc.moc.kw.users/I.B.K. Ed. Amro Mohie Al-din. Circ: 1,500.

332.1 SDN ISSN 0073-7356
INDUSTRIAL BANK OF SUDAN. BOARD OF DIRECTORS. ANNUAL REPORT. Text in Arabic, English. 1962. a. free. **Document type:** *Corporate.*
Published by: Industrial Bank of Sudan, Research Department, P O Box 1722, Khartoum, Sudan. TELEX 22456 SINAI SD. Ed. Mohamed Amara.

332.1 JOR
INDUSTRIAL DEVELOPMENT BANK. ANNUAL REPORT AND BALANCE SHEET/BANK AL-INMA AL-SINAI. ANNUAL REPORT AND BALANCE SHEET. Text in Arabic. 1967. a. free. charts; illus.
Published by: Industrial Development Bank, Schools of the Islamic College St., P O Box 1982, Amman, Jordan. TEL 06-642216, FAX 06-647821, TELEX 21349 IDB JO. Circ: 2,000.

332.1 KEN
INDUSTRIAL DEVELOPMENT BANK LIMITED. ANNUAL REPORT AND ACCOUNTS. Text in English. 1974. a. illus.; stat. **Document type:** *Corporate.*
Published by: Industrial Development Bank Ltd., National Bank Bldg., PO Box 44036, Nairobi, Kenya. FAX 254-2-334594.

332.1 IND ISSN 0073-7372
INDUSTRIAL DEVELOPMENT BANK OF INDIA. ANNUAL REPORT. Text in English; Text occasionally in Hindi. 1965. a. free. **Document type:** *Corporate.*
Published by: Industrial Development Bank of India, N227 Backbay Reclamation, Nariman Bhavan,, Nariman Point, Mumbai, Maharashtra 400 021, India.

INDUSTRIAL ECONOMIST. see *BUSINESS AND ECONOMICS—Production Of Goods And Services*

332 USA
INDUSTRIAL PRODUCTION AND CAPACITY UTILIZATION. Text in English. m. USD 15. **Document type:** *Government.*
Related titles: Diskette ed.
Indexed: AmStI.
Published by: U.S. Federal Reserve System, Board of Governors, Publications Services, Rm MS 138, Washington, DC 20551. TEL 202-452-3244, FAX 202-728-5886.

332.1 SWE ISSN 1401-3967
INFLATION REPORT. Text in English. 1993. q. free. charts. back issues avail. **Document type:** *Bulletin, Academic/Scholarly.*
Formerly (until 1996): Inflation and Inflation Expectations in Sweden (1400-1624)
Related titles: ♦ Swedish ed.: Inflationsrapport. ISSN 1401-3959.
Published by: Sveriges Riksbank, Brunkebergstorg 11, Stockholm, 10337, Sweden. TEL 46-8-7870000, FAX 46-8-210531, registratorn@riksbank.se, http://www.riksbank.se. Circ: 1,200 (controlled).

332 SWE ISSN 1401-3959
INFLATIONSRAPPORT. Text in Swedish. 1993. q. **Document type:** *Journal, Trade.*
Formerly (until 1996): Inflation och Inflationsfoervaltningar i Sverige (1400-1616)
Related titles: Online - full text ed.; ♦ English ed.: Inflation Report. ISSN 1401-3967.
Published by: Sveriges Riksbank, Brunkebergstorg 11, Stockholm, 10337, Sweden. TEL 46-8-7870000, FAX 46-8-210531, registratorn@riksbank.se, http://www.riksbank.se. Circ: 1,200 (controlled).

INFORMACOES F I P E. see *BUSINESS AND ECONOMICS*

332 DEU
INFORMATION SOURCES IN FINANCE AND BANKING. Text in English. 1994. irreg., latest vol.2, 1996. GBP 86 domestic; USD 125 in North America. bibl. **Document type:** *Directory, Bibliography.* **Description:** Covers traditional and computerized sources on all aspects of the financial system and evaluates them. Includes historic sources, money markets, central banks, laws, and regulations.
Related titles: ♦ Series: Information Sources for the Press and Broadcast Media; ♦ Information Sources in Chemistry; ♦ Information Sources in the Life Sciences; ♦ Information Sources in Grey Literature; ♦ Information Sources in Physics; ♦ Guides to Information Sources Series; ♦ Information Sources in Architecture and Construction; ♦ Information Sources in Development Studies; ♦ Information Sources in Engineering; ♦ Information Sources in Environmental Protection; ♦ Information Sources in Law; ♦ Information Sources in Official Publications.
Published by: K.G. Saur Verlag GmbH (Subsidiary of: Gale Group), Ortlerstr 8, Munchen, 81373, Germany. TEL 49-89-769020, FAX 49-89-76902150, info@saur.de, http://www.saur.de. **Orders in Central Europe to:** Postfach 701620, Munich 81316, Germany. TEL 49-89-76902-232, FAX 49-89-76902-250.

INFORMAZIONE MEDITERRANEA. see *BUSINESS AND ECONOMICS—Economic Situation And Conditions*

332.7 COL
INFORME COYUNTURA ESTABLECIMIENTOS DE CREDITO. Text in Spanish. 1992. q. free.
Published by: Superintendencia Bancaria, Apartado Aereo 3460, Bogota, CUND, Colombia. TEL 57-1-2804060, FAX 57-1-2800864. Circ: 500.

368 COL
INFORME COYUNTURA SEGUROS Y CAPITALIZACION. Text in Spanish. 1992. q. free.
Published by: Superintendencia Bancaria, Apartado Aereo 3460, Bogota, CUND, Colombia. TEL 57-1-2804060, FAX 57-1-2800864. Circ: 500.

332 COL
INFORME COYUNTURA SERVICIOS FINANCIEROS. Text in Spanish. 1992. q. free.
Published by: Superintendencia Bancaria, Apartado Aereo 3460, Bogota, CUND, Colombia. TEL 57-1-2804060, FAX 57-1-2800864. Circ: 500.

332.1 CHL ISSN 0716-243X
HC191
INFORME ECONOMICO Y FINANCIERO. Text in Spanish. 1982. s-m. CLP 60,000, USD 400 (effective 1999). charts; stat. **Document type:** *Government.* **Description:** Contains Chilean economic survey with statistical tables.
Published by: Banco Central de Chile, Casilla 967, Santiago, Chile. TEL 56-2-670-2000, FAX 56-2-698-4847. Circ: 800.

332 COL
INFORME FINANCIERO SEMANAL. Text in Spanish. 1988. w.
Published by: Superintendencia Bancaria, Apartado Aereo 3460, Bogota, CUND, Colombia. TEL 57-1-2804060, FAX 57-1-2800864. Circ: 450.

332 USA ISSN 1092-423X
INSIDE M B S & A B S. Text in English. 1985. w. (48/yr). USD 1,295 (effective 2000). charts; stat. back issues avail. **Document type:** *Trade.* **Description:** Covers mortgage-related and asset-backed securities, as well as the secondary mortgage market. Focuses on market, regulatory and legislative developments.
Former titles: Inside Mortgage Securities (1076-3716); Inside Mortgage Capital Markets (1059-1397)
Published by: Inside Mortgage Finance Publications, PO Box 42387, Washington, DC 20015. TEL 301-951-1240, FAX 301-656-1709, http://www.imfpubs.com. Ed. John Bancroft. Pub. Guy D Cecala. R&P Didi Parks.

332 USA ISSN 8756-0003
INSIDE MORTGAGE FINANCE. Text in English. 1984. 48/yr. USD 889 (effective 2005). stat. **Document type:** *Magazine, Trade.* **Description:** Contains complete coverage and analysis of trends and developments affecting residential mortgage finance. Studies regulatory, legislative and market developments affecting lending, servicing and securitization.
Indexed: BLI.
Published by: Inside Mortgage Finance Publications, PO Box 42387, Washington, DC 20015. TEL 301-951-1240, FAX 301-656-1709, http://www.imfpubs.com. Ed. John Bancroft. Pub. Guy D Cecala. R&P Didi Parks.

332 USA ISSN 1093-4030
INSIDE MORTGAGE FINANCE'S INSIDE B&C LENDING. Variant title: Inside B&C Lending. Text in English. 1996. bi-w. USD 597 (effective 2000). **Document type:** *Trade.* **Description:** Focuses on the business of lending to borrowers with less than perfect credit ratings. Explains loan grading approaches, regulatory developments and activity among the top market players.
Published by: Inside Mortgage Finance Publications, PO Box 42387, Washington, DC 20015. TEL 301-951-1240, FAX 301-656-1709, http://www.imfpubs.com. Ed. John Bancroft. Pub. Guy D Cecala. R&P Didi Parks.

332 USA ISSN 1098-5727
HG2040.5.U5
INSIDE MORTGAGE FINANCE'S INSIDE MORTGAGE COMPLIANCE. Variant title: Inside Mortgage Compliance. Text in English. 1990. bi-w. USD 495 (effective 2000). **Document type:** *Newsletter.* **Description:** Coverage and analysis of fair lending and consumer compliance issues, as well as legislative developments.
Former titles (until 1998): Inside Fair Lending; (until 1996): C R A - H M D A Update (1059-1400)
Published by: Inside Mortgage Finance Publications, PO Box 42387, Washington, DC 20015. TEL 301-951-1240, FAX 301-656-1709, http://www.imfpubs.com. Ed. George Brooks. Pub. Guy D Cecala. R&P Didi Parks.

332 USA ISSN 1544-9343
INSIDE MORTGAGE PROFITABILITY. Variant title: Inside Mortgage Finance's Inside Mortgage Profitability. Text in English. 2002 (Oct.). 25/yr. USD 686 (effective 2003).
Published by: Inside Mortgage Finance Publications, 7910 Woodmont Ave. Ste. 1010, Bethesda, MD 20814. TEL 301-951-1240, FAX 301-656-1709, http://www.imfpubs.com. Pub. Guy D Cecala.

332 USA ISSN 1093-4049
INSIDE MORTGAGE TECHNOLOGY. Text in English. 1997. bi-w. USD 525 (effective 2000). **Document type:** *Trade.* **Description:** Reports on mortgage technology developments surfacing in today's residential mortgage market.
Published by: Inside Mortgage Finance Publications, PO Box 42387, Washington, DC 20015. TEL 301-951-1240, FAX 301-656-1709, http://www.imfpubs.com. Ed. Guy D Cecala. Pub. John Bancroft. R&P Didi Parks.

332.3 USA ISSN 1546-3958
INSIDE THE G S E S. (Government Sponsored Enterprises) Text in English. 2002. bi-w. USD 727 (effective 2004).
Published by: Inside Mortgage Finance Publications, 7910 Woodmont Ave. Ste. 1010, Bethesda, MD 20814. TEL 301-951-1240, FAX 301-656-1709, IGSE@imfpubs.com, http://www.imfpubs.com. Ed., Pub. Guy D Cecala.

332 USA
INSIDERS' QUARTERLY✶. Text in English. q. USD 250.
Published by: Thomson Financial Services Company, One State St Plaza, New York, NY 10004. TEL 800-733-4371, FAX 301-654-1678.

332.7 346 GBR
INSOLVENCY BULLETIN. Text in English. 10/yr. GBP 245, USD 385 (effective 1999). adv. back issues avail. **Document type:** *Newsletter.*
Published by: L L L Ltd., Flat 69, Telephone House, 69-77 Paul St, London, EC2A 4LQ, United Kingdom. TEL 44-171-553-1815, FAX 44-171-553-1106. Ed. Hannah Doran. Pub. Richard Armstrong. Adv. contact Matt Fenton.

332 DNK
INSTITUT FOR FINANSIERING OG KREDITVAESEN. KOMPENDIUM. Text in Danish. irreg., latest vol.10, 1982. price varies. illus.
Published by: Institut for Finansiering og Kreditvaesen, Handelshoejskolen i Aarhus, Aarhus, Denmark. **Dist. by:** Handelsvidenskabelig Boghandel, Fuglesangs Alle 4, Aarhus V 8210, Denmark.

332 346.066 CHE
INSTITUT FUER FINANZWIRTSCHAFT UND FINANZRECHT. SCHRIFTENREIHE. Text in German. 1971. irreg., latest vol.100, 2000. price varies. **Document type:** *Monographic series, Academic/Scholarly.*
Formerly: Schriftenreihe Finanzwirtschaft und Finanzrecht
Published by: (Institut fuer Finanzwirtschaft und Finanzrecht), Paul Haupt AG, Falkenplatz 14, Bern, 3001, Switzerland. TEL 41-31-3012425, FAX 41-31-3014669, verlag@haupt.ch, http://www.haupt.ch.

INSTITUT FUER FINANZWISSENSCHAFT UND STEUERRECHT. GELBE BRIEFE. see *BUSINESS AND ECONOMICS—Public Finance, Taxation*

INSTITUT FUER FINANZWISSENSCHAFT UND STEUERRECHT. MITTEILUNGSBLATT. see *BUSINESS AND ECONOMICS—Public Finance, Taxation*

332.1 PAK ISSN 0073-8999
INSTITUTE OF BANKERS IN PAKISTAN. COUNCIL. REPORT AND ACCOUNTS. Text in English. s-a.
Indexed: WBA.
Published by: Institute of Bankers in Pakistan, Karachi, Pakistan.

INSTITUTE OF BANKERS OF SRI LANKA. JOURNAL. see *OCCUPATIONS AND CAREERS*

332 GBR ISSN 0269-3933
INSTITUTE OF EUROPEAN FINANCE. SCHOOL OF ACCOUNTING, BANKING AND ECONOMICS. RESEARCH PAPERS IN BANKING AND FINANCE. Text in English. 1986. irreg. GBP 100 (effective 1999). **Document type:** *Monographic series, Academic/Scholarly.*
—BLDSC (7755.034450), ingenta.
Published by: (University of Wales, Bangor), Institute of European Finance, School of Accounting, Banking and Economics, Bangor, Gwynedd, United Kingdom. TEL 44-1248-382277, FAX 1248-364760, ief@bangor.ac.uk. Eds. E P M Gardener, P Molyneux.

332.0715 TZA
INSTITUTE OF FINANCE MANAGEMENT. PROSPECTUS. Text in English. 1974. biennial. free. **Document type:** *Academic/Scholarly.* **Description:** Carries subjects taught and their syllabuses on finance, management, banking, accounting, insurance, social security, computers, and related areas.
Published by: Institute of Finance Management, Library, PO Box 3918, Dar Es Salaam, Tanzania. TEL 255-51-112931, TELEX 41969 TZ, ifm@costech.gn.apc.org. Ed. J P M Masome. Circ: 2,000.

332 USA
INSTITUTIONAL BROKERS ESTIMATE SYSTEM✶. Short title: I-B-E-S. Text in English. 1971. d. price varies. back issues avail.
Related titles: Magnetic Tape ed.: 1971.
Published by: I-B-E-S Inc., 1 World Trade Ctr, Lbby 18, New York, NY 10048-0202. TEL 212-243-3335, FAX 212-727-1386. Circ: 900.

INSTITUTIONAL INVESTMENT REVIEW (YEAR). see *BUSINESS AND ECONOMICS—Investments*

THE INSTITUTIONAL PHARMACY ACQUISITION REPORT. see *PHARMACY AND PHARMACOLOGY*

INSURANCE FINANCE AND INVESTMENT. see *INSURANCE*

332.1 338.9 USA
INTER-AMERICAN DEVELOPMENT BANK. ANNUAL REPORT. Text in English. 1960. a. free. charts; stat. **Document type:** *Corporate.* **Description:** Reports on the bank's activities.
Formerly: Inter-American Development Bank. Report (0074-087X); Incorporates: Inter-American Development Bank. Statement of Loans
Related titles: Microfiche ed.: (from CIS); French ed.; Portuguese ed.; Spanish ed.: Banco Interamericano de Desarollo. Informe Anual.
Indexed: IIS.
Published by: Inter-American Development Bank/Banco Interamericano de Desarrollo, 1300 New York Ave, N W, Washington, DC 20577. TEL 202-623-1709, FAX 202-623-1753, http://www.iadb.org/exr/pub/engcatalog/Pages/anpubs.htm. Ed. Barbara Rierveld TEL 202-623-1154.

332.1 338.9 USA ISSN 0074-0861
INTER-AMERICAN DEVELOPMENT BANK. BOARD OF GOVERNORS. PROCEEDINGS OF THE MEETING. Text in English. 1960. irreg., latest 1996. free. **Document type:** *Proceedings.* **Description:** Reports on various meetings at the Bank.
Related titles: Portuguese ed.; Spanish ed.: Banco Interamericano de Desarollo. Junta Directiva. Anales de la Reunion; French ed.
Published by: Inter-American Development Bank/Banco Interamericano de Desarrollo, 1300 New York Ave, N W, Washington, DC 20577. TEL 202-623-1709, http://www.iadb.org. Ed. Barbara Rierveld TEL 202-623-1154.

332.2 USA
INTER-AMERICAN DEVELOPMENT BANK. OCCASIONAL PAPERS. Text in English, Spanish. 1989. irreg., latest vol.12. USD 8 per issue (effective 2000). back issues avail. **Document type:** *Monographic series.* **Description:** Reports on issues regarding the financing of projects throughout Latin America.
Published by: Inter-American Development Bank/Banco Interamericano de Desarrollo, 1300 New York Ave, N W, Washington, DC 20577. TEL 202-623-1709, FAX 202-623-1753, http://www.iadb.org. Ed. Barbara Rierveld TEL 202-623-1154.

332.2 USA
INTER-AMERICAN DEVELOPMENT BANK. WORKING PAPERS SERIES. Text in English. irreg. price varies. back issues avail. **Document type:** *Monographic series.* **Description:** Reports on issues regarding projects throughout Latin America being or to be financed through the Inter-American Development Bank.
Related titles: French ed.; Portuguese ed.; Spanish ed.
Published by: Inter-American Development Bank/Banco Interamericano de Desarrollo, 1300 New York Ave, N W, Washington, DC 20577. TEL 202-623-1709, FAX 202-623-1753, http://www.iadb.org. Ed. Barbara Rierveld TEL 202-623-1154.

332 ESP
INTERCOGUI; boletin internacional. Text in Spanish. 1973. m. free. **Document type:** *Bulletin.*
Published by: Banco Guipuzcoano, Departamento Internacional, Avda Libertad, 21, San Sebastian-donostia, Guipuzcoa 20004, Spain. FAX 43-426828, TELEX 36369. Circ: 2,500.

332 USA
INTEREST MAGAZINE. Text in English. 1960. q. USD 1 to members (effective 2005). back issues avail. **Document type:** *Magazine, Trade.* **Description:** Features news for and about Ohio credit unions.
Formerly (until 2001): High Spots (0885-2138)
Related titles: Online - full text ed.
Published by: Ohio Credit Union League, 5815 Wall St, Dublin, OH 43017. TEL 614-336-2894, 800-486-2917, FAX 614-336-2895, oculmail@ohiocul.org, halheim@ohiocul.org, http://www.ohiocul.org/Interest.htm. Ed. Scott Biggs. Circ: 5,100 (paid).

332.4 GBR ISSN 0308-9002
INTEREST RATE SERVICE. Text in English. 1977. 10/yr. GBP 450 domestic; GBP 950 foreign (effective 2003). back issues avail. **Document type:** *Trade.* **Description:** Surveys global interest rates and monetary developments for corporate, financial sector and private investors.
Published by: World Reports Ltd., 108 Horseferry Rd, London, SW1P 2EF, United Kingdom. TEL 44-20-72223836, FAX 44-20-72330185, subs@worldreports.org, http://www.worldreports.org. Ed. Christopher Story. **US subscr. to:** 280 Madison Ave, Ste 280, New York, NY 10016-0802. TEL 212-679-0095, FAX 212-679-1094.

332.1 RUS ISSN 1523-245X
INTERFAX. BANKING AND FINANCE REPORT. Variant title: Banking and Finance Report. Text in English. w. USD 1,820. **Description:** Contains news of mergers, investment projects, banking services, and ratings. Provides information on Western banks and financial companies operating in Russia, the CIS, and Baltic states. Also contains macroeconomic analysis of the budgets of the newly independent states, foreign debt, and loans provided by international financial organizations.
Formerly (until 1998): Interfax. Financial Report (Weekly) (1072-2637)
Published by: Interfax Ltd., 1-ya Tverskaya-Yamskaya 2, Moscow, 127006, Russian Federation. TEL 7-095-2509840, FAX 7-095-2509727. **Dist. Germany, Austria and Switzerland by:** Interfax Deutschland GmbH, IndustriestraBe 6, Kronberg/Tx 61476 , Germany. TEL 49-61-7361369, FAX 49-61-7361206; **Dist. elsewhere by:** Interfax America, Inc.,

B

3025 S Parker Rd, Ste 737, Aurora, CO 80014-2925. TEL 303-825-1510, 852-2537-2262, FAX 303-825-1513, 852-2537-2264, america@interfax.com, http://www.interfax.com; **Dist. in Western Europe by:** Interfax Europe Ltd., 1st Fl, 50 Hans Crescent, Knightsbridge, London SW1X 0N, United Kingdom. TEL 44-20-7581-5550, FAX 44-20-7581-4490.

330 NLD ISSN 0020-5605
INTERMEDIAIR. Text in Dutch. 1965. w. adv. bk.rev. bibl.; illus.; stat. index. **Description:** Covers current developments affecting the world of business and industry, including scientific, political, economic and management issues.
Indexed: ELLIS, ExcerpMed, KES.
—IE, Infotrieve, KNAW. **CCC.**
Published by: V N U Business Publications (Netherlands), Postbus 9194, Amsterdam, 1006 CC, Netherlands. TEL 31-206175137. Circ: 20,000 (paid); 195,000 (controlled).

INTERNATIONAL ACCOUNTANT. see *BUSINESS AND ECONOMICS—Accounting*

332.1 CAN ISSN 0020-6113
HG3
INTERNATIONAL BANK CREDIT ANALYST. Text in English. 1962. m. price varies. abstr.; charts. **Description:** Provides a forecast and analysis for the principal countries of interest rates, equity markets, gold and commodity prices, economic trends and currency movements.
—IE. **CCC.**
Published by: B C A Research, 1002 Sherbrooke St W, Ste 1600, Montreal, PQ H3A 3L6, Canada. TEL 514-499-9706, 800-724-2942, FAX 514-499-9709, http://www.bcaresearch.com.

332 GBR ISSN 0965-674X
INTERNATIONAL BANKING SYSTEMS. Text in English. 1991. 10/yr. GBP 395 in Europe; GBP 495 elsewhere (effective 2005). index. 12 p./no.; back issues avail.; reprints avail. **Document type:** *Journal, Trade.* **Description:** Looks at wholesale back office systems and their suppliers.
Incorporates: Retail & Private Banking Systems (1740-1232); Formerly (until 2003): Retail Banking Systems (1465-8917)
Related titles: CD-ROM ed.; Online - full text ed.
Published by: I B S Publishing, 11 Mount St, Hythe, Kent CT21 5NT, United Kingdom. TEL 44-1303-262636, FAX 44-1303-262646, enquries@ibspublishing.com, http://www.ibspublishing.com/ibs_journal.htm. Ed., Pub. Martin Whybrow.

332 GBR
THE INTERNATIONAL BANKING SYSTEMS MARKET REPORT (YEAR). Text in English. 1993. a. GBP 595 per issue (effective 2005). back issues avail. **Document type:** *Trade.* **Description:** Provides supplier and system profiles on wholesale bank office systems.
Related titles: CD-ROM ed.; Online - full text ed.
Published by: I B S Publishing, 11 Mount St, Hythe, Kent CT21 5NT, United Kingdom. TEL 44-1303-262636, FAX 44-1303-262646, enquries@ibspublishing.com, http://www.ibspublishing.com/publications_2005/IBSMarketReport2005.htm. Ed., Pub. Martin Whybrow.

332 USA ISSN 1085-6374
INTERNATIONAL CAPITAL MARKETS. Text in English. 1980. a. free. **Document type:** *Magazine, Trade.*
—**CCC.**
Published by: International Monetary Fund, Publication Services, 700 19th St, N W, Ste 12-607, Washington, DC 20431.

332.1 TWN
INTERNATIONAL COMMERCIAL BANK OF CHINA. ANNUAL REPORT. Text in English. 1960. a. free. stat. **Document type:** *Corporate.*
Formerly: Chung-Kuo Yin Hang. Annual Report
Published by: International Commercial Bank of China, Head Office-Economic Research Department, 100 Chi Lin Rd, Taipei, Taiwan 10424, Taiwan. TEL 886-2-5633156, FAX 886-2-25611216. Ed. Heh Song Wang. Circ: 4,500.

▼ **INTERNATIONAL CORPORATE RESCUE.** see *LAW—Corporate Law*

332 GBR ISSN 1361-6048
INTERNATIONAL CORRESPONDENT BANKING REVIEW (YEARS). Text in English. a. GBP 95, USD 170 (effective 1998). **Description:** Covers the international correspondent banking market, with country reviews contributed by leading banking experts worldwide.
Published by: Euromoney Publications plc, Nestor House, Playhouse Yard, London, EC4V 5EX, United Kingdom. TEL 44-207-7798673, FAX 44-20-77798541.

INTERNATIONAL COUNTRY RISK GUIDE. see *BUSINESS AND ECONOMICS—Economic Situation And Conditions*

INTERNATIONAL COUNTRY RISK GUIDE ANNUAL. VOL. 1, THE AMERICAS. see *BUSINESS AND ECONOMICS—Economic Situation And Conditions*

INTERNATIONAL COUNTRY RISK GUIDE ANNUAL. VOL. 2, EUROPE (EUROPEAN UNION). see *BUSINESS AND ECONOMICS—Economic Situation And Conditions*

INTERNATIONAL COUNTRY RISK GUIDE ANNUAL. VOL. 3, EUROPE (NON-EUROPEAN UNION). see *BUSINESS AND ECONOMICS—Economic Situation And Conditions*

INTERNATIONAL COUNTRY RISK GUIDE ANNUAL. VOL. 5, SUB-SAHARAN AFRICA. see *BUSINESS AND ECONOMICS—Economic Situation And Conditions*

INTERNATIONAL COUNTRY RISK GUIDE ANNUAL. VOL. 6, ASIA & THE PACIFIC. see *BUSINESS AND ECONOMICS—Economic Situation And Conditions*

INTERNATIONAL COUNTRY RISK GUIDE ANNUAL. VOL. 7, RISK RATINGS & STATISTICS. see *BUSINESS AND ECONOMICS—Economic Situation And Conditions*

332.4 GBR ISSN 0020-6490
HG3881
INTERNATIONAL CURRENCY REVIEW. Text in English. 1969. q. GBP 235 domestic; GBP 475 foreign (effective 2003). back issues avail. **Document type:** *Journal.* **Description:** Reviews global currency developments, financial and economic affairs, with country/currency reports.
Indexed: CREJ, KES, PAIS, PCI, RASB, WBA.
—BLDSC (4539.500500), IE, Infotrieve, ingenta. **CCC.**
Published by: World Reports Ltd., 108 Horseferry Rd, London, SW1P 2EF, United Kingdom. TEL 44-20-72223836, FAX 44-20-72330185, subs@worldreports.org, http://www.worldreports.org. Ed. Christopher Story. **US subscr. to:** 280 Madison Ave, Ste 280, New York, NY 10016-0802. TEL 212-679-0095, FAX 212-679-1094.

INTERNATIONAL EQUITY REVIEW. see *BUSINESS AND ECONOMICS—Investments*

INTERNATIONAL ESTATE PLANNING. see *LAW—Estate Planning*

332 382 GBR ISSN 1367-0271
HG3879
➤ **INTERNATIONAL FINANCE.** Text in English. 1998. 3/yr., latest vol.5, no.3, 2002. EUR 99 combined subscription in Europe to individuals print & online eds.; USD 111 combined subscription in the Americas to individuals & Caribbean, print & online eds.; GBP 66 combined subscription elsewhere to individuals print & online eds.; USD 692 combined subscription in the Americas to institutions & Caribbean, print & online eds.; GBP 412 combined subscription elsewhere to institutions print & online eds. (effective 2006). reprint service avail. from PSC. **Document type:** *Journal, Academic/Scholarly.* **Description:** Addresses issues affecting market performance and the international economy. Incorporates macro and micro analysis, finance and international economics. Aims to bridge the gap between theory and policy.
Related titles: Online - full text ed.: ISSN 1468-2362. USD 657 in the Americas to institutions & Caribbean; GBP 391 elsewhere to institutions (effective 2006) (from Blackwell Synergy, EBSCO Publishing, Gale Group, IngentaConnect, O C L C Online Computer Library Center, Inc., Swets Information Services).
Indexed: ABIn, GEOBASE, JEL, PAIS.
—BLDSC (4540.188450), IE, Infotrieve, ingenta. **CCC.**
Published by: Blackwell Publishing Ltd., 9600 Garsington Rd, Oxford, OX4 2ZG, United Kingdom. TEL 44-1865-776868, FAX 44-1865-714591, customerservices@oxon.blackwellpublishing.com, http://www.blackwellpublishing.com/journals/INFI. Ed. Dr. Benn Steil.

332 382 USA ISSN 1092-1605
HG1
INTERNATIONAL FINANCE & TREASURY. Text in English. 1972. s-m. USD 1,334 domestic; USD 1,384 foreign (effective 2005). adv. **Document type:** *Newsletter, Trade.* **Description:** For international treasury managers. Demonstrates cash management techniques to manage worldwide financial resources, such as cross-border pooling, multilateral netting, regional invoicing, and the use of various electronic applications.
Former titles (until 1995): Finance & Treasury (1070-9215); (until 1992): Business International Money Report (0161-0384)
—**CCC.**
Published by: WorldTrade Executive, Inc., 2250 Main St, Ste 100, PO Box 761, Concord, MA 01742. TEL 978-287-0301, FAX 978-287-0302, smuhapatra@wtexec.com, info@wtexec.com, http://www.wtexecutive.com/cms/content.jsp?id=com.tms.cms.section.Section_1025, http://www.wtexec.com. Pub. Gary A Brown. Adv. contact Jay Stanley. page USD 975.

332 USA
HG3881
INTERNATIONAL FINANCE CORPORATION. ANNUAL REPORT. Text in English. 1957. a. free. **Document type:** *Corporate.*
Related titles: Microfiche ed.; (from CIS).
Indexed: IIS.
—CISTI.
Published by: International Finance Corporation, 2121 Pennsylvania Ave, N W, Washington, DC 20433. TEL 202-473-7711, FAX 202-473-4384, http://www.ifc.org.

332 USA ISSN 1073-2500
INTERNATIONAL FINANCE DISCUSSION PAPERS. Text in English. 1972. irreg. **Document type:** *Government.*
Related titles: Online - full content ed.
—BLDSC (4540.188700), IE, ingenta.
Published by: Board of Governors of the Federal Reserve System, c/o Secretary, Mailstop 16, Federal Reserve Board, Washington, DC 20551. http://www.federalreserve.gov/pubs/ifdp/.

336.76 GBR ISSN 1569-3767
INTERNATIONAL FINANCE REVIEW. Text in English. 2000. irreg., latest vol.4, 2003. **Document type:** *Monographic series, Academic/Scholarly.*
Related titles: Online - full text ed.: (from ScienceDirect).
—BLDSC (4540.188790).
Published by: Elsevier Ltd. (Subsidiary of: Elsevier Science & Technology), The Boulevard, Langford Ln, Kidlington, Oxford, OX5 1GB, United Kingdom. TEL 44-1865-843000, FAX 44-1865-843010, nlinfo-f@elsevier.nl, http://www.elsevier.com/locate/issn/15693767.

INTERNATIONAL FINANCE: TAX & REGULATION ADVISOR. see *BUSINESS AND ECONOMICS—Public Finance, Taxation*

INTERNATIONAL FINANCIAL LAW REVIEW. see *LAW—International Law*

INTERNATIONAL FINANCIAL LAW REVIEW 1000. see *LAW—International Law*

332.1 GBR ISSN 1469-6509
INTERNATIONAL FINANCIAL OUTLOOK. Text in English. 1994. m.
Published by: Barclays Bank plc., Economics Department, Barclays House, 1 Wimborne Rd, PO Box 12, Poole, Dorset BH15 2BB, United Kingdom. TEL 44-1202-334023, FAX 44-1202-402303.

332 USA ISSN 0271-2423
INTERNATIONAL FINANCIER. Text in English. 1979. m. USD 1,000 membership. adv. bk.rev. **Description:** Covers major domestic and international financial projects and transactions.
Published by: International Society of Financiers, PO Box 398, Naples, NC 28760-0398. Ed. Ronald I Gershen. Circ: 500 (controlled).

332 GBR ISSN 0953-0223
HG3879
INTERNATIONAL FINANCING REVIEW. Abbreviated title: I F R. Text in English. 1974. w. USD 4,595 (effective 2004). adv. index. **Document type:** *Magazine, Trade.* **Description:** Provides incisive analysis of the week's events in the global capital markets and reports on all primary market transactions.
Related titles: Online - full content ed.; Online - full text ed.: (from EBSCO Publishing).
—**CCC.**
Published by: I F R Publishing (Subsidiary of: Thomson Financial Services Ltd.), Aldgate House, 33 Aldgate High St, London, EC3N 1DL, United Kingdom. TEL 44-20-7369-7521, FAX 44-20-7369-7397, mullink@ifr.pub.com, http://www.ifrweb.com/. Ed. Keith Mullin TEL 44-20-73697566. Adv. contact Sylvie Grassin.

332 GBR
INTERNATIONAL FINANCING REVIEW ASIA. Abbreviated title: I F R Asia. Text in English. w. **Document type:** *Trade.* **Description:** Provides incisive analysis of the week's events in the global capital market and reports on all primary market transactions.
Published by: I F R Publishing (Subsidiary of: Thomson Financial Services Ltd.), Aldgate House, 33 Aldgate High St, London, EC3N 1DL, United Kingdom. TEL 44-20-7369-7000, FAX 44-20-7369-7525, marinosm@ifrpub.com, http://www.ifrpub.com. Ed. Simon Timms. Pub. Anne O'Brien. Adv. contact Henry Krzymuski.

332.6327 GBR
INTERNATIONAL FUND INVESTMENT. Text in English. 1992. bi-m. USD 140 (effective 2000). adv. **Description:** Includes articles on investments markets and the international fund industry.
Address: 10 Hans Crescent, 5th Fl, London, SW1X 0NB, United Kingdom. TEL 44-20-7225-2567, FAX 44-20-7823-7233, http://www.fundmap.com. Ed. Simon Osborn. Pub. Adam Jacot. adv.: B&W page GBP 6,750, color page GBP 8,000. Circ: 8,570.

THE INTERNATIONAL GUIDE TO THE TAXATION OF TRUSTS. see *BUSINESS AND ECONOMICS—Public Finance, Taxation*

B

332.7 346.066 GBR ISSN 1180-0518
CODEN: IINRES
➤ **INTERNATIONAL INSOLVENCY REVIEW.** Variant title: Insol International Review. Text in English. 1992. 3/yr. USD 755 to institutions; USD 831 combined subscription to institutions print & online eds. (effective 2006). adv. back issues avail.; reprint service avail. from PSC. **Document type:** *Journal, Academic/Scholarly.* **Description:** Provides analysis and commentary on key insolvency issues across major jurisdictions in Europe and the EC, Eastern Europe, the US, the Far East, Asia and Australia.
Related titles: Microform ed.: (from PQC); Online - full content ed.: ISSN 1099-1107. 1999. USD 755 to institutions (effective 2006); Online - full text ed.: (from EBSCO Publishing, Swets Information Services, Wiley InterScience).
Indexed: CLI, LRI.
—BLDSC (4541.305000), IE, Infotrieve, ingenta. **CCC.**
Published by: (International Association of Insolvency Practitioners), John Wiley & Sons Ltd. (Subsidiary of: John Wiley & Sons, Inc.), The Atrium, Southern Gate, Chichester, West Sussex PO19 8SQ, United Kingdom. TEL 44-1243-779777, FAX 44-1243-775878, customer@wiley.co.uk, http://www.wiley.co.uk. adv.: B&W page GBP 650, color page GBP 1,550; trim 160 x 235. **Subscr. to:** John Wiley & Sons, Inc., 111 River St, Hoboken, NJ 07030-5774. TEL 201-748-6645, FAX 201-748-6088, subinfo@wiley.com.

➤ **INTERNATIONAL JOURNAL OF APPLIED ECONOMETRICS AND QUANTITATIVE STUDIES.** see *POLITICAL SCIENCE*

330 GBR ISSN 0265-2323
CODEN: IJBMES
➤ **THE INTERNATIONAL JOURNAL OF BANK MARKETING.** Text in English. 1982. 7/yr. EUR 13,755.79 in Europe; USD 13,539 in North America; AUD 16,409 in Australasia; GBP 9,166.54 in UK & elsewhere (effective 2006). reprint service avail. from PSC. **Document type:** *Journal, Academic/Scholarly.* **Description:** Aims to present the latest innovations and research findings of relevance to bank marketers. Focuses on the adoption and implementation of marketing planning and management in personal, corporate and international banking.
Related titles: CD-ROM ed.; Online - full text ed.: (from EBSCO Publishing, Emerald Group Publishing Limited, Gale Group, IngentaConnect, O C L C Online Computer Library Center, Inc., ProQuest Information & Learning, Swets Information Services).
Indexed: ABIn, BLI, C&CSA, CPM, EmerIntel, Emerald, Inspec, WBA.
—BLDSC (4542.127000), AskIEEE, IE, Infotrieve, ingenta. **CCC.**
Published by: Emerald Group Publishing Limited, 60-62 Toller Ln, Bradford, W Yorks BD8 9BY, United Kingdom. TEL 44-1274-777700, FAX 44-1274-785200, help@emeraldinsight.com, infomation@emeraldinsight.com, http://www.emeraldinsight.com/ijbm.htm. Ed. Christine Ennew. **Subscr. addr. in N America:** Emerald Group Publishing Ltd., 44 Brattle St, 4th Fl, Cambridge, MA 02138. TEL 617-497-2175, 888-622-0075, FAX 617-354-6875.

➤ **INTERNATIONAL JOURNAL OF BUSINESS.** see *BUSINESS AND ECONOMICS—International Commerce*

▼ ➤ **INTERNATIONAL JOURNAL OF BUSINESS STRATEGY.** see *BUSINESS AND ECONOMICS—Management*

▼ ➤ **INTERNATIONAL JOURNAL OF BUSINESS STUDIES.** see *BUSINESS AND ECONOMICS—International Commerce*

332 GBR ISSN 1325-9547
HG3881
INTERNATIONAL JOURNAL OF COMMUNITY CURRENCY RESEARCH. Text in English. 1997. irreg. **Description:** Provides a forum for the dissemination of knowledge and understanding about the emerging array of community currencies being used throughout the world both at present and in the past.
Media: Online - full text.
Published by: University of Leicester, Department of Geography, University Rd, Leicester, Leics LE1 7RH, United Kingdom. TEL 44-116-2522522, FAX 44-116-2522200, http://www.geog.le.ac.uk/ijccr/. Eds. Colin C Williams, Graham R Irwin.

INTERNATIONAL JOURNAL OF DEVELOPMENT BANKING. see *BUSINESS AND ECONOMICS—International Development And Assistance*

▼ **INTERNATIONAL JOURNAL OF DISCLOSURE AND GOVERNANCE.** see *BUSINESS AND ECONOMICS—Management*

332 USA ISSN 1041-2743
➤ **INTERNATIONAL JOURNAL OF FINANCE.** Text in English. 1988. 4/yr. USD 40 domestic to individuals; USD 45 foreign to individuals; USD 125 domestic to institutions; USD 140 foreign to institutions (effective 2004). adv. bk.rev. illus. Index. reprints avail. **Document type:** *Academic/Scholarly.* **Description:** Publishes original contributions, theoretical, as well as empirical, in the field of corporate finance, investment, financial institutions, international finance and financial economics.
Related titles: Online - full text ed.: (from EBSCO Publishing).
—BLDSC (4542.251000), IE, ingenta.
Address: 206 Rabbit Run Dr, Cherry Hill, NJ 08003. Ed. Dilip K Ghosh.

332 GBR ISSN 1076-9307
HG3879 CODEN: IJFEEO
➤ **INTERNATIONAL JOURNAL OF FINANCE AND ECONOMICS.** Text in English. 1996. q. USD 635 to institutions; USD 699 combined subscription to institutions print & online eds. (effective 2006). adv. bk.rev. illus. reprint service avail. from PSC. **Document type:** *Journal, Academic/Scholarly.*
Related titles: Online - full content ed.: ISSN 1099-1158. USD 635 to institutions (effective 2006); Online - full text ed.: (from EBSCO Publishing, ProQuest Information & Learning, Swets Information Services, Wiley InterScience).
Indexed: ABIn, BLI, CurCont, GEOBASE, JEL, SSCI.
—BLDSC (4542.251200), IDS, IE, Infotrieve, ingenta. **CCC.**
Published by: John Wiley & Sons Ltd. (Subsidiary of: John Wiley & Sons, Inc.), The Atrium, Southern Gate, Chichester, West Sussex PO19 8SQ, United Kingdom. TEL 44-1243-779777, FAX 44-1243-775878, customer@wiley.co.uk, http://www.wiley.com/WileyCDA/WileyTitle/productCd-IJFE.html, http://www.wiley.co.uk. Eds. Keith Cuthbertson, Mark P Taylor, Michael P Dooley. adv.: B&W page GBP 650, color page GBP 1,550; trim 200 x 260. **Subscr. in the Americas to:** John Wiley & Sons, Inc., 111 River St, Hoboken, NJ 07030-5774. TEL 201-748-6645, FAX 201-748-6088, subinfo@wiley.com.

332 658 GBR ISSN 1743-9132
▼ ➤ **INTERNATIONAL JOURNAL OF MANAGERIAL FINANCE.** Text in English. 2005. 3/yr. EUR 760.16 in Europe; USD 879 in North America; AUD 1,199 in Australasia; GBP 531.79 in the UK and elsewhere (effective 2006). **Document type:** *Journal, Academic/Scholarly.*
Media: Online - full content. **Related titles:** Online - full text ed.: (from Emerald Group Publishing Limited).
Published by: Emerald Group Publishing Limited, 60-62 Toller Ln, Bradford, W Yorks BD8 9BY, United Kingdom. TEL 44-1274-777700, FAX 44-1274-785200, ijmf@adelaide.edu.au, infomation@emeraldinsight.com, http://www.emeraldinsight.com/ijmf.htm.

332 GBR ISSN 1474-7332
▼ ➤ **INTERNATIONAL JOURNAL OF REVENUE MANAGEMENT.** Text in English. 2005. q. EUR 430, USD 450 to institutions print or online ed.; EUR 520, USD 545 combined subscription to institutions print & online eds. (effective 2005). **Document type:** *Journal, Academic/Scholarly.*
Related titles: Online - full content ed.
Published by: Inderscience Publishers, IEL Editorial Office, PO Box 735, Olney, Bucks MK46 5WB, United Kingdom. TEL 44-1234-240519, FAX 44-1234-240515, ijrm@inderscience.com, editor@inderscience.com, http://www.inderscience.com/ijrm. **Subscr. to:** World Trade Centre Bldg, 29 route de Pre-Bois, Case Postale 896, Geneva 15 1215, Switzerland. FAX 41-22-7910885, subs@inderscience.com.

▼ ➤ **INTERNATIONAL JOURNAL OF STRATEGIC MANAGEMENT.** see *BUSINESS AND ECONOMICS—Management*

332.1 SGP ISSN 0219-0249
HG41
➤ **INTERNATIONAL JOURNAL OF THEORETICAL AND APPLIED FINANCE.** Abbreviated title: I J T A F. Text in English. 1998. 8/yr. SGD 347, USD 204, EUR 186 to individuals; SGD 843, USD 496, EUR 450 combined subscription to institutions print & online eds.; SGD 520, USD 306, EUR 278 combined subscription in developing nations to institutions print & online eds. (effective 2006). back issues avail. **Document type:** *Journal, Academic/Scholarly.* **Description:** Covers financial mathematics and financial engineering; decision theory; probability theory; optimization; statistical analysis; data analysis; modelling; computer algorithms and simulations; numerical methods; calibration and institutional implementation of models; regulatory aspects of the financial markets; emerging markets.
Related titles: Online - full text ed.: (from EBSCO Publishing, Gale Group, O C L C Online Computer Library Center, Inc., Swets Information Services).
Indexed: ABIn, CCMJ, ESPM, IBSS, JEL, MathR, MathSciNet, RiskAb.
—BLDSC (4542.694750), IE, Infotrieve, ingenta. **CCC.**
Published by: World Scientific Publishing Co. Pte. Ltd., 5 Toh Tuck Link, Singapore, 596224, Singapore. TEL 65-466-5775, FAX 65-467-7667, wspc@wspc.com.sg, http://www.worldscinet.com/ijtaf/ijtaf.shtml, http://www.worldscientific.com. **Subscr. to:** Farrer Rd, PO Box 128, Singapore 912805, Singapore. sales@wspc.com.sg. **Dist. by:** World Scientific Publishing Co., Inc., 1060 Main St, River Edge, NJ 07661. TEL 201-487-9655, 800-227-7562, FAX 201-487-9656, 888-977-2665.; World Scientific Publishing Ltd., 57 Shelton St, London WC2H 9HE, United Kingdom. TEL 44-20-78360888, FAX 44-20-78362020, sales@wspc.co.uk.

346.078 341.7 USA
INTERNATIONAL LOAN WORKOUTS AND BANKRUPTCIES. Text in English. 1989. 2 base vols. plus a. updates. looseleaf. USD 160. Supplement avail. **Description:** Presents practical analysis and information in question and answer format. Topics covered include general enforcement of secured and unsecured claims, bankruptcy and insolvency proceedings, conflict of laws and recognition of foreign judgements, and practical hazards.
Published by: LexisNexis (Subsidiary of: LexisNexis North America), PO Box 7587, Charlottesville, VA 22906-7587. TEL 804-972-7600, 800-562-1197, FAX 804-972-7666, llp.customer.support@lexis-nexis.com, http://www.lexislawpublishing.com. Eds. Richard A Gitlin, Rona R Mears.

332 330.9 CAN
INTERNATIONAL MARKET REVIEW. Text in English. 1985. m. free. charts; stat. **Document type:** *Newsletter.* **Description:** Covers expected short-term financial and exchange rate developments in the principal industrial countries.
Published by: Bank of Montreal, Economics Department, First Canadian Place, 21st Fl, Toronto, ON M5X 1A1, Canada. TEL 416-867-7842, FAX 416-867-5401.

332 USA ISSN 0250-7498
HG3881
INTERNATIONAL MONETARY FUND. ANNUAL REPORT OF THE EXECUTIVE BOARD. Text in English. 1947. a. free. reprint service avail. from PQC. **Description:** Reviews the fund's activities, policies, organization, and administration and surveys the world economy, with special emphasis on balance of payments problems, exchange rates, world trade, international liquidity, and developments in the international monetary system.
Formerly: International Monetary Fund. Annual Report of the Executive Directors (0085-2171)
Related titles: Microfiche ed.: (from CIS, WSH); Microfilm ed.: (from BHP); French ed.: Fonds Monetaire International. Rapport Annuel du Conseil d'Administration. ISSN 0250-7501; German ed.: Internationaler Waehrungsfonds. Jahresbericht der Exekutivdirektoren. ISSN 0250-7528; Spanish ed.: Fondo Monetario Internacional. Informe Anual del Directorio Ejectivo. ISSN 0250-751X.
Indexed: IIS, RASB, WBA.
—BLDSC (1311.550000), CISTI. **CCC.**
Published by: International Monetary Fund, Publication Services, 700 19th St, N W, Ste 12-607, Washington, DC 20431. TEL 202-623-7430, FAX 202-623-7201, publications@imf.org, http://www.imf.org.

332 USA ISSN 0250-7366
K4440.A13
INTERNATIONAL MONETARY FUND. ANNUAL REPORT ON EXCHANGE ARRANGEMENTS AND EXCHANGE RESTRICTIONS. Text in English. 1950. a. USD 110 (effective 2004 & 2005). reprint service avail. from PQC. **Description:** Contains country-by-country descriptions of the exchange systems and related measures in operation in all Fund member countries.
Formerly: International Monetary Fund. Annual Report on Exchange Restrictions (0085-2163)
Related titles: Microform ed.: (from PQC).
Indexed: RASB.
—**CCC.**
Published by: International Monetary Fund, Publication Services, 700 19th St, N W, Ste 12-607, Washington, DC 20431. TEL 202-623-7430, FAX 202-623-7201.

332.4 USA ISSN 0250-7307
K4452.A47
INTERNATIONAL MONETARY FUND. BY-LAWS RULES AND REGULATIONS. Text in English. 1947. irreg., latest vol.59, 2003. free (effective 2004).
Related titles: Online - full text ed.: ISSN 1607-9426.
Published by: International Monetary Fund, Publication Services, 700 19th St, N W, Ste 12-607, Washington, DC 20431. TEL 202-623-7430, FAX 202-623-7201, publications@imf.org, http://www.imf.org.

332.1 338.9 USA ISSN 1729-701X
INTERNATIONAL MONETARY FUND. GLOBAL FINANCIAL STABILITY REPORT. Text in English. 2000. s-a. USD 49 per edition (effective 2004 & 2005). **Document type:** *Journal, Government.* **Description:** provides comprehensive coverage of mature and emerging financial markets and seeks to identify potential fault lines in the global financial system that could lead to crisis. It.
Formerly (until 2001): International Capital Markets. Developments and Prospects (1016-0345)
Related titles: Online - full content ed.; ♦ Series of: International Monetary Fund. World Economic and Financial Surveys. ISSN 0258-7440.
Published by: International Monetary Fund, Publication Services, 700 19th St, N W, Ste 12-607, Washington, DC 20431. TEL 202-623-8300, FAX 202-623-6149, publications@imf.org, http://www.imf.org/external/pubs/ft/gfsr/.

B

▼ *new title* ➤ *refereed* ✶ *unverified* ♦ *full entry avail.*

332 USA ISSN 0251-6365
HG230.3 CODEN: TITADP
INTERNATIONAL MONETARY FUND. OCCASIONAL PAPERS. Text in English. 1980. irreg., latest vol.177, 1999. USD 25 (effective 2004 & 2005). back issues avail. **Description:** Contains studies on a variety of economic and financial subjects of importance to the work of the Fund.
Related titles: Microform ed.: (from PQC); ♦ Series: International Monetary Fund. World Economic and Financial Surveys. ISSN 0258-7440.
Indexed: GEOBASE.
—BLDSC (6217.477500), CISTI, IE, ingenta. **CCC.**
Published by: International Monetary Fund, Publication Services, 700 19th St, N W, Ste 12-607, Washington, DC 20431. TEL 202-623-7430, FAX 202-623-7201, publications@imf.org, http://www.imf.org.

332 USA ISSN 0538-8759
INTERNATIONAL MONETARY FUND. PAMPHLET SERIES. Text in English. 1964. irreg., latest vol.57, 1999. free. reprint service avail. from PQC.
Related titles: Microform ed.: (from PQC); ♦ French ed.: Fonds Monetaire International. Serie des Brochures. ISSN 0252-2985; ♦ Spanish ed.: Fondo Monetario Internacional. Serie de Folletos. ISSN 0252-2993.
—**CCC.**
Published by: International Monetary Fund, Publication Services, 700 19th St, N W, Ste 12-607, Washington, DC 20431. TEL 202-623-7430, FAX 202-623-7201. Ed. Ian S McDonald.

332 USA ISSN 1020-8313
INTERNATIONAL MONETARY FUND. RESEARCH BULLETIN. Text in English. 2000. q. free. **Document type:** *Bulletin, Trade.*
Related titles: Online - full content ed.: ISSN 1607-9515.
—**CCC.**
Published by: International Monetary Fund, Publication Services, 700 19th St, N W, Ste 12-607, Washington, DC 20431. TEL 202-623-8300, FAX 202-623-6149, publications@imf.org, http://www.imf.org/external/pubs/ft/irb/archive.htm.

332.1 USA ISSN 1087-4275
HG3881
INTERNATIONAL MONETARY FUND. SELECTED DECISIONS AND SELECTED DOCUMENTS OF THE INTERNATIONAL MONETARY FUND. Text in English. 1972. irreg. free. index. reprint service avail. from PQC.
Former titles (until 198?): International Monetary Fund. Selected Decisions of the International Monetary Fund and Selected Documents (0094-1735); (until 1972): International Monetary Fund. Selected Decisions of the Executive Directors (0535-1472)
Related titles: Online - full text ed.: ISSN 1607-9450.
Published by: International Monetary Fund, Publication Services, 700 19th St, N W, Ste 12-607, Washington, DC 20431. TEL 202-623-7430, FAX 202-623-7201.

332.4 USA ISSN 1020-7635
HG3810
➤ **INTERNATIONAL MONETARY FUND. STAFF PAPERS.** Text in English. 1950. q. USD 56; USD 28 to students (effective 1999). adv. charts; illus. index, cum.index. reprint service avail. from PQC. **Document type:** *Academic/Scholarly.* **Description:** Contains theoretical studies on monetary and financial problems prepared by Fund staff. Subjects covered include balance of payments and exchange rates, monetary systems and analysis, national monetary and fiscal policies, and international liquidity.
Formerly (until 1998): International Monetary Fund. Staff Papers (0020-8027)
Related titles: Microform ed.: (from CIS, PQC); Online - full text ed.: ISSN 1564-5150. 1998. free (effective 2005) (from Chadwyck-Healey Inc., EBSCO Publishing, Florida Center for Library Automation, Gale Group, H.W. Wilson, O C L C Online Computer Library Center, Inc., ProQuest Information & Learning).
Indexed: ABIn, APEL, ASCA, AgeL, AmH&L, BAS, BLI, BPI, BusI, CPM, CurCont, EIP, ELLIS, HistAb, IBR, IBSS, IBZ, IIS, IndIslam, JEL, MEA&I, PAA&I, PAIS, PCI, RASB, RRTA, SSCI, SSI, T&II, WAE&RSA, WBA.
—BLDSC (4369.269000), CISTI, IDS, IE, Infotrieve, ingenta. **CCC.**
Published by: International Monetary Fund, Publication Services, 700 19th St, N W, Ste 12-607, Washington, DC 20431. TEL 202-623-7430, FAX 202-623-7201, publications@imf.org, http://www.imf.org. Ed. Ian S McDonald. Circ: 5,000.

330 USA ISSN 0074-7025
HG3881.5.I58
INTERNATIONAL MONETARY FUND. SUMMARY PROCEEDINGS OF THE ANNUAL MEETING OF THE BOARD OF GOVERNORS. Text in English. 1946. a. free. reprint service avail. from PQC. **Document type:** *Proceedings, Corporate.* **Description:** Contains the opening and closing addresses of the Chairman of the Board of Governors, presentation of the Annual Report by the Managing Director, statements of Governors, committee reports, resolutions, and a list of delegates.
Related titles: Microfilm ed.: (from BHP); Microform ed.: (from BHP, PQC).
—BLDSC (8531.160000). **CCC.**
Published by: International Monetary Fund, Publication Services, 700 19th St, N W, Ste 12-607, Washington, DC 20431. TEL 202-623-7430, FAX 202-623-7201.

332.1 338.9 USA ISSN 0258-7440
INTERNATIONAL MONETARY FUND. WORLD ECONOMIC AND FINANCIAL SURVEYS. Text in English. irreg. (8-9/yr.). price varies. **Description:** Contains periodic studies covering monetary and financial issues of importance to the world economy. The core elements in the series are the semiannual World Economic Outlook report and the Global Financial Stability Report. Other studies cover such topics as developments in international trade policies, export credit policies, exchange and payment systems, and international financial markets.
Related titles: Microfiche ed.: (from CIS); ♦ French ed.: Fonds Monetaire International. Etudes Economiques et Financieres. ISSN 1020-5101; ♦ Series of: International Monetary Fund. Occasional Papers. ISSN 0251-6365; ♦ Series of: International Monetary Fund. World Economic Outlook. ISSN 0256-6877; ♦ Series: International Monetary Fund. Global Financial Stability Report. ISSN 1729-701X; Supplement(s): Staff Studies for the World Economic Outlook. ISSN 1016-0361. 1986.
Indexed: IIS.
—BLDSC (4195.398550). **CCC.**
Published by: International Monetary Fund, Publication Services, 700 19th St, N W, Ste 12-607, Washington, DC 20431. TEL 202-623-6639, FAX 202-623-7201.

332 GBR ISSN 0958-3785
INTERNATIONAL MONEY MARKETING. Text in English. 1987. m. **Document type:** *Newspaper, Trade.* **Description:** For marketers and distributors of international investment products and services.
Formerly (until 1989): Offshore Money (0955-6133)
Related titles: Online - full text ed.: (from EBSCO Publishing, Gale Group, H.W. Wilson, LexisNexis, Northern Light Technology, Inc., O C L C Online Computer Library Center, Inc., ProQuest Information & Learning).
Indexed: ABIn, BPI.
—**CCC.**
Published by: Centaur Publishing, St Giles House, 50 Poland St, London, W1V 4AX, United Kingdom. TEL 44—20-7970-4000, FAX 44-20-7970-4009.

INTERNATIONAL OIL & GAS FINANCE REVIEW (YEAR). see *PETROLEUM AND GAS*

332 ZAF
INTERNATIONAL PERSONAL FINANCE. Text in English. 1985. m. USD 213 (effective 2000). **Document type:** *Newsletter.* **Description:** Provides international investment information for individuals with particular focus for South Africans and others still subject to exchange control.
Published by: Prescon Publishing Corporation (Pty) Ltd., PO Box 84004, Greenside, Johannesburg 2034, South Africa. TEL 27-11-7829229, FAX 27-11-7822025, prescon@iafrica.com. Ed. Martin C Spring. R&P Jenny Bell.

INTERNATIONAL PETROLEUM FINANCE; earnings, finances and management strategies in the petroleum industry. see *PETROLEUM AND GAS*

332 GBR ISSN 1367-6512
INTERNATIONAL POWER FINANCE REVIEW (YEARS). Text in English. 1997. a. GBP 95, USD 170 (effective 1998). **Description:** Aimed at the international power finance market, featuring contributions from experts within the field of project and power finance.
—**CCC.**
Published by: Euromoney Publications plc, Nestor House, Playhouse Yard, London, EC4V 5EX, United Kingdom. TEL 44-207-7798673, FAX 44-20-77798541.

INTERNATIONAL PRESS CUTTING SERVICE: TAXATION - FINANCE - COMPANY LAW. see *BUSINESS AND ECONOMICS—Public Finance, Taxation*

INTERNATIONAL REVIEW OF ECONOMICS & FINANCE. see *BUSINESS AND ECONOMICS—Economic Situation And Conditions*

332 GBR ISSN 1369-412X
HG11
➤ **INTERNATIONAL REVIEW OF FINANCE.** Text in English. 1999. q. EUR 51 combined subscription in Europe to individuals print & online eds.; USD 49 combined subscription in the Americas to individuals & Caribbean, print & online eds.; GBP 34 combined subscription elsewhere to individuals print & online eds.; USD 324 combined subscription in the Americas to institutions & Caribbean, print & online eds.; GBP 214 combined subscription elsewhere to institutions print & online eds. (effective 2006). **Document type:** *Journal, Academic/Scholarly.* **Description:** Publishes research in all areas of financial economics. Welcomes research in financial markets and institutions of emerging markets, and articles that will contribute to understanding Asia Pacific markets and economies.
Related titles: Online - full text ed.: ISSN 1468-2443. USD 308 in the Americas to institutions & Caribbean; GBP 203 elsewhere to institutions (effective 2006) (from Blackwell Synergy, EBSCO Publishing, Gale Group, IngentaConnect, O C L C Online Computer Library Center, Inc., Swets Information Services).
Indexed: ABIn.
—BLDSC (4547.155000), IE, Infotrieve, ingenta. **CCC.**
Published by: (Asia Pacific Finance Association), Blackwell Publishing Ltd., 9600 Garsington Rd, Oxford, OX4 2ZG, United Kingdom. TEL 44-1865-776868, FAX 44-1865-714591, customerservices@oxon.blackwellpublishing.com, http://www.blackwellpublishing.com/journals/IRFI. **Co-sponsor:** Nippon Finance Association.

332 NLD ISSN 1057-5219
HG1
➤ **INTERNATIONAL REVIEW OF FINANCIAL ANALYSIS.** Text in English. 1991. 5/yr. EUR 359 in Europe to institutions; JPY 47,700 in Japan to institutions; USD 402 elsewhere to institutions (effective 2006). illus. Index. back issues avail.; reprints avail. **Document type:** *Journal, Academic/Scholarly.* **Description:** Provides an outlet for high quality financial research.
Related titles: Microform ed.: (from PQC); Online - full text ed.: (from EBSCO Publishing, Gale Group, IngentaConnect, ScienceDirect, Swets Information Services).
Indexed: ABIn, BAS, BLI, JEL.
—BLDSC (4547.160000), IE, Infotrieve, ingenta. **CCC.**
Published by: Elsevier BV, North-Holland (Subsidiary of: Elsevier Science & Technology), Sara Burgerhartstraat 25, Amsterdam, 1055 KV, Netherlands. TEL 31-20-485-3911, FAX 31-20-485-2457, nlinfo-f@elsevier.nl, http://www.elsevier.com/locate/irfa, http://www.elsevier.nl. Eds. C. Kearney, D. K. Ding, Thomas A. Fetherston. **Subscr. to:** Elsevier BV, PO Box 211, Amsterdam 1000 AE, Netherlands. TEL 31-20-485-3757, FAX 31-20-485-3432, http://www.elsevier.nl.

➤ **INTERNATIONAL RISK MANAGEMENT.** see *BUSINESS AND ECONOMICS*

332 GBR ISSN 1470-4005
INTERNATIONAL SECURITIES FINANCE. Abbreviated title: I S F. Text in English. 1992. q. GBP 350 combined subscription domestic print & online eds.; EUR 535 combined subscription in Europe print & online eds.; USD 595 combined subscription elsewhere print & online eds. (effective 2005). adv. **Document type:** *Trade.*
Formerly (until Mar. 2000): International Securities Lending (0964-9301)
Related titles: Online - full text ed.: (from EBSCO Publishing, Gale Group, O C L C Online Computer Library Center, Inc.).
Indexed: ABIn.
—BLDSC (4548.895220), IE, ingenta. **CCC.**
Published by: Euromoney Institutional Investor Plc., Nestor House, Playhouse Yard, London, EC4V 5EX, United Kingdom. TEL 44-20-7779-8673, FAX 44-20-7779-8541, http://www.isfmagazine.com, http://www.euromoney.com. Ed. Anuj Gangahar TEL 44-20-77798390. Pub. Will Goodhart TEL 44-20-77798989. Adv. contact Elliot Jacobs TEL 44-20-7779-8432. **Dist. in U.S. by:** American Educational Systems, PO Box 246, New York, NY 10024-0246. TEL 800-431-1579, aesbooks@aol.com.

INTERNATIONAL SMART CARD INDUSTRY GUIDE. see *COMPUTERS—Computer Industry*

332 NLD ISSN 1385-3074
K9
INTERNATIONAL TRANSFER PRICING JOURNAL. Text in English. 1993. bi-m. USD 450 (effective 2002). back issues avail. **Document type:** *Trade.* **Description:** Covers major current issues in international transfer pricing, including case reports and news of worldwide developments.
Related titles: Online - full text ed.: (from Swets Information Services).
Indexed: ELJI, LJI.
—IE.
Published by: (International Bureau of Fiscal Documentation), I B F D Publications BV, H J E Wenckebachweg 210, PO Box 20237, Amsterdam, 1000 HE, Netherlands. TEL 31-20-554-0100, FAX 31-20-620-8626, info@ibfd.nl, http://www.ibfd.nl. **customer service in N. America:** I B F D Publications USA, Inc, PO Box 805, Valatie, NY 12184-0805. TEL 518-758-2245, FAX 518-758-2246.

332 USA ISSN 1075-5691
INTERNATIONAL TREASURER★; the journal of global treasury and financial risk management. Text in English. 1994. s-m. USD 595. **Document type:** *Trade.* **Description:** Covers the treasury function and its role in the multinational corporation.
Related titles: Online - full text ed.
Address: 305 Madison Ave, Ste 1146, New York, NY 10165. itmail@intltreasurer.com, http://www.intltreasurer.com.

332 ZAF
INTERNATIONAL WERKS. Text in English. 1993. irreg. adv. **Document type:** *Bulletin.* **Description:** Discusses issues relating to foreign investment in South Africa.
Published by: Werksmans, PO Box 927, Johannesburg, 2000, South Africa. Ed. Charles Butler. R&P, Adv. contact Kandy Wright.

B

INTERNET & TECHNOLOGY FINANCE. see COMMUNICATIONS

332   USA
▼ ➤ **THE INTERNET JOURNAL OF FINANCE.** Text in English. 2004. irreg. free to individuals; USD 500 to institutions (effective 2005). **Document type:** *Journal, Academic/Scholarly.*
Media: Online - full content.
Published by: Internet Scientific Publications, L.L.C., 23 Rippling Creek Dr, Sugar Land, TX 77479. TEL 832-443-1193, FAX 281-240-1533, wenker@ispub.com, http://www.ispub.com/ostia/index.php?xmlFilePath=journals/ijfin/front.xml.

332   CHE   ISSN 1024-1663
CJ3
INVENTAR DER FUNDMUENZEN DER SCHWEIZ. BULLETIN/INVENTAIRE DES TROUVAILLES MONETAIRES SUISSES. BULLETIN/INVERATRIO DEI RITROVAMENTI MONETALI SVIZZERI. BULLETIN. Cover title: Bulletin I F S. Text in French, German, Italian. 1994. a. CHF 10 (effective 2000). **Document type:** *Bulletin.*
Published by: Inventar der Fundmuenzen der Schweiz, Aarbergergasse 30, Postfach 6855, Bern, 3001, Switzerland. TEL 41-31-3113424, FAX 41-31-3113425.

332   SCG
INVESTBANKA; list radne zajednice investbanka. Text in Serbo-Croatian. 1964. m. free. adv. charts; illus.
Address: Terazije 9, Postanski Fah 152, Belgrade, 11001. TEL 011 658-582, FAX 320-617, TELEX 11147. Ed. Ljubisa Stojiljkovic.

332   SCG
INVESTBANKA. ANNUAL REPORT. Text in Serbo-Croatian. 1956. a. free. **Document type:** *Corporate.*
Formerly: Yugoslovenska Investiciona Banka. Annual Report (0075-4536)
Published by: Investbanka, Terazije 9, Postanski Fah 152, Belgrade, 11001. TEL 38-11-656-842, FAX 38-11-320-617. Ed. Ljubisa K Plavsic. Circ: 1,200.

332   FRA   ISSN 0759-7673
INVESTIR. Text in French. 1974. w. adv. **Document type:** *Newspaper.*
Published by: Societe d'Information Economique et Financiere, Investir Publications, 48 rue Notre-Dame-des-Victoires, Paris, Cedex 2 75081, France. TEL 33-1-44884800, FAX 33-1-44884801, http://www.investir.fr. Ed. Jean Claude Regnier. Adv. contact Fabrice Larue. Circ: 116,265 (controlled).

332.1   MWI
INVESTMENT AND DEVELOPMENT BANK OF MALAWI. ANNUAL REPORT AND ACCOUNTS. Text in English. 1973. a. **Document type:** *Corporate.*
Published by: Investment and Development Bank of Malawi Ltd., PO Box 358, Blantyre, Malawi. TEL 265-620055, FAX 265-623353, TELEX 45201 MI, indebank@malawi.net. Ed. Webster Nyengo. Circ: 500.

INVESTMENT FUNDS. see BUSINESS AND ECONOMICS—Public Finance, Taxation

332 332.62   GBR   ISSN 0267-3770
INVESTMENT MANAGEMENT. Text in English. 1985. 10/yr. adv. back issues avail. **Document type:** *Trade.*
Published by: Mitre House Publishing Ltd., 154 Graham Rd, Wimbledon, London, SW19 3SJ, United Kingdom. http://www.mitrehousepublishing.co.uk/. Ed. Richard Blausten. Adv. contact Joseph Gaydecki. Circ: 8,000 (controlled).

346.078   DEU
INVO - INSOLVENZ UND VOLLSTRECKUNG. Text in German. 1996. m. EUR 158; EUR 13 newsstand/cover (effective 2004). adv. **Document type:** *Journal, Trade.*
Published by: Deutscher Anwaltverlag GmbH, Wachsbleiche 7, Bonn, 53111, Germany. TEL 49-228-919110, FAX 49-228-9191123, kontakt@anwaltverlag.de, http://www.anwaltverlag.de. adv.: B&W page EUR 700, color page EUR 1,390. Circ: 2,000 (paid and controlled).

332   SAU   ISSN 1319-0830
AL-IQTISADIYYAH; jaridat al-arab al-iqtisadiyyah al-duwaliyyah - the international Arab business daily. Variant title: Al Eqtisadiah. Text in Arabic. 1992. d. adv. bk.rev. 12 p./no. 8 cols./p.; **Document type:** *Newspaper, Consumer.*
Description: Covers business and investment opportunities, market trends, financial issues, with a particular focus on the Gulf region.
Published by: Saudi Research & Publishing Co., PO Box 4556, Jeddah, 21412, Saudi Arabia. TEL 966-2-669-1888, FAX 966-2-667-1650, http://www.alkhaleejiahadv.com.sa/srpc/. adv.: page SAR 33,900; 14 x 21. Circ: 57,647 (paid and controlled).

332   IRL   ISSN 0790-066X
IRISH BANK OFFICIALS ASSOCIATION NEWSHEET. Text in English. 1919. m. USD 25 (effective 1999). adv. bk.rev. **Document type:** *Newsletter.*
Published by: Irish Bank Officials Association, 93 St, St Stephen's Green, Dublin, 2, Ireland. TEL 353-1-4755908, FAX 353-1-4780567. Ed., R&P Ken Doyle. Adv. contact Gillian Morgan. Circ: 15,000 (controlled).

332.1   IRL   ISSN 0021-1060
HC257.I6
IRISH BANKING REVIEW. Text in English. 1957. q. **Document type:** *Trade.* **Description:** Encourages discussion of economic and development issues, including monetary systems, private sector projects and macro-economic policies.
Indexed: CREJ, IBSS, JEL, KES, LJI, PAIS, RRTA, WAE&RSA, WBA.
—BLDSC (4569.500000), IE, Infotrieve, ingenta.
Published by: Irish Bankers' Federation, Nassau House, 40 Nassau St., Dublin, 2, Ireland. TEL 353-1-6715311, FAX 353-1-6796680, TELEX 93957. Ed. F O'Regan. Circ: 4,000.

332.153   SAU   ISSN 1319-1314
ISLAMIC DEVELOPMENT BANK. ANNUAL REPORT. Text in English. 1975. a. free; free. **Document type:** *Corporate.* **Description:** Covers world economic developments and their impacts, economic cooperation, major policy developments and operations, details on financing and trade operations of the bank.
Related titles: Microfilm ed.; Arabic ed.; French ed.
Published by: Islamic Development Bank, P O Box 5925, Jeddah, 21432, Saudi Arabia. TEL 966-2-6361400, FAX 966-2-6366871, TELEX 601137 ISDB SJ, archives@isdb.org.sa, http://www.isdb.org. Circ: 15,000.

ISLAMIC ECONOMIC STUDIES. see RELIGIONS AND THEOLOGY—Islamic

332   GBR
ISLAMIC FINANCE. Text in English. w. (50x/yr). GBP 650 combined subscription domestic print & online eds.; USD 980 combined subscription foreign print & online eds. (effective 2004).
Published by: Euromoney Institutional Investor Plc., Nestor House, Playhouse Yard, London, EC4V 5EX, United Kingdom. TEL 44-20-7779-8673, information@euromoneyplc.com, http://www.islamicfinanceweekly.com, http://www.euromoneyplc.com. Ed. Jacqueline Grosch Lobo.

332.1   ISR   ISSN 0334-2093
HG3260.A5
ISRAEL'S BANKING SYSTEM. Text in English. a. ILS 81 (effective 2000).
Related titles: Hebrew ed.
Published by: Bank of Israel, Kiryath Ben Gurion, P O Box 780, Jerusalem, 91007, Israel. http://www.bankisrael.gov.il.

J A S S A. see BUSINESS AND ECONOMICS—Investments

332   JPN
J B I C I REVIEW. (Japan Bank for International Cooperation Institute) Text in English. 1980; N.S. 2000. s-a. **Document type:** *Government.* **Description:** Contains selection of surveys and studies conducted at the Research Institute for Development and Finance.
Formerly: J B I C Review (1345-5710); Which was formed by the merger of (1980-1999): EX-IM Review (Export-Import) (0914-5451); (1995-1999): Journal of Development Assistance (1341-3953)
Indexed: PAIS.
—BLDSC (4663.437200), IE, ingenta.
Published by: Japan Bank for International Cooperation, Research Institute for Development and Finance, 4-1 Ohtemachi 1-chome, Chiyoda-ku, Tokyo, 100-8144, Japan.

332 388   GBR   ISSN 1351-1211
JANE'S TRANSPORT FINANCE. Text in English. 24/yr. GBP 1,150, USD 1,840, AUD 2,990 (effective 2004). adv. **Document type:** *Magazine, Trade.* **Description:** Briefs readers on the transferability of financing techniques across the transport sector.
Related titles: CD-ROM ed.: 2000 (May). GBP 1,770, USD 2,830, AUD 4,600 (effective 2004); Online - full text ed.: GBP 1,950, USD 3,120, AUD 5,070 (effective 2004).
Published by: Jane's Information Group, Sentinel House, 163 Brighton Rd, Coulsdon, Surrey CR5 2YH, United Kingdom. TEL 44-20-87003700, FAX 44-20-87631006, info@janes.co.uk, http://jtf.janes.com/, http://www.janes.com. Dist. by: Jane's Information Group Asia, 60 Albert St, #15-01 Albert Complex, Singapore 189969, Singapore. TEL 65-331-6280, FAX 65-336-9921, info@janes.com.sg; Jane's Information Group Australia, PO Box 3502, Rozelle, NSW 2039, Australia. TEL 61-2-8587-7900, FAX 61-2-8587-7901, info@janes.thomson.com.au; 1340 Braddock Pl, Ste 300, Alexandria, VA 22314-1651. TEL 703-683-3700, 800-824-0768, FAX 703-836-0297, 800-836-0297, info@janes.com.

346.082   USA
JAPANESE BANKING, SECURITIES AND ANTI-MONOPOLY LAW. Text in English. 1988. base vol. plus a. updates. USD 85. Supplement avail.
Published by: LexisNexis (Subsidiary of: LexisNexis North America), PO Box 7587, Charlottesville, VA 22906-7587. TEL 804-972-7600, 800-562-1197, FAX 804-972-7666, llp.customer.support@lexis-nexis.com, http://www.lexislawpublishing.com. Ed. Hiroshi Oda.

332 338   JPN   ISSN 0385-2369
HG41
JAPANESE FINANCE AND INDUSTRY: QUARTERLY SURVEY. Text in English. 1949. q. free. charts; stat.
Formerly: Quarterly Survey of Japanese Finance and Industry (0039-6249)
Indexed: BAS, KES, PAIS.
Published by: Industrial Bank of Japan/Nippon Kogyo Ginko, 3-3, Marunouchi 1-chome, Chiyoda-ku, Tokyo, 100-8210, Japan. TEL 81-3-3214-1111, FAX 81-3-3201-7643, http://www.ibjbank.co.jp/.

332   CHN
JIANGXI CHENGSHI JINRONG/JIANGXI URBAN FINANCE. Text in Chinese. m.
Published by: Jiangxi Sheng Chengshi Jinrong Xuehui/Jiangxi Urban Finance Society, No 23 Tie Jie, Nanchang, Jiangxi 330008, China. TEL 51918. Ed. Tu Yide.

332   CHN
JINRONG SHIBAO/FINANCIAL NEWS. Text in Chinese. d. USD 314.70, CNY 156.60. **Document type:** *Newspaper, Consumer.*
Contact Dist.: China Books & Periodicals Inc TEL 415-282-2994, FAX 415-282-0994. **Dist. by:** China International Book Trading Corp, 35 Chegongzhuang Xilu, Haidian District, PO Box 399, Beijing 100044, China. TEL 86-10-68412045, FAX 86-10-68412023, cibtc@mail.cibtc.com.cn, http://www.cibtc.com.cn.

332   CHN   ISSN 0529-2794
JINRONG YANJIU/BANKING AND FINANCE STUDIES. Text in Chinese. m.
Published by: Zhongguo Jinrong Xuehui/Chinese Society of Banking and Finance, 1 Baiguanglu Toutiao, Beijing, 100053, China. TEL 6014422. Ed. Zhao Haixian.

368.854   CHN   ISSN 1005-4383
HG187.C6
JINRONG YU BAOXIAN/FINANCE AND INSURANCE. Text in Chinese. m. CNY 192 (effective 2004). **Document type:** *Journal, Academic/Scholarly.* **Description:** Covers Chinese currency, banking and finance, insurance, investment and security issues.
Indexed: RASB.
Published by: Zhongguo Renmin Daxue, Shubao Zilio Zhongxin/Renmin University of China, Information Center for Social Server, Dongcheng-qu, 3, Zhangzizhong Lu, Beijing, 100007, China. TEL 86-10-64039458, FAX 86-10-64015080, kyes@163.net, http://www.confucius.cn.net/bkdetail.asp?fzt=F62. **Dist. in US by:** China Publications Service, PO Box 49614, Chicago, IL 60649. TEL 312-288-3291, FAX 312-288-8570; **Dist. by:** China International Book Trading Corp, 35 Chegongzhuang Xilu, Haidian District, PO Box 399, Beijing 100044, China. TEL 86-10-68412045, FAX 86-10-68412023, cibtc@mail.cibtc.com.cn, http://www.cibtc.com.cn.

THE JOURNAL OF 21ST CENTURY ACCOUNTING. see BUSINESS AND ECONOMICS—Accounting

JOURNAL OF ACCOUNTING AND FINANCE RESEARCH. see BUSINESS AND ECONOMICS—Accounting

332.1 630   USA   ISSN 1542-5606
JOURNAL OF AGRICULTURAL LENDING. Text in English. 1987. q. USD 110 to non-members; USD 75 to members (effective 2002). **Description:** Supplies current information on agricultural lending, including annual Farm Credit Situation Survey results; and profiles of prominent industry figures.
Related titles: Microform ed.: (from PQC); Online - full text ed.: USD 60 (effective 2002).
Published by: (American Bankers Association, Center for Agricultural and Rural Banking), Countryside Marketing, 1212 S Naper Blvd Ste 119, P M B 285, Naperville, IL 60540. TEL 630-637-0199, FAX 630-637-0198, cmerry@countryside-marketing.com, http://www.agricultural-lending.com/. Pub. Carroll Merry.

332.1   USA   ISSN 1078-1196
HG4001
➤ **JOURNAL OF APPLIED CORPORATE FINANCE.** Text in English. 1988. q. USD 95 combined subscription in the Americas to individuals print & online eds.; EUR 80 combined subscription in Europe to individuals print & online eds.; GBP 53 combined subscription elsewhere to individuals print & online eds.; USD 324 combined subscription in the Americas to institutions print & online eds.; BSD 198 combined subscription elsewhere to institutions print & online eds.; USD 432 combined subscription in the Americas to corporations print & online eds.; GBP 263 combined subscription elsewhere to corporations print & online eds.; USD 50 combined subscription in the Americas to students print & online eds.; EUR 42 combined subscription in Europe to students print & online eds. (effective 2006). illus. cum.index. back issues avail.; reprints avail. **Document type:** *Journal, Academic/Scholarly.*
Formerly: Continental Bank Journal of Applied Corporate Finance (0898-4484)

B

Related titles: Online - full text ed.: ISSN 1745-6622. USD 308 in the Americas to institutions; GBP 188 elsewhere to institutions (effective 2006) (from Blackwell Synergy, Gale Group, IngentaConnect, O C L C Online Computer Library Center, Inc., Swets Information Services).
Indexed: ATI, BLI, ESPM, Emerald, RiskAb.
—BLDSC (4942.375000), IE, Infotrieve, ingenta. **CCC.**
Published by: (Morgan Stanley), Blackwell Publishing, Inc. (Subsidiary of: Blackwell Publishing Ltd.), Commerce Place, 350 Main St, Malden, MA 02148. TEL 781-388-8206, FAX 781-388-8232, subscrip@blackwellpub.com, http://www.blackwellpublishing.com/subs.asp?ref=1078-1196. Ed. Donald H Chew Jr.

332 USA ISSN 1534-6668
HG152
➤ **JOURNAL OF APPLIED FINANCE**; theory, practice, education. Text in English. 1991. s-a. USD 95 to individual members; USD 40 to libraries (effective 2003). adv. **Document type:** *Journal, Academic/Scholarly.* **Description:** Covers topics relevant to both financial practice and financial education in the fields of financial management, investments, and financial institutions and markets.
Formerly (until 2001): Financial Practice and Education (1082-0698)
Related titles: Online - full text ed.: (from EBSCO Publishing, O C L C Online Computer Library Center, Inc., ProQuest Information & Learning).
Indexed: ABIn, BAS, BLI, JEL, RefZh.
—BLDSC (4942.608500), IE, ingenta. **CCC.**
Published by: Financial Management Association International, University of South Florida, College of Business Administration, Ste 3331, Tampa, FL 33620-5500. TEL 813-974-2084, FAX 813-974-3318, fma@coba.usf.edu, http://www.fma.org. Ed. Raj Aggrawal. Circ: 4,500.

332 NLD ISSN 0378-4266
CODEN: JBFIDO
➤ **JOURNAL OF BANKING & FINANCE.** Text in English. 1977. 12/yr. EUR 136 in Europe to individuals; JPY 18,500 in Japan to individuals; USD 145 to individuals except Europe and Japan; EUR 2,308 in Europe to institutions; JPY 306,500 in Japan to institutions; USD 2,582 to institutions except Europe and Japan (effective 2006). adv. bk.rev. charts; illus. index. back issues avail.; reprints avail. **Document type:** *Academic/Scholarly.* **Description:** Provides an outlet for the increasing flow of scholarly research concerning financial institutions and the money and capital markets within which they function.
Incorporates (1985-1989): Studies in Banking and Finance (0169-6939)
Related titles: Microform ed.: (from PQC); Online - full text ed.: (from EBSCO Publishing, Gale Group, IngentaConnect, ScienceDirect, Swets Information Services).
Indexed: ABIn, ASCA, ATI, BAS, BLI, BPI, BPIA, BusI, CPM, CREJ, CurCont, ELLIS, ESPM, Emerald, IBSS, JCQM, JEL, ManagCont, PAIS, RiskAb, SSCI, T&II, WBA.
—BLDSC (4951.112000), IDS, IE, Infotrieve, ingenta. **CCC.**
Published by: (Universita degli Studi di Bergamo ITA), Elsevier BV, North-Holland (Subsidiary of: Elsevier Science & Technology), Sara Burgerhartstraat 25, Amsterdam, 1055 KV, Netherlands. TEL 31-20-485-3911, FAX 31-20-485-2457, nlinfo-f@elsevier.nl, http://www.elsevier.com/locate/jbf, http://www.elsevier.nl. **Subscr. to:** Elsevier BV, PO Box 211, Amsterdam 1000 AE, Netherlands. TEL 31-20-485-3757, FAX 31-20-485-3432, http://www.elsevier.nl.

332 346 AUS ISSN 1034-3040
K10
JOURNAL OF BANKING AND FINANCE - LAW AND PRACTICE. Text in English. q. AUD 395 (effective 2004). **Document type:** *Journal, Trade.* **Description:** Contains articles of topical interest on legislative and case law developments affecting banking and finance law and practice.
Related titles: Online - full text ed.
Indexed: CLI, LRI.
—BLDSC (4951.113000), IE, ingenta.
Published by: (Banking Law Association), Lawbook Co. (Subsidiary of: Thomson Legal & Regulatory Ltd.), PO Box 3502, Rozelle, NSW 2039, Australia. TEL 61-2-85877000, FAX 61-2-85877100, LRA.Service@thomson.com, http://onlineecom01.thomson.com.au/thomson/Catalog.asp?EES_CMD=SI&EES_ID=100217, http://www.lawbookco.com.au/. Eds. Gregory Burton, Robert Baxt.

332.1 342.066 GBR ISSN 1745-6452
K10
JOURNAL OF BANKING REGULATION. Text in English. 1999. q. GBP 95 in Europe to individuals; USD 150 in North America to individuals; GBP 110 elsewhere to individuals; GBP 320 in Europe to institutions; USD 500 in North America to institutions; GBP 335 elsewhere to institutions (effective 2005). back issues avail.; reprint service avail. from PSC. **Document type:** *Journal, Trade.* **Description:** Provides a forum for analysis from leading representatives of regulation, practice and banking. Covers banking regulation in its broadest sense, across the full field of financial services, from the protection of ordinary citizens' savings on the one hand to the regulation of multi-national financial institutions with a taste for huge risk and high profit on the other.
Formerly (until 2005): Journal of International Banking Regulation (1465-4830)
Related titles: Online - full text ed.: (from EBSCO Publishing, O C L C Online Computer Library Center, Inc., ProQuest Information & Learning).
Indexed: ABIn, BLI.
—BLDSC (4951.114500), IE, ingenta.
Published by: Palgrave Macmillan Ltd. (Subsidiary of: Macmillan Publishers Ltd.), Houndmills, Basingstoke, Hants RG21 6XS, United Kingdom. TEL 44-1256-329242, FAX 44-1256-810526, journal-info@palgrave.com, http://www.palgrave-journals.com/. Eds. Geoffrey Wood, Dr. Mads Andenas, Dr. Rosa Maria Lastra, William Blair.

THE JOURNAL OF BEHAVIORAL FINANCE. see *PSYCHOLOGY*

332 USA ISSN 1075-6124
JOURNAL OF BUSINESS (SPOKANE). Variant title: Spokane Journal of Business. Text in English. 1986. bi-w. USD 34 (effective 2005). adv. reprints avail. **Document type:** *Newspaper, Trade.* **Description:** Covers local business news for Spokane, Washington, Coeur d'Alene and other north Idaho and eastern Washington markets.
Related titles: E-mail ed.; Microform ed.: (from PQC); Online - full text ed.: (from EBSCO Publishing, O C L C Online Computer Library Center, Inc., ProQuest Information & Learning).
Indexed: ABIn, AcaI, BusDate, CurCont, ManagCont.
Published by: Northwest Business Press, Inc., 429 E Third Ave, Spokane, WA 99202. TEL 509-456-5257, journal@spokanejournal.com, http://www.spokanejournal.com. Ed. Richard Ripley. Pub. Greg Bever. Adv. contact Jonelle Opitz. page USD 2,180; 9.75 x 14.5. Circ: 15,000.

332 USA ISSN 1544-0028
HG1
➤ **JOURNAL OF COMMERCIAL BANKING AND FINANCE.** Text in English. 2002. a. **Document type:** *Journal, Academic/Scholarly.*
Related titles: Online - full text ed.
Published by: (Academy of Commercial Banking and Finance), Allied Academies, 145 Travis Rd., P. O. Box 2689, Cullowhee, NC 28723. http://www.alliedacademies.org/banking/acbf.html. Ed. Jim Bexley.

➤ **JOURNAL OF CONTEMPORARY BUSINESS ISSUES.** see *BUSINESS AND ECONOMICS—Management*

332 NLD ISSN 0929-1199
HG4001
➤ **JOURNAL OF CORPORATE FINANCE.** Text in English. 1994. 5/yr. EUR 52 in Europe to individuals; JPY 7,000 in Japan to individuals; USD 54 to individuals except Europe and Japan; EUR 410 in Europe to institutions; JPY 54,500 in Japan to institutions; USD 460 to institutions except Europe and Japan (effective 2006). adv. abstr. index. back issues avail.; reprints avail. **Document type:** *Academic/Scholarly.* **Description:** Publishes empirical and theoretical papers that combine the disciplines of financial economics, industrial organization, corporate law, accounting, and applied econometrics in analyzing the contractual underpinnings of firms.
Related titles: Microform ed.: (from PQC); Online - full text ed.: (from EBSCO Publishing, Gale Group, IngentaConnect, ScienceDirect, Swets Information Services).
Indexed: CurCont, IBR, IBZ, Inspec, JEL, SSCI.
—BLDSC (4965.336300), IE, Infotrieve, ingenta. **CCC.**
Published by: Elsevier BV, North-Holland (Subsidiary of: Elsevier Science & Technology), Sara Burgerhartstraat 25, Amsterdam, 1055 KV, Netherlands. TEL 31-20-485-3911, FAX 31-20-485-2457, nlinfo-f@elsevier.nl, http://www.elsevier.com/locate/jcorpfin, http://www.elsevier.nl. Eds. A. Poulsen, J. Netter. **Subscr. to:** Elsevier BV, PO Box 211, Amsterdam 1000 AE, Netherlands. TEL 31-20-485-3757, FAX 31-20-485-3432, http://www.elsevier.nl.

332 USA ISSN 1074-1240
HG6024.A3
JOURNAL OF DERIVATIVES. Text in English. 1993. q. USD 370 combined subscription domestic print & online eds.; USD 445 combined subscription foreign print & online eds. (effective 2005). adv. illus. Index. reprints avail. **Document type:** *Magazine, Trade.* **Description:** Bridges the gap between academic theory and practical application. Includes analysis of the market.
Related titles: Online - full text ed.: (from EBSCO Publishing, Florida Center for Library Automation, Gale Group, H.W. Wilson, O C L C Online Computer Library Center, Inc., ProQuest Information & Learning).
Indexed: ABIn, BLI, BPI, JEL.
—BLDSC (4968.758000), IE, Infotrieve, ingenta. **CCC.**
Published by: Institutional Investor, Journals (Subsidiary of: Euromoney Institutional Investor Plc.), 225 Park Ave S, 7th Fl., New York, NY 10003-1605. TEL 212-224-3800, FAX 212-224-3563, info@iijournals.com, http://www.iijournals.com/JOD. Ed. Stephen Figlewski. Pub. Allison Adams TEL 212-224-3584. adv.: B&W page USD 4,500, color page USD 7,700.

332 USA ISSN 1543-0464
JOURNAL OF ECONOMICS AND FINANCE EDUCATION. Text in English. 2002. s-a.
Media: Online - full content.
Published by: The Academy of Economics and Finance, c/o MBA Office, 316 Combs Academic Bld., Eastern Kentucky University, Richmond, KY 40475. http://www.jeandfe.org, http://www.economics-finance.org. Eds. Luther D. Lawson, Richard Cebula.

332 341 USA ISSN 1083-9798
HG5993
➤ **JOURNAL OF EMERGING MARKETS.** Text in English. 1996. 3/yr. USD 45 to individuals; USD 95 to institutions; USD 75 to libraries (effective 2004). adv. bk.rev. back issues avail. **Document type:** *Journal, Academic/Scholarly.* **Description:** Focuses on emerging markets, status of borrowers in these markets, country analyses, and use of emergency debt and equity for portfolio investers.
Indexed: BAS, JEL.
—BLDSC (4977.455000), IE, ingenta.
Published by: (Emerging Markets Traders Association), Center for Global Education, 800 Utopia Parkway, Jamaica, NY 11439. TEL 718-990-1951, FAX 718-990-2321, globalstudies@stjohns.edu, http://www.stjohns.edu/pls/portal30/sjudev.school.home?p_siteid=40&p_navbar=379&p_id=51369. Eds., Adv. contacts Francis Lees, Maximo Eng. page USD 195. Circ: 140 (paid).

332 519 NLD ISSN 0927-5398
HG23 CODEN: JEFIEC
➤ **JOURNAL OF EMPIRICAL FINANCE.** Text in English. 1993. 5/yr. EUR 52 in Europe to individuals; JPY 7,000 in Japan to individuals; USD 54 elsewhere to individuals; EUR 458 in Europe to institutions; JPY 60,700 in Japan to institutions; USD 512 elsewhere to institutions (effective 2006). adv. bk.rev. stat.; abstr. back issues avail. **Document type:** *Academic/Scholarly.* **Description:** Publishes empirical studies dealing with econometric analyses of financial markets and data, including forecasting, risk measurement, nonlinear dynamic models, and applications in corporate finance, asset pricing, and bond markets.
Related titles: Microform ed.: (from PQC); Online - full text ed.: (from EBSCO Publishing, Gale Group, IngentaConnect, ScienceDirect, Swets Information Services).
Indexed: IBSS, JEL.
—BLDSC (4977.630000), IE, Infotrieve, ingenta. **CCC.**
Published by: Elsevier BV, North-Holland (Subsidiary of: Elsevier Science & Technology), Sara Burgerhartstraat 25, Amsterdam, 1055 KV, Netherlands. TEL 31-20-485-3911, FAX 31-20-485-2457, nlinfo-f@elsevier.nl, http://www.elsevier.com/locate/jempfin, http://www.elsevier.nl. Eds. G Bekaert, R T Baillie, W. Ferson. **Subscr. to:** Elsevier BV, PO Box 211, Amsterdam 1000 AE, Netherlands. TEL 31-20-485-3757, FAX 31-20-485-3432, http://www.elsevier.nl.

332 USA ISSN 0022-1082
HG1 CODEN: JLFIAN
➤ **THE JOURNAL OF FINANCE.** Text in English. 1946. bi-m. USD 350 combined subscription in the Americas to institutions & Caribbean, print & online eds.; USD 393 combined subscription in Canada & Mexico to institutions print & online eds.; GBP 272 combined subscription elsewhere to institutions print & online eds.; USD 390 combined subscription in the Americas to corporations & Caribbean, print & online eds.; USD 455 combined subscription in Canada & Mexico to corporations print & online eds.; GBP 316 combined subscription elsewhere to corporations print & online eds.; USD 10 combined subscription in the Americas to students & Caribbean, print & online eds.; USD 15 combined subscription in Canada & Mexico to students print & online eds.; EUR 15 combined subscription in Europe to students print & online eds.; GBP 10 combined subscription elsewhere to students print & online eds. (effective 2006). adv. bk.rev. illus. index. back issues avail.; reprint service avail. from PSC. **Document type:** *Journal, Academic/Scholarly.* **Description:** Publishes original research into the field of finance.
Related titles: Microform ed.: (from MIM, PQC); Online - full text ed.: ISSN 1540-6261. USD 333 in the Americas to institutions & Caribbean; USD 373 in Canada & Mexico to institutions; GBP 258 elsewhere to institutions (effective 2006) (from Blackwell Synergy, EBSCO Publishing, Gale Group, IngentaConnect, JSTOR (Web-based Journal Archive), O C L C Online Computer Library Center, Inc., Swets Information Services).
Indexed: ABIn, ASCA, ATI, BLI, BPI, BPIA, BRI, BusI, CBRI, CIS, CPM, CREJ, CurCont, DIP, ESPM, Emerald, IBR, IBSS, IBZ, JCQM, JEL, KES, M&MA, ManagCont, MathR, PAIS, PCI, RASB, RiskAb, SCIMP, SSCI, T&II, WBA.
—BLDSC (4984.220000), CISTI, IDS, IE, Infotrieve, ingenta. **CCC.**
Published by: (American Finance Association), Blackwell Publishing, Inc. (Subsidiary of: Blackwell Publishing Ltd.), Commerce Place, 350 Main St, Malden, MA 02148. TEL 781-388-8206, FAX 781-388-8232, subscrip@blackwellpub.com, http://www.blackwellpublishing.com/journals/JOF. Ed. Robert F Stambaugh. Circ: 8,000.

332 USA ISSN 1527-5426
HG1
JOURNAL OF FINANCE CASE RESEARCH. Text in English. 1999 (Fall). s-a. USD 45 to individuals; USD 70 to institutions (effective 2002).
Published by: Hampton University, Department of Banking & Finance, Hampton, VA 23668. TEL 757-727-5605, editor@jfcr.org, http://www.jfcr.org/jfcr2.html.

658 USA ISSN 0022-1090
CODEN: JFQAAC

➤ **JOURNAL OF FINANCIAL AND QUANTITATIVE ANALYSIS.** Text in English. 1966. q. USD 70 domestic to individuals; USD 80 foreign to individuals; USD 150 domestic to libraries; USD 160 foreign to libraries; USD 25 domestic to students; USD 30 foreign to students (effective 2005). adv. charts; stat.; illus. index. back issues avail.; reprint service avail. from PQC,SCH. **Document type:** *Journal, Academic/Scholarly.* **Description:** Furthers advanced research in finance.
Related titles: Microform ed.: (from PQC); Online - full text ed.: (from EBSCO Publishing, JSTOR (Web-based Journal Archive), ProQuest Information & Learning).
Indexed: ABIn, ASCA, ATI, BLI, BPI, BPIA, CIS, CPM, CREJ, CurCont, Emerald, IBR, IBSS, IBZ, JCQM, JEL, LibLit, ManagCont, ORMS, PAIS, QC&AS, RefZh, SSCI, T&II, WBA.
—BLDSC (4984.230000), IDS, IE, Infotrieve, ingenta.
Published by: University of Washington, School of Business Administration, 115 Lewis Hall, Box 353200, Seattle, WA 981953200. TEL 206-543-4598, FAX 206-616-1894, jfqa@flqa.org, http://www.jfqa.org/. Eds. Hank Bessembinder, Paul Malatesta, Stephen Brown. adv.: page USD 375. Circ: 3,200 (paid).

332 USA ISSN 1065-1853
HG1
➤ **THE JOURNAL OF FINANCIAL AND STRATEGIC DECISIONS**✶ . Text in English. 1988. 3/yr. free. back issues avail. **Document type:** *Academic/Scholarly.* **Description:** Dedicated to academic and financial professionals.
Related titles: Online - full text ed.
Published by: Journal of Financial and Strategic Decisions, 402 N Dijon Ct, Tucson, AZ 85748-1946. TEL 239-768-9303, FAX 239-768-3699, sharon@tmag.com, http://www.tmag.com/jfsd/. Ed. Sharon H Garrison.

➤ **JOURNAL OF FINANCIAL CRIME.** see *LAW—Criminal Law*

332 GBR ISSN 1479-8409
HB139
JOURNAL OF FINANCIAL ECONOMETRICS. Text in English. 2002. q. GBP 381, USD 648, EUR 572 to institutions; GBP 254, USD 432, EUR 381 academics; GBP 401, USD 682, EUR 602 combined subscription to institutions print & online eds.; GBP 267, USD 454, EUR 401 combined subscription academics; print & online eds. (effective 2006). **Document type:** *Journal, Academic/Scholarly.* **Description:** Addresses substantive statistical issues raised by the tremendous growth of the financial industry; aims to advance the relationship between econometrics and finance at the methodological and empirical levels.
Related titles: Online - full text ed.: ISSN 1479-8417. GBP 361, USD 614, EUR 542 to corporations; GBP 240, USD 408, EUR 360 academics (effective 2006) (from EBSCO Publishing, Gale Group, HighWire Press, IngentaConnect, O C L C Online Computer Library Center, Inc., Oxford University Press Online Journals).
—BLDSC (4984.238000). **CCC.**
Published by: Oxford University Press, Great Clarendon St, Oxford, OX2 6DP, United Kingdom. TEL 44-1865-556767, FAX 44-1865-556646, enquiry@oup.co.uk, http://jfec.oxfordjournals.org/, http://www.oup.co.uk/. Eds. Eric Renault, Rene Garcia.

332 IND ISSN 0970-4205
HG4001 CODEN: JFANE9
➤ **JOURNAL OF FINANCIAL MANAGEMENT AND ANALYSIS**; international review of finance. Text in English. 1988. s-a. USD 108 to institutions (effective 2006). adv. bk.rev. charts; stat.; abstr. 115 p./no. 2 cols./p.; back issues avail. **Document type:** *Journal, Academic/Scholarly.* **Description:** Provides a bridge between financial management theory and practice in line with demands of today's techno-economic corporate, cooperative and public-sector business environments to find solutions to critical issues in financial management in the context of techno-economic development of MNC-parented developed vis-a-vis MNC-controlled developing countries.
Related titles: CD-ROM ed.; Magnetic Tape ed.; Microform ed.: (from PQC); Online - full text ed.: (from EBSCO Publishing, O C L C Online Computer Library Center, Inc., ProQuest Information & Learning).
Indexed: ABIn, BLI, JEL.
—BLDSC (4984.260000), IE, Infotrieve.
Published by: Om Sai Ram Centre for Financial Management Research, 15 Prakash Co-operative Housing Society, Relief Rd., Santacruz(west), Mumbai, 400 054, India. TEL 91-022-6607715, jfmaosr@indiatimes.com, http://www.scientificpub.com/bookdetails.php?booktransid=471&bookid=467. Ed., R&P M R K Swamy. Circ: 2,500 (paid and controlled). **Subscr. to:** Scientific Publishers, 5-A New Pali Rd., Near Hotel Taj Hari Mahal, PO Box 91, Jodhpur, Rajasthan 342 003, India.

332 NLD ISSN 1386-4181
HG4523
➤ **JOURNAL OF FINANCIAL MARKETS.** Text in English. 1998. 4/yr. EUR 50 in Europe to individuals; JPY 7,000 in Japan to individuals; USD 54 to individuals except Europe and Japan; EUR 298 in Europe to institutions; JPY 39,600 in Japan to institutions; USD 334 to institutions except Europe and Japan (effective 2006). bk.rev. back issues avail. **Document type:** *Academic/Scholarly.* **Description:** Contains research on applied and theoretical issues related to securities trading and pricing.
Related titles: Online - full text ed.: (from EBSCO Publishing, Gale Group, IngentaConnect, ScienceDirect, Swets Information Services).
Indexed: CurCont, JEL, SSCI.
—BLDSC (4984.260300), IE, Infotrieve, ingenta. **CCC.**
Published by: Elsevier BV, North-Holland (Subsidiary of: Elsevier Science & Technology), Sara Burgerhartstraat 25, Amsterdam, 1055 KV, Netherlands. TEL 31-20-485-3911, FAX 31-20-485-2457, nlinfo-f@elsevier.nl, http://www.elsevier.com/locate/finmar, http://www.elsevier.nl. Eds. A. Subrahmanyam, B. Lehmann, Matthew Spiegel. **Subscr. to:** Elsevier BV, PO Box 211, Amsterdam 1000 AE, Netherlands.

332 340 GBR ISSN 1358-1988
➤ **JOURNAL OF FINANCIAL REGULATION AND COMPLIANCE.** Text in English. 1992. q. GBP 429 (effective 2006). adv. back issues avail.; reprint service avail. from PSC. **Document type:** *Journal, Academic/Scholarly.* **Description:** Publishes articles and notes that enhance an understanding of, and thinking on, the practice, systems, and theory of financial regulation and compliance.
Formerly (until 1993): Regulatory Law and Practice (0968-087X)
Related titles: Online - full text ed.: ISSN 1740-0279 (from EBSCO Publishing, Gale Group, IngentaConnect, O C L C Online Computer Library Center, Inc., ProQuest Information & Learning, Swets Information Services).
Indexed: ABIn, BLI.
—BLDSC (4984.264000), IE, ingenta. **CCC.**
Published by: Emerald Group Publishing Limited, 60-62 Toller Ln, Bradford, W Yorks BD8 9BY, United Kingdom. TEL 44-1274-777700, FAX 44-1274-785200, subscriptions@emeraldinsight.com, infomation@emeraldinsight.com, http://www.emeraldinsight.com, http://www.emeraldinsight.com/. Ed. Oonagh McDonald. R&P Mr. John Eggleton. Circ: 1,000 (paid).

➤ **JOURNAL OF FINANCIAL RESEARCH.** see *BUSINESS AND ECONOMICS*

332 USA ISSN 1537-1816
HG8751
➤ **JOURNAL OF FINANCIAL SERVICE PROFESSIONALS.** Text in English. 1946. bi-m. USD 86 domestic to individuals; USD 101 foreign to individuals; USD 99 domestic to institutions; USD 114 foreign to institutions (effective 2005). adv. charts; illus.; stat.; abstr. cum.index. 96 p./no.; back issues avail.; reprint service avail. from PQC. **Document type:** *Journal, Academic/Scholarly.*
Former titles (until 1999): American Society of C L U & Ch F C. Journal (1052-2875); (until 1986): American Society of C L U. Journal (0742-9517); (until 1984): C L U Journal (0007-8573)
Related titles: Microform ed.: (from PQC); Online - full text ed.: included with print subscr. (from EBSCO Publishing, O C L C Online Computer Library Center, Inc., ProQuest Information & Learning).
Indexed: ABIn, AgeL, BPI, BPIA, BusI, CLI, FamI, ILP, LRI, PAIS, PSI, T&II.
—BLDSC (4984.265200), IE, ingenta.
Published by: Society of Financial Service Professionals, 17 Campus Blvd., Ste. 201, Newtown Sq, PA 19073-3230. TEL 800-392-6900, journal@financialpro.org, custserv@financialpro.org, http://www.financialpro.org/adv_mkt/journal/about.cfm. Ed. Kenn B Tacchino. Pub. Joseph Frack. R&P Mary Anne Mennite. adv.: color page USD 6,630, B&W page USD 4,900; trim 7.125 x 10. Circ: 36,500 (paid and controlled). **Dist. by:** Cadmus. http://www.cadmus.com.

➤ **JOURNAL OF FINANCIAL SERVICES MARKETING.** see *BUSINESS AND ECONOMICS—Marketing And Purchasing*

332 USA ISSN 0920-8550
HG1 CODEN: JFSRE9
➤ **JOURNAL OF FINANCIAL SERVICES RESEARCH.** Text in English. 1987. bi-m. EUR 658, USD 675, GBP 415 combined subscription to institutions print & online eds. (effective 2005). adv. illus. Index. reprint service avail. from PQC,PSC. **Document type:** *Journal, Academic/Scholarly.* **Description:** Publishes original research dealing with private and public policy questions arising from the evolution of the financial services sector.
Related titles: Microform ed.: (from PQC); Online - full text ed.: ISSN 1573-0735 (from EBSCO Publishing, Gale Group, IngentaConnect, Kluwer Online, O C L C Online Computer Library Center, Inc., ProQuest Information & Learning, Springer LINK, Swets Information Services).
Indexed: ABIn, ASCA, BLI, BibLing, CurCont, ESPM, Emerald, IBSS, JEL, RASB, RefZh, RiskAb, SSCI.
—BLDSC (4984.266000), IDS, IE, Infotrieve, ingenta. **CCC.**
Published by: Springer-Verlag New York, Inc. (Subsidiary of: Springer Science+Business Media), 233 Spring St, New York, NY 10013. TEL 212-460-1500, FAX 212-460-1575, service@springer-ny.com, http://springerlink.metapress.com/openurl.asp?genre=journal&issn=0920-8550, http://www.springer-ny.com. **Subscr. to:** Journal Fulfillment, PO Box 2485, Secaucus, NJ 07096-2485. TEL 201-348-4033, FAX 201-348-4505, journals@springer-ny.com.

➤ **THE JOURNAL OF HOSPITALITY FINANCIAL MANAGEMENT.** see *HOTELS AND RESTAURANTS*

➤ **JOURNAL OF INTERNATIONAL BANKING LAW AND REGULATION.** see *LAW—Corporate Law*

▼ ➤ **JOURNAL OF INTERNATIONAL BUSINESS STRATEGY.** see *BUSINESS AND ECONOMICS—International Commerce*

332 USA ISSN 1555-6336
▼ ➤ **JOURNAL OF INTERNATIONAL FINANCE AND ECONOMICS.** Abbreviated title: J I F E. Text in English. forthcoming 2006 (Jan.). s-a. USD 100 (effective 2006). **Document type:** *Journal, Academic/Scholarly.* **Description:** Contains scholarly research in international finance and economics.
Published by: Academy of International Business and Economics, 983 Woodland Dr, Turlock, CA 95382-7281. TEL 209-656-7084, Review@aibe.org, http://www.aibe.org; http://www.jife.org.

B

332 GBR ISSN 0954-1314
HG4027.5
➤ **JOURNAL OF INTERNATIONAL FINANCIAL MANAGEMENT AND ACCOUNTING.** Abbreviated title: J I F M A. Text in English. 1988. 3/yr., latest vol.13, no.3, 2002. GBP 83, EUR 125 combined subscription in Europe to individuals print & online eds.; USD 148 combined subscription in the Americas to individuals & Caribbean, print & online eds.; GBP 88 combined subscription elsewhere to individuals print & online eds.; GBP 318 combined subscription in Europe to institutions print & online eds.; USD 600 combined subscription in the Americas to institutions & Caribbean, print & online eds.; GBP 357 combined subscription elsewhere to institutions print & online eds. (effective 2006). bk.rev. illus. reprint service avail. from PSC. **Document type:** *Journal, Academic/Scholarly.*
Related titles: Online - full text ed.: ISSN 1467-646X. GBP 305 in Europe to institutions; USD 570 in the Americas to institutions & Caribbean; GBP 339 elsewhere to institutions (effective 2006) (from Blackwell Synergy, EBSCO Publishing, Gale Group, IngentaConnect, O C L C Online Computer Library Center, Inc., Swets Information Services).
Indexed: ABIn, ATI, BPI, IBSS.
—BLDSC (5007.661200), IE, Infotrieve, ingenta. **CCC.**
Published by: Blackwell Publishing Ltd., 9600 Garsington Rd, Oxford, OX4 2ZG, United Kingdom. TEL 44-1865-776868, FAX 44-1865-714591, customerservices@oxon.blackwellpublishing.com, http://www.blackwellpublishing.com/journals/JIFMA. Eds. Frederick Choi TEL 212-998-4010, Richard Levich TEL 212-998-0422. Circ: 600.

332.04505 NLD ISSN 1042-4431
HG3879
➤ **JOURNAL OF INTERNATIONAL FINANCIAL MARKETS, INSTITUTIONS & MONEY.** Text in English. 1991. 5/yr. EUR 301 in Europe to institutions; JPY 40,000 in Japan to institutions; USD 337 elsewhere to institutions (effective 2006). back issues avail.; reprints avail. **Document type:** *Academic/Scholarly.* **Description:** Includes original articles dealing with the international aspects of financial markets, institutions, and money.
Related titles: Microform ed.: (from PQC); Online - full text ed.: (from EBSCO Publishing, Gale Group, IngentaConnect, ScienceDirect, Swets Information Services).
Indexed: CPM, IBSS, JEL.
—BLDSC (5007.661300), IE, Infotrieve, ingenta. **CCC.**
Published by: Elsevier BV, North-Holland (Subsidiary of: Elsevier Science & Technology), Sara Burgerhartstraat 25, Amsterdam, 1055 KV, Netherlands. TEL 31-20-485-3911, FAX 31-20-485-2457, nlinfo-f@elsevier.nl, http://www.elsevier.com/locate/intfin, http://www.elsevier.nl. Eds. C J Neely, I Mathur. **Subscr. to:** Elsevier BV, PO Box 211, Amsterdam 1000 AE, Netherlands. TEL 31-20-485-3757, FAX 31-20-485-3432, http://www.elsevier.nl.

332 GBR ISSN 0261-5606
HG3879
➤ **JOURNAL OF INTERNATIONAL MONEY AND FINANCE.** Text in English. 1982. 8/yr. EUR 88 in Europe to individuals; JPY 12,300 in Japan to individuals; USD 99 to individuals except Europe and Japan; EUR 986 in Europe to institutions; JPY 130,900 in Japan to institutions; USD 1,104 to institutions except Europe and Japan (effective 2006). bk.rev. illus. index. back issues avail.; reprints avail. **Document type:** *Academic/Scholarly.* **Description:** Covers foreign exchange, balance of payments, international interactions of prices, incomes and money, multinational corporate finance, foreign aid, and international economic institutions.
Related titles: Microform ed.: (from PQC); Online - full text ed.: (from EBSCO Publishing, Gale Group, IngentaConnect, ScienceDirect, Swets Information Services).

▼ *new title* ➤ *refereed* ✶ *unverified* ♦ *full entry avail.*

Indexed: ABIn, APEL, ASCA, BLI, BPIA, BibInd, CPM, CurCont, ESPM, IBSS, JEL, PAIS, PCI, RASB, RiskAb, SSCI.
—BLDSC (5007.677000), IDS, IE, Infotrieve, ingenta. **CCC.**
Published by: Pergamon (Subsidiary of: Elsevier Science & Technology), The Boulevard, Langford Ln, East Park, Kidlington, Oxford OX5 1GB, United Kingdom. TEL 44-1865-843000, FAX 44-1865-843010, http://www.elsevier.com/locate/jimf. Eds. James R Lothian, Michael T Melvin. **Subscr. to:** Elsevier BV, PO Box 211, Amsterdam 1000 AE, Netherlands. TEL 31-20-485-3757, FAX 31-20-485-3432, nlinfo-f@elsevier.nl, http://www.elsevier.nl.

332 CAN ISSN 1204-5357
HG1708.7
JOURNAL OF INTERNET BANKING AND COMMERCE. Text in English. bi-m. **Document type:** *Journal, Academic/Scholarly.* **Description:** Provides a forum for discussion and informs professionals on recent trends and developments in electronic banking and commerce.
Media: Online - full content.
Indexed: C&CSA, ESPM, RiskAb.
Published by: Array Development TEL 613-723-1581, FAX 613-723-8938, http://www.arraydev.com/commerce/jibc/announce.htm, http://www.infop.com/karoma. Ed. Gord Jenkins TEL 613-723-1581.

B

332.6 USA ISSN 1545-9144
HJ4529
▼ ➤ **JOURNAL OF INVESTMENT MANAGEMENT.** Text in English. 2003. q. USD 250 combined subscription domestic print & online; USD 275 combined subscription foreign print & online (effective 2005). **Document type:** *Journal, Academic/Scholarly.*
Related titles: Online - full text ed.: ISSN 1545-9152.
—BLDSC (5008.053000), IE.
Published by: Stallion Press, 3658 Mt. Diablo Blvd. Ste. 200, Lafayette, CA 94549. TEL 925-299-7800, FAX 925-299-7815, http://www.joim.com. Ed. H. Gifford Fong. Circ: 13,000.

➤ **JOURNAL OF MANAGEMENT & GOVERNANCE.** see *BUSINESS AND ECONOMICS—Management*

332 USA ISSN 1527-4314
HG178.3
JOURNAL OF MICROFINANCE. Text in English. 1999. s-a. USD 45 to individuals; USD 125 to libraries (effective 2005). adv. **Description:** Provides a forum for information related to microfinance and microenterprise development. Focuses on case studies from the field.
Related titles: Online - full text ed.: (from ProQuest Information & Learning).
Indexed: ABIn, BLI.
—**CCC.**
Published by: Brigham Young University, Marriott School of Management, 790 TNRB, Provo, UT 84602. TEL 801-378-1770, FAX 801-378-8975, http://www.microjournal.com/. adv.: page USD 350.

JOURNAL OF MODERN BUSINESS. see *BUSINESS AND ECONOMICS—Management*

332 NLD ISSN 0304-3932
CODEN: JMOEDW
➤ **JOURNAL OF MONETARY ECONOMICS.** Text in English. 1975. 8/yr. EUR 98 in Europe to individuals; JPY 13,100 in Japan to individuals; USD 99 to individuals except Europe and Japan; EUR 1,618 in Europe to institutions; JPY 214,800 in Japan to institutions; USD 1,810 to institutions except Europe and Japan; EUR 58 in Europe to students; JPY 7,700 in Japan to students; USD 64 to students except Europe and Japan (effective 2006). adv. illus. Index. back issues avail.; reprint service avail. from ISI. **Document type:** *Academic/Scholarly.* **Description:** Discusses problems in the broader field of monetary economics, with particular emphasis on monetary analysis.
Incorporates (1978-2002): Carnegie-Rochester Conference Series on Public Policy (0167-2231)
Related titles: Microform ed.: (from PQC); Online - full text ed.: (from EBSCO Publishing, Gale Group, IngentaConnect, ScienceDirect, Swets Information Services).
Indexed: ABIn, ASCA, BLI, BPIA, BusI, CPM, CREJ, CurCont, DIP, ELLIS, ESPM, IBR, IBSS, IBZ, JEL, LRI, ManagCont, PAIS, RASB, RiskAb, SSCI, T&II, WBA.
—BLDSC (5020.860000), IDS, IE, Infotrieve, ingenta. **CCC.**
Published by: Elsevier BV, North-Holland (Subsidiary of: Elsevier Science & Technology), Sara Burgerhartstraat 25, Amsterdam, 1055 KV, Netherlands. TEL 31-20-485-3911, FAX 31-20-485-2457, nlinfo-f@elsevier.nl, http://www.elsevier.com/locate/jme, http://www.elsevier.nl. Eds. Charles Plosser, Robert G. King. **Subscr. to:** Elsevier BV, PO Box 211, Amsterdam 1000 AE, Netherlands. TEL 31-20-485-3757, FAX 31-20-485-3432, http://www.elsevier.nl.

332 USA ISSN 0022-2879
HG201 CODEN: JMCBBT
➤ **JOURNAL OF MONEY, CREDIT & BANKING.** Text in English. 1969. 8/yr. USD 79 domestic to individuals; USD 221 domestic to institutions; USD 111.53 in Canada to individuals; USD 263.47 in Canada to institutions; USD 106 foreign to individuals; USD 248 foreign to institutions; USD 310 combined subscription domestic to institutions print & online eds.; USD 358.70 combined subscription in Canada to institutions print & online eds.; USD 337 combined subscription foreign to institutions print & online eds. (effective 2005). adv. bk.rev. illus. index. back issues avail.; reprint service avail. from SCH. **Document type:** *Journal, Academic/Scholarly.* **Description:** Reports major findings in the study of financial institutions, financial markets, monetary and fiscal policy, credit markets, money and banking.
Related titles: CD-ROM ed.: (from ProQuest Information & Learning); Microfiche ed.: (from PQC); Online - full text ed.: ISSN 1538-4616. USD 221 domestic to institutions; USD 236.47 in Canada to institutions; USD 221 elsewhere to institutions (effective 2005) (from EBSCO Publishing, Florida Center for Library Automation, Gale Group, H.W. Wilson, JSTOR (Web-based Journal Archive), O C L C Online Computer Library Center, Inc., Project MUSE, ProQuest Information & Learning, Swets Information Services).
Indexed: ABIn, APEL, ASCA, ATI, BLI, BPI, BPIA, BusI, CPM, CREJ, CurCont, DIP, ESPM, IBR, IBSS, IBZ, JEL, ManagCont, PAIS, RASB, RiskAb, SSCI, SSI, WBA.
—BLDSC (5020.880000), IDS, IE, Infotrieve, ingenta. **CCC.**
Published by: Ohio State University Press, 180 Pressey Hall, 1070 Carmack Rd, Columbus, OH 43210-1002. TEL 614-292-6930, FAX 614-292-2065, jmcb@ecolan.sbs.ohio-state.edu, ohiostatepress@osu.edu, http://www.ohiostatepress.org. Eds. Kenneth West, Masao Osaki. Circ: 3,500 (paid).

364.168 GBR ISSN 1368-5201
K10
➤ **JOURNAL OF MONEY LAUNDERING CONTROL.** Text in English. 1997. q. GBP 349 to institutions (effective 2006). adv. back issues avail.; reprint service avail. from PSC. **Document type:** *Journal, Academic/Scholarly.* **Description:** Keeps readers abreast of the latest techniques, ideas and practices in the prevention and identification of money laundering.
Related titles: Online - full text ed.: (from EBSCO Publishing, ProQuest Information & Learning).
Indexed: ABIn, BLI, CJPI.
—BLDSC (5020.890000), IE, ingenta. **CCC.**
Published by: Emerald Group Publishing Limited, 60-62 Toller Ln, Bradford, W Yorks BD8 9BY, United Kingdom. TEL 44-1274-777700, FAX 44-1274-785200, subscriptions@emeraldinsight.com, infomation@emeraldinsight.com, http://www.emeraldinsight.com, http://www.emeraldinsight.com/. Eds. Barry Rider, Chizu Nakajima. R&P Mr. John Eggleton. Circ: 900 (paid).

➤ **JOURNAL OF MULTINATIONAL FINANCIAL MANAGEMENT.** see *BUSINESS AND ECONOMICS—Management*

332 USA ISSN 1071-846X
HG4930
JOURNAL OF MUTUAL FUND SERVICES. Text in English. 8/yr. USD 795; USD 895 foreign. adv. back issues avail. **Document type:** *Trade.*
Formerly (until 1993): F A C S - Funds Agents, Custodians, Suppliers (0887-8161)
Published by: Securities Data Publishing (Subsidiary of: Thomson Financial / I M G Media), 195 Broadway, New York, NY 10007. TEL 212-765-5311, FAX 212-765-6123. Ed. Elizabeth Pease. Adv. contact Kelly Doherty.

332 657 USA
HG1616.C6
JOURNAL OF PERFORMANCE MANAGEMENT. Text in English. 1985. 3/yr. USD 100 in North America; USD 110 elsewhere (effective 2000). **Document type:** *Academic/Scholarly.* **Description:** Covers issues and practice advances affecting cost and management accounting in the financial services industry.
Formerly: Journal of Bank Cost & Management Accounting (1070-941X)
Related titles: Microform ed.: (from PQC); Online - full text ed.: (from Northern Light Technology, Inc.).
Indexed: ATI.
—BLDSC (5030.542300), IE, ingenta.
Published by: Association for Management Information in Financial Services, 7950 E La Junta Rd, Scottsdale, AZ 85255-2798. FAX 480-515-2101, ami@amifs.org, http://www.amifs.org. R&P Nancy Basinger. Circ: 600.

332 USA ISSN 1540-6717
HG179
JOURNAL OF PERSONAL FINANCE. Text in English. 2002 (Sept.). s-a. USD 55 domestic to individuals; USD 68 foreign to individuals; USD 98 domestic to institutions; USD 115 foreign to institutions (effective 2002).
Published by: International Association of Registered Financial Consultants, 2507 N. Verity Pkwy, Middleton, OH 45042. TEL 800-532-9060, FAX 513-424-5752, http://www.iarfc.org.

JOURNAL OF REAL ESTATE FINANCE AND ECONOMICS. see *REAL ESTATE*

332 SGP ISSN 0219-869X
▼ ➤ **JOURNAL OF RESTRUCTURING FINANCE.** Text in English. 2004 (Mar.). q. SGD 180, USD 105, EUR 99 to individuals; SGD 595, USD 347, EUR 327 combined subscription to institutions print & online eds. (effective 2006). back issues avail. **Document type:** *Journal, Academic/Scholarly.* **Description:** Covers the business reorganization processes, turnaround and reinvention and also, to research on economic reform and transformation.
Related titles: Online - full content ed.; Online - full text ed.: (from EBSCO Publishing, O C L C Online Computer Library Center, Inc., Swets Information Services).
Indexed: ESPM, RiskAb.
—BLDSC (5052.038600).
Published by: World Scientific Publishing Co. Pte. Ltd., 5 Toh Tuck Link, Singapore, 596224, Singapore. TEL 65-466-5775, FAX 65-467-7667, editor.jrf@gmx.de, wspc@wspc.com.sg, http://www.worldscinet.com/jrf/jrf.shtml, http://www.worldscientific.com. Ed. Mamouda Mbemap. **Dist. by:** World Scientific Publishing Co., Inc., 1060 Main St, River Edge, NJ 07661. TEL 201-487-9655, FAX 201-487-9656, 888-977-2665; World Scientific Publishing Ltd., 57 Shelton St, London WC2H 9HE, United Kingdom. TEL 44-20-78360888, FAX 44-20-78362020, sales@wspc.co.uk.

332 332.6 GBR ISSN 1465-1211
➤ **THE JOURNAL OF RISK.** Text in English. 1999. q. GBP 80 domestic to qualified personnel; EUR 128 in Europe to qualified personnel; USD 148 in United States to qualified personnel; GBP 90 elsewhere to qualified personnel; GBP 315 domestic to institutions; EUR 502 in Europe to institutions; USD 535 in United States to institutions; USD 355 elsewhere to institutions (effective 2004). **Document type:** *Journal, Trade.* **Description:** Provides a dedicated medium for the dissemination of research into financial risk management, with contributions from leading academics and practitioners in the field.
Indexed: ABIn.
—BLDSC (5052.095000), IE, ingenta. **CCC.**
Published by: Risk Waters Group (Subsidiary of: Incisive Media Plc.), Haymarket House, 28-29 Haymarket, London, SW1Y 4RX, United Kingdom. TEL 44-20-74849700, FAX 44-20-79302238, http://www.riskwaters.com/jrisk/, http://www.incisivemedia.com/. Ed. Philippe Jorion. **Subscr. in the US & Canada to:** Incisive Media Plc., 270 Lafayette St, Ste 700, New York, NY 10012. TEL 212-925-6990, FAX 212-925-7585, customerservices@incisivemedia.com.

332 USA ISSN 1551-9783
HG5993
JOURNAL OF STRUCTURED FINANCE. Text in English. 1995. q. USD 365 combined subscription domestic print & online eds.; USD 440 combined subscription foreign print & online eds. (effective 2005). back issues avail. **Document type:** *Magazine, Trade.* **Description:** Provides articles and case studies on specific aspects of project finance deals.
Former titles (until 2004): Journal of Structured and Project Finance (1538-3830); (until 2001): Journal of Project Finance (1082-3220)
Related titles: Online - full text ed.: (from EBSCO Publishing, Florida Center for Library Automation, Gale Group, H.W. Wilson, O C L C Online Computer Library Center, Inc.).
Indexed: ABIn, BPI.
—BLDSC (5066.890600), IE, ingenta. **CCC.**
Published by: Institutional Investor, Journals (Subsidiary of: Euromoney Institutional Investor Plc.), 225 Park Ave S, 7th Fl., New York, NY 10003-1605. TEL 212-224-3800, FAX 212-224-3563, info@iijournals.com, http://www.iijspf.com, http://www.iijournals.com. Ed. Jonathan S. Saiger. Pub. Allison Adams TEL 212-224-3584.

332 336 USA ISSN 1547-3996
KF6495.B2
JOURNAL OF TAXATION AND REGULATION OF FINANCIAL INSTITUTION. Text in English. 1987. bi-m. USD 284 domestic; USD 314 foreign (effective 2005). **Document type:** *Journal, Trade.* **Description:** Provides in-depth guidance from the country's leading experts on current regulations and opportunities for tax benefits in the pipeline.
Former titles (until Nov.2003): Journal of Taxation of Financial Institutions (1532-544X); (until 2000): Journal of Bank Taxation (0895-4720)
Related titles: Online - full text ed.: (from O C L C Online Computer Library Center, Inc.).
Indexed: ABIn, ATI.
—BLDSC (5068.202000), IE, ingenta. **CCC.**
Published by: Civic Research Insitute, 4490 US Route 27, PO Box 585, Kingston, NJ 08528. TEL 609-683-4450, FAX 609-683-7291, order@civicresearchinstitute.com, http://www.civicresearchinstitute.com/tax2.html. Ed. John J Ensminger. Circ: 1,500.

JUMBO FLASH REPORT. see *BUSINESS AND ECONOMICS—Investments*

332.6 USA ISSN 8756-2332
JUMBO RATE NEWS. Text in English. 1983. w. USD 445 (effective 2001). charts; stat. 8 p./no. 2 cols./p.; back issues avail. **Document type:** *Newsletter, Trade.* **Description:** Covers investments at pre-screened credit-worthy banks and thrifts for jumbo CD investors.
Related titles: E-mail ed.; Fax ed.
Published by: Bauer Financial Newsletters, Inc, 2655 LeJeune Rd, PH-1A, Drawer 145510, Coral Gables, FL 33114-5510. TEL 305-445-9500, 800-388-6686, FAX 305-445-6775, http://www.jumboratenews.com, http://www.bauerfinancial.com. Ed., Pub. Paul A Bauer. R&P Caroline P Jervey TEL 305-445-9500. Circ: 3,500 (paid).

JURIDISQUE FISCAL. see *LAW*

332.3 SWE ISSN 1651-1484
JUSTITIA; kreditinformation fraan D & B. Text in Swedish. 1893. 45/yr. SEK 1,695 Paper ed. Includes Svensk Handelstidning Justitia; SEK 1,295 Online ed. Includes Svensk Handelstidning Justitia (effective 2004).
Supersedes in part (in 2002): Svensk Handelstidning Justitia (0039-6575); Which was formerly (until 1941): Justitia, Svensk Handelstidning
Related titles: Online - full text ed.
Published by: Svensk Handelstidning Justitia A-B (Subsidiary of: Dun & Bradstreet Corporation), Sveavaegen 151, Stockholm, 11346, Sweden. TEL 46-8-6955424, FAX 46-8-6193535, http://www.shj.se.

332 BEL ISSN 1374-2124
K B C ECONOMIC AND FINANCIAL BULLETIN. Text in English. 1988. m. EUR 10 (effective 2000). charts. index. **Document type:** *Bulletin, Trade.*
Former titles (until 1998): Kredietbank. Monthly Bulletin (0778-421X); (until 1991): Kredietbank. Weekly Bulletin (0023-4583)
Related titles: French ed.: K B C Courrier Economique et Financier. ISSN 1374-2108. 1946; Dutch ed.: K B C Economisch Financiele Berichten. ISSN 1374-2132. 1946; German ed.: K B C Wirtschafts- und Finanzberichte. ISSN 1374-2116.
Indexed: PAIS.
Published by: K B C Bank, Havenlaan 1, Brussels, 1080, Belgium. Ed. E de Boeck.

K D B REPORT. see *BUSINESS AND ECONOMICS*

332.7 CHE
K-GELD. Text in German. 2000. bi-m. CHF 28 (effective 2001). adv. **Document type:** *Magazine, Consumer.* **Description:** Provides information and advice on banking and finance, investments, stocks, insurance, mortgages, and taxes.
Published by: K I Media GmbH, Hottingerstr 12, Postfach 75, Zurich, 8024, Switzerland. TEL 41-1-2538383, FAX 41-1-2538484, redaktion@k-geld.ch, administration@k-tip.ch, http://www.k-geld.ch, http://www.ki-media.ch.

332.1 USA ISSN 0022-8478
THE KANSAS BANKER. Text in English. 1911. m. USD 12 (effective 2005). adv. 32 p./no.; **Document type:** *Magazine, Trade.*
Related titles: Online - full text ed.: (from Northern Light Technology, Inc., ProQuest Information & Learning).
Indexed: ABIn, BLI.
Published by: Kansas Bankers Association, 610 S W Corporate View, PO Box 4407, Topeka, KS 66604-0407. TEL 785-232-3444, FAX 785-232-3484, klynch@ksbankers.com, kers.com. Ed. Kristin Keeney. Adv. contact Sara Blubaugh. Circ: 1,500.

332.1 DNK ISSN 1603-9947
KAPITAL. Text in Danish. 1900. biennial. DKK 250 includes Kapital Nyt (effective 2005). adv. bk.rev. charts; illus.; stat. **Document type:** *Monographic series, Trade.*
Former titles (until 2004): Finans og Samfund (0905-9415); (until 1990): Sparekassen (0107-9530); (until 1971): Sparekassetidende (0038-6529)
Published by: Finansraadet/The Danish Bankers Association, Finansraadets Hus, Amaliegade 7, Copenhagen K, 1256, Denmark. TEL 45-33-701000, FAX 45-33-930260, mail@finansraadet.dk, http://www.finansraadet.dk. Ed. Mikael Winkler.

336 HRV ISSN 1330-6537
KAPITAL. Text in Croatian. 1994. m. **Document type:** *Magazine, Trade.*
Published by: Kapital d.d., Savska 141, Zagreb, 10000, Croatia. TEL 385-1-6190728, FAX 385-1-6190728. Ed. Ratko Boskovic.

332.1 DNK ISSN 1603-9955
▼ **KAPITAL NYT.** Text in Danish. 2005. 10/yr. DKK 250 includes Kapital (effective 2005). adv. **Document type:** *Newsletter, Trade.*
Related titles: E-mail ed.: ISSN 1604-5645.
Published by: Finansraadet/The Danish Bankers Association, Finansraadets Hus, Amaliegade 7, Copenhagen K, 1256, Denmark. TEL 45-33-701000, FAX 45-33-930260, mail@finansraadet.dk, http://www.finansraadet.dk. Ed. Mikael Winkler. Circ: 4,500.

332 SWE
KAPITALMARKNADEN. Text in Swedish. 2000. 11/yr.
Formerly (until 2003): Aktiemarknaden (1650-2345); Which was formed by the merger of (1985-2000): Utlaendska Aktiemarknader (1400-3058); (1980-2000): Svensk Aktiemarknad
Published by: Svenska Handelsbanken, Kungstraedgaardsgatan 2, Stockholm, 10670, Sweden. TEL 46-8-7011000, http://www.handelsbanken.se.

KARRIEREFUEHRER FINANZDIENSTLEISTUNGEN; Berufseinstieg fuer Hochschulabsolventen. see *OCCUPATIONS AND CAREERS*

332 DEU ISSN 0937-597X
KARTEN/CARDS/CARTES. Text in German. 1990. q. EUR 89.72; EUR 21 newsstand/cover (effective 2004). adv. **Document type:** *Magazine, Trade.*
Related titles: ♦ Supplement to: Bank und Markt. ISSN 1433-5204.
Published by: Fritz Knapp Verlag GmbH, Postfach 111151, Frankfurt Am Main, 60046, Germany. TEL 49-69-9708330, FAX 49-69-7078400, verlagsleitung@kreditwesen.de, http://www.kreditwesen.de. Ed. Swantje Benkelberg. adv.: B&W page EUR 4,120, color page EUR 6,220. Circ: 4,060 (paid and controlled).

332.1 USA ISSN 0023-0111
KENTUCKY BANKER. Text in English. 1938 (no.151). bi-m. adv. illus. **Document type:** *Magazine, Trade.* **Description:** Contains financial related articles on compliance, accounting, legal and legislative issues related to the banking industry.
Related titles: Online - full text ed.: (from Northern Light Technology, Inc., ProQuest Information & Learning).
Indexed: ABIn, BLI.
Published by: Kentucky Bankers Association, Ste 1000, Waterfront Plaza, 325 W Main St, Louisville, KY 40202. TEL 502-582-2453, FAX 502-584-6390, jprice@kybanks.comom. Ed., R&P, Adv. contact Joe Price. Circ: 900.

332.1 USA
KENTUCKY BANKING AND RELATED LAWS AND RULES ANNOTATED. Text in English. irreg., latest 1994. 366 p./no.;
Related titles: Diskette ed.; Online - full text ed.
Published by: (Kentucky Banker's Association), LexisNexis (Subsidiary of: LexisNexis North America), PO Box 7587, Charlottesville, VA 22906-7587. TEL 804-972-7566, 800-562-1197, FAX 800-643-1280, llp.customer.support@lexisnexis.com, http://www.lexislawpublishing.com. Ed. George Harley.

332 KEN
KENYA COMMERCIAL BANK. DIRECTOR'S REPORT AND ACCOUNTS AND EXECUTIVE CHAIRMAN'S STATEMENT. Text in English. a.
Published by: Kenya Commercial Bank, PO Box 48400, Nairobi, Kenya.

332 338 GBR
KEY NOTE MARKET ASSESSMENT. COMMERCIAL DYNAMICS IN FINANCIAL SERVICES. Variant title: Commercial Dynamics in Financial Services Market Assessment. Text in English. irreg., latest 2001, Sept. GBP 730 per issue (effective 2002). **Description:** Market analysis of the forces which are continually reshaping the financial services industry. Provides an overview including industry structure, market size and trends, developments, prospects, and major company profiles.
Published by: Key Note Ltd., Field House, 72 Oldfield Rd, Hampton, Mddx TW12 2HQ, United Kingdom. TEL 44-20-8481-8750, FAX 44-20-8783-0049, info@keynote.co.uk, http://www.keynote.co.uk. Ed. Simon Taylor.

332 338 GBR
KEY NOTE MARKET ASSESSMENT. DIRECT MORTGAGES. Text in English. 199?. irreg., latest 2001, Dec. GBP 730 per issue (effective 2002). **Description:** Provides an in-depth strategic analysis across a broad range of industries and contains an examination on the scope, dynamics and shape of key UK markets in the consumer, financial, lifestyle and business to business sectors.
Formerly (until 2001): M A P S Strategic Market Report. Direct Mortgages (1366-736X)
Published by: Key Note Ltd., Field House, 72 Oldfield Rd, Hampton, Mddx TW12 2HQ, United Kingdom. TEL 44-20-8481-8750, FAX 44-20-8783-0049, info@keynote.co.uk, http://www.keynote.co.uk. Ed. Simon Taylor.

332.1 332.102 338 GBR
KEY NOTE MARKET ASSESSMENT. ELECTRONIC BANKING. Text in English. irreg., latest 2000, Apr. GBP 730 per issue (effective 2002). **Description:** Provides an in-depth strategic analysis across a broad range of industries and contains an examination on the scope, dynamics and shape of key UK markets in the consumer, financial, lifestyle and business to business sectors.
Published by: Key Note Ltd., Field House, 72 Oldfield Rd, Hampton, Mddx TW12 2HQ, United Kingdom. TEL 44-20-8481-8750, FAX 44-20-8783-0049, info@keynote.co.uk, http://www.keynote.co.uk.

332 338 GBR
KEY NOTE MARKET ASSESSMENT. FINANCIAL SERVICES MARKETING TO A BS. Text in English. 2001. irreg., latest 2001, June. GBP 730 per issue (effective 2002). **Description:** Provides an in-depth strategic analysis across a broad range of industries and contains an examination on the scope, dynamics and shape of key UK markets in the consumer, financial, lifestyle and business to business sectors.
Published by: Key Note Ltd., Field House, 72 Oldfield Rd, Hampton, Mddx TW12 2HQ, United Kingdom. TEL 44-20-8481-8750, FAX 44-20-8783-0049, info@keynote.co.uk, http://www.keynote.co.uk. Ed. Simon Taylor.

332 338 GBR
KEY NOTE MARKET ASSESSMENT. FINANCIAL SERVICES MARKETING TO C1C2DE. Text in English. 2001. irreg., latest 2001, July. GBP 730 per issue (effective 2002). **Description:** Provides an in-depth strategic analysis across a broad range of industries and contains an examination on the scope, dynamics and shape of key UK markets in the consumer, financial, lifestyle and business to business sectors.
Published by: Key Note Ltd., Field House, 72 Oldfield Rd, Hampton, Mddx TW12 2HQ, United Kingdom. TEL 44-20-8481-8750, FAX 44-20-8783-0049, info@keynote.co.uk, http://www.keynote.co.uk. Ed. Simon Taylor.

B

332 338 GBR
KEY NOTE MARKET ASSESSMENT. INDEPENDENT FINANCIAL ADVISORS. Text in English. 1997. irreg., latest 2001, June. GBP 730 per issue (effective 2002). **Description:** Provides an in-depth strategic analysis across a broad range of industries and contains an examination on the scope, dynamics and shape of key UK markets in the consumer, financial, lifestyle and business to business sectors.
Formerly (until 2001): M A P S Strategic Market Report. Independent Financial Advisers (1461-2178)
Published by: Key Note Ltd., Field House, 72 Oldfield Rd, Hampton, Mddx TW12 2HQ, United Kingdom. TEL 44-20-8481-8750, FAX 44-20-8783-0049, info@keynote.co.uk, http://www.keynote.co.uk.

332.2 332.6 GBR
KEY NOTE MARKET ASSESSMENT. SAVINGS & INVESTMENTS. Text in English. irreg., latest 2002, June. GBP 730 per issue (effective 2002). **Description:** Provides an in-depth strategic analysis across a broad range of industries and contains an examination on the scope, dynamics and shape of key UK markets in the consumer, financial, lifestyle and business to business sectors.
Published by: Key Note Ltd., Field House, 72 Oldfield Rd, Hampton, Mddx TW12 2HQ, United Kingdom. TEL 44-20-8481-8750, FAX 44-20-8783-0049, info@keynote.co.uk, http://www.keynote.co.uk.

332 338 GBR
KEY NOTE MARKET REPORT: CREDIT & OTHER FINANCE CARDS. Variant title: Credit & Other Finance Cards Market Report. Text in English. irreg. (12th Edition), latest 1999, Dec. GBP 340 per issue (effective 2002). **Document type:** *Trade.* **Description:** Provides an overview of the UK credit and other finance cards market, including industry structure, market size and trends, developments, prospects, and major company profiles.
Formerly (until 1995): Key Note Report: Credit and Other Finance Cards (1352-6545)
Related titles: CD-ROM ed.; Online - full text ed.
Published by: Key Note Ltd., Field House, 72 Oldfield Rd, Hampton, Mddx TW12 2HQ, United Kingdom. TEL 44-20-8481-8750, FAX 44-20-8783-0049, http://www.keynote.co.uk. Ed. Emma Clarke.

332 GBR
KEY NOTE MARKET REPORT: DEBT MANAGEMENT (COMMERCIAL & CONSUMER). Variant title: Debt Management (Commercial & Consumer) Market Report. Text in English. 2001. irreg., latest 2001, Mar. GBP 340 per issue (effective 2002). **Description:** Provides an overview of a specific UK market segment and includes executive summary, market definition, market size, industry background, competitor analysis, current issues, forecasts, company profiles, and more.
Published by: Key Note Ltd., Field House, 72 Oldfield Rd, Hampton, Mddx TW12 2HQ, United Kingdom. TEL 44-20-8481-8750, FAX 44-20-8783-0049, info@keynote.co.uk, http://www.keynote.co.uk. Ed. Emma Wiggin.

332 GBR
KEY NOTE MARKET REPORT: DEBT MANAGEMENT & FACTORING. Variant title: Debt Management & Factoring Market Report. Text in English. irreg. (13th Edition), latest 1999, Nov. GBP 340 per issue (effective 2002). **Document type:** *Trade.* **Description:** Provides an overview of the UK debt management & factoring market, including industry structure, market size and trends, developments, prospects, and major company profiles.
Formerly: Key Note Report: Debt Management and Factoring
Related titles: CD-ROM ed.; Online - full text ed.
Published by: Key Note Ltd., Field House, 72 Oldfield Rd, Hampton, Mddx TW12 2HQ, United Kingdom. TEL 44-20-8481-8750, FAX 44-20-8783-0049, info@keynote.co.uk, http://www.keynote.co.uk. Ed. Nick Bardsley.

B

332 **GBR**
KEY NOTE MARKET REPORT: FACTORING & INVOICE DISCOUNTING. Variant title: Factoring & Invoice Discounting Market Report. Text in English. 2001. irreg., latest 2001, Oct. GBP 340 per issue (effective 2002). **Description:** Provides an overview of a specific UK market segment and includes executive summary, market definition, market size, industry background, competitor analysis, current issues, forecasts, company profiles, and more.
Published by: Key Note Ltd., Field House, 72 Oldfield Rd, Hampton, Mddx TW12 2HQ, United Kingdom. TEL 44-20-8481-8750, FAX 44-20-8783-0049, info@keynote.co.uk, http://www.keynote.co.uk. Ed. Dominic Fenn.

332 338 **GBR** **ISSN 1367-2398**
KEY NOTE MARKET REPORT: FINANCE HOUSES. Text in English. 1984. irreg., latest 2000, Mar. GBP 340 per issue (effective 2002). **Document type:** Trade. **Description:** Provides an overview of a specific UK market segment and includes executive summary, market definition, market size, industry background, competitor analysis, current issues, forecasts, company profiles, and more.
Formerly (until 1996): Key Note Report: Finance Houses (0951-6689)
Related titles: CD-ROM ed.; Online - full text ed.
Published by: Key Note Ltd., Field House, 72 Oldfield Rd, Hampton, Mddx TW12 2HQ, United Kingdom. TEL 44-20-8481-8750, FAX 44-20-8783-0049, info@keynote.co.uk, http://www.keynote.co.uk.

KEY NOTE MARKET REPORT: FOOTBALL CLUBS & FINANCE. see SPORTS AND GAMES—Ball Games

332 658.8 **GBR** **ISSN 1368-4043**
KEY NOTE MARKET REPORT: MORTGAGE FINANCE. Variant title: Mortgage Finance. Text in English. 1994. irreg. (3rd Edition), latest 1999, June. GBP 340 per issue (effective 2002). **Document type:** Trade. **Description:** Provides and overview of a specific UK market segment and includes executive summary, market definition, market size, industry background, competitor analysis, current issues, forecasts, company profiles, and more.
Formerly (until 1997): Key Note Report: Mortgage Finance (1354-2141)
Related titles: CD-ROM ed.; Online - full text ed.
Published by: Key Note Ltd., Field House, 72 Oldfield Rd, Hampton, Mddx TW12 2HQ, United Kingdom. TEL 44-20-8481-8750, FAX 44-20-8783-0049, info@keynote.co.uk, http://www.keynote.co.uk. Ed. Jane Griffiths.

332 **GBR** **ISSN 1467-5684**
KEY NOTE MARKET REPORT: PERSONAL BANKING. Text in English. 1993. irreg., latest 2000, Dec. GBP 340 per issue (effective 2002). **Document type:** Trade. **Description:** Provides an overview of a specific UK market segment and includes executive summary, market definition, market size, industry background, competitor analysis, current issues, forecasts, company profiles, and more.
Former titles (until 1999): Key Note Market Report: Retail Branch Banking (1461-5142); (until 1997): Key Note Report: Retail Branch Banking (1352-6987)
Related titles: CD-ROM ed.; Online - full text ed.
Published by: Key Note Ltd., Field House, 72 Oldfield Rd, Hampton, Mddx TW12 2HQ, United Kingdom. TEL 44-20-8481-8750, FAX 44-20-8783-0049, info@keynote.co.uk, http://www.keynote.co.uk. Ed. Jenny Baxter.

KEY NOTE MARKET REPORT: RUGBY CLUBS & FINANCE. see SPORTS AND GAMES—Ball Games

332 **GBR**
KEY NOTE MARKET REVIEW: PERSONAL FINANCE IN THE U K. Variant title: Personal Finance in the U K. Text in English. irreg. (5th Edition), latest 1996, Feb. GBP 565 per issue (effective 2002). **Document type:** Trade. **Description:** Designed to keep you up to date with the developments and opportunities across entire industry sectors. They provide a comprehensive analysis of the industry by drawing together key related market segments under one cover.
Related titles: CD-ROM ed.; Online - full text ed.
Published by: Key Note Ltd., Field House, 72 Oldfield Rd, Hampton, Mddx TW12 2HQ, United Kingdom. TEL 44-20-8481-8750, FAX 44-20-8783-0049, info@keynote.co.uk, http://www.keynote.co.uk. Ed. Richard Caines.

332.1 **JPN** **ISSN 0287-5306**
KINYU KENKYU/MONETARY AND ECONOMIC STUDIES. Text in Japanese. 4/yr. JPY 1,050 per issue (effective 1998). 200 p./no.; **Description:** Contains research papers written by staff of the Institute or by visiting scholars from Japan and overseas, on monetary and economic theory, as well as institutional and historical issues. Also includes minutes of conferences and various symposiums.
Related titles: ♦ English ed.: Monetary and Economic Studies. ISSN 1348-7787.
Indexed: IBSS, JEL.
—BLDSC (5908.335050), ingenta.

Published by: (Institute for Monetary and Economic Studies), Bank of Japan/Nippon Ginko, c/o Public Relations Department, 2-1-1 Hongoku-cho-Nihonbashi, Chuo-ku, Tokyo, 1030000, Japan. TEL 81-3-3279-1111, FAX 81-3-3510-1374, TELEX JPTCO J27161, http://www.boj.or.jp/en.index.htm. **Dist. by:** Tokiwa Sohgoh Service Co. Ltd., Publication and Research Department, Kyodo Bldg, 2-4 Hongokucho, Nihonbashi 3-chome, Chuo-ku, Tokyo 103-0027, Japan. TEL 81-3-3270-5713, FAX 81-3-3270-5710; **Overseas Dist. by:** Japan Publications Trading Co., Ltd., Book Export II Dept, PO Box 5030, Tokyo International, Tokyo 101-3191, Japan. TEL 81-3-32923753, FAX 81-3-32920410.

332 **JPN** **ISSN 1345-3033**
KIN'YU ZAISEI JIJO/FINANCIAL ECONOMIST WEEKLY. Text in Japanese. 1950. w. JPY 25,200 (effective 2001). adv. bk.rev. 66 p./no.; back issues avail. **Document type:** Magazine, Trade.
Published by: Institute for Financial Affairs, Inc., 19 Minami-Moto-machi, Shinjuku-ku, Tokyo, 160-8519, Japan. TEL 81-3-3355-1711, 81-3-3358-0011, FAX 81-3-3357-7416, 81-3-3358-0052, weekly@kinzai.or.jp, http://www.kinzai.com/KW/. Ed. Atsushi Asmi. Pub. Isao Kurata. R&P Shigeru Abe TEL 81-3-3355-1619. Adv. contact tomoko Harada TEL 81-3-3358-1161. Circ: 63,000.

332.024 **USA** **ISSN 1528-9729**
HC101 **CODEN: KPFMEA**
KIPLINGER'S PERSONAL FINANCE. Abbreviated title: K P F. Text in English. 1947. m. USD 23.95 domestic; USD 39.95 foreign; USD 3.50 newsstand/cover (effective 2005). adv. bk.rev.; rec.rev. charts; illus.; mkt.; stat.; tr.lit. index. reprint service avail. from PQC. **Document type:** Magazine, Consumer. **Description:** Contains advice on personal finance, including home, job, and health.
Former titles (until 2000): Kiplinger's Personal Finance Magazine (1056-697X); (until 1991): Changing Times (0009-143X)
Related titles: Braille ed.; CD-ROM ed.: (from ProQuest Information & Learning); Microfiche ed.: (from NBI, PQC); Online - full text ed.: (from bigchalk, EBSCO Publishing, Factiva, Florida Center for Library Automation, Gale Group, H.W. Wilson, LexisNexis, Northern Light Technology, Inc., O C L C Online Computer Library Center, Inc., ProQuest Information & Learning, The Dialog Corporation).
Indexed: ABIn, ARG, ATI, Acal, AgeL, BPI, BRI, CBRI, CHNI, CINAHL, Consl, CurPA, HlthInd, JHMA, MASUSE, MEDLINE, MagInd, PAIS, RGAb, RGPR, RehabLit, TOM.
—IDS. **CCC.**
Published by: Kiplinger Washington Editors, Inc., 1729 H St, N W, Washington, DC 20006. TEL 888-419-0424, FAX 202-331-1206, magazine@kiplinger.com, http://www.kiplinger.com/. Eds. Fred Frailey, Knight A Kiplinger, Kevin McCormally. Pub. Robert Kelly. Adv. contacts Alex S McKenna, Roger Steckle. B&W page USD 43,650, color page USD 63,450; trim 7 x 10. Circ: 850,000 (paid). **Dist. in UK by:** Seymour Distribution Ltd, 86 Newman St, London W1T 3EX, United Kingdom.

332 340 **DEU** **ISSN 0932-6782**
KOMMENTIERTE FINANZ RECHTSPRECHUNG; aktuelle Darstellung - Analyse - Empfehlungen. Abbreviated title: K F R. Text in German. 1987. m. EUR 126; EUR 13 newsstand/cover (effective 2002). **Document type:** Journal, Academic/Scholarly.
Published by: Verlag Neue Wirtschafts-Briefe GmbH & Co., Eschstr 22, Herne, 44629, Germany. TEL 49-2323-141900, FAX 49-2323-141123, info@nwb.de, http://www.nwb.de. Eds. Hermann-Ulrich Viskorf, Stephan Hettler. Circ: 2,000 (paid).

332.1 **KOR** **ISSN 0075-6806**
KOREA DEVELOPMENT BANK: ITS FUNCTIONS AND ACTIVITIES. Text in English. 1965. a. free.
Published by: Korea Development Bank, 10-2 Kwanch'ol-dong, Chongno-gu, C.P.O. Box 28, Seoul, Korea, S. Ed. Min Beoung Yun.

332 **KOR**
KOREA ECONOMIC RESEARCH INSTITUTE. RESEARCH PAPER. FINANCIAL STUDIES. Text in Korean. 1995. irreg. (3-4/yr.)
Published by: Korea Economic Research Institute, Yeongdungpo-ku, 28-1 Yoido dong, Seoul, 150756, Korea, S. TEL 82-2-3771-0001, FAX 82-2-785-0270, http://www.keri.org.

332 **KOR**
KOREA EXCHANGE BANK. QUARTERLY REVIEW. Text in English. 1967. q. free. charts; mkt.; stat. **Document type:** Bulletin.
Former titles (until 1991): Korea Exchange Bank. Monthly Review (0023-3889); Foreign Exchange Bank of Korea
Indexed: KES, PAIS, WBA.
Published by: Korea Exchange Bank, 1 Ulgiro, Chung-ku, Seoul, 100, Korea, S. Ed. Jong Mo Yun. Pub. Myung Sun Chang. Circ: 5,500.

332 **KOR**
KOREA INSTITUTE OF FINANCE. FINANCIAL STUDIES. Variant title: Financial Studies. Text in Korean. q. **Document type:** Academic/Scholarly. **Description:** Specializes in financial and monetary economics.

Published by: Korea Institute of Finance, 4 1 1 Ga Myong dong, Chung-gu, Seoul, 100012, Korea, S. TEL 82-2-3705-6300, FAX 82-2-3705-6309, wmaster@sun.kif.re.kr, http://www.kif.re.kr.

KOREA INSTITUTE OF FINANCE. QUARTERLY FINANCIAL REVIEW; analysis and forecast. see BUSINESS AND ECONOMICS—Economic Situation And Conditions

332 **KOR**
KOREA INSTITUTE OF FINANCE. WEEKLY FINANCIAL REVIEW. Variant title: Weekly Financial Review. Text in Korean. w. **Description:** Analyzes economic issues and changes in the domestic financial markets. Provides financial statistics as well as policy advice on relevant financial issues.
Published by: Korea Institute of Finance, 4 1 1 Ga Myong dong, Chung-gu, Seoul, 100012, Korea, S. TEL 82-2-3705-6300, FAX 82-2-3705-6309, wmaster@sun.kif.re.kr, http://www.kif.re.kr.

332 **KOR**
KOREA INSTITUTE OF FINANCE. WEEKLY INTERNATIONAL FINANCIAL REVIEW. Variant title: Weekly International Financial Review. Text in Korean. w. **Description:** Analyzes current development in the world economy and international financial markets. Discusses economy and financial prospects.
Published by: Korea Institute of Finance, 4 1 1 Ga Myong dong, Chung-gu, Seoul, 100012, Korea, S. TEL 82-2-3705-6300, FAX 82-2-3705-6309, wmaster@sun.kif.re.kr, http://www.kif.re.kr.

KOREAN ECONOMIC AND FINANCIAL OUTLOOK. see BUSINESS AND ECONOMICS—Economic Situation And Conditions

332 **KOR** **ISSN 1225-9462**
HG187.K62
KOREAN FINANCIAL REVIEW. Text in English. 1993. q. **Description:** Provides analysis and forecast of the domestic financial markets.
Indexed: BAS, IBSS.
Published by: Korea Institute of Finance, 4 1 1 Ga Myong dong, Chung-gu, Seoul, 100012, Korea, S. TEL 82-2-3705-6300, FAX 82-2-3705-6309, wmaster@sun.kif.re.kr, http://www.kif.re.kr. **Subscr. to:** KPO Box 1267, Seoul, Korea, S.

332 **DEU** **ISSN 0023-4591**
HG999.5
KREDIT UND KAPITAL. Text in English, German; Summaries in English, French, German. 1968. q. EUR 78; EUR 62.40 to students; EUR 22 newsstand/cover (effective 2006). adv. bk.rev. abstr.; stat. index. reprints avail. **Document type:** Journal, Academic/Scholarly.
Related titles: ♦ Supplement(s): Beihefte zu Kredit und Kapital. ISSN 0720-6801.
Indexed: CREJ, DIP, ELLIS, IBR, IBSS, IBZ, JEL, PAIS, PCI, RASB.
—BLDSC (5118.151000), IE, Infotrieve, ingenta. **CCC.**
Published by: Duncker und Humblot GmbH, Carl-Heinrich-Becker-Weg 9, Berlin, 12165, Germany. TEL 49-30-7900060, FAX 49-30-79000631, info@duncker-humblot.de, http://www.kredit-und-kapital.de, http://www.duncker-humblot.de. adv.: page EUR 550; trim 115 x 185. Circ: 900 (paid and controlled).

332.7 **SWE** **ISSN 1103-0895**
KREDITGUIDE; kreditinformation foer penningmarknaden. Text in Swedish. 1990. q. SEK 3,000 (effective 1998).
Published by: Standard & Poor's AB, Fack 1753, Stockholm, 11187, Sweden.

332 **DEU** **ISSN 0939-3722**
KREDITWESENGESETZ. Text in German. 1963. irreg. looseleaf. price varies. **Document type:** Monographic series, Trade.
Published by: Erich Schmidt Verlag GmbH & Co. (Berlin), Genthiner Str 30G, Berlin, 10785, Germany. TEL 49-30-250085-0, FAX 49-30-25008521, vertrieb@esvmedien.de, http://www.erich-schmidt-verlag.de.

332 **DEU** **ISSN 1861-0765**
▼ **KRISEN-, SANIERUNGS- UND INSOLVENZBERATUNG.** Variant title: K S I. Text in German. 2005. bi-m. EUR 96; EUR 19.80 newsstand/cover (effective 2006). **Document type:** Journal, Trade.
Published by: Erich Schmidt Verlag GmbH & Co. (Berlin), Genthiner Str 30G, Berlin, 10785, Germany. TEL 49-30-2500850, FAX 49-30-250085305, esv@esvmedien.de, http://www.esv.info.

332 **DEU**
KURS; Monatszeitschrift fuer Finanzdienstleistung. Text in German. m. **Document type:** Trade.
Indexed: RASB.
Published by: Verlagsgruppe Handelsblatt GmbH, Kasernenstr 67, Duesseldorf, 40213, Germany. TEL 49-211-887-0, FAX 49-211-133522.

332 **KWT**
KUWAIT INTERIM ECONOMIC AND FINANCIAL REPORT. Text in English. q.

Published by: National Bank of Kuwait, Economic Research and Planning Division, P O Box 95, Safat, 13001, Kuwait. TEL 2422011, FAX 2429442, TELEX 2204322451-NATBANK-KT.

332 KWT
KUWAIT INVESTMENT COMPANY (REPORT). Text in English. a.
Published by: Kuwait Investment Company, P O Box 1005, Safat, Kuwait.

L A R F REPORT. ANNUAL. see *BUSINESS AND ECONOMICS*

L I M R A'S VISION; effective strategy for tomorrow's leaders. see *BUSINESS AND ECONOMICS—Management*

THE L T C ANCILLARY SERVICES ACQUISITION REPORT. see *MEDICAL SCIENCES*

332 FRA ISSN 1257-1660
LAMY DROIT DU FINANCEMENT; haut de bilan, tresorerie, relations banque entreprise. Text in French. 1990. base vol. plus m. updates. EUR 585.53 print & CD-ROM eds. (effective 2004). Supplement avail.
Related titles: CD-ROM ed.: ISSN 1284-117X. FRF 3,290; Online - full text ed.: EUR 214 (effective 2003).
Published by: Lamy S.A. (Subsidiary of: Wolters Kluwer France), 21/23 rue des Ardennes, Paris, 75935 Cedex 19, France. TEL 33-1-825080800, FAX 33-1-44721388, lamy@lamy.fr, http://www.lamy.fr. Ed. Jean Deveze.

LAMY FISCAL; l'outil pratique pour connaitre et exploiter la reglementation fiscale. see *LAW*

LAMY SOCIETES COMMERCIALES. see *LAW—Corporate Law*

332.1 IND ISSN 0970-8472
LAND BANK JOURNAL. Text in English. 1963. q. INR 25. adv. bk.rev.
Former titles (until 1975): All India Central Land Development Bank Cooperative Union. Journal (0569-0196); (until 1966): All India Central Land Mortgage Bank Cooperative Union. Journal
Published by: National Cooperative Agriculture and Rural Development Banks' Federation, Shivshakti 2nd Fl., B.G. Kher Rd., Worli, Mumbai, Maharashtra 400 018, India. TEL 22-4934349. Ed. P V Prabhu. Circ: 2,000.

332 DEU
LANDESZENTRALBANK IN HESSEN. VIERTELJAHRESBERICHTE. Text in German. 1949. q.
Published by: Landeszentralbank in Hessen, Taunusanlage 5, Frankfurt Am Main, 60329, Germany.

LATIN AMERICAN FINANCE EXECUTIVE REPORT. see *BUSINESS AND ECONOMICS—Investments*

LATIN AMERICAN INFORMES ESPECIALES. see *BUSINESS AND ECONOMICS—Investments*

332 USA ISSN 1048-535X
HG185.L3
LATINFINANCE. Text in English. 1988. 10/yr. USD 235 domestic membership; USD 255 foreign membership (effective 2004); print & online eds. subscr. incld. with membership. adv. Website rev. charts; stat. **Document type:** *Magazine, Trade.*
Description: Covers business, finance, cross-border investments and capital markets in Latin America.
Related titles: Online - full text ed.: (from EBSCO Publishing, Factiva, Florida Center for Library Automation, Gale Group, H.W. Wilson, LexisNexis, O C L C Online Computer Library Center, Inc., ProQuest Information & Learning); ♦ Supplement(s): Private Banking & Money Management in Latin America. ISSN 1098-0415.
Indexed: ABIn, B&I, BLI, BPI, PAIS.
—IE, Infotrieve. **CCC.**
Published by: Latin American Financial Publications, Inc. (Subsidiary of: Euromoney Institutional Investor Plc.), 2121 Ponce de Leon Blvd, 1020, Coral Gables, FL 33134. TEL 305-357-4232, FAX 305-448-0718, advertising@latinfinace.com, editorial@latinfinance.com, subscriptions@latinfinance.com, http://www.latinfinance.com. Ed., R&P John Barham. adv.: color page USD 13,845; 8 x 10.75. Circ: 35,000.

332.1 340 USA
THE LAW AND REGULATION OF FINANCIAL INSTITUTIONS. Text in English. a. USD 115; USD 166.95 foreign. **Document type:** *Trade.*
Formerly: Bank Officers Handbook of Commercial Banking Law
Published by: W G & L Financial Reporting & Management Research (Subsidiary of: R I A), 395 Hudson St, New York, NY 10014. TEL 212-367-6300, FAX 212-367-6178. **Subscr. to:** The Park Square Bldg., 31 St James Ave, Boston, MA 02116-4112. TEL 800-950-1207.

341.751 GBR
THE LAW AND REGULATION OF INTERNATIONAL FINANCE. Text in English. 1991. irreg. (in 1 vol.), latest 2004, 2nd ed. GBP 150 (effective 2003). Supplement avail.
Published by: Butterworths (Croydon) (Subsidiary of: LexisNexis UK (Scottish Office)), Tolley House, 2 Addiscombe Rd, Croydon, Surrey CR9 5AF, United Kingdom. TEL 44-181-686-9141, FAX 44-181-287-3337, http://www.butterworths.co.uk. Ed. Ravi C Tennekoon.

332 340 USA
LAW OF BANK DEPOSITS, COLLECTIONS AND CREDIT CARDS (SUPPLEMENT). Text in English. base vol. plus s-a. updates. USD 115; USD 166.95 foreign. **Document type:** *Trade.*
Published by: W G & L Financial Reporting & Management Research (Subsidiary of: R I A), 395 Hudson St, New York, NY 10014. TEL 212-367-6300, FAX 212-367-6178. **Subscr. to:** The Park Square Bldg., 31 St James Ave, Boston, MA 02116-4112. TEL 800-950-1207.

332 340 GBR
LAW OF LOANS & BORROWING. Text in English. 1989. base vol. plus updates 2/yr. looseleaf. GBP 388 (effective 2006). **Document type:** *Journal, Trade.*
Published by: Sweet & Maxwell Ltd., 100 Avenue Road, London, NW3 3PF, United Kingdom. TEL 44-20-74491111, FAX 44-20-74491144, customer.services@sweetandmaxwell.co.uk, http://www.sweetandmaxwell.co.uk. **Subscr. to:** Cheriton House, North Way, Andover, Hants SP10 5BE, United Kingdom.

THE LAW RELATING TO BANKER AND CUSTOMER IN AUSTRALIA. see *LAW*

LAWS OF VIRGINIA RELATED TO FINANCIAL INSTITUTIONS. see *LAW—Corporate Law*

332 USA ISSN 1045-2508
HD9800.4.U6
LEASING SOURCEBOOK; the directory of the U S capital equipment leasing industry. Text in English. 1986. irreg. (approx. every 12-18 m.), latest 2001, May. USD 135 (effective 2001). **Document type:** *Directory, Trade.*
Description: Directory of firms engaged in capital equipment leasing or providing services to the capital equipment leasing industry.
Published by: Bibliotechnology Systems & Publishing Co, PO Box 657, Lincoln, MA 01773. TEL 781-259-0524, FAX 781-259-9861, http://www.leasingsourcebook.com, bibliotech@leasingsourcebook.com. Ed., Pub. Barbara B Low.

332 657 USA ISSN 1058-7101
LEDGER QUARTERLY. Text in English. 1989. q. looseleaf. USD 67 (effective 2002). **Document type:** *Newsletter, Trade.*
Description: Provides financial and accounting information to community associations.
Published by: Community Associations Institute, 225 Reinekers Lane, Ste. 300, Alexandria, VA 22314. TEL 703-548-8600, FAX 703-836-6907, http://www.caionline.com, http://www.caionline.org. Ed. Gary Porter. Circ: 2,650.

LEGALINES: SALES & SECURED TRANSACTIONS KEYED TO THE SPEIDEL CASEBOOK. see *LAW—Corporate Law*

331 USA
LEGALINES: SECURITIES REGULATION KEYED TO THE JENNINGS CASEBOOK. Text in English. irreg., latest vol.7. USD 22.95 per vol.. **Document type:** *Trade.*
Published by: Gilbert Law Summaries (Subsidiary of: B A R / B R I Group), 111 W Jackson, 7th Fl, Chicago, IL 60604. TEL 312-853-3662, 800-787-8717, FAX 312-853-3622, http://www.gilbertlaw.com.

332 USA
LEGISLATIVE AND REGULATORY UPDATE. Text in English. 12/yr. USD 395 domestic to non-members; USD 474 foreign to non-members; USD 245 domestic to members. adv. **Document type:** *Newsletter, Trade.*
Related titles: ♦ Supplement to: A B A Bank Compliance. ISSN 0887-0187.
Published by: American Bankers Association, 1120 Connecticut Ave NW, Washington, DC 20036-3971. TEL 202-663-5268, 800-338-0626, FAX 202-828-4540, custserv@aba.com, http://www.aba.com. Ed. Cris Naser. Adv. contact Laurence Price TEL 202-663-5378. Circ: 4,500 (paid).

LENDER LIABILITY. see *LAW—Corporate Law*

LENDER LIABILITY LAW AND LITIGATION. see *LAW—Corporate Law*

LENDER LIABILITY LAW REPORT. see *LAW—Corporate Law*

332 USA
LENDING INTELLIGENCE MAGAZINE. Text in English. bi-m. USD 49.95 (effective 2002). **Document type:** *Magazine, Trade.* **Description:** Provides in-depth coverage of all aspects of consumer lending, from origination techniques to bleeding-edge technology updates.
Related titles: Online - full text ed.: Lendingintelligence.com.
Published by: Royal Media Group, 1359 Broadway, Ste 1512, New York, NY 10018. TEL 800-320-4418, FAX 212-564-8973, info@lendingintelligence.com, http://www.lendingintelligence.com.

332.1 LSO
LESOTHO BANK. ANNUAL REPORT. Text in English. a. charts. **Document type:** *Corporate.* **Description:** Reports on financial highlights, international economic scene, past and present financial performance, and financial statements.
Published by: Lesotho Bank, Lesotho Development Bank, Lesotho Bank Centre, Kingways St, PO Box 999, Maseru, 100, Lesotho. TEL 266-314333, FAX 266-326119, TELEX LESBANK 4366 LO.

332 ITA ISSN 0391-7711
LETTERA FINANZIARIA. Text in Italian. 52/yr.
Address: Via Giovanni de Alessandri, 11, Milan, MI 20144, Italy. TEL 39-02-4986250. Ed. Antonio Calabro.

LETTERS OF CREDIT. see *LAW*

LETTERS OF CREDIT. see *LAW*

LA LETTRE DE L'EXPANSION. see *BUSINESS AND ECONOMICS—Production Of Goods And Services*

332.1 DEU
LFA-REPORT. Text in German. q. **Document type:** *Magazine, Trade.*
Published by: (LfA Foerderbank Bayern), BurdaYukom Publishing GmbH (Subsidiary of: Hubert Burda Media Holding GmbH & Co. KG), Schleissheimer Str 141, Munich, 80797, Germany. TEL 49-89-306200, FAX 49-89-30620100, info@burdayukom.de, http://www.yukom.de. Circ: 20,000 (controlled).

332 FRA
LES LIAISONS FINANCIERES. Text in French. 1966. a. adv.
Former titles: Collection Radiographie du Capital - Les Liaisons Financieres; Liaisons Financieres en France (0075-8957)
Published by: D A F S A, 42 rue Emeriau, Paris, 75015, France. FAX 40-60-51-51, TELEX 206 065.

LIST OF STOCK EXCHANGE PARTICIPANTS. see *BUSINESS AND ECONOMICS—Investments*

332 GBR
LLOYDS TSB. ECONOMIC BULLETIN. Text in English. 1979. q. GBP 12. **Document type:** *Bulletin.* **Description:** Provides an analysis of trends in major industrialized countries, along with statistics and forecasts.
Formerly: Lloyds Bank Economic Bulletin (0261-0175)
Indexed: WBA.
—**CCC.**
Published by: Lloyds TSB, 71 Lombard St, London, EC3P 3BS, United Kingdom. TEL 44-171-356-1994, FAX 44-171-356-1997, http://www.lloydstsbcommercial.com. Ed. Patrick Foley. Circ: 32,000.

332 USA
LOAN COLLECTIONS & TECHNOLOGY MAGAZINE. Text in English. m. USD 295 (effective 2002). **Document type:** *Magazine, Trade.* **Description:** Covers repossessions, foreclosure, bankruptcy, and regulatory changes in all 50 states.
Published by: Royal Media Group, 1359 Broadway, Ste 1512, New York, NY 10018. TEL 800-320-4418, FAX 212-564-8973, info@lendingintelligence.com.

332 USA ISSN 1049-2240
THE LOAN INVESTOR✶ . Text in English. fortn.
Published by: Loan Pricing Corporation, 500 Seventh Ave, 12th Fl, New York, NY 10018. americas@loanpricing.com. Ed. Floyd Loomis.

332 USA ISSN 1529-5680
LOAN MARKET WEEK; the newsweekly of the loan syndication, trading and investment markets. Text in English. 1977. w. (51x/yr). USD 2,420 combined subscription domestic print & online eds.; USD 2,495 combined subscription foreign print & online eds. (effective 2005). adv. reprint service avail. from PQC. **Document type:** *Newsletter, Trade.* **Description:** Contains current news on primary issuance and detailed coverage of the secondary market as well as the emergence of new nonbank investors and loan-investment vehicles.
Formerly (until 199?): Bank Letter
Related titles: CD-ROM ed.; Online - full text ed.: (from Florida Center for Library Automation, Gale Group, O C L C Online Computer Library Center, Inc.).
—**CCC.**
Published by: Institutional Investor News (Subsidiary of: Euromoney Institutional Investor Plc.), 225 Park Ave S, 7th Fl, New York, NY 10003-1605. TEL 212-224-3800, FAX 212-224-3491, info@iiplatinum.com, http://www.loanmarketweek.com, http://www.iinews.com. Pub. Nanzeen Kanga TEL 212-224-3005. **Subscr. to:** New Orders, PO Box 5063, Brentwood, TN 37024. TEL 615-377-3322, 800-945-2034, 800-715-9197, FAX 615-337-0525, vlockridge@sunbeltfs.com.

332 USA
LOANS AND SECURITIES AT ALL COMMERCIAL BANKS. Text in English. m. USD 5. **Document type:** *Government.*

▼ new title ➤ refereed ✶ unverified ♦ full entry avail.

Published by: U.S. Federal Reserve System, Board of Governors, Publications Services, Rm MS 138, Washington, DC 20551. TEL 202-452-3244, FAX 202-728-5886.

L'OBSERVATEUR DE L'IMMOBILIER. see *HOUSING AND URBAN PLANNING*

332 340 GBR
LOCAL GOVERNMENT FINANCE: LAW & PRACTICE. Text in English. 1994. 2 base vols. plus updates 2/yr. looseleaf. GBP 315 base vol(s).; GBP 157, EUR 236 updates in Europe; GBP 165, USD 300 updates elsewhere (effective 2006). **Document type:** *Journal, Trade.*
Published by: Sweet & Maxwell Ltd., 100 Avenue Road, London, NW3 3PF, United Kingdom. TEL 44-20-74491111, FAX 44-20-74491144, customer.services@sweetandmaxwell.co.uk, http://www.sweetandmaxwell.co.uk. **Subscr. to:** Cheriton House, North Way, Andover, Hants SP10 5BE, United Kingdom.

332 ITA
LOMBARD. Text in Italian. 1987. bi-m. EUR 200 (effective 2005). adv. **Document type:** *Magazine, Consumer.*
Related titles: Online - full text ed.
Indexed: PAIS.
Published by: (Lombard Editori Srl), Class Editori, Via Marco Burigozzo 5, Milan, MI 20122, Italy. TEL 39-02-582191, http://www.classeditori.com. Ed. Ettore Mazzotti. Adv. contact Danilo Della Mura. Circ: 21,851.

332 GBR ISSN 0307-0360
LONDON CURRENCY REPORT. Text in English. 1972. 10/yr. GBP 450 domestic; USD 950 foreign (effective 2003). back issues avail. **Document type:** *Trade.* **Description:** From a geostrategic perspective, covers global currency and economic developments, with regional and country reports.
Incorporates (1980-1999): Gold and Silver Survey (0196-3546)
Published by: World Reports Ltd., 108 Horseferry Rd, London, SW1P 2EF, United Kingdom. TEL 44-20-72223836, FAX 44-20-72330185, subs@worldreports.org, http://www.worldreports.org. Ed. Christopher Story. **US subscr. to:** 280 Madison Ave, Ste 280, New York, NY 10016-0802. TEL 212-679-0095, FAX 212-679-1094.

332 GBR
LONDON SCHOOL OF ECONOMICS AND POLITICAL SCIENCE. FINANCIAL MARKETS GROUP. QUARTERLY REVIEW. Text in English. q. **Document type:** *Academic/Scholarly.*
Published by: London School of Economics and Political Science, Financial Markets Group, Houghton St, London, WC2A 2AE, United Kingdom. p.maddicott@lse.ac.uk, http://fmg.lse.ac.uk/publications/reviews/reviews.htm.

332 GBR ISSN 1359-9151
LONDON SCHOOL OF ECONOMICS AND POLITICAL SCIENCE, FINANCIAL MARKETS GROUP. SPECIAL PAPER. Text in English. 1987. irreg.
—BLDSC (8368.310000), IE, ingenta.
Published by: London School of Economics and Political Science, Financial Markets Group, Houghton St, London, WC2A 2AE, United Kingdom.

332 USA
A LONG CYCLE OBSERVER. Text in English. m. USD 36. **Document type:** *Newsletter.* **Description:** Provides financial advice and discusses issues relating to financial markets.
Published by: Long Cycle Observer, PO Box 4132, White River Junction, VT 05001. Ed. Andrew Ralph.

332 GBR ISSN 0958-0654
LOUGHBOROUGH UNIVERSITY BANKING CENTRE. RESEARCH PAPER SERIES. Cover title: L U B C Research Monograph. Text in English. 1987. irreg. **Document type:** *Monographic series.*
Indexed: RefZh.
—BLDSC (5914.655170).
Published by: Loughborough University Banking Centre, Loughborough University, Business School, Loughborough, United Kingdom. TEL 44-1509-223118, J.B.Howcroft@lboro.ac.uk, http://www.lboro.ac.uk/departments/bs/research/rgbankce.html.

332.1 USA ISSN 1050-379X
LOUISIANA BANKER. Text in English. 1934. s-m. USD 15 (effective 2005). adv. **Document type:** *Newsletter, Trade.*
Formerly (until 1989): L B A Banker (0895-1640)
Indexed: BLI.
Published by: Louisiana Bankers Association, PO Box 2871, Baton Rouge, LA 70821. TEL 225-387-3282, FAX 225-343-3159, foster@lba.org, http://www.lba.org. Ed., Pub. Jayme Foster. Circ: 2,500 (paid).

LOUISIANA BUSINESS CREDIT DIRECTORY. see *BUSINESS AND ECONOMICS—Trade And Industrial Directories*

332 USA
LOUISIANA COMMERCIAL FINANCING FORMS. Text in English. 1991. 2-3 updates/yr), 2 base vols. plus irreg. updates. looseleaf. USD 170.
Published by: LexisNexis (Subsidiary of: LexisNexis North America), PO Box 7587, Charlottesville, VA 22906-7587. TEL 804-972-7600, 800-562-1197, FAX 804-972-7666, llp.customer.support@lexis-nexis.com, http://www.lexislawpublishing.com. Eds. James A Stuckey, Philip Claverie.

LUMBERMENS RED BOOK; reference book of the Lumbermens Credit Association. see *FORESTS AND FORESTRY—Lumber And Wood*

332 DEU ISSN 0941-1089
M & A REVIEW. (Mergers & Acquisitions) Text in English, German. 1990. m. adv. bk.rev. charts; illus.; stat. back issues avail. **Document type:** *Trade.*
Related titles: Online - full text ed.
Indexed: DIP, IBR, IBZ.
Published by: Verlagsgruppe Handelsblatt GmbH, Kasernenstr 67, Duesseldorf, 40213, Germany. TEL 49-211-887-0, FAX 49-211-133522, mar@unisg.ch.

333.33 GBR
M I R A S LENDERS MANUAL. Text in English. base vol. plus irreg. updates. looseleaf. GBP 200 to non-members; GBP 85 to members. **Document type:** *Trade.* **Description:** Covers practical and legal aspects of mortgage lending and borrowing.
Published by: Council of Mortgage Lenders, 3 Savile Row, London, W1X 1AF, United Kingdom. TEL 44-20-74370075, FAX 44-207-4343791.

M P T REVIEW; specializing in modern portfolio theory. (Modern Portfolio Theory) see *BUSINESS AND ECONOMICS—Investments*

332 737 USA ISSN 1055-3851
HG353
M R I BANKERS' GUIDE TO FOREIGN CURRENCY. Text in English, French, German, Portuguese, Spanish. 1991. q. USD 225 (effective 2001). adv. 256 p./no.; back issues avail. **Document type:** *Trade.* **Description:** Provides information on the monetary units and currency regulations, along with description and full color illustration of all current banknotes of all countries of the world.
Published by: Monetary Research Institute, 1014 Witte Rd, 200, P O Box 3174, Houston, TX 77253-3174. TEL 713-827-1796, FAX 713-827-8665, aefron@mriguide.com, info@mriguide.com, http://www.mriguide.com, http://www.mriguide.com. Ed., Pub., Adv. contact Arnoldo Efron. Circ: 13,000.

332.1 IND ISSN 0076-2563
MAHARASHTRA STATE FINANCIAL CORPORATION. ANNUAL REPORT. Text in English. 1963. a. free. charts; stat. **Document type:** *Corporate.*
Published by: Maharashtra State Financial Corporation, New Excelsior Bldg., 7, 8 & 9 th Floors, Amrit Keshav Nayak Marg, Fort, Mumbai, Maharashtra 400 001, India.

MAINE GOVERNMENT REGISTER. see *PUBLIC ADMINISTRATION*

MAJOR FINANCIAL INSTITUTIONS OF EUROPE. see *BUSINESS AND ECONOMICS—Trade And Industrial Directories*

MAJOR FINANCIAL INSTITUTIONS OF EUROPE (YEAR). see *BUSINESS AND ECONOMICS—Trade And Industrial Directories*

MAJOR FINANCIAL INSTITUTIONS OF THE ARAB WORLD (YEAR). see *BUSINESS AND ECONOMICS—Trade And Industrial Directories*

MAJOR FINANCIAL INSTITUTIONS OF THE FAR EAST & AUSTRALASIA (YEAR). see *BUSINESS AND ECONOMICS—Trade And Industrial Directories*

MAJOR FINANCIAL INSTITUTIONS OF THE WORLD (YEAR). see *BUSINESS AND ECONOMICS—Trade And Industrial Directories*

332 USA
MAJOR NONDEPOSIT FUNDS OF COMMERCIAL BANKS. Text in English. m. USD 5. **Document type:** *Government.*
Published by: U.S. Federal Reserve System, Board of Governors, Publications Services, Rm MS 138, Washington, DC 20551. TEL 202-452-3244, FAX 202-728-5886.

332.1 MWI ISSN 0076-3322
MALAWI. POST OFFICE SAVINGS BANK. ANNUAL REPORT. Text in English. 1964. a. **Document type:** *Government.*
Published by: Post Office Savings Bank, PO Box 521, Blantyre, Malawi. Circ: 300.

THE MANAGED CARE ACQUISITION REPORT. see *BUSINESS AND ECONOMICS*

MANAGING 401K PLANS YEARBOOK. see *BUSINESS AND ECONOMICS—Personnel Management*

332 USA
MANAGING CREDIT, RECEIVABLES & COLLECTIONS YEARBOOK. Text in English. a. USD 224.95 print & online eds. (effective 2003). **Description:** Provides information on successful collections techniques, how to minimize bad debt ratios, and the latest ideas on enhancing the quality of your receivable and more.
Related titles: Online - full text ed.: USD 219 (effective 2003); ♦ Cumulative ed. of: I O M A's Report on Managing Credit, Receivables and Collections. ISSN 1074-8903.
Published by: Institute of Management & Administration, Inc., 3 Park Ave, New York, NY 10016-5902. TEL 212-244-0360, FAX 212-564-0465, subserve@ioma.com, http://www.ioma.com. Ed. Mary Schaeffer.

332.1 USA ISSN 1062-1709
MANAGING TECHNOLOGY. Text in English. 1987. a.
Former titles (until 1990): Technology, the Big Gamble (1051-2985); (until 1989): Managing Technology (1042-8992)
Related titles: ♦ Supplement to: American Banker. ISSN 0002-7561.
Published by: Thomson Financial Media, One State St Plaza, 27th Fl, New York, NY 10004-1549. TEL 212-803-8200, FAX 212-292-5216, custserv@thomsonmedia.com, http://www.thomsonmedia.com.

▼ **MANAGING THE MARGIN**; strategies for generating new revenue and controlling costs. see *HEALTH FACILITIES AND ADMINISTRATION*

332 CAN ISSN 0848-5542
MANITOBA. CO-OPERATIVE LOANS AND LOANS GUARANTEE BOARD. ANNUAL REPORT. Text in English. 1971. a. free. **Document type:** *Government.*
Published by: Co-Operative Loans and Loans Guarantee Board, 155 Carlton St, 7th Fl, Winnipeg, MB R3C 3H8, Canada. FAX 204-945-2302. Circ: 100.

658.15 USA ISSN 1524-5853
KF889
MANUAL OF CREDIT AND COMMERCIAL LAWS. Text in English. 1898. a. USD 125 to non-members (effective 1999). **Document type:** *Trade.*
Formerly (until 1997): Credit Manual of Commercial Laws (0070-1467)
Indexed: ATI.
—CCC.
Published by: National Association of Credit Management, 8840 Columbia 100 Parkway, Columbia, MD 21045. TEL 410-740-5560, FAX 410-740-5574. Ed. Megan Snyder. R&P Karron Davis.

332.1 ISR ISSN 0076-4515
MARITIME BANK OF ISRAEL. ANNUAL REPORT✶ /BANK HA-SAPANUT LE-YISRAEL. ANNUAL REPORT. Text in English, Hebrew. a. free. **Document type:** *Corporate.*
Published by: Maritime Bank of Israel Ltd., 16 Ahad Ha an St., P O Box 29373, Tel Aviv, 65142, Israel.

332.1 OMN
AL-MARKAZI. Text in Arabic, English. 1975. bi-m. free. **Document type:** *Newspaper.* **Description:** Highlights current economic and banking issues and economic activities in Oman.
Published by: Central Bank of Oman, P O Box 1161, Muscat, 112, Oman. TEL 702222, FAX 707913, TELEX 3794. Ed. Fuaad Sajwani.

332 GBR
THE MARKET DATA INDUSTRY. Short title: M D I. Text in English. q. USD 4,995 (effective 2000). **Document type:** *Trade.* **Description:** Contains facts and analyses on the strategies and positioning of the major market data vendors.
Published by: Risk Waters Group (Subsidiary of: Incisive Media Plc.), Haymarket House, 28-29 Haymarket, London, SW1Y 4RX, United Kingdom. TEL 44-20-74849700, FAX 44-20-74849833.

332.45 GBR ISSN 1358-0779
MARKET INSIGHT. EMERGING MARKETS SERVICE. Text in English. 1993. 3/m. GBP 395, USD 595 for fax edition. **Document type:** *Newsletter.*
Supersedes in part (in 1995): Market Insight
Related titles: E-mail ed.
Published by: Markets International Ltd., Aylworth, Naunton, Cheltenham, Glos GL54 3AH, United Kingdom. TEL 44-1451-850367, FAX 44-1451-850055, marketsinternational@compuserve.com.

332.45 GBR ISSN 1358-0787
MARKET INSIGHT. WEEKLY MAJOR MARKETS SERVICE. Text in English. 1993. w. GBP 395, USD 695 for fax edition. **Document type:** *Newsletter.*
Supersedes in part (in 1995): Marketing Insight
Related titles: E-mail ed.
Published by: Markets International Ltd., Aylworth, Naunton, Cheltenham, Glos GL54 3AH, United Kingdom. TEL 44-1451-850367, FAX 44-1451-850055, marketsinternational@compuserve.com.

332 SGP
MARKETWATCH. Text in English. 1926. m. free. stat.

Formerly (until 1987): Fraser's Circular (0016-0083)
Indexed: WBA.
Published by: Fraser Roach & Co. Pte. Ltd., Maxwell Rd, P.O. Box 789, Singapore, 9015, Singapore. FAX 65-5351745, TELEX RS21433-FRASA. Circ: 2,250.

MARYLAND BUSINESS CREDIT DIRECTORY. see *BUSINESS AND ECONOMICS—Trade And Industrial Directories*

MASSACHUSETTS BUSINESS CREDIT DIRECTORY. see *BUSINESS AND ECONOMICS—Trade And Industrial Directories*

510 USA ISSN 0960-1627
HF5691
➤ **MATHEMATICAL FINANCE**; an international journal of mathematics, statistics and financial economics. Text in English. 1991. q. USD 149 combined subscription in the Americas to individuals & Caribbean, print & online eds.; EUR 183 combined subscription in Europe to individuals print & online eds.; GBP 122 combined subscription elsewhere to individuals print & online eds.; USD 841 combined subscription in the Americas to institutions & Caribbean, print & online eds.; GBP 657 combined subscription elsewhere to institutions print & online eds. (effective 2006). adv. bk.rev. illus. Index. reprint service avail. from PSC. **Document type:** *Journal, Academic/Scholarly.* **Description:** Presents the latest theoretical studies, focusing on finance theory, finance engineering, and the related mathematical and statistical techniques.
Related titles: Online - full text ed.: ISSN 1467-9965. 1997. USD 799 in the Americas to institutions & Caribbean; GBP 624 elsewhere to institutions (effective 2006) (from Blackwell Synergy, EBSCO Publishing, Gale Group, IngentaConnect, O C L C Online Computer Library Center, Inc., Swets Information Services).
Indexed: ABIn, CCMJ, CIS, CMCI, CurCont, IBSS, JEL, MathR, MathSciNet, SSCI, ST&MA, ZentMath.
—BLDSC (5401.975000), IDS, IE, Infotrieve, ingenta. **CCC.**
Published by: Blackwell Publishing, Inc. (Subsidiary of: Blackwell Publishing Ltd.), Commerce Place, 350 Main St, Malden, MA 02148. TEL 781-388-8206, FAX 781-388-8232, subscrip@blackwellpub.com, http://www.blackwellpublishing.com/journal.asp?ref=0960-1627&site=1. Ed. Robert A Jarrow. Circ: 800.

332.1 MUS
MAURITIUS POST OFFICE SAVINGS BANK. ANNUAL REPORT. Text in English. irreg. free. **Document type:** *Corporate.*
Formerly: Post Office Savings Bank. Annual Report
Related titles: Online - full content ed.
Published by: Mauritius Post Office Savings Bank Ltd., No 1, Sir William Newton St., Port Louis, Mauritius. TEL 320-2139430, FAX 230-2087270, http://www.mpcb.mu/annual.aspx?pageid=7.

MEDIA FINANCE. see *COMMUNICATIONS*

332 338.83 362 615 USA
THE MEDICAL TECHNOLOGY ACQUISITION RECORD. Text in English. 2002. q. USD 695 worldwide (effective 2002). **Document type:** *Trade.*
Published by: Irving Levin Associates, Inc., 268-1/2 Main Ave, Norwalk, CT 06851. TEL 203-846-6800, 800-248-1668, FAX 203-846-8300, general@levinassociates.com, http://www.levinassociates.com. Ed. Sanford B Steever. Pub. Ms. Eleanor B Meredith.

332.7 DEU ISSN 0025-8792
MEIN EIGENHEIM. Text in German. 1927. 4/yr. EUR 0.85 newsstand/cover (effective 2005). adv. bk.rev. illus. index. **Document type:** *Magazine, Consumer.*
Published by: (Bausparkasse Wuestenrot), Die Publikation GmbH, Hohenzollernstr 46, Ludwigsburg, 71638, Germany. TEL 49-7141-971492, FAX 49-7141-971499, widmann@gruppe-mein-eigenheim.de, http://www.gruppe-mein-eigenheim.de. Adv. contact Manfred Widmann. B&W page EUR 29,940, color page EUR 50,900; trim 195 x 261. Circ: 2,511,745 (paid and controlled).

332 ESP
MEMORIA DE RESPONSABILIDAD SOCIAL CORPORATIVA (YEAR). Text in Spanish. a.
Published by: Grupo Santander, Plaza de Canalejas no.1, Madrid, 28014, Spain.

332 BRA
MENSAGEM ECONOMICA/ECONOMIC MESSAGE. Text in Portuguese. 1952. m. adv.
Published by: Associacao Comercial de Minas, Av Afonso Pena, 172, Centro, Belo Horizonte, MG 30130-001, Brazil. Circ: 6,000.

332 USA ISSN 1539-6444
MERGENT BANK & FINANCE MANUAL. Text in English. 1928. a. USD 1,750 (effective 1999); includes s-w. Moody's Bank & Finance News Reports. reprints avail. **Description:** Covers full financial and operating data on 20,000 financial institutions in U.S.
Formerly (until 2001): Moody's Bank and Finance Manual (0545-0152)
Related titles: Microfiche ed.
—**CCC.**
Published by: Mergent, 5250 77 Center Dr, Ste 150, Charlotte, NC 28217. customerservice@mergent.com, http://www.mergent.com.

MERGERS & ACQUISITIONS CONSULTANT; the management report and information resource. see *BUSINESS AND ECONOMICS—Management*

332 MEX
MEXICAN FINANCIAL REPORT✶. Text in English. 1974. m. MXP 375, USD 30. charts; stat.
Published by: Publicaciones Marynka S.A., SALAVERRY 1204, Col Zacatenco, Mexico City, DF 07360, Mexico.

332.1 MEX ISSN 0185-1675
HG2711
MEXICO. COMISION NACIONAL BANCARIA. BOLETIN ESTADISTICO. Text in Spanish. 1925. m. **Document type:** *Bulletin, Government.*
Published by: (Mexico. Secretaria de Hacienda y Credito Publico), Comision Nacional Bancaria, Av. de los Insurgentes 1971, Plaza Inn Torre 2 Norte, Piso 10, Mexico City, DF 01020, Mexico.

346.082 USA
MICHIE ON BANKS AND BANKING. Text in English. 1955. irreg. (w/ current supplement) (in 13 vols.). USD 480 base vol(s). (effective 2003). **Description:** An encyclopedic treatise based on exhaustive and continuous study of the case law involving the organization, functions, rights, powers, duties, and liabilities of banks and other financial institutions.
Published by: Michie Company (Subsidiary of: LexisNexis North America), 701 E Water St, Charlottesville, VA 22902-5389. TEL 434-972-7600, 800-446-3410, FAX 434-972-7677, http://www.michie.com.

MICHIGAN BUSINESS CREDIT DIRECTORY. see *BUSINESS AND ECONOMICS—Trade And Industrial Directories*

332 GBR
HG3256.A5
MIDDLE EAST FINANCIAL GUIDE. Text in English. a. GBP 120 (effective 2000). adv. index. back issues avail. **Document type:** *Directory.* **Description:** Country by country listing of financial institutions in the Middle East.
Former titles (until 2000): M E E D/T A I C Middle East Financial Directory (0266-2094); (until 1984): M E E D Middle East Financial Directory (0264-2727)
Published by: M E E D - Emap Communications (Subsidiary of: Emap Business Communications Ltd.), 33-39 Bowling Green Lane, London, EC1R 0DA, United Kingdom. TEL 44-20-7470-6200, FAX 44-20-7837-8271.

332 GBR
MIDLAND GROUP NEWS. Text in English. 1971. 12/yr. free. adv. back issues avail.
Formerly: Midland Bank Group Newspaper
Published by: Midland Bank, 79 Hoyle St, Sheffield, S Yorks S3 7EW, United Kingdom. TEL 0742 528620. Ed. Eric Walker. Circ: 60,500.

MIDWEST CLEARING CORPORATION AND MIDWEST SECURITIES TRUST COMPANY. DIRECTORY OF PARTICIPANTS. see *BUSINESS AND ECONOMICS—Trade And Industrial Directories*

338.23 622 GBR ISSN 1364-4440
MINING FINANCE. Text in English. 1996. bi-m. **Document type:** *Trade.* **Description:** Provides coverage of all aspects of the mining industry.
Published by: I F R Publishing (Subsidiary of: Thomson Financial Services Ltd.), Aldgate House, 33 Aldgate High St, London, EC3N 1DL, United Kingdom. TEL 44-20-7369-7572, FAX 44-20-7369-7572.

MINNESOTA BUSINESS CREDIT DIRECTORY. see *BUSINESS AND ECONOMICS—Trade And Industrial Directories*

332 640.73 RUS
MIR TSEN. Text in Russian. bi-m. USD 129.95 in United States.
Published by: Tsena-Konsalting, Vorotnikovskii per 11, str 3, Moscow, 103006, Russian Federation. TEL 7-095-2997026, FAX 7-095-9247848. **US dist. addr.:** East View Information Services, 3020 Harbor Ln. N., Minneapolis, MN 55447. TEL 612-550-0961.

332.1 USA ISSN 0026-6159
MISSISSIPPI BANKER. Text in English. 1914. m. USD 25; USD 5 newsstand/cover (effective 2005). adv. illus. 48 p./no.; **Document type:** *Magazine, Trade.*
Published by: Mississippi Bankers Association, 640 N State St, PO Box 37, Jackson, MS 39205. TEL 601-948-6366, FAX 601-355-6461, msbankers@msbankers.com, http://www.msbankers.com. Ed., Adv. contact Kristen Kern. B&W page USD 460, color page USD 910. Circ: 1,500 (paid).

MISSISSIPPI GOVERNMENT REGISTER. see *PUBLIC ADMINISTRATION*

MISSOURI BUSINESS CREDIT DIRECTORY. see *BUSINESS AND ECONOMICS—Trade And Industrial Directories*

332 SWE ISSN 1100-4738
MODERN BANKING; tidskrift foer anstaellda inom bank- och finansindustrin. Text in Swedish. 1988. q.
Published by: Eventor Konsult, Fack 6911, Stockholm, 10239, Sweden.

332.1 USA
MODERN BANKING CHECKLISTS (SUPPLEMENT). Text in English. base vol. plus s-a. updates. USD 165; USD 231.95 foreign (effective 1995). **Document type:** *Trade.*
Published by: W G & L Financial Reporting & Management Research (Subsidiary of: R I A), 395 Hudson St, New York, NY 10014. TEL 212-367-6300, FAX 212-367-6718. **Subscr. to:** The Park Square Bldg., 31 St James Ave, Boston, MA 02116-4112. TEL 800-950-1207.

332.024 333.33 USA
MODERN ESTATE PLANNING. Text in English. 1981. 7 base vols. plus updates 3/yr. looseleaf. USD 1,210 base vol(s). (effective 2002). **Description:** A unified, transactional approach to estate and financial planning covering estate, gift, and income taxes.
Related titles: CD-ROM ed.
Published by: Matthew Bender & Co., Inc. (Subsidiary of: LexisNexis North America), 1275 Broadway, Albany, NY 12204. international@bender.com, http://bender.lexisnexis.com.

332.1 ITA ISSN 0026-9506
MONDO BANCARIO; rassegna bimestrale illustrata di cultura, di studi e di documentazione. Text in Italian. 1959. bi-m. EUR 65 domestic; EUR 100 foreign (effective 2003). adv. bk.rev. bibl.; charts; illus.; mkt.; maps; stat.; tr.lit. index. **Document type:** *Monographic series, Academic/Scholarly.*
Indexed: PAIS.
Published by: Futura 2000 SpA, Via Jacopo Sannazzaro, 6-8, Rome, RM 00141, Italy. TEL 39-06-8260326, FAX 39-06-8260270, mondobancario@mondobancario.it, http://www.mondobancario.it. Ed. G Girardi. Circ: 9,000 (paid).

330.9 PRI
MONEDA. Text in Spanish. 1978. bi-w. USD 20. adv. back issues avail.
Indexed: PAIS.
Published by: Moneda Inc., 1614 San Mateo, Santurce, 00912, Puerto Rico. TEL 787-721-7977, FAX 787-721-7991. Ed. Martha Dreyer Duperray. Circ: 30,000.

332 ESP ISSN 0026-959X
HB9
MONEDA Y CREDITO✶; revista de economia. Text in Spanish. 1942. q. bk.rev.
Indexed: AmH&L, HistAb, IBR, JEL, PAIS, PCI.
—CINDOC, IE, Infotrieve.
Address: Ave. de America, 32 - 6o, Madrid, 28028, Spain. TEL 34-91-3377433. Ed. Prof Gonzalo Anes. Circ: 1,500.

332 ARG
MONEDA Y FINANZAS DEL CONO SUR. CUADERNOS. Text in Spanish. q. ARS 24 domestic; USD 13 foreign. **Description:** Covers research and analysis of various aspects in banking, business and finance.
Indexed: PAIS.
Published by: Universidad Nacional de Lujan, C.C. 221, Lujan, Buenos Aires 6700, Argentina. Ed. Jose Luis Moreno.

332 ITA ISSN 0026-9611
HG19
MONETA E CREDITO. Text in Italian. 1948. q. EUR 62 domestic to individuals; EUR 68 foreign to individuals; EUR 41 domestic to students; EUR 45 foreign to students (effective 2003). adv. bk.rev. charts. index. back issues avail. **Document type:** *Academic/Scholarly.* **Description:** Articles by leading economists on macroeconomic theory and policy, international trade and finance, the evolution of national monetary and financial institutions and allied topics.
Indexed: ELLIS, JEL, PAIS, RASB.
Published by: (Banca Nazionale del Lavoro), B N L Edizioni SpA (Subsidiary of: Gruppo BNL), Via San Basilio 48, Rome, 00187, Italy. TEL 39-06-42012918, FAX 39-06-42012921, sliberati@bnledizioni.com. Ed. Alessandro Roncaglia. Adv. contact Filippo Cucuccio. Circ: 5,000.

332.1 MEX ISSN 0185-1136
HG185.L3
MONETARIA. Text in Spanish. 1978. q. USD 60. adv. bk.rev. index. **Document type:** *Bulletin.*
Related titles: Online - full text ed.: (from EBSCO Publishing).
Indexed: IBR, IBSS, PAIS, PCI.
—IE, Infotrieve.
Published by: Centro de Estudios Monetarios Latinoamericanos, A.C., Durango 54, Mexico City, DF 06700, Mexico. TEL 905-5330-300, FAX 525-4432. Ed. Juan Manuel Rodriguez Sierra. Pub. Juan Manuel Rodriguez. R&P Luis A Giorgio Burzilla TEL 525-514-3165. Adv. contact Claudio Antonovich. Circ: 1,000.

332.1 JPN ISSN 1348-7787
MONETARY AND ECONOMIC STUDIES. Text in English. 1983. q. **Document type:** *Journal.*

B

Formerly (until 1996): Bank of Japan Monetary and Economic Studies (0288-8432)
Related titles: ◆ Japanese ed.: Kinyu Kenkyu. ISSN 0287-5306.
Indexed: JEL, SSCI.
—BLDSC (5908.335050), IE.
Published by: Institute for Monetary and Economic Studies (Subsidiary of: Bank of Japan/Nippon Ginko), 2-1-1 Nihonbashi-Hongokucho, Chuo-ku, Tokyo, 103-8660, Japan. TEL 81-3-32791111, FAX 81-3-35101265, http://www.imes.boj.or.jp/english/publication/mes/mes03.html.

332   USA
MONETARY POLICY AND RESERVE REQUIREMENTS HANDBOOK. Text in English. a. USD 75. **Document type:** *Government.*
Published by: U.S. Federal Reserve System, Board of Governors, Publications Services, Rm MS 137, 20th and Constitution Ave, N W, Washington, DC 20551. FAX 202-728-5886, pipubs@ny.frb.org.

332   ZAF   ISSN 1609-3194
HG1351
MONETARY POLICY REVIEW. Text in English. 2001. s-a. free.
Published by: South African Reserve Bank/Suid-Afrikaanse Reserwebank, PO Box 427, Pretoria, 0001, South Africa. TEL 27-12-313-3911, FAX 27-12-313-3197, info@gwisel.resbank.co.za, http://www.resbank.co.za.

332   NLD   ISSN 0925-4129
**   CODEN: IJATB7**
MONEY. Text in Dutch. 1990. 10/yr. EUR 49.50 (effective 2003). illus. **Document type:** *Magazine, Consumer.*
Indexed: AgeL.
Published by: Reed Business Information bv (Subsidiary of: Reed Business), Hanzestraat 1, Doetinchem, 7006 RH, Netherlands. TEL 31-314-349911, FAX 31-314-343839, info@reedbusiness.nl, http://www.money.nl, http://www.reedbusiness.nl.

332   USA   ISSN 0149-4953
HG179   CODEN: MNEYAB
MONEY (NEW YORK). Text in English. 1972. 13/yr. USD 39.89 domestic; USD 39.95 in Canada; USD 99.99 elsewhere; USD 3.99 per issue (effective 2005). adv. bk.rev. illus. s-a. index. reprints avail. **Document type:** *Magazine, Consumer.*
Description: Guide for individual investors, featuring in-depth coverage of stocks, funds, the markets and the economy as well as the best things money can buy.
Related titles: CD-ROM ed.: (from ProQuest Information & Learning); Diskette ed.; Microform ed.: (from CIS, PQC); Online - full text ed.: CNN/Money (from EBSCO Publishing, Florida Center for Library Automation, Gale Group, H.W. Wilson, LexisNexis, O C L C Online Computer Library Center, Inc., ProQuest Information & Learning, The Dialog Corporation).
Indexed: ABIn, ATI, BLI, BPI, BPIA, BRI, BusI, CBRI, ConsI, EnvAb, LRI, MASUSE, MagInd, PAIS, PMR, PSI, RGAb, RGPR, T&II, TOM.
—BLDSC (5908.358000), IE, Infotrieve, ingenta.
Published by: Time, Inc (Subsidiary of: Time Warner, Inc.), Time & Life Bldg., Rockefeller Center, 29th Fl, 1271 Ave of the Americas, New York, NY 10020-1393. TEL 212-522-1212, FAX 212-522-1796, money_letters@moneymail.com, http://money.cnn.com/, http://www.money.cnn.com. Eds. Norman Pearlstine, John Huey. Pub. Michael Dukmejian. R&P Joe Mattern. adv.: B&W page USD 87,415, color page USD 122,292. Circ: 1,900,000 (paid). **Subscr. to:** Money, PO Box 60001, Tampa, FL 33630-0001. TEL 800-633-9970.

332 ·   MEX   ISSN 0187-7615
MONEY AFFAIRS. Text in Spanish. 1988. s-a. USD 20. adv. bk.rev. index. **Document type:** *Bulletin.*
Related titles: Online - full text ed.: (from EBSCO Publishing).
Indexed: IBSS, PAIS.
Published by: Centro de Estudios Monetarios Latinoamericanos, A.C., Durango 54, Mexico City, DF 06700, Mexico. TEL 905-5330-300, FAX 525-4432. Ed. Juan Manuel Rodriguez Sierra. Pub. Juan Manuel Rodriguez. R&P Luis A Giorgio Burzilla TEL 525-514-3165. Adv. contact Claudio Antonovich. Circ: 300.

MONEY FUND REPORT. see *BUSINESS AND ECONOMICS—Investments*

332   JPN   ISSN 0911-9353
MONEY JAPAN. Text in Japanese. 1985. m. JPY 6,600 (effective 2005). adv. Supplement avail. **Document type:** *Magazine, Trade.* **Description:** Offers the latest financial information. Topics include shopping, travel, marriage, educational expenses, mortgages, health and retirement funds.
Published by: Kadokawa S.S. Communications Inc., 3rd Fl., Sankin Bldg., 3-18-3 Kanda-nisiki-mach, Chiyoda-ku, Tokyo, 101-8467, Japan. TEL 81-3-52830220, FAX 81-3-52830229, mj@sscom.co.jp, http://www.sscom.co.jp/money/. Ed. Kenji Morita. Circ: 400,000.

MONEY LAUNDERING ALERT. see *CRIMINOLOGY AND LAW ENFORCEMENT*

MONEY LAUNDERING LAW REPORT. see *LAW—Corporate Law*

332   USA
MONEY LINES MAGAZINE. Text in English. 1988. q. USD 5.99 per issue (effective 2000). back issues avail. **Document type:** *Consumer.* **Description:** Covers a range of investment opportunities, from how to get rich to mutual funds to tips on selling; provides the reader with information on what, where, how and why.
Formerly: Financial Planning Series
Published by: Frederick Fell Publishers, Inc., 2131 Hollywood Blvd., Hollywood, CA 33020. TEL 954-925-0555, FAX 954-925-5244, info@fellpub.com, http://www.fellpub.com. Ed. Brian Feinblum. Pub. Donald Lessne. Circ: 50,000.

332   AUS   ISSN 1444-6219
MONEY MAGAZINE. Text in English. 1999. m. AUD 55 domestic; AUD 80 in New Zealand; AUD 95 elsewhere; AUD 5.95 newsstand/cover (effective 2004). adv. **Document type:** *Magazine, Consumer.* **Description:** Provides a source of information for ideas and advice on personal finance.
Related titles: Online - full text ed.: (from EBSCO Publishing).
Published by: A C P Publishing Pty. Ltd., 54-58 Park St, Sydney, NSW 1028, Australia. TEL 61-2-92828000, FAX 61-2-92674361, info@acp.com.au, http://finance.ninemsn.com.au/money, http://www.acp.com.au. Ed. Pam Walkley. Adv. contact Andrew Cook. Circ: 54,668.

332   AUS   ISSN 1322-7254
MONEY MANAGEMENT; the newspaper for the personal investment professional. Text in English. fortn. AUD 172.10 (effective 2001). adv. **Document type:** *Newspaper, Trade.* **Description:** Covers finance and investment topics including life insurance, managed funds, shares, financial planning and advisory services, taxation, banking, pensions and mortgages.
Related titles: Online - full text ed.: (from EBSCO Publishing, ProQuest Information & Learning).
Published by: Reed Business Information Pty Ltd (Subsidiary of: Reed Business Information International), Locked Bag 2999, Chatswood, NSW 2067, Australia. customerservice@reedbusiness.com.au, http://www.reedbusiness.com.au. Ed. Stuart Engel. Pub. Jeremy Knibbs TEL 61-2-9422-2930. Adv. contact Brad Lawson. Circ: 5,500.

332   GBR   ISSN 1463-1911
HG11
MONEY MANAGEMENT; the professional's independent adviser. Text in English. 1963. m. GBP 65 domestic; GBP 135 foreign; GBP 5.95 newsstand/cover (effective 1999). adv. stat. **Document type:** *Trade.* **Description:** Publishes in-depth surveys covering transfer plans, P.E.P.s, I.F.A. training, and long-term care insurance. Also covers every aspect of the intermediary and insurance markets and financial news.
Former titles (until 1988): Money Management and Unitholder (0028-6052); Unitholder (0041-7106)
Related titles: Microform ed.: (from PQC); Online - full text ed.: (from Factiva, Gale Group).
Indexed: ABIX.
—BLDSC (5908.366000), IE, ingenta.
Published by: Financial Times Business Ltd. (Subsidiary of: Financial Times Group), Maple House, 149 Tottenham Court Rd, London, W1P 9LL, United Kingdom. TEL 44-20-7896-2525, FAX 44-20-7896-2592, janet.walford@ft.com. Ed. Janet Walford. Pub. Nick Collard. Adv. contact Mark Lister. Circ: 19,094 (paid). **Dist. by:** Seymour Distribution Ltd, 86 Newman St, London W1T 3EX, United Kingdom. FAX 44-207-396-8002, enquiries@seymour.co.uk.

MONEY MANAGEMENT LETTER; bi-weekly newsletter covering the pensions & money management industry. see *BUSINESS AND ECONOMICS—Investments*

332   USA   ISSN 0736-6051
HG4509
MONEY MARKET DIRECTORY OF PENSION FUNDS AND THEIR INVESTMENT MANAGERS. Text in English. 1970. a. USD 1,095 (effective 2002). adv. index. 2000 p./no.; **Document type:** *Directory.*
Former titles: Money Market Directory of Pension Funds and Their Investment Advisors; Money Market Directory (0077-0388)
Media: Magnetic Tape. Related titles: CD-ROM ed.; Diskette ed.; Print ed.
Published by: Money Market Directories, Inc., PO Box 1608, Charlottesville, VA 22902. TEL 804-977-1450, 800-446-2810, FAX 804-979-9962. Ed. Jehu Martin. Pub. Thomas A Lupd. Adv. contact Jay Josey. Circ: 8,500.

332   GBR   ISSN 0958-3769
MONEY MARKETING. Text in English. 1985. w. GBP 75 in United Kingdom; GBP 120 overseas (effective 2001). **Document type:** *Newspaper.* **Description:** Aims to meet the information needs of independent financial advisers and the communication needs of those that serve them.
Related titles: Online - full text ed.: (from bigchalk, EBSCO Publishing, Gale Group, H.W. Wilson, LexisNexis, Northern Light Technology, Inc., O C L C Online Computer Library Center, Inc.).
Indexed: BPI.
Published by: Centaur Publishing, St Giles House, 50 Poland St, London, W1V 4AX, United Kingdom. TEL 44-20-7970-4000, http://www.moneymarketing.co.uk, http://www.centaur.co.uk/.

332.6   ZAF   ISSN 1562-7586
MONEY MARKETING. Text in English. m. ZAR 406 domestic; ZAR 493 foreign (effective 2003). **Document type:** *Newsletter.*
Published by: Primedia Publishing, 366 Pretoria Ave, Ferndale, Randburg, Transvaal 2194, South Africa. TEL 27-11-787-5725, FAX 27-11-787-5776, http://www.primemags.co.za.

332   GBR
MONEY MARKETING UNIT TRUST INDEX. Text in English. 1987. q. GBP 100 (effective 1998). adv. **Document type:** *Trade.* **Description:** For investment intermediaries in the U.K. Lists fund management groups.
Related titles: Microform ed.: (from PQC).
Published by: Centaur Publishing, St Giles House, 50 Poland St, London, W1V 4AX, United Kingdom. TEL 44—20-7970-4000, FAX 44-20-7970-4009. Ed. Jane Green. Circ: 4,419.

362.41   GBR
MONEY MATTERS. Text in English. bi-m. GBP 12 (effective 2000). **Document type:** *Consumer.* **Description:** Covers all aspects of personal finance, including insurance and investments.
Media: Braille. Related titles: Diskette ed.
Published by: Royal National Institute for the Blind, PO Box 173, Peterborough, Cambs PE2 6WX, United Kingdom. TEL 44-1733-370777, FAX 44-1733-371555, webmaster@rnib.org.uk, webmaster@rnib.org.uk, http://www.rnib.org.uk.

332   GBR
MONEY MEDIA. Text in English. 1989. m. GBP 12 (effective 2001). **Document type:** *Magazine, Trade.* **Description:** Contains news and views from both the financial and the industrial sectors of the Island.
Published by: Mannin Media Group Limited, Spring Valley Industrial Estate, Braddan, Isle of Man, United Kingdom. TEL 44-162-462-6018, FAX 44-162-466-1655, mail@manninmedia.co.im, http://www.manninmedia.co.im/media.html. Ed. Jane Kidd. Adv. contact Jane Watkins. Circ: 6,000.

332   ZAF
MONEY NEWSLETTER. Text in English. 1984. m. USD 100. **Document type:** *Newsletter.* **Description:** Provides personal financial advice for middle income individuals.
Formerly: Money Magazine
Published by: Prescon Publishing Corporation (Pty) Ltd., PO Box 84004, Greenside, Johannesburg 2034, South Africa. TEL 27-11-7829229, FAX 27-11-7822025, prescon@iafrica.com. Ed. Leon J Kok.

332   IND
MONEY OPPORTUNITIES✶**.** Text in English. 1985. w. INR 5 newsstand/cover. adv. 8 cols./p.
Published by: Ross Murarka Finance Ltd., c/o Kshitij Consultancy Services, 8 Old Pont Office, Kolkata, West Bengal 700 001, India. TEL 91-22-4949766, 91-22-4928146, FAX 91-22-4932134, TELEX 011 76884. Ed. Lynn Deas. Adv. contact Nimal Parekh. Circ: 53,186.

332   USA
MONEY STOCK, LIQUID ASSETS, AND DEBT MEASURES. Text in English. w. USD 35. **Document type:** *Government.*
Published by: U.S. Federal Reserve System, Board of Governors, Publications Services, Rm MS 138, Washington, DC 20551. TEL 202-452-3244, FAX 202-728-5886.

MONEYEXTRA. see *BUSINESS AND ECONOMICS—Investments*

MONEYLETTER (ASHLAND). see *BUSINESS AND ECONOMICS—Investments*

332   POL
MONITOR RACHUNKOWOSCI I FINANSOW. Text in Polish. 2002. m. PLZ 312 domestic (effective 2005). **Document type:** *Journal, Trade.*
Published by: Wydawnictwo C.H. Beck, ul Gen. Zajaczka 9, Warsaw, 01518, Poland. TEL 48-22-3377600, FAX 48-22-3377601, redakcja@mrf.pl, redakcja@beck.pl, http://mrf.pl, http://wydawnictwo.beck.pl. **Co-publisher:** Verlag C.H. Beck.

332   GBR   ISSN 1357-0676
MONKS U.K. BOARD EARNINGS (YEAR). Text in English. a. **Document type:** *Corporate.*
Published by: Monks Partnership Ltd., Monks Partnership, The Mill House, Royston Rd, Wendens Ambo, Saffron Walden, Essex CB11 4JX, United Kingdom. TEL 44-1799-542222, FAX 44-1799-541805, info@monkspartnership.co.uk. R&P David Atkins.

332 340   GBR
MONROE & NOCK ON THE LAW OF STAMP DUTIES. Text in English. 1989. 2 base vols. plus updates 3/yr. looseleaf. GBP 460 base vol(s).; GBP 445, EUR 669 updates in Europe; GBP 460, USD 836 updates elsewhere (effective 2006). **Document type:** *Journal, Trade.*

Published by: Sweet & Maxwell Ltd., 100 Avenue Road, London, NW3 3PF, United Kingdom. TEL 44-20-74491111, FAX 44-20-74491144, customer.services@sweetandmaxwell.co.uk, http://www.sweetandmaxwell.co.uk. **Subscr. to:** Cheriton House, North Way, Andover, Hants SP10 5BE, United Kingdom.

MONTANA. OFFICE OF THE LEGISLATIVE AUDITOR. STATE OF MONTANA BOARD OF INVESTMENTS. REPORT ON EXAMINATION OF FINANCIAL STATEMENTS. see *PUBLIC ADMINISTRATION*

332 JPN ISSN 0388-0605
HG41
MONTHLY FINANCE REVIEW. Text in English. 1973. m. free. **Document type:** *Government.*
Published by: Ministry of Finance, Institute of Fiscal and Monetary Policy/Okura-sho, 3-1-1 Kasumigaseki, Chiyoda-ku, Tokyo, 100-0013, Japan. Circ: 1,060.

MORGAN STANLEY CENTRAL BANK DIRECTORY (YEAR). see *BUSINESS AND ECONOMICS—Trade And Industrial Directories*

332 USA
THE MORNING REPORT. Text in English. d. **Description:** Provides with daily insights on stock market, S&P 500, mutual funds and related issues.
Media: Online - full text.
Published by: Money.net, 155 Spring St. 3rd Fl, New York, NY 10012. TEL 212-445-4000, FAX 888-254-8904, support@money.net, http://www.money.net/.

332 USA ISSN 1055-4696
KF695
MORTGAGE AND CONSUMER LOAN DISCLOSURE HANDBOOK; a step-by-step guide with forms. Text in English. 1987. a., latest 2002. USD 390 subscr - carrier delivery print & CD-ROM eds. (effective 2004). **Document type:** *Trade.* **Description:** Provides sample forms and detailed information on the disclosure requirements lenders must meet under federal laws and regulations.
Related titles: CD-ROM ed.
Published by: Thomson West (Subsidiary of: Thomson Corporation, The), 610 Opperman Dr, Eagan, MN 55123-1396. TEL 651-687-8000, 800-328-4880, FAX 651-687-7302, http://west.thomson.com/product/14048113/product.asp. Eds. Cameron Cowan, Kenneth G Lore.

332.7 USA ISSN 0730-0212
HG2051.U5 CODEN: MOBAAX
MORTGAGE BANKING; the magazine of real estate finance managers and employees. Text in English. 1939. m. USD 69.95 domestic to non-members; USD 60 domestic to members; USD 74.95 foreign (effective 2005). adv. illus. Index. 120 p./no.; back issues avail.; reprints avail. **Document type:** *Magazine, Trade.*
Former titles (until 1981): Mortgage Banker (0027-1241); M B A News Review
Related titles: Microfiche ed.: (from CIS); Microform ed.: (from PQC); Online - full text ed.: (from EBSCO Publishing, Factiva, Florida Center for Library Automation, Gale Group, H.W. Wilson, Northern Light Technology, Inc., O C L C Online Computer Library Center, Inc., ProQuest Information & Learning).
Indexed: ABIn, ATI, BLI, BPI, BPIA, BusI, ManagCont, PAIS, SRI, T&II.
—BLDSC (5967.465000), IE, ingenta. **CCC.**
Published by: Mortgage Bankers Association, 1919 Pennsylvania Ave NW, Washington, DC 20006-3438. TEL 202-557-2700, FAX 202-721-0245, janet_hewitt@mbaa.org, http://www.mortgagebankingmagazine.com, http://www.mbaa.org. Eds. Janet Hewitt, Janet Hewitt. R&P Susan Edgar. Adv. contact Christine Rene. B&W page USD 3,353, color page USD 4,453. Circ: 10,023.

332.1 333.333 GBR ISSN 0964-7988
MORTGAGE FINANCE GAZETTE✶. Text in English. 1869. m. GBP 65. adv. bk.rev. illus.; stat.; tr.lit. index. **Document type:** *Trade.*
Formerly (until 1990): Building Societies' Gazette (0007-3652)
Indexed: RICS, WBA.
—BLDSC (5967.466300), IE, ingenta. **CCC.**
Published by: Franey and Co. Ltd., 100 Avenue Rd, London, N14 4EA, United Kingdom. Ed. Neil Madden. Circ: 5,000.

MORTGAGE LAW AND PRACTICE MANUAL. see *LAW*

332 USA ISSN 1553-8214
MORTGAGE LENDING COMPLIANCE MONITOR. Text in English. 2001 (Jan). m. USD 425 (effective 2005). **Document type:** *Newsletter.*
Published by: AlexInformation, 807 Las Cimas Pkwy Ste 300, Austin, TX 78746. TEL 512-652-4400, FAX 512-652-4499, inforeply@alexinformation.com, http://www.alexinformation.com.

332 USA ISSN 1528-1779
MORTGAGE MARKET UPDATE. Text in English. 1988. m. USD 465 (effective 2000). **Document type:** *Trade.* **Description:** Detailed summary of important issues related to selling and servicing of residential mortgages.
Formerly (until 1999): Seller - Servicer Update (1059-1389)
Published by: Inside Mortgage Finance Publications, PO Box 42387, Washington, DC 20015. TEL 301-951-1240, FAX 301-656-1709, http://www.imfpubs.com. Ed. John Bancroft. Pub. Guy D Cecala. R&P Didi Parks.

MORTGAGE NEWS. see *REAL ESTATE*

332.7 USA
MORTGAGE NEWS. Text in English. w. **Document type:** *Newsletter, Consumer.* **Description:** Contains the latest mortgage news and rates information.
Media: E-mail.
Published by: Bankrate Inc., 11811 US Hwy 1, North Palm Beach, FL 33408. TEL 561-630-2400, FAX 561-625-4540, webmaster@bankrate.com, http://bankrate.process9.com/bankrate/subscribe.html, http://www.bankrate.com.

MORTGAGE ORIGINATOR. see *REAL ESTATE*

332.3 USA ISSN 1093-1252
MORTGAGE SERVICING NEWS. Text in English. 1997. m. USD 98 domestic; USD 108 in Canada; USD 128 elsewhere (effective 2005). adv. **Document type:** *Magazine, Trade.* **Description:** Provides expert coverage and analysis of new technologies, emerging trends, and serving opportunities.
Related titles: Online - full text ed.: (from EBSCO Publishing, Factiva, Florida Center for Library Automation, Gale Group, O C L C Online Computer Library Center, Inc., ProQuest Information & Learning).
Indexed: BLI.
—CCC.
Published by: Source Media, Inc., One State St Plaza, 27th Fl, New York, NY 10004. TEL 212-803-6077, 800-221-1809, FAX 212-747-1154, custserv@sourcemedia.com, http://www.mortgageservicingnews.com, http://www.sourcemedia.com. adv.: B&W page USD 3,495, color page USD 4,545; trim 15 x 10.

332 ESP ISSN 0300-3884
HC381
EL MUNDO FINANCIERO; gran revista grafica de economia y finanzas. Text in Spanish. 1946. m. USD 28. adv. bk.rev. bibl.; illus.; stat. **Document type:** *Newspaper, Trade.*
Related titles: Microfilm ed.
Published by: Mundo Financiero, Hermosilla, 93 1o Izq., Apdo. de Correo 6119, Madrid, 28001, Spain. TEL 34-1-5773376, mundofinanciero@nauta.es, http://www.nauta.es/mundof/. Ed., R&P Jose Luis Barcelo. Pub. Miguel A Martinez. Adv. contact Pilar Vicente. Circ: 100,000.

MUNICIPAL FINANCIAL INFORMATION. see *PUBLIC ADMINISTRATION—Municipal Government*

332 346.078 USA
N A B TALK. Text in English. q. **Document type:** *Newsletter.* **Description:** Discusses bankruptcy issues and ways to manage a bankruptcy practice more efficiently.
Published by: National Association of Bankruptcy Trustees, 1 Windsor Cv., Ste. 305, Columbia, SC 29223-1833. TEL 803-252-5646.

N A S D A Q FACT BOOK. (National Association of Securities Dealers Automated Quotations) see *BUSINESS AND ECONOMICS—Investments*

N A S D A Q SUBSCRIBER BULLETIN. (National Association of Securities Dealers Automated Quotations) see *BUSINESS AND ECONOMICS—Investments*

N A S D ANNUAL REPORT. see *BUSINESS AND ECONOMICS—Investments*

N A S D REGULATORY AND COMPLIANCE ALERT. see *BUSINESS AND ECONOMICS—Investments*

332 LBR
N B L REVIEW. (National Bank of Liberia) Text in English. 1984. q. **Description:** Covers news of the National Bank of Liberia and the events it sponsors.
Published by: National Bank of Liberia, E.G. King Plaza, Broad St., P.O. Box 2048, Monrovia, Liberia. TEL 231-222580, TELEX NATBANK, 44215 MONROVIA. Ed. James Monxhwedey.

332 USA
N I B E S A NEWS. Text in English. 1980. m. membership. adv. **Document type:** *Newsletter.*
Published by: National Independent Bank Equipment & Systems Association, 1411 Peterson Ave, Ste 101, Park Ridge, IL 60068. TEL 847-825-8419, 800-843-6082, FAX 847-825-8445. Ed., Adv. contact Ann Walk. Circ: 400.

332.72 USA
N.Y. MORTGAGE REPORT. Text in English. 1986. m. USD 30 (effective 1998). adv. **Document type:** *Trade.*
Published by: Source One Communications, Inc., 57 Manorhaven Blvd, Port Washington, NY 11050-1627. TEL 516-379-7200, FAX 516-379-6654. Ed. Susan Pechman. Pub. Andy Cohen. R&P Elaine Wilk. Adv. contact Mark Kasper. B&W page USD 1,225; trim 15 x 10.5. Circ: 15,500.

332 MEX ISSN 0185-4968
NACIONAL FINANCIERA. ANNUAL REPORT. Text in Spanish. a. **Document type:** *Corporate.*
Published by: Nacional Financiera S.N.C., Subdireccion de Informacion Tecnica y Publicaciones, INSURGENTES SUR 1971, Nivel Fuente, Col Guadalupe Inn, Mexico City, DF 01020, Mexico. TEL 52-5-3256047.

332.09 SCG ISSN 0351-3211
NARODNA BANKA JUGOSLAVIJE. BILTEN. Text in Serbo-Croatian. 1973. m. (English ed. q.). free. **Document type:** *Bulletin.* **Description:** Economic and monetary developments.
Related titles: English ed.: National Bank of Yugoslavia. Quarterly Bulletin. ISSN 0350-4484.
Indexed: KES.
Published by: Narodna Banka Jugoslavije, Bulevar Revolucije 15, Postanski Fah 1010, Belgrade, 11001. TEL 381-11-3248841. Ed. Jovan Petrovic. Circ: 375.

NARODNA BANKA JUGOSLAVIJE. GODISNJI IZVESTAJ. see *BUSINESS AND ECONOMICS—Economic Situation And Conditions*

332 POL ISSN 1230-0020
NARODOWY BANK POLSKI. BIULETYN INFORMACYJNY (MONTHLY). Text in Polish. 1990. m. free. charts; stat. back issues avail. **Document type:** *Bulletin.* **Description:** Covers the economic and financial situation of Polish economy and monetary policy.
Formerly (until 1991): Narodowy Bank Polski. Miesieczny Biuletyn Informacyjny (0867-2423)
Related titles: English ed.: National Bank of Poland. Information Bulletin. ISSN 1230-0101.
Published by: Narodowy Bank Polski, ul Swietokrzyska 11-21, Warsaw, 00919, Poland. TEL 48-22-6532571, FAX 48-22-6531321, nbpgpno@telbank.pl, nbp@nbp.pl, http://www.nbp.pl. Ed. Stefan peikarczyk. Circ: 1,300.

332 POL ISSN 0239-7013
NARODOWY BANK POLSKI. DZIENNIK URZEDOWY. Text in Polish. 1982. irreg., latest vol.3, 2003.
Published by: Grupa Wydawnicza INFOR Sp. z o.o., Ul Okopowa 58/72, Warsaw, 01042, Poland. TEL 48-22-7613030, FAX 48-22-7613031, bok@infor.pl, http://www.infor.pl.

337 POL
NARODOWY BANK POLSKI. INFORMACJA WSTEPNA. Text in Polish. irreg.
Published by: Narodowy Bank Polski, ul Swietokrzyska 11-21, Warsaw, 00919, Poland. TEL 48-22-6532571, FAX 48-22-6531321. R&P Iwona Stefaniak TEL 48-22-6532571.

332 POL ISSN 1427-0277
HG3138
NARODOWY BANK POLSKI. RAPORT ROCZNY. Text in Polish. 1968. a. free. charts; illus.; stat. back issues avail. **Document type:** *Bulletin, Trade.*
Formerly (until 1995): Narodowy Bank Polski. Biuletyn Informacyjny (Annual) (1230-6290); Supersedes in part (in 1990): Narodowy Bank Polski. Annual Report (1230-008X); Which was formerly (until 1988): Narodowy Bank Polski. Information Bulletin (0239-3395)
Related titles: ♦ English ed.: National Bank of Poland. Annual Report. ISSN 1427-0285.
Published by: Narodowy Bank Polski, ul Swietokrzyska 11-21, Warsaw, 00919, Poland. TEL 48-22-6532571, FAX 48-22-6531321, nbpgpno@telbank.pl, nbp@nbp.pl, http://www.nbp.pl. Circ: 1,000.

332 FRA
NATIONAL ACCOUNTS OF O E C D COUNTRIES. (Organization for Economic Cooperation and Development) Text in English. a. price varies. **Document type:** *Monographic series.*
Related titles: ♦ Series: National Accounts of O E C D Countries. Volume 1 Main Aggregates. ISSN 0256-758X; ♦ National Accounts of O E C D Countries. Volume 2 Detailed Tables. ISSN 0256-7571; ♦ National Accounts of O E C D Countries. Volume 3, Financial Accounts; ♦ National Accounts of O E C D Countries. Volume 4, General Government Accounts.
Published by: Organization for Economic Cooperation and Development, 2 Rue Andre Pascal, Paris, 75775 Cedex 16, France. TEL 33-1-45248200, FAX 33-1-45248500, http://www.oecd.org.

330 FRA
NATIONAL ACCOUNTS OF O E C D COUNTRIES. VOLUME 3, FINANCIAL ACCOUNTS/COMPTES NATIONAUX DES PAYS DE L'O C D E. VOLUME III - COMPTES FINANCIERS. (Organization for Economic Cooperation and Development) Text in English, French. a. price varies. **Document type:** *Monographic series.*
Related titles: ♦ Series of: National Accounts of O E C D Countries.
Published by: Organization for Economic Cooperation and Development, 2 Rue Andre Pascal, Paris, 75775 Cedex 16, France. TEL 33-1-45248200, FAX 33-1-45248500, http://www.oecd.org. **Dist. by:** O E C D Turpin North America, PO Box 194, Downingtown, PA 19335-0194. TEL 610-524-5361, 800-456-6323, FAX 610-524-5417, bookscustomer@turpinna.com.

B

332.1 TZA
NATIONAL BANK OF COMMERCE. ANNUAL REPORT AND ACCOUNTS. Text in English, Swahili. 1967. a. free. **Document type:** *Corporate.*
Published by: National Bank of Commerce, PO Box 1863, Dar Es Salaam, Tanzania. Circ: 3,000.

NATIONAL BANK OF EGYPT. ECONOMIC BULLETIN. see *BUSINESS AND ECONOMICS—Economic Situation And Conditions*

332 ETH ISSN 1015-2717
HG3389.A7
NATIONAL BANK OF ETHIOPIA. ANNUAL REPORT. Text in English. 1964. a. USD 2.50. **Document type:** *Government.*
Published by: National Bank of Ethiopia, c/o Documentation Division, PO Box 5550, Addis Ababa, Ethiopia.

330.9 ETH ISSN 0027-8750
HC845.A1
NATIONAL BANK OF ETHIOPIA. QUARTERLY BULLETIN. Text in English. 1964. q. USD 20. charts; mkt. **Document type:** *Bulletin, Government.*
Supersedes: State Bank of Ethiopia. Report on Economic Conditions and Market Trends
Published by: (Economic Research and Planning Division), National Bank of Ethiopia, c/o Documentation Division, PO Box 5550, Addis Ababa, Ethiopia.

B

332.1 GRC ISSN 0077-3514
NATIONAL BANK OF GREECE. ANNUAL REPORT/ETHNIKE TRAPEZA TES HELLADOS. APOLOGISMOS. Text in English. 1843. a. free. **Document type:** *Corporate.*
Related titles: Greek ed.
—BLDSC (1362.469200).
Published by: (Economic Research and Planning Department), National Bank of Greece, 86 Eolou St, Athens, 102 32, Greece. Circ: 8,500.

332 KWT
NATIONAL BANK OF KUWAIT. ANNUAL REPORT OF THE BOARD OF DIRECTORS AND ACCOUNTS. Text in English. 1953. a. free. **Document type:** *Corporate.* **Description:** Covers the international economy as it applies to Kuwait, proceedings of the Gulf Corporation Council, economic developments in Kuwait as well as all other financial reports.
Published by: National Bank of Kuwait S.A.K., Economic Research & Planning Division, Abdullah al-Salim St., P O Box 95, Kuwait City, Kuwait.

332.1 LBR
NATIONAL BANK OF LIBERIA. ANNUAL REPORT. Text in English. 1974. a. charts; stat. **Document type:** *Corporate.*
Published by: National Bank of Liberia, E.G. King Plaza, Broad St., P.O. Box 2048, Monrovia, Liberia. TEL 231-222580, TELEX NATBANK, 44215 MONROVIA.

332 LBR
NATIONAL BANK OF LIBERIA. QUARTERLY STATISTICAL BULLETIN. Text in English. q. **Document type:** *Bulletin.*
Published by: National Bank of Liberia, Research Department, E.G. King Plaza, Broad St., P O Box 2048, Monrovia, Liberia. TEL 231-222580, TELEX NATBANK, 44215 MONROVIA.

332 PAK
NATIONAL BANK OF PAKISTAN. ANNUAL REPORT. Text in English. a. **Document type:** *Corporate.*
Published by: National Bank of Pakistan, I.I. Chundrigar Rd., Karachi 2, Pakistan.

332 PAK
NATIONAL BANK OF PAKISTAN. MONTHLY ECONOMIC LETTER. Text in English. 1975. m. free.
Indexed: KES, WBA.
Published by: National Bank of Pakistan, Planning & Research Division, I.I. Chundrigar Rd., P O Box 4973, Karachi, Pakistan. TEL 2416164, FAX 021-2416157, TELEX 23732 NBPPK. Ed. Muhammad Naeemuddin. Circ: 2,700.

332.1 PAK ISSN 0077-3522
NATIONAL BANK OF PAKISTAN. REPORT AND STATEMENT OF ACCOUNTS. Text in English. a. **Document type:** *Corporate.*
Published by: National Bank of Pakistan, I.I. Chundrigar Rd., Karachi 2, Pakistan.

336.711 POL ISSN 1427-0285
NATIONAL BANK OF POLAND. ANNUAL REPORT. Text in English. 1968. a. free. charts; illus.; stat. back issues avail. **Document type:** *Bulletin, Trade.*
Formerly (until 1994): Narodowy Bank Polski. Information Bulletin (Annual) (1230-6282); Supersedes in part (in 1990): Narodowy Bank Polski. Annual Report (1230-008X); Which was formerly (until 1988): Narodowy Bank Polski. Information Bulletin (0239-3395)
Related titles: ♦ Polish ed.: Narodowy Bank Polski. Raport Roczny. ISSN 1427-0277.
Published by: Narodowy Bank Polski, ul Swietokrzyska 11-21, Warsaw, 00919, Poland. TEL 48-22-6532571, FAX 48-22-6531321, TELEX 814681 NBP PL, nbpgpno@telbank.pl, nbp@nbp.pl, http://www.nbp.pl. Ed. Boguslaw Pietrzak. R&P Iwona Stefaniak TEL 48-22-6532571. Circ: 1,750.

336.711 POL ISSN 1640-0755
NATIONAL BANK OF POLAND. INFLATION REPORT. Text in English. 1998. q.
Related titles: ♦ Polish ed.: Raport o Inflacji. ISSN 1640-0747.
Published by: Narodowy Bank Polski, ul Swietokrzyska 11-21, Warsaw, 00919, Poland.

NATIONAL BANK OF YUGOSLAVIA. ANNUAL REPORT. see *BUSINESS AND ECONOMICS—Economic Situation And Conditions*

332.1 CAN ISSN 0822-1081
NATIONAL BANKING LAW REVIEW; banking business and the law. Text in English. 1982. bi-m. CND 285 (effective 2003). back issues avail. **Document type:** *Newsletter.* **Description:** Provides information and comments on current legal trends affecting the banking industry.
Indexed: ICLPL.
Published by: LexisNexis Butterworths Canada Inc. (Subsidiary of: LexisNexis North America), 123 Commerce Valley Dr E, Ste 700, Markham, ON L3T 7W8, Canada. TEL 905-479-2665, FAX 905-479-2826, http://www.lexisnexis.ca/nationalbankinglawreview.htm. Ed. Robert Elliot.

332.3 DMA
NATIONAL COMMERCIAL & DEVELOPMENT BANK. ANNUAL REPORT AND FINANCIAL STATEMENTS. Text in English. a. illus. **Document type:** *Corporate.*
Formerly: Dominica Agricultural and Industrial Development Bank. Annual Report and Financial Statements
Published by: National Commercial & Development Bank, Hillsborough St 64, Roseau, Dominica. **Affiliate:** A I D Bank.

332 USA ISSN 0146-6046
NATIONAL CREDIT UNION ADMINISTRATION. ANNUAL REPORT. Text in English. 1970. a.
—CISTI.
Published by: National Credit Union Administration, 1775 Duke St, Alexandria, VA 22314-3428. TEL 703-518-6300, FAX 703-518-6660, http://www.ncua.gov.

332.7 CAN ISSN 0829-2019
NATIONAL CREDITOR-DEBTOR REVIEW. Text in English. 1986. q. CND 210 (effective 2003). back issues avail. **Document type:** *Newsletter.* **Description:** Provides commentary, case reviews and articles on creditors' and debtors' obligations and rights.
Indexed: ICLPL.
Published by: LexisNexis Butterworths Canada Inc. (Subsidiary of: LexisNexis North America), 123 Commerce Valley Dr E, Ste 700, Markham, ON L3T 7W8, Canada. TEL 905-479-2665, FAX 905-479-2826, http://www.butterworths.ca/.

332.1 SLE
NATIONAL DEVELOPMENT BANK. ANNUAL REPORT AND ACCOUNTS. Text in English. 1969. a. free. stat. **Document type:** *Corporate.*
Published by: National Development Bank, Leone House, Siaka Stevens St 21-23, Freetown, Sierra Leone. FAX 232-22-24468, TELEX 3589 NATDEV. Circ: 450.

332 340 USA ISSN 1073-953X
NATIONAL FINANCING LAW DIGEST; case digests of court decisions affecting secured and unsecured financial transactions. Text in English. 1988. m. USD 527 domestic; USD 557 in Canada; USD 582 elsewhere (effective 2004). index. back issues avail. **Document type:** *Newsletter.* **Description:** Offers complete coverage of workouts, bankruptcy, lender's liability, and the growing number of court decisions related to the changing economic situation.
Related titles: Online - full text ed.: (from LexisNexis).
Published by: Strafford Publications, Inc., 590 Dutch Valley Rd, N E, Postal Drawer 13729, Atlanta, GA 30324-0729. TEL 404-881-1141, FAX 404-881-0074, editors@straffordpub.com, custserv@straffordpub.com, http://www.straffordpub.com. Ed. Jennifer F Vaughan. Pub. Richard M Ossoff.

332 CAN ISSN 0822-2584
NATIONAL INSOLVENCY REVIEW. Text in English. bi-m. CND 252 (effective 2001). back issues avail. **Document type:** *Newsletter.* **Description:** Reviews recent laws and cases in the area of insolvency, bankruptcy and creditors' rights.
Indexed: ICLPL.
Published by: LexisNexis Butterworths Canada Inc. (Subsidiary of: LexisNexis North America), 123 Commerce Valley Dr E, Ste 700, Markham, ON L3T 7W8, Canada. TEL 905-479-2665, FAX 905-479-2826, http://www.lexisnexis.ca/nationalinsolvencyreview.htm.

332 797.1 USA
NATIONAL MARINE BANKERS ASSOCIATION. SUMMARY ANNUAL REPORT. Text in English. a. USD 295. **Document type:** *Corporate.* **Description:** Describes activities, programs and trends in the recreational boat loan marketplace and includes statistics on delinquencies, charge-offs, average transactions, terms, turnover.
Published by: National Marine Bankers Association, 200 E Randolph St, Ste 5100, Chicago, IL 60601-6528.

NATIONAL MORTGAGE BROKER. see *REAL ESTATE*

332.3 USA ISSN 1050-3331
HG2150
NATIONAL MORTGAGE NEWS; the newsweekly for america's mortgage industry. Text in English. 1976. w. USD 228 domestic; USD 238 in Canada; USD 258 elsewhere (effective 2005). adv. bk.rev. back issues avail. **Document type:** *Newspaper, Trade.* **Description:** News of developments in the banking, finance and real estate sectors for an executive audience.
Former titles (until 1990): National Thrift and Mortgage News (1045-9766); (until 1989): National Thrift News (0193-287X)
Related titles: Microfiche ed.: (from PQC); Online - full text ed.: National Mortgage News Daily (from EBSCO Publishing, Factiva, Florida Center for Library Automation, Gale Group, LexisNexis, Northern Light Technology, Inc., O C L C Online Computer Library Center, Inc., ProQuest Information & Learning).
Indexed: ABIn, B&I, BLI.
—CCC.
Published by: Source Media, Inc., One State St Plaza, 27th Fl, New York, NY 10004. TEL 212-803-6077, 800-221-1809, FAX 212-747-1154, custserv@sourcemedia.com, http://www.nationalmortgagenews.com, http://www.sourcemedia.com. Circ: 12,000. **Co-publisher:** Deutsche Bank.

332 332.6 CAN ISSN 1494-1988
NATIONAL POST BUSINESS. Text in English. 1972. m. adv. **Document type:** *Magazine, Trade.* **Description:** Tells how to get your financial life in order. Covers investment, taxation, retirement and the basic aspects of intelligent financial planning. Includes special worksheets and a directory of services.
Former titles (until 1999): Financial Post Magazine (1184-7824); (until 1990): Financial Post Magazine for the Moneywise (1182-0713); (until 1990): Financial Post Moneywise (0843-2317); (until 1988): Financial Post Moneywise Magazine (0833-9481); (until 1986): Financial Post Magazine (0384-0360); (until 1976): Impetus (0384-0352); (until 1973): Financial Post Magazine (0384-0344)
Related titles: Microfiche ed.: (from MML); Microform ed.: (from MML); Online - full text ed.: (from Micromedia ProQuest); Special ed(s).: Financial Post Moneyplanner.
Indexed: CBPI, CPerl.
—CCC.
Published by: Financial Post Datagroup, 300-1450 Don Mills Rd, Don Mills, ON M3B 3R5, Canada. TEL 416-383-2300, FAX 416-383-2443, http://www.canada.com/national/nationalpost/info/. Ed. Wayne Gooding. Adv. contact Victoria Petrolo. color page CND 17,707; trim 8 x 10.75.

332.62 CAN
(YEAR) NATIONAL PROFILE DIRECTORY OF INDEPENDENT AGENTS AND BROKERS. Text in English. a. USD 199.95 (effective 2000).
Published by: International Press Publications Inc, 90 Nolan Ct, Ste 21, Markham, ON L3R 4L9, Canada. TEL 905-946-9588, ipp@interlog.com, http://www.interlof.com/~ipp, http://www.interlog.com/~ipp.

333.33 USA
NATIONAL SECOND MORTGAGE ASSOCIATION. LEGISLATIVE REPORT✱ . Text in English. 1980. 2/yr. looseleaf. membership. back issues avail. **Description:** Covers legislative activity at the state level regarding mortgage lending, mortgage insurance, and relevant developments in consumer protection.
Published by: National Second Mortgage Association, 3833 Schaefer Ave, Ste K, Chino, CA 91710-5456. TEL 909-941-2080, FAX 909-941-8248. Ed. Jeffrey Zeltzer. Circ: 350.

332 NLD ISSN 0169-0922
DE NEDERLANDSCHE BANK N.V. ANNUAL REPORT. Text in Dutch. a. free (effective 2005). **Document type:** *Corporate.*
Formerly: Nederlandsche Bank. Report (0167-3998)
Related titles: Online - full text ed.
Indexed: BibLing.
—CCC.
Published by: Nederlandsche Bank N.V., Postbus 98, Amsterdam, 1000 AB, Netherlands. TEL 31-20-5249111, http://www.dnb.nl.

332 NLD ISSN 0922-6184
HC321
DE NEDERLANDSCHE BANK N.V. QUARTERLY BULLETIN/DUTCH CENTRAL BANK. QUARTERLY BULLETIN. Text in English. 1972. q. free. **Document type:** *Bulletin.*

Formerly (until 1983): Nederlandsche Bank N.V. Quarterly Statistics (0166-9400).
Related titles: Dutch ed.: Nederlandsche Bank N.V. Kwartaalbericht. ISSN 0166-915X.
Indexed: PAIS.
—CCC.
Published by: Nederlandsche Bank N.V., Postbus 98, Amsterdam, 1000 AB, Netherlands. TEL 31-20-5249111, http://www.dnb.nl.

332   MEX   ISSN 0028-2456
NEGOCIOS Y BANCOS. Short title: Negobancos. Text in Spanish. 1951. 24/yr. USD 60. illus.; stat.
Related titles: Online - full text ed.
Published by: Publicaciones Importantes, S.A., Bolivar 8-601, Apdo. Postal 1907, Mexico City, DF 06000, Mexico. TEL 5-510-1884, FAX 5-512-9411. Ed. Alfredo Farrugia Reed. adv.: B&W page USD 3,000, color page USD 3,750. Circ: 18,000.

NELSON INFORMATION'S DIRECTORY OF INVESTMENT RESEARCH. see BUSINESS AND ECONOMICS—Trade And Industrial Directories

NELSON'S DIRECTORY OF INVESTMENT MANAGERS. see BUSINESS AND ECONOMICS—Trade And Industrial Directories

332   NPL
NEPAL BANK LIMITED. ANNUAL REPORT AND BALANCE SHEET. Text in English, Nepali. a. charts; stat. Document type: Corporate.
Published by: Nepal Bank Limited, Dharma Path, Kathmandu, Nepal.

332   NPL
NEPAL BANK PATRIKA/NEPAL BANK BULLETIN. Text in English. 1968. m. free. charts; illus.; stat. Document type: Bulletin.
Related titles: Nepali ed.
Published by: Nepal Bank Limited, Dharma Path, Kathmandu, Nepal. Ed. Chiranjivi Dutt. Circ: 2,500.

332.1   NPL   ISSN 1016-7544
NEPAL RASTRA BANK. ANNUAL REPORT. Text in English. 1957. a. free (effective 2000). Document type: Corporate.
Description: Financial report of the bank.
Formerly: Nepal Rastra Bank. Report of the Board of Directors (0077-6580)
Published by: Nepal Rastra Bank, Research Department, Baluwatar, Kathmandu, Nepal.

332.1   NPL
NEPAL RASTRA BANK. ECONOMIC REVIEW. Text and summaries in English. 1987. a. price varies. Document type: Trade. Description: Provides articles dealing with problems related to economics, especially the banking sector. Its main purpose is to provide opportunities to publish articles based on the bank staff's understanding of the subject matter.
Published by: Nepal Rastra Bank, Baluwatar, P O Box 73, Kathmandu, Nepal. TEL 977-1-419806, FAX 977-1-414553, TELEX 2207 RABA NP. Ed. Deependra Bahadur Kshetry.

NETHERLANDS. CENTRAAL BUREAU VOOR DE STATISTIEK. STATISTIEK FINANCIEN VAN ONDERNEMINGEN. see BUSINESS AND ECONOMICS—Abstracting, Bibliographies, Statistics

332.1 338.9   NLD
NETHERLANDS INVESTMENT BANK FOR DEVELOPING COUNTRIES. REPORT/NEDERLANDSE INVESTERINGSBANK VOOR ONTWIKKELINGSLANDEN. VERSLAG. Text in Dutch, English. 1965. a. free. Document type: Corporate. Description: Includes development aid budget, list of bank loans and grants to the different countries, funding, profit and loss account as well as a balance sheet.
Formerly: Netherlands Investment Bank for Developing Countries. Annual Report (0077-7560)
Published by: Netherlands Investment Bank for Developing Countries/Nederlandse Investeringsbank voor Ontwikkelingslanden N.V., SE Carmegicplein, PO Box 380, The Hague, 2501 BH, Netherlands. TEL 31-70-3425425, FAX 31-70-3657815, TELEX 32089 NIO NL. Circ: 2,000.

332   USA   ISSN 1528-0799
NETWORK MARKETING LIFESTYLES. Text in English. 1999. m. USD 29.97 domestic; USD 39.97 in Canada & Mexico; USD 44.97 elsewhere (effective 2001). adv. software rev.; Website rev. 96 p./no.; back issues avail.; reprints avail. Document type: Magazine, Consumer. Description: Contains news, technology bulletins, trends, legal and regulatory updates, tips, recruiting strategies and financial management advice.
Published by: Network Marketing Publications, Inc., 221 N. Figueroa St., Los Angeles, CA 90012-2639. TEL 818-947-4444, FAX 818-947-4440, http://www.nmlifestyles.com. Pub. N Ridgeley Goldsborough. R&P Michael Rubin TEL 212-219-1201 ext 15. Adv. contact Barton Smith TEL 818-947-4444 ext 112. B&W page USD 9,000, color page USD 11,000; 8.25 x 10.25. Circ: 60,000 (paid); 10,000 (controlled).

NEW ENGLAND ACCOUNTING RESEARCH STUDIES (NO.). see BUSINESS AND ECONOMICS—Accounting

332   USA
NEW ENGLAND FINANCIAL DIRECTORY. Text in English. s-a. Document type: Directory, Trade. Description: Lists financial information for banks, bank holding companies, thrifts and major credit union institutions for the following states: Connecticut, Maine, Massachusetts, New Hampshire, Rhode Island, and Vermont.
Published by: Thomson Financial Services Company, 4709 W Golf Rd, Skokie, IL 60076-1256. TEL 847-676-9600, 800-321-3373, FAX 847-933-8101, prodinfo@tfp.com, customerservice@tfp.com, http://www.tfp.com/banks.

332   USA
NEW ENGLAND FISCAL FACTS. Text in English. 1991. 3/yr. free (effective 2003). Document type: Journal, Trade.
Related titles: Online - full text ed.
Published by: Federal Reserve Bank of Boston, Research Department, 55882, Boston, MA 02205-5882. TEL 617-973-3397, FAX 617-973-4221, http://www.bos.frb.org/economic/neff/neff.htm, http://www.bos.fsb.org. Ed. Robert Tannenwald. Circ: 3,500.

NEW HAMPSHIRE GOVERNMENT REGISTER. see PUBLIC ADMINISTRATION

332.1   GBR   ISSN 0955-095X
HG3368
NEW HORIZON. Text in English. 1975. m. GBP 45; GBP 55 rest of world (effective 2000). adv. bk.rev. back issues avail. Description: Concerns the interests and activities of those involved with Islamic (interest-free) banking and insurance.
Indexed: PerIslam.
—BLDSC (6084.237910).
Published by: Institute of Islamic Banking & Insurance, 144-146 King's Cross Rd, London, WC1X 9DH, United Kingdom. TEL 44-171-833-8275, FAX 44-171-278-4797, icis@iibi.demon.co.uk, http://www.islamic-banking.com. Ed. S Ghazanfar Ali. adv.: B&W page GBP 700, color page GBP 800; trim 210 x 294. Circ: 7,000 (paid).

NEW JERSEY ADMINISTRATIVE CODE. BANKING. see LAW

NEW JERSEY BUSINESS CREDIT DIRECTORY. see BUSINESS AND ECONOMICS—Trade And Industrial Directories

332.1   USA
NEW JERSEY. DEPARTMENT OF BANKING. ANNUAL REPORT. Text in English. 1895. a. USD 10. Document type: Government.
Formed by the merger of: New Jersey. Division of Savings and Loan Associations. Annual Report (0098-8073); New Jersey. Division of Banking. Annual Report (0098-7409)
Related titles: Microfiche ed.: (from CIS).
Published by: Department of Banking, PO Box CN040, Trenton, NJ 08625. TEL 609-984-2772, FAX 609-292-5455. Ed. Gerald Trimble. Circ: 1,300.

332.1   USA
NEW JERSEY LEAGUE NEWS. Text in English. 1922. 3/yr. free. adv. stat. Document type: Trade.
Former titles: New Jersey Savings League News; New Jersey Savings League Guide (0300-6115)
Published by: New Jersey League of Community & Savings Bankers, 411 North Ave E, Cranford, NJ 07016. TEL 908-272-8500, FAX 908-272-6626. Ed. Samuel J Damiano. Adv. contact James Meredith. Circ: 2,000 (controlled).

332   USA
NEW JERSEY STATE BAR ASSOCIATION. BANKING LAW SECTION. NEWSLETTER. Text in English. 1977. irreg. membership. bk.rev. back issues avail. Document type: Newsletter.
Published by: (Banking Law Section), New Jersey State Bar Association, One Constitution Sq, New Brunswick, NJ 08901-1520. TEL 732-249-5000, FAX 732-828-0034. Ed. Cheryl Baisden TEL 732-937-7521. Circ: 800.

332 340   USA
NEW JERSEY STATE BAR ASSOCIATION. CREDITOR AND DEBTOR RELATIONS SECTION. NEWSLETTER. Text in English. 1966. irreg. free to members. Document type: Newsletter.
Published by: (Creditor and Debtor Relations Section), New Jersey State Bar Association, One Constitution Sq, New Brunswick, NJ 08901-1520. TEL 732-249-5000, FAX 732-828-0034. Ed. Cheryl Baisden TEL 732-937-7521.

332.1 340   USA
NEW YORK BANKING LAW. Text in English. a. USD 50.
Published by: New York Legal Publishing Corp., 136 Railroad Ave., Albany, NY 12205-5786. TEL 800-541-2681, FAX 518-456-0828.

NEW YORK BUSINESS CREDIT DIRECTORY. see BUSINESS AND ECONOMICS—Trade And Industrial Directories

332   USA
NEW YORK UNIVERSITY. SALOMON CENTER. NEWSLETTER. Text in English. 1971. q. bibl. Document type: Newsletter. Description: Focuses on research projects, conferences and the Center's objectives. Lists recent business monographs, working papers and occasional papers.
Formerly (until 1990): New York University Salomon Brothers Center for the Study of Financial Institutions. Newsletter —ingenta.
Published by: New York University, Salomon Center, Stern School of Business, 44 W Fourth St, New York, NY 10012. TEL 212-998-0700. Ed. Ingo Walter.

332   USA
NEW YORK UNIVERSITY. SALOMON CENTER. OCCASIONAL PAPERS. Text in English. 1979. irreg., latest vol.9, 1989. price varies. Description: Series devoted to work-in-progress that has important current applications.
Formerly (until 1990): Salomon Brothers Center for the Study of Financial Institutions. Occasional Papers
Published by: New York University, Salomon Center, Stern School of Business, 44 W Fourth St, New York, NY 10012. TEL 212-998-0700. Ed. Ingo Walter. Circ: 1,000.

332   USA   ISSN 0884-318X
HG1
NEW YORK UNIVERSITY. SALOMON CENTER. OCCASIONAL PAPERS IN BUSINESS AND FINANCE. Text in English. irreg. USD 10 per issue (effective 1999).
Former titles (until 1990): Salomon Brothers Center for the Study of Financial Institutions. Occasional Papers in Business and Finance; Occasional Papers in Metropolitan Business and Finance
Published by: New York University, Salomon Center, Stern School of Business, 44 W Fourth St, New York, NY 10012. TEL 212-998-0700.

332   USA
NEW YORK UNIVERSITY. SALOMON CENTER. WORKING PAPERS SERIES. Text in English. 1971. irreg. USD 100 (effective 1999). Document type: Monographic series.
Formerly (until 1990): Salomon Brothers Center for the Study of Financial Institutions. Working Paper Series
—BLDSC (9350.870500).
Published by: New York University, Salomon Center, Stern School of Business, 44 W Fourth St, New York, NY 10012. TEL 212-998-0700. Ed. Ingo Walter. Circ: 500.

332   NGA   ISSN 0794-6430
HG3431
NIGERIA BANKING, FINANCE & COMMERCE. Text in English. 1985. a. NGN 500. Document type: Directory. Description: Lists Nigerian banks and nonbank financial institutions, as well as regulatory bodies. Profiles companies and compiles financial statistics.
Published by: Research & Data Services Ltd., Marina, 54-55 Taiwo St off Abibu Oki St, PO Box 2720, Lagos, Nigeria. TEL 234-2-664639, FAX 234-2-660926. Ed. Amade Abalaka. adv.: page NGN 17,500.

332 336   NGA
NIGERIA FINANCE YEARBOOK. Text in English. 1992. a. NGN 350. Description: Contains essential facts and information on the companies, institutions, and activities in the finance sector.
Published by: Goldstar Publishers (Nigeria) Ltd., Ajao Estate, Isolo, Ikoyi, 13-15 Osolo Way, PO Box 51699, Lagos, Nigeria. TEL 234-1-522530.

332.1   NGA   ISSN 0549-2734
HG3399.N53
NIGERIAN INDUSTRIAL DEVELOPMENT BANK. ANNUAL REPORT AND ACCOUNTS. Text in English. 1963. a. free. bk.rev. illus. Document type: Corporate.
Published by: Nigerian Industrial Development Bank, 63-71 Broad St, PO Box 2357, Lagos, Nigeria. TEL 234-1-2662259, TELEX 21774. Ed. Segun Talabi. Circ: 2,000.

333   NGA   ISSN 0189-3319
NIGERIAN JOURNAL OF FINANCIAL MANAGEMENT∗: international review of finance. Text in English. s-a. NGN 25, USD 40. adv. bk.rev. Document type: Academic/Scholarly.
Published by: Centre for Financial Management and Research, Institute of Management and Technology, PMB 1079, Nsukka, Enugu State, Nigeria. Ed. M R K Swamy. Circ: 1,500.

332   JPN
NIKKEI. ANNUAL CORPORATION REPORTS (LISTED COMPANIES). Text in Japanese. a. JPY 69,300 (effective 2005). Document type: Directory, Trade. Description: Contains entries on all companies listed on Japan's eight stock exchanges and major extracts from financial statements, including balance sheets and statements of profit and loss.
Published by: Nihon Keizai Shimbun Inc., 1-9-5 Ote-Machi, Chiyoda-ku, Tokyo, 100-0004, Japan. TEL 81-3-52552825, FAX 81-3-32462861, pub_sp@nikkei.co.jp, http://www.nikkei-bookdirect.com/.

▼ new title   ➤ refereed   ∗ unverified   ◆ full entry avail.

B

332 JPN
NIKKEI. ANNUAL CORPORATION REPORTS (UNLISTED COMPANIES). Text in Japanese. a. JPY 69,300 (effective 2005). **Document type:** *Directory, Trade.* **Description:** Covers more than 18,000 unlisted companies. Provides information on finance, financial indices, profitability, and capital formation.
Published by: Nihon Keizai Shimbun Inc., 1-9-5 Ote-Machi, Chiyoda-ku, Tokyo, 100-0004, Japan. TEL 81-3-52552825, FAX 81-3-32462861, pub_sp@nikkei.co.jp, http://www.nikkei-bookdirect.com/.

332 JPN
NIKKEI ANNUAL FINANCIAL REPORT. Text in Japanese. a. **Document type:** *Corporate.* **Description:** Publishes rankings and management indices for 1,600 leading financial and securities institutions.
Published by: Nihon Keizai Shimbun Inc., 1-9-5 Ote-Machi, Chiyoda-ku, Tokyo, 100-0004, Japan. TEL 81-3-32700251, FAX 81-3-52552661.

332 JPN
NIKKEI FINANCIAL ANALYSIS (LISTED COMPANIES). Text in Japanese. a. **Document type:** *Trade.* **Description:** Analysis of various data and 107 indices for 2,100 nonfinancial companies listed on Japan's eight stock exchanges.
Published by: Nihon Keizai Shimbun Inc., 1-9-5 Ote-Machi, Chiyoda-ku, Tokyo, 100-0004, Japan. TEL 81-3-32700251, FAX 81-3-52552661.

332 JPN
NIKKEI FINANCIAL ANALYSIS (UNLISTED COMPANIES). Text in Japanese. a. **Document type:** *Trade.* **Description:** Analysis of 4,900 leading unlisted Japanese companies.
Published by: Nihon Keizai Shimbun Inc., 1-9-5 Ote-Machi, Chiyoda-ku, Tokyo, 100-0004, Japan. TEL 81-3-32700251, FAX 81-3-52552661.

332 JPN
NIKKEI KINYU SHIMBUN/NIKKEI FINANCIAL DAILY. Text in Japanese. 1987. 6/w. adv. **Document type:** *Newspaper.* **Description:** Covers the international capital and money markets. Provides in-depth analysis of the strategies and financial performances of both Japanese and foreign companies.
Indexed: B&I.
Published by: Nihon Keizai Shimbun Inc., 1-9-5 Ote-Machi, Chiyoda-ku, Tokyo, 100-0004, Japan. TEL 81-3-32700251, FAX 81-3-52552661. Ed. Takashi Kageyama. Adv. contact Masahiro Matsui. B&W page JPY 1,095,000; trim 533 x 385. Circ: 61,864.

332 USA ISSN 1087-8718
HG3755.7
THE NILSON REPORT. Text in English. 1970. 23/yr. USD 995 (effective 2004). back issues avail. **Document type:** *Newsletter, Trade.*
Published by: The Nilson Report., 1110 Eugenia Place, Ste 100, Carpinteria, CA 93013-9921. TEL 805-684-8800, FAX 805-684-8825, info@nilsonreport.com, http://www.nilsonreport.com. Ed. H Spencer Nilson.

332 JPN
NIPPON GINKO CHOSA GEPPO/BANK OF JAPAN MONTHLY BULLETIN. Text in Japanese. m. JPY 790 per issue (effective 1998). 130 p./no.; **Document type:** *Bulletin.* **Description:** Contains articles on the Bank's operations and the Japanese financial system, research papers on finance and the economy of Japan, various statistics, and a chronology of financial events in Japan.
Formerly (until Apr. 1998): Nippon Ginko Geppo (0917-2165)
Indexed: RASB.
Published by: Bank of Japan/Nippon Ginko, c/o Public Relations Department, 2-1-1 Hongoku-cho-Nihonbashi, Chuo-ku, Tokyo, 1030000, Japan. TEL 81-3-3279-1111, FAX 81-3-3510-1374, http://www.boj.or.jp/en.index.htm. **Dist. by:** Tokiwa Songoh Service Co. Ltd., Publication and Research Department, Kyodo Bldg, 2-4 Hongokucho, Nihonbashi 3-chome, Chuo-ku, Tokyo 103-0027, Japan. TEL 81-3-3270-5713, FAX 81-3-3270-5710; **Overseas dist. by:** Japan Publications Trading Co., Ltd., Book Export II Dept, PO Box 5030, Tokyo International, Tokyo 101-3191, Japan. TEL 81-3-32923753, FAX 81-3-32920410.

332 JPN
NIPPON GINKO SEISAKU IINKAI GEPPO/BANK OF JAPAN. POLICY BOARD. MONTHLY REPORT. Text in Japanese. m. free. 60 p./no.; **Description:** Covers decisions on monetary policy and other matters by the Policy Board. Includes "Minutes of the Monetary Policy Meeting" and "Monthly Report of Recent Economic and Financial Developments".
Formerly: Seisaku Iinkai Geppo
Published by: Bank of Japan/Nippon Ginko, c/o Public Relations Department, 2-1-1 Hongoku-cho-Nihonbashi, Chuo-ku, Tokyo, 1030000, Japan. TEL 81-3-3279-1111, FAX 81-3-3510-1374, http://www.boj.or.jp/en/index.htm.

332 JPN ISSN 1345-1308
NIPPON SEISAKU TOSHI GINKO. CHOSABU. CHOSA/DEVELOPMENT BANK OF JAPAN. RESEARCH REPORT. Text in Japanese. 1952. irreg. free.
Former titles (until no.262, 1999): Nihon Kaihatsu Ginko. Chosabu. Chosa (0285-5887); (until 1973): Nihon Kaihatsu Ginko. Chosa Geppo (0285-5879)
—BLDSC (3181.579000).
Published by: Development Bank of Japan/Nippon Seisaku Toshi Ginko, 9-1, Otemachi 1-chome, Chiyoda-ku, Tokyo, 100-0004, Japan. TEL 81-3-3244-1770, FAX 81-3-3245-0954, TELEX J24342, http://www.jdb.go.jp/. Circ: 3,000.

NOLEGGIO. see *BUILDING AND CONSTRUCTION*

NORDRHEIN-WESTFALEN. FINANZMINISTERIUM. FINANZ REPORT. see *PUBLIC ADMINISTRATION*

332.1 NOR ISSN 0800-8507
HG3166
NORGES BANK. BERETNING OG REGNSKAP. Text in Norwegian. 1817. a. free.
Related titles: ♦ English ed.: Norges Bank. Report and Accounts. ISSN 0078-1185.
Published by: Norges Bank, Postboks 1179, Sentrum, Oslo, 0107, Norway. TEL 47-22-31-60-00, central.bank@norges-bank.no, http://www.norges-bank.no.

332 NOR ISSN 1502-2749
NORGES BANK. FINANCIAL STABILITY. Text in English. 2000. s-a.
Related titles: Online - full text ed.; Norwegian ed.: ISSN 1502-2765.
Indexed: ABIn.
Published by: Norges Bank, Bankplassen 2, Postboks 1179, Sentrum, Oslo, 0107, Norway. TEL 47-22-31-60-00, central.bank@norges-bank.no, http://www.norges-bank.no.

332 NOR ISSN 0332-5598
HG1115
NORGES BANK. PENGER OG KREDITT. Text in Norwegian. 1973. q. NOK 250 (effective 2003). charts; illus.; stat. **Document type:** *Journal, Academic/Scholarly.*
Related titles: Online - full text ed.
Published by: Norges Bank, Postboks 1179, Sentrum, Oslo, 0107, Norway. TEL 47-22-31-60-00, FAX 47-22-31-64-10, central.bank@norges-bank.no, http://www.norges-bank.no. Ed. Svein Gjedrem.

332.1 NOR ISSN 0078-1185
NORGES BANK. REPORT AND ACCOUNTS. Cover title: Norges Bank. Annual Report. Text in English. 1955. a. free. **Document type:** *Corporate.* **Description:** Provides an overview of Norway's economic activity, monetary policy and international cooperative efforts and a detailed report about its accounts.
Related titles: Online - full text ed.; ♦ Norwegian ed.: Norges Bank. Beretning og Regnskap. ISSN 0800-8507.
Published by: Norges Bank, Postboks 1179, Sentrum, Oslo, 0107, Norway. TEL 47-22-31-60-00, FAX 47-22-41-31-05, TELEX 56-71-369 NBANK N, central.bank@norges-bank.no, http://www.norges-bank.no. Pub. Svein Gjedrem.

332.1 NOR ISSN 1502-5780
NORGES BANK. WORKING PAPERS. Text in English. 1985. irreg.
Formerly (until 2001): Arbeidsnotat (0801-2504)
Related titles: Online - full text ed.
Published by: Norges Bank, Bankplassen 2, Postboks 1179, Sentrum, Oslo, 0107, Norway. TEL 47-22-31-60-00, central.bank@norges-bank.no, http://www.norges-bank.no/english/publications.

332 RUS
NORMATIVNYE AKTY DLYA BUKHGALTERA. Text in Russian. s-m. RUR 2,160 domestic to individuals; RUR 3,000 domestic to institutions (effective 2002).
Indexed: RASB.
Published by: Berator-Press, Ul Khalturinskaya 2, str 2, Moscow, 107392, Russian Federation. TEL 7-095-3639542, http://www.berator.ru. **US dist. addr.:** East View Information Services, 3020 Harbor Ln. N., Minneapolis, MN 55447. TEL 612-550-0961.

332 BLR
NORMATIVNYE DOKUMENTY PO FINANSAM, NALOGAM, BUKHGALTERSKOMY UCHETU. Text in Russian. m. USD 189 in United States. **Document type:** *Government.*
Published by: Ministry of Finance, Information and Calculation Center, Minsk, Belarus. TEL 375-172-223-6951. Ed. A V Kozlyakov. **US dist. addr.:** East View Information Services, 3020 Harbor Ln. N., Minneapolis, MN 55447. TEL 612-550-0961.

332 UKR
NORMATYVNI AKTY Z FINANSIV, PODATKIV, STRAKHUVANNYA TA BUKHALTERS'KOHO OBLIKU. Text in Ukrainian. m. USD 155 in United States.
Address: Ul Degtyarevskaya 38-42, Kiev, Ukraine. TEL 380-44-211-0390. **US dist. addr.:** East View Information Services, 3020 Harbor Ln. N., Minneapolis, MN 55447. TEL 612-550-0961.

NORTH AMERICAN FINANCIAL INSTITUTIONS DIRECTORY. see *BUSINESS AND ECONOMICS—Trade And Industrial Directories*

THE NORTH AMERICAN JOURNAL OF ECONOMICS AND FINANCE. see *BUSINESS AND ECONOMICS—Economic Situation And Conditions*

NORTH CAROLINA BUSINESS CREDIT DIRECTORY. see *BUSINESS AND ECONOMICS—Trade And Industrial Directories*

NORTH SEA LETTER. see *PETROLEUM AND GAS*

332 USA ISSN 0007-6554
NORTHERN TRUST BUSINESS COMMENT. Variant title: Business Comment. Text in English. a.
Indexed: ABIn.
Published by: Northern Trust Company, 50 S La Salle St, Chicago, IL 60690. TEL 312-630-6000, http://www.htrs.com/.

332 USA ISSN 1042-1254
HF1
NORTHWESTERN FINANCIAL REVIEW. Text in English. 1988. s-m. USD 89 (effective 2005). illus.; mkt. **Document type:** *Magazine, Trade.* **Description:** For the banking and finance industry in the Upper Midwest.
Formed by the merger of (1901-1988): Commercial West (0010-3144); (1902-1988): Michigan Investor (1040-0389)
Related titles: Online - full text ed.: (from EBSCO Publishing, Northern Light Technology, Inc., ProQuest Information & Learning).
Indexed: BLI.
Address: 3109 W. 50th St., # 125, Minneapolis, MN 55410-2102. tom-bengston@nfrcom.com, http://www.nfrcom.com. Ed., Pub., R&P Tom Bengtson. Adv. contacts Jackie Hilgert, Tom Bengtson. Circ: 3,000 (paid).

NORTON BANKRUPTCY LAW AND PRACTICE. see *LAW*

338.47 GBR
NORWAY FINANCIAL ANALYSIS SERVICE. Text in English. s-a. GBP 7,500 for single users; GBP 5,000 renewals for single users. **Document type:** *Trade.* **Description:** Calculates discounted pre- and post-tax cashflow by field and company for Norway.
Media: Diskette.
Published by: Petroleum Services Group (Subsidiary of: Andersen), 1 Surrey St, London, WC2R 2NE, United Kingdom. TEL 44-171-438-3888, FAX 44-171-438-3881. Eds. David Baker, Mike Coulten.

332 FRA ISSN 0399-1636
LES NOUVELLES FISCALES. Text in French. 1957. bi-m. FRF 1,895 (effective 1997). **Document type:** *Trade.*
Formerly (until 1973): Aide - Memoire Fiscal (0995-9106)
Published by: Groupe Liaisons S.A. (Subsidiary of: Wolters Kluwer BV), 1 Avenue Edouard Belin, Rueil Malmaison, Cedex 92856, France. TEL 33-1-41299696, FAX 33-1-41299880.

332 SVN
NOVICE; glasilo delovne skupnosti Jugobanke. Text in Slovenian. 1974. m. SIT 7.30 per issue.
Published by: Banka D.D. Ljubljana, Titova 32, Ljubljana, Slovenia. Ed. Maja Tejkal. Circ: 500.

O C C BULLETINS. (Office of the Comptroller of the Currency) see *BUSINESS AND ECONOMICS—Public Finance, Taxation*

382 332 FRA ISSN 0474-5655
O E C D CODE OF LIBERALIZATION OF CAPITAL MOVEMENTS/O C D E CODE DE LA LIBERATION DES MOUVEMENTS DE CAPITAUX. Text in English. irreg. price varies.
Related titles: French ed.
Published by: Organization for Economic Cooperation and Development, 2 Rue Andre Pascal, Paris, 75775 Cedex 16, France. TEL 33-1-45248200, FAX 33-1-45248500, http://www.oecd.org.

332 GBR
O I E S PAPERS. FINANCE. Text in English. 1984. irreg., latest vol.8, 2003. price varies. **Document type:** *Monographic series, Academic/Scholarly.*
Published by: Oxford Institute for Energy Studies, 57 Woodstock Rd, Oxford, Oxfords OX2 6FA, United Kingdom. TEL 44-1865-311377, FAX 44-1865-310527, publications@oxfordenergy.org, http://www.oxfordenergy.org/.

O S F I ANNUAL REPORT. see *PUBLIC ADMINISTRATION*

332 COL
OASIS. Text in Spanish. a. COP 30,000 domestic; USD 19 foreign (effective 2003). **Description:** Collects studies on countries and regions that are at the dawning of their globalization process.
Published by: Universidad Externado de Colombia, Departamento de Publicaciones, Calle 12, No 0-38 Este, Apartado Aereo 034141, Santafe de Bogota, Colombia. publicaciones@uexternado.edu.co, http://www.uexternado.edu.co.

332.1 USA
OBERWEIS REPORT: A MONTHLY REVIEW. Text in English. 1976. m. USD 169 (effective 1999). back issues avail. **Document type:** *Newsletter.*
Former titles: Oberweis Securities Monthly Review; Oberweis Management Monthly Review
Related titles: Fax ed.: USD 299 (effective 1999).
Published by: Oberweis Asset Management, Inc., 3333 Warrenville Rd., Ste. 500, Lisle, IL 60532-1498. TEL 630-801-6000, 800-323-6166, FAX 630-896-5282, http://www.oberweisfunds.com. Ed. James W Oberweis. Circ: 3,000 (paid); 2,000 (controlled).

332 FRA ISSN 1285-5138
L'OBSERVATOIRE DES PRODUITS BANCAIRES. Text in French. 1997. m. (11/yr). EUR 509 domestic; EUR 564 foreign (effective 2000). **Document type:** *Newsletter.* **Description:** Informs readers on all the launches and regular updates of the various banking products including savings, credit, services, insurance, and payment systems.
Published by: Publi-News, 47 rue Aristide Briand, Levallois-Perret, 92300, France. TEL 33-1-41499360, FAX 33-1-47573725, publi.news@wanadoo.fr. Ed. Ange Galula.

332 FRA
L'OBSERVATOIRE DES PRODUITS D'ASSURANCES. Text in French. 1998. m. (11/yr). EUR 409 domestic; EUR 457 foreign (effective 2000). **Document type:** *Newsletter.* **Description:** Features the latest news on life insurance and damage cover insurance, including launches of new products, product descriptions, commercial positioning, regular updates, as well as articles from renowned writers in the insurance field.
Published by: Publi-News, 47 rue Aristide Briand, Levallois-Perret, 92300, France. TEL 33-1-41499360, FAX 33-1-47573725, publi.news@wanadoo.fr. Ed. Ange Galula.

332 AUT ISSN 1563-4604
DER OEFFENTLICHE SEKTOR; Forschungsmemoranden. Text in German. 1975. q. EUR 16 domestic; EUR 18.20 foreign (effective 2005). bk.rev. **Document type:** *Journal, Academic/Scholarly.*
Published by: Technische Universitaet Wien, Institut fuer Finanzwissenschaft und Infrastrukturpolitik, Resselgasse 5/2/2, Vienna, W 1040, Austria. TEL 43-1-5880126701, FAX 43-1-5880126799, ifip@tuwien.ac.at, http://www.ifip.tuwien.ac.at/publikationen.htm. Ed. Wolfgang Blaas. Circ: 300.

332.1 AUT
OESTERREICHISCHE BANKWISSENSCHAFTLICHE GESELLSCHAFT. BANKWISSENSCHAFTLICHE SCHRIFTENREIHE. Text in German. 1953. irreg., latest vol.86, 1997. price varies. **Document type:** *Monographic series.*
Published by: (Oesterreichische Bankwissenschaftliche Gesellschaft), Bank Verlag, Wallnerstrasse 1, Vienna, W 1010, Austria. TEL 43-1-5335050, FAX 43-1-53127247. Ed. Otto Lucius.

332 AUT
OESTERREICHISCHE NATIONALBANK. BERICHTE UND STUDIEN. Text in German. 1990. q. free. **Document type:** *Bulletin.* **Description:** Covers the Austrian economy and banking sector.
Related titles: English ed.
Published by: Oesterreichische National Bank, Otto-Wagner-Platz 3, Vienna, W 1090, Austria. http://www.oenb.at. Ed. Wolfdietrich Grau. Circ: 2,500.

332.1 AUT
OESTERREICHISCHE NATIONALBANK. GESCHAEFTSBERICHT UEBER DAS GESCHAEFTSJAHR MIT JAHRESABSCHLUSS - ANNUAL REPORT. Text in German. 1956. a. free. **Document type:** *Corporate.* **Description:** Covers the Austrian and international economy. Includes balance sheet, profit and loss account, tables, and graphs.
Formerly: Oesterreichische Nationalbank, Bericht ueber das Geschaeftsjahr mit Rechnungsabschluss - Annual Report (0078-3528)
Related titles: English ed.
Published by: Oesterreichische National Bank, Otto-Wagner-Platz 3, Vienna, W 1090, Austria. http://www.oenb.co.at, http://www.oenb.at. Ed. Wolfdietrich Grau. Circ: 2,500.

332.4 AUT
HG3014
OESTERREICHISCHE NATIONALBANK. STATISTISCHES MONATSHEFT. Text in German. 1926. m. charts. index. **Description:** Statistics on the Austrian Central Bank, Austria's money and credit market, interest rates, capital markets, notes and coin, public finance, economic development, etc.
Formerly: Oesterreichische Nationalbank. Mitteilungen des Direktoriums (0029-9332)
Indexed: PROMT.
Published by: Oesterreichische National Bank, Otto-Wagner-Platz 3, Vienna, W 1090, Austria. http://www.oenb.co.at, http://www.oenb.at. Ed. Wolfdietrich Grau.

332.2 AUT
OESTERREICHISCHE SPARKASSENZEITUNG. Text in German. fortn. **Document type:** *Bulletin.*
Published by: Hauptverband der Oesterreichischen Sparkassen, Postfach 256, Vienna, W 1011, Austria. TEL 0222-71169, FAX 0222-7138926.

332 AUT ISSN 0472-5859
OESTERREICHISCHES FORSCHUNGSINSTITUT FUER SPARKASSENWESEN. SCHRIFTENREIHE. Text in German. 1961. q. charts; stat. **Document type:** *Journal, Academic/Scholarly.*
Indexed: PAIS.
Published by: Oesterreichisches Forschungsinstitut fuer Sparkassenwesen, Neuer Platz 14, Klagenfurt, 9020, Austria. TEL 43-50100-30674, GrossH@KaerntnerSparkasse.at. Circ: 550.

332.1 GBR ISSN 1353-422X
HG4538
OFFSHORE FINANCE YEARBOOK (YEARS). Text in English. 1993. a., latest vol.8, 2001. GBP 135 per vol. in United Kingdom; USD 215 per vol. elsewhere (effective 2001). **Document type:** *Directory.* **Description:** Serves as a guide to the international offshore finance industry. Provides individual reviews of offshore jurisdictions with legal and tax information.
Published by: Euromoney Institutional Investor Plc., Nestor House, Playhouse Yard, London, EC4V 5EX, United Kingdom. TEL 44-20-7779-8673, FAX 44-20-7779-8541, http://www.euromoneyplc.com. Ed. Adrian Hornbrook. **Dist. by:** Portica, Portica House, Addison Road, Sudbury, Suffolk CO10 2YW, United Kingdom. TEL 44-1787-319-933, FAX 44-870-242-9430.

332 361.7 338.85 GBR ISSN 0954-0628
OFFSHORE INVESTMENT. Text in English. 1986. 10/yr. GBP 290 in Europe to individuals; USD 720 in United States to individuals; GBP 399 rest of world to individuals; GBP 1,450 in Europe to institutions; USD 3,600 in United States to institutions; GBP 1,995 rest of world to institutions (effective 2005). adv. bk.rev. charts; illus.; tr.lit. index. 64 p./no.; back issues avail. **Document type:** *Magazine, Trade.* **Description:** Presents current information regarding offshore incorporation, investment, domicile, and tax issues.
Related titles: Online - full text ed.: O I Archive.
—CCC.
Published by: European Magazine Services Ltd., Lombard House, 10-20 Lombard St, Belfast, BT1 1BW, United Kingdom. TEL 44-2890-328777, FAX 44-2890-328555, subscriptions@offshoreinvestment.com, http://www.offshoreinvestment.com. Ed. Charles A Cain. Pub., R&P Barry C Bingham. Adv. contact Robert Ayres. B&W page GBP 2,900, color page GBP 3,700. Circ: 10,000.

OHIO BUSINESS CREDIT DIRECTORY. see *BUSINESS AND ECONOMICS—Trade And Industrial Directories*

332.1 USA
OHIO RECORD. Text in English. 1908. q. USD 25 to members; USD 50 to non-members (effective 2005). adv. **Document type:** *Magazine, Trade.*
Formerly: Ohio Banker (0030-0802)
Related titles: Online - full text ed.
Indexed: BLI.
Published by: Ohio Bankers League, 4249 Easton Way, Columbus, OH 43219-4170. TEL 614-340-7595, FAX 614-340-7596, mwachtman@ohiobankersleague.com, webmaster@ohiobankersleague.com, http://www.ohiobankersleague.com. Ed., Adv. contact James Thurston. B&W page USD 650, color page USD 1,150. Circ: 3,200 (paid and free).

346.065 332.6327 USA
OHIO SECURITIES LAW AND PRACTICE HANDBOOK. Text in English. a. USD 70 per vol. (effective 2005).
Published by: Anderson Publishing Co (Subsidiary of: LexisNexis North America), 9443 Springboro Pike, Miamisburg, OH 45342-4425. TEL 513-421-4142, 800-582-7295, FAX 513-562-8116, mail@andersonpublishing.com, http://bookstore.lexis.com/bookstore/catalog?action=product&prod_id=45150, http://www.andersonpublishing.com. Ed. Howard M. Friedman.

332.1 USA ISSN 0030-1647
OKLAHOMA BANKER. Text in English. 1909. bi-w. USD 35 membership (effective 2005). adv. bk.rev. illus. **Document type:** *Newspaper, Trade.*
Indexed: BLI.
Published by: Oklahoma Bankers Association, PO Box 18246, Oklahoma City, OK 73154-0246. TEL 405-424-5252, FAX 405-424-4518, info@oba.com, http://www.oba.com. Ed. Jeremy Cowen. Circ: 3,000.

330 DEU
ON TOP. Text in German. q. **Document type:** *Magazine, Consumer.*
Published by: (Deutscher Sparkassenverlag GmbH), G & J Corporate Media GmbH (Subsidiary of: Gruner und Jahr AG & Co.), Griegstr 75, Hamburg, 22763, Germany. TEL 49-40-88303401, FAX 49-40-88303402, http://www.guj-corporate-media.de. Ed. Regine Smith-Thyme. Circ: 180,000 (controlled).

332 NLD
ONDERNEMINGSANALYSES BANKEN. Text in Dutch. a. **Description:** Provides information on the financial performance of the banking and finance sectors in the Netherlands.
Published by: Reed Business Information bv (Subsidiary of: Reed Business), Postbus 16400, Den Haag, 2500 BK, Netherlands. TEL 31-70-3624800, FAX 31-70-3605606.

332 USA ISSN 1095-2829
ONLINE BANKING REPORT. Text in English. 1994. m. USD 795 (effective 2005). **Document type:** *Newsletter, Trade.*
Indexed: BLI.
Published by: Jim Bruene, 4739 University Way, N E, Ste 1002, Seattle, WA 98105. TEL 206-517-5021, FAX 206-524-0351, info@onlinebankingreport.com, http://www.onlinebankingreport.com. Ed. Jim Bruene.

332.1 USA
OPERATING BANKS AND BRANCHES. DATA BOOK 5: IOWA, KANSAS, MINNESOTA, MISSOURI, NEBRASKA, NORTH DAKOTA, SOUTH DAKOTA; summary of deposits in all FDIC BIF-insured commercial and savings banks and US branches of foreign banks. Spine title: F D I C Data Book 5 - IA, KS, MN, MO, NE, ND, SD. Text in English. a. free. **Document type:** *Government.*
Indexed: RefZh.
Published by: U.S. Federal Deposit Insurance Corp., Division of Insurance and Research, Reports Analysis and Quality Control Section, 550 17th Street, N.W., Washington, DC 20429. http://www2.fdic.gov/sod/sodPublications.asp?barItem=5.

332 USA
OPERATIONS ALERT (CHICAGO)✶. Text in English. 1981. bi-w. USD 200 to non-members. **Description:** Covers information on the latest operating developments and practices in the savings institution business.
Published by: United States League of Savings Institutions, 900 19th St, N W, 900, Washington, DC 20006-2105. TEL 312-644-3100. Eds. Edward T Maney, William T Marshall. Circ: 9,000.

330 FRA ISSN 0989-1900
OPTION FINANCE. Text in French. 1988. w. (48/yr.). adv. 60 p./no.; back issues avail. **Document type:** *Magazine, Consumer.* **Description:** Looks at corporations, financial techniques, and the stock market.
Address: 91 bis Rue du Cherche-Midi, Paris, 75006 , France. TEL 33-1-53635555, FAX 33-1-53635550, redaction@optionfinance.fr. Ed. Valerie Nau. Pub., R&P Francois Fahys TEL 33-1-46-48-49-35. Adv. contact Michele Fenetre TEL 33-1-46-48-49-40. Circ: 20,000 (paid).

332.7 IND
OPTIONS. Text in English. 1994. q. free.
Published by: Magna Publishing Company Ltd., Magna House, 100 E Old Prabhadevi Rd., Prabhadevi, Mumbai, Maharashtra 400 025, India. TEL 91-22-436-2270, FAX 91-22-430-6523. Ed. Ashvina Vakil. adv.: B&W page INR 15,000, color page INR 30,000; trim 203 x 267. Circ: 106,250.

332.3 333.33 USA ISSN 1083-8481
ORIGINATION NEWS. Text in English. 1990. m. USD 78 domestic; USD 88 in Canada; USD 108 elsewhere (effective 2005). adv. back issues avail. **Document type:** *Newspaper, Trade.* **Description:** General management publication for mortgage brokers, wholesale lenders, and managers.
Formerly: Managing Mortgages (1060-9318)
Related titles: Microform ed.: (from PQC); Online - full text ed.: (from Factiva, Florida Center for Library Automation, Gale Group, O C L C Online Computer Library Center, Inc., ProQuest Information & Learning).
Indexed: ABIn, BLI.
—CCC.
Published by: Source Media, Inc., One State St Plaza, 27th Fl, New York, NY 10004. TEL 212-803-6077, FAX 212-747-1154, custserv@sourcemedia.com, http://www.originationnews.com, http://www.sourcemedia.com. Circ: 18,998.

332.1 IND
OUTLOOK MONEY; making every rupee count. Text in English. 1998. fortn. INR 215 domestic; INR 1,400 in Bhutan, Bangladesh, Nepal & Pakistan; INR 2,100 elsewhere (effective 2003). adv. **Document type:** *Magazine, Consumer.* **Description:** Advises readers on how to invest well, borrow wisely and spend smartly in simple and friendly language.
Formerly: Intelligent Investor
Related titles: Online - full text ed.
Published by: Hathway Investments Pvt. Ltd., AB-10, SJ Enclave, New Delhi, 110 029, India. TEL 91-11-6191421, FAX 91-11-6191420, mahesh@outlookindia.com, outlook@outlookindia.com, http://www.outlookmoney.com.

332 NLD ISSN 0928-8503
HJ54
OVERHEIDSMANAGEMENT; vakblad voor financien automatisering en personeel & organisatie. Text in Dutch. 1925. 11/yr. EUR 94 (effective 2005). adv. bk.rev. stat.; illus. **Document type:** *Trade.* **Description:** Covers developments in finance, computers, personnel and management of interest to management at all levels.

B

▼ new title ➤ refereed ✶ unverified ◆ full entry avail.

Former titles (until 1992): Financieel Overheidsmanagement (0922-1026); (until 1988): Financieel Overheidsbeheer (0015-2072)
Indexed: KES.
—IE, Infotrieve.
Published by: Reed Business Information bv (Subsidiary of: Reed Business), Postbus 16500, Den Haag, 2500 BM, Netherlands. TEL 31-70-4415000, FAX 31-70-4415917, dorien.eldering@reedbusiness.nl, info@reedbusiness.nl, http://www.overheidsmanagement.nl/, http://www.reedbusiness.nl. adv.: B&W page EUR 1,523, color page EUR 2,771; trim 215 x 285. Circ: 1,705.

P M E; le magazine de l'entrepreneurship du Quebec. (Petites et Moyennes Entreprises) see *BUSINESS AND ECONOMICS—Small Business*

330.9 PHL
P N B INTERNATIONAL✶. Text in English. q. free. illus.
Published by: Philippine National Bank, PNB Financial Center, CCP Complex, Pres. Diosdado P. Macapagal Boulevard, Pasay City, 1300, Philippines. Ed. E P Patanne.

332 USA
▼ **P N C DIRECTIONS.** Text in English. 2003. **Document type:** *Consumer.*
Related titles: Online - full text ed.
Published by: P N C Financial Services Group, Inc., 249 Fifth Ave., 23rd Fl, Pittsburgh, PA 15222. pncdirections@pncbank.com, http://www.pncbank.com.

332 NZL ISSN 0114-0582
HF5601
PACIFIC ACCOUNTING REVIEW. Text in English. s-a. (Jun. & Dec.). NZD 30 (effective 2002). **Document type:** *Journal, Academic/Scholarly.* **Description:** Contains articles on a variety of accounting and related issues and topics from a variety of perspectives of interest to an academic, practitioner and student audience.
Related titles: Online - full text ed.: (from EBSCO Publishing, ProQuest Information & Learning).
Indexed: ATI.
—BLDSC (6328.400000).
Published by: Pacific Accounting Review Trust, c/o Pat Piper, Dept of Accounting, University of Waikato, Private Bag 3105, Hamilton, New Zealand. http://www.mngt.waikato.ac.nz/par/. Eds. Keitha Dunstan, Martin Lally, Tony Van Zijl.

332 NLD ISSN 0927-538X
HG5980.7.A2 CODEN: PBFJEQ
➤ **PACIFIC-BASIN FINANCE JOURNAL.** Text in English. 1993. 5/yr. EUR 50 in Europe to individuals; JPY 7,000 in Japan to individuals; USD 52 to individuals except Europe and Japan; EUR 478 in Europe to institutions; JPY 63,600 in Japan to institutions; USD 536 to institutions except Europe and Japan (effective 2006). **Document type:** *Journal, Academic/Scholarly.* **Description:** Publishes original empirical and theoretical research on capital markets of the Asia Pacific countries.
Related titles: Microform ed.: (from PQC); Online - full text ed.: (from EBSCO Publishing, Gale Group, IngentaConnect, ScienceDirect, Swets Information Services).
Indexed: APEL, BAS, JEL.
—BLDSC (6328.784000), IE, Infotrieve, ingenta. **CCC.**
Published by: Elsevier BV, North-Holland (Subsidiary of: Elsevier Science & Technology), Sara Burgerhartstraat 25, Amsterdam, 1055 KV, Netherlands. TEL 31-20-485-3911, FAX 31-20-485-2457, nlinfo-f@elsevier.nl, http://www.elsevier.com/locate/pacfin, http://www.elsevier.nl. Eds. K. Chan, S Ghon Rhee. **Subscr. to:** Elsevier BV, PO Box 211, Amsterdam 1000 AE, Netherlands. TEL 31-20-485-3757, FAX 31-20-485-3432, http://www.elsevier.nl.

332.1 CHE
PANORAMA. Text in English. 10/yr. **Document type:** *Bulletin.* **Description:** Information bulletin for Swiss banking customers.
Published by: Kretz AG, Postfach, Feldmeilen, 8706, Switzerland. TEL 41-1-9237656, FAX 41-1-9237657, kretz_ag@bluewin.ch. Circ: 183,647 (controlled).

332.1 BRA
PANORAMA ESTATISTICO DE SETOR BANCARIA. Text in Portuguese. 1971. q. stat.
Published by: Sindicato dos Bancos do Estado da Guanabara, Assessoria Economica, Av Rio Branco, 81, Centro, Rio De Janeiro, RJ 20040-004, Brazil.

332 PNG
PAPUA NEW GUINEA BANKING CORPORATION. ANNUAL REPORT. Text in English. a. **Document type:** *Corporate.*
Published by: Papua New Guinea Banking Corporation, Cnr. Musgrave & Douglas St., Port Moresby, Papua New Guinea. TEL 675-211999, FAX 675-222867, TELEX BACKCOR 22160.

332 339 BGR ISSN 0861-5608
PARI; businessdaily. Text in Bulgarian; Section in English. 1991. 5/w. BGL 336 (effective 2005). back issues avail. **Document type:** *Newspaper, Trade.* **Description:** Contains news, analysis, comments on the daily events in the economy, financial sector, industries.
Related titles: CD-ROM ed.; E-mail ed.; Online - full content ed.; ◆ English ed.: Bulgarian Economic Review (Online Edition).
Published by: Roubicon ITK PARI AD, 47A Tsarigradsko Shaussee Blvd, Sofia, 1504, Bulgaria. TEL 359-2-9433646, 359-2-9433651, 359-2-9433147, FAX 359-2-9433646, office@pari.bg, vpan@mail.pari.bg, kiril@pari.bg, http://www.pari.bg/. Ed. Vladimir Sabev. Pub. Valentin Panayotov. Adv. contact Elka Kamenova.

332 GBR
PARIBAS CENTRAL BANK AND MINISTRY OF FINANCE YEARBOOK (YEAR). Text in English. a. GBP 95, USD 170 (effective 1998). **Document type:** *Corporate.*
Published by: (Paribas Capital Markets), Euromoney Institutional Investor Plc., Nestor House, Playhouse Yard, London, EC4V 5EX, United Kingdom. TEL 44-20-7779-8673, FAX 44-20-7779-8541, http://www.euromoney.com. Ed. Guy Norton. Pub. Chris Brown.

PARKER'S (YEAR) TEXAS UNIFORM COMMERCIAL CODE. see *LAW—Corporate Law*

PARTNERS IN BUSINESS. see *BUSINESS AND ECONOMICS—Management*

332 USA
THE PAYMENT SYSTEM HANDBOOK. Text in English. a. USD 75. **Document type:** *Government.*
Published by: U.S. Federal Reserve System, Board of Governors, Publications Services, Rm MS 137, 20th and Constitution Ave, N W, Washington, DC 20551. TEL 202-452-3244, FAX 202-728-5886.

332 FRA ISSN 1636-6891
PAYMENT SYSTEMS NEWS. Text in English. 1999. m. (11/yr). EUR 640 domestic; EUR 761 foreign (effective 2000). **Document type:** *Newsletter.* **Description:** Contains the latest developments in electronic purses, Internet payments, multi-application cards.
Formerly (until 2000): New Payment Systems
Published by: Publi-News, 47 rue Aristide Briand, Levallois-Perret, 92300, France. TEL 33-1-41499360, FAX 33-1-47573725, publi.news@wanadoo.fr. Ed. Ange Galula.

332 USA ISSN 0162-1610
PAYROLL MANAGEMENT GUIDE. Text in English. 1943. 8 base vols. plus w. updates. looseleaf. USD 689 base vol(s). (effective 2004). **Document type:** *Trade.* **Description:** Helps to resolve day-to-day payroll issues and guides us in effective payroll planning. This reporter instructs how to implement proactive, efficient payroll procedures while ensuring compliance with federal, state and local requirements.
Related titles: CD-ROM ed.: USD 669 (effective 2004); Online - full text ed.: USD 669 (effective 2004).
Indexed: ATI.
—CCC.
Published by: C C H Inc., 2700 Lake Cook Rd, Riverwoods, IL 60015. TEL 847-267-7000, 800-449-6439, cust_serv@cch.com, http://www.cch.com. Pub. Catherine Wolfe.

332 SWE ISSN 1650-5468
PENGAR; en journal foer penningreform. Text in Swedish. 2000. q. SEK 180 (effective 2002). **Document type:** *Consumer.*
Published by: J A K Medlemsbank, Vasagatan 14, Skoevde, 54150, Sweden. TEL 46-500-46-45-00, FAX 46-500-46-45-61. Ed. Simon Goldin. Pub. Oskar Kjellberg.

332 USA ISSN 0252-3108
PER JACOBSSON FOUNDATION. LECTURES. Text in English. 1964. a. free. **Document type:** *Journal, Academic/Scholarly.*
Former titles: Per Jacobsson Foundation. Proceedings (0079-0761); Per Jacobsson Memorial Lecture (0079-077X)
Related titles: French ed.; Spanish ed.
Published by: Per Jacobsson Foundation, International Monetary Fund Bldg, Washington, DC 20431. TEL 202-623-4207, FAX 202-623-6694, nsalah@imf.org, http://www.perjacobsson.org. Circ: 2,000. **Affiliate:** International Monetary Fund.

332.3 USA
PERCEPTIONS (DULUTH). Text in English. q. adv.
Published by: Georgia Credit Union Affiliates, 2400 Pleasant Hill Rd, Ste 300, Duluth, GA 30136-5200. TEL 404-476-9625. Ed. Sherrie Futch. Circ: 3,200.

332 ZAF
PERSONAL FINANCE. Text in English. 1980. m. USD 253 (effective Mar. 2000). bk.rev. **Document type:** *Newsletter.* **Description:** Gives specific advice on all aspects of personal finance for upper-income individuals, including investments, taxation, insurance, retirement planning and more.
Incorporates (in 1993): Business Success; Which was formerly (until 1989): Independent Business
Published by: Prescon Publishing Corporation (Pty) Ltd., PO Box 84004, Greenside, Johannesburg 2034, South Africa. TEL 27-11-7829229, FAX 27-11-7822025, prescon@iafrica.com. Ed. Martin C Spring.

332 CAN ISSN 1203-7109
PERSONAL FINANCE. Text in English. 1995. m. CND 64.15 (effective 2002). 20 p./no.; **Document type:** *Journal.*
Related titles: Online - full text ed.: (from Gale Group).
Indexed: CPerI.
Published by: Lombardi Publishing Corp., 185 Woodbridge Ave, Woodbridge, ON L4L 2S9, Canada. TEL 905-264-2995, FAX 905-264-9619, http://www.lombardipublishing.com/. Ed. Don Sutton.

332 GBR ISSN 1351-9018
PERSONAL FINANCE (LONDON); make the most of your money. Text in English. 1994. q. GBP 19.95; GBP 2.60 newsstand/cover (effective 2001). adv. bk.rev.; software rev.; Website rev. back issues avail.; reprints avail. **Document type:** *Magazine, Consumer.* **Description:** Covers all one's savings and investments options, explaining all the complexities in everyday jargon-free language.
—CCC.
Published by: Charterhouse Communications Group Ltd., Arnold House, 36-41 Holywell Ln, London, EC2A 3ET, United Kingdom. TEL 44-20-7827-5454, FAX 44-20-7827-0567, martin.fagan@charterhouse-communications.co.uk, info@themoneypages.com, http://www.pfmagazine.co.uk, http://www.moneypages.com, http://www.charterhouse-communications.co.uk. Ed. Martin Fagan. Pub. Ramesh Sharma. Adv. contact Samantha Brierley TEL 44-20-7827-5459. **Dist. by:** Seymour Distribution Ltd, 86 Newman St, London W1T 3EX, United Kingdom. TEL 44-20-73968000, FAX 44-20-73968002.

332 GBR
PERSONAL FINANCE INTELLIGENCE. Text in English. 1985. q. GBP 3,100 (effective 1999). back issues avail. **Document type:** *Trade.* **Description:** Contains reports aiming to provide insight into consumer attitudes towards developments in financial services and institutions.
Related titles: CD-ROM ed.; Online - full text ed.
Published by: Mintel International Group Ltd., 18-19 Long Ln., London, EC1A 9PL, United Kingdom. TEL 44-20-76064533, FAX 44-20-76065932. Ed. Lance Close.

332 USA
PERSONAL FINANCE ONLINE. Text in English. 2001. bi-m. USD 3.99 newsstand/cover (effective 2003). adv. **Document type:** *Magazine, Consumer.*
Published by: Highbury House Communications, Inc. (Subsidiary of: Highbury House Communications PLC), Barrett Court, Ste 23, 1925 Vaughn Rd, NW, Kennesaw, GA 30144. TEL 770-422-3225, http://www.hhc.co.uk/personalfinanceonlinemagazine. Ed. David Pritchard TEL 770-422-3225 ext 229.

332 USA ISSN 1535-413X
HG179
PERSONAL FINANCIAL PLANNING MONTHLY. Text in English. 2001 (June). m. USD 210 (effective 2002). **Description:** Provides the in-depth analysis and advice you need to maintain a successful practice and to keep up with advances in the financial planning field.
Related titles: Online - full text ed.: (from Florida Center for Library Automation, Gale Group).
Indexed: ABIn, ATI.
Published by: Aspen Publishers, Inc. (Subsidiary of: Wolters Kluwer N.V.), 111Eighth Ave., 7th Fl, New York, NY 10011. TEL 212-771-0600, FAX 212-771-0885, http://www.aspenpub.com. Eds. Nina Festa, Jeffrey Rattiner, Elaine Stattler. Pub. Louis Lucarelli.

332 USA ISSN 0883-5608
PERSONAL IDENTIFICATION NEWS✶. Abbreviated title: P I N. Text in English. 1985. m. USD 345; USD 370 foreign. bk.rev. index. back issues avail. **Document type:** *Newsletter.* **Description:** Publishes executive-level summaries of business developments in smart card and advanced security technology.
Published by: Warfel & Miller, Inc., 7200 Wisonsin Ave, Ste 308, Bethesda, MD 20814-4829. Ed. Ben Miller.

332 AUT
PERSONEN-COMPASS. Text in German. a. adv. **Document type:** *Directory, Trade.*
Published by: Compass Verlag, Matznergasse 17, Vienna, W 1141, Austria. TEL 43-1-98116-0, FAX 43-1-98116148, office@compass.at, http://www.compass.at. Ed. Karin Schraml. R&P Nikoalaus Futter. Adv. contact Michael Bayer TEL 43-1-98116160.

332 ESP ISSN 1132-9564
HC381
PERSPECTIVAS DEL SISTEMA FINANCIERO. Text in Spanish. 1983. 3/yr. EUR 46 domestic; EUR 63 foreign (effective 2003). abstr.; bibl.; charts; maps; stat. **Document type:** *Monographic series.*
Formerly (until 1992): Papeles de Economia Espanola. Suplementos sobre el Sistema Financiero (0212-5994)
Related titles: Online - full content ed.
Indexed: PCI.
—CINDOC.
Published by: Fundacion de las Cajas de Ahorros Confederadas para la Investigacion Economica y Social, Juan Hurtado de Mendoza, 19, Madrid, 28036, Spain. TEL 34-91-3507907, FAX 34-91-3508040, publica@funcas.ceca.es, http://www.funcas.ceca.es. Ed., R&P Fernando Gonzalez Olivares. Pub. Victorio Valle Sanchez. Circ: 2,800.

332 BEL
PERSPECTIVES. Text in English, French, German. 1970. 8/yr.
Description: Discusses economic issues affecting the EU.
Supersedes (in 1995): E U F I Journal; Incorporates (in 1991): E E - Epargne Europe (0046-0869)
Indexed: WBA.
Published by: European Savings Banks Group/Groupement Europeen des Caisses d'Epargne, Av Marie Therese 11, Brussels, 1000, Belgium. TEL 32-2-211111, FAX 32-2-211199. Pub. C De Noose. **Co-sponsor:** World Savings Bank Institute - Institut Mondial des Caisses d'Epargnes.

332 338.91 USA
PERSPECTIVES (MADISON). Text in English. 1991. bi-m. looseleaf. free. back issues avail. **Document type:** *Newsletter.*
Published by: World Council of Credit Unions Inc., 5710 Mineral Pt Rd, Box 2982, Madison, WI 53701. TEL 608-231-7130, FAX 608-238-8020, TELEX 467918. Ed. Karen Kaplan. Circ: 4,200.

332 USA
THE PETER DAG PORTFOLIO STRATEGY AND MANAGEMENT. Text in English. 1977. s-m. looseleaf. USD 389 (effective 2005). bk.rev. charts; stat. 6 p./no.; back issues avail. **Document type:** *Newsletter.* **Description:** Provides stock market forecasts, outlook for short-term interest rates, bonds, foreign equity markets, gold and energy stocks and US dollar. Includes a model portfolio of no-load mutual funds (Vanguard) and exclusive Equity-10 portfolio of 10 stocks.
Formerly (until 1995): Peter Dag Investment Letter (0196-9323)
Related titles: Online - full content ed.
—CCC.
Published by: Peter Dag & Associates, Inc., 65 Lake Front Dr, Akron, OH 44319-3698. gdagnino@peterdag.com, http://www.peterdag.com. Ed. George Dagnino. Circ: 2,000 (paid).

332.1 PHL
PHILIPPINE NATIONAL BANK. ECONOMIC BRIEF✶. Text in English. m. charts; illus.; stat.
Published by: Philippine National Bank, PNB Financial Center, CCP Complex, Pres. Diosdado P. Macapagal Boulevard, Pasay City, 1300, Philippines.

332.6029 PHL ISSN 0115-3005
DS666.C5
PHILIPPINES YEARBOOK OF THE FOOKIEN TIMES. Text in English. 1936. a. PHP 1,200, USD 35 (effective 2001). adv. back issues avail. **Description:** Includes annual reports of all major government offices; economic analyses; special features on the country's leading corporations; environment; health; science and technology; education.
Indexed: IPP.
Published by: Fookien Times Yearbook Publishing Co., Inc., P.O. Box 747, Port Area, Manila, Philippines. TEL 632-527-5818, 632-527-7901-15, FAX 632-527-2411, vernongo@webquest.com, vernongo@vasia.com, yearbook@pacific.net.ph. Ed. Vernon Go. Pub. Grace Glory Go. Adv. contact Betsy Velasco TEL 63-2-524-6585. B&W page PHP 42,000, color page PHP 52,000; trim 243 x 296. Circ: 60,000.

THE PHYSICIAN MEDICAL GROUP ACQUISITION REPORT. see *BUSINESS AND ECONOMICS*

332 ESP ISSN 1017-4567
PIGNUS. Text in Spanish. 1990. s-a.
Indexed: RILM.
—CINDOC.
Published by: Asociacion Internacional de Establecimientos Publicos de Credito Pignoraticio, Plaza Celenque, 2, Madrid, 28013, Spain.

332 GBR ISSN 0032-0668
PLANNED SAVINGS; a review of personal finance & saving. Text in English. 1968. m. GBP 62; GBP 70 in Europe; GBP 80 elsewhere (effective Jun. 1999). adv. bk.rev. charts; illus. **Document type:** *Trade.*
Indexed: WBA.
—BLDSC (6508.800000).
Published by: Emap Finance (Subsidiary of: Emap Business Communications Ltd.), 33-39 Bowling Green Ln, London, EC1R 0DA, United Kingdom. TEL 44-171-505-8000, FAX 44-171-505-8185, http://www.emap.com. Ed. Julia Dodd. Circ: 6,386.

PLUNKETT'S FINANCIAL SERVICES INDUSTRY ALMANAC. see *BUSINESS AND ECONOMICS—Trade And Industrial Directories*

332.1 FRA ISSN 1299-2798
POINT BANQUE. Text in French. 1986. bi-m. EUR 84 domestic; EUR 100 foreign (effective 2000). adv. **Document type:** *Trade.* **Description:** Covers the latest developments in banking; new delivery channels, the latest technologies, new products, the people behind the news. Also contains features on online banking, cash management, and investment banking.
Formerly (until 2000): Technologies Bancaires Magazine (0768-7702)
Published by: Publi-News, 47 rue Aristide Briand, Levallois-Perret, 92300, France. TEL 33-1-41499360, FAX 33-1-47573725, publi.news@wanadoo.fr. Ed., Pub. Ange Galula. Adv. contact Ziva Galula. Circ: 10,000.

POLITICAL RISK LETTER. see *BUSINESS AND ECONOMICS—International Commerce*

332 382 USA
JQ1871.A1
POLITICAL RISK YEARBOOK (SET). Text in English. 1987. a. USD 1,295 for 8 vol. set (effective 2001). **Description:** Contains complete reports on more than 100 countries.
Related titles: CD-ROM ed.; Online - full text ed.: (from Data-Star); ♦ Series: Political Risk Yearbook. Volume 1: North & Central America. ISSN 0897-8557; ♦ Political Risk Yearbook. Volume 2: Middle East & North Africa. ISSN 0897-8530; ♦ Political Risk Yearbook. Volume 3: South America. ISSN 0897-8549; ♦ Political Risk Yearbook. Volume 4: Sub-Saharan Africa. ISSN 0889-2725; ♦ Political Risk Yearbook. Volume 5: East Asia & the Pacific. ISSN 1522-2500; ♦ Political Risk Yearbook. Volume 6: West Europe. ISSN 1522-2462; ♦ Political Risk Yearbook. Volume 7: East Europe. ISSN 1522-2470; ♦ Political Risk Yearbook. Volume 8: Central and South Africa. ISSN 1522-2489.
Published by: The P R S Group, Inc., PO Box 248, East Syracuse, NY 13057-0248. TEL 315-431-0511, FAX 315-431-0200, custserv@prsgroup.com, http://www.prsgroup.com.

332 382 USA ISSN 0897-8557
JL1416
POLITICAL RISK YEARBOOK. VOLUME 1: NORTH & CENTRAL AMERICA. Text in English. 1987. a. USD 345 (effective 2001).
Related titles: CD-ROM ed.; Online - full text ed.: (from Data-Star); ♦ Series of: Political Risk Yearbook (Set).
Published by: The P R S Group, Inc., PO Box 248, East Syracuse, NY 13057-0248. TEL 315-431-0511, FAX 315-431-0200, custserv@prsgroup.com, http://www.prsgroup.com.

332 382 USA ISSN 0897-8530
JQ1858.A1
POLITICAL RISK YEARBOOK. VOLUME 2: MIDDLE EAST & NORTH AFRICA. Text in English. 1987. a. USD 345 (effective 2001).
Related titles: CD-ROM ed.; Online - full text ed.: (from Data-Star); ♦ Series of: Political Risk Yearbook (Set).
Published by: The P R S Group, Inc., PO Box 248, East Syracuse, NY 13057-0248. TEL 315-431-0511, FAX 315-431-0200, custserv@prsgroup.com, http://www.prsgroup.com.

332 382 USA ISSN 0897-8549
JL1866
POLITICAL RISK YEARBOOK. VOLUME 3: SOUTH AMERICA. Text in English. 1987. a. USD 345 (effective 2001).
Related titles: CD-ROM ed.; Online - full text ed.: (from Data-Star); ♦ Series of: Political Risk Yearbook (Set).
Published by: The P R S Group, Inc., PO Box 248, East Syracuse, NY 13057-0248. TEL 315-431-0511, FAX 315-431-0200, custserv@prsgroup.com, http://www.prsgroup.com.

332 382 USA ISSN 0889-2725
JQ1871
POLITICAL RISK YEARBOOK. VOLUME 4: SUB-SAHARAN AFRICA. Text in English. 1987. a. USD 345 (effective 2001).
Related titles: CD-ROM ed.; Online - full text ed.: (from Data-Star); ♦ Series of: Political Risk Yearbook (Set).
Published by: The P R S Group, Inc., PO Box 248, East Syracuse, NY 13057-0248. TEL 315-431-0511, FAX 315-431-0200, custserv@prsgroup.com, http://www.prsgroup.com.

332 382 USA ISSN 1522-2500
JQ21.A1
POLITICAL RISK YEARBOOK. VOLUME 5: EAST ASIA & THE PACIFIC. Text in English. 1987. a. USD 345 (effective 2001).
Formerly (until 1999): Political Risk Yearbook. Volume 5: Asia & the Pacific (0897-8565)
Related titles: CD-ROM ed.; Online - full text ed.: (from Data-Star); ♦ Series of: Political Risk Yearbook (Set).
Published by: The P R S Group, Inc., PO Box 248, East Syracuse, NY 13057-0248. TEL 315-431-0511, FAX 315-431-0200, custserv@prsgroup.com, http://www.prsgroup.com.

332 382 USA ISSN 1522-2462
JN12
POLITICAL RISK YEARBOOK. VOLUME 6: WEST EUROPE. Text in English. 1996. a. USD 345 (effective 2001).
Supersedes in part (in 1999): Political Risk Yearbook. Volume 6: Europe (1522-2497); Which was formed by the merger of (1987-1996): Political Risk Yearbook. Volume 6: Europe - Countries of the European Union (1080-0174); Which was formerly (until 1995): Political Risk Yearbook. Volume 6: Europe - Countries of the E C (1053-8771); (until 1991): Political Risk Yearbook. Volume 6: Western Europe (0897-8522); (1987-1996): Political Risk Yearbook. Volume 7: Europe - Outside the European Union (1080-0182); Which was formerly (until 1995): Political Risk Yearbook. Volume 7: Europe - Outside the E C (1053-878X); (until 1991): Political Risk Yearbook. Volume 7: Eastern Europe (0897-8514)
Related titles: CD-ROM ed.; Online - full text ed.: (from Data-Star); ♦ Series of: Political Risk Yearbook (Set).
Published by: The P R S Group, Inc., PO Box 248, East Syracuse, NY 13057-0248. TEL 315-431-0511, FAX 315-431-0200, custserv@prsgroup.com, http://www.prsgroup.com.

332 382 USA ISSN 1522-2470
JN12
POLITICAL RISK YEARBOOK. VOLUME 7: EAST EUROPE. Text in English. 1996. a. USD 345 (effective 2001).
Supersedes in part (in 1999): Political Risk Yearbook. Volume 6: Europe; Which was formed by the merger of (1987-1996): Political Risk Yearbook. Volume 6: Europe - Countries of the European Union (1080-0174); Which was formerly (until 1995): Political Risk Yearbook. Volume 6: Europe - Countries of the E C (1053-8771); (until 1991): Political Risk Yearbook. Volume 6: Western Europe (0897-8522); (1987-1996): Political Risk Yearbook. Volume 7: Europe - Outside the European Union (1080-0182); Which was formerly (until 1995): Political Risk Yearbook. Volume 7: Europe - Outside the E C (1053-878X); (until 1991): Political Risk Yearbook. Volume 7: Eastern Europe (0897-8514)
Related titles: CD-ROM ed.; Online - full text ed.; ♦ Series of: Political Risk Yearbook (Set).
Published by: The P R S Group, Inc., PO Box 248, East Syracuse, NY 13057-0248. TEL 315-431-0511, FAX 315-431-0200, custserv@prsgroup.com, http://www.prsgroup.com.

332 382 USA ISSN 1522-2489
JQ21.A1
POLITICAL RISK YEARBOOK. VOLUME 8: CENTRAL AND SOUTH AFRICA. Text in English. 1999. a. USD 1,200 (effective 2001).
Related titles: CD-ROM ed.; Online - full text ed.; ♦ Series of: Political Risk Yearbook (Set).
Published by: The P R S Group, Inc., PO Box 248, East Syracuse, NY 13057-0248. TEL 315-431-0511, FAX 315-431-0200, custserv@prsgroup.com, http://www.prsgroup.com.

POLK'S FINANCIAL INSTITUTIONS BUYER'S GUIDE AND SERVICES DIRECTORY. see *BUSINESS AND ECONOMICS—Trade And Industrial Directories*

332 332.6 GBR ISSN 0957-1973
PORTFOLIO INTERNATIONAL. Text in English. m. adv. mkt.; stat.
Related titles: E-mail ed.; Fax ed.
—CCC.
Published by: Southern Magazines, 30 Cannon St, London, EC4M 6YJ, United Kingdom. TEL 44-20-7618-3456, FAX 44-20-7618-3499, gavin@portfolioint.co.uk. Ed. Gavin Serkin. Circ: 9,787.

332 658 USA ISSN 1529-6652
POWER, FINANCE & RISK. Text in English. 1998. w. (51x/yr). USD 2,195 combined subscription print & online eds. (effective 2005). **Document type:** *Newsletter, Trade.* **Description:** Covers corporate finance, investment banking and risk management in global power markets.
Related titles: Online - full text ed.: (from Florida Center for Library Automation, Gale Group, O C L C Online Computer Library Center, Inc., ProQuest Information & Learning).
Indexed: ABIn.
—CCC.
Published by: Institutional Investor News (Subsidiary of: Euromoney Institutional Investor Plc.), 225 Park Ave S, 7th Fl, New York, NY 10003-1605. TEL 212-224-3800, FAX 212-224-3491, info@iiplatinum.com, http://www.iipower.com, http://www.iinews.com. Pub. Elayne Glick. **Subscr. to:** New Orders, PO Box 5063, Brentwood, TN 37024. TEL 615-377-3322, 800-945-2034, 800-715-9197, FAX 615-337-0525, vlockridge@sunbeltfs.com.

332 GBR ISSN 1467-1492
HG939.5
PRACTICAL ISSUES ARISING FROM THE EURO. Text in English. 1996. irreg. **Document type:** *Corporate.*
Formerly (until 1999): Practical Issues Arising from the Introduction of the Euro (1365-9707)
—BLDSC (6594.614000).
Published by: Bank of England, HO-3, Threadneedle St, London, EC2R 8AH, United Kingdom. TEL 44-20-7601-5191, FAX 44-20-7601-3217.

332 340 GBR
PRACTICAL LENDING & SECURITY PRECEDENTS. Text in English. 1992. 2 base vols. plus updates 2/yr. looseleaf. GBP 435 (effective 2006).

B

Published by: Sweet & Maxwell Ltd., 100 Avenue Road, London, NW3 3PF, United Kingdom. TEL 44-20-74491111, FAX 44-20-74491144, customer.services@sweetandmaxwell.co.uk, http://www.sweetandmaxwell.co.uk. **Subscr. to:** Cheriton House, North Way, Andover, Hants SP10 5BE, United Kingdom.

346.078 USA
THE PRACTITIONER'S GUIDE TO CONSUMER BANKRUPTCY. Text in English. 1996. base vol. plus a. updates. USD 95. **Description:** Traces the origins of the current Bankruptcy Code and offers detailed analysis of the 1994 amendments.
Published by: LexisNexis (Subsidiary of: LexisNexis North America), PO Box 7587, Charlottesville, VA 22906-7587. TEL 804-972-7600, 800-562-7600, FAX 804-972-7666, llp.customer.support@lexis-nexis.com, http://www.lexislawpublishing.com. Ed. Lee E Woodard.

332.1 658 IND ISSN 0970-8448
➤ **PRAJNAN (PUNE)**; journal of social and management sciences. Text in English. 1972. q. INR 200 domestic; USD 45 foreign. adv. bk.rev.; film rev.; software rev. bibl.; illus. index, cum.index: 1972-1987. reprints avail. **Document type:** *Academic/Scholarly.* **Description:** Encourages new thinking on concepts and theoretical frameworks in the various disciplines of social, administrative and management sciences, which have relevance to the workings and development of banking and financial institutions.
Published by: National Institute of Bank Management, NIBM Post Office, Kondhwe Khurd, Pune, Maharashtra 411 048, India. TEL 91-212-673080, FAX 91-212-674478, TELEX 145 7256 NIBM IN, sankar@nibm.ernet.in, http://www.nibmindia.com. Ed. T S Ravisankar. adv.: page INR 2,500.

B

332 658 USA
HG1615.25
PRATT'S BANK ASSET/LIABILITY MANAGEMENT. Text in English. 1985. m. USD 375 (effective 2005). **Document type:** *Newsletter, Trade.* **Description:** For bankers concerned with balancing an asset and liability portfolio. Helps bankers reduce exposure to interest rate volatility.
Formerly: Bank Asset - Liability Management (0896-6230)
Related titles: Microform ed.: 1985 (from PQC); Online - full text ed.
Indexed: BLI.
—CCC.
Published by: A.S. Pratt & Sons, Inc., 1911 Fort Myer Dr, Arlington, VA 22209. TEL 703-528-0145, FAX 703-528-1736, http://www.sheshunoff.com/store/805.html. Ed. Alan Rice.

PRATT'S BANK SECURITY REPORT. see *CRIMINOLOGY AND LAW ENFORCEMENT—Security*

332.1 USA ISSN 1540-451X
PRATT'S DIRECTORS NEWSLETTER. Text in English. 1996. m. USD 205 (effective 2005). **Document type:** *Newsletter.*
Published by: A.S. Pratt & Sons, Inc., 1911 Fort Myer Dr, Arlington, VA 22209. TEL 703-528-0145, 800-572-2797, FAX 703-528-1736, pratt.info@thomsonmedia.com, http://www.aspratt.com/.

332 USA ISSN 1540-4412
PRATT'S LETTER. Text in English. w. USD 245. **Document type:** *Newsletter.*
Related titles: Online - full content ed.: ISSN 1540-3769.
Published by: A.S. Pratt & Sons, Inc., 1911 Fort Myer Dr, Arlington, VA 22209. TEL 703-528-0145, FAX 703-528-1736, pratt.info@thomsonmedia.com, http://www.sheshunoff.com/store/083.html, http://www.aspratt.com/. Ed. Alan Rice.

332 USA ISSN 1540-398X
PRATT'S MORTGAGE COMPLIANCE LETTER. Text in English. 2001. m. USD 425 (effective 2005). **Document type:** *Newsletter.*
Published by: A.S. Pratt & Sons, Inc., 1911 Fort Myer Dr, Arlington, VA 22209. TEL 703-528-0145, 800-572-2797, FAX 703-528-1736, pratt.info@thomsonmedia.com, http://www.aspratt.com/. Ed. Goodwin Procter.

332.1 332.63 DEU
PRAXISHANDBUCH AELDAULAGE. Text in German. 1998. irreg. looseleaf. **Document type:** *Trade.*
Published by: W R S Verlag GmbH & Co. KG (Subsidiary of: Rudolf Haufe Verlag GmbH & Co. KG), Fraunhoferstr 5, Planegg, 82152, Germany. info@wrs.de, http://www.wrs.de.

332.1 USA ISSN 1049-3883
HG2401
PRENTICE HALL BANKING YEARBOOK✱ . Text in English. 1990. a.
Published by: Prentice Hall, Business & Professional Division, 405 Murray Hill Pkwy., E Rutherford, NJ 07073-2136.

PREVISIONS GLISSANTES DETAILLEES EN PERSPECTIVES SECTORIELLES (VOL.33): BANQUES. see *BUSINESS AND ECONOMICS—Economic Situation And Conditions*

PRICE INDEXES MONTHLY. see *BUSINESS AND ECONOMICS—Abstracting, Bibliographies, Statistics*

332.1 USA ISSN 1522-1334
PRICEWATERHOUSECOOPERS REGULATORY HANDBOOK SERIES. Text in English. 1993. a. (in 7 vols.). price varies. **Document type:** *Trade.*
Formerly (until 1997): PricewaterhouseCoopers Compliance Handbook Series
Related titles: ♦ Series: The Trust Regulatory Handbook. ISSN 1090-2511; ♦ The Regulatory Risk Management Handbook. ISSN 1090-2554; ♦ The Consumer Banking Regulatory Handbook. ISSN 1090-2546; ♦ The Commercial Banking Regulatory Handbook. ISSN 1090-2538; ♦ The Securities Regulatory Handbook. ISSN 1090-252X; ♦ The Regulatory Reporting Handbook. ISSN 1090-2562; ♦ Compliance Link. ISSN 1522-0664.
Published by: (PricewaterhouseCoopers), M.E. Sharpe, Inc., 80 Business Park Dr, Armonk, NY 10504. TEL 914-273-1800, 800-541-6563, FAX 914-273-2106, custserv@mesharpe.com, http://www.mesharpe.com.

332.1 FRA
LES PRINCIPALES PROCEDURES DE FINANCEMENT - ENTREPRISES ET MENAGES. Text in French. 1989. a. EUR 38.11 (effective 2003).
Former titles: Principales Procedures de Financement des Besoins des Entreprises et des Menages; Principaux Mecanismes de Distribution de Credit
Related titles: CD-ROM ed.; Online - full text ed.; ♦ Series of: Banque de France. Service de l'Information. Collection Notes d'Information.
Published by: Banque de France, Service Relations avec le Public, 48 rue Croix-des-Petits-Champs, Paris, 75049, France. http://www.banque-france.fr.

332 GBR ISSN 0953-7031
PRIVATE BANKER INTERNATIONAL. Text in English. 1987. m. GBP 997, EUR 1,597, USD 1,697 (effective 2005). **Document type:** *Bulletin.* **Description:** Gives news, information and advice on maintaining affluent client relationships.
Related titles: Online - full text ed.: (from Gale Group, LexisNexis, O C L C Online Computer Library Center, Inc., ProQuest Information & Learning).
Indexed: B&I, BLI.
Published by: Lafferty Publications Ltd., The Colonnades, 82 Bishops Bridge Rd, London, W2 6BB, United Kingdom. TEL 44-20-75635700, FAX 44-20-75635701, cuserv@lafferty.com, http://www.lafferty.com/newsletter_publication.php?id=12. Ed. John Evans.

332 USA ISSN 1098-0415
HG2031.L29
PRIVATE BANKING & MONEY MANAGEMENT IN LATIN AMERICA. Text in English. 1995. a.
Related titles: ♦ Supplement to: LatinFinance. ISSN 1048-535X.
Published by: Latin American Financial Publications, Inc. (Subsidiary of: Euromoney Institutional Investor Plc.), 2121 Ponce de Leon Blvd, 1020, Coral Gables, FL 33134. TEL 305-357-4232, FAX 305-448-0718.

332 340 GBR
PRIVATE EQUITY TRANSACTIONS. Text in English. 2000. base vol. plus updates 2/yr. looseleaf. GBP 310 base vol(s).; GBP 265, EUR 399 updates in Europe; GBP 275, USD 500 updates elsewhere (effective 2006). **Document type:** *Bulletin, Trade.*
Published by: Sweet & Maxwell Ltd., 100 Avenue Road, London, NW3 3PF, United Kingdom. TEL 44-20-74491111, FAX 44-20-74491144, customer.services@sweetandmaxwell.co.uk, http://www.sweetandmaxwell.co.uk. **Subscr. to:** Cheriton House, North Way, Andover, Hants SP10 5BE, United Kingdom.

332 USA ISSN 1099-341X
PRIVATE EQUITY WEEK. Text in English. 1994. w. USD 1,575 in US & Canada; USD 1,650 elsewhere (effective 2005). adv. **Document type:** *Newsletter, Trade.*
Related titles: Online - full text ed.: (from EBSCO Publishing, Florida Center for Library Automation, Gale Group, LexisNexis, O C L C Online Computer Library Center, Inc.).
Indexed: B&I.
Published by: Source Media, Inc., PO Box 95512, Chicago, IL 60694-5512. TEL 646-822-3220, 800-607-4463, FAX 646-822-4945, custserv@sourcemedia.com, http://www.privateequityweek.com, http://www.sourcemedia.com. Ed. Lawrence Aragon.

332.1 USA ISSN 1099-3401
PRIVATE PLACEMENT LETTER. Text in English. 1982. w. (49/yr.). USD 1,395 domestic; USD 1,504 foreign (effective 2005). adv. **Document type:** *Newsletter, Trade.* **Description:** Covers buying, selling, and trading unregistered securities.
Formerly: Private Placements (0735-9950)
Related titles: Online - full text ed.: (from Florida Center for Library Automation, Gale Group, LexisNexis, O C L C Online Computer Library Center, Inc.).
Indexed: B&I.
—CCC.
Published by: Source Media, Inc., One State St Plaza, 27th Fl, New York, NY 10004. TEL 212-803-6077, 800-221-1809, FAX 212-747-1154, custserv@sourcemedia.com, http://www.privateplacementletter.com, http://www.sourcemedia.com. Ed. Ronald Cooper TEL 212-803-8722. Pub. John Toth TEL 212-803-6565. Adv. contact James MacDonald TEL 212-803-8749.

332 USA ISSN 1094-8996
PRIVATE PLACEMENT REPORT. Text in English. 1993. 48/yr. USD 895; USD 995 foreign. adv. **Document type:** *Newsletter, Trade.* **Description:** Covers buying, selling and trading unregistered securities. Includes deal structure and pricing, covenant packages and spreads; surveillance and the "new" private placement market in post-144A environment; stories affecting the marketplace.
Incorporates (in 1999): Financial Services Document Watch - Insurance Edition; Which superseded in part: Insurance Document Watch; Formerly: Private Placement Reporter
Related titles: Online - full text ed.: (from EBSCO Publishing, Florida Center for Library Automation, Gale Group, O C L C Online Computer Library Center, Inc., The Dialog Corporation).
Indexed: B&I.
Published by: Securities Data Publishing (Subsidiary of: Thomson Financial / I M G Media), 195 Broadway, New York, NY 10007. TEL 212-765-5311, FAX 212-765-6123, glicke@tfn.com, sdp@tfn.com. Ed. Bonnie McGeer. Adv. contact Hans Winberg.

PRIVATLIQUIDATION AKTUELL. see *LAW—Corporate Law*

332 340 USA ISSN 0734-6638
HG2573
PROFILE OF STATE CHARTERED BANKING. Text in English. 1965. a. **Document type:** *Journal, Trade.*
Published by: Conference of State Bank Supervisors, 1155 Connecticut Ave, NW, 5th Fl, Washington, DC 20036. TEL 202-296-2840, FAX 202-296-1928, http://www.csbs.org. Ed., R&P Montrice Yakimov.

332.1 PRI
PROGRESO ECONOMICO/ECONOMIC PROGRESS. Text in English, Spanish. 1965. q. free. **Document type:** *Newsletter.* **Description:** Reports economic and financial data related to Puerto Rico and the U.S.
Formerly: Progress in Puerto Rico
Published by: Banco Popular de Puerto Rico, Strategic Planning Division, Banco Popular Center, P O Box 362708, San Juan, 00936-2708, Puerto Rico. TEL 787-754-7639, FAX 787-758-2714, ffernandez@bppr.com. Ed. Frances Fernandez. Circ: 5,000.

332 382 GBR ISSN 1462-0014
PROJECT FINANCE. Text in English. 1997. 10/yr. GBP 595 combined subscription domestic print & online eds.; EUR 885 combined subscription in Europe print & online eds.; USD 995 combined subscription elsewhere print & online eds. (effective 2005). adv. charts; stat.; illus. index. reprints avail. **Document type:** *Magazine, Trade.* **Description:** Keeps exporters and their bankers worldwide informed of the major trends in the provision of term financing for domestic and overseas projects and for wholesale trade deals.
Formed by the merger of (1992-1997): Infrastructure Finance (1063-0260); (1990-1997): Project and Trade Finance (London, 1989) (1350-2700); Which was formerly (until 1990): Trade Finance and Banker International (0960-1740); Which was formed by the 1989 merger of: Trade Finance; Banker International (0951-5739); Which was formerly (until 1987): Euromoney Bank Report (0266-9919)
Related titles: Fax ed.; Microform ed.: (from PQC); Online - full text ed.: (from EBSCO Publishing, Factiva, Gale Group, O C L C Online Computer Library Center, Inc., ProQuest Information & Learning); ♦ Supplement(s): Project Finance Book of Lists (Years); ♦ World Export Credit Guide. ISSN 1354-9847.
Indexed: ABIn, B&I, BLI, BPIA, WBA.
—BLDSC (6924.844620), Infotrieve. **CCC.**
Published by: Euromoney Institutional Investor Plc., Nestor House, Playhouse Yard, London, EC4V 5EX, United Kingdom. TEL 44-20-7779-8673, FAX 44-20-7779-8541, information@euromoneyplc.com, http://www.projectfinancemagazine.com, http://www.euromoney.com. Ed. Tom Nelthorpe TEL 212-224-3554. Adv. contact Gary Parker TEL 44-20-77798848. Circ: 6,000. **Subscr. to:** American Educational Systems, PO Box 246, New York, NY 10024-0246. TEL 800-431-1579, aesbooks@aol.com.

PROJECT FINANCE BOOK OF LISTS (YEARS). see *BUSINESS AND ECONOMICS—Abstracting, Bibliographies, Statistics*

332 GBR ISSN 0967-5914
PROJECT FINANCE INTERNATIONAL. Text in English. 1989. s-m. adv. back issues avail. **Document type:** *Magazine, Trade.* **Description:** Informs readers of the progression of deals, regulatory changes, legal developments and the financial structure of deals.
Formerly (until 1992): Project Finance (0961-818X)
Related titles: CD-ROM ed.; Online - full text ed.: (from EBSCO Publishing).
—CCC.

Published by: I F R Publishing (Subsidiary of: Thomson Financial Services Ltd.), Aldgate House, 33 Aldgate High St, London, EC3N 1DL, United Kingdom. TEL 44-20-7369-7692, FAX 44-20-7369-7395, maria.ryan@tfeurope.com, http://www.ifr.pub, http://www.ifrweb.com. Ed. Rod Morrison TEL 44-20-73697570. Adv. contact Maria Ryan. page GBP 1,500. Circ: 2,500.

332   GBR   ISSN 1352-4062
PROJECT FINANCE INTERNATIONAL DIRECTORY. Text in English. 1993. a. **Document type:** *Directory.*
Published by: I F R Publishing (Subsidiary of: Thomson Financial Services Ltd.), 11 New Fetter Ln, London, EC4A 1JN, United Kingdom. TEL 44-20-7815-3900, FAX 44-20-7815-3856.

332   GBR
PROJECT FINANCE REGIONAL REPORTS. Text in English. irreg. GBP 595, USD 995. **Description:** Provides data on individual projects within a region, including country and borrower details, industry and sector information as well as project scheduling and size.
Published by: Euromoney Institutional Investor Plc., Nestor House, Playhouse Yard, London, EC4V 5EX, United Kingdom. TEL 44-20-7779-8673, FAX 44-20-7779-8541.

332   GBR
PROJECT FINANCE SECTOR REPORTS. Text in English. irreg. GBP 495, USD 795 (effective 1998). **Description:** Provides in-depth information on individual projects within a particular project finance sector.
Published by: Euromoney Institutional Investor Plc., Nestor House, Playhouse Yard, London, EC4V 5EX, United Kingdom. TEL 44-20-7779-8673, FAX 44-20-7779-8541.

332   GBR   ISSN 0968-2279
HD75.8
PROJECT FINANCE YEARBOOK (YEARS). Text in English. a. GBP 115; USD 195 foreign. **Document type:** *Directory, Trade.* **Description:** Examines ways in which projects can be financed in the current market, listing more than 1600 companies in the field of project finance.
—BLDSC (6924.844800).
Published by: Euromoney Institutional Investor Plc., Nestor House, Playhouse Yard, London, EC4V 5EX, United Kingdom. TEL 44-20-7779-8673, FAX 44-20-7779-8541, http://www.euromoney.com. Ed. Adrian Hornbrook. **Dist. in U.S. by:** American Educational Systems, PO Box 246, New York, NY 10024-0246. TEL 800-431-1579, aesbooks@aol.com; **Orders to:** Plymbridge Distributors Ltd, Plymbridge House, Estover Rd, Plymouth, Devon PL6 7PY, United Kingdom. TEL 44-1752-202300, FAX 44-1752-202330, enquiries@plymbridge.com, http://www.plymbridge.com.

332   MEX
PRONTUARIO INTERNACIONAL. Text in Spanish. d. MXP 250 domestic.
Published by: Banco de Mexico, Subdireccion de Investigacion Economica y Bancaria, 06059 Mexico, Mexico, Ave. JUAREZ 90, Centro Urbano Benito Juarez, Del. Cuauhtemoc, Ciudad De Mexico, DF 06059, Mexico. TEL 525-761-8588.

336   DEU   ISSN 0033-3476
HJ101
➤ **PUBLIC FINANCE/FINANCES PUBLIQUES.** Text in English. 1946. q. EUR 139.10 to individuals; EUR 288.90 to institutions (effective 2003). adv. bk.rev. bibl.; charts; stat. index. 130 p./no.; back issues avail.; reprint service avail. from PQC. **Document type:** *Journal, Academic/Scholarly.* **Description:** Covers the study of public economics theory and policy and related problems.
Related titles: Microfiche ed.: (from PQC).
Indexed: ASCA, CJA, CurCont, DIP, IBR, IBSS, IBZ, JEL, MEA&I, PAA&I, PAIS, PCI, RASB, SSCI.
—IDS, IE. **CCC.**
Published by: Foundation Journal Public Finance, c/o Prof. Dieter Biehl, Goethestr 13, Koenigstein, 61462, Germany. TEL 49-6174-23370, FAX 49-6174-23370. Ed., R&P, Adv. contact Dieter Biehl. Circ: 1,300.

332 336 351   GBR   ISSN 1742-0334
PUBLIC-PRIVATE FINANCE. Text in English. 1996. m. adv. stat.; tr.lit. back issues avail. **Document type:** *Magazine, Trade.*
Description: Provides information on the development of private finance initiative and public and private partnership projects in the UK and abroad. Also contains technical articles, case studies and a database.
Formerly (until 2002): P F I Report (1364-7768)
Related titles: Online - full text ed.: (from EBSCO Publishing, Gale Group, O C L C Online Computer Library Center, Inc.).
Published by: Centaur Publishing, St Giles House, 50 Poland St, London, W1V 4AX, United Kingdom. TEL 44-20-79704000, nickforrest@centaur.co.uk, http://www.publicprivatefinance.com/, http://www.centaur.co.uk. Ed., R&P Quentin Carruthers. Pub. Nigel Roby. Circ: 450.

332   PRI   ISSN 0270-126X
HC154.5.A1
PUERTO RICO BUSINESS REVIEW. Text in English. 1976. q. free. charts; illus.; stat. cum.index: 1976-1988. Supplement avail. **Document type:** *Magazine, Consumer.* **Description:** Provides business-related articles of interest to the financial community, economists, and the private and public sectors.

Indexed: PAIS.
Published by: Government Development Bank for Puerto Rico, PO Box 42001, Minillas Sta, San Juan, 00940-2001, Puerto Rico. TEL 787-728-9200, 787-722-2525, FAX 787-268-5496, http://www.gdb-pur.com. Eds. Anabel Hernandez, Maria Socorro Rosario-Claudio. Circ: 11,000.

332.1   IND   ISSN 0304-8101
HG3290.D44
PUNJAB NATIONAL BANK. ANNUAL REPORT. Key Title: Annual Report - Punjab National Bank. Text in English. a. **Document type:** *Corporate.*
Published by: Punjab National Bank, Ltd., 5 Parliament St., New Delhi, 100 001, India.

PURCHASING GROUP USERS' HANDBOOK. see *INSURANCE*

332   USA   ISSN 1536-2329
THE PURE FUNDAMENTALIST. Text in English. m. USD 19.95 per month; USD 55, USD 195 (effective 2005). **Document type:** *Newsletter, Trade.*
Published by: Horizon Publishing Co., L L C, 7412 Calumet Ave., Hammond, IN 46324-2692. TEL 800-233-5922, FAX 219-931-6487, http://www.thepurefundamentalist.com. Ed. Al Toral.

332   QAT
QATAR NATIONAL BANK (S.A.Q.). REPORT OF THE DIRECTORS AND BALANCE SHEET. Text in English. a. **Document type:** *Corporate.*
Published by: Qatar National Bank (S.A.Q.), P O Box 1000, Doha, Qatar.

QUADRO DI SINTESI DEL BOLLETTINO STATISTICO; dati territoriali sul credito, la finanza e i tassi di interesse bancari. see *BUSINESS AND ECONOMICS—Abstracting, Bibliographies, Statistics*

332   GBR   ISSN 1469-7688
HG11   CODEN: QFUIAV
➤ **QUANTITATIVE FINANCE.** Text in English. 2001. bi-m. GBP 490, USD 959 combined subscription to institutions print & online eds. (effective 2006). adv. bk.rev. a.index. back issues avail.; reprint service avail. from PSC. **Document type:** *Journal, Academic/Scholarly.* **Description:** Publishes articles that reflect the increasing use of quantitative methods in finance and the growth in practical applications of financial engineerings, such as asset creation, pricing and risk management. It also covers new developments such as agent-based modelling and evolutionary game theory.
Related titles: Microfiche ed.; Online - full text ed.: ISSN 1469-7696. GBP 466, USD 911 to institutions (effective 2006) (from EBSCO Publishing, Gale Group, IngentaConnect, Swets Information Services).
Indexed: ABIn, CMCI, CurCont, Inspec, JEL, MathR, MathSciNet, RefZh, SSCI.
—BLDSC (7168.333200), Infotrieve. **CCC.**
Published by: Routledge (Subsidiary of: Taylor & Francis Group), 4 Park Sq, Milton Park, Abingdon, Oxon OX14 4RN, United Kingdom. TEL 44-1235-828600, FAX 44-1235-829000, Quant@tandf.co.uk, journals@routledge.com, http://www.tandf.co.uk/journals/titles/14697688.asp, http://www.routledge.com. Eds. Jean-Philippe Bouchaud, Michael Dempster. adv.: page GBP 1,495; trim 210 x 286.

332   USA
QUARTERLY BANK DIGEST✱. Text in English. m. USD 699. **Description:** Data publication for commercial banks.
Formerly: Bank Portfolio Strategist
Published by: S N L Financial LC, 212 7th St NE, Charlottesvle, VA 22902-5307. TEL 434-977-1600, FAX 804-977-4466, subscriptions@shlnet.com, customerservice@snl.com, http://www.snlnet.com. Ed. Mona Thompson. Pub. Reid Nagle.

QUARTERLY BUSINESS FAILURES. see *BUSINESS AND ECONOMICS—Economic Situation And Conditions*

332.10973   USA
QUARTERLY FINANCIAL INSTITUTION RATINGS. Abbreviated title: Q F I R. Text in English. 1989. q. USD 349.95.
Description: Features comprehensive coverage of 12,000 commercial and savings banks, 2,600 savings and loans, 2,500 credit unions and the 100 largest bank holding companies, including information on assets, income, liquidity, asset quality, capital and earnings.
Formerly: Quarterly Bank, Savings and Loan Rating Service (1051-8010)
Related titles: CD-ROM ed.; Diskette ed.
Published by: L A C E Financial Corp., 118 N Court St, Frederick, MD 21701. TEL 301-662-1011. Ed. Barron Putnam. Pub. Clara Smith.

332   IND   ISSN 0536-8014
QUARTERLY STATISTICS OF THE WORKING OF CAPITAL ISSUES CONTROL. Text in English. q. INR 6, USD 2.16. charts; stat.
Published by: Government of India, Department of Publications, Civil Lines, New Delhi, 110 054, India. TEL 2517409.

332   JPN
R & I COUNTRY RISK SURVEY. (Ratings & Investment) Text in Japanese. 1982. s-a. (plus w. fax newsletter). JPY 40,000 (effective 2000). adv. **Document type:** *Newsletter.*
Description: Carries the results of a multi-faceted analysis and evaluation of investment risk in 100 countries around the world.
Formerly: Nikkei Country Risk Report
Published by: Japan Rating and Investment Information Inc., TT-2 Bldg, 3-8-1 Nihonbashiningyo-cho, Chuo-ku, Tokyo, 103-0013, Japan. TEL 81-3-5644-3450, FAX 81-3-5644-3452, TELEX J22308 NIKKEI. Ed., R&P, Adv. contact Toshio Iezumi TEL 81-3-5644-3470.

332.1 330.9   CAN
HC111
R B C LETTER. (Royal Bank of Canada) Text in English. 1920. q. free. **Document type:** *Newsletter.* **Description:** Presents subjects of general interest; instruction, self betterment, history and economics have been key areas.
Former titles (until 2002): Royal Bank Letter (0229-0243); (until July 1980): Royal Bank of Canada. Monthly Letter (0035-8770)
Related titles: Microform ed.: (from MML); French ed.: ISSN 0227-5961.
Indexed: CBCARef, CBPI, CPerl, IFP, PAIS.
—BLDSC (7298.983220), CISTI. **CCC.**
Published by: Royal Bank of Canada, Public Affairs Department, c/o Marsha Tanti, Ste 935, 9th Fl, South Tower, 200 Bay St, Toronto, ON M5J 2J5, Canada. TEL 416-974-5816, FAX 416-974-6023, rbcletter@rbc.com, http://www.rbc.com/community/letter/. Ed. Robert Stewart. R&P Marsha Tanti. Circ: 150,000 (controlled).

332   FRA   ISSN 1772-6638
HG1505
R B. REVUE BANQUE. Text in French. 1926. m. EUR 260 domestic; EUR 290 foreign (effective 2005). adv. bk.rev. stat. index. reprint service avail. from SCH. **Document type:** *Magazine, Consumer.*
Former titles (until 2005): Banque Magazine (1299-3174); (until 1999): Banque (0005-5581)
Indexed: ELLIS, PAIS, RASB, SCIMP.
—BLDSC (7891.530500), IE, Infotrieve, ingenta. **CCC.**
Published by: Revue Banque, 18 Rue La Fayette, Paris, 75009, France. TEL 33-1-49600661, FAX 33-1-48241297, revuebanque@abocom.fr, http://www.revue-banque.fr. Ed. Elisabeth Coulomb. Circ: 20,000.

332   ZWE
R B Z WEEKLY ECONOMIC HIGHLIGHTS. Text in English. w. ZWD 520. charts; stat. **Document type:** *Journal, Trade.*
Description: Contains reports and statistics on financial news and trends regarding the economy of Zimbabwe.
Published by: Reserve Bank of Zimbabwe, Economic Research and Policy Division, PO Box 1283, Harare, Zimbabwe. TEL 263-4-703000, FAX 263-4-707800.

332 650   USA   ISSN 1545-7699
HF5681.B2
R M A ANNUAL STATEMENT STUDIES. Text in English. 1923. a. USD 135 to non-members; USD 29 to members (effective 2000). index. **Document type:** *Corporate.* **Description:** Contains corporate balance sheets, income data and ratios on over 500 different industries. Includes trend data for the past five years for most of these industries, as well as data sorted by asset size and sales size.
Formerly (until 1977): Risk Management Association. Annual Statement Studies (0080-3340)
Related titles: CD-ROM ed.: ISSN 1551-6067; Microfiche ed.: (from CIS).
Indexed: SRI.
—CCC.
Published by: Risk Management Association, One Liberty Place, Ste 2300, 1650 Market St, Philadelphia, PA 19103-7398. TEL 215-446-4000, FAX 215-446-4101, studies@rmahq.org. Ed. Sue Wharton. Circ: 40,000.

332.7   USA   ISSN 1531-0558
HG1507
THE R M A JOURNAL. Text in English. 1918. 10/yr. USD 85 in US & Canada to non-members; USD 140 elsewhere to non-members; USD 60 in US & Canada to members; USD 95 elsewhere to members (effective 2005). adv. bk.rev. charts; illus.; stat. index, cum.index. back issues avail.; reprints avail. **Document type:** *Magazine, Trade.* **Description:** Covers issues relating to commercial lending, risk management and related topics.
Former titles (until Sep. 2000): The Journal of Lending & Credit Risk Management (1088-7261); (until 1996): Journal of Commercial Lending (1062-6271); (until 1992): Journal of Commercial Bank Lending (0021-986X); (until 1967): Robert Morris Associates Bulletin
Related titles: Microfiche ed.; Online - full text ed.: (from Florida Center for Library Automation, Gale Group, O C L C Online Computer Library Center, Inc.).
Indexed: ABIn, ATI, BLI, BPI, BPIA, BusI, CPM, CurCont, ESPM, IPARL, ManagCont, PAIS, RiskAb, SRI, T&II, WBA.
—BLDSC (7993.952800), IE, Infotrieve, ingenta. **CCC.**

▼ *new title*   ➤ *refereed*   ✱ *unverified*   ◆ *full entry avail.*

Published by: Risk Management Association, One Liberty Place, Ste 2300, 1650 Market St, Philadelphia, PA 19103-7398. TEL 215-446-4000, FAX 215-446-4101, bfoster@rmahq.org, http://www.rmahq.org. Ed. Beverly Foster. Adv. contact Jennifer Germanotta TEL 215-448-4098. B&W page USD 2,500, color page USD 3,500; trim 8 x 10.88. Circ: 20,000 (paid).

332 USA
R T C WATCH✶. Text in English. w. USD 465 domestic; USD 495 foreign; USD 645 renewals domestic; USD 675 renewals foreign.
Related titles: Online - full text ed.
Published by: Thomson Financial Services Company, One State St Plaza, New York, NY 10004. TEL 800-733-4371, FAX 301-654-1678.

332 GBR ISSN 0898-1515
R T F I: THE REAL-TIME FINANCIAL INFORMATION INDEX. Text in English. 1988. base vol. plus updates 4/yr. USD 2,495 (effective 2000). **Document type:** *Directory.* **Description:** Documents key features and data coverage of real-time market data services in North America and Europe; reviews key financial services vendors.
—CCC.
Published by: Risk Waters Group (Subsidiary of: Incisive Media Plc.), Haymarket House, 28-29 Haymarket, London, SW1Y 4RX, United Kingdom. TEL 44-20-74849700, FAX 44-20-74849833, http://www.watersinfo.com.

R UND V REPORT. see *INSURANCE*

332 CHE
RAIFFEISEN. Text in German. m.
Published by: Schweizer Verband der Raiffeisenkassen, Vadianstr. 17, Sankt Gallen, CH-9001, Switzerland. TEL 219111.

332 ISR
RASHUT NEYAROT EREKH. ANNUAL REPORT/ISRAEL SECURITIES AUTHORITY. ANNUAL REPORT. Text in Hebrew. a. free. **Document type:** *Corporate.*
Published by: Rashut Neyarot Erekh/Israel Securities Authority, 22 Kanfe Nesharim St, Jerusalem, 95464, Israel. TEL 972-2-6556555, FAX 972-2-6513169. Circ: 1,000.

332 USA ISSN 1539-8099
HG179
READINGS IN FINANCIAL PLANNING. Text in English. 1996. irreg.
Published by: American College, 270 S Bryn Mawr Ave., Bryn Mawr, PA 19010. TEL 610-526-1000, http://www.amercoll.edu. Ed. David M. Cordell.

REAL ESTATE FINANCE AND INVESTMENT. see *REAL ESTATE*

REAL ESTATE FINANCE JOURNAL. see *REAL ESTATE*

REAL ESTATE FINANCING - TEXT, FORMS, TAX ANALYSIS. see *REAL ESTATE*

REAL MONEY. see *BUSINESS AND ECONOMICS—Investments*

332 USA ISSN 1548-3347
▼ **REAL WEALTH REPORT.** Text in English. 2004. m. USD 189 (effective 2004).
Related titles: Online - full content ed.: ISSN 1548-3355.
Published by: Weiss Research, Inc., 15430 Endeavour Dr., Jupiter, FL 33478. TEL 561-627-3300, http://www.weissgroupinc.com/research/. Eds. Larry Edelson, Jill Talbot.

332 GBR
RECAP. Text in English. 1998. m. free. **Document type:** *Bulletin, Trade.* **Description:** For members of the organization and the financial and business press.
Related titles: E-mail ed.; Fax ed.
Published by: Scottish Financial Enterprise, 91 George St, Edinburgh, EH2 3ES, United Kingdom. TEL 44-131-225-6990, FAX 44-131-220-1353, info@sfe.org.uk, http://www.sfe.org.uk. Ed., R&P Derek Elder. Circ: 400 (controlled).

332 USA
RECENT DEVELOPMENTS IN INTERNATIONAL BANKING AND FINANCE. Text in English. a. price varies. **Document type:** *Monographic series.*
Published by: Blackwell Publishing, Inc. (Subsidiary of: Blackwell Publishing Ltd.), Commerce Place, 350 Main St, Malden, MA 02148. TEL 781-388-8206, FAX 781-388-8232, subscrip@blackwellpub.com, http://www.blackwellpublishing.com.

332 DEU
RECHT DER KREDITWIRTSCHAFT. Text in German. irreg. (2-3/yr). looseleaf. adv. **Document type:** *Trade.*
Published by: Walhalla Fachverlag, Haus an der Eisernen Bruecke, Regensburg, 93042, Germany. TEL 49-941-5684-0, FAX 49-941-5684111, walhalla@walhalla.de, http://www.walhalla.de. Eds. Hannelore Grill, Wolfgang Grill. Circ: 1,500.

REDALERT; petitions, receiverships and resolution service. see *LAW*

332 USA ISSN 1045-3369
THE REGION MAGAZINE. Text in English. 1987. q. free (effective 2005). bk.rev. back issues avail. **Document type:** *Magazine, Consumer.* **Description:** Includes economic annalysis, interviews, bank reviews, and a column by the Minneapolis Federal Reserve president.
Media: Online - full content. **Related titles:** Online - full text ed.: (from O C L C Online Computer Library Center, Inc., ProQuest Information & Learning).
Indexed: ABIn, BLI, PAIS.
Published by: Federal Reserve Bank of Minneapolis, c/o The Region, Box 291, Minneapolis, MN 55480-0291. TEL 612-204-5255, paeditor@res.mpls.fnb.fed.us, http://minneapolisfed.org. Ed. David Fettig. Circ: 12,000 (free).

332 USA ISSN 1556-4045
THE REGISTER (MIDDLETOWN). Variant title: I A R F C Register. Text in English. 2000. m. USD 99 to non-members; free to members; USD 9 per issue (effective 2006). **Document type:** *Newsletter, Trade.*
Published by: International Association of Registered Financial Consultants, 2507 N. Verity Pkwy, Middleton, OH 45042. TEL 800-532-9060, FAX 513-424-5752, http://www.iarfc.org. Ed. Wendy M. Kennedy.

REGULATION OF FOREIGN BANKS; United States and international. see *LAW—International Law*

332.1 USA ISSN 1090-2562
KF1030.R3
THE REGULATORY REPORTING HANDBOOK. Text in English. 1993. a. price varies. **Document type:** *Trade.*
Formerly (until 1997): Regulatory Reporting Compliance Handbook (1084-5054)
Related titles: ♦ Series of: PricewaterhouseCoopers Regulatory Handbook Series. ISSN 1522-1334.
Published by: (PricewaterhouseCoopers), M.E. Sharpe, Inc., 80 Business Park Dr, Armonk, NY 10504. TEL 914-273-1800, 800-541-6563, FAX 914-273-2106, custserv@mesharpe.com, http://www.mesharpe.com.

332.1 USA ISSN 1090-2554
KF974
THE REGULATORY RISK MANAGEMENT HANDBOOK. Text in English. 1997. a. price varies. **Document type:** *Trade.*
Related titles: ♦ Series of: PricewaterhouseCoopers Regulatory Handbook Series. ISSN 1522-1334.
Published by: (PricewaterhouseCoopers), M.E. Sharpe, Inc., 80 Business Park Dr, Armonk, NY 10504. TEL 914-273-1800, 800-541-6563, FAX 914-273-2106, mesinfo@usa.net, custserv@mesharpe.com, http://www.mesharpe.com.

330 USA
REGULATORY RISK MONITOR. Text in English. bi-w. USD 349 (effective 2005). back issues avail. **Document type:** *Newsletter, Trade.*
Published by: Argosy Group (Subsidiary of: United Communications Group), 11300 Rockville Pike, Ste 1100, Rockville, MD 20852. TEL 888-287-2223, FAX 301-816-8945, http://www.rrmonitor.com/frcjsp/index.jsp, http://www.ucg.com/argosy.html. Ed. Fran Fanshel TEL 301-287-2245.

REIMBURSEMENT ADVISOR. see *HEALTH FACILITIES AND ADMINISTRATION*

332 ESP ISSN 0034-4184
REMANSO. Text in Spanish. 1958. bi-m. free.
Published by: Caja de Ahorros y Monte de Piedad de Zaragoza, Aragon y Rioja, San Jorge, 8, Zaragoza, 50001, Spain. Ed. Manuel Cabeza Munoz. Circ: 1,500.

332.152 CAN ISSN 0849-3235
REPORT ON OPERATIONS UNDER THE BRETTON WOODS AND RELATED AGREEMENTS ACT. Text in English, French. 19??. a.
Former titles (until 1986): Report on Operations under the Bretton Woods Agreements Act and International Development Association Act (0703-6396); (until 196?): Report on Operations under the Bretton Woods Agreement Act (0703-640X)
Related titles: Online - full text ed.: ISSN 1487-0568.
—CISTI.
Published by: Canada. Department of Finance, Distribution Centre, West Tower, Rm P-135, 300 Laurier Ave W, Ottawa, ON K1A 0G5, Canada. TEL 613-995-2855, FAX 613-996-0518, services-distribution@fin.gc.ca, http://www.fin.gc.ca/purl/bretwd-e.html.

332 USA
REPORT ON THE TERMS OF CREDIT CARD PLAN. Text in English. s-a. USD 5. **Document type:** *Government.*
Published by: U.S. Federal Reserve System, Board of Governors, Publications Services, Rm MS 138, Washington, DC 20551. TEL 202-452-3244, FAX 202-728-5886.

332 USA ISSN 0080-1380
HG3879
REPRINTS IN INTERNATIONAL FINANCE. Text in English. 1965. irreg., latest vol.29, 1996. USD 45 (effective 2000); includes Essays in International Finance; Studies in International Finance; Special Papers in International Economics. back issues avail.; reprint service avail. from PQC. **Document type:** *Monographic series.* **Description:** Reprints of articles and essays by staff members of the International Finance Section that have appeared in other publications.
Published by: Princeton University, International Finance Section, c/o Margaret B Riccardi, Ed, Department of Economics, Fisher Hall, Princeton, NJ 08544-1021. TEL 609-258-4048, FAX 609-258-1374, ifs@princeton.edu. Ed. Margaret B Riccardi. Circ: 2,000.

332 COL
LA REPUBLICA; el diario empresarial y financiero de Colombia. Text in Spanish. d. adv. Supplement avail.; back issues avail. **Document type:** *Newspaper, Consumer.*
Media: Online - full text.
Published by: Diario La Republica, Cra 43B No 14-10, Edif. Colinas del Poblado, Medellin, Colombia. TEL 57-4-268-8190, FAX 57-4-266-5955, repumed@medellin.cetcol.net.co, http://www.la-republica.com.co/. Ed. Natalia Yoria.

332 USA ISSN 0196-3821
HG1
RESEARCH IN FINANCE. Text in English. 1979. a., latest vol.21, 2005. price varies. back issues avail. **Document type:** *Monographic series, Academic/Scholarly.*
Related titles: Online - full text ed.: (from ScienceDirect); ♦ Supplement(s): Research in Finance. Supplement. ISSN 0882-3138.
—BLDSC (7741.035000), IE, ingenta. **CCC.**
Published by: J A I Press Inc. (Subsidiary of: Elsevier Science & Technology), 360 Park Ave S, New York, NY 10010-1710. TEL 212-989-5800, FAX 212-633-3990, usinfo-f@elsevier.com, http://www.elsevier.com/wps/find/bookdescription.cws_home/BS_REF/description#description. Ed. Andrew H Chen.

332 USA ISSN 0882-3138
HG136
RESEARCH IN FINANCE. SUPPLEMENT. Text in English. 1984. irreg., latest vol.2, 1996. price varies. **Document type:** *Monographic series, Academic/Scholarly.*
Related titles: ♦ Supplement to: Research in Finance. ISSN 0196-3821.
Published by: J A I Press Inc. (Subsidiary of: Elsevier Science & Technology), 360 Park Ave S, New York, NY 10010-1710. TEL 212-989-5800, FAX 212-633-3990, usinfo-f@elsevier.com, http://www.elsevier.com. Ed. Andrew H Chen.

332.1 USA ISSN 1052-7788
RESEARCH IN FINANCIAL SERVICES. Text in English. 1989. a., latest vol.15, 2003. price varies. back issues avail. **Document type:** *Monographic series, Academic/Scholarly.*
—BLDSC (7741.036000). **CCC.**
Published by: J A I Press Inc. (Subsidiary of: Elsevier Science & Technology), 360 Park Ave S, New York, NY 10010-1710. TEL 212-989-5800, FAX 212-633-3990, usinfo-f@elsevier.com, http://www.elsevier.com/wps/find/bookseriesdescription.cws_home/BS_RFSPPP/description. Ed. G G Kaufman.

332 CAN ISSN 0833-1677
RESEARCH MONEY. Text in English. 1987. 20/yr. CND 575 (effective 1999). **Document type:** *Directory.* **Description:** Covers funding issues in industry, university and government programs.
Related titles: Online - full text ed.: (from bigchalk, Micromedia ProQuest, Northern Light Technology, Inc., ProQuest Information & Learning).
—CISTI.
Published by: Evert Communications Ltd., 1296 Carling Ave, 2nd Fl, Ottawa, ON K1Z 7K8, Canada. TEL 613-728-4621, FAX 613-728-0385, services@evert.com, http://www.evert.com. Ed. Mark Henderson.

332.1 AUS ISSN 0484-5412
HG3446
RESERVE BANK OF AUSTRALIA. ANNUAL REPORT. Text in English. 1960. a. free. **Document type:** *Corporate.* **Description:** Contains annual report and financial statement.
Related titles: Online - full text ed.
Published by: Reserve Bank of Australia, 65 Martin Place, PO Box 3947, Sydney, NSW 2001, Australia. TEL 61-2-9551-8111, FAX 61-2-9551-8000, rbainfo@rba.gov.au, http://www.rba.gov.au/. Circ: 3,599.

RESERVE BANK OF AUSTRALIA. BULLETIN. see *BUSINESS AND ECONOMICS—Abstracting, Bibliographies, Statistics*

332.1 330.9 AUS ISSN 0080-178X
RESERVE BANK OF AUSTRALIA. OCCASIONAL PAPERS. Text in English. 1970. irreg., latest vol.15, 1997. price varies.
Related titles: Diskette ed.
Published by: Reserve Bank of Australia, 65 Martin Place, PO Box 3947, Sydney, NSW 2001, Australia. TEL 61-2-9551-8111, FAX 61-2-9551-8000, rbainfo@rba.gov.au, http://www.rba.gov.au/.

332 AUS ISSN 1442-939X
HG3441
RESERVE BANK OF AUSTRALIA. PAYMENTS SYSTEM BOARD. ANNUAL REPORT. Text in English. 1999. a. **Document type:** *Consumer.*
Related titles: Online - full text ed.
Published by: Reserve Bank of Australia, 65 Martin Place, PO Box 3947, Sydney, NSW 2001, Australia. TEL 61-2-9551-8111, FAX 61-2-9551-8000, rbainfo@rba.gov.au, http://www.rba.gov.au/.

332 330.9 AUS ISSN 1320-7229
RESERVE BANK OF AUSTRALIA. RESEARCH DISCUSSION PAPER. Text in English. 1969. irreg. abstr.; bibl. back issues avail. **Document type:** *Academic/Scholarly.* **Description:** Presents preliminary results of economic research.
Related titles: Online - full text ed.: 1993.
—BLDSC (7738.874000).
Published by: Reserve Bank of Australia, 65 Martin Place, PO Box 3947, Sydney, NSW 2001, Australia. TEL 61-2-9551-8111, FAX 61-2-9551-8000, ecpubs@rbs.gov.au, http://www.rba.gov.au/.

RESERVE BANK OF FIJI. ANNUAL REPORT. see *BUSINESS AND ECONOMICS—Economic Situation And Conditions*

RESERVE BANK OF FIJI. MONTHLY ECONOMIC BULLETIN. see *BUSINESS AND ECONOMICS—Economic Situation And Conditions*

RESERVE BANK OF FIJI. NEWS REVIEW. see *BUSINESS AND ECONOMICS—Economic Situation And Conditions*

RESERVE BANK OF FIJI. QUARTERLY REVIEW. see *BUSINESS AND ECONOMICS—Economic Situation And Conditions*

332 IND ISSN 0080-1801
RESERVE BANK OF INDIA. ANNUAL REPORT. Short title: R B I Annual Report. Text in English, Hindi. 1936. a. free. **Document type:** *Corporate.*
Indexed: RASB.
Published by: (India. Division of Reports, Reviews & Publications), Reserve Bank of India, Department of Economic Analysis & Policy, New Central Office Bldg., Shahid Bhagat Singh Rd., P O Box 1036, Mumbai, Maharashtra 400 023, India. TEL 22-2862524. Ed. A Seshan. Circ: 8,500.

332 IND ISSN 0034-5512
HG188.I6
RESERVE BANK OF INDIA. BULLETIN. Text in English, Hindi. 1947. m. USD 550 to institutions (effective 2005). adv. charts. index. **Document type:** *Bulletin, Academic/Scholarly.*
Indexed: BAS, IBSS, KES, PAIS, RASB, RDA, WAE&RSA.
Published by: (India. Reserve Bank of India, India. Department of Economic Analysis & Policy), Scientific Publishers, 5-A New Pali Rd., Near Hotel Taj Hari Mahal, PO Box 91, Jodhpur, Rajasthan 342 003, India. TEL 91-291-2433323, FAX 91-291-2512580, info@scientificpub.com, http://www.scientificpub.com/bookdetails.php?booktransid=347&bookid=343. Circ: 5,300.

332 IND
RESERVE BANK OF INDIA. BULLETIN. WEEKLY STATISTICAL SUPPLEMENT. Text in English. 1949. w. INR 50, USD 17. charts; stat. **Document type:** *Bulletin.*
Indexed: RASB.
Published by: (India. Division of Reports, Reviews & Publications), Reserve Bank of India, Department of Economic Analysis & Policy, New Central Office Bldg., Shahid Bhagat Singh Rd., P O Box 1036, Mumbai, Maharashtra 400 023, India. TEL 22-2862524. Circ: 1,400.

332.1 IND
RESERVE BANK OF INDIA. OCCASIONAL PAPERS. Text in English. 1980. 4/yr. INR 40, USD 14. adv. **Document type:** *Monographic series, Government.*
Indexed: BAS, PAA&I.
Published by: (India. Division of Reports, Reviews & Publications), Reserve Bank of India, Department of Economic Analysis & Policy, New Central Office Bldg., Shahid Bhagat Singh Rd., P O Box 1036, Mumbai, Maharashtra 400 023, India. TEL 91-22-2862524. Ed. S H Shetty. Circ: 1,000.

332 IND
RESERVE BANK OF INDIA. REPORT ON CURRENCY AND FINANCE. (Issued in two sections: Economic Reviews; Statistical Statements) Text in English, Hindi. 1936. a. INR 100, USD 40.
Indexed: RASB.
Published by: (India. Division of Reports, Reviews & Publications), Reserve Bank of India, Department of Economic Analysis & Policy, New Central Office Bldg., Shahid Bhagat Singh Rd., P O Box 1036, Mumbai, Maharashtra 400 023, India. TEL 22-2862524. Ed. S J Salvi. Circ: 3,000.

RESERVE BANK OF MALAWI. FINANCIAL AND ECONOMIC REVIEW. see *BUSINESS AND ECONOMICS—Economic Situation And Conditions*

332 MWI ISSN 0486-5383
HG3407.A7
RESERVE BANK OF MALAWI. REPORT AND ACCOUNTS. Text in English. a. free. charts; stat.; maps. **Document type:** *Corporate.* **Description:** Analyzes the financial and economic performance of various sectors of the economy.
Formerly: Reserve Bank of Malawi. Annual Report and Statement of Account
Published by: (Research Department), Reserve Bank of Malawi, PO Box 30063, Lilongwe, Malawi. TEL 265-780600.

332.1 NZL ISSN 0110-7070
HG3466
RESERVE BANK OF NEW ZEALAND. ANNUAL REPORT. Text in English. a. free. **Document type:** *Corporate.*
Published by: Reserve Bank of New Zealand, Public Affairs & Information Service Section, 2 The Terrace, PO Box 2498, Wellington, New Zealand. TEL 64-4-4722029, FAX 64-4-4738554, rbnz-info@rbnz.govt.nz, http://www.rbnz.govt.nz/about/Whatwedo/0094054.html.

332.1 330.9 NZL ISSN 1174-7943
HC621
RESERVE BANK OF NEW ZEALAND BULLETIN. Text in English. 1938. q. NZD 48 (effective 2005). charts; stat. cum.index: 1950-1959, 1969-1979. **Document type:** *Bulletin, Corporate.* **Description:** Covers wide range of issues related to both central banking and the New Zealand economy.
Former titles (until 1997): Reserve Bank Bulletin (0112-871X); (until 1982): Reserve Bank of New Zealand. Bulletin (0034-5539)
Related titles: Online - full text ed.: (from Gale Group).
Indexed: ABIX, IBR, IBZ, INZP, KES, PAIS.
—CCC.
Published by: Reserve Bank of New Zealand, Public Affairs & Information Service Section, 2 The Terrace, PO Box 2498, Wellington, New Zealand. TEL 64-4-4722029, FAX 64-4-4738554, rbnz-info@rbnz.govt.nz, http://www.rbnz.govt.nz/research/bulletin/index.html. Ed. Bernard Hodgetts TEL 64-4-4713781. Circ: 1,500.

332 ZWE ISSN 1024-2732
HG3402.A7
RESERVE BANK OF ZIMBABWE. ANNUAL REPORT. Key Title: Reserve Bank of Zimbabwe. Annual Report and Statements of Accounts for the Year. Text in English. 1994. a. ZWD 25 domestic; USD 15 in Africa; USD 20 elsewhere. **Document type:** *Corporate.*
Published by: Reserve Bank of Zimbabwe, Economic Research and Policy Division, PO Box 1283, Harare, Zimbabwe. TEL 263-4-703000, FAX 263-4-707800. Ed. W Manungo.

332 ZWE ISSN 1024-2740
RESERVE BANK OF ZIMBABWE. MONTHLY BULLETIN. Text in English. 1980. m. ZWD 150 domestic; USD 55 in Africa; USD 70 elsewhere. **Document type:** *Bulletin, Trade.*
Published by: Reserve Bank of Zimbabwe, Economic Research and Policy Division, PO Box 1283, Harare, Zimbabwe. TEL 263-4-703000, FAX 263-4-707800, TELEX 26033 RESZIM ZW.

332 ZWE ISSN 0251-1819
RESERVE BANK OF ZIMBABWE. QUARTERLY ECONOMIC AND STATISTICAL REVIEW. Text in English. 1980. q. ZWD 90 domestic; USD 35 in Africa; USD 50 elsewhere. charts; stat. **Document type:** *Corporate.*
Published by: Reserve Bank of Zimbabwe, Economic Research and Policy Division, PO Box 1283, Harare, Zimbabwe. TEL 263-4-703000, FAX 263-4-707800.

332 DEU
RESULTS; das Firmenkunden-Magazin der Deutschen Bank. Text in German. q. **Document type:** *Magazine, Consumer.*
Published by: (Deutsche Bank), Hoffmann und Campe Verlag (Subsidiary of: Ganske Verlagsgruppe), Harvestehuder Weg 42, Hamburg, 20149, Germany. TEL 49-40-44188-0, FAX 49-40-44188236, email@hoca.de, http://www.hoca.de.

332 GBR ISSN 0261-1740
RETAIL BANKER INTERNATIONAL. Text in English. 1982. 20/yr. GBP 997, EUR 1,597, USD 1,697 (effective 2005). adv. back issues avail. **Document type:** *Newsletter.* **Description:** Directed to senior management in the consumer financial services industry.
Related titles: Online - full text ed.: GBP 800 (effective 1999) (from Gale Group, LexisNexis, O C L C Online Computer Library Center, Inc., ProQuest Information & Learning).
Indexed: B&I, BLI.
Published by: Lafferty Publications Ltd., The Colonnades, 82 Bishops Bridge Rd, London, W2 6BB, United Kingdom. TEL 44-20-75635700, FAX 44-20-75635701, cuserv@lafferty.ie, cuserv@lafferty.com, http://www.lafferty.com/newsletter_publication.php?id=4. Ed. Gerard Lysaght. adv.: B&W page GBP 3,330; trim 210 x 297.

332 USA ISSN 1085-9020
HG1660.U5
RETAIL BANKING SURVEY REPORT. Text in English. a. USD 265 to non-members; USD 175 to members. charts; stat. **Document type:** *Trade.* **Description:** Informs on how banks can benefit from focusing on the small-business market by furnishing information on product and service offerings, securities and annuities sales, and expenses per FTE.
Former titles: Retail Banking Report (1058-885X); (until 1991): Retail Deposit Services Report (0270-2762)
Published by: American Bankers Association, Retail Service Center, 1120 Connecticut Ave, N W, Washington, DC 20036. TEL 202-663-5430, FAX 202-663-7543, http://www.aba.org. **Subscr. to:** PO Box 630544, Baltimore, MD 21263-0544.

332 GBR
THE RETAIL BANKING SYSTEMS MARKET REPORT (YEAR). Text in English. a. GBP 525 per issue (effective 2005). **Document type:** *Trade.* **Description:** Provides supplier and system profiles on retail bank office systems.
Related titles: Online - full text ed.
Published by: I B S Publishing, 11 Mount St, Hythe, Kent CT21 5NT, United Kingdom. TEL 44-1303-262636, FAX 44-1303-262646, enquries@ibspublishing.com, http://www.ibspublishing.com/. Pub. Martin Whybrow.

B

330 GBR ISSN 1468-1196
RETAIL FINANCE STRATEGIES. Text in English. 1999. m. adv. **Document type:** *Magazine, Trade.*
Related titles: Online - full text ed.: (from Gale Group, O C L C Online Computer Library Center, Inc.).
Published by: Centaur Publishing, St Giles House, 50 Poland St, London, W1V 4AX, United Kingdom. TEL 44-20-79704000, FAX 44-20-7970-4191, joannap@centaur.co.uk, http://www.centaur.co.uk.

332.1 USA
REVIEW OF BANK PERFORMANCE. Text in English. a.
Published by: Salomon Brothers, Inc., Marketing Department, 7 World Trade Center, New York, NY 10048. TEL 212-747-7000.

332 USA ISSN 1051-1741
KF967
THE REVIEW OF BANKING & FINANCIAL SERVICES; an analysis of current laws and regulations affecting banking and related industries. Text in English. 1985. s-m. (22/yr.). USD 560. index. **Document type:** *Newsletter, Trade.* **Description:** Focuses on practical analyses of regulations in banking and related fields, discussing the strengths and weaknesses of recent legislation and how they affect attorneys' clients and practice.
Formerly (until 1989): Review of Financial Services Regulation (0897-1196)
Related titles: Online - full text ed.: (from LexisNexis, ProQuest Information & Learning).
Indexed: BLI.
—CCC.
Published by: Standard & Poor's (Subsidiary of: McGraw-Hill Companies, Inc.), 55 Water St, New York, NY 10041. TEL 212-208-8000. Ed. Michael O Finkelstein.

332 USA ISSN 1380-6645
HG6024.A3 CODEN: RDREF6
➤ **REVIEW OF DERIVATIVES RESEARCH.** Text in English. 1996. 3/yr. EUR 295, USD 296, GBP 184 combined subscription to institutions print & online eds. (effective 2005). adv. reprint service avail. from PSC. **Document type:** *Academic/Scholarly.* **Description:** Publishes academic research articles dealing with the pricing and hedging of derivative assets on any underlying asset.
Related titles: Online - full text ed.: ISSN 1573-7144 (from EBSCO Publishing, Gale Group, IngentaConnect, Kluwer Online, O C L C Online Computer Library Center, Inc., ProQuest Information & Learning, Springer LINK, Swets Information Services).
Indexed: ABIn, BLI, BibLing, JEL, RefZh.
—BLDSC (7790.161600), IE, Infotrieve, ingenta. **CCC.**
Published by: Springer-Verlag New York, Inc. (Subsidiary of: Springer Science+Business Media), 233 Spring St, New York, NY 10013. TEL 212-460-1500, FAX 212-460-1575, service@springer-ny.com, http://springerlink.metapress.com/openurl.asp?genre=journal&issn=1380-6645, http://www.springer-ny.com. Eds. Marti G Subrahmanyam, Menachem Brenner. **Subscr. to:** Journal Fulfillment, PO Box 2485, Secaucus, NJ 07096-2485. TEL 201-348-4033, FAX 201-348-4505, journals@springer-ny.com.

332 341 USA ISSN 1572-3097
CODEN: EFREFD
➤ **REVIEW OF FINANCE**; the journal of the European Finance Association. Text in English. 1997. 4/yr. EUR 418, USD 428, GBP 278 combined subscription to institutions print & online eds. (effective 2005). adv. reprint service avail. from PSC. **Document type:** *Journal, Academic/Scholarly.* **Description:** Publishes original articles and research in all areas of finance, both applied and theoretical.
Formerly (until 2004): European Finance Review (1382-6662)
Related titles: Online - full text ed.: ISSN 1573-692X (from EBSCO Publishing, Gale Group, IngentaConnect, Kluwer Online, O C L C Online Computer Library Center, Inc., ProQuest Information & Learning, Springer LINK, Swets Information Services).

▼ *new title* ➤ *refereed* ✶ *unverified* ♦ *full entry avail.*

Indexed: ABIn, BLI, BibLing, ESPM, Inspec, JEL, RefZh, RiskAb.
—BLDSC (7790.563700), IE, Infotrieve, ingenta. **CCC.**
Published by: Springer-Verlag New York, Inc. (Subsidiary of: Springer Science+Business Media), 233 Spring St, New York, NY 10013. TEL 212-460-1500, FAX 212-460-1575, service@springer-ny.com, http://springerlink.metapress.com/openurl.asp?genre=journal&issn=1572-3097, http://www.springer-ny.com. Eds. Josef Zechner, Marco Pagano. **Subscr. to:** Journal Fulfillment, PO Box 2485, Secaucus, NJ 07096-2485. TEL 201-348-4033, FAX 201-348-4505, journals@springer-ny.com.

332 GBR ISSN 0893-9454
HG1
➤ **THE REVIEW OF FINANCIAL STUDIES.** Text in English. 1988. q. GBP 413, USD 620, EUR 620 to institutions; GBP 165, USD 248, EUR 248 academic; GBP 435, USD 653, EUR 653 combined subscription to institutions print & online eds.; GBP 174, USD 261, EUR 261 combined subscription academic; print & online eds. (effective 2006). adv. bk.rev. bibl.; illus. back issues avail.; reprint service avail. from PSC. **Document type:** *Journal, Academic/Scholarly.* **Description:** Covers new research in financial economics. Strives to maintain a balance between theoretical and empirical studies.
Related titles: Online - full text ed.: ISSN 1465-7368. GBP 392, USD 588, EUR 588 to institutions; GBP 157, USD 236, EUR 236 academic (effective 2006) (from EBSCO Publishing, Gale Group, HighWire Press, IngentaConnect, JSTOR (Web-based Journal Archive), O C L C Online Computer Library Center, Inc., Oxford University Press Online Journals, ProQuest Information & Learning, Swets Information Services).
Indexed: ABIn, ASCA, AgeL, BLI, CPM, CurCont, ESPM, IBSS, JEL, RiskAb, SSCI, ST&MA.
—BLDSC (7790.565000), IDS, IE, Infotrieve, ingenta. **CCC.**
Published by: Oxford University Press, Great Clarendon St, Oxford, OX2 6DP, United Kingdom. TEL 44-1865-556767, FAX 44-1865-556646, rfins@cornell.edu, jnl.orders@oup.co.uk, http://rfs.oxfordjournals.org/, http://www.oxfordjournals.org/. Ed. Maureen O'Hara. Pub. Erich Staib. Adv. contact Helen Pearson. B&W page GBP 205, B&W page USD 295; 110 x 175. Circ: 2,750.

332 SGP ISSN 0219-0915
➤ **REVIEW OF PACIFIC BASIN FINANCIAL MARKETS AND POLICIES.** Abbreviated title: R P B F M P. Text in English. 1998. q. SGD 165, USD 94, EUR 91 to individuals; SGD 415, USD 238, EUR 229 combined subscription to institutions print & online eds.; SGD 297, USD 175, EUR 161 combined subscription in developing nations to institutions print & online eds. (effective 2006). back issues avail. **Document type:** *Journal, Academic/Scholarly.* **Description:** Concentrates on global interdisciplinary research in finance, economics and accounting. Emphasizes the economic and financial relationships among Pacific Rim countries.
Related titles: Online - full text ed.: (from EBSCO Publishing, O C L C Online Computer Library Center, Inc., Swets Information Services).
Indexed: ESPM, GEOBASE, IBSS, RiskAb.
—IE. **CCC.**
Published by: World Scientific Publishing Co. Pte. Ltd., 5 Toh Tuck Link, Singapore, 596224, Singapore. TEL 65-466-5775, FAX 65-467-7667, wspc@wspc.com.sg, http://www.worldscinet.com/rpbfmp/rpbfmp.shtml, http://www.worldscientific.com. Ed. Cheng Few Lee. **Subscr. to:** Farrer Rd, PO Box 128, Singapore 912805, Singapore. sales@wspc.com.sg. **Dist. by:** World Scientific Publishing Co., Inc., 1060 Main St, River Edge, NJ 07661. TEL 201-487-9655, 800-227-7562, FAX 201-487-9656, 888-977-2665.; World Scientific Publishing Ltd., 57 Shelton St, London WC2H 9HE, United Kingdom. TEL 44-20-78360888, FAX 44-20-78362020, sales@wspc.co.uk.

➤ **REVIEW OF QUANTITATIVE FINANCE AND ACCOUNTING.** see *BUSINESS AND ECONOMICS—Accounting*

332.1 GTM
REVISTA BANCA CENTRAL. Text in Spanish. q. adv. charts; illus.; stat.
Published by: Banco de Guatemala, 7a Av. 22-01, ZONA, 1, Guatemala, 01001, Guatemala. TEL 535932. Ed. Francisco Albizurez.

332.1 BRA ISSN 0034-706X
HC186
REVISTA BANCARIA BRASILEIRA. Text in Portuguese. 1933. m. USD 150 (effective 1997). adv. stat.
Indexed: PAIS.
Address: Centro, ZC-00, Caixa Postal 2291, Rio De Janeiro, RJ 20001-970, Brazil. TEL 55-21-2407275, FAX 55-21-5330447, boucas@centroin.com.br. Ed. Oyama Pereira Teixeira. Adv. contact Ronaldo Boucas. B&W page BRL 500, color page BRL 900; 260 x 185. Circ: 15,000.

REVISTA DE CIENCIAS ECONOMICAS. see *BUSINESS AND ECONOMICS—Accounting*

332 ESP ISSN 0211-6138
REVISTA DE DERECHO BANCARIO Y BURSATIL. Text in Spanish. 1981. q.
—CINDOC.
Published by: Centro de Documentacion Bancaria y Bursatil, Colombia, 61, Madrid, 28016, Spain.

REVISTA DE DERECHO FINANCIERO Y DE HACIENDA PUBLICA. see *LAW*

336 ESP ISSN 0212-4610
REVISTA DE HACIENDA AUTONOMICA Y LOCAL. Text in Spanish. 1971. 3/yr. USD 98.
Formerly (until 1982): Revista de Economia y Hacienda Local (0210-2404)
Indexed: ChemAb.
Published by: Editoriales de Derecho Reunidas S.A., Valverde, 32, 1o izda., Madrid, 28004, Spain. TEL 521-02-46, FAX 521-05-39. Ed. Julio Banacloche.

332 ARG
REVISTA DEL INSTITUTO DE ESTUDIOS COOPERATIVOS. Text in Spanish. q.
Indexed: PAIS.
Published by: Universidad Nacional de la Plata, Facultad de Ciencias Economicas, Biblioteca, 6 Esq. 47, La Plata, Buenos Aires 1900, Argentina.

REVISTA ECUATORIANA DE HISTORIA ECONOMICA. see *BUSINESS AND ECONOMICS*

332 ESP ISSN 0210-2412
REVISTA ESPANOLA DE FINANCIACION Y CONTABILIDAD. Text in Spanish. 1972. q. USD 118. index. back issues avail.
Published by: Editoriales de Derecho Reunidas S.A., Valverde, 32, 1o izda., Madrid, 28004, Spain. TEL 521-02-46, FAX 521-05-39.

332 MEX ISSN 0556-6835
HG6
REVISTA MEXICANA DE FIANZAS. Text in Spanish. 1964. a. MXP 10, USD 7. adv.
Published by: (Mexican Bond Companies and Bancomer, S.N.C.), Fernando Castaneda Alatorre Ed. & Pub., PUEBLA 383, Col Roma, Mexico City, DF 06700, Mexico. Circ: 1,000.

332 MEX
REVISTA MEXICANA DE SEGUROS FIANZAS Y FINANZAS★. Text in Spanish. 1948. m. USD 75. adv. bk.rev. **Document type:** *Trade.*
Published by: Revista Mexicana de Seguros y Fianzas S.A. de C.V., PUELLA 383, Col Roma, Mexico City, DF 06700, Mexico. Ed. Marivel Campos. Circ: 15,000.

332 COL
REVISTA UNIVERSIDAD COOPERATIVA DE COLOMBIA. Text in Spanish. q.
Indexed: PAIS.
Published by: Universidad Cooperativa de Colombia, Calle 50, No 41-70, Medellin, Colombia.

332 ESP ISSN 1577-4163
HC387
REVISTA VALENCIANA DE ECONOMIA Y HACIENDA. Text in Spanish. 1987. 3/yr.
Supersedes (in 2001): Palau 14 (0214-6819)
—CINDOC.
Published by: Generalitat Valenciana, Conselleria d'Economia, Hisenda i Ocupacio, Palau, 14, Valencia, 46003, Spain. TEL 34-96-1964300, FAX 34-96-1964301, http://www.gva.es/.

332 CAN ISSN 0829-4011
REVUE CANADIENNE DE GESTION DE TRESORERIE. Text in French. 1984. bi-m.
Related titles: ◆ English ed.: Canadian Treasury Management Review. ISSN 0829-4003.
Published by: Royal Bank of Canada, S Tower, 9th Fl, Royal Bank Plaza, Toronto, ON M5J 2J5, Canada. TEL 416-974-2274, FAX 416-974-0365.

332 BEL ISSN 0772-7801
REVUE DE LA BANQUE. CAHIER. Text in French. 1936. m.
Related titles: ◆ Supplement to: Financieel Forum. Bank - en Financiewezen. ISSN 1376-7720; ◆ Supplement to: Financieel Forum. Bank - en Finacieel Recht. ISSN 1377-8013.
Published by: Forum Financier Belge/Belgisch Financeel Forum, Ravensteinstraat 36 B-5, Brussels, 1000, Belgium. FAX 32-2-5125861, jv@abb-bvb.be.

332 FRA ISSN 0987-3368
HG15
REVUE D'ECONOMIE FINANCIERE. Text in French. 1987. 6/yr. **Description:** Promotes analytical studies of economic finance.
Indexed: ELLIS, JEL.
Published by: (Association d'Economie Financiere), Editions Juridiques Associees, 14 rue Pierre et Marie Curie, Paris, 75005, France. TEL 33-1-44419710, FAX 33-1-43547821, TELEX EJA203918F. Ed. Youssef Achour.

332 CAN ISSN 0035-2284
REVUE DESJARDINS. Text in English. 1935. 5/yr. CND 14. adv. bk.rev. charts; illus. index. **Document type:** *Catalog, Trade.*
Indexed: PdeR.
Published by: Confederation des Caisses Populaires et d'Economie Desjardins du Quebec, 100 Ave. des Commandeurs, Levis, PQ G6V 7N5, Canada. TEL 418-835-8444 ext 2203, FAX 418-835-3809. Ed. Pierre Goulet. Adv. contact Yvan Forest. Circ: 25,000.

330 FRA ISSN 0223-0143
➤ **LA REVUE DU FINANCIER.** Text in French; Abstracts in English; Summaries in French, English. 1979. 5/yr. EUR 170 domestic; EUR 230 foreign (effective 2005). bk.rev. bibl.; illus. index. back issues avail. **Document type:** *Academic/Scholarly.*
Related titles: CD-ROM ed.; Online - full text ed.
Published by: Revue du Financier, 9-11av. Franklin D. Roosevelt, Paris, 75008, France. TEL 33-1-42562597, FAX 33-1-42259537, revue.du.financier@cybel.fr, http://www.cybel.fr/html/Communaute/rdf/index_rdf.htm. Pub., Adv. contact Thierry Vagne. Circ: 2,000.

➤ **LA REVUE JURIDIQUE, POLITIQUE ET ECONOMIQUE DU MAROC.** see *LAW—Judicial Systems*

336 MAR ISSN 0851-3058
REVUE MAROCAINE DE FINANCES PUBLIQUES ET D'ECONOMIE. Text in French. 1985. a.
Indexed: PAIS.
Published by: Ministere de l'Enseignement Superieur, de la Formation des Cadres et de la Recherche Scientifique, Avenue des Nations Unies, B.P. 721 Agdal, Rabat, Morocco.

RHODE ISLAND GOVERNMENT REGISTER. see *PUBLIC ADMINISTRATION*

RIGHTS GUIDE FOR HOME OWNERS. see *SOCIAL SERVICES AND WELFARE*

332 GBR ISSN 0952-8776
HG4502
RISK. Text in English. 1987. m. GBP 615, EUR 985, USD 985 (effective 2003). adv. bk.rev. illus. back issues avail.; reprints avail. **Document type:** *Magazine, Trade.* **Description:** An international journal of financial risk management covering currencies, interest rates, equities, commodities and credit.
Related titles: Online - full text ed.: (from EBSCO Publishing); Ed.: Risk.net.
Indexed: ABIn, ESPM, RiskAb.
—BLDSC (7972.581300), IE, Infotrieve, ingenta. **CCC.**
Published by: Risk Waters Group (Subsidiary of: Incisive Media Plc.), Haymarket House, 28-29 Haymarket, London, SW1Y 4RX, United Kingdom. TEL 44-20-74849700, FAX 44-20-79302238, customerservices@incisivemedia.com, http://www.risk.net/, http://www.incisivemedia.com/. Ed. Nicholas Dunbar. adv.: B&W page GBP 5,895, color page GBP 6,995; trim 230 x 297. **Subscr. in US & Canada to:** Incisive Media Plc., 270 Lafayette St, Ste 700, New York, NY 10012. TEL 212-925-6990, FAX 212-925-7585, customerservices@incisivemedia.com.

332 AUS ISSN 0812-8901
RISK MEASUREMENT SERVICE. Text in English. q. AUD 450 (effective 2000). stat. back issues avail. **Document type:** *Corporate.* **Description:** Provides estimates of systematic or beta risk for investors in Australian listed stocks. Used by investors managing the risk of portfolios and also those wanting to calculate the cost of equity capital.
Published by: A G S M Ltd, Australian Graduate School of Management, University of New South Wales, Sydney, NSW 2052, Australia. TEL 61-2-9931-9276, FAX 61-2-9662-7621, crif@agsm.unsw.edu.au.

332 GBR ISSN 0261-3344
RISK MEASUREMENT SERVICE. Text in English. 1979. q. GBP 350 to corporations; GBP 250 to institutions (effective 1999). adv. illus. **Document type:** *Bulletin.* **Description:** Provides the information used by investment professionals and corporate executives to analyze the risks of UK shares and portfolios.
Related titles: Diskette ed.
Published by: (London Business School), L B S Financial Services, Sussex Pl, Regent's Park, London, NW1 4SA, United Kingdom. TEL 44-171-2625050, FAX 44-171-7243317, rfrost@london.edu, http://www.london.edu/ifa/Risk_Measurement/RMS/rms.html, http://www.lbs.ac.uk/ifa/rms.htm. Eds. Elroy Dimson, Paul Marsh. R&P Ann Busfield TEL 44-171-7066807. Adv. contact Anna Bousfield. Circ: 600.

RISK RETENTION GROUP DIRECTORY AND GUIDE. see *INSURANCE*

RISK RETENTION REPORTER. see *INSURANCE*

332 ITA ISSN 0035-5615
IL RISPARMIO. Text in Italian. 1953. 3/yr. bk.rev. bibl.; charts; stat. index. **Description:** Addresses current matters in the field of banking.
Indexed: ELLIS, IBSS, JEL, PAIS.
Published by: (Associazione fra le Casse di Risparmio Italiane), Casa Editrice Dott. A. Giuffre (Subsidiary of: LexisNexis Europe and Africa), Via Busto Arsizio, 40, Milan, MI 20151, Italy. TEL 39-02-28089200, FAX 39-02-38009582, giuffre@giuffre.it, http://www.giuffre.it. Ed. M Talamona. Circ: 3,400.

332 ITA ISSN 0035-578X
RIVISTA BANCARIA - MINERVA BANCARIA. Text in Italian. 1936. bi-m. EUR 78 domestic; EUR 130 foreign (effective 2004). **Document type:** *Magazine, Consumer.*
Formed by the merger of (1926-1935): Rivista Bancaria (0392-8802); (1928-1935): Minerva Bancaria (0392-8799)
Indexed: PAIS, RASB.
Published by: Istituto di Cultura Bancaria Milano, Via Montevideo, 18, Rome, RM 00198, Italy. http://www.rivistabancaria.it. Ed. Francesco Parrillo.

332 340 ITA ISSN 0035-6131
RIVISTA DI DIRITTO FINANZIARIO E SCIENZA DELLE FINANZE. Text in Italian. 1949. q. EUR 72.30 in the European Union; EUR 108.46 elsewhere (effective 2002). bk.rev. bibl.; charts. index. **Description:** Offers a panorama of finance and economic studies, including essays on finance laws, economics, and contributions on concrete aspects of new tax laws.
Indexed: ELLIS, IBR, IBSS, IBZ.
—IE, Infotrieve.
Published by: Casa Editrice Dott. A. Giuffre (Subsidiary of: LexisNexis Europe and Africa), Via Busto Arsizio, 40, Milan, MI 20151, Italy. TEL 39-02-28089200, FAX 39-02-38009582, giuffre@giuffre.it, http://www.giuffre.it. Ed. Emilio Gerelli. Circ: 1,300.

332 ITA ISSN 0035-676X
CODEN: BSGCA5
RIVISTA INTERNAZIONALE DI SCIENZE SOCIALI. Text in English, French, Italian. 1893. q. EUR 68 domestic; EUR 101 foreign (effective 2005). bk.rev. bibl.; charts; illus.; stat. index. **Document type:** *Journal, Academic/Scholarly.* **Description:** Covers various areas in social sciences, with emphasis on economics.
Indexed: AmH&L, DIP, HistAb, IBR, IBSS, IBZ, IPSA, JEL, PAIS, PCI, RASB.
—IE. **CCC.**
Published by: (Universita Cattolica del Sacro Cuore, Istituto di Economia), Vita e Pensiero, Largo Gemelli 1, Milan, 20123, Italy. TEL 39-02-72342335, FAX 39-02-72342260, redazione.vp@mi.unicatt.it, http://www.vitaepensiero.it/riviste/pagcoml/riss.asp?titolo=RISS. Ed. Dr. Gian Carlo Mazzocchi. Circ: 900.

RIV'ON HESHEV. see *BUSINESS AND ECONOMICS—Marketing And Purchasing*

332 ISR
➤ **RIV'ON LE-VANKA'UT/QUARTERLY BANKING REVIEW.** Text in Hebrew. 1962. q. ILS 90. bk.rev. **Document type:** *Academic/Scholarly.*
Formerly: Revon Lebankaut - Banking Quarterly (0557-1480)
Indexed: IHP.
Published by: Association of Banks in Israel, P O Box 2258, Tel Aviv, 61021, Israel. TEL 972-3-5609019, FAX 972-3-5660317. Ed. Freddy Wieder. Circ: 2,000 (paid).

332 TTO
ROYAL BANK OF TRINIDAD AND TOBAGO. ANNUAL REPORT. Text in English. a. **Document type:** *Corporate.*
Published by: Royal Bank of Trinidad and Tobago, Royal Ct, 19-21 Park St, Port-of-Spain, Trinidad, Trinidad & Tobago. TEL 868-623-1322, FAX 868-625-3764, TELEX 22678 ROYIBD, rpyalinfo@rbtt.co.tt, http://www.rbtt.co.tt.

336 USA
ROYALTY RATE REPORT FOR THE PHARMACEUTICAL & BIOTECHNOLOGY INDUSTRIES. Text in English. a. USD 895; USD 250 renewals. adv. **Document type:** *Monographic series.* **Description:** Contains financial information about technology transfers. Presents financial details about pharmaceutical and biotechnology intellectual-property strategic alliances, primarily focusing on license fees and royalty rates.
Published by: Intellectual Property Research Associates, 1004 Buckinghamway, Yardley, PA 19067. TEL 215-428-1163, FAX 215-428-1163. Ed., R&P Russell L Parr. Adv. contact Jane J Parr.

RYNOK. see *BUSINESS AND ECONOMICS—Investments*

RYNOK TSENNYKH BUMAG/SECURITIES MARKET; analiticheskii zhurnal. see *BUSINESS AND ECONOMICS—Investments*

332.1 ZAF ISSN 0038-2000
HG3399.S7
➤ **S A BANKER.** (South African) Text in English. 1904. q. ZAR 90 domestic; ZAR 150 foreign (effective 2003). adv. bk.rev. illus.; charts; stat.; tr.lit.; bibl. index. 36 p./no.; back issues avail. **Document type:** *Journal, Academic/Scholarly.*
Formerly (until 1968): South African Banker's Journal
Related titles: Braille ed.
Indexed: ISAP, PAIS, WBA.
Published by: Institute of Bankers in South Africa, PO Box 61420, Marshalltown, Johannesburg 2107, South Africa. TEL 27-11-8321371, FAX 27-11-8346592, iobinfo@iob.co.za, http://www.iob.co.za. Ed. Paula Cockburn. Adv. contact Linda Erasmus. Circ: 20,000.

➤ **S A P FINANCIALS EXPERT.** (System Application Programming) see *COMPUTERS—Computer Systems*

332.1 ZAF
S A S B O NEWS/S A S B O NUUS. Text in Afrikaans, English. m. adv. illus.
Published by: South African Society of Bank Officials, SASBO House, 97 Simmonds St, Braamfontein, Johannesburg 2000, South Africa. Ed. B J Smith. Circ: 39,000.

332.2 332.3 USA
S & L QUARTERLY. (Savings and Loan) Text in English. 1986. q. USD 349. **Description:** Lists 30 key figures and ratios for every federally insured savings and loan, and federal savings bank in America.
Published by: United Communications Group, 11300 Rockville Pike Ste 1100, Rockville, MD 20852-3030. TEL 301-816-8950, FAX 301-816-8945. Ed. Martin Zook.

S B I C DIRECTORY AND HANDBOOK OF SMALL BUSINESS FINANCE. see *BUSINESS AND ECONOMICS—Small Business*

332 AUT
S JOURNAL. Text in German. q. **Document type:** *Bulletin.*
Published by: Sparkassenverlag GmbH, Grimmelshausengasse 1, Vienna, W 1030, Austria. TEL 43-1-71170-0, FAX 43-1-71170237. Ed. Paul Holy. Circ: 24,000.

332 USA ISSN 1522-1296
S N L BANK & THRIFT WEEKLY (NORTHEASTERN ED.). Text in English. w. USD 295 (effective 2002).
Media: E-mail. **Related titles:** Fax ed.; Regional ed(s).: S N L Bank & Thrift Weekly (Midwestern ed.). ISSN 1522-130X. USD 295 (effective 2002); S N L Bank & Thrift Weekly (Southern ed.). ISSN 1522-1288. USD 295 (effective 2002); S N L Bank & Thrift Weekly (Western ed.). ISSN 1522-127X. USD 295 (effective 2002).
Published by: S N L Financial LC, 212 7th St NE, Charlottesvle, VA 22902-5307. TEL 434-977-1600, FAX 434-293-0407, http://www.snl.com.

332.1 USA ISSN 1522-1261
S N L BANK DAILY. Text in English. d. price varies.
Media: E-mail. **Related titles:** Fax ed.
Published by: S N L Financial LC, 212 7th St NE, Charlottesvle, VA 22902-5307. TEL 434-977-1600, FAX 434-293-0407, http://www.snl.com.

332 USA ISSN 1074-6668
S N L CONVERSIONWATCH. Text in English. irreg. USD 1,200 (effective 2002).
Media: E-mail. **Related titles:** Fax ed.
Published by: S N L Financial LC, 212 7th St NE, Charlottesvle, VA 22902-5307. TEL 434-977-1600, FAX 434-293-0407, http://www.snl.com.

S N L DAILY THRIFTWATCH. see *BUSINESS AND ECONOMICS—Investments*

332 USA ISSN 1074-5904
HG2401
S N L QUARTERLY BANK DIGEST. Text in English. 1990. q. USD 799 (effective 2002).
Published by: S N L Financial LC, 212 7th St NE, Charlottesvle, VA 22902-5307. TEL 434-977-1600, FAX 434-293-0407, http://www.snl.com.

332.2 USA ISSN 1074-5920
HG1921
S N L QUARTERLY THRIFT DIGEST. Text in English. 1987. q. USD 799 (effective 2002).
Published by: S N L Financial LC, 212 7th St NE, Charlottesvle, VA 22902-5307. TEL 434-977-1600, FAX 434-293-0407, http://www.snl.com.

332 004.6 GBR ISSN 1365-6813
S T P MAGAZINE. (Straight Through Processing) Text in English. 1996. m. USD 495 (effective 2001). back issues avail. **Document type:** *Magazine, Trade.* **Description:** Covers issues regarding automated transaction processing in the capital markets and payments arenas.
Related titles: Online - full text ed.
—IE.
Published by: STP Information Services, Ltd., 11 Plough Yard, Ste 6, London, EC2A 3LP, United Kingdom. TEL 44-20-73750756, FAX 44-20-7375 0758, post@stpinfo.com, http://www.stpinfo.com/stp_journal/home.html.

332 ESP ISSN 0409-9192
SA NOSTRA CAIXA DE BALEARS. MEMORIA. Text in Spanish. irreg. illus.; charts; stat.
Formerly: Caja de Ahorros y Monte de Piedad de las Baleares. Memoria
Published by: "Sa Nostra" Caixa de Balears, Ramon Llull, 2, Palma De Mallorca, Baleares 07001, Spain. Ed. Pedro Batle Mayol.

332.1 USA ISSN 0036-2379
THE SAFE DEPOSIT BULLETIN. Text in English. 1911. q. free to members. adv. bk.rev. 30 p./no.; **Document type:** *Bulletin, Trade.* **Description:** Includes information about safe and sound practice for banks involved in all aspects of the safe deposit business.
Published by: New York State Safe Deposit Association, c/o Paul J Sanchez, Ed, Box 5074, Rockefeller Center, New York, NY 10185. TEL 212-484-2260, 516-883-2390, FAX 516-883-8429. Ed., R&P, Adv. contact Paul J Sanchez. page USD 600; 8.5 x 11.

332 KNA
ST. KITTS NEVIS ANGUILLA NATIONAL BANK LIMITED AND ITS SUBSIDIARIES. ANNUAL REPORT AND ACCOUNTS. Text in English. a. **Document type:** *Corporate.*
Published by: St. Kitts Nevis Anguilla National Bank Limited, Church St., Basseterre, St Kitts, St. Kitts & Nevis.

332 BEL ISSN 0778-1288
SAMSOM GELD EN ONDERNEMING. Variant title: Geld en Onderneming. Text in Flemish. 1986. s-m. Supplement avail. **Description:** For financial directors, chief accountants and banking houses. Examines business transactions from a fiscal perspective.
Published by: C E D Samsom (Subsidiary of: Wolters Samsom Belgie n.v.), Kouterveld 14, Diegem, 1831, Belgium. TEL 32-2-7231111.

SAN JOSE POST-RECORD; daily legal, & commercial real estate & financial news. see *LAW*

332.1 JPN
SANWA BANK. CORPORATE COMMUNICATIONS DEPARTMENT. ANNUAL REPORT. Text in Japanese. a. **Document type:** *Corporate.*
Published by: Sanwa Bank Ltd., Corporate Communications Department, 1-1-1 Ote-Machi, Chiyoda-ku, Tokyo, 100-0004, Japan. TEL 03-216-3111.

SATELLITE FINANCE. see *COMMUNICATIONS*

332 SAU ISSN 0581-8672
SAUDI ARABIAN MONETARY AGENCY. STATISTICAL SUMMARY. Text in Arabic. a. charts; stat. **Document type:** *Government.* **Description:** Reviews major economic developments in Saudi Arabia such as money and banking, cost of living, government budget and oil developments.
Published by: Saudi Arabian Monetary Agency, Research and Statistics Department, PO Box 2992, Riyadh, 11169, Saudi Arabia. TEL 966-1-463-3000, TELEX 401734.

332 ITA ISSN 0393-4551
HC59.72.S3
SAVINGS AND DEVELOPMENT. Text in English; Summaries in French. 1977. q. EUR 75 in the European Union and ACP countries; EUR 110 elsewhere (effective 2002). adv. bk.rev. charts; stat. index, cum.index. 130 p./no.; back issues avail. **Document type:** *Academic/Scholarly.*
Formerly (until 1977): Finafrica Bulletin (0393-456X)
Related titles: ♦ Supplement(s): African Review of Money Finance and Banking. ISSN 1124-3163.
Indexed: ARDT, ASD, GEOBASE, IBSS, ILD, MaizeAb, PHN&I, PerIslam, RASB, RDA, RRTA, WAE&RSA, WBA.
—BLDSC (8077.254000), IE, Infotrieve, ingenta.
Published by: Giordano dell'Amore Foundation, Via San Vigilio, 10, Milan, MI 20142, Italy. TEL 39-02-8135341, FAX 39-02-8137481, http://www.fgda.org. Ed. Arnaldo Mauri. Pub. Felice Tambussi. R&P, Adv. contact Cinzia Raimondi. Circ: 2,500.

332 USA ISSN 1054-3805
HG1921
SAVINGS BANKS OF AMERICA. Text in English. 1989. a. **Document type:** *Trade.*
Published by: Sheshunoff Information Services Inc., 807 Las Cimas Pkwy, Ste 300, Austin, TX 78746. TEL 512-472-2244, 800-456-2340, FAX 512-305-6575, customercare.sis@sheshunoff.com, http://www.sheshunoff.com.

332 RUS
SBEREGATEL'NOE DELO ZA RUBEZHOM. Text in Russian. q. USD 85 in United States.
Published by: Finansovaya Gruppa Nika, Ul Narvskaya 23, k 306, 113, Moscow, 125493, Russian Federation. TEL 7-095-1557135, FAX 7-095-4521720, vikiniki@aha.ru. Ed. V N Volodina. **US dist. addr.:** East View Information Services, 3020 Harbor Ln. N., Minneapolis, MN 55447. TEL 612-550-0961.

336 DEU ISSN 0720-6755
SCHRIFTEN ZUM BANK- UND BOERSENWESEN. Text in German. 1975. irreg., latest vol.6, 1985. price varies. **Document type:** *Monographic series, Academic/Scholarly.*
Published by: Duncker und Humblot GmbH, Carl-Heinrich-Becker-Weg 9, Berlin, 12165, Germany. TEL 49-30-7900060, FAX 49-30-79000631, info@duncker-humblot.de, http://www.duncker-humblot.de.

B

▼ new title ➤ refereed ✶ unverified ♦ full entry avail.

332 DEU ISSN 1435-6244
SCHRIFTEN ZUR KONZERNSTEUERUNG. Text in German. 1993. irreg., latest vol.9, 2001. price varies. **Document type:** *Monographic series, Academic/Scholarly.*
Published by: Verlag Dr. Kovac, Arnoldstr 49, Hamburg, 22763, Germany. TEL 49-40-3988800, FAX 49-40-39888055, info@verlagdrkovac.de, http://www.verlagdrkovac.de/3-4.htm.

332 CHE ISSN 1010-5808
SCHWEIZER BANK. Text in German. 1986. m. CHF 110 domestic; CHF 129 in Europe; CHF 138 elsewhere (effective 2001). adv. **Document type:** *Journal, Trade.* **Description:** For executives in the banking and financial business.
Indexed: RASB.
Published by: HandelsZeitung Fachverlag AG, Seestr 344, Zuerich, 8027, Switzerland. TEL 41-1-2889414, FAX 41-1-2889301, verlag@handelszeitung.ch, http://www.handelszeitung.ch. Ed. Brigitte Strebel-Aerni. Adv. contact Jean-Claude Page TEL 41-1-2889410. Circ: 11,000 (paid and controlled).

B

332 CHE
SCHWEIZERISCHE BANKPERSONAL ZEITUNG. Text in German. 22/yr.
Published by: Zentralsekretariat, Postfach 8235, Bern, 3001, Switzerland. TEL 031-454311, FAX 031-459874. Ed. Urs Tschumi. Circ: 30,000.

332 CHE ISSN 1424-7046
HC395
SCHWEIZERISCHE NATIONALBANK. BANKENSTATISTISCHES QUARTALSHEFT. Text in German. 1990. q. **Document type:** *Bulletin, Government.*
Former titles (until 2000): Schweizerische Nationalbank. Bankenstatistisches Monatsheft (1422-5336); (until 1998): Schweizerische Nationalbank. Monatsbericht. Bankenstatistisches Beiheft (1420-1925)
Published by: Schweizerische Nationalbank/Banque Nationale Suisse, Boersenstr. 15, Postfach, Zurich, 8022, Switzerland. TEL 41-1-6313111, FAX 41-1-6313911, snb@snb.ch, http://www.snb.ch.

332 CHE ISSN 1421-5497
SCHWEIZERISCHE NATIONALBANK. GESCHAEFTSBERICHT. Text in German. 1909. a. **Document type:** *Yearbook, Government.*
Related titles: French ed.: Banque Nationale Suisse. Rapport de Gestion. ISSN 1421-5500; Italian ed.: Banca Nazionale Svizzera. Rapporto di Gestione. ISSN 1421-5489; English ed.: Swiss National Bank. Annual Report. ISSN 1421-6477.
Published by: Schweizerische Nationalbank/Banque Nationale Suisse, Boersenstr. 15, Postfach, Zurich, 8022, Switzerland. TEL 41-1-6313111, FAX 41-1-6313911, snb@snb.ch, http://www.snb.ch.

332 CHE ISSN 1423-3789
HC395
SCHWEIZERISCHE NATIONALBANK. QUARTALSHEFT. Text in German. 1983. q. **Document type:** *Bulletin, Government.*
Supersedes in part (in 1997): Geld, Wahrung und Konjunktur (0257-4616)
Indexed: JEL.
Published by: Schweizerische Nationalbank/Banque Nationale Suisse, Boersenstr. 15, Postfach, Zurich, 8022, Switzerland. TEL 41-1-6313111, FAX 41-1-6313911, snb@snb.ch, http://www.snb.ch.

332 CHE ISSN 1422-5298
HC395
SCHWEIZERISCHE NATIONALBANK. STATISTISCHES MONATSHEFT/BANQUE NATIONALE SUISSE. BULLETIN MENSUEL DE STATISTIQUES ECONOMIQUES. Text in French, German. 1926. m. charts; mkt.; stat. **Document type:** *Bulletin, Government.*
Formerly (until 1998): Schweizerische Nationalbank. Monatsbericht (0036-7729); Which was formed by the merger of (1907-1926): Monatsausweise der Schweizerischen Nationalbank und Zentraler Notenbanken des Auslandes (1421-3060); Which was formerly (until 1921): Wochenausweise der Schweizerischen Nationalbank und Zentraler Notenbanken des Auslandes (1421-3095); (until 1911): Wochenausweise der Schweizerischen Nationalbank (und der Schweizerischen Emissionsbanken) und einiger Zentralen Notenbanken des Auslandes (1421-3087); (1907-1926): Diskontosaetze und Wechselkurse (1421-3036); Which was formerly (until 1911): Statistik der Diskontosaetze und Wechselkurse (1421-3079); (1907-1926): Statistik des Edelmetallverkehrs der Schweiz (1421-3028); (1907-1926): Uebersicht der Hauptzahlen der Handelsstatistik (1421-3052); (1907-1926): Monatlicher Durchschnitt der Geldkurse fuer Devisen (1421-3044)
Published by: Schweizerische Nationalbank/Banque Nationale Suisse, Boersenstr. 15, Postfach, Zurich, 8022, Switzerland. TEL 41-1-6313111, FAX 41-1-6313911, snb@snb.ch, http://www.snb.ch. Circ: 3,600.

332 CAN
SCOTIA NEWS. Text in English. 12/yr. free. **Document type:** *Newsletter.*
Formerly (until June 1998): Scotiabanker
Published by: Scotia Economics, 44 King St W., Scotia Plaza, Toronto, ON M5W 2X6, Canada. TEL 416-933-2927, FAX 416-866-7281. Ed. Sue Lavigne. Circ: 40,000.

332.1 GBR
SCOTTISH BANKER. Text in English. 1909. bi-m. GBP 20 (effective 2002). adv. bk.rev. illus. index. **Document type:** *Trade.*
Formerly: Scottish Bankers Magazine (0036-9128)
Indexed: CPM, PAIS, WBA.
—BLDSC (8206.095000), ingenta.
Published by: Chartered Institute of Bankers in Scotland, Drumsheugh House, 38 Drumsheugh Gardens, Edinburgh, Midlothian EH3 7SW, United Kingdom. TEL 44-131-473-7777, FAX 44-131-473-7788, charles@ciobs.org.uk, http://www.ciobs.org.uk. Ed. Charles W Munn. Adv. contact Laura Tervit. Circ: 12,000.

332 332.6 658 GBR ISSN 0952-1488
SCOTTISH BUSINESS INSIDER. Variant title: Insider. Text in English. 1984. m. GBP 36 domestic; GBP 52 in Europe; GBP 59 in United States; GBP 3 newsstand/cover (effective 2001). adv. back issues avail. **Document type:** *Trade.* **Description:** Covers the major sectors of business, commerce and industry in Scotland, including corporate and management issues.
Indexed: B&I.
Published by: Insider Publications Ltd., 43 Queensferry St Ln, Edinburgh, Midlothian EH2 4PF, United Kingdom. TEL 44-131-225-8323, FAX 44-131-220-1203, editor-sbi@insider.co.uk. Ed. Bill Millar. Adv. contact David Roulstone. Circ: 17,301 (paid).

SCREEN FINANCE. see *MOTION PICTURES*

332 USA ISSN 0891-2947
SECONDARY MARKETING EXECUTIVE; the journal for mortgage banking professionals. Text in English. 1986. m. USD 48 (effective 2005). adv. charts; illus.; tr.lit. index. back issues avail. **Document type:** *Magazine, Trade.* **Description:** Provides how-to information and trends analysis for buyers and sellers of mortgage loans and servicing rights on the secondary market.
Related titles: Online - full text ed.
Published by: Zackin Publications, PO Box 2180, Waterbury, CT 06722-2180. info@sme-online.com, info@zackin.com, http://www.sme-online.com/sme/, http://www.zackin.com. Eds. Mike King, Neil Morse. Pub. Paul Zackin. Circ: 22,000.

332 USA ISSN 0888-255X
HF5565
SECURED LENDER. Text in English. 1945. bi-m. USD 28 to members; USD 56 to non-members (effective 2005). adv. bk.rev. **Document type:** *Trade.*
Former titles (until 1986): Journal: Asset-Based Financial Services Industry (0278-9353); (until 1980): Commercial Finance Journal (0160-5178); Commercial Financing (0010-2962); Incorporates: National Commercial Finance Association. Journal
Related titles: Online - full text ed.: (from EBSCO Publishing, Northern Light Technology, Inc., O C L C Online Computer Library Center, Inc., ProQuest Information & Learning).
Indexed: ABIn, ATI, BLI, PAIS, WBA.
—BLDSC (8216.988000), IE, ingenta.
Published by: Commercial Finance Association, 225 W 34th St, Rm 1815, New York, NY 10122-0008. TEL 212-594-3490, FAX 212-564-6053, http://www.cfa.com/The_Secured_Lender/securedlender.asp. Ed., Pub. Bruce H Jones. R&P Michele Ocejo TEL 212-594-3490. Adv. contacts Bruce H Jones, Michele Ocejo TEL 212-594-3490. Circ: 5,400.

332.1 HKG
SECURITIES (DISCLOSURE OF INTERESTS) NOTIFICATIONS HISTORY REPORTS. Text in English. irreg. HKD 200 per issue domestic; HKD 205 per issue in Asia; HKD 210 per issue elsewhere (effective 2001).
Formerly: Stock Exchange of Hong Kong. Securities (Disclosure of Interests) Notification History Reports
Related titles: Online - full content ed.
Published by: Hong Kong Exchanges and Clearing Ltd., Corporate Communications, 12/F, One International Finance Centre, 1 Harbour View St, Hong Kong, Hong Kong. TEL 852-2522-1122, FAX 852-2845-3554, info@sehk.com.hk, info@hkex.com.hk, http://www.sehk.com.hk, http://www.hkex.com.hk.

332 USA
SECURITIES HANDBOOK SERIES. MORTGAGE-BACKED SECURITIES; developments and trends in the secondary mortgage market. Text in English. a., latest 2002. USD 275 per vol. (effective 2004). **Document type:** *Trade.* **Description:** Covers the legal, tax, and business considerations affecting the sale of mortgage-backed securities.
Published by: Thomson West (Subsidiary of: Thomson Corporation, The), 610 Opperman Dr, Eagan, MN 55123-1396. TEL 651-687-8000, 800-328-4880, FAX 651-687-7302, http://west.thomson.com/product/14610644/product.asp. Ed. Kenneth G Lore.

332 340 USA ISSN 0080-8474
KF1066.A32
SECURITIES LAW REVIEW. Text in English. 1969. a., latest 2004. USD 365 per vol. (effective 2005). reprint service avail. from WSH. **Document type:** *Trade.* **Description:** Covers the latest developments in securities law.
Related titles: Online - full text ed.
Indexed: ATI, CLI, ILP, LRI.
Published by: Thomson West (Subsidiary of: Thomson Corporation, The), 610 Opperman Dr, Eagan, MN 55123-1396. TEL 651-687-8000, 800-328-4880, FAX 651-687-7302, customer.service@westgroup.com, http://west.thomson.com/product/14806123/product.asp. Ed. Donald C Langevoort.

SECURITIES PRO NEWSLETTER; the authority on African Americans in finance. see *ETHNIC INTERESTS*

SECURITIES REFORM ACT LITIGATION REPORTER. see *LAW—Corporate Law*

332.1 USA ISSN 1090-252X
KF975
THE SECURITIES REGULATORY HANDBOOK. Text in English. 1994. a. price varies. **Document type:** *Trade.*
Formerly (until 1997): Securities Compliance Handbook (1084-5070)
Related titles: ♦ Series of: PricewaterhouseCoopers Regulatory Handbook Series. ISSN 1522-1334.
Published by: (PricewaterhouseCoopers), M.E. Sharpe, Inc., 80 Business Park Dr, Armonk, NY 10504. TEL 914-273-1800, 800-541-6563, FAX 914-273-2106, custserv@mesharpe.com, http://www.mesharpe.com.

332 USA
SECURITIES TRANSACTIONS HANDBOOK. Text in English. a. USD 75. **Document type:** *Government.*
Published by: U.S. Federal Reserve System, Board of Governors, Publications Services, Rm MS 137, 20th and Constitution Ave, N W, Washington, DC 20551. TEL 202-452-3244, FAX 202-728-5886.

332 340 GBR
SECURITIES TRANSACTIONS IN EUROPE. Text in English. 1997. base vol. plus updates 4/yr. looseleaf. GBP 665 base vol(s).; GBP 560, EUR 842 updates in Europe; GBP 580, USD 1,054 updates elsewhere (effective 2006). **Document type:** *Journal, Trade.*
Published by: Sweet & Maxwell Ltd., 100 Avenue Road, London, NW3 3PF, United Kingdom. TEL 44-20-74491111, FAX 44-20-74491144, http://www.sweetandmaxwell.co.uk. **Subscr. to:** Cheriton House, North Way, Andover, Hants SP10 5BE, United Kingdom.

332 340 USA
SECURITIZATION: ASSET-BACKED AND MORTGAGE-BACKED SECURITIES. Text in English. 1991. irreg. (in 1 vol.). looseleaf. USD 135 base vol(s). (effective 2003). **Description:** Covers all federal and state regulatory and tax provisions governing securitized transactions, including rules of accounting and rating agency requirements.
Published by: Michie Company (Subsidiary of: LexisNexis North America), 701 E Water St, Charlottesville, VA 22902-5389. TEL 434-972-7600, 800-446-3410, FAX 434-972-7677, http://www.michie.com. Ed. Ronald S Borod.

SEDMICHEN ZAKONNIK. see *BUSINESS AND ECONOMICS—Accounting*

332 USA
SELECTED BORROWINGS IN IMMEDIATELY AVAILABLE FUNDS OF LARGE COMMERCIAL BANKS. Text in English. w. USD 20. **Document type:** *Government.*
Published by: U.S. Federal Reserve System, Board of Governors, Publications Services, Rm MS 138, Washington, DC 20551. TEL 202-452-3244, FAX 202-728-5886.

332 USA
SELECTED INTEREST RATES. Text in English. w. (and m. releases). USD 20 for w. release; USD 5 for m. release. **Document type:** *Government.*
Indexed: AmStI.
Published by: U.S. Federal Reserve System, Board of Governors, Publications Services, Rm MS 138, Washington, DC 20551. TEL 202-452-3244, FAX 202-728-5886.

SELECTED LAWS AND REGULATIONS OF TENNESSEE FINANCIAL INSTITUTIONS. see *LAW—Corporate Law*

332 MEX
SEMANARIO PARA EL INVERSIONISTA. Text in Spanish. w. MXP 7 newsstand/cover (effective 2000).
Address: Blvd Rodriguez No 20, Col Centro, Hermosillo, Sonora, Mexico. TEL 52-62-121694, FAX 52-16-121649. Ed. Luz Mercedes Moreno Lara.

THE SENIOR CARE ACQUISITION REPORT. see *BUSINESS AND ECONOMICS*

THE SENIORCARE INVESTOR. see *BUSINESS AND ECONOMICS*

SENTINEL INVESTMENT LETTER. see *BUSINESS AND ECONOMICS—Investments*

510 SGP
SERIES IN MATHEMATICAL FINANCE. Text in English. 1996. irreg., latest vol.1. price varies. **Document type:** *Monographic series, Academic/Scholarly.*
Published by: World Scientific Publishing Co. Pte. Ltd., 5 Toh Tuck Link, Singapore, 596224, Singapore. TEL 65-466-5775, FAX 65-467-7667, wspc@wspc.com.sg, series@wspc.com.sg, http://www.wspc.com.sg/books/series/smf_series.shtml, http://www.worldscientific.com. Eds. M Avallaneda, P G Zhang, Z H Chen. **Dist. by:** World Scientific Publishing Co., Inc., 1060 Main St, River Edge, NJ 07661. TEL 201-487-9655, 800-227-7562, FAX 201-487-9656, 888-977-2665; World Scientific Publishing Ltd., 57 Shelton St, London WC2H 9HE, United Kingdom. TEL 44-20-78360888, FAX 44-20-78362020.

332 510 SGP
SERIES ON MATHEMATICAL ECONOMICS AND GAME THEORY. Text in English. irreg. price varies. **Document type:** *Monographic series, Academic/Scholarly.* **Description:** Publishes original monographs in descriptive or normative economic theory, game-theoretical foundations of economic theory, and mathematics designed to facilitate economic or game-theoretical analyses.
Published by: World Scientific Publishing Co. Pte. Ltd., 5 Toh Tuck Link, Singapore, 596224, Singapore. TEL 65-466-5775, FAX 65-467-7667, series@wspc.com.sg, http://www.wspc.com/books/series/megt_series.shtml, http://www.worldscientific.com. Ed. Tatsuro Ichiishi. **Subscr. to:** Farrer Rd, PO Box 128, Singapore 912805, Singapore. TEL 65-382-5663, FAX 65-382-5919.

332 FRA ISSN 0037-2595
SERVICE ECONOMIQUE & FINANCIER "SECOFI". Text in French. 1942. w. adv. bibl.; stat. index, cum.index.
Published by: (Express Documents), Groupe Revenu Francais, 1 bis av. de la Republique, Paris, 75011, France. TEL 33-1-49293000, FAX 33-1-43559141. Ed. Robert Monteux. Circ: 15,000.

332 USA ISSN 1044-1077
SERVICING MANAGEMENT. Text in English. 1989. m. USD 48 (effective 2005). adv. charts; illus.; tr.lit. index. back issues avail. **Document type:** *Magazine, Trade.* **Description:** Provides how-to information and trends analysis for executives and managers of mortgage servicing operations.
Published by: Zackin Publications, PO Box 2180, Waterbury, CT 06722-2180. fabrini@sm-online.com, info@zackin.com, http://www.sm-online.com/sm, http://www.zackin.com. Ed. Michael Bates. Pub. Paul Zackin. Adv. contact Linda Zackin. B&W page USD 3,360. Circ: 23,000 (paid and controlled).

332.1 USA
SHAREHOLDERS, FORM 10-K. BANKING SUPPLEMENT. Text in English. 1983. s-a. free. stat.
Former titles (until 1988): S E C Annual Reports. Banking Supplement; S E C Annual Reports
Indexed: ATI.
Published by: Ernst & Young, 5 Times Sq., New York, NY 10036-6530. TEL 212-773-6000. Circ: 3,675.

332.7 USA ISSN 0730-1936
KF1515.5
SHEPARD'S BANKRUPTCY CITATIONS. Text in English. 1985. m. USD 1,030 (effective 2000). **Description:** Contains citations to bankruptcy court decisions, statutes and other legal sources.
Related titles: CD-ROM ed.; Online - full text ed.
Published by: Shepard's (Subsidiary of: LexisNexis North America), 555 Middle Creek Pkwy, Colorado Springs, CO 80921. TEL 719-488-3000, customer_service@shepards.com, http://www.lexis.com.

332 340 USA
SHESHUNOFF COMPLIANCE AND LAW SERIES. Text in English. 198?. a. (plus irreg. updates). looseleaf. USD 1,950. index. back issues avail. **Document type:** *Trade.* **Description:** Provides important reference data for compliance managers at banks.
Published by: Sheshunoff Information Services Inc., 807 Las Cimas Pkwy, Ste 300, Austin, TX 78746. TEL 512-472-2244, 800-456-2340, FAX 512-305-6575, customercare.sis@sheshunoff.com, http://www.sheshunoff.com.

332 USA
SHESHUNOFF FINANCIAL MANAGEMENT SERIES. Text in English. irreg. price varies. back issues avail. **Document type:** *Directory, Trade.*
Published by: Sheshunoff Information Services Inc., 807 Las Cimas Pkwy, Ste 300, Austin, TX 78746. TEL 512-472-2244, 800-456-2340, FAX 512-305-6575, customercare.sis@sheshunoff.com, http://www.sheshunoff.com.

332 USA
SHESHUNOFF REGULATORY REPORTING SERIES. Text in English. irreg. price varies. **Document type:** *Directory, Trade.* **Description:** Offers bank management guidance in regulations governing disclosure.
Published by: Sheshunoff Information Services Inc., 807 Las Cimas Pkwy, Ste 300, Austin, TX 78746. TEL 512-472-2244, 800-456-2340, FAX 512-305-6575, customercare.sis@sheshunoff.com, http://www.sheshunoff.com.

332 USA
SHESHUNOFF TRAINING SERIES. Text in English. irreg. price varies. back issues avail. **Document type:** *Directory, Trade.*
Published by: Sheshunoff Information Services Inc., 807 Las Cimas Pkwy, Ste 300, Austin, TX 78746. TEL 512-472-2244, 800-456-2340, FAX 512-305-6575, customercare.sis@sheshunoff.com, http://www.sheshunoff.com.

SHIPPING FINANCE ANNUAL. see *TRANSPORTATION—Ships And Shipping*

332 380 CHN ISSN 1004-9339
SHUIWU YU JINGJI/TAXATION AND ECONOMY. Text in Chinese; Contents page in English. 1979. bi-m. CNY 35, USD 30. bk.rev. back issues avail. **Document type:** *Academic/Scholarly.* **Description:** Contains papers on taxation theory, financial strategy and policy, enterprise management, relations between state and private enterprise, financial regulation and reform, joint ventures, accounting principles, and related topics.
Formerly (until Jan. 1993): Jilin Caimao Xueyuan Xuebao/Jilin Institute of Finance and Trade. Journal (1001-4586)
Related titles: Online - full text ed.: (from East View Information Services).
Published by: Changchun Institute of Taxation, Journal Editorial Department, 102 Renmin St, Changchun, Jilin 130021, China. TEL 86-431-8919931-3406. Ed. Shangguan Shuyan. Circ: 4,000. **Dist. outside China by:** China Educational Books Import & Export Corporation, 15 Xueyuan Lu, Haidian-qu, Beijing, China.

332 CHN
SICHUAN CAIZHENG YANJIU/SICHUAN FINANCE RESEARCH. Text in Chinese. m.
Published by: Sichuan Caizheng Ting/Sichuan Bureau of Finance, 37 Nanxin Jie, Chengdu, Sichuan 610016, China. TEL 22353.

332 CHN
SICHUAN JINRONG/SICHUAN FINANCE. Text in Chinese. m.
Published by: Sichuan Finance Society, Yinhang Dasha (Bank Building), Shudu Dadao, Chengdu, Sichuan 610016, China. TEL 554360. **Co-sponsor:** Chinese People's Bank, Sichuan Branch.

332 COL
SIMPOSIO SOBRE MERCADO DE CAPITALES. Text in Spanish. 1974 (no.3). a. USD 11 (effective 1990).
Published by: Asociacion Bancaria de Colombia, Carrera 7 No. 17-01 Piso 3, Bogota, DE, Colombia. TEL 57-1-281-3501, FAX 57-1-281-3017.

332.4 SGP
SINGAPORE. BOARD OF COMMISSIONERS OF CURRENCY. ANNUAL REPORT AND ACCOUNTS. Text in English. 1967. a.
Formerly: Singapore. Board of Commissioners of Currency. Annual Report
Published by: Board of Commissioners of Currency, 79 Robinson Rd 01-01, Singapore, 068897, Singapore. TEL 2222211, FAX 2257671, TELEX SINWANG RS 24722. Circ: 800.

332 GBR
SINGLE CURRENCY NEWSLETTER. Text in English. q. **Document type:** *Newsletter.*
Published by: Lovell White Durrant, 65 Holburn Viaduct, London, EC1A 2DY, United Kingdom. TEL 44-20-7236-0066, FAX 44-20-7248-4212, publications@lovellwhitedurrant.com, http://www.lovellwhitedurrant.com.

332 COL
SISTEMA FINANCIERO INFORME TRIMESTRAL. Text in Spanish. 1990. q. free.
Published by: Superintendencia Bancaria, Apartado Aereo 3460, Bogota, CUND, Colombia. TEL 57-1-2804060, FAX 57-1-2800864. Circ: 500.

332.2 USA
SMALL BIZ NEWS. Text in English. w. **Document type:** *Newsletter, Consumer.* **Description:** Contains current information on small business financial issues.
Media: E-mail.
Published by: Bankrate Inc., 11811 US Hwy 1, North Palm Beach, FL 33408. TEL 561-630-2400, FAX 561-625-4540, webmaster@bankrate.com, http://bankrate.process9.com/bankrate/subscribe.html, http://www.bankrate.com.

SMALL BUSINESS BANKING NEWS. see *BUSINESS AND ECONOMICS—Small Business*

332 GBR
SMALL BUSINESSES AND THEIR BANKS. Text in English. 1988. biennial. **Document type:** *Academic/Scholarly.*
Published by: Forum of Private Business, Ruskin Chambers, Drury Ln, Knutsford, Ches WA16 6HA, United Kingdom. TEL 44-1565-634467, FAX 44-1565-650059.

332.6 USA ISSN 1069-2851
HG179
SMARTMONEY; the Wall Street Journal magazine of personal business. Variant title: Smart Money. Text in English. 1992. m. USD 15 domestic; USD 30 foreign (effective 2005). adv. bk.rev. illus.; tr.lit. Index. reprints avail. **Document type:** *Magazine, Consumer.* **Description:** Covers a variety of personal finance topics for upscale readers, including retirement planning, investment strategies, financial planning for education, and related life-style issues.
Related titles: ◆ Online - full content ed.: Smartmoney.com; Online - full text ed.: (from EBSCO Publishing).
Indexed: ASIP, AgeL, BPI.
Published by: Dow Jones Company, 200 Liberty St, New York, NY 10281. TEL 212-416-2700, FAX 212-416-2829, editors@smartmoney.com, http://www.smartmoney.com/mag/. Eds. Robert Hunter, Edwin A Finn, Andrew Seibert. Pub. Jay McGill. adv.: B&W page USD 40,170, color page USD 54,290; trim 10.75 x 9. Circ: 600,000 (paid).

332.6 USA
SMARTMONEY.COM. Text in English. 1997. d. adv. **Description:** Contains information and resources for all aspects of personal finance and investment.
Media: Online - full content. **Related titles:** Online - full text ed.: (from EBSCO Publishing); ◆ Print ed.: SmartMoney. ISSN 1069-2851.
Published by: Hearst Corporation, 1755 Broadway, 2nd Fl, New York, NY 10019. TEL 212-373-9300, FAX 212-245-7276, http://www.smartmoney.com.

332 BEL ISSN 0081-1114
SOCIETE GENERALE DE BELGIQUE. RAPPORT - REPORT. Text in French. 1822. a. free.
Related titles: English ed.
Published by: Societe Generale de Belgique, Communications Department, Rue Royale 30, Brussels, 1000, Belgium.

332.1 USA
SOLUTIONS. Variant title: Centura Solutions. Text in English. m. **Document type:** *Newsletter, Consumer.* **Description:** Contains articles and information for customers of Centura Bank.
—BLDSC (8327.800500).
Published by: Hammock Publishing, Inc., 3322 W End Ave, Ste 700, Nashville, TN 37203. TEL 615-690-3400, FAX 615-690-3401, info@hammock.com, http://www.hammock.com.

332 USA ISSN 1543-5733
HG179.5
▼ **SOLUTIONS (DENVER);** your business, your profession, your success. Text in English. 2003 (Mar.). bi-m.
—CCC.
Published by: Financial Planning Association, 4100 E Mississippi Ave Ste 400, Denver, CO 80246.

SOURCE O C D E. ECONOMIES EN TRANSITION. (Organisation de Cooperation et de Developpement Economiques) see *BUSINESS AND ECONOMICS*

332 FRA ISSN 1683-237X
SOURCE O C D E. FINANCE ET INVESTISSEMENT / ASSURANCE ET RETRAITES. (Organisation de Cooperation et de Developpement Economiques) Text in French. irreg. EUR 1,244, USD 1,430, GBP 820, JPY 168,000 (effective 2005).
Related titles: Online - full content ed.: ISSN 1684-3029. EUR 871, USD 1,001, GBP 575, JPY 117,600 (effective 2005); Online - full text ed.: (from EBSCO Publishing, Gale Group, IngentaConnect, Swets Information Services); ◆ English ed.: Source O E C D. Finance & Investment / Insurance & Pensions. ISSN 1608-022X.
Published by: Organization for Economic Cooperation and Development, 2 Rue Andre Pascal, Paris, 75775 Cedex 16, France. TEL 33-1-45248200, FAX 33-1-45248500, http://www.oecd.org. **Dist. by:** Extenza - Turpin, Pegasus Dr, Stratton Business Park, Biggleswade, Beds SG18 8TQ, United Kingdom. TEL 44-1462-687552, FAX 44-1462-480947, subscriptions@extenza-turpin.com; O E C D Turpin North America, PO Box 194, Downingtown, PA 19335-0194. TEL 610-524-5361, 800-456-6323, FAX 610-524-5417, journalscustomer@turpinna.com.

332 FRA ISSN 1608-022X
SOURCE O E C D. FINANCE & INVESTMENT / INSURANCE & PENSIONS. Text in English. irreg. EUR 1,244, USD 1,430, GBP 820, JPY 168,000 (effective 2005). **Description:** Studies on FDI flows and policies and on pensions and insurance.
Related titles: Online - full content ed.: ISSN 1681-200X. EUR 871, USD 1,001, GBP 575, JPY 117,600 (effective 2005); [3ba] Online - full text ed.: 2000 (from EBSCO Publishing, Gale Group, IngentaConnect, Swets Information Services); ◆ French ed.: Source O C D E. Finance et Investissement / Assurance et Retraites. ISSN 1683-237X.

B

Published by: Organization for Economic Cooperation and Development, 2 Rue Andre Pascal, Paris, 75775 Cedex 16, France. TEL 33-1-45248200, FAX 33-1-45248500, http://www.oecd.org. **Dist. by:** Extenza - Turpin, Pegasus Dr, Stratton Business Park, Biggleswade, Beds SG18 8TQ, United Kingdom. TEL 44-1462-687552, FAX 44-1462-480947, subscriptions@extenza-turpin.com; O E C D Turpin North America, PO Box 194, Downingtown, PA 19335-0194. TEL 610-524-5361, 800-456-6323, FAX 610-524-5417, journalscustomer@turpinna.com.

SOURCE O E C D. TRANSITION ECONOMIES. see *BUSINESS AND ECONOMICS*

332 GBR ISSN 1359-3501
SOUTH. Text in English. 1995. m. GBP 20 in United Kingdom; USD 40 in developing nations; USD 55 elsewhere.
Indexed: ESPM.
Published by: Global News Network, 50 Portland Pl, London, W1N 3DG, United Kingdom. FAX 44-171-580-7623.

332 ZAF ISSN 0049-1403
SOUTH AFRICAN FINANCIAL GAZETTE. Cover title: Financial Gazette. Text in English. 1964. w. ZAR 18. adv. film rev.; play rev. charts; stat.
Published by: South African Financial Gazette Ltd., PO Box 8161, Johannesburg, 2000, South Africa. Ed. Otto Krause. Circ: 15,000.

332 ZAF ISSN 0038-2620
HG3399.S7
SOUTH AFRICAN RESERVE BANK. QUARTERLY BULLETIN/SUID-AFRIKAANSE RESERWEBANK. KWARTAALBLAD. Text in Afrikaans, English. 1946. q. ZAR 120 (effective 1999). charts; stat. **Document type:** *Bulletin.* **Description:** Reports on the banks economic situation and outlook.
Formerly: South African Reserve Bank. Quarterly Bulletin of Statistics
Indexed: PROMT, RASB, WBA.
Published by: South African Reserve Bank/Suid-Afrikaanse Reserwebank, PO Box 427, Pretoria, 0001, South Africa. TEL 27-12-313-3911, FAX 27-12-313-3197, info@gwisel.resbank.oc.za, info@gwisel.resbank.co.za, http://www.resbank.co.za. Circ: 3,000.

332.1 ZAF
SOUTH AFRICAN RESERVE BANK. REPORT OF THE ORDINARY GENERAL MEETING OF SHAREHOLDERS/ SUID-AFRIKAANSE RESERWEBANK. VERSLAG VAN DIE GEWONE ALGEMENE VERGADERING VAN AANDEELHOUERS. Text in Afrikaans, English. 1922. a. free. **Document type:** *Corporate.* **Description:** Report covers economic development, monetary policy, payment systems, maintenance of currency supply, and international relations. Includes balance sheet, charts and more.
Published by: South African Reserve Bank/Suid-Afrikaanse Reserwebank, PO Box 427, Pretoria, 0001, South Africa. TEL 27-12-313-3911, FAX 27-12-313-3197, info@gwisel.resbank.co.za, http://www.resbank.co.za. Ed., R&P J J Rossouw TEL 27-12-3133723. Circ: 3,120.

332.1 USA ISSN 0734-7812
HG2441
SOUTHERN BANKERS DIRECTORY. Text in English. 1937. s-a. USD 134 (effective 2001). adv. **Document type:** *Directory, Trade.* **Description:** Lists financial information for banks, bank holding companies, thrifts, and major credit unions for the following states: Alabama, Arkansas, District of Columbia, Florida, Georgia, Kentucky, Louisiana, Maryland, Mississippi, North Carolina, South Carolina, Tennessee, Virginia, and West Virginia.
Published by: Thomson Financial Services Company, 4709 W Golf Rd, Skokie, IL 60076-1256. TEL 847-676-9600, 800-321-3373, FAX 847-933-8101, prodinfo@tfp.com, customerservice@tfp.com, http://www.tfp.com/banks. Circ: 6,105.

332.6029 USA ISSN 1082-8923
SOUTHWESTERN FINANCIAL DIRECTORY. Variant title: McFadden Southwestern Financial Directory. Text in English. 1995. s-a. USD 104 (effective 2001). **Description:** Lists financial information for banks, bank holding companies, thrifts and major credit union institutions for the following states: Arkansas, Louisiana, New Mexico, Oklahoma, and Texas.
Published by: Thomson Financial Services Company, 4709 W Golf Rd, Skokie, IL 60076-1256. TEL 847-676-9600, 800-321-3373, FAX 847-933-8101, customerservice@tfp.com, http://www.tfp.com/.

SOVEREIGN ASSESSMENT MONTHLY. see *BUSINESS AND ECONOMICS—Investments*

332.1 NOR ISSN 0038-6502
SPAREBANKBLADET/NORWEGIAN SAVINGS BANK NEWS. Text in Norwegian. 1917. m. NOK 210 (effective 1997). adv. bk.rev. charts; stat.
—CCC.
Published by: Sparebankforeningens Publikasjoner AS, Postboks 6772, St Olavs Plass, Oslo, 0130, Norway. TEL 47-22-11-00-75, FAX 47-22-36-25-33, firmapost@sparebankforeningen.no, http://www.sparebankforeningen.no. Ed. Ragnar Falck. Circ: 7,500 (controlled).

332.1 DEU ISSN 0038-6561
HG1939.G2
SPARKASSE. Text in German. 1881. m. adv. bk.rev. charts; illus.; stat. index. **Document type:** *Magazine, Trade.*
Indexed: PAIS, RASB.
—CCC.
Published by: (Deutscher Sparkassen- und Giroverband e.V.), Deutscher Sparkassenverlag GmbH, Am Wallgraben 115, Stuttgart, 70565, Germany. TEL 49-711-7820, FAX 49-711-7821709, webredaktion@dsv-gruppe.de, http://www.dsv-gruppe.de. Ed. Arnulf Sauter. Circ: 7,000.

330 DEU ISSN 1435-8379
SPARKASSEN-MAGAZIN. Text in German. 1976. m. adv. **Document type:** *Magazine, Consumer.*
Published by: Deutscher Sparkassenverlag GmbH, Am Wallgraben 115, Stuttgart, 70565, Germany. TEL 49-711-7820, FAX 49-711-7821709, webredaktion@dsv-gruppe.de, http://www.dsv-gruppe.de. adv.: B&W page EUR 2,800, color page EUR 4,630. Circ: 11,600 (controlled).

332.1 DEU ISSN 1612-3743
DIE SPARKASSEN-ZEITUNG. Text in German. 1924. 2/w. charts; illus.; stat. index, cum.index. **Document type:** *Newsletter, Trade.*
Formerly (until 2000): Deutsche Sparkassenzeitung (0012-0766)
—CCC.
Published by: (Deutscher Sparkassen- und Giroverband e.V.), Deutscher Sparkassenverlag GmbH, Am Wallgraben 115, Stuttgart, 70565, Germany. TEL 49-711-7820, FAX 49-711-7821709, webredaktion@dsv-gruppe.de, http://www.dsv-gruppe.de. Ed. George Clegg. Circ: 23,000.

332.1 DEU
SPARKASSENFACHBUCH (YEAR). Text in German. a. **Document type:** *Trade.*
Published by: Deutscher Sparkassenverlag GmbH, Am Wallgraben 115, Stuttgart, 70565, Germany.

332 USA ISSN 1547-1136
HG181
SPECIALTY FINANCE. Text in English. m. USD 496 (effective 2002).
Formerly (until 2002): Specialty Lender (1091-7179)
Published by: S N L Financial LC, 212 7th St NE, Charlottesvle, VA 22902-5307. TEL 434-977-1600, FAX 434-293-0407, http://www.snl.com.

332 USA
SPECIALTY FINANCE QUARTERLY. Text in English. 1999. q. USD 696 (effective 2002).
Formerly (until 2002): Specialty Lender Quarterly (1525-4453); Which superseded in part (in 1999): S N L Financial Services Quarterly (1074-5912)
Published by: S N L Financial LC, 212 7th St NE, Charlottesvle, VA 22902-5307. TEL 434-977-1600, FAX 434-293-0407, http://www.snl.com.

332 USA
SPECIALTY FINANCE WEEKLY. Text in English. w. USD 396 (effective 2002).
Media: E-mail. **Related titles:** Fax ed.
Published by: S N L Financial LC, 212 7th St NE, Charlottesvle, VA 22902-5307. TEL 434-977-1600, FAX 434-293-0407, http://www.snl.com.

332 USA
STANDARD & POOR'S DIVIDEND RECORD (ANNUAL). Text in English. q. looseleaf. USD 26. reprints avail.
Related titles: Microfiche ed.
Published by: Standard & Poor's (Subsidiary of: McGraw-Hill Companies, Inc.), 55 Water St, New York, NY 10041. Ed. Anthony Onofrio.

332 USA ISSN 1530-678X
HG5993
STANDARD & POOR'S EMERGING STOCK MARKETS FACTBOOK. Text in English. 1986. a. **Document type:** *Journal, Trade.* **Description:** Provides both fundamental economic information and vital data on market size, liquidity, and valuations.
Formerly (until 2000): Emerging Stock Markets Factbook (1012-8115)
Related titles: Microfiche ed.: (from CIS).
Indexed: IIS.
—BLDSC (8430.252420).
Published by: (Capital Market Dept.), International Finance Corporation, 2121 Pennsylvania Ave, N W, Washington, DC 20433. TEL 202-473-9520, FAX 202-974-4805, emdb@ifc.org, http://www.ifc.org. Circ: 5,000.

STANDARD & POOR'S FINANCIAL INSTITUTIONS RATINGS (QUARTERLY EDITION). see *BUSINESS AND ECONOMICS—Abstracting, Bibliographies, Statistics*

332.1 GBR
STANDARD CHARTERED. FACT BOOK. Text in English. a. **Document type:** *Directory, Corporate.* **Description:** Presents basic information on Chartered Bank divisions throughout the world.
Published by: Standard Chartered Bank, 1 Aldermanbury Sq, London, EC2V 7SB, United Kingdom. TEL 44-171-280-7500, FAX 44-171-280-7791.

332 CAN ISSN 0829-7460
STANDING SENATE COMMITTEE ON BANKING, TRADE AND COMMERCE. PROCEEDINGS. Text in English, French. 1969. irreg.
Incorporates (1969-1976): Deliberations du Comite Senatorial Permanent des Banques et du Commerce (0829-7479)
Related titles: Online - full content ed.: ISSN 1494-0353; French ed.: Deliberations du Comite Senatorial Permanent des Banques et du Commerce. ISSN 1494-0361.
Published by: Canada, Senate Standing Committee on Banking, Trade and Commerce, The Senate, Ottawa, ON K1A 0A4, Canada. TEL 613-990-0088, FAX 613-990-6666, banking_banques@sen.parl.gc.ca, http://www.parl.gc.ca/common/Committee_SenProceed.asp?Language=E&Parl=37&Ses=3&comm_id=3, http://www.parl.gc.ca/common/Committee_SenHome.asp?Language=E&Parl=37&Ses=3&comm_id=3.

332 IND
STATE BANK OF INDIA. ANNUAL REPORT. Text in English. 1955. a. **Document type:** *Corporate.*
Supersedes: State Bank of India. Report of the Central Board of Directors (0585-0991); Report for the Half Year of the Imperial Bank of India
Published by: State Bank of India, Economic Research Department, Central Office, New Administration Bldg., Backbay Reclamation, Mumbai, Maharashtra 400 021, India.

332.1 PAK ISSN 0081-444X
STATE BANK OF PAKISTAN. ANNUAL REPORT. Text in English. 1949. a. **Document type:** *Government.*
Published by: State Bank of Pakistan, Central Directorate, Public Relations Department, I.I. Chundrigar Rd, PO Box 4456, Karachi, Pakistan. TEL 92-21-2414141, FAX 92-21-9217865, TELEX 21774 SBPK PK. Circ: 2,500.

332 PAK ISSN 0039-0011
HC440.5
STATE BANK OF PAKISTAN. BULLETIN. Text in English. 1950. m. PKR 600, USD 84 (effective 2000). **Document type:** *Bulletin, Government.* **Description:** Provides information on prices, labor, and national accounts in Pakistan.
Indexed: WBA.
Published by: State Bank of Pakistan, Central Directorate, Public Relations Department, I.I. Chundrigar Rd, PO Box 4456, Karachi, Pakistan. TEL 92-21-9212400, FAX 92-21-9212436, TELEX 21774 SBPK PK. Circ: 727.

332 PAK ISSN 0561-8738
STATE BANK OF PAKISTAN. STATE BANK NEWS. Text in English. 1963. s-m. **Document type:** *Newsletter, Government.* **Description:** Provides information of relevance to bank employees.
Published by: State Bank of Pakistan, Central Directorate, Public Relations Department, I.I. Chundrigar Rd, PO Box 4456, Karachi, Pakistan. TEL 92-21-9212400, FAX 92-21-9212436, TELEX 21774 SBPK PK.

332.1 USA ISSN 1053-3435
HG2571
STATE OF THE STATE BANKING SYSTEM. Text in English. 1965. a., latest vol.15, 1994. USD 60.
Published by: Conference of State Bank Supervisors, 1155 Connecticut Ave, NW, 5th Fl, Washington, DC 20036. TEL 202-296-2840, FAX 202-296-1928, http://www.csbs.org. Ed., R&P Ellen Lamb.

334.2 USA
STATELINE. Text in English. 1975. m. membership (effective 1999). **Document type:** *Newsletter.* **Description:** Covers the credit union financial industry.
Published by: National Association of State Credit Union Supervisors, 1555 N Fort Myer Dr, Ste 300, Arlington, VA 22209. TEL 703-528-0669, FAX 703-528-3248, offices@nascus.org, http://www.nascus.org. Ed. Ronda Combs. R&P Ronda Coombs. Circ: 1,000.

332 IND
STOCK MARKET YEARBOOK; an easy reference to 200 companies. Text in English. 1989. a. INR 150.
Published by: Quantum Financial Services Pvt. Ltd., 2 Jay Mahal, A Rd., Mumbai, Maharashtra 400 020, India. TEL 91-22-283-0322, FAX 91-22-285-4318, TELEX 011-4529 MCTC IN. Ed., R&P Ajit Dayal.

STOCK SUMMARY (MONTHLY EDITION). see *BUSINESS AND ECONOMICS—Investments*

323.3 333.33 USA
STRATEGIC: HOUSING, FINANCIAL, COMMUNITY PARTNERS. Text in English. q. free. adv. **Document type:** *Corporate.*
Formerly: Community Enterprise

Published by: Federal Home Loan Bank of Atlanta, 1475 Peachtree St, Atlanta, GA 30309. TEL 800-536-9650. Ed. Jim McDougall. Adv. contact Avis McGhee.

332 GBR ISSN 1467-0607
STRUCTURED FINANCE INTERNATIONAL. Text in English. 1999. bi-m. GBP 1,215 combined subscription domestic print & online eds.; EUR 1,945 combined subscription in Europe print & online eds.; USD 1,945 combined subscription foreign print & online eds. (effective 2005). adv. **Document type:** *Magazine, Trade.* **Description:** Covers structured finance and securitization.
Related titles: Online - full text ed.: (from Gale Group, O C L C Online Computer Library Center, Inc.).
Published by: Euromoney Institutional Investor Plc., Nestor House, Playhouse Yard, London, EC4V 5EX, United Kingdom. TEL 44-20-7779-8673, FAX 44-20-7779-8541, http://www.ew-sfi.com, http://www.euromoney.com. Ed. John Hay. **Subscr. to:** Eclipse, The In-house Fulfillment Bureau, PO Box 18083, London EC4V 5JS, United Kingdom. TEL 44-20-7779-8610, FAX 44-20-7779-8602, CustomerService@euromoneyplc.com.

THE STUDENT AID AUDIO GUIDE. see *EDUCATION*

THE STUDENT GUIDE. see *EDUCATION*

330 DEU ISSN 0939-5113
STUDIEN ZU FINANZEN, GELD UND KAPITAL. Text in German. 1991. irreg., latest vol.13, 2001. price varies. **Document type:** *Monographic series, Academic/Scholarly.*
Published by: Duncker und Humblot GmbH, Carl-Heinrich-Becker-Weg 9, Berlin, 12165, Germany. TEL 49-30-7900060, FAX 49-30-79000631, info@duncker-humblot.de, http://www.duncker-humblot.de.

332 DEU
STUDIEN ZU FUNDMUENZEN DER ANTIKE. Text in German. irreg., latest vol.14, 1997. price varies. **Document type:** *Monographic series, Academic/Scholarly.*
Published by: Verlag Philipp von Zabern GmbH, Philipp-von-Zabern-Platz 1-3, Mainz, 55116, Germany. TEL 49-6131-287470, FAX 49-6131-223710, zabern@zabern.de, http://www.zabern.de.

332 SGP
STUDIES IN APPLIED INTERNATIONAL ECONOMICS. Text in English. 1998. irreg., latest vol.1. price varies. **Document type:** *Monographic series, Academic/Scholarly.*
Published by: World Scientific Publishing Co. Pte. Ltd., 5 Toh Tuck Link, Singapore, 596224, Singapore. TEL 65-466-5775, FAX 65-467-7667, wspc@wspc.com.sg, series@wspc.com.sg, http://www.wspc.com/books/series/saie_series.shtml, http://www.worldscientific.com. Ed. P Pauly. **Dist. by:** World Scientific Publishing Co., Inc., 1060 Main St, River Edge, NJ 07661. TEL 201-487-9655, 800-227-7562, FAX 201-487-9656, 888-977-2665; World Scientific Publishing Ltd., 57 Shelton St, London WC2H 9HE, United Kingdom. TEL 44-20-78360888, FAX 44-20-78362020.

346.082 AUS
STUDIES IN AUSTRALIAN BANKING & FINANCE SERIES. BANKING AND FINANCIAL INSTITUTIONS LAW. Text in English. irreg., latest 2001, 5th ed. AUD 99.95 (effective 2004). 573 p./no.; **Document type:** *Monographic series.* **Description:** Covers the laws regulating financial institutions, regulated markets and instruments, financial market instruments and other facilities, and other related issues.
Published by: Lawbook Co. (Subsidiary of: Thomson Legal & Regulatory Ltd.), PO Box 3502, Rozelle, NSW 2039, Australia. LRA.Service@thomson.com, http://onlineecom01.thomson.com.au/thomson/Catalog.asp?EES_CMD=SI&EES_ID=100184, http://www.lawbookco.com.au/. Eds. Anna Everett, Sheeleagh McCracken.

332 GBR ISSN 1086-7376
HB1
➤ **STUDIES IN ECONOMICS AND FINANCE.** Text in English. 1977. s-a. GBP 20 domestic to individuals; USD 30 foreign to individuals; GBP 50 domestic to institutions & libraries; USD 75 foreign to institutions & libraries (effective 2005). adv. abstr.; bibl.; charts. cum.index. back issues avail. **Document type:** *Journal, Academic/Scholarly.* **Description:** Publishes original articles in finance, economics such as corporate finance, financial markets, investments, risk management, international economics & finance, etc.
Formerly: Studies in Economic Analysis (0198-8263)
Related titles: Microform ed.: (from PQC); Online - full text ed.: (from O C L C Online Computer Library Center, Inc., ProQuest Information & Learning).
Indexed: ABIn, BPIA, JEL, PAIS.
—BLDSC (8490.441000).
Published by: Robert Gordon University, Aberdeen Business School, Garthdee Rd, Aberdeen, AB10 7QG, United Kingdom. TEL 44-1224-263103, FAX 44-1224-263143, sieaf@rgu.ac.uk, http://www.abs.ac.uk/sieaf. Ed., R&P Mahendra Raj. adv.: B&W page GBP 100. Circ: 200 (paid).

332 USA ISSN 0081-8070
STUDIES IN INTERNATIONAL FINANCE. Text in English. 1950. irreg., latest vol.84, 1998. price varies. back issues avail.; reprint service avail. from PQC,PSC. **Document type:** *Monographic series, Academic/Scholarly.* **Description:** Research studies in the field of international finance problems that are too technical or too specialized to appear in "Essays in International Finance".
—CCC.
Published by: Princeton University, International Finance Section, c/o Margaret B Riccardi, Ed, Department of Economics, Fisher Hall, Princeton, NJ 08544-1021. TEL 609-258-4048, FAX 609-258-1374, ifs@princeton.edu. Ed. Margaret B Riccardi. Circ: 2,000.

SUARA N U B E. see *LABOR UNIONS*

332 658 USA ISSN 1523-6196
SUCCESSFUL OFFICER CALL STRATEGIES. Text in English. 1998. m. USD 329 (effective 2000). index. back issues avail. **Document type:** *Newsletter.* **Description:** Profiles strategies officers use to increase sales and cross-sales.
Published by: Siefer Consultants, Inc., 525 Cayuga St, Storm Lake, IA 50588. TEL 712-732-7340, FAX 712-732-7906, siefer@ncn.net. Ed. Steve Herron. Circ: 1,400.

332 SDN
SUDAN COMMERCIAL BANK. REPORT OF THE BOARD OF DIRECTORS. Text in English. irreg. **Document type:** *Corporate.*
Published by: Sudan Commercial Bank, P O Box 1116, Khartoum, Sudan.

332 JPN ISSN 0910-1403
SUMITOMO BANK. ANNUAL REPORT. Text in English. 1951. a. free. **Document type:** *Corporate.*
Formerly (until 1968): Sumitomo Bank. Half-yearly Report (0910-139X)
Published by: Sumitomo Bank, Ltd., Economic Department, C.P.O. Box 4, Tokyo, 100-91, Japan.

332 FIN ISSN 1456-4718
EURO & TALOUS. Text in Finnish; Text occasionally in Swedish. 1993. q. free. **Document type:** *Trade.*
Formerly (until 1998): Markka ja Talous (1236-4231)
Related titles: Online - full text ed.: ISSN 1456-5862. 1999.
Published by: Suomen Pankki/Bank of Finland, P O Box 160, Helsinki, 00101, Finland. TEL 358-9-183-2566, FAX 358-9-174-872, publications@bof.fi, http://www.bof.fi/env/rhinden.htm. Ed. Matti Vanhala. Circ: 6,600.

332 FIN ISSN 1239-9329
SUOMEN PANKKI. VUOSIKERTOMUS. Text in Finnish. 1997. a. free. charts. **Description:** Covers economic developments, monetary policy, payment systems and maintenance of currency supply, international relations, balance sheet, charts, tables and more.
Formerly (until 1997): Vuosikirja - Suomen Pankki (0355-5925)
Related titles: Online - full text ed.: ISSN 1456-5773; ♦ English ed.: Bank of Finland. Annual Report. ISSN 1239-9345; ♦ Swedish ed.: Finlands Bank. Aarsberaettelse. ISSN 1239-9337.
Published by: Suomen Pankki/Bank of Finland, P O Box 160, Helsinki, 00101, Finland. TEL 358-9-183-2566, FAX 358-9-174-872, publications@bof.fi, http://www.bof.fi/env/rhinden.htm. Circ: 8,000.

332 AUS ISSN 1324-5295
SUPER REVIEW. Text in English. 1986. m. AUD 162.31 (effective 2001). adv. **Document type:** *Trade.* **Description:** Provides in-depth coverage of superannuation policy, compliance, administration and investment issues.
Formerly (until 1994): Australian Super Review (0819-341X)
Related titles: Online - full text ed.: (from Gale Group, LexisNexis).
Indexed: ABIX.
Published by: Reed Business Information Pty Ltd (Subsidiary of: Reed Business Information International), Locked Bag 2999, Chatswood, NSW 2067, Australia. customerservice@reedbusiness.com.au, http://www.reedbusiness.com.au. Ed. Zilla Efrat. Pub. Jeremy Knibbs TEL 61-2-9422-2930. Adv. contact Brad Lawson. Circ: 4,438.

332 CHL
SUPERINTENDENCIA DE BANCOS E INSTITUCIONES FINANCIERAS. INFORME ANUAL. Text in Spanish. a. back issues avail.
Related titles: Online - full text ed.
Published by: Superintendencia de Bancos e Instituciones Financieras, Moneda 1123, Santiago, Chile. TEL 56-2-4426200, http://www.sbif.cl/.

332 CHL
SUPERINTENDENCIA DE BANCOS E INSTITUCIONES FINANCIERAS. INFORME DE GESTION. Text in Spanish. a. back issues avail.
Related titles: Online - full text ed.
Published by: Superintendencia de Bancos e Instituciones Financieras, Moneda 1123, Santiago, Chile. TEL 56-2-4426200, http://www.sbif.cl/.

332 CHL
SUPERINTENDENCIA DE BANCOS E INSTITUCIONES FINANCIERAS. MEMORIA. Text in Spanish. a.
Related titles: Online - full text ed.
Published by: Superintendencia de Bancos e Instituciones Financieras, Moneda 1123, Santiago, Chile. TEL 56-2-4426200, http://www.sbif.cl/.

332 CAN ISSN 0839-9115
SUPERINTENDENT OF FINANCIAL INSTITUTIONS. REPORT; investment companies to which certificates have been granted under the Investment Companies Act. Text in English, French. 1973. a.
Former titles (until 1985): Superintendent of Insurance on the Administration of the Investment Companies Act. Report (0839-9093); (until 1986): Superintendent of Insurance for Canada. Report (0839-9107)
Published by: Canada. Office of the Superintendent of Financial Institutions, 255 Albert St, 13th Flr, Ottawa, ON K1A 0H2, Canada. TEL 613-990-7655, FAX 613-952-8219, pub@osfi-bsif.gc.ca, http://www.osfi-bsif.gc.ca.

SURGICAL NEWS (ONLINE). see *EDUCATION—Higher Education*

332 USA
SURVEY OF TERMS OF BANK LENDING. Text in English. q. USD 5. **Document type:** *Government.*
Published by: U.S. Federal Reserve System, Board of Governors, Publications Services, Rm MS 138, Washington, DC 20551. TEL 202-452-3244, FAX 202-728-5886.

332.1 SWE ISSN 0081-9913
SVENSKA HANDELSBANKEN. ANNUAL REPORT. Variant title: Svenska Handelsbanken. Annual Report and Auditors' Report. Text in Swedish. 1871. a. free. **Document type:** *Corporate.*
Related titles: English ed.: 1955.
—BLDSC (1464.300000).
Published by: Svenska Handelsbanken, Kungstraedgaardsgatan 2, Stockholm, 10670, Sweden. TEL 46-8-7011000, http://www.handelsbanken.se. Circ: 8,000.

332.1 SWE ISSN 1403-7262
SVENSKA HANDELSBANKEN. INTERIM REPORT. Text in English. q.
—BLDSC (4533.922500).
Published by: Svenska Handelsbanken, Kungstraedgaardsgatan 2, Stockholm, 10670, Sweden. TEL 46-8-7011000, http://www.handelsbanken.se.

336.7 SWE ISSN 1400-4259
SVERIGES RIKSBANK. AARSBERAETTELSE. Variant title: Sveriges Riksbank. Aarsredovisning. Text in Swedish. 1994. a. charts; illus. 70 p./no. 2 cols./p.; back issues avail. **Document type:** *Yearbook, Government.*
Published by: Sveriges Riksbank, Brunkebergstorg 11, Stockholm, 10337, Sweden. TEL 46-8-7870000, FAX 46-8-210531, registratorn@riksbank.se, http://www.riksbank.se. Ed. Leif Jacobson. Circ: 1,000 (controlled).

332 SWE ISSN 0347-5042
SVERIGES RIKSBANK. ANNUAL REPORT. Text in English. 1962. a.
Formerly (until 1972): Sveriges Riksbank. Yearbook (1102-710X)
Related titles: Online - full text ed.
Published by: Sveriges Riksbank, Brunkebergstorg 11, Stockholm, 10337, Sweden. TEL 46-8-7870000, FAX 46-8-210531, registratorn@riksbank.se, http://www.riksbank.se. Circ: 800.

332.1 SWE ISSN 1100-5815
SVERIGES RIKSBANK. PENNING- OCH VALUTAPOLITIK. Text in Swedish. 1979. q. free. charts. index. back issues avail. **Document type:** *Bulletin, Government.*
Formerly (until 1989): Sveriges Riksbank. Kredit- och valutaoeversikt (0348-5153)
Related titles: Online - full text ed.; English ed.: Sveriges Riksbank. Economic Review. ISSN 1404-6768. 1979.
Indexed: ELLIS, PAIS.
Published by: (Sveriges Riksbank, Information Department), Sveriges Riksbank, Brunkebergstorg 11, Stockholm, 10337, Sweden. TEL 46-8-7870000, FAX 46-8-210531, registratorn@riksbank.se, http://www.riksbank.se. Ed. Stefan Viotti. Circ: 1,500. **Subscr. to:** Quarterly Review - Sveriges Riksbank, Information Secretariat, Stockholm 10337, Sweden.

332 SCG ISSN 0354-3463
SVET FINANSIJA. Text in Serbo-Croatian. 1994. a. **Document type:** *Magazine, Trade.*
Formerly (until 1992): Vojvodanska Banka. Annual Report (0353-7714)
Related titles: Russian ed.: 1994.
Published by: Vojvodanska Banka, Trg Slobode 5-7, Novi Sad, 21000. TEL 381-21-4886600, FAX 381-21-624859, nivetic@voban.co.yu, http://www.voban.co.yu/sr/svetfinansija.htm. Ed. Natasa Ivetic TEL 381-21-614035.

332 SWZ
SWAZILAND. MINISTRY OF FINANCE. CAPITAL FUND ESTIMATES. Text in English. a. free. **Document type:** *Government.*

Formerly: Swaziland. Central Statistical Office. Capital Fund Estimates
Published by: Ministry of Finance Office, PO Box 443, Mbabane, Swaziland. TEL 268-4048145-9, FAX 268-404-3187.

332 CHE
SWISS BANK CORPORATION. REPORT OF THE BOARD OF DIRECTORS TO THE ANNUAL GENERAL MEETING OF SHAREHOLDERS. Text in English. a. **Document type:** *Corporate.*
Indexed: WBA.
Published by: Schweizerischer Bankverein/Swiss Bank Corporation, 6 Aeschenplatz, Basel, 4002, Switzerland. TEL 41-61-288-2020, FAX 41-61-2883708. R&P Rainer Skierka.

332.1 CHE ISSN 1422-9366
SWISS SECTORAL TRENDS. Text in English. 1947. a.
Description: Provides an overview and analysis of structural trends and perspectives of the Swiss economy.
Former titles (until 1999): Sectoral Trends in the Swiss Economy (1422-7967); (until 1995): Economic Trends in Switzerland (1422-2604); (until 1989): Economic Survey of Switzerland (1422-2566); (until 1972): Switzerland Economic Survey (0586-2442)
Published by: Union Bank of Switzerland, Private and Corporate Clients Division, Economic Information Center, GHDE CK9K-AUL, Bahnhofstrasse 45, Zurich, 8098, Switzerland. TEL 41-1-2341111, http://www.ubs.com/e/ubs_ch/bb_ch/market_information/industries_outlook.html.

332 FRA ISSN 1261-7733
SYSTEMES DE PAIEMENT. Text in French. 1995. m. EUR 543 domestic; EUR 564 foreign (effective 2000). **Document type:** *Newsletter.* **Description:** Covers the marketing of credit and debit cards.
Published by: Publi-News, 47 rue Aristide Briand, Levallois-Perret, 92300, France. TEL 33-1-41499360, FAX 33-1-47573725, publi.news@wanadoo.fr. Ed. Ange Galula.

332 TWN
THE TAIWAN ECONOMIC NEWS. Text in Chinese. d. USD 160 (effective 2000). **Document type:** *Newspaper.* **Description:** Provides the only English language daily on-line economic news service on Taiwanese industries.
Formerly: Economic News Daily Bulletin
Media: Online - full text.
Published by: China Economic News Service, 555 Chunghsiao E. Rd Sec 4, Taipei, 110, Taiwan. TEL 886-2-2642-2629, FAX 886-2-2642-7422, webmaster@www.cens.com, http://www.news.cens.com. Ed., R&P Philip Liu. Pub. Wang Pi Ly.

332.1 TWN ISSN 0256-3169
HG3883.T28
TAIWAN, REPUBLIC OF CHINA. CENTRAL BANK OF CHINA. BALANCE OF PAYMENTS. Text in English. 1981. q. USD 5.
Published by: Central Bank of China, 2 Roosevelt Rd, Sec 1, Taipei, 107, Taiwan. FAX 886-2-23571974, http://www.cbc.gov.tw. Circ: 2,000.

332 TWN
TAIWAN, REPUBLIC OF CHINA. MINISTRY OF FINANCE. BUREAU OF MONETARY AFFAIRS. ANNUAL REPORT. Text in Chinese, English. a.
Published by: Ministry of Finance, Bureau of Monetary Affairs, 4th Fl, 1 Nanhai Rd, Taipei, Taiwan. TEL 886-2-3055000, FAX 886-2-3977506. Ed. Mu Tsai Chen.

332 658.15 FIN ISSN 1455-6308
TALOUSSANOMAT. Text in Finnish. 1997. 5/w. **Document type:** *Newspaper, Trade.* **Description:** Finnish financial daily.
Published by: Startel Oy (Subsidiary of: Sanoma Magazines Finland Corporation), Toolonlahdenkatu 2, PL 35, Helsinki, 00089, Finland. TEL 358-9-1221, FAX 358-9-1224070, taloussanomat.startel@sanoma.fi, http://www.taloussanomat.fi. Eds. Antti Pekka Pietila, Markku Hurmeranta.

332.1 TZA ISSN 0856-2687
TANZANIA HOUSING BANK. ANNUAL REPORT AND STATEMENT OF ACCOUNTS/BENKI YA NYUMBA TANZANIA. RIPOTI YA MWAKA. Text in English, Swahili. 1974. a. **Document type:** *Corporate.* **Description:** Aims to provide the public with information to give them confidence in continuing to invest in the bank.
Published by: Tanzania Housing Bank, Planning and Research Department, PO Box 1723, Dar Es Salaam, Tanzania. TEL 255-51-3112, FAX 255-51-3119, TELEX 41831. Circ: 600.

332.1 TZA ISSN 0856-2423
TANZANIA INVESTMENT BANK. ANNUAL REPORT. Text in English, Swahili. 1971. a. **Document type:** *Corporate.*
Published by: Tanzania Investment Bank, PO Box 9373, Dar Es Salaam, Tanzania.

332 TZA
TANZANIAN BANKERS JOURNAL. Text in English. 1986. irreg., latest vol.3, 1990.
Indexed: PLESA.
Published by: National Bank of Commerce, PO Box 1863, Dar Es Salaam, Tanzania.

332 HKG
TARGET INTELLIGENCE REPORT. Text in English. 1973. m. HKD 7,000 domestic; HKD 1,500 in Asia; HKD 1,700 elsewhere. **Document type:** *Corporate.* **Description:** Presents financial analysis, investigations and surveys.
Incorporates: Target Financial Service
Published by: Target Newspapers Ltd., 4-F, Wah Tao Bldg, 42 Wood Rd, Wanchai, Hong Kong, Hong Kong. TEL 852-2573-0379, FAX 852-2838-1597, targnews@hkstar.com, http://www.targetnewspapers.com. Circ: 120,000.

TAX & BUSINESS ADVISER. see *BUSINESS AND ECONOMICS—Accounting*

TAX ASPECTS OF BANKRUPTCY LAW AND PRACTICE. see *LAW*

TAX, ESTATE & FINANCIAL PLANNING FOR THE ELDERLY. see *GERONTOLOGY AND GERIATRICS*

TAX, ESTATE & FINANCIAL PLANNING FOR THE ELDERLY: FORMS AND PRACTICE. see *GERONTOLOGY AND GERIATRICS*

332 USA ISSN 8756-1360
KF6296.A15
TAX MANAGEMENT FINANCIAL PLANNING JOURNAL. Text in English. 1985. m. USD 478 (effective 2005). index. back issues avail. **Document type:** *Trade.* **Description:** Provides coverage on the state of financial planning today, including legislative, regulatory, and economic developments.
Incorporates (1985-1999): Tax Management Financial Planning (Supplement)
Related titles: Online - full text ed.: (from Northern Light Technology, Inc., ProQuest Information & Learning, The Bureau of National Affairs, Inc.); Series of: Tax Management Financial Planning Series.
Indexed: ATI, CLI, FamI, LRI.
—CCC.
Published by: Tax Management Inc. (Subsidiary of: The Bureau of National Affairs, Inc.), 1231 25th St, N W, Washington, DC 20037. TEL 202-452-4200, 800-372-1033, FAX 202-785-7195, http://www.bnatax.com. Ed. Glenn B Davis.

TAXATION OF FINANCIAL INSTITUTIONS. see *BUSINESS AND ECONOMICS—Public Finance, Taxation*

332 332.6 USA ISSN 1556-8326
HC79.H53
▼ **TECH CONFIDENTIAL.** Text in English. 2005 (May/June). bi-m. **Description:** Focuses on the global intersection of technology, strategy and finance. Designed to explain the interchange between business and finance decision-making in an era defined by efficiency and innovation on a global scale.
Published by: The Deal, LLC (Subsidiary of: A L M), 105 Madison Ave, 5th Fl, New York, NY 10016. TEL 212-313-9238, 888-667-3325, FAX 212-313-9293, http://www.thedeal.com/.

332 GBR
TECHNICAL TAX PROPOSALS. Text in English. a. GBP 20.
Formerly: Technical Budget Representations
Published by: Confederation of British Industry, Centre Point, 103 New Oxford St, London, WC1A 1DU, United Kingdom. TEL 44-71-379-7400, FAX 44-71-240-1578.

332 FRA ISSN 0765-3069
TECHNOLOGIES BANCAIRES. Text in French. 1984. m. EUR 543 domestic; EUR 567 foreign (effective 2000). **Document type:** *Newsletter.* **Description:** Presents information technology in the banking sector.
Published by: Publi-News, 47 rue Aristide Briand, Levallois-Perret, 92300, France. TEL 33-1-41499360, FAX 33-1-47573725, publi.news@wanadoo.fr. Ed. Ange Galula.

332 RUS
TEKUSHCHIE TENDENTSII V DENEZHNO-KREDITNOI SFERE. Text in Russian. m. USD 425 in United States.
Indexed: RASB.
Published by: Tsentral'nyi Bank Rossiiskoi Federatsii, Myasnitskaya ul 43, Moscow, 101000, Russian Federation. TEL 7-095-2072500, FAX 7-095-2071177. **US dist. addr.:** East View Information Services, 3020 Harbor Ln. N., Minneapolis, MN 55447. TEL 612-550-0961.

TELECOM FINANCE. see *BUSINESS AND ECONOMICS—International Commerce*

332.1 GBR ISSN 0955-4327
TELERATE - DOW JONES BANK REGISTER (YEAR). Text in English. 1986. a. GBP 170, USD 300; includes index. index. back issues avail. **Document type:** *Directory.* **Description:** Gives full contact details on more than 12,000 institutions in 180 countries, as well as information on correspondent banks, subsidiaries, and ownership.
Formerly: Telerate Bank Register (Year)
—CCC.
Published by: Euromoney Publications plc, Nestor House, Playhouse Yard, London, EC4V 5EX, United Kingdom. TEL 44-207-7798673, FAX 44-20-77798541. Circ: 5,000. **Orders to:** Plymbridge Distributors Ltd, Plymbridge House, Estover Rd, Plymouth, Devon PL6 7PY, United Kingdom. TEL 44-1752-202300, FAX 44-1752-202330, enquiries@plymbridge.com, http://www.plymbridge.com.

332 USA ISSN 1077-4343
TELLER SENSE. Text in English. 1970. s-m. USD 26 to individuals; USD 1 newsstand/cover (effective 2002). **Document type:** *Newsletter, Trade.* **Description:** Includes tips and techniques tellers can apply to their own jobs.
Related titles: Online - full text ed.: (from EBSCO Publishing, Florida Center for Library Automation, Gale Group, ProQuest Information & Learning).
Indexed: BLI.
Published by: Bureau of Business Practice (Subsidiary of: Aspen Publishers, Inc.), 1185 Avenue of the Americas, 37th Fl, New York, NY 10036. TEL 860-442-4365, 800-243-0876, FAX 860-437-3555, rebecca_armitage@prenhall.com, http://www.bbpnews.com. Ed. Jeanne Moorton. Pub. Peter Garabedian. R&P Kathryn Mennone.

332 USA ISSN 0895-1039
TELLER VISION. Text in English. 1984. s-m. USD 158 (effective 2004). index. back issues avail. **Document type:** *Newsletter.* **Description:** Features interview-based training for tellers, customer service reps, and other front-line personnel in the banking field. Includes tips and advice to help banking employees fine-tune their skills.
Related titles: Online - full text ed.: (from EBSCO Publishing, Florida Center for Library Automation, Gale Group, ProQuest Information & Learning).
Indexed: BLI.
—CCC.
Published by: Bureau of Business Practice (Subsidiary of: Aspen Publishers, Inc.), 1185 Avenue of the Americas, 37th Fl, New York, NY 10036. TEL 860-442-4365, 800-243-0876, FAX 860-437-3555, rebecca_armitage@prenhall.com, http://www.bbpnews.com. Ed. Jeanne Moorton. Pub. Peter Garabedian. R&P Kathryn Mennone.

332.1 USA ISSN 0040-3199
THE TENNESSEE BANKER. Text in English. 1913. m. USD 30 to members; USD 43 to non-members (effective 2005). adv. illus. 36 p./no.; **Document type:** *Magazine, Trade.* **Description:** Educates, informs, and guides readers about the activities and projects of their banks, fellow bankers, and the T.B.A.
Related titles: Online - full text ed.
Indexed: BLI.
Published by: Tennessee Bankers Association, 201 Venture Cir, Nashville, TN 37228-1603. TEL 615-244-4871, FAX 615-244-0995, dymartin@TNBankers.org, http://www.tnbankers.org. Ed. Dianne W Martin. adv.: B&W page USD 685, color page USD 1,395; trim 11 x 8.5. Circ: 2,500 (paid and free).

332 USA ISSN 0885-6907
HG1507
TEXAS BANKING. Text in English. 1911. m. USD 35 to non-members; free to members (effective 2005). adv. bk.rev. **Document type:** *Magazine, Trade.*
Formerly (until 1985): Texas Bankers Record (0738-7652)
Related titles: Online - full text ed.: (from Northern Light Technology, Inc., O C L C Online Computer Library Center, Inc., ProQuest Information & Learning).
Indexed: ABIn, BLI.
—BLDSC (8798.672700), IE, ingenta.
Published by: Texas Bankers Association, 1102 West Ave., Austin, TX 78701-2020. olivia@texasbankers.com, http://www.texasbankers.com. adv.: B&W page USD 980. Circ: 5,000 (paid and controlled).

332.1 USA
TEXAS BANKING RED BOOK. Text in English. 1946. s-a. looseleaf. USD 26. adv.
Related titles: Diskette ed.
Published by: Texas Red Book, Inc., PO Box 29156, Shawnee Msn, KS 66201-9156. TEL 800-336-1120. Ed. William Baker. Circ: 20,000.

332 USA ISSN 1063-0376
TEXAS FINANCE REPORT. Text in English. 1956. w. USD 60.
Published by: Report Publications, Inc., PO Box 12368, Austin, TX 78711. TEL 512-478-5663, FAX 512-478-2345. Ed. Bill Kidd. Circ: 290.

THOMSON BANK DIRECTORY. see *BUSINESS AND ECONOMICS—Trade And Industrial Directories*

332.3 USA ISSN 1061-1681
HG2037
THOMSON CREDIT UNION DIRECTORY. Text in English. 1986. s-a. USD 179; USD 149 to members CUNA (effective 2001). adv. stat. **Document type:** *Directory, Trade.* **Description:** Lists all credit unions in the U.S., including routing numbers, wire transfer information and key personnel.
Formerly: Rand McNally Credit Union Directory

Published by: (Credit Union National Association, Inc.), Thomson Financial Services Company, 4709 W Golf Rd, Skokie, IL 60076-1256. TEL 847-676-9600, 800-321-3373, FAX 847-933-8101, prodinfo@tfp.com, customerservice@tfp.com, http://www.tfp.com/banks. Ed., R&P Beth Swann. Adv. contact Hugh Boyd.

332 USA ISSN 1064-5357
THOMSON REGULATION C C DIRECTORY. (Check Clearinghouse) Variant title: Thomson Regulation Check Clearinghouse Directory. Text in English. 1988. s-a. USD 129 domestic (effective 2001). adv. **Document type:** *Directory, Trade.* **Description:** Matches bank routing numbers with direct telephone numbers for checks and return-items contacts.
Published by: Thomson Financial Services Company, 4709 W Golf Rd, Skokie, IL 60076-1256. TEL 847-676-9600, 800-321-3373, FAX 847-933-8101, prodinfo@tfp.com, http://www.tfp.com/banks. Ed., R&P Beth Swann. Adv. contact Hugh Boyd.

THOMSON SAVINGS DIRECTORY. see *BUSINESS AND ECONOMICS—Trade And Industrial Directories*

THOMSON WORLD BANK DIRECTORY. 1-VOL EDITION. see *BUSINESS AND ECONOMICS—Trade And Industrial Directories*

332.1 USA ISSN 1078-8522
HG1616.E7
THOMSON'S BLUE BOOK; the banker's guide to product and service providers. Text in English. 1993. a. adv. **Document type:** *Directory, Trade.* **Description:** Lists only those providers who have the products, knowledge, skills, and resources to provide you with the latest advancements in the financial industry.
Formerly (until 1993): Thomson's Blue Book of Bank Suppliers (1070-9452)
Related titles: Online - full text ed.
Published by: Thomson Financial Services Company, 4709 W Golf Rd, Skokie, IL 60076-1256. TEL 847-676-9600, 800-321-3373, FAX 847-933-8101, support@bankinfo.com. Ed. Jeffrey Lomax. Pub. Elizabeth F Swann. Adv. contact Tobi Chunowitz.

332 USA ISSN 0196-7762
HG1626
THORNDIKE ENCYCLOPEDIA OF BANKING AND FINANCIAL TABLES. Text in English. a. USD 175.95; USD 253.45 foreign. **Document type:** *Trade.* **Description:** Covers all aspects of interest rate calculation.
Published by: W G & L Financial Reporting & Management Research (Subsidiary of: R I A), 395 Hudson St, New York, NY 10014. TEL 212-367-6300, FAX 212-367-6718. Ed. David Thorndike. **Subscr. to:** The Park Square Bldg., 31 St James Ave, Boston, MA 02116-4112. TEL 800-950-1207.

THRIFT INVESTOR. see *BUSINESS AND ECONOMICS—Investments*

TIJDSCHRIFT CONTROLLING. see *BUSINESS AND ECONOMICS—Accounting*

332 CAN ISSN 0838-5769
TIMELY DISCLOSURE. Text in English. 1987. m. CND 20, USD 30. **Description:** News affecting Canada's securities industry.
Published by: Timely Disclosure Inc., 5027 Cenabar Crt, Burlington, ON L7L 4Y6, Canada. TEL 416-847-1617. Ed. Mario Carr. Circ: 13,455.

332 USA
TIMELY TIPS MAGAZINE. Text in English. 1925. m. USD 10 domestic; USD 12 in Canada. adv. back issues avail. **Document type:** *Trade.*
Published by: Mc Enterprises, PO Box 603, Marshall, MI 49068. TEL 616-966-9890, karlenterprise@corp.com, http://www.karlenterprise.com. Ed., Pub. Carl Eisenlord. adv.: B&W page USD 160. Circ: 10,000 (paid).

332 JPN ISSN 1342-2340
TOKYO - MITSUBISHI REVIEW. Text in English. 1996. m.
Formed by the merger of (1970-1996): Mitsubishi Bank Review (0300-3914); (1976-1996): Tokyo Financial Review (0387-6896); Which incorporated (1847-1978): Bank of Tokyo Weekly Review (0005-5379)
Published by: Bank of Tokyo - Mitsubishi Ltd., Research Office, 7-1 Marunouchi 2-chome, Chiyoda-ku, Tokyo, Japan. TEL 81-3-32401111, TELEX J22358, http://www.btm.co.jp/report/ecorev2001e/index.htm.

TOLLEY'S V A T PLANNING (YEAR). (Value Added Tax) see *BUSINESS AND ECONOMICS—Public Finance, Taxation*

TOP SUPER FUNDS. see *BUSINESS AND ECONOMICS—Trade And Industrial Directories*

332 GBR ISSN 1464-8873
HG3753
TRADE FINANCE. Text in English. 10/yr. GBP 380 combined subscription domestic print & online eds.; EUR 562 combined subscription in Europe print & online eds.; USD 649 combined subscription elsewhere print & online eds. (effective 2005). **Document type:** *Magazine, Corporate.* **Description:** Covers global commodity finance, countertrade, documentation, pre-export and export finance developments. Designed for trade and finance executives.
Related titles: Online - full content ed.: (from Florida Center for Library Automation); Online - full text ed.: (from EBSCO Publishing, Gale Group, O C L C Online Computer Library Center, Inc.); ◆ Supplement(s): World Export Credit Guide. ISSN 1354-9847.
Indexed: PAIS.
—IE.
Published by: Euromoney Institutional Investor Plc., Nestor House, Playhouse Yard, London, EC4V 5EX, United Kingdom. TEL 44-20-7779-8673, FAX 44-20-7779-8541, http://www.tradefinancemagazine.com, http://www.euromoney.com. Ed. Jonathan Bell TEL 44-20-7779-8428. Adv. contact Daniel Morris TEL 44-20-7779-8099.

332 USA ISSN 0894-7295
HG4928.5
TRADERS MAGAZINE; the magazine for the professional securities trader. Text in English. 1987. m. USD 60 domestic; USD 79 in Canada & Mexico; USD 99 elsewhere (effective 2005). adv. bk.rev. charts; stat.; tr.lit. back issues avail. **Document type:** *Magazine, Trade.* **Description:** Directed to the investment community with profiles of individuals, reports on conventions, securities laws, and news.
Related titles: Online - full text ed.: (from EBSCO Publishing, Florida Center for Library Automation, Gale Group, LexisNexis, O C L C Online Computer Library Center, Inc., ProQuest Information & Learning); (from Northern Light Technology, Inc.).
Indexed: ABIn, B&I, BLI.
—CCC.
Published by: Source Media, Inc., One State St Plaza, 27th Fl, New York, NY 10004. TEL 212-803-6077, 800-221-1809, FAX 212-747-1154, custserv@sourcemedia.com, http://www.tradersmagazine.com, http://www.sourcemedia.com. Ed. John Byrne. Circ: 4,000 (controlled).

332 USA
TRANSMITTER (OKLAHOMA CITY). Text in English. bi-m. free (effective 2005). **Document type:** *Newsletter, Consumer.*
Related titles: E-mail ed.
Published by: Weokie Credit Union, 8100 W Reno Ave, Oklahoma City, OK 73127. TEL 405-235-3030, FAX 405-787-2898, http://www.weokie.org.

332 388 624 GBR ISSN 1461-7498
TRANSPORTATION EQUIPMENT & INFRASTRUCTURE REVIEW (YEARS). Text in English. 1997. a. GBP 95, USD 170. **Description:** Serves as a guide to the financing of large scale transportation equipment and infrastructure projects.
Published by: Euromoney Publications plc, Nestor House, Playhouse Yard, London, EC4V 5EX, United Kingdom. TEL 44-207-7798673, FAX 44-20-77798541.

332 381 382 GBR ISSN 0264-0937
THE TREASURER; the official journal of the Association of Corporate Treasurers. Text in English. 1979. m. GBP 190 in Europe; GBP 220 elsewhere (effective 2002). adv. charts; illus.; stat.; tr.lit. 72 p./no.; back issues avail. **Document type:** *Magazine, Trade.* **Description:** Contains treasury and finance information. Targets finance directors, CFOs, and company treasurers.
Indexed: Emerald.
—BLDSC (9045.860000), IE, ingenta.
Published by: Association of Corporate Treasurers, Ocean House, 10-12 Little Trinity Ln, London, EC4V 2DJ, United Kingdom. TEL 44-20-7213-9728, FAX 44-20-7248-2591, http://www.treasurers.org. Ed. Mike Henigan TEL 44-20-7213-0723. R&P Nicola Harvey TEL 44-20-7213-0706. Adv. contact Chantal Feduchin-Pate TEL 44-20-7213-0701. B&W page GBP 3,160, color page GBP 5,470; trim. Circ: 4,800 (paid and controlled).

332 GBR ISSN 0961-2092
THE TREASURER'S HANDBOOK; the official handbook of the Association of Corporate Treasurers. Text in English. 1990. a., latest vol.12, 2002. GBP 150 (effective 2002). adv. Website rev. charts; mkt.; stat. Index. back issues avail. **Document type:** *Trade.* **Description:** Practical guide to all aspects of treasury, including corporate finance, capital markets funding, risk management, cash management and systems.
Published by: Association of Corporate Treasurers, Ocean House, 10-12 Little Trinity Ln, London, EC4V 2DJ, United Kingdom. TEL 44-20-7213-9728, FAX 44-20-7248-2591, enquiries@treasurers.co.uk, http://www.treasurers.org. Ed., Pub. Mike Henigan TEL 44-20-7213-0723. R&P Nicola Harvey TEL 44-20-7213-0706. Adv. contact Chantal Feduchin-Pate TEL 44-20-7213-0701. B&W page GBP 3,350, color page GBP 5,050; trim 171.5 x 245.5. Circ: 200 (paid); 3,200 (controlled).

332 AUT
TREASURYLOG. Text in German. 1991. 5/yr. **Document type:** *Bulletin, Trade.* **Description:** Information, experiences and contributions for and from treasury professionals.
Related titles: Online - full text ed.
Published by: Go Public Relations, Badnerstrasse 3-21, Baden Bei Wien, N 2500, Austria. sabina.schwabe@go-public.com, http://www.go-public.com/treasurylog. Ed. Sabina Schwabe. Circ: 14,000 (controlled).

332.1 DEU
TREFFPUNKT SPARKASSE. Text in German. 1952. bi-m. adv. **Document type:** *Magazine, Consumer.*
Published by: Deutscher Sparkassenverlag GmbH, Am Wallgraben 115, Stuttgart, 70565, Germany. TEL 49-711-7820, FAX 49-711-7821709, webredaktion@dsv-gruppe.de, http://www.dsv-gruppe.de. adv.: B&W page EUR 5,540, color page EUR 7,100. Circ: 127,592 (controlled).

346.73059 USA ISSN 1090-2511
KF731
THE TRUST REGULATORY HANDBOOK. Text in English. 1993. a. price varies. **Document type:** *Trade.*
Formerly (until 1997): Trust Compliance Handbook (1084-5089)
Related titles: ◆ Series of: PricewaterhouseCoopers Regulatory Handbook Series. ISSN 1522-1334.
Published by: (PricewaterhouseCoopers), M.E. Sharpe, Inc., 80 Business Park Dr, Armonk, NY 10504. TEL 914-273-1800, 800-541-6563, FAX 914-273-2106, custserv@mesharpe.com, http://www.mesharpe.com.

332.1 USA ISSN 1068-4301
TRUST REGULATORY NEWS. Text in English. 1992. m. looseleaf. USD 395 (effective 1999). adv. index, cum.index every 5 yrs. **Document type:** *Newsletter.* **Description:** Covers regulatory, legal and legislative issues: federal banking regulators, Department of Labor, and state and federal courts. Of interest to fiduciaries: primarily trust bankers, attorneys, and auditors, but also insurance and securities executives.
Published by: A.M. Publishing, Inc., PO Box 1110, Chicago, IL 60690-1110. TEL 773-784-1818, FAX 773-561-2462, trustnews@aol.com. Ed., Pub. Bernard Garbo. R&P, Adv. contact Todd Schmidt.

332 USA *
TRUTH-IN-LENDING MANUAL. Text in English. base vol. plus s-a. updates. USD 185.95; USD 287.45 foreign (effective 1995). **Document type:** *Trade.*
Published by: W G & L Financial Reporting & Management Research (Subsidiary of: R I A), 395 Hudson St, New York, NY 10014. TEL 212-367-6300, FAX 212-367-6718. **Subscr. to:** The Park Square Bldg., 31 St James Ave, Boston, MA 02116-4112. TEL 800-950-1205.

332.1 AZE
TURAN-FINANCE. Text in English. 3/w. **Document type:** *Bulletin.*
Related titles: Russian ed.
Published by: Turan Information Agency/Turna Informasiya Agentilyi, Khagani ul 33, Baku, 370000, Azerbaijan. TEL 994-12-984226, 994-12-935967, FAX 994-12-983817, root@turan.baku.az, http://www.turaninfo.com.

332 TUR ISSN 0041-4336
HG3216
TURKIYE CUMHURIYET MERKEZ BANKASI. AYLIK BULTEN/CENTRAL BANK OF THE REPUBLIC OF TURKEY. QUARTERLY BULLETIN. Text in English, Turkish. 1931. bi-m. free. mkt.; stat. **Document type:** *Bulletin, Government.* **Description:** Covers credit statistics of the Central Bank of Turkey.
Indexed: PROMT, RASB.
Published by: Central Bank of the Republic of Turkey, General Directorate of Planning and Research, Directorate of Documentation, Ankara, Turkey. FAX 90-312-3116685.

332.1 TUR ISSN 0073-7402
HG3729.T82
TURKIYE SINAI KALKINMA BANKASI. ANNUAL STATEMENT/INDUSTRIAL DEVELOPMENT BANK OF TURKEY. ANNUAL STATEMENT. Cover title: Turkiye Sinai Kalkinma Bankasi Annual Report. Text in English. a. illus.; stat. **Document type:** *Corporate.* **Description:** Reports on the financial status of the bank, with a review of the economic environment and operations in different sectors of activity.
Published by: Turkiye Sinai Kalkinma Bankasi A.S./Industrial Development Bank of Turkey, Meclisi Mebusan Cad. No. 137, Findikli - Istanbul, 80040, Turkey. TEL 90-212-2512792, FAX 90-212-2432975, TELEX 24344 TSKB TR.

332 CHE
U B S INTERNATIONAL FINANCE. Text in English. q. free. **Document type:** *Bulletin.*
Indexed: PAIS.
Published by: Union Bank of Switzerland, Bahnhofstr 45, Zurich, 8021, Switzerland. TEL 41-1-2346544, FAX 41-1-2346190. Circ: 25,000 (controlled).

U C B INVESTOR'S HANDBOOK. see *BUSINESS AND ECONOMICS—Investments*

B

B

332.1 GBR
U K CLEARINGS DIRECTORY; directory of offices of banks and other financial institutions participating in the payment clearings operations. Text in English. 1967. a., latest 2003. GBP 21.75 per vol. domestic; GBP 26.50 per vol. foreign (effective 2003). **Document type:** *Directory.*
Formerly: Sorting Code Numbers
Related titles: Magnetic Tape ed.
—BLDSC (9082.655206).
Published by: (Association for Payment Clearing Services), Reed Business Information Ltd. (Subsidiary of: Reed Business), Windsor Ct., East Grinstead, W Sussex RH19 1XA, United Kingdom. TEL 44-1342-326972, FAX 44-1342-335860, rbi.subscriptions@qss-uk.com, http://www.reedbusiness.co.uk/. Ed. R Phelps. Circ: 155,000.

U K DIRECTORY OF PROPERTY DEVELOPERS, INVESTORS & FINANCIERS. see *REAL ESTATE*

332 USA
U S A A MAGAZINE. Text in English. 5/yr. **Document type:** *Magazine, Consumer.*
Published by: (United Services Automobile Association), Pohly & Partners Inc., 27 Melcher St., 2nd Fl., Boston, MA 02210. TEL 617-451-1700, FAX 617-338-7767, http://www.usaa.com, http://www.pohlypartners.com. Ed. Rhonda A Crawford. Circ: 3,200,000 (controlled).

U S BANKER. see *BUSINESS AND ECONOMICS—Investments*

U.S. DEPARTMENT OF EDUCATION. NATIONAL CENTER FOR EDUCATION STATISTICS. STUDENT FINANCING OF GRADUATE AND FIRST-PROFESSIONAL EDUCATION. see *EDUCATION—Higher Education*

U.S. DEPARTMENT OF HEALTH AND HUMAN SERVICES. FOOD AND DRUG ADMINISTRATION. PRESCRIPTION DRUG USER FEE ACT. FINANCIAL REPORT TO CONGRESS. see *PUBLIC ADMINISTRATION*

332 USA ISSN 0364-1015
U.S. DEPARTMENT OF THE TREASURY. BUREAU OF PUBLIC DEBT. MONTHLY STATEMENT OF THE PUBLIC DEBT OF THE UNITED STATES. Text in English. 1974. m. **Document type:** *Government.* **Description:** Summarizes the financial activities of the Federal Government and off-budget Federal entities in accordance with the Budget of the U.S. Government. It presents receipts and outlays, the surplus or deficit, and means of financing on a modified cash basis.
Formerly (until 2001): U.S. Department of the Treasury. Financial Management Service. Monthly Statement of Treasury Securities of the United States
Related titles: Online - full text ed.: ISSN 1555-0184.
Published by: U.S. Department of the Treasury, Bureau of Public Debt, 999 E St Ste 501, Washington, DC 20239-0001. OAdmin@bpd.treas.gov, http://www.publicdebt.treas.gov/. **Subscr. to:** U.S. Government Printing Office, Superintendent of Documents, PO Box 371954, Pittsburgh, PA 15250-7954. TEL 202-512-1800, FAX 202-512-2250, orders@gpo.gov, http://www.access.gpo.gov.

332 USA
U.S. DEPARTMENT OF THE TREASURY. FINANCIAL MANAGEMENT SERVICE. FINANCIAL CONNECTION. Text in English. 1991. q. free.
Published by: U.S. Department of the Treasury, Financial Management Service, 401 14th St, S W, Washington, DC 20227.

U.S. DEPARTMENT OF THE TREASURY. FINANCIAL MANAGEMENT SERVICE. FINANCIAL REPORT OF THE UNITED STATES GOVERNMENT. see *PUBLIC ADMINISTRATION*

332.4 USA ISSN 0364-1007
HJ10.2
U.S. DEPARTMENT OF THE TREASURY. FINANCIAL MANAGEMENT SERVICE. MONTHLY TREASURY STATEMENT OF RECEIPTS AND OUTLAYS OF THE UNITED STATES GOVERNMENT. Text in English. m. USD 50 (effective 2001). **Document type:** *Government.*
Former titles: U.S. Department of the Treasury. Bureau of Government Financial Operations. Monthly Treasury Statement of Receipts and Outlays of the United States Government; U.S. Department of the Treasury. Bureau of Government Financial Operations. Monthly Statement of Receipts and Outlays of the United States Government
Related titles: Online - full text ed.: ISSN 1555-0222.
Indexed: AmStI.
Published by: U.S. Department of the Treasury, Financial Management Service, Budget Reports Branch, 3700 E West Highway, Rm 518D, Hyattsville, MD 20782 . TEL 202-874-9880, 202-874-9890, Budget.Reports@fms.sprint.com, budget.reports@fms.treas.gov, http://www.fms.treas.gov/mts/index.html. **Subscr. to:** U.S. Government Printing Office, Superintendent of Documents, PO Box 371954, Pittsburgh, PA 15250-7954. TEL 202-512-1800, FAX 202-512-2250, orders@gpo.gov, http://www.access.gpo.gov.

332.4 USA ISSN 0041-2155
U.S. DEPARTMENT OF THE TREASURY. FINANCIAL MANAGEMENT SERVICE. TREASURY BULLETIN. Variant title: Treasury Bulletin. Text in English. 1939. q. USD 45 domestic; USD 45.01 foreign (effective 2004). charts; stat. back issues avail.; reprint service avail. from CIS. **Document type:** *Bulletin, Government.* **Description:** Contains a mix of narrative, tables, and charts on Treasury issues, federal financial operations, international statistics, and special reports on liabilities currency and coins in circulation.
Incorporates (in 1945): Annual Report on the Financial Condition and results of the Operations of the Highway Trust Fund (0749-0054)
Related titles: Microfiche ed.: (from CIS); Microform ed.: (from PMC); Online - full text ed.: ISSN 1555-0168 (from O C L C Online Computer Library Center, Inc., ProQuest Information & Learning).
Indexed: ABIn, AmStI, BLI, RASB.
Published by: (Directives Management Branch), U.S. Department of the Treasury, Financial Management Service, 3700 East West Highway, Rm 515C, Hyattsville, MD 20782. treasury.bulletin@fms.treas.gov, http://fms.treas.gov/bulletin/overview.html, http://www.fms.treas.gov. Circ: 1,900. **Subscr. to:** U.S. Government Printing Office, Superintendent of Documents, PO Box 371954, Pittsburgh, PA 15250-7954. TEL 202-512-1800, FAX 202-512-2250, orders@gpo.gov, http://www.access.gpo.gov.

332.1 USA ISSN 0884-1187
HG1662.U5
U.S. FEDERAL DEPOSIT INSURANCE CORPORATION. MERGER DECISIONS. Text in English. a. free (effective 2005). **Document type:** *Government.*
Supersedes in part (in 1981): Federal Deposit Insurance Corporation. Annual Report (0741-2665)
Published by: U.S. Federal Deposit Insurance Corp., Public Information Center, 801 17th St., N.W., Washington, DC 20434-0001t. TEL 202-416-6940, 877-275-3342, FAX 202-416-2076, publicinfo@fdic.gov, http://www.fdic.gov/bank/individual/merger/.

332 USA
U.S. FEDERAL DEPOSIT INSURANCE CORPORATION. NEWS RELEASES. Text in English. irreg.
Published by: U.S. Federal Deposit Insurance Corp., 550 17th St, N W, Washington, DC 20429. TEL 202-393-8400.

332 USA ISSN 0278-5692
HG4345
U.S. FEDERAL DEPOSIT INSURANCE CORPORATION. TRUST ASSETS OF BANKS AND TRUST COMPANIES. Text in English. a.
Formerly: U.S. Federal Deposit Insurance Corporation. Trust Assets of Insured Commercial Banks (0149-8274)
Published by: U.S. Federal Deposit Insurance Corp., 550 17th St, N W, Washington, DC 20429. TEL 202-389-4221.

332.1 USA ISSN 0083-0887
U.S. FEDERAL RESERVE SYSTEM. ANNUAL REPORT. Text in English. 1914. a. price varies. back issues avail. **Document type:** *Government.*
Published by: U.S. Federal Reserve System, Board of Governors, Publications Services, Rm MS 138, Washington, DC 20551. TEL 202-452-3244, FAX 202-728-5886. Circ: 10,000.

332.1 USA ISSN 0148-4338
HG181.A1
U.S. FEDERAL RESERVE SYSTEM. ANNUAL STATISTICAL DIGEST. Key Title: Annual Statistical Digest - Board of Governors of the Federal Reserve System. Text in English. 1981. a. price varies. **Document type:** *Government.*
Published by: U.S. Federal Reserve System, Board of Governors, Publications Services, Rm MS 138, Washington, DC 20551. TEL 202-452-3244, FAX 202-728-5886.

U.S. FEDERAL RESERVE SYSTEM. RESEARCH LIBRARY - RECENT ACQUISITIONS. see *BIBLIOGRAPHIES*

332.1 USA ISSN 0364-8370
HG3863
U.S. FEDERAL RESERVE SYSTEM. SELECTED INTEREST AND EXCHANGE RATES. WEEKLY SERIES OF CHARTS. Text in English. w. USD 30; USD 35 foreign. reprint service avail. from CIS. **Document type:** *Government.*
Related titles: Microfiche ed.: (from CIS).
Indexed: AmStI.
Published by: U.S. Federal Reserve System, Board of Governors, Publications Services, Rm MS 138, Washington, DC 20551. TEL 202-452-3244, FAX 202-728-5886.

332 USA
U.S. FEDERAL RESERVE SYSTEM. STAFF STUDIES. Text in English. 1985 (vol.146). irreg. (approx. 1-4/yr.). **Document type:** *Monographic series, Government.* **Description:** Examines economic and financial matters of general interest.
Published by: U.S. Federal Reserve System, Board of Governors, Publications Services, Rm MS 138, Washington, DC 20551. TEL 202-452-3244, FAX 202-728-5886.

332 USA
U S INTERNATIONAL TRANSFER PRICING. Text in English. 8/yr. USD 295; USD 408.45 foreign (effective 1999). **Document type:** *Newsletter.*
Published by: W G & L Financial Reporting & Management Research (Subsidiary of: R I A), 90 Fifth Ave, New York, NY 10011. TEL 212-645-4800, FAX 212-337-4280.

334.2 USA
U.S. NATIONAL CREDIT UNION ADMINISTRATION. ANNUAL REPORT. Text in English. a. USD 3.50. **Document type:** *Corporate.*
Published by: U.S. National Credit Union Administration, 1775 Duke St, Alexandria, VA 22316. TEL 202-537-1000. Circ: 8,000. **Orders to:** N C U A, Office of Administration, 1775 Duke St, Alexandria, VA 22314-3428. TEL 703-518-6340.

332 USA
U.S. NATIONAL CREDIT UNION ADMINISTRATION. RULES AND REGULATIONS. Text in English. base vol. plus irreg. updates. looseleaf. USD 130 for basic manual and updates of indeterminate periods (effective 2001). **Document type:** *Government.* **Description:** Incorporates all amendments and revisions to the rules and regulations that have been finalized.
Published by: U.S. National Credit Union Administration, 1776 G St, N W, Washington, DC 20456. **Subscr. to:** U.S. Government Printing Office, Superintendent of Documents, PO Box 371954, Pittsburgh, PA 15250-7954. TEL 202-512-1800, FAX 202-512-2250, orders@gpo.gov, http://www.access.gpo.gov.

U.S. OFFICE OF THE COMPTROLLER OF THE CURRENCY. INTERPRETATIONS AND ACTIONS. see *BUSINESS AND ECONOMICS—Public Finance, Taxation*

U.S. OFFICE OF THE COMPTROLLER OF THE CURRENCY. QUARTERLY JOURNAL. see *BUSINESS AND ECONOMICS—Public Finance, Taxation*

332 658.8 USA
U S TRANSACTIONS MONTHLY. Text in English. m. back issues avail. **Document type:** *Trade.* **Description:** Surveys and analyzes consumer research for the banking and financial services industry.
Published by: U S Transactions, 2285 Peachtree Rd NE, Ste 222, Atlanta, GA 30309. TEL 404-350-7200, FAX 800-582-5200, info@ustrans.com, http://www.ustrans.com.

332 658.8 USA
U S TRANSACTIONS PRIME CUSTOMER QUARTERLY. Text in English. q. back issues avail. **Document type:** *Trade.* **Description:** Surveys and analyzes consumer research for the banking and financial services industry, targeting customers with bank deposits of at least $50,000 and with household incomes of at least $75,000.
Published by: U S Transactions, 2285 Peachtree Rd NE, Ste 222, Atlanta, GA 30309. TEL 404-350-7200, FAX 800-582-5200, info@ustrans.com, http://www.ustrans.com.

332 658.8 USA
U S TRANSACTIONS SMALL BUSINESS QUARTERLY. Text in English. q. back issues avail. **Document type:** *Trade.* **Description:** Surveys and analyzes consumer research for the banking and financial services industry, targeting small business firms ranging in sales from $500,000 to 10 million annually.
Published by: U S Transactions, 2285 Peachtree Rd NE, Ste 222, Atlanta, GA 30309. TEL 404-350-7200, FAX 800-582-5200, info@ustrans.com, http://www.ustrans.com.

U.S. VIRGIN ISLANDS GOVERNMENT REGISTER. see *PUBLIC ADMINISTRATION*

332 USA
U25; a magazine for young adult USAA members. Text in English. q. **Document type:** *Magazine, Consumer.*
Published by: United Services Automobile Association, 9800 Fredericksburg Rd., San Antonio, TX 78288. TEL 210-498-8080, 800-531-8646, FAX 210-498-0030, u25@usaa.com, http://www.usaa.com. Ed. Carol Barnes.

332.1 UGA
UGANDA COMMERCIAL BANK. ANNUAL REPORT. Text in English. 1966. a. **Document type:** *Corporate.* **Description:** Facts of the Ugandan economy and how it affects the banking industry there. Gives the environment in which banking activities are carried out, disclosing the final accounts to shareholders, depositors and borrowers.
Published by: Uganda Commercial Bank, PO Box 973, Kampala, Uganda. Circ: 2,000.

332 UGA
UGANDA COMMERCIAL BANK. QUARTERLY ECONOMIC REVIEW. Text in English. 1983. q. **Description:** Presents analytic data on Uganda's economy. Attempts to promote public consciousness of the factors that influence the economy.
Indexed: ASD.
Published by: Uganda Commercial Bank, PO Box 973, Kampala, Uganda. TEL 234710, FAX 259012. Circ: 2,000.

332   USA
THE UNDERGROUND SHOPPER. Text in English. m.
Published by: Talk Productions, 2002 Academy Ln., Ste. 200, Dallas, TX 75234-9235. editor@undergroundshopper.com. Ed. Kit King.

332   FIN   ISSN 0355-0133
UNION BANK OF FINLAND. ANNUAL REPORT. Text in Finnish. 1952. a. **Document type:** Corporate.
Indexed: RASB.
Published by: Union Bank of Finland, Publications, PO Box 160, Helsinki, 00101, Finland. FAX 358-0-1652648.

332   GBR   ISSN 0503-2628
UNIT TRUST YEAR BOOK (YEAR). Text in English. 1964. a. GBP 97 domestic; GBP 110 overseas. adv. **Document type:** Academic/Scholarly. **Description:** Contains a comprehensive listing of U.K. authorized units and editorials on industry and legislative changes.
Supersedes: Directory of Unit Trusts
Published by: (Association of Unit Trust and Investment Funds), Financial Times Business Information, Management Reports (Subsidiary of: Financial Times Group), 102-108 Clerkenwell Rd, London, EC1M 5SA, United Kingdom. TEL 44-171-215-9321, FAX 44-171-251-9321. Ed. Christine Stopp. Adv. contact Colin Clarke. B&W page GBP 2,150, color page GBP 2,600. Circ: 3,500. **Orders to:** F T B I, 126 Jermyn St, London, Mddx SW1Y 4UJ, United Kingdom. TEL 44-1209-612493, FAX 44-1209-612811.

UNITE DE PROGRAMMATION DU MINISTERE. BULLETIN DE CONJONCTURE. see BUSINESS AND ECONOMICS— Economic Situation And Conditions

332.6   UAE
UNITED ARAB EMIRATES. AL-MASRAF AL-MARKAZI. AL-NASHRAH AL-IQTISADIYYAH/UNITED ARAB EMIRATES. CENTRAL BANK. ECONOMIC BULLETIN. Text in Arabic. 1974. a. charts; stat.
Formerly: United Arab Emirates. Central Bank. Publication
Published by: Central Bank, P O Box 854, Abu Dhabi, United Arab Emirates. TEL 652220, FAX 668483. Circ: (controlled).

UNITED KINGDOM. AUDIT COMMISSION. HEALTH INFORMATION BULLETIN. see PUBLIC ADMINISTRATION— Municipal Government

UNITED KINGDOM. AUDIT COMMISSION. LOCAL GOVERNMENT INFORMATION BULLETIN. see PUBLIC ADMINISTRATION—Municipal Government

332.1   GBR
UNITED KINGDOM. AUDIT COMMISSION. LOCAL GOVERNMENT REPORTS. Text in English. irreg. (approx. 35-50/yr.). GBP 600 (effective 1999). **Document type:** Monographic series, Government.
Published by: Audit Commission for Local Authorities and the National Health Service in England and Wales, 1 Vincent Sq, London, SW1P 2PN, United Kingdom. TEL 44-207- 8281212, http://www.audit-commission.gov.uk. **Orders to:** Bookpoint. FAX 44-1235-404454.

352.14   GBR
UNITED KINGDOM. AUDIT COMMISSION. REPORT & ACCOUNTS (YEAR). Text in English. 1981. a. GBP 9. **Document type:** Government.
Published by: Audit Commission for Local Authorities and the National Health Service in England and Wales, 1 Vincent Sq, London, SW1P 2PN, United Kingdom. TEL 44-20-7828-1212, http://www.audit-commission.gov.uk. **Dist. by:** Bookpoint, 39 Milton Park, Milton, Abingdon, Oxon OX14 4TD, United Kingdom. TEL 44-1235-400400, FAX 44-1235-400454.

332.1   GBR
UNITED KINGDOM. AUDIT COMMISSION. REPORTS. Text in English. irreg. price varies. adv. **Document type:** Monographic series, Government.
Supersedes (in 1999): Audit Commission. Occasional Papers (0959-2571)
Published by: Audit Commission for Local Authorities and the National Health Service in England and Wales, 1 Vincent Sq, London, SW1P 2PN, United Kingdom. TEL 44-20-7828-1212, http://www.audit-commission.gov.uk. Adv. contact B Dewar. **Orders to:** Bookpoint, 39 Milton Park, Milton, Abingdon, Oxon OX14 4TD, United Kingdom. TEL 44-123-5400400, FAX 44-123-5400454.

332.2   USA
UNITED STATES LEAGUE OF SAVINGS INSTITUTIONS. MEMBERSHIP BULLETIN. Text in English. bi-m. membership. **Document type:** Bulletin.
Published by: United States League of Savings Institutions, 900 19th St, N W, 900, Washington, DC 20006-2105. TEL 312-644-3100.

332.4   USA   ISSN 0160-1210
HG451
UNITED STATES MINT. ANNUAL REPORT OF THE DIRECTOR OF THE MINT. Text in English. 1873. a. USD 3. **Document type:** Government.
Formerly: U.S. Department of the Treasury. Bureau of the Mint. Annual Report of the Director of the Mint

Published by: United States Mint, 633 Third St, N W, Washington, DC 20220. TEL 202-566-2000. **Subscr. to:** U.S. Government Printing Office, Superintendent of Documents.

UNITED STATES SENATE. COMMITTEE ON BANKING, HOUSING, AND URBAN AFFAIRS. LEGISLATIVE CALENDAR. see PUBLIC ADMINISTRATION

332   USA   ISSN 0364-4162
KF21
UNITED STATES SENATE. COMMITTEE ON FINANCE. LEGISLATIVE CALENDAR. Text in English. a.
Published by: (U.S. Senate, Committee on Finance), U.S. Government Printing Office, 732 N Capitol St NW, Washington, DC 20401. TEL 888-293-6498, FAX 202-512-1262, gpoaccess@gpo.gov, http://www.gpo.gov.

332.1   DEU   ISSN 1613-5032
▼ **UNIVERSITAET BAYREUTH. FORSCHUNGSSTELLE FUER BANKRECHT UND BANKPOLITIK. SCHRIFTENREIHE.** Variant title: Schriftenreihe der Forschungsstelle fuer Bankrecht und Bankpolitik an der Universitaet Bayreuth. Text in German. 2004. irreg., latest vol.4, 2005. price varies. **Document type:** Monographic series, Academic/Scholarly.
Published by: (Universitaet Bayreuth, Forschungsstelle fuer Bankrecht und Bankpolitik), Verlag Dr. Kovac, Arnoldstr 49, Hamburg, 22763, Germany. TEL 49-40-3988800, FAX 49-40-39888055, info@verlagdrkovac.de, http://www.verlagdrkovac.de/3-18.htm.

332   AUT
UNIVERSITAET INNSBRUCK. FINANZWISSENSCHAFTLICHE STUDIEN∗. Text in German. 1969. irreg., latest vol.9, 1970. price varies.
Related titles: Series of: Universitaet Innsbruck. Veroeffentlichungen.
Published by: (Universitaet Innsbruck), Oesterreichische Kommissionsbuchhandlung, Glasmalereistr 6, Innsbruck, T 6020, Austria. TEL 43-512-587039, FAX 43-512-5870394, oekobuch@aon.at, http://www.oekobuch.com. Ed. Clemens August Andreae.

UNIVERSITY OF ESSEX. DEPARTMENT OF ACCOUNTING AND FINANCIAL MANAGEMENT. WORKING PAPER SERIES. see BUSINESS AND ECONOMICS—Accounting

UNIVERSITY OF NEW ENGLAND. DEPARTMENT OF ACCOUNTING & FINANCIAL MANAGEMENT. WORKING PAPERS. see BUSINESS AND ECONOMICS—Accounting

UNIVERSITY OF NORTH CAROLINA SCHOOL OF LAW BANKING INSTITUTE. see LAW

332.1   DEU   ISSN 1616-9247
UNTERNEHMENSRECHNUNG UND INSOLVENZWESEN. Text in German. 2001. irreg., latest vol.4, 2005. price varies. **Document type:** Monographic series, Academic/Scholarly.
Published by: Verlag Dr. Kovac, Arnoldstr 49, Hamburg, 22763, Germany. TEL 49-40-3988800, FAX 49-40-39888055, info@verlagdrkovac.de, http://www.verlagdrkovac.de/3-14.htm.

336.7   DEU   ISSN 0720-7336
UNTERSUCHUNGEN UEBER DAS SPAR-, GIRO- UND KREDITWESEN. ABTEILUNG A: WIRTSCHAFTSWISSENSCHAFT. Text in German. 1958. irreg., latest vol.175, 2002. price varies. **Document type:** Monographic series, Academic/Scholarly.
Formerly (until 1972): Untersuchungen ueber das Spar-, Giro und Kreditwesen (0566-2745)
Published by: Duncker und Humblot GmbH, Carl-Heinrich-Becker-Weg 9, Berlin, 12165, Germany. TEL 49-30-7900060, FAX 49-30-79000631, info@duncker-humblot.de, http://www.duncker-humblot.de.

336.7   DEU   ISSN 0720-7352
UNTERSUCHUNGEN UEBER DAS SPAR-, GIRO- UND KREDITWESEN. ABTEILUNG B: RECHTSWISSENSCHAFT. Text in German. 1973. irreg., latest vol.151, 2003. price varies. **Document type:** Monographic series, Academic/Scholarly.
Published by: Duncker und Humblot GmbH, Carl-Heinrich-Becker-Weg 9, Berlin, 12165, Germany. TEL 49-30-7900060, FAX 49-30-79000631, info@duncker-humblot.de, http://www.duncker-humblot.de.

332   USA
UPPER MIDWEST FINANCIAL DIRECTORY. Text in English. s-a. USD 110 (effective 2001). **Document type:** Directory, Trade. **Description:** Lists financial information for banks, bank holding companies, thrifts and major credit union institutions for the following states: Michigan, Minnesota, Montana, North Dakota, South Dakota, and Wisconsin.
Published by: Thomson Financial Services Company, 4709 W Golf Rd, Skokie, IL 60076-1256. TEL 847-676-9600, 800-321-3373, FAX 847-933-8101, prodinfo@tfp.com, customerservice@tfp.com, http://www.tfp.com/banks.

332 340   GBR
USE OF OFFSHORE JURISDICTIONS. Text in English. base vol. plus updates 2/yr. looseleaf. GBP 540 base vol(s).; GBP 529, EUR 796 updates in Europe; GBP 540, USD 981 updates elsewhere (effective 2006). **Document type:** Trade.

Published by: Sweet & Maxwell Ltd., 100 Avenue Road, London, NW3 3PF, United Kingdom. TEL 44-20-74491111, FAX 44-20-74491144, customer.services@sweetandmaxwell.co.uk, http://www.sweetandmaxwell.co.uk. **Subscr. to:** Cheriton House, North Way, Andover, Hants SP10 5BE, United Kingdom.

V W D - FINANZ- UND WIRTSCHAFTSSPIEGEL. see BUSINESS AND ECONOMICS—Investments

VANUATU. STATISTICS OFFICE. MONETARY AND BANKING STATISTICS. see BUSINESS AND ECONOMICS— Abstracting, Bibliographies, Statistics

332   GBR   ISSN 1369-1066
HG4961
➤ **VENTURE CAPITAL;** an international journal of entrepreneurial finance. Text in English. 1999. q. GBP 354, USD 584 combined subscription to institutions print & online eds. (effective 2006). reprint service avail. from PSC. **Document type:** Journal, Academic/Scholarly. **Description:** Publishes research-based papers from academics and practitioners on all aspects of private equity finance and the venture capital process.
Related titles: Online - full text ed.: ISSN 1464-5343. GBP 336, USD 555 to institutions (effective 2006) (from EBSCO Publishing, Gale Group, IngentaConnect, O C L C Online Computer Library Center, Inc., Swets Information Services).
Indexed: IBSS, JEL.
—BLDSC (9154.533900), IE, ingenta. **CCC.**
Published by: Routledge (Subsidiary of: Taylor & Francis Group), 4 Park Sq, Milton Park, Abingdon, Oxon OX14 4RN, United Kingdom. TEL 44-1235-828600, FAX 44-1235-829000, info@routledge.co.uk, http://www.tandf.co.uk/journals/titles/13691066.asp, http://www.routledge.co.uk. Eds. Colin Mason, Richard T Harrison. **Subscr. addr. in Europe:** Taylor & Francis Ltd, Journals Customer Service, Rankine Rd, Basingstoke, Hants RG24 8PR, United Kingdom. TEL 44-1256-813000, FAX 44-1256-330245, enquiry@tandf.co.uk; **Subscr. in N. America to:** Taylor & Francis Inc., Customer Services Dept, 325 Chestnut St, 8th Fl, Philadelphia, PA 19106. TEL 215-625-8900, 800-354-1420, FAX 215-625-8914.

332 600   USA   ISSN 1550-5804
THE VENTURE CAPITAL ANALYST: TECHNOLOGY EDITION. Text in English. 2002. m. USD 1,195 domestic; USD 1,270 foreign (effective 2004). **Document type:** Magazine, Trade.
Formed by the merger of (1998-2002): Venture Capital & Information Technology (1099-9302); (1997-2002): VentureEdge (1093-8893)
—**CCC.**
Published by: Alternative Investor, 170 Linden St, 2nd Fl, Wellesley, MA 02482. TEL 781-304-1400, FAX 781-304-1440, info@assetnews.com, http://www.assetnews.com. Ed. Russ Garland.

VENTURE CAPITAL & PRIVATE EQUITY YEARBOOK (YEARS). see BUSINESS AND ECONOMICS—Investments

332   NLD
VENTURE CAPITAL GIDS - N V P JAARBOEK. Text in Dutch. a. **Description:** Provides an overview of developments in the venture capital sector of the banking industry in the Netherlands.
Formerly: Nederlandse Venture Capital Gids - N V P Jaarboek
Published by: (Nederlandse Vereniging van Participatiemaatschappijen), Reed Business Information bv (Subsidiary of: Reed Business), Postbus 16400, Den Haag, 2500 BK, Netherlands. TEL 31-70-3624800, FAX 31-70-3605606.

332   USA
VENTURES. Text in English. 3/yr. **Document type:** Newsletter.
Media: Online - full content.
Published by: Accion International, 56 Roland St, 300, Boston, MA 02129. TEL 617-625-7080, FAX 617-625-7020.

332   DEU   ISSN 1437-0441
VERMOGEN & STEUERN. Text in German. 1998. 10/yr. EUR 142.08; EUR 12.70 newsstand/cover (effective 2004). adv. **Document type:** Magazine, Trade. **Description:** Publishes articles on banking and finance, taxation and other business issues.
Indexed: IBR, IBZ.
Published by: Helmut Richardi Verlag GmbH, Postfach 111151, Frankfurt Am Main, 60046, Germany. TEL 49-69-970833-0, FAX 49-69-7078400, verlagsleitung@kreditwesen.de, http://www.kreditwesen.de. adv.: B&W page EUR 2,950, color page EUR 4,090. Circ: 1,982 (paid and controlled).

368.094   USA
HG2411
VERMONT. COMMISSIONER OF BANKING INSURANCE AND SECURITIES. ANNUAL REPORT OF THE BANK COMMISSIONER. Text in English. 1880. a. free. **Document type:** Government.
Formerly: Vermont. Commissioner of Banking and Insurance. Annual Reports of the Bank Commissioner (0083-5730)
Related titles: Microfiche ed.: (from CIS).
Indexed: SRI.

B

▼ *new title*   ➤ *refereed*   ∗ *unverified*   ♦ *full entry avail.*

Published by: Department of Banking Insurance and Securities, Division of Banking, 89 Main St, Drawer 20, Montpelier, VT 05620. TEL 802-828-3301. Ed. Thomas J Candon. Circ: 1,700 (controlled).

VERMONT GOVERNMENT REGISTER. see *PUBLIC ADMINISTRATION*

330 DEU ISSN 1610-8019
VERSICHERUNG UND ALLFINANZ. Text in German. 2002. bi-m. adv. **Document type:** *Magazine, Trade.*
Published by: BAUVE AG i.G., Kirchdorfer Str 87, Bad Woerishofen, 86825, Germany. TEL 49-82473800, FAX 49-8247-380100, information@bauve.de, http://www.bauve.de. adv.: B&W page EUR 2,530, color page EUR 3,910.

332 RUS
VESTNIK BANKA ROSII. Text in Russian. w. USD 995 in United States.
Indexed: RASB.
Published by: Vestnik Banka Rossii, Zubovskii bulv 4, Moscow, 121019, Russian Federation. TEL 7-095-2018199, FAX 7-095-2014323. **US dist. addr.:** East View Information Services, 3020 Harbor Ln. N., Minneapolis, MN 55447. TEL 612-550-0961.

332 MAR ISSN 0505-4885
VIE ECONOMIQUE. Text in French. 1921. w. USD 60. adv.
Indexed: KES, PAIS, RASB, WBSS.
Published by: Societe Fermiere de Presse et Publicite, 5 bd. Abdellah ben Yacine, Casablanca, Morocco. TEL 307332, FAX 304542, TELEX 28045. Ed. Marcel Herzog. Circ: 22,000.

332.1 IND ISSN 0970-8456
VINIMAYA/BANK MANAGEMENT EDUCATION. Text in English. 1979. bi-m. INR 150; USD 24 foreign. **Document type:** *Academic/Scholarly.* **Description:** Presents conceptual and practical viewpoints of both the bankers and management educationists on bank management which has relevance to the workings and development of banking and financial institutions.
Published by: National Institute of Bank Management, NIBM Post Office, Kondhwe Khurd, Pune, Maharashtra 411 048, India. TEL 91-212-673080, FAX 91-212-674478, kalyan@nibm.ernet.in, http://www.nibmindia.com. Ed. Kalyam Swarup.

332 USA
VIRGINIA BANKING. Text in English. bi-m. free domestic membership (effective 2005). adv. **Document type:** *Newsletter.* **Description:** Devoted to legal, legislative and informational articles related to Virginia's banking industry. Also spotlights human interest stories of bankers in the state and also devotes pages to recent bank promotions, new hires as well as new associate members.
Contact Owner: Virginia Bankers Association, 700 E Main St, Ste 1411, Richmond, VA 23219. TEL 804-643-7469, FAX 804-643-6308, fford@vabankers.org, http://www.vabankers.org.

VIRGINIA REGISTER INDEX. see *PUBLIC ADMINISTRATION*

332 DEU
VORTEIL. Text in German. q. **Document type:** *Magazine, Consumer.* **Description:** Contains articles and features of interest to customers of Bavarian banks.
Published by: (Bayerische Raiffeisen und Volksbanken Verlag GmbH), BurdaYukom Publishing GmbH (Subsidiary of: Hubert Burda Media Holding GmbH & Co. KG), Schleissheimer Str 141, Munich, 80797, Germany. TEL 49-89-306200, FAX 49-89-30620100, info@burdayukom.de, http://www.yukom.de. Circ: 10,000 (controlled).

332 330.9 DEU ISSN 0172-2530
VORTEILHAFTE GELDANLAGEN; Handbuch fuer Anleger, Berater und Vermittler. Text in German. 1978. m. **Document type:** *Trade.*
Published by: Rudolf Haufe Verlag GmbH & Co. KG, Hindenburgstr 64, Freiburg Im Breisgau, 79102, Germany. TEL 49-761-3683-0, online@haufe.de.

332 AUT
W I F - WIRTSCHAFT, INFORMATION, FORTBILDUNG. Text in German. 4/yr. **Document type:** *Bulletin.*
Formerly: Wirtschaft in Form
Published by: Sparkassenverlag GmbH, Grimmelshausengasse 1, Vienna, W 1030, Austria. TEL 43-1-71170-0, FAX 43-1-71170310. Ed. Klaus Orthaber. Circ: 15,000.

W I K - ZEITSCHRIFT FUER DIE SICHERHEIT DER WIRTSCHAFT. see *CRIMINOLOGY AND LAW ENFORCEMENT*

332 DEU ISSN 0342-6874
W M ALLGEMEINE VERLOSUNGSTABELLE. (Wertpapier-Mitteilungen) Text in German. w. looseleaf. index. back issues avail. **Document type:** *Bulletin.*
Related titles: Magnetic Tape ed.
Published by: Herausgebergemeinschaft Wertpapier-Mitteilungen Keppler Lehmann GmbH & Co., Postfach 110932, Frankfurt Am Main, 60044, Germany. TEL 49-69-2732-0, FAX 49-69-232264, TELEX 412066-BZFFM.

332 DEU
W M TEIL I: SAMMELLISTE MIT OPPOSITION BELEGTE WERTPAPIERE. (Wertpapier-Mitteilungen) Text in German. d. **Document type:** *Bulletin.*
Published by: Herausgebergemeinschaft Wertpapier-Mitteilungen Keppler Lehmann GmbH & Co., Postfach 110932, Frankfurt Am Main, 60044, Germany. TEL 49-69-2732-0, FAX 49-69-232264.

332 DEU ISSN 0342-6939
W M TEIL II: NACHRICHTEN UEBER DEUTSCHE FESTVERZINSLICHE WERTE. (Wertpapier-Mitteilungen) Text in German. w. **Document type:** *Bulletin.*
Published by: Herausgebergemeinschaft Wertpapier-Mitteilungen Keppler Lehmann GmbH & Co., Postfach 110932, Frankfurt Am Main, 60044, Germany. TEL 49-69-2732-0, FAX 49-69-232264.

332 DEU
W M TEIL IIA: NEUEMISSIONEN - SCHNELLDIENST. (Wertpapier-Mitteilungen) Text in German. d. looseleaf. index. **Document type:** *Bulletin.*
Published by: Herausgebergemeinschaft Wertpapier-Mitteilungen Keppler Lehmann GmbH & Co., Postfach 110932, Frankfurt Am Main, 60044, Germany. TEL 49-69-2732-0, FAX 49-69-232264.

332 DEU ISSN 0170-5458
W M TEIL IIB: SAMMELLISTE GEKUENDIGTER UND VERLOSTER WERTPAPIERE. (Wertpapier-Mitteilungen) Text in German. w. looseleaf. index. back issues avail. **Document type:** *Bulletin.*
Published by: Herausgebergemeinschaft Wertpapier-Mitteilungen Keppler Lehmann GmbH & Co., Postfach 110932, Frankfurt Am Main, 60044, Germany. TEL 49-69-2732-0, FAX 49-69-232264.

332 DEU ISSN 0342-6955
W M TEIL III: NACHRICHTEN UEBER DEUTSCHE AKTIEN, ANTEILE, GENUSSSCHEINE, KUXE. (Wertpapier-Mitteilungen) Text in German. w. looseleaf. index. back issues avail. **Document type:** *Bulletin.*
Related titles: Magnetic Tape ed.
Published by: Herausgebergemeinschaft Wertpapier-Mitteilungen Keppler Lehmann GmbH & Co., Postfach 110932, Frankfurt Am Main, 60044, Germany. TEL 49-69-2732-0, FAX 49-69-232264.

W M TEIL IV: ZEITSCHRIFT FUER WIRTSCHAFTS- UND BANKRECHT. (Wertpapier-Mitteilungen) see *LAW*

332 DEU ISSN 0342-6998
W M TEIL VA: NACHRICHTEN UEBER AUSLAENDISCHE AKTIEN UND AKTIENAEHNLICHE WERTE. (Wertpapier-Mitteilungen) Text in German. w. looseleaf. index. back issues avail. **Document type:** *Bulletin.*
Related titles: Magnetic Tape ed.
Published by: Herausgebergemeinschaft Wertpapier-Mitteilungen Keppler Lehmann GmbH & Co., Postfach 110932, Frankfurt Am Main, 60044, Germany. TEL 49-69-2732-0, FAX 49-69-232264.

332 DEU
W M TEIL VB: NACHRICHTEN UEBER AUSLAENDISCHE FESTVERZINSLICHE WERTPAPIERE. (Wertpapier Mitteilungen) Text in German. w. **Document type:** *Bulletin.*
Published by: Herausgebergemeinschaft Wertpapier-Mitteilungen Keppler Lehmann GmbH & Co., Postfach 110932, Frankfurt Am Main, 60044, Germany. TEL 49-69-2732-0, FAX 49-69-232264, TELEX 4123-066-BZFFM.

332 DEU ISSN 0937-4108
W M TEIL VI: NACHRICHTEN UEBER OPTIONEN UND FUTURES. (Wertpapier Mitteilungen) Text in German. w. **Document type:** *Bulletin.*
Published by: Herausgebergemeinschaft Wertpapier-Mitteilungen Keppler Lehmann GmbH & Co., Postfach 110932, Frankfurt Am Main, 60044, Germany. TEL 49-69-2732-0, FAX 49-69-232264.

332 DEU ISSN 0342-6882
W M: WERTPAPIERBERATUNG. Text in German. w. looseleaf. index. back issues avail. **Document type:** *Bulletin.*
Related titles: Magnetic Tape ed.
Published by: Herausgebergemeinschaft Wertpapier-Mitteilungen Keppler Lehmann GmbH & Co., Postfach 110932, Frankfurt Am Main, 60044, Germany. TEL 49-69-2732-0, FAX 49-69-232264, TELEX 412066-BZFFM.

332 330.9 USA ISSN 0899-0530
WALL STREET DIGEST. Text in English. 1977. m. USD 150 (effective 2005). bk.rev. **Document type:** *Newsletter.*
Published by: Wall Street Digest, Inc., 8830 South Tamiami Trail, Ste 100, Sarasota, FL 34238-3130. TEL 941-954-5500, FAX 941-364-8447, editor@wallstreetdigest.com, http://www.wallstreetdigest.com. Ed., Pub., R&P Donald H Rowe. Circ: 25,000.

332.6 USA ISSN 1092-0935
WALL STREET JOURNAL (CENTRAL EDITION). Text in English. 1997. d. (Mon.-Fri.). adv. **Document type:** *Newspaper, Consumer.*
Formed by the 1997 merger of: Wall Street Journal (Midwest Edition) (0163-089X); Wall Street Journal (Southwest Edition) (0193-225X)
Related titles: Online - full text ed.: Wall Street Journal Online. USD 79 (effective 2004) (from bigchalk, Factiva, O C L C Online Computer Library Center, Inc., ProQuest Information & Learning).
—CCC.
Published by: Dow Jones Company, 1155 Ave of the Americas 3rd Fl, New york, NY 10036. TEL 212-597-5716, newswires@dowjones.com, http://www.dowjones.com/.

332 USA ISSN 0099-9660 CODEN: WSJOAF
WALL STREET JOURNAL (EASTERN EDITION). Text in English. 1889. d. (Mon.-Fri). USD 198; USD 1 newsstand/cover (effective 2005). adv. illus. reprint service avail. from PQC. **Document type:** *Newspaper, Consumer.* **Description:** Provides detailed news and commentary on political, economic, and social issues worldwide affecting the world of business.
Supersedes (in 1959): Wall Street Journal
Related titles: Online - full text ed.: Wall Street Journal Online. USD 79 (effective 2004) (from bigchalk, Factiva, O C L C Online Computer Library Center, Inc., ProQuest Information & Learning); ♦ Regional ed(s).: Wall Street Journal (Midwest Edition). ISSN 0163-089X; ♦ Wall Street Journal (Southwest Edition). ISSN 0193-225X; ♦ Wall Street Journal (Western Edition). ISSN 0193-2241; ♦ Supplement(s): Encore: A Guide to Life After 55; ♦ Breakaway: A Focus on Small Business.
Indexed: ABIn, ATI, Agr, B&I, BLI, BPI, BRI, CADCAM, CBRI, CHNI, CIN, ChemAb, ChemTitl, CompD, CompIU, EIA, FutSurv, GardL, HlthInd, Inpharma, LogistBibl, MCR, NewsAb, ORMS, PAIS, PCR2, PE&ON, PersLit, QC&AS, RASB, RI-1, RI-2, Reac, TTI, TelAb, Telegen.
—CASDDS, CISTI. **CCC.**
Published by: Dow Jones Company, 200 Liberty St, New York, NY 10281. TEL 212-416-2000, 800-223-2274, wsj.service@dowjones.com, http://www.wallstreetjournal.com, http://www.wsj.com. Eds. Robert L Bartley, Robert L. Bartley. Pubs. Karen Elliott House, Neil F. Budde. Adv. contacts Annette St Vincent, Steve Howe. page USD 70,454. Circ: 1,857,050 (paid). Wire service: AP.

332.6 USA ISSN 0193-2241
WALL STREET JOURNAL (WESTERN EDITION). Text in English. 5/w. USD 189; USD 1 newsstand/cover (effective 2003). adv. **Document type:** *Newspaper.* **Description:** Offers detailed news and commentary on global economic, political, and social issues affecting the world of business.
Related titles: Online - full text ed.: Wall Street Journal Online. USD 79 (effective 2004) (from bigchalk, Factiva, O C L C Online Computer Library Center, Inc., ProQuest Information & Learning); ♦ Regional ed(s).: Wall Street Journal (Eastern Edition). ISSN 0099-9660; ♦ Wall Street Journal (Midwest Edition). ISSN 0163-089X; ♦ Wall Street Journal (Southwest Edition). ISSN 0193-225X; ♦ Supplement(s): Encore: A Guide to Life After 55; ♦ Breakaway: A Focus on Small Business.
Indexed: BRI, ChPerl, LRI, MagInd.
—CCC.
Published by: Dow Jones & Company, Inc. (San Francisco) (Subsidiary of: Dow Jones Company), 201 California St, Ste 1350, San Francisco, CA 94111-5077. TEL 415-986-6886, FAX 415-391-4534, 415-398-0929, http://www.wsj.com, http://www.advertising.wsj.com. Ed. Robert Bartley. Adv. contact Chris Windbiel. B&W page USD 37,847. Circ: 409,000 (paid).

332 BEL ISSN 0921-9986 CODEN: WSJEAJ
THE WALL STREET JOURNAL EUROPE; global business news for Europe. Text in English. 1983. d. EUR 440 domestic (effective 2004). adv. bk.rev. **Document type:** *Newspaper.*
Related titles: Microfilm ed.: (from PQC); Online - full text ed.: (from O C L C Online Computer Library Center, Inc.).
Indexed: ABC, B&I, IPackAb, M&MA.
—CCC.
Published by: Dow Jones Publishing Co. Europe, Bd Brand Whitlock 87, Brussels, 1200, Belgium. TEL 32-2-7411211, FAX 32-2-7321102. Ed. Philip Revzin. Adv. contact Anne Renton. page USD 28,664.64. Circ: 61,500 (paid). **Subscr. to:** Wall Street Journal Circulation Department, In de Cramer 37, PO Box 2845, Heerlen 6401 DH, Netherlands. TEL 31-45-5761222, FAX 31-45-5714722.

332 USA ISSN 1042-9840
HG1
THE WALL STREET JOURNAL INDEX. Text in English. 1958. a. (plus m. updates). illus. reprints avail. **Document type:** *Abstract/Index.* **Description:** Abstracts and indexes articles and columns from the Wall Street Journal.
Related titles: CD-ROM ed.; Diskette ed.; Online - full text ed.; ♦ Includes: Barron's Index. ISSN 0360-8379.
—CCC.
Published by: ProQuest Information & Learning, 300 N Zeeb Rd., PO Box 1346, Ann Arbor, MI 48106-1346. TEL 313-761-4700, 800-521-0600, FAX 800-864-0019.

332 USA ISSN 1068-1477
THE WASATCH LETTER. Text in English. 1992. q. USD 25 (effective 1999). back issues avail. **Document type:** *Newsletter.*

Published by: Wasatch Planning and Publishing Corp., 3495 S Medford Dr, Bountiful, UT 84010-5823. TEL 801-296-6005, FAX 801-292-6927. Ed. Mary Flood.

332 USA
WASHINGTON PERSPECTIVE. Text in English. 1983. w. USD 510 to non-members; USD 220 to members (effective 1999). back issues avail. **Document type:** *Newsletter.* **Description:** Provides up-to-date coverage of new laws and final regulations that affect savings and commercial banking institutions.
Formed by the 1992 merger of: Washington Notes (0195-525X); Washington Memo (Washington) (0882-2247)
Published by: America's Community Bankers, 900 19th St, N W, Ste 400, Washington, DC 20006. TEL 202-857-3100, FAX 202-296-8716, http://www.acbankers.org, http://www.americascommunitybankers.org. R&P James Eberle. Circ: 4,000.

332 340 USA
WASHINGTON STATE BAR ASSOCIATION. CREDITOR - DEBTOR LAW SECTION NEWSLETTER. Text in English. 1974. q. USD 17.50 (effective 2000). **Document type:** *Newsletter.*
Published by: Washington State Bar Association, 2101 Fourth Ave, Ste 400, Seattle, WA 98121-2330. TEL 206-727-8239, FAX 206-727-8320. Circ: 680.

332 GBR ISSN 1742-1748
▼ **WEALTH.** Text in English. 2003. 3/yr. free to qualified personnel (effective 2005). adv. **Document type:** *Magazine, Trade.* **Description:** Pan-European publication that is designed to act as a business tool in providing information to the chain of key decision-makers who are primarily involved in the distribution of financial products & services for wealthy and high-net worth investors.
Published by: Risk Waters Group (Subsidiary of: Incisive Media Plc.), Haymarket House, 28-29 Haymarket, London, SW1Y 4RX, United Kingdom. TEL 44-20-74849700, FAX 44-20-79302238, customerservices@incisivemedia.com, http://www.incisivemedia.com/. Ed. Julian Marr TEL 44-20-74849771. Pub. Susanne Petrie TEL 44-20-74849806. Adv. contact Jonathan Greene TEL 44-20-74849867. Circ: 10,000 (controlled).

THE WEBSTER AGRICULTURAL LETTER. see *AGRICULTURE*

332 USA
WEEKLY CONSOLIDATED CONDITION REPORT OF LARGE COMMERCIAL BANKS AND DOMESTIC SUBSIDIARIES. Text in English. w. USD 14. **Document type:** *Government.*
Published by: U.S. Federal Reserve System, Board of Governors, Publications Services, Rm MS 138, Washington, DC 20551. TEL 202-452-3244, FAX 202-728-5886.

WEIL'S ARKANSAS GOVERNMENT REGISTER. see *PUBLIC ADMINISTRATION*

WEIL'S CONNECTICUT GOVERNMENT REGISTER. see *PUBLIC ADMINISTRATION*

WEIL'S GEORGIA GOVERNMENT REGISTER. see *PUBLIC ADMINISTRATION*

WEIL'S HAWAII GOVERNMENT REGISTER. see *PUBLIC ADMINISTRATION*

WEIL'S WYOMING GOVERNMENT REGISTER. see *PUBLIC ADMINISTRATION*

WEISS RATINGS' GUIDE TO BROKERAGE FIRMS. see *BUSINESS AND ECONOMICS—Investments*

332.1 USA
WESTERN BANKING. Text in English. bi-m. USD 36 domestic (effective 2002).
Published by: Bank News, Inc., PO Box 29156, Shawnee Mission, KS 66201-9156. TEL 800-336-1120.

322 346.066 USA
WESTERN LEAGUE OF SAVINGS INSTITUTIONS. REGULATORY CHECKLIST✶. Text in English. s-m. looseleaf. USD 35 to non-members; USD 25 to members. **Document type:** *Newsletter.* **Description:** Informs employees of savings and loans industry in California of changes in regulations that affect the operating of their financial institution.
Former titles (until 1994): California League of Savings Institutions. Regulatory Checklist; (until 1992): California League of Savings Institutions. Legislation and Regulation Update
Published by: Western League of Savings Institutions, 9841 Airport Blvd, Ste 418, Los Angeles, CA 90045. TEL 310-414-8300, FAX 310-414-8399. Ed. Cathy Moran. Circ: 700.

WEST'S BANKRUPTCY DIGEST. see *LAW*

332.7 USA ISSN 0199-5782
KF1515.A2
WEST'S BANKRUPTCY REPORTER. Text in English. 1980. 319 base vols. plus w. updates. USD 174.50 per vol.; USD 5,364 319 vol. set (effective 2005).
Published by: Thomson West (Subsidiary of: Thomson Corporation, The), 610 Opperman Dr, Eagan, MN 55123-1396. TEL 800-328-9352, FAX 651-687-6674, 651-687-7302, customer.service@westgroup.com, http://west.thomson.com/product/22064327/product.asp.

WEST'S BANKRUPTCY SERIES. see *LAW*

WETBOEK FINANCIEEL RECHT. see *LAW—Corporate Law*

332 GBR
WHAT FINANCE✶. Text in English. 1983. bi-m. GBP 9.
Published by: Charterhouse Communications Group Ltd., Arnold House, 36-41 Holywell Ln, London, EC2A 3ET, United Kingdom. TEL 44-20-7827-5454. Circ: 30,000.

323 GBR ISSN 0305-3954
WHO OWNS WHAT IN WORLD BANKING. Text in English. 1971. a. GBP 192 domestic; GBP 202 foreign. adv. stat. **Document type:** *Trade.* **Description:** Summarizes recent events in world banking, enumerates main parent banks worldwide with their subsidiaries and affiliates, and lists consortium banks and their participants.
Published by: Financial Times Business Information, Management Reports (Subsidiary of: Financial Times Group), 102-108 Clerkenwell Rd, London, EC1M 5SA, United Kingdom. TEL 44-171-251-9321, FAX 44-171-251-4686. **Orders to:** F T B I, 126 Jermyn St, London, Mddx SW1Y 4UJ, United Kingdom. TEL 44-1209-612493, FAX 44-1209-612811.

332 GBR
WHO'S WHO IN CENTRAL BANKING. Text in English. a. GBP 85; GBP 230 foreign. adv. **Document type:** *Directory.*
Published by: Central Banking Publications Ltd., Fifth Fl, Tavistock House, Tavistock Sq, London, WC1H 9JZ, United Kingdom. TEL 44-20-73880006, FAX 44-20-73889040, info@centralbanking.co.uk, httpf:/www.centralbanking.co.uk, http://www.centralbanking.co.uk/. Ed., Pub. Robert Pringle. Adv. contact Jean Somerville.

WHO'S WHO IN INTERNATIONAL BANKING. see *BIOGRAPHY*

WHO'S WHO IN MORTGAGE FINANCE. see *BUSINESS AND ECONOMICS—Trade And Industrial Directories*

332.1 USA
WILMINGTON TRUST BRIEFINGS. Text in English. q.
Published by: Wilmington Trust Company, Trust Department, Wilmington, DE 19890.

332 USA ISSN 1540-6962
HG106
WILMOTT MAGAZINE. Text in English. bi-m. USD 650 (effective 2006). **Document type:** *Journal, Academic/Scholarly.* **Description:** On the subject of quantitative analysis, it offers cutting-edge research, innovative models, new products, useful software, in-depth analysis, and solutions. The latest quantitative finance theories are put to the test with practical, jargon-free examples.
Related titles: Online - full text ed.: ISSN 1541-8286 (from Wiley InterScience).
—CCC.
Published by: John Wiley & Sons, Inc., 111 River St, Hoboken, NJ 07030-5774. TEL 201-748-6000, 800-825-7550, FAX 201-748-5915, http://www.wiley.com/WileyCDA/WileyTitle/productCd-WILM.html. Ed. Paul Wilmott. **Subscr. to:** PO Box 5597, Somerset, NJ 08875. TEL 732-650-4630, FAX 732-650-4623, subinfo@wiley.com.

332 AUT
WIRTSCHAFT HEUTE. Text in German. q.
Published by: Landesverband der Sparkassen Oberoesterreichs, Promenade 11-13, Linz, O 4041, Austria. TEL 0732-2391-2500.

WIRTSCHAFTSDIENST FUER VERSICHERUNGS- UND BAUSPARKAUFLEUTE. see *INSURANCE*

332.1 USA
WISCONSIN BANKING NEWS. Text in English. 1971. m. USD 67.50 (effective 1999). adv. **Document type:** *Trade.*
Published by: Public Relations Enterprises, Inc., PO Box 12236, Lansing, MI 48901-2236. TEL 517-484-0775, FAX 517-484-4676. Ed., Pub., R&P, Adv. contact Jerry O'Neil. Circ: 590 (paid).

WOMEN'S BUSINESS JOURNAL. see *WOMEN'S INTERESTS*

332 330.9 GBR
WORKING PAPER. Text in English. irreg.
Related titles: Online - full text ed.
Published by: University of Durham, Dept of Economics & Finance, University of Durham, 23-26 Old Elvet, Durham, DH1 3HY, United Kingdom. TEL 44-191-374-7270, FAX 44-191-374-7289, P.A.Wears@durham.ac.uk, http://www.dur.ac.uk/Economics/wopec.html.

332.72 USA
▼ **WORKOUTWIRE.** Text in English. 2005. s-m. USD 495 (effective 2005). **Document type:** *Newsletter.* **Description:** Provides you the latest news and analysis on all aspects of the mortgage workout market.
Media: E-mail.
Published by: Source Media, Inc., One State St Plaza, 27th Fl, New York, NY 10004. TEL 212-803-6077, 800-221-1809, FAX 212-747-1154, custserv@sourcemedia.com, http://www.nationalmortgagenews.com/wow, http://www.sourcemedia.com.

WORLD BANK. E D I DEVELOPMENT STUDY. see *BUSINESS AND ECONOMICS—International Development And Assistance*

332 USA
WORLD BANK GROUP DIRECTORY. Text in English. 2/yr. USD 22 per issue (effective 1999). **Document type:** *Directory.*
Indexed: IIS.
Published by: World Bank Group, PO Box 960, Herndon, VA 20172-0960. TEL 703-661-1580, FAX 703-661-1501, books@worldbank.org, http://www.imf.org/.

332.1 USA ISSN 0253-2131
WORLD BANK. REPRINT SERIES. Text in English. 1971. irreg., latest vol.481, 1996. **Document type:** *Monographic series.*
—CCC.
Published by: World Bank Group, 1818 H St, NW, Washington, DC 20433. TEL 703-661-1580, 202-473-1000, FAX 703-661-1501, 202-477-6391, books@worldbank.org, http://www.worldbank.org.

332.1 GBR ISSN 0257-3032
HD72
➤ **WORLD BANK RESEARCH OBSERVER.** Text in English. 1986. s-a. GBP 104, USD 164, EUR 156 to institutions; GBP 69, USD 109, EUR 104 academic; GBP 109, USD 172, EUR 164 combined subscription to institutions print & online eds.; GBP 73, USD 115, EUR 110 combined subscription academic; print & online eds. (effective 2006). adv. illus. back issues avail.; reprint service avail. from PSC. **Document type:** *Journal, Academic/Scholarly.* **Description:** Covers policy-relevant development economics for noneconomists.
Related titles: Microfiche ed.: (from CIS); Microform ed.: (from PQC); Online - full text ed.: ISSN 1564-6971. GBP 98, USD 155, USD 147 to institutions; GBP 66, USD 104, EUR 99 academic (effective 2006) (from EBSCO Publishing, Gale Group, H.W. Wilson, HighWire Press, IngentaConnect, Northern Light Technology, Inc., O C L C Online Computer Library Center, Inc., Oxford University Press Online Journals, ProQuest Information & Learning, Swets Information Services, The Dialog Corporation).
Indexed: ABIn, ABS&EES, APEL, ASCA, AbAn, BPI, CurCont, FamI, ForAb, GEOBASE, I&DA, IBSS, IIS, IndIslam, JEL, PAA&I, PAIS, PGegResA, RASB, RDA, REE&TA, S&F, SSCI, TDB, TriticAb, WAE&RSA.
—BLDSC (9352.928500), IDS, IE, Infotrieve, ingenta. **CCC.**
Published by: (World Bank Group USA), Oxford University Press, Great Clarendon St, Oxford, OX2 6DP, United Kingdom. TEL 44-1865-556767, FAX 44-1865-556646, researchobserver@worldbank.org, jnl.orders@oup.co.uk, http://wbro.oxfordjournals.org/, http://www.oxfordjournals.org/. Ed. Shantayanan Devarajan. Pub. Erich Staib. Circ: 10,600.

➤ **WORLD BANK SERIES ON EVALUATION AND DEVELOPMENT.** see *BUSINESS AND ECONOMICS—International Development And Assistance*

016.3321 GBR ISSN 0265-9484
HG1505
WORLD BANKING ABSTRACTS; the international journal of the financial services industry. Text in English. 1984. bi-m. USD 1,943 combined subscription in the Americas to institutions & Caribbean (print & online eds.); GBP 1,157 combined subscription elsewhere to institutions print & online eds. (effective 2006). reprints avail. **Document type:** *Abstract/Index.*
Related titles: CD-ROM ed.; Microform ed.: (from PQC); Online - full text ed.: ISSN 1467-9698. USD 1,846 in the Americas to institutions & Caribbean; GBP 1,099 elsewhere to institutions (effective 2006).
—BLDSC (9352.938200). **CCC.**
Published by: (Institute of European Finance), Blackwell Publishing Ltd., 9600 Garsington Rd, Oxford, OX4 2ZG, United Kingdom. TEL 44-1865-776868, FAX 44-1865-714591, customerservices@oxon.blackwellpublishing.com, http://www.wbaonline.co.uk/, http://www.blackwellpublishing.com. Eds. E P M Gardener TEL 44-1248-382168, Philip Molyneux.

332 USA
WORLD COUNCIL OF CREDIT UNIONS. ANNUAL AND STATISTICAL REPORT. Text in English, French, Spanish. a. charts; stat. **Document type:** *Corporate.*

B

Former titles: World Council of Credit Unions. International Annual Report; World Council of Credit Unions Yearbook
Published by: World Council of Credit Unions Inc., 5710 Mineral Pt Rd, Box 2982, Madison, WI 53701. TEL 608-231-7130, FAX 608-238-8020, info@woccu.org, http://www.woccu.org. Ed. Karen Kaplan. Circ: 4,000.

332 GBR ISSN 1354-9847
WORLD EXPORT CREDIT GUIDE. Text in English. 1992. a., latest 2001. GBP 100, USD 160 per vol. (effective 2001).
Related titles: ♦ Supplement to: Project Finance. ISSN 1462-0014; ♦ Supplement to: Trade Finance. ISSN 1464-8873.
—BLDSC (9354.866000). **CCC.**
Published by: Euromoney Institutional Investor Plc., Nestor House, Playhouse Yard, London, EC4V 5EX, United Kingdom. TEL 44-20-7779-8673, FAX 44-20-7779-8541, http://www.euromoney.com.

332 USA ISSN 0190-2083
HG1
WORLD FINANCIAL MARKETS. Text in English. 1970. q.
Published by: J.P. Morgan Chase & Co., 23 Wall St, New York, NY 10015. TEL 212-270-6000, http://www.jpmorgan.com.

WORLD LEASING YEARBOOK (YEAR). see *BUSINESS AND ECONOMICS—Economic Situation And Conditions*

332 658 SGP
WORLD SCIENTIFIC ASIAN ECONOMIC PROFILES. Text in English. 1998. irreg., latest 1998. price varies. **Document type:** *Monographic series, Academic/Scholarly.*
Published by: World Scientific Publishing Co. Pte. Ltd., 5 Toh Tuck Link, Singapore, 596224, Singapore. TEL 65-466-5775, FAX 65-467-7667, wspc@wspc.com.sg, series@wspc.com.sg, http://www.wspc.com/books/series/wsaep_series.shtml, http://www.worldscientific.com. **Dist. by:** World Scientific Publishing Co., Inc., 1060 Main St, River Edge, NJ 07661. TEL 201-487-9655, 800-227-7562, FAX 201-487-9656, 888-977-2665; World Scientific Publishing Ltd., 57 Shelton St, London WC2H 9HE, United Kingdom. TEL 44-20-78360888, FAX 44-20-78362020.

332 AUT
WUESTENROT MAGAZIN. Text in German. 1930. 3/yr. free. adv. bk.rev. illus.; stat. **Document type:** *Magazine, Consumer.*
Formerly: Wuestenrot-Heim (0043-9622)
Published by: Bausparkasse Wuestenrot, Alpenstr 70, Postfach 155, Salzburg, Sa 5033, Austria. TEL 43-57070-100373, FAX 43-57070-100577, presse@wuestenrot.co.at, http://www.wuestenrot.at. Ed. Josef Mayer. Pub. Herbert Moser. Adv. contact Alexander Viehauser. B&W page EUR 9,374, color page EUR 12,354; trim 185 x 245. Circ: 920,000 (controlled).

332 CHN
XIN JINRONG/NEW FINANCE. Text in Chinese; Abstracts in English. 1988. m. CNY 280, USD 50. adv. **Document type:** *Academic/Scholarly.* **Description:** Covers the theory and practice of banking and finance, and the administration and operation of Chinese commercial banks.
Published by: Bank of Communications, c/o Head Office, 18 Xianxia Rd, Shanghai, 200335, China. TEL 86-21-6275-7261, FAX 86-21-6275-5462. Ed. Feng Song. Pub. Yiming Lin. Adv. contact Cuiting Wang. Circ: 17,000.

332.1 TUR
YAPI VE KREDI BANKASI. ANNUAL REPORT. Text in English. a.
Published by: Yapi ve Kredi Bankasi, Istiklal Caddesi, Korsan Cikmazi 1, Beyoglu, P O Box 250, Istanbul, Turkey.

368.854 GBR
YOUR MONEY (LONDON); options explained. Text in English. 1993. bi-m. GBP 2.50 newsstand/cover (effective 2005). adv. **Document type:** *Magazine, Consumer.* **Description:** Serves as a guide to personal finance by phone. Covers pensions, personal loans, mortgages, Internet banking, house and contents insurance, health insurance, and travel insurance.
Former titles (until 2003): Your Money Savings and Investments (1474-1350); (until 2001): Your Money Direct (1369-6912); (until 1997): Money Direct (1364-7938); (until 1996): Your Savings and Investment (1357-4361); (until 1995): Which Savings (0969-9597)
Related titles: Online - full content ed.
—**CCC.**
Published by: Matching Hat Ltd. (Subsidiary of: Incisive Media Plc.), Aldwych House, 71-91 Aldwych, London, WC2B 4HN, United Kingdom. TEL 44-20-74043123, FAX 44-20-74043123, info@matchinghat.com, http://www.yourmoney.com, http://www.matching-hat.co.uk/. Ed. Paula John TEL 44-20-74305123. Pub. Bharat Sagar TEL 44-20-74305116. Adv. contact Lorraine Meek TEL 44-20-74305152. Circ: 50,000 (paid).

332 GBR ISSN 1357-4353
YOUR MORTGAGE. Text in English. 1986. m. GBP 31.20 (effective 2005). adv. charts. back issues avail.; reprints avail. **Document type:** *Magazine, Consumer.* **Description:** Contains all information consumers need to purchase and finance a home. Lists mortgage interest rates.
Formerly (until 1995): Which Mortgage (0963-7044)
Related titles: Online - full content ed.
—**CCC.**
Published by: Matching Hat Ltd. (Subsidiary of: Incisive Media Plc.), Aldwych House, 71-91 Aldwych, London, WC2B 4HN, United Kingdom. TEL 44-20-74043123, FAX 44-20-74043123, info@matchinghat.com, http://www.yourmortgage.co.uk, http://www.matching-hat.co.uk/. Ed. Paula John TEL 44-20-74305123. Pub. Bharat Sagar TEL 44-20-74305116. Adv. contact Iain Cartlidge TEL 44-20-74305122. B&W page GBP 3,680, color page GBP 5,040. Circ: 18,000.

332 333.33 AUS ISSN 1039-0081
YOUR MORTGAGE MAGAZINE. Text in English. 1993. bi-m. AUD 59.70 domestic; AUD 120 newsstand/cover foreign; AUD 9.95 newsstand/cover domestic (effective 2004). adv. bk.rev. back issues avail. **Document type:** *Magazine, Consumer.* **Description:** Features articles specializing in home loan interest rates, buying and selling property, financing and banking for the residential and investment property markets in Australia. Includes a complete, independent, national interest rate table comparing mortgage products from various lenders.
Related titles: E-mail ed.; Online - full content ed.
Published by: H W W Limited, PO Box 996, Darlinghurst, NSW 2010, Australia. TEL 61-2-8268-8268, FAX 61-2-8268-8267, info@hww.com.au, http://www.yourmortgage.com.au. Ed. Alex Holoyda. Pub. Stephen Wall. R&P Gregan McMahon. Adv. contact Peri Beecraft. color page AUD 2,700; trim 206 x 276. Circ: 20,000 (paid).

332 JPN
ZAIKAI/FINANCIAL WORLD. Text in Japanese. 1953. fortn.
Published by: Zaikai Kenkyujo, Akasaka-Tokyu Bldg, 2-14-3 Nagata-cho, Chiyoda-ku, Tokyo, 100-0014, Japan. TEL 81-3-3582-6771, FAX 81-3-3581-6777. Ed. Akira Kanemitsu. Circ: 120,000.

ZEITSCHRIFT FUER BANK- UND KAPITALMARKTRECHT. see *BUSINESS AND ECONOMICS—Investments*

332.1 DEU ISSN 0936-2800
KK2188.A13
ZEITSCHRIFT FUER BANKRECHT UND BANKWIRTSCHAFT. Text in German. q.
Indexed: IBR, IBZ.
Published by: Verlag Kommunikationsforum GmbH Recht Wirtschaft Steuern, Aachener Str 217, Cologne, 50931, Germany. TEL 0221-40088-0, FAX 0221-4008828.

332.7 DEU ISSN 0341-4019
HG17
ZEITSCHRIFT FUER DAS GESAMTE KREDITWESEN. Text in German. 1948. s-m. EUR 309.12; EUR 17.90 newsstand/cover (effective 2004). adv. bk.rev. charts; stat. s-a. index, cum.index: 1948-1967. reprints avail. **Document type:** *Magazine, Trade.*
Indexed: DIP, ELLIS, IBR, IBZ, KES, PAIS, RASB.
—IE, Infotrieve. **CCC.**
Published by: Fritz Knapp Verlag GmbH, Postfach 111151, Frankfurt Am Main, 60046, Germany. TEL 49-69-9708330, FAX 49-69-7078400, verlagsleitung@kreditwesen.de, http://www.kreditwesen.de. Ed. Berthold Morschhaeuser. Adv. contact Werner Scholz. B&W page EUR 4,220, color page EUR 6,320. Circ: 2,925 (paid and controlled).

332.7 DEU
ZEITSCHRIFT FUER DAS GESAMTE SCHULDRECHT. Text in German. m. EUR 120 (effective 2004). adv. **Document type:** *Magazine, Trade.*
Published by: Z A P - Verlag fuer die Rechts- und Anwaltspraxis GmbH und Co., Postfach 101953, Recklinghausen, 45619, Germany. TEL 49-2361-91420, FAX 49-2361-914235, hotline@zap-verlag.de, http://www.zap-verlag.de. adv.: B&W page EUR 1,200, color page EUR 1,950; trim 170 x 263. Circ: 6,000 (controlled).

332 340 AUT ISSN 1024-6096
ZEITSCHRIFT FUER INSOLVENZRECHT UND KREDITSCHUTZ. Text in German. 1995. bi-m. EUR 89; EUR 18.40 newsstand/cover (effective 2005). adv. bk.rev. 36 p./no.; **Document type:** *Magazine, Trade.*
Published by: LexisNexis Verlag ARD Orac GmbH & Co. KG (Subsidiary of: LexisNexis Europe and Africa), Marxergasse 25, Vienna, W 1030, Austria. TEL 43-1-534520, FAX 43-1-53452141, verlag@orac.at, http://www.lexisnexis.at/. Ed. Andreas Konecny. Adv. contact Malgorzata Leitliner TEL 43-1-534521115. Circ: 1,500 (paid).

ZEITSCHRIFT FUER WIRTSCHAFTSRECHT - Z I P. see *LAW*

332 CHN ISSN 0578-1485
HG201
ZHONGGUO JINRONG/CHINA FINANCE. Text in Chinese; Contents page in English. m. CNY 19.20, USD 45.80. adv. charts; illus.
Related titles: Online - full text ed.: (from East View Information Services).
Published by: (Zhongguo Renmin Yinhang Zonghang/Head Office of China People's Bank), Zhongguo Jinrong Chubanshe, 17 Xijiaomin Xiang, Beijing, 100031, China. TEL 653858. Ed. Xu Shuxin. **Dist. in US by:** China Books & Periodicals Inc, 360 Swift Ave., Ste. 48, S San Fran, CA 94080-6220. TEL 415-282-2994; **Dist. outside China by:** China International Book Trading Corp, 35 Chegongzhuang Xilu, Haidian District, PO Box 399, Beijing 100044, China. TEL 86-10-68412045, FAX 86-10-68412023, cibtc@mail.cibtc.com.cn, http://www.cibtc.com.cn.

332 CHN ISSN 1001-5841
HG3331
ZHONGGUO JINRONG NIANJIAN/CHINA FINANCE YEAR BOOK. Text in Chinese. a.
Published by: Zhongguo Jinrong Xuehui/Chinese Society of Banking and Finance, 1 Baiguanglu Toutiao, Beijing, 100053, China. TEL 363428. Ed. Chen Yuan.

332 630 CHN
ZHONGGUO NONGCUN JINRONG/CHINA RURAL FINANCE. Text in Chinese. m.
Published by: Zhongguo Nongcun Jinrong Zazhishe, 25 Fuxing Lu, Beijing, 100036, China. TEL 8211639. Ed. Zhang Fan.

ZHONGNAN CAIJING DAXUE XUEBAO/CENTRAL-SOUTH UNIVERSITY OF FINANCE AND ECONOMICS. JOURNAL. see *BUSINESS AND ECONOMICS—Economic Systems And Theories, Economic History*

332 TWN ISSN 1017-9623
ZHONGYANG YINHANG JIKAN. Text in Chinese. 1979. q. **Document type:** *Government.*
Published by: Zhongyang Yinhang/Central Bank of China, 2, Roosevelt Road, Section 1, Taipei, Taiwan. TEL 886-2-23936161, 886-2-23936253, FAX 886-2-23571974, http://www.cbc.gov.tw/economic/publication/maga2/.

332 ROM ISSN 1454-2641
ZIARUL FINANCIAR. Text in Romanian. 1998. d. adv. **Document type:** *Newspaper, Consumer.*
Published by: Publimedia International, Str. Luterana nr. 11, bloc CINOR, et. 5, Bucharest, Romania. TEL 40-21-3033907, FAX 40-21-3033958, zf@zf.ro, http://www.zf.ro.

332 ZWE
ZIMBABWE FINANCIAL HOLDINGS LIMITED. ANNUAL REPORT. Text in English. 1967. a. **Document type:** *Journal, Corporate.* **Description:** Reports on group corporate activities in the commercial and merchant banking fields in Zimbabwe and Botswana.
Supersedes (in 1993): Zimbabwe Banking Corporation. Group Annual Report
Published by: Zimbabwe Financial Holdings Limited, PO Box 3198, Harare, Zimbabwe. TEL 263-4-756671, 263-4-751168/75, FAX 263-4-756674, 263-4-757497, rtaruvinga@finhold.co.zw, http://www.finhold.co.zw.

332 CHE
ZUERCHER BANKANGESTELLTE. Text in German. bi-m.
Published by: Zuercher Bankpersonalverband, Schanzeneggstr 1, Zuerich, 8002, Switzerland. TEL 01-2012421. Circ: 5,500.

20-20 INSIGHT. see *BUSINESS AND ECONOMICS—Investments*

332.1 USA ISSN 0885-4777
100 HIGHEST YIELDS. Text in English. 1983. w. looseleaf. USD 124 (effective 2005). charts; mkt.; stat. **Document type:** *Newsletter.* **Description:** Lists high-yielding CD's and money markets offered by federally-insured institutions nationwide.
Published by: Bankrate, Inc., 11760 US Highway One, Ste 500, N Palm Beach, FL 33408. TEL 561-630-2400, FAX 561-625-4540, webmaster@bankrate.com, http://www.bankrate.com. Circ: 860 (paid); 15 (controlled).

BUSINESS AND ECONOMICS—Banking And Finance—Computer Applications

ADVANCES IN MATHEMATICAL PROGRAMMING AND FINANCIAL PLANNING. see *MATHEMATICS—Computer Applications*

THE AIRLINE INDUSTRY: AN INDUSTRY OVERVIEW. see *TRANSPORTATION—Air Transport*

330.9 USA ISSN 1387-2834
HG41
➤ **ASIA - PACIFIC FINANCIAL MARKETS.** Text in English. 1994. q. USD 414, EUR 414, GBP 241 combined subscription to institutions print & online eds. (effective 2005). adv. back issues avail.; reprint service avail. from PSC. **Document type:** *Academic/Scholarly.* **Description:** Publishes empirical and theoretical research on the Japanese financial markets, in all areas of financial econometrics and financial engineering.
Formerly (until 1998): Financial Engineering and the Japanese Markets (1380-2011)

Related titles: Online - full text ed.: ISSN 1573-6946 (from EBSCO Publishing, Gale Group, IngentaConnect, Kluwer Online, O C L C Online Computer Library Center, Inc., ProQuest Information & Learning, Springer LINK, Swets Information Services).
Indexed: ABIn, BAS, BibLing, JEL, RefZh.
—BLDSC (1742.260385), IE, Infotrieve, ingenta. **CCC.**
Published by: (Japanese Association of Financial Econometrics and Engineering NLD), Springer-Verlag New York, Inc. (Subsidiary of: Springer Science+Business Media), 233 Spring St, New York, NY 10013. TEL 212-460-1500, FAX 212-473-6272, journals@springer-ny.com, http://springerlink.metapress.com/openurl.asp?genre=journal&issn=1387-2834, http://www.springer-ny.com. Ed. Ryozo Miura. **Subscr. to:** Journal Fulfillment, PO Box 2485, Secaucus, NJ 07096-2485. TEL 201-348-4033, FAX 201-348-4505.

332.1 USA
BANK DATA PROCESSING POLICIES AND PROCEDURES. Text in English. 1991. base vol. plus s-a. updates. looseleaf. USD 415; USD 265 renewals (effective 2004). **Document type:** *Directory, Trade.* **Description:** Informs bank data personnel about regulations and assists them in implementing policies in security and risk management, short- and long-range planning, internal and external audits, and computer operations.
Related titles: ♦ Series of: Compliance Officer's Management Manual.
Published by: Sheshunoff Information Services Inc., 505 Barton Springs Rd, Ste 1100, Austin, TX 78704. TEL 512-472-2244, 800-456-2340.

BANK WAGE-HOUR & PERSONNEL REPORT. see *LAW—Corporate Law*

332.1 GBR ISSN 1360-0842
BANKING ON WINDOWS N T. Text in English. 1995. s-a. adv. software rev. illus. **Document type:** *Trade.* **Description:** Covers banking applications based on the Microsoft Windows NT platform.
—BLDSC (1861.930590).
Published by: (Microsoft Corp. USA), I B C Business Publishing Ltd., Gilmoora House, 57-61 Mortimer St, London, W1N 7TD, United Kingdom. TEL 44-20-7637-4383, FAX 44-20-7636-6414, http://www.microsoft.com/industry/finserv. Ed. Martin Whybrow.

332.1 DEU
BANKING ONLINE. Text in German. m. **Document type:** *Magazine, Consumer.*
Published by: W E K A Computerzeitschriften-Verlag GmbH, Gruberstr 46a, Poing, 85586, Germany. TEL 49-8121-951001, FAX 49-8121-951199, redaktion@b-onl.de, http://www.b-onl.de, http://www.wekanet.de.

332.1 USA
BANKLINE. Text in English. m. looseleaf. USD 16 to members; USD 32 to non-members. adv. back issues avail. **Document type:** *Newsletter.* **Description:** Contains banking and finance news for CEOs and CFOs of independent and community banks.
Formerly: Newsline Newsletter
Published by: Western Independent Bankers, 550 Montgomery St, Ste 600, San Francisco, CA 94111-2537. TEL 415-352-2323, FAX 415-352-2314, wibank@aol.com, http://www.wib.org. Ed. Nancy Jennings. Circ: 1,300.

332.1 AUT
BANKTECHNIK; Das Magazin fuer innovative Banker. Text in German. 11/yr. EUR 36 domestic; EUR 51 foreign (effective 2004). adv. **Document type:** *Magazine, Trade.*
Published by: Oesterreichischer Agrarverlag GmbH, Achauer Str 49a, Leopoldsdorf, N 2333, Austria. TEL 43-2235-4040, FAX 43-2235-404929, office@agrarverlag.at, http://www.agrarverlag.at/banktechnik/index.html. Ed. Kurt Quendler. Adv. contact Johanna Kolbert. B&W page EUR 2,262, color page EUR 4,017; trim 175 x 260. Circ: 6,300 (paid and controlled).

332.1 FRA ISSN 0248-9708
BANQUE ET INFORMATIQUE. Text in French. 1981. m. adv. **Document type:** *Consumer.*
Published by: B.I. Magazine, 14 rue du Champ de Mars, Paris, 75007, France. TEL 33-1-45556052, FAX 33-1-45561576. Ed., R&P Gilles Benay. Adv. contact Karin Alexandra. Circ: 10,000.

BROKER. see *BUSINESS AND ECONOMICS—Banking And Finance*

C A A S NEWS; newsletter on computer-assisted appraisal. (Computer-Assisted Appraisal Section) see *REAL ESTATE*

332.1 DEU ISSN 1437-2207
CARD-FORUM. Text in German. 1994. 10/yr. adv. **Document type:** *Magazine, Trade.*
Published by: Every Card Verlags GmbH, Luener Rennbahn 7, Lueneburg, 21339, Germany. TEL 49-4131-98340, info@card-forum.com, http://www.card-forum.com. Ed., Pub. Hans Huber. Adv. contact Ines Krafft. color page EUR 2,500. Circ: 2,500 (controlled).

332.1 DEU
CARD-FORUM INTERNATIONAL. Text in English. 1997. bi-m. adv. **Document type:** *Magazine, Trade.*
Published by: Every Card Verlags GmbH, Luener Rennbahn 7, Lueneburg, 21339, Germany. TEL 49-4131-98340, info@card-forum.com, http://www.card-forum.com. Ed., Pub. Hans Huber. Adv. contact Ines Krafft. color page EUR 2,500. Circ: 6,000 (controlled).

332 GBR ISSN 0956-5558
CARDS INTERNATIONAL. Text in English. 1989. fortn. GBP 1,297, EUR 2,097, USD 2,197 (effective 2005). adv. **Document type:** *Trade.* **Description:** Worldwide briefing on the plastic card industry.
Related titles: Online - full text ed.: (from Gale Group, LexisNexis, O C L C Online Computer Library Center, Inc., ProQuest Information & Learning).
Indexed: B&I, BLI.
Published by: Lafferty Publications Ltd., The Colonnades, 82 Bishops Bridge Rd, London, W2 6BB, United Kingdom. TEL 44-20-75635700, FAX 44-20-75635701, cuserv@lafferty.com, http://www.lafferty.com/newsletter_publication.php?id=5. Eds. Theodore Iacobuzio, Tony Morbin. adv.: B&W page GBP 3,330; trim 184 x 243.

332.1 USA
COMPUTING CHANNELS. Text in English. 1985. m. **Description:** Provides articles on how to manage a microcomputer or software sales organization more efficiently and effectively.
Former titles: A Better Channel; Association of Better Computer Dealers Newsletter
Published by: COMPTIA, 450 E 22nd St, Ste 230, Lombard, IL 60148-6158. TEL 630-268-1818, FAX 630-268-1384. Ed. Kate Nemchausky. adv.: B&W page USD 1,125, color page USD 1,500. Circ: 2,800.

332.1 USA ISSN 1054-7304
HG2037
CREDIT UNION TECHNOLOGY; the magazine for credit union technology decision makers. Text in English. 1991. bi-m. USD 36. adv. bk.rev. index. back issues avail. **Document type:** *Trade.*
Published by: Credit Union Technology, Inc., 110-64 Queens Blvd., Ste. 106, Forest Hills, NY 11375-6347. TEL 718-793-9400, FAX 718-793-9414. Ed. Andrew B Mallon. Circ: 6,000.

332.1 USA ISSN 1744-0416
DEALING WITH TECHNOLOGY. Text in English. 1988. w. (50/yr.). USD 2,025 (effective 2005). **Document type:** *Newsletter, Trade.* **Description:** Aimed at those involved with dealing with technology, both vendors and users.
Formed by the merger of (1997-2003): Trading Technology Week (1096-2638); (1987-2003): Trading Systems Technology (0892-5542); (1995-2003): Dealing & Investment Systems (1079-4107)
Published by: Incisive R W G (Subsidiary of: Incisive Media Plc.), 270 Lafayette St., Ste. 700, New York, NY 10012. TEL 212-925-6990, FAX 212-925-7585, http://www.dealingwithtechnology.com, http://www.incisivemedia.com/. Ed. Eugene Grygo TEL 212-634-4817. Pub. Adrian Goulbourn TEL 212-484-9950. **Subscr. in US to:** Incisive Media Plc., Haymarket House, 28-29 Haymarket, London SW1Y 4RX, United Kingdom. TEL 44-870-2408859, FAX 44-20-74849800.

332.1 GBR ISSN 1461-5215
DERIVATIVES & RISK TECHNOLOGY. Text in English. 1992. bi-w. USD 795 (effective 2000). **Document type:** *Newsletter.* **Description:** Delivers behind-the-scenes reports on the latest software, systems, and networks supporting leading-edge financial engineering and risk management.
Formerly (until 1997): Derivatives Engineering and Technology (0967-3989)
—CCC.
Published by: Risk Waters Group (Subsidiary of: Incisive Media Plc.), Haymarket House, 28-29 Haymarket, London, SW1Y 4RX, United Kingdom. TEL 44-20-74849700, FAX 44-20-74849833, http://www.watersinfo.com.

332.1 USA ISSN 0195-7287
E F T REPORT. (Electronic Funds Transfer) Text in English. 1978. bi-w. USD 995 (effective 2005). back issues avail. **Document type:** *Newsletter, Trade.* **Description:** Publishes for administrators and bankers interested in the electronic funds transfer market. Contains reports on automated teller machine systems, personal identification systems, home banking, home security, and regional and national networks.
Incorporates (1996-2000): Retail Delivery Systems News (1086-2137); (1989-1998): Bank Automation News
Related titles: Online - full text ed.: (from Gale Group, ProQuest Information & Learning, The Dialog Corporation).
Indexed: ABIn, BLI, PROMT.
—CCC.
Published by: Access Intelligence, LLC (Subsidiary of: Veronis, Suhler & Associates Inc.), 1201 Seven Locks Rd, Ste 300, Potomac, MD 20854. TEL 301-354-2000, 800-777-5006, FAX 301-340-1451, jscheinman@phillips.com, clientservices@accessintel.com, http://www.pbimedia.com,. Ed. Lurdes da Maia-Abruscato. **Dist. by:** Publications Resource Group, 121 Union St., Box 792, North Adams, MA 01247. TEL 413-664-6185, FAX 413-664-9343.

332.1 DEU ISSN 1612-1007
EBANKER. Text in German. 2000. bi-m. EUR 10 newsstand/cover (effective 2005). adv. **Document type:** *Magazine, Trade.*
Published by: H & T Verlag GmbH & Co. KG (Subsidiary of: Verlagsgruppe Handelsblatt GmbH), Konrad-Zuse-Platz 1, Munich, 81829, Germany. TEL 49-89-4447870, FAX 49-89-44478710, es@htverlag.de, info@htverlag.de, http://www.ebanker.de, http://www.htverlag.de. Ed. Eva Schulz. adv.: page EUR 4,000. Circ: 39,800 (paid and controlled).

332 658 USA ISSN 1089-3059
HF5548.32
ELECTRONIC COMMERCE ADVISOR. Text in English. 1997. bi-m. USD 190 domestic; USD 247 foreign (effective 1999). bk.rev.; software rev. charts; illus.; stat.; tr.lit. **Document type:** *Trade.* **Description:** Covers business, marketing and technical issues pertaining to electronic commerce, the Internet and the Web.
—CCC.
Published by: W G & L Financial Reporting & Management Research (Subsidiary of: R I A), 395 Hudson St, New York, NY 10014. TEL 212-367-6300, FAX 212-367-6718, wglcorpfinance@riag.com, http://www.wghcorpfinance.com. Ed. Richard H Gamble. Pub. Jean Mary Levy. Circ: 3,500 (paid). **Subscr. to:** The Park Square Bldg 31 St James Ave, Boston, MA 02116-4112.

B

332.1 GBR ISSN 0954-0393
ELECTRONIC PAYMENTS INTERNATIONAL. Text in English. 1986. m. GBP 997, EUR 1,597, USD 1,697 (effective 2005). **Document type:** *Bulletin.* **Description:** Global intelligence on the electronic payments industry, covering marketplace and technology developments in retail EFT services, EDI, homebanking and interbank payment systems.
Formerly (until 1988): RBI EFTPOS International (0269-459X)
Related titles: Online - full text ed.: (from Gale Group, LexisNexis, Northern Light Technology, Inc., O C L C Online Computer Library Center, Inc., ProQuest Information & Learning).
Indexed: B&I, BLI.
Published by: Lafferty Publications Ltd., The Colonnades, 82 Bishops Bridge Rd, London, W2 6BB, United Kingdom. TEL 44-20-75635700, FAX 44-20-75635701, cuserv@lafferty.com, http://www.lafferty.com/newsletter_publication.php?id=6. Ed. Tony Morbin.

332.0285 GBR ISSN 1742-0024
▼ **FINANCIAL COMPUTING.** Text in English. 2003. m. **Document type:** *Magazine, Trade.*
Published by: Penton Media Europe (Subsidiary of: Penton Media, Inc.), Penton House, 288-290 Worton Rd, Isleworth, Mddx TW7 6EL, United Kingdom. TEL 44-20-8232-1600, FAX 44-20-8232-1650, information@penton.com, http://www.penton.com.

332 GBR ISSN 1358-8664
FINANCIAL SECTOR TECHNOLOGY. Text in English. 1995. bi-m. GBP 98 domestic; GBP 128 foreign (effective 2005). adv. **Document type:** *Magazine, Trade.* **Description:** Computer magazine for banks, insurance companies, building societies, and trading houses.
Published by: Perspective Publishing Ltd., 408 Fruit & Wool Exchange, Brushfield St, London, E1 6EP, United Kingdom. TEL 44-20-74260636, FAX 44-20-74260123, muir@perspectivepublishing.com, http://www.fstech.co.uk/, http://www.perspectivepublishing.com/. Ed. Neil Ainger TEL 44-20-74260424. Adv. contact Oliver Morgan TEL 44-20-74260101.

FINANCIAL SOFTWARE AND SYSTEMS GUIDE. see *COMPUTERS—Software*

332.1 GBR ISSN 0957-6177
FINANCIAL SYSTEMS. Text in English. q. GBP 26; GBP 42 foreign. adv. back issues avail. **Document type:** *Trade.* **Description:** Provides information on the advancing technologies for financial service companies and banks such as e-commerce, Internet, telecommunications, and computer systems.
—BLDSC (3926.992600).
Published by: Mitre House Publishing Ltd., 154 Graham Rd, Wimbledon, London, SW19 3SJ, United Kingdom. http://www.mitrehousepublishing.co.uk/. Ed., Pub., R&P Richard Blausten. Adv. contact Ian Holdom.

332 GBR ISSN 0265-1661
FINANCIAL TECHNOLOGY BULLETIN; the international review of IT in the banking industry. Variant title: Financial Technology International Bulletin. Text in English. 1983. 21/yr. GBP 410, USD 720 (effective 1999). bk.rev. index. back issues avail. **Document type:** *Newsletter, Trade.* **Description:** Key source of information for strategic management and IT professionals in the financial sector. Covers developments in financial technology.
Related titles: Online - full text ed.: (from EBSCO Publishing, O C L C Online Computer Library Center, Inc., ProQuest Information & Learning).
Indexed: ABIn, BLI, Inspec.
—BLDSC (3926.993070). **CCC.**

▼ *new title* ➤ *refereed* ✶ *unverified* ♦ *full entry avail.*

Published by: I B C Business Publishing Ltd., Gilmoora House, 57-61 Mortimer St, London, W1N 7TD, United Kingdom. TEL 44-20-7637-4383, FAX 44-20-7636-6414, kburger@mfi.com, http://www.financetech.com/fti.htm. Ed. Frances Maguire. **Subscr. in the US to:** I B C (USA), 290 Eliot St, Box 91004, Ashland, MA 01721-9104. TEL 508-881-2800, 508-881-0982, FAX 508-881-0982.

FINANCIAL TECHNOLOGY INSIGHT. see *BUSINESS AND ECONOMICS—Computer Applications*

332.1 DEU
G & D REPORT. Text in English, German. 2/yr. **Document type:** *Magazine, Trade.* **Description:** Contains articles and information on the latest electronic credit and payment products available from Giesecke & Devrient.
Published by: (Giesecke & Devrient GmbH), BurdaYukom Publishing GmbH (Subsidiary of: Hubert Burda Media Holding GmbH & Co. KG), Schleissheimer Str 141, Munich, 80797, Germany. TEL 49-89-306200, FAX 49-89-30620100, info@burdayukom.de, http://www.yukom.de. Circ: 10,000 (controlled).

B

332.1 DEU
I T - BANKEN UND VERSICHERUNG. Text in German. 2000. bi-m. EUR 10 newsstand/cover (effective 2004). adv. **Document type:** *Magazine, Trade.*
Formerly: I T Banker (1616-5853)
Published by: BAUVE AG i.G., Kirchdorfer Str 87, Bad Woerishofen, 86825, Germany. TEL 49-82473800, FAX 49-8247-380100, information@bauve.de, http://www.bauve.de. adv.: B&W page EUR 2,530, color page EUR 3,910. Circ: 6,488 (paid and controlled).

330 CAN ISSN 1498-9549
I T FOR INDUSTRY. (Information Technology) Text in English. 2000. m. CND 39 domestic; CND 95.88 foreign (effective 2003). adv. **Document type:** *Magazine, Trade.* **Description:** Dedicated to helping Canadian manufacturers implement information technology solutions so they can cut costs and improve their productivity.
Related titles: Online - full text ed.: (from Micromedia ProQuest, ProQuest Information & Learning).
Indexed: ABIn.
Published by: Rogers Media Publishing Ltd, One Mount Pleasant Rd, 11th Fl, Toronto, ON M4Y 2Y5, Canada. TEL 416-764-2000, FAX 416-764-3941, http://www.bizlink.com/itforindustry.htm, http://www.rogers.com. Ed. Adam Pletsch. Pub. Lesley Mellor. Adv. contact Ken McMillan.

332.1 BGR
INFORMATION TECHNOLOGIES IN BANKING. Text in Bulgarian. 2/yr. adv. **Document type:** *Magazine, Trade.* **Description:** Focuses on the development and implementation of information technologies in Bulgarian banks.
Published by: I D G Bulgaria Ltd., 1 Hristo Smirnenski blvd, etazh 11, Sofia, 1421, Bulgaria. TEL 359-2-9630886, FAX 359-2-9632841, idg@mbox.digsys.bg, http://www.idg.bg. adv.: B&W page USD 580, color page USD 875; trim 205 x 285.

332.10285 GBR ISSN 1047-2908
INSIDE MARKET DATA; the newsletter of real-time market data. Text in English. 1985. 50/yr. GBP 1,125, EUR 1,685, USD 2,025 (effective 2005). **Document type:** *Newsletter, Trade.* **Description:** Reports news and analysis on electronic information services and databases used by financial market professionals.
Formerly: Micro Ticker Report (0885-2510)
Related titles: Online - full text ed.: (from Factiva).
—CCC.
Published by: Risk Waters Group (Subsidiary of: Incisive Media Plc.), Haymarket House, 28-29 Haymarket, London, SW1Y 4RX, United Kingdom. TEL 44-20-74849700, FAX 44-20-79302238, customerservices@incisivemedia.com, http://www.watersinfo.com/news/imd/index_home.asp, http://www.incisivemedia.com/. Ed. Samara Zwanger.

332.1 GBR ISSN 1095-0672
INSTITUTIONAL TRADING TECHNOLOGY. Text in English. 1997. bi-w. **Document type:** *Newsletter, Trade.* **Description:** Covers the business and technology of buy-to-sell-side connectivity and provides analysis of the latest trading technologies that are of interest to money managers, brokers and system professionals.
—CCC.
Published by: Risk Waters Group (Subsidiary of: Incisive Media Plc.), Haymarket House, 28-29 Haymarket, London, SW1Y 4RX, United Kingdom. TEL 44-20-74849700, http://www.watersinfo.com.

INTELLIGENT SYSTEMS IN ACCOUNTING, FINANCE & MANAGEMENT. see *BUSINESS AND ECONOMICS—Computer Applications*

332.1 USA ISSN 1553-8206
INTERNET BANKING COMMENTARY; the bankers information resource. Text in English. 2001 (May). m. USD 375 (effective 2005). **Document type:** *Newsletter.*
Published by: AlexInformation, 807 Las Cimas Pkwy Ste 300, Austin, TX 78746. TEL 512-652-4400, FAX 512-652-4499, ibn@alexinformation.com, inforeply@alexinformation.com, http://www.alexinformation.com. Ed. Caroline Wilson.

332 USA ISSN 1533-9939
INTERNET BANKING GROWTH STRATEGIES. Text in English. 2000. m. USD 279 (effective 2004). **Document type:** *Newsletter, Trade.* **Description:** Describes the ways in which financial institutions are using the Internet to increase deposits and loans, expand their market share, introduce new high-tech services, reduce operating costs, provide new fee income and build customer loyalty.
Indexed: BLI.
Published by: Siefer Consultants, Inc., 525 Cayuga St, Storm Lake, IA 50588. TEL 712-732-7340, FAX 712-732-7906, siefer@ncn.net, http://www.siefer.com. Ed. Shere Siefer.

332.1 657 USA ISSN 1532-8805
HJ5709.5.U6
INTERNET TAX ADVISOR. Text in English. 2000. m. USD 205 (effective 2004). 12 p./no.; **Document type:** *Newsletter, Trade.* **Description:** Written for tax attorneys, state and local tax or e-commerce departments of accounting firms, CPA's and accountants, it covers the ins and outs of taxation and proposed taxation of e-commerce.
Related titles: Online - full text ed.: (from EBSCO Publishing, Florida Center for Library Automation, Gale Group).
Indexed: ATI.
Published by: C C H Inc., 2700 Lake Cook Rd, Riverwoods, IL 60015. TEL 847-267-7000, 800-449-6439, cust_serv@cch.com, http://www.cch.com.

KENYA. MINISTRY OF FINANCE AND PLANNING. BUDGET SPEECH BY MINISTER FOR FINANCE AND PLANNING. see *PUBLIC ADMINISTRATION*

KNOWLEDGE MANAGEMENT; the magazine for knowledge professionals. see *COMPUTERS*

332.1 UKR ISSN 1605-5470
KORPORATIVNYE SISTEMY. Text and summaries in Russian. 1995. q. UAK 170 domestic; USD 60 foreign (effective 2001). software rev. **Document type:** *Magazine, Trade.*
Formerly (until 1999): Bankovskie Tekhnologii: Komp'iutery i Programmy
Published by: Dekabr Ltd, Vossoedineniya pr-t 15, 7 etazh, Kiev, 02160, Ukraine. TEL 380-44-5533986, FAX 380-44-5531940, cs_secretary@comizdat.com, http://www.cs.comizdat.com. Ed. Igor Solov'ev. Pub. Sergei Kostyukov. **US dist. addr.:** East View Information Services, 3020 Harbor Ln. N., Minneapolis, MN 55447. TEL 612-550-0961.

LAW AND ELECTRONIC COMMERCE. see *LAW*

332.1 USA
THE LAW OF ELECTRONIC FUNDS TRANSFER. Text in English. 1992. irreg. looseleaf. USD 130 (effective 1999).
Published by: Matthew Bender & Co., Inc. (Subsidiary of: LexisNexis North America), 1275 Broadway, Albany, NY 12204. international@bender.com, http://bender.lexisnexis.com. Ed. Benjamin Geva.

332.10285 USA
MICROBANKER BANKING TECHNOLOGY STRATEGIES NEWSLETTER; the research letter on financial end-user computing. Text in English. 1981. 24/yr., latest vol.2. USD 395 domestic; USD 435 foreign (effective 2001). bk.rev. 12 p./no.; back issues avail. **Document type:** *Newsletter.* **Description:** For bankers using microcomputers. Articles cover banking operations, related programs and software packages.
Formerly: Microbanker (0738-7156)
Related titles: E-mail ed.; Microform ed.: (from PQC); Online - full content ed.
Published by: Microbanker, Inc., PO Box 708, Lake George, NY 12845. TEL 518-745-7071, FAX 518-745-7009, webmaster@microbanker.com, http://www.microbanker.com. Eds. Nancy Davis, Roy W Urrico. Pub. Nancy R Davis. Circ: 2,000.

332.72 USA
MORTGAGE INDUSTRY DIRECTORY. Text in English. 1984. biennial, latest 10th ed. USD 495 per issue (effective 2005). adv. 1000 p./no.; **Document type:** *Directory.* **Description:** Source of industry statistics, rankings, company profiles, and contact information.
Former titles: Mortgage Technology Directory; (until 1998): Guide to Real Estate and Mortgage Banking Software
Published by: Source Media, Inc., One State St Plaza, 27th Fl, New York, NY 10004. TEL 212-803-6077, 800-221-1809, FAX 212-747-1154, custserv@sourcemedia.com, http://www.nationalmortgagenews.com/directory, http://www.sourcemedia.com.

MORTGAGE SERVICING NEWS. see *BUSINESS AND ECONOMICS—Banking And Finance*

332.1 USA ISSN 1096-1879
HG3879
➤ **MULTINATIONAL FINANCE JOURNAL.** Abbreviated title: M F J. Text in English. 1997. q. USD 40 domestic to individuals; USD 60 foreign to individuals; USD 80 domestic to institutions; USD 100 foreign to institutions (effective 2001). adv. back issues avail. **Document type:** *Journal, Academic/Scholarly.* **Description:** Disseminates high-quality research on capital markets, financial institutions, investment management, and corporate finance, especially in a global context.
Related titles: Online - full text ed.: (from EBSCO Publishing, Northern Light Technology, Inc., O C L C Online Computer Library Center, Inc., ProQuest Information & Learning).
Indexed: ABIn, BLI, JEL.
—BLDSC (5983.158000). **CCC.**
Published by: (Rutgers University, Camden, School of Business), Multinational Finance Society, c/o Rutgers University, School of Business, 227 Penn St, Camden, NJ 08102. TEL 856-225-6594, FAX 856-225-6632, http://mfs.rutgers.edu/journal.html. Ed. Panayiotis Theodossiou. adv.: page USD 150; 4 x 7.

332.1 AUS ISSN 1328-2360
OPEN LEARNING DEFERRED PAYMENT SCHEME. Text in English. 1998.
Media: Online - full text.
Published by: AusInfo, GPO Box 1920, Canberra Mc, ACT 2610, Australia. http://www.deetya.gov.au/highered/pubs/oldps/contents.htm.

332.1 USA
P C BUSINESS PRODUCTS. Text in English. 1989. m. USD 150 in North America; USD 165 elsewhere (effective 2001). bk.rev. back issues avail. **Document type:** *Newsletter, Trade.* **Description:** Provides the latest news and information on software, hardware, supplies, and services for individuals and companies using microcomputers for business applications. Contains detailed product information, prices, and evaluations to help microcomputer users select products that will best meet their needs.
Related titles: Online - full text ed.: (from Data-Star, The Dialog Corporation).
Published by: Worldwide Videotex, PO Box 3273, Boynton Beach, FL 33424-3273. TEL 561-738-2276, markedit@juno.com, http://www.wvpubs.com. Ed., Pub. Mark Wright.

332.1 657 USA
PAYMENTS SYSTEM REPORT✶. Text in English. m. USD 150 to non-members; USD 95 to members. adv. **Document type:** *Newsletter.*
Formerly: Automated Payments Update (0897-6457)
Related titles: Microform ed.: (from PQC); Online - full text ed.
Published by: National Automated Clearing House Association, 13665 Dulles Technology Dr, Ste 300, Herndon, VA 20171-4603. TEL 703-742-9190, FAX 703-787-0996, psr@nacha.org. Ed., R&P Brian Ragan. Adv. contact Geirgie Goldston. Circ: 3,500.

351.0285 USA ISSN 1094-673X
HC110.H53
TECH CAPITAL; technology business and finance. Text in English. 1997. bi-m. free to qualified personnel. illus. **Document type:** *Newspaper, Trade.* **Description:** Reports on technology issues in business and finance, both in the federal government and private industry.
Related titles: Online - full text ed.: (from Gale Group, O C L C Online Computer Library Center, Inc.).
Published by: Post - Newsweek Tech Media Group (Subsidiary of: Washington Post Co.), 10 G St, N E, Ste 500, Washington, DC 20002-4228. TEL 202-772-2500, 888-345-7624; FAX 202-772-2511, account_support@posnewsweektech.com, http://www.techcapital.com, http://www.pnbi.com. Circ: 50,000 (controlled).

332 USA
▼ **THOMSON MERGER NEWS.** Text in English. 2005. d. **Description:** Carries reports on the most significant pan-European M&A developments as well as editorial from other Thomson Financial publications.
Media: E-mail.
Published by: Thomson Financial Media, One State St Plaza, 27th Fl, New York, NY 10004-1549. TEL 212-803-8200, FAX 212-292-5216, custserv@thomsonmedia.com, http://www.thomsonmedia.com.

332.1 USA ISSN 1060-989X
HG4515.5 CODEN: WSTEE5
WALL STREET & TECHNOLOGY; for senior-level executives in technology and information management in securities and investment firms. Text in English. 1983. m. USD 85 domestic; USD 105 in Canada; USD 125 elsewhere; free to qualified personnel (effective 2005). adv. bk.rev. illus. Index. back issues avail.; reprints avail. **Document type:** *Magazine, Trade.* **Description:** Publishes information on new and emerging technologies in the global securities and investment management industries.
Formerly (until 1992): Wall Street Computer Review (0738-4343); Which Incorporated (in 1991): Wall Street Computer Review. Buyer's Guide (1042-7171)

Related titles: Online - full text ed.: (from bigchalk, Factiva, Florida Center for Library Automation, Gale Group, H.W. Wilson, LexisNexis, O C L C Online Computer Library Center, Inc., ProQuest Information & Learning).
Indexed: ABIn, BPI, CompC, CompD, Inspec, LRI, Microcompind, PAIS, PCR2, SoftBase.
—BLDSC (9261.479300), AskIEEE, IE, Infotrieve, ingenta. **CCC.**
Published by: C M P Media LLC (Subsidiary of: United News & Media), 3 Park Ave., New York, NY 10016-5902. wst@halldata.com, http://www.wallstreetandtech.com/, http://www.cmp.com. Ed. Kerry Massaro. Pub. John Ecke. adv.: B&W page USD 11,474, color page USD 13,653. Circ: 25,000 (controlled).

332.1 004 GBR
WATERS. Text in English. m. USD 150 (effective 2003). **Document type:** *Trade.* **Description:** For technology professionals at securities firms, banks, institutional investors and exchanges in the US and Canada.
Related titles: Online - full text ed.
Published by: Risk Waters Group (Subsidiary of: Incisive Media Plc.), Haymarket House, 28-29 Haymarket, London, SW1Y 4RX, United Kingdom. TEL 44-20-74849700, FAX 44-20-74849833, usinfo@watersinfo.com, http:// www.watersinfo.com.

BUSINESS AND ECONOMICS—Chamber Of Commerce Publications

A C C R A COST OF LIVING INDEX. (Association for Applied Community Research) see *BUSINESS AND ECONOMICS—Abstracting, Bibliographies, Statistics*

330.9 USA
A C C R A RESEARCH IN REVIEW; promoting excellence in research for community & economic development. (Association for Applied Community Research) Text in English. 1968. q. looseleaf. USD 95 (effective 2000). bk.rev.; software rev. **Document type:** *Newsletter.* **Description:** Covers community and economic development research techniques, and association membership news.
Formerly: A C C R A Newsletter (0899-2304)
Published by: A C C R A, 3401 N Fairfax Dr 3B1, P O Box 407, Arlington, VA 22210-0407. TEL 703-522-4980, FAX 730-522-4985, http://www.accra.org. R&P Kenneth E Poole. Circ: 450.

380.14 AUS ISSN 1328-7699
A C M BULLETIN. Text in English. 1973. m. AUD 80 to members. adv. back issues avail. **Document type:** *Trade.*
Former titles (until 1995): Australian Chamber of Manufactures. Bulletin (1320-2472); (until 1991): A C M Bulletin (Victorian Edition) (1035-395X); (until 1990): File; (until 1984): V.C.M. File (0311-127X)
Published by: Australian Industry Group, 20 Queens Rd, Melbourne, VIC 8004, Australia. TEL 61-3-98670111, FAX 61-3-98670199, helpdesk@aigroup.asn.au, http://www.aigroup.asn.au/. Ed. H. Leek. Adv. contact H Leek.

380 UAE
ABU DHABI. Text in Arabic, English. 1969. m. AED 100. **Description:** Covers local, Arab, and international economic affairs.
Formerly: Abu Dhabi Chamber of Commerce and Industry. Review
Published by: Abu Dhabi Chamber of Commerce and Industry/Ghurfat Tijarah wa-Sina'ah Abu Dhabi, P O Box 662, Abu Dhabi, United Arab Emirates. TEL 2-214000, FAX 2-215867, TELEX 22449 TIJARA EM. Ed. Salem Hamdan Al Amiri.

953 UAE
ABU DHABI CHAMBER OF COMMERCE AND INDUSTRY. ANNUAL REPORT/GHURFAT TIJARAH WA-SINA'AH ABU DHABI. AL-TAQRIR AL-SANAWI. Text in Arabic, English. 1969. a. **Description:** Covers news and activities of the chamber, with an overview of the economic situation in Abu Dhabi.
Published by: Abu Dhabi Chamber of Commerce and Industry/Ghurfat Tijarah wa-Sina'ah Abu Dhabi, P O Box 662, Abu Dhabi, United Arab Emirates. TEL 2-214000, FAX 2-215867, TELEX 22449 TIJARAH EM. Ed. Salem Hamdan Al Amiri. Circ: 500 (controlled).

382 CAN ISSN 0318-7306
ACTION CANADA FRANCE✶. Text in English. 1976. 4/yr. CND 10; CND 15 foreign. adv. bk.rev. charts; illus. **Document type:** *Trade.* **Description:** Deals with commercial, industrial and financial exchanges between France and Canada.
Supersedes: Chambre de Commerce Francaise au Canada. Revue (0045-6306)
Indexed: PAIS.
Published by: Chambre De Commerce Francaise, 500 Place D, Armes, Ste 1510, Montreal, PQ H2Y 2W2, Canada. TEL 514-281-1246, FAX 514-289-9594. Ed. Jean Francois Pichard Du Page. Adv. contact Raphael Benbassa. Circ: 4,500.

944 FRA
ACTIONS LIMOGES✶. Text in French. m.
Published by: Publiclair, 16 Place Jourdan, B.P. 403, Limoges, Cedex 87011, France. TEL 42-66-25-54, FAX 47-42-06-17. Circ: 12,000.

963 ETH
ADDIS ABABA CHAMBER OF COMMERCE. CHAMBER NEWS. Text in Amharic, English. 1981. irreg. free. adv.
Published by: Addis Ababa Chamber of Commerce, c/o Ethiopian Chamber of Commerce, PO Box 517, Addis Ababa, Ethiopia. Ed. Solomon Asfaow. Circ: 2,500.

382 UAE ISSN 1024-266X
HC498.A1
➤ **AFAQ IQTISADIYYAH/ECONOMIC HORIZONS.** Text and summaries in Arabic, English. 1980. q. AED 80 domestic to institutions; USD 45 foreign to institutions (effective 2002). adv. bk.rev.; software rev. abstr.; bibl. back issues avail.; reprints avail. **Document type:** *Journal, Academic/Scholarly.* **Description:** Covers U.A.E. and regional business matters, economic cooperation and development, and chamber activities.
Published by: Federation of U A E Chambers of Commerce and Industry/Ittihad Ghuraf al-Tijarah wal-Sina'ah fi Dawlat al-Imarat al-Arabiyyah al-Muttahidah, PO Box 3014, Abu Dhabi, United Arab Emirates. TEL 971-2-6214144, FAX 971-2-6339210, TELEX 23883 GHURFA EM, fcciauh@emirates.net.ae. Ed. Dr. Abdulrazaq Faris Al-Faris. Circ: 800 (paid); 200 (controlled).

381 USA ISSN 1524-007X
AGENDA (MEMPHIS); the magazine of Memphis success. Text in English. 1990. bi-m. USD 18 (effective 2000); USD 3.95 newsstand/cover. adv. back issues avail. **Document type:** *Consumer.* **Description:** Contains business profiles, pen portraits, stories and reviews designed to highlight noteworthy businesses, organizations, and individuals in Memphis and the Mid-South.
Formerly: Memphis Business
Related titles: Online - full text ed.
Published by: (Memphis Area Chamber of Commerce), Towery Publishing, Inc., 1835 Union Ave, Memphis, TN 38104. TEL 901-251-7000, FAX 901-251-7001, agenda@towery.com, http://www.towery.com. Ed. Melissa Haller. Pub. J Robert Towery. R&P J. Robert Towery. Adv. contact Gigi Phillips. Circ: 20,000 (controlled).

953 UAE
AJMAN. Text in Arabic. q. **Description:** Covers chamber news and activities and examines local and international economic issues.
Formerly: Ajman Chamber of Commerce and Industry. Magazine
Published by: Ajman Chamber of Commerce and Industry, P O Box 662, Ajman, United Arab Emirates. TEL 422177, TELEX 69523 TIJARA EM. Ed. Naeim Ahmed Jumaa. Circ: 1,000 (controlled).

917.6 346.066 USA ISSN 0745-5771
ALABAMA TODAY. Text in English. 1986. m. membership. adv. **Document type:** *Newsletter.* **Description:** Informs members of the council of legislative and regulatory actions, reports on BCA events, membership news, general business news, chamber of commerce news, calendar of events, and new member listings.
Published by: Business Council of Alabama, 2 N Jackson St, Ste 500, Box 76, Montgomery, AL 36101-0076. TEL 334-834-6000, FAX 334-262-7371, http://www.bcatoday.org. Ed., R&P, Adv. contact Marty Ellis. Circ: 6,500.

976.8 USA
ALASKA ACTION. Text in English. m. free. **Document type:** *Newsletter.*
Published by: Alaska State Chamber of Commerce, 217 Second St, Ste 201, Juneau, AK 99801. TEL 907-586-2323, FAX 907-463-5515, asccjuno@ptialaska.net, http:// www.alaskachamber.com. Ed., R&P Pamela LaBolle. Circ: 800.

382 BEL
AMCHAM BUSINESS JOURNAL. Text in English. 1950. q. free. adv. bk.rev. **Document type:** *Magazine, Consumer.* **Description:** Contains a variety of business interest articles as well as information on chamber activities.
Formerly (until 2003): AmCham Magazine; Which superseded in part: AmCham (0778-2624); Which was formerly (until 1990): Commerce in Belgium (0775-2695)
Indexed: ELLIS, HongKongiana, KES.
—BLDSC (0809.229810).
Published by: American Chamber of Commerce in Belgium, Av des Arts 50, Brussels, 1000, Belgium. TEL 32-2-5136770, FAX 32-2-5133590, cbi@post1.amcham.be, http://www.amcham.be. Ed. Carole Hazlewood. Circ: 2,500.

382 HKG
AMCHAM MAGAZINE. Text in English. m. USD 90; USD 9 newsstand/cover. adv. **Document type:** *Consumer.*
Published by: American Chamber of Commerce in Hong Kong, GPO Box 355, Hong Kong, Hong Kong. TEL 852-2526-0165, FAX 852-2810-1289, http://www.amcham.org.hk. Ed. Fred Armentrout. Adv. contact Brian Smith. B&W page HKD 12,200, color page HKD 16,200; trim 215 x 280. Circ: 6,000.

382 MAR ISSN 0065-7689
AMCHAM MOROCCO✶. Cover title: American Chamber of Commerce in Morocco. Annual Review. Text in English, French. 1966. a. free. adv.
Published by: American Chamber of Commerce in Morocco, c/o Fed. des Chambres de Commerce du Maroc, 6 rue d'Erfoud, Rabat Agdal, Morocco.

993.1 NZL ISSN 1173-034X
AMCHAM NEW ZEALAND MEMBERSHIP AND TRADE DIRECTORY. Text in English. a. USD 150 (effective 2001). **Document type:** *Directory.* **Description:** Listing of members, who's who in US business in New Zealand. Includes New Zealand - U.S. trade statistics.
Formerly (until 1990): American Chamber of Commerce in New Zealand. Annual Directory (0113-9495)
Published by: American Chamber of Commerce in New Zealand, P.O. Box 106-002, Auckland, New Zealand. TEL 64-9-3099140, FAX 64-9-3091090, amcham@amcham.co.nz. Ed., R&P Mike Hearn.

382 CHL
AMCHAM NEWS. Text in Spanish. m. adv. **Document type:** *Newsletter, Trade.* **Description:** Reports on the chamber's activities and business opportunities for U.S. and foreign companies entering the market in Chile.
Published by: Chilean - American Chamber of Commerce, Avda Kennedy 5735, of 201, Torre Poniente, Las Condes, Santiago, Chile. TEL 56-2-2909700, FAX 56-2-2120515, amcham@amchamchile.cl, http://www.amchamchile.cl/publicat/ newslett.htm.

382 BEL
AMCHAM NEWSLETTER. Text in English. 1950. bi-m. adv. bk.rev.
Supersedes in part: AmCham (0778-2624); Formerly (until Dec. 1990): Commerce in Belgium (0775-2695)
Published by: American Chamber of Commerce in Belgium, Av des Arts 50, Brussels, 1000, Belgium. TEL 32-2-5136770, FAX 32-2-5133590, http://www.amcham.be. Ed. Carole Hazlewood. Circ: 2,500.

382 NLD ISSN 0001-1878
AMCHAM NEWSLETTER. Text in English. 1962. m. membership. bk.rev. bibl.; charts; illus.; stat. **Document type:** *Newsletter, Trade.* **Description:** Consists of updates on upcoming events, new publications, seminars and conferences of relevance to members.
Published by: American Chamber of Commerce in the Netherlands, Burg van Karnebeeklaan 14, The Hague, 2585 BB, Netherlands. TEL 31-70-3659808, FAX 31-70-3646992, office@amcham.nl, http://www.amcham.nl/newsletter.htm. Ed. Simon Paul. Circ: 1,700.

382 BRA ISSN 0065-7662
AMERICAN CHAMBER OF COMMERCE FOR BRAZIL. ANNUAL DIRECTORY. Text in Portuguese. 1917. a. membership. adv. **Document type:** *Directory.*
Published by: American Chamber of Commerce for Brazil, Praca Pio X, 15 Andar 5, Centro, Caixa Postal 916, Rio De Janeiro, RJ 20040-020, Brazil. FAX 55-21-2032477, achambr@amchamrio.com.br, http://www.amchamrio.br. Ed. Ronaldo Lapa. Adv. contact Mario Simoes. Circ: 2,200.

382 FRA ISSN 0065-7670
AMERICAN CHAMBER OF COMMERCE IN FRANCE. DIRECTORY. Text in French. 1896. a. USD 165 in United States (effective 2001). adv. **Document type:** *Directory.*
Incorporates: List of American Firms in France
Published by: American Chamber of Commerce in France, 156 boul Haussmann, Paris, 75008, France. TEL 33-1-56434567, FAX 33-1-56434560.

382 USA ISSN 0172-9799
AMERICAN CHAMBER OF COMMERCE IN GERMANY. MEMBERSHIP DIRECTORY AND YEARBOOK. Text in English. a. USD 190. **Document type:** *Directory.*
Former titles (until 1978): American Chamber of Commerce in Germany. Directory and Yearbook (0173-2641); (until 1970): American Chamber of Commerce in Germany. Annual Report and Directory (0569-3640); (until 1967): American Chamber of Commerce in Germany. Yearbook (0569-3659)
Published by: (American Chamber of Commerce in Germany e.V.), European Business Publications, Inc., PO Box 891, Darien, CT 06820-9859. TEL 203-656-2701.

382 ITA ISSN 0569-3667
AMERICAN CHAMBER OF COMMERCE IN ITALY. DIRECTORY. Text in Italian. 1964. a. EUR 120 domestic to non-members; USD 175 foreign to non-members; free to members (effective 2005). adv. **Document type:** *Directory, Trade.* **Description:** Covers American trade in Italy and Italian trade in the US.
Published by: American Chamber of Commerce in Italy, Via Cesare Cantu 1, Milan, MI 20123, Italy. TEL 39-02-8690661, FAX 39-02-8057737, amcham@amcham.it, http://www.amcham.it. adv.: color page EUR 1,750; 17.7 x 24.7. Circ: 3,000.

B

▼ new title ➤ refereed ✶ unverified ◆ full entry avail.

382 ITA
AMERICAN CHAMBER OF COMMERCE IN ITALY. NEWSLETTER. Text in English, Italian. 1964. m. free to members. adv. **Document type:** *Newsletter, Consumer.* **Description:** News of upcoming events and American Chamber of Commerce activities in Italy.
Published by: American Chamber of Commerce in Italy, Via Cesare Cantu 1, Milan, MI 20123, Italy. TEL 39-02-8690661, FAX 39-02-8057737, amcham@amcham.it, http://www.amcham.it. adv.: B&W page EUR 500; 17.7 x 24.7. Circ: 30,000.

382 JPN ISSN 0002-7847
HF41
AMERICAN CHAMBER OF COMMERCE IN JAPAN. JOURNAL. Text in Japanese. 1964. m. JPY 75,000 membership to individuals; JPY 180,000 membership to institutions (effective 2005). adv. bk.rev. charts; illus.; stat. **Document type:** *Journal, Trade.* **Description:** Provides information about living and doing business in Japan.
Related titles: Online - full text ed.: (from Gale Group, LexisNexis, O C L C Online Computer Library Center, Inc.).
Indexed: B&I, KES, PAIS.
—BLDSC (4684.400000), IE, ingenta.
Published by: American Chamber of Commerce in Japan, Masonic 39 MT Bldg. 10F, 2-4-5 Azabudai, Minato-ku, Tokyo, 106-0041, Japan. TEL 81-3-34335381, FAX 81-3-34338454, info@accj.or.jp, http://www.accj.or.jp/content/offerings/pub/journal. Circ: 4,500.

382 MAR
AMERICAN CHAMBER OF COMMERCE IN MOROCCO. BULLETIN✶ . Text in English, French. m. **Document type:** *Bulletin.*
Published by: American Chamber of Commerce in Morocco, c/o Fed. des Chambres de Commerce du Maroc, 6 rue d'Erfoud, Rabat Agdal, Morocco.

993.1 NZL
AMERICAN CHAMBER OF COMMERCE IN NEW ZEALAND. NEWSLETTER. Text in English. 8/yr. USD 150 to members (effective 1999). adv. **Document type:** *Newsletter, Trade.* **Description:** Covers US-New Zealand trade topics.
Related titles: E-mail ed.; Fax ed.
Published by: American Chamber of Commerce in New Zealand, P.O. Box 106-002, Auckland, New Zealand. TEL 64-9-3099140, FAX 64-9-3091090, amcham@amcham.co.nz. Ed. Mike Hearn.

382 THA
AMERICAN CHAMBER OF COMMERCE IN THAILAND. HANDBOOK DIRECTORY. Text in Thai. biennial. USD 20. **Document type:** *Directory.*
Published by: American Chamber of Commerce in Thailand, 140 Wireless Rd, Bangkok, Thailand.

382 UKR
AMERICAN CHAMBER OF COMMERCE IN UKRAINE. ELECTRONIC BI-WEEKLY BULLETIN. Text in English. bi-w. membership. **Document type:** *Bulletin.* **Description:** Delivers news of the American Chamber of Commerce to members every second Monday.
Media: Online - full text.
Published by: American Chamber of Commerce in Ukraine, Shovkovychna vul 42-44 LL 2, Kiev, 252004, Ukraine. TEL 380-44-490-5800. Ed. Jorge Zukoski.

AMERICAN CHAMBER OF COMMERCE IN UKRAINE. MEMBERSHIP DIRECTORY. see *BUSINESS AND ECONOMICS—Trade And Industrial Directories*

381 PHL ISSN 0115-3188
AMERICAN CHAMBER OF COMMERCE OF THE PHILIPPINES. WEEKLY EXECUTIVE UPDATE. Short title: Weekly Executive Update (W E U). Variant title: AmCham W E U. Text in English. w. USD 165. adv. **Document type:** *Consumer.*
Formerly: American Chamber of Commerce of the Philippines. Weekly Business Letter
Published by: American Chamber of Commerce of the Philippines, C.P.O. Box 2562, Makati City Mm, 1299, Philippines. TEL 818-79-11, FAX 816-63-59. Ed. L P Gonzaga. R&P Robert M Sears. Adv. contact Lynn A Acejas. Circ: 5,000.

382 GRC ISSN 0065-8529
AMERICAN - HELLENIC CHAMBER OF COMMERCE. BUSINESS DIRECTORY/ELLINOAMERIKANIKON EMBORIKON EPIMELITIRION. BUSINESS DIRECTORY. Text in English. 1960. a. USD 100, EUR 110.01 (effective 2001). adv. charts; stat.; tr.lit. 500 p./no. 3 cols./p.; **Document type:** *Directory, Trade.*
Related titles: ◆ Supplement(s): American - Hellenic Chamber of Commerce. Business Directory. Special Issue. ISSN 0065-8537.
Published by: American - Hellenic Chamber of Commerce, 109-111 Messoghion Ave., Athens, 115 26, Greece. TEL 01-699-3559, info@amcham.gr, http://www.amcham.gr. Ed. Raymond Matera. Pub. Sotiris Yannopoulos. Adv. contacts Dimitris Papaevaggelopoulos, Nikos Psomiades.

338 USA ISSN 0272-1953
HG4057
AMERICAN SUBSIDIARIES OF GERMAN FIRMS/ AMERIKANISCHE TOCHTERGESELLSCHAFTEN DEUTSCHER UNTERNEHMEN. Text in English. 1968. a. USD 100 to non-members; USD 80 to members. adv. **Document type:** *Directory.*
Published by: German American Chamber of Commerce, 12 E 49th St, 24th Fl, New York, NY 10017. info@gaccny.com, http://www.gaccny.com. Ed. Armin Kkrueger. Adv. contact Benigna Kirsten. Circ: 1,500.

382 AUT
AMERIKANISCHE HANDELSKAMMER IN OESTERREICH. AUSTRIA IN U S A/AMERICAN CHAMBER OF COMMERCE IN AUSTRIA. AUSTRIA IN U S A. Text in German, English. 1998. irreg. EUR 30 newsstand/cover to members; EUR 40 newsstand/cover to non-members (effective 2001). 118 p./no.; **Document type:** *Directory, Trade.* **Description:** Presents an alphabetical listing of approximately 550 Austrian companies with subsidiaries, branch offices, and joint ventures or representations in the US, including complete address of the Austrian company and its US counterpart, chief executive officer, and nature of business.
Related titles: CD-ROM ed.: EUR 108 newsstand/cover to members; EUR 138 newsstand/cover to non-members (effective 2001).
Published by: Amerikanische Handelskammer in Oesterreich/American Chamber of Commerce in Austria, Porzellangasse 35, Vienna, W 1090, Austria. TEL 43-1-3195751, FAX 43-1-3195151, office@amcham.or.at, http://www.amcham.or.at. Ed. Patricia Helletzgruber.

382 AUT
AMERIKANISCHE HANDELSKAMMER IN OESTERREICH. EAST WEST TRADE/AMERICAN CHAMBER OF COMMERCE IN AUSTRIA. EAST WEST TRADE. Text in English, German. 1995. irreg. EUR 30 newsstand/cover to members; EUR 40 newsstand/cover to non-members (effective 2001). back issues avail. **Document type:** *Directory, Trade.* **Description:** Presents a selected list of more than 290 AmCham members, US subsidiaries and representatives active in east west trade in 16 countries in Eastern and Central Europe.
Related titles: CD-ROM ed.: EUR 108 newsstand/cover to members; EUR 138 newsstand/cover to non-members (effective 2001).
Published by: Amerikanische Handelskammer in Oesterreich/American Chamber of Commerce in Austria, Porzellangasse 35, Vienna, W 1090, Austria. TEL 43-1-3195751, FAX 43-1-3195151, office@amcham.or.at, http://www.amcham.or.at. Ed. Patricia A Helletzgruber.

382 AUT
AMERIKANISCHE HANDELSKAMMER IN OESTERREICH. NEWSLETTER. Text in English, German. 1960. m. looseleaf. bk.rev.; play rev. stat.; tr.lit. back issues avail. **Document type:** *Newsletter, Trade.* **Description:** Concerns economic and membership news and announcements.
Formerly: Magazine Oesterreich - U S A
Published by: Amerikanische Handelskammer in Oesterreich/American Chamber of Commerce in Austria, Porzellangasse 35, Vienna, W 1090, Austria. TEL 43-1-3195751, FAX 43-1-3195151, office@amcham.or.at, http://www.amcham.or.at. Ed. Patricia Helletzgruber. Adv. contact Patricia A Helletzgruber. Circ: 700.

382 AUT
AMERIKANISCHE HANDELSKAMMMER IN OESTERREICH. U.S. LIST/AMERICAN CHAMBER OF COMMERCE IN AUSTRIA. U.S. LIST. Text in English, German. 1985. irreg. EUR 30 newsstand/cover to members; EUR 40 newsstand/cover to non-members (effective 2001). 92 p./no.; **Document type:** *Directory, Trade.* **Description:** Provides an alphabetical listing of more than 370 US firms, subsidiaries, affiliates and licensees in Austria. Includes the name and address of the American company and its Austrian counterpart, along with telephone and fax numbers, chief executive officers, and the nature of the business.
Related titles: CD-ROM ed.: EUR 108 newsstand/cover to members; EUR 138 newsstand/cover to non-members (effective 2001).
Published by: Amerikanische Handelskammer in Oesterreich/American Chamber of Commerce in Austria, Porzellangasse 35, Vienna, W 1090, Austria. TEL 43-1-3195751, FAX 43-1-3195151, office@amcham.or.at, http://www.amcham.or.at. Ed. Patricia Helletzgruber.

380 338 GRC
ANAPTIXI. Text in Greek. 1920. m. free. adv. bk.rev. charts; mkt.; pat.; tr.lit.; tr.mk.; illus.; stat. 100 p./no. 3 cols./p.; back issues avail. **Document type:** *Bulletin, Trade.*
Formerly (until 1994): Athens Chamber of Commerce and Industry. Monthly Bulletin (0004-6612)
Related titles: Online - full text ed.: 2000.
Published by: Athens Chamber of Commerce and Industry, 7 Akadimias St, Athens, 106 71, Greece. TEL 30-210-3604815, FAX 30-210-3616464, info@acci.gr, http://www.acci.gr/anaptixi. Ed. Theodore Vamvakaris. Pub. Drakoulis Fountoukakos. R&P Panagiotis Koutsikos. Adv. contact Spyros Zervos TEL 3-01-3615149. Circ: 50,000 (controlled).

382 GBR
ANGLO-SPANISH TRADE DIRECTORY/DIRECTORIO COMERCIAL HISPANO BRITANICO. Text in English. a. adv. **Document type:** *Directory.*
Published by: (Spanish Chamber of Commerce in Great Britain), Kogan Page Ltd., 120 Pentonville Rd, London, N1 9JN, United Kingdom. FAX 44-20-7837-6348. R&P Caroline Gomm. Adv. contact Linda Batham.

330.9 FRA
ANJOU ECONOMIQUE. Text in French. 1966. 5/yr. adv. **Document type:** *Newsletter.*
Published by: Chambre de Commerce et d'Industrie d'Angers, 8 bd. du Roi Rene, BP 626, Angers, Cedex 1 49006, France. TEL 33-2-41205420, FAX 33-2-41205414. Ed. Alain Ratour. R&P Dominique Gruson. Adv. contact Pascal Tauvel. Circ: 12,500.

381 FRA ISSN 0066-2798
ANNUAIRE DES CHAMBRES DE COMMERCE ET D'INDUSTRIE. Text in French. 1963. triennial. adv. **Document type:** *Directory.*
Published by: Assemblee des Chambres Francaises de Commerce et d'Industrie (ACFCI), 45 av. d'Iena, Paris, 75116, France. TEL 33-1-40693700, FAX 33-1-47206128, TELEX 610-396, http://www.cci.fr.

382 FRA ISSN 0066-3115
ANNUAIRE FRANCO-ITALIEN. Text in French. 1964. biennial. adv.
Published by: Chambre de Commerce Italienne de Paris, 134 rue du Faubourg Saint- Honore, Paris, 75008, France. Circ: 2,000.

944 330 FRA
ANNUAIRE TELEXPORT; les exportateurs et importateurs francais. Text in English, French, German, Spanish. 1990. a. **Description:** Provides address, telephone, fax and telex numbers, top management, exports and imports and geographic ranges for 38000 French companies.
Related titles: CD-ROM ed.; Online - full text ed.: (from Data-Star).
Published by: (Association Telexport), Chambre de Commerce et d'Industrie de Paris (CEDIP), 27 av. de Friedland, Paris, 75008, France. TEL 33-1-42897240, FAX 33-1-42897281.

946 ESP
ANUARIO INDUSTRIAL DE LA PROVINCIA. Text in Spanish. a.
Published by: Camara Oficial de Comercio, Industria y Navegacion de Tarragona, Av Pau Casals 17, Tarragona, 43003, Spain. TEL 34-977-21967, FAX 34-977-240900.

382 GBR ISSN 1351-0495
ARAB - BRITISH TRADE. Text in Arabic, English. bi-m. free. adv. bk.rev. **Document type:** *Trade.* **Description:** Contains Arab and UK sectorial reports, business opportunities, Arab country reports and regional news, UK economic reports.
Formerly: Arab - British Commerce
Published by: Arab - British Chamber of Commerce, 6 Belgrave Sq, London, SW1X 8PH, United Kingdom. TEL 44-171-235-4363, FAX 44-171-253-1748, abt@abccbims.force9.co.uk. Ed. Simon Bland. adv.: color page GBP 2,750. Circ: 15,000.

382 CHE
ARAB - SWISS CHAMBER OF COMMERCE AND INDUSTRY. ANNUAL DIRECTORY. Text in English. a. CHF 120. adv. **Document type:** *Directory.*
Published by: Arab - Swiss Chamber of Commerce and Industry, 70 route de Florissant, PO Box 304, Geneva 12, 1211, Switzerland. TEL 41-22-3473202, FAX 41-22-3473870. Ed. Elias Attia. Adv. contact Elias Ettia. B&W page CHF 3,190, color page CHF 5,720; trim 185 x 270.

382 CHE
ARAB - SWISS CO-OPERATION. Text in English. 1975. q. free. adv. **Document type:** *Trade.*
Published by: Arab - Swiss Chamber of Commerce and Industry, 70 route de Florissant, PO Box 304, Geneva 12, 1211, Switzerland. TEL 41-22-3473202, FAX 41-22-3473870. Ed., Adv. contact Elias Attia. B&W page CHF 2,700, color page CHF 3,410; trim 185 x 270. Circ: 6,000.

944 FRA ISSN 0335-0088
ARDENNE ECONOMIQUE (CARLEVILLE-MEZIERES). Text in French. 1966. 4/yr.
Address: 18A av. G. Corneau, B.P. 389, Carleville-Mezieres, 08106, France. TEL 24-56-62-62, FAX 24-56-62-22, TELEX 840 016 CHAMCO. Ed. B Lebeau. Circ: 6,000.

330 ITA ISSN 0004-363X
ARTI E MERCATURE. Text in Italian. 1866. bi-m. adv. illus. **Document type:** *Bulletin.*
Related titles: Online - full text ed.
Published by: Camera di Commercio Industria e Agricoltura di Firenze, Piazza dei Giudici 3, Florence, FI 50122, Italy. TEL 39-055-27951, FAX 39-055-2795259, info@camcom.it, http://www.fi.camcom.it/camcom.asp. Ed. Francesco Barbolla.

338.1   TZA
ARUSHA CHAMBER OF COMMERCE AND AGRICULTURE. BULLETIN TO MEMBERS. Text in English. bi-m. **Document type:** *Bulletin.*
Published by: Arusha Chamber of Commerce and Agriculture, PO Box 141, Arusha, Tanzania. TEL 255-3722.

956   ISR
ASAKIM & KALKALA. Text in Hebrew. 1973. q. adv.
Former titles (until May 1993): Kalkala Umischar (0334-7753); (until 1985): Bakalkalah Umischar (0334-3006)
Published by: Igud Lishkot Hamischar Be-Israel/Federation of Israeli Chambers of Commerce, P O Box 20027, Tel Aviv, 61200, Israel. TEL 972-3-5631010, FAX 972-3-5612614, TELEX 33484. Ed. Yosef Shostak. Circ: 5,000.

381   USA
ASHEVILLE REPORT. Text in English. 1943. bi-m. USD 12. adv. illus. **Document type:** *Newsletter.* **Description:** Covers chamber news, industry spotlights, education and local government.
Former titles: Asheville Area Chamber of Commerce. Report; Sky News Report
Published by: Asheville Area Chamber of Commerce, PO Box 1010, Asheville, NC 28802. TEL 704-258-6131, FAX 704-251-0926, http://www.ashevillechamber.org. Ed., R&P, Adv. contact Lynn Schroeder. Pub. Jay Garner. Circ: 2,500 (controlled).

380.106   USA
ASIAN SUNEWS. Text in English. 1994. m. USD 25 (effective 1999). adv.
Published by: Asian Chamber of Commerce, 626 W Indian School, Phoenix, AZ 85013-3150. TEL 602-271-9500, FAX 602-870-7562, asiansun@aol.com, http://www.asianchamber.org/. Ed. Madeline Ong-Sakata. Pub. Madeline Ong Sakata. Adv. contact James Rocky Tang.

381   ERI
ASMARA CHAMBER OF COMMERCE. TRADE AND DEVELOPMENT BULLETIN. Text in English, Tigrinya. 1979. q. USD 16. adv. stat. **Document type:** *Bulletin.*
Supersedes (1972 - Dec. 1977): Chamber of Commerce, Industry and Agriculture of Eritrea. Trade and Development Bulletin
Published by: Asmara Chamber of Commerce, PO Box 856, Asmara, Eritrea. TEL 110814, TELEX 42079. Ed. Taame Foto. Circ: 1,500.

382   IND
ASSO CHAM BULLETIN✱ . Variant title: Associated Chambers of Commerce and Industry of India. Bulletin. Text in English. m. INR 1,000, USD 100. **Document type:** *Bulletin.*
Published by: Associated Chambers of Commerce and Industry of India, c/o Federation of Indian Chambers of Commerce and Industry, Federation H S C, Tansen Marg, New Delhi, 110 001, India. TEL 91-11-3360704, FAX 91-11-3342193, raghuraman@sansad.nic.in, http://www.assocham.org. Ed. T S Sampat Kuman. Circ: 1,500.

382   IND
ASSO CHAM NEWS & VIEWS✱ . Text in English. w. INR 1,500, USD 200.
Published by: Associated Chambers of Commerce and Industry of India, c/o Federation of Indian Chambers of Commerce and Industry, Federation H S C, Tansen Marg, New Delhi, 110 001, India. TEL 91-11-3360704, FAX 91-11-3342193, raghuraman@sansad.nic.in, http://www.assocham.org. Circ: 1,500.

382   IND
ASSO CHAM PARLIAMENTARY DIGEST✱ . Text in English. w. INR 3,000, USD 200. **Document type:** *Corporate.*
Published by: Associated Chambers of Commerce and Industry of India, c/o Federation of Indian Chambers of Commerce and Industry, Federation H S C, Tansen Marg, New Delhi, 110 001, India. TEL 91-11-3360704, FAX 91-11-3342193, raghuraman@sansad.nic.in, http://www.assocham.org. Ed. T S Sampat Kuman. Circ: 1,000.

380   BRA   ISSN 0004-5217
ASSOCIACAO COMERCIAL DO AMAZONAS. BOLETIM✱ . Text in Portuguese. 1968. s-m. free. mkt.; stat. **Document type:** *Bulletin.*
Media: Duplicated (not offset).
Published by: Associacao Comercial do Amazona, Rua Guilherme Moreira, 281, Centro, Manaus, AM 69005-300, Brazil. aca@aca.org.br, http://www.aca.org.br/.

967   MWI
ASSOCIATED CHAMBERS OF COMMERCE AND INDUSTRY OF MALAWI. NEWSLETTER. Text in English. m. **Document type:** *Newsletter, Trade.*
Published by: Associated Chamber of Commerce and Industry of Malawi, PO Box 258, Blantyre, Malawi. TEL 265-671988, FAX 265-671147.

968.91   ZWE
ASSOCIATED CHAMBERS OF COMMERCE OF ZIMBABWE. COMMERCE. Text in English. m.
Published by: Associated Chambers of Commerce of Zimbabwe, Equity House, Rezende St, PO Box 1934, Harare, Zimbabwe.

382   MYS
ASSOCIATED CHINESE CHAMBER OF COMMERCE. TRADE DIRECTORY. Text in English. **Document type:** *Directory.*
Published by: Associated Chinese Chamber of Commerce, 24th 1st Fl Jalan Green Hill, Kuching, Sazawak 93100, Malaysia. FAX 082-429950.

381   GBR
ASSOCIATED KENT CHAMBERS OF COMMERCE & INDUSTRY DIRECTORY. Text in English. a. GBP 60 (effective 2001). **Document type:** *Directory.*
Formerly: Kent Chambers of Commerce Directory
Published by: (Association of Kent Chambers of Commerce), Kemps Publishing Ltd., 11 Swan Courtyard, Charles Edward Rd, Birmingham, W Mids B26 1BU, United Kingdom. TEL 44-121-765-4144, FAX 44-121-706-6210.

330   ITA   ISSN 0004-6078
ASTI INFORMAZIONI ECONOMICHE. Text in Italian. 1946. m. stat. **Description:** Features economic news.
Published by: Camera di Commercio Industria Artigianato e Agricoltura di Asti, Piazza Medici, 8, Asti, AT 14100, Italy. Circ: 1,200.

382   GBR
ATLANTIC. Text in English. 1978 (vol.17). m. GBP 40, USD 88. adv. bk.rev. **Description:** Contains a broad-ranging review of transatlantic business for directors of UK and US companies in Britain.
Formerly: Anglo-American Trade News (0003-3316)
Related titles: Online - full text ed.: (from The Dialog Corporation).
Indexed: Acal, BRD, CBPI, IPARL, MEA&I, MRD, MagInd, PAIS, PMR.
Published by: American Chamber of Commerce (UK), 75 Brook St, London, W1Y 2EB, United Kingdom. TEL 071-493-0381, FAX 071-493-2394, TELEX 23675-AMCHAM-G. Ed. Mara Papathedorou. Circ: 5,000.

382   ITA
ATTUALITA ITALIA - AUSTRALIA. Text in Italian. 1988. 6/yr. adv. **Document type:** *Trade.* **Description:** Covers Australian culture, industry, business, finance, art, science, and fashion.
Published by: Italian - Australian Association, Via Barberini, 86, Rome, RM 00187, Italy. TEL 39-06-4743565, FAX 39-02-233201031, austral@mbox.thunder.it, http://www.australiaitalia.it. Ed. Alberto Olivero. Pub. Vincenzo Romiti. Adv. contact Pietro Friggi. B&W page AUD 1,000, color page AUD 1,300; trim 190 x 265. Circ: 80,000 (controlled).

943   DEU
AUSSENWIRTSCHAFT AKTUELL. Text in German. 1947. s-m. membership. bk.rev. **Description:** Chamber of Commerce publication concerned with foreign trade worldwide. Includes list of fairs and exhibitions.
Formerly (until 1986): Aussenhandelsrundschreiben
Published by: Industrie- und Handelskammer Nuernberg, Hauptmarkt 25-27, Nuernberg, 90403, Germany. TEL 0911-1335-0, FAX 0911-1335488. Circ: 860.

382 332.6   GBR
AUSTRALIA IN BRITAIN. Text in English. a. GBP 25 to non-members. **Document type:** *Directory.* **Description:** Lists Australian and U.K. government agencies, Australian companies and their subsidiaries in the UK.
Published by: Australian British Chamber of Commerce (UK), Morley House, Ste. 10-16, 3rd Fl., 314-322 Regent St, London, W1R 5AE, United Kingdom. TEL 44-171-636-4525. Pub. Nick Came.

382   USA
AUSTRIAN BUSINESS. Text in English. 1975 (vol.27). q. USD 28. adv. illus.
Indexed: BAS.
Published by: United States Austrian Chamber of Commerce, 165 W 46th St, New York, NY 10036. TEL 212-819-0117, FAX 212-819-0117. Ed. Erika N Borozan.

381   GBR
B N. (Business North) Text in English. m.
Formerly: Leeds, Bradford, York and North Yorkshire Chambers of Commerce. Journal
Published by: Leeds, Bradford, York and North Yorkshire Chambers of Commerce, Phoenix House, Rushton Ave, Bradford, W Yorks BD3 7BH, United Kingdom. TEL 44-1274-772777, FAX 44-1274-771081, information@cms.chamber.uk, http://www.cms.chamber.uk. Ed. Susan Pape.

330   IRQ
BAGHDAD CHAMBER OF COMMERCE & INDUSTRY. MONTHLY BULLETIN✱ . Text in Arabic, English. 1950. m. IQD 7,000. adv. bk.rev. **Document type:** *Bulletin.* **Description:** Covers trade and economic news, index prices, and laws and regulations.
Formerly: Baghdad Chamber of Commerce. Weekly Bulletin (0005-3899)
Indexed: ZooRec.

Published by: (Studies and Statistics Department), Baghdad Chamber of Commerce & Industry, Federation of Iraqi Chambers of Commerce, Mustansir St., Baghdad, Iraq. TELEX 212821 GHURFA IK. Circ: 5,000.

970   BHS
BAHAMAS. CHAMBER OF COMMERCE. ANNUAL DIRECTORY. Text in English. 1960. a. USD 8 (effective 1999). adv. **Document type:** *Directory.*
Published by: Chamber of Commerce, Attn: Executive Dir., PO Box N 665, Nassau, Bahamas. TEL 242-322-2145, FAX 242-322-4649. Ed., Adv. contact Ruby Lee Sweeting. Circ: 10,000 (controlled).

380   BHR
BAHRAIN CHAMBER OF COMMERCE AND INDUSTRY. COMMERCE REVIEW/AL-HAYA AL-TIJARIYA. Text in Arabic, English. 1961. m. BHD 10 (effective 2000). adv. bk.rev. **Document type:** *Trade.*
Published by: Bahrain Chamber of Commerce and Industry, PO Box 248, Manama, Bahrain. TEL 973-229555, FAX 973-224985, TELEX 8691 GHURFA BN, bahcci@batelco.com.bh, http://www.bahchamber.com. Ed., Adv. contact Khalil Yousuf. Circ: 7,000.

949.4   CHE
BASLER HANDELSKAMMER. INFO AND B H K NEWS. Text in German. 1976. m. membership. **Document type:** *Bulletin.*
Formerly: Basler Handelskammer. Info and Bulletin
Published by: Basler Handelskammer, Postfach 1548, Basel, 4001, Switzerland. TEL 41-61-2721888, FAX 41-61-2726228, 101320,3471@compuserve.com.

381   DEU   ISSN 0171-9416
BAYERISCH-SCHWAEBISCHE WIRTSCHAFT. Text in German. 1945. m. adv. bk.rev.; film rev. bibl.; charts; stat. index. back issues avail. **Document type:** *Magazine, Trade.* **Description:** Concerned with industry, retail trade and services, business and regional economic development.
Published by: (Industrie- und Handelskammer fuer Augsburg und Schwaben), V M M Wirtschaftsverlag GmbH & Co. KG, Maximilianstr 9, Augsburg, 86150, Germany. TEL 49-821-44050, FAX 49-821-4405409, bsw@augsburg.ihk.de, info@vmm-wirtschaftsverlag.de, http://www.vmm-wirtschaftsverlag.de. Ed. Hans Ulrich Rohde. Adv. contact Sabine Sokoll. B&W page EUR 3,810, color page EUR 4,840; trim 210 x 297. Circ: 52,000 (controlled).

382   GBR   ISSN 1357-6879
BELGO-LUXEMBOURG CHAMBER OF COMMERCE IN GREAT BRITAIN. JOURNAL. Text in English. 1978. 6/yr. membership. adv. bk.rev. charts; illus.; tr.lit. **Document type:** *Trade.* **Description:** Interviews with business leaders, embassy news and events, new member profiles, and a list of trade fairs.
Former titles: Business Contact; Belgian Chamber of Commerce in Great Britain Journal (0005-8378)
Published by: Belgo-Luxembourg Chamber of Commerce in Great Britain, Berkeley House, 2nd Fl, 73 Upper Richmond Rd, London, SW15 2SZ, United Kingdom. TEL 44-181-877-3025, FAX 44-181-877-3961. Ed. D Maeremans. Adv. contact Annelies Vangysegem. B&W page GBP 515, color page GBP 710. Circ: 3,500.

380   DEU   ISSN 0944-7350
BERGISCHE WIRTSCHAFT. Text in German. s-m. adv. bk.rev. abstr.; pat.; stat.; tr.lit.; tr.mk. index. **Document type:** *Magazine, Trade.*
Former titles (until 1993): Bergische Wirtschaft in Wuppertal, Solingen und Remscheid (0343-821X); (until 1977): I H K Wuppertal. Wirtschaftliche Mitteilungen (0343-8295)
Published by: (Industrie- und Handelskammer Wuppertal - Solingen - Remscheid), Bergische Verlagsgesellschaft Menzel GmbH & Co. KG, Neumarktstr 10, Wuppertal, 42103, Germany. TEL 49-202-451654, FAX 49-202-450086, info@bvg-menzel.de, http://www.bvg-menzel.de. adv.: B&W page EUR 1,264, color page EUR 1,992.58; trim 185 x 260. Circ: 9,500 (controlled).

382   DEU   ISSN 0939-4443
BERLIN - BRANDENBURGISCHE HANDWERK. Text in German. 1986. fortn. EUR 46.02; EUR 2.56 newsstand/cover (effective 2004). adv. **Document type:** *Journal, Academic/Scholarly.*
Formerly (until 1990): Berliner Handwerk (0931-3206)
Published by: (Handwerkskammer Berlin), Westkreuz Verlag GmbH Berlin-Bonn, Buehlenstr 10-14, Bad Muenstereifel, 53902, Germany. TEL 49-2257-811, FAX 49-2257-7853, verlag@westkreuz.de, http://www.westkreuz.de. Ed. Christian Schmaling. Adv. contact Erika Broeschke. B&W page EUR 2,400, color page EUR 4,200. Circ: 28,334 (paid and controlled).

943   DEU   ISSN 0405-5756
DIE BERLINER WIRTSCHAFT. Text in German. 1950. m. EUR 2.50 newsstand/cover (effective 2004). adv. charts; illus. index. **Document type:** *Magazine, Trade.*
Indexed: RASB.
Published by: Industrie- und Handelskammer zu Berlin, Fasanenstr 85, Berlin, 10623, Germany. TEL 49-30-315100, FAX 49-30-31510166, service@berlin.ihk.de, http://www.berlin.ihk24.de. Ed. Egbert Steinke. adv.: B&W page EUR 3,514, color page EUR 5,973. Circ: 53,000 (controlled).

B

943 DEU
BERUFSBILDUNGSBRIEF. Text in German. 1965. q. free. back issues avail. **Document type:** *Bulletin.* **Description:** Information on vocational training affairs.
Published by: Industrie- und Handelskammer zu Dortmund, Maerkische Str 120, Dortmund, 44141, Germany. TEL 49-231-5417-260, FAX 49-231-5417-329, weibert@dortmund.ihk.de, info@dortmund.ihk.de. Ed. Claus Dieter Weibert. Circ: 7,000.

382 PRT
BILATERAL. Text in English, Portuguese. 1951. q. bk.rev. charts; illus.; stat. **Document type:** *Trade.*
Former titles (until 1994): Camara de Comercio Luso-Britanica. Revista Bimestral (0872-1572); (until 1986): British-Portuguese Chamber of Commerce Magazine (0872-9832); British-Portuguese Chamber of Commerce. Monthly Bulletin (0007-165X)
Published by: British-Portuguese Chamber of Commerce, Rua da Estrela, 8, Lisbon, 1200-669, Portugal. TEL 351-213-942020, FAX 351-213-942029, info@bpcc.pt, http://www.bpcc.pt. Ed., Pub. David Sampson. R&P Chris Barton. Adv. contact Emi Dasilva. Circ: 4,000.

B

976 USA ISSN 0006-369X
BIRMINGHAM. Text in English. 1961. m. USD 15; USD 2.95 newsstand/cover (effective 2005). adv. bk.rev. **Document type:** *Magazine, Trade.* **Description:** General interest city magazine.
Published by: Birmingham Area Chamber of Commerce, 505 N 20th St, Ste 151, Birmingham, AL 35203-2605. TEL 205-241-8180, bham_mag@snsnet.net, http://www.bhammag.com. Ed. Joe O'Donnell TEL 205-241-8186. adv.: B&W page USD 2,420, color page USD 3,250. Circ: 18,000. **Subscr. to:** 505 20th St N., Birmingham, AL 35203-2605.

917.6 USA ISSN 0888-403X
BIRMINGHAM BUSINESS. Text in English. m. USD 6 to non-members. back issues avail. **Description:** Reports on chamber activities and programs; provides calendar of events.
Related titles: Online - full text ed.
Published by: Birmingham Area Chamber of Commerce, 505 N 20th St, Ste 151, Birmingham, AL 35203-2605. TEL 205-250-7653. Ed. Kristi Gilmore. Circ: 5,000.

943 DEU
BLICKPUNKT WIRTSCHAFT (GIESSEN). Text in German. 1956. m. membership. adv. bk.rev. **Document type:** *Journal, Trade.*
Published by: Industrie- und Handelskammer Giessen/Chamber of Industry and Commerce Giessen, Lonystr 7, PO Box 111220, Giessen, 35390, Germany. Circ: 6,300.

330 DEU ISSN 0944-3606
BLICKPUNKT WIRTSCHAFT (TRIER). Text in German. 1991. m. EUR 1.53 newsstand/cover (effective 2004). adv. **Document type:** *Magazine, Trade.*
Published by: Industrie- und Handelskammer Trier, Herzogenbuscher Str 12, Trier, 54292, Germany. TEL 49-651-97770, FAX 49-651-9777150, info@trier.ihk.de, http://www.ihk-trier.de. adv.: B&W page EUR 1,303.02, color page EUR 2,084.83. Circ: 20,800 (paid and controlled).

381.06 USA
BOISE METRO BUSINESS TODAY. Text in English. 1974. m. free membership; USD 24 to non-members (effective 2005). **Document type:** *Magazine, Trade.* **Description:** Features Chamber news and events, new members, small business feature articles and monthly training and event calendar.
Formerly: Boise Business Today
Published by: Boise Metro Chamber of Commerce, PO Box 2368, Boise, ID 83701. TEL 208-472-5200, FAX 208-472-5201, info@boisechamber.org, http://www.boisechamber.org. Pub. Nancy Vannorsdel. Circ: 5,000 (controlled).

380 ESP ISSN 0211-1268
BOLETIN DE COYUNTURA Y ESTADISTICA DEL PAIS VASCO. Text in Spanish, Basque. 1969-1978; resumed. q. charts. **Document type:** *Bulletin.*
Formed by the merger of: Camaras Oficiales de Comercio, Industria y Navegacion de la Region Vasconavarra. Coyuntura Industrial Regional; Utilizacion de la Capacidad Productiva Regional
Published by: Camara Oficial de Comercio e Industria de Alava, Dato 38, Vitoria, 01005, Spain. TEL 34-45-141800, FAX 34-45-143156, cocia@jet.es, http://www.jet.es/camara. Ed. Lorenzo Bergareche Capa. Circ: 2,000.

986 COL
BOLETIN INTERNACIONAL DE OPORTUNIDADES. Text in Spanish. 1971. w. USD 60.
Published by: Camara de Comercio de Bogota, Carrera 26 68D-35, Bogota, Colombia. Circ: 800.

BOLLETTINO COMMERCIO ESTERO. see *BUSINESS AND ECONOMICS—International Commerce*

945 ITA
BOLLETTINO DEI PROTESTI. Text in Italian. fortn.
Published by: Camera di Commercio Industria Artigianato e Agricoltura di Vicenza, Corso Antonio Fogazzaro, 37, Vicenza, VI 36100, Italy. TEL 39-444-994811, FAX 39-444-994834.

330 ITA ISSN 0006-6796
BOLLETTINO ECONOMICO. Text in Italian. 1946. m. free. adv. **Document type:** *Bulletin, Government.*
Indexed: NumL.
Published by: Camera di Commercio, Industria, Artigianato e Agricoltura di Ancona, 1 Piazza 24 Maggio, Ancona, AN, Italy. TEL 071-58981. Ed. Roberto Ronchitelli. Circ: 600.

380 ARG ISSN 0325-4984
BOLSA. Text in Spanish. 1905. irreg. USD 3 per issue. adv. illus.; mkt.; stat.
Formerly (until 1968): Bolsa de Comercio de Buenos Aires. Boletin (0006-6923)
Related titles: ♦ Supplement(s): Bolsa. Suplemento. ISSN 0325-4992; ♦ Bolsa. Suplemento Semanal. ISSN 0325-500X.
Published by: Bolsa de Comercio de Buenos Aires, Sarmiento, 299, Capital Federal, Buenos Aires 1041, Argentina.

982 ARG
BOLSA DE COMERCIO DE MENDOZA. CENTRO DE INFORMACIONES. BOLETIN. Text in Spanish. 1975 (no.152). m. ARS 100. adv. bk.rev. **Document type:** *Bulletin.*
Published by: Bolsa de Comercio de Mendoza, Sarmiento 199, Mendoza, Argentina. Ed. Ernesto Diez Miralles.

380 ARG ISSN 0006-6931
BOLSA DE COMERCIO DE ROSARIO. REVISTA. Text in Spanish. 1913. 3/yr. free. adv. mkt.; stat. **Document type:** *Trade.*
Indexed: PAIS.
Published by: Bolsa de Comercio de Rosario, Cordoba, 1402, Rosario, Santa Fe 2000, Argentina. TEL 54-341-4213437, FAX 54-341-4241019, TELEX 41894 BOROS AR, prensa@bcr.com.ar, http://www.bolsarosario.com. Ed. Nicanor Sodiro. R&P, Adv. contact Carolina Rolle. Circ: 5,000.

380 ARG ISSN 0325-4992
BOLSA. SUPLEMENTO. Text in Spanish. 1905. irreg.
Related titles: ♦ Supplement to: Bolsa. ISSN 0325-4984.
Published by: Bolsa de Comercio de Buenos Aires, Sarmiento, 299, Capital Federal, Buenos Aires 1041, Argentina.

380 ARG ISSN 0325-500X
BOLSA. SUPLEMENTO SEMANAL. Text in Spanish. 1905. w.
Related titles: ♦ Supplement to: Bolsa. ISSN 0325-4984.
Published by: Bolsa de Comercio de Buenos Aires, Sarmiento, 299, Capital Federal, Buenos Aires 1041, Argentina.

381 FRA ISSN 0988-9590
BOULOGNE INFORMATIONS. Text in French. 1951. 2/m. bk.rev. **Document type:** *Trade.*
Formerly (until 1970): Revue de Bologne et de la Region (0988-9582)
Published by: Chambre de Commerce et d'Industrie de Boulogne, 98 quai Leon Gambetta, BP 269, Boulogne-sur-Mer, Cedex 62204, France. FAX 33-3-21996201. Ed. Michel Baillieu. Adv. contact Bruno Leleu. Circ: 9,000.

382 USA ISSN 0300-7464
BRAZILIAN AMERICAN CHAMBER OF COMMERCE NEWS BULLETIN. Text in English. 1977 (vol.7). m. USD 120 (effective 2000). charts; stat. **Document type:** *Directory, Trade.*
Media: Duplicated (not offset).
Published by: Brazilian - American Chamber of Commerce, Inc, 509 Madison Ave, Ste 304, New York, NY 10022-5501. TEL 212-751-4691, FAX 212-751-7692, info@brazilcham.com, http://www.brazilcham.com. Ed. Monica Rocha. R&P Sueli Christina Bonaperte. Circ: 1,200.

944 FRA ISSN 0153-6028
BRETAGNE ECONOMIQUE. Text in French. 1979. 9/yr. adv.
Published by: Editions Bretagne Economique, 1 rue du General Guillaudot, Rennes, Cedex 35044, France. TEL 33-2-99254137, FAX 33-2-99633528, TELEX 730 020, bret_eco@iway.fr. Ed. Elizabeth Pantou Vincent. Pub. Jean Claude Crocq. Adv. contact Veronique Maignant. Circ: 13,000.

339.1 ROM ISSN 1454-6558
BREVIARUL AGENTILOR ECONOMICI DIN JUDETUL BRASOV. Text in Romanian. a. **Document type:** *Magazine, Trade.*
Formerly (until 1994): Camera de Comert si Industrie Brasov. Anuarul Societatilor Comerciale
Published by: Tipotex, Str. Traian Grozavescu nr. 7, Brasov, Romania. TEL 40-68-410845, FAX 40-68-410865.

941 GBR
BRISTOL CHAMBER OF COMMERCE AND AFFILIATED CHAMBERS. MEMBERS DIRECTORY. Text in English. a. GBP 60 (effective 2001). adv. **Document type:** *Directory.*
Former titles: Directory of the Bristol and Western Chambers of Commerce; Bristol Business Reference Book; (until 1993): Bristol Chamber of Commerce and Industry Directory
Published by: (Bristol Chamber of Commerce & Industry), Kemps Publishing Ltd., 11 Swan Courtyard, Charles Edward Rd, Birmingham, W Mids B26 1BU, United Kingdom. TEL 44-121-765-4144, FAX 44-121-706-6210.

382 THA
BRITISH CHAMBER OF COMMERCE. MONTHLY INFORMATION SERVICE. Text in Thai. m.
Published by: British Chamber of Commerce, Bangkok Insurance Bldg, 302 Silom Rd, Bangkok, 10500, Thailand. TEL 2341140.

382 TUR ISSN 0007-0416
BRITISH CHAMBER OF COMMERCE OF TURKEY. TRADE JOURNAL. Text in Turkish. 1908. m. USD 61. adv. mkt.; stat. index.
Published by: British Chamber of Commerce of Turkey, Karakoy, P K 190, Istanbul, Turkey. FAX 152-55-51, TELEX 24-881 ITOD TR. Ed. Ilter Koral. Circ: 700.

381 ARG
BUENOS AIRES. CAMARA DE COMERCIO. INFORMATIVO MENSUAL. Text in Spanish. 1913. m. free. bk.rev. illus.
Published by: Camara de Comercio, piso 4, Florida, Buenos Aires 1602, Argentina. Circ: 1,000.

381 BFA
BULLETIN ECONOMIQUE ET FISCAL DU BURKINA FASO. Text in French. 1971. bi-m. XOF 16,000 (effective 1999). stat. cum.index. back issues avail. **Description:** Contains legislative and statutory notices.
Former titles: Bulletin Economique et Fiscal de la Haute Volta; (until 1975): Chambre de Commerce, d'Agriculture et d'Industrie de Haute-Volta. Bulletin Douanier et Fiscal
Published by: Chambre de Commerce d'Industrie et d'Artisanat, PO Box 502, Ouagadougou, 01, Burkina Faso. TEL 30-61-15, FAX 30-61-16. Circ: 350.

382 AUT
BURGENLANDS WIRTSCHAFT. Text in German. fortn. adv. **Document type:** *Newspaper, Trade.*
Formerly: Burgenlandischer Wirtschaftsdienst
Published by: Wirtschaftskammer Burgenland, Robert-Graf-Platz 1, Eisenstadt, B 7000, Austria. TEL 43-590-907, wkbgld@wkbgld.at, http://wko.at/bgld. adv.: B&W page EUR 1,565, color page EUR 2,200; trim 186 x 258. Circ: 13,500 (controlled).

338 GBR
THE BUSINESS; industry in the Tayside region. Text in English. 1958. m. GBP 1.50 per issue (effective 2000). adv. **Document type:** *Newspaper.*
Former titles (until 1999): Dundee Tayside (0306-0241); Dundee Chamber of Commerce Journal (0012-7124)
—BLDSC (3631.125300).
Published by: Dundee and Tayside Chamber of Commerce and Industry, Chamber of Commerce Bldgs, Dundee, Panmure St, Dundee, DD1 1ED, United Kingdom. Ed., R&P Maggie Lennon. Adv. contact Julie Christie. Circ: 6,000 (controlled).

381 USA ISSN 0887-7904
BUSINESS (LITTLE ROCK). Text in English. 1977. m. USD 225 to non-members. adv. stat. back issues avail.
Superseded: Little Rock Currents
Published by: Greater Little Rock Chamber of Commerce, 1 Chamber Plaza, Little Rock, AR 72201. TEL 501-374-4871. Ed. Gary Newton. Circ: 2,430.

382 COL ISSN 0122-249X
BUSINESS COLOMBIA COMERCIO COLOMBO AMERICANO. Text in English. 1969. q. USD 75 (effective 2001).
Published by: Camara de Comercio Colombo-Americana, Calle 98 No. 22-64 Ofic. 1209, Apartado Aereo 8008, Bogota, CUND, Colombia. TEL 57-1-6237088, FAX 57-1-6216838, publicaciones@amchamcolombia.com.co, http://www.amchamcolombia.com.co. Ed. Joseph Finin.

381.029 USA
BUSINESS DESK REFERENCE. Text in English. a. USD 150 to non-members (effective 2000). adv. **Document type:** *Directory.* **Description:** Includes 2800 business listings with contact name, title, business address, phone and fax. Organized alphabetically and by type of business.
Published by: Hampton Roads Chamber of Commerce, 420 Bank St, Norfolk, VA 23510. TEL 757-622-2312, FAX 757-622-5563, http://www.hrccva.com. Ed., R&P, Adv. contact Amy Bull TEL 757-664-2530. Pub. John A Hornbeck Jr. Circ: 10,000.

968 ZAF
BUSINESS FOCUS. Variant title: Chamber News. Text in English. m.
Formerly: Zululand Chamber of Commerce and Industry. News
Published by: Zululand Chamber of Business, PO Box 1133, Empangeni, Zululand 3880, South Africa. TEL 27-351-25335, info@zululandchamber.co.za. Ed. Helen Ludwig.

382 USA
BUSINESS GUIDE TO SWITZERLAND. Text in English. bi-m. adv. **Document type:** *Magazine, Trade.* **Description:** Dedicated to the promotion of Swiss products, technologies, specialties, companies, research and trade fairs.
Published by: Pyramid Media Group, 666 Fifth Ave, Ste 230, New York, NY 10103. TEL 212-332-0909, FAX 212-315-1534, info@pyramid.ch, http://www.pyramid.ch. Ed., Pub. Aram Gesar. Adv. contact Martin Brennan. Circ: 40,000 (controlled).

382 HTI
BUSINESS HAITI. Text in French. q. USD 10.
Published by: Haitian-American Chamber of Commerce and Industry, Scotiabank Bldg., 82 rte. de Delmas, PO Box 13486 DELMAS, Port-au-Prince, Haiti.

974 USA
BUSINESS INSIDER. Text in English. m. USD 25. adv. back issues avail. **Document type:** *Newsletter.* **Description:** Aimed at the business community of the Niagara Falls area.
Published by: Niagara Falls Area Chamber of Commerce, 345 Third St, Niagara Falls, NY 14303-1117. TEL 716-285-9141, FAX 716-285-0941. Pub. Charles Steiner. Adv. contact Fred Caso Jr. Circ: 3,000.

BUSINESS INTELLIGENCE REPORT; strategies and trends for the successful business. see *BUSINESS AND ECONOMICS—Small Business*

381 IRL ISSN 1649-1890
BUSINESS IRELAND MAGAZINE. Text in English. 1952. q. adv.
Former titles (until 2002): Business Contact (0791-9182); (until 1988): Industry and Commerce (0791-8259); (until 1980): Chamber of Commerce Journal (0790-0465)
Published by: (Dublin Chamber of Commerce), Ashville Media Group, Apollo House, Tara St., Dublin, 2, Ireland. TEL 353-1-4322200, FAX 353-1-6727100, info@ashville.com, http://www.ashville.com. Adv. contact Brian Kearns. page EUR 2,750. Circ: 3,300.

382 PHL ISSN 0116-452X
HC451
BUSINESS JOURNAL. Text in English. 1921. m. PHP 385; USD 27 foreign. adv. **Document type:** *Trade.*
Indexed: BAS, IPP, PAIS, PROMT.
Published by: American Chamber of Commerce of the Philippines, C.P.O. Box 2562, Makati City Mm, 1299, Philippines. TEL 63-818-79-11, FAX 63-816-63-59. Ed. Katherine D Mayo. Adv. contact Linda A Acejas. B&W page USD 350; 10 x 7.5. Circ: 5,000.

338 USA ISSN 0007-6945
BUSINESS MEMO FROM BELGIUM. Text in English. 1957. q. free. **Document type:** *Newsletter.* **Description:** Focuses on Belgium's legal and economic environment, available investment opportunities, and foreign companies operating in the country.
Media: Duplicated (not offset). **Related titles:** Online - full text ed.: (from Gale Group).
Indexed: PROMT.
Published by: Embassy of Belgium, Investments Office, 3330 Garfield St N W, Washington, DC 20008. TEL 202-625-5887, FAX 202-625-7567, washington@diplobel.org, http://www.diplobel.org/usa. Ed. Walter Stevens. Circ: 50,000 (controlled).

382 MEX ISSN 0187-1455
HF3231
BUSINESS MEXICO. Text in English. 1981. m. USD 134 (effective 2003). adv. bk.rev.; software rev. charts; illus. index. back issues avail. **Document type:** *Magazine, Corporate.* **Description:** Comprehensive view of Mexico's economics, investment, trade, environment and industries.
Formed by the merger of (1981): American Chamber of Commerce of Mexico. Quarterly Economic Report; (1939-1981): Mexican-American Review (0026-1696)
Related titles: CD-ROM ed.: (from ProQuest Information & Learning); Microform ed.: (from PQC); Online - full text ed.: (from bigchalk, EBSCO Publishing, Florida Center for Library Automation, Gale Group, H.W. Wilson, LexisNexis, Northern Light Technology, Inc., O C L C Online Computer Library Center, Inc., ProQuest Information & Learning).
Indexed: ABIn, B&I, BPI, HAPI, KES, PAIS.
—BLDSC (2934.286000), IE, ingenta.
Published by: American Chamber of Commerce of Mexico A.C., Lucerna 78, Col. Juarez, Mexico City, D F 06600, Mexico. TEL 52-55-51413800, FAX 52-55-57032911, amchamm@amcham.com.mx, http://www.amcham.com.mx/. Eds. Armando Saliba, Matthew Brayman. R&P Diana H de Hernandez. Adv. contact Rommy Strevel. Circ: 11,000.

381 GBR
BUSINESS NEWS BRIEF. Text in English. 1918. q. membership. adv. **Document type:** *Newsletter.*
Formerly: Edinburgh Chamber of Commerce and Manufactures Journal
Published by: Edinburgh Chamber of Commerce and Enterprise, 27 Melville Street, Edinburgh, EH3 7JF, United Kingdom. TEL 44-131-4777000, FAX 44-131-4777002, information@ecce.org, http://www.ecce.org/. Ed. Maureen Munn. R&P, Adv. contact Mark Ellison. Circ: 3,000.

381.029 USA
BUSINESS REVIEW - DIRECTORY. Text in English. a. USD 75 (effective 2000). **Document type:** *Directory, Trade.* **Description:** Listing of Chamber members and economic-statistical information on Brazil.
Published by: Brazilian - American Chamber of Commerce, Inc, 509 Madison Ave, Ste 304, New York, NY 10022-5501. TEL 212-751-4691, FAX 212-751-7692, info@brazilcham.com, http://www.brazilcham.com. Ed. Monica Rocha. R&P Sueli Christina Bonaperte. Circ: 1,500.

382 BRA
BUSINESS ROUND-UP. Text in Portuguese. m.
Published by: American Chamber of Commerce for Brazil, Praca Pio X, 15 Andar 5, Centro, Caixa Postal 916, Rio De Janeiro, RJ 20040-020, Brazil. TEL 55-21-2032477, achambr@amchamrio.com.br, http://www.amchamrio.com.br.

380.1 USA ISSN 1043-5336
BUSINESS TODAY (ST. PAUL)✶. Text in English. 1975. bi-m. USD 20. bk.rev. **Document type:** *Newsletter.*
Former titles (until 1989): Chamberview (0885-0828); Saint Paul Area Chamber of Commerce Dialogue
Published by: St. Paul Area Chamber of Commerce, 332 Minnesota St., Ste. N205, St. Paul, MN 55101-2701. TEL 612-223-5000, FAX 612-223-5119. Circ: 3,000.

382 VEN ISSN 0045-3641
BUSINESS VENEZUELA. Text in English. 1968. 10/yr. USD 250. adv. reprint service avail. from PQC.
Related titles: Microform ed.: (from PQC).
Indexed: HAPI, KES, PAIS.
Published by: Venezuelan - American Chamber of Commerce and Industry/Camara Venezolano-Americana de Comercio e Industria, Torre Credival-PL., 2da Avenida de Campo Alegre, Caracas, DF 1010-A, Venezuela. TEL 58-2-2630833, FAX 58-2-2630586, TELEX 28399, skivilevic@venamcham.org. Ed. Antonio Herrera Vaillant. R&P, Adv. contact Shalom Kivilevic. Circ: 30,000.

944 FRA
C C I MAGAZINE. Text in French. 4/yr. **Document type:** *Bulletin.*
Published by: Chambre de Commerce et d'Industrie de Cherbourg-Cotentin, Hotel Atlantique, Bd. Felix Amiot, BP 839, Cherbourg, Cedex 50108, France. TEL 33-2-33233200, FAX 33-2-33233228, TELEX 170 849 F. Ed. Rene Moirand. Circ: 5,000.

380 EGY
CAIRO CHAMBER OF COMMERCE. JOURNAL/GHURFAT AL-TIGARA AL-QAHIRA. MAGALLA. Text in Arabic. m. EGP 26.70.
Published by: Cairo Chamber of Commerce/Ghurfat al-Tigara al-Qahira, 4 Midan al-Falaky, Cairo, Egypt. TEL 02-3558261, FAX 02-3563603, TELEX 92453. Ed. Rafaat Amin.

979.4 USA ISSN 0882-0929
CALIFORNIA CHAMBER OF COMMERCE ALERT. Text in English. 1972. 34/yr. membership only. **Document type:** *Newsletter.* **Description:** Provides updates on legislation, regulations and policy issues of concern to California employers.
Formerly: Pacific Alert (0048-2617)
Indexed: EEA.
Published by: California Chamber of Commerce, PO Box 1736, Sacramento, CA 95812-1736. TEL 916-444-6670, FAX 916-444-6685, alert@calchamber.com, http://www.calchamber.com. Ed., R&P Ann S Amioka. Pub. Allan Zaremberg. Circ: 24,000.

975.9 USA
CAMACOL NEWS. Text in English. m.
Published by: Latin Chamber of Commerce/Camara de Comercio Latina, 1417 W Flagler, Miami, FL 33135.

380.1 ESP ISSN 1130-832X
LA CAMARA. Text in Spanish. 1944. m. adv. bk.rev. illus.
Formerly (until Dec. 1989): Comercio Industria y Navegacion (0211-1578)
Published by: Camara Oficial de Comercio Industria y Navegacion de Valencia, Poeta Querol, 15, Valencia, 46002, Spain. TEL 34-6-3511301, FAX 34-6-3516349. Ed. Jose M Gil Suay. Circ: 15,000.

382 CHL
CAMARA CHILENO - ALEMANA DE COMERCIO E INDUSTRIA. ANNUAL REPORT. Text in Spanish. a.
Published by: Camara Chileno - Alemana de Comercio e Industria/Deutsch - Chilenische Industrie- und Handelskammer, Av El Bosque Norte 0440, Oficina 601 - Las Condes, Santiago, Chile. TEL 56-2-2035325, TELEX 56-2-2035320.

382 PRT
CAMARA DE COMERCIO AMERICANA. BOLETIM. Text in Portuguese. 1956. 9/yr. adv. charts; illus. index. **Document type:** *Bulletin.*
Former titles: Camara de Comercio Luso-Americana. Boletim (0008-1906); Camara de Comercio dos Estados Unidos da America do Norte em Portugal. Boletim
Related titles: Special ed(s).: Camara de Comercio Americana. Directorio.
Published by: Camara de Comercio Americana, Rua de Dona Estefania, 155-5 Esq, Lisbon, 1000-154, Portugal. TEL 351-21-3572561, FAX 351-21-3572580, nop37676@mail.telepac.pt. Ed. Henrique Brito Do Rio. Circ: 2,000.

382 ARG
CAMARA DE COMERCIO ARGENTINO-BRITANICA. BULLETIN. Text in English. 1914. m. adv. **Document type:** *Newsletter, Trade.* **Description:** Provides data on new members, bilateral commerce data, news of members and general business news. Includes a calendar of coming activities and trade shows.
Formerly: British Chamber of Commerce in the Argentine Republic. Bulletin
Published by: Camara de Comercio Argentino-Britanica, Avda. Corrientes, 457, Capital Federal, Buenos Aires 1043, Argentina. TEL 54-114-3942318, FAX 54-114-3942282. Ed. John D Wilson. Circ: 500.

330 COL ISSN 0008-185X
CAMARA DE COMERCIO DE BOGOTA. BOLETIN. Text in Spanish. 1916. fortn. USD 38. adv. **Document type:** *Bulletin.*
Published by: Camara de Comercio de Bogota, Carrera 26 68D-35, Bogota, Colombia. Ed. Mario Suarez Melo.

338 980 COL ISSN 0120-4289
HF6
CAMARA DE COMERCIO DE BOGOTA. REVISTA. Text in Spanish. 1970. q. USD 50. bk.rev. bibl.
Indexed: KES, PAIS, RASB.
Published by: Camara de Comercio de Bogota, Carrera 26 68D-35, Bogota, Colombia. Ed. Mario Suarez Melo.

381 COL
CAMARA DE COMERCIO DE BOGOTA. SERVICIO INFORMATIVO. Text in Spanish. 1969. m.
Former titles: Camara de Comercio de Bogota. Servicio Informativo Mensual; Camara de Comercio de Bogota. Servicio Informativo Quincenal
Published by: Camara de Comercio de Bogota, Carrera 26 68D-35, Bogota, Colombia. Ed. Mario Suarez.

972.86 CRI
CAMARA DE COMERCIO DE COSTA RICA. MAGAZINE. Text in Spanish.
Published by: Camara de Comercio de Costa Rica, Barrio Tournon, Apdo. 1114, San Jose, Costa Rica.

330 NIC
CAMARA DE COMERCIO DE NICARAGUA. BOLETIN COMERCIAL. Text in Spanish. 1928. m. NIC 42, USD 6. adv. charts; mkt. **Document type:** *Bulletin.*
Former titles: Camara Nacional de Comercio de Managua. Boletin (0008-1922); Camara Nacional de Comercio e Industrias de Managua. Boletin
Published by: Camara de Comercio de Nicaragua, Apartado Postal 135 C 001, Managua, Nicaragua. Circ: 2,500.

381 ECU
CAMARA DE COMERCIO DE QUITO. BOLETIN DE INFORMACION COMERCIAL. Text in Spanish. 1977 (no.78). m. **Document type:** *Bulletin.*
Published by: Camara de Comercio de Quito, Avenidas Amazonas y de la Republica, Apdo 202, Quito, Pichincha, Ecuador. TEL 453-011.

382 BOL
CAMARA DE COMERCIO E INDUSTRIA BOLIVIANO - ALEMANA. BULLETIN BOLIVIA - GERMANY. Text in Spanish. bi-m. USD 80 (effective 2000). adv. **Document type:** *Bulletin.*
Published by: Camara de Comercio e Industria Boliviano - Alemana/Deutsch - Bolivianische Industrie- und Handelskammer, Casilla 2722, Ave. Villazon, 1966, La Paz, Bolivia. TEL 591-2-411774, FAX 413321, cambolal@datacom-bo.net, info@ahkboe.com. Ed. Petra Kleinschmidt. Adv. contact Fabrizio Velasco Velazquez.

382 PRT
CAMARA DE COMERCIO E INDUSTRIA LUSO - ALEMA. INFORMATIONEN✶. Text in Portuguese. m.
Published by: Camara de Comercio e Industria Luso - Alema, c/o Camara de Comercio e Industria Portuguesa, Rua das Portas de Santo Antao, 89, Lisbon, 1194, Portugal. TEL 1-772587, TELEX 16469.

987 VEN
CAMARA DE COMERCIO, INDUSTRIA Y AGRICULTURA VENEZOLANO-ITALIANO. Text in Spanish. 1954. q. USD 50.
Published by: Camara de Comercio Industria y Agricultura Venezolano-Italiano, Ave. Andres Bello, Centro Andres Bello, Torre Oeste p. 14 Ofs. 143-144, Apdo 14204, Caracas, DF 1050, Venezuela.

382 ARG
CAMARA DE COMERCIO, INDUSTRIA Y PRODUCCION DE LA REPUBLICA ARGENTINA. BOLETIN INFORMATIVO. Text in Spanish. irreg. free. **Description:** Includes news and information related to the Chamber of Commerce in Argentina.
Published by: Camara de Comercio Industria y Produccion de la Republica Argentina, Florida, 1 / 15 Piso 4, Buenos Aires, 1005, Argentina. TEL 54-11-43310813, FAX 54-11-43319116, cacipra@houseware.com.ar, http://www.houseware.com.ar/cacipra. Ed. Maria Arsenia Tula.

382 PRY
CAMARA DE COMERCIO PARAGUAYO - ALEMANA. Text in Spanish. 8/yr.
Address: J E O'Leary, 409, Oficina 316, PO Box 919, Asuncion, Paraguay. TEL 21-46594.

382 ARG
CAMARA DE COMERCIO SUIZA-ARGENTINA. BULLETIN. Text in Spanish. m. **Document type:** *Bulletin.*
Published by: Camara de Comercio Suiza-Argentina, Avda. Leandro N. Alem, 1074, Capital Federal, Buenos Aires 1001, Argentina. TEL 54-114-3117187.

989 URY
CAMARA DE COMERCIO URUGUAY - U S A. REVISTA. Text in Spanish. s-a.
Published by: Camara de Comercio Uruguay - USA, Casilla 809, Montevideo, Uruguay. TEL 2-986934.

382 ARG ISSN 0008-2112
CAMARA DE INDUSTRIA Y COMERCIO ARGENTINO-ALEMANA. BOLETIN/DEUTSCH-ARGENTINISCHE INDUSTRIE- UND HANDELSKAMMER. MITTEILUNGEN. Text in German, Spanish. 1951. 6/yr. adv. bk.rev. bibl. **Document type:** *Bulletin, Trade.*
Indexed: KES.
Published by: Camara de Industria y Comercio Argentino-Alemana/Deutsch-Argentinische Industrie- und Handelskammer, Av Corrientes 327, no 23, Buenos Aires, Buenos Aires 1043, Argentina. TEL 54-11-52194000, FAX 54-11-52194001, info@cadicaa.com.ar, http://www.cadicaa.com.ar. Circ: 800.

983 CHL
CAMARA NACIONAL DE COMERCIO DE CHILE. BOLETIN DE INFORMES COMERCIALES. Text in Spanish. w.
Published by: Camara Nacional de Comercio de Chile, Santa Lucia, 302, Santiago, Chile. TEL 394744, TELEX 560264.

983 CHL
CAMARA NACIONAL DE COMERCIO DE CHILE. INFORMATIVO. Text in Spanish. w.
Published by: Camara Nacional de Comercio de Chile, Santa Lucia, 302, Santiago, Chile. TEL 396639.

989 URY ISSN 0797-5686
CAMARA NACIONAL DE COMERCIO. INFORME ANUAL. Text in Spanish. a. **Document type:** *Corporate.*
Published by: Camara Nacional de Comercio, Misiones, 1400, Montevideo, 11006, Uruguay. TEL 96-12-77, FAX 5982-961243.

989 URY
CAMARA NACIONAL DE COMERCIO. PUBLICACIONES. Text in Spanish. irreg. **Document type:** *Monographic series.*
Published by: Camara Nacional de Comercio, Misiones, 1400, Montevideo, 11006, Uruguay. TEL 96-12-77, FAX 5982-961243.

989 URY ISSN 0797-2989
HF300.U8
CAMARA NACIONAL DE COMERCIO. REVISTA. Text in Spanish. 1979. bi-m. membership. charts; stat. **Document type:** *Bulletin.*
Published by: Camara Nacional de Comercio, Misiones, 1400, Montevideo, 11006, Uruguay. TEL 96-12-77, FAX 5982-961243.

381 ESP
CAMARA OFICIAL DE COMERCIO E INDUSTRIA DE ALAVA. BOLETIN INFORMATIVO. Text in Spanish. m. free. adv. charts; illus.; stat. Supplement avail.
Published by: Camara Oficial de Comercio e Industria de Alava, Dato 38, Vitoria, 01005, Spain. TEL 34-45-141800, FAX 34-45-143156, cocia@jet.es, http://www.jet.es/camara. Ed. Lorenzo Bergareche Capa. Circ: 4,000.

380 ESP ISSN 0008-1930
CAMARA OFICIAL DE COMERCIO, INDUSTRIA Y NAVEGACION DE BARCELONA. BOLETIN/CAMBRA OFICIAL DE COMERC, INDUSTRIA I NAVEGACIO DE BARCELONA. BUTLLETI. Text in Spanish. 1967. 4/yr. free. adv. bk.rev. charts; mkt.; stat. **Document type:** *Bulletin.*
Formed by the merger of (1918-1966): Comercio y Navegacion (0210-8216); (1916-1966): Camara Oficial de la Industria. Boletin Informativo (0404-9241); Which was formerly (until 1955): Industria Espanola (Barcelona) (1131-5547)
Published by: Cambra Oficial de Comerc Industria i Navegacio de Barcelona, Avinguda Diagonal, 452, Barcelona, 08006, Spain. TEL 34-3-4169300, FAX 34-3-4169301. Ed. Carmen Miro. Adv. contact Oriol Prats. Circ: 25,000.

946 ESP
CAMARA OFICIAL DE COMERCIO, INDUSTRIA Y NAVEGACION DE SANTA CRUZ DE TENERIFE. BOLETIN INFORMATIVO. Text in Spanish. 1954. 12/yr. adv. **Document type:** *Bulletin.*
Published by: Camara Oficial de Comercio, Industria y Navegacion de Santa Cruz de Tenerife, Plaza Candelaria 6, 4o, Santa Cruz De Tenerife, Canary Islands 38003, Spain. TEL 34-22-245384, FAX 34-22-240364. Ed. Rafael Espejo Castro. Adv. contact Adela Sosa Santana. Circ: 1,500.

382 VEN
CAMARA VENEZOLANO-BRITANICA DE COMERCIO E INDUSTRIA. ANUARIO. Text in English, Spanish. 1972. a. VEB 900. adv.
Formerly: Asociacion Venezolano-Britanica de Comercio e Industria. Anuario (0084-6848)
Published by: Camara Venezolano-Britanica de Comercio e Industria, Torre Britanica piso 10,, Altamira Sur, Caracas, DF 1060, Venezuela. TEL 58-2-2673112, FAX 58-2-2630362. Ed. Tim Duhan. Circ: 2,000.

338 338.1 ITA ISSN 0008-2147
CAMERA DI COMMERCIO, INDUSTRIA, ARTIGIANATO E AGRICOLTURA DI BELLUNO. RASSEGNA ECONOMICA. Text in Italian. 1953. 3/yr. EUR 26 (effective 2004). adv. illus.; stat. back issues avail. **Document type:** *Magazine, Consumer.*
Published by: Camera di Commercio Industria Artigianato e Agricoltura di Belluno, Piazza S Stefano 15-17, Belluno, BL 32100, Italy. TEL 39-0437-955111, FAX 39-0437-955250, http://www.bl.camcom.it. Ed. Armando Mosca. Circ: 500.

338 ITA ISSN 0391-7436
CAMERA DI COMMERCIO, INDUSTRIA, ARTIGIANATO E AGRICOLTURA DI CUNEO. NOTIZIARIO ECONOMICO. Text in Italian. 1946. bi-m. adv. charts; illus.; stat. **Description:** Covers the tourism and agricultural industries and climate of Cuneo.
Published by: Camera di Commercio Industria Artigianato e Agricoltura di Cuneo, Via Emanuele Filiberto 3, Cuneo, CN, Italy. TEL 39-0171-318728, FAX 39-0171-318829, http://www.cn.camcom.it. Ed. Rinaldo Chiabra. Circ: 4,250.

945 ITA ISSN 1120-3900
CAMERA DI COMMERCIO, INDUSTRIA, ARTIGIANATO E AGRICOLTURA DI FERRARA. LISTINO DEI PREZZI ALL'INGROSSO. Text in Italian. 1954. w. EUR 67.14 (effective 2001).
Published by: Camera di Commercio Industria Artigianato e Agricoltura di Ferrara, Via Borgoleoni, 11, Ferrara, FE 44100, Italy. TEL 39-0532-783711, FAX 39-0532-240204, prezzi.protesti@fe.camcom.it, http://www.fe.camcom.it. Ed. Dr. Bruno Baldazzi.

338 ITA ISSN 1120-3943
CAMERA DI COMMERCIO, INDUSTRIA, ARTIGIANATO E AGRICOLTURA DI FERRARA. NOTIZIARIO MENSILE. Text in Italian. 1981. m. EUR 168 (effective 2004).
Published by: Camera di Commercio Industria Artigianato e Agricoltura di Ferrara, Via Borgoleoni, 11, Ferrara, FE 44100, Italy. TEL 39-0532-783711, FAX 39-0532-240204, riccardo.bedeschi@fe.camcom.it, http://www.fe.camcom.it. Ed. Dr. Bruno Baldazzi.

CAMERA DI COMMERCIO, INDUSTRIA, ARTIGIANATO E AGRICOLTURA DI FORLI. LISTINO SETTIMANALE PREZZI. see *BUSINESS AND ECONOMICS—Domestic Commerce*

381 ITA
CAMERA DI COMMERCIO, INDUSTRIA, ARTIGIANATO E AGRICOLTURA DI PADOVA. RAPPORTI. Text in Italian. 1983. irreg. free. stat. **Document type:** *Monographic series, Trade.*
Published by: Camera di Commercio, Industria, Artigianato e Agricoltura di Padova, Via E. Filiberto 34, Padua, PD, Italy. TEL 39-049-8208111, FAX 39-049-8208290, studi@pd.camcom.it, http://www.pd.camcom.it. Ed. Giampaolo Redivo. Circ: 280.

382 BRA
CAMERA DI COMMERCIO ITALIANA DI RIO DE JANEIRO. QUARTERLY REVIEW. Text in Portuguese. q.
Published by: Camera di Commercio Italiana di Rio de Janeiro, Av Presidente Antonio Carlos, 40, Centro, Rio De Janeiro, RJ 20020-010, Brazil. TEL 2208417.

382 CAN ISSN 0045-4214
CANADA JAPAN TRADE COUNCIL. NEWSLETTER. Text in English. 1963. bi-m. free. **Document type:** *Newsletter.*
Related titles: Microform ed.: (from PQC).
—CISTI.
Published by: Canada Japan Trade Council, Fuller Bldg, Ste 903, 75 Albert St, Ottawa, ON K1P 5E7, Canada. TEL 613-233-4047. Ed. K H Pringsheim. Circ: 3,000.

382 GBR ISSN 1361-7494
CANADA U.K. LINK. Text in English. 1921. bi-m. membership. adv. **Document type:** *Newsletter.*
Former titles (until 1995): Can - U.K. Link (0267-4319); (until 1984): Canada - U.K. Trade News (0045-4281); (until 1971): Canada - United Kingdom Trade News (0591-0897)
Published by: Canada - United Kingdom Chamber of Commerce, 38 Grosvenor St, London, W1X 0DP, United Kingdom. TEL 44-171-258-6572, FAX 44-171-258-6594. Ed. C Lengyel. Circ: 1,600.

382 GBR ISSN 0309-0329
CANADA - U.K. YEAR BOOK. Text in English. 1925. a. GBP 10.60.
Published by: (Canada-United Kingdom Chamber of Commerce), Rank Zerox Ltd., 2 Brewers Green, London, SW1H 0RH, United Kingdom. Ed. G F Bacon. Circ: 550.

944 FRA
CANTALE ECO. Text in French. 8/yr. adv. **Document type:** *Newspaper.*
Published by: Chambre de Commerce & d Industrie d Aurillac et du, 44 bd. du Pont Rouge, Aurillac, Cedex 15013, France. TEL 71-45-40-40, FAX 71-48-48-12, TELEX 393 160. Ed. M Delzangles. Adv. contact Robert Lafeuille. Circ: 6,000.

382 USA
CAPITOLINE. Text in English. w. (Jan.-May). membership. **Document type:** *Newsletter, Trade.*
Related titles: Fax ed.
Published by: Colorado Association of Commerce and Industry, 1600 Broadway, Ste 1000, Denver, CO 80202. TEL 303-831-7411, FAX 303-860-1439, http://www.businesscolorado.com. Ed. Marilyn Holmes.

382 ESP ISSN 0213-9286
CATALUNYA EXPORTA - CATALUNYA IMPORTA. Text in Spanish. 1964. a. adv.
Formerly (until 1984): Catalunya Exporta (0069-1178)
Published by: Cambra Oficial de Comerc Industria i Navegacio de Barcelona, Avinguda Diagonal, 452, Barcelona, 08006, Spain. Ed. Joan Ramon Rovira. Adv. contact Oriol Prats. Circ: 1,000.

972.9 CYM
CAYMAN ISLANDS CHAMBER OF COMMERCE DIRECTORY. Text in English. 1984. a. adv. **Document type:** *Directory, Trade.*
Published by: Chamber of Commerce, P O Box 1000, George Town, Grand Cayman, Cayman Isl. TEL 345-949-8090, FAX 345-949-0220, chamber@candw.ky, http://www.caymanchamber.ky. Ed., Adv. contact Wil Pineav. Circ: 5,000.

972.9 CYM
CAYMAN ISLANDS CHAMBER OF COMMERCE NEWSLETTER. Text in English. 1986. m. adv. **Document type:** *Newsletter, Trade.*
Published by: Chamber of Commerce, P O Box 1000, George Town, Grand Cayman, Cayman Isl. TEL 345-949-8090, FAX 345-949-0220, chamber@candw.ky, http://www.caymanchamber.ky. Ed., Adv. contact Wil Pineau. Circ: 2,000.

972 USA ISSN 0887-0594
F1421
CENTRAL AMERICA NEWSPAK; a bi-weekly news & resource update. Text in English. 1986. fortn. USD 42 (effective 1998). back issues avail.
Published by: Human Rights Documentation Exchange, PO Box 2327, Austin, TX 78768-2327. TEL 512-476-9841, FAX 512-476-0130. Ed. Donna Woodwell. Circ: 400 (paid).

971 CAN
CENTRAL NOVA BUSINESS NEWS. Text in English. m.
Published by: (Truro and District Chamber of Commerce), Gordon Publishing and Printing, 228 Main St., Bible Hill, NS B2N 4H2, Canada. TEL 902-895-7948, FAX 902-893-1427. Ed. Peter Heckbert. adv.: B&W page CND 180. Circ: 2,200.
Subscr. to: P O Box 946, Truro, NS B2N 5G7, Canada.

381 GBR
CENTRAL SCOTLAND CHAMBER OF COMMERCE BULLETIN. Text in English. 1973 (vol.15). bi-m. GBP 1 in United Kingdom to non-members; GBP 1.50 in Europe to non-members; GBP 2.50 elsewhere to non-members (effective 1999 - 2000). adv. **Description:** Covers business information, current legislation, health and safety, members news, training news, commercial services, members success stories, features, guest columns and profiles.
Former titles (until 1997): Central Scotland Chamber of Commerce Quarterly Bulletin; Forth Valley Chamber of Commerce Quarterly Bulletin (0015-8100)
Published by: Central Scotland Chamber of Commerce, Haypark Business Centre, Marchmont Ave, Polmont, Falkirk, Stirlingshire FK2 0NZ, United Kingdom. TEL 44-1324-716868, FAX 44-1324-719899, commerce@post.almac.co.uk, http://www.central-chamber.co.uk. Ed. Bob Ness. Circ: 1,000 (controlled).

944 FRA
CENTRE ECONOMIQUE MAGAZINE. Text in French. 1955. 6/yr. **Document type:** *Bulletin.*
Address: 15 bd. Carnot, BP 3248, Montlucon, Cedex 03106, France. TEL 33-4-70025000, FAX 33-4-70025059, TELEX CHAMCO 990 029 F. Ed., R&P Bruno Paugam TEL 33-4-70025035. Pub. Yves Laval. Circ: 10,000.

381 LKA
CEYLON CHAMBER OF COMMERCE. ANNUAL REVIEW OF BUSINESS AND TRADE (YEAR). Text in English. 1839. a., latest 1991. USD 30. charts; stat.
Published by: Ceylon Chamber of Commerce, Chamber of Commerce Bldg., P O Box 274, Colombo, 2, Sri Lanka. FAX 941-449352.

381 LKA
CEYLON CHAMBER OF COMMERCE. REGISTER OF MEMBERS. Text in English. 1981. biennial. USD 30.

Published by: Ceylon Chamber of Commerce, Chamber of Commerce Bldg., P O Box 274, Colombo, 2, Sri Lanka. FAX 941-449352.

381 GBR ISSN 0266-4127
CHACOM. Text in English. 1984. m. GBP 18 to members. adv. bk.rev. stat. **Document type:** *Newsletter.* **Description:** Contains a mixture of business information, news, statistics, and member news relating to business and commerce.
Formerly: Forum for Commerce and Industry
Published by: Central & West Lancashire Chamber of Commerce and Industry, 9-10 Eastway Business Village, Oliver's Pl, Fulwood, Preston PR2 9WT, United Kingdom. TEL 44-1772-653000, FAX 44-1772-655544, cwicci@aol.com. Ed. Hugh Evans. R&P Babs Murphy. Adv. contact Nick Wilson. Circ: 3,500.

914.4 FRA
CHAMBER DE COMMERCE ET D'INDUSTRIE DE MEURTHE ET MOSELLE. DOSSIERS. Text in French. q. **Description:** Covers activities in the import-export industry and international commerce.
Published by: Chambre de Commerce et d'Industrie de Meurthe et Moselle, 40 av. Henri Poincare, Nancy, 54042, France. Ed. Gerard Barthier.

973 USA ISSN 0884-8114
CHAMBER EXECUTIVE. Text in English. 1985. m. USD 87; USD 135 foreign. adv. **Description:** Covers official news of the Chamber of Commerce and its executives.
Related titles: Microform ed.
Published by: American Chamber of Commerce Executives, 4875 Eisenhower Ave., Ste. 250, Alexandria, VA 22304-4850. TEL 703-998-0072, FAX 703-931-5624. Ed. Marlies Mulckhuyse. Circ: 5,100.

977 USA ISSN 1070-2342
CHAMBER EXECUTIVE NETWORK. Text in English. 1984. m. looseleaf. USD 110 (effective 1998). back issues avail. **Document type:** *Newsletter.* **Description:** Advisory newsletter for Chamber of Commerce managers in U.S. and Canada.
Formerly: Community Development Executive (0747-7503)
Published by: Hakes Publications, PO Box 603, Storm Lake, IA 50588. TEL 712-732-7718, hakesd@bvu.edu. Ed., Pub., R&P Richard L Hakes. Circ: 800 (paid).

973 USA
CHAMBER JOBWATCH. Text in English. s-m. USD 80 to non-members; USD 40 to members. bk.rev. back issues avail. **Description:** Lists chamber of commerce job openings across the United States.
Related titles: Online - full text ed.
Published by: American Chamber of Commerce Executives, 4875 Eisenhower Ave., Ste. 250, Alexandria, VA 22304-4850. TEL 703-998-0072, FAX 703-931-5624. Ed. Lisa Raspino. Circ: 250 (paid).

381 USA ISSN 0897-7917
CHAMBER JOURNAL. Text in English. bi-m. membership. adv. index. back issues avail. **Document type:** *Newsletter.* **Description:** Informs business people of the New Orleans region about Chamber events. Includes items of interest and general news.
Formerly: New Orleans Area Chamber of Commerce. Journal
Related titles: Diskette ed.; Microfilm ed.: (from BHP).
Published by: New Orleans Area Chamber of Commerce, New Orleans and the River Region, 601 Poydras St, Ste 1700, New Orleans, LA 70130. TEL 504-527-6921, FAX 504-527-6970, journal@www.gnofn.org. Ed., Adv. contact Sarah Shaw.

381.06 USA
THE CHAMBER L.I.N.C. (Legislative Information Network Community Development) Text in English. q. free domestic to members. **Document type:** *Newsletter, Trade.*
Formerly: In-Between
Published by: Kansas City Kansas Area Chamber of Commerce, 727 Minnesota Ave., Kansas City, KS 66101. TEL 913-371-3070, FAX 913-371-3732. Ed. Cindy Cash. Circ: 1,100 (free).

975 USA
CHAMBER NEWS. Text in English. 1986. m. membership. **Document type:** *Newsletter.* **Description:** News items, information, and announcements on the members and activities of the Chamber of Commerce of Greater Hartsville, South Carolina.
Formerly: Greater Hartsville Chamber of Commerce Newsletter
Published by: Greater Hartsville Chamber of Commerce, PO Box 578, Hartsville, SC 29551. TEL 803-332-6401, FAX 803-332-8017. Ed. Nancy Truesdale. Circ: 600 (controlled).

380.1 IDN
CHAMBER OF COMMERCE AND INDUSTRY IN WEST JAVA. MEMBER LIST/KAMAR DAGANG DAN INDUSTRI DI JAWA BARAT. DAFTAR ANGGOTA. Text in English, Indonesian. a.
Published by: Chamber of Commerce and Industry in West Java, Jl. Sunaiaraja 3, Bandung, West Java, Indonesia.

954.9 PAK
CHAMBER OF COMMERCE AND INDUSTRY. TRADE JOURNAL. Text in English. bi-w.
Published by: Karachi Chamber of Commerce and Industry, Aiwan-e-Tijarat Rd., Shahrah-e-Liaquat, Karachi, 74000, Pakistan.

381 SLE ISSN 0080-9527
CHAMBER OF COMMERCE OF SIERRA LEONE. JOURNAL✶. Text in English. 1965. m. adv.
Published by: Chamber of Commerce of Sierra Leone, Industry & Agriculture Dept, Guma Bldg, 5th Fl, Lamina Sankoh St, PO Box 502, Freetown, Sierra Leone. TEL 26305. Ed. F Iscandari. Circ: 1,000.

989 URY
CHAMBER OF COMMERCE OF THE U S A IN URUGUAY. NEWSLETTER. Text in Spanish. bi-m. **Document type:** *Newsletter.*
Published by: Camara de Comercio Uruguay - USA, Casilla 809, Montevideo, Uruguay. TEL 986934, TELEX 853.

381 CAN
CHAMBER ONLINE. Text in English. m. free (effective 2004). **Document type:** *Newsletter.* **Description:** Covers material pertinent to the local business community. Includes updates of important issues, events and business promotions.
Media: Online - full content.
Published by: Edmonton Chamber of Commerce, Ste 600, 10123 99 St, Edmonton, AB T5J 3G9, Canada. TEL 780-426-4620, FAX 780-424-7946, info@edmontonchamber.com, http://www.edmontonchamber.com.

950 NPL
CHAMBER PATRIKA; economic and business affairs in Nepal. Text in Nepali. fortn. charts. **Description:** Covers economic and business news in Nepal, as it affects both domestic and international trade.
Published by: Nepal Chamber of Commerce (N.C.C.), Kantipath, P O Box 198, Kathmandu, Nepal. TEL 977-1-222890, FAX 977-1-229998. Ed. Yagya Narayan Shrestha. adv.: page NPR 1,800.

977 USA
CHAMBER REVIEW. Text in English. 1980. fortn. USD 15 (effective 1999). adv. **Document type:** *Newsletter.*
Formerly: Update (LaCrosse)
Published by: Greater LaCrosse Area Chamber of Commerce, 712 Main St., Box 219, Lacrosse, WI 54602-0219. TEL 608-784-4880. Ed., R&P Timothy Tracy. Adv. contact Kerry Lucchini. Circ: 1,500.

330 USA ISSN 0279-0785
THE CHAMBER TODAY. Text in English. 1916. m. free (effective 2005). illus. **Document type:** *Newsletter, Consumer.*
Formerly (until 1980): San Antonian (0036-3952)
Published by: Greater San Antonio Chamber of Commerce, 602 E Commerce St, PO Box 1628, San Antonio, TX 78296. TEL 210-229-2100, FAX 210-229-1600, newsletter@sachamber.org, http://www.sachamber.org. Ed. Joseph R Krier. Circ: 4,000 (controlled).

380.1 USA
CHAMBER UPDATE. Text in English. 1965. m. USD 12. adv. 8 p./no.; **Document type:** *Newsletter.*
Supersedes (in 197?): Working Together for a Greater Yakima
Published by: Greater Yakima Chamber of Commerce, PO Box 1490, Yakima, WA 98907-1490. TEL 509-248-2021, FAX 509-248-0601, chamber@yakima.org, http://www.yakima.org. Ed., R&P Gary W Webster. Adv. contact Theresa Shields. Circ: 1,500.

382 USA
CHAMBER VISION. Text in English. m. free to members. 8 p./no. 3 cols./p.; back issues avail. **Document type:** *Newsletter, Trade.*
Published by: Greater Cincinnati Chamber of Commerce, 441 Vine St., Ste. 300, Cincinnati, OH 45202-2812. TEL 513-579-3100, FAX 513-579-3101, dbedwell@gccc.com, http://www.cincinnatichamber.com. Ed. Don Bedwell. Circ: 7,000 (controlled and free).

381.06 USA
CHAMBERLETTER. Text in English. m. free to members (effective 2005). **Document type:** *Newsletter.*
Contact Owner: Fort Worth Chamber of Commerce, 777 Taylor St, Ste 900, Fort Worth, TX 76102-4997 . TEL 817-336-2491, FAX 817-877-4034, http://www.fortworthchamber.com/. Circ: 130,000 (free).

380.106 USA
CHAMBERWAY GERMANY-MIDWEST. Text in English, German. 1982. bi-m. USD 25 (effective 2003). adv. bk.rev. charts; stat. back issues avail. **Document type:** *Journal, Trade.* **Description:** Features business, market and product developments, economic commentaries, company profiles, statistics on Germany and the U.S. as well as the European Union.
Former titles (until 1996): German American Business Journal Midwest; (until 1995): Focus Germany-Midwest
Published by: German American Chamber of Commerce of the Midwest, 401 N. Michigan Ave., Ste. 3330, Chicago, IL 60611-4236. info@gaccom.org, http://www.gaccom.org. Ed., Pub. Christian J Roehr. R&P Jodi M Schmaltz. Adv. contact Beth Saltz. B&W page USD 920; trim 11 x 7.5. Circ: 6,000. **Dist. by:** IPC Communications, 501 Colonial Dr., St. Joseph, MI 49085. TEL 616-983-7105, FAX 616-983-8749.

966.1 MRT
CHAMBRE DE COMMERCE, D'AGRICULTURE, D'ELEVAGE, D'INDUSTRIE ET DES MINES DE LA REPUBLIQUE ISLAMIQUE DE MAURITANIE. BULLETIN. Text in French. m. **Document type:** *Bulletin.*
Published by: Chambre de Commerce d'Agriculture d'Elevage d'Industrie et des Mines de la Republique Islamique de Mauritanie, BP 215, Nouakchott, Mauritania.

964.26 NER
CHAMBRE DE COMMERCE, D'AGRICULTURE, D'INDUSTRIE ET D'ARTISANAT DU NIGER. WEEKLY BULLETIN. Text in French. 1960. w. adv. **Document type:** *Bulletin.*
Published by: Chambre de Commerce d'Agriculture d'Industrie et d'Artisanat du Niger, BP 209, Niamey, Niger. TEL 732210, FAX 734668, TELEX 5242 NI. Ed. Hassane Almoctar. Adv. contact Idrissa Harouna Maimouna Ko. Circ: 170 (controlled).

967.2 GAB ISSN 0045-6276
CHAMBRE DE COMMERCE, D'AGRICULTURE, D'INDUSTRIE ET DES MINES DU GABON. BULLETIN. Text in French. m. XOF 25,000. adv. charts; stat.
Media: Duplicated (not offset).
Indexed: PAIS.
Published by: Chambre de Commerce d'Agriculture d'Industrie et des Mines du Gabon, BP 2234, Libreville, Gabon. TEL 72-20-64, TELEX 5554.

960 TCD
CHAMBRE DE COMMERCE, D'AGRICULTURE ET D'INDUSTRIE. INFORMATIONS ECONOMIQUES. Text in French. w.
Published by: Chambre de Commerce, d'Agriculture et d'Industrie, BP 458, N'djamena, Chad.

960 COG
CHAMBRE DE COMMERCE DE BRAZZAVILLE. BULLETIN MENSUEL. Text in French. m.
Published by: Chambre de Commerce de Brazzaville, BP 92, Brazzaville, Congo, Republic.

381 TUN
CHAMBRE DE COMMERCE DE TUNIS. BULLETIN. Text in Arabic, English. m. TND 1. charts; stat. **Document type:** *Bulletin.*
Indexed: KES.
Published by: Chambre de Commerce de Tunis, 1 rue des Entrepreneurs, Tunis, Tunisia.

960 COD
CHAMBRE DE COMMERCE, D'INDUSTRIE ET D'AGRICULTURE DE LITTURI. BULLETIN. Text in French. m. adv. **Document type:** *Bulletin.*
Published by: Chambre de Commerce, d'Industrie et d'Agriculture, BP 38, Bunia, Congo, Dem. Republic.

960 COD
CHAMBRE DE COMMERCE, D'INDUSTRIE ET D'AGRICULTURE DU KISAI. BULLETIN. Text in French. m. adv. **Document type:** *Bulletin.*
Published by: Chambre de Commerce, d'Industrie et d'Agriculture du Kisai Occidental, Av. Commandant Michaux, BP 194, Luluabourg, Congo, Dem. Republic.

381 BFA
CHAMBRE DE COMMERCE, D'INDUSTRIE ET D'ARTISANAT DU BURKINA FASO. ANNUAIRE DES ENTREPRISES. Text in French. 1980. a. XOF 10,000 (effective 1999). adv. bk.rev. **Document type:** *Directory.*
Former titles: Chambre de Commerce, d'Industrie et d'Artisanat du Burkina Faso. Annuaire; Chambre de Commerce, d'Artisanat et d'Industrie de Haute-Volta. Annuaire
Published by: Chambre de Commerce d'Industrie et d'Artisanat, PO Box 502, Ouagadougou, 01, Burkina Faso. FAX 30-61-16. Circ: 2,500.

382 BFA
CHAMBRE DE COMMERCE, D'INDUSTRIE ET D'ARTISANAT. REPERTOIRE NATIONAL DES ENTREPRISES. Text in French. a.
Published by: Chambre de Commerce d'Industrie et d'Artisanat, Direction des Etudes et de l'Information, BP 502, Ouagadougou, 01, Burkina Faso. TEL 30-61-14, FAX 30-61-16, TELEX 5268 BF.

916.4 338 CMR ISSN 0008-2198
CHAMBRE DE COMMERCE, D'INDUSTRIE ET DES MINES DU CAMEROUN. BULLETIN D'INFORMATION. Text in French. 1967-1975; resumed 1980. m. XAF 100 per issue. adv. illus.; stat. **Document type:** *Bulletin.*
Published by: Chambre de Commerce d'Industrie et des Mines du Cameroun, BP 4011, Douala, Cameroun. TEL 237-42-6855, FAX 237-42-5596. Ed. Saidou A Bobboy. Pub. Claude Juimo Monthe.

B

B

380.1   CMR
CHAMBRE DE COMMERCE, D'INDUSTRIE ET DES MINES DU CAMEROUN. COMPTE-RENDU D'ACTIVITES. Text in French. irreg. Document type: Corporate.
Published by: Chambre de Commerce d'Industrie et des Mines du Cameroun, BP 4011, Douala, Cameroon. TEL 237-42-6855, FAX 237-42-5596. Ed. Saidou A Bobboy. Pub. Claude Juimo Monthe.

966.11   CMR
CHAMBRE DE COMMERCE, D'INDUSTRIE ET DES MINES DU CAMEROUN. IMPORT EXPORT. Text in French. m.
Published by: Chambre de Commerce d'Industrie et des Mines du Cameroun, BP 4011, Douala, Cameroon. TEL 237-42-6855, FAX 237-42-5596.

381   BEL
CHAMBRE DE COMMERCE ET D'INDUSTRIE D'ANVERS. BULLETIN. Text in French. m.
Related titles: ♦ Dutch ed.: Kamer van Koophandel en Nijverheid van Antwerpen. Bulletin. ISSN 0022-8087.
Published by: Kamer van Koophandel en Nijverheid van Antwerpen/Antwerp Chamber of Commerce and Industry, Markgravestraat 12, Antwerp, 2000, Belgium.

944   FRA   ISSN 1247-4312
CHAMBRE DE COMMERCE ET D'INDUSTRIE D'AUXERRE. ACTION CONSULAIRE. Text in French. 1964. 6/yr. adv. bk.rev. Document type: Bulletin.
Formerly (until 1993): Chambre de Commerce et d'Industrie d'Auxerre. Documentation Economique (0183-4037).
Published by: Chambre de Commerce et d'Industrie d'Auxerre, Informations Economiques, 26 rue Etienne Dolet, Auxerre, Cedex 89015, France. TEL 33-3-86494000, FAX 33-3-86494009. Ed., Pub., R&P, Adv. contact Patrick Ardisson. Circ: 8,500.

961   MAR
CHAMBRE DE COMMERCE ET D'INDUSTRIE DE CASABLANCA. REVUE MENSUELLE. Text in French. m. adv.
Published by: Chambre de Commerce et d'Industrie de Casablanca, B P 423, Casablanca, Morocco. Ed. Abdlah Souiri.

966.68   CIV
CHAMBRE DE COMMERCE ET D'INDUSTRIE DE COTE D'IVOIRE. BULLETIN QUOTIDIEN. Text in French. 1928. d. Document type: Bulletin, Consumer.
Former titles: Chambre de Commerce et d'Industrie de la Republique de Cote d'Ivoire. Bulletin; (until 1992): Chambre de Commerce de la Republique de Cote d'Ivoire. Bulletin
Published by: Chambre de Commerce et d'Industrie de Cote d'Ivoire, BP 1399, Abidjan, Ivory Coast. TEL 225-20-331600, FAX 225-20323942, info@cci-ci.org, http://www.cci-ci.org.

380   BEN
CHAMBRE DE COMMERCE ET D'INDUSTRIE DE LA REPUBLIQUE POPULAIRE DE BENIN. NOTE HEBDOMADAIRE. Text in French. w. XOF 12,000. stat.
Formerly: Chambre de Commerce et d'Industrie du Dahomey. Note Hebdomadaire; Chambre de Commerce, d'Agriculture et d'Industrie du Dahomey. Note Hebdomadaire
Indexed: KES.
Published by: Chambre de Commerce et d'Industrie de la Republique Populaire de Benin, Ave du General de Gaulle, BP 31, Cotonou, Benin.

944   FRA
CHAMBRE DE COMMERCE ET D'INDUSTRIE DE MEAUX. REVUE. Text in French. 4/yr.
Published by: Chambre de Commerce et d'Industrie de Meaux, 12 bd. Jean Rose, BP 216, Meaux, Cedex 77104, France. TEL 33-1-64363257, FAX 33-1-64334115. Ed. Daniel Retournard. Pub. Pierre Py.

944   FRA
CHAMBRE DE COMMERCE ET D'INDUSTRIE DE PARIS. LE NOUVEAU COURRIER. Text in French. 9/yr. Document type: Magazine, Consumer.
Formerly: Chambre de Commerce et d'Industrie de Paris. Courrier
Published by: Chambre de Commerce et d'Industrie de Paris (CEDIP), 27 av. de Friedland, Paris, 75008, France. TEL 33-1-55657033, FAX 33-1-55657067, http://www.infomediatheque.ccip.fr. Ed. Jilliane De La Laurencie. Circ: 255,000 (paid).

381   GLP   ISSN 1141-7978
CHAMBRE DE COMMERCE ET D'INDUSTRIE DE POINTE-A-PITRE. LETTRE. Text in French. irreg.
Formerly (until 1989): Chambre de Commerce et d'Industrie de Pointe-a-Pitre. Lettre d'Information (0750-4233).
Published by: Chambre de Commerce et d'Industrie de Pointe-a-Pitre, BP 64, Pointe-a-Pitre, Cedex 97152, Guadeloupe. TEL 90-08-08, FAX 90-21-87, TELEX 919 780 GL. Ed. Patricia Merino.

380 338   FRA   ISSN 0986-2013
CHAMBRE DE COMMERCE ET D'INDUSTRIE DE ROUEN. BULLETIN ECONOMIQUE. Text in French. 1948. m. free. bk.rev. charts; illus.; stat. Document type: Bulletin.

Formerly: Bulletin Economique (0009-1227)
Published by: Chambre de Commerce et d'Industrie de Rouen, B.P. 641, Rouen, 76000, France. TEL 33-2-35143737, FAX 33-2-35708092, http://www.rouen.cci.fr. Ed. Yves Poyeton. Adv. contact Annaick Seve. Circ: 17,500.

943   BEL
CHAMBRE DE COMMERCE ET D'INDUSTRIE DU CENTRE. BULLETIN. Text in French. 1928. bi-m. membership. Document type: Bulletin.
Published by: Chambre de Commerce et d'Industrie du Centre, Av des Croix du Feu 9, La Louviere, 7100, Belgium. TEL 064-222349, FAX 064-282382.

381   TUN   ISSN 0330-9584
HC547.T8
CHAMBRE DE COMMERCE ET D'INDUSTRIE DU SUD. BULLETIN. Text in French. 1949. s-m. TND 15. adv. Document type: Bulletin. Description: Covers activities of the Chamber as well as supply, demands and proposals of societies.
Formerly: Chambre de Commerce du Sud de la Tunisie. Bulletin Economique (0045-6292)
Related titles: Microform ed.
Published by: Chambre de Commerce et d'Industrie du Sud/Chamber of Commerce and Industry of the South, 127 Rue Haffouz, B P 794, Sfax, 3018, Tunisia. TEL 04-96-120, FAX 04-96-121, TELEX 40767. Ed. Mohamed Amous. Circ: 720.

382   BEL
CHAMBRE DE COMMERCE ET D'INDUSTRIE FRANCAISE POUR LA BELGIQUE ET LE GRAND-DUCHE LUXEMBOURG COMMERCE EXTERIEUR✱. Text in French. m.
Published by: Chambre de Commerce et d'Industrie Francaise pour la Belgique et le Grand-Duche de Luxembourg, c/o Chambre de Commerce et d'Industrie de Bruxelles, Av Louise 500, Brussels, 1050, Belgium. TEL 02-2302250.

944   FRA
CHAMBRE DE COMMERCE ET D'INDUSTRIE. LA LETTRE; Chambre de Commerce et d'Industrie d'Eure-et-Loir. Text in French. 1987. m. adv. illus. Document type: Newsletter. Description: Includes information on commerce, industry, environment, international business relations and documentation from the Chartres Chamber of Commerce and Industry.
Published by: Chambre de Commerce et Industrie (Chartres), 1 rue de l'Etroit Degre, BP 62, Chartres, Cedex 28002, France. TEL 33-2-37842828, FAX 33-2-37842829, cci28@wanadoo.fr, http://www.eureetloir.cci.fr. Ed. Jean Paul Vidal. Circ: 11,000.

382   ISR
CHAMBRE DE COMMERCE ISRAEL - FRANCE. BULLETIN. Text in French. m. free. Document type: Bulletin. Description: News about bilateral trade, chamber activities, business proposals and more.
Published by: Chambre de Commerce Israel - France, 28 Siderot David Hamelech, Tel Aviv, 64954, Israel. TEL 972-3-6960816, FAX 972-3-6960825, TELEX 342315 PCENT IL. Circ: 1,000.

382   FRA   ISSN 0069-2565
CHAMBRE DE COMMERCE JAPONAISE EN FRANCE. ANNUAIRE✱. Text in French. 1968. a.
Published by: Chambre de Commerce Japonaise en France, 1 av. de Friedland, Paris, 75008, France.

944   FRA
CHAMBRE DE METIERS DE L'AIN. BULLETIN. Text in French. 6/yr.
Indexed: RefZh.
Published by: Chambre de Metiers de l, 3 rue Paul Pioda, Bourg-en-Bresse, 01000, France. TEL 74-23-33-01, FAX 74-23-24-18. Ed. Jean Garcia. Circ: 13,000.

381   MAR   ISSN 0528-8231
CHAMBRE FRANCAISE DE COMMERCE ET D'INDUSTRIE DU MAROC. REVUE CONJONCTURE. Text in French. 1962. s-m. USD 54. adv. bk.rev.
Indexed: RASB.
Published by: Chambre Francaise de Commerce et d'Industrie du Maroc, 15 Av. Mers Sultan, Casablanca, Morocco. FAX 27-37-86, TELEX 24652 M. Circ: 2,000.

382   DZA
CHAMBRE FRANCAISE DE COMMERCE ET D'INDUSTRIE EN ALGERIE. ECONOMIC NEWS BULLETIN. Text in French. 1968. m. Document type: Bulletin.
Published by: Chambre Francaise de Commerce et d'Industrie en Algerie, 1 Rue du Languedoc, Alger, Algeria. TEL 632525, TELEX 53719.

382   FRA
CHAMBRE FRANCO ALLEMANDE DE COMMERCE ET D'INDUSTRIE. LISTE DES MEMBRES. Text in French. 1966. a.
Formerly: Chambre Officielle Franco Allemande de Commerce et d'Industrie. Liste des Membres (0069-2581)
Published by: Chambre Franco Allemande de Commerce et d'Industrie, 18 rue Balard, Paris, 75015, France. TEL 33-1-40583535, FAX 33-1-45754739.

967   DJI
CHAMBRE INTERNATIONALE DE COMMERCE ET D'INDUSTRIE DE DJIBOUTI. BULLETIN PERIODIQUE. Text in French. m.
Formerly (until 1979): Chambre de Commerce et d'Industrie de Djibouti. Bulletin Periodique
Published by: Chambre Internationale de Commerce et d'Industrie de Djibouti, BP 84, Djibouti, Djibouti.

381   FRA
CHAMBRE REGIONALE DE COMMERCE ET D'INDUSTRIE D'ALSACE. RAPPORT SUR LES ACTIVITES. Text in French. a.
Published by: Chambre Regionale de Commerce et d'Industrie d'Alsace, 42 rue Schweighaeuser, Strasbourg, 67000, France. TEL 33-3-88607475, FAX 33-3-88615354.

944   FRA   ISSN 0220-9241
CHAMBRE REGIONALE DE COMMERCE ET D'INDUSTRIE PROVENCE - ALPES - COTE D'AZUR - CORSE. CONJONCTURE. Text in French. 1973. s-a.
Formerly (until 1978): Chambre Regionale de Commerce et d'Industrie Provence - Cote d'Azur - Corse. Conjoncture (0220-9233)
Published by: Chambre Regionale de Commerce et d'Industrie Provence - Alpes - Cote d'Azur - Corse, 8 rue Neuve Saint Martin, BP 1880, Marseille, Cedex 1 13222, France. TEL 33-4-91144200, FAX 33-4-91144245, crci1@pacac-cci.fr.

382 961.1   TUN
CHAMBRE TUNISO-FRANCAISE DE COMMERCE ET D'INDUSTRIE. BULLETIN D'INFORMATION. Text in French. q.
Published by: Chambre Tuniso - Francaise de Commerce et d'Industrie (CTFCI), 14 Rue de la Monnaie, Tunis, 1001, Tunisia. TEL 01-253545, TELEX 14463.

384   FRA   ISSN 1629-3576
CHAMP'ECO; magazine mensuel d'information economique des Chambres de Commerce et d'Industrie de la Marne. Text in French. 1946. 9/yr. free. bk.rev. back issues avail. Document type: Monographic series, Trade. Description: Contains practical information on various industrial, commercial and service businesses in the Marne region. Includes contributions on the organization's financial status.
Formerly (until 2000): La Champagne Economique (1146-8599)
Published by: Chambre de Commerce et d'Industrie de Reims et d'Epernay, 5 rue des Marmouzets, BP 2511, Reims, Cedex 51070, France. TEL 33-3-26506200, FAX 33-3-26506289, info@reims.cci.fr, cci.chalons.champ@wanadoo.fr. Ed. Michel Clary. Pub. Jean Pierre Appert. Adv. contact Ghislaine Cartier. Circ: 17,000.

381   GBR
CITY AND COUNTY✱. Text in English. 1934. m. adv. bk.rev. illus.; stat. index.
Formerly: Leicester and County Chamber of Commerce Journal (0024-0648)
Published by: Leicester & County Chamber of Commerce, 4-6 New St, Leicester, LE1 5HT, United Kingdom. Ed. A H Green. Circ: 2,000.

382   COL
COLOMBIAN - AMERICAN BUSINESS ANNUAL DIRECTORY. Text in English, Spanish. 1956. a. USD 50. Document type: Directory. Description: Lists members with relevant data, organizations in Colombia, Latin America and the U.S. that are useful contacts, and general economic and visa information for both countries.
Formerly: Who's Who of Colombian - American Business
Published by: Camara de Comercio Colombo-Americana, Calle 98 No. 22-64 Ofic. 1209, Apartado Aereo 8008, Bogota, CUND, Colombia. TEL 57-1-6237088, FAX 57-1-6216838, publicaciones@amchamcolombia.com.co, http://www.amchamcolombia.com.co. Ed. Joseph Finin. Circ: 1,000 (paid).

382   USA
COLORADO BUSINESS RESOURCE DIRECTORY. Text in English. a. USD 35 per vol. to non-members (effective 2000); included with membership. Document type: Directory, Trade. Description: Provides a comprehensive business-to-business resource for firms of all types in Colorado.
Published by: Colorado Association of Commerce and Industry, 1600 Broadway, Ste 1000, Denver, CO 80202. TEL 303-831-7411, FAX 303-860-1439, caci@businesscolorado.com, http://www.businesscolorado.com/membership/memdir.html.

380   ECU   ISSN 0008-1868
COMERCIANTE✱. Text in Spanish. 1965. m. ECS 100, USD 10. adv. abstr.; illus.; stat.
Supersedes: Camara de Comercio de Guayaquil. Revista
Media: Microform.
Address: Ave. OLMEDO, 414, Guayaquil, Guayas, Ecuador.

330   CRI
COMERCIO. Text in Spanish. 1975. q. free.
Formerly: Camara de Comercio. Boletin Informativo (0010-9630)
Published by: Camara de Comercio de Costa Rica, Barrio Tournon, Apdo. 1114, San Jose, Costa Rica.

380 HND ISSN 0010-2245
COMERCIO. Text in Spanish. 1970. m. free. adv. bk.rev.
Published by: (Camara de Comercio e Industrias de Tegucigalpa), Honduras Industrial S. A., Apartado Postal 17 G, Tegucigalpa DC, Honduras. TEL 32-8210, FAX 31-2049. Ed. Jorge Mejia Ortega. Circ: 3,500.

380 ECU ISSN 0010-2296
COMERCIO ECUATORIANO. Text in Spanish. 1906. m. ECS 300, USD 10 to members. adv. stat.
Published by: Camara de Comercio de Quito, Avenidas Amazonas y de la Republica, Apdo 202, Quito, Pichincha, Ecuador. TEL 453-011, TELEX 2638. Ed. Marcelo Eguez Toro.

946.9 ESP
COMERCIO EXTERIOR DE LA COMUNIDAD VALENCIANA. Text in Spanish. 1973. a. **Document type:** *Trade.*
Formerly (until 1986): Region Exporta (0211-8866)
Published by: Camara Oficial de Comercio Industria y Navegacion de Valencia, Poeta Querol, 15, Valencia, 46002, Spain. TEL 34-96-351-1301, FAX 34-96-351-6349.
Co-sponsor: Camaras Oficiales de Comercio, Industria y Navegacion de Alcoy, Alicante, Castellon, Orihuela.

382 GBR ISSN 0010-2326
COMERCIO HISPANO BRITANICO. Text in English, Spanish. 1908. bi-m. free. adv. bk.rev. stat. **Document type:** *Newsletter.*
Published by: Spanish Chamber of Commerce in Great Britain, 5 Cavendish Sq, London, WIM 0DP, United Kingdom. TEL 44-171-637-9061, FAX 44-171-436-7188, TELEX 8811583-CAMCOE-G. Ed. J Fernandez Bragado. Adv. contact V Lorente. B&W page GBP 550, color page GBP 750; trim 210 x 297. Circ: 1,000.

380 PRT
COMERCIO, INDUSTRIA, SERVICOS. Text in Portuguese. 1939. 4/yr. membership. adv. illus.; stat.
Formerly (until 1975): Comercio Portugues (0010-2334)
Published by: Associacao Comercial de Lisboa, Camara de Comercio e Industria Portuguesa, Rua das Portas de Santo Antao 89, Lisbon Codex, 1194, Portugal. TEL 363355. Ed. Sergio Texeira de Queiroz. Circ: 3,000.

380 338 PER ISSN 0008-1892
COMERCIO Y PRODUCCION. Text in Spanish. 1929. w. adv. mkt.; stat. index.
Incorporates: Camara de Comercio de Lima. Boletin Semanal - Informativo Legal; Which was formed by the merger of: Camara de Comercio de Lima. Boletin Semanal (0008-1884); Camara de Comercio de Lima. Informativo Legal; Formerly: Camara de Comercio de Lima. Revista Mensual
Published by: Camara de Comercio de Lima, Ave. Gregorio Escobedo, 398, Jesus Maria, Lima, 11, Peru. TEL 51-14619864, FAX 51-14633686. Ed. Pedro A Flores Polo. Circ: 2,500.

380 338 PRI ISSN 0010-2350
COMERCIO Y PRODUCCION. Text in English, Spanish. 1960. bi-m. adv. charts; illus.; stat.; tr.lit.
Indexed: PAIS.
Published by: Chamber of Commerce of Puerto Rico, PO Box 9024033, San Juan, 00902-4033, Puerto Rico. TEL 787-721-6060, http://www.camarapr.org. Ed. Sixto Toro Cintron. Circ: 1,500 (controlled).

380 338 DOM ISSN 0010-2342
COMERCIO Y PRODUCCION. Text in Spanish. 1943. m. DOP 3.60. adv. bk.rev.
Published by: Camara de Comercio Agricultura e Industria del Distrito Nacional Inc., Apdo. Postal 815, Calle Arzobispo Nouel 206, Santo Domingo, Dominican Republic. Ed. Virgilio Hoepelman. Circ: 1,500.

382 ARG ISSN 0010-2660
COMMENTS ON ARGENTINE TRADE. Text in English. 1919. bi-m. USD 35 domestic; USD 75 foreign. adv. bk.rev. illus.; stat.; tr.lit. index. **Document type:** *Trade.*
Formerly: AmCham Weekly News
Indexed: PAIS, RASB.
Published by: American Chamber of Commerce in Argentina, Viamonte, 1133 Piso 8, Capital Federal, Buenos Aires 1053, Argentina. TEL 54-114-3714500, FAX 54-114-3718400. Ed., R&P Antonio Lofeudo. Adv. contact Mariana Urrestarazu. Circ: 2,500.

381 USA
COMMERCE (BATON ROUGE). Text in English. 1951. q. USD 12 to non-members; free to members (effective 2005). adv. illus.; stat. **Document type:** *Newsletter, Trade.* **Description:** Covers Chamber activities updates as well as technology and business tips.
Former titles: Action Newsletter (Baton Rouge); Baton Rouge (0005-6324)
Published by: The Chamber of Greater Baton Rouge, PO Box 3217, Baton Rouge, LA 70821. info@brchamber.org, http://www.brchamber.org. Ed. Amy Delaney. adv.: B&W page USD 569; trim 7.5 x 10. Circ: 3,200 (free).

382 USA
COMMERCE (WINSTON-SALEM). Text in English. 2000. 3/yr. free to members. back issues avail. **Document type:** *Newsletter, Consumer.* **Description:** Contains feature stories on Chamber members' businesses and news wire stories on timely business topics.
Former titles (until 2004): Strategy; Entrepreneur
Related titles: Supplement(s): City Vision.
Published by: Greater Winston - Salem Chamber of Commerce, PO Box 1408, Winston-Salem, NC 27102. TEL 336-728-9200, FAX 336-721-2209, http://www.winstonsalem.com. Ed. Emily Smoot. Circ: 8,000 (free).

380 CAN
COMMERCE COMMENTS. Text in English. 1968. m. CND 25.68 membership (effective 2000). adv. illus. **Document type:** *Newsletter.* **Description:** Serving the business community of Calgary.
Former titles: Calgary Commerce (0707-8064); Calgary Business; Calgary Chamber of Commerce. Business News (0382-7887)
Related titles: Online - full text ed.: (from Micromedia ProQuest, ProQuest Information & Learning).
Indexed: BusDate.
Published by: Calgary Chamber of Commerce, 517 Center St S, Calgary, AB T2G 2C4, Canada. TEL 403-750-0400, FAX 403-266-3413, esonntag@chamber.calgary.ab.ca, http://www.chamber.calgary.ab.ca/. Ed. Erin Sonntag. adv.: page CND 600;. Circ: 4,500.

944 FRA ISSN 0996-1860
COMMERCE ET INDUSTRIE DE L'INDRE. Text in French. 1952. 5/yr. **Document type:** *Trade.*
Published by: Commerce et Industrie de l, 24 Place Gambetta, Chateauroux, Cedex 36028, France. TEL 33-2-54535251, FAX 33-2-54341777, TELEX 750 534. Ed. Andre Blanc Bernard. Circ: 8,000.

382 FRA
COMMERCE EXTERIEUR DES REGIONS PROVENCE, COTE D'AZUR ET CORSE. Text in French. 1968. a. illus.
Published by: Chambre de Commerce et d'Industrie de Marseille, Immeuble CMCI, 2 rue Henri Barbusse, Marseille, Cedex 1 13241, France. Ed. Rene Delboy. Circ: 600.

382 CHE ISSN 0010-2830
COMMERCE FRANCO-SUISSE. Text in French. 1894. 4/yr. membership. adv. bk.rev. bibl.; illus.; pat.; stat.; tr.lit.; tr.mk. index.
Indexed: KES.
Published by: Chambre France - Suisse pour le Commerce et l'Industrie, 32 Av de Frontenex, Geneva 6, 1211, Switzerland. Circ: 5,000.

COMMERCE IN GERMANY. see *BUSINESS AND ECONOMICS*

382 ZWE
COMMERCE - ZIMBABWE. Text in English. m. ZWD 181.20; ZWD 250.80 foreign (effective 1999). adv. **Document type:** *Trade.*
Formerly: Commerce - Rhodesia
Published by: (Zimbabwe National Chamber of Commerce), Thomson Publications Zimbabwe (Pvt) Ltd., Thomson House, PO Box 1683, Harare, Zimbabwe. TEL 263-4-736835, FAX 263-4-752390.

380 MLT ISSN 0010-2938
COMMERCIAL COURIER. Text in English. 1947. m. adv. bk.rev. **Document type:** *Bulletin, Trade.* **Description:** Official organ of the Malta Chamber of Commerce.
Indexed: KES.
Published by: Malta Chamber of Commerce, The Exchange, Republic St., Valletta, VLT 05, Malta. FAX 356-245223. Ed., R&P Kevin J Borg. Circ: 1,500.

977 USA ISSN 1092-3780
COMMUNITY IMPROVEMENT PROJECTS & FUNDING. Text in English. 1995. m. looseleaf. USD 119 (effective 2004). back issues avail. **Document type:** *Newsletter, Trade.* **Description:** Contains concise articles emphasizing practical community projects and programs with proven success records across the U.S. and Canada.
Published by: White Pine Press, 7475 E. Donnywood Cir., Britt, MN 55710-8018. hakesd@bvu.edu, whitepine@frontiernet.net. Ed., Pub., R&P Barbara J Booton. Circ: 250 (paid).

382 UKR
COMPASS; quarterly newsletter. Text in English. q. membership. **Document type:** *Newsletter.* **Description:** Includes Chamber of Commerce, international, and community news; committee reports, announcements, member news, and a calendar.
Published by: American Chamber of Commerce in Ukraine, Shovkovychna vul 42-44 LL 2, Kiev, 252004, Ukraine. TEL 380-44-490-5800, FAX 380-44-490-5801. Ed. Jorge Zukoski.

381 COL
CONFEDERACION COLOMBIANA DE CAMARAS DE COMERCIO. ASAMBLEA GENERAL. INFORME FINAL✶. Text in Spanish. 1970. irreg. free.
Published by: Confederacion Colombiana de Camaras de Comercio, Carrera 13 no. 27-47, Oficina 502, PO Box 29750, Bogota, CUND, Colombia. Circ: 1,000.

380 COL
CONFEDERACION COLOMBIANA DE CAMARAS DE COMERCIO. SINTESIS MENSUAL✶. Text in Spanish. 1969. m. COP 400, USD 10. illus.
Published by: Confederacion Colombiana de Camaras de Comercio, Carrera 13 no. 27-47, Oficina 502, PO Box 29750, Bogota, CUND, Colombia. Ed. Alvaro Garcia. Circ: 8,000.

CONFEDERATION OF ZIMBABWE INDUSTRIES. REGISTER & BUYERS GUIDE. see *BUSINESS AND ECONOMICS—Trade And Industrial Directories*

382 FRA ISSN 0753-5724
CONTACT - CHAMBRE OFFICIELLE FRANCO-ALLEMANDE DE COMMERCE ET D'INDUSTRIE/ZEITSCHRIFT DER DEUTSCH-FRANZOESISCHEN WIRTSCHAFT. Text in French, German. 6/yr. EUR 67. adv. bk.rev. bibl.; pat.; stat.
Formerly (until 1981): Revue Economique Franco-Allemande (0048-8038)
Published by: Chambre Franco Allemande de Commerce et d'Industrie, 18 rue Balard, Paris, 75015, France. TEL 45-75-62-56, FAX 45-75-47-39, TELEX 203-738 CFACI. Circ: 6,000.

382 ITA
CONTACTS FRANCO-ITALIENS. Text in French, Italian. 1885. bi-m. adv. bk.rev. **Document type:** *Magazine, Trade.* **Description:** Forum covering articles on the economic life in Italy and France. Includes monthly letters, French subsidiaries and a list of members.
Published by: Chambre Francaise de Commerce et d'Industrie en Italie/Camera Francese di Commercio ed Industria in Italia, Via Cusani 5, Milan, MI 20121, Italy. TEL 39-02-725371, FAX 39-02-865593, http://www.chambre.it. Ed. Eric Sauvaire. Circ: 1,500.

945 ITA
CORRIERE DEL COMMERCIO. Text in Italian. 20/yr. adv.
Published by: Associazione Commercianti della Provincia di Bologna, Strada Maggiore, 23, Bologna, BO 40125, Italy. Ed. Franco Fabbri. Circ: 20,000.

338 916 BFA ISSN 0574-3370
COURRIER CONSULAIRE DU BURKINA FASO. Text in French. 1960. m. XOF 14,000 (effective 1999). charts; stat. **Description:** Contains legislative and statutory notices.
Formerly: Courrier Consulaire de la Haute Volta
Published by: Chambre de Commerce d'Industrie et d'Artisanat, PO Box 502, Ouagadougou, 01, Burkina Faso. TEL 30-61-14, FAX 30-61-16, TELEX 5268 BF.

381 GBR
COVENTRY & WARWICKSHIRE CHAMBER OF COMMERCE. TRAINING & ENTERPRISE DIRECTORY. Text in English. a. GBP 60 (effective 2001). **Document type:** *Directory.*
Published by: Kemps Publishing Ltd., 11 Swan Courtyard, Charles Edward Rd, Birmingham, W Mids B26 1BU, United Kingdom. TEL 44-121-765-4144, FAX 44-121-706-6210.

946 ESP
COYUNTURA INDUSTRIAL. BOLETIN. Text in Spanish. m. **Document type:** *Bulletin.*
Published by: Camara Oficial de Comercio, Industria y Navegacion de Tarragona, Av Pau Casals 17, Tarragona, 43003, Spain. TEL 34-977-21967, FAX 34-977-240900.

330.9 TGO
LA CROISIERE DES OPERATEURS ECONOMIQUES. Text in French. q. XOF 16,000 domestic; XOF 20,000 in Africa and France; XOF 23,000 in Europe; XOF 28,000 in the Americas; XOF 30,000 in Australasia (effective 2005). adv. bk.rev. charts; stat. 70 p./no.; **Document type:** *Bulletin, Corporate.* **Description:** News of commercial, agricultural and industrial activities of the chamber.
Former titles (until 2000): Chambre de Commerce, d'Agriculture et d'Industrie du Togo. Bulletin Bimestriel; Chambre de Commerce, d'Agriculture et d'Industrie du Togo. Bulletin Mensuel
Published by: Chambre de Commerce et d'Industrie du Togo, Angle Av. de La Presidence et Av. Georges Pompidou, BP 360, Lome, Togo. TEL 228-2217065, FAX 228-2214730, ccit@rdd.tg, http://www.ccit.tg. Circ: 450.

382 FRA
CROSS CHANNEL. Text in French. 1952. bi-m. FRF 250. adv. bk.rev. **Document type:** *Directory.*
Formerly (until 1992): Cross Channel Trade (0983-1487)
Published by: Franco-British Chamber of Commerce and Industry, 31 rue Boissy d'Anglas, Paris, 75008, France. TEL 33-1-53308130, FAX 33-1-53308135. Ed., R&P, Adv. contact Catherine Le Yaouanc. Circ: 2,000.

338 GBR
CROYDON CHAMBER OF COMMERCE AND INDUSTRY DIRECTORY. Text in English. a. GBP 45 (effective 2001). **Document type:** *Directory.*

▼ new title ➤ refereed ✶ unverified ◆ full entry avail.

Former titles (until 2000): Croydon and South London Chamber of Commerce and Industry Directory (1354-0149); (until 1994): Croydon Chamber of Commerce and Industry Directory (0144-2996); (until 1979): Croydon Chamber of Commerce and Industry. Members List; Southern Home Counties Chamber of Commerce Directory; Southern Home Counties Directory
Published by: Kemps Publishing Ltd., 11 Swan Courtyard, Charles Edward Rd, Birmingham, W Mids B26 1BU, United Kingdom. TEL 44-121-765-4144, FAX 44-121-706-6210.

382 CUB ISSN 0864-3857
HF300.C9
CUBA FOREIGN TRADE. Text in English, Spanish. 1988. q. USD 20 domestic; USD 30 foreign (effective 2000). adv. illus. index. **Document type:** *Trade.*
Published by: Camara de Comercio de la Republica de Cuba/Chamber of Commerce of Cuba, Calle 21 No. 661, esq. A, Apartado 370, Vedado, La Habana, Cuba. TEL 53-303356, FAX 53-333042, TELEX 51-1752, correo@camara.com.cu. Ed., R&P Miriam Martinez Delgado. Adv. contact Vivian Hernandez. B&W page USD 600, color page USD 1,200; trim 275 x 210. Circ: 4,000.

382 380.1029 NZL ISSN 1175-0200
CURRENT DIRECTORY OF INTERNATIONAL CHAMBERS OF COMMERCE AND INDUSTRY. Text in English. 1999. irreg., latest 1999-2000. looseleaf. USD 150 newsstand/cover foreign (effective 2001). 234 p./no.; **Document type:** *Directory, Trade.* **Description:** Provides information on more than 3,200 international chambers of commerce and industry selected from major cities in more than 165 countries and territories in the world. Countries covers Afghanistan to Zimbabwe, Cities include Accra to Zurich. Typical entries include these basic information: Name of organization; Full address; Phone number; Fax number; E-mail address; and Name of Chief Executive Officer.
Published by: Current Pacific Ltd., PO Box 36-536, Northcote, Auckland, New Zealand.

381.029 IND
D C C TRADE DIRECTORY. Text in English. 1982. a. free to members. adv. **Document type:** *Directory.* **Description:** Renders service to importers and exporters in the world.
Published by: Delhi Chamber of Commerce, Sodhbans Chambers, Paharganj, 9104 D.B. Gupta Rd., New Delhi, 110 055, India. TEL 91-11-7516421, FAX 91-11-7528847. Circ: 3,000.

382 AUT
D H K MAGAZIN. Text in German. 1964. 7/yr. membership. bk.rev. charts; illus.; stat.; tr.lit. **Document type:** *Magazine, Trade.*
Former titles: D H K Wirtschaftsspiegel; Deutsche Handelskammer in Oesterreich. Bulletin (0012-0251)
Related titles: Cards ed.
Published by: Deutsche Handelskammer in Oesterreich, Wiedner Hauptstr 142, Vienna, W 1050, Austria. TEL 43-1-5451417, FAX 43-1-5452259, office@dhk.at, http://www.dhk.at/magazin.html. Ed. Steffen Lenke. Adv. contact Corina Kaltenhauser. Circ: 12,000 (controlled).

972 MEX ISSN 0185-1985
DECISION; comercio, servicios y turismo. Text in Spanish. 1979. m. MXP 100 domestic; USD 50 in the Americas; USD 55 elsewhere. adv. bk.rev. **Description:** Publishes economic, political, commercial, and tourism and service industry information.
Published by: Confederacion de Camaras Nacionales de Comercio, Servicios y Turismo, Balderas 144, 2o Piso, Apdo. Postal 113, Mexico City, DF 06079, Mexico. TEL 709-15-59 ext. 249, FAX 709-11-52. Ed. Carlos Arrieta Davila. Adv. contact Nelia Sanchez Mendez. Circ: 30,000.

954 IND
DELHI CHAMBER OF COMMERCE. BULLETIN. Text in English. bi-w. free to members. adv. **Document type:** *Bulletin.* **Description:** Renders service to importers and exporters world wide.
Published by: Delhi Chamber of Commerce, Sodhbans Chambers, Paharganj, 9104 D.B. Gupta Rd., New Delhi, 110 055, India. TEL 91-11-7516421, FAX 91-11-7528847, TELEX 31-61826 DCC IN. Circ: 1,200.

381 USA ISSN 0011-9709
DETROITER. Text in English. 1910. 8/yr. USD 18 to non-members; USD 14 to members (effective 2005). adv. bk.rev. illus. back issues avail.; reprints avail. **Document type:** *Magazine, Trade.* **Description:** Covers the southeastern Michigan business community.
Incorporates: Chamber Business News (1061-1649); Formerly: Detroiter Business News
Related titles: Microform ed.: (from PQC); Online - full text ed.: (from Florida Center for Library Automation, Gale Group, Northern Light Technology, Inc., ProQuest Information & Learning).
Indexed: BusDate, MMI.
Published by: Detroit Regional Chamber, One Woodward Ave, Ste 1900, Box 33840, Detroit, MI 48232-0840. TEL 313-596-0373, FAX 313-964-0531, cmead@detroitchamber.com, http://www.detroitchamber.com/detroiter. Ed. Chris Mead. Pub. Richard E Blouse Jr. Adv. contact Robert Bowers. B&W page USD 1,800, color page USD 2,900. Circ: 10,000 (paid and controlled).

944 FRA ISSN 0184-878X
DIEPPE INFO. Text in French. q. free.
Former titles (until 1977): Doc Info (0184-8771); (until 1975): Via Dieppe (0335-2935)
Address: 4 bd. du General de Gaulle, Dieppe, Cedex 76374, France. TEL 35-06-50-50, FAX 35-06-50-51, TELEX 180 770 CHAMLOM. Ed. Corinne Emo. Pub. Christophe Maurel. Circ: 3,800.

980 SLV
DIRECTORIO COMERCIAL E INDUSTRIAL. Text and summaries in English, Spanish. 1970. a. USD 12. adv. index.
Published by: (Camara de Comercio e Industria de El Salvador), Ediciones Culturales Publicitarias, S.A., 57 Avenida Norte No. 114, Colonia Escalon, San Salvador, El Salvador. Circ: 2,000.
Subscr. to: 9a Avenida Norte y 5a, Calle Poniente, San Salvador, El Salvador.

382 MEX
DIRECTORY OF AMERICAN COMPANIES. Text in English, Spanish. a., latest 2003. USD 750 (effective 2003). **Document type:** *Trade.* **Description:** Supplies details on 2900 US firms operating in Mexico, Mexican companies, products and services manufactured, sold or offered by representative firms, and US locations.
Published by: American Chamber of Commerce of Mexico A.C., Lucerna 78, Col. Juarez, Mexico City, D F 06600, Mexico. TEL 52-55-51413800, FAX 52-55-57032911, amchamm@amcham.com.mx, http://www.amcham.com.mx/. Ed. Alma Soots. R&Ps Diana H de Hernandez, Mariana Prado.

381 LKA
DIRECTORY OF EXPORTERS. Text in English. 1975. biennial. USD 25. adv. **Document type:** *Directory.*
Published by: (Export Section), Ceylon Chamber of Commerce, Chamber of Commerce Bldg., P O Box 274, Colombo, 2, Sri Lanka. FAX 941-449352.

DIRECTORY OF INDUSTRIAL PRODUCTS: SHARJAH, UNITED ARAB EMIRATES/DALEEL AL MONTAJAT AL SINA'IAH: AL SHARIQAH. see *BUSINESS AND ECONOMICS—Trade And Industrial Directories*

986.1 COL
DOCTRINA MERCANTIL. Text in Spanish. a.
Published by: Camara de Comercio de Bogota, Carrera 26 68D-35, Bogota, Colombia.

987 382 VEN
DOING BUSINESS IN VENEZUELA. Text in Spanish, English. 1999. q. VEB 10, USD 15. adv. **Document type:** *Trade.*
Formerly: Business Guide to Venezuela
Published by: Venezuelan - American Chamber of Commerce and Industry/Camara Venezolano-Americana de Comercio e Industria, Torre Credival-PL., 2da Avenida de Campo Alegre, Caracas, DF 1010-A, Venezuela. TEL 58-2-2630833, FAX 58-2-2630586, skivilevic@venamcham.org. Ed. Antonio Herrera Vaillant. Adv. contact Shalom Kivilevic.

381 USA
DULUTH AREA CHAMBER OF COMMERCE OFFICIAL BUSINESS & COMMUNITY GUIDE. Text in English. a. **Document type:** *Directory.*
Published by: Duluth Area Chamber of Commerce, 5 W. 1st St., Ste. 101, Duluth, MN 55802-2115. TEL 218-722-5501, FAX 218-722-3223, http://www.duluthchamber.com. Circ: 1,850.

381 USA ISSN 0012-7116
DULUTHIAN. Text in English. 1965. bi-m. USD 5 to non-members; free to members (effective 2000 - 2001). adv. bk.rev. charts; illus.; tr.lit. index. **Document type:** *Newsletter, Trade.*
Related titles: Microform ed.: (from PQC); Online - full text ed.: (from Northern Light Technology, Inc., ProQuest Information & Learning).
Indexed: ABIn, BusDate.
Published by: Duluth Area Chamber of Commerce, 5 W. 1st St., Ste. 101, Duluth, MN 55802-2115. TEL 218-722-5501, FAX 218-722-3223, http://www.duluthchamber.com. Ed., R&P Nancy LeMay Nebel. Pub. David Ross. Circ: 4,000.

381.029 GBR
DUNDEE AND TAYSIDE CHAMBER OF COMMERCE AND INDUSTRY. BUYER'S GUIDE AND TRADE DIRECTORY. Text in English. 1958. a. GBP 7.50 (effective 2000). **Document type:** *Directory.*
Formerly: Dundee Chamber of Commerce. Buyer's Guide and Trade Directory
Published by: Dundee and Tayside Chamber of Commerce and Industry, Chamber of Commerce Bldgs, Dundee, Panmure St, Dundee, DD1 1ED, United Kingdom. Ed., R&P Maggie Lennon. Adv. contact Julie Christie. Circ: 1,800 (controlled).

944 FRA ISSN 0243-2633
DUNKERQUE EXPANSION. Text in French. 36/yr. adv. **Document type:** *Newspaper.*
Address: 1 rue du Rempart, Dunkerque, 59140, France. TEL 33-3-28664761, FAX 33-3-28662104, TELEX 820 970. Ed., Adv. contact Laurence Desbischop. Circ: 6,000.

381 ZAF ISSN 1021-0067
DURBAN CHAMBER OF COMMERCE AND INDUSTRY. CHAMBER DIGEST. Text in English. 1953. fortn. adv. **Document type:** *Bulletin.*
Formerly (until 1992): Durban Regional Chamber of Business. Information Digest (0250-1740)
Indexed: ISAP.
Published by: Durban Chamber of Commerce and Industry, PO Box 1506, Durban, KwaZulu-Natal 4000, South Africa. TEL 27-31-335-1000, chamber@durbanchamber.co.za, http://www.durbanchamber.co.za. R&P Nadia Thomson. Adv. contact Lorraine Wheal.

380 GBR
EAST MERCIA CHAMBER OF COMMERCE & INDUSTRY DIRECTORY. Text in English. a. GBP 50 (effective 2001). **Document type:** *Directory.*
Formerly: Walsall Chamber of Commerce & Industry Directory (0141-6626)
Published by: Kemps Publishing Ltd., 11 Swan Courtyard, Charles Edward Rd, Birmingham, W Mids B26 1BU, United Kingdom. TEL 44-121-765-4144, FAX 44-121-706-6210.

381 GBR ISSN 1356-529X
HF3519.M53
EAST MIDLANDS CHAMBER OF COMMERCE DIRECTORY. Text in English. 1983. a. GBP 70 (effective 2001). **Document type:** *Directory.* **Description:** Highlights principal industrial and commercial companies in the English East Midlands.
Former titles (until 1993): East Midlands Business Directory (0962-9491); East Midlands Chamber of Commerce Regional Directory (0263-404X)
Published by: (East Midlands Chambers of Commerce), Kemps Publishing Ltd., 11 Swan Courtyard, Charles Edward Rd, Birmingham, W Mids B26 1BU, United Kingdom. TEL 44-121-765-4144, FAX 44-121-706-6210.

381 USA ISSN 0012-8538
EAST SIDE CHAMBER OF COMMERCE NEWSLETTER. Text in English. 1956. bi-m. free. adv. charts. **Document type:** *Newsletter, Trade.*
Published by: East Side Chamber of Commerce, PO Box 3380, New York, NY 10008-3380. TEL 212-233-1925, FAX 212-233-1965. Ed., Adv. contact Sidney Baumgarten. Circ: 500.

382 DEU ISSN 0723-2179
ECONOMIA; Zeitschrift der Italienischen Handelskammer fuer Deutschland. Text in German, Italian. 1950. q. bk.rev. **Document type:** *Magazine, Trade.*
Formerly (until 1982): Informazioni Economiche Italo-Germaniche (0723-225X)
Indexed: ELLIS.
Published by: Italienische Handelskammer fuer Deutschland/Camera di Commercio Italiana per la Germania, Kettenhofweg 65, Frankfurt Am Main, 60325, Germany. TEL 49-69-97145210, FAX 49-69-97145299, info@ccig.de, http://www.itkam.de. Adv. contact Kathrin Walter. Circ: 3,000 (controlled).

330.9 ESP ISSN 0568-8876
HC387.A53
ECONOMIA ALAVESA. Text in Spanish. a. index.
Published by: Camara Oficial de Comercio e Industria de Alava, Dato 38, Vitoria, 01005, Spain. TEL 34-45-141800, FAX 34-45-143156, cocia@jet.es, http://www.jet.es/camara. Ed. D Lorenzo Bergareche Capa. Circ: 1,000.

330 ITA ISSN 0012-9747
ECONOMIA ARETINA. Text in Italian. 1922. m. adv. bk.rev. charts; illus.; mkt.; stat. **Document type:** *Bulletin.*
Formerly: Rassegna Economica (Arezzo)
Published by: Camera di Commercio Industria Artigianato e Agricoltura di Arezzo, Viale Giotto, 4, Arezzo, AR 52100, Italy. TEL 0575-3030, FAX 0575-300953. Ed. Lodovico Lodovichi. R&P, Adv. contact Piero Innocenti. Circ: 1,050.

330 ITA
ECONOMIA DELLA MARCA TREVIGIANA. Text in Italian. 1903. w. free. adv.
Related titles: Online - full text ed.
Published by: Camera di Commercio Industria Artigianato e Agricoltura di Treviso, Piazza della Borsa, Treviso, TV 31100, Italy. TEL 39-0422-5951, FAX 39-0422-412625, segreteria.generale@tv.camcom.it, http://www.tv.camcom.it. Ed. Renato Chahinian. Circ: 5,200.

330 ESP ISSN 0211-4763
ECONOMIA GUIPUZCOANA. Text in Spanish. 1965. 4/yr. free. adv. abstr.; illus.; stat. **Document type:** *Bulletin.*
Published by: Camara Oficial de Comercio Industria y Navegacion de Guipuzcoa, Ramon Maria Lili, 6, San Sebastian, Spain. TEL 43-27-2100, FAX 43-29-3105, TELEX 36529 CAMIN E. Ed. Felix Iraola. Circ: 12,000 (controlled).

382 ITA ISSN 0012-981X
HB7
ECONOMIA INTERNAZIONALE. Text in English, French, Italian, Spanish. 1948. q. EUR 100; EUR 28 per issue (effective 2005). bk.rev. bibl.; charts. index. back issues avail.
Document type: *Magazine, Consumer.* **Description:** Presents articles in several languages about international economic relations.
Indexed: APEL, BAS, CREJ, CurCont, DIP, IBR, IBSS, IBZ, JEL, KES, PAIS, PCI, RRTA, ST&MA, WAE&RSA.
—BLDSC (3650.860000), CISTI, IE, Infotrieve, ingenta.
Published by: Camera di Commercio di Genova, Via Garibaldi 4, Genoa, GE 16124, Italy. TEL 39-010-27041, FAX 39-010-2704300, http://www.ge.camcom.it, camera.genova@ge.camcom.it. Circ: 1,000.

945 ITA
ECONOMIA ISONTINA. Text in Italian. 1960. m. adv. **Document type:** *Bulletin, Consumer.* **Description:** Covers the Chamber's activities, domestic economic system, and economic relations with Eastern European countries.
Published by: Camera di Commercio Industria Agricoltura e Artigianato (Gorizia), Via Francesco Crispi 10, Gorizia, GO 34170, Italy. TEL 39-0481-3841, FAX 39-0481-533176, http://www.go.camcom.it. Ed. Renato Chahinian.

330 ITA ISSN 0391-6359
ECONOMIA PESARESE. Text in Italian. 1948. bi-m. adv.
Document type: *Magazine, Consumer.* **Description:** Includes articles on economic subjects and activities of the organization.
Published by: Camera di Commercio Industria Artigianato e Agricoltura di Pesaro e Urbino, Corso XI Settembre 116, Pesaro, PS 61100, Italy. FAX 39-0721-31015, 39-0721-3571, http://www.ps,camcom.it. Ed. Paolo Lamaro. Circ: 1,500.

330 ITA ISSN 0012-9879
ECONOMIA TRENTINA. Text in Italian. 1952. q. adv.
Former titles (until 1954): Economia Atesina (1123-3567); (until 1952): Camera di Commercio Industria Artigianato e Agricola. Trento. Notiziario Economico (1123-3575)
Indexed: PAIS.
—BLDSC (3651.130000).
Published by: Camera di Commercio Industria Artigianato e Agricoltura di Trento, Via Calepina, 13, Trento, TN 38100, Italy. TEL 39-0461-887111, FAX 39-0461-986356, http://www.tn.camcom.it. Ed. Enzo Dematte. Adv. contact Giorgio Baldi. Circ: 900.

330 IND ISSN 0970-6453
ECONOMIC TRENDS. Text in English. 1957. s-m. INR 1,000, USD 90. adv. bk.rev. bibl.; charts; stat.; tr.lit. reprints avail.
Document type: *Trade.*
Formerly (until 1971): Federation of Indian Chambers of Commerce and Industry. Fortnightly Review (0014-9470)
Media: Duplicated (not offset). **Related titles:** Supplement(s): Parliament News.
Indexed: CRIA.
Published by: Federation of Indian Chambers of Commerce and Industry, Federation House, Tansen Marg, New Delhi, 110 001, India. TEL 91-11-331-9251, FAX 91-11-332-0714, TELEX 031-61768. Circ: 3,000.

381 CHE
ECONOMIE LAUSANNOISE. Text in French. q.
Address: Case Postale 62, Lausanne, 1018, Switzerland. TEL 021-361704. Circ: 2,500.

330 LBN ISSN 0013-0540
ECONOMIE LIBANAISE ET ARABE*. Text in French. 1970 (vol.19). bi-m. LBP 40, USD 20. adv. charts; illus.; stat.
Description: Survey of economic developments in Lebanon.
Published by: Chambre de Commerce et d'Industrie de Beyrouth, Rue Allenby, Immeuble Avass, P O Box 1801, Beirut, Lebanon. Ed. Sami N Atiyeh.

969.82 MUS
ECONOMY IN FIGURES. Text in English. a. free. **Document type:** *Trade.*
Formerly: Facts and Figures
Published by: Mauritius Chamber of Commerce and Industry, 3 Royal St, Port Louis, Mauritius. TEL 230-208-3301, FAX 230-208-0076, mcci@intnet.mu. Circ: 1,200.

382 ECU
ECUADOR BUSINESS & COMMERCE. Text in Spanish. m. USD 3 per issue. **Document type:** *Consumer.*
Formerly: Comercio Ecuatoriano Americano - Ecuadorian American Business
Published by: Ecuadorian - American Chamber of Commerce, Edif. Multicentro, 4P, La Nina y 6 Diciembre, Quito, Pichincha, Ecuador. TEL 5932-507-450, FAX 5932-504-571. Circ: 2,000.

382 ECU
ECUADORIAN - AMERICAN CHAMBER OF COMMERCE. ANNUAL DIRECTORY. Text in Spanish. a. USD 40.
Document type: *Directory.*
Published by: Ecuadorian - American Chamber of Commerce, Edif. Multicentro, 4P, La Nina y 6 Diciembre, Quito, Pichincha, Ecuador. TEL 5932-507-450, FAX 5932-504-571. Circ: 1,000.

381 CAN ISSN 0704-8017
EDMONTON CHAMBER OF COMMERCE. COMMERCE NEWS. Text in English. 1976. 10/yr. CND 24.95 to non-members; free to members (effective 2004). adv. bk.rev. illus. **Document type:** *Newsletter, Trade.* **Description:** Reports on major stories of interest to business.
Related titles: Online - full text ed.: (from Micromedia ProQuest, ProQuest Information & Learning).
Indexed: BusDate.
Published by: Edmonton Chamber of Commerce, Ste 600, 10123 99 St, Edmonton, AB T5J 3G9, Canada. TEL 780-426-4620, FAX 780-424-7946, info@edmontonchamber.com, http://www.edmontonchamber.com. Ed. Michel Proule. Pub. Martin Salloum. Adv. contact Rita Boyce. page CND 1,850; trim 13.5 x 11.25. Circ: 30,000 (controlled).

380 EGY
EGYPTIAN CHAMBER OF COMMERCE. BULLETIN. Text in English. m. **Document type:** *Bulletin.*
Published by: Egyptian Chamber of Commerce, 4 Midan Falaki, Cairo, Egypt.

956.1 TUR
EKONOMI/ECONOMY. Text in Turkish. 1978. w. **Document type:** *Newspaper.*
Published by: Turkish Cypriot Chamber of Commerce, Bedrettin Demirel Ave., Lefkosa, P O Box 718, Mersin 10, Turkey. TEL 90-392-2283760, FAX 90-392-2283089, TELEX 57511. Circ: 3,000.

332 ITA ISSN 0013-6050
ELENCO UFFICIALE DEI PROTESTI CAMBIARI LEVATI NELLA PROVINCIA DI TORINO. Text in Italian. 1955. fortn.
Published by: Camera di Commercio Industria Artigianato e Agricoltura di Torino, Via carlo Alberto 16, Turin, TO 10123, Italy. info@to.camcom.it, http://www.to.camcom.it. Ed. Franco Alunno. Circ: 1,300.

382 SGP
ENQUIRES. Text in English. bi-w.
Published by: Singapore Indian Chamber of Commerce, 101 Cecil St, 23-01 Tong Eng Bldg, Singapore, 069533, Singapore. FAX 65-223-1707.

338 974 USA
ENRICH!; information bank briefings for network members. Text in English. 1985. m. USD 69 (effective 2000). adv. bk.rev. charts; illus. back issues avail. **Description:** Provides business plan formats, results and analysis, plus next-step guidelines for women in business, and pay range reports for women in salaried positions.
Published by: National Chamber of Commerce for Women, 10 Waterside Plaza, Ste 6H, New York, NY 10010. TEL 212-685-3454. Ed. M. Rinaldi. Pub. R. Wright. R&P M Rinaldi. Adv. contact R Wright. Circ: 4,700.

330 GBR
ENTERPRISE. Text in English. 1978. m. free. adv.
Formerly: Central Midland Enterprise
Published by: Coventry and Warwickshire Chamber of Commerce Training and Enterprise, Oak Tree Court, Binley Business Park, Harry Weston Rd, Coventry, CV3 2UN, United Kingdom. Ed. Alan Robinson.

330 BEL ISSN 0770-2264
ENTREPRENDRE/DYNAMIEK. Text in French. 1875. 11/yr. free membership (effective 2005). adv. bibl.; charts. index.
Document type: *Trade.*
Formerly (until vol.106, no.3, 1980): Chambre de Commerce de Bruxelles. Bulletin Officiel (0009-1197)
Indexed: PdeR.
Published by: Chambre de Commerce de Bruxelles, Av Louise 500, Brussels, 1050, Belgium. ccibrussels@cci.be, http://www.500.be/site/fr/maison_des_entreprises/publications/entreprendre/index_htm, http://www.ccib.be. Ed. Philippe D'Hondt. Adv. contact Robert Demarcke. B&W page EUR 1,360, color page EUR 1,935; bleed 210 x 297. Circ: 10,000.

944 FRA ISSN 1634-9113
ENTREPRISE ET METIERS. Text in French. 1959. bi-m. adv.
Former titles (until 2001): Metiers Reussite 01 (1248-9468); (until 1993): Metiers (1248-945X); (until 1972): Chambre de Metiers de l'Ain. Bulletin (1248-9441)
Published by: Chambre de Metiers de l, 3 rue P. Piola, Bourg, (Ain), France. Circ: 7,800.

960 CIV
L'ENTREPRISE IVOIRIENNE. Text in French. a.
Published by: Chambre de Commerce et d'Industrie de Cote d'Ivoire, BP 1399, Abidjan, Ivory Coast. TEL 225-20-331600, FAX 225-20323942, info@cci-ci.org, http://www.cci-ci.org.

381 CHE ISSN 1013-3089
ENTREPRISE ROMANDE. Text in French. 1933. 46/yr.
Document type: *Newspaper, Consumer.*
Formerly (until 1983): Ordre Professionnel (1013-3070)
Address: 98 Rue de St Jean, Geneva 11, 1211, Switzerland. TEL 41-22-7153244, FAX 41-22-7153214, er@fsp.ch. Ed. Didier Fleck. Circ: 19,937.

944 FRA ISSN 0755-6306
ENTREPRISES MIDI-PYRENEES. Text in French. 1983. 11/yr.
Address: 11 bd. des Recollets, Toulouse, Cedex 4 31078, France. TEL 33-0561144200, FAX 33-0561144201, emp@entreprises-midpyrenees.com. Ed. Emma Bao. Circ: 10,000.

380 338 GBR
ESSEX BUSINESS MAGAZINE. Text in English. 1970. m. membership. adv. illus. index. **Document type:** *Directory.*
Former titles: Chamber Impact; South Essex Chamber of Commerce, Trade and Industry. Southend. Monthly Journal; Southend-on-Sea and District Chamber of Commerce, Trade and Industry. Monthly Journal; Southend-on-Sea and District Chamber of Trade and Industry. Monthly Journal (0038-3724)
Published by: South Essex Chamber of Commerce Trade & Industry (Southend) Ltd., 845 London Rd, Westcliff-on-Sea, Essex SS0 9SZ, United Kingdom. TEL 44-1702-716000, FAX 44-1702-716001. Ed. D J Horsley. R&P W E F March. Circ: 700 (controlled).

ETHIOPIAN TRADE DIRECTORY. see *BUSINESS AND ECONOMICS—Trade And Industrial Directories*

963 ETH
ETHIOPIAN TRADE JOURNAL. Text in English. 1967-1970; resumed 1981. q. USD 16. **Document type:** *Trade.*
Published by: Ethiopian Chamber of Commerce, PO Box 517, Addis Ababa, Ethiopia. Ed. Getachew Zicke. Circ: 3,000.

052 BEL
EXPAT DIRECTORY. Text in English. a. **Document type:** *Directory, Consumer.* **Description:** Provides a source of information for expatriates living in Belgium.
Published by: Ackroyd Publications, Ch de Waterloo 1038, Brussels, 1180, Belgium. TEL 32-2-373-9909, FAX 32-2-375-9822, info@ackroyd.be, http://www.ackroyd.be/expat/index.html. Circ: 20,000 (controlled and free).

382 SGP ISSN 0129-5225
EXPATRIATE LIVING COSTS IN SINGAPORE. Text in English. 1970. a. SGD 13 per issue. **Document type:** *Consumer.*
Description: Regularly updated guide on the cost of living of expatriate families in Singapore.
Published by: Singapore International Chamber of Commerce, John Hancock Tower, 6 Raffles Quay 10-01, Singapore, 048580, Singapore. TEL 65-2241255, FAX 65-2242785, TELEX RS 25235 INTCHAM, singicc@asianconnect.com, http://www.sicc.com.sg. Circ: 8,000 (paid).

382 GBR ISSN 1351-4601
EXPORT HANDBOOK (YEAR). Text in English. 1992. a. GBP 30. adv. **Document type:** *Directory.*
Published by: (London Chamber of Commerce and Industry), Kogan Page Ltd., 120 Pentonville Rd, London, N1 9JN, United Kingdom. FAX 44-20-7837-6348. R&P Caroline Gomm. Adv. contact Linda Batham.

382 954 IND
F A P C C I REVIEW. Text in English. w. (40/yr. plus m. special issues). INR 200 to non-members; free to members.
Document type: *Trade.* **Description:** Covers information on matters pertaining to trade, commerce and industry.
Published by: Federation of Andhra Pradesh Chambers of Commerce & Industry, 11 - 6 - 841 Red Hills, P O Box 14, Hyderabad, Andhra Pradesh 500 004, India. TEL 91-40-3393428, info@fapcci.org. Ed. B V Chalapathi. Pub. B.V. Chalapathi.

944 FRA ISSN 0985-0074
FACE. Text in French. 9/yr.
Published by: Chambre de Commerce et Industrie de Lille, Place du Theatre, BP 121, Lille, Cedex 59001, France. TEL 33-3-20637866, FAX 33-3-20637863. Ed. Dominique Louvet. Circ: 35,000.

956.45 CYP
FAMAGUSTA CHAMBER OF COMMERCE AND INDUSTRY. TRADE INFORMATION BULLETIN. Text in English. q.
Document type: *Bulletin.*
Published by: Famagusta Chamber of Commerce and Industry, Stylianides Bldg, 3rd Fl, Koumandarias St, PO Box 347, Limassol, Cyprus. TEL 357-5-170165.

382 COD
FEDERATION DES ENTREPRISES DU CONGO. ANNUAIRE DES ENTREPRISES DU ZAIRE. Text in French. 1984. a. adv.
Description: Provides information on Congolese economic agents: names, addresses, telex, fax and telephone numbers, business, number of employees, names of top executives, some official addresses and the Congo investment code.
Published by: Federation des Entreprises du Congo, 10 av. des Aviateurs, BP 7247, Kinshasa, Congo, Dem. Republic. TEL 242-22286. Ed. Athanase Matenda Kyelu. Adv. contact Joseph Muicanya. Circ: 3,000.

330 COD
FEDERATION DES ENTREPRISES DU CONGO. CIRCULAIRE D'INFORMATION. Text in French. 1959. m. USD 85 to non-members; USD 75 to members (effective 1999). adv.
Description: Reprints, entirely or in abstracts, any laws, regulations, rules or decisions relating to business or trade carried out in Congo. Provides tenders for joint ventures and bids.

B

Former titles: Association Nationale des Entreprises Zairoises. Circulaire d'Information; Federation Nationale des Chambres de Commerce, d'Industrie et d'Agriculture de la Republique du Zaire. Circulaire d'Information (0085-0497)
Published by: Federation des Entreprises du Congo, 10 av. des Aviateurs, BP 7247, Kinshasa, Congo, Dem. Republic. TEL 242-22286. Ed. Athanase Matenda Kyelu. Adv. contact Joseph Mukanya. Circ: 1,000.

381   BGD
FEDERATION OF BANGLADESH CHAMBERS OF COMMERCE AND INDUSTRY. FEDERATION JOURNAL. Text in English. q.
Published by: Federation of Bangladesh Chambers of Commerce and Industry, 60 Motijheel Commercial Area, Dhaka, 1000, Bangladesh. FAX 880-2-7176030, fbcci@bol-online.com, http://www.fbcci-bd.org.

956.95   JOR
FEDERATION OF JORDANIAN CHAMBERS OF COMMERCE. MAGAZINE. Text in Arabic. q.
Related titles: Online - full text ed.
Published by: Federation of Jordanian Chambers of Commerce, P O Box 7029, Amman, Jordan. TEL 962-6-5665492, 962-6-5674495, FAX 962-6-5685997, fjcc@nets.com.jo, fjcc@go.com.jo, http://www.fjcc.com.

381   NPL
FEDERATION OF NEPALESE CHAMBERS OF COMMERCE AND INDUSTRY. NEWSLETTER. Text in Nepali. 1992. m. USD 6 (effective 2000). bk.rev. **Document type:** *Newsletter.*
Published by: Federation of Nepalese Chambers of Commerce and Industry, Teku, P O Box 269, Kathmandu, Nepal. TEL 977-1-262218, FAX 977-1-261022, fincci@mos.com.np, fncci@mos.com.np, http://www.fncci.org. Ed. Rameshwor Acharya. R&P Rameswar Acharya.

954.9   PAK
FEDERATION OF PAKISTAN CHAMBERS OF COMMERCE AND INDUSTRY. ANNUAL REPORT. Text in English. a.
Published by: Federation of Pakistan Chambers of Commerce and Industry, Sharea Firdousi, Main Clifton, PO Box 13875, Karachi, 75600, Pakistan. TEL 534621, TELEX 25370 FPCCI PK.

381   PAK   ISSN 0071-4429
FEDERATION OF PAKISTAN CHAMBERS OF COMMERCE AND INDUSTRY. BRIEF REPORT OF ACTIVITIES. Text in English. a. PKR 100.
Published by: Federation of Pakistan Chambers of Commerce and Industry, Sharea Firdousi, Main Clifton, PO Box 13875, Karachi, 75600, Pakistan.

FEDERATION OF PAKISTAN CHAMBERS OF COMMERCE AND INDUSTRY. DIRECTORY OF EXPORTERS. see *BUSINESS AND ECONOMICS—Trade And Industrial Directories*

954.9   PAK
FEDERATION OF PAKISTAN CHAMBERS OF COMMERCE AND INDUSTRY. TRADE BULLETIN. Text in English. bi-w.
Published by: Federation of Pakistan Chambers of Commerce and Industry, Sharea Firdousi, Main Clifton, PO Box 13875, Karachi, 75600, Pakistan. TEL 534621.

945   ITA   ISSN 1120-396X
FERRARA ECONOMICA. Text in Italian. 1987. a. free; free.
Published by: Camera di Commercio Industria Artigianato e Agricoltura di Ferrara, Via Borgoleoni, 11, Ferrara, FE 44100, Italy. TEL 39-0532-783711, FAX 39-0532-240204, corrado.padovan@fe.camcom.it, http://www.fe.camcom.it. Ed. Dr. Bruno Baldazzi.

382   CHE
FLASH INFORMATION∗ . Text in English. bi-m.
Published by: Chambre de Commerce Belgo-Luxembourgeoise en Suisse/Belgisch-Luxemburgische Handelskammer fuer die Schweiz, c/o Zuercher Handelskammer, Boersengebaeude, Bleicherweg 5, Postfach 4031, Zuerich, 8022, Switzerland.

338 380   GBR
FOCUS (STOKE-ON-TRENT). Text in English. 1952. bi-m. GBP 30. adv. bk.rev. illus. **Document type:** *Newsletter.*
Former titles: Focus on Industry and Commerce (0015-5098); North Staffordshire Focus on Industry and Commerce
Published by: (North Staffordshire Chamber of Commerce and Industry), Tudored Publishing Ltd., Brook St, Leek, Staffs ST13 5JL, United Kingdom. TEL 44-1538-399998, FAX 44-1538-399967. Ed. David Cliffe. Adv. contact Angela Smith. B&W page GBP 600, color page GBP 900; 185 x 275. Circ: 3,500.

975 330   USA
FOCUS ON BUSINESS. Text in English. 1997. q. USD 12 (effective 2000). adv. illus.; stat.
Published by: Roanoke Regional Chamber of Commerce, 212 S Jefferson St, Roanoke, VA 24011. TEL 540-983-0700, FAX 540-983-0723, business@roanokechamber.org, http://www.roanokechamber.org. Ed. Linda Scarborough. Adv. contact Shimilia Wright. Circ: 3,400.

381   USA   ISSN 1056-1919
FORT WORTH MAGAZINE. Text in English. 1928. m. USD 24. adv. bk.rev. illus.
Formerly (until 1990): Fort Worth (0015-8089)
Related titles: Online - full text ed.: (from ProQuest Information & Learning).
Published by: Fort Worth Chamber of Commerce, 777 Taylor St, Ste 900, Fort Worth, TX 76102-4997 . TEL 817-336-2491, http://www.fortworthchamber.com/. Ed. Yale Youngblood. Circ: 9,000.

381.06   DEU
FORUM (AUGSBURG); das Brandenburger Wirtschaftsmagazin. Text in German. 2000. m. EUR 8 newsstand/cover (effective 2004). adv. **Document type:** *Magazine, Trade.*
Published by: V M M Wirtschaftsverlag GmbH & Co. KG, Maximilianstr 9, Augsburg, 86150, Germany. TEL 49-821-44050, FAX 49-821-4405409, info@vmm-wirtschaftsverlag.de, http://www.vmm-wirtschaftsverlag.de. Adv. contact Michael Schupke. B&W page EUR 4,300, color page EUR 5,600. Circ: 65,000 (controlled).

382   JPN   ISSN 1342-369X
➤ **FRANCE JAPON ECO**; vie et affaires au Japon. Text in French. q. adv. bk.rev. 80 p./no.; **Document type:** *Magazine, Academic/Scholarly.*
Published by: Chambre de Commerce et d'Industrie Francaise du Japon/Zai-Nichi Furansu Shoko Kaigisho, IIDA Bldg, 5-5 Roku-Ban-cho, Chiyoda-ku, Tokyo, 102-0085, Japan. TEL 81-3-3288-9621, FAX 81-3288-9558, lemait_c@ccifj.or.jp, http://www.ccifj.or.jp/FJE-index.html. Ed., R&P Catherine Lemaitre. Adv. contact Isabelle Brochard. Circ: 6,000 (paid).

382.029   FRA   ISSN 0995-2209
FRANCO-BRITISH CHAMBER OF COMMERCE AND INDUSTRY. TRADE DIRECTORY. Text in French. 1874. a. FRF 375. adv. **Document type:** *Directory.*
Former titles: Franco-British Chamber of Commerce and Industry. Year Book (0766-7000); British Chamber of Commerce in France. Year Book (0068-1415)
Published by: Franco-British Chamber of Commerce and Industry, 31 rue Boissy d'Anglas, Paris, 75008, France. Circ: 1,500.

FRANCO-BRITISH TRADE DIRECTORY. see *BUSINESS AND ECONOMICS—Trade And Industrial Directories*

974   USA
FRENCH - AMERICAN NEWS. Text in English. bi-m. looseleaf. membership. adv. bk.rev. **Document type:** *Newsletter.* **Description:** Covers business and other news of interest to the French - American business community.
Published by: French - American Chamber of Commerce, 1350 Ave of the Americas, 6th Fl, New York, NY 10019-4702. TEL 212-765-4460, FAX 212-765-4650. Ed. Serge Bellanger. R&P, Adv. contact Erica Robbins. Circ: 650 (controlled).

946   ESP
FULLS INFORMATIUS. Text in Spanish. m.
Published by: Camara Oficial de Comercio, Industria y Navegacion de Tarragona, Av Pau Casals 17, Tarragona, 43003, Spain. TEL 34-977-21967, FAX 34-977-240900.

381   GBR
FUTURE∗ . Text in English. m. adv. **Document type:** *Bulletin.*
Published by: Leeds Junior Chamber of Commerce, 102 Wellington St, Leeds, W Yorks LS1 4LT, United Kingdom. TEL 44-113-247-0000, FAX 44-113-247-1111, http://www.leedsjc.org. Ed. Nora Harrigan.

338.025   USA
FUTURE 50 LIST. Text in English. a. free. **Description:** Lists 50 young and growing companies in the metro Milwaukee area, including a description of the businesses.
Published by: Metropolitan Milwaukee Association of Commerce, Council of Small Business Executives, 756 N Milwaukee St, Milwaukee, WI 53202. TEL 414-287-4100.

381   GRD
G C I C ANNUAL REPORT. Text in English. 1986. a. USD 5. **Document type:** *Corporate.*
Published by: Grenada Chamber of Industry and Commerce, Mt. Gay, St. George's, Grenada. TEL 809-440-2937, FAX 809-440-6627, gcic@caribsurf.com. Ed., R&P Cheryl Kirton. Circ: 200.

GERMAN AMERICAN TRADE. see *BUSINESS AND ECONOMICS—International Commerce*

382   EGY   ISSN 0072-1433
GERMAN ARAB TRADE. Text in Arabic. irreg. membership.
Published by: Deutsch-Arabische Handelskammer/German-Arab Chamber of Commerce, 2 Sherif St., Cairo, Egypt.

381.029   THA
GERMAN-THAI CHAMBER OF COMMERCE HANDBOOK AND DIRECTORY. Text in Thai. 1978. a. USD 140 (effective 1999). adv. **Document type:** *Directory.* **Description:** Contains information about German-Thai trade relations and opportunities and German investment opportunities in Thailand.; also provides short profiles of all its member companies.
Formerly: German-Thai Chamber of Commerce Handbook
Related titles: CD-ROM ed.; Online - full text ed.
Published by: (German-Thai Chamber of Commerce), Chamber Publications LP, 25th Fl, Empire Tower 3, 195 S Sathorn Rd, Bangkok, 10120, Thailand. TEL 662-6700-600, FAX 662-6700-601, ahkbkk@box1.a-net.net.th, http://www.gtcc.org. Ed. Paul Strunk. R&P Stefan Buerkle. Adv. contact Eupaporn S Ayuthaya. Circ: 2,500.

382   CHE
GESCHAEFTE MIT OESTERREICH∗ . Text in German. 1977. 9/yr.
Published by: Oesterreichischer Handelsdelegierter fuer die Schweiz und Liechtenstein, Talstr 65, Zuerich, 8039, Switzerland. Ed. Peter Schneider.

966.7   GHA
GHANA NATIONAL CHAMBER OF COMMERCE. ANNUAL REPORT. Text in English. 1962. a. USD 10. adv. **Document type:** *Corporate.*
Published by: Ghana National Chamber of Commerce, PO Box 2325, Accra, Ghana. TEL 233-21-662427, FAX 233-21-662210, TELEX 2687 GH. Ed. John B K Amanfu. Adv. contact Daniel Armah.

381.029   GHA
GHANA NATIONAL CHAMBER OF COMMERCE. BUSINESS DIRECTORY. Text in English. 1992. biennial. USD 55. adv. **Document type:** *Directory.*
Published by: Ghana National Chamber of Commerce, PO Box 2325, Accra, Ghana. TEL 233-21-662427, FAX 233-21-662210, TELEX 2687-GH. Ed. John B K Amanfu. Adv. contact Daniel Armah.

382   OMN
AL-GHDRFA/OMAN COMMERCE. Text in Arabic, English. bi-m. OMR 10 (effective 2001). 76 p./no. 3 cols./p.; **Document type:** *Magazine, Trade.*
Published by: Oman Chamber of Commerce and Industry, Ruwi-112, 1400, Muscat, Oman. TEL 968-707684, FAX 968-708497, pubrel@omanchamber.org, http://www.omanchamber.org. Ed. Maqboul bin Ali bin Sultan. Circ: 10,500 (controlled).

330 915.357   UAE
AL-GHURFA. Text in Arabic. 1971. 4/yr. per issue exchange basis. **Description:** Covers local business and agricultural news, provides official listings of company registrations and business legislation.
Published by: Ras al-Khaimah Chamber of Commerce Industry and Agriculture, PO Box 87, Ras Al Khaimah, United Arab Emirates. TEL 33511, FAX 30233, TELEX 99140 TEJARA EM. Ed. Zaki Hassan Saqr. Circ: 500.

330   ITA   ISSN 0017-0429
GIORNALE ECONOMICO. Text in Italian. 1966 (no.78). bi-m. adv. charts; illus.; stat.
Indexed by: PAIS.
Published by: Camera di Commercio Industria Artigianato e Agricoltura di Venezia, Via 22 Marzo 2032, Venice, VE, Italy. Ed. Filippo Lo Torto.

380   GBR
GLASGOW CHAMBER OF COMMERCE. ANNUAL REPORT. Text in English. a. charts; illus. **Document type:** *Corporate.*
Published by: Glasgow Chamber of Commerce, 30 George Sq, Glasgow, G2 1EQ, United Kingdom. TEL 44-141-204-2121, FAX 44-141-221-2336.

380   GBR
GLASGOW CHAMBER OF COMMERCE. INFORMATION NEWSLETTER. Text in English. m. **Document type:** *Newsletter.*
Published by: Glasgow Chamber of Commerce, 30 George Sq, Glasgow, G2 1EQ, United Kingdom. TEL 44-141-204-2121, FAX 44-141-221-2336.

380   GBR   ISSN 0017-0860
GLASGOW CHAMBER OF COMMERCE. JOURNAL. Text in English. 1918. m. GBP 30. adv. bk.rev. illus.
Published by: Glasgow Chamber of Commerce, 30 George Sq, Glasgow, G2 1EQ, United Kingdom. TEL 44-141-204-2121, FAX 44-141-221-2336, TELEX 777967 CHACOM G. Ed. James Carson. Circ: 5,000.

954   IND
GOA CHAMBER OF COMMERCE AND INDUSTRY. BULLETIN. Text in English. m. **Document type:** *Bulletin.*
Published by: Goa Chamber of Commerce and Industry, Ormuz Rd., P O Box 59, Punjim, Goa 403 001, India. TEL 3420-4223.

968 ZAF
GOING CONCERNS. Text in English. 1975. bi-m. membership. adv. bk.rev. **Document type:** *Newsletter, Trade.* **Description:** Business information, including international trade, lobby of government at local (metro), provincial and national levels, etc.
Former titles: Chamber Bulletin; J C C Bulletin; J C C News
Published by: Johannesburg Chamber of Commerce & Industry, JCC House, Private Bag 34, Auckland Park, Johannesburg 2006, South Africa. TEL 27-11-726-5300, FAX 27-11-482-2000, brady@jcci.co.za, http://www.jcci.co.za. Ed. Maureen Brady. Circ: 5,000.

GOOD NEWS. see *BUSINESS AND ECONOMICS*

GREATER BATON ROUGE MANUFACTURERS DIRECTORY. see *BUSINESS AND ECONOMICS—Trade And Industrial Directories*

380 USA
GREATER LOUISVILLE INK. Text in English. 1968. m. USD 5.20 to members. **Document type:** *Newsletter.*
Former titles: Update (Louisville); Action (0001-737X)
Published by: (Louisville Chamber of Commerce), Greater Louisville Ink, 600 W Main St, Louisville, KY 40202. TEL 502-625-0000, FAX 502-625-0010, mogburn@greaterlouisville.com, http://www.greaterlouisville.com. Ed. Mike Ogburn. Pub. Robert H Gayle Jr. Circ: 4,000.

975 USA
GREATER WASHINGTON BOARD OF TRADE PROGRESS REPORT. Text in English. a. membership. back issues avail. **Description:** Outlines goals for the year and how they were met. Lists board of directors and staff. Describes each committee and its purpose.
Published by: Greater Washington Board of Trade, 1725 I St, NW, Ste 200, Washington, DC 20006-2427. TEL 202-857-5900, FAX 202-223-2648. Ed. Moira Saucer. Circ: 6,700 (controlled).

382 GRC ISSN 0046-6379
GREEK - AMERICAN TRADE. Text in Greek, English. 1966. bi-m. USD 100. charts. 64 p./no. 3 cols./p.; back issues avail. **Document type:** *Magazine, Trade.*
Published by: American - Hellenic Chamber of Commerce, 109-111 Messoghion Ave., Athens, 115 26, Greece. TEL 01-699-3559, info@amcham.gr, http://www.amcham.gr. Ed. Raymond Matera. Adv. contact Dimitris Papaevaggelopoulos. Circ: 5,000.

949.5 GRC
GREEK EXPORT DIRECTORY. Text in English, French, German, Greek. 1953. a. free. adv. illus. 800 p./no. 3 cols./p.; **Document type:** *Directory, Trade.*
Related titles: CD-ROM ed.: 1998; Online - full text ed.: 2001.
Published by: Athens Chamber of Commerce and Industry, 7 Akadimias St, Athens, 106 71, Greece. TEL 30-210-3604815, FAX 30-210-3616464, info@acci.gr, http://www.icap.gr/acci, http://www.acci.gr. Ed. Pavlos Giannokopoulos. R&P Dimitrios Golemis. Circ: 8,000.

380 ESP ISSN 0211-4917
GUIA DEL COMERCIO Y DE LA INDUSTRIA DE MADRID. Text in Spanish. 1960. biennial (in 10 vols.). adv.
Formerly: Catalogo de la Industria de Madrid y Su Provincia (0528-2438)
Published by: Camara Oficial de Comercio e Industria de Madrid, Huertas, 13, Madrid, 28012, Spain. TEL 5383513, FAX 5383677, cpd2@camaramadrid.es, http://www.camaramadrid.es. Circ: 2,000.

954 IND
GUJARAT CHAMBER OF COMMERCE AND INDUSTRY. ANNUAL REPORT. Text in English. a.
Published by: Gujarat Chamber of Commerce and Industry, Ranchhodlal Marg, Navarangpura, P O Box 4045, Ahmedabad, Gujarat 380009, India. TEL 402301.

954 IND
GUJARAT CHAMBER OF COMMERCE AND INDUSTRY. BULLETIN. Text in English. m. **Document type:** *Bulletin.*
Published by: Gujarat Chamber of Commerce and Industry, Ranchhodlal Marg, Navarangpura, P O Box 4045, Ahmedabad, Gujarat 380009, India. TEL 402301.

382 HRV
H G K INFO. Text in Croatian. 2/m. **Document type:** *Magazine, Trade.*
Published by: Hrvatska Gospodarska Komora, Rooseveltov trg 2, Zagreb, 10000, Croatia. TEL 385-1-4561555, FAX 385-1-4561534, hgk@hgk.hr, http://www.hgk.hr. Ed. Sanja Kapetanic.

330 DEU ISSN 0935-0594
HAMBURGER WIRTSCHAFT; Mitteilungen der Handelskammer Hamburg. Text in German. 1946. m. EUR 30; EUR 2.50 newsstand/cover (effective 2005). adv. illus.; stat.; tr.lit. index. **Document type:** *Magazine, Trade.*
Formerly (until 1974): Handelskammer Hamburg. Mitteilungen (0017-730X)
Related titles: Online - full text ed.: (from G B I).
Indexed: RASB, RefZh.
Published by: Handelskammer Hamburg, Adolphsplatz 1, Hamburg, 20457, Germany. TEL 49-40-36138138, FAX 49-40-36138401, hamburger.wirtschaft@hk24.de, service@hk24.de, http://www.hamburger-wirtschaft.de, http://www.hk24.de. Adv. contact Tanya Kumst. Circ: 33,400.

948.5 SWE
HANDELSKAMMAREN. Text in Swedish. 1991. bi-m.
Media: Online - full content.
Published by: Vaestsvenska Industri- och Handelskammaren/ West Sweden Chamber of Commerce & Industry, Maessans Gata 18, PO Box 5253, Goeteborg, 40225, Sweden. TEL 46-31-83 59 00, FAX 46-31-83 59 36, info@handelskammaren.net, http://www.handelskammaren.net.

330 SWE ISSN 0345-4495
HANDELSKAMMARTIDNINGEN. Abbreviated title: H K T. Text in Swedish. 1917. 8/yr. SEK 350 (effective 2001). adv. bk.rev. charts; illus. index. **Document type:** *Magazine, Trade.*
Formerly (until vol.3, 1973): Meddelanden fraan Stockholms Handelskammare (0039-1654)
Published by: Stockholms Handelskammare/Stockholm Chamber of Commerce, Vaestra Traedgaardsgatan 9, Fack 16050, Stockholm, 10321, Sweden. TEL 46-8-55510000, FAX 46-8-56631605, lena.lindstedt@chamber.se, http://www.chamber.se. Ed., R&P Karl Melin. Adv. contact Niklas Nilsson. B&W page SEK 11,000, color page SEK 14,800; trim 188 x 255. Circ: 5,000.

382 CHE
HANDELSKAMMER FINNLAND-SCHWEIZ. BULLETIN✶. Text in German. q. **Document type:** *Bulletin.*
Published by: Handelskammer Finnland - Schweiz/Chambre de Commerce Finno - Suisse, Forchstr 45, Zuerich, 8032, Switzerland. TEL 2023630.

944 FRA
HAUTE LOIRE ECONOMIQUE. Text in French. 5/yr.
Published by: Chambre de Commerce et d'Industrie le Puy-en-Velay - Yssingeaux, BP 127, Le Puy en Velay, Cedex 43004, France. TEL 71-02-11-46, FAX 71-02-77-58, TELEX 393 934 F. Ed. Guy Quemener. Circ: 8,000.

382 USA
HAWAII'S INTERNATIONAL FESTIVAL OF THE PACIFIC. Text in English. a.
Published by: Japanese Chamber of Commerce and Industry of Hawaii, 400 Hualani St, Ste 20 B, Hilo, HI 96720. TEL 808-949-5531.

381 USA ISSN 0894-6434
JK5601
HERE IS YOUR INDIANA GOVERNMENT. Text in English. 1944. biennial. USD 12.50 (effective 2001). **Description:** Covers form and function of state and local government.
Published by: Indiana State Chamber of Commerce, 115 W Washington St, No 850S, Indianapolis, IN 46204-3407. TEL 317-264-3110, FAX 317-264-6855, bschreiber@indianachamber.com, http://www.indianachamber.com. Eds. Danielle Emerson, Jessica Richards. Circ: 25,000.

382 ZAF
HILITE. Text in English. 1977. m. ZAR 2. adv. bk.rev. stat. index. back issues avail. **Document type:** *Bulletin.*
Contact Corp. Auth.: Border Chamber of Business, Box 11179, Southernwoo, E London, 5213, South Africa. TEL 27-431-438-438, FAX 27-431-432-249. Ed. P M Miles. Adv. contact Kim Vanrooyen. Circ: 1,200.

330 IND ISSN 0971-1066
HINDUSTAN CHAMBER REVIEW. Text in English. 1965. m. free. bk.rev. **Description:** Covers Indian policies relating to trade, industry and commerce as well as important labor and consumer cases.
Published by: Hindustan Chamber of Commerce, 8 Kondi Chetty St., Chennai, Tamil Nadu 600 001, India. TEL 583134, FAX 568063. Ed. P Gopalakrishna. Circ: (controlled).

382 CHE
HOLLAND - SCHWEIZ✶. Text in German. 1917. bi-m. free. adv. **Document type:** *Newsletter.*
Published by: Zuercher Handelskammer, Bleicherweg 5, Postfach 4031, Zurich, 8022, Switzerland. Circ: 2,000.

382 USA
HOLLAND - U S A. Text in English. 1942. 4/yr. free. adv. bk.rev. charts; stat. index, cum.index. **Document type:** *Newsletter.* **Description:** Focuses on economics, commercial legislation, cultural events and historical buildings and estates.
Formerly: Holland - U S A and Netherlands News; Supersedes: Netherlands - American Trade (0028-2855)
Indexed: KES.
Published by: Netherlands Chamber of Commerce in U.S., 303 E Wacker Dr, Ste 412, Chicago, IL 60601. TEL 312-938-9050, FAX 312-938-8949. Ed. Michael Donahue. Circ: 7,000.

951.25 HKG
HONG KONG GENERAL CHAMBER OF COMMERCE. ANNUAL REPORT. Text in Chinese. a. **Document type:** *Corporate.*
Published by: Hong Kong General Chamber of Commerce, 22/F United Centre, 95 Queensway, Admiralty, Hong Kong, Hong Kong. TEL 852-2529-9229, FAX 852-2527-9843, malcom@chamber.org.hk, http://www.hkgcc.org.hk/bus_suite/the_bulletin/bulletin_index.htm. Ed. Malcolm Ainsworth. Adv. contact Jeremy Orritt.

950 HKG
HONG KONG GENERAL CHAMBER OF COMMERCE BULLETIN. Text in Chinese. 1970. m. HKD 360, USD 30 to non-members (effective 2000). adv. **Document type:** *Trade.* **Description:** Covers economic and business issues affecting HK businesses and chamber activities.
Published by: Hong Kong General Chamber of Commerce, 22/F United Centre, 95 Queensway, Admiralty, Hong Kong, Hong Kong. TEL 852-2529-9229, FAX 852-2527-9843, TELEX 83535-TRIND-HK, malcom@chamber.org.hk, http://www.hkgcc.org.hk/bus_suite/the_bulletin/bulletin_index.htm. Ed. Malcolm Ainsworth. Adv. contact Jeremy Orritt. B&W page HKD 8,240, color page HKD 12,760; trim 210 x 286. Circ: 8,000.

382 341.5 FRA ISSN 1017-284X
THE I C C INTERNATIONAL COURT OF ARBITRATION BULLETIN. Text in English. 1990. s-a. (plus supplement). EUR 280 (effective 2005). **Description:** This bulletin is at the forefront of information on dispute resolution practice in international trade.
Related titles: French ed.: La Cour Internationale d'Arbitrage de la C C I. Bulletin. ISSN 1017-2831.
—CCC.
Published by: I C C Publishing, 38 Cours Albert 1er, Paris, 75008, France. TEL 33-1-49532828, FAX 33-1-49535774, pub@iccwbo.org, http://www.iccbooks.com/TopBannerSites/bulletin.asp.

380 TUR ISSN 1300-3720
I C O C✶. Key Title: ICOC. Text in English. 1881. q. free. adv. **Description:** Covers the Turkish economy and Turkish industries, including textiles, mining, marble, ceramics.
Formerly (until 1982): Istanbul Ticaret Odasi Mecmuasi - Istanbul Chamber of Commerce. Journal
Published by: Istanbul Chamber of Commerce, Ragip Gumuspala, Cad. 84, 34378, Eminonu, Istanbul, Turkey. TEL 90-1-5266215, TELEX 22682 ODA TR. Ed. Cengiz Ersun. Circ: 5,000.

943.1 DEU
I H K LIPPE INFO. Text in German. m. adv. **Document type:** *Bulletin.*
Formerly: Informationen fuer die Lippische Wirtschaft
Published by: Industrie- und Handelskammer Lippe zu Detmold, Willi-Hofmann-Str 5, Detmold, 32756, Germany. TEL 05231-76010, FAX 05231-760157. Ed. Michael Swoboda.

382 DEU ISSN 1433-8610
I H K REPORT SUEDHESSEN. Text in German. 1947. 11/yr. EUR 11 (effective 2005). adv. bk.rev. back issues avail. **Document type:** *Bulletin, Trade.*
Former titles (until 1997): Starkenburger Wirtschaft (0722-4249); (until 1982): Industrie- und Handelskammer Darmstadt. Nachrichten (0722-4230)
Published by: (Industrie- und Handelskammer Darmstadt), Druck- und Verlagshaus Zarbock, Sontraer Str 6, Frankfurt Am Main, 60386, Germany. TEL 49-69-42090344, FAX 49-69-42090370, info@darmstadt.ihk.de, verlag@zarbock.de, http://ihk.darmstadt.de, http://www.zarbock.de. Ed. Barbara Becker. Adv. contact Martina Koerner. B&W page EUR 3,100, color page EUR 4,600; trim 185 x 260. Circ: 41,500 (controlled).

338 DEU ISSN 1434-5072
I H K WIRTSCHAFT. (Industrie- und Handelskammer) Text in German. 1949. q. **Document type:** *Newspaper, Trade.*
Former titles (until 1997): I H K Journal (0944-4491); (until 1993): Industrie und Handel. Ausgabe A (0930-3081); (until 1977): Industrie und Handel (0930-3073)
Published by: (Industrie- und Handelskammer Muenchen), BurdaYukom Publishing GmbH (Subsidiary of: Hubert Burda Media Holding GmbH & Co. KG), Schleissheimer Str 141, Munich, 80797, Germany. TEL 49-89-306200, FAX 49-89-30620100, info@burdayukom.de, http://www.yukom.de. Circ: 145,000 (controlled).

338 380 DEU
I H K WIRTSCHAFTSFORUM. Text in German. 1878. m. bk.rev. charts; illus. index. **Document type:** *Proceedings, Trade.*
Former titles: Wirtschaftsregion Frankfurt - Rhein-Main (1435-4926); (until 1997): Industrie- und Handelskammer Frankfurt am Main. Mitteilungen (0427-394X)
Published by: Industrie- und Handelskammer Frankfurt am Main, Boersenplatz 4, Frankfurt Am Main, 60313, Germany. TEL 49-69-21971280, FAX 49-69-21971424, info@frankfurt-main.ihk.de, http://www.frankfurt-main.ihk.de/presse/ihk-wirtschaftsforum/. Ed. Petra Menke. Circ: 60,284.

382 DEU
I H K WIRTSCHAFTSSPIEGEL. Text in German. m. adv. **Document type:** *Bulletin, Trade.*

B

Published by: (Industrie- und Handelskammer Muenster), Aschendorff Medien GmbH & Co. KG, Soester Str 13, Muenster, 48155, Germany. TEL 49-251-6900, FAX 49-251-6904570, ksc@aschendorff.de, http://www.aschendorff.de. Ed. Peter Schnepper. Adv. contact Achim Hartkopf. B&W page EUR 3,288, color page EUR 5,436; trim 185 x 252. Circ: 63,000 (controlled).

330 DEU ISSN 1438-5740
I H K - ZEITUNG. (Industrie- und Handelskammer) Text in German. 1998. 2/m. adv. **Document type:** *Magazine, Trade.*
Formed by the merger of (1960-1998): Unsere Wirtschaft (0042-0549); (1954-1998): Industrie- und Handelskammer Duesseldorf. Schnelldienst (1438-5732)
Published by: (Industrie- und Handelskammer zu Duesseldorf), Bergische Verlagsgesellschaft Menzel GmbH & Co. KG, Neumarktstr 10, Wuppertal, 42103, Germany. TEL 49-202-451654, FAX 49-202-450086, info@bvg-menzel.de, http://www.bvg-menzel.de. adv.: B&W page EUR 2,475; trim 185 x 268.

382 USA
ILLINOIS BUSINESS. Text in English. 1995. q. USD 7.95 (effective 2000). adv. **Description:** Contains news, columns, and feature stories about Illinois businesses and state chamber members; legislative and business issues affecting large and small businesses in Illinois.
Published by: (Illinois Chamber of Commerce), CommunityLink, a publishing service of Craig Williams Creative Inc., 201 E Ozburn, PO Box 306, Pinckneyville, IL 62274. Ed. Jim Hale. Pub. Craig Williams. Adv. contact Amy Yates. Circ: 25,000 (controlled).

974.1 USA ISSN 1055-3029
IMPACT (AUGUSTA). Text in English. 1989. w. USD 25 (effective 2000). adv. **Document type:** *Newsletter.* **Description:** Deals with legislative and regulatory issues facing Maine business.
Former titles: Maine Chamber of Commerce and Industry. Newsletter (1045-6902); Maine Business Newsletter (8750-8443)
Published by: Maine State Chamber of Commerce, 7 University Dr, Augusta, ME 04330-9412. TEL 207-623-4568, FAX 207-622-7723, impact@mainechamber.org, http://www.mainechamber.org. Ed., R&P Melanie Baillargeon. Pub. Dana F Connors. Adv. contact Melody Rousseau. Circ: 1,400 (paid).

381 ITA ISSN 1123-5519
IMPRESA & STATO. Text in Italian. 1988. q. EUR 42 domestic; EUR 62 foreign (effective 2003). bibl.; charts; illus.; stat. Index. back issues avail. **Document type:** *Magazine, Trade.*
Supersedes (in 1988): Realta Economica (0557-6946); Which was formerly (until 1969): Camera di Commercio di Milano (0008-2120)
Related titles: Online - full text ed.
Indexed: PAIS.
Published by: (Camera di Commercio Industria Artigianato e Agricoltura di Milano), Franco Angeli Edizioni, Viale Monza 106, Milan, 20127, Italy. TEL 39-02-2837141, FAX 39-02-26144793, impresa.stato@mi.camcom.it, redazioni@francoangeli.it, http://www.francoangeli.it. Ed. Piero Bassetti. R&P, Adv. contact Patrizio Surace. Circ: 3,000.

944 FRA ISSN 1152-3263
IMPULSION. Text in French. 1966. 4/yr.
Former titles (until 1989): Info C C I (1148-7283); (until 1983): Bulletin Economique de la Valle du Commerce (0338-3601); (until 1974): Chambre de Commerce et d'Industrie de Bolbec, Lillebonne et Notre Dame de Gravenvchon. Bulletin de Liaison (0338-3598)
Published by: Chambre de Commerce et d'Industrie de Bolbec-Lillebonne, 16 bis, av. Foch, BP 11, Bolbec, 76210, France. TEL 35-31-00-78, FAX 35-31-20-55. Ed. Annie Lemasurier. Circ: 2,000.

954 IND
INDO-AMERICAN CHAMBER OF COMMERCE. NEWSLETTER. Text in English. m. **Document type:** *Newsletter.*
Published by: Indo-American Chamber of Commerce, Vulcan Insurance Bldg., Veer Nariman Rd., P O Box 11057, Mumbai, Maharashtra 400 020, India.

382 IND
INDO - U S BUSINESS. Text in English. 1970. m. adv. bk.rev.
Formerly (until 1987): I A C C Newsletter
Published by: Indo-American Chamber of Commerce, Vulcan Insurance Bldg., Veer Nariman Rd., P O Box 11057, Mumbai, Maharashtra 400 020, India. Ed. V Rangaraj. Circ: 1,800 (controlled).

989.5 URY
INDUSTRIA EN EL URUGUAY. Text in Spanish. a. **Document type:** *Monographic series.*
Published by: (Departamento de Estudios Economicos), Camara de Industrias del Uruguay, Av. Lib. Brig. Gral. Lavalleja 1672, Montevideo, Uruguay. TEL 9023402 ext. 222.

338 380 DEU
INDUSTRIE- UND HANDELSKAMMER HANNOVER-HILDESHEIM. YEARBOOK - STATISTICS. Text in German. 1949. a. free. adv. bk.rev. stat.; tr.lit. index. **Document type:** *Corporate.*
Former titles: Industrie- und Handelskammer Hannover-Hildesheim. Yearbook - Information Kommentaire; Industrie- und Handelskammer Hannover-Hildesheim. Information-Kommentaire (0171-1016)
Published by: Industrie- und Handelskammer Hannover-Hildesheim, Schiffgraben 49, Hannover, 30175, Germany. TEL 0511-3107-268. Ed. Martin Rudolph. Circ: 8,000.

943.1 DEU
INDUSTRIE- UND HANDELSKAMMER LUENEBURG-WOLFSBURG. MITTEILUNGEN. Text in German. m.
Published by: Industrie- und Handelskammer Lueneburg-Wolfsburg, Am Sande 1, Lueneburg, 21335, Germany. TEL 7090, FAX 709180.

943 DEU
INDUSTRIE- UND HANDELSKAMMER ZU AACHEN. WIRTSCHAFTLICHE NACHRICHTEN. Text in German. 1919. m. EUR 20 to non-members (effective 2005). adv. bk.rev. **Document type:** *Magazine, Trade.*
Published by: Industrie- und Handelskammer zu Aachen, Theaterstr 6-10, Aachen, 52062, Germany. TEL 49-241-44600, FAX 49-241-4460259, info@aachen.ihk.de, http://www.aachen.ihk.de. adv.: B&W page EUR 1,815, color page EUR 3,348; trim 185 x 260. Circ: 30,000 (controlled).

382 GBR
INFO (LONDON). Text and summaries in English, French. bi-m. GBP 35. index, cum.index. **Description:** Promoting Franco-British business relations.
Former titles: Franco - British Trade Journal; Franco-British Trade Review (0015-9867)
Published by: French Chamber of Commerce in Great Britain, 21 Dartmouth St, London, SW1H 9BP, United Kingdom. Ed. Annie Lavnois. Circ: 2,000.

330 BGR ISSN 1310-9332
INFOBUSINESS - ECONOMIC NEWS OF BULGARIA. Text in English. 1959. m. USD 49 in Europe; USD 59 elsewhere (effective 2002). illus. **Description:** Presents Bulgaria's export, import and customs regulations, taxation, banking, foreign investment, privatization as well as individual firms, and offers for business contacts.
Formerly (until 1996): Economic News of Bulgaria (0205-1400)
Indexed: KES, PROMT.
Published by: Bulgarska Turgovsko-Promishlena Palata/Bulgarian Chamber of Commerce and Industry, 42 Parchevich ul, Sofia, 1058, Bulgaria. TEL 359-2-9872631, FAX 359-2-9873209, bcci@bcci.bg, http://www.bcci.bg/. Ed. L Mikhailov. Circ: 3,000.

944 FRA ISSN 1764-6510
L'INFORMATEUR ECONOMIQUE DU CHOLETAIS. Text in French. 1956. a. **Document type:** *Corporate.*
Former titles (until 2003): L' Informateur (0992-7514); (until 1988): Informateur Economique du Choletais (0995-6735)
Published by: Chambre de Commerce et Industrie (Cholet), 34 rue Nationale, BP 2116, Cholet, Cedex 49321, France. TEL 33-2-41491000, FAX 33-2-41491010. Ed. Samuel Leblond. Pub. Xavier Coiffard. Circ: 5,000.

944 FRA ISSN 0996-1488
INFORMATION ECONOMIQUE DU LOIRET. Text in French. 1945. 9/yr. adv. **Document type:** *Newspaper.*
Published by: Information Economique du, 23 Place du Martroi, Orleans, Cedex 1 45044, France. TEL 33-2-38777777, FAX 33-2-38530978, comceil@cybercable.fr, http://www.loiret.cci.fr. Ed. Alain Souche. Pub. Francois Huvelin. Circ: 15,000.

943 DEU
INFORMATIONEN FUER DIE WIRTSCHAFT. Text in German. m. adv. **Document type:** *Magazine, Trade.*
Published by: (Industrie- und Handelskammer Nordschwarzwald), Pruefer Medienmarketing, Lichtentaler Str 33, Baden-Baden, 76530, Germany. TEL 49-7221-21190, FAX 49-7221-211915, werbeagentur@pruefer.com, http://www.pruefer.com. adv.: B&W page EUR 2,283, color page EUR 3,196. Circ: 28,000 (controlled).

330.9 ESP ISSN 0211-5468
HC387.A68
INFORME ECONOMICO DE ARAGON. Text in Spanish. 1980. a. **Description:** Contains economic information on the region of Aragon. Includes general information, national and international, about the preceding year.
Former titles (until 1978): Provincia de Zaragoza. Informe Economico; (until 1976): Desarrollo Industrial y Mercantil en la Provincia de Zaragoza
Published by: Consejo de Camaras de Comercio e Industria de Aragon, Paseo Isabel 1a Catolica, 2, Zaragoza, 50009, Spain. FAX 35-79-45, TELEX 58-072 CACIN E. Circ: 1,000.

946.9 ESP ISSN 0211-8734
INFORME ECONOMICO REGIONAL. Text in Spanish. a. bk.rev.
Formerly (until 1972): Camara Oficial de Comercio, Industria y Navegacion de Valencia (0211-8750)
Published by: Camara Oficial de Comercio Industria y Navegacion de Valencia, Poeta Querol, 15, Valencia, 46002, Spain. TEL 34-6-3511301, FAX 34-6-3516349, TELEX 62243 COCIN E. Circ: 1,000. **Co-sponsor:** Camaras Oficiales de Comercio, Industria y Navegacion de Alcoy, Alicante, Castellon, Orihuela.

382 MEX ISSN 0020-5192
INTER-CAMBIO. Text in English. 1943. 6/yr. USD 20 to non-members. adv. bk.rev. illus.; pat. index. **Document type:** *Magazine, Trade.* **Description:** Covers Anglo-Mexican business topics.
Indexed: PAIS.
Published by: Camara de Comercio Britanica A.C./British Chamber of Commerce, RIO DE LA PLATA 30, Col Cuauhtemoc, Mexico City, DF 06500, Mexico. FAX 52-5-2115451. Ed., R&P, Adv. contact Lourdes G Loyola TEL 52-5-2560901. B&W page MXP 4,800, color page MXP 6,600; trim 280 x 215. Circ: 2,000.

381 FRA ISSN 0988-5838
INTERCONSULAIRE FRANCE REGIONS. Text in French. 1973. m. illus.; stat. **Document type:** *Trade.*
Formerly (until 1987): France Regions (0988-582X)
Published by: Chambres de Commerce et d'Industrie, 45 avenue d'Iena, Paris, 75116, France. Ed. Francois de la Maisonneuve.

382 NLD ISSN 1567-1860
INTERFACE. Text in Dutch, French. 1980. q. adv. 36 p./no.; **Document type:** *Magazine, Trade.* **Description:** Covers French and Dutch economy, exhibitions, technology and scientific research, and commercial exchange between the two countries.
Formerly (until 1999): I N F (0921-2701)
Published by: Chambre Francaise de Commerce et d'Industrie aux Pays-Bas/French Chamber of Commerce and Industry in the Netherlands, Wibautstraat 129, Amsterdam, 1091 GL, Netherlands. TEL 31-20-562-8200, FAX 31-20-562-8222, cfci@cfci.nl, http://www.cfci.nl. Ed. Josee Focke. Circ: 3,000.

941 AUS
INTERNATIONAL BUSINESS JOURNAL. Text in English. q. AUD 30 domestic to non-members; AUD 70 foreign to non-members; free to members. adv. **Document type:** *Newsletter, Trade.*
Formerly: A B C C Newsletter
Published by: (Australian British Chamber of Commerce), Verandah Press Pty. Ltd., PO Box 835, Epping, NSW 2121, Australia. TEL 02-876-5046, FAX 02-867-4059. Ed. Richard Stanton. adv.: page AUD 975.

974 USA
INTERNATIONAL LABOR AFFAIRS REPORT. Text in English. bi-m. **Document type:** *Newsletter.*
Media: Online - full text.
Published by: United States Council for International Business, 1212 Ave of the Americas, New York, NY 10036. TEL 212-354-4480, FAX 212-575-0327. Ed. William J Sibravy.

INVESTOR'S GUIDE TO SINGAPORE. see *BUSINESS AND ECONOMICS—Investments*

382 IRN
IRAN CHAMBER OF COMMERCE, INDUSTRIES AND MINES. DIRECTORY. Text in Persian, Modern. 19??. biennial. adv. **Document type:** *Directory, Trade.*
Related titles: Diskette ed.
Published by: Iran Chamber of Commerce, Industries and Mines, Public Relations, 254 Taleghanni Ave., Tehran, 15875-4671, Tehran, Iran. TEL 98-21-8846031, FAX 98-21-8825111, TELEX 213382 TCIM.

330 IRN ISSN 1023-1838
HF3770.2
IRAN COMMERCE. Text in English. q. USD 30. **Document type:** *Government.*
Published by: Iran Chamber of Commerce, Industries and Mines, Public Relations, 254 Taleghanni Ave., Tehran, 15875-4671, Tehran, Iran. TEL 98-21-8846031, FAX 98-21-8825111, http://www.neda.net/ibr/ircom.html. adv.: B&W page USD 750, color page USD 1,750.

330.9561 TUR ISSN 1300-3712
HC491
ISTANBUL CHAMBER OF COMMERCE. ECONOMIC REPORT✶. Key Title: Economic Report. Text in English. 1983. a.
Related titles: Turkish ed.: Ekonomik Rapor. ISSN 1300-3704.
Published by: Istanbul Chamber of Commerce, Ragip Gumuspala, Cad. 84, 34378, Eminonu, Istanbul, Turkey. TEL 90-1-5266215.

956.1 TUR
ISTANBUL CHAMBER OF COMMERCE. MAGAZINE✶. Text in Turkish. q.
Published by: Istanbul Chamber of Commerce, Ragip Gumuspala, Cad. 84, 34378, Eminonu, Istanbul, Turkey. TEL 90-1-5266215.

381 TUR ISSN 1300-3666
HC493.I88
ISTANBUL TICARET GAZETESI✶. Text in Turkish. 1958. w.
Published by: Istanbul Chamber of Commerce, Ragip Gumuspala, Cad. 84, 34378, Eminonu, Istanbul, Turkey.

380 CAN ISSN 0225-1140
ITALCOMMERCE. Text in English, French, Italian. 1964. 4/yr. CND 12 to non-members. adv. bk.rev. **Document type:** *Trade.* **Description:** Canada-Italy business exchanges magazine and guide.

Formerly: Italian Chamber of Commerce Bulletin (0318-7985)
Published by: Italian Chamber of Commerce in Canada-Montreal, 550 Sherbrooke Ouest, 680, Montreal, PQ H3A 1B9, Canada. TEL 514-844-4249, 800-263-4372, FAX 514-844-4875, info.montreal@italchambers.net, http://www.italchambers.net/montreal. Eds. Joyce Pillarella, Marianna Simeone. adv.: B&W page CND 1,200, color page CND 1,500. Circ: 6,000.

382 ITA ISSN 0021-2873
ITALIAN AMERICAN BUSINESS. Text in English, Italian. 1956. bi-m. free to members. adv. charts; illus.; mkt. **Document type:** *Magazine, Consumer.* **Description:** News from the United States, the EEC and Italy on the legal, economic and fiscal aspects of doing business in Italy and the United States.
Indexed: PAIS.
Published by: American Chamber of Commerce in Italy, Via Cesare Cantu 1, Milan, MI 20123, Italy. TEL 39-02-8690661, FAX 39-02-8057737, amcham@amcham.it, http://www.amcham.it. Ed. Gabriella Gabet. adv.: color page EUR 1,200; 17.7 x 24.7. Circ: 30,000.

382 USA ISSN 0021-2903
ITALIAN AMERICAN CHAMBER OF COMMERCE OF CHICAGO. BULLETIN. Text in English. 1907. bi-m. USD 24 (effective 2000). adv. bibl.; illus.; stat. **Document type:** *Bulletin.*
Published by: Italian American Chamber of Commerce, 30 S Michigan Ave, Ste 504, Chicago, IL 60603. TEL 312-553-9137, FAX 312-553-9142, italchgo@interaccess.com, http:www.italy-america-chamber.com. Ed. Leonora Lipuma. Circ: 1,600.

382 CAN ISSN 0021-3098
ITALY CANADA TRADE. Text in English, Italian; Summaries in English. 1964. q. free to qualified personnel. adv. illus. **Document type:** *Trade.*
Published by: Italian Chamber of Commerce of Toronto, 901 Lawrence Ave W, Ste 306, Toronto, ON M6A 1C3, Canada. TEL 416-789-7169, FAX 416-789-7160, mail@italchamber-tor.on.ca, http://www.italchamber-tor.on.ca. Ed., Adv. contact Giuseppe Mancini. Circ: 10,000.

382 GBR
ITALY - U K - TRADE - MONTHLY PUBLICATION. Text in English. m. membership. adv. stat. **Document type:** *Newsletter.* **Description:** Contains economic information, business contacts, chamber news, and statistics.
Formerly: Italian Chamber of Commerce for Great Britain. Information Bulletin
Published by: Italian Chamber of Commerce and Industry for the U.K., Walmar House, 296 Regent St, London, W1R 6AE, United Kingdom. TEL 44-171-637-3153, FAX 44-171-436-6037. Ed., R&P, Adv. contact Antonino Leone TEL 44-171-436-4742. Circ: 1,000.

382 TUR ISSN 0021-3357
IZMIR TICARET ODASI DERGISI/IZMIR CHAMBER OF COMMERCE REVIEW. Text in Turkish. 1926. bi-m. USD 11.50 (effective 1998). adv. bk.rev. charts; illus.; mkt.; stat.; tr.lit. index. **Document type:** *Newspaper, Trade.* **Description:** Promotes commercial relations with other countries. Examines Turkey's import-export activities.
Published by: Izmir Ticaret Odasi/Izmir Chamber of Commerce, Ataturk Cad. no.126, Izmir, Turkey. TEL 90-232-4417777, FAX 90-232-4837853, TELEX 52331 IODA TR, http://www.izto.org.tr. Ed., Pub., Adv. contact Cengiz Ural. R&P Ilter Akat. Circ: 2,000.

382 TUR
IZMIR TICARET ODASI HABER GAZETESI. Text in Turkish. 1989. m. free. adv. **Document type:** *Newspaper.* **Description:** Provides news of foreign trade and domestic trade.
Supersedes: Izmir Ticaret Odasi Bulten
Published by: Izmir Ticaret Odasi/Izmir Chamber of Commerce, Ataturk Cad. no.126, Izmir, Turkey. TEL 90-232-4417777, FAX 90-232-4837853, TELEX 134119, http://www.izto.org.tr. R&P Ilter Akat. Adv. contact Cengiz Ural.

330 JAM ISSN 0021-4094
JAMAICA CHAMBER OF COMMERCE JOURNAL. Text in English. 1973 (vol.29). s-a. free. adv. bk.rev. illus.
Published by: Jamaica Chamber of Commerce, 7-8 E. Parade, P.O. Box 172, Kingston, Jamaica. TEL 809-922-0150, FAX 809-924-9056. Ed. Chester Burgess. Circ: 2,000.

382 USA
JAPANESE CHAMBER OF COMMERCE AND INDUSTRY OF HAWAII. NEWSBULLETIN. Text in English. m.
Published by: Japanese Chamber of Commerce and Industry of Hawaii, 400 Hualani St, Ste 20 B, Hilo, HI 96720. TEL 808-949-5531.

382 CHL
THE JOURNAL. Text in English. m. adv. **Document type:** *Journal, Trade.* **Description:** Reports on topical issues about Chile's foreign relations, economic progress and social development.
Published by: Chilean - American Chamber of Commerce, Avda Kennedy 5735, of 201, Torre Poniente, Las Condes, Santiago, Chile. TEL 56-2-2909700, FAX 56-2-2120515, amcham@amchamchile.cl, http://www.amchamchile.cl/publicat/journal.htm.

944 FRA ISSN 1246-8576
JOURNAL DES ENTREPRISES DE SAINT-DENIS. Text in French. 4/yr.
Address: 2 place Victor Hugo, St Denis, 93200, France. TEL 48-20-63-83, FAX 48-09-02-39. Ed. Dominique Sanchez. Circ: 50,000.

951.9 KOR
K C C I BUSINESS JOURNAL. Text in English. 1986. q. free. **Document type:** *Newsletter.*
Former titles (until 1996): K C C I Quarterly Review; Korea Chamber of Commerce and Industry. News
Published by: Korea Chamber of Commerce and Industry, 45 Namdaemunno 4 ga Chung gu, PO Box 25, Seoul, 100743, Korea, S. TEL 82-2-316-3536, FAX 82-2-757-9475, trade@kcci.or.kr, http://www.kcci.or.kr. Ed. Kim Hyo Sung. Pub. Kim Song Ha.

381 NLD
KAMER VAN KOOPHANDEL EN FABRIEKEN VOOR AMSTERDAM. JAARREDE. Text in Dutch. 1812. a.
Published by: Kamer van Koophandel en Fabrieken voor Amsterdam/Chamber of Commerce, De Ruyterkade 5, Amsterdam, 1013 AA, Netherlands. TEL 31-20-5236600, FAX 31-20-5236677, TELEX 18888AMTRA. Circ: 5,000.

949.2 NLD ISSN 0167-1138
KAMER VAN KOOPHANDEL EN FABRIEKEN VOOR EEMLAND. KAMER VAN KOOPHANDEL. Text in Dutch. m.
Published by: Kamer van Koophandel en Fabrieken voor Eemland, Stationsplein 25, Amersfoort, 3818 LE, Netherlands. TEL 12964.

381 BEL ISSN 0022-8087
KAMER VAN KOOPHANDEL EN NIJVERHEID VAN ANTWERPEN. BULLETIN. Key Title: Bulletin - Kamer van Koophandel en Nijverheid van Antwerpen. Text in Dutch. 1908. m. adv. bk.rev. illus. **Document type:** *Bulletin.*
Formerly (until 1969): Kamer van Koophandel van Antwerpen. Bulletin (0772-7593)
Related titles: ♦ French ed.: Chambre de Commerce et d'Industrie d'Anvers. Bulletin.
Indexed: ELLIS, KES.
Published by: Kamer van Koophandel en Nijverheid van Antwerpen/Antwerp Chamber of Commerce and Industry, Markgravestraat 12, Antwerp, 2000, Belgium. FAX 32-3-2336442. Ed., R&P Lieve Noels. Pub. Luc Luwel. Adv. contact Liesbeth Detaevernier. Circ: 2,500.

381 NLD
KAMERKRANT (LANDELIJKE EDITIE); informatiekrant van de Kamer van Koophandel. (26 regional editions also avail.: Amersfoort; Amsterdam - Haarlem; Apeldoorn; Arnhem - Nijmegen - Doetinchem - Ede; Den Bosch; Breda; Dordrecht; Drenthe; Eindhoven; Enschede; Flevoland; Gouda; Groningen; The Hague - Delft; Hilversum; Leiden; Middelburg; Noordwest Holland; Roermond; Terneuzen; Tiel; Tilburg; Utrecht; Venlo; Zuid-Limburg; Zwolle) Text in Dutch. 1979. 10/yr. EUR 22.50; free to qualified personnel (effective 2005). adv. **Document type:** *Newspaper.*
Formerly (until 1994): Kamer van Koophandel
Published by: Stichting K v K Media, Postbus 265, Woerden, 3110 AG, Netherlands. TEL 31-348-426911, FAX 31-348-424368, info@vvk.kvk.nl, http://www.kvk.nl. adv.: B&W page EUR 32,000. Circ: 683,060.

382 DEU ISSN 0722-6470
DIE KAMMER. Variant title: Industrie- und Handelskammer Mittlerer Niederrhein. Die Kammer. Text in German. 1944. m. EUR 2 newsstand/cover (effective 2002). adv. **Document type:** *Magazine, Trade.*
Published by: (Industrie- und Handelskammer Mittlerer Niederrhein), Neusser Druckerei und Verlag GmbH, Moselstr 14, Neuss, 41464, Germany. TEL 49-2131-40402, FAX 49-2131-404283, info@ndv.de, http://www.ndv.de. adv.: B&W page EUR 2,688, color page EUR 3,633. Circ: 54,000 (controlled).

330 AUT ISSN 0022-8184
KAMMER NACHRICHTEN. Text in German. 1947. w. EUR 1.45 newsstand/cover (effective 2005). adv. bk.rev. abstr.; charts; illus.; stat. index. **Document type:** *Journal, Trade.*
Published by: Wirtschaftskammer Oberoesterreich, Hessenplatz 3, Linz, O 4020, Austria. TEL 43-732-7800361, FAX 43-732-7800395, medien@wkooe.wk.or.at, medien@wkooe.at, http://www.wko.at/ooe, http://wko.at/ooe. Ed. Johann Grosswindhager. Adv. contact Greif Werbung. page EUR 4,100; trim 192 x 258. Circ: 60,100.

381 IND ISSN 0300-4074
KANARA CHAMBER OF COMMERCE & INDUSTRY JOURNAL. Text in English, Kannada. 1971. m. INR 180 (effective 2003). adv. bk.rev. illus.; stat. **Document type:** *Bulletin, Trade.* **Description:** Contains information useful to trade, commerce and industry, including the description, dissemination and clarification of the latest government notifications, clarifications, laws and rules, amendments, statistics and market reports, as well as discussions and topical articles on current issues relating to trade, commerce and industry.
Published by: Kanara Chamber of Commerce & Industry, Bunder, P O Box 116, Mangalore, Karnataka 575 001, India. TEL 91-824-2442718, FAX 91-824-2420669, kanarachamber@sancharnet.in, http://www.commodityindia.com/kcci. Ed. Santhosh D'Souza. Adv. contact K N S Shetty TEL 91-824-2442718. Circ: 6,600 (paid and controlled).

978 USA ISSN 0274-9912
KANSAS CITIAN. Text in English. 1910. s-m. USD 50 to non-members; USD 25 to members. adv. **Document type:** *Newsletter.* **Description:** Contains articles on activities, events, and issues relevant to the Chamber.
Published by: Greater Kansas City Chamber of Commerce, 911 Main, 2600 Commerce Tower, Kansas City, MO 64105. TEL 816-221-2424, FAX 816-221-7440, http://www.kcity.com. Ed., R&P Pamela Kingsolver. Adv. contact Liz Wheeler. Circ: 6,200.

B

380.1 PAK ISSN 0047-3197
HF41
KARACHI. CHAMBER OF COMMERCE AND INDUSTRY; fortnightly trade journal. Text in English. 1975. fortn. PKR 50 domestic to members; PKR 500 foreign (effective 2002). adv. tr.lit. back issues avail. **Document type:** *Journal, Trade.*
Published by: Karachi Chamber of Commerce and Industry, Aiwan-e-Tijarat Rd., Shahrah-e-Liaquat, Karachi, 74000, Pakistan. TEL 9221-2416091, FAX 9221-2416095, ccikar@cyber.net.pk, http://karachichamber.com. Ed. Muhammad Rauf. Pub. Nazir Ali. Adv. contact Usman Ghani. B&W page PKR 100.

338 PAK ISSN 0075-5079
KARACHI. CHAMBER OF COMMERCE AND INDUSTRY. ANNUAL REPORT. Text in English. a. free.
Formerly: Karachi. Chamber of Commerce and Industry. Report
Published by: Karachi Chamber of Commerce and Industry, Aiwan-e-Tijarat Rd., Shahrah-e-Liaquat, Karachi, 74000, Pakistan.

954 PAK
KARACHI. CHAMBER OF COMMERCE AND INDUSTRY. NEWS BULLETIN. Text in English. fortn. free for members. **Document type:** *Bulletin.*
Published by: Karachi Chamber of Commerce and Industry, Aiwan-e-Tijarat, Nicol Rd., P O Box 4258, Karachi 2, Pakistan.

380.1029 KEN
KENYA NATIONAL CHAMBER OF COMMERCE AND INDUSTRY. TRADE AND INDUSTRY GUIDE. Text in English. a. KES 50. stat. **Document type:** *Directory.*
Formerly: Kenya National Chamber of Commerce and Industry. Annual Report
Published by: Kenya National Chamber of Commerce and Industry, Nairobi, Kenya. TEL 254-2-220867, FAX 254-2-340664. Ed. Peter G Muiruri. Circ: 9,000.

952 JPN
KYOTO BUSINESS DIRECTORY. Text in Japanese. s-a. **Document type:** *Directory.*
Published by: Kyoto Chamber of Commerce and Industry, 240 Shoshoi-cho-Karasuma-Dori-Ebisugawagaru, Nakagyo-ku, Kyoto-shi, 604-0000, Japan. TEL 075-231-0181.

381 USA
L A J C C SCENE. Text in English. m. free domestic to members (effective 2005). back issues avail.; reprints avail. **Document type:** *Newsletter, Consumer.*
Formerly: Profile
Published by: Los Angeles Junior Chamber of Commerce, 350 S. Bixel, Ste. 100, Los Angeles, CA. TEL 213-482-1311, FAX 213-580-1490, http://www.lajcc.org/lajcc/scene. Ed. Ramona Vargas. Circ: 750 (controlled).

954 PAK
LAHORE CHAMBER OF COMMERCE & INDUSTRY. WEEKLY CHAMBER CIRCULAR. Text in English, Urdu. 1972. w.
Published by: Lahore Chamber of Commerce and Industry, 11 Aiwan-i-Tijarat, P O Box 597, Lahore, Pakistan. Ed. M A Hameed. Circ: 5,000.

975.9 USA
LATIN CHAMBER OF COMMERCE. DIRECTORIO COMERCIAL. Text in English. a.
Published by: Latin Chamber of Commerce/Camara de Comercio Latina, 1417 W Flagler, Miami, FL 33135.

382 340 BRA
LAW AND YOU. Text in Portuguese. m.

▼ new title ➤ refereed ✶ unverified ♦ full entry avail.

Published by: American Chamber of Commerce for Brazil, Praca Pio X, 15 Andar 5, Centro, Caixa Postal 916, Rio De Janeiro, RJ 20040-020, Brazil. TEL 55-21-2032477, achambr@amchamrio.com.br, http://www.amchamrio.com.br.

381 CAN ISSN 1480-4638
LEADERSHIP MONTREAL. Text in English, French. 1998. 9/yr. CND 25. adv. **Document type:** *Trade.*
Formerly (until 1998): Montreal Plus (1196-1651)
Published by: Board of Trade of Metropolitan Montreal/Chambre de Commerce du Montreal Metropolitain, 5 Ville Marie Place, Ste 12500, Plaza Level, Montreal, PQ H3B 4Y2, Canada. TEL 514-871-4000, FAX 514-871-1255. Ed. Madeleine Murdock. R&P Luce Des Marais. Adv. contact Johanne Gagne. B&W page CND 2,800, color page CND 3,640; trim 15.25 x 9.84. Circ: 15,000.

330 GBR ISSN 1353-5552
LEEDS, BRADFORD, YORK AND NORTH YORKSHIRE CHAMBER OF COMMERCE. JOURNAL. Text in English. 1924. m. GBP 20; GBP 2.50 newsstand/cover (effective 1999). adv. bk.rev. stat. **Document type:** *Trade.*
Former titles (until 1994): Leeds and Bradford Journal (1351-0584); (until 1993): Leeds Journal (0024-0273)
Published by: Leeds, Bradford, York and North Yorkshire Chambers of Commerce, Phoenix House, Rushton Ave, Bradford, W Yorks BD3 7BH, United Kingdom. TEL 44-1274-772777, FAX 44-1274-771108. Ed. Peter Embling. Adv. contact Richard Henley. Circ: 4,200.

338 GBR
LEICESTERSHIRE CHAMBER OF COMMERCE & INDUSTRY DIRECTORY. Text in English. a. GBP 60 (effective 2001). **Document type:** *Directory.* **Description:** Lists all Chamber members and many others within the county of Leicestershire.
Formerly: Leicester & County Chamber of Commerce & Industry Directory
Published by: Kemps Publishing Ltd., 11 Swan Courtyard, Charles Edward Rd, Birmingham, W Mids B26 1BU, United Kingdom. TEL 44-121-765-4144, FAX 44-121-706-6210.

944 FRA ISSN 1150-4706
LA LETTRE D'ACTIVITES EN PAYS BASQUE. Text in French. q. free. bk.rev. **Document type:** *Newsletter.*
Formerly (until 1990): Activites en Pays Basque (0400-4450)
Published by: Bayonne and Basque country's Chamber of Commerce, 50-51 allees Marines, B.P. 215, Bayonne, Cedex 64102, France. TEL 33-5-59465999, FAX 33-5-59594279, TELEX 570 001 CHAMCO. Ed. Gerard Eder. Circ: 11,000 (controlled).

966.62 LBR
LIBERIAN TRADE TOPICS AND NEWSLETTER AND FORECASTS. Text in English. m.
Published by: Liberia Chamber of Commerce, P O Box 92, Monrovia, Liberia.

943 LIE
LIECHTENSTEINISCHE INDUSTRIE- UND HANDELSKAMMER. ANNUAL REPORT. Text in German. a. **Document type:** *Corporate.*
Published by: Liechtensteinische Industrie- und Handelskammer, Josef Rheinberger Strasse 11, Postfach 232, Vaduz, 9490, Liechtenstein. TEL 423-2375511.

945 ITA
LIGURIA TRE - RAPPORTO ANNUALE; andamento socio economico della regione. Text in Italian. 1972. a. free. bk.rev.
Formerly: Liguria Tre
Published by: Unioncamere Liguri, Via San Lorenzo, 15, Genoa, GE 16123, Italy. FAX 39-10-290422. Circ: 2,000.

382 ECU
LIVING IN ECUADOR. Text in Spanish. a. USD 40.
Published by: Ecuadorian - American Chamber of Commerce, Edif. Multicentro, 4P, La Nina y 6 Diciembre, Quito, Pichincha, Ecuador. TEL 5932-507-450, FAX 5932-504-571. Circ: 1,000.

LIVING IN VENEZUELA. see *TRAVEL AND TOURISM*

381 GBR
LONDON CHAMBER OF COMMERCE AND INDUSTRY. ANNUAL REVIEW. Text in English. 1882. a. free membership (effective 2005). adv. **Document type:** *Directory.*
Former titles: London Chamber of Commerce. Annual Review; London Chamber of Commerce and Industry. Annual Review
Published by: London Chamber of Commerce and Industry, 33 Queen St, London, EC4R 1AP, United Kingdom. TEL 44-20-72484444, FAX 44-20-74890391, lc@londonchamber.co.uk, http://www.londonchamber.co.uk/. Ed. Vincent Burke. Circ: 4,000.

381 GBR ISSN 0142-9728
LONDON CHAMBER OF COMMERCE AND INDUSTRY DIRECTORY. Text in English. 1882. a. GBP 75 (effective 2001). adv. **Document type:** *Directory.*
Incorporates: Westminster Chamber of Commerce Directory; Formerly: London Chamber of Commerce and Industry. (0076-0528)
Published by: (London Chamber of Commerce and Industry), Kemps Publishing Ltd., 11 Swan Courtyard, Charles Edward Rd, Birmingham, W Mids B26 1BU, United Kingdom. TEL 44-121-765-4144, FAX 44-121-706-6210.

943.1 DEU
M E O; das Magazin der Industrie- und Handelskammer fuer Essen - Muelheim an der Ruhr - Oberhausen. Text in German. m. adv. stat. 58 p./no.; back issues avail. **Document type:** *Magazine, Trade.*
Formerly (until 1999): Wirtschaft und Kammer (0178-8337)
Published by: Industrie- und Handelskammer fuer Essen Muelheim an der Ruhr Oberhausen zu Essen, Am Waldthausenpark 2, Essen, 45127, Germany. TEL 49-201-18920, FAX 49-201-1892173. Ed. Susanne Herrmann. Adv. contact H Leindecker TEL 49-201-226376. Circ: 37,000 (paid and controlled).

382 MYS
M I C C I BULLETIN. Text in English. m. free. **Document type:** *Newsletter.*
Formerly: M I C C I Digest (0127-5739)
Published by: Malaysian International Chamber of Commerce and Industry/Dewan Perniagaan dan Perindustrian Antarabangsa, 10th Fl Wisma Damansara, Jalan Semantan, PO Box 12921, Kuala Lumpur, 50792, Malaysia. TEL 60-3-254-2677, FAX 60-3-255-4946, micci@micci.po.my, http://www.micci.com.my. Ed. P J L Jenkins.

382 ITA ISSN 0394-347X
MADE IN ITALY; rivista del commercio estero. Text in English, French, German, Italian, Spanish. 1946. m. USD 60. adv. illus.
Published by: Camera di Commercio Italiana per l'Estero, Corso Vittorio Emanuele II, 15, Milan, MI 20122, Italy. TEL 2-76-02-02-69, FAX 2-76-00-49-82. Ed. Marco Polenghi.

974 USA
MADISON TOWN GUIDE. Text in English. 1982. a. free. adv. illus. **Description:** Directory designed to serve as a direct guide for shopping and as a survey of opportunities for community involvement.
Formerly: Madison, Connecticut - A Pictorial Guide
Published by: Madison Chamber of Commerce, Inc., PO Box 706, Madison, CT 06443-0906. TEL 203-318-0403, FAX 203-245-3419, http://www.madisonct.com. Ed. Ruth Desabo. Circ: 13,750.

943.1 DEU
MAGAZIN WIRTSCHAFT. Text in German. 1972. m. adv. **Document type:** *Trade.*
Formerly: Mittlerer Neckar
Published by: Industrie- und Handelskammer Region Stuttgart, Postfach 102444, Stuttgart, 70020, Germany. TEL 0711-2005-0, FAX 0711-2005327. Ed. Guenter Huhndorf. Adv. contact Peter Schmidt. Circ: 98,000.

954 IND
MAHARASHTRA CHAMBER PATRIKA. Text in English. bi-w.
Published by: Maharashtra Chamber of Commerce, 12 Rampart Row, Mumbai, Maharashtra 400 023, India. TEL 22-244548.

944 FRA
MAINE ECO. Text in French. 1983. 6/yr. EUR 30 (effective 2003). adv. 48 p./no.; **Description:** Covers local industry, trade, services, tourism.
Formerly (until 2002): Maine Economie (1269-6633)
Related titles: Online - full text ed.
Published by: Maine Economie, 1 bd. Rene Levasseur, BP 22385, Le Mans, Cedex 1 72002, France. TEL 33-2-43210000, FAX 33-2-43210050, maine.editions@wanadoo.fr, http://www.lemans.cci.fr/. Ed. Maryse Gauthier. Pub. Auffret Plessix. Adv. contact Pascal Tauvel TEL 33-02-43242342. Circ: 13,500.

381 USA
MAINSAIL. Text in English. m. **Document type:** *Newsletter.*
Published by: Duluth Area Chamber of Commerce, 5 W. 1st St., Ste. 101, Duluth, MN 55802-2115. TEL 218-722-5501, FAX 218-722-3223, http://www.duluthchamber.com. Circ: 1,850.

953 UAE
MAJALLAT AL-TIJARA WAL-SINA'A/TRADE AND INDUSTRY. Text in Arabic. 1975. m. **Document type:** *Government.* **Description:** Covers the business and economic situation in Dubai, the Gulf, and the Arab world.
Published by: Dubai Chamber of Commerce and Industry, P O Box 1457, Dubai, United Arab Emirates. TEL 971-4-280000, FAX 971-4-211646, TELEX 45997 TIJARA EM. Ed. Abdul Rahman G Al Mutawee. Circ: 7,500.

976 USA
MAJOR EMPLOYERS DIRECTORY. Text in English. a. USD 20. **Document type:** *Directory.* **Description:** Lists companies in the Birmingham MSA that employ 100 or more people.
Published by: Birmingham Area Chamber of Commerce, 505 N 20th St, Ste 151, Birmingham, AL 35203-2605. TEL 205-250-7653.

330 GBR ISSN 0025-1992
MANCHESTER CHAMBER OF COMMERCE. RECORD. Text in English. 1890. 10/yr. GBP 190 (effective 1999 & 2000). adv. bk.rev. mkt.; stat.; tr.lit. index. 36 p./no. 8 cols./p.; back issues avail. **Document type:** *Newspaper.* **Description:** Covers information on chamber of commerce members, hotels and manchester airport.
Indexed: WTA.
Published by: Manchester Chamber of Commerce and Industry, Churchgate House, 56 Oxford St, Manchester, M60 7HJ, United Kingdom. TEL 44-161-236-3210, FAX 44-161-236-4160, http://www.manchester2002-uk.com/business/chambers.html. Ed. David Allaby. adv.: B&W page GBP 3,200, color page GBP 4,800. Circ: 8,000.

914 ITA ISSN 0025-2506
MANTOVA. Text in Italian. 1905. q. adv. bk.rev.
Published by: Camera di Commercio Industria e Agricoltura di Mantova, Via P.F. Calvi 28, Mantua, MN, Italy. TEL 76-322371, FAX 76-361883, TELEX 300686.

381 DEU ISSN 0721-9148
MARKT & WIRTSCHAFT. Text in German. 1955. m. EUR 15 (effective 2005). adv. **Document type:** *Magazine, Trade.*
Former titles (until 1981): I H K Mitteilungen (0341-146X); (until 1976): Industrie- und Handelskammer zu Koeln. Mitteilungen (0341-1451)
Related titles: Online - full text ed.
Published by: Industrie- und Handelskammer zu Koeln, Unter Sachsenhausen 10-26, Cologne, 50667, Germany. TEL 49-221-1640130, FAX 49-221-1640129, service@koeln.ihk.de, http://www.ihk-koeln.de/Service/Presse/MarktUndWirtschaft/Onlineversion.jsp. Ed. Michael Sallmann. Circ: 119,000 (paid and controlled).

968.91 ZWE
MASHONALAND CHAMBER OF INDUSTRIES. ANNUAL REPORT. Text in English. a.
Published by: Mashonaland Chamber of Industries (MCI), Rotten Row 109, PO Box 3794, Harare, Zimbabwe. TEL 702431, TELEX 2073.

945 ITA
MATERA. Text in Italian. bi-m.
Published by: Camera di Commercio Industria e Agricoltura di Matera, Matera, MT 75100, Italy.

967 MUS
MAURITIUS CHAMBER OF COMMERCE AND INDUSTRY. ANNUAL REPORT. Text in English. 1950. a. free. **Document type:** *Corporate.*
Published by: Mauritius Chamber of Commerce and Industry, 3 Royal St, Port Louis, Mauritius. TEL 230-208-3301, FAX 230-208-0076, mcci@intnet.mu, http://www.mcci.org. Circ: 800.

382 URY ISSN 0797-2733
MERCADO. Text in Spanish; Text occasionally in German. 1987. q. **Document type:** *Magazine, Trade.*
Published by: Camara de Comercio Uruguayo-Alemana/Deutsch-Uruguayische Handelskammer, Pza Independencia 831, Edificio Plaza Mayor, Montevideo, 11100, Uruguay. TEL 598-2-9010575, FAX 598-2-9085666, camural@ahkurug.com.uy, http://www.ahk-uruguay.com. Circ: 1,000.

380.1 USA ISSN 0194-9101
HF1
MERCER BUSINESS MAGAZINE. Text in English. 1924. m. USD 25; USD 3 newsstand/cover (effective 2005). adv. bk.rev. stat. 56 p./no. 3 cols./p.; reprints avail. **Document type:** *Magazine, Trade.* **Description:** A monthly business features magazine covering activities in the Princeton-Trenton, New Jersey metro-market.
Formerly (until 1979): Trenton (0041-2449)
Related titles: Microform ed.: (from PQC); Online - full text ed.: (from O C L C Online Computer Library Center, Inc., ProQuest Information & Learning, The Dialog Corporation); Supplement(s): Mercer County Tourism Guide.
Indexed: ABIn, BusDate, PAIS.
Published by: Greater Mercer County Chamber of Commerce, 214 W State St, Trenton, NJ 08608. TEL 609-586-2056, 609-586-2056, 609-393-1032, FAX 609-586-8052, donnak@mercerbusiness.com, http://www.mercerchamber.org. Ed. Maggi Hill. Pub. Timothy Losch. adv.: B&W page USD 1,345, color page USD 1,740. Circ: 600 (free); 7,826 (paid and controlled).

381 BGD
METROPOLITAN CHAMBER OF COMMERCE AND INDUSTRY, DHAKA. CHAMBER NEWS. Text in English. 1978. m. BDT 50. adv. bk.rev.
Formerly: Narayanganj Chambers of Commerce & Industry. Chamber News
Indexed: KES.
Published by: Metropolitan Chamber of Commerce and Industry, Chamber Bldg 4th Fl, 122-124 Motijheel C.A., Dhaka, 1000, Bangladesh. Circ: 400.

METROPOLITAN MILWAUKEE ASSOCIATION OF COMMERCE. MEMBERSHIP DIRECTORY & BUYERS' GUIDE (YEAR). see *BUSINESS AND ECONOMICS—Trade And Industrial Directories*

944 FRA ISSN 0755-7078
MEUSE ECONOMIQUE. Text in French. q. adv. **Document type:** *Bulletin.*
Published by: Chambre de Commerce et d Industrie de la, 6 Parc Bradfer, Bar-le-Duc, 55000, France. TEL 33-3-29768300, FAX 33-3-29454742, cci.meuse@wanadoo.fr, http://www.perso.wanadoo.fr/cci-meuse/. Ed. Francois Godinot. R&P Pascale Rollinger. Adv. contact Marie Claude Bertaud. Circ: 4,800.

972 USA ISSN 1068-2074
HC131
MEXICO NEWSPAK; a bi-weekly news & resource update. Text in English. 1993. fortn. USD 42 (effective 1998). back issues avail.
Published by: Human Rights Documentation Exchange, PO Box 2327, Austin, TX 78768-2327. TEL 512-476-9841, FAX 512-476-0130. Ed. Donna Woodwell. Circ: 250 (paid).

381.06 USA ISSN 0540-4428
MISSOURI BUSINESS. Text in English. 1952. 12/yr. free to members; USD 40 to non-members (effective 2004). adv. **Document type:** *Newsletter, Consumer.*
Published by: Missouri Chamber of Commerce, PO Box 149, Jefferson City, MO 65102-0149. TEL 573-634-3511, FAX 573-634-8855, mchamber@computerland.net, http://www.mochamber.org. Pub. Daniel P Mehan. Circ: 4,000 (paid).

053.1 DEU
MITTEILUNGEN "BERUFSBILDUNG". Text in German. 1959. m. **Document type:** *Bulletin.*
Published by: Industrie- und Handelskammer zu Muenster, Sentmaringer Weg 61, Muenster, 48151, Germany. TEL 49-251-707-261, FAX 49-251-707-325. Circ: 10,700.

382 DEU
MITTELDEUTSCHE WIRTSCHAFT. Text in German. 1990. 10/yr. EUR 20 (effective 2003). adv. **Document type:** *Magazine, Trade.*
Published by: Industrie- und Handelskammer Halle - Dessau, Franckestr 5, Halle, 06110, Germany. TEL 49-345-21260, FAX 49-345-2029649, info@halle.ihk.de, http://www.halle.ihk.de. adv.: B&W page EUR 2,504, color page EUR 4,007. Circ: 31,700 (controlled).

382 USA
MOBILE AREA CHAMBER OF COMMERCE MEMBERSHIP DIRECTORY AND BUYER'S GUIDE. Text in English. a., latest 2001. USD 20 to non-members. adv. 400 p./no.; **Document type:** *Directory, Corporate.* **Description:** Business directory and information guide for the city of Mobile.
Formerly (since 1979): Who's Who in the Mobile Area
Published by: Mobile Area Chamber of Commerce, 451 Government St, Box 2187, Mobile, AL 36652. TEL 251-433-6951, FAX 251-431-8608, info@mobilechamber.com. Pub., R&P Leigh Perry Herndon TEL 251-431-8645. Adv. contact Carolyn Golson TEL 251-431-8622. Circ: 5,000.

330 ITA ISSN 0391-6626
MODENA ECONOMICA. Text in Italian. 1892. 9/yr. adv. bk.rev. illus.; mkt.; stat.
Formerly: Modena (0026-7430)
Published by: Camera di Commercio Industria Artigianato e Agricoltura di Modena, Via Ganaceto, 134, Modena, MO 41100, Italy. TEL 208111, FAX 211035. Ed. Giorgio Bertolani. Circ: 7,000.

320 ITA
MONDO PADANO. Text in Italian. 1981. fortn. adv. **Document type:** *Newspaper.*
Related titles: Online - full text ed.
Published by: Societa Servizi Editoriali, Via delle Industrie 2, Cremona, CR 26100, Italy. TEL 39-0372-4981, FAX 39-0372-28487, mondopadano@cremonmaonline.it, http://www.mondopadano.it. Ed. Antonio Leoni. Circ: 27,000.

949.4 CHE ISSN 1420-0422
MONTAGNA. Text in French, German, Italian. 1865. m. CHF 60 (effective 2000). adv. bk.rev. back issues avail. **Document type:** *Newspaper, Trade.*
Former titles (until 1990): Blaue (0006-4610); (until 1977): Alpwirthschaftliche Monatsblaetter (1421-0401); (until 1891): Alpen- und Jura-Chronik (1421-0398); (until 1887): Alp- und Milchwirthschaftliche Monatsblaetter (1421-038X); (until 1883): Alpwirthschaftliche Monatsblaetter (1421-0371); (until 1867): Schweizerischer Alpwirtschaftlicher Verein. Jahresbericht (1421-0363)
—CCC.
Published by: Schweizerische Arbeitsgemeinschaft fuer die Berggebiete, Laurstr 10, Brugg Ag, 5200, Switzerland. TEL 41-56-4423012, FAX 41-56-4413642, sab@sab.ch, sabll@pop.agri.ch, http://www.sab.ch. Ed. Berchtold Lehnherr. Circ: 6,000.

382 954 PAK
MONTHLY EXPORT TRENDS✶ ; monitor of Pakistan's export trade. Text in English. 1986. m. PKR 180. adv. bk.rev.
Published by: Federation of Pakistan Chambers of Commerce and Industry, Sharea Firdousi, Main Clifton, PO Box 13875, Karachi, 75600, Pakistan. TEL 92-21-5873691-94, TELEX 23862 DABH PK. Ed. Agha Masood. Circ: 5,000.

945 ITA
MOVIMENTO ANAGRAFE DITTE. Text in Italian. 1991. m. **Document type:** *Directory, Trade.* **Description:** Lists new and ceased firms in the province of Pesaro.
Published by: Camera di Commercio Industria Artigianato e Agricoltura di Pesaro e Urbino, Corso XI Settembre 116, Pesaro, PS 61100, Italy. FAX 39-0721-31015, 39-0721-3571, http://www.ps,camcom.it. Ed. Paolo Lamaro. Circ: 720 (controlled).

381 USA
MT. OLIVE TODAY. Text in English. 1991. q. free. adv. **Document type:** *Newsletter.* **Description:** Discusses the Chamber's activities and ambitions; promotes active participation in the organization.
Published by: Mt. Olive Area Chamber of Commerce, 100 Rte 46, Village Green Annex, PO Box 192, Budd Lake, NJ 07828-9998. TEL 973-691-0109, FAX 973-691-0110. Ed. Dolores Ortiz.

380 IND ISSN 0027-559X
MYSORE COMMERCE. Text in English. 1944. m. INR 6. adv. bk.rev. bibl.; charts; illus.; pat.; stat.
Published by: Federation of Karnataka Chambers of Commerce & Industry, K.G. Rd., P O Box 9996, Bangalore, Karnataka 560 009, India. Ed. B N Narayan. Circ: 2,000.

382 NLD ISSN 0927-703X
HF3611
N C H TRADELETTER. Text in Dutch. 1948. 8/yr. USD 45. abstr.; pat.; stat.; tr.lit. **Document type:** *Newsletter.*
Formerly (until 1992): N C H Newsletter (0923-3911); Incorporates (in 1992): Oost Europa - U S S R Bulletin (0924-3410); Which was formed by the 1988 merger of: Oost Europa (0924-3429); Nederland - U S S R Instituut. Maandberichten (0028-2022); Incorporates (in 1992): Afrika - Midden-Oosten Bulletin (0923-3377); Which was formed by the merger of (1970-1988): Afrika in het Nieuws (0165-8026); (1970-1988): Midden Oosten (0923-8654); Incorporates (in 1992): Israel Bulletin (0924-2821); Which was formerly (1951-1988): Nederland-Israel (0028-2014); Incorporates (in 1992): Latijns-Amerika Bulletin (0923-3431); Which was formerly (until 1988): Noticias Economics (0923-344X); Incorporates (in 1992): West-Europa Bulletin (0924-3380); Which was formerly (1977-1988): Noord-Europa (0924-3399)
Indexed: KES, RASB.
Published by: Nederlands Centrum voor Handelsbevordering, Postbus 10, The Hague, 2501 CA, Netherlands. Ed. W F van der Hooft. Circ: 400.

381 338 ZAF
N.T.C.I. CURRENT AFFAIRS UPDATE. Text in English. 1993. 7/yr.
Indexed: ISAP.
Published by: Northern Transvaal Chamber of Industries, PO Box 933, Pretoria, 0001, South Africa.

330 IRN ISSN 1024-3011
HC471
NAMAH-'I UTAQ-I BAZARGANI. Text in Persian, Modern. m. USD 50.
Published by: Iran Chamber of Commerce, Industries and Mines, Public Relations, 254 Taleghanni Ave., Tehran, 15875-4671, Tehran, Iran. TEL 98-21-8846031, FAX 98-21-8825111. adv.: B&W page USD 500, color page USD 1,500.

382 AUS
NARRABEEN CHAMBER NEWS. Text in English. 1996. q.
Media: Online - full text.
Published by: Narrabeen Lakes Chamber of Commerce, PO Box 245, Narrabeen, NSW 2101, Australia. TEL 61-2-9971-6439, http://www.interweb.com.au/narrabeen/narrnews.htm. Ed., Pub. Marlene Regimbal.

382 USA ISSN 1064-9913
HF1416.5
NATIONAL TRADE DATA BANK. Short title: N T D B. Text in English. 1990. m. USD 575 in North America; USD 775 elsewhere (effective 2001). **Description:** Contains trade and export promotion data collected by 14 federal agencies. Includes information on international economics, foreign trade, export regulations, policies, and promotion programs.
Media: CD-ROM.
Indexed: AmStl.
Published by: (United States. Economics and Statistics Administration), Department of Commerce, Office of Business Analysis, c/o U S National Technical Information Service, 5825 Port Royal Rd, Springfield, VA 22161.

382.029 NLD
NETHERLANDS-AMERICAN TRADE DIRECTORY. Text in English. 1969. biennial. EUR 90 domestic to non-members; USD 140 foreign (effective 2001). stat. **Document type:** *Directory, Trade.* **Description:** Listings of members, US firms with Netherlands subsidiaries, Netherlands firms with US subsidiaries, classification of firms by SIC-code, state or region. Includes related organizations in US and Netherlands, and statistical information on trade between the US and the Netherlands.
Published by: American Chamber of Commerce in the Netherlands, Burg van Karnebeeklaan 14, The Hague, 2585 BB, Netherlands. TEL 31-70-3659808, FAX 31-70-3646992, amchamnl@wxs.nl, http://www.amcham.nl. Ed. M van den Berg.

NETHERLANDS-BRITISH TRADE DIRECTORY. see *BUSINESS AND ECONOMICS—Trade And Industrial Directories*

338 GBR
NETWORK NOTTINGHAMSHIRE. Text in English. 1917. m. (10 issues excludes January and August). GBP 50 (effective 2001). adv. illus.; tr.lit. index. 40 p./no. 5 cols./p.; **Document type:** *Magazine, Newspaper-distributed.*
Formerly (untill 2000): Industrial Nottinghamshire (0019-8579)
Published by: Nottinghamshire Chamber of Commerce and Industry, 309 Hagdn Road, Nottingham, NG5 1DL, United Kingdom. TEL 0115-962-4624, FAX 0115-985-6612, sderbyshine@nottschamber.co.uk, http://www.nottschamberco.uk. Ed. Stephen Derbgshine. Circ: 3,200 (controlled).

381 NPL
NEWS & NEWS. Text in Nepali. 1992. m. USD 2. adv. bk.rev.
Published by: Federation of Nepalese Chambers of Commerce and Industry, Teku, P O Box 269, Kathmandu, Nepal. TEL 977-1-262061, FAX 977-1-261011, fincci@mos.com.np, fncci@mos.com.np.

381 USA
NEWTON - NEEDHAM BUSINESS. Text in English. 1959. 10/yr. USD 25. **Document type:** *Newsletter.* **Description:** Covers news and issues of interest to the local business community.
Published by: Newton - Needham Chamber of Commerce, Inc., PO Box 268, Newton, MA 02159-0002. TEL 617-244-5300, FAX 617-244-5302. Ed. Martin Cohn.

974 USA
NIAGARA FALLS AREA CHAMBER OF COMMERCE. MEMBERSHIP DIRECTORY & BUYERS' GUIDE. Text in English. a. USD 25. adv. **Document type:** *Directory.* **Description:** Listing of Chamber members, contact personnel, financial institutions and local industry.
Formerly: Niagara Falls Area Chamber of Commerce. Business - Industrial Directory
Published by: Niagara Falls Area Chamber of Commerce, 345 Third St, Niagara Falls, NY 14303-1117. TEL 716-285-9141, FAX 716-285-0941. Ed., R&P, Adv. contact Fred Caso Jr. Pub. Charles Steiner. Circ: 2,500.

943.1 DEU
NIEDERBAYERISCHE WIRTSCHAFT. Text in German. 1947. m. free to members (effective 2005). adv. **Document type:** *Magazine, Trade.*
Published by: Industrie- und Handelskammer fuer Niederbayern in Passau, Nibelungenstr 15, Passau, 94032, Germany. TEL 49-851-507251, FAX 49-851-507280, niwi@passau.ihk.de, http://www.passau.ihk.de/service/pub/niwi/zeitschrift.html. Ed. Martin Brunner. Adv. contact Brigitte Pfaffinger. B&W page EUR 1,820, color page EUR 2,660; trim 185 x 267. Circ: 38,000 (controlled).

380 NGA ISSN 0189-5036
NIGERIAN BUSINESS JOURNAL. Text in English. 1950. a. adv. bk.rev. **Document type:** *Trade.*
Formerly: Commerce in Nigeria (0069-6633)
Published by: Lagos Chamber of Commerce and Industry, 1 Idowu Taylor St., PO Box 109, Victoria Island., Lagos State, Nigeria. Ed. S B Akande. Circ: 5,000.

944 FRA ISSN 0243-8860
NORD SEINE ET MARNE INFORMATIONS. Text in French. 1960. 4/yr.
Formerly (until 1980): Chambre de Commerce et d'Industrie de Meaux-Coulommiers. Bulletin Trimestriel (0243-8739)
Published by: Chambre de Commerce et d'Industrie de Meaux, 12 bd. Jean Rose, BP 216, Meaux, Cedex 77104, France. TEL 33-1-64363257, FAX 33-1-64334115, TELEX 691 142 F. Ed. Daniel Retournard.

941.6 GBR
NORTHERN IRELAND CHAMBER OF COMMERCE AND INDUSTRY YEARBOOK. Text in English. a.
Published by: Northern Ireland Chamber of Commerce and Industry, 22 Great Victoria St, Belfast, Bl2 7BJ, United Kingdom.

382 USA ISSN 0803-1134
NORWAY AT YOUR SERVICE. Text in English. 2/yr. membership.
Published by: Norwegian American Chamber of Commerce, Inc., 655 3rd Ave., Rm. 1810, New York, NY 10017-9111. TEL 212-421-9210.

382 USA ISSN 0891-2890
NORWEGIAN TRADE BULLETIN. Text in English. 8/yr. free. **Document type:** *Bulletin.*
Published by: Norwegian American Chamber of Commerce, Inc., 655 3rd Ave., Rm. 1810, New York, NY 10017-9111. TEL 212-421-9210.

▼ new title ➤ refereed ✶ unverified ♦ full entry avail.

941 GBR ISSN 0953-5470
NORWICH AND NORFOLK CHAMBER OF COMMERCE AND INDUSTRY. DIRECTORY. Text in English. 1981. a. GBP 35 to non-members. adv. illus. **Document type:** *Directory.*
Description: Gives current data on the region with membership listings under alphabetical and classified headings.
Related titles: French ed.; German ed.
Published by: Norwich and Norfolk Chamber of Commerce, Norfolk, 112 Barrack St, Norwich, Norfolk NR3 1UB, United Kingdom. TEL 0603-625977, FAX 0603-633032, TELEX CHACOM-G-975247. Ed. Deb Jackson. Circ: 3,500.

380.1 COL ISSN 0120-615X
NOTICIA COMERCIAL DEL ORIENTE. Text in Spanish. 1979. m. USD 17. adv. charts; illus.; stat.
Supersedes: Noticiero Mercantil; Organizacion Mercantil (0030-5049)
Published by: Camara de Comercio de Bogota, Carrera 26 68D-35, Bogota, Colombia. Ed. Alba Maria Rueda Vasquez. Circ: 1,000.

945 ITA
NOTIZIARIO COMMERCIO ESTERO. Text in Italian. 1960. m. free. **Document type:** *Trade.* **Description:** Contains articles on international trade and business opportunities.
Published by: Camera di Commercio Industria Artigianato e Agricoltura di Vicenza, Corso Antonio Fogazzaro, 37, Vicenza, VI 36100, Italy. TEL 39-444-994811, FAX 39-444-994834, TELEX 480496 VICAM I. Ed. Antonio Bellin. Circ: 3,800.

330 ITA
NOTIZIE DELL'ECONOMIA. Text in Italian. 1945. m. adv. **Document type:** *Magazine, Consumer.*
Published by: Camera di Commercio Industria Artigianato e Agricoltura di Teramo, Via Savini 48-50, Teramo, TE 64100, Italy. TEL 39-0861-3351, FAX 39-0861-246142, camera.commercio@te.camcom.it, http://www.camcom.te.it. Ed. Luciotti R Gianni.

381 GBR ISSN 0963-1437
NOTTINGHAMSHIRE BUSINESS DIRECTORY. Text in English. a. GBP 60 (effective 2001). **Document type:** *Directory.*
Published by: Kemps Publishing Ltd., 11 Swan Courtyard, Charles Edward Rd, Birmingham, W Mids B26 1BU, United Kingdom. TEL 44-121-765-4144, FAX 44-121-706-6210.

330 ITA ISSN 0029-6171
NUOVA ECONOMIA. Text in Italian. m. abstr.; bibl.; charts; illus.; stat.
Published by: Camera di Commercio Industria Artigianato e Agricoltura di Perugia, Piazza Italia, 1, Perugia, PG 06121, Italy. Circ: 1,000.

945 ITA
NUOVO COMMERCIO. Text in Italian. 1963. m. adv.
Published by: Confesercenti del Comprensorio di Cesena, Via Roverella, 1, Cesena, FO 47023, Italy. TEL 547-22771. Ed. Dino Amadori. Circ: 9,000.

338 DEU ISSN 0029-7496
OBERFRAENKISCHE WIRTSCHAFT. Text in German. 1910. m. adv. bk.rev. charts; illus.; stat.; tr.lit. **Document type:** *Consumer.*
Published by: Industrie- und Handelskammer fuer Oberfranken, Bahnhofstr 25-27, Bayreuth, 95444, Germany. Ed. Bodo Schultheiss. Adv. contact Monika Oberst. Circ: 38,000.

382 AUT ISSN 0029-8751
OESTERREICH-NEDERLAND. Text in German. 1961. irreg. (approx. 5/yr.). membership. adv. bk.rev. abstr.; bibl.; charts; illus.; stat.; tr.lit.
Published by: Niederlaendische Handelskammer fuer Oesterreich, Schwarzenbergplatz 10, Postfach 160, Vienna, W 1041, Austria. TEL 0222-5055708, FAX 0222-5055700. Circ: 3,000.

381.06 USA
OHIO MATTERS. Text in English. 1995. bi-m. free domestic membership (effective 2005). **Document type:** *Magazine, Trade.* **Description:** Distributed to members throughout the state, including state legislators, government officials and more than 325 local chambers and includes timely features on current business issues and policy debates.
Published by: Ohio Chamber of Commerce, 230 E Town St, Columbus, OH 43215-0159. TEL 614-228-4201, FAX 614-228-6403, occ@ohiochamber.com, http://www.ohiochamber.com/Events/ohiomatters.asp. Ed. Julie Feasel. Circ: 6,500 (paid and free).

382 NLD
OOSTENRIJKSE ECONOMISCHE BERICHTEN. Text in Dutch. 1950. m. free. adv. illus.; tr.lit.
Supersedes: Oostenrijkse Handelsdelegatie in Nederland (0030-3291)
Published by: Oostenrijkse Handelsdelegatie in Nederland/Oesterreichische Aussenhandelsstelle in den Niederlanden, Lange Voorhout 58a, The Hague, 2514 EG, Netherlands. Circ: 3,000. **Affiliate:** Bundeshandelskammer, Vienna.

382 FRA ISSN 0249-5163
OPPORTUNITES INDUSTRIELLES BULLETIN. Text in French. q. **Document type:** *Bulletin.*
Published by: Chambre Regionale de Commerce et d'Industrie d'Alsace, 42 rue Schweighaeuser, Strasbourg, 67000, France. TEL 33-3-88607475, FAX 33-3-88615354.

380.15 ESP ISSN 0212-7385
ORIENTACION ECONOMICA Y FINANCIERA. Text in Spanish. 1943. q.
—CINDOC.
Published by: Camara Oficial de Comercio, Industria y Navegacion de la Coruna, Alameda, 30-32, Coruna, Spain. TEL 34-981-216072, FAX 34-981-225208, ccincoruna@camerdata.es, camerdata.es/coruna.

330 DEU ISSN 0720-4868
OSTSEEJAHRBUCH. Text in German. 1934. a. price varies. **Document type:** *Bulletin.*
Former title: Wirtschaft im Ostseeraum (0084-0483)
Published by: Industrie- und Handelskammer zu Luebeck, Fackenburger Allee 2, Luebeck, 23554, Germany. FAX 49-451-7085284, ihk@luebeck-ihk.de, http://www.ihk-luebeck.de. Ed. Hans-Jochen Arndt. R&P Hans Jochen Arndt. Circ: 1,200.

943 DEU
OSTWESTFAELISCHE WIRTSCHAFT. Text in German. m. adv. bk.rev. **Document type:** *Bulletin.*
Published by: (Industrie- und Handelskammer Ostwestfalen zu Bielefeld), Panorama Verlags- und Werbegesellschaft mbH, Sudbrackstr 14-18, Bielefeld, 33611, Germany. TEL 49-521-58540, FAX 49-521-585308.

380 GBR
OXFORDSHIRE COMMERCIAL & INDUSTRIAL DIRECTORY. Text in English. a. GBP 40 (effective 2001). **Document type:** *Directory.*
Published by: Kemps Publishing Ltd., 11 Swan Courtyard, Charles Edward Rd, Birmingham, W Mids B26 1BU, United Kingdom. TEL 44-121-765-4144, FAX 44-121-706-6210.

382 ITA
PADOVA IMPRESA. Text in Italian. 1999. 6/yr. free. illus.; mkt.; stat. **Document type:** *Newsletter, Corporate.*
Published by: Camera di Commercio, Industria, Artigianato e Agricoltura di Padova, Via E. Filiberto 34, Padua, PD, Italy. TEL 39-049-8208111, FAX 39-049-8208290, studi@pd.camcom.it, http://www.pd.camcom.it. Ed. Alessandro Selmin. Circ: 90,000.

338 PAK
PAKISTAN DIRECTORY OF TRADE AND INDUSTRY. Text in English. 1976. a. **Document type:** *Directory.*
Published by: Lahore Chamber of Commerce and Industry, 11 Aiwan-i-Tijarat, P O Box 597, Lahore, Pakistan.

330 ITA ISSN 0391-8319
PAVIA ECONOMICA. Text in Italian. 1946. q. adv. bk.rev. index. **Document type:** *Magazine, Trade.*
Formerly (until 1961): Informazioni Economiche
Published by: Camera di Commercio Industria Artigianato e Agricoltura di Pavia, Via Mentana 27, Pavia, PV 27100, Italy. TEL 39-0382-393260, FAX 39-0382-393238, http://www.pv.camcom.it. Ed. G Pallavicini.

381 USA
PENNSYLVANIA CHAMBER OF BUSINESS AND INDUSTRY. STATE & REGIONAL DIRECTORY✶. Text in English. a. USD 40 to non-members; USD 25 to members. **Document type:** *Directory.*
Former titles: Pennsylvania Chamber of Commerce. State and Regional Directory; Pennsylvania Chamber of Commerce. Directory of State, Regional and Commercial Organizations (0098-5368)
Published by: Pennsylvania Chamber of Business and Industry, 417 Walnut St, Harrisburg, PA 17101. TEL 717-255-3252, FAX 717-255-3298. Ed. John Eichorn. Circ: 650.

982 ARG ISSN 0325-5069
PENSAMIENTO ECONOMICO. Text in Spanish. 1925. q.
Formerly (until 1975): Camara Argentina de Comercio. Revista
Published by: Camara Argentina de Comercio, Avda. Leandro N. Alem, 36, Capital Federal, Buenos Aires 1003, Argentina. TEL 54-114-3318051, TELEX 18542. Ed. Pedro Naon Argerich.

382 ESP ISSN 1135-5891
PERSPECTIVES; magazine of the French chambers of commerce and industry in Spain. Text in Spanish. 1969. 4/yr. adv. **Document type:** *Monographic series.* **Description:** Each issue presents a complete approach to a theme of Spanish economy, with concrete examples, written by Spanish and French professionals.
Published by: Chambre Franco-Espagnole de Commerce et d'Industrie de Madrid/Camara Francesa de Comercio e Industria de Madrid, Ruiz de Alarcon, 7, Madrid, 28014, Spain. TEL 34-1-5226742, FAX 34-1-5233642, chambre@teleline.es, http://www.lachambre.es. Ed. B Barthelemy. Adv. contact Maria Luz Mena. Circ: 2,200 (controlled). **Subscr. to:** Chambre de Commerce et d'Industrie Francaise, Passeig De Gracia, 2, Barcelona 08007, Spain. TEL 34-3-3176738, FAX 34-3-3171139.

338 ITA ISSN 0031-9570
LA PIANURA. Text in Italian. 1964. 3/yr. free. adv. charts; illus.; stat.
Indexed: RefZh, ZooRec.
Published by: Camera di Commercio Industria Artigianato e Agricoltura di Ferrara, Via Borgoleoni, 11, Ferrara, FE 44100, Italy. TEL 39-0532-783711, FAX 39-0532-240204, corrado.padovan@fe.camcom.it, http://www.fe.camcom.it. Ed. Dr. Bruno Baldazzi.

944 FRA ISSN 0180-6084
PLEIN OUEST; informations economiques Nantes Atlantique. Text in French. 1977. bi-m. adv. illus. **Document type:** *Consumer.* **Description:** Covers the economic news of the Pays de la Loire.
Published by: Chambres de Commerce et d'Industrie de Nantes et de Saint-Nazaire, Centre des Salorges, 16 quai Ernest Renaud, BP 90517, Nantes, Cedex 4 44105, France. TEL 33-2-40446347, FAX 33-2-40446125. Ed. Philippe Hervouet. R&P Aurele Salmon. Adv. contact Catherine Manceron TEL 33-02-40735051. Circ: 30,000.

PLYMOUTH COUNTY BUSINESS REVIEW. see *BUSINESS AND ECONOMICS—Domestic Commerce*

381 USA ISSN 1075-6264
THE POINT!. Text in English. 1916. bi-w. USD 25. adv. charts; illus. reprint service avail. from PQC. **Document type:** *Newsletter, Trade.*
Former titles (until 1994): O K C Action (1043-4259); (until 1989): Oklahoma (0030-1639)
Related titles: Microform ed.: (from PQC).
Published by: Oklahoma City Chamber of Commerce, 123 Park Ave, Oklahoma City, OK 73102-9031. TEL 405-297-8900, FAX 405-297-8916. R&P, Adv. contact Jeffrey A Knight. Circ: 5,000.

380.1 FRA ISSN 1629-436X
LE POINT ECO. Text in French. 1971. 8/yr. adv. bk.rev.
Formerly (until 2000): Point Economique (0758-573X)
Published by: Chambre de Commerce et d'Industrie de Strasbourg et du Bas-Rhin, 10 place Gutenberg, Strasbourg, Cedex 67081, France. TEL 33-3-88752525, FAX 33-3-33223120, TELEX 870068 F CHAMCO. Ed. Francois Frieh. Circ: 25,000.

382 CHE
POINT ECONOMIQUE. Text in French. 10/yr.
Published by: Chambre France - Suisse pour le Commerce et l'Industrie, 32 Av de Frontenex, Geneva 6, 1211, Switzerland.

944 FRA ISSN 0981-1869
PRESENCES. Text in French. 1987. 10/yr. adv. **Document type:** *Newspaper.*
Address: 1 place Andre Malraux, BP 297, Grenoble, Cedex 1 38016, France. TEL 76-28-28-76, FAX 76-28-28-60, TELEX CECOMEX 320 824 F. Ed. Jacques Baillieux. Pub., Adv. contact Odile Brasseur. Circ: 40,000.

382 VEN
PRESENZA ECONOMICA. Text in Spanish. m.?. adv. charts; illus.
Published by: Camara de Comercio Industria y Agricultura Venezolano-Italiano, Ave. Andres Bello, Centro Andres Bello, Torre Oeste p. 14 Ofs. 143-144, Apdo 14204, Caracas, DF 1050, Venezuela. TEL 02-781-5213, FAX 7813731, TELEX 28676 CAMCO VC.

382 ITA ISSN 1120-3919
PREZZI DEI MATERIALI E DELLE OPERE EDILI IN FERRARA. Text in Italian. 1968. s-a. adv.
Formerly: Inserite Nuove Voci e Miglioramenti Tipografici
Published by: Camera di Commercio Industria Artigianato e Agricoltura di Ferrara, Via Borgoleoni, 11, Ferrara, FE 44100, Italy. TEL 39-0532-783711, FAX 39-0532-240204, prezzi.protesti@fe.camcom.it, http://www.fe.camcom.it. Ed. Dr. Bruno Baldazzi.

330 HRV ISSN 0350-9427
PRIVREDA (OSIJEK); casopis za privredna pitanja Slavonije i Baranje. Text in Croatian. 1957. m.
Formerly: Privreda Kotara Osijek (0032-8960)
Published by: Privredna Komora Slavonije i Baranje, Bulevar JNA 13, Osijek, 54000, Croatia. Ed. Petar Djidara. Circ: 1,100.

381 USA ISSN 1048-2989
PROFILE (LOS ANGELES). Text in English. 1925. bi-m. USD 1; to members only. illus. **Document type:** *Newsletter.*
Formerly (until 1989): Headlines (0300-7782)
Published by: Los Angeles Junior Chamber of Commerce, 404 S Bixel St, Los Angeles, CA 90017. TEL 213-482-1311, FAX 213-482-0865. Ed. Bob Levey. Circ: 1,500.

380.1 USA ISSN 0162-5241
PROFILE (OMAHA). Text in English. 1973 (vol.33). s-m. USD 40 to non-members; free to members (effective 2005). adv. illus. **Document type:** *Newsletter.* **Description:** News items, information, and announcements of the activities and issues pertaining to the Chamber of Commerce.
Formerly: Omaha Profile (0030-221X)

B

Published by: Greater Omaha Chamber of Commerce, 1301 Harney, Omaha, NE 68102-1832. gocc@accessomaha.com, cburke@accessomaha.com, http://www.omahachamber.net, http://www.accessomaha.com. Ed. Elizabeth Perry. Circ: 5,000 (free).

PROVINCIA DI FORLI IN CIFRE. see *BUSINESS AND ECONOMICS—Economic Situation And Conditions*

381   USA   ISSN 0033-6068
HF296
QUEENSBOROUGH. Text in English. 1914. a. USD 200 to members. adv. illus. **Document type:** *Newsletter.*
Published by: Queens Chamber of Commerce, 75-20 Astoria Blvd., Ste. 140, Jackson Heights, NY 11370. TEL 718-898-8500, FAX 718-898-8599, http://www.queenschamber.org. Ed., R&P Eric P Robinson. Pub. Lucy Nunziato. Adv. contact Marilyn McAndrews. Circ: 1,500.

R C G A'S DIRECTORY OF ST. LOUIS LARGE EMPLOYERS. see *BUSINESS AND ECONOMICS—Trade And Industrial Directories*

945   ITA
RASSEGNA ECONOMICA DELLA PROVINCIA DI SONDRIO. Text in Italian. 1948. bi-m. adv. bk.rev.
Published by: Camera di Commercio Industria Artigianato e Agricoltura di Sondrio, Sondrio, SO 23100, Italy. Circ: 7,000.

380.1   FRA   ISSN 0223-5730
REALITES FRANC-COMTOISES. Text in French. 1957. m. FRF 300 (effective 2000). adv. **Document type:** *Trade.*
Indexed: PAIS.
Published by: Chambre de Commerce et d'Industrie du Doubs, 46 av. Villarceau, Besancon, Cedex 25042, France. TEL 33-3-81252525, FAX 33-3-81252500, http://www.doubs.cci.fr. Ed. David Patrice. Adv. contact P M Conseil. Circ: 3,500.

946.9   ESP
REPERTORIO DE EXPORTADORES. Text in Spanish. 1942. s-a. adv.
Formerly: Catalogo de Exportadores
Published by: Camara Oficial de Comercio Industria y Navegacion de Valencia, Poeta Querol, 15, Valencia, 46002, Spain.

946.9   ESP
REPERTORIO DE IMPORTADORES. Text in Spanish. 1982. s-a.
Formerly: Catalogo de Importadores
Published by: Camara Oficial de Comercio Industria y Navegacion de Valencia, Poeta Querol, 15, Valencia, 46002, Spain. TEL 34-6-3511301, FAX 34-6-3516349.

382   COL
REVISTA SUIZA. Text in French, German, Spanish. 1985. q. free. adv. **Document type:** *Trade.* **Description:** Covers the economic situations of Switzerland and Colombia.
Former titles (until 1993): Bitacora Colombo Suizo; Circulo Colombo Suizo. Boletin Informativo
Published by: Camara de Comercio Colombo Suiza, Apartado Aereo 11232, Bogota, CUND, Colombia. TEL 57-1-288-5079, FAX 57-1-316-7590, suizacam@colomsat.net.co. Ed. Jacqueline Made.

382   FRA   ISSN 0753-3098
REVUE DE PRESSE ET DE DOCUMENTATION ALLEMANDE. Text in French. m.
Published by: Chambre Regionale de Commerce et d'Industrie d'Alsace, 42 rue Schweighaeuser, Strasbourg, 67000, France. TEL 33-3-88607475, FAX 33-3-88615354.

971   CAN
REVUE ECONOMIQUE. Text in English. 1984. 3/yr. adv. reprints avail. **Document type:** *Trade.*
Published by: Chambre de Commerce de Laval, 1555 Chomedy Blvd, Ste 200, Laval, PQ H7V 3Z1, Canada. TEL 514-682-5255, FAX 514-682-5735. Ed. Roger Desautels. Circ: 17,712.

382   FRA
REVUE ECONOMIQUE SUISSE EN FRANCE. Text in French. 1920. q. adv. bibl.; illus. index.
Formerly (until 1996): Revue Economique Franco Suisse (0035-2799)
Indexed: ELLIS, PAIS, RASB.
—BLDSC (7898.850000).
Published by: Chambre de Commerce Suisse en France, 10 rue des Messageries, Paris, 75010, France. TEL 33-1-48010077, FAX 33-1-48010575. Ed. Olivier Julliard. Adv. contact Dominique Barue.

338.9   FRA   ISSN 0080-2506
REVUE FRANCAISE DE COOPERATION ECONOMIQUE AVEC ISRAEL. Text in French. 1969. bi-m. bk.rev. **Document type:** *Directory, Trade.*
Formerly (until 1969): Revue Economique France-Israel
Published by: Chambre de Commerce France-Israel, 64 av. Marceau, Paris, 75008, France. TEL 33-1-44433506, FAX 33-1-44433500, ccfi@wanadoo.fr. Ed. L Stoleru. R&P, Adv. contact Eric Chicheportiche. Circ: 5,000.

956.95   JOR
RISALAT AL SINA'A/AMMAN CHAMBER OF INDUSTRY. BIMONTHLY INDUSTRIAL BULLETIN. Text in Arabic. bi-m. USD 24. adv. **Description:** Reviews legislation, regulations, statistics, and information concerning industry and trade opportunities.
Published by: Amman Chamber of Industry, P O Box 1800, Amman, Jordan. TEL 643001, FAX 647852, TELEX 22079 INDUST JO. Circ: 1,750.

382   CHE
RIVISTA DEGLI SCAMBI ITALO-SVIZZERI∗ . Text in Italian. m.
Published by: Zuericher Handelskammer, Boersengebaeude, Bleicherweg 5, Postfach 4031, Zuerich, 8022, Switzerland. TEL 1-471080, TELEX 57509 COMITALIA.

670.29   USA
(YEAR) ROANOKE METROPOLITAN AREA INDUSTRIAL DIRECTORY. Text in English. q. USD 12 (effective 2000). **Document type:** *Directory.*
Former titles: Roanoke Regional Chamber of Commerce. Industrial Directory; Roanoke Valley Chamber of Commerce. Industrial Directory
Published by: Roanoke Regional Chamber of Commerce, 212 S Jefferson St, Roanoke, VA 24011. TEL 540-983-0700, FAX 540-983-0723, business@roanokechamber.org, http://www.roanokechamber.org. Ed. Linda Scarborough. Circ: 2,000.

380   USA   ISSN 0036-293X
HC108.S2
ST. LOUIS COMMERCE MAGAZINE. Text in English. 1918. m. USD 30 (effective 2005). adv. illus. reprint service avail. from PQC. **Document type:** *Newsletter, Consumer.*
Formerly: St. Louis Commerce
Related titles: Microform ed.: (from PQC); Online - full text ed.: (from Northern Light Technology, Inc.).
Indexed: BusDate, PAIS.
Published by: (St. Louis Regional Chamber & Growth Association), Commerce Magazine, Inc., 1 Metropolitan Sq, Ste 1300, St Louis, MO 63102-2733. TEL 314-231-5555, FAX 314-206-3222, cschwab@stlrcga.org, http://www.stlcommercemagazine.com. Ed. Carol Schwab. Pubs. Richard C D Fleming, Richard C.D. Flemming. Adv. contacts Gloria Jarvis, Gloria Jarvis. Circ: 11,000.

330   AUT   ISSN 0036-3677
SALZBURGER WIRTSCHAFT. Text in German. 1947. w. adv. bk.rev. **Document type:** *Journal, Government.*
Published by: Wirtschaftskammer Salzburg, Julius Raab Platz 1, Salzburg, Sa 5027, Austria. TEL 43-662-8888346, FAX 43-662-878513, wirtschaftskammer@wks.at, at/sbg. Ed. Kurt Oberholzer. Circ: 36,000.

954   IND
SAMRUDDHI. Text in English. m.
Published by: Southern Gujarat Chamber of Commerce and Industry, Samruddhi, Nanpura, Surat, Gujarat 395 001, India.

SAN FRANCISCO COUNTY COMMERCE AND INDUSTRY DIRECTORY. see *BUSINESS AND ECONOMICS—Trade And Industrial Directories*

SAN MATEO COUNTY COMMERCE AND INDUSTRY DIRECTORY. see *BUSINESS AND ECONOMICS—Trade And Industrial Directories*

SANTA CLARA COUNTY COMMERCE AND INDUSTRY DIRECTORY. see *BUSINESS AND ECONOMICS—Trade And Industrial Directories*

382   BRA
SAO PAULO YEARBOOK. Text in Portuguese. 1946. a. USD 175 (effective 1997). adv.
Published by: American Chamber of Commerce for Brazil, Praca Pio X, 15 Andar 5, Centro, Caixa Postal 916, Rio De Janeiro, RJ 20040-020, Brazil. TEL 55-21-2032477, achambr@amchamrio.com.br, http://www.amchamrio.com.br. Ed. Elizabeth Mortlock. Circ: 4,500.

330   ITA   ISSN 0036-4770
SARDEGNA ECONOMICA. Text in Italian. 1963. bi-m. free (effective 2005). adv. illus. **Document type:** *Magazine, Consumer.*
Indexed: PAIS.
Published by: Camera di Commercio di Cagliari, Largo Felice 72, Cagliari, 09124, Italy. TEL 39-070-605121, FAX 39-070-60512435, http://www.ca.camcom.it. Ed. A Petti.

380   GBR
SCOTLAND CHAMBERS OF COMMERCE. NATIONAL DIRECTORY. Text in English. a. GBP 48. adv. index. **Document type:** *Directory.*
Former titles: Glasgow Chamber of Commerce. Directory; Glasgow Chamber of Commerce. Regional Directory; Glasgow Chamber of Commerce. Industrial Index to Glasgow and West of Scotland
Published by: Glasgow Chamber of Commerce, 30 George Sq, Glasgow, G2 1EQ, United Kingdom. TEL 44-141-204-2121, FAX 44-141-221-2336. Circ: 10,000.

941   GBR
SCOTTISH CHAMBERS OF COMMERCE NATIONAL DIRECTORY. Text in English. 1948. a. GBP 85 (effective 2001). **Document type:** *Directory.*
Formerly (until 1984): Glasgow Chamber of Commerce and Manufactures Regional Directory (0260-0641)
Published by: (Scottish Chambers of Commerce), Kemps Publishing Ltd., 11 Swan Courtyard, Charles Edward Rd, Birmingham, W Mids B26 1BU, United Kingdom. TEL 44-121-765-4144, FAX 44-121-706-6210.

382   GBR   ISSN 1369-4065
SCOTTISH COUNCIL DEVELOPMENT AND INDUSTRY. ANNUAL REPORT AND ACCOUNTS. Text in English. 1947. a. **Document type:** *Corporate.*
Formerly (until 1996): Scottish Council Development and Industry. Annual Report (0307-4900)
Published by: Scottish Council Development and Industry, 23 Chester St, Edinburgh, EH3 7ET, United Kingdom. TEL 44-131-225-7911, FAX 44-131-220-2116.

SHARJAH COMMERCIAL DIRECTORY/DALIL AL-SHARQAH AL-TIJARI. see *BUSINESS AND ECONOMICS—Trade And Industrial Directories*

SHARJAH EXPORTER - IMPORTER DIRECTORY/DALEEL AL SARIQAH LIL MOSADDIREEN WA AL-MOSTAWRIDEEN. see *BUSINESS AND ECONOMICS—Trade And Industrial Directories*

954.9   PAK
SHIPPERS' DIGEST. Text in English. bi-w.
Published by: Federation of Pakistan Chambers of Commerce and Industry, Sharea Firdousi, Main Clifton, PO Box 13875, Karachi, 75600, Pakistan. TEL 534621, TELEX 25370 FEDCOMERC.

959.52   SGP   ISSN 0129-5179
SHOWCASE. Text in English. 1975. a.
Published by: Hagley & Hoyle Pte. Ltd., 70 Shenton Way, 03-03 Marina House, Singapore, 079118, Singapore. TEL 2240688, FAX 2246998.

382   SGP
SINGAPORE INDIAN CHAMBER OF COMMERCE. CIRCULARS. Text in English. m.
Published by: Singapore Indian Chamber of Commerce, 101 Cecil St, 23-01 Tong Eng Bldg, Singapore, 069533, Singapore. FAX 65-223-1707.

382   SGP   ISSN 0037-5659
HC445.8.A1
SINGAPORE INTERNATIONAL CHAMBER OF COMMERCE. ECONOMIC BULLETIN. Text in English. 1960. m. SGD 98 (effective 1999). adv. charts; mkt.; stat.; tr.lit. **Document type:** *Bulletin.* **Description:** Provides business features and regional news of interest as well as the latest available trade statistics and trade enquiries to businessmen and industrialists.
Indexed: APEL, PAIS.
Published by: Singapore International Chamber of Commerce, John Hancock Tower, 6 Raffles Quay 10-01, Singapore, 048580, Singapore. TEL 65-2241255, FAX 65-2242785, singicc@asianconnect.com, http://www.sicc.com.sg. Circ: 3,200.

382   SGP   ISSN 0377-449X
HF331.S58
SINGAPORE INTERNATIONAL CHAMBER OF COMMERCE. REPORT. Text in English. 1837. a. SGD 29 per issue. stat. **Document type:** *Corporate.* **Description:** Reviews the performance of various sectors of the Singapore economy each year.
Published by: Singapore International Chamber of Commerce, John Hancock Tower, 6 Raffles Quay 10-01, Singapore, 048580, Singapore. TEL 65-2241255, FAX 65-2242785, singicc@asianconnect.com, http://www.sicc.com.sg. Circ: 1,400.

949.4   CHE
SOLOTHURNISCHE HANDELSKAMMER. JAHRESBERICHT. Text in German. a. **Document type:** *Bulletin.*
Published by: Solothurnische Handelskammer, Grabackerstr 6, Solothurn, 4502, Switzerland. TEL 41-32-6262424, FAX 41-32-6262426.

949.4   CHE
SOLOTHURNISCHE HANDELSKAMMER. MITTEILUNGEN. Text in German. bi-m. **Document type:** *Bulletin.*
Published by: Solothurnische Handelskammer, Grabackerstr 6, Solothurn, 4502, Switzerland. TEL 41-32-6262424, FAX 41-32-6262426.

338   AUS   ISSN 0818-4674
SOUTH AUSTRALIA IN BUSINESS. Text in English. 1911. m. AUD 30. adv. bk.rev. illus.
Formerly: Journal of Industry (0022-1872)
Indexed: BAS, CISA.
Published by: Chamber of Commerce & Industry S.A. Inc., Entreprise House, 136 Greenhill Rd, Unley, SA 5061, Australia. TEL 08-373-1422, FAX 08-272-9662. Ed. Ian Dove. Circ: 4,500.

382 GBR
SOUTH WALES BUSINESS DIRECTORY. Text in English. a. GBP 50 (effective 2001). **Document type:** *Directory.*
Former titles: Wales Business Directory; Available from Wales
Published by: (South Wales Chambers of Commerce Inc.), Kemps Publishing Ltd., 11 Swan Courtyard, Charles Edward Rd, Birmingham, W Mids B26 1BU, United Kingdom. TEL 44-121-765-4144, FAX 44-121-706-6210.

338 GBR
SOUTHAMPTON AND FAREHAM CHAMBER OF COMMERCE AND INDUSTRY DIRECTORY. Text in English. a. GBP 70 (effective 2001). **Document type:** *Directory.* **Description:** Directory of business in the Southampton area. Includes local chamber news, membership lists and classified section.
Former titles: Confederation of Chambers of Commerce Central Southern England Directory; Southampton Chamber of Commerce Regional Directory
Published by: Kemps Publishing Ltd., 11 Swan Courtyard, Charles Edward Rd, Birmingham, W Mids B26 1BU, United Kingdom. TEL 44-121-765-4144, FAX 44-121-706-6210.

381.06 USA
SOUTHEAST TEXAS BUSINESS MONTHLY. Text in English. m. USD 25; free domestic to members (effective 2004). adv. **Document type:** *Magazine, Consumer.*
Published by: Beaumont Chamber of Commerce, PO Box 3150, Beaumont, TX 77704. TEL 409-838-2816, FAX 409-838-2865, http://www.beaumontenterprise.com. Ed. David Pero.

SOUTHERN CALIFORNIA BUSINESS DIRECTORY AND BUYERS GUIDE. see *BUSINESS AND ECONOMICS—Trade And Industrial Directories*

SPAIN: THE BUSINESS LINK. see *BUSINESS AND ECONOMICS—International Commerce*

382 AUS
SPANISH OFFICIAL CHAMBER OF COMMERCE IN AUSTRALIA. SPANISH - AUSTRALIAN TRADE. Text in English. q. AUD 150. adv. **Document type:** *Newsletter.*
Published by: Spanish Official Chamber of Commerce in Australia, Ste. 205, Edgecliff Centre, 203 New South Head Rd, Edgecliff, NSW 2027, Australia. TEL 61-2-3623168, FAX 61-2-3624074. Ed., Pub., R&P, Adv. contact Sara Lopez.

380 ITA ISSN 0391-7983
LA SPEZIA OGGI. Text in Italian. 1946. m. bk.rev. stat.
Former titles (until 1972): Rassegna Commerciale della Spezia (1128-7349); (until 1952): Rassegna Commerciale (0033-9350)
Published by: Camera di Commercio Industria Artigianato e Agricoltura della Spezia, Via Vittorio Veneto, 28, La Spezia, SP 19124, Italy. Ed. Pier E Macchiavelli. Circ: 1,200.

380.1 USA
SPOKANE AREA CHAMBER OF COMMERCE. DIRECTORY OF ORGANIZATIONS. Text in English. a. USD 20 to non-members; USD 12 to members. **Document type:** *Directory.* **Description:** Lists more than 400 social, fraternal, patriotic, and service organizations in Spokane, WA.
Published by: Spokane Area Chamber of Commerce, PO Box 2147, Spokane, WA 99210. TEL 509-624-1393, FAX 509-747-0077, http://www.spokane.org.

380.1 USA ISSN 1074-3065
SPOKANE BUSINESS INTERACTION. Text in English. 1924. m. USD 25 to non-members. adv. bk.rev. illus.; stat. **Document type:** *Newsletter.* **Description:** Focuses on public meetings, business affairs seminars, political issues and new members.
Formerly (until 1994): Spokane Affairs (0038-7681)
Published by: (Marketing Department), Spokane Area Chamber of Commerce, PO Box 2147, Spokane, WA 99210. TEL 509-624-1393, FAX 509-747-0077, http://www.spokane.org. Ed. Stacy Baker. Circ: 4,000.

381 LKA
SRI LANKA IN BRIEF. Text in English. 1977. a. USD 8.
Published by: Ceylon Chamber of Commerce, Chamber of Commerce Bldg., P O Box 274, Colombo, 2, Sri Lanka. FAX 941-449352.

382 DEU
SUEDTHUERINGISCHE WIRTSCHAFT. Text in German. 1990. 9/yr. adv. **Document type:** *Magazine, Trade.*
Published by: (Industrie- und Handelskammer Suedthueringen), V H I Verlagsgesellschaft fuer Handel und Industrie, Mauergasse 4a, Meiningen, 98617, Germany. TEL 49-3693-847412, FAX 49-3693-847415. adv.: B&W page EUR 1,210, color page EUR 1,620; trim 185 x 255. Circ: 13,300 (controlled).

330 DEU ISSN 0039-4637
SUEDWESTFAELISCHE WIRTSCHAFT. Text in German. 1964. m. adv. bk.rev. abstr.; bibl.; charts; illus.; stat. index.
Published by: (Suedwestfaelische Industrie- und Handelskammer zu Hagen), V.D. Linnepe Verlagsgesellschaft KG, Bahnhofstr 28, Hagen, 58119, Germany. TEL 02331-32078, FAX 02331-32090. Circ: 1,000.

990 AUS ISSN 1039-4761
SURVEY OF AUSTRALIAN MANUFACTURING. Text in English. 1980. q. AUD 143 to members; AUD 165 to non-members; AUD 38.50 per issue to members; AUD 44 per issue to non-members (effective 2004). back issues avail. **Document type:** *Trade.* **Description:** Trends in Australian manufacturing.
Former titles: Survey of Victorian Manufacturing (1033-9094); (until 1988): Pulse Survey of Victorian Manufacturing (0158-9857)
Published by: Australian Industry Group, 20 Queens Rd, Melbourne, VIC 8004, Australia. TEL 61-3-98670111, FAX 61-3-98670199, helpdesk@aigroup.asn.au, http://www.aigroup.asn.au/. Ed. Tony Pensabene. Circ: 250.

380 USA ISSN 0069-2441
HF294
SURVEY OF LOCAL CHAMBERS OF COMMERCE. Text in English. a. USD 55 to non-members; USD 45 to members (effective 1999). **Document type:** *Trade.* **Description:** Examines income sources, staff salaries and staff benefits.
Indexed: SRI.
Published by: Chamber of Commerce of the U.S., 1615 H St, N W, Washington, DC 20062. TEL 202-463-5580. Ed. Richard Loomis.

382 ITA
SVIZZERA INDUSTRIALE E COMMERCIALE. Text in Italian. 1938. m. (11/yr.). free to members. adv. **Document type:** *Magazine, Consumer.*
Published by: Camera di Commercio Svizzera in Italia/Swiss Chamber of Commerce in Italy, Via Palestro 2, Milan, 20121, Italy. http://www.ccsi.it/. Ed. Bernardo Cerutti. Circ: 2,500.

949.2 NLD
SWISS MATE. Text in Dutch. q.
Published by: Zwitserse Kamer van Koophandel in Nederland, Koningsplein 11, Amsterdam, 1017 BB, Netherlands. TEL 249436.

382 JPN
SWISS MINUTES. Text in Japanese. 3/yr. membership only. **Document type:** *Newsletter.*
Formerly: Swiss Chamber of Commerce and Industry in Japan. Newsletter
Published by: Swiss Chamber of Commerce and Industry in Japan/Zainichi Suisu Shoko Kaigisho, Toranomon No2 Waiko Bldg, 2-6 Toranomon 5-chome Minato-ku, Tokyo, 105-0001, Japan. TEL 81-3-5408-7569, FAX 81-3-3433-6066, sccij@gol.com, http://www.gol.com/swiss/.

380.1 USA
TACOMA - PIERCE COUNTY CHAMBER OF COMMERCE UPDATE. Text in English. 1926. m. USD 25 (effective 2000). adv. bk.rev. **Document type:** *Newsletter.* **Description:** Features information of community and business issues as well as chamber programs and activities.
Formerly: Tacoma Area Progress
Published by: Tacoma-Pierce County Chamber of Commerce, 950 Pacific Ave, Ste 300, Box 1933, Tacoma, WA 98401. TEL 253-627-2175, FAX 253-597-7305. Ed., R&P Dennis Johnson. Adv. contact Judie Latham Lloyd. Circ: 3,500 (controlled).

951.9 KOR
TAEGU CHAMBER OF COMMERCE AND INDUSTRY. MONTHLY. Text in Korean. m.
Published by: Taegu Chamber of Commerce and Industry, 107, 3-gu Sincheon-dong, Dong-gu, Taegu, 635, Korea, S. TEL 053-730041-6, TELEX 54343.

954 IND
TAMIL CHAMBER OF COMMERCE. JOURNAL*. Text in English. bi-m.
Published by: Tamil Chamber of Commerce, c/o Madras Chamber of Commerce, Karumuttu Centre, 498 Anna Salai, Chennai, Tamil Nadu 600 035, India.

382 AUS
TASMANIAN BUSINESS REPORTER. Text in English. 1981. m. adv. **Document type:** *Newspaper.* **Description:** Aims to accurately inform business management about current trends, government action affecting business, new products, marketing trends, overseas news, real estate, the computer world, trade appointments, people in the news, import-export opportunities, transport and travel.
Formerly: T C I News
Published by: Tasmanian Chamber of Commerce and Industry, GPO Box 793 H, Hobart, TAS 7001, Australia. TEL 61-3-6234-5933, FAX 61-3-6231-1278, admin@tcci.org.au. Ed., R&P Heidi Murphy. Adv. contact Dong Williams. Circ: 16,400 (controlled).

382 THA ISSN 0125-0191
THAI-AMERICAN BUSINESS. Text in Thai. 1967. bi-m. THB 400, USD 20. adv. illus.
Formerly: American Chamber of Commerce in Thailand. Review (0002-7855)
Published by: American Chamber of Commerce in Thailand, 140 Wireless Rd, Bangkok, Thailand. Ed. Tom Seale. Circ: 3,000.

382.029 THA
THAI CHAMBER OF COMMERCE. DIRECTORY (YEAR). Text in English. a. USD 40 per issue. illus. **Document type:** *Directory.* **Description:** Covers the member companies of Thai Chamber of Commerce, including company profiles and a view on Thai economy.
Former titles: Thai Chamber of Commerce. Handbook (Year); (until 1983): Thai Chamber of Commerce. Business Directory (0563-3400)
Published by: (Thai Chamber of Commerce), Cosmic Group of Companies, 4th Fl Phyathai Bldg, Rajthevi, 31 Phyathai Rd, Bangkok, 10400, Thailand. TEL 662-2453850, FAX 662-2461710. adv.: color page USD 1,200. Circ: 5,000 (controlled).

954 THA
THAI CHAMBER OF COMMERCE. JOURNAL. Text in Thai, English. m.
Published by: (Thai Chamber of Commerce), Bamrung Nukoulkit Press, 83 Bamrung Muang Rd, Bangkok, Thailand. Ed. L Chara.

382 959.3 THA
THAI - CHINESE CHAMBER OF COMMERCE. NEWS. Variant title: Chamber News. Text in Thai. q.
Published by: Thai - Chinese Chamber of Commerce, 233 South Sathorn Rd, Bangkok, Thailand.

382.029 THA
THAI-KOREAN CHAMBER OF COMMERCE HANDBOOK & DIRECTORY. Text in English. 1995. a. adv. illus. **Document type:** *Directory.* **Description:** Covers the member companies of Thai-Korean Chamber of Commerce, including company profiles and a view on the Thai and Korean economies.
Published by: Cosmic Group of Companies, 4th Fl Phyathai Bldg, Rajthevi, 31 Phyathai Rd, Bangkok, 10400, Thailand. TEL 662-2453850, FAX 662-2461710. adv.: color page USD 1,000. Circ: 2,000 (controlled).

382 GBR
THAMES VALLEY CHAMBER OF COMMERCE AND INDUSTRY MEMBER'S DIRECTORY. Text in English. a. GBP 75 (effective 2001). adv. illus.; tr.lit. **Document type:** *Directory.*
Former titles: Thames Valley Business Directory; Thames Valley Chamber of Commerce and Industry Directory; Thames-Chiltern Chamber of Commerce and Industry Directory; South Bucks and East Berks Chamber of Commerce and Industry Directory
Published by: (Thames Valley Chamber of Commerce & Industry), Kemps Publishing Ltd., 11 Swan Courtyard, Charles Edward Rd, Birmingham, W Mids B26 1BU, United Kingdom. TEL 44-121-765-4144, FAX 44-121-706-6210.

380.1 USA
THE/CHAMBER VOICE. Text in English. 1923. q. free; USD 17.34 subscr - mailed (effective 2005). adv. bk.rev. charts; illus.; stat. **Document type:** *Newspaper.*
Former titles (until 2005): Southern California Business Trends (1098-9692); (until 2004): Southern California Business (0038-3880)
Related titles: Microfilm ed.: (from LIB); Online - full text ed.: (from Gale Group, Northern Light Technology, Inc., ProQuest Information & Learning).
Indexed: BusDate.
Published by: Los Angeles Area Chamber of Commerce, 350 S Bixel St, Los Angeles, CA 90017. TEL 213-580-7571, FAX 213-580-7586. Ed. Marie O Condron. Circ: 10,000 (controlled).

338 380 DEU ISSN 0945-2397
THEMA WIRTSCHAFT. Text in German. 1945. 11/yr. EUR 28.60; EUR 2.60 newsstand/cover (effective 2005). adv. bk.rev. charts; illus.; stat. index. **Document type:** *Magazine, Trade.*
Former titles (until 1993): NiederrheinKammer (0174-5700); (until 1977): Niederrheinishe Industrie- und Handelskammer Duisberg Wesel zu Duisberg. Wirtschaftliche Mitteilungen (0028-9752); Niederrheinische Industrie- und Handelskammer Duisberg Wesel. Mitteilungen (0174-5719)
Published by: (Niederrheinische Industrie- und Handelskammer Duisburg - Wesel - Kleve zu Duisburg), Neusser Druckerei und Verlag GmbH, Moselstr 14, Neuss, 41464, Germany. TEL 49-2131-40402, FAX 49-2131-404283, info@ndv.de, http://www.ndv.de. Ed. Markus Vorpeil. Adv. contact Wolfgang Hoewener. B&W page EUR 2,664; trim 185 x 260. Circ: 43,000 (paid and controlled).

953 UAE
AL-TIJARAH. Text in Arabic, English. 1971. m. USD 85 in the Middle East; USD 145 elsewhere (effective 2001). adv. **Description:** Discusses chamber activities and related news affecting economic development in Sharjah, al-Dhaid, Khor Fakkan and Kalba, as well as regional and international development issues.
Published by: Sharjah Chamber of Commerce and Industry, P O Box 580, Sharjah, United Arab Emirates. TEL 971-6-5088600, FAX 971-6-5541119, scci@sharjah.gov.ae, http://www.sharjah.gov.ae. Ed. Ahmed Mohamed Al-Midfa'a. R&P Saeed O Al Jarwan. Adv. contact Saeed Al Najjar. Circ: 50,000.

382 SAU
AL-TIJARAH (JEDDAH). Text in Arabic. 1960. m.

Published by: Jeddah Chamber of Commerce and Industry, P O Box 1264, Jeddah, Saudi Arabia. TEL 966-2-4711000, FAX 966-2-6484603. Ed. Abdullah S Dahlan. Circ: 8,000.

944 FRA ISSN 1637-9837
TOURAINE ECONOMIQUE. Text in French. 9/yr. adv. illus. **Document type:** *Trade.*
Published by: Chambre de Commerce et d'Industrie de Touraine, B.P. 1028, Tours, Cedex 1 37010, France. TEL 33-2-47472022, TELEX CHAMCO-TOURS 750 020. Ed. Laurent Blain. Pub. Pascal Rivet. Circ: 16,000.

961 ETH
TRADE FOCUS. Text in English. q.
Published by: Addis Ababa Chamber of Commerce, c/o Ethiopian Chamber of Commerce, PO Box 517, Addis Ababa, Ethiopia. Ed. Solomon Asfaon.

382.029 TWN
TRADE OPPORTUNITY. Text in Chinese. 35/yr.
Published by: Chinese National Association of Industry and Commerce, 4th Fl, No 7 Roosevelt Rd, Sec 1, Taipei, Taiwan.

TRADE UNIONS INTERNATIONAL OF CHEMICAL, OIL AND ALLIED WORKERS. INFORMATION BULLETIN. see *LABOR UNIONS*

382 GRC ISSN 0041-0543
HF37.G7
TRADE WITH GREECE. Text in English. 1959. q. free. adv. illus.; mkt.; stat.; tr.mk.; charts. 100 p./no. 3 cols./p.; back issues avail. **Document type:** *Magazine, Trade.*
Incorporates: Data from the Greek Economic Life (0007-4462)
Related titles: Online - full text ed.
Indexed: KES, PROMT, RASB, RefZh.
—BLDSC (8880.580000).
Published by: Athens Chamber of Commerce and Industry, 7 Akadimias St, Athens, 106 71, Greece. TEL 30-210-3604815, FAX 30-210-3616464, info@acci.gr, http://www.acci.gr/trade. Ed. Theodore Vamvakaris. Pub. Drakoulis Fountoukakos. R&P Panagiotis Koutsikos. Adv. contact Spyros Zervos TEL 3-01-3615149. Circ: 4,000 (controlled).

382 USA ISSN 0041-0551
HF1
TRADE WITH ITALY. Text in English. 1946. bi-m. USD 60 (effective 2000). adv. bk.rev. charts; illus.; mkt. index. **Document type:** *Trade.*
Published by: Italy - America Chamber of Commerce, Inc., 730 Fifth Ave, New York, NY 10019. TEL 212-459-0044, FAX 212-459-0090. Ed., Pub. Franco De Angelis. R&P, Adv. contact Federico Zozzi. Circ: 4,000.

974 USA ISSN 0893-2107
U K & U S A; the British-American magazine. Text in English. 1987. q. USD 30. bk.rev. stat. 44 p./no.; **Document type:** *Magazine, Consumer.* **Description:** Subjects of interest to Anglo-American business people.
Published by: (British - American Chamber of Commerce), Forbes Custom Communications Partners, 38 Newbury St, 5th Fl, Boston, MA 02116. TEL 617-437-9977, 617-638-9020, FAX 617-437-0196, frontdesk@custcomm.com, http://www.babinc.org/memberservices/mn_uk_usa.html, http://www.custcomm.com/. Ed. Christine Verdi TEL 212-367-4135. R&P Maria Allen TEL 212-661-4060. Adv. contact Julia Scheel TEL 212-367-4117. Circ: 12,000.

382.029 GBR
HF54.G7
U K - U S TRADE DIRECTORY (YEAR). Text in English. 1916. a. GBP 90, USD 170. adv. **Document type:** *Directory.* **Description:** Lists more than 18,000 British and American companies that have transatlantic business links with each other.
Formerly (until 1996): Anglo-American Trade Directory (Year) (0066-1813)
Published by: American Chamber of Commerce (UK), 75 Brook St, London, W1Y 2EB, United Kingdom. TEL 44-171-493-0381, FAX 44-171-493-2394, TELEX 23675 AMCHAM G, acc@amcham.demon.co.uk. Ed. Shahpari Dolatshahi.

U.S. CHAMBER OF COMMERCE. (YEAR) EMPLOYEE BENEFITS STUDY. see *BUSINESS AND ECONOMICS—Personnel Management*

381 USA
U.S. CHAMBER OF COMMERCE. ASSOCIATION AGENDA. Text in English. 1958. m. **Document type:** *Newsletter.* **Description:** Contains news and information of interest to members.
Formerly: U.S. Chamber of Commerce. Chamber Memo
Published by: U.S. Chamber of Commerce, Business Information and Development Dept., 1615 H St N W, Washington, DC 20062-2000. TEL 202-463-5560, FAX 202-463-3190. Ed. Gary A Labranche. Circ: 1,200 (controlled).

U S FIRMS IN GERMANY/AMERIKANISCHE UNTERNEHMEN IN DEUTSCHLAND. see *BUSINESS AND ECONOMICS—Trade And Industrial Directories*

950 NPL
UDYOG BANIHYA PATRIKA. Text in Nepali. 1967. s-a. USD 3.50. adv. bk.rev. **Document type:** *Newsletter.*
Published by: Federation of Nepalese Chambers of Commerce and Industry, Teku, P O Box 269, Kathmandu, Nepal. TEL 977-1-262061, FAX 977-1-261022, fincci@mos.com.np, fncci@mos.com.np. Ed. Rameshwor Acharya. R&P Rameswar Acharya. Circ: 1,000.

974 USA
UNITED STATES COUNCIL FOR INTERNATIONAL BUSINESS. NEWSLETTER. Text in English. bi-m. **Document type:** *Newsletter.*
Published by: United States Council for International Business, 1212 Ave of the Americas, New York, NY 10036. TEL 212-354-4480, FAX 212-575-0327. Ed. Christina Sherchik.

382 USA
UNITED STATES - GERMAN ECONOMIC YEARBOOK (YEAR). Text in English. a. USD 50 (effective 2005). adv. **Document type:** *Magazine, Trade.* **Description:** Provides an in-depth view of U.S.-German politics, economics and finance.
Related titles: German ed.: Deutsch - Amerikanisches Wirtschaftsjahrbunch (Year).
Indexed: SRI.
Published by: German American Chamber of Commerce, 12 E 49th St, 24th Fl, New York, NY 10017. TEL 212-974-8830, FAX 212-974-8867, info@gaccny.com, http://www.gaccny.com. Ed. Richard Jacob. Adv. contact Benigna Kirsten.

UNITED STATES - ITALY TRADE DIRECTORY. see *BUSINESS AND ECONOMICS—Trade And Industrial Directories*

382 THA
UP-DATE. Text in Thai. q. USD 75 in United States. adv. charts; illus.; stat. **Document type:** *Bulletin.* **Description:** For members of the German-Thai Chamber of Commerce as internal news bulletin giving internal news as well as articles of more general interest.
Published by: (German-Thai Chamber of Commerce), Chamber Publications LP, 25th Fl, Empire Tower 3, 195 S Sathorn Rd, Bangkok, 10120, Thailand. TEL 662-6700-600, FAX 662-6700-601, ahkbkk@box1.a-net.net.th, http://www.gtcc.org. Ed., Pub. Paul Strunk. R&P Stefan Buerkle. Adv. contact Eupaporn S Ayuthaya. Circ: 700.

330 USA ISSN 0732-3115
UPPER MIDWEST REPORT✶. Text in English. 1981 (vol.2). bi-m. free.
Published by: Upper Midwest Council, Federal Reserve Bank Bldg, PO Box 291, Minneapolis, MN 55480-0291. TEL 612-340-9666. Ed. Molly MacGregor.

989 URY
URUGUAY - INFO. Text in Spanish. m.
Published by: Camara de Comercio Uruguayo-Alemana/Deutsch-Uruguayische Handelskammer, Pza Independencia 831, Edificio Plaza Mayor, Montevideo, 11100, Uruguay. TEL 598-2-9007965, FAX 598-2-9085666, camural@ahkurug.com.uy. Ed. Sven Heldt.

330 IRN
UTAQ-I BAZARGANI VA SANAYI' VA MA'ADIN-I IRAN. HAFTAH'NAMAH. Text in English, Persian, Modern. 1970. w. **Document type:** *Trade.*
Published by: Iranian Chamber of Commerce, Industries and Mines, P O Box 15875-4671, Tehran, Iran.

943 DEU
V D C - NACHRICHTEN. Text in German. s-a.
Published by: Verband Deutscher Chemo Techniker und Chemisch - Technischer Association, Mulhauser Str 61, Kempen, 47906, Germany. TEL 02152 3503.

954 IND
VAIBHAV. Text in English. m.
Published by: Maharashtra Chamber of Commerce, 12 Rampart Row, Mumbai, Maharashtra 400 023, India. TEL 22-244548.

944 FRA ISSN 0994-1258
VENDEE MAGAZINE. Text in French. 1988. 11/yr.
Published by: P A M, 4 rue Marechal-Foch, La Roche-sur-Yon, 85000, France. TEL 51-36-34-37, FAX 51-46-03-56. Ed. Claude Grimaud. Circ: 11,000.

987 382 VEN
VENEZUELAN - AMERICAN CHAMBER OF COMMERCE AND INDUSTRY YEARBOOK. Text in Spanish. 1999. a. VEB 75, USD 90 (effective 1999). adv. **Description:** Consists of biographies of Venezuelan business leaders cross-indexed by product, service and trademark.
Published by: Venezuelan - American Chamber of Commerce and Industry/Camara Venezolano-Americana de Comercio e Industria, Torre Credival-PL., 2da Avenida de Campo Alegre, Caracas, DF 1010-A, Venezuela. TEL 58-2-2630833, FAX 58-2-2630586. Ed. Antonio Herrera Vaillant. Adv. contact Shalom Kivilevic.

382 VEN
VENEZUELAN - AMERICAN CHAMBER OF COMMERCE AND INDUSTRY. YEARBOOK AND MEMBERSHIP DIRECTORY. Text in Spanish. 1961. a. USD 75. adv. reprint service avail. from PQC. **Document type:** *Directory.*
Formerly: American Chamber of Commerce of Venezuela. Yearbook and Membership Directory (0065-7697)
Published by: Venezuelan - American Chamber of Commerce and Industry/Camara Venezolano-Americana de Comercio e Industria, Apdo 5181, Caracas, DF 1010-A, Venezuela. TEL 58-2-2630833, FAX 58-2-2631829, TELEX 28399. Circ: 5,000.

943 DEU
VERBAND ANGESTELLTER AKADEMIKER UND LEITENDER ANGESTELLTER DER CHEMISCHEN INDUSTRIE. INFO. Short title: Info. Text in German. 8/yr.
Published by: Verband Angestellter Akademiker und Leitender Angestellter der Chemischen Industrie, Kattenbug 2, Cologne, 50667, Germany.

945 ITA
VICENZA ECONOMICA. Text in Italian. m.
Published by: Camera di Commercio Industria Artigianato e Agricoltura di Vicenza, Corso Antonio Fogazzaro, 37, Vicenza, VI 36100, Italy. TEL 39-444-994811, FAX 39-444-994834.

944 FRA
VIE ECO SAONE ET LOIRE. Text in French. 8/yr.
Published by: J.P. Doiteau et Associes, 42 quai Joseph Gillet, Lyon, 69004, France. TEL 78-29-18-33, FAX 78-29-66-14. Circ: 8,000.

941.5 IRL
WATERFORD CHAMBER OF COMMERCE. NEWS LETTER. Text in English. 1997. q. adv. **Document type:** *Newsletter.*
Published by: Waterford Chamber of Commerce, George's St., Waterford, Ireland. TEL 353-51-872639, FAX 353-51-876002, waterfordchamber@tinet.ie. Ed. Frank O'Donognde.

381 GBR
WEST MERCIA BUSINESS DIRECTORY. Text in English. a. GBP 50 (effective 2001).
Published by: Kemps Publishing Ltd., 11 Swan Courtyard, Charles Edward Rd, Birmingham, W Mids B26 1BU, United Kingdom. TEL 44-121-765-4144, FAX 44-121-706-6210.

381 GBR
HF302
WEST MIDLANDS CHAMBER OF COMMERCE DIRECTORY. Text in English. 1905. a. GBP 90 (effective 2001). **Document type:** *Directory.*
Formerly: Birmingham & West Midlands Chamber of Commerce Directory (0307-0158)
Published by: (Birmingham Chamber of Industry & Commerce), Kemps Publishing Ltd., 11 Swan Courtyard, Charles Edward Rd, Birmingham, W Mids B26 1BU, United Kingdom. TEL 44-121-765-4144, FAX 44-121-706-6210.

975 USA
WEST VIRGINIA: AN ECONOMIC-STATISTICAL PROFILE. Text in English. 1982. irreg. (every 3-4 yrs). USD 26.19. stat. back issues avail. **Document type:** *Trade.*
Published by: West Virginia Chamber of Commerce, PO Box 2789, Charleston, WV 25330. TEL 304-342-1115. Circ: 1,500.

974 USA ISSN 0888-3459
WESTCHESTER COMMERCE; the official newsmagazine of the County Chamber of Commerce, Inc. Text in English. 1986. bi-m. USD 9.95 to non-members; USD 5 to members (effective 2001). adv. bk.rev. back issues avail. **Document type:** *Magazine, Consumer.* **Description:** Reports on business topics and issues of interest to County business and professional leaders.
Published by: (County Chamber of Commerce, Inc.), Suburban Publishing, Inc., 100 Clearbrook Rd, Elmsford, NY 10523. TEL 914-345-3055. Ed. John Jordan. Pub., Adv. contact John Seng TEL 914-592-0896. R&P Ralph Martinelli TEL 914-345-6726. B&W page USD 1,620, color page USD 2,395. Circ: 10,000 (controlled). **Subscr. to:** Westchester Commerce, 222 Mamaroneck Ave., Ste. 100, White Plains, NY 10605-1304. TEL 914-948-2110, FAX 914-948-0122.

380.1 SWE
WESTERN SWEDEN CHAMBER OF COMMERCE. MEMBERSHIP DIRECTORY. Text in Swedish. 1953. biennial. free. adv. **Document type:** *Directory.*
Former titles: Gothenburg and Western Sweden Chamber of Commerce. Membership Directory; Trade Directory of Western Sweden
Published by: Western Sweden Chamber of Commerce/ Vaestsvenska Handelskammaren, Fack 5253, Goeteborg, 40225, Sweden. TEL 46-31-835900, FAX 46-31-835936, TELEX 27430 GOTCHAM. Circ: 5,000.

382 DEU
WIRTSCHAFT. Text in German. m. EUR 28 (effective 2005). adv. **Document type:** *Journal, Trade.* **Description:** Covers local business news and events in the Saxony region of Germany.

▼ new title ➤ refereed ✶ unverified ♦ full entry avail.

Published by: (Industrie- und Handelskammer zu Leipzig), Leipziger Verlagsanstalt GmbH, Paul-Gruner-Str 62, Leipzig, 04107, Germany. TEL 49-341-678770, FAX 49-341-6787712, info@leipziger-verlagsanstalt.de, http://www.leipziger-verlagsanstalt.de.

943 DEU ISSN 0173-329X
WIRTSCHAFT AM BAYERISCHEN UNTERMAIN. Text in German. 1946. m. adv. bk.rev. back issues avail. **Document type:** *Corporate.*
Published by: Industrie- und Handelskammer Aschaffenburg, Kerschensteinerstr 9, Aschaffenburg, 63741, Germany. TEL 06021-880-117, FAX 06021-87981, TELEX 04188867. Ed. Juergen Parr. Circ: 15,000.

334 DEU ISSN 0724-4142
WIRTSCHAFT IM REVIER. Text in German. 1983. m. EUR 2.05 newsstand/cover (effective 2003). adv. **Document type:** *Magazine, Trade.*
Published by: Schuermann & Klagges GmbH & Co. KG, Industriestr 34, Bochum, 44894, Germany. TEL 49-234-92140, FAX 49-234-9214100, sk@skala.de, http://www.skala.de. adv.: B&W page EUR 1,841, color page EUR 3,806. Circ: 22,000 (controlled).

943.1 DEU
WIRTSCHAFT IM SUEDOESTLICHEN WESTFALEN. Text in German. m. adv. bk.rev. **Document type:** *Newsletter.*
Formerly (until 1993): Wirtschaft in Suedostwestfalen
Published by: Industrie- und Handelskammer fuer das Suedostliche Westfalen zu Arnsberg, Koenigstr 18-20, Arnsberg, 59821, Germany. TEL 02931-878154, FAX 02931-21427. Ed. Ralf Huess. Circ: 11,500.

943 DEU ISSN 0931-2196
WIRTSCHAFT IN BREMEN. Text in German. 1948. m. EUR 22.80; EUR 2.30 newsstand/cover (effective 2005). adv. **Document type:** *Magazine, Trade.*
Former titles (until 1986): Handelskammer Bremen. Nachrichten und Kommentare (0931-2188); (until 1968): Handelskammer Bremen. Mitteilungen (0520-8912)
Published by: (Handelskammer Bremen), Carl Ed. Schuenemann KG, Zweite Schlachpforte 7, Bremen, 28195, Germany. TEL 49-421-3690372, FAX 49-421-3690334, zeitschriften@schuenemann-verlag.de, http://www.schuenemann-verlag.de. Ed. Christine Backhaus. Adv. contact Karin Wachendorf. B&W page EUR 2,295, color page EUR 3,665; trim 190 x 261. Circ: 13,833 (paid).

381 DEU ISSN 1437-7071
WIRTSCHAFT IN MITTELFRANKEN. Text in German. 1944. m. EUR 24 (effective 2005). adv. bk.rev. **Document type:** *Magazine, Trade.*
Formerly (until 1997): Mittelfraenkische Wirtschaft (0949-4677)
Published by: (Industrie- und Handelskammer Nuernberg fuer Mittelfranken), Hofmann Druck Nuernberg GmbH & Co. KG, Postfach 120260, Nuernberg, 90402, Germany. TEL 49-911-52030, FAX 0911/5203148, sander@hofmann-infocom.de, http://www.ihk-nuernberg.de. Ed. Kurt Hesse. Pub. Guenter Hofmann. R&P Dieter Goessner. Adv. contact Ruediger Sander. page EUR 4,530; trim 188 x 260. Circ: 90,000 (controlled).

380 DEU ISSN 0938-8230
WIRTSCHAFT IN OSTWUERTTEMBERG. Text in German. 1970. m. EUR 25; EUR 2.30 newsstand/cover (effective 2004); free to members. adv. bk.rev. **Document type:** *Journal, Trade.*
Formerly (until 1973): Ostschwaebische Wirtschaft (0019-8994)
Published by: Industrie- und Handelskammer Ostwuerttemberg, Ludwig-Erhard-Str 1, Heidenheim, 89520, Germany. TEL 49-7321-3240, FAX 49-7321-324169, gring@ostwuerttemberg.ihk.de, http://www.ostwuerttemberg.ihk.de. Ed. Peter Gring. adv.: B&W page EUR 1,443, color page EUR 1,804; trim 185 x 250. Circ: 9,000 (controlled).

330 DEU
WIRTSCHAFT - NECKAR - ALB; Magazin der IHK Reutlingen. Text in German. 1946. m. adv. bk.rev. illus.; stat. **Document type:** *Trade.*
Formerly (until 1980): Industrie- und Handelskammer Reutlingen. Mitteilungen (0026-6892)
Published by: Industrie- und Handelskammer Reutlingen, Postfach 1944, Reutlingen, 72709, Germany. TEL 49-7121-201-0, FAX 49-7121-4120, ihk@reutlingen.ihk.de. Ed., R&P Ulrike Fleischle TEL 49-7121-201172. Adv. contact Helmut Gollmer TEL 49-7123-978537. Circ: 27,500.

941.1 DEU ISSN 0940-4449
WIRTSCHAFT NORDHESSEN. Text in German. 1946. m. adv. bk.rev. **Document type:** *Bulletin.* **Description:** Provides reports and information about general and regional economic and other affairs for the owners and managers of enterprises in the area of North Hesse.
Formerly: Kurhessische Wirtschaft
Published by: Industrie- und Handelskammer Kassel, Kurfuerstenstr 9, Kassel, 34117, Germany. TEL 49-561-78910, FAX 49-561-7891290, russ@kassel.ihk.de. Ed. Walter Russ-Rohlfs. Circ: 32,000 (controlled).

382 DEU
WIRTSCHAFT ZWISCHEN ALB UND BODENSEE. Text in German. m. adv. **Document type:** *Magazine, Trade.*
Published by: Ebner Verlag GmbH, Karlstr 41, Ulm, 89073, Germany. TEL 49-731-1520151, FAX 49-731-68503, gl@ebnerverlag.de, http://www.ebnerverlag.de. adv.: B&W page EUR 2,357, color page EUR 3,065. Circ: 29,481 (controlled).

943 DEU ISSN 1616-0746
WIRTSCHAFT ZWISCHEN OSTSEE UND ELBE. Text in German. 1948. m. EUR 16.87; EUR 1.28 newsstand/cover (effective 2005). adv. bk.rev. index. back issues avail. **Document type:** *Bulletin, Trade.*
Formerly (until 2000): I H K Aktuell (0946-4557)
Published by: Industrie- und Handelskammer zu Luebeck, Fackenburger Allee 2, Luebeck, 23554, Germany. TEL 49-451-60060, FAX 49-451-6006999, ihk@luebeck-ihk.de, http://www.wirtschaftostseeelbe.de, http://www.ihk-luebeck.de. R&P Hans Jochen Arndt. Adv. contact Christiane Kermel. Circ: 35,500 (paid and controlled).

382 DEU
WIRTSCHAFTSDIENST (DRESDEN). Text in German. 10/yr. EUR 16; EUR 1.60 newsstand/cover (effective 2003). adv. **Document type:** *Magazine, Trade.*
Published by: Industrie- und Handelskammer Dresden, Langer Weg 4, Dresden, 01239, Germany. TEL 49-351-28020, FAX 49-351-2802280, internetredaktion@dresden.ihk.de, http://www.dresden.ihk.de. adv.: B&W page EUR 3,117, color page EUR 4,988. Circ: 62,200 (controlled).

943 DEU
WIRTSCHAFTSMAGAZIN PFALZ. Text in German. 10/yr. EUR 31 (effective 2005). adv. **Document type:** *Magazine, Trade.*
Formerly: I H K Magazin
Published by: Industrie- und Handelskammer fuer die Pfalz, Ludwigsplatz 2-4, Ludwigshafen Am Rhein, 67059, Germany. TEL 49-621-59040, FAX 49-621-59041204, info@pfalz.ihk24.de. Ed. Sabine Fuchs-Hilbruch. adv.: page EUR 2,740; trim 185 x 250. Circ: 40,000 (controlled).

943 DEU ISSN 1434-1573
WIRTSCHAFTSMAGAZIN RHEIN-NECKAR. Text in German. m. adv. bk.rev. **Document type:** *Magazine, Trade.*
Formerly (until 1995): Wirtschaft
Published by: (Industrie- und Handelskammer Rhein-Neckar), Pruefer Medienmarketing, Lichtentaler Str 33, Baden-Baden, 76530, Germany. TEL 49-7221-21190, FAX 49-7221-211915, werbeagentur@pruefer.com, http://www.pruefer.com. Ed. Christa Bender. R&P Andrea Kiefer. adv.: B&W page EUR 2,750, color page EUR 3,080; trim 185 x 250. Circ: 48,600 (controlled).

943.1 DEU
WIRTSCHAFTSRAUM HANAU KINZIGTAL. Text in German. 1872. m. adv. bk.rev. **Document type:** *Bulletin.*
Formerly: Wirtschaft im Raum Hanau Kinzigtal
Published by: Industrie- und Handelskammer Hanau - Gelnhausen - Schluchtern, Am Pedro-Jung-Park 14, Hanau, 63450, Germany. TEL 49-6181-929014, FAX 49-6181-929078, knips@hanau.ihk.de.

338 DEU ISSN 1435-8425
WIRTSCHAFTSREPORT RHEINHESSEN. Text in German. 1910. m. adv. bk.rev. **Document type:** *Trade.*
Formerly: Rheinhessische Wirtschaft (0035-4449)
Published by: Industrie- und Handelskammer fuer Rheinhessen, Schillerplatz 7, Mainz, 55116, Germany. TEL 49-6131-262-0, FAX 49-6131-262169. Eds. Richard Patzke, Stefan Linden. Circ: 27,000.

382 AUT
WIRTSCHAFTSRUNDSCHAU. Text in German. m.
Published by: Schweizerische Handelskammer in Oesterreich, Neuer Markt 4, Vienna, W 1010, Austria. TEL 0222-525959.

382 AUT
WIRTSCHAFTSRUNDSCHAU ITALIA - OESTERREICH. Text in German. q.
Published by: Italienische Handelskammer fuer Oesterreich, Reisnerstrasse 20, Vienna, W 1030, Austria. TEL 0222-7158782, FAX 0222-7158789.

380 USA ISSN 1048-2849
HF294 CODEN: WCCDE9
WORLD CHAMBER OF COMMERCE DIRECTORY. Text in English. 1967. a. USD 40 per issue (effective 2000). **Document type:** *Directory.* **Description:** Lists addresses, phone numbers, and the name of person in charge; population; and the number of members of chambers of commerce throughout the world. Includes embassies.
Formerly: Worldwide Chamber of Commerce Directory (0893-326X)
—CASDDS.
Address: PO Box 1029, Loveland, CO 80539. TEL 970-663-3231, FAX 970-663-6187, worldchamberdirectory@compuserve.com. Ed. Jan Pierce. Circ: 12,000.

966.9 NGA
WORLD TRADE CENTER OF NIGERIA. NEWSLETTER. Text in English. 1988. q. USD 10. charts; stat.; tr.lit. back issues avail. **Document type:** *Newsletter.*
Published by: Apple Academy Press, 63 Coker St, PO Box 3445, Lagos, Ilupeju, Nigeria. Ed. John Adeyemi Adeleke. Circ: 4,500.

968.9 ZWE
Z N C C NEWSLETTER. Text in English. 1981. m. free. adv. bk.rev. back issues avail. **Document type:** *Newsletter.*
Formerly: A C C O Z News
Published by: Zimbabwe National Chamber of Commerce, PO Box 1934, Harare, Zimbabwe. Ed. E Mpundu. Circ: 2,000.

ZIMBABWE NATIONAL CHAMBER OF COMMERCE DIRECTORY. see *BUSINESS AND ECONOMICS—Trade And Industrial Directories*

BUSINESS AND ECONOMICS—Computer Applications

A B S E L NEWS & VIEWS. see *COMPUTERS—Computer Simulation*

330 USA ISSN 1046-8188
HF5548.2 CODEN: ATISET
➤ **A C M TRANSACTIONS ON INFORMATION SYSTEMS.** Short title: T O I S. Text in English. 1983. q. USD 185 domestic to non-members; USD 199 foreign to non-members; USD 44 domestic to members; USD 58 foreign to members; USD 39 domestic to students; USD 53 foreign to students; USD 222 combined subscription domestic to non-members print & online eds.; USD 236 combined subscription foreign to non-members print & online eds.; USD 53 combined subscription domestic to members print & online eds.; USD 67 combined subscription foreign to members print & online eds.; USD 47 combined subscription domestic to students print & online eds.; USD 61 combined subscription foreign to students print & online eds. (effective 2006). adv. illus. back issues avail.; reprints avail. **Document type:** *Journal, Academic/Scholarly.* **Description:** Serves corporate and academic researchers who have broad interests in information systems.
Formerly (until 1988): Transactions on Office Information Systems (0734-2047)
Related titles: Microform ed.; Online - full text ed.: USD 148 to non-members; USD 35 to members; USD 31 to students (effective 2006) (from Association for Computing Machinery, Inc., EBSCO Publishing, Florida Center for Library Automation, Gale Group).
Indexed: ABIn, AHCI, AS&TI, ASCA, ArtHuCI, BrCerAb, C&CSA, C&ISA, CADCAM, CMCI, CerAb, CompAb, CompD, CompLI, CompR, CorrAb, CurCont, E&CAJ, EMA, EngInd, ErgAb, IAA, ISR, InfoSAb, Inspec, JOF, LISA, M&TEA, MBF, METADEX, RefZh, SCI, SSCI, SolStAb, TelAb, WAA.
—BLDSC (0578.668000), AskIEEE, CASDDS, CISTI, Ei, IDS, IE, Infotrieve, ingenta, Linda Hall. **CCC.**
Published by: Association for Computing Machinery, Inc., 1515 Broadway, 17th Fl, New York, NY 10036-5701. TEL 212-626-0520, 800-342-6626, FAX 212-944-1318, usacm@acm.org, sigs@acm.org, http://www.acm.org/tois. adv.: B&W page USD 4,870, color page USD 6,600; trim 8.13 x 10.88. Circ: 4,573 (paid).

➤ **ACCOUNTING TECHNOLOGY.** see *BUSINESS AND ECONOMICS—Accounting*

330 510 NLD ISSN 0929-130X
➤ **ADVANCES IN COMPUTATIONAL ECONOMICS.** Text in English. 1993. irreg., latest vol.19, 2004. price varies. back issues avail. **Document type:** *Monographic series, Academic/Scholarly.*
Indexed: CCMJ, ZentMath.
—BLDSC (0704.103700), IE, ingenta.
Published by: Springer-Verlag Dordrecht (Subsidiary of: Springer Science+Business Media), Van Godewijckstraat 30, Dordrecht, 3311 GX, Netherlands. TEL 31-78-6576050, FAX 31-78-6576474, http://www.springeronline.com. Eds. Anna Nagurney, Hans M Amman.

343 USA ISSN 1555-5941
KF872
ANDREWS LITIGATION REPORTER: E-BUSINESS LAW BULLETIN. Text in English. 1999. m. USD 485 (effective 2005). **Document type:** *Newsletter, Trade.* **Description:** Provides a forum for emerging issues and strategies in e-commerce law, discussions on possible legal strategies and summaries of court decisions involving jurisdiction issues, legal liability for linking, framing and caching, and contract issues.
Formerly (until 2004): Andrews E-Business Law Bulletin (1536-7037)
Published by: Andrews Publications (Subsidiary of: Thomson West), 175 Strafford Ave, Ste 140, Wayne, PA 19087. TEL 610-225-0510, 800-345-1101, FAX 610-225-0501, http://www.andrewsonline.com.

330 GBR ISSN 1369-4200
APPLICATION DEVELOPMENT ADVISOR. Text in English. 1995. bi-m. GBP 20 domestic; GBP 35 in Europe; GBP 45 elsewhere; GBP 3.95 newsstand/cover. adv. bk.rev.
Document type: *Trade.* **Description:** Presents information relevant to both academia and business regarding the application of computer technology.
Formerly: Object Expert (1360-3426)
Related titles: Online - full text ed.
Indexed: Inspec.
—BLDSC (1570.511410), IE, ingenta. **CCC.**
Published by: Sigs Ltd., Brocus House, Parkgate Rd,, Newdigate, Surrey RH5 5AH, United Kingdom. TEL 44-181-4598169, danny@itjournalist.com, subscriptions@sigs.com, http://www.appdevadvisor.com. Ed. Danny Bradbury. Adv. contact Gary Cunningham. **Subscr. to:** Tower Publishing Services Ltd., Tower House, Sovereign Park, Market Harborough, Leics LE16 9EF, United Kingdom. TEL 44-1858-435301, FAX 44-1858-434958. **Dist. by:** Comag, Mercury Centre, Central Way, Feltham, Middx TW14 0RX, United Kingdom. TEL 44-181-844-1000.

AUTOMOTIVE MANAGEMENT INFORMATION SYSTEMS COUNCIL NEWSLETTER. see *BUSINESS AND ECONOMICS—Office Equipment And Services*

B I T - BUSINESS INFORMATION TECHNOLOGY. see *BUSINESS AND ECONOMICS—Office Equipment And Services*

BANK SYSTEMS & TECHNOLOGY; for senior-level executives in perations and technology management. see *BUSINESS AND ECONOMICS—Banking And Finance*

BERUFS- UND KARRIERE-PLANER. I T UND E-BUSINESS. see *OCCUPATIONS AND CAREERS*

BERUFSPLANUNG FUER DEN I T NACHWUCHS. see *OCCUPATIONS AND CAREERS*

658 004 USA ISSN 0178-5001
BETRIEBS- UND WIRTSCHAFTSINFORMATIK. Text in English. 1982. irreg. price varies. **Document type:** *Academic/Scholarly.*
Published by: Springer-Verlag New York, Inc. (Subsidiary of: Springer Science+Business Media), 233 Spring St, New York, NY 10013. TEL 212-460-1500, FAX 212-473-6272.

651 HRV ISSN 1330-4097
BIROTREND. Text in Croatian. 1994. m. **Document type:** *Magazine, Trade.*
Published by: Trend d.o.o., Trg Petra Svacica 12-II, Zagreb, 10000, Croatia. TEL 385-1-4856895, FAX 385-1-4554536.

DER BUEROMASCHINEN- UND BUEROBEDARFSHANDEL. see *BUSINESS AND ECONOMICS—Office Equipment And Services*

BUILDERS' COMPUTER NEWSLETTER. see *BUILDING AND CONSTRUCTION*

330 ROM ISSN 1454-993X
BURSA I T. (Information Technology) Variant title: Bursa - Tehnologia Informatiei. Text in Romanian. 1998. s-a. ROL 65,000 (effective 2002). adv. **Document type:** *Magazine, Trade.*
Published by: Ring Media, Str. Popa Tatu nr. 71, sector 1, Bucharest, Romania. TEL 40-21-3154356, FAX 40-21-3124556.

004.68 GBR
▼ **BUSINESS & I T SUPPORT.** Text in English. 2004. bi-m. **Document type:** *Magazine, Trade.*
Published by: Penton Media Europe (Subsidiary of: Penton Media, Inc.), Penton House, 288-290 Worton Rd, Isleworth, Mddx TW7 6EL, United Kingdom. TEL 44-20-8232-1600, FAX 44-20-8232-1650, information@penton.com, http://www.penton.com.

330 GBR ISSN 1351-3680
BUSINESS & TECHNOLOGY MAGAZINE. Text in English. 1993. m. GBP 48 domestic; GBP 120, USD 180 elsewhere (effective 2000). adv. back issues avail. **Document type:** *Trade.*
Description: Delivers high-profile interviews, topical business critiques, and far-sighted technical analysis for those who make and shape IT decisions in large corporate organizations.
Related titles: ♦ Supplement(s): Corporate Networks. ISSN 1369-7382.
Indexed: Inspec.
—**CCC.**
Published by: Reed Business Information Ltd. (Subsidiary of: Reed Business), Quadrant House, The Quadrant, Brighton Rd, Sutton, Surrey SM2 5AS, United Kingdom. TEL 44-208-652-3500, FAX 44-208-652-8977, rbi.subscriptions@qss-uk.com, http://www.reedbusiness.co.uk/. Ed. Jim Mortleman TEL 44-20-8652-2080. Adv. contact Nick Ratnieks TEL 44-20-8652-8570. color page GBP 3,300. Circ: 30,000. **Subscr. to:** Quadrant Subscription Services, PO Box 302, Haywards Heath, W Sussex RH16 3YY, United Kingdom. TEL 44-1444-445566, FAX 44-1444-445447.

330 IND
BUSINESS COMPUTER. Text in English. 1986. m.
Published by: Nariman Point Building Services & Trading Pvt. Ltd., 920 Tulsiani Chambers, Nariman Point, Mumbai, Maharashtra 400 021, India. Ed. Maneck Davar. adv.: B&W page INR 9,000, color page INR 18,000; trim 165 x 240.

330 USA
▼ **BUSINESS COMPUTING.** (delivered as a PDF file; broadband Internet connection required for subscription.) Text in English. 2005 (Jul.). m. free to qualified personnel (effective 2005). adv. **Document type:** *Magazine, Trade.* **Description:** Covers business computing from the SBMB/SOHO business owner's standpoint.
Media: Online - full content.
Published by: Possibility Media, 10400 N.W. 33rd St., Ste. 270, Miami, FL 33172. TEL 786-206-8880, FAX 786-206-8884, info@possibilitymedia.com, http://www.businesscomputingmagazine.com/, http://www.possibilitymedia.com/. Adv. contact Terry Logan TEL 786-206-8880 ext 103. page USD 2,855.

686.8 BEL ISSN 1373-9832
BUSINESS I C T. (Information Communication Technology) Text in French. 1985. 9/yr. EUR 57 (effective 2004). adv. software rev. illus. **Document type:** *Magazine, Trade.* **Description:** Contains market analyses, user surveys, interviews, news and case studies on business information and communications technology.
Former titles (until 1998): B I Technology (1371-1792); (until 1994): B M B Bureau Informatique (0777-9208); (until 1990): B M B Bureau Magazine (0777-9186)
Related titles: Dutch ed.: Business I C T (Nederlandse Ed.). ISSN 1373-9840.
Published by: Roularta Media Group, Research Park, Zellik, 1731, Belgium. TEL 32-2-4675611, FAX 32-2-4675757, communication@roularta.be, http://www.roularta.be. Circ: 20,100 (paid and controlled).

330 USA ISSN 1465-5896 CODEN: OBINE8
BUSINESS INFORMATION TESTDRIVE. Text in English. 1985. m. (except Jul.). GBP 385 combined subscription domestic print & online eds.; EUR 625 combined subscription in Europe print & online eds.; USD 595 combined subscription elsewhere print & online eds. (effective 2003). adv. bk.rev.; software rev. cum.index. Supplement avail.; back issues avail.; reprints avail. **Document type:** *Newsletter, Trade.* **Description:** Evaluates electronic databases for business.
Former titles (until 1998): Online - CD-ROM Business Information (1352-0490); (until 1994): Online Business Information (0267-9515)
Related titles: Online - full text ed.: (from Gale Group).
Indexed: Inspec.
—BLDSC (2933.810700), AskIEEE, IE, Infotrieve.
Published by: C S A Journal Division (Subsidiary of: Cambridge Information Group), 7200 Wisconsin Ave, Ste 715, Bethesda, MD 20814. TEL 301-961-6798, 800-843-7751, FAX 301-961-6799, journals@csa.com, http://www.csa.com. Circ: 500.

330 BRA
BUSINESS STANDARD BRAZIL. Text in Portuguese. m. adv. **Document type:** *Magazine, Trade.* **Description:** Contains up-to-date articles and information on the companies, business models and people running the Internet-driven New Economy.
Published by: I D G Computerworld do Brasil, Rua Tabapua, 145-3 e 4 andar, Itaim Bibi, Sao Paulo, 04533-010, Brazil. TEL 55-11-3049-2000, FAX 55-11-3071-4022, negocios@idg.com.br, http://www.businessstandard.com.br, http://www.idg.com.br. adv.: color page USD 9,900; 210 x 280.

330 USA
BUSINESS TECHNOLOGY JOURNAL. Text in English. d. **Document type:** *Trade.* **Description:** Provides recommendations and frameworks that help business leaders translate technology into competitive edge.
Media: Online - full text.
Published by: Gartner Inc., 56 Top Gallant Rd, Stamford, CT 06904-2212. TEL 203-316-1111, 800-544-7337, FAX 203-316-6300, jwhitney@info-edge.com, http://www.gartner3.gartnerweb.com.

330 CZE ISSN 1213-1709
BUSINESS WORLD. Text in Czech, Slovak. 1998. m. CZK 400, SKK 450 (effective 2002). adv. **Document type:** *Magazine, Trade.* **Description:** Contains articles concerned with the management of information systems and with the economic aspects of their implementation and installation.
Related titles: Online - full text ed.
Published by: I D G Czech, a.s., Seydlerova 2451-11, Prague 5, 158 00, Czech Republic. TEL 420-2-57088111, FAX 420-2-6520812, info@idg.cz, http://www.businessworld.cz, http://www.idg.cz. Ed. Karel Taschner. Adv. contact Jitka Vyhlidkova TEL 420-2-57088181. color page USD 2,156; trim 210 x 295. Circ: 15,000 (paid and controlled).

330 USA ISSN 0894-9301
T58.6 CODEN: CIOOEQ
C I O; the magazine for information executives. (Chief Information Officer) Text in English. 1987. s-m. (23/yr.). USD 95 in US & Canada; USD 195 elsewhere; free to qualified personnel (effective 2005). adv. bk.rev. illus. back issues avail.; reprints avail. **Document type:** *Magazine, Trade.* **Description:** Business publication covering information technology for top-level information executives.
Incorporates (1995-1997): WebMaster (1091-0743)
Related titles: Microform ed.; Online - full text ed.: (from Factiva, O C L C Online Computer Library Center, Inc., ProQuest Information & Learning); Supplement(s): ISSN 1088-5455.
Indexed: ABIn, CompLI, Inspec, LogistBibl, MicrocompInd, SoftBase.
—BLDSC (3198.667000), AskIEEE, IE, Infotrieve, ingenta. **CCC.**
Published by: C X O Media Inc. (Subsidiary of: I D G Communications Inc.), 492 Old Connecticut Path, PO Box 9208, Framingham, MA 01701-9208. TEL 508-872-0080, 800-788-4605, FAX 508-879-7784, denisep@cio.com, lundberg@cio.com, http://www.cio.com/. Ed. Abbie Lundberg. Pub. Gary J Beach. R&P Bill Kerber. Adv. contact Michael Masters. B&W page USD 21,300. Circ: 140,000 (paid and controlled).

330 FRA ISSN 1636-0575
C I O (FRANCE). (Chief Information Officer) Text in French. 2002. bi-m. EUR 80 foreign (effective 2005). **Document type:** *Magazine, Trade.*
Published by: I D G Communications France, 5 rue Chantecoq, Puteaux, 92808, France. TEL 33-1-4197-6161, FAX 33-1-4197-6160, http://www.idg.fr/cio.

658.403805 GBR
HD30.2
C I O AGENDA; aligning IT with business. (Chief Information Officer) Text in English. 2000. s-a. GBP 19.95 per issue (effective 2003). adv. **Document type:** *Journal, Trade.* **Description:** Brings together a range of voices with shared visions to demonstrate the importance of aligning a strategy that considers business needs and the role of IT in developing a company's services.
Formerly: C I O Technology International (1469-7564)
Published by: Quasar International Communications Ltd. (Subsidiary of: Sterling Publishing Group Plc.), Brunel House, 55-57 North Wharf Rd, London, W2 1LA, United Kingdom. TEL 44-20-79159717, FAX 44-20-79159763, info@quasar.uk.net, http://www.cioagenda.com, http://www.quasar.uk.net. Pub. Sarah Woddis. Circ: 10,000 (controlled).

330 SGP
C I O ASIA. (Chief Information Officer) Text in English. m. adv. **Document type:** *Magazine, Trade.* **Description:** Delivers analysis and tips from some of the world's best business thinkers on cutting-edge management ideas and the role technology plays in them.
Related titles: Online - full text ed.
Published by: Communication Resources Pte. Ltd., Blk. 1008, Tao Payoh North, No. 07-01, Singapore, 318996, Singapore. TEL 65-256-6201, FAX 65-251-0348, http://www.cio-asia.com, http://www.idg.com.sp. adv.: color page USD 6,200; trim 205 x 275. Circ: 13,000 (paid and controlled).

330 AUS
C I O AUSTRALIA. (Chief Information Officer) Text in English. m. AUD 95 domestic; AUD 150 in New Zealand; AUD 200 elsewhere (effective 2002). adv. **Document type:** *Magazine, Trade.* **Description:** Provides information about the benefits of technology and how it can streamline business processes and enhance profitability.
Related titles: Online - full text ed.
Published by: I D G Communications Pty. Ltd., 88 Christie St, St Leonards, NSW 2065, Australia. TEL 61-2-94395133, FAX 61-2-94395512, heidi_woof@idg.com.au, http://cio.idg.com.au/, http://www.idg.com.au. Ed., Pub. Linda Kennedy. Adv. contact Julian Zipparo. color page USD 4,046; trim 205 x 275. Circ: 10,329 (paid).

380.10285 NOR ISSN 1503-6189
C I O BUSINESS STANDARD NORWAY; tidsskriftet for e-business, IT og ledelse. Text in Norwegian. 2000. 11/yr. NOK 795 (effective 2004). adv. **Document type:** *Magazine, Trade.* **Description:** Provides useful coverage of the people, companies and business models that are forming the Internet economy as well as new IT solutions.
Formerly (until 2003): Business Standard Norway (1502-363X)
Related titles: Online - full text ed.
Published by: I D G Communications Norge, PO Box 9090, Gronland, Oslo, 0133, Norway. TEL 47-22-053000, FAX 47-22-053001, http://www.cio.idg.no, http://www.idg.no. Eds. Michael Oreld TEL 47-22-053015, Arne Uppheim TEL 47-22-053023. Adv. contact Rune Antonsen TEL 47-22-053043. B&W page NOK 32,200, color page NOK 40,400; trim 225 x 297. Circ: 23,000 (paid).

330 CAN ISSN 1195-6097
C I O CANADA. (Chief Information Officer) Text in English. 1993. 10/yr. CND 95 domestic; CND 195 foreign; free to qualified personnel (effective 2005). adv. **Document type:** *Magazine, Trade.* **Description:** Directed to CIO, CEO, VP of MIS, all those looking for information technology solutions as applied in their business strategies.
Related titles: Online - full text ed.: (from Micromedia ProQuest).
Indexed: CBCABus.
—CISTI. **CCC.**
Published by: I T World Canada, Inc., No.302 - 55 Town Centre Court, Scarborough, ON M1P 4X4, Canada. TEL 416-290-0240, FAX 416-290-0238, info@itworldcanada.com, http://www.cio.com/, http://www.itworldcanada.com. Ed. Abbie Lundberg. adv.: color page CND 5,616; trim 8.13 x 10.88. Circ: 7,012 (controlled).

330 USA ISSN 1554-7515
HD30.213
▼ **C I O DECISIONS.** (Chief Information Officer) Text in English. 2005 (Apr.). m. USD 90; USD 10 per issue (effective 2005). adv. **Document type:** *Magazine, Trade.* **Description:** Contains information for CIOs and senior IT executives involved in setting their organizations' IT budgets and priorities.
Related titles: Online - full text ed.
Published by: TechTarget, 117 Kendrick St, Ste 800, Needham, MA 02494. TEL 781-657-1000, 888-274-4111, FAX 781-657-1100, info@techtarget.com, http://www.ciodecisions.com, http://www.techtarget.com/. Ed. Maryfran Johnson. Pub. Joseph Levy. adv.: B&W page USD 14,900, color page USD 16,900; trim 8 x 10.875. Circ: 60,000 (controlled).

330 DEU ISSN 1618-3487
C I O GERMANY; IT-Strategie fuer Manager. (Chief Information Officer) Text in German. 2001. m. EUR 65 domestic; EUR 85 foreign; EUR 6.50 newsstand/cover (effective 2004). adv. **Document type:** *Magazine, Trade.*
Related titles: Online - full text ed.
Published by: Computerwoche Verlag GmbH, Brabanter Str 4, Munich, 80805, Germany. TEL 49-89-360860, FAX 49-89-36086118, redaktion@cio-media.de, http://www.cio-magazin.de. Ed. Heinrich Seeger. Adv. contact Marie-Henriette von Wangenheim. page EUR 10,850. Circ: 36,942 (paid and controlled).

330 IND
C I O INDIA. Text in English. m. adv. **Document type:** *Magazine, Trade.* **Description:** Provides technical insight for business CIOs, IT directors in the corporate and public sectors, CEOs, and other members of management teams.
Published by: Technology Media Group Pvt. Ltd., No. 3540, Hal II Stage, Indiranagar, Bangalore, 560 038, India. TEL 91-80-521-0309, FAX 91-80-521-0362, click@tmgpower.com, http://www.indianitonline.com/cio.asp, http://www.tmgpower.com. adv.: color page USD 1,875; bleed 209 x 274. Circ: 10,000 (paid and controlled).

330 USA ISSN 1535-0096
T1
C I O INSIGHT. (Chief Information Officer) Text in English. 2001 (May). m. free to qualified personnel. adv. back issues avail. **Document type:** *Magazine, Trade.* **Description:** Serves the strategic information technology and business information needs of today's critical senior-level technology executives.
Related titles: Online - full text ed.: (from EBSCO Publishing, Gale Group, H.W. Wilson, O C L C Online Computer Library Center, Inc., ProQuest Information & Learning).
Indexed: BPI.
Published by: Ziff Davis Media Inc., 28 E 28th St, New York, NY 10016-7930. TEL 212-503-3500, FAX 212-503-5420, info@ziffdavis.com, http://www.cioinsight.com/, http://www.ziffdavis.com. Eds. Edward H Baker, Ellen Pearlman. Pub. Stephen Veith. adv.: B&W page USD 12,900, color page USD 14,850. Circ: 50,000 (controlled).

330 JPN
C I O JAPAN. (Chief Information Officer) Text in Japanese. m. adv. **Document type:** *Magazine, Trade.* **Description:** Targeted at senior level IT executives from multinational and large firms who exercise influence on corporate IT strategy and purchasing decisions.
Related titles: Online - full text ed.
Published by: I D G Japan, Inc., Hongo 3-4-5, Bunkyo-ku, Tokyo, 1130033, Japan. TEL 81-3-5800-3111, FAX 81-3-5800-3590, http://www.idg.co.jp/CIO/. adv.: color page USD 7,566; trim 210 x 277. Circ: 15,600 (paid and controlled).

330 KOR
C I O KOREA. (Chief Information Officer) Text in Korean. s-m. adv. **Document type:** *Magazine, Trade.* **Description:** Contains details on management trends, success stories, strategies, and articles that discuss the challenges facing information executives and their senior management.
Related titles: Online - full text ed.
Published by: C I O Communications, Inc., Kora Bldg., 4th Fl., 92-4 Dangsan-Dong, Ga Yongdungpo-Gu, Seoul, 150806, Korea, S. TEL 82-2-2632-7561, FAX 82-2-676-3509, webmaster@ciokorea.com, http://www.ciokorea.com. adv.: color page USD 2,652; trim 206 x 273. Circ: 20,225 (paid and controlled).

658.40380 NZL ISSN 1174-992X
C I O NEW ZEALAND. (Chief Information Officer) Text in English. 1999. m. NZD 89 domestic; NZD 105 in Australasia; NZD 120 elsewhere (effective 2002). adv. **Document type:** *Magazine, Trade.* **Description:** Informs readers about innovation, technology directions, partnering, people, and the issues that turn complex technology choices such as ERP into profitable business decisions.
Related titles: Online - full text ed.
Published by: I D G Communications Ltd., Wellesley St., PO Box 6813, Auckland, 1036, New Zealand. TEL 64-9-377-9902, FAX 64-9-377-4604, idg@idg.co.nz, http://cio.co.nz/, http://www.idg.net.nz. adv.: B&W page USD 1,088, color page USD 1,477; trim 205 x 275. Circ: 1,995 (paid and controlled).

330 TWN
C I O TAIWAN. (Chief Information Officer) Text in Chinese. w. adv. **Document type:** *Magazine, Trade.* **Description:** Provides the latest news and in-depth analysis of IT management, applications and solutions.
Published by: I D G Communications, Taiwan, 8F, No. 131, Sec. 3, Nanking E. Rd., Taipei, 104, Taiwan. TEL 886-2-2715-3000, FAX 886-2-2547-0601, http://www.infopro.com.tw. adv.: color page USD 3,130; 190 x 260. Circ: 25,000 (paid and controlled).

330 USA ISSN 1557-2315
▼ **C I O TODAY.** Text in English. 2005. m. free to qualified personnel (effective 2003).
Related titles: Online - full text ed.
Published by: NewsFactor Network, 21700 Oxnard St, Ste 2040, Woodland Hills, CA 91367. TEL 818-593-2200, FAX 818-593-2203, http://www.ciotoday.com/, http://www.newsfactor.com/.

330 657 USA ISSN 1550-4743
THE C P A TECHNOLOGY ADVISOR. (Certified Public Accountant) Text in English. 1991. 8/yr. USD 48; USD 74.90 in Canada & Mexico; USD 99 elsewhere (effective 2004). adv. bk.rev.; software rev. 80 p./no. 5 cols./p.; back issues avail.; reprints avail. **Document type:** *Magazine, Trade.* **Description:** Includes articles to assist CPAs with computer software, installing computers, client write-up, tax software, spreadsheets, and accounting software.
Former titles (until 2004): The C P A Software News (1068-8285); (until 1991): N S P A Software News
Related titles: Online - full text ed.: (from Gale Group, ProQuest Information & Learning).
Indexed: ATI.
—**CCC.**
Published by: Cygnus Business Media, Inc., 110 N Bell St., Ste 300, Shawnee, OK 74801. TEL 405-275-3100, FAX 405-275-3101, www.cpasoftwarenews.com, http://www.cygnusb2b.com/index.cfm. Ed. Gregory LaFollette. Pub., Adv. contact Shari Dodgen TEL 800-456-0864 Ext 108. B&W page USD 5,495, color page USD 6,995; trim 14 x 11.5. Circ: 51,343.

330 POL
C X O; magazyn kadry zarzadzajacej. Text in Polish. 2001. bi-m. PLZ 75 (effective 2002). adv. **Document type:** *Magazine, Trade.*
Related titles: Online - full text ed.
Published by: I D G Poland S.A., ul Jordanowska 12, PO Box 73, Warsaw, 04-204, Poland. TEL 48-22-3217800, FAX 48-22-3217888, idg@idg.com.pl, http://www.cxo.pl, http://www.idg.pl. adv.: color page PLZ 14,500; trim 225 x 275.

338 001.6 FRA ISSN 0985-0791
CENTRE D'INFORMATION DES UTILISATEURS DE PROGICIELS. CATALOGUE. Text in French. 1976. a. adv. **Document type:** *Catalog, Directory.* **Description:** Provides information on 14000 software packages available in a database on Minitel.
Former titles: Guide Europeen des Progiciels (0294-0701); Guide Europeen des Produits Logiciels (0395-2061)
Published by: Centre d'Experimentation des Progiciels (CXP), 19-21 rue du Rocher, Paris, 75008, France. TEL 43-87-90-28, FAX 44-70-91-10. Eds. Alain Pauly, Isabelle Jahn. Circ: 8,000.

330 ZAF
THE CHANNEL. Text in English. 1997. m. adv. **Document type:** *Magazine, Trade.* **Description:** Targets key issues in the information technology channel and provides in-depth analysis of related news, people and products.
Formerly: The Weekly Channel (1608-0092)
Published by: T M L Business Publishing (Subsidiary of: Times Media Ltd.), PO Box 182, Pinegowrie, Gauteng 2123, South Africa. TEL 27-11-789-2144, FAX 27-11-789-3196. adv.: color page USD 756; trim 210 x 297. Circ: 3,271 (paid and controlled).

CHRISTIAN MANAGEMENT REPORT. see *BUSINESS AND ECONOMICS—Management*

330 USA
COMDISCO. ANNUAL REPORT. Text in English. a. **Document type:** *Yearbook, Corporate.* **Description:** Provides financial highlights, a review of operations and other information concerning Comdisco.
Published by: Comdisco Inc., 5600 N. River Rd., Ste. 800, Rosemont, IL 60018-5166. TEL 800-321-1111, http://comdisco.com, http://comdisco.com/.

COMMUNICATIONS NEWSFILE. see *COMMUNICATIONS*

330 USA ISSN 1087-7118
COMPENSATION & BENEFITS SOFTWARE CENSUS. Text in English. 1993. a. USD 79.95 (effective 2000). **Document type:** *Directory.* **Description:** Covers compensation and employee benefits software with listings for over 800 products. Includes 125-word feature descriptions, platform information, price, and vendor contact information. Also systems consulting firms and annotated listings of 100 compensation and benefits Web sites.
Formerly: Compensation and Benefits Software Locator (1072-1428)
Related titles: CD-ROM ed.; E-mail ed.
Published by: Advanced Personnel Systems, 1247, Roseville, CA 95678-8247. TEL 916-781-2900, FAX 916-781-2901, frantz@hrcensus.com, http://www.hrcensus.com. Ed., Pub. Richard B Frantzreb. Circ: 1,000 (paid).

330 USA ISSN 0927-7099
HB143.5 CODEN: CNOMEL
➤ **COMPUTATIONAL ECONOMICS.** Text in English. 1988. 8/yr. (in 2 vols.). EUR 798, USD 818, GBP 488 combined subscription to institutions print & online eds. (effective 2005). adv. reprint service avail. from PSC. **Document type:** *Journal, Academic/Scholarly.* **Description:** Serves as an interface for work which integrates computer science with economic or management science.
Formerly (until vol.6, 1993): Computer Science in Economics and Management (0921-2736)
Related titles: Microform ed.: (from PQC); Online - full text ed.: ISSN 1572-9974 (from EBSCO Publishing, Gale Group, IngentaConnect, Kluwer Online, O C L C Online Computer Library Center, Inc., ProQuest Information & Learning, Springer LINK, Swets Information Services).
Indexed: ABIn, BibLing, CompR, EngInd, IBSS, Inspec, JEL, MathR, RASB, RefZh, ZentMath.
—BLDSC (3390.585000), AskIEEE, EI, IE, Infotrieve, ingenta. **CCC.**
Published by: Springer-Verlag New York, Inc. (Subsidiary of: Springer Science+Business Media), 233 Spring St, New York, NY 10013. TEL 212-460-1500, FAX 212-460-1575, service@springer-ny.com, http://springerlink.metapress.com/openurl.asp?genre=journal&issn=0927-7099, http://www.springer-ny.com. Ed. Hans M Amman. **Subscr. to:** Journal Fulfillment, PO Box 2485, Secaucus, NJ 07096-2485. TEL 201-348-4033, FAX 201-348-4505, journals@springer-ny.com.

658 DEU ISSN 1619-697X
▼ ➤ **COMPUTATIONAL MANAGEMENT SCIENCE.** Text in English. 2003. q. EUR 170 combined subscription to institutions print & online eds. (effective 2005). adv. **Document type:** *Journal, Academic/Scholarly.* **Description:** Aims to provide a forum for novel research results, and occasional surveys, in computational methods, models and empirical analysis for decision making in economics, finance, management, and related aspects of engineering.
Related titles: Online - full text ed.: ISSN 1619-6988 (from EBSCO Publishing, Springer LINK).
Indexed: JEL.
—BLDSC (3390.608500), IE. **CCC.**
Published by: Springer-Verlag (Subsidiary of: Springer Science+Business Media), Tiergartenstr 17, Heidelberg, 69121, Germany. TEL 49-6221-3450, FAX 49-6221-345229, http://link.springer.de/link/service/journals/10287/index.htm. Eds. Berc Rustem, Hans Amman, Istvan Maros, Panos Pardalos. Adv. contact Stephan Kroeck TEL 49-30-827875739. **Subscr. to:** Springer-Verlag New York, Inc., Journal Fulfillment, PO Box 2485, Secaucus, NJ 07096-2485. TEL 800-777-4643, 201-348-4033, FAX 201-348-4505, journals@springer-ny.com, http://www.springer-ny.com; Springer GmbH Auslieferungsgesellschaft, Haberstr 7, Heidelberg 69126, Germany. TEL 49-6221-345-0, FAX 49-6221-345-4229, subscriptions@springer.de.

330 657 CAN ISSN 0843-8072
COMPUTER ACCOUNTING LETTER. Text in English. 1989. q. CND 25. **Description:** Aimed at the end-user of financial applications such as accounting, tax and financial analysis; provides news, reviews and strategies.
Published by: Morochove & Associates Inc., 390 Bay St, Ste 2000, Toronto, ON M5H 2Y2, Canada. TEL 416-947-1427, FAX 416-923-3938. Ed. Richard Morochove. Circ: 2,000.

COMPUTER AUDIT NEWS AND DEVELOPMENTS. see *BUSINESS AND ECONOMICS—Accounting*

330 USA ISSN 1095-1377
COMPUTER CURRENTS. ATLANTA. Text in English. 1989. m. USD 19.95 (effective 1999). adv. software rev. illus. **Document type:** *Trade.* **Description:** Covers computing and computer products for the business community in the Atlanta metropolitan area.
Formerly: Atlanta Computer Currents (1040-6034)

Published by: ComputerUser.com, Inc., 1563 Solano Ave, Berkeley, CA 94707-2116. TEL 510-527-0333, 800-365-7773, FAX 510-527-4106, editorial@computercurrents.com, http://www.computercurrents.com, http://www.computeruser.com. Pub., Adv. contact Stan Politi. Circ: 75,000.

330 USA ISSN 1520-4030
COMPUTER ECONOMICS NETWORKING STRATEGIES. Text in English. 1996. m. USD 395 (effective 2005). **Document type:** *Newsletter.* **Description:** Enables readers to maximize enterprise network investments by aligning intranet, networking, and open systems strategies with business objectives.
Formerly (until 1998): Intranet and Networking Strategies Report (1089-9405); Formed by the merger of (1994-1996): Open Systems Economics Letter (1071-6394); (1993-1996): Network Economics Letter (1069-126X)
Related titles: CD-ROM ed.
Indexed: Inspec.
—BLDSC (3393.905000), AskIEEE, IE. **CCC.**
Published by: Computer Economics, Inc., 2082 Business Center Dr., Ste 240, Irvine, CA 92612. TEL 949-831-8700, FAX 949-442-7688, editor@compecon.com, http://www.computereconomics.com. Ed. Anne Zalatan. Pub. Bruno Bassi.

COMPUTER FINANCE. see *BUSINESS AND ECONOMICS—Banking And Finance*

658 DEU
COMPUTER IM UNTERNEHMEN. Text in German. 1997. 2/yr. adv. **Document type:** *Magazine, Trade.*
Published by: V M M Wirtschaftsverlag GmbH & Co. KG, Maximilianstr 9, Augsburg, 86150, Germany. TEL 49-821-44050, FAX 49-821-4405409, info@vmm-wirtschaftsverlag.de, http://www.vmm-wirtschaftsverlag.de. adv.: color page EUR 30,575. Circ: 1,005,000 (controlled).

COMPUTERIZED INVESTING. see *BUSINESS AND ECONOMICS—Investments*

004.16 USA
COMPUTERLAND MAGAZINE✶. Text in English. 1985. 8/yr. free to qualified personnel. adv. back issues avail. **Description:** Presents innovative applications of computers - hardware and software.
Media: Microfiche.
Indexed: SoftBase.
Published by: ComputerLand Corporation, 3797 Spinnaker Ct, Fremont, CA 94538-6537. TEL 510-734-4087, FAX 510-734-4802. Ed. David Gancher. Circ: 270,000 (controlled).

004 621.39 NLD ISSN 0166-3615
TS155.A1 CODEN: CINUD4
➤ **COMPUTERS IN INDUSTRY.** Text in English. 1980. 9/yr. EUR 1,048 in Europe to institutions; JPY 139,200 in Japan to institutions; USD 1,174 to institutions except Europe and Japan (effective 2006). adv. bk.rev. illus. index. back issues avail.; reprints avail. **Document type:** *Academic/Scholarly.* **Description:** Contains case studies, reviews and survey papers on computer applications and computing techniques in industry. Focuses on computer-aided design and manufacturing, production planning and control, and material and control management.
Related titles: Microform ed.: (from PQC); Online - full text ed.: (from EBSCO Publishing, Gale Group, IngentaConnect, ScienceDirect, Swets Information Services).
Indexed: ABIn, AIA, AS&TI, ASCA, BrCerAb, C&ISA, CADCAM, CEA, CMCI, CerAb, CivEngAb, CompAb, CompC, CompD, CompLI, CompR, CorrAb, CurCont, E&CAJ, EIA, EMA, EngInd, EnvAb, ErgAb, IAA, ICEA, IPackAb, ISMEC, ISR, Inspec, M&TEA, MBF, METADEX, ORMS, QC&AS, RefZh, RoboAb, SSCI, SoftAbEng, SolStAb, WAA.
—BLDSC (3394.923000), AskIEEE, CISTI, Ei, IDS, IE, Infotrieve, ingenta, Linda Hall. **CCC.**
Published by: Elsevier BV (Subsidiary of: Elsevier Science & Technology), Radarweg 29, Amsterdam, 1043 NX, Netherlands. TEL 31-20-4853911, FAX 31-20-4852457, nlinfo-f@elsevier.nl, http://www.elsevier.com/locate/compind, http://www.elsevier.nl. Ed. J. C. Wortmann.

330 IRL ISSN 0790-7281
COMPUTERSCOPE; defining technology for business. Text in English. 1985. 11/yr. free to qualified personnel. adv. **Document type:** *Magazine, Trade.* **Description:** Covers PCs, minis, mainframes, datacomms, internet, networks and trade news and analysis for business computer users and professionals.
Related titles: Online - full text ed.
Published by: Scope Communications Ltd., Prospect House, 3 Prospect Rd., Glasnevin, Dublin, 9, Ireland. TEL 353-1-8824407, FAX 353-1-8300888, info@scope.ie, http://www.techcentral.ie/. Ed. David D'Arcy. Pub. Frank Quinn. R&P, Adv. contact Brenda Smith. B&W page EUR 3,900, color page EUR 4,315; trim 280 x 405. Circ: 10,000.

330 USA
COMPUTERWORLD R O I. Text in English. 2001. bi-m. adv. **Document type:** *Magazine, Trade.* **Description:** Focuses on the value technology brings to business results.
Published by: Computerworld, Inc. (Subsidiary of: I D G Communications Inc.), 500 Old Connecticut Path, Box 9171, Framingham, MA 01701-9171. TEL 508-879-0700, 800-669-1002, FAX 508-875-8931, roi@computerworld.com, http://www.computerworld.com/roi. Ed. Ellen Fanning.

COMPUTING & CONTROL ENGINEERING. see *ENGINEERING—Computer Applications*

658 JPN
COMPUTING JAPAN. Text in English. 1999. m. adv. **Document type:** *Trade.* **Description:** Covers the entire spectrum of the IT scene in Japan, including hardware, software, networking, telecommunications, and bilingual computing.
Media: Online - full text.
Indexed: Emerald.
Published by: LINC Media Inc., Odakyu Minami-Aoyama Bldg 8F, 7-8-1 Minami Aoyama, Minato-ku, Tokyo, 107-0062, Japan. TEL 81-3-3499-2099, FAX 81-3-3499-2199, steve@japaninc.net, http://www.computingjapan.com. Ed. Daniel Scuka. Pub. Terrie Lloyd.

658.8 DEU
CONFIDENZ-DEPESCHE; Bonner Nachrichten Dienst. Text in German. m. EUR 184 (effective 2000). adv. **Document type:** *Trade.*
Media: Online - full text.
Published by: Verlag Ralph Tegtmeier Nachf., Postfach 73, Hellenthal, 53938, Germany. TEL 49-6557-931122, FAX 49-6557-931123, cdredaktion@confidenz-depesche.com, http://confidenz-depesche.com. Ed., Pub. Ralph Tegtmeier.

330 DEU
▼ **CONTENT MANAGEMENT MAGAZIN;** Die Fachzeitschrift zur Content-basierenden Technologien. Text in German. 2003. 8/yr. EUR 72; EUR 10 newsstand/cover (effective 2004). adv. **Document type:** *Magazine, Trade.*
Published by: K.E. Lomey Fachverlag fuer Neue Technologien, Frankfurter Ring 193a, Munich, 80807, Germany. TEL 49-89-255575914, FAX 49-89-255575915, info@cmmag.de, info@kelomey.de, http://www.cmmag.de, http://www.kelomey.de. Ed. Joerg Dennis Krueger. adv.: color page EUR 1,950; trim 210 x 297. Circ: 3,000 (paid and controlled).

330 600 USA
[CONTEXT]; where strategy and technology meet. Text in English. 1998. bi-m. USD 39 domestic; USD 59 in Canada; USD 6.50 newsstand/cover domestic; USD 9.50 newsstand/cover in Canada (effective 2001). **Document type:** *Magazine, Trade.* **Description:** Offers provocative writing and lively debate on how technology is transforming the business world.
Related titles: Online - full text ed.
Published by: Diamond Technology Partners, Inc., 875 N Michigan Ave, Ste 3000, Chicago, IL 60611. TEL 312-255-5550, FAX 312-255-6000, info@contextmag.com, http://www.contextmag.com. Ed. Paul Carroll. Pub. Lisa Laing.

CUSTOMER RELATIONSHIP TECHNOLOGY IN FINANCE; for customer centric banking and insurance. see *BUSINESS AND ECONOMICS—Banking And Finance*

004.068 GBR ISSN 1366-9680
CUSTOMER SERVICE NEWS. Text in English. 1997. m. **Document type:** *Magazine, Trade.*
Published by: Penton Media Europe (Subsidiary of: Penton Media, Inc.), Penton House, 288-290 Worton Rd, Isleworth, Mddx TW7 6EL, United Kingdom. TEL 44-20-8232-1600, FAX 44-20-8232-1650, information@penton.com, http://www.penton.com.

658.8 POL ISSN 1642-8951
CYBIZ. Text in Polish. 2001. m. adv. **Document type:** *Magazine, Trade.*
Published by: Polskie Wydawnictwo Fachowe Sp. Z o.o. (Subsidiary of: Deutscher Fachverlag GmbH), Jadzwingow 14, Warsaw, 02-692, Poland. FAX 48-22-8536702, pwf@pwf.com.pl, http://www.cybiz.pl, http://www.pwf.com.pl. adv.: page PLZ 9,800.

658.8 DEU
CYBIZ; das Fachmagazin fuer Erfolg mit E-Commerce. Text in German. 1999. 10/yr. EUR 44; EUR 6 newsstand/cover (effective 2004). adv. **Document type:** *Magazine, Trade.* **Description:** Provides information on the latest trends and strategies in the world of e-commerce and e-business.
Related titles: ♦ Online - full text ed.: CYbiz.de.
Published by: Deutscher Fachverlag GmbH, Mainzer Landstr 251, Frankfurt Am Main, 60326, Germany. TEL 49-69-759501, FAX 49-69-75952999, info@cybiz.de, info@dfv.de, http://www.cybiz.de, http://www.dfv.de. Ed. Rainer Miserre. Adv. contact Sabine Strauss. page EUR 6,900; trim 175 x 246. Circ: 20,569 (paid and controlled).

658.8 DEU
CYBIZ.DE. Text in German. d. adv.
Media: Online - full text. **Related titles:** ♦ Print ed.: CYbiz.
Published by: B2B Online GmbH, Mainzer Landstr 251, Frankfurt Am Main, 60326, Germany. TEL 49-69-759501, FAX 49-69-75952999, info@cybiz.de, info@b2b-online-gmbh.de, http://www.cybiz.de.

330 DEU ISSN 1612-0957
D O Q. Text in German. 1999. bi-m. EUR 60; EUR 10 newsstand/cover (effective 2005). adv. **Document type:** *Magazine, Trade.*
Published by: H & T Verlag GmbH & Co. KG (Subsidiary of: Verlagsgruppe Handelsblatt GmbH), Konrad-Zuse-Platz 1, Munich, 81829, Germany. TEL 49-89-4447870, FAX 49-89-44478710, egr@htverlag.de, info@htverlag.de, http://www.doq.de, http://www.htverlag.de. Ed. Elisabeth Grenzebach. adv.: page EUR 3,500; trim 180 x 266. Circ: 14,683 (paid and controlled).

DECISION SUPPORT SYSTEMS. see *BUSINESS AND ECONOMICS—Management*

330 DEU
DETECON MANAGEMENT REPORT. Text in German. 1971. q. adv. **Document type:** *Magazine, Trade.*
Formerly (until 2003): Diebold Management Report (0341-3683)
—IE, Infotrieve.
Published by: Detecon International GmbH, Frankfurterstr 27, Eschborn, 65760, Germany. TEL 49-6196-9030, FAX 49-6196-903465, info@detecon.com, http://www.detecon.com/en/publications/dmr_magazine.php?sid=a23e939ea48de600497dcaff7a265e12. Circ: 2,200 (paid).

DEVELOPMENTS IN BUSINESS SIMULATION & EXPERIENTIAL EXERCISES. see *COMPUTERS—Computer Simulation*

330 CHN
DIGITAL FORTUNE CHINA. Variant title: Industry Standard China. Text in Chinese. fortn. adv. **Document type:** *Magazine, Trade.* **Description:** Covers news, phenomenon and problems in the development of the New Economy, especially on the VC, hi-tech capital market and investment in the hi-tech sector.
Related titles: Online - full text ed.
Published by: I D G China, Rm. 616, Tower A, COFCO Plaza, Jianguomennei Dajie, Beijing, 100005 , China. TEL 86-10-6526-0959, FAX 86-10-6526-0866, dumin@idg.com.cn, http://www.digitalfortune.com.cn, http://www.idgchina.com. adv.: color page USD 6,500; trim 206 x 271. Circ: 60,000 (paid and controlled).

330 RUS ISSN 1680-8177
DIREKTOR INFORMACIONNOJ SLUZBY. Text in Russian. 2001. m. RUR 1,430 domestic; RUR 110 per issue domestic (effective 2004). adv. **Document type:** *Magazine, Trade.*
Published by: Izdatel'stvo Otkrytye Sistemy/Open Systems Publications, ul Rustaveli, dom 12A, komn 117, Moscow, 127254, Russian Federation. TEL 7-095-9563306, FAX 7-095-2539204, cio@osp.ru, info@osp.ru, http://www.osp.ru/cio. Ed. Pavel Khristov. Circ: 7,000.

330 AUT
E A N AUSTRIA INFORMATION. Text in German. q. adv. **Document type:** *Bulletin.*
Published by: E A N Austria Gesellschaft fuer Kooperative Logistik GmbH, Mayerhofgasse 1-15, Vienna, W 1040, Austria. TEL 01-5058601. Ed. Peter Franzmair. Adv. contact Renate Pardatscher. Circ: 6,000.

381 USA ISSN 1525-4178
E.BILL; source for electronic delivery & payment. Text in English. 1999. bi-m. adv. **Document type:** *Magazine.*
—IE.
Published by: R B Publishing, Inc., 2901 International Ln, Ste 200, Madison, WI 53704-3177. TEL 608-241-8777, 800-536-1992, FAX 608-241-8666, rbpub@rbpub.com, http://www.ebillmag.com, http://www.rbpub.com. Ed. Elizabeth Gooding. Pub. Ron Brent TEL 608-241-8777 ext 204.

330 CZE ISSN 1213-063X
E-BIZ; byznys, management a technologie. Text in Czech. 2000. m. CZK 399 (effective 2003). adv. **Document type:** *Magazine, Trade.*
Related titles: Online - full text ed.
Published by: Computer Press a.s., Pod Vinici 23, Prague 4, 143 11, Czech Republic. TEL 420-2-225273930, FAX 420-2-225273934, ebiz@cpress.cz, webmaster@cpress.cz, http://www.ebiz.cz, http://www.cpress.cz. Ed. Libuse Mohelska. Adv. contact Miroslava Doubkova. page CZK 150,000; trim 210 x 280.

E C MGT.COM EZINE. (Electronic Commerce Management) see *COMPUTERS—Internet*

E-COMMERCE IN FINANCE. see *COMPUTERS—Data Communications And Data Transmission Systems*

658.8 DEU ISSN 1436-8021
E-COMMERCE MAGAZIN; Geschaeftserfolg im Internet. Text in German. 1998. 7/yr. EUR 45.50; EUR 7.50 newsstand/cover (effective 2005). adv. **Document type:** *Magazine, Trade.* **Description:** Provides information and advice on how to succeed and profit from the Internet.
Incorporates (1994-2000): P C Mobil und Kommunikation (0949-8427); (2000-2000): Digital Enterprise (1439-7692)
Related titles: Online - full text ed.

Published by: W I N - Verlag GmbH & Co. KG, Johann-Sebastian-Bach Str 5, Vaterstetten, 85591, Germany. TEL 49-8106-3500, FAX 49-8106-350190, info@win-verlag.de, http://www.e-commerce-magazin.de/, http://www.win-verlag.de. Ed. Peter von Bechen. Pub. Hans-J. Grohmann. Adv. contact Gabi Koenig TEL 49-8106-350100. color page EUR 6,880. Circ: 10,417 (paid and controlled).

330 USA
E-COMMERCE MINUTE. Text in English. d. **Document type:** *Newsletter, Trade.*
Media: E-mail.
Published by: NewsFactor Network, 21700 Oxnard St, Ste 2040, Woodland Hills, CA 91367. TEL 818-593-2200, FAX 818-593-2203, http://www.newsfactor.com/. Pub. Richard Kern.

330 CAN
E D G E. (Executives in a Digital Gobal Economy) Text in English. 1995. m. CND 80 domestic; USD 115 in United States; USD 155 elsewhere; free to qualified personnel (effective 2003). **Document type:** *Magazine, Trade.*
Formerly (until Sep.2002): InfoSystems Executive (1482-9185)
Published by: Transcontinental Media, Inc. (Subsidiary of: Transcontinental, Inc.), 25 Sheppard Ave West, Ste 100, Toronto, ON M2N 6S7, Canada. TEL 416-733-7600, FAX 416-218-3544, info@transcontinental.ca, http://www.transcontinental-gtc.com/en/home.html, http://www.itbusiness.ca. Circ: 19,000 (controlled).

E D M REPORT; Data-Management-Magazin. see *COMPUTERS—Data Base Management*

330 DEU ISSN 0943-4542
E D V BERATER. Text in German. 1993. m. looseleaf. **Document type:** *Bulletin.* **Description:** Information related to computers for office use.
Incorporates: Telekommunikations-Berater (0943-9110)
Published by: V N R Verlag fuer die Deutsche Wirtschaft AG, Theodor-Heuss-Str 2-4, Bonn, 53095, Germany. TEL 49-228-8205-0, FAX 49-228-364411. Ed. Eduard Altmann.

330 GBR ISSN 1474-5127
E.LEARNING AGE; the magazine for the learning organisation. Variant title: E Learning Age. Text in English. 2001. m. free in United Kingdom; GBP 80 in Europe; GBP 120 rest of world (effective 2001). adv. bk.rev.; Website rev. charts; illus.; stat.; tr.lit. back issues avail.; reprints avail. **Document type:** *Magazine, Corporate.* **Description:** Aimed at those working for, or within, learning organizations and those that are seeking to become learning organizations.
Related titles: Online - full text ed.: (from EBSCO Publishing, ProQuest Information & Learning).
Published by: Bizmedia, Royal Station Court, Station Rd, Twyford, Reading, Berks RG10 9NF, United Kingdom. TEL 44-118-960-2820, FAX 44-118-960-2821, admin@bizmedia.co.uk, http://www.elearningage.co.uk/, http://www.bizmedia.co.uk/. Ed. Peter Williams. Pub. Melanie Williams. Adv. contact Nigel Clear TEL 44-118-960-2823. page GBP 2,500; trim 210 x 297. **Dist. by:** Jordan and Co, Units 3, 4 & 5, Parkside, Station Lane, Witney, Oxford OX8 6YF, United Kingdom. TEL 44-1993-772-644, FAX 44-1993-772-676, orders@jordanandco.co.uk, http://www.jordanandco.co.uk.

330 UAE
E MAGAZINE. Text in English. m. USD 150 (effective 2002). **Document type:** *Magazine, Trade.*
Published by: Corporate Publishing International, PO Box 13700, Dubai, United Arab Emirates. TEL 971-4-351-5316, FAX 971-4-359-8486, cpi@emirates.net.ae, http://www.cpilive.net.

332 DEU ISSN 1612-2569
ECOMPANY. Text in German. 2002. bi-m. **Document type:** *Magazine, Trade.*
Published by: H & T Verlag GmbH & Co. KG (Subsidiary of: Verlagsgruppe Handelsblatt GmbH), Konrad-Zuse-Platz 1, Munich, 81829, Germany. TEL 49-89-4447870, FAX 49-89-44478710, hd@htverlag.de, info@htverlag.de, http://www.ecompany-online.ch, http://www.htverlag.de. Ed. Henrik Daeschner.

330 GBR ISSN 0962-2780
HB143.5 CODEN: EFNCFL
ECONOMIC & FINANCIAL COMPUTING; a quarterly international journal. Text in English. 1991. q. GBP 109 in Europe; GBP 205 elsewhere (effective 2005). adv. bk.rev. **Document type:** *Journal, Academic/Scholarly.* **Description:** Provides a forum to present recent advances on the measurement aspects of economic and financial problems. Focuses on both the methodological and practical facets of quantitative and computational techniques.
Indexed: Inspec.
—BLDSC (3651.446500), IE, Infotrieve, ingenta. **CCC.**
Published by: European Economics and Financial Centre, 20 Guilford St, London, WC1N 1DZ, United Kingdom. TEL 44-20-72290402, FAX 44-20-72215118, eefc@eefc.com, http://www.eefc.com/efcsubfo.htm. Ed. H M Scobie. Adv. contact Brian Allan. **Subscr. to:** Publications Department, PO Box 2498, London W2 4LE, United Kingdom.

330 GBR ISSN 1350-7419
ECONOMIC & FINANCIAL MODELLING. Text in English. 1994. q. GBP 190 in Europe; GBP 205 elsewhere (effective 2005). adv. **Document type:** *Journal, Academic/Scholarly.* **Description:** Presents recent advances in all aspects of economic modelling.
Indexed: JEL.
—BLDSC (3651.447500).
Published by: European Economics and Financial Centre, 20 Guilford St, London, WC1N 1DZ, United Kingdom. TEL 44-20-72290402, FAX 44-20-72215118, eefc@eefc.com, http://www.eefc.com/efmsubfo.htm. Ed. H M Scobie. Adv. contact Brian Allan. **Subscr. to:** Publications Department, PO Box 2498, London W2 4LE, United Kingdom.

330 USA
▼ **ELEARNING!.** Text in English. 2004. q. USD 49.95; USD 9.95 per issue (effective 2005); free to qualified personnel. adv. **Document type:** *Magazine, Trade.* **Description:** Focuses on senior level executives who drive enterprise-wide knowledge management solutions.
Published by: B2B Media Co., PO Box 77694, Corona, CA 92881. TEL 888-201-2841, http://www.elearning.b2bmediaco.com/index.php. Ed. Larry Tuck. Pub. Catherine Upton. adv.: color page USD 5,500; trim 8.75 x 10.8. Circ: 10,000 (controlled).

ELECTRONIC COMMERCE NEWS. see *BUSINESS AND ECONOMICS—Domestic Commerce*

381 USA ISSN 1092-0366
HF5548.33 CODEN: ECWOFD
ELECTRONIC COMMERCE WORLD; business solutions through technology integration. Text in English. 1991. m. adv. **Document type:** *Magazine, Trade.*
Incorporates (1989-1999): E D I Forum (1048-3047); Formerly: E D I World (1055-0399)
Related titles: Online - full text ed.: (from Gale Group, O C L C Online Computer Library Center, Inc.).
Indexed: CompLI, Inspec, SoftBase.
—BLDSC (3700.285000), IE, Linda Hall. **CCC.**
Published by: E C Media Group, 2021 Coolidge St, Hollywood, FL 33020. TEL 954-925-5900, 954-336-4887, FAX 305-925-7533, http://www.ecomworld.com. Ed. Paul Demery. Pub., R&P Rick D'Allesandro. Adv. contact Eileen Baldwin. **Subscr. to:** Faulkner & Gray, Inc., PO Box 87271, Chicago, IL 60680. TEL 212-967-7000, FAX 212-967-7155, faulknerygray@msn.com.

ELECTRONIC MARKETS/ELEKTRONISCHE MAERKTE. see *BUSINESS AND ECONOMICS—Marketing And Purchasing*

384.33 AUS
ELECTRONIC TRADING MARKETS. Text in English. 1984. a. USD 425 domestic (effective 2001); USD 445 in United States; USD 480 in Europe. stat. **Document type:** *Directory.* **Description:** Covers fax, e-mail, interactive voice response, voice mail, EDI, EFTPOS, computer reservation systems. Includes information on developments and trends in Australia.
Former titles: Electronic Trading Markets Australia and New Zealand (1326-6780); (until 1997): Messaging and Transaction Services Market (Years); Which superseded in part: Directory of Electronic Services and Communications Networks in Australia and New Zealand (1322-350X)
Published by: Paul Budde Communication Pty. Ltd., 2643 George Downes Dr, Bucketty, NSW 2250, Australia. TEL 61-2-4998-8144, FAX 61-2-4998-8247, sally@budde.com.au, http://www.budde.com.au. Ed. Paul Budde. Circ: 150.

332 DEU ISSN 1612-1015
EMANAGER. Text in German. 2001. bi-m. **Document type:** *Magazine, Trade.*
Published by: H & T Verlag GmbH & Co. KG (Subsidiary of: Verlagsgruppe Handelsblatt GmbH), Konrad-Zuse-Platz 1, Munich, 81829, Germany. TEL 49-89-4447870, FAX 49-89-44478710, info@htverlag.de, http://www.htverlag.de. Ed. Eva Schulz. Circ: 62,000 (controlled).

EMARKETECT MAGAZINE; the journal for emarketplace builders, owners and operators. see *COMPUTERS—Internet*

ENTERPRISE. see *BUSINESS AND ECONOMICS—Small Business*

330 DEU
ENTSCHEIDER MAGAZIN MITTELSTAND; das Magazin fuer den Mittelstand. Abbreviated title: e m mittelstand. Text in German. 2002. q. adv. **Document type:** *Magazine, Trade.*
Related titles: Online - full text ed.
Published by: W I N - Verlag GmbH & Co. KG, Johann-Sebastian-Bach Str 5, Vaterstetten, 85591, Germany. TEL 49-8106-350-0, FAX 49-8106-350190, sm@iwtnet.de, info@win-verlag.de, http://www.entscheider-magazin.de, http://www.win-verlag.de. Ed. Rainer Miserre. Pub. Hans-J. Grohmann. Adv. contact Gabi Koenig TEL 49-8106-350100. page EUR 4,397; trim 204 x 288.

330 DEU ISSN 1619-7941
DER ENTWICKLER. Text in German. 1995. bi-m. EUR 29.50; EUR 5.50 newsstand/cover (effective 2005). adv. **Document type:** *Magazine, Trade.*
Published by: Software & Support Verlag GmbH, Kennedyallee 87, Frankfurt am Main, 60596, Germany. TEL 49-69-6300890, FAX 49-69-63008989, redaktion@derentwickler.de, info@software-support.biz, http://www.derentwickler.de, http://www.software-support.biz. Adv. contact Patrik Baumann. B&W page EUR 2,340, color page EUR 3,360. Circ: 20,000 (controlled).

681.3 PRT ISSN 0873-4798
EXAME INFORMATICA. Text in Portuguese. 1995. 8/yr. EUR 73.68 (effective 2004). adv. **Document type:** *Magazine, Trade.*
Published by: Edimpresa Editora Lda., Rua Calvet de Magalhaes 242, Laveiras, Paco de Arcos, 2770-022, Portugal. TEL 351-21-4698000, FAX 351-21-4698501, edimpresa@edimpresa.pt, http://www.edimpresa.pt. adv.: page EUR 3,090; trim 205 x 275. Circ: 37,532 (paid).

330 USA
EXECUTIVE EDGE. Text in English. d. free. adv. **Document type:** *Newsletter, Trade.* **Description:** Focuses on how IT can lead to effective business decisions.
Media: Online - full text.
Published by: Gartner Inc., 56 Top Gallant Rd, Stamford, CT 06904-2212. TEL 203-316-1111, 800-544-7337, FAX 203-316-6300, executiveedge@forbes.com, http://www.ee-online.com. Adv. contact Philip Alia. **Co-publisher:** Forbes, Inc.

EXECUTIVE REPORT; analysbrevet om hela it-industrin. see *BUSINESS AND ECONOMICS—Management*

005 USA ISSN 1082-7471
QA76.753
F A C C T. (Faulkner's Advisory on Computer and Communications Technologies) Text in English. d. **Document type:** *Trade.* **Description:** Provides web-based IT and communications reports that serve the information needs of professional service and manufacturing firms, technology providers, research libraries, and government agencies around the world.
Formerly (until 1995): MicroData Infodisk (1070-5902)
Media: Online - full content.
Published by: Faulkner Information Services, Inc. (Subsidiary of: Information Today, Inc.), 116 Cooper Center, 7905 Browning Rd, Pennsauken, NJ 08109-4319. TEL 856-662-2070, 800-843-0460, FAX 856-662-3380, faulkner@faulkner.com, http://www.faulkner.com/showcase/faccts.htm.

330 658 USA ISSN 1538-6023
CODEN: FETAAA
FAIRCHILD'S EXECUTIVE TECHNOLOGY. Variant title: Executive Technology. Text in English. m. free to qualified personnel. adv. **Document type:** *Trade.* **Description:** Reports on how top-level executives in the retailing industry can use information technology to maximize their profits.
Related titles: Online - full text ed.: (from EBSCO Publishing, ProQuest Information & Learning).
Indexed: TTI.
—**CCC.**
Published by: Fairchild Publications, Inc., 7 W 34th St, New York, NY 10001-8191. TEL 212-630-3700, millstem@fairchildpub.com, http://www.executivetechnology.com, http://www.fairchildpub.com. Ed. Marc Millstein. Pub. Tia Potter. Adv. contact Peter Lewine. Circ: 47,000 (controlled).

FIELD FORCE AUTOMATION. see *BUSINESS AND ECONOMICS—Marketing And Purchasing*

FIERCEENTERPRISE; the crm & enterprise it daily monitor. see *BUSINESS AND ECONOMICS—Management*

330 GBR ISSN 0961-5342
HG1709
FINANCIAL TECHNOLOGY INSIGHT✶. Text in English. 1990. m. GBP 300, USD 447 (effective 1995). bk.rev. charts; stat. back issues avail. **Document type:** *Bulletin, Trade.* **Description:** Provides information on the latest technology and policy implications of advanced automation and the globalization of banking and financial services.
Incorporates (1991-1993): E D I in Finance Newsletter (0960-4634); Formed by the merger of (1984-1990): Electronic Banking and Finance (0265-9239); (19??-1990): Online Finance
Related titles: Microform ed.: (from PQC); Online - full text ed.: (from Data-Star, Factiva, The Dialog Corporation).
Indexed: BLI, Inspec.
—AskIEEE. **CCC.**
Published by: Pergamon (Subsidiary of: Elsevier Science & Technology), The Boulevard, Langford Ln, East Park, Kidlington, Oxford OX5 1GB, United Kingdom. TEL 44-1865-843000, FAX 44-1865-843010. Ed. J Meyer. **Subscr. to:** Elsevier BV, PO Box 211, Amsterdam 1000 AE, Netherlands. TEL 31-20-485-3757, FAX 31-20-485-3432, nlinfo-f@elsevier.nl, http://www.elsevier.nl.

330 USA
▼ **FORRESTER.** Text in English. 2005. 3/yr. free for Forrester clients. **Document type:** *Magazine, Trade.* **Description:** Aims to provide ideas and advice that would become a permanent part of CEOs business libraries.

B

Published by: Forrester Research, Inc., 400 Technology Sq, Cambridge, MA 02139. resourcecenter@forrester.com, press@forrester.com, http://www.forrester.com/mag. Ed. Jimmy Guterman. Circ: 40,000 (controlled).

330 DEU ISSN 1435-6260
FORSCHUNGSERGEBNISSE ZUR INFORMATIK. Text in German. 1997. irreg., latest vol.61, 2002. price varies. **Document type:** *Monographic series, Academic/Scholarly.*
Published by: Verlag Dr. Kovac, Arnoldstr 49, Hamburg, 22763, Germany. TEL 49-40-3988800, FAX 49-40-39888055, info@verlagdrkovac.de, http://www.verlagdrkovac.de/4-1.htm.

330 ROM ISSN 1222-7129
G INFO - GAZETA DE INFORMATICA. Text in Romanian. 1991. 8/yr. ROL 120,000 (effective 2002). adv. **Document type:** *Magazine, Trade.*
Related titles: Online - full text ed.
Published by: Agora Media, Str. Tudor Vladimirescu nr. 63, ap. 9, CP 230-1, Targu Mures, 4300, Romania. TEL 40-65-166516, FAX 40-65-166290, office@agora.ro, http://www.ginfo.ro, http://www.agora.ro. Circ: 4,000 (paid and controlled).

331.11 600 USA
THE H R INTERNET AND TECHNOLOGY LETTER. Text in English. 1999. m. USD 197 (effective 1999). **Document type:** *Newsletter, Trade.* **Description:** Helps human resource professionals and employers better employ online resources. Includes recruiting trends and opportunities, privacy and liability issues associated with workplace technologies, reviews of HR-related Web sites, product information, case studies, and other news related to the the convergence of personnel functions and online capabilities.
Published by: Thompson Publishing Group, 1725 K St, N W, Ste 700, Washington, DC 20006. TEL 202-739-9698, 800-677-3789, http://www.thompson.com.

330 658.3 USA
HD9696.C63
H R - P C (ONLINE); computer technology for human resource management. Text in English. 1985. USD 117 (effective 2001). adv. bk.rev.; software rev. index. **Document type:** *Journal, Trade.*
Formerly (until 2000): H R - P C (Print) (0884-9129)
Media: Online - full content.
Published by: D G M Associates, PO Box 10639, Marina, CA 90295-6639. TEL 310-578-1428, dgm@hrworld.com, http://www.hrworld.com/. Ed. David G Mahal.

330 USA
HARLOW REPORT: GEOGRAPHIC INFORMATION SYSTEMS (ONLINE). Text in English. 1978. m. looseleaf. USD 125 (effective 2005). bk.rev. Index. back issues avail. **Document type:** *Newsletter, Trade.* **Description:** Presents current reports on the use of computers and computer graphics for managing geographic information systems. Written for engineers, planners, systems developers, cartographers, and others interested in the management of geographic information systems and facilities. The publication can be read and printed through Adobe Acrobat Reader.
Former titles (until 2001): Harlow Report: Geographic Information Systems (Print) (1043-6146); (until 1989): F - M Automation Newsletter (Facilities Management) (0742-468X)
Media: Online - full text.
Published by: Advanced Information Management Group, Inc., 905 Thistledown Ln., Hoover, AL 35244-3361. TEL 205-982-9203, charlow@charter.net, http://www.theharlowreport.com. Ed., Pub. Chris Harlow. Circ: 1,000 (paid).

HIGH TECHNOLOGY AND OTHER GROWTH STOCKS. see *BUSINESS AND ECONOMICS—Investments*

HONG KONG SPECIAL ADMINISTRATIVE REGION OF CHINA. CENSUS AND STATISTICS DEPARTMENT. REPORT ON ANNUAL SURVEY ON INFORMATION TECHNOLOGY USAGE AND PENETRATION IN THE BUSINESS SECTOR. see *BUSINESS AND ECONOMICS—Abstracting, Bibliographies, Statistics*

330 GBR
CODEN: ICLTEG
I D G NEWS SERVICE. Text in English. 1985. m. free. bk.rev. illus. back issues avail.
Formerly: I C L Today (0268-5957)
Related titles: Online - full text ed.
Indexed: Inspec.
—AskIEEE.
Published by: I.D.G. Communications Ltd., 2 Stone Rd, Bromley, Kent BR2 9AU, United Kingdom. TEL 0181-460-0944, http://www.idg.com/. Ed. Ron Condon. Circ: 16,000.

629.8029 USA ISSN 1043-8319
HD9801.6.P763
I D SYSTEMS BUYERS GUIDE. Text in English. 1983. a. adv. **Document type:** *Directory, Trade.* **Description:** Lists companies and products for the automated data collection industry.
Former titles (until 1989): Automatic Identification Manufacturers and Services Directory (1042-4512); (until 1987): Bar Code Manufacturers and Services Directory (8755-7851)

Published by: Helmers Publishing, Inc., 174 Concord St, Peterborough, NH 03458-0874. TEL 603-924-9631, FAX 603-924-7408. Pub. Dan Rodrigues. adv.: B&W page USD 4,795; trim 10.88 x 8.13. Circ: 67,500.

I E E E SYMPOSIUM ON MASS STORAGE SYSTEMS. DIGEST OF PAPERS. see *COMPUTERS*

I N T I X NEWSLETTER. see *BUSINESS AND ECONOMICS—Marketing And Purchasing*

658 SWE ISSN 1402-0963
I T.BRANSCHEN; affaerstidningen foer hela it-industrin. Text in Swedish. 20/yr. SEK 795 (effective 2002). adv. **Document type:** *Magazine, Trade.*
Related titles: Online - full text ed.; ◆ Supplement(s): AV - Magasinet.
Published by: I D G AB (Subsidiary of: I D G Communications Inc.), Sturegatan 11, Stockholm, 10678, Sweden. TEL 46-8-4536000, FAX 46-8-4536005, itbranschen@idg.se, http://itbranschen.idg.se, http://www.idg.se. Ed. Fredrik Arvidsson. Adv. contact Rickard Carlsson. page SEK 46,500; trim 178 x 240. Circ: 17,500 (paid).

658 DEU
I T - BUSINESS DAY. (Information Technology) Text in German. d. **Document type:** *Newsletter, Trade.* **Description:** Presents up-to-date news on all aspects of the information technology business world.
Media: Online - full text.
Published by: Vogel IT-Medien GmbH, Gutermannstr 25, Augsburg, 86154, Germany. TEL 49-821-21770, FAX 49-821-2177150, http://www.it-business.net.

658 DEU ISSN 1435-7046
I T - BUSINESS NEWS; Wochenzeitung fuer IT-Reseller und E-Solution-Provider. (Information Technology) Text in German. 1990. w. EUR 99; EUR 3 newsstand/cover (effective 2003). adv. **Document type:** *Newspaper, Trade.* **Description:** Contains news and information on the latest products and services available for the information technology industry.
Former titles (until 1998): E H Z - E D V Handelszeitung (1435-7119); (until 1993): E D V Handelszeitung (0938-7544)
Related titles: Online - full text ed.; ◆ Supplement(s): I T - Sources Weekly.
Published by: Vogel IT-Medien GmbH, Gutermannstr 25, Augsburg, 86154, Germany. TEL 49-821-21770, FAX 49-821-2177150, abo@it-business.net, marliese_bernhardt@vogel-medien.de, http://www.it-business.net, http://www.vogel-it.de. adv.: B&W page EUR 6,800, color page EUR 8,600; trim 320 x 480. Circ: 33,290 (paid and controlled).

330 GBR
I T DECISIONS EUROPE. Text in English. a. free to qualified personnel (effective 2005). adv. **Document type:** *Journal, Trade.* **Description:** Presents information on the latest technologies, trends and best-practice solutions relevant to all participants within the IT decision making process.
Published by: S P G Media Ltd. (Subsidiary of: Sterling Publishing Group Plc.), Brunel House, 55-57 North Wharf Rd, London, W2 1LA, United Kingdom. TEL 44-20-79159600, FAX 44-20-77242089, info@sterlingpublications.com, http://www.itdecisions.co.uk/, http://www.spgmedia.com/. adv.: B&W page GBP 6,700, color page GBP 6,900. Circ: 10,600 (controlled).

330 POL
I T PARTNER. (Information Technology) Text in Polish. d. (Mon.-Fri.). **Document type:** *Trade.*
Media: Online - full content.
Published by: I D G Poland S.A., ul Jordanowska 12, PO Box 73, Warsaw, 04-204, Poland. TEL 48-22-3217800, FAX 48-22-3217888, idg@idg.com.pl, http://www.itpartner.pl, http://www.idg.pl.

658 DEU ISSN 1435-7054
I T - SOURCES. (Information Technology) Text in German. 1998. m. adv. **Document type:** *Magazine, Trade.*
Published by: Vogel IT-Medien GmbH, Gutermannstr 25, Augsburg, 86154, Germany. TEL 49-821-21770, FAX 49-821-2177150, marliese_bernhardt@vogel-medien.de, http://www.it-business.net, http://www.vogel-it.de. adv.: B&W page EUR 970, color page EUR 1,300; trim 220 x 290.

658 DEU
I T - SOURCES WEEKLY. (Information Technology) Text in German. 1998. w. adv. **Document type:** *Newspaper, Trade.*
Formerly: I T - Sales Week (1435-7062)
Related titles: ◆ Supplement to: I T - Business News. ISSN 1435-7046.
Published by: Vogel IT-Medien GmbH, Gutermannstr 25, Augsburg, 86154, Germany. TEL 49-821-21770, FAX 49-821-2177150, marliese_bernhardt@vogel-medien.de, http://www.vogel-it.de. adv.: color page EUR 1,600; trim 320 x 480.

681.3 FIN ISSN 1457-0025
I T VIIKKO. (Information Technology) Text in Finnish. 1999. w. EUR 95 (effective 2004). adv. **Document type:** *Magazine, Trade.* **Description:** Covers information technology current events and trends occuring both in Finland and the rest of the world.
Published by: Sanoma Magazines Finland Corporation, Hoylaamotie 1 D, P.O. Box 100, Helsinki, 00040, Finland. TEL 358-9-1201, FAX 358-9-1205171, webmaster@ITviikko.fi, info@sanomamagazines.fi, http://www.itviikko.fi, http://www.sanomamagazines.fi. adv.: B&W page EUR 5,090, color page EUR 7,600. Circ: 45,000 (paid and controlled).

330 GBR
I T WEEK (ONLINE EDITION). (Information Technology) Text in English. d. **Document type:** *Trade.* **Description:** Provides IT technical and informed product coverage with comprehensive UK and world analysis.
Media: Online - full text (from Gale Group). **Related titles:** ◆ Print ed.: I T Week (Print Edition). ISSN 1462-396X.
Published by: ZDNet UK Ltd., International House, 1 St Katharine's Way, London, E1W 1XQ, United Kingdom. TEL 44-20-7903-6800, FAX 44-20-7903-6000, itweek@zd.com, http://www.zdnet.co.uk/itweek. Ed. Eugene Lacey TEL 44-20-7903-6857. Adv. contact Martin Taylor TEL 44-20-7903-6915.

330 GBR ISSN 1462-396X
I T WEEK (PRINT EDITION); the newsweekly for the connected enterprise. (Information Technology) Text in English. 1982. w. free to qualified personnel. adv. back issues avail. **Document type:** *Magazine, Trade.* **Description:** Provides news and features related to the needs of IT management and personnel.
Former titles (until 2000): Information Week (1460-0498); (until 1997): P C User (0263-5720)
Related titles: ◆ Online - full text ed.: I T Week (Online Edition).
Indexed: CompC, CompD, ICEA, Inspec, PCR2, SoftAbEng.
—AskIEEE, CISTI, IE. **CCC.**
Published by: V N U Business Publications Ltd., 32-34 Broadwick St, London, W1A 2HG, United Kingdom. TEL 44-20-7316-9000, FAX 44-20-7316-9003, itweek@zd.com, http://www.itweek.co.uk, http://www.vnunet.co.uk, http://www.itweekmedia.co.uk/. Ed. Toby Wolpe. adv.: page GBP 4,380. Circ: 55,000.

ICONOMY; Wirtschaftsmagazin fuer IT- und EBusiness-Strategien. see *BUSINESS AND ECONOMICS—Management*

005.74 GBR ISSN 0263-5577
HD28 CODEN: IMDSD8
➤ **INDUSTRIAL MANAGEMENT & DATA SYSTEMS.** Text in English. 1980. 9/yr. EUR 9,177.41 in Europe; USD 9,249 in North America; AUD 11,619 in Australasia; GBP 6,328.16 in UK & elsewhere (effective 2006). bk.rev. illus.; abstr. back issues avail.; reprint service avail. from PSC. **Document type:** *Journal, Academic/Scholarly.* **Description:** Aims to improve skills by promoting awareness of new products, processes, training techniques and management concepts. Covers the full range of managerial activity: personnel, production, communications, marketing.
Formed by the merger of (1967-1980): Data Systems (0011-6912); (1970-1980): Industrial Management (0007-6929)
Related titles: CD-ROM ed.; Online - full text ed.: (from EBSCO Publishing, Emerald Group Publishing Limited, Florida Center for Library Automation, Gale Group, IngentaConnect, O C L C Online Computer Library Center, Inc., ProQuest Information & Learning, Swets Information Services).
Indexed: ABIn, ADPA, AIA, ASCA, ASEANManA, BMT, BPI, BrTechI, CMCI, CPM, CompC, CompD, CompLI, CurCont, ETA, EmerIntel, Emerald, EngInd, ErgAb, Inspec, M&MA, T&II.
—BLDSC (4457.715000), AskIEEE, Ei, IDS, IE, Infotrieve, ingenta. **CCC.**
Published by: Emerald Group Publishing Limited, 60-62 Toller Ln, Bradford, W Yorks BD8 9BY, United Kingdom. TEL 44-1274-777700, FAX 44-1274-785200, infomation@emeraldinsight.com, http://www.emeraldinsight.com/imds.htm. Ed. Binshan Lin.

384.0285 USA ISSN 1533-8746
INFOCOMMERCE REPORT. Text in English. 2000. m. USD 199 domestic; USD 249 foreign (effective 2002). **Document type:** *Newsletter, Trade.* **Description:** Contains the latest news and trends in business and marketing information communications and technologies along with profiles of content providers and distributors.
Related titles: Online - full text ed.
Published by: The Perkins Group Ltd., 2 Penn Center Plaza, 1500 JFK Blvd., Ste. 200, Philadelphia, PA 19102-1706. TEL 215-735-8900, FAX 215-735-5281, info@perkinsgroup.net, http://www.infocommercereport.com, http://www.perkinsgroup.net.

330 USA ISSN 1040-2179
INFOCUS (PORTLAND); the newsletter on products, services and trends in forms and systems. Text in English. 1988. m. (10/yr.). USD 50; USD 65 foreign. bk.rev. back issues avail. **Document type:** *Newsletter.* **Description:** Covers industry news, events and hardware and software for forms and records design. Includes tips on ways of improving forms and systems.

B

Published by: Business Forms Management Association, Inc., 319 S W Washington St, Ste 710, Portland, OR 97204-2604. TEL 503-227-3393, FAX 503-274-7667, Paul@bfma.org, http://www.bfma.org/~bfma/. R&P Paul Telles. Circ: 2,000.

THE INFORMATION ADVISOR. see *LIBRARY AND INFORMATION SCIENCES—Computer Applications*

INFORMATION AND ORGANIZATION. see *BUSINESS AND ECONOMICS—Accounting*

658.4 GBR ISSN 1479-9774
INFORMATION SECURITY MANAGEMENT. Text in English. 2001. m. adv. **Document type:** *Magazine, Trade.*
Published by: Penton Media Europe (Subsidiary of: Penton Media, Inc.), Penton House, 288-290 Worton Rd, Isleworth, Mddx TW7 6EL, United Kingdom. TEL 44-20-8232-1600, FAX 44-20-8232-1650, information@penton.com, http://www.infosecuritymanagement.com/index.cfm?cat=MH&siteheader=m, http://www.penton.com. Ed. Rob Gallagher. Circ: 23,000 (paid and controlled).

INFORMATION TECHNOLOGY ADVISER. see *BUSINESS AND ECONOMICS—Management*

330 POL ISSN 1506-5774
INFORMATOR I T. Text in Polish. 1999. a. **Document type:** *Directory, Trade.*
Related titles: Online - full text ed.
Published by: I D G Poland S.A., ul Jordanowska 12, PO Box 73, Warsaw, 04-204, Poland. TEL 48-22-3217800, FAX 48-22-3217888, idg@idg.com.pl, http://www.informator.idg.pl, http://www.idg.pl.

681.3 HRV ISSN 1330-0393
INFOTREND. Text in Croatian. 1992. bi-m. **Document type:** *Magazine, Trade.*
Related titles: Online - full text ed.: ISSN 1332-6414. 1996.
Published by: Trend d.o.o., Trg Petra Svacica 12-II, Zagreb, 10000, Croatia. TEL 385-1-4856895, FAX 385-1-4554536.

INPUT - OUTPUT STUDIEN. see *BUSINESS AND ECONOMICS*

330 657 GBR ISSN 1550-1949
HF5679 CODEN: IJAMEN
➤ **INTELLIGENT SYSTEMS IN ACCOUNTING, FINANCE & MANAGEMENT.** Text in English. 198?. q. USD 695 to institutions; USD 765 combined subscription to institutions print & online eds. (effective 2006). adv. back issues avail.; reprint service avail. from PSC. **Document type:** *Journal, Academic/Scholarly.* **Description:** Publishes original material concerned with all aspects of intelligent systems in business-based applications with an aim of providing a forum for advancing theory and application of intelligent systems in business theory.
Former titles (until 2004): International Journal of Intelligent Systems in Accounting, Finance & Management (1055-615X); (until 1992): Expert Systems Review for Business & Accounting (1059-3640)
Related titles: Microform ed.: (from PQC); Online - full content ed.: ISSN 1099-1174. USD 695 to institutions (effective 2006); Online - full text ed.: (from EBSCO Publishing, Gale Group, IngentaConnect, ProQuest Information & Learning, Swets Information Services, Wiley InterScience).
Indexed: ABIn, BrCerAb, C&ISA, CerAb, CompLI, CorrAb, E&CAJ, EMA, IAA, Inspec, M&TEA, MBF, METADEX, SolStAb, WAA.
—BLDSC (4531.832101), AskIEEE, IE, Infotrieve, ingenta. **CCC.**
Published by: John Wiley & Sons Ltd. (Subsidiary of: John Wiley & Sons, Inc.), The Atrium, Southern Gate, Chichester, West Sussex PO19 8SQ, United Kingdom. TEL 44-1243-779777, FAX 44-1243-775878, customer@wiley.co.uk, http://www.wiley.co.uk. adv.: B&W page GBP 650, color page GBP 1,550; trim 200 x 260. **Subscr. in the Americas to:** John Wiley & Sons, Inc., 111 River St, Hoboken, NJ 07030-5774. TEL 201-748-6645, FAX 201-748-6088, subinfo@wiley.com.

➤ **INTERNATIONAL JOURNAL OF ACCOUNTING INFORMATION SYSTEMS.** see *BUSINESS AND ECONOMICS—Accounting*

330 GBR ISSN 1740-2107
▼ ➤ **INTERNATIONAL JOURNAL OF ADAPTIVE INFRASTRUCTURES.** Text in English. forthcoming 2006. q. USD 450 to institutions; USD 545 combined subscription to institutions print & online eds. (effective 2005). **Document type:** *Journal, Academic/Scholarly.*
Related titles: Online - full text ed.: ISSN 1740-2115. forthcoming 2006. USD 450 to institutions (effective 2005).
Published by: Inderscience Publishers, IEL Editorial Office, PO Box 735, Olney, Bucks MK46 5WB, United Kingdom. TEL 44-1234-240519, FAX 44-1234-240515, ijais@inderscience.com, info@inderscience.com, http://www.inderscience.com/ijais. Ed. Peter T Rayson. **Subscr. to:** World Trade Centre Bldg, 29 route de Pre-Bois, Case Postale 896, Geneva 15 1215, Switzerland. FAX 41-22-7910885, subs@inderscience.com.

▼ ➤ **INTERNATIONAL JOURNAL OF AGILE SYSTEMS AND MANAGEMENT.** see *BUSINESS AND ECONOMICS—Management*

▼ ➤ **INTERNATIONAL JOURNAL OF BUSINESS DATA COMMUNICATIONS AND NETWORKING.** see *COMPUTERS—Data Communications And Data Transmission Systems*

330 GBR ISSN 1743-8195
▼ ➤ **INTERNATIONAL JOURNAL OF BUSINESS INTELLIGENCE AND DATA MINING.** Text in English. 2005. 4/yr. USD 450; USD 545 combined subscription print & online eds. (effective 2005). **Document type:** *Journal, Academic/Scholarly.* **Description:** Publishes original research results, surveys and tutorials of important areas and techniques, detailed descriptions of significant applications, technical advances and news items concerning use of intelligent data analysis technique in business applications.
Related titles: Online - full text ed.: ISSN 1743-8187. USD 450 (effective 2005).
Published by: Inderscience Publishers, IEL Editorial Office, PO Box 735, Olney, Bucks MK46 5WB, United Kingdom. TEL 44-1234-240519, FAX 44-1234-240515, ijbidm@inderscience.com, info@inderscience.com, http://www.inderscience.com/ijbidm. Ed. David Taniar.

330 USA ISSN 1548-0623
▼ **INTERNATIONAL JOURNAL OF CASES ON ELECTRONIC COMMERCE.** Text in English. 2005. q. USD 85 to individuals; USD 195 to institutions (effective 2005). **Document type:** *Journal, Academic/Scholarly.*
Related titles: Online - full text ed.: ISSN 1548-0615. 2005.
Indexed: C&ISA, E&CAJ, IAA.
Published by: (Information Resources Management Association), Idea Group Publishing (Subsidiary of: Idea Group Inc.), 701 E Chocolate Ave, Ste 200, Hershey, PA 17033-1240. TEL 717-533-8845, FAX 717-533-7115, cust@idea-group.com, http://www.idea-group.com/journals/details.asp?id=4285. Ed. Rabbi Mehdi Khosrow-Pour. R&P Jan Travers.

330 USA ISSN 1553-4685
▼ **INTERNATIONAL JOURNAL OF E-BUSINESS.** Text in English. 2005 (Mar.). s-a.
Published by: International Academy of Business and Economics, 983 Woodland Dr, Turlock, CA 95382-7281. TEL 209-667-3074, FAX 209-667-3210, AKhade@iabe.org, http://www.iabe.org.

330 004.678 USA ISSN 1548-1131
▼ **INTERNATIONAL JOURNAL OF E-BUSINESS RESEARCH.** Text in English. 2005. q. USD 85 to individuals; USD 195 to institutions (effective 2005). **Document type:** *Journal.* **Description:** Provides an international forum for researchers and practitioners to advance the knowledge and practice of all facets of electronic business. Emerging e-business theories, architectures, and technologies are emphasized to stimulate and disseminate cutting-edge information into research and business communities in a timely fashion.
Related titles: Online - full text ed.: ISSN 1548-114X. 2005.
Indexed: C&ISA, E&CAJ, IAA.
—BLDSC (4542.189600).
Published by: (Information Resources Management Association), Idea Group Publishing (Subsidiary of: Idea Group Inc.), 701 E Chocolate Ave, Ste 200, Hershey, PA 17033-1240. TEL 717-533-8845, FAX 717-533-7115, cust@idea-group.com, http://www.idea-group.com/journals/details.asp?id=4294. Ed. In Lee.

330 GBR ISSN 1470-6067
➤ **INTERNATIONAL JOURNAL OF ELECTRONIC BUSINESS.** Abbreviated title: I J E B. Text in English. 2002. 6/yr. USD 540 to institutions; USD 685 combined subscription to institutions print & online eds. (effective 2005). back issues avail.; reprints avail. **Document type:** *Journal, Academic/Scholarly.* **Description:** Aims to develop, promote and coordinate the development and practice of electronic business methods.
Related titles: Online - full content ed.: ISSN 1741-5063. USD 540 to institutions (effective 2005); Online - full text ed.: (from EBSCO Publishing).
Indexed: ABIn, BrCerAb, C&ISA, CerAb, CompLI, CorrAb, E&CAJ, EMA, IAA, Inspec, M&TEA, MBF, METADEX, WAA.
—BLDSC (4542.230500), IE, Linda Hall.
Published by: Inderscience Publishers, IEL Editorial Office, PO Box 735, Olney, Bucks MK46 5WB, United Kingdom. TEL 44-1234-240519, FAX 44-1234-240515, ijeb@inderscience.com, editor@inderscience.com, http://www.inderscience.com/ijeb. Ed. Dr. Eldon Y Li TEL 805-756-2964. R&P Jeanette Brooks. Adv. contact Cheryl Busby. **Subscr. to:** World Trade Centre Bldg, 29 route de Pre-Bois, Case Postale 896, Geneva 15 1215, Switzerland. FAX 41-22-7910885.

380.10285 USA ISSN 1086-4415
HF5548.32 CODEN: IJECFE
➤ **INTERNATIONAL JOURNAL OF ELECTRONIC COMMERCE.** Text in English. 1996. q. USD 87 domestic to individuals; USD 101 foreign to individuals; USD 599 combined subscription domestic to institutions print & online eds.; USD 641 combined subscription foreign to institutions print & online eds. (effective 2006). adv. bk.rev. **Document type:** *Journal, Academic/Scholarly.* **Description:** Offers an integrated view of the field covering the areas of management information systems, computer science, economics, sociology, and related disciplines.
Related titles: Online - full text ed.: 2000 (Sep.) (from EBSCO Publishing, Gale Group, H.W. Wilson, O C L C Online Computer Library Center, Inc., Swets Information Services).
Indexed: ABIn, BPI, CMCI, CompLI, CurCont, Inspec, SSCI.
—BLDSC (4542.231000), IDS, IE, Infotrieve, ingenta. **CCC.**
Published by: M.E. Sharpe, Inc., 80 Business Park Dr, Armonk, NY 10504. TEL 914-273-1800, 800-541-6563, FAX 914-273-2106, custserv@mesharpe.com, http://www.mesharpe.com/mall/results1.asp. Ed. Vladimir Zwass. Pub. Evelyn M Fazio. Adv. contact Barbara Ladd TEL 914-273-1800 ext 121. B&W page USD 300; trim 9 x 6.

330 GBR ISSN 1460-6712
➤ **INTERNATIONAL JOURNAL OF FINANCIAL SERVICES MANAGEMENT.** Abbreviated title: I J F S M. Text in English. 2000. q. USD 450 to institutions; USD 545 combined subscription to institutions print & online eds. (effective 2005). **Document type:** *Journal, Academic/Scholarly.* **Description:** Provides an international forum for experts, researchers and practitioners in financial services, banking, insurance, financial accounting, corporate finance, fund management and related disciplines.
Related titles: Online - full content ed.: ISSN 1741-8062. USD 450 (effective 2005).
Published by: Inderscience Publishers, IEL Editorial Office, PO Box 735, Olney, Bucks MK46 5WB, United Kingdom. TEL 44-1234-240519, FAX 44-1234-240515, ijfsm@inderscience.com, editor@inderscience.com, http://www.inderscience.com/ijfsm. Ed. Dr. Mohammed A Dorgham. **Subscr. to:** World Trade Centre Bldg, 29 route de Pre-Bois, Case Postale 896, Geneva 15 1215, Switzerland. FAX 41-22-7910885, subs@inderscience.com.

330 GBR ISSN 1740-2085
▼ ➤ **INTERNATIONAL JOURNAL OF INTELLIGENT COLLABORATIVE ENTERPRISE.** Text in English. 2005. q. USD 450 to institutions; USD 545 combined subscription to institutions print & online eds. (effective 2005). **Document type:** *Journal, Academic/Scholarly.*
Related titles: Online - full text ed.: ISSN 1740-2093. 2005. USD 450 to institutions (effective 2005).
Published by: Inderscience Publishers, IEL Editorial Office, PO Box 735, Olney, Bucks MK46 5WB, United Kingdom. TEL 44-1234-240519, FAX 44-1234-240515, ijice@inderscience.com, info@inderscience.com, http://www.inderscience.com/ijice. Ed. Peter T Rayson. **Subscr. to:** World Trade Centre Bldg, 29 route de Pre-Bois, Case Postale 896, Geneva 15 1215, Switzerland. FAX 41-22-7910885, subs@inderscience.com.

338 658 GBR ISSN 0263-7863
T56.8
➤ **INTERNATIONAL JOURNAL OF PROJECT MANAGEMENT.** Text in English. 1983. 8/yr. EUR 217 in Europe to individuals; JPY 28,800 in Japan to individuals; USD 244 to individuals except Europe and Japan; EUR 998 in Europe to institutions; JPY 132,500 in Japan to institutions; USD 1,116 to institutions except Europe and Japan (effective 2006). bk.rev. index. back issues avail. **Document type:** *Journal, Academic/Scholarly.* **Description:** Offers guidance to practicing managers striving to complete projects on time, to meet project requirements and to stay within budget.
Related titles: Microform ed.: (from PQC); Online - full text ed.: (from EBSCO Publishing, Gale Group, IngentaConnect, ScienceDirect, Swets Information Services).
Indexed: ABIn, BPIA, CivEngAb, Emerald, EngInd, EnvAb, ExcerpMed, FLUIDEX, GEOBASE, IAOP, ICEA, Inspec, ORMS, QC&AS, RASB, RDA, RefZh, SCIMP.
—BLDSC (4542.487100), AskIEEE, CISTI, Ei, IE, Infotrieve, ingenta. **CCC.**
Published by: (International Project Management Association (INTERNET)), Pergamon (Subsidiary of: Elsevier Science & Technology), The Boulevard, Langford Ln, East Park, Kidlington, Oxford OX5 1GB, United Kingdom. TEL 44-1865-843000, FAX 44-1865-843010, ijpm@europrojex.com, http://www.elsevier.com/locate/ijproman. Ed. J Rodney Turner. **Subscr. to:** Elsevier BV, PO Box 211, Amsterdam 1000 AE, Netherlands. TEL 31-20-485-3757, FAX 31-20-485-3432, nlinfo-f@elsevier.nl, http://www.elsevier.nl.

330   GBR   ISSN 1460-6720
                             CODEN: IJSTCU
➤ **INTERNATIONAL JOURNAL OF SERVICES TECHNOLOGY AND MANAGEMENT.** Abbreviated title: I J S T M. Text in English. 1998. 6/yr. EUR 515, USD 540 to institutions print & online ed.; EUR 650, USD 685 combined subscription to institutions print & online eds.. **Document type:** *Journal, Academic/Scholarly.* **Description:** Covers a wide range of operations and functions, such as human aspects of healthcare, and technological aspects of public services design and management, as well as services provided by the manufacturing sector, information services and the associated cultural, ethical, legal and political aspects.
Related titles: Online - full text ed.: ISSN 1741-525X. USD 540 to institutions (effective 2005) (from EBSCO Publishing).
Indexed: ABIn, BrCerAb, C&ISA, CerAb, CompLI, CorrAb, E&CAJ, EMA, IAA, Inspec, M&TEA, MBF, METADEX, SolStAb, WAA.
—BLDSC (4542.544690), Linda Hall.
Published by: Inderscience Publishers, IEL Editorial Office, PO Box 735, Olney, Bucks MK46 5WB, United Kingdom. TEL 44-1234-240519, FAX 44-1234-240515, ijstm@inderscience.com, editor@inderscience.com, http://www.inderscience.com/ijstm. Ed. Dr. Mohammed A Dorgham. **Subscr. to:** World Trade Centre Bldg, 29 route de Pre-Bois, Case Postale 896, Geneva 15 1215, Switzerland. FAX 41-22-7910885, subs@inderscience.com.

330   GBR   ISSN 1740-2123
▼ ➤ **INTERNATIONAL JOURNAL OF SIMULATION AND PROCESS MODELLING.** Text in English. 2005. q. USD 450 to institutions print or online ed.; USD 545 combined subscription to institutions print & online eds. (effective 2005). **Document type:** *Journal, Academic/Scholarly.* **Description:** Aims to provide a unified discussion forum for academics, researchers and practitioners interested in the modelling and simulation of business processes, production processes, service and administrative processes and public sector processes.
Related titles: Online - full text ed.: ISSN 1740-2131. 2005.
Indexed: C&ISA, E&CAJ, IAA.
Published by: Inderscience Publishers, IEL Editorial Office, PO Box 735, Olney, Bucks MK46 5WB, United Kingdom. TEL 44-1234-240519, FAX 44-1234-240515, ijspm@inderscience.com, info@inderscience.com, http://www.inderscience.com/ijspm. **Subscr. to:** World Trade Centre Bldg, 29 route de Pre-Bois, Case Postale 896, Geneva 15 1215, Switzerland. FAX 41-22-7910885, subs@inderscience.com.

330   AUT   ISSN 1726-4529
➤ **INTERNATIONAL JOURNAL OF SIMULATION MODELLING.** Text in English. 2002. q. EUR 120 (effective 2005). adv. charts; illus. back issues avail. **Document type:** *Journal, Academic/Scholarly.* **Description:** Provides a global forum for the publication of all forms of simulation modelling research work in academic institutions, in industry or in consultancy.
Indexed: C&ISA, E&CAJ, IAA, Inspec.
Published by: D A A A M International Vienna, Karlsplatz 13-311, Vienna, 1040, Austria. TEL 43-1-5880131121, FAX 43-1-5880131199, president@daaam.com, http://www.ijsimm.com, http://www.daaam.com. Ed., R&P, Adv. contact Borut Buchmeister. Pub. Branko Katalinic. B&W page EUR 150; trim 205 x 290. Circ: 280 (paid and controlled).

▼ ➤ **INTERNATIONAL JOURNAL OF TECHNOLOGY MARKETING.** see *BUSINESS AND ECONOMICS—Marketing And Purchasing*

330.1   NLD   ISSN 0924-5235
➤ **INTERNATIONAL SERIES IN ECONOMIC MODELING.** Text in English. 1986. irreg., latest vol.3, 1986. price varies. **Document type:** *Monographic series, Academic/Scholarly.*
Published by: Springer-Verlag Dordrecht (Subsidiary of: Springer Science+Business Media), Van Godewijckstraat 30, Dordrecht, 3311 GX, Netherlands. TEL 31-78-6576050, FAX 31-78-6576474, http://www.springeronline.com.

658.8   NLD
INTERNATIONAL SERIES IN OPERATIONS RESEARCH AND MANAGEMENT SCIENCE. Text in English. 1982. irreg., latest vol.82, 2005. price varies. back issues avail. **Document type:** *Monographic series, Abstract/Index.* **Description:** Encompasses the following four areas of operations research and management science: mathematical programming, applied probability, production and operations management, and applications of operations research and management science.
Formerly (until 1987): International Series in Management Science/Operations Research (0884-8289)
Indexed: CCMJ, ZentMath.
—BLDSC (4549.270300), ingenta. **CCC.**
Published by: Springer-Verlag Dordrecht (Subsidiary of: Springer Science+Business Media), Van Godewijckstraat 30, Dordrecht, 3311 GX, Netherlands. TEL 31-78-6576050, FAX 31-78-6576474, http://www.springeronline.com. Ed. Frederick S Hillier.

INTERNET LAW & REGULATION. see *LAW—Computer Applications*

025.04029   USA   ISSN 1548-9019
Z480.D57
INTERNET YELLOW PAGES (YEAR): BUSINESS MODELS AND MARKET OPPORTUNITIES. Text in English. a. USD 2,095 (effective 2000). **Document type:** *Trade.* **Description:** Helps users sort through online services and identify the potential risks and rewards of venturing onto the internet.
Formerly: Electronic Yellow and White Pages: Review, Trends and Forecast
Published by: SIMBA Information (Subsidiary of: R.R. Bowker LLC), 60 Long Ridge Rd., Ste 300, Stamford, CT 06902. TEL 203-325-8193, 800-307-2529, 888-269-5372, FAX 203-325-8915, info@simbanet.com, http://www.simbanet.com.

004.68   USA   ISSN 1546-3087
TK5105.875.I6
INTRANETS; enterprise strategies and solutions. Text in English. 1998. bi-m. USD 149.95 domestic; USD 161 in Canada & Mexico; USD 172 elsewhere (effective 2005). **Document type:** *Newsletter,, Trade.* **Description:** Designed for libraries and research centers that need to plan for, design and implement intranet technologies and knowledge management practices. Articles are written to be easily understood by non-technical library supervisors, yet contain sufficient technical detail to satisfy the needs of systems and technical staff.
Formerly (until 2004): Intranet Professional (1098-7142)
Indexed: CINAHL, InfoSAb, MicrocompInd.
—BLDSC (4557.479420). **CCC.**
Published by: Information Today, Inc., 143 Old Marlton Pike, Medford, NJ 08055-8750. http://www.infotoday.com/IP/default.shtml. Ed. Michelle Manafy. **Subscr. outside US to:** Learned Information Europe Ltd., Woodside, Hinksey Hill, Oxford, Oxon OX1 5BE, United Kingdom. TEL 44-1865-388000, FAX 44-1865-736354.

330   GBR   ISSN 1366-9435
IT CONSULTANT. (Information Technology) Text in English. 1996. m. adv. **Document type:** *Magazine, Trade.* **Description:** Provides trade and product information for independent IT advisors.
—CCC.
Published by: Penton Media Europe (Subsidiary of: Penton Media, Inc.), Penton House, 288-290 Worton Rd, Isleworth, Mddx TW7 6EL, United Kingdom. TEL 44-20-8232-1600, FAX 44-20-8232-1650, information@penton.com, http://www.itconsultantmagazine.com, http://www.penton.com. Ed. Luke Turton. Adv. contact Karen Hewitt. page GBP 3,860; trim 210 x 297. Circ: 15,000 (paid and controlled).

ITBEAT MAGAZINE. see *BUSINESS AND ECONOMICS—Office Equipment And Services*

332.1   GBR   ISSN 1460-1559
HG174
THE JOURNAL OF COMPUTATIONAL FINANCE. Text in English. 1997. q. GBP 229, USD 389, EUR 329 (effective 2000). back issues avail. **Document type:** *Journal, Academic/Scholarly.* **Description:** Focuses on advances in numerical and computational techniques in pricing, hedging and risk management of financial instruments.
Indexed: JEL.
—BLDSC (4963.465000), IE, ingenta. **CCC.**
Published by: Risk Waters Group (Subsidiary of: Incisive Media Plc.), Haymarket House, 28-29 Haymarket, London, SW1Y 4RX, United Kingdom. TEL 44-20-74849700, FAX 44-20-79302238, market@risk.co.uk, customerservices@incisivemedia.com, http://www.thejournalofcomputationalfinance.com/, http://www.incisivemedia.com/. Ed. Mark Broadie. **Subscr. in US & Canada to:** Incisive Media Plc., 270 Lafayette St, Ste 700, New York, NY 10012. TEL 212-925-6990, FAX 212-925-7585, customerservices@incisivemedia.com.

658   GBR   ISSN 1741-2439
HF5415.126
▼ ➤ **THE JOURNAL OF DATABASE MARKETING & CUSTOMER STRATEGY MANAGEMENT.** Text in English. 1993. q. GBP 245 in Europe to institutions; USD 370 in North America to institutions; GBP 260 elsewhere to institutions (effective 2004). adv. bk.rev.; software rev. charts; illus.; abstr. 96 p./no. 2 cols./p.; back issues avail.; reprint service avail. from PSC. **Document type:** *Journal, Academic/Scholarly.* **Description:** Provides systematic, comprehensive coverage of the latest techniques, ideas and developments in data sourcing.
Formerly (until 2003): The Journal of Database Marketing (1350-2328)
Related titles: Online - full text ed.: ISSN 1741-2447 (from EBSCO Publishing, Gale Group, IngentaConnect, O C L C Online Computer Library Center, Inc., ProQuest Information & Learning, Swets Information Services).
Indexed: ABIn, Emerald.
—BLDSC (4967.816300), IE, ingenta. **CCC.**
Published by: Palgrave Macmillan Ltd. (Subsidiary of: Macmillan Publishers Ltd.), Houndmills, Basingstoke, Hants RG21 6XS, United Kingdom. TEL 44-1256-329242, FAX 44-1256-810526, journal-info@palgrave.com, http://www.palgrave-journals.com/. Ed. John Ozimek. Circ: 800 (paid).

658   USA   ISSN 1531-0981
HF5548.32
THE JOURNAL OF E-BUSINESS AND INFORMATION TECHNOLOGY. Text in English. 2000 (Fall). a. USD 32 domestic to individuals; USD 42 foreign to individuals; USD 120 domestic to libraries; USD 140 foreign to libraries (effective 2004). **Document type:** *Journal, Academic/Scholarly.*
Published by: (American Institute of Management and Information Technology), Pace University, School of Computer Science and Information Systems, 186 Bedford Rd., Pleasantville, NY 10570. http://csis.pace.edu/csis/index.html. Ed. Bel G. Raggad.

381   USA   ISSN 1539-2937
HF5548.32   CODEN: JECOBC
▼ ➤ **JOURNAL OF ELECTRONIC COMMERCE IN ORGANIZATIONS;** the international journal of electronic commerce in modern organizations. Text in English. 2003. q. USD 90 combined subscription to individuals print & online eds.; USD 225 combined subscription to institutions print & online eds. (effective 2005). adv. bk.rev. Index. back issues avail. **Document type:** *Journal, Academic/Scholarly.* **Description:** Designed to provide comprehensive coverage and understanding of the social, cultural, organizational and cognitive impacts of e-commerce technologies and advances on organizations around the world.
Related titles: Online - full text ed.: ISSN 1539-2929. 2003. USD 68 to individuals; USD 148 to institutions (effective 2004) (from O C L C Online Computer Library Center, Inc., ProQuest Information & Learning).
Indexed: ABIn, BrCerAb, C&ISA, CerAb, CompLI, CorrAb, E&CAJ, EMA, IAA, Inspec, M&TEA, MBF, METADEX, SolStAb, WAA.
—BLDSC (4974.905000), IE, Linda Hall. **CCC.**
Published by: (Information Resources Management Association), Idea Group Publishing (Subsidiary of: Idea Group Inc.), 701 E Chocolate Ave, Ste 200, Hershey, PA 17033-1240. TEL 717-533-8845, 866-342-6657, FAX 717-533-7115, jeco@idea-group.com, cust@idea-group.com, http://www.idea-group.com/journals/details.asp?id=471. Ed. Rabbi Mehdi Khosrow-Pour. Pub., R&P Jan Travers. adv.: B&W page USD 350; trim 7 x 10.

330 658   GBR   ISSN 1047-8310
HD62.37   CODEN: JTMRE9
➤ **THE JOURNAL OF HIGH TECHNOLOGY MANAGEMENT RESEARCH.** Text in English. 1990. 2/yr. EUR 128 in Europe to individuals; JPY 16,800 in Japan to individuals; USD 141 to individuals except Europe and Japan; EUR 346 in Europe to institutions; JPY 46,000 in Japan to institutions; USD 387 to institutions except Europe and Japan (effective 2006). back issues avail. **Document type:** *Academic/Scholarly.* **Description:** Promotes interdisciplinary research regarding special problems and opportunities related to marketing and managing emerging technologies, their products, services, and companies.
Related titles: Microform ed.: (from PQC); Online - full text ed.: (from EBSCO Publishing, Gale Group, IngentaConnect, ScienceDirect, Swets Information Services).
Indexed: ABIn, Emerald, SOPODA.
—BLDSC (4998.565000), IE, Infotrieve, ingenta. **CCC.**
Published by: Pergamon (Subsidiary of: Elsevier Science & Technology), The Boulevard, Langford Ln, East Park, Kidlington, Oxford OX5 1GB, United Kingdom. TEL 44-1865-843000, FAX 44-1865-843010, http://www.elsevier.com/locate/hitech. Ed. Luis R. Gomez-Mejia. **Subscr. to:** Elsevier BV, PO Box 211, Amsterdam 1000 AE, Netherlands. TEL 31-20-485-3757, FAX 31-20-485-3432, nlinfo-f@elsevier.nl, http://www.elsevier.nl.

330   USA   ISSN 1533-2861
HF5548.32   CODEN: JICOA5
➤ **JOURNAL OF INTERNET COMMERCE.** Abbreviated title: J I C O M. Text in English. 2002 (Spring). q. USD 315 combined subscription domestic to institutions print & online eds.; USD 425.25 combined subscription in Canada to institutions print & online eds.; USD 456.75 combined subscription elsewhere to institutions print & online eds. (effective 2006). adv. bk.rev. charts. 120 p./no. 1 cols./p.; back issues avail.; reprint service avail. from HAW. **Document type:** *Journal, Academic/Scholarly.* **Description:** Offers a solid, ongoing forum for researchers and practitioners to disseminate high-quality materials and issues related to conducting business on the Internet.
Related titles: Online - full text ed.: ISSN 1533-287X. free to institutions (effective 2003); free with print subs. (from EBSCO Publishing, O C L C Online Computer Library Center, Inc., Swets Information Services).
Indexed: BrCerAb, C&ISA, CerAb, CorrAb, E&CAJ, EMA, ESPM, IAA, Inspec, M&TEA, MBF, METADEX, PAIS, RefZh, RiskAb, WAA.
—BLDSC (5007.693150), Haworth, IE, ingenta, Linda Hall. **CCC.**

Published by: Best Business Books (Subsidiary of: Haworth Press, Inc.), 10 Alice St, Binghamton, NY 13904. TEL 607-722-5857, 800-429-6784, FAX 607-771-0012, 800-896-0582, getinfo@haworthpress.com, http://www.haworthpress.com/web/JICOM. Ed. Ronald Berry. Pub. William Cohen. R&P Ruth Ann Heath TEL 607-722-5857 ext 316. Adv. contact Rebecca Miller-Baum TEL 607-722-5857 ext 337. B&W page USD 315, color page USD 550; trim 4.375 x 7.125. Circ: 32 (paid). **Co-publisher:** Internet Practice Press.

➤ **JOURNAL OF MANAGEMENT INFORMATION SYSTEMS.** see *COMPUTERS—Information Science And Information Theory*

330 USA ISSN 1091-9392
HD30.2 CODEN: JOCEFM
JOURNAL OF ORGANIZATIONAL COMPUTING AND ELECTRONIC COMMERCE. Text in English. 1991. q. USD 500 in US & Canada to institutions; USD 530 elsewhere to institutions; USD 525 combined subscription in US & Canada to institutions print & online eds.; USD 555 combined subscription elsewhere to institutions print & online eds. (effective 2006). adv. abstr.; bibl. back issues avail.; reprint service avail. from PSC. **Document type:** *Journal, Academic/Scholarly.* **Description:** Publishes original research articles concerned with the impact of computer and communication technology on organizational design, operations, and performance.
Formerly (until 1996): Journal of Organizational Computing (1054-1721)
Related titles: Online - full text ed.: ISSN 1532-7744. USD 475 worldwide to institutions (effective 2006) (from EBSCO Publishing, Gale Group, O C L C Online Computer Library Center, Inc., Swets Information Services).
Indexed: ABIn, CMCI, CompLI, CurCont, ErgAb, ISR, Inspec, PsycInfo, PsycholAb, SCI.
—BLDSC (5027.090000), AskIEEE, IE, ingenta. **CCC.**
Published by: (Association for Information Systems), Lawrence Erlbaum Associates, Inc., 10 Industrial Ave, Mahwah, NJ 07430-2262. TEL 201-258-2200, 800-926-6579, FAX 201-236-0072, journals@erlbaum.com, http://www.leaonline.com/loi/joce. Ed. Andrew B Whinston. adv.: page USD 275; trim 6 x 9.

658.8 USA
▼ ➤ **JOURNAL OF STRATEGIC E-COMMERCE.** Text in English. 2003 (Fall). s-a. **Document type:** *Journal, Academic/Scholarly.*
Related titles: Online - full text ed.
Published by: (Academy for Strategic e-Commerce), Allied Academies, 145 Travis Rd., P. O. Box 2689, Cullowhee, NC 28723. http://www.alliedacademies.org/e-commerce/ase.html. Ed. David C Wyld.

➤ **JOURNALS OF CASES ON INFORMATION TECHNOLOGY.** see *BUSINESS AND ECONOMICS—Management*

➤ **JYVASKYLA STUDIES IN COMPUTER SCIENCE, ECONOMICS AND STATISTICS.** see *COMPUTERS*

004.68 USA
K M WORLD & INTRANETS (YEAR) CONFERENCE PROCEEDINGS. (Knowledge Management) Text in English. a. USD 35 (effective 2005). **Document type:** *Proceedings, Trade.*
Published by: Information Today, Inc., 143 Old Marlton Pike, Medford, NJ 08055-8750. TEL 609-654-6266, FAX 609-654-4309, custserv@infotoday.com, http://www.infotoday.com.

330 DEU
KOMPETENZ. Text in German. q. **Document type:** *Newsletter.*
Published by: (Detecon International GmbH), Vereinigte Verlagsanstalten GmbH, Hoeherweg 278, Duesseldorf, 40231, Germany. TEL 49-211-7357589, FAX 49-211-7357507, am@vva.de, info@vva.de, http://www.vva.de. Circ: 10,000 (controlled).

330 657.6 657.2 RUS
KOMP'YUTER V BUKHGALTERSKOM UCHETE I AUDITE. Text in Russian. 1994. q. **Document type:** *Magazine, Trade.*
Published by: Optim.Ru, ul Amundsena, 15/ 1-7, Moscow, 129343, Russian Federation. TEL 7-095-1800201, audit@optim.ru, http://www.optim.ru/comp. Ed. V Yu Chistyakov TEL 7-095-9324709. Circ: 3,000.

330 JPN ISSN 0913-5545
KOSHIEN UNIVERSITY. COLLEGE OF BUSINESS ADMINISTRATION AND INFORMATION SCIENCE. BULLETIN. Text in English, Japanese; Summaries in English. 1986 (no.14). a. **Document type:** *Bulletin.*
Indexed: CCMJ, MathSciNet, ZentMath.
Published by: Koshien University, College of Business Administration and Information Science, 10-1 Momijigaoka, Takarazuka-shi, Hyogo-ken 665-0006, Japan. TEL 0797-87-5111. Ed. Hiroyuki Masutani. Circ: 500.

384.0285 DEU ISSN 0173-6213
LOGISTIK HEUTE. Text in German. 1979. 10/yr. EUR 148; EUR 16.80 newsstand/cover (effective 2004). adv. bk.rev. index. back issues avail. **Document type:** *Journal, Trade.*
Description: Methods and plans for using computers and communications to build chains of goods and material flow.
Incorporates (1985-1991): Produktions-Logistik (0178-8663)
—IE, Infotrieve.
Published by: (Bundesvereinigung Logistik e.V.), Huss-Verlag GmbH, Joseph-Dollinger-Bogen 5, Munich, 80807, Germany. TEL 49-89-323910, FAX 49-89-32391416, anzeigen@logistik-heute.de, management@huss-verlag.de, http://www.logistik-heute.de, http://www.huss-verlag.de. Ed. Petra Seebauer. Adv. contact Vera Sebastian. B&W page EUR 5,780, color page EUR 8,480; trim 185 x 270. Circ: 38,713 (paid and controlled).

330 AUS ISSN 1447-2457
MARKETING ST. KILDA. Text in English. 1986. m. AUD 80 domestic; AUD 120 foreign (effective 2004). adv. illus.; mkt. **Document type:** *Magazine, Trade.* **Description:** Explores the strategic challenges and issues facing businesses large and small from leading industry specialists.
Former titles (until 2002): Marketing and e-Business (1441-7863); (until 1998): Marketing (0819-1131); Which incorporated (1983-1988): Marketing World (0812-9983)
Indexed: ABIX.
Published by: Niche Media Pty Ltd (Subsidiary of: Waivcom Worldwide Ltd.), 165 Fitzroy St, St Kilda, VIC 3182, Australia. TEL 61-3-95255566, 800-804-160, FAX 61-3-95255628, subscription@niche.com.au, http://www.niche.com.au. Ed. Grant Arnott. Adv. contact Ben Cohen. color page AUD 3,300; trim 225 x 275.

MEALEY'S LITIGATION REPORT: CYBER TECH & E-COMMERCE. see *LAW—Corporate Law*

330 USA
MICROCOMPUTER INVESTOR. Text in English. 1977. 2/yr. looseleaf. bk.rev. back issues avail. **Document type:** *Newsletter, Trade.*
Published by: MicroComputer Investors Association, 902 Anderson Dr, Fredericksburg, VA 22045. TEL 703-371-5474. Ed. Jack M Williams.

MICROVIEW; journal for micro users in business. see *COMPUTERS—Microcomputers*

MIND YOUR OWN BUSINESS. see *BUSINESS AND ECONOMICS—Office Equipment And Services*

005.5 USA
MOODY'S COMPANY DATA. Short title: M C D. Text in English. m. USD 6,000 (effective 1999). **Description:** Allows for access to in-depth information on more than 10,000 public companies listed on the NYSE, AMEX, and NASDAQ exchanges.
Incorporates: Moody's 5000 Plus; Moody's O T C Plus
Published by: Mergent, 5250 77 Center Dr, Ste 150, Charlotte, NC 28217. customerservice@mergent.com, http://www.mergent.com.

THE MUSHROOM. see *BUSINESS AND ECONOMICS*

658.8 DEU ISSN 0342-4006
NEW BUSINESS. Text in German. 197?. 50/yr. EUR 35 per month (effective 2004). adv. **Document type:** *Magazine, Trade.*
—IE.
Published by: New Business Verlag GmbH, Eidelstedter Weg 22, Hamburg, 20255, Germany. TEL 49-40-6090090, FAX 49-40-60900977, redaktion@new-business.de, info@new-business.de, http://www.new-business.de. Ed. Harald Nebel. Pub. Peter Strahlendorf. Adv. contact Jens Jansen. color page EUR 2,675; trim 180 x 240. Circ: 1,518 (paid and controlled).

330 025.04 USA ISSN 1051-5984
NEW YORK METRO COMPUTERUSER; for business & IT professionals. Text in English. 1995. m. USD 24.99 (effective 2005). adv. **Document type:** *Newspaper, Trade.* **Description:** Helps business and IT professionals broaden their resources and skills.
Published by: ComputerUser.com, Inc., 29 John St, Ste 503, New York, NY 10038. TEL 212-385-0716, FAX 212-385-0650, http://www.userweb.com. Ed. James Mathewson. Pub. Paulson Ambookan. Adv. contact Jennifer Brown. Circ: 60,000 (controlled).

330 JPN
NIKKEI NET TRADING. Text in Japanese. 2000. m. JPY 780 (effective 2000). adv. **Document type:** *Consumer.*
Description: Contains information on how to make use of PCs for online trading and in-depth knowledge for investing online.
Published by: Nikkei Business Publications Inc. (Subsidiary of: Nihon Keizai Shimbun, Inc.), 2-7-6 Hirakawa-cho, Chiyoda-ku, Tokyo, 102-8622, Japan. TEL 81-3-5210-8311, FAX 81-3-5210-8530, info@nikkeibp-america.com, http://www.nikkeipb.com. Ed. Kenji Tamura. Pub. Tamio Oota. adv.: B&W page JPY 495,000, color page JPY 800,000.

330 384.33 RUS ISSN 1606-156X
NOVOSTI E-KOMMERTSII. Text in Russian. 2000. w. free (effective 2004). **Document type:** *Consumer.*
Media: Online - full text.
Published by: Al'yans Midiya, Bolotnaya ul 12, str 3, Moscow, 115035, Russian Federation. TEL 7-095-2345380, FAX 7-095-2345363, allmedia@allmedia.ru, http://www.businesspress.ru, http://allmedia.ru.

330 IRL
NUA MAKING IT WORK. Text in English. 1996. bi-m. free. adv. **Document type:** *Newsletter.* **Description:** Examines the impact that technology brings to business.
Media: Online - full text.
Published by: Nua Ltd., Merrion House, Merrion Road, Dublin, 4, Ireland. TEL 353-1-676-8996, FAX 353-1-283-9988, antoin@nua.ie, http://www.nua.ie/nuathinking/. Ed. Antoin O'Lachtnain. R&P Antoine O'Lachtnain. Adv. contact Oriana LoLacona.

330 USA ISSN 1537-2308
OPTIMIZE; ideas. action. results. Text in English. m. USD 195 domestic; USD 225 in Canada; USD 275 elsewhere; free to qualified personnel (effective 2005). adv. back issues avail. **Document type:** *Magazine, Trade.*
Related titles: Online - full text ed.: (from H.W. Wilson, O C L C Online Computer Library Center, Inc., ProQuest Information & Learning).
Indexed: ABIn, BPI, MicrocompInd.
—**CCC.**
Published by: C M P Media LLC (Subsidiary of: United News & Media), 600 Community Dr, Manhasset, NY 11030. http://www.optimizemag.com/, http://www.cmp.com. Ed. Brian Gillooly. Pub. Scott Vaughan. adv.: B&W page USD 10,140, color page USD 12,090. Circ: 70,000 (controlled and free).

ORGANIZACJA I KIEROWANIE/ORGANIZATION AND MANAGEMENT. see *BUSINESS AND ECONOMICS—Management*

330 DEU
P C BUSINESS; Produkte und Loesungen fuer Ihr Unternehmen. Text in German. 2000. bi-m. EUR 7.80 newsstand/cover (effective 2003). adv. **Document type:** *Magazine, Trade.*
Description: Provides information on professional office applications, network solutions, telecommunications, office technology, e-business solutions as well as on financial topics.
Related titles: Online - full text ed.
Published by: W E K A Computerzeitschriften-Verlag GmbH, Gruberstr 46a, Poing, 85586, Germany. TEL 49-8121-950, FAX 49-8121-951621, http://www.pcbusiness-online.de, http://www.wekanet.de. Ed. Andreas Eichelsdoerfer. Pub. Stephan Quinkertz. Adv. contact Roy Decker. B&W page EUR 5,400, color page EUR 6,500. Circ: 27,629 (paid and controlled).

330 IRL ISSN 1393-0591
P C LIVE!; ireland's pc and internet magazine. Text in English. 1994. m. EUR 49.50; EUR 4.90 newsstand/cover (effective 2002). adv. **Document type:** *Magazine, Consumer.*
Description: Covers a wide range of computing topics that are both authoritative and informative for the small to medium-size business PC user and the SOHO (small office, home office) market.
Related titles: Online - full text ed.
Published by: Scope Communications Ltd., Prospect House, 3 Prospect Rd., Glasnevin, Dublin, 9, Ireland. TEL 353-1-8824407, FAX 353-1-8300888, info@pclive.ie, info@scope.ie, http://www.techcentral.ie. Ed. Stephen Cawley. Pub. Frank Quinn. R&P, Adv. contact Eimear Nealon. B&W page EUR 2,666, color page EUR 3,047; trim 210 x 297. Circ: 18,000.

004.16 GBR ISSN 0269-0640
P C MANAGEMENT; corporate strategy, connectivity and analysis. Text in English. 1984. m. back issues avail. **Document type:** *Trade.*
Indexed: Inspec.
—**CCC.**
Published by: E M A P Computing (Subsidiary of: E M A P Business Communications), 33-39 Bowling Green Ln, London, EC1R 0DA, United Kingdom. TEL 44-20-7837-1212, FAX 44-207-278-4008. Circ: 15,000.

005.5 USA
P M S TODAY*✱*. Text in English. 1977. 12/yr. free to qualified personnel.
Published by: Policy Management Systems Corp., PO Box 10, Columbia, SC 29202. TEL 803-735-4000. Ed. Carl Harrison. Circ: 6,000.

PERSONNEL SOFTWARE CENSUS. VOL. 1: DEPARTMENTAL SOFTWARE. see *BUSINESS AND ECONOMICS—Personnel Management*

PERSONNEL SOFTWARE CENSUS. VOL. 2: HUMAN RESOURCE INFORMATION SYSTEMS. see *BUSINESS AND ECONOMICS—Personnel Management*

330 USA
▼ **PORTALS MAGAZINE.** Text in English. 2003. q. **Document type:** *Magazine, Trade.* **Description:** Covers corporate portal strategy and solutions.
Related titles: Online - full content ed.
Published by: Line56 Media, Inc., 10940 Wilshire Blvd, Ste 600, Los Angeles, CA 90024. TEL 310-443-4226, FAX 310-443-4230, info@line56.com, http://www.line56.com/. Ed. Sarah Witt.

PROCESS EQUIPMENT NEWS; new products for busy managers. see *ENGINEERING*

330 DEU ISSN 1437-2592
PROFESSIONAL SYSTEM. Text in German. 1999. bi-m. adv. **Document type:** *Magazine, Trade.*
Published by: Musik - Media Verlag GmbH, An der Wachsfabrik 8, Cologne, 50996, Germany. TEL 49-2236-96217-0, FAX 49-2236-962175, redaktion@professional-system.de, info@musikmedia.de, http://www1.professional-system.de, http://www.musikmedia.de. Eds. Detlef Hoepfner, Walter Werhan. Adv. contact Angelika Mueller.

QUICK SOLUTIONS. see *BUSINESS AND ECONOMICS—Small Business*

650.0285 USA
QUICKBYTES; business + technology. Text in English. 1998. m. free. adv.
Related titles: Online - full text ed.
Published by: Stewart Consultants, PO Box 61493, Denver, CO 80206. TEL 303-358-9147, FAX 800-863-2869, sfarnham@stewartconsultants.com, http://www.stewartconsultants.com/quickbyte.htm. Ed. Susan Farnham. Adv. contact Mia Chambers.

621.382 FRA
R F I D IN EUROPE NEWSLETTER. (Radio Frequency Identification) Text in English. 24/yr. EUR 750 (effective 2003). **Document type:** *Trade.* **Description:** Supplies reports on the markets, technologies, businesses and people shaping the radio frequency identification industries and players.
Media: E-mail.
Address: 6 rue Voltaire, Grenoble, 38000, France. rfid@rfidineurope.com, http://www.rfidineurope.com. Ed. Claudia Wolosin.

▼ **R T EJOURNAL**; forum fuer rapid technologie. (Rapid Technology) see *BUSINESS AND ECONOMICS—Production Of Goods And Services*

332.1 658 FRA ISSN 0982-3085
HF5415.125
REPERTOIRE INTERNATIONAL DES BANQUES DE DONNEES POUR LE MARKETING ET LES ETUDES. Text in French. 1987. irreg., latest vol.2, 1994. adv. **Document type:** *Directory.* **Description:** Lists databases useful for marketing and studies.
Published by: Editions F L A Consultants, 27 rue de la Vistule, Paris, 75013, France. TEL 33-1-45827575, FAX 33-1-45824604, flabases@iway.fr, http://www.fla-consultants.fr. Eds. Anne Sophie Kandel, Francois Libmann. Adv. contact Beatrice Riou.

650.0285 004 USA ISSN 1060-3808
RETAIL INFO SYSTEMS NEWS; fusing technology solutions to corporate vision. Variant title: R I S News. Text in English. 1988. m. USD 190 domestic; USD 225 in Canada; USD 250 elsewhere; free to qualified personnel (effective 2005). adv. charts; illus.; stat. back issues avail.; reprints avail. **Document type:** *Magazine, Trade.* **Description:** Demonstrates how technology tools can enable a successful and forward-thinking retail environment.
Formerly: R I S (1044-6796)
Related titles: Online - full text ed.
—CCC.
Published by: Edgell Communications, Inc., 4 Middlebury Blvd, Randolph, NJ 07869-4214. edgell@edgellmail.com, http://www.risnews.com, http://www.edgellcommunications.com. Ed. Joe Skorupa. Pub. Andrew Gaffney. Circ: 20,000 (controlled).

338.0029 USA
RETAIL INFO SYSTEMS NEWS DIRECTORY. Text in English. 1989. a. adv. **Document type:** *Directory, Trade.* **Description:** Provides systems solutions for corporate management, operations and MIS management functions at retail.
Published by: Edgell Communications, Inc., 4 Middlebury Blvd, Randolph, NJ 07869-4214. TEL 973-252-0100, FAX 973-252-9020, http://www.risnews.com. Ed. Dennis Eskow.

330 GBR ISSN 1369-5037
RETAIL SYSTEMS; first choice for IT makers in retail. Text in English. 1997. bi-m. GBP 88 domestic; GBP 130 foreign (effective 2005). adv. **Document type:** *Magazine, Trade.* **Description:** Contains detailed news from the sector, broken down in to general news, product news, news from the US market.
Published by: Perspective Publishing Ltd., 408 Fruit & Wool Exchange, Brushfield St, London, E1 6EP, United Kingdom. TEL 44-20-74260636, FAX 44-20-74260123, muir@perspectivepublishing.com, http://www.retail-systems.com/, http://www.perspectivepublishing.com/. Ed. John Broy. Adv. contacts Chris Paul, Neil Howman.

REVIEW OF BUSINESS INFORMATION SYSTEMS. see *BUSINESS AND ECONOMICS—Accounting*

658.8 GBR ISSN 1460-5953
REVOLUTION; the magazine for news-media marketing. Text in English. 1997. m. GBP 65 domestic; GBP 47 in Europe; GBP 109 elsewhere (effective 2005). adv. illus. back issues avail. **Document type:** *Magazine, Trade.* **Description:** Offers marketing professionals advice on how to put new telecommunication technologies to their advantage.
Related titles: Online - full text ed.: (from Gale Group, LexisNexis, O C L C Online Computer Library Center, Inc., ProQuest Information & Learning).
Indexed: ABIn, M&MA.
—CCC.
Published by: Haymarket Business Publications Ltd., 174 Hammersmith Rd, London, W6 7JP, United Kingdom. TEL 44-20-8267-4940, FAX 44-20-8267-4927, stovin@revolution.haynet.com, http://www.revolution.haynet.com. Ed. Philip Smith. Pub. Jane Macken. Circ: 75,000. **Subscr. to:** WDIS Ltd., W D I S Ltd, Publishing House, 652 Victoria Rd, Ruislip, Mddx HA4 0SX, United Kingdom. TEL 44-20-8841-3970.

RUTGERS COMPUTER & TECHNOLOGY LAW JOURNAL. see *LAW—Computer Applications*

330 USA
S I GECOM NEWSLETTER. (Special Interest Group Electronic Commerce) Text in English. q. USD 30 (effective 2004). **Document type:** *Newsletter.* **Description:** Encourages research and advanced applications relating to electronic commerce and to the sharing of new electronic ideas and experiences.
Media: Online - full text.
Published by: Association for Computing Machinery, Inc., 1515 Broadway, 17th Fl, New York, NY 10036-5701. TEL 212-626-0500, 212-626-0520, 800-342-6626, usacm@acm.org, http://www.acm.org/sigecom/.

330 SGP
S M E - I T GUIDE; information technology for a successful business. (Small and Medium-Sized Enterprise - Information Technology) Text in English. m. adv. **Document type:** *Magazine, Trade.* **Description:** Focuses on both business and information technology related issue that impact on the operations of small and medium sized businesses.
Related titles: Online - full text ed.
Published by: Communication Resources Pte. Ltd., Blk. 1008, Tao Payoh North, No. 07-01, Singapore, 318996, Singapore. TEL 65-256-6201, FAX 65-251-0348, marketing@comres.com.sg, http://www.cio-asia.com/dev/idgsme.nsf, http://www.idg.com.sp. adv.: B&W page USD 3,087, color page USD 3,816; trim 205 x 275. Circ: 13,000 (paid and controlled).

004.6 USA
S O H O MARKET ANALYSIS & FORECAST: TARGETING THE SMALL OFFICE - HOME OFFICE ONLINE USER. Text in English. 1996. a. USD 1,295 (effective 2000). **Description:** Details how information publishers and technology companies can effectively target and profit from the burgeoning audience of small businesses and work-at-home professionals.
Published by: SIMBA Information (Subsidiary of: R.R. Bowker LLC), 60 Long Ridge Rd., Ste 300, Stamford, CT 06902. TEL 203-325-8193, 800-307-2529, 888-269-5372, FAX 203-325-8915, info@simbanet.com, http://www.simbanet.com.

SALES ARENA; improving sales and marketing success through technology, business images and people. see *BUSINESS AND ECONOMICS—Marketing And Purchasing*

681.31 CHE ISSN 1424-1706
DIE SCHWEIZERISCHE INFORMATIK REVUE. Abbreviated title: S I R. Text in German. 1994. bi-m. CHF 55 domestic; CHF 75 foreign; CHF 11 newsstand/cover (effective 2002). adv. **Document type:** *Magazine, Trade.*
Published by: Trend Verlags AG, Steinenvorstadt 67, Basel, 4001, Switzerland. TEL 41-61-2262626, FAX 41-61-2262600, redaktion@trendverlag.ch, http://www.trendverlag.ch. Ed., Pub. Bruno Ruessli. Adv. contact Barbara Hopf. B&W page CHF 5,100, color page CHF 6,375; trim 210 x 297. Circ: 17,000 (paid and controlled).

SIMULATION & GAMING; an international journal of theory, design and research. see *COMPUTERS—Computer Simulation*

330 USA
THE SMALL BUSINESS ADVISOR: SOFTWARE NEWS. Text in English. 1996. 6/yr. USD 39.95. adv. **Document type:** *Trade.*
Published by: The Software News, Inc., 400 Ginger Ct., South Lake, TX 76092. TEL 817-416-6650, FAX 405-275-3101, trose@softwarenews.net. Ed., R&P T. Allen Rose. Pub. T Allen Rose. Circ: 30,000.

330 IRL
SMART COMPANY; business technology & the internet made easy. Text in English. 2002. q. free to qualified personnel. adv. **Document type:** *Magazine, Trade.* **Description:** Explains the business benefits of technology in simple, concise terms to managers and decision makers in small and medium sized businesses throughout Ireland.
Related titles: Online - full text ed.
Published by: Scope Communications Ltd., Prospect House, 3 Prospect Rd., Glasnevin, Dublin, 9, Ireland. TEL 353-1-8824407, FAX 353-1-8300888, info@scope.ie, http://www.smartcompany.ie, http://www.techcentral.ie. Ed. Stephen Cawley. Pub. Frank Quinn. R&P, Adv. contact Eimear Nealon. B&W page EUR 5,000, color page EUR 6,000. Circ: 50,000 (paid and controlled).

330 MEX ISSN 0188-8048
SOLUCIONES AVANZADAS; tecnologias de informacion y estrategias de negocios. Text in Spanish. 1992. bi-m. MXP 150, USD 100. adv. bk.rev. back issues avail. **Document type:** *Trade.*
Related titles: Online - full text ed.
Published by: Xview S.A. de C.V., TUXPAN 2 Desp. 603, Col Roma Sur, Mexico City, DF 06760, Mexico. TEL 52-5-5646211, FAX 52-5-5745318, solucion@servidor.unam.mx, http://www.fciencias.unam.mx/revista/soluciones.html. Ed. Carlos Vizcaino. Adv. contact Oscar Guerrero B. Circ: 5,000.

SOUTHERN BUSINESS & ECONOMIC JOURNAL. see *BUSINESS AND ECONOMICS*

330 DEU ISSN 1435-6295
STUDIEN ZUR WIRTSCHAFTSINFORMATIK. Text in German. 1989. irreg., latest vol.15, 2005. price varies. **Document type:** *Monographic series, Academic/Scholarly.*
Published by: Verlag Dr. Kovac, Arnoldstr 49, Hamburg, 22763, Germany. TEL 49-40-3988800, FAX 49-40-39888055, info@verlagdrkovac.de, http://www.verlagdrkovac.de/4-4.htm.

629.8 USA ISSN 1539-865X
HF5416 CODEN: IDSYE5
SUPPLY CHAIN SYSTEMS; the resource for supply chain automation. Text in English. 1981. m. USD 55; free to qualified personnel (effective 2005). adv. tr.lit. reprints avail. **Document type:** *Magazine, Trade.* **Description:** ID systems is the authoritative source of information for users and implementers of data collection technologies throughout the supply chain, providing reliable and in-depth information on improving accuracy and efficiency in all aspects of the movement of information and products.
Former titles (until 2001): I D Systems (0892-676X); (until 1987): Bar Code News (8750-8702)
Related titles: Online - full text ed.
Indexed: ABIPC, BrCerAb, C&ISA, CerAb, CorrAb, E&CAJ, EMA, EngInd, IAA, IPackAb, Inspec, LogistBibl, M&TEA, MBF, METADEX, SoftBase, WAA.
—BLDSC (8547.630680), CASDDS, Ei. **CCC.**
Published by: Helmers Publishing, Inc., 174 Concord St, Peterborough, NH 03458-0874. TEL 603-924-9631, FAX 603-924-7408, editors@idsystems.com, dandrews@helmers.com, http://www.scs-mag.com, http://www.helmers.com/. Eds. Mark Reynolds, David L Andrews. Pub. David L Andrews. adv.: B&W page USD 5,450, color page USD 8,035. Circ: 53,000 (paid and controlled).

330 GBR
SUPPORT INSIGHT; the first place for training news. Text in English. 2001. d. free. adv. Website rev. bibl.; charts; illus.; maps; stat.; tr.lit. back issues avail. **Document type:** *Newsletter, Trade.* **Description:** Provides information on IT support, CRN, call centers, e-Learning, e-Government, IT training and certification.
Formerly (until Oct. 2001): Training in Focus
Media: Online - full content. **Related titles:** E-mail ed.
Address: 37 Evelyn Rd, Dunstable, Bedfordshire LU5 4NG, United Kingdom. TEL 44-1582-696911, FAX 44-1582-696913, editor@supportinsight.com, http://www.supportinsight.com. Ed. Claire Sankey. Pub. Peter Friedman. R&Ps Claire Sankey, Peter Friedman.

330 640.73 USA
SURVIVE & WIN✶. Text in English. 1988. m. USD 50. adv. bk.rev. back issues avail. **Description:** Survival information and tips using hi-tech tactics and strategies.
Published by: Consumertronics, PO Box 23097, Albuquerque, NM 87192-1097. TEL 505-434-0234. Ed. John Williams. Circ: 21,000.

651.3 DEU ISSN 0341-2024
T B REPORT; Archivierung und Datensicherung im Technischen Buero. (Technische Buero) Text in German. 1970. q. EUR 31 domestic; EUR 47.80 foreign (effective 2002). **Document type:** *Magazine, Trade.*
Indexed: DIP.
Published by: B I T Verlag Weinbrenner GmbH & Co. KG, Fasanenweg 18, Leinfelden-Echterdingen, 70771, Germany. TEL 49-711-75910, FAX 49-711-7591336, info@bitverlag.de, http://www.bitverlag.de.

B

384.0285　　　　　USA　　　　ISSN 1054-979X
TECHSCAN NEWSLETTER; the manager's guide to technology.
Text in English. 1990. m. USD 87.50 domestic; USD 111.50
foreign (effective 2004). bk.rev. bibl.; charts; illus.; stat. back
issues avail. **Document type:** *Newsletter.* **Description:**
Informs business professionals about technological
developments and applications, design techniques, and
products used to solve business problems.
Formerly: Intelligent Systems
Published by: Richmond Research, Inc., PO BOX 537, VILLAGE
STA, New York, NY 10014-0537. TEL 212-741-0045, FAX
212-243-7356, techscan@pipeline.com, http://
www.techscan.com. Ed., R&P Mr. Louis Giacalone. Circ: 2,500
(paid).

TEL-COM - BRIEF; Telekommunikation, Datenverarbeitung und
Organisation. see *BUSINESS AND ECONOMICS—Office
Equipment And Services*

**THEORY AND DECISION LIBRARY. SERIES C: GAME
THEORY, MATHEMATICAL PROGRAMMING AND
OPERATIONS RESEARCH.** see *MATHEMATICS—Computer
Applications*

U K ONLINE INVESTING NEWS. see *BUSINESS AND
ECONOMICS—Investments*

U K ONLINE INVESTING REPORT. see *BUSINESS AND
ECONOMICS—Investments*

UNIGRAM.X; the weekly information newsletter for the UNIX
community worldwide. see *COMPUTERS—Software*

UNLIMITED; inspiring business. see *BUSINESS AND
ECONOMICS—Management*

WEBBUSINESS. see *COMPUTERS—Internet*

330　　　　　　GBR
THE WHARTON REPORT. Text in English. m. GBP 249 domestic;
GBP 269 foreign (effective 2000). **Document type:** *Consumer.*
Description: Various detailed reports on a specific topic within
the information technology environment.
Former titles: Wharton Market Report; Market Report
Indexed: AESIS, Inspec.
—BLDSC (9309.555500).
Published by: Wharton Information Systems, 11 Beaumont Ave,
Richmond, Surrey TW9 2HE, United Kingdom. TEL
44-20-8332-1120, n_wharton@compuserve.com. Ed. Keith
Wharton.

332　　　　　DEU　　　　ISSN 0720-6992
WIRTSCHAFTSKYBERNETIK UND SYSTEMANALYSE. Text in
German. 1971. irreg., latest vol.21, 2002. price varies.
Document type: *Monographic series, Academic/Scholarly.*
Published by: Duncker und Humblot GmbH, Carl-Heinrich-
Becker-Weg 9, Berlin, 12165, Germany. TEL 49-30-7900060,
FAX 49-30-79000631, info@duncker-humblot.de,
http://www.duncker-humblot.de.

3 C MALL/E-SHIDAI QUANFANGWEI QINGBAO ZHI. see
COMPUTERS—Internet

BUSINESS AND ECONOMICS—Cooperatives

A C D I - V O C A WORLD REPORT. see *BUSINESS AND
ECONOMICS—International Development And Assistance*

334　　　　　HUN　　　　ISSN 1217-7040
A F E S Z MAGAZIN. Text in Hungarian. 1922. w. **Document
type:** *Newspaper.*
Former titles (until 1993): Uj Szovetkezet (0865-6940); (until
1989): Szovetkezet (0133-1612); (until 1948): Magyar
Szovetkezes (0324-2641); (until 1922): Orszagos Kozponti
Hitelszovetkezeti Ertesito (0324-3990)
Indexed: WAE&RSA.
Published by: Altalanos Fogyasztasi es Ertekesito
Szovetkezetek/National Council of Consumers' Cooperative
Societies, Szabadsag ter 14, Budapest, 1054, Hungary. TEL
36-1-131-3132, TELEX 224862. Ed. Attila Kovacs. Circ:
85,000.

A G P MITTEILUNGEN; Zeitschrift fuer Partnerschaft in der
Wirtschaft. see *BUSINESS AND ECONOMICS—Labor And
Industrial Relations*

334　　　　　NLD
AALSMEER NIEUWS. Text in Dutch. fortn. free to qualified
personnel. **Document type:** *Newspaper.*
Formerly: V B A Bode (Verenigde Bloemveilingen Aalsmeer)
Published by: Bloemenveiling Aalsmeer, Legmeerdijk 313,
Aalsmeer, 1431 GB, Netherlands. TEL 31-297-393939, FAX
31-297-390021. Circ: 12,500.

630　　　　　GRC　　　　ISSN 1105-1213
AGROTICOS SYNERGATISMOS. Text in Greek. 1945. m. USD
20. adv. bk.rev.
Former titles (until 1982): Agroticos Cosmos K Synergatismos;
(until 1979): Voice of the Cooperatives

Published by: Panhellenic Confederation of Unions of Agricultural
Cooperatives, 16 Kifissias Ave, Athens, 115 26, Greece. TEL
30-210-749-9400, FAX 30-210-777-9313, pasegsyd@otenet.gr,
http://www.paseges.gr/en/magazines.asp. Ed. Nikolaos G
Gotsinas. Circ: 8,000.

334　　　　　DEU
AKTUELLES FUER DEN LANDWIRT. Text in German. m.
Document type: *Trade.*
Published by: Genossenschaftsverband Bayern e.V., Tuerkenstr
16, Munich, 80333, Germany. TEL 089-21342925, FAX
089-21342928.

ALTERNATIVE CURRENTS. see *BUSINESS AND
ECONOMICS—Banking And Finance*

ALTERNATIVE TRADING NEWS. see *BUSINESS AND
ECONOMICS—International Development And Assistance*

334　　　　　COL
AMERICA COOPERATIVA. Text in Spanish. 1964. 3/yr. looseleaf.
USD 20. illus.
Formerly: Cooperative America (0002-7057)
Published by: Organization of the Cooperatives of
America/Organizacion de las Cooperativas de America,
Carrera 11, 86-32 Ofc 101, Bogota, DE 241263, Colombia.
TEL 2181295, FAX 057-1-610-19-12, TELEX 45103
FICOP-CO. OCA. Ed. Carlos Julio Pineda Suarez. adv.: B&W
page COP 70,000, color page COP 150,000; trim 280 x 210.
Circ: 5,000 (controlled).

334　　　　　USA　　　　ISSN 0065-793X
HD3443
AMERICAN COOPERATION YEARBOOK. Text in English. 1925.
a. USD 35 hardcover ed.; USD 30 softcover ed.. index.
Document type: *Trade.* **Description:** Presents an annual
review of the year in cooperatives including key trades and
issues.
Indexed: Agr, RI-1, RI-2.
Published by: National Council of Farmer Cooperatives, 50 F St,
N W, Ste 900, Washington, DC 20001. TEL 202-626-8700,
FAX 202-626-8722, http://www.ncfc.org. Ed. Lisa Smith. Circ:
1,800.

320.54095694　　　　　ISR
AMUDIM; bulletin of the religious kibbutzim. Text in Hebrew. 1955.
11/yr. ILS 144 domestic; USD 40 foreign (effective 1999). adv.
bk.rev. **Document type:** *Bulletin.* **Description:** Covers
questions and personalities in current religious Zionism and
kibbutzim.
Published by: Religious Kibbutz Movement/Ha'Kibbutz Hadati, 7
Dubnov St, Tel Aviv, 64732, Israel. TEL 972-3-6957231, FAX
972-3-6957039. Ed., R&P, Adv. contact Techiya Tamari. Circ:
500 (paid); 2,500 (controlled).

334 630　　　　　DNK　　　　ISSN 0003-2913
CODEN: ANBLAT
ANDELSBLADET. Text in Danish. 1900. 24/yr. DKK 300 (effective
2004). adv. bk.rev. cum.index: 1900-1939. **Document type:**
Newsletter, Corporate.
Related titles: Online - full text ed.
Indexed: DSA, WAE&RSA, WeedAb.
Published by: Danske Andelsselskaber/Federation of Danish
Co-Operatives, Vesterbrogade 4 A 2, Copenhagen V, 1620,
Denmark. TEL 45-33-394500, FAX 45-33-394515,
andel@andelsselskab.dk, http://www.andelsselskab.dk. Ed.
Torsten Buhl TEL 45-33-394509. Circ: 8,300.

334　　　　　GBR　　　　ISSN 1370-4788
HD3840
➤ **ANNALS OF PUBLIC AND COOPERATIVE ECONOMICS.**
Text in English, French, German. 1908. q. EUR 99 combined
subscription in Europe to individuals print & online eds.; USD
111 combined subscription in the Americas to individuals &
Caribbean (print & online eds.); GBP 66 combined
subscription elsewhere to individuals print & online eds.; GBP
192 combined subscription in Europe to institutions print &
online eds.; USD 344 combined subscription in the Americas
to institutions & Caribbean (print & online eds.); GBP 205
combined subscription elsewhere to institutions print & online
eds. (effective 2006). bk.rev. bibl. back issues avail.; reprint
service avail. from PSC. **Document type:** *Journal,
Academic/Scholarly.* **Description:** Contains research on
theoretical and empirical developments in public, cooperative
or non-profit economics.
Former titles (until 1989): Annals of Public and Co-operative
Economy (0770-8548); Annales de l'Economie Publique,
Sociale et Cooperative (0379-3699); (until 1964): Annales de
l'Economie Collective (0003-407X)
Related titles: Online - full text ed.: ISSN 1467-8292. GBP 182 in
Europe to institutions; USD 328 in the Americas to institutions
& Caribbean; GBP 195 elsewhere to institutions (effective
2006) (from Blackwell Synergy, EBSCO Publishing, Gale
Group, IngentaConnect, O C L C Online Computer Library
Center, Inc., Swets Information Services).
Indexed: ABIn, BAS, CREJ, DIP, DSA, ELLIS, IBR, IBSS, IBZ,
ILD, JEL, MEA&I, NutrAb, PAIS, PCI, RASB, RRTA, SSCI,
WAE&RSA.
—BLDSC (1043.590000), IE, Infotrieve, ingenta. **CCC.**

Published by: (International Centre of Research and Information
on Public and Cooperative Economy ISR), Blackwell
Publishing Ltd., 9600 Garsington Rd, Oxford, OX4 2ZG,
United Kingdom. TEL 44-1865-776868, FAX 44-1865-714591,
jnlinfo@blackwellpublishers.co.uk,
customerservices@oxon.blackwellpublishing.com,
http://www.blackwellpublishing.com/journals/APCE. Ed.
Fabienne Fecher.

➤ **ANNOTATED BIBLIOGRAPHY OF LITERATURE ON
COOPERATIVE MOVEMENTS IN SOUTH-EAST ASIA.** see
BIBLIOGRAPHIES

➤ **ANNUAIRE GENERAL DES COOPERATIVES FRANCAISES
ET DE LEURS FOURNISSEURS.** see *BUSINESS AND
ECONOMICS—Domestic Commerce*

334　　　　　DEU
BAYERISCHES RAIFFEISENBLATT. Text in German. m.
Published by: Genossenschaftsverband Bayern e.V., Tuerkenstr
22-24, Munich, 80333, Germany.

334　　　　　ESP　　　　ISSN 0006-6273
BOLETIN DE FORMACION COOPERATIVA✱. Text in Spanish.
1972 (no.67). bi-m. bk.rev. charts; illus.
Published by: Asociacion de Estudios Cooperativos, Heroes del
10 de Agosto 5 4 Andar, Madrid, 28022, Spain. Ed. Rafael
Monge Simon.

334　　　　　DEU
BONUS. Text in German. 1991. m. adv. **Document type:**
Magazine, Consumer.
Published by: Deutscher Genossenschafts-Verlag eG, Leipziger
Str 35, Wiesbaden, 65191, Germany. TEL 49-611-50660, FAX
49-611-50661500, direct@dgverlag.de, http://www.dgverlag.de.
adv.: B&W page EUR 5,790, color page EUR 9,264. Circ:
165,885 (controlled).

334　　　　　BWA
**BOTSWANA. MINISTRY OF AGRICULTURE. DIVISION OF
CO-OPERATIVE DEVELOPMENT. ANNUAL REPORT
(YEAR).** (Includes: Cooperative Statistic of Cooperative
Societies in the last three years 1986-1988) Text in English. a.
illus.; stat.
Published by: Ministry of Agriculture, Division of Planning and
Statistics, Private Bag 0033, Gaborone, Botswana.

C H F NEWSBRIEFS. see *HOUSING AND URBAN PLANNING*

C U E S - FOR YOUR INFORMATION. see *BUSINESS AND
ECONOMICS—Banking And Finance*

C U I S. (Credit Union Information Service) see *BUSINESS AND
ECONOMICS—Banking And Finance*

334　　　　　FRA
**CAISSE FRANCAISE DE DEVELOPPEMENT. RAPPORT
ANNUEL.** Text in English, French. 1947. a. free. adv. illus.
Former titles: Caisse Centrale de Cooperation Economique.
Rapport Annuel; Caisse Centrale de Cooperation Economique.
Rapport d'Activite (0575-1632)
Published by: Caisse Francaise de Developpement, 35-37 rue
Boissy d'Anglas, Cite du Retiro, Paris, Cedex 8 75379,
France. FAX 40-06-40-85, TELEX 212 632 F. Adv. contact
Denis Castaing. Circ: 8,000.

334　　　　　USA　　　　ISSN 0743-605X
JK1
CATO POLICY REPORT. Text in English. 1977. 6/yr. bk.rev.
Document type: *Academic/Scholarly.* **Description:** Contains
original articles on public policy issues.
Formerly: Policy Report (0190-325X)
Related titles: Online - full text ed.
Indexed: EnvAb, IPSA, PAIS.
—BLDSC (3093.275200), IE, Infotrieve.
Published by: Cato Institute, 1000 Massachusetts Ave, N W,
Washington, DC 20077-0172. TEL 202-842-0200, FAX
202-842-3490, cato@cato.org, http://www.cato.org/. Ed. David
Boaz. Circ: 20,000.

CAYAPA; revista venezolana de economia social. see
SOCIOLOGY

**CHECKLISTS AND ILLUSTRATIVE FINANCIAL STATEMENTS
FOR CREDIT UNIONS.** see *BUSINESS AND
ECONOMICS—Accounting*

334　　　　　JPN
CO-OP JAPAN INFORMATION. Text in Japanese. q. free.
Document type: *Newsletter.* **Description:** Provides
information about current situation of consumer co-ops in
Japan.
Published by: Japanese Consumers Cooperative Union/Nihon
Seikatsu Kyodokumiai Rengokai, Seikyo Kaikan, 4-1-13
Sendagaya, Shibuya-ku, Tokyo, 151-0051, Japan. TEL
81-3-3470-9103, FAX 81-3-3470-2924,
jccu-int@mxb.meshnet.or.jp, http://www.co-op.or.jp/. Ed. Boku
Nakano. Circ: 400.

334 GBR ISSN 0009-9821
CODEN: FMADEI
CO-OPERATIVE NEWS; official organ of the Co-operative Movement. Text in English. 1871. w. (51/yr.). GBP 43; GBP 65 in Europe; GBP 86 elsewhere. adv. bk.rev. illus. **Document type:** *Newspaper.* **Description:** Organ of Britain's coop movement.
Incorporates: Co-Operative News (Scottish Edition); Which was formerly: Scottish Cooperator (0048-976X)
Indexed: RASB.
Published by: Co-Operative Press Ltd., Progress House, Co-Operative Press Ltd, Chester Rd, Manchester, M16 9HP, United Kingdom. TEL 44-161-872-2991, FAX 44-161-872-6366. Ed. Geoffrey Whiteley. Adv. contact Keith Sidebotham.

334 GBR
CO-OPERATIVE STATISTICS. Text in English. 1879. a. GBP 79 (effective 1999). **Description:** Statistics of all British co-operative societies showing membership, sources and uses of funds, and other information.
Published by: Co-operative Union Ltd., Co-Operative Union Ltd, Holyoake House, Hanover St, Manchester, Lancs M60 0AS, United Kingdom. TEL 44-161-832-4300, FAX 44-161-831-7684, info@co-opunion.org.uk, http://www.co-op.co.uk/UKCM/Union/index.html. Ed. I V Williamson. Circ: 400.

334 GBR
CO-OPERATIVE UNION. ANNUAL REPORT. Text in English. 1869. a. GBP 5 (effective 1999). back issues avail. **Document type:** *Corporate.* **Description:** Publishes the reports and transactions of committees and departments of the British Co-operative Union.
Supersedes in part: Co-operative Union. Annual Report and Financial Statements
Published by: Co-operative Union Ltd., Co-Operative Union Ltd, Holyoake House, Hanover St, Manchester, Lancs M60 0AS, United Kingdom. TEL 44-0161-832-4300, FAX 44-0161-831-7684, info@co-opunion.org.uk, http://www.co-op.co.uk/UKCM/Union/index.html. Ed. I V Williamson. Circ: 1,200.

334 GBR
CO-OPERATIVE UNION. FINANCIAL STATEMENTS. Text in English. 1869. a. GBP 5 (effective 1999). back issues avail. **Document type:** *Corporate.* **Description:** Publishes the transactions of committees and departments of the British Co-operative Union.
Supersedes in part: Co-operative Union. Annual Report and Financial Statements
Published by: Co-operative Union Ltd., Co-Operative Union Ltd, Holyoake House, Hanover St, Manchester, Lancs M60 0AS, United Kingdom. FAX 0161-831-7684, info@co-opunion.org.uk, http://www.co-op.co.uk/UKCM/Union/index.html. Ed. I V Williamson. Circ: 1,200.

334 TWN ISSN 0009-9856
CO-OPERATIVES QUARTERLY✶. Text in Chinese, English. 1969 (vol.7). q. charts; stat.
Published by: Cooperative Bank of Taiwan, 75-1 Kuan Chien Rd, Taipei, Taiwan.

334 647.9 FRA ISSN 1281-3788
COLLECTIVITES EXPRESS. Text in French. 1953. 9/yr. adv. **Description:** Details administration of collective institutions.
Former titles (until 1996): Collectivites Hotellerie et Restauration (1242-2126); (until 1992): Collectivites - Express (0010-0811)
Published by: Editions Max Brezol, 9 rue Labie, Paris, Cedex 17 75838, France. TEL 45-74-21-62, FAX 45-74-01-03. Ed. Georges Golan.

COMMUNITY ASSOCIATION LAW REPORTER; a newsletter on the emerging law of condominium and homeowner associations and cooperatives. see *HOUSING AND URBAN PLANNING*

334 USA ISSN 1045-4322
COMMUNITY ECONOMICS. Text in English. 1983. 3/yr. USD 25 to institutions. bk.rev. **Description:** Covers community based developments, land reform, community land trusts, preserving permanently affordable housing and community investing.
Published by: Institute for Community Economics, 57 School St, Springfield, MA 01105-1331. TEL 413-746-8660, FAX 413-746-8862. Ed. Kirby White. Circ: 6,500.

CONCLUSIONSONLINE. see *BUSINESS AND ECONOMICS—Banking And Finance*

334 ITA ISSN 0391-6278
COOP ITALIA. Text in Italian. 1966. bi-m. adv.
Address: Viale Famagosta, 75, Milan, MI 20142, Italy. Ed. Bruno Cremascoli. Circ: 5,000.

334 NGA ISSN 0794-7763
COOP NEWS. Text in English. 1985. m. NGN 36 (effective 1991). adv. bk.rev.
Published by: Co-operative Federation of Nigeria, PMB 5533, Ibadan, Oyo, Nigeria. TEL 234-22-711276, TELEX 31621 COEDPRO NG. Ed. 'Sola Osola. Circ: 4,000.

334 CHE
COOP - ZEITUNG. Text in German. 1902. w. CHF 39. adv. **Document type:** *Newspaper.*
Published by: Coop Schweiz, Postfach 2550, Basel, 4002, Switzerland. TEL 41-61-3367118, FAX 41-61-3367072. Ed. Urs Knapp. Adv. contact Karl Voegeli. Circ: 1,082,409 (controlled).

334 NLD ISSN 1389-7462
COOPERATIE. Text in Dutch. 1935. q. EUR 23 (effective 2005). bk.rev. bibl.; stat. index. 25 p./no. 2 cols./p.; **Document type:** *Magazine, Corporate.* **Description:** Contains information on all aspects of agricultural and horticultural cooperatives.
Former titles (until 1996): Cooperatie Magazine (0928-3048); (until 1991): Cooperatie (0009-9783)
Indexed: KES.
Published by: Nationale Cooperatieve Raad voor Land- en Tuinbouw/National Co-operative Council for Agriculture and Horticulture, Straatweg 25, Breukelen, 3621 BG, Netherlands. TEL 31-346-295600, abonnement@cooperatie.nl, ncr@cooperatie.nl, http://www.cooperatie.nl, 31-346-295610. Circ: 2,700 (controlled).

334 CHE
COOPERATION. Text in English. w. adv. **Document type:** *Newspaper.*
Published by: Coop Schweiz, Postfach 2550, Basel, 4002, Switzerland. TEL 41-61-3367117, FAX 41-61-3367072. Ed. J C Aeschlimann. Adv. contact Karl Voegeli. Circ: 287,994.

334 TUR ISSN 1300-1477
COOPERATION IN TURKIYE. Text in English, German. 1984. 2/yr. USD 14 (effective 2003). adv. bk.rev.; Website rev. charts; illus.; stat. back issues avail. **Document type:** *Bulletin, Academic/Scholarly.* **Description:** Covers activities of economic cooperative organizations in Turkey, including legislative issues and historical discussions.
Formerly (until 1991): Cooperation in Turkey
Published by: Turk Kooperatifcilik Kurumu/Turkish Cooperative Association, Mithatpasa Caddesi no.38-A, 06420 Kizilay, Ankara, Turkey. TEL 90-312-4359899, FAX 90-312-4304292, http://www.koopkur.org/. Eds., Pubs. Celal Er, Rasih Demirci.

THE COOPERATIVE ACCOUNTANT. see *BUSINESS AND ECONOMICS—Accounting*

334 USA ISSN 0896-9426
COOPERATIVE PARTNERS. Text in English. 1925. 8/yr. USD 6; free to qualified personnel (effective 2005). adv. charts; illus. **Document type:** *Magazine, Trade.* **Description:** Communicates innovative thinking that contributes to Land O'Lakes and Cenex customers' profitability and the quality of rural life.
Formerly (until 1987): Cooperative Builder (0010-8413)
Related titles: Microfilm ed.
Published by: Cenex - Land O'Lakes, 5500 Cenex Dr, Inver Grove Heights, MN 55077. TEL 651-355-5035, FAX 651-355-4310, lpede@cnxlol.com, http://www.co-oppartners.com. Ed. Linda Tank. Circ: 230,000.

334 IND
COOPERATIVE SUGAR PRESS NEWS. Text in English. w. —ingenta.
Published by: National Federation of Co-operative Sugar Factories, 82 Nehru Pl., New Delhi, 110 019, India. TEL 011-6412868, TELEX 314561.

380.1029 IND ISSN 0069-9837
COOPERATIVE TRADE DIRECTORY FOR SOUTHEAST ASIA. Text in English. 1964. irreg., latest vol.3, 1970. INR 20, USD 3. Supplement avail. **Document type:** *Directory.*
Published by: International Cooperative Alliance, Regional Office and Education Centre for South-East Asia, 43 Friends Colony, P O Box 3312, New Delhi, 110 014, India. Ed. M V Madane. Circ: 300.

334 IND ISSN 0010-8464
COOPERATOR. Text in English. 1963. m. INR 150, USD 50. adv. charts; illus.
Published by: National Cooperative Union of India, Panchshila Marg (Behind Hauz Khas), 3 Siri Institutional Area, New Delhi, 110 016, India. Ed. M L Sharma. Circ: 2,700.

334 CHE
COOPERAZIONE. Text in Italian. w. adv. **Document type:** *Newspaper.*
Published by: Coop Schweiz, Postfach 2550, Basel, 4002, Switzerland. TEL 41-61-3367149, FAX 41-61-3367072. Ed. Orazio Martinetti. Adv. contact Karl Voegeli. Circ: 58,331.

334 621.393 USA ISSN 0747-0592
COUNTRY LIVING (COLUMBUS). (Published in 25 regional editions) Text in English. 1958. m. USD 7.50 (effective 2005). adv. 40 p./no.; back issues avail. **Document type:** *Magazine, Consumer.* **Description:** For members of consumer-owned electric cooperatives. Publishes energy-related articles, columns, and rural life features.
Published by: Ohio Rural Electric Cooperatives, Inc., 6677 Busch Blvd, Box 26036, Columbus, OH 43226-0036. TEL 614-846-5757, FAX 614-846-7108, http://www.buckeyepower.com. R&P Jeff Brehm. Circ: 285,000 (paid).

CREDIT UNION MAGAZINE; for credit union elected officials, managers and employees. see *BUSINESS AND ECONOMICS—Banking And Finance*

CREDIT UNION NEWS. see *BUSINESS AND ECONOMICS—Banking And Finance*

CREDIT UNION REPORT. see *BUSINESS AND ECONOMICS—Banking And Finance*

▼ **CREDIT UNION TELLER/M S R REPORT.** (Member Service Representative) see *BUSINESS AND ECONOMICS—Banking And Finance*

CREDIT UNION WAY. see *BUSINESS AND ECONOMICS—Banking And Finance*

334.2 ITA
CREDITO COOPERATIVO; rivista di cultura cooperativa. Text in Italian. 1948. m. EUR 36 domestic; EUR 72 foreign (effective 2005). adv. bk.rev. stat. index. **Document type:** *Magazine, Consumer.* **Description:** Includes technical and general articles about the Italian system of BCC - credit cooperative banks.
Former titles: Credito e Cooperazione; Cooperazione di Credito (0010-8480)
Published by: (Federazione Nazionale delle Casse Rurali e Artigiane), Edizioni ECRA, Via Massimo d'Azeglio 33, Rome, 00184, Italy. TEL 39-06-4741157, info_ecra@ecra.bcc.it, http://www.bcc.it. Ed. Giuseppe Vannucci. Circ: 34,000.

B

334 ESP
CUADERNOS DE ESTUDIOS COOPERATIVOS. Text in Spanish. 1958. 4/yr. bibl.
Published by: Instituto Sindical de Formacion Cooperativa, Paseo del Prado, 18, Madrid, Spain.

330.9 CHL ISSN 0252-2195
CUADERNOS DE LA C E P A L. Text in Spanish; Text occasionally in English. 1981. irreg., latest vol.84, 1998. price varies. back issues avail.
Indexed: RASB.
Published by: Comision Economica para America Latina y el Caribe/Economic Commission for Latin America and the Caribbean, Ave Dag Hammarskjold 3477, Vitacura, Santiago de Chile, Chile. TEL 56-2-471-2000, FAX 56-2-208-0252, publications@eclac.cl, http://www.eclac.cl. **Subscr. to:** United Nations Publications, Distribution and Sales Section, Palais des Nations, Rm C-116, 8-14 av de la Paix, Geneva 1211, Switzerland; United Nations Publications, Rm DC2-853, United Nations Bldg, 2 United Nations Plaza, New York, NY 10017. TEL 205-995-1567, FAX 205-995-1588.

DIE DEUTSCHEN GENOSSENSCHAFTEN. STATISTIK. see *BUSINESS AND ECONOMICS—Abstracting, Bibliographies, Statistics*

334 DEU ISSN 1619-1064
DIALOG (HANNOVER, 1994). Text in German. 1994. m. EUR 78; EUR 8 newsstand/cover (effective 2005). adv. **Document type:** *Magazine, Trade.*
Published by: Genossenschaftsverband Norddeutschland e.V., Hannoversche Str 149, Hannover, 30627, Germany. TEL 49-511-95740, FAX 49-511-9574348, info@geno-verband.de, http://www.geno-verband.de. Ed. Joachim Prahat. adv.: B&W page EUR 2,408, color page EUR 2,759. Circ: 6,000 (paid and controlled).

334.021 COL
DIRECTORIO NACIONAL DE ENTIDADES COOPERATIVOS. Text in Spanish. irreg.
Published by: Departamento Administrativo Nacional de Estadistica, Banco Nacional de Datos, Centro Administrativo Nacional (CAN), Avenida Eldorado, Apartado Aereo 80043, Bogota, CUND, Colombia.

DOCUMENTATION BULLETIN FOR SOUTH-EAST ASIA. see *BIBLIOGRAPHIES*

DUCA POST. see *BUSINESS AND ECONOMICS—Banking And Finance*

334 LUX ISSN 1680-1687
HC240.A1
ECONOMIC PORTRAIT OF THE EUROPEAN UNION. Text in English. 2000. a. EUR 30 (effective 2004).
Published by: European Commission, Office for Official Publications of the European Union, 2 Rue Mercier, Luxembourg, L-2985, Luxembourg. FAX 352-2929-1, opoce-info-info@cec.eu.int, http://publications.eu.int.

334 CAN ISSN 1484-8031
HD3450.A3 CODEN: CDEVEU
ECONOMIE ET SOLIDARITES. Text mainly in French; Text occasionally in English. 1968. s-a. CND 28, USD 36 (effective 2000). bk.rev. bibl.; charts; stat. back issues avail.
Description: Studies the characteristics of cooperatives, their role as agent of socio-economic development, their economy, management and the main sectors of activity where they are involved.

▼ new title ➤ refereed ✶ unverified ◆ full entry avail.

Former titles (until 1996): Cooperatives et Developpement (0712-2748); (until 1983): Revue du C.I.R.I.E.C. (0831-876X); (until 1977): Revue Canadienne d'Economie Publique et Cooperative (0384-8744); (until 1971): Revue du C.I.R.I.E.C. Canadien (0045-6063)
Indexed: PSA, PdeR, SOPODA, SSA, SociolAb.
—CISTI.
Published by: Universite du Quebec a Hull, C P 1250, succ B, Hull, PQ J8X 3X7, Canada. revue_ciriec@uqah.uquebec.ca, http://www.unites.uqam.ca/ciriec/. Ed. Louis Favreau. Pub. Yvan Comeau. Circ: 1,000.

334 FIN
ELANTO. Text in Finnish. 9/yr. adv.
Published by: (Elanto Cooperative Society), Oy Kaupparengas AB, Haemeentie 11, Helsinki, 00530, Finland.

334 DEU
EMSCHERGENOSSENSCHAFT. JAHRESBERICHTE. Text in German. 1906. a. **Document type:** *Corporate.*
Published by: Emschergenossenschaft, Kronprinzenstr 24, Essen, 45128, Germany. TEL 0201-1042216.

B

334 JPN
FACTS AND FIGURES. Text in Japanese. a. **Document type:** *Corporate.* **Description:** Provides statistics on consumer co-ops in Japan.
Published by: Japanese Consumers Cooperative Union/Nihon Seikatsu Kyodokumiai Rengokai, Seikyo Kaikan, 4-1-13 Sendagaya, Shibuya-ku, Tokyo, 151-0051, Japan. TEL 81-3-3497-9103, FAX 81-3-3470-2924, TELEX 2423380 NCOOP J, jccu-int@mxb.meshnet.or.jp, http://www.co-op.or.jp/. Ed. Syakagori Katuyuki.

FARM CREDIT ADMINISTRATION. ANNUAL REPORT. see *AGRICULTURE—Agricultural Economics*

334 658.8 CHE
FEDERATION OF MIGROS COOPERATIVES. DOCUMENTATION AND INFORMATION; report of the Board of Directors to the Assembly of Delegates. Text in English. 1956. a. free. adv. bk.rev. **Document type:** *Corporate.*
Formerly: Federation of Migros Cooperatives. Annual Report (0071-4410)
Related titles: French ed.: 1941; German ed.: 1941; Italian ed.: 1982.
Published by: Federation of Migros Cooperatives, Limmatstr 152, Postfach 266, Zuerich, 8031, Switzerland. TEL 41-1-2772111, FAX 41-1-2772525, http://www.mgb.ch. Circ: 6,000.

334.2 USA ISSN 0094-0240
FIRST FRIDAY. Text in English. 1973. m. USD 35. bk.rev. charts; stat. back issues avail.
Published by: A S C U, PO Box 5488, Madison, WI 53705. Ed. Walter Polner. Circ: 1,450.

334 DEU ISSN 0933-9477
GENOSSENSCHAFTS-HANDBUCH. Text in German. 1973. irreg. looseleaf. price varies. **Document type:** *Monographic series, Trade.*
Published by: Erich Schmidt Verlag GmbH & Co. (Berlin), Genthiner Str 30G, Berlin, 10785, Germany. TEL 49-30-250085-0, FAX 49-30-25008521, vertrieb@esvmedien.de, http://www.erich-schmidt-verlag.de.

334 DEU ISSN 0942-847X
GESUND UND SICHER. Key Title: G & S. Gesund und Sicher. Text in German. m. bk.rev. 32 p./no.; **Document type:** *Journal, Trade.*
Formerly (until 1991): Nordwestliche (0176-3652)
Published by: Norddeutsche Metall-Berufsgenossenschaft, Seligmannallee 4, Hannover, 30173, Germany. TEL 49-511-811836, FAX 49-511-8118358, klaus.taubitz@nmbg.de, http://www.nmbg.de.

334 AUT
GEWERBLICHE GENOSSENSCHAFT. Text in German. q.
Published by: Oesterreichischer Genossenschaftsverband, Schottengasse 10, Vienna, W 1010, Austria. TELEX 114268.

GRASSROOTS ECONOMIC ORGANIZING NEWSLETTER. see *OCCUPATIONS AND CAREERS*

334 ISR
HAIFA UNIVERSITY. INSTITUTE FOR STUDY AND RESEARCH OF THE KIBBUTZ AND THE COOPERATIVE IDEA. DISCUSSION PAPERS. Text in English, Hebrew. irreg.
Published by: Haifa University, Institute for Study and Research of the Kibbutz and the Cooperative Idea, Hacarmel, Haifa, 31999, Israel. FAX 4-342104, TELEX 46660-UVIH.

334 KEN
HARAMBEE. Text in English. q.
Published by: Harambee Co-operative Savings and Credit Society Ltd., Shankardas House Moi Ave., PO Box 47815, Nairobi, Kenya.

HARVEST STATES AGRIVISIONS. see *AGRICULTURE*

334 IND ISSN 0017-8233
HARYANA COOPERATION. Text in English, Hindi. 1970 (vol.4). q. INR 6. adv. charts.
Published by: Haryana Cooperative Union Ltd., No. 96, Sector 18-A, Chandigarh, Haryana, India. Ed. Prem Singh.

HOME & FAMILY FINANCE; a guide to family finance and consumer action. see *BUSINESS AND ECONOMICS—Banking And Finance*

334 IND
I C A REGIONAL BULLETIN. (International Cooperative Alliance) Text in English. 1968. q. free. bk.rev.
Formerly: I C A Information Bulletin (0018-8743)
Published by: International Cooperative Alliance, Regional Office and Education Centre for South-East Asia, 43 Friends Colony, P O Box 3312, New Delhi, 110 014, India. Ed. A H Ganesan. Circ: 2,000.

334 GBR ISSN 0309-3298
IN THE MAKING; directory of radical cooperation. Text in English. 1973. biennial. GBP 1, USD 6. bk.rev.
Address: 44 Albion Rd, Sutton, Surrey SM2 5TF, United Kingdom. Ed. D Bollen. Circ: 2,000.

334 IND ISSN 0019-4581
INDIAN COOPERATIVE REVIEW. Text in English. 1963. q. INR 40, USD 10. adv. bk.rev. bibl. index.
Indexed: AEA, ARDT, BAS, DSA, FPA, HortAb, NutrAb, PHN&I, RASB, RDA, RiceAb, S&F, SIA, TDB, WAE&RSA.
Published by: National Cooperative Union of India, Panchshila Marg (Behind Hauz Khas), 3 Siri Institutional Area, New Delhi, 110 016, India. Ed. M L Sharma. Circ: 2,000.

334 NER ISSN 0534-4697
INTER-AFRICAN CONFERENCE ON CO-OPERATIVE SOCIETIES MEETING. REUNION*. Text in Niger-Congo. irreg. **Document type:** *Proceedings.*
Published by: (Commission for Technical Co-Operation in Africa South of the Sahara), Maison de l'Afrique, BP 878, Niamey, Niger.

334 IND ISSN 0074-4255
INTERNATIONAL COOPERATIVE ALLIANCE. COOPERATIVE SERIES*. Text in English. 1965. irreg.
Published by: International Cooperative Alliance, Regional Office and Education Centre for South-East Asia, 43 Friends Colony, P O Box 3312, New Delhi, 110 014, India. Circ: 2,000.

334 ISR ISSN 0080-1313
ISRAEL. MINISTRY OF LABOUR. REGISTRAR OF COOPERATIVE SOCIETIES. REPORT ON THE COOPERATIVE MOVEMENT IN ISRAEL. Text in English. 1964. a.
Published by: (Israel. Registrar of Cooperative Societies), Ministry of Labour and Social Affairs, 10 Yad Harutzim St., Talpiod, P O Box 1260, Jerusalem, Israel. Circ: 1,200.
Co-sponsor: Women's Society & Welfare League of Israel.

334 ITA ISSN 0391-7150
L'ITALIA COOPERATIVA. Text in Italian. 1946. fortn. **Document type:** *Magazine, Trade.*
Published by: (Confederazione Cooperativa Italiana), Editrice Tecnostudi Srl, Piazza della Citta Leonina 9, Rome, 00193, Italy. TEL 39-06-6879907, FAX 39-06-6540212. Ed. Dario Mengozzi. Circ: 65,000.

334 JPN
J A - ZENCHU NEWS. Text in Japanese. 1961. bi-m. free. **Document type:** *Newsletter.*
Former titles (until Jun. 1995): J A - Zenchu Farm News; Zenchu Farm News; Japan Agricultural Coop News (0447-5240)
Published by: Central Union of Agricultural Co-operatives/Zenchu, 1-8-3 Ote-Machi, Chiyoda-ku, Tokyo, 100-0004, Japan. TEL 03-245-7565, FAX 03-5255-7358, TELEX CUAC-J33809.

334 GBR ISSN 0961-5784
➤ **JOURNAL OF CO-OPERATIVE STUDIES.** Text in English. 3/yr. in United Kingdom membership individuals & institutions; GBP 20 in Europe to individuals; GBP 25 elsewhere to individuals; GBP 50 in Europe to institutions; GBP 60 elsewhere to institutions (effective until Mar. 2003). bk.rev. **Document type:** *Academic/Scholarly.* **Description:** Contains articles about co-operatives and other third sector organizations and the issues affecting them.
Indexed: IBSS.
Published by: Society for Co-operative Studies, c/o Frank Dent, 18 Macclesfield Rd, Buxton, Derbys SK17 9AH, United Kingdom. TEL 44-1298-79277, frankdent@email.msn.com. Ed. J Birchall. Circ: 600 (paid).

➤ **THE JOURNAL OF COMMUNITY ASSOCIATION LAW.** see *HOUSING AND URBAN PLANNING*

334 ISR ISSN 0377-7480
HD1491.A1 CODEN: JRCOE4
➤ **JOURNAL OF RURAL COOPERATION.** Text in English. 1973. s-a. USD 28 (effective 2004). adv. bk.rev. bibl. Index. 90 p./no.; back issues avail.; reprints avail. **Document type:** *Journal, Academic/Scholarly.* **Description:** Focuses on subjects relating to the study of rural cooperatives, particularly the dynamics of cooperative-community reciprocity and relations. Special emphasis is given to the role of cooperatives vis-a-vis privatization and global competition.
Indexed: BAS, GEOBASE, IBSS, RDA, RRTA, RiceAb, SOPODA, SSA, SociolAb, WAE&RSA.
—BLDSC (5052.127000), IE, ingenta.
Published by: International Research Center on Rural Cooperative Communities (CIRCOM), Yad Tabenkin, Ramat Efal, 52960, Israel. TEL 972-3-7500054, FAX 972-3-5346376, yalevi@netvision.net.il. Ed. Dr. Yair Levi. R&P Daphna Bar-Nes. Circ: 450.

334 TUR ISSN 1300-1450
HD3531
KARINCA; Kooperatif Postasi. Text in Turkish. 1931. m. USD 24 (effective 2002). bk.rev.; Website rev. bibl.; illus. back issues avail. **Document type:** *Newsletter, Corporate.* **Description:** Information on cooperatives and related subjects.
Published by: Turk Kooperatifcilik Kurumu/Turkish Cooperative Association, Mithatpasa Caddesi no.38-A, 06420 Kizilay, Ankara, Turkey. TEL 90-312-4359899, FAX 90-312-4304292, http://www.koopkur.org/. Eds., Pubs. Celal Er, Rasih Demirci. R&P Celal Er. Circ: 5,000.

334.683 IND
KERALA CO-OPERATIVE JOURNAL. Text in English, Malayalam. 1959. m. INR 12. adv. charts.
Published by: State Co-Operative Union, P O Box 35, Thiruvananthapuram, Kerala 695 001, India. Ed. C K Mani. Circ: 4,500.

334 DEU ISSN 0721-4596
KERAMIK UND GLAS. Text in German. q. membership. **Document type:** *Newsletter.*
Published by: Berufsgenossenschaft der Keramischen und Glas-Industrie, Riemenschneiderstr 2, Wuerzburg, 97072, Germany. TEL 49-931-7943-0, FAX 49-931-7943804. Ed. Friedrich Muenzer.

334 USA
KIBBUTZ JOURNAL (NEW YORK). Text in English. 1983. a. donation. back issues avail. **Document type:** *Newsletter, Academic/Scholarly.*
Published by: Kibbutz Aliya Desk, 633 3d Ave, 21st Fl, New York, NY 10017. TEL 212-318-6130, FAX 212-318-6134, kibbutzdsk@aol.com. Circ: 14,000.

334 ISR ISSN 0792-7290
HX742.2.A3
KIBBUTZ TRENDS. Text in English. 1974. s-a. ILS 35 domestic; USD 24 foreign (effective 2003). bk.rev. 64 p./no.; back issues avail.; reprints avail. **Document type:** *Journal, Academic/Scholarly.*
Former titles (until 1991): K C. Kibbutz Currents (0792-3163); (until 1987): Shdemot (0334-4363)
Indexed: IJP.
Published by: Yad Tabenkin, C/o Ruth Sobol, Efal, 52960, Israel. TEL 972-3-5301217, FAX 972-3-5346376, yadtab@inter.net.il. Eds. Idit Paz, Neil Harris, Rochelle Mass. R&P Ruth Sobol TEL 972-3-5301217. Circ: 1,200.

KODIN PELLERVO. see *AGRICULTURE*

334 DEU ISSN 0930-6439
KOMMUNALER BESCHAFFUNGS-DIENST. Text in German. 1980. 10/yr. EUR 5 newsstand/cover (effective 2004). adv. **Document type:** *Magazine, Trade.*
Published by: Verlag Dieter A. Kuberski GmbH, Ludwigstr 26, Stuttgart, 70176, Germany. TEL 49-711-2388611, FAX 49-711-2388633, norbert.mueller@kbd.de. adv.: B&W page EUR 2,920, color page EUR 4,120; trim 185 x 280. Circ: 10,520 (paid and controlled).

334 DNK ISSN 0023-382X
KOOPERATIONEN. Text in Danish. 1923. 5/yr. DKK 195 domestic (effective 2000). bk.rev. charts; illus. index. **Document type:** *Trade.*
Published by: Kooperative Faellesforbund i Danmark, Reventlowsgade 14 2, Copenhagen V, 1651, Denmark. TEL 45-33-31-22-62, FAX 45-33-31-30-41, dkf@dkf.dk, http://www.dkf.dk. Ed. Jes Bastholm. Circ: 2,400 (paid).

334 SWE ISSN 0283-9210
KOOPERATIV HORISONT. Text in Swedish. 1986. 4/yr. free.
Related titles: E-mail ed.; Online - full text ed.
Published by: Kooperativa Institutet, Oestgoetagatan 90, PO Box 20063, Stockholm, 10460, Sweden. TEL 46-08-772-8990, FAX 46-08-642-8106, http://www.koopi.se/index_horisont_2002_1.shtml. Ed. Ulla Loord-Gynne.

334 BGR
KOOPERATSIA. Text in Bulgarian. bi-w. USD 84 foreign (effective 2002). **Document type:** *Newspaper.*

Published by: Central Cooperative Union, 11, Dondoukov Blvd., Bitov Kombinat, Sofia, 1040, Bulgaria. TEL 359-2-883848, FAX 359-2-870320. **Dist. by:** Sofia Books, ul Silivria 16, Sofia 1404, Bulgaria. TEL 359-2-9586257, info@sofiabooks-bg.com, http://www.sofiabooks-bg.com.

L O A. see *AGRICULTURE*

334 SWE ISSN 0024-015X
LEDARFORUM. Text in Swedish. 1925. 10/yr. SEK 550. adv. bk.rev. illus.; tr.lit. index.
Former titles (until 1971): K F F; (until 1944): K F F Medlemsblad (0023-3838)
Published by: Kooperativa Ledares Foerbund, Fack 5200, Stockholm, 10465, Sweden. Circ: 8,000.

334.008 FRA ISSN 1019-1518
LETTRE DE LA FRANCOPHONIE. Text in French. 1990. m.
Description: Covers the various activities of the Agency in the fields of education, culture and communications, technical cooperation and economic development, judicial cooperation in Francophone countries.
Published by: Agence de Cooperation Culturelle et Technique, 13 quai Andre Citroen, Paris, 75015, France. TEL 33-1-44-37-33-00. Ed. Jean Louis Roy.

334 ISR
MA'ANIT. Text in Hebrew. q.
Published by: Union of Moshavim of Hapoal Hamizrachi, 166 Even Giverol St., Tel Aviv, Israel. TEL 03-441224. Ed. Shlomo Zis.

334 IND ISSN 0025-0430
HD2951
THE MAHARASHTRA CO-OPERATIVE QUARTERLY. Text in English. 1918 (Jul.). q. INR 100 domestic to individuals; USD 30, GBP 15 foreign; INR 25 newsstand/cover domestic (effective 2000). adv. bk.rev. charts; stat. index.
Published by: Maharashtra Rajya Sahakari Sangh Maryadit/Maharashtra State Co-Operative Union, 5 B J Rd., Pune, Maharashtra 411 001, India. TEL 91-20-622640, FAX 91-20-609033. Ed., Pub. Krishna L Fale. adv.: page USD 4,000. Circ: 2,000.

334 MUS
MAURITIUS. MINISTRY OF CO-OPERATIVES AND CO-OPERATIVE DEVELOPMENT. ANNUAL REPORT. Text in English. irreg.
Published by: Government Printing Office, Elizabeth II Ave, Port Louis, Mauritius.

658.7 FIN ISSN 0025-6269
AP80
ME. Text in Finnish. 1916. 12/yr. adv. bk.rev. **Document type:** *Magazine, Consumer.*
Former titles (until 1970): Me Kuluttajat (1235-5909); (until 1965): Kuluttaja (0451-0569); (until 1957): Kuluttajain Lehti
Indexed: RASB.
Published by: Tradeka Oy, Hameentie 19, PO Box 72, Helsinki, 00501, Finland. TEL 358-9-7331, FAX 358-9-7332120, http://www.tradeka.fi. Ed. Riitta Raasakka. adv.: color page EUR 5,800, B&W page EUR 4,600. Circ: 810,000 (controlled).

N A F C U'S CREDIT UNION REGULATORY COMPLIANCE REPORT. (National Association of Federal Credit Unions) see *LAW—Corporate Law*

334 USA ISSN 1065-7207
N C B A COOPERATIVE BUSINESS JOURNAL. Text in English. 1978. 10/yr. USD 15 domestic; USD 25 foreign (effective 2005). adv. **Document type:** *Newspaper, Trade.*
Former titles (until 199?): Cooperative Business Journal (0893-3391); (until 1987): In League (0164-8500)
Published by: National Cooperative Business Association, 1401 New York Ave, N W, Ste 1100, Washington, DC 20005. TEL 202-638-6222, FAX 202-638-1374, ncba@ncba.coop, ncba@ncba.org, http://www.ncba.org, http://www.cooperative.org. Ed. Judith Bennett. Adv. contact Jill Stevenson. B&W page USD 1,315. Circ: 10,000 evening (paid).

334 IND ISSN 0027-6278
N C D C BULLETIN. Text in English, Hindi. 1967. bi-m. free. bk.rev. bibl.; charts; stat. 48 p./no. 3 cols./p.; **Document type:** *Bulletin, Government.*
Published by: National Cooperative Development Corporation, Hauz Khas, 4 Siri Institutional Area, New Delhi, 110 016, India. TEL 91-11-6569246, FAX 0-11-6962370, 0-11-6516032, TELEX 31-73059 NCDC IN, editor@ncdc.de1hi.nic.in. Ed., Pub. Archna Sood. Circ: 7,000.

334 COL
O C A NEWS. Text in Spanish. m.
Published by: Organization of the Cooperatives of America/Organizacion de las Cooperativas de America, Carrera 11, 86-32 Ofc 101, Bogota, DE 241263, Colombia. TEL 2181295, FAX 057-1-610-19-12.

334 FIN ISSN 1236-4835
HD3517.3
O T. OSUUSTOIMINTA-LEHTI. Text in Finnish. 1909. 8/yr. adv. illus. index. **Document type:** *Magazine, Trade.*
Former titles (until 1993): Osuustoiminta (0783-800X); (until 1986): Suomen Osuustoimintalehti (0039-5609)
Published by: Pellervo-Seura ry/Confederation of Finnish Cooperatives, Simonkatu 6, PO Box 77, Helsinki, 00101, Finland. TEL 358-9-4767501, FAX 358-9-6948845, finnvoop@pellervo.fi, http://www.pellervo.fi/otlehti/index.htm. Ed. Mauno-Markus Karjalainen TEL 358-9-47675588. adv.: color page EUR 1,200; 210 x 297. Circ: 8,500.

PRAWO SPOLEK. see *LAW*

334 AUS
PRIMARY PRODUCERS' GUIDE. Text in English. a.
Published by: Primac Association Limited, South, 109 Melbourne St, Brisbane, QLD 4001, Australia. TEL 07-840-5555, FAX 07-844-7530, TELEX AA41889.

334 PAK
PUNJAB COOPERATIVE UNION. REVIEW. Text in English. 1963. q. PKR 15, USD 3.25.
Formerly: Pakistan Cooperative Review; Supersedes (vol. 6, July 1974): West Pakistan Cooperative Review (0511-6147)
Published by: Punjab Cooperative Union, 5 Court St., Lahore, Pakistan. Ed. Khalida Saeed.

R UND V REPORT. see *INSURANCE*

334 DEU
RAIFFEISEN; Informationen des Deutschen Raiffeisenverbandes. Text in German. 1974. bi-m. free membership (effective 2005). bk.rev. **Document type:** *Bulletin, Trade.*
Published by: Deutscher Raiffeisenverband e.V., Adenauerallee 127, Bonn, 53113, Germany. TEL 49-228-1060, FAX 49-228-106266, info@drv.raiffeisen.de, presse@drv.raiffeisen.de, http://www.raiffeisen.de. Ed. Monika Windbergs. Adv. contact Waltraud Roder. Circ: 30,000 (controlled).

334 AUT
RAIFFEISENZEITUNG. Text in German. 1904. w. adv. bk.rev. **Document type:** *Newspaper, Trade.*
Published by: Oesterreichischer Raiffeisenverband, Friedrich-Wilhelm-Raiffeisen-Platz 1, Vienna, W 1020, Austria. TEL 43-1-211360, FAX 43-1-211362559, ferdinand.maier@oerv.raiffeisen.at, http://www.raiffeisenverband.at. Ed. Kurt Ceipek. Adv. contact Bernd Sibitz. Circ: 48,000.

334 PER
REVISTA DE ASESORIA PARA COOPERATIVAS. Variant title: Revista Tecnica de Cooperativismo en el Peru. Text in Spanish. s-w. PEN 220 (effective 1997).
Published by: Asesorandina Publicaciones, Ave. Salaverry, 674 Of 403, Casilla 11-0059, Jesus Maria, Lima, 11, Peru. TEL 51-14-237730, FAX 51-14-378430. Ed. Carlos Torres.

334 FRA ISSN 1626-1682
REVUE INTERNATIONALE DE L'ECONOMIE SOCIALE. Text in French; Abstracts in English. 1948. q. EUR 70 domestic; EUR 80 foreign; EUR 50 to students (effective 2004). adv. bk.rev. index. reprints avail. **Document type:** *Academic/Scholarly.*
Description: Covers cooperatives, economic systems and theories.
Former titles (until 1999): Revue des Etudes Cooperatives, Mutualistes et Associatives (0299-1624); (until 1986): Revue des Etudes Cooperatives (0035-2020); Which superseded in part (in 1950): Annee Politique, Economique et Cooperative (1149-8064); Which was formerly (until 1949): Annee Politique et Revue des Etudes Cooperatives, Res Publica (1149-8072); Which was formed by the merger of (1921-1948): Revue des Etudes Cooperatives (1149-8056); (1925-1948): Annee Politique Francaise et Etrangere (1149-0152); (1931-1948): Res Publica (1153-5911)
Indexed: IBSS, PAIS, PCI, RASB, RDA, RRTA, WAE&RSA.
Published by: R.E.C.M.A., 43 rue de Liege, Paris, 75008, France. TEL 33-1-4387-0010, FAX 33-1-4387-0027, http://www.recma.org. Ed. Jean Francois Draperi. Pub. Alain Magnier. R&P Sylvie Cleaud TEL 33-1-49542607. Circ: 1,200.

RURAL COOPERATIVES. see *AGRICULTURE*

334 USA ISSN 0164-8578
RURAL MISSOURI. Text in English. 1948. m. USD 6 (effective 2005). adv. bk.rev. illus. **Document type:** *Magazine, Consumer.* **Description:** Includes news items pertaining to electrification and regional issues, as well as general articles, recipes and classifieds.
Formerly: Rural Electric Missourian (0048-8801)
Related titles: Braille ed.
Published by: Association of Missouri Electric Cooperatives, Inc., 2722 E McCarty, PO Box 1645, Jefferson City, MO 65102. TEL 573-635-6857 ext 3423, FAX 573-636-9499, mailbag@ruralmissouri.coop, http://www.ruralmissouri.coop. Ed. Jim McCarty. Adv. contact Mary Davis. Circ: 480 (paid).

334 DEU ISSN 0948-9908
DER SACHVERSTAENDIGE; Fachzeitschrift fuer Sachverstaendige, Kammern, Gerichte und Behoerden. Text in German. 1974. m. EUR 80; EUR 8 newsstand/cover (effective 2005). adv. bk.rev. **Document type:** *Journal, Trade.*
Formerly (until 1995): Der Oeffentlich Bestellte und Vereidigte Sachverstaendige (0341-2016)
Published by: Oeffentlich Bestellte und Vereidigte Sachverstaendige, Lindenstr 76, Berlin, 10969, Germany. TEL 49-30-2559380, FAX 49-30-25593814, info@bvs-ev.de, http://www.bvs-ev.de. adv.: B&W page EUR 1,500, color page EUR 2,625. Circ: 3,787 (paid and controlled).

334 640.73 FIN ISSN 0036-3715
SAMARBETE. Text in Swedish. 1909. m. adv. illus. **Document type:** *Consumer.*
Published by: Helsinki Media Company Oy, PL 2, Helsinki, 00040, Finland. TEL 358-9-1201, FAX 358-9-120-5988. Ed. Pentii Tormala. Circ: 23,132.

334 LKA
SAMUPAKARA VIGRAHAYA. Text in Singhalese. 3/yr.
Published by: National Cooperation Board, 455 Galle Rd., Colombo, 3, Sri Lanka.

334 ISR
HA-SHAVU'A. Text in Hebrew. w. membership. bk.rev.
Published by: Ha-Kibbutz ha-Artzi, P O Box 40009, Tel Aviv, 61400, Israel. TEL 03-435328. Ed. Mira Narkis.

334 ISR ISSN 0037-4008
SHITUF/COOPERATION. Text in Hebrew. 1948. bi-m. USD 8. bk.rev. charts; illus.; stat.
Published by: Central Union of Industrial Transport & Services Co-Operative Societies in Israel, 24 Haarbaa St., (Hakirya), P O Box 7151, Tel Aviv, Israel. Ed. L Losh. Circ: 12,500.

334 DEU
SICHERHEIT FUER HAUS UND HOF. Text in German. 1966. q. free. **Document type:** *Bulletin.*
Incorporates (1962-1999): Hilf Mit!
Published by: Landwirtschaftliche Berufsgenossenschaft Oberbayern Unterfranken und Niederbayern - Oberpfalz, Neumarkter Str 35, Munich, 81673, Germany. TEL 49-89-45480-0, FAX 49-89-436639813, bernhard.richter@lsv-obb.de, http://www.lsv-obb.de. Ed. Norbert Gradl.

334 USA ISSN 0038-4003
SOUTHERN COOPERATOR✶. Text in English. 1970. irreg. USD 5. adv. charts; illus.
Published by: Federation of Southern Cooperatives, Education Dept, Box 95, Epes, AL 35460. Ed. Alice Paris. Circ: 6,000.

STATELINE. see *BUSINESS AND ECONOMICS—Banking And Finance*

334 IND ISSN 0377-8002
HD3537
TAMIL NADU JOURNAL OF CO-OPERATION. Text in English. 1909. m. INR 30. adv. bk.rev.
Continues: Madras Journal of Co-operation
Indexed: BAS, ILD.
Published by: Tamil Nadu Co-operative Union, TNCU Bldg., Near Walajah Bridge, Chennai, Tamil Nadu 600 009, India. Ed. Thiru C M Rajan. Circ: 3,000.

334 333.79 USA
TEXAS CO-OP POWER. Text in English. 1944. m. USD 15 (effective 2005). adv. bk.rev. 40 p./no.; **Document type:** *Magazine, Trade.* **Description:** Covers primarily general interest with features on Texas and Texans. Includes news about electric industry issues, electrotechnology and electric co-ops.
Published by: Association of Texas Electric Cooperatives, 2550 S IH-35, Austin, TX 78704. TEL 512-454-0311, FAX 512-486-6254, kayen@texas-ec.org, http://www.texas-ec.org/publications. Ed., R&P Kaye Northcott TEL 512-486-6242. Adv. contact Martin Bevins. page USD 9,750. Circ: 880,000.

U.S. NATIONAL CREDIT UNION ADMINISTRATION. ANNUAL REPORT. see *BUSINESS AND ECONOMICS—Banking And Finance*

334 DNK ISSN 0109-1328
UDDELERBLADET. Text in Danish. 1905. 50/yr. adv. bk.rev. **Document type:** *Trade.*
Former titles (until 1983): Brugslederen (0106-5599); (until 1973): Uddelerbladet (0903-4935); (until 1927): Medlemsblad for Foreningen Danmarks Uddelere
Published by: Danmarks Uddelerforening, Markvangen 3, Viby J, 8260, Denmark. TEL 45-86-147781. Ed. Joergen Nielsen. Circ: 7,500.

334 FIN ISSN 0356-1364
UNIVERSITY OF HELSINKI. INSTITUTE FOR CO-OPERATIVE STUDIES. PUBLICATIONS. Text in English, Finnish, German. 1967. irreg. price varies.
—BLDSC (9110.360000).

Published by: University of Helsinki, Institute for Co-operative Studies, Franseninkatu 13, University of Helsinki, PL 25, Helsinki, 00014, Finland. TEL 358-0-1911, FAX 358-0-191-7000. Circ: 150.

334 DEU ISSN 0566-2753
UNTERSUCHUNGEN UEBER GRUPPEN UND VERBAENDE. Text in German. 1964. irreg., latest vol.14, 1978. price varies. **Document type:** *Monographic series, Academic/Scholarly.*
Published by: Duncker und Humblot GmbH, Carl-Heinrich-Becker-Weg 9, Berlin, 12165, Germany. TEL 49-30-7900060, FAX 49-30-79000631, info@duncker-humblot.de, http://www.duncker-humblot.de.

VAIKUNTH MEHTA NATIONAL INSTITUTE OF COOPERATIVE MANAGEMENT. PUBLICATIONS. see *BUSINESS AND ECONOMICS—Management*

334 JOR
VOICE OF COOPERATION/SAWT UL-TA'WUN. Text in Arabic. 1957. m. free to qualified personnel. adv. bk.rev.
Published by: Jordan Cooperative Organization, P O Box 1343, Amman, Jordan. Ed. Marwan A Dudin. Circ: 1,000.

WUERTTEMBERGISCHE BAU-BERUFSGENOSSENSCHAFT. JAHRESBERICHT. see *BUILDING AND CONSTRUCTION*

334 FIN ISSN 0044-0396
YHTEISHYVA. Text in Finnish. 1905. m. adv. bk.rev. illus.; stat. **Document type:** *Magazine, Consumer.*
Published by: Sanoma Magazines Finland Corporation, Hoylaamotie 1 D, P.O. Box 100, Helsinki, 00040, Finland. TEL 358-9-1201, FAX 358-9-1205171, info@sanomamagazines.fi, http://www.sanomamagazines.fi. Circ: 653,092.

334 334 ZMB
ZAMBIA. MINISTRY OF COOPERATIVES. ANNUAL REPORT. Text in English. a. ZMK 100. stat. **Document type:** *Government.* **Description:** Annual paper on the coordination of agricultural input supply services.
Formerly: Zambia. Department of Cooperatives. Annual Report (0514-5430)
Published by: (Zambia. Ministry of Cooperatives), Government Printing Department, PO Box 30136, Lusaka, Zambia.

334 DEU ISSN 0174-1136
ZEITSCHRIFT FUER KOMMUNALFINANZEN. Text in German. 1951. m. EUR 205.60; EUR 21.20 newsstand/cover (effective 2005). adv. **Document type:** *Journal, Trade.*
Formerly (until 1980): Deutsche Gemeindesteuer-Zeitung (0341-6801); Incorporates (1990-2003): Finanzwirtschaft (0863-2499); Which was formerly (until 1990): Sozialistische Finanzwirtschaft (0012-0103); (1956-1969): Deutsche Finanzwirtschaft (0323-7257)
Indexed: IBR, IBZ.
—CCC.
Published by: Stollfuss Verlag GmbH & Co. KG, Dechenstr 7, Bonn, 53115, Germany. TEL 49-228-7240, FAX 49-228-72491181, info@stollfuss.de, http://www.stollfuss.de/programm/products/0400100.htm. adv.: B&W page EUR 1,435, color page EUR 2,255. Circ: 2,500 (paid and controlled).

ZEITSCHRIFT FUER OEFFENTLICHE UND GEMEINWIRTSCHAFTLICHE UNTERNEHMEN. see *PUBLIC ADMINISTRATION*

BUSINESS AND ECONOMICS—Domestic Commerce

380 635.2 NLD ISSN 0169-653X
AARDAPPELWERELD MAGAZINE. Text in Dutch. 1985. m. adv. bk.rev. charts; illus.; stat. **Document type:** *Journal, Trade.* **Description:** Discusses the cultivation and marketing of potato crops.
Formed by the merger of (1974-1985): Pootaardappelwereld (0165-6031); (1974-1985): Pootaardappelhandel (0921-5700); Which superseded (1948-1974): Nederlandse Federatie voor de Handel in Pootaardappelen. Vakblad (0032-4337)
Indexed: FCA, KES, PotatoAb.
—CISTI.
Published by: Aardappelwereld BV, Van Stolkweg 31, Postbus 84102, The Hague, 2508 AC, Netherlands. TEL 31-70-358-9331, redactie@aardappelenwereld.nl, redactie@aardappelwereld, http://www.aardappelenwereld.nl, http://www.aardappelwereld.nl. Ed. M van Delft. Adv. contact H L Vorst. Circ: 5,000.

381 FRA ISSN 1141-7102
ACTUALITES COMMERCE. Text in French. 1964. 3/yr. adv. **Document type:** *Academic/Scholarly.*
Former titles (until 1971): Contact (1141-7110); (until 1967): Actualites Commerce (0567-8684)
Published by: Ecole des Cadres, La Defense 1, 70 Galerie des Damiers, Courbevoie, 92400, France. TEL 46-93-02-93, FAX 47-75-99-80. Ed. Alexis Saccardo. Pub. Christian Regnier. Circ: 35,000.

387.0021 330.21 GBR ISSN 0265-4113
AEROSPACE AND ELECTRONICS COST INDICES. Cover title: Economy. Aerospace and Electronics Cost Indices. Variant title: Cost Indices for the Aerospace and Radio and Electronic Capital Goods Industries. Text in English. 1983. m.
—BLDSC (0729.853600).
Published by: Office for National Statistics, Government Buildings, Cardiff Rd, Newport, Gwent NP9 1XG, United Kingdom. TEL 44-1633-812973, FAX 44-1633-81599, library@ons.govk, http://www.statistics.gov.uk.

380 GBR ISSN 1462-964X
THE AGENTS NEWS. Text in English. 1908. bi-m. GBP 35. adv. **Document type:** *Bulletin.*
Formerly (until 1997): Manufacturers' Agent (0025-2522)
Published by: Manufacturers Agents Association, Somers House, 1 Somers Rd, Reigate, Surrey RH2 9DU, United Kingdom. TEL 44-1737-241025, FAX 44-1737-224537. Ed. A P Lindsey Renton. adv.: B&W page GBP 190; trim 180 x 250. Circ: 650.

381 ESP
ALMERIA ECONOMICA. Text in Spanish. 12/yr.
Address: Paseo De Almeria, 59 1o, Almeria, 04001, Spain. TEL 51-23-44-33, FAX 51-23-48-50. Ed. J M Cosano Perez.

AMCHAM BUSINESS JOURNAL. see *BUSINESS AND ECONOMICS—Chamber Of Commerce Publications*

AMCHAM NEWSLETTER. see *BUSINESS AND ECONOMICS—Chamber Of Commerce Publications*

381 FRA ISSN 1258-732X
ANNUAIRE GENERAL DES COOPERATIVES FRANCAISES ET DE LEURS FOURNISSEURS. Text in French. 1956. a. EUR 97 (effective 2005). adv. **Document type:** *Directory, Trade.* **Description:** Classifies geographically and by activity about 8,000 agricultural, manufacturing, retail and trading cooperatives. Suppliers classified by products.
Formerly: Annuaire General des Cooperatives Francaises et de leurs Fournisseurs: France, Afrique et Marche Commun (0066-3182)
Published by: Agence Generale de Publication, 32 Rue de la Bienfaisance, Paris, 75008, France. TEL 33-1-40268124, FAX 33-1-40263440, agp-gerverau@wanadoo.fr. Adv. contact Martine Tissier.

L'ANTENNE; seul quotidien francais des transports. see *TRANSPORTATION—Ships And Shipping*

381 FRA
ARDENNE ECONOMIQUE (CHALONS-SUR-MARNE). Text in French. q.
Published by: Chambre Regionale de Commerce et d'Industrie Champagne - Ardenne, Direction de la Communication, 10 rue de Chastillon, B.P. 537, Chalons-sur-Marne, Cedex 51011, France. TEL 33-3-26693340, FAX 33-3-26693369.

381 ESP
ASTURIAS. Text in Spanish. 12/yr. membership only.
Published by: Centro Asturiano de Madrid, Farmacia, 2, Madrid, 28004, Spain. TEL 34-1-5328245, FAX 34-1-5328256. Ed. Cosme Sordo Obeso. Circ: 100,000.

381 CAN
ATLANTIC BUSINESS MAGAZINE. Text in English. 1990. bi-m. CND 17.25 domestic; CND 23 in United States; CND 32 elsewhere; CND 3.95 newsstand/cover (effective 2000). adv. back issues avail. **Document type:** *Consumer.* **Description:** Promotes the entrepreneurial achievements of New Brunswick, Prince Edward Island, Nova Scotia, Newfoundland and Labrador and highlights the character and determination of Atlantic Canadian business community and the success of their initiatives in the global marketplace.
Formerly: Atlantic Lifestyle Business (1184-051X)
Published by: Communications Ten Ltd., 197 Water St., P O Box 2356, Sta. C, St. John's, NF A1C 6E7, Canada. TEL 709-726-9300, FAX 709-726-3013. Ed. Dawn Chafe. Pub. Hubert Hutton. R&P Edwina Hutton. Adv. contact Tonia Caines. Circ: 500 (paid); 29,500 (controlled).

AVANCE DE INFORMACION ECONOMICA. ENCUESTA SOBRE ESTABLECIMIENTOS COMERCIALES. CIUDADES DE: MEXICO, GUADALAJARA Y MONTERREY. see *BUSINESS AND ECONOMICS—Abstracting, Bibliographies, Statistics*

658.8 380 DEU
B A G - HANDELSMAGAZIN. Text in German. 1961. m. adv. bk.rev. charts; illus.; stat. **Document type:** *Magazine, Trade.*
Formerly (until 1992): B A G - Nachrichten (0005-2639)
Published by: Bundesarbeitsgemeinschaft der Mittel- und Grossbetriebe des Einzelhandels e.V., Atrium Friedrichstr 60, Berlin, 10117, Germany. TEL 49-30-206120-0, FAX 49-30-20612088, handelsmagazin@bag.de, handelsverband@bag.de, http://www.bag.de. Circ: 10,000.

B B I A NEWSLINE. see *SPORTS AND GAMES—Ball Games*

381 CAN ISSN 0704-6278
B C MANUFACTURER'S DIRECTORY. Text in English. a. CND 45 (effective 1997). stat. **Document type:** *Government.* **Description:** Publicizes the availability of locally manufactured products for the benefit of buyers and sellers.
—CISTI.
Published by: Ministry of Finance and Corporate Relations, B C Stats, Sta Prov Govt, P O Box 9410, Victoria, BC V8W 9V1, Canada. TEL 250-387-0359, FAX 250-387-0380, bcstats@fincc04.fin.gov.bc.ca, http://www.bcstats.gov.bc.ca.

381.15 AUS ISSN 1039-0553
BARB'S FACTORY SHOPPING GUIDE (YEAR). Text in English. 1991. a. AUD 11 (effective 2004).
Published by: Universal Magazines Pty. Ltd., Unite 5, 6-8 Byfield St, North Ryde, NSW 2113, Australia. TEL 61-2-98870399, FAX 61-2-98050714, info@universalmagazines.com.au, http://www.universalmagazines.com.au/.

BARGAIN SHOPPER'S GUIDE TO MELBOURNE. see *CONSUMER EDUCATION AND PROTECTION*

BARGAIN SHOPPERS GUIDE TO SYDNEY. see *CONSUMER EDUCATION AND PROTECTION*

381 ESP
BASQUE ENTERPRISE. Text in Spanish. 4/yr.
Published by: Spri S.A., Gran Via 35, 3o, Bilbao, 48009, Spain. TEL 4-415-82-88, FAX 4-416-96-23. Ed. Mikel Pulgarin.

381 DEU ISSN 0722-4893
BAYERISCHER EINZELHANDEL. Text in German. m.
Published by: Wirtschaftshilfe des Bayerischen Einzelhandels, Brienner Str 45, Munich, 80333, Germany. Circ: 21,027.

381 ESP
BOLETIN DE INFORMACION ECONOMICA ALTOARAGONES. Text in Spanish. 11/yr.
Address: Angel de la Guarda 7, Huesca, 22005, Spain. TEL 74-21-27-46.

381 978.8 USA ISSN 1528-6320
THE BOULDER COUNTY BUSINESS REPORT. Text in English. 1981. bi-w. USD 29.97 in state; USD 39.97 out of state; USD 50 elsewhere (effective 2001). adv. illus. back issues avail. **Document type:** *Newspaper, Trade.* **Description:** Reports on issues and opinions of interest to the Boulder County and metropolitan Denver business communities.
Related titles: Online - full text ed.: (from O C L C Online Computer Library Center, Inc., ProQuest Information & Learning).
Indexed: ABIn, BusDate.
Published by: Boulder County Business Report, 3180 Sterling Court, Ste 201, Boulder, CO 80301-2338. TEL 303-440-4950, FAX 303-440-4950, http://www.bcbr.com/. Adv. contact Jeff Schott. B&W page USD 2,495, color page USD 3,095; trim 11.25 x 15. Circ: 10,000.

381 910.09 IDN ISSN 0216-0412
BULLETIN EKONOMI INDONESIA✶ . Text in Indonesian. 1970. 2/w.
Published by: Gabungan Importir Nasional Seluruh Indonesia/National Importers Association of Indonesia, Wisma Nusantara Bldg., Jalan Majapahit No. 1, Jakarta, Indonesia. TEL 021-360-643, FAX 62-021-367269. Circ: 20,000.

382 CAN
BUSINESS CENTRAL. Text in English. 1983. bi-m. CND 19 (effective 2000). adv. bk.rev. back issues avail. **Document type:** *Trade.*
Formerly (until 1998): Red Deer Commerce
Published by: Sylvester Publications Ltd., 304-4820 Gaetz Ave, Red Deer, AB T4N 4A4, Canada. TEL 403-309-5587, FAX 403-346-3044. Ed., Pub., R&P, Adv. contact Donald Sylvester. B&W page CND 1,480. Circ: 10,000.

381 USA
THE BUSINESS JOURNAL (LIMA); West Central Ohio's leading business publication. Text in English. 1992. m. USD 10. charts; stat. 4 cols./p.; back issues avail. **Document type:** *Newspaper, Trade.* **Description:** Reports on business and management news and issues in west central Ohio.
Formerly: Business Journal of West Central Ohio
Related titles: Online - full text ed.
Published by: American City Business Journals, Inc. (Lima), PO Box 388, Lima, OH 45802-0388. TEL 419-999-4762, 800-370-2351, FAX 419-991-6839. Ed., Pub. Ronald Freed. Circ: 15,000.

381 USA ISSN 1046-9575
HF3161.N45
BUSINESS N H MAGAZINE. Key Title: Business New Hampshire Magazine. Text in English. 1983. m. USD 28 (effective 2005). adv. 60 p./no.; back issues avail.; reprints avail. **Document type:** *Magazine, Trade.* **Description:** Aimed at the New Hamshire business community. Covers acquisitions, marketing, banking, profiles, and construction and growth trends.
Former titles (until 1989): Business of New Hampshire (1042-7511); Joliecoeur's Business N H (0897-8093); Business N H (0893-4800)

Related titles: Online - full text ed.: (from EBSCO Publishing, Gale Group).
Indexed: BusDate, T&II.
Published by: Millyard Communications, 670 N Commercial St, Ste 110, Manchester, NH 03101. TEL 603-626-6354, FAX 603-626-6359, edit@businessnhmagazine.com, http://www.businessnhmagazine.com. Pub. Sean Mahoney. adv.: B&W page USD 2,195, color page USD 2,695; trim 10.88 x 8.13. Circ: 15,000 (paid and controlled).

381　　　　　　USA
BUSINESS PULSE. Text in English. 1987. m. USD 12. adv.
Description: Informs Skagit County businesspersons of the people, news, ideas, trends, and opinions affecting their businesses.
Published by: Westbourne Newspapers, PO Box 589, Burlington, WA 98284-0589. TEL 360-755-0195, FAX 360-755-1279. Ed., R&P Michael Barrett. Adv. contact Paula Gordon. Circ: 5,000.

BUTTERWORTHS E C BRIEF. see BUSINESS AND ECONOMICS—Economic Situation And Conditions

CALIFORNIA CORPORATIONS CODE AND CORPORATE SECURITIES RULES. see LAW—Corporate Law

CAMARA DE COMERCIANTES EN ARTEFACTOS PARA EL HOGAR. REVISTA. see INTERIOR DESIGN AND DECORATION—Furniture And House Furnishings

381　　　　　　ITA
CAMERA DI COMMERCIO, INDUSTRIA, ARTIGIANATO E AGRICOLTURA DI FORLI. LISTINO SETTIMANALE PREZZI. Text in English. w.
Published by: Camera di Commercio Industria Artigianato e Agricoltura di Forli-Cesena, Corso della Repubblica 5, Forli', FC 47100, Italy. TEL 39-0547-21901, FAX 39-0547-23157, http://www.fo.camcom.it.

381　　　　　　CAN　　　　　ISSN 0575-8823
HD2807
CANADA. STATISTICS CANADA. INTER-CORPORATE OWNERSHIP/CANADA. STATISTIQUE CANADA. LIENS DE PARENTE ENTRE SOCIETES. Text in English. 1975. biennial. CND 350 domestic (effective 1999); USD 420 domestic; USD 490 foreign. **Document type:** Government. **Description:** Information about Canadian corporations and subsidiaries, including foreign-controlled corporations in Canada.
Related titles: CD-ROM ed.: ISSN 1198-0753. CND 3,000; Microform ed.: (from MML); Online - full text ed.: (from F P Infomart Ltd.).
Published by: Statistics Canada, Operations and Integration Division, Circulation Management, Jean Talon Bldg, 2 C12, Tunney's Pasture, Ottawa, ON K1A 0T6, Canada. TEL 613-951-7277, 800-267-6677, FAX 613-951-1584, http://www.statcan.ca.

332.6 381　　　　　　CAN　　　　　ISSN 0828-0622
CANADIAN CAPITAL PROJECTS. Text in English. 1981. q. CND 622 (effective 2000). Supplement avail. **Description:** Provides detailed records of major investment projects: speculative, planned or underway; classified by province and industry. Includes location, owners, value, timing, political, business or financial risks.
Related titles: Diskette ed.
—CISTI.
Published by: Informetrica Limited, P O Box 828, Sta B, Ottawa, ON K1P 5P9, Canada. TEL 613-238-4831, FAX 613-238-7698. Ed. Stan Kustec. Circ: 200.

CANADIAN COMPETITION RECORD. see LAW

381　　　　　　USA
CAROLINA BUSINESS & COMMERCE. Text in English. 1986. m. USD 12; USD 1 newsstand/cover (effective 2005). **Document type:** Newspaper.
Published by: Ed Bolin, 7650 Ovaldale Dr., Charleston, SC 29418. TEL 843-766-4422, FAX 843-763-2592, editor@carolina -news-line.com, http://www.carolina-news-line.com. Ed., Pub. Ed Bolin. Circ: 10,700 (controlled and free). Wire service: CNS.

381　　　　　　FRA　　　　　ISSN 0069-1100
CATALOGUE DES PRODUITS AGREES PAR QUALITE-FRANCE. Text in French. 1963 (2nd ed.). irreg.
Published by: Association Nationale pour la Promotion et le Controle de la Qualite, 18 rue Volney, Paris, 75002, France.

381　　　　　　LKA
CEYLON COMMERCE. Text in English. 1965. m. USD 40. bk.rev. 30 p./no. 2 cols./p.; **Document type:** Magazine, Trade.
Published by: National Chamber of Commerce of Sri Lanka, 450, D.R.Wijewardene Mawatha, Main St., P O Box 1375, Colombo, 10, Sri Lanka. TEL 94-1-689603, FAX 94-1-689596, nccsl@slt.lk, http://www.nccsl.lk. Ed. Neil Sabaratham.

381　　　　　　FRA
CHALLENGES HAUTE-MARNE. Text in French. 6/yr.
Published by: Chambre Regionale de Commerce et d'Industrie Champagne - Ardenne, Direction de la Communication, 10 rue de Chastillon, B.P. 537, Chalons-sur-Marne, Cedex 51011, France. TEL 33-3-266-3340, FAX 33-3-26693369.

CHILE. INSTITUTO NACIONAL DE ESTADISTICAS. ANUARIO DE COMERCIO INTERIOR Y SERVICIOS. see BUSINESS AND ECONOMICS—Abstracting, Bibliographies, Statistics

CHILE. INSTITUTO NACIONAL DE ESTADISTICAS. ANUARIO DE PRECIOS. see BUSINESS AND ECONOMICS—Abstracting, Bibliographies, Statistics

CHINA'S CUSTOMS STATISTICS. see BUSINESS AND ECONOMICS—Abstracting, Bibliographies, Statistics

381　　　　　　USA　　　　　ISSN 0732-071X
HF5429.4.C6
COLORADO CITY RETAIL SALES BY STANDARD INDUSTRIAL CLASSIFICATION. Text in English. 1965. q. (plus a.). USD 75 domestic; USD 90 foreign (effective 2001); includes Colorado County and State Retail Sales.
Supersedes in part: Colorado County and City Retail Sales by Standard Industrial Classification (0091-4789)
Published by: University of Colorado, Business Research Division, Campus Box 420, Boulder, CO 80309-0420. TEL 303-492-8227, FAX 303-492-3620. Ed. Cindy Dipersio.

381　　　　　　PER　　　　　ISSN 0010-2253
COMERCIO. Text in Spanish. 1892. d. PEN 49; PEN 20 Sat.-Sun. (effective 2005). adv. bk.rev. **Document type:** Newspaper, Consumer.
Related titles: Online - full text ed.: ISSN 1605-3052. 199?.
Indexed: RASB.
Published by: Empresa Editorial Cusco S.A., Casilla 70, Cuzco, Peru. TEL 51-1-3116500, suscriptores@comercio.com.pe, http://www.elcomercioperu.com.pe/. Ed. Carlos Lujan. Pub. Beatriz Hernandez. Circ: 60,000.

381　　　　　　ESP
COMERCIO 45. Text in Spanish. 6/yr.
Address: Alameda Recalde, 50, Bilbao, Vizcaya 48008, Spain. TEL 4-4444054, FAX 4-4434145, TELEX 32783 CCINB. Circ: 19,086.

381　　　　　　PRT
COMERCIO DE GAIA. Text in Portuguese. 26/yr.
Address: RUA JOAQUIM NICOLAU DE ALMEIDA, 127, Vila Nova De Gaia, 4400, Portugal. TEL 2-301912.

381　　　　　　CHE
LE COMMERCANT. Text in French. bi-m. membership. adv. **Document type:** Bulletin, Trade.
Published by: Societe des Jeunes Commercants, Rue Haldimand 18, Case Postale 494, Lausanne 17, 1000, Switzerland. TEL 41-21-3134411, FAX 41-21-3134419. Ed., R&P, Adv. contact Claude Vouilloz. B&W page CHF 2,200. Circ: 3,200.

380　　　　　　NPL
COMMERCE; English monthly. Text in English. 1972. m. USD 25 (effective 2003). adv. bk.rev.; film rev. charts; illus.; stat.; abstr.; bibl. reprints avail. **Document type:** Magazine, Trade. **Description:** Covers trade, commerce, industry, and the economy.
Published by: Nepal Economic and Commerce Research Centre, 7/358, Kohity Bahal, P O Box 285, Kathmandu, Nepal. TEL 977-1-4279636, FAX 977-1-4279544, manju_sakya@hotmail.com. Ed., Pub., R&P Manju Ratna Sakya. Adv. contact Mr. Kamal Shrestha. Circ: 20,000.

381　　　　　　CAN　　　　　ISSN 1482-6283
　　　　　　　　　　　　　　　　　CODEN: WCIMEW
COMMERCE & INDUSTRY MAGAZINE. Text in English. 1949. bi-m. CND 45 domestic to individuals; CND 49.50 foreign to individuals (effective 1999). adv. illus. **Document type:** Trade. **Description:** Trade magazine for construction, manufacturing and resource industries in Canada.
Former titles: Western Commerce and Industry Magazine (0043-3624); Western Construction and Building
Related titles: Microfiche ed.: (from MML); Microform ed.: (from MML).
—CISTI.
Published by: Mercury Publications Ltd., 1839 Inkster Blvd, Winnipeg, MB R2X 1R3, Canada. TEL 204-954-2085, FAX 204-954-2057, mp@mercury.mp.ca. Ed. Kelly Gray. Pub., Adv. contact Frank Yeo. Circ: 16,200.

382　　　　　　LBN　　　　　ISSN 0010-2814
COMMERCE DU LEVANT. Text in French. 1929-1975; resumed 1979. s-w. USD 225. adv. charts; illus.; stat.
Indexed: PAIS, RASB.
Published by: Societe de la Presse Economique, Immeuble de Commerce et Financement, Rue Kantari, P O Box 687, Beirut, Lebanon. TEL 1-297770. Ed. Maroun Akl. Circ: 1,500.

380　　　　　　IND　　　　　ISSN 0010-3012
COMMERCIAL HERALD. Text in English. 1966. s-m. INR 53.
Address: c/o Sudarshan Paul Bahri, Ed., 75-C Saheed Udhamsingh Nagar, Civil Lines, Ludhiana, Punjab, India.

380　　　　　　IND　　　　　ISSN 0010-3039
COMMERCIAL JOURNAL. Text in English. 1934. m. USD 50. adv. bk.rev. stat.
Published by: All India Commercial Association, Daryaganj, New Delhi, 110 006, India. TEL 3272040, FAX 3271294. Ed. J K Soni. Circ: 3,000.

380　　　　　　ITA
COMMERCIANTE∗. Text in Italian. 1956. m. adv. **Document type:** Trade.
Published by: Associazione Commercianti di Reggio Emilia, Via Roma, 13, Reggio Emilia, RE 42100, Italy. Ed. Paolo Ferraboschi. Circ: 7,500.

381 910.09　　　　　　ITA
COMMERCIO E TURISMO ROMAGNOLO. Text in Italian. m. **Document type:** Trade.
Address: Via Grado, 2, Forli', FO 47100, Italy. TEL 39-0543-34930. Circ: 11,000.

380　　　　　　IND　　　　　ISSN 0010-3160
COMMERCIUM. Text in English. 1970 (vol.6). s-a. adv. bk.rev. charts; stat.
Indexed: KES.
Published by: University of Rajasthan, School of Commerce, Gandhi Nagar, Jaipur, Rajasthan 302 004, India.

380　　　　　　BRA
CONFEDERACAO NACIONAL DO COMERCIO. ASSESSORIA JURIDICA. BOLETIM INFORMATIVO. Text in Portuguese. 1977 (vol.28). w. free.
Formerly: Confederacao Nacional do Comercio. Divisao Juridico-Legislativa. Boletim
Published by: Confederacao Nacional do Comercio, Av General Justo, 307, Andar 6, Centro, Rio de Janeiro, RJ 20021-130, Brazil.

338　　　　　　BRA　　　　　ISSN 0101-4315
HF6
CONFEDERACAO NACIONAL DO COMERCIO. CONSELHO TECNICO CONSULTIVO. CARTA MENSAL. Text in Portuguese. 1955. m. free. illus.
Formerly: Confederacao Nacional do Comercio. Divisao de Divulgacao. Carta Mensal (0588-9979)
Indexed: AgBio, FPA, ForAb, HortAb, I&DA, MaizeAb, PAIS, PBA, RDA, RPP, RRTA, RiceAb, S&F, SIA, SoyAb, WAE&RSA.
Published by: Confederacao Nacional do Comercio, Av General Justo, 307, Andar 6, Centro, Rio de Janeiro, RJ 20021-130, Brazil. Ed. Paulo Godoy.

381　　　　　　ESP
CONFEDERACION DE EMPRESARIOS DE CASTELLON. Text in Spanish. 12/yr.
Address: Escultor Viciano 1, 6o, Castellon De La Plana, 12002, Spain. TEL 64-22-62-12. Circ: 50,000.

330.9746　　　　　　USA
THE CONNECTICUT ECONOMY. Text in English. 1993. q. USD 50 (effective 2000). charts; illus.; mkt.; maps; stat. cum.index: 1972-1996. back issues avail. **Document type:** Newsletter. **Description:** Includes economic indicators of Connecticut for the press, state legislators, superintendents of schools, libraries, and the general public.
Published by: University of Connecticut, Connecticut Center for Economic Analysis, 341 Mansfield Rd., U-63C, Storrs, CT 06269-1063. TEL 860-486-0263, FAX 860-486-4463, http://www.lib.uconn.edu/Economics/review.html. Ed., R&P William A McEachern. Circ: 4,000.

380.1 338　　　　　　USA
CONSULTANTS BULLETIN∗; a newsletter for certified professional consultants. Text in English. 1989. 6/yr. USD 200 to members. bk.rev. Index. back issues avail. **Document type:** Bulletin, Trade. **Description:** Deals with industry trade issues.
Published by: National Bureau of Certified Consultants, 2728 5th Ave., San Diego, CA 92103. TEL 619-297-2207, FAX 619-296-3580, nationalbureau@att.net, http://www.national-bureau.com. Ed. Vito Tanzi.

381.34　　　　　　USA
CONSUMER E-NEWS ALERT. Text in English. 1999. bi-w. back issues avail. **Document type:** Newsletter. **Description:** Covers consumer protection and consumer rights.
Media: Online - full text.
Published by: Sheller Ludwig & Badey, P.C., 1528 Walnut St, 3rd Fl, Philadelphia, PA 19102. TEL 215-790-7300, 800-883-2299, FAX 215-546-0942, jshub@sheller.com, http://www.sheller.com/enews.htm. Ed. Jonathan Shub.

CORPORATE COUNSEL'S GUIDE TO DOMESTIC JOINT VENTURES. see LAW—Corporate Law

381 382 346　　　　　　USA
CORPORATE COUNSEL'S GUIDE TO EXPORT CONTROLS. Text in English. 1993. irreg. USD 165 (effective 2001).
Published by: Business Laws, Inc., 11630 Chillicothe Rd, Chesterland, OH 44026. TEL 440-729-7996, FAX 440-729-0645, http://www.businesslaws.com.

381 346　　　　　　USA
CORPORATE COUNSEL'S GUIDE TO IMPORTING UNDER THE U.S. CUSTOMS LAWS. Text in English. 1992. irreg. USD 210 (effective 2001).
Published by: Business Laws, Inc., 11630 Chillicothe Rd, Chesterland, OH 44026. TEL 440-729-7996, FAX 440-729-0645, http://www.businesslaws.com.

▼ new title　　　▶ refereed　　　∗ unverified　　　◆ full entry avail.

688.76 USA ISSN 0736-0703
HD9992.U5
COST OF DOING BUSINESS FOR RETAIL SPORTING GOODS STORES. Text in English. 1968. biennial. USD 125.
Document type: *Trade.* **Description:** Provides key performance ratios (profitability, productivity and financial management), as well as pro-forma income statements and balance sheets for various types of sporting goods stores.
Indexed: SRI.
Published by: National Sporting Goods Association, 1601 Feehanville Dr, Ste 300, Mt. Prospect, IL 60056-6305. TEL 800-815-5422, nsga1699@aol.com, http://www.nsga.org. Ed. Thomas B Doyle.

CRAIN'S CLEVELAND BUSINESS. see *BUSINESS AND ECONOMICS—Economic Situation And Conditions*

380 HND ISSN 0011-2836
CULTURAL COMERCIAL✶. Text in Spanish. 1959. m. adv.
Address: Apdo. Postal 239, Tegucigalpa D C, Honduras.

658.8 381 USA ISSN 0363-8553
HF105
CURRENT BUSINESS REPORTS: MONTHLY WHOLESALE TRADE, SALES AND INVENTORIES. Text in English. 1936. m. USD 17 (effective 1999). Supplement avail.; back issues avail.; reprint service avail. from CIS. **Document type:** *Government.* **Description:** Compiles monthly wholesalers' sales and inventories, by type of business and geographic area.
Related titles: Microfiche ed.: (from CIS); Online - full text ed.
Indexed: AmStI, PROMT, RASB.
Published by: U.S. Bureau of the Census (Subsidiary of: U.S. Department of Commerce), Customer Services, Washington, DC 20233. TEL 301-457-4100, FAX 301-457-4714, http://www.census.gov/. **Subscr. to:** U.S. Government Printing Office, Superintendent of Documents.

658.87 SWE ISSN 1403-2759
DAGENS HANDEL. Text in Swedish. 1908. 11/yr. adv. bk.rev. charts; mkt.; stat.; tr.mk. **Document type:** *Magazine, Trade.*
Former titles (until 1997): Koepmannen (0023-2688); (until 1912): Meddelanden fraan Sveriges Minuthandlares Riksfoerbund
Related titles: E-mail ed.; Online - full text ed.
Published by: Svensk Handel, Blasieholmsgatan 4B, Stockholm, 10329, Sweden. TEL 46-8-50556234, red@dagenshandel.se, http://www.dagenshandel.se, http://www.svenskhandel.se. Eds. Bjoern Englund, Yvonne Ingman TEL 46-8-7627703. Adv. contact Lennart Ekblom TEL 46-8-879700. B&W page SEK 29,000, color page SEK 35,000; trim 252 x 358. Circ: 28,000.

338.642 USA ISSN 0896-8012
DAILY JOURNAL OF COMMERCE (PORTLAND). Text in English. 1872. d. USD 180; USD 1 newsstand/cover (effective 2005). adv. back issues avail. **Document type:** *Newspaper, Trade.*
Formerly: New Orleans Daily Journal of Commerce
Related titles: CD-ROM ed.: (from The Dialog Corporation); Online - full text ed.: (from Newsbank, Inc., ProQuest Information & Learning).
Indexed: ABIn.
Published by: Dolan Media Co., 2840 NW 35th Ave, Portland, OR 97210. TEL 503-226-1311, FAX 503-224-7140, http://www.djc-or.com/Editorial/index.cfm. Ed., Pub. Brian Hunt. Adv. contact Chris Shulz. Circ: 5,000 morning (paid). Wire service: RN.

381 GBR ISSN 1355-7483
THE DEALER. Text in English. 1990. m. GBP 18 in United Kingdom; GBP 40 rest of Europe; GBP 70 rest of world; GBP 1.50 newsstand/cover (effective 2000). adv. **Document type:** *Consumer.* **Description:** Features trading information about the following items of interest: jewelry, watches, toys and fancy goods, electrical notions, clothing, plus business opportunities.
Former titles: Trading Place; Trading Post
Published by: Trinity Publications Ltd.., 1st Fl, Edward House, 92-93 Edward St, Birmingham, B1 2RA, United Kingdom. TEL 44-121-233-8712, FAX 44-121-233-8715, andrews@trinitypub.co.uk. Ed. Andrew Shorter. Adv. contact Stephen Playfoot. **Dist. by:** M M C Ltd., Octagon House, White Hart Meadows, Ripley, Woking, Surrey GU23 6HR, United Kingdom. TEL 44-1483-211222, FAX 44-1483-224541.

DETAILBLADET. see *BUSINESS AND ECONOMICS—Marketing And Purchasing*

381 JPN ISSN 0385-7360
DIAMOND INDUSTRIA; Japan's economic journal. Text in English. 1971. m. JPY 9,960, USD 55. back issues avail.
Description: Devoted to business and economy and of interest to business people and investors. Includes articles on companies, their activities, industry trends and newly developed products.
Formerly: Diamond's Industria
Indexed: RASB.
Published by: Diamond Inc., 4-2 Kasumigaseki 1-chome, Chiyoda-ku, Tokyo, 100-0013, Japan. TEL 03-504-6791, FAX 03-504-6798, TELEX J-26145 DLED. Ed. Natsuki Mori. Circ: 47,000.

DIRECTORY OF BUILDING PRODUCTS & HARDLINES DISTRIBUTORS. see *BUSINESS AND ECONOMICS—Trade And Industrial Directories*

381 346 ITA ISSN 1722-3792
DISCIPLINA DEL COMMERCIO E SERVIZI. Text in Italian. 2002. q. EUR 152 (effective 2005).
Formed by the merger of (1992-2001): Commercio e Servizi (1121-340X); (1981-2001): Disciplina del Commercio (1594-5227)
Published by: Maggioli Editore, Via del Carpino 8/10, Santarcangelo di Romagna, RN 47822, Italy. TEL 39-0541-628111, FAX 39-0541-622020, editore@maggioli.it, http://www.maggioli.it.

DOLLARS & CENTS OF CONVENIENCE CENTERS. see *REAL ESTATE*

DOLLARS & CENTS OF RENOVATED - EXPANDED SHOPPING CENTERS. see *REAL ESTATE*

DOLLARS & CENTS OF SHOPPING CENTERS IN THE TOP 20 METROPOLITAN AREAS. see *REAL ESTATE*

DOLLARS & CENTS OF SMALL TOWN - NONMETROPOLITAN SHOPPING CENTERS. see *REAL ESTATE*

DOMESTIC WATERBORNE TRADE OF THE UNITED STATES. see *TRANSPORTATION—Ships And Shipping*

381 338 DOM
DOMINICAN REPUBLIC. SECRETARIA DE ESTADO DE INDUSTRIA Y COMERCIO. REVISTA. Text in Spanish. 1948. 2/yr. charts; stat.
Former titles (until 1954): Dominican Republic. Secretaria de Estado de Trabajo, Economia y Comercio. Revista; (until 1952): Dominican Republic. Secretaria de Estado de Economia y Comercio. Revista; (until 1950): Dominican Republic. Secretaria de Estado de Economia Nacional. Revista
Published by: Secretaria de Estado de Industria y Comercio, Santo Domingo, Dominican Republic.

▼ **DRUG DELIVERY & COMMERCE.** see *PHARMACY AND PHARMACOLOGY*

EBIZCHRONICLE; the business of e-business. see *COMPUTERS—Internet*

381 USA ISSN 1529-7470
HC121
ECONOMIA (WASHINGTON, D.C.). Text in English. 2000. s-a. USD 46 domestic to individuals; USD 58 foreign to individuals; USD 70 domestic to institutions; USD 82 foreign to institutions (effective 2005); USD 92.40 combined subscription to institutions print & online eds. (effective 2004). **Document type:** *Journal, Academic/Scholarly.* **Description:** Provides a forum for economists and policymakers from Latin America and the Caribbean to share research directly applied to policy issues within and among those countries of the region.
Related titles: Online - full text ed.: ISSN 1533-6239. 2000 (from EBSCO Publishing, O C L C Online Computer Library Center, Inc., Project MUSE, Swets Information Services).
Indexed: ABIn, JEL.
—IE. **CCC.**
Published by: (Latin American and Caribbean Economic Association), Brookings Institution Press, 1775 Massachusetts Ave, NW, Washington, DC 20036-2188. TEL 202-797-6258, 800-275-1447, FAX 202-797-6004, http://www.brook.edu/press/books/economia.htm.

381 GBR
ECONOMIC BRIEFING. Text in English. 1993. m. **Document type:** *Government.*
Indexed: M&MA.
Published by: H M Treasury, Information Division, Parliament St, London, SW1A 2NU, United Kingdom.

ECUADOR. INSTITUTO NACIONAL DE ESTADISTICA Y CENSOS. ENCUESTA ANUAL DE COMERCIO INTERNO. see *BUSINESS AND ECONOMICS—Abstracting, Bibliographies, Statistics*

381 ECU
ECUADOR. MINISTERIO DE INDUSTRIAS, COMERCIO E INTEGRACION. DOCUMENTO. Text in Spanish. 1975. a.
Published by: Ministerio de Industrias Comercio e Integracion, Quito, Pichincha, Ecuador.

381 ECU
ECUADOR. MINISTERIO DE INDUSTRIAS, COMERCIO E INTEGRACION. INFORME A LA NACION. Text in Spanish. 1974. a. illus.
Published by: Ministerio de Industrias Comercio e Integracion, Quito, Pichincha, Ecuador.

381 CAN ISSN 0702-7435
EDMONTON COMMERCE AND INDUSTRY. Text in English. 1974. m. CND 5; CND 10 in United States; CND 12 elsewhere. adv. illus. **Description:** Contains up-to-date reports on transportation, mining, construction and building developments, as well as articles and reports on local, regional and national economic, legislative and business trends.
Formerly (until 1976): Edmonton Commerce (0702-7443)
Published by: Homersham Advertising Agency, 214 11802 124th St, Edmonton, AB T5L 0M3, Canada. TEL 403-454-5625, FAX 403-453-2553. Ed. Doug Homersham. Adv. contact Colleen McCullough. Circ: 4,300.

ELECTRICAL MACHINERY: LATIN AMERICAN INDUSTRIAL REPORT. see *ENGINEERING—Electrical Engineering*

380 CAN
ELECTRONIC COMMERCE. Text in English. 1998. q.
Published by: Industry Canada/Industrie Canada, Distribution Services, Communications & Marketing Branch, Rm 268D, West Tower, C.D. Howe Bldg, 235 Queen St, Ottawa, ON K1A 0H5, Canada. TEL 613-947-7466, FAX 613-954-6436, publications@ic.gc.ca, http://www.ic.gc.ca.

332.6420285 USA
ELECTRONIC COMMERCE NEWS. Text in English. 1996. bi-w. USD 997 (effective 2005). **Document type:** *Newsletter, Trade.* **Description:** Reporting on electronic commerce technologies, strategy and alliances with focus on e-security, electronic payments and supply chain.
Formerly: Electronic Commerce Technology News (1086-2870); Incorporates (1983-2001): Corporate E F T Report (0272-0299); Which incorporated (in Mar.1993): Treasury Watch; Which incorporated (in 1992): Treasury Manager (0896-2987); Which was formerly (197?-1987): Cash Manager (0197-7075); Incorporates (1996-2000): C T I News (1090-5510); (1988-1999): Video Technology News (1040-2772); (1989-1998): Electronic Messaging News (1044-9892); (1993-1997): Treasury Manager's Report (1071-8532)
Related titles: Online - full text ed.: (from Gale Group, LexisNexis, O C L C Online Computer Library Center, Inc., ProQuest Information & Learning).
Indexed: ABIn, BLI, Microcompind.
—IE. **CCC.**
Published by: Access Intelligence, LLC (Subsidiary of: Veronis, Suhler & Associates Inc.), 1201 Seven Locks Rd, Ste 300, Potomac, MD 20854. TEL 301-354-2000, 800-777-5006, FAX 301-340-1451, clientservices@accessintel.com, http://www.pbimedia.com/cgi/catalog/info?ECTN. Ed. Mary Crowley.

381 332 USA
ENERGY IN THE NEWS. Text in English. 1978. q. free. adv. charts; stat.; tr.lit. 32 p./no.; **Document type:** *Magazine, Trade.* **Description:** Devoted to fundamental and technical energy market conditions, and futures and options trading strategies.
Published by: New York Mercantile Exchange, Corporate Communications Department, One North End Ave, World Financial Center, New York, NY 10282-1101. TEL 212-299-2777, FAX 212-301-4700, exchangeinfo@nymex.com, http://www.nymex.com. Ed. James Conmy. R&P Jenifer Semenza TEL 212-299-2433. Adv. contact Linda Mieszowski TEL 212-299-2432. Circ: 35,000 (controlled).

380.1 TGO
ENQUETE SUR LES ENTREPRISES INDUSTRIELLES ET COMMERCIALES DU TOGO. Text in French. a. XOF 5,000. stat.
Published by: Direction de la Statistique, BP 118, Lome, Togo.

381 AUS ISSN 0085-0268
ENTERPRISE (KENSINGTON)✶. Text in English. 1963. a. free.
Published by: University of New South Wales, Sydney, NSW 2052, Australia.

ETAGE; Chef-Informationen. see *BUSINESS AND ECONOMICS*

381 LUX ISSN 1560-8492
EUROSTAT. EXTERNAL TRADE AND BALANCE OF PAYMENTS. MONTHLY STATISTICS. Text in English. 1961. m.
Formerly (until 1992): Eurostat. External Trade. Monthly Statistics (English Edition) (1017-6004); Which superseded in part (in 1991): Eurostat. External Trade. Monthly Statistics (1016-5770); Which was formerly (until 1990): Eurostat. Monthly External Trade Bulletin (0378-3723)
Published by: European Commission, Statistical Office of the European Communities, Rue Alcide de Gasperi, Luxembourg, 2920, Luxembourg. eurostat-infodesk@cec.eu.int, http://www.europa.eu.int/comm/eurostat.

F T C - JAPAN VIEWS: INFORMATION & OPINION FROM THE FAIR TRADE COMMISSION OF JAPAN. see *BUSINESS AND ECONOMICS—International Commerce*

381 346.065 RUS
FAKT; informatsionno-analiticheskii zhurnal. Text in Russian. 1997. s-a. **Document type:** *Journal.*
Media: Online - full content.

Published by: Spetsial'naya Informatsionnaya Sluzhba, ul Abramtsevskaya 10, Moscow, 127576, Russian Federation. TEL 7-095-4003710, FAX 7-095-9088392, fact@sinshost.sins.ru, http://www.fact.ru, http://www.sins.ru. Ed. A Parfenov.

FINANCE AND COMMERCE. see *BUSINESS AND ECONOMICS—Banking And Finance*

381 USA ISSN 1534-8857
FINGER LAKES BUSINESS ALMANAC. Text in English. 1994. m. USD 38.75; USD 3.50 newsstand/cover (effective 2001). adv. 20 p./no. 4 cols./p.; **Document type:** *Newspaper.*
Formerly: Credibility Newsletter
Published by: Onpoint Publishing, 144 Genesee, Auburn, NY 13021. TEL 315-252-9675. Ed., Pub., R&P David Connelly. Adv. contact Mel Buttorff TEL 315-253-4573. page USD 800. Circ: 1,100 (paid); 1,300.

614.84 330 USA ISSN 8755-4372
FIREWORKS BUSINESS. Text in English. 1983. m. USD 32.95 domestic; USD 39 foreign (effective 2000). adv. bk.rev. **Document type:** *Newsletter.* **Description:** Covers business news for the fireworks trade and fireworks enthusiasts.
Published by: American Fireworks News, HC67 Box 30, Dingmans Ferry, PA 18328. TEL 570-828-8417, FAX 717-828-8695, afn@98.net, http://www.fireworksnews.com. Ed. John M Drewes. R&P John Eric. Adv. contact E V Musselwhite. Circ: 500 (paid).

FOCUS: AN ECONOMIC PROFILE OF THE APPAREL INDUSTRY. see *CLOTHING TRADE*

380 USA ISSN 0015-8097
K6
FORT WORTH COMMERCIAL RECORDER. Text in English. 1903. d. (Mon.-Fri.). USD 150 (effective 2005). adv. bk.rev. **Document type:** *Newspaper, Trade.*
Published by: Recorder Publishing Co., PO Box 11038, Ft. Worth, TX 76110. TEL 817-926-5351, FAX 817-926-5377, recorder@flash.net, http://www.commercialrecorder.com. Circ: 600 (paid).

380 IND ISSN 0015-864X
FORWARD MARKETS BULLETIN. Text in English. 1959. q. INR 20, USD 4.70. adv. charts; stat. index.
Published by: Forward Markets Commission, Government of India, 100 Marine Dr., Mumbai, Maharashtra, India. Ed. Smt R M Pavaskar.

381 FRA ISSN 0220-9896
KJV5595.A15
FRANCE. MINISTERE DE L'ECONOMIE, DES FINANCES ET DE L'INDUSTRIE. REVUE DE LA CONCURRENCE ET DE LA CONSOMMATION. Text in French. 6/yr. EUR 61.10 domestic; EUR 63.20 in the European Union; EUR 66.20 DOM-TOM; EUR 67.20 elsewhere (effective 2003). back issues avail. **Document type:** *Government.*
Related titles: Microfiche ed.
Indexed: ELLIS.
Published by: (France. Ministere de l'Economie, des Finances et de l'Industrie, France. Direction Generale de la Concurrence, de la Consommation et de la Repression des Fraudes), Documentation Francaise, 29-31 quai Voltaire, Paris, Cedex 7 75344, France. FAX 33-1-40157230.

FRANCE. SERVICE D'ETUDE DES STRATEGIES ET DES STATISTIQUES INDUSTRIELLES. L'IMPLANTATION ETRANGERE DANS L'INDUSTRIE. see *BUSINESS AND ECONOMICS—Abstracting, Bibliographies, Statistics*

381.41 ZAF
FRESH PRODUCE MARKET, JOHANNESBURG. REPORT OF THE DIRECTOR. Text in English. 1913. irreg.
Supersedes: National Fresh Produce Market, Johannesburg. Annual Report of the Director
Media: Duplicated (not offset).
Published by: Fresh Produce Market, PO Box 86007, City Deep, 2049, South Africa. TEL 27-11-6132049, FAX 27-11-6135346. Ed. Daan Spengler. Circ: 350.

381 DNK ISSN 1395-5411
G D S - INFO. (Goer Det Selv) Text in Danish. 1994. 8/yr. free. adv. back issues avail. **Document type:** *Trade.*
Published by: Odsgard AS, Stationsparken 25, Glostrup, 2600, Denmark. TEL 45-43-43-29-00, FAX 45-43-43-13-28, odsgard@odsgard.dk. Ed. Peter Odsgard. adv.: B&W page DKK 9,530; trim 262 x 185. Circ: 3,195 (controlled).

381 BRA ISSN 1415-2649
HE199.B6
GLOBAL; comercio exterior e transporte. Text in Portuguese. 1997. m. USD 70 (effective 1998). adv. back issues avail.
Related titles: ♦ Supplement(s): Guia Maritimo. ISSN 1414-0438.
Published by: Editora Update do Brasil Ltda., Av. Faria Lima 1234 - CJ 53, Sao Paulo SP, SP 01452-000, Brazil. TEL 55-11-815-9900, FAX 55-11-815-8259, http://www.ceol.com.br/global.html. Ed. Cassia Schitini. Pub., Adv. contact Tadeusz Polakiewicz. page USD 3,200. Circ: 12,000.

GOVERNO DA REGIAO ADMINISTRATIVA ESPECIAL DE MACAU. DIRECCAO DOS SERVICOS DE ESTATISTICA E CENSOS. REVISAO DO PERIODO BASE DO INDICE DE PRECOS NO CONSUMIDOR/GOVERNMENT OF MACAO SPACIAL ADMINISTRATIVE REGION. STATISTICS AND CENSUS SERVICE. REBASING OF CONSUMER PRICE INDEX. see *BUSINESS AND ECONOMICS—Abstracting, Bibliographies, Statistics*

330 USA ISSN 1045-4055
GRAND RAPIDS BUSINESS JOURNAL. Text in English. 1979. w. USD 52 (effective 2005). adv. charts; illus.; pat.; stat. **Document type:** *Newspaper.*
Related titles: Online - full text ed.: (from EBSCO Publishing, Northern Light Technology, Inc., O C L C Online Computer Library Center, Inc., ProQuest Information & Learning, The Dialog Corporation).
Indexed: ABIn, BusDate.
—CCC.
Published by: Gemini Publications, 549 Ottawa Ave N W, Ste 201, Grand Rapids, MI 49503-1444. TEL 616-459-4545, FAX 616-459-4800, info@geminipub.com, http://www.geminipub.com. Ed. Carole Valade. Pub. John H Zwarensteyn. Adv. contact Randy Prichand. Circ: 7,000.

381 338 GBR ISSN 1365-5949
GREAT BRITAIN. DEPARTMENT OF TRADE AND INDUSTRY. ENERGY PAPER. Text in English. 1992. irreg. **Document type:** *Monographic series.*
—BLDSC (3747.695000), IE, ingenta.
Published by: (Great Britain. Department of Trade and Industry), Home Office, 50 Queen Anne's Gate, London, SW1 9AT, United Kingdom. http://www.open.gov.uk.

380 USA ISSN 0274-5496
GREATER WASHINGTON BOARD OF TRADE NEWS; a regional Chamber of Commerce for the District of Columbia, Northern Virginia and suburban Maryland. Text in English. 1946. bi-m. USD 120 (effective 2005). adv. illus. **Document type:** *Newspaper, Trade.* **Description:** News, articles, features, editorials, and announcements pertaining to the members and activities of the Board, representing the interaction between and the integration of business and the community in the District of Columbia, Northern Virginia, and suburban Maryland.
Formerly: Metropolitan Washington Board of Trade News (0026-1599)
Published by: Greater Washington Board of Trade, 1725 I St, NW, Ste 200, Washington, DC 20006-2427. TEL 202-857-5900, FAX 202-223-2648, info@bot.org, http://www.bot.org. Ed. Sandra Rubenstein. Pub. Berta Maginniss. adv.: B&W page USD 1,650; trim 10.5 x 15. Circ: 5,875 (controlled).

381.416 630 DNK ISSN 0106-6382
GROVVARELEDEREN. Text in Danish. 1973. 9/yr. DKK 350 (effective 2004). adv. bk.rev. **Document type:** *Trade.*
Published by: Landsforeningen den Lokale Andel, Centerhavnsvej 13, Fredericia, 7000, Denmark. TEL 45-79-212121, FAX 45-79-212179, post@dla.dk, http://www.dla.dk. Circ: 107,000.

381 ITA
GUIDA MONACI. ANNUARIO GENERALE. Text in Italian. 1871. a. adv. index. **Document type:** *Directory, Consumer.* **Description:** Directory of Italian commercial and industrial activities.
Former titles: Guida Monaci. Annuario Generale Italiano (1122-8504); (until 1967): Guida Monaci (1123-0991); (until 1909): Guida Commerciale, Scientifica, Artistica ed Industriale della Citta di Roma (1126-2893); (until 1872): Guida Scientifica, Artistica e Commerciale della Citta di Roma (1123-0983)
Related titles: CD-ROM ed.
Published by: Guida Monaci SpA, Via Salaria 1319, Rome, 00138, Italy. TEL 39-06-8887777, FAX 39-06-8889996, guida.monaci@italybygm.it, http://www.italybygm.it.

GUIDE TO SPRINGFIELD; an encyclopedia of facts and figures on the queen city of the Ozarks. see *GEOGRAPHY*

381 MEX ISSN 0533-5469
GUIDE TO THE MEXICAN MARKETS✶. Text in Spanish. 1959. a. USD 53.
Published by: Publicaciones Marynka S.A., SALAVERRY 1204, Col Zacatenco, Mexico City, DF 07360, Mexico.

380 DEU ISSN 0936-9856
H V - JOURNAL. Text in German. 1949. s-m. EUR 83.40 domestic; EUR 92 foreign; EUR 7.50 newsstand/cover (effective 2005). adv. bk.rev. 48 p./no. 4 cols./p.; **Document type:** *Magazine, Trade.*
Formerly (until 1989): Handelsvertreter und Handelsmakler (0046-6808)
Published by: (Zentralvereinigung Deutscher Wirtschaftsverbaende fuer Handelsvermittlung und Vertrieb), Siegel Verlag Otto Mueller GmbH, Mainzer Landstr 238, Frankfurt Am Main, 60326, Germany. TEL 49-69-75890950, FAX 49-69-75890960, hv-journal@svffm.de, info@svffm.de, http://www.svffm.de/hvl/index.htm. Ed. Andreas Paffhausen. Adv. contact Peter Holzberger TEL 49-69-75890952. B&W page EUR 3,080, color page EUR 4,490; trim 184 x 255. Circ: 16,832 (paid and controlled).

338 DEU ISSN 0017-7229
DER HANDEL; das Wirtschaftsmagazin fuer Handelsmanagement. Text in German. 1951. m. EUR 36.80 domestic; EUR 37.25 in the European Union; EUR 38.95 elsewhere (effective 2003). adv. bk.rev. illus. **Document type:** *Magazine, Trade.* **Description:** Business magazine for management in trade and commerce in Germany. Features retail stores, department stores, display of goods, office and communications technology, transportation, finances, personnel management, and current trends.
Incorporates (in 1999): Der Handel (0942-4881); Incorporates (1971-1991): D F Z Wirtschaftsmagazin (0341-549X); Which was formerly (until 1976): D F Z Magazin (0342-3727)
Indexed: KES, PAIS, RASB, RefZh.
Published by: Deutscher Fachverlag GmbH, Mainzer Landstr 251, Frankfurt Am Main, 60326, Germany. TEL 49-69-759501, FAX 49-69-75952999, Schneider@derhandel.de, info@dfv.de, http://www.derhandel.de, http://www.dfv.de. Ed. Uwe Rosmanith. Adv. contact Ernst Ludwig Schneider. B&W page EUR 11,220, color page EUR 13,000; trim 175 x 246. Circ: 94,439 (paid and controlled).

380 DEU
HANDEL IM FOKUS. Text in German. 1949. q. EUR 100; EUR 30 newsstand/cover (effective 2003). charts; stat. index. back issues avail. **Document type:** *Journal, Academic/Scholarly.*
Formerly: Universitaet zu Koeln. Institut fuer Handelsforschung. Mitteilungen (0531-030X)
Indexed: IBR, IBZ, KES, PAIS.
Published by: Institut fuer Handelsforschung (Subsidiary of: Universitaet zu Koeln), Saeckinger Str. 5, Cologne, 50935, Germany. TEL 49-221-9436070, FAX 49-221-94360799, info@ifhkoeln.de, http://www.ifhkoeln.de. Circ: 3,500.

381 POL ISSN 0438-5403
HF37.P6
HANDEL WEWNETRZNY. Text in Polish. 1974 (vol.20). bi-m. EUR 37 foreign (effective 2005). bk.rev. bibl. **Document type:** *Journal, Academic/Scholarly.* **Description:** Devoted to the subject matters of the market, marketing and enterprises.
Indexed: AgrLib, RASB.
Published by: Instytut Rynku Wewnetrznego i Konsumpcji, Al Jerozolimskie 87, Warsaw, 02001, Poland. TEL 48-22-6285585, FAX 48-22-6282479, irwik@irwik.waw.pl, http://www.irwik.waw.pl. **Dist. by:** Ars Polona, Krakowskie Przedmiescie 7, Warsaw, Poland. TEL 48-22-9263914, FAX 48-22-9265334, arspolona@arspolona.com.pl, http://www.arspolona.com.pl.

380 DEU ISSN 0017-7296
HANDELSBLATT; Deutschlands Wirtschafts- und Finanzzeitung. Text in German. 1946. d. (Mon.-Fri.). EUR 398; EUR 80 to students (effective 2005). adv. reprint service avail. from PQC. **Document type:** *Newspaper, Consumer.*
Incorporated: Industriekurier
Related titles: Microfiche ed.: (from PQC); Microfilm ed.: (from ALP, PQC); Online - full text ed.
Indexed: B&I, CBNB, KES, PROMT, RASB.
—CCC.
Published by: Verlagsgruppe Handelsblatt GmbH, Kasernenstr 67, Duesseldorf, 40213, Germany. TEL 49-211-8870, FAX 49-211-371792, handelsblatt@vhb.de, fachverlag@vhb.de, http://www.handelsblatt.com, http://www.vhb.de. Eds. Rainer Nahrendorf, Waldemar Schaefer. Adv. contact Andreas Formen. B&W page EUR 36,600, color page EUR 53,200; trim 371 x 528. Circ: 150,000 (paid and controlled).

381 DEU ISSN 0941-0716
HANDELSJOURNAL; das Wirtschaftsmagazin fuer den deutschen Einzelhandel. Text in German. 1974. m. EUR 32; EUR 2.70 newsstand/cover (effective 2005). adv. **Document type:** *Journal, Trade.*
Formerly (until 1991): Einzelhandels-Report (0938-958X)
Published by: Verlagsgruppe Handelsblatt GmbH, Kasernenstr 67, Duesseldorf, 40213, Germany. TEL 49-211-8870, FAX 49-211-371792, fachverlag@vhb.de, http://www.vhb.de/handelsjournal/. Adv. contact Sigrid Dethloff. B&W page EUR 7,854, color page EUR 10,404; trim 210 x 297.

HANDELSNYTT. see *LABOR UNIONS*

381 DEU ISSN 1437-6199
HANNOVER-JOURNAL. Text in German. 1984. 3/yr. EUR 11 domestic; EUR 26 foreign; EUR 5 newsstand/cover (effective 2003). adv. **Document type:** *Magazine, Trade.*
Published by: Verlagsgesellschaft Gruetter GmbH & Co. KG, Postfach 910708, Hannover, 30427, Germany. TEL 49-511-4609300, FAX 49-511-4609320, info@gruetter.de, http://www.hannover-journal.de, http://www.gruetter.de. adv.: page EUR 4,300; trim 196 x 251. Circ: 28,818 (paid and controlled).

381 CHN
HEBEI SHANGYE YANJIU/HEBEI COMMERCE. Text in Chinese. m.
Published by: Hebei Sheng Shangye Zhuanke Xuexiao, 6, Huaibei Zhonglu, Shijiazhuang, Hebei 050011, China. TEL 612601. Ed. Zhong Xing.

381 LAO
HENG NGAN. Text in Laotian. fortn.
Published by: Lao Federation of Trade Unions, 87 ave Lane Xang, BP 780, Vientiane, Laos. TEL 4151. Ed. Bouapheng Bounsoulinh.

381 HKG
HONG KONG INDUSTRIALIST. Text in Chinese, English. 1962. m. HKD 400, USD 90. adv. stat. **Document type:** *Trade.*
Description: Covers investment and trade trends, economic and industrial policies, and company profiles.
Formerly: Industrial News
Related titles: Online - full text ed.
Indexed: B&I.
Published by: Federation of Hong Kong Industries, 4-F, Hankow Centre, 5-15 Hankow Rd, Tsim Sha Tsui, Kowloon, Hong Kong. TEL 852-2732-3188, FAX 852-2721-3494, TELEX 30101 FHKI HX, fhki@fhki.org.hk, http://www.fhki.org.hk. Ed. Mark Tindall. adv.: B&W page HKD 7,920, color page HKD 10,900; trim 210 x 285. Circ: 35,000.

381 CAN ISSN 0822-6482
HJ7662
HOW OTTAWA SPENDS. Text in English. 1981. a. CND 27.95 (effective 1997). **Description:** Analyses 11 areas of government policy, including economic management, national unity, social policies and ethics.
Former titles (until 1992): How Ottawa Spends Your Tax Dollars (0711-4990); (1981): Spending Tax Dollars. Federal Expenditures (0226-1723)
—CISTI.
Published by: McGill-Queens's University Press, 3430 McTavish St, Montreal, PQ H3A 1X9, Canada. TEL 514-398-3750, FAX 514-398-4333, mqup@mqup.mcgill.ca, orderbook@cupserv.org, http://www.mcgill.ca/mqup/ordinfo.htm. Ed. Gene Swimmer.

381 FIN ISSN 1235-8509
HYVA SUOMI!. Text in Finnish. 1961. 5/yr. adv. charts; illus.; stat. 24 p./no. 4 cols./p.; **Document type:** *Newspaper, Consumer.*
Formerly (until 1992): Tuotantouutiset (0357-4520)
Related titles: Online - full text ed.
Published by: Suomalaisen Tyon Liitto/Association for Finnish Work, Mikonkatu 17 A, Helsinki, 00101, Finland. TEL 358-9-6962430, FAX 358-9-69924333, stl@avainlippu.fi, http://www.avainlippu.fi/. Ed., R&P Lars Collin. Adv. contact Bouser Oy. Circ: 500 (paid); 22,000 (controlled).

380 GBR ISSN 1462-2475
HD28 CODEN: BUSAB6
I B A NEWS. Text in English. 1949. 3/yr. GBP 4; GBP 5.50 foreign (effective 2001). adv. bk.rev. abstr.; charts; illus.; stat.; tr.lit. index. 16 p./no. 4 cols./p.; reprints avail. **Document type:** *Journal, Trade.*
Former titles (until 1997): Business Administrator (1360-1318); British Society of Commerce. Review (0007-1781)
Published by: Institute of Chartered Secretaries and Administration (I C S A), 16 Park Crescent, London, W1N 1AH, United Kingdom. TEL 44-20-7580-4741, FAX 44-20-7612-7034, iba-uk@dial.pipex.com, http://www.ibauk.org. Ed. Jonathan Presse. Adv. contact Steven Poss. Circ: 2,000.

381 ISR
I B T. (Israel Business Today) Text in English. 1986. m. ILS 756.70, USD 249 (effective 1999). adv. **Document type:** *Newsletter.*
Formerly: I C E N - Israel Commercial Economic Newsletter (0792-3465)
Related titles: Online - full text ed.: (from Gale Group).
Published by: Economic News Ltd., P O Box 145, Tel Aviv, 61001, Israel. TEL 972-3-6397196, FAX 972-3-6397195. Ed. Barry Davis. Pub., R&P Ralph Kronenthal. Adv. contact Zehava Stepak. B&W page USD 1,900, color page USD 2,750; trim 178 x 245.

381 KEN
I C D C NEWS. Text in English. 1975. 3/yr.
Published by: Industrial and Commercial Development Corporation, PO Box 45519, Nairobi, Kenya.

381 DEU ISSN 0939-9909
I K; Zeitschrift fuer Industriekaufleute. Text in German. 1979. m. EUR 43.80; EUR 3.65 newsstand/cover (effective 2003). adv. **Document type:** *Magazine, Trade.*
Formerly (until 1990): Industriekaufmann (0173-6612)
—IE, Infotrieve. **CCC.**
Published by: Friedrich Kiehl Verlag GmbH, Pfaustr 13, Ludwigshafen, 67063, Germany. TEL 49-621-635020, FAX 49-621-6350222, info@kiehl.de, http://www.kiehl.de/zeitschr/ik/default.htm. adv.: B&W page EUR 720, color page EUR 1,368; trim 186 x 260. Circ: 5,766 (paid).

381 ESP
IMAGEN VASCA ONLINE. Text in Spanish. 1987. m. adv. **Document type:** *Newspaper.*
Formerly: Magazine de los Negocios - Imagen Vasca
Media: Online - full text.
Published by: Codeco, Comercial de Comunicaciones, S.L., Trasera de Burgos 8, Bilbao, 48014, Spain. TEL 34-94-4478414, FAX 34-94-4761187, imagenvasca@codeconet.com, http://www.codeconet.com/imagenvasca. Ed. Javier Bustamante. Adv. contact Rafael Vallejo.

381 USA ISSN 0192-7450
IN BUSINESS (MADISON); Dane county's business magazine. Text in English. 1978. m. USD 36 (effective 2005). adv. charts; illus.; stat. back issues avail. **Document type:** *Magazine, Consumer.* **Description:** Dane county's source for business news, targeting business decision makers. Designed for position-qualified, management-level business executives and government officials.
Published by: Magna Publications, Inc., 200 River Pl, Ste 250, Madison, WI 53716. TEL 608-204-9655, FAX 608-204-9656, custserv@magnapubs.com, http://www.inbusinessmagazine.com, http://www.magnapubs.com. Ed. Paul Zukowski. Pub. Jody Anderson. Adv. contact Julie O'Gara. Circ: 15,000.

381 IND
INDEX OF WHOLESALE PRICES IN INDIA. Text in English. m. INR 1,200, USD 139.92. **Document type:** *Government.*
Published by: Ministry of Urban Development, Department of Publications, Civil Lines, New Delhi, 110 054, India. TEL 11-2512527.

381 IND
INDIAN INDUSTRY REVIEW. Text in English. 1993. a. INR 250, USD 55 (effective 2000). adv. abstr.; charts; illus. reprint service avail. from PQC. **Document type:** *Trade.*
Related titles: Microfilm ed.: (from PQC).
Published by: Technical Press Publications, Eucharistic Congress Bldg. No.1, 5/1 Convent St, Colaba, Mumbai, Maharashtra 400 039, India. TEL 91-22-2021446, FAX 91-22-2871499. Ed., Pub. J P de Sousa. adv.: B&W page INR 1,750, color page INR 2,250; trim 18 x 23. Circ: 12,000.

380 IND ISSN 0019-512X
HF41
INDIAN JOURNAL OF COMMERCE. Text in English. 1960. q. INR 33, USD 8. adv. bk.rev.
Indexed: BAS.
Published by: Indian Commerce Association, B.Y.K. College of Commerce, Nasik, Maharashtra 5, India. Ed. M S Gosavi.

380 IND ISSN 0019-5901
INDIAN MERCHANTS' CHAMBER. JOURNAL. Text in English. 1907. bi-m. INR 60, USD 15. adv. bk.rev. illus.
Published by: Indian Merchants' Chamber, Indian Merchants' Chamber Bldg., 76 Veer Nariman Rd., Churchgate, Mumbai, Maharashtra 400 020, India. Ed. Shri Ramu Pandit. Circ: 3,000.

380 IND ISSN 0019-6444
INDIAN TRADE JOURNAL. Text in English, Hindi. 1906. w. (except Jun.). INR 600, USD 216. adv. bibl.; mkt.; stat. index. Supplement avail.
Indexed: ChemAb.
Published by: Government of India, Department of Publications, Civil Lines, New Delhi, 110 054, India. TEL 28-3111, TELEX DGCS IN 21-7902. Circ: 2,322.

330 USA ISSN 0274-4929
HF5065.I6
INDIANAPOLIS BUSINESS JOURNAL. Text in English. 1980. w. USD 74; USD 1.50 newsstand/cover (effective 2005). adv. stat. back issues avail.; reprints avail. **Document type:** *Magazine, Trade.* **Description:** Covers business news in Indianapolis and surrounding areas.
Related titles: Online - full text ed.: (from Florida Center for Library Automation, Gale Group, Northern Light Technology, Inc., O C L C Online Computer Library Center, Inc., ProQuest Information & Learning).
Indexed: ABIn, BusDate, LRI, T&II.
—**CCC.**
Published by: I B J Corp., 41 E Washington St, Ste 200, Indianapolis, IN 46204-3592. TEL 317-634-6200, FAX 317-263-5060, info-ibj@ibj.com, http://www.ibj.com. Ed. Tom Harton. Pub. Chris Katterjohn. Adv. contact Lisa Schenkel Bradley. B&W page USD 5,425. Circ: 17,000 (paid).

381.021 PRT ISSN 0870-2616
INDICE DE PRECOS NO CONSUMIDOR. Text in Portuguese. 1975. m. EUR 30.72 (effective 2005). **Description:** Provides statistical data on inflation and price changes.
Published by: Instituto Nacional de Estatistica, Ave. Antonio Jose de Almeida 2, Lisbon, 1000-043, Portugal. TEL 351-21-8426100, FAX 351-21-8426380, ine@ine.pt, http://www.ine.pt/.

380.1 IDN ISSN 0377-0001
HF41
INDONESIAN COMMERCIAL NEWSLETTER. Key Title: Indonesian Commercial Newsletters. Text in English. 1974. fortn. IDR 561,000 per issue domestic; IDR 320 per issue in ASEAN countries; IDR 370 per issue in Asia in ASEAN countries; IDR 410 per issue in Europe in ASEAN countries; IDR 530 per issue in US & Canada in ASEAN countries (effective 2004). **Document type:** *Newsletter, Trade.*
Related titles: Online - full text ed.: (from Gale Group, Northern Light Technology, Inc., O C L C Online Computer Library Center, Inc.).
Indexed: B&I, KES.
Published by: PT Data Consult Inc., Jalan Kramat Raya No. 5-L, Jakarta Pusat, Indonesia. TEL 62-21-3904711, FAX 62-21-3901878, datacon@idola.net.id, http://www.datacon.co.id/. Ed. Sulaeman Krisnandhi.

381 MEX ISSN 0188-4603
INDUSTRIA. Text in Spanish. 1955. m. USD 30. adv. bk.rev.
Formerly (until June 1988): ConCamIn
Published by: Confederacion de Camaras Industriales de los Estados Unidos Mexicanos, MANUEL MA CONTRERAS 133 Piso 1,, Col Cuauhtemoc, Del. Cuauhtemoc, Mexico City, DF 06597, Mexico. TEL 592-0529, FAX 535-6871, TELEX 1772789 CCINMEX. Ed. Andres Senosiain Ruiloba. Circ: 25,000.

381 KEN
INDUSTRIAL AND COMMERCIAL DEVELOPMENT CORPORATION. ANNUAL REPORT AND ACCOUNTS. Text in English. a. **Document type:** *Corporate.*
Published by: Industrial and Commercial Development Corporation, PO Box 45519, Nairobi, Kenya.

381 JPN
INDUSTRIAL GROUPINGS IN JAPAN; the anatomy of the Keiretsu. Text in English. 1973. biennial. USD 800. index. **Description:** Covers the 3,500 leading Japanese companies in 28 major industries. Provides information on annual sales, sales rankings, capital, major shareholders, and outstanding loans for 700 group companies. Classified by industry and conglomerates.
Published by: Dodwell Marketing Consultants, Kowa no 35 Bldg, 14-14 Akasaka 1-chome, Minato-ku, Tokyo, 107-0052, Japan. TEL 03-3589-0207, FAX 03-5570-7132, TELEX J22274 DODWELL J. Circ: 1,000.

381 ESP
INFORMACION. Text in Spanish. 12/yr.
Address: Alameda Recalde, 50, Bilbao, Vizcaya 48008, Spain. TEL 4-444-40-54, FAX 4-443-61-71, TELEX 32783 CCINB. Ed. Juan Carlos Landeta.

380 ESP ISSN 0213-3768
INFORMACION COMERCIAL ESPANOLA. BOLETIN ECONOMICO. Text in Spanish. 1940. w. (45/yr.). adv.
Formerly: Informacion Comercial Espanola. Boletin Semanal (0019-9761)
Indexed: ELLIS, KES.
—CINDOC.
Published by: Ministerio de Industria Comercio y Turismo, Paseo Castellana, 162, Planta 16, Madrid, 28046, Spain. TEL 34-1-349-36-47, FAX 34-1-349-36-34. Ed. Maria Eugenia Caumel. Circ: 6,000.

380 ESP
INFORMACION COMERCIAL ESPANOLA. REVISTA DE ECONOMIA. Text in Spanish. 1898. m. (11/yr.). adv. bk.rev.
Formerly: Informacion Comercial Espanola. Revista Mensual (0019-977X)
Indexed: ELLIS, IBR, IBSS, JEL, PAIS, RASB, SCIMP.
—BLDSC (4478.945000), CINDOC, IE, ingenta.
Published by: Ministerio de Industria Comercio y Turismo, Paseo Castellana, 162, Planta 16, Madrid, 28046, Spain. TEL 34-1-349-36-47, FAX 34-1-349-36-34. Circ: 8,900.

381 GBR
INSTITUTE OF LOGISTICS. MEMBERS' DIRECTORY. Text in English. 1994. 10/yr. GBP 72; GBP 10 newsstand/cover (effective 1999). adv. bk.rev. illus.; tr.lit. back issues avail. **Document type:** *Trade.*
Formerly (until 1995): Institute of Logistics. Yearbook (1353-0267)
—**CCC.**
Published by: Institute of Logistics and Transport, Logistics and Transport Centre, PO Box 5787, Corby, Northants NN17 4XQ, United Kingdom. TEL 44-1536-740100, FAX 44-1536-740101, enquiry@iolt.org.uk, http://www.iolt.org.uk. Ed. Gerald Fisher. Adv. contact Christine Guy TEL 44-1536-740118. Circ: 25,000 (paid).

▼ **INSTORE BUYER.** see *FOOD AND FOOD INDUSTRIES*

381 IRN ISSN 0074-1213
INTERNAL TRADE OF IRAN. Text in English, Persian, Modern. 1965. a. free. **Document type:** *Government.*
Published by: (Bureau of Statistics), Ministry of Finance and Economic Affairs, Teheran, Iran.

INTERNATIONAL JOURNAL OF ADVERTISING; the quarterly review of marketing communications. see *ADVERTISING AND PUBLIC RELATIONS*

381 USA ISSN 8750-6645
IOWA COMMERCE. Text in English. 1984. m. USD 15 to non-members. adv. stat. back issues avail. **Description:** Business and industry news.
Published by: Heartland Construction Group, Inc., 1003 Central Ave, Fort Dodge, IA 50501. TEL 515-955-1600, 800-247-2000, FAX 800-247-2000. Ed. Jeanne Lightly. Pub. Ann M Foster. Adv. contact Ann Wahl. Circ: 10,000.

IRELAND. CENTRAL STATISTICS OFFICE. RETAIL SALES INDEX. see *BUSINESS AND ECONOMICS—Abstracting, Bibliographies, Statistics*

IRELAND. CENTRAL STATISTICS OFFICE. VEHICLES LICENSED FOR THE FIRST TIME (MONTH). see *BUSINESS AND ECONOMICS—Abstracting, Bibliographies, Statistics*

ITALY. ISTITUTO NAZIONALE DI STATISTICA. STATISTICHE DEL COMMERCIO INTERNO. see *BUSINESS AND ECONOMICS—Abstracting, Bibliographies, Statistics*

381 HTI
JOURNAL DE COMMERCE. Text in French. w.
Address: B.P. 1569, 49 rue Traversiere, Port-au-Prince, Haiti. TEL 1-7-3008. Ed. Gerard Allen. Circ: 4,000.

380 CAN ISSN 0709-1230
JOURNAL OF COMMERCE. Text in English. 1978. s-w. CND 895 (effective 2005). adv. charts; illus. **Document type:** *Journal, Trade.*
Formed by the merger of (19??-1978): Journal of Commerce. Wednesday Edition (0318-837X); Which was formerly (until 1975): Journal of Commerce. Wednesday Report (0318-8361); (until 1972): Journal of Commerce. Mid-Weekly (0318-8353); (1973-1978): Journal of Commerce. Western Canada Edition (0709-1249); (1911-1978): Journal of Commerce. B.C. Yukon Edition (0318-8345); Which was formerly (until 1973): Journal of Commerce. British Columbia Edition (0318-8337); (until 1950): British Columbia Journal of Commerce and Building Record (0845-2237); (until 1928): Journal of Commerce and Building Record (0845-2229); (until 1922): British Columbia Record (0845-2210); (until 1916): British Columbia Building Record (0845-2202); (until 19??): Daily Building Record (0845-2199)
Related titles: Online - full text ed.: (from LexisNexis, Micromedia ProQuest, Northern Light Technology, Inc.).
Indexed: BusI, CBCABus, CBPI, T&II.
—CISTI. **CCC.**
Published by: Journal of Commerce Ltd. (Subsidiary of: Construction Market Data Canada Inc.), 4285 Way, Burnaby, BC V5G 1H2, Canada. TEL 604-433-8164, 888-878-2121, FAX 604-433-9549, jofc@lynx.bc.ca, http://www.joconl.com/. Ed. Frank Lillquist. Pub., R&P Brian Martin. Adv. contact Dan Gnocato. Circ: 4,301.

381 382 USA ISSN 1542-3867
CODEN: JOCOFI
THE JOURNAL OF COMMERCE. Variant title: JoC Week. Text in English. 1827. w. USD 195 domestic (effective 2005). adv. charts; mkt. **Document type:** *Magazine, Consumer.*
Formerly (until 2002, vol.3, issue 42): J o C Week (1530-7557); Which was superseded in part (until 2000): Journal of Commerce (1088-7407); Which was formerly (until 1996): Journal of Commerce and Commercial (0361-5561); (until 1927): Journal of Commerce (0021-9827)
Related titles: Microfilm ed.: (from PQC); Online - full text ed.: Journal of Commerce Online. USD 200 foreign (effective 2003) (from EBSCO Publishing, Gale Group, H.W. Wilson, O C L C Online Computer Library Center, Inc., The Dialog Corporation).
Indexed: BPI, CIN, ChemAb, ChemTitl, HlthInd, KES, LRI, LogistBibl, PAIS, PROMT, RASB, T&II.
—BLDSC (4669.792000), CASDDS. **CCC.**
Published by: Journal of Commerce, Inc. (Subsidiary of: Commonwealth Business Media, Inc.), 33 Washington St, 13th Fl, Newark, NJ 07102. TEL 973-848-7000, 800-215-6084, editor@mail.joc.com, http://www.joc.com. Circ: 22,000 (paid).

380 338 LBR ISSN 0303-9293
HC591.L6
JOURNAL OF COMMERCE, INDUSTRY & TRANSPORTATION✶ Text in English. 1967. q. USD 6. adv. charts; illus.; stat.
Formerly: Journal of Commerce and Industry (0021-9843)
Published by: Ministry of Commerce Industry and Transportation, PO Box 9041, Monrovia, Liberia. Eds. Richard M Morris, William E Dennis Jr. Circ: 7,000. **Subscr. to:** African Development, Wheatsheaf House, Carmelite St., London EC4Y 0AX, United Kingdom.

381 332.6 ITA ISSN 1593-2052
CODEN: RIMEDE
JOURNAL OF COMMODITY SCIENCE. Text in Italian, English. 1962. q. **Document type:** *Magazine, Trade.*
Former titles (until 1997): Rivista di Merceologia (0392-064X); (until 1978): Quaderni di Merceologia (0523-9559)
Indexed: AbHyg, AgBio, AgrForAb, AnBrAb, CIN, CPA, ChemAb, ChemTitl, DSA, FS&TA, ForAb, HortAb, NutrAb, PBA, PGegResA, PGrRegA, PHN&I, RA&MP, RDA, RM&VM, RPP, S&F, SIA, SeedAb, SoyAb, TriticAb, WAE&RSA, WeedAb.
—BLDSC (7990.750000), CASDDS, IE, ingenta.
Published by: Casa Editrice C L U E B, Via Marsala 31, Bologna, BO 40126, Italy. TEL 39-051-220736, FAX 39-051-237758, clueb@clueb.com, http://www.clueb.com.

JOURNAL OF ECONOMICS, BUSINESS AND LAW. see *BUSINESS AND ECONOMICS*

381 KEN
K I R D I ANNUAL REPORT AND STATEMENT OF ACCOUNTS. Text in English. 1982. a.
Published by: Kenya Industrial Research and Development Institute, PO Box 30650, Nairobi, Kenya. Circ: 1,000.

381 NGA
KANO (STATE). MARKET CALENDAR. Text in English. 1980. a. free. **Document type:** *Government.*
Published by: Budget & Economic Planning Directorate, Ministry of Finance, Audu Bako Secretariat, PMB 3291, Kano, Kano State, Nigeria.

381 JPN ISSN 1344-8455
KANSAI UNIVERSITY REVIEW OF BUSINESS AND COMMERCE. Variant title: Review of Business and Commerce. Text in English. 1999. s-a. **Document type:** *Academic/Scholarly.*
Supercedes in part (in 1998): Review of Economics and Business (0302-6574)
Indexed: APEL, BAS, RASB.
—BLDSC (5085.535400), CISTI.
Published by: Kansai University, Faculty of Commerce, 3-3-35, Yamate-cho, Suita City, Osaka 564-8680, Japan. Circ: 600.

381 DEU ISSN 0022-9474
KAUFHAUS UND WARENHAUS. Text in German. 1966. q. EUR 40 (effective 2001). adv. bk.rev. charts; stat.; tr.lit. **Document type:** *Magazine, Trade.*
Published by: Zeitungs- und Zeitschriftenverlag Heinrichs, Brueggekamp 1, Barsinghausen, 30890, Germany. TEL 49-5105-2289. Ed., Pub. Gerhard Heinrichs.

381 KEN ISSN 0304-7202
HF3899.K42
KENYA NATIONAL TRADING CORPORATION. ANNUAL REPORT. Text in English. a.
Published by: Kenya National Trading Corporation Ltd., PO Box 30587, Nairobi, Kenya.

381 GBR ISSN 1364-7997
KEY NOTE MARKET REPORT: MIXED RETAIL BUSINESSES. Text in English. 1982. irreg. (7th Edition), latest 1996, May. GBP 340 per issue (effective 2002). **Document type:** *Trade.* **Description:** Provides and overview of a specific UK market segment and includes executive summary, market definition, market size, industry background, competitor analysis, current issues, forecasts, company profiles, and more.
Formerly (until 1996): Key Note Report. Mixed Retail Business (0951-6743)
Published by: Key Note Ltd., Field House, 72 Oldfield Rd, Hampton, Mddx TW12 2HQ, United Kingdom. TEL 44-20-8481-8750, FAX 44-20-8783-0049, info@keynote.co.uk, http://www.keynote.co.uk. Ed. Kim Potts.

381 GBR
KEY NOTE MARKET REPORT: NEW TRENDS IN RETAILING. Variant title: New Trends in Retailing. Text in English. irreg., latest vol.2, 1990. GBP 265 (effective 1999). **Document type:** *Trade.*
Published by: Key Note Ltd., Field House, 72 Oldfield Rd, Hampton, Mddx TW12 2HQ, United Kingdom. TEL 44-20-8481-8750, FAX 44-20-8783-0049, info@keynote.co.uk, http://www.keynote.co.uk.

658.87 SWE ISSN 1103-3142
KOEPMANNEN VAEST. Text in Swedish. 1941. 7/yr. SEK 100 (effective 1993).
Formerly (until 1992): Goeteborgskoepmannen
Published by: Koepmannfoerbunden i Goeteborg och Vaestergoetland, Fack 53200, Goeteborg, 40015, Sweden.

381 346 USA ISSN 1541-8197
L A B I ENTERPRISE. Text in English. q. membership. adv. back issues avail. **Document type:** *Trade.* **Description:** Covers developments in the political, legislative and judicial areas. Includes profiles of member businesses.
Formerly (until 1997): L A B I Report (0164-8446)
Published by: Louisiana Association of Business and Industry, 3113 Valley Creek Dr, Box 80258, Baton Rouge, LA 70898-0258. TEL 225-928-5388, FAX 225-929-6054, labi@labi.org, http://www.labi.org. Ed. Cindy Capello. Pub., R&P Mona Davis. Adv. contact A J Heine.

381 DEU
L G A NACHRICHTEN✶. Text in German. bi-m.
Published by: Landesverband des Bayerischen Gross- und Aussenhandels, Max-Joseph-Str 4, Munich, 80333, Germany.

LATIN AMERICAN METAL MECHANIC & ELECTRONIC INDUSTRY DIRECTORY. see *MACHINERY*

381 330.9 331 340.5 USA
LITIGATION ECONOMICS DIGEST. Text in English. 1995. s-a. USD 60 (effective 2000). software rev. **Description:** Features new data available for economic research, the status of work done by the NAFE Committee and case studies and articles on a wide range of issues in the field of forensic economics, including commercial litigation, employment litigation, securities fruad, environmental litigation and valuing financial assets and businesses.
Indexed: IBZ.
Published by: National Association of Forensic Economics, PO Box 30067, Kansas City, MO 64112. TEL 816-235-2833, FAX 816-235-5263, umkcnafe@umkc.edu, http://www.nafe.net. Eds. Michael J Piette, Steven Shapiro. R&P, Adv. contact Nancy Eldredge TEL 816-235-2833. Circ: 800 (paid).

381 GBR
LIVERPOOL COTTON ASSOCIATION. RAW COTTON REPORT AND VALUE DIFFERENCES FOR SHIPMENT CIRCULAR. Text in English. fortn. **Document type:** *Trade.*
Formed by the merger of: Liverpool Cotton Association. Weekly Raw Cotton Report; Liverpool Cotton Association. Weekly Value Differences Circular
Published by: Liverpool Cotton Association Ltd., 620 Cotton Exchange Bldgs, Liverpool, Merseyside L3 9LH, United Kingdom. TEL 44-151-236-6041, FAX 44-151-255-0174, TELEX 627849, staff@ics.org.uk. Circ: 300.

B

381 GBR ISSN 1466-836X
HF5415.7
LOGISTICS & TRANSPORT FOCUS. Text in English. 1993. m. (except Jan. & Aug.). free to members. adv. bk.rev. illus.; tr.lit. back issues avail. **Document type:** *Trade.* **Description:** Provides information to logistics and transport professionals working within the supply-chain.
Formerly (until 1999): Logistics Focus (1350-6293); Which was formed by the merger of (1982-1993): Logistics Today (0262-4354); (1987-1993): Focus on Physical Distribution and Logistics Management (0952-2190); Which was formerly: Focus on Logistics and Distribution Management
Related titles: Online - full text ed.: (from EBSCO Publishing).
Indexed: ABIn, Emerald, ICEA, Inspec, M&MA.
—BLDSC (5292.314800), AskIEEE, IE, ingenta. **CCC.**
Published by: Institute of Logistics and Transport, Logistics and Transport Centre, PO Box 5787, Corby, Northants NN17 4XQ, United Kingdom. TEL 44-1536-740100, FAX 44-1536-740101, enquiry@iolt.org.uk, http://www.iolt.org.uk. Ed. Gerald Fisher. R&P, Adv. contact Christine Guy TEL 44-1536-740118. B&W page GBP 1,355, color page GBP 2,010. Circ: 23,000 (paid).

381 BRA
LOJAS & LOJISTAS. Text in Portuguese. m. illus.
Published by: Sindicato dos Lojistas do Comercio de Sao Paulo, Rua Xavier de Toledo, 99-2 andar, Sao Paulo, SP, Brazil.

M D - MARKETING DIGEST; Fachbereichszeitschrift der Fachhochschule fuer Wirtschaft, Pforzheim. see *BUSINESS AND ECONOMICS—Marketing And Purchasing*

380 NZL
M.G. BUSINESS. (Mercantile Gazette) Text in English. 1876. fortn. NZD 162 (effective 2000). adv. charts; stat. **Document type:** *Newspaper.*
Former titles: New Zealand Mercantile Gazette (0111-3321); Mercantile Gazette of New Zealand (0025-9799)
Published by: Mercantile Gazette Marketing, PO Box 20-034, Christchurch 5, New Zealand. FAX 64-3-3584490. Circ: 20,000.

381 USA
M M A C MILWAUKEE COMMERCE HOT-LINE ANNUAL REPORT. (Metropolitan Milwaukee Association of Commerce) Text in English. a. free to members. **Description:** Provides yearly review of the MMAC's activities and accomplishments.
Published by: Metropolitan Milwaukee Association of Commerce, Council of Small Business Executives, 756 N Milwaukee St, Milwaukee, WI 53202. TEL 414-287-4100.

381 HUN
M T I ECONEWS. Text in English. 1988. d. (5/w.). USD 960 (effective 2001). adv. 16 p./no.; **Document type:** *Bulletin.* **Description:** Covers the Hungarian economy, companies, banking and finance, economic trends and government economic and financial policy.
Related titles: E-mail ed.; Online - full text ed.
Published by: M T I - E C O Ltd., Pl Naphegy ter 8, Budapest, 1016, Hungary. TEL 36-1-3188204, FAX 36-1-2012209, info@mtieco.hu, http://www.mtieco.hu. Ed. Adam Danko. R&P Emese Gyuracz. Adv. contact Krisztina Segesdi. Circ: 400.

MACAO. DIRECCAO DOS SERVICOS DE ESTATISTICA E CENSOS. C A M CLASSIFICACAO DAS ACTIVIDADES ECONOMICAS DE MACAU/MACAO. CENSUS AND STATISTICS DEPARTMENT. C A M CLASSIFICATION OF ECONOMIC ACTIVITIES OF MACAO. see *BUSINESS AND ECONOMICS—Abstracting, Bibliographies, Statistics*

MACAO. DIRECCAO DOS SERVICOS DE ESTATISTICA E CENSOS. INDICE DE PRECOS NO CONSUMIDOR/MACAO. CENSUS AND STATISTICS DEPARTMENT. CONSUMER PRICE INDEX. see *BUSINESS AND ECONOMICS—Abstracting, Bibliographies, Statistics*

B

MACAO. DIRECCAO DOS SERVICOS DE ESTATISTICA E CENSOS. INDICE DE PRECOS NO CONSUMIDOR (RELATORIO ANUAL)/MACAO. CENSUS AND STATISTICS DEPARTMENT. CONSUMER PRICE INDEX (ANNUAL REPORT). see *BUSINESS AND ECONOMICS—Abstracting, Bibliographies, Statistics*

381 ITA
MADE IN VARESE. Text in Italian. 6/yr.
Address: Viale Milano, 5, Varese, VA 21100, Italy. TEL 332-25-61-11, FAX 332-25-62-00, TELEX 316893 ASARVA I. Ed. Vito Artioli. Circ: 5,000.

381 MYS
MALAYSIA. DEPARTMENT OF INLAND REVENUE. ANNUAL REPORT/MALAYSIA. JABATAN HASIL DALAM NEGERI. LAPURAN TAHUNAN. Text in Malay. 1972. a.
Published by: Department of Inland Revenue, Kuala Lumpur, Malaysia.

381 DEU ISSN 0946-9214
MANNESMANN MAGAZIN. Text in German. 1994. m. **Document type:** *Trade.*
Formed by the merger of (1972-1994): Mannesmann Illustrierte (0946-9222); (1956-1994): Mannesmann Post (0933-3150); Which was formerly (until 1985): Rohr-Post (0485-3598)
Related titles: English ed.
—BLDSC (5361.038000).
Published by: Mannesmann AG, Mannesmannufer 2, Duesseldorf, 40213, Germany. TEL 49-211-8202841, FAX 49-211-8201846, http://www.mannesmann.com. Ed. Georg Lohmann. Circ: 27,000.

MARKETING I PRAKTIKA PREDPRINIMATEL'STVA. see *BUSINESS AND ECONOMICS—Marketing And Purchasing*

381 MEX
MARYNKA: MERCADOS DE MEXICO EN ACCION. Text in Spanish. 1971. a.
Published by: Publicaciones Marynka S.A., SALAVERRY 1204, Col Zacatenco, Mexico City, DF 07360, Mexico. TEL 574-13-81. Circ: 5,000.

381.1 USA
MASS RETAILERS' EXECUTIVE PERQUISITE REPORT✶. Text in English. biennial. USD 85 to non-members; USD 40 to members. **Document type:** *Bulletin.*
Indexed: SRI.
Published by: Retail Industry Leaders Association, 1700 N Moore St, Ste 2250, Arlington, VA 22209-1903. TEL 703-841-2300, http://www.imra.org.

381 FRA
MERCURE 10. Text in French. 6/yr.
Published by: Chambre Regionale de Commerce et d'Industrie Champagne - Ardenne, Direction de la Communication, 10 rue de Chastillon, B.P. 537, Chalons-sur-Marne, Cedex 51011, France. TEL 33-3-26693340, FAX 33-3-26693369.

381 ISR
MICHERON SHERUTIM FINANTSIYIM UMISCHARIYIM. Text in Hebrew. q.
Published by: Cheshev Ltd., P O Box 40021, Tel Aviv, 61400, Israel. TEL (03)216291.

MID-MISSOURI BUSINESS JOURNAL. see *BUSINESS AND ECONOMICS—Small Business*

381 USA ISSN 0746-6706
MILWAUKEE COMMERCE HOT-LINE. Text in English. 1980. 3/m. free to members (effective 2005). **Document type:** *Newsletter, Consumer.* **Description:** Provides news, and upcoming events schedules of interest to members.
Formed by the merger of (1923-1984): Milwaukee Commerce (0026-4342); (1923-1984): Commerce Hotline (0746-6714); Which incorporated (1980-1984): Metropolitan Milwaukee Association of Commerce. Trends in Selected Economic Indicators (0076-7069)
Published by: Metropolitan Milwaukee Association of Commerce, Council of Small Business Executives, 756 N Milwaukee St, Milwaukee, WI 53202. TEL 414-287-4100, FAX 414-271-7753. Ed. Julie Granger. Circ: 3,750.

388.044 USA ISSN 0273-5822
HF5487
MINI-STORAGE MESSENGER. Text in English. 1979. 13/yr. USD 59.95 domestic; USD 79 in Canada & Mexico; USD 108 elsewhere; USD 7.95 per issue (effective 2005). adv. **Document type:** *Magazine, Trade.* **Description:** Trade magazine for owners, operators and managers of self-storage facilities.
Published by: Minico, Inc., 2531 W Dunlap Ave, Phoenix, AZ 85021. TEL 602-678-3574, 800-352-4636, 800-824-6864, FAX 602-678-3511, messenger@minico.com, http://www.minico.com. Adv. contact Lauri Longstrom. B&W page USD 1,877, color page USD 2,391; trim 10.88 x 8.38. Circ: 6,000 (paid and free).

381 CAN ISSN 1185-2186
MISSISSAUGA BUSINESS TIMES. Text in English. 1983. m. free. adv. **Document type:** *Newspaper.*
Formerly: Mississauga Business (0826-4139)
Related titles: Microfilm ed.: (from CML, SOC).
Published by: Metroland Printing, Publishing and Distributing Ltd., 3145 Wolfedale Rd, Mississauga, ON L5C 3A9, Canada. TEL 905-273-8222, FAX 905-273-8118. Ed. R Drenna. Pub. Ron Lenyk TEL 905-273-8119. Adv. contact Andrew Luke. B&W page CND 1,912, color page CND 2,762; trim 15.5 x 10. Circ: 21,055.

380 DEU ISSN 0931-5934
MITTEILUNGEN AUS DER F F H BERLIN. Text in German. 1959. q. bk.rev. abstr.; bibl. index. **Document type:** *Bulletin.*
Formerly (until 1986): F F H Mitteilungen (0014-5831)
—BLDSC (5842.190000). **CCC.**
Published by: Forschungsstelle fuer den Handel Berlin e.V., Fehrbelliner Platz 3, Berlin, 10707, Germany. TEL 49-30-863094-0, FAX 49-30-86309444. Ed. Andrea Woelk.

381 ITA
MODENA - MONDO. Text in Italian. 1989. 10/yr. free (effective 2005). adv. **Document type:** *Trade.*
Published by: (Associazione Industriali di Modena), S.A.I.M.O. s.r.l., Via Bellinzona, 27 A, Modena, MO 41100, Italy. TEL 39-059-448311, FAX 39-059-448310, http://www.pubbli.it/momondo1.htm. Ed. Marzia Barbieri. Circ: 10,000.

MONEY SAVER. see *CONSUMER EDUCATION AND PROTECTION*

MOSKVA: MER I BIZNES. see *PUBLIC ADMINISTRATION*

381 658 USA ISSN 1055-8268
NATIONAL AUCTIONS & SALES✶. Text in English. 1991. q. USD 29.99. adv. Supplement avail. **Document type:** *Consumer.* **Description:** Reviews major auctions and sales throughout the nation and provides information on upcoming events.
Announced as: Government Auctions Update
Published by: Publishing & Business Consultants, 4427 W Slauson Ave, Los Angeles, CA 90043-2717. TEL 213-732-3477, FAX 213-732-9123. Ed. Andeson Napoleon Atia. Circ: 120,000.

381 USA ISSN 0164-8152
NEW HAMPSHIRE BUSINESS REVIEW; the granite state's business resource. Text in English. 1978. bi-w. USD 33; USD 1.75 newsstand/cover (effective 2005). adv. bk.rev. **Document type:** *Newspaper, Trade.*
Related titles: Microform ed.: (from PQC); Online - full text ed.: (from bigchalk, EBSCO Publishing, Florida Center for Library Automation, Gale Group, Northern Light Technology, Inc., O C L C Online Computer Library Center, Inc., ProQuest Information & Learning).
Indexed: ABIn, BusDate, T&II.
Published by: McLean Communications, Inc., 150 Dow St., Manchester, NH 03101. TEL 603-624-1442, FAX 603-624-1310, smeyers@nhbr.com, http://www.nhbr.com. Ed. Jeff Feingold TEL 603-624-1442 ext 18. Pub., R&P Sharon R McCarthy. adv.: B&W page USD 1,965, color page USD 2,465. Circ: 13,000 (paid).

051 USA ISSN 1059-4140
NEW MIAMI✶. Text in English. 1988. m. USD 18. adv. bk.rev. **Description:** Covers community and business issues and profiles business leaders.
Related titles: Online - full text ed.
Indexed: BusDate.
Published by: New Miami, Inc., 100 N W 37th Ave, Miami, FL 33123-4844. TEL 305-649-0100, FAX 305-372-1669. Ed. Mike Seemuth. Circ: 20,000.

381 NIC ISSN 0078-0510
NICARAGUA. DIRECCION GENERAL DE ADUANAS. MEMORIA. Text in Spanish. 1918. a. USD 7. stat.
Published by: Direccion General de Aduanas, Managua, Nicaragua. Circ: 200.

NORTH AMERICAN POST/HOKUBEI HOCHI. see *ETHNIC INTERESTS*

381 USA ISSN 1063-2875
F251
NORTH CAROLINA MAGAZINE. Text in English. 1943. m. USD 21.40 (effective 2005). adv. bk.rev. **Document type:** *Magazine, Trade.*
Formerly: We the People of North Carolina
Related titles: Microform ed.: (from PQC); Online - full text ed.
Published by: North Carolina Citizens for Business and Industry, 225 Hillsborough, Ste 460, PO Box 2508, Raleigh, NC 27602. TEL 919-836-1400, FAX 919-836-1425, stuttle@nccbi.org, http://www.nccbi.org. Ed., R&P A Steve Tuttle TEL 919-836-1411. Pub. Phillip J Kirk Jr. Adv. contact Stephen Wissink. page USD 2,889. Circ: 17,200 (paid).

381 GBR ISSN 0306-5650
NORTH WEST BUSINESS. Text in English. 1968. m. GBP 19.50. adv. bk.rev. **Document type:** *Trade.*
Former titles: North West Business Monthly; (until 1985): North West and North Wales Industrial Review
Published by: Business Magazine Group, Adamsway, Mansfield, Notts NG18 4FP, United Kingdom. TEL 44-1623-450500, FAX 44-1623-454560. Ed. Anabella McIntyre Brown. Circ: 11,818.

381 978.8 USA ISSN 1094-8198
THE NORTHERN COLORADO BUSINESS REPORT; the voice of northern Colorado business. Text in English. 1995. bi-w. USD 29.97; USD 50 foreign (effective 2000). adv. illus. back issues avail. **Document type:** *Newspaper, Trade.* **Description:** Reports on news and trends about and affecting businesses in northern Colorado.
Related titles: Online - full text ed.: (from Northern Light Technology, Inc.).
Indexed: BusDate.
Published by: Northern Colorado Business Report, 201 S. College Ave., Ste. 300, Ft. Collins, CO 80524-2810. TEL 970-221-5400, FAX 970-221-5432, publisher@ncbr.com, ncbr@aol.com, http://www.ncbr.com/. Ed. Tom Hacker. Pub., R&P Christopher Wood. Adv. contact Jeff Nuttall. B&W page USD 2,375, color page USD 2,975; trim 14 x 10.25. Circ: 12,000 (paid and controlled).

380 NOR
NORWAY. MINISTRY OF INDUSTRY. REPORTS TO THE STORTING. Text in Norwegian. irreg. price varies.
Published by: Ministry of Industry, Postboks 8014, Dep, Oslo, 0030, Norway.

381 PRT ISSN 0870-2047
NOTICIAS DO COMERCIO. Text in Portuguese. 1938. 6/yr.
Address: Rua da Palma, 284, 2o Dto., Lisbon, 1100, Portugal. TEL 860912.

381 ITA
NOTIZIE F A I D. Text in Italian. bi-m. **Document type:** *Newsletter, Trade.*
Related titles: Online - full text ed.
Published by: Federazione Associazione Imprese Distribuzione, Viale Majno 42, Milan, MI 20129, Italy. TEL 39-02-653333, FAX 39-02-6551169, info@faidfederdistribuzione.com, http://www.faidfederdistribuzione.com.

381 SCG ISSN 0469-0281
NOVA TRGOVINA. Text in Serbo-Croatian. 1948. m. YUN 600.
Indexed: RASB.
Published by: Privredni Pregled, Marsala Birjuzova 3-5, Belgrade, 11000. Ed. Ljubodrag Jozic.

381 ESP
NUEVA DIMENSION. Text in Spanish. 11/yr.
Address: Lillo, 1, Madrid, 28041, Spain. TEL 1-217-96-59. Ed. Fidel Astudillo. Circ: 5,000.

OFFICE - DATA PROCESSING MACHINES: LATIN AMERICAN INDUSTRIAL REPORT. see *COMPUTERS—Computer Industry*

381 GBR
OLD BEN NEWS. Text in English. 1975. q. GBP 5. adv. bk.rev.
Published by: Newsvendors' Benevolent Institution, News Vendors Benevolent Institution, PO Box 306, Dunmow, Essex CM6 1HY, United Kingdom. Ed. Leonard Stall. Circ: 46,000 (controlled).

381 POL ISSN 1641-8077
ORGANIZACJA I ZARZADZANIE W REGIONIE NADMORSKIM. Text in Polish. 2001. a. **Document type:** *Monographic series, Academic/Scholarly.*
Published by: (Polska Akademia Nauk, Oddzial w Gdansku, Komisja Organizacji i Zarzadzania), Polska Akademia Nauk, Oddzial w Gdansku/Polish Academy of Sciences, Section in Gdansk, ul Jaskowa Dolina 31, Gdansk, 80286, Poland. o1pan@ibwpan.gda.pl.

OUTSTATE BUSINESS; the magazine of Michigan business & industry. see *BUSINESS AND ECONOMICS—Economic Situation And Conditions*

PALESTINE BUSINESS REPORT. see *BUSINESS AND ECONOMICS—Economic Situation And Conditions*

381 918.6 PAN ISSN 1011-3940
PANAMA NOW. Text in English. 1986. biennial. USD 40 (effective 1999). adv. index. **Document type:** *Consumer.* **Description:** Portrait of the nation in yearbook form. Includes many color photos.
Related titles: Spanish ed.: Panama Hoy. ISSN 1011-3959.
Published by: Focus Publications (Int.) S.A., Apdo. 6-3287, El Dorado, Panama City, Panama. TEL 507-225-6638, FAX 507-225-0466, focusint@sinfo.net, http://focuspublicationsint.com. Ed. Kenneth J Jones. Circ: 10,000.

338 380 PRY ISSN 0031-1685
PARAGUAY INDUSTRIAL Y COMERCIAL✶. Text in Spanish. 1944. m. adv. charts; illus.
Published by: Ministerio de Industria y Comercio, C.C. 1772, Ave. ESPANA, 374, Asuncion, Paraguay.

381 332.62 332.66 340.56 BGR
PAZAR I PRAVO. Text in Bulgarian. m. BGL 88.80 (effective 2002). **Description:** Publishes articles concerning capital market, exchange, competition; trade activity and market terms.
Related titles: CD-ROM ed.
Published by: Izdatelski Kompleks Trud i Pravo/Labour and Law Publishing House, Pl. Makedonia 1, Fl. 7, Sofia, 1040, Bulgaria. TEL 359-2-9875110, FAX 359-2-9870612, office@trudipravo.bg, http://www.trudipravo.bg.

PEDDLER. see *CONSUMER EDUCATION AND PROTECTION*

PETROLEUM: LATIN AMERICAN INDUSTRIAL REPORT. see *PETROLEUM AND GAS*

PHARMACEUTICAL: LATIN AMERICAN INDUSTRIAL REPORT. see *PHARMACY AND PHARMACOLOGY*

381 USA
THE PHILADELPHIA HISPANIC BUSINESS JOURNAL. Text in English. 1997. m.
Published by: Grupo Bogota, Inc., 198 W Chew Ave, Philadelphia, PA 19120. TEL 215-424-1200, FAX 215-424-6064, phbj@aol.com.

PHILIPPINE JOURNAL OF DEVELOPMENT. see *BUSINESS AND ECONOMICS—Public Finance, Taxation*

PHILIPPINES. DEPARTMENT OF TRADE AND INDUSTRY. ANNUAL REPORT. see *BUSINESS AND ECONOMICS— International Commerce*

381 382 PHL
PHILIPPINES. NATIONAL STATISTICS OFFICE. COMMODITY FLOW IN THE PHILIPPINES. Text in English. a. 398 p./no.; **Document type:** *Government.* **Description:** Comprehensive statistics on regional commodity flow of domestic trade by mode of transport.
Related titles: Diskette ed.
Published by: National Statistics Office, Ramon Magsaysay Blvd, PO Box 779, Manila, Philippines. FAX 63-2-610794.

381 ITA ISSN 0393-9448
PIAZZA MERCATO. Text in Italian. 1983. m.
Published by: Promodis Italia Editrice s.r.l., Via Creta, 56, Brescia, BS 25124, Italy. TEL 030-220261, FAX 030-225868, TELEX 305362 PROMED I. Ed. Argentino Albori. Circ: 33,640.

381 ESP
PLACA GRAN. Text in Spanish. 52/yr.
Address: Roger de Lluria 1, Granollers, Barcelona 08400, Spain. TEL 3-870-47-09.

381 USA
PLYMOUTH COUNTY BUSINESS REVIEW. Text in English. 1982. s-a. USD 4. adv. **Description:** Describes the economic climate of Plymouth County.
Related titles: Microform ed.: (from PQC); Online - full text ed.
Indexed: BusDate.
Published by: Plymouth County Development Council, PO Box 1620, Pembroke, MA 02359. TEL 781-826-3136, FAX 781-826-0444, info@plymouth-1620.com, http://www.plymouth-1620.com/. Ed. David Kindy. Pub. Brooks Kelly. Adv. contact Janet Ramsay. Circ: 5,000 (controlled).

381 332.6 IND
PONDICHERRY INDUSTRIAL PROMOTION, DEVELOPMENT AND INVESTMENT CORPORATION. ANNUAL REPORTS AND ACCOUNTS. Text in English. 1975. a.
Published by: Pondicherry Industrial Promotion Development and Investment Corporation Ltd., 38 Romain Rolland St., Pondicherry, Tamil Nadu 605 001, India. Circ: (controlled).

381 DEU ISSN 0343-415X
POSITION. Text in German. q.
—CCC.
Published by: Deutscher Industrie- und Handelstag, Adenauerallee 148, Bonn, 53113, Germany. TEL 0228-1040, TELEX 886805.

PRINTING & PUBLISHING: LATIN AMERICAN INDUSTRIAL REPORT. see *PUBLISHING AND BOOK TRADE*

381 MDA
PRIVAT-REVIU/PRIVATE REVIEW. Text in Russian. w. **Document type:** *Newspaper, Consumer.* **Description:** Covers problems of privatization, analysis and work experience of privatized ventures, investing funds, work of exchanges and other market structures.
Published by: Nezavisimaya Moldova, Ul Pushkin 22, Chisinau, 2012, Moldova. TEL 373-2-233605, FAX 373-2-233141, tis@nemo.moldova.su, http://www.mldnet.com/nezmold/index.html. Ed. Ivan Koretsky TEL 373-2-233178.

381 IND
PRODUCTION OF SELECTED INDUSTRIES IN INDIA. Text in English. m. INR 120, USD 43.20.
Published by: Government of India, Department of Publications, Civil Lines, New Delhi, 110 054, India. TEL 11-2512527.

R S A JOURNAL. see *ART*

REPORT ON ELECTRONIC COMMERCE; online business, financial and consumer strategies and trends. see *COMPUTERS—Internet*

RETAIL DETAILS. see *BUSINESS AND ECONOMICS—Marketing And Purchasing*

381 JPN
RETAIL DISTRIBUTION IN JAPAN. Text in English. irreg., latest 1991, Oct. USD 600 per issue. **Document type:** *Directory.* **Description:** Information on socioeconomic changes and characteristics of the Japanese distribution system. Covers retailers, wholesalers, distribution channels for imported products. Includes company profiles.
Published by: Dodwell Marketing Consultants, Kowa no 35 Bldg, 14-14 Akasaka 1-chome, Minato-ku, Tokyo, 107-0052, Japan. TEL 81-3-3589-0207, FAX 81-3-5570-7132.

381 340 EGY ISSN 1110-1377
THE REVIEW OF THE FACULTY OF COMMERCE/AL-MAGALLAT AL-'LMIYYAT LI-KOLIYYAT AL-TIGAARAT. Text in English. 1981. s-a. **Document type:** *Journal, Academic/Scholarly.*
Published by: Assiut University, Faculty of Commerce, Souhag, Assiut, Egypt. TEL 20-93-601807, FAX 20-93-604820, http://derp.sti.sci.eg/data/0187.htm. Eds. Dr. Esmaeil Sabri Maqlad, Dr. Authman Muhammad Yasin.

381 PRT
REVISTA COMERCIO PORTUENSE. Text in Portuguese. 6/yr.
Address: Avenina Rodrigues de Freitas, 200, Porto, 4000, Portugal. TEL 57-41-48, FAX 580423, TELEX 22758 ASCOP P.

381 CUB
REVISTA DEL COMERCIO. Text in Spanish. 3/yr. USD 15 in North America; USD 17 in South America; USD 18 in Europe.
Published by: (Cuba. Ministerio del Comercio Interior), Ediciones Cubanas, Obispo No. 527, Apdo. 605, Havana, Cuba.

380 CAN ISSN 0380-9811
HC111
REVUE COMMERCE. Text in French. 1896. m. CND 27.95 domestic; CND 65 in United States (effective 2005). adv. illus. index. **Document type:** *Magazine, Trade.* **Description:** Aimed at managers in the province of Quebec.
Formerly: Commerce (0010-2725); Which incorporates (1968-1982): Point (0316-7852)
Related titles: Microfilm ed.
Indexed: AIAP, CBCARef, CBPI, CPerl, PAIS, PdeR.
—CCC.
Published by: Transcontinental Media, Inc. (Subsidiary of: Transcontinental, Inc.), 1100 Blvd Rene Levesque W, 24th Fl, Montreal, PQ H3B 4X9, Canada. TEL 514-392-9000, FAX 514-392-1489, info@transcontinental.ca, http://www.transcontinental-gtc.com/en/home.html. Ed. Pierre Duhamel. Adv. contact Lucie Leduc. Circ: 42,426 (paid).

381 FRA ISSN 1631-1132
LA REVUE DE L'ATELIER. strategies, technologies et business. Text in French. 1987. 8/yr.
Formerly (until 2001): Le Journal de l'Atelier (0299-3570)
—IE.
Published by: Editions La Perouse, 37 rue La Pelouse, Paris, 75116, France. Pub. Jean-Michel Billaut.

381 MDG
REVUE DE L'OCEAN INDIEN. ECONOMIE. Text in French. 1982. q. USD 29. adv. bk.rev.
Published by: Communication et Media Ocean Indien, BP 46, Antananarivo, Madagascar. TEL 26120-22536, FAX 26120-34534. Ed. Georges Ranaivosoa. Circ: 3,000.

RIV'ON HESHEV. see *BUSINESS AND ECONOMICS—Marketing And Purchasing*

381 USA
ROUTE 202 REVIEW✳ ; serving Chester, Montgomery & Delaware County business community along the Route 202 corridor. Text in English. 1984. bi-m. USD 42. adv. bk.rev. **Document type:** *Newspaper.* **Description:** News and features on lifestyles in the regional business community.
Formerly: Great Valley Business News
Published by: Montgomery Newspapers, 290 Commerce Dr, Ft, Washington, PA 19034-2400. TEL 610-647-8082, FAX 610-647-8180. Ed. Todd Palmer. Pub. Arthur Howe. Adv. contact Betsy Wilson. Circ: 15,000.

RURAL INDIA. see *AGRICULTURE—Agricultural Economics*

381 FRA
SACHEZ-LE ENVIRONNEMENT. Text in French. m.
Published by: Chambre Regionale de Commerce et d'Industrie Champagne - Ardenne, Direction de la Communication, 10 rue de Chastillon, B.P. 537, Chalons-sur-Marne, Cedex 51011, France. TEL 33-3-26693340, FAX 33-3-26693369.

381 SWE ISSN 0346-2560
SAELJAREN. Text in Swedish. 1965. 10/yr. SEK 375 (effective 2001). adv. 32 p./no. 3 cols./p.; **Document type:** *Magazine, Trade.*
Published by: Saeljarnas Riksfoerbund, Box 12668, Stockholm, 11293, Sweden. TEL 46-8-617-02-00, FAX 46-8-652-15-10, info@saljarnas-riksforbund.se, http://www.saljarnas-riksforbund.se. Ed. Britt-Marie Ericson. Pub. Rolf Laurelli. Adv. contact Britta Hjort Ekstroem. B&W page SEK 11,650, color page SEK 14,950; trim 185 x 265. Circ: 10,500.

381.09 CAN ISSN 1184-731X
SAINT JOHN BUSINESS TODAY. Text in English. 1976. m. adv. bk.rev.
Formerly: Saint John Today (0705-1905)
Published by: Saint John Board of Trade, 39 King St, P O Box 6037, Saint John, NB E2L 4R5, Canada. TEL 506-634-8111, FAX 506-632-2008. Ed. Brian McLaughlin. Circ: 1,000.

381 USA ISSN 0890-0337
HF3163
SAN FRANCISCO BUSINESS TIMES. Text in English. 1986. w. (Fri.). USD 89 (effective 2005). adv. back issues avail. **Document type:** *Newspaper, Trade.*
Formerly: California Business Times
Related titles: Online - full text ed.: (from Florida Center for Library Automation, Gale Group, Northern Light Technology, Inc., O C L C Online Computer Library Center, Inc., ProQuest Information & Learning).
Indexed: ABIn, BusDate, LRI.
—CCC.
Address: 275 Battery St, Ste 940, San Francisco, CA 94111. TEL 415-989-2522, FAX 415-398-2494, sanfrancisco@buzjournals.com, http://www.bizjournals.com/sanfrancisco/. Circ: 16,000.

381 CHE
SCHWEIZERISCHES HANDELSAMTSBLATT/FEUILLE OFFICIELLE SUISSE DU COMMERCE/FOGLIO UFFICIALE SVIZZERO DI COMMERCIO. Text in French, German, Italian. 5/w. CHF 115 domestic; CHF 195 foreign (effective 2000). **Document type:** *Newspaper, Government.*
Published by: Staatssekretariat fuer Wirtschaft, Eidgenoessischen Volkswirtschaftsdepartment, Effingerstr 1, Postfach 8164, Bern, 3001, Switzerland. TEL 41-31-3240992, FAX 41-31-3240961, shab@seco.admin.ch. Ed., Pub., R&P Markus Tanner.

338.044 658.7 USA
SELF-STORAGE ALMANAC. Text in English. 1991. a. USD 99.95 (effective 2001). adv. **Document type:** *Trade.*
Published by: Minico, Inc., 2531 W Dunlap Ave, Phoenix, AZ 85021. TEL 602-870-1711, 800-352-4636, FAX 602-861-1094, http://www.minico.com. Ed., R&P Denise Nunez. Pub. Hardy Good. Adv. contact Lauri Longstrom. B&W page USD 1,400, color page USD 2,000. Circ: 3,500.

388.044 USA
SELF-STORAGE NOW. Text in English. 1991. bi-m. adv. illus. **Document type:** *Trade.* **Description:** Each issue focuses on a particular topic linked to current events and seasonal activities in self-storage.
Published by: MiniCo, Inc., Publishing Division, 2531 W Dunlap Ave, Phoenix, AZ 85021. TEL 602-870-1711, 800-528-1056, FAX 602-8611094, http://www.minico.com. Ed., R&P Heather Samee. Adv. contact Bob Rodgers. B&W page USD 1,430, color page USD 1,875; trim 9.75 x 7.5. Circ: 30,000 (controlled).

SENTINEL INVESTMENT LETTER. see *BUSINESS AND ECONOMICS—Investments*

330.9710021 CAN ISSN 1480-8382
SERVICES INDICATORS (ONLINE)/INDICATEURS DES SERVICES. Text in English, French. 1994. quadrennial. **Document type:** *Government.*
Formerly: Services Indicators (Print) (1195-5961)
Media: Online - full content.
Published by: Statistics Canada, Publications Sales and Services, Ottawa, ON K1A 0T6, Canada. TEL 613-951-7277, FAX 613-951-1582, http://www.statcan.ca/english/IPS/Data/63-016-XIB.htm.

381 CHN ISSN 1004-7808
SHANGHAI QIYE/SHANGHAI ENTERPRISE. Text in Chinese. 1981. m. CNY 69.60 (effective 2004). adv. 48 p./no.; **Document type:** *Magazine, Trade.* **Description:** Covers the experiences of business management, and information on economic reform.
Related titles: Online - full text ed.: (from East View Information Services).
Published by: Shanghai Shi Qiye Guanli Xiehui, 2623, Gonghexin Lu, Fu-4-Luo, Shanghai, 200072, China. adv.: page CNY 5,000. Circ: 20,000. **Dist. outside of China by:** China International Book Trading Corp, 35 Chegongzhuang Xilu, Haidian District, PO Box 399, Beijing 100044, China. TEL 86-10-68412045, FAX 86-10-68412023, cibtc@mail.cibtc.com.cn, http://www.cibtc.com.cn/.

381 658 CHN ISSN 1009-1580
SHANGYE JINGJI/COMMERICAL ECONOMY. Text in Chinese. m. 136 p./no.; **Description:** Covers domestic commerce, market studies and marketing management.
Former titles: Shangye Jingji, Wuzi Jingji (1005-4359); (until 1993): Shangye Jingji, Shangye Qiye Guanli (1001-3415)
Contact Dist.: China International Book Trading Corp/Zhongguo Guoji Tushu Maoyi Zonggongsi, 35 Chegongzhuang Xilu, Haidian District, PO Box 399, Beijing, 100044, China. TEL 86-10-68412045, FAX 86-10-68412023, cibtc@mail.cibtc.com.cn, http://www.cibtc.com.cn.

381 GBR ISSN 1360-1822
SHOPPING CENTRE AND RETAIL DIRECTORY. Text in English. 1994. a. GBP 189 per issue (effective 2003). **Document type:** *Directory.*
Related titles: Online - full content ed.
Published by: William Reed Directories (Subsidiary of: William Reed Publishing Ltd.), Broadfield Park, Brighton Rd, Pease Pottage, Crawley, W Sussex RH11 9RT, United Kingdom. TEL 44-1293-610488, FAX 44-1293-610322, directories@william-reed.co.uk, http://www.wrdirectories.co.uk/scd, http://www.william-reed.co.uk/directories/. Adv. contact Ms. Marianne Ripsher TEL 44-1293-610209.

381 CAN ISSN 0843-1507
SHOPPING CENTRE NEWS. Text in English. 1981. s-m. **Document type:** *Newsletter, Trade.* **Description:** Focuses on development plans for new centres and expansions, leasing opportunities, latest events and trends in Canada's shopping centre industry.
Formerly (until 1988): Shopping Centre News and Construction Update (0712-1245)
Related titles: Online - full text ed.: (from Micromedia ProQuest, ProQuest Information & Learning).
Published by: Rogers Media Publishing Ltd, One Mount Pleasant Rd, 11th Fl, Toronto, ON M4Y 2Y5, Canada. TEL 416-764-2000, FAX 416-764-3941, http://www.retailinfonet.com, http://www.rogers.com.

380 SLE ISSN 0037-4768
SIERRA LEONE TRADE JOURNAL. Text in English. 1961. q. adv. illus.; mkt.; pat.; stat. **Document type:** *Trade.*
Indexed: RASB.
Published by: (Sierra Leone. Government Information Services), Ministry of Information and Broadcasting, Lightfoot Boston St, Freetown, Sierra Leone.

381 GBR ISSN 0264-8814
SIGNS MAGAZINE. Text in English. 1981. 8/yr. GBP 48. adv. bk.rev. back issues avail.; reprints avail. **Document type:** *Trade.*
Indexed: Acal, SSI.
Published by: (British Sign Association), Angwin Associates, Lenton, Leengate, Nottingham, NG7 2LX, United Kingdom. FAX 44-1602-420407. Ed. Val Hirst. Adv. contact Dawn Seager. Circ: 4,306.

380 IND ISSN 0300-4546
SOCIETY AND COMMERCE; for balanced social change. Text in English. 1972. m. INR 20, USD 8. adv. bk.rev. bibl.; charts; illus.
Published by: Society & Commerce Publications (Pvt) Ltd., 2 Waterloo St., Kolkata, West Bengal 700 069, India. Ed. Parimal Mookerjea. Circ: 1,000.

381.1 709.2 USA ISSN 0267-6915
SOTHEBY'S INTERNATIONAL PREVIEW. Text in English. 1975. 7/yr. adv. **Description:** Provides coverage of the most exceptional artworks sold in Sotheby's auction rooms in locations around the world, such as London, New York, Hong Kong, Geneva and Amsterdam. It features a variety of historic sales from Europe, the US and Asia as well as articles by experts with unrivaled knowledge.
Former titles (until 1984): Sotheby's Preview (0144-8277); (until 1980): Sotheby's Preview Calendar of Sales (0308-3691)
Published by: Pohly & Partners Inc., 1334 York St, New York, NY 10021. TEL 212-606-7000, http://www.sothebys.com. adv.: color page USD 8,225; trim 9.0625 x 11.3125. Circ: 76,947 (controlled); 3,053 (paid).

381 GBR ISSN 1365-9693
SOUTH EAST BUSINESS. Text in English. 1982 (June). m. GBP 50 domestic; GBP 70 foreign (effective 2003). adv. tr.lit. back issues avail. **Document type:** *Trade.* **Description:** Contains news and intelligence for business in southeastern England.
Formerly (until 1990): Business South East (0262-8597)
Published by: Evegate Publishing Ltd., PO Box 53, Ashford, Kent TN23 1WE, United Kingdom. TEL 44-1233-656644, publish@southeastbusiness.net, http://www.southeastbusiness.net. Ed. Nick Mercer. Circ: 14,500.

SPACE R & D ALERT. see *AERONAUTICS AND SPACE FLIGHT*

381 ESP
SPAIN. DIRECCION GENERAL DE COMERCIO EXTERIOR. COLECCION CUADERNOS DE INFORMATION DEL SOIVRE. Text in Spanish. irreg., latest vol.13, 1994. price varies.
Published by: (Spain. Direccion General de Comercio Exterior), Ministerio de Comercio y Turismo, Paseo Castellana, 162, pl. 16, Madrid, 28046, Spain. TEL 34-1-349-36-47, FAX 34-1-349-36-34.

381 ESP
SPAIN. DIRECCION GENERAL DE COMERCIO INTERIOR. COLECCION ESTUDIOS. Text in Spanish. irreg., latest vol.54, 1994. price varies.
Published by: (Spain. Direccion General de Comercio Interior), Ministerio de Comercio y Turismo, Paseo Castellana, 162, pl. 16, Madrid, 28046, Spain. TEL 34-1-349-36-47, FAX 34-1-349-36-34.

381 USA ISSN 1535-4113
SUCCESSFUL TRADE SHOW STRATEGIES; profitable tips and ideas for the trade show exhibitor. Text in English. 2001 (Jul.). m.
Published by: Strategic Business Information, LLC, 3230 La Costa Circle Ste. 206, Naples, FL 34105. TEL 941-263-9777, FAX 941-263-9444. Pub. Ted Epstein.

SUDAN. DEPARTMENT OF STATISTICS. INTERNAL TRADE AND OTHER STATISTICS. see *BUSINESS AND ECONOMICS—Abstracting, Bibliographies, Statistics*

381 SDN
SUDANESE BUSINESS. Text in English. 1988. w. USD 80. adv. **Description:** Concerned with business in Sudan's private sector.
Address: P O Box 3219, Khartoum, Sudan. TELEX 22288 SMAGP. Circ: 2,000.

SURVEY OF AUSTRALIAN MANUFACTURING. see *BUSINESS AND ECONOMICS—Chamber Of Commerce Publications*

381 AUT
SURVEY OF THE AUSTRIAN ECONOMY/OESTERREICHS WIRTSCHAFT IM UEBERBLICK. Text in German. 1972. a. EUR 11 (effective 2005). adv. **Document type:** *Bulletin, Trade.*
Published by: Wirtschafts-Studio des Oesterreichen Gesellschafts und Wirtschaftsmuseums, Vogelsanggasse 36, Vienna, W 1050, Austria. TEL 43-1-5452551, FAX 43-1-545255155, wirtschaftsmuseum@oegwm.ac.at, http://www.wirtschaftsmuseum@oegwm.ac.at. Ed. Heinz Brunner. Adv. contact Andreas Herlinger. Circ: 20,000.

381 MDA
SVOBODNAYA ZONA/FREE ZONE. Text in Russian. w. **Document type:** *Newspaper, Consumer.* **Description:** Contains general news of Moldovian economics and information on work experience of free enterprise zones, collaboration between them.
Published by: Nezavisimaya Moldova, Ul Pushkin 22, Chisinau, 2012, Moldova. TEL 373-2-233605, FAX 373-2-233141, tis@nemo.moldova.su, http://www.mldnet.com/nezmold/index.html. Ed. Boris Belen'kii TEL 373-2-233324.

380 AUS ISSN 0011-1716
T T P I TRADE GAZETTE. Text in English. 1932. fortn. AUD 38. adv.
Published by: (Tasmanian Trade Protective Institute), Cromptons Collection Service, 84 Charles St, Launceston, TAS 7250, Australia. Ed. Stanley A Guy.

381 ESP ISSN 1130-8338
TESON. Text in Spanish. 1953. m.
Address: Alonso Quintanilla, 3 2o H, Oviedo, Asturias 33002, Spain. TEL 8-251-00-47, FAX 8-251-89-22. Ed. D Martin Ibanez.

381.029 THA ISSN 0857-7277
HG4244.655
THAILAND COMPANY INFORMATION (YEAR). Text and summaries in English, Thai. 1988. a. THB 2,500 domestic; USD 150 foreign (effective 1999); THB 2,500 newsstand/cover. adv. **Document type:** *Directory, Government.* **Description:** Provides collection of annual balance sheets and income statements of the top 1,600 companies in Thailand, classified by business type. Also lists over 2,000 newly registered companies with over one million baht registered capital.
Indexed: RASB.
Published by: (India. Ministry of Commerce IND), Advanced Research Group Co. Ltd., AR Bldg Klongsan, 27 Charoen Nakorn 14 Rd, Bangkok, 10600, Thailand. TEL 66-2-439-4600, FAX 66-2-439-4616, kid@ar.co.th, http://www.ar.co.th/tci. Ed., R&P Siriporn Promrat. Pub. Patchara Kiatnuntavimon. Adv. contact Vanida Siraklow. color page THB 50,000. Circ: 50,000. **Dist. by:** Current Pacific Ltd., PO Box 36-536, Northcote, Auckland, New Zealand. TEL 64-9-480-1388, FAX 64-9-480-1387, info@cplnz.com, http://www.cplnz.com.

381 GRL ISSN 1399-4859
HC110.5.A1
THIS IS GREENLAND. Text in English. 1999. a.
Published by: (Denmark. Udenrigsministeriet, Kommunikationsenhed/Royal Danish Ministry of Foreign Affairs, Department of Press and Information DNK), Greenland Resources AS, Tuapannguit 38, PO Box 821, Nuuk, 3900, Greenland. TEL 299-3-27913, FAX 299-3-27914, green.sources@greennet.gl, http://www.resources.gl.

381 VNM ISSN 0868-2712
THUONG MAI/COMMERCE. Text in Vietnamese. 1990. w. VND 104,000. **Description:** Provides information on state policies and guidelines in commerce and trade. Also covers business experiences of local and foreign companies.
Published by: Ministry of Commerce and Tourism, 100 Lo Duc St, Hanoi, Viet Nam. TEL 63150, FAX 84-204696, TELEX 411 525 BNT VY. Circ: 30,000.

551.46 USA
TIDINGS (CAMDEN). Text in English. 1965. q. looseleaf. membership. adv. **Document type:** *Newsletter.* **Description:** Covers activities of the association and industry news.
Former titles: News Waves; N M R A Newsletter
Related titles: Online - full text ed.
Published by: National Marine Representatives Association, PO Box 360, Gurnee, IL 60031-0360. TEL 901-584-0203, FAX 901-584-0420, nmra95@aol.com, http://www.nmra.com. Ed. David McCloskey. Circ: 400.

TOBACCO: LATIN AMERICAN INDUSTRIAL REPORT. see *TOBACCO*

TOLLEY'S V A T CASES (YEAR). (Value Added Tax) see *BUSINESS AND ECONOMICS—Public Finance, Taxation*

TOLLEY'S VALUE ADDED TAX. see *BUSINESS AND ECONOMICS—Public Finance, Taxation*

381 RUS ISSN 1606-1497
TORGOVAYA NEDELIA. Text in Russian. 1999. w. free (effective 2004). back issues avail. **Document type:** *Consumer.*
Media: Online - full text.
Published by: Al'yans Midiya, Bolotnaya ul 12, str 3, Moscow, 115035, Russian Federation. TEL 7-095-2345380, FAX 7-095-2345363, allmedia@allmedia.ru, http://www.businesspress.ru, http://allmedia.ru.

381 RUS ISSN 0869-5660
HF25
TORGOVLYA. Text in Russian. 1926. m. USD 60 (effective 1997). adv. bk.rev. bibl.; illus.; stat. index.
Formerly (until 1992): Sovetskaya Torgovlya (0371-1927)
Related titles: Microform ed.
Indexed: CDSP, RASB.
Published by: (Ministerstvo Torgovli i Material'nykh Resursov), Torgovlya, Berezhkovskaya nab 6, Moscow, 121864, Russian Federation. TEL 7-95-2404837. Ed. M M Lysov. Circ: 50,000.

TORGOVLYA V ROSSII (YEAR). see *BUSINESS AND ECONOMICS—Abstracting, Bibliographies, Statistics*

381 382 USA
TRADE ACTION MONITORING SYSTEM. Text in English. m. USD 225 in North America; USD 450 elsewhere (effective 1999). **Description:** Provides the facility to trace the various petitions on the 1974 Trade Act, such as Escape Clause (Section 201), antidumping, countervailing duties (Section 301), and unfair trading practices (Section 337). Illustrates the process and position of each case in the process of determining the final decision.
Published by: (Executive Office of the President, U.S. Trade Representative), U.S. Department of Commerce, National Technical Information Service, 5285 Port Royal Rd, Springfield, VA 22161. TEL 703-605-6000, info@ntis.gov, http://www.ntis.gov.

380 CAN ISSN 0049-4321
HC111
TRADE AND COMMERCE. Text in English. 1906. 5/yr. CND 30. adv. **Document type:** *Directory.*
Related titles: Microfiche ed.: (from MML); Microform ed.: (from MML).
Indexed: BPIA, CBCARef, CBPI, PAIS.
Published by: Sanford Evans Research Group A Subsidiary of Sun Media Corporation, 1700 Church Ave, P O Box 6900, Winnipeg, MB R3C 3B1, Canada. TEL 204-632-2606, FAX 204-632-4250. Pub. George Mitchell. Circ: 10,000.

380 CAN ISSN 1496-1938
TRADE AND INVESTMENT MONITOR. Text in English. 2000. s-a. back issues avail.
Related titles: Online - full text ed.: ISSN 1496-1946; French ed.: Moniteur du Commerce et de l'investissement. ISSN 1496-1970. 1999.
Published by: Industry Canada/Industrie Canada, Distribution Services, Communications & Marketing Branch, Rm 268D, West Tower, C.D. Howe Bldg, 235 Queen St, Ottawa, ON K1A 0H5, Canada. TEL 613-947-7466, FAX 613-954-6436, publications@ic.gc.ca, http://strategis.ic.gc.ca/epic/internet/ineas-aes.nsf/en/h_ra01873e.html, http://www.ic.gc.ca.

381 346.07 USA ISSN 1045-5191
KF1605.A2
TRADE CASES. Text in English. s-a.
—CCC.
Published by: C C H Inc., 2700 Lake Cook Rd, Riverwoods, IL 60015. TEL 847-267-7000, 800-248-3248, 800-449-6439, FAX 800-224-8299, cust_serv@cch.com, http://www.cch.com.

381 IND
TRADE COMMERCE & INDUSTRY WEEKLY BULLETIN. Text in English. 1951. w. membership. adv.
Published by: Indian Merchants' Chamber, Indian Merchants' Chamber Bldg., 76 Veer Nariman Rd., Churchgate, Mumbai, Maharashtra 400 020, India. Ed. Shri S I Padhya. Circ: 3,000.

380.1 USA
TRADE MONITOR. Text in English. q. **Description:** Aimed at state economic development directors and commissioners.
Published by: National Association of State Development Agencies, 750 First St, N E, Ste 710, Washington, DC 20002. TEL 202-898-1302.

381 USA ISSN 1064-9263
HF1731
TRADE POLICY AGENDA AND ANNUAL REPORT OF THE PRESIDENT OF THE UNITED STATES ON THE TRADE AGREEMENTS PROGRAM. Text in English. 1976. a.
Formerly (until 1989): Annual Report of the President of the United States on the Trade Agreements Program (0190-3098)
Published by: Office of the U. S. Trade Representative (Subsidiary of: Executive Office of the President), 600 17th St, N W, Washington, DC 20508. TEL 888-473-8787, contactustr@ustr.gov, http://www.ustr.gov.

381 USA
TRADE REGULATION REPORTER. Text in English. 7 base vols. plus w. updates. looseleaf. USD 2,735 base vol(s). (effective 2004). **Description:** Provides U.S. antitrust cases, texts, and pending U.S. consent decrees. Perhaps its most important feature is the full-text reporting of court decisions in both government and private antitrust litigation.
Formerly: Trade Regulation Reports (0572-9912)
Related titles: CD-ROM ed.: USD 2,785 (effective 2004); Online - full text ed.: USD 2,863 (effective 2003).
—CCC.
Published by: C C H Inc., 2700 Lake Cook Rd, Riverwoods, IL 60015. TEL 847-267-7000, 800-449-6439, cust_serv@cch.com, http://www.cch.com. Pub. Stacey Caywood.

380 NZL ISSN 1171-2961
TRANS TASMAN. Text in English. 1968. w. NZD 27 in New Zealand; AUD 240 in Australia; USD 240 elsewhere (effective 2000). **Document type:** *Newsletter.*
—BLDSC (884.659500).
Published by: Trans-Tasman News Service Ltd., PO Box 377, Wellington, New Zealand. FAX 64-4-4733691. Ed., Pub., R&P Ian Templeton. Circ: 1,000 (paid).

381 346 USA
TRANSNATIONAL JOINT VENTURES. Text in English. 1989. irreg. USD 400 (effective 2001).
Published by: Business Laws, Inc., 11630 Chillicothe Rd, Chesterland, OH 44026. TEL 440-729-7996, FAX 440-729-0645, http://www.businesslaws.com.

TRANSPORTATION: LATIN AMERICAN INDUSTRIAL REPORT. see *TRANSPORTATION*

THE TREASURER; the official journal of the Association of Corporate Treasurers. see *BUSINESS AND ECONOMICS—Banking And Finance*

381 DEU ISSN 0947-0301
TUEBINGER VOLKSWIRTSCHAFTLICHE STUDIEN. Text in German. 1991. irreg., latest vol.21, 2002. price varies. back issues avail. **Document type:** *Monographic series, Academic/Scholarly.* **Description:** Studies ethnic issues from a social, cultural, or philosophic perspective.
Published by: A. Francke Verlag GmbH, Postfach 2560, Tuebingen, 72015, Germany. TEL 49-7071-9797-0, FAX 49-7071-75288, http://www.francke.de. Ed. Adolf Wagner Alfred Ott.

381 USA ISSN 0083-0917
HD2775
U.S. FEDERAL TRADE COMMISSION. ANNUAL REPORT. Key Title: Annual Report of the Federal Trade Commission. Text in English. 1915. a. price varies. **Document type:** *Government.*
—CISTI.
Published by: U.S. Federal Trade Commission, Office of Public Affairs, Sixth St and Pennsylvania Ave, N W, Washington, DC 20580. TEL 202-655-4000. **Subscr. to:** U.S. Government Printing Office, Superintendent of Documents.

381 USA
U.S. FEDERAL TRADE COMMISSION. COURT DECISIONS PERTAINING TO THE FEDERAL TRADE COMMISSION. Text in English. a. price varies. **Document type:** *Government.*
Formerly: U.S. Federal Trade Commission. Statutes and Court Decisions Pertaining to the Federal Trade Commission. Supplements (0083-0933)
Published by: U.S. Federal Trade Commission, Public Reference Branch, Sixth St & Pennsylvania Ave, N W, Washington, DC 20580. TEL 202-655-4000. **Subscr. to:** U.S. Government Printing Office, Superintendent of Documents. TEL 202-783-3238, FAX 202-512-2233.

381 USA
U.S. FEDERAL TRADE COMMISSION. FEDERAL TRADE COMMISSION DECISIONS, FINDINGS, ORDERS AND STIPULATIONS. Text in English. 1915. a. price varies. reprints avail. **Document type:** *Government.*
Formerly: U.S. Federal Trade Commission. Federal Trade Commission Decisions (0891-7515)
Related titles: Microfilm ed.: (from BHP).
Published by: U.S. Federal Trade Commission, Public Reference Branch, Sixth St & Pennsylvania Ave, N W, Washington, DC 20580. TEL 202-655-4000. **Subscr. to:** U.S. Government Printing Office, Superintendent of Documents. TEL 202-783-3238, FAX 202-512-2233.

346.06 380 USA ISSN 0503-1966
K25
UNIFORM COMMERCIAL CODE LAW LETTER. Variant title: U C C Law Letter. Text in English. 1967. m. USD 183.75; USD 252.45 foreign. **Document type:** *Newsletter.* **Description:** Covers important state and federal case decisions and offers practical advice for conducting business under the Uniform Commercial Code.
Related titles: Microform ed.: (from PQC).
—CCC.
Published by: W G & L Financial Reporting & Management Research (Subsidiary of: R I A), One Penn Plaza, New York, NY 10119. TEL 212-367-6300, FAX 212-367-6718. Ed. Thomas Quinn. **Subscr. to:** The Park Square Bldg., 31 St James Ave, Boston, MA 02116-4112. TEL 800-950-1207.

381 AUS ISSN 1323-787X
UNIVERSITY OF NEW SOUTH WALES. HANDBOOK: COMMERCE AND ECONOMICS. Text in English. 1989. a. AUD 5. **Document type:** *Trade.*
Formerly (until 1993): University of New South Wales. Faculty Handbooks: Commerce and Economics (0811-7616)
Published by: University of New South Wales, Sydney, NSW 2052, Australia. TEL 61-9-2385-2840, FAX 61-9-2662-2163.

381 ZAF ISSN 0379-6191
HC905.A1
UNIVERSITY OF STELLENBOSCH. BUREAU FOR ECONOMIC RESEARCH. TRENDS. Key Title: Trends (Stellenbosch). Text in English. q. ZAR 760 (effective Jul. 2003). **Description:** Presents statistical data on changes and developments in the South African economy.
Related titles: Online - full text ed.
Published by: Universiteit Stellenbosch, Bureau for Economic Research/Stellenbosch University, University, Private Bag 5050, Stellenbosch, 7599, South Africa. TEL 27-21-8872810, FAX 27-21-8899225, hhman@maties.sun.ac.za, http://www.journals.co.za/ej/ejour_trends.html, http://www.sun.ac.za/. Ed. G M Pellissier. Circ: 550.

381 CAN ISSN 0083-517X
VANCOUVER BOARD OF TRADE. ANNUAL REPORT. Text in English. 1887. a. free. adv. **Document type:** *Corporate.*
Published by: Board of Trade, World Trade Centre, Ste 400, 999 Canada Pl, Vancouver, BC V6C 3E1, Canada. TEL 604-641-1270, FAX 604-681-0437. Ed. Davey Rezac. Adv. contact Michelle Brazeau. Circ: 5,000.

VEHICLE NEWS NEWSLETTER. see *TRANSPORTATION—Abstracting, Bibliographies, Statistics*

381 PRT
VENTO NORTE. Text in Portuguese. 12/yr.
Address: Pc. Marques Pombal 78, Porto, Portugal.

381 CHE
VERKAUF SCHWEIZ∗. Text in German. w. CHF 1.10 per issue. **Document type:** *Bulletin.*
Formerly: Merkur
Address: Roetihalde 8, Walchenwil, 8220, Switzerland. TEL 41-1-7806995. Eds. Christian Koepfer, Pascal Streit. Circ: 15,348.

381 FRA ISSN 1298-1133
LA VIE FINANCIERE. Text in French. 1945. w. EUR 66.50 domestic; EUR 123.50 in the European Union; EUR 143.50 in US & Canada; EUR 213.50 in Africa (effective 2005). adv.
Formerly (until 1999): La Vie Francaise (0220-5858)
Related titles: Online - full text ed.
Indexed: AmH&L, ELLIS, RASB.
Published by: Groupe Express-Expansion (Subsidiary of: Socpresse), 17 rue de l'Arrivee, Paris Cede, 75733, France. TEL 33-1-53911111, http://www.laviefinanciere.com, http://www.groupe-expansion.com. Circ: 85,000.

381 USA
VIRGINIA'S LOCAL ECONOMIES: ACCOMACK-NORTHAMPTON, P D NO. 22 (EASTERN SHORE AREA)∗. (Planning District) Text in English. a. USD 7.32.
Published by: University of Virginia, Center for Public Service, 918 Emmet St N Ste 300, Charlottesville, VA 22903-4832. TEL 804-924-3396.

381 USA
VIRGINIA'S LOCAL ECONOMIES: BRISTOL M S A∗. (Metropolitan Statistical Area) Text in English. a. USD 7.32.
Published by: University of Virginia, Center for Public Service, 918 Emmet St N Ste 300, Charlottesville, VA 22903-4832. TEL 804-924-3396.

381 975.5 USA
VIRGINIA'S LOCAL ECONOMIES: CENTRAL SHENANDOAH, P D NO. 6 (SHENANDOAH VALLEY AREA). (Planning District) Text in English. a. USD 12.
Published by: University of Virginia, Weldon Cooper Center for Public Service, 918 Emmet St N Ste 300, Charlottesville, VA 22903-4832. TEL 804-924-3396, knapp@virginia.edu, http://www.virginia.edu/cpserv/.

381 USA
VIRGINIA'S LOCAL ECONOMIES: CENTRAL VIRGINIA, P D NO. 11 (LYNCHBURG AREA)∗. (Planning District) Text in English. a. USD 7.32.
Published by: University of Virginia, Center for Public Service, 918 Emmet St N Ste 300, Charlottesville, VA 22903-4832. TEL 804-924-3396.

381 USA
VIRGINIA'S LOCAL ECONOMIES: CHARLOTTESVILLE M S A∗. (Metropolitan Statistical Area) Text in English. a. USD 7.32.
Published by: University of Virginia, Center for Public Service, 918 Emmet St N Ste 300, Charlottesville, VA 22903-4832. TEL 804-924-3396.

381 USA
VIRGINIA'S LOCAL ECONOMIES: CRATER, P D NO. 19 (PETERSBURG AREA)∗. (Planning District) Text in English. a. USD 7.32.
Published by: University of Virginia, Center for Public Service, 918 Emmet St N Ste 300, Charlottesville, VA 22903-4832. TEL 804-924-3396.

381 USA
VIRGINIA'S LOCAL ECONOMIES: CUMBERLAND PLATEAU, P D NO. 2 (TAZEWELL AREA)∗. (Planning District) Text in English. a. USD 7.32.
Published by: University of Virginia, Center for Public Service, 918 Emmet St N Ste 300, Charlottesville, VA 22903-4832. TEL 804-924-3396.

381 USA
VIRGINIA'S LOCAL ECONOMIES: DANVILLE M S A. (Metropolitan Statistical Area) Text in English. a. USD 12.
Published by: University of Virginia, Center for Public Service, 918 Emmet St N Ste 300, Charlottesville, VA 22903-4832. TEL 804-924-3396, FAX 804-982-5524, jec8y@virginia, http://www.virginia.edu/cpseru. Ed. John Knapp.

381 USA
VIRGINIA'S LOCAL ECONOMIES: FIFTH, P D NO. 5 (ROANOKE AREA)∗. (Planning District) Text in English. a. USD 7.32.
Published by: University of Virginia, Center for Public Service, 918 Emmet St N Ste 300, Charlottesville, VA 22903-4832. TEL 804-924-3396.

381 USA
VIRGINIA'S LOCAL ECONOMIES: LENOWISCO, P D NO. 1 (NORTON AREA)∗. (Planning District) Text in English. a. USD 7.32.
Published by: University of Virginia, Center for Public Service, 918 Emmet St N Ste 300, Charlottesville, VA 22903-4832. TEL 804-924-3396.

381 USA
VIRGINIA'S LOCAL ECONOMIES: LORD FAIRFAX, P D NO. 7 (WINCHESTER AREA). (Planning District) Text in English. a. USD 7.32.
Published by: University of Virginia, Center for Public Service, 918 Emmet St N Ste 300, Charlottesville, VA 22903-4832. TEL 804-924-3396.

381 USA
VIRGINIA'S LOCAL ECONOMIES: LYNCHBURG M S A∗. (Metropolitan Statistical Area) Text in English. a. USD 7.32.
Published by: University of Virginia, Center for Public Service, 918 Emmet St N Ste 300, Charlottesville, VA 22903-4832. TEL 804-924-3396.

381 USA
VIRGINIA'S LOCAL ECONOMIES: MIDDLE PENINSULA, P D NO. 18∗. (Planning District) Text in English. a. USD 7.32.
Published by: University of Virginia, Center for Public Service, 918 Emmet St N Ste 300, Charlottesville, VA 22903-4832. TEL 804-924-3396.

381 USA
VIRGINIA'S LOCAL ECONOMIES: MOUNT ROGERS, P D NO. 3 (BRISTOL - GALAX AREA). (Planning District) Text in English. a. USD 12 per issue.

B

▼ new title ➤ refereed ∗ unverified ♦ full entry avail.

B

Published by: University of Virginia, Weldon Cooper Center for Public Service, 918 Emmet St N Ste 300, Charlottesville, VA 22903-4832. TEL 804-982-5522, FAX 804-982-5524, knapp@virginia.edu, Http://www.virginiaedu//ctserv. Ed. John Knapp.

381   USA
VIRGINIA'S LOCAL ECONOMIES: NEW RIVER VALLEY, P D NO. 4 (BLACKSBURG - REDFORD AREA)∗ . (Planning District) Text in English. a. USD 7.32.
Published by: University of Virginia, Center for Public Service, 918 Emmet St N Ste 300, Charlottesville, VA 22903-4832. TEL 804-924-3396.

381   USA
VIRGINIA'S LOCAL ECONOMIES: NORFOLK - NEWPORT NEWS - VIRGINIA BEACH M S A∗ . (Metropolitan Statistical Area) Text in English. a. USD 7.32.
Published by: University of Virginia, Center for Public Service, 918 Emmet St N Ste 300, Charlottesville, VA 22903-4832. TEL 804-924-3396.

381   USA
VIRGINIA'S LOCAL ECONOMIES: NORTHERN NECK, P D NO. 17∗ . (Planning District) Text in English. a. USD 7.32.
Published by: University of Virginia, Center for Public Service, 918 Emmet St N Ste 300, Charlottesville, VA 22903-4832. TEL 804-924-3396.

381   USA
VIRGINIA'S LOCAL ECONOMIES: NORTHERN VIRGINIA M S A∗ . (Metropolitan Statistical Area) Text in English. a. USD 7.32.
Published by: University of Virginia, Center for Public Service, 918 Emmet St N Ste 300, Charlottesville, VA 22903-4832. TEL 804-924-3396.

381   USA
VIRGINIA'S LOCAL ECONOMIES: NORTHERN VIRGINIA, P D NO. 8∗ . (Planning District) Text in English. a. USD 7.32.
Published by: University of Virginia, Center for Public Service, 918 Emmet St N Ste 300, Charlottesville, VA 22903-4832. TEL 804-924-3396.

381   USA
VIRGINIA'S LOCAL ECONOMIES: PENINSULA, P D NO. 21 (NEWPORT NEWS - HAMPTON AREA)∗ . (Planning District) Text in English. a. USD 7.32.
Published by: University of Virginia, Center for Public Service, 918 Emmet St N Ste 300, Charlottesville, VA 22903-4832. TEL 804-924-3396.

381   USA
VIRGINIA'S LOCAL ECONOMIES: PIEDMONT, P D NO. 14 (FARMVILLE AREA)∗ . (Planning District) Text in English. a. USD 7.32.
Published by: University of Virginia, Center for Public Service, 918 Emmet St N Ste 300, Charlottesville, VA 22903-4832. TEL 804-924-3396.

381   USA
VIRGINIA'S LOCAL ECONOMIES: RADCO, P D NO. 16 (FREDERICKSBURG AREA)∗ . (Planning District) Text in English. a. USD 7.32.
Published by: University of Virginia, Center for Public Service, 918 Emmet St N Ste 300, Charlottesville, VA 22903-4832. TEL 804-924-3396.

381   USA
VIRGINIA'S LOCAL ECONOMIES: RAPPAHANNOCK - RAPIDAN, P D NO. 9 (CULPEPER AREA)∗ . (Planning District) Text in English. a. USD 7.32.
Published by: University of Virginia, Center for Public Service, 918 Emmet St N Ste 300, Charlottesville, VA 22903-4832. TEL 804-924-3396.

381   USA
VIRGINIA'S LOCAL ECONOMIES: RICHMOND - PETERSBURG M S A. (Metropolitan Statistical Area) Text in English. a. USD 12.
Published by: University of Virginia, Center for Public Service, 918 Emmet St N Ste 300, Charlottesville, VA 22903-4832. TEL 804-982-5522, FAX 804-982-5524, ccpsuva@virginia.edu, http://www.virginia edu/~cpseru. Ed. John Knapp.

381   USA
VIRGINIA'S LOCAL ECONOMIES: RICHMOND REGIONAL, P D NO. 15∗ . (Planning District) Text in English. a. USD 7.32.
Published by: University of Virginia, Center for Public Service, 918 Emmet St N Ste 300, Charlottesville, VA 22903-4832. TEL 804-924-3396.

381   USA
VIRGINIA'S LOCAL ECONOMIES: ROANOKE M S A∗ . (Metropolitan Statistical Area) Text in English. a. USD 7.32.
Published by: University of Virginia, Center for Public Service, 918 Emmet St N Ste 300, Charlottesville, VA 22903-4832. TEL 804-924-3396.

381   USA
VIRGINIA'S LOCAL ECONOMIES: SOUTHEASTERN VIRGINIA, P D NO. 20 (NORFOLK - VIRGINIA BEACH AREA)∗ . (Planning District) Text in English. a. USD 7.32.
Published by: University of Virginia, Center for Public Service, 918 Emmet St N Ste 300, Charlottesville, VA 22903-4832. TEL 804-924-3396.

381   USA
VIRGINIA'S LOCAL ECONOMIES: SOUTHSIDE, P D NO. 13 (SOUTH BOSTON AREA). (Planning District) Text in English. a. USD 12.
Published by: University of Virginia, Center for Public Service, 918 Emmet St N Ste 300, Charlottesville, VA 22903-4832. TEL 804-982-5522, FAX 804-982-5524, knapp@virginia.edu.

381   USA
VIRGINIA'S LOCAL ECONOMIES: THOMAS JEFFERSON, P D NO. 10 (CHARLOTTESVILLE AREA)∗ . (Planning District) Text in English. a. USD 7.32.
Published by: University of Virginia, Center for Public Service, 918 Emmet St N Ste 300, Charlottesville, VA 22903-4832. TEL 804-924-3396.

381   USA
VIRGINIA'S LOCAL ECONOMIES: WEST PIEDMONT, P D NO. 12 (DANVILLE AREA)∗ . (Planning District) Text in English. a. USD 7.32.
Published by: University of Virginia, Center for Public Service, 918 Emmet St N Ste 300, Charlottesville, VA 22903-4832. TEL 804-924-3396.

380 338   FRA   ISSN 1630-3792
LA VOLONTE DES P M E. (Petites et Moyennes Entreprises) Text in French. 1945. m. FRF 240. adv. bk.rev. back issues avail.
Former titles (until 2001): Volonte de l'Industrie, du Commerce et des Prestataires de Services (0753-0056); (until 1980): Volonte du Commerce, de l'Industrie et des Prestataires de Services (0151-8631); Volonte du Commerce et de l'Industrie (0042-8612)
Published by: (Confederation des Petites et Moyennes Enterprises), Societe d'Edition et de Publication des P.M.E., 30 rue des Jeuneurs, Paris, 75002, France. Ed. G Lazaro. Circ: 125,000.

380 338   IND
VYAVASAYA KERALAM. Text in English, Malayalam. 1962. m. INR 150 domestic (effective 2001). adv. charts; illus. 40 p./no.; **Document type:** Magazine.
Formerly: Kerala Commerce and Industry (0023-0499)
Indexed: RPP.
Published by: Department of Industries and Commerce, Vikas Bhavan, Trivandrum, Kerala 695 033, India. TEL 91-471-322789, FAX 91-471-305493, dictvm@sanchar.net.in, dictvm@md5.vsnl.net.in, http://www.keralaindustry.org. Eds. L Radhakrishnan, R Rengaraja Iyengar. Circ: 7,100 (paid).

381   JPN   ISSN 0387-3404
HF41
WASEDA SHOGAKU/WASEDA COMMERCIAL REVIEW. Text in Japanese. 1925. 4/yr. JPY 400. bk.rev. **Document type:** Academic/Scholarly.
Indexed: IBSS, RASB.
Published by: Waseda Shogaku Doukoukai, 1-6-1 Nishi-waseda, Shinjuku-ku, Tokyo, 169-8050, Japan. TEL 81-3-3203-4141. Ed. Muneharu Otsuka. Circ: 2,500.

381   GBR
WEST COUNTRY BUSINESS REVIEW. Text in English. 1987. m. GBP 30. adv. back issues avail. **Document type:** Newspaper.
Description: Contains a wide variety of local business news, ideas and information relevant to industry and commerce in Devonshire.
Formerly: Devon Business Review
Published by: Herald Express Publications Ltd., Harmsworth House, Barton Hill Rd, Torquay, Devon TQ2 8JN, United Kingdom. TEL 44-1803-676000, FAX 44-1803-676579. Ed. Julia Snow. Adv. contact Marc Overton. Circ: 10,000.

381   AUS
WESTERN AUSTRALIA. INDUSTRIAL GAZETTE. Text in English. m. AUD 261 in state; AUD 311 out of state; AUD 435 foreign (effective 2000). **Document type:** Government.
Description: Serves as a medium for news and notices of an industrial relations theme from the Industrial Commission of Western Australia.
Published by: State Law Publisher, Ground Fl, 10 William St, Perth, W.A. 6000, Australia. TEL 61-8-9321-7688, FAX 61-9-9321-7536. Circ: 188.

381   CHE
WIR KAUFLEUTE. Text in German. 11/yr.
Published by: Kaufmaennischer Verband Zuerich, Pelikanstr 18, Zuerich, 8023, Switzerland. TEL 01-2113322, FAX 01-2210913. Ed. Peter Volanthen. Circ: 18,000.

381   DEU
WIRTSCHAFT UND VERKEHR IM BAYERISCHEN DREILAENDERECK. Text in German. 1947. m. adv. bk.rev. stat.; tr.lit. back issues avail. **Document type:** Bulletin.

Published by: Industrie- und Handelskammer Lindau - Bodensee, Postfach 1365, Lindau, 88103, Germany. TEL 49-8382-93830, FAX 49-8382-938373, ihklindau@t-online.de, http://www.lindau.ihk.de. Circ: 4,000.

381   BGR   ISSN 0861-8445
WIRTSCHAFTSBLATT. Text in German. 1992. m. USD 188 foreign (effective 2002). **Document type:** Magazine, Trade.
Description: Contains information on business relations, promotions, and company presentations in Bulgaria.
Related titles: Online - full content ed.; Online - full text ed.: (from LexisNexis).
Published by: Verlags Business, Tsar Assen St. 31, Sofia, 1000, Bulgaria. TEL 359-2-9809505, FAX 359-2-9815331, wirtbl@online.bg, http://www.online.bg/wb/. **Dist. by:** Sofia Books, ul Silivria 16, Sofia 1404, Bulgaria. TEL 359-2-9586257, info@sofiabooks-bg.com, http://www.sofiabooks-bg.com.

381 338.642   USA   ISSN 1063-6595
WORCESTER BUSINESS JOURNAL. Text in English. 1990. fortn. USD 49.95 (effective 2005). adv. charts; illus.; stat. 32 p./no. 5 cols./p.; back issues avail. **Document type:** Newspaper. **Description:** Covers news and other issues of interest to owners and executives of small- and medium-sized businesses in central Massachusetts.
—CCC.
Published by: Worcester Publishing, Inc., 172 Shrewsbury St, Worcester, MA 01604. TEL 508-755-8004, FAX 508-755-8860, http://www.wbjournal.com/. Ed. Steven Jones-D'Agostino. Pub. Peter Stanton. Adv. contact Jeffrey Forts. Circ: 12,000.

ZEITSCHRIFT FUER WIRTSCHAFTSRECHT - Z I P. see LAW

381   CHN   ISSN 1002-9699
ZHONGGUO GONGSHANG BAO/CHINESE INDUSTRY & COMMERCE NEWS. Text in Chinese. m. CNY 54. 48 p./no.; **Document type:** Newspaper.
Related titles: Online - full text ed.: (from East View Information Services).
Published by: Zhonghua Quanguo Gongshangye Lianhehui/All-China Industry and Commerce Federation, No 93 Beiheyan Dajie, Beijing, 100006, China. TEL 86-10-5136677, FAX 86-10-5135286. **Dist. overseas by:** China International Book Trading Corp, 35 Chegongzhuang Xilu, Haidian District, PO Box 399, Beijing 100044, China. http://www.cibtc.com.cn.

381   CHN   ISSN 1006-5040
ZHONGGUO GUONEI MAOYI NIANJIAN/ALMANAC OF CHINA'S DOMESTIC TRADE. Text in Chinese. 1988. a. CNY 200 newsstand/cover (effective 2005). adv. **Document type:** Trade, Government.
Formerly (until 1994): Zhongguo Shangye Nianjian/Almanac of China's Commerce (1002-591X)
Related titles: Online - full text ed.: (from WanFang Data Corp.).
Published by: (Guonei Maoyi Ju), Zhongguo Guonei Maoyi Nianjian She/China's Domestic Trade Publishing House, 45 Fuxingmennei Dajie, Beijing, 100801, China. TEL 86-10-66018407, nianjianshe@163.net, http://zggnmynj.periodicals.net.cn/. Ed. Hai Huang. adv.: color page CNY 5,000.

381   CHN
ZHONGGUO MINBAN KEJI SHIYE/CHINESE PRIVATELY OWNED SCIENCE AND TECHNOLOGY ENTERPRISES. Text in Chinese. m.
Published by: Zhongguo Minban Keji Shiyejia Xiehui/Chinese Association of Private Science and Technology Entrepreneurs, Xibianmen Bldg. 10 Rm. 1307, Xuanwu-qu, Beijing, 100053, China. TEL 3010247. Ed. Bao Ke.

BUSINESS AND ECONOMICS—Economic Situation And Conditions

330.9   NLD   ISSN 0928-9933
HC321
A B N AMRO ECONOMIC REVIEW. Text in English. 1967. q. free. stat.
Incorporated (in 1991): Netherlands Economic Report (0922-0720); Former titles (until 1991): A B N Economic Review (0169-5363); (until 1983): Algemene Bank Netherlands. Economic Review (0928-9992); (until 1976): A B N Economic Review (0044-7269)
Indexed: PAIS.
Published by: A B N Amro Bank N.V., PO Box 283, Amsterdam, 1000 EA, Netherlands.

A C C R A RESEARCH IN REVIEW; promoting excellence in research for community & economic development. (Association for Applied Community Research) see BUSINESS AND ECONOMICS—Chamber Of Commerce Publications

A G A FINANCIAL QUARTERLY REVIEW. see ENERGY

330.9   UAE
A M E INFO MIDDLE EAST BUSINESS INFORMATION. Text in English. d.

Published by: A M E INFO F Z, L L C, Dubai Media City, Phase II, Building 4, Office 204, PO Box 502100, Dubai, United Arab Emirates. TEL 971-4-3902700, FAX 971-4-3908015, http://www.ameinfo.com/.

330.9 BRA
A N D I M A RETROSPECTIVA. Text in English, Portuguese. 1985. a. **Document type:** *Corporate.* **Description:** Records the developments of the market during the year. Includes statistics on assets, monetary indicators, price indices, the privatization program and government policies.
Published by: Associacao Nacional das Instituicoes do Mercado Aberto, Av Republica do Chile, 230 Andar 12, Centro, Rio De Janeiro, RJ 20031-170, Brazil. TEL 55-21-220-5412, FAX 55-21-220-7537.

330.9 GBR
A O N CITYSCOPE; a survey of economic & investment forecasts. Text in English. 1979. m. free. **Document type:** *Bulletin.*
Former titles (until 1996): Godwins Cityscope; (until 1990): Cityscope (0260-0293)
Published by: Godwins Ltd., Briarcliff House, Kingsmead, Farnborough, Hants GU14 7TE, United Kingdom. TEL 44-1252-544484, FAX 44-1252-522206. Ed. Mark Chandler. Circ: 200.

330.9 AUT
A P A - JOURNAL. ECONOMIST. Text in German. w. EUR 380 combined subscription for print & online eds. (effective 2003). **Document type:** *Journal, Trade.*
Related titles: Online - full text ed.
Published by: Austria Presse Agentur, Gunoldstr 14, Vienna, W 1190, Austria. TEL 43-1-360600, FAX 43-1-360603099, kundenservice@apa.at, http://www.apa.at.

330.9 AUT
A P A - JOURNAL. ECONOMIST - KONJUNKTUR. Text in German. w. EUR 380 combined subscription for print & online eds. (effective 2003). **Document type:** *Journal, Trade.*
Related titles: Online - full text ed.
Published by: Austria Presse Agentur, Gunoldstr 14, Vienna, W 1190, Austria. TEL 43-1-360600, FAX 43-1-360603099, kundenservice@apa.at, http://www.apa.at.

330.9 AUT
A P A - JOURNAL. EMERGING MARKETS - ASIEN. Text in German. w. EUR 380 combined subscription for print & online eds. (effective 2003). **Document type:** *Journal, Trade.*
Related titles: Online - full text ed.
Published by: Austria Presse Agentur, Gunoldstr 14, Vienna, W 1190, Austria. TEL 43-1-360600, FAX 43-1-360603099, kundenservice@apa.at, http://www.apa.at.

330.9 AUT
A P A - JOURNAL. EMERGING MARKETS - OSTEUROPA. Text in German. w. EUR 380 combined subscription for print & online eds. (effective 2003). **Document type:** *Journal, Trade.*
Related titles: Online - full text ed.
Published by: Austria Presse Agentur, Gunoldstr 14, Vienna, W 1190, Austria. TEL 43-1-360600, FAX 43-1-360603099, kundenservice@apa.at, http://www.apa.at.

330.9 AUT
A P A - JOURNAL. EUROPA. Text in German. w. EUR 380 combined subscription for print & online eds. (effective 2003). **Document type:** *Journal, Trade.*
Related titles: Online - full text ed.
Published by: Austria Presse Agentur, Gunoldstr 14, Vienna, W 1190, Austria. TEL 43-1-360600, FAX 43-1-360603099, kundenservice@apa.at, http://www.apa.at.

330.9 AUT
A P A - JOURNAL. FUEHRUNGSKRAEFTE-BUERO. Text in German. w. EUR 380 combined subscription for print & online eds. (effective 2003). **Document type:** *Journal, Trade.*
Related titles: Online - full text ed.
Published by: Austria Presse Agentur, Gunoldstr 14, Vienna, W 1190, Austria. TEL 43-1-360600, FAX 43-1-360603099, kundenservice@apa.at, http://www.apa.at.

330.9 AUT
A P A - JOURNAL. TERMINVORSCHAU. Text in German. w. EUR 380 combined subscription for print & online eds. (effective 2003). **Document type:** *Journal, Trade.*
Related titles: Online - full text ed.
Published by: Austria Presse Agentur, Gunoldstr 14, Vienna, W 1190, Austria. TEL 43-1-360600, FAX 43-1-360603099, kundenservice@apa.at, http://www.apa.at.

330 BRA ISSN 0001-2181
HC186
A P E C. (Analise e Perspectiva Economica) Text in English, Portuguese. 1962. fortn. USD 200. bk.rev. charts; stat. **Document type:** *Academic/Scholarly.*
Published by: Associacao Promotora de Estudos de Economia, Av Rio Branco, 156, n-1833, Rio De Janeiro, RJ 20040-003, Brazil. FAX 55-21-2623901. Ed. Ernane Galveas. Circ: 2,000.

338.9 HKG ISSN 0251-2521
A S E A N BRIEFING. Text in Chinese. 1978. m. USD 125. back issues avail. **Document type:** *Newsletter.*
Indexed: RASB.
Published by: (Association of Southeast Asian Nations IND), Asia Letter Group, GPO Box 10874, Hong Kong, Hong Kong. TEL 852-526-2950, FAX 852-526-7131. Ed. Charles R Smith.

330.9 MDA
ACADEMIA DE STIINTE A REPUBLICII MOLDOVA. BULETINUL. ECONOMIE SI SOCIOLOGIE/AKADEMIYA NAUK RESPUBLIKI MOLDOVA. IZVESTIYA. EKONOMIKA I SOTSIOLOGIYA. Text in Romanian, Russian. 1951. 3/yr. USD 44 (effective 1998). bk.rev. **Document type:** *Bulletin, Academic/Scholarly.* **Description:** Devoted to the economic and social problems related to the transition to a free market economy.
Formerly: Academia de Stiinte a R.S.S. Moldova. Buletinul. Economie se Sociologie (0236-3070); Supersedes in part (in 1990): Akademiya Nauk Moldavskoi S.S.R. Izvestiya. Seriya Obshchestvennykh Nauk (0321-1681)
Indexed: RASB.
Published by: Academia de Stiinte a Moldovej, Biblioteca Stiintifica Centrala, Bd Stefan cel Mare 1, Chisinau, 2001, Moldova. http://www.asm.md/altstruc/library. Circ: 750. **Dist. by:** M K - Periodica, ul Gilyarovskogo 39, Moscow 129110, Russian Federation. TEL 7-095-2845008, FAX 7-095-2813798, info@periodicals.ru, http://www.mkniga.ru.

330 ESP ISSN 0001-7655
HC381.A1
ACTUALIDAD ECONOMICA. Text in Spanish. 1957. w. EUR 102.32 domestic; EUR 247.59 in Europe; EUR 336.18 elsewhere (effective 2002). adv. bibl.; charts; illus.; mkt.; pat.; stat. **Document type:** *Trade.*
Related titles: CD-ROM ed.: (from Chadwyck-Healey Inc.); Online - full text ed.: (from Factiva).
Indexed: ELLIS, PAIS, RASB.
—BLDSC (0677.030000), IE, Infotrieve, ingenta.
Published by: Recoletos Compania Editorial S.A (Subsidiary of: Pearson Publishing Group), Paseo Recoletos, 1 5o, Madrid, 28001, Spain. TEL 34-91-3373220, FAX 34-91-3373266, expansion@recoletos.es, http://www.actualidad-economica.com, http://www.recoletos.es. Circ: 22,697.

330.9 ITA
ADRIATICO. Text in Italian. 2001. q. EUR 26 (effective 2003). **Description:** This journal covers the the economy and cultures of the regions on the Adriatic Sea.
Published by: Rubbettino Editore, Viale Rosario Rubbettino 10, Soveria Mannelli, CZ 88049, Italy. TEL 39-0968-662034, FAX 39-0968-662055, segreteria@rubettino.it, http://www.rubbettino.it. Ed. Rosario Pavia.

ADVANCES IN BEHAVIORAL ECONOMICS. see *PSYCHOLOGY*

330.9 USA ISSN 0731-9053
HB139
ADVANCES IN ECONOMETRICS. Text in English. 1982. irreg., latest vol.19, 2005. price varies. back issues avail. **Document type:** *Monographic series, Academic/Scholarly.* **Description:** Serves as a research tool for economists and business analysts desiring to incorporate the latest developments in econometric methodology in their work.
Related titles: Online - full text ed.: (from ScienceDirect); Supplement(s): ISSN 1045-0661.
Indexed: SSCI.
—BLDSC (0704.542000), IE, ingenta. **CCC.**
Published by: J A I Press Inc. (Subsidiary of: Elsevier Science & Technology), 360 Park Ave S, New York, NY 10010-1710. TEL 212-989-5800, FAX 212-633-3990, usinfo-f@elsevier.com, http://www.elsevier.com/wps/find/bookdescription.cws_home/BS_AE/description#description. Eds. R Carter Hill, T Fomby.

330.9 USA ISSN 1048-4736
HB615
ADVANCES IN THE STUDY OF ENTREPRENEURSHIP, INNOVATION, AND ECONOMIC GROWTH. Text in English. 1986. irreg., latest vol.16, 2005. price varies. back issues avail. **Document type:** *Monographic series, Academic/Scholarly.* **Description:** Aims to present the latest research on entrepreneurship and innovation and the impact on economic performance.
Related titles: Online - full text ed.: (from ScienceDirect); Supplement(s): Advances in the Study of Entrepreneurship, Innovation, and Economic Growth. Supplement. ISSN 1046-896X. 1988.
—BLDSC (0711.593200). **CCC.**
Published by: J A I Press Inc. (Subsidiary of: Elsevier Science & Technology), 360 Park Ave S, New York, NY 10010-1710. TEL 212-989-5800, FAX 212-633-3990, usinfo-f@elsevier.com, http://www.elsevier.com/wps/find/bookdescription.cws_home/BS_SEIEG/description#description. Ed. Gary Libecap.

ADVERTISING EXPENDITURE FORECASTS. see *ADVERTISING AND PUBLIC RELATIONS*

ADVISOR (NEW YORK). see *BUSINESS AND ECONOMICS—Marketing And Purchasing*

330.9 GBR ISSN 0950-902X
HG46
AFRICA ANALYSIS; fortnightly bulletin on financial and political trends. Text in English. 1986. fortn. GBP 300 to corporations; GBP 210 to academics (effective 2005). adv. bk.rev. illus. reprints avail. **Document type:** *Bulletin.* **Description:** Explains financial and political trends of African nations, including trade and finance, contracts, currencies, exchange controls, and country-by-country statistics.
Incorporates: Southern Africa Business Intelligence (0967-5019)
Related titles: Online - full text ed.: (from Florida Center for Library Automation, ProQuest Information & Learning, SoftLine Information).
Indexed: ENW, IIBP.
Published by: Africa Analysis Ltd., Diamond House, Ste 2F, 36-38 Hatton Garden, London, EC1N 8EB, United Kingdom. TEL 44-20-74044321, FAX 44-20-74044351, aa@africaanalysis.com, http://www.africaanalysis.com. Ed. Ahmed Rajab. Pub. Richard Hall. Circ: 1,000.

330 GBR ISSN 0144-8234
HC800.A1
AFRICA ECONOMIC DIGEST✶ ; weekly business news, analysis and forecast. Text in English. 1980. w. GBP 225, USD 400. adv. bk.rev. illus. Index. reprints avail. **Description:** News articles and analysis of economic trends in the 50 member countries of the Organization of African Unity, and their relationship to domestic and international foreign and military policy, with market reports and lists of business opportunities by country.
Related titles: Online - full text ed.
Indexed: IIBP, KES, RASB.
—IE.
Published by: Concord Press of Nigeria, 26-32 Whistler St, London, N5 1NJ, United Kingdom. TELEX 262505, jon.ansah@which.net. Ed. Eddie Momoh. Circ: 240.

AFRICA INSIGHT. see *HISTORY—History Of Africa*

AFRICA INSTITUTE. OCCASIONAL PUBLICATIONS. see *HISTORY—History Of Africa*

AFRICA INSTITUTE. RESEARCH PAPER. see *HISTORY—History Of Africa*

330.961 GBR ISSN 1472-1791
HC805.A1
AFRICA MONITOR. NORTH AFRICA. Text in English. 1996. m. GBP 325, USD 540, EUR 490 (effective 2003). **Document type:** *Journal, Trade.* **Description:** Covers political risk, the business environment, and economic prospects in Morocco, Algeria, Tunisia, and Libya.
Formerly (until 2000): North Africa Monitor (1362-4415)
Related titles: Online - full text ed.: (from EBSCO Publishing).
—**CCC.**
Published by: Business Monitor International Ltd., Mermaid House, 2 Puddle Dock, Blackfriars, London, EC4V 3DS, United Kingdom. TEL 44-20-72480468, FAX 44-20-72480467, subs@businessmonitor.com, https://www.businessmonitor.com/bmi/africamonitor_order.html, http://www.businessmonitor.com.

330.968 GBR ISSN 1472-1805
HC900.A1
AFRICA MONITOR. SOUTHERN AFRICA. Text in English. 1996. m. GBP 325, USD 540, EUR 490 (effective 2003). **Document type:** *Journal, Trade.* **Description:** Covers political risk, the business environment, and economic prospects in South Africa, Zimbabwe, Zambia, Namibia, Angola, Botswana, Malawi, and Mozambique.
Formerly (until 2000): Southern Africa Monitor (1362-4423)
Related titles: Online - full text ed.: (from EBSCO Publishing).
—CISTI. **CCC.**
Published by: Business Monitor International Ltd., Mermaid House, 2 Puddle Dock, Blackfriars, London, EC4V 3DS, United Kingdom. TEL 44-20-72480468, FAX 44-20-72480467, marketing@businessmonitor.com, https://www.businessmonitor.com/bmi/africamonitor_order.html, http://www.businessmonitor.com.

330.966005 GBR ISSN 1472-2038
HC1000.A1
AFRICA MONITOR. WEST & CENTRAL AFRICA. Text in English. 2000. m. GBP 325, USD 540, EUR 490 (effective 2003). **Document type:** *Journal, Trade.*
Related titles: Online - full text ed.: (from EBSCO Publishing).
—**CCC.**
Published by: Business Monitor International Ltd., Mermaid House, 2 Puddle Dock, Blackfriars, London, EC4V 3DS, United Kingdom. TEL 44-20-72480468, FAX 44-20-72480467, marketing@businessmonitor.com, https://www.businessmonitor.com/bmi/africamonitor_order.html, http://www.businessmonitor.com.

330.9 USA
HC800.A1
➤ **AFRICA RENEWAL.** Text in English. 1985. q. USD 20 to individuals; USD 35 to institutions (effective 2004). back issues avail. **Document type:** *Journal.* **Description:** Provides news and analysis on the economic and development challenges facing the African continent.

B

▼ new title ➤ refereed ✶ unverified ♦ full entry avail.

Former titles (until vol.18,no.3, 2004): Africa Recovery (1014-0255); (until 1987): Africa Emergency Report (1014-0271)
Related titles: Online - full text ed.; Supplement(s): Africa Recovery. Briefing Paper. ISSN 1564-491X; Afrique Relance. Document d'Information. ISSN 1564-4928.
Indexed: M&GPA.
Published by: United Nations, Department of Public Information. Strategic Communications Division, United Nations Bldg, Rm S-931, New York, NY 10017. TEL 212-963-6857, FAX 212-963-4556, africa-recovery@un.org, http://www.un.org/ecosocdev/geninfo/afrec/. Ed. Julie I Thompsen.

960 GBR ISSN 0001-9852
AFRICA RESEARCH BULLETIN. ECONOMIC, FINANCIAL AND TECHNICAL SERIES. Text in English. 1964. m. GBP 677 combined subscription in Europe to institutions print & online eds.; GBP 440 combined subscription in Africa to institutions print & online eds.; USD 1,285 combined subscription in the Americas to institutions & Caribbean (print & online eds.); GBP 765 combined subscription elsewhere to institutions print & online eds.; GBP 207, EUR 311 combined subscription in Europe to students print & online eds.; GBP 134 combined subscription in Africa to students print & online eds.; USD 391 combined subscription in the Americas to students print & online eds.; GBP 233 combined subscription elsewhere to students print & online eds. (effective 2006). adv. maps; stat.; illus. index. back issues avail.; reprints avail. **Document type:** *Journal, Academic/Scholarly.* **Description:** Provides impartial summaries and extensive reports on political and economic developments throughout Africa.
Related titles: Online - full text ed.: ISSN 1467-6346. GBP 643 in Europe to institutions; GBP 418 in Africa to institutions; USD 1,221 in the Americas to institutions & Caribbean; GBP 727 elsewhere to institutions (effective 2006) (from Blackwell Synergy, EBSCO Publishing, Gale Group, IngentaConnect, O C L C Online Computer Library Center, Inc., Swets Information Services).
Indexed: RASB.
—IE, Infotrieve. **CCC.**
Published by: Blackwell Publishing Ltd., 9600 Garsington Rd, Oxford, OX4 2ZG, United Kingdom. TEL 44-1865-776868, FAX 44-1865-714591, customerservices@oxon.blackwellpublishing.com, http://www.blackwellpublishing.com/journals/ARBE. Ed. Pita Adams.

320 GBR ISSN 0269-3844
HC501
AFRICA REVIEW. Text in English. 1977. a. GBP 50, USD 75 per issue (effective 2005). adv. illus.; stat.; maps. back issues avail. **Document type:** *Journal, Trade.* **Description:** Analytical, interpretative overview of events, trends & developments in every African country. For academic, business & governmental audience.
Formerly (until 1985): Africa Guide (0308-678X)
Related titles: CD-ROM ed.; Online - full text ed.
—BLDSC (0732.186500), IE.
Published by: World of Information, 2 Market St, Saffron Walden, Essex CB10 1HZ, United Kingdom. TEL 44-1799-521150, FAX 44-1799-524805, info@worldinformation.com, http://worldofinformation.safeshopper.com/4/cat4.htm?547, http://www.worldinformation.com. Ed., Pub., R&P Anthony Axon. adv.: B&W page GBP 2,950, color page GBP 2,950; trim 210 x 217. Circ: 7,000 (paid). **Orders in USA:** PO Box 830840, Birmingham, AL 35283-0430. TEL 800-633-4931, FAX 205-995-1588, heather@exchange.ebsco.com.

AFRICA SOUTH OF THE SAHARA (YEAR). see *POLITICAL SCIENCE*

330.9 338.91 CIV
AFRICAN DEVELOPMENT BANK. ECONOMIC RESEARCH PAPERS. Text in French. irreg. **Document type:** *Academic/Scholarly.*
Published by: African Development Bank, 01 BP 1387, Abidjan, Ivory Coast. TEL 225-20-44-44, FAX 225-20-49-48, TELEX 225-23717.

330.9 338.91 USA ISSN 1020-2927
HC800.A1
AFRICAN DEVELOPMENT INDICATORS. Text in English. 1989. a.
Formerly (until 1992): African Economic and Financial Data (1020-2919)
Published by: International Bank for Reconstruction and Development, 1818 H St N W, Washington, DC 20433. TEL 202-473-1000, FAX 202-477-6391, http://www.worldbank.org.

330.9 KEN
AFRICAN ECONOMIC DEVELOPMENT NEWS. Text in English, French. 1984. m.
Address: PO Box 46854, Nairobi, Kenya. TEL 254-2-331402. Ed. Kul Bhushan.

AFRIKA JAHRBUCH. see *POLITICAL SCIENCE*

AFRIKA SPECTRUM; Zeitschrift fuer gegenwartsbezogene Afrikaforschung. see *POLITICAL SCIENCE*

330 TUN
AFRIQUE ECONOMIE. Text in French. 1960. m. USD 50 (effective 2000). bk.rev. charts; illus.; stat. **Description:** Financial, political and economic news covering the Middle East and Africa, including new economic activity.
Formerly: Information Economique Africaine (0020-0050)
Indexed: KES, PAIS, RASB.
Published by: Societe I E A, 16 rue de Rome, Tunis, 1015, Tunisia. TEL 216-1-347441, FAX 216-1-353172, iea@planet.tn. Ed. Mohamed Zerzeri. Circ: 40,000.

AGRICULTURAL REVIEW FOR EUROPE. see *AGRICULTURE—Agricultural Economics*

AGRICULTURAL TRADE IN EUROPE. see *AGRICULTURE—Agricultural Economics*

AGRIFACK. see *AGRICULTURE*

AIRLINE ECONOMIC RESULTS AND PROSPECTS. see *TRANSPORTATION—Air Transport*

330.9 DEU ISSN 1611-8006
DER AKTIENSAMMLER. Text in English, German. 1980. bi-m. EUR 36 domestic; EUR 42 foreign (effective 2005). adv. **Document type:** *Magazine, Consumer.*
Former titles (until 2001): H P - Magazin fuer Historische Wertpapiere (1660-4989); (until 1993): H P - Magazin fuer Historische Wertpapiere und Gueltige Nebenwerte (1660-4970); (until 1990): H P - Magazin fuer Historische Papiere (1023-6414); (until 1984): H P (1423-2944)
Published by: Aktiensammler GmbH, Wacholderweg 38, Bremerhaven, 27578, Germany. TEL 49-471-9690431, FAX 49-471-9690431, info@deraktiensammler.de, http://www.deraktiensammler.de. Ed. Juergen Baral. adv.: B&W page EUR 450; trim 205 x 287. Circ: 800 (paid and controlled).

AKTUELL EKONOMI. see *BUSINESS AND ECONOMICS—Macroeconomics*

330.9 USA
ALABAMA ECONOMIC OUTLOOK. Text in English. 1980. a. USD 18 (effective 2000). **Description:** Examines current economic conditions and trends and their likely effects on the national and Alabama economies in the coming year.
Related titles: Microfiche ed.: (from CIS).
Indexed: SRI.
Published by: Center for Business and Economic Research, University of Alabama, Box 870221, Tuscaloosa, AL 35487-0221. TEL 205-348-6191, FAX 205-348-2951, dhamilto@cba.ua.edu, http://www.cber.ua.edu/~cber. Ed. Deborah Hamilton.

650 USA ISSN 0002-4392
ALAM ATTIJARAT; the business magazine of the Arab world. Text in Arabic. 1966. 12/yr. USD 60. adv. illus.
Published by: Keller International Publishing Corp., 150 Great Neck Rd, Great Neck, NY 11021. TEL 516-829-9210, FAX 516-824-5414, http://www.kellerpubs.com. Ed. Nadim Makdisi. Circ: 25,000.

338.9 USA ISSN 1072-8139
ALASKA ECONOMIC REPORT. Text in English. 1974. fortn. USD 275 (effective 2000). **Document type:** *Newsletter.*
Published by: Information & Research Service, 3037 South Circle, Anchorage, AK 99507. TEL 907-349-7711, FAX 907-522-1761. Ed., R&P Tim Bradner. Pub. Mike Bradner. Circ: 550.

330 USA ISSN 0160-3345
HD8053.A4
ALASKA ECONOMIC TRENDS. Text in English. 1965. m. free. charts; stat. back issues avail. **Document type:** *Government.* **Description:** Addresses the current economic and demographic conditions of Alaska including regional economic analysis, labor force data by region, nonagricultural wage and salary employment, and average hours and earnings in selected industries.
Former titles: Alaska Employment Trends; Trends in Alaska's Employment and Economy
Related titles: Microfiche ed.: (from CIS); Online - full text ed.
Indexed: PAIS, SRI.
Published by: Department of Labor, PO Box 21149, Juneau, AK 99802-1149. TEL 907-465-6018, FAX 907-465-1888, joanne_erskine@labor.state.ak.us, http://www.labor.state.ak.us/trends/trends.htm. Ed. Joanne Erskine. Circ: 4,000.

330.9 USA ISSN 0162-5403
HC107.A45
ALASKA REVIEW OF SOCIAL AND ECONOMIC CONDITIONS. Text in English. 1964. irreg. free. charts; illus. index. **Document type:** *Government.*
Former titles (until Dec. 1977): Alaska Review of Business and Economic Conditions (0034-6462); Review of Business and Economic Conditions in Alaska
Related titles: Microfiche ed.: (from CIS).
Indexed: PAIS, RASB, RRTA, SRI, WAE&RSA.
—CISTI.
Published by: University of Alaska, Institute of Social and Economic Research, 3211 Providence Dr, Anchorage, AK 99508-4614. TEL 907-786-7710, FAX 907-786-7739. Ed. Linda Leask. Circ: 3,000.

330.94965 ALB
ALBANIAN DAILY NEWS. Text in English. 1991. d. **Document type:** *Newspaper, Consumer.* **Description:** Keeps one informed about Albania in economic, political, financial, social and culture fields.
Formerly (until 1994): Tribuna Ekonomike Shqiptare (1021-9099)
Related titles: Online - full text ed.
Published by: Independent Albanian Economic Tribune Ltd., Str Qemal Stafa, Pall 195 Shk1 Ap 8, Tirana, Albania. TEL 355-42-235-02, http://www.albaniannews.com/.

330.9 USA ISSN 1046-5480
ALL ABOUT BUSINESS IN HAWAII. Text in English. 1972. a. USD 19.95. adv. **Description:** Covers life in Hawaii - its economy, people, government, market, real estate, education, taxes, labor force, agriculture, and commerce.
Published by: Crossroads Press, Inc., PO Box 833, Honolulu, HI 96808. TEL 808-521-0021, FAX 808-526-3273. Ed. Michelle Yamaguchi. Circ: 22,000.

330.9 ARG
AMERICA FINANCIERA. Text in Spanish. 1992. q.?.
Published by: Centro de Estudios de America Latina, Of. 18, Sarmiento, 944 Piso 8, Capital Federal, Buenos Aires 1041, Argentina.

330.9 ECU ISSN 1390-1230
F1401
AMERICA LATINA EN MOVIMIENTO. Text in Spanish. 1977. 20/yr., latest vol.25. USD 30 in Latin America to individuals; USD 60 rest of world to individuals; USD 55 in Latin America to institutions; USD 100 rest of world to institutions (effective 2001). index. back issues avail. **Document type:** *Newsletter.*
Former titles (until Feb. 1999): A L A I Servicio Informativo (1390-0544); (until Feb. 1992): A L A I Servicio Mensual de Informacion y Documentacion (0827-5564); (until Aug. 1984): Agencia Latino-Americana de Informacion. Servicio Informativo (0821-5014)
Indexed: RASB.
Published by: Agencia Latino-Americana de Informacion, Oficina Regional Andina, Casilla 17-12-877, 12 de Octubre N18-24, Quito, Ecuador. TEL 593-2-505074, 593-2-528716, FAX 593-2-505073, info@alai.ecuanex.net.ec, http://www.alainet.org. Circ: 2,000.

AMERICA LATINA - INTERNACIONAL. see *POLITICAL SCIENCE*

330.9 336 USA
AMERICA REPORT. Text in English. 1994. a. USD 5.95. back issues avail. **Document type:** *Consumer.* **Description:** Aims to educate tax payers. Shows how the tax dollars citizens "invest" each year are being spent and what government is accomplishing with these tax dollars.
Published by: Blue Heron Press, S Starlight Farm, Phoenix, MD 21131. TEL 410-472-4573, FAX 410-771-4213. Ed. Lyle A Brecht.

330.9 USA ISSN 0363-566X
AMERICAN BUSINESS* . Text in English. 1976. q. USD 25. adv. bk.rev. back issues avail.
Indexed: PMR, RASB.
Published by: Avant-Garde Media, Inc., 80 Central Park West, Ste 168, New York, NY 10023-5200. Ed., Pub. Ralph Ginzburg. Circ: 275,000.

330.9 USA ISSN 0065-812X
AMERICAN ECONOMIC ASSOCIATION. PAPERS AND PROCEEDINGS OF THE ANNUAL MEETING. Text in English. 1886. a. USD 270 domestic; USD 300 foreign; USD 15 newsstand/cover (effective 2005). **Document type:** *Academic/Scholarly.*
Related titles: ◆ Supplement to: The American Economic Review (Print Edition). ISSN 0002-8282.
—**CCC.**
Published by: American Economic Association, 2014 Broadway, Ste 305, Nashville, TN 37203. TEL 615-322-2595, FAX 615-343-7590, http://www.vanderbilt.edu/AEA/paprsg.htm.

330.9 USA
AMERICAN ECONOMIC DEVELOPMENT COUNCIL. COUNCIL NEWS. Text in English. 6/yr. membership only. back issues avail. **Document type:** *Newsletter.*
Published by: American Economic Development Council, 734 15th St NW., Ste 900, Washington, DC 20005-1013. TEL 202-223-7800, FAX 202-223-4745, aedc@interaccess.com, aedc@aedc.com, http://www.aedc.org/hqtrs, http://www.iedconline.org. Ed., R&P Marion Morgan. Circ: 2,700 (controlled).

330.9 USA
THE AMERICAN ECONOMIC REVIEW (ONLINE EDITION). Text in English. 1999. q. USD 240 (effective 2005).

Media: Online - full text (from EBSCO Publishing, Gale Group, IngentaConnect, JSTOR (Web-based Journal Archive), O C L C Online Computer Library Center, Inc., ProQuest Information & Learning). **Related titles:** Microform ed.: (from MIM, PMC, PQC); ♦ Print ed.: The American Economic Review (Print Edition). ISSN 0002-8282.
Published by: American Economic Association, 2014 Broadway, Ste 305, Nashville, TN 37203. TEL 615-322-2595, FAX 615-343-7590, http://www.e-aer.org/, http://www.vanderbilt.edu/AEA/.

330.9 USA ISSN 0002-8282
HB1
➤ **THE AMERICAN ECONOMIC REVIEW (PRINT EDITION).** Text in English. 1911. 5/yr. USD 270 domestic to institutions; USD 330 foreign to institutions (effective 2005); includes Journal of Economic Literature and Journal of Economic Perspectives. adv. charts; illus.; stat. index. reprint service avail. from PQC. **Document type:** *Journal, Academic/Scholarly.* **Description:** Contains articles and short papers on economic subjects.
Formed by the 1911 merger of: American Economic Association Quarterly (1532-5059); Economic Bulletin
Related titles: Microform ed.: (from MIM, PMC, PQC); ♦ Online - full text ed.: The American Economic Review (Online Edition); ♦ Supplement(s): American Economic Association. Papers and Proceedings of the Annual Meeting. ISSN 0065-812X.
Indexed: ABIn, ABS&EES, ASCA, ATI, Acal, AgeL, Agr, AmH&L, ArtHuCI, BAS, BLI, BPI, BPIA, BRD, BRI, BibAg, BusI, CBRI, CIS, CPM, CREJ, CurCont, DIP, ESPM, Emerald, EnvAb, ExcerpMed, FamI, HistAb, IBR, IBSS, IBZ, ILD, IPARL, IPSA, JEL, KES, LRI, M&MA, MEA&I, MEDLINE, MagInd, MaizeAb, ORMS, PAA&I, PAIS, PCI, PopulInd, QC&AS, RASB, RI-1, RI-2, RRTA, RiskAb, SCIMP, SRRA, SSCI, SSI, SWA, T&II, WAE&RSA, WBA.
—BLDSC (0813.500000), CISTI, IDS, IE, Infotrieve, ingenta, Linda Hall. **CCC.**
Published by: American Economic Association, 2014 Broadway, Ste 305, Nashville, TN 37203. aeainfo@ctrvax.vanderbilt.edu, http://www.vanderbilt.edu/AEA/. Ed. Ben S Bernanke. R&P Edda B Leithner. Circ: 27,000.

330.9 USA ISSN 0569-4345
➤ **AMERICAN ECONOMIST.** Text in English. 1956. s-a. USD 20 domestic to individuals; USD 45 foreign to individuals; USD 40 domestic to institutions; USD 50 foreign to institutions (effective 2004). bk.rev. abstr.; bibl.; charts; stat. 100 p./no. 2 cols./p.; back issues avail.; reprints avail. **Document type:** *Journal, Academic/Scholarly.*
Related titles: Microform ed.: (from PQC); Online - full text ed.: (from EBSCO Publishing, Florida Center for Library Automation, Gale Group, H.W. Wilson, Northern Light Technology, Inc., O C L C Online Computer Library Center, Inc., ProQuest Information & Learning).
Indexed: ABIn, ABS&EES, AgeL, BPI, BPIA, ESPM, JEL, ORMS, PAIS, RASB, RefZh, RiskAb, SSCI, SSI, T&II, WorkRelAb.
—BLDSC (0813.550000), IE, Infotrieve, ingenta.
Published by: Omicron Delta Epsilon, PO Box 1486, Hattiesburg, MS 39403-1486. TEL 601-264-3115, FAX 601-264-3669, odecf@aol.com, http://webpage.pace.edu/cfar/. Ed. Michael Szenberg. Adv. contact Irene Gunther TEL 601-264-3115. Circ: 6,500 (paid).

330.9 USA ISSN 0897-8964
E838
THE AMERICAN FORECASTER ALMANAC. Text in English. 1983. a. USD 28.95 (effective 2001). 312 p./no.; **Description:** Includes information about business and consumer trends in the United States.
Formerly (until 1989): American Forecaster (0893-7710)
Published by: The American Forecaster, 2546 S Broadway, Denver, CO 80210-5703. TEL 303-722-8669, FAX 303-722-9005, contact@americanforecaster.com, http://www.americanforecaster.com. Ed. Kim Long.

330.9 USA ISSN 1087-4410
THE AMERICAN FORECASTER NEWSLETTER. Text in English. 1996. 11/yr. USD 129 (effective 2001). **Description:** Covers news about emerging topics, technology, and trends.
Published by: The American Forecaster, 2546 S Broadway, Denver, CO 80210-5703. TEL 303-722-8669, FAX 303-722-9005, contact@americanforecaster.com, http://www.americanforecaster.com.

AMERICAN LAW AND ECONOMICS REVIEW. see *LAW*

330.9 GBR ISSN 1351-4571
HC121
AMERICAS REVIEW. Text in English. 1979. a. GBP 50, USD 75 per issue (effective 2005). adv. illus.; stat. **Document type:** *Journal, Trade.* **Description:** An analytical, interpretative overview of events, trends & developments in every country of the Americas, North, South & the Caribbean. For academic, business & governmental audience.
Former titles: Latin America and Caribbean Review; (until 1985): Latin America and Caribbean (0262-5415); (until 1981): Latin America Annual Review and the Caribbean
Related titles: CD-ROM ed.; Online - full text ed.
Indexed: RASB.
Published by: World of Information, 2 Market St, Saffron Walden, Essex CB10 1HZ, United Kingdom. TEL 44-1799-521150, FAX 44-1799-524805, info@worldinformation.com, http://worldofinformation.safeshopper.com/4/cat4.htm?547, http://www.worldinformation.com. Ed., Pub., R&P Anthony Axon. adv.: B&W page GBP 2,950, color page GBP 2,950; trim 210 x 217. Circ: 7,000 (paid). **Orders in USA:** PO Box 830840, Birmingham, AL 35283-0430. TEL 800-633-4931, FAX 205-995-1588, heather@exchange.ebsco.com.

330.9 DNK ISSN 1397-6141
AMTERNES OEKONOMI. BUDGETPUBLIKATION. Text in Danish. 1978. a. illus. **Description:** Reports on the budget of the 14 Danish counties. Provides information about income and expenditure.
Former titles (until 1997): Amternes Oekonomi (0109-7822); (until 1984): Amtskommunernes Oekonomi (0105-8509); (until 1978): Oekonomisk Oversigt for Amtskommunerne
Published by: Amtsraadsforeningen, Dampfaergevej 22, Copenhagen OE, 2593, Denmark. TEL 45-35-298100, FAX 45-35-298300.

AMUSEMENT BUSINESS; international live entertainment and amusement industry newsletter. see *THEATER*

ANALISIS DEL TIEMPO. see *POLITICAL SCIENCE*

330.9 ECU
ANALISIS SEMANAL. Text in Spanish. w. USD 480 (effective 1999). bk.rev. index. **Document type:** *Newsletter.*
Related titles: ♦ English ed.: Weekly Analysis of Ecuadorian Issues. ISSN 0252-2659.
Published by: Walter R. Spurrier Ed. & Pub., ELIZALDE, 119 10o, Apdo 4925, Guayaquil, Guayas, Ecuador. FAX 4-326-842. Circ: 1,000.

380 332 PER ISSN 0251-2491
HC226
ANDEAN REPORT. Text in English. 1908. w. USD 520. adv. charts; stat. index. **Document type:** *Newsletter.* **Description:** Covers economics, finance, development and politics in Peru.
Former titles (until 1975): Peruvian Times; (until 1940): West Coast Leader; (until 1912): Peru Today
Related titles: Online - full text ed.: (from ProQuest Information & Learning).
Indexed: ABIn, PROMT, RASB.
Published by: Andean Air Mail & Peruvian Times S.A., Pasaje Los Pinos, 156 Piso B Of 6, Miraflores, Lima 18, Peru. TEL 51-14-453761, FAX 51-14-467888, perutimes@amauta.rcp.net.pe. Pub. Eleanor Zuniga. Adv. contact Luisa Perbuli. Circ: 4,000.

330.9 USA
ANDEAN WEEKLY FAX BULLETIN. Text in English. w. USD 595 worldwide (effective Sep. 2000). stat. 4 p./no.; back issues avail. **Document type:** *Bulletin, Consumer.* **Description:** Reports on political, economic, and business events in Chile, Colombia, Peru, and Venezuela.
Media: Fax. **Related titles:** E-mail ed.; Online - full text ed.
Published by: Orbis Publications, LLC, 1924 47th St NW, Washington, DC 20007-1901. TEL 202-298-7936, FAX 202-298-7938, sfoster@orbispub.com, http://www.orbispublications.com. Ed., Pub. Stephen Foster. R&P David Mosedale.

330 FRA ISSN 1252-3224
ANIMER; le Magazine rural. Text in French. 1966. q. EUR 8 to members; EUR 12 to non-members (effective 2003). adv. bk.rev. 63 p./no.; **Document type:** *Magazine, Academic/Scholarly.*
Former titles (until 1991): Animer mon Village, mon Pays (0244-4046); (until 1981): Federation Nationale des Foyers Riraux de France. Bulletin d'Information (0180-2410); (until 1972): Federation Nationale des Foyers Ruraux de France. Foyer Rural Informations. (0071-4364)
Published by: Federation Nationale des Foyers Ruraux, 1 Rue Sainte Lucie, Paris, 75015, France. TEL 33-1-45780178, FAX 33-1-45756894, FNFR@mouvement-rural.org, http://www.mouvement-rural.org. Ed. Philippe Cahen. Pub., Adv. contact Jean Marie Lavergne.

330.954 GBR ISSN 1353-4734
ANNUAL COUNTRY FORECAST REPORT. INDIA. Text in English. a. GBP 270, USD 450 (effective 1999). **Document type:** *Trade.* **Description:** Provides a comprehensive assessment of the Indian government, economy and business environment over the next 30 months. Helps to identify opportunities and reduce risk, and answers key questions facing executives at this time.
Published by: Business Monitor International Ltd., Mermaid House, 2 Puddle Dock, Blackfriars, London, EC4V 3DS, United Kingdom. TEL 44-20-72480468, FAX 44-20-72480467, busmon@dial.pipex.com, http://www.businessmonitor.com.

330 ZWE ISSN 1012-6236
ANNUAL ECONOMIC REVIEW OF ZIMBABWE. Text in English. a. ZWD 5. **Document type:** *Government.*
Former titles (until 1981): Economic Survey of Rhodesia (0070-8739); (until 1965): Review of the Economy of Rhodesia (0080-1992)
Indexed: RASB.
Published by: Department of Printing and Stationery, Causeway, PO Box 8062, Harare, Zimbabwe.

330.9 JPN
ANNUAL REPORT ON NATIONAL ACCOUNTS. Text in Japanese. a. JPY 4,100 (effective 2000). **Document type:** *Government.*
Published by: (Japan. Economic Planning Agency/Keizai Keikaku-kyoku), Ministry of Finance, Printing Bureau, 2-2-4 Toranomon, Minato-ku, Tokyo, 105-0001, Japan.

330.9 JAM
ANNUAL REPORT ON THE JAMAICAN ECONOMY (YEAR). Text in English. 1985. a. JMD 600, USD 20 domestic; USD 28 foreign (effective 2000). adv. back issues avail. **Description:** Review of economic activity in the Jamaican economy during the review year. Includes sectoral activity and outcomes on GDP as well as the effects of monetary and fiscal policies on economic activity.
Formerly (until 1990): Economic Review (Year) (0259-9171)
Published by: Private Sector Organisation of Jamaica, 39 Hope Rd, PO Box 236, Kingston, 10, Jamaica. TEL 876-927-6238, FAX 876-927-5137, psoj@cwjamaica.com. Ed., R&P, Adv. contact Charles Ross. Circ: 750.

ANUARIO JURIDICO Y ECONOMICO ESCURIALENSE. see *LAW*

330.9 332 GBR ISSN 0960-3107
HG11
➤ **APPLIED FINANCIAL ECONOMICS.** Text in English. 1991. 18/yr. GBP 1,466, USD 2,404 combined subscription to institutions print & online eds. (effective 2006). illus. Index. back issues avail.; reprint service avail. from PSC. **Document type:** *Journal, Academic/Scholarly.* **Description:** Provides an international forum for applied research on financial markets, including the bond and equity markets, derivative securities markets, the foreign exchange market, corporate finance, market microstructure and cognate areas.
Related titles: Online - full text ed.: ISSN 1466-4305. GBP 1,393, USD 2,284 to institutions (effective 2006) (from EBSCO Publishing, Gale Group, IngentaConnect, O C L C Online Computer Library Center, Inc., Swets Information Services); ♦ Supplement to: Applied Economics. ISSN 0003-6846.
Indexed: ABIn, BAS, BPI, CurCont, ESPM, Emerald, GEOBASE, IBR, IBSS, IBZ, JEL, RASB, RiskAb.
—BLDSC (1572.555000), CISTI, IE, Infotrieve, ingenta. **CCC.**
Published by: Routledge (Subsidiary of: Taylor & Francis Group), 4 Park Sq, Milton Park, Abingdon, Oxon OX14 4RN, United Kingdom. econjournals@gwmail.warwick.ac.uk, info@routledge.co.uk, http://www.tandf.co.uk/journals/routledge/09603107.html, http://www.routledge.com. Eds. Lucio Sarno, Mark Taylor. R&P Ms. Sarah King. **Subscr. in N America to:** Taylor & Francis Inc., Customer Services Dept, 325 Chestnut St, 8th Fl, Philadelphia, PA 19106. TEL 800-354-1420, FAX 215-625-8914; **Subscr. to:** Taylor & Francis Ltd, Journals Customer Service, Rankine Rd, Basingstoke, Hants RG24 8PR, United Kingdom. enquiry@tandf.co.uk, http://www.tandf.co.uk/journals.

330.9 388 DEU ISSN 0939-8872
ARBEITSPLAETZE IN UMSCHLAG- UND LAGERANLAGEN VON SPEDITIONSUNTERNEHMEN. Text in German. 1991. irreg. price varies. **Document type:** *Monographic series, Trade.*
Published by: Erich Schmidt Verlag GmbH & Co. (Berlin), Genthiner Str 30G, Berlin, 10785, Germany. TEL 49-30-250085-0, FAX 49-30-25008521, vertrieb@esvmedien.de, http://www.erich-schmidt-verlag.de.

ARCHIV DER GEGENWART; die weltweite Dokumentation fuer Politik und Wirtschaft. see *POLITICAL SCIENCE*

ARGENTINA. INSTITUTO NACIONAL DE ESTADISTICA Y CENSOS. CENSO NACIONAL ECONOMICO (YEAR). AVANCE DE RESULTADOS. see *BUSINESS AND ECONOMICS—Abstracting, Bibliographies, Statistics*

ARGENTINA. INSTITUTO NACIONAL DE ESTADISTICA Y CENSOS. CENSO NACIONAL ECONOMICO (YEAR). SERIE A. RESULTADOS DEFINITIVOS. see *BUSINESS AND ECONOMICS—Abstracting, Bibliographies, Statistics*

330.9 ARG
ARGENTINA. MINISTERIO DE ECONOMIA. ECONOMIC REPORT. SUMMARY. Text in Spanish. 1973. q. stat.
Continues: Argentina. Ministerio de Hacienda y Finanzas. Economic Report. Summary
Published by: Argentina. Ministerio de Economia, Servicio de Prensa, 501, Balcarce, 136 Piso 5, Capital Federal, Buenos Aires 1064, Argentina. TEL 54-114-3495079, FAX 54-114-3495730, http://www.mecon.gov.ar/.

330.9 ARG ISSN 0325-383X
HC171
ARGENTINA. MINISTERIO DE ECONOMIA, HACIENDA Y FINANZAS. BOLETIN SEMANAL DE ECONOMIA. Text in Spanish. 1975 (no.77). w. charts; stat.
Formerly (until no.393, Jun. 1981): Argentina. Ministerio de Economia. Boletin Semanal

B

Published by: (Argentina. Subsecretaria de Coordinacion de Informacion Economica), Argentina. Ministerio de Economia, Servicio de Prensa, 501, Balcarce, 136 Piso 5, Capital Federal, Buenos Aires 1064, Argentina. TEL 54-114-3495079, FAX 54-114-3495730, http://www.mecon.gov.ar/.

330 ARG
ARGENTINA. MINISTERIO DE ECONOMIA Y OBRAS Y SERVICIOS PUBLICOS. INFORME ECONOMICO. RESUMEN✶. Text in Spanish. 1973. q. stat. **Document type:** *Government.*
Former titles: Argentina. Ministerio de Economia. Informe Economico. Resumen; Argentina. Ministerio de Hacienda y Finanzas. Informe Economico. Resumen
Published by: (Argentina. Secretaria de Estudios Economicos), Argentina. Ministerio de Economia, Servicio de Prensa, 501, Balcarce, 136 Piso 5, Capital Federal, Buenos Aires 1064, Argentina. TEL 54-114-3495079, FAX 54-114-3495730, http://www.mecon.gov.ar/.

330.982 GBR ISSN 1470-7438
F2849.2
ARGENTINA QUARTERLY FORECAST REPORT. Text in English. 1985. 3/yr. GBP 330, USD 495, EUR 450 (effective 2003). **Document type:** *Journal, Trade.* **Description:** Provides a comprehensive assessment of the Argentine government, economy and business environment over the next 30 months. Helps to identify opportunities and reduce risk, and answers key questions facing executives at this time.
Formerly (until 2000): Annual Country Forecast Report. Argentina (0267-9949)
Related titles: Online - full text ed.: (from EBSCO Publishing).
—CCC.
Published by: Business Monitor International Ltd., Mermaid House, 2 Puddle Dock, Blackfriars, London, EC4V 3DS, United Kingdom. TEL 44-20-72480468, FAX 44-20-72480467, marketing@businessmonitor.com, http://www.businessmonitor.com/argentinaforecast.html.

330.982 USA
ARGENTINA WEEKLY FAX BULLETIN. Text in English. 1992. w. USD 595 (effective 2005). stat. 2 p./no.; back issues avail. **Document type:** *Bulletin, Consumer.* **Description:** Reports on political, economic, and business events in Argentina.
Media: Fax. **Related titles:** E-mail ed.; Online - full text ed.
Published by: Brazil Watch Publications, 8218 Wisconsin Ave, Ste 307, Bethesda, MD 20814. TEL 301-718-3080, FAX 301-718-3081, bw@brazilwatch.com, http://www.brazilwatch.com. Pub. Richard W Foster.

330.9 ARG
ARGENTINE ECONOMIC DEVELOPMENT. Text in English, French. biennial.
Published by: Argentina. Ministerio de Economia, Servicio de Prensa, 501, Balcarce, 136 Piso 5, Capital Federal, Buenos Aires 1064, Argentina. TEL 54-114-3495079, FAX 54-114-3495730, http://www.mecon.gov.ar/.

320.9 ARG
ARGENTINE LETTER. Text in Spanish. 1988. m. USD 250.
Address: PB "A", Ayacucho, 1370, Capital Federal, Buenos Aires 1111, Argentina. FAX 54-114-3114385. Eds. Arturo Meyer, Javier Gonzalez Fraga. Circ: 500. **Subscr. to:** PO Box 855, Bethesda, MD 20817.

330.9 DEU
ARGUMENTE ZU MARKTWIRTSCHAFT UND POLITIK. Text in German. 1985. irreg. (approx. 5/yr.). free. **Document type:** *Journal, Academic/Scholarly.*
Formerly (until 1998): Argumente zur Wirtschaftspolitik
Published by: Frankfurter Institut Stiftung Marktwirtschaft und Politik, Charlottenstr 60, Berlin, 10117, Germany. TEL 49-30-2060570, FAX 49-30-20605757, info@stiftung-marktwirtschaft.de, http://www.frankfurter-institut.de.

330.9 USA
ARIZONA ECONOMIC PROFILE. Text in English. a.
Published by: Arizona State University, Center for Business Research, College of Business, Box 874406, Tempe, AZ 85287-4406. TEL 602-965-3961, FAX 602-965-5458, asucbr@asuvm.inre.asu.edu.

ARIZONA STATISTICAL ABSTRACT. see *BUSINESS AND ECONOMICS—Abstracting, Bibliographies, Statistics*

330.9 USA
ARIZONA'S ECONOMY. Text in English. 1979. 4/yr. free domestic; USD 12 foreign (effective 2000). **Description:** Provides current analysis of business conditions and forecasts of future economic activity in Arizona.
Indexed: PAIS.
Published by: University of Arizona, College of Business and Public Administration, Economic and Business Research Program, McClelland Hall 204, Tucson, AZ 85721. TEL 520-621-2155, FAX 520-621-2150, pmontoya@bpa.arizona.edu. Ed. Diana Hunter. Circ: 6,300.

ARIZONA'S WORKFORCE. see *BUSINESS AND ECONOMICS—Labor And Industrial Relations*

AS A MATTER OF FACT. see *BUSINESS AND ECONOMICS—Investments*

330.9 MEX
EL ASESOR DE MEXIO. Text in Spanish. w. MXP 550 (effective 2002). adv.
Related titles: Online - full text ed.: ISSN 1607-0178. 1999.
Published by: Crain Communications, Inc. (Mexico), Holbein 217, Torre Detroit 9-101, Col. Ciudad de los Deportes, Mexico, D.F., 03710, Mexico. TEL 525-5630341, FAX 525-6113819, http://www.elasesor.com.mx/, http://www.crain.com. Ed. Jorge Monjaras. Pub. Ana Luz De Alba.

330.9 GBR ISSN 1351-458X
HC411
ASIA & PACIFIC REVIEW; the business and economic report. Text in English. 1980. a. GBP 50, USD 75 per issue (effective 2005). adv. illus.; stat.; maps. back issues avail. **Document type:** *Journal, Trade.* **Description:** An analytical and interpretative overview of events, trends, developments in every Asian & Pacific state and country. For an academic, business and governmental audience.
Former titles (until 1985): Asia and Pacific (0262-5407); (until 1981): Asia and Pacific Annual Review
Related titles: CD-ROM ed.; Online - full content ed.
Indexed: APEL, SPPI.
Published by: World of Information, 2 Market St, Saffron Walden, Essex CB10 1HZ, United Kingdom. TEL 44-1799-521150, FAX 44-1799-524805, info@worldinformation.com, http://worldofinformation.safeshopper.com/4/cat4.htm?547, http://www.worldinformation.com. Ed., Pub., R&P Anthony Axon. adv.: B&W page GBP 2,950, color page GBP 2,950; trim 210 x 217. Circ: 7,000 (paid). **Subscr. in USA:** PO Box 830840, Birmingham, AL 35283-0430. TEL 800-633-4931, FAX 205-995-1588, heather@exchange.ebsco.com.

330.95 DEU
▼ **ASIA BRIDGE MIT ASIEN-CONTACT**; Das Informationsforum fuer das Deutsche Asiengeschaeft. Text in German. 2004. m. adv. **Document type:** *Magazine, Trade.*
Formed by the merger of (1996-2004): Asia Bridge; (1997-2004): Asien-Contact
Published by: V W D - Vereinigte Wirtschaftsdienste GmbH, Niederurseler Allee 8-10, Eschborn, 65760, Germany. TEL 49-6196-4050, FAX 49-6196-405303, feedback@vwd.de, http://www.vwd.de. adv.: B&W page EUR 2,250, color page EUR 3,100; trim 180 x 265. Circ: 3,685 (controlled).

330.9 HKG
ASIA CORPORATE PROFILE AND NATIONAL FINANCE✶. Text in Chinese. a. USD 60.
Published by: Dataline Asia - Pacific Ltd., 3rd Fl Hollywood Centre, 233 Hollywood Rd, Hong Kong, Hong Kong. TEL 8155221, FAX 8542794. Ed. Amitabha Chowdury.

650 HKG ISSN 0004-4466
DS1
ASIA LETTER; a weekly newsletter containing an authoritative analysis of Asian affairs. Text in Chinese. 1964. w. USD 225. bk.rev. **Document type:** *Newsletter.*
Indexed: KES, RASB.
Published by: Asia Letter Group, GPO Box 10874, Hong Kong, Hong Kong. TEL 852-526-2950, FAX 852-526-7131, TELEX HX-61166-HKNW. Ed. Charles R Smith.

330.951 GBR ISSN 1474-5615
HC427.95
ASIA MONITOR. CHINA & NORTH EAST ASIA. Text in English. 1994. m. GBP 325, USD 495, USD 430 (effective 2003). **Document type:** *Journal, Trade.* **Description:** Provides country-by-country analysis of the most recent changes to the political and business environment in China, Hong Kong, Taiwan, North Korea and South Korea.
Former titles (until 2001): Asia Monitor. China & North Asia (1470-5184); (until 2000): China & North Asia Monitor (1353-4688)
Related titles: Online - full text ed.: (from EBSCO Publishing).
—CCC.
Published by: Business Monitor International Ltd., Mermaid House, 2 Puddle Dock, Blackfriars, London, EC4V 3DS, United Kingdom. TEL 44-20-72480468, FAX 44-20-72480467, subs@businessmonitor.com, https://www.businessmonitor.com/bmi/asiamonitor_order.html, http://www.businessmonitor.com. **Dist. by:** Abraham Book Centre, Rm.1203, Hong Kong Plaza, 188 Connaught Rd W, Hong Kong, Hong Kong. TEL 852-2856-9484, FAX 852-2565-8749.

338.954 GBR ISSN 1479-5744
HC430.6.A1
ASIA MONITOR. SOUTH ASIA. Text in English. 1995. m. GBP 325, USD 495, EUR 430 (effective 2003). **Document type:** *Journal, Trade.* **Description:** Provides country-by-country analysis of the most recent changes to the political and business environment in India, Pakistan, Sri Lanka, and Bangladesh.
Former titles (until 2003): Asia Monitor. Indian Subcontinent (1470-5176); (until 2000): Indian Subcontinent Monitor (1358-152X)
Related titles: Online - full text ed.: (from EBSCO Publishing).
—CCC.
Published by: Business Monitor International Ltd., Mermaid House, 2 Puddle Dock, Blackfriars, London, EC4V 3DS, United Kingdom. TEL 44-20-72480468, FAX 44-20-72480467, marketing@businessmonitor.com, http://www.businessmonitor.com. **Dist. by:** Abraham Book Centre, 2902 Admiralty Centre, Tower One, 18 Harcourt Rd, Hong Kong, Hong Kong. TEL 852-2856-9484, FAX 852-2565-8749.

330.959 GBR ISSN 1470-7810
HC441.A1
ASIA MONITOR. SOUTH EAST ASIA. Text in English. 1990. m. GBP 325, USD 495, EUR 430 (effective 2003). **Document type:** *Journal, Trade.* **Description:** Provides country-by-country analysis of the most recent changes to the political and business environment in Indonesia, Philippines, Singapore, Malaysia, Thailand, Myanmar, Vietnam, Cambodia, and Loas.
Formerly (until 2000): South East Asia Monitor (0959-2601)
Related titles: Online - full text ed.: (from EBSCO Publishing).
Indexed: PerIslam.
—CCC.
Published by: Business Monitor International Ltd., Mermaid House, 2 Puddle Dock, Blackfriars, London, EC4V 3DS, United Kingdom. TEL 44-20-72480468, FAX 44-20-72480467, marketing@businessmonitor.com, http://www.businessmonitor.com. Ed. Anthony Beachey. **Dist. by:** Abraham Book Centre, Rm.1203, Hong Kong Plaza, 188 Connaught Rd W, Hong Kong, Hong Kong. TEL 852-2856-9484, FAX 852-2565-8749.

330.9 GBR ISSN 1351-0967
HC460.5.A1
ASIA PACIFIC CONSENSUS FORCASTS. Text in English. 1995. m. GBP 399, USD 629 (effective 2003). 32 p./no.; back issues avail. **Document type:** *Journal, Academic/Scholarly.* **Description:** Covers growth, inflation, foreign trade, and exchange rates. Includes individual and consensus forecasts, historical and trade data, country analysis and special surveys.
Related titles: Diskette ed.; E-mail ed.; Fax ed.
—CCC.
Published by: Consensus Economics Inc., 53 Upper Brook St, London, W1K 2LT, United Kingdom. TEL 44-20-7491-3211, FAX 44-20-7409-2331, editors@consensuseconomics.com, http://www.consensuseconomics.com. Ed. Suyin Kan. Pub. Philip M Hubbard.

338 THA ISSN 1020-1246
HC411.U4
➤ **ASIA - PACIFIC DEVELOPMENT JOURNAL.** Text in English. 1956. s-a. USD 17.50 per issue (effective 2003). back issues avail.; reprint service avail. from PQC. **Document type:** *Bulletin, Government.* **Description:** Examines economic issues and trends affecting the Pacific Rim.
Former titles (until 1994): Economic Bulletin for Asia and the Pacific (0378-455X); Economic Bulletin for Asia and the Far East (0041-6371)
Related titles: Microfiche ed.: (from CIS); Microfilm ed.: (from PQC).
Indexed: APEL, BAS, CREJ, EI, IBSS, IIS, ILD, JEL, KES, MEA&I, PAIS, PROMT.
—CISTI, IE. **CCC.**
Published by: United Nations Economic and Social Commission for Asia and the Pacific, United Nations Bldg., Rajadamnern Ave., Bangkok, 10200, Thailand. unescap@unescap.org, http://www.unescap.org/drpad/publication/journal_9_2/apdj_9_2.pdf. **Dist. by:** United Nations Publications, Distribution and Sales Section, Palais des Nations, Rm C-116, 8-14 av de la Paix, Geneva 1211, Switzerland; United Nations Publications, Rm DC2-853, United Nations Bldg, 2 United Nations Plaza, New York, NY 10017; Conference Services Unit, Conference Services Unit, ESCAP, Bangkok 10200, Thailand. TEL 662-288-1174, 662-288-2313, FAX 662-288-3022.

330.9 PHL
ASIA RECOVERY REPORT (YEAR). Text in English. 2000 (Mar.). s-a. (with occasional updates). free. stat.; charts. **Description:** Covers Asia's recovery from economic crisis with analysis supported by high-frequency indicators compiled under the ARIC Indicators section of the ARIC website.
Media: Online - full content.
Published by: Asian Development Bank, Regional Economic Monitoring Unit, 6 ADB Ave, Mandaluyong City, Metro Manila, 0401, Philippines. TEL 63-2-632-5458, FAX 63-2-636-2183, aric_info@adb.org, http://www.aric.adb.org.

330.95 GBR ISSN 1475-5203
ASIA WEEKLY FINANCIAL ALERT. Text in English. 48/yr. GBP 665, USD 995, EUR 995 (effective 2003). **Document type:** *Journal, Trade.* **Description:** Provides briefings on key business and finance developments as well as the week's significant new economic indicator. Highlights the change in political risk.
Formerly: Asia Weekly Economic Alert (1460-504X)
Related titles: E-mail ed.; Fax ed.; Online - full text ed.: (from EBSCO Publishing).
—CCC.
Published by: Business Monitor International Ltd., Mermaid House, 2 Puddle Dock, Blackfriars, London, EC4V 3DS, United Kingdom. TEL 44-20-72480468, FAX 44-20-72480467, subs@businessmonitor.com, https://www.businessmonitor.com/bmi/awfa_order.html, http://www.businessmonitor.com.

330.9 MYS ISSN 0127-3337
ASIAN AND PACIFIC DEVELOPMENT CENTRE NEWSLETTER. Text in English. 1980. 3/yr. free. bk.rev. **Document type:** *Newsletter.*
Formerly: Asian and Pacific Development Administration Centre. Occasional Papers Series
Published by: Asian and Pacific Development Centre, PO Box 12224, Kuala Lumpur, 50770, Malaysia. TEL 60-3-254-8088, FAX 60-3-255-0316, TELEX MA-30676-APDEC, info@apdc.po.my, http://www.apdc.co.my/apdc. Ed. Yap Chin Yean. Circ: 1,600.

ASIAN ENTERPRISE. see *BUSINESS AND ECONOMICS—Small Business*

339.5 DEU
ASIEN-PAZIFIK. WIRTSCHAFTSHANDBUCH. Variant title: Wirtschaftshandbuch Asien, Pazifik. Text in German. 1986. a. EUR 70 per issue (effective 2005). **Document type:** *Yearbook, Academic/Scholarly.*
Formerly: Asien-Pazifik (0936-3572)
Published by: Institut fuer Asienkunde, Rothenbaumchaussee 32, Hamburg, 20148, Germany. TEL 49-40-4288740, FAX 49-40-4107945, ifa@ifa.duei.de, http://www.duei.de/ifa/de/content/aktuelles/pdf/gesamt-pazifik.pdf.

330.9 COL ISSN 0122-6657
ASOBANCARIA SEMANA ECONOMICA. Text in Spanish. w. USD 350 (effective 1998). **Description:** Follows up on the main short-term indicators of the economy.
Published by: Asociacion Bancaria y de Entidades Financieras, Apartado Aereo 13994, Bogota, CUND, Colombia. TEL 57-1-2114811, FAX 57-1-2119915, info@asobancaria.com, http://www.asobancaria.com/.

330.9 COL
ASOCIACION NACIONAL DE INSTITUCIONES FINANCIERAS. CARTA FINANCIERA. Text in Spanish. 1974. bi-m. COP 23,000 domestic; USD 45 foreign. adv.
Published by: Asociacion Nacional de Instituciones Financieras, Calle 35 No. 4-89, Apartado Aereo 29677, Bogota, CUND, Colombia. TEL 57-1-2128200, FAX 57-1-2355947. Circ: 4,000.

ASSET FINANCE INTERNATIONAL. see *BUSINESS AND ECONOMICS—Investments*

330.9 LBN
ASSOCIATION DES BANQUES DU LIBAN. RAPPORT DU CONSEIL. Cover title: Association des Banques du Liban. Rapport Annuel. Text in Arabic, French. a. USD 25 (effective 1999). stat. **Document type:** *Corporate.*
Published by: Association of Banks in Lebanon, DORA Centre Moucarri, P O Box 80536, Beirut, Lebanon.

ASTUTE INVESTOR. see *BUSINESS AND ECONOMICS—Investments*

330.9 USA ISSN 0164-8071
ATLANTA BUSINESS CHRONICLE. Text in English. 1978. w. (Fri.). USD 90 (effective 2005). adv. bk.rev. illus.; stat. **Document type:** *Newspaper, Trade.*
Related titles: Online - full text ed.: Atlanta Business Journal (from Florida Center for Library Automation, Gale Group, O C L C Online Computer Library Center, Inc., ProQuest Information & Learning).
Indexed: ABIn, BusDate, LRI, T&II.
—CCC.
Address: 1801 Peachtree St, 150, Atlanta, GA 30339-1859. TEL 404-249-1000, FAX 404-249-1058, atlanta@bizjournals.com, http://www.bizjournals.com/atlanta/, http://www.amcity.com/atlanta. Ed. David Rubinger. Pub. Ed Baker. R&P Melissa Bower TEL 404-249-1006. Adv. contact Nancy Kenerly. Circ: 26,000 (paid). Wire service: PR.

330.1 CAN ISSN 0067-0162
HC117.M35
ATLANTIC PROVINCES ECONOMIC COUNCIL. ANNUAL REPORT. Text in English. 1966. a. membership. **Document type:** *Corporate.*
Published by: Atlantic Provinces Economic Council, 5121 Sackville St, Ste 500, Halifax, NS B3J 1K1, Canada. TEL 902-422-6516, FAX 902-429-6803, info@apec-econ.ca, http://www.apec-econ.ca. R&P Elizabeth Beale. Circ: 1,000.

330 CAN ISSN 0004-6841
HC117.A88 CODEN: ATRPEV
ATLANTIC REPORT. Text in English. 1966. q. membership. charts; stat.
Related titles: Microfiche ed.: (from MML); Microfilm ed.: (from MML); Online - full text ed.: (from Micromedia ProQuest).
Indexed: CBCABus, CBCARef, CBPI, CPerI.
—CISTI.
Published by: Atlantic Provinces Economic Council, 5121 Sackville St, Ste 500, Halifax, NS B3J 1K1, Canada. TEL 902-422-6516, FAX 902-429-6803, info@apec-econ.ca, http://www.apec-econ.ca/publicat.htm#Atlrep. Ed. Elizabeth Beale. Circ: 1,300.

330.9 332.6 USA ISSN 1064-3184
AURA WEALTH NEWSLETTER; economic survival in perilous times. Text in English, Spanish. 1979. s-m. USD 2,400; includes fax service 5/w. & e-mail advisories. adv. bk.rev.; software rev.; Website rev. charts; illus. cum.index: 1979-1994; 1995-2001. 80 p./no. 2 cols./p.; **Document type:** *Newsletter, Trade.* **Description:** Covers the discovery and evolution of international wealth building opportunities and their sensitivity to taxation in the Western democracies.
Related titles: Diskette ed.
Published by: Aura Publishing Co., PO Box 1367, Scarsdale, NY 10583. TEL 914-337-5552, FAX 775-254-1961, info@aural.com, http://www.aura.com. Ed. Richard A Sandell. Pub. Arnold P Josevie. Adv. contact Marcel Aurevie. Circ: 2,950 (paid); 300 (controlled).

AUSSENHANDEL. see *BUSINESS AND ECONOMICS—International Commerce*

330.9 AUS ISSN 1324-0935
HT395.A78
➤ **AUSTRALASIAN JOURNAL OF REGIONAL STUDIES.** Text in English. 1987. 3/yr., latest vol.3, 2001. AUD 80 to individual members; AUD 165 to institutional members (effective 2002). adv. bk.rev. Yes. 100 p./no. 1 cols./p.; back issues avail. **Document type:** *Journal, Academic/Scholarly.* **Description:** Provides a forum for the discussion of regional development and regional policy; includes papers from the Annual Meeting.
Formerly (until no.8, 1994): Australian Journal of Regional Studies (1030-7923)
Indexed: CJA, JEL.
—BLDSC (1795.160000).
Published by: Regional Science Association, Australian and New Zealand Section, c/o Linda Pink, Dep. of Economics, University Of Queensland, St. Lucia, QLD 4072, Australia. TEL 61-7-38248935, FAX 61-7-38248936, anzrsai@uq.net.au, http://www.uq.net.aul~zzanzrsa. Ed. John Mangan. R&P, Adv. contact Linda Pink. Circ: 300.

➤ **AUSTRALIA AND THE ASIAN DEVELOPMENT BANK.** see *BUSINESS AND ECONOMICS—International Development And Assistance*

➤ **AUSTRALIA. BUREAU OF STATISTICS. AUSTRALIAN BUSINESS REGISTER, A N Z S I C INDUSTRY CLASS BY STATE.** see *BUSINESS AND ECONOMICS—Abstracting, Bibliographies, Statistics*

➤ **AUSTRALIA. BUREAU OF STATISTICS. AUSTRALIAN INDUSTRY.** see *BUSINESS AND ECONOMICS—Abstracting, Bibliographies, Statistics*

➤ **AUSTRALIA. BUREAU OF STATISTICS. BUSINESS OPERATIONS AND INDUSTRY PERFORMANCE, AUSTRALIA, PRELIMINARY.** see *BUSINESS AND ECONOMICS—Abstracting, Bibliographies, Statistics*

➤ **AUSTRALIA. BUREAU OF STATISTICS. BUSINESS REGISTER CONSULTANCY - LOCATIONS.** see *BUSINESS AND ECONOMICS—Abstracting, Bibliographies, Statistics*

➤ **AUSTRALIA. BUREAU OF STATISTICS. BUSINESS REGISTER CONSULTANCY - MANAGEMENT UNITS.** see *BUSINESS AND ECONOMICS—Abstracting, Bibliographies, Statistics*

➤ **AUSTRALIA. BUREAU OF STATISTICS. EXPERIMENTAL ESTIMATES, AUSTRALIAN INDUSTRY, A STATE PERSPECTIVE.** see *BUSINESS AND ECONOMICS—Abstracting, Bibliographies, Statistics*

➤ **AUSTRALIA. BUREAU OF STATISTICS. GOVERNMENT FINANCE STATISTICS, AUSTRALIA.** see *BUSINESS AND ECONOMICS—Abstracting, Bibliographies, Statistics*

➤ **AUSTRALIA. BUREAU OF STATISTICS. MEASURING AUSTRALIA'S ECONOMY.** see *BUSINESS AND ECONOMICS—Abstracting, Bibliographies, Statistics*

➤ **AUSTRALIA. BUREAU OF STATISTICS. MEASURING AUSTRALIA'S PROGRESS.** see *BUSINESS AND ECONOMICS—Abstracting, Bibliographies, Statistics*

➤ **AUSTRALIA. BUREAU OF STATISTICS. MODELLERS' DATABASE.** see *BUSINESS AND ECONOMICS—Abstracting, Bibliographies, Statistics*

➤ **AUSTRALIA. BUREAU OF STATISTICS. OCCASIONAL PAPER: AUSTRALIAN BUSINESS REGISTER - A SNAPSHOT.** see *BUSINESS AND ECONOMICS—Abstracting, Bibliographies, Statistics*

➤ **AUSTRALIA. BUREAU OF STATISTICS. TREASURY MODEL OF THE AUSTRALIAN ECONOMY - DOCUMENTATION.** see *BUSINESS AND ECONOMICS—Abstracting, Bibliographies, Statistics*

➤ **AUSTRALIA. BUREAU OF STATISTICS. TREASURY MODEL OF THE AUSTRALIAN ECONOMY - TSP VERSION.** see *BUSINESS AND ECONOMICS—Abstracting, Bibliographies, Statistics*

330.9 USA
AUSTRALIA COUNTRY MONITOR. Text in English. 1998. m.
Related titles: Online - full text ed.
Published by: W E F A, 530, 5th Ave, New York, NY 10016. TEL 212-884-9500, http://www.wefa.com.

350 AUS ISSN 1032-4054
AUSTRALIA. DEPARTMENT OF PRIMARY INDUSTRIES AND ENERGY. ANNUAL REPORT. Text in English. 1979. a. AUD 39.95.
Formerly: Australia. Department of Primary Industry. Annual Report (0158-1309)
Indexed: AESIS, EIA.
Published by: Department of Primary Industries and Energy, GPO Box 858, Canberra, ACT 2600, Australia.

330.9 AUS ISSN 0728-9405
AUSTRALIA. DEPARTMENT OF THE TREASURY. ANNUAL REPORT. Text in English. 1979. a. charts; stat. back issues avail. **Document type:** *Government.* **Description:** Describes the overall Treasury Portfolio program structure and provides a corporate overview of the program.
Related titles: Online - full text ed.
Published by: (Australia. Department of the Treasury), AusInfo, GPO Box 1920, Canberra Mc, ACT 2610, Australia. TEL 61-2-6295-4512, FAX 61-2-6295-4455, http://www.ausinfo.gov.au, http://www.treasury.gov.au. **Orders to:** AusInfo Mail Order Sales, GPO Box 84, Canberra, ACT 2601, Australia. FAX 61-2-6295-4888.

B

330.9 336.3 AUS ISSN 0810-5677
AUSTRALIA. DEPARTMENT OF THE TREASURY. BUDGET. Text in English. 1982. a. charts; stat. back issues avail. **Document type:** *Government.*
Related titles: Online - full text ed.
Published by: (Australia. Department of the Treasury), AusInfo, GPO Box 1920, Canberra MC, ACT 2610, Australia. TEL 61-2-6295-4512, FAX 61-2-6295-4455. **Orders to:** AusInfo Mail Order Sales, GPO Box 84, Canberra, ACT 2601, Australia. FAX 61-2-6295-4888.

AUSTRALIA. DEPARTMENT OF THE TREASURY. ECONOMIC ROUND-UP. see *BUSINESS AND ECONOMICS—Abstracting, Bibliographies, Statistics*

AUSTRALIA. DEPARTMENT OF THE TREASURY. MID - YEAR ECONOMIC FISCAL OUTLOOK. see *BUSINESS AND ECONOMICS—Abstracting, Bibliographies, Statistics*

AUSTRALIA. DEPARTMENT OF THE TREASURY. NATIONAL FISCAL OUTLOOK. see *BUSINESS AND ECONOMICS—Abstracting, Bibliographies, Statistics*

AUSTRALIA. DEPARTMENT OF THE TREASURY. PRE-ELECTION ECONOMIC AND FISCAL OUTLOOK. see *BUSINESS AND ECONOMICS—Abstracting, Bibliographies, Statistics*

AUSTRALIA. DEPARTMENT OF THE TREASURY. TAX EXPENDITURES STATEMENT. see *BUSINESS AND ECONOMICS—Public Finance, Taxation*

330.9 AUS
AUSTRALIA. DEPARTMENT OF THE TREASURY. TREASURY ECONOMIC PAPERS. Text in English. irreg., latest vol.17. price varies. charts. back issues avail. **Document type:** *Monographic series, Government.* **Description:** Reports on the Australian Commonwealth Government fiscal policy and procedure.
Related titles: Online - full text ed.
Published by: (Australia. Department of the Treasury), AusInfo, GPO Box 1920, Canberra MC, ACT 2610, Australia. TEL 61-2-6295-4512, FAX 61-2-6295-4455, TELEX AA2013, http://www.ausinfo.gov.au, http://www.treasury.gov.au. **Orders to:** AusInfo Mail Order Sales, GPO Box 84, Canberra, ACT 2601, Australia. FAX 61-2-6295-4888.

330.9 AUS ISSN 1323-9546
AUSTRALIA. DEPARTMENT OF THE TREASURY. TREASURY RESEARCH PAPERS. Abbreviated title: T R P. Text in English. 1990. irreg., latest vol.10. price varies. charts; stat. back issues avail. **Document type:** *Monographic series, Government.* **Description:** Publishes valuable contributions to public debate on major economic issues of concern to Australia.
Related titles: Online - full text ed.
Published by: (Australia. Department of the Treasury), AusInfo, GPO Box 1920, Canberra Mc, ACT 2610, Australia. TEL 61-2-6295-4512, FAX 61-2-6295-4455. **Orders to:** AusInfo Mail Order Sales, GPO Box 84, Canberra, ACT 2601, Australia. FAX 61-2-6295-4888.

330.9 AUS
AUSTRALIA. PRODUCTIVITY COMMISSION. ANNUAL REPORT SERIES. Text in English. 1997. a. price varies. back issues avail. **Document type:** *Government.* **Description:** Reports on the state of economic conditions and indicators in Australia.

▼ new title ➤ refereed ✶ unverified ◆ full entry avail.

Supersedes in part (in 1998): Australia. Economic Planning Advisory Commission. Annual Report (1325-9067); Which was formerly (1984-1995): Australia. Economic Planning Advisory Council. Annual Report (0814-8570); Incorporated in part (in 1998): Australia. Industry Commission. Annual Report Publications (1035-5243); Which was formed by the merger of (1974-1990): Australia. Industries Assistance Commission. Annual Report (0311-6271); (1984-1990): Australia. Inter-State Commission. Annual Report (0814-2831)
Related titles: Online - full text ed.
Published by: Productivity Commission, Media and Publications Section, Locked Bag 2, Collins St E., Melbourne, VIC 8003, Australia. TEL 61-3-9653-2100, FAX 61-3-9653-2199, maps@pc.gov.au, http://www.pc.gov.au. **Orders to:** AusInfo, GPO Box 1920, Canberra Mc, ACT 2610, Australia. TEL 61-2-6275-3442, FAX 61-2-6295-4888.

330.9 AUS
AUSTRALIA. PRODUCTIVITY COMMISSION. CONFERENCE PROCEEDINGS. Text in English. irreg. price varies. back issues avail. **Document type:** *Proceedings, Government.* **Description:** Publishes papers on economic topics in Australia presented at conferences.
Formerly: Australia. Productivity Commission. Conference Papers
Related titles: Online - full text ed.
Published by: Productivity Commission, Media and Publications Section, Locked Bag 2, Collins St E., Melbourne, VIC 8003, Australia. TEL 61-3-9653-2100, FAX 61-3-9653-2199, maps@pc.gov.au, http://www.pc.gov.au. **Orders to:** AusInfo, GPO Box 1920, Canberra Mc, ACT 2610, Australia. TEL 61-2-6275-3442, FAX 61-2-6295-4888.

330.9 AUS
AUSTRALIA. PRODUCTIVITY COMMISSION. INQUIRY REPORTS. DRAFT REPORT. Text in English. irreg. price varies. back issues avail. **Document type:** *Monographic series, Government.* **Description:** Presents Productivity Commission approved studies on various economic and business issues affecting economic productivity in Australia.
Related titles: Online - full text ed.
Published by: Productivity Commission, Media and Publications Section, Locked Bag 2, Collins St E., Melbourne, VIC 8003, Australia. TEL 61-3-9653-2100, FAX 61-3-9653-2199, maps@pc.gov.au, http://www.pc.gov.au. **Orders to:** AusInfo, GPO Box 1920, Canberra Mc, ACT 2610, Australia. TEL 61-2-6275-3442, FAX 61-2-6295-4888.

330.9 AUS
AUSTRALIA. PRODUCTIVITY COMMISSION. INQUIRY REPORTS. FINAL REPORT. Text in English. 1974. irreg., latest Report no.13. price varies. back issues avail. **Document type:** *Monographic series, Government.* **Description:** Presents commissioned approved studies on various business, social and issues affecting economic productivity in Australian industry.
Supersedes in part (in 1998): Australia. Industry Commission. Final Report; (until 1990): Australia. Industries Assistance Commission. Final Report
Related titles: Online - full text ed.
Published by: Productivity Commission, Media and Publications Section, Locked Bag 2, Collins St E., Melbourne, VIC 8003, Australia. TEL 61-3-9653-2100, FAX 61-3-9653-2199, maps@pc.gov.au, http://www.pc.gov.au. **Orders to:** AusInfo, GPO Box 1920, Canberra Mc, ACT 2610, Australia. TEL 61-2-6275-3442, FAX 61-2-6295-4888.

330.9 AUS ISSN 1443-6671
AUSTRALIA. PRODUCTIVITY COMMISSION. P C UPDATE. Text in English. 1990. q. free. back issues avail. **Document type:** *Newsletter, Government.* **Description:** Discusses Productivity Commission activities and key events.
Former titles (until 1997): Australia. Productivity Commission. Bulletin (1327-3868); (until 1996): Australia. Industry Commission. Bulletin (1322-6932)
Related titles: Online - full text ed.
Published by: Productivity Commission, Media and Publications Section, Locked Bag 2, Collins St E., Melbourne, VIC 8003, Australia. TEL 61-3-9653-2100, FAX 61-3-9653-2199, maps@pc.gov.au, http://www.pc.gov.au/commission/pcupdate/index.html.

330.9 AUS
AUSTRALIA. PRODUCTIVITY COMMISSION. RESEARCH REPORT. Variant title: Australia. Productivity Commission. Commissioned Studies. Text in English. 1978. irreg., latest 2001, Jul. price varies. **Document type:** *Monographic series, Government.* **Description:** Publishes commissioned research in all aspects of national business and economics, includes international benchmarks and labour market research series.
Supersedes in part (in 1998): Australia. Bureau of Industry Economics. Research Report (0156-3394)
Related titles: Online - full text ed.
—CCC.
Published by: Productivity Commission, Media and Publications Section, Locked Bag 2, Collins St E., Melbourne, VIC 8003, Australia. TEL 61-3-9653-2100, FAX 61-3-9653-2199, maps@pc.gov.au, http://www.pc.gov.au. **Orders to:** AusInfo, GPO Box 1920, Canberra Mc, ACT 2610, Australia. TEL 61-2-6275-3442, FAX 61-2-6295-4888.

330.9 AUS
AUSTRALIA. PRODUCTIVITY COMMISSION. STAFF RESEARCH PAPERS. Text in English. 1998. irreg. price varies. back issues avail. **Document type:** *Government.* **Description:** Publishes staff research papers on a variety of economic topics in Australia.
Related titles: Online - full text ed.
Published by: Productivity Commission, Media and Publications Section, Locked Bag 2, Collins St E., Melbourne, VIC 8003, Australia. TEL 61-3-9653-2100, FAX 61-3-9653-2199, maps@pc.gov.au, http://www.pc.gov.au. **Orders to:** AusInfo, GPO Box 1920, Canberra Mc, ACT 2610, Australia. TEL 61-2-6275-6442, FAX 61-2-6295-4888.

330.9 AUS
AUSTRALIAN ECONOMIC POLICY; updated articles from the Ecodate collection. Text in English. 1993. irreg. AUD 14.25 (effective 2002). charts; stat. back issues avail. **Document type:** *Academic/Scholarly.* **Description:** Provides information on recent developments in Australian economics. Covers economic problems and issues, recent policy approaches, current statistics and data.
Published by: Warringal Publications, 116 Argyle St, Fitzroy, VIC 3065, Australia. TEL 61-3-94160200, FAX 61-3-94160402, http://www.edassist.com.au. Ed. Ted Kramer. Pub. Maree Prince. Circ: 3,000.

330.994 AUS ISSN 0812-2261
THE AUSTRALIAN ECONOMY; a student's guide to current economic conditions. Text in English. 1982. a. AUD 14.25 (effective 2002). charts; stat. back issues avail. **Document type:** *Academic/Scholarly.* **Description:** Provides commentary on developments in the economy over the past year.
Published by: Warringal Publications, 116 Argyle St, Fitzroy, VIC 3065, Australia. TEL 61-3-94160200, FAX 61-3-94160402. Ed. Ted Kramer. Pub. Maree Prince. Circ: 5,000.

330.994 AUS ISSN 1442-8636
HC601
AUSTRALIAN NATIONAL UNIVERSITY. CENTRE FOR ECONOMIC POLICY RESEARCH DISCUSSION PAPERS. Text in English. 1980. irreg. AUD 10 per issue (effective 2005). adv. **Document type:** *Academic/Scholarly.* **Description:** Covers studies of relevance to economic policy undertaken by the Economics Group research staff, visitors and students, and research presented at conferences held under the auspices of the Centre.
Formerly (until 1999): Australian National University. Centre for Economic Policy Research. Discussion Papers (0725-430X)
Media: Duplicated (not offset). **Related titles:** Online - full text ed.: 1999.
Indexed: WAE&RSA.
Published by: Australian National University, Centre for Economic Policy Research, Research School of Social Sciences, Coombs Bldg 9, Fellows Rd, Canberra, ACT 0200, Australia. TEL 61-2-61252118, FAX 61-2-61250182, cepr@anu.edu.au, http://cepr.anu.edu.au/discussionpapers.htm. Ed. Bruce Chapman. Adv. contact Chatherine Bairo.

AUSTRALIEN AKTUELL. see *POLITICAL SCIENCE—International Relations*

330.9 AUT ISSN 1605-4709
AUSTRIAN ECONOMIC QUARTERLY. Text in English. 199?. q. EUR 78 (effective 2005). adv. charts; mkt.; stat. index. **Document type:** *Bulletin, Trade.* **Description:** Covers all aspects of the Austrian economy and its relations with the European Union and Eastern Europe.
Media: Online - full content.
Published by: Oesterreichisches Institut fuer Wirtschaftsforschung/Austrian Institute of Economic Research, Postfach 91, Vienna, W 1103, Austria. TEL 43-1-79826010, FAX 43-1-7989386, office@wifo.ac.at, http://www.wifo.ac.at. Ed. Wolfgang Pollan. Adv. contact Christine Kautz.

330.9 AUT
AUSTRIAN INDUSTRIES. ANNUAL REPORT. Text in English. a. **Document type:** *Corporate.*
Published by: Austrian Industries AG, Kantgasse 1, Vienna, W 1015, Austria. TEL 01-71114, FAX 01-71114-245.

AUSZUEGE AUS PRESSEARTIKELN. see *BUSINESS AND ECONOMICS—Abstracting, Bibliographies, Statistics*

AUTOMOTIVE ECONOMY. see *TRANSPORTATION—Automobiles*

330 FRA ISSN 0045-1142
AUVERGNE ECONOMIQUE. Text in French. 1968. 8/yr. adv. bk.rev. illus.
Published by: Association Auvergne Economique, Aeroport de Clermont-Ferrand, Immeuble de Bureaux, Aulnat, 63510, France. TEL 33-4-73918181, FAX 33-4-73929364. Ed. Gerard Duval. Circ: 11,000.

AVANCE DE INFORMACION ECONOMICA. PRODUCTO INTERNO BRUTO TRIMESTRAL. see *BUSINESS AND ECONOMICS—Abstracting, Bibliographies, Statistics*

AVANTE; periodismo de analisis. see *POLITICAL SCIENCE*

330.9 USA
AVERAGE ANNUAL PAY LEVELS IN METROPOLITAN AREAS (YEAR). Text in English. a.?. **Document type:** *Government.*
Related titles: ◆ Series of: U.S. Bureau of Labor Statistics. National Office News Releases.
Published by: U.S. Department of Labor, Bureau of Labor Statistics, Postal Square Bldg., 2 Massachusetts Ave, NE, Washington, DC 20212-0001 . TEL 202-691-5200, http://www.bls.gov. **Subscr. to:** U.S. Government Printing Office, Superintendent of Documents.

AVERAGE RETAIL PRICES OF GOODS AND SERVICES BY RURAL AREAS. see *BUSINESS AND ECONOMICS—Abstracting, Bibliographies, Statistics*

AVIS ET DECISIONS DU CONSEIL DE LA CONCURRENCE. see *BUSINESS AND ECONOMICS—Banking And Finance*

330.9 KAZ
AZIYA-EKONOMIKA I ZHIZN'. Text in Russian. w. USD 295 in United States.
Address: Ul Furmanovo 103, Almaty, 480000, Kazakstan. TEL 3272-625233, yroslslav@almaty.kz. Ed. G G Dil'dyaev. **US dist. addr.:** East View Information Services, 3020 Harbor Ln. N., Minneapolis, MN 55447. TEL 612-550-0961.

330.9 DEU
B A W - MONATSBERICHT. (Bremer Ausschuss fuer Wirtschaftsforschung) Text in German. 1978. m. back issues avail. **Document type:** *Bulletin, Academic/Scholarly.*
Formerly (until 1986): Konjunkturspiegel
Related titles: Online - full text ed.
Published by: B A W Institut fuer Wirtschaftsforschung, Wilhelm-Herbst-Str 5, Bremen, 28359, Germany. TEL 49-421-206990, FAX 49-421-2069999, info@baw-bremen.de, http://www.baw.uni-bremen.de. Ed. Martha Pohl. Circ: 1,200.

330.9 GBR ISSN 1473-4400
B B C MONITORING GLOBAL NEWSLINE. AFRICA ECONOMIC. Text in English. d. **Document type:** *Newspaper, Consumer.*
Media: Online - full text.
Published by: B B C Monitoring, Caversham Park, Peppard Rd, Reading, Berks RG4 8TZ, United Kingdom. TEL 44-118-948-6289, FAX 44-118-946-3823, marketing@monitor.bbc.co.uk, http://www.monitor.bbc.co.uk.

B B C MONITORING GLOBAL NEWSLINE. AFRICA POLITICAL. see *POLITICAL SCIENCE*

330.9 GBR ISSN 1473-446X
B B C MONITORING GLOBAL NEWSLINE. ASIA PACIFIC ECONOMIC. Text in English. d.
Media: Online - full content.
Published by: B B C Monitoring, Caversham Park, Peppard Rd, Reading, Berks RG4 8TZ, United Kingdom. TEL 44-118-948-6289, FAX 44-118-946-3823, marketing@monitor.bbc.co.uk, http://www.monitor.bbc.co.uk.

B B C MONITORING GLOBAL NEWSLINE. ASIA PACIFIC POLITICAL. see *POLITICAL SCIENCE*

330.9 GBR ISSN 1473-4486
B B C MONITORING GLOBAL NEWSLINE. CENTRAL ASIA ECONOMIC. Text in English. d.
Media: Online - full content.
Published by: B B C Monitoring, Caversham Park, Peppard Rd, Reading, Berks RG4 8TZ, United Kingdom.

B B C MONITORING GLOBAL NEWSLINE. CENTRAL ASIA POLITICAL. see *POLITICAL SCIENCE*

330.9 GBR ISSN 1473-4508
B B C MONITORING GLOBAL NEWSLINE. EUROPE ECONOMIC. Text in English. d.
Media: Online - full content.
Published by: B B C Monitoring, Caversham Park, Peppard Rd, Reading, Berks RG4 8TZ, United Kingdom. http://www.monitor.bbc.co.uk.

B B C MONITORING GLOBAL NEWSLINE. EUROPE POLITICAL. see *POLITICAL SCIENCE*

330.9 GBR ISSN 1473-4524
B B C MONITORING GLOBAL NEWSLINE. FORMER SOVIET UNION ECONOMIC. Text in English. d.
Media: Online - full content.
Published by: B B C Monitoring, Caversham Park, Peppard Rd, Reading, Berks RG4 8TZ, United Kingdom. TEL 44-118-948-6289, FAX 44-118-946-3823, marketing@monitor.bbc.co.uk, http://www.monitor.bbc.co.uk.

B B C MONITORING GLOBAL NEWSLINE. LATIN AMERICA AND THE CARIBBEAN POLITICAL AND ECONOMIC. see *POLITICAL SCIENCE*

330.9 GBR ISSN 1473-4559
B B C MONITORING GLOBAL NEWSLINE. MIDDLE EAST ECONOMIC. Text in English. d.
Media: Online - full content.

B

Published by: B B C Monitoring, Caversham Park, Peppard Rd, Reading, Berks RG4 8TZ, United Kingdom. TEL 44-118-948-6289, FAX 44-118-946-3823, marketing@monitor.bbc.co.uk, http://www.monitor.bbc.co.uk.

B B C MONITORING GLOBAL NEWSLINE. MIDDLE EAST POLITICAL. see *POLITICAL SCIENCE*

330.9 GBR ISSN 1473-4605
B B C MONITORING GLOBAL NEWSLINE. SOUTH ASIA ECONOMIC. Text in English. d.
Media: Online - full content.
Published by: B B C Monitoring, Caversham Park, Peppard Rd, Reading, Berks RG4 8TZ, United Kingdom. TEL 44-118-948-6289, FAX 44-118-946-3823, marketing@monitor.bbc.co.uk, http://www.monitor.bbc.co.uk.

B B C MONITORING GLOBAL NEWSLINE. SOUTH ASIA POLITICAL. see *POLITICAL SCIENCE*

330.9 CAN
HC117.B8
B C FINANCIAL AND ECONOMIC REVIEW. (British Columbia Financial and Economic Review) Text in English. a. CND 25 (effective 1997). charts; maps. **Document type:** *Government.* **Description:** Describes BC's physical and institutional structure as well as presents information on provincial government programs and finances, economic developments and demographic trends.
Formerly: B C Economic and Statistical Review (0847-1525); Which was formed by the merger of: British Columbia. Ministry of Finance and Corporate Relations. Financial and Economic Review; British Columbia. Ministry of Finance and Corporate Relations. Facts and Statistics
Published by: Ministry of Finance and Corporate Relations, Sta Prov Govt, P O Box 9410, Victoria, BC V8W 9V1, Canada. TEL 250-387-0359, FAX 250-387-0380, kris_ovens@fincc04.fin.gov.bc.ca, bcstats@fincc04.fin.gov.bc.ca, http://www.bcstats.gov.bc.ca.

318 USA
B E B R MONOGRAPHS. Text in English. irreg., latest vol.8. USD 17. **Document type:** *Government.* **Description:** Provides in-depth analyses of topics relevant to an understanding of the Florida economy and business situation.
Published by: University of Florida, Bureau of Economic and Business Research, Warrington College of Business Administration, PO Box 117145, Gainesville, FL 32611-7145. TEL 352-392-0171, FAX 352-392-4739. **Co-sponsor:** College of Business Administration.

330.9 NZL ISSN 1170-4861
B E R L FORECASTS. Text in English. 1957. q. NZD 612.50 domestic; NZD 550 foreign (effective 2000). charts; illus.; stat. back issues avail. **Document type:** *Bulletin.* **Description:** Provides analysis, data, commentary and forecasts for the New Zealand economy; includes assessment of recent policy changes and proposals and impacts on employment, inflation, exports and industry.
Published by: Business & Economic Research Ltd., Level 5, 108 the Terrace, Wellington, New Zealand. TEL 64-4-4705550, FAX 64-4-4733276, innovate@bert.co.nz, http://www.berl.co.nz. Ed., R&P Ganesh Nana. Pub. Bryan Philpott. Circ: 200.

330.9 DEU
B F A I NEWS. Text in German. 4/yr. adv. **Document type:** *Bulletin, Government.*
Published by: Bundesagentur fuer Aussenwirtschaft, Agrippastr 87-93, Cologne, 50676, Germany. TEL 49-221-20570, FAX 49-221-2057212, info@bfai.de, http://www.bfai.com. adv.: B&W page EUR 4,900, color page EUR 5,900. Circ: 60,000 (controlled).

330.9 USA
B L S RELEASES: DEMOGRAPHIC DATA BOOK FOR STATES AND LARGE METROPOLITAN AREAS. Text in English. a. **Document type:** *Government.*
Related titles: ♦ Series of: U.S. Bureau of Labor Statistics. National Office News Releases.
Published by: U.S. Department of Labor, Bureau of Labor Statistics, Postal Square Bldg., 2 Massachusetts Ave, NE, Washington, DC 20212-0001 . http://www.bls.gov. **Subscr. to:** U.S. Government Printing Office, Superintendent of Documents, PO Box 371954, Pittsburgh, PA 15250-7954. TEL 202-512-1800, FAX 202-512-2250, gpoaccess@gpo.gov, http://www.access.gpo.gov.

330.9 USA ISSN 1058-7365
KJC6411.3
B N A'S EASTERN EUROPE REPORTER. Variant title: Eastern Europe Reporter. Text in English. 1991. bi-w. USD 1,295 (effective 1999). back issues avail. **Document type:** *Trade.* **Description:** Covers legislative, regulatory, and legal developments affecting business, trade, and investment in Eastern Europe and Russia.
Related titles: Online - full text ed.: (from The Bureau of National Affairs, Inc.).
—IE. CCC.
Published by: The Bureau of National Affairs, Inc., 1231 25th St., NW, Washington, DC 20037. TEL 202-452-4200, 800-372-1033, 800-452-7773, FAX 202-822-8092, customercare@bna.com, bnaplus@bna.com, http://www.bna.com. Ed. Linda G Botsford. Pub. Greg C McCaffery.

B N L BASIC STATISTICS ON THE ITALIAN ECONOMY. see *BUSINESS AND ECONOMICS—Abstracting, Bibliographies, Statistics*

330.9 FIN ISSN 1456-4564
B O F I T DISCUSSION PAPERS. Text in English. 1999. irreg. free. **Document type:** *Corporate.*
Related titles: ♦ Online - full text ed.: B O F I T Discussion Papers (Online Edition). ISSN 1456-5889.
Indexed: IBSS.
Published by: Bank of Finland, Institute for Economies in Transition (BOFIT), PL 160, Helsinki, 0010, Finland. TEL 358-9-183-2268, FAX 358-9-183-2294, bofit@bof.fi, http://www.bof.fi/bofit. Ed. Jukka Pirttila.

330.9 FIN ISSN 1456-5889
B O F I T DISCUSSION PAPERS (ONLINE EDITION). Text in English. 1999. irreg. free. **Document type:** *Academic/Scholarly.*
Media: Online - full text. **Related titles:** ♦ Print ed.: B O F I T Discussion Papers. ISSN 1456-4564.
Published by: Bank of Finland, Institute for Economies in Transition (BOFIT), P O Box 160, Helsinki, 00101, Finland. TEL 358-9-183-2268, FAX 358-9-183-2294, bofit@bof.fi, http://www.bof.fi/bofit. Ed. Jukka Pirttila.

330.9 FIN ISSN 1456-811X
B O F I T ONLINE. (Bank of Finland Institute for Economies in Transition) Text in English, Finnish. 1999. irreg. free. **Document type:** *Academic/Scholarly.*
Media: Online - full text.
Published by: Bank of Finland, Institute for Economies in Transition (BOFIT), P O Box 160, Helsinki, 00101, Finland. TEL 358-9-183-2268, FAX 358-9-183-2294, bofit@bof.fi, http://www.bof.fi/bofit. Eds. Iikka Korhonen, Tuomas Komulainen.

330.947 FIN
B O F I T RUSSIA REVIEW (ONLINE EDITION). Text in English. 1998. m. free (effective 2004). 4 p./no.; **Document type:** *Corporate.* **Description:** Focuses exclusively on recent developments in the Russian economy, public finances, and financial markets. In addition to this regular coverage, each issue contains commentary from an expert.
Formerly (until 2004): Russian Economy (Online Edition) (1456-5897)
Media: Online - full text. **Related titles:** ♦ Print ed.: Russian Economy. ISSN 1455-7355.
Published by: Bank of Finland, Institute for Economies in Transition (BOFIT), P O Box 160, Helsinki, 00101, Finland. TEL 358-9-183-2268, FAX 358-9-183-2294, bofit@bof.fi, http://www.bof.fi/bofit. Ed. Seija Lainela.

330.9 SLE
B S L BULLETIN. Text in English. 1995. s-a. free. bk.rev. charts; stat. **Document type:** *Bulletin, Trade.* **Description:** Discusses economic issues affecting Sierra Leone. Publishes speeches on various financial topics by prominent Bank of Sierra Leone officials and contains public notices.
Formed by the Jan. 1995 merger of: Bank of Sierra Leone. Economic Trends; Bank of Sierra Leone. Economic Review; Bank of Sierra Leone. Economic Report
Related titles: Online - full text ed.
Indexed: PAIS.
Published by: Bank of Sierra Leone, Siaka Stevens St, PO Box 30, Freetown, Sierra Leone. TEL 232-22-226501, FAX 232-22-224764, research@bankofsierraleone.org, http://www.bankofsierraleone.org. Ed. Andrina Coker. Circ: 400.

BAHAMAS DATELINE. see *BUSINESS AND ECONOMICS—Investments*

330.9 BHS ISSN 0067-2912
F1650
BAHAMAS HANDBOOK AND BUSINESSMAN'S ANNUAL. Text in English. 1960. a. USD 28 softcover; USD 39.95 hardcover (effective 2000). adv. index. **Description:** Leisure and vacation, business and finance in the Bahamas. Includes two A-Z listings of facts and figures.
Published by: Etienne Dupuch Jr. Publications Ltd., PO Box N 7513, Nassau, Bahamas. TEL 242-3235665, FAX 242-3235728, dupuch@bahamasnet.com, http://www.bahamasnet.com. Ed. Sylvia Dupuch. R&P S P Dupuch. Adv. contact Etienne Dupuch.

650 BHS ISSN 0005-397X
BAHAMIAN REVIEW. Text in English. 1952. 10/yr. USD 50. adv. bk.rev. charts; illus.
Published by: Bahamian Review Ltd., PO Box 494, Nassau, Bahamas. TEL 809-32-6-7416. Ed. William W Cartwright. Circ: 50,000.

338.9 CHL ISSN 1014-7810
HC121
BALANCE PRELIMINAR DE LAS ECONOMIAS DE AMERICA LATINA Y EL CARIBE (YEAR). Text in Spanish. 1985. a. USD 15 (effective 1999). back issues avail.
Formerly (until 1987): Balance Preliminar de la Economia Latinoamericana (1012-506X)
Related titles: ♦ English ed.: Preliminary Overview of the Economies of Latin America and the Caribbean. ISSN 1014-7802.
Published by: Comision Economica para America Latina y el Caribe/Economic Commission for Latin America and the Caribbean, Ave Dag Hammarskjold 3477, Vitacura, Santiago de Chile, Chile. TEL 56-2-471-2000, FAX 56-2-208-0252, publications@eclac.cl, http://www.eclac.cl. **Subscr. to:** United Nations Publications, Distribution and Sales Section, Palais des Nations, Rm C-116, 8-14 av de la Paix, Geneva 1211, Switzerland; United Nations Publications, Rm DC2-853, United Nations Bldg, 2 United Nations Plaza, New York, NY 10017.

330.9 FIN ISSN 1456-4963
BALTIC ECONOMIES; the quarter in review. Text in English. 1999. q. free. **Document type:** *Newsletter, Corporate.*
Related titles: ♦ Online - full text ed.: Baltic Economies (Online Edition). ISSN 1456-5900.
Published by: Bank of Finland, Institute for Economies in Transition (BOFIT), P O Box 160, Helsinki, 00101, Finland. TEL 358-9-183-2268, FAX 358-9-183-2294, bofit@bof.fi, http://www.bof.fi/bofit. Ed. Iikka Korhonen.

330.9 FIN ISSN 1456-5900
BALTIC ECONOMIES (ONLINE EDITION); the quarterly review. Text in English. 1999. q. free. **Document type:** *Corporate.*
Media: Online - full text. **Related titles:** ♦ Print ed.: Baltic Economies. ISSN 1456-4963.
Published by: Bank of Finland, Institute for Economies in Transition (BOFIT), P O Box 160, Helsinki, 00101, Finland. TEL 358-9-183-2268, FAX 358-9-183-2294, bofit@bof.fi, http://www.bof.fi/bofit. Ed. Iikka Korhonen.

330.9 ITA ISSN 0393-2400
HC301
BANCA D'ITALIA. BOLLETTINO ECONOMICO. Text in Italian. 1983. 2/yr. free. back issues avail. **Document type:** *Bulletin.*
Related titles: Online - full text ed.; English ed.: Banca d'Italia. Economic Bulletin. ISSN 0393-7704. 1985.
Indexed: PAIS, WBA.
Published by: Banca d'Italia, Via Nazionale 187, Rome, 00184, Italy. TEL 39-06-47922333, FAX 39-06-47922059, http://www.bancaditalia.it. Ed. Giancarlo Morcaldo. Circ: 16,000.

BANCO CENTRAL DE CHILE. BOLETIN MENSUAL. see *BUSINESS AND ECONOMICS—Banking And Finance*

BANCO CENTRAL DE CHILE. MEMORIA ANUAL. see *BUSINESS AND ECONOMICS—Banking And Finance*

330 HND
BANCO CENTRAL DE HONDURAS. INFORME ECONOMICO. Text in Spanish. 1960. a. charts; stat.
Published by: Banco Central de Honduras, Departamento de Estudios Economicos, 6a y 7a Avda. 1a Calle, Tegucigalpa D.C., Honduras.

330.9 HND
BANCO CENTRAL DE HONDURAS. MEMORIA (YEAR). Text in Spanish. 1950. a. charts; stat.
Former titles: Banco Central de Honduras. Memoria Anual (Year); Banco Central de Honduras. Memoria (0067-3218)
Published by: Banco Central de Honduras, Departamento de Estudios Economicos, 6a y 7a Avda., 1a Calle, Tegucigalpa D C, Honduras.

BANCO CENTRAL DE NICARAGUA. CARTA QUINCENAL. see *BUSINESS AND ECONOMICS—Banking And Finance*

330.9 NIC
BANCO CENTRAL DE NICARAGUA. DEPARTAMENTO DE ESTUDIOS ECONOMICOS. INDICADORES ECONOMICOS ✶. Text in Spanish. 1976. irreg. charts; stat.
Published by: Ministerio de Comercio Exterior (MICE), Apdo 2412, Managua, Nicaragua.

330.9 VEN ISSN 0067-3250
HC236
BANCO CENTRAL DE VENEZUELA. INFORME ECONOMICO. Text in Spanish. 1962. a. USD 13 (effective 2000).
Published by: Banco Central de Venezuela, Av Urdaneta Esq Las Carmelitas, Caracas, 1010, Venezuela. FAX 582-8611646, info@bcv.org.ve, http://www.bcv.org.ve.

330.9 918.6 ECU
BANCO CENTRAL DEL ECUADOR. CUENTAS NACIONALES ANUALES. Text in Spanish. 1981. a. free.
Formerly (until 1987): Banco Central del Ecuador. Division Tecnica. Cuentas Nacionales del Ecuador
Published by: Banco Central del Ecuador, Avenida 10 de Agosto y Briceno, Quito, Ecuador. TEL 593-2-2580158, uweb@uio.bce.fin.ec, http://www.bce.fin.ec. Circ: 6,000.

B

B

BANCO CENTRAL DEL PARAGUAY. GERENCIA DE ESTUDIOS ECONOMICOS. ESTADISTICAS ECONOMICAS. see
BUSINESS AND ECONOMICS—Abstracting, Bibliographies, Statistics

330.9   URY
BANCO CENTRAL DEL URUGUAY. CUENTAS NACIONALES.
Text in Spanish. a. free.
Published by: (Departamento de Estadisticas Economicas), Banco Central del Uruguay, Casilla 1467, Paysando y Florida, Montevideo, Uruguay. TEL 598-2-921782. Ed. Ariel E Collazo.

330   URY
BANCO CENTRAL DEL URUGUAY. SELECCION DE TEMAS.
Text in Spanish. q. free. charts; stat.
Formerly: Banco Central del Uruguay. Seleccion de Temas Economicos (0005-4755); Which superseded: Banco de la Republica Oriental del Uruguay. Boletin Mensual. Seleccion de Temas Economicos
Published by: Banco Central del Uruguay, Departamento de Estadisticas Economicas, Casilla 1467, Paysando y Florida, Montevideo, Uruguay.

330.9   ESP
BANCO DE BILBAO. ECONOMIC REPORT. Text in English. a. charts; stat.
Published by: (Servicio de Estudios), Banco de Bilbao, Gran via, 12, Bilbao, Spain.

330.9   ESP   ISSN 0522-1315
HG3190.B54
BANCO DE BILBAO. INFORME ECONOMICO. Text in Spanish. 1950. a. charts; stat.
Published by: Banco de Bilbao, Servicio de Estudios, Apartado 21, Bilbao, Vizcaya 48070, Spain.

330.9   ESP   ISSN 0210-3737
HC381
BANCO DE ESPANA. BOLETIN ECONOMICO. Text in Spanish. m. **Document type:** Bulletin.
Related titles: ◆ Supplement(s): Banco de Espana. Boletin Estadistico. ISSN 0005-4798.
Indexed: ELLIS.
—CINDOC.
Published by: Banco de Espana, Alcala 50, Madrid, 28014, Spain. TEL 34-91-3385180, FAX 34-91-3385320, http://www.bde.es.

330.946   ESP
BANCO DE ESPANA. CUENTAS FINANCIERAS. Text in Spanish. q.
Related titles: Online - full text ed.
Published by: Banco de Espana, Alcala 50, Madrid, 28014, Spain. TEL 34-91-3385180, FAX 34-91-3385320, http://www.bde.es/estadis/ccff/ccff.htm.

330.9   ESP   ISSN 1130-4987
HC381
BANCO DE ESPANA. ECONOMIC BULLETIN. Text in English. 1990. q. charts; stat. **Document type:** Bulletin.
Indexed: JEL.
Published by: Banco de Espana, Alcala 50, Madrid, 28014, Spain. TEL 34-91-3385180, FAX 34-91-3385320, http://www.bde.es.

330.946   ESP
BANCO DE ESPANA. ESTABILIDAD FINANCIERA. Text in Spanish. s-a.
Related titles: Online - full text ed.
Published by: Banco de Espana, Alcala 50, Madrid, 28014, Spain. TEL 34-91-3385180, FAX 34-91-3385320, http://www.bde.es.

330.946   ESP   ISSN 0213-2699
BANCO DE ESPANA. ESTUDIOS ECONOMICOS. serie azul.
Text in Spanish. 1972. irreg., latest vol.43, 1987.
Published by: Banco de Espana, Alcala 50, Madrid, 28014, Spain. TEL 34-91-3385180, FAX 34-91-3385320, http://www.bde.es.

BANCO DE LA REPUBLICA. REVISTA. see BUSINESS AND ECONOMICS—Banking And Finance

330.9   MEX
BANCO DE MEXICO. INDICADORES ECONOMICOS. Text in Spanish. 1972. m. MXP 800; USD 240 in the Americas; USD 300 in Europe; USD 360 elsewhere. charts; stat. **Description:** Contains statistics on monetary indicators, public finance, production, price and salary indexes.
Published by: Banco de Mexico, Subdireccion de Investigacion Economica y Bancaria, 06059 Mexico, Mexico, Ave. JUAREZ 90, Centro Urbano Benito Juarez, Del. Cuauhtemoc, Ciudad De Mexico, DF 06059, Mexico. TEL 525-761-8588.

BANCO DE MEXICO. INFORME ANUAL. see BUSINESS AND ECONOMICS—Banking And Finance

330.9   PRT   ISSN 0872-9794
BANCO DE PORTUGAL. BOLETIM ECONOMICO. Text in Portuguese. 1995. q.

Related titles: English ed.: Bank of Portugal. Economic Bulletin. ISSN 0872-9786.
Published by: Banco de Portugal, Rua do Ouro 27, Lisbon, 1100-150, Portugal. TEL 351-21-3213200, FAX 351-21-3464843, http://www.bportugal.pt.

338.9   BRA
BANCO DO NORDESTE DO BRASIL. SERIE ESTUDOS ECONOMICOS E SOCIAIS. Text in Portuguese. 1975. irreg.
Published by: Banco do Nordeste do Brasil, Celula da Administracao da Documentacao e Informacao, Av Paranjana, 5700, Passare, Fortaleza, CE 60740-000, Brazil. TEL 55-85-2993137, FAX 55-85-2993524.

330.9   ECU
BANCO NACIONAL DE FOMENTO. INFORME DE LABORES.
Text in Spanish. a. charts; illus.; stat.
Published by: (Departamento de Relaciones Publicas), Banco Nacional de Fomento, Apdo 685, Quito, Pichincha, Ecuador.

330.9   BRA
BANCO REGIONAL DE DESENVOLVIMENTO DO EXTREMO SUL. ANNUAL REPORT. Text in Portuguese. 1962. a. free. illus. **Document type:** Corporate.
Formed by the merger of: Banco Regional de Desenvolvimento do Extremo Sul. Relatorio da Diretoria (0522-2079); Banco Regional de Desenvolvimento do Extremo Sul. Relatorio Annual
Published by: Banco Regional de Desenvolvimento do Extremo Sul, Centro, Caixa Postal 139, Porto Alegre, RGS 90001-970, Brazil. TEL 55-051-225-5000, FAX 55-051-215-5050, TELEX 51-1229 BRDE BR. Circ: 1,000.

BANGKO SENTRAL REVIEW. see BUSINESS AND ECONOMICS—Banking And Finance

330.9   BGD   ISSN 0304-9345
HC440.8.A1
BANGLADESH BANK. BULLETIN. Text in English. 1973. m. BDT 50, USD 36.
Published by: (Department of Public Relations and Publications), Bangladesh Bank, Motijheel Commercial Area, Dhaka, 2, Bangladesh.

338 304.6   BGD   ISSN 0304-095X
HC440.8.A1
BANGLADESH DEVELOPMENT STUDIES. Text in English. 1973. q. BDT 200, USD 50. adv. bk.rev. charts; illus. index. reprints avail. **Document type:** Academic/Scholarly.
Supersedes: Bangladesh Economic Review (0304-2553)
Indexed: BAS, CTFA, EIP, I&DA, IBSS, JEL, KES, PAIS, PerIslam, PopulInd, RASB, RDA, REE&TA, RRTA, S&F, TriticAb, WAE&RSA.
—BLDSC (1861.620000), IE.
Published by: Bangladesh Unnayan Gobeshona Protishthan/Bangladesh Institute of Development Studies, E-17 Agargaon, Sher-e-Banglanagar, GPO Box 3854, Dhaka, 1207, Bangladesh. TEL 880-2-316959, FAX 880-2-833212, TELEX 642460 BHL BJ. Circ: 1,500.

338   BGD
BANGLADESH INSTITUTE OF DEVELOPMENT STUDIES. ANNUAL REPORT. Text in English. 1975. a. price varies.
Description: Discusses progress of current projects and plans for future research.
Formerly: Report on the Background, Current Programmes and Planned Development of the Bangladesh Institute of Development Studies
Published by: Bangladesh Unnayan Gobeshona Protishthan/Bangladesh Institute of Development Studies, E-17 Agargaon, Sher-e-Banglanagar, GPO Box 3854, Dhaka, 1207, Bangladesh. TEL 325401.

BANGLADESH NEWS. see ETHNIC INTERESTS

330   BGD
BANGLADESH: SELECTED ECONOMIC INDICATORS. Text in English. 1972. w.
Published by: (Department of Public Relations and Publications), Bangladesh Bank, Motijheel Commercial Area, Dhaka, 2, Bangladesh.

332   USA   ISSN 1540-3912
BANK CONTROLLERS REPORT. Text in English. m. USD 375 (effective 2004). **Document type:** Newsletter, Trade.
Description: Covers bank management, industry performance, investments, technology, and accounting developments for bank controllers.
Indexed: ABIn.
Published by: Sheshunoff Information Services Inc., 807 Las Cimas Pkwy, Ste 300, Austin, TX 78746. TEL 512-472-2244, 800-456-2340, FAX 512-305-6575, customercare.sis@sheshunoff.com, http://www.sheshunoff.com/store/821.html. Ed. Ruth Razook.

BANK MARKAZI JOMHOURI ISLAMI IRAN. BULLETIN. see BUSINESS AND ECONOMICS—Banking And Finance

330.9   IRN
BANK MARKAZI JOMHOURI ISLAMI IRAN. SURVEY OF THE LARGE MANUFACTURING INDUSTRIES. Text in Persian, Modern. q.
Formerly (until 1983): Bank Markazi Iran. Survey of the Large Manufacturing Industries
Published by: (Iran. Economic Statistics Department), Bank Markazi Jomhouri Islami Iran/Central Bank of the Islamic Republic of Iran, P O Box 11365-8531, Tehran, Iran. FAX 98-21-390323.

330.9   MYS
BANK NEGARA MALAYSIA. ANNUAL REPORT. Text in English, Malay. a. USD 45 in Asia; USD 55 in Europe; USD 60 in Africa. charts; stat. **Description:** Features a comprehensive material on economic developments and trends in Malaysia. Includes information on money and credit, public finance, real sector development (production, prices, wages and employment), and external sector developments (exchange rate, trade and balance of payments).
Published by: Bank Negara Malaysia/Central Bank of Malaysia, Jalan Dato'Onn, PO Box 10922, Kuala Lumpur, 50480, Malaysia. TEL 2988044, FAX 2912990. Circ: (controlled).

330.9   MYS   ISSN 0005-5115
HC445.5.A1
BANK NEGARA MALAYSIA. BULLETIN EKONOMI SUKU TAHUNAN/BANK NEGARA MALAYSIA. QUARTERLY ECONOMIC BULLETIN. Text in English, Malay. 1968. 3/yr. USD 60; USD 77 in Asia; USD 77 in Australasia; USD 77 in Europe; USD 85 in Africa; USD 85 in the Americas. charts; stat. **Document type:** Bulletin. **Description:** Covers international economic environment and Malaysian economy with major indicators such as annual change in GDP and monetary aggregates.
Indexed: BAS, KES, WBA.
—BLDSC.
Published by: Bank Negara Malaysia/Central Bank of Malaysia, Jalan Dato'Onn, PO Box 10922, Kuala Lumpur, 50480, Malaysia. TEL 03-2988044, FAX 03-2912990, TELEX MA 30201. Circ: (controlled).

BANK NEGARA MALAYSIA. STATISTICAL BULLETIN. see BUSINESS AND ECONOMICS—Abstracting, Bibliographies, Statistics

330.9   GBR   ISSN 1353-6737
HC251
BANK OF ENGLAND. INFLATION REPORT. Text in English. 1993. q. GBP 10.50 domestic; GBP 13 foreign; GBP 7 domestic to academics (UK only); GBP 3 newsstand/cover domestic; GBP 4 newsstand/cover foreign; GBP 2 newsstand/cover domestic to academics (UK only); GBP 27 domestic with Quarterly Bulletin; GBP 33 foreign with Quarterly Bulletin; GBP 18 domestic with Quarterly Bulletin (to academics (UK only)) (effective 2003). charts. 80 p./no. 2 cols./p.; back issues avail. **Document type:** Bulletin. **Description:** Seeks greater openness in explaining the basis of monetary policy. Analyzes inflationary trends and pressures and examines the range of intermediate indicators that help gauge the future path of inflation.
Related titles: Online - full text ed.
—BLDSC (4478.846300), IE, Infotrieve.
Published by: (Inflation Report Division), Bank of England, Publications Group, Threadneedle St, London, EC2R 8AH, United Kingdom. TEL 44-20-76014030, FAX 44-20-76013298, mapublications@bankofengland.co.uk, http://www.bankofengland.co.uk/.

330.9   GBR   ISSN 0005-5166
HG2994
BANK OF ENGLAND QUARTERLY BULLETIN. Text in English. 1960. q. GBP 21 domestic; GBP 25 in Europe; GBP 35 in Australasia, Japan, China, the Philippines & Korea; GBP 34 elsewhere; GBP 14 domestic to academics (UK only); GBP 6 newsstand/cover domestic; GBP 7 newsstand/cover in Europe; GBP 9 newsstand/cover elsewhere; GBP 4 newsstand/cover domestic to academics (UK only); GBP 27 domestic with Inflation Report; GBP 33 in Europe with Inflation Report; GBP 45 with Inflation Report (in Australasia, Japan, China, the Philippines & Korea); GBP 43 elsewhere with Inflation Report; GBP 18 domestic with Inflation Report (to academics (UK only)) (effective 2003). abstr.; stat.; charts. 2 cols./p.; back issues avail.; reprint service avail. from PQC,SCH. **Document type:** Bulletin. **Description:** Describes and assesses recent economic and financial developments at home and abroad.
Related titles: Microform ed.: (from PQC); Online - full text ed.: (from EBSCO Publishing, Northern Light Technology, Inc., ProQuest Information & Learning).
Indexed: ABIn, BPIA, CPM, CREJ, ELLIS, Emerald, IBSS, JEL, KES, M&MA, PAIS, RASB, WBA.
—BLDSC (7171.400000), IE, Infotrieve, ingenta. **CCC.**
Published by: (Inflation Report Division), Bank of England, Publications Group, Threadneedle St, London, EC2R 8AH, United Kingdom. TEL 44-20-76014030, FAX 44-20-76013298, mapublications@bankofengland.co.uk, http://www.bankofengland.co.uk/qb/index.htm.

330.9   GHA   ISSN 0855-0964
HG517.G6
BANK OF GHANA. QUARTERLY ECONOMIC BULLETIN. Text in English. 1961. q. free. charts; stat. **Document type:** *Bulletin.*
Published by: Bank of Ghana, Information Documentation and Publications Services Department, Accra, Ghana. TEL 233-21-66902-8, TELEX 2052 GHBANK. Circ: 3,000.

330.9   USA   ISSN 0893-0732
HC687.H3
BANK OF HAWAII BUSINESS TRENDS; a newsletter report of business and economic conditions in Hawaii. Text in English. 1956. bi-m. free. stat. back issues avail. **Document type:** *Newsletter.*
Former titles: Bank of Hawaii. Review of Business and Economic Conditions; Bank of Hawaii Monthly Review (0005-5204)
Related titles: Online - full text ed.
Published by: Bank of Hawaii, Economics Department, PO Box 2900, Honolulu, HI 96846. TEL 808-537-8307, FAX 808-536-9433, http://www.boh.com/econ/. Ed. Paul H Brewbaker. Circ: 13,000.

332   IND   ISSN 0005-5212
BANK OF INDIA. BULLETIN. Text in English. 1962. m. INR 12. charts; stat. **Document type:** *Bulletin.*
Published by: Bank of India, Express Towers, Nariman Point, Mumbai, Maharashtra 400 021, India. TEL 203-3020, FAX 202-2831, TELEX 011-2281 IN. Ed. S A Shetty. Circ: 6,000.

332   ISR   ISSN 0334-441X
BANK OF ISRAEL. ECONOMIC REVIEW. Text in English. 1955. irreg., latest vol.72. ILS 33 (effective 2000). stat.
Formerly: Bank of Israel. Bulletin (0005-5220)
Related titles: Hebrew ed.
Indexed: IHP, JEL, KES, PAIS, WBA.
Published by: (Research Department), Bank of Israel, Kiryath Ben Gurion, P O Box 780, Jerusalem, 91007, Israel. Eds. Alan Hercberg, Dorothea Shefer. Circ: 1,000.

330   ISR   ISSN 0333-7073
BANK OF ISRAEL. RECENT ECONOMIC DEVELOPMENTS. Text in English, Hebrew. q. ILS 18 (effective 2000).
Indexed: WBA.
Published by: (Research Department), Bank of Israel, Kiryath Ben Gurion, P O Box 780, Jerusalem, 91007, Israel. http://www.bankisrael.gov.il/.

330.9   KOR
BANK OF KOREA. QUARTERLY ECONOMIC REVIEW. Text in English. 1969. q.
Formerly: Bank of Korea. Quarterly Economic Report
Indexed: APEL, BAS, IBSS, PAIS, WBA.
Published by: Bank of Korea, Research Department, 110 3 Ka Namdaemun Ro, Chung-Ku, Seoul, 100794, Korea, S. TEL 82-2759-4172, FAX 82-2-752-0946, bokdrar@bok.or.kr, http://www.bok.or.kr. Ed. Seong Tae Lee.

BANK OF KOREA. RESEARCH DEPARTMENT. ECONOMIC PAPERS. see *BUSINESS AND ECONOMICS—Banking And Finance*

330.9   LBY   ISSN 0067-3714
BANK OF LIBYA. ANNUAL REPORT OF THE BOARD OF DIRECTORS∗ . Text in English. 1957. a. free. **Document type:** *Corporate.*
Related titles: Arabic ed.: 1957.
Published by: (Economic Research Division), Bank of Libya, P O Box 1103, Tripoli, Libya.

330.9   LBY   ISSN 0005-5271
BANK OF LIBYA. ECONOMIC RESEARCH DIVISION. ECONOMIC BULLETIN∗ . Text in Arabic, English. 1961. bi-m. free. charts; mkt. **Document type:** *Bulletin.*
Indexed: PAIS.
Published by: Bank of Libya, P O Box 1103, Tripoli, Libya. Circ: 2,000.

332.1   SLE
BANK OF SIERRA LEONE. ANNUAL REPORT AND STATEMENT OF ACCOUNTS. Text in English. a. free. charts; illus. **Document type:** *Corporate.* **Description:** Reports on the fiscal indicators for the Bank of Sierra Leone.
Formerly: Bank of Sierra Leone. Annual Report (0067-3730)
Related titles: Online - full text ed.
Published by: Bank of Sierra Leone, Siaka Stevens St, PO Box 30, Freetown, Sierra Leone. TEL 232-22-226501, FAX 232-22-224764, research@bankofsierraleone.org, http://www.bankofsierraleone.org. Circ: 400.

332   SDN
BANK OF SUDAN. ECONOMIC AND FINANCIAL STATISTICS REVIEW. Text in English. 1960. q. free. charts; stat. **Description:** Details Sudan's economic conditions through tables showing the trade balance, balance of payments, the deficit, loans, foreign reserves, imports and exports by commodity, and industrial production and consolidation sheet.
Formerly (until vol.17, no.2, 1976): Bank of Sudan. Economic and Financial Bulletin (0005-5336)
Media: Duplicated (not offset). **Related titles:** Arabic ed.
Indexed: NumL.

Published by: (Statistics Dept.), Bank of Sudan, P O Box 313, Khartoum, Sudan. TEL 78064, TELEX 22559 ELBNK SD. Circ: 1,000.

332   TWN   ISSN 0005-5344
HC430.5
BANK OF TAIWAN QUARTERLY. Key Title: Taiwan Yinhang Jikan. Text in Chinese. 1947. q. TWD 150. charts; illus.; stat. index. **Document type:** *Academic/Scholarly.*
Published by: Bank of Taiwan, Economic Research Department, 198 Chung Hua Rd, Sec 1, Taipei, 108, Taiwan. TEL 383211, FAX 3895294. Ed. Y T Ting. Pub. M S Tsai. Circ: 1,500. **Dist. by:** Chung-Hwa Book Co. Ltd., 94 Chungking S. Rd Sec 1, Taipei, Taiwan.

330 332   TZA   ISSN 0067-3757
BANK OF TANZANIA. ECONOMIC AND OPERATIONS REPORT (YEAR). Text in English. a. free. charts; stat. **Document type:** *Corporate.* **Description:** Details economic developments and operations for the year.
Formerly: Bank of Tanzania. Economic Report (0067-3765)
Published by: Bank of Tanzania, Research Department, PO Box 2939, Dar es Salaam, Tanzania. TEL 255-51-110495-7, FAX 255-51-113325, TELEX 41024 TZ. Circ: 3,000.

330.9   TZA   ISSN 0856-101X
BANK OF TANZANIA. ECONOMIC BULLETIN. Text in English. 1969. q. free or on exchange basis. charts; stat. **Document type:** *Bulletin, Trade.* **Description:** Discusses finance, credit, trade, and development in Tanzania.
Indexed: KES.
Published by: Bank of Tanzania, Research Department, PO Box 2939, Dar es Salaam, Tanzania. TEL 255-51-110495-7, FAX 255-51-113325, TELEX 41024 TZ. Circ: 2,500.

330   THA
BANK OF THAILAND. ANNUAL ECONOMIC REPORT. Text in Thai. a. USD 11; USD 11.50 in Asia; USD 13 to Europe, Africa & Oceania; USD 14.50 in the Americas (effective 2000). **Document type:** *Corporate.*
Published by: Bank of Thailand, Information & Public Relations Group, PO Box 154, Hua Lamphong BPC, 10331, Thailand. TEL 662-283-5619, FAX 662-280-4591. Circ: 1,800.

330.9   THA   ISSN 0125-605X
HG3300.55
BANK OF THAILAND. QUARTERLY BULLETIN. Text in Thai. 1961. q. USD 23; USD 29 in Asia; USD 33 in Europe, Africa & Oceania; USD 37 in the Americas; USD 5.75 per issue; USD 7.25 per issue in Asia; USD 8.25 per issue in Europe, Africa & Oceania; USD 9.25 per issue in the Americas (effective 2000). index. **Document type:** *Bulletin.*
Former titles (until 1981): Bank of Thailand. Monthly Bulletin (0005-5352); Bank of Thailand Monthly Report
Indexed: APEL, KES, PAIS, RASB, RefZh, WBA.
Published by: Bank of Thailand, Information & Public Relations Group, PO Box 154, Hua Lamphong BPC, 10331, Thailand. TEL 662-283-5619, FAX 662-280-4591. Circ: 1,700.

330.9   USA
BANK ONE ARIZONA BLUE CHIP ECONOMIC FORECAST. Text in English. 1984. m. USD 99 (effective 1998). illus. back issues avail. **Document type:** *Newsletter.* **Description:** Contains consensus economic forecasts by month for Arizona, given by 22 economists representing banks, universities, companies and state agencies.
Formerly: Arizona Blue Chip Economic Forecast (1042-6787)
Related titles: ◆ Supplement(s): Greater Phoenix Blue Chip Economic Forecast. ISSN 1093-8931.
Indexed: SRI.
Published by: Arizona State University, Bank One Economic Outlook Center, PO Box 874406, Tempe, AZ 85287-4406. TEL 602-965-5543, 800-448-0432, FAX 602-965-5458, ruth.mcclarnon@asu.edu. Ed. Tracy Clark. Circ: 790.

330.9   IDN
BANK PEMBANGUNAN INDONESIA. BULLETIN EKONOMI BAPINDO. Text in Indonesian. m.
Published by: Bank Pembangunan Indonesia/Development Bank of Indonesia, 2-4 Jalan Gondangdia Lama, P.O. Box 140, Jakarta, Indonesia.

330.9   DEU
BANKGESELLSCHAFT BERLIN. DEVISENBRIEF. Text in German. 1983. fortn. free. **Document type:** *Bulletin, Trade.*
Published by: Bankgesellschaft Berlin AG, Alexanderplatz 2, Berlin, 10178, Germany. TEL 49-30-31092860, FAX 49-30-31095031. Circ: 4,600 (controlled).

330.9   DEU
BANKGESELLSCHAFT BERLIN. WIRTSCHAFTSBERICHT. Text in German. 1951. 2/yr. free. charts; stat. **Document type:** *Corporate.*
Formerly: Berliner Bank. Wirtschaftsbericht (0005-9277)
Published by: Bankgesellschaft Berlin AG, Alexanderplatz 2, Berlin, 10178, Germany. TEL 49-30-31092860, FAX 49-30-31095031. Circ: 12,100.

BANQUE DE FRANCE. BULLETIN. see *BUSINESS AND ECONOMICS—Banking And Finance*

BANQUE DE FRANCE. BULLETIN. SUPPLEMENT STATISTIQUES. see *BUSINESS AND ECONOMICS— Banking And Finance*

330.9   FRA   ISSN 0242-5815
BANQUE DE FRANCE. ENQUETE MENSUELLE DE CONJONCTURE. Text in French; Summaries in English. 1965. m. (11/yr.). looseleaf. EUR 91 (effective 2002). charts; stat.
Formerly: Situation Economique (0037-5926)
Related titles: ◆ Series of: Collection Conjoncture. ISSN 1152-4952.
Indexed: PAIS.
Published by: Banque de France, Service Relations avec le Public, 48 rue Croix-des-Petits-Champs, Paris, 75049, France. TEL 33-1-42923908, FAX 33-1-42923940, http://www.banque-france.fr. Ed. M Cauchi.

330.9   FRA   ISSN 0429-338X
BANQUE DE FRANCE. LA ZONE FRANC. RAPPORT ANNUEL (YEAR). Variant title: Banque de France. La Zone Franc. Rapport. Text in French. 1953. a. EUR 22 (effective 2003).
Published by: Banque de France, Service Relations avec le Public, 48 rue Croix-des-Petits-Champs, Paris, 75049, France. TEL 33-1-42923908, FAX 33-1-42923940, http://www.banque-france.fr.

330.9   EGY   ISSN 0005-5603
BANQUE DE PORT-SAID. REVUE ECONOMIQUE TRIMESTRIELLE. Text in French. 1929. q. free. charts; mkt.; stat.
Related titles: Arabic ed.: 1961.
Published by: Banque de Port-Said, 18 Rue Talaat Harb, Alexandria, Egypt. Ed. Mahmoud Sami Mohamed El Adawy.

BANQUE NATIONALE DE BELGIQUE. BULLETIN STATISTIQUE. see *BUSINESS AND ECONOMICS—Banking And Finance*

330.9   FRA
BANQUE SUDAMERIS. ETUDES ECONOMIQUES. Text in English, French, Italian, Spanish. 1954. irreg. (2-3/yr.). free. charts; stat. **Document type:** *Bulletin.* **Description:** Comprises an examination of economic situations in Latin American countries.
Formerly: Banque Francaise et Italienne. Etudes Economiques (0014-2042)
Indexed: PAIS.
Published by: Banque SudAmeris, 4 rue Meyerbeer, Paris, Cedex 9 75429, France. TEL 33-1-42463213, FAX 33-1-48017987, TELEX SUDIR 641669. Ed. Jean Luc Chalumeau.

330.9   BRB
BARBADOS. MINISTRY OF FINANCE AND ECONOMIC AFFAIRS. ECONOMIC REPORT. Text in English. 1977. a. USD 7.50 (effective 1995). **Document type:** *Government.*
Formerly (until 1988): Barbados. Ministry of Finance and Planning. Economic Report
Published by: Ministry of Finance and Economic Affairs, Government Printery, Bay St., St Michael, Barbados. Circ: 500.

330.9   USA   ISSN 1092-3608
BARTERNEWS. Text in English. 1979. q. USD 40 domestic; USD 54 foreign; USD 10 newsstand/cover (effective 2001). adv. bk.rev. 100 p./no. 3 cols./p.; back issues avail. **Document type:** *Trade.* **Description:** Contains how-to information as well as scores of barter contacts & unique trades.
Published by: BarterNews Publications, PO Box 3024, Mission Viejo, CA 92690. TEL 949-831-0607, FAX 949-831-9378, bmeyer@barternews.com, http://www.barternews.com. Ed., Pub., R&P, Adv. contact Bob Meyer. page USD 4,000; trim 8 x 10. Circ: 32,500 (paid and controlled).

330.9   USA   ISSN 0094-1115
HC107.I2
BASIC ECONOMIC DATA FOR IDAHO. Text in English. a. stat. **Document type:** *Government.*
Supersedes in part: Labor Force in Idaho and Basic Economic Data for Idaho
Related titles: Microfiche ed.: (from CIS).
Indexed: SRI.
Published by: Idaho Department of Labor, Public Affairs, 317 W Main St, Boise, ID 83735. TEL 208-334-6168, http://www.labor.state.id.us. Ed. Janeel Hyer.

330.9   CHN
BEIJING JINGJI BAO/BEIJING ECONOMIC INFORMATION NEWS. Text in Chinese. w. (6/week). CNY 14 per month (effective 2004). **Document type:** *Newspaper, Consumer.*
Address: 21, Kuotaimen Hutong, Beijing Xuanwucai Shi, 100052, China. TEL 86-10-63031803. **Dist. by:** China International Book Trading Corp, 35 Chegongzhuang Xilu, Haidian District, PO Box 399, Beijing 100044, China. TEL 86-10-68412045, FAX 86-10-68412023, cibtc@mail.cibtc.com.cn, http://www.cibtc.com.cn.

BEKNOPT OVERZICHT VAN DE SOCIALE ZEKERHEID IN BELGIE/SURVEY OF SOCIAL SECURITY IN BELGIUM. see *PUBLIC ADMINISTRATION*

B

▼ *new title*   ➤ *refereed*   ∗ *unverified*   ◆ *full entry avail.*

B

BELGIUM. FEDERAAL MINISTERIE VAN SOCIALE ZAKEN, VOLKSGEZONDHEID EN LEEFMILIEU. HANIDGIDS/GUIDE OF THE DISABLED PERSON. see *HANDICAPPED*

BELGIUM. INSTITUT NATIONAL DE STATISTIQUE. COMMUNIQUE HEBDOMADAIRE. see *BUSINESS AND ECONOMICS—Abstracting, Bibliographies, Statistics*

BELGIUM. INSTITUT NATIONAL DE STATISTIQUE. EMPLOI ET CHOMAGE. ENQUETE SUR LES FORCES DE TRAVAIL (YEAR). see *BUSINESS AND ECONOMICS—Abstracting, Bibliographies, Statistics*

BELGIUM. INSTITUT NATIONAL DE STATISTIQUE. ENQUETE SUR LES BUDGETS DES MENAGES. see *BUSINESS AND ECONOMICS—Abstracting, Bibliographies, Statistics*

BELGIUM. INSTITUT NATIONAL DE STATISTIQUE. INDUSTRIE ET CONSTRUCTION. see *BUSINESS AND ECONOMICS—Abstracting, Bibliographies, Statistics*

BELGIUM. INSTITUT NATIONAL DE STATISTIQUE. MEDIA. NOMBRE DE LICENCES D'APPAREILS DE RADIO SUR VEHICULE ET DE TELEVISION. see *BUSINESS AND ECONOMICS—Abstracting, Bibliographies, Statistics*

BELGIUM. INSTITUT NATIONAL DE STATISTIQUE. NOUVELLES ECONOMIQUES. see *BUSINESS AND ECONOMICS—Abstracting, Bibliographies, Statistics*

BELGIUM. INSTITUT NATIONAL DE STATISTIQUE. STATISTIQUES DU TRANSPORT. PARC DES VEHICULES A MOTEUR AU (YEAR). see *TRANSPORTATION—Abstracting, Bibliographies, Statistics*

BELGIUM. NATIONAAL INSTITUUT VOOR DE STATISTIEK. ECONOMISCHE NIEUWS. see *BUSINESS AND ECONOMICS—Abstracting, Bibliographies, Statistics*

BELGIUM. NATIONAAL INSTITUUT VOOR DE STATISTIEK. INDUSTRIE EN BOUWNIJVERHEID. see *BUSINESS AND ECONOMICS—Abstracting, Bibliographies, Statistics*

BELGIUM. NATIONAAL INSTITUUT VOOR DE STATISTIEK. MEDIA. AANTAL VERGUNNINGEN VOOR AUTORADIO'S EN TELEVISIETOESTELLEN. see *BUSINESS AND ECONOMICS—Abstracting, Bibliographies, Statistics*

BELGIUM. NATIONAAL INSTITUUT VOOR DE STATISTIEK. VERVOERSTATISTIEKEN. MOTORVOERTUIGENPARK OP (YEAR). see *TRANSPORTATION—Abstracting, Bibliographies, Statistics*

BELGIUM. NATIONAAL INSTITUUT VOOR DE STATISTIEK. WEEKBERICHT. see *BUSINESS AND ECONOMICS—Abstracting, Bibliographies, Statistics*

BELGIUM. NATIONAAL INSTITUUT VOOR DE STATISTIEK. WERKGELEGENHEID EN WERKLOOSHEID. ENQUETE NAAR DE ARBEIDSKRACHTEN (YEAR). see *BUSINESS AND ECONOMICS—Abstracting, Bibliographies, Statistics*

330.9 DEU
➤ **BERNHARD-HARMS-VORLESUNGEN.** Text in German, English. irreg., latest vol.19, 2000. EUR 6 (effective 2002). **Document type:** *Monographic series, Academic/Scholarly.* **Description:** Contains lectures distinguished by having been awarded the Bernhard Harms Prize.
Published by: Institut fuer Weltwirtschaft, Duesternbrooker Weg 120, Kiel, 24105, Germany. TEL 49-431-8814305, FAX 49-431-85853, info@ifw.uni-kiel.de, http://www.uni-kiel.de/ifw. Ed. Horst Siebert.

330.9 DEU ISSN 0939-415X
HJ1150.A2
BETRIEB UND WIRTSCHAFT; Zeitschrift fuer Rechnungswesen, Steuern, Wirtschafts-, Arbeits- und Sozialrecht im Betrieb. Text in German. 1947. fortn. EUR 99 domestic; EUR 141 foreign; EUR 6 newsstand/cover (effective 2004). adv. bk.rev. index, cum.index. 50 p./no.; **Document type:** *Newspaper, Trade.* **Description:** Covers all aspects of the financial economy in eastern Germany, such as social insurance, productivity, rationalization, financial planning, labor efficiency, and government policies.
Former titles: Sozialistische Finanzwirtschaft (0012-0103); Deutsche Finanzwirtschaft
Indexed: PAIS, RASB, RefZh.
—BLDSC (1946.809000), IE, Infotrieve.
Published by: Huss-Medien GmbH, Am Friedrichshain 22, Berlin, 10407, Germany. TEL 49-30-42151381, FAX 49-30-4215123, verlag.wirtschaft@hussberlin.de, http://www.betrieb-und-wirtschaft.de, http://www.huss-medien.de. Ed. Brigitte Gebhardt. Adv. contact Kathrin Pobering TEL 49-30-42151343. B&W page EUR 1,740, color page EUR 2,970; trim 182 x 265. Circ: 8,000 (controlled).

330 IND ISSN 0006-0488
BHARAT SEVAK✶. Text in English. 1966. m. INR 6. adv. charts; illus.; stat.
Address: House No. 600, Sector 16-D, Chandigarh, Chandigarh 17, India. Ed. B D Nanda.

330.9 BRA
BIBLIOTECA DE ECONOMIA✶. Text in Portuguese. 1977. irreg.
Published by: Edicoes Graal Ltda., Rua Hermenegildo de Barros 31A, Gloria, RJ 20240, Brazil.

330.9 CHE ISSN 0772-4861
BILAN; le magazine economique suisse. Text in French. 1989. m. adv. bk.rev. **Document type:** *Magazine, Trade.*
Related titles: Online - full text ed.; ♦ Dutch ed.: Balans. ISSN 0772-4853.
Published by: Agedip S.A., 33 av de la Gare, Lausanne, 1001, Switzerland. TEL 41-21-3494822, FAX 41-21-3494830, bilan@bilan.ch, http://www.bilan.ch. Ed., R&P Alain Jeannet. adv.: B&W page CHF 6,100, color page CHF 9,750; trim 187 x 253. Circ: 18,453 (paid).

330.9 CHE ISSN 1022-3487
BILANZ; Schweizer Wirtschafts Magazin. Text in French. 1960. m. CHF 132 domestic; CHF 167 in Europe; CHF 254.50 elsewhere; CHF 12 newsstand/cover (effective 2002). adv. bk.rev. illus. **Document type:** *Magazine, Consumer.*
Supersedes (in 1977): Wirtschaftsrevue (0510-5528); (in 1962): Schweizerische Wirtschaftszeitung
Related titles: Online - full text ed.
Published by: Jean Frey AG, Foerrlibuckstr 10, Zuerich, 8021, Switzerland. TEL 41-1-4487221, FAX 41-1-4487665, verlag@bilanz.ch, http://www2.bilanz.ch/home/index.cfm. Ed. Medard Meier. adv.: page CHF 17,700; trim 187 x 240. Circ: 57,110 (paid).

330.9 ETH
BIRRITU. Text in Amharic, English. 1981. bi-m. per issue exchange basis. adv. **Document type:** *Government.* **Description:** Includes articles, features and news on banking and insurance. Provides a forum for intelligent informed debates.
Supersedes: Financial Institutions Forum
Published by: National Bank of Ethiopia, c/o Documentation Division, PO Box 5550, Addis Ababa, Ethiopia. Circ: 6,000.

330.9 RUS
BIZNES I POLITIKA. Text in Russian. m. (US $129.95).
Related titles: Microform ed.: (from EVP).
Indexed: RASB.
Published by: Firma Ankil, Elizavetinskii pr-d 6-1, ofis 23, Moscow, 107005, Russian Federation. TEL 7-095-4349395, FAX 7-095-2653718. Ed. I G Kosikov. **US dist. addr.:** East View Information Services, 3020 Harbor Ln. N., Minneapolis, MN 55447. TEL 612-550-0961.

330.9 TJK
BIZNES I POLITIKA. Text in Russian. w. USD 299 in United States.
Indexed: RASB.
Address: Sherozi pr 16, Dushanbe, 734018, Tajikistan. TEL 7-33-43-96. Ed. Nina Pak. **US dist. addr.:** East View Information Services, 3020 Harbor Ln. N., Minneapolis, MN 55447. TEL 612-550-0961.

330.9 CAN ISSN 0381-7245
HF3223
BLUE BOOK OF CANADIAN BUSINESS (YEAR). Text in English. 1954. a. CND 189.95 domestic; USD 189.95 foreign (effective 2002). illus. back issues avail. **Document type:** *Directory, Trade.* **Description:** Provides current facts and figures on Canada's leading business enterprises.
Former titles (until 1976): National Reference Book (0470-2190); (until 1956): National Reference Book on Canadian Business Personalities with Other General Information for Library, Newspaper and Individual Use (0702-3693)
Related titles: Online - full content ed.: 1999. CND 299.90 domestic; USD 299.90 foreign (effective 1999 & 2000).
—CISTI.
Published by: Canadian Newspaper Services International Ltd, 8130 Sheppard Ave E, Ste 208, Toronto, ON M1B 3W2, Canada. TEL 416-752-1992, 888-422-4742, FAX 416-752-8303, 888-422-4749, info@bluebook.ca, http://www.bluebook.ca/. Circ: 2,800.

330.9 USA ISSN 0193-4600
BLUE CHIP ECONOMIC INDICATORS; what top economists are saying about the US outlook for the year ahead. Text in English. 1975. m. USD 665; USD 789 combined subscription print & online eds (effective 2005). **Document type:** *Newsletter.* **Description:** Provides current economic forecasts for top management, corporate planners, market research directors, economists, bankers, brokers and investors.
Related titles: E-mail ed.: USD 665 (effective 2005).
Indexed: PROMT.
Published by: Aspen Publishers, Inc. (Subsidiary of: Wolters Kluwer N.V.), 111Eighth Ave., 7th Fl, New York, NY 10011. TEL 212-771-0600, FAX 212-771-0885, customer.service@aspenpubl.com, http://www.aspenpublishers.com/Product.asp?catalog%5Fname=Aspen&category%5Fname=&product%5Fid=SS01934600&Mode=SEARCH&ProductType=L. Ed. Randell Moore. **Subscr. to:** Customer Care, 7201 McKinney Circle, Frederick, MD 21704. TEL 800-234-1660, FAX 800-901-9075.

330.9 USA ISSN 1062-9327
HD5723
BLUE CHIP JOB GROWTH UPDATE; ranking the states and MSAs. Text in English. 1990. m. USD 79 (effective 1998). back issues avail. **Document type:** *Newsletter.* **Description:** Presents nonagricultural establishment survey data ranked according to the percentage change in jobs for each of the major employment sectors.
Formerly (until 1992): Job Growth Update (1051-5615)
Published by: Arizona State University, Bank One Economic Outlook Center, PO Box 874406, Tempe, AZ 85287-4406. TEL 602-965-5543, 800-448-0432, FAX 602-965-5458, ruth.mcclarnon@asu.edu. Eds. Lee Mepheters, Yolanda Strozier. Circ: 135.

330.9 GBR
BOARD EARNINGS IN FT-SE 100 COMPANIES. Text in English. a. **Document type:** *Corporate.*
Published by: Monks Partnership Ltd., Monks Partnership, The Mill House, Royston Rd, Wendens Ambo, Saffron Walden, Essex CB11 4JX, United Kingdom. TEL 44-1799-542222, FAX 44-1799-541805, info@monkspartnership.co.uk. R&P David Atkins.

BOLETIM CONJUNTURAL DO NORDESTE DO BRASIL. see *BUSINESS AND ECONOMICS—Abstracting, Bibliographies, Statistics*

330.9 BRA
BOLETIM DE CONJUNTURA (SAO PAULO). Text in Portuguese. 1996. m. free. adv. **Document type:** *Newsletter.* **Description:** Provides macroeconomic analysis and coverage of economic policies.
Related titles: E-mail ed.
Published by: Pontificia Universidade Catolica de Sao Paulo, Faculdade de Fonoaudiologia, Rua Monte Alegre, 984, Perdizes, Sao Paulo, SP 05014-001, Brazil. TEL 55-11-3670-8136, FAX 55-11-3670-8503, boltim@uol.com.br. Pub. Rubens R Samata.

330.9 CUB
BOLETIN DE INFORMACION SOBRE ECONOMIA CUBANA. Text in Spanish; Contents page in English, Spanish. 1991. q. USD 40 for 2 yrs.. bk.rev. bibl.; stat. **Document type:** *Bulletin.* **Description:** Contains feature articles on the Cuban economy.
Formerly (until 1991): Boletin de Informacion sobre Estudios Cubanos
Related titles: Diskette ed.
Published by: Centro de Investigaciones de la Economia Mundial, Quinta Ave., No. 2010, Esquina a 22, Miramar, La Playa, Ciudad de La Habana, Cuba. TEL 537-242507. Ed. George Carriazo Moreno. Circ: 300.

330.9 ESP ISSN 0212-6621
BOLETIN ECONOMICO DE ANDALUCIA. Text in Spanish. 1983. s-a.
—CINDOC.
Published by: Junta de Andalucia, Consejeria de Economia y Hacienda, Edif. Torretriana, Isla de Cartuja, Sevilla, 41092, Spain. TEL 34-955-065000, http://www.ceh.junta-andalucia.es.

330.9 ESP ISSN 0210-1947
BOLETIN ECONOMICO DE LA CONSTRUCCION. Text in Catalan, Spanish. 1940. q. **Document type:** *Bulletin.*
Address: Emancipacio, 28-30, Barcelona, 08022, Spain. TEL 2112121, FAX 2112204. Ed. Balcells Gorina.

338 MWI
BOMA LATHU. 1964-1969; resumed 1973. m. free. adv. **Description:** Development information on the island country of Malawi.
Formerly: Malawi Mwezi Uno-Malawi This Month (0025-1240)
Published by: Department of Information, PO Box 494, Blantyre, Malawi. TEL 265-620266. Ed. J C Tumbwe. Circ: 150,000.

650 IND ISSN 0006-6974
BOMBAY MARKET. Text in English. 1970 (vol.34). fortn. INR 60. adv. illus.; mkt.; stat.
Address: 505 Arun Chambers, Tardeo Rd., Mumbai, Maharashtra 400 034, India. Ed. K Multani.

330.9 USA
BOOT COVE ECONOMIC FORECAST. Text in English. 1978. m. USD 380. back issues avail.
Related titles: Online - full text ed.
Published by: Voight Industries, Inc., PO Box 200, Lubec, ME 04652. TEL 207-733-5593. Ed. R O Voight.

BOTSWANA. CENTRAL STATISTICS OFFICE. CONSUMER PRICE STATISTICS. see *BUSINESS AND ECONOMICS—Abstracting, Bibliographies, Statistics*

BOTSWANA. CENTRAL STATISTICS OFFICE. DEMOGRAPHIC AND HEALTH SURVEY. see *BUSINESS AND ECONOMICS—Abstracting, Bibliographies, Statistics*

BOTSWANA. CENTRAL STATISTICS OFFICE. EDUCATION STATISTICS. see *EDUCATION—Abstracting, Bibliographies, Statistics*

BOTSWANA. CENTRAL STATISTICS OFFICE. EXTERNAL TRADE STATISTICS. see *BUSINESS AND ECONOMICS—Abstracting, Bibliographies, Statistics*

BOTSWANA. CENTRAL STATISTICS OFFICE. HOUSEHOLD INCOME AND EXPENDITURE SURVEY. see *BUSINESS AND ECONOMICS—Abstracting, Bibliographies, Statistics*

BOTSWANA. CENTRAL STATISTICS OFFICE. INDUSTRIAL STATISTICS. see *BUSINESS AND ECONOMICS—Abstracting, Bibliographies, Statistics*

BOTSWANA. CENTRAL STATISTICS OFFICE. LABOUR FORCE SURVEY. see *BUSINESS AND ECONOMICS—Abstracting, Bibliographies, Statistics*

BOTSWANA. CENTRAL STATISTICS OFFICE. LABOUR STATISTICS. see *BUSINESS AND ECONOMICS—Abstracting, Bibliographies, Statistics*

BOTSWANA. CENTRAL STATISTICS OFFICE. STATISTICAL BULLETIN. see *BUSINESS AND ECONOMICS—Abstracting, Bibliographies, Statistics*

BOTSWANA. CENTRAL STATISTICS OFFICE. TRANSPORT STATISTICS. see *TRANSPORTATION*

BOTSWANA. MINISTRY OF AGRICULTURE. FARM MANAGEMENT SURVEY RESULTS. see *AGRICULTURE—Agricultural Economics*

330.9 BRA ISSN 0103-3921
HG4109.5
BRAZIL COMPANY HANDBOOK. Text in English. 1987. a. USD 69.95 (effective 2005). charts; stat. back issues avail. **Document type:** *Directory, Trade.* **Description:** Profiles 90 of Brazil's major companies and 60 money managers and investment advisors. Provides hard-to-find information on the economic conditions in Brazil.
—CCC.
Published by: I M F Editora Ltda., Av Almirante Barroso, 63, Grupo 409, Centro, Rio De Janeiro, RJ 20031-003, Brazil. TEL 55-21-240-4347, FAX 55-21-262-7570. **Dist. worldwide by:** Reference Press Inc.. TEL 512-454-7778, FAX 512-454-9401.

330.9 USA ISSN 1540-0794
HC186
BRAZIL COUNTRY REPORT. Text in English. 1995. a. looseleaf. USD 475 (effective 2001). charts; illus.; mkt.; stat. 150 p./no.; **Document type:** *Yearbook, Consumer.* **Description:** Reviews the previous year's events politically and economically, and forecasts the coming year's events.
Published by: Orbis Publications, LLC, 1924 47th St NW, Washington, DC 20007-1901. TEL 202-298-7936, FAX 202-298-7938, sfoster@orbispub.com, http://www.orbispublications.com. Ed., Pub., R&P Richard W Foster. Circ: 125 (paid).

330.981 GBR ISSN 1470-7411
HC186
BRAZIL QUARTERLY FORECAST REPORT. Text in English. 1985. 3/yr. GBP 330, USD 495, EUR 450 (effective 2003). **Document type:** *Journal, Trade.* **Description:** Provides a comprehensive assessment of the Brazilian government, economy and business environment over the next 30 months. Helps to identify opportunities and reduce risk, and answers key questions facing executives at this time.
Formerly (until 2000): Annual Country Forecast Report. Brazil (0267-9965)
Related titles: Online - full text ed.: (from EBSCO Publishing).
—CCC.
Published by: Business Monitor International Ltd., Mermaid House, 2 Puddle Dock, Blackfriars, London, EC4V 3DS, United Kingdom. TEL 44-20-72480468, FAX 44-20-72480467, marketing@businessmonitor.com, http://www.businessmonitor.com/brazilforecast.html.

338.9 GBR ISSN 0143-5272
HC186
BRAZIL REPORT. Variant title: Latin American Regional Report - Brazil Report. Text in English. 1979. 10/yr. GBP 155, USD 218 to individuals; GBP 88, USD 116 to institutions (effective 2001). back issues avail. **Document type:** *Newsletter.* **Description:** Covers in detail political, business, economic, and financial events in Brazil.
Related titles: Online - full text ed.
Indexed: RASB.
—IE, Infotrieve.
Published by: Latin American Newsletters (Subsidiary of: Lettres (U.K.) Ltd.), 61 Old St, London, EC1V 9HW, United Kingdom. TEL 44-20-7251-0012, FAX 44-20-7253-8193, subs@latinnews.com, http://www.latinnews.com. Ed. Colin Harding. R&P Alex McHallam TEL 44-20-7251-0012.

330.9 BRA
BRAZIL. SUPERINTENDENCIA DO DESENVOLVIMENTO DO NORDESTE. RELATORIO ANUAL. Text in Portuguese. irreg., latest 1986. per issue exchange basis. charts; stat. **Document type:** *Government.*
Published by: Superintendencia do Desenvolvimento do Nordeste, Praca Ministro J. Goncalves de Souza, Edf. Sudene, Cidade Universitaria, Recife, PE 50670900, Brazil. TEL 2711044, FAX 4531277.

330.981 USA ISSN 0897-3067
HC186
BRAZIL WATCH. Text in English. 1984. s-m. looseleaf. USD 855; USD 1,610 to corporations (effective 2005). charts; illus.; mkt.; stat. back issues avail. **Document type:** *Newsletter, Consumer.* **Description:** Reports on political, economic and business events in Brazil.
Related titles: E-mail ed.: USD 545 in US & Canada (effective 2001).
Published by: Brazil Watch Publications, 8218 Wisconsin Ave, Ste 307, Bethesda, MD 20814. TEL 301-718-3080, FAX 301-718-3081, bw@brazilwatch.com, http://www.brazilwatch.com. Pub. Richard W Foster. Circ: 465 (paid and free).

330.982 USA
BRAZIL WATCH FAX BULLETIN. Text in English. 1991. w. USD 595 (effective 2005). 2 p./no.; **Document type:** *Trade.*
Media: Fax.
Published by: Brazil Watch Publications, 8218 Wisconsin Ave, Ste 307, Bethesda, MD 20814. TEL 301-718-3080, FAX 301-718-3081, bw@brazilwatch.com, http://www.brazilwatch.com. Pub. Richard W Foster.

330 FRA ISSN 0006-9566
BREF RHONE - ALPES; lettre hebdomadaire d'informations economiques. Text in French. 1966. 45/yr. EUR 435 (effective 2004); Includes Entreprises Rhone-Alpes. **Document type:** *Newsletter, Consumer.*
Published by: Societe des Medias Economiques, Immeuble Les Lauriers, 513 Rue du Saint-Souci, Limonest, 69579, France. TEL 33-4-37497790, FAX 33-4-78645169, bref@smebref.com, http://www.brefonline.com.

BRENNPUNKT LATEINAMERIKA. see *POLITICAL SCIENCE*

BRIEFING. see *POLITICAL SCIENCE*

BRITISH ACTUARIAL JOURNAL. see *INSURANCE*

330.9 USA ISSN 0163-2000
HJ2051
THE BUDGET OF THE UNITED STATES GOVERNMENT. Text in English. 1936. a.
Related titles: Online - full text ed.
—CISTI.
Published by: Executive Office of the President of the United States, Office of Management and Budget, 725 17th St., NW, Washington, DC 20503. TEL 202-395-3080, FAX 202-395-3888, http://w3.access.gpo.gov/usbudget/fy2001/maindown.html, http://www.whitehouse.gov/omb/index.html. **Subscr. to:** U.S. Government Printing Office, Superintendent of Documents, PO Box 371954, Pittsburgh, PA 15250-7954. TEL 202-512-1800, FAX 202-512-2250, orders@gpo.gov, http://www.access.gpo.gov.

BULLETIN L A R F. see *BUSINESS AND ECONOMICS—Banking And Finance*

330 GBR ISSN 0007-4918
HC446
➤ **BULLETIN OF INDONESIAN ECONOMIC STUDIES.** Text in English. 1965. 3/yr. GBP 156, USD 253, AUD 301 combined subscription to institutions print & online eds. (effective 2006). adv. bk.rev. charts; illus.; stat. cum.index. reprint service avail. from PSC. **Document type:** *Journal, Academic/Scholarly.* **Description:** Contains a survey of recent developments in the economy, 3 or 4 articles by specialist writers, and notes on special topics.
Related titles: Online - full text ed.: ISSN 1472-7234. GBP 148, USD 240, AUD 286 to institutions (effective 2006) (from EBSCO Publishing, Gale Group, IngentaConnect, O C L C Online Computer Library Center, Inc., R M I T Publishing, Swets Information Services).
Indexed: ABIn, AEA, APEL, ASCA, AgrForAb, BAS, CREJ, CurCont, DSA, EI, EIA, EnerInd, ForAb, GEOBASE, HortAb, I&DA, IBR, IBSS, ILD, IndIslam, JEL, KES, MaizeAb, NutrAb, PAIS, PHN&I, PerIslam, PopulInd, RASB, RDA, RiceAb, S&F, SSCI, TDB, WAE&RSA.
—BLDSC (2862.060000), IDS, IE, Infotrieve, ingenta. **CCC.**
Published by: (Australian National University AUS, Economics Division, Indonesia Project AUS), Routledge (Subsidiary of: Taylor & Francis Group), 4 Park Sq, Milton Park, Abingdon, Oxon OX14 4RN, United Kingdom. TEL 44-1235-828600, FAX 44-1235-829000, info@routledge.co.uk, http://www.tandf.co.uk/journals/titles/00074918.asp, http://www.routledge.com. Ed. Ross H McLeod TEL 61-2-6125-2370. Circ: 1,200. **Subscr. in N. America to:** Taylor & Francis Inc., Customer Services Dept, 325 Chestnut St, 8th Fl, Philadelphia, PA 19106. TEL 215-625-8900, 800-354-1420, FAX 215-625-8914, customerservice@taylorandfrancis.com; **Subscr. to:** Taylor & Francis Ltd, Journals Customer Service, Rankine Rd, Basingstoke, Hants RG24 8PR, United Kingdom. TEL 44-1256-813000, FAX 44-1256-330245, enquiry@tandf.co.uk.

338.9 LUX ISSN 0068-4120
BULLETIN OF THE EUROPEAN COMMUNITIES AND SUPPLEMENTS. Text in Danish, Dutch, English, French, German, Greek, Italian, Spanish, Portuguese. 1968. 11/yr. USD 255. **Document type:** *Bulletin.* **Description:** Features official texts adopted by the commission (communications to the council, programmes, reports, proposals).
Related titles: Microfiche ed.: (from CIS).
Indexed: IIS, RASB.
Published by: (European Commission BEL), European Commission, Office for Official Publications of the European Union, 2 Rue Mercier, Luxembourg, L-2985, Luxembourg. **Dist. in U.S. by:** Bernan Associates, Bernan, 4611-F Assembly Dr., Lanham, MD 20706-4391. TEL 301-459-0056, 800-274-4447.

382 338 USA ISSN 0968-4468
HC800.A1
BUSINESS AFRICA. Text in English. s-m. USD 1,095 print or online ed.; USD 85 newsstand/cover print or online ed. (effective 2005). **Document type:** *Newsletter.* **Description:** Provides business information, intelligence and assessments. Covers developments throughout the continent (with the exception of Egypt and Libya).
Incorporates (in Jan. 1993): South Africa Alert - Issues Monitors; Aid Finance Update Africa; Africa Markets Monitor (0968-1442); Which was formerly: Africa Letter
Related titles: ♦ CD-ROM ed.: E I U International Business Newsletters on Disc; Microform ed.: (from PQC); Online - full text ed.: E I U International Business Newsletters (from EBSCO Publishing, Florida Center for Library Automation, ProQuest Information & Learning, SilverPlatter Information, Inc., The Dialog Corporation).
Indexed: ABIn.
—CCC.
Published by: Economist Intelligence Unit, 111 W 57th St, New York, NY 10019. TEL 212-554-0600, FAX 212-586-1181, newyork@eiu.com, http://www.eiu.com. Ed. Daniel Franklin.

BUSINESS AND THE ENVIRONMENT; monthly global news and analysis. see *ENVIRONMENTAL STUDIES*

382 338 USA ISSN 0572-7545
BUSINESS ASIA; fortnightly report to managers of Asia operations index. Text in English. 1970. bi-w. USD 1,055 print or online; USD 85 newsstand/cover print or online (effective 2004). illus. reprints avail. **Document type:** *Newsletter.* **Description:** Provides up-to-the-minute coverage of what is happening throughout Asia and why, and what can be done about it for profit.
Related titles: ♦ CD-ROM ed.: E I U International Business Newsletters on Disc; Microform ed.: (from PQC); Online - full text ed.: E I U International Business Newsletters (from EBSCO Publishing, Florida Center for Library Automation, ProQuest Information & Learning, SilverPlatter Information, Inc., The Dialog Corporation).
Indexed: ABIX, ABIn, HongKongiana, KES.
—IE. **CCC.**
Published by: Economist Intelligence Unit, 111 W 57th St, New York, NY 10019. TEL 212-554-0600, FAX 212-586-1181, http://www.eiu.com.

382 ZAF
BUSINESS BRIEF. Text in English. 1975. q. free. illus.
Former titles: Barclays Business Brief (0250-2402); Barclays National Review (0302-6809); Barclays Trade Review (0005-5913)
Indexed: BusI.
Published by: First National Bank Ltd., Economics Department, PO Box 1153, Johannesburg, 2000, South Africa. Ed. C Bruggemans. Circ: 5,000.

382 338 USA ISSN 1016-9776
BUSINESS CHINA; fortnightly report to managers of China operations. Text in English. 1975. bi-w. USD 1,055 print or online; USD 85 newsstand/cover print or online (effective 2004). charts; maps; stat. index, cum.index. **Document type:** *Newsletter.* **Description:** Analyzes economic trends and new policies, and forecasts the effects on businesses. Identifies unfolding opportunities and competition through regular reviews of industrial sectors and reports on major transactions, joint ventures, licensing agreements and other developments in key industries.
Related titles: ♦ CD-ROM ed.: E I U International Business Newsletters on Disc; Microform ed.: (from PQC); Online - full text ed.: E I U International Business Newsletters (from EBSCO Publishing, Florida Center for Library Automation, ProQuest Information & Learning, SilverPlatter Information, Inc., The Dialog Corporation).
Indexed: ABIn, KES, RASB.
—CCC.
Published by: (Business International Asia Pacific Ltd HKG), Economist Intelligence Unit, 111 W 57th St, New York, NY 10019. TEL 212-554-0600, FAX 212-586-1181, http://www.eiu.com.

330.9 MYS ISSN 0127-0001
BUSINESS CONDITIONS MALAYSIA. Text in English. 1980. q. free. **Document type:** *Newsletter.*
Published by: Sime Bank Berhad, PO Box 12006, Kuala Lumpur, 50935, Malaysia. TEL 60-3-230-9866, FAX 60-3-232-2627, TELEX MA-33707 SIMEBK. Ed. Ng Goo Phai. Circ: 1,500.

B

330.9 USA ISSN 1088-7857
HB3743
BUSINESS CYCLE INDICATORS; a monthly report from the Conference Board. Text in English. 1921. m. USD 130 (effective 2003). illus. reprints avail. **Document type:** *Academic/Scholarly.*
Supersedes in part (in 1996): Survey of Current Business (0039-6222)
—CCC.
Published by: Conference Board, Inc., 845 Third Ave, New York, NY 10022. TEL 212-759-0900, FAX 212-980-7014, http://www.conference-board.org.

382 338 USA ISSN 1351-8763
HF3500.7
BUSINESS EASTERN EUROPE. Text in English. 1972. w. USD 1,530 print or online ed.; USD 85 newsstand/cover print or online ed. (effective 2005). charts; stat. **Document type:** *Newsletter.* **Description:** Provides strategies for financing, countertrade, cooperation agreements, licensing and marketing in the six Comecon countries and Yugoslavia, from contacting foreign trade organizations to negotiating contracts, clinching deals and securing payments.
Formerly: Eastern Europe Report
Related titles: ◆ CD-ROM ed.: E I U International Business Newsletters on Disc; Microform ed.: (from PQC); Online - full text ed.: E I U International Business Newsletters (from EBSCO Publishing, Florida Center for Library Automation, ProQuest Information & Learning, SilverPlatter Information, Inc., The Dialog Corporation).
Indexed: ABIn, KES.
—CCC.
Published by: Economist Intelligence Unit, 111 W 57th St, New York, NY 10019. TEL 212-554-0600, FAX 212-586-1181, newyork@eiu.com, http://www.eiu.com.

338.0071 USA ISSN 1060-0663
LC1085.2
BUSINESS - EDUCATION INSIDER; how business can reform education. Text in English. 1990. m. USD 3.50 newsstand/cover. back issues avail.; reprints avail.
Related titles: Online - full text ed.
Published by: Heritage Foundation, 214 Massachusetts Ave, N E, Washington, DC 20002. TEL 202-546-4400, FAX 202-543-9647, info@heritage.org. Ed. Allyson Tucker. Circ: 4,000.

382 338 USA ISSN 0007-6724
BUSINESS EUROPE. Text in English. 1960. bi-w. USD 1,395; USD 85 newsstand/cover (effective 2005). **Document type:** *Newsletter.* **Description:** Management advisory report for executives responsible for European operations, with latest issues, trends, policies, and corporate strategies in 16 countries, EEC developments and forecasts for each country and industrial sector. Covers finance, marketing, taxation, personnel, organization, politics and actual corporate experience.
Incorporates: Management Europe
Related titles: ◆ CD-ROM ed.: E I U International Business Newsletters on Disc; Microform ed.: (from PQC); Online - full text ed.: E I U International Business Newsletters (from EBSCO Publishing, Florida Center for Library Automation, ProQuest Information & Learning, SilverPlatter Information, Inc., The Dialog Corporation).
Indexed: ABIn, CPM, ELLIS, KES, PAIS.
—CCC.
Published by: Economist Intelligence Unit, 111 W 57th St, New York, NY 10019. TEL 212-554-0600, FAX 212-586-1181, info@businesseurope.com, http://www.businesseurope.com/, http://www.eiu.com.

330.9 USA
BUSINESS FAILURE RECORD. Text in English. a. free; free. **Description:** Provides number of failures and liabilities by state and region, by major industry group and by age of business, plus historical failures data.
Related titles: Online - full text ed.: free.
Indexed: SRI.
Published by: Dun & Bradstreet, Economic Analysis Department (Subsidiary of: Dun & Bradstreet Corporation), c/o Judy Webb, 3 Sylvan Way, Parsippany, NJ 07054. FAX 973-254-4063, http://www.dnb.com. R&P Judy Webb.

650 USA ISSN 0007-683X
BUSINESS IN NEBRASKA. Text in English. 1948. m. USD 10. charts; illus.; stat. reprints avail. **Document type:** *Newsletter.*
Related titles: Microfiche ed.: (from CIS).
Indexed: PAIS, SRI.
Published by: University of Nebraska at Lincoln, Bureau of Business Research, 114 C B A, Lincoln, NE 68588-0408. TEL 402-472-2334, FAX 402-472-3878. Ed. F Charles Lamphear. R&P F. Charles Lamphear. Circ: 9,000.

338 THA ISSN 0125-0140
HF41
BUSINESS IN THAILAND. Text in English. 1969. m. THB 500, USD 52. adv. bk.rev. charts; illus.; stat. index. **Description:** An analysis of Thailand's business, focusing on economics, commerce, industry, and trade.
Indexed: KES, RASB.
Published by: Business in Thailand Co. Ltd., New Rd, Opp G P O, 185 Soi Putta O Soth, Bangkok, 10500, Thailand. TEL 2-235-6049, FAX 2-237-1517, TELEX 20932 BIT TH. Ed. William Than. Pub. Suphat Busayapong. Adv. contact Paitoon Na Songihla. Circ: 7,500. **Subscr. to:** PO Box 1332, Bangkok Mail Center, Bangkok 10000, Thailand.

330.9 USA ISSN 1525-5115
THE BUSINESS JOURNAL. Text in English. 1980. w. USD 88; USD 1.50 newsstand/cover (effective 2005). adv. reprints avail. **Document type:** *Newspaper, Trade.* **Description:** Covers business news in Hillsborough and Pinellas counties in Florida. Covers areas such as law, economic development, technology, retail, tourism, hospitality, advertising and marketing, trade, finance, health care, and government regulation for management and professionals.
Former titles (until 1999): Tampa Bay Business Journal (0896-467X); (until 198?): Tampa Bay Business (0273-5830)
Related titles: Online - full text ed.: (from Florida Center for Library Automation, Gale Group, Northern Light Technology, Inc.).
Indexed: BusDate, LRI, T&II.
—CCC.
Published by: American City Business Journals, Inc. (Tampa), 4350 W Cypress St, Ste 800, Tampa, FL 33607. TEL 813-873-8225, FAX 813-876-1827, tampabay@bizjournals.com, http://tampabay.bizjournals.com/tampabay/. Ed. Alexis Muellner. Pub. Arthur Porter. Circ: 13,000 (paid).

THE BUSINESS JOURNAL (PHOENIX); serving Phoenix & the Valley of the Sun. see *BUSINESS AND ECONOMICS*

330.9 USA ISSN 0742-6550
BUSINESS JOURNAL (PORTLAND); serving greater Portland. Text in English. 1984. w. (Fri.). USD 89; USD 158 for 2 yrs.; USD 211 for 3 yrs. (effective 2005). charts; illus.; pat.; stat. **Document type:** *Newspaper.* **Description:** Covers business and economics in the Portland area.
Formerly: The Portland Business Journal
Related titles: Online - full text ed.: (from Florida Center for Library Automation, Gale Group, O C L C Online Computer Library Center, Inc., ProQuest Information & Learning).
Indexed: ABIn, BusDate, LRI.
—CCC.
Published by: American City Business Journals, Inc. (Portland), PO Box 14490, Portland, OR 97214. TEL 503-274-8733, FAX 503-227-2650, portland@bizjournal.com, http://www.bizjournals.com/portland/. Ed. Steven D Jones. Pub. Candace Clement. Adv. contact Matt Tolbert. Circ: 10,900 (paid); 4,100 (controlled). Wire service: PR.

382 338 USA ISSN 0007-6880
HF6
BUSINESS LATIN AMERICA; weekly report to managers of Latin American operations. Text in English. 1966. w. USD 1,330 print or online; USD 85 newsstand/cover print or online (effective 2004). illus. back issues avail.; reprints avail. **Document type:** *Newsletter.* **Description:** Interprets and evaluates changing political, economic and business-related trends, government policy changes, regulatory developments, regional integration moves and actions taken by governments and leading agencies to cope with the region's debt.
Related titles: ◆ CD-ROM ed.: E I U International Business Newsletters on Disc; Microform ed.: (from PQC); Online - full text ed.: E I U International Business Newsletters (from EBSCO Publishing, Florida Center for Library Automation, ProQuest Information & Learning, SilverPlatter Information, Inc., The Dialog Corporation).
Indexed: ABIn, KES, RASB.
—IE, Infotrieve. **CCC.**
Published by: Economist Intelligence Unit, 111 W 57th St, New York, NY 10019. TEL 212-554-0600, 800-938-4685, FAX 212-586-1181, marcus@interpart.net, newyork@eiu.com, http://www.eiu.com/2x605brid/catalog/country/samer.html. Eds. Steven Murphy, Anna Szterenfeld.

382 338 USA ISSN 1350-7354
HF3756
BUSINESS MIDDLE EAST. Text in English. 1946. bi-w. USD 1,095 print or online ed.; USD 85 newsstand/cover print or online ed. (effective 2005). **Document type:** *Newsletter.* **Description:** Identifies and tracks business issues to keep companies abreast of changes, developments and opportunities in the Middle East. For decision makers who wish to enter the market or expand their presence there.
Incorporates (in Jan. 1993): Iran Monitor (0969-1626); Which was formerly: Business International Iran Service; Saudi Arabia Monitor (0969-1634); B I - Turkey Monitor (0969-157X); Which was formerly: Turkey Monitor
Related titles: ◆ CD-ROM ed.: E I U International Business Newsletters on Disc; Microform ed.: (from PQC); Online - full text ed.: E I U International Business Newsletters (from EBSCO Publishing, Florida Center for Library Automation, ProQuest Information & Learning, SilverPlatter Information, Inc., The Dialog Corporation).
—IE. **CCC.**
Published by: Economist Intelligence Unit, 111 W 57th St, New York, NY 10019. TEL 212-554-0600, FAX 212-586-1181, http://www.eiu.com. Ed. David Johnson.

BUSINESS MONITOR. RETAIL PRICES INDEX. see *BUSINESS AND ECONOMICS—Abstracting, Bibliographies, Statistics*

330.9 ESP
BUSINESS OPPORTUNITIES IN SPAIN. Text in English. a.
Related titles: French ed.; Spanish ed.
Published by: Banco de Santander, Publicidad y Estudios, Paseo Pereda, 9-12, Santander, Cantabria 39004, Spain.

330.9 USA
BUSINESS OUTLOOK FOR WEST MICHIGAN. Text in English. 1984. q. USD 25 (effective 2003). stat. back issues avail. **Document type:** *Academic/Scholarly.* **Description:** Provides economic analysis, statistics, and forecasts for western Michigan.
Former titles (until 198?): Business Outlook (0748-4216); (until 1984): Business Conditions in the Kalamazoo Area (0732-5487)
Related titles: Online - full text ed.
Published by: W.E. Upjohn Institute for Employment Research, 300 S Westnedge Ave, Kalamazoo, MI 49007. TEL 616-343-5541, FAX 616-343-7310, http://www.upjohninst.org. R&P George A Erickcek. Circ: 600.

BUSINESS RATIO. BUS AND COACH OPERATORS. see *TRANSPORTATION*

BUSINESS RATIO. CONSTRUCTIONAL STEELWORK MANUFACTURERS. see *BUILDING AND CONSTRUCTION*

BUSINESS RATIO. MEAT PROCESSORS. see *AGRICULTURE—Poultry And Livestock*

BUSINESS RATIO. MEAT WHOLESALERS. see *AGRICULTURE—Poultry And Livestock*

BUSINESS RATIO. THE FILM AND TELEVISION INDUSTRY; film & tv producers & distributors. see *MOTION PICTURES*

BUSINESS RATIO. THE LIGHTING EQUIPMENT INDUSTRY. see *INTERIOR DESIGN AND DECORATION*

330.9 PAK ISSN 1563-9436
BUSINESS RECORDER; Pakistan's national business and financial daily. Text in English. d. back issues avail.
Media: Online - full text.
Address: recorder@fascom.com, http://www.brecorder.com/. Ed. M A Zuberi.

330.9 THA ISSN 0125-0477
HF5001
BUSINESS REVIEW. Text in English. 1972. m. USD 60 in Asia; USD 93 in Europe; USD 111 in the Americas. adv. bk.rev. illus.
Indexed: BAS, KES, PAIS, PROMT, RASB.
Published by: Nation Publishing Group Co., Km 4.5 Bangna Prakanong, 44 Moo 10 Bagna Trat Rd, Bangkok, 10260, Thailand. TEL 317-1365, FAX 317-1384, TELEX 20326 NATION TH. Ed. Laurie Rosenthal. adv.: page THB 33,000; 273 x 203. Circ: 20,000. **Dist. in Hong Kong by:** In Group Publications Ltd., B26 Seven Seas Commercial Centre, 121 King's Rd, Hong Kong, Hong Kong. TEL 5-887-1830.

330.9 GBR ISSN 0144-6096
HC257.S4
BUSINESS SCOTLAND; a monthly review of national and international business. Text in English. 1947. m. GBP 36 domestic; GBP 42.75 foreign (effective Oct. 1999). adv. bk.rev. **Document type:** *Trade.*
Formerly: Scotland (0036-9055)
Indexed: PAIS, RASB.
Published by: Business Magazine Group, Adamsway, Mansfield, Notts NG18 4FP, United Kingdom. TEL 44-1623-450500, FAX 44-1623-454560, bmg@bmgonline.co.uk, http://www.bmgroup.co.uk. Circ: 15,167.

330.9 USA ISSN 0895-4615
HD2346.U5
BUSINESS STARTS RECORD. Text in English. a. free. charts. **Document type:** *Trade.* **Description:** Provides number of starts and total employees by state and region and by major industry group. Includes city data, graphs and industry trends by state.
Related titles: Online - full text ed.: free.
Published by: Dun & Bradstreet, Economic Analysis Department (Subsidiary of: Dun & Bradstreet Corporation), c/o Judy Webb, 3 Sylvan Way, Parsippany, NJ 07054. FAX 973-254-4063, http://www.dnb.com. R&P Judy Webb.

BUSINESS T I P S ON CUBA. (Technological Information Promotion System) see *BUSINESS AND ECONOMICS—International Commerce*

330.9 CAN ISSN 1713-8701
BUSINESS TIMES. Text in English. m.
Former titles (until 2004): Huronia Business Times (1194-9384); (until 1992): Huronia Business Journal (1194-9376)
—CCC.

Published by: Huronia Business Times, 169 Dufferin St, Unit 22, Alliston, ON L9R 1E6, Canada. TEL 705-435-5552, FAX 705-435-3342, businesstimes@simcoe.com, http://www.simcoe.com/sc/business/. Ed. Bruce Hain. Adv. contact Josie Tytus. Circ: 11,000.

330.9   USA   ISSN 0744-172X
BUSINESS TIMES. Text in English. 1978. m. USD 36; USD 3 newsstand/cover (effective 2005). adv. bk.rev. back issues avail. **Document type:** *Newspaper, Trade.* **Description:** Statewide business to business publication reaching top level business executives, CFOs, presidents, business owners. Focuses on issues in banking and finance, telecommunications, healthcare, higher education and technology.
Formerly: Connecticut Business Times (0161-6102)
Related titles: Online - full text ed.: (from Northern Light Technology, Inc., O C L C Online Computer Library Center, Inc., ProQuest Information & Learning).
Indexed: ABIn, BusDate, KES, T&II.
Published by: Choice Media, 315 Peck St, Box 580, New Haven, CT 06513-0580. TEL 203-782-1420, FAX 203-782-3793, cbtimes@ctbusinesstimes.com. Ed., Pub. Joel MacClaren. adv.: B&W page USD 2,400, color page USD 7,900; trim 13.5 x 9.5. Circ: 22,400 (paid and controlled).

330.9   MYS
BUSINESS TRENDS ASIA REPORT: INDONESIA. Text in English. 1979. irreg. USD 30. bk.rev. stat.
Published by: M P R C (Asia) Sdn. Berhad, PO Box 10706, Kuala Lumpur, 50722, Malaysia. TEL 60-3-2217762, FAX 60-3-7564478. Ed. Paul Markandan. Circ: (controlled).

330.9   GHA
BUSINESS WEEKLY. Text in English. 1966. w. adv. **Document type:** *Trade.*
Indexed: RASB.
Published by: Business Publication, Ring Road West Industrial Area, PO Box 2351, Accra, Ghana. Ed. Mark Botsio. Circ: 3,000.

330.9   URY   ISSN 0797-2008
BUSQUEDA. Text in Spanish. 1972. w. USD 225.
Published by: (Sociedad Interamericana de Prensa), Editorial Agora S.A., Av. Uruguay, 1146, Montevideo, 11105, Uruguay. TEL 598-2-922666, FAX 598-2-922036. Ed. Danilo Arbilla Frachia. Circ: 25,000.

334 381   GBR   ISSN 0955-8888
BUTTERWORTHS E C BRIEF. Text in English. 1989. w. GBP 459 (effective 2000). **Document type:** *Trade.* **Description:** Covers EU directives, ComDocs, regulations and activities.
Related titles: Online - full text ed.
Published by: Butterworths Tolley (Subsidiary of: LexisNexis UK (Scottish Office)), Halsbury House, 35 Chancery Ln, London, Mddx WC2A 1EL, United Kingdom. TEL 44-20-74002500, FAX 44-20-74002583, order.line@butterworths.co.uk, http://www.butterworths.co.uk/.

330.9   AUT
C A QUARTERLY; facts and figures on Austria's economy. Text in German. 1982. q. **Document type:** *Bulletin.* **Description:** Covers Austria's business cycle, Austrian economy and banking system, international economic information, and indicators of economic development.
Indexed: WBA.
Published by: Creditanstalt-Bankverein, Schottengasse 6, Vienna, W 1010, Austria. TEL 01-53131-0. Ed. Manfred Weidmann.

338   USA   ISSN 0199-686X
       CODEN: CHRGB7
C B I A NEWS. Text in English. 1923. m. USD 9 to members; free (effective 2005). bk.rev. illus. **Document type:** *Magazine.* **Description:** Keeps business people informed about business trends, state politics, legislative actions, economic forecasts, regulatory changes and small-business issues. Covers basic business management skills and social changes affecting state businesses.
Former titles: Connecticut Business and Industry; Connecticut Industry (0010-6135)
Indexed: PAIS.
Published by: (Connecticut Business and Industry Association), Connecticut Business & Industry Association, 350 Church St, Hartford, CT 06103-1106. TEL 860-244-1900, FAX 860-278-8562. Ed., R&P Diane Friend Edwards TEL 860-244-1958. Circ: 10,000.

330.9   GBR   ISSN 0142-6419
C B I ECONOMIC SITUATION REPORT. Text in English. 8/yr. GBP 366 to non-members; GBP 208 to members. adv. **Description:** Summarizes CBI's views of economic trends and offers an assessment of developments in the UK and world economies.
Indexed: CREJ.
Published by: Confederation of British Industry, Centre Point, 103 New Oxford St, London, WC1A 1DU, United Kingdom. TEL 44-171-395-8164, FAX 44-171-240-1578, TELEX 21332. Ed. Sudhair Junankar. R&P Wendy Hayes TEL 44-171-395-8036. Adv. contact Frances Hughes.

330.9   AUS
C E D A INFORMATION PAPERS (I P SERIES). Text in English. 1979. irreg. price varies.
Published by: Committee for Economic Development of Australia, 123 Lonsdale St, Melbourne, VIC 3000, Australia. FAX 61-3-9663-7271.

338   CHL   ISSN 0251-2920
HC121
C E P A L REVIEW. Text in Spanish. 1976. 3/yr. USD 35 (effective 2005). stat. index. back issues avail.; reprint service avail. from PSC.
Formerly: Economic Bulletin for Latin America (0424-2661)
Related titles: Microfiche ed.: (from CIS); Online - full text ed.: ISSN 1684-0348. 1995; ♦ Spanish ed.: Revista de la C E P A L. ISSN 0252-0257.
Indexed: ABIn, ARDT, CREJ, HAPI, I&DA, IBR, IBSS, IBZ, IIS, ILD, JEL, KES, PAIS, RDA, RRTA, WAE&RSA.
—BLDSC (3113.689000), CISTI, IE, Infotrieve, ingenta. **CCC.**
Published by: Comision Economica para America Latina y el Caribe/Economic Commission for Latin America and the Caribbean, Ave Dag Hammarskjold 3477, Vitacura, Santiago de Chile, Chile. TEL 56-2-471-2000, FAX 56-2-208-0252, publications@eclac.cl, http://www.eclac.cl. **Subscr. to:** United Nations Publications, PO Box 361, Birmingham, AL 35201-0361. TEL 205-995-1567, 205-995-1588, FAX 205-995-1588.

330.9   FRA   ISSN 0243-1947
C.E.P.I.I. LETTRE. Text in French. 1979. 11/yr. EUR 51.50 domestic; EUR 54.50 in the European Union; EUR 55.50 DOM-TOM; EUR 57.70 elsewhere (effective 2003). back issues avail. **Document type:** *Bulletin.* **Description:** Looks at basic economic problems from a world perspective.
Related titles: Microfiche ed.
Indexed: RASB.
Published by: (France. Centre d'Etudes Prospectives et d'Informations Internationales), Documentation Francaise, 29-31 quai Voltaire, Paris, Cedex 7 75344, France. FAX 33-1-40157230.

330   USA   ISSN 0196-9021
C E P REPORT. Text in English. 1975. irreg. **Document type:** *Monographic series.*
Indexed: ABIn.
Published by: Council on Economic Priorities, 30 Irving Pl, New York, NY 10003. TEL 212-420-1133, 800-729-4237, FAX 212-420-0988.

334   ESP   ISSN 0213-8093
C I R I E C ESPANA; revista de economia publica, social y cooperativa. (Centro Internacional de Investigacion e Informacion sobre la Economia Publica, Social y Cooperativa) Text in Spanish; Abstracts in English, French. 1987. 3/yr. USD 400 (effective 2003). 300 p./no.; **Document type:** *Journal, Academic/Scholarly.*
Indexed: HortAb, IBSS, JEL, PHN&I, PotatoAb, RRTA, WAE&RSA.
—CINDOC.
Published by: C I R I E C - Espana, Ave de los Naranjos, s-n, Edif. Dep. Oriental 2P21, Valencia, 46022, Spain. TEL 34-96-3828489, FAX 34-96-3828492, ciriec@uv.es, reciriec@uv.es, http://www.ciriec.es, http://www.uv.es/~reciriec. Ed. Rafael Chaves.

330.9   FRA   ISSN 1269-9772
C N R S ECONOMIE. (Centre Nationale de la Recherche Scientifique) Text in French. 1995. irreg. price varies.
Document type: *Monographic series, Academic/Scholarly.*
Published by: (France. Centre National de la Recherche Scientifique), C N R S Editions, 15 Rue Malebranche, Paris, 75005, France. TEL 33-1-53102700, FAX 33-1-53102727, http://www.cnrseditions.fr.

C O M E T. (Companies Markets Economic Trends) see *PAINTS AND PROTECTIVE COATINGS*

330.9 300   GBR
C R E S R LECTURE SERIES. Text in English. irreg., latest vol.6, 1993. **Document type:** *Monographic series.*
Published by: Sheffield Hallam University, Centre for Regional Economic and Social Research, City Campus, Pond St, Sheffield, S Yorks S1 1WB, United Kingdom. TEL 44-114-225-3073, FAX 44-114-225-2197.

330.9   GBR
C R E S R PLANNING AND PROPERTY SERIES. Text in English. irreg., latest vol.5, 1996. **Document type:** *Monographic series.*
Published by: Sheffield Hallam University, Centre for Regional Economic and Social Research, City Campus, Pond St, Sheffield, S Yorks S1 1WB, United Kingdom. TEL 44-114-225-3073, FAX 44-114-225-2197.

330.9 300   GBR
C R E S R RESEARCH PAPER. Text in English. irreg., latest vol.5, 1993. **Document type:** *Monographic series.*
Published by: Sheffield Hallam University, Centre for Regional Economic and Social Research, City Campus, Pond St, Sheffield, S Yorks S1 1WB, United Kingdom. TEL 44-114-225-3073, FAX 44-114-225-2197.

330.9   GBR
C R E S R SUPERTRAM IMPACT SERIES. Text in English. irreg., latest vol.28, 1996. **Document type:** *Monographic series.*
Published by: Sheffield Hallam University, Centre for Regional Economic and Social Research, City Campus, Pond St, Sheffield, S Yorks S1 1WB, United Kingdom. TEL 44-114-225-3073, FAX 44-114-225-2197.

338   NOR
C R O P NEWSLETTER. Text in English. q.
Indexed: PAIS.
Published by: Comparative Research Programme on Poverty, Fosswinckelsgate 7, Bergen, N-5007, Norway.

330.981   BRA   ISSN 0102-2040
CADERNOS P U C. (Pontificia Universidade Catolica) Text in Portuguese. 1980. s-a. BRL 10. **Document type:** *Monographic series, Academic/Scholarly.*
Published by: Pontificia Universidade Catolica de Sao Paulo, Rua Monte Alegre 984, Sao Paolo, 05010-001, Brazil. TEL 55-11-38733359, boltim@uol.com.br. Ed. Anita Kon. Pub. Monica Landi.

CAHIERS AFRICAINS/AFRIKA STUDIES. see *HISTORY—History Of Africa*

CAHIERS DE SOCIOLOGIE ECONOMIQUE ET CULTURELLE. see *SOCIOLOGY*

330.9 301   FRA   ISSN 0758-2412
CAHIERS LILLOIS D'ECONOMIE ET DE SOCIOLOGIE. Variant title: C L E S. Cahiers Lillois d'Economie et de Sociologie. Text in French. 1983. s-a. **Document type:** *Journal, Academic/Scholarly.*
Published by: (Universite de Lille I (Sciences et Technologies)), L' Harmattan, 5 rue de l'Ecole Polytechnique, Paris, 75005, France. TEL 33-1-43257651, FAX 33-1-43258203, http://www.editions-harmattan.fr.

CAIJING KEXUE/FINANCE AND ECONOMICS. see *BUSINESS AND ECONOMICS—Banking And Finance*

330.9   USA   ISSN 0364-2895
HC107.C2
CALIFORNIA ECONOMIC INDICATORS. Text in English. 1968. bi-m. USD 8. charts. **Document type:** *Government.* **Description:** Summarizes economic trends and data relating to the state of California.
Indexed: SRI.
Published by: Department of Finance, Economic Research Section, 915 L St, 8th Fl, Sacramento, CA 95814-3701. TEL 916-322-2263, FAX 916-327-0213. Circ: 350. **Subscr. to:** PO Box 151, Sacramento, CA 95801.

330.9   USA
CALIFORNIA LABOR MARKET BULLETIN. Text in English. 1971. m. USD 15 (effective 1997). stat. Supplement avail. **Document type:** *Bulletin, Government.* **Description:** Provides labor market information (labor force, employment and unemployment rate) for the counties and the state.
Related titles: Microfiche ed.: (from CIS); Online - full text ed.
Indexed: SRI.
Published by: Employment Development Department, Labor Market Information Division, 7000 Franklin Blvd, 1100, Sacramento, CA 95823. TEL 916-262-2162, FAX 916-262-2443, http://www.calmis.cahwnet.gov. Circ: 7,000.

330.9   USA
CANADA COUNTRY MONITOR. Text in English. 1998. m.
Published by: W E F A, 800 Baldwin Tower, Eddystone, PA 19022. http://www.wefa.com.

CANADA. STATISTICS CANADA. CANADIAN ECONOMIC OBSERVER/OBSERVATEUR ECONOMIQUE CANADIEN. see *BUSINESS AND ECONOMICS—Abstracting, Bibliographies, Statistics*

CANADA. STATISTICS CANADA. PROVINCIAL ECONOMIC ACCOUNTS. ANNUAL ESTIMATES, TABLES AND ANALYTICAL DOCUMENT/CANADA. STATISTIQUE CANADA. COMPTES ECONOMIQUES PROVINCIAUX ESTIMATIONS ANNUELLES. see *BUSINESS AND ECONOMICS—Abstracting, Bibliographies, Statistics*

CANADIAN ENERGYTRENDS QUARTERLY. see *ENERGY*

330   CAN   ISSN 0576-5501
CANADIAN INTELLIGENCE SERVICE. Text in English. m. CND 25. bk.rev. **Document type:** *Newsletter.*
Media: Duplicated (not offset).
Published by: Canadian Intelligence Publications, 55 Eight Ave, High River, AB T1V 1E8, Canada. TEL 403-652-4200, FAX 403-652-7940. Pub. Ron Gostick.

B

▼ *new title*   ➤ *refereed*   ✶ *unverified*   ♦ *full entry avail.*

B

330.9 338 CAN
CANADIAN OFFICE GUIDE. Text in English, French. 1998. a. CND 9.95 (effective 2000). adv. charts; illus.; mkt.; maps; stat.; tr.lit. back issues avail. **Document type:** *Trade.*
Description: Publishes information in fields of technology, accounting, banking, finance, law and insurance for decisionmakers in those fields.
Related titles: E-mail ed.; Fax ed.; Online - full text ed.
Published by: Royal LePage Commercial Inc., 5770 Hurontario St, Ste. 200, Mississaiga, ON L5R365, Canada. TEL 905-501-6466, FAX 905-568-9444, sdavies@royallepage.com. Ed., Pub., R&P, Adv. contact Sheryl Davies. B&W page USD 3,539, color page USD 5,039; trim 10.88 x 8.13. Circ: 37,000.

330 CAN ISSN 0829-8416
CANADIAN OUTLOOK, ECONOMIC FORECAST. Text in English. 1974. q. CND 2,500 to non-members. charts. **Document type:** *Bulletin.*
Formerly (until 1986): Conference Board of Canada. Quarterly Canadian Forecast (0713-0406)
Related titles: Online - full text ed.
Indexed: CSI.
—CISTI.
Published by: Conference Board of Canada, 255 Smyth Rd, Ste 100, Ottawa, ON K1H 8M7, Canada. TEL 613-526-3280, FAX 613-526-4857.

330.971 CAN ISSN 0832-0500
CANADIAN OUTLOOK, EXECUTIVE SUMMARY. Text in English. 1970. q.
Formerly (until 1985): Quarterly Canadian Forescast. Executive Summary (0829-1128)
Published by: Conference Board of Canada, 255 Smyth Rd, Ste 100, Ottawa, ON K1H 8M7, Canada. TEL 613-526-3280, FAX 613-526-4857, corpcomm@conferenceboard.ca, http://www.conferenceboard.ca/.

330 CAN ISSN 0317-0861
➤ **CANADIAN PUBLIC POLICY/ANALYSE DE POLITIQUES.** Text in English, French. 1975. q. CND 55 domestic to individuals; USD 55 foreign to individuals; CND 115 domestic to institutions; USD 115 foreign to institutions; CND 25 domestic to students; CND 20 per issue (effective 2005). adv. bk.rev. charts; illus. Index. 192 p./no.; back issues avail.; reprints avail. **Document type:** *Journal, Academic/Scholarly.*
Description: Discusses current social and economic policy issues and proposals.
Related titles: Microfiche ed.: (from MML); Microform ed.: (from MML); Online - full text ed.
Indexed: ABIn, ASCA, ASG, AgeL, AmH&L, ArtHuCI, CBCARef, CBPI, CPerl, CREJ, CWPI, CurCont, DIP, DSA, EAA, EIA, EnerInd, FPA, ForAb, FutSurv, GEOBASE, HRA, HistAb, IBR, IBZ, ICLPL, IPSA, JEL, MAB, NutrAb, PAIS, PSA, RASB, RRTA, RefZh, SOPODA, SPAA, SRRA, SSA, SSCI, SUSA, SWA, SociolAb, WAE&RSA.
—BLDSC (3044.210000), CISTI, IDS, IE, Infotrieve, ingenta. CCC.
Published by: University of Toronto Press, Journals Division, 5201 Dufferin St, Toronto, ON M3H 5T8, Canada. TEL 416-667-7810, FAX 416-667-7881, cpp@qsilver.queensu.ca, journals@utpress.utoronto.ca, http://www.utpjournals.com/cpp. Ed. Kenneth J McKenzie. Adv. contact Audrey Greenwood. Circ: 1,800 (paid).

338.9 GBR
HC151.A1
CARIBBEAN & CENTRAL AMERICA REPORT. Text in English. 1979. 10/yr. GBP 155, USD 218 to individuals; GBP 88, USD 116 to institutions (effective 2001). back issues avail. **Document type:** *Newsletter.*
Former titles: Latin America & Caribbean Report (0968-2732); (until 1992): Caribbean Report (0143-523X)
Related titles: Online - full text ed.
Indexed: RASB.
Published by: Latin American Newsletters (Subsidiary of: Lettres (U.K.) Ltd.), 61 Old St, London, EC1V 9HW, United Kingdom. TEL 44-20-7251-0012, FAX 44-20-7253-8193, subs@latinnews.com, http://www.latinnews.com. Ed. Colin Harding. R&P Alex McHallam TEL 44-20-7251-0012.

330.9 GUY ISSN 0254-962X
HC151.A1
CARIBBEAN COMMUNITY PERSPECTIVE. Key Title: CARICOM Perspective. Text in English. 1980. a. free. back issues avail.
Published by: Caribbean Community Secretariat, Bank of Guyana Bldg., PO Box 10827, Georgetown, Guyana. TEL 592-269281, FAX 592-2-67816, carisec1@caricom.org. Circ: 6,000.

CARIBBEAN DATELINE. see *BUSINESS AND ECONOMICS—Investments*

CARIBBEAN NEWSLETTER. see *POLITICAL SCIENCE—International Relations*

CARIBBEAN UPDATE. see *BUSINESS AND ECONOMICS—International Commerce*

330.9 BRA
CARTA DA AMAZONIA. Text in Portuguese. 1978 (vol.6). bi-m.
Published by: Banco da Amazonia S.A., Av. Presidente. Vargas 800, Belen, Para, Brazil.

330.9 BRA ISSN 1517-7246
➤ **CARTA DE CONJUNTURA.** Text in English. m. charts; stat. 8 p./no.; **Document type:** *Bulletin, Academic/Scholarly.*
Media: Online - full text. **Related titles:** ◆ Portuguese ed.: Carta de Conjuntura F E E. ISSN 1517-7262.
Published by: Fundacao de Economia e Estatistica, Rua Duque de Caxias, 1691, Andar 8, Centro, Porto Alegre, RS 90010-283, Brazil. TEL 55-51-3216-9008, FAX 55-51-3225-0006, diretoria@fee.tche.br, http://www.fee.tche.br.

330.9 BRA ISSN 1517-7262
CARTA DE CONJUNTURA F E E. Text in Portuguese. 1991. m. free (effective 2003). charts; stat. 8 p./no.; **Document type:** *Bulletin.* **Description:** Analyzes the economic status of the country and the region. Presents recent and relevant economic events.
Related titles: Online - full content ed.; ◆ English ed.: Carta de Conjuntura. ISSN 1517-7246.
Published by: Fundacao de Economia e Estatistica, Rua Duque de Caxias, 1691, Andar 8, Centro, Porto Alegre, RS 90010-283, Brazil. TEL 55-51-3216-9008, FAX 55-21-2250006, conjuntura@fee.tche.br, diretoria@fee.tche.br, http://www.fee.tche.br. Circ: 2,100 (controlled).

330.9 USA
CASCADE (PHILADELPHIA). Text in English. s-a. **Document type:** *Newsletter.* **Description:** Covers consumer credit and community redevelopment.
Published by: Federal Reserve Bank of Philadelphia, 10 Independence Mall, Philadelphia, PA 19106. http://www.phil.frb.org/.

CASH; die Wirtschaftszeitung der Schweiz. see *BUSINESS AND ECONOMICS—Banking And Finance*

330.9 USA ISSN 1040-8452
HC59.69
CENTER FOR INTERNATIONAL AND COMPARATIVE STUDIES. IOWA INTERNATIONAL PAPERS. Text in English. 1989. a. price varies. **Document type:** *Academic/Scholarly.*
Published by: University of Iowa, Center for International and Comparative Studies, 226 International Center, Iowa City, IA 52242. TEL 319-335-0368, FAX 319-335-0280. Ed. Douglas Midgett.

330.9 BRB ISSN 0304-6796
HG2846.B3
CENTRAL BANK OF BARBADOS. ANNUAL REPORT. Text in English. 1973. a. free. charts; stat. **Document type:** *Bulletin, Corporate.* **Description:** This is a report on the economic activity during the year - with tables and charts on selected economic indicators; the Bank's operations and administration, along with its financial statement.
Published by: Central Bank of Barbados, Research Department, Spry St., PO Box 1016, Bridgetown, Barbados. TEL 246-4366870, FAX 246-4271431, cbblibr@caribsurf.com, cbb.libr@caribsurf.com, http://www.centralbank.org.bb. R&P Neville Pollard. Circ: 1,400.

330.9 EGY ISSN 0008-9249
HF46
CENTRAL BANK OF EGYPT. ECONOMIC REVIEW. Key Title: Economic Review - Central Bank of Egypt. Text in English. 1961. q. free. charts; stat. **Description:** Deals with economic development in Egypt and abroad.
Related titles: Arabic ed.
Indexed: ASD, PROMT, RRTA, S&F, WAE&RSA, WBA.
—BLDSC (3654.920000).
Published by: Central Bank of Egypt, Research Department, 31 Sharia Kasr-el Nil, Cairo, Egypt. Eds. Mahasen Abdel Rehim, Mohamed Saad Badr. Circ: 2,500.

CENTRAL BANK OF IRAQ. QUARTERLY BULLETIN. see *BUSINESS AND ECONOMICS—Banking And Finance*

CENTRAL BANK OF JORDAN. MONTHLY STATISTICAL BULLETIN. see *BUSINESS AND ECONOMICS—Abstracting, Bibliographies, Statistics*

330.9 KEN
CENTRAL BANK OF KENYA. MONTHLY ECONOMIC REVIEWS. Text in English. 1968. m. charts; stat. **Document type:** *Government.* **Description:** Examines various economic indicators for Kenya, including inflation, interest rates, exchange rates, balance of payment and domestic debt, the stock market, and economic growth.
Formerly: Central Bank of Kenya. Economic and Financial Review
Related titles: Online - full text ed.
Indexed: WBA.
Published by: Central Bank of Kenya, Research Department, PO Box 60000, Nairobi, Kenya. cbk-resd@africaonline.co.ke, http://www.africaonline.co.ke/cbk.

330.9 KWT ISSN 1029-4554
HC497.K8
CENTRAL BANK OF KUWAIT. ECONOMIC REPORT. Text in English. a. free. charts; stat. **Document type:** *Government.* **Description:** Covers issues related to the State of Kuwait's overall financial and monetary sector as well as economical indicators. Topics such as external trade, prices, stock market movements monetary policy etc. are covered.
Related titles: Arabic ed.: Taqrir al-Iqtisadi - Bank al-Kuwayt al-Markazi. ISSN 1029-4570.
Published by: Central Bank of Kuwait, Economic Research Department/Bank al-Kuwayt al-Markazi, Idarat al-Buhuth al-ektisadia, P O Box 526, Safat, 13006, Kuwait. TEL 965-2449200, FAX 965-2440887, cbk@cbk.gov.kw, http://www.cbk.gov.kw. R&P Sami H Al-Anbaee TEL 965-2403257.

CENTRAL BANK OF KUWAIT. MONTHLY MONETARY STATISTICS. see *BUSINESS AND ECONOMICS—Abstracting, Bibliographies, Statistics*

CENTRAL BANK OF KUWAIT. QUARTERLY STATISTICAL BULLETIN/BANK AL-KUWAYT AL-MARKAZI. AL-NASHRAH AL-IHSA'IYYAH AL-FASLIYYAH. see *BUSINESS AND ECONOMICS—Abstracting, Bibliographies, Statistics*

330.9 NGA ISSN 0008-9281
HG46
CENTRAL BANK OF NIGERIA. ECONOMIC AND FINANCIAL REVIEW. Text in English. 1963. irreg., latest vol.16, no.2, 1978. free. charts; stat.
Indexed: KES, PAIS.
Published by: Central Bank of Nigeria, Tinubu Sq., PMB 12194, Lagos, Nigeria. Circ: 4,000.

330.9 LKA
CENTRAL BANK OF SRI LANKA. BULLETIN. Text in English, Singhalese, Tamil. 1950. m. LKR 375, USD 30. charts; stat. index. back issues avail. **Document type:** *Bulletin.*
Description: Reviews economic trends and developments in Sri Lanka.
Formerly: Central Bank of Ceylon. Bulletin (0008-9222)
Indexed: PAIS.
Published by: Central Bank of Sri Lanka, Janadhipathi Mawatha, P O Box 590, Colombo, 1, Sri Lanka. TEL 94-1-346275, FAX 94-1-346289. Circ: 875.

330 332 SYR ISSN 0377-3213
CENTRAL BANK OF SYRIA. QUARTERLY BULLETIN. Text in Arabic, English; Text occasionally in French. 1963. q. free. charts; stat. **Document type:** *Bulletin.*
Formerly: Banque Centrale de Syrie. Bulletin Periodique (0067-3846)
Indexed: RASB, WBA.
Published by: (Research Department), Central Bank of Syria/Banque Centrale de Syrie, 29, Ayar Sq., Damascus, Syria. TEL 963-11-216801, FAX 963-11-2227109, TELEX 411910.

330.9 GMB ISSN 0796-0220
HG3399.G3
CENTRAL BANK OF THE GAMBIA. QUARTERLY BULLETIN. Text in English. 1971. q. free. **Document type:** *Bulletin.*
Supersedes: Gambia. Currency Board. Report
Indexed: RASB.
Published by: Central Bank of the Gambia, Economic Research Department, 1-2 Buckle St, Banjul, Gambia. TEL 228103, FAX 226969, TELEX 2218 GAMBANK GV. Ed. Buah Saidy. Circ: 200.

CENTRAL BANK OF TRINIDAD AND TOBAGO. ECONOMIC BULLETIN. see *BUSINESS AND ECONOMICS—Abstracting, Bibliographies, Statistics*

330.947 GBR ISSN 1469-5278
HC244.A1
CENTRAL EUROPE MONITOR. Key Title: Emerging Europe Monitor. Central Europe. Text in English. 2000. m. GBP 265, USD 435 (effective 1999). **Document type:** *Journal, Trade.*
Description: Covers political risk, the business environment, and economic prospects in Central European countries.
Supersedes in part (1994-2000): Central and South East Europe Monitor (1466-3937); Which was formerly (until 1999): Eastern Europe Monitor (1353-4696)
Related titles: Online - full text ed.: (from EBSCO Publishing).
—IE. CCC.
Published by: Business Monitor International Ltd., Mermaid House, 2 Puddle Dock, Blackfriars, London, EC4V 3DS, United Kingdom. TEL 44-20-72480468, FAX 44-20-72480467, busmon@dial.pipex.com, http://www.businessmonitor.com.

330.943 BEL ISSN 1025-7969
CENTRAL EUROPEAN ECONOMIC REVIEW. Text in English. m.
Description: Covers economic changes in the countries in eastern Europe as they adapt to post-Communist conditions.
Related titles: Online - full text ed.
Published by: Dow Jones Publishing Co. Europe, Bd Brand Whitlock 87, Brussels, 1200, Belgium. TEL 32-2-7411211, FAX 32-2-7411600. Ed. Fred Kempe.

CENTRAL INTELLIGENCE AGENCY. MONOGRAPHS. see *POLITICAL SCIENCE—International Relations*

CENTRAL INTELLIGENCE AGENCY. MONOGRAPHS. ALL COMMUNIST COUNTRIES REPORTS. see *POLITICAL SCIENCE—International Relations*

CENTRAL INTELLIGENCE AGENCY. MONOGRAPHS. ALL COUNTRIES REPORTS. see *POLITICAL SCIENCE—International Relations*

CENTRAL INTELLIGENCE AGENCY. MONOGRAPHS. ALL INTERNATIONAL COUNTRIES REPORTS. see *POLITICAL SCIENCE—International Relations*

CENTRAL INTELLIGENCE AGENCY. MONOGRAPHS. CHINA REPORTS. see *POLITICAL SCIENCE—International Relations*

CENTRAL INTELLIGENCE AGENCY. MONOGRAPHS. COMMONWEALTH OF INDEPENDENT STATES REPORT. see *POLITICAL SCIENCE—International Relations*

CENTRAL INTELLIGENCE AGENCY. MONOGRAPHS. MAPS ONLY. see *POLITICAL SCIENCE—International Relations*

330.9 USA ISSN 1050-3005
CENTRAL NEW YORK BUSINESS JOURNAL. Text in English. 1986. w. (Fri.). USD 69 (effective 2005). adv. bk.rev. illus.; stat. index. 4 cols./p.; **Document type:** *Newspaper.*
Formerly (until 1989): The Business Journal (0894-5675); Incorporates (in 1987): Central New York Business Review (0890-1015)
Related titles: Online - full text ed.: (from EBSCO Publishing, Northern Light Technology, Inc., The Dialog Corporation).
Indexed: BusDate, LRI, T&II.
Published by: C N Y Business Journal, 231 Walton St, Syracuse, NY 13202-1230. TEL 315-472-3104, FAX 315-478-8166, arombel@cnybi.com, http://www.cnybi.com. Ed. Charles McChesney. Pub. Norman Poltenson. Adv. contact Bill Browning. Circ: 8,000 (paid).

330.9 CHL ISSN 0716-1123
HC191
CENTRO DE ESTUDIOS PUBLICOS. DOCUMENTO DE TRABAJO. Text in Spanish; Text occasionally in English. 1981. m. **Document type:** *Academic/Scholarly.*
Published by: Centro de Estudios Publicos, Monsenor Sotero Sanz 162, Providencia, Santiago 9, Chile. TEL 56-2-3282400, FAX 56-2-3282440, biblioteca@cepchile.cl, http://www.depchile.cl. Ed. Arturo Fontaine Talavera. Pub. Maria Teresa Miranda. Circ: 1,000.

330.9 BOL
CENTRO DE INVESTIGACION Y PROMOCION DEL CAMPESINADO. CUADERNOS DE INVESTIGACION. Text in Spanish. 1973. irreg.
Published by: Centro de Investigacion y Promocion del Campesinado, Casilla 5854, La Paz, Bolivia.

330 ITA ISSN 0065-6151
CENTRO DOCUMENTAZIONE E RICERCHE ECONOMICO-SOCIALI. QUADERNI. Cover title: Quaderni Ce D R E S. Text in Italian. 1963. irreg., latest vol.119, 1982. free. bk.rev.
Published by: Centro Documentazione e Ricerche Economico-Sociali, Via Galimberti, 2-A, Alessandria, AL 15100, Italy. Ed. Carlo Beltrame. Circ: 1,000.

382 338 BEL
CHALLENGE EUROPE. Text in English. m.
Media: Online - full content.
Published by: The European Policy Centre, Residence Palace, 155 Rue de la Loi, Brussels, 1040, Belgium. TEL 32-2-2310340, FAX 32-2-2310704, http://www.theepc.be/challenge/. Ed. John Palmer.

CHAMBRE DE COMMERCE ET D'INDUSTRIE DE CASABLANCA. REVUE MENSUELLE. see *BUSINESS AND ECONOMICS—Chamber Of Commerce Publications*

CHENGSHI GAIGE YU FAZHAN/URBAN REFORM AND DEVELOPMENT. see *HOUSING AND URBAN PLANNING*

330.973 USA ISSN 0895-0164
HC107.A14
CHICAGO FED LETTER. Text in English. 1996. m. free (effective 2005). **Document type:** *Newsletter, Trade.* **Description:** Features essays on economic policy issues of regional and national interest.
Related titles: Online - full text ed.: (from EBSCO Publishing, O C L C Online Computer Library Center, Inc., ProQuest Information & Learning).
Indexed: ABIn, BLI, PAIS.
—CISTI.
Published by: Federal Reserve Bank of Chicago, 230 South LaSalle St, Chicago, IL 60604-1413. TEL 312-322-5322, http://www.chicagofed.org/publications/fedletter/cflaug2004_205.pdf. Ed. Karl A Scheld.

330.9 PAK
CHIEF EXECUTIVES THINK TANK. ECONOMIC RESEARCH REPORTS. Text in English. 1960. bi-m. PKR 1,500. stat.
Former titles (until 1986): Chief Executive; (until 1981): Chief Executive's Guide
Indexed: BusI, M&MA.
Published by: Shaikhconsults International, Saddar, P O Box 8560, Karachi 3, Pakistan. TEL 469635. Ed. S Shaukat Ali.

330.983 GBR ISSN 1474-144X
CHILE QUARTERLY FORECAST REPORT. Text in English. 1990. 3/yr. GBP 330, USD 495, EUR 450 (effective 2003). **Document type:** *Journal, Trade.* **Description:** Provides a comprehensive assessment of the Chilean government, economy and business environment. Helps to identify opportunities and reduce risk, and answers key questions facing executives at this time.
Formerly (until 2001): Annual Country Forecast Report. Chile (0960-5282)
Related titles: CD-ROM ed.: GBP 410, USD 675 (effective 2000); Online - full text ed.: (from EBSCO Publishing).
—CCC.
Published by: Business Monitor International Ltd., Mermaid House, 2 Puddle Dock, Blackfriars, London, EC4V 3DS, United Kingdom. TEL 44-20-72480468, FAX 44-20-72480467, subs@businessmonitor.com, http://www.businessmonitor.com/chileforecast.html.

CHIMERA. see *POLITICAL SCIENCE*

330.9 USA
CHINA COUNTRY REPORT. Text in English. 1999. a. looseleaf. USD 475 (effective 2001). charts; stat.; illus. 150 p./no.; back issues avail. **Document type:** *Yearbook, Consumer.* **Description:** Reviews political and economic events of the previous year in China, and forecasts the coming year's events.
Published by: Orbis Publications, LLC, 1924 47th St NW, Washington, DC 20007-1901. TEL 202-298-7936, FAX 202-298-7938, sfoster@orbispub.com, http://www.orbispublications.com. Ed. Derek Scissors. Pub., R&P Stephen Foster. Circ: 110 (paid).

330.9 HKG ISSN 1011-2898
CHINA ECONOMIC EXPRESS (JAPANESE EDITION). Text in Japanese. w. HKD 2,900, USD 430.
Related titles: ♦ Chinese ed.: China Economic Express (Korean Edition). ISSN 1013-5375.
Published by: Economic Information & Agency, 342 Hennessy Rd 10th Fl, 10 th Fl, Wanchai, Hong Kong. TEL 852-573-8217, FAX 852-838-8304.

330.9 HKG ISSN 1013-5375
CHINA ECONOMIC EXPRESS (KOREAN EDITION). Text in Chinese. w. HKD 2,265, USD 310.
Related titles: ♦ Japanese ed.: China Economic Express (Japanese Edition). ISSN 1011-2898.
Published by: Economic Information & Agency, 342 Hennessy Rd 10th Fl, 10 th Fl, Wanchai, Hong Kong. TEL 852-573-8217, FAX 852-838-8304.

330.9 NLD ISSN 1043-951X
HC426
➤ **CHINA ECONOMIC REVIEW (AMSTERDAM).** Text in English. 1989. 4/yr. EUR 95 in Europe to individuals; JPY 13,100 in Japan to individuals; USD 99 elsewhere to individuals; EUR 335 in Europe to institutions; JPY 44,500 in Japan to institutions; USD 376 elsewhere to institutions (effective 2006). back issues avail. **Document type:** *Journal, Academic/Scholarly.* **Description:** Focuses on the economic development of the People's Republic of China.
Related titles: Microform ed.: (from PQC); Online - full text ed.: (from EBSCO Publishing, Florida Center for Library Automation, Gale Group, IngentaConnect, ScienceDirect, Swets Information Services).
Indexed: APEL, ASCA, BPI, CurCont, ESPM, FamI, JEL, PAIS, RiskAb, SSCI.
—BLDSC (3180.138100), IE, Infotrieve, ingenta. **CCC.**
Published by: Elsevier BV, North-Holland (Subsidiary of: Elsevier Science & Technology), Sara Burgerhartstraat 25, Amsterdam, 1055 KV, Netherlands. TEL 31-20-485-3911, FAX 31-20-485-2457, nlinfo-f@elsevier.nl, http://www.elsevier.com/locate/chieco, http://www.elsevier.nl. Ed. C. Chang.

330.9 CHN
CHINA INFRASTRUCTURE. Text in English. m. USD 495 (effective 2001). adv. 12 p./no.; **Document type:** *Newsletter, Trade.* **Description:** Provides information and analysis of mainland China's power, transportation, water and construction industries.
Related titles: E-mail ed.
Published by: Clear Thinking Corp., 2-F Profit Tower, 17 Chaoyangmenwai Ave, Beijing, 100020, China. TEL 86-1-65991631, 86-1-65991634, FAX 86-1-65991639, marketing@clearthinking.com, http://www.clearthinking.com/publications/aboutci.asp.

330 HKG ISSN 0379-2862
CHINA LETTER. Text in Chinese. 1971. m. USD 225. bk.rev. **Document type:** *Newsletter.* **Description:** Keeps business executives up to date on the processes of change in China and on the evolution of the China market.
Indexed: RASB.
Published by: Asia Letter Group, GPO Box 10874, Hong Kong, Hong Kong. TEL 852-526-2950, FAX 852-526-7131. Ed. Charles R Smith.

330.9 HKG ISSN 0258-3054
CHINA MARKET. Variant title: China Market Monthly. Text in English. 1982. m. HKD 300, USD 80.
Indexed: KES, PAIS.

Published by: Economic Information & Agency, 342 Hennessy Rd 10th Fl, 10 th Fl, Wanchai, Hong Kong. TEL 852-573-8217, FAX 852-838-8304, TELEX 86990 EIA HX.

330.951 GBR ISSN 1470-7381
DS779.15
CHINA QUARTERLY FORECAST REPORT. Text in English. 1993. 3/yr. GBP 330, USD 495, EUR 450 (effective 2003). **Document type:** *Journal, Trade.* **Description:** Provides a comprehensive assessment of the Chinese government, economy and business environment over the next 30 months. Helps to identify opportunities and reduce risk, and answers key questions facing executives at this time.
Formerly (until 2000): Annual Country Forecast Report. China (0969-5184)
Related titles: Online - full text ed.: (from EBSCO Publishing).
—CCC.
Published by: Business Monitor International Ltd., Mermaid House, 2 Puddle Dock, Blackfriars, London, EC4V 3DS, United Kingdom. TEL 44-20-72480468, FAX 44-20-72480467, marketing@businessmonitor.com, http://www.businessmonitor.com/chinaforecast.html.

330.9 USA ISSN 1093-5126
HC427.92
CHINA WATCH. Text in English. 1998. m. looseleaf. USD 425 worldwide (effective 2005). charts; stat. back issues avail. **Document type:** *Newsletter, Consumer.* **Description:** Reports on political, economic, and business events in China.
Related titles: E-mail ed.; Online - full text ed.
Published by: Orbis Publications, LLC, 1924 47th St NW, Washington, DC 20007-1901. TEL 202-298-7936, FAX 202-298-7938, orbis@orbispub.com, http://www.orbispublications.com. Ed. Derek Scissors. Pub., R&P Stephen Foster. Circ: 200 (paid).

330.951 USA
CHINA WEEKLY FAX BULLETIN. Text in English. w. looseleaf. USD 545 in US & Canada; USD 595 elsewhere (effective Sep. 2000). 2 p./no.; back issues avail. **Document type:** *Bulletin, Consumer.* **Description:** Reports on political, economic, and business events in China.
Media: Fax. **Related titles:** E-mail ed.; Online - full text ed.
Published by: Orbis Publications, LLC, 1924 47th St NW, Washington, DC 20007-1901. TEL 202-298-7936, FAX 202-298-7938, sfoster@orbispub.com, http://www.orbispublications.com. Ed. Derek Scissors. Pub., R&P Stephen Foster.

330.9 USA
CHINAONLINE. Text in English. d. USD 150 (effective 2002). adv. **Description:** Includes news and analysis providing business information of China.
Media: Online - full content.
Published by: ChinaOnline, Inc, 900 N. Michigan Ave, Ste 2180, Chicago, IL 60611. TEL 312-335-8881, 312-335-8881, FAX 312-335-9299, info@chinaonline.com, http://www.chinaonline.com/. Pub. Lyric Hughes. Circ: 10,000.

330.9 USA
CHINESE BUSINESS JOURNAL. Text in English. 1989. fortn. USD 7.50 (effective 1998). adv. back issues avail. **Document type:** *Newspaper.* **Description:** Provides information on business, finance and investment for the greater Seattle area.
Address: 3469, Seattle, WA 98114-3469. TEL 206-624-8781, FAX 206-624-7437. Ed. Hung Szeto. Circ: 10,000.

330.9 KOR
CHONGYONGNYON✶. Text in Korean. 1976. m. free. adv. bk.rev.
Published by: Federation of Korean Industries, c/o Korean Chamber of Commerce & Industry, 45, 4-ka Namdaemun-no, CPO Box 25, Chung-ku, Seoul, Korea, S. Ed. Bong Shik Shin. Circ: 13,000.

330.9 USA
CITY LINE NEWS✶. Text in English. 1985. w. USD 65 (effective 2001). adv. bk.rev. illus. cum.index. 6 cols./p.; back issues avail. **Document type:** *Newspaper.* **Description:** Covers all facets of business, dining and entertainment, and community news.
Address: 857 Montgommery Ave, 2nd Fl, Narberth, PA 19072-1541. TEL 610-667-6623, FAX 610-667-6624. Ed., Adv. contact Leslie Swan TEL 610-667-6623. Pub., R&P Robert Klein. B&W page USD 990; trim 10.375 x 13.975. Circ: 20,000 (controlled).

330 ARG ISSN 0009-8256
CLARIN ECONOMICO. Text in Spanish. 1960. m. USD 52. charts; stat.; tr.lit.
Published by: Arte Grafico Editorial Argentino S.A., Piedras, 1743, Capital Federal, Buenos Aires 1140, Argentina. Ed. Ernestina Laura Herrera de Noble.

330.9 333.33 USA ISSN 1047-6083
THE CLAYTON - FILLMORE REPORT✶; perspectives on economics and real estate. Text in English. 1983. m. USD 175; USD 200 foreign (effective 1996). cum.index: 1984-1992. back issues avail. **Document type:** *Trade.* **Description:** Describes real estate and economic conditions in three metro areas throughout the US in each issue; contains feature articles on a particular US region.

▼ *new title* ➤ *refereed* ✶ *unverified* ♦ *full entry avail.*

Related titles: Online - full text ed.: (from Florida Center for Library Automation, Gale Group).
Published by: Clayton-Fillmore, Ltd., 125 Dorset Ct., Castle, CO 80211. TEL 303-433-5323, FAX 303-433-5363. Ed. Howard Treibitz. Circ: 550 (paid).

330.9 USA ISSN 0009-8892
CLEVELANDER. Text in English. 1926. m. USD 12. adv.
Document type: *Newsletter.*
Indexed: PAIS.
Published by: Greater Cleveland Growth Association, 50 Public Sq, Cleveland, OH 44113-2291. TEL 216-621-3300, FAX 216-621-6013. Circ: 17,500.

CLINICAL TRIALS INSIGHT CLASSICS. PHARMACOECONOMICS. see *PHARMACY AND PHARMACOLOGY—Abstracting, Bibliographies, Statistics*

330.9 USA
COBBLE HILL NEWS. Text in English. w. USD 25.
Published by: Brooklyn Journal Publications, Inc., 129 Montague St, Brooklyn, NY 11201. TEL 718-624-6033, FAX 718-875-5302.

COLABORACION INTERNACIONAL. see *BUSINESS AND ECONOMICS—International Commerce*

330.944 FRA ISSN 1152-4952
COLLECTION CONJONCTURE. Text in French. 1991. irreg.
Related titles: ◆ Series: Banque de France. Enquete Mensuelle de Conjoncture. ISSN 0242-5815.
Published by: Banque de France, Service Relations avec le Public, 48 rue Croix-des-Petits-Champs, Paris, 75049, France. FAX 33-1-42922954, cdoc@banque-france.fr. Ed. R Raymond.

330.9 070.5 USA
COLLEGE PUBLISHING MARKET FORECAST (YEAR). Text in English. biennial. USD 1,995 per vol. (effective 2003 & 2004).
Document type: *Trade.*
Published by: SIMBA Information (Subsidiary of: R.R. Bowker LLC), 60 Long Ridge Rd., Ste 300, Stamford, CT 06902. TEL 203-325-8193, 800-307-2529, FAX 203-325-8915, info@simbanet.com, http://www.simbanet.com.

330.9861 GBR ISSN 1474-1458
COLOMBIA QUARTERLY FORECAST REPORT. Text in English. 1992. 3/yr. GBP 330, USD 495, EUR 450 (effective 2003).
Document type: *Journal, Trade.* **Description:** Provides a comprehensive assessment of the Colombian government, economy and business environment. Helps to identify opportunities and reduce risk, and answers key questions facing executives at this time.
Formerly (until 2001): Annual Country Forecast Report. Colombia (0966-8179)
Related titles: CD-ROM ed.: GBP 410, USD 675 (effective 2000); Online - full text ed.: (from EBSCO Publishing).
—CCC.
Published by: Business Monitor International Ltd., Mermaid House, 2 Puddle Dock, Blackfriars, London, EC4V 3DS, United Kingdom. TEL 44-20-72480468, FAX 44-20-72480467, subs@businessmonitor.com, http://www.businessmonitor.com/colombiaforecast.html.

COLORADO AGRIBUSINESS ROUNDUP. see *AGRICULTURE—Agricultural Economics*

330.9 USA ISSN 1536-6766
TN210 CODEN: CSEREL
COLORADO SCHOOL OF MINES QUARTERLY REVIEW. Text in English. 1905. q. USD 65 domestic; USD 70 foreign (effective 2005). bibl.; charts; illus.; stat. cum.index: 1906-1998. back issues avail. **Document type:** *Academic/Scholarly.*
Former titles (until 1999): Colorado School of Mines Quarterly Review of Engineering, Science, Education and Research (1068-2937); (until 1992): Colorado School of Mines Quarterly (0163-9153); (until 1979): Colorado School of Mines. Quarterly (0010-1753)
Related titles: Microform ed.: (from PQC).
Indexed: AESIS, ApMecR, CIN, ChemAb, ChemTitl, E&PHSE, EIA, EngInd, EnvAb, F&EA, GP&P, GeotechAb, IMMAb, Inspec, PetrolAb, RefZh.
—CASDDS, CIS, CISTI, Linda Hall, PADDS. **CCC.**
Published by: Colorado School of Mines, 1500 Illinois, Golden, CO 80401-1887. TEL 303-273-3595, FAX 303-273-3199, lpang@mines.edu, http://www.mines.edu/Academic/affairs/quarthp.html. Ed., R&P Laura Jarnagin Pang. Circ: 1,500.

330.9 USA
COLORADO SKI INDUSTRY; highlights of the (years) season. Text in English. a. USD 25 (effective 2001). **Document type:** *Bulletin.* **Description:** Annual synopsis of the ski conditions in Colorado.
Published by: University of Colorado, Business Research Division, Campus Box 420, Boulder, CO 80309-0420. TEL 303-492-8227, FAX 303-492-3620.

330.9 USA ISSN 1523-6366
HC107.C7
COLORADOBIZ. Text in English. 1973. m. USD 24; USD 3.95 newsstand/cover (effective 2005). adv. illus. **Document type:** *Magazine, Trade.*
Former titles (until 1999): Colorado Business Magazine (0898-6363); (until 1986): Colorado Business (0092-5071)
Related titles: Microform ed.: (from PQC); Online - full text ed.: (from EBSCO Publishing, Florida Center for Library Automation, Gale Group, O C L C Online Computer Library Center, Inc., The Dialog Corporation).
Indexed: BusDate, BusI, LRI, MagInd, PAIS, T&II.
Published by: Wiesner Publishing, LLC, 7009 S Potomac St, Ste 200, Centennial, CO 80112. TEL 303-397-7600, FAX 303-397-7619, rschwab@cobizmag.com, http://cobizmag.com/, http://www.wiesnerpublishing.com. Ed. Robert Schwab. Pub. Tamara W Patterson. Circ: 20,019 (paid).

330 CHL ISSN 0716-4025
COMENTARIOS SOBRE LA SITUACION ECONOMICA. Text in Spanish. 1971. s-a. USD 15. charts; stat. **Document type:** *Academic/Scholarly.*
Published by: Universidad de Chile, Facultad de Ciencias Economicas y Administrativas, Ave. Ranacagua, 257, Santiago, Chile. Ed. Luis Riveros.

330.9 CHL
COMISION ECONOMICA PARA AMERICA LATINA Y EL CARIBE. SERIE REFORMAS DE POLITICA PUBLICA. Text in Chinese. irreg., latest vol.57. price varies. back issues avail.
Document type: *Monographic series.*
Published by: Comision Economica para America Latina y el Caribe/Economic Commission for Latin America and the Caribbean, Ave Dag Hammarskjold 3477, Vitacura, Santiago de Chile, Chile. TEL 56-2-471-2000, FAX 56-2-208-0252, publications@eclac.cl, http://www.eclac.cl. Circ: (controlled).

380 CHE
COMMERCE EXTERIEUR SUISSE/SCHWEIZER AUSSENWIRTSCHAFT. Text in French, German. 1922. m. adv. bk.rev. abstr.; bibl.; stat.; tr.lit. **Document type:** *Trade.*
Former titles (until 1995): Exportation en Pratique; Marches Etrangers - Auslandmaerkte; Wirtschaftliche Mitteilungen - Informations Economiques (0043-6186)
Indexed: KES.
Published by: Swiss Office for Trade Promotion, Stampfenbachstr 85, Zuerich, 8035, Switzerland. TEL 41-1-3655151, FAX 41-1-3655221, info.zurich@osec.ch, http://www.osec.ch. Circ: 6,000.

330 332 USA
COMMERSANT WEEKLY. Text in Russian. w. USD 495; USD 545 foreign (effective 1998). adv. **Description:** Covers business opportunities, the availability of funding, reliable local contacts, and other essential trade and investment information related to Russia and Eastern Europe.
Related titles: ◆ English ed.: East - West Commersant. ISSN 1081-8421.
Published by: WorldTrade Executive, Inc., 2250 Main St, Ste 100, PO Box 761, Concord, MA 01742. TEL 978-287-0301, FAX 978-287-0302, info@wtexec.com, http://www.wtexec.com. Pub. Gary A Brown. adv.: page USD 975; 9.5 x 7.5.

330.9 USA ISSN 0273-1886
COMMITTEE FOR ECONOMIC DEVELOPMENT. ANNUAL REPORT. Text in English. 1943. a.
Former titles (until 1976): Committee for Economic Development. Report on Activities (0573-0392); (until 1960): Committee for Economic Development. Annual Report (0196-7266)
Related titles: Online - full text ed.
Published by: Committee for Economic Development, 261 Madison Ave., Flr. 25, New York, NY 10016-2303. TEL 212-296-5860, FAX 212-223-0776, http://www.ced.org/about/annual.shtml.

330.9 AUS
COMMONWEALTH COMPETITIVE NEUTRALITY ANNUAL REPORT. Text in English. 1996. a. charts; stat. back issues avail. **Document type:** *Government.* **Description:** Reports on efforts by the Australian Commonwealth Government to enforce the provisions of the Competition Principles Agreement of 1995.
Related titles: Online - full text ed.
Published by: (Australia. Department of the Treasury), AusInfo, GPO Box 1920, Canberra Mc, ACT 2610, Australia. TEL 61-2-6295-4512, FAX 61-2-6295-4455, http://www.ausinfo.gov.au, http://www.treasury.gov.au. **Orders to:** AusInfo Mail Order Sales, GPO Box 84, Canberra, ACT 2601, Australia. FAX 61-2-6295-4888.

330.9 AUS
COMMONWEALTH LEGISLATION REVIEW ANNUAL REPORT. Text in English. 1996. a. charts; stat. **Description:** Reviews activities by the Australian Commonwealth Government to enact and enforce legislation under the Competition Principles Agreement of 1995.
Related titles: Online - full text ed.
Published by: (Australia. Department of the Treasury), AusInfo, GPO Box 1920, Canberra Mc, ACT 2610, Australia. TEL 61-2-6295-4512, FAX 61-2-6295-4455, http://www.ausinfo.gov.au, http://www.treasury.gov.au. **Orders to:** AusInfo Mail Order Sales, GPO Box 84, Canberra, ACT 2601, Australia. FAX 61-2-6295-4888.

COMMONWEALTH LETTERS; for investors in single family homes. see *REAL ESTATE*

COMMUNICATIONS MARKETS ANALYSIS. see *COMMUNICATIONS*

COMMUNICATIONS MARKETS IN EASTERN EUROPE (YEAR). see *COMMUNICATIONS*

330.9 USA ISSN 0896-9159
COMMUNITY CHANGE. Text in English. 1986. irreg. bk.rev. back issues avail. **Document type:** *Newsletter.* **Description:** For community organizations working in low-income neighborhoods and individuals concerned about poverty. Focuses on poverty and what can be done about poverty-related problems, such as the need for affordable housing.
Published by: Center for Community Change, 1536 U St NW, Washington, DC 20009-3912. info@communitychange.org, http://www.communitychange.org/. Ed. Tim Saasta. Circ: 2,800.

COMPETITIVENESS REVIEW; an international business journal. see *BUSINESS AND ECONOMICS—International Commerce*

330.9 PYF
COMPTES ECONOMIQUES DE LA POLYNESIE FRANCAISE. Text in French. irreg. **Document type:** *Government.*
Published by: Institut Territorial de la Statistique, BP 395, Papeete, Tahiti Cedex 98713, French Polynesia. TEL 689-54-32-32, FAX 689-42-72-52.

COMPUTATIONAL ECONOMICS. see *BUSINESS AND ECONOMICS—Computer Applications*

330 ESP ISSN 0210-0738
CONFEDERACION ESPANOLA DE CAJAS DE AHORROS. COYUNTURA ECONOMICA. Text in Spanish. 1977. m.
Published by: Confederacion Espanola de Cajas de Ahorros, Servicio de Estudios, Alcala, 276, Madrid, 28014, Spain.

330.9 ITA
CONGIUNTURA INDUSTRIALE IN EMILIA-ROMAGNA. Text in Italian. 1984. q. **Document type:** *Bulletin.*
Published by: Unione Regionale dfelle Camere di Commercio dell'Emilia-Romagna, Via Aldo Moro 62, Bologna, BO 40127, Italy. TEL 39-051-6377011, FAX 39-051-6377050, staff@rer.camcom.it, http://www.rer.camcom.it. Ed. Claudio Pasini. Circ: 6,000.

CONGO. CENTRE NATIONAL DE LA STATISTIQUE ET DES ETUDES ECONOMIQUES. ANNUAIRE STATISTIQUE. see *BUSINESS AND ECONOMICS—Abstracting, Bibliographies, Statistics*

CONGO. CENTRE NATIONAL DE LA STATISTIQUE ET DES ETUDES ECONOMIQUES. BULLETIN DE STATISTIQUE. see *BUSINESS AND ECONOMICS—Abstracting, Bibliographies, Statistics*

CONGO. CENTRE NATIONAL DE LA STATISTIQUE ET DES ETUDES ECONOMIQUES. BULLETIN TRIMESTRIEL DE LA CONJONCTURE. see *BUSINESS AND ECONOMICS—Abstracting, Bibliographies, Statistics*

330.9 TUN
CONJONCTURE/AL-ALAM AL-IQTISADIY; etudes et informations economiques de Tunisie - dirasat wa mu'atiyat iqtisadiyyah 'an Tunis. Text in Arabic, French. 1971. m. TND 1.50 per issue. adv. bk.rev. charts; illus.; stat.
Indexed: PAIS, RASB.
Published by: Ministere de l'Economie Nationale, Publication des Ministeres du Commerce & Ministere de l'Industrie et d'Energie, 37, Av Kherredine Pacha, Tunis, 1002, Tunisia. TEL 289-801. Eds. Ahmed Souibgui, Kamel Gharbi. Circ: 3,000.

330.9 BRA ISSN 1413-1536
HC188.B3
CONJUNTURA & PLANEJAMENTO. Text in Portuguese. 1994. m. BRL 3 per issue (effective 2002).
Published by: Superintendencia de Estudos Economicos e Sociais da Bahia, Ave Luiz Vianna Filho s/n, Salvador, Bahia 41 750-300, Brazil. TEL 55-71-3704847, FAX 55-71-371853, http://www.sei.ba.gov.br.

330.9 BRA ISSN 0010-5945
HC186
CONJUNTURA ECONOMICA. Text in Portuguese. 1947. m. USD 235 (effective 2000). adv. charts; stat. index. **Document type:** *Academic/Scholarly.* **Description:** Analyzes the national economy, profiles national accounts, contains price indices in different sectors, and presents the latest research in the economic area.
Indexed: ILD, KES, PAIS, RASB.
—BLDSC (3417.565000).
Published by: (Instituto Brasileiro de Economia), Fundacao Getulio Vargas, 190 Praia de Botafogo, Rio de Janeiro, RJ 22253-53-900, Brazil. TEL 55-21-2559-5544, FAX 55-21-2559-5541, assine@fgv.br. Ed. Roberto Fendt. Adv. contact Else Flejlau. Circ: 16,000.

B

330.9   ESP   ISSN 1130-3530
CONSEJERIA DE OBRAS PUBLICAS Y ORDENACION DEL TERRITORIO. BOLETIN ESTADISTICO. Text in Spanish. 1989. q.
—CINDOC.
Published by: Region de Murcia, Consejeria de Obras Publicas y Ordenacion del Territorio, Plaza Santona s-n, Poligono de la Fama, Murcia, 30071, Spain. TEL 34-968-362531, FAX 34-968-362392, http://www.carm.es/cpt/orga/.

330.9   GBR   ISSN 0957-0950
HC10
CONSENSUS FORECASTS; a worldwide survey. Text in English. 1984. m. GBP 370, USD 565 (effective 2003). adv. 32 p./no.; back issues avail. **Document type:** *Journal, Academic/Scholarly.* **Description:** Presents and discusses individual and consensus forecasts for the G-10 countries along with historical data, analysis, foreign exchange and oil price forecasts and a special topical survey.
Formerly: Economic Forecasts (0169-1767)
Related titles: Diskette ed.; E-mail ed.; Fax ed.; Microform ed.: (from PQC).
—IE. **CCC.**
Published by: Consensus Economics Inc., 53 Upper Brook St, London, W1K 2LT, United Kingdom. TEL 44-20-7491-3211, FAX 44-20-7409-2331, editors@consensuseconomics.com, http://www.consensuseconomics.com. Ed. Claire V M Hubbard. Pub. Philip M Hubbard.

330.9   USA
CONSOLIDATED FEDERAL FUNDS REPORT. Text in English. 1981. a. price varies. **Document type:** *Government.*
Related titles: CD-ROM ed.; Online - full text ed.
Published by: U.S. Bureau of the Census (Subsidiary of: U.S. Department of Commerce), Customer Services, Washington, DC 20233. TEL 301-457-4100, FAX 301-457-4714, http://www.census.gov/. Circ: 7,000. **Co-sponsor:** Office of Management and Budget.

330.9   USA
CONSUMER EXPENDITURE SURVEY. Text in English. a.?. free. **Document type:** *Government.* **Description:** Presents detailed statistics on consumer spending.
Related titles: Diskette ed.; ◆ Series of: U.S. Bureau of Labor Statistics. Bulletin. ISSN 0082-9021.
Published by: U.S. Department of Labor, Bureau of Labor Statistics, Postal Square Bldg., 2 Massachusetts Ave, NE, Washington, DC 20212-0001 . TEL 202-691-5200, http://www.bls.gov. **Subscr. to:** U.S. Government Printing Office, Superintendent of Documents, PO Box 371954, Pittsburgh, PA 15250-7954. TEL 202-512-1800, FAX 202-512-2250, orders@gpo.gov, http://www.access.gpo.gov.

331.1   USA
CONSUMER EXPENDITURE SURVEY: QUARTERLY DATA FROM THE INTERVIEW SURVEY. Text in English. q.
Document type: *Government.* **Description:** Reports on historical consumer spending patterns.
Related titles: ◆ Series of: U.S. Bureau of Labor Statistics. Reports.
Indexed by: AmStl.
Published by: U.S. Department of Labor, Bureau of Labor Statistics, Postal Square Bldg., 2 Massachusetts Ave, NE, Washington, DC 20212-0001 . TEL 202-691-5200, http://www.bls.gov. **Subscr. to:** U.S. Government Printing Office, Superintendent of Documents.

330.9   USA
CONSUMER EXPENDITURES IN (YEAR). Text in English. a. free. **Document type:** *Government.*
Related titles: ◆ Series of: U.S. Bureau of Labor Statistics. National Office News Releases.
Published by: U.S. Department of Labor, Bureau of Labor Statistics, Postal Square Bldg., 2 Massachusetts Ave, NE, Washington, DC 20212-0001 . TEL 202-691-5200, http://www.bls.gov. **Subscr. to:** U.S. Government Printing Office, Superintendent of Documents.

CONSUMER PRICE INDEX OF BELIZE. see *BUSINESS AND ECONOMICS—Abstracting, Bibliographies, Statistics*

CONSUMER PRICE INDICES OF ETHIOPIA AT COUNTRY, RURAL AND URBAN LEVELS. see *BUSINESS AND ECONOMICS—Abstracting, Bibliographies, Statistics*

330.9   ESP   ISSN 1577-1369
HC387.M2
CONTABILIDAD REGIONAL DE LA COMUNIDAD DE MADRID. Text in Spanish. 1999. a.
Related titles: Online - full text ed.
Published by: Comunidad de Madrid, Consejeria de Economia e Innovacion Tecnologica. Instituto de Estadistica, Principe de Vargara, 108, Madrid, 28002, Spain. TEL 34-91-5802540, jestadis@madrid.org, http://www.madrid.org/iestadis/index.htm.

338.9   GBR   ISSN 0951-4937
HN398.W26
➤ **CONTEMPORARY WALES;** an annual review of economic and social research. Text in English. 1987. a., latest vol.15. GBP 7.50, USD 14 per vol. (effective 2004). adv. stat. back issues avail. **Document type:** *Academic/Scholarly.*
Description: Contains an authoritative analysis of economic and social development in Wales.
Related titles: Online - full text ed.: (from Gale Group, IngentaConnect).
—BLDSC (3425.315000). **CCC.**
Published by: (Board of Celtic Studies), University of Wales Press, 10 Columbus Walk, Brigantine Pl, Cardiff, CF10 4UP, United Kingdom. TEL 44-29-2049-6899, FAX 44-29-2049-6108, journals@press.wales.ac.uk, http://www.uwp.co.uk. Eds. Andrew Thompson, Jonathan Scourfield, Paul Jones. Circ: 300 (paid).

330.9   GBR   ISSN 0277-5921
HB1
➤ **CONTRIBUTIONS TO POLITICAL ECONOMY.** Text in English. 1980. a., latest vol.22. GBP 50, USD 90, EUR 75 to institutions; GBP 20, USD 36, EUR 30 in developing nations to institutions; GBP 53, USD 95, EUR 80 combined subscription to institutions print & online eds. (effective 2006). bk.rev. 128 p./no.; back issues avail.; reprint service avail. from PSC. **Document type:** *Journal, Academic/Scholarly.* **Description:** Contains scholarly economic research and analysis on issues on vital concern to business government, and other decision makers, including three Nobel laureates, are among the journal's authors.
Related titles: Online - full text ed.: ISSN 1464-3588. GBP 43; USD 72 9 (effective 2004) (from Chadwyck-Healey Inc., EBSCO Publishing, Gale Group, HighWire Press, IngentaConnect, O C L C Online Computer Library Center, Inc., Oxford University Press Online Journals, ProQuest Information & Learning, Swets Information Services).
Indexed by: ABIn, IBSS, JEL, PAIS, PCI, PSA, RASB, SSCI.
—BLDSC (3461.119000), IE, Infotrieve, ingenta. **CCC.**
Published by: (The Western Economic Association International), Oxford University Press, Great Clarendon St, Oxford, OX2 6DP, United Kingdom. TEL 44-1865-556767, FAX 44-1865-556646, jnl.orders@oup.co.uk, http:// cpe.oxfordjournals.org/, http://www.oxfordjournals.org/. Eds. Giancarlo de Vivo, John Eatwell, Murray Milgate. Pub. Martin Green. R&P Fiona Bennett. Circ: 650.

330.9 346   USA
CORPORATE COUNSEL'S GUIDE TO DOING BUSINESS IN RUSSIA. Text in English. 2000. irreg. USD 185 (effective 2001).
Published by: Business Laws, Inc., 11630 Chillicothe Rd, Chesterland, OH 44026. TEL 440-729-7996, FAX 440-729-0645, http://www.businesslaws.com.

330   MEX   ISSN 0010-9118
CORREO ECONOMICO. Text in Spanish. 1963. w. MXP 250, USD 25. adv. bk.rev. bibl.; charts; illus.; stat.
Published by: (Informacion Nacional y Publicidad), Ediciones Correo S.A., CADIZ 53, Col Alamos, Mexico City, DF 03400, Mexico. Circ: 19,000.

341.7   LUX   ISSN 0377-466X
COUNCIL OF THE EUROPEAN COMMUNITIES. REVIEW OF THE COUNCIL'S WORK. Text in English. a. USD 25. **Document type:** *Monographic series.*
Indexed by: IIS.
Published by: (Council of the European Union), European Commission, Office for Official Publications of the European Union, 2 Rue Mercier, Luxembourg, L-2985, Luxembourg.
Dist. in the U.S. by: Bernan Associates, Bernan, 4611-F Assembly Dr., Lanham, MD 20706-4391. TEL 301-459-0056, 800-274-4447.

330   USA   ISSN 1475-1321
HC59
COUNTRY BY COUNTRY. Text in English. 1969. a. USD 525 per issue print or online (effective 2004). **Description:** Forecasts the political and economic trends in over 180 countries.
Formerly (until 2001): E I U World Outlook (0424-3331)
Related titles: Online - full text ed.: (from ProQuest Information & Learning).
Indexed by: ABIn, RASB.
—CCC.
Published by: Economist Intelligence Unit, 111 W 57th St, New York, NY 10019. TEL 212-554-0600, 800-938-4685, FAX 212-586-1182, http://www.eiu.com.

COUNTRY FORECAST. AFRICA. see *POLITICAL SCIENCE*

COUNTRY FORECAST. ALGERIA. see *POLITICAL SCIENCE*

COUNTRY FORECAST. ARGENTINA. see *POLITICAL SCIENCE*

COUNTRY FORECAST. ASIA. see *POLITICAL SCIENCE*

COUNTRY FORECAST. AUSTRALIA. see *POLITICAL SCIENCE*

COUNTRY FORECAST. AUSTRIA. see *POLITICAL SCIENCE*

COUNTRY FORECAST. BELGIUM. see *POLITICAL SCIENCE*

COUNTRY FORECAST. BRAZIL. see *POLITICAL SCIENCE*

COUNTRY FORECAST. BULGARIA. see *POLITICAL SCIENCE*

COUNTRY FORECAST. CANADA. see *POLITICAL SCIENCE*

COUNTRY FORECAST. CHILE. see *POLITICAL SCIENCE*

COUNTRY FORECAST. CHINA. see *POLITICAL SCIENCE*

COUNTRY FORECAST. COLOMBIA. see *POLITICAL SCIENCE*

COUNTRY FORECAST. CZECH REPUBLIC. see *POLITICAL SCIENCE*

COUNTRY FORECAST. DENMARK. see *POLITICAL SCIENCE*

COUNTRY FORECAST. EASTERN EUROPE. see *POLITICAL SCIENCE*

COUNTRY FORECAST. ECUADOR. see *POLITICAL SCIENCE*

COUNTRY FORECAST. EGYPT. see *POLITICAL SCIENCE*

COUNTRY FORECAST. EUROPE. see *POLITICAL SCIENCE*

COUNTRY FORECAST. FINLAND. see *POLITICAL SCIENCE*

COUNTRY FORECAST. FRANCE. see *POLITICAL SCIENCE*

COUNTRY FORECAST. GERMANY. see *POLITICAL SCIENCE*

COUNTRY FORECAST. GLOBAL OUTLOOK. see *POLITICAL SCIENCE*

COUNTRY FORECAST. GREECE. see *POLITICAL SCIENCE*

COUNTRY FORECAST. HONG KONG. see *POLITICAL SCIENCE*

COUNTRY FORECAST. HUNGARY. see *POLITICAL SCIENCE*

COUNTRY FORECAST. INDIA. see *POLITICAL SCIENCE*

COUNTRY FORECAST. INDONESIA. see *POLITICAL SCIENCE*

COUNTRY FORECAST. IRAN. see *POLITICAL SCIENCE*

COUNTRY FORECAST. IRAQ. see *POLITICAL SCIENCE*

COUNTRY FORECAST. IRELAND. see *POLITICAL SCIENCE*

COUNTRY FORECAST. ISRAEL. see *POLITICAL SCIENCE*

COUNTRY FORECAST. ITALY. see *POLITICAL SCIENCE*

COUNTRY FORECAST. JAPAN. see *POLITICAL SCIENCE*

COUNTRY FORECAST. LATIN AMERICA. see *POLITICAL SCIENCE*

COUNTRY FORECAST. MALAYSIA. see *POLITICAL SCIENCE*

COUNTRY FORECAST. MEXICO. see *POLITICAL SCIENCE*

COUNTRY FORECAST. MIDDLE EAST. see *POLITICAL SCIENCE*

COUNTRY FORECAST. NETHERLANDS. see *POLITICAL SCIENCE*

COUNTRY FORECAST. NEW ZEALAND. see *POLITICAL SCIENCE*

COUNTRY FORECAST. NIGERIA. see *POLITICAL SCIENCE*

COUNTRY FORECAST. NORWAY. see *POLITICAL SCIENCE*

COUNTRY FORECAST. PAKISTAN. see *POLITICAL SCIENCE*

COUNTRY FORECAST. PERU. see *POLITICAL SCIENCE*

COUNTRY FORECAST. PHILIPPINES. see *POLITICAL SCIENCE*

COUNTRY FORECAST. POLAND. see *POLITICAL SCIENCE*

COUNTRY FORECAST. PORTUGAL. see *POLITICAL SCIENCE*

COUNTRY FORECAST. ROMANIA. see *POLITICAL SCIENCE*

COUNTRY FORECAST. RUSSIA. see *POLITICAL SCIENCE*

COUNTRY FORECAST. SAUDI ARABIA. see *POLITICAL SCIENCE*

COUNTRY FORECAST. SINGAPORE. see *POLITICAL SCIENCE*

B

▼ *new title*   ➤ *refereed*   ✶ *unverified*   ◆ *full entry avail.*

B

COUNTRY FORECAST. SLOVAKIA. see *POLITICAL SCIENCE*

COUNTRY FORECAST. SOUTH AFRICA. see *POLITICAL SCIENCE*

COUNTRY FORECAST. SOUTH KOREA. see *POLITICAL SCIENCE*

COUNTRY FORECAST. SPAIN. see *POLITICAL SCIENCE*

COUNTRY FORECAST. SRI LANKA. see *POLITICAL SCIENCE*

COUNTRY FORECAST. SWEDEN. see *POLITICAL SCIENCE*

COUNTRY FORECAST. SWITZERLAND. see *POLITICAL SCIENCE*

COUNTRY FORECAST. TAIWAN. see *POLITICAL SCIENCE*

COUNTRY FORECAST. THAILAND. see *POLITICAL SCIENCE*

COUNTRY FORECAST. TURKEY. see *POLITICAL SCIENCE*

COUNTRY FORECAST. UNITED KINGDOM. see *POLITICAL SCIENCE*

COUNTRY FORECAST. UNITED STATES OF AMERICA. see *POLITICAL SCIENCE*

COUNTRY FORECAST. VENEZUELA. see *POLITICAL SCIENCE*

COUNTRY FORECAST. VIETNAM. see *POLITICAL SCIENCE*

COUNTRY FORECAST. WORLD. see *POLITICAL SCIENCE*

382 338   USA   ISSN 1528-4530
HD2755.5   CODEN: CSSBE9
COUNTRY MONITOR. Text in English. 1993. w. USD 1,055 print
or online; USD 85 per issue print or online (effective 2004).
adv. **Document type:** *Trade.* **Description:** Stay informed of
trends, outlooks and strategies for doing business in 195
countries worldwide.
Former titles (until 1999): Crossborder Monitor (1070-5961); (until
1993): Crossborder (1070-5953)
Related titles: ♦ CD-ROM ed.: E I U International Business
Newsletters on Disc; Microform ed.: (from PQC); Online - full
text ed.: E I U International Business Newsletters (from
EBSCO Publishing, Florida Center for Library Automation,
ProQuest Information & Learning, SilverPlatter Information,
Inc., The Dialog Corporation).
Indexed: ABIn.
—BLDSC (3481.892650), IE. **CCC.**
Published by: Economist Intelligence Unit, 111 W 57th St, New
York, NY 10019. TEL 212-554-0600, 800-938-4685, FAX
212-586-1182, http://www.eiu.com. Ed. Nico Cilchester. Pub.
Debra Langley. Adv. contact Leslie Magee.

COUNTRY PROFILE. AFGHANISTAN; annual survey of political
and economic background. see *POLITICAL SCIENCE*

COUNTRY PROFILE. ALBANIA; annual survey of political and
economic background. see *POLITICAL SCIENCE*

COUNTRY PROFILE. ALGERIA; annual survey of political and
economic background. see *POLITICAL SCIENCE*

COUNTRY PROFILE. ANGOLA; annual survey of political and
economic background. see *POLITICAL SCIENCE*

COUNTRY PROFILE. ARGENTINA; annual survey of political and
economic background. see *POLITICAL SCIENCE*

COUNTRY PROFILE. ARMENIA; annual survey of political and
economic background. see *POLITICAL SCIENCE*

COUNTRY PROFILE. ARUBA; annual survey of political and
economic background. see *POLITICAL SCIENCE*

COUNTRY PROFILE. AUSTRALIA; annual survey of political and
economic background. see *POLITICAL SCIENCE*

COUNTRY PROFILE. AUSTRIA; annual survey of political and
economic background. see *POLITICAL SCIENCE*

COUNTRY PROFILE. AZERBAIJAN; annual survey of political
and economic background. see *POLITICAL SCIENCE*

COUNTRY PROFILE. BAHAMAS; annual survey of political and
economic background. see *POLITICAL SCIENCE*

COUNTRY PROFILE. BAHRAIN; annual survey of political and
economic background. see *POLITICAL SCIENCE*

COUNTRY PROFILE. BANGLADESH; annual survey of political
and economic background. see *POLITICAL SCIENCE*

COUNTRY PROFILE. BELARUS; annual survey of political and
economic background. see *POLITICAL SCIENCE*

COUNTRY PROFILE. BELGIUM; annual survey of political and
economic background. see *POLITICAL SCIENCE*

COUNTRY PROFILE. BELIZE; annual survey of political and
economic background. see *POLITICAL SCIENCE*

COUNTRY PROFILE. BENIN; annual survey of political and
economic background. see *POLITICAL SCIENCE*

COUNTRY PROFILE. BERMUDA; annual survey of political and
economic background. see *POLITICAL SCIENCE*

COUNTRY PROFILE. BOLIVIA; annual survey of political and
economic background. see *POLITICAL SCIENCE*

COUNTRY PROFILE. BOSNIA-HERCEGOVINA; annual survey of
political and economic background. see *POLITICAL SCIENCE*

COUNTRY PROFILE. BOTSWANA; annual survey of political and
economic background. see *POLITICAL SCIENCE*

COUNTRY PROFILE. BRAZIL; annual survey of political and
economic background. see *POLITICAL SCIENCE*

COUNTRY PROFILE. BULGARIA; annual survey of political and
economic background. see *POLITICAL SCIENCE*

COUNTRY PROFILE. BURKINA FASO; annual survey of political
and economic background. see *POLITICAL SCIENCE*

COUNTRY PROFILE. BURUNDI; annual survey of political and
economic background. see *POLITICAL SCIENCE*

COUNTRY PROFILE. CAMBODIA; annual survey of political and
economic background. see *POLITICAL SCIENCE*

COUNTRY PROFILE. CAMEROON; annual survey of political and
economic background. see *POLITICAL SCIENCE*

COUNTRY PROFILE. CANADA; annual survey of political and
economic background. see *POLITICAL SCIENCE*

COUNTRY PROFILE. CAPE VERDE; annual survey of political
and economic background. see *POLITICAL SCIENCE*

COUNTRY PROFILE. CAYMAN ISLANDS; annual survey of
political and economic background. see *POLITICAL SCIENCE*

COUNTRY PROFILE. CENTRAL AFRICAN REPUBLIC; annual
survey of political and economic background. see *POLITICAL
SCIENCE*

COUNTRY PROFILE. CHAD; annual survey of political and
economic background. see *POLITICAL SCIENCE*

COUNTRY PROFILE. CHILE; annual survey of political and
economic background. see *POLITICAL SCIENCE*

COUNTRY PROFILE. CHINA; annual survey of political and
economic background. see *POLITICAL SCIENCE*

COUNTRY PROFILE. COLOMBIA; annual survey of political and
economic background. see *POLITICAL SCIENCE*

COUNTRY PROFILE. COMOROS; annual survey of political and
economic background. see *POLITICAL SCIENCE*

COUNTRY PROFILE. CONGO; annual survey of political and
economic background. see *POLITICAL SCIENCE*

COUNTRY PROFILE. COSTA RICA; annual survey of political
and economic background. see *POLITICAL SCIENCE*

COUNTRY PROFILE. COTE D'IVOIRE; annual survey of political
and economic background. see *POLITICAL SCIENCE*

COUNTRY PROFILE. CROATIA; annual survey of political and
economic background. see *POLITICAL SCIENCE*

COUNTRY PROFILE. CUBA; annual survey of political and
economic background. see *POLITICAL SCIENCE*

COUNTRY PROFILE. CYPRUS; annual survey of political and
economic background. see *POLITICAL SCIENCE*

COUNTRY PROFILE. CZECH REPUBLIC; annual survey of
political and economic background. see *POLITICAL SCIENCE*

COUNTRY PROFILE. DEMOCRATIC REPUBLIC OF CONGO;
annual survey of political and economic background. see
POLITICAL SCIENCE

COUNTRY PROFILE. DENMARK; annual survey of political and
economic background. see *POLITICAL SCIENCE*

COUNTRY PROFILE. DJIBOUTI; annual survey of political and
economic background. see *POLITICAL SCIENCE*

COUNTRY PROFILE. DOMINICAN REPUBLIC; annual survey of
political and economic background. see *POLITICAL SCIENCE*

COUNTRY PROFILE. ECUADOR; annual survey of political and
economic background. see *POLITICAL SCIENCE*

COUNTRY PROFILE. EGYPT; annual survey of political and
economic background. see *POLITICAL SCIENCE*

COUNTRY PROFILE. EL SALVADOR; annual survey of political
and economic background. see *POLITICAL SCIENCE*

COUNTRY PROFILE. EQUATORIAL GUINEA; annual survey of
political and economic background. see *POLITICAL SCIENCE*

COUNTRY PROFILE. ERITREA; annual survey of political and
economic background. see *POLITICAL SCIENCE*

COUNTRY PROFILE. ESTONIA; annual survey of political and
economic background. see *POLITICAL SCIENCE*

COUNTRY PROFILE. ETHIOPIA; annual survey of political and
economic background. see *POLITICAL SCIENCE*

COUNTRY PROFILE. EUROPEAN UNION; annual survey of
political and economic background. see *POLITICAL SCIENCE*

COUNTRY PROFILE. FINLAND; annual survey of political and
economic background. see *POLITICAL SCIENCE*

COUNTRY PROFILE. FRANCE; annual survey of political and
economic background. see *POLITICAL SCIENCE*

COUNTRY PROFILE. GABON; annual survey of political and
economic background. see *POLITICAL SCIENCE*

COUNTRY PROFILE. GEORGIA; annual survey of political and
economic background. see *POLITICAL SCIENCE*

COUNTRY PROFILE. GERMANY; annual survey of political and
economic background. see *POLITICAL SCIENCE*

COUNTRY PROFILE. GHANA; annual survey of political and
economic background. see *POLITICAL SCIENCE*

COUNTRY PROFILE. GREECE; annual survey of political and
economic background. see *POLITICAL SCIENCE*

COUNTRY PROFILE. GUATEMALA; annual survey of political
and economic background. see *POLITICAL SCIENCE*

COUNTRY PROFILE. GUINEA; annual survey of political and
economic background. see *POLITICAL SCIENCE*

COUNTRY PROFILE. GUINEA-BISSAU; annual survey of political
and economic background. see *POLITICAL SCIENCE*

COUNTRY PROFILE. GUYANA; annual survey of political and
economic background. see *POLITICAL SCIENCE*

COUNTRY PROFILE. HAITI; annual survey of political and
economic background. see *POLITICAL SCIENCE*

COUNTRY PROFILE. HONDURAS; annual survey of political and
economic background. see *POLITICAL SCIENCE*

COUNTRY PROFILE. HONG KONG; annual survey of political
and economic background. see *POLITICAL SCIENCE*

COUNTRY PROFILE. HUNGARY; annual survey of political and
economic background. see *POLITICAL SCIENCE*

COUNTRY PROFILE. ICELAND; annual survey of political and
economic background. see *POLITICAL SCIENCE*

COUNTRY PROFILE. INDIA; annual survey of political and
economic background. see *POLITICAL SCIENCE*

COUNTRY PROFILE. INDONESIA; annual survey of political and
economic background. see *POLITICAL SCIENCE*

COUNTRY PROFILE. IRAN; annual survey of political and
economic background. see *POLITICAL SCIENCE*

COUNTRY PROFILE. IRAQ; annual survey of political and
economic background. see *POLITICAL SCIENCE*

COUNTRY PROFILE. IRELAND; annual survey of political and
economic background. see *POLITICAL SCIENCE*

COUNTRY PROFILE. ISRAEL, PALESTINIAN TERRITORIES.
see *POLITICAL SCIENCE*

COUNTRY PROFILE. ITALY; annual survey of political and
economic background. see *POLITICAL SCIENCE*

COUNTRY PROFILE. JAMAICA, BELIZE, ORGANISATION OF EASTERN CARIBBEAN STATES, WINDWARD AND LEEWARD ISLANDS. see *POLITICAL SCIENCE*

COUNTRY PROFILE. JAPAN; annual survey of political and economic background. see *POLITICAL SCIENCE*

COUNTRY PROFILE. JORDAN; annual survey of political and economic background. see *POLITICAL SCIENCE*

COUNTRY PROFILE. KAZAKHSTAN; annual survey of political and economic background. see *POLITICAL SCIENCE*

COUNTRY PROFILE. KENYA; annual survey of political and economic background. see *POLITICAL SCIENCE*

COUNTRY PROFILE. KUWAIT; annual survey of political and economic background. see *POLITICAL SCIENCE*

COUNTRY PROFILE. KYRGYZ REPUBLIC; annual survey of political and economic background. see *POLITICAL SCIENCE*

COUNTRY PROFILE. LAOS; annual survey of political and economic background. see *POLITICAL SCIENCE*

COUNTRY PROFILE. LATVIA; annual survey of political and economic background. see *POLITICAL SCIENCE*

COUNTRY PROFILE. LEBANON; annual survey of political and economic background. see *POLITICAL SCIENCE*

COUNTRY PROFILE. LESOTHO; annual survey of political and economic background. see *POLITICAL SCIENCE*

COUNTRY PROFILE. LIBERIA; annual survey of political and economic background. see *POLITICAL SCIENCE*

COUNTRY PROFILE. LIBYA; annual survey of political and economic background. see *POLITICAL SCIENCE*

COUNTRY PROFILE. LITHUANIA; annual survey of political and economic background. see *POLITICAL SCIENCE*

COUNTRY PROFILE. LUXEMBOURG; annual survey of political and economic background. see *POLITICAL SCIENCE*

COUNTRY PROFILE. MACAU; annual survey of political and economic background. see *POLITICAL SCIENCE*

COUNTRY PROFILE. MACEDONIA; annual survey of political and economic background. see *POLITICAL SCIENCE*

COUNTRY PROFILE. MADAGASCAR; annual survey of political and economic background. see *POLITICAL SCIENCE*

COUNTRY PROFILE. MALAWI; annual survey of political and economic background. see *POLITICAL SCIENCE*

COUNTRY PROFILE. MALAYSIA; annual survey of political and economic background. see *POLITICAL SCIENCE*

COUNTRY PROFILE. MALI; annual survey of political and economic background. see *POLITICAL SCIENCE*

COUNTRY PROFILE. MALTA; annual survey of political and economic background. see *POLITICAL SCIENCE*

COUNTRY PROFILE. MAURITANIA; annual survey of political and economic background. see *POLITICAL SCIENCE*

COUNTRY PROFILE. MAURITIUS; annual survey of political and economic background. see *POLITICAL SCIENCE*

COUNTRY PROFILE. MEXICO; annual survey of political and economic background. see *POLITICAL SCIENCE*

COUNTRY PROFILE. MOLDOVA; annual survey of political and economic background. see *POLITICAL SCIENCE*

COUNTRY PROFILE. MONGOLIA; annual survey of political and economic background. see *POLITICAL SCIENCE*

COUNTRY PROFILE. MOROCCO; annual survey of political and economic background. see *POLITICAL SCIENCE*

COUNTRY PROFILE. MOZAMBIQUE; annual survey of political and economic background. see *POLITICAL SCIENCE*

COUNTRY PROFILE. MYANMAR; annual survey of political and economic background. see *POLITICAL SCIENCE*

COUNTRY PROFILE. NAMIBIA; annual survey of political and economic background. see *POLITICAL SCIENCE*

COUNTRY PROFILE. NEPAL; annual survey of political and economic background. see *POLITICAL SCIENCE*

COUNTRY PROFILE. NETHERLANDS; annual survey of political and economic background. see *POLITICAL SCIENCE*

COUNTRY PROFILE. NETHERLANDS ANTILLES; annual survey of political and economic background. see *POLITICAL SCIENCE*

COUNTRY PROFILE. NEW ZEALAND; annual survey of political and economic background. see *POLITICAL SCIENCE*

COUNTRY PROFILE. NICARAGUA; annual survey of political and economic background. see *POLITICAL SCIENCE*

COUNTRY PROFILE. NIGER; annual survey of political and economic background. see *POLITICAL SCIENCE*

COUNTRY PROFILE. NIGERIA; annual survey of political and economic background. see *POLITICAL SCIENCE*

COUNTRY PROFILE. NORTH KOREA; annual survey of political and economic background. see *POLITICAL SCIENCE*

COUNTRY PROFILE. NORWAY; annual survey of political and economic background. see *POLITICAL SCIENCE*

COUNTRY PROFILE. OMAN; annual survey of political and economic background. see *POLITICAL SCIENCE*

COUNTRY PROFILE. PACIFIC ISLANDS: FIJI, NEW CALEDONIA, SAMOA, SOLOMON ISLANDS, VANUATU, TONGA; annual survey of political and economic background. see *POLITICAL SCIENCE*

COUNTRY PROFILE. PAKISTAN; annual survey of political and economic background. see *POLITICAL SCIENCE*

COUNTRY PROFILE. PANAMA; annual survey of political and economic background. see *POLITICAL SCIENCE*

COUNTRY PROFILE. PAPUA NEW GUINEA; annual survey of political and economic background. see *POLITICAL SCIENCE*

COUNTRY PROFILE. PARAGUAY; annual survey of political and economic background. see *POLITICAL SCIENCE*

COUNTRY PROFILE. PERU; annual survey of political and economic background. see *POLITICAL SCIENCE*

COUNTRY PROFILE. PHILIPPINES; annual survey of political and economic background. see *POLITICAL SCIENCE*

COUNTRY PROFILE. POLAND; annual survey of political and economic background. see *POLITICAL SCIENCE*

COUNTRY PROFILE. PORTUGAL; annual survey of political and economic background. see *POLITICAL SCIENCE*

COUNTRY PROFILE. PUERTO RICO; annual survey of political and economic background. see *POLITICAL SCIENCE*

COUNTRY PROFILE. QATAR; annual survey of political and economic background. see *POLITICAL SCIENCE*

COUNTRY PROFILE. ROMANIA; annual survey of political and economic background. see *POLITICAL SCIENCE*

COUNTRY PROFILE. RUSSIA; annual survey of political and economic background. see *POLITICAL SCIENCE*

COUNTRY PROFILE. RWANDA; annual survey of political and economic background. see *POLITICAL SCIENCE*

COUNTRY PROFILE. SAO TOME AND PRINCIPE; annual survey of political and economic background. see *POLITICAL SCIENCE*

COUNTRY PROFILE. SAUDI ARABIA; annual survey of political and economic background. see *POLITICAL SCIENCE*

COUNTRY PROFILE. SENEGAL; annual survey of political and economic background. see *POLITICAL SCIENCE*

COUNTRY PROFILE. SERBIA-MONTENEGRO; annual survey of political and economic background. see *POLITICAL SCIENCE*

COUNTRY PROFILE. SEYCHELLES; annual survey of political and economic background. see *POLITICAL SCIENCE*

COUNTRY PROFILE. SIERRA LEONE; annual survey of political and economic background. see *POLITICAL SCIENCE*

COUNTRY PROFILE. SINGAPORE; annual survey of political and economic background. see *POLITICAL SCIENCE*

COUNTRY PROFILE. SLOVAKIA; annual survey of political and economic background. see *POLITICAL SCIENCE*

COUNTRY PROFILE. SLOVENIA; annual survey of political and economic background. see *POLITICAL SCIENCE*

COUNTRY PROFILE. SOMALIA; annual survey of political and economic background. see *POLITICAL SCIENCE*

COUNTRY PROFILE. SOUTH AFRICA; annual survey of political and economic background. see *POLITICAL SCIENCE*

COUNTRY PROFILE. SOUTH KOREA; annual survey of political and economic background. see *POLITICAL SCIENCE*

COUNTRY PROFILE. SPAIN; annual survey of political and economic background. see *POLITICAL SCIENCE*

COUNTRY PROFILE. SRI LANKA; annual survey of political and economic background. see *POLITICAL SCIENCE*

COUNTRY PROFILE. SUDAN; annual survey of political and economic background. see *POLITICAL SCIENCE*

COUNTRY PROFILE. SURINAME; annual survey of political and economic background. see *POLITICAL SCIENCE*

COUNTRY PROFILE. SWAZILAND; annual survey of political and economic background. see *POLITICAL SCIENCE*

COUNTRY PROFILE. SWEDEN; annual survey of political and economic background. see *POLITICAL SCIENCE*

COUNTRY PROFILE. SWITZERLAND; annual survey of political and economic background. see *POLITICAL SCIENCE*

COUNTRY PROFILE. SYRIA; annual survey of political and economic background. see *POLITICAL SCIENCE*

COUNTRY PROFILE. TAIWAN; annual survey of political and economic background. see *POLITICAL SCIENCE*

COUNTRY PROFILE. TAJIKISTAN; annual survey of political and economic background. see *POLITICAL SCIENCE*

COUNTRY PROFILE. TANZANIA; annual survey of political and economic background. see *POLITICAL SCIENCE*

COUNTRY PROFILE. THAILAND; annual survey of political and economic background. see *POLITICAL SCIENCE*

COUNTRY PROFILE. THE GAMBIA; annual survey of political and economic background. see *POLITICAL SCIENCE*

COUNTRY PROFILE. THE PALESTINIAN TERRITORIES; annual survey of political and economic background. see *POLITICAL SCIENCE*

COUNTRY PROFILE. TOGO; annual survey of political and economic background. see *POLITICAL SCIENCE*

COUNTRY PROFILE. TRINIDAD AND TOBAGO; annual survey of political and economic background. see *POLITICAL SCIENCE*

COUNTRY PROFILE. TUNISIA; annual survey of political and economic background. see *POLITICAL SCIENCE*

COUNTRY PROFILE. TURKEY; annual survey of political and economic background. see *POLITICAL SCIENCE*

COUNTRY PROFILE. TURKMENISTAN; annual survey of political and economic background. see *POLITICAL SCIENCE*

COUNTRY PROFILE. TURKS AND CAICOS ISLANDS; annual survey of political and economic background. see *POLITICAL SCIENCE*

COUNTRY PROFILE. UGANDA; annual survey of political and economic background. see *POLITICAL SCIENCE*

COUNTRY PROFILE. UKRAINE; annual survey of political and economic background. see *POLITICAL SCIENCE*

COUNTRY PROFILE. UNITED ARAB EMIRATES; annual survey of political and economic background. see *POLITICAL SCIENCE*

COUNTRY PROFILE. UNITED KINGDOM; annual survey of political and economic background. see *POLITICAL SCIENCE*

COUNTRY PROFILE. UNITED STATES OF AMERICA; annual survey of political and economic background. see *POLITICAL SCIENCE*

COUNTRY PROFILE. URUGUAY; annual survey of political and economic background. see *POLITICAL SCIENCE*

COUNTRY PROFILE. UZBEKISTAN; annual survey of political and economic background. see *POLITICAL SCIENCE*

B

▼ *new title*   ➤ *refereed*   ✳ *unverified*   ◆ *full entry avail.*

COUNTRY PROFILE. VENEZUELA; annual survey of political and economic background. see *POLITICAL SCIENCE*

COUNTRY PROFILE. VIETNAM; annual survey of political and economic background. see *POLITICAL SCIENCE*

COUNTRY PROFILE. WINDWARD AND LEEWARD ISLANDS; annual survey of political and economic background. see *POLITICAL SCIENCE*

COUNTRY PROFILE. YEMEN; annual survey of political and economic background. see *POLITICAL SCIENCE*

COUNTRY PROFILE. ZAMBIA; annual survey of political and economic background. see *POLITICAL SCIENCE*

COUNTRY PROFILE. ZIMBABWE; annual survey of political and economic background. see *POLITICAL SCIENCE*

330.9549 USA ISSN 1478-0364
HC416
COUNTRY REPORT. AFGHANISTAN; analysis of economic and political trends every quarter. Text in English. q. USD 485 print or online; USD 230 per issue print or online (effective 2004). illus.; stat. **Document type:** *Trade.* **Description:** Analyzes the current political and economic climate, as well as short-term economic projections.
Supersedes in part (in 2001): Country Report. Pakistan, Afghanistan (0269-7173)
Published by: Economist Intelligence Unit, 111 W 57th St, New York, NY 10019. TEL 212-554-0600, FAX 212-586-1181, newyork@eiu.com, http://www.eiu.com.

330.94965 USA ISSN 1366-4018
HC402.A1
COUNTRY REPORT. ALBANIA; analysis of economic and political trends every quarter. Text in English. q. USD 485 print or online; USD 230 per issue print or online (effective 2004). charts; stat. **Document type:** *Trade.* **Description:** Analyzes the current political and economic climate of Albania and provides short-term economic projections.
Supersedes in part (in 1997): Country Report. Bulgaria, Albania (1356-4110); Which superseded in part (in 1995): Country Report. Romania, Bulgaria, Albania (0269-5669); Which was formerly: Quarterly Economic Review of Romania, Bulgaria, Albania (0142-4068)
Related titles: ♦ CD-ROM ed.: E I U Country Reports on Disc: Eastern Europe; Online - full text ed.: E I U Country Reports: Eastern Europe (from Central Institute for Scientific & Technical Information, SilverPlatter Information, Inc., The Dialog Corporation).
—BLDSC (3481.897045).
Published by: Economist Intelligence Unit, 111 W 57th St, New York, NY 10019. TEL 212-554-0600, FAX 212-586-1181, newyork@eiu.com, http://www.eiu.com.

330.965 USA ISSN 0269-5723
HC815.A1
COUNTRY REPORT. ALGERIA; analysis of economic and political trends every quarter. Text in English. 1952. q. USD 485 print or online; USD 230 per issue print or online (effective 2004). illus.; stat. **Document type:** *Trade.* **Description:** Analyzes Algeria's current political and economic climate, as well as short-term economic projections.
Formerly: Quarterly Economic Review of Algeria (0142-4130)
Related titles: ♦ CD-ROM ed.: E I U Country Reports on Disc: Middle East - North Africa; Online - full text ed.: E I U Country Reports: Middle East-North Africa.
Indexed: RASB.
—CCC.
Published by: Economist Intelligence Unit, 111 W 57th St, New York, NY 10019. TEL 212-554-0600, FAX 212-586-1181, newyork@eiu.com, http://www.eiu.com.

330.9673 USA ISSN 0969-7985
HC950.A1
COUNTRY REPORT. ANGOLA; analysis of economic and political trends every quarter. Text in English. 1952. q. USD 485 print or online; USD 230 per issue print or online (effective 2004). illus.; stat. **Document type:** *Trade.* **Description:** Analyzes the current political and economic climate, as well as short-term economic projections.
Supersedes in part (in 1994): Country Report. Angola, Botswana, Namibia, Lesotho, Swaziland; Which was formed by the 1992 merger of part of: Country Report. Angola, Sao Tome and Principe (0269-4344); part of: Country Report. Namibia, Botswana, Lesotho, Swaziland (0269-6746); Which was formerly: Quarterly Economic Review of Angola, Sao Tome and Principe (0266-9781); Quarterly Economic Review of Namibia, Botswana, Lesotho, Swaziland (0144-896X)
Related titles: ♦ CD-ROM ed.: E I U Country Reports on Disc: Sub-Saharan Africa; Online - full text ed.: E I U Country Reports: Sub-Saharan Africa (from SilverPlatter Information, Inc., The Dialog Corporation).
Indexed: RASB.
—CCC.
Published by: Economist Intelligence Unit, 111 W 57th St, New York, NY 10019. TEL 212-554-0600, FAX 212-586-1181, newyork@eiu.com, http://www.eiu.com.

330.982 USA ISSN 0269-4212
HC171
COUNTRY REPORT. ARGENTINA; analysis of economic and political trends every quarter. Text in English. 1952. q. USD 485 print or online; USD 230 per issue print or online (effective 2004). illus.; stat. **Document type:** *Trade.* **Description:** Analyzes Argentina's current political and economic climate, as well as short-term economic projections.
Formerly: Quarterly Economic Review of Argentina (0142-4149)
Related titles: ♦ CD-ROM ed.: E I U Country Reports on Disc: The Americas; Online - full text ed.: E I U Country Reports: The Americas; (from EBSCO Publishing).
Indexed: RASB.
—CCC.
Published by: Economist Intelligence Unit, 111 W 57th St, New York, NY 10019. TEL 212-554-0600, FAX 212-586-1181, newyork@eiu.com, http://www.eiu.com.

330.9549 USA ISSN 1478-0321
HC415.17.A1
COUNTRY REPORT. ARMENIA; analysis of economic and political trends every quarter. Text in English. q. USD 485 print or online; USD 230 per issue print or online (effective 2004). illus.; stat. **Document type:** *Journal, Trade.* **Description:** Analyzes the current political and economic climate, as well as short-term economic projections.
Supersedes in part (in 2001): Country Report: Georgia, Armenia (1366-4069); Which superseded in part (in 1997): Country Report. Georgia, Armenia, Azerbaijan (1356-4080); (in 1995): Country Report. Georgia, Armenia, Azerbaijan, Kazakhstan, Central Asian Republics (1352-2930); Which was formerly (until 1993): Country Report. Georgia, Armenia, Azerbaijan, Central Asian Republics (1350-7206); Which superseded in part (in 1992): Country Report. Commonwealth of Independent States (0968-8242); Which was formerly (until 1992): Country Report. U S S R (0269-5480); (until 1986): Quarterly Economic Review of U S S R (0142-3967); (until 1976): Q E R - U S S R
Published by: Economist Intelligence Unit, 111 W 57th St, New York, NY 10019. TEL 212-554-0600, FAX 212-586-1181, newyork@eiu.com, http://www.eiu.com.

330.9549 USA
COUNTRY REPORT. ARUBA; analysis of economic and political trends every quarter. Text in English. q. USD 485 print or online; USD 230 per issue print or online (effective 2004). illus.; stat. **Document type:** *Journal, Trade.*
Supersedes in part: Country Report. Bahamas, Barbados, Bermuda, British Virgin Islands, Netherlands Antilles, Aruba, Turks and Caicos Islands, Cayman Islands (1462-687X); Which superseded in part (in 1998): Country Report. Trinidad & Tobago, Guyana, Windward & Leeward Islands, Suriname, Netherlands Antilles, Aruba (1351-1270); Which superseded in part (in 1993): Country Report. Venezuela, Suriname, Netherlands Antilles (0269-6754); Which was formerly (until 1986): Quarterly Economic Review of Venezuela, Suriname, Netherlands Antilles (0264-9675); (until 1983): Quarterly Economic Review of Venezuela, Netherlands Antilles, Suriname (0264-8458); (until 1982): Quarterly Economic Review of Venezuela, Surinam, Netherlands Antilles (0142-4017); (until 1976): Q E R Venezuela
Published by: Economist Intelligence Unit, 111 W 57th St, New York, NY 10019. TEL 212-554-0600, FAX 212-586-1181, newyork@eiu.com, http://www.eiu.com.

330.994 USA ISSN 0269-7106
HC601
COUNTRY REPORT. AUSTRALIA; analysis of economic and political trends every quarter. Text in English. 1952. q. USD 485 print or online; USD 230 per issue print or online (effective 2004). illus.; stat. **Document type:** *Trade.* **Description:** Analyzes Australia's current political and economic climate, as well as short-term economic projections.
Formerly: Quarterly Economic Review of Australia (0266-9587)
Related titles: ♦ CD-ROM ed.: E I U Country Reports on Disc: Asia-Pacific; Online - full text ed.: E I U Country Reports: Asia-Pacific (from EBSCO Publishing); (from EBSCO Publishing).
Indexed: RASB, WBA, WMB.
—CCC.
Published by: Economist Intelligence Unit, 111 W 57th St, New York, NY 10019. TEL 212-554-0600, FAX 212-586-1181, newyork@eiu.com, http://www.eiu.com.

330.946 USA ISSN 0269-5170
HC261
COUNTRY REPORT. AUSTRIA; analysis of economic and political trends every quarter. Text in English. 1952. q. USD 485 print or online; USD 230 per issue print or online (effective 2004). illus.; stat. **Document type:** *Trade.* **Description:** Analyzes Austria's current political and economic climate, as well as short-term economic projections.
Formerly: Quarterly Economic Review of Austria (0142-3711)
Related titles: ♦ CD-ROM ed.: E I U Country Reports on Disc: Western Europe; Online - full text ed.: E I U Country Reports: Western Europe (from SilverPlatter Information, Inc., The Dialog Corporation); (from EBSCO Publishing).
—CCC.
Published by: Economist Intelligence Unit, 111 W 57th St, New York, NY 10019. TEL 212-554-0600, FAX 212-586-1181, newyork@eiu.com, http://www.eiu.com.

330.94754 USA ISSN 1366-4077
HC415.18.A1
COUNTRY REPORT. AZERBAIJAN; analysis of economic and political trends every quarter. Text in English. q. USD 485 print or online; USD 230 per issue print or online (effective 2004). charts. **Document type:** *Trade.* **Description:** Analyzes the current Azerbaijani political and economic climate and provides short-term economic projections.
Supersedes in part (in 1997): Country Report. Georgia, Armenia, Azerbaijan (1356-4080); Which superseded in part (in 1995): Country Report. Georgia, Armenia, Azerbaijan, Central Asian Republics (1350-7206); Which superseded in part (in 1992): Country Report. Commonwealth of Independent States; Which was formerly (until 1991): Country Report. U S S R (0269-5480); Quarterly Economic Review of U S S R (0142-3967)
Related titles: ♦ CD-ROM ed.: E I U Country Reports on Disc: Eastern Europe; Online - full text ed.: E I U Country Reports: Eastern Europe (from Central Institute for Scientific & Technical Information, SilverPlatter Information, Inc., The Dialog Corporation).
Indexed: ABIn.
Published by: Economist Intelligence Unit, 111 W 57th St, New York, NY 10019. TEL 212-554-0600, FAX 212-586-1181, newyork@eiu.com, http://www.eiu.com.

330.9549 USA
COUNTRY REPORT. BAHAMAS; analysis of economic and political trends every quarter. Text in English. q. USD 485 print or online; USD 230 per issue print or online (effective 2004). illus.; stat. **Document type:** *Trade.*
Supersedes in part: Country Report. Bahamas, Barbados, Bermuda, British Virgin Islands, Netherlands Antilles, Aruba, Turks and Caicos Islands, Cayman Islands (1462-687X); Which superseded in part (in 1998): Country Report. Jamaica, Barbados, Belize, Bahamas, Bermuda, Cayman Islands, Turks and Caicos Islands (1368-9142); Which was formerly (until 1997): Country Report. Jamaica, Belize, Bahamas, Bermuda, Barbados (1460-3543); (until 1994): Country Report. Jamaica, Belize, Bahamas, Bermuda, Barbados, Cayman Islands (1354-2699); (until 1993): Country Report. Jamaica, Belize, Bahamas, Bermuda, Barbados (1351-8674); (until 1993): Country Report. Jamaica, Belize, Bahamas, Bermuda (0269-7130); (until 1986): Quarterly Economic Review of Jamaica, Belize, Bahamas, Bermuda (0266-9617); Which superseded in part (in 1985): Quarterly Economic Review of the West Indies, Belize, Bahamas, Bermuda, Guyana (0142-3738); Which was formerly (until 1976): Q E R West Indies, Belize, Bahamas, Bermuda, Guyana
Published by: Economist Intelligence Unit, 111 W 57th St, New York, NY 10019. TEL 212-554-0600, FAX 212-586-1181, newyork@eiu.com, http://www.eiu.com.

330.9536 USA ISSN 1473-8937
HC415.38.A1
COUNTRY REPORT. BAHRAIN; analysis of economic and political trends every quarter. Text in English. 1952. q. USD 485 print or online; USD 230 per issue print or online (effective 2004). illus.; stat. **Document type:** *Trade.* **Description:** Analyzes Bahrain's and Qatar's current political and economic climates, as well as short-term economic projections.
Supersedes in part (in 2001): Country Report. Bahrain, Qatar (1351-8682); Which superseded in part (in 1992): Country Report. Bahrain, Qatar, Oman, Yemen (0269-5707); Which was formerly: Quarterly Economic Review of Bahrain, Qatar, Oman, Yemen (0142-4114)
Related titles: ♦ CD-ROM ed.: E I U Country Reports on Disc: Middle East - North Africa; Online - full text ed.: E I U Country Reports: Middle East-North Africa.
Indexed: RASB.
Published by: Economist Intelligence Unit, 111 W 57th St, New York, NY 10019. TEL 212-554-0600, FAX 212-586-1181, newyork@eiu.com, http://www.eiu.com.

330.95492 USA ISSN 0269-431X
HC440.8.A1
COUNTRY REPORT. BANGLADESH; analysis of economic and political trends every quarter. Text in English. 1952. q. USD 485 print or online; USD 230 per issue print or online (effective 2004). illus.; stat. **Document type:** *Trade.* **Description:** Analyzes Bangladesh's current political and economic climate, as well as short-term economic projections.
Formerly: Quarterly Economic Review of Bangladesh (0266-9668)
Related titles: ♦ CD-ROM ed.: E I U Country Reports on Disc: Asia-Pacific; Online - full text ed.: E I U Country Reports: Asia-Pacific (from EBSCO Publishing).
Indexed: RASB.
—CCC.
Published by: Economist Intelligence Unit, 111 W 57th St, New York, NY 10019. TEL 212-554-0600, FAX 212-586-1181, newyork@eiu.com, http://www.eiu.com.

330.9549 USA
COUNTRY REPORT. BARBADOS; analysis of economic and political trends every quarter. Text in English. q. USD 485 print or online; USD 230 per issue print or online (effective 2004). illus.; stat. **Document type:** *Trade.*

Supersedes in part: Country Report. Bahamas, Barbados, Bermuda, British Virgin Islands, Netherlands Antilles, Aruba, Turks and Caicos Islands, Cayman Islands (1462-687X); Which superseded in part (in 1998): Country Report. Jamaica, Barbados, Belize, Bahamas, Bermuda, Cayman Islands, Turks and Caicos Islands (1368-9142); Which was formerly (until 1997): Country Report. Jamaica, Belize, Bahamas, Bermuda, Barbados (1460-3543); (until 1994): Country Report. Jamaica, Belize, Bahamas, Bermuda, Barbados, Cayman Islands (1354-2699); (until 1993): Country Report. Jamaica, Belize, Bahamas, Bermuda, Barbados (1351-8674); (until 1993): Country Report. Jamaica, Belize, Bahamas, Bermuda (0269-7130); (until 1986): Quarterly Economic Review of Jamaica, Belize, Bahamas, Bermuda (0266-9617); Which superseded in part (in 1985): Quarterly Economic Review of the West Indies, Belize, Bahamas, Bermuda, Guyana (0142-3738); Which was formerly (until 1976): Q E R West Indies, Belize, Bahamas, Bermuda, Guyana
Published by: Economist Intelligence Unit, 111 W 57th St, New York, NY 10019. TEL 212-554-0600, FAX 212-586-1181, newyork@eiu.com, http://www.eiu.com.

330.9476 USA ISSN 1478-0291
COUNTRY REPORT. BELARUS; analysis of economic and political trends every quarter. Text in English. q. USD 485 print or online; USD 230 per issue print or online (effective 2004). charts; stat. **Document type:** *Trade.* **Description:** Analyzes the current political and economic climates of Belarus, also providing short-term economic projections.
Supersedes in part (in 2001): Country Report. Belarus, Moldova (1356-4137); Which superseded in part (in 1995): Country Report. Ukraine, Belarus, Moldova (1350-7192); Which superseded in part (in 1992): Country Report. Commonwealth of Independent States; Which was formerly (until 1991): Country Report. U S S R (0269-5480); Quarterly Economic Review of U S S R (0142-3967)
Related titles: ◆ CD-ROM ed.: E I U Country Reports on Disc: Eastern Europe; Online - full text ed.: E I U Country Reports: Eastern Europe (from Central Institute for Scientific & Technical Information, SilverPlatter Information, Inc., The Dialog Corporation).
Indexed: ABIn.
Published by: Economist Intelligence Unit, 111 W 57th St, New York, NY 10019. TEL 212-554-0600, FAX 212-586-1181, newyork@eiu.com, http://www.eiu.com.

330.94935 USA ISSN 1473-9062
HC311
COUNTRY REPORT. BELGIUM; analysis of economic and political trends every quarter. Text in English. 1952. q. USD 485 print or online; USD 230 per issue print or online (effective 2004). illus.; stat. **Document type:** *Trade.* **Description:** Analyzes Belgium's and Luxembourg's current political and economic climates, as well as short-term economic projections.
Supersedes in part (in 2001): Country Report. Belgium, Luxembourg (0269-4158); Which was formerly (until 1986): Quarterly Economic Review of Belgium, Luxembourg (0142-372X); (until 1976): Q E R Belgium, Luxembourg
Related titles: ◆ CD-ROM ed.: E I U Country Reports on Disc: Western Europe; Online - full text ed.: E I U Country Reports: Western Europe (from SilverPlatter Information, Inc., The Dialog Corporation); (from EBSCO Publishing).
Published by: Economist Intelligence Unit, 111 W 57th St, New York, NY 10019. TEL 212-554-0600, FAX 212-586-1181, newyork@eiu.com, http://www.eiu.com.

330.9549 USA
COUNTRY REPORT. BELIZE; analysis of economic and political trends every quarter. Text in English. q. USD 485 print or online; USD 230 per issue print or online (effective 2004). illus.; stat. **Document type:** *Trade.*
Supersedes in part: Country Report. Jamaica, Belize, Organisation of Eastern Caribbean States (Windward and Leeward Islands) (1463-7219); Which was formerly (until 1998): Country Report. Jamaica, Belize, Windward and Leeward Islands (1462-6861); Which superseded in part (in 1998): Country Report. Jamaica, Barbados, Belize, Bahamas, Bermuda, Cayman Islands, Turks and Caicos Islands (1368-9142); Which was formerly (until 1997): Country Report. Jamaica, Belize, Bahamas, Bermuda, Barbados (1460-3543); (until 1994): Country Report. Jamaica, Belize, Bahamas, Bermuda, Barbados, Cayman Islands (1354-2699); (until 1994): Country Report. Jamaica, Belize, Bahamas, Bermuda, Barbados (1351-8674); (until 1993): Country Report. Jamaica, Belize, Bahamas, Bermuda (0269-7130); (until 1986): Quarterly Economic Review of Jamaica, Belize, Bahamas, Bermuda (0266-9617); Which superseded in part (in 1985): Quarterly Economic Review of the West Indies, Belize, Bahamas, Bermuda, Guyana (0142-3738); Which was formerly (until 1976): Q E R West Indies, Belize, Bahamas, Bermuda, Guyana
Published by: Economist Intelligence Unit, 111 W 57th St, New York, NY 10019. TEL 212-554-0600, FAX 212-586-1181, newyork@eiu.com, http://www.eiu.com.

330.9549 USA
COUNTRY REPORT. BENIN. Text in English. q. USD 485 print or online; USD 230 per issue print or online (effective 2004). illus.; stat. **Document type:** *Trade.*
Supersedes in part (in 2001): Country Report. Togo, Benin (1366-4107)
Published by: Economist Intelligence Unit, 111 W 57th St, New York, NY 10019. TEL 212-554-0600, FAX 212-586-1181, newyork@eiu.com, http://www.eiu.com.

330.9549 USA
COUNTRY REPORT. BERMUDA; analysis of economic and political trends every quarter. Text in English. q. USD 485 print or online; USD 230 per issue print or online (effective 2004). illus.; stat. **Document type:** *Trade.*
Supersedes in part: Country Report. Bahamas, Barbados, Bermuda, British Virgin Islands, Netherlands Antilles, Aruba, Turks and Caicos Islands, Cayman Islands (1462-687X); Which superseded in part (in 1998): Country Report. Jamaica, Barbados, Belize, Bahamas, Bermuda, Cayman Islands, Turks and Caicos Islands (1368-9142); Which was formerly (until 1997): Country Report. Jamaica, Belize, Bahamas, Bermuda, Barbados (1460-3543); (until 1994): Country Report. Jamaica, Belize, Bahamas, Bermuda, Barbados, Cayman Islands (1354-2699); (until 1994): Country Report. Jamaica, Belize, Bahamas, Bermuda, Barbados (1351-8674); (until 1993): Country Report. Jamaica, Belize, Bahamas, Bermuda (0269-7130); (until 1986): Quarterly Economic Review of Jamaica, Belize, Bahamas, Bermuda (0266-9617); Which superseded in part (in 1985): Quarterly Economic Review of the West Indies, Belize, Bahamas, Bermuda, Guyana (0142-3738); Which was formerly (until 1976): Q E R West Indies, Belize, Bahamas, Bermuda, Guyana
Published by: Economist Intelligence Unit, 111 W 57th St, New York, NY 10019. TEL 212-554-0600, FAX 212-586-1181, newyork@eiu.com, http://www.eiu.com.

330.984 USA ISSN 1356-4072
HC181
COUNTRY REPORT. BOLIVIA; analysis of economic and political trends every quarter. Text in English. q. USD 485 print or online; USD 230 per issue print or online (effective 2004). charts; stat. **Document type:** *Trade.* **Description:** Analyzes Bolivia's current political and economic climate, as well as short-term economic projections.
Supersedes in part (in 1995): Country Report. Peru, Bolivia (0269-543X); Which was formerly: Quarterly Economic Review of Peru, Bolivia (0142-3916)
Related titles: ◆ CD-ROM ed.: E I U Country Reports on Disc: The Americas; Microform ed.; Online - full text ed.: E I U Country Reports: The Americas.
Indexed: RASB.
—CCC.
Published by: Economist Intelligence Unit, 111 W 57th St, New York, NY 10019. TEL 212-554-0600, FAX 212-586-1181, newyork@eiu.com, http://www.eiu.com.

330.949742 USA ISSN 1462-673X
HC402.5.A1
COUNTRY REPORT. BOSNIA-HERCEGOVINA; analysis of economic and political trends every quarter. Text in English. 1952. q. USD 485 print or online; USD 230 per issue print or online (effective 2004). illus.; stat. **Document type:** *Trade.* **Description:** Analyzes the current political and economic climate and provides short-term economic projections for the former Yugoslav republics.
Supersedes in part (in 1998): Country Report. Bosnia and Hercegovina, Croatia (1366-4123); Which superseded in part (in 1997): Country Report. Bosnia-Hercegovina, Croatia, Slovenia (1361-1453); Which superseded in part (in 1995): Country Report. Bosnia-Hercegovina, Croatia, Macedonia, Serbia-Montenegro, Slovenia (1350-7222); Which was formerly (until 1993): Country Report. Yugoslav Republics (0968-7734); (1986-1992): Country Report. Yugoslavia (0269-4190); (1976-1986): Economic Review of Yugoslavia. Quarterly (0142-3983); Q E R Yugoslavia
Related titles: Online - full text ed.
Published by: Economist Intelligence Unit, 111 W 57th St, New York, NY 10019. TEL 212-554-0600, FAX 212-586-1181, newyork@eiu.com, http://www.eiu.com.

330.9688 USA
COUNTRY REPORT. BOTSWANA; analysis of economic and political trends every quarter. Text in English. q. USD 485 print or online; USD 230 per issue print or online (effective 2004). charts; stat. **Document type:** *Trade.* **Description:** Analyzes the current political and economic climates of Botswana and Lesotho, as well as short-term economic projections.
Supersedes in part: Country Report. Botswana, Lesotho (1356-4021); Which superseded in part (in 1994): Country Report. Botswana, Namibia, Lesotho, Swaziland (1351-8658); Which was formerly: Country Report. Namibia, Botswana, Lesotho, Swaziland (0269-6746); Quarterly Economic Review of Angola, Sao Tome and Principe (0266-9781); (until 1986): Quarterly Economic Review of Namibia, Botswana, Lesotho, Swaziland (0144-896X); Which superseded in part (in 1982): Quarterly Economic Review of Southern Africa, Republic of South Africa, Namibia, Botswana, Lesotho, Swaziland (0142-4475)
Related titles: ◆ CD-ROM ed.: E I U Country Reports on Disc: Sub-Saharan Africa; Online - full text ed.: E I U Country Reports: Sub-Saharan Africa (from SilverPlatter Information, Inc., The Dialog Corporation).
—CCC.
Published by: Economist Intelligence Unit, 111 W 57th St, New York, NY 10019. TEL 212-554-0600, FAX 212-586-1181, newyork@eiu.com, http://www.eiu.com.

330.981 USA ISSN 0269-5731
HC186
COUNTRY REPORT. BRAZIL; analysis of economic and political trends every quarter. Text in English. 1952. q. USD 485 print or online; USD 230 per issue print or online (effective 2004). illus.; stat. **Document type:** *Trade.* **Description:** Analyzes Brazil's current political and economic climate, as well as short-term economic projections.
Formerly: Quarterly Economic Review of Brazil (0142-4165)
Related titles: ◆ CD-ROM ed.: E I U Country Reports on Disc: The Americas; Online - full text ed.: E I U Country Reports: The Americas; (from EBSCO Publishing).
Indexed: RASB.
—CCC.
Published by: Economist Intelligence Unit, 111 W 57th St, New York, NY 10019. TEL 212-554-0600, FAX 212-586-1181, newyork@eiu.com, http://www.eiu.com.

330.9549 USA
COUNTRY REPORT. BRUNEI; analysis of economic and political trends every quarter. Text in English. q. USD 485 print or online; USD 230 per issue print or online (effective 2004). illus.; stat. **Document type:** *Trade.*
Supersedes in part: Country Report. Malaysia, Brunei (0269-6703); Which was formerly (until 1986): Quarterly Economic Review of Malaysia, Brunei (0144-8919); Which superseded in part (in 1982): Quarterly Economic Review of Malaysia, Singapore, Brunei (0142-3894); Which was formerly (until 1976): Q E R Malaysia, Singapore, Brunei
Related titles: Online - full text ed.: (from EBSCO Publishing).
—BLDSC (3481.898850).
Published by: Economist Intelligence Unit, 111 W 57th St, New York, NY 10019. TEL 212-554-0600, FAX 212-586-1181, newyork@eiu.com, http://www.eiu.com.

B

330.9499 USA ISSN 1366-400X
HC403.A1
COUNTRY REPORT. BULGARIA; analysis of economic and political trends every quarter. Text in English. q. USD 485 print or online; USD 230 per issue print or online (effective 2004). charts; stat. **Document type:** *Trade.* **Description:** Analyzes the current political and economic climate of Bulgaria and provides short-term economic projections.
Supersedes in part (in 1997): Country Report. Bulgaria, Albania (1356-4110); Which superseded in part (in 1995): Country Report. Romania, Bulgaria, Albania (0269-5669); Which was formerly: Quarterly Economic Review of Romania, Bulgaria, Albania (0142-4068)
Related titles: ◆ CD-ROM ed.: E I U Country Reports on Disc: Eastern Europe; Microform ed.; Online - full text ed.: E I U Country Reports: Eastern Europe (from Central Institute for Scientific & Technical Information, SilverPlatter Information, Inc., The Dialog Corporation).
Published by: Economist Intelligence Unit, 111 W 57th St, New York, NY 10019. TEL 212-554-0600, FAX 212-586-1181, newyork@eiu.com, http://www.eiu.com.

330.9549 USA
COUNTRY REPORT. BURKINA FASO; analysis of economic and political trends every quarter. Text in English. q. USD 485 print or online; USD 230 per issue print or online (effective 2004). illus.; stat. **Document type:** *Trade.*
Supersedes in part: Country Report. Niger, Burkina Faso (1366-4115); Which superseded in part (in 1996): Country Report. Togo, Niger, Benin, Burkina Faso (1466-0318); Which was formerly (until 1994): Country Report. Togo, Niger, Benin, Burkina (0269-7262); (until 1986): Quarterly Economic Review of Togo, Niger, Benin, Burkina (0266-9773); Which superseded in part (in 1984): Quarterly Economic Review of Ivory Coast, Togo, Benin, Niger, Upper Volta (0142-4513); Which was formerly (until 1976): Q E R. Ivory Coast, Togo, Dahomey, Niger, Upper Volta (0302-3389)
Published by: Economist Intelligence Unit, 111 W 57th St, New York, NY 10019. TEL 212-554-0600, FAX 212-586-1181, newyork@eiu.com, http://www.eiu.com.

330.9549 USA
COUNTRY REPORT. BURUNDI. Text in English. q. USD 485 print or online; USD 230 per issue print or online (effective 2004). illus.; stat. **Document type:** *Trade.*
Supersedes in part (in 2001): Country Report. Uganda, Rwanda, Burundi (0969-8817)
Published by: Economist Intelligence Unit, 111 W 57th St, New York, NY 10019. TEL 212-554-0600, FAX 212-586-1181, newyork@eiu.com, http://www.eiu.com.

330.959 USA
HC442.A1
COUNTRY REPORT. CAMBODIA; analysis of economic and political trends every quarter. Text in English. 1952. q. USD 485 print or online; USD 230 per issue print or online (effective 2004). illus.; stat. **Document type:** *Trade.* **Description:** Analyzes the current political and economic climate, as well as short-term economic projections.
Supersedes in part: Country Report. Cambodia, Laos (1361-1437); Which superseded in part (in 1996): Country Report. Cambodia, Laos, Myanmar (1356-4048); Which superseded in part (in 1995): Country Report. Indochina: Vietnam, Laos, Cambodia (0269-5677); Which was formerly: Quarterly Economic Review of Indochina: Vietnam, Laos, Cambodia (0142-4076); (until 1976): Q E R Indochina. South Vietnam, North Vietnam, Cambodia, Laos

▼ *new title* ➤ *refereed* ✶ *unverified* ◆ *full entry avail.*

Related titles: ♦ CD-ROM ed.: E I U Country Reports on Disc: Asia-Pacific; Microfiche ed.; Online - full text ed.: E I U Country Reports: Asia-Pacific (from EBSCO Publishing).
Indexed: RASB.
Published by: Economist Intelligence Unit, 111 W 57th St, New York, NY 10019. TEL 212-554-0600, FAX 212-586-1181, newyork@eiu.com, http://www.eiu.com.

330.967   USA
HC995.A1
COUNTRY REPORT. CAMEROON; analysis of economic and political trends every quarter. Text in English. 1952. q. USD 485 print or online; USD 230 per issue print or online (effective 2004). illus.; stat. **Document type:** *Trade.* **Description:** Analyzes the current political and economic climate, as well as short-term economic projections.
Supersedes in part (in 2001): Country Report. Cameroon, C.A.R., Chad (0269-4336); Which was formerly (until 1986): Quarterly Economic Review of Cameroon, Central African Republic, Chad (0266-9757)
Related titles: ♦ CD-ROM ed.: E I U Country Reports on Disc: Sub-Saharan Africa; Online - full text ed.: E I U Country Reports: Sub-Saharan Africa (from SilverPlatter Information, Inc., The Dialog Corporation).
Indexed: RASB.
Published by: Economist Intelligence Unit, 111 W 57th St, New York, NY 10019. TEL 212-554-0600, FAX 212-586-1181, newyork@eiu.com, http://www.eiu.com.

330.971   USA   ISSN 0269-4166
HC111
COUNTRY REPORT. CANADA; analysis of economic and political trends every quarter. Text in English. 1952. q. USD 485 print or online; USD 230 per issue print or online (effective 2004). illus.; stat. **Document type:** *Trade.* **Description:** Analyzes Canada's current political and economic climate, as well as short-term economic projections.
Formerly: Quarterly Economic Review of Canada (0142-3762)
Related titles: ♦ CD-ROM ed.: E I U Country Reports on Disc: The Americas; Online - full text ed.: E I U Country Reports: The Americas; (from EBSCO Publishing).
—CCC.
Published by: Economist Intelligence Unit, 111 W 57th St, New York, NY 10019. TEL 212-554-0600, FAX 212-586-1181, newyork@eiu.com, http://www.eiu.com.

330.9549   USA
COUNTRY REPORT. CAPE VERDE; analysis of economic and political trends every quarter. Text in English. q. USD 485 print or online; USD 230 per issue print or online (effective 2004). illus.; stat. **Document type:** *Trade.*
Supersedes in part (in 2001): Country Report. Congo, Sao Tome and Principe, Guinea-Bissau, Cape Verde (1350-7028)
Published by: Economist Intelligence Unit, 111 W 57th St, New York, NY 10019. TEL 212-554-0600, FAX 212-586-1181, newyork@eiu.com, http://www.eiu.com.

330.9549   USA
COUNTRY REPORT. CENTRAL AFRICAN REPUBLIC; analysis of economic and political trends every quarter. Text in English. q. USD 485 print or online; USD 230 per issue print or online (effective 2004). illus.; stat. **Document type:** *Trade.*
Supersedes in part (in 2001): Country Report. Cameroon, C.A.R., Chad (0269-4336)
Published by: Economist Intelligence Unit, 111 W 57th St, New York, NY 10019. TEL 212-554-0600, FAX 212-586-1181, newyork@eiu.com, http://www.eiu.com.

330.9549   USA
COUNTRY REPORT. CHAD; analysis of economic and political trends every quarter. Text in English. q. USD 485 print or online; USD 230 per issue print or online (effective 2004). illus.; stat. **Document type:** *Trade.*
Supersedes in part (in 2001): Country Report. Cameroon, C.A.R., Chad (0269-4336)
Published by: Economist Intelligence Unit, 111 W 57th St, New York, NY 10019. TEL 212-554-0600, FAX 212-586-1181, newyork@eiu.com, http://www.eiu.com.

330.983   USA   ISSN 0269-5197
HC191
COUNTRY REPORT. CHILE; analysis of economic and political trends every quarter. Text in English. 1952. q. USD 485 print or online; USD 230 per issue print or online (effective 2004). illus.; stat. **Document type:** *Trade.* **Description:** Analyzes Chile's current political and economic climate, as well as short-term economic projections.
Formerly: Quarterly Economic Review of Chile (0142-3789)
Related titles: ♦ CD-ROM ed.: E I U Country Reports on Disc: The Americas; Online - full text ed.: E I U Country Reports: The Americas.
Indexed: RASB.
—CCC.
Published by: Economist Intelligence Unit, 111 W 57th St, New York, NY 10019. TEL 212-554-0600, FAX 212-586-1181, newyork@eiu.com, http://www.eiu.com.

330.951   USA   ISSN 1473-897X
HC426
COUNTRY REPORT. CHINA; analysis of economic and political trends every quarter. Text in English. 1952. q. USD 500 print or online; USD 235 per issue print or online (effective 2005). illus.; stat. **Document type:** *Trade.* **Description:** Analyzes China's and Mongolia's current political and economic climates, as well as short-term economic projections.
Supersedes in part (in 2001): Country Report. China, Mongolia (1350-7109); Which superseded in part (in 1993): Country Report. China, North Korea (0269-6231); Which was formerly (until 1986): Quarterly Economic Review of China, North Korea (0144-8854); Which superseded in part (in 1981): Quarterly Economic Review of China, Hong Kong, North Korea (0142-3797); Which was formerly (until 1976): Q E R China, Hong Kong, North Korea
Related titles: ♦ CD-ROM ed.: E I U Country Reports on Disc: Asia-Pacific; Online - full text ed.: E I U Country Reports: Asia-Pacific (from EBSCO Publishing).
Indexed: RASB, WMB.
—CCC.
Published by: Economist Intelligence Unit, 111 W 57th St, New York, NY 10019. TEL 212-554-0600, FAX 212-586-1181, newyork@eiu.com, http://www.eiu.com.

330.9861   USA   ISSN 0269-7157
HC196
COUNTRY REPORT. COLOMBIA; analysis of economic and political trends every quarter. Text in English. 1952. q. USD 485 print or online; USD 230 per issue print or online (effective 2004). illus.; stat. **Document type:** *Trade.* **Description:** Analyzes Colombia's current political and economic climate, as well as short-term economic projections.
Formerly: Quarterly Economic Review of Colombia (0266-9633)
Related titles: ♦ CD-ROM ed.: E I U Country Reports on Disc: The Americas; Online - full text ed.: E I U Country Reports: The Americas; (from EBSCO Publishing).
Indexed: RASB.
—CCC.
Published by: Economist Intelligence Unit, 111 W 57th St, New York, NY 10019. TEL 212-554-0600, FAX 212-586-1181, newyork@eiu.com, http://www.eiu.com.

330.9549   USA
COUNTRY REPORT. COMOROS; analysis of economic and political trends every quarter. Text in English. q. USD 485 print or online; USD 230 per issue print or online (effective 2004). illus.; stat. **Document type:** *Trade.*
Published by: Economist Intelligence Unit, 111 W 57th St, New York, NY 10019. TEL 212-554-0600, FAX 212-586-1181, newyork@eiu.com, http://www.eiu.com.

330.967   USA
HC980.A1
COUNTRY REPORT. CONGO (BRAZZAVILLE); analysis of economic and political trends every quarter. Text in English. 1984. q. USD 485 print or online; USD 230 per issue print or online (effective 2004). illus.; stat. **Document type:** *Trade.* **Description:** Analyzes the current political and economic climate, as well as short-term economic projections.
Supersedes in part (in 2001): Country Report. Congo, Sao Tome and Principe, Guinea-Bissau, Cape Verde (1350-7028); Which was formed by the merger of part of (198?-1992): Country Report. Congo, Gabon, Equatorial Guinea (0269-7246); Which was formerly: Quarterly Economic Review of Congo, Gabon, Equatorial Guinea (0266-9749); (until 1985): Quarterly Economic Review of Gabon, Congo, Cameroon, CAR, Chad, Equatorial Guinea; part of (1986-1992): Country Report. Angola, Sao Tome and Principe (0269-4344); part of (1984-1992): Country Report. Senegal, The Gambia, Guinea-Bassau, Cape Verde (0269-719X); Which was formerly (until 1986): Quarterly Economic Review of Senegal, The Gambia, Guinea-Bassau, Cape Verde (0266-9684); Which was formed by the merger of part of (19??-1984): Quarterly Economic Review of Ghana, Sierra Leone, Gambia, Liberia (0142-3746); Which was formerly (until 1976): Q E R Ghana, Sierra Leone, Gambia, Liberia; (19??-1984): Quarterly Economic Review of Angola, Guinea Bissau, Cape Verde, Sao Tome and Proncipe (0142-4521); Which was formerly (until 1978): Quarterly Economic Review of Angola, Mozambique; (19??-1984): Quarterly Economic Review of Senegal, Mali, Mauritania, Guinea (0142-3991); Which was formerly (until 1978): Q E R Senegal, Mali, Mauritania, Guinea
Related titles: ♦ CD-ROM ed.: E I U Country Reports on Disc: Sub-Saharan Africa; Online - full text ed.: E I U Country Reports: Sub-Saharan Africa (from SilverPlatter Information, Inc., The Dialog Corporation).
Indexed: RASB.
Published by: Economist Intelligence Unit, 111 W 57th St, New York, NY 10019. TEL 212-554-0600, FAX 212-586-1181, newyork@eiu.com, http://www.eiu.com.

330.97286   USA   ISSN 1366-4026
HC143.A1
COUNTRY REPORT. COSTA RICA; analysis of economic and political trends every quarter. Text in English. q. USD 485 print or online; USD 230 per issue print or online (effective 2004). illus.; stat. **Document type:** *Trade.* **Description:** Analyzes Costa Rica's current political and economic climate and provides short-term economic projections.

Supersedes in part (in 1997): Country Report. Costa Rica, Panama (1350-7125); Which superseded in part (in 1992): Country Report. Nicaragua, Costa Rica, Panama (0269-4247); Which was formerly: Quarterly Economic Review of Nicaragua, Costa Rica, Panama (0142-4300)
Related titles: ♦ CD-ROM ed.: E I U Country Forecasts on Disc: The Americas; Online - full text ed.: E I U Country Forecasts: The Americas.
Published by: Economist Intelligence Unit, 111 W 57th St, New York, NY 10019. TEL 212-554-0600, FAX 212-586-1181, newyork@eiu.com, http://www.eiu.com.

330.966   USA
HC1025.A1
COUNTRY REPORT. COTE D'IVOIRE; analysis of economic and political trends every quarter. Text in English. 1952. q. USD 485 print or online; USD 230 per issue print or online (effective 2004). illus.; stat. **Document type:** *Trade.* **Description:** Analyzes the current political and economic climate, as well as short-term economic projections.
Supersedes in part (in 2000): Country Report. Cote d'Ivoire, Mali (0969-4730); Which was formerly (until 1992): Country Report. Cote d'Ivoire (0956-1218); (until 1986): Country Report. Ivory Coast (0269-7254); Quarterly Economic Review of Cote d'Ivoire (0266-9765); Which superseded in part (in 1984): Quarterly Economic Review of Ivory Coast, Togo, Benin, Niger, Upper Volta (0142-4513); Which was formerly (until 1976): Q E R. Ivory Coast, Togo, Dahomey, Niger, Upper Volta (0302-3389)
Related titles: ♦ CD-ROM ed.: E I U Country Reports on Disc: Sub-Saharan Africa; Online - full text ed.: E I U Country Reports: Sub-Saharan Africa (from SilverPlatter Information, Inc., The Dialog Corporation).
Indexed: RASB.
—CCC.
Published by: Economist Intelligence Unit, 111 W 57th St, New York, NY 10019. TEL 212-554-0600, FAX 212-586-1181, newyork@eiu.com, http://www.eiu.com. **Subscr. to:** Economist Intelligence Unit Ltd., Harold Hill, Romford, PO Box 200, Essex RM3 8UX, United Kingdom. TEL 44-1708-381444, FAX 44-1708-371850.

330.9549   USA   ISSN 1462-6748
HC404.A1
COUNTRY REPORT. CROATIA; analysis of economic and political trends every quarter. Text in English. q. USD 485 print or online; USD 230 per issue print or online (effective 2004). illus.; stat. **Document type:** *Trade.*
Supersedes in part (in 1998): Country Report. Bosnia-Hercegovina, Croatia and Slovenia (1366-4123); Which superseded in part (in 1997): Country Report. Bosnia-Hercegovina, Croatia, Slovenia (1361-1453); Which superseded in part (in 1996): Country Report. Bosnia-Hercegovina, Croatia, Macedonia, Serbia-Montenegro, Slovenia (1350-7222); Which was formerly (until 1993): Country Report. Yugoslav Republics (0968-7734); (until 1992): Country Report. Yugoslavia (0269-4190); (until 1986): Quarterly Economic Review of Yugoslavia (0142-3983); (until 1976): Q E R Yugoslavia
Published by: Economist Intelligence Unit, 111 W 57th St, New York, NY 10019. TEL 212-554-0600, FAX 212-586-1181, newyork@eiu.com, http://www.eiu.com.

330.9729   USA   ISSN 1465-6388
HC152.5.A1
COUNTRY REPORT. CUBA; analysis of economic and political trends every quarter. Text in English. 1952. q. USD 485 print or online; USD 230 per issue print or online (effective 2004). illus.; stat. **Document type:** *Trade.* **Description:** Analyzes the current political and economic climate, as well as short-term economic projections.
Supersedes in part (in 1998): Country Report. Cuba, Dominican Republic, Haiti, Puerto Rico (0269-5251); Which was formerly (until 1986): Quarterly Economic Review of Cuba, Dominican Republic, Haiti, Puerto Rico (0142-3819); (until 1976): Q E R Cuba, Dominican Republic, Haiti, Puerto Rico
Related titles: ♦ CD-ROM ed.: E I U Country Reports on Disc: The Americas; Online - full text ed.: E I U Country Reports: The Americas.
Indexed: RASB.
Published by: Economist Intelligence Unit, 111 W 57th St, New York, NY 10019. TEL 212-554-0600, FAX 212-586-1181, newyork@eiu.com, http://www.eiu.com.

330.95693   USA
COUNTRY REPORT. CYPRUS; analysis of economic and political trends every quarter. Text in English. 1952. q. USD 485 print or online; USD 230 per issue print or online (effective 2004). illus.; stat. **Document type:** *Trade.* **Description:** Analyzes Cyprus's and Malta's current political and economic climates, as well as short-term economic projections.
Supersedes in part: Country Report. Cyprus, Malta (1350-715X); Which superseded in part (in 1992): Country Report. Lebanon, Cyprus (0269-5693); Which was formerly (until 1986): Quarterly Economic Review of Lebanon, Cyprus (0142-4106); Which superseded in part (in 1978): Quarterly Economic Review of Syria, Lebanon, Cyprus (0959-5368)
Related titles: ♦ CD-ROM ed.: E I U Country Reports on Disc: Western Europe; Online - full text ed.: E I U Country Reports: Western Europe (from SilverPlatter Information, Inc., The Dialog Corporation).
Indexed: RASB.

B

Published by: Economist Intelligence Unit, 111 W 57th St, New York, NY 10019. TEL 212-554-0600, FAX 212-586-1181, newyork@eiu.com, http://www.eiu.com.

330.9437   USA   ISSN 1366-4042
HC270.2
COUNTRY REPORT. CZECH REPUBLIC; analysis of economic and political trends every quarter. Text in English. 1952. q. USD 485 print or online; USD 230 per issue print or online (effective 2004). illus.; stat. **Document type:** *Trade.* **Description:** Analyzes the current political and economic climate, as well as short-term economic projections.
Supersedes in part (in 1997): Country Report. Czech Republic, Slovakia (1350-7214); Which superseded in part (in 1992): Country Report. Czechoslovakia (0269-4298); Which was formerly: Quarterly Economic Review of Czechoslovakia (0144-8978)
Related titles: Microfilm ed.; Online - full text ed.
Published by: Economist Intelligence Unit, 111 W 57th St, New York, NY 10019. TEL 212-554-0600, FAX 212-586-1181, newyork@eiu.com, http://www.eiu.com.

330.9549   USA   ISSN 1478-0380
HC955.A1
COUNTRY REPORT. DEMOCRATIC REPUBLIC OF CONGO; analysis of economic and political trends every quarter. Text in English. q. USD 455; USD 215 newsstand/cover (effective 2003). illus.; stat. **Document type:** *Journal, Trade.*
Supersedes in part (in 2001): Country Report: Zambia, Democratic Republic of Congo (1369-4839); Which was formerly (until 1997): Country Report. Zambia, Zaire (1350-7087); (until 1992): Country Report. Zambia (0269-4271); (until 1986): Quarterly Economic Review of Zambia (0142-4467); (until 1976): Q E R Zambia (0306-5022); Which superseded in part (in 1974): Quarterly Economic Review Tanzania, Zambia
Published by: Economist Intelligence Unit, 111 W 57th St, New York, NY 10019. TEL 212-554-0600, FAX 212-586-1181, newyork@eiu.com, http://www.eiu.com.

330.948   USA   ISSN 1473-9046
HC351   CODEN: PUCEAN
COUNTRY REPORT. DENMARK; analysis of economic and political trends every quarter. Text in English. 1952. q. USD 485 print or online; USD 230 per issue print or online (effective 2004). illus.; stat. **Document type:** *Trade.* **Description:** Analyzes Denmark's and Iceland's current political and economic climates, as well as short-term economic projections.
Supersedes in part (in 2001): Country Report. Denmark, Iceland (0269-574X); Which was formerly (until 1986): Quarterly Economic Review of Denmark, Iceland (0142-4181); (until 1976): Q E R Denmark, Iceland (0481-1569)
Related titles: ♦ CD-ROM ed.: E I U Country Reports on Disc: Western Europe; Online - full text ed.: E I U Country Reports: Western Europe (from SilverPlatter Information, Inc., The Dialog Corporation).
Published by: Economist Intelligence Unit, 111 W 57th St, New York, NY 10019. TEL 212-554-0600, FAX 212-586-1181, newyork@eiu.com, http://www.eiu.com.

330.9549   USA
COUNTRY REPORT. DJIBOUTI; analysis of economic and political trends every quarter. Text in English. q. USD 485 print or online; USD 230 per issue print or online (effective 2004). illus.; stat. **Document type:** *Trade.*
Supersedes in part: Country Report. Ethiopia, Eritrea, Somalia, Djibouti (1352-2922); Which was formerly (until 1993): Country Report. Ethiopia, Somalia, Djibouti (1350-7036); Which superseded in part (in 1992): Country Report. Uganda, Ethiopia, Somalia, Djibouti (0269-5685); Which was formerly (until 1986): Quarterly Economic Review of Uganda, Ethiopia, Somalia, Djibouti (0142-4092); (until 1978): Quarterly Economic Review of Uganda, Ethiopia, Somalia
Published by: Economist Intelligence Unit, 111 W 57th St, New York, NY 10019. TEL 212-554-0600, FAX 212-586-1181, newyork@eiu.com, http://www.eiu.com.

330.9549   USA
COUNTRY REPORT. DOMINICAN REPUBLIC; analysis of economic and political trends every quarter. Text in English. q. USD 485 print or online; USD 230 per issue print or online (effective 2004). illus.; stat. **Document type:** *Trade.*
Supersedes in part: Country Report. Dominican Republic, Haiti, Puerto Rico (1465-6396); Which superseded in part (in 1998): Country Report. Cuba, Dominican Republic, Haiti, Puerto Rico (0269-5251); Which was formerly (until 1986): Quarterly Economic Review of Cuba, Dominican Republic, Haiti, Puerto Rico (0142-3819); (until 1976): Q E R Cuba, Dominican Republic, Haiti, Puerto Rico
Published by: Economist Intelligence Unit, 111 W 57th St, New York, NY 10019. TEL 212-554-0600, FAX 212-586-1181, newyork@eiu.com, http://www.eiu.com.

330.9866   USA   ISSN 0269-7165
HC201
COUNTRY REPORT. ECUADOR; analysis of economic and political trends every quarter. Text in English. 1952. q. USD 485 print or online; USD 230 per issue print or online (effective 2004). illus.; stat. **Document type:** *Trade.* **Description:** Analyzes Ecuador's current political and economic climate, as well as short-term economic projections.

Formerly: Quarterly Economic Review of Ecuador (0266-9641)
Related titles: ♦ CD-ROM ed.: E I U Country Reports on Disc: The Americas; Online - full text ed.: E I U Country Reports: The Americas.
Indexed: RASB.
—CCC.
Published by: Economist Intelligence Unit, 111 W 57th St, New York, NY 10019. TEL 212-554-0600, FAX 212-586-1181, newyork@eiu.com, http://www.eiu.com. **Subscr. to:** Economist Intelligence Unit Ltd., Harold Hill, Romford, PO Box 200, Essex RM3 8UX, United Kingdom. TEL 44-1708-381444, FAX 44-1708-371850.

330.962   USA   ISSN 0269-526X
HC830.A1
COUNTRY REPORT. EGYPT; analysis of economic and political trends every quarter. Text in English. 1952. q. USD 485 print or online; USD 230 per issue print or online (effective 2004). illus.; stat. **Document type:** *Trade.* **Description:** Analyzes Egypt's current political and economic climate, as well as short-term economic projections.
Formerly: Quarterly Economic Review of Egypt (0142-3827)
Related titles: ♦ CD-ROM ed.: E I U Country Reports on Disc: Middle East - North Africa; Online - full text ed.: E I U Country Reports: Middle East-North Africa.
Indexed: IBR, IBZ, RASB.
—CCC.
Published by: Economist Intelligence Unit, 111 W 57th St, New York, NY 10019. TEL 212-554-0600, FAX 212-586-1181, newyork@eiu.com, http://www.eiu.com.

330.9549   USA   ISSN 1473-9038
HC148.A1
COUNTRY REPORT. EL SALVADOR; analysis of economic and political trends every quarter. Text in English. q. USD 485 print or online; USD 230 per issue print or online (effective 2004). illus.; stat. **Document type:** *Trade.*
Supersedes in part (in 2001): Country Report. Guatemala, El Salvador (0969-8752); Which superseded in part (in 1993): Country Report. Guatemala, El Salvador, Honduras (0269-4220); Which was formerly (until 1986): Quarterly Economic Review of Guatemala, El Salvador, Honduras (0142-4211); (until 1976): Q E R. Guatemala, El Salvador, Honduras (0306-7491); Which superseded in part (in 1974): Q E R. Central America (0481-147X)
Published by: Economist Intelligence Unit, 111 W 57th St, New York, NY 10019. newyork@eiu.com, http://www.eiu.com.

330.9549   USA
COUNTRY REPORT. EQUATORIAL GUINEA; analysis of economic and political trends every quarter. Text in English. q. USD 485 print or online; USD 230 per issue print or online (effective 2004). illus.; stat. **Document type:** *Trade.*
Supersedes in part: Country Report. Gabon, Equatorial Guinea (1350-7044); Which superseded in part (in 1993): Country Report. Congo, Gabon, Equatorial Guinea (0269-7246); Which was formerly (until 1986): Quarterly Economic Review of Congo, Gabon, Equatorial Guinea (0266-9749); Which superseded in part (in 1985): Quarterly Economic Review of Gabon, Congo, Cameroon, CAR, Chad, Equatorial Guinea
Published by: Economist Intelligence Unit, 111 W 57th St, New York, NY 10019. TEL 212-554-0600, FAX 212-586-1181, newyork@eiu.com, http://www.eiu.com.

330.9549   USA
COUNTRY REPORT. ERITREA; analysis of economic and political trends every quarter. Text in English. 1978. q. USD 485 print or online; USD 230 per issue print or online (effective 2004). illus.; stat. **Document type:** *Trade.*
Supersedes in part: Country Report. Ethiopia, Eritrea, Somalia, Djibouti (1352-2922); Which was formerly (until 1993): Country Report. Ethiopia, Somalia, Djibouti (1350-7036); Which superseded in part (in 1993): Country Report. Uganda, Ethiopia, Somalia, Djibouti (0269-5685); Which was formerly (until 1986): Quarterly Economic Review of Uganda, Ethiopia, Somalia, Djibouti (0142-4092)
Published by: Economist Intelligence Unit, 111 W 57th St, New York, NY 10019. TEL 212-554-0600, FAX 212-586-1181, newyork@eiu.com, http://www.eiu.com.

330.9549   USA   ISSN 1462-6705
HC340.4.A1
COUNTRY REPORT. ESTONIA; analysis of economic and political trends every quarter. Text in English. q. USD 485 print or online; USD 230 per issue print or online (effective 2004). illus.; stat. **Document type:** *Trade.*
Supersedes in part (in 1998): Country Report. Baltic Republics: Lithuania, Latvia, Estonia (1360-9459); Which was formerly (until 1995): Country Report. Baltic Republics (1350-7176); Which superseded in part (in 1993): Country Report. Commonwealth of Independent States (0968-8242); Which was formerly (until 1991): Country Report. U S S R (0269-5480); (until 1986): Quarterly Economic Review of U S S R (0142-3967); (until 1976): Q E R. U S S R
Indexed: ABIn.
Published by: Economist Intelligence Unit, 111 W 57th St, New York, NY 10019. TEL 212-554-0600, FAX 212-586-1181, newyork@eiu.com, http://www.eiu.com.

330.963   USA
HC845.A1
COUNTRY REPORT. ETHIOPIA; analysis of economic and political trends every quarter. Text in English. q. USD 485 print or online; USD 230 per issue print or online (effective 2004). illus.; stat. **Document type:** *Trade.* **Description:** Analyzes the current political and economic climate, as well as short-term economic projections.
Supersedes in part: Country Report. Ethiopia, Eritrea, Somalia, Djibouti (1352-2922); Which was formerly (until 1993): Country Report. Ethiopia, Somalia, Djibouti (1350-7036); Which superseded in part (in 1992): Country Report. Uganda, Ethiopia, Somalia, Djibouti (0269-5685); Which was formerly (until 1986): Quarterly Economic Review of Uganda, Ethiopia, Somalia, Djibouti (0142-4092); (until 1978): Quarterly Economic Review of Uganda, Ethiopia, Somalia
Related titles: ♦ CD-ROM ed.: E I U Country Reports on Disc: Sub-Saharan Africa; Online - full text ed.: E I U Country Reports: Sub-Saharan Africa (from SilverPlatter Information, Inc., The Dialog Corporation).
Indexed: RASB.
Published by: Economist Intelligence Unit, 111 W 57th St, New York, NY 10019. TEL 212-554-0600, FAX 212-586-1181, newyork@eiu.com, http://www.eiu.com.

330.940   USA   ISSN 1365-3989
HC240.A1
COUNTRY REPORT. EUROPEAN UNION. Text in English. 1997. q. USD 485 print or online; USD 230 per issue print or online (effective 2004). **Document type:** *Magazine, Trade.* **Description:** Analyzes the current political and economic climates in the European Union, as well as short-term economic projections.
Related titles: Online - full text ed.: (from EBSCO Publishing).
Indexed: MASUSE, WBA.
Published by: Economist Intelligence Unit, 111 W 57th St, New York, NY 10019. TEL 212-554-0600, FAX 212-586-1181, newyork@eiu.com, http://www.eiu.com.

330.9965   USA
HC681.A1
COUNTRY REPORT. FIJI; analysis of economic and political trends every quarter. Text in English. q. USD 485 print or online; USD 230 per issue print or online (effective 2004). illus.; stat.
Supersedes in part: Country Report. Pacific Islands: Fiji, New Caledonia, Samoa, Solomon Islands, Tonga, Vanuatu (1460-7077); Which was formerly (until 1997): Country Report. Pacific Islands: Fiji, New Caledonia, Solomon Islands, Tonga, Vanuatu, Western Samoa (1366-4093); Which superseded in part (in 1996): Country Report. Pacific Islands: Papua New Guinea, Fiji, Solomon Islands, Western Samoa, Vanuatu, Tonga (0269-7122); Which was formerly (until 1986): Quarterly Economic Review of Pacific Islands: Papua New Guinea, Fiji, Solomon Islands, Western Samoa, Vanuatu, Tonga (0266-9609); Which superseded in part (in 1984): Quarterly Economic Review of Australia, Papua New Guinea (0142-4157); Which was formerly (until 1976): Q E R. Australia, Papua, New Guinea (0306-4786)
Related titles: CD-ROM ed.: (from SilverPlatter Information, Inc.); Online - full text ed.: (from SilverPlatter Information, Inc., The Dialog Corporation).
Indexed: RASB.
Published by: Economist Intelligence Unit, 111 W 57th St, New York, NY 10019. TEL 212-554-0600, FAX 212-586-1181, newyork@eiu.com, http://www.eiu.com.

330.94897   USA   ISSN 0269-5901
HC340.2.A1
COUNTRY REPORT. FINLAND; analysis of economic and political trends every quarter. Text in English. 1952. q. USD 485 print or online; USD 230 per issue print or online (effective 2004). illus.; stat. **Document type:** *Trade.* **Description:** Analyzes Finland's current political and economic climate, as well as short-term economic projections.
Formerly: Quarterly Economic Review of Finland (0142-419X)
Related titles: ♦ CD-ROM ed.: E I U Country Reports on Disc: Western Europe; Online - full text ed.: E I U Country Reports: Western Europe (from SilverPlatter Information, Inc., The Dialog Corporation).
—CCC.
Published by: Economist Intelligence Unit, 111 W 57th St, New York, NY 10019. TEL 212-554-0600, FAX 212-586-1181, newyork@eiu.com, http://www.eiu.com.

330.944   USA   ISSN 0269-5286
HC271
COUNTRY REPORT. FRANCE; analysis of economic and political trends every quarter. Text in English. 1952. q. USD 485 print or online; USD 230 per issue print or online (effective 2004). illus.; stat. **Document type:** *Trade.* **Description:** Analyzes France's current political and economic climate, as well as short-term economic projections.
Formerly: Quarterly Economic Review of France (0142-3843)
Related titles: ♦ CD-ROM ed.: E I U Country Reports on Disc: Western Europe; Online - full text ed.: E I U Country Reports: Western Europe (from SilverPlatter Information, Inc., The Dialog Corporation); (from EBSCO Publishing).
—CCC.
Published by: Economist Intelligence Unit, 111 W 57th St, New York, NY 10019. TEL 212-554-0600, FAX 212-586-1181, newyork@eiu.com, http://www.eiu.com.

B

330.967 USA
COUNTRY REPORT. GABON; analysis of economic and political trends every quarter. Text in English. q. USD 485 print or online; USD 230 per issue print or online (effective 2004). illus.; stat. **Document type:** Trade. **Description:** Analyzes the current political and economic climates, as well as short-term economic projections for Gabon and Equatorial Guinea.
Supersedes in part: Country Report. Gabon, Equatorial Guinea (1350-7044); Which superseded in part (in 1993): Country Report. Congo, Gabon, Equatorial Guinea (0269-7246); Which was formerly (until 1986): Quarterly Economic Review of Congo, Gabon, Equatorial Guinea (0266-9749); Which superseded in part (in 1985): Quarterly Economic Review of Gabon, Congo, Cameroon, CAR, Chad, Equatorial Guinea.
Related titles: ♦ CD-ROM ed.: E I U Country Reports on Disc: Sub-Saharan Africa; Online - full text ed.: E I U Country Reports: Sub-Saharan Africa (from SilverPlatter Information, Inc., The Dialog Corporation).
Published by: Economist Intelligence Unit, 111 W 57th St, New York, NY 10019. TEL 212-554-0600, FAX 212-586-1181, newyork@eiu.com, http://www.eiu.com.

330.9475 USA ISSN 1478-0313
HC415.19.A1
COUNTRY REPORT. GEORGIA; analysis of economic and political trends every quarter. Text in English. q. USD 485 print or online; USD 230 per issue print or online (effective 2004). charts; stat. **Document type:** Journal, Trade. **Description:** Analyzes the current political and economic climates, as well as short-term economic projections for Georgia.
Supersedes in part (in 2001): Country Report. Georgia, Armenia (1366-4069); Which superseded in part (in 1997): Country Report. Georgia, Armenia, Azerbaijan (1356-4080); Which superseded in part (in 1995): Country Report. Georgia, Armenia, Azerbaijan, Central Asian Republics (1350-7206); Which superseded in part (in 1992): Country Report. Commonwealth of Independent States; Which was formerly (until 1991): Country Report. U S S R (0269-5480); Quarterly Economic Review of U S S R (0142-3967)
Related titles: ♦ CD-ROM ed.: E I U Country Reports on Disc: Eastern Europe; Online - full text ed.: E I U Country Reports: Eastern Europe (from Central Institute for Scientific & Technical Information, SilverPlatter Information, Inc., The Dialog Corporation).
Indexed: ABIn.
Published by: Economist Intelligence Unit, 111 W 57th St, New York, NY 10019. TEL 212-554-0600, FAX 212-586-1181, newyork@eiu.com, http://www.eiu.com.

330.943 USA ISSN 0965-1365
HC281
COUNTRY REPORT. GERMANY; analysis of economic and political trends every quarter. Text in English. 1952. q. USD 485 print or online; USD 230 per issue print or online (effective 2004). illus.; stat. **Document type:** Trade. **Description:** Analyzes Germany's current political and economic climate, as well as short-term economic projections.
Formerly: Quarterly Economic Review of Germany (0142-3975); Formed by the 1990 merger of: Country Report. West Germany (0269-5499); Country Report. East Germany (0269-6207); Which was formerly: Quarterly Economic Review of East Germany (0144-8889)
Related titles: ♦ CD-ROM ed.: E I U Country Reports on Disc: Western Europe; Online - full text ed.: E I U Country Reports: Western Europe (from SilverPlatter Information, Inc., The Dialog Corporation); (from EBSCO Publishing).
—CCC.
Published by: Economist Intelligence Unit, 111 W 57th St, New York, NY 10019. TEL 212-554-0600, FAX 212-586-1181, newyork@eiu.com, http://www.eiu.com.

330.9667 USA ISSN 1350-7052
HC1060.A1
COUNTRY REPORT. GHANA; analysis of economic and political trends every quarter. Text in English. q. USD 485 print or online; USD 230 per issue print or online (effective 2004). illus.; stat. **Document type:** Trade. **Description:** Analyzes Ghana's current political and economic climate, as well as short-term economic projections.
Supersedes in part (in 1992): Country Report. Ghana, Sierra Leone, Liberia (0269-7181); Which was formerly: Quarterly Economic Review of Ghana, Sierra Leone, Liberia (0266-9676)
Related titles: ♦ CD-ROM ed.: E I U Country Reports on Disc: Sub-Saharan Africa; Online - full text ed.: E I U Country Reports: Sub-Saharan Africa (from SilverPlatter Information, Inc., The Dialog Corporation).
Indexed: RASB.
—CCC.
Published by: Economist Intelligence Unit, 111 W 57th St, New York, NY 10019. TEL 212-554-0600, FAX 212-586-1181, newyork@eiu.com, http://www.eiu.com.

330.9495 USA ISSN 0269-591X
HC291
COUNTRY REPORT. GREECE; analysis of economic and political trends every quarter. Text in English. 1952. q. USD 500 print or online; USD 235 per issue print or online (effective 2005). illus.; stat. **Document type:** Trade. **Description:** Analyzes Greece's current political and economic climate, as well as short-term economic projections.
Formerly: Quarterly Economic Review of Greece (0142-4203)

Related titles: ♦ CD-ROM ed.: E I U Country Reports on Disc: Western Europe; Online - full text ed.: E I U Country Reports: Western Europe (from SilverPlatter Information, Inc., The Dialog Corporation).
—BLDSC (3481.898010). **CCC.**
Published by: Economist Intelligence Unit, 111 W 57th St, New York, NY 10019. TEL 212-554-0600, FAX 212-586-1181, newyork@eiu.com, http://www.eiu.com.

330.9728 USA ISSN 1473-902X
HC144.A1
COUNTRY REPORT. GUATEMALA; analysis of economic and political trends every quarter. Text in English. 1952. q. USD 485 print or online; USD 230 per issue print or online (effective 2004). illus.; stat. **Document type:** Trade. **Description:** Analyzes the current political and economic climate, as well as short-term economic projections for Guatemala and El Salvador.
Supersedes in part (in 2001): Country Report. Guatemala, El Salvador (0969-8752); Which superseded in part (in 1992): Country Report. Guatemala, El Salvador, Honduras (0269-4220); Which was formerly (until 1986): Quarterly Economic Review of Guatemala, El Salvador, Honduras (0142-4211); Which superseded in part (in 1976): Q E R. Guatemala, El Salvador, Honduras (0306-7491); Which superseded in part (in 1974): Q E R. Central America (0481-147X)
Related titles: ♦ CD-ROM ed.: E I U Country Reports on Disc: The Americas; Online - full text ed.: E I U Country Reports: The Americas.
Indexed: RASB.
Published by: Economist Intelligence Unit, 111 W 57th St, New York, NY 10019. TEL 212-554-0600, FAX 212-586-1181, newyork@eiu.com, http://www.eiu.com.

330.966 USA
HC1030.A1
COUNTRY REPORT. GUINEA; analysis of economic and political trends every quarter. Text in English. 1952. q. USD 485 print or online; USD 230 per issue print or online (effective 2004). illus.; stat. **Document type:** Trade. **Description:** Analyzes the current political and economic current, as well as short-term economic projections.
Supersedes in part (in 2001): Country Report. Guinea, Sierra Leone, Liberia (0969-4692); Which was formed by the 1992 merger of part of: Country Report. Ghana, Sierra Leone, Liberia (0269-7181); part of: Country Report. Guinea, Mali, Mauritania (0269-7203); Which was formerly: Quarterly Economic Review of Ghana, Sierra Leone, Liberia (0266-9676); (until 1986): Quarterly Economic Review of Guinea, Mali, Mauritania (0266-9692)
Related titles: ♦ CD-ROM ed.: E I U Country Reports on Disc: Sub-Saharan Africa; Online - full text ed.: E I U Country Reports: Sub-Saharan Africa (from SilverPlatter Information, Inc., The Dialog Corporation).
Indexed: RASB.
Published by: Economist Intelligence Unit, 111 W 57th St, New York, NY 10019. TEL 212-554-0600, FAX 212-586-1181, newyork@eiu.com, http://www.eiu.com.

330.9549 USA
COUNTRY REPORT. GUINEA-BISSAU; analysis of economic and political trends every quarter. Text in English. q. USD 485 print or online; USD 230 per issue print or online (effective 2004). illus.; stat. **Document type:** Trade.
Supersedes in part (1993-2001): Country Report. Congo, Sao Tome and Principe, Guinea-Bissau, Cape Verde (1350-7028)
Published by: Economist Intelligence Unit, 111 W 57th St, New York, NY 10019. TEL 212-554-0600, FAX 212-586-1181, newyork@eiu.com, http://www.eiu.com.

330.9549 USA
COUNTRY REPORT. GUYANA; analysis of economic and political trends every quarter. Text in English. q. USD 485 print or online; USD 230 per issue print or online (effective 2004). illus.; stat. **Document type:** Trade.
Supersedes in part: Country Report. Trinidad and Tobago, Guyana, Suriname (1462-6659); Which superseded in part (in 1998): Country Report. Trinidad & Tobago, Guyana, Windward & Leeward Islands, Suriname, Netherlands Antilles, Aruba (1351-1270); Which superseded in part (in 1993): Country Profile. Guyana, Barbados, Windward & Leeward Islands (0269-8110); Which superseded in part (in 1986): Quarterly Economic Review of Trinidad & Tobago, Guyana, Barbados, Windward & Leeward Islands. Annual Supplement
Related titles: Online - full text ed.: (from Gale Group).
Published by: Economist Intelligence Unit, 111 W 57th St, New York, NY 10019. TEL 212-554-0600, FAX 212-586-1181, newyork@eiu.com, http://www.eiu.com.

330.9549 USA
COUNTRY REPORT. HAITI; analysis of economic and political trends every quarter. Text in English. q. USD 485 print or online; USD 230 per issue print or online (effective 2004). illus.; stat. **Document type:** Trade.
Supersedes in part: Country Report. Dominican Republic, Haiti, Puerto Rico (1465-6396); Which superseded in part (in 1999): Country Report. Cuba, Dominican Republic, Haiti, Puerto Rico (0269-5251); Which was formerly (until 1986): Quarterly Economic Review of Cuba, Dominican Republic, Haiti, Puerto Rico (0142-3819); (until 1976): Q E R Cuba, Dominican Republic, Haiti, Puerto Rico

Published by: Economist Intelligence Unit, 111 W 57th St, New York, NY 10019. TEL 212-554-0600, FAX 212-586-1181, newyork@eiu.com, http://www.eiu.com.

330.9549 USA ISSN 1473-9011
HC145.A1
COUNTRY REPORT. HONDURAS; analysis of economic and political trends every quarter. Text in English. 1974. q. USD 485 print or online; USD 230 per issue print or online (effective 2004). illus.; stat. **Document type:** Trade.
Supersedes in part (in 2001): Country Report. Nicaragua, Honduras (0969-8809); Which superseded in part (in 1993): Country Report. Guatemala, El Salvador, Honduras (0269-4220); Which was formerly (until 1986): Quarterly Economic Review of Guatemala, El Salvador, Honduras (0142-4211); (until 1976): Q E R - Guatemala, El Salvador, Honduras (0306-7491)
Published by: Economist Intelligence Unit, 111 W 57th St, New York, NY 10019. TEL 212-554-0600, FAX 212-586-1181, newyork@eiu.com, http://www.eiu.com.

330.95125 USA
HC470.3.A1
COUNTRY REPORT. HONG KONG; analysis of economic and political trends every quarter. Text in English. 1952. q. USD 485 print or online; USD 230 per issue print or online (effective 2004). illus.; stat. **Document type:** Trade. **Description:** Analyzes the current political and economic climate, as well as short-term economic projections.
Supersedes in part (in 2000): Country Report. Hong Kong, Macau (0269-6762); Which was formerly (until 1986): Quarterly Economic Review of Hong Kong, Macau (0265-6906); (until 1984): Quarterly Economic Review of Hong Kong (0144-8862); Which superseded in part (in 1982): Quarterly Economic Review of China, Hong Kong, North Korea (0142-3797); Which was formerly (until 1976): Q E R China, Hong Kong, North Korea
Related titles: ♦ CD-ROM ed.: E I U Country Reports on Disc: Asia-Pacific; Online - full text ed.: E I U Country Reports: Asia-Pacific (from EBSCO Publishing); (from EBSCO Publishing, ProQuest Information & Learning).
Indexed: ABIn, RASB.
—CCC.
Published by: Economist Intelligence Unit, 111 W 57th St, New York, NY 10019. TEL 212-554-0600, FAX 212-586-1181, newyork@eiu.com, http://www.eiu.com.

330.9439 USA ISSN 0269-4301
HC300.2
COUNTRY REPORT. HUNGARY; analysis of economic and political trends every quarter. Text in English. 1952. q. USD 485 print or online; USD 230 per issue print or online (effective 2004). illus.; stat. **Document type:** Trade. **Description:** Analyzes Hungary's current political and economic climate, as well as short-term economic projections.
Formerly: Quarterly Economic Review of Hungary (0144-8986)
Related titles: Online - full text ed.: (from EBSCO Publishing).
—CCC.
Published by: Economist Intelligence Unit, 111 W 57th St, New York, NY 10019. TEL 212-554-0600, FAX 212-586-1181, newyork@eiu.com, http://www.eiu.com.

330.9549 USA ISSN 1473-9054
HC360.5.A1
COUNTRY REPORT. ICELAND; analysis of economic and political trends every quarter. Text in English. 1952. q. USD 485 print or online; USD 230 per issue print or online (effective 2004). illus.; stat. **Document type:** Trade.
Supersedes in part (in 2001): Country Report. Denmark, Iceland (0269-574X); Which was formerly (until 1986): Quarterly Economic Review of Denmark, Iceland (0142-4181); (until 1976): Q E R Denmark, Iceland (0481-1569)
Published by: Economist Intelligence Unit, 111 W 57th St, New York, NY 10019. TEL 212-554-0600, FAX 212-586-1181, newyork@eiu.com, http://www.eiu.com.

330.954 USA ISSN 1473-8953
HC435.2
COUNTRY REPORT. INDIA. Text in English. 1952. q. USD 485 print or online; USD 230 per issue print or online (effective 2004). illus.; stat. **Document type:** Trade. **Description:** Analyzes the current political and economic climate, as well as short-term economic projections for India and Nepal.
Supersedes in part (in 2000): Country Report. India, Nepal (0269-5294); Which was formerly (until 1986): Quarterly Economic Review of India, Nepal (0142-3851)
Related titles: ♦ CD-ROM ed.: E I U Country Reports on Disc: Asia-Pacific; Online - full text ed.: E I U Country Reports: Asia-Pacific (from EBSCO Publishing); (from EBSCO Publishing).
Indexed: RASB.
Published by: Economist Intelligence Unit, 111 W 57th St, New York, NY 10019. TEL 212-554-0600, FAX 212-586-1181, newyork@eiu.com, http://www.eiu.com.

330.9598 USA ISSN 0269-5413
HC446
COUNTRY REPORT. INDONESIA; analysis of economic and political trends every quarter. Text in English. 1952. q. USD 485 print or online; USD 230 per issue print or online (effective 2004). illus.; stat. **Document type:** *Trade.* **Description:** Analyzes Indonesia's current political and economic climate, as well as short-term economic projections.
Formerly: Quarterly Economic Review of Indonesia (0142-3878)
Related titles: ♦ CD-ROM ed.: E I U Country Reports on Disc: Asia-Pacific; Online - full text ed.: E I U Country Reports: Asia-Pacific (from EBSCO Publishing); (from EBSCO Publishing).
Indexed: BAS, RASB, WBA, WMB.
—CCC.
Published by: Economist Intelligence Unit, 111 W 57th St, New York, NY 10019. TEL 212-554-0600, FAX 212-586-1181, newyork@eiu.com, http://www.eiu.com.

330.955 USA ISSN 0269-5448
HC471
COUNTRY REPORT. IRAN; analysis of economic and political trends every quarter. Text in English. 1952. q. USD 485 print or online; USD 230 per issue print or online (effective 2004). illus.; stat. **Document type:** *Trade.* **Description:** Analyzes Iran's current political and economic climate, as well as short-term economic projections.
Formerly: Quarterly Economic Review of Iran (0142-3924)
Related titles: ♦ CD-ROM ed.: E I U Country Reports on Disc: Middle East - North Africa; Online - full text ed.: E I U Country Reports: Middle East-North Africa.
Indexed: RASB.
—CCC.
Published by: Economist Intelligence Unit, 111 W 57th St, New York, NY 10019. TEL 212-554-0600, FAX 212-586-1181, newyork@eiu.com, http://www.eiu.com.

330.9567 USA ISSN 0269-5502
HC415.4.A1
COUNTRY REPORT. IRAQ; analysis of economic and political trends every quarter. Text in English. 1952. q. USD 485 print or online; USD 230 per issue print or online (effective 2004). illus.; stat. **Document type:** *Trade.* **Description:** Analyzes Iraq's current political and economic climate as well as short-term economic projections.
Formerly: Quarterly Economic Review of Iraq (0142-4009)
Related titles: ♦ CD-ROM ed.: E I U Country Reports on Disc: Middle East - North Africa; Online - full text ed.: E I U Country Reports: Middle East-North Africa.
Indexed: RASB.
—BLDSC (3481.898330). **CCC.**
Published by: Economist Intelligence Unit, 111 W 57th St, New York, NY 10019. TEL 212-554-0600, FAX 212-586-1181, newyork@eiu.com, http://www.eiu.com.

330.9417 USA ISSN 0269-5278
HC260.5.A1
COUNTRY REPORT. IRELAND; analysis of economic and political trends every quarter. Text in English. 1952. q. USD 485 print or online; USD 230 per issue print or online (effective 2004). illus.; stat. **Document type:** *Trade.* **Description:** Analyzes Ireland's current political and economic climate, as well as short-term economic projections.
Formerly: Quarterly Economic Review of Ireland (0142-3835)
Related titles: ♦ CD-ROM ed.: E I U Country Reports on Disc: Western Europe; Online - full text ed.: E I U Country Reports: Western Europe (from SilverPlatter Information, Inc., The Dialog Corporation).
—CCC.
Published by: Economist Intelligence Unit, 111 W 57th St, New York, NY 10019. TEL 212-554-0600, FAX 212-586-1181, newyork@eiu.com, http://www.eiu.com.

330.95694 USA
HC415.25.A1
COUNTRY REPORT. ISRAEL; analysis of economic and political trends every quarter. Text in English. 1952. q. USD 485 print or online; USD 230 per issue print or online (effective 2004). illus.; stat. **Document type:** *Trade.* **Description:** Analyzes Israel's current political and economic climate, as well as short-term economic projections.
Supersedes in part (in 2001): Country Report. Israel, the Occupied Territories (1353-3142); Which was formerly (until 1993): Country Report. Israel (0269-5928); (until 1986): Quarterly Economic Review of Israel (0142-4238); (until 1976): Q E R Israel (0481-1755)
Related titles: ♦ CD-ROM ed.: E I U Country Reports on Disc: Middle East - North Africa; Online - full text ed.: E I U Country Reports: Middle East-North Africa; (from EBSCO Publishing).
Indexed: RASB.
Published by: Economist Intelligence Unit, 111 W 57th St, New York, NY 10019. TEL 212-554-0600, FAX 212-586-1181, newyork@eiu.com, http://www.eiu.com.

330.945 USA ISSN 0269-5421
HC301
COUNTRY REPORT. ITALY; analysis of economic and political trends every quarter. Text in English. 1952. q. USD 485 print or online; USD 230 per issue print or online (effective 2004). illus.; stat. **Document type:** *Trade.* **Description:** Analyzes Italy's current political and economic climate, as well as short-term economic projections.
Formerly: Quarterly Economic Review of Italy (0142-3886)
Related titles: ♦ CD-ROM ed.: E I U Country Reports on Disc: Western Europe; Online - full text ed.: E I U Country Reports: Western Europe (from SilverPlatter Information, Inc., The Dialog Corporation); (from EBSCO Publishing).
—CCC.
Published by: Economist Intelligence Unit, 111 W 57th St, New York, NY 10019. TEL 212-554-0600, FAX 212-586-1181, newyork@eiu.com, http://www.eiu.com.

330.9729 USA
HC154.A1
COUNTRY REPORT. JAMAICA; analysis of economic and political trends every quarter. Text in English. 1952. q. USD 485 print or online; USD 230 per issue print or online (effective 2004). illus.; stat. **Document type:** *Trade.* **Description:** Analyzes the current political and economic climate, as well as short-term economic projections.
Supersedes in part: Country Report. Jamaica, Belize, Bahamas, Bermuda, Barbados (1351-8674); Which was formed by the 1992 merger of part of: Country Report. Jamaica, Belize, Bahamas, Bermuda (0269-7130); part of: Country Report. Trinidad and Tobago, Guyana, Barbados, Windward and Leeward Islands (0269-7149); Which was formerly: Quarterly Economic Review of Jamaica, Belize, Bahamas, Bermuda (0266-9617); Quarterly Economic Review of Trinidad and Tobago, Guyana, Barbados, Windward and Leeward Islands (0266-9625)
Related titles: ♦ CD-ROM ed.: E I U Country Reports on Disc: The Americas; Online - full text ed.: E I U Country Reports: The Americas.
Indexed: RASB.
Published by: Economist Intelligence Unit, 111 W 57th St, New York, NY 10019. TEL 212-554-0600, FAX 212-586-1181, newyork@eiu.com, http://www.eiu.com.

330.952 USA ISSN 0269-6681
HC461
COUNTRY REPORT. JAPAN; analysis of economic and political trends every quarter. Text in English. 1952. q. USD 485 print or online; USD 230 per issue print or online (effective 2004). illus.; stat. **Document type:** *Trade.* **Description:** Analyzes Japan's current political and economic climate, as well as short-term economic projections.
Formerly: Quarterly Economic Review of Japan (0144-8897)
Related titles: ♦ CD-ROM ed.: E I U Country Reports on Disc: Asia-Pacific; Online - full text ed.: E I U Country Reports: Asia-Pacific (from EBSCO Publishing); (from EBSCO Publishing).
Indexed: MASUSE, RASB, WBA, WMB.
—CCC.
Published by: Economist Intelligence Unit, 111 W 57th St, New York, NY 10019. TEL 212-554-0600, FAX 212-586-1181, newyork@eiu.com, http://www.eiu.com.

330.95695 USA ISSN 0269-722X
HC415.26.A1
COUNTRY REPORT. JORDAN; analysis of economic and political trends every quarter. Text in English. 1952. q. USD 485 print or online; USD 230 per issue print or online (effective 2004). illus.; stat. **Document type:** *Trade.* **Description:** Analyzes Jordan's political and economic climate, as well as short-term economic projections.
Formerly: Quarterly Economic Review of Jordan (0266-9714)
Related titles: ♦ CD-ROM ed.: E I U Country Reports on Disc: Middle East - North Africa; Online - full text ed.: E I U Country Reports: Middle East-North Africa.
Indexed: RASB.
—CCC.
Published by: Economist Intelligence Unit, 111 W 57th St, New York, NY 10019. TEL 212-554-0600, FAX 212-586-1181, newyork@eiu.com, http://www.eiu.com.

330.95845 USA ISSN 1361-147X
HC420.5.A1
COUNTRY REPORT. KAZAKHSTAN. Text in English. q. USD 485 print or online; USD 230 per issue print or online (effective 2004). illus.; stat. **Document type:** *Trade.* **Description:** Analyzes the Kazach current political and economic climate, as well as short-term economic projections.
Supersedes in part: Country Report. Central Asian Republics: Kazakhstan, Kyrgyz Republic, Tajikistan, Turkmenistan, Uzbekistan; Which superseded in part (in 1995): Country Report. Georgia, Armenia, Azerbaijan, Central Asian Republics (1350-7206); Which superseded in part (in 1992): Country Report. Commonwealth of Independent States; Which was formerly (until 1991): Country Report. U S S R (0269-5480); Quarterly Economic Review of U S S R (0142-3967)
Related titles: ♦ CD-ROM ed.: E I U Country Forecasts on Disc: Eastern Europe; Online - full text ed.: E I U Country Forecasts: Eastern Europe (from EBSCO Publishing).
Indexed: ABIn.
Published by: Economist Intelligence Unit, 111 W 57th St, New York, NY 10019. TEL 212-554-0600, FAX 212-586-1181, newyork@eiu.com, http://www.eiu.com.

330.96762 USA ISSN 0269-4239
HC865.A1
COUNTRY REPORT. KENYA; analysis of economic and political trends every quarter. Text in English. 1952. q. USD 485 print or online; USD 230 per issue print or online (effective 2004). illus.; stat. **Document type:** *Trade.* **Description:** Analyzes Kenya's current political and economic climate, as well as short-term economic projections.
Formerly: Quarterly Economic Review of Kenya (0142-4254)
Related titles: ♦ CD-ROM ed.: E I U Country Reports on Disc: Sub-Saharan Africa; Online - full text ed.: E I U Country Reports: Sub-Saharan Africa (from SilverPlatter Information, Inc., The Dialog Corporation).
Indexed: RASB.
—CCC.
Published by: Economist Intelligence Unit, 111 W 57th St, New York, NY 10019. TEL 212-554-0600, FAX 212-586-1181, newyork@eiu.com, http://www.eiu.com.

330.95367 USA ISSN 0269-5715
HC415.39.A1
COUNTRY REPORT. KUWAIT; analysis of economic and political trends every quarter. Text in English. 1952. q. USD 485 print or online; USD 230 per issue print or online (effective 2004). illus.; stat. **Document type:** *Trade.* **Description:** Analyzes Kuwait's current political and economic climate, as well as short-term economic projections.
Formerly: Quarterly Economic Review of Kuwait
Related titles: ♦ CD-ROM ed.: E I U Country Reports on Disc: Middle East - North Africa; Online - full text ed.: E I U Country Reports: Middle East-North Africa.
Indexed: RASB.
—CCC.
Published by: Economist Intelligence Unit, 111 W 57th St, New York, NY 10019. TEL 212-554-0600, FAX 212-586-1181, newyork@eiu.com, http://www.eiu.com.

330.958 USA ISSN 1478-0399
HC420.7.A1
COUNTRY REPORT. KYRGYZ REPUBLIC; analysis of economic and political trends every quarter. Text in English. q. USD 485 print or online; USD 230 per issue print or online (effective 2004). charts; stat. **Document type:** *Trade.* **Description:** Analyzes the current political and economic climate and provides short-term economic projections.
Supersedes in part (in 2001): Country Report. Kyrgyz Republic, Tajikistan, Turkmenistan (1366-414X); Which superseded in part (in 1997): Country Report. Kyrgyz Republic, Tajikistan, Turkmenistan, Uzbekistan (1361-1488); Which superseded in part (in 1996): Country Report. Kazakhstan, Kyrgyz Republic, Tajikistan, Turkmenistan, Uzbekistan (1360-9467); Which superseded in part (in 1995): Country Report. Georgia, Armenia, Azerbaijan, Central Asian Republics; Superseded in part (in 1992): Country Report. Commonwealth of Independent States; Which was formerly (until 1991): Country Report. U S S R (0269-5480); Quarterly Economic Review of U S S R (0142-3967)
Related titles: ♦ CD-ROM ed.: E I U Country Reports on Disc: Eastern Europe; Online - full text ed.: E I U Country Reports: Eastern Europe (from Central Institute for Scientific & Technical Information, SilverPlatter Information, Inc., The Dialog Corporation).
Indexed: ABIn.
Published by: Economist Intelligence Unit, 111 W 57th St, New York, NY 10019. TEL 212-554-0600, FAX 212-586-1181, newyork@eiu.com, http://www.eiu.com.

330.9549 USA
COUNTRY REPORT. LAOS; analysis of economic and political trends every quarter. Text in English. q. USD 485 print or online; USD 230 per issue print or online (effective 2004). illus.; stat. **Document type:** *Trade.*
Supersedes in part: Country Report. Cambodia, Laos (1361-1437)
Published by: Economist Intelligence Unit, 111 W 57th St, New York, NY 10019. TEL 212-554-0600, FAX 212-586-1181, newyork@eiu.com, http://www.eiu.com.

330.9549 USA ISSN 1462-6713
HC340.5.A1
COUNTRY REPORT. LATVIA; analysis of economic and political trends every quarter. Text in English. q. USD 485 print or online; USD 230 per issue print or online (effective 2004). illus.; stat. **Document type:** *Journal, Trade.* **Description:** Analyzes Latvia's current political and economic climates, as well as short-term economic projections.
Supersedes in part (in 1998): Country Report. Lithuania, Latvia, Estonia (1360-9459); Which was formerly (until 1995): Country Report. Baltic Republics (1350-7176); Which superseded in part (in 1993): Country Report. Commonwealth of Independent States (0968-8242); Which was formerly (until 1992): Country Report. U S S R (0269-5480); (until 1986): Quarterly Economic Review of U S S R (0142-3967); (until 1976): Q E R - U S S R
Indexed: ABIn.
Published by: Economist Intelligence Unit, 111 W 57th St, New York, NY 10019. TEL 212-554-0600, FAX 212-586-1181, newyork@eiu.com, http://www.eiu.com.

330.95692 USA ISSN 1350-7141
HC415.24.A1
COUNTRY REPORT. LEBANON; analysis of economic and political trends every quarter. Text in English. 1952. q. USD 485 print or online; USD 230 per issue print or online (effective 2004). illus.; stat. **Document type:** *Trade.* **Description:** Analyzes Lebanon's current political and economic climate, as well as short-term economic projections.
Supersedes (in 1992): Country Report. Lebanon, Cyprus (0269-5693); Which was formerly: Quarterly Economic Review of Lebanon, Cyprus (0142-4106)

B

▼ new title ➤ refereed ✶ unverified ♦ full entry avail.

Related titles: ♦ CD-ROM ed.: E I U Country Reports on Disc: Middle East - North Africa; Online - full text ed.: E I U Country Reports: Middle East-North Africa.
Indexed: RASB.
—CCC.
Published by: Economist Intelligence Unit, 111 W 57th St, New York, NY 10019. TEL 212-554-0600, FAX 212-586-1181, newyork@eiu.com, http://www.eiu.com.

330.9549 USA
COUNTRY REPORT. LESOTHO; analysis of economic and political trends every quarter. Text in English. q. USD 485 print or online; USD 230 per issue print or online (effective 2004). illus.; stat. **Document type:** *Trade.*
Supersedes in part: Country Report. Botswana, Lesotho
Published by: Economist Intelligence Unit, 111 W 57th St, New York, NY 10019. TEL 212-554-0600, FAX 212-586-1181, newyork@eiu.com, http://www.eiu.com.

B

330.9549 USA
COUNTRY REPORT. LIBERIA; analysis of economic and political trends every quarter. Text in English. 1976. q. USD 485 print or online; USD 230 per issue print or online (effective 2004). illus.; stat. **Document type:** *Trade.*
Supersedes in part (in 2001): Country Report. Guinea, Sierra Leone, Liberia (0969-4692); Which was formerly (until 1993): Country Report. Guinea, Mali, Mauritania (0269-7203); (until 1986): Quarterly Economic Review of Guinea, Mali, Mauritania (0266-9692); Which superseded in part (in 1985): Quarterly Economic Review of Senegal, Mali, Mauritania, Guinea (0142-3991)
Published by: Economist Intelligence Unit, 111 W 57th St, New York, NY 10019. TEL 212-554-0600, FAX 212-586-1181, newyork@eiu.com, http://www.eiu.com.

330.9612 USA ISSN 0269-4328
HC825.A1
COUNTRY REPORT. LIBYA; analysis of economic and political trends every quarter. Text in English. 1952. q. USD 485 print or online; USD 230 per issue print or online (effective 2004). illus.; stat. **Document type:** *Trade.* **Description:** Analyzes Libya's current political and economic climate, as well as short-term economic projections.
Formerly: Quarterly Economic Review of Libya (0266-9722)
Related titles: ♦ CD-ROM ed.: E I U Country Reports on Disc: Middle East - North Africa; Online - full text ed.: E I U Country Reports: Middle East-North Africa.
Indexed: RASB.
—CCC.
Published by: Economist Intelligence Unit, 111 W 57th St, New York, NY 10019. TEL 212-554-0600, FAX 212-586-1181, newyork@eiu.com, http://www.eiu.com.

330.9479 USA ISSN 1462-6721
HC340.6.A1
COUNTRY REPORT. LITHUANIA; analysis of economic and political trends every quarter. Text in English. 1952. q. USD 485 print or online; USD 230 per issue print or online (effective 2004). illus.; stat. **Document type:** *Trade.* **Description:** Analyzes the current political and economic climate, as well as short-term economic projections for the Baltic republics.
Supersedes in part (in 1998): Country Report. Estonia, Latvia, Lithuania (1360-9459); Which was formerly (until 1995): Country Report. Baltic Republics (1350-7176); Which superseded in part (in 1992): Country Report. Commonwealth of Independent States (0968-8242); Which was formerly (until 1991): Country Report. U S S R (0269-5480); (until 1986): Quarterly Economic Review of U S S R (0142-3967); (until 1976): Q E R - U S S R
Related titles: Online - full text ed.
Indexed: ABIn.
Published by: Economist Intelligence Unit, 111 W 57th St, New York, NY 10019. TEL 212-554-0600, FAX 212-586-1181, newyork@eiu.com, http://www.eiu.com.

330.9549 USA ISSN 1473-9070
HC330.A1
COUNTRY REPORT. LUXEMBOURG; analysis of economic and political trends every quarter. Text in English. q. USD 485 print or online; USD 230 per issue print or online (effective 2004). illus.; stat. **Document type:** *Trade.*
Supersedes in part: Country Report. Belgium, Luxembourg (0269-4158)
Related titles: Online - full text ed.: (from EBSCO Publishing).
Published by: Economist Intelligence Unit, 111 W 57th St, New York, NY 10019. TEL 212-554-0600, FAX 212-586-1181, newyork@eiu.com, http://www.eiu.com.

330.9549 USA
COUNTRY REPORT. MACAU; analysis of economic and political trends every quarter. Text in English. q. USD 485 print or online; USD 230 per issue print or online (effective 2004). illus.; stat. **Document type:** *Trade.*
Supersedes in part (in 2000): Country Report. Hong Kong, Macau (0269-6762)
Related titles: Online - full text ed.: (from EBSCO Publishing, ProQuest Information & Learning).
Published by: Economist Intelligence Unit, 111 W 57th St, New York, NY 10019. TEL 212-554-0600, FAX 212-586-1181, newyork@eiu.com, http://www.eiu.com.

330.9497 USA ISSN 1462-6691
HC404.5.A1
COUNTRY REPORT. MACEDONIA; analysis of economic and political trends every quarter. Text in English. q. USD 485 print or online; USD 230 per issue print or online (effective 2004). charts; stat. **Document type:** *Trade.* **Description:** Analyzes the current political and economic situations, as well as short-term economic projections for Serbia-Montenegro and Macedonia.
Supersedes in part (in 1998): Country Report. Yugoslavia (Serbia-Montenegro), Macedonia (1361-1461); Which was formerly (until 1996): Country Report. Macedonia, Serbia-Montenegro (1363-4658); Which superseded in part (in 1995): Country Report. Bosnia-Hercegovina, Croatia, Macedonia, Serbia-Montenegro, Slovenia (1350-7222); Which superseded in part (in 1993): Country Report. Yugoslav Republics (0968-7734); Which was formerly (until 1992): Country Report. Yugoslavia (0269-4190); (until 1986): Quarterly Economic Review of Yugoslavia (0142-3983)
Related titles: ♦ CD-ROM ed.: E I U Country Reports on Disc: Eastern Europe; Online - full text ed.: E I U Country Reports: Eastern Europe (from Central Institute for Scientific & Technical Information, SilverPlatter Information, Inc., The Dialog Corporation).
Published by: Economist Intelligence Unit, 111 W 57th St, New York, NY 10019. TEL 212-554-0600, FAX 212-586-1181, newyork@eiu.com, http://www.eiu.com.

330.9549 USA
COUNTRY REPORT. MADAGASCAR; analysis of economic and political trends every quarter. Text in English. 2001. q. USD 485 print or online; USD 230 per issue print or online (effective 2004). illus.; stat. **Document type:** *Trade.*
Supersedes in part (in 2001): Country Report. Mauritius, Madagascar, Seychelles (1350-7060); Which superseded in part (in 1992): Country Report. Madagascar, Mauritius, Seychelles, Comoros (0269-5154); Which was formerly (until 1986): Quarterly Economic Review of Madagascar, Mauritius, Seychelles, Comoros (0141-8092)
Related titles: Online - full text ed.: (from Gale Group).
Published by: Economist Intelligence Unit, 111 W 57th St, New York, NY 10019. TEL 212-554-0600, FAX 212-586-1181, newyork@eiu.com, http://www.eiu.com.

330.9549 USA ISSN 1478-0283
HC935.A1
COUNTRY REPORT. MALAWI; analysis of economic and political trends every quarter. Text in English. 2001. q. USD 485 print or online; USD 230 per issue print or online (effective 2004). illus.; stat. **Document type:** *Trade.*
Supersedes in part (in 2001): Country Report. Mozambique, Malawi (1351-8089); Which was formerly (until 1993): Country Report. Tanzania, Mozambique (0269-6223); (until 1986): Quarterly Economic Review of Tanzania, Mozambique (0142-4505)
Published by: Economist Intelligence Unit, 111 W 57th St, New York, NY 10019. TEL 212-554-0600, FAX 212-586-1181, newyork@eiu.com, http://www.eiu.com.

330.9595 USA
HC445.5.A1
COUNTRY REPORT. MALAYSIA; analysis of economic and political trends every quarter. Text in English. 1952. q. USD 485 print or online; USD 230 per issue print or online (effective 2004). illus.; stat. **Document type:** *Trade.* **Description:** Analyzes the current political and economic climate, as well as short-term economic projections for Malaysia and Brunei Darussalam.
Supersedes in part: Country Report. Malaysia, Brunei (0269-6703); Which was formerly (until 1986): Quarterly Economic Review of Malaysia, Brunei (0144-8919)
Related titles: ♦ CD-ROM ed.: E I U Country Reports on Disc: Asia-Pacific; Online - full text ed.: (from EBSCO Publishing).
Indexed: BAS, RASB, WMB.
—BLDSC (3481.898850).
Published by: Economist Intelligence Unit, 111 W 57th St, New York, NY 10019. TEL 212-554-0600, FAX 212-586-1181, newyork@eiu.com, http://www.eiu.com.

330.9549 USA
COUNTRY REPORT. MALI; analysis of economic and political trends every quarter. Text in English. q. USD 485 print or online; USD 230 per issue print or online (effective 2004). illus.; stat. **Document type:** *Trade.*
Supersedes in part (in 2000): Country Report. Cote d'Ivoire, Mali (0969-4730)
Published by: Economist Intelligence Unit, 111 W 57th St, New York, NY 10019. TEL 212-554-0600, FAX 212-586-1181, newyork@eiu.com, http://www.eiu.com.

330.9549 USA
COUNTRY REPORT. MALTA; analysis of economic and political trends every quarter. Text in English. q. USD 485 print or online; USD 230 per issue print or online (effective 2004). illus.; stat. **Document type:** *Trade.*
Supersedes in part: Country Report. Cyprus, Malta (1350-715X)
Published by: Economist Intelligence Unit, 111 W 57th St, New York, NY 10019. TEL 212-554-0600, FAX 212-586-1181, newyork@eiu.com, http://www.eiu.com.

330.9549 USA
COUNTRY REPORT. MAURITANIA; analysis of economic and political trends every quarter. Text in English. 2001. q. USD 485 print or online; USD 230 per issue print or online (effective 2004). illus.; stat. **Document type:** *Trade.*
Supersedes in part (in 2001): Country Report. Senegal, The Gambia, Mauritania (1350-7079); Which was formed by the 1993 merger of part of: Country Report. Senegal, the Gambia, Guinea-Bissau, Cape Verde (0269-719X); Which was formerly (1985-1986): Quarterly Economic Review of Senegal, the Gambia, Guinea-Bissau, Cape Verde (0266-9684); part of: Country Report. Guinea, Mali, Mauritania (0269-7203); Which was formerly (1985-1986): Quarterly Economic Review of Guinea, Mali, Mauritania (0266-9692)
Published by: Economist Intelligence Unit, 111 W 57th St, New York, NY 10019. TEL 212-554-0600, FAX 212-586-1181, newyork@eiu.com, http://www.eiu.com.

330.969 USA
HC597.5.A1
COUNTRY REPORT. MAURITIUS; analysis of economic and political trends every quarter. Text in English. 2001. q. USD 485 print or online; USD 230 per issue print or online (effective 2004). illus.; stat. **Document type:** *Trade.* **Description:** Anaylyzes the current political and economic currents, as well as short-term economic projections for these island nations.
Supersedes in part (1993-2001): Country Report. Mauritius, Madagascar, Seychelles (1350-7060); Which superseded in part (1978-1993): Country Report. Madagascar, Mauritius, Seychelles, Comoros (0269-5154); Which was formerly (until 1986): Quarterly Economic Review of Madagascar, Mauritius, Seychelles, Comoros (0141-8092)
Related titles: ♦ CD-ROM ed.: E I U Country Reports on Disc: Sub-Saharan Africa; Online - full text ed.: E I U Country Reports: Sub-Saharan Africa (from SilverPlatter Information, Inc., The Dialog Corporation); (from Gale Group).
Published by: Economist Intelligence Unit, 111 W 57th St, New York, NY 10019. TEL 212-554-0600, FAX 212-586-1181, newyork@eiu.com, http://www.eiu.com.

330.972 USA ISSN 0269-5936
HC131
COUNTRY REPORT. MEXICO; analysis of economic and political trends every quarter. Text in English. 1952. q. USD 500 print or online; USD 235 per issue print or online (effective 2005). illus.; stat. **Document type:** *Trade.* **Description:** Analyzes Mexico's current political and economic climate, as well as short-term economic projections.
Formerly: Quarterly Economic Review of Mexico (0142-4270)
Related titles: ♦ CD-ROM ed.: E I U Country Reports on Disc: The Americas; Online - full text ed.: E I U Country Reports: The Americas; (from EBSCO Publishing, ProQuest Information & Learning).
Indexed: ABIn, RASB.
—CCC.
Published by: Economist Intelligence Unit, 111 W 57th St, New York, NY 10019. TEL 212-554-0600, FAX 212-586-1181, newyork@eiu.com, http://www.eiu.com.

330.9549 USA ISSN 1478-0305
COUNTRY REPORT. MOLDOVA; analysis of economic and political trends every quarter. Text in English. q. USD 485 print or online; USD 230 per issue print or online (effective 2004). illus.; stat. **Document type:** *Trade.*
Supersedes in part (in 2001): Country Report: Belarus, Moldova (1356-4137); Which superseded in part (in 1995): Country Report. Ukraine, Belarus, Moldova (1350-7192); Which superseded in part (in 1993): Country Report. Commonwealth of Independent States (0968-8242); Which was formerly (until 1992): Country Report. U S S R (0269-5480); (until 1986): Quarterly Economic Review of U S S R (0142-3967); (until 1976): Q E R - U S S R
Published by: Economist Intelligence Unit, 111 W 57th St, New York, NY 10019. TEL 212-554-0600, FAX 212-586-1181, newyork@eiu.com, http://www.eiu.com.

330.9549 USA
COUNTRY REPORT. MONGOLIA; analysis of economic and political trends every quarter. Text in English. q. USD 485 print or online; USD 230 per issue print or online (effective 2004). illus.; stat. **Document type:** *Trade.*
Supersedes in part (in 2000): Country Report. China, Mongolia (1350-7109)
Related titles: Online - full text ed.: (from EBSCO Publishing).
Published by: Economist Intelligence Unit, 111 W 57th St, New York, NY 10019. TEL 212-554-0600, FAX 212-586-1181, newyork@eiu.com, http://www.eiu.com.

330.964 USA ISSN 0269-6126
HC810.A1
COUNTRY REPORT. MOROCCO; analysis of economic and political trends every quarter. Text in English. 1952. q. USD 485 print or online; USD 230 per issue print or online (effective 2004). illus.; stat. **Document type:** *Trade.* **Description:** Analyzes Morocco's current political and economic climate, as well as short-term economic projections.
Formerly: Quarterly Economic Review of Morocco (0142-4289)
Related titles: ♦ CD-ROM ed.: E I U Country Reports on Disc: Middle East - North Africa; Online - full text ed.: E I U Country Reports: Middle East-North Africa.
Indexed: RASB.
—CCC.

Published by: Economist Intelligence Unit, 111 W 57th St, New York, NY 10019. TEL 212-554-0600, FAX 212-586-1181, newyork@eiu.com, http://www.eiu.com.

330.967 USA ISSN 1478-0275
HC890.A1
COUNTRY REPORT. MOZAMBIQUE; analysis of economic and political trends every quarter. Text in English. 2002. q. USD 485 print or online; USD 230 per issue print or online (effective 2004). illus.; stat. **Document type:** *Trade.* **Description:** Analyzes the current political and economic climates, as well as short-term economic projections for Mozambique and Malawi.
Supersedes in part (in 2001): Country Report. Mozambique, Malawi (1351-8089); Which was formed by the merger of part of (1978-1992): Country Report. Tanzania, Mozambique (0269-6223); Which was formerly (until 1986): Quarterly Economic Review of Tanzania, Mozambique (0142-4505); part of (1980-1992): Country Report. Zimbabwe, Malawi (0269-4255); Which was formerly (until 1986): Quarterly Economic Review of Zimbabwe, Malawi (0266-4372)
Related titles: ♦ CD-ROM ed.: E I U Country Reports on Disc: Sub-Saharan Africa; Online - full text ed.: E I U Country Reports: Sub-Saharan Africa (from SilverPlatter Information, Inc., The Dialog Corporation).
Indexed: RASB.
Published by: Economist Intelligence Unit, 111 W 57th St, New York, NY 10019. TEL 212-554-0600, FAX 212-586-1181, newyork@eiu.com, http://www.eiu.com.

330.9591 USA ISSN 1361-1445
HC422.A1
COUNTRY REPORT. MYANMAR; analysis of economic and political trends every quarter. Text in English. q. USD 485 print or online; USD 230 per issue print or online (effective 2004). charts; stat. **Document type:** *Trade.* **Description:** Analyzes the Burmese current political and economic climate, as well as short-term economic projections.
Supersedes in part: Country Report. Cambodia, Laos, Myanmar (1356-4048); Which was formed by the 1995 merger of part of: Country Report. Indochina: Vietnam, Laos, Cambodia (0269-5677); Which was formerly: Quarterly Economic Review of Indochina: Vietnam, Laos, Cambodia (0142-4076); (in part of): Country Report. Thailand, Myanmar (1350-7117); Which was formerly: Country Report. Thailand, Burma (0269-5189); Quarterly Economic Review of Thailand, Burma (0142-3754)
Related titles: ♦ CD-ROM ed.: E I U Country Reports on Disc: Asia-Pacific; Online - full text ed.: E I U Country Reports: Asia-Pacific (from EBSCO Publishing).
Indexed: RASB.
—CCC.
Published by: Economist Intelligence Unit, 111 W 57th St, New York, NY 10019. TEL 212-554-0600, FAX 212-586-1181, newyork@eiu.com, http://www.eiu.com.

330.9688 USA
COUNTRY REPORT. NAMIBIA; analysis of economic and political trends every quarter. Text in English. 1982. q. USD 485 print or online; USD 230 per issue print or online (effective 2004). charts; stat. **Document type:** *Trade.* **Description:** Analyzes the current political and economic climates, as well as short-term economic projections for Namibia and Swaziland.
Supersedes in part: Country Report. Namibia, Swaziland (1356-4218); Which superseded in part (in 1995): Country Report. Botswana, Namibia, Lesotho, Swaziland (1351-8658); Which was formerly (until 1994): Country Report. Namibia, Botswana, Lesotho, Swaziland (0269-6746); (until 1986): Quarterly Economic Review of Namibia, Botswana, Lesotho, Swaziland (0144-896X)
Related titles: ♦ CD-ROM ed.: E I U Country Reports on Disc: Sub-Saharan Africa; Online - full text ed.: E I U Country Reports: Sub-Saharan Africa (from SilverPlatter Information, Inc., The Dialog Corporation).
Indexed: RASB.
Published by: Economist Intelligence Unit, 111 W 57th St, New York, NY 10019. TEL 212-554-0600, FAX 212-586-1181, newyork@eiu.com, http://www.eiu.com.

330.9549 USA
COUNTRY REPORT. NEPAL; analysis of economic and political trends every quarter. Text in English. q. USD 485 print or online; USD 230 per issue print or online (effective 2004). illus.; stat. **Document type:** *Trade.*
Supersedes in part (in 2000): Country Report. India, Nepal (0269-5294)
Related titles: Online - full text ed.: (from EBSCO Publishing).
Published by: Economist Intelligence Unit, 111 W 57th St, New York, NY 10019. TEL 212-554-0600, FAX 212-586-1181, newyork@eiu.com, http://www.eiu.com.

330.9492 USA ISSN 0269-6134
HC321
COUNTRY REPORT. NETHERLANDS; analysis of economic and political trends every quarter. Text in English. 1952. q. USD 485 print or online; USD 230 per issue print or online (effective 2004). illus.; stat. **Document type:** *Trade.* **Description:** Analyzes the Netherlands's current political and economic climate, as well as short-term economic projections.
Formerly: Quarterly Economic Review of Netherlands (0142-4297)
Related titles: ♦ CD-ROM ed.: E I U Country Reports on Disc: Western Europe; Online - full text ed.: E I U Country Reports: Western Europe (from SilverPlatter Information, Inc., The Dialog Corporation); (from EBSCO Publishing).
—CCC.
Published by: Economist Intelligence Unit, 111 W 57th St, New York, NY 10019. TEL 212-554-0600, FAX 212-586-1181, newyork@eiu.com, http://www.eiu.com.

330.9549 USA
COUNTRY REPORT. NETHERLANDS ANTILLES; analysis of economic and political trends every quarter. Text in English. q. USD 485 print or online; USD 230 per issue print or online (effective 2004). illus.; stat. **Document type:** *Trade.*
Supersedes in part: Country Report. Trinidad & Tobago, Guyana, Windward & Leeward Islands, Suriname, Netherlands Antilles, Aruba (1351-1270)
Published by: Economist Intelligence Unit, 111 W 57th St, New York, NY 10019. TEL 212-554-0600, FAX 212-586-1181, newyork@eiu.com, http://www.eiu.com.

330.9549 USA
COUNTRY REPORT. NEW CALEDONIA; analysis of economic and political trends every quarter. Text in English. q. USD 485 print or online; USD 230 per issue print or online (effective 2004). illus.; stat. **Document type:** *Trade.*
Supersedes in part: Country Report. Pacific Islands: Fiji, New Caledonia, Samoa, Solomon Islands, Tonga, Vanuatu (1460-7077)
Published by: Economist Intelligence Unit, 111 W 57th St, New York, NY 10019. TEL 212-554-0600, FAX 212-586-1181, newyork@eiu.com, http://www.eiu.com.

330.993 USA ISSN 0269-7114
HC661
COUNTRY REPORT. NEW ZEALAND; analysis of economic and political trends every quarter. Text in English. 1952. q. USD 485 print or online; USD 230 per issue print or online (effective 2004). illus.; stat. **Document type:** *Trade.* **Description:** Analyzes New Zealand's current political and economic climate, as well as short-term economic projections.
Formerly: Quarterly Economic Review of New Zealand (0266-9595)
Related titles: ♦ CD-ROM ed.: E I U Country Reports on Disc: Asia-Pacific; Online - full text ed.: E I U Country Reports: Asia-Pacific (from EBSCO Publishing); (from EBSCO Publishing).
Indexed: RASB, WBA, WMB.
—CCC.
Published by: Economist Intelligence Unit, 111 W 57th St, New York, NY 10019. TEL 212-554-0600, FAX 212-586-1181, newyork@eiu.com, http://www.eiu.com.

330.9728 USA ISSN 1473-9003
HC146.A1
COUNTRY REPORT. NICARAGUA; analysis of economic and political trends every quarter. Text in English. 1952. q. USD 485 print or online; USD 230 per issue print or online (effective 2004). illus.; stat. **Document type:** *Trade.* **Description:** Analyzes the current political and economic climate, as well as short-term economic projections.
Supersedes in part (in 2000): Country Report. Nicaragua, Honduras (0969-8809); Which was formed by the 1993 merger of part of: Country Report. Nicaragua, Costa Rica, Panama (0269-4247); Which was formerly (until 1986): Quarterly Economic Review of Nicaragua, Costa Rica, Panama (0142-4300); (1975-1976): Q E R. Nicaragua, Costa Rica, Panama (0306-8978); part of: Country Report. Guatemala, El Salvador, Honduras (0269-4220); Which was formerly (until 1986): Quarterly Economic Review of Guatemala, El Salvador, Honduras (0142-4211); (1974-1976): Q E R. Guatemala, El Salvador, Honduras (0306-7491)
Related titles: ♦ CD-ROM ed.: E I U Country Reports on Disc: The Americas; Online - full text ed.: E I U Country Reports: The Americas.
Indexed: RASB.
Published by: Economist Intelligence Unit, 111 W 57th St, New York, NY 10019. TEL 212-554-0600, FAX 212-586-1181, newyork@eiu.com, http://www.eiu.com.

330.9662 USA
HC1020.A1
COUNTRY REPORT. NIGER; analysis of economic and political trends every quarter. Text in English. q. USD 485 print or online; USD 230 per issue print or online (effective 2004). charts. **Document type:** *Trade.* **Description:** Analyzes the current political and economic climate and provides short-term economic projections for Niger and Burkina Faso.
Supersedes in part: Country Report. Niger, Burkina Faso (1366-4115); Which superseded in part (in 1997): Country Report. Togo, Niger, Benin, Burkina Faso (0269-7262); Which was formerly: Quarterly Economic Review of Togo, Niger, Benin, Burkina Faso (0266-9773)
Related titles: CD-ROM ed.: (from SilverPlatter Information, Inc.); Online - full text ed.: (from SilverPlatter Information, Inc., The Dialog Corporation).
Published by: Economist Intelligence Unit, 111 W 57th St, New York, NY 10019. TEL 212-554-0600, FAX 212-586-1181, newyork@eiu.com, http://www.eiu.com.

330.9669 USA ISSN 0269-4204
HC1055.A1
COUNTRY REPORT. NIGERIA; analysis of economic and political trends every quarter. Text in English. 1952. q. USD 485 print or online; USD 230 per issue print or online (effective 2004). illus.; stat. **Document type:** *Trade.* **Description:** Analyzes Nigeria's current political and economic climate, as well as short-term economic projections.
Formerly: Quarterly Economic Review of Nigeria (0142-4033)
Related titles: ♦ CD-ROM ed.: E I U Country Reports on Disc: Sub-Saharan Africa; Online - full text ed.: E I U Country Reports: Sub-Saharan Africa (from SilverPlatter Information, Inc., The Dialog Corporation).
Indexed: RASB.
—CCC.
Published by: Economist Intelligence Unit, 111 W 57th St, New York, NY 10019. TEL 212-554-0600, FAX 212-586-1181, newyork@eiu.com, http://www.eiu.com.

330.9549 USA ISSN 1478-033X
COUNTRY REPORT. NORTH KOREA; analysis of economic and political trends every quarter. Text in English. q. USD 485 print or online; USD 230 per issue print or online (effective 2004). illus.; stat. **Document type:** *Trade.*
Supersedes in part (in 2001): Country Report. South Korea, North Korea (1350-6900); Which was formerly (until 1992): Country Report. South Korea (0269-669X); (until 1986): Quarterly Economic Review of South Korea (0144-8900); Which superseded in part (1952-1982): Quarterly Economic Review of Japan, South Korea (0142-4246); Which was formerly (until 1976): Q E R Japan, South Korea (0481-1771)
Related titles: Online - full text ed.: (from EBSCO Publishing).
Published by: Economist Intelligence Unit, 111 W 57th St, New York, NY 10019. TEL 212-554-0600, FAX 212-586-1181, newyork@eiu.com, http://www.eiu.com.

330.9481 USA ISSN 0269-4182
HC361
COUNTRY REPORT. NORWAY; analysis of economic and political trends every quarter. Text in English. 1952. q. USD 485 print or online; USD 230 per issue print or online (effective 2004). illus.; stat. **Document type:** *Trade.* **Description:** Analyzes Norway's current political and economic climate, as well as short-term economic projections.
Formerly: Quarterly Economic Review of Norway (0142-3908)
Related titles: ♦ CD-ROM ed.: E I U Country Reports on Disc: Western Europe; Online - full text ed.: E I U Country Reports: Western Europe (from SilverPlatter Information, Inc., The Dialog Corporation); (from EBSCO Publishing).
Indexed: WBA, WMB.
—CCC.
Published by: Economist Intelligence Unit, 111 W 57th St, New York, NY 10019. TEL 212-554-0600, FAX 212-586-1181, newyork@eiu.com, http://www.eiu.com.

330.953 USA ISSN 1462-6667
HC415.35.A1
COUNTRY REPORT. OMAN; analysis of economic and political trends every quarter. Text in English. q. USD 485 print or online; USD 230 per issue print or online (effective 2004). illus.; stat. **Document type:** *Trade.* **Description:** Analyzes Oman's and Yemen's current political and economic climates, as well as short-term economic projections.
Supersedes in part (in 1998): Country Report. Oman, Yemen (1351-8690); Which superseded in part (in 1992): Country Report. Bahrain, Qatar, Oman, Yemen (0269-5707); Which was formerly: Quarterly Economic Review of Bahrain, Qatar, Oman, Yemen (0142-4114)
Related titles: ♦ CD-ROM ed.: E I U Country Forecasts on Disc: Middle East-Africa; Online - full text ed.: E I U Country Forecasts: Middle East-Africa.
Published by: Economist Intelligence Unit, 111 W 57th St, New York, NY 10019. TEL 212-554-0600, FAX 212-586-1181, newyork@eiu.com, http://www.eiu.com.

330.9549 USA ISSN 1478-0356
HV440.5.A1
COUNTRY REPORT. PAKISTAN; analysis of economic and political trends every quarter. Text in English. 1952. q. USD 485 print or online; USD 230 per issue print or online (effective 2004). illus.; stat. **Document type:** *Trade.* **Description:** Analyzes the current political and economic climate, as well as short-term economic projections.
Supersedes in part (in 2001): Country Report. Pakistan, Afghanistan (0269-7173); Which was formerly (until 1986): Quarterly Economic Review of Pakistan, Afghanistan (0266-965X); Which superseded in part (in 1985): Quarterly Economic Review of Pakistan, Bangladesh, Afghanistan (0142-436X); Which was formerly (until 1976): Q E R. Pakistan, Bangladesh, Afghanistan (0306-2422); (until 1972): Quarterly Economic Review Pakistan, Afghanistan (0481-1844)
Related titles: ♦ CD-ROM ed.: E I U Country Reports on Disc: Asia-Pacific; Online - full text ed.: E I U Country Reports: Asia-Pacific (from EBSCO Publishing).
Indexed: RASB.
Published by: Economist Intelligence Unit, 111 W 57th St, New York, NY 10019. TEL 212-554-0600, FAX 212-586-1181, newyork@eiu.com, http://www.eiu.com.

B

320.97287 USA ISSN 1366-4034
HC147.A1
COUNTRY REPORT. PANAMA; analysis of economic and political trends every quarter. Text in English. q. USD 485 print or online; USD 230 per issue print or online (effective 2004). charts; stat. **Document type:** *Trade.* **Description:** Analyzes the current political and economic climate of Panama and provides short-term economic projections.
Supersedes in part (in 1997): Country Report. Costa Rica, Panama (1350-7125); Which superseded in part (in 1992): Country Report. Nicaragua, Costa Rica, Panama (0269-4247); Which was formerly: Quarterly Economic Review of Nicaragua, Costa Rica, Panama (0142-4300)
Related titles: ♦ CD-ROM ed.: E I U Country Reports on Disc: The Americas; Online - full text ed.: E I U Country Reports: The Americas.
Indexed: RASB.
Published by: Economist Intelligence Unit, 111 W 57th St, New York, NY 10019. TEL 212-554-0600, FAX 212-586-1181, newyork@eiu.com, http://www.eiu.com.

330.9953 USA ISSN 1366-4085
HC683.5.A1
COUNTRY REPORT. PAPUA NEW GUINEA; analysis of economic and political trends every quarter. Text in English. 1952. q. USD 485 print or online; USD 230 per issue print or online (effective 2004). illus.; stat. **Document type:** *Trade.* **Description:** Analyzes the current political and economic climate, as well as short-term economic projections.
Supersedes in part (in 1996): Country Report. Pacific Islands: Papua New Guinea, Fiji, Solomon Islands, Western Samoa, Vanuatu, Tonga (0269-7122); Which was formerly (until 1986): Quarterly Economic Review of Pacific Islands: Papua New Guinea, Fiji, Solomon Islands, Western Samoa, Vanuatu, Tonga (0266-9609)
Related titles: ♦ CD-ROM ed.: E I U Country Reports on Disc: Asia-Pacific; Online - full text ed.: E I U Country Reports: Asia-Pacific (from EBSCO Publishing).
Published by: Economist Intelligence Unit, 111 W 57th St, New York, NY 10019. TEL 212-554-0600, FAX 212-586-1181, newyork@eiu.com, http://www.eiu.com.

330.9549 USA ISSN 1473-8996
HC221
COUNTRY REPORT. PARAGUAY; analysis of economic and political trends every quarter. Text in English. q. USD 485 print or online; USD 230 per issue print or online (effective 2004). illus.; stat. **Document type:** *Trade.*
Supersedes in part (in 2000): Country Report. Uruguay, Paraguay (0269-6177); Which was formerly (until 1986): Quarterly Economic Review of Uruguay, Paraguay (0142-4440)
Published by: Economist Intelligence Unit, 111 W 57th St, New York, NY 10019. TEL 212-554-0600, FAX 212-586-1181, newyork@eiu.com, http://www.eiu.com.

330.985 USA ISSN 1356-4064
HC226
COUNTRY REPORT. PERU; analysis of economic and political trends every quarter. Text in English. 1952. q. USD 485 print or online; USD 230 per issue print or online (effective 2004). illus.; stat. **Document type:** *Trade.* **Description:** Analyzes Peru's current political and economic climate, as well as short-term economic projections.
Supersedes in part (in 1995): Country Report. Peru, Bolivia (0269-543X); Which was formerly: Quarterly Economic Review of Peru, Bolivia (0142-3916)
Related titles: ♦ CD-ROM ed.: E I U Country Reports on Disc: The Americas; Microform ed.; Online - full text ed.: E I U Country Reports: The Americas.
Indexed: RASB.
—CCC.
Published by: Economist Intelligence Unit, 111 W 57th St, New York, NY 10019. TEL 212-554-0600, FAX 212-586-1181, newyork@eiu.com, http://www.eiu.com.

330.9599 USA ISSN 0269-428X
HC451
COUNTRY REPORT. PHILIPPINES; analysis of economic and political trends every quarter. Text in English. 1952. q. USD 485 print or online; USD 230 per issue print or online (effective 2004). illus.; stat. **Document type:** *Trade.* **Description:** Analyzes the Philippines's current political and economic climate, as well as short-term economic projections.
Formerly: Quarterly Economic Review of Philippines (0144-8935)
Related titles: ♦ CD-ROM ed.: E I U Country Reports on Disc: Asia-Pacific; Online - full text ed.: E I U Country Reports: Asia-Pacific (from EBSCO Publishing); (from EBSCO Publishing).
Indexed: BAS, RASB, WBA, WMB.
—CCC.
Published by: Economist Intelligence Unit, 111 W 57th St, New York, NY 10019. TEL 212-554-0600, FAX 212-586-1181, newyork@eiu.com, http://www.eiu.com.

330.9438 USA ISSN 0269-6193
HC340.3.A1
COUNTRY REPORT. POLAND; analysis of economic and political trends every quarter. Text in English. 1952. q. USD 485 print or online; USD 230 per issue print or online (effective 2004). illus.; stat. **Document type:** *Trade.* **Description:** Analyzes Poland's current political and economic climate, as well as short-term economic projections.
Formerly: Quarterly Economic Review of Poland (0144-8870)
Related titles: Online - full text ed.
—BLDSC (3481.900330). **CCC.**
Published by: Economist Intelligence Unit, 111 W 57th St, New York, NY 10019. TEL 212-554-0600, FAX 212-586-1181, newyork@eiu.com, http://www.eiu.com.

330.9469 USA ISSN 0269-5456
HC391
COUNTRY REPORT. PORTUGAL; analysis of economic and political trends every quarter. Text in English. 1952. q. USD 485 print or online; USD 230 per issue print or online (effective 2004). illus.; stat. **Document type:** *Trade.* **Description:** Analyzes Portugal's current political and economic climate, as well as short-term economic projections.
Formerly: Quarterly Economic Review of Portugal (0142-3932)
Related titles: ♦ CD-ROM ed.: E I U Country Reports on Disc: Western Europe; Online - full text ed.: E I U Country Reports: Western Europe (from SilverPlatter Information, Inc., The Dialog Corporation).
Indexed: RASB.
—CCC.
Published by: Economist Intelligence Unit, 111 W 57th St, New York, NY 10019. TEL 212-554-0600, FAX 212-586-1181, newyork@eiu.com, http://www.eiu.com.

330.9549 USA
COUNTRY REPORT. PUERTO RICO; analysis of economic and political trends every quarter. Text in English. q. USD 485 print or online; USD 230 per issue print or online (effective 2004). illus.; stat. **Document type:** *Trade.*
Supersedes in part (in 1998): Country Report. Cuba, Dominican Republic, Haiti, Puerto Rico (0269-5251); Which was formerly (until 1986): Quarterly Economic Review of Cuba, Dominican Republic, Haiti, Puerto Rico (0142-3819)
Published by: Economist Intelligence Unit, 111 W 57th St, New York, NY 10019. TEL 212-554-0600, FAX 212-586-1181, newyork@eiu.com, http://www.eiu.com.

330.9549 USA ISSN 1473-8945
HC415.37.A1 CODEN: TDABCX
COUNTRY REPORT. QATAR; analysis of economic and political trends every quarter. Text in English. 2001. q. USD 485 print or online; USD 230 per issue print or online (effective 2004). illus.; stat. **Document type:** *Trade.*
Supersedes in part (in 2001): Country Report. Bahrain, Qatar (1351-8682); Which superseded in part (1978-1991): Country Report. Bahrain, Qatar, Oman, the Yemens (0269-5707); Which was formerly (until 1986): Quarterly Economic Review of Bahrain, Qatar, Oman, the Yemens (0142-4114)
Published by: Economist Intelligence Unit, 111 W 57th St, New York, NY 10019. TEL 212-554-0600, FAX 212-586-1181, newyork@eiu.com, http://www.eiu.com.

330.9498 USA ISSN 1356-4102
HC405.A1
COUNTRY REPORT. ROMANIA; analysis of economic and political trends every quarter. Text in English. 1952. q. USD 485 print or online; USD 230 per issue print or online (effective 2004). illus.; stat. **Document type:** *Trade.* **Description:** Analyzes the current political and economic climate, as well as short-term economic projections.
Supersedes in part (in 1995): Country Report. Romania, Bulgaria, Albania (0269-5669); Which was formerly: Quarterly Economic Review of Romania, Bulgaria, Albania (0142-4068)
Related titles: Online - full text ed.
Published by: Economist Intelligence Unit, 111 W 57th St, New York, NY 10019. TEL 212-554-0600, FAX 212-586-1181, newyork@eiu.com, http://www.eiu.com.

330.947 USA ISSN 1350-7184
HC340.12.A1
COUNTRY REPORT. RUSSIA; analysis of economic and political trends every quarter. Text in English. q. USD 485 print or online; USD 230 per issue print or online (effective 2004). illus.; stat. **Document type:** *Trade.* **Description:** Analyzes Russia's current political and economic climate, as well as short-term economic projections.
Supersedes in part (in 1992): Country Report. Commonwealth of Independent States; Which was formerly (until 1991): Country Report. U S S R (0269-5480); Quarterly Economic Review of U S S R (0142-3967)
Related titles: ♦ CD-ROM ed.: E I U Country Forecasts on Disc: Eastern Europe; Online - full text ed.: E I U Country Forecasts: Eastern Europe (from EBSCO Publishing).
Indexed: ABIn, RASB.
—CCC.
Published by: Economist Intelligence Unit, 111 W 57th St, New York, NY 10019. TEL 212-554-0600, FAX 212-586-1181, newyork@eiu.com, http://www.eiu.com.

330.9549 USA
COUNTRY REPORT. RWANDA; analysis of economic and political trends every quarter. Text in English. q. USD 485 print or online; USD 230 per issue print or online (effective 2004). illus.; stat. **Document type:** *Trade.*
Supersedes in part (in 2001): Country Report. Rwanda, Burundi (1465-6418); Which superseded in part (in 1999): Country Report. Uganda, Rwanda, Burundi (0969-8817); Which was formed by the 1999 merger of part of: Country Report. Zaire, Rwanda, Burundi (0269-5510); Which was formerly (until 1986): Quarterly Economic Review of Zaire, Rwanda, Burundi (0142-4025); (until 1976): Q E R Zaire, Rwanda, Burundi; and part of: Country Report. Uganda, Ethiopia, Somalia, Djibouti (0269-5685); Which was formerly (until 1986): Quarterly Economic Review of Uganda, Ethiopia, Somalia, Djibouti (0142-4092); (until 1978): Quarterly Economic Review of Uganda, Ethiopia, Somalia
Published by: Economist Intelligence Unit, 111 W 57th St, New York, NY 10019. TEL 212-554-0600, FAX 212-586-1181, newyork@eiu.com, http://www.eiu.com.

330.9549 USA
COUNTRY REPORT. SAMOA; analysis of economic and political trends every quarter. Text in English. q. USD 485 print or online; USD 230 per issue print or online (effective 2004). illus.; stat. **Document type:** *Trade.*
Supersedes in part: Country Report. Pacific Islands: Fiji, New Caledonia, Samoa, Solomon Islands, Tonga, Vanuatu (1460-7077)
Published by: Economist Intelligence Unit, 111 W 57th St, New York, NY 10019. TEL 212-554-0600, FAX 212-586-1181, newyork@eiu.com, http://www.eiu.com.

330.9549 USA
COUNTRY REPORT. SAO TOME AND PRINCIPE; analysis of economic and political trends every quarter. Text in English. 1985. q. USD 485 print or online; USD 230 per issue print or online (effective 2004). illus.; stat. **Document type:** *Trade.*
Supersedes in part (in 2001): Country Report. Congo, Sao Tome and Principe, Guinea-Bissau, Cape Verde (1350-7028); Which was formed by the 1992 merger of part of: Country Report. Congo, Gabon, Equatorial Guinea (0269-7246); Which was formerly (1985-1986): Quarterly Economic Review of Congo, Gabon, Equatorial Guinea (0266-9749); part of: Country Report. Angola, Sao Tome & Principe (0269-4344); Which was formerly (1985-1986): Quarterly Economic Review of Angola, Sao Tome and Procipe (0266-9781); part of: Country Report. Senegal, the Gambia, Guinea-Bissau, Cape Verde (0269-719X); Which was formerly (1985-1986): Quarterly Economic Review of Senegal, the Gambia, Guinea-Bissau, Cape Verde (0266-9684)
Published by: Economist Intelligence Unit, 111 W 57th St, New York, NY 10019. TEL 212-554-0600, FAX 212-586-1181, newyork@eiu.com, http://www.eiu.com.

330.9538 USA ISSN 0269-6215
HC415.33.A1
COUNTRY REPORT. SAUDI ARABIA; analysis of economic and political trends every quarter. Text in English. 1952. q. USD 485 print or online; USD 230 per issue print or online (effective 2004). illus.; stat. **Document type:** *Trade.* **Description:** Analyzes Saudi Arabia's current political and economic climate, as well as short-term economic projections.
Formerly: Quarterly Economic Review of Saudi Arabia (0142-4491)
Related titles: ♦ CD-ROM ed.: E I U Country Reports on Disc: Middle East - North Africa; Online - full text ed.: E I U Country Reports: Middle East-North Africa.
Indexed: RASB.
—CCC.
Published by: Economist Intelligence Unit, 111 W 57th St, New York, NY 10019. TEL 212-554-0600, FAX 212-586-1181, newyork@eiu.com, http://www.eiu.com.

330.96 USA
HC1045.A1
COUNTRY REPORT. SENEGAL; analysis of economic and political trends every quarter. Text in English. 2001. q. USD 485 print or online; USD 230 per issue print or online (effective 2004). illus.; stat. **Document type:** *Trade.* **Description:** Analyzes the current political and economic currents, as well as short-term economic projections.
Supersedes in part (1993-2001): Country Report. Senegal, The Gambia, Mauritania (1350-7079); Which was formed by the merger of (1985-1993): Country Report. Senegal, The Gambia, Guinea-Bassau, Cape Verde (0269-719X); Which was formerly (until 1986): Quarterly Economic Review of Senegal, The Gambia, Guinea-Bassau, Cape Verde (0266-9684); (1985-1993): Country Report. Guinea, Mali, Mauritania (0269-7203); Which was formerly (until 1986): Quarterly Economic Review of Guinea, Mali, Mauritania (0266-9692)
Related titles: ♦ CD-ROM ed.: E I U Country Reports on Disc: Sub-Saharan Africa; Online - full text ed.: E I U Country Reports: Sub-Saharan Africa (from SilverPlatter Information, Inc., The Dialog Corporation).
Indexed: RASB.
Published by: Economist Intelligence Unit, 111 W 57th St, New York, NY 10019. TEL 212-554-0600, FAX 212-586-1181, newyork@eiu.com, http://www.eiu.com.

330.9549 USA
COUNTRY REPORT. SEYCHELLES; analysis of economic and political trends every quarter. Text in English. 2001. q. USD 485 print or online; USD 230 per issue print or online (effective 2004). illus.; stat. **Document type:** *Trade.*
Supersedes in part (in 2001): Country Report. Mauritius, Madagascar, Seychelles (1350-7060); Which superseded in part (1978-1993): Country Report. Madagascar, Mauritius, Seychelles, Comoros (0269-5154); Which was formerly (until 1986): Quarterly Economic Review of Madagascar, Mauritius, Seychelles, Comoros (0141-8092)
Related titles: Online - full text ed.: (from Gale Group).

Published by: Economist Intelligence Unit, 111 W 57th St, New York, NY 10019. TEL 212-554-0600, FAX 212-586-1181, newyork@eiu.com, http://www.eiu.com.

330.9549 USA
COUNTRY REPORT. SIERRA LEONE; analysis of economic and political trends every quarter. Text in English. q. USD 485 print or online; USD 230 per issue print or online (effective 2004). illus.; stat. **Document type:** *Trade.*
Supersedes in part (in 2001): Country Report. Guinea, Sierra Leone, Liberia (0969-4692)
Published by: Economist Intelligence Unit, 111 W 57th St, New York, NY 10019. TEL 212-554-0600, FAX 212-586-1181, newyork@eiu.com, http://www.eiu.com.

330.95957 USA ISSN 0269-6711
HC445.8.A1
COUNTRY REPORT. SINGAPORE; analysis of economic and political trends every quarter. Text in English. 1952. q. USD 485 print or online; USD 230 per issue print or online (effective 2004). illus.; stat. **Document type:** *Trade.*
Description: Analyzes Singapore's current political and economic climate, as well as short-term economic projections.
Formerly: Quarterly Economic Review of Singapore (0144-8927)
Related titles: ♦ CD-ROM ed.: E I U Country Reports on Disc: Asia-Pacific; Online - full text ed.: E I U Country Reports: Asia-Pacific (from EBSCO Publishing); (from EBSCO Publishing).
Indexed: RASB.
—CCC.
Published by: Economist Intelligence Unit, 111 W 57th St, New York, NY 10019. TEL 212-554-0600, FAX 212-586-1181, newyork@eiu.com, http://www.eiu.com.

330.943733 USA ISSN 1366-4050
HC270.3.A1
COUNTRY REPORT. SLOVAKIA; analysis of economic and political trends every quarter. Text in English. 1952. q. USD 485 print or online; USD 230 per issue print or online (effective 2004). illus.; charts; stat. **Document type:** *Trade.*
Description: Analyzes the current political and economic climate of Slovakia and provides short-term economic projections.
Supersedes in part (in 1997): Country Report. Czech Republic, Slovakia (1350-7214); Which superseded in part (in 1992): Country Report. Czechoslovakia (0269-4298); Which was formerly: Quarterly Economic Review of Czechoslovakia (0144-8978)
Related titles: ♦ CD-ROM ed.: E I U Country Reports on Disc: Eastern Europe; Online - full text ed.: E I U Country Reports: Eastern Europe (from Central Institute for Scientific & Technical Information, SilverPlatter Information, Inc., The Dialog Corporation).
Published by: Economist Intelligence Unit, 111 W 57th St, New York, NY 10019. TEL 212-554-0600, FAX 212-586-1181, newyork@eiu.com, http://www.eiu.com.

330.9549 USA ISSN 1366-4131
HC406.A1
COUNTRY REPORT. SLOVENIA; analysis of economic and political trends every quarter. Text in English. q. USD 485 print or online; USD 230 per issue print or online (effective 2004). illus.; stat. **Document type:** *Trade.*
Supersedes in part (in 1996): Country Report. Bosnia-Hercegovina, Croatia and Slovenia (1361-1453)
Published by: Economist Intelligence Unit, 111 W 57th St, New York, NY 10019. TEL 212-554-0600, FAX 212-586-1181, newyork@eiu.com, http://www.eiu.com.

330.9549 USA
COUNTRY REPORT. SOLOMON ISLANDS; analysis of economic and political trends every quarter. Text in English. q. USD 485 print or online; USD 230 per issue print or online (effective 2004). illus.; stat. **Document type:** *Trade.*
Supersedes in part: Country Report. Pacific Islands: Fiji, New Caledonia, Samoa, Solomon Islands, Tonga, Vanuatu (1460-7077)
Published by: Economist Intelligence Unit, 111 W 57th St, New York, NY 10019. TEL 212-554-0600, FAX 212-586-1181, newyork@eiu.com, http://www.eiu.com.

330.9549 USA
COUNTRY REPORT. SOMALIA; analysis of economic and political trends every quarter. Text in English. q. USD 485 print or online; USD 230 per issue print or online (effective 2004). illus.; stat. **Document type:** *Trade.*
Supersedes in part: Country Report. Ethiopia, Eritrea, Somalia, Djibouti (1352-2922); Which was formerly (until 1993): Country report. Ethiopia, Somalia, Djibouti (1350-7036)
Published by: Economist Intelligence Unit, 111 W 57th St, New York, NY 10019. TEL 212-554-0600, FAX 212-586-1181, newyork@eiu.com, http://www.eiu.com.

330.968 USA ISSN 0269-6738
HC905.A1
COUNTRY REPORT. SOUTH AFRICA; analysis of economic and political trends every quarter. Text in English. 1952. q. USD 485 print or online; USD 230 per issue print or online (effective 2004). illus.; stat. **Document type:** *Trade.*
Description: Analyzes South Africa's current political and economic climate, as well as short-term economic projections.
Formerly: Quarterly Economic Review of South Africa (0144-8951)
Related titles: ♦ CD-ROM ed.: E I U Country Reports on Disc: Sub-Saharan Africa; Online - full text ed.: E I U Country Reports: Sub-Saharan Africa (from SilverPlatter Information, Inc., The Dialog Corporation); (from EBSCO Publishing).
Indexed: RASB, WBA, WMB.
—BLDSC (3481.900570). **CCC.**
Published by: Economist Intelligence Unit, 111 W 57th St, New York, NY 10019. TEL 212-554-0600, FAX 212-586-1181, newyork@eiu.com, http://www.eiu.com.

330.9519 USA ISSN 1478-0348
HC466
COUNTRY REPORT. SOUTH KOREA; analysis of economic and political trends every quarter. Text in English. 2001. q. USD 500 print or online; USD 235 per issue print or online (effective 2005). illus.; stat. **Document type:** *Trade.*
Description: Analyzes the current political and economic climate, as well as short-term economic projections.
Supersedes in part (in 2002): Country Report. South Korea, North Korea (1350-6900); Which was formed by the merger of (1952-1993): Country Report. South Korea (0269-669X); Which was formerly (until 1986): Quarterly Economic Review of South Korea (0144-8900); Which superseded in part (in 1982): Quarterly Economic Review of Japan, South Korea (0142-4246); Which was formerly (until 1976): Q E R Japan, South Korea (0481-1771); part of (1986-1993): Country Report. China, North Korea (0269-6231)
Related titles: ♦ CD-ROM ed.: E I U Country Reports on Disc: Asia-Pacific; Online - full text ed.: E I U Country Reports: Asia-Pacific (from EBSCO Publishing); (from EBSCO Publishing).
Indexed: RASB, WMB.
—CCC.
Published by: Economist Intelligence Unit, 111 W 57th St, New York, NY 10019. TEL 212-554-0600, FAX 212-586-1181, newyork@eiu.com, http://www.eiu.com.

330.946 USA ISSN 0269-4263
HC381
COUNTRY REPORT. SPAIN; analysis of economic and political trends every quarter. Text in English. 1952. q. USD 485 print or online; USD 230 per issue print or online (effective 2004). illus.; stat. **Document type:** *Trade.* **Description:** Analyzes Spain's current political and economic climate, as well as short-term economic projections.
Formerly: Quarterly Economic Review of Spain (0142-4394)
Related titles: ♦ CD-ROM ed.: E I U Country Reports on Disc: Western Europe; Online - full text ed.: E I U Country Reports: Western Europe (from SilverPlatter Information, Inc., The Dialog Corporation); (from EBSCO Publishing).
—BLDSC (3481.900650). **CCC.**
Published by: Economist Intelligence Unit, 111 W 57th St, New York, NY 10019. TEL 212-554-0600, FAX 212-586-1181, newyork@eiu.com, http://www.eiu.com.

330.95493 USA ISSN 0269-4174
HC424.A1
COUNTRY REPORT. SRI LANKA; analysis of economic and political trends every quarter. Text in English. 1952. q. USD 485 print or online; USD 230 per issue print or online (effective 2004). illus.; stat. **Document type:** *Trade.*
Description: Analyzes Sri Lanka's current political and economic climate, as well as short-term economic projections.
Formerly: Quarterly Economic Review of Sri Lanka (0142-3770)
Related titles: ♦ CD-ROM ed.: E I U Country Reports on Disc: Asia-Pacific; Online - full text ed.: E I U Country Reports: Asia-Pacific (from EBSCO Publishing).
Indexed: RASB.
—CCC.
Published by: Economist Intelligence Unit, 111 W 57th St, New York, NY 10019. TEL 212-554-0600, FAX 212-586-1181, newyork@eiu.com, http://www.eiu.com.

330.9624 USA ISSN 0269-6150
HC835.A1
COUNTRY REPORT. SUDAN; analysis of economic and political trends every quarter. Text in English. 1952. q. USD 485 print or online; USD 230 per issue print or online (effective 2004). illus.; stat. **Document type:** *Trade.* **Description:** Analyzes the Sudan's current political and economic climate, as well as short-term economic projections.
Formerly: Quarterly Economic Review of Sudan (0142-4408)
Related titles: ♦ CD-ROM ed.: E I U Country Reports on Disc: Middle East - North Africa; Online - full text ed.: E I U Country Reports: Middle East-North Africa.
Indexed: RASB.
—CCC.
Published by: Economist Intelligence Unit, 111 W 57th St, New York, NY 10019. TEL 212-554-0600, FAX 212-586-1181, newyork@eiu.com, http://www.eiu.com.

330.9549 USA
COUNTRY REPORT. SURINAME; analysis of economic and political trends every quarter. Text in English. q. USD 485 print or online; USD 230 per issue print or online (effective 2004). illus.; stat. **Document type:** *Trade.*
Supersedes in part: Country Report. Trinidad & Tobago, Guyana, Windward & Leeward Islands, Suriname, Netherlands Antilles, Aruba (1351-1270)
Published by: Economist Intelligence Unit, 111 W 57th St, New York, NY 10019. TEL 212-554-0600, FAX 212-586-1181, newyork@eiu.com, http://www.eiu.com.

330.9549 USA
COUNTRY REPORT. SWAZILAND; analysis of economic and political trends every quarter. Text in English. q. USD 485 print or online; USD 230 per issue print or online (effective 2004). illus.; stat. **Document type:** *Trade.*
Supersedes in part: Country Report. Namibia, Swaziland (1356-4218)
Published by: Economist Intelligence Unit, 111 W 57th St, New York, NY 10019. TEL 212-554-0600, FAX 212-586-1181, newyork@eiu.com, http://www.eiu.com.

330.9485 USA ISSN 0269-6142
HC371
COUNTRY REPORT. SWEDEN; analysis of economic and political trends every quarter. Text in English. 1952. q. USD 485 print or online; USD 230 per issue print or online (effective 2004). illus.; stat. **Document type:** *Trade.* **Description:** Analyzes Sweden's current political and economic climate, as well as short-term economic projections.
Formerly: Quarterly Economic Review of Sweden (0142-4416)
Related titles: ♦ CD-ROM ed.: E I U Country Reports on Disc: Western Europe; Online - full text ed.: E I U Country Reports: Western Europe (from SilverPlatter Information, Inc., The Dialog Corporation); (from EBSCO Publishing).
Indexed: WBA, WMB.
—CCC.
Published by: Economist Intelligence Unit, 111 W 57th St, New York, NY 10019. TEL 212-554-0600, FAX 212-586-1181, newyork@eiu.com, http://www.eiu.com.

330.9494 USA ISSN 0269-6169
HC395
COUNTRY REPORT. SWITZERLAND; analysis of economic and political trends every quarter. Text in English. 1952. q. USD 485 print or online; USD 230 per issue print or online (effective 2004). illus.; stat. **Document type:** *Trade.*
Description: Analyzes Switzerland's current political and economic climate, as well as short-term economic projections.
Formerly: Quarterly Economic Review of Switzerland (0142-4424)
Related titles: ♦ CD-ROM ed.: E I U Country Reports on Disc: Western Europe; Online - full text ed.: E I U Country Reports: Western Europe (from SilverPlatter Information, Inc., The Dialog Corporation).
—CCC.
Published by: Economist Intelligence Unit, 111 W 57th St, New York, NY 10019. TEL 212-554-0600, FAX 212-586-1181, newyork@eiu.com, http://www.eiu.com.

330.95691 USA ISSN 0269-7211
HC415.23.A1
COUNTRY REPORT. SYRIA; analysis of economic and political trends every quarter. Text in English. 1952. q. USD 485 print or online; USD 230 per issue print or online (effective 2004). illus.; stat. **Document type:** *Trade.* **Description:** Analyzes Syria's current political and economic climate, as well as short-term economic projections.
Formerly: Quarterly Economic Review of Syria (0266-9706)
Related titles: ♦ CD-ROM ed.: E I U Country Reports on Disc: Middle East - North Africa; Online - full text ed.: E I U Country Reports: Middle East-North Africa.
Indexed: RASB.
—CCC.
Published by: Economist Intelligence Unit, 111 W 57th St, New York, NY 10019. TEL 212-554-0600, FAX 212-586-1181, newyork@eiu.com, http://www.eiu.com.

330.951249 USA ISSN 0269-672X
HC430.5.A1
COUNTRY REPORT. TAIWAN; analysis of economic and political trends every quarter. Text in English. 1952. q. USD 485 print or online; USD 230 per issue print or online (effective 2004). illus.; stat. **Document type:** *Trade.* **Description:** Analyzes Taiwan's current political and economic climate, as well as short-term economic projections.
Formerly: Quarterly Economic Review of Taiwan (0144-8943)
Related titles: ♦ CD-ROM ed.: E I U Country Reports on Disc: Asia-Pacific; Online - full text ed.: E I U Country Reports: Asia-Pacific (from EBSCO Publishing); (from EBSCO Publishing).
—BLDSC (3481.900890). **CCC.**
Published by: Economist Intelligence Unit, 111 W 57th St, New York, NY 10019. TEL 212-554-0600, FAX 212-586-1181, newyork@eiu.com, http://www.eiu.com.

330.9549 USA ISSN 1478-0402
HC421.3.A1
COUNTRY REPORT. TAJIKISTAN; analysis of economic and political trends every quarter. Text in English. q. USD 485 print or online; USD 230 per issue print or online (effective 2004). illus.; stat. **Document type:** *Trade.*
Supersedes in part (in 2001): Country Report. Kyrgyz Republic, Tajikistan (1462-6756); Which superseded in part (in 1998): Country Report. Kyrgyz Republic, Tajikistan, Turkmenistan (1366-414X); Which superseded in part (in 1997): Country Report. Kyrgyz Republic, Tajikistan, Turkmenistan, Uzbekistan (1361-1488); Which superseded in part (in 1996): Country Report. Kazakhstan, Kyrgyz Republic, Tajikistan, Turkmenistan, Uzbekistan (1360-9467); Which was formerly

(until 1995): Country Report. Central Asian Republics: Kazakhstan, Kyrgyz Republic, Tajikistan, Uzbekistan (1356-4099); Which superseded in part (in 1994): Country Report. Georgia, Armenia, Azerbaijan, Kazakhstan, Central Asian Republics (1352-2930); Which was formerly (until 1993): Country Report. Georgia, Armenia, Azerbaijan, Central Asian Republics (1350-7206); Which superseded in part (in 1993): Country Report. Commonwealth of Independent States (0968-8242); Which was formerly (until 1992): Country Report. U S S R (0269-5480); (until 1986): Quarterly Economic Review of U S S R (0142-3967); (until 1976): Q E R. U S S R
Published by: Economist Intelligence Unit, 111 W 57th St, New York, NY 10019. TEL 212-554-0600, FAX 212-586-1181, newyork@eiu.com, http://www.eiu.com.

330.9678 USA
HC885.A1
COUNTRY REPORT. TANZANIA; analysis of economic and political trends every quarter. Text in English. 1993. q. USD 485 print or online; USD 230 per issue print or online (effective 2004). illus.; stat. **Document type:** *Trade.* **Description:** Analyzes the current political and economic current in Tanzania and the Comoros Islands, along with short-term economic projections.
Supersedes in part (in 2001): Country Report. Tanzania, Comoros (0969-6776); Which was formed by the 1993 merger of part of: Country Report. Tanzania, Mozambique (0269-6223); Which was formerly (1978-1986): Quarterly Economic Review of Tanzania, Mozambique (0142-4505); part of: Country Report. Madagascar, Mauritius, Seychelles, Comoros (0269-5154); Which was formerly (until 1986): Quarterly Economic Review of Madagascar, Mauritius, Seychelles, Comoros (0141-8092); Which superseded in part (in 1978): Q E R. Tanzania, Mauritius (0306-5804)
Related titles: ♦ CD-ROM ed.: E I U Country Reports on Disc: Sub-Saharan Africa; Online - full text ed.: E I U Country Reports: Sub-Saharan Africa (from SilverPlatter Information, Inc., The Dialog Corporation).
Indexed: RASB.
—CCC.
Published by: Economist Intelligence Unit, 111 W 57th St, New York, NY 10019. TEL 212-554-0600, FAX 212-586-1181, newyork@eiu.com, http://www.eiu.com.

330.9593 USA ISSN 1356-4056
HC445.A1
COUNTRY REPORT. THAILAND; analysis of economic and political trends every quarter. Text in English. 1952. q. USD 485 print or online; USD 230 per issue print or online (effective 2004). illus.; stat. **Document type:** *Trade.* **Description:** Analyzes Thailand's current political and economic climate, as well as short-term economic projections.
Supersedes in part (in 1995): Country Report. Thailand, Myanmar (1350-7117); Formerly (until 1992): Country Report. Thailand, Burma (0269-5189); Quarterly Economic Review of of Thailand, Burma (0142-3754)
Related titles: ♦ CD-ROM ed.: E I U Country Reports on Disc: Asia-Pacific; Online - full text ed.: E I U Country Reports: Asia-Pacific (from EBSCO Publishing).
Indexed: RASB.
—CCC.
Published by: Economist Intelligence Unit, 111 W 57th St, New York, NY 10019. TEL 212-554-0600, FAX 212-586-1181, newyork@eiu.com, http://www.eiu.com.

330.9549 USA
COUNTRY REPORT. THE GAMBIA; analysis of economic and political trends every quarter. Text in English. 2001. q. USD 485 print or online; USD 230 per issue print or online (effective 2004). illus.; stat. **Document type:** *Trade.*
Supersedes in part (in 2001): Country Report. Senegal, The Gambia, Mauritania (1350-7079); Which superseded in part (in 1993): Country Report. Senegal, the Gambia, Guinea-Bissau, Cape Verde (0269-719X); Which was formerly (until 1986): Quarterly Economic Review of Senegal, the Gambia, Guinea-Bissau, Cape Verde (0266-9684); (1985-1993): Country Report. Guinea, Mali, Mauritania (0269-7203); Which was formerly (until 1986): Quarterly Economic Review of Guinea, Mali, Mauritania (0266-9692)
Published by: Economist Intelligence Unit, 111 W 57th St, New York, NY 10019. TEL 212-554-0600, FAX 212-586-1181, newyork@eiu.com, http://www.eiu.com.

330.9549 USA
COUNTRY REPORT. THE PALESTINIAN TERRITORIES; analysis of economic and political trends every quarter. Text in English. 2001. q. USD 485 print or online; USD 230 per issue print or online (effective 2004). illus.; stat. **Document type:** *Trade.*
Supersedes in part (in 2001): Country Report. Israel, the Occupied Territories (1353-3142); Which was formerly (until 1993): Country Report. Israel (0269-5928); (until 1986): Quarterly Economic Review of Israel (0142-4238); (until 1976): Q E R Israel (0481-1755)
Related titles: Online - full text ed.: (from EBSCO Publishing).
Published by: Economist Intelligence Unit, 111 W 57th St, New York, NY 10019. TEL 212-554-0600, FAX 212-586-1181, newyork@eiu.com, http://www.eiu.com.

330.96681 USA
HC1020.A1
COUNTRY REPORT. TOGO; analysis of economic and political trends every quarter. Text in English. 1952. q. USD 485 print or online; USD 230 per issue print or online (effective 2004). illus.; stat. **Description:** Analyzes the current political and economic climate and offers short-term economic projections for Togo and Benin.
Supersedes in part (in 2001): Country Report. Togo, Benin (1366-4107); Which superseded in part (in 1996): Country Report. Togo, Niger, Benin, Burkina Faso (1466-0318); Which was formerly (until 1994): Country Report. Togo, Niger, Benin, Burkina Faso (0269-7262); (until 1986): Quarterly Economic Review of Togo, Niger, Benin, Burkina Faso (0266-9773); . Which superseded in part (in 1985): Quarterly Economic Review of Ivory Coast, Togo, Benin, Niger, Upper Volta (0142-4513); Which was formerly (until 1976): Q E R. Ivory Coast, Togo, Dahomey, Niger, Upper Volta (0302-3389)
Related titles: ♦ CD-ROM ed.: E I U Country Reports on Disc: Sub-Saharan Africa; Online - full text ed.: E I U Country Reports: Sub-Saharan Africa (from SilverPlatter Information, Inc., The Dialog Corporation).
Indexed: RASB.
—BLDSC (3481.901000).
Published by: Economist Intelligence Unit, 111 W 57th St, New York, NY 10019. TEL 212-554-0600, FAX 212-586-1181, newyork@eiu.com, http://www.eiu.com.

330.9549 USA
COUNTRY REPORT. TONGA; analysis of economic and political trends every quarter. Text in English. q. USD 485 print or online; USD 230 per issue print or online (effective 2004). illus.; stat. **Document type:** *Trade.*
Supersedes in part: Country Report. Pacific Islands: Fiji, New Caledonia, Somoa, Solomon Islands, Tonga, Vanuatu (1460-7077)
Published by: Economist Intelligence Unit, 111 W 57th St, New York, NY 10019. TEL 212-554-0600, FAX 212-586-1181, newyork@eiu.com, http://www.eiu.com.

330.9729 USA
HC151.A1
COUNTRY REPORT. TRINIDAD & TOBAGO; analysis of economic and political trends every quarter. Text in English. 1992. q. USD 485 print or online; USD 230 per issue print or online (effective 2004). illus.; stat. **Description:** Analyzes the current political and economic climate, as well as short-term economic projections.
Supersedes in part (in 1998): Country Report. Trinidad & Tobago, Guyana, Windward & Leeward Islands, Suriname, Netherlands Antilles, Aruba (1351-1270); Which was formed by the 1992 merger of part of: Country Report. Trinidad and Tobago, Guyana, Barbados, Windward and Leeward Islands (0269-7149); part of: Country Report. Venezuela, Suriname, Netherlands Antilles (0269-6754); Which was formerly: Quarterly Economic Review of Trinidad and Tobago, Guyana, Barbados, Windward and Leeward Islands (0266-9625); Quarterly Economic Review of Venezuela, Suriname, Netherlands Antilles (0264-9675)
Related titles: ♦ CD-ROM ed.: E I U Country Reports on Disc: The Americas; Online - full text ed.: E I U Country Reports: The Americas.
Indexed: RASB.
Published by: Economist Intelligence Unit, 111 W 57th St, New York, NY 10019. TEL 212-554-0600, FAX 212-586-1181, newyork@eiu.com, http://www.eiu.com.

330.9611 USA ISSN 1350-7168
HC820.A1
COUNTRY REPORT. TUNISIA; analysis of economic and political trends every quarter. Text in English. 1952. q. USD 485 print or online; USD 230 per issue print or online (effective 2004). illus.; stat. **Document type:** *Trade.* **Description:** Analyzes Tunisia's current political and economic climate, as well as short-term economic projections.
Former titles (until 1992): Country Report. Tunisia, Malta (0269-7238); Quarterly Economic Review of Tunisia, Malta (0266-9730)
Related titles: ♦ CD-ROM ed.: E I U Country Reports on Disc: Middle East - North Africa; Online - full text ed.: E I U Country Reports: Middle East-North Africa.
Indexed: RASB.
—CCC.
Published by: Economist Intelligence Unit, 111 W 57th St, New York, NY 10019. TEL 212-554-0600, FAX 212-586-1181, newyork@eiu.com, http://www.eiu.com.

330.9561 USA ISSN 0269-5464
HC491
COUNTRY REPORT. TURKEY; analysis of economic and political trends every quarter. Text in English. 1952. q. USD 485 print or online; USD 230 per issue print or online (effective 2004). illus.; stat. **Document type:** *Trade.* **Description:** Analyzes Turkey's current political and economic climate, as well as short-term economic projections.
Formerly: Quarterly Economic Review of Turkey
Related titles: ♦ CD-ROM ed.: E I U Country Reports on Disc: Western Europe; Online - full text ed.: E I U Country Reports: Western Europe (from SilverPlatter Information, Inc., The Dialog Corporation); (from EBSCO Publishing).
Indexed: RASB.
—BLDSC (3481.901130). **CCC.**

Published by: Economist Intelligence Unit, 111 W 57th St, New York, NY 10019. TEL 212-554-0600, FAX 212-586-1181, newyork@eiu.com, http://www.eiu.com.

330.9549 USA ISSN 1462-6764
HC420.3.A1
COUNTRY REPORT. TURKMENISTAN; analysis of economic and political trends every quarter. Text in English. 1998. q. USD 485 print or online; USD 230 per issue print or online (effective 2004). illus.; stat. **Document type:** *Trade.*
Supersedes in part (in 1998): Country Report. Kyrgyz Republic, Tajikistan, Turkmenistan (1366-414X); Which superseded in part (in 1997): Country Report. Kyrgyz Republic, Tajikistan, Turkmenistan, Uzbekistan (1361-1488); Which superseded in part (in 1996): Country Report. Kazakhstan, Kyrgyz Republic, Tajikistan, Turkmenistan, Uzbekistan (1360-9467); Which was formerly (until 1995): Country Report. Central Asian Republics: Kazakhstan, Kyrgyz Republic, Tajikistan, Uzbekistan (1356-4099); Which superseded in part (in 1994): Country Report. Georgia, Armenia, Azerbaijan, Kazakhstan, Central Asian Republics (1352-2930); Which was formerly (until 1993): Country Report. Georgia, Armenia, Azerbaijan, Central Asian Republics (1350-7206); Which superseded in part (in 1992): Country Report. Commonwealth of Independent States (0968-8242); Which was formerly (until 1992): Country Report. U S S R (0269-5480); (until 1986): Quarterly Economic Review of U S S R (0142-3967); (until 1976): Q E R. U S S R
Published by: Economist Intelligence Unit, 111 W 57th St, New York, NY 10019. TEL 212-554-0600, FAX 212-586-1181, newyork@eiu.com, http://www.eiu.com.

330.968 USA ISSN 1465-640X
HC870.A1
COUNTRY REPORT. UGANDA; analysis of economic and political trends every quarter. Text in English. 1952. q. USD 485 print or online; USD 230 per issue print or online (effective 2004). illus.; stat. **Description:** Analyzes the current political and economic current in Uganda, Rwanda, and Burundi and provides short-term economic projections.
Supersedes in part (in 1999): Country Report. Uganda, Rwanda, Burundi (0969-8817); Which was formed by the 1992 merger of part of: Country Report. Uganda, Ethiopia, Somalia, Djibouti (0269-5685); Which was formerly (until 1986): Quarterly Economic Review of Uganda, Ethiopia, Somalia, Djibouti (0142-4092); (until 1978): Quarterly Economic Review of Uganda, Ethiopia, Somalia; part of: Country Report. Zaire, Rwanda, Burundi (0269-5510); Which was formerly (until 1986): Quarterly Economic Review of Zaire, Rwanda, Burundi (0142-4025); (until 1976): Q E R Zaire, Rwanda, Burundi
Related titles: ♦ CD-ROM ed.: E I U Country Reports on Disc: Sub-Saharan Africa; Online - full text ed.: E I U Country Reports: Sub-Saharan Africa (from SilverPlatter Information, Inc., The Dialog Corporation).
Indexed: RASB.
Published by: Economist Intelligence Unit, 111 W 57th St, New York, NY 10019. TEL 212-554-0600, FAX 212-586-1181, newyork@eiu.com, http://www.eiu.com.

330.9477 USA ISSN 1356-4129
HC340.19.A1
COUNTRY REPORT. UKRAINE; analysis of economic and political trends every quarter. Text in English. q. USD 500 print or online; USD 235 per issue print or online (effective 2005). illus.; stat. **Document type:** *Trade.* **Description:** Analyzes the current political and economic climate as, well as short-term economic projections.
Supersedes in part (in 1995): Country Report. Ukraine, Belarus, Moldova (1350-7192); Which superseded in part (in 1992): Country Report. Commonwealth of Independent States; Which was formerly (until 1991): Country Report. U S S R (0269-5480); Quarterly Economic Review of U S S R (0142-3967)
Related titles: ♦ CD-ROM ed.: E I U Country Forecasts on Disc: Eastern Europe; Online - full text ed.: E I U Country Forecasts: Eastern Europe (from EBSCO Publishing).
Indexed: ABIn.
—CCC.
Published by: Economist Intelligence Unit, 111 W 57th St, New York, NY 10019. TEL 212-554-0600, FAX 212-586-1181, newyork@eiu.com, http://www.eiu.com.

330.95357 USA ISSN 0269-5162
HC415.36.A1
COUNTRY REPORT. UNITED ARAB EMIRATES; analysis of economic and political trends every quarter. Text in English. 1952. q. USD 485 print or online; USD 230 per issue print or online (effective 2004). illus.; stat. **Document type:** *Trade.* **Description:** Analyzes the current political and economic climate, as well as short-term economic projections for the United Arab Emirates.
Formerly: Quarterly Economic Review of United Arab Emirates (0141-8416)
Related titles: ♦ CD-ROM ed.: E I U Country Reports on Disc: Middle East - North Africa; Online - full text ed.: E I U Country Reports: Middle East-North Africa.
Indexed: RASB.
—CCC.
Published by: Economist Intelligence Unit, 111 W 57th St, New York, NY 10019. TEL 212-554-0600, FAX 212-586-1181, newyork@eiu.com, http://www.eiu.com.

330.941 USA ISSN 0269-5472
HC251
COUNTRY REPORT. UNITED KINGDOM; analysis of economic and political trends every quarter. Text in English. 1952. q. USD 485 print or online; USD 230 per issue print or online (effective 2004). illus.; stat. **Document type:** *Trade.*
Description: Analyzes the United Kingdom's current political and economic climate, as well as short-term economic projections.
Formerly: Quarterly Economic Review of United Kingdom (0142-3959)
Related titles: ♦ CD-ROM ed.: E I U Country Reports on Disc: Western Europe; Online - full text ed.: E I U Country Reports: Western Europe (from SilverPlatter Information, Inc., The Dialog Corporation); (from EBSCO Publishing).
Indexed: WBA, WMB.
—CCC.
Published by: Economist Intelligence Unit, 111 W 57th St, New York, NY 10019. TEL 212-554-0600, FAX 212-586-1181, newyork@eiu.com, http://www.eiu.com.

330.973 USA ISSN 1367-8876
HC101
COUNTRY REPORT. UNITED STATES OF AMERICA; analysis of economic and political trends every quarter. Text in English. 1952. q. USD 485 print or online; USD 230 per issue print or online (effective 2004). illus.; stat. **Document type:** *Trade.*
Description: Analyzes the US current political and economic climate, as well as short-term economic projections.
Former titles (until 1994): Country Report. U S A (0269-6185); (until 1986): Quarterly Economic Review of U S A (0142-4459); Q E R - U S A (0481-2018)
Related titles: ♦ CD-ROM ed.: E I U Country Reports on Disc: The Americas; Online - full text ed.: E I U Country Reports: The Americas; (from EBSCO Publishing).
Indexed: MASUSE, RASB, WBA, WMB.
—CCC.
Published by: Economist Intelligence Unit, 111 W 57th St, New York, NY 10019. TEL 212-554-0600, FAX 212-586-1181, newyork@eiu.com, http://www.eiu.com.

330.989 USA ISSN 1473-8988
HC231
COUNTRY REPORT. URUGUAY; analysis of economic and political trends every quarter. Text in English. 1952. q. USD 485 print or online; USD 230 per issue print or online (effective 2004). illus.; stat. **Document type:** *Trade.*
Description: Analyzes Paraguay's and Uruguay's current political and economic climates, as well as their short-term economic projections.
Supersedes in part (in 2000): Country Report. Uruguay, Paraguay (0269-6177); Which was formerly (until 1986): Quarterly Economic Review of Uruguay, Paraguay (0142-4440)
Related titles: ♦ CD-ROM ed.: E I U Country Reports on Disc: The Americas; Online - full text ed.: E I U Country Reports: The Americas.
Indexed: RASB.
Published by: Economist Intelligence Unit, 111 W 57th St, New York, NY 10019. TEL 212-554-0600, FAX 212-586-1181, newyork@eiu.com, http://www.eiu.com.

330.9587 USA ISSN 1366-4158
HC421.7.A1
COUNTRY REPORT. UZBEKISTAN; analysis of economic and political trends every quarter. Text in English. q. USD 485 print or online; USD 230 per issue print or online (effective 2004). charts. **Document type:** *Trade.*
Supersedes in part (in 1997): Country Report. Kyrgyz Republic, Tajikistan, Turkmenistan, Uzbekistan (1361-1488); Which superseded in part (in 1996): Country Report. Kazakhstan, Kyrgyz Republic, Tajikistan, Turkmenistan, Uzbekistan (1360-9467); Which superseded in part (in 1995): Country Report. Georgia, Armenia, Azerbaijan, Central Asian Republics; Superseded in part (in 1992): Country Report. Commonwealth of Independent States; Which was formerly (until 1991): Country Report U S S R (0269-5480); Quarterly Economic Review of U S S R (0142-3967)
Related titles: ♦ CD-ROM ed.: E I U Country Reports on Disc: Eastern Europe; Online - full text ed.: E I U Country Reports: Eastern Europe (from Central Institute for Scientific & Technical Information, SilverPlatter Information, Inc., The Dialog Corporation).
Indexed: ABIn.
Published by: Economist Intelligence Unit, 111 W 57th St, New York, NY 10019. TEL 212-554-0600, FAX 212-586-1181, newyork@eiu.com, http://www.eiu.com.

330.9549 USA
COUNTRY REPORT. VANUATU; analysis of economic and political trends every quarter. Text in English. q. USD 485 print or online; USD 230 per issue print or online (effective 2004). illus.; stat. **Document type:** *Trade.*
Supersedes in part: Country Report. Pacific Islands: Fiji, New Caledonia, Samoa, Solomon Islands, Tonga, Vanuatu (1460-7077)
Published by: Economist Intelligence Unit, 111 W 57th St, New York, NY 10019. TEL 212-554-0600, FAX 212-586-1181, newyork@eiu.com, http://www.eiu.com.

330.87 USA ISSN 1350-7133
HC236
COUNTRY REPORT. VENEZUELA; analysis of economic and political trends every quarter. Text in English. 1952. q. USD 485 print or online; USD 230 per issue print or online (effective 2004). illus.; stat. **Document type:** *Trade.*
Description: Analyzes Venezuela's current political and economic climate, as well as short-term economic projections.
Supersedes in part (in 1992): Country Report. Venezuela, Suriname, Netherlands Antilles (0269-6754); Which was formerly: Quarterly Economic Review of Venezuela, Suriname, Netherlands Antilles (0264-9675)
Related titles: ♦ CD-ROM ed.: E I U Country Reports on Disc: The Americas; Online - full text ed.: E I U Country Reports: The Americas.
Indexed: RASB.
—CCC.
Published by: Economist Intelligence Unit, 111 W 57th St, New York, NY 10019. TEL 212-554-0600, FAX 212-586-1181, newyork@eiu.com, http://www.eiu.com.

330.9597 USA ISSN 1356-403X
HC444.A1
COUNTRY REPORT. VIETNAM; analysis of economic and political trends every quarter. Text in English. q. USD 485 print or online; USD 230 per issue print or online (effective 2004). charts; stat. **Document type:** *Trade.* **Description:** Analyzes Vietnam's current political and economic climate, as well as short-term economic projections.
Supersedes in part (in 1995): Country Report. Indochina: Vietnam, Laos, Cambodia (0269-5677); Which was formerly: Quarterly Economic Review of Indochina: Vietnam, Laos, Cambodia (0142-4076)
Related titles: ♦ CD-ROM ed.: E I U Country Reports on Disc: Asia-Pacific; Online - full text ed.: E I U Country Reports: Asia-Pacific (from EBSCO Publishing).
Indexed: RASB.
—CCC.
Published by: Economist Intelligence Unit, 111 W 57th St, New York, NY 10019. TEL 212-554-0600, FAX 212-586-1181, newyork@eiu.com, http://www.eiu.com.

330.9549 USA
COUNTRY REPORT. WINDWARD & LEEWARD ISLANDS; analysis of economic and political trends every quarter. Text in English. q. USD 485 print or online; USD 230 per issue print or online (effective 2004). illus.; stat. **Document type:** *Trade.*
Supersedes in part (in 1998): Country Report. Trinidad & Tobago, Guyana, Windward & Leeward Islands, Netherlands Antilles, Aruba (1351-1270)
Published by: Economist Intelligence Unit, 111 W 57th St, New York, NY 10019. TEL 212-554-0600, FAX 212-586-1181, newyork@eiu.com, http://www.eiu.com.

330.9549 USA ISSN 1462-6675
HC415.34.A1
COUNTRY REPORT. YEMEN; analysis of economic and political trends every quarter. Text in English. 1998. q. USD 485 print or online; USD 230 per issue print or online (effective 2004). illus.; stat. **Document type:** *Trade.*
Supersedes in part (in 1998): Country Report. Oman, Yemen (1351-8690); Which superseded in part (in 1993): Country Report. Bahrain, Qatar, Oman, the Yemens (0269-5707); Which was formerly (until 1986): Quarterly Economic Review of Bahrain, Qatar, Oman, the Yemens (0142-4114)
Published by: Economist Intelligence Unit, 111 W 57th St, New York, NY 10019. TEL 212-554-0600, FAX 212-586-1181, newyork@eiu.com, http://www.eiu.com.

330.9549 USA ISSN 1462-6683
HC407.A1
COUNTRY REPORT. YUGOSLAVIA (SERBIA-MONTENEGRO); analysis of economic and political trends every quarter. Text in English. 1976. q. USD 485 print or online; USD 230 per issue print or online (effective 2004). illus.; stat. **Document type:** *Trade.*
Supersedes in part (in 1998): Country Report. Yugoslavia (Serbia-Montenegro), Macedonia (1361-1461); Which was formerly (until 1996): Country Report. Macedonia, Serbia-Montenegro (1363-4658); Which superseded in part (in 1995): Country Report. Bosnia-Hercegovina, Croatia, Macedonia, Serbia-Montenegro, Slovenia (1350-7222); Which superseded in part (in 1993): Country Report. Yugoslav Republics (0968-7734); Which was formerly (until 1992): Country Report. Yugoslavia (0269-4190); (until 1986): Quarterly Economic Review of Yugoslavia (0142-3983)
Published by: Economist Intelligence Unit, 111 W 57th St, New York, NY 10019. TEL 212-554-0600, FAX 212-586-1181, newyork@eiu.com, http://www.eiu.com.

330.96894 USA ISSN 1478-0372
HC915.A1
COUNTRY REPORT. ZAMBIA; analysis of economic and political trends every quarter. Text in English. 1952. q. USD 485 print or online; USD 230 per issue print or online (effective 2004). illus.; stat. **Document type:** *Trade.* **Description:** Analyzes the current political and economic climates, as well as short-term economic projections for Zambia and the Democratic Republic of the Congo.
Supersedes in part (in 2001): Country Report. Zambia, Democratic Republic of Congo (1369-4839); Which superseded in part (in 1997): Country Report. Zambia, Zaire (1350-7087); Which was formed by the merger of (19??-1992): Country Report. Zambia (0269-4271); Which was formerly (until 1986): Quarterly Economic Review of Zambia (0142-4467); (until 1976): Q E R Zambia (0306-5022); Which superseded in part (in 1974): Quarterly Economic Review Tanzania, Zambia; part of (1976-1992): Country Report. Zaire, Rwanda, Burundi (0269-5510); Which was formerly (until 1986): Quarterly Economic Review of Zaire, Rwanda, Burundi (0142-4025)
Related titles: ♦ CD-ROM ed.: E I U Country Reports on Disc: Sub-Saharan Africa; Online - full text ed.: E I U Country Reports: Sub-Saharan Africa (from SilverPlatter Information, Inc., The Dialog Corporation).
Indexed: RASB.
Published by: Economist Intelligence Unit, 111 W 57th St, New York, NY 10019. TEL 212-554-0600, FAX 212-586-1181, newyork@eiu.com, http://www.eiu.com.

330.96891 USA ISSN 1350-7095
HC910.A1
COUNTRY REPORT. ZIMBABWE; analysis of economic and political trends every quarter. Text in English. 1952. q. USD 485 print or online; USD 230 per issue print or online (effective 2004). illus.; stat. **Document type:** *Trade.*
Supersedes in part (in 1992): Country Report. Zimbabwe, Malawi (0269-4255); Which was formerly: Quarterly Economic Review of Zimbabwe, Malawi (0266-4372)
Related titles: ♦ CD-ROM ed.: E I U Country Reports on Disc: Sub-Saharan Africa; Online - full text ed.: E I U Country Reports: Sub-Saharan Africa (from SilverPlatter Information, Inc., The Dialog Corporation).
Indexed: RASB.
—CCC.
Published by: Economist Intelligence Unit, 111 W 57th St, New York, NY 10019. TEL 212-554-0600, FAX 212-586-1181, newyork@eiu.com, http://www.eiu.com.

330.9581 304.6 USA ISSN 1520-2070
COUNTRY REVIEW. AFGHANISTAN. Text in English. a. USD 39.95 (effective 2004). **Description:** Covers demographic, political, economic, social, corporate, cultural, and environmental information.
Related titles: Online - full text ed.: USD 39.95 single country; USD 99 standard - 192 countries (effective 2004).
Published by: Commercial Data International, CountryWatch, Two Riverway, Ste 1770, Houston, TX 77056. TEL 713-355-6500, FAX 713-355-2008, 800-879-3885, editor@countrywatch.com, http://www.countrywatch.com/.

330.94965 304.6 USA ISSN 1520-2089
COUNTRY REVIEW. ALBANIA. Text in English. a. USD 39.95 (effective 2004). **Description:** Covers demographic, political, economic, social, corporate, cultural, and environmental information.
Related titles: Online - full text ed.: USD 39.95 single country; USD 99 standard - 192 countries (effective 2004).
Published by: Commercial Data International, CountryWatch, Two Riverway, Ste 1770, Houston, TX 77056. TEL 713-355-6500, FAX 713-355-2008, 800-879-3885, editor@countrywatch.com, http://www.countrywatch.com/.

330.965 304.6 USA ISSN 1520-2097
COUNTRY REVIEW. ALGERIA. Text in English. a. USD 39.95 (effective 2004). **Description:** Covers demographic, political, economic, social, corporate, cultural, and environmental information.
Related titles: Online - full text ed.: USD 39.95 single country; USD 99 standard - 192 countries (effective 2004).
Published by: Commercial Data International, CountryWatch, Two Riverway, Ste 1770, Houston, TX 77056. TEL 713-355-6500, FAX 713-355-2008, 800-879-3885, editor@countrywatch.com, http://www.countrywatch.com/.

330.94679 USA ISSN 1520-2100
COUNTRY REVIEW. ANDORRA. Text in English. a. USD 39.95 (effective 2004). **Description:** Covers demographic, political, economic, social, corporate, cultural, and environmental information.
Related titles: Online - full text ed.: USD 39.95 single country; USD 99 standard - 192 countries (effective 2004).
Published by: Commercial Data International, CountryWatch, Two Riverway, Ste 1770, Houston, TX 77056. TEL 713-355-6500, FAX 713-355-2008, 800-879-3885, editor@countrywatch.com, http://www.countrywatch.com/.

330.9673 304.6 USA ISSN 1520-2119
COUNTRY REVIEW. ANGOLA. Text in English. a. USD 39.95 (effective 2004). **Description:** Covers demographic, political, economic, social, corporate, cultural, and environmental information.
Related titles: Online - full text ed.: USD 39.95 single country; USD 99 standard - 192 countries (effective 2004).
Published by: Commercial Data International, CountryWatch, Two Riverway, Ste 1770, Houston, TX 77056. TEL 713-355-6500, FAX 713-355-2008, 800-879-3885, editor@countrywatch.com, http://www.countrywatch.com/.

B

330.972974 USA ISSN 1520-2127
COUNTRY REVIEW. ANTIGUA BARBUDA. Text in English. a. USD 39.95 (effective 2004). **Description:** Covers demographic, political, economic, social, corporate, cultural, and environmental information.
Related titles: Online - full text ed.: USD 39.95 single country; USD 99 standard - 192 countries (effective 2004).
Published by: Commercial Data International, CountryWatch, Two Riverway, Ste 1770, Houston, TX 77056. TEL 713-355-6500, FAX 713-355-2008, 800-879-3885, editor@countrywatch.com, http://www.countrywatch.com/.

330.982 USA ISSN 1520-2135
COUNTRY REVIEW. ARGENTINA. Text in English. a. USD 39.95 (effective 2004). **Description:** Covers demographic, political, economic, social, corporate, cultural, and environmental information.
Related titles: Online - full text ed.: USD 39.95 single country; USD 99 standard - 192 countries (effective 2004).
Published by: Commercial Data International, CountryWatch, Two Riverway, Ste 1770, Houston, TX 77056. TEL 713-355-6500, FAX 713-355-2008, 800-879-3885, editor@countrywatch.com, http://www.countrywatch.com/.

330.93955 USA ISSN 1520-2143
COUNTRY REVIEW. ARMENIA. Text in English. a. USD 39.95 (effective 2004). **Description:** Covers demographic, political, economic, social, corporate, cultural, and environmental information.
Related titles: Online - full text ed.: USD 39.95 single country; USD 99 standard - 192 countries (effective 2004).
Published by: Commercial Data International, CountryWatch, Two Riverway, Ste 1770, Houston, TX 77056. TEL 713-355-6500, FAX 713-355-2008, 800-879-3885, editor@countrywatch.com, http://www.countrywatch.com/.

330.994 USA ISSN 1520-2151
COUNTRY REVIEW. AUSTRALIA. Text in English. a. USD 39.95 (effective 2004). **Description:** Covers demographic, political, economic, social, corporate, cultural, and environmental information.
Related titles: Online - full text ed.: USD 39.95 single country; USD 99 standard - 192 countries (effective 2004).
Published by: Commercial Data International, CountryWatch, Two Riverway, Ste 1770, Houston, TX 77056. TEL 713-355-6500, FAX 713-355-2008, 800-879-3885, editor@countrywatch.com, http://www.countrywatch.com/.

330.9436 USA ISSN 1520-216X
COUNTRY REVIEW. AUSTRIA. Text in English. a. USD 39.95 (effective 2004). **Description:** Covers demographic, political, economic, social, corporate, cultural, and environmental information.
Related titles: Online - full text ed.: USD 39.95 single country; USD 99 standard - 192 countries (effective 2004).
Published by: Commercial Data International, CountryWatch, Two Riverway, Ste 1770, Houston, TX 77056. TEL 713-355-6500, FAX 713-355-2008, 800-879-3885, editor@countrywatch.com, http://www.countrywatch.com/.

330.94754 USA ISSN 1520-2178
COUNTRY REVIEW. AZERBAIJAN. Text in English. a. USD 39.95 (effective 2004). **Description:** Covers demographic, political, economic, social, corporate, cultural, and environmental information.
Related titles: Online - full text ed.: USD 39.95 single country; USD 99 standard - 192 countries (effective 2004).
Published by: Commercial Data International, CountryWatch, Two Riverway, Ste 1770, Houston, TX 77056. TEL 713-355-6500, FAX 713-355-2008, 800-879-3885, editor@countrywatch.com, http://www.countrywatch.com/.

330.97296 USA ISSN 1520-2186
COUNTRY REVIEW. BAHAMAS. Text in English. a. USD 39.95 (effective 2004). **Description:** Covers demographic, political, economic, social, corporate, cultural, and environmental information.
Related titles: Online - full text ed.: USD 39.95 single country; USD 99 standard - 192 countries (effective 2004).
Published by: Commercial Data International, CountryWatch, Two Riverway, Ste 1770, Houston, TX 77056. TEL 713-355-6500, FAX 713-355-2008, 800-879-3885, editor@countrywatch.com, http://www.countrywatch.com/.

330.95365 USA ISSN 1520-2194
COUNTRY REVIEW. BAHRAIN. Text in English. a. USD 39.95 (effective 2004). **Description:** Covers demographic, political, economic, social, corporate, cultural, and environmental information.
Related titles: Online - full text ed.: USD 39.95 single country; USD 99 standard - 192 countries (effective 2004).
Published by: Commercial Data International, CountryWatch, Two Riverway, Ste 1770, Houston, TX 77056. TEL 713-355-6500, FAX 713-355-2008, 800-879-3885, editor@countrywatch.com, http://www.countrywatch.com/.

330.95492 USA ISSN 1520-2208
COUNTRY REVIEW. BANGLADESH. Text in English. a. USD 39.95 (effective 2004). **Description:** Covers demographic, political, economic, social, corporate, cultural, and environmental information.
Related titles: Online - full text ed.: USD 39.95 single country; USD 99 standard - 192 countries (effective 2004).
Published by: Commercial Data International, CountryWatch, Two Riverway, Ste 1770, Houston, TX 77056. TEL 713-355-6500, FAX 713-355-2008, 800-879-3885, editor@countrywatch.com, http://www.countrywatch.com/.

330.972981 USA ISSN 1520-2216
COUNTRY REVIEW. BARBADOS. Text in English. a. USD 39.95 (effective 2004). **Description:** Covers demographic, political, economic, social, corporate, cultural, and environmental information.
Related titles: Online - full text ed.: USD 39.95 single country; USD 99 standard - 192 countries (effective 2004).
Published by: Commercial Data International, CountryWatch, Two Riverway, Ste 1770, Houston, TX 77056. TEL 713-355-6500, FAX 713-355-2008, 800-879-3885, editor@countrywatch.com, http://www.countrywatch.com/.

330.9478 USA ISSN 1520-2224
COUNTRY REVIEW. BELARUS. Text in English. a. USD 39.95 (effective 2004). **Description:** Covers demographic, political, economic, social, corporate, cultural, and environmental information.
Related titles: Online - full text ed.: USD 39.95 single country; USD 99 standard - 192 countries (effective 2004).
Published by: Commercial Data International, CountryWatch, Two Riverway, Ste 1770, Houston, TX 77056. TEL 713-355-6500, FAX 713-355-2008, 800-879-3885, editor@countrywatch.com, http://www.countrywatch.com/.

330.9493 USA ISSN 1520-2232
COUNTRY REVIEW. BELGIUM. Text in English. a. USD 39.95 (effective 2004). **Description:** Covers demographic, political, economic, social, corporate, cultural, and environmental information.
Related titles: Online - full text ed.: USD 39.95 single country; USD 99 standard - 192 countries (effective 2004).
Published by: Commercial Data International, CountryWatch, Two Riverway, Ste 1770, Houston, TX 77056. TEL 713-355-6500, FAX 713-355-2008, 800-879-3885, editor@countrywatch.com, http://www.countrywatch.com/.

330.97282 USA ISSN 1520-2240
COUNTRY REVIEW. BELIZE. Text in English. a. USD 39.95 (effective 2004). **Description:** Covers demographic, political, economic, social, corporate, cultural, and environmental information.
Related titles: Online - full text ed.: USD 39.95 single country; USD 99 standard - 192 countries (effective 2004).
Published by: Commercial Data International, CountryWatch, Two Riverway, Ste 1770, Houston, TX 77056. TEL 713-355-6500, FAX 713-355-2008, 800-879-3885, editor@countrywatch.com, http://www.countrywatch.com/.

330.96683 USA ISSN 1520-2259
COUNTRY REVIEW. BENIN. Text in English. a. USD 39.95 (effective 2004). **Description:** Covers demographic, political, economic, social, corporate, cultural, and environmental information.
Related titles: Online - full text ed.: USD 99 standard - 192 countries; USD 39.95 single country (effective 2004).
Published by: Commercial Data International, CountryWatch, Two Riverway, Ste 1770, Houston, TX 77056. TEL 713-355-6500, FAX 713-355-2008, 800-879-3885, editor@countrywatch.com, http://www.countrywatch.com/.

330.95498 USA ISSN 1520-2267
COUNTRY REVIEW. BHUTAN. Text in English. a. USD 39.95 (effective 2004). **Description:** Covers demographic, political, economic, social, corporate, cultural, and environmental information.
Related titles: Online - full text ed.: USD 39.95 single country; USD 99 standard - 192 countries (effective 2004).
Published by: Commercial Data International, CountryWatch, Two Riverway, Ste 1770, Houston, TX 77056. TEL 713-355-6500, FAX 713-355-2008, 800-879-3885, editor@countrywatch.com, http://www.countrywatch.com/.

330.984 USA ISSN 1520-2275
COUNTRY REVIEW. BOLIVIA. Text in English. a. USD 39.95 (effective 2004). **Description:** Covers demographic, political, economic, social, corporate, cultural, and environmental information.
Related titles: Online - full text ed.: USD 39.95 single country; USD 99 standard - 192 countries (effective 2004).
Published by: Commercial Data International, CountryWatch, Two Riverway, Ste 1770, Houston, TX 77056. TEL 713-355-6500, FAX 713-355-2008, 800-879-3885, editor@countrywatch.com, http://www.countrywatch.com/.

330.949742 USA ISSN 1520-2283
COUNTRY REVIEW. BOSNIA HERZEGOVINA. Text in English. a. USD 39.95 (effective 2004). **Description:** Covers demographic, political, economic, social, corporate, cultural, and environmental information.
Related titles: Online - full text ed.: USD 39.95 single country; USD 99 standard - 192 countries (effective 2004).
Published by: Commercial Data International, CountryWatch, Two Riverway, Ste 1770, Houston, TX 77056. TEL 713-355-6500, FAX 713-355-2008, 800-879-3885, editor@countrywatch.com, http://www.countrywatch.com/.

330.96883 USA ISSN 1520-2291
COUNTRY REVIEW. BOTSWANA. Text in English. a. USD 39.95 (effective 2004). **Description:** Covers demographic, political, economic, social, corporate, cultural, and environmental information.
Related titles: Online - full text ed.: USD 39.95 single country; USD 99 standard - 192 countries (effective 2004).
Published by: Commercial Data International, CountryWatch, Two Riverway, Ste 1770, Houston, TX 77056. TEL 713-355-6500, FAX 713-355-2008, 800-879-3885, editor@countrywatch.com, http://www.countrywatch.com/.

330.981 USA ISSN 1520-2305
COUNTRY REVIEW. BRAZIL. Text in English. a. USD 39.95 (effective 2004). **Description:** Covers demographic, political, economic, social, corporate, cultural, and environmental information.
Related titles: Online - full text ed.: USD 39.95 single country; USD 99 standard - 192 countries (effective 2004).
Published by: Commercial Data International, CountryWatch, Two Riverway, Ste 1770, Houston, TX 77056. TEL 713-355-6500, FAX 713-355-2008, 800-879-3885, editor@countrywatch.com, http://www.countrywatch.com/.

330.95955 USA ISSN 1520-2313
COUNTRY REVIEW. BRUNEI. Text in English. a. USD 39.95 (effective 2004). **Description:** Covers demographic, political, economic, social, corporate, cultural, and environmental information.
Related titles: Online - full text ed.: USD 39.95 single country; USD 99 standard - 192 countries (effective 2004).
Published by: Commercial Data International, CountryWatch, Two Riverway, Ste 1770, Houston, TX 77056. TEL 713-355-6500, FAX 713-355-2008, 800-879-3885, editor@countrywatch.com, http://www.countrywatch.com/.

330.9499 USA ISSN 1520-2321
COUNTRY REVIEW. BULGARIA. Text in English. a. USD 39.95 (effective 2004). **Description:** Covers demographic, political, economic, social, corporate, cultural, and environmental information.
Related titles: Online - full text ed.: USD 39.95 single country; USD 99 standard - 192 countries (effective 2004).
Published by: Commercial Data International, CountryWatch, Two Riverway, Ste 1770, Houston, TX 77056. TEL 713-355-6500, FAX 713-355-2008, 800-879-3885, editor@countrywatch.com, http://www.countrywatch.com/.

330.96625 USA ISSN 1520-233X
COUNTRY REVIEW. BURKINA FASO. Text in English. a. USD 39.95 (effective 2004). **Description:** Covers demographic, political, economic, social, corporate, cultural, and environmental information.
Related titles: Online - full text ed.: USD 39.95 single country; USD 99 standard - 192 countries (effective 2004).
Published by: Commercial Data International, CountryWatch, Two Riverway, Ste 1770, Houston, TX 77056. TEL 713-355-6500, FAX 713-355-2008, 800-879-3885, editor@countrywatch.com, http://www.countrywatch.com/.

330.967572 USA ISSN 1520-2348
COUNTRY REVIEW. BURUNDI. Text in English. a. USD 39.95 (effective 2004). **Description:** Covers demographic, political, economic, social, corporate, cultural, and environmental information.
Related titles: Online - full text ed.: USD 39.95 single country; USD 99 standard - 192 countries (effective 2004).
Published by: Commercial Data International, CountryWatch, Two Riverway, Ste 1770, Houston, TX 77056. TEL 713-355-6500, FAX 713-355-2008, 800-879-3885, editor@countrywatch.com, http://www.countrywatch.com/.

338.9596 USA ISSN 1520-2356
COUNTRY REVIEW. CAMBODIA. Text in English. a. USD 39.95 (effective 2004). **Description:** Covers demographic, political, economic, social, corporate, cultural, and environmental information.
Related titles: Online - full text ed.: USD 39.95 single country; USD 99 standard - 192 countries (effective 2004).
Published by: Commercial Data International, CountryWatch, Two Riverway, Ste 1770, Houston, TX 77056. TEL 713-355-6500, FAX 713-355-2008, 800-879-3885, editor@countrywatch.com, http://www.countrywatch.com/.

330.96711 USA ISSN 1520-2364
CODEN: C
COUNTRY REVIEW. CAMEROON. Text in English. a. USD 39.95 (effective 2004). **Description:** Covers demographic, political, economic, social, corporate, cultural, and environmental information.
Related titles: Online - full text ed.: USD 99 standard - 192 countries; USD 39.95 single country (effective 2004).
Published by: Commercial Data International, CountryWatch, Two Riverway, Ste 1770, Houston, TX 77056. TEL 713-355-6500, FAX 713-355-2008, 800-879-3885, editor@countrywatch.com, http://www.countrywatch.com/.

330.971 USA ISSN 1520-2372
COUNTRY REVIEW. CANADA. Text in English. a. USD 39.95 (effective 2004). **Description:** Covers demographic, political, economic, social, corporate, cultural, and environmental information.

Related titles: Online - full text ed.: USD 39.95 single country; USD 99 standard - 192 countries (effective 2004).
Published by: Commercial Data International, CountryWatch, Two Riverway, Ste 1770, Houston, TX 77056. TEL 713-355-6500, FAX 713-355-2008, 800-879-3885, editor@countrywatch.com, http://www.countrywatch.com/.

330.96658 USA ISSN 1520-2380
COUNTRY REVIEW. CAPE VERDE. Text in English. a. USD 39.95 (effective 2004). **Description:** Covers demographic, political, economic, social, corporate, cultural, and environmental information.
Related titles: Online - full text ed.: USD 39.95 single country; USD 99 standard - 192 countries (effective 2004).
Published by: Commercial Data International, CountryWatch, Two Riverway, Ste 1770, Houston, TX 77056. TEL 713-355-6500, FAX 713-355-2008, 800-879-3885, editor@countrywatch.com, http://www.countrywatch.com/.

330.9674 USA
COUNTRY REVIEW. CENTRAL AFRICAN REPUBLIC. Text in English. a. USD 39.95 (effective 2004).
Related titles: Online - full content ed.: USD 39.95 single country; USD 99 standard- 192 countries (effective 2004).
Published by: Commercial Data International, CountryWatch, Two Riverway, Ste 1770, Houston, TX 77056. TEL 713-355-6500, FAX 713-355-2008, 800-879-3885, editor@countrywatch.com, http://www.countrywatch.com/.

330.96743 USA ISSN 1520-2402
COUNTRY REVIEW. CHAD. Text in English. a. USD 39.95 (effective 2004). **Description:** Covers demographic, political, economic, social, corporate, cultural, and environmental information.
Related titles: Online - full text ed.: USD 39.95 single country; USD 99 standard - 192 countries (effective 2004).
Published by: Commercial Data International, CountryWatch, Two Riverway, Ste 1770, Houston, TX 77056. TEL 713-355-6500, FAX 713-355-2008, 800-879-3885, editor@countrywatch.com, http://www.countrywatch.com/.

330.983 USA ISSN 1520-2429
COUNTRY REVIEW. CHILE. Text in English. a. USD 39.95 (effective 2004). **Description:** Covers demographic, political, economic, social, corporate, cultural, and environmental information.
Related titles: Online - full text ed.: USD 39.95 single country; USD 99 standard - 192 countries (effective 2004).
Published by: Commercial Data International, CountryWatch, Two Riverway, Ste 1770, Houston, TX 77056. TEL 713-355-6500, FAX 713-355-2008, 800-879-3885, editor@countrywatch.com, http://www.countrywatch.com/.

330.951 USA ISSN 1520-2437
COUNTRY REVIEW. CHINA. Text in English. a. USD 39.95 (effective 2004). **Description:** Covers demographic, political, economic, social, corporate, cultural, and environmental information.
Related titles: Online - full text ed.: USD 39.95 single country; USD 99 standard - 192 countries (effective 2004).
Published by: Commercial Data International, CountryWatch, Two Riverway, Ste 1770, Houston, TX 77056. TEL 713-355-6500, FAX 713-355-2008, 800-879-3885, editor@countrywatch.com, http://www.countrywatch.com/.

330.9861 USA ISSN 1520-2445
COUNTRY REVIEW. COLOMBIA. Text in English. a. USD 39.95 (effective 2004). **Description:** Covers demographic, political, economic, social, corporate, cultural, and environmental information.
Related titles: Online - full text ed.: USD 39.95 single country; USD 99 standard - 192 countries (effective 2004).
Published by: Commercial Data International, CountryWatch, Two Riverway, Ste 1770, Houston, TX 77056. TEL 713-355-6500, FAX 713-355-2008, 800-879-3885, editor@countrywatch.com, http://www.countrywatch.com/.

330.96941 USA ISSN 1520-2453
COUNTRY REVIEW. COMOROS. Text in English. a. USD 39.95 (effective 2004). **Description:** Covers demographic, political, economic, social, corporate, cultural, and environmental information.
Related titles: Online - full text ed.: USD 39.95 single country; USD 99 standard - 192 countries (effective 2004).
Published by: Commercial Data International, CountryWatch, Two Riverway, Ste 1770, Houston, TX 77056. TEL 713-355-6500, FAX 713-355-2008, 800-879-3885, editor@countrywatch.com, http://www.countrywatch.com/.

330.96724 USA ISSN 1520-2488
COUNTRY REVIEW. CONGO. Text in English. a. USD 39.95 (effective 2004). **Description:** Covers demographic, political, economic, social, corporate, cultural, and environmental information.
Related titles: Online - full text ed.: USD 39.95 single country; USD 99 standard - 192 countries (effective 2004).
Published by: Commercial Data International, CountryWatch, Two Riverway, Ste 1770, Houston, TX 77056. TEL 713-355-6500, FAX 713-355-2008, 800-879-3885, editor@countrywatch.com, http://www.countrywatch.com/.

330.96751 USA ISSN 1520-2461
COUNTRY REVIEW. CONGO DEMOCRATIC REPUBLIC. Text in English. a. USD 39.95 (effective 2004). **Description:** Covers demographic, political, economic, social, corporate, cultural, and environmental information.
Related titles: Online - full text ed.: USD 99 standard - 192 countries; USD 39.95 single country (effective 2004).
Published by: Commercial Data International, CountryWatch, Two Riverway, Ste 1770, Houston, TX 77056. TEL 713-355-6500, FAX 713-355-2008, 800-879-3885, editor@countrywatch.com, http://www.countrywatch.com/.

330.7286 USA ISSN 1520-2496
COUNTRY REVIEW. COSTA RICA. Text in English. a. USD 39.95 (effective 2004). **Description:** Covers demographic, political, economic, social, corporate, cultural, and environmental information.
Related titles: Online - full text ed.: USD 39.95 single country; USD 99 standard - 192 countries (effective 2004).
Published by: Commercial Data International, CountryWatch, Two Riverway, Ste 1770, Houston, TX 77056. TEL 713-355-6500, FAX 713-355-2008, 800-879-3885, editor@countrywatch.com, http://www.countrywatch.com/.

330.6668 USA ISSN 1520-250X
COUNTRY REVIEW. COTE D'IVOIRE. Text in English. a. USD 39.95 (effective 2004). **Description:** Covers demographic, political, economic, social, corporate, cultural, and environmental information.
Related titles: Online - full text ed.: USD 39.95 single country; USD 99 standard - 192 countries (effective 2004).
Published by: Commercial Data International, CountryWatch, Two Riverway, Ste 1770, Houston, TX 77056. TEL 713-355-6500, FAX 713-355-2008, 800-879-3885, editor@countrywatch.com, http://www.countrywatch.com/.

330.94972 USA ISSN 1520-2410
COUNTRY REVIEW. CROATIA. Text in English. a. USD 39.95 (effective 2004). **Description:** Covers demographic, political, economic, social, corporate, cultural, and environmental information.
Related titles: Online - full text ed.: USD 39.95 single country; USD 99 standard - 192 countries (effective 2004).
Published by: Commercial Data International, CountryWatch, Two Riverway, Ste 1770, Houston, TX 77056. TEL 713-355-6500, FAX 713-355-2008, 800-879-3885, editor@countrywatch.com, http://www.countrywatch.com/.

330.97291 USA ISSN 1520-2518
COUNTRY REVIEW. CUBA. Text in English. a. USD 39.95 (effective 2004). **Description:** Covers demographic, political, economic, social, corporate, cultural, and environmental information.
Related titles: Online - full text ed.: USD 99 standard - 192 countries; USD 39.95 single country (effective 2004).
Published by: Commercial Data International, CountryWatch, Two Riverway, Ste 1770, Houston, TX 77056. TEL 713-355-6500, FAX 713-355-2008, 800-879-3885, editor@countrywatch.com, http://www.countrywatch.com/.

330.95693 USA ISSN 1520-2526
COUNTRY REVIEW. CYPRUS. Text in English. a. USD 39.95 (effective 2004). **Description:** Covers demographic, political, economic, social, corporate, cultural, and environmental information.
Related titles: Online - full text ed.: USD 39.95 single country; USD 99 standard - 192 countries (effective 2004).
Published by: Commercial Data International, CountryWatch, Two Riverway, Ste 1770, Houston, TX 77056. TEL 713-355-6500, FAX 713-355-2008, 800-879-3885, editor@countrywatch.com, http://www.countrywatch.com/.

330.94371 USA ISSN 1520-2534
COUNTRY REVIEW. CZECH REPUBLIC. Text in English. a. USD 39.95 (effective 2004). **Description:** Covers demographic, political, economic, social, corporate, cultural, and environmental information.
Related titles: Online - full text ed.: USD 39.95 standard - 192 countries; USD 99 single country (effective 2004).
Published by: Commercial Data International, CountryWatch, Two Riverway, Ste 1770, Houston, TX 77056. TEL 713-355-6500, FAX 713-355-2008, 800-879-3885, editor@countrywatch.com, http://www.countrywatch.com/.

330.9489 USA ISSN 1520-2542
COUNTRY REVIEW. DENMARK. Text in English. a. USD 39.95 (effective 2004). **Description:** Covers demographic, political, economic, social, corporate, cultural, and environmental information.
Related titles: Online - full text ed.: USD 39.95 single country; USD 99 standard - 192 countries (effective 2004).
Published by: Commercial Data International, CountryWatch, Two Riverway, Ste 1770, Houston, TX 77056. TEL 713-355-6500, FAX 713-355-2008, 800-879-3885, editor@countrywatch.com, http://www.countrywatch.com/.

330.96771 USA ISSN 1520-2550
COUNTRY REVIEW. DJIBOUTI. Text in English. a. USD 39.95 (effective 2004). **Description:** Covers demographic, political, economic, social, corporate, cultural, and environmental information.
Related titles: Online - full text ed.: USD 39.95 single country; USD 99 standard - 192 countries (effective 2004).
Published by: Commercial Data International, CountryWatch, Two Riverway, Ste 1770, Houston, TX 77056. TEL 713-355-6500, FAX 713-355-2008, 800-879-3885, editor@countrywatch.com, http://www.countrywatch.com/.

330.9729841 USA ISSN 1520-2569
COUNTRY REVIEW. DOMINICA. Text in English. a. USD 39.95 (effective 2004). **Description:** Covers demographic, political, economic, social, corporate, cultural, and environmental information.
Related titles: Online - full text ed.: USD 39.95 single country; USD 99 standard - 192 countries (effective 2004).
Published by: Commercial Data International, CountryWatch, Two Riverway, Ste 1770, Houston, TX 77056. TEL 713-355-6500, FAX 713-355-2008, 800-879-3885, editor@countrywatch.com, http://www.countrywatch.com/.

330.97293 USA ISSN 1520-2577
COUNTRY REVIEW. DOMINICAN REPUBLIC. Text in English. a. USD 39.95 (effective 2004). **Description:** Covers demographic, political, economic, social, corporate, cultural, and environmental information.
Related titles: Online - full text ed.: USD 39.95 single country; USD 99 standard - 192 countries (effective 2004).
Published by: Commercial Data International, CountryWatch, Two Riverway, Ste 1770, Houston, TX 77056. TEL 713-355-6500, FAX 713-355-2008, 800-879-3885, editor@countrywatch.com, http://www.countrywatch.com/.

330.95987 USA
COUNTRY REVIEW. EAST TIMOR. Text in English. a. USD 39.95 (effective 2004).
Related titles: Online - full text ed.: USD 39.95 single country; USD 99 standard - 192 countries (effective 2004).
Published by: Commercial Data International, CountryWatch, Two Riverway, Ste 1770, Houston, TX 77056. TEL 713-355-6500, FAX 713-355-2008, 800-879-3885, editor@countrywatch.com, http://www.countrywatch.com/.

330.9866 USA ISSN 1520-1708
COUNTRY REVIEW. ECUADOR. Text in English. a. USD 39.95 (effective 2004). **Description:** Covers demographic, political, economic, social, corporate, cultural, and environmental information.
Related titles: Online - full text ed.: USD 39.95 single country; USD 99 standard - 192 countries (effective 2004).
Published by: Commercial Data International, CountryWatch, Two Riverway, Ste 1770, Houston, TX 77056. TEL 713-355-6500, FAX 713-355-2008, 800-879-3885, editor@countrywatch.com, http://www.countrywatch.com/.

330.962 USA ISSN 1520-1716
COUNTRY REVIEW. EGYPT. Text in English. a. USD 39.95 (effective 2004). **Description:** Covers demographic, political, economic, social, corporate, cultural, and environmental information.
Related titles: Online - full text ed.: USD 39.95 single country; USD 99 standard - 192 countries (effective 2004).
Published by: Commercial Data International, CountryWatch, Two Riverway, Ste 1770, Houston, TX 77056. TEL 713-355-6500, FAX 713-355-2008, 800-879-3885, editor@countrywatch.com, http://www.countrywatch.com/.

330.97284 USA ISSN 1520-1724
COUNTRY REVIEW. EL SALVADOR. Text in English. a. USD 39.95 (effective 2004). **Description:** Covers demographic, political, economic, social, corporate, cultural, and environmental information.
Related titles: Online - full text ed.: USD 39.95 single country; USD 99 standard - 192 countries (effective 2004).
Published by: Commercial Data International, CountryWatch, Two Riverway, Ste 1770, Houston, TX 77056. TEL 713-355-6500, FAX 713-355-2008, 800-879-3885, editor@countrywatch.com, http://www.countrywatch.com/.

330.96718 USA ISSN 1520-1759
COUNTRY REVIEW. EQUATORIAL GUINEA. Text in English. a. USD 39.95 (effective 2004). **Description:** Covers demographic, political, economic, social, corporate, cultural, and environmental information.
Related titles: Online - full text ed.: USD 39.95 single country; USD 99 standard - 192 countries (effective 2004).
Published by: Commercial Data International, CountryWatch, Two Riverway, Ste 1770, Houston, TX 77056. TEL 713-355-6500, FAX 713-355-2008, 800-879-3885, editor@countrywatch.com, http://www.countrywatch.com/.

330.9635 USA ISSN 1520-1732
COUNTRY REVIEW. ERITREA. Text in English. a. USD 39.95 (effective 2004). **Description:** Covers demographic, political, economic, social, corporate, cultural, and environmental information.
Related titles: Online - full text ed.: USD 39.95 single country; USD 99 standard - 192 countries (effective 2004).
Published by: Commercial Data International, CountryWatch, Two Riverway, Ste 1770, Houston, TX 77056. TEL 713-355-6500, FAX 713-355-2008, 800-879-3885, editor@countrywatch.com, http://www.countrywatch.com/.

B

330.94798 USA ISSN 1520-1740
COUNTRY REVIEW. ESTONIA. Text in English. a. USD 39.95 (effective 2004). **Description:** Covers demographic, political, economic, social, corporate, cultural, and environmental information.
Related titles: Online - full text ed.: USD 39.95 single country; USD 99 standard - 192 countries (effective 2004).
Published by: Commercial Data International, CountryWatch, Two Riverway, Ste 1770, Houston, TX 77056. TEL 713-355-6500, FAX 713-355-2008, 800-879-3885, editor@countrywatch.com, http://www.countrywatch.com/.

330.963 USA ISSN 1520-1767
COUNTRY REVIEW. ETHIOPIA. Text in English. a. USD 39.95 (effective 2004). **Description:** Covers demographic, political, economic, social, corporate, cultural, and environmental information.
Related titles: Online - full text ed.: USD 39.95 single country; USD 99 standard - 192 countries (effective 2004).
Published by: Commercial Data International, CountryWatch, Two Riverway, Ste 1770, Houston, TX 77056. TEL 713-355-6500, FAX 713-355-2008, 800-879-3885, editor@countrywatch.com, http://www.countrywatch.com/.

330.99611 USA ISSN 1520-1775
COUNTRY REVIEW. FIJI. Text in English. a. USD 39.95 (effective 2004). **Description:** Covers demographic, political, economic, social, corporate, cultural, and environmental information.
Related titles: Online - full text ed.: USD 39.95 single country; USD 99 standard - 192 countries (effective 2004).
Published by: Commercial Data International, CountryWatch, Two Riverway, Ste 1770, Houston, TX 77056. TEL 713-355-6500, FAX 713-355-2008, 800-879-3885, editor@countrywatch.com, http://www.countrywatch.com/.

330.94897 USA ISSN 1520-1783
COUNTRY REVIEW. FINLAND. Text in English. a. USD 39.95 (effective 2004). **Description:** Covers demographic, political, economic, social, corporate, cultural, and environmental information.
Related titles: Online - full text ed.: USD 39.95 single country; USD 99 standard - 192 countries (effective 2004).
Published by: Commercial Data International, CountryWatch, Two Riverway, Ste 1770, Houston, TX 77056. TEL 713-355-6500, FAX 713-355-2008, 800-879-3885, editor@countrywatch.com, http://www.countrywatch.com/.

330.944 USA ISSN 1520-1791
COUNTRY REVIEW. FRANCE. Text in English. a. USD 39.95 (effective 2004). **Description:** Covers demographic, political, economic, social, corporate, cultural, and environmental information.
Related titles: Online - full text ed.: USD 39.95 single country; USD 99 standard - 192 countries (effective 2004).
Published by: Commercial Data International, CountryWatch, Two Riverway, Ste 1770, Houston, TX 77056. TEL 713-355-6500, FAX 713-355-2008, 800-879-3885, editor@countrywatch.com, http://www.countrywatch.com/.

330.96721 USA ISSN 1520-1805
COUNTRY REVIEW. GABON. Text in English. a. USD 39.95 (effective 2004). **Description:** Covers demographic, political, economic, social, corporate, cultural, and environmental information.
Related titles: Online - full text ed.: USD 39.95 single country; USD 99 standard - 192 countries (effective 2004).
Published by: Commercial Data International, CountryWatch, Two Riverway, Ste 1770, Houston, TX 77056. TEL 713-355-6500, FAX 713-355-2008, 800-879-3885, editor@countrywatch.com, http://www.countrywatch.com/.

330.96651 USA
COUNTRY REVIEW. GAMBIA. Text in English. a. USD 39.95 (effective 2004).
Related titles: Online - full text ed.: USD 39.95 single country; USD 99 standard - 192 countries (effective 2004).
Published by: Commercial Data International, CountryWatch, Two Riverway, Ste 1770, Houston, TX 77056. TEL 713-355-6500, FAX 713-355-2008, 800-879-3885, editor@countrywatch.com, http://www.countrywatch.com/.

330.9758 USA ISSN 1520-1821
COUNTRY REVIEW. GEORGIA. Text in English. a. USD 39.95 (effective 2004). **Description:** Covers demographic, political, economic, social, corporate, cultural, and environmental information.
Related titles: Online - full text ed.: USD 39.95 single country; USD 99 standard - 192 countries (effective 2004).
Published by: Commercial Data International, CountryWatch, Two Riverway, Ste 1770, Houston, TX 77056. TEL 713-355-6500, FAX 713-355-2008, 800-879-3885, editor@countrywatch.com, http://www.countrywatch.com/.

330.943 USA ISSN 1520-183X
COUNTRY REVIEW. GERMANY. Text in English. a. USD 39.95 (effective 2004). **Description:** Covers demographic, political, economic, social, corporate, cultural, and environmental information.
Related titles: Online - full text ed.: USD 39.95 single country; USD 99 standard - 192 countries (effective 2004).
Published by: Commercial Data International, CountryWatch, Two Riverway, Ste 1770, Houston, TX 77056. TEL 713-355-6500, FAX 713-355-2008, 800-879-3885, editor@countrywatch.com, http://www.countrywatch.com/.

330.9667 USA ISSN 1520-1848
COUNTRY REVIEW. GHANA. Text in English. a. USD 39.95 (effective 2004). **Description:** Covers demographic, political, economic, social, corporate, cultural, and environmental information.
Related titles: Online - full text ed.: USD 39.95 single country; USD 99 standard - 192 countries (effective 2004).
Published by: Commercial Data International, CountryWatch, Two Riverway, Ste 1770, Houston, TX 77056. TEL 713-355-6500, FAX 713-355-2008, 800-879-3885, editor@countrywatch.com, http://www.countrywatch.com/.

330.9495 USA ISSN 1520-1856
COUNTRY REVIEW. GREECE. Text in English. a. USD 39.95 (effective 2004). **Description:** Covers demographic, political, economic, social, corporate, cultural, and environmental information.
Related titles: Online - full text ed.: USD 39.95 single country; USD 99 standard - 192 countries (effective 2004).
Published by: Commercial Data International, CountryWatch, Two Riverway, Ste 1770, Houston, TX 77056. TEL 713-355-6500, FAX 713-355-2008, 800-879-3885, editor@countrywatch.com, http://www.countrywatch.com/.

330.9729845 USA ISSN 1520-1864
COUNTRY REVIEW. GRENADA. Text in English. a. USD 39.95 (effective 2004). **Description:** Covers demographic, political, economic, social, corporate, cultural, and environmental information.
Related titles: Online - full text ed.: USD 39.95 single country; USD 99 standard - 192 countries (effective 2004).
Published by: Commercial Data International, CountryWatch, Two Riverway, Ste 1770, Houston, TX 77056. TEL 713-355-6500, FAX 713-355-2008, 800-879-3885, editor@countrywatch.com, http://www.countrywatch.com/.

330.97281 USA ISSN 1520-1872
COUNTRY REVIEW. GUATEMALA. Text in English. a. USD 39.95 (effective 2004). **Description:** Covers demographic, political, economic, social, corporate, cultural, and environmental information.
Related titles: Online - full text ed.: USD 39.95 single country; USD 99 standard - 192 countries (effective 2004).
Published by: Commercial Data International, CountryWatch, Two Riverway, Ste 1770, Houston, TX 77056. TEL 713-355-6500, FAX 713-355-2008, 800-879-3885, editor@countrywatch.com, http://www.countrywatch.com/.

330.96652 USA ISSN 1520-1880
COUNTRY REVIEW. GUINEA. Text in English. a. USD 39.95 (effective 2004). **Description:** Covers demographic, political, economic, social, corporate, cultural, and environmental information.
Related titles: Online - full text ed.: USD 39.95 single country; USD 99 standard - 192 countries (effective 2004).
Published by: Commercial Data International, CountryWatch, Two Riverway, Ste 1770, Houston, TX 77056. TEL 713-355-6500, FAX 713-355-2008, 800-879-3885, editor@countrywatch.com, http://www.countrywatch.com/.

330.96657 USA ISSN 1520-1899
COUNTRY REVIEW. GUINEA-BISSAU. Text in English. a. USD 39.95 (effective 2004). **Description:** Covers demographic, political, economic, social, corporate, cultural, and environmental information.
Related titles: Online - full text ed.: USD 39.95 single country; USD 99 standard - 192 countries (effective 2004).
Published by: Commercial Data International, CountryWatch, Two Riverway, Ste 1770, Houston, TX 77056. TEL 713-355-6500, FAX 713-355-2008, 800-879-3885, editor@countrywatch.com, http://www.countrywatch.com/.

330.9881 USA ISSN 1520-1902
COUNTRY REVIEW. GUYANA. Text in English. a. USD 39.95 (effective 2004). **Description:** Covers demographic, political, economic, social, corporate, cultural, and environmental information.
Related titles: Online - full text ed.: USD 39.95 single country; USD 99 standard - 192 countries (effective 2004).
Published by: Commercial Data International, CountryWatch, Two Riverway, Ste 1770, Houston, TX 77056. TEL 713-355-6500, FAX 713-355-2008, 800-879-3885, editor@countrywatch.com, http://www.countrywatch.com/.

330.97294 USA ISSN 1520-1910
COUNTRY REVIEW. HAITI. Text in English. a. USD 39.95 (effective 2004). **Description:** Covers demographic, political, economic, social, corporate, cultural, and environmental information.
Related titles: Online - full text ed.: USD 39.95 single country; USD 99 standard - 192 countries (effective 2004).
Published by: Commercial Data International, CountryWatch, Two Riverway, Ste 1770, Houston, TX 77056. TEL 713-355-6500, FAX 713-355-2008, 800-879-3885, editor@countrywatch.com, http://www.countrywatch.com/.

330.945634 USA ISSN 1520-1929
COUNTRY REVIEW. HOLY SEE. Text in English. a. USD 39.95 (effective 2004). **Description:** Covers demographic, political, economic, social, corporate, cultural, and environmental information.
Related titles: Online - full text ed.: USD 39.95 single country; USD 99 standard - 192 countries (effective 2004).
Published by: Commercial Data International, CountryWatch, Two Riverway, Ste 1770, Houston, TX 77056. TEL 713-355-6500, FAX 713-355-2008, 800-879-3885, editor@countrywatch.com, http://www.countrywatch.com/.

330.97283 USA ISSN 1520-1937
COUNTRY REVIEW. HONDURAS. Text in English. a. USD 39.95 (effective 2004). **Description:** Covers demographic, political, economic, social, corporate, cultural, and environmental information.
Related titles: Online - full text ed.: USD 39.95 single country; USD 99 standard - 192 countries (effective 2004).
Published by: Commercial Data International, CountryWatch, Two Riverway, Ste 1770, Houston, TX 77056. TEL 713-355-6500, FAX 713-355-2008, 800-879-3885, editor@countrywatch.com, http://www.countrywatch.com/.

330.9739 USA ISSN 1520-1945
COUNTRY REVIEW. HUNGARY. Text in English. a. USD 39.95 (effective 2004). **Description:** Covers demographic, political, economic, social, corporate, cultural, and environmental information.
Related titles: Online - full text ed.: USD 39.95 single country; USD 99 standard - 192 countries (effective 2004).
Published by: Commercial Data International, CountryWatch, Two Riverway, Ste 1770, Houston, TX 77056. TEL 713-355-6500, FAX 713-355-2008, 800-879-3885, editor@countrywatch.com, http://www.countrywatch.com/.

330.94912 USA ISSN 1520-1953
COUNTRY REVIEW. ICELAND. Text in English. a. USD 39.95 (effective 2004). **Description:** Covers demographic, political, economic, social, corporate, cultural, and environmental information.
Related titles: Online - full text ed.: USD 39.95 single country; USD 99 standard - 192 countries (effective 2004).
Published by: Commercial Data International, CountryWatch, Two Riverway, Ste 1770, Houston, TX 77056. TEL 713-355-6500, FAX 713-355-2008, 800-879-3885, editor@countrywatch.com, http://www.countrywatch.com/.

330.954 USA ISSN 1520-1961
COUNTRY REVIEW. INDIA. Text in English. a. USD 39.95 (effective 2004). **Description:** Covers demographic, political, economic, social, corporate, cultural, and environmental information.
Related titles: Online - full text ed.: USD 39.95 single country; USD 99 standard - 192 countries (effective 2004).
Published by: Commercial Data International, CountryWatch, Two Riverway, Ste 1770, Houston, TX 77056. TEL 713-355-6500, FAX 713-355-2008, 800-879-3885, editor@countrywatch.com, http://www.countrywatch.com/.

330.9598 USA
COUNTRY REVIEW. INDONESIA. Text in English. a. USD 39.95 (effective 2004). **Description:** Covers demographic, political, economic, social, corporate, cultural, and environmental information.
Related titles: Online - full text ed.: USD 39.95 single country; USD 99 standard - 192 countries (effective 2004).
Published by: Commercial Data International, CountryWatch, Two Riverway, Ste 1770, Houston, TX 77056. TEL 713-355-6500, FAX 713-355-2008, 800-879-3885, editor@countrywatch.com, http://www.countrywatch.com/.

330.955 USA ISSN 1520-1988
COUNTRY REVIEW. IRAN. Text in English. a. USD 39.95 (effective 2004). **Description:** Covers demographic, political, economic, social, corporate, cultural, and environmental information.
Related titles: Online - full text ed.: USD 39.95 single country; USD 99 standard - 192 countries (effective 2004).
Published by: Commercial Data International, CountryWatch, Two Riverway, Ste 1770, Houston, TX 77056. TEL 713-355-6500, FAX 713-355-2008, 800-879-3885, editor@countrywatch.com, http://www.countrywatch.com/.

330.9567 USA ISSN 1520-1996
COUNTRY REVIEW. IRAQ. Text in English. a. USD 39.95 (effective 2003). **Description:** Covers demographic, political, economic, social, corporate, cultural, and environmental information.
Related titles: Online - full text ed.: USD 39.95 single country; USD 99 standard - 192 countries (effective 2004).
Published by: Commercial Data International, CountryWatch, Two Riverway, Ste 1770, Houston, TX 77056. TEL 713-355-6500, FAX 713-355-2008, 800-879-3885, editor@countrywatch.com, http://www.countrywatch.com/.

330.9417 USA ISSN 1520-2003
COUNTRY REVIEW. IRELAND. Text in English. a. USD 39.95 (effective 2004). **Description:** Covers demographic, political, economic, social, corporate, cultural, and environmental information.

Related titles: Online - full text ed.: USD 39.95 single country; USD 99 standard - 192 countries (effective 2004).
Published by: Commercial Data International, CountryWatch, Two Riverway, Ste 1770, Houston, TX 77056. TEL 713-355-6500, FAX 713-355-2008, 800-879-3885, editor@countrywatch.com, http://www.countrywatch.com/.

330.95694 USA ISSN 1520-2011
COUNTRY REVIEW. ISRAEL. Text in English. a. USD 39.95 (effective 2004). **Description:** Covers demographic, political, economic, social, corporate, cultural, and environmental information.
Related titles: Online - full text ed.: USD 39.95 single; USD 99 standard - 192 countries (effective 2004).
Published by: Commercial Data International, CountryWatch, Two Riverway, Ste 1770, Houston, TX 77056. TEL 713-355-6500, FAX 713-355-2008, 800-879-3885, editor@countrywatch.com, http://www.countrywatch.com/.

330.945 USA ISSN 1520-202X
COUNTRY REVIEW. ITALY. Text in English. a. USD 39.95 (effective 2004). **Description:** Covers demographic, political, economic, social, corporate, cultural, and environmental information.
Related titles: Online - full text ed.: USD 39.95 single country; USD 99 standard - 192 countries (effective 2004).
Published by: Commercial Data International, CountryWatch, Two Riverway, Ste 1770, Houston, TX 77056. TEL 713-355-6500, FAX 713-355-2008, 800-879-3885, editor@countrywatch.com, http://www.countrywatch.com/.

330.97292 USA ISSN 1520-2038
COUNTRY REVIEW. JAMAICA. Text in English. a. USD 39.95 (effective 2004). **Description:** Covers demographic, political, economic, social, corporate, cultural, and environmental information.
Related titles: Online - full text ed.: USD 39.95 single country; USD 99 standard - 192 countries (effective 2004).
Published by: Commercial Data International, CountryWatch, Two Riverway, Ste 1770, Houston, TX 77056. TEL 713-355-6500, FAX 713-355-2008, 800-879-3885, editor@countrywatch.com, http://www.countrywatch.com/.

330.952 USA ISSN 1520-2046
COUNTRY REVIEW. JAPAN. Text in English. a. USD 39.95 (effective 2004). **Description:** Covers demographic, political, economic, social, corporate, cultural, and environmental information.
Related titles: Online - full text ed.: USD 39.95 single country; USD 99 standard - 192 countries (effective 2004).
Published by: Commercial Data International, CountryWatch, Two Riverway, Ste 1770, Houston, TX 77056. TEL 713-355-6500, FAX 713-355-2008, 800-879-3885, editor@countrywatch.com, http://www.countrywatch.com/.

330.95695 USA ISSN 1520-2054
COUNTRY REVIEW. JORDAN. Text in English. a. USD 39.95 (effective 2004). **Description:** Covers demographic, political, economic, social, corporate, cultural, and environmental information.
Related titles: Online - full text ed.: USD 39.95 single country; USD 99 standard - 192 countries (effective 2004).
Published by: Commercial Data International, CountryWatch, Two Riverway, Ste 1770, Houston, TX 77056. TEL 713-355-6500, FAX 713-355-2008, 800-879-3885, editor@countrywatch.com, http://www.countrywatch.com/.

330.95845 USA ISSN 1520-2062
COUNTRY REVIEW. KAZAKHSTAN. Text in English. a. USD 39.95 (effective 2004). **Description:** Covers demographic, political, economic, social, corporate, cultural, and environmental information.
Related titles: Online - full text ed.: USD 39.95 single country; USD 99 standard - 192 countries (effective 2004).
Published by: Commercial Data International, CountryWatch, Two Riverway, Ste 1770, Houston, TX 77056. TEL 713-355-6500, FAX 713-355-2008, 800-879-3885, editor@countrywatch.com, http://www.countrywatch.com/.

330.96762 USA ISSN 1520-1619
COUNTRY REVIEW. KENYA. Text in English. a. USD 39.95 (effective 2004). **Description:** Covers demographic, political, economic, social, corporate, cultural, and environmental information.
Related titles: Online - full text ed.: USD 39.95 single country; USD 99 standard - 192 countries (effective 2004).
Published by: Commercial Data International, CountryWatch, Two Riverway, Ste 1770, Houston, TX 77056. TEL 713-355-6500, FAX 713-355-2008, 800-879-3885, editor@countrywatch.com, http://www.countrywatch.com/.

330.9681 USA ISSN 1520-1627
COUNTRY REVIEW. KIRIBATI. Text in English. a. USD 39.95 (effective 2004). **Description:** Covers demographic, political, economic, social, corporate, cultural, and environmental information.
Related titles: Online - full text ed.: USD 39.95 single country; USD 99 standard - 192 countries (effective 2004).
Published by: Commercial Data International, CountryWatch, Two Riverway, Ste 1770, Houston, TX 77056. TEL 713-355-6500, FAX 713-355-2008, 800-879-3885, editor@countrywatch.com, http://www.countrywatch.com/.

330.95367 USA ISSN 1520-1651
COUNTRY REVIEW. KUWAIT. Text in English. a. USD 39.95 (effective 2004). **Description:** Covers demographic, political, economic, social, corporate, cultural, and environmental information.
Related titles: Online - full text ed.: USD 39.95 single country; USD 99 standard - 192 countries (effective 2004).
Published by: Commercial Data International, CountryWatch, Two Riverway, Ste 1770, Houston, TX 77056. TEL 713-355-6500, FAX 713-355-2008, 800-879-3885, editor@countrywatch.com, http://www.countrywatch.com/.

330.95843 USA ISSN 1520-166X
COUNTRY REVIEW. KYRGYZSTAN. Text in English. a. USD 39.95 (effective 2004). **Description:** Covers demographic, political, economic, social, corporate, cultural, and environmental information.
Related titles: Online - full text ed.: USD 39.95 single country; USD 99 standard - 192 countries (effective 2004).
Published by: Commercial Data International, CountryWatch, Two Riverway, Ste 1770, Houston, TX 77056. TEL 713-355-6500, FAX 713-355-2008, 800-879-3885, editor@countrywatch.com, http://www.countrywatch.com/.

330.9594 USA ISSN 1520-1678
COUNTRY REVIEW. LAOS. Text in English. a. USD 39.95 (effective 2004). **Description:** Covers demographic, political, economic, social, corporate, cultural, and environmental information.
Related titles: Online - full text ed.: USD 39.95 single country; USD 99 standard - 192 countries (effective 2004).
Published by: Commercial Data International, CountryWatch, Two Riverway, Ste 1770, Houston, TX 77056. TEL 713-355-6500, FAX 713-355-2008, 800-879-3885, editor@countrywatch.com, http://www.countrywatch.com/.

330.94796 USA ISSN 1520-1686
COUNTRY REVIEW. LATVIA. Text in English. a. USD 39.95 (effective 2004). **Description:** Covers demographic, political, economic, social, corporate, cultural, and environmental information.
Related titles: Online - full text ed.: USD 39.95 single country; USD 99 standard - 192 countries (effective 2004).
Published by: Commercial Data International, CountryWatch, Two Riverway, Ste 1770, Houston, TX 77056. TEL 713-355-6500, FAX 713-355-2008, 800-879-3885, editor@countrywatch.com, http://www.countrywatch.com/.

330.95692 USA ISSN 1520-1694
COUNTRY REVIEW. LEBANON. Text in English. a. USD 39.95 (effective 2004). **Description:** Covers demographic, political, economic, social, corporate, cultural, and environmental information.
Related titles: Online - full text ed.: USD 39.95 single country; USD 99 standard - 192 countries (effective 2004).
Published by: Commercial Data International, CountryWatch, Two Riverway, Ste 1770, Houston, TX 77056. TEL 713-355-6500, FAX 713-355-2008, 800-879-3885, editor@countrywatch.com, http://www.countrywatch.com/.

330.96885 USA ISSN 1520-0752
COUNTRY REVIEW. LESOTHO. Text in English. a. USD 39.95 (effective 2004). **Description:** Covers demographic, political, economic, social, corporate, cultural, and environmental information.
Related titles: Online - full text ed.: USD 39.95 single country; USD 99 standard - 192 countries (effective 2004).
Published by: Commercial Data International, CountryWatch, Two Riverway, Ste 1770, Houston, TX 77056. TEL 713-355-6500, FAX 713-355-2008, 800-879-3885, editor@countrywatch.com, http://www.countrywatch.com/.

330.96662 USA ISSN 1520-0760
COUNTRY REVIEW. LIBERIA. Text in English. a. USD 39.95 (effective 2004). **Description:** Covers demographic, political, economic, social, corporate, cultural, and environmental information.
Related titles: Online - full text ed.: USD 39.95 single country; USD 99 standard - 192 countries (effective 2004).
Published by: Commercial Data International, CountryWatch, Two Riverway, Ste 1770, Houston, TX 77056. TEL 713-355-6500, FAX 713-355-2008, 800-879-3885, editor@countrywatch.com, http://www.countrywatch.com/.

330.9612 USA ISSN 1520-0779
COUNTRY REVIEW. LIBYA. Text in English. a. USD 39.95 (effective 2004). **Description:** Covers demographic, political, economic, social, corporate, cultural, and environmental information.
Related titles: Online - full text ed.: USD 39.95 single country; USD 99 standard - 192 countries (effective 2004).
Published by: Commercial Data International, CountryWatch, Two Riverway, Ste 1770, Houston, TX 77056. TEL 713-355-6500, FAX 713-355-2008, 800-879-3885, editor@countrywatch.com, http://www.countrywatch.com/.

330.943648 USA ISSN 1520-0787
COUNTRY REVIEW. LIECHTENSTEIN. Text in English. a. USD 39.95 (effective 2004). **Description:** Covers demographic, political, economic, social, corporate, cultural, and environmental information.
Related titles: Online - full text ed.: USD 39.95 single country; USD 99 standard - 192 countries (effective 2004).
Published by: Commercial Data International, CountryWatch, Two Riverway, Ste 1770, Houston, TX 77056. TEL 713-355-6500, FAX 713-355-2008, 800-879-3885, editor@countrywatch.com, http://www.countrywatch.com/.

330.94793 USA ISSN 1520-0795
COUNTRY REVIEW. LITHUANIA. Text in English. a. USD 39.95 (effective 2004). **Description:** Covers demographic, political, economic, social, corporate, cultural, and environmental information.
Related titles: Online - full text ed.: USD 39.95 single country; USD 99 standard - 192 countries (effective 2004).
Published by: Commercial Data International, CountryWatch, Two Riverway, Ste 1770, Houston, TX 77056. TEL 713-355-6500, FAX 713-355-2008, 800-879-3885, editor@countrywatch.com, http://www.countrywatch.com/.

330.94935 USA ISSN 1520-0809
COUNTRY REVIEW. LUXEMBOURG. Text in English. a. USD 39.95 (effective 2004). **Description:** Covers demographic, political, economic, social, corporate, cultural, and environmental information.
Related titles: Online - full text ed.: USD 39.95 single country; USD 99 standard - 192 countries (effective 2004).
Published by: Commercial Data International, CountryWatch, Two Riverway, Ste 1770, Houston, TX 77056. TEL 713-355-6500, FAX 713-355-2008, 800-879-3885, editor@countrywatch.com, http://www.countrywatch.com/.

330.94976 USA ISSN 1520-0817
COUNTRY REVIEW. MACEDONIA. Text in English. a. USD 39.95 (effective 2004). **Description:** Covers demographic, political, economic, social, corporate, cultural, and environmental information.
Related titles: Online - full text ed.: USD 39.95 single country; USD 99 standard - 192 countries (effective 2004).
Published by: Commercial Data International, CountryWatch, Two Riverway, Ste 1770, Houston, TX 77056. TEL 713-355-6500, FAX 713-355-2008, 800-879-3885, editor@countrywatch.com, http://www.countrywatch.com/.

330.9691 USA ISSN 1520-0825
COUNTRY REVIEW. MADAGASCAR. Text in English. a. USD 39.95 (effective 2004). **Description:** Covers demographic, political, economic, social, corporate, cultural, and environmental information.
Related titles: Online - full text ed.: USD 39.95 single country; USD 99 standard - 192 countries (effective 2004).
Published by: Commercial Data International, CountryWatch, Two Riverway, Ste 1770, Houston, TX 77056. TEL 713-355-6500, FAX 713-355-2008, 800-879-3885, editor@countrywatch.com, http://www.countrywatch.com/.

330.96897 USA ISSN 1520-0833
COUNTRY REVIEW. MALAWI. Text in English. a. USD 39.95 (effective 2004). **Description:** Covers demographic, political, economic, social, corporate, cultural, and environmental information.
Related titles: Online - full text ed.: USD 39.95 single country; USD 99 standard - 192 countries (effective 2004).
Published by: Commercial Data International, CountryWatch, Two Riverway, Ste 1770, Houston, TX 77056. TEL 713-355-6500, FAX 713-355-2008, 800-879-3885, editor@countrywatch.com, http://www.countrywatch.com/.

330.9595 USA ISSN 1520-0841
COUNTRY REVIEW. MALAYSIA. Text in English. a. USD 39.95 (effective 2004). **Description:** Covers demographic, political, economic, social, corporate, cultural, and environmental information.
Related titles: Online - full text ed.: USD 39.95 single country; USD 99 standard - 192 countries (effective 2004).
Published by: Commercial Data International, CountryWatch, Two Riverway, Ste 1770, Houston, TX 77056. TEL 713-355-6500, FAX 713-355-2008, 800-879-3885, editor@countrywatch.com, http://www.countrywatch.com/.

330.95495 USA ISSN 1520-085X
COUNTRY REVIEW. MALDIVES. Text in English. a. USD 39.95 (effective 2004). **Description:** Covers demographic, political, economic, social, corporate, cultural, and environmental information.
Related titles: Online - full text ed.: USD 39.95 single country; USD 99 standard - 192 countries (effective 2004).
Published by: Commercial Data International, CountryWatch, Two Riverway, Ste 1770, Houston, TX 77056. TEL 713-355-6500, FAX 713-355-2008, 800-879-3885, editor@countrywatch.com, http://www.countrywatch.com/.

330.96623 USA ISSN 1520-0868
COUNTRY REVIEW. MALI. Text in English. a. USD 39.95 (effective 2004). **Description:** Covers demographic, political, economic, social, corporate, cultural, and environmental information.
Related titles: Online - full text ed.: USD 39.95 single country; USD 99 standard - 192 countries (effective 2004).
Published by: Commercial Data International, CountryWatch, Two Riverway, Ste 1770, Houston, TX 77056. TEL 713-355-6500, FAX 713-355-2008, 800-879-3885, editor@countrywatch.com, http://www.countrywatch.com/.

B

▼ *new title* ➤ *refereed* ✶ *unverified* ♦ *full entry avail.*

330.94585 USA ISSN 1520-0876
COUNTRY REVIEW. MALTA. Text in English. a. USD 39.95 (effective 2004). **Description:** Covers demographic, political, economic, social, corporate, cultural, and environmental information.
Related titles: Online - full text ed.: USD 39.95 single country; USD 99 standard - 192 countries (effective 2004).
Published by: Commercial Data International, CountryWatch, Two Riverway, Ste 1770, Houston, TX 77056. TEL 713-355-6500, FAX 713-355-2008, 800-879-3885, editor@countrywatch.com, http://www.countrywatch.com/.

330.99683 USA ISSN 1520-0892
COUNTRY REVIEW. MARSHALL ISLANDS. Text in English. a. USD 39.95 (effective 2004). **Description:** Covers demographic, political, economic, social, corporate, cultural, and environmental information.
Related titles: Online - full text ed.: USD 39.95 single country; USD 99 standard - 192 countries (effective 2004).
Published by: Commercial Data International, CountryWatch, Two Riverway, Ste 1770, Houston, TX 77056. TEL 713-355-6500, FAX 713-355-2008, 800-879-3885, editor@countrywatch.com, http://www.countrywatch.com/.

330.9661 USA ISSN 1520-0906
COUNTRY REVIEW. MAURITANIA. Text in English. a. USD 39.95 (effective 2004). **Description:** Covers demographic, political, economic, social, corporate, cultural, and environmental information.
Related titles: Online - full text ed.: USD 39.95 single country; USD 99 standard - 192 countries (effective 2004).
Published by: Commercial Data International, CountryWatch, Two Riverway, Ste 1770, Houston, TX 77056. TEL 713-355-6500, FAX 713-355-2008, 800-879-3885, editor@countrywatch.com, http://www.countrywatch.com/.

330.96982 USA ISSN 1520-0914
COUNTRY REVIEW. MAURITIUS. Text in English. a. USD 39.95 (effective 2004). **Description:** Covers demographic, political, economic, social, corporate, cultural, and environmental information.
Related titles: Online - full text ed.: USD 39.95 single country; USD 99 standard - 192 countries (effective 2004).
Published by: Commercial Data International, CountryWatch, Two Riverway, Ste 1770, Houston, TX 77056. TEL 713-355-6500, FAX 713-355-2008, 800-879-3885, editor@countrywatch.com, http://www.countrywatch.com/.

330.972 USA ISSN 1520-0922
COUNTRY REVIEW. MEXICO. Text in English. a. USD 39.95 (effective 2004). **Description:** Covers demographic, political, economic, social, corporate, cultural, and environmental information.
Related titles: Online - full text ed.: USD 39.95 single country; USD 99 standard - 192 countries (effective 2004).
Published by: Commercial Data International, CountryWatch, Two Riverway, Ste 1770, Houston, TX 77056. TEL 713-355-6500, FAX 713-355-2008, 800-879-3885, editor@countrywatch.com, http://www.countrywatch.com/.

330.9965 USA ISSN 1520-0949
COUNTRY REVIEW. MICRONESIA. Text in English. a. USD 39.95 (effective 2004). **Description:** Covers demographic, political, economic, social, corporate, cultural, and environmental information.
Related titles: Online - full text ed.: USD 39.95 single country; USD 99 standard - 192 countries (effective 2004).
Published by: Commercial Data International, CountryWatch, Two Riverway, Ste 1770, Houston, TX 77056. TEL 713-355-6500, FAX 713-355-2008, 800-879-3885, editor@countrywatch.com, http://www.countrywatch.com/.

330.9476 USA ISSN 1520-0957
COUNTRY REVIEW. MOLDOVA. Text in English. a. USD 39.95 (effective 2004). **Description:** Covers demographic, political, economic, social, corporate, cultural, and environmental information.
Related titles: Online - full text ed.: USD 39.95 single country; USD 99 standard - 192 countries (effective 2004).
Published by: Commercial Data International, CountryWatch, Two Riverway, Ste 1770, Houston, TX 77056. TEL 713-355-6500, FAX 713-355-2008, 800-879-3885, editor@countrywatch.com, http://www.countrywatch.com/.

330.944949 USA ISSN 1520-0973
COUNTRY REVIEW. MONACO. Text in English. a. USD 39.95 (effective 2004). **Description:** Covers demographic, political, economic, social, corporate, cultural, and environmental information.
Related titles: Online - full text ed.: USD 39.95 single country; USD 99 standard - 192 countries (effective 2004).
Published by: Commercial Data International, CountryWatch, Two Riverway, Ste 1770, Houston, TX 77056. TEL 713-355-6500, FAX 713-355-2008, 800-879-3885, editor@countrywatch.com, http://www.countrywatch.com/.

330.95173 USA ISSN 1520-0965
COUNTRY REVIEW. MONGOLIA. Text in English. a. USD 39.95 (effective 2004). **Description:** Covers demographic, political, economic, social, corporate, cultural, and environmental information.
Related titles: Online - full text ed.: USD 39.95 single country; USD 99 standard - 192 countries (effective 2004).
Published by: Commercial Data International, CountryWatch, Two Riverway, Ste 1770, Houston, TX 77056. TEL 713-355-6500, FAX 713-355-2008, 800-879-3885, editor@countrywatch.com, http://www.countrywatch.com/.

330.964 USA ISSN 1520-0930
COUNTRY REVIEW. MOROCCO. Text in English. a. USD 39.95 (effective 2004). **Description:** Covers demographic, political, economic, social, corporate, cultural, and environmental information.
Related titles: Online - full text ed.: USD 39.95 single country; USD 99 standard - 192 countries (effective 2004).
Published by: Commercial Data International, CountryWatch, Two Riverway, Ste 1770, Houston, TX 77056. TEL 713-355-6500, FAX 713-355-2008, 800-879-3885, editor@countrywatch.com, http://www.countrywatch.com/.

330.9679 USA ISSN 1520-0981
COUNTRY REVIEW. MOZAMBIQUE. Text in English. a. USD 39.95 (effective 2004). **Description:** Covers demographic, political, economic, social, corporate, cultural, and environmental information.
Related titles: Online - full text ed.: USD 39.95 single country; USD 99 standard - 192 countries (effective 2004).
Published by: Commercial Data International, CountryWatch, Two Riverway, Ste 1770, Houston, TX 77056. TEL 713-355-6500, FAX 713-355-2008, 800-879-3885, editor@countrywatch.com, http://www.countrywatch.com/.

330.9591 USA ISSN 1520-099X
COUNTRY REVIEW. MYANMAR. Text in English. a. USD 39.95 (effective 2004). **Description:** Covers demographic, political, economic, social, corporate, cultural, and environmental information.
Related titles: Online - full text ed.: USD 39.95 single country; USD 99 standard - 192 countries (effective 2004).
Published by: Commercial Data International, CountryWatch, Two Riverway, Ste 1770, Houston, TX 77056. TEL 713-355-6500, FAX 713-355-2008, 800-879-3885, editor@countrywatch.com, http://www.countrywatch.com/.

330.96881 USA ISSN 1520-1007
COUNTRY REVIEW. NAMIBIA. Text in English. a. USD 39.95 (effective 2004). **Description:** Covers demographic, political, economic, social, corporate, cultural, and environmental information.
Related titles: Online - full text ed.: USD 39.95 single country; USD 99 standard - 192 countries (effective 2004).
Published by: Commercial Data International, CountryWatch, Two Riverway, Ste 1770, Houston, TX 77056. TEL 713-355-6500, FAX 713-355-2008, 800-879-3885, editor@countrywatch.com, http://www.countrywatch.com/.

330.99685 USA ISSN 1520-1015
COUNTRY REVIEW. NAURU. Text in English. a. USD 39.95 (effective 2004). **Description:** Covers demographic, political, economic, social, corporate, cultural, and environmental information.
Related titles: Online - full text ed.: USD 39.95 single country; USD 99 standard - 192 countries (effective 2004).
Published by: Commercial Data International, CountryWatch, Two Riverway, Ste 1770, Houston, TX 77056. TEL 713-355-6500, FAX 713-355-2008, 800-879-3885, editor@countrywatch.com, http://www.countrywatch.com/.

330.95496 USA ISSN 1520-1023
COUNTRY REVIEW. NEPAL. Text in English. a. USD 39.95 (effective 2004). **Description:** Covers demographic, political, economic, social, corporate, cultural, and environmental information.
Related titles: Online - full text ed.: USD 39.95 single country; USD 99 standard - 192 countries (effective 2004).
Published by: Commercial Data International, CountryWatch, Two Riverway, Ste 1770, Houston, TX 77056. TEL 713-355-6500, FAX 713-355-2008, 800-879-3885, editor@countrywatch.com, http://www.countrywatch.com/.

330.9492 USA ISSN 1520-104X
COUNTRY REVIEW. NETHERLANDS. Text in English. a. USD 39.95 (effective 2004). **Description:** Covers demographic, political, economic, social, corporate, cultural, and environmental information.
Related titles: Online - full text ed.: USD 39.95 single country; USD 99 standard - 192 countries (effective 2004).
Published by: Commercial Data International, CountryWatch, Two Riverway, Ste 1770, Houston, TX 77056. TEL 713-355-6500, FAX 713-355-2008, 800-879-3885, editor@countrywatch.com, http://www.countrywatch.com/.

330.993 USA ISSN 1520-1058
COUNTRY REVIEW. NEW ZEALAND. Text in English. a. USD 39.95 (effective 2004). **Description:** Covers demographic, political, economic, social, corporate, cultural, and environmental information.
Related titles: Online - full text ed.: USD 39.95 single country; USD 99 standard - 192 countries (effective 2004).
Published by: Commercial Data International, CountryWatch, Two Riverway, Ste 1770, Houston, TX 77056. TEL 713-355-6500, FAX 713-355-2008, 800-879-3885, editor@countrywatch.com, http://www.countrywatch.com/.

330.97285 USA ISSN 1520-1066
COUNTRY REVIEW. NICARAGUA. Text in English. a. USD 39.95 (effective 2004). **Description:** Covers demographic, political, economic, social, corporate, cultural, and environmental information.
Related titles: Online - full text ed.: USD 39.95 single country; USD 99 standard - 192 countries (effective 2004).
Published by: Commercial Data International, CountryWatch, Two Riverway, Ste 1770, Houston, TX 77056. TEL 713-355-6500, FAX 713-355-2008, 800-879-3885, editor@countrywatch.com, http://www.countrywatch.com/.

330.96626 USA ISSN 1520-1074
COUNTRY REVIEW. NIGER. Text in English. a. USD 39.95 (effective 2004). **Description:** Covers demographic, political, economic, social, corporate, cultural, and environmental information.
Related titles: Online - full text ed.: USD 39.95 single country; USD 99 standard - 192 countries (effective 2004).
Published by: Commercial Data International, CountryWatch, Two Riverway, Ste 1770, Houston, TX 77056. TEL 713-355-6500, FAX 713-355-2008, 800-879-3885, editor@countrywatch.com, http://www.countrywatch.com/.

330.9669 USA ISSN 1520-1082
COUNTRY REVIEW. NIGERIA. Text in English. a. USD 39.95 (effective 2004). **Description:** Covers demographic, political, economic, social, corporate, cultural, and environmental information.
Related titles: Online - full text ed.: USD 39.95 single country; USD 99 standard - 192 countries (effective 2004).
Published by: Commercial Data International, CountryWatch, Two Riverway, Ste 1770, Houston, TX 77056. TEL 713-355-6500, FAX 713-355-2008, 800-879-3885, editor@countrywatch.com, http://www.countrywatch.com/.

330.95193 USA ISSN 1520-1635
COUNTRY REVIEW. NORTH KOREA. Text in English. a. USD 39.95 (effective 2004). **Description:** Covers demographic, political, economic, social, corporate, cultural, and environmental information.
Related titles: Online - full text ed.: USD 39.95 single country; USD 99 standard - 192 countries (effective 2004).
Published by: Commercial Data International, CountryWatch, Two Riverway, Ste 1770, Houston, TX 77056. TEL 713-355-6500, FAX 713-355-2008, 800-879-3885, editor@countrywatch.com, http://www.countrywatch.com/.

330.9481 USA ISSN 1520-1090
COUNTRY REVIEW. NORWAY. Text in English. a. USD 39.95 (effective 2004). **Description:** Covers demographic, political, economic, social, corporate, cultural, and environmental information.
Related titles: Online - full text ed.: USD 39.95 single country; USD 99 standard - 192 countries (effective 2004).
Published by: Commercial Data International, CountryWatch, Two Riverway, Ste 1770, Houston, TX 77056. TEL 713-355-6500, FAX 713-355-2008, 800-879-3885, editor@countrywatch.com, http://www.countrywatch.com/.

330.95353 USA ISSN 1520-1104
COUNTRY REVIEW. OMAN. Text in English. a. USD 39.95 (effective 2004). **Description:** Covers demographic, political, economic, social, corporate, cultural, and environmental information.
Related titles: Online - full text ed.: USD 39.95 single country; USD 99 standard - 192 countries (effective 2004).
Published by: Commercial Data International, CountryWatch, Two Riverway, Ste 1770, Houston, TX 77056. TEL 713-355-6500, FAX 713-355-2008, 800-879-3885, editor@countrywatch.com, http://www.countrywatch.com/.

330.95491 USA
COUNTRY REVIEW. PAKISTAN. Text in English. a. USD 39.95 (effective 2004). **Description:** Covers demographic, political, economic, social, corporate, cultural, and environmental information.
Related titles: Online - full text ed.: USD 39.95 single country; USD 99 standard - 192 countries (effective 2004).
Published by: Commercial Data International, CountryWatch, Two Riverway, Ste 1770, Houston, TX 77056. TEL 713-355-6500, FAX 713-355-2008, 800-879-3885, editor@countrywatch.com, http://www.countrywatch.com/.

330.9966 USA ISSN 1520-1112
COUNTRY REVIEW. PALAU. Text in English. a. USD 39.95 (effective 2004). **Description:** Covers demographic, political, economic, social, corporate, cultural, and environmental information.
Related titles: Online - full text ed.: USD 39.95 single country; USD 99 standard - 192 countries (effective 2004).
Published by: Commercial Data International, CountryWatch, Two Riverway, Ste 1770, Houston, TX 77056. TEL 713-355-6500, FAX 713-355-2008, 800-879-3885, editor@countrywatch.com, http://www.countrywatch.com/.

330.97287 USA ISSN 1520-1120
COUNTRY REVIEW. PANAMA. Text in English. a. USD 39.95 (effective 2004). **Description:** Covers demographic, political, economic, social, corporate, cultural, and environmental information.

Related titles: Online - full text ed.: USD 39.95 single country; USD 99 standard - 192 countries (effective 2004).
Published by: Commercial Data International, CountryWatch, Two Riverway, Ste 1770, Houston, TX 77056. TEL 713-355-6500, FAX 713-355-2008, 800-879-3885, editor@countrywatch.com, http://www.countrywatch.com/.

330.9953 USA ISSN 1520-1139
COUNTRY REVIEW. PAPUA NEW GUINEA. Text in English. a. USD 39.95 (effective 2004). **Description:** Covers demographic, political, economic, social, corporate, cultural, and environmental information.
Related titles: Online - full text ed.: USD 39.95 single country; USD 99 standard - 192 countries (effective 2004).
Published by: Commercial Data International, CountryWatch, Two Riverway, Ste 1770, Houston, TX 77056. TEL 713-355-6500, FAX 713-355-2008, 800-879-3885, editor@countrywatch.com, http://www.countrywatch.com/.

330.9892 USA ISSN 1520-1147
COUNTRY REVIEW. PARAGUAY. Text in English. a. USD 39.95 (effective 2004). **Description:** Covers demographic, political, economic, social, corporate, cultural, and environmental information.
Related titles: Online - full text ed.: USD 39.95 single country; USD 99 standard - 192 countries (effective 2004).
Published by: Commercial Data International, CountryWatch, Two Riverway, Ste 1770, Houston, TX 77056. TEL 713-355-6500, FAX 713-355-2008, 800-879-3885, editor@countrywatch.com, http://www.countrywatch.com/.

330.985 USA ISSN 1520-1155
COUNTRY REVIEW. PERU. Text in English. a. USD 39.95 (effective 2004). **Description:** Covers demographic, political, economic, social, corporate, cultural, and environmental information.
Related titles: Online - full text ed.: USD 39.95 single country; USD 99 standard - 192 countries (effective 2004).
Published by: Commercial Data International, CountryWatch, Two Riverway, Ste 1770, Houston, TX 77056. TEL 713-355-6500, FAX 713-355-2008, 800-879-3885, editor@countrywatch.com, http://www.countrywatch.com/.

330.9599 USA ISSN 1520-1163
COUNTRY REVIEW. PHILIPPINES. Text in English. a. USD 39.95 (effective 2004). **Description:** Covers demographic, political, economic, social, corporate, cultural, and environmental information.
Related titles: Online - full text ed.: USD 39.95 single country; USD 99 standard - 192 countries (effective 2004).
Published by: Commercial Data International, CountryWatch, Two Riverway, Ste 1770, Houston, TX 77056. TEL 713-355-6500, FAX 713-355-2008, 800-879-3885, editor@countrywatch.com, http://www.countrywatch.com/.

330.9438 USA ISSN 1520-1171
COUNTRY REVIEW. POLAND. Text in English. a. USD 39.95 (effective 2004). **Description:** Covers demographic, political, economic, social, corporate, cultural, and environmental information.
Related titles: Online - full text ed.: USD 39.95 single country; USD 99 standard - 192 countries (effective 2004).
Published by: Commercial Data International, CountryWatch, Two Riverway, Ste 1770, Houston, TX 77056. TEL 713-355-6500, FAX 713-355-2008, 800-879-3885, editor@countrywatch.com, http://www.countrywatch.com/.

330.9469 USA ISSN 1520-118X
COUNTRY REVIEW. PORTUGAL. Text in English. a. USD 39.95 (effective 2004). **Description:** Covers demographic, political, economic, social, corporate, cultural, and environmental information.
Related titles: Online - full text ed.: USD 39.95 single country; USD 99 standard - 192 countries (effective 2004).
Published by: Commercial Data International, CountryWatch, Two Riverway, Ste 1770, Houston, TX 77056. TEL 713-355-6500, FAX 713-355-2008, 800-879-3885, editor@countrywatch.com, http://www.countrywatch.com/.

330.9563 USA ISSN 1520-1198
COUNTRY REVIEW. QATAR. Text in English. a. USD 39.95 (effective 2004). **Description:** Covers demographic, political, economic, social, corporate, cultural, and environmental information.
Related titles: Online - full text ed.: USD 39.95 single country; USD 99 standard - 192 countries (effective 2004).
Published by: Commercial Data International, CountryWatch, Two Riverway, Ste 1770, Houston, TX 77056. TEL 713-355-6500, FAX 713-355-2008, 800-879-3885, editor@countrywatch.com, http://www.countrywatch.com/.

330.9498 USA ISSN 1520-1201
COUNTRY REVIEW. ROMANIA. Text in English. a. USD 39.95 (effective 2004). **Description:** Covers demographic, political, economic, social, corporate, cultural, and environmental information.
Related titles: Online - full text ed.: USD 39.95 single country; USD 99 standard - 192 countries (effective 2004).
Published by: Commercial Data International, CountryWatch, Two Riverway, Ste 1770, Houston, TX 77056. TEL 713-355-6500, FAX 713-355-2008, 800-879-3885, editor@countrywatch.com, http://www.countrywatch.com/.

330.947 USA ISSN 1520-121X
COUNTRY REVIEW. RUSSIA. Text in English. a. USD 39.95 (effective 2004). **Description:** Covers demographic, political, economic, social, corporate, cultural, and environmental information.
Related titles: Online - full text ed.: USD 39.95 single country; USD 99 standard - 192 countries (effective 2004).
Published by: Commercial Data International, CountryWatch, Two Riverway, Ste 1770, Houston, TX 77056. TEL 713-355-6500, FAX 713-355-2008, 800-879-3885, editor@countrywatch.com, http://www.countrywatch.com/.

330.967571 USA ISSN 1520-1228
COUNTRY REVIEW. RWANDA. Text in English. a. USD 39.95 (effective 2004). **Description:** Covers demographic, political, economic, social, corporate, cultural, and environmental information.
Related titles: Online - full text ed.: USD 39.95 single country; USD 99 standard - 192 countries (effective 2004).
Published by: Commercial Data International, CountryWatch, Two Riverway, Ste 1770, Houston, TX 77056. TEL 713-355-6500, FAX 713-355-2008, 800-879-3885, editor@countrywatch.com, http://www.countrywatch.com/.

330.9729844 USA ISSN 1520-1252
COUNTRY REVIEW. SAIN VICENT AND THE GRENADINES. Text in English. a. USD 39.95 (effective 2004). **Description:** Covers demographic, political, economic, social, corporate, cultural, and environmental information.
Related titles: Online - full text ed.: USD 39.95 single country; USD 99 standard - 192 countries (effective 2004).
Published by: Commercial Data International, CountryWatch, Two Riverway, Ste 1770, Houston, TX 77056. TEL 713-355-6500, FAX 713-355-2008, 800-879-3885, editor@countrywatch.com, http://www.countrywatch.com/.

330.972973 USA ISSN 1520-1236
COUNTRY REVIEW. SAINT KITTS NEVIS. Text in English. a. USD 39.95 (effective 2004). **Description:** Covers demographic, political, economic, social, corporate, cultural, and environmental information.
Related titles: Online - full text ed.: USD 39.95 single country; USD 99 standard - 192 countries (effective 2004).
Published by: Commercial Data International, CountryWatch, Two Riverway, Ste 1770, Houston, TX 77056. TEL 713-355-6500, FAX 713-355-2008, 800-879-3885, editor@countrywatch.com, http://www.countrywatch.com/.

330.9729843 USA ISSN 1520-1244
COUNTRY REVIEW. SAINT LUCIA. Text in English. a. USD 39.95 (effective 2004). **Description:** Covers demographic, political, economic, social, corporate, cultural, and environmental information.
Related titles: Online - full text ed.: USD 39.95 single country; USD 99 standard - 192 countries (effective 2004).
Published by: Commercial Data International, CountryWatch, Two Riverway, Ste 1770, Houston, TX 77056. TEL 713-355-6500, FAX 713-355-2008, 800-879-3885, editor@countrywatch.com, http://www.countrywatch.com/.

330.959 USA
COUNTRY REVIEW. SAMOA. Text in English. a. USD 39.95 (effective 2004).
Related titles: Online - full text ed.: USD 39.95 single country; USD 99 standard - 192 countries (effective 2004).
Published by: Commercial Data International, CountryWatch, Two Riverway, Ste 1770, Houston, TX 77056. TEL 713-355-6500, FAX 713-355-2008, 800-879-3885, editor@countrywatch.com, http://www.countrywatch.com/.

330.94549 USA ISSN 1520-1260
COUNTRY REVIEW. SAN MARINO. Text in English. a. USD 39.95 (effective 2004). **Description:** Covers demographic, political, economic, social, corporate, cultural, and environmental information.
Related titles: Online - full text ed.: USD 39.95 single country; USD 99 standard - 192 countries (effective 2004).
Published by: Commercial Data International, CountryWatch, Two Riverway, Ste 1770, Houston, TX 77056. TEL 713-355-6500, FAX 713-355-2008, 800-879-3885, editor@countrywatch.com, http://www.countrywatch.com/.

330.96715 USA
COUNTRY REVIEW. SAO TOME & PRINCIPE. Text in English. a. USD 39.95 (effective 2004).
Related titles: Online - full text ed.: USD 39.95 single country; USD 99 standard - 192 countries (effective 2004).
Published by: Commercial Data International, CountryWatch, Two Riverway, Ste 1770, Houston, TX 77056. TEL 713-355-6500, FAX 713-355-2008, 800-879-3885, editor@countrywatch.com, http://www.countrywatch.com/.

330.9538 USA ISSN 1520-1287
COUNTRY REVIEW. SAUDI ARABIA. Text in English. a. USD 39.95 (effective 2004). **Description:** Covers demographic, political, economic, social, corporate, cultural, and environmental information.
Related titles: Online - full text ed.: USD 39.95 single country; USD 99 standard - 192 countries (effective 2004).
Published by: Commercial Data International, CountryWatch, Two Riverway, Ste 1770, Houston, TX 77056. TEL 713-355-6500, FAX 713-355-2008, 800-879-3885, editor@countrywatch.com, http://www.countrywatch.com/.

330.9663 USA ISSN 1520-1295
COUNTRY REVIEW. SENEGAL. Text in English. a. USD 39.95 (effective 2004). **Description:** Covers demographic, political, economic, social, corporate, cultural, and environmental information.
Related titles: Online - full text ed.: USD 39.95 single country; USD 99 standard - 192 countries (effective 2004).
Published by: Commercial Data International, CountryWatch, Two Riverway, Ste 1770, Houston, TX 77056. TEL 713-355-6500, FAX 713-355-2008, 800-879-3885, editor@countrywatch.com, http://www.countrywatch.com/.

330.94971 USA ISSN 1520-1309
COUNTRY REVIEW. SERBIA AND MONTENEGRO. Text in English. a. USD 39.95 (effective 2004). **Description:** Covers demographic, political, economic, social, corporate, cultural, and environmental information.
Related titles: Online - full text ed.: USD 39.95 single country; USD 99 standard - 192 countries (effective 2004).
Published by: Commercial Data International, CountryWatch, Two Riverway, Ste 1770, Houston, TX 77056. TEL 713-355-6500, FAX 713-355-2008, 800-879-3885, editor@countrywatch.com, http://www.countrywatch.com/.

B

330.9696 USA ISSN 1520-0744
COUNTRY REVIEW. SEYCHELLES. Text in English. a. USD 39.95 (effective 2004). **Description:** Covers demographic, political, economic, social, corporate, cultural, and environmental information.
Related titles: Online - full text ed.: USD 39.95 single country; USD 99 standard - 192 countries (effective 2004).
Published by: Commercial Data International, CountryWatch, Two Riverway, Ste 1770, Houston, TX 77056. TEL 713-355-6500, FAX 713-355-2008, 800-879-3885, editor@countrywatch.com, http://www.countrywatch.com/.

330.9664 USA ISSN 1520-1317
COUNTRY REVIEW. SIERRA LEONE. Text in English. a. USD 39.95 (effective 2004). **Description:** Covers demographic, political, economic, social, corporate, cultural, and environmental information.
Related titles: Online - full text ed.: USD 39.95 single country; USD 99 standard - 192 countries (effective 2004).
Published by: Commercial Data International, CountryWatch, Two Riverway, Ste 1770, Houston, TX 77056. TEL 713-355-6500, FAX 713-355-2008, 800-879-3885, editor@countrywatch.com, http://www.countrywatch.com/.

330.94373 USA ISSN 1520-1333
COUNTRY REVIEW. SLOVAKIA. Text in English. a. USD 39.95 (effective 2004). **Description:** Covers demographic, political, economic, social, corporate, cultural, and environmental information.
Related titles: Online - full text ed.: USD 39.95 single country; USD 99 standard - 192 countries (effective 2004).
Published by: Commercial Data International, CountryWatch, Two Riverway, Ste 1770, Houston, TX 77056. TEL 713-355-6500, FAX 713-355-2008, 800-879-3885, editor@countrywatch.com, http://www.countrywatch.com/.

330.94973 USA ISSN 1520-1341
COUNTRY REVIEW. SLOVENIA. Text in English. a. USD 39.95 (effective 2004). **Description:** Covers demographic, political, economic, social, corporate, cultural, and environmental information.
Related titles: Online - full text ed.: USD 39.95 single country; USD 99 standard - 192 countries (effective 2004).
Published by: Commercial Data International, CountryWatch, Two Riverway, Ste 1770, Houston, TX 77056. TEL 713-355-6500, FAX 713-355-2008, 800-879-3885, editor@countrywatch.com, http://www.countrywatch.com/.

330.99593 USA ISSN 1520-135X
COUNTRY REVIEW. SOLOMON ISLANDS. Text in English. a. USD 39.95 (effective 2004). **Description:** Covers demographic, political, economic, social, corporate, cultural, and environmental information.
Related titles: Online - full text ed.: USD 39.95 single country; USD 99 standard - 192 countries (effective 2004).
Published by: Commercial Data International, CountryWatch, Two Riverway, Ste 1770, Houston, TX 77056. TEL 713-355-6500, FAX 713-355-2008, 800-879-3885, editor@countrywatch.com, http://www.countrywatch.com/.

330.96773 USA ISSN 1520-1368
COUNTRY REVIEW. SOMALIA. Text in English. a. USD 39.95 (effective 2004). **Description:** Covers demographic, political, economic, social, corporate, cultural, and environmental information.
Related titles: Online - full text ed.: USD 39.95 single country; USD 99 standard - 192 countries (effective 2004).
Published by: Commercial Data International, CountryWatch, Two Riverway, Ste 1770, Houston, TX 77056. TEL 713-355-6500, FAX 713-355-2008, 800-879-3885, editor@countrywatch.com, http://www.countrywatch.com/.

▼ *new title* ➤ *refereed* ✶ *unverified* ◆ *full entry avail.*

330.968 USA ISSN 1520-1376
COUNTRY REVIEW. SOUTH AFRICA. Text in English. a. USD 39.95 (effective 2004). **Description:** Covers demographic, political, economic, social, corporate, cultural, and environmental information.
Related titles: Online - full text ed.: USD 39.95 single country; USD 99 standard - 192 countries (effective 2004).
Published by: Commercial Data International, CountryWatch, Two Riverway, Ste 1770, Houston, TX 77056. TEL 713-355-6500, FAX 713-355-2008, 800-879-3885, editor@countrywatch.com, http://www.countrywatch.com/.

330.95195 USA ISSN 1520-1643
COUNTRY REVIEW. SOUTH KOREA. Text in English. a. USD 39.95 (effective 2004). **Description:** Covers demographic, political, economic, social, corporate, cultural, and environmental information.
Related titles: Online - full text ed.: USD 39.95 single country; USD 99 standard - 192 countries (effective 2004).
Published by: Commercial Data International, CountryWatch, Two Riverway, Ste 1770, Houston, TX 77056. TEL 713-355-6500, FAX 713-355-2008, 800-879-3885, editor@countrywatch.com, http://www.countrywatch.com/.

B

330.946 USA ISSN 1520-1384
COUNTRY REVIEW. SPAIN. Text in English. a. USD 39.95 (effective 2004). **Description:** Covers demographic, political, economic, social, corporate, cultural, and environmental information.
Related titles: Online - full text ed.: USD 39.95 single country; USD 99 standard - 192 countries (effective 2004).
Published by: Commercial Data International, CountryWatch, Two Riverway, Ste 1770, Houston, TX 77056. TEL 713-355-6500, FAX 713-355-2008, 800-879-3885, editor@countrywatch.com, http://www.countrywatch.com/.

330.95493 USA ISSN 1520-1392
COUNTRY REVIEW. SRI LANKA. Text in English. a. USD 39.95 (effective 2004). **Description:** Covers demographic, political, economic, social, corporate, cultural, and environmental information.
Related titles: Online - full text ed.: USD 39.95 single country; USD 99 standard - 192 countries (effective 2004).
Published by: Commercial Data International, CountryWatch, Two Riverway, Ste 1770, Houston, TX 77056. TEL 713-355-6500, FAX 713-355-2008, 800-879-3885, editor@countrywatch.com, http://www.countrywatch.com/.

330.9624 USA ISSN 1520-1406
COUNTRY REVIEW. SUDAN. Text in English. a. USD 39.95 (effective 2004). **Description:** Covers demographic, political, economic, social, corporate, cultural, and environmental information.
Related titles: Online - full text ed.: USD 39.95 single country; USD 99 standard - 192 countries (effective 2004).
Published by: Commercial Data International, CountryWatch, Two Riverway, Ste 1770, Houston, TX 77056. TEL 713-355-6500, FAX 713-355-2008, 800-879-3885, editor@countrywatch.com, http://www.countrywatch.com/.

330.9883 USA ISSN 1520-1414
COUNTRY REVIEW. SURINAME. Text in English. a. USD 39.95 (effective 2004). **Description:** Covers demographic, political, economic, social, corporate, cultural, and environmental information.
Related titles: Online - full text ed.: USD 39.95 single country; USD 99 standard - 192 countries (effective 2004).
Published by: Commercial Data International, CountryWatch, Two Riverway, Ste 1770, Houston, TX 77056. TEL 713-355-6500, FAX 713-355-2008, 800-879-3885, editor@countrywatch.com, http://www.countrywatch.com/.

330.96887 USA ISSN 1520-0736
COUNTRY REVIEW. SWAZILAND. Text in English. a. USD 39.95 (effective 2004). **Description:** Covers demographic, political, economic, social, corporate, cultural, and environmental information.
Related titles: Online - full text ed.: USD 39.95 single country; USD 99 standard - 192 countries (effective 2004).
Published by: Commercial Data International, CountryWatch, Two Riverway, Ste 1770, Houston, TX 77056. TEL 713-355-6500, FAX 713-355-2008, 800-879-3885, editor@countrywatch.com, http://www.countrywatch.com/.

330.9485 USA ISSN 1520-1422
COUNTRY REVIEW. SWEDEN. Text in English. a. USD 39.95 (effective 2004). **Description:** Covers demographic, political, economic, social, corporate, cultural, and environmental information.
Related titles: Online - full text ed.: USD 39.95 single country; USD 99 standard - 192 countries (effective 2004).
Published by: Commercial Data International, CountryWatch, Two Riverway, Ste 1770, Houston, TX 77056. TEL 713-355-6500, FAX 713-355-2008, 800-879-3885, editor@countrywatch.com, http://www.countrywatch.com/.

330.9494 USA ISSN 1520-1430
COUNTRY REVIEW. SWITZERLAND. Text in English. a. USD 39.95 (effective 2004). **Description:** Covers demographic, political, economic, social, corporate, cultural, and environmental information.
Related titles: Online - full text ed.: USD 39.95 single country; USD 99 standard - 192 countries (effective 2004).
Published by: Commercial Data International, CountryWatch, Two Riverway, Ste 1770, Houston, TX 77056. TEL 713-355-6500, FAX 713-355-2008, 800-879-3885, editor@countrywatch.com, http://www.countrywatch.com/.

330.95691 USA ISSN 1520-1449
COUNTRY REVIEW. SYRIA. Text in English. a. USD 39.95 (effective 2004). **Description:** Covers demographic, political, economic, social, corporate, cultural, and environmental information.
Related titles: Online - full text ed.: USD 39.95 single country; USD 99 standard - 192 countries (effective 2004).
Published by: Commercial Data International, CountryWatch, Two Riverway, Ste 1770, Houston, TX 77056. TEL 713-355-6500, FAX 713-355-2008, 800-879-3885, editor@countrywatch.com, http://www.countrywatch.com/.

330.9586 USA ISSN 1520-1457
COUNTRY REVIEW. TAJIKISTAN. Text in English. a. USD 39.95 (effective 2004). **Description:** Covers demographic, political, economic, social, corporate, cultural, and environmental information.
Related titles: Online - full text ed.: USD 39.95 single country; USD 99 standard - 192 countries (effective 2004).
Published by: Commercial Data International, CountryWatch, Two Riverway, Ste 1770, Houston, TX 77056. TEL 713-355-6500, FAX 713-355-2008, 800-879-3885, editor@countrywatch.com, http://www.countrywatch.com/.

330.9678 USA ISSN 1520-1465
COUNTRY REVIEW. TANZANIA. Text in English. a. USD 39.95 (effective 2004). **Description:** Covers demographic, political, economic, social, corporate, cultural, and environmental information.
Related titles: Online - full text ed.: USD 39.95 single country; USD 99 standard - 192 countries (effective 2004).
Published by: Commercial Data International, CountryWatch, Two Riverway, Ste 1770, Houston, TX 77056. TEL 713-355-6500, FAX 713-355-2008, 800-879-3885, editor@countrywatch.com, http://www.countrywatch.com/.

330.9593 USA
COUNTRY REVIEW. THAILAND. Text in English. a. USD 39.95 (effective 2004). **Description:** Covers demographic, political, economic, social, corporate, cultural, and environmental information.
Related titles: Online - full text ed.: USD 39.95 single country; USD 99 standard - 192 countries (effective 2004).
Published by: Commercial Data International, CountryWatch, Two Riverway, Ste 1770, Houston, TX 77056. TEL 713-355-6500, FAX 713-355-2008, 800-879-3885, editor@countrywatch.com, http://www.countrywatch.com/.

330.96681 USA ISSN 1520-1473
COUNTRY REVIEW. TOGO. Text in English. a. USD 39.95 (effective 2004). **Description:** Covers demographic, political, economic, social, corporate, cultural, and environmental information.
Related titles: Online - full text ed.: USD 39.95 single country; USD 99 standard - 192 countries (effective 2004).
Published by: Commercial Data International, CountryWatch, Two Riverway, Ste 1770, Houston, TX 77056. TEL 713-355-6500, FAX 713-355-2008, 800-879-3885, editor@countrywatch.com, http://www.countrywatch.com/.

330.99612 USA ISSN 1520-1481
COUNTRY REVIEW. TONGA. Text in English. a. USD 39.95 (effective 2004). **Description:** Covers demographic, political, economic, social, corporate, cultural, and environmental information.
Related titles: Online - full text ed.: USD 39.95 single country; USD 99 standard - 192 countries (effective 2004).
Published by: Commercial Data International, CountryWatch, Two Riverway, Ste 1770, Houston, TX 77056. TEL 713-355-6500, FAX 713-355-2008, 800-879-3885, editor@countrywatch.com, http://www.countrywatch.com/.

330.972983 USA ISSN 1520-149X
COUNTRY REVIEW. TRINIDAD AND TOBAGO. Text in English. a. USD 39.95 (effective 2004). **Description:** Covers demographic, political, economic, social, corporate, cultural, and environmental information.
Related titles: Online - full text ed.: USD 39.95 single country; USD 99 standard - 192 countries (effective 2004).
Published by: Commercial Data International, CountryWatch, Two Riverway, Ste 1770, Houston, TX 77056. TEL 713-355-6500, FAX 713-355-2008, 800-879-3885, editor@countrywatch.com, http://www.countrywatch.com/.

330.9611 USA ISSN 1520-1503
COUNTRY REVIEW. TUNISIA. Text in English. a. USD 39.95 (effective 2004). **Description:** Covers demographic, political, economic, social, corporate, cultural, and environmental information.
Related titles: Online - full text ed.: USD 39.95 single country; USD 99 standard - 192 countries (effective 2004).
Published by: Commercial Data International, CountryWatch, Two Riverway, Ste 1770, Houston, TX 77056. TEL 713-355-6500, FAX 713-355-2008, 800-879-3885, editor@countrywatch.com, http://www.countrywatch.com/.

330.9561 USA ISSN 1520-1511
COUNTRY REVIEW. TURKEY. Text in English. a. USD 39.95 (effective 2004). **Description:** Covers demographic, political, economic, social, corporate, cultural, and environmental information.
Related titles: Online - full text ed.: USD 39.95 single country; USD 99 standard - 192 countries (effective 2004).
Published by: Commercial Data International, CountryWatch, Two Riverway, Ste 1770, Houston, TX 77056. TEL 713-355-6500, FAX 713-355-2008, 800-879-3885, editor@countrywatch.com, http://www.countrywatch.com/.

330.9585 USA ISSN 1520-152X
COUNTRY REVIEW. TURKMENISTAN. Text in English. a. USD 39.95 (effective 2004). **Description:** Covers demographic, political, economic, social, corporate, cultural, and environmental information.
Related titles: Online - full text ed.: USD 39.95 single country; USD 99 standard - 192 countries (effective 2004).
Published by: Commercial Data International, CountryWatch, Two Riverway, Ste 1770, Houston, TX 77056. TEL 713-355-6500, FAX 713-355-2008, 800-879-3885, editor@countrywatch.com, http://www.countrywatch.com/.

330.99682 USA ISSN 1520-1538
COUNTRY REVIEW. TUVALU. Text in English. a. USD 39.95 (effective 2004). **Description:** Covers demographic, political, economic, social, corporate, cultural, and environmental information.
Related titles: Online - full text ed.: USD 39.95 single country; USD 99 standard - 192 countries (effective 2004).
Published by: Commercial Data International, CountryWatch, Two Riverway, Ste 1770, Houston, TX 77056. TEL 713-355-6500, FAX 713-355-2008, 800-879-3885, editor@countrywatch.com, http://www.countrywatch.com/.

330.96761 USA ISSN 1520-1546
COUNTRY REVIEW. UGANDA. Text in English. a. USD 39.95 (effective 2004). **Description:** Covers demographic, political, economic, social, corporate, cultural, and environmental information.
Related titles: Online - full text ed.: USD 39.95 single country; USD 99 standard - 192 countries (effective 2004).
Published by: Commercial Data International, CountryWatch, Two Riverway, Ste 1770, Houston, TX 77056. TEL 713-355-6500, FAX 713-355-2008, 800-879-3885, editor@countrywatch.com, http://www.countrywatch.com/.

330.9477 USA ISSN 1520-1554
COUNTRY REVIEW. UKRAINE. Text in English. a. USD 39.95 (effective 2004). **Description:** Covers demographic, political, economic, social, corporate, cultural, and environmental information.
Related titles: Online - full text ed.: USD 39.95 single country; USD 99 standard - 192 countries (effective 2004).
Published by: Commercial Data International, CountryWatch, Two Riverway, Ste 1770, Houston, TX 77056. TEL 713-355-6500, FAX 713-355-2008, 800-879-3885, editor@countrywatch.com, http://www.countrywatch.com/.

330.95357 USA ISSN 1520-1562
COUNTRY REVIEW. UNITED ARAB EMIRATES. Text in English. a. USD 39.95 (effective 2004). **Description:** Covers demographic, political, economic, social, corporate, cultural, and environmental information.
Related titles: Online - full text ed.: USD 39.95 single country; USD 99 standard - 192 countries (effective 2004).
Published by: Commercial Data International, CountryWatch, Two Riverway, Ste 1770, Houston, TX 77056. TEL 713-355-6500, FAX 713-355-2008, 800-879-3885, editor@countrywatch.com, http://www.countrywatch.com/.

330.941 USA ISSN 1520-1570
COUNTRY REVIEW. UNITED KINGDOM. Text in English. a. USD 39.95 (effective 2004). **Description:** Covers demographic, political, economic, social, corporate, cultural, and environmental information.
Related titles: Online - full text ed.: USD 39.95 single country; USD 99 standard - 192 countries (effective 2004).
Published by: Commercial Data International, CountryWatch, Two Riverway, Ste 1770, Houston, TX 77056. TEL 713-355-6500, FAX 713-355-2008, 800-879-3885, editor@countrywatch.com, http://www.countrywatch.com/.

330.973 USA ISSN 1520-1589
COUNTRY REVIEW. UNITED STATES. Text in English. a. USD 39.95 (effective 2004). **Description:** Covers demographic, political, economic, social, corporate, cultural, and environmental information.
Related titles: Online - full text ed.: USD 39.95 single country; USD 99 standard - 192 countries (effective 2004).
Published by: Commercial Data International, CountryWatch, Two Riverway, Ste 1770, Houston, TX 77056. TEL 713-355-6500, FAX 713-355-2008, 800-879-3885, editor@countrywatch.com, http://www.countrywatch.com/.

330.9895 USA ISSN 1520-1597
COUNTRY REVIEW. URUGUAY. Text in English. a. USD 39.95 (effective 2004). **Description:** Covers demographic, political, economic, social, corporate, cultural, and environmental information.

Related titles: Online - full text ed.: USD 39.95 single country; USD 99 standard - 192 countries (effective 2004).
Published by: Commercial Data International, CountryWatch, Two Riverway, Ste 1770, Houston, TX 77056. TEL 713-355-6500, FAX 713-355-2008, 800-879-3885, editor@countrywatch.com, http://www.countrywatch.com/.

330.9587 USA ISSN 1520-1600
COUNTRY REVIEW. UZBEKISTAN. Text in English. a. USD 39.95 (effective 2004). **Description:** Covers demographic, political, economic, social, corporate, cultural, and environmental information.
Related titles: Online - full text ed.: USD 39.95 single country; USD 99 standard - 192 countries (effective 2004).
Published by: Commercial Data International, CountryWatch, Two Riverway, Ste 1770, Houston, TX 77056. TEL 713-355-6500, FAX 713-355-2008, 800-879-3885, editor@countrywatch.com, http://www.countrywatch.com/.

330.99595 USA ISSN 1520-0663
COUNTRY REVIEW. VANUATU. Text in English. a. USD 39.95 (effective 2004). **Description:** Covers demographic, political, economic, social, corporate, cultural, and environmental information.
Related titles: Online - full text ed.: USD 39.95 single country; USD 99 standard - 192 countries (effective 2004).
Published by: Commercial Data International, CountryWatch, Two Riverway, Ste 1770, Houston, TX 77056. TEL 713-355-6500, FAX 713-355-2008, 800-879-3885, editor@countrywatch.com, http://www.countrywatch.com/.

330.987 USA ISSN 1520-0884
COUNTRY REVIEW. VENEZUELA. Text in English. a. USD 39.95 (effective 2004). **Description:** Covers demographic, political, economic, social, corporate, cultural, and environmental information.
Related titles: Online - full text ed.: USD 39.95 single country; USD 99 standard - 192 countries (effective 2004).
Published by: Commercial Data International, CountryWatch, Two Riverway, Ste 1770, Houston, TX 77056. TEL 713-355-6500, FAX 713-355-2008, 800-879-3885, editor@countrywatch.com, http://www.countrywatch.com/.

330.9597 USA ISSN 1520-0671
COUNTRY REVIEW. VIETNAM. Text in English. a. USD 39.95 (effective 2004). **Description:** Covers demographic, political, economic, social, corporate, cultural, and environmental information.
Related titles: Online - full text ed.: USD 39.95 single country; USD 99 standard - 192 countries (effective 2004).
Published by: Commercial Data International, CountryWatch, Two Riverway, Ste 1770, Houston, TX 77056. TEL 713-355-6500, FAX 713-355-2008, 800-879-3885, editor@countrywatch.com, http://www.countrywatch.com/.

330.9533 USA ISSN 1520-0698
COUNTRY REVIEW. YEMEN. Text in English. a. USD 39.95 (effective 2004). **Description:** Covers demographic, political, economic, social, corporate, cultural, and environmental information.
Related titles: Online - full text ed.: USD 39.95 single country; USD 99 standard - 192 countries (effective 2004).
Published by: Commercial Data International, CountryWatch, Two Riverway, Ste 1770, Houston, TX 77056. TEL 713-355-6500, FAX 713-355-2008, 800-879-3885, editor@countrywatch.com, http://www.countrywatch.com/.

330.96894 USA ISSN 1520-0701
COUNTRY REVIEW. ZAMBIA. Text in English. a. USD 39.95 (effective 2004). **Description:** Covers demographic, political, economic, social, corporate, cultural, and environmental information.
Related titles: Online - full text ed.: USD 39.95 single country; USD 99 standard - 192 countries (effective 2004).
Published by: Commercial Data International, CountryWatch, Two Riverway, Ste 1770, Houston, TX 77056. TEL 713-355-6500, FAX 713-355-2008, 800-879-3885, editor@countrywatch.com, http://www.countrywatch.com/.

330.96891 USA ISSN 1520-071X
COUNTRY REVIEW. ZIMBABWE. Text in English. a. USD 39.95 (effective 2004). **Description:** Covers demographic, political, economic, social, corporate, cultural, and environmental information.
Related titles: Online - full text ed.: USD 39.95 single country; USD 99 standard - 192 countries (effective 2004).
Published by: Commercial Data International, CountryWatch, Two Riverway, Ste 1770, Houston, TX 77056. TEL 713-355-6500, FAX 713-355-2008, 800-879-3885, editor@countrywatch.com, http://www.countrywatch.com/.

330.9 332 USA
COUNTRY RISK SERVICE. (Covers 82 countries) Text in English. m. USD 735 print or online; USD 410 per issue print or online (effective 2004). **Document type:** *Trade.* **Description:** Two-year forecasting service assesses the solvency of 82 developing and indebted countries. Focuses on predicting growth, budget deficits, trade and current accounts, foreign financing requirements and sources, and debt service for each country.
Related titles: CD-ROM ed.: E I U Country Risk Service on Disc (from SilverPlatter Information, Inc.); Online - full text ed.: E I U Country Risk Service (from SilverPlatter Information, Inc.).
Published by: Economist Intelligence Unit, 111 W 57th St, New York, NY 10019. TEL 212-554-0600, FAX 212-586-1181, newyork@eiu.com, http://www.eiu.com.

330.9 332 USA ISSN 1351-6752
HC815.A1
COUNTRY RISK SERVICE. ALGERIA. Text in English. 1988. q. USD 735 print or online; USD 410 per issue print or online (effective 2004). charts; stat. **Document type:** *Trade.* **Description:** Focuses on predicting growth, budget deficits, trade and current accounts, foreign financing requirements and sources, and debt service for Algeria.
Related titles: ♦ CD-ROM ed.: E I U Country Risk Service on Disc: Middle East-North Africa; Diskette ed.; Online - full text ed.: E I U Country Risk Service: Middle East-North Africa.
Published by: Economist Intelligence Unit, 111 W 57th St, New York, NY 10019. TEL 212-554-0600, FAX 212-586-1181, newyork@eiu.com, http://www.eiu.com.

330.9 332 USA ISSN 1351-6760
HC950.A1
COUNTRY RISK SERVICE. ANGOLA. Text in English. 1988. q. USD 735 print or online; USD 410 per issue print or online (effective 2004). charts; stat. **Document type:** *Trade.* **Description:** Focuses on predicting growth, budget deficits, trade and current accounts, foreign financing requirements and sources, and debt service for Angola.
Related titles: ♦ CD-ROM ed.: E I U Country Risk Service on Disc: Sub-Saharan Africa; Diskette ed.; Online - full text ed.: E I U Country Risk Service: Sub-Saharan Africa (from SilverPlatter Information, Inc.).
Published by: Economist Intelligence Unit, 111 W 57th St, New York, NY 10019. TEL 212-554-0600, FAX 212-586-1181, newyork@eiu.com, http://www.eiu.com.

330.9 332 USA ISSN 1351-6779
HC171
COUNTRY RISK SERVICE. ARGENTINA. Text in English. 1988. q. USD 735 print or online; USD 410 per issue print or online (effective 2004). charts; stat. **Document type:** *Trade.* **Description:** Focuses on predicting growth, budget deficits, trade and current accounts, foreign financing requirements and sources, and debt service for Argentina.
Related titles: ♦ CD-ROM ed.: E I U Country Risk Service on Disc: Latin America; Diskette ed.; Online - full text ed.: E I U Country Risk Service: Latin America.
Published by: Economist Intelligence Unit, 111 W 57th St, New York, NY 10019. TEL 212-554-0600, FAX 212-586-1181, newyork@eiu.com, http://www.eiu.com.

330.9 332 USA ISSN 1351-6787
HC601
COUNTRY RISK SERVICE. AUSTRALIA. Text in English. 1991. q. USD 735 print or online; USD 410 per issue print or online (effective 2004). charts; stat. **Document type:** *Trade.* **Description:** Focuses on predicting growth, budget deficits, trade and current accounts, foreign financing requirements and sources, and debt service for Australia.
Related titles: CD-ROM ed.; Online - full content ed.
Published by: Economist Intelligence Unit, 111 W 57th St, New York, NY 10019. TEL 212-554-0600, FAX 212-586-1181, newyork@eiu.com, http://www.eiu.com.

330.9 332 USA ISSN 1365-4756
HC415.38.A1
COUNTRY RISK SERVICE. BAHRAIN. Text in English. 1994. q. USD 735 print or online; USD 410 per issue print or online (effective 2004). charts; stat. **Document type:** *Trade.* **Description:** Focuses on predicting growth, budget deficits, trade and current accounts, foreign financing requirements and sources, and debt service for Bahrain.
Supersedes in part (in 1997): Country Risk Service. Bahrain, Oman, Qatar (1354-5639)
Related titles: ♦ CD-ROM ed.: E I U Country Risk Service on Disc: Middle East-North Africa; Diskette ed.; Online - full text ed.: E I U Country Risk Service: Middle East-North Africa.
Published by: Economist Intelligence Unit, 111 W 57th St, New York, NY 10019. TEL 212-554-0600, FAX 212-586-1181, newyork@eiu.com, http://www.eiu.com.

330.9 332 USA ISSN 1351-6809
HC440.8.A1
COUNTRY RISK SERVICE. BANGLADESH. Text in English. 1988. q. USD 735 print or online; USD 410 per issue print or online (effective 2004). charts; stat. **Document type:** *Trade.* **Description:** Focuses on predicting growth, budget deficits, trade and current accounts, foreign financing requirements and sources, and debt service for Bangladesh.
Related titles: CD-ROM ed.: (from SilverPlatter Information, Inc.); Diskette ed.; Online - full text ed.: (from SilverPlatter Information, Inc.).
Published by: Economist Intelligence Unit, 111 W 57th St, New York, NY 10019. TEL 212-554-0600, FAX 212-586-1181, newyork@eiu.com, http://www.eiu.com.

330.9 332 USA ISSN 1351-6817
HC181
COUNTRY RISK SERVICE. BOLIVIA. Text in English. 1988. q. USD 735 print or online; USD 410 per issue print or online (effective 2004). charts; stat. **Document type:** *Trade.* **Description:** Focuses on predicting growth, budget deficits, trade and current accounts, foreign financing requirements and sources, and debt service for Bolivia.
Related titles: ♦ CD-ROM ed.: E I U Country Risk Service on Disc: Latin America; Diskette ed.; Online - full text ed.: E I U Country Risk Service: Latin America.
Published by: Economist Intelligence Unit, 111 W 57th St, New York, NY 10019. TEL 212-554-0600, FAX 212-586-1181, newyork@eiu.com, http://www.eiu.com.

330.9 332 USA ISSN 1354-5647
HC930.A1
COUNTRY RISK SERVICE. BOTSWANA. Text in English. 1994. q. USD 735 print or online; USD 410 per issue print or online (effective 2004). charts; stat. **Document type:** *Trade.* **Description:** Focuses on predicting growth, budget deficits, trade and current accounts, foreign financing requirements and sources, and debt service for Botswana.
Related titles: ♦ CD-ROM ed.: E I U Country Risk Service on Disc: Sub-Saharan Africa; Online - full text ed.: E I U Country Risk Service: Sub-Saharan Africa (from SilverPlatter Information, Inc.).
Published by: Economist Intelligence Unit, 111 W 57th St, New York, NY 10019. TEL 212-554-0600, FAX 212-586-1181, newyork@eiu.com, http://www.eiu.com.

B

330.9 332 USA ISSN 1351-6825
HC186
COUNTRY RISK SERVICE. BRAZIL. Text in English. 1988. q. USD 735 print or online; USD 410 per issue print or online (effective 2004). charts; stat. **Document type:** *Trade.* **Description:** Focuses on predicting growth, budget deficits, trade and current accounts, foreign financing requirements and sources, and debt service for Brazil.
Related titles: ♦ CD-ROM ed.: E I U Country Risk Service on Disc: Latin America; Diskette ed.; Online - full text ed.: E I U Country Risk Service: Latin America.
Published by: Economist Intelligence Unit, 111 W 57th St, New York, NY 10019. TEL 212-554-0600, FAX 212-586-1181, newyork@eiu.com, http://www.eiu.com.

330.9 332 USA ISSN 1351-6833
HC403.A1
COUNTRY RISK SERVICE. BULGARIA. Text in English. 1988. q. USD 735 print or online; USD 410 per issue print or online (effective 2004). charts; stat. **Document type:** *Trade.* **Description:** Focuses on predicting growth, budget deficits, trade and current accounts, foreign financing requirements and sources, and debt service for Bulgaria.
Related titles: ♦ CD-ROM ed.: E I U Country Risk Service on Disc: Europe; Diskette ed.; Online - full text ed.: E I U Country Risk Service: Europe (from SilverPlatter Information, Inc.).
Published by: Economist Intelligence Unit, 111 W 57th St, New York, NY 10019. TEL 212-554-0600, FAX 212-586-1181, newyork@eiu.com, http://www.eiu.com.

330.9 332 USA ISSN 1351-6841
HC995.A1
COUNTRY RISK SERVICE. CAMEROON. Text in English. 1988. q. USD 735 print or online; USD 410 per issue print or online (effective 2004). charts; stat. **Document type:** *Trade.* **Description:** Focuses on predicting growth, budget deficits, trade and current accounts, foreign financing requirements and sources, and debt service for Cameroon.
Related titles: ♦ CD-ROM ed.: E I U Country Risk Service on Disc: Sub-Saharan Africa; Diskette ed.; Online - full text ed.: E I U Country Risk Service: Sub-Saharan Africa (from SilverPlatter Information, Inc.).
Published by: Economist Intelligence Unit, 111 W 57th St, New York, NY 10019. TEL 212-554-0600, FAX 212-586-1181, newyork@eiu.com, http://www.eiu.com.

330.9 332 USA ISSN 1351-685X
HC191
COUNTRY RISK SERVICE. CHILE. Text in English. 1988. q. USD 735 print or online; USD 410 per issue print or online (effective 2004). charts; stat. **Document type:** *Trade.* **Description:** Focuses on predicting growth, budget deficits, trade and current accounts, foreign financing requirements and sources, and debt service for Chile.
Related titles: ♦ CD-ROM ed.: E I U Country Risk Service on Disc: Latin America; Diskette ed.; Online - full text ed.: E I U Country Risk Service: Latin America.
Published by: Economist Intelligence Unit, 111 W 57th St, New York, NY 10019. TEL 212-554-0600, FAX 212-586-1181, newyork@eiu.com, http://www.eiu.com.

330.9 332 USA ISSN 1351-6868
HC426
COUNTRY RISK SERVICE. CHINA. Text in English. 1988. q. USD 735 print or online; USD 410 per issue print or online (effective 2004). charts; stat. **Document type:** *Trade.* **Description:** Focuses on predicting growth, budget deficits, trade and current accounts, foreign financing requirements and sources, and debt service for China.

Related titles: CD-ROM ed.: (from SilverPlatter Information, Inc.); Diskette ed.; Online - full text ed.: (from SilverPlatter Information, Inc.).
Published by: Economist Intelligence Unit, 111 W 57th St, New York, NY 10019. TEL 212-554-0600, FAX 212-586-1181, newyork@eiu.com, http://www.eiu.com.

330.9 332 USA ISSN 1351-6876
HC196
COUNTRY RISK SERVICE. COLOMBIA. Text in English. 1988. q. USD 735 print or online; USD 410 per issue print or online (effective 2004). charts; stat. **Document type:** *Trade.*
Description: Focuses on predicting growth, budget deficits, trade and current accounts, foreign financing requirements and sources, and debt service for Colombia.
Related titles: ♦ CD-ROM ed.: E I U Country Risk Service on Disc: Latin America; Diskette ed.; Online - full text ed.: E I U Country Risk Service: Latin America.
Published by: Economist Intelligence Unit, 111 W 57th St, New York, NY 10019. TEL 212-554-0600, FAX 212-586-1181, newyork@eiu.com, http://www.eiu.com.

330.9 332 USA ISSN 1351-6884
COUNTRY RISK SERVICE. CONGO. Text in English. 1988. q. USD 735 print or online; USD 410 per issue print or online (effective 2004). charts; stat. **Document type:** *Trade.*
Description: Focuses on predicting growth, budget deficits, trade and current accounts, foreign financing requirements and sources, and debt service for the Congo.
Related titles: ♦ CD-ROM ed.: E I U Country Risk Service on Disc: Sub-Saharan Africa; Diskette ed.; Online - full text ed.: E I U Country Risk Service: Sub-Saharan Africa (from SilverPlatter Information, Inc.).
Published by: Economist Intelligence Unit, 111 W 57th St, New York, NY 10019. TEL 212-554-0600, FAX 212-586-1181, newyork@eiu.com, http://www.eiu.com.

330.9 332 USA ISSN 1351-6892
HC143.A1
COUNTRY RISK SERVICE. COSTA RICA. Text in English. 1988. q. USD 735 print or online; USD 410 per issue print or online (effective 2004). charts; stat. **Document type:** *Trade.*
Description: Focuses on predicting growth, budget deficits, trade and current accounts, foreign financing requirements and sources, and debt service for Costa Rica.
Related titles: ♦ CD-ROM ed.: E I U Country Risk Service on Disc: Latin America; Diskette ed.; Online - full text ed.: E I U Country Risk Service: Latin America.
Published by: Economist Intelligence Unit, 111 W 57th St, New York, NY 10019. TEL 212-554-0600, FAX 212-586-1181, newyork@eiu.com, http://www.eiu.com.

330.9 332 USA ISSN 1351-6906
HC1025.A1
COUNTRY RISK SERVICE. COTE D'IVOIRE. Text in English. 1988. q. USD 735 print or online; USD 410 per issue print or online (effective 2004). charts; stat. **Document type:** *Trade.*
Description: Focuses on predicting growth, budget deficits, trade and current accounts, foreign financing requirements and sources, and debt service for Cote d'Ivoire.
Related titles: ♦ CD-ROM ed.: E I U Country Risk Service on Disc: Sub-Saharan Africa; Diskette ed.; Online - full text ed.: E I U Country Risk Service: Sub-Saharan Africa (from SilverPlatter Information, Inc.).
Published by: Economist Intelligence Unit, 111 W 57th St, New York, NY 10019. TEL 212-554-0600, FAX 212-586-1181, newyork@eiu.com, http://www.eiu.com.

330.9 332 USA ISSN 1368-3454
HC152.5.A1
COUNTRY RISK SERVICE. CUBA. Text in English. 1997. q. USD 735 print or online; USD 410 per issue print or online (effective 2004). charts; stat. **Document type:** *Trade.*
Published by: Economist Intelligence Unit, 111 W 57th St, New York, NY 10019. TEL 212-554-0600, FAX 212-586-1181, newyork@eiu.com, http://www.eiu.com.

330.9 332 USA ISSN 1351-6914
HC415.2.A1
COUNTRY RISK SERVICE. CYPRUS. Text in English. 1988. q. USD 735 print or online; USD 410 per issue print or online (effective 2004). charts; stat. **Document type:** *Trade.*
Description: Focuses on predicting growth, budget deficits, trade and current accounts, foreign financing requirements and sources, and debt service for Cyprus.
Related titles: CD-ROM ed.: (from SilverPlatter Information, Inc.); Diskette ed.; Online - full text ed.: (from SilverPlatter Information, Inc.).
Published by: Economist Intelligence Unit, 111 W 57th St, New York, NY 10019. TEL 212-554-0600, FAX 212-586-1181, newyork@eiu.com, http://www.eiu.com.

330.9 332 USA ISSN 1351-6922
HC271.2
COUNTRY RISK SERVICE. CZECH REPUBLIC. Text in English. 1993. q. USD 735 print or online; USD 410 per issue print or online (effective 2004). charts; stat. **Document type:** *Trade.*
Description: Focuses on predicting growth, budget deficits, trade and current accounts, foreign financing requirements and sources, and debt service for the Czech Republic.
Related titles: ♦ CD-ROM ed.: E I U Country Risk Service on Disc: Europe; Diskette ed.; Online - full text ed.: E I U Country Risk Service: Europe (from SilverPlatter Information, Inc.).
Published by: Economist Intelligence Unit, 111 W 57th St, New York, NY 10019. TEL 212-554-0600, FAX 212-586-1181, newyork@eiu.com, http://www.eiu.com.

330.9 332 USA ISSN 1351-6930
HC153.5.A1
COUNTRY RISK SERVICE. DOMINICAN REPUBLIC. Text in English. 1988. q. USD 735 print or online; USD 410 per issue print or online (effective 2004). charts; stat. **Document type:** *Trade.* **Description:** Focuses on predicting growth, budget deficits, trade and current accounts, foreign financing requirements and sources, and debt service for the Dominican Republic.
Related titles: ♦ CD-ROM ed.: E I U Country Risk Service on Disc: Latin America; Diskette ed.; Online - full text ed.: E I U Country Risk Service: Latin America.
Published by: Economist Intelligence Unit, 111 W 57th St, New York, NY 10019. TEL 212-554-0600, FAX 212-586-1181, newyork@eiu.com, http://www.eiu.com.

330.9 332 USA ISSN 1351-6949
HC201
COUNTRY RISK SERVICE. ECUADOR. Text in English. 1988. q. USD 735 print or online; USD 410 per issue print or online (effective 2004). charts; stat. **Document type:** *Trade.*
Description: Focuses on predicting growth, budget deficits, trade and current accounts, foreign financing requirements and sources, and debt service for Ecuador.
Related titles: ♦ CD-ROM ed.: E I U Country Risk Service on Disc: Latin America; Diskette ed.; Online - full text ed.: E I U Country Risk Service: Latin America.
Published by: Economist Intelligence Unit, 111 W 57th St, New York, NY 10019. TEL 212-554-0600, FAX 212-586-1181, newyork@eiu.com, http://www.eiu.com.

330.9 332 USA ISSN 1351-6957
HC830.A1
COUNTRY RISK SERVICE. EGYPT. Text in English. 1988. q. USD 735 print or online; USD 410 per issue print or online (effective 2004). charts; stat. **Document type:** *Trade.*
Description: Focuses on predicting growth, budget deficits, trade and current accounts, foreign financing requirements and sources, and debt service for Egypt.
Related titles: ♦ CD-ROM ed.: E I U Country Risk Service on Disc: Middle East-North Africa; Diskette ed.; Online - full text ed.: E I U Country Risk Service: Middle East-North Africa.
Published by: Economist Intelligence Unit, 111 W 57th St, New York, NY 10019. TEL 212-554-0600, FAX 212-586-1181, newyork@eiu.com, http://www.eiu.com.

330.9 332 USA ISSN 1351-6965
HC148.A1
COUNTRY RISK SERVICE. EL SALVADOR. Text in English. 1988. q. USD 735 print or online; USD 410 per issue print or online (effective 2004). charts; stat. **Document type:** *Trade.*
Description: Focuses on predicting growth, budget deficits, trade and current accounts, foreign financing requirements and sources, and debt service for El Salvador.
Related titles: ♦ CD-ROM ed.: E I U Country Risk Service on Disc: Latin America; Diskette ed.; Online - full text ed.: E I U Country Risk Service: Latin America.
Published by: Economist Intelligence Unit, 111 W 57th St, New York, NY 10019. TEL 212-554-0600, FAX 212-586-1181, newyork@eiu.com, http://www.eiu.com.

330.9 332 USA ISSN 1461-6157
HC340.4.A1
COUNTRY RISK SERVICE. ESTONIA. Text in English. 199?. q. USD 735 print or online; USD 410 per issue print or online (effective 2004). illus.; stat. **Document type:** *Trade.*
Description: Focuses on predicting growth, budget deficits, trade and current accounts, foreign financing requirements and sources, and debt service for the Baltic Republics.
Supersedes in part (in 1998): Country Risk Service. The Baltic Republics: Latvia, Estonia, Lithuania (1351-6795)
Published by: Economist Intelligence Unit, 111 W 57th St, New York, NY 10019. TEL 212-554-0600, FAX 212-586-1181, newyork@eiu.com, http://www.eiu.com.

330.9 332 USA ISSN 1351-6973
HC975.A1
COUNTRY RISK SERVICE. GABON. Text in English. 1988. q. USD 735 print or online; USD 410 per issue print or online (effective 2004). charts; stat. **Document type:** *Trade.*
Description: Focuses on predicting growth, budget deficits, trade and current accounts, foreign financing requirements and sources, and debt service for Gabon.
Related titles: ♦ CD-ROM ed.: E I U Country Risk Service on Disc: Sub-Saharan Africa; Diskette ed.; Online - full text ed.: E I U Country Risk Service: Sub-Saharan Africa (from SilverPlatter Information, Inc.).
Published by: Economist Intelligence Unit, 111 W 57th St, New York, NY 10019. TEL 212-554-0600, FAX 212-586-1181, newyork@eiu.com, http://www.eiu.com.

330.9 332 USA ISSN 1351-6981
HC291
COUNTRY RISK SERVICE. GHANA. Text in English. 1988. q. USD 735 print or online; USD 410 per issue print or online (effective 2004). charts; stat. **Document type:** *Trade.*
Description: Focuses on predicting growth, budget deficits, trade and current accounts, foreign financing requirements and sources, and debt service for Ghana.
Related titles: ♦ CD-ROM ed.: E I U Country Risk Service on Disc: Sub-Saharan Africa; Diskette ed.; Online - full text ed.: E I U Country Risk Service: Sub-Saharan Africa (from SilverPlatter Information, Inc.).
Published by: Economist Intelligence Unit, 111 W 57th St, New York, NY 10019. TEL 212-554-0600, FAX 212-586-1181, newyork@eiu.com, http://www.eiu.com.

330.9 332 USA ISSN 1351-699X
COUNTRY RISK SERVICE. GREECE. Text in English. 1991. q. USD 735 print or online; USD 410 per issue print or online (effective 2004). charts; stat. **Document type:** *Trade.*
Description: Focuses on predicting growth, budget deficits, trade and current accounts, foreign financing requirements and sources, and debt service for Greece.
Related titles: CD-ROM ed.: (from SilverPlatter Information, Inc.); Diskette ed.; Online - full text ed.: (from SilverPlatter Information, Inc.).
Published by: Economist Intelligence Unit, 111 W 57th St, New York, NY 10019. TEL 212-554-0600, FAX 212-586-1181, newyork@eiu.com, http://www.eiu.com.

330.9 332 USA ISSN 1351-7007
HC144.A1
COUNTRY RISK SERVICE. GUATEMALA. Text in English. 1988. q. USD 735 print or online; USD 410 per issue print or online (effective 2004). charts; stat. **Document type:** *Trade.*
Description: Focuses on predicting growth, budget deficits, trade and current accounts, foreign financing requirements and sources, and debt service for Guatemala.
Related titles: ♦ CD-ROM ed.: E I U Country Risk Service on Disc: Latin America; Diskette ed.; Online - full text ed.: E I U Country Risk Service: Latin America.
Published by: Economist Intelligence Unit, 111 W 57th St, New York, NY 10019. TEL 212-554-0600, FAX 212-586-1181, newyork@eiu.com, http://www.eiu.com.

330.9 332 USA ISSN 1351-7015
HC145.A1
COUNTRY RISK SERVICE. HONDURAS. Text in English. 1988. q. USD 735 print or online; USD 410 per issue print or online (effective 2004). charts; stat. **Document type:** *Trade.*
Description: Focuses on predicting growth, budget deficits, trade and current accounts, foreign financing requirements and sources, and debt service for Honduras.
Related titles: ♦ CD-ROM ed.: E I U Country Risk Service on Disc: Latin America; Diskette ed.; Online - full text ed.: E I U Country Risk Service: Latin America.
Published by: Economist Intelligence Unit, 111 W 57th St, New York, NY 10019. TEL 212-554-0600, FAX 212-586-1181, newyork@eiu.com, http://www.eiu.com.

330.9 332 USA ISSN 1351-7023
HC470.3.A1
COUNTRY RISK SERVICE. HONG KONG. Text in English. 1988. q. USD 735 print or online; USD 410 per issue print or online (effective 2004). charts; stat. **Document type:** *Trade.*
Description: Focuses on predicting growth, budget deficits, trade and current accounts, foreign financing requirements and sources, and debt service for Hong Kong.
Related titles: CD-ROM ed.: (from SilverPlatter Information, Inc.); Diskette ed.; Online - full text ed.: (from SilverPlatter Information, Inc.).
Published by: Economist Intelligence Unit, 111 W 57th St, New York, NY 10019. TEL 212-554-0600, FAX 212-586-1181, newyork@eiu.com, http://www.eiu.com.

330.9 332 USA ISSN 1351-7031
HC300.2
COUNTRY RISK SERVICE. HUNGARY. Text in English. 1988. q. USD 735 print or online; USD 410 per issue print or online (effective 2004). charts; stat. **Document type:** *Trade.*
Description: Focuses on predicting growth, budget deficits, trade and current accounts, foreign financing requirements and sources, and debt service for Hungary.
Related titles: ♦ CD-ROM ed.: E I U Country Risk Service on Disc: Europe; Diskette ed.; Online - full text ed.: E I U Country Risk Service: Europe (from SilverPlatter Information, Inc.).
Published by: Economist Intelligence Unit, 111 W 57th St, New York, NY 10019. TEL 212-554-0600, FAX 212-586-1181, newyork@eiu.com, http://www.eiu.com.

330.9 332 USA ISSN 1351-704X
HC431
COUNTRY RISK SERVICE. INDIA. Text in English. 1988. q. USD 735 print or online; USD 410 per issue print or online (effective 2004). charts; stat. **Document type:** *Trade.*
Description: Focuses on predicting growth, budget deficits, trade and current accounts, foreign financing requirements and sources, and debt service for India.
Related titles: CD-ROM ed.: (from SilverPlatter Information, Inc.); Diskette ed.; Online - full text ed.: (from SilverPlatter Information, Inc.).

B

Published by: Economist Intelligence Unit, 111 W 57th St, New York, NY 10019. TEL 212-554-0600, FAX 212-586-1181, newyork@eiu.com, http://www.eiu.com.

330.9 332 USA ISSN 1351-7058
HC446
COUNTRY RISK SERVICE. INDONESIA. Text in English. 1988. q. USD 735 print or online; USD 410 per issue print or online (effective 2004). charts; stat. **Document type:** *Trade.*
Description: Focuses on predicting growth, budget deficits, trade and current accounts, foreign financing requirements and sources, and debt service for Indonesia.
Related titles: CD-ROM ed.: (from SilverPlatter Information, Inc.); Diskette ed.; Online - full text ed.: (from SilverPlatter Information, Inc.).
Published by: Economist Intelligence Unit, 111 W 57th St, New York, NY 10019. TEL 212-554-0600, FAX 212-586-1181, newyork@eiu.com, http://www.eiu.com.

330.9 332 USA ISSN 1351-7066
HC471
COUNTRY RISK SERVICE. IRAN. Text in English. 1988. q. USD 735 print or online; USD 410 per issue print or online (effective 2004). charts; stat. **Document type:** *Trade.*
Description: Focuses on predicting growth, budget deficits, trade and current accounts, foreign financing requirements and sources, and debt service for Iran.
Related titles: ♦ CD-ROM ed.: E I U Country Risk Service on Disc: Middle East-North Africa; Diskette ed.; Online - full text ed.: E I U Country Risk Service: Middle East-North Africa.
Published by: Economist Intelligence Unit, 111 W 57th St, New York, NY 10019. TEL 212-554-0600, FAX 212-586-1181, newyork@eiu.com, http://www.eiu.com.

330.9 332 USA ISSN 1351-7074
HC415.4.A1
COUNTRY RISK SERVICE. IRAQ. Text in English. 1988. q. USD 735 print or online; USD 410 per issue print or online (effective 2004). charts; stat. **Document type:** *Trade.*
Description: Focuses on predicting growth, budget deficits, trade and current accounts, foreign financing requirements and sources, and debt service for Iraq.
Related titles: ♦ CD-ROM ed.: E I U Country Risk Service on Disc: Middle East-North Africa; Diskette ed.; Online - full text ed.: E I U Country Risk Service: Middle East-North Africa.
Published by: Economist Intelligence Unit, 111 W 57th St, New York, NY 10019. TEL 212-554-0600, FAX 212-586-1181, newyork@eiu.com, http://www.eiu.com.

330.9 332 USA ISSN 1351-7082
HC415.25.A1
COUNTRY RISK SERVICE. ISRAEL. Text in English. 1988. q. USD 735 print or online; USD 410 per issue print or online (effective 2004). charts; stat. **Document type:** *Trade.*
Description: Focuses on predicting growth, budget deficits, trade and current accounts, foreign financing requirements and sources, and debt service for Israel.
Related titles: ♦ CD-ROM ed.: E I U Country Risk Service on Disc: Middle East-North Africa; Diskette ed.; Online - full text ed.: E I U Country Risk Service: Middle East-North Africa.
Published by: Economist Intelligence Unit, 111 W 57th St, New York, NY 10019. TEL 212-554-0600, FAX 212-586-1181, newyork@eiu.com, http://www.eiu.com.

330.9 332 USA ISSN 1351-7090
HC154.A1
COUNTRY RISK SERVICE. JAMAICA. Text in English. 1988. q. USD 735 print or online; USD 410 per issue print or online (effective 2004). charts; stat. **Document type:** *Trade.*
Description: Focuses on predicting growth, budget deficits, trade and current accounts, foreign financing requirements and sources, and debt service for Jamaica.
Related titles: ♦ CD-ROM ed.: E I U Country Risk Service on Disc: Latin America; Diskette ed.; Online - full text ed.: E I U Country Risk Service: Latin America.
Published by: Economist Intelligence Unit, 111 W 57th St, New York, NY 10019. TEL 212-554-0600, FAX 212-586-1181, newyork@eiu.com, http://www.eiu.com.

330.9 332 USA ISSN 1351-7104
HC415.26.A1
COUNTRY RISK SERVICE. JORDAN. Text in English. 1988. q. USD 735 print or online; USD 410 per issue print or online (effective 2004). charts; stat. **Document type:** *Trade.*
Description: Focuses on predicting growth, budget deficits, trade and current accounts, foreign financing requirements and sources, and debt service for Jordan.
Related titles: ♦ CD-ROM ed.: E I U Country Risk Service on Disc: Middle East-North Africa; Diskette ed.; Online - full text ed.: E I U Country Risk Service: Middle East-North Africa.
Published by: Economist Intelligence Unit, 111 W 57th St, New York, NY 10019. TEL 212-554-0600, FAX 212-586-1181, newyork@eiu.com, http://www.eiu.com.

330.9 332 USA ISSN 1351-7112
HC420.5.A1
COUNTRY RISK SERVICE. KAZAKHSTAN. Text in English. 199?. q. USD 735 print or online; USD 410 per issue print or online (effective 2004). charts; stat. **Document type:** *Trade.*
Description: Focuses on predicting growth, budget deficits, trade and current accounts, foreign financing requirements and sources, and debt service for Kazakhstan.
Related titles: ♦ CD-ROM ed.: E I U Country Risk Service on Disc: Europe; Diskette ed.; Online - full text ed.: E I U Country Risk Service: Europe (from SilverPlatter Information, Inc.).
Published by: Economist Intelligence Unit, 111 W 57th St, New York, NY 10019. TEL 212-554-0600, FAX 212-586-1181, newyork@eiu.com, http://www.eiu.com.

330.9 332 USA ISSN 1351-7120
HC865.A1
COUNTRY RISK SERVICE. KENYA. Text in English. 1988. q. USD 735 print or online; USD 410 per issue print or online (effective 2004). charts; stat. **Document type:** *Trade.*
Description: Focuses on predicting growth, budget deficits, trade and current accounts, foreign financing requirements and sources, and debt service for Kenya.
Related titles: ♦ CD-ROM ed.: E I U Country Risk Service on Disc: Sub-Saharan Africa; Diskette ed.; Online - full text ed.: E I U Country Risk Service: Sub-Saharan Africa (from SilverPlatter Information, Inc.).
Published by: Economist Intelligence Unit, 111 W 57th St, New York, NY 10019. TEL 212-554-0600, FAX 212-586-1181, newyork@eiu.com, http://www.eiu.com.

330.9 332 USA ISSN 1351-7139
HC415.39.A1
COUNTRY RISK SERVICE. KUWAIT. Text in English. 1988. q. USD 735 print or online; USD 410 per issue print or online (effective 2004). charts; stat. **Document type:** *Trade.*
Description: Focuses on predicting growth, budget deficits, trade and current accounts, foreign financing requirements and sources, and debt service for Kuwait.
Related titles: ♦ CD-ROM ed.: E I U Country Risk Service on Disc: Middle East-North Africa; Diskette ed.; Online - full text ed.: E I U Country Risk Service: Middle East-North Africa.
Published by: Economist Intelligence Unit, 111 W 57th St, New York, NY 10019. TEL 212-554-0600, FAX 212-586-1181, newyork@eiu.com, http://www.eiu.com.

330.9 332 USA ISSN 1461-6165
HC340.5.A1
COUNTRY RISK SERVICE. LATVIA. Text in English. 199?. q. USD 735 print or online; USD 410 per issue print or online (effective 2004). charts; stat. **Document type:** *Trade.*
Description: Focuses on predicting growth, budget deficits, trade and current accounts, foreign financing requirements and sources, and debt service for the Baltic Republics.
Supersedes in part (in 1998): Country Risk Service. The Baltic Republics (1351-6795)
Related titles: CD-ROM ed.: (from SilverPlatter Information, Inc.); Diskette ed.; Online - full text ed.: E I U Country Risk Service: Europe (from SilverPlatter Information, Inc.).
Published by: Economist Intelligence Unit, 111 W 57th St, New York, NY 10019. TEL 212-554-0600, FAX 212-586-1181, newyork@eiu.com, http://www.eiu.com.

330.9 332 USA ISSN 1351-7147
HC825.A1
COUNTRY RISK SERVICE. LIBYA. Text in English. 1988. q. USD 735 print or online; USD 410 per issue print or online (effective 2004). charts; stat. **Document type:** *Trade.*
Description: Focuses on predicting growth, budget deficits, trade and current accounts, foreign financing requirements and sources, and debt service for Libya.
Related titles: ♦ CD-ROM ed.: E I U Country Risk Service on Disc: Middle East-North Africa; Diskette ed.; Online - full text ed.: E I U Country Risk Service: Middle East-North Africa.
Published by: Economist Intelligence Unit, 111 W 57th St, New York, NY 10019. TEL 212-554-0600, FAX 212-586-1181, newyork@eiu.com, http://www.eiu.com.

330.9 332 USA ISSN 1461-6173
HC340.6.A1
COUNTRY RISK SERVICE. LITHUANIA. Text in English. 199?. m. USD 735 print or online; USD 410 per issue print or online (effective 2004). illus.; stat. **Document type:** *Trade.*
Description: Focuses on predicting growth, budget deficits, trade and current accounts, foreign financing requirements and sources, and debt service for the Baltic Republics.
Supersedes in part (in 1998): Country Risk Service. The Baltic Republics (1351-6795)
Published by: Economist Intelligence Unit, 111 W 57th St, New York, NY 10019. TEL 212-554-0600, FAX 212-586-1181, newyork@eiu.com, http://www.eiu.com.

330.9 332 USA ISSN 1461-6076
HC404.5.A1
COUNTRY RISK SERVICE. MACEDONIA. Text in English. 1993. q. USD 735 print or online; USD 410 per issue print or online (effective 2004). charts; stat. **Document type:** *Trade.*
Description: Focuses on predicting growth, budget deficits, trade and current accounts, foreign financing requirements and sources, and debt service for the former Yugoslav Republics.
Supersedes in part: Country Risk Service. Former Yugoslav Republics: Serbia, Montenegro, Macedonia (1366-4301); Which was formerly: Country Risk Service. Former Yugoslav Republics (1351-7538); Country Risk Service. Yugoslav Republics
Related titles: ♦ CD-ROM ed.: E I U Country Risk Service on Disc: Europe; Diskette ed.; Online - full text ed.: E I U Country Risk Service: Europe (from SilverPlatter Information, Inc.).
Published by: Economist Intelligence Unit, 111 W 57th St, New York, NY 10019. TEL 212-554-0600, FAX 212-586-1181, newyork@eiu.com, http://www.eiu.com.

330.9 332 USA ISSN 1351-7155
HC935.A1
COUNTRY RISK SERVICE. MALAWI. Text in English. 1988. q. USD 735 print or online; USD 410 per issue print or online (effective 2004). charts; stat. **Document type:** *Trade.*
Description: Focuses on predicting growth, budget deficits, trade and current accounts, foreign financing requirements and sources, and debt service for Malawi.
Related titles: ♦ CD-ROM ed.: E I U Country Risk Service on Disc: Sub-Saharan Africa; Diskette ed.; Online - full text ed.: E I U Country Risk Service: Sub-Saharan Africa (from SilverPlatter Information, Inc.).
Published by: Economist Intelligence Unit, 111 W 57th St, New York, NY 10019. TEL 212-554-0600, FAX 212-586-1181, http://www.eiu.com.

330.9 332 USA ISSN 1351-7163
HC445.5.A1
COUNTRY RISK SERVICE. MALAYSIA. Text in English. 1988. q. USD 735 print or online; USD 410 per issue print or online (effective 2004). charts; stat. **Document type:** *Trade.*
Description: Focuses on predicting growth, budget deficits, trade and current accounts, foreign financing requirements and sources and debt service for Malaysia.
Related titles: CD-ROM ed.: (from SilverPlatter Information, Inc.); Diskette ed.; Online - full text ed.: (from SilverPlatter Information, Inc.).
Published by: Economist Intelligence Unit, 111 W 57th St, New York, NY 10019. TEL 212-554-0600, FAX 212-586-1181, newyork@eiu.com, http://www.eiu.com.

330.9 332 USA ISSN 1461-7943
HC597.5.A1
COUNTRY RISK SERVICE. MAURITIUS. Text in English. 1998. q. USD 735 print or online; USD 410 per issue print or online (effective 2004). charts; stat. **Document type:** *Trade.*
Published by: Economist Intelligence Unit, 111 W 57th St, New York, NY 10019. http://www.eiu.com.

330.9 332 USA ISSN 1351-7171
HC131
COUNTRY RISK SERVICE. MEXICO. Text in English. 1988. q. USD 735 print or online; USD 410 per issue print or online (effective 2004). charts; stat. **Document type:** *Trade.*
Description: Focuses on predicting growth, budget deficits, trade and current accounts, foreign financing requirements and sources, and debt service for Mexico.
Related titles: ♦ CD-ROM ed.: E I U Country Risk Service on Disc: Latin America; Diskette ed.; Online - full text ed.: E I U Country Risk Service: Latin America.
Published by: Economist Intelligence Unit, 111 W 57th St, New York, NY 10019. TEL 212-554-0600, FAX 212-586-1181, newyork@eiu.com, http://www.eiu.com.

330.9 332 USA ISSN 1461-7951
COUNTRY RISK SERVICE. MOLDOVA. Text in English. 1998. q. USD 735 print or online; USD 410 per issue print or online (effective 2004). charts; stat. **Document type:** *Trade.*
Published by: Economist Intelligence Unit, 111 W 57th St, New York, NY 10019. TEL 212-554-0600, FAX 212-586-1181, newyork@eiu.com, http://www.eiu.com.

330.9 332 USA ISSN 1351-718X
HC810.A1
COUNTRY RISK SERVICE. MOROCCO. Text in English. 1988. q. USD 735 print or online; USD 410 per issue print or online (effective 2004). charts; stat. **Document type:** *Trade.*
Description: Focuses on predicting growth, budget deficits, trade and current accounts, foreign financing requirements and sources, and debt service for Morocco.
Related titles: ♦ CD-ROM ed.: E I U Country Risk Service on Disc: Middle East-North Africa; Diskette ed.; Online - full text ed.: E I U Country Risk Service: Middle East-North Africa.
Published by: Economist Intelligence Unit, 111 W 57th St, New York, NY 10019. TEL 212-554-0600, FAX 212-586-1181, newyork@eiu.com, http://www.eiu.com.

330.9 332 USA ISSN 1351-7198
HC940.A1
COUNTRY RISK SERVICE. NAMIBIA. Text in English. 1988. q. USD 735 print or online; USD 410 per issue print or online (effective 2004). charts; stat. **Document type:** *Trade.*
Description: Focuses on predicting growth, budget deficits, trade and current accounts, foreign financing requirements and sources, and debt service for Namibia.
Related titles: ♦ CD-ROM ed.: E I U Country Risk Service on Disc: Sub-Saharan Africa; Diskette ed.; Online - full text ed.: E I U Country Risk Service: Sub-Saharan Africa (from SilverPlatter Information, Inc.).
Published by: Economist Intelligence Unit, 111 W 57th St, New York, NY 10019. TEL 212-554-0600, 800-938-4685, FAX 212-586-1182, newyork@eiu.com, http://www.eiu.com.

B

▼ *new title* ➤ *refereed* ✶ *unverified* ♦ *full entry avail.*

330.9 332 USA ISSN 1351-7201
HC661
COUNTRY RISK SERVICE. NEW ZEALAND. Text in English. 1991. q. USD 735 print or online; USD 410 per issue print or online (effective 2004). charts; stat. **Document type:** *Trade.*
Description: Focuses on predicting growth, budget deficits, trade and current accounts, foreign financing requirements and sources and debt service for New Zealand.
Related titles: ♦ CD-ROM ed.: E I U Country Risk Service on Disc: Asia-Pacific; Diskette ed.; Online - full text ed.: E I U Country Risk Service: Asia-Pacific (from SilverPlatter Information, Inc.).
Published by: Economist Intelligence Unit, 111 W 57th St, New York, NY 10019. TEL 212-554-0600, FAX 212-586-1181, newyork@eiu.com, http://www.eiu.com.

330.9 332 USA ISSN 1351-721X
HC146.A1
COUNTRY RISK SERVICE. NICARAGUA. Text in English. 1988. q. USD 735 print or online; USD 410 per issue print or online (effective 2004). charts; stat. **Document type:** *Trade.*
Description: Focuses on predicting growth, budget deficits, trade and current accounts, foreign financing requirements and sources, and debt service for Nicaragua.
Related titles: ♦ CD-ROM ed.: E I U Country Risk Service on Disc: Latin America; Diskette ed.; Online - full text ed.: E I U Country Risk Service: Latin America.
Published by: Economist Intelligence Unit, 111 W 57th St, New York, NY 10019. TEL 212-554-0600, FAX 212-586-1181, newyork@eiu.com, http://www.eiu.com.

330.9 332 USA ISSN 1351-7228
HC1055.A1
COUNTRY RISK SERVICE. NIGERIA. Text in English. 1988. q. USD 735 print or online; USD 410 per issue print or online (effective 2004). charts; stat. **Document type:** *Trade.*
Description: Focuses on predicting growth, budget deficits, trade and current accounts, foreign financing requirements and sources, and debt service for Nigeria.
Related titles: ♦ CD-ROM ed.: E I U Country Risk Service on Disc: Sub-Saharan Africa; Diskette ed.; Online - full text ed.: E I U Country Risk Service: Sub-Saharan Africa (from SilverPlatter Information, Inc.).
Published by: Economist Intelligence Unit, 111 W 57th St, New York, NY 10019. TEL 212-554-0600, FAX 212-586-1181, newyork@eiu.com, http://www.eiu.com.

330.9 332 USA ISSN 1365-4764
HC415.35.A1
COUNTRY RISK SERVICE. OMAN. Text in English. 1994. q. USD 735 print or online; USD 410 per issue print or online (effective 2004). charts; stat. **Document type:** *Trade.*
Description: Focuses on predicting growth, budget deficits, trade and current accounts, foreign financing requirements and sources, and debt service for the Sultanate of Oman.
Supersedes in part (in 1997): Country Risk Service. Bahrain, Oman, Qatar
Related titles: CD-ROM ed.: (from SilverPlatter Information, Inc.); Online - full text ed.: (from SilverPlatter Information, Inc.).
Published by: Economist Intelligence Unit, 111 W 57th St, New York, NY 10019. TEL 212-554-0600, FAX 212-586-1181, newyork@eiu.com, http://www.eiu.com.

330.9 332 USA ISSN 1351-7236
HC440.5.A1
COUNTRY RISK SERVICE. PAKISTAN. Text in English. 1988. q. USD 735 print or online; USD 410 per issue print or online (effective 2004). charts; stat. **Document type:** *Trade.*
Description: Focuses on predicting growth, budget deficits, trade and current accounts, foreign financing requirements and sources and debt service for Pakistan.
Related titles: ♦ CD-ROM ed.: E I U Country Risk Service on Disc: Asia-Pacific; Diskette ed.; Online - full text ed.: E I U Country Risk Service: Asia-Pacific (from SilverPlatter Information, Inc.).
Published by: Economist Intelligence Unit, 111 W 57th St, New York, NY 10019. TEL 212-554-0600, FAX 212-586-1181, newyork@eiu.com, http://www.eiu.com.

330.9 332 USA ISSN 1351-7244
HC147.A1
COUNTRY RISK SERVICE. PANAMA. Text in English. 1988. q. USD 735 print or online; USD 410 per issue print or online (effective 2004). charts; stat. **Document type:** *Trade.*
Description: Focuses on predicting growth, budget deficits, trade and current accounts, foreign financing requirements and sources, and debt service for Panama.
Related titles: ♦ CD-ROM ed.: E I U Country Risk Service on Disc: Latin America; Diskette ed.; Online - full text ed.: E I U Country Risk Service: Latin America.
Published by: Economist Intelligence Unit, 111 W 57th St, New York, NY 10019. TEL 212-554-0600, FAX 212-586-1181, newyork@eiu.com, http://www.eiu.com.

330.9 332 USA ISSN 1351-7252
HC683.5.A1
COUNTRY RISK SERVICE. PAPUA NEW GUINEA. Text in English. 1988. q. USD 735 print or online; USD 410 per issue print or online (effective 2004). charts; stat. **Document type:** *Trade.* **Description:** Focuses on predicting growth, budget deficits, trade and current accounts, foreign financing requirements and sources, and debt service for Papua New Guinea.
Related titles: ♦ CD-ROM ed.: E I U Country Risk Service on Disc: Asia-Pacific; Diskette ed.; Online - full text ed.: E I U Country Risk Service: Asia-Pacific (from SilverPlatter Information, Inc.).
Published by: Economist Intelligence Unit, 111 W 57th St, New York, NY 10019. TEL 212-554-0600, FAX 212-586-1181, newyork@eiu.com, http://www.eiu.com.

330.9 332 USA ISSN 1351-7260
HC221
COUNTRY RISK SERVICE. PARAGUAY. Text in English. 1988. q. USD 735 print or online; USD 410 per issue print or online (effective 2004). charts; stat. **Document type:** *Trade.*
Description: Focuses on predicting growth, budget deficits, trade and current accounts, foreign financing requirements and sources, and debt service for Paraguay.
Related titles: ♦ CD-ROM ed.: E I U Country Risk Service on Disc: Latin America; Diskette ed.; Online - full text ed.: E I U Country Risk Service: Latin America.
Published by: Economist Intelligence Unit, 111 W 57th St, New York, NY 10019. TEL 212-554-0600, FAX 212-586-1181, newyork@eiu.com, http://www.eiu.com.

330.9 332 USA ISSN 1351-7279
HC226
COUNTRY RISK SERVICE. PERU. Text in English. 1988. q. USD 735 print or online; USD 410 per issue print or online (effective 2004). charts; stat. **Document type:** *Trade.*
Description: Focuses on predicting growth, budget deficits, trade and current accounts, foreign financing requirements and sources, and debt service for Peru.
Related titles: ♦ CD-ROM ed.: E I U Country Risk Service on Disc: Latin America; Diskette ed.; Online - full text ed.: E I U Country Risk Service: Latin America.
Published by: Economist Intelligence Unit, 111 W 57th St, New York, NY 10019. TEL 212-554-0600, FAX 212-586-1181, newyork@eiu.com, http://www.eiu.com.

330.9 332 USA ISSN 1351-7287
HC451
COUNTRY RISK SERVICE. PHILIPPINES. Text in English. 1988. q. USD 735 print or online; USD 410 per issue print or online (effective 2004). charts; stat. **Document type:** *Trade.*
Description: Focuses on predicting growth, budget deficits, trade and current accounts, foreign financing requirements and sources and debt service for the Philippines.
Related titles: ♦ CD-ROM ed.: E I U Country Risk Service on Disc: Asia-Pacific; Diskette ed.; Online - full text ed.: E I U Country Risk Service: Asia-Pacific (from SilverPlatter Information, Inc.).
Published by: Economist Intelligence Unit, 111 W 57th St, New York, NY 10019. TEL 212-554-0600, FAX 212-586-1181, newyork@eiu.com, http://www.eiu.com.

330.9 332 USA ISSN 1351-7295
HC340.3.A1
COUNTRY RISK SERVICE. POLAND. Text in English. 1988. q. USD 735 print or online; USD 410 per issue print or online (effective 2004). charts; stat. **Document type:** *Trade.*
Description: Focuses on predicting growth, budget deficits, trade and current accounts, foreign financing requirements and sources, and debt service for Poland.
Related titles: ♦ CD-ROM ed.: E I U Country Risk Service on Disc: Europe; Diskette ed.; Online - full text ed.: E I U Country Risk Service: Europe (from SilverPlatter Information, Inc.).
Published by: Economist Intelligence Unit, 111 W 57th St, New York, NY 10019. TEL 212-554-0600, FAX 212-586-1181, ewyork@eiu.com, http://www.eiu.com.

330.9 332 USA ISSN 1351-7309
HC391
COUNTRY RISK SERVICE. PORTUGAL. Text in English. 1991. q. USD 735 print or online; USD 410 per issue print or online (effective 2004). charts; stat. **Document type:** *Trade.*
Description: Focuses on predicting growth, budget deficits, trade and current accounts, foreign financing requirements and sources, and debt service for Portugal.
Related titles: CD-ROM ed.: (from SilverPlatter Information, Inc.); Diskette ed.; Online - full text ed.: (from SilverPlatter Information, Inc.).
Published by: Economist Intelligence Unit, 111 W 57th St, New York, NY 10019. TEL 212-554-0600, FAX 212-586-1181, ewyork@eiu.com, http://www.eiu.com.

330.9 332 USA ISSN 1365-4772
HC415.37.A1
COUNTRY RISK SERVICE. QATAR. Text in English. 1996. q. USD 735; USD 410 per issue (effective 2004). charts; stat. **Document type:** *Trade.* **Description:** Focuses on predicting growth, budget deficits, trade and current accounts, foreign financing requirements and sources, and debt service for Qatar.
Supersedes in part (in 1997): Country Risk Service. Bahrain, Oman, Qatar
Related titles: CD-ROM ed.: (from SilverPlatter Information, Inc.); Online - full text ed.: (from SilverPlatter Information, Inc.).
Published by: Economist Intelligence Unit, 111 W 57th St, New York, NY 10019. TEL 212-554-0600, FAX 212-586-1181, ewyork@eiu.com, http://www.eiu.com.

330.9 332 USA ISSN 1351-7317
HC405.A1
COUNTRY RISK SERVICE. ROMANIA. Text in English. 1988. q. USD 735 print or online; USD 410 per issue print or online (effective 2004). charts; stat. **Document type:** *Trade.*
Description: Focuses on predicting growth, budget deficits, trade and current accounts, foreign financing requirements and sources, and debt service for Romania.
Related titles: ♦ CD-ROM ed.: E I U Country Risk Service on Disc: Europe; Diskette ed.; Online - full text ed.: E I U Country Risk Service: Europe (from SilverPlatter Information, Inc.).
Published by: Economist Intelligence Unit, 111 W 57th St, New York, NY 10019. TEL 212-554-0600, FAX 212-586-1181, ewyork@eiu.com, http://www.eiu.com.

330.9 332 USA ISSN 1351-7325
HC340.12.A1
COUNTRY RISK SERVICE. RUSSIA. Text in English. 199?. q. USD 735 print or online; USD 410 per issue print or online (effective 2004). charts; stat. **Document type:** *Trade.*
Description: Focuses on predicting growth, budget deficits, trade and current accounts, foreign financing requirements and sources, and debt service for Russia.
Related titles: ♦ CD-ROM ed.: E I U Country Risk Service on Disc: Europe; Diskette ed.; Online - full text ed.: E I U Country Risk Service: Europe (from SilverPlatter Information, Inc.).
Published by: Economist Intelligence Unit, 111 W 57th St, New York, NY 10019. TEL 212-554-0600, FAX 212-586-1181, ewyork@eiu.com, http://www.eiu.com.

330.9 332 USA ISSN 1351-7333
HC415.33.A1
COUNTRY RISK SERVICE. SAUDI ARABIA. Text in English. 1988. q. USD 735 print or online; USD 410 per issue print or online (effective 2004). charts; stat. **Document type:** *Trade.*
Description: Focuses on predicting growth, budget deficits, trade and current accounts, foreign financing requirements and sources, and debt service for Saudi Arabia.
Related titles: ♦ CD-ROM ed.: E I U Country Risk Service on Disc: Middle East-North Africa; Diskette ed.; Online - full text ed.: E I U Country Risk Service: Middle East-North Africa.
Published by: Economist Intelligence Unit, 111 W 57th St, New York, NY 10019. TEL 212-554-0600, FAX 212-586-1181, ewyork@eiu.com, http://www.eiu.com.

330.9 332 USA ISSN 1351-7341
HC1045.A1
COUNTRY RISK SERVICE. SENEGAL. Text in English. 1988. q. USD 735 print or online; USD 410 per issue print or online (effective 2004). charts; stat. **Document type:** *Trade.*
Description: Focuses on predicting growth, budget deficits, trade and current accounts, foreign financing requirements and sources, and debt service for Senegal.
Related titles: ♦ CD-ROM ed.: E I U Country Risk Service on Disc: Sub-Saharan Africa; Diskette ed.; Online - full text ed.: E I U Country Risk Service: Sub-Saharan Africa (from SilverPlatter Information, Inc.).
Published by: Economist Intelligence Unit, 111 W 57th St, New York, NY 10019. TEL 212-554-0600, FAX 212-586-1181, ewyork@eiu.com, http://www.eiu.com.

330.9 332 USA ISSN 1351-735X
HC445.8.A1
COUNTRY RISK SERVICE. SINGAPORE. Text in English. 1988. q. USD 735 print or online; USD 410 per issue print or online (effective 2004). charts; stat. **Document type:** *Trade.*
Description: Focuses on predicting growth, budget deficits, trade and current accounts, foreign financing requirements and sources, and debt service for Singapore.
Related titles: CD-ROM ed.: (from SilverPlatter Information, Inc.); Diskette ed.; Online - full text ed.: (from SilverPlatter Information, Inc.).
Published by: Economist Intelligence Unit, 111 W 57th St, New York, NY 10019. TEL 212-554-0600, FAX 212-586-1181, ewyork@eiu.com, http://www.eiu.com.

332 330.9 USA ISSN 1354-5663
COUNTRY RISK SERVICE. SLOVAKIA. Text in English. 1994. q. USD 735 print or online; USD 410 per issue print or online (effective 2004). back issues avail. **Document type:** *Trade.*
Related titles: Online - full content ed.
Published by: Economist Intelligence Unit, 111 W 57th St, New York, NY 10019. TEL 212-554-0600, FAX 212-586-1181, newyork@eiu.com, http://www.eiu.com.

330.9 332 USA ISSN 1351-7368
HC406.A1
COUNTRY RISK SERVICE. SLOVENIA. Text in English. 199?. q. USD 735 print or online; USD 410 per issue print or online (effective 2004). charts; stat. **Document type:** *Trade.*
Description: Focuses on predicting growth, budget deficits, trade and current accounts, foreign financing requirements and sources, and debt service for Slovenia.

Related titles: ♦ CD-ROM ed.: E I U Country Risk Service on Disc: Europe; Diskette ed.; Online - full text ed.: E I U Country Risk Service: Europe (from SilverPlatter Information, Inc.).
Published by: Economist Intelligence Unit, 111 W 57th St, New York, NY 10019. TEL 212-554-0600, FAX 212-586-1181, ewyork@eiu.com, http://www.eiu.com.

330.9 332　　　USA　　　ISSN 1351-7376
HC905.A1
COUNTRY RISK SERVICE. SOUTH AFRICA. Text in English. 1988. q. USD 735 print or online; USD 410 per issue print or online (effective 2004). charts; stat. **Document type:** *Trade.*
Description: Focuses on predicting growth, budget deficits, trade and current accounts, foreign financing requirements and sources, and debt service for South Africa.
Related titles: ♦ CD-ROM ed.: E I U Country Risk Service on Disc: Sub-Saharan Africa; Diskette ed.; Online - full text ed.: E I U Country Risk Service: Sub-Saharan Africa (from SilverPlatter Information, Inc.).
Published by: Economist Intelligence Unit, 111 W 57th St, New York, NY 10019. TEL 212-554-0600, FAX 212-586-1181, ewyork@eiu.com, http://www.eiu.com.

330.9 332　　　USA　　　ISSN 1351-7384
HC466
COUNTRY RISK SERVICE. SOUTH KOREA. Text in English. 1988. q. USD 735 print or online; USD 410 per issue print or online (effective 2004). charts; stat. **Document type:** *Trade.*
Description: Focuses on predicting growth, budget deficits, trade and current accounts, foreign financing requirements and sources, and debt service for South Korea.
Related titles: CD-ROM ed.: (from SilverPlatter Information, Inc.); Diskette ed.; Online - full text ed.: (from SilverPlatter Information, Inc.).
Published by: Economist Intelligence Unit, 111 W 57th St, New York, NY 10019. TEL 212-554-0600, FAX 212-586-1181, ewyork@eiu.com, http://www.eiu.com.

330.9 332　　　USA　　　ISSN 1351-7392
HC381
COUNTRY RISK SERVICE. SPAIN. Text in English. 1991. q. USD 735 print or online; USD 410 per issue print or online (effective 2004). charts; stat. **Document type:** *Trade.*
Description: Focuses on predicting growth, budget deficits, trade and current accounts, foreign financing requirements and sources, and debt service for Spain.
Related titles: CD-ROM ed.: (from SilverPlatter Information, Inc.); Diskette ed.; Online - full text ed.: (from SilverPlatter Information, Inc.).
Published by: Economist Intelligence Unit, 111 W 57th St, New York, NY 10019. TEL 212-554-0600, FAX 212-586-1181, ewyork@eiu.com, http://www.eiu.com.

330.9 332　　　USA　　　ISSN 1351-7406
HC424.A1
COUNTRY RISK SERVICE. SRI LANKA. Text in English. 1988. q. USD 735 print or online; USD 410 per issue print or online (effective 2004). charts; stat. **Document type:** *Trade.*
Description: Focuses on predicting growth, budget deficits, trade and current accounts, foreign financing requirements and sources, and debt service for Sri Lanka.
Related titles: CD-ROM ed.: (from SilverPlatter Information, Inc.); Diskette ed.; Online - full text ed.: (from SilverPlatter Information, Inc.).
Published by: Economist Intelligence Unit, 111 W 57th St, New York, NY 10019. TEL 212-554-0600, FAX 212-586-1181, ewyork@eiu.com, http://www.eiu.com.

330.9 332　　　USA　　　ISSN 1351-7414
HC835.A1
COUNTRY RISK SERVICE. SUDAN. Text in English. 1988. q. USD 735 print or online (effective 2004). charts; stat. **Document type:** *Trade.* **Description:** Focuses on predicting growth, budget deficits, trade and current accounts, foreign financing requirements and sources, and debt service for Sudan.
Related titles: ♦ CD-ROM ed.: E I U Country Risk Service on Disc: Middle East-North Africa; Diskette ed.; Online - full text ed.: E I U Country Risk Service: Middle East-North Africa.
Published by: Economist Intelligence Unit, 111 W 57th St, New York, NY 10019. TEL 212-554-0600, FAX 212-586-1181, ewyork@eiu.com, http://www.eiu.com.

330.9 332　　　USA　　　ISSN 1351-7422
HC415.23.A1
COUNTRY RISK SERVICE. SYRIA. Text in English. 1988. q. USD 735 print or online; USD 410 per issue print or online (effective 2004). charts; stat. **Document type:** *Trade.*
Description: Focuses on predicting growth, budget deficits, trade and current accounts, foreign financing requirements and sources, and debt service for Syria.
Related titles: ♦ CD-ROM ed.: E I U Country Risk Service on Disc: Middle East-North Africa; Diskette ed.; Online - full text ed.: E I U Country Risk Service: Middle East-North Africa.
Published by: Economist Intelligence Unit, 111 W 57th St, New York, NY 10019. TEL 212-554-0600, FAX 212-586-1181, ewyork@eiu.com, http://www.eiu.com.

330.9 332　　　USA　　　ISSN 1351-7430
HC430.5.A1
COUNTRY RISK SERVICE. TAIWAN. Text in English. 1988. q. USD 735 print or online; USD 410 per issue print or online (effective 2004). charts; stat. **Document type:** *Trade.*
Description: Focuses on predicting growth, budget deficits, trade and current accounts, foreign financing requirements and sources, and debt service for Taiwan.
Related titles: ♦ CD-ROM ed.: (from SilverPlatter Information, Inc.); Diskette ed.; Online - full text ed.: (from SilverPlatter Information, Inc.).
Published by: Economist Intelligence Unit, 111 W 57th St, New York, NY 10019. TEL 212-554-0600, FAX 212-586-1181, ewyork@eiu.com, http://www.eiu.com.

330.9 332　　　USA
COUNTRY RISK SERVICE. TAJIKISTAN. Text in English. q. USD 735 print or online; USD 410 per issue print or online (effective 2004). charts; stat. **Document type:** *Trade.*
Published by: Economist Intelligence Unit, 111 W 57th St, New York, NY 10019. TEL 212-554-0600, FAX 212-586-1181, ewyork@eiu.com, http://www.eiu.com.

330.9 332　　　USA　　　ISSN 1351-7449
HC445.A1
COUNTRY RISK SERVICE. THAILAND. Text in English. 1988. q. USD 735 print or online; USD 410 per issue print or online (effective 2004). charts; stat. **Document type:** *Trade.*
Description: Focuses on predicting growth, budget deficits, trade and current accounts, foreign financing requirements and sources, and debt service for Thailand.
Related titles: CD-ROM ed.: (from SilverPlatter Information, Inc.); Diskette ed.; Online - full text ed.: (from SilverPlatter Information, Inc.).
Published by: Economist Intelligence Unit, 111 W 57th St, New York, NY 10019. TEL 212-554-0600, FAX 212-586-1181, ewyork@eiu.com, http://www.eiu.com.

330.9 332　　　USA　　　ISSN 1351-7457
HC157.3.A1
COUNTRY RISK SERVICE. TRINIDAD AND TOBAGO. Text in English. 1988. q. USD 735 print or online; USD 410 per issue print or online (effective 2004). charts; stat. **Document type:** *Trade.* **Description:** Focuses on predicting growth, budget deficits, trade and current accounts, foreign financing requirements and sources, and debt service for Trinidad and Tobago.
Related titles: ♦ CD-ROM ed.: E I U Country Risk Service on Disc: Latin America; Diskette ed.; Online - full text ed.: E I U Country Risk Service: Latin America.
Published by: Economist Intelligence Unit, 111 W 57th St, New York, NY 10019. TEL 212-554-0600, FAX 212-586-1181, ewyork@eiu.com, http://www.eiu.com.

330.9 332　　　USA　　　ISSN 1351-7465
HC820.A1
COUNTRY RISK SERVICE. TUNISIA. Text in English. 1988. q. USD 735 print or online; USD 410 per issue print or online (effective 2004). charts; stat. **Document type:** *Trade.*
Description: Focuses on predicting growth, budget deficits, trade and current accounts, foreign financing requirements and sources, and debt service for Tunisia.
Related titles: ♦ CD-ROM ed.: E I U Country Risk Service on Disc: Middle East-North Africa; Diskette ed.; Online - full text ed.: E I U Country Risk Service: Middle East-North Africa.
Published by: Economist Intelligence Unit, 111 W 57th St, New York, NY 10019. TEL 212-554-0600, FAX 212-586-1181, ewyork@eiu.com, http://www.eiu.com.

330.9 332　　　USA　　　ISSN 1351-7473
HC491
COUNTRY RISK SERVICE. TURKEY. Text in English. 1988. q. USD 735 print or online; USD 410 per issue print or online (effective 2004). charts; stat. **Document type:** *Trade.*
Description: Focuses on predicting growth, budget deficits, trade and current accounts, foreign financing requirements and sources, and debt service for Turkey.
Related titles: CD-ROM ed.: (from SilverPlatter Information, Inc.); Diskette ed.; Online - full text ed.: (from SilverPlatter Information, Inc.).
Published by: Economist Intelligence Unit, 111 W 57th St, New York, NY 10019. TEL 212-554-0600, FAX 212-586-1181, ewyork@eiu.com, http://www.eiu.com.

330.9 332　　　USA　　　ISSN 1351-7481
HC340.19.A1
COUNTRY RISK SERVICE. UKRAINE. Text in English. 199?. q. USD 735 print or online; USD 410 per issue print or online (effective 2004). charts; stat. **Document type:** *Trade.*
Description: Focuses on predicting growth, budget deficits, trade and current accounts, foreign financing requirements and sources, and debt service for the Ukraine.
Related titles: ♦ CD-ROM ed.: E I U Country Risk Service on Disc: Europe; Diskette ed.; Online - full text ed.: E I U Country Risk Service: Europe (from SilverPlatter Information, Inc.).
Published by: Economist Intelligence Unit, 111 W 57th St, New York, NY 10019. TEL 212-554-0600, FAX 212-586-1181, ewyork@eiu.com, http://www.eiu.com.

330.9 332　　　USA　　　ISSN 1351-749X
HC415.36.A1
COUNTRY RISK SERVICE. UNITED ARAB EMIRATES. Text in English. 1988. q. USD 735 print or online; USD 410 per issue print or online (effective 2004). charts; stat. **Document type:** *Trade.* **Description:** Focuses on predicting growth, budget deficits, trade and current accounts, foreign financing requirements and sources, and debt service for the United Arab Emirates.
Related titles: ♦ CD-ROM ed.: E I U Country Risk Service on Disc: Middle East-North Africa; Diskette ed.; Online - full text ed.: E I U Country Risk Service: Middle East-North Africa.
Published by: Economist Intelligence Unit, 111 W 57th St, New York, NY 10019. TEL 212-554-0600, FAX 212-586-1181, ewyork@eiu.com, http://www.eiu.com.

330.9 332　　　USA　　　ISSN 1351-7503
HC231
COUNTRY RISK SERVICE. URUGUAY. Text in English. 1988. q. USD 735 print or online; USD 410 per issue print or online (effective 2004). charts; stat. **Document type:** *Trade.*
Description: Focuses on predicting growth, budget deficits, trade and current accounts, foreign financing requirements and sources, and debt service for Uruguay.
Related titles: ♦ CD-ROM ed.: E I U Country Risk Service on Disc: Latin America; Diskette ed.; Online - full text ed.: E I U Country Risk Service: Latin America.
Published by: Economist Intelligence Unit, 111 W 57th St, New York, NY 10019. TEL 212-554-0600, FAX 212-586-1181, ewyork@eiu.com, http://www.eiu.com.

330.9 332　　　USA　　　ISSN 1366-4328
HC421.7.A1
COUNTRY RISK SERVICE. UZBEKISTAN. Text in English. 1997. q. USD 735 print or online; USD 410 per issue print or online (effective 2004). charts; stat. **Document type:** *Trade.*
Published by: Economist Intelligence Unit, 111 W 57th St, New York, NY 10019. TEL 212-554-0600, FAX 212-586-1181, ewyork@eiu.com, http://www.eiu.com.

330.9 332　　　USA　　　ISSN 1351-7511
HC236
COUNTRY RISK SERVICE. VENEZUELA. Text in English. 1988. q. USD 735 print or online; USD 410 per issue print or online (effective 2004). charts; stat. **Document type:** *Trade.*
Description: Focuses on predicting growth, budget deficits, trade and current accounts, foreign financing requirements and sources, and debt service for Venezuela.
Related titles: ♦ CD-ROM ed.: E I U Country Risk Service on Disc: Latin America; Diskette ed.; Online - full text ed.: E I U Country Risk Service: Latin America.
Published by: Economist Intelligence Unit, 111 W 57th St, New York, NY 10019. TEL 212-554-0600, FAX 212-586-1181, ewyork@eiu.com, http://www.eiu.com.

330.9 332　　　USA　　　ISSN 1354-5655
HC444.A1
COUNTRY RISK SERVICE. VIETNAM. Text in English. 1994. q. USD 735 print or online; USD 410 per issue print or online (effective 2004). charts; stat. **Document type:** *Trade.*
Description: Focuses on predicting growth, budget deficits, trade and current accounts, foreign financing requirements and sources, and debt service for Vietnam.
Related titles: ♦ CD-ROM ed.: E I U Country Risk Service on Disc: Asia-Pacific; Diskette ed.; Online - full text ed.: E I U Country Risk Service: Asia-Pacific (from SilverPlatter Information, Inc.).
Published by: Economist Intelligence Unit, 111 W 57th St, New York, NY 10019. TEL 212-554-0600, FAX 212-586-1181, newyork@eiu.com, http://www.eiu.com.

330.9 332　　　USA　　　ISSN 1351-752X
HC415.34.A1
COUNTRY RISK SERVICE. YEMEN. Text in English. 1988. q. USD 735 print or online; USD 410 per issue print or online (effective 2004). charts; stat. **Document type:** *Trade.*
Description: Focuses on predicting growth, budget deficits, trade and current accounts, foreign financing requirements and sources, and debt service for Yemen.
Related titles: ♦ CD-ROM ed.: E I U Country Risk Service on Disc: Middle East-North Africa; Diskette ed.; Online - full text ed.: E I U Country Risk Service: Middle East-North Africa.
Published by: Economist Intelligence Unit, 111 W 57th St, New York, NY 10019. TEL 212-554-0600, FAX 212-586-1181, newyork@eiu.com, http://www.eiu.com.

330.9 332　　　USA　　　ISSN 1468-9731
COUNTRY RISK SERVICE. YUGOSLAVIA (SERBIA-MONTENEGRO). Text in English. 1998. q. USD 735 print or online; USD 410 per issue print or online (effective 2004). illus.; stat. **Document type:** *Trade.*
Former titles (until 1998): Country Risk Service. Yugoslavia (1461-6068); Superseded in part: Country Risk Service. Yugoslavia Macedonia (1366-4301); Which superseded in part (in 1997): Country Risk Service. Former Yugoslav Republics (1351-7538)
Published by: Economist Intelligence Unit, 111 W 57th St, New York, NY 10019. TEL 212-554-0600, FAX 212-586-1181, newyork@eiu.com, http://www.eiu.com.

330.9 332 USA ISSN 1351-7546
HC955.A1
COUNTRY RISK SERVICE. ZAIRE. Text in English. 1988. q. USD 735 print or online; USD 410 per issue print or online (effective 2004). charts; stat. **Document type:** *Trade.*
Description: Focuses on predicting growth, budget deficits, trade and current accounts, foreign financing requirements and sources, and debt service for Zaire.
Related titles: ◆ CD-ROM ed.: E I U Country Risk Service on Disc: Sub-Saharan Africa; Diskette ed.; Online - full text ed.: E I U Country Risk Service: Sub-Saharan Africa (from SilverPlatter Information, Inc.).
Published by: Economist Intelligence Unit, 111 W 57th St, New York, NY 10019. TEL 212-554-0600, FAX 212-586-1181, newyork@eiu.com, http://www.eiu.com.

330.9 332 USA ISSN 1351-7554
HC915.A1
COUNTRY RISK SERVICE. ZAMBIA. Text in English. 1988. q. USD 735 print or online; USD 410 per issue print or online (effective 2004). charts; stat. **Document type:** *Trade.*
Description: Focuses on predicting growth, budget deficits, trade and current accounts, foreign financing requirements and sources, and debt service for Zambia.
Related titles: ◆ CD-ROM ed.: E I U Country Risk Service on Disc: Sub-Saharan Africa; Diskette ed.; Online - full text ed.: E I U Country Risk Service: Sub-Saharan Africa (from SilverPlatter Information, Inc.).
Published by: Economist Intelligence Unit, 111 W 57th St, New York, NY 10019. TEL 212-554-0600, FAX 212-586-1181, newyork@eiu.com, http://www.eiu.com.

330.9 332 USA ISSN 1351-7562
HC910.A1
COUNTRY RISK SERVICE. ZIMBABWE. Text in English. 1988. q. USD 735 print or online; USD 410 per issue print or online (effective 2004). charts; stat. **Document type:** *Trade.*
Description: Focuses on predicting growth, budget deficits, trade and current accounts, foreign financing requirements and sources, and debt service for Zimbabwe.
Related titles: ◆ CD-ROM ed.: E I U Country Risk Service on Disc: Sub-Saharan Africa; Diskette ed.; Online - full text ed.: E I U Country Risk Service: Sub-Saharan Africa (from SilverPlatter Information, Inc.).
Published by: Economist Intelligence Unit, 111 W 57th St, New York, NY 10019. TEL 212-554-0600, FAX 212-586-1181, newyork@eiu.com, http://www.eiu.com.

330.9 320 USA
COUNTRY VIEWSWIRE. (60 separate country reports available.) Text in English. d. USD 750; USD 300 per issue (effective 2004). illus.; stat. **Document type:** *Trade.* **Description:** Tracks the latest global developments and industry trends.
Media: Online - full content.
Published by: Economist Intelligence Unit, 111 W 57th St, New York, NY 10019. TEL 212-554-0600, FAX 212-586-1182, newyork@eiu.com, http://www.viewswire.com.

COUNTRYSIDE FOCUS; working for people and places in rural England. see *CONSERVATION*

330.9 USA
COUNTY ECONOMIC INDICATORS. Text in English. a. charts; stat. **Document type:** *Trade.*
Media: Online - full text.
Published by: Oregon Economic Development Department, 775 Summer St, N E, Salem, OR 97310. TEL 503-373-1290, FAX 503-581-5115, http://www.econ.state.or.us.

330.9 MAR ISSN 0752-1855
COURRIER ECONOMIQUE. Text in French. w. adv.
Address: 22 av. de l'Armee Royale, Casablanca, Morocco.

330.9 USA
COWLES FOUNDATION. DISCUSSION PAPERS (ONLINE). Text in English. 1955. irreg.
Formerly (until 1989): Cowles Foundation. Discussion Papers (Print)
Media: Online - full text.
—BLDSC (3486.120000), ingenta.
Published by: Yale University, Cowles Foundation for Research in Economics, 30 Hillhouse Ave, New Haven, CT 06511. http://cowles.econ.yale.edu.

330.9 ESP ISSN 0214-7343
COYUNTURA ECONOMICA DE ANDALUCIA. Text in Spanish. 1989. q.
Related titles: Online - full text ed.
—CINDOC.
Published by: Junta de Andalucia, Consejeria de Economia y Hacienda, Edif. Torretriana, Isla de Cartuja, Sevilla, 41092, Spain. TEL 34-955-065000, http://www.ceh.junta-andalucia.es/web/economia/situacion/coyuntura/coyuntura.htm.

330.9 ESP ISSN 1134-4636
HC387.V3
COYUNTURA ECONOMICA VALENCIANA. Text in Spanish, Catalan. 1992. bi-m. back issues avail.
Formerly (until 1994): Coyuntura Economica (1134-4628)
—CINDOC.
Published by: Generalitat Valenciana, Conselleria d'Economia, Hisenda i Ocupacio, Palau, 14, Valencia, 46003, Spain. TEL 34-96-1964300, FAX 34-96-1964301, http://www.gva.es/coyuntura/.

330.9 COL ISSN 0121-2532
HN301
COYUNTURA SOCIAL. Text in Spanish. 1989. s-a. COP 53,000 domestic; USD 293 foreign (effective 2001). adv. bk.rev. stat. **Document type:** *Journal, Academic/Scholarly.*
Related titles: Supplement(s): Debates de Coyuntura Social.
Indexed: IBSS.
Published by: Fedesarrollo (Fundacion para la Educacion Superior y el Desarrollo), Calle 78, N1 9-91, Apartado Aereo 75074, Bogota, Santa Fe, Colombia. TEL 57-1-312-5300, FAX 57-1-212-6073, administrator@fedesarrollo.org.co, http://www.fedesarrollo.org.co. Ed. Olga Lucia Acosta Navarro. R&P, Adv. contact Maria Mercedes Carrasquilla. B&W page COP 1,084,000, color page COP 1,459,780.

330.9 USA ISSN 0197-2375
CRAIN'S CLEVELAND BUSINESS. Text in English. 1980. w. (Mon.). USD 59 in state; USD 102 out of state (effective 2005). adv. bk.rev. charts; illus. 38 p./no.; reprint service avail. from PQC. **Document type:** *Newspaper, Trade.* **Description:** Provides news, commentary, in-depth analysis and features in technology, health care, manufacturing, real estate, finance and other industries for the Greater Cleveland business community.
Related titles: Microform ed.: (from PQC); Online - full text ed.: CrainsCleveland.com (from bigchalk, EBSCO Publishing, Florida Center for Library Automation, Gale Group, H.W. Wilson, LexisNexis, Northern Light Technology, Inc., O C L C Online Computer Library Center, Inc., ProQuest Information & Learning, The Dialog Corporation).
Indexed: ABIn, B&I, BPI, BusDate, LRI, T&II.
—CCC.
Published by: Crain Communications, Inc., 1155 Gratiot Ave, Detroit, MI 48207-2997. clevedit@crain.com, http://www.crainscleveland.com, http://www.crain.com. Eds. Mark Dodosh, Brian Tucker. Pub. Brian Tucker. adv.: page USD 7,000. Circ: 22,400 (paid).

CREATING QUALITY CITIES. see *PUBLIC ADMINISTRATION—Municipal Government*

CRED-ALERT. see *BUSINESS AND ECONOMICS—Banking And Finance*

330.9 ITA
CREDIT AND FINANCE IN ITALY. QUARTERLY BULLETIN. Text in English. 1970 (no.16). q. free. charts; stat. **Document type:** *Bulletin.*
Formerly: Cassa di Risparmio delle Provincie Lombarde Quarterly (0008-7408)
Published by: Cassa di Risparmio delle Provincie Lombarde, Via Monte Di Pieta', 8, Milan, MI 20121, Italy. http://www.cariplo.it. Ed. Renzo G Avesani.

330.9 DEU
CREDIT-CURIER. Text in German. 1983. m. adv. bk.rev. **Document type:** *Journal, Trade.*
Published by: Creditreform Neuss Frommann KG, Hellersbergstr 14, Neuss, 41460, Germany. TEL 49-2131-22030, FAX 49-2131-220312, Info@Neuss.Creditreform.de, http://www.creditreform.de/vc/neuss/. Ed. Norbert Becker Harzheim. Circ: 4,400.

CREDIT SUISSE. BULLETIN. see *BUSINESS AND ECONOMICS—Banking And Finance*

CRITICA PERIODISMO EN SONORA. see *POLITICAL SCIENCE*

330.9 MEX ISSN 0186-0445
HC131
CUADERNO DE INFORMACION OPORTUNA. Text in Spanish. 1978. m. MXP 900 (effective 1999).
Published by: Instituto Nacional de Estadistica, Geografia e Informatica, Secretaria de Programacion y Presupuesto, Prol. Heroe de Nacozari 2301 Sur, Puerta 11, Acceso, Aguascalientes, 20270, Mexico. TEL 52-4-918-19488, FAX 52-4-918-0739, http://www.inegi.gob.mx. Circ: 1,150.

330.9 MEX ISSN 0186-047X
CUADERNO DE INFORMACION OPORTUNA REGIONAL. Text in Spanish. 1984. q. MXP 90 (effective 1999).
Published by: Instituto Nacional de Estadistica, Geografia e Informatica, Secretaria de Programacion y Presupuesto, Prol. Heroe de Nacozari 2301 Sur, Puerta 11, Acceso, Aguascalientes, 20270, Mexico. TEL 52-4-918-1948, FAX 52-4-918-0739, http://www.inegi.gob.mx. Circ: 500.

330.9 ESP ISSN 0211-0865
CUADERNOS ARAGONESES DE ECONOMIA. Text in Spanish. 1976. q. EUR 21 domestic to individuals; USD 40 foreign to individuals; EUR 24 domestic to institutions; USD 50 foreign to institutions (effective 2002).
Related titles: Online - full text ed.
—CINDOC.
Published by: Universidad de Zaragoza, Facultad de Ciencias Economicas y Empresariales, Dr. Cerrada, 1-E, Zaragoza, Aragon 50005, Spain. TEL 34-976-76100, FAX 34-976-761770, http://siempre.unizar.es/. Ed. Jose Mariano Moneva Abadia.

330.9 ESP ISSN 0214-6002
CUADERNOS DE ECONOMIA MURCIANA. Text in Spanish. 1988. 3/yr.
—CINDOC.
Published by: Murcia. Consejeria de Economia y Hacienda, Alejandro Seiquer, 11 2o., Murcia, 30001, Spain. informatica@carm.es, http://www.carm.es/chac.

330.9 ARG ISSN 0327-9693
CUADERNOS DE ECONOMIA POLITICA. Text in Spanish. 1985. 3/yr. **Description:** Presents research works and analysis on diverse aspects of the contemporary economic situation.
Published by: Universidad Nacional de Lujan, C.C. 221, Lujan, Buenos Aires 6700, Argentina. Ed. Felix Marcos.

320.9 MEX ISSN 1605-0355
CUARTO PODER. Text in Spanish. d.
Media: Online - full text.
Published by: Cuarto Poder de Chiapas http://www.cuarto-poder.com.mx/.

320.9 MEX ISSN 1605-4873
CUARTO PODER DE MICHOACAN; objetividad, veracidad y profesionalismo. Variant title: 4o Poder de Michoacan. Text in Spanish. w.
Media: Online - full text.
Address: TEL 52-434-23631, cuartopoder@ml.com.mx, http://www.ml.com.mx/4to-poder/. Ed. Raul Garcia Aguirre.

330.9 ARG ISSN 0328-8951
CUENTAS NACIONALES OFERTA Y DEMANDA GLOBALES. Text in Spanish. 1996. a. **Document type:** *Directory, Government.*
Published by: Argentina. Ministerio de Economia, Servicio de Prensa, 501, Balcarce, 136 Piso 5, Capital Federal, Buenos Aires 1064, Argentina. TEL 54-114-3495079, FAX 54-114-3495730, mpqonz@mecon.gov.ar, http://www.mecon.gov.ar/.

CUESTIONES ECONOMICAS. see *BUSINESS AND ECONOMICS—Banking And Finance*

381 ANT
CURACAO TRADE AND INDUSTRY ASSOCIATION. NEWSLETTER. Text in English. 1972. m. **Document type:** *Newsletter.*
Formerly: Trade and Industry of Curacao. Monthly Publication
Published by: Curacao Trade and Industry Association, Pietermaai 21, Willemstad, Curacao, Netherlands Antilles. Ed. V M Oenes.

330.9 ROM ISSN 1220-4684
CURIERUL NATIONAL. Text in Romanian. 1990. d. ROL 64,296 (effective 1998). adv. tel.rev. mkt. 16 p./no. 9 cols./p.; **Document type:** *Newspaper, Consumer.* **Description:** Covers economics for private economists, businessmen, bankers and politicians.
Related titles: Microfilm ed.
Published by: (Editura Presa Libera), Curierul National S.A., Str. Ministerului 2-4, Bucharest, Romania. TEL 40-1-3159512, FAX 40-1-3152570, TELEX 10250, curiernr@bx.logicnet.ro, http://domingo.kappa.ro/e-media. Ed. Valentin Paunescu. Adv. contact Silvia Feir. page USD 20,000. Circ: 50,000. **Dist. by:** Rodipet S.A., Piata Presei Libere 1, sector 1, PO Box 33-57, Bucharest 3, Romania. TEL 40-21-2224126, 40-21-2226407, rodipet@rodipet.ro.

CURRENT POLITICS AND ECONOMICS OF ASIA. see *POLITICAL SCIENCE*

CURRENT POLITICS AND ECONOMICS OF EUROPE. see *POLITICAL SCIENCE*

330.9 CYP ISSN 0253-8555
HC415.2.A1
CYPRUS. DEPARTMENT OF STATISTICS AND RESEARCH. MONTHLY ECONOMIC INDICATORS. Text in English. 1978. bi-m. CYP 4 (effective 1999). **Document type:** *Government.*
Description: Brings together selected economic indicators to provide a picture of significant short-term developments in the Cypriot economy.
Supersedes: Cyprus. Department of Statistics and Research. Short-Term Industrial Indicators
Published by: Ministry of Finance, Department of Statistics and Research, 13 Andreas Araouzos St, Nicosia, 1444, Cyprus. TEL 357-2-309318, FAX 357-2-374830, cydsr@cytanet.com.cy, http://www.pio.gov.cy/dsr.

330.9 CYP
CYPRUS. FIVE YEAR PLANS. Variant title: Emergency Economic Action Plans. Text in English, Greek. 1961. quinquennial. free. **Document type:** *Government.*
Published by: Planning Bureau Office, Nicosia, Cyprus. TEL 357-2-302202, FAX 357-2-303175. Circ: 2,000.

330   BRA
D E S E D* . (Departamento Geral de Selecao e Desenvolvimento do Pessoal) Text in Portuguese. 1965. q. free. bk.rev. illus. Supplement avail.
Published by: Banco do Brasil S.A., Departamento Geral de Selecao e Desenvolvimento do Pessoal, Setor Bancario Sul, LOTE, 23, Bloco C, A Sul (P Piloto), Caixa Postal 562, Brasilia, DF 70359-970, Brazil. Circ: 113,000.

332   JPN   ISSN 0385-2350
D K B ECONOMIC REPORT. (Dai-Ichi Kangyo Bank) Text in English. 1971. m. free. charts; illus.; stat. **Document type:** *Newsletter, Corporate.*
Formerly: N K B Research Monthly (0027-6774)
Published by: D K B Research Institute Corp., 1-1-5 Uchisaiwai-cho, Chiyoda-ku, Tokyo, 100-0011, Japan. FAX 81-3-3596-3198. Ed., R&P Masato Nagasawa. Circ: 10,500.

330.9   GBR   ISSN 0958-1383
D P P WORKING PAPER. (Development Policy & Practice) Text in English. 198?. irreg., latest vol.45. **Document type:** *Monographic series.*
Indexed: GEOBASE.
Published by: Open University, Faculty of Technology, Walton Hall, Milton Keynes, MK7 6AA, United Kingdom. TEL 44-1908-652103, FAX 44-1908-654825, dpp@open.ac.uk, http://dpp.open.ac.uk/workdocs.htm.

330.9   USA
D R I - MCGRAW-HILL COST AND PRICE REVIEW. Key Title: Cost and Price Review. Text in English. q. back issues avail.
Formed by the merger of: D R I McGraw-Hill Cost and Price Review: U.S. Long-Range Focus (1052-1283); D R I - McGraw-Hill Cost and Price Review: U S Short-Range Focus (1052-1704); Formerly: U S Cost Forecasting Service Long-Term Review
Published by: D R I - McGraw-Hill, 24 Hartwell Ave, Lexington, MA 02173. TEL 617-863-5100, FAX 617-860-6332. Ed. Mark Ulmer.

330.9   USA   ISSN 1052-1690
HB231
D R I - MCGRAW-HILL COST AND PRICE REVIEW: INTERNATIONAL FOCUS. Key Title: Cost and Price Review: International Focus. Text in English. q. **Document type:** *Trade.*
Formerly: International Cost Forecasting Service Review
Published by: D R I - McGraw-Hill, 24 Hartwell Ave, Lexington, MA 02173. TEL 617-863-5100, FAX 617-860-6332. Ed. Mark Ulmer.

330.9   USA   ISSN 1054-495X
HD3881
D R I - MCGRAW-HILL COST AND PRICE REVIEW: UTILITY FOCUS. Key Title: Cost and Price Review: Utility Focus. Text in English. q. back issues avail. **Document type:** *Trade.*
Formerly: Utility Cost Forecasting Service Review
Published by: D R I - McGraw-Hill, 24 Hartwell Ave, Lexington, MA 02173. TEL 617-863-5100, FAX 617-860-6332, TELEX 200 284. Ed. Nariman Behravesh.

330.9 339   USA
D R I - MCGRAW-HILL COUNTRY REPORTS. Text in English. q. **Document type:** *Trade.*
Former titles (until 1992): D R I - McGraw-Hill European Review; Data Resources European Review; European Review (0276-7430); D R I European Review (0362-4730)
Published by: D R I - McGraw-Hill, 24 Hartwell Ave, Lexington, MA 02173. TEL 617-863-5100, FAX 617-860-6332. Ed. Nariman Behravesh.

D R I - MCGRAW-HILL ENERGY REVIEW. see *ENERGY*

330.9   USA
D R I - MCGRAW-HILL EUROPEAN INDUSTRY REVIEW. Text in English. q. **Document type:** *Trade.*
Former titles (until 1992): D R I - McGraw-Hill Industry Review; European Sectoral Service Review
Published by: D R I - McGraw-Hill, 24 Hartwell Ave, Lexington, MA 02173. TEL 617-863-5100, FAX 617-860-6332. Ed. Elizabeth Waelbroeck Rocha.

330.9 339   USA
D R I - MCGRAW-HILL GLOBAL RISK REPORT. Text in English. s-a. back issues avail. **Document type:** *Trade.*
Former titles: D R I - McGraw-Hill Latin American Country Reports; D R I - McGraw-Hill Latin American Review; Data Resources Latin American Review
Published by: D R I - McGraw-Hill, 24 Hartwell Ave, Lexington, MA 02173. TEL 617-863-5100, FAX 617-860-6332. Ed. Eric Rice.

330.9 339   USA   ISSN 0743-7323
HC106.6
D R I - MCGRAW-HILL REVIEW OF THE U S ECONOMY. Key Title: Review of the U S Economy. Text in English. 1972. m. **Document type:** *Trade.*
Former titles: Data Resources Review of the U S Economy (0197-6966); (until 1979): Data Resources Review (0092-5482)

Published by: D R I - McGraw-Hill, 24 Hartwell Ave, Lexington, MA 02173. TEL 617-863-5100, FAX 617-863-5100. Ed. Cynthia Latta.

330.9 339   USA
D R I - MCGRAW-HILL REVIEW OF THE U S ECONOMY: LONG RANGE FOCUS. Key Title: Review of the U S Economy: Long Range Focus. Text in English. 1976. s-a. **Document type:** *Trade.*
Former titles: D R I - McGraw-Hill U S Long-Term Review; Data Resources U S Long-Term Review; Data Resources U S Long-Term Bulletin (0362-6199)
Published by: D R I - McGraw-Hill, 24 Hartwell Ave, Lexington, MA 02173. TEL 617-863-5100, FAX 617-860-6332. Ed. Cynthia Latta.

330.9 339   USA
D R I - MCGRAW-HILL U S FORECAST SUMMARY. Text in English. m. back issues avail. **Document type:** *Trade.*
Related titles: Online - full text ed.
Published by: D R I - McGraw-Hill, 24 Hartwell Ave, Lexington, MA 02173. TEL 617-863-5100, FAX 617-860-6332. Ed. Cynthia Latta.

D R I - MCGRAW-HILL U S MARKETS REVIEW: INDUSTRY FOCUS. see *BUSINESS AND ECONOMICS—Production Of Goods And Services*

D R I - MCGRAW-HILL U S MARKETS REVIEW: METRO FOCUS. see *BUSINESS AND ECONOMICS—Production Of Goods And Services*

D R I - MCGRAW-HILL U S MARKETS REVIEW: MIDWEST. STATE FOCUS. see *BUSINESS AND ECONOMICS—Production Of Goods And Services*

D R I - MCGRAW-HILL U S MARKETS REVIEW: NORTHEAST. METRO FOCUS. see *BUSINESS AND ECONOMICS—Production Of Goods And Services*

D R I - MCGRAW-HILL U S MARKETS REVIEW: NORTHEAST. STATE FOCUS. see *BUSINESS AND ECONOMICS—Production Of Goods And Services*

D R I - MCGRAW-HILL U S MARKETS REVIEW: REGIONAL FORECAST SUMMARY. see *BUSINESS AND ECONOMICS—Production Of Goods And Services*

D R I - MCGRAW-HILL U S MARKETS REVIEW: REGIONAL PREVIEW. see *BUSINESS AND ECONOMICS—Production Of Goods And Services*

D R I - MCGRAW-HILL U S MARKETS REVIEW: SOUTH. STATE FOCUS. see *BUSINESS AND ECONOMICS—Production Of Goods And Services*

D R I - MCGRAW-HILL U S MARKETS REVIEW: WEST. METRO FOCUS. see *BUSINESS AND ECONOMICS—Production Of Goods And Services*

D R I - MCGRAW-HILL U S MARKETS REVIEW: WEST. STATE FOCUS. see *BUSINESS AND ECONOMICS—Production Of Goods And Services*

DAILY BULLETIN (BROOKLYN); a daily newspaper serving professionals. see *LAW*

330.9   DNK   ISSN 0419-9480
DANSK OEKONOMI/DANISH ECONOMY. Variant title: Vismandsrapporten. Text in Danish; Summaries in English. 1968. 2/yr. price varies. **Description:** Economic analyses and policy statements on fiscal and monetary policies, includes forecast of the Danish economy for the next 2-3 years.
Related titles: Online - full text ed.: ISSN 1398-585X. 199?. free.
Published by: Det Oekonomiske Raad/Danish Economic Council, Adelgade 13, Copenhagen K, 1304, Denmark. TEL 45-33-135128, FAX 45-33-329029, dors@dors.dk, http://www.dors.dk/rapp/.

DATAFILE OF ASIA-PACIFIC TELECOMMUNICATIONS. see *COMMUNICATIONS*

DATAFILE OF EASTERN EUROPEAN COMMUNICATIONS. see *COMMUNICATIONS*

DATAFILE OF EUROPEAN TELECOMMUNICATIONS. see *COMMUNICATIONS*

DATAFILE OF LATIN AMERICAN TELECOMMUNICATIONS. see *COMMUNICATIONS*

330.9   JAM
DATAPAC CARIBBEAN BUSINESS TRENDS. Text in English. 1983. q. JMD 600, USD 50. **Document type:** *Academic/Scholarly.* **Description:** Contains current information on economic trends in commerce, industry and finance throughout the Caribbean.
Formerly: DataPac Caribbean

Published by: Data Resource Systems International Ltd., 7 Oxford Park Ave, PO Box 193, Kingston, 5, Jamaica. TEL 809-968-0813, FAX 809-968-0826. Ed. Huntley Manhertz. adv.: B&W page JMD 7,000, color page JMD 11,000; 7.5 x 10.5. Circ: 2,000.

330   USA
DELTA BUSINESS JOURNAL; business news for the mississippi delta. Text in English. 1998. m. USD 28 (effective 2004). adv. **Document type:** *Magazine, Trade.* **Description:** Contains news items and major articles on Delta business and industry.
Published by: Coopwood Publishing Group, Inc., PO Box 117, Cleveland, MS 38732. TEL 662-843-2700, FAX 662-843-0505, scott@coopwoodpublishinggroup.com, http:// www.deltabusinessjournal.com, http:// www.coopwoodpublishinggroup.com. Ed. Joe Meek. Pub. J. Scott Coopwood.

DEMOKRATIE UND GESCHICHTE. see *HISTORY—History Of Europe*

DENMARK. DANMARKS STATISTIK. NATIONALREGNSKABSSTATISTIK/NATIONAL ACCOUNTS STATISTICS. see *BUSINESS AND ECONOMICS— Abstracting, Bibliographies, Statistics*

DENMARK. MINISTERIET FOR FOEDEVARER, LANDBRUG OG FISKERI. FOEDEVAREMINISTERIETS AARSRAPPORT; politik, produktion og forbrug. see *AGRICULTURE— Agricultural Economics*

330.9   USA
DEPARTMENT STORE INVENTORIES. Text in English. m. **Document type:** *Government.*
Related titles: ♦ Series of: U.S. Bureau of Labor Statistics. National Office News Releases.
Published by: U.S. Department of Labor, Bureau of Labor Statistics, Postal Square Bldg., 2 Massachusetts Ave, NE, Washington, DC 20212-0001 . TEL 202-691-5200, http://www.bls.gov. **Subscr. to:** U.S. Government Printing Office, Superintendent of Documents.

DEUTSCHE BANK BULLETIN; current economic and monetary issues. see *BUSINESS AND ECONOMICS—Banking And Finance*

330.9   DEU
DEUTSCHER WARENHANDEL. Text in German. 1966. q. EUR 40 (effective 2001). adv. **Document type:** *Magazine, Trade.*
Published by: Zeitungs- und Zeitschriftenverlag Heinrichs, Brueggekamp 1, Barsinghausen, 30890, Germany. TEL 49-5105-2289. Ed., Pub. Gerhard Heinrichs.

330.9   DEU   ISSN 0012-1304
DEUTSCHES INSTITUT FUER WIRTSCHAFTSFORSCHUNG. WOCHENBERICHT. Variant title: D I W Wochenbericht. Text in German. 1928. w. EUR 108; EUR 10 newsstand/cover (effective 2003). charts; stat. **Document type:** *Journal, Academic/Scholarly.*
Indexed: CIN, ELLIS, KES, PAIS, RefZh. —BLDSC (9341.730000), IE, ingenta. **CCC.**
Published by: (Deutsches Institut fuer Wirtschaftsforschung), Duncker und Humblot GmbH, Carl-Heinrich-Becker-Weg 9, Berlin, 12165, Germany. TEL 49-30-7900060, FAX 49-30-79000361, info@duncker-humblot.de, http://www.duncker-humblot.de. Ed. Klaus Henkner.

330   EGY
DEVELOPMENT & SOCIO-ECONOMIC PROGRESS. Text in Arabic, English, French. 1977. q. bk.rev. back issues avail. **Description:** Spreads awareness in Asia and Africa on the economic factor, not only with regard to building national economies, but also in consolidation of national independence.
Indexed: IBSS, PerIslam, RASB, RDA, WAE&RSA.
Published by: Afro-Asian Peoples' Solidarity Organization, 89 Abdel Aziz Al Saoud St., Manial, Cairo, Egypt. TEL 84 54 95. Ed. Nouri Abdel Razzak. Circ: 5,000.

330.9   USA
HC106.8
DEVELOPMENT REPORT CARD FOR THE STATES (ONLINE). Text in English. 1987. a. free. **Document type:** *Directory.* **Description:** Comparison and ranking of each of the 50 states on 50 socio-economic indicators key to state economics and economic development. Includes brief analysis of each state, U.S. as a whole, and regions.
Former titles (until 2000): Development Report Card for the States (Print) (1053-3672); Making the Grade (1045-4691)
Media: Online - full content.
Indexed: SRI.
Published by: Corporation for Enterprise Development, 777 N Capitol St, N E, Ste 410, Washington, DC 20002. TEL 202-408-9788, FAX 202-408-9793, http://www.cfed.org. Ed. Daphne Clones. R&P Linda Keenex.

DIALOGO CIENTIFICO; revista semestral de investigaciones alemanas sobre sociedad, derecho y economia. see *LAW*

B

330 BRA ISSN 0101-4218
DIGESTO ECONOMICO. Text in Portuguese. 1944. bi-m. BRL 60,000. adv. bk.rev.
Indexed: PAIS, RASB.
Published by: Associacao Comercial de Sao Paulo, Rua Boa Vista, 51 Andar 10, Centro, Sao Paulo, SP 01014-001, Brazil. TEL 11-234-3322, FAX 11-239-0067, TELEX 11-23355. Ed. Joao de Scantimburgo. Circ: 10,000.

330.9025 ESP ISSN 1577-1342
HF3689.M26
DIRECTORIO DE UNIDADES DE ACTIVIDAD ECONOMICA DE LA COMUNIDAD DE MADRID. Text in Spanish. 1999. a. free. back issues avail.
Related titles: CD-ROM ed.: ISSN 1578-7699; ♦ Abridged ed.: Directorio de Unidades de Actividad Economica de la Comunidad de Madrid (Abridge Edition). ISSN 1579-3907.
Published by: Comunidad de Madrid, Consejeria de Economia e Innovacion Tecnologica. Instituto de Estadistica, Principe de Vargara, 108, Madrid, 28002, Spain. TEL 34-91-5802540, jestadis@madrid.org, http://www.madrid.org/iestadis/index.htm.

330.9025 ESP ISSN 1579-3907
DIRECTORIO DE UNIDADES DE ACTIVIDAD ECONOMICA DE LA COMUNIDAD DE MADRID (ABRIDGE EDITION). Text in Spanish. 2001. a.
Related titles: ♦ Abridged ed. of: Directorio de Unidades de Actividad Economica de la Comunidad de Madrid. ISSN 1577-1342.
Published by: Comunidad de Madrid, Consejeria de Economia e Innovacion Tecnologica. Instituto de Estadistica, Principe de Vargara, 108, Madrid, 28002, Spain. TEL 34-91-5802540, jestadis@madrid.org, http://www.madrid.org/iestadis/index.htm.

DISCUSSION PAPERS IN INTERNATIONAL INVESTMENT AND MANAGEMENT. see *BUSINESS AND ECONOMICS—Investments*

330.968 ZAF
DOING BUSINESS IN SOUTH AFRICA. Text in English. 1994. a.
Published by: Kessel Feinstein, PO Box 6610, Johannesburg, 2000, South Africa.

330.9 382 CZE ISSN 1211-0949
DOING BUSINESS IN THE CZECH REPUBLIC. Text in English. 1995. a. USD 55 (effective 1999). **Document type:** *Trade.* **Description:** Summarizes economic, business and practical information for foreign partners of Czech companies.
Published by: P.P. Agency, V Jircharich 150-8, Prague 1, 110 00, Czech Republic. TEL 420-2-24912185, FAX 420-2-24912355, orders@ppagency.cz, http://www.ppagency.cz.

DOKHODY, RASKHODY I POTREBLENIE DOMASHNIKH KHOZYAISTV/INCOMES, EXPENDITURES AND CONSUMPTION OF HOUSEHOLDS. see *BUSINESS AND ECONOMICS—Abstracting, Bibliographies, Statistics*

330.9 910.03 USA ISSN 0012-5245
DOLLARS & SENSE (CAMBRIDGE); the magazine of economic justice. Text in English. 1974. bi-m. USD 18.95 domestic to individuals; USD 28 in Canada to institutions; USD 42 elsewhere to institutions; USD 4.50 newsstand/cover (effective 2005). adv. bk.rev. charts; illus.; stat. Index. 44 p./no.; back issues avail.; reprints avail. **Document type:** *Magazine, Consumer.* **Description:** Provides analysis of the US and international economies, from health care to trade agreements, welfare reform, and environmental regulations.
Related titles: Microform ed.: (from PQC); Online - full text ed.: (from EBSCO Publishing, Florida Center for Library Automation, Gale Group, O C L C Online Computer Library Center, Inc., ProQuest Information & Learning).
Indexed: AgeL, AltPI, ChPerI, DIP, IBR, IBZ, LeftInd, NPI, PAIS, RASB, SOPODA, SSA.
—BLDSC (3616.581000), IE, ingenta. **CCC.**
Published by: Economic Affairs Bureau, Inc., 29 Winter St, Boston, MA 02108. TEL 617-447-2177, FAX 617-447-2179, dollars@dollarsandsense.org, http://www.dollarsandsense.org. Eds. Adria Scharf, Amy Gluckman. Pub., Adv. contact Maryalice Guilford. Circ: 6,000 (paid).

330.9 USA
DOLLARS & SENSE (NEW YORK). Text in English. 1997. m. free. **Document type:** *Newsletter.* **Description:** Offers investment advice and discusses US and global financial issues.
Published by: Muriel Siebert & Co., Inc., 885 Third Ave, 17th Fl, New York, NY 10022. TEL 800-872-0444, http:// www.msiebert.com. Pub. Muriel Siebert.

DOMINICA. MINISTRY OF FINANCE. CENTRAL STATISTICAL OFFICE. CONSUMER PRICE INDICES. see *BUSINESS AND ECONOMICS—Abstracting, Bibliographies, Statistics*

DOMINICA. MINISTRY OF FINANCE. CENTRAL STATISTICAL OFFICE. NATIONAL ACCOUNTS AND BALANCE OF PAYMENTS. see *BUSINESS AND ECONOMICS—Abstracting, Bibliographies, Statistics*

DOMINICA. MINISTRY OF FINANCE. CENTRAL STATISTICAL OFFICE. QUARTERLY ECONOMIC INDICATORS. see *BUSINESS AND ECONOMICS—Abstracting, Bibliographies, Statistics*

330.9 DMA
DOMINICA. MINISTRY OF FINANCE. CENTRAL STATISTICAL OFFICE. STATISTICAL DIGEST. Text in English. a. USD 14.89. **Document type:** *Government.*
Former titles: Dominica. Ministry of Finance and Development. Statistical Division. Digest; Dominica. Ministry of Finance and Development. Statistical Digest
Published by: Ministry of Finance, Central Statistical Office, Kennedy Ave., Roseau, Dominica.

330.9 USA ISSN 1556-4037
DR. MARK SKOUSEN'S FORECASTS & STRATEGIES. Text in English. 1980. m. USD 99.95 (effective 2005). bk.rev. **Document type:** *Newsletter.* **Description:** Specific recommendations on a broad range of investments, with discussion of tax, financial privacy and other issues.
Former titles (until 200?): Mark Skousen's Forecasts & Strategies on Inflation, Taxes and Government Controls (0272-0868); (until Sept. 1980): Price Controls Alert (0199-9893)
—CCC.
Published by: Phillips International, Inc., 1 Massachusetts Ave., NW, Washington, DC 20001. TEL 202-216-0600, 800-930-6801, FAX 202-216-0611, http:// www.markskousen.com. Ed. Mark Skousen.

330.9 USA
DUN & BRADSTREET LOOKS AT BUSINESS. Text in English. irreg. free. **Description:** Business and economic highlights based on proprietary information of the Dun & Bradstreet Corporation and its divisions.
Published by: Dun & Bradstreet (Subsidiary of: Dun & Bradstreet Corporation), 103 John F Kennedy Pkwy., Short Hills, NJ 07078-2708. FAX 908-665-5418.

330.9 USA ISSN 1082-1937
HG3766
DUN & BRADSTREET MONTHLY BUSINESS FAILURES. Text in English. 1900. m. USD 30 (effective 2000). **Document type:** *Trade.* **Description:** Provides number of failures and liabilities in over 100 lines of business. Data are broken down by liability size, major industry group, state and region, and by selected cities.
Former titles: Dun and Bradstreet Record of Business Closings. Monthly Business Failures (1052-2808); (until 1986): Monthly Business Failures (0027-027X)
Indexed: SRI.
Published by: Dun & Bradstreet, Economic Analysis Department (Subsidiary of: Dun & Bradstreet Corporation), c/o Judy Webb, 3 Sylvan Way, Parsippany, NJ 07054. FAX 973-254-4063, http://www.dnb.com. R&P Judy Webb.

330.9561 TUR
E B A NEWSLETTER. Text in Turkish. 1969. d. adv. **Document type:** *Newsletter.*
Formerly: T E B A Haber (1300-2724)
Published by: Ekonomik Basin Ajansi, Bestekar Sokak 59-3, Kavaklidere - Ankara, 06680, Turkey. TEL 90-312-4685376, FAX 90-312-4684114, ebainfo@superonline.com, http://www.ebanews.com. Ed. Yavuz Tolun. Pub., R&P, Adv. contact Melek Tolun TEL 90-312-4685380.

330.9 TUR
E B A REPORT. Text in Turkish. 1972. w. USD 560 (effective 1998). adv. **Document type:** *Newsletter.* **Description:** Covers business and investment, international tenders and contracts in Turkey.
Published by: Ekonomik Basin Ajansi, Bestekar Sokak 59-3, Kavaklidere - Ankara, 06680, Turkey. TEL 90-312-4685376, FAX 90-312-4684114, ebainfo@superonline.com, http://www.ebanews.com. Ed. Yavuz Tolun. Adv. contact Melek Tolun TEL 90-312-4685380.

E-BUSINESS. see *COMPUTERS—Internet*

330.9 KOR ISSN 1329-1149
E D A P JOINT POLICY STUDIES. (Economic Development Management in Asia and the Pacific) Text in English. 1997. q. **Document type:** *Academic/Scholarly.*
Indexed: GEOBASE.
Published by: Korea Development Institute (Subsidiary of: United Nations), 207-43 Dongdaemun-ku, Cheongnyangri-dong, PO Box 184, Seoul, 140 032, Korea, S. Ed. Maree Tait.

330.9 PAK
E I P ECONOMIC FORECASTING SERVICE. Text in English. 1981. forth. looseleaf. PKR 5,000, USD 400 (effective 1999). adv. charts; stat. **Document type:** *Trade.*
Formerly (until 1986): E I P Labour Research Service
Published by: Economic and Industrial Publications, Al-Masiha, 47, Abdullah Haroon Rd., P O Box 7843, Karachi, 74400, Pakistan. TEL 92-21-7728434. Ed., Pub., R&P Iqbal Haidari TEL 92-21-7728963. Adv. contact K N Viqar. Circ: 1,000.

E I U COUNTRY FORECASTS ON DISC: ASIA-PACIFIC. (Economist Intelligence Unit) see *POLITICAL SCIENCE*

E I U COUNTRY FORECASTS ON DISC: EASTERN EUROPE. (Economist Intelligence Unit) see *POLITICAL SCIENCE*

E I U COUNTRY FORECASTS ON DISC: MIDDLE EAST-AFRICA. (Economist Intelligence Unit) see *POLITICAL SCIENCE*

E I U COUNTRY FORECASTS ON DISC: THE AMERICAS. (Economist Intelligence Unit) see *POLITICAL SCIENCE*

E I U COUNTRY FORECASTS ON DISC: WESTERN EUROPE. (Economist Intelligence Unit) see *POLITICAL SCIENCE*

330.95 USA
E I U COUNTRY REPORTS ON DISC: ASIA-PACIFIC. (Economist Intelligence Unit) Text in English. 1993. m. USD 7,500. charts; stat. **Document type:** *Trade.* **Description:** Provides a full, country-specific overview of the latest economic, political, and market conditions for the following nations: Afghanistan, Australia, Bangladesh, Brunei Darussalam, Cambodia, China, Fiji, Hong Kong, India, Indonesia, Japan, Laos, Macao, Malaysia, Mongolia, Myanmar (Burma), Nepal, New Zealand, North Korea, Pakistan, Papua New Guinea, Philippines, Singapore, Solomon Islands, South Korea, Sri Lanka, Taiwan, Thailand, Tonga, Vanuatu, Vietnam, Western Samoa.
Media: CD-ROM (from SilverPlatter Information, Inc.). **Related titles:** Online - full text ed.: (from SilverPlatter Information, Inc.); E I U Country Reports: Asia-Pacific (from EBSCO Publishing); ♦ Print ed.: Country Report. Pakistan. ISSN 1478-0356; ♦ Country Report. India. ISSN 1473-8953; ♦ Country Report. Japan. ISSN 0269-6681; ♦ Country Report. Australia. ISSN 0269-7106; ♦ Country Report. China. ISSN 1473-897X; ♦ Country Report. Hong Kong; ♦ Country Report. Cambodia; ♦ Country Report. Indonesia. ISSN 0269-5413; ♦ Country Report. Malaysia; ♦ Country Report. New Zealand. ISSN 0269-7114; ♦ Country Report. Papua New Guinea. ISSN 1366-4085; ♦ Country Report. Philippines. ISSN 0269-428X; ♦ Country Report. Singapore. ISSN 0269-6711; ♦ Country Report. South Korea. ISSN 1478-0348; ♦ Country Report. Taiwan. ISSN 0269-672X; ♦ Country Report. Thailand. ISSN 1356-4056; ♦ Country Report. Sri Lanka. ISSN 0269-4174; ♦ Country Report. Bangladesh. ISSN 0269-431X; ♦ Country Report. Vietnam. ISSN 1356-403X; ♦ Country Report. Myanmar. ISSN 1361-1445.
Published by: SilverPlatter Information, Incorporated (Subsidiary of: Ovid Technologies, Incorporated), 100 River Ridge Dr., Norwood, MA 02062. TEL 800-343-0064, FAX 781-769-87632, info@silverplatter.com, sales@ovid.com, http:// www.silverplatter.com, http://www.ovid.com.

330.947 USA
E I U COUNTRY REPORTS ON DISC: EASTERN EUROPE. (Economist Intelligence Unit) Text in English. 1993. m. USD 6,900. charts; stat. **Document type:** *Trade.* **Description:** Provides a full, country-specific overview of the latest economic, political, and market conditions for the following nations: Albania, Armenia, Azerbaijan, Belarus, Bosnia-Hercegovina, Bulgaria, Croatia, Czech Republic, Estonia, Georgia, Hungary, Kazakhstan, Kyrgyzstan, Latvia, Lithuania, Macedonia, Moldova, Poland, Romania, Russia, Serbia-Montenegro, Slovakia, Slovenia, Tajikistan, Turkmenistan, Ukraine, and Uzbekistan.
Media: CD-ROM (from SilverPlatter Information, Inc.). **Related titles:** ♦ Print ed.: Country Report. Belarus. ISSN 1478-0291; ♦ Country Report. Bulgaria. ISSN 1366-400X; ♦ Country Report. Kyrgyz Republic. ISSN 1478-0399; ♦ Country Report. Georgia. ISSN 1478-0313; ♦ Country Report. Macedonia. ISSN 1462-6691; ♦ Country Report. Albania. ISSN 1366-4018; ♦ Country Report. Slovakia. ISSN 1366-4050; ♦ Country Report. Azerbaijan. ISSN 1366-4077; ♦ Country Report. Uzbekistan. ISSN 1366-4158.
Published by: SilverPlatter Information, Incorporated (Subsidiary of: Ovid Technologies, Incorporated), 100 River Ridge Dr., Norwood, MA 02062. TEL 781-769-8763, 800-343-0064, info@silverplatter.com, sales@ovid.com, http:// www.silverplatter.com, http://www.ovid.com.

330.956 USA
E I U COUNTRY REPORTS ON DISC: MIDDLE EAST - NORTH AFRICA. (Economist Intelligence Unit) Text in English. 1993. m. USD 6,400. charts; stat. **Document type:** *Trade.* **Description:** Provides a full, country-specific overview of the latest economic, political, and market conditions for the following nations: Algeria, Bahrain, Egypt, Iran, Iraq, Israel (including the Occupied Territory), Jordan, Kuwait, Lebanon, Libya, Morocco, Oman, Qatar, Saudi Arabia, Sudan, Syria, Tunisia, United Arab Emirates, Yemen.
Media: CD-ROM (from SilverPlatter Information, Inc.). **Related titles:** Online - full text ed.: (from EBSCO Publishing); ♦ Print ed.: Country Report. Morocco. ISSN 0269-6126; ♦ Country Report. Bahrain. ISSN 1473-8937; ♦ Country Report. Saudi Arabia. ISSN 0269-6215; ♦ Country Report. Iraq. ISSN 0269-5502; ♦ Country Report. United Arab Emirates. ISSN 0269-5162; ♦ Country Report. Iran. ISSN 0269-5448; ♦ Country Report. Egypt. ISSN 0269-526X; ♦ Country Report.

Sudan. ISSN 0269-6150; ♦ Country Report. Tunisia. ISSN 1350-7168; ♦ Country Report. Syria. ISSN 0269-7211; ♦ Country Report. Algeria. ISSN 0269-5723; ♦ Country Report. Israel; ♦ Country Report. Jordan. ISSN 0269-722X; ♦ Country Report. Kuwait. ISSN 0269-5715; ♦ Country Report. Lebanon. ISSN 1350-7141; ♦ Country Report. Libya. ISSN 0269-4328.
Published by: SilverPlatter Information, Incorporated (Subsidiary of: Ovid Technologies, Incorporated), 100 River Ridge Dr., Norwood, MA 02062. TEL 800-343-0064, FAX 781-769-87632, info@silverplatter.com, sales@ovid.com, http://www.silverplatter.com, http://www.ovid.com.

330.967 USA
E I U COUNTRY REPORTS ON DISC: SUB-SAHARAN AFRICA. (Economist Intelligence Unit) Text in English. 1993. m. USD 7,850. charts; stat. **Document type:** *Trade.* **Description:** Provides a full, country-specific overview of the latest economic, political, and market conditions for the following nations: Angola, Benin, Burkina Faso, Burundi, Botswana, Cameroon, Cape Verde, Central African Republic (Republique Centafricaine), Chad, Comoros, Congo, Democratic Republic of the Congo (Zaire), Cote d'Ivoire, Djibouti, Equatorial Guinea, Guinea-Bissau, Kenya, Lesotho, Liberia, Madagascar, Malawi, Mali, Mauritania, Mauritius, Mozambique, Namibia, Niger, Nigeria, Rwanda, Sao Tome Principe, Senegal, Seychelles, Sierra Leone, Somalia, South Africa, Swaziland, Tanzania, Togo, Uganda, Zambia, Zimbabwe.
Media: CD-ROM (from SilverPlatter Information, Inc.). **Related titles:** Online - full text ed.: (from EBSCO Publishing); (from Gale Group); ♦ Print ed.: Country Report. Kenya. ISSN 0269-4239; ♦ Country Report. Zimbabwe. ISSN 1350-7095; ♦ Country Report. Zambia. ISSN 1478-0372; ♦ Country Report. Uganda. ISSN 1465-640X; ♦ Country Report. Togo; ♦ Country Report. Guinea; ♦ Country Report. Congo (Brazzaville); ♦ Country Report. Angola. ISSN 0969-7985; ♦ Country Report. Ghana. ISSN 1350-7052; ♦ Country Report. Namibia; ♦ Country Report. Botswana; ♦ Country Report. Gabon; ♦ Country Report. Mozambique. ISSN 1478-0275; ♦ Country Report. Ethiopia; ♦ Country Report. Nigeria. ISSN 0269-4204; ♦ Country Report. Cameroon; ♦ Country Report. Cote d'Ivoire; ♦ Country Report. Tanzania; ♦ Country Report. South Africa. ISSN 0269-6738; ♦ Country Report. Senegal; ♦ Country Report. Mauritius.
Published by: SilverPlatter Information, Incorporated (Subsidiary of: Ovid Technologies, Incorporated), 100 River Ridge Dr., Norwood, MA 02062. TEL 800-343-0064, FAX 781-769-87632, info@silverplatter.com, sales@ovid.com, http://www.silverplatter.com, http://www.ovid.com.

330.98 USA
E I U COUNTRY REPORTS ON DISC: THE AMERICAS. (Economist Intelligence Unit) Text in English. 1993. m. USD 6,900. charts; stat. **Document type:** *Trade.* **Description:** Provides a full, country-specific overview of the latest economic, political, and market conditions for the following nations: Argentina, Aruba, Bahamas, Barbados, Belize, Bermuda, Bolivia, Brazil, Canada, Chile, Colombia, Costa Rica, Cuba, Dominican Republic, Ecuador, El Salvador, Guatemala, Guyana, Haiti, Honduras, Jamaica, Leeward Islands, Mexico, Netherlands Antilles, Nicaragua, Panama, Paraguay, Peru, Puerto Rico, Surinam, Trinidad and Tobago, United States, Uruguay, Venezuela, Windward Islands.
Media: CD-ROM (from SilverPlatter Information, Inc.). **Related titles:** Online - full text ed.: (from SilverPlatter Information, Inc.); (from EBSCO Publishing); ProQuest Information & Learning); ♦ Print ed.: Country Report. Venezuela. ISSN 1350-7133; ♦ Country Report. Nicaragua. ISSN 1473-9003; ♦ Country Report. Argentina. ISSN 0269-4212; ♦ Country Report. Mexico. ISSN 0269-5936; ♦ Country Report. Brazil. ISSN 0269-5731; ♦ Country Report. Chile. ISSN 0269-5197; ♦ Country Report. Colombia. ISSN 0269-7157; ♦ Country Report. Cuba. ISSN 1465-6388; ♦ Country Report. Ecuador. ISSN 0269-7165; ♦ Country Report. Guatemala. ISSN 1473-902X; ♦ Country Report. Jamaica; ♦ Country Report. Peru. ISSN 1356-4064; ♦ Country Report. Trinidad & Tobago; ♦ Country Report. Uruguay. ISSN 1473-8988; ♦ Country Report. Canada. ISSN 0269-4166; ♦ Country Report. United States of America. ISSN 1367-8876; ♦ Country Report. Bolivia. ISSN 1356-4072; ♦ Country Report. Panama. ISSN 1366-4034.
Published by: SilverPlatter Information, Incorporated (Subsidiary of: Ovid Technologies, Incorporated), 100 River Ridge Dr., Norwood, MA 02062. TEL 800-343-0064, FAX 781-769-87632, info@silverplatter.com, sales@ovid.com, http://www.silverplatter.com, http://www.ovid.com.

320.94 USA
E I U COUNTRY REPORTS ON DISC: WESTERN EUROPE. Text in English. m.
Media: CD-ROM (from SilverPlatter Information, Inc.). **Related titles:** Online - full text ed.: (from EBSCO Publishing); (from EBSCO Publishing); ♦ Print ed.: Country Report. Turkey. ISSN 0269-5464; ♦ Country Report. Germany. ISSN 0965-1365; ♦ Country Report. Austria. ISSN 0269-5170; ♦ Country Report. Belgium. ISSN 1473-9062; ♦ Country Report. Denmark. ISSN 1473-9046; ♦ Country Report. Finland. ISSN 0269-5901; ♦ Country Report. France. ISSN 0269-5286; ♦ Country Report. Greece. ISSN 0269-591X; ♦ Country Report. Ireland. ISSN 0269-5278; ♦ Country Report. Italy. ISSN 0269-5421; ♦ Country Report. Netherlands. ISSN 0269-6134; ♦ Country Report. Norway. ISSN 0269-4182; ♦ Country Report. Portugal. ISSN 0269-5456; ♦ Country Report. Spain. ISSN 0269-4263; ♦ Country Report. Sweden. ISSN 0269-6142; ♦ Country Report. Switzerland. ISSN 0269-6169; ♦ Country Report. United Kingdom. ISSN 0269-5472; ♦ Country Report. Cyprus.
Published by: SilverPlatter Information, Incorporated (Subsidiary of: Ovid Technologies, Incorporated), 100 River Ridge Dr., Norwood, MA 02062. TEL 781-769-2599, 800-343-0064, FAX 781-769-8763, sales@ovid.com, http://www.ovid.com.

320.94 USA
E I U COUNTRY RISK SERVICE ON DISC: ASIA-PACIFIC. Text in English. m.
Media: CD-ROM (from SilverPlatter Information, Inc.). **Related titles:** Diskette ed.; Online - full text ed.: E I U Country Risk Service: Asia-Pacific (from SilverPlatter Information, Inc.); ♦ Print ed.: Country Risk Service. New Zealand. ISSN 1351-7201; ♦ Country Risk Service. Pakistan. ISSN 1351-7236; ♦ Country Risk Service. Papua New Guinea. ISSN 1351-7252; ♦ Country Risk Service. Vietnam. ISSN 1354-5655; ♦ Country Risk Service. Philippines. ISSN 1351-7287.
Published by: SilverPlatter Information, Incorporated (Subsidiary of: Ovid Technologies, Incorporated), 100 River Ridge Dr., Norwood, MA 02062. TEL 781-769-2599, 800-343-0064, FAX 781-769-8763, sales@ovid.com, http://www.ovid.com.

330.9 332 USA
E I U COUNTRY RISK SERVICE ON DISC: EUROPE. (Economist Intelligence Unit) Text in English. 1997. m. USD 11,300. charts; stat. **Document type:** *Trade.* **Description:** Projects for the next 2 years the trade and current-account balances, financing requirements, and debt-service ratios for the following nations: Azerbaijan, Bulgaria, Croatia, Cyprus, Czech Republic, Estonia, Greece, Hungary, Italy, Kazakhstan, Latvia, Lithuania, Macedonia, Poland, Portugal, Romania, Russia, Slovakia, Slovenia, Spain, Turkey, Ukraine, Uzbekestan, Yugoslavia (Serbia-Montenegro).
Media: CD-ROM. **Related titles:** Diskette ed.; Online - full text ed.: E I U Country Risk Service: Europe (from SilverPlatter Information, Inc.); ♦ Print ed.: Country Risk Service. Bulgaria. ISSN 1351-6833; ♦ Country Risk Service. Czech Republic. ISSN 1351-6922; ♦ Country Risk Service. Hungary. ISSN 1351-7031; ♦ Country Risk Service. Kazakhstan. ISSN 1351-7112; ♦ Country Risk Service. Poland. ISSN 1351-7295; ♦ Country Risk Service. Romania. ISSN 1351-7317; ♦ Country Risk Service. Russia. ISSN 1351-7325; ♦ Country Risk Service. Slovenia. ISSN 1351-7368; ♦ Country Risk Service. Ukraine. ISSN 1351-7481; ♦ Country Risk Service. Macedonia. ISSN 1461-6076.
Published by: SilverPlatter Information, Incorporated (Subsidiary of: Ovid Technologies, Incorporated), 100 River Ridge Dr., Norwood, MA 02062. TEL 800-343-0064, FAX 781-769-87632, info@silverplatter.com, sales@ovid.com, http://www.silverplatter.com, http://www.ovid.com.

330.9 332 USA
E I U COUNTRY RISK SERVICE ON DISC: LATIN AMERICA. (Economist Intelligence Unit) Text in English. 1997. m. USD 10,500. charts; stat. **Document type:** *Trade.* **Description:** Projects for the next 2 years the trade and current-account balances, financing requirements, and debt-service rations for the following nations: Argentina, Brazil, Chile, Colombia, Costa Rica, Cuba, Dominican Republic, Ecuador, El Salvador, Guatemala, Honduras, Jamaica, Mexico, Nicaragua, Panama, Paraguay, Peru, Trinidad & Tobago, Uruguay, Venezuela.
Media: CD-ROM. **Related titles:** Diskette ed.; Online - full text ed.: E I U Country Risk Service: Latin America; ♦ Print ed.: Country Risk Service. Argentina. ISSN 1351-6779; ♦ Country Risk Service. Bolivia. ISSN 1351-6817; ♦ Country Risk Service. Brazil. ISSN 1351-6825; ♦ Country Risk Service. Chile. ISSN 1351-685X; ♦ Country Risk Service. Colombia. ISSN 1351-6876; ♦ Country Risk Service. Costa Rica. ISSN 1351-6892; ♦ Country Risk Service. Dominican Republic. ISSN 1351-6930; ♦ Country Risk Service. Ecuador. ISSN 1351-6949; ♦ Country Risk Service. El Salvador. ISSN 1351-6965; ♦ Country Risk Service. Guatemala. ISSN 1351-7007; ♦ Country Risk Service. Honduras. ISSN 1351-7015; ♦ Country Risk Service. Jamaica. ISSN 1351-7090; ♦ Country Risk Service. Mexico. ISSN 1351-7171; ♦ Country Risk Service. Nicaragua. ISSN 1351-721X; ♦ Country Risk Service. Panama. ISSN 1351-7244; ♦ Country Risk Service. Paraguay. ISSN 1351-7260; ♦ Country Risk Service. Peru. ISSN 1351-7279; ♦ Country Risk Service. Trinidad and Tobago. ISSN 1351-7457; ♦ Country Risk Service. Uruguay. ISSN 1351-7503; ♦ Country Risk Service. Venezuela. ISSN 1351-7511.
Published by: SilverPlatter Information, Incorporated (Subsidiary of: Ovid Technologies, Incorporated), 100 River Ridge Dr., Norwood, MA 02062. TEL 800-343-0064, FAX 781-769-87632, info@silverplatter.com, sales@ovid.com, http://www.silverplatter.com, http://www.ovid.com.

330.9 332 USA
E I U COUNTRY RISK SERVICE ON DISC: MIDDLE EAST-NORTH AFRICA. (Economist Intelligence Unit) Text in English. 1997. m. USD 9,400. charts; stat. **Document type:** *Trade.* **Description:** Projects for the next 2 years the trade and current-account balances, financing requirements, and debt-service ratios for the following nations: Algeria, Bahrain, Egypt, Iran, Iraq, Israel, Jordan, Kuwait, Lebanon, Libya, Morocco, Oman, Qatar, Saudi Arabia, Sudan, Syria, Tunesia, United Arab Emirates, Yemen.
Media: CD-ROM. **Related titles:** Diskette ed.; Online - full text ed.: E I U Country Risk Service: Middle East-North Africa; ♦ Print ed.: Country Risk Service. Algeria. ISSN 1351-6752; ♦ Country Risk Service. Egypt. ISSN 1351-6957; ♦ Country Risk Service. Iran. ISSN 1351-7066; ♦ Country Risk Service. Iraq. ISSN 1351-7074; ♦ Country Risk Service. Israel. ISSN 1351-7082; ♦ Country Risk Service. Jordan. ISSN 1351-7104; ♦ Country Risk Service. Kuwait. ISSN 1351-7139; ♦ Country Risk Service. Libya. ISSN 1351-7147; ♦ Country Risk Service. Morocco. ISSN 1351-718X; ♦ Country Risk Service. Saudi Arabia. ISSN 1351-7333; ♦ Country Risk Service. Sudan. ISSN 1351-7414; ♦ Country Risk Service. Syria. ISSN 1351-7422; ♦ Country Risk Service. Tunisia. ISSN 1351-7465; ♦ Country Risk Service. United Arab Emirates. ISSN 1351-749X; ♦ Country Risk Service. Yemen. ISSN 1351-752X; ♦ Country Risk Service. Bahrain. ISSN 1365-4756.
Published by: SilverPlatter Information, Incorporated (Subsidiary of: Ovid Technologies, Incorporated), 100 River Ridge Dr., Norwood, MA 02062. TEL 781-769-8763, 800-343-0064, info@silverplatter.com, sales@ovid.com, http://www.silverplatter.com, http://www.ovid.com.

330.9 332 USA
E I U COUNTRY RISK SERVICE ON DISC: SUB-SAHARAN AFRICA. (Economist Intelligence Unit) Text in English. 1997. m. USD 7,950. charts; stat. **Document type:** *Trade.* **Description:** Projects for the next 2 years the trade and current-account balances, financing requirements, and debt-service ratios for the following nations: Angola, Botswana, Cameroon, Cote d'Ivoire, Gabon, Ghana, Kenya, Malawi, Nigeria, Namibia, Senegal, South Africa, Tanzania, Zambia, Zimbabwe.
Media: CD-ROM. **Related titles:** Diskette ed.; Online - full text ed.: E I U Country Risk Service: Sub-Saharan Africa (from SilverPlatter Information, Inc.); (from SilverPlatter Information, Inc.); E I U Country Risk Service: Sub-Saharan Africa (from SilverPlatter Information, Inc.); ♦ Print ed.: Country Risk Service. Angola. ISSN 1351-6760; ♦ Country Risk Service. Cameroon. ISSN 1351-6841; ♦ Country Risk Service. Congo. ISSN 1351-6884; ♦ Country Risk Service. Cote d'Ivoire. ISSN 1351-6906; ♦ Country Risk Service. Gabon. ISSN 1351-6973; ♦ Country Risk Service. Ghana. ISSN 1351-6981; ♦ Country Risk Service. Kenya. ISSN 1351-7120; ♦ Country Risk Service. Malawi. ISSN 1351-7155; ♦ Country Risk Service. Namibia. ISSN 1351-7198; ♦ Country Risk Service. Nigeria. ISSN 1351-7228; ♦ Country Risk Service. Senegal. ISSN 1351-7341; ♦ Country Risk Service. South Africa. ISSN 1351-7376; ♦ Country Risk Service. Zaire. ISSN 1351-7546; ♦ Country Risk Service. Zambia. ISSN 1351-7554; ♦ Country Risk Service. Zimbabwe. ISSN 1351-7562; ♦ Country Risk Service. Botswana. ISSN 1354-5647.
Published by: SilverPlatter Information, Incorporated (Subsidiary of: Ovid Technologies, Incorporated), 100 River Ridge Dr., Norwood, MA 02062. TEL 800-343-0064, FAX 781-769-87632, info@silverplatter.com, sales@ovid.com, http://www.silverplatter.com, http://www.ovid.com.

382 338 USA
E I U INTERNATIONAL BUSINESS NEWSLETTERS ON DISC. (Economist Intelligence Unit) Text in English. m. **Document type:** *Newsletter, Trade.* **Description:** Reports on developments on all business fronts: economic and political developments, regulatory changes, financial markets, industry trends, labor conditions, and corporate strategies. Publishes the full text of Business Africa, Business Asia, Business China, Business Eastern Europe, Business Europe, Business Latin America, Business Middle East, and Country Monitor.
Media: CD-ROM. **Related titles:** ♦ Print ed.: Business Latin America. ISSN 0007-6880; ♦ Business Asia. ISSN 0572-7545; ♦ Business China. ISSN 1016-9776; ♦ Business Eastern Europe. ISSN 1351-8763; ♦ Business Europe. ISSN 0007-6724; ♦ Business Middle East. ISSN 1350-7354; ♦ Business Africa. ISSN 0968-4468; ♦ Country Monitor. ISSN 1528-4530.
Published by: SilverPlatter Information, Incorporated (Subsidiary of: Ovid Technologies, Incorporated), 100 River Ridge Dr., Norwood, MA 02062. TEL 800-343-0064, FAX 781-769-87632, info@silverplatter.com, sales@ovid.com, http://www.silverplatter.com, http://www.ovid.com.

330.9 USA
E N A. (Economic News from Austria) Text in English. q. free. **Document type:** *Newsletter.*
Related titles: Online - full text ed.
Published by: Austrian Press and Information Service, 3524 International Ct, N W, Washington, DC 20008-3035. TEL 202-895-6775, FAX 202-895-6772, http://www.austria.org/.

330.9 PHL ISSN 1655-5236
E R D TECHNICAL NOTE SERIES. Text in English. 2002 (Feb.). irreg., latest no.11, 2004, Feb.
Related titles: Online - full text ed.

B

Published by: Asian Development Bank, Economics and Research Department, 6 ADB Avenue, Mandaluyong City, Metro Manila, 1550, Philippines. TEL 632-632-4444, FAX 632-636-2444, information@adb.org, http://www.adb.org/economics/erd_technical_notes.asp.

330.9 PHL ISSN 1655-5252
E R D WORKING PAPER SERIES. Text in English. 2002. irreg., latest no.69, May, 2005.
Related titles: Online - full text ed.
Published by: Asian Development Bank, Economics and Research Department, 6 ADB Avenue, Mandaluyong City, Metro Manila, 1550, Philippines. TEL 632-632-4444, FAX 632-636-2444, information@adb.org, http://www.adb.org/economics/erd_working_papers.asp.

E U I REVIEW. see *POLITICAL SCIENCE*

E U I WORKING PAPERS. (European University Institute) see *POLITICAL SCIENCE*

330.9 DEU ISSN 0946-4689
HC241.2
E U MAGAZIN. (Europaeische Union) Text in German. 1976. m. (10/yr.). EUR 40; EUR 20 to students; EUR 5 newsstand/cover (effective 2004). adv. charts. 54 p./no. 3 cols./p.; **Document type:** *Magazine, Consumer.* **Description:** Reports on economics, politics and culture in the European Union.
Formerly (until 1994): E G Magazin (0343-6667)
Indexed: DIP, IBR, IBZ.
Published by: (Kommission der Europaeischen Gemeinschaften), Nomos Verlagsgesellschaft mbH und Co. KG, Waldseestr 3-5, Baden-Baden, 76530, Germany. TEL 49-7221-2104-0, FAX 49-7221-210427, nomos@nomos.de, marketing@nomos.de, http://www.nomos.de. adv.: B&W page EUR 2,400, color page EUR 4,200; trim 190 x 255.

330.9 USA ISSN 0272-1589
KNC242.A15
EAST ASIAN EXECUTIVE REPORTS. Text in English. 1978. m. USD 455 foreign (effective 2004). adv. bk.rev. cum.index. reprints avail. **Document type:** *Magazine, Trade.* **Description:** Designed for international business executives involved in East Asia trade, contracting, marketing and investment.
Related titles: Online - full text ed.: (from Northern Light Technology, Inc., O C L C Online Computer Library Center, Inc., ProQuest Information & Learning, Thomson West).
Indexed: ABIn, BPIA, CCME, CLI, IPARL, KES, LRI.
—BLDSC (3645.935700), IE, ingenta. **CCC.**
Published by: International Executive Reports, Ltd., 717 D St, N W, Ste 300, Washington, DC 20004-2807. TEL 202-628-6900, FAX 202-628-6618, pub@ili.org, http://www.his.com/~ili/pubeaer.html, http://www.his.com/~ili/index.htm. Circ: 800.

EAST TENNESSEE DEVELOPMENT DISTRICT ECONOMIC STATISTICS. see *STATISTICS*

330.9 USA ISSN 1065-6790
HF3626.5 CODEN: EBTREX
EAST - WEST BUSINESS AND TRADE✶; with news from Russia, the Baltics, Central & Eastern Europe. Text in English. 1972. s-m. looseleaf. USD 367.20 domestic to institutions; USD 377.20 in Canada & Mexico to institutions; USD 397.20 elsewhere to institutions; USD 459 domestic to corporations; USD 469 in Canada & Mexico to corporations; USD 489 elsewhere to corporations (effective 1999). adv. bk.rev. stat.; tr.lit. back issues avail. **Document type:** *Newsletter.* **Description:** Provides news and analysis on business and economic developments throughout the former Soviet Union.
Incorporates (in 1994): East - West Technology Digest (0145-1421); Which was formerly (until 1976): Soviet Technology Digest; Formerly (until 1992): Soviet Business and Trade (0731-7727); Which superseded in part: Business and Trade (0196-8602); Which was formerly: Soviet Business and Trade (0092-4695)
Indexed: CIN, ChemAb, ChemTitl, PROMT.
—CASDDS.
Published by: Welt Publishing Co., 1524 18th St, NW, Washington, DC 20036-1333. TEL 202-371-0555, 800-898-INTL, FAX 202-408-9369. Ed., Pub. Leo G.B. Welt. Circ: 3,500.

330 IND ISSN 0012-8767
HC431
EASTERN ECONOMIST. Text in English. 1943. w. INR 125, USD 30. adv. bk.rev. mkt.; stat. index. reprint service avail. from PQC.
Related titles: Microfilm ed.: (from PQC).
Indexed: BAS, MEA&I, PAIS, PROMT, RRTA, WAE&RSA.
Published by: Eastern Economist Ltd., UCO Bank Bldg., Parliament St., P O Box 34, New Delhi, 110 001, India. Ed. V Balasubramanian. Circ: 7,000.

330.9 GBR ISSN 0965-0350
EASTERN EUROPE ANALYST. Text in English. 1978. q. GBP 235 domestic; USD 365 foreign (effective 2003). back issues avail. **Document type:** *Academic/Scholarly.* **Description:** Economic news on the former Soviet empire and sphere of influence, the economies of Eastern European countries, and world developments in light of policy changes in Moscow.
Formerly (until 1991): Comecon Reports (0142-0763)
Indexed: PAIS.
Published by: World Reports Ltd., 108 Horseferry Rd, London, SW1P 2EF, United Kingdom. TEL 44-20-72223836, FAX 44-20-72330185, subs@worldreports.org, http://www.worldreports.org. Ed. Christopher Story. **US subscr. to:** 280 Madison Ave, Ste 280, New York, NY 10016-0802. TEL 212-679-0095, FAX 212-679-1094.

330.9 GBR ISSN 1462-4001
EASTERN EUROPE CONSENSUS FORECASTS. Text in English. 1998. bi-m. GBP 337, USD 497 (effective 2003). adv. 32 p./no.; back issues avail. **Document type:** *Journal, Academic/Scholarly.* **Description:** Contains detailed coverage of the Czech Republic, Hungary, Poland, Russia, Turkey, Romania, Slovakia and the Ukraine featuring both individual and consensus (average) forecasts for 10-13 economic indicators each. Also includes consensus forecasts for three variables each for eleven other countries in the region (Azerbaijan, Belarus, Bulgaria, Croatia, Estonia, Kazakhstan, Latvia, Lithuania, Moldova, Slovenia and Uzbekistan). Plus: historical data, graphs and text, special surveys, foreign exchange forecasts, oil price forecasts, significant changes in the consensus, monthly inflation forecasts, interest rates and regional aggregates.
Related titles: Diskette ed.; E-mail ed.
Published by: Consensus Economics Inc., 53 Upper Brook St, London, W1K 2LT, United Kingdom. TEL 44-20-7491-3211, FAX 44-20-7409-2331, editors@consensuseconomics.com, http://www.consensuseconomics.com. Ed. Che-wing Pang. Pub. Philip M Hubbard.

330.9 IRN
ECHO OF IRAN. Text in Persian, Modern. m. USD 300 each bulletin (effective 2005). adv.
Published by: Echo Publications, Av. Hafez, Kuche Hurtab No. 4, P O Box 11365-5551, Teheran, Iran.

330.9 FRA
LES ECHOS; le quotidien de l'economie. Text in French. 1908. 5/w. EUR 373.35; EUR 449.72 combined subscription print & online eds. (effective 2001). adv. **Document type:** *Newspaper.* **Description:** Provides news and information on business, finance and trade development at home and abroad.
Related titles: CD-ROM ed.; Microfilm ed.: (from PQC, RPI); Online - full text ed.
Indexed: B&I, KES, PROMT.
Published by: Les Echos (Subsidiary of: Financial Times), 46 rue la Boetie, Paris, Cedex 8 75381, France. TEL 33-1-49536565, FAX 33-1-45614892, TELEX 640 331 F, http://www.lesechos.fr. Ed. Nicolas Beytout. Pub. David Guiraud. Circ: 140,000.

330.9 USA ISSN 0747-4938
HB139 CODEN: ECREEP
ECONOMETRIC REVIEWS. Text in English. 1982. q. USD 1,092, GBP 661 combined subscription to institutions print & online eds. (effective 2006). adv. illus. reprint service avail. from PSC. **Document type:** *Journal, Academic/Scholarly.* **Description:** Features retrospective, critical, and readable surveys of current economic conditions that determine where future efforts should be directed.
Formerly (until 1984): Communications in Statistics: Econometric Reviews (0731-1761)
Related titles: Microform ed.: (from RPI); Online - full text ed.: ISSN 1532-4168. GBP 628, USD 1,037 to institutions (effective 2006) (from EBSCO Publishing, O C L C Online Computer Library Center, Inc., Swets Information Services).
Indexed: ABIn, CCMJ, CIS, CurCont, IBSS, JCQM, JEL, MathR, MathSciNet, RefZh, ST&MA, ZentMath.
—BLDSC (3650.080000), IE, Infotrieve, ingenta. **CCC.**
Published by: Taylor & Francis Inc. (Subsidiary of: Taylor & Francis Group), 325 Chestnut St, Ste 800, Philadelphia, PA 19016. TEL 215-625-8900, 800-354-1420, FAX 215-625-2940, info@taylorandfrancis.com, http://www.tandf.co.uk/journals/titles/07474938.asp, http://www.taylorandfrancis.com. Ed. Esfandiar Maasoumi. Adv. contact Sharon Moran. B&W page USD 600. Circ: 625.

338.9 BRA ISSN 0424-2386
ECONOMIA BRASILEIRA E SUAS PERSPECTIVAS - A P E C A O. Text in English, Portuguese. 1962. a. USD 200.
Published by: Associacao Promotora de Estudos de Economia, Av Rio Branco, 156, n-1833, Rio De Janeiro, RJ 20040-003, Brazil. FAX 021-262-3901. Ed. Ernane Galveas. Circ: 10,000.

330.9 COL ISSN 0422-2733
ECONOMIA COLOMBIANA Y COYUNTURA POLITICA; revista de la Contraloria General de la Republica. Text in Spanish. 1958. bi-m. COP 40,000 domestic; USD 13 foreign (effective 2003). adv. bk.rev. abstr.; bibl.; charts; illus.; stat. 120 p./no.; back issues avail. **Document type:** *Magazine, Academic/Scholarly.*
Formerly: Economia Colombiana (0120-4998)
Related titles: Online - full content ed.: 2002. free.
Indexed: PAIS.
Published by: Contraloria General de la Republica, Carrera 10 No. 17-18, Bogota, CUND, Colombia. TEL 57-1-2868344, FAX 57-1-3360815, revista-economia@contraloriagen.gov.co, http://www.contraloria.gov.co/. Ed. Cesar Parra. Adv. contact Margarita Henad.

330.9 CUB
ECONOMIA CUBANA. Text in Spanish. a. stat.
Related titles: English ed.: Cuban Economy.
Published by: Comite Estatal de Estadisticas, Centro de Informacion Cientifico-Tecnica, Almendares No. 156, esq. a Desague, Gaveta Postal 6016, Havana, Cuba.

330.9 MOZ ISSN 0012-9755
HC578.M6
ECONOMIA DE MOCAMBIQUE. Text in Portuguese. m. adv.
Indexed: PAIS.
Published by: Companhia Editoria de Mocambique, C.P. 81, Beira, Mozambique. Ed. Antonia de Almeida.

338 PRT ISSN 0870-4635
HC391
ECONOMIA E C. Text in Portuguese. 1976. bi-m.
Indexed: PAIS.
Published by: Editorial Caminho, S.A., Alameda de St. Antonio dos Couchos, 6-B, Lisbon, 1100, Portugal.

330.9 PRT ISSN 0870-6026
➤ **ECONOMIA E SOCIOLOGIA.** Text in Portuguese. 1965. 2/yr., latest vol.71. EUR 4 per issue (effective 2003). bk.rev. bibl.; illus.; maps; stat. **Document type:** *Academic/Scholarly.*
Formerly (until 1968): Estudos Erborenses
Indexed: PAIS.
Published by: Instituto Superior Economico e Social, Rua Vasco da Gama 15, Evora, 7000-941, Portugal. TEL 351-266703327, FAX 351-266747243. Ed. Agostinho Moreira Ferraz. Pub. Augusto da Silva. R&P Manuel Ferreira da Lima Bello. Circ: 580 (paid).

330 BRA ISSN 1413-6090
➤ **ECONOMIA EM REVISTA.** Text in Portuguese; Summaries in English, Portuguese. 1993. s-a. BRL 16 domestic; USD 8 foreign (effective 2000). bk.rev. abstr.; bibl.; charts; stat. index. back issues avail. **Document type:** *Academic/Scholarly.* **Description:** Presents the results of research activities of the faculty members. Covers a wide range of topics in economics.
Published by: (Universidade Estadual de Maringa, Departamento de Economia), Universidade Estadual de Maringa, Av. Colombo, 5.790, Maringa, Parana 87020-900, Brazil. TEL 55-44-2614253, FAX 55-44-2222754, http://www.uem.br. Ed. Marcos Roberto Vasconcelos. R&P Marcos R Vasconcelos. Circ: 150.

330.9 ITA
ECONOMIA EMILIA-ROMAGNA. Text in Italian. 1994. m. free. **Document type:** *Trade.*
Published by: Unione Regionale dfelle Camere di Commercio dell'Emilia-Romagna, Via Aldo Moro 62, Bologna, BO 40127, Italy. TEL 39-051-6377011, FAX 39-051-6377050, staff@rer.camcom.it, http://www.rer.camcom.it. Ed. Claudio Pasini.

330.9 PER ISSN 1682-4342
ECONOMIA Y SOCIEDAD. Text in Spanish. 1997. quadrennial. back issues avail.
Formerly (until 2000): Boletin de Opinion
Media: Online - full text.
Published by: Consorcio de Investigacion Economica y Social, C. Antero Aspillaga No. 584, San Isidro, Lima, 27, Peru. TEL 51-1-4218082, http://www.consorcio.org/bol.asp.

330 IND
ECONOMIC AGE. Text in English. 1974 (vol.7). m. INR 0.75 per issue. adv. bk.rev.
Indexed: BAS.
Published by: Siba Prosad Banerjee Ed. & Pub., P-36 India Exchange Place, 2nd Fl. Rm.40, Kolkata, West Bengal 700 001, India. Ed. Sib Banerji. Circ: 29,000.

330.9 ESP ISSN 1579-1475
ECONOMIC ANALYSIS WORKING PAPERS/DOCUMENTOS DE TRABAJO EN ANALISIS ECONOMICO. Text in Multiple languages. 2002. m. free (effective 2005). **Document type:** *Journal, Academic/Scholarly.* **Description:** Aims to provide economic analyses in different areas of the economy.
Media: Online - full text.
Published by: Colegio de Economistas de La Coruna/Economists Association of La Coruna, Calle Caballeros 29-1, La Coruna, 15009, Spain. FAX 34-981-154323, http://eawp.economistascoruna.org.

330.973 USA ISSN 0737-8866
THE ECONOMIC AND BUDGET OUTLOOK; an update. Text in English. a. **Document type:** *Government.* **Description:** Presents a series of reports on the state of the economy and the budget.
Formerly (until 1980): The Economic Outlook at Midyear (0272-4618)
Media: Online - full text.
Published by: U S Congress, Congressional Budget Office, Ford House Bldg, Second and D St, S W, Washington, DC 20515. TEL 202-226-2600, FAX 202-226-2714, webmaster@cbo.gov, http://www.cbo.gov/.

338 338.9 IND ISSN 0970-0560
ECONOMIC AND COMMERCIAL NEWS. Text in English. 1971. w. INR 50, USD 22.
Indexed: KES.

Published by: Trade Fair Authority of India, Administrative Block-Pragati Maidan, Lal Bahadur Shastri Marg, New Delhi, 110 001, India. Ed. Shri N N Kesar. Circ: 1,950.

330.9 CHE ISSN 0256-3525
ECONOMIC AND FINANCIAL PROSPECTS. Text in English. 1947. bi-m. free. charts; illus.; stat. Supplement avail.; reprint service avail. from PQC. **Document type:** *Bulletin.* **Description:** Provides information about economic and financial issues, and issues affecting the banking community.
Former titles (until 1983): Prospects (0552-3648); (until 1955): Swiss Bank Corporation. Bulletin (0039-7466)
Related titles: Microform ed.: (from PQC).
Indexed: PAIS.
Published by: Schweizerischer Bankverein/Swiss Bank Corporation, 6 Aeschenplatz, Basel, 4002, Switzerland. TEL 41-61-288-2020, FAX 41-61-288-4424. Ed., R&P Daniel Witschi. Circ: 30,000.

330.9 332 KWT
ECONOMIC & FINANCIAL QUARTERLY. Text in English. q. free. stat. **Document type:** *Bulletin.* **Description:** Provides an overview of the current state of the Kuwaiti economy, information on the oil and banking sectors, foreign trade, and the outlook for the future.
Published by: National Bank of Kuwait S.A.K., Economic Research Division, P O Box 95, Safat, 13001, Kuwait. TEL 965-2422011, FAX 965-2465098.

338.9 CAN
HJ13
ECONOMIC AND FISCAL POLICY. Text in English. 1954. a. free.
Formerly: Saskatchewan Economic and Finance Position (0080-6676)
Published by: Saskatchewan Finance, 2350 Albert St, Regina, SK S4P 4S6, Canada. TEL 306-787-6768, FAX 306-787-3982. Circ: 1,500.

ECONOMIC & SHIPPING REVIEW. see *TRANSPORTATION—Ships And Shipping*

330.9 USA ISSN 0095-2850
HC125
ECONOMIC AND SOCIAL PROGRESS IN LATIN AMERICA. REPORT. Text in English. 1961. a. USD 24.95 (effective 2000). charts. back issues avail. **Document type:** *Corporate.* **Description:** Offers a regional and country-by-country overview of social and economic conditions throughout Latin America and the Caribbean.
Formerly (until 1972): Socio-Economic Progress in Latin America. Annual Report (0160-4902)
Related titles: Microfiche ed.: (from CIS); French ed.: Progres Economique et Social en Amerique Latine. Rapport. ISSN 0252-9319; Portuguese ed.: Progresso Socio-Economico na America Latina. Relatorio. ISSN 0253-6021; Spanish ed.: Progreso Economico y Social en America Latina. Informe. ISSN 0253-6013.
Indexed: IIS.
Published by: Inter-American Development Bank/Banco Interamericano de Desarrollo, 1300 New York Ave, N W, Washington, DC 20577. TEL 202-623-1709, http://www.iadb.org/exr/pub/engcatalog/Pages/anpubs.htm. Ed. Barbara Rierveld TEL 202-623-1154. **Subscr. to:** The Johns Hopkins University Press, Journals Publishing Division, PO Box 19966, Baltimore, MD 21211. TEL 410-516-6987, 800-548-1784, FAX 410-516-6968, jlorder@jhunix.hcf.jhu.edu.

338.9 THA ISSN 0252-5704
HC411
ECONOMIC AND SOCIAL SURVEY OF ASIA AND THE PACIFIC. Text in English. 1948. a., latest 2002. USD 50 (effective 2003). back issues avail. **Document type:** *Bulletin, Government.* **Description:** Emphasizes economic and social policy issues through an analysis of economic and social developments in the Pacific Rim.
Formerly: Economic Survey of Asia and the Far East (0070-8690)
Related titles: Microfiche ed.: (from CIS).
Indexed: ARDT, IIS.
—BLDSC (3651.533000), CISTI.
Published by: United Nations Economic and Social Commission for Asia and the Pacific, United Nations Bldg., Rajadamnern Ave., Bangkok, 10200, Thailand. TEL 662-2881174, FAX 662-2883022, TELEX 82392 ESCAP TH, unescap@unescap.org. **Subscr. to:** United Nations Publications, Distribution and Sales Section, Palais des Nations, Rm C-116, 8-14 av de la Paix, Geneva 1211, Switzerland. **Dist. by:** United Nations Publications, Rm DC2-853, United Nations Bldg, 2 United Nations Plaza, New York, NY 10017. http://www.un.org/Pubs.

330.9 USA ISSN 1075-8631
ECONOMIC BULLETIN (SAN DIEGO). Text in English. 1953. m. USD 250; USD 25 per issue (effective 2005). back issues avail.; reprint service avail. from PQC. **Document type:** *Newsletter, Bibliography.*
Former titles: San Diego Economic Bulletin (0558-3918); San Diego Bulletin
Related titles: Microfiche ed.: (from PQC); Microfilm ed.: (from PQC).
Indexed: PROMT.
Published by: San Diego Regional Chamber of Commerce, 402 W Broadway, Ste 1000, San Diego, CA 92101-3585. TEL 619-544-1300, FAX 619-234-0571, webinfo@sdchamber.org, http://www.sdchamber.org. Ed. Kelly Cunningham. Circ: 6,000 (paid and free).

330.9 USA ISSN 1573-9414
HC10
➤ **ECONOMIC CHANGE AND RESTRUCTURING**; an international journal devoted to the study of comparative economics, planning and development. Text in English. 1960. 4/yr. EUR 418, USD 428, GBP 265 combined subscription to institutions print & online eds. (effective 2005). adv. bk.rev. reprint service avail. from PSC. **Document type:** *Journal, Academic/Scholarly.* **Description:** Covers the study of micro- and macroeconomic planning, related techniques, and analysis of recent changes in economies traditionally associated with central planning.
Formerly (until 2004): Economics of Planning (0013-0451); Which incorporated (1990-2001): M O C T - M O S T (1120-7388)
Related titles: Microform ed.: (from PQC); Online - full text ed.: ISSN 1574-0277 (from EBSCO Publishing, Gale Group, IngentaConnect, Kluwer Online, O C L C Online Computer Library Center, Inc., ProQuest Information & Learning, Springer LINK).
Indexed: ABIn, ASCA, AgeL, BAS, BibLing, CREJ, CurCont, GEOBASE, IBR, IBSS, IBZ, IPSA, JEL, RRTA, RefZh, SSCI, WAE&RSA.
—BLDSC (3657.100000), IDS, IE, Infotrieve, ingenta. **CCC.**
Published by: Springer-Verlag New York, Inc. (Subsidiary of: Springer Science+Business Media), 233 Spring St, New York, NY 10013. TEL 212-460-1500, FAX 212-460-1575, service@springer-ny.com, http://springerlink.metapress.com/openurl.asp?genre=journal&issn=1573-9414, http://www.springer-ny.com. Eds. Roberta Benini, Wojciech W Charemza. **Subscr. to:** Journal Fulfillment, PO Box 2485, Secaucus, NJ 07096-2485. TEL 201-348-4033, FAX 201-348-4505, journals@springer-ny.com.

➤ **ECONOMIC COMMENTARY.** see *BUSINESS AND ECONOMICS*

330 CAN ISSN 0070-8488
HC111
ECONOMIC COUNCIL OF CANADA. ANNUAL REVIEW✶. Text in English, French. 1964. a. price varies.
—CISTI.
Published by: Government of Canada Publications, Publishing and Depository Services, Public Works and Government Services Canada, Ottawa, ON K1A 0S9, Canada. TEL 819-997-2560, FAX 613-952-2171. Circ: 3,500.

330.9 USA
ECONOMIC DEVELOPMENT DIGEST. Text in English. 1991. 10/yr. free. bk.rev. illus.; stat. back issues avail. **Document type:** *Newsletter.* **Description:** Covers rural economic and community development in US.
Related titles: Online - full text ed.
Published by: (Research Foundation), National Association of Development Organizations, 444 N Capitol St, N W, Ste 630, Washington, DC 20001. TEL 202-624-7806, FAX 202-624-8813, nado@sso.org, http://www.nado.org. Ed. Laurie Thompson. R&P Melissa Levy. Circ: 10,000.

338.9 USA
ECONOMIC DEVELOPMENT - STATE CAPITALS. Cover title: State Capitals Newsletters. Economic Development. Text in English. 1946. 48/yr. USD 275 in US & Canada; USD 295 elsewhere (effective 2005). back issues avail. **Document type:** *Newsletter.* **Description:** Covers such economic-development issues such as economic incentives and disincentives, environmental requirements, mass transportation, enterprise zones, utility rates, parkland development, taxes, licensing and fees, and labor laws.
Formerly: From the State Capitals. Economic Development (1061-9712); Which incorporated: From the State Capitals. Construction Policies (0749-2766); Which incorporated: Construction - Institutional (0741-3491); From the State Capitals. Parks and Recreational Trends (0749-2804); Which incorporated: Fish and Game Regulations (0734-1067); From the State Capitals. Tourist Business Promotion (0734-1199); From the State Capitals. Transportation Policies (0749-2774); Which was formed by the merger of: Urban Transit (0741-3564); Which was formerly: Urban Transit and Bus Transportation (0734-7210); Parking Regulations (0741-3513); Off-Street Parking (0734-161X); From the State Capitals. Urban Development (0741-3483); Which was formerly: Housing and Redevelopment (0734-1075); From the State Capitals. Industrial Development (0016-1721); Airport Construction and Financing (0734-1636); School Construction (0734-1164)
Related titles: Online - full text ed.
—CCC.
Published by: State Capitals Newsletters, PO Box 7376, Alexandria, VA 22307-7376. TEL 703-768-9600, FAX 703-768-9690, newsletters@statecapitals.com, http://www.statecapitals.com. Pub. Keyes Walworth.

ECONOMIC DEVELOPMENT TODAY. see *BUSINESS AND ECONOMICS—Abstracting, Bibliographies, Statistics*

330.9 336 USA
ECONOMIC EDGE. Text in English. 1996. q. free. back issues avail. **Document type:** *Newsletter.* **Description:** Provides a quarterly forecast of Illinois economy.
Related titles: Online - full text ed.
Published by: Institute of Govt. & Public Affairs, University of Illinois, 1007 W Nevada, Urbana, IL 61801. TEL 217-333-3340, FAX 217-244-4817, http://www.igpa.uillinois.edu. Ed. Robert W Resek. Circ: 1,000.

330.9 CAN ISSN 1482-471X
ECONOMIC FREEDOM OF THE WORLD ANNUAL REPORT. Text in English. 1996. a.
Related titles: Online - full text ed.: ISSN 1495-4982.
Published by: Fraser Institute, 1770 Burrard St, 4th floor, Vancouver, BC V6J 3G7, Canada. TEL 604-688-0221, FAX 604-688-8539, freetheworld@fraserinstitute.ca, http://www.freetheworld.com/release.html, http://www.fraserinstitute.ca.

330.9 USA ISSN 0278-8381
HA203
ECONOMIC INDICATORS (CHARLESTON). Text in English. 1981. quinquennial. looseleaf. USD 25 (effective 2001). **Description:** Presents quantitative data comparing important public policy functions in West Virginia and all states.
Indexed: MagInd.
Published by: West Virginia Research League Inc., PO Box 11176, Charleston, WV 25339-1176. TEL 304-766-9496, wvrl1@aol.com. Ed. Sarah F Roach.

330 USA ISSN 0013-0125
HC101 CODEN: ECINA3
ECONOMIC INDICATORS (WASHINGTON). Text in English. 1948. m. USD 58 domestic; USD 81.20 foreign (effective 2004). charts; mkt.; stat. back issues avail.; reprint service avail. from PQC. **Document type:** *Government.* **Description:** Publishes data on prices, wages, production, business activity, purchasing power, credit, money and federal finance.
Related titles: Microform ed.: (from PQC); Online - full text ed.: (from EBSCO Publishing, Florida Center for Library Automation, Gale Group, O C L C Online Computer Library Center, Inc., ProQuest Information & Learning).
Indexed: AcaI, MASUSE, MagInd, PAIS, SRI, T&II.
—CISTI.
Published by: U.S. Executive Office of the President, Council of Economic Advisers, Executive Office Bldg, Washington, DC 20502. TEL 202-395-5062, http://www.whitehouse.gov/WH/EOP/CEA/html/. **Subscr. to:** U.S. Government Printing Office, Superintendent of Documents, PO Box 371954, Pittsburgh, PA 15250-7954. TEL 202-512-1800, FAX 202-512-2250, orders@gpo.gov, http://www.access.gpo.gov.

330 ARG ISSN 0325-2388
HC171
ECONOMIC INFORMATION ON ARGENTINA✶. Text in English. 1983 (no.130). m. free to qualified personnel. illus.; charts; stat.
Indexed: PAIS, PROMT.
Published by: (Secretaria de Estado de Programacion y Coordinacion Economica), Argentina. Ministerio de Economia, Servicio de Prensa, 501, Balcarce, 136 Piso 5, Capital Federal, Buenos Aires 1064, Argentina. TEL 54-114-3495079, FAX 54-114-3495730, http://www.mecon.gov.ar/. Ed. Ana M Luro Rivarola. Circ: (controlled).

ECONOMIC ISSUES. see *BUSINESS AND ECONOMICS—Economic Systems And Theories, Economic History*

330.9 LBN
ECONOMIC LETTER. Text in English. m. **Description:** Includes a brief analysis of the Lebanese economy, with a statistical appendix.
Published by: Association of Banks in Lebanon, DORA Centre Moucarri, P O Box 80536, Beirut, Lebanon.

ECONOMIC LOGIC. see *BUSINESS AND ECONOMICS—Investments*

330.9 DNK
ECONOMIC MONTHLY. Text in English. 1938. q. free. mkt.; stat. index.
Former titles (until 1999): Danish Economy - A Quarterly Review (0908-3138); (until 1993): Denmark (0906-7906); (until 1988): Denmark Quarterly Review (0011-8427); (until 1984): Denmark (0902-235X)
Related titles: German ed.
Indexed: PROMT.
Published by: Danske Bank Aktieselskab, Communications, Holmens Kanal 2-12, Copenhagen K, 1092, Denmark. TEL 45-33-44-00-00, FAX 45-39-18-58-73, TELEX 27000. Ed. Steen Reeslev.

330.9 USA ISSN 0013-0206
ECONOMIC OPPORTUNITY REPORT; the independent weekly source for news of all economic opportunity programs. Text in English. 1965. w. looseleaf. USD 337 in US & Mexico; USD 355 elsewhere; USD 387 combined subscription print & email eds. (effective 2005); Includes School-to-Career Report. back issues avail.; reprints avail. **Document type:** *Newsletter, Consumer.* **Description:** Provides inside news from Washington on money, trends, innovations, and research results for antipoverty administrators.
Incorporates (in 2002): School-to-Career Report (1540-9929)
Related titles: E-mail ed.: ISSN 1545-4746. USD 277 (effective 2005); Online - full text ed.: (from Gale Group).
—CCC.
Published by: Business Publishers, Inc., 8737 Colesville Rd., Flr. 10, Silver Spring, MD 20910-3976. TEL 800-274-6737, bpinews@bpinews.com, custserv@bpinews.com, http://www.bpinews.com. Eds. Marcy Levin-Epstein, Charlotte Wright. Pub. L A Eiserer.

330 PAK
ECONOMIC OUTLOOK. Text in English. 1969. m. PKR 1,200, USD 80 (effective 2003). bk.rev. charts; stat.; tr.lit. 60 p./no.; **Document type:** *Magazine, Trade.* **Description:** Covers topics in economic development and technological change in Pakistan and around the world.
Indexed: BAS.
Published by: Pakistan Press International, Press Centre, Shahrah-e-Kamal Attaturk, Karachi, Pakistan. TEL 92-21-2627850, FAX 92-21-2631125, owais.ali@post.harvard.edu. Eds. Fazal Qureshi, T H Siddique. R&P, Adv. contact Fazal Qureshi. Circ: 5,000.

332 GBR ISSN 0140-489X
➤ **ECONOMIC OUTLOOK.** Text in English. 1977. q. USD 1,403 combined subscription in the Americas to institutions & Caribbean (print & online eds.); GBP 835 combined subscription elsewhere to institutions print & online eds. (effective 2006). **Document type:** *Journal, Academic/Scholarly.* **Description:** Provides a combination of independent analysis, commentary, and forecasts of the UK, as well as other major world economies previously incorporated in the International Economic Outlook. The emphasis alternates between the UK and the international economy. Designed for corporate executives, business libraries, corporate planners and government and policy-making institutions.
Incorporates: International Economic Outlook (0960-8869)
Related titles: Online - full text ed.: ISSN 1468-0319. USD 1,332 in the Americas to institutions & Caribbean; GBP 793 elsewhere to institutions (effective 2006) (from bigchalk, Blackwell Synergy, EBSCO Publishing, IngentaConnect, Northern Light Technology, Inc., O C L C Online Computer Library Center, Inc., Swets Information Services).
Indexed: ABIn, Emerald, GEOBASE, IBSS, KES, M&MA, PAIS, SCIMP.
—BLDSC (3653.934700), CISTI, IE, Infotrieve, ingenta. **CCC.**
Published by: (Oxford Economic Forecasting Ltd. USA, London Business School, Centre for Economic Forecasting), Blackwell Publishing Ltd., 9600 Garsington Rd, Oxford, OX4 2ZG, United Kingdom. TEL 44-1865-776868, FAX 44-1865-714591, customerservices@oxon.blackwellpublishing.com, http://www.blackwellpublishing.com/journals/ECOL. Ed. Adrian Cooper. Circ: 1,200.

➤ **ECONOMIC OUTLOOK**; a newsletter on economic issues for financial institutions. see *BUSINESS AND ECONOMICS—Banking And Finance*

330.9 USA ISSN 1048-115X
HC101
ECONOMIC PERSPECTIVES (CHICAGO). Text in English. 1917. q. free. charts; stat. index. reprint service avail. from CIS,PQC. **Document type:** *Journal, Academic/Scholarly.*
Former titles (until 1989): F R B Chicago Economic Perspectives (0884-7576); (until 1983): Economic Perspectives (0164-0682); (until Jan. 1977): Business Conditions (0007-6589)
Related titles: Microfiche ed.: (from CIS); Microform ed.: (from PQC); Online - full text ed.: (from EBSCO Publishing, Gale Group, O C L C Online Computer Library Center, Inc.).
Indexed: ABIn, AmStI, BAS, BLI, BPIA, JEL, PAIS, SRI.
—BLDSC (3654.078000), CISTI, IE, ingenta.
Published by: Federal Reserve Bank of Chicago, Public Information Center, PO Box 834, Chicago, IL 60690. TEL 312-322-5111, FAX 312-322-5515, http://www.chicagofed.org. Ed. Helen Koshy. Circ: 14,000.

330 USA
ECONOMIC PROFILE OF OREGON. Text in English. a. charts. **Document type:** *Government.*
Former titles: Oregon, a Statistical Profile; Oregon, an Economic Profile
Media: Online - full text.
Published by: Oregon Economic Development Department, 775 Summer St, N E, Salem, OR 97310. TEL 503-373-1290, FAX 503-581-5115, http://www.econ.state.or.us.

330 USA ISSN 0193-1180
HC106.5
ECONOMIC REPORT OF THE PRESIDENT. Text in English. 1947. a. USD 35 domestic; USD 49 foreign (effective 2005). reprints avail. **Document type:** *Government.* **Description:** Presents the Annual Report of the Council of Economic Advisers as well as the Economic Report of the President.
Formerly: U.S. Executive Office of the President. Economic Report of the President
Related titles: CD-ROM ed.; Microfiche ed.: (from BHP); Online - full text ed.
—CISTI.
Published by: U.S. Executive Office of the President, Council of Economic Advisers, Executive Office Bldg, Washington, DC 20502. TEL 202-395-7332, wwwadmin@gpo.gov, http://www.gpoaccess.gov/eop/, http://www.whitehouse.gov/WH/EOP/CEA/html/. **Subscr. to:** U.S. Government Printing Office, Superintendent of Documents, PO Box 371954, Pittsburgh, PA 15250-7954. TEL 202-512-1800, FAX 202-512-2250, orders@gpo.gov, http://www.access.gpo.gov.

330 SCG ISSN 0013-0303
ECONOMIC REVIEW. Text in Serbo-Croatian. 1955. m. YUN 24, USD 18. adv. charts; illus.; stat.
Published by: Privredni Pregled, Marsala Birjuzova 3-5, Belgrade, 11000. Ed. Vladimir Kacanski.

330 LBN ISSN 0013-032X
ECONOMIC REVIEW OF THE ARAB WORLD; argus of Arab economy. Text in English. 1966. m. USD 300 (effective 2001). charts; stat. **Document type:** *Bulletin.* **Description:** Round-up of economic and financial developments in the Arab world covering trade agreements, imports and exports, customs and taxation, and banking regulations.
Incorporates: Argus Pharma Report
Indexed: MEA&I, Perislam.
Published by: Bureau of Lebanese and Arab Documentation - Argus, Sodeco St, P O Box 165403, Beirut, Lebanon. TEL 961-1-219113, FAX 961-1-219955.

330.9 GRC ISSN 1105-252X
ECONOMIC REVIEW OF THE YEAR - THE GREEK ECONOMY. Text in Greek. 1983. a. adv. **Description:** Comprehensive review and analysis of all aspects of the Greek economy, with quantitative socio-economic data for all 10 regions and 52 departments of Greece.
Related titles: ◆ Supplement to: Epilogi. ISSN 1105-2503.
Published by: Electra Press, 4 Stadiou St, Athens, 105 64, Greece. TEL 323-3203, FAX 323-5160. Ed. Christos Papaioannou. Circ: 11,000.

330.9 346 USA
ECONOMIC SANCTIONS AND EMBARGOES. Text in English. 1996. irreg. USD 165 (effective 2001).
Published by: Business Laws, Inc., 11630 Chillicothe Rd, Chesterland, OH 44026. TEL 440-729-7996, FAX 440-729-0645, http://www.businesslaws.com.

330.9 DEU ISSN 0431-6045
HC286.5
ECONOMIC SITUATION IN THE FEDERAL REPUBLIC OF GERMANY. Text in English. m. charts; illus.; stat. **Document type:** *Government.*
Published by: Bundesministerium der Finanzen, Adenauerallee 99-103, Bonn, 53105, Germany. FAX 49-228-6824629. Circ: 1,500.

338.9 CHE ISSN 0070-8712
HC240.A1
ECONOMIC SURVEY OF EUROPE. Text in English, Russian. 1948. 2/yr. price varies. **Document type:** *Bulletin, Government.* **Description:** Reports on the economic condition of the UN ECE nations in the world economy.
Related titles: Microfiche ed.: (from CIS); Online - full text ed.: (from EBSCO Publishing).
Indexed: IIS, MASUSE.
—BLDSC (3656.200000), IE, ingenta.
Published by: United Nations, Economic Commission for Europe (ECE), Palais des Nations, Geneva 10, 1211, Switzerland. TEL 41-22-9174444, FAX 41-22-9170505, info.ece@unece.org, http://www.unece.org.

330.9 CHL ISSN 0257-2184
HC161
ECONOMIC SURVEY OF LATIN AMERICA AND THE CARIBBEAN. Text in English. 1948. a.
Formerly (until 1981): Economic Survey of Latin America (0070-8720)
Related titles: CD-ROM ed.: ISSN 1811-6191. 2001; Online - full text ed.: ISSN 1681-0384. 2000; ◆ Spanish ed.: Estudio Economico de America Latina y el Caribe. ISSN 0257-2176.
Published by: Comision Economica para America Latina y el Caribe/Economic Commission for Latin America and the Caribbean, Ave Dag Hammarskjold 3477, Vitacura, Santiago de Chile, Chile. TEL 56-2-471-2000, FAX 56-2-208-0252, publications@eclac.cl, http://www.eclac.cl.

330.9 CHL ISSN 1681-0597
ECONOMIC SURVEY OF LATIN AMERICA AND THE CARIBBEAN. SUMMARY. Text in English. 1986. a.
Formerly (until 1997): Economic Panorama of Latin America (0259-241X)
Related titles: Online - full text ed.: ISSN 1681-0600.
Published by: United Nations Economic Commission for Latin America and the Caribbean, Av. Dag Hammarskjold 3477, Vitacura, Casilla 179-D, Santiago de Chile, Chile. TEL 56-2-471-2000, FAX 56-2-208-0252, dpisantiago@eclac.cl, http://www.eclac.cl.

330.9 LBR ISSN 0303-853X
HA2171
ECONOMIC SURVEY OF LIBERIA✶. Text in English. a. USD 5. stat.
Published by: Ministry of Planning and Economic Affairs, PO Box 9016, Monrovia, Liberia.

330 IND
ECONOMIC SURVEY OF MAHARASHTRA. Text in English, Marathi. 1962. a. free.
Former titles: Economic Survey of India; Maharashtra: An Economic Review (0076-2539)
Published by: Directorate of Economics and Statistics, MHADA Bldg., Kalanagar Bandra (E), Mumbai, Maharashtra 400 051, India. TEL 91-22-6438781, FAX 91-22-6438781. Ed. B M Nagrale.

ECONOMIC TIMES. see *BUSINESS AND ECONOMICS—Banking And Finance*

ECONOMIC TIMES. see *BUSINESS AND ECONOMICS—Banking And Finance*

330 BGD
ECONOMIC TRENDS. Text in English. 1976. m. reprints avail.
Indexed: RefZh.
Published by: (Department of Public Relations and Publications), Bangladesh Bank, Motijheel Commercial Area, Dhaka, 2, Bangladesh.

330 GBR ISSN 0013-0400
HC251
ECONOMIC TRENDS. Text in English. 1953. m. GBP 196. charts; stat. reprint service avail. from SCH. **Document type:** *Government.* **Description:** Brings all the main economic indicators together in graphs and statistical tables, which are analyzed in articles. Also covers quarterly national accounts and balance of payment.
Related titles: Microform ed.: (from PQC); ◆ Supplement(s): United Kingdom. Office for National Statistics. United Kingdom Economic Accounts.
Indexed: IBR, IBZ, PAIS, PROMT, RRTA, WAE&RSA, WBA.
—BLDSC (3656.700000), CISTI, IE. **CCC.**
Published by: Office for National Statistics, c/o Phil Lewin, Room B110, Pimlico, London, SW1V 2QQ, United Kingdom. TEL 44-20-7533-6165, FAX 44-20-7533-6185, library@ons.gov.uk, http://www.statistics.gov.uk. **Orders to:** Stationery Office, PO Box 276, London SW8 5DT, United Kingdom. TEL 44-20-7873-9090, FAX 44-207-873-8200.

330.9 IRN
ECONOMIC TRENDS. Text in English. q. **Document type:** *Bulletin.*
Formerly: Central Bank of the Islamic Republic of Iran. Economic Report and Balance Sheet (0259-9902)
—BLDSC (3654.448000).
Published by: (Iran. Economic Research Department), Bank Markazi Jomhouri Islami Iran/Central Bank of the Islamic Republic of Iran, P O Box 11365-8531, Tehran, Iran. FAX 98-21-390323.

330 USA ISSN 0748-2922
HC101
ECONOMIC TRENDS (CLEVELAND). Text in English. 1979. m. free (effective 2005). back issues avail.; reprint service avail. from CIS. **Document type:** *Newsletter.* **Description:** Covers patterns and trends in the U.S. economy in terms of the gross national product, interest rates, capital investment, money aggregates, financial markets, and foreign exchange markets, with a specific emphasis on the economic conditions of and outlook for the state of Ohio.
Supersedes: Economic Presentation
Related titles: Microfiche ed.: (from CIS); Online - full text ed.: (from EBSCO Publishing, Florida Center for Library Automation, Gale Group).
Indexed: AmStI.
Published by: Federal Reserve Bank of Cleveland, PO Box 6387, Cleveland, OH 44101. TEL 216-579-3079, FAX 216-579-3172. Eds. Michele Lachman, Monica Crabtree-Reuser. R&P Lee Faulhaber TEL 216-579-2961. Circ: 15,300.

330.9 JPN
ECONOMIC TRENDS: JAPAN. Text in English. s-a. reprints avail.
Published by: Embassy of the United States in Japan, 1-10-5 Akasaka, Minato-ku, Tokyo, 107-0052, Japan.

330.9 USA
ECONOMIC UPDATE. Text in English. 1993. irreg. free. **Document type:** *Government.* **Description:** Covers the State's current economic conditions and financial plan.
Published by: Ways & Means Committee, Economic Group, State Capitol, Rm 412, Albany, NY 12248. TEL 518-455-4026, FAX 518-455-3040, priestd@Assembly.state.ny.us, http://www.assembly.state.ny.us/reports/. Ed. Edward Cupoli. Circ: 5,000.

330.9 CHN ISSN 1529-7373
HB1
ECONOMICS AND FINANCE. ANNALS. Text in English. 2000. s-a.
Indexed: JEL.
—BLDSC (1040.367000), IE.
Published by: Peking University Press, 205 Chengfu Rd, Zhongguancun, Beijing, 100037, China. TEL 86-10-62556201, FAX 86-10-62752036.

330.9 GBR ISSN 0266-2671
HB1
➤ **ECONOMICS AND PHILOSOPHY.** Text in English. 1985. 3/yr. USD 182 in North America to institutions; GBP 110 elsewhere to institutions; USD 198 combined subscription in North America to institutions print & online eds.; GBP 118 combined subscription elsewhere to institutions print & online eds. (effective 2006). adv. bk.rev. illus. Index. back issues avail.; reprint service avail. from PSC. **Document type:** *Journal, Academic/Scholarly.* **Description:** Explores the foundations of economics as both a predictive or explanatory enterprise and a normative one.
Related titles: Microform ed.: (from PQC); Online - full text ed.: ISSN 1474-0028. USD 174 in North America to institutions; GBP 105 elsewhere to institutions (effective 2006) (from EBSCO Publishing, O C L C Online Computer Library Center, Inc., Swets Information Services).
Indexed: ABIn, ASCA, CREJ, CurCont, IBSS, IPB, JEL, PCI, PhilInd, SOPODA, SSCI.
—BLDSC (3656.930900), IDS, IE, Infotrieve, ingenta. **CCC.**
Published by: Cambridge University Press, The Edinburgh Bldg, Shaftesbury Rd, Cambridge, CB2 2RU, United Kingdom. TEL 44-1223-312393, FAX 44-1223-315052, journals@cambridge.org, http://uk.cambridge.org/journals/eap/. Eds. Geoffrey Brennan, Luc Bovens, Peter Vallentyne. R&P Linda Nicol TEL 44-1223-325757. Adv. contact Rebecca Curtis TEL 44-1223-325757. **Subscr. addr. in N America:** Cambridge University Press, 100 Brook Hill Dr, West Nyack, NY 10994. TEL 845-353-7500, FAX 845-353-4141, journals_subscriptions@cup.org

330.9 AUS ISSN 1446-1978
ECONOMICS MONITOR. Text in English. 1972. m. AUD 545.
Formerly (until 2001): Economics Monitor on Australia and the World (1441-0060); (until 1998): Corporate Brief on Australia and the World; (until 1995): Corporate Brief; Syntec Business Outlook
Indexed: CBCABus.
Published by: Access Economics, Level 3, 39 Brisbane Ave, Barton, ACT 2600, Australia. TEL 61-2-6273-1222, FAX 61-2-6273-1223, info@AccessEconomics.com.au, http://www.accesseconomics.com.au/. Circ: 1,700.

330 DZA
ECONOMIE. Text in French. 1962. m.
Formerly: Algerie Economique
Published by: Algerie Presse Service (A.P.S.), 7 bd. Che Guevara, Algiers, Algeria. TEL 2-71-24-36, FAX 2-57-85-08, TELEX 65761. Ed. B A Djaballah. Circ: 700.

330.9 REU ISSN 0750-0769
HC598.A1
L'ECONOMIE DE LA REUNION. Text in French. 1982. q. bk.rev. charts; illus.; maps; stat. **Document type:** *Magazine.*
Indexed: ASD.
Published by: Institut National de la Statistique et des Etudes Economiques, Direction Regionale de la Reunion, 15 rue de L'Ecole, B P 13, St. Denis Messag, Cedex 9 97408, Reunion. TEL 02-62-488900, FAX 02-62-488989. Ed. Gaillard Jean. Circ: 1,800.

330 TUN ISSN 0070-878X
ECONOMIE DE LA TUNISIE EN CHIFFRES. Text in Arabic, French. 1960. a. TND 2,000 (effective 2000).
Published by: Institut National de la Statistique, 70 Rue Ech-Cham, B P 260, Tunis, Tunisia. TEL 216-1-891002, FAX 216-1-792559.

330.9 BEL ISSN 1373-8496
➤ **ECONOMIE PUBLIQUE**; etudes et recherches. Text in French. 1998. s-a. EUR 60 in France to institutions; EUR 66.35 to institutions (effective 2005). bk.rev. abstr. 160 p./no.; back issues avail. **Document type:** *Monographic series, Academic/Scholarly.* **Description:** Examines various economic topics, often in the context of environmental issues.
Indexed: IBR, IBZ.
Published by: De Boeck Universite, Fond Jean-Paques 4, Louvain-la-Neuve, 1348, Belgium. TEL 32-10-482511, FAX 32-10-482519, info@universite.deboeck.com, http://universite.deboeck.com/revues/ep. Ed. Alain Trannoy. **Subscr. to:** Acces S.P.R.L.. TEL 32-10-482570, acces+cde@deboeck.be.

➤ **ECONOMIE RURALE**; agricultures - alimentation - territoires. see *AGRICULTURE—Agricultural Economics*

330.9 FRA
ECONOMIES ET SOCIETES. SERIE R. THEORIES DE LA REGULATION. Text in French. irreg.
Published by: Les Presses de l'I S M E A, BP 22, Paris, Cedex 13 75622, France. TEL 33-1-55489076, FAX 33-1-55489071, http://www.ismea.org. Ed. Gerard de Bernis.

330 NLD ISSN 0013-0583
HC10
ECONOMISCH-STATISTISCHE BERICHTEN. Text in Dutch. 1916. w. EUR 102 to individuals; EUR 203 to institutions; EUR 66 to students (effective 2005). adv. bk.rev. bibl.; stat. index. **Document type:** *Academic/Scholarly.* **Description:** Professional publication for economists. Covers current economic trends and information, analysis of economic issues, national and international news, business news and politics. Includes positions available.
Related titles: Online - full text ed.
Indexed: ExcerpMed, KES, SCIMP, WBSS.
—IE, Infotrieve.
Published by: Nederlands Economisch Instituut/Netherlands Economic Institute, Postbus 3320, Utrecht, 3502 GH, Netherlands. TEL 31-30-2192462, FAX 31-30-2512496, redactie-esb@economie.nl, http://www.economie.nl. adv.: B&W page EUR 1,231; 180 x 250. Circ: 5,500.

330 JPN ISSN 0013-0621
ECONOMIST. Text in Japanese. 1923. w. JPY 280. adv.
Related titles: Online - full text ed.
Indexed: BLI, BRD, CPerI, CurCont, M&MA, PROMT, SSCI, SSI, T&II, Telegen.
Published by: Mainichi Shinbunsha/Mainichi Newspapers, 1-1-1 Hitotsubashi, Chiyoda-ku, Tokyo, 100-8051, Japan. TEL 81-3-3212-0321, FAX 81-3-3211-0895, TELEX 22324. Ed. Saburo Zushi. Circ: 117,000. **Order from:** Oversea Courier Service Inc., Osaka Branch Office, 3-28 Nozatonishi, Nishiyodogawa, Osaka-shi 541, Japan.

330.9 GBR ISSN 0013-0613
HG11 CODEN: EONOEH
THE ECONOMIST. Text in English. 1843. w. (51/yr.). GBP 92 domestic; USD 129 in United States; USD 180 in Mexico; CND 189 in Canada (effective 2004); includes access to the Online Edition. adv. bk.rev. charts; illus.; stat. q. index; a. cum.index. reprints avail. **Document type:** *Magazine, Consumer.* **Description:** Offers reporting, commentary, and analysis on world politics, finance, and business trends. Also covers science and technology, literature and the arts.
Related titles: ◆ CD-ROM ed.: The Economist on CD-ROM; Microform ed.: (from PQC); Online - full text ed.: (from Florida Center for Library Automation); (from EBSCO Publishing, Gale Group, LexisNexis, Micromedia ProQuest, Newsbank, Inc., O C L C Online Computer Library Center, Inc., ProQuest Information & Learning); Regional ed(s).: The Economist (North American Edition); The Economist (European Edition); Supplement(s): Technology Quarterly.
Indexed: ABIn, AEA, AESIS, AbHyg, AcaI, AgBio, AgeL, B&I, BAS, BLI, BMT, BPI, BRD, BRI, BrCerAb, BrHumI, BrTechI, CADCAM, CBNB, CBRI, CPerI, ChPerI, DSA, Emerald, EnvAb, FutSurv, HECAB, HortAb, I&DA, IAA, ILD, IndBusRep, IndVet, Inpharma, Inspec, KES, LogistBibl, M&MA, M&TEA, MASUSE, MEA&I, MagInd, MaizeAb, NutrAb, PAIS, PBA, PE&ON, PROMT, RAPRA, RASB, RDA, RI-1, RI-2, RRTA, Reac, RefZh, RoboAb, S&F, SPPI, SRRA, SSI, SoyAb, T&II, TDB, TOM, TTI, TriticAb, WAE&RSA, WBA, WMB, WTA.
—BLDSC (3659.410000), CASDDS, CISTI, IDS, IE, Infotrieve, ingenta, Linda Hall. **CCC.**
Published by: Economist Newspaper Ltd, 25 St James's St, London, SW1A 1HG, United Kingdom. TEL 44-20-7830-7000, FAX 44-20-7930-0458, TELEX 24344 ECON G, inquiries@economist.com, letters@economist.com, http://www.economist.com. Ed. Bill Emmott. Pub., Adv. contact David Hanger. B&W page GBP 8,650, color page GBP 12,550; trim 180 x 240. Circ: 722,984 (paid). **Subscr. to:** Harold Hill, PO Box 14, Romford, Essex RM3 8EQ, United Kingdom.

016.33 GBR ISSN 1358-247X
ECONOMIST. ANNUAL INDEX. Text in English. a. back issues avail. **Document type:** *Abstract/Index.*
Related titles: CD-ROM ed.: (from Chadwyck-Healey Inc.).
Indexed: CBCARef.
—IE.
Published by: Economist Newspaper Ltd, 25 St James's St, London, SW1A 1HG, United Kingdom. FAX 44-20-7839-2968.

330.9 USA
THE ECONOMIST ON CD-ROM. Text in English. q. USD 595 (effective 1999). back issues avail. **Description:** Provides electronic access to the full text of The Economist magazine and its index. Archival disks cover material from 1987-1994.
Media: CD-ROM (from Chadwyck-Healey Inc.). **Related titles:** ◆ Print ed.: The Economist. ISSN 0013-0613.
Published by: ProQuest Information & Learning, 300 N Zeeb Rd., PO Box 1346, Ann Arbor, MI 48106-1346. FAX 703-683-7589, info@il.proquest.com, http://www.chadwyck.com.

330 EGY ISSN 0013-0672
L'ECONOMISTE EGYPTIEN. Text in Arabic. 1901. w. looseleaf. adv. mkt.; pat.; stat.; tr.lit.; tr.mk.
Published by: Margaret & Joffre Hosni, Ed. & Pub., 11 Sharia de la Poste, P O Box 847, Alexandria, Egypt.

330.9 UGA
THE ECONOMY. Text in English. 1979. w. UGX 600.
Published by: Economy Publications Ltd., PO Box 6787, Kampala, Uganda. Ed. Roland Mutale. Circ: 25,000.

330.971 CAN ISSN 0712-2012
ECONOSCOPE. Text in English. 1977. m. **Description:** Provides coverage of the Canadian economic landscape.
Published by: Royal Bank of Canada, Economics Department, PO Box 1, Toronto, ON M5J 2J5, Canada. http://rbcc.royalbank.com/rt/gss.nsf/Policies+and+Procedures+Home?OpenForm.

ECOSTAT ECONOMIC BULLETIN. see *ENGINEERING—Chemical Engineering*

330 ECU
ECUADOR; carta de noticias. Text in Spanish. 1975. w. free. charts; illus.; stat. **Description:** General and economic news of Ecuador.
Published by: Ministerio de Relaciones Exteriores, Quito, Pichincha, Ecuador. Ed. Abelardo Posso. Circ: 1,200.

330.9 ECU
ECUADOR. CORPORACION FINANCIERA NACIONAL. BOLETIN ESTADISTICO. Text in Spanish. 1978 (no.6). irreg., latest 1996. charts. **Document type:** *Bulletin, Government.* **Description:** Reviews statistical information from the past four years.
Published by: Corporacion Financiera Nacional, Juan Leon Mera 130 y Av Patria, Quito, Ecuador. TEL 593-2-564900, FAX 593-2-223823, http://www.cfn.fin.ec/.

330.9 GBR
EDINBURGH ECONOMIC REVIEW. Text in English. 1986. q. free. bibl.; charts; illus.; stat. back issues avail. **Document type:** *Government.* **Description:** Stimulates debate and interest about local economic and employment issues. Includes statistical summary.
Formerly: Edinburgh Economic and Employment Review
Related titles: Braille ed.; Diskette ed.; Large type ed.
Published by: City of Edinburgh District Council, Department of Economic Development and Estates, 375 High St, Edinburgh, EH1 1QE, United Kingdom. TEL 44-131-5293417, FAX 44-131-5293737. Ed. G S Callaghan. Circ: 3,000.

334 IDN ISSN 0852-0747
EDISI CHUSUS BULLETIN KOPERASI. Variant title: Bulletin Koperasi. Text in Indonesian. 1966. q. free. charts; stat.
Description: Provides cooperative information such as government policy, operational instructions, and successful examples of cooperative societies to various provincial and district offices and universities in Indonesia.
Published by: Department of Cooperatives, Directorate General of the Institutional Promotion for Cooperatives - Direktorat Bina Penyuluhan Koperasi, Jalan H R Rasuna Said Kav 3-5, Jakarta, 12940, Indonesia. TEL 5204382. Ed. Rosdiana Sipayung. Circ: 7,500 (controlled).

330.9 CAN ISSN 0824-409X
EDMONTON REPORT ON ECONOMIC DEVELOPMENT. Text in English. q. free. back issues avail. **Description:** Responsible for the initiation of economic development programs on behalf of Edmonton.
Published by: Economic Development Edmonton, 9797 Jasper Ave, Edmonton, AB T5J 1N9, Canada. TEL 403-424-7870, 800-661-6965, FAX 403-426-0535. Ed. Janice Dewar. Circ: 13,500.

330.962 GBR ISSN 1470-7365
EGYPT QUARTERLY FORECAST REPORT. Text in English. 1993. 3/yr. GBP 330, USD 495, EUR 450 (effective 2003). **Document type:** *Journal, Trade.* **Description:** Provides a comprehensive assessment of the Egyptian government, economy and business environment over the next 30 months. Helps to identify opportunities and reduce risk, and answers key questions facing executives at this time.
Formerly (until 2000): Annual Country Forecast Report. Egypt (0969-5176)
Related titles: Online - full text ed.: (from EBSCO Publishing).
—**CCC.**
Published by: Business Monitor International Ltd., Mermaid House, 2 Puddle Dock, Blackfriars, London, EC4V 3DS, United Kingdom. TEL 44-20-72480468, FAX 44-20-72480467, marketing@businessmonitor.com, http://www.businessmonitor.com/egyptforecast.html.

330.96205 GBR ISSN 1468-1846
THE EGYPT REPORT. Text in English. 1999. q. GBP 290 (effective 2002). adv. **Document type:** *Magazine, Trade.* **Description:** Provides an in-depth analysis of political and economic trends in Egypt.
Published by: M E E D - Emap Communications (Subsidiary of: Emap Business Communications Ltd.), 33-39 Bowling Green Lane, London, EC1R 0DA, United Kingdom. TEL 44-20-7470-6406, FAX 44-207-470-6406, customerservice@meed.com, http://www.meed.com. Ed. David Butter.

330.9 EGY
EGYPT. SPECIALISED NATIONAL COUNCILS. MAGAZINE. Text in Arabic. 1976. q.
Indexed: PAIS.
Published by: Specialised National Councils, Arab Socialist Union Bldg., Nile Corniche, Cairo, Egypt. Ed. A Anis.

B

330.9 ESP ISSN 0213-3865
HC387.P28
EKONOMIAZ; revista de economia vasca. Text in Spanish. 1985. 4/yr. **Document type:** *Magazine, Consumer.*
Indexed: JEL.
—CINDOC.
Published by: Eusko Jaurlaritzaren Argitalpen-Zerbitzu Nagusia/Servicio Central de Publicaciones del Gobierno Vasco, Donostia-San Sebastian, 1, Vitoria-gasteiz, Alava 01010, Spain. TEL 34-945-018561, FAX 34-945-189709, hac-sabd@ej-gv.es.

300 330.9 RUS
EKONOMICHESKIE I SOTSIAL'NYE PROBLEMY ROSSII. Text in Russian. 1997. s-a. USD 59 (effective 2004). **Document type:** *Journal.*
Published by: Rossiiskaya Akademiya Nauk, Institut Nauchnoi Informatsii po Obshchestvennym Naukam, Nakhimovskii pr-t 51/21, Moscow, 117997, Russian Federation. TEL 7-095-1288930, FAX 7-095-4202261, info@inion.ru, http://www.inion.ru. **Dist. by:** East View Information Services, 3020 Harbor Ln. N., Minneapolis, MN 55447. TEL 800-477-1005, FAX 800-800-3839, eastview@eastview.com, http://www.eastview.com.

EKONOMICHESKIE POKAZATELI RAZVITIYA RAYONOV KRAINEGO SEVERA I PRIRAVNENNYKH K NIM MESTNOSTEI/ECONOMIC INDICATORS OF THE DEVELOPMENT OF THE FAR NORTH AND OTHER SIMILAR AREAS. see *BUSINESS AND ECONOMICS—Abstracting, Bibliographies, Statistics*

EKONOMICHESKOE I SOTSIAL'NOE RAZVITIE KORENNYKH MALOCHISLENNYKH NARODOV SEVERA/ECONOMIC AND SOCIAL DEVELOPMENT OF INDIGENOUS SMALL NATIONALITIES OF THE FAR NORTH. see *BUSINESS AND ECONOMICS—Abstracting, Bibliographies, Statistics*

EKONOMIKA UKRAINY/UKRAINE'S ECONOMY. see *BUSINESS AND ECONOMICS—Economic Systems And Theories, Economic History*

330.9 SLV
EL SALVADOR, INFORME ECONOMICO Y SOCIAL. Text in Spanish. 1975. a. free. stat. **Description:** Includes comparative data for previous years.
Formerly: Economia Salvadorena (San Salvador, 1975)
Media: Duplicated (not offset).
Published by: Ministerio de Planificacion y Coordinacion del Desarrollo Economico y Social, Biblioteca Tecnica "Hector Humberto Zelaya", 10 Av. Sur y Calle Mexico, Barrio San Jacinto, San Salvador, 1505, El Salvador. Circ: 88.

330.9 SLV
EL SALVADOR. MINISTERIO DE PLANIFICACION Y COORDINACION DEL DESARROLLO ECONOMICO Y SOCIAL. MEMORIA DE LABORES. Text in Spanish. 1976. irreg.
Published by: Ministerio de Planificacion y Coordinacion del Desarrollo Economico y Social, Biblioteca Tecnica "Hector Humberto Zelaya", 10 Av. Sur y Calle Mexico, Barrio San Jacinto, San Salvador, 1505, El Salvador.

ELECTRONIC COMMERCE RESEARCH AND APPLICATIONS. see *COMPUTERS—Information Science And Information Theory*

EMERGING EUROPE MARKET REVIEW. see *BUSINESS AND ECONOMICS—Investments*

330.947 GBR ISSN 1472-4103
HC336.27
EMERGING EUROPE MONITOR. RUSSIA, C I S & BALTICS. Text in English. 1997. m. GBP 325, USD 540, EUR 490 (effective 2003). **Document type:** *Journal, Trade.* **Description:** Covers political risk, the business environment, and economic prospects in Russia, Ukraine, Central Asian Republics (Kazakhstan, Uzbekistan, Turkmenistan, Azerbaijan, Georgia, etc.), and the Baltic States (Estonia, Latvia, and Lithuania).
Formerly (until 2000): Russia & Former Soviet Union Monitor (1368-2512); Which incorporated (1992-1999): Russian Far East Update (1061-5679)
Related titles: Online - full text ed.: (from EBSCO Publishing).
—**CCC.**
Published by: Business Monitor International Ltd., Mermaid House, 2 Puddle Dock, Blackfriars, London, EC4V 3DS, United Kingdom. TEL 44-20-72480468, FAX 44-20-72480467, marketing@businessmonitor.com, https://www.businessmonitor.com/bmi/euromonitor_order.html, http://www.businessmonitor.com.

332.0947 GBR ISSN 1461-6572
EMERGING EUROPEAN MARKETS. Text in English. 1997. m. **Document type:** *Journal, Trade.*
Formed by the merger of (1991-1997): Finance East Europe (0965-9560); (1981-1997): East European Markets (0262-0456)
Related titles: Online - full text ed.
Published by: Financial Times Business Ltd. (Subsidiary of: Financial Times Group), Maple House, 149 Tottenham Court Rd, London, W1P 9LL, United Kingdom. TEL 44-20-7896-2525, FAX 44-20-7896-2587, http://www.ft.com.

330.9 GBR
EMERGING MARKET TRENDS. Text in English. 1977. q. **Document type:** *Trade.* **Description:** Provides a broad explanation of and forecast for the economic background against which investment decisions are being taken.
Formerly (until 1997): Asian Monetary Monitor (1010-416X)
Indexed: PAIS.
Published by: L G T Asset Management plc, Economic Research Unit, Alban Gate 14th Fl, 125 London Wall, London, EC2Y 5AS, United Kingdom. TEL 44-171-710-4567.

330.9 POL ISSN 1233-3115
HC244.A1
➤ **EMERGO.** Text in English. 1994. q. EUR 76 foreign (effective 2005). **Document type:** *Journal, Academic/Scholarly.* **Description:** Deals with such topics as: industrial policy, the redesign of fiscal systems, the reorganization of social welfare, company valuation in the privatisation process, the emergence of real estate markets, public administration in transition economies of the countries of the Eastern Europe.
—BLDSC (3733.443000), IE, ingenta.
Published by: Akademia Ekonomiczna, Krakow, ul Rakowicka 27, Krakow, 31510, Poland. TEL 48-12-2935200, http://www.emergo-journal.pro.onet.pl/Emergo.html, http://www.ae.krakow.pl. **Dist. by:** Ars Polona, Krakowskie Przedmiescie 7, Warsaw, Poland. TEL 48-22-9263914, FAX 48-22-9265334, arspolona@arspolona.com.pl, http://www.arspolona.com.pl.

330.9 USA ISSN 0340-8744
H62.5.A9
EMPIRICA. Text in Dutch. 1974. q. EUR 398, USD 408, GBP 248 combined subscription to institutions print & online eds. (effective 2005). adv. reprint service avail. from PSC. **Document type:** *Journal, Academic/Scholarly.* **Description:** Publishes applied articles and papers dealing with all kinds of problems relevant to economic policy, with particular emphasis on industrial economics, economic integration and relevant international economic issues.
Related titles: Online - full text ed.: ISSN 1573-6911 (from EBSCO Publishing, Gale Group, IngentaConnect, Kluwer Online, O C L C Online Computer Library Center, Inc., ProQuest Information & Learning, Springer LINK, Swets Information Services).
Indexed: ABIn, BibLing, GEOBASE, IBR, IBSS, IBZ, JEL, PAIS, PSA, RefZh, SOPODA.
—BLDSC (3737.005000), IE, Infotrieve, ingenta. **CCC.**
Published by: (Oesterreichisches Institut fuer Wirtschaftsforschung/Austrian Institute of Economic Research AUT), Springer-Verlag New York, Inc. (Subsidiary of: Springer Science+Business Media), 233 Spring St, New York, NY 10013. TEL 212-460-1500, FAX 212-460-1575, service@springer-ny.com, http://springerlink.metapress.com/openurl.asp?genre=journal&issn=0340-8744, http://www.springer-ny.com. Eds. Jurgen Weigand, Pierre Pestieau, Robert Holzmann. Circ: 800. **Subscr. to:** Journal Fulfillment, PO Box 2485, Secaucus, NJ 07096-2485. TEL 201-348-4033, FAX 201-348-4505, journals@springer-ny.com. **Co-sponsor:** Austrian Economic Association.

331.1 USA
EMPLOYMENT AND EARNINGS: CHARACTERISTICS OF FAMILIES. Text in English. q. **Document type:** *Government.*
Related titles: ◆ Series of: U.S. Bureau of Labor Statistics. National Office News Releases.
Published by: U.S. Department of Labor, Bureau of Labor Statistics, Postal Square Bldg., 2 Massachusetts Ave, NE, Washington, DC 20212-0001 . TEL 202-655-4000. **Subscr. to:** U.S. Government Printing Office, Superintendent of Documents.

331.125 USA
EMPLOYMENT AND THE ECONOMY. ATLANTIC COASTAL REGION. Text in English. 1969. q. free. **Document type:** *Government.* **Description:** Describes current labor market and economic conditions in Atlantic, Cape May, Monmouth and Ocean counties.
Published by: Department of Labor, Division of Labor Market and Demographic Research, CN 057, Trenton, NJ 08625-0057. TEL 609-292-2145. Ed. Jan J Dejong. Circ: 1,300.

330.9 USA
EMPLOYMENT AND THE ECONOMY. NORTHERN NEW JERSEY REGION. Text in English. 1969. q. free. **Document type:** *Government.* **Description:** Describes current labor market and economic development conditions in Bergen, Essex, Hudson, Hunterdon, Middlesex, Morris, Passaic, Somerset, Sussex, Union, and Warren counties.
Published by: Department of Labor, Division of Labor Market and Demographic Research, CN 057, Trenton, NJ 08625-0057. TEL 609-292-2145. Ed. Jan J Dejong. Circ: 1,300.

330.9 USA
EMPLOYMENT AND THE ECONOMY. SOUTHERN NEW JERSEY REGION. Text in English. 1969. q. free. **Document type:** *Newsletter, Government.* **Description:** Describes current labor market and economic conditions in Burlington, Camden, Cumberland, Glouster, Mercer and Salem counties.
Published by: Department of Labor, Division of Labor Market and Demographic Research, CN 057, Trenton, NJ 08625-0057. TEL 609-292-2145. Ed. Jan J Dejong. Circ: 1,300.

331 USA
EMPLOYMENT COST INDEXES AND LEVELS. Text in English. 1975. irreg. price varies. **Document type:** *Government.* **Description:** Analyzes employee compensation, using the Employment Cost Index and Employer Costs Employee Compensation data.
Related titles: ◆ Series of: U.S. Bureau of Labor Statistics. Bulletin. ISSN 0082-9021.
Published by: U.S. Department of Labor, Bureau of Labor Statistics, Postal Square Bldg., 2 Massachusetts Ave, NE, Washington, DC 20212-0001 . TEL 202-691-5200, http://www.bls.gov. **Subscr. to:** U.S. Government Printing Office, Superintendent of Documents.

EMPLOYMENT IN EUROPE. see *BUSINESS AND ECONOMICS—Labor And Industrial Relations*

EMPLOYMENT OPPORTUNITIES (WASHINGTON). see *OCCUPATIONS AND CAREERS*

EMPLOYMENT OUTLOOK SURVEY. see *BUSINESS AND ECONOMICS—Labor And Industrial Relations*

330.9 USA ISSN 0364-491X
THE EMPLOYMENT SITUATION. Text in English. m. reprint service avail. from CIS. **Document type:** *Government.*
Related titles: Microfiche ed.: (from CIS); ◆ Series of: U.S. Bureau of Labor Statistics. National Office News Releases.
Indexed: AmStI.
Published by: U.S. Department of Labor, Bureau of Labor Statistics, Postal Square Bldg., 2 Massachusetts Ave, NE, Washington, DC 20212-0001 . TEL 202-691-5200, FAX 202-691-6325, http://www.bls.gov. Circ: 4,000. **Subscr. to:** U.S. Government Printing Office, Superintendent of Documents.

330.9 GRC ISSN 1106-658X
EMPORIKE TRAPEZA TES ELLADOS. OIKONOMIKO DELTIO/COMMERCIAL BANK OF GREECE. ECONOMIC BULLETIN. Text in English, Greek. 1994. bi-m. free. stat.; charts. **Document type:** *Bulletin.*
Formed by the merger of (1954-1994): Emporike Trapeza tes Ellados. Oikonomiko Deltio (Greek Edition) (1105-218X); (1944-1994): Commercial Bank of Greece. Economic Bulletin (English Edition) (0013-0036)
Indexed: ELLIS, KES, PAIS, PROMT.
Published by: (Economic Research Department), Commercial Bank of Greece, Sofokleous 11, Athens, 105 56, Greece. Ed. G Valais. Circ: 3,000.

330.9 ESP ISSN 1138-9702
EMPRENDEDORES. Text in Spanish. 1997. m. EUR 25 domestic; EUR 2.60 newsstand/cover; EUR 58.56 in Europe; EUR 62.16 elsewhere (effective 2005). adv. back issues avail. **Document type:** *Magazine, Consumer.*
Related titles: Online - full text ed.
Published by: Hachette Filipacchi SA, Avda Cardenal Herrera Oria 3, Madrid, 28034, Spain. TEL 34-91-7287000, FAX 34-91-3585473, emprendedores@hachette.es, comunicacion@hachette.es, http://www.emprendedoresrevista.com/, http://www.hachette.es. Ed. Javier Inaraja. Adv. contact Coral Garelly. color page EUR 5,900; 228 x 297. Circ: 72,454.

ENERGY ECONOMIST; an international analysis. see *ENERGY*

363.6 333.7 GBR ISSN 0958-1324
ENERGY INFORMATION CENTRE NEWS. Short title: Centre News. Text in English. 1976. bi-m. GBP 90 (effective 2001). adv. stat.; mkt. 30 p./no.; back issues avail. **Description:** Provides informed, independent commentary about the utility markets and environmental trends and developments.
Former titles (until vol. 6, no. 1, 1997): Executive Energy and Environment (0967-5027); (until 1992): Energy for Industry and Commerce
—CISTI.
Published by: Energy Information Centre, Rosemary House, Lanwades Business Park, Kennett, Newmarket, CB8 7PW, United Kingdom. TEL 44-01638-751400, FAX 44-01638-751801, info@eic.co.uk, http://www.eic.co.uk. Adv. contact Rachel Wilbourn. Circ: 800 (paid); 1,200 (controlled).

330.9861 COL ISSN 0121-117X
ENSAYOS DE ECONOMIA. Text in Spanish. 1989. s-a. COP 12,000; USD 60 foreign. **Description:** Publishes articles about Colombian economic affairs.
Published by: (Departamento de Economia), Universidad Nacional de Colombia, Facultad de Ciencias Humanas, Apartado Aereo 3840, Medellin, ANT, Colombia. Ed. Ramiro Restrepo Uribe.

330.9 LUX ISSN 1680-0516
ENTERPRISE EUROPE. Text in English. q.
Formerly (until 2000): Euro Info (1681-9535)
Related titles: Online - full text ed.
—BLDSC (3776.621350).
Published by: European Commission, Office for Official Publications of the European Union, 2 Rue Mercier, Luxembourg, L-2985, Luxembourg. FAX 352-2929-1. Ed. Robert Verrue.

330.9 DEU ISSN 0177-9303
KK2050.5
ENTSCHEIDUNGEN ZUM WIRTSCHAFTSRECHT - E W I R. Text in German. 1980. s-m. adv. bk.rev.
Formerly (until 1985): Zeitschrift fuer Wirtschaftsrecht - Z I P
—IE, Infotrieve.
Published by: Verlag Kommunikationsforum GmbH Recht Wirtschaft Steuern, Aachener Str 217, Cologne, 50931, Germany. TEL 0221-40088-0. Ed. Bruno M Kuebler.

354 USA
EQUALITY STATE ALMANAC. Text in English. a. free. charts; stat. **Document type:** *Government.* **Description:** Compiles detailed demographic, economic, and physical information for each county in Wyoming.
Formerly: Wyoming Data Handbook
Indexed: SRI.
Published by: Department of Administration and Information, Economic Analysis Division, 327 E Emerson Bldg, Cheyenne, WY 82002. TEL 307-777-7504. Circ: 1,300.

330.9 331 DNK ISSN 1603-7618
▼ **ERHVERVNORD**; profilavis. Variant title: Erhverv Nord. Text in Danish. 2003. 5/yr. adv. **Document type:** *Newsletter, Trade.* **Description:** Regional business newsletter for Northern Jutland, Denmark.
Address: Kloevermarksvej 4, Hjoerring, 9800, Denmark. ctryk@mail.dk, http://www.erhvervnord.dk. Ed. Lars Joergensen. Circ: 13,400 (controlled and free).

330.9 CHE
ERWERBSTAETIGER- UND BESCHAEFTIGUNGSSTATISTIK/ STATISTIQUE DE LA POPULATION ACTIVE OCCUPEE ET STATISTIQUE DE L'EMPLOI. Text in French, German. 1986. q. CHF 25 (effective 2001). **Document type:** *Government.*
Former titles (until 2000): Beschaeftigungsstatistik; (until 1995): Beschaeftigungs- und Erwerbstaetigenstatistik
Published by: Bundesamt fuer Statistik, Espace de l'Europe 10, Neuchatel, 2010, Switzerland. TEL 41-32-7136011, FAX 41-32-7136012, information@bfs.admin.ch, http://www.admin.ch/bfs.

330.9 300 SDN
ESSAYS ON THE ECONOMY AND SOCIETY OF THE SUDAN. Text in English. 1977. irreg., latest vol.2, 1986. bibl.
Published by: National Council for Research, Economic and Social Research Council, P O Box 1166, Khartoum, Sudan. TEL 78805. Ed. Ali Mohamed El Hassan.

330.9 ITA ISSN 0046-256X
EST - OVEST. Text in English, French, Italian; Summaries in English. 1970. 6/yr. EUR 100 domestic; EUR 125 foreign (effective 2003). adv. bk.rev. stat. index. **Document type:** *Academic/Scholarly.* **Description:** Deals with socio-economic and political-institutional aspects of Central and Eastern European countries, with particular reference to the Danubian-Balkan area and the enlargement of the European Community.
Indexed: ABCPolSci, AmH&L, HistAb, ILD, IPSA, IndIslam, PAIS, PSA.
Published by: I S D E E - Istituto di Studi e Documentazione sull'Europa Comunitaria e l'Europa Orientale, Corso Italia 27, Trieste, 34122, Italy. TEL 39-040-639130, FAX 39-040-634248, isdee@spin.it, http://www.isdee.it. Ed., R&P Tito Favaretto. Adv. contact Miro Bisiach. Circ: 400.

ESTADISTICA PANAMENA. INDICADORES ECONOMICOS. SECCION 011. see *BUSINESS AND ECONOMICS—Abstracting, Bibliographies, Statistics*

ESTADISTICA PANAMENA. SITUACION DEMOGRAFICA. SECCION 231. MOVIMIENTO INTERNACIONAL DE PASAJEROS. see *POPULATION STUDIES—Abstracting, Bibliographies, Statistics*

ESTADISTICA PANAMENA. SITUACION ECONOMICA. SECCION 314, 323, 324, 325, 353. INDUSTRIA. see *BUSINESS AND ECONOMICS—Abstracting, Bibliographies, Statistics*

ESTADISTICA PANAMENA. SITUACION ECONOMICA. SECCION 321. INDUSTRIA MANUFACTURERA. see *BUSINESS AND ECONOMICS—Abstracting, Bibliographies, Statistics*

ESTADISTICA PANAMENA. SITUACION ECONOMICA. SECCION 331. COMERCIO. ANUARIO DE COMERCIO EXTERIOR. see *BUSINESS AND ECONOMICS—Abstracting, Bibliographies, Statistics*

ESTADISTICA PANAMENA. SITUACION ECONOMICA. SECCION 342. CUENTAS NACIONALES. see *BUSINESS AND ECONOMICS—Abstracting, Bibliographies, Statistics*

ESTADISTICA PANAMENA. SITUACION ECONOMICA. SECCION 343. HACIENDA PUBLICA. see *BUSINESS AND ECONOMICS—Abstracting, Bibliographies, Statistics*

ESTADISTICA PANAMENA. SITUACION ECONOMICA. SECCION 344. FINANZAS. see *BUSINESS AND ECONOMICS—Abstracting, Bibliographies, Statistics*

ESTADISTICA PANAMENA. SITUACION ECONOMICA. SECCION 351. INDICE DE PRECIOS AL POR MAYOR Y AL CONSUMIDOR. see *BUSINESS AND ECONOMICS—Abstracting, Bibliographies, Statistics*

ESTRATEGICA SOBRE NUEVO LEON EN UNA EPOCA DE CAMBIO. see *TECHNOLOGY: COMPREHENSIVE WORKS*

338.9 CHL ISSN 0257-2176
HC161
ESTUDIO ECONOMICO DE AMERICA LATINA Y EL CARIBE. Text in Spanish. 1948. a. USD 50. stat. index. back issues avail. **Document type:** *Academic/Scholarly.*
Formerly (until 1981): Estudio Economico de America Latina (0252-2217)
Related titles: CD-ROM ed.: ISSN 1811-4970. 2001; Microfiche ed.: (from CIS); Online - full text ed.: ISSN 1681-0392. 2000; ♦ English ed.: Economic Survey of Latin America and the Caribbean. ISSN 0257-2184.
Indexed: IIS.
—CISTI.
Published by: Comision Economica para America Latina y el Caribe/Economic Commission for Latin America and the Caribbean, Ave Dag Hammarskjold 3477, Vitacura, Santiago de Chile, Chile. TEL 56-2-471-2000, FAX 56-2-208-0252, publications@eclac.cl, http://www.eclac.cl. **Subscr. to:** United Nations Publications, Distribution and Sales Section, Palais des Nations, Rm C-116, 8-14 av de la Paix, Geneva 1211, Switzerland; United Nations Publications, Rm DC2-853, United Nations Bldg, 2 United Nations Plaza, New York, NY 10017. TEL 205-995-1567, FAX 205-995-1588.

330.9 MEX ISSN 0185-5271
ESTUDIOS DE CASO. SERIE ESTADOS UNIDOS. Text in Spanish. 1984. irreg. **Document type:** *Monographic series, Academic/Scholarly.*
Indexed: AnthLit.
Published by: Centro de Investigacion y Docencia Economicas, Carretera Mexico-Toluca Km. 16.5, Apdo. Postal 116-114, Mexico City, DF 01130, Mexico. TEL 52-5-7279885, FAX 52-5-7279875, http://www.cide.mx.

330.9 ESP ISSN 1133-3197
ESTUDIOS DE ECONOMIA APLICADA. Text in Spanish. 1993. 3/yr.
Indexed: JEL.
—CINDOC.
Published by: Asociacion de Economia Aplicadad, C. Juan Ramon Jimenez, 43, Madrid, 28036, Spain. presidente@aspelt.org, http://www.asepelt.org/. Ed. Bernardo Pena Trapero.

330.9 ESP ISSN 0214-2236
ESTUDIOS DE HISTORIA SOCIAL Y ECONOMICA DE AMERICA. Text in Spanish. 1985. a.
Indexed: PCI.
—CINDOC.
Published by: Universidad de Alcala de Henares, Area de Historia de America, Plaza de San Diego, s-n, Alcala de Henares, Madrid, 28801, Spain. TEL 34-94-8554066, FAX 34-91-8854580, http://www2.alcala.es/historia2/revista.htm. Ed. Manuel Casado Arbonies.

330.9 ESP ISSN 1578-4479
ESTUDIOS ECONOMICOS DE DESARROLLO INTERNATIONAL. Text in Spanish. 2001. s-a. EUR 15 per issue (effective 2005). **Document type:** *Journal, Academic/Scholarly.* **Description:** Aims to foster international cooperation between Europe and America for improving the economic development of Latin American countries and other areas.
Related titles: Online - full text ed.: EUR 15 to individuals; EUR 30 to institutions (effective 2005).
Indexed: JEL.
Published by: Asociacion Euro-Americana de Estudios del Desarrollo Economico/Euro-American Association of Economic Development Studies, Ave. Burgo Nacionales s/n, Santiago de Compostela, 15704, Spain. TEL 34-981-563100, FAX 34-981-563676, http://www.usc.es/econometi/eedi.htm, http://www.usc.es/~economet/eaa.htm. Ed. Maria-Carmen Guisan.

330.9 ESP ISSN 1578-4460
ESTUDIOS ECONOMICOS REGIONALES Y SECTORIALES/ REGIONAL AND SECTORAL ECONOMIC STUDIES. Text in Spanish. 2001. s-a. EUR 15 per issue (effective 2005). **Document type:** *Journal, Academic/Scholarly.*
Related titles: Online - full text ed.: EUR 15 to individuals; EUR 30 to institutions (effective 2005).
Indexed: JEL.
Published by: Asociacion Euro-Americana de Estudios del Desarrollo Economico/Euro-American Association of Economic Development Studies, Ave. Burgo Nacionales s/n, Santiago de Compostela, 15704, Spain. TEL 34-981-563100, FAX 34-981-563676, http://www.usc.es/economet/eers.htm, http://www.usc.es/~economet/eaa.htm. Ed. Maria-Carmen Guisan.

330.9 COL ISSN 0120-0747
ESTUDIOS RURALES LATINOAMERICANOS/LATIN AMERICAN RURAL STUDIES. Text in Spanish. 1978. 3/yr. adv. bk.rev. index. back issues avail. **Document type:** *Academic/Scholarly.*
Related titles: Online - full text ed.
Indexed: CTFA, HAPI, IBR, ILD, RDA.
Published by: Fundacion Estudios Rurales Latinoamericanos, Apartado Aereo 11386, Bogota, CUND, Colombia. TEL 57-1-2837771. Circ: 2,000.

330.9 ESP ISSN 0214-1590
HC387.B16 CODEN: MIITEJ
ESTUDIS D'HISTORIA ECONOMICA. Text in Spanish. 1987. s-a.
—CINDOC.
Published by: Prensa Universitaria, Apdo de Correso 5100, Mallorca, 07080, Spain. TEL 34-91-905915, prensa_univeristaria@yahoo.es.

EURAZJA. see *POLITICAL SCIENCE—International Relations*

330.9489 DNK ISSN 0906-6039
EURO - POSTEN; Danmarks EU-avis. Text in Danish. 1986. d. adv. **Document type:** *Newspaper.*
Formerly (until 1991): Erhvervs - Posten (0904-1486)
Published by: E P Erhverv, Media Huset ApS, Jyllingevej 57, PO Box 1670, Vanlose, 2720, Denmark. TEL 45-38-79-34-00, FAX 45-38-79-34-10. Ed. Ib Helge. Adv. contact Ib Rasch. B&W page DKK 34,460, color page DKK 42,100; trim 265 x 360. Circ: 25,100.

330.94 ITA
EUROMEDIA. Text in Italian. 1997. d. **Document type:** *Newspaper.* **Description:** Covers business and economic events in Europe and Southern Italy.
Published by: (Agenzia di Stampa Quotidiana e di Servizi per la Comunicazione), Mare s.r.l. Editrice, Centro Direzionale Is. X G1, Naples, NA 80143, Italy. TEL 39-81-205948, FAX 39-81-5536574, pisanti@tin.it. Ed. Amedeo Pisanti.

330.9 DEU ISSN 0931-5233
EUROPAEISCHE GEGENWART. Text in English, German. 1980. bi-m. USD 5. **Document type:** *Bulletin.*
Published by: Verlag fuer Wirtschaftliche Informationen, Malvenweg 4, Cologne, 51061, Germany. TEL 49-221-963564-0, FAX 49-221-96356427. Circ: 10,000.

EUROPAEISCHE RUNDSCHAU. see *POLITICAL SCIENCE—International Relations*

▼ **EUROPE INFORMATION SOCIAL (ED. FRANCAISE).** see *POLITICAL SCIENCE—International Relations*

EUROPE INFORMATION SOCIAL (ENGLISH EDITION). see *POLITICAL SCIENCE—International Relations*

320 GBR ISSN 0269-3852
HC240
EUROPE REVIEW. Text in English. 1985. a. USD 50, USD 75 per issue (effective 2005). adv. illus.; stat.; maps. back issues avail. **Document type:** *Journal, Trade.* **Description:** An analytical, interpretative overview of events, trends & developments in every European state and territory. For an academic, business & governmental audience.
Related titles: CD-ROM ed.; Online - full text ed.
Published by: World of Information, 2 Market St, Saffron Walden, Essex CB10 1HZ, United Kingdom. TEL 44-1799-521150, FAX 44-1799-524805, info@worldinformation.com, http://worldofinformation.safeshopper.com/4/cat4.htm?547, http://www.worldinformation.com. Ed., Pub., R&P Anthony Axon. adv.: B&W page GBP 2,950, color page GBP 2,950; trim 210 x 217. Circ: 7,000 (paid). **Subscr. in USA:** PO Box 830840, Birmingham, AL 35283-0430. TEL 800-633-4931, FAX 205-995-1588, heather@exchange.ebsco.com.

338 LUX ISSN 0379-0991
HC241.2
EUROPEAN ECONOMY. (Supplements avail.) Text in English. 1978. q. USD 125. reprint service avail. from SCH. **Description:** Contains annual economic reports, communications from the Commission to the Council and the Parliament on significant economic developments and borrowing and lending activities of the Community.
Formed by the merger of: Graphs and Notes on the Economic Situation in the Community (0017-3487); Economic Situation in the Community (0013-0346)
Related titles: Supplement(s): European Economy. Special Report. ISSN 1684-033X. 2002.
Indexed: ECI, IIS, M&MA, PAIS, PROMT, WAE&RSA.
—BLDSC (3829.697330), CISTI, IE, Infotrieve, ingenta.

B

Published by: European Commission, Office for Official Publications of the European Union, 2 Rue Mercier, Luxembourg, L-2985, Luxembourg. **Dist. in the U.S. by:** Unipub, 4611-F Assembly Drive, Lanham, MD 20706-4391. TEL 301-459-0056, 800-274-4888.

338   LUX
EUROPEAN ECONOMY. SERIES A: RECENT ECONOMIC TRENDS. Text in English. 1979. m. USD 65. stat.
Formerly: European Economy. Supplement A: Recent Economic Trends (0379-2056)
Related titles: Microfiche ed.: (from CIS); Online - full text ed.
Indexed: IIS, WBA.
—BLDSC (3829.697400), CISTI, IE, ingenta.
Published by: (European Commission BEL), European Commission, Office for Official Publications of the European Union, 2 Rue Mercier, Luxembourg, L-2985, Luxembourg. **Dist. in U.S. by:** Bernan Associates, Bernan, 4611-F Assembly Dr., Lanham, MD 20706-4391. TEL 301-459-0056, 800-274-4447.

338   LUX
EUROPEAN ECONOMY. SERIES B: BUSINESS AND CONSUMER SURVEY RESULTS. Text in English. m. USD 65. stat.
Formed by the merger of: European Economy. Supplement B: Economic Prospects - Business Survey Results (0379-2110); European Economy. Supplement C: Economic Prospects - Consumer Survey Results (0379-217X)
Related titles: Microfiche ed.: (from CIS); Online - full text ed.; French ed.; German ed; Italian ed.
Indexed: IIS.
—BLDSC (3829.697500), CISTI.
Published by: (European Commission BEL), European Commission, Office for Official Publications of the European Union, 2 Rue Mercier, Luxembourg, L-2985, Luxembourg. **Dist. in U.S. by:** Bernan Associates, Bernan, 4611-F Assembly Dr., Lanham, MD 20706-4391. TEL 301-459-0056, 800-274-4447.

EUROPEAN INTEGRATION ONLINE PAPERS. see *POLITICAL SCIENCE—International Relations*

338   BEL   ISSN 0030-3593
EUROPEAN INTELLIGENCE; a review of the European business economy: fortnightly report on company initiatives E E C (mergers, affiliations etc.) plus community news and articles. Text in English. 1964. m. (11/yr.). EUR 555 (effective 2000).
Document type: *Bulletin, Trade.* **Description:** Presents updates on the completion of the Single Market.
Formerly (until 1969): Opera Mundi-Europe
Related titles: Online - full text ed.; French ed.: Europe Entreprises. ISSN 1021-4194. 1993.
Published by: Europe Information Service SA, Av Adolphe Lacomble 66-68, Brussels, 1030, Belgium. TEL 32-2-737-7709, FAX 32-2-732-6757, eis@eis.be, http://www.eis.be. Ed. R P Eliot. Pub. Eric Damiens.

382 338   USA   ISSN 1364-2758
HC241.2
EUROPEAN POLICY ANALYST. Text in English. 1964. q. USD 655 print or online; USD 380 per issue print or online (effective 2004).
Formerly (until 1996): European Trends (0014-3162)
Related titles: Online - full text ed.: (from EBSCO Publishing).
Indexed: ABIn, PAIS.
—BLDSC (3829.788050), IE, Infotrieve, ingenta. **CCC.**
Published by: Economist Intelligence Unit, 111 W 57th St, New York, NY 10019. TEL 212-554-0600, FAX 212-586-1181, newyork@eiu.com, http://www.eiu.com.

382 338   BEL
THE EUROPEAN POLICY CENTRE. ANNUAL REPORT. Text in English. a.
Published by: The European Policy Centre, Residence Palace, 155 Rue de la Loi, Brussels, 1040, Belgium. TEL 32-2-2310340, FAX 32-2-2310704, http://www.theepc.be.

382 338   BEL
THE EUROPEAN POLICY CENTRE. CONFERENCE REPORTS. Text in English. irreg.
Published by: The European Policy Centre, Residence Palace, 155 Rue de la Loi, Brussels, 1040, Belgium. TEL 32-2-2310340, FAX 32-2-2310704, http://www.theepc.be.

382 338   BEL
THE EUROPEAN POLICY CENTRE. NEWSLETTER. Text in English. bi-m.
Related titles: Online - full text ed.
Published by: The European Policy Centre, Residence Palace, 155 Rue de la Loi, Brussels, 1040, Belgium. TEL 32-2-2310340, FAX 32-2-2310704, http://www.theepc.be.

382 338   BEL
THE EUROPEAN POLICY CENTRE. OCCASIONAL PAPERS. Text in English. irreg.
Published by: The European Policy Centre, Residence Palace, 155 Rue de la Loi, Brussels, 1040, Belgium. TEL 32-2-2310340, FAX 32-2-2310704, http://www.theepc.be.

382 338   BEL
THE EUROPEAN POLICY CENTRE. POSITION PAPERS. Text in English. irreg.
Published by: The European Policy Centre, Residence Palace, 155 Rue de la Loi, Brussels, 1040, Belgium. TEL 32-2-2310340, FAX 32-2-2310704, http://www.theepc.be.

330.9   DEU   ISSN 0961-2998
EUROPEAN REGIONAL INCENTIVES. Text in English. 1980. a. 472 p./no.; **Document type:** *Directory, Trade.* **Description:** Provides a comprehensive review of the main regional incentives in each of the European Union countries and Norway.
—BLDSC (3829.857000).
Published by: (University of Strathclyde GBR), K.G. Saur Verlag GmbH (Subsidiary of: Gale Group), Ortlerstr 8, Munchen, 81373, Germany. TEL 49-89-769020, FAX 49-89-76902150, info@saur.de, http://www.saur.de. Circ: 500.

330.9   GBR   ISSN 0969-4595
HC240
EUROPEAN REGIONAL PROSPECTS (ABRIDGED EDITION). (Base vol. full report also avail.) Text in English. 1991. a. GBP 80. **Document type:** *Academic/Scholarly.*
—BLDSC (3829.890000), IE, ingenta.
Published by: (European Economic Research Consortium (ERECO)), Cambridge Econometrics Ltd., 13-15 Covent Garden, Cambridge, Cambs CB1 2HS, United Kingdom. TEL 44-1223-460760, FAX 44-1223-464378, info@camecon.com, http://www.camecon.demon.co.uk/europros.htm. Ed. Richard Lewney. Circ: 135 (paid).

338   LUX   ISSN 1025-4005
HC241.2   CODEN: BEUCBC
EUROPEAN UNION. BULLETIN. Text in English. 1958. 11/yr. USD 210. charts; tr.lit. index. **Document type:** *Bulletin.* **Description:** Covers main events, developments in community policies, external relations, financing of community activities, European political cooperation, relations between the community's institutions, and activities of the institutions.
Former titles (until 1993): European Communities. Bulletin (0378-3693); (until 1968): European Economic Community. Bulletin (0531-3430); Which incorporated (1979-1981): Euroforum (Brussels); Industry and Society (0304-1646); Weekly Industry Research and Technology
Related titles: Microfiche ed.: (from CIS); Online - full content ed.; French ed.: Union Europeenee. Bulletin. ISSN 1023-4357; Finnish ed.: Euroopan Unionin Tiedote. ISSN 1025-0441; Portuguese ed.: Uniao Europeia. Boletim. ISSN 1606-2191; Italian ed.: Unione Europea. Bollettino. ISSN 1605-7783; German ed.: Europaischen Union. Bulletin. ISSN 1606-2205; Spanish ed.: Union Europea. Boletin. ISSN 1606-2213; Danish ed.: Europaeiske Unie. Bulletin. ISSN 1606-2221; Dutch ed.: Europese Unie. Bulletin. ISSN 1606-223X; Greek ed.: Europaikes Enoses. Deltio. ISSN 1606-2248; Swedish ed.: Europeiska Unionens. Bulletin. ISSN 1025-045X; ♦ Supplement(s): European Union. Bulletin. Supplement. ISSN 1027-6424.
Indexed: CBNB, ECI, IIS, M&MA, MEA&I, P&BA, PAIS, RASB, RRTA, TriticAb, WAE&RSA.
—BLDSC (2853.694900), CISTI.
Published by: (European Commission BEL), European Commission, Office for Official Publications of the European Union, 2 Rue Mercier, Luxembourg, L-2985, Luxembourg. http://europa.eu.int/abc/doc/off/bull/en/welcome.htm. **Dist. in the U.S. by:** Bernan Associates, Bernan, 4611-F Assembly Dr., Lanham, MD 20706-4391. TEL 301-459-0056, 800-274-4447.

338   LUX   ISSN 1027-6424
EUROPEAN UNION. BULLETIN. SUPPLEMENT. Text in English.
Formerly (until 1993): European Communities. Bulletin. Supplement (1016-8702)
Related titles: ♦ Supplement to: European Union. Bulletin. ISSN 1025-4005.
Indexed: PAIS.
Published by: European Commission, Office for Official Publications of the European Union, 2 Rue Mercier, Luxembourg, L-2985, Luxembourg. TEL 352-43031, FAX 352-43032500.

THE EUROPEAN UNION REVIEW. see *POLITICAL SCIENCE—International Relations*

EUROSTAT STATISTICS IN FOCUS. ECONOMY AND FINANCE. see *BUSINESS AND ECONOMICS—Abstracting, Bibliographies, Statistics*

EUROSTAT STATISTICS IN FOCUS. INDUSTRY, TRADE AND SERVICES. see *BUSINESS AND ECONOMICS—Abstracting, Bibliographies, Statistics*

EUROSTAT STATISTICS IN FOCUS. POPULATION AND SOCIAL CONDITIONS. see *BUSINESS AND ECONOMICS—Abstracting, Bibliographies, Statistics*

EUROSTAT STATISTIK KURZ GEFASST. BEVOELKERUNG UND SOZIALE BEDINGUNGEN. see *BUSINESS AND ECONOMICS—Abstracting, Bibliographies, Statistics*

EUROSTAT STATISTIK KURZ GEFASST. INDUSTRIE, HANDEL UND DIENSTLEISTUNGEN. see *BUSINESS AND ECONOMICS—Abstracting, Bibliographies, Statistics*

EUROSTAT STATISTIK KURZ GEFASST. WIRTSCHAFT UND FINANZEN. see *BUSINESS AND ECONOMICS—Abstracting, Bibliographies, Statistics*

EUROSTAT STATISTIQUES EN BREF. ECONOMIE ET FINANCES. see *BUSINESS AND ECONOMICS—Abstracting, Bibliographies, Statistics*

EUROSTAT STATISTIQUES EN BREF. INDUSTRIE, COMMERCE ET SERVICES. see *BUSINESS AND ECONOMICS—Abstracting, Bibliographies, Statistics*

EUROSTAT STATISTIQUES EN BREF. POPULATION ET CONDITIONS SOCIALES. see *BUSINESS AND ECONOMICS—Abstracting, Bibliographies, Statistics*

330.9   USA   ISSN 1528-0160
THE EVERETT BUSINESS JOURNAL. Text in English. 1998. m. USD 20 (effective 2003). **Document type:** *Journal, Trade.* **Description:** Contains the latest business news, trends and leader profiles within the greater Everett area.
Related titles: Online - full text ed.: (from Gale Group).
Published by: The Everett Business Journal, 8213 State Ave., # A, Marysville, WA 98270-3405. ebjedit@businessjournal.org, http://www.businessjournal.org/ebj/. Ed. Myke Folger. Adv. contact Dawn Joao.

330   MEX   ISSN 0014-3960
HC131
EXAMEN DE LA SITUACION ECONOMICA DE MEXICO. Text in English, Spanish. 1925. m. free. charts; illus.; stat. index, cum.index: 1925-1969, 1970-1979, 1980-1993, 1994-1997.
Description: Examines economic conditions affecting Mexico. Includes information on all aspects of the economy, from the gold market and cattle industry, to public-sector enterprise and the commercial banking system.
Related titles: English ed.: Review of the Economic Situation of Mexico. ISSN 0187-3407.
Indexed: ILD, KES, PROMT.
Published by: Banco Nacional de Mexico S.A., Department of Economic Research, VENUSTIANO CARRANZA 64,Mezz, Col Centro, Mexico City, DF 06000, Mexico. TEL 525-2256633, FAX 525-2255111, oavila@banamex.com, http:// www.banamex.com. Ed. Alberto Gomez. Circ: 13,500 (controlled).

330.9   KEN   ISSN 0251-0332
EXECUTIVE; Kenya's premier business journal. Text in English. 1980. m. KES 2,000 domestic; USD 84 in Europe; USD 92 in the Middle East; USD 102 in Australasia (effective 2000). adv.
Document type: *Trade.* **Description:** Directed to decision makers.
Published by: Space Sellers Ltd., Chepkerio Rd., PO Box 47186, Nairobi, Kenya. TEL 254-2-555811, FAX 254-2-557815. Ed. Parselelo Kantai. Pub., R&P Sylvia King TEL 254-2-530598. Adv. contact Carole Argwins-Kodhek. Circ: 8,000.

330.9   GBR
EXECUTIVE NORTH EAST. Text in English. 1973. s-m. GBP 12. adv. bk.rev. back issues avail.
Published by: Executive North East Magazine, 30 Queen St, Redcar, Cleveland TS10 1BD, United Kingdom. TEL 0642-477155, FAX 0642-477143. Ed. John Malkin. Circ: 10,000 (controlled).

EXPANSION. see *BUSINESS AND ECONOMICS*

EXPANSION EN CD-ROM. see *BUSINESS AND ECONOMICS*

330.9   GRC
EXPRESS; daily financial newspaper. Text in Greek; Summaries in English. 1962. d. USD 450 in United States. adv. bk.rev.; film rev.; music rev.; play rev.; software rev.; tel.rev. charts; illus.; mkt.; stat. back issues avail. **Document type:** *Newspaper.* **Description:** A financial, political, and professional publication providing detailed information, analysis, and in-depth feature articles on all aspects of the Greek and world economies. The audience is comprised of executives, managers, and owners of all types of enterprises.
Related titles: Online - full text ed.
Published by: Hellenews Ltd., 39 Amaroussiou-Halandriou Rd., Maroussi, Athens, Greece. TEL 30-1-6899400, FAX 30-1-6899430, http://www.kapatel.gr/express. Ed. Dimitris Christou. Pub. D G Kalofolias N S Galeos. Adv. contact Elias Maniatis. B&W page GRD 2,200,000. Circ: 27,500 (paid).

EXTERNAL TRADE STATISTICS OF GHANA (ANNUAL). see *BUSINESS AND ECONOMICS—Abstracting, Bibliographies, Statistics*

EXTERNAL TRADE STATISTICS OF GHANA (HALF-YEARLY). see *BUSINESS AND ECONOMICS—Abstracting, Bibliographies, Statistics*

EXTERNAL TRADE STATISTICS OF GHANA (QUARTERLY). see *BUSINESS AND ECONOMICS—Abstracting, Bibliographies, Statistics*

330.9 USA ISSN 0162-3184
EXTRAORDINARY CONTRACTUAL RELIEF REPORTER. Text in English. 1973. a. USD 230. **Description:** Reports on government contracts.
Published by: Federal Publications Inc., 901 Fifteenth St, N W, Ste 200, Washington, DC 20005. TEL 202-377-7000, 800-922-4330, FAX 202-842-7565, webmaster@fedpub.com, info@fedpub.com, http://www.fedpub.com.

330.9 IRL
F A S/E S R I MANPOWER FORECASTING STUDIES. (Foras Aiseanna Saothair/Economic and Social Research Institute) Text in English. 1991. irreg., latest vol.11, 2004. price varies. charts. **Document type:** *Monographic series, Academic/Scholarly.*
Published by: Economic and Social Research Institute, 4 Burlington Rd., Dublin, 4, Ireland. TEL 353-1-6671525, FAX 353-1-6686231, admin@esri.ie, http://www.esri.ie.

330.9 USA
F C C DAILY DIGEST. (Federal Communications Commission Daily Digest) Text in English. 1994. d. free (effective 2002). back issues avail. **Document type:** *Newsletter.*
Media: Online - full text. **Related titles:** E-mail ed.
Published by: F-D-C Reports, Inc. (Subsidiary of: Elsevier Health Sciences), 5550 Friendship Blvd, Ste One, Chevy Chase, MD 20815-7278. TEL 301-657-9830, 800-332-2181, FAX 301-656-3094, http://www.fcc.gov/Daily_Releases/Daily-Digest, http://www.fdcreports.com. Ed. Karl Uhlendorf.

330.9 320.9 BRA
F G V BRAZIL FORECAST. (Fundacao Getulio Vargas) Text in English. 2001. q. USD 1,920; USD 620 per issue (effective 2002). **Description:** View from Brazil of current trends and most likely scenarios for politics, government policy and markets in the years ahead. A tool especially designed for strategic business planning and risk analysis in Brazil.
Published by: Fundacao Getulio Vargas, 190 Praia de Botafogo, Rio de Janeiro, RJ 22253-53-900, Brazil. gvpreve@fgv.br, http://www.fgv.br/editora/.

330.9 SLV
F U S A D E S CARTA INFORMATIVA. Text in Spanish. bi-m.
Published by: Fundacion Salvadorena para el Desarrollo Economico y Social, Urb. Santa Elena, Antiguo Cuscatlan, Dept. de la Libertad, C. Chaparrastique y Blvd. Santa Elena, San Salvador, El Salvador. TEL 503-78-3366, FAX 503-78-3356.

330.9 332.6 USA
F X C NEWSLETTER. Text in English. 1972. s-m. looseleaf. USD 119 (effective 2005). adv. back issues avail. **Document type:** *Newsletter, Trade.* **Description:** Provides conservative and speculative recommendations, allocated to six categories: asset play, growth, hi-tech, income, special and turnaround situations.
Formerly: F X C Report
Published by: F X C Investors Corp., 1366, Selden, NY 11784-0994. TEL 800-392-0992. Ed. Francis Xavier Curzio. Circ: 2,000 (paid).

330.9 BEL
FACTS AND FIGURES OF THE CHEMICAL INDUSTRY IN BELGIUM. Cover title: Facts & Figures. Text in English. 1928. a. free.
Supersedes in part (in 1998): Federation des Industries Chimiques de Belgique. Rapport Annuel (0085-0489)
Related titles: Online - full content ed.
Published by: Federation des Industries Chimiques de Belgique, Sq Marie Louise 49, Brussels, 1000, Belgium. TEL 32-2-2389711, FAX 32-2-2311301, http://www.fedichem.be. Ed. J M Biot.

338 USA ISSN 0898-9818
FAIRFIELD COUNTY BUSINESS JOURNAL. Text in English. 1967. w. (Mon.). USD 60 (effective 2005). adv. bk.rev. charts; illus.; mkt.; pat.; stat. 40 p./no. 4 cols./p.; back issues avail. **Document type:** *Newspaper, Trade.* **Description:** Deals with local business news and information especially economic forecasts and profiles for upper management executives, professionals, entrepreneurs and business-owners.
Former titles (until 1988): Southern Connecticut Business Journal (0894-976X); (until 198?): Connecticut Business Journal (0889-5325); (until 1985): Connecticut Business (0887-2252); (until 198?): Connecticut Business Journal (0300-7529); Southern Connecticut Business Journal (0038-3988)
Related titles: Online - full text ed.: (from EBSCO Publishing, Florida Center for Library Automation, Gale Group, Northern Light Technology, Inc., O C L C Online Computer Library Center, Inc., ProQuest Information & Learning).
Indexed: ABIn, BusDate, EngInd, T&II.
Published by: Westfair Communications, Inc., 3 Gannett Dr, White Plains, NY 10604-3407. TEL 914-694-3600, FAX 914-694-3699, mills@westfairinc.com, http://www.businessjrnls.com. Ed. Dan Strempel. Pub. Dee Delbello. R&P Bruce Spring TEL 914-694-3003. Adv. contact Barbara Hanlon. B&W page USD 2,240, color page USD 3,460. Circ: 13,000.

FAR EAST AND AUSTRALASIA (YEAR). see *POLITICAL SCIENCE*

330 HKG ISSN 0014-7591
HC411 CODEN: FEERAK
FAR EASTERN ECONOMIC REVIEW. Text in English. 1946. 10/yr. USD 100; USD 50 to students (effective 2005). adv. bk.rev. stat.; illus. q. index. reprint service avail. from SCH. **Document type:** *Magazine, Consumer.* **Description:** Reports and interprets business, finance, stock market, and political and investment trends in Asia.
Related titles: CD-ROM ed.; Microfilm ed.: (from PQC, RPI); Online - full text ed.: ISSN 1563-9339 (from O C L C Online Computer Library Center, Inc., ProQuest Information & Learning).
Indexed: ABIX, ABIn, AESIS, APEL, AcaI, BAS, BPI, BPIA, CBNB, Emerald, GdIns, HRIR, HongKongiana, ILD, IndBusRep, KES, M&MA, MEA&I, PAIS, PCI, PSI, RASB, RRTA, SPPI, SSI, WAE&RSA, WBA, WMB.
—BLDSC (3865.920000), IE, Infotrieve, ingenta. **CCC.**
Published by: Review Publishing Co. Ltd. (Subsidiary of: Dow Jones Company), GPO Box 160, Hong Kong, Hong Kong. TEL 852-25737121, FAX 852-25031530, review@feer.com, subscription@feer.com, https://www.feer.com, http://www.feer.com. Ed. Hugo Restall. adv.: B&W page USD 11,532, color page USD 15,580; trim 206 x 276. Circ: 20,000 (paid).

330.9 DEU ISSN 0343-9062
HC281
FEDERAL REPUBLIC OF GERMANY - PARTNER OF THE WORLD; documentation of economy and export. Text in German. 1966. a. USD 12. adv. **Document type:** *Bulletin.*
Published by: Verlag fuer Wirtschaftliche Informationen, Malvenweg 4, Cologne, 51061, Germany. TEL 49-221-963564-0, FAX 49-221-96356427. Circ: 20,000.

330.9 USA ISSN 0732-1813
HC107.A13 CODEN: ECRWDA
FEDERAL RESERVE BANK OF ATLANTA. ECONOMIC REVIEW. Text in English. 1915. q. free. charts; illus.; stat. index. back issues avail.; reprint service avail. from CIS. **Document type:** *Academic/Scholarly.*
Incorporates (in Mar. 1981): Caribbean Basin Economic Survey; Formerly (1975-1981): Federal Reserve Bank of Atlanta. Monthly Review (0014-9144)
Related titles: Microfiche ed.: (from CIS); Microform ed.: (from MIM, PQC); Online - full text ed.: (from bigchalk, EBSCO Publishing, Florida Center for Library Automation, Gale Group, O C L C Online Computer Library Center, Inc., ProQuest Information & Learning).
Indexed: ABIn, Agr, AmStI, BLI, BPIA, FiP, IBR, IBZ, Inspec, JEL, PAIS, PROMT, WBA.
—BLDSC (3654.928000), IE, Infotrieve, ingenta.
Published by: Federal Reserve Bank of Atlanta, 1000 Peachtree St NE, Atlanta, GA 30309-3904. TEL 404-521-8020, http://www.frbatlanta.org. Ed. Joycelyn Woolfolk. Circ: 23,000.

330.9 USA ISSN 0899-6571
FEDERAL RESERVE BANK OF ATLANTA. REGIONAL UPDATE. Text in English. 1988. q. free. reprint service avail. from CIS. **Document type:** *Newsletter.*
Related titles: Microfiche ed.: (from CIS); Online - full text ed.: (from Gale Group, H.W. Wilson).
Indexed: AmStI.
Published by: Federal Reserve Bank of Atlanta, 1000 Peachtree St NE, Atlanta, GA 30309-3904. TEL 404-521-8020, http://www.frbatlanta.org. Ed. Pierce Nelson. Circ: 6,900.

330.9 USA ISSN 0361-8714
FEDERAL RESERVE BANK OF BOSTON. CONFERENCE SERIES. Text in English. 1969. a. free ten copies or less (effective 2003). bibl.; charts; tr.lit. reprint service avail. from PQC. **Document type:** *Proceedings, Academic/Scholarly.*
Related titles: Microform ed.: (from PQC); Online - full text ed.: (from ProQuest Information & Learning).
Indexed: BLI, FiP, WBA.
—BLDSC (3409.948000), IE, ingenta.
Published by: Federal Reserve Bank of Boston, Research Department, 55882, Boston, MA 02205-5882. TEL 617-973-3397, FAX 617-973-4221, http://www.bos.frb.org/economic/conf/index.htm. Circ: 5,000.

330.9 USA ISSN 1062-1865
HC107.A11
FEDERAL RESERVE BANK OF BOSTON. REGIONAL REVIEW. Text in English. 1991. q. free (effective 2005). back issues avail. **Document type:** *Magazine, Trade.* **Description:** Contains essays on New England's economy for the general business audience.
Related titles: Online - full text ed.: (from EBSCO Publishing, Gale Group, H.W. Wilson, O C L C Online Computer Library Center, Inc., ProQuest Information & Learning).
Indexed: AmStI, BLI, BPI, PAIS.
Published by: Federal Reserve Bank of Boston, Research Department, 55882, Boston, MA 02205-5882. TEL 617-973-3397, FAX 617-973-4221, jane.katz@bos.frb.org, http://www.bos.frb.org/economic/nerr/regrev.htm. Ed. Jane Katz. Circ: 15,000.

330 USA ISSN 1552-2814
HD72 CODEN: NWEEAP
➤ **FEDERAL RESERVE BANK OF BOSTON. RESEARCH REVIEW.** Text in English. 1920. q. free. charts; illus.; stat.; abstr. index, cum.index: 1969-1984. back issues avail.; reprint service avail. from CIS,PQC. **Document type:** *Journal, Government.* **Description:** Provides an overview of recent research by economists of the Federal Reserve Bank of Boston, containing summaries of scholarly papers, staff briefings, and Bank-sponsored research conferences, together with a list of articles, books, and speeches recently published externally by Bank economists.
Supersedes in part (in 2004): New England Economic Review (0028-4726); Which was formerly (until 1969): New England Business Review (0548-4405)
Related titles: Microfiche ed.: (from CIS); Microform ed.: (from MIM, PQC); Online - full text ed.: ISSN 1552-2822 (from bigchalk, EBSCO Publishing, Florida Center for Library Automation, Gale Group, H.W. Wilson, Northern Light Technology, Inc., O C L C Online Computer Library Center, Inc., ProQuest Information & Learning).
Indexed: ABIn, ASCA, ASG, AgeL, AmStI, BLI, BPI, BPIA, CurCont, FiP, GEOBASE, IBSS, JEL, PAIS, RASB, SSCI.
—BLDSC (6083.850000), IDS, IE, ingenta.
Published by: Federal Reserve Bank of Boston, Research Library-D, 600 Atlantic Ave., Boston, MA 02210. TEL 617-973-3397, FAX 617-973-4221, boston.library@bos.frb.org, http://www.bos.frb.org/economic/ResearchReview/index.htm. Ed. Suzanne Lorant. Circ: 13,000.

B

330.9 USA ISSN 0161-2387
HC107.A17 CODEN: ERKCDK
FEDERAL RESERVE BANK OF KANSAS CITY. ECONOMIC REVIEW. Text in English. 1914. q. free. reprints avail. **Document type:** *Journal, Academic/Scholarly.*
Formerly (until 1978): Federal Reserve Bank of Kansas City. Monthly Review (0014-9152)
Related titles: Online - full text ed.: (from bigchalk, EBSCO Publishing, Gale Group, H.W. Wilson, O C L C Online Computer Library Center, Inc., ProQuest Information & Learning).
Indexed: ABIn, Agr, AmStI, AnBrAb, BLI, BPI, BPIA, CREJ, FiP, ForAb, IPARL, JEL, PAIS, PN&I, PROMT, RDA, RRTA, S&F, WAE&RSA, WBA.
—BLDSC (3654.932000), IE, ingenta.
Published by: Federal Reserve Bank of Kansas City, 925 Grand Blvd, Kansas City, MO 64198-0001. TEL 816-881-2683, FAX 816-881-2569. Ed. Craig S Hakkio. Circ: 29,000.

FEDERAL RESERVE BANK OF NEW YORK. CURRENT ISSUES IN ECONOMICS AND FINANCE. see *BUSINESS AND ECONOMICS—Banking And Finance*

330.9 USA
HC101 CODEN: FRYMAQ
FEDERAL RESERVE BANK OF NEW YORK. ECONOMIC POLICY REVIEW. Text in English. 1976. q. free. charts; stat. reprint service avail. from CIS,PQC,SCH. **Description:** Describes patterns and trends in banking, investment, and capital market activities.
Former titles (until 1995): Federal Reserve Bank of New York. Quarterly Review (0147-6580); (until 1976): Federal Reserve Bank of New York. Monthly Review (0014-9160); (until 1958): Monthly Review of Credit and Business Conditions in the Second Federal Reserve District (0361-9826)
Related titles: Microfiche ed.: (from CIS); Microform ed.: (from PQC); Online - full text ed.: (from EBSCO Publishing, Gale Group, H.W. Wilson, O C L C Online Computer Library Center, Inc., ProQuest Information & Learning, The Dialog Corporation).
Indexed: ABIn, AgeL, AmStI, BLI, BPI, BPIA, BusI, CREJ, FiP, IBSS, IFP, JEL, MEA&I, PAIS, PROMT, RASB, SPAA, SUSA, T&II, WBA.
—BLDSC (3654.094000).
Published by: Federal Reserve Bank of New York, Public Information, 33 Liberty St, New York, NY 10045-0001. TEL 212-720-6150, http://www.newyorkfed.org. Circ: 38,000.

330.9 USA
FEDERAL RESERVE BANK OF PHILADELPHIA. BANKING BRIEF. Text in English. q. stat. back issues avail. **Document type:** *Government.* **Description:** Analyzes recent banking trends, focusing on Pennsylvania, New Jersey, and Delaware. Includes comparison of financial ratios in the tr-state area to those throughout the nation.
Related titles: Online - full content ed.
Published by: Federal Reserve Bank of Philadelphia, 10 Independence Mall, Philadelphia, PA 19106. TEL 215-574-6431, http://www.phil.frb.org/econ/bb/index.html. R&P Victoria Geyfman.

330 332 USA ISSN 0007-7011
CODEN: FRBPBN
FEDERAL RESERVE BANK OF PHILADELPHIA. BUSINESS REVIEW. Key Title: Business Review (Philadelphia). Text in English. 1918. q. free. charts; illus.; stat. index, cum.index. reprint service avail. from CIS,PQC. **Document type:** *Journal.* **Description:** Presents articles written by staff economists and dealing with economic policy, financial economics and banking, and regional economic issues.

▼ new title ➤ refereed ✶ unverified ◆ full entry avail.

Related titles: Microfiche ed.: (from CIS); Microform ed.: (from MIM, PQC); Online - full text ed.: (from bigchalk, EBSCO Publishing, Florida Center for Library Automation, Gale Group, H.W. Wilson, O C L C Online Computer Library Center, Inc., ProQuest Information & Learning).
Indexed: ABIn, AmStI, BLI, BPI, BPIA, CREJ, FiP, IFP, JEL, PAIS, PROMT, WBA.
—BLDSC (2934.690000).
Published by: (Research Department), Federal Reserve Bank of Philadelphia, PO Box 66, Philadelphia, PA 19105. FAX 215-574-4364, http://www.phil.frb.org/econ/br/index.html. Ed. Sarah Burke. Circ: 10,000.

330.9 USA
FEDERAL RESERVE BANK OF PHILADELPHIA. RESEARCH DEPARTMENT. WORKING PAPERS. Text in English. irreg. **Document type:** *Monographic series.*
Formerly: Federal Reserve Bank of Philadelphia. Economic Research Division. Working Papers
Related titles: Online - full content ed.
—BLDSC (9349.850250).
Published by: (Economic Research Division), Federal Reserve Bank of Philadelphia, PO Box 66, Philadelphia, PA 19105. http://www.phil.frb.org.

B

330.9 USA ISSN 1069-7225
HC107.A13
FEDERAL RESERVE BANK OF RICHMOND. ECONOMIC QUARTERLY. Text in English. 1914. q. free. bibl.; charts; stat. back issues avail.; reprint service avail. from CIS. **Document type:** *Journal, Academic/Scholarly.* **Description:** Articles on monetary theory and policy, banking and finance.
Former titles (until 1992): Federal Reserve Bank of Richmond. Economic Review (0094-6893); (until 1974): Federal Reserve Bank of Richmond. Monthly Review (0014-9179)
Related titles: Microfiche ed.: (from CIS); Microform ed.: (from PQC); Online - full text ed.: (from bigchalk, EBSCO Publishing, Florida Center for Library Automation, Gale Group, H.W. Wilson, O C L C Online Computer Library Center, Inc., ProQuest Information & Learning).
Indexed: ABIn, AmStI, BLI, BPI, BPIA, FiP, JEL, PAIS, WBA.
—BLDSC (3654.140000), IE, ingenta.
Published by: Federal Reserve Bank of Richmond, Research Department, 701 E Byrd St, Richmond, VA 23219. TEL 804-697-8000, FAX 804-697-8287, eg@rich.frb.org, http://www.rich.frb.org. Ed. Thomas M Humphrey. R&P Elaine Mandaleris TEL 804-697-8144. Circ: 15,000. **Subscr. to:** Public Affairs, PO Box 27622, Richmond, VA 23261. TEL 804-697-8111.

330.9 USA
FEDERAL RESERVE BANK OF ST. LOUIS. ANNUAL REPORT. Text in English. a. **Document type:** *Corporate.*
Published by: (Public Affairs), Federal Reserve Bank of St. Louis, PO Box 442, St. Louis, MO 63166. TEL 314-444-8808, http://www.stls.frb.org/fred.

330.9 USA ISSN 0430-1978
HG2563
FEDERAL RESERVE BANK OF ST. LOUIS. MONETARY TRENDS. Text in English. m. free. charts; stat. **Document type:** *Newsletter.* **Description:** Reviews U.S. monetary and financial conditions, with an emphasis on alternative measures of the stance of monetary policy. Includes a short essay on a current topic on money, financial markets or a related issue.
Indexed: AmStI.
Published by: Federal Reserve Bank of St. Louis, PO Box 422, St. Louis, MO 63166. TEL 314-444-8320. Ed. William Gavin. R&P Alice Dames TEL 314-444-8593.

330.9 USA ISSN 0430-1986
HC101 CODEN: PRSQAG
FEDERAL RESERVE BANK OF ST. LOUIS. NATIONAL ECONOMIC TRENDS. Text in English. m. free. charts. **Document type:** *Newsletter.* **Description:** Data on national output, employment, inflation and selected federal budget measures along with a brief analysis of an issue of current interest.
Indexed: AmStI, BLI.
Published by: Federal Reserve Bank of St. Louis, PO Box 244, St. Louis, MO 63166. TEL 314-444-8320.

330.9 USA ISSN 0014-9187
HC107.A15 CODEN: FRBRDV
FEDERAL RESERVE BANK OF ST. LOUIS. REVIEW. Text in English. 1917. bi-m. free. charts; stat. index. reprint service avail. from CIS,PQC. **Description:** Contains articles about national and international economic developments, particularly their monetary aspects.
Formerly (until 1961): Federal Reserve Bank of St. Louis. Monthly Review (0362-3491)
Related titles: Microfiche ed.: (from CIS); Microform ed.: (from PQC); Online - full text ed.: (from EBSCO Publishing, Gale Group, H.W. Wilson, O C L C Online Computer Library Center, Inc., ProQuest Information & Learning).
Indexed: ABIn, AmStI, BLI, BPI, BPIA, CurCont, FiP, IBR, IBSS, IBZ, JEL, MagInd, PAIS, PROMT, RASB, RRTA, SSCI, WAE&RSA.
—BLDSC (7786.125000), IE, ingenta.
Published by: Federal Reserve Bank of St. Louis, PO Box 442, St. Louis, MO 63166. TEL 314-444-8320. Ed. Daniel P Brennan. Circ: 25,000.

330.9 USA
FEDERAL RESERVE BANK OF SAN FRANCISCO. ECONOMIC LETTER. Text in English. 38/yr. free domestic; USD 50 foreign (effective 2000). charts; stat. **Document type:** *Newsletter.*
Former titles: Federal Reserve Bank of San Francisco. Weekly Letter (0890-927X); Federal Reserve Bank of San Francisco. Business and Financial Letter
Related titles: Online - full text ed.: (from EBSCO Publishing).
Indexed: FiP, PROMT, WBA.
Published by: Federal Reserve Bank of San Francisco, PO Box 7702, San Francisco, CA 94120. TEL 415-974-3230, FAX 415-974-3341, http://www.frbsf.org. Ed. Judith Goff. R&P Anita Todd. Circ: 9,000.

330.9 USA ISSN 0363-0021
HC101
FEDERAL RESERVE BANK OF SAN FRANCISCO. ECONOMIC REVIEW. Text in English. 1974. a. free. charts; illus. index. reprint service avail. from CIS. **Document type:** *Journal, Academic/Scholarly.*
Former titles: Federal Reserve Bank of San Francisco. Business Review (0093-8262); Federal Reserve Bank of San Francisco. Monthly Review (0014-9195)
Related titles: Microfiche ed.: (from CIS); Online - full text ed.: (from bigchalk, EBSCO Publishing, H.W. Wilson, O C L C Online Computer Library Center, Inc., ProQuest Information & Learning).
Indexed: ABIn, AmStI, BLI, BPI, CREJ, FiP, IBR, IBZ, JEL, PAIS, PROMT, WBA.
—BLDSC (3654.940000), IE, ingenta.
Published by: Federal Reserve Bank of San Francisco, PO Box 7702, San Francisco, CA 94120. TEL 415-974-3230, FAX 415-974-3341, http://www.frbsf.org. Ed. Judith Goff. R&P Anita Todd. Circ: 8,000.

330.9 USA
FEDERAL RESERVE BASIC INSTRUCTIONS. Text in English. irreg. USD 50 in North America; USD 100 elsewhere (effective 1999). **Description:** Covers the following categories: insured commercial banks with domestic and foreign offices, domestic offices only and total assets of $300 million or more, domestic offices only and total assets between $100 and $300 million, domestic offices only with total assets of less than $100 million.
Published by: (Federal Reserve System, Board of Governors), U.S. Department of Commerce, National Technical Information Service, 5285 Port Royal Rd, Springfield, VA 22161. TEL 703-605-6000, info@ntis.gov, http://www.ntis.gov.

333 USA
FEDERAL RESERVE BOARD. BEIGE BOOK. Text in English. 8/yr. back issues avail. **Document type:** *Government.* **Description:** Summarizes economic conditions in the US via information gathered by individual Federal Reserve districts, market experts, economists, and other sources. The report is organized by Federal Reserve District.
Published by: U.S. Federal Reserve System, Board of Governors, Publications Services, Rm MP 510, Washington, DC 20551. http://www.federalreserve.gov/FOMC/BeigeBook.

330.9 USA
FEDERAL RESERVE INSTRUCTIONS. Text in English. (Merged with: Federal Reserve Forms to form: Federal Reserve Forms and Instructions). irreg. USD 50 in North America; USD 100 elsewhere (effective 1999).
Published by: (Federal Reserve System, Board of Governors), U.S. Department of Commerce, National Technical Information Service, 5285 Port Royal Rd, Springfield, VA 22161. TEL 703-605-6000, info@ntis.gov, http://www.ntis.gov.

330.9 332 USA ISSN 0190-6313
FEDERAL RESERVE SYSTEM. BOARD OF GOVERNORS. ANNUAL REPORT. Text in English. 1966. a.
Published by: Federal Reserve System, Board of Governors, Publications Services, Rm MS 127, 20th and Constitution Ave, N W, Washington, DC 20551. TEL 202-452-3244, FAX 202-728-5886.

330.9 USA
HC110.P63
FEDERAL SPENDING IN THE NORTHEAST - MIDWEST. Text in English. 1979. a. price varies. charts; illus. **Document type:** *Academic/Scholarly.* **Description:** Analyzes the flow of federal funds into the states by examining per-capita federal spending and the rate of return on federal tax dollars.
Supersedes: Guide to State and Federal Resources for Economic Development (0894-4202)
Published by: (Center for Regional Policy), Northeast - Midwest Institute, 218 D St, S E, Washington, DC 20003. TEL 202-544-5200, FAX 202-544-0043, http://www.nemw.org. Ed. Richard Munson. R&P Tim Kay.

330.9 BEL
FEDERATIE VAN DE CHEMISCHE INDUSTRIE VAN BELGIE. ACTIVITEITENVERSLAG FEDICHEM. Text in Dutch. 1928. a. free.
Supersedes in part (in 1998): Federation des Industries Chimiques de Belgique. Rapport Annuel (0085-0489)
Related titles: Online - full content ed.; ♦ French ed.: Federation des Industries Chimiques de Belgique. Rapport d'Activites.
Published by: Federation des Industries Chimiques de Belgique, Sq Marie Louise 49, Brussels, 1000, Belgium. TEL 32-2-2389711, FAX 32-2-2311301. Ed. J M Biot.

660.28 330.9 BEL
FEDERATION DES INDUSTRIES CHIMIQUES DE BELGIQUE. RAPPORT D'ACTIVITES. Text in French. 1928. a. free. **Document type:** *Corporate.* **Description:** Describes the economic situation, the results, and the perspectives of the Belgian chemical industry.
Supersedes in part (in 1998): Federation des Industries Chimiques de Belgique. Rapport Annuel (0085-0489)
Related titles: Online - full content ed.; ♦ Dutch ed.: Federatie van de Chemische Industrie van Belgie. Activiteitenverslag Fedichem.
Published by: Federation des Industries Chimiques de Belgique, Sq Marie Louise 49, Brussels, 1000, Belgium. TEL 32-2-2389711, FAX 32-2-2311301. Ed. J M Biot.

330.9 USA ISSN 1045-3334
HC107.A14
FEDGAZETTE: FEDERAL RESERVE BANK OF MINNEAPOLIS REGIONAL BUSINESS & ECONOMICS NEWSPAPER. Text in English. 1985. bi-m. free. charts; illus.; stat. 20 p./no.; reprint service avail. from CIS. **Document type:** *Newspaper, Consumer.* **Description:** Focuses on economic issues affecting the states in the Ninth Federal Reserve District. Incorporates national and district economic data. Includes opinion poll results and business news.
Incorporates (1985-1988): Federal Reserve Bank of Minneapolis. District Economic Conditions (0882-410X)
Related titles: Microfiche ed.: (from CIS); Online - full text ed.: (from bigchalk, EBSCO Publishing, O C L C Online Computer Library Center, Inc., ProQuest Information & Learning).
Indexed: ABIn, AmStI.
Published by: (Public Affairs Department), Federal Reserve Bank of Minneapolis, Public Affairs Department, PO Box 291, Minneapolis, MN 55480-0291. TEL 612-204-5255, paeditor@mpls.frb.org, http://minneapolisfed.org, http://woodrow.mpls.frb.fed.us. Ed. Ronald A. Wirtz. Circ: 18,000.

330.9 LBR
FINANCE BULLETIN. Text in English. 1979. 3/yr. USD 7.50; includes Ministry of Finance Annual Report. charts; stat.
Published by: Office of Fiscal Policy and Planning, Borad St., Monrovia, Liberia.

FINANCIAL MANAGEMENT SURVEY. see *BUSINESS AND ECONOMICS—Management*

330.9 GBR ISSN 1080-9821
HG3810
FINANCIAL TIMES CURRENCY FORECASTER★ ; consensus forecasts of the worldwide currency and economic outlook. Text in English. 1981. m. **Document type:** *Trade.* **Description:** Presents forecasts analysis for 40 major international currencies and key economic variables for the 20 largest industrialized countries.
Former titles (until 1995): Currency Forecaster's Digest; (until 1987): Blue Chip Economic WorldScan (0741-8337)
Related titles: Supplement(s): Mid-Month Global Financial Report.
Published by: Financial Times Professional Publishing (Subsidiary of: Financial Times Group), Maple House, 149 Tottenham Court Rd, London, W1P 9LL, United Kingdom. TEL 44-20-7896-2222, FAX 44-20-7896-2276. Circ: 2,000.

FINANSI NA PREDPRIATIATA. see *STATISTICS*

330.9 948.97 FIN ISSN 0430-5221
FINLAND. VALTIOVARAINMINISTERIO. ECONOMIC SURVEY. Text in English. 1950. a. **Document type:** *Government.*
Related titles: ♦ English ed.: Finland. Valtiovarainministerio. Taloudellinen Katsaus. ISSN 0071-5271; Swedish ed.: Finland. Valtiovarainministerio. Ekonomisk Oeversikt. ISSN 0430-523X. 1948.
Published by: Valtiovarainministerio, Kansantalousosasto/Ministry of Finance. Economics Department, PO Box 28, Helsinki, 00023, Finland. TEL 358-9-16001, FAX 358-9-16033123, valtiovarainministerio@vm.fi, http://www.vm.fi.

330 948.97 FIN ISSN 0071-5271
HC337.F5
FINLAND. VALTIOVARAINMINISTERIO. TALOUDELLINEN KATSAUS. Text in English, Finnish, Swedish. 1948. a. Supplement avail. **Document type:** *Government.*
Formerly (until 1955): Finland. Kansantalousosasto. Taloudellinen Tilannekatsaus (0784-7521)
Related titles: ♦ English ed.: Finland. Valtiovarainministerio. Economic Survey. ISSN 0430-5221; Swedish ed.: Finland. Valtiovarainministerio. Ekonomisk Oeversikt. ISSN 0430-523X. 1948.
Published by: Valtiovarainministerio, Kansantalousosasto/Ministry of Finance. Economics Department, PO Box 28, Helsinki, 00023, Finland. TEL 358-9-16001, FAX 358-9-16033123, valtiovarainministerio@vm.fi, http://www.vm.fi.

330.9 658.7 338 USA
FLORIDA COUNTY MIGRATION FLOWS 1981-1996. Text in English. 1994. a. looseleaf. USD 25; USD 25 foreign (effective 1999). stat. back issues avail. **Document type:** *Government.* **Description:** Presents Florida annual county migration flows (in, out and net) in tabular form.
Related titles: Diskette ed.
Published by: University of Florida, Bureau of Economic and Business Research, Warrington College of Business Administration, PO Box 117145, Gainesville, FL 32611-7145. TEL 352-392-0171, FAX 352-392-4739, jgalvez@ufl.edu, http//www:bebr.ufl.edu, http://www.bebr.ufl.edu. Ed. June Noegel. Pub. Janet Galvez. Circ: 20.

338 USA ISSN 0015-4326
HC107.F6
FLORIDA TREND; magazine of Florida business. Text in English. 1958. m. free (effective 2005). adv. illus. back issues avail.; reprint service avail. from PQC. **Document type:** *Magazine, Consumer.* **Description:** Contains articles, informational items, features, and photography on marketing, business, finance and economy in the state.
Related titles: Microform ed.: (from PQC); Online - full text ed.: (from bigchalk, Florida Center for Library Automation, Gale Group, Northern Light Technology, Inc., O C L C Online Computer Library Center, Inc., ProQuest Information & Learning, The Dialog Corporation).
Indexed: ABIn, AgeL, BusDate, PAIS, T&II.
—BLDSC (3956.172000), IE. **CCC.**
Published by: Trend Magazine, Inc., PO Box 611, St. Petersburg, FL 33731. FAX 727-822-5083, http://www.floridatrend.com. Pub. Lynda Keever. R&P Jill South TEL 813-892-2613. Adv. contact Lynn Lotkowictz TEL 727-892-2612. B&W page USD 8,210, color page USD 10,650. Circ: 50,000.

330.9 USA ISSN 0364-0655
HC110.F55
FLOW OF FUNDS ACCOUNT. Text in English. q. USD 960 in North America; USD 1,920 elsewhere (effective 1999). reprint service avail. from CIS. **Description:** Contains annual data 45-51, quarterly data 52-87 in three forms: levels outstanding at end of period, unadjusted flows, and quarterly seasonally adjusted flows.
Media: Magnetic Tape. **Related titles:** Microfiche ed.: (from CIS).
Indexed: AmStI.
Published by: (Federal Reserve System), U.S. Department of Commerce, National Technical Information Service, 5285 Port Royal Rd, Springfield, VA 22161. TEL 703-605-6000, info@ntis.gov, http://www.ntis.gov.

FOCUS AFRIKA; I A K Diskussionsbeitraege. see *POLITICAL SCIENCE*

380.102 DNK ISSN 1601-9776
HF3641
FOCUS DENMARK (ENGLISH EDITION); business and investment news. Text in English. 1961. q. free (effective 2003). back issues avail. **Document type:** *Journal, Government.*
Formerly (until 2001): Denmark Review. Business News from Denmark (0418-6745)
Related titles: Online - full text ed.; Japanese ed.: Focus Denmark (Japanese edition). ISSN 1602-7361. 2001; Chinese ed.: Focus Denmark (Chinese edition); Spanish ed.: Revista Danesa. ISSN 0107-5837.
Indexed: KES, PROMT.
—**CCC.**
Published by: Udenrigsministeriet, Danmarks Exportraad/Royal Danish Ministry of Foreign Affairs. Danish Trade Council, Asiatisk Plads 2, Copenhagen K, 1448, Denmark. TEL 45-33-920000, FAX 45-32-540533, http://www.exportraadet.dk/view.asp?ID=194. Circ: 20,000 (controlled and free).

FOLIO: FIRST DAY FINANCIAL REPORT. see *PUBLISHING AND BOOK TRADE*

330 ESP ISSN 1137-4128
HC381
FOMENTO DEL TRABAJO. HORIZONTE EMPRESARIAL. Text in Spanish. 1889. m. adv. bk.rev. bibl.; mkt.; stat. **Document type:** *Consumer.*
Former titles (until 1993): Horizonte Empresarial (0212-0607); (until 1978): Fomento del Trabajo Nacional. Economia Nacional, Internacional de la Empresa (0041-0233); (until 1970): Trabajo Nacional (0212-0593)
Indexed: ELLIS, PAIS.
Published by: Fomento del Trabajo Nacional, Via Layetana 32-34, Barcelona, 08003, Spain. TEL 34-93-484-1200, FAX 34-93-484-1230, rev@foment.com, http://www.foment.com. Circ: 4,500.

FOREIGN EXCHANGE CONSENSUS FORECASTS. see *BUSINESS AND ECONOMICS—Banking And Finance*

330.9 GBR ISSN 0305-9936
FRAMEWORK FORECAST FOR THE E E C ECONOMIES*. Variant title: Framework Forecast for the European Economic Community's Economies. Text in English. 1977. q. GBP 700. **Description:** Review of current business climates with five-year forecasts for each EEC economy.
Published by: Henley Centre for Forecasting Ltd., 9 Bridewell Pl, London, EC4Y 6AY, United Kingdom. Ed. Stephen Radley.

FRANCE. INSTITUT NATIONAL DE LA STATISTIQUE ET DES ETUDES ECONOMIQUES. CONJONCTURE IN FRANCE; a bi-annual short term economic report by INSEE. see *BUSINESS AND ECONOMICS—Abstracting, Bibliographies, Statistics*

330.9 FRA
FRANCE. MINISTERE DE L'ECONOMIE, DES FINANCES ET DE L'INDUSTRIE. NOTE TRIMESTRIELLE DE CONJONCTURE. Text in French. q. **Document type:** *Government.*
Indexed: PAIS.
Published by: Ministere de l'Economie, des Finances, et de l'Industrie, 139 rue de Bercy, Paris, Cedex 12 75572, France. TEL 33-1-53188815, http://www.finances.gouv.fr.

FRANCE. SERVICE D'ETUDE DES STRATEGIES ET DES STATISTIQUES INDUSTRIELLES. LA SITUATION DE L'INDUSTRIE: RESULTATS AGREGES. see *BUSINESS AND ECONOMICS—Abstracting, Bibliographies, Statistics*

FRANCE. SERVICE D'ETUDE DES STRATEGIES ET DES STATISTIQUES INDUSTRIELLES. LA SITUATION DE L'INDUSTRIE: RESULTATS DETAILLES. see *BUSINESS AND ECONOMICS—Abstracting, Bibliographies, Statistics*

330.9 CAN ISSN 0827-7893
FRASER FORUM. Text in English. 1985. m. CND 5.95 per issue (effective 2005). back issues avail. **Document type:** *Magazine.* **Description:** Studies market solutions for public policy problems.
Incorporates (1988-1995): On Balance (0840-612X)
Related titles: CD-ROM ed.
Indexed: AgBio, CBCARef, FPA, ForAb, PAIS, PBA, ProtozoAb, RRTA, RefZh, S&F, TDB, WAE&RSA.
—**CCC.**
Published by: Fraser Institute, 1770 Burrard St, 4th floor, Vancouver, BC V6J 3G7, Canada. TEL 604-688-0221, FAX 604-688-8539, http://www.fraserinstitute.ca. Ed. Michael A Walker. R&P Kristin McCahon. Circ: 6,000.

330.9 CHN ISSN 1000-8780
FUJIAN LUNTAN (JINGJI BAN)/FUJIAN TRIBUNE (ECONOMICS EDITION). Text in Chinese. 1981. m. USD 32.20. **Document type:** *Academic/Scholarly.*
Related titles: Online - full text ed.: (from East View Information Services).
Published by: Fujian Shehui Kexueyuan/Fujian Academy of Social Sciences, 18, Liuhe Lu, Fuzhou, 350001, China. Ed. Lin Qiping. Circ: 60,000. **Subscr. to:** China International Book Trading Corp, 35 Chegongzhuang Xilu, Haidian District, PO Box 399, Beijing 100044, China. TEL 86-10-68412045, FAX 86-10-68412023, cibtc@mail.cibtc.com.cn, http://www.cibtc.com.cn.

330.9 ARG ISSN 0537-3468
FUNDACION DE INVESTIGACIONES ECONOMICAS LATINOAMERICANAS. INDICADORES DE COYUNTURA. Text in Spanish. 1966. m. USD 340. adv. bk.rev. stat.
Indexed: PAIS.
Published by: Fundacion de Investigaciones Economicas Latinoamericanas, Esmeralda, 320 Piso 4, Capital Federal, Buenos Aires 1343, Argentina. TEL 54-114-3962387, FAX 54-114-3962727. Ed. Juan Luis Bour. Circ: 2,000.

338.9 DOM
FUNDACION DOMINICANA DE DESARROLLO. INFORME ANUAL. Text in Spanish. a. charts; illus.
Published by: Fundacion Dominicana de Desarrollo, Apdo. 857, Z.P.1, Santo Domingo, Dominican Republic.

330.9 ARG ISSN 0329-7489
FUNDAMENTOS (RIO CUARTO). Text in Spanish. 1995. q.
Published by: Universidad Nacional del Rio Cuarto, Facultad de Ciencias Economicas, Ruta Nacional 36 Km. 601, Rio Cuarto, Cordoba 5800, Argentina. TEL 54-358-4676200, FAX 54-358-4680280, webmaster@unrc.edu.ar, http://www.unrc.edu.ar/. Ed. Huber Costantino.

338.5 GBR ISSN 0016-3287
HB3730 CODEN: FUTUBD
➤ **FUTURES.** Text in English. 1968. 10/yr. EUR 225 in Europe to individuals; JPY 29,700 in Japan to individuals; USD 252 to individuals except Europe and Japan; EUR 923 in Europe to institutions; JPY 122,400 in Japan to institutions; USD 1,033 to institutions except Europe and Japan (effective 2006). adv. bk.rev. charts; illus. index. back issues avail.; reprints avail. **Document type:** *Journal, Academic/Scholarly.* **Description:** Features studies, analyses and projections of the future, for those in business, industrial R&D, academic research, defense planning, international relations, and public affairs.
Related titles: Microform ed.: (from PQC); Online - full text ed.: (from EBSCO Publishing, Gale Group, IngentaConnect, ScienceDirect).
Indexed: ABC, ABIn, AIAP, ArtHuCI, BPIA, CISA, CLOSS, CPM, CurCont, DIP, ESPM, Emerald, EngInd, FCA, FamI, FutSurv, GEOBASE, HerbAb, HortAb, IBR, IBZ, ILD, InfoSAb, LID&ISL, M&MA, PSA, PerIslam, PhilInd, RASB, RRTA, RefZh, RiskAb, SCIMP, SOPODA, SSA, SSCI, SSI, SociolAb, WAE&RSA.
—BLDSC (4060.650000), CISTI, IDS, IE, Infotrieve, ingenta, Linda Hall. **CCC.**
Published by: Pergamon (Subsidiary of: Elsevier Science & Technology), The Boulevard, Langford Ln, East Park, Kidlington, Oxford OX5 1GB, United Kingdom. TEL 44-1865-843000, FAX 44-1865-843010, futures@ziasardar.com, http://www.elsevier.com/locate/futures. Ed. Zia Sardar. **Subscr. to:** Elsevier BV, PO Box 211, Amsterdam 1000 AE, Netherlands. TEL 31-20-485-3757, FAX 31-20-485-3432, nlinfo-f@elsevier.nl, http://www.elsevier.nl.

330.9 550 MEX
GACETA INFORMATIVA I N E G I. Text in Spanish. 1978. q. free or exchange basis. charts; illus.
Formerly (until 1989): Gaceta Informativa (0185-0679)
Published by: Instituto Nacional de Estadistica, Geografia e Informatica, Secretaria de Programacion y Presupuesto, Prol. Heroe de Nacozari 2301 Sur, Puerta 11, Acceso, Aguascalientes, 20270, Mexico. TEL 52-4-918-1948, FAX 52-4-918-0739, http://www.inegi.gob.mx. Circ: 9,000.

GALE COUNTRY AND WORLD RANKINGS REPORTER. see *BUSINESS AND ECONOMICS—Abstracting, Bibliographies, Statistics*

GALE STATE RANKINGS REPORTER. see *BUSINESS AND ECONOMICS—Abstracting, Bibliographies, Statistics*

330.9 GRC
THE GAMES. Text in Greek. fortn. **Document type:** *Newspaper, Trade.* **Description:** Contains all business news and opportunities involving the Olympic Games 2004.
Published by: Liberis Publications S.A./Ekdoseon Lymperi A.E., Ioannou Metaxa 80, Karelas, Koropi 19400, Greece. TEL 30-1-6198000, FAX 30-1-6198608, info@liberis.gr, http://www.liberis.gr.

GAZETTEER; alphabetical list of localities with statistics on population, number of houses and main source of water supply. see *BUSINESS AND ECONOMICS—Abstracting, Bibliographies, Statistics*

330 LUX ISSN 0259-3963
HC241.2
GENERAL REPORT ON THE ACTIVITIES OF THE EUROPEAN COMMUNITIES. Text in Dutch, English, French, German, Italian. 1968. a. USD 50. **Document type:** *Monographic series.* **Description:** Comprehensive source book on the history of European integration.
Indexed: IIS.
—BLDSC (4111.117520).
Published by: (European Commission BEL), European Commission, Office for Official Publications of the European Union, 2 Rue Mercier, Luxembourg, L-2985, Luxembourg. TELEX PUBOF LU 1324 B. **Dist. in U.S. by:** Bernan Associates, Bernan, 4611-F Assembly Dr., Lanham, MD 20706-4391. TEL 301-459-0056, 800-274-4447.

330.9 GBR ISSN 1607-8616
GENEVA REPORTS ON THE WORLD ECONOMY. Text in English. irreg.
—BLDSC (4115.562500).
Published by: Centre for Economic Policy Research, 90-98 Goswell Rd, London, EC1V 7RR, United Kingdom. TEL 44-20-78782900, FAX 44-20-78782999, http://www.cepr.org. **Co-publisher:** International Center for Monetary and Banking Studies.

330.972 MEX
GENTE SUR; un nuevo periodismo. Text in Spanish. 1996. m. MXP 10 newsstand/cover (effective 2000). illus.; charts. **Document type:** *Magazine, Trade.* **Description:** Includes in-depth articles about the political and economic situation of Mexico.
Related titles: Online - full text ed.: ISSN 1605-5659.
Published by: Gente Sur Ediciones, Apartado Postal 7-935, Col. Roma, Mexico, D F 06700, Mexico. TEL 52-5-5599129, gentesur@acnet.net, http://www.gentesur.com.mx/. Ed. Claudia Val Castro.

GEOGRAPHIE, ECONOMIE, SOCIETE. see *GEOGRAPHY*

330.9 GBR ISSN 1465-6485
HB1
GERMAN ECONOMIC REVIEW. Text in English. 2000. q. EUR 53 combined subscription in Europe to individuals print & online eds.; USD 53 combined subscription in the Americas to individuals & Caribbean, print & online eds.; GBP 35 combined subscription elsewhere to individuals print & online eds.; USD 154 combined subscription in the Americas to institutions & Caribbean, print & online eds.; GBP 100 combined subscription elsewhere to institutions print & online eds. (effective 2006). adv. bk.rev. reprints avail. **Document type:** *Journal, Academic/Scholarly.* **Description:** Aims at publishing original and rigorous research of general interest in a broad range of economic disciplines, including macro and microeconomics, economic policy, international economics, public economics, finance, and business administration. The scope of research approaches includes theoretical, empirical and experimental work.

B

Related titles: Microform ed.; Online - full text ed.: ISSN 1468-0475. USD 1 in the Americas to institutions & Caribbean; GBP 88 elsewhere to institutions (effective 2006) (from Blackwell Synergy, EBSCO Publishing, Gale Group, IngentaConnect, O C L C Online Computer Library Center, Inc., Swets Information Services).
Indexed: ABIn, CCMJ, GEOBASE, JEL, MathR, MathSciNet, PAIS, PSA, RefZh, SociolAb.
—BLDSC (4162.087000), IE, Infotrieve, ingenta.
Published by: (Verein fuer Socialpolitik DEU), Blackwell Publishing Ltd., 9600 Garsington Rd, Oxford, OX4 2ZG, United Kingdom. TEL 44-1865-776868, FAX 44-1865-714591, customerservices@oxon.blackwellpublishing.com, http://www.blackwellpublishing.com/journals/GEER.

330.9 332.6 GBR ISSN 1368-0439
GERMAN INVESTMENT WORLD. Text in English; Summaries in English, German. 1976. 4/yr. GBP 270, USD 530 (effective 1999). adv. bk.rev. index. back issues avail. **Document type:** *Trade.* **Description:** Serves as an international information service for business, finance and government. Covers legislation and policies affecting trade and investment. Examines opportunities offered and threats posed by governments to international business. Contains research analysing corporate investment intentions of interest to governments.
Former titles (until 1997): Government World (1361-8792); Economic Development Briefing (0268-2184); Annual Investment File
Published by: Urban Publishing Co., Hampstead, PO Box 625, London, NW3 2TZ, United Kingdom. TEL 44-2082-091722, FAX 44-2084-554107. Ed. Tann von Hove. Adv. contact Guy Kervella. B&W page USD 1,000, color page USD 2,000; trim 210 x 270. Circ: 4,200.

B

330.9 GHA ISSN 0435-9348
GHANA COMMERCIAL BANK. ANNUAL REPORT. Text in English. a. free. **Document type:** *Corporate.*
Published by: Ghana Commercial Bank, Research Department, PO Box 134, Accra, Ghana.

330 GHA ISSN 0855-0417
HC517.G6
GHANA COMMERCIAL BANK. QUARTERLY ECONOMIC REVIEW. Text in English. 1970. q. free. stat. **Document type:** *Corporate.*
Supersedes (in 1978): Ghana Commercial Bank. Monthly Economic Bulletin
Published by: Ghana Commercial Bank, Research Department, PO Box 134, Accra, Ghana. Circ: 2,000.

GHANA INDUSTRIAL CENSUS. DIRECTORY OF INDUSTRIAL ESTABLISHMENTS. see *BUSINESS AND ECONOMICS—Abstracting, Bibliographies, Statistics*

GHANA INDUSTRIAL CENSUS. PHASE II REPORT. see *BUSINESS AND ECONOMICS—Abstracting, Bibliographies, Statistics*

GHANA LIVING STANDARDS SURVEY. ROUND REPORT. see *BUSINESS AND ECONOMICS—Abstracting, Bibliographies, Statistics*

GHANA LIVING STANDARDS SURVEY. RURAL COMMUNITIES IN GHANA. see *BUSINESS AND ECONOMICS—Abstracting, Bibliographies, Statistics*

GHANA. STATISTICAL SERVICE. CONSUMER PRICE INDEX NUMBERS. see *BUSINESS AND ECONOMICS—Abstracting, Bibliographies, Statistics*

GHANA. STATISTICAL SERVICE. ECONOMIC SURVEY. see *BUSINESS AND ECONOMICS—Abstracting, Bibliographies, Statistics*

GHANA. STATISTICAL SERVICE. MOTOR VEHICLE REGISTRATION. see *TRANSPORTATION—Abstracting, Bibliographies, Statistics*

GHANA. STATISTICAL SERVICE. POPULATION CENSUS - DEMOGRAPHIC AND ECONOMIC CHARACTERISTICS. see *POPULATION STUDIES—Abstracting, Bibliographies, Statistics*

GHANA. STATISTICAL SERVICE. POPULATION CENSUS - SPECIAL REPORT ON LOCALITIES. see *POPULATION STUDIES—Abstracting, Bibliographies, Statistics*

GHANA. STATISTICAL SERVICE. QUARTERLY DIGEST OF STATISTICS. see *STATISTICS*

330.9 332.1 GBR ISSN 0968-820X
GLOBAL ECONOMIC FORECASTS✶. Text in English. 1993. q. GBP 900, USD 1,350 (effective 1994). charts; stat. Supplement avail. **Document type:** *Trade.* **Description:** Monitors the economic condition of nations and markets worldwide and provides currency forecasts for 23 nations.
Published by: Henley Centre for Forecasting Ltd., 9 Bridewell Pl, London, EC4Y 6AY, United Kingdom. Eds. Filippo Dell'Osso, Stephen Radley.

GLOBAL INVESTOR. see *BUSINESS AND ECONOMICS—Banking And Finance*

330.9 CAN ISSN 1495-6764
GLOBAL OUTLOOK. Text in English. 1983. q. free to qualified personnel. **Description:** Reports on the global economy.
Former titles (until 2000): Global Economic Outlook (0820-5167); (until 1987): Regional and Industrial Outlook (0820-5159); (until 1985): Economic Outlook (0831-3563)
Related titles: Online - full content ed.; Online - full text ed.: (from bigchalk, Micromedia ProQuest, O C L C Online Computer Library Center, Inc., ProQuest Information & Learning).
Indexed: ABIn, CPerI.
Published by: Scotia Economics, 44 King St W., Scotia Plaza, Toronto, ON M5W 2X6, Canada. TEL 416-866-6253, FAX 416-866-2829, http://www.scotiabank.co/eccomm.htm.

330.9 332.6 USA
▼ **GLOBAL S T M MARKET ANALYSIS & FORECAST (YEAR).** Text in English. 2003. biennial. USD 8,195 (effective 2005). **Document type:** *Directory, Trade.*
Published by: SIMBA Information (Subsidiary of: R.R. Bowker LLC), 60 Long Ridge Rd., Ste 300, Stamford, CT 06902. TEL 203-325-8193, 800-307-2529, FAX 203-325-8915, info@simbanet.com, http://www.simbanet.com/publications/report_gstm.htm.

330.9 300 MEX ISSN 1605-5519
JZ1318
GLOBALIZACION; revista web mensual de economia, sociedad y cultura. Text in Spanish. 1997. m. free. **Document type:** *Bulletin.* **Description:** Review on world economy, social movements and cultural criticism.
Media: Online - full text.
Address: Mexico. fegarc@mailcity.com, http://www.rcci.net/globalizacion/. Ed. Federico Garcia Morales.

338.5 CAN ISSN 0017-1212
GLOBE AND MAIL REPORT ON BUSINESS. Text in English. 1962. d. adv. bk.rev. **Document type:** *Newspaper.*
Related titles: Microfilm ed.; Online - full text ed.
Indexed: CBCARef, CBPI, CLitI, RASB.
Published by: Globe and Mail Publishing, 444 Front St W, Toronto, ON M5V 2S9, Canada.

330.9 IND
GOA, DAMAN, AND DIU. DIRECTORATE OF ECONOMICS, STATISTICS, AND EVALUATION. EVALUATION REPORT. Text in English. 1969. irreg. stat. **Document type:** *Government.*
Published by: Directorate of Economics, Statistics, and Evaluation, Panaji, Goa, Goa, India. Circ: 150.

330.9 CHN
GONGREN RIBAO/WORKER'S DAILY. Text in Chinese. d. CNY 298.20 (effective 2004). adv. **Document type:** *Newspaper, Consumer.* **Description:** Covers China's economic issues and news.
Related titles: Cumulative ed(s).: Gongren Ribao Hedingben. CNY 380 (effective 2004).
Published by: Gongren Ribaoshe, Andingmen, Liupukang, Beijing, 100718, China. TEL 86-10-64211561 ext 1651, FAX 86-10-64214570, http://www.grrb.com.cn/. Circ: 960,000. **Dist. by:** China International Book Trading Corp, 35 Chegongzhuang Xilu, Haidian District, PO Box 399, Beijing 100044, China. TEL 86-10-68412045, FAX 86-10-68412023, cibtc@mail.cibtc.com.cn, http://www.cibtc.com.cn.

330.9 POL ISSN 0867-0005
HC337.P7
➤ **GOSPODARKA NARODOWA.** Text in Polish. 1946. m. PLZ 300 domestic; EUR 127 foreign (effective 2005). adv. bk.rev. charts; stat. index. **Document type:** *Journal, Academic/Scholarly.* **Description:** Covers domestic and international economy from a theoretical and political perspective.
Formerly (until 1990): Gospodarka Planowa (0017-2421)
Indexed: AgrLib, IBSS, RASB.
Published by: Szkola Glowna Handlowa w Warszawie, Al Niepodleglosci 162, Warsaw, 02554, Poland. TEL 48-22-3379000, FAX 48-22-8495312, informacja@sgh.waw.pl, http://www.sgh.waw.pl/informacje/gospodarka_narodowa. Circ: 600 (paid). **Dist. by:** Ars Polona, Krakowskie Przedmiescie 7, Warsaw, Poland. TEL 48-22-9263914, FAX 48-22-9265334, arspolona@arspolona.com.pl, http://www.arspolona.com.pl.

330.9 BGR
GOVERNMENT DEBT MANAGEMENT. Text in English. m. USD 78 foreign (effective 2002).
Published by: (Bulgaria. Ministerstvo na Finansite), Bulgarska Narodna Banka/Bulgarian National Bank, 1 Alexander Batterberg Sq, Sofia, 1000, Bulgaria. TEL 359-2-91459, FAX 359-2-9802425, press_office@bnbank.org, http://www.bnb.bg. **Dist. by:** Sofia Books, ul Silivria 16, Sofia 1404, Bulgaria. TEL 359-2-9586257, info@sofiabooks-bg.com, http://www.sofiabooks-bg.com.

330 TWN ISSN 1017-9631
GRAPHICAL SURVEY OF THE ECONOMY OF TAIWAN DISTRICT, REPUBLIC OF CHINA. Key Title: Zhongua Minguo Taiwan Diqu Jingji Tongji Tubiao. Text in Chinese, English. 1972. a. USD 5.
Published by: Central Bank of China, 2 Roosevelt Rd, Sec 1, Taipei, 107, Taiwan. TEL 886-2-23936161. Circ: 2,000.

330.9 GBR
GREAT BRITAIN. H M TREASURY. FORECASTS FOR THE U K ECONOMY; a comparison of independent forecasts. Text in English. irreg., latest vol.93, 1995, January. GBP 75. **Document type:** *Government.* **Description:** Summarizes published material reflecting the views of economic forecasting organizations.
Published by: H M Treasury, Economic Briefing Unit, Publishing Unit, 4, Rm 53A-4, Parliament St, London, SW1A 2NU, United Kingdom. TEL 44-171-270-5607.

330.9 USA ISSN 0747-4652
THE GREATER BATON ROUGE BUSINESS REPORT. Variant title: Baton Rouge Business Report. Text in English. 1982. bi-w. USD 59.80 in state (effective 2005). adv. bk.rev. **Document type:** *Magazine, Trade.* **Description:** Covers local, state and national business news, issues and trends, with emphasis on local Baton Rouge news.
Related titles: Online - full text ed.: (from Florida Center for Library Automation, Gale Group, O C L C Online Computer Library Center, Inc., ProQuest Information & Learning).
Indexed: ABIn, BusDate.
Published by: Louisiana Business Inc., 445 North Blvd, Ste 210, Baton Rouge, LA 70802. TEL 225-928-1700, FAX 225-923-3448, editors@businessreport.com, http://www.businessreport.com. Ed. Paulette Senior. Pub. Rolfe McCollister. R&P Michelle Gros. Adv. contact Debi Brand. Circ: 11,500 (controlled and free).

330.9 USA ISSN 1093-8931
GREATER PHOENIX BLUE CHIP ECONOMIC FORECAST. Text in English. 1988. q. USD 39 (effective 1998). **Document type:** *Newsletter.* **Description:** Provides economic and real estate forecasts for the metropolitan Phoenix area.
Formerly (until 1997): Metro Phoenix Blue Chip Economic Forecast (1042-6825)
Related titles: ♦ Supplement to: Bank One Arizona Blue Chip Economic Forecast.
Published by: Arizona State University, Bank One Economic Outlook Center, PO Box 874406, Tempe, AZ 85287-4406. TEL 602-965-5543, 800-448-0432, FAX 602-965-5458, ruth.mcclarnon@asu.edu. Ed. Tracy L Clark.

THE GREEN SHEET. see *PHARMACY AND PHARMACOLOGY*

330.9 USA ISSN 0278-1468
GROUP OF THIRTY. OCCASIONAL PAPER. Text in English. 1980. irreg., latest vol.70, 2004. USD 125; USD 75 to non-profit organizations; USD 10 per issue (effective 2005).
—BLDSC (6217.331000), IE, ingenta.
Published by: Group of Thirty, 1990 M St, Ste 450, Washington, DC 20236. TEL 202-331-2472, FAX 202-785-9423, info@group30.org, http://www.group30.org.

330.973 USA ISSN 0894-1297
GROWTH STRATEGIES. Text in English. 1976. m. looseleaf. USD 146 domestic; USD 195 foreign (effective 2001). bk.rev. back issues avail. **Document type:** *Newsletter.* **Description:** Reports on economic, social, political, technological, demographic, life-style, consumer, business, management, work force, and marketing trends.
Formerly: Futurescan (1088-7822)
Related titles: Online - full text ed.
Published by: FutureScan, 2118 Wilshire Blvd, Ste 826, Santa Monica, CA 90403. TEL 310-451-2990, FAX 310-828-0427, rogerselbert@aol.com. Ed., Pub. Roger Selbert.

330 BRA
GUANABARA: O BALANCO ECONOMICO. Text in Portuguese. 1972. a. free. illus.; stat.
Published by: Instituto de Desenvolvimento da Guanabara, Av Calogeras, 15 Andar 3, Centro, Rio De Janeiro, RJ 20030-070, Brazil. Circ: 1,000.

330.9 HKG
GUANGZHOU YEARBOOK (YEAR). Text in Chinese. 1992. a. HKD 350, USD 72.
Published by: Economic Information & Agency, 342 Hennessy Rd 10th Fl, 10 th Fl, Wanchai, Hong Kong. TEL 852-573-8217, FAX 852-838-8304.

GUATEMALA. BANCO NACIONAL DE DESARROLLO AGRICOLA. MEMORIA. see *AGRICULTURE—Agricultural Economics*

338 BOL
GUIA BOLIVIA; industria, comercio, ganaderia. Text in Spanish. 1976. irreg.
Published by: Editora Nacional, Bolivar, 3235, Cochabamba, Bolivia.

330.9 CHN ISSN 1009-7384
GUOJI JINGJI WENZHAI KA/INTERNATIONAL ECONOMICS ABSTRACTS ON CARDS. Text in Chinese. q. CNY 20 (effective 2004). 112 p./no.; **Document type:** *Abstract/Index.* **Description:** Covers world economic situations.
Media: Cards.
Published by: Zhongguo Renmin Daxue, Shubao Zilio Zhongxin/Renmin University of China, Information Center for Social Server, Dongcheng-qu, 3, Zhangzizhong Lu, Beijing, 100007, China. TEL 86-10-64039458, FAX 86-10-64015080, kyes@163.net, http://www.confucius.cn.net/bkdetail.asp?fzt=WF8. **Dist. in US by:** China Publications Service, PO Box 49614, Chicago, IL 60649. TEL 312-288-3291, FAX 312-288-8570; **Dist. by:** China International Book Trading Corp.

GUOJI WENTI YANJIU/INTERNATIONAL STUDIES. see *POLITICAL SCIENCE—International Relations*

330.9 GBR
H M TREASURY ECONOMIC BRIEFING. (Her Majesty) Text in English. irreg.
Former titles: Economic Progress Report (0262-5067); (until 1970): D E A Progress Report (0436-3906)
Related titles: Online - full text ed.: (from Gale Group).
Published by: H M Treasury, 1 Horse Guards Rd, London, SW1A 2HQ, United Kingdom. TEL 44-20-72705000, FAX 44-20-72704558, http://www.hm-treasury.gov.uk/.

HAMBURG AFRICAN STUDIES/ETUDES AFRICAINES HAMBOURGEOISES. see *POLITICAL SCIENCE*

330.9 USA ISSN 1043-6685
HC107.H3
HAWAII ANNUAL ECONOMIC REPORT. Text in English. 1968. a. stat. back issues avail. **Description:** Contains analysis and table of statistics of Hawaii's economy, including outlook and forecast for the coming year.
Former titles: Hawaii Annual Economic Review (0067-3633); Economy of Hawaii
Indexed: PAIS.
—BLDSC (1085.020000).
Published by: Bank of Hawaii, Economics Department, PO Box 2900, Honolulu, HI 96846. TEL 808-537-8307, FAX 808-536-9433. Ed. Paul H Brewbaker. Circ: 12,000.

338 USA ISSN 0440-5056
HC687
HAWAII BUSINESS. Text in English. 1955. m. USD 29.95 domestic; USD 49 foreign (effective 2005). adv. charts; illus. index. back issues avail. **Document type:** *Magazine, Trade.*
Formerly: Hawaii Business and Industry
Related titles: Online - full text ed.: (from bigchalk, EBSCO Publishing, Florida Center for Library Automation, Gale Group, Northern Light Technology, Inc., O C L C Online Computer Library Center, Inc., ProQuest Information & Learning, The Dialog Corporation).
Indexed: ABIn, BusDate, PAIS, T&II.
Published by: Pacific Basin Communications Inc., 1000 Bishop St, Ste 405, Honolulu, HI 96813. TEL 808-537-9500, FAX 808-537-6455, hbeditorial@pacificbasin.net, info@pacificbasin.net, http://www.hawaiibusiness.com. Ed. Kelli A Trifonovitch. Pub. Hoyt Zia. Adv. contact Meredith Low. B&W page USD 1,990, color page USD 2,590; trim 8.13 x 10.88. Circ: 12,966 (paid and controlled). **Dist by:** Andersen News, 3375 Koapaka St, Honolulu, HI 96819. TEL 808-836-5555, FAX 808-836-2772.

330.9 658 USA ISSN 0739-8034
RA410.53
HEALTH CARE COSTS. Text in English. 1981. q.
Published by: D R I - McGraw-Hill, 24 Hartwell Ave, Lexington, MA 02173. TEL 617-863-5100, FAX 617-860-6332. Ed. Sheila Smith.

330.9 GBR ISSN 0305-9928
HENLEY CENTRE FOR FORECASTING. COSTS & PRICES. Text in English. 1975. q. USD 730. **Description:** Forecasts and analysis for five years ahead of key costs and prices movements in the UK economy.
Published by: Henley Centre for Forecasting, 2 Tudor St, Blackfriars, London, EC4Y 0AA, United Kingdom. TEL 01-353 9961. Ed. Mark Mitchell.

330.9 GBR ISSN 0952-5467
HENLEY CENTRE FOR FORECASTING. DIRECTOR'S REPORT✶. Text in English. 1976. m. GBP 220, USD 330 (effective 1994). charts; stat. **Document type:** *Trade.* **Description:** Provides an overview of economic and social developments in the U.K. and worldwide.
Former titles: Henley Centre for Forecasting. Director's Guide to the U.K. Economy (0263-2721); Henley Centre for Forecasting. Director's Guide (0140-9719)
Published by: Henley Centre for Forecasting Ltd., 9 Bridewell Pl, London, EC4Y 6AY, United Kingdom. TEL 0171-353-9961, FAX 0171-353-2899. Ed. Katie Munson.

330.9 GBR ISSN 1469-4816
HERIOT-WATT UNIVERSITY. DEPARTMENT OF ECONOMICS. DISCUSSION PAPER IN ECONOMICS. Text in English. irreg. **Document type:** *Monographic series.*
Formerly: Centre for Economic Reform and Transformation. Discussion Paper
Published by: Heriot-Watt University, Department of Economics, PO Box 807, Edinburg, EH14 4AT, United Kingdom. TEL 44-131-449-5111, FAX 44-131-451-3498, r.cameron@hw.ac.uk, http://www.hw.ac.uk/cert/.

HERNE IN ZAHLEN. JAHRBUCH (YEAR). see *BUSINESS AND ECONOMICS—Abstracting, Bibliographies, Statistics*

HERNE IN ZAHLEN. MONATSBERICHT. see *BUSINESS AND ECONOMICS—Abstracting, Bibliographies, Statistics*

HERNE IN ZAHLEN. VIERTELJAHRESBERICHTE. see *BUSINESS AND ECONOMICS—Abstracting, Bibliographies, Statistics*

334.788 DEU
HESSISCHE WIRTSCHAFT. Text in German. m. EUR 30.68 domestic; EUR 100 foreign (effective 2004). adv. **Document type:** *Magazine, Trade.*
Published by: Bauer Publications GmbH, Marktplatz 13, Wiesbaden, 65183, Germany. TEL 49-611-360980, FAX 49-611-3609877, info@chmielorz.de, http://www.chmielorz.de. adv.: B&W page EUR 1,749, color page EUR 2,798. Circ: 18,000 (paid and controlled).

HIMAL SOUTH ASIAN. see *POLITICAL SCIENCE*

HONG KONG ECONOMIC TRENDS. see *BUSINESS AND ECONOMICS—Abstracting, Bibliographies, Statistics*

330.9 HKG
HONG KONG SOCIAL AND ECONOMIC TRENDS. Text in Chinese, English. 1973. biennial. HKD 78 (effective 2001). stat. **Document type:** *Government.* **Description:** Aims to present selected major annual data series relating to various social and economic aspects of Hong Kong for analysis. With the Use of tables and charts, plus commentaries, this publication is meant to give readers an overall view of Hong Kong's social and economic trends in the past decade.
Related titles: Online - full text ed.
Published by: Census and Statistics Department/Zhengfu Tongjichu, General Statistics Sections 2(B), 21/F Wanchai Tower, 12 Harbour Rd, Wan Chai, Hong Kong. TEL 852-2582-4734, FAX 852-2119-0161, g2b_1@censtatd.gov.hk, http://www.info.gov.hk/censtatd, http://www.statisticalbookstore.gov.hk. **Subscr. to:** Information Services Department, Publications Sales Section, 4/F, Murray Bldg, Garden Rd, Hong Kong, Hong Kong. puborder@isd.gcn.gov.hk, http://www.info.gov.hk/isd/book_e.htm. **Subscr. to:** Government Publications Centre, Low Block, Ground Fl, Queensway Government Offices, 66 Queensway, Hong Kong, Hong Kong.

HONG KONG SPECIAL ADMINISTRATIVE REGION OF CHINA. CENSUS AND STATISTICS DEPARTMENT. EMPLOYMENT AND VACANCIES STATISTICS (DETAILED TABLES) SERIES C. INDUSTRIAL SECTORS. see *BUSINESS AND ECONOMICS—Abstracting, Bibliographies, Statistics*

330.1 HKG
HONG KONG SPECIAL ADMINISTRATIVE REGION OF CHINA. ECONOMIC ANALYSIS DIVISION, FINANCIAL SERVICES BUREAU. ECONOMIC BACKGROUND. Text in Chinese. a. HKD 100.40 per issue domestic for 1998 ed.. **Document type:** *Government.*
Published by: Financial Services Bureau, Economic Analysis Division, 18/F Tower 1, Admiralty Centre, 18 Harbour Rd, Hong Kong, Hong Kong. TEL 852-2528-9155, FAX 852-2866-8869.

330.1 HKG
HONG KONG SPECIAL ADMINISTRATIVE REGION OF CHINA. ECONOMIC ANALYSIS DIVISION, FINANCIAL SERVICES BUREAU. ECONOMIC PROSPECTS. Text in Chinese. a. HKD 42.20 per issue domestic for 1999 ed.. **Document type:** *Government.*
Related titles: English ed.
Published by: Financial Services Bureau, Economic Analysis Division, 18/F Tower 1, Admiralty Centre, 18 Harbour Rd, Hong Kong, Hong Kong. TEL 852-2528-9155, FAX 852-2866-8869.

330.1 HKG
HONG KONG SPECIAL ADMINISTRATIVE REGION OF CHINA. ECONOMIC ANALYSIS DIVISION, FINANCIAL SERVICES BUREAU. ECONOMIC REPORT. Text in Chinese. q. HKD 76.40 per issue domestic First Quarter Economic Report 1999. **Document type:** *Government.* **Description:** Provides a review of Hong Kong's economic development, including a detailed analysis on topics such as Gross Domestic Product, external trade, finance, labour and prices.
Related titles: English ed.
Published by: Financial Services Bureau, Economic Analysis Division, 18/F Tower 1, Admiralty Centre, 18 Harbour Rd, Hong Kong, Hong Kong. TEL 852-2528-9155, FAX 852-2866-8869.

330.9 UGA
HORIZON INTERNATIONAL. Text in English. 1979. m. UGX 1,200. film rev.; play rev. charts; illus.
Published by: Economy Publications Ltd., PO Box 6787, Kampala, Uganda. Ed. Roland Mutale. Circ: 25,000.

HOUSING & FINANCE - JAMAICA. see *HOUSING AND URBAN PLANNING*

330.9 USA
HOUSTON BUSINESS. Text in English. 1989. every 6 wks. free. back issues avail. **Document type:** *Newsletter, Consumer.* **Description:** Discusses issues concerning the Texas Gulf Coast economy, with emphasis on Houston.
Formerly: Houston Business Briefs
Related titles: Online - full text ed.
Published by: Federal Reserve Bank of Dallas, 2200 N Pearl St, Dallas, TX 75201-2272. TEL 214-922-6000, FAX 214-922-5268, Kay.Champagne@dal.frb.org, http://www.dallasfed.org. Ed. Kay Champagne. Circ: 1,250.

330.9 665 USA ISSN 0277-4976
HOUSTON BUSINESS JOURNAL; strictly Houston, strictly business. Text in English. 1971. w. USD 87 (effective 2005); USD 1.75 newsstand/cover (effective 2001). adv. bk.rev. illus.; stat. 140 p./no.; back issues avail.; reprint service avail. from PQC. **Document type:** *Newspaper, Trade.* **Description:** Covers marketing and other business issues in the greater Houston area. Profiles prominent businesspersons.
Related titles: Microform ed.: (from PQC); Online - full text ed.: (from Florida Center for Library Automation, Gale Group, The Dialog Corporation).
Indexed: BusDate, T&II.
—CCC.
Published by: American City Business Journals, Inc. (Houston), 1233 West Loop S, Ste 1300, Houston, TX 77027-9100. TEL 713-688-8811, FAX 713-963-0482, houston@bizjournals.com, http://www.bizjournals.com/houston. adv.: B&W page USD 5,325. Circ: 115,000. Wire service: PR.

330.9 USA
HUMAN RESOURCES MANAGEMENT - STATE EMPLOYMENT LAWS. Text in English. m. USD 599 online or CD-ROM ed. (effective 2004).
Media: Online - full text. **Related titles:** CD-ROM ed.
Published by: C C H Inc., 2700 Lake Cook Rd, Riverwoods, IL 60015. TEL 847-267-7000, 800-449-6439, FAX 800-224-8299, cust_serv@cch.com, http://www.cch.com.

330.9 HUN ISSN 1215-2439
HF13 CODEN: HECRE2
HUNGARIAN ECONOMIC REVIEW. Text in English. 1990. bi-m. HUF 900, USD 42. adv. back issues avail. **Description:** Contains analyses on financial trends, news and business offers.
Published by: Magyar Kereskedelmi Kamara, Kossuth Lajos ter 608, Budapest, 1055, Hungary. TEL 36-1-153333, FAX 36-1-1531285. Ed. Endre Aczel. Circ: 10,000. **Subscr. to:** Forka Communications, Herman Otto utca 41, Budapest 1026, Hungary. TEL 361-156-2812.

330.982 GBR ISSN 1474-1431
HUNGARY QUARTERLY FORECAST REPORT. Text in English. 1999. 3/yr. GBP 330, USD 495, EUR 450 (effective 2003). **Document type:** *Journal, Trade.* **Description:** Examines political risk, macroeconomic performance and outlook, industry, capital markets, and the business climate, helping to lower risks and maximize opportunities in Hungary.
Formerly (until 2001): Annual Country Forecast Report. Hungary (1465-556X)
Related titles: CD-ROM ed.: GBP 410, USD 675 (effective 2000); Online - full text ed.: (from EBSCO Publishing).
—CCC.
Published by: Business Monitor International Ltd., Mermaid House, 2 Puddle Dock, Blackfriars, London, EC4V 3DS, United Kingdom. TEL 44-20-72480468, FAX 44-20-72480467, subs@businessmonitor.com, http://www.businessmonitor.com/hungaryforecast.html.

HUNTER VALLEY RESEARCH FOUNDATION. WORKING PAPERS. see *STATISTICS*

I A E E NEWSLETTER. see *ENERGY*

330.9 USA ISSN 0738-3398
HC10
I B C D: INTERNATIONAL BUSINESS CONDITIONS DIGEST✶. Text in English. 1983. q. USD 120 to institutions; USD 80 to libraries.
Published by: International Business Resources, Inc., Economics Department, 67 Newmarket Rd, Derham, NH 03824. TEL 603-862-3363. Ed. Evangelos O Simos.

330.9 JPN
I B J MONTHLY REPORT; economic & industrial trends in Japan. Text in English. 1969. m. free. charts; stat. **Document type:** *Corporate.*
Related titles: Online - full text ed.
Indexed: WBA.

Published by: Industrial Bank of Japan/Nippon Kogyo Ginko, 3-3, Marunouchi 1-chome, Chiyoda-ku, Tokyo, 100-8210, Japan. TEL 81-3-3214-1111, FAX 81-3-3201-7643, http://www.ibjbank.co.jp/English/month_report.html.

I C S C RESEARCH QUARTERLY. see *REAL ESTATE*

330.9   DEU   ISSN 0946-7920
I F O DRESDEN STUDIEN. Text in German. 1994. irreg., latest vol.20, 1998. price varies. **Document type:** *Monographic series.*
Published by: I F O Institut fuer Wirtschaftsforschung, Poschingerstr 5, Munich, 81679, Germany. TEL 49-89-9224-0, FAX 49-89-985369, ifo@ifo.de, http://www.ifo.de.

330.9   DEU   ISSN 0176-8689
I F O - G F K KONSUMREPORT. Text in German. 1984. m. EUR 75; EUR 7 newsstand/cover (effective 2004). **Document type:** *Bulletin, Trade.*
Published by: I F O Institut fuer Wirtschaftsforschung, Poschingerstr 5, Munich, 81679, Germany. TEL 49-89-9224-0, FAX 49-89-985369, ifo@ifo.de, http://www.ifo.de. **Co-sponsor:** G f K Marktforschung.

330.9   DEU   ISSN 0938-6955
I F O STUDIEN ZUR EUROPAEISCHEN WIRTSCHAFT. Text in German. 1990. irreg., latest vol.9, 1996. price varies. **Document type:** *Monographic series.*
Published by: I F O Institut fuer Wirtschaftsforschung, Poschingerstr 5, Munich, 81679, Germany. TEL 49-89-9224-0, FAX 49-89-985369, ifo@ifo.de, http://www.ifo.de.

330.9   DEU   ISSN 0930-9551
I F O STUDIEN ZUR JAPANFORSCHUNG. Text in German. 1986. irreg., latest vol.14, 1998. price varies. **Document type:** *Monographic series.*
Published by: I F O Institut fuer Wirtschaftsforschung, Poschingerstr 5, Munich, 81679, Germany. TEL 49-89-9224-0, FAX 49-89-985369, ifo@ifo.de, http://www.ifo.de.

330.9   DEU
I F O STUDIEN ZUR OSTEUROPA- UND TRANSFORMATIONSFORSCHUNG. Text in German. 1988. irreg., latest vol.33, 1998. price varies. **Document type:** *Monographic series.*
Formerly: I F O Studien zur Ostforschung
Published by: (I F O Institut fuer Wirtschaftsforschung), Weltforum Verlag, Hohenzollernplatz 3, Bonn, 53173, Germany. TEL 49-228-368243-0, FAX 49-228-3682439, ifo@ifo.de.

330.9   DEU
I F O STUDIEN ZUR REGIONAL- UND STADTOEKONOMIE. Text in German. 1991. irreg., latest vol.12, 1999. price varies. **Document type:** *Monographic series.*
Published by: I F O Institut fuer Wirtschaftsforschung, Poschingerstr 5, Munich, 81679, Germany. TEL 49-89-9224-0, FAX 49-89-985369, ifo@ifo.de, http://www.ifo.de.

330.9   CHE   ISSN 1011-4971
I L O MULTINATIONAL ENTERPRISES PROGRAMME. WORKING PAPER. Text in English. 1979. irreg., latest vol.76, 1994. CHF 15, USD 12. **Document type:** *Monographic series.*
Related titles: French ed.: B I T Programme des Entreprises Multinationales. Documents de Travail. ISSN 1011-4963; Spanish ed.: O I T Programa de Empresas Multinacionales. Documentos de Trabajo. ISSN 1011-498X; German ed.: I A O Programm der Multinationale Unternehmen. Arbeitspapiere. ISSN 1011-4998.
—BLDSC (9349.605000), IE, ingenta.
Published by: (International Labour Office), I L O Publications, 4 route des Morillons, Geneva 22, 1211, Switzerland. TEL 41-22-799-6111, FAX 41-22-799-6358. Ed. Casimiro Miranda. **Dist. in US by:** I L O Publications Center, 9 Jay Gould Court, Ste. CT, PO Box 753, Waldorf, MD 20604. TEL 301-638-3152, FAX 301-843-0159, ilopubs@tasco1.com.

330.9   USA
I M F ECONOMIC FORUMS AND INTERNATIONAL SEMINARS. (International Monetary Fund) Text in English. 10/yr.
Published by: International Monetary Fund, Publication Services, 700 19th St, N W, Ste 12-607, Washington, DC 20431. TEL 202-623-7430, 202-623-6639, http://www.imf.org.

330.9   USA   ISSN 1020-6779
I M F. ECONOMIC REVIEWS. PRESS INFORMATION NOTICES. (International Monetary Fund) Text in English. 3/yr.
Former titles (until 1998): I M F. Economic Reviews (1020-0576); (until 1992): International Monetary Fund. Economic Review (1607-176X)
—CISTI. **CCC.**
Published by: International Monetary Fund, 700 19th St, N W, Washington, DC 20431. TEL 202-623-6639, FAX 202-623-7201, publications@imf.org, http://www.imf.org.

330.9   USA
I M F FINANCIAL RESOURCES AND LIQUIDITY POSITION. (International Monetary Fund) Text in English. m.
Media: Online - full content.

Published by: International Monetary Fund, Publication Services, 700 19th St, N W, Ste 12-607, Washington, DC 20431. TEL 202-623-7430, FAX 202-623-7201, publications@imf.org, http://www.imf.org/external/pubs/pubs/per.htm.

330.9   USA   ISSN 1564-5193
I M F POLICY DISCUSSION PAPERS. Text in English. 10/yr. —CCC.
Published by: International Monetary Fund, Publication Services, 700 19th St, N W, Ste 12-607, Washington, DC 20431. TEL 202-623-7430, FAX 202-623-7201, publications@imf.org, http://www.imf.org.

330.9   USA
I M F QUARTERLY REPORT ON THE ASSESSMENTS OF STANDARDS AND CODES. (International Monetary Fund) Text in English. q.
Published by: International Monetary Fund, Publication Services, 700 19th St, N W, Ste 12-607, Washington, DC 20431. TEL 202-623-7430, FAX 202-623-7201, publications@imf.org, http://www.imf.org.

330.9   USA   ISSN 1564-5169
I M F STAFF COUNTRY REPORT. (International Monetary Fund) Text in English. 15/m. back issues avail. **Document type:** *Monographic series.* **Description:** Covers economic developments in I M F member countries. —CCC.
Published by: International Monetary Fund, Publication Services, 700 19th St, N W, Ste 12-607, Washington, DC 20431. TEL 202-623-7430, FAX 202-623-7201, http://www.imf.org.

330.9   USA
I M F VIEWS AND COMMENTARIES. Text in English. 3/m. back issues avail. **Document type:** *Monographic series.*
Published by: International Monetary Fund, Publication Services, 700 19th St, N W, Ste 12-607, Washington, DC 20431. TEL 202-623-7430, FAX 202-623-7201, publications@imf.org, http://www.imf.org.

330.9   USA   ISSN 1018-5941
I M F WORKING PAPERS. (International Monetary Fund) Text in English. 15/m.
Published by: International Monetary Fund, Publication Services, 700 19th St, N W, Ste 12-607, Washington, DC 20431. TEL 202-623-7430, FAX 202-623-7201, publications@imf.org, http://www.imf.org.

330   FRA   ISSN 1279-1733
HA37.F8
I N S E E ACTUALITES. Text in French. 1997. q. free. **Document type:** *Bibliography.* **Description:** Presents information on all of the available INSEE publications.
Published by: (INSEE Division Marketing et Commercialisation), Institut National de la Statistique et des Etudes Economiques, 18 bd. Adolphe Pinard, Paris, Cedex 14 75675, France. TEL 33-1-41175050, FAX 33-1-41176204, inseeactualites@insee.fr.

I N S E E PICARDIE DOSSIERS. see *BUSINESS AND ECONOMICS—Abstracting, Bibliographies, Statistics*

I N S E E PICARDIE PREMIERE. see *BUSINESS AND ECONOMICS—Abstracting, Bibliographies, Statistics*

I N S E E PICARDIE RELAIS. see *BUSINESS AND ECONOMICS—Abstracting, Bibliographies, Statistics*

I P E A SERIE P N P E. see *BUSINESS AND ECONOMICS*

330   IND
I S E C MONOGRAPH. Text in English. 1976 (no.4). irreg. INR 20, USD 4.50. **Document type:** *Monographic series.*
Published by: (Institute for Social and Economic Change), World Press Ltd., 37 A College St., Kolkata, West Bengal 700 073, India. Ed. F Rao.

I S E R CONFERENCE PAPER. see *SOCIOLOGY*

I S E R OCCASIONAL PAPERS. (Institute of Social and Economic Research) see *SOCIAL SCIENCES: COMPREHENSIVE WORKS*

I S E R REPORT. see *SOCIOLOGY*

I S E R RESEARCH AND POLICY PAPERS. see *SOCIOLOGY*

330.9   DEU   ISSN 0941-6838
I W TRENDS; Analysen, Dokumentationen, Prognosen. Text in German. 1974. q. EUR 50.75; EUR 20 newsstand/cover (effective 2004). **Document type:** *Journal, Trade.*
Indexed: IBR, IBZ, PAIS.
Published by: Deutscher Instituts Verlag GmbH, Gustav-Heinemann-Ufer 84-88, Cologne, 50968, Germany. TEL 49-221-4981452, FAX 49-221-4981445, div@iwkoeln.de, http://www.iwkoeln.de. Ed. Michael Groemling. Circ: 2,000.

INCENTIVE TAXATION. see *HOUSING AND URBAN PLANNING*

INDIA INTERNATIONAL CENTRE QUARTERLY. see *POLITICAL SCIENCE—International Relations*

INDIA NEWS. see *POLITICAL SCIENCE*

330   IND   ISSN 0019-4948
INDIAN INSTITUTE OF PUBLIC OPINION. QUARTERLY ECONOMIC REPORT. Text in English. 1953. q. INR 400, USD 90. charts. reprint service avail. from PQC. **Description:** Details results of studies on a variety of socio-economic and political subjects.
Related titles: Microform ed.: (from PQC).
Indexed: BAS, PAIS.
Published by: Indian Institute of Public Opinion Private Ltd., Parliament St., 2-A National Insurance Bldg., P O Box 288, New Delhi, 110 001, India. Ed. E P W da Costa.

330.9   IND   ISSN 0019-4999
HC435.2
INDIAN INVESTMENT CENTRE. MONTHLY NEWSLETTER. Text in English. 1963. m. INR 200, USD 40 (effective 1992). illus.; stat. index. **Document type:** *Newsletter.* **Description:** Provides information on industrial licenses, letters of intent issued and foreign collaborations approved by the government. Also gives facts on current economic developments in India.
Indexed: CRIA, CRICC.
Published by: Indian Investment Centre, Jeevan Vihar Bldg., Sansad Marg, New Delhi, 110 001, India. TEL 91-11-351673, FAX 91-11-351205, TELEX 031-63176 ICHO IN. Ed. K K Trivedi. Circ: 3,000.

INDIAN OCEAN NEWSLETTER. see *POLITICAL SCIENCE—International Relations*

650   USA   ISSN 1060-4154
HF107.I6
INDIANA BUSINESS MAGAZINE. Text in English. 1957. m. USD 9.50 (effective 1998). adv. illus. **Document type:** *Trade.* **Description:** Profiles Indiana business people, firms, and industry. Explores trends and issues affecting Indiana business, and focuses on a specific region in each issue. Annual supplement includes top 3,000 firms in the state.
Former titles (until 1992): Indiana Business (0273-7930); (until 1971): Indiana Business and Industry (0019-6533)
Related titles: Microform ed.: (from PQC); Online - full text ed.: (from bigchalk, EBSCO Publishing, Florida Center for Library Automation, Gale Group, Northern Light Technology, Inc., O C L C Online Computer Library Center, Inc., ProQuest Information & Learning, The Dialog Corporation); Supplement(s): Indiana Corporate Directory.
Indexed: ABIn, BusDate, T&II.
Published by: Curtis Magazine Group, Inc., 1000 Waterway Blvd, Indianapolis, IN 46202-2157. TEL 317-692-1200, FAX 317-692-4250, http://www.indianabusiness.com. Ed., R&P Steve Kaelble. Pub. Eric Senaas. Adv. contact Amy Krieg. Circ: 30,000.

338.9   GTM
INDICADORES ECONOMICOS CENTROAMERICANOS. Text in Spanish. 1967. q.
Published by: Secretaria Permanente del Tratado General de Integracion Economica Centroamericana, 4a Avda. 10-25, ZONA, 14, PO Box 1237, Guatemala City, 01901, Guatemala. TEL 502-3682151, FAX 502-3681071, sieca@pronet.net.gt.

338.9   PRI
INDICADORES ECONOMICOS MENSUALES DE PUERTO RICO/MONTHLY ECONOMIC INDICATORS OF PUERTO RICO. Text in English, Spanish. 1976. m. USD 3.50. charts; stat. **Document type:** *Government.*
Published by: Planning Board, Area of Economic and Social Planning, Minillas Governmental Center, Box 41119, San Juan, 00940-9985, Puerto Rico. FAX 787-724-5598. Circ: 400.

INDICADORES ECONOMICOS Y SOCIALES DE PANAMA. see *BUSINESS AND ECONOMICS—Abstracting, Bibliographies, Statistics*

330.9   MAR   ISSN 1114-0097
HN782.A58
LES INDICATEURS SOCIAUX (YEAR). Text in French. 1993. a. MAD 165 foreign (effective 2000). **Document type:** *Government.*
Published by: Morocco. Direction de la Statistique, B P 178, Rabat, Morocco. TEL 212-7-77-36-06, FAX 212-7-773042, dvistat@wizarat.sukkan, http://sukkan.gov.ma.

330.9   ITA
INDICI MENSILI PIROLA. Text in Italian. 1983. m. USD 75. bk.rev.
Published by: Pirola Editore SpA, Via Parabiago, 19, Milan, MI 20151, Italy. TEL 2-30-221, FAX 2-380-11-205. Circ: 8,000.

INDIEN WIRTSCHAFTSNACHRICHTEN. see *POLITICAL SCIENCE—International Relations*

330.9   HKG   ISSN 0019-7297
DS611
INDONESIA LETTER. Text in Chinese. 1969. m. USD 225. bk.rev. **Document type:** *Newsletter.* **Description:** Covers Indonesian affairs for business executives.
Indexed: KES.

Published by: Asia Letter Group, GPO Box 10874, Hong Kong, Hong Kong. TEL 852-526-2950, FAX 852-526-7131, TELEX HX-61166-HKNW. Ed. Charles R Smith.

330.9598   GBR   ISSN 1470-7403
INDONESIA QUARTERLY FORECAST REPORT. Text in English. 1993. 3/yr. GBP 330, USD 495, EUR 450 (effective 2003). **Document type:** *Journal, Trade.* **Description:** Provides a comprehensive assessment of the Indonesian government, economy and business environment over the next 30 months. Helps to identify opportunities and reduce risk, and answers key questions facing executives at this time.
Formerly (until 2000): Annual Country Forecast Report. Indonesia (0966-8209)
Related titles: Online - full text ed.: (from EBSCO Publishing). —CCC.
Published by: Business Monitor International Ltd., Mermaid House, 2 Puddle Dock, Blackfriars, London, EC4V 3DS, United Kingdom. TEL 44-20-72480468, FAX 44-20-72480467, marketing@businessmonitor.com, http://www.businessmonitor.com/indonesiaforecast.html.

330.9 338.91   ITA   ISSN 1460-6682
INDUSTRIAL DEVELOPMENT POLICY DISCUSSION PAPER. Text in English. 1997. irreg. **Document type:** *Monographic series.*
—BLDSC (4449.496250).
Published by: Universita degli Studi di Ferrara, Facolta di Economia, Via del Gregorio 13, Ferrara, 44100, Italy. TEL 39-532-293000, FAX 39-532-293012, facolta@economia.unife.it, http://www.economia.unife.it.

330.9   CIV   ISSN 0019-9230
INDUSTRIEL DE COTE D'IVOIRE. Text in French. m.
Published by: Syndicat des Industriels de la Cote d'Ivoire, BP 1340, Abidjan, Ivory Coast.

330.9   CAN
INDUSTRY CANADA. DIRECTOR OF INVESTIGATION AND RESEARCH. ANNUAL REPORT. Text in English, French. a. free. **Document type:** *Government.*
Formerly: Canada. Department of Consumer and Corporate Affairs. Director of Investigation and Research. Annual Report (0837-4279)
Published by: Industry Canada/Industrie Canada, Distribution Services, Communications & Marketing Branch, Rm 268D, West Tower, C.D. Howe Bldg, 235 Queen St, Ottawa, ON K1A 0H5, Canada. TEL 613-947-7466.

330.9   USA
INDUSTRY FORECASTS. Text in English. USD 450 (effective 2003). **Description:** Provides five-year forecasts for eight key industries, along with relevant background information. This series covers the 60 major economies that account for more than 95% of world output and trade. The forecasts are based on the latest data and in-depth analysis of sectoral trends. It also includes information on a country's political structure; economic policy and business issues; foreign investment, foreign trade and taxation policies and trends; and macroeconomic outlook.
Published by: Economist Intelligence Unit, 111 W 57th St, New York, NY 10019. newyork@eiu.com, http://www.eiu.com.

330.9   USA   ISSN 8755-2396
HF5681.R25
INDUSTRY NORMS AND KEY BUSINESS RATIOS. Text in English. a. (in 5 vols.).
Formerly: Industry Norms and Key Business Ratios. Library Edition
Related titles: Diskette ed.: USD 530 per vol.; USD 2,115 per vol. whole set.
Indexed: ATI.
Published by: Dun & Bradstreet Information Services (Murray Hill) (Subsidiary of: Dun & Bradstreet, Inc.), 103 John F Kennedy Pkwy., Short Hills, NJ 07078-2708. TEL 800-223-0141.

330.9   CAN
INDUSTRY REPORT. Text in English. w. CND 59.95 (effective 2001). **Document type:** *Newsletter, Consumer.* **Description:** Covers in 61 major occupational categories to show the top 25 employers & job opportunities.
Related titles: E-mail ed.
Published by: Mediacorp Canada Inc., 21 New St, Toronto, ON M5R 1P7, Canada. TEL 416-964-6069, FAX 416-964-3202, info@mediacorp2.com, http://www.mediacorp2.com.

330.9   GBR   ISSN 1473-0960
INFOCONOMIST. Text in English. 2000. m. adv. **Document type:** *Magazine, Trade.* **Description:** Provides analysis, data and commentary for Europe's rapidly growing community of technology managers, executives and investors.
Related titles: Online - full text ed.: (from Gale Group). —CCC.
Published by: Infoconomy Ltd, 17-18 Margaret St, London, W1W 8RP, United Kingdom. TEL 44-20-76129300, FAX 44-20-74369188, edit@infoconomy.com, news@infoconomy.com, http://www.infoconomy.com.

330.9   PRT   ISSN 0871-7338
INFORMACAO ECONOMICA. Text in Portuguese. N.S. 1990. q. charts; stat. back issues avail.; reprints avail. **Document type:** *Government.*
Related titles: Online - full text ed.: free (effective 2005).
Published by: Ministerio do Ambiente, do Ordenamento do Territorio e do Desenvolvimento Regional, Departamento de Prospectiva e Planeamento, Avda. D. Carlos I, 126, Lisbon, 1249-079, Portugal. TEL 351-21-3935200, FAX 351-21-3935209, nic@dpp.pt, http://www.dpp.pt/home_dpp.html.

330.9   ESP   ISSN 0210-2633
INFORMACION COMERCIAL ESPANOLA. CUADERNOS ECONOMICOS. Text in Spanish. 1977. 3/yr.
Indexed: ELLIS, JEL, PCI.
—CINDOC, IE.
Published by: Ministerio de Comercio y Turismo, Paseo Castellana, 162, pl. 16, Madrid, 28046, Spain. TEL 34-1-349-36-47, FAX 34-1-349-36-34. Ed. Maria Eugenia Caumel. Circ: 3,000.

330.9   BOL
INFORMACION POLITICA Y ECONOMICA. Text in Spanish. w.
Address: Casilla 2484o, Calle Comerci, La Paz, Bolivia. Ed. Gonzalo Lopez Munoz.

330.9   REU   ISSN 1296-2058
L'INFORMATION EN DETAIL. Variant title: Info en Detail. Text in French. 1982. irreg. charts; stat. **Document type:** *Monographic series.*
Formerly (until 1998): Dossiers de l'Economie Reunionnaise (0292-6792)
Published by: Institut National de la Statistique et des Etudes Economiques, Direction Regionale de la Reunion, 15 rue de L'Ecole, B P 13, St. Denis Messag, Cedex 9 97408, Reunion. TEL 02-62-488900, FAX 02-62-488989. Ed. Gaillard Jean.

330.9   BRA
INFORMATION ON PARANA. Text in Portuguese. 1973. irreg. free. illus.
Related titles: ◆ Portuguese ed.: Parana Informacoes.
Published by: Banco de Desenvolvimento do Parana, S.A., Av. Vicente Machado, 445, Cx. Postal 6042, Curitiba, PARANA, Brazil. Ed. Luiz Fernando Osti Magalhaes.

330.9   AZE
INFORMATSIONNOE AGENTSTVO TURAN. EKONOMICHESKII BYULLETEN'. Text in Russian. 260/yr. USD 1,199 in United States.
Related titles: Azerbaijani ed.; ◆ English ed.: Turan Information Agency. Daily Economic Bulletin.
Published by: Turan Information Agency/Turna Informasiya Agentilyi, Khagani ul 33, Baku, 370000, Azerbaijan. TEL 994-12-984226. Ed. Mekhman Aliev.

INFORMATSIYA O SOTSIAL'NO-EKONOMICHESKOM POLOZHENII ROSSII/INFORMATION ON SOCIAL AND ECONOMIC SITUATION OF RUSSIA. see *BUSINESS AND ECONOMICS—Abstracting, Bibliographies, Statistics*

330   ITA   ISSN 0020-0794
INFORMAZIONE MEDITERRANEA. Text in Italian. 1958. w.
Published by: Carlo de Leva Ed. & Pub., Via Giovanni Campolo, 49, Palermo, PA 90145, Italy.

330.9   ESP
INFORME ANUAL INTEGRADO DE LA HACIENDA VASCA. Text in Spanish. a.
Published by: (Basque Region. Organo de Coordinacion Tributaria de Euskadi), Eusko Jaurlaritzaren Argitalpen-Zerbitzu Nagusia/Servicio Central de Publicaciones del Gobierno Vasco, Donostia-San Sebastian, 1, Vitoria-gasteiz, Alava 01010, Spain. TEL 34-945-018561, FAX 34-945-018709, hac-sabd@ej-gv.es, http://www.ej-gv.net/publicaciones. Circ: 3,500.

330.9   ESP
INFORME ECONOMICO. Text in Spanish. free.
Related titles: English ed.; French ed.; German ed.
Indexed: KES.
Published by: Banco de Santander, Publicidad y Estudios, Paseo Pereda, 9-12, Santander, Cantabria 39004, Spain.

330.9   ESP
INFORME ECONOMICO DE ANDALUCIA. Text in Spanish. 1998. a.
Media: Online - full text.
Published by: Junta de Andalucia, Consejeria de Economia y Hacienda, Edif. Torretriana, Isla de Cartuja, Sevilla, 41092, Spain. TEL 34-955-065000, http://www.ceh.junta-andalucia.es/web/economia/situacion/informes/informes.htm.

338.9   GBR   ISSN 0263-5372
INFORME LATINOAMERICANO. Text in Spanish. 1982. w. GBP 316, USD 425 (effective 2001). bk.rev. **Document type:** *Newsletter.* **Description:** News and analysis on Latin American issues.
Supersedes (in 1982): America Latina Informe de Mercados (0261-3751); America Latina Informe Economico (0261-3735); America Latina Informe Politico (0261-3743)

Related titles: Online - full text ed.: (from EBSCO Publishing). —IE, Infotrieve.
Published by: Latin American Newsletters (Subsidiary of: Lettres (U.K.) Ltd.), 61 Old St, London, EC1V 9HW, United Kingdom. TEL 44-20-7251-0012, FAX 44-20-7253-8193, subs@latinnews.com, http://www.latinnews.com. Ed. Eduardo Crawley. R&P Alex McHallam TEL 44-20-7251-0012.

INOSTRANNAYA PECHAT' OB EKONOMICHESKOM, NAUCHNO-TEKHNICHESKOM I VOENNOM POTENTSIALE GOSUDARSTV-UCHASTNIKOV SNG I TEKHNICHESKIKH SREDSTVAKH EGO VYIAVLENIYA. SERIYA: EKONOMICHESKII I NAUCHNO-TEKHNICHESKII POTENTSIAL. see *BUSINESS AND ECONOMICS—Abstracting, Bibliographies, Statistics*

INOSTRANNAYA PECHAT' OB EKONOMICHESKOM, NAUCHNO-TEKHNICHESKOM I VOENNOM POTENTSIALE GOSUDARSTV-UCHASTNIKOV SNG I TEKHNICHESKIKH SREDSTVAKH EGO VYIAVLENIYA. SERIYA: TEKHNICHESKIE SREDSTVA RAZVEDYVATELNYKH SLUZHB ZARUBEZHNYKH GOSUDARSTV. see *BUSINESS AND ECONOMICS—Abstracting, Bibliographies, Statistics*

INOSTRANNAYA PECHAT' OB EKONOMICHESKOM, NAUCHNO-TEKHNICHESKOM I VOENNOM POTENTSIALE GOSUDARSTV-UCHASTNIKOV SNG I TEKHNICHESKIKH SREDSTVAKH EGO VYIAVLENIYA. SERIYA: VOORUZHENNYE SILY I VOENNO-PROMYSHLENNYI POTENTSIAL. see *BUSINESS AND ECONOMICS— Abstracting, Bibliographies, Statistics*

INSTITUT DER DEUTSCHEN WIRTSCHAFT. FORUM. see *BUSINESS AND ECONOMICS—Management*

INSTITUT FUER AFRIKA-KUNDE. ARBEITEN. see *POLITICAL SCIENCE*

330.9   DEU
INSTITUT FUER WELTWIRTSCHAFT. ANNUAL REPORT. Text in German. a. **Document type:** *Yearbook, Corporate.* **Description:** Contains reports on research and other activities conducted at the Institute.
Published by: Institut fuer Weltwirtschaft, Duesternbrooker Weg 120, Kiel, 24105, Germany. TEL 49-431-8814305, FAX 49-431-85853, info@ifw.uni-kiel.de, http://www.uni-kiel.de/ifw.

330.9   SGP
INSTITUTE OF SOUTHEAST ASIAN STUDIES. PROCEEDINGS OF INTERNATIONAL CONFERENCES. Text in English. 1973. irreg., latest vol.108, 2003. price varies. **Document type:** *Proceedings.* **Description:** Politics and economics pertaining to present day Southeast Asia.
Published by: Institute of Southeast Asian Studies, 30 Heng Mui Keng Terrace, Pasir Panjang, Singapore, 119614, Singapore. TEL 65-6870-2447, FAX 65-6775-6259, pubsunit@iseas.edu.sg, http://www.iseas.edu.sg/. R&P Mrs. Triena Ong TEL 65-6870-2449.

330.9   BRA
INSTITUTO DE ECONOMIA DO SETOR PUBLICO. NOTAS TECNICAS. Text in Portuguese. irreg., latest vol.5, 1994.
Published by: Instituto de Economia do Setor Publico, Rua Bandeira Paulista, 716, I Bibi, Sao Paulo, SP 04532-002, Brazil. TEL 55-11-8298955, FAX 55-11-8298743. **Co-sponsor:** Fundacao do Desenvolvimento Administrativo.

330.9   ESP   ISSN 0210-9565
HC381
INSTITUTO DE ESTUDIOS ECONOMICOS. REVISTA. Key Title: Revista del Instituto de Estudios Economicos. Text in Spanish. 1980. q.
Indexed: PAIS.
—CINDOC.
Published by: Instituto de Estudios Economicos, Castello, 128 6o. Planta, Madrid, 28006, Spain. TEL 34-91-7820580, FAX 34-91-5623613, iee@ieemadrid.ecom, http://www.ieemadrid.com. Ed. Juan E Iranzo.

338.9   PER   ISSN 1019-4509
INSTITUTO DE ESTUDIOS PERUANOS. ANALISIS ECONOMICO. Text in Spanish. 1964. irreg., latest vol.18, 1998. price varies. back issues avail. **Document type:** *Monographic series, Academic/Scholarly.*
Published by: (Instituto de Estudios Peruanos), I E P Ediciones (Subsidiary of: Instituto de Estudios Peruanos), Horacio Urteaga 694, Jesus Maria, Lima, 11, Peru. TEL 51-14-3326194, FAX 51-14-3326173, libreria@iep.org.pe, http://iep.peruculturalorg.pe.

INSTITUTO DE ESTUDIOS PERUANOS. DOCUMENTOS DE TRABAJO. SERIE TALLERES. see *BUSINESS AND ECONOMICS—Production Of Goods And Services*

330.9   ARG
HC175
INSTITUTO DE ESTUDIOS SOBRE LA REALIDAD ARGENTINA Y LATINOAMERICANA. ESTUDIOS. Text in Spanish. 1978. q. USD 30 (effective 1999); free to qualified personnel or on exchange basis. adv. **Document type:** *Academic/Scholarly.*

B

Formerly: Instituto de Estudios Economicos sobre la Realidad Argentina y Latinoamericana. Estudios (0325-6928)
Indexed: PAIS.
Published by: (Instituto de Estudios sobre la Realidad Argentina y Latinoamericana), Fundacion Mediterranea, Campillo, 394, Cordoba, 5000, Argentina. FAX 54-51-724625, TELEX 51811 IERAL AR. Ed., R&P Aldo Arnaudo. Adv. contact Olga Krajczy. Circ: 1,000.

330.9 BRA
INSTITUTO DO DESENVOLVIMENTO ECONOMICO-SOCIAL DO PARA. COMERCIO VAREJISTA. Text in Portuguese. 1986. m. donation.
Published by: Instituto do Desenvolvimento Economico Social do Para, Av Nazare, 871, Nazare, Belem, Para 66035170, Brazil. TEL 55-91-2244411, FAX 55-91-2253414.

330.9 BRA ISSN 0103-5282
INSTITUTO DO DESENVOLVIMENTO ECONOMICO-SOCIAL DO PARA. INDICADORES DA SOCIO-ECONOMIA PARAENSE. Text in Portuguese. 1984. irreg. USD 1. bibl.; charts; stat. **Document type:** *Government.* **Description:** Covers the economy of the Brazilian state.
Published by: Instituto do Desenvolvimento Economico Social do Para, Av Nazare, 871, Nazare, Belem, Para 66035170, Brazil. TEL 55-91-2244411, FAX 55-91-2253414.

330.9 BRA
INSTITUTO DO DESENVOLVIMENTO ECONOMICO-SOCIAL DO PARA. INDICE DO CUSTO DE VIDA. Text in Portuguese. 1976. m. donation.
Published by: Instituto do Desenvolvimento Economico Social do Para, Av Nazare, 871, Nazare, Belem, Para 66035170, Brazil. TEL 55-91-2244411, FAX 55-91-2253414.

330.9 338.91 BRA ISSN 0553-1721
HC188.P3
INSTITUTO DO DESENVOLVIMENTO ECONOMICO-SOCIAL DO PARA. PARA DESENVOLVIMENTO. Text in Portuguese. 1965. s-a. USD 1. bibl.; charts; stat. **Description:** Covers relevant areas related to the socio-economic transformation of the state of Para, contains technical, scientific and research articles. Also includes interviews, studies, depositions and other materials of interest.
Published by: Instituto do Desenvolvimento Economico Social do Para, Av Nazare, 871, Nazare, Belem, Para 66035170, Brazil. TEL 55-91-2244411, FAX 55-91-2283414.

INSTITUTO NACIONAL DE INVESTIGACIONES FORESTALES, AGRICOLAS Y PECUARIAS. FOLLETOS DE INVESTIGACION. see *AGRICULTURE*

330.9 CUB
INTEGRACION ECONOMICA SOCIALISTA. Text in Spanish. m. USD 18.
Published by: (Council for Mutual Economic Assistance), Prensa Latina Agencia Informativa Latinoamericana, Calle 23 No. 201,, Vedado, La Habana, Cuba.

330 COL
INTEGRACION FINANCIERA; pasado, presente y futuro de las finanzas en Colombia y el mundo. Text in Spanish. 1984. bi-m. COP 30,000, USD 50. adv. illus. **Description:** News on the development of the financial sector of Colombia and Latin America. Presents important information to businessmen. Includes principals of the different activities relating to banking, financing, insurance, stocks and more in the economic field.
Published by: Medios & Medios Publicidad Cia Ltda., Calle 63, 11-45 Of 802, PO Box 036943, Bogota, CUND, Colombia. TEL 57-1-255-0992, FAX 57-1-249-4696. Ed. Raul Rodriguez Puerto.

330.968 ZAF ISSN 1022-8314
INTELLIGENCE. Text in English. 1994. m. ZAR 240 (effective 2005). illus. **Document type:** *Magazine, Consumer.* **Description:** Offers insightful analysis of life in the information age and examines the implications for business and society of emerging and converging technologies.
Related titles: Online - full text ed.
Indexed: ISAP, e-psyche.
Published by: Intelligence Publishing, PO Box 2917, Parklands, Johannesburg 2917, South Africa. TEL 27-11-442-6006, editor@intelligence.co.za, http://www.intelligence.co.za, http://www.intelligence.co.za/isite/current.html. Ed. Michael Herman. Pub. Martyn Samuels. Adv. contact Lisa McCallum.

INTERIEUR SYSTEMES; la construction seche en action. see *BUSINESS AND ECONOMICS—Management*

330.9 USA
INTERNATIONAL CENTER FOR ECONOMIC GROWTH. NEWSLETTER. Text in English. 1987. q. free. adv. bk.rev. **Document type:** *Newsletter.* **Description:** Covers new research progress and timely information on growth and developmental issues.
Media: Online - full text. **Related titles:** E-mail ed.; French ed.; Spanish ed.
Indexed: RASB.
Published by: International Center for Economic Growth, 1 Sansome St, Ste 2000, San Francisco, CA 94104-4432. TEL 415-984-3193, FAX 415-984-3196, ntruitt@iceq.org, http://www.iceq.org. Ed. Nancy Truitt. Adv. contact Rachel Levine.

330.9 TWN ISSN 0013-029X
HC464.F7
INTERNATIONAL COMMERCIAL BANK OF CHINA. ECONOMIC REVIEW. Text in Chinese. 1950. bi-m. free. index.
Description: Articles on economic development, planning, and conditions in the Republic of China.
Incorporates (1973-1997): International Commercial Bank of China. Monthly Economic Survey (1013-9893)
Indexed: APEL, BAS, BusI, JEL, PAIS.
—BLDSC (3654.943000).
Published by: International Commercial Bank of China, Head Office-Economic Research Department, 100 Chi Lin Rd, Taipei, Taiwan 10424, Taiwan. TEL 886-2-25633156, FAX 886-2-25611216, TELEX 11300 INCOBK. Ed. Heh Song Wang.

338.9 USA ISSN 0278-6680
HG3891.5
INTERNATIONAL COUNTRY RISK GUIDE. (Published in several editions: Asia & the Pacific; Europe; Statistical Section; Sub-Saharan Africa; The Americas) Text in English. 1980. m. USD 3,795 (effective 2001). stat. **Description:** Provides data and analysis on events in 130 countries throughout the world. Each issue includes extended analysis of 65-80 countries, with detailed coverage of political trends, economic developments and financial risks.
Related titles: CD-ROM ed.: USD 4,595 (effective 2001); Online - full text ed.: USD 4,595 (effective 2001) (from Data-Star, The Dialog Corporation).
Published by: The P R S Group, Inc., PO Box 248, East Syracuse, NY 13057-0248. TEL 315-431-0511, FAX 315-431-0200, custserv@prsgroup.com, http://www.countrydata.com, http://www.prsgroup.com. Ed. Tom Sealy.

338.9 USA ISSN 1539-9699
HC94.A1
INTERNATIONAL COUNTRY RISK GUIDE ANNUAL. VOL. 1, THE AMERICAS. Text in English. 2002 (Sep.). a. **Document type:** *Trade.*
Related titles: ♦ Regional ed(s).: International Country Risk Guide Annual. Vol. 2, Europe (European Union). ISSN 1539-9788; ♦ International Country Risk Guide Annual. Vol. 3, Europe (Non-European Union). ISSN 1539-9796; ♦ International Country Risk Guide Annual. Vol. 5, Sub-Saharan Africa. ISSN 1539-9818; ♦ International Country Risk Guide Annual. Vol. 7, Risk Ratings & Statistics. ISSN 1539-9834; ♦ International Country Risk Guide Annual. Vol. 6, Asia & the Pacific. ISSN 1539-9826; International Country Risk Guide Annual. Vol. 4, North Africa. ISSN 1539-980X. 2002 (Sep.).
Published by: The P R S Group, Inc., PO Box 248, East Syracuse, NY 13057-0248. TEL 315-431-0511, FAX 315-431-0200, custserv@prsgroup.com, http://www.prsgroup.com. **Subscr. to:** 6320 Fly Rd, Ste 102, East Syracuse, NY 13057-0248.

338.9 USA ISSN 1539-9788
HC240.A1
INTERNATIONAL COUNTRY RISK GUIDE ANNUAL. VOL. 2, EUROPE (EUROPEAN UNION). Text in English. 2002 (Sep.). a. **Document type:** *Trade.*
Related titles: ♦ Regional ed(s).: International Country Risk Guide Annual. Vol. 1, the Americas. ISSN 1539-9699; ♦ International Country Risk Guide Annual. Vol. 3, Europe (Non-European Union). ISSN 1539-9796; ♦ International Country Risk Guide Annual. Vol. 5, Sub-Saharan Africa. ISSN 1539-9818; ♦ International Country Risk Guide Annual. Vol. 7, Risk Ratings & Statistics. ISSN 1539-9834; ♦ International Country Risk Guide Annual. Vol. 6, Asia & the Pacific. ISSN 1539-9826; International Country Risk Guide Annual. Vol. 4, North Africa. ISSN 1539-980X. 2002 (Sep.).
Published by: The P R S Group, Inc., PO Box 248, East Syracuse, NY 13057-0248. TEL 315-431-0511, FAX 315-431-0200, custserv@prsgroup.com, http://www.prsgroup.com. **Subscr. to:** 6320 Fly Rd, Ste 102, East Syracuse, NY 13057-0248.

338.9 USA ISSN 1539-9796
HC240.A1
INTERNATIONAL COUNTRY RISK GUIDE ANNUAL. VOL. 3, EUROPE (NON-EUROPEAN UNION). Text in English. 2002 (Sep.). a. **Document type:** *Trade.*
Related titles: ♦ Regional ed(s).: International Country Risk Guide Annual. Vol. 1, the Americas. ISSN 1539-9699; ♦ International Country Risk Guide Annual. Vol. 2, Europe (European Union). ISSN 1539-9788; ♦ International Country Risk Guide Annual. Vol. 5, Sub-Saharan Africa. ISSN 1539-9818; ♦ International Country Risk Guide Annual. Vol. 7, Risk Ratings & Statistics. ISSN 1539-9834; ♦ International Country Risk Guide Annual. Vol. 6, Asia & the Pacific. ISSN 1539-9826; International Country Risk Guide Annual. Vol. 4, North Africa. ISSN 1539-980X. 2002 (Sep.).
Published by: The P R S Group, Inc., PO Box 248, East Syracuse, NY 13057-0248. TEL 315-431-0511, FAX 315-431-0200, custserv@prsgroup.com, http://www.prsgroup.com. **Subscr. to:** 6320 Fly Rd, Ste 102, East Syracuse, NY 13057-0248.

338.9 USA ISSN 1539-9818
HC800.A1
INTERNATIONAL COUNTRY RISK GUIDE ANNUAL. VOL. 5, SUB-SAHARAN AFRICA. Text in English. 2002 (Sep.). a. **Document type:** *Trade.*
Related titles: ♦ Regional ed(s).: International Country Risk Guide Annual. Vol. 1, the Americas. ISSN 1539-9699; ♦ International Country Risk Guide Annual. Vol. 2, Europe (European Union). ISSN 1539-9788; ♦ International Country Risk Guide Annual. Vol. 3, Europe (Non-European Union). ISSN 1539-9796; ♦ International Country Risk Guide Annual. Vol. 7, Risk Ratings & Statistics. ISSN 1539-9834; ♦ International Country Risk Guide Annual. Vol. 6, Asia & the Pacific. ISSN 1539-9826; International Country Risk Guide Annual. Vol. 4, North Africa. ISSN 1539-980X. 2002 (Sep.).
Published by: The P R S Group, Inc., PO Box 248, East Syracuse, NY 13057-0248. TEL 315-431-0511, FAX 315-431-0200, custserv@prsgroup.com, http://www.prsgroup.com. **Subscr. to:** 6320 Fly Rd, Ste 102, East Syracuse, NY 13057-0248.

338.9 USA ISSN 1539-9826
HC411
INTERNATIONAL COUNTRY RISK GUIDE ANNUAL. VOL. 6, ASIA & THE PACIFIC. Text in English. 2002 (Sep.). a. **Document type:** *Trade.*
Related titles: ♦ Regional ed(s).: International Country Risk Guide Annual. Vol. 1, the Americas. ISSN 1539-9699; ♦ International Country Risk Guide Annual. Vol. 2, Europe (European Union). ISSN 1539-9788; ♦ International Country Risk Guide Annual. Vol. 3, Europe (Non-European Union). ISSN 1539-9796; ♦ International Country Risk Guide Annual. Vol. 7, Risk Ratings & Statistics. ISSN 1539-9834; ♦ International Country Risk Guide Annual. Vol. 5, Sub-Saharan Africa. ISSN 1539-9818; International Country Risk Guide Annual. Vol. 4, North Africa. ISSN 1539-980X. 2002 (Sep.).
Published by: The P R S Group, Inc., PO Box 248, East Syracuse, NY 13057-0248. TEL 315-431-0511, FAX 315-431-0200, custserv@prsgroup.com, http://www.prsgroup.com. **Subscr. to:** 6320 Fly Rd, Ste 102, East Syracuse, NY 13057-0248.

338.9 USA ISSN 1539-9834
HB3730
INTERNATIONAL COUNTRY RISK GUIDE ANNUAL. VOL. 7, RISK RATINGS & STATISTICS. Text in English. 2002 (Sep.). a. **Document type:** *Trade.*
Related titles: ♦ Regional ed(s).: International Country Risk Guide Annual. Vol. 1, the Americas. ISSN 1539-9699; ♦ International Country Risk Guide Annual. Vol. 2, Europe (European Union). ISSN 1539-9788; ♦ International Country Risk Guide Annual. Vol. 3, Europe (Non-European Union). ISSN 1539-9796; ♦ International Country Risk Guide Annual. Vol. 6, Asia & the Pacific. ISSN 1539-9826; ♦ International Country Risk Guide Annual. Vol. 5, Sub-Saharan Africa. ISSN 1539-9818; International Country Risk Guide Annual. Vol. 4, North Africa. ISSN 1539-980X. 2002 (Sep.).
Published by: The P R S Group, Inc., PO Box 248, East Syracuse, NY 13057-0248. TEL 315-431-0511, FAX 315-431-0200, custserv@prsgroup.com, http://www.prsgroup.com. **Subscr. to:** 6320 Fly Rd, Ste 102, East Syracuse, NY 13057-0248.

330.9 USA ISSN 0738-1425
INTERNATIONAL DEVELOPMENT RESOURCE BOOKS. Text in English. 1984. irreg. price varies. **Document type:** *Monographic series, Academic/Scholarly.*
Published by: Greenwood Publishing Group Inc. (Subsidiary of: Harcourt International), 88 Post Rd W, PO Box 5007, Westport, CT 06881. TEL 203-226-3571, FAX 203-226-1502, bookinfo@greenwood.com, http://www.greenwood.com.

330.9 GBR ISSN 1016-8737
HB1.A1
➤ **INTERNATIONAL ECONOMIC JOURNAL.** Text in Korean. 1987. q. GBP 170, USD 282 combined subscription to institutions print & online eds. (effective 2006). adv. back issues avail.; reprint service avail. from PSC. **Document type:** *Journal, Academic/Scholarly.* **Description:** Devoted to publishing high-quality papers and sharing original economics research worldwide.
Related titles: CD-ROM ed.; Online - full text ed.: ISSN 1743-517X. GBP 162, USD 268 to institutions (effective 2006) (from EBSCO Publishing, Gale Group, IngentaConnect, O C L C Online Computer Library Center, Inc., Swets Information Services).
Indexed: APEL, BAS, IBSS, JEL.
—BLDSC (4539.770000), IE, Infotrieve, ingenta.
Published by: (Seoul University, College of Social Sciences, Division of Economics KOR), Routledge (Subsidiary of: Taylor & Francis Group), 4 Park Sq, Milton Park, Abingdon, Oxon OX14 4RN, United Kingdom. TEL 44-1235-828600, FAX 44-1235-829000, info@routledge.co.uk, http://www.tandf.co.uk/journals/titles/10168737.asp, http://www.routledge.co.uk. Eds. Jaymin Lee, Sunwoong Kim. Circ: 1,000.

330.9 USA ISSN 0895-7185
INTERNATIONAL ECONOMIC REVIEW (WASHINGTON DC). Text in English. bi-m. back issues avail. **Document type:** *Journal, Government.*
Related titles: Online - full text ed.

Published by: U.S. International Trade Commission, Publications Office, 500 E St, S W, Rm 112A, Washington, DC 20436. TEL 202-205-2000, http://www.usitc.gov/ier.htm.

330.9 USA ISSN 0270-045X
INTERNATIONAL ECONOMIC SCOREBOARD. Text in English. 1979. q. USD 295 to non-members; USD 145 to members (effective 2005). **Document type:** *Newsletter, Trade.* **Description:** Forecasts of economic performance of major industrial countries.
Related titles: Microfiche ed.: (from CIS); Online - full text ed.
Indexed: PROMT, SRI.
—CISTI. **CCC.**
Published by: Conference Board, Inc., 845 Third Ave, New York, NY 10022. TEL 212-759-0900, FAX 212-836-9740, rgtaylor@prodigy.net, http://www.conference-board.org. Ed. Robert G Taylor.

330.9 USA
HG3863
INTERNATIONAL ECONOMIC TRENDS. Text in English. 1978. q. free. **Document type:** *Journal, Trade.* **Description:** Contains data on US transactions and economic developments for major trading partners of the US. Data on money supply, price indexes, unemployment, real GDP, merchandise trade, interest rates and exchange rates.
Formerly (until 1995): International Economic Conditions (0190-7085); Which was formed by the merger of (19??-1978): Rates of Change in Economic Data for Ten Industrial Countries (0149-9092); (19??-1978): U.S. International Transactions and Currency Review (0145-4153)
Related titles: Special ed(s).
Published by: Federal Reserve Bank of St. Louis, PO Box 442, St. Louis, MO 63166. TEL 314-444-8320.

330.9 USA ISSN 0307-4951
INTERNATIONAL FINANCIAL BULLETIN. Text in English. 1987. 8/yr. **Document type:** *Trade.*
Formerly: International Business and Financial Outlook
—IE.
Published by: D R I - McGraw-Hill, 24 Hartwell Ave, Lexington, MA 02173. TEL 617-863-5100, FAX 617-860-6332. Ed. N Behravesh.

650 JPN
INTERNATIONAL HERALD TRIBUNE - THE ASAHI SHIMBUN. Text in Japanese. 1966. d. JPY 43,200 (effective 2005). adv. charts; illus.; stat. **Document type:** *Newspaper, Consumer.*
Former titles: Asahi Evening News International (0025-2816); March of Japan's Economy
Related titles: Online - full text ed.: (from ProQuest Information & Learning).
Published by: Asahi Shimbun Publishing Co., 5-3-2 Tsukiji, Chuo-ku, Tokyo, 104-8011, Japan. TEL 81-3-35450131, FAX 81-3-55418696, http://www.asahi.com/. Circ: 20,000.

338.9 USA ISSN 1523-9748
➤ **INTERNATIONAL JOURNAL OF ECONOMIC DEVELOPMENT.** Text in English. 1999. q. USD 25 to individuals; USD 175 to institutions (effective 2003). adv. bk.rev. back issues avail. **Document type:** *Journal, Academic/Scholarly.* **Description:** Deals with economic development issues from an interdisciplinary perspective at both the national and local levels.
Media: Online - full text.
—CCC.
Published by: Southern Public Administration Education Foundation, Inc., 2103 Fairway Ln, Harrisburg, PA 17112. TEL 717-540-5477, FAX 717-893-1763, spaef@spaef.com, http://www.spaef.com/. Eds. Jack Rabin, K Tom Liou. R&P, Adv. contact Jack Rabin.

➤ **INTERNATIONAL JOURNAL OF ENERGY, ENVIRONMENT AND ECONOMICS.** see *ENERGY*

330.9 NLD ISSN 0169-2070
H61.4 CODEN: IJFOEK
➤ **INTERNATIONAL JOURNAL OF FORECASTING.** Text in English, French. 1985. 4/yr. EUR 563 in Europe to institutions; JPY 74,600 in Japan to institutions; USD 630 elsewhere to institutions (effective 2006). adv. bk.rev. back issues avail.; reprints avail. **Document type:** *Journal, Academic/Scholarly.* **Description:** Publishes papers covering all aspects of forecasting.
Related titles: Microform ed.: (from PQC); Online - full text ed.: (from EBSCO Publishing, Gale Group, IngentaConnect, ScienceDirect, Swets Information Services).
Indexed: ABIn, ASCA, BAS, CIS, CPM, CREJ, CurCont, ESPM, Emerald, FPA, Faml, IAOP, IBSS, Inspec, JCQM, JEL, PAIS, PCI, PSA, RASB, RefZh, RiskAb, SSCI, ST&MA.
—BLDSC (4542.255000), AskIEEE, IDS, IE, Infotrieve, ingenta. **CCC.**
Published by: (International Institute of Forecasters), Elsevier BV, North-Holland (Subsidiary of: Elsevier Science & Technology), Sara Burgerhartstraat 25, Amsterdam, 1055 KV, Netherlands. http://www.elsevier.com/locate/ijforecast. Ed. Rob J. Hyndman. **Subscr. to:** Elsevier BV, PO Box 211, Amsterdam 1000 AE, Netherlands. TEL 31-20-485-3757, FAX 31-20-485-3432, http://www.elsevier.nl.

▼ ➤ **INTERNATIONAL JOURNAL OF TECHNOLOGY AND GLOBALISATION**; economy, sustainability and security. see *TECHNOLOGY: COMPREHENSIVE WORKS*

➤ **INTERNATIONAL MARKET REVIEW.** see *BUSINESS AND ECONOMICS—Banking And Finance*

330.9 USA ISSN 0256-6877
HC10
INTERNATIONAL MONETARY FUND. WORLD ECONOMIC OUTLOOK. Text in Arabic, English, French, Spanish. 1980. s-a. USD 49 per edition (effective 2004). stat. **Description:** Discusses the problems of balance of payments adjustment by major groups of countries, the key policy options available to them, issues of inflation and interest rates, debt, and capital flows. Details scenarios for the evolution of the world economy over the medium term under various policy options.
Related titles: Microform ed.: (from CIS, PQC); Online - full text ed.: ISSN 1564-5215 (from Florida Center for Library Automation, Gale Group, Northern Light Technology, Inc.); Arabic ed.; French ed.; Spanish ed.; ♦ Series: International Monetary Fund. World Economic and Financial Surveys. ISSN 0258-7440.
Indexed: IIS.
—BLDSC (9354.297000), CISTI, IE, ingenta. **CCC.**
Published by: International Monetary Fund, Publication Services, 700 19th St, N W, Ste 12-607, Washington, DC 20431. TEL 202-623-7430, FAX 202-623-7201, TELEX RCA 248331 IMF UR, publications@imf.org, http://www.imf.org. Circ: 8,000.

330.9 332 NLD ISSN 1059-0560
HB1
➤ **INTERNATIONAL REVIEW OF ECONOMICS & FINANCE.** Text in English. 1991. 4/yr. EUR 337 in Europe to institutions; JPY 44,600 in Japan to institutions; USD 377 to institutions except Europe and Japan (effective 2006). bk.rev. illus. Index. back issues avail.; reprints avail. **Document type:** *Journal, Academic/Scholarly.* **Description:** Devoted to the publication of high-quality theoretical and empirical papers on all aspects of economics and finance.
Related titles: Microform ed.: (from PQC); Online - full text ed.: (from EBSCO Publishing, Gale Group, IngentaConnect, ScienceDirect, Swets Information Services).
Indexed: ABIn, BAS, BLI, JEL.
—BLDSC (4547.095000), IE, Infotrieve, ingenta. **CCC.**
Published by: Elsevier BV, North-Holland (Subsidiary of: Elsevier Science & Technology), Sara Burgerhartstraat 25, Amsterdam, 1055 KV, Netherlands. TEL 31-20-485-3911, FAX 31-20-485-2457, nlinfo-f@elsevier.nl, http://www.elsevier.com/locate/iref, http://www.elsevier.nl. Eds. C. R. Chen, H. Beladi. **Subscr. to:** Elsevier BV, PO Box 211, Amsterdam 1000 AE, Netherlands. TEL 31-20-485-3757, FAX 31-20-485-3432, http://www.elsevier.nl.

➤ **INTERNEWSLETTER AFRIQUE**; la seule revue de presse Americaine en Francais sur l'Afrique. see *POLITICAL SCIENCE—International Relations*

338 USA ISSN 1076-6456
HD72
INTLEC CD-ROM✶ . Key Title: IntlEc CD-ROM. Variant title: Index to International Economics, Development and Finance. Text in English. q. USD 989 (effective 1999). **Document type:** *Abstract/Index.* **Description:** Provides bibliographic information on international development and related economic issues.
Media: CD-ROM (from Chadwyck-Healey Inc.).
Published by: (Joint Bank-Fund Library), ProQuest Information & Learning, 300 N Zeeb Rd., PO Box 1346, Ann Arbor, MI 48106-1346. TEL 800-752-0515, FAX 703-683-7589, mktg@chadwyck.com, info@il.proquest.com, http://www.chadwyck.com. Adv. contact Lauri Wooley. **Co-sponsors:** International Monetary Fund; International Bank for Reconstruction and Development.

INVESTING IN KWAZULU NATAL. see *BUSINESS AND ECONOMICS—Investments*

297.57 UAE
AL-IQTISAD AL-ISLAMI/ISLAMIC ECONOMY. Text in Arabic. 1981. m. **Description:** Comprehensive treatment of Islamic economic issues.
Published by: Bank Dubai al-Islami, PO Box 1080, Dubai, United Arab Emirates. TEL 285538, FAX 237243, TELEX 48772 ISLAMI EM. Ed. Muhammed Abdul Hakim Zuair. Circ: 5,000.

330.955 GBR ISSN 1474-1474
IRAN QUARTERLY FORECAST REPORT. Text in English. 1992. 3/yr. GBP 330, USD 495, EUR 450 (effective 2003). **Document type:** *Journal, Trade.* **Description:** Provides a comprehensive assessment of the Iranian government, economy and business environment. Helps to identify opportunities and reduce risk, and answers key questions facing executives at this time.
Formerly (until 2001): Annual Country Forecast Report. Iran (0966-8152)
Related titles: CD-ROM ed.: GBP 410, USD 675 (effective 2000); Online - full text ed.: (from EBSCO Publishing).
—CCC.
Published by: Business Monitor International Ltd., Mermaid House, 2 Puddle Dock, Blackfriars, London, EC4V 3DS, United Kingdom. TEL 44-20-72480468, FAX 44-20-72480467, subs@businessmonitor.com, http://www.businessmonitor.com.

330 GBR ISSN 1468-4691
HC471
IRAN REPORT. Text in English. 1989. q. GBP 290 per issue (effective 2002). adv. **Document type:** *Newsletter, Trade.* **Description:** Provides in-depth analysis of political and economic trends in Iran.
Formerly (until 1999): Iran Quarterly (0960-6475)
—BLDSC (4567.525500), IE.
Published by: M E E D - Emap Communications (Subsidiary of: Emap Business Communications Ltd.), 33-39 Bowling Green Lane, London, EC1R 0DA, United Kingdom. TEL 44-20-7470-6200, FAX 44-20-7837-8271, customerservice@meed.com, http://www.meed.com. Ed. David Butter.

330.9 IRN
IRAN TRADE & INDUSTRY ANNUAL REVIEW. Text in English. a. adv.
Published by: Echo Publications, Ave. Shiras, Kuche Khalhali No. 4, P O Box 2008, Teheran, Iran.

IRELAND. CENTRAL STATISTICS OFFICE. CENSUS OF INDUSTRIAL PRODUCTION. see *BUSINESS AND ECONOMICS—Abstracting, Bibliographies, Statistics*

IRELAND. CENTRAL STATISTICS OFFICE. CENSUS OF INDUSTRIAL PRODUCTION. PROVISIONAL RESULTS. see *BUSINESS AND ECONOMICS—Abstracting, Bibliographies, Statistics*

IRELAND. CENTRAL STATISTICS OFFICE. CONSUMER PRICE INDEX. see *BUSINESS AND ECONOMICS—Abstracting, Bibliographies, Statistics*

IRELAND. CENTRAL STATISTICS OFFICE. COUNTY INCOMES AND REGIONAL GDP. see *BUSINESS AND ECONOMICS—Abstracting, Bibliographies, Statistics*

IRELAND. CENTRAL STATISTICS OFFICE. INDUSTRIAL EARNINGS AND HOURS WORKED. see *BUSINESS AND ECONOMICS—Abstracting, Bibliographies, Statistics*

IRELAND. CENTRAL STATISTICS OFFICE. INDUSTRIAL EMPLOYMENT. see *BUSINESS AND ECONOMICS—Abstracting, Bibliographies, Statistics*

IRELAND. CENTRAL STATISTICS OFFICE. INDUSTRIAL PRODUCTION AND TURNOVER. see *BUSINESS AND ECONOMICS—Abstracting, Bibliographies, Statistics*

IRELAND. CENTRAL STATISTICS OFFICE. LABOUR COSTS SURVEY - IN INDUSTRY, DISTRIBUTION, CREDIT AND INSURANCE. see *BUSINESS AND ECONOMICS—Abstracting, Bibliographies, Statistics*

IRELAND. CENTRAL STATISTICS OFFICE. LIVE REGISTER ANALYSIS. see *BUSINESS AND ECONOMICS—Abstracting, Bibliographies, Statistics*

IRELAND. CENTRAL STATISTICS OFFICE. NATIONAL INCOME AND EXPENDITURE. FIRST RESULTS. see *BUSINESS AND ECONOMICS—Abstracting, Bibliographies, Statistics*

IRELAND. CENTRAL STATISTICS OFFICE. PRODCOM PRODUCT SALES. see *BUSINESS AND ECONOMICS—Abstracting, Bibliographies, Statistics*

IRELAND. CENTRAL STATISTICS OFFICE. PUBLIC SECTOR EMPLOYMENT EARNINGS. see *BUSINESS AND ECONOMICS—Abstracting, Bibliographies, Statistics*

IRELAND. CENTRAL STATISTICS OFFICE. WHOLESALE PRICE INDEX. see *BUSINESS AND ECONOMICS—Abstracting, Bibliographies, Statistics*

338.1 IRL
S219
IRELAND. DEPARTMENT OF AGRICULTURE AND FOOD. ANNUAL REPORT. Text in English. a. charts; stat. **Document type:** *Government.* **Description:** Presents the year's statistical information and reports on agricultural (both crop and livestock) production.
Former titles: Ireland. Minister for Agriculture, Food and Forestry. Annual Report (1393-0648); (until 1994): Ireland. Minister for Agriculture and Food. Annual Report (0791-0177); (until 1988): Ireland. Minister for Agriculture. Annual Report (0332-1088); (until 1977): Ireland. Minister for Agriculture and Fisheries. Annual Report (0075-0646)
Related titles: Online - full text ed.
Indexed: AnBrAb.
—CISTI.

Published by: Department of Agriculture, Food & Rural Development/An Roinn Talmhaiochta Bia Agus Forbartha Tuaithe, Agriculture House, Kildare St, Dublin, Dublin 2, Ireland. TEL 353-1-607-2000, information@daff.irlgov.ie, http://www.irlgov.ie/daff, http://www.irlgov.ie/daff/. Ed. Joe Walsh.

338.1 IRL
IRELAND. DEPARTMENT OF AGRICULTURE AND FOOD. ANNUAL REVIEW AND OUTLOOK; for agriculture and the food industry. Text in English. a. charts; stat. **Document type:** *Government.*
Related titles: Online - full text ed.
Published by: Department of Agriculture, Food & Rural Development/An Roinn Talmhaiochta Bia Agus Forbartha Tuaithe, Agriculture House, Kildare St, Dublin, Dublin 2, Ireland. TEL 353-1-607-2000, information@daff.irlgov.ie, http://www.irlgov.ie/daff/. Ed. Joe Walsh.

330.1 IRL ISSN 0791-7252
S3
IRELAND. DEPARTMENT OF AGRICULTURE AND FOOD. SCHEMES AND SERVICES (YEAR). Text in English. 1959. a. charts; stat. **Document type:** *Government.* **Description:** Reports on agricultural production in each area.
Former titles (until 1993): Ireland. Department of Agriculture and Food. Schemes and Services in Agriculture (1393-1954); (until 1991): Ireland. Department of Agriculture. Specially for the Farmer (0790-603X)
Related titles: Online - full text ed.
—CISTI.
Published by: Department of Agriculture, Food & Rural Development/An Roinn Talmhaiochta Bia Agus Forbartha Tuaithe, Agriculture House, Kildare St, Dublin, Dublin 2, Ireland. TEL 353-1-607-2000, information@daff.irlgov.ie, http://www.irlgov.ie/daff/. Ed. Joe Walsh.

ISSUES & VIEWS; an open forum on issues affecting the black community. see *ETHNIC INTERESTS*

330 ITA ISSN 0075-1995
ITALY. MINISTERO DEL BILANCIO E DELLA PROGRAMMAZIONE ECONOMICA. RELAZIONE GENERALE SULLA SITUAZIONE ECONOMICA DEL PAESE. Text in Italian. 1951. a. free.
Published by: Ministero del Bilancio, Via 20 Settembre, 97, Rome, RM, Italy. TELEX 626432.

330.9 ITA
ITALY. MINISTERO DEL BILANCIO E DELLA PROGRAMMAZIONE ECONOMICA. RELAZIONE PREVISIONALE E PROGRAMMATICA. Text in Italian. 1965. a. free.
Published by: Ministero del Bilancio e della Programmazione Economica, Via Venti Settembre, 97, Rome, RM 00187, Italy. TELEX 626432.

IVORY COAST. DIRECTION DE LA STATISTIQUE. BULLETIN MENSUEL DE STATISTIQUES. see *BUSINESS AND ECONOMICS—Abstracting, Bibliographies, Statistics*

330 AUT
JAHRBUCH DER OESTERREICHISCHEN WIRTSCHAFT. Text in German. 1969. a. free. **Document type:** *Government.*
Published by: Wirtschaftskammer Oesterreich, Wiedner Hauptstr 63, Vienna, 1045, Austria. Ed. Werner Filek-Wittinghausen.

330.9 DEU ISSN 0945-1749
HC462.95
JAPAN ANALYSEN PROGNOSEN. Text in German. 1986. m. **Document type:** *Bulletin, Academic/Scholarly.*
Published by: I F O Institut fuer Wirtschaftsforschung, Poschingerstr 5, Munich, 81679, Germany. TEL 49-89-9224-0, FAX 49-89-985369, ifo@ifo.de, http://www.ifo.de.

JAPAN AND THE WORLD ECONOMY. see *BUSINESS AND ECONOMICS—Economic Systems And Theories, Economic History*

JAPAN ECONOMIC ALMANAC; an annual in-depth report on the state of the Japanese economy. see *BUSINESS AND ECONOMICS—Production Of Goods And Services*

330.9 JPN ISSN 0449-4636
JAPAN ECONOMIC REVIEW✶. Text in English. 1969. m. USD 7. illus. reprints avail.
Related titles: Microfilm ed.: 1969.
Indexed: MEA&I, RASB.
Address: c/o Kyodo Tsushinsha, 9-20, Asaka 1-chome, Minato-ku, Tokyo, 107, Japan.

338 952 HKG ISSN 0379-2889
JAPAN LETTER. Text in Chinese. 1971. s-m. USD 195. **Document type:** *Newsletter.* **Description:** Covers business in Japan and the Japanese market.
Indexed: KES.
Published by: Asia Letter Group, GPO Box 10874, Hong Kong, Hong Kong. TEL 852-526-2950, FAX 852-526-7131. Ed. Charles R Smith.

338.9 USA
JAPAN TRADE CENTER INFORMATION SERVICE. MONTHLY ECONOMIC REPORT✶. Text in English. 1977 (no.150). m. free. charts; stat.
Published by: Ruder, Finn & Rotman, 301 E 57th St, New York, NY 10022. Circ: 200.

JAVERIANA. see *POLITICAL SCIENCE*

330.9 FRA ISSN 0982-1856
JEUNE AFRIQUE ECONOMIE. Text in French. 1981. m. FRF 630 domestic; FRF 420 in Africa; FRF 700 elsewhere. adv. **Document type:** *Newspaper.* **Description:** Reviews the politics and economies of the different countries in Africa.
Former titles (until 1986): Journal de l'Economie Africaine (0769-377X); (until 1985): Jeune Afrique Economie (0292-7357)
Indexed: IBR, IBZ, PAIS, RASB.
—IE. **CCC.**
Published by: Gideppe S.A., 58 rue de Lisbonne, Paris, 75008, France. gideppe@gideppe.fr. Ed. Blaise Pascal Talla. Adv. contact Jerome Millan. Circ: 50,000.

330 HKG ISSN 0013-0265
HC59
JINGJI DAOBAO/ECONOMIC REPORTER. Text in Chinese. 1947. w. HKD 720; HKD 950 in China; HKD 950 in Macau; USD 180 elsewhere. adv. charts; illus.; stat.
Indexed: BAS, HongKongiana, PAIS, RASB.
Published by: Economic Information & Agency, 342 Hennessy Rd 10th Fl, 10 th Fl, Wanchai, Hong Kong. TEL 852-573-8217, FAX 852-838-8304, TELEX 86990-EIA-HX. Ed. Chan Pak Kwan. Circ: 15,000.

JINGJI DILI/ECONOMIC GEOGRAPHY. see *GEOGRAPHY*

338.951 CHN ISSN 1000-7989
JINGJI GAIGE/ECONOMIC REFORM. Text in Chinese. 1985. bi-m. USD 24.80. adv. bk.rev. **Description:** Covers the theories and practices of the Chinese economic reform and management systems.
Related titles: Microfiche ed.
Published by: Shaanxi Sheng Shehui Kexueyuan/Shaanxi Academy of Social Sciences, No 7, Lingyuan Nanduan, Xi'an, Shaanxi 710061, China. TEL 029-54006. Ed. Yang Peiying. Circ: 8,000. **Dist. in US by:** China Books & Periodicals Inc, 360 Swift Ave., Ste. 48, S San Fran, CA 94080-6220. TEL 415-282-2994.

JINGJI YU GUANLI YANJIU/RESEARCH ON ECONOMICS AND MANAGEMENT. see *BUSINESS AND ECONOMICS—Management*

JINRONG SHIBAO/FINANCIAL NEWS. see *BUSINESS AND ECONOMICS—Banking And Finance*

THE JOINT ECONOMIC REPORT. see *PUBLIC ADMINISTRATION*

330.9 SVN ISSN 1580-4615
➤ **JOURNAL FOR INSTITUTIONAL INNOVATION, DEVELOPMENT AND TRANSITION.** Text in English. 1997. a. EUR 15 per issue (effective 2004). **Description:** Publishes papers dealing with Slovenian's economic and social development.
Formerly (until 1999): I B Review (1408-2136)
Related titles: Online - full text ed.: (from EBSCO Publishing).
Published by: Institute of Macroeconomic Analysis and Development, Gregorciceva 27, Ljubljana, 1000, Slovenia. TEL 386 1 478 1012, FAX 386 1 478 1070, gp.umar@gov.si, http://www.sigov.si/zmar/apublic/jiidt/ajiidt.php, http://www.sigov.si/zmar/apublic/ajiidt.php. Ed. Reiner Eichenberger.

➤ **JOURNAL OF ACCOUNTING AND ECONOMICS.** see *BUSINESS AND ECONOMICS—Accounting*

330.9 GBR ISSN 0963-8024
HC800.A1 CODEN: JAFECO
➤ **JOURNAL OF AFRICAN ECONOMIES.** Text in English. 1992. q. GBP 217, USD 401, EUR 326 to institutions; GBP 30, USD 56, EUR 45 in developing nations to institutions; GBP 228, USD 422, EUR 342 combined subscription to institutions print & online eds. (effective 2006). adv. bk.rev. illus. back issues avail.; reprint service avail. from PSC. **Document type:** *Journal, Academic/Scholarly.* **Description:** Aims to be a vehicle to carry rigorous economic analysis, focused entirely on Africa, for Africans and anyone interested in the continent.
Related titles: Online - full text ed.: ISSN 1464-3723. GBP 205, USD 379, EUR 308 to institutions (effective 2006) (from EBSCO Publishing, Gale Group, HighWire Press, IngentaConnect, O C L C Online Computer Library Center, Inc., Oxford University Press Online Journals, ProQuest Information & Learning, Swets Information Services).
Indexed: ABIn, ASD, BibInd, CJA, CurCont, GEOBASE, HelmAb, HerbAb, HortAb, I&DA, IBSS, IndVet, JEL, MaizeAb, RASB, RDA, RRTA, RiceAb, S&F, SSCI, TDB, TriticAb, WAE&RSA.
—BLDSC (4919.989500), IDS, IE, Infotrieve, ingenta. **CCC.**
Published by: (Centre for the Study of African Economies), Oxford University Press, Great Clarendon St, Oxford, OX2 6DP, United Kingdom. TEL 44-1865-556767, FAX 44-1865-556646, csaepub@economics.ox.ac.uk, jnl.orders@oup.co.uk, http://jae.oxfordjournals.org/, http://www.oxfordjournals.org/. Ed. Marcel Fafchamps. Pub. Martin Green. R&P Fiona Bennett. Adv. contact Helen Pearson. B&W page GBP 250, B&W page USD 420; 110 x 195. Circ: 700.

338.91 300 USA ISSN 1068-0055
HF3790.8
➤ **JOURNAL OF ASIAN BUSINESS.** Text in English. 1983. q. USD 45 domestic to individuals; USD 54 foreign to individuals; USD 60 domestic to institutions; USD 9 foreign to institutions (effective 2004). bk.rev. illus. reprints avail. **Document type:** *Journal, Academic/Scholarly.* **Description:** Covers political, economic, business, industrial, and cultural news, analysis, and commentary about Asia for American or other business academic-oriented studies.
Former titles: Journal of Southeast Asia Business (1055-2073); Southeast Asia Business (0886-6651)
Indexed: ABIn, APEL, BAS, BPI, IBSS.
—BLDSC (4947.234000), IE, Infotrieve, ingenta.
Published by: Southeast Asia Business Program, University of Michigan, 914 Hill St, Ann Arbor, MI 48109-1234. TEL 734-998-7276, FAX 734-936-1721, jab@umich.edu, http://www.umich.edu/~cibe/JAB/. Eds. Jason Eyster, Linda E Lim. Circ: 1,000.

330.9 NLD ISSN 1049-0078
HC460.5.A1
➤ **JOURNAL OF ASIAN ECONOMICS.** Text in English. 1990. 6/yr. EUR 95 in Europe to individuals; JPY 13,100 in Japan to individuals; USD 99 to individuals except Europe and Japan; EUR 417 in Europe to institutions; JPY 55,200 in Japan to institutions; USD 465 to institutions except Europe and Japan (effective 2006). adv. illus. back issues avail.; reprints avail. **Document type:** *Journal, Academic/Scholarly.* **Description:** Disseminates the increasingly growing body of research in Asian economic studies, examining special issues in adaptive innovation paradigms in Asian economic regimes, studies relative to unique dimensions of Asian economic paradigms, comparative studies of development paradigms of developing nations, the emerging pattern of comparative advantages between Asian countries and North America, and the emerging economic dimensions following the EU single-currency reforms.
Related titles: Microform ed.: (from PQC); Online - full text ed.: (from EBSCO Publishing, Gale Group, IngentaConnect, ScienceDirect, Swets Information Services).
Indexed: APEL, BAS, IndIslam, Inspec, JEL, PAIS, RDA.
—BLDSC (4947.238000), IE, Infotrieve, ingenta. **CCC.**
Published by: (American Committee on Asian Economic Studies GBR), Elsevier BV, North-Holland (Subsidiary of: Elsevier Science & Technology), Sara Burgerhartstraat 25, Amsterdam, 1055 KV, Netherlands. TEL 31-20-485-3911, FAX 31-20-485-2457, nlinfo-f@elsevier.nl, http://www.elsevier.com/locate/asieco, http://www.elsevier.nl. Ed. M. Dutta. **Subscr. to:** Elsevier BV, PO Box 211, Amsterdam 1000 AE, Netherlands. TEL 31-20-485-3757, FAX 31-20-485-3432, http://www.elsevier.nl.

330 AUS ISSN 0156-5826
➤ **JOURNAL OF AUSTRALIAN POLITICAL ECONOMY.** Text in English. 1977. s-a. AUD 25 (effective 2003). adv. bk.rev. **Document type:** *Journal, Academic/Scholarly.* **Description:** Presents progressive views on Australian economic, labor and social policy.
Related titles: Online - full text ed.: (from R M I T Publishing).
Indexed: AusPAIS, IBSS, JEL.
—BLDSC (4949.470000).
Published by: University of Sydney, School of Economics and Political Sciences, Rm 384, Merewether Bldg, Corner City Rd and Butlin Ave, Sydney, NSW 2006, Australia. TEL 61-2-9351-6625, FAX 61-2-9351-6635, n.towart@labor.org.au, economics@bullwinkle.econ.usyd.edu.au, http://www.jape.org. Ed. Frank Stilwell. Circ: 500 (paid).

➤ **JOURNAL OF BUSINESS AND ECONOMIC STATISTICS.** see *BUSINESS AND ECONOMICS—Abstracting, Bibliographies, Statistics*

▼ ➤ **JOURNAL OF BUSINESS CHEMISTRY.** see *CHEMISTRY*

330.9 GBR ISSN 1476-5284
▼ ➤ **JOURNAL OF CHINESE ECONOMICS AND BUSINESS STUDIES.** Text in English. 2003. 3/yr. GBP 206, USD 340 combined subscription to institutions print & online eds. (effective 2006). adv. **Document type:** *Journal, Academic/Scholarly.* **Description:** Aims to publish current and relevant findings from cutting edge research in Chinese economic, business and related issues.
Related titles: Online - full text ed.: ISSN 1476-5292. GBP 196, USD 323 to institutions (effective 2006) (from EBSCO Publishing, Gale Group, IngentaConnect, O C L C Online Computer Library Center, Inc., Swets Information Services).
Indexed: IBSS, JEL.
—BLDSC (4958.039000), IE.

Published by: (The Chinese Economic Association), Routledge (Subsidiary of: Taylor & Francis Group), 4 Park Sq, Milton Park, Abingdon, Oxon OX14 4RN, United Kingdom. TEL 44-1235-828600, FAX 44-1235-829000, info@routledge.co.uk, http://www.tandf.co.uk/journals/titles/14765284.asp, http://www.routledge.co.uk. **Subscr. to:** Taylor & Francis Ltd, Journals Customer Service, Rankine Rd, Basingstoke, Hants RG24 8PR, United Kingdom. TEL 44-1256-813000, FAX 44-1256-330245, enquiry@tandf.co.uk.

330 THA ISSN 0125-0566
JOURNAL OF COMMERCE. Text in English, Thai. 1976. m. THB 120. **Description:** Monthly report of consumer prices in Thailand.
Incorporates: Consumer Price Indexes for Thailand
Related titles: Online - full text ed.: (from Northern Light Technology, Inc.).
Published by: Department of Business Economics, Bangkok, Thailand.

330.9 AUS ISSN 1323-6903
HF5292
➤ **JOURNAL OF CONTEMPORARY ISSUES IN BUSINESS AND GOVERNMENT.** Text in English. 1995. s-a. AUD 44 domestic; AUD 50 foreign (effective 2000). back issues avail. **Document type:** *Academic/Scholarly.*
Related titles: Online - full text ed.
—BLDSC (4965.232000).
Published by: Curtin University of Technology, Curtin Business School, PO Box U1985, Perth, W.A. 6845, Australia. TEL 61-8-9266-7113, FAX 61-8-9266-2378, http://www.cbs.curtin.edu.au/mkt/journals/jcibg/index.htm. Ed. Allan Peachment.

330.9 GBR ISSN 1468-2702
HF1021
➤ **JOURNAL OF ECONOMIC GEOGRAPHY.** Text in English. 2000 (Dec). 5/yr. GBP 240, USD 444, EUR 360 to institutions; GBP 253, USD 468, EUR 380 combined subscription to institutions print & online eds. (effective 2006). adv. bk.rev. back issues avail.; reprint service avail. from PSC. **Document type:** *Journal, Academic/Scholarly.* **Description:** Focuses on the topics of the intersection between economics and geography, such as spatial agglomeration, regional patterns of growth and specialization, globalization, and the future of cities and regions with an editorial team drawn from economists and geographers. This journal seeks to be a forum for the exchange of ideas between the two disciplines.
Related titles: Online - full text ed.: ISSN 1468-2710. GBP 228, USD 422, EUR 342 to institutions (effective 2006) (from EBSCO Publishing, Gale Group, HighWire Press, IngentaConnect, O C L C Online Computer Library Center, Inc., Oxford University Press Online Journals, ProQuest Information & Learning, Swets Information Services).
Indexed: ABIn, CurCont, GEOBASE, JEL, SSCI.
—BLDSC (4973.010000), IE, Infotrieve. **CCC.**
Published by: Oxford University Press, Great Clarendon St, Oxford, OX2 6DP, United Kingdom. TEL 44-1865-556767, FAX 44-1865-556646, joeg.editor@utoronto.ca, jnl.orders@oup.co.uk, http://joeg.oxfordjournals.org/, http://www.oxfordjournals.org/. Eds. Diego Puga, Neil Wrigley. Pub. Martin Green. R&P Fiona Bennett. Adv. contact Helen Pearson. B&W page GBP 320, B&W page USD 520; 160 x 260. Circ: 350.

320.9 USA ISSN 1569-1721
HM548
▼ **THE JOURNAL OF ECONOMIC INEQUALITY.** Text in English. 2003 (Apr.). 3/yr. EUR 242, USD 242, GBP 152 combined subscription to institutions print & online eds. (effective 2005). bk.rev. reprint service avail. from PSC. **Document type:** *Academic/Scholarly.* **Description:** Includes articles about inequality of earnings as well as of household incomes. Provides a forum for a rigorous analysis of these issues, both at the theoretical and at the empirical level, as well as for a discussion of the policy implications of the research findings in this field.
Related titles: Online - full text ed.: ISSN 1573-8701 (from EBSCO Publishing, Gale Group, IngentaConnect, Kluwer Online, O C L C Online Computer Library Center, Inc., ProQuest Information & Learning, Springer LINK, Swets Information Services).
Indexed: ABIn, BibLing.
—BLDSC (4973.050500), IE. **CCC.**
Published by: Springer-Verlag New York, Inc. (Subsidiary of: Springer Science+Business Media), 233 Spring St, New York, NY 10013. TEL 212-460-1500, FAX 212-460-1575, service@springer-ny.com, http://springerlink.metapress.com/openurl.asp?genre=journal&issn=1569-1721, http://www.springer-ny.com. Ed. Jacques Silber. **Subscr. to:** Journal Fulfillment, PO Box 2485, Secaucus, NJ 07096-2485. TEL 201-348-4033, FAX 201-348-4505, journals@springer-ny.com.

JOURNAL OF EMERGING MARKETS. see *BUSINESS AND ECONOMICS—Banking And Finance*

JOURNAL OF ENVIRONMENT & DEVELOPMENT; a review of international policy. see *ENVIRONMENTAL STUDIES*

JOURNAL OF EUROPEAN INTEGRATION HISTORY/REVUE D'HISTOIRE DE L'INTEGRATION EUROPEENNE/ ZEITSCHRIFT FUER GESCHICHTE DER EUROPAEISCHEN INTEGRATION. see *POLITICAL SCIENCE—International Relations*

JOURNAL OF FINANCIAL MANAGEMENT AND ANALYSIS; international review of finance. see *BUSINESS AND ECONOMICS—Banking And Finance*

JOURNAL OF INTERNATIONAL RELATIONS AND DEVELOPMENT. see *POLITICAL SCIENCE—International Relations*

330.9 GBR ISSN 1354-7860
HC411
➤ **JOURNAL OF THE ASIA PACIFIC ECONOMY.** Text in English. 1995. 4/yr. GBP 358, USD 584 combined subscription to institutions print & online eds. (effective 2006). bk.rev. reprint service avail. from PSC. **Document type:** *Journal, Academic/Scholarly.* **Description:** Includes analyses that range from overview articles spanning the region to ones with a detailed focus on particular economic issues facing individual countries.
Related titles: Online - full text ed.: ISSN 1469-9648. GBP 340, USD 555 to institutions (effective 2006) (from EBSCO Publishing, Gale Group, IngentaConnect, O C L C Online Computer Library Center, Inc., Swets Information Services).
Indexed: ABIn, APEL, BAS, BrHumI, GEOBASE, IBR, IBSS, IBZ, IPSA, IndIslam, JEL.
—BLDSC (4947.219500), IE, Infotrieve, ingenta. **CCC.**
Published by: Routledge (Subsidiary of: Taylor & Francis Group), 4 Park Sq, Milton Park, Abingdon, Oxon OX14 4RN, United Kingdom. TEL 44-1235-828600, FAX 44-1235-829000, info@routledge.co.uk, http://www.tandf.co.uk/journals/titles/13547860.asp, http://www.routledge.co.uk. Eds. Anis Chowdhury, Iyanatul Islam. R&P Sally Sweet. **Subscr. to:** Taylor & Francis Ltd, Journals Customer Service, Rankine Rd, Basingstoke, Hants RG24 8PR, United Kingdom. TEL 44-1256-813000, FAX 44-1256-330245, enquiry@tandf.co.uk.

330.9 332.6 USA
JUDGE'S RETIREMENT SYSTEM. ANNUAL FINANCIAL REPORT AND REPORT OF OPERATIONS. Text in English. a. free. **Document type:** *Government.*
Published by: Judge's Retirement System, 400 P St, Rm 3450, Sacramento, CA 95814. TEL 916-326-3688. Circ: 3,000.

JURECO. see *LAW*

330.9 MYS ISSN 0127-1962
HC445.5.A1
JURNAL EKONOMI MALAYSIA. Short title: J E M. Text in English, Malay. 1980. s-a. USD 15.
Indexed: APEL, BAS.
Published by: Penerbit Universiti Kebangsaan Malaysia, Ukm Bangi, Selangor 43600, Malaysia. FAX 603-825-6484. Ed. Osman Rani. Circ: 500.

K D B REPORT. see *BUSINESS AND ECONOMICS*

330.9 JPN ISSN 0389-3030
HB9
KAGAWA DAIGAKU KEIZAI RONSO/KAGAWA UNIVERSITY ECONOMIC REVIEW. Text in Japanese. 1949. q. **Document type:** *Academic/Scholarly.*
—BLDSC (5081.136300).
Published by: (Kagawa Daigaku Keizai Kenkyusho/Institute of Economic Research), Kagawa Daigaku Keizai Gakkai/Economic Society Kagawa University, 2-1, Saiwai-cho, Takamatsu-shi, 760-0016, Japan.

330.9 CHN
KAIFA BAO/DEVELOPMENT NEWS. Text in Chinese. w. USD 46.50. **Document type:** *Newspaper.*
Address: 287 Heping Lu, Tianjin, China. TEL 31-6426. **Dist. in US by:** China Books & Periodicals Inc, 360 Swift Ave., Ste. 48, S San Fran, CA 94080-6220; **Dist. outside China by:** China International Book Trading Corp, 35 Chegongzhuang Xilu, Haidian District, PO Box 399, Beijing 100044, China.

363.7 JPN ISSN 0288-089X
KAIHATSU RONSHU/JOURNAL OF DEVELOPMENT POLICY STUDIES. Text in Japanese; Contents page in English. 1965. s-a. index. back issues avail. **Document type:** *Bulletin.* **Description:** Academic research in regional development policies.
Published by: Hokkai-Gakuen University, Center for Development Policy Studies, 4 Asahi-Machi, Toyohira-ku, Sapporo-shi, Hokkaido 062-0911, Japan. TEL 81-11-841-1161. Ed. Kyoshi Koda. R&P Kiyoshi Koda. Circ: 800.

330.9 NGA
KANO (STATE). DIRECTORY OF INDUSTRIAL & COMMERCIAL ESTABLISHMENTS. Text in English. 1985. quinquennial. USD 30 (effective 1996). **Document type:** *Government.*
Published by: Budget & Economic Planning Directorate, Ministry of Finance, Audu Bako Secretariat, PMB 3291, Kano, Kano State, Nigeria.

KANO (STATE). LOCAL GOVERNMENT SURVEY OF TOWNS, VILLAGES AND HAMLETS. see *BUSINESS AND ECONOMICS—Abstracting, Bibliographies, Statistics*

KANO (STATE). PRICES OF SELECTED COMMODITIES IN SOME TOWNS IN KANO STATE. see *BUSINESS AND ECONOMICS—Abstracting, Bibliographies, Statistics*

KANO (STATE). STATISTICAL YEAR - BOOK. see *BUSINESS AND ECONOMICS—Abstracting, Bibliographies, Statistics*

330.9 JPN ISSN 1344-8463
HB1
KANSAI UNIVERSITY REVIEW OF ECONOMICS. Variant title: Review of Economics. Text in English. 1999. a.
Supersedes in part (in 1998): Review of Economics and Business (0302-6574)
—BLDSC (5085.535500), CISTI.
Published by: Kansai University, Faculty of Economics, 3-3-35, Yamate-cho, Suita City, Osaka 564-8680, Japan.

330.9 USA ISSN 0734-2748
THE KANSAS CITY BUSINESS JOURNAL. Text in English. 1982. w. (Fri.). USD 90 (effective 2005). adv. **Document type:** *Newspaper.*
Related titles: Microform ed.: (from PQC); Online - full text ed.: (from Florida Center for Library Automation, Gale Group).
Indexed: BusDate, T&II.
—CCC.
Published by: American City Business Journals, Inc. (Kansas City), 1100 Main St., Ste. 210, Kansas City, MO 64105-5123. kansascity@bizjournlas.com, http://www.bizjournals.com/kansascity/. Eds. Paul Wenske, Brian Kaberline. Adv. contact Randy Grossert. Circ: 11,500 (paid). Wire service: PR.

330.9 USA
➤ **KANSAS ECONOMIC REPORT & KANSAS ECONOMIC INDICATORS.** Text in English. 1971. q. USD 50 (effective 2002). charts; stat. Supplement avail.; back issues avail. **Document type:** *Academic/Scholarly.* **Description:** Includes articles concerning business information and economic conditions and forecasts for the Wichita MSA, Kansas and the United States. Includes U.S., Kansas and Wichita economic indicators for the quarter.
Former titles (until Jan. 1998): Business and Economic Report and Kansas Economic Indicators; Kansas Economic Indicators; Business and Economic Report (1043-6227)
Related titles: Microfiche ed.: (from CIS); Online - full text ed.
Indexed: PAIS, SRI.
—BLDSC (5085.610000).
Published by: Center for Economic Development and Business Research (Subsidiary of: Wichita State University, W. Frank Barton School of Business), 2nd Floor, Devlin Hall, 1845 Fairmount, Wichita, KS 67260-0121. TEL 316-978-3225, FAX 316-978-3950, cedbr@wichita.edu, http://www.webs.wichita.edu/cedbr/. Eds. Janet Harrah, Mary Jane Townsend. R&P, Adv. contact Janet Harrah. Circ: 635.

330 JPN
KEIDANREN CLIP. Text in Japanese. 1951. bi-w. membership.
Formerly: Keidanren Shuho
Published by: Japan Federation of Economic Organizations/Keizai Dantai Rengokai (KEIDANREN), 9-4 Ote-Machi 1-chome, Chiyoda-ku, Tokyo, 100-0004, Japan. TEL 81-3-3279-1411, FAX 81-3-5255-6255. Circ: 5,000.

330 JPN
KEIDANREN SHIRYO. Text in Japanese. 1947. irreg. USD 10. charts; illus.; stat.
Formerly: Keidanren Keizai Shiryo
Published by: Japan Federation of Economic Organizations/Keizai Dantai Rengokai (KEIDANREN), 9-4 Ote-Machi 1-chome, Chiyoda-ku, Tokyo, 100-0004, Japan. TEL 81-3-3279-1411, FAX 81-3-5255-6255.

330.9 KEN
KENYA BUSINESS SPOTLIGHT. Text in English. 1983. m.
Published by: Native Publishers Ltd., PO Box 18379, Nairobi, Kenya. Ed. Christopher Mulei. **Dist. by:** Kenya Times Ltd., PO Box 30958, Nairobi, Kenya.

330.9 KEN ISSN 0075-5842
HC517.K4
KENYA. CENTRAL BUREAU OF STATISTICS. ECONOMIC SURVEY. Key Title: Economic Survey. Text in English. 1956. a. KES 850 (effective 2001). stat. back issues avail. **Document type:** *Government.*
Published by: Ministry of Finance and Planning, Central Bureau of Statistics, PO Box 30266, Nairobi, Kenya. TEL 254-2-333970, 254-2-317011, FAX 254-2-333030, http://www.treasury.go.ke.cbs. **Subscr. to:** Government Press, Haile Selaissie Ave., PO Box 30128, Nairobi, Kenya. TEL 254-2-334075.

330.9 GBR
KENYA YEARBOOK. Text in English. a. GBP 10, USD 30. adv. charts; illus.
Published by: New Product Newsletter Co. Ltd., 1a Chesterfield St, London, W1X 7HF, United Kingdom.

B

▼ new title ➤ refereed ✶ unverified ◆ full entry avail.

330.9 IND ISSN 0453-7440
➤ **KERALA; AN ECONOMIC REVIEW.** Text in English. 1959. a. price varies. charts; maps; stat. **Document type:** *Academic/Scholarly.* **Description:** Reports on the Development Plans of the Kerala State Planning Board, such as the Five Year Plans and the different aspects of the state's economy to support the planning process.
Published by: Kerala State Planning Board, Pattom, Thiruvananthapuram, Kerala 695 004, India. Circ: 2,000 (controlled).

330.9 USA
KERN COUNTY BUSINESS. Text in English. 1970. m. free. back issues avail. **Document type:** *Newsletter.* **Description:** Reports on local economic development, filmmaking, tourism and county government.
Published by: Kern County Board of Trade, 2101 Oak St., Bakersfield, CA 93301-3012. TEL 661-861-2367, FAX 661-861-2017, kerninfo@co.kern.ca.us, http://www.visitkern.com/. Ed., R&P Barry Zoeller. Adv. contact Aimee Barajas. Circ: 2,800.

330.9 CAN ISSN 0708-1553
KEY BUSINESS RATIOS. Text in English, French. 1965. a.
Formerly (until 1974): Key Business Ratios in Canada (0316-4217)
Published by: D & B Companies of Canada Ltd., 5770 Hurontario St, Mississauga, ON L5R 3GH, Canada. TEL 905-568-6000, 800-463-6362, FAX 905-568-6197, 800-668-7800, cic@dnb.com, http://www.dnb.ca.

330.9 LBN
KEY INDICATORS. Text in Arabic, English. m. **Description:** Includes statitics on a number of closely watched economic indicators.
Published by: Association of Banks in Lebanon, DORA Centre Moucarri, P O Box 80536, Beirut, Lebanon.

KEY NOTE MARKET ASSESSMENT. ABC1 CONSUMER. see *SOCIOLOGY*

330.9 GBR
KEY NOTE MARKET REPORT: PLANT HIRE. Variant title: Plant Hire. Text in English. irreg., latest 2001, Feb. GBP 340 per issue (effective 2002). **Document type:** *Trade.* **Description:** Provides an overview of a specific UK market segment and includes executive summary, market definition, market size, industry background, competitor analysis, current issues, forecasts, company profiles, and more.
Formerly: Key Note Report: Plant Hire
Related titles: CD-ROM ed.; Online - full text ed.
Published by: Key Note Ltd., Field House, 72 Oldfield Rd, Hampton, Mddx TW12 2HQ, United Kingdom. TEL 44-20-8481-8750, FAX 44-20-8783-0049, info@keynote.co.uk, http://www.keynote.co.uk. Ed. Dominic Fenn.

KEY STATISTICS OF THAILAND (YEAR). see *BUSINESS AND ECONOMICS—Abstracting, Bibliographies, Statistics*

KIA ECONOMIC RESEARCH INSTITUTE. ECONOMIC FORUM. see *TRANSPORTATION—Automobiles*

330.9 DEU ISSN 0342-0787
HB5
➤ **KIELER ARBEITSPAPIERE/KIEL WORKING PAPERS.** Text in English, German. 1973. irreg. EUR 6 per issue (effective 2002). abstr.; bibl. **Document type:** *Monographic series, Academic/Scholarly.* **Description:** Presents preliminary results of research projects within the Kiel Institute.
Indexed: AgBio, ForAb, PGegResA, RDA, RRTA, S&F, WAE&RSA.
—BLDSC (9349.640000), IE, ingenta.
Published by: Institut fuer Weltwirtschaft, Duesternbrooker Weg 120, Kiel, 24105, Germany. TEL 49-431-8814305, FAX 49-431-85853, TELEX 292479-WELTW-D, info@ifw.uni-kiel.de, http://www.uni-kiel.de/ifw. Ed. Horst Siebert. R&P Dr. Harmen Lehment. Circ: 150.

330.9 DEU ISSN 0455-0420
HB44
➤ **KIELER DISKUSSIONSBEITRAEGE/KIEL DISCUSSION PAPERS.** Text in English, German. 1969. irreg., latest vol.388, 2002. EUR 8 per issue (effective 2002). **Document type:** *Monographic series, Academic/Scholarly.* **Description:** Deals with current economic problems.
Indexed: DIP, IBR, IBZ, RASB, RefZh.
—BLDSC (5094.680000).
Published by: Institut fuer Weltwirtschaft, Duesternbrooker Weg 120, Kiel, 24105, Germany. TEL 49-431-8814305, FAX 49-431-85853, info@ifw.uni-kiel.de, http://www.uni-kiel.de/ifw. Ed. Horst Siebert. R&P Dr. Harmen Lehment. Circ: 900.

330.9 DEU ISSN 0173-5241
HF1410
➤ **KIELER KURZBERICHTE.** Text in German. irreg. **Document type:** *Bulletin, Academic/Scholarly.*
Published by: Institut fuer Weltwirtschaft, Duesternbrooker Weg 120, Kiel, 24105, Germany. TEL 49-431-8814305, FAX 49-431-85853, info@ifw.uni-kiel.de, http://www.uni-kiel.de/ifw. Ed. Dietmar Gebert. R&P Dr. Harmen Lehment.

330.9 DEU ISSN 0340-6970
➤ **KIELER VORTRAEGE.** Text in German, English. a. EUR 6 (effective 2002). reprint service avail. from SCH. **Document type:** *Monographic series, Academic/Scholarly.*
Published by: Institut fuer Weltwirtschaft, Duesternbrooker Weg 120, Kiel, 24105, Germany. TEL 49-431-8814305, FAX 49-431-85853, info@ifw.uni-kiel.de, http://www.uni-kiel.de/ifw. Ed. Horst Siebert. R&P Dr. Harmen Lehment.

338 NLD ISSN 0023-1363
HC321
KIJK OP HET NOORDEN/OUTLOOK ON THE NORTH; signalement van de economische ontwikkeling in de provincies Groningen, Friesland en Drenthe. Text in Dutch. 1969. 10/yr. EUR 40 (effective 2002). adv. Website rev. tr.lit. **Document type:** *Magazine, Consumer.*
—IE, Infotrieve.
Published by: Uitgeverij Ten Brink, Postbus 41, Meppel, 7940 AA, Netherlands. TEL 31-522-855306, FAX 31-522-855300. Ed. Tjakko Kars. R&P Harriet Koning. Adv. contact B Althusius. Circ: 10,000.

332 USA ISSN 1531-7692
KIPLINGER BUSINESS FORECASTS. Text in English. 2000. d. USD 84 (effective 2003). **Document type:** *Trade.*
Media: Online - full content. **Related titles:** Online - full text ed.: (from Gale Group).
Published by: Kiplinger Washington Editors, Inc., 1729 H St, N W, Washington, DC 20006. TEL 202-887-6400, FAX 202-778-8976, letterresponse@kiplinger.com, http://special.kiplinger.com/home/, http://www.kiplinger.com.

KOMPASS ITALIA - ANNUARIO GENERALE DELL'ECONOMIA ITALIANA. see *BUSINESS AND ECONOMICS—Abstracting, Bibliographies, Statistics*

338 DEU ISSN 1610-7586
▼ **KONJUNKTUR;** Studien zur innovativen Konjunktur- und Wachstumsforschung. Text in German. 2003. irreg., latest vol.2, 2003. price varies. **Document type:** *Monographic series, Academic/Scholarly.*
Published by: Verlag Dr. Kovac, Arnoldstr 49, Hamburg, 22763, Germany. TEL 49-40-3988800, FAX 49-40-39888055, info@verlagdrkovac.de, http://www.verlagdrkovac.de/15-4.htm.

330.9 DEU
KONJUNKTUR IN BAYERN. Text in German. 1981. m. free. stat. **Document type:** *Government.* **Description:** Survey of the business climate of Bavarian industry, and other economic indicators.
Formerly (until 1994): Bericht zur Aktuellen Konjunkturlage im Bundesgebiet und in Bayern
Published by: Staatsministerium fuer Wirtschaft Verkehr und Technologie, Prinzregentenstr 28, Munich, 80525, Germany. FAX 49-89-2162-2614, http://www.stmwvt.bayern.de, http://www.stmwvt.bayern.de/bayerns-wirtschaft-in-zahlen/konjunktur. Circ: 900.

330.9 SWE ISSN 0282-9967
KONJUNKTUREN. Text in Swedish. 1980. 4/yr. SEK 600 (effective 2000). **Document type:** *Journal, Trade.* **Description:** Contains a report from the Department of Economic and Fiscal Policy.
Formerly (until 1985): SIKonjunkturen (0349-4845)
Published by: Industrifoerbundet/Federation of Swedish Industries, Fack 5501, Stockholm, 11485, Sweden. Ed. Lena Hagman.

KOREA (REPUBLIC). NATIONAL STATISTICAL OFFICE. ANNUAL REPORT ON CONSUMER PRICE INDEX/MULGA YONBO. see *BUSINESS AND ECONOMICS—Abstracting, Bibliographies, Statistics*

KOREA (REPUBLIC). NATIONAL STATISTICAL OFFICE. ANNUAL REPORT ON THE FAMILY INCOME AND EXPENDITURE SURVEY. see *BUSINESS AND ECONOMICS—Abstracting, Bibliographies, Statistics*

330 KOR ISSN 0017-744X
KOREA DEVELOPMENT BANK. MONTHLY ECONOMIC REVIEW. Text in Korean. 1964. m. free. charts; stat. cum.index.
Published by: Korea Development Bank, 10-2 Kwanch'ol-dong, Chongno-gu, C.P.O. Box 28, Seoul, Korea, S. Ed. Beoung Yun Min.

330.9 KOR
KOREA ECONOMIC QUARTERLY. Text in Korean. 1995. q.
Published by: Korea Economic Research Institute, Yeongdungpo-ku, 28-1 Yoido dong, Seoul, 150756, Korea, S. TEL 82-2-3771-0001, FAX 82-2-785-0270, http://www.keri.com.

KOREA ECONOMIC REPORT. see *BUSINESS AND ECONOMICS*

330.9 KOR
KOREA ECONOMIC WEEKLY. Text in English. 1988. w. KRW 60,000 domestic in Central & S. America, Africa; USD 170 in China, Taiwan, Hong Kong, Macao, Japan; USD 200 in Thailand, the Philippines, Singapore, Malaysia, Indonesia; USD 220 in Central & S. America, Africa; USD 210 elsewhere (effective 2000). **Document type:** *Newspaper.* **Description:** Provides indepth coverage of wide range of world issues, analysis, and reports.
Media: Online - full text.
Published by: Korea Economic Daily Co. Ltd., 4th Fl WISE-Naeil Venture Center, 154-11 Samsung-dong, Kangnam-gu, Seoul, 154-11, Korea, S. TEL 82-2-3430-2177, FAX 82-2-3430-2170, subscription@koreaeconomy.com, http://eco.ked.co.kr/h-kew.html, http://www.koreaeconomy.com. Ed. Timothy M Chung. Pub. Kim Tae-han.

330.9 KOR
KOREA INSTITUTE OF FINANCE. PANEL DISCUSSIONS FOR THE ANALYSIS OF THE KOREAN ECONOMY. PROCEEDINGS. Text in Korean. irreg. **Description:** Discusses current issues concerning the Korean economy and formulate policy recommendations.
Published by: Korea Institute of Finance, 4 1 1 Ga Myong dong, Chung-gu, Seoul, 100012, Korea, S. TEL 82-2-3705-6300, FAX 82-2-3705-6309, wmaster@sun.kif.re.kr, http://www.kif.re.kr.

330.9 KOR
KOREA INSTITUTE OF FINANCE. QUARTERLY FINANCIAL REVIEW; analysis and forecast. Variant title: Quarterly Financial Review. Text in Korean. q. **Description:** Provides analysis and forecasts on the performance and development of the international financial markets, the macro economy of Korea, and domestic financial markets.
Published by: Korea Institute of Finance, 4 1 1 Ga Myong dong, Chung-gu, Seoul, 100012, Korea, S. TEL 82-2-3705-6300, FAX 82-2-3705-6309, wmaster@sun.kif.re.kr, http://www.kif.re.kr.

KOREA POLICY SERIES. see *POLITICAL SCIENCE*

330.9 KOR
KOREAN ECONOMIC AND FINANCIAL OUTLOOK. Text in English. 1996. bi-m. **Description:** Analyzes and forecasts macroeconomic performances and developments in the money and financial markets in Korea and abroad.
Published by: Korea Institute of Finance, 4 1 1 Ga Myong dong, Chung-gu, Seoul, 100012, Korea, S. TEL 82-2-3705-6300, FAX 82-2-3705-6309, wmaster@sun.kif.re.kr, http://www.kif.re.kr. **Subscr. to:** KPO Box 1267, Seoul, Korea, S.

KRATKOSROCHNYE EKONOMICHESKIE POKAZATELI ROSSIISKOI FEDERATSII/SHORT-TERM INDICATORS OF THE RUSSIA'S ECONOMY. see *BUSINESS AND ECONOMICS—Abstracting, Bibliographies, Statistics*

330.9 KWT ISSN 1016-4278
KUWAIT & GULF ECONOMIC AND FINANCIAL BULLETIN. Key Title: Kuwait & Gulf Cooperation Council. Economic & Financial Bulletin. Text in English. 1982. q. free. back issues avail.
Former titles (until 1987): Kuwait Economic and Financial Bulletin (1016-426X); Economics and Financial Quarterly; Kuwait Economic and Financial Quarterly
Indexed: WBA.
Published by: National Bank of Kuwait S.A.K., Economic Research and Planning Division, P O Box 95, Safat, 13001, Kuwait. TEL 965-2422011, FAX 965-2466260, TELEX 22451. Circ: 6,000.

KYKLOS; internationale Zeitschrift fuer Sozialwissenschaften. see *SOCIOLOGY*

L A R F REPORT. ANNUAL. see *BUSINESS AND ECONOMICS*

330.9 FRA ISSN 1260-8556
L A T E C. DOCUMENT DE TRAVAIL. (Laboratoire d'Analyse et de Techniques Economiques) Text in French. 199?. irreg.
Published by: (France. Centre National de la Recherche Scientifique), Universite de Bourgogne, Faculte de Science Economique et de Gestion, BP 26611, Dijon, 21066 Cedex, France. http://ungaro.u-bourgogne.fr/pagelatec/DOCUMENT/ECONOMIE/Economie.htm.

L S M S WORKING PAPER. (Living Standards Measurement Study) see *BUSINESS AND ECONOMICS—International Development And Assistance*

330.9 USA
LA CROSSE AREA BUSINESS AND ECONOMIC REVIEW. Text in English. 1977. q. donation. **Document type:** *Trade.*
Former titles: La Crosse - Winona Business and Economic Review; La Crosse Economic Indicators
Published by: University of Wisconsin at La Crosse, 1725 State St, La Crosse, WI 54601. TEL 608-785-8782. Ed. Jan Gallagher.

B

330.9 USA ISSN 1048-2822
LAFAYETTE BUSINESS DIGEST. Text in English. 1983. w. USD 43.95 (effective 1999). adv. cum.index: 1983-1990. back issues avail. **Document type:** *Newspaper.* **Description:** Includes business news, trends, and features highlighting business and industry in Tippecanoe County and surrounding area.
Related titles: Microfilm ed.: (from PQC); Online - full text ed.: (from Northern Light Technology, Inc., O C L C Online Computer Library Center, Inc., ProQuest Information & Learning).
Indexed: ABIn, BusDate.
Published by: Kapp Crowell Communications, PO Box 587, Lafayette, IN 47902. TEL 765-742-6918, FAX 765-423-8133. Pub. Jennifer Kapp. Circ: 2,000.

352.14 GBR
LANCASHIRE COUNTY COUNCIL. PLANNING REPORT. Text in English. irreg., latest vol.5, 1995. GBP 10. **Document type:** *Government.*
Published by: Lancashire County Council, East Cliff County Office, Lancashire County Council, P O Box 160, Preston, PR1 3EX, United Kingdom.

330.9 MYS
LAPORAN KETUA ODIT NEGARA. KERAJAAN PERSEKUTUAN. Text in Malay. a.
Published by: Jabatan Percetakan Negara, Kuala Lumpur, Malaysia.

330.98 GBR ISSN 1475-519X
HG183.L3
LATIN AMERICA FINANCIAL ALERT. Text in English. 50/yr. GBP 585, USD 950 (effective 2000). **Document type:** *Trade.* **Description:** Provides briefings on key business and finance developments as well as the week's significant new economic indicator. Highlights the change in political risk.
Formerly: Latin America Weekly Economic Alert (1460-5031)
Related titles: E-mail ed.; Fax ed.; Online - full text ed.: (from EBSCO Publishing, Florida Center for Library Automation).
—CCC.
Published by: Business Monitor International Ltd., Mermaid House, 2 Puddle Dock, Blackfriars, London, EC4V 3DS, United Kingdom. TEL 44-20-72480468, FAX 44-20-72480467, subs@businessmonitor.com, busmon@dial.pipex.com, http://www.businessmonitor.com.

THE LATIN AMERICA MINING RECORD/PERIODICO DE MINERIA LATINO AMERICANA. see *MINES AND MINING INDUSTRY*

330.98 GBR ISSN 0265-9093
LATIN AMERICA MONITOR. ANDEAN GROUP. Text in English. m. GBP 180, USD 295 (effective 2000). **Document type:** *Trade.* **Description:** Provides analysis of the most recent changes to the political and business environment in Bolivia, Colombia, Ecuador, Peru, and Venezuela.
Related titles: Online - full text ed.: (from EBSCO Publishing, Florida Center for Library Automation).
Indexed: RASB.
—CISTI. **CCC.**
Published by: Business Monitor International Ltd., Mermaid House, 2 Puddle Dock, Blackfriars, London, EC4V 3DS, United Kingdom. TEL 44-20-72480468, FAX 44-20-72480467, subs@businessmonitor.com, http://www.businessmonitor.com.

330.981 GBR ISSN 0969-5966
LATIN AMERICA MONITOR. BRAZIL. Text in English. 1993. m. GBP 180, USD 295 (effective 2000). **Document type:** *Trade.* **Description:** Provides analysis of the most recent changes to the political and business environment.
Supersedes in part (1984-1993): Latin American Monitor. 1, Mexico and Brazil (0265-6841)
Related titles: Online - full text ed.: (from EBSCO Publishing, Florida Center for Library Automation).
Indexed: RASB.
—CISTI. **CCC.**
Published by: Business Monitor International Ltd., Mermaid House, 2 Puddle Dock, Blackfriars, London, EC4V 3DS, United Kingdom. TEL 44-20-72480468, FAX 44-20-72480467, busmon@dial.pipex.com, subs@businessmonitor.com, http://www.businessmonitor.com.

330.9729 GBR ISSN 0265-9115
LATIN AMERICA MONITOR. CARIBBEAN. Text in English. m. GBP 180, USD 295 (effective 2000). **Document type:** *Trade.* **Description:** Provides analysis of the most recent changes to the political and business environment in the Bahamas, Barbados, Belize, Cuba, Dominican Republic, East Caribbean, Guyana, Haiti, Jamaica, Puerto Rico, Suriname, and Trinidad and Tobago.
Related titles: Online - full text ed.: (from EBSCO Publishing, Florida Center for Library Automation).
Indexed: RASB.
—CISTI. **CCC.**
Published by: Business Monitor International Ltd., Mermaid House, 2 Puddle Dock, Blackfriars, London, EC4V 3DS, United Kingdom. TEL 44-20-72480468, FAX 44-20-72480467, subs@businessmonitor.com, busmon@dial.pipex.com, http://www.businessmonitor.com.

330.9728 GBR ISSN 0265-9085
LATIN AMERICA MONITOR. CENTRAL AMERICA. Text in English. m. GBP 180, USD 295 (effective 2000). **Document type:** *Trade.* **Description:** Provides analysis of the most recent changes to the political and business environment in Costa Rica, El Salvador, Guatemala, Honduras, Nicaragua, and Panama.
Related titles: Online - full text ed.: (from EBSCO Publishing, Florida Center for Library Automation).
Indexed: RASB.
—CISTI. **CCC.**
Published by: Business Monitor International Ltd., Mermaid House, 2 Puddle Dock, Blackfriars, London, EC4V 3DS, United Kingdom. TEL 44-20-72480468, FAX 44-20-72480467, subs@businessmonitor.com, busmon@dial.pipex.com, http://www.businessmonitor.com.

330.972 GBR ISSN 0969-5974
LATIN AMERICA MONITOR. MEXICO. Text in English. 1993. m. GBP 180, USD 295 (effective 2000). **Document type:** *Trade.* **Description:** Provides analysis of the most recent changes to the political and business environment.
Supersedes in part (1983-1993): Latin American Monitor. 1, Mexico and Brazil (0265-6841)
Related titles: Online - full text ed.: (from EBSCO Publishing).
Indexed: RASB.
—CISTI. **CCC.**
Published by: Business Monitor International Ltd., Mermaid House, 2 Puddle Dock, Blackfriars, London, EC4V 3DS, United Kingdom. TEL 44-20-72480468, FAX 44-20-72480467, subs@businessmonitor.com, busmon@dial.pipex.com, http://www.businessmonitor.com.

330.98 GBR ISSN 0265-9107
LATIN AMERICA MONITOR. SOUTHERN CONE. Text in English. m. GBP 180, USD 295 (effective 2000). **Document type:** *Trade.* **Description:** Provides analysis of the most recent changes to the political and business environment in Argentina, Chile, Paraguay, and Uruguay.
Related titles: Online - full text ed.: (from EBSCO Publishing).
Indexed: RASB.
—CISTI. **CCC.**
Published by: Business Monitor International Ltd., Mermaid House, 2 Puddle Dock, Blackfriars, London, EC4V 3DS, United Kingdom. TEL 44-20-72480468, FAX 44-20-72480467, subs@businessmonitor.com, http://www.businessmonitor.com.

330.9 GBR ISSN 0968-4972
HC121
LATIN AMERICAN CONSENSUS FORECASTS. Text in English. m. GBP 363, USD 573 (effective 2003). back issues avail. **Document type:** *Journal, Academic/Scholarly.* **Description:** Covers growth, inflation, and trade forecasts. Includes special surveys, foreign exchange forecasts, country analysis and historical data.
Related titles: Diskette ed.; E-mail ed.
—IE.
Published by: Consensus Economics Inc., 53 Upper Brook St, London, W1K 2LT, United Kingdom. TEL 44-20-7491-3211, FAX 44-20-7409-2331, editors@consensuseconomics.com, http://www.consensuseconomics.com. Eds. Claire V M Hubbard, Suyin Kan. Pub. Philip M Hubbard.

LATIN AMERICAN FINANCE EXECUTIVE REPORT. see *BUSINESS AND ECONOMICS—Investments*

338.9 GBR ISSN 0143-5248
HC161
LATIN AMERICAN REGIONAL REPORTS - ANDEAN GROUP. Text in English. 10/yr. GBP 155, USD 215 (effective 2001). back issues avail. **Document type:** *Trade.* **Description:** News and analysis on the Andean Group Countries.
Related titles: Online - full text ed.
Indexed: RASB.
—IE, Infotrieve.
Published by: Latin American Newsletters (Subsidiary of: Lettres (U.K.) Ltd.), 61 Old St, London, EC1V 9HW, United Kingdom. TEL 44-20-7251-0012, FAX 44-20-7253-8193, subs@latinnews.com, http://www.latinnews.com. Ed. Eduardo Crawley. R&P Alex McHallam TEL 44-20-7251-0012.

338.9 GBR ISSN 0143-5280
F1401
LATIN AMERICAN WEEKLY REPORT. Text in English. 1967. w. (50/yr.). GBP 708, USD 955 (effective 2001). adv. back issues avail. **Document type:** *Newsletter.* **Description:** Weekly report on Latin American issues.
Related titles: Online - full text ed.
Indexed: KES, RASB.
—IE, Infotrieve.
Published by: Latin American Newsletters (Subsidiary of: Lettres (U.K.) Ltd.), 61 Old St, London, EC1V 9HW, United Kingdom. TEL 44-20-7251-0012, FAX 44-20-7253-8193, subs@latinnews.com, http://www.latinnews.com. Ed. Eduardo Crawley. R&P Alex McHallam TEL 44-20-7251-0012.

330.9 658.8 CAN ISSN 0834-3586
LEADS. Text in English. 1981. bi-m. price varies. bk.rev. **Description:** Follows the rebirth of free enterprise in the explosive multi-level marketing industry, provides opportunity for secondary incomes seekers, promotes barter, educates the new breed of shop-at-home consumer and advocates monetary reform.
Address: P O Box 9333, Ottawa, ON K1G 3V1, Canada. TEL 800-927-1527, FAX 1-613-746-2053. Ed. Tom Kennedy. Circ: 2,000.

LEBANON REPORT. see *POLITICAL SCIENCE—International Relations*

LECTURAS DE ECONOMIA. see *BUSINESS AND ECONOMICS—Abstracting, Bibliographies, Statistics*

LEISURE FUTURES. see *LEISURE AND RECREATION*

330.9 LSO
LESOTHO NATIONAL DEVELOPMENT CORPORATION. NEWSLETTER. Text in English. irreg. **Document type:** *Newsletter.*
Published by: Lesotho National Development Corporation, PO Box 666, Maseru, Lesotho.

330.9 FRA ISSN 1261-7903
LA LETTRE DE L'INSERTION PAR L'ACTIVITE ECONOMIQUE. Text in French. 1995. m. EUR 38.90 per issue domestic; EUR 45.70 per issue in Europe; EUR 45.70 per issue French speaking Africa; EUR 53.40 per issue elsewhere (effective 2002).
Published by: Alternatives Economiques, 28 rue du Sentier, Paris, 75002, France. TEL 33-01-44882890, FAX 33-01-40284358, http://www.alternatives-economiques.fr.

330.9 ISR ISSN 0334-9160
LEUMI REVIEW; Israel: macroperspectives. Text in English. 1952. irreg. (approx. 3/yr.). free. charts; mkt.; stat. **Document type:** *Trade.*
Formed by the merger of: Bank Leumi Israel Macroperspectives; Bank Leumi Economic Review (0034-6519); Formerly: Review of Economic Conditions in Israel
Indexed: WBA.
Published by: Bank Leumi Le-Israel, Economics Department, P O Box 2, Tel Aviv, 61000, Israel. TEL 972-3-5148737, FAX 972-3-5147375, shifron@bll.co.il, http://www.bankleumi.co.il/english/. Eds. Eyal Raz, Gad Shifron. Circ: 8,000.

338 USA
THE LEVY INSTITUTE FORECAST. Text in English. 1949. 12/yr. looseleaf. USD 295 (effective 1998). charts. back issues avail. **Document type:** *Newsletter.* **Description:** Newsletter on financial, business, and economic indicators and prospects, based on production, housing, inventory, and other key statistics.
Formerly: Industry Forecast
Published by: Bard College, Jerome Levy Economics Institute, Forecasting Center, 69 S. Moger Ave., Mount Kisko, NY 10549. TEL 888-244-8617, FAX 914-666-0725. Eds. David A Levy, S Jay Levy. R&P David A Levy.

LEXIKON DES STEUER- UND WIRTSCHAFTSRECHTS. see *LAW*

330.9 CHN
LIAONING JINGJI RIBAO/LIAONING ECONOMIC DAILY. Text in Chinese. d. CNY 110.16. adv. **Document type:** *Newspaper.*
Formerly: Liaoning Jinji Bao - Liaoning Economic Weekly
Published by: Liaoning Jingji Ribao She, Shenyang, Liaoning, China. TEL 86-24-2484-5784. Ed. Feng Chang Jiang. Adv. contact Xiao Peng Chen. **Dist. in US by:** China International Book Trading Corp, 35 Chegongzhuang Xilu, Haidian District, PO Box 399, Beijing 100044, China. TEL 86-10-68412045, FAX 86-10-68412023, cibtc@mail.cibtc.com.cn, http://www.cibtc.com.cn.

330.9 GBR ISSN 0267-7164
LIBERTARIAN ALLIANCE. ECONOMIC NOTES. Text in English. 1985. irreg. GBP 15, USD 30. adv. bk.rev.; film rev. bibl. back issues avail. **Document type:** *Monographic series.*
Published by: Libertarian Alliance, 2 Landsdowne Row, Ste 35, London, W1J 6HL, United Kingdom. TEL 44-20-7821-5502, FAX 44-20-7834-2031, liberty@capital.demon.co.uk, nigel@libertarian.co.uk, http://www.digiweb.com/igeldard/la. Ed. Brian Micklethwait. Pub. Chris Tame. Circ: 1,000.

330.9 USA
LIBERTY AT BAY; issues impacting on freedom in our time. Text in English, Spanish. 1982. bi-w. looseleaf. USD 685 (effective 2002). adv. bk.rev.; film rev.; software rev.; Website rev. charts. cum.index: 1982-1994. 5 p./no. 2 cols./p.; **Document type:** *Newsletter.* **Description:** Analysis of international economic and political issues affecting wealthy individuals.
Related titles: Microfiche ed.
Published by: Aura Publishing Co., PO Box 1367, Scarsdale, NY 10583. TEL 914-337-5552, FAX 775-254-1961, rsandell@aura.com, info@aural.com, http://www.aura1.com, http://www.aura.com. Ed. Richard A Sandell. Pub. Arnold P Josevie. Adv. contact Marcel Aurevie. Circ: 2,400 (paid); 280 (controlled).

B

▼ new title ➤ refereed ✶ unverified ◆ full entry avail.

LINE56.COM. see *COMPUTERS—Internet*

LINE56 E-BUSINESS JOURNAL. see *COMPUTERS—Internet*

LINK; Israel's international business magazine. see *BUSINESS AND ECONOMICS—International Commerce*

LIST OF ITALIAN STOCKS. see *BUSINESS AND ECONOMICS—Investments*

LITIGATION ECONOMICS DIGEST. see *BUSINESS AND ECONOMICS—Domestic Commerce*

LOCAL WORK. see *BUSINESS AND ECONOMICS—Labor And Industrial Relations*

330.9 JPN
LONG-TERM ECONOMIC FORECAST. Text in Japanese; Summaries in English. 1970. a. JPY 13,500 (effective 2000).
Description: Focuses on specific topics in the Japanese and world economy.
Published by: (Publications Department), Japan Center for Economic Research, Nikkei Kayabacho Bldg, 6-1 Nihonbashikayaba-cho 2-chome, Chuo-ku, Tokyo, 103-0025, Japan. TEL 81-3-3639-2801, FAX 81-3-3639-2839.

330.9 USA ISSN 0194-2603
LOS ANGELES BUSINESS JOURNAL. Text in English. 1979. w. (Mon.). USD 99.95 combined subscription print & online eds. (effective 2005). adv. back issues avail. **Document type:** *Newspaper.* **Description:** Carries comprehensive coverage of local business news as well as vital statistics on the economy.
Related titles: Microform ed.: (from PQC); Online - full text ed.: (from Florida Center for Library Automation, Gale Group, Northern Light Technology, Inc., ProQuest Information & Learning).
Indexed: BusDate, T&II.
—CCC.
Published by: California Business Journals, 5700 Wilshire Blvd, Ste 170, Los Angeles, CA 90036. TEL 213-549-5225, FAX 213-549-5255, http://www.labusinessjournal.com/. Eds. Mark Lacter, Mark Lacter. Pubs. Matt Toledo, Matthew Toledo. R&P Mark Lacter. Adv. contact Harry Jigmanian. Circ: 40,000.

LOTHIAN & EDINBURGH LABOUR MARKET ASSESSMENT. see *BUSINESS AND ECONOMICS—Labor And Industrial Relations*

LUXEMBOURG. SERVICE CENTRAL DE LA STATISTIQUE ET DES ETUDES ECONOMIQUES. NOTE DE CONJONCTURE. see *BUSINESS AND ECONOMICS—Abstracting, Bibliographies, Statistics*

330.9 332.6 USA
M A R PERFORMANCE & EVALUATION DIRECTORY. Text in English. 1982. q. looseleaf. USD 395; USD 525 foreign (effective 1998). back issues avail. **Description:** Includes statistical reports updating performance of future money managers and future funds.
Formerly: Quarterly Performance Report
Published by: Managed Account Reports LLC, 1250 Broadway, 26th Fl, New York, NY 10001. TEL 212-213-6202, FAX 212-213-1870.

330 GBR ISSN 0963-5572
M E E D INDEX. (Middle East Economic Digest) Text in English. 1957. w. price varies. **Document type:** *Trade.*
Published by: M E E D - Emap Communications (Subsidiary of: Emap Business Communications Ltd.), 33-39 Bowling Green Lane, London, EC1R 0DA, United Kingdom. TEL 44-20-7470-6200, FAX 44-20-7837-8271.

330 GBR
M E E D PLUS. Text in English. 2001. w. GBP 497 in Europe; GBP 472 in the Middle East; GBP 537 elsewhere (effective 2002). adv. **Document type:** *Newsletter, Trade.* **Description:** Contains news articles and analysis of economic trends in the 21 Arab states and their relationship to domestic and international foreign and military policy.
Related titles: Online - full text ed.
Published by: M E E D - Emap Communications (Subsidiary of: Emap Business Communications Ltd.), 33-39 Bowling Green Lane, London, EC1R 0DA, United Kingdom. TEL 44-20-7470-6200, FAX 44-20-7837-8271, customerservice@meed.com, http://www.meed.com. Ed. David Butter. Pub. Edmund O'Sullivan TEL 44-207-470-6200. Circ: 700 (paid and controlled).

330 EGY ISSN 0024-8118
AP9
M E N ECONOMIC WEEKLY. Text in English. w. USD 150. charts; stat. **Description:** Covers economic activities in Egypt and all Arab countries.
Formerly: M E N Weekly Review of World and Arab Affairs
Indexed: RASB.
Published by: Middle East News Agency, Hoda Sha'Rawi St., Attaba, P O Box 1165, Cairo, 11511, Egypt. Ed. Zeinab Wahby.

338 EGY
M E O BULLETIN. Text in Arabic. 32/yr. **Document type:** *Bulletin.*
Published by: Middle East Observer, 41 Sherif St., Cairo, Egypt. TEL 20-2-3939732, FAX 20-2-3606804.

330 JPN ISSN 0026-6809
M E R I'S MONTHLY CIRCULAR; survey of economic conditions in Japan. Text in English. 1923. m. USD 40, GBP 28, EUR 45 (effective 2003). adv. charts; mkt.; stat. **Document type:** *Academic/Scholarly.* **Description:** Explains and analyzes the principal moves of the Japanese economy with the main object of affording a better understanding abroad of the Japanese economy.
Indexed: RASB.
Published by: Mitsubishi Economic Research Institute, 10-14 Yushima 4-chome, Bunkyo-ku, Tokyo, 113-0034, Japan. TEL 81-3-5802-8670, TELEX J 27161 JPTCO, meri@meri.or.jp, http://www.meri.or.jp. Ed. Akira Tanaka. Circ: 2,670. **Dist. by:** Japan Publications Trading Co., Ltd., Book Export II Dept, PO Box 5030, Tokyo International, Tokyo 101-3191, Japan.

330.9 MYS
M P R C REPORT ON FINANCE, COMMERCE, INDUSTRY: INDONESIA. Text in English. 1972. irreg. USD 30. bk.rev. stat.
Published by: M P R C (Asia) Sdn. Berhad, PO Box 10706, Kuala Lumpur, 50722, Malaysia. TEL 60-3-2217762, FAX 60-3-7564478. Ed. Paul Markandan. Circ: (controlled).

330.9 MYS
M P R C REPORT ON FINANCE, COMMERCE, INDUSTRY: INDONESIA. SUPPLEMENT. Text in English. 1974. irreg. USD 15. bk.rev. stat.
Published by: M P R C (Asia) Sdn. Berhad, PO Box 10706, Kuala Lumpur, 50722, Malaysia. TEL 60-3-2217762, FAX 60-3-7564478. Ed. Paul Markandan.

330.9 MYS
M P R C REPORT ON FINANCE, COMMERCE, INDUSTRY: SINGAPORE. Text in English. 1972. irreg. USD 15. bk.rev. stat.
Published by: M P R C (Asia) Sdn. Berhad, PO Box 10706, Kuala Lumpur, 50722, Malaysia. TEL 60-3-2217762, FAX 60-3-7564478. Ed. Paul Markandan. Circ: (controlled).

330.9 MYS
M P R C REPORT ON FINANCE, COMMERCE, INDUSTRY: SOUTH EAST ASIA. Text in English. 1977. irreg. USD 30. bk.rev. stat.
Published by: M P R C (Asia) Sdn. Berhad, PO Box 10706, Kuala Lumpur, 50722, Malaysia. TEL 60-3-2217762, FAX 60-3-7564478. Ed. Paul Markandan. Circ: (controlled).

330.9 MYS
M P R C REPORT ON FINANCE, COMMERCE, INDUSTRY: THAILAND. Text in English. 1973. irreg. USD 30. bk.rev. stat.
Published by: M P R C (Asia) Sdn. Berhad, PO Box 10706, Kuala Lumpur, 50722, Malaysia. TEL 60-2-2217762, FAX 60-3-7564478. Ed. Paul Markandan. Circ: (controlled).

MACHINERY: LATIN AMERICAN INDUSTRIAL REPORT. see *MACHINERY*

330.9 MEX
MACROPOLITICS DE MEXICO. Text in English. 1996. w.
Media: Online - full content.
Address: http://spoin.com.mx/~igutierreze/macropolitica/ingles.html. Ed. Luis Esparza.

330 GBR ISSN 1467-5749
HC805.A1
MAGHREB REPORT. Text in English. 1991. q. GBP 290 (effective 2002). adv. **Document type:** *Magazine, Trade.* **Description:** Provides an in-depth analysis of political and economic trends in the Islamic north African nations.
Formerly (until 1999): Maghreb Quarterly (0961-9836)
Published by: M E E D - Emap Communications (Subsidiary of: Emap Business Communications Ltd.), 33-39 Bowling Green Lane, London, EC1R 0DA, United Kingdom. TEL 44-20-7470-6200, FAX 44-20-7837-8271, customerservice@meed.com, http://www.meed.com. Ed. David Butter.

330.9 IND
MAHARASHTRA ECONOMIC DEVELOPMENT COUNCIL. MONTHLY ECONOMIC DIGEST FOR BUSINESS EXECUTIVES. Text in English. 1972. m. membership. adv. bk.rev.
Published by: Maharashtra Economic Development Council, 106 Nagindas Master Rd., Mumbai, Maharashtra 400 001, India. TEL 274660. Ed. S B Sakhalkar. Circ: 2,000.

330.9 NPL
MAIN ECONOMIC INDICATORS. Text in English. m. charts; stat. **Document type:** *Newsletter.* **Description:** Monthly notes on the economic activities of Nepal.
Indexed: RASB.
Published by: Nepal Rastra Bank, Research Department, Baluwatar, Kathmandu, Nepal. TEL 977-1-411638.

338.5 USA ISSN 0025-0619
HC107.M2
MAINE BUSINESS INDICATORS. Text in English. 1956. q. free. charts; stat. **Document type:** *Newsletter.* **Description:** Contains Maine-oriented articles on economic development and analysis, industry studies, and economic public policy. It also maintains the Maine Business Index as a measure of changes in the level of Maine's economy.
Published by: University of Southern Maine, Center for Business and Economic Research, c/o Stanley M. Max, P O Box 9300, Portland, ME 04104-9300. TEL 207-780-4187, FAX 207-780-4046, http://www.usm.maine.edu/~cber/. R&P Stanley M Max TEL 207-780-4179. Circ: 1,100.

330.9 USA ISSN 0160-2985
HD8051
MAJOR PROGRAMS. Text in English. irreg. free. **Document type:** *Government.*
Published by: U.S. Department of Labor, Bureau of Labor Statistics, Postal Square Bldg., 2 Massachusetts Ave, NE, Washington, DC 20212-0001 . TEL 202-691-5200, FAX 202-691-6325, http://www.bls.gov. **Subscr. to:** U.S. Government Printing Office, Superintendent of Documents.

MAKING WAVES; Canada's community economic development magazine. see *SOCIAL SERVICES AND WELFARE*

330.1 MWI ISSN 0076-3101
HC517.M3
MALAWI ECONOMIC REPORT. Text in English. a. **Document type:** *Government.*
Published by: Government Printer, PO Box 37, Zomba, Malawi.

MALAYSIA. DEPARTMENT OF STATISTICS. BALANCE OF PAYMENTS REPORT, MALAYSIA/MALAYSIA. JABATAN PERANGKAAN. LAPORAN IMBANGAN PEMBAYARAN, MALAYSIA. see *BUSINESS AND ECONOMICS—Abstracting, Bibliographies, Statistics*

MALAYSIA. DEPARTMENT OF STATISTICS. CENSUS OF SELECTED SERVICE INDUSTRIES, MALAYSIA/MALAYSIA. JABATAN PERANGKAAN. PERANGKAAN AKAUN NEGARA, MALAYSIA. see *BUSINESS AND ECONOMICS—Abstracting, Bibliographies, Statistics*

MALAYSIA. DEPARTMENT OF STATISTICS. INDEX OF INDUSTRIAL PRODUCTION, MALAYSIA/MALAYSIA. JABATAN PERANGKAAN. INDEKS PENGELUARAN PERIDUSTRIAN, MALAYSIA. see *BUSINESS AND ECONOMICS—Abstracting, Bibliographies, Statistics*

MALAYSIA. DEPARTMENT OF STATISTICS. MONTHLY EXTERNAL TRADE STATISTICS, MALAYSIA/MALAYSIA. JABATAN PERANGKANN. PERANGKAAN PERDAGANGAN LUAR NEGERI BULANAN, MALAYSIA. see *BUSINESS AND ECONOMICS—Abstracting, Bibliographies, Statistics*

MALAYSIA. DEPARTMENT OF STATISTICS. MONTHLY RUBBER STATISTICS, MALAYSIA/MALAYSIA. JABATAN PERANGKAAN. PERANGKAAN GETAH BULANAN, MALAYSIA. see *RUBBER—Abstracting, Bibliographies, Statistics*

MALAYSIA. DEPARTMENT OF STATISTICS. SPECIAL RELEASE 2 - FOR BUILDING WORKS, PENINSULAR MALAYSIA/MALAYSIA. JABATAN PERANGKAAN. SIARAN KHAS 2 - UNTUK KERJA-KERJA PEMBINAAN, SEM. MALAYSIA. see *BUILDING AND CONSTRUCTION—Abstracting, Bibliographies, Statistics*

MALAYSIA. DEPARTMENT OF STATISTICS. SPECIAL RELEASE 2 - FOR BUILDING WORKS, SABAH/MALAYSIA. JABATAN PERANGKAAN. SIARAN KHAS 2 - UNTUK KERJA-KERJA PEMBINAAN, SABAH. see *BUILDING AND CONSTRUCTION—Abstracting, Bibliographies, Statistics*

MALAYSIA. DEPARTMENT OF STATISTICS. YEARBOOK OF STATISTICS, SABAH/MALAYSIA. JABATAN PERANGKAAN. BUKU TAHUNAN PERANGKAAN, SABAH. see *BUSINESS AND ECONOMICS—Abstracting, Bibliographies, Statistics*

MALAYSIA. DEPARTMENT OF STATISTICS. YEARBOOK OF STATISTICS, SARAWAK/MALAYSIA. JABATAN PERANGKAAN. BUKU TAHUNAN PERANGKAAN, SARAWAK. see *BUSINESS AND ECONOMICS—Abstracting, Bibliographies, Statistics*

330.9595 GBR ISSN 1470-739X
MALAYSIA QUARTERLY FORECAST REPORT. Text in English. 1993. 3/yr. GBP 330, USD 495, EUR 450 (effective 2003). **Document type:** *Journal, Trade.* **Description:** Provides a comprehensive assessment of the Malaysian government, economy and business environment over the next 30 months. Helps to identify opportunities and reduce risk, and answers key questions facing executives at this time.
Formerly (until 2000): Annual Country Forecast Report. Malaysia (0966-8195)
Related titles: Online - full text ed.: (from EBSCO Publishing).
—CCC.

B

Published by: Business Monitor International Ltd., Mermaid House, 2 Puddle Dock, Blackfriars, London, EC4V 3DS, United Kingdom. TEL 44-20-72480468, FAX 44-20-72480467, marketing@businessmonitor.com, http://www.businessmonitor.com/malaysiaforecast.html.

330.9 MLT
MALTA. MINISTRY OF FINANCE AND COMMERCE. ECONOMIC SURVEY. Text in English. 1969. a. MTL 1.50, USD 6. **Document type:** *Government.*
Formerly: Malta. Central Office of Statistics. Economic Survey
Published by: (Malta. Central Office of Statistics), Ministry of Finance and Commerce, Economic Planning Division, St. Calcedonius Square, Floriana, CMRO2, Malta. TEL 356-250550, FAX 356-237170. Circ: 1,000. **Subscr. to:** Information Division, Auberge de Castille, Valletta CMRO2, Malta.

MANAGEMENT. see *BUSINESS AND ECONOMICS—Management*

MARKET: AFRICA - MID-EAST. see *BUSINESS AND ECONOMICS—International Commerce*

330.9549 USA
MARKET INDICATORS AND FORECASTS. (60 separate country reports available.) Text in English. m. USD 230 (effective 2004). charts; stat. **Document type:** *Trade.* **Description:** Includes historic and forecast data on different market conditions, from industry trends to labor market competitiveness.
Formerly (until 2003): Country Indicators
Media: Online - full content.
Published by: Economist Intelligence Unit, 111 W 57th St, New York, NY 10019. http://www.eiu.com.

330.9 GBR
MARKET RESEARCH MONITOR. Variant title: Market Research Monitor on the Internet. Text in English. 2001. m. GBP 7,725 domestic; EUR 12,375 in Europe; USD 12,375 elsewhere (effective 2003). **Document type:** *Trade.* **Description:** Provides a comprehensive and strategic review of consumer markets from a global perspective.
Media: Online - full content.
Published by: Euromonitor, 60-61 Britton St, London, EC1 5UX, United Kingdom. TEL 44-20-7251-8024, FAX 44-20-7608-3149, info@euromonitor.com, http://www.euromonitor.com.

330.9 USA
MARKET TIMING REPORT. Text in English. 1978. m. USD 100 (effective 1997 & 1998). **Document type:** *Newsletter.*
Address: 1539 E Waverly St, Tucson, AZ 85719. TEL 520-795-9552, tearle@primenet.com. Ed., R&P Ted C Earle. **Subscr. to:** PO Box 225, Tucson, AZ 85702.

330.9 MAR ISSN 0851-0857
MAROC MAGAZINE. Text in French. 1975. w. adv.
Address: 34 rue Mohamed Smiha, Casablanca, Morocco. Ed. Ahmed Alaoui. Circ: 50,000.

330.9 USA ISSN 1553-2925
HC107.A19
MARPLE'S PACIFIC NORTHWEST NEWSLETTER; inside the Pacific Northwest economy. Text in English. 1949. bi-w. USD 125 (effective 2005). stat. index. back issues avail. **Document type:** *Newsletter, Consumer.* **Description:** Covers business trends affecting the Pacific Northwest, with company profiles, news of recent acquisitions, demographic issues, and evaluation of international business conditions.
Former titles (until 2002): Marple's Business Newsletter (0279-960X); (until 1974): Marple's Business Roundup (0025-391X)
—CCC.
Published by: Newsletter Publishing Corp., 117 W Mercer St, Ste 200, Seattle, WA 98119-3960. TEL 206-281-9609, FAX 206-285-8035, marples@compuserve.com, http://www.marples.com, http://marples.com. Ed., Pub. Michael J Parks. Circ: 2,100 (paid).

330.9 332.6 USA ISSN 1086-251X
HG4501
MARTIN WEISS' SAFE MONEY REPORT. Text in English. 1971. m. USD 189 (effective 2005). charts. 8 p./no.; back issues avail.; reprints avail. **Document type:** *Newsletter, Consumer.* **Description:** A forum for investors that deals with high returns, maximum liquidity, and speculative strategies along with bank, insurance, and brokerage safety.
Former titles (until 1993): The Safe Money Report (1068-4034); Money and Markets (1047-9821)
Related titles: Online - full text ed.
Published by: Weiss Research, Inc., 15430 Endeavour Dr., Jupiter, FL 33478. TEL 561-627-3300, 800-844-1773, clara@weissinc.com, http://www.martinweiss.com. Ed., Pub. Martin Weiss. Circ: 180,000 (paid).

330.9 NZL ISSN 1174-474X
MASSEY UNIVERSITY. CENTRE FOR APPLIED ECONOMICS AND POLICY STUDIES. DISCUSSION PAPER IN NATURAL RESOURCE AND ENVIRONMENTAL ECONOMICS. Text in English. 1977. irreg., latest vol.23, 2002. price varies. **Document type:** *Monographic series.*
Formerly (until 1993): Massey University. Centre for Applied Economics and Policy Studies. Discussion Paper in Natural Resource Economics (0110-2044)
Indexed: WAE&RSA.
Published by: Massey University, Centre for Applied Economics and Policy Studies, Palmerston North, New Zealand. TEL 64-6-3505799, FAX 64-6-3505660, J.Fisher@massey.ac.nz, http://econ.massey.ac.nz/caps, http://econ.massey.ac.nz/caps/. Ed. Anton O Meister.

MAURITIUS. CENTRAL STATISTICAL OFFICE. ANNUAL DIGEST OF STATISTICS. see *BUSINESS AND ECONOMICS—Abstracting, Bibliographies, Statistics*

MAURITIUS. CENTRAL STATISTICAL OFFICE. BUSINESS ACTIVITY STATISTICS. see *BUSINESS AND ECONOMICS—Abstracting, Bibliographies, Statistics*

MAURITIUS. CENTRAL STATISTICAL OFFICE. DIGEST OF AGRICULTURAL STATISTICS. see *AGRICULTURE—Abstracting, Bibliographies, Statistics*

MAURITIUS. CENTRAL STATISTICAL OFFICE. DIGEST OF DEMOGRAPHIC STATISTICS. see *POPULATION STUDIES—Abstracting, Bibliographies, Statistics*

MAURITIUS. CENTRAL STATISTICAL OFFICE. DIGEST OF EDUCATIONAL STATISTICS. see *EDUCATION—Abstracting, Bibliographies, Statistics*

MAURITIUS. CENTRAL STATISTICAL OFFICE. DIGEST OF INDUSTRIAL STATISTICS. see *BUSINESS AND ECONOMICS—Abstracting, Bibliographies, Statistics*

MAURITIUS. CENTRAL STATISTICAL OFFICE. DIGEST OF INTERNATIONAL TRAVEL AND TOURISM STATISTICS. see *TRAVEL AND TOURISM—Abstracting, Bibliographies, Statistics*

MAURITIUS. CENTRAL STATISTICAL OFFICE. DIGEST OF LABOUR STATISTICS. see *BUSINESS AND ECONOMICS—Abstracting, Bibliographies, Statistics*

MAURITIUS. CENTRAL STATISTICAL OFFICE. DIGEST OF PRODUCTIVITY AND COMPETITIVENESS STATISTICS. see *BUSINESS AND ECONOMICS—Abstracting, Bibliographies, Statistics*

MAURITIUS. CENTRAL STATISTICAL OFFICE. DIGEST OF PUBLIC FINANCE STATISTICS. see *BUSINESS AND ECONOMICS—Abstracting, Bibliographies, Statistics*

MAURITIUS. CENTRAL STATISTICAL OFFICE. DIGEST OF ROAD TRANSPORT & ROAD ACCIDENTS STATISTICS. see *TRANSPORTATION—Abstracting, Bibliographies, Statistics*

MAURITIUS. CENTRAL STATISTICAL OFFICE. HOUSEHOLD BUDGET SURVEY. see *HOME ECONOMICS—Abstracting, Bibliographies, Statistics*

MAURITIUS. CENTRAL STATISTICAL OFFICE. HOUSING AND POPULATION CENSUS (YEAR). RESULTS. see *HOUSING AND URBAN PLANNING—Abstracting, Bibliographies, Statistics*

MAURITIUS. CENTRAL STATISTICAL OFFICE. HOUSING AND POPULATION CENSUS. CENSUS OF ECONOMIC ACTIVITIES (YEAR). see *BUSINESS AND ECONOMICS—Abstracting, Bibliographies, Statistics*

MAURITIUS. CENTRAL STATISTICAL OFFICE. STATISTICS ON RODRIGUES. see *BUSINESS AND ECONOMICS—Abstracting, Bibliographies, Statistics*

MCGRAW-HILL'S POWER MARKETS WEEK. see *ENERGY—Electrical Energy*

MEAT SHEET. see *AGRICULTURE—Poultry And Livestock*

MEDIA SELECTION; Nachrichten und Meinungen der internationalen Presse. see *BUSINESS AND ECONOMICS—International Commerce*

MEDICAL BUSINESS REVIEW; medical business analysis for the doctor-executive. see *BUSINESS AND ECONOMICS—Management*

MELHORES E MAIORES. see *BUSINESS AND ECONOMICS—Production Of Goods And Services*

MEMBERSHIP DIRECTORY. see *ENERGY*

330.982 ARG ISSN 0325-0687
HC171
MERCADO/BUSINESS. Text in Spanish. 1969. m. adv. bk.rev. illus.
Related titles: Online - full text ed.
Published by: Editorial Coyuntura S.A., Rivaldavia 877 2do Piso, Buenos Aires, 1002, Argentina. TEL 54-11-51669400, FAX 54-114-3423475, http://www.mercado.com.ar/. Ed. Dolores Valle. Pub. Miguel Angel Diez. Adv. contact Juan C Milillo. B&W page USD 4,900, color page USD 6,200; 250 x 175. Circ: 18,350 (paid).

MERCOSUR; sinopsis estadistica. see *BUSINESS AND ECONOMICS—Abstracting, Bibliographies, Statistics*

330.9 GBR ISSN 1363-9684
MERCOSUR CRITIQUE. Text in English. 1996. q. USD 450 (effective 1999). bk.rev. index. **Document type:** *Newsletter.* **Description:** Examines economic, financial, political, and social conditions in Brazil, Argentina, Uruguay, Paraguay, Chile and Bolivia.
Published by: Urban Publishing Co., Hampstead, PO Box 625, London, NW3 2TZ, United Kingdom. TEL 44-2082-091722, FAX 44-2084-554107. Ed. Paulo Botas. Pub. Tann von Hove.

330.9 339 GBR ISSN 1368-1427
MERSEYSIDE BUSINESS PROSPECT. Text in English. 1986. s-a. GBP 30 to individuals; GBP 50 to institutions (effective 2001). charts. **Document type:** *Bulletin, Trade.* **Description:** Provides a macroeconomic overview with forecasts and regional commentary, along with a news diary of job losses and gains in the region and feature articles of interest to each region.
Formerly (until 1995): Merseyside Economic and Business Prospect (1368-1419); Which was formed by the 1989 merger of: Merseyside Economic Prospect (0952-0732); Merseyside Business Survey
Published by: (University of Liverpool, Department of Economics and Accounting), Liverpool Macroeconomic Research Ltd, 5 Cable Rd, Whiston, Liverpool, L35 5AN, United Kingdom. TELEX 627095-UNILPL-G, jfnw36652@cableinet.co.uk, http://www.euro-know.org/lmr.html. Ed., R&P Patrick Minford. **Subscr. to:** c/o Jane Francis, 131 Mount Pleasant, Liverpool L3 5TF, United Kingdom.

977 USA
METROPOLITAN MILWAUKEE ECONOMIC FACT BOOK. Variant title: Economic Fact Book on Metropolitan Milwaukee. Text in English. 1965. a. USD 80 to non-members; USD 40 to members (effective 1999). **Description:** Provides information on the economic characteristics of metro Milwaukee, labor force, population, U.S. Census tracts, transportation and education.
Formerly: Metropolitan Milwaukee Association of Commerce. Economic Studies (0076-7077)
Published by: Metropolitan Milwaukee Association of Commerce, Council of Small Business Executives, 756 N Milwaukee St, Milwaukee, WI 53202. TEL 414-287-4100. Circ: 300.

330.9 MEX
MEXICAN ECONOMY. Text in Spanish. a. MXP 85; USD 20 in United States; USD 25 in Europe; USD 30 elsewhere.
Published by: Banco de Mexico, Subdireccion de Investigacion Economica y Bancaria, 06059 Mexico, Mexico, Ave. JUAREZ 90, Centro Urbano Benito Juarez, Del. Cuauhtemoc, Ciudad De Mexico, DF 06059, Mexico. TEL 525-761-8588.

338.9 GBR ISSN 0968-2724
HC131
MEXICO & N A F T A REPORT. (North American Free Trade Agreement) Variant title: Latin American Regional Report - Mexico & N A F T A Report. Text in English. 1979. m. GBP 218, USD 298 (effective 2001). back issues avail. **Document type:** *Newsletter.* **Description:** Addresses the dynamic developments of the new Mexican political and economic environment, with expanded coverage of NAFTA.
Formerly (until 1993): Mexico and Central America Report (0143-5264)
Related titles: Online - full text ed.
Indexed: RASB.
—IE, Infotrieve.
Published by: Latin American Newsletters (Subsidiary of: Lettres (U.K.) Ltd.), 61 Old St, London, EC1V 9HW, United Kingdom. TEL 44-20-7251-0012, FAX 44-20-7253-8193, subs@latinnews.com, http://www.latinnews.com. Ed. Eduardo Crawley. R&P Alex McHallam TEL 44-20-7251-0012.

330.9 BRA
MEXICO COMPANY HANDBOOK. Text in English. a. USD 29.95. charts; stat. **Document type:** *Trade.* **Description:** Profiles the economy, trade situation and investment climate of Mexico, along with 75 of its largest public companies and 60 mutual funds.
Published by: I M F Editora Ltda., Av Almirante Barroso, 63, Grupo 409, Centro, Rio De Janeiro, RJ 20031-003, Brazil. TEL 55-21-240-4347, FAX 55-21-262-7570. **Dist. worldwide by:** Reference Press Inc.. TEL 512-454-7778, FAX 512-454-9401.

330.9 USA ISSN 1068-8307
HC131
MEXICO CONSENSUS ECONOMIC FORECAST/CONSENSO DE PRONOSTICOS ECONOMICOS. Text in English. 1993. q. USD 20 (effective 1998). **Document type:** *Newsletter.* **Description:** Provides forecasts and an analysis of the Mexican economy.
Related titles: Online - full text ed.

▼ new title ➤ refereed ✶ unverified ♦ full entry avail.

Indexed: SRI.
Published by: Arizona State University, Bank One Economic Outlook Center, PO Box 874406, Tempe, AZ 85287-4406. TEL 602-965-5543, 800-448-0432, FAX 602-964-5458, http://www.cob.asu.edu/seid/eoc/eocmex.html. Ed. Lee R Mepheters.

330.9 USA
MEXICO COUNTRY REPORT. Text in English. 1996. a. looseleaf. USD 475 (effective 2001). charts; stat. **Document type:** *Yearbook, Consumer.* **Description:** Reviews previous year's events politically and economically; and forecasts the coming year's events in Mexico.
Published by: Orbis Publications, LLC, 1924 47th St NW, Washington, DC 20007-1901. TEL 202-298-7936, FAX 202-298-7938, sfoster@orbispub.com, http://www.orbispublications.com. Ed. Jeffrey A. Wright. Pub., R&P Stephen Foster. Circ: 100 (paid).

330.9 MEX ISSN 0188-8714
MEXICO: INFORMACION ECONOMICA Y SOCIAL; revista internacional del Inegi. Text in Spanish. 1989. 3/yr. free or exchange basis. charts; illus.; stat.
Published by: Instituto Nacional de Estadistica, Geografia e Informatica, Secretaria de Programacion y Presupuesto, Prol. Heroe de Nacozari 2301 Sur, Puerta 11, Acceso, Aguascalientes, 20270, Mexico. TEL 52-4-918-1948, FAX 52-4-918-0739, http://www.inegi.gob.mx. Circ: 3,500.

330.972 GBR ISSN 1470-742X
HC131
MEXICO QUARTERLY FORECAST REPORT. Text in English. 1985. 3/yr. GBP 330, USD 495, EUR 450 (effective 2003). **Document type:** *Journal, Trade.* **Description:** Provides a comprehensive assessment of the Mexican government, economy and business environment over the next 30 months. Helps to identify opportunities and reduce risk, and answers key questions facing executives at this time.
Formerly (until 2000): Annual Country Forecast Report. Mexico (0267-9973)
Related titles: Online - full text ed.: (from EBSCO Publishing).
—CCC.
Published by: Business Monitor International Ltd., Mermaid House, 2 Puddle Dock, Blackfriars, London, EC4V 3DS, United Kingdom. TEL 44-20-72480468, FAX 44-20-72480467, marketing@businessmonitor.com, http://www.businessmonitor.com/mexicoforecast.html.

330.972 USA
MEXICO WATCH (WASHINGTON). Text in English. m. USD 395 (effective 2004). abstr.; charts; mkt.; stat. back issues avail. **Document type:** *Newsletter, Academic/Scholarly.* **Description:** Reports on political, economic, and business events in Mexico.
Related titles: E-mail ed.; Fax ed.: Mexico Weekly Fax Bulletin. USD 545 in US & Canada (effective 2001).
Published by: Orbis Publications, LLC, 1924 47th St NW, Washington, DC 20007-1901. TEL 202-298-7936, FAX 202-298-7938, orbis@orbispub.com, http://www.orbismexico.com/mexwatch.htm, http://www.orbispublications.com. Ed. Jeffrey A. Wright. Pub., R&P Stephen Foster.

380 USA ISSN 1044-1948
MICHIGAN BANKER; the news magazine of Michigan's banking industry. Text in English. 1971. m. USD 92.50 (effective 2005); incl. Bank Holding Company Directory. illus. 40 p./no. 2 cols./p.; **Document type:** *Magazine, Trade.* **Description:** Advises executives, officers and staff members of Michigan bank and executives of companies providing services and products.
Former titles (until 1983): Michigan Banking and Business News (0193-0257); Michigan Tradesman (0026-248X)
Related titles: Microform ed.: (from PQC); Online - full text ed.: (from Northern Light Technology, Inc., ProQuest Information & Learning).
Indexed: ABIn, BLI, MMI.
Address: PO Box 12236, Lansing, MI 48901-2236. TEL 517-484-0775, FAX 517-484-4676, billperry@michiganbankermag.com, http://www.michiganbankermag.com. Ed. Bill Perry. Pub. Jerome O'Neil. Circ: 750 (paid).

338 USA ISSN 0193-2047
MID-AMERICA COMMERCE & INDUSTRY. Text in English. 1973. m. USD 18 (effective 2005). adv. bk.rev. back issues avail. **Document type:** *Magazine, Trade.* **Description:** News, announcements, and advertisements on manufacturing firms in this U.S. region, targeted toward executives, purchasers, plant managers, and industrial engineers.
Related titles: Microform ed.: (from PQC); Online - full text ed.: (from Northern Light Technology, Inc., O C L C Online Computer Library Center, Inc., ProQuest Information & Learning).
Indexed: ABIn, BusDate.
Published by: M A C I Inc., 2432 S W Pepperwood Rd, Topeka, KS 66614. TEL 785-272-5280, FAX 785-272-3729, maci@maci-mag.com, http://www.maci-mag.com. Ed., Pub. N Ray Lippe. R&P, Adv. contact David Lippe. B&W page USD 1,100, color page USD 1,640; trim 11 x 8.5. Circ: 8,500 (paid and controlled).

330.9 JPN
MID-TERM FORECAST OF JAPANESE ECONOMY. Text in Japanese. a. JPY 13,500 (effective 2000). **Description:** Mid-term economic forecast analyzes and predicts the general economic trends and changes in Japan's economic structure in 5-year span. Provides guidelines for policy formation by both government and the private sector.
Formerly: Japan's Economic Outlook
Published by: (Publications Department), Japan Center for Economic Research, Nikkei Kayabacho Bldg, 6-1 Nihonbashikayaba-cho 2-chome, Chuo-ku, Tokyo, 103-0025, Japan. TEL 81-3-3639-2801, FAX 81-3-3639-2839.

330.9 GBR ISSN 1475-5211
MIDDLE EAST & AFRICA FINANCIAL ALERT. Text in English. 2001. w.
Related titles: Online - full text ed.: (from EBSCO Publishing).
—CCC.
Published by: Business Monitor International Ltd., Mermaid House, 2 Puddle Dock, Blackfriars, London, EC4V 3DS, United Kingdom. TEL 44-20-72480468, FAX 44-20-72480467, http://www.businessmonitor.com.

MIDDLE EAST AND NORTH AFRICA (YEAR); survey and directory of lands of Middle East and North Africa. see *POLITICAL SCIENCE*

330.9 GBR ISSN 1363-3740
MIDDLE EAST BUSINESS REVIEW. Text in English. 1996. q. GBP 34 to individuals; GBP 94 to institutions. **Document type:** *Academic/Scholarly.*
Published by: University of London, School of Management, Royal Holloway, Egham, Surrey TW20 0EX, United Kingdom. TEL 44-1784-443780, FAX 44-1784-439854, a.alshamali@rhbnc.ac.uk, http://sun.rhbnc.ac.uk/mgt/mbr.html.

330 GBR ISSN 0047-7230
CODEN: MEEDDO
MIDDLE EAST ECONOMIC DIGEST; the Middle East business weekly. Abbreviated title: M E E D. Text in English. 1957. w. GBP 410 in Europe; GBP 387, USD 670 in the Middle East; GBP 450, USD 778 elsewhere; GBP 513.17 combined subscription in Europe print & online; GBP 190.17, USD 848.50 combined subscription in the Middle East print & online; GBP 553.17, USD 956.50 combined subscription elsewhere print & online (effective 2004). adv. bk.rev. stat. index. **Document type:** *Magazine, Trade.* **Description:** Contains news articles and analysis of economic trends in the 21 Arab states and their relationship to domestic and international foreign and military policy.
Related titles: Online - full text ed.: (from EBSCO Publishing, Gale Group, H.W. Wilson, O C L C Online Computer Library Center, Inc.).
Indexed: BPI, ILD, KES, MEA&I, PAIS, RASB, RICS.
—BLDSC (5536.111000), CASDDS, IE. **CCC.**
Published by: M E E D - Emap Communications (Subsidiary of: Emap Business Communications Ltd.), 33-39 Bowling Green Lane, London, EC1R 0DA, United Kingdom. TEL 44-20-74706200, FAX 44-20-74706641, customerservice@meed.com, http://www.meed.com. Ed. Tom Everett-Heath. Circ: 12,340. **Subscr. to:** Tower House, Sovereign Park, Market Harborough LE16 9EF, United Kingdom. TEL 44-1858-438837, FAX 44-1858-461739, jigisha@meed-dubai.com, meed@subscription.co.uk.

330 LBN ISSN 0026-3117
MIDDLE EAST EXPRESS✶. Text in English. 1971. m. stat.
Published by: Societe de la Presse Economique S.A.L., P O Box 11 0687, Beirut, Lebanon. Ed. A Debian.

330.956 GBR ISSN 1469-526X
MIDDLE EAST MONITOR. EAST MED. Text in English. 1991. m. GBP 325, EUR 490, USD 540 (effective 2003). **Document type:** *Journal, Trade.* **Description:** Provides information on economic and financial trends and competitive intelligence on company and industry-wide developments and opportunities involving Egypt, Turkey, Israel, Lebanon, Jordan, Syria, and Palestine.
Supersedes in part (in 2000): Middle East Monitor (0961-8724)
Related titles: Online - full text ed.: (from EBSCO Publishing).
—IE. **CCC.**
Published by: Business Monitor International Ltd., Mermaid House, 2 Puddle Dock, Blackfriars, London, EC4V 3DS, United Kingdom. TEL 44-20-72480468, FAX 44-20-72480467, marketing@businessmonitor.com, https://www.businessmonitor.com/bmi/meastmonitor_order.html, http://www.businessmonitor.com.

330.956 GBR ISSN 1469-5251
MIDDLE EAST MONITOR. THE GULF. Text in English. 1991. m. GBP 325, USD 540, EUR 490 (effective 2003). **Document type:** *Journal, Trade.* **Description:** Covers political risk, the business environment, and economic prospects in Saudi Arabia, UAE, Iran, Oman, Kuwait, Bahrain, Qatar, Iraq, and Yemen.
Supersedes in part (in 2000): Middle East Monitor (0961-8724)
Related titles: Online - full text ed.: (from EBSCO Publishing).
—IE. **CCC.**
Published by: Business Monitor International Ltd., Mermaid House, 2 Puddle Dock, Blackfriars, London, EC4V 3DS, United Kingdom. TEL 44-20-72480468, FAX 44-20-72480467, marketing@businessmonitor.com, https://www.businessmonitor.com/bmi/meastmonitor_order.html, http://www.businessmonitor.com.

330.9 GBR ISSN 1351-4717
HC410.7.A1
MIDDLE EAST REVIEW. Text in English. 1974. a. GBP 50, USD 75 per issue (effective 2005). adv. illus.; stat.; maps. **Document type:** *Journal, Trade.* **Description:** Overview of events, trends & developments in every Middle Eastern country. For an academic, business & governmental audience.
Formerly (until 1981): Middle East Annual Review (0305-3210)
Related titles: CD-ROM ed.; Online - full text ed.
Indexed: HRIR, PAIS.
—BLDSC (5761.401300).
Published by: World of Information, 2 Market St, Saffron Walden, Essex CB10 1HZ, United Kingdom. TEL 44-1799-521150, FAX 44-1799-524805, info@worldinformation.com, http://worldofinformation.safeshopper.com/4/cat4.htm?547, http://www.worldinformation.com. Ed., Pub., R&P Anthony Axon. adv.: B&W page GBP 2,950, color page GBP 2,950; trim 210 x 217. Circ: 7,000 (paid). **Subscr. addr. in the US:** PO Box 830840, Birmingham, AL 35283-0430. TEL 800-633-4931, FAX 205-995-1588, heather@exchange.ebsco.com.

330.9 USA
MIDDLE TENNESSEE STATE UNIVERSITY. BUSINESS AND ECONOMIC RESEARCH CENTER. CONFERENCE PAPER. Text in English. 1975. irreg. price varies. **Document type:** *Academic/Scholarly.*
Published by: Middle Tennessee State University, Business and Economic Research Center, PO Box 102, Bus N216, Murfreesboro, TN 37132. TEL 615-898-2610, FAX 615-818-5045. Ed., R&P Reuben Kyle.

330 USA
MIDSTATE ECONOMIC INDICATORS. Text in English. 1991. q. free. adv. **Document type:** *Newsletter, Academic/Scholarly.* **Description:** Provides an analysis of current economic conditions in Middle Tennessee.
Published by: Middle Tennessee State University, College of Business, 1301 E Main St, MTSU Box 102, Murfreesboro, TN 37132. TEL 615-898-2387, FAX 615-898-5045, http://www.mtsu.edu/~berc/publications.html. Ed., Adv. contact Albert E De Prince. R&P Sally Govan. Circ: 4,000.

330.9 USA ISSN 1523-4282
HC101
THE MILKEN INSTITUTE REVIEW; a journal of economic policy. Text in English. 1999. q. USD 29 (effective 2005). **Document type:** *Academic/Scholarly.* **Description:** Encourages discussion of current issues of economic policy relating to economic growth, job creation and capital formation.
—BLDSC (5773.115000), IE, ingenta.
Published by: Milken Institute Press, 1250 Fourth St, Santa Monica, CA 90401. TEL 310-998-2600, FAX 310-998-2627, info@milkeninstitute.org, http://www.milkeninstitute.org/publications/publications.taf?function=list&cat=mir. Ed. Peter Passell. Pub. Joel Kurtzman.

338 GBR
THE MILLENNIUM PROJECTS REVIEW. Text in English. 1997. irreg. adv. **Document type:** *Bulletin.*
—BLDSC (5773.949700).
Published by: P P F Publications Ltd., Roman House, 296 Golders Green Rd, London, NW11 9PY, United Kingdom. TEL 44-181-455-1166, FAX 44-171-573-7819. Ed. Jennifer Francis. Adv. contact Sharon Hand.

MINERALS: LATIN AMERICAN INDUSTRY REPORT. see *MINES AND MINING INDUSTRY*

330.9 USA
MINNESOTA. DEPARTMENT OF ECONOMIC SECURITY. MINNESOTA ECONOMIC TRENDS. Text in English. 1974. q. free. **Document type:** *Government.*
Formerly: Minnesota. Department of Jobs and Training. Labor Market Trends; Incorporates (1974-1993): Minnesota. Department of Jobs and Training. Review of Labor and Economic Conditions
Related titles: Online - full text ed.
Indexed: SRI.
Published by: Department of Economic Security, Research and Statistics Office, 390 N. Robert St., St. Paul, MN 55101. TEL 612-296-3324, 888-234-1114, FAX 612-282-5429, http://www.des.state.mn.us. Ed. Julia Pool. Circ: 5,200.

330.9 USA ISSN 1530-5546
HC107.M7
MISSISSIPPI ECONOMICS REVIEW & OUTLOOK. Text in English. 199?. s-a. (June & Dec.). free to qualified personnel; USD 10 to individuals; USD 20 to institutions (effective 2004). **Document type:** *Magazine, Government.*
Formerly: Mississippi Research & Development Center

B

Contact Owner: Mississippi Institutions of Higher Learning, 3825 Ridgewood Rd., 8th Fl Tower, Jackson, MS 39211. TEL 601-432-6742, FAX 601-432-6117, dbridges@ihl.state.ms.us, http://www.ihl.state.ms.us/publicaffairs/publications.html. Circ: 675 (paid and free).

330.9 USA ISSN 0195-6159
HC107.M8
MISSOURI ECONOMIC INDICATORS. Text in English. 1976. q. USD 25 (effective 1999). **Document type:** *Academic/Scholarly.*
Published by: University of Missouri at Columbia, Business and Public Administration Research Center, 10 Professional Bldg, Columbia, MO 65211. TEL 573-882-4805, FAX 573-882-5563. Ed. Edward Robb. Pub. Vickie Stokes. Circ: 300.

MONEDA. see *BUSINESS AND ECONOMICS—Banking And Finance*

330.9 CAN ISSN 1201-8783
HG651
MONETARY POLICY REPORT/RAPPORT SUR LA POLITIQUE MONETAIRE. Text in English, French. 1995. s-a. (plus 2 upds). free. adv. bk.rev. charts. back issues avail. **Document type:** *Government.* **Description:** Covers the Canadian economy, monetary policy and inflation.
Related titles: Online - full text ed.
—BLDSC (5908.338000).
Published by: Bank of Canada, Publications Distribution, Communications Services, 234 Wellington St, Ottawa, ON K1A 0G9, Canada. TEL 613-782-8248, FAX 613-782-8874, publications@bank-banque-canada.ca, http://www.bankofcanada.ca. Circ: 4,400.

330.9 USA
MONEY WATCH BULLETIN. Text in English. 1984. m. USD 95 (effective 2005). bk.rev. back issues avail. **Document type:** *Bulletin, Trade.* **Description:** Provides information on 100 lenders for real estate, business and other income-producing activities.
Published by: International Wealth Success, Inc., 24 Cantebury Rd, Rockville Centre, NY 11570-1310. admin@iws-inc.com, http://www.iwsmoney.com/money.htm. Ed., Pub. Tyler G Hicks.

MONITOR MONEY REVIEW. see *BUSINESS AND ECONOMICS—Investments*

330.9 SCG ISSN 1451-3617
MONTENEGRO ECONOMIC TRENDS. Text in Serbo-Croatian. 1999. irreg.
Related titles: Online - full text ed.: (from EBSCO Publishing).
Published by: Institute for Strategic Studies and Prognoses, Naselje pod Ljubovic, Lamela C (1 i 2), Podgorica - Montenegro, 81000. TEL 381-81-634-338, FAX 381-81-634-329, ISSP@cg.yu, http://www.isspm.org.

330.9 USA
MONTHLY BUSINESS STARTS. Text in English. 1986-1987; N.S. 1996. m. USD 30 (effective 2000). **Document type:** *Trade.* **Description:** Provides number of starts and total employees in over 100 lines of business. Data are broken down by employment size, major industry group, state and region, and by selected cities.
Published by: Dun & Bradstreet, Economic Analysis Department (Subsidiary of: Dun & Bradstreet Corporation), c/o Judy Webb, 3 Sylvan Way, Parsippany, NJ 07054. FAX 973-254-4063, http://www.dnb.com. R&P Judy Webb.

330 IND ISSN 0027-030X
MONTHLY COMMENTARY ON INDIAN ECONOMIC CONDITIONS. Text in English. 1959. m. INR 250, USD 40. adv. bk.rev. charts. Supplement avail. **Description:** Clarifies government statistics and economic indicators in the Indian economy.
Formerly: Monthly Statistical Commentary on Indian Economic Conditions
Published by: Indian Institute of Public Opinion Private Ltd., Parliament St., 2-A National Insurance Bldg., P O Box 288, New Delhi, 110 001, India. Ed. E P W da Costa.

330.9 SLE
MONTHLY ECONOMIC REVIEW. Text in English. 1999. m. free. charts; stat. **Document type:** *Corporate.* **Description:** Reports on the Bank of Sierra Leone's balance of payments for the preceeding year.
Published by: Bank of Sierra Leone, Siaka Stevens St, PO Box 30, Freetown, Sierra Leone. TEL 232-22-226501, FAX 232-22-224764, research@bankofsierraleone.org, http://www.bankofsierraleone.org. Circ: 400.

330.9 KEN
MONTHLY MARKET BULLETIN. Text in English. m. KES 100. **Document type:** *Government.*
Published by: Ministry of Agriculture, Livestock Development and Marketing, Marketing Information Branch, PO Box 30028, Nairobi, Kenya.

MUJERES AVANTE/WOMEN ON FORWARD. see *POLITICAL SCIENCE*

330.9 USA
N A B E INDUSTRY SURVEY. Text in English. q. free to members (effective 2004). stat. **Description:** Survey of a special panel of NABE members on business conditions within their company and industry. Questions are asked on changes in demand, employment, inventories, and capital spending.
Media: Online - full content.
Indexed: SRI.
Published by: National Association for Business Economics, 1233 20th St, N W, Ste 505, Washington, DC 20036-2304. TEL 202-463-6223, FAX 202-463-6239, nabe@nabe.com, http://www.nabe.com.

330.9 339 USA ISSN 0745-3205
N A B E NEWS. Text in English. bi-m. free to members (effective 2005). adv. back issues avail. **Document type:** *Newsletter.* **Description:** Features economic articles, reviews of seminars and annual meetings, news from local chapters and roundtables and personal notes.
Media: Online - full text.
—CCC.
Published by: National Association for Business Economics, 1233 20th St, N W, Ste 505, Washington, DC 20036-2304. TEL 202-463-6223, FAX 202-463-6239, nabe@nabe.com, http://www.nabe.com. Ed. Anne Picker. Circ: 3,700.

330.9 USA
N A B E OUTLOOK & POLICY SURVEY. Text in English. q. free to members (effective 2004). stat. **Description:** Survey of a special panel of NABE members on the outlook for selected macroeconomic variables including GNP, CPI, auto sales, housing starts, and unemployment.
Formed by the Feb. 1994 merger of: N A B E Outlook; N A B E Policy Survey
Media: Online - full content.
Indexed: SRI.
Published by: National Association for Business Economics, 1233 20th St, N W, Ste 505, Washington, DC 20036-2304. TEL 202-463-6223, FAX 202-463-6239, nabe@nabe.com, http://www.nabe.com.

330.9 USA
N A D O NEWS. Text in English. w. membership. **Document type:** *Newsletter.* **Description:** Addresses concerns of economic development in small rural towns.
Published by: National Association of Development Organizations, 444 N Capitol St, N W, Ste 630, Washington, DC 20001. TEL 202-624-7806, FAX 202-624-8813, nado@sso.org, http://www.nado.org. Ed., Pub. Aliceann Wohlbruck.

330.9 USA
N A D O SPECIAL REPORT. Text in English. irreg. (3-4 yr.). membership. **Document type:** *Newsletter.* **Description:** Addresses concerns of economic development in small rural towns.
Published by: National Association of Development Organizations, 444 N Capitol St, N W, Ste 630, Washington, DC 20001. TEL 202-624-7806, FAX 202-624-8813, nado@sso.org, http://www.nado.org. Ed. Aliceann Wohlbruck.

338.9 USA
N A S D A DIRECTORY OF DEVELOPMENT AGENCIES AND OFFICIALS. Text in English. q. **Document type:** *Directory.* **Description:** Aimed at state economic development directors and commissioners.
Published by: National Association of State Development Agencies, 750 First St, N E, Ste 710, Washington, DC 20002. TEL 202-898-1302.

338.9 USA
N A S D A LETTER. Text in English. irreg. (6-9/yr.). **Document type:** *Newsletter.* **Description:** Aimed at state economic development directors and commissioners.
Published by: National Association of State Development Agencies, 750 First St, N E, Ste 710, Washington, DC 20002. TEL 202-898-1302.

338.9 USA
N A S D A STATE ENTERPRISE ZONE ROUNDUP. Text in English. a. **Description:** Aimed at state economic development directors and commissioners.
Published by: National Association of State Development Agencies, 750 First St, N E, Ste 710, Washington, DC 20002. TEL 202-898-1302.

330.9 USA ISSN 1073-5534
N B I A REVIEW. Text in English. 1985. bi-m. USD 175 (effective 1999). adv. bk.rev. back issues avail. **Document type:** *Newsletter.* **Description:** Offers information of interest to persons developing and managing business incubators and other support systems for enterpreneurial firms.
Published by: National Business Incubation Association, 20 E. Circle Dr., Ste. 37198, Athens, OH 45701-7198. TEL 614-593-4331, FAX 614-593-1996. Ed., Adv. contact Sally Lindner. Circ: 560.

338 NZL
N B R BUSINESS ALMANAC. (National Business Review) Text in English. a. **Document type:** *Directory, Consumer.*
Published by: Liberty Holdings, PO Box 1734, Auckland 1, New Zealand. TEL 64-9-307-1629, http://www.nbr.co.nz.

330.9 IRL ISSN 1393-4201
N E S F FORUM OPINION. Text in English. 1995. irreg., latest vol.8, 2000. price varies. adv. **Document type:** *Monographic series, Government.*
Related titles: Online - full content ed.
—BLDSC (4024.094540).
Published by: National Economic and Social Forum, First Fl, Frederick House, 19 S Frederick St, Dublin, 2, Ireland. TEL 353-1-6369280, FAX 353-1-6713526, secretariat@nesf.ie, http://www.nesf.ie. Ed. Sean O'hEigeartaigh. Pub., Adv. contact Abel Print.

330.9 IRL ISSN 1393-421X
N E S F FORUM REPORT. Text in English. 1993. irreg., latest vol.20, 2001. price varies. adv. **Document type:** *Government.*
Related titles: Online - full content ed.
—BLDSC (4024.102000).
Published by: National Economic and Social Forum, First Fl, Frederick House, 19 S Frederick St, Dublin, 2, Ireland. TEL 353-1-6369280, FAX 353-1-6713526, secretariat@nesf.ie, http://www.nesf.ie. Ed. Sean O'hEigeartaigh. Pub., Adv. contact Abel Print.

330 SCG ISSN 0352-3314
NARODNA BANKA JUGOSLAVIJE. GODISNJI IZVESTAJ. Text in Serbo-Croatian. 1958. a. **Document type:** *Corporate.*
Related titles: ♦ English ed.: National Bank of Yugoslavia. Annual Report. ISSN 0077-2798.
Published by: Narodna Banka Jugoslavije, Bulevar Revolucije 15, Postanski Fah 1010, Belgrade, 11001. TEL 381-11-3248841. Circ: 350.

NATIONAL ACCOUNTS E S A - AGGREGATES (YEARS). see *BUSINESS AND ECONOMICS*

330.9 EGY ISSN 0304-274X
HC531
NATIONAL BANK OF EGYPT. ECONOMIC BULLETIN. Text in English. 1948. q. free. charts; stat. **Document type:** *Bulletin.* **Description:** Provides coverage of domestic and international economic issues and developments, statistics of economic activities, and in-depth studies of specific topics.
Related titles: Arabic ed.
Indexed: ASD, KES, PAIS, PROMT, RRTA, RefZh, WAE&RSA, WBA.
—BLDSC (3651.910000).
Published by: National Bank of Egypt, Economic Research Department, 1187 Corniche El Nile, P O Box 11611, Cairo, Egypt. TEL 20-2-5748144, FAX 20-2-5747168, TELEX 20069 NBE UN. R&P Inas El Hagrasy. Circ: 6,000.

NATIONAL BANK OF ETHIOPIA. QUARTERLY BULLETIN. see *BUSINESS AND ECONOMICS—Banking And Finance*

330.9 HUN ISSN 1216-4879
HG3020.5.A7
NATIONAL BANK OF HUNGARY. MONTHLY REPORT. Text in English. 1992. m. USD 100. **Document type:** *Bulletin, Corporate.*
Formed by the merger of (1986-1991): National Bank of Hungary. Market Letter (0209-9268); (1983-1991): National Bank of Hungary. Quarterly Review (0231-3456)
Related titles: Hungarian ed.: Magyar Nemzeti Bank. Havi Jelentes. ISSN 1216-4860.
Indexed: RASB.
Published by: National Bank of Hungary, Information Department, Szabadsag ter 8-9, Budapest, 1850, Hungary. TEL 36-1-3023000, http://www.mnb.hu.

330 SCG ISSN 0077-2798
NATIONAL BANK OF YUGOSLAVIA. ANNUAL REPORT. Text in English. a.
Related titles: ♦ Serbo-Croatian ed.: Narodna Banka Jugoslavije. Godisnji Izvestaj. ISSN 0352-3314.
Published by: Narodna Banka Jugoslavije, Bulevar Revolucije 15, Postanski Fah 1010, Belgrade, 11001.

338 NZL ISSN 0110-6813
NATIONAL BUSINESS REVIEW. Text in English. 1970. w. (Fridays). NZD 336 domestic; NZD 625 in Australia & S Pacific; NZD 695 in Asia; NZD 725 elsewhere (effective 2001). adv. bk.rev. illus. 72 p./no. 6 cols./p.; back issues avail. **Document type:** *Newspaper.* **Description:** Covers business and financial news.
Incorporates (1964-1973): Advertising and Marketing News (0001-8910)
Related titles: Online - full text ed.; ♦ Supplement(s): N B R Personal Investor. ISSN 1173-5384.
Indexed: Inpharma, PE&ON, Reac.
—CCC.
Published by: Liberty Holdings, PO Box 1734, Auckland 1, New Zealand. TEL 64-9-307-1629, FAX 64-9-373-3997, http://www.nbr.co.nz. Ed., R&P Nevil Gibson. Pub. Barry Colman. Adv. contact Dianne Driver. B&W page NZD 3,510, color page NZD 5,376. Circ: 14,023.

330.9 PAK
NATIONAL DEVELOPMENT FINANCE CORPORATION. QUARTERLY REVIEW. Text in English. 1975. q. illus.
Formerly: National Development Finance Corporation. Monthly Economic Report

Published by: (Economics Division), National Development Finance Corporation, Finance and Trade Center, 2nd Fl., Shahrah-e Faisal, Karachi, Pakistan. FAX 525310, TELEX 23842 NDFC PK. Ed. Nader E Morshed. Circ: 1,200 (controlled).

330.9 IRN ISSN 0572-5941
NATIONAL INCOME OF IRAN. Text in Persian, Modern. 1974. irreg., latest 1977. free.
Published by: (Iran. Economic Statistics Department), Bank Markazi Jomhouri Islami Iran/Central Bank of the Islamic Republic of Iran, P O Box 11365-8531, Tehran, Iran. FAX 98-21-390323.

330 USA
NATIONAL POLICY ASSOCIATION REPORTS. Text in English. 1934. irreg., latest vol.290. USD 100. stat.
Formerly (until 1997): National Planning Association Reports —BLDSC (7568.096000), ingenta.
Published by: National Policy Association, 3424 Porter St NW, Washington, DC 20016-3126. TEL 202-265-7685, FAX 202-797-5516, npa@npa1.org, http://www.npa1.org. Ed. Martha L Benz. R&P Marlene Thompson. Circ: 2,000.

NATSIONAL'NYE SCHETA ROSSII. see *BUSINESS AND ECONOMICS—Abstracting, Bibliographies, Statistics*

THE NATURAL GAS LOOKOUT. see *PETROLEUM AND GAS*

330 USA ISSN 0890-6092
NEBRASKA DEVELOPMENT NEWS. Text in English. 1974. 11/yr. free. charts; stat. 8 p./no. 3 cols./p.; back issues avail. **Document type:** *Newsletter, Government.* **Description:** Aimed at companies and developers interested in relocating in Nebraska.
Former titles (until 1986): Nebraska Economic Times (0889-406X); (until 1986): Nebraska Economic Developments (8750-9032); (until 198?): Nebraska Now
Published by: Nebraska Department of Economic Development, 301 Centennial Mall S, Lincoln, NE 68509-4666. TEL 402-471-3987, 800-426-6505, FAX 402-471-7889. Ed. Susan M Sitzmann. Circ: 8,000.

330.968 ZAF
NEDCOR ECONOMIC PROFILE. Text in English. q. **Document type:** *Bulletin.*
Former titles (until 1998): Nedcor Monthly Economic Profile; Monthly Economic Profile
Related titles: Afrikaans ed.: Nedcor Ekonomiese Profiel.
Published by: Nedcor Economic Unit/Nedcor Ekonomiese Eenheid, PO Box 582, Johannesburg, 2000, South Africa. TEL 27-11-480-1048, FAX 27-11-480-1044, abdullas@nib.co.za, http://www.nedcor.co.za. Ed. Dennis M Dykes.

330.9 ZAF ISSN 1023-7097
NEDCOR GUIDE TO THE ECONOMY/NEDCOR GIDS TOT DIE EKONOMIE. Text in English. 1986. q. free. 8 p./no.; **Document type:** *Bulletin.* **Description:** Presents analytical articles on the South African economy.
Former titles (until 1994): Nedbank Quarterly Guide to the Economy; (until 1992): Nedbank Guide to the Economy; (until 1990): Nedcor Group. Guide to the Economy (0258-6754); Which was formed by the 1986 merger of: Nedbank Economic Roundup & Executive Guide to the Economy; Which was formerly: U A L Executive Guide to the Economy
Related titles: Afrikaans ed.
Indexed: ISAP.
Published by: Nedcor Economic Unit/Nedcor Ekonomiese Eenheid, PO Box 582, Johannesburg, 2000, South Africa. TEL 27-11-480-1048, FAX 27-11-480-1044, abdullas@nib.co.za, http://www.nedcor.co.za. Ed. Dennis M Dykes. Circ: 10,000.

330.9 NPL
NEPAL. RASHTRIYA PANCAYATA. ARTHIKA SAMITI. Text in Nepali. a.
Published by: Rashtriya Panchayat Sachivalaya, Rashtriya Panchayat Bhavan, Singhdarbar, Kathmandu, Nepal.

330.9 NPL ISSN 0028-274X
NEPAL RASTRA BANK. QUARTERLY ECONOMIC BULLETIN. Text in English. 1966. q. free (effective 2000). charts; stat. **Document type:** *Bulletin.* **Description:** Data on money, credit, government finance, foreign trade and payments statistics.
Published by: Nepal Rastra Bank, Research Department, Baluwatar, Kathmandu, Nepal. TEL 977-1-411638.

330.9 ANT
NETHERLANDS ANTILLES. CENTRAL BUREAU OF STATISTICS. NATIONALE REKENINGEN. Text and summaries in Dutch. 1980. a. ANG 25. **Document type:** *Government.*
Published by: Central Bureau of Statistics, Fort Amsterdam z/n, Willemstad, Curacao, Netherlands Antilles. TEL 599-9-611031, FAX 599-9-611696, ank0004@ibm.net. Circ: 250.

NETHERLANDS. CENTRAAL BUREAU VOOR DE STATISTIEK. BUDGETONDERZOEK. KERNCIJFERS (YEAR). see *BUSINESS AND ECONOMICS—Abstracting, Bibliographies, Statistics*

NETHERLANDS. CENTRAAL BUREAU VOOR DE STATISTIEK. DEMOGRAFISCHE KERNCIJFERS PER GEMEENTE. see *POPULATION STUDIES—Abstracting, Bibliographies, Statistics*

NETHERLANDS. CENTRAAL BUREAU VOOR DE STATISTIEK. ENQUETE BEROEPSBEVOLKING. see *POPULATION STUDIES—Abstracting, Bibliographies, Statistics*

NETHERLANDS. CENTRAAL BUREAU VOOR DE STATISTIEK. GEBRUIKERSHANDBOEK BUDGETONDERZOEK, METHODOLOGIE: ENQUETEDOCUMENTEN. see *BUSINESS AND ECONOMICS—Abstracting, Bibliographies, Statistics*

NETHERLANDS. CENTRAAL BUREAU VOOR DE STATISTIEK. INDEX, FEITEN EN CIJFERS OVER ONZE SAMENLEVING. see *POPULATION STUDIES—Abstracting, Bibliographies, Statistics*

NETHERLANDS. CENTRAAL BUREAU VOOR DE STATISTIEK. JAARBOEK WELVAARTSVERDELING. see *BUSINESS AND ECONOMICS—Abstracting, Bibliographies, Statistics*

NETHERLANDS. CENTRAAL BUREAU VOOR DE STATISTIEK. JEUGD: FEITEN EN CIJFERS. see *POPULATION STUDIES—Abstracting, Bibliographies, Statistics*

NETHERLANDS. CENTRAAL BUREAU VOOR DE STATISTIEK. LEEFTIJDSOPBOUW PER GEMEENTE, KERNCIJFERS (YEAR). see *POPULATION STUDIES—Abstracting, Bibliographies, Statistics*

NETHERLANDS. CENTRAAL BUREAU VOOR DE STATISTIEK. LEEFTIJDSOPBOUW PER GEMEENTE OP 1 JANUARI (YEAR). see *POPULATION STUDIES—Abstracting, Bibliographies, Statistics*

NETHERLANDS. CENTRAAL BUREAU VOOR DE STATISTIEK. NIET-NEDERLANDERS IN NEDERLAND OP 1 JANUARI (YEAR). see *POPULATION STUDIES—Abstracting, Bibliographies, Statistics*

NETHERLANDS. CENTRAAL BUREAU VOOR DE STATISTIEK. SOCIAAL-ECONOMISCHE TRENDS. see *SOCIAL SERVICES AND WELFARE—Abstracting, Bibliographies, Statistics*

NETHERLANDS. CENTRAAL BUREAU VOOR DE STATISTIEK. STATISTISCH BULLETIN. see *BUSINESS AND ECONOMICS—Abstracting, Bibliographies, Statistics*

NETHERLANDS. CENTRAAL BUREAU VOOR DE STATISTIEK. STATISTISCH JAARBOEK/NETHERLANDS. CENTRAL BUREAU OF STATISTICS. POCKET YEARBOOK. see *POPULATION STUDIES—Abstracting, Bibliographies, Statistics*

NETHERLANDS. SOCIAAL EN CULTUREEL PLANBUREAU. SOCIALE EN CULTUREEL RAPPORT. see *SOCIOLOGY*

330.9 CAN ISSN 0548-4073
THE NEW BRUNSWICK ECONOMY. Text in English. 1964. a.
Formerly (until 1965): New Brunswick. Office of the Economic Advisor. Statistical Report on the New Brunswick Economy (0383-3194)
—CISTI.
Published by: (New Brunswick.Office of the Economic Advisor), New Brunswick. Department of Finance, Centennial Bldg, PO Box 6000, Fredericton, NB E3B 5H1, Canada. TEL 506-453-2451, FAX 506-457-4989, http://www.gnb.ca/0024/index-e.asp.

330.9 USA
NEW BUSINESS AND EXPANSION REPORT. Text in English. m. USD 50 (effective 2001). **Description:** Lists new and expanding businesses in the Wichita area and relocations.
Related titles: Online - full content ed.
Published by: (Center for Economic Development and Business Research), Wichita State University, W. Frank Barton School of Business, 2nd Floor, Devlin Hall, 1845 Fairmount, Wichita, KS 67260-0121. TEL 316-978-3225, FAX 316-978-3950, cedbr@wichita.edu, http://www.webs.wichita.edu/cedbr.

330.9 USA ISSN 0548-4448
NEW ENGLAND ECONOMIC INDICATORS. Text in English. 1969. m. free (effective 2003). back issues avail.; reprint service avail. from CIS. **Document type:** *Bulletin, Trade.* **Description:** Provides analysis of New England economy.
Related titles: Microfiche ed.: (from CIS); Online - full text ed.: (from Northern Light Technology, Inc., ProQuest Information & Learning).
Indexed: AmStI, BLI, FiP.
Published by: Federal Reserve Bank of Boston, Research Department, 55882, Boston, MA 02205-5882. TEL 617-973-3397, FAX 617-973-4221, http://www.bos.frb.org/economic/neei/neei.htm. Ed. Tom DeCoff. Circ: 6,000 (controlled).

NEW ENGLAND JOURNAL OF PUBLIC POLICY. see *PUBLIC ADMINISTRATION—Municipal Government*

330.9 320 GRC ISSN 1106-8299
D1050
NEW EUROPE; the European weekly. (Avail. in 3 editions: Central European Edition; International Edition; USA Edition) Text in English. 1993. w. EUR 350 in the European Union; EUR 395 elsewhere (effective 2005). adv. bk.rev. 48 p./no.; **Document type:** *Newspaper, Consumer.* **Description:** Provides news and news analysis stories on countries in Central Europe, Eastern Europe, the Balkans, and Eurasia.
Formerly (until 1995): Balkan News and East European Report (1106-0905)
Related titles: E-mail ed.
Published by: News Corporation, 3D Stefanias Ave, Palea Pendeli, Attiki, Athens, 152 36, Greece. TEL 30-21-6136999, FAX 30-21-6136899, editor@new-europe.info, http://www.new-europe.info/new-europe/Index.asp. Ed., R&P Basil A Coronakis. Pub. Anastasia Bouyiatiotis. adv.: B&W page EUR 9,800, color page EUR 11,700; trim 290 x 390. Circ: 84,460.

320 USA ISSN 1043-2264
NEW FEDERALIST. Text in English. 1987. w. USD 20 for 50 issues; USD 35 for 100 issues (effective 2001). adv. bk.rev. back issues avail. **Document type:** *Newspaper.* **Description:** Independent coverage of the national and world economy, traditional American system economics, including features on historical and scientific topics. Features work of Lyndon LaRouche, Jr. and his associates.
Address: PO Box 889, Leesburg, VA 20178. TEL 703-777-9451, FAX 703-771-3099, 703-771-9492. Ed. Nancy Spannaus. R&Ps Bonnie James, Bonnies James TEL 703-777-9451 ext 551. Adv. contact Michele Steinberg TEL 703-777-9451 ext 402. Circ: 105,000 (paid).

330.9 USA
NEW JERSEY. DEPARTMENT OF LABOR. LABOR MARKET REVIEW. SOUTHERN N.J. REGION. Text in English. 1981. biennial. USD 10. **Document type:** *Government.* **Description:** Analyzes significant labor market and economic developments within Burlington, Camden, Cumberland, Glouster, Mercer and Salem counties.
Published by: Department of Labor, Division of Labor Market and Demographic Research, CN 057, Trenton, NJ 08625-0057. TEL 609-292-2145. Ed. Jan J Dejong. Circ: 1,600.

330.9 USA ISSN 1064-5942
HC107.N5
NEW JERSEY ECONOMIC INDICATORS. Text in English. 1963. m. free. charts; stat. **Document type:** *Government.* **Description:** Disseminates the most comprehensive set of current economic statistics available in the state.
Incorporates: Commercial and Industrial Construction Plans Approved (0098-0285); Supersedes: Employment in Nonagricultural Establishments; Hours and Earnings of Production Workers; Production Workers in Manufacturing Establishments by Two-Digit Industry
Related titles: Microfiche ed.: (from CIS).
Indexed: SRI.
Published by: Department of Labor, Division of Labor Market and Demographic Research, CN 057, Trenton, NJ 08625-0057. TEL 609-633-6434. Ed. Mary Ann R Unger. Circ: 2,800.

NEW MEDIT. see *AGRICULTURE*

330.9 USA ISSN 1090-5693
➤ **NEW YORK ECONOMIC REVIEW.** Text in English. 1971. s-a. USD 20 (effective 2001). adv. bk.rev. **Document type:** *Academic/Scholarly.* **Description:** Publishes theoretical and empirical articles on topics in economics, with interpretative reviews of the current literature in the field.
Formerly (until 1985): New York State Economics Association. Journal
Published by: New York State Economic Association, c/o William O Dea, Ed, Dept of Economics and Business, SUNY, Oneonta, NY 13820. TEL 607-436-2127, FAX 607-436-2107. Ed., R&P, Adv. contact William O'Dea. Circ: 400.

330.9 382 USA
NEW YORK MERCANTILE EXCHANGE GUIDE. Text in English. base vol. plus m. updates. USD 415 base vol(s). (effective 2004). **Description:** Cover issues relating to the complex world of stock exchanges.
Related titles: CD-ROM ed.: USD 385 (effective 2004); Online - full text ed.: USD 375 (effective 2004).
Published by: C C H Inc., 2700 Lake Cook Rd, Riverwoods, IL 60015. TEL 847-267-7000, 800-449-6439, cust_serv@cch.com, http://www.cch.com. Pub. Stacey Caywood.

NEW ZEALAND. STATISTICS NEW ZEALAND. CONSUMER EXPENDITURE. see *BUSINESS AND ECONOMICS—Abstracting, Bibliographies, Statistics*

NEWS FROM GREECE. see *POLITICAL SCIENCE*

338.9 FRA ISSN 0258-6347
NEWS FROM O E C D. Text in English. 1975. m. free.
Supersedes: O E C D Activities
Related titles: French ed.: Nouvelles de l'O.C.D.E.. ISSN 0251-1835; German ed.; Italian ed.

Published by: Organization for Economic Cooperation and Development, 2 Rue Andre Pascal, Paris, 75775 Cedex 16, France. TEL 33-1-45248200, FAX 33-1-45248500, http://www.oecd.org.

330.9 USA ISSN 0738-2650
HC110.L3
NEWS, PRODUCTIVITY AND COSTS; business, nonfarm business, manufacturing, and nonfinancial corporations. Text in English. q. **Document type:** *Government.*
Related titles: ♦ Series of: U.S. Bureau of Labor Statistics. National Office News Releases.
Indexed: AmStI.
Published by: U.S. Department of Labor, Bureau of Labor Statistics, Postal Square Bldg., 2 Massachusetts Ave, NE, Washington, DC 20212-0001 . TEL 202-691-5200, http://www.bls.gov. **Subscr. to:** U.S. Government Printing Office, Superintendent of Documents.

330 DEU ISSN 0341-1982
NIEDERSAECHSISCHE WIRTSCHAFT. Text in German. 1922. m. adv. bk.rev. charts; illus. index. **Document type:** *Journal, Trade.*
—CCC.
Published by: Schluetersche GmbH und Co. KG, Hans-Boeckler-Allee 7, Hannover, 30173, Germany. TEL 49-511-85500, FAX 49-511-85502405, anzeigen@schluetersche.de, http://www.schluetersche.de. Ed. M Rudolph. Circ: 35,372 (paid); 1,342 (controlled).

338 NGA ISSN 0048-038X
NIGERIAN BUSINESS DIGEST✶. Text in English. 1970. m. NGN 60 domestic; NGN 40 in Africa; NGN 42 in Europe; NGN 50 elsewhere. adv. charts; illus. reprint service avail. from PQC. **Description:** Reviews Nigeria's commerce, industry, finance, and economic development.
Related titles: Microfilm ed.: 1970 (from PQC).
Published by: Universal Publications Ltd., Ebute - Metta, 115 Griffith St, PO Box 1959, Lagos, Nigeria. Ed. Alhaji Lateef Teniola. Circ: 40,000.

330.9 NGA
NIGERIAN BUSINESSMAN'S MAGAZINE. Text in English. m. adv. **Document type:** *Trade.*
Published by: Nigerian Businessman Publications, 39 Mabo St., Surulere, Lagos State, Nigeria.

338 JPN ISSN 0029-0491
HF5001
NIKKEI BIJINESU/NIKKEI BUSINESS. Text in Japanese. 1969. w. USD 300 in North America; JPY 30,000 elsewhere (effective 2005). adv. bk.rev. **Document type:** *Magazine, Trade.* **Description:** Covers business developments in Japan and overseas, focusing on corporate strategies and management.
Related titles: Online - full content ed.
Published by: Nikkei Business Publications Inc. (Subsidiary of: Nihon Keizai Shimbun, Inc.), 2-7-6 Hirakawa-cho, Chiyoda-ku, Tokyo, 102-8622, Japan. TEL 813-52108502, FAX 813-52108119, subscript@nikkeibusiness.com, info@nikkeibp.com, http://nb.nikkeibp.co.jp/, http://www.nikkeibp.com. Ed. Osamu Kobayashi. Pub. Masaaki Sato. Adv. contact Tatsuo Ito. B&W page JPY 1,670,000, color page JPY 2,520,000; trim 210 x 280. Circ: 330,732. **Dist. in America by:** Nikkei Business Publications America Inc., 575 Fifth Ave, 20th Fl, New York, NY 10017. TEL 212-599-3331, 800-964-5534, FAX 212-599-3636, 800-266-4553.

NORDIC NEWS NETWORK; international newsletter. see *POLITICAL SCIENCE*

332.1 NOR ISSN 0029-1676
HG3166
NORGES BANK. ECONOMIC BULLETIN/PENGER OG KREDITT. Text in English. 1925. q. free. charts; mkt.; stat. cum.index every 3 yrs. **Document type:** *Bulletin, Academic/Scholarly.* **Description:** Includes current financial and economic statistics.
Formerly (until 1965): Norges Bank. Bulletin (0802-5282)
Related titles: Online - full text ed.: (from Florida Center for Library Automation, Gale Group, O C L C Online Computer Library Center, Inc., ProQuest Information & Learning).
Indexed: ABIn, IBSS, KES, PAIS, WBA.
—CCC.
Published by: Norges Bank, Bankplassen 2, Postboks 1179, Sentrum, Oslo, 0107, Norway. TEL 47-22-31-60-00, FAX 47-22-31-64-10, TELEX 56-71-369 NBANK N, central.bank@norges-bank.no, http://www.norges-bank.no. Ed. Svein Gjedrem.

NORGES BANK. FINANCIAL STABILITY. see *BUSINESS AND ECONOMICS—Banking And Finance*

332.1 NOR ISSN 1501-2794
HD9575.N6
NORGES BANK. FORVALTNING AV STATENS PETROLEUMSFOND. ARSRAPPORT/NORGES BANK. GOVERNMENT PETROLEUM FUND. ANNUAL REPORT. Text in Norwegian. 1998. a. **Document type:** *Trade.*
Related titles: Online - full text ed.
Published by: Norges Bank, Postboks 1179, Sentrum, Oslo, 0107, Norway. TEL 47-22-31-60-00, FAX 47-22-41-31-05, central.bank@norges-bank.no, http://www.norges-bank.no.

332.1 NOR ISSN 1502-2730
HG1111
NORGES BANK. INFLATION REPORT. Text in Norwegian, English. 2000. 3/yr.
Related titles: Online - full text ed.; Norwegian ed.: ISSN 0807-8521.
Published by: Norges Bank, Bankplassen 2, Postboks 1179, Sentrum, Oslo, 0107, Norway. TEL 47-22-31-60-00, central.bank@norges-bank.no, http://www.norges-bank.no.

332.1 NOR ISSN 0802-7188
NORGES BANK. SKRIFTSERIE/NORGES BANK. OCCASIONAL PAPERS. Text in English, Norwegian. 1973. irreg., latest vol.30, 2002. free. back issues avail. **Document type:** *Monographic series, Trade.*
Published by: Norges Bank, Postboks 1179, Sentrum, Oslo, 0107, Norway. TEL 47-22-31-60-00, FAX 47-22-41-31-05, central.bank@norges-bank.no, http://www.norges-bank.no.

NORGES BANK. WORKING PAPERS. see *BUSINESS AND ECONOMICS—Banking And Finance*

330.97 332 NLD ISSN 1062-9408
HC95
➤ **THE NORTH AMERICAN JOURNAL OF ECONOMICS AND FINANCE.** Text in English. 1988. 3/yr. EUR 95 in Europe to individuals; JPY 13,100 in Japan to individuals; USD 99 to individuals except Europe and Japan; EUR 382 in Europe to institutions; JPY 50,700 in Japan to institutions; USD 427 to institutions except Europe and Japan (effective 2006). adv. bk.rev. **Document type:** *Academic/Scholarly.* **Description:** Publishes interdisciplinary research for economists and finance professionals in academic, governmental, and other organizations.
Formerly (until 1992): North American Review of Economics and Finance (1042-752X)
Related titles: Microform ed.: (from PQC); Online - full text ed.: (from EBSCO Publishing, Gale Group, IngentaConnect, ScienceDirect, Swets Information Services).
Indexed: ABIn, BLI, JEL.
—BLDSC (6148.168800), IE, Infotrieve, ingenta. **CCC.**
Published by: (North American Economics and Finance Association USA), Elsevier BV, North-Holland (Subsidiary of: Elsevier Science & Technology), Sara Burgerhartstraat 25, Amsterdam, 1055 KV, Netherlands. TEL 31-20-485-3911, FAX 31-20-485-2457, nlinfo-f@elsevier.nl, http://www.elsevier.com/locate/najef, http://www.elsevier.nl/homepage/about/us/regional_sites.htt, http://www.elsevier.nl. Eds. J. Boyd, M. A. Zaidi. **Subscr. to:** Elsevier BV, PO Box 211, Amsterdam 1000 AE, Netherlands. TEL 31-20-485-3757, FAX 31-20-485-3432.

➤ **NORTH AMERICAN TRADE GUIDE.** see *BUSINESS AND ECONOMICS—International Commerce*

330.9 USA ISSN 1081-1214
NORTHERN NEW JERSEY BUSINESS. Text in English. 1993. fortn. adv. **Document type:** *Magazine, Trade.*
Formerly (until 1994): Northern Business (1071-281X)
Related titles: Online - full text ed.: (from EBSCO Publishing, ProQuest Information & Learning).
Published by: Snowden Publications Inc., 104 Church St, New Brunswick, NJ 08901-2002. TEL 732-246-7677, FAX 732-249-8886.

NORTHWEST REPORT (ST PAUL). see *ENVIRONMENTAL STUDIES*

330.9 NOR ISSN 0800-4110
HC370.I52
NORWAY. STATISTISK SENTRALBYRAA. OEKONOMISKE ANALYSER. Text in Norwegian. 1976. 6/yr. NOK 540 to individuals; NOK 1,000 to institutions; NOK 170 per issue (effective 2004). back issues avail. **Document type:** *Magazine, Government.*
Incorporates (1936-1985): Norway. Statistisk Sentralbyraa. Oekonomisk Utsyn over Aaret (0078-1924); (1976-1985): Norway. Statistisk Sentralbyraa. Konjunkturtendensene (0800-160X)
Related titles: E-mail ed.; English ed.; English ed.: Norway. Central Bureau of Statistics. Economic Survey. ISSN 0801-8324.
Indexed: PAIS.
—CISTI.
Published by: Statistisk Sentralbyraa/Statistics Norway, Kongensgate 6, Postboks 8131, Dep, Oslo, 0033, Norway. TEL 47-21-090000, FAX 47-21-094973, ssb@ssb.no, http://www.ssb.no/emner/08/05/10/oa/. Ed. Aadue Cappelen.

338 CHL
NOTAS DE LA C E P A L. (Notas de la Comision Economica para America Latina y el Caribe) Text in Spanish, English, French. 1998. bi-m. back issues avail.
Related titles: Online - full text ed.
—CINDOC.
Published by: Comision Economica para America Latina y el Caribe/Economic Commission for Latin America and the Caribbean, Ave Dag Hammarskjold 3477, Vitacura, Santiago de Chile, Chile. TEL 56-2-471-2000, FAX 56-2-208-0252, publications@eclac.cl, http://www.eclac.cl.

330.9 FRA
HJ47
LES NOTES BLEUES DE BERCY (ONLINE EDITION). Text in French. 1980. 2/m. free. adv. charts; stat. cum. index: (1995-1998). back issues avail. **Document type:** *Bulletin, Government.* **Description:** Provides information about economic, financial, tax and budgetary news from the French Ministries of the Economy, Finance and Industry, a series of indicators for France and its major partner, and information about changeover to the single currency.
Former titles: Les Notes Bleues de Bercy (Print Edition) (1168-9021); (until 1992): France. Ministere de l'Economie, des Finances et du Budget. Notes Bleues (0244-1179); Which was formed by the merger of (1978-1980): Allocutions Ministerielles - Ministere du Budget (0244-1233); (1978-1980): Allocutions Ministerielles - Ministere de l'Economie (0244-1195); (1979-1980): Allocutions Ministerielles - Ministere de l'Economie - Ministere du Budget (0244-1241); (1978-1980): Mesures Nouvelles - Ministere de l'Economie - Ministere du Budget (0290-0475); (1978-1980): Documents - Ministere de l'Economie (0244-1071); (1979-1980): Documents - Ministere du Budget (0244-1292); (1978-1980): Etudes et Bilans - Ministere de l'Economie (0244-1098); (1979-1980): Etudes et Bilans - Ministere du Budget (0224-108X); (1979-1981): Etudes et Bilans - Ministere de l'Economie - Ministere du Commerce Exterieure (0244-1101); (1978-1981): Etudes et Bilans - Ministere de l'Economie (0244-1217); (1978-1980): Mesures Nouvelles - Ministere du Budget (0244-1209); (1978-1980): Syntheses. Budget (0244-1160); (1978-1980): Syntheses. Economie (0244-1152)
Media: Online - full text. **Related titles:** Online - full text ed.
Indexed: PAIS.
Published by: Ministere de l'Economie, des Finances, et de l'Industrie, 139 rue de Bercy, Paris, Cedex 12 75572, France. TEL 33-1-53188815, www.minefi.gouv.fr/notes_bleues, http://www.finances.gouv.fr, http://lekiosque.finances.gouv.fr. Ed. Jerome Chevaillier. Pub. Michel le Clainche. Circ: 7,200 (paid); 10,000. **Subscr. to:** Centre de Documentation Economie - Finances, 12 place du Bataillon-du-Pacifique, Paris Cedex 12 75572, France. TEL 33-1-40249930, FAX 33-1-43444067.

330 FRA ISSN 0029-4004
D411
NOTES ET ETUDES DOCUMENTAIRES. Text in French. 1949. 15/yr. price varies. adv. charts; stat. **Document type:** *Government.* **Description:** Stories covering political, judicial, economic, social and cultural themes. Also contains graphs, statistical tables and bibliography section.
Related titles: Microfiche ed.
Indexed: ELLIS, ILD, IPSA, KES, PAIS, PdeR, RASB, RRTA, WAE&RSA.
—IE, Infotrieve.
Published by: Documentation Francaise, 29-31 quai Voltaire, Paris, Cedex 7 75344, France. FAX 33-1-40157230. Ed. Isabelle Crucifix. Circ: 6,000.

338 330.9 USA
NOTICEN; Central American & Caribbean political and economic affairs, including Cuba. Text in English. 1996. w. USD 95 to individuals; USD 375 to institutions (effective 2005). back issues avail. **Document type:** *Bulletin, Academic/Scholarly.* **Description:** Covers news relating to sustainable development, politics and economic issues in Central America and the Caribbean.
Formerly (until Feb. 1999): EcoCentral (1089-1560)
Media: Online - full text (from The Dialog Corporation). **Related titles:** CD-ROM ed.: (from National Information Services Corp. (N I S C)); E-mail ed.
Published by: Latin America Database, University Of New Mexico, Latin American And Iberian Institute, MSC 02 1690, 1 University of New Mexico, Albuquerque, NM 87131-0001. TEL 505-277-6839, FAX 505-277-5989, info@ladb.unm.edu, http://ladb.unm.edu/noticen/.

334.73 ESP ISSN 1131-6454
NOTICIAS DE LA ECONOMIA PUBLICA, SOCIAL Y COOPERATIVA. Variant title: Revista Noticias del CIDEC. Text in Spanish. 1991. 3/yr.
—CINDOC.
Published by: C I R I E C - Espana, Ave de los Naranjos, s-n, Edif. Dep. Oriental 2P21, Valencia, 46022, Spain. TEL 34-96-3828489, FAX 34-96-3828492, ciriec@uv.es, http://www.ciriec.es. Ed. Jose Juan Cabezuelo.

NOTISUR; South American political and economic affairs. see *POLITICAL SCIENCE*

LE NOUVEL AFRIQUE ASIE. see *POLITICAL SCIENCE*

330 FRA ISSN 1278-9038
NOUVELLES DES ENTREPRISES COMMERCIALES, INDUSTRIELLES ET DE SERVICES. Text in French. 1954. bi-m. adv. bk.rev. bibl.; illus.; stat.

B

Former titles (until 1995): Nouvelles Industrielles et Commerciales (1278-902X); (until 1986): Nouvelles Industrielles et Commerciales de la Chambre de Commerce et d'Industrie de Toulouse (0992-6046); (until 1985): Nouvelles Industrielles et Commerciales (0338-3725)
Published by: Centre d'Etudes et d'Editions Patronales, Palais Consulaire, B.P. 1506, Toulouse, France.

330.9 VEN
NUEVA CIENCIA✱. Text in Spanish. 1975. irreg. USD 10.
Published by: Universidad Central de Venezuela, Facultad de Ciencias Economicas y Sociales, Ciudad Universitaria, ZP 104, Los Chaguaramos, Caracas, DF 1040, Venezuela.

330.9 FRA ISSN 0304-3363
O C D E. ETUDES ECONOMIQUES. (Organisation de Cooperation et de Developpement Economiques) Variant title: Etudes Economiques de l'O C D E. Text in French. 1961. a. EUR 554, USD 637, GBP 364, GBP 74,800 (effective 2005).
Description: Provides a detailed analysis of recent developments in demand, production, employment, prices and wages, conditions in the money and capital markets, and developments in the balance of payments, for each member country.
Related titles: Online - full text ed.: ISSN 1684-3428. EUR 394, USD 453, GBP 261, JPY 53,200 (effective 2005) (from EBSCO Publishing, Gale Group, IngentaConnect, Swets Information Services); ♦ English ed.: O E C D Economic Surveys. ISSN 0376-6438.
—Infotrieve.
Published by: Organization for Economic Cooperation and Development, 2 Rue Andre Pascal, Paris, 75775 Cedex 16, France. TEL 33-1-45248200, FAX 33-1-45248500, http://www.oecd.org. **Dist. by:** Extenza - Turpin, Pegasus Dr, Stratton Business Park, Biggleswade, Beds SG18 8TQ, United Kingdom. TEL 44-1462-687552, FAX 44-1462-480947, subscriptions@extenza-turpin.com; O E C D Turpin North America, PO Box 194, Downingtown, PA 19335-0194. TEL 610-524-5361, 800-456-6323, FAX 610-524-5417, journalscustomer@turpinna.com.

330.9 USA
O C METRO. (Orange County) Text in English. 1982. bi-w. USD 26 (effective 2004). adv. bk.rev. back issues avail. **Document type:** *Consumer.*
Formerly: Orange County Metropolitan
Related titles: Online - full text ed.
Indexed: BusDate.
Published by: Churm Publishing, 1451 Quail St, Ste 201, Newport Beach, CA 92660. TEL 949-757-1404, FAX 949-757-1996, ocmetro@earthlink.net, info@churmpublishing.com, http://www.churmpublishing.com. Ed. Craig Reem. Pub. Steve Churm. R&P Brian O'Neil. Adv. contact Mike Caron. Circ: 80,000.

338 FRA ISSN 0474-5574
HC10 CODEN: OEEOA8
O E C D ECONOMIC OUTLOOK. Text in English. 1967. s-a. EUR 115, USD 132, GBP 75, JPY 15,500 (effective 2005). charts; stat. **Description:** Surveys the latest economic developments in the OECD area and, by means of an integrated set of quantitative forecasts, assesses future prospects.
Related titles: Diskette ed.; Online - full content ed.: ISSN 1609-7408. USD 84 (effective 2004) (from Florida Center for Library Automation); Online - full text ed.: (from Chadwyck-Healey Inc., EBSCO Publishing, Gale Group, IngentaConnect, O C L C Online Computer Library Center, Inc., ProQuest Information & Learning, Swets Information Services); ♦ French ed.: Perspectives Economiques de l'O E C D. ISSN 0304-3274.
Indexed: ABIn, BMT, BPIA, Cadscan, IIS, LeadAb, PCI, PROMT, RAPRA, RASB, SCIMP, T&II, WBA, Zincscan.
—BLDSC (6235.251000), IE, Infotrieve. **CCC.**
Published by: Organization for Economic Cooperation and Development, 2 Rue Andre Pascal, Paris, 75775 Cedex 16, France. TEL 33-1-45248200, FAX 33-1-45248500, http://www.oecd.org. **Subscr. in N. America to:** O E C D Turpin North America, PO Box 194, Downingtown, PA 19335-0194. TEL 610-524-5361, 800-456-6323, FAX 610-524-5417, journalscustomer@turpinna.com.

338 FRA ISSN 0255-0822
HC10
O E C D ECONOMIC STUDIES. Text in French. 1983. s-a. EUR 97, USD 111, GBP 63, JPY 13,100 (effective 2005).
Description: Focuses on the area of applied macroeconomic and statistical analyses, generally with an international or cross-country dimension.
Formerly (until 1983): Organization for Economic Cooperation and Development. Economic Outlook Occasional Studies (0259-4528)
Related titles: Online - full content ed.: ISSN 1609-7491. EUR 68, USD 78, GBP 46, JPY 9,200 (effective 2005) (from Florida Center for Library Automation); Online - full text ed.: (from EBSCO Publishing, Gale Group, IngentaConnect, O C L C Online Computer Library Center, Inc., Swets Information Services); ♦ French ed.: Revue Economique de l'O C D E. ISSN 0255-0830.
Indexed: ABIn, APEL, BAS, CREJ, ELLIS, IBR, IBSS, IBZ, IIS, ILD, JEL, PAIS, PCI, RASB, WBA.
—BLDSC (6235.251280), CISTI, IE, Infotrieve, ingenta. **CCC.**
Published by: Organization for Economic Cooperation and Development, 2 Rue Andre Pascal, Paris, 75775 Cedex 16, France. TEL 33-1-45248200, FAX 33-1-45248500, http://www.oecd.org/document/59/0,2340,en_2649_201185_2744443_1_1_1_1,00.html.

330 FRA ISSN 0376-6438
HC186
O E C D ECONOMIC SURVEYS. Text in English. 1961. 18/yr. (in 25 vols.). EUR 554, USD 637, GBP 364, JPY 74,800 (effective 2005). stat. **Document type:** *Government.*
Description: Provides a detailed analysis of recent developments in demand, production, employment, prices and wages, conditions in the money and capital markets, and developments in the balance of payments, for each member country.
Related titles: CD-ROM ed.: USD 395 (effective 1999); Online - full content ed.: ISSN 1609-7513. EUR 394, USD 453, GBP 261, JPY 53,200 (effective 2005); Online - full text ed.: (from EBSCO Publishing, IngentaConnect, O C L C Online Computer Library Center, Inc., Swets Information Services); ♦ French ed.: O C D E. Etudes Economiques. ISSN 0304-3363.
Indexed: ATI, IIS, RASB.
—CISTI, IE, Infotrieve. **CCC.**
Published by: Organization for Economic Cooperation and Development, 2 Rue Andre Pascal, Paris, 75775 Cedex 16, France. TEL 33-1-45248200, FAX 33-1-45248500, http://www.oecd.org. **Dist. in Europe by:** Extenza - Turpin, Pegasus Dr, Stratton Business Park, Biggleswade, Beds SG18 8TQ, United Kingdom. TEL 44-1462-687552, FAX 44-1462-480947, subscriptions@extenza-turpin.com; **Dist. in N. America by:** O E C D Turpin North America, PO Box 194, Downingtown, PA 19335-0194. TEL 610-524-5361, 800-456-6323, FAX 610-524-5417, journalscustomer@turpinna.com.

330.9 FRA
O E C D ECONOMIC SURVEYS: AUSTRALIA. Text in French. a. price varies. illus.; stat. **Document type:** *Journal, Trade.*
Related titles: CD-ROM ed.: USD 395 (effective 1999).
Indexed: IIS.
Published by: Organization for Economic Cooperation and Development, 2 Rue Andre Pascal, Paris, 75775 Cedex 16, France. TEL 33-1-45248200, FAX 33-1-45248500, http://www.oecd.org. **Dist. in N. America by:** O E C D Turpin North America, PO Box 194, Downingtown, PA 19335-0194. TEL 610-524-5361, 800-456-6323, FAX 610-524-5417, bookscustomer@turpinna.com.

330 FRA ISSN 0474-5124
HC261
O E C D ECONOMIC SURVEYS: AUSTRIA. Text in French. 1959. a. price varies.
Supersedes in part: Organization for Economic Cooperation and Development. Economic Conditions in Austria and Switzerland
Related titles: Online - full text ed.: (from Florida Center for Library Automation, Gale Group).
Indexed: IIS.
—CISTI.
Published by: Organization for Economic Cooperation and Development, 2 Rue Andre Pascal, Paris, 75775 Cedex 16, France. TEL 33-1-45248200, FAX 33-1-45248500, http://www.oecd.org. **Dist. in N. America by:** O E C D Turpin North America, PO Box 194, Downingtown, PA 19335-0194. TEL 610-524-5361, 800-456-6323, FAX 610-524-5417, bookscustomer@turpinna.com.

330 FRA ISSN 0474-5132
HC315
O E C D ECONOMIC SURVEYS: BELGIUM - LUXEMBOURG. Text in French. 1960. a. price varies.
Related titles: CD-ROM ed.: USD 395 (effective 1999); Online - full text ed.: (from Gale Group).
Indexed: IIS.
Published by: Organization for Economic Cooperation and Development, 2 Rue Andre Pascal, Paris, 75775 Cedex 16, France. TEL 33-1-45248200, FAX 33-1-45248500, http://www.oecd.org. **Dist. in N. America by:** O E C D Turpin North America, PO Box 194, Downingtown, PA 19335-0194. TEL 610-524-5361, 800-456-6323, FAX 610-524-5417, bookscustomer@turpinna.com.

330 FRA ISSN 0474-5140
HC111
O E C D ECONOMIC SURVEYS: CANADA. Text in French. 1959. a.
Related titles: Online - full text ed.: (from Florida Center for Library Automation, Gale Group).
Indexed: IIS.
—CISTI. **CCC.**
Published by: Organization for Economic Cooperation and Development, 2 Rue Andre Pascal, Paris, 75775 Cedex 16, France. TEL 33-1-45248200, FAX 33-1-45248500, http://www.oecd.org. **Dist. in N. American by:** O E C D Turpin North America, PO Box 194, Downingtown, PA 19335-0194. TEL 610-524-5361, 800-456-6323, FAX 610-524-5417, bookscustomer@turpinna.com.

330.9 FRA ISSN 0474-5159
HC351
O E C D ECONOMIC SURVEYS: DENMARK. Text in French. 1960. a.
Related titles: Online - full text ed.: (from Florida Center for Library Automation, Gale Group).
Indexed: IIS.
—CISTI.
Published by: Organization for Economic Cooperation and Development, 2 Rue Andre Pascal, Paris, 75775 Cedex 16, France. TEL 33-1-45248200, FAX 33-1-45248500, http://www.oecd.org. **Dist. in N. America by:** O E C D Turpin North America, PO Box 194, Downingtown, PA 19335-0194. TEL 610-524-5361, 800-456-6323, FAX 610-524-5417, bookscustomer@turpinna.com.

330.9 FRA
O E C D ECONOMIC SURVEYS: FINLAND. Text in French. a. **Document type:** *Journal, Trade.*
Related titles: CD-ROM ed.: USD 395 (effective 1999).
Indexed: IIS.
Published by: Organization for Economic Cooperation and Development, 2 Rue Andre Pascal, Paris, 75775 Cedex 16, France. TEL 33-1-45248200, FAX 33-1-45248500, http://www.oecd.org. **Dist. in N. America by:** O E C D Turpin North America, PO Box 194, Downingtown, PA 19335-0194. TEL 610-524-5361, 800-456-6323, FAX 610-524-5417, bookscustomer@turpinna.com.

330 FRA ISSN 0474-5167
O E C D ECONOMIC SURVEYS: FRANCE. Text in French. 1953. a. **Document type:** *Journal, Trade.*
Related titles: CD-ROM ed.: USD 395 (effective 1999).
Indexed: IIS.
—IE.
Published by: Organization for Economic Cooperation and Development, 2 Rue Andre Pascal, Paris, 75775 Cedex 16, France. TEL 33-1-45248200, FAX 33-1-45248500, http://www.oecd.org. **Dist. N. America by:** O E C D Turpin North America, PO Box 194, Downingtown, PA 19335-0194. TEL 610-524-5361, 800-456-6323, FAX 610-524-5417, bookscustomer@turpinna.com.

330 FRA ISSN 0474-5175
O E C D ECONOMIC SURVEYS: GERMANY. Text in French. 1953. a. **Document type:** *Journal, Trade.*
Related titles: CD-ROM ed.: USD 365 (effective 1999); Online - full text ed.: (from Gale Group).
Indexed: IIS.
Published by: Organization for Economic Cooperation and Development, 2 Rue Andre Pascal, Paris, 75775 Cedex 16, France. TEL 33-1-45248200, FAX 33-1-45248500, http://www.oecd.org. **Dist. in N. America by:** O E C D Turpin North America, PO Box 194, Downingtown, PA 19335-0194. TEL 610-524-5361, 800-456-6323, FAX 610-524-5417, bookscustomer@turpinna.com.

330 FRA ISSN 0474-5183
HC291
O E C D ECONOMIC SURVEYS: GREECE. Text in French. 1954. a. **Document type:** *Journal, Trade.*
Related titles: CD-ROM ed.: USD 395 (effective 1999); Online - full text ed.: (from Gale Group).
Indexed: IIS.
Published by: Organization for Economic Cooperation and Development, 2 Rue Andre Pascal, Paris, 75775 Cedex 16, France. TEL 33-1-45248200, FAX 33-1-45248500, http://www.oecd.org. **Dist. in N. America by:** O E C D Turpin North America, PO Box 194, Downingtown, PA 19335-0194. TEL 610-524-5361, 800-456-6323, FAX 610-524-5417, bookscustomer@turpinna.com.

330 FRA
O E C D ECONOMIC SURVEYS: HUNGARY. Text in French. 1991. a.
Related titles: Series of: Partners in Transition.
Indexed: IIS.
Published by: (Center for Cooperation with European Economies in Transition), Organization for Economic Cooperation and Development, 2 Rue Andre Pascal, Paris, 75775 Cedex 16, France. TEL 33-1-45248200, FAX 33-1-45248500, http://www.oecd.org. **Dist. in N. America by:** O E C D Turpin North America, PO Box 194, Downingtown, PA 19335-0194. TEL 610-524-5361, 800-456-6323, FAX 610-524-5417, bookscustomer@turpinna.com.

330.9 FRA ISSN 0474-5191
HC360.5
O E C D ECONOMIC SURVEYS: ICELAND. Text in French. 1960. a.
Related titles: Online - full text ed.: (from Florida Center for Library Automation, Gale Group).
—CISTI.
Published by: Organization for Economic Cooperation and Development, 2 Rue Andre Pascal, Paris, 75775 Cedex 16, France. TEL 33-1-45248200, FAX 33-1-45248500, http://www.oecd.org. **Dist. in N. America by:** O E C D Turpin North America, PO Box 194, Downingtown, PA 19335-0194. TEL 610-524-5361, 800-456-6323, FAX 610-524-5417, bookscustomer@turpinna.com.

330 FRA ISSN 0474-5205
O E C D ECONOMIC SURVEYS: IRELAND. Text in French. 1960. a. **Document type:** *Journal, Trade.*
Related titles: CD-ROM ed.: USD 395 (effective 1999).
Indexed: IIS.

Published by: Organization for Economic Cooperation and Development, 2 Rue Andre Pascal, Paris, 75775 Cedex 16, France. TEL 33-1-45248200, FAX 33-1-45248500, http://www.oecd.org. **Dist. in N. America by:** O E C D Turpin North America, PO Box 194, Downingtown, PA 19335-0194. TEL 610-524-5361, 800-456-6323, FAX 610-524-5417, bookscustomer@turpinna.com.

330 FRA ISSN 0474-5213
O E C D ECONOMIC SURVEYS: ITALY. Text in French. 1953-1978; resumed 1979. a. **Document type:** *Journal, Trade.*
Related titles: CD-ROM ed.: USD 395 (effective 1999).
Indexed: IIS.
—**CCC.**
Published by: Organization for Economic Cooperation and Development, 2 Rue Andre Pascal, Paris, 75775 Cedex 16, France. TEL 33-1-45248200, FAX 33-1-45248500, http://www.oecd.org. **Dist. in N. America by:** O E C D Turpin North America, PO Box 194, Downingtown, PA 19335-0194. TEL 610-524-5361, 800-456-6323, FAX 610-524-5417, bookscustomer@turpinna.com.

330 FRA ISSN 0474-5221
HC461.A1
O E C D ECONOMIC SURVEYS: JAPAN. Text in French. 1964. a. **Document type:** *Journal, Trade.*
Related titles: CD-ROM ed.: USD 395 (effective 1999); Online - full text ed.: (from Gale Group).
Indexed: IIS.
—CISTI.
Published by: Organization for Economic Cooperation and Development, 2 Rue Andre Pascal, Paris, 75775 Cedex 16, France. TEL 33-1-45248200, FAX 33-1-45248500, http://www.oecd.org. **Dist. in N. America by:** O E C D Turpin North America, PO Box 194, Downingtown, PA 19335-0194. TEL 610-524-5361, 800-456-6323, FAX 610-524-5417, bookscustomer@turpinna.com.

330.9 FRA
O E C D ECONOMIC SURVEYS: MEXICO. Text in French. a.
Indexed: IIS.
Published by: Organization for Economic Cooperation and Development, 2 Rue Andre Pascal, Paris, 75775 Cedex 16, France. TEL 33-1-45248200, FAX 33-1-45248500, http://www.oecd.org. **Dist. in N. America by:** O E C D Turpin North America, PO Box 194, Downingtown, PA 19335-0194. TEL 610-524-5361, 800-456-6323, FAX 610-524-5417, bookscustomer@turpinna.com.

330 FRA ISSN 0474-523X
O E C D ECONOMIC SURVEYS: NETHERLANDS. Text in French. 1954. a. **Document type:** *Journal, Trade.*
Related titles: CD-ROM ed.: USD 395 (effective 1999).
Indexed: IIS.
Published by: Organization for Economic Cooperation and Development, 2 Rue Andre Pascal, Paris, 75775 Cedex 16, France. TEL 33-1-45248200, FAX 33-1-45248500, http://www.oecd.org. **Dist. in N. America by:** O E C D Turpin North America, PO Box 194, Downingtown, PA 19335-0194. TEL 610-524-5361, 800-456-6323, FAX 610-524-5417, bookscustomer@turpinna.com.

330 FRA
O E C D ECONOMIC SURVEYS: NEW ZEALAND. Text in French. a. **Document type:** *Journal, Trade.*
Indexed: IIS.
Published by: Organization for Economic Cooperation and Development, 2 Rue Andre Pascal, Paris, 75775 Cedex 16, France. TEL 33-1-45248200, FAX 33-1-45248500, http://www.oecd.org. **Dist. in N. America by:** O E C D Turpin North America, PO Box 194, Downingtown, PA 19335-0194. TEL 610-524-5361, 800-456-6323, FAX 610-524-5417, bookscustomer@turpinna.com.

330 FRA ISSN 0474-5248
O E C D ECONOMIC SURVEYS: NORWAY. Text in French. 1960. a. **Document type:** *Journal, Trade.*
Related titles: CD-ROM ed.: USD 395 (effective 1999).
Indexed: IIS.
Published by: Organization for Economic Cooperation and Development, 2 Rue Andre Pascal, Paris, 75775 Cedex 16, France. TEL 33-1-45248200, FAX 33-1-45248500, http://www.oecd.org. **Dist. in N. America by:** O E C D Turpin North America, PO Box 194, Downingtown, PA 19335-0194. TEL 610-524-5361, 800-456-6323, FAX 610-524-5417, bookscustomer@turpinna.com.

330 FRA
O E C D ECONOMIC SURVEYS: POLAND. Text in French. a.
Related titles: Series of: Partners in Transition.
—ingenta.
Published by: (Center for Cooperation with European Economies in Transition), Organization for Economic Cooperation and Development, 2 Rue Andre Pascal, Paris, 75775 Cedex 16, France. TEL 33-1-45248200, FAX 33-1-45248500, http://www.oecd.org. **Dist. in N. America by:** O E C D Turpin North America, PO Box 194, Downingtown, PA 19335-0194. TEL 610-524-5361, 800-456-6323, FAX 610-524-5417, bookscustomer@turpinna.com.

330 FRA ISSN 0474-5256
O E C D ECONOMIC SURVEYS: PORTUGAL. Text in French. 1960. a. **Document type:** *Journal, Trade.*
Related titles: CD-ROM ed.: USD 395 (effective 1999).
Indexed: IIS.
Published by: Organization for Economic Cooperation and Development, 2 Rue Andre Pascal, Paris, 75775 Cedex 16, France. TEL 33-1-45248200, FAX 33-1-45248500, http://www.oecd.org. **Dist. in N. America by:** O E C D Turpin North America, PO Box 194, Downingtown, PA 19335-0194. TEL 610-524-5361, 800-456-6323, FAX 610-524-5417, bookscustomer@turpinna.com.

330 FRA ISSN 0474-5272
O E C D ECONOMIC SURVEYS: SPAIN. Text in French. 1958. a. **Document type:** *Journal, Academic/Scholarly.*
Related titles: Online - full text ed.: (from Gale Group).
Indexed: IIS.
Published by: Organization for Economic Cooperation and Development, 2 Rue Andre Pascal, Paris, 75775 Cedex 16, France. TEL 33-1-45248200, FAX 33-1-45248500, http://www.oecd.org. **N. American orders to:** O E C D Turpin North America, PO Box 194, Downingtown, PA 19335-0194. TEL 610-524-5361, 800-456-6323, FAX 610-524-5417, bookscustomer@turpinna.com.

330 FRA ISSN 0474-5280
O E C D ECONOMIC SURVEYS: SWEDEN. Text in French. 1954. a. **Document type:** *Journal, Trade.*
Related titles: CD-ROM ed.
Indexed: IIS.
—IE. **CCC.**
Published by: Organization for Economic Cooperation and Development, 2 Rue Andre Pascal, Paris, 75775 Cedex 16, France. TEL 33-1-45248200, FAX 33-1-45248500, http://www.oecd.org. **Dist. in N. America by:** O E C D Turpin North America, PO Box 194, Downingtown, PA 19335-0194. TEL 610-524-5361, 800-456-6323, FAX 610-524-5417, bookscustomer@turpinna.com.

330 FRA ISSN 0474-5299
HC395
O E C D ECONOMIC SURVEYS: SWITZERLAND. Text in French. 1959. a.
Related titles: CD-ROM ed.: USD 395 (effective 1999); Online - full text ed.: (from Gale Group).
Indexed: IIS.
Published by: Organization for Economic Cooperation and Development, 2 Rue Andre Pascal, Paris, 75775 Cedex 16, France. TEL 33-1-45248200, FAX 33-1-45248500, http://www.oecd.org. **Dist. in N. America by:** O E C D Turpin North America, PO Box 194, Downingtown, PA 19335-0194. TEL 610-524-5361, 800-456-6323, FAX 610-524-5417, bookscustomer@turpinna.com.

330 FRA
O E C D ECONOMIC SURVEYS: THE CZECH REPUBLIC. Text in English. a.
Incorporates in part: O E C D Economic Surveys: The Czech and Slovak Republics; O E C D Economic Surveys: Czech and Slovak Federal Republic
Related titles: CD-ROM ed.; French ed.; Series of: Partners in Transition.
—BLDSC (3656.519000).
Published by: (Center for Cooperation with European Economies in Transition), Organization for Economic Cooperation and Development, 2 Rue Andre Pascal, Paris, 75775 Cedex 16, France. TEL 33-1-45248200, FAX 33-1-45248500, http://www.oecd.org. **Dist. in N. America by:** O E C D Turpin North America, PO Box 194, Downingtown, PA 19335-0194. TEL 610-524-5361, 800-456-6323, FAX 610-524-5417, bookscustomer@turpinna.com.

330 FRA
O E C D ECONOMIC SURVEYS: THE SLOVAK REPUBLIC. Text in English. a.
Incorporates in part: O E C D Economic Surveys: The Czech and Slovak Republics; O E C D Economic Surveys: Czech and Slovak Federal Republic
Related titles: CD-ROM ed.: USD 395 for complete series; French ed.; Series of: Partners in Transition.
—BLDSC (3656.607000).
Published by: (Center for Cooperation with European Economies in Transition), Organization for Economic Cooperation and Development, 2 Rue Andre Pascal, Paris, 75775 Cedex 16, France. TEL 33-1-45248200, FAX 33-1-45248500, http://www.oecd.org. **Dist. in N. America by:** O E C D Turpin North America, PO Box 194, Downingtown, PA 19335-0194. TEL 610-524-5361, 800-456-6323, FAX 610-524-5417, bookscustomer@turpinna.com.

330 FRA ISSN 0474-5302
O E C D ECONOMIC SURVEYS: TURKEY. Text in French. 1954-1978; resumed 1979. a. **Document type:** *Journal, Trade.*
Related titles: CD-ROM ed.: USD 395 (effective 1999); Online - full text ed.: (from Gale Group).
Indexed: IIS.

Published by: Organization for Economic Cooperation and Development, 2 Rue Andre Pascal, Paris, 75775 Cedex 16, France. TEL 33-1-45248200, FAX 33-1-45248500, http://www.oecd.org. **Dist. in N. America by:** O E C D Turpin North America, PO Box 194, Downingtown, PA 19335-0194. TEL 610-524-5361, 800-456-6323, FAX 610-524-5417, bookscustomer@turpinna.com.

330 FRA ISSN 0474-5310
O E C D ECONOMIC SURVEYS: UNITED KINGDOM. Text in French. 1953. a. **Document type:** *Journal, Trade.*
Indexed: IIS.
—**CCC.**
Published by: Organization for Economic Cooperation and Development, 2 Rue Andre Pascal, Paris, 75775 Cedex 16, France. TEL 33-1-45248200, FAX 33-1-45248500, http://www.oecd.org. **Dist. in N. America by:** O E C D Turpin North America, PO Box 194, Downingtown, PA 19335-0194. TEL 610-524-5361, 800-456-6323, FAX 610-524-5417, bookscustomer@turpinna.com.

330 FRA ISSN 0474-5329
HC106.5
O E C D ECONOMIC SURVEYS: UNITED STATES. Text in French. 1953. a.
Related titles: CD-ROM ed.: USD 395 (effective 1999); Online - full text ed.: (from Florida Center for Library Automation, Gale Group).
Indexed: IIS.
—CISTI.
Published by: Organization for Economic Cooperation and Development, 2 Rue Andre Pascal, Paris, 75775 Cedex 16, France. TEL 33-1-45248200, FAX 33-1-45248500, http://www.oecd.org. **Dist. in N. America by:** O E C D Turpin North America, PO Box 194, Downingtown, PA 19335-0194. TEL 610-524-5361, 800-456-6323, FAX 610-524-5417, bookscustomer@turpinna.com.

330 FRA ISSN 1013-0241
O E C D EMPLOYMENT OUTLOOK. Text in English. 1983. a. price varies. **Document type:** *Monographic series.* **Description:** Presents OECD's latest review of labor market trends and issues.
Related titles: Online - full content ed.; French ed.: O C D E Perspectives de l'Emploi. ISSN 0256-6192.
Indexed: IIS.
—BLDSC (6235.251500), IE. **CCC.**
Published by: Organization for Economic Cooperation and Development, 2 Rue Andre Pascal, Paris, 75775 Cedex 16, France. TEL 33-1-45248200, FAX 33-1-45248500, http://www.oecd.org. **Dist. in N. America by:** O E C D Turpin North America, PO Box 194, Downingtown, PA 19335-0194. TEL 610-524-5361, 800-456-6323, FAX 610-524-5417, bookscustomer@turpinna.com.

330.9 FRA ISSN 0474-5523
HF1016
O E C D MAIN ECONOMIC INDICATORS/O C D E PRINCIPAUX INDICATEURS ECONOMIQUES. Text in English, French. 1960. m. EUR 510, USD 586, GBP 334, JPY 68,900 (effective 2005). charts; stat. **Description:** Designed to provide at a glance a picture of the most recent changes in the economy of the OECD countries, and a collection of international statistics on the economic developments affecting the OECD area in the past few years.
Related titles: CD-ROM ed.: ISSN 1726-930X. 2002. EUR 995, USD 1,144, GBP 656, JPY 134,300 (effective 2005); Diskette ed.; Online - full content ed.: ISSN 1609-7319. EUR 357, USD 410, GBP 235, JPY 48,200 (effective 2005); Online - full text ed.: (from EBSCO Publishing, Gale Group, IngentaConnect, O C L C Online Computer Library Center, Inc., Swets Information Services).
Indexed: IIS, RASB, WBA.
—BLDSC (5351.800000), CISTI, IE, Infotrieve. **CCC.**
Published by: Organization for Economic Cooperation and Development, 2 Rue Andre Pascal, Paris, 75775 Cedex 16, France. TEL 33-1-45248200, FAX 33-1-45248500, http://www.oecd.org. **Dist. in N. America by:** O E C D Turpin North America, PO Box 194, Downingtown, PA 19335-0194. TEL 610-524-5361, 800-456-6323, FAX 610-524-5417, journalscustomer@turpinna.com.

338 FRA ISSN 0029-7054
HC240.A1
O E C D OBSERVER. Text in English. 1962. bi-m. EUR 55, USD 63, GBP 35, JPY 7,300 (effective 2005). adv. bk.rev. charts; illus. Index. back issues avail.; reprint service avail. from PQC. **Document type:** *Magazine, Trade.* **Description:** Coverage of the most important problems dealt with by the O.E.C.D. - economic growth, employment and unemployment, social problems, agriculture, energy, financial markets, fiscal policy, multinational enterprises, environment, science and technology, aid to and trade with the developing world.
Related titles: Online - full text ed.: ISSN 1561-5529 (from Chadwyck-Healey Inc., EBSCO Publishing, Florida Center for Library Automation, Gale Group, H.W. Wilson, IngentaConnect, O C L C Online Computer Library Center, Inc., ProQuest Information & Learning, Swets Information Services); French ed.: Observateur de l'O C D E. ISSN 0304-3398.

B

Indexed: ABIn, ASFA, BPI, BPIA, BusI, CIJE, Cadscan, DSA, EIA, EIP, ELLIS, ERA, ESPM, EnvAb, EnvInd, ExcerpMed, F&EA, FutSurv, GEOBASE, IBR, IBZ, IIS, ILD, INIS AtomInd, KES, LeadAb, MEA, MEA&I, NutrAb, PAA&I, PAIS, PROMT, PdeR, PollutAb, RASB, RDA, RRTA, SEA, SWA, T&II, TelAb, Telegen, TriticAb, WAE&RSA, WTA, Zincscan.
—BLDSC (6235.255000), CISTI, IE, Infotrieve, ingenta. **CCC.**
Published by: Organization for Economic Cooperation and Development, 2 Rue Andre Pascal, Paris, 75775 Cedex 16, France. TEL 33-1-45248200, FAX 33-1-45248500, http://www.oecd.org/publications/observer/. Circ: 25,000. **Dist. in N. America by:** O E C D Turpin North America, PO Box 194, Downingtown, PA 19335-0194. TEL 610-524-5361, 800-456-6323, FAX 610-524-5417, bookscustomer@turpinna.com, journalscustomer@turpinna.com.

338 FRA ISSN 1609-1914
HD72
O E C D PAPERS. Text in English. m. EUR 695, USD 799, GBP 459, JPY 93,800 (effective 2005). **Document type:** *Journal, Trade.* **Description:** Contains the most recent research, analyses, forecasts, policy reviews and statistics produced by OECD experts.
Formerly (until 2000): O E C D Working Papers (1022-2227)
Related titles: Online - full content ed.: ISSN 1681-2328. 2001. free (effective 2004); Online - full text ed.: (from EBSCO Publishing, Gale Group, IngentaConnect, O C L C Online Computer Library Center, Inc., Swets Information Services).
Indexed: ABIn.
—CISTI, Infotrieve.
Published by: Organization for Economic Cooperation and Development, 2 Rue Andre Pascal, Paris, 75775 Cedex 16, France. TEL 33-1-45248200, FAX 33-1-45248500, http://www.oecd.org. **Dist. by:** Extenza - Turpin, Pegasus Dr, Stratton Business Park, Biggleswade, Beds SG18 8TQ, United Kingdom. TEL 44-1462-687552, FAX 44-1462-480947, subscriptions@extenza-turpin.com; O E C D Turpin North America, PO Box 194, Downingtown, PA 19335-0194. TEL 610-524-5361, 800-456-6323, FAX 610-524-5417, journalscustomer@turpinna.com.

O E C S ANNUAL DIGEST OF STATISTICS. see *STATISTICS*

330.9 011 ATG ISSN 1021-7312
O E C S CURRENT AWARENESS BULLETIN. Text in English. 1985. q. XEC 60, USD 24. back issues avail. **Document type:** *Bulletin, Abstract/Index.* **Description:** Listing of recently acquired documents and journal articles relevant to the OECS Work Programme.
Published by: Organisation of Eastern Caribbean States, Economic Affairs Secretariat, PO Box 822, St John's, Antigua. TEL 809-462-3500, FAX 809-462-1537. Circ: 75.

O E C S DIGEST OF EXTERNAL TRADE STATISTICS. see *BUSINESS AND ECONOMICS—Abstracting, Bibliographies, Statistics*

O E C S NATIONAL ACCOUNTS DIGEST. see *STATISTICS*

330.9 011 ATG ISSN 1021-7304
O E C S SELECT BIBLIOGRAPHY. Text in English. 1988. irreg. (approx. 2/yr.). XEC 25, USD 10. **Document type:** *Bibliography.*
Published by: Organisation of Eastern Caribbean States, Economic Affairs Secretariat, PO Box 822, St John's, Antigua. TEL 809-462-3500, FAX 809-462-1537, TELEX 2157 ECON SEC AK. Circ: 100.

O E C S STATISTICAL POCKET DIGEST. see *STATISTICS*

O T C BULLETIN; the business newsletter for Europe's consumer healthcare industry. (Over the Counter) see *PHARMACY AND PHARMACOLOGY*

330.9489 DNK ISSN 0909-1165
HC351
OEKONOMISK UGEBREV. Text in Danish. 1994. w. DKK 5,950 (effective 2001). adv. **Document type:** *Trade.* **Description:** Contains issues of importance to players and decision makers with a professional interest in Denmark and the Danish economy and finance, including trends, interest rates, currencies, bonds, etc.
Published by: Boersen Magasiner A-S, Moentergade 19, PO Box 2242, Copenhagen K, 1019, Denmark. TEL 45-33-32-44-00, 45-33-32-01-02, FAX 45-33-32-13-90, http://www.ugebrev.dk. Eds. Ejlif F. Thomasen TEL 45-33-76-95-56, Tage Otkjaer. adv.: B&W page DKK 9,600; 187 x 250.

330.9 AUT ISSN 0029-9898
HG17
OESTERREICHISCHES INSTITUT FUER WIRTSCHAFTSFORSCHUNG. MONATSBERICHTE. Text in German. 1927. m. EUR 212; EUR 21.20 newsstand/cover (effective 2005). adv. charts; mkt.; stat. index, cum.index: 1927-1996. back issues avail. **Document type:** *Bulletin, Academic/Scholarly.* **Description:** Covers all aspects of the Austrian economy, featuring the economic outlook, state of markets, revenues and expenditures, unemployment, manufacturing industry, trade, statistics and more.
Indexed: ELLIS, FPA, IBR, IBSS, IBZ, RASB, RefZh.
Published by: Oesterreichisches Institut fuer Wirtschaftsforschung/Austrian Institute of Economic Research, Postfach 91, Vienna, W 1103, Austria. TEL 43-1-79826010, FAX 43-1-7989386, office@wifo.ac.at, http://www.wifo.ac.at. Ed. Wolfgang Pollan. Adv. contact Christine Kautz. Circ: 3,300.

330.9861 COL ISSN 0121-070X
OIKOS; estudiantes de economia. Text in Spanish. 1987. a. COP 10,000 domestic (effective 2003). **Document type:** *Journal, Academic/Scholarly.* **Description:** Presents academic articles on diferent areas of economy.
Indexed: SoyAb, WAE&RSA.
Published by: Universidad de Antioquia, Facultad de Ciencias Economicas, Apdo. Aereo 1226, Medellin, Colombia. http://caribe.udea.edu.co/~oikos.

ON PRINCIPLE. see *POLITICAL SCIENCE*

330.9 CAN ISSN 1483-5967
ONTARIO ECONOMIC OUTLOOK AND FISCAL REVIEW. Text in English. 1986. a.
Former titles (until 1996): Ontario. Ministry of Finance. Fiscal and Economic Statement (1483-5959); (until 1995): Ontario's Economic Outlook (1184-9118); (until 1990): Ontario. Economic Outlook and Fiscal Review (0837-7529); (until 1987): Province of Ontario. Economic and Fiscal Review (0837-7510)
—CISTI.
Published by: Ontario Ministry of Finance, Frost Bldg S, 7th Flr, 7 Queen's Park Cres, Toronto, ON M7A 1Y7, Canada. TEL 800-263-7965, FAX 905-433-6777, http://www.gov.on.ca/FIN/english/engoutlook.htm, http://www.gov.on.ca/fin.

330.9 CAN ISSN 0846-5142
OPPORTUNITY. Text in English. 1974. q. CND 20 per issue. adv. illus.
Formerly: Opportunity in Northern Canada
Published by: Fleet Publications Inc., P O Box 1679, Winnipeg, MB R3C 2Z6, Canada. TEL 204-788-4884, FAX 204-786-5038. Ed., R&P Ann Wiens. Pub., Adv. contact George Derksen.

338 USA ISSN 1051-7480
ORANGE COUNTY BUSINESS JOURNAL; weekly journal of commerce & industry. Text in English. 1967. w. USD 89 (effective 2005). adv. bk.rev. illus.; stat. **Document type:** *Journal, Trade.*
Formerly (until 1978): Orange County Business (0030-4255)
Related titles: Online - full text ed.: 1967 (from EBSCO Publishing, Factiva, Gale Group, Northern Light Technology, Inc., O C L C Online Computer Library Center, Inc., ProQuest Information & Learning, The Dialog Corporation).
Indexed: ABIn, BusDate, LRI, PAIS, T&II.
Address: 2600 Michelson Dr, Ste 170, Irvine, CA 92612-1550. TEL 714-833-8373, FAX 714-833-8751, http://www.ocbj.com. Ed. Rick Reiff. Circ: 25,000.

330.9 ITA ISSN 1122-2980
ORIZZONTE SICILIA. Text in Italian. 1979. q. free to qualified personnel. bk.rev. bibl.; charts; illus.; stat. back issues avail. **Document type:** *Corporate.*
Published by: Banca Popolare Sant'Angelo, Via Ruggiero VII, 78, Palermo, PA 90141, Italy. TEL 39-91-332922, FAX 39-91-584923. Ed. Pietro Busetta. R&P Alessandro La Monica. Circ: (controlled).

339 DEU ISSN 0344-7030
OST-WIRTSCHAFTSREPORT. Text in German. 1973. w. EUR 636 (effective 2005). reprint service avail. from PQC. **Document type:** *Journal, Trade.*
—IE, Infotrieve. **CCC.**
Published by: Vereinigte Wirtschaftsdienste GmbH, Niederurseler Allee 8-10, Eschborn, 65760, Germany. TEL 49-6196-4050, FAX 49-6196-405303, feedback@vwd.de, http://www.vwd-ostwirtschaftsreport.de, http://www.vwd.de. Circ: 1,200.

OTKRYTAYA POLITYKA; zhurnal rossiiskoi politicheskoi zhizni. see *POLITICAL SCIENCE*

OTTAWA LETTER. see *PUBLIC ADMINISTRATION*

330.9 USA ISSN 1064-3621
HC107.M5
OUTSTATE BUSINESS; the magazine of Michigan business & industry. Text in English. 1987. q. USD 10. adv. **Description:** Serves the economic interests of business and commerce in Michigan. Reaches manufacturers with more than five employees, all public utilities and the Fortune 500 CEOs in the Midwest.
Formerly (until 1992): North Force (0895-0024)
Related titles: Microfiche ed.: (from PQC); Online - full text ed.: (from ProQuest Information & Learning).
Indexed: BusDate.
Published by: Harbor House Publishers, Inc., 221 Water St., Boyne City, MI 49712. TEL 231-582-2814, FAX 231-582-3392, harbor@harborhouse.com, http://www.harborhouse.com/. Ed. David L Knight. Pub. Michelle Cortright. Circ: 10,000.

330.9 CAN ISSN 0700-3617
OVERVIEW. Text in English. 1976. 6/yr. CND 135 (effective 2000). bk.rev. **Document type:** *Newsletter.*
Published by: National Citizens' Coalition, 501 27 Queen St E, Toronto, ON M5C 2M6, Canada. TEL 416-869-3838. Ed. Jeffrey R A Ball. Circ: 10,000.

330 CUB ISSN 0030-7920
P E L: PANORAMA ECONOMICO LATINOAMERICANO. Text in Spanish. 1960. 24/yr. USD 86 in South America; USD 90 in North America; USD 94 elsewhere. adv. bk.rev. illus.; stat. reprint service avail. from PQC.
Related titles: Microfilm ed.: (from PQC).
Indexed: RASB.
Published by: Ediciones Cubanas, Obispo No. 527, Apdo. 605, Havana, Cuba. Ed. Jose Bodes Gomez. Circ: 3,000.

330.9 MDG
P M E MADAGASCAR. Text in French. 1989. m.
Address: Rue Hughes Rabesahala, BP 953, Antananarivo, Antsakaviro 101, Madagascar. TEL 22536, FAX 34534, TELEX 22261. Ed. Romain Andrianarisoa. Circ: 3,500.

P N B INTERNATIONAL. see *BUSINESS AND ECONOMICS—Banking And Finance*

330.9 658 USA ISSN 1040-8169
P-O-P TIMES. (Point-of-Purchase) Text in English. 1988. 12/yr. USD 60 domestic; USD 80 in Canada & Mexico; USD 190 elsewhere (effective 2005); free to qualified personnel. adv. **Document type:** *Magazine, Trade.* **Description:** Presents corporate developments, point-of-purchase campaigns, research, new technologies and personnel to consumer marketers who use point-of-purchase ads and displays.
Published by: Hoyt Publishing Co., 7400 Skokie Blvd, Skokie, IL 60077-3339. TEL 847-675-7400, FAX 847-675-7494, poptimes@hoytpub.com, getinfo@hoytpub.com, http://www.hoytpub.com/poptimes/. Ed. William Schober. Pub., R&P, Adv. contact Harold Fischer. B&W page USD 4,709, color page USD 5,729; trim 9.5 x 13.5. Circ: 20,000.

330.965 USA ISSN 1054-5220
THE P R S GROUP. COUNTRY REPORTS: ALGERIA. (Political Risk Services) Key Title: Algeria (Syracuse, N.Y.). Text in English. 1979. a. USD 395 (effective 2001). stat. **Description:** In-depth analysis and forecasts of political and economic conditions.
Related titles: CD-ROM ed.; Diskette ed.; Online - full text ed.: (from Data-Star).
Published by: The P R S Group, Inc., PO Box 248, East Syracuse, NY 13057-0248. TEL 315-431-0511, FAX 315-431-0200, custserv@prsgroup.com, http://www.countrydata.com, http://www.prsgroup.com.

330.9673 USA
THE P R S GROUP. COUNTRY REPORTS: ANGOLA. Text in English. 1993. a. USD 395 (effective 2001). **Description:** Provides analysis and forecasts of political and economic conditions.
Formerly: Political Risk Services. Executive Reports: Angola (1067-7976)
Related titles: CD-ROM ed.; Online - full content ed.
Published by: The P R S Group, Inc., PO Box 248, East Syracuse, NY 13057-0248. TEL 315-431-0511, FAX 315-431-0200, custserv@prsgroup.com, http://www.countrydata.com, http://www.prsgroup.com.

330.982 USA ISSN 1054-5239
THE P R S GROUP. COUNTRY REPORTS: ARGENTINA. (Political Risk Services) Text in English. 1979. a. USD 395 (effective 2001). **Description:** In-depth analysis and forecasts of political and economic conditions.
Related titles: CD-ROM ed.; Diskette ed.; Online - full text ed.: (from Data-Star).
Published by: The P R S Group, Inc., PO Box 248, East Syracuse, NY 13057-0248. TEL 315-431-0511, FAX 315-431-0200, custserv@prsgroup.com, http://www.countrydata.com, http://www.prsgroup.com.

330.994 USA
THE P R S GROUP. COUNTRY REPORTS: AUSTRALIA. (Political Risk Services) Text in English. 1979. a. USD 395 (effective 2001). **Description:** In-depth analysis and forecasts of political and economic conditions.
Former titles: P R S Group. Executive Reports. Australia (1054-5247); Political Risk Services. Country Reports. Australia
Related titles: CD-ROM ed.; Diskette ed.; Online - full text ed.: (from Data-Star).
Published by: The P R S Group, Inc., PO Box 248, East Syracuse, NY 13057-0248. TEL 315-431-0511, FAX 315-431-0200, custserv@prsgroup.com, http://www.countrydata.com, http://www.prsgroup.com.

330.9436 USA
THE P R S GROUP. COUNTRY REPORTS: AUSTRIA. (Political Risk Services) Text in English. 1979. a. USD 395 (effective 2001). **Description:** In-depth analysis and forecasts of political and economic conditions.
Former titles: P R S Group. Executive Reports: Austria (1054-5255); Political Risk Services. Country Reports: Austria

Related titles: CD-ROM ed.; Diskette ed.; Online - full text ed.: (from Data-Star).
Published by: The P R S Group, Inc., PO Box 248, East Syracuse, NY 13057-0248. TEL 315-431-0511, FAX 315-431-0200, custserv@prsgroup.com, http://www.countrydata.com, http://www.prsgroup.com.

330.4754 USA
THE P R S GROUP. COUNTRY REPORTS: AZERBAIJAN. Text in English. a. USD 395 (effective 2001). **Document type:** *Trade.*
Related titles: CD-ROM ed.; Online - full content ed.
Published by: The P R S Group, Inc., PO Box 248, East Syracuse, NY 13057-0248. TEL 315-431-0511, FAX 315-431-0200, custserv@prsgroup.com, http://www.prsgroup.com.

330.95492 USA
THE P R S GROUP. COUNTRY REPORTS: BANGLADESH. (Political Risk Services) Text in English. 1993. a. USD 395 (effective 2001). **Description:** Provides analysis and forecasts of political and economic conditions.
Formerly: P R S Group. Executive Reports: Bangladesh (1067-7984)
Related titles: CD-ROM ed.; Online - full content ed.
Published by: The P R S Group, Inc., PO Box 248, East Syracuse, NY 13057-0248. TEL 315-431-0511, FAX 315-431-0200, custserv@prsgroup.com, http://www.countrydata.com, http://www.prsgroup.com.

330.9493 USA
THE P R S GROUP. COUNTRY REPORTS: BELGIUM. (Political Risk Services) Text in English. 1979. a. USD 395 (effective 2001). **Description:** In-depth analysis and forecasts of political and economic conditions.
Former titles: P R S Group. Executive Reports: Belgium (1054-5263); Political Risk Services. Country Reports: Belgium
Related titles: CD-ROM ed.; Diskette ed.; Online - full text ed.: (from Data-Star).
Published by: The P R S Group, Inc., PO Box 248, East Syracuse, NY 13057-0248. TEL 315-431-0511, FAX 315-431-0200, custserv@prsgroup.com, http://www.countrydata.com, http://www.prsgroup.com.

330.984 USA ISSN 1054-5271
THE P R S GROUP. COUNTRY REPORTS: BOLIVIA. (Political Risk Services) Text in English. 1979. a. USD 395 (effective 2001). **Description:** Provides in-depth analysis and forecasts of political and economic conditions.
Related titles: CD-ROM ed.; Diskette ed.; Online - full text ed.: (from Data-Star).
Published by: The P R S Group, Inc., PO Box 248, East Syracuse, NY 13057-0248. TEL 315-431-0511, FAX 315-431-0200, custserv@prsgroup.com, http://www.countrydata.com, http://www.prsgroup.com.

330.96883 USA
THE P R S GROUP. COUNTRY REPORTS: BOTSWANA. (Political Risk Services) Text in English. 1993. a. USD 395 (effective 2001). **Description:** Provides analysis and forecasts of political and economic conditions.
Formerly: P R S Group. Executive Reports: Botswana (1067-7992)
Related titles: CD-ROM ed.; Online - full content ed.
Published by: The P R S Group, Inc., PO Box 248, East Syracuse, NY 13057-0248. TEL 315-431-0511, FAX 315-431-0200, custserv@prsgroup.com, http://www.countrydata.com, http://www.prsgroup.com.

330.981 USA ISSN 1054-528X
THE P R S GROUP. COUNTRY REPORTS: BRAZIL. (Political Risk Services) Key Title: Brazil (Syracuse, N.Y.). Text in English. 1979. a. USD 395 (effective 2001). **Description:** In-depth analysis and forecasts of political and economic conditions.
Related titles: CD-ROM ed.; Diskette ed.; Online - full text ed.: (from Data-Star).
Published by: The P R S Group, Inc., PO Box 248, East Syracuse, NY 13057-0248. TEL 315-431-0511, FAX 315-431-0200, custserv@prsgroup.com, http://www.countrydata.com, http://www.prsgroup.com.

330.9499 USA ISSN 1054-5298
THE P R S GROUP. COUNTRY REPORTS: BULGARIA. (Political Risk Services) Key Title: Bulgaria (Syracuse, N.Y.). Text in English. 1979. a. USD 395 (effective 2001). **Description:** In-depth analysis and forecasts of political and economic conditions.
Related titles: CD-ROM ed.; Diskette ed.; Online - full text ed.: (from Data-Star).
Published by: The P R S Group, Inc., PO Box 248, East Syracuse, NY 13057-0248. TEL 315-431-0511, FAX 315-431-0200, custserv@prsgroup.com, http://www.countrydata.com, http://www.prsgroup.com.

330.96711 USA ISSN 1054-5301
THE P R S GROUP. COUNTRY REPORTS: CAMEROON. (Political Risk Services) Key Title: Cameroon (Syracuse, N.Y.). Text in English. 1979. a. USD 395 (effective 2001). **Description:** In-depth analysis and forecasts of political and economic conditions.
Related titles: CD-ROM ed.; Diskette ed.; Online - full text ed.: (from Data-Star).
Published by: The P R S Group, Inc., PO Box 248, East Syracuse, NY 13057-0248. TEL 315-431-0511, FAX 315-431-0200, custserv@prsgroup.com, http://www.countrydata.com, http://www.prsgroup.com.

330.971 USA
THE P R S GROUP. COUNTRY REPORTS: CANADA. Text in English. 1979. a. USD 395 (effective 2001). **Description:** Provides in-depth analysis and forecasts of political and economic conditions.
Former titles: P R S Group. Executive Reports: Canada (1054-531X); Political Risk Services. Country Reports: Canada
Related titles: CD-ROM ed.; Diskette ed.; Online - full text ed.: (from Data-Star).
Published by: The P R S Group, Inc., PO Box 248, East Syracuse, NY 13057-0248. TEL 315-431-0511, FAX 315-431-0200, custserv@prsgroup.com, http://www.countrydata.com, http://www.prsgroup.com.

330.983 USA ISSN 1054-5328
THE P R S GROUP. COUNTRY REPORTS: CHILE. (Political Risk Services) Key Title: Chile (Syracuse, N.Y.). Text in English. 1979. a. USD 395 (effective 2001). **Description:** In-depth analysis and forecasts of political and economic conditions.
Related titles: CD-ROM ed.; Diskette ed.; Online - full text ed.: (from Data-Star).
Published by: The P R S Group, Inc., PO Box 248, East Syracuse, NY 13057-0248. TEL 315-431-0511, FAX 315-431-0200, custserv@prsgroup.com, http://www.countrydata.com, http://www.prsgroup.com.

330.951 USA ISSN 1054-5336
THE P R S GROUP. COUNTRY REPORTS: CHINA. (Political Risk Services) Key Title: China (Syracuse, N.Y.). Text in English. 1979. a. USD 395 (effective 2001). **Description:** In-depth analysis and forecasts of political and economic conditions.
Related titles: CD-ROM ed.; Diskette ed.; Online - full text ed.: (from Data-Star).
Published by: The P R S Group, Inc., PO Box 248, East Syracuse, NY 13057-0248. TEL 315-431-0511, FAX 315-431-0200, custserv@prsgroup.com, http://www.countrydata.com, http://www.prsgroup.com.

330.9861 USA ISSN 1054-5344
THE P R S GROUP. COUNTRY REPORTS: COLOMBIA. (Political Risk Services) Key Title: Colombia (Syracuse, N.Y.). Text in English. 1979. a. USD 395 (effective 2001). **Description:** In-depth analysis and forecasts of political and economic conditions.
Related titles: CD-ROM ed.; Diskette ed.; Online - full text ed.: (from Data-Star).
Published by: The P R S Group, Inc., PO Box 248, East Syracuse, NY 13057-0248. TEL 315-431-0511, FAX 315-431-0200, custserv@prsgroup.com, http://www.countrydata.com, http://www.prsgroup.com.

330.96724 USA
THE P R S GROUP. COUNTRY REPORTS: CONGO (BRAZZAVILLE). (Political Risk Services) Text in English. 1993. a. USD 395 (effective 2001). **Description:** Provides analysis and forecasts of political and economic conditions.
Formerly: P R S Group. Executive Reports: Congo (Brazzaville) (1067-8018)
Related titles: CD-ROM ed.; Online - full content ed.
Published by: The P R S Group, Inc., PO Box 248, East Syracuse, NY 13057-0248. TEL 315-431-0511, FAX 315-431-0200, custserv@prsgroup.com, http://www.countrydata.com, http://www.prsgroup.com.

330.96751 USA
THE P R S GROUP. COUNTRY REPORTS: CONGO (KINSHASA). (Political Risk Services) Text in English. 1979. a. USD 395 (effective 2000). **Description:** In-depth analysis and forecasts of political and economic conditions.
Formerly: Political Risk Services Group. Country Reports: Zaire (1054-6316)
Related titles: CD-ROM ed.; Diskette ed.; Online - full text ed.: (from Data-Star).
Published by: The P R S Group, Inc., PO Box 248, East Syracuse, NY 13057-0248. TEL 315-431-0511, FAX 315-431-0200, custserv@prsgroup.com, http://www.countrydata.com, http://www.prsgroup.com.

330.97286 USA ISSN 1054-5352
THE P R S GROUP. COUNTRY REPORTS: COSTA RICA. (Political Risk Services) Key Title: Costa Rica (Syracuse, N.Y.). Text in English. 1979. a. USD 395 (effective 2001). **Description:** In-depth analysis and forecasts of political and economic conditions.
Related titles: CD-ROM ed.; Diskette ed.; Online - full text ed.: (from Data-Star).
Published by: The P R S Group, Inc., PO Box 248, East Syracuse, NY 13057-0248. TEL 315-431-0511, FAX 315-431-0200, custserv@prsgroup.com, http://www.countrydata.com, http://www.prsgroup.com.

330.9668 USA ISSN 1054-5670
THE P R S GROUP. COUNTRY REPORTS: COTE D'IVOIRE. (Political Risk Services) Key Title: Cote d'Ivoire (Syracuse, N.Y.). Text in English. 1979. a. USD 395 (effective 2001). **Description:** In-depth analysis and forecasts of political and economic conditions.
Related titles: CD-ROM ed.; Diskette ed.; Online - full text ed.: (from Data-Star).
Published by: The P R S Group, Inc., PO Box 248, East Syracuse, NY 13057-0248. TEL 315-431-0511, FAX 315-431-0200, custserv@prsgroup.com, http://www.countrydata.com, http://www.prsgroup.com.

330.97291 USA
THE P R S GROUP. COUNTRY REPORTS: CUBA. (Political Risk Services) Text in English. 1993. a. USD 395 (effective 2001). **Description:** Provides analysis and forecasts of political and economic conditions.
Formerly: P R S Group. Executive Reports: Cuba (1067-8026)
Related titles: CD-ROM ed.; Online - full content ed.
Published by: The P R S Group, Inc., PO Box 248, East Syracuse, NY 13057-0248. TEL 315-431-0511, FAX 315-431-0200, custserv@prsgroup.com, http://www.countrydata.com, http://www.prsgroup.com.

330.94371 USA ISSN 1072-8163
THE P R S GROUP. COUNTRY REPORTS: CZECH REPUBLIC. (Political Risk Services) Key Title: Czech Republic (Syracuse, N.Y.). Text in English. 1979. a. USD 395 (effective 2001). **Description:** In-depth analysis and forecasts of political and economic conditions.
Formerly: Political Risk Services Group. Country Reports: Czechoslovakia (1054-5360)
Related titles: CD-ROM ed.; Diskette ed.; Online - full text ed.: (from Data-Star).
Published by: The P R S Group, Inc., PO Box 248, East Syracuse, NY 13057-0248. TEL 315-431-0511, FAX 315-431-0200, custserv@prsgroup.com, http://www.countrydata.com, http://www.prsgroup.com.

330.9489 USA
THE P R S GROUP. COUNTRY REPORTS: DENMARK. (Political Risk Services) Text in English. 1979. a. USD 395 (effective 2001). **Description:** In-depth analysis and forecasts of political and economic conditions.
Former titles: P R S Group. Executive Reports: Denmark (1054-5379); Political Risk Services. Country Reports: Denmark
Related titles: CD-ROM ed.; Diskette ed.; Online - full text ed.: (from Data-Star).
Published by: The P R S Group, Inc., PO Box 248, East Syracuse, NY 13057-0248. TEL 315-431-0511, FAX 315-431-0200, custserv@prsgroup.com, http://www.countrydata.com, http://www.prsgroup.com.

330.97293 USA ISSN 1054-5387
THE P R S GROUP. COUNTRY REPORTS: DOMINICAN REPUBLIC. (Political Risk Services) Key Title: Dominican Republic (Syracuse, N.Y.). Text in English. 1979. a. USD 395 (effective 2001). **Description:** In-depth analysis and forecasts of political and economic conditions.
Related titles: CD-ROM ed.; Diskette ed.; Online - full text ed.: (from Data-Star).
Published by: The P R S Group, Inc., PO Box 248, East Syracuse, NY 13057-0248. TEL 315-431-0511, FAX 315-431-0200, custserv@prsgroup.com, http://www.countrydata.com, http://www.prsgroup.com.

330.9866 USA ISSN 1054-5395
THE P R S GROUP. COUNTRY REPORTS: ECUADOR. (Political Risk Services) Key Title: Ecuador (Syracuse, N.Y.). Text in English. 1979. a. USD 395 (effective 2001). **Description:** In-depth analysis and forecasts of political and economic conditions.
Related titles: CD-ROM ed.; Diskette ed.; Online - full text ed.: (from Data-Star).
Published by: The P R S Group, Inc., PO Box 248, East Syracuse, NY 13057-0248. TEL 315-431-0511, FAX 315-431-0200, custserv@prsgroup.com, http://www.countrydata.com, http://www.prsgroup.com.

330.962 USA ISSN 1054-5484
THE P R S GROUP. COUNTRY REPORTS: EGYPT. (Political Risk Services) Key Title: Egypt (Syracuse, N.Y.). Text in English. 1979. a. USD 395 (effective 2001). **Description:** In-depth analysis and forecasts of political and economic conditions.
Related titles: CD-ROM ed.; Diskette ed.; Online - full text ed.: (from Data-Star).
Published by: The P R S Group, Inc., PO Box 248, East Syracuse, NY 13057-0248. TEL 315-431-0511, FAX 315-431-0200, custserv@prsgroup.com, http://www.countrydata.com, http://www.prsgroup.com.

330.97284 USA ISSN 1054-5492
THE P R S GROUP. COUNTRY REPORTS: EL SALVADOR. (Political Risk Services) Key Title: El Salvador (Syracuse, N.Y.). Text in English. 1979. a. USD 395 (effective 2001). **Description:** In-depth analysis and forecasts of political and economic conditions.
Related titles: CD-ROM ed.; Diskette ed.; Online - full text ed.: (from Data-Star).

B

Published by: The P R S Group, Inc., PO Box 248, East Syracuse, NY 13057-0248. TEL 315-431-0511, FAX 315-431-0200, custserv@prsgroup.com, http://www.countrydata.com, http://www.prsgroup.com.

330.94897 USA
THE P R S GROUP. COUNTRY REPORTS: FINLAND. (Political Risk Services) Text in English. 1979. a. USD 395 (effective 2001). **Description:** In-depth analysis and forecasts of political and economic conditions.
Former titles: P R S Group. Executive Reports: Finland (1054-5506); Political Risk Services. Country Reports: Finland
Related titles: CD-ROM ed.; Diskette ed.; Online - full text ed.: (from Data-Star).
Published by: The P R S Group, Inc., PO Box 248, East Syracuse, NY 13057-0248. TEL 315-431-0511, FAX 315-431-0200, custserv@prsgroup.com, http://www.countrydata.com, http://www.prsgroup.com.

330.94897 USA
THE P R S GROUP. COUNTRY REPORTS: FRANCE. (Political Risk Services) Text in English. 1979. a. USD 395 (effective 2001). **Description:** In-depth analysis and forecasts of political and economic conditions.
Former titles: P R S Group. Executive Reports: France (1054-5514); Political Risk Services. Country Reports: France
Related titles: CD-ROM ed.; Diskette ed.; Online - full text ed.: (from Data-Star).
Published by: The P R S Group, Inc., PO Box 248, East Syracuse, NY 13057-0248. TEL 315-431-0511, FAX 315-431-0200, custserv@prsgroup.com, http://www.countrydata.com, http://www.prsgroup.com.

330.96721 USA ISSN 1054-5522
THE P R S GROUP. COUNTRY REPORTS: GABON. (Political Risk Services) Key Title: Gabon (Syracuse, N.Y.). Text in English. 1979. a. USD 395 (effective 2001). **Description:** In-depth analysis and forecasts of political and economic conditions.
Related titles: CD-ROM ed.; Diskette ed.; Online - full text ed.: (from Data-Star).
Published by: The P R S Group, Inc., PO Box 248, East Syracuse, NY 13057-0248. TEL 315-431-0511, FAX 315-431-0200, custserv@prsgroup.com, http://www.countrydata.com, http://www.prsgroup.com.

330.943 USA
THE P R S GROUP. COUNTRY REPORTS: GERMANY. (Political Risk Services) Text in English. 1991. a. USD 395 (effective 2001). **Description:** In-depth analysis and forecasts of political and economic conditions.
Former titles: P R S Group. Executive Reports: Germany (1056-4721); Political Risk Services. Country Reports: Germany
Related titles: CD-ROM ed.; Diskette ed.; Online - full text ed.: (from Data-Star).
Published by: The P R S Group, Inc., PO Box 248, East Syracuse, NY 13057-0248. TEL 315-431-0511, FAX 315-431-0200, custserv@prsgroup.com, http://www.countrydata.com, http://www.prsgroup.com.

330.9667 USA
THE P R S GROUP. COUNTRY REPORTS: GHANA. (Political Risk Services) Text in English. 1993. a. USD 395 (effective 2001). **Description:** Provides analysis and forecasts of political and economic conditions.
Formerly: P R S Group. Executive Reports: Ghana (1067-8034)
Related titles: CD-ROM ed.; Online - full content ed.
Published by: The P R S Group, Inc., PO Box 248, East Syracuse, NY 13057-0248. TEL 315-431-0511, FAX 315-431-0200, custserv@prsgroup.com, http://www.countrydata.com, http://www.prsgroup.com.

330.9495 USA
THE P R S GROUP. COUNTRY REPORTS: GREECE. Text in English. 1979. a. USD 395 (effective 2001). **Description:** Provides in-depth analysis and forecasts of political and economic conditions.
Former titles: P R S Group. Executive Reports: Greece (1054-5530); Political Risk Services. Country Reports: Greece
Related titles: CD-ROM ed.; Diskette ed.; Online - full text ed.: (from Data-Star).
Published by: The P R S Group, Inc., PO Box 248, East Syracuse, NY 13057-0248. TEL 315-431-0511, FAX 315-431-0200, custserv@prsgroup.com, http://www.countrydata.com, http://www.prsgroup.com.

330.97281 USA ISSN 1054-5549
THE P R S GROUP. COUNTRY REPORTS: GUATEMALA. (Political Risk Services) Key Title: Guatemala (Syracuse, N.Y.). Text in English. 1979. a. USD 395 (effective 2001). **Description:** In-depth analysis and forecasts of political and economic conditions.
Related titles: CD-ROM ed.; Diskette ed.; Online - full text ed.: (from Data-Star).
Published by: The P R S Group, Inc., PO Box 248, East Syracuse, NY 13057-0248. TEL 315-431-0511, FAX 315-431-0200, custserv@prsgroup.com, http://www.countrydata.com, http://www.prsgroup.com.

330.96652 USA ISSN 1054-5557
THE P R S GROUP. COUNTRY REPORTS: GUINEA. (Political Risk Services) Key Title: Guinea (Syracuse, N.Y.). Text in English. 1979. a. USD 395 (effective 2001). **Description:** In-depth analysis and forecasts of political and economic conditions.
Related titles: CD-ROM ed.; Diskette ed.; Online - full text ed.: (from Data-Star).
Published by: The P R S Group, Inc., PO Box 248, East Syracuse, NY 13057-0248. TEL 315-431-0511, FAX 315-431-0200, custserv@prsgroup.com, http://www.countrydata.com, http://www.prsgroup.com.

330.9881 USA
THE P R S GROUP. COUNTRY REPORTS: GUYANA. (Political Risk Services) Text in English. 1993. a. USD 395 (effective 2001). **Description:** Provides analysis and forecasts of political and economic conditions.
Formerly: P R S Group. Executive Reports: Guyana (1067-8042)
Related titles: CD-ROM ed.; Online - full content ed.
Published by: The P R S Group, Inc., PO Box 248, East Syracuse, NY 13057-0248. TEL 315-431-0511, FAX 315-431-0200, custserv@prsgroup.com, http://www.countrydata.com, http://www.prsgroup.com.

330.97294 USA ISSN 1054-5565
THE P R S GROUP. COUNTRY REPORTS: HAITI. (Political Risk Services) Key Title: Haiti (Syracuse, N.Y.). Text in English. 1979. a. USD 395 (effective 2001). **Description:** In-depth analysis and forecasts of political and economic conditions.
Related titles: CD-ROM ed.; Diskette ed.; Online - full text ed.: (from Data-Star).
Published by: The P R S Group, Inc., PO Box 248, East Syracuse, NY 13057-0248. TEL 315-431-0511, FAX 315-431-0200, custserv@prsgroup.com, http://www.countrydata.com, http://www.prsgroup.com.

330.97283 USA ISSN 1054-5573
THE P R S GROUP. COUNTRY REPORTS: HONDURAS. (Political Risk Services) Key Title: Honduras (Syracuse, N.Y.). Text in English. 1979. a. USD 395 (effective 2001). **Description:** In-depth analysis and forecasts of political and economic conditions.
Related titles: CD-ROM ed.; Diskette ed.; Online - full text ed.: (from Data-Star).
Published by: The P R S Group, Inc., PO Box 248, East Syracuse, NY 13057-0248. TEL 315-431-0511, FAX 315-431-0200, custserv@prsgroup.com, http://www.countrydata.com, http://www.prsgroup.com.

330.95125 USA ISSN 1054-5581
THE P R S GROUP. COUNTRY REPORTS: HONG KONG. (Political Risk Services) Key Title: Hong Kong (Syracuse, N.Y.). Text in English. 1979. a. USD 395 (effective 2001). **Description:** In-depth analysis and forecasts of political and economic conditions.
Related titles: CD-ROM ed.; Diskette ed.; Online - full text ed.: (from Data-Star).
Published by: The P R S Group, Inc., PO Box 248, East Syracuse, NY 13057-0248. TEL 315-431-0511, FAX 315-431-0200, custserv@prsgroup.com, http://www.countrydata.com, http://www.prsgroup.com.

330.9439 USA ISSN 1054-559X
THE P R S GROUP. COUNTRY REPORTS: HUNGARY. (Political Risk Services) Key Title: Hungary (Syracuse, N.Y.). Text in English. 1979. a. USD 395 (effective 2001). **Description:** In-depth analysis and forecasts of political and economic conditions.
Related titles: CD-ROM ed.; Diskette ed.; Online - full text ed.: (from Data-Star).
Published by: The P R S Group, Inc., PO Box 248, East Syracuse, NY 13057-0248. TEL 315-431-0511, FAX 315-431-0200, custserv@prsgroup.com, http://www.countrydata.com, http://www.prsgroup.com.

330.954 USA ISSN 1054-5603
THE P R S GROUP. COUNTRY REPORTS: INDIA. (Political Risk Services) Key Title: India (Syracuse, N.Y.). Text in English. 1979. a. USD 395 (effective 2001). **Description:** Provides in-depth analysis and forecasts of political and economic issues.
Related titles: CD-ROM ed.; Diskette ed.; Online - full text ed.: (from Data-Star).
Published by: The P R S Group, Inc., PO Box 248, East Syracuse, NY 13057-0248. TEL 315-431-0511, FAX 315-431-0200, custserv@prsgroup.com, http://www.countrydata.com, http://www.prsgroup.com.

330.9598 USA ISSN 1054-5611
THE P R S GROUP. COUNTRY REPORTS: INDONESIA. (Political Risk Services) Key Title: Indonesia (Syracuse, N.Y.). Text in English. 1979. a. USD 395 (effective 2001). **Description:** In-depth analysis and forecasts of political and economic conditions.
Related titles: CD-ROM ed.; Diskette ed.; Online - full text ed.: (from Data-Star).
Published by: The P R S Group, Inc., PO Box 248, East Syracuse, NY 13057-0248. TEL 315-431-0511, FAX 315-431-0200, custserv@prsgroup.com, http://www.countrydata.com, http://www.prsgroup.com.

330.955 USA ISSN 1054-562X
THE P R S GROUP. COUNTRY REPORTS: IRAN. (Political Risk Services) Key Title: Iran (Syracuse, N.Y.). Text in English. 1979. a. USD 395 (effective 2001). **Description:** In-depth analysis and forecasts of political and economic conditions.
Related titles: CD-ROM ed.; Diskette ed.; Online - full text ed.: (from Data-Star).
Published by: The P R S Group, Inc., PO Box 248, East Syracuse, NY 13057-0248. TEL 315-431-0511, FAX 315-431-0200, custserv@prsgroup.com, http://www.countrydata.com, http://www.prsgroup.com.

330.9567 USA ISSN 1054-5638
THE P R S GROUP. COUNTRY REPORTS: IRAQ. (Political Risk Services) Key Title: Iraq (Syracuse, N.Y.). Text in English. 1979. a. USD 395 (effective 2001). **Description:** In-depth analysis and forecasts of political and economic conditions.
Related titles: CD-ROM ed.; Diskette ed.; Online - full text ed.: (from Data-Star).
Published by: The P R S Group, Inc., PO Box 248, East Syracuse, NY 13057-0248. TEL 315-431-0511, FAX 315-431-0200, custserv@prsgroup.com, http://www.countrydata.com, http://www.prsgroup.com.

330.9417 USA
THE P R S GROUP. COUNTRY REPORTS: IRELAND. (Political Risk Services) Text in English. 1979. a. USD 395 (effective 2001). **Description:** In-depth analysis and forecasts of political and economic conditions.
Former titles: P R S Group. Executive Reports: Ireland (1054-5646); Political Risk Services. Country Reports: Ireland
Related titles: CD-ROM ed.; Diskette ed.; Online - full text ed.: (from Data-Star).
Published by: The P R S Group, Inc., PO Box 248, East Syracuse, NY 13057-0248. TEL 315-431-0511, FAX 315-431-0200, custserv@prsgroup.com, http://www.countrydata.com, http://www.prsgroup.com.

330.95694 USA ISSN 1054-5662
THE P R S GROUP. COUNTRY REPORTS: ISRAEL. (Political Risk Services) Key Title: Israel (Syracuse, N.Y.). Text in English. 1979. a. USD 395 (effective 2001). **Description:** In-depth analysis and forecasts of political and economic conditions.
Related titles: CD-ROM ed.; Diskette ed.; Online - full text ed.: (from Data-Star).
Published by: The P R S Group, Inc., PO Box 248, East Syracuse, NY 13057-0248. TEL 315-431-0511, FAX 315-431-0200, custserv@prsgroup.com, http://www.countrydata.com, http://www.prsgroup.com.

330.945 USA
THE P R S GROUP. COUNTRY REPORTS: ITALY. (Political Risk Services) Text in English. 1979. a. USD 395 (effective 2001). **Description:** In-depth analysis and forecasts of political and economic conditions.
Former titles: P R S Group. Executive Reports: Italy (1054-5654); Political Risk Services. Country Reports: Italy
Related titles: CD-ROM ed.; Diskette ed.; Online - full text ed.: (from Data-Star).
Published by: The P R S Group, Inc., PO Box 248, East Syracuse, NY 13057-0248. TEL 315-431-0511, FAX 315-431-0200, custserv@prsgroup.com, http://www.countrydata.com, http://www.prsgroup.com.

330.97292 USA ISSN 1054-5689
THE P R S GROUP. COUNTRY REPORTS: JAMAICA. (Political Risk Services) Key Title: Jamaica (Syracuse, N.Y.). Text in English. 1979. a. USD 395 (effective 2001). **Description:** In-depth analysis and forecasts of political and economic conditions.
Related titles: CD-ROM ed.; Diskette ed.; Online - full text ed.: (from Data-Star).
Published by: The P R S Group, Inc., PO Box 248, East Syracuse, NY 13057-0248. TEL 315-431-0511, FAX 315-431-0200, custserv@prsgroup.com, http://www.countrydata.com, http://www.prsgroup.com.

330.952 USA
THE P R S GROUP. COUNTRY REPORTS: JAPAN. (Political Risk Services) Text in English. 1979. a. USD 395 (effective 2001). **Description:** In-depth analysis and forecasts of political and economic conditions.
Former titles: P R S Group. Executive Reports: Japan (1054-5697); Political Risk Services. Country Reports: Japan
Related titles: CD-ROM ed.; Diskette ed.; Online - full text ed.: (from Data-Star).
Published by: The P R S Group, Inc., PO Box 248, East Syracuse, NY 13057-0248. TEL 315-431-0511, FAX 315-431-0200, custserv@prsgroup.com, http://www.countrydata.com, http://www.prsgroup.com.

300.5845 USA
THE P R S GROUP. COUNTRY REPORTS: KAZAKSTAN. Text in English. a. USD 395 (effective 2001). **Document type:** *Trade.*
Related titles: CD-ROM ed.; Online - full content ed.
Published by: The P R S Group, Inc., PO Box 248, East Syracuse, NY 13057-0248. TEL 315-431-0511, FAX 315-431-0200, custserv@prsgroup.com, http://www.prsgroup.com.

330.96762   USA   ISSN 1054-5700
THE P R S GROUP. COUNTRY REPORTS: KENYA. (Political Risk Services) Key Title: Kenya (Syracuse, N.Y.). Text in English. 1979. a. USD 395 (effective 2001). **Description:** In-depth analysis and forecasts of political and economic conditions.
Related titles: CD-ROM ed.; Diskette ed.; Online - full text ed.: (from Data-Star).
Published by: The P R S Group, Inc., PO Box 248, East Syracuse, NY 13057-0248. TEL 315-431-0511, FAX 315-431-0200, custserv@prsgroup.com, http://www.countrydata.com, http://www.prsgroup.com.

330.95367   USA   ISSN 1055-9434
THE P R S GROUP. COUNTRY REPORTS: KUWAIT. (Political Risk Services) Key Title: Kuwait (Syracuse, N.Y.). Text in English. 1979. a. USD 395 (effective 2001). **Description:** In-depth analysis and forecasts of political and economic conditions.
Related titles: CD-ROM ed.; Diskette ed.; Online - full text ed.: (from Data-Star).
Published by: The P R S Group, Inc., PO Box 248, East Syracuse, NY 13057-0248. TEL 315-431-0511, FAX 315-431-0200, custserv@prsgroup.com, http://www.countrydata.com, http://www.prsgroup.com.

300.5843   USA
THE P R S GROUP. COUNTRY REPORTS: KYRGYZSTAN. Text in English. a. USD 395 (effective 2001). **Document type:** Trade.
Related titles: CD-ROM ed.; Online - full content ed.
Published by: The P R S Group, Inc., PO Box 248, East Syracuse, NY 13057-0248. TEL 315-431-0511, FAX 315-431-0200, custserv@prsgroup.com, http://www.prsgroup.com.

330.9612   USA   ISSN 1054-5719
THE P R S GROUP. COUNTRY REPORTS: LIBYA. (Political Risk Services) Key Title: Libya (Syracuse, N.Y.). Text in English. 1979. a. USD 395 (effective 2001). **Description:** In-depth analysis and forecasts of political and economic conditions.
Related titles: CD-ROM ed.; Diskette ed.; Online - full text ed.: (from Data-Star).
Published by: The P R S Group, Inc., PO Box 248, East Syracuse, NY 13057-0248. TEL 315-431-0511, FAX 315-431-0200, custserv@prsgroup.com, http://www.countrydata.com, http://www.prsgroup.com.

330.94793   USA   ISSN 1099-2286
THE P R S GROUP. COUNTRY REPORTS: LITHUANIA. Key Title: Lithuania (Syracuse, N.Y.). Text in English. a. USD 395 (effective 2001). **Description:** Offers in-depth analysis and forecasts of political and economic conditions.
Related titles: CD-ROM ed.; Online - full content ed.
Published by: The P R S Group, Inc., PO Box 248, East Syracuse, NY 13057-0248. TEL 315-431-0511, FAX 315-431-0200, custserv@prsgroup.com, http://www.countrydata.com, http://www.prsgroup.com.

330.9595   USA   ISSN 1054-5727
THE P R S GROUP. COUNTRY REPORTS: MALAYSIA. (Political Risk Services) Key Title: Malaysia (Syracuse, N.Y.). Text in English. 1979. a. USD 395 (effective 2001). **Description:** In-depth analysis and forecasts of political and economic conditions.
Related titles: CD-ROM ed.; Diskette ed.; Online - full text ed.: (from Data-Star).
Published by: The P R S Group, Inc., PO Box 248, East Syracuse, NY 13057-0248. TEL 315-431-0511, FAX 315-431-0200, custserv@prsgroup.com, http://www.countrydata.com, http://www.prsgroup.com.

330.972   USA   ISSN 1054-5735
THE P R S GROUP. COUNTRY REPORTS: MEXICO. (Political Risk Services) Key Title: Mexico (Syracuse, N.Y.). Text in English. 1979. a. USD 395 (effective 2001). **Description:** In-depth analysis and forecasts of political and economic conditions.
Related titles: CD-ROM ed.; Diskette ed.; Online - full text ed.: (from Data-Star).
Published by: The P R S Group, Inc., PO Box 248, East Syracuse, NY 13057-0248. TEL 315-431-0511, FAX 315-431-0200, custserv@prsgroup.com, http://www.countrydata.com, http://www.prsgroup.com.

330.964   USA   ISSN 1054-5743
THE P R S GROUP. COUNTRY REPORTS: MOROCCO. (Political Risk Services) Key Title: Morocco (Syracuse, N.Y.). Text in English. 1979. a. USD 395 (effective 2001). **Description:** In-depth analysis and forecasts of political and economic conditions.
Related titles: CD-ROM ed.; Diskette ed.; Online - full text ed.: (from Data-Star).
Published by: The P R S Group, Inc., PO Box 248, East Syracuse, NY 13057-0248. TEL 315-431-0511, FAX 315-431-0200, custserv@prsgroup.com, http://www.countrydata.com, http://www.prsgroup.com.

330.9591   USA
THE P R S GROUP. COUNTRY REPORTS: MYANMAR. (Political Risk Services) Text in English. 1993. a. USD 395 (effective 2001). **Description:** Provides analysis and forecasts of political and economic conditions.
Former titles: P R S Group. Executive Reports: Myanmar; Political Risk Services. Executive Reports: Burma (1067-800X)
Related titles: CD-ROM ed.; Online - full content ed.
Published by: The P R S Group, Inc., PO Box 248, East Syracuse, NY 13057-0248. TEL 315-431-0511, FAX 315-431-0200, custserv@prsgroup.com, http://www.countrydata.com, http://www.prsgroup.com.

330.9494   USA
THE P R S GROUP. COUNTRY REPORTS: NETHERLANDS. (Political Risk Services) Text in English. 1979. a. USD 395 (effective 2001). **Description:** In-depth analysis and forecasts of political and economic conditions.
Former titles: P R S Group. Executive Reports: Netherlands (1054-5751); Political Risk Services. Country Reports: Netherlands
Related titles: CD-ROM ed.; Diskette ed.; Online - full text ed.: (from Data-Star).
Published by: The P R S Group, Inc., PO Box 248, East Syracuse, NY 13057-0248. TEL 315-431-0511, FAX 315-431-0200, custserv@prsgroup.com, http://www.countrydata.com, http://www.prsgroup.com.

330.993   USA
THE P R S GROUP. COUNTRY REPORTS: NEW ZEALAND. (Political Risk Services) Text in English. 1979. a. USD 395 (effective 2001). **Description:** In-depth analysis and forecasts of political and economic conditions.
Former titles: P R S Group. Executive Reports: New Zealand (1054-5778); Political Risk Services. Country Reports: New Zealand
Related titles: CD-ROM ed.; Diskette ed.; Online - full text ed.: (from Data-Star).
Published by: The P R S Group, Inc., PO Box 248, East Syracuse, NY 13057-0248. TEL 315-431-0511, FAX 315-431-0200, custserv@prsgroup.com, http://www.countrydata.com, http://www.prsgroup.com.

330.97285   USA   ISSN 1054-5786
THE P R S GROUP. COUNTRY REPORTS: NICARAGUA. (Political Risk Services) Key Title: Nicaragua (Syracuse, N.Y.). Text in English. 1979. a. USD 395 (effective 2001). **Description:** In-depth analysis and forecasts of political and economic conditions.
Related titles: CD-ROM ed.; Diskette ed.; Online - full text ed.: (from Data-Star).
Published by: The P R S Group, Inc., PO Box 248, East Syracuse, NY 13057-0248. TEL 315-431-0511, FAX 315-431-0200, custserv@prsgroup.com, http://www.countrydata.com, http://www.prsgroup.com.

330.9669   USA   ISSN 1054-576X
THE P R S GROUP. COUNTRY REPORTS: NIGERIA. (Political Risk Services) Key Title: Nigeria (Syracuse, N.Y.). Text in English. 1979. a. USD 395 (effective 2001). **Description:** In-depth analysis and forecasts of political and economic conditions.
Related titles: CD-ROM ed.; Diskette ed.; Online - full text ed.: (from Data-Star).
Published by: The P R S Group, Inc., PO Box 248, East Syracuse, NY 13057-0248. TEL 315-431-0511, FAX 315-431-0200, custserv@prsgroup.com, http://www.countrydata.com, http://www.prsgroup.com.

330.9481   USA
THE P R S GROUP. COUNTRY REPORTS: NORWAY. (Political Risk Services) Text in English. 1979. a. USD 395 (effective 2001). **Description:** In-depth analysis and forecasts of political and economic conditions.
Former titles: P R S Group. Executive Reports: Norway (1054-5794); Political Risk Services. Country Reports: Norway
Related titles: CD-ROM ed.; Diskette ed.; Online - full text ed.: (from Data-Star).
Published by: The P R S Group, Inc., PO Box 248, East Syracuse, NY 13057-0248. TEL 315-431-0511, FAX 315-431-0200, custserv@prsgroup.com, http://www.countrydata.com, http://www.prsgroup.com.

330.95353   USA   ISSN 1054-5808
THE P R S GROUP. COUNTRY REPORTS: OMAN. (Political Risk Services) Key Title: Oman (Syracuse, N.Y.). Text in English. 1979. a. USD 395 (effective 2001). **Description:** In-depth analysis and forecasts of political and economic conditions.
Related titles: CD-ROM ed.; Diskette ed.; Online - full text ed.: (from Data-Star).
Published by: The P R S Group, Inc., PO Box 248, East Syracuse, NY 13057-0248. TEL 315-431-0511, FAX 315-431-0200, custserv@prsgroup.com, http://www.countrydata.com, http://www.prsgroup.com.

330.95491   USA   ISSN 1054-6030
THE P R S GROUP. COUNTRY REPORTS: PAKISTAN. (Political Risk Services) Key Title: Pakistan (Syracuse, N.Y.). Text in English. 1979. a. USD 395 (effective 2001). **Description:** In-depth analysis and forecasts of political and economic conditions.

Related titles: CD-ROM ed.; Diskette ed.; Online - full text ed.: (from Data-Star).
Published by: The P R S Group, Inc., PO Box 248, East Syracuse, NY 13057-0248. TEL 315-431-0511, FAX 315-431-0200, custserv@prsgroup.com, http://www.countrydata.com, http://www.prsgroup.com.

330.97287   USA   ISSN 1054-6049
THE P R S GROUP. COUNTRY REPORTS: PANAMA. (Political Risk Services) Key Title: Panama (Syracuse, N.Y.). Text in English. 1979. a. USD 395 (effective 2001). **Description:** In-depth analysis and forecasts of political and economic conditions.
Related titles: CD-ROM ed.; Diskette ed.; Online - full text ed.: (from Data-Star).
Published by: The P R S Group, Inc., PO Box 248, East Syracuse, NY 13057-0248. TEL 315-431-0511, FAX 315-431-0200, custserv@prsgroup.com, http://www.countrydata.com, http://www.prsgroup.com.

330.9953   USA
THE P R S GROUP. COUNTRY REPORTS: PAPUA NEW GUINEA. (Political Risk Services) Text in English. 1993. a. USD 395 (effective 2001). **Description:** Provides analysis and forecasts of political and economic conditions.
Formerly: P R S Group. Executive Reports: Papua New Guinea (1067-8050)
Related titles: CD-ROM ed.; Online - full content ed.
Published by: The P R S Group, Inc., PO Box 248, East Syracuse, NY 13057-0248. TEL 315-431-0511, FAX 315-431-0200, custserv@prsgroup.com, http://www.countrydata.com, http://www.prsgroup.com.

330.9892   USA
THE P R S GROUP. COUNTRY REPORTS: PARAGUAY. (Political Risk Services) Text in English. 1993. a. USD 395 (effective 2001). **Description:** Provides analysis and forecasts of political and economic conditions.
Formerly: P R S Group. Executive Reports: Paraguay (1067-8069)
Related titles: CD-ROM ed.; Online - full content ed.
Published by: The P R S Group, Inc., PO Box 248, East Syracuse, NY 13057-0248. TEL 315-431-0511, FAX 315-431-0200, custserv@prsgroup.com, http://www.countrydata.com, http://www.prsgroup.com.

330.985   USA   ISSN 1054-6057
THE P R S GROUP. COUNTRY REPORTS: PERU. (Political Risk Services) Key Title: Peru (Syracuse, N.Y.). Text in English. 1979. a. USD 395 (effective 2001). **Description:** In-depth analysis and forecasts of political and economic conditions.
Related titles: CD-ROM ed.; Diskette ed.; Online - full text ed.: (from Data-Star).
Published by: The P R S Group, Inc., PO Box 248, East Syracuse, NY 13057-0248. TEL 315-431-0511, FAX 315-431-0200, custserv@prsgroup.com, http://www.countrydata.com, http://www.prsgroup.com.

330.9599   USA   ISSN 1054-6065
THE P R S GROUP. COUNTRY REPORTS: PHILIPPINES. (Political Risk Services) Key Title: Philippines (Syracuse, N.Y.). Text in English. 1979. a. USD 395 (effective 2001). **Description:** In-depth analysis and forecasts of political and economic conditions.
Related titles: CD-ROM ed.; Diskette ed.; Online - full text ed.: (from Data-Star).
Published by: The P R S Group, Inc., PO Box 248, East Syracuse, NY 13057-0248. TEL 315-431-0511, FAX 315-431-0200, custserv@prsgroup.com, http://www.countrydata.com, http://www.prsgroup.com.

330.9438   USA   ISSN 1054-6073
THE P R S GROUP. COUNTRY REPORTS: POLAND. (Political Risk Services) Key Title: Poland (Syracuse, N.Y.). Text in English. 1979. a. USD 395 (effective 2001). **Description:** In-depth analysis and forecasts of political and economic conditions.
Related titles: CD-ROM ed.; Diskette ed.; Online - full text ed.: (from Data-Star).
Published by: The P R S Group, Inc., PO Box 248, East Syracuse, NY 13057-0248. TEL 315-431-0511, FAX 315-431-0200, custserv@prsgroup.com, http://www.countrydata.com, http://www.prsgroup.com.

330.9469   USA
THE P R S GROUP. COUNTRY REPORTS: PORTUGAL. (Political Risk Services) Text in English. 1979. a. USD 395 (effective 2001). **Description:** In-depth analysis and forecasts of political and economic conditions.
Former titles: P R S Group. Executive Reports: Portugal (1054-6081); Political Risk Services. Country Reports: Portugal
Related titles: CD-ROM ed.; Diskette ed.; Online - full text ed.: (from Data-Star).
Published by: The P R S Group, Inc., PO Box 248, East Syracuse, NY 13057-0248. TEL 315-431-0511, FAX 315-431-0200, custserv@prsgroup.com, http://www.countrydata.com, http://www.prsgroup.com.

B

330.97295 USA
THE P R S GROUP. COUNTRY REPORTS: PUERTO RICO. (Political Risk Services) Text in English. 1979. a. USD 395 (effective 2001). **Description:** In-depth analysis and forecasts of political and economic conditions.
Former titles: P R S Group. Executive Reports: Puerto Rico (1054-609X); Political Risk Services. Country Reports: Puerto Rico
Related titles: CD-ROM ed.; Diskette ed.; Online - full text ed.: (from Data-Star).
Published by: The P R S Group, Inc., PO Box 248, East Syracuse, NY 13057-0248. TEL 315-431-0511, FAX 315-431-0200, custserv@prsgroup.com, http://www.countrydata.com, http://www.prsgroup.com.

330.95363 USA
THE P R S GROUP. COUNTRY REPORTS: QATAR. (Political Risk Services) Text in English. 1993. a. USD 395 (effective 2001). **Description:** Provides analysis and forecasts of political and economic conditions.
Formerly: P R S Group. Executive Reports: Qatar (1067-8077)
Related titles: CD-ROM ed.; Online - full content ed.
Published by: The P R S Group, Inc., PO Box 248, East Syracuse, NY 13057-0248. TEL 315-431-0511, FAX 315-431-0200, custserv@prsgroup.com, http://www.countrydata.com, http://www.prsgroup.com.

330.9498 USA ISSN 1054-6103
THE P R S GROUP. COUNTRY REPORTS: ROMANIA. (Political Risk Services) Key Title: Romania (Syracuse, N.Y.). Text in English. 1979. a. USD 395 (effective 2001). **Description:** In-depth analysis and forecasts of political and economic conditions.
Related titles: CD-ROM ed.; Diskette ed.; Online - full text ed.: (from Data-Star).
Published by: The P R S Group, Inc., PO Box 248, East Syracuse, NY 13057-0248. TEL 315-431-0511, FAX 315-431-0200, custserv@prsgroup.com, http://www.countrydata.com, http://www.prsgroup.com.

330.947 USA ISSN 1060-8753
THE P R S GROUP. COUNTRY REPORTS: RUSSIA. (Political Risk Services) Key Title: Russia (Syracuse, N.Y.). Text in English. 1992. a. USD 395 (effective 2001). **Description:** In-depth analysis and forecasts of political and economic conditions.
Supersedes in part (1984-1991): U S S R (Syracuse, N.Y.) (1054-6243)
Related titles: CD-ROM ed.; Diskette ed.; Online - full text ed.: (from Data-Star).
Published by: The P R S Group, Inc., PO Box 248, East Syracuse, NY 13057-0248. TEL 315-431-0511, FAX 315-431-0200, custserv@prsgroup.com, http://www.countrydata.com, http://www.prsgroup.com.

330.9538 USA ISSN 1054-6111
THE P R S GROUP. COUNTRY REPORTS: SAUDI ARABIA. (Political Risk Services) Key Title: Saudi Arabia (Syracuse, N.Y.). Text in English. 1979. a. USD 395 (effective 2001). **Description:** In-depth analysis and forecasts of political and economic conditions.
Related titles: CD-ROM ed.; Diskette ed.; Online - full text ed.: (from Data-Star).
Published by: The P R S Group, Inc., PO Box 248, East Syracuse, NY 13057-0248. TEL 315-431-0511, FAX 315-431-0200, custserv@prsgroup.com, http://www.countrydata.com, http://www.prsgroup.com.

330.95957 USA ISSN 1054-612X
THE P R S GROUP. COUNTRY REPORTS: SINGAPORE. (Political Risk Services) Key Title: Singapore (Syracuse, NY). Text in English. 1979. a. USD 395 (effective 2001). **Description:** In-depth analysis and forecasts of political and economic conditions.
Related titles: CD-ROM ed.; Diskette ed.; Online - full text ed.: (from Data-Star).
Published by: The P R S Group, Inc., PO Box 248, East Syracuse, NY 13057-0248. TEL 315-431-0511, FAX 315-431-0200, custserv@prsgroup.com, http://www.countrydata.com, http://www.prsgroup.com.

330.94373 USA ISSN 1531-4707
THE P R S GROUP. COUNTRY REPORTS: SLOVAK REPUBLIC. Key Title: Slovak Republic (Syracuse, N.Y.). Text in English. a. USD 395 (effective 2001). **Description:** Offers in-depth analysis and forecasts of political and economic conditions.
Related titles: CD-ROM ed.; Online - full content ed.
Published by: The P R S Group, Inc., PO Box 248, East Syracuse, NY 13057-0248. TEL 315-431-0511, FAX 315-431-0200, custserv@prsgroup.com, http://www.countrydata.com, http://www.prsgroup.com.

330.968 USA ISSN 1054-6138
THE P R S GROUP. COUNTRY REPORTS: SOUTH AFRICA. (Political Risk Services) Key Title: South Africa (Syracuse, N.Y.). Text in English. 1979. a. USD 395 (effective 2001). **Description:** In-depth analysis and forecasts of political and economic conditions.
Related titles: CD-ROM ed.; Diskette ed.; Online - full text ed.: (from Data-Star).
Published by: The P R S Group, Inc., PO Box 248, East Syracuse, NY 13057-0248. TEL 315-431-0511, FAX 315-431-0200, custserv@prsgroup.com, http://www.countrydata.com, http://www.prsgroup.com.

330.95195 USA ISSN 1054-6146
THE P R S GROUP. COUNTRY REPORTS: SOUTH KOREA. (Political Risk Services) Key Title: South Korea (Syracuse, N.Y.). Text in English. 1979. a. USD 395 (effective 2001). **Description:** In-depth analysis and forecasts of political and economic conditions.
Related titles: CD-ROM ed.; Diskette ed.; Online - full text ed.: (from Data-Star).
Published by: The P R S Group, Inc., PO Box 248, East Syracuse, NY 13057-0248. TEL 315-431-0511, FAX 315-431-0200, custserv@prsgroup.com, http://www.countrydata.com, http://www.prsgroup.com.

330.946 USA
THE P R S GROUP. COUNTRY REPORTS: SPAIN. (Political Risk Services) Text in English. 1979. a. USD 395 (effective 2001). **Description:** In-depth analysis and forecasts of political and economic conditions.
Former titles: P R S Group. Executive Reports: Spain (1054-6154); Political Risk Services. Country Reports: Spain
Related titles: CD-ROM ed.; Diskette ed.; Online - full text ed.: (from Data-Star).
Published by: The P R S Group, Inc., PO Box 248, East Syracuse, NY 13057-0248. TEL 315-431-0511, FAX 315-431-0200, custserv@prsgroup.com, http://www.countrydata.com, http://www.prsgroup.com.

330.95493 USA ISSN 1054-6162
THE P R S GROUP. COUNTRY REPORTS: SRI LANKA. (Political Risk Services) Key Title: Sri Lanka (Syracuse, N.Y.). Text in English. 1979. a. USD 395 (effective 2001). **Description:** In-depth analysis and forecasts of political and economic conditions.
Related titles: CD-ROM ed.; Diskette ed.; Online - full text ed.: (from Data-Star).
Published by: The P R S Group, Inc., PO Box 248, East Syracuse, NY 13057-0248. TEL 315-431-0511, FAX 315-431-0200, custserv@prsgroup.com, http://www.countrydata.com, http://www.prsgroup.com.

330.9624 USA ISSN 1054-6170
THE P R S GROUP. COUNTRY REPORTS: SUDAN. (Political Risk Services) Key Title: Sudan (Syracuse, N.Y.). Text in English. 1979. a. USD 395 (effective 2001). **Description:** In-depth analysis and forecasts of political and economic conditions.
Related titles: CD-ROM ed.; Diskette ed.; Online - full text ed.: (from Data-Star).
Published by: The P R S Group, Inc., PO Box 248, East Syracuse, NY 13057-0248. TEL 315-431-0511, FAX 315-431-0200, custserv@prsgroup.com, http://www.countrydata.com, http://www.prsgroup.com.

330.9883 USA
THE P R S GROUP. COUNTRY REPORTS: SURINAME. (Political Risk Services) Text in English. 1993. a. USD 395 (effective 2001). **Description:** Provides analysis and forecasts of political and economic conditions.
Formerly: P R S Group. Executive Reports: Suriname (1067-8085)
Related titles: CD-ROM ed.; Online - full content ed.
Published by: The P R S Group, Inc., PO Box 248, East Syracuse, NY 13057-0248. TEL 315-431-0511, FAX 315-431-0200, custserv@prsgroup.com, http://www.countrydata.com, http://www.prsgroup.com.

330.9494 USA
THE P R S GROUP. COUNTRY REPORTS: SWITZERLAND. (Political Risk Services) Text in English. 1993. a. USD 395 (effective 2001). **Description:** Provides analysis and forecasts of political and economic conditions.
Formerly: P R S Group. Executive Reports: Switzerland (1067-8093)
Related titles: CD-ROM ed.; Online - full content ed.
Published by: The P R S Group, Inc., PO Box 248, East Syracuse, NY 13057-0248. TEL 315-431-0511, FAX 315-431-0200, custserv@prsgroup.com, http://www.countrydata.com, http://www.prsgroup.com.

330.95691 USA ISSN 1054-6197
THE P R S GROUP. COUNTRY REPORTS: SYRIA. (Political Risk Services) Key Title: Syria (Syracuse, N.Y.). Text in English. 1979. a. USD 395 (effective 2001). **Description:** In-depth analysis and forecasts of political and economic conditions.
Related titles: CD-ROM ed.; Diskette ed.; Online - full text ed.: (from Data-Star).
Published by: The P R S Group, Inc., PO Box 248, East Syracuse, NY 13057-0248. TEL 315-431-0511, FAX 315-431-0200, custserv@prsgroup.com, http://www.countrydata.com, http://www.prsgroup.com.

330.951249 USA ISSN 1054-6200
THE P R S GROUP. COUNTRY REPORTS: TAIWAN. (Political Risk Services) Key Title: Taiwan (Syracuse, N.Y.). Text in English. 1979. a. USD 395 (effective 2001). **Description:** In-depth analysis and forecasts of political and economic conditions.
Related titles: CD-ROM ed.; Diskette ed.; Online - full text ed.: (from Data-Star).
Published by: The P R S Group, Inc., PO Box 248, East Syracuse, NY 13057-0248. TEL 315-431-0511, FAX 315-431-0200, custserv@prsgroup.com, http://www.countrydata.com, http://www.prsgroup.com.

330.9593 USA ISSN 1054-6219
THE P R S GROUP. COUNTRY REPORTS: THAILAND. (Political Risk Services) Key Title: Thailand (Syracuse, N.Y.). Text in English. 1979. a. USD 395 (effective 2001). **Description:** In-depth analysis and forecasts of political and economic conditions.
Related titles: CD-ROM ed.; Diskette ed.; Online - full text ed.: (from Data-Star).
Published by: The P R S Group, Inc., PO Box 248, East Syracuse, NY 13057-0248. TEL 315-431-0511, FAX 315-431-0200, custserv@prsgroup.com, http://www.countrydata.com, http://www.prsgroup.com.

330.972983 USA
THE P R S GROUP. COUNTRY REPORTS: TRINIDAD & TOBAGO. (Political Risk Services) Text in English. 1993. a. USD 395 (effective 2001). **Description:** Provides analysis and forecasts of political and economic conditions.
Formerly: P R S Group. Executive Reports: Trinidad and Tobago (1067-8107)
Related titles: CD-ROM ed.; Online - full content ed.
Published by: The P R S Group, Inc., PO Box 248, East Syracuse, NY 13057-0248. TEL 315-431-0511, FAX 315-431-0200, custserv@prsgroup.com, http://www.countrydata.com, http://www.prsgroup.com.

330.9611 USA ISSN 1054-6227
THE P R S GROUP. COUNTRY REPORTS: TUNISIA. (Political Risk Services) Key Title: Tunisia (Syracuse, N.Y.). Text in English. 1979. a. USD 395 (effective 2001). **Description:** In-depth analysis and forecasts of political and economic conditions.
Related titles: CD-ROM ed.; Diskette ed.; Online - full text ed.: (from Data-Star).
Published by: The P R S Group, Inc., PO Box 248, East Syracuse, NY 13057-0248. TEL 315-431-0511, FAX 315-431-0200, custserv@prsgroup.com, http://www.countrydata.com, http://www.prsgroup.com.

330.9561 USA ISSN 1054-6235
THE P R S GROUP. COUNTRY REPORTS: TURKEY. (Political Risk Services) Key Title: Turkey (Syracuse, N.Y.). Text in English. 1979. a. USD 395 (effective 2001). **Description:** In-depth analysis and forecasts of political and economic conditions.
Related titles: CD-ROM ed.; Diskette ed.; Online - full text ed.: (from Data-Star).
Published by: The P R S Group, Inc., PO Box 248, East Syracuse, NY 13057-0248. TEL 315-431-0511, FAX 315-431-0200, custserv@prsgroup.com, http://www.countrydata.com, http://www.prsgroup.com.

330.9585 USA ISSN 1099-2308
THE P R S GROUP. COUNTRY REPORTS: TURKMENISTAN. Key Title: Turkmenistan (Syracuse, N.Y.). Text in English. a. USD 395 (effective 2001). **Description:** Offers in-depth analysis and forecasts of political and economic conditions.
Related titles: CD-ROM ed.; Online - full content ed.
Published by: The P R S Group, Inc., PO Box 248, East Syracuse, NY 13057-0248. TEL 315-431-0511, FAX 315-431-0200, custserv@prsgroup.com, http://www.countrydata.com, http://www.prsgroup.com.

330.9477 USA ISSN 1061-1304
THE P R S GROUP. COUNTRY REPORTS: UKRAINE. (Political Risk Services) Key Title: Ukraine (Syracuse, N.Y.). Text in English. 1992. a. USD 395 (effective 2001). **Description:** In-depth analysis and forecasts of political and economic conditions.
Supersedes in part (1984-1991): U S S R (Syracuse, N.Y.) (1054-6243)
Related titles: CD-ROM ed.; Diskette ed.; Online - full text ed.: (from Data-Star).
Published by: The P R S Group, Inc., PO Box 248, East Syracuse, NY 13057-0248. TEL 315-431-0511, FAX 315-431-0200, custserv@prsgroup.com, http://www.countrydata.com, http://www.prsgroup.com.

330.95357 USA ISSN 1054-6251
THE P R S GROUP. COUNTRY REPORTS: UNITED ARAB EMIRATES. (Political Risk Services) Key Title: United Arab Emirates (Syracuse, N.Y.). Text in English. 1979. a. USD 395 (effective 2001). **Description:** Provides in-depth analysis and forecasts of political and economic conditions.
Related titles: CD-ROM ed.; Diskette ed.; Online - full text ed.: (from Data-Star).

Published by: The P R S Group, Inc., PO Box 248, East Syracuse, NY 13057-0248. TEL 315-431-0511, FAX 315-431-0200, custserv@prsgroup.com, http://www.countrydata.com, http://www.prsgroup.com.

330.941 USA
THE P R S GROUP. COUNTRY REPORTS: UNITED KINGDOM. (Political Risk Services) Text in English. 1979. a. USD 395 (effective 2001). **Description:** In-depth analysis and forecasts of political and economic conditions.
Former titles: P R S Group. Executive Reports: United Kingdom (1054-626X); Political Risk Services. Country Reports: United Kingdom
Related titles: CD-ROM ed.; Diskette ed.; Online - full text ed.: (from Data-Star).
Published by: The P R S Group, Inc., PO Box 248, East Syracuse, NY 13057-0248. TEL 315-431-0511, FAX 315-431-0200, custserv@prsgroup.com, http://www.countrydata.com, http://www.prsgroup.com.

330.973 USA
THE P R S GROUP. COUNTRY REPORTS: UNITED STATES. (Political Risk Services) Text in English. 1979. a. USD 395 (effective 2001). **Description:** In-depth analysis and forecasts of political and economic conditions.
Former titles: P R S Group. Executive Reports: United States (1054-6278); Political Risk Services. Country Reports: United States
Related titles: CD-ROM ed.; Diskette ed.; Online - full text ed.: (from Data-Star).
Published by: The P R S Group, Inc., PO Box 248, East Syracuse, NY 13057-0248. TEL 315-431-0511, FAX 315-431-0200, custserv@prsgroup.com, http://www.countrydata.com, http://www.prsgroup.com.

330.9895 USA ISSN 1054-6286
THE P R S GROUP. COUNTRY REPORTS: URUGUAY. (Political Risk Services) Key Title: Uruguay (Syracuse, N.Y.). Text in English. 1979. a. USD 395 (effective 2001). **Description:** In-depth analysis and forecasts of political and economic conditions.
Related titles: CD-ROM ed.; Diskette ed.; Online - full text ed.: (from Data-Star).
Published by: The P R S Group, Inc., PO Box 248, East Syracuse, NY 13057-0248. TEL 315-431-0511, FAX 315-431-0200, custserv@prsgroup.com, http://www.countrydata.com, http://www.prsgroup.com.

330.9587 USA ISSN 1099-226X
THE P R S GROUP. COUNTRY REPORTS: UZBEKISTAN. Text in English. a. USD 395 (effective 2001). **Description:** Offers in-depth analysis and forecasts of political and economic conditions.
Related titles: CD-ROM ed.; Online - full content ed.
Published by: The P R S Group, Inc., PO Box 248, East Syracuse, NY 13057-0248. TEL 315-431-0511, FAX 315-431-0200, custserv@prsgroup.com, http://www.countrydata.com, http://www.prsgroup.com.

330.987 USA ISSN 1054-6294
THE P R S GROUP. COUNTRY REPORTS: VENEZUELA. (Political Risk Services) Key Title: Venezuela (Syracuse, N.Y.). Text in English. 1979. a. USD 395 (effective 2001). **Description:** Provides in-depth analysis and forecasts of political and economic conditions.
Related titles: CD-ROM ed.; Diskette ed.; Online - full text ed.: (from Data-Star).
Published by: The P R S Group, Inc., PO Box 248, East Syracuse, NY 13057-0248. TEL 315-431-0511, FAX 315-431-0200, custserv@prsgroup.com, http://www.countrydata.com, http://www.prsgroup.com.

330.9597 USA ISSN 1058-3831
THE P R S GROUP. COUNTRY REPORTS: VIETNAM. (Political Risk Services) Key Title: Vietnam (Syracuse, N.Y.). Text in English. 1990. a. USD 395 (effective 2001). **Description:** In-depth analysis and forecasts of political and economic conditions.
Related titles: CD-ROM ed.; Diskette ed.; Online - full text ed.: (from Data-Star, Factiva, Florida Center for Library Automation).
Published by: The P R S Group, Inc., PO Box 248, East Syracuse, NY 13057-0248. TEL 315-431-0511, FAX 315-431-0200, custserv@prsgroup.com, http://www.countrydata.com, http://www.prsgroup.com.

320 USA
THE P R S GROUP. COUNTRY REPORTS: WORLD SERVICE. (Political Risk Services) Text in English. 1979. 100/yr. (7-9 reports/m.). USD 6,995 (effective 2001); includes 100 Country Reports, Monthly Updates, Country Forecasts, Political Risk Letter, unlimited 30 minute consultations with PRS Group country experts.. **Description:** Covers political and economic risk factors for international business. Executive Reports provide up-to-date summaries and overviews of the situation in a country; Country Reports provide greater depth and detail.
Formerly: World Country Report Service
Related titles: CD-ROM ed.: USD 7,995 (effective 2000); Online - full text ed.: USD 7,995 for single user licenses (effective 2000) (from Data-Star).

Published by: The P R S Group, Inc., PO Box 248, East Syracuse, NY 13057-0248. TEL 315-431-0511, FAX 315-431-0200, custserv@prsgroup.com, http://www.countrydata.com, http://www.prsgroup.com.

330.9533 USA
THE P R S GROUP. COUNTRY REPORTS: YEMEN. (Political Risk Services) Text in English. 1993. a. USD 395 (effective 2001). **Description:** Provides analysis and forecasts of political and economic conditions.
Formerly: P R S Group. Executive Reports: Yemen (1067-8115)
Related titles: CD-ROM ed.; Online - full content ed.
Published by: The P R S Group, Inc., PO Box 248, East Syracuse, NY 13057-0248. TEL 315-431-0511, FAX 315-431-0200, custserv@prsgroup.com, http://www.countrydata.com, http://www.prsgroup.com.

330.96894 USA ISSN 1054-6324
THE P R S GROUP. COUNTRY REPORTS: ZAMBIA. (Political Risk Services) Key Title: Zambia (Syracuse, N.Y.). Text in English. 1979. a. USD 395 (effective 2001). **Description:** In-depth analysis and forecasts of political and economic conditions.
Related titles: CD-ROM ed.; Diskette ed.; Online - full text ed.: (from Data-Star).
Published by: The P R S Group, Inc., PO Box 248, East Syracuse, NY 13057-0248. TEL 315-431-0511, FAX 315-431-0200, custserv@prsgroup.com, http://www.countrydata.com, http://www.prsgroup.com.

330.96891 USA ISSN 1054-6332
THE P R S GROUP. COUNTRY REPORTS: ZIMBABWE. Key Title: Zimbabwe (Syracuse, N.Y.). Text in English. 198?. a. USD 395 (effective 2001). **Description:** Offers in-depth analysis and forecasts of political and economic conditions.
Related titles: CD-ROM ed.; Diskette ed.; Online - full text ed.: (from Data-Star).
Published by: The P R S Group, Inc., PO Box 248, East Syracuse, NY 13057-0248. TEL 315-431-0511, FAX 315-431-0200, custserv@prsgroup.com, http://www.countrydata.com, http://www.prsgroup.com.

330.9485 USA
THE P R S GROUP. EXECUTIVE REPORTS: SWEDEN. Text in English. 1979. a. USD 395 (effective 2001). **Description:** Provides in-depth analysis and forecasts of political and economic conditions.
Former titles: P R S Group. Executive Reports: Sweden (1054-6189); Political Risk Services. Country Reports: Sweden
Related titles: CD-ROM ed.; Diskette ed.; Online - full text ed.: (from Data-Star).
Published by: The P R S Group, Inc., PO Box 248, East Syracuse, NY 13057-0248. TEL 315-431-0511, FAX 315-431-0200, custserv@prsgroup.com, http://www.countrydata.com, http://www.prsgroup.com.

051 USA ISSN 1543-6195
PACIFIC COAST BUSINESS TIMES. Text in English. w. USD 49.99; USD 1.50 newsstand/cover (effective 2005). adv. **Document type:** *Magazine, Trade.* **Description:** Concentrates on issues of interest to the business communities of Ventura and Santa Barbara counties.
Address: 14 E Carrillo St, Ste A, Santa Barbara, CA 73101. TEL 805-560-6950, FAX 805-560-8399, gwolverton@pacbiztimes.com, http://www.pacbiztimes.com. Ed. Henry Dubross. adv.: B&W page USD 2,270; trim 11 x 13.75.

330.9 338.91 AUS ISSN 0817-8038
HC681.A1 CODEN: PEBUEQ
➤ **PACIFIC ECONOMIC BULLETIN.** Text in English. 1986. s-a. AUD 20 per issue (effective 2005). bk.rev. stat. back issues avail. **Document type:** *Bulletin, Academic/Scholarly.* **Description:** Describes the economies and economic problems of the South Pacific for public servants, academics and businesses.
Related titles: Online - full content ed.
Indexed: APEL, FPA, FS&TA, ForAb, GEOBASE, HortAb, IBSS, JEL, NutrAb, PHN&I, PSA, RDA, RRTA, SIA, SOPODA, SSA, SociolAb, TDB, WAE&RSA.
—BLDSC (6329.150000).
Published by: (Australian National University, Asia Pacific School of Economics and Management), Asia Pacific Press, The Crawford Bldg, Ellery Circuit, The Australian National University, Canberra, ACT 0200, Australia. TEL 61-2-61250178, FAX 61-2-62572886, books@asiapacificpress.com, http://www.asiapacificpress.com/. Eds. Maree Tait, Ron Duncan. Circ: 700.

330.9 AUS
PACIFIC ECONOMIC OUTLOOK. Text in English. a., latest 2004-2005. AUD 25 per issue (effective 2005). charts; stat. back issues avail. **Description:** Provides annual economic forecasts for 20 economies in the Pacific region.
Published by: (Pacific Economic Cooperation Council), Asia Pacific Press, The Crawford Bldg, Ellery Circuit, The Australian National University, Canberra, ACT 0200, Australia. TEL 61-2-61250178, FAX 61-2-62572886, books@asiapacificpress.com, http://www.pacificeconomicoutlook.com, http://www.asiapacificpress.com/. Adv. contact Maree Tait.

330.9 AUS ISSN 1361-374X
H1
➤ **PACIFIC ECONOMIC REVIEW.** Text in English. 1961. q. USD 75 combined subscription in the Americas to individuals print & online eds.; EUR 77 combined subscription in Europe to individuals print & online eds.; GBP 51 combined subscription elsewhere to individuals print & online eds.; USD 391 combined subscription in the Americas to institutions print & online eds.; GBP 270 combined subscription elsewhere to institutions print & online eds. (effective 2006). reprint service avail. from PSC. **Document type:** *Journal, Academic/Scholarly.* **Description:** Analyzes economic issues in the Pacific Rim area.
Formerly (until 199?): Hong Kong Economic Papers (1025-8884)
Related titles: Online - full text ed.: ISSN 1468-0106. USD 371 in the Americas to institutions; GBP 257 elsewhere to institutions (effective 2006) (from Blackwell Synergy, EBSCO Publishing, Gale Group, IngentaConnect, O C L C Online Computer Library Center, Inc., Swets Information Services).
Indexed: AmH&L, BAS, CREJ, GEOBASE, IBSS, JEL, PAIS, ST&MA.
—BLDSC (6329.187000), IE, Infotrieve, ingenta. **CCC.**
Published by: (Hong Kong Economic Association HKG), Blackwell Publishing Asia (Subsidiary of: Blackwell Publishing Ltd.), 550 Swanston St, Carlton South, VIC 3053, Australia. TEL 61-383591011, FAX 61-383591120, subs@blackwellpublishingasia.com, http://www.blackwellpublishing.com/journals/PER. Eds. K C Fung, Kenneth S Chan.

B

330 PAK ISSN 0078-8082
PAKISTAN ECONOMIC SURVEY. Text in English. 1962. a. price varies. index.
Published by: Finance Division, Islamabad, Pakistan. **Dist. by:** Manager of Publications.

330 PAK ISSN 0254-9204
HB1
➤ **PAKISTAN JOURNAL OF APPLIED ECONOMICS.** Text in English. 1982. s-a. PKR 150 domestic to individuals; USD 30 foreign to individuals; PKR 200 domestic to institutions; USD 50 foreign to institutions (effective 2000). adv. bk.rev. charts; illus.; stat. back issues avail.; reprints avail. **Document type:** *Academic/Scholarly.*
Supersedes (1974-1982): Journal of Economic Studies; Which was formerly: Federal Economic Review (0428-1128)
Indexed: CREJ, HortAb, IBSS, JEL, NutrAb, PAIS, PerIslam, RDA, RiceAb, TDB, WAE&RSA.
—BLDSC (6340.896000).
Published by: University of Karachi, Applied Economics Research Centre, P O Box 8403, Karachi, 75270, Pakistan. TEL 92-21-474749, FAX 92-21-4969729, pjae@aerc.its.super.net.pk. Ed. Nuzhat Ahmad. R&P, Adv. contact Tufail Hakem. Circ: 800.

330.9 381 ISR ISSN 0793-8241
HC415.254.A1
PALESTINE BUSINESS REPORT. Text in English. 1996. m. USD 80 domestic; USD 90 in Europe; USD 95 elsewhere (effective 2002). adv. stat.; tr.lit. back issues avail. **Document type:** *Bulletin, Trade.* **Description:** Contains information on important changes and special events taking place within the business sector of the Palestinians.
Published by: European Palestinian Chamber of Commerce, 19 Nablus Road, P O Box 51219, East Jerusalem, Israel. TEL 972-2-6273293, FAX 972-2-6264975, info@epcc-jerusalem.org, http://www.epcc-jerusalem.org/. Ed. Maher Abukhater. Pub. Hanna Siniora. adv.: page USD 500; trim 23 x 16.5. Circ: 1,000 (paid).

PANAMA EN CIFRAS. see *BUSINESS AND ECONOMICS—Abstracting, Bibliographies, Statistics*

330.9 PAN
PANAMA. MINISTERIO DE PLANIFICACION Y POLITICA ECONOMICA. INFORME ECONOMICO. Text in Spanish. a. stat.
Published by: Ministerio de Planificacion y Politica Economica, Direccion de Planificacion Economica y Social, Panama City, Panama.

PANEUROPA DEUTSCHLAND. see *POLITICAL SCIENCE—International Relations*

330.9 MEX ISSN 0479-4346
PANORAMA ECONOMICO. Text in Spanish. 1966. bi-m. free. charts; stat. **Description:** Covers the Mexican economy, with emphasis on the automotive and textile industries.
Related titles: English ed.: Economic Panorama. ISSN 0013-0214.
Indexed: PAIS.
Published by: Bancomer, Sociedad Nacional Credito, Grupo Investigaciones Economicas, Universidad Avenue 1200, Mexico City, DF 03339, Mexico. TEL 534-00-34 ext. 5245. Ed. Eduardo Millan Lozano. Circ: 5,000.

330.9 CUB ISSN 1028-4397
PANORAMA ECONOMICO LATINOAMERICANO. Text in Spanish. 1996. m.
Media: Online - full text.

Published by: Prensa Latina Agencia Informativa Latinoamericana, Calle 23 No. 201,, Vedado, La Habana, Cuba. TEL 53-78-4127902, http://www.prensa-latina.org/. Ed. Edilberto Mendez Amador.

330.9 CHL ISSN 1020-5152
HN110.5
PANORAMA SOCIAL DE AMERICA LATINA (YEAR). Text in Spanish. 1994. a. USD 20 (effective 1998). back issues avail.
Related titles: ♦ English ed.: Social Panorama of Latin America (Year). ISSN 1020-5160.
Published by: Comision Economica para America Latina y el Chile/Economic Commission for Latin America and the Caribbean, Casilla 179-D, Santiago, Chile. TEL 56-2-210-2048, FAX 56-2-210-2069, publications@eclac.cl, http://www.eclac.cl. **Subscr. to:** United Nations Publications, Distribution and Sales Section, Palais des Nations, Rm C-116, 8-14 av de la Paix, Geneva 1211, Switzerland; United Nations Publications, Rm DC2-853, United Nations Bldg, 2 United Nations Plaza, New York, NY 10017.

330.9 ESP ISSN 0210-9107
HC381
PAPELES DE ECONOMIA ESPANOLA. Text in Spanish. 1980. q. EUR 53 domestic; EUR 91 foreign (effective 2003). abstr.; illus.; bibl.; maps; stat. **Document type:** *Magazine, Academic/Scholarly.* **Description:** Offers information on the economic problems of Spain through research done by the foundation.
Indexed: IBSS, JEL, PCI, RASB, SCIMP.
—BLDSC (6358.493000), CINDOC, IE, ingenta.
Published by: Fundacion de las Cajas de Ahorros Confederadas para la Investigacion Economica y Social, Juan Hurtado de Mendoza, 19, Madrid, 28036, Spain. TEL 34-91-3507907, FAX 34-91-3508040, publica@funcas.ceca.es, http://www.funcas.ceca.es. Ed., R&P Fernando Gonzalez Olivares. Pub. Victorio Valle Sanchez. Circ: 7,000.

330.9 ESP ISSN 1137-7186
PAPELES DE TRABAJO. ECONOMIA. Text in Spanish. 1987. irreg. price varies. **Document type:** *Monographic series, Academic/Scholarly.*
Published by: Fundacion Jose Ortega y Gasset, Fortuny 53, Madrid, 28010, Spain. TEL 34-91-7004139, FAX 34-91-7003530, http://www.ortegaygasset.edu/.

338 BRA ISSN 0031-174X
PARANA EM PAGINAS✶. Text in Portuguese. 1969 (vol.4). m. free. adv. charts; illus.; stat.
Address: Rua Augusto Stellfeld, 70 Curitiba, Curitiba, Parana, Brazil. Ed. Candido Gomes Chagas.

330.9 BRA
PARANA INFORMACOES. Text in Portuguese. irreg.
Related titles: ♦ Portuguese ed.: Information on Parana.
Published by: Banco de Desenvolvimento do Parana, S.A., Av. Vicente Machado, 445, Cx. Postal 6042, Curitiba, PARANA, Brazil.

338 GBR
PARLIAMENTARY AND COMMON MARKET NEWS BULLETIN. Text in English. 1947. w. GBP 37. **Document type:** *Bulletin.*
Published by: Parliamentary and Common Market News Services, 19 Kingsdowne Rd, Surbiton, KT6 6JZ, United Kingdom.

PATRIKA. see *POLITICAL SCIENCE—International Relations*

330.9 ESP ISSN 0212-0208
HC121
PENSAMIENTO IBEROAMERICANO; revista de economia politica. Text in Spanish. 1982. s-a. adv. bk.rev. **Document type:** *Academic/Scholarly.* **Description:** Covers articles and research papers in the field of economics, as it pertains to Spain and the rest of the world.
Indexed: HAPI, IBR, IBSS, ILD, IPSA, JEL, PAIS, PCI, RASB.
—CINDOC, IE.
Published by: (Sociedad Estatal Quinto Centenario), Agencia Espanola de Cooperacion Internacional, Instituto de Cooperacion Iberoamericana, Avda Reyes Catolicos 4, Madrid, 28040, Spain. TEL 34-91-5838399, FAX 34-91-5838310, http://www.aeci.es. Ed. Osvaldo Sunkel. Circ: 4,000. **Co-sponsor:** United Nations Comision Economica para America Latina y el Caribe.

330.9 COL
▼ **PERFIL DE COYUNTURA ECONOMICA.** Text in Spanish. 2003. s-a.
Published by: Universidad de Antioquia, Facultad de Ciencias Economicas, Apdo. Aereo 1226, Medellin, Colombia.

330.9 USA ISSN 1052-5254
THE PERRYMAN TEXAS LETTER. Text in English. 1990. m. looseleaf. adv. charts; stat. back issues avail. **Document type:** *Newsletter, Trade.* **Description:** Analyzes the political, social, and economic trends in Texas, bringing readers an insider's perspective on the latest news from job trends to legislative activity.
Incorporates: Texas Economic Forecast (0748-0008); Which was formerly (1982-1984): Trends in the Texas Economy (0737-3317)
Related titles: Online - full text ed.: (from EBSCO Publishing).
Published by: Texas Economic Publishers, Inc., 510 N Valley Mills Dr, Ste 300, Waco, TX 76710-6076. TEL 254-751-7411, FAX 254-751-7855, info@perrymangroup.com, http://www.perrymangroup.com. Ed. Nancy Cunningham. R&P, Adv. contact Eugene Baker. Circ: 2,000. **Subscr. to:** Fulfillment, PO Box 1943, Birmingham, AL 35201-1943. TEL 800-433-4931, FAX 205-995-1588.

PERSPECTIVAS EN POLITICA, ECONOMIA Y GESTION. see *POLITICAL SCIENCE*

330.9 USA
HD28
PERSPECTIVES ON BUSINESS AND GLOBAL CHANGE. Text in English. 1987. q. USD 64. adv. bk.rev. illus. reprints avail. **Document type:** *Academic/Scholarly.* **Description:** Discusses how business can be a creative, positive force for resolving the pressing issues facing global society today.
Formerly: World Business Academy Perspectives (1061-9917)
—BLDSC (6428.138650), IE. **CCC.**
Published by: Berrett-Koehler Publishers, Inc., 235 Montgomery St., Ste. 650, San Francisco, CA 94104-2916. TEL 415-288-0260, FAX 415-362-2512, bkpub@aol.com. Ed. Maya Porter. Adv. contact Robin Donovan. Circ: 400 (paid).

330.9 GBR ISSN 1465-6493
HB5
PERSPEKTIVEN DER WIRTSCHAFTSPOLITIK. Text in German. 2000. q. EUR 41 combined subscription in Europe to individuals print & online eds.; USD 41 combined subscription in the Americas to individuals & Caribbean, print & online eds.; GBP 27 combined subscription elsewhere to individuals print & online eds.; USD 154 combined subscription in the Americas to institutions & Caribbean, print & online eds.; GBP 100 combined subscription elsewhere to institutions print & online eds. (effective 2006). adv. bk.rev. **Document type:** *Journal, Academic/Scholarly.* **Description:** Covers the whole field of economics and neighboring disciplines and in particular includes business theory.
Related titles: Online - full text ed.: ISSN 1468-2516. USD 137 in the Americas to institutions & Caribbean; GBP 88 elsewhere to institutions (effective 2006) (from Blackwell Synergy, EBSCO Publishing, Gale Group, IngentaConnect, O C L C Online Computer Library Center, Inc., Swets Information Services).
Indexed: GEOBASE, PSA.
—BLDSC (6428.181595), IE, Infotrieve. **CCC.**
Published by: Blackwell Publishing Ltd., 9600 Garsington Rd, Oxford, OX4 2ZG, United Kingdom. TEL 44-1865-776868, FAX 44-1865-714591, customerservices@oxon.blackwellpublishing.com, http://www.blackwellpublishing.com/journals/PERS. Ed. Friedrich Schneider.

330.9 PER ISSN 1018-0621
PERU ECONOMICO. Text in Spanish. 1979. m. USD 560 (effective 1997). bk.rev.
Formerly (until 1986): Peruvian Quarterly Report
Indexed: KES.
Published by: Apoyo Comunicaciones S.A., Juan De La Fuente, 625, Miraflores, Lima 18, Peru. TEL 51-14-445555, FAX 51-14-445240. Ed. Augusto Alvarez Rodrich. Circ: 2,500.

330.985 GBR ISSN 1474-855X
PERU QUARTERLY FORECAST REPORT. Text in English. q. GBP 295, USD 485 (effective 1999). **Document type:** *Trade.* **Description:** Provides a comprehensive assessment of the Peruvian government, economy and business environment over the next 30 months. Helps to identify opportunities and reduce risk, and answers key questions facing executives at this time.
Formerly (until 2000): Annual Country Forecast Report. Peru (1353-470X)
Related titles: Online - full text ed.: (from EBSCO Publishing).
Published by: Business Monitor International Ltd., Mermaid House, 2 Puddle Dock, Blackfriars, London, EC4V 3DS, United Kingdom. TEL 44-20-72480468, FAX 44-20-72480467, busmon@dial.pipex.com, http://www.businessmonitor.com.

THE PETROLEUM ECONOMICS MONTHLY. see *PETROLEUM AND GAS*

PHARMACEUTICAL COMPANIES ANALYSIS. see *PHARMACY AND PHARMACOLOGY*

PHARMACEUTICAL STRATEGIC ALLIANCES; the drug and biotech alliances reference guide. see *PHARMACY AND PHARMACOLOGY*

330.5 USA ISSN 0744-3587
PHILADELPHIA BUSINESS JOURNAL. Text in English. 1982. w. (Fri.). USD 94 (effective 2005). adv. **Document type:** *Newspaper, Trade.*
Related titles: Microfilm ed.: 1982; Online - full text ed.: ISSN 1549-1919. 1982 (from CompuServe Inc., Data-Star, Florida Center for Library Automation, Gale Group, O C L C Online Computer Library Center, Inc., ProQuest Information & Learning, The Dialog Corporation).
Indexed: ABIn, BusDate, LRI, T&II.
—**CCC.**
Published by: American City Business Journals, Inc. (Philadelphia), 400 Market St, Ste 300, Philadelphia, PA 19106. TEL 215-238-1450, FAX 215-238-9489, philadelphia@bizjournals.com, http://www.bizjournals.com/philadelphia, http://www.amcity.com. Ed. Bernard Dagenais TEL 215-238-5134. adv.: B&W page USD 4,780, color page USD 5,655. Circ: 19,000; 13,990 (paid).

330.9 HKG ISSN 0379-2870
PHILIPPINE LETTER. Text in English. 1978. s-m. USD 195. bk.rev. **Document type:** *Newsletter.*
Published by: Asia Letter Group, GPO Box 10874, Hong Kong, Hong Kong. TEL 852-526-2950, FAX 852-526-7131, TELEX HX 61166 HKNW. Ed. Charles R Smith.

330.9599 GBR ISSN 1474-1407
PHILIPPINES QUARTERLY FORECAST REPORT. Text in English. 199?. 3/yr. GBP 330, USD 495, EUR 450 (effective 2003). **Document type:** *Journal, Trade.* **Description:** Provides a comprehensive assessment of the Filipino government, economy and business environment over the next 30 months. Helps to identify opportunities and reduce risk, and answers key questions facing executives at this time.
Formerly (until 2001): Annual Country Forecast Report. Philippines (0969-5192)
Related titles: CD-ROM ed.: GBP 410, USD 675 (effective 2000); Online - full text ed.: (from EBSCO Publishing).
—**CCC.**
Published by: Business Monitor International Ltd., Mermaid House, 2 Puddle Dock, Blackfriars, London, EC4V 3DS, United Kingdom. TEL 44-20-72480468, FAX 44-20-72480467, marketing@businessmonitor.com, http://www.businessmonitor.com/philippinesforecast.html.

IL PICENTINO. see *AGRICULTURE*

330.9 USA ISSN 0846-1066
PICTOU COUNTY BUSINESS DIRECTORY. Text in English. 1988. a. **Document type:** *Directory.*
Published by: Target Marketing, Inc., 1 Liberty Bell Circle, Ste 200, Liberty, MO 64068. TEL 816-781-7557, FAX 816-792-3892.

330.9 NOR ISSN 0805-083X
HD4811
PLAN; tidsskrift for samfunnsplanlegging, byplan og regional utvikling. Text in Norwegian. 1965. bi-m. NOK 450 to individuals; NOK 690 to institutions; NOK 200 to students; NOK 75 per issue (effective 2004). adv. bk.rev. index. **Document type:** *Journal, Academic/Scholarly.* **Description:** Focuses on community development, regional planning and employment.
Former titles (until 1995): Plan og Arbeid (0032-0609); Arbeidsmarkedet (0332-7043)
Published by: Universitetsforlaget AS/Scandinavian University Press (Subsidiary of: Aschehoug & Co.), Sehesteds Gate 3, Postboks 508, Oslo, 0105, Norway. TEL 47-24-147500, FAX 47-24-147501, post@universitetsforlaget.no, http://www.universitetsforlaget.no/tidsskrifter/article.jhtml?articleID=285, http://www.universitetesforlaget.no. Ed. Jens Fredrik Nystad. Adv. contact Vidar Roeggen. Circ: 2,500.

330.9 GBR ISSN 0308-7751
PLANNING CONSUMER MARKETS✶. Text in English. 1975. q. GBP 1,100, USD 1,650 (effective 1994). charts; stat. **Document type:** *Trade.* **Description:** Analyzes and forecasts key macroeconomic and consumer trends affecting U.K. markets.
Related titles: Online - full text ed.: 1975.
Published by: Henley Centre for Forecasting Ltd., 9 Bridewell Pl, London, EC4Y 6AY, United Kingdom. TEL 0171-353-9961, FAX 0171-353-2899. Ed. Richard Woods.

331.11 USA
PLANNING GUIDE: ECONOMIC DATA - CLIENT DATA. Text in English. 1979. a. free. **Document type:** *Government.*
Former titles: Planning Guide: Bridgeport - Norwalk - Stamford - Valley Service Delivery Area; Planning Guide: Statewide and Nine Service Delivery Areas Including Bridgeport - Norwalk - Stamford - Valley; Planning Guide: Bridgeport - Norwalk - Stamford - Valley Service Delivery Area; Annual Planning Information: Bridgeport - Norwalk - Stamford - Valley Service Delivery Area; Annual Planning Information for Stamford Labor Market Area; Stamford Annual Planning Information
Published by: (Office of Research), Labor Department, 200 Folly Brook Blvd, Wethersfield, CT 06109. TEL 860-263-6275, FAX 860-263-6263, http://www.ctdol.state.ct.us/imi/index.htm. Ed. John Tirinzonie. Circ: 350.

PLATINUM (YEAR). see *METALLURGY*

330.9 DEU ISSN 1431-3863
DER PLATOW BRIEF. Text in German. 1946. 3/w. EUR 495 combined subscription print & online eds. (effective 2005). bk.rev. **Document type:** *Newsletter, Trade.* **Description:** Contains news and information on various economic and market events and trends.
Related titles: Online - full text ed.: EUR 466 (effective 2005).

Published by: Verlag Aktuelle Information GmbH (Subsidiary of: Springer Science+Business Media), Postfach 111926, Frankfurt Am Main, 60054, Germany. TEL 49-69-2426390, FAX 49-69-236909, info.platow@bertelsmann.de, http://www.platowbriefe.de/ind_brief.htm, http://www.platow.de. Ed. Frank Mahlmeister. Pub. Albrecht Schirmacher.

330.9　　　　　　DEU
PLATOW PROGNOSE. Text in German. 1950. a. **Document type:** Directory, Trade.
Published by: Verlag Aktuelle Information GmbH (Subsidiary of: Springer Science+Business Media), Postfach 111926, Frankfurt Am Main, 60054, Germany. TEL 49-69-2426390, FAX 49-69-236909, info.platow@bertelsmann.de, http://www.platow.de.

PODER. see COMPUTERS—Internet

330.9438　　　　GBR　　　　ISSN 1470-7454
POLAND QUARTERLY FORECAST REPORT. Text in English. 1995. 3/yr. GBP 330, USD 495, EUR 450 (effective 2003). **Document type:** Journal, Trade. **Description:** Provides a comprehensive assessment of the Polish government, economy and business environment over the next 30 months. Helps to identify opportunities and reduce risk, and answers key questions facing executives at this time.
Formerly (until 2000): Annual Country Forecast Report. Poland (1359-7159)
Related titles: Online - full text ed.: (from EBSCO Publishing). —CCC.
Published by: Business Monitor International Ltd., Mermaid House, 2 Puddle Dock, Blackfriars, London, EC4V 3DS, United Kingdom. TEL 44-20-72480468, FAX 44-20-72480467, marketing@businessmonitor.com, http://www.businessmonitor.com/polandforecast.html.

330　　　POL　　　　ISSN 0208-9904
HC340.3.A1
POLISH ECONOMIC NEWS. Text in English. 1962. fortn. USD 21.60. bk.rev. stat.
Formerly (until 1982): Polish Economic Survey (0032-2849)
Related titles: French ed.: Revue de l'Economie Polonaise. ISSN 0208-7537; German ed.: Polnischer Wirtschaftsanzeuger. ISSN 0208-7529; Russian ed.: Pol'skii Ekonomicheskii Obzor. ISSN 0208-9912.
Published by: AGPOL - Polexportpress, Ul Kierbedzia 4, Warsaw, 00957, Poland. Ed. Danuta Gasiorowska. Circ: 6,000. **Dist. by:** Ars Polona, Krakowskie Przedmiescie 7, Warsaw, Poland.

330.9　　　POL　　　　ISSN 1507-3157
POLISH ECONOMIC OUTLOOK; trends, analyses, forecasts. Text in English. 1999. q. PLZ 3,400 (effective 2005). **Description:** Written by the CASE's economists - experts in macroeconomics and econometrics, it serves as a source of independent opinions and short- and medium-term forecasts.
Related titles: Online - full text ed.; ♦ Translation of: Polska Gospodarka. ISSN 1507-3149.
Published by: Centrum Analiz Spoleczno-Ekonomicznych/Center for Social and Economic Resarch, ul Sienkiewicza 12, Warsaw, 00010, Poland. TEL 48-22-6226627, FAX 48-22-8286069, case@case.com.pl, http://www.case.com.pl.

330.9　　　ITA　　　　ISSN 1120-9496
HB7
POLITICA ECONOMICA; rivista di studi e ricerche per la politica economica. Text in Italian. 1985. 3/yr. EUR 55 domestic to individuals; EUR 84 foreign to individuals; EUR 102 domestic to institutions print & online eds.; EUR 135 foreign to institutions print & online eds. (effective 2004). adv. index. back issues avail. **Document type:** Academic/Scholarly.
Related titles: Online - full text ed.
Indexed: JEL, PAIS, PCI, RefZh.
Published by: Societa Editrice Il Mulino, Strada Maggiore 37, Bologna, 40125, Italy. TEL 39-051-256011, FAX 39-051-256034, riviste@mulino.it, http://www.mulino.it. Ed. Paolo Bosi. Adv. contact M Luisa Vezzali. Circ: 1,000.

330.9　　　ITA　　　　ISSN 0393-7844
POLITICA MERIDIONALISTA; rivistadi cultura, economia e informazione. Text in Italian. 1972. q. EUR 10 domestic; EUR 25 foreign (effective 2005). adv. bk.rev. back issues avail. **Document type:** Magazine, Consumer. **Description:** Deals with Italian culture, the Italian economy and current events, specifically focused on southern Italy.
Published by: Politica Meridionalista Editrice, Corso Umberto I, 22, Naples, NA 80138, Italy. TEL 39-81-5527744, FAX 39-81-5527744, pisanti@email.it. Ed., Adv. contact Dr. Antonio Pisanti TEL 39-81-5527744. Pub., R&P Dr. Nicola Squitieri TEL 39-06-36001891. Circ: 5,000 (paid and controlled).

330.9　　　POL　　　　ISSN 1507-3149
POLSKA GOSPODARKA; tendencje, oceny, prognozy. Text in Polish. 1999. q. PLZ 2,400 (effective 2005). **Description:** Written by the CASE's economists - experts in macroeconomics and econometrics, it serves as a source of independent opinions and short- and medium-term forecasts.
Related titles: Online - full text ed.; ♦ English Translation: Polish Economic Outlook. ISSN 1507-3157.

Published by: Centrum Analiz Spoleczno-Ekonomicznych/Center for Social and Economic Resarch, ul Sienkiewicza 12, Warsaw, 00010, Poland. TEL 48-22-6226627, FAX 48-22-8286069, case@case.com.pl, http://www.case-doradcy.com.pl/index.php?pID=3512, http://www.case.com.pl.

330.9　　　ECU
PONTIFICIA UNIVERSIDAD CATOLICA DEL ECUADOR. INSTITUTO DE INVESTIGACIONES ECONOMICAS. DOCUMENTOS. Text in Spanish. 1983. 3/yr. adv.
Published by: Pontificia Universidad Catolica del Ecuador, Instituto de Investigaciones Economicas, Casilla 17012184, Quito, Pichincha, Ecuador. FAX 593-2567117.

POPULATION RESEARCH AND POLICY REVIEW. see POPULATION STUDIES

330.9　　　COL
PORTAFOLIO; diario de economia y negocios. Text in Spanish. d. **Description:** Covers economics, marketing and political issues about Colombia.
Related titles: Online - full text ed.
Indexed: B&I.
Published by: Casa Editorial El Tiempo, Edif. World Business Port, Carrera 69, 43-B Piso 2, Bogota, CUND, Colombia. TEL 57-1-410-4555, FAX 57-1-410-6178, info@portafolio.com.co, http://www.portafolio.com.co/hoy/. Ed. Fernando Quijano.

330.9　　　COD
PORTEFEUILLE; revue des entreprises. Text in French. 1971. irreg.
Indexed: PAIS.
Published by: Departement du Portefeuille, BP 3473, Kinhasa-Gombe, Congo, Dem. Republic. Ed. Atunaku Adunagow.

PORTLAND ALLIANCE. see LABOR UNIONS

330.9　　　DEU　　　　ISSN 1617-982X
HB1
➤ **PORTUGUESE ECONOMIC JOURNAL.** Text in English. 2002. 3/yr. EUR 130 combined subscription to institutions print & online eds. (effective 2005). adv. **Document type:** Journal, Academic/Scholarly. **Description:** Publishes theoretical, empirical, applied and policy-oriented research papers on any field in economics.
Related titles: Online - full text ed.: ISSN 1617-9838 (from EBSCO Publishing, ProQuest Information & Learning, Springer LINK, Swets Information Services).
Indexed: ABIn, IBSS.
—BLDSC (6557.260000), IE. **CCC.**
Published by: Springer-Verlag (Subsidiary of: Springer Science+Business Media), Tiergartenstr 17, Heidelberg, 69121, Germany. Ed. Paulo MB Brito. Adv. contact Stephan Kroeck TEL 49-30-827875739. **Subscr. to:** Springer GmbH Auslieferungsgesellschaft, Haberstr 7, Heidelberg 69126, Germany. TEL 49-6221-345-0, FAX 49-6221-345-4229, subscriptions@springer.de; Springer-Verlag New York, Inc., Journal Fulfillment, PO Box 2485, Secaucus, NJ 07096-2485. TEL 800-777-4643, 201-348-4033, FAX 201-348-4505, journals@springer-ny.com, http://www.springer-ny.com.

330.9　　　USA　　　　ISSN 1060-586X
HC335
➤ **POST-SOVIET AFFAIRS.** Text in English. 1985. 4/yr. USD 72 in North America to individuals; USD 305 in North America to institutions; USD 319 elsewhere to institutions (effective 2005). abstr.; charts; illus.; stat. index. back issues avail.; reprints avail. **Document type:** Journal, Academic/Scholarly.
Formerly (until 1992): Soviet Economy (0882-6994)
Related titles: Online - full text ed.: (from Gale Group, IngentaConnect).
Indexed: ABIn, ABS&EES, ASCA, CurCont, GEOBASE, IBSS, IPSA, JEL, PAIS, PCI, RASB, SSCI, WBA, WMB.
—BLDSC (6559.600000), IDS, IE, Infotrieve, ingenta. **CCC.**
Published by: Bellwether Publishing, Ltd., 8640 Guilford Rd, Ste 200, Columbia, MD 21046. TEL 410-290-3870, FAX 410-290-8726, bellpub@bellpub.com, http://www.bellpub.com. Ed. George Breslauer. Circ: 500. **Co-sponsors:** Social Science Research Council; American Council of Learned Societies.

➤ **POWER ECONOMICS.** see ENERGY

338.9　　　CHL　　　　ISSN 1014-7802
HC121
PRELIMINARY OVERVIEW OF THE ECONOMIES OF LATIN AMERICA AND THE CARIBBEAN. Text in English. 1988. a.
Related titles: ♦ Spanish ed.: Balance Preliminar de las Economias de America Latina y el Caribe (Year). ISSN 1014-7810.
Published by: Comision Economica para America Latina y el Caribe/Economic Commission for Latin America and the Caribbean, Ave Dag Hammarskjold 3477, Vitacura, Santiago de Chile, Chile. TEL 56-2-471-2000, FAX 56-2-208-0252, publications@eclac.cl, http://www.eclac.cl.

330.9　　　ARG　　　　ISSN 0032-7433
PRENSA CONFIDENCIAL. Text in Spanish. 1966. w. looseleaf. ARS 5,500, USD 25.
Address: No. 1, Avda. Corrientes, 1894, Capital Federal, Buenos Aires 1045, Argentina. Ed. Jorge Vago. Circ: 6,000.

331　　　USA　　　　ISSN 1524-2803
E184.S75
PRENSA LATINA. Text in English. q. **Description:** A vehicle for exploring equal opportunity/affirmative action issues as they affect those of Latino heritage and businesses owned or operated by Latinos.
Published by: E M Publishing Enterprises, Inc, 19456 Ventura Blvd, 200, Tarzana, CA 91356. TEL 818-654-0870, FAX 818-654-0874, empei@aol.com.

330.968　　　ZAF
PRESCON SOUTH AFRICAN NEWSLETTER. Text in English. 1977. m. USD 100 (effective 1999 & 2000). **Document type:** Newsletter. **Description:** Presents information, analysis and commentary on political, economic and sociological issues relating to South Africa.
Formerly: South African Newsletter
Published by: Prescon Publishing Corporation (Pty) Ltd., PO Box 84004, Greenside, Johannesburg 2034, South Africa. TEL 27-11-7829229, FAX 27-11-7822025, prescon@iafrica.com. Ed. Leon J Kok.

330.9 658　　　BEL　　　　ISSN 0779-8881
PRESENCES IN BUSINESS. Text in French. 1960. q. adv. bk.rev.
Formerly (until 1990): Presences (0779-8873)
Published by: Association Royale des Ingenieurs Commercieux Licencies et Docteurs de Mons-Warocque (A.I.C.M.), Av Louise 438, BP 12, Brussels, 1050, Belgium. FAX 32-2-6487366. Ed. Michel Rousille. Circ: 2,500.

330.9　　　FRA　　　　ISSN 1291-8334
PREVISIONS GLISSANTES DETAILLEES. Text in French. 1959. irreg. (in 42 vols.). charts; stat.
Supersedes: Economie Francaise en Perspectives Sectorielles (Vols. 1-5); Prevision a Un An de l'Economie Francaise; Economie Francaise consisted of 5 vols.: Vol.1: Donnees d'Encadrement; Vol.2: Filiere Agro-Alimentaire, Industrie de Consommation; Which was formerly: Industries de Biens de Consommation; Vol.3: Industries d'Equipement; Vol.4: Energie et Industries Intermediaires; Which was formerly: Industries de Biens Intermediaires; Vol.5: Filiere Batiment, Travaux Publics, Materiaux et Produits de Construction; Which was formerly: Filiere Batiment, Genie Civil, Materiaux de Construction
Published by: B I P E Conseil, L'Atrium - 6 Place Abel Gance, Boulogne-Billancourt, Cedex 92652, France. TEL 33-1-46944522, FAX 33-1-46944599. Circ: 450.

330.9　　　FRA
PREVISIONS GLISSANTES DETAILLEES EN PERSPECTIVES A MOYEN TERME. Text in French. 1959. s-a. charts; stat.
Supersedes in part: Economie Francaise en Perspectives Sectorielles (Vols.1-5); Which supersedes in part: Prevision a Un An de l'Economie Francaise
Published by: B I P E Conseil, L'Atrium - 6 Place Abel Gance, Boulogne-Billancourt, Cedex 92652, France. TEL 33-1-46944522, FAX 33-1-46944599.

330.9　　　FRA
PREVISIONS GLISSANTES DETAILLEES EN PERSPECTIVES MACROECONOMIQUES A COURT ET MOYEN TERME (YEAR). Text in French. 1959. irreg. charts; stat.
Supersedes in part: Economie Francaise en Perspectives Sectorielles (Vols.1-5); Which supersedes in part: Prevision a Un An de l'Economie Francaise
Published by: B I P E Conseil, L'Atrium - 6 Place Abel Gance, Boulogne-Billancourt, Cedex 92652, France. TEL 33-1-46944522, FAX 33-1-46944599.

330.9　　　FRA
PREVISIONS GLISSANTES DETAILLEES EN PERSPECTIVES SECTORIELLES (VOL.1): AGRICULTURE. Text in French. 1959. irreg. charts; stat.
Supersedes in part: Economie Francaise en Perspectives Sectorielles (Vols.1-5); Which supersedes in part: Prevision a Un An de l'Economie Francaise
Published by: B I P E Conseil, L'Atrium - 6 Place Abel Gance, Boulogne-Billancourt, Cedex 92652, France. TEL 33-1-46944522, FAX 33-1-46944599.

330.9 621.3　　　FRA
PREVISIONS GLISSANTES DETAILLEES EN PERSPECTIVES SECTORIELLES (VOL.10): CONSTRUCTION ELECTRIQUE ET ELECTRONIQUE GRAND-PUBLIC. Text in French. 1959. irreg. charts; stat.
Supersedes in part: Economie Francaise en Perspectives Sectorielles (Vols.1-5); Which supersedes in part: Prevision a Un An de l'Economie Francaise
Published by: B I P E Conseil, L'Atrium - 6 Place Abel Gance, Boulogne-Billancourt, Cedex 92652, France. TEL 33-1-46944522, FAX 33-1-46944599.

330.9 621.3　　　FRA
PREVISIONS GLISSANTES DETAILLEES EN PERSPECTIVES SECTORIELLES (VOL.11): CONSTRUCTION ELECTRIQUE PROFESSIONNELLE. Text in French. 1959. irreg. charts; stat.
Supersedes in part: Economie Francaise en Perspectives Sectorielles (Vols.1-5); Which supersedes in part: Prevision a Un An de l'Economie Francaise
Published by: B I P E Conseil, L'Atrium - 6 Place Abel Gance, Boulogne-Billancourt, Cedex 92652, France. TEL 33-1-46944522, FAX 33-1-46944599.

B

330.9 621.3 FRA
PREVISIONS GLISSANTES DETAILLEES EN PERSPECTIVES SECTORIELLES (VOL.12): CONSTRUCTION ELECTRONIQUE PROFESSIONNELLE. Text in French. 1959. irreg. charts; stat.
Supersedes in part: Economie Francaise en Perspectives Sectorielles (Vols.1-5); Which supersedes in part: Prevision a Un An de l'Economie Francaise
Published by: B I P E Conseil, L'Atrium - 6 Place Abel Gance, Boulogne-Billancourt, Cedex 92652, France. TEL 33-1-46944522, FAX 33-1-46944599.

621.382 FRA
PREVISIONS GLISSANTES DETAILLEES EN PERSPECTIVES SECTORIELLES (VOL.14): TELECOMMUNICATIONS. Text in French. 1959. irreg. charts; stat.
Supersedes in part: Economie Francaise en Perspectives Sectorielles (Vols.1-5); Which supersedes in part: Prevision a Un An de l'Economie Francaise
Published by: B I P E Conseil, L'Atrium - 6 Place Abel Gance, Boulogne-Billancourt, Cedex 92652, France. TEL 33-1-46944522, FAX 33-1-46944599.

330.9 629 FRA
PREVISIONS GLISSANTES DETAILLEES EN PERSPECTIVES SECTORIELLES (VOL.15): CONSTRUCTION AUTOMOBILE. Text in French. 1959. irreg. charts; stat.
Supersedes in part: Economie Francaise en Perspectives Sectorielles (Vols.1-5); Which supersedes in part: Prevision a Un An de l'Economie Francaise
Published by: B I P E Conseil, L'Atrium - 6 Place Abel Gance, Boulogne-Billancourt, Cedex 92652, France. TEL 33-1-46944522, FAX 33-1-46944599.

330.9 FRA
PREVISIONS GLISSANTES DETAILLEES EN PERSPECTIVES SECTORIELLES (VOL.16): CONSTRUCTION AEROSPATIALE. Text in French. 1959. irreg. charts; stat.
Supersedes in part: Economie Francaise en Perspectives Sectorielles (Vols.1-5); Which supersedes in part: Prevision a Un An de l'Economie Francaise
Published by: B I P E Conseil, L'Atrium - 6 Place Abel Gance, Boulogne-Billancourt, Cedex 92652, France. TEL 33-1-46944522, FAX 33-1-46944599.

330.9 333.79 FRA
PREVISIONS GLISSANTES DETAILLEES EN PERSPECTIVES SECTORIELLES (VOL.17): ENERGIE. Text in French. 1959. irreg. charts; stat.
Supersedes in part: Economie Francaise en Perspectives Sectorielles (Vols.1-5); Which supersedes in part: Prevision a Un An de l'Economie Francaise
Published by: B I P E Conseil, L'Atrium - 6 Place Abel Gance, Boulogne-Billancourt, Cedex 92652, France. TEL 33-1-46944522, FAX 33-1-46944599.

330.9 669.1 FRA
PREVISIONS GLISSANTES DETAILLEES EN PERSPECTIVES SECTORIELLES (VOL.18): SIDERURGIE ET PREMIERE TRANSFORMATION DE L'ACIER. Text in French. 1959. irreg. charts; stat.
Supersedes in part: Economie Francaise en Perspectives Sectorielles (Vols.1-5); Which supersedes in part: Prevision a Un An de l'Economie Francaise
Published by: B I P E Conseil, L'Atrium - 6 Place Abel Gance, Boulogne-Billancourt, Cedex 92652, France. TEL 33-1-46944522, FAX 33-1-46944599.

330.9 669 FRA
PREVISIONS GLISSANTES DETAILLEES EN PERSPECTIVES SECTORIELLES (VOL.19): INDUSTRIE DES NON-FERREUX. Text in French. 1959. irreg. charts; stat.
Supersedes in part: Economie Francaise en Perspectives Sectorielles (Vols.1-5); Which supersedes in part: Prevision a Un An de l'Economie Francaise
Published by: B I P E Conseil, L'Atrium - 6 Place Abel Gance, Boulogne-Billancourt, Cedex 92652, France. TEL 33-1-46944522, FAX 33-1-46944599.

338 FRA
PREVISIONS GLISSANTES DETAILLEES EN PERSPECTIVES SECTORIELLES (VOL.2): INDUSTRIES AGRO-ALIMENTAIRES. Text in French. 1959. irreg. charts; stat.
Supersedes in part: Economie Francaise en Perspectives Sectorielles (Vols.1-5); Which supersedes in part: Prevision a Un An de l'Economie Francaise
Published by: B I P E Conseil, L'Atrium - 6 Place Abel Gance, Boulogne-Billancourt, Cedex 92652, France. TEL 33-1-46944522, FAX 33-1-46944599.

330.9 546 FRA
PREVISIONS GLISSANTES DETAILLEES EN PERSPECTIVES SECTORIELLES (VOL.20): CHIMIE MINERALE. Text in French. 1959. irreg. charts; stat.
Supersedes in part: Economie Francaise en Perspectives Sectorielles (Vols.1-5); Which supersedes in part: Prevision a Un An de l'Economie Francaise
Published by: B I P E Conseil, L'Atrium - 6 Place Abel Gance, Boulogne-Billancourt, Cedex 92652, France. TEL 33-1-46944522, FAX 33-1-46944599.

330.9 547 FRA
PREVISIONS GLISSANTES DETAILLEES EN PERSPECTIVES SECTORIELLES (VOL.21): CHIMIE ORGANIQUE. Text in French. 1959. irreg. charts; stat.
Supersedes in part: Economie Francaise en Perspectives Sectorielles (Vols.1-5); Which supersedes in part: Prevision a Un An de l'Economie Francaise
Published by: B I P E Conseil, L'Atrium - 6 Place Abel Gance, Boulogne-Billancourt, Cedex 92652, France. TEL 33-1-46944522, FAX 33-1-46944599.

330.9 615.19 FRA
PREVISIONS GLISSANTES DETAILLEES EN PERSPECTIVES SECTORIELLES (VOL.22): PARACHIMIE. Text in French. 1959. irreg. charts; stat.
Formerly: Previsions Glissantes Detaillees en Perspectives Sectorielles (Vol.19): Parachimie et Pharmacie; Supersedes in part: Economie Francaise en Perspectives Sectorielles (Vols.1-5); Which supersedes in part: Prevision a Un An de l'Economie Francaise
Published by: B I P E Conseil, L'Atrium - 6 Place Abel Gance, Boulogne-Billancourt, Cedex 92652, France. TEL 33-1-46944522, FAX 33-1-46944599.

330.9 668.4 678.2 FRA
PREVISIONS GLISSANTES DETAILLEES EN PERSPECTIVES SECTORIELLES (VOL.23): TRANSFORMATION DU CAOUTCHOUC ET DES MATIERES PLASTIQUES. Text in French. 1959. irreg. charts; stat.
Supersedes in part: Economie Francaise en Perspectives Sectorielles (Vols.1-5); Which supersedes in part: Prevision a Un An de l'Economie Francaise
Published by: B I P E Conseil, L'Atrium - 6 Place Abel Gance, Boulogne-Billancourt, Cedex 92652, France. TEL 33-1-46944522, FAX 33-1-46944599.

330.9 666.1 FRA
PREVISIONS GLISSANTES DETAILLEES EN PERSPECTIVES SECTORIELLES (VOL.24): INDUSTRIE DU VERRE. Text in French. 1959. irreg. charts; stat.
Supersedes in part: Economie Francaise en Perspectives Sectorielles (Vols.1-5); Which supersedes in part: Prevision a Un An de l'Economie Francaise
Published by: B I P E Conseil, L'Atrium - 6 Place Abel Gance, Boulogne-Billancourt, Cedex 92652, France. TEL 33-1-46944522, FAX 33-1-46944599.

330.9 676 FRA
PREVISIONS GLISSANTES DETAILLEES EN PERSPECTIVES SECTORIELLES (VOL.25): INDUSTRIE DES PATES, PAPIERS ET CARTONS. Text in French. 1959. irreg. charts; stat.
Supersedes in part: Economie Francaise en Perspectives Sectorielles (Vols.1-5); Which supersedes in part: Prevision a Un An de l'Economie Francaise
Published by: B I P E Conseil, L'Atrium - 6 Place Abel Gance, Boulogne-Billancourt, Cedex 92652, France. TEL 33-1-46944522, FAX 33-1-46944599.

330.9 676 FRA
PREVISIONS GLISSANTES DETAILLEES EN PERSPECTIVES SECTORIELLES (VOL.26): EMBALLAGES. Text in French. 1959. irreg. charts; stat.
Supersedes in part: Economie Francaise en Perspectives Sectorielles (Vols.1-5); Which supersedes in part: Prevision a Un An de l'Economie Francaise
Published by: B I P E Conseil, L'Atrium - 6 Place Abel Gance, Boulogne-Billancourt, Cedex 92652, France. TEL 33-1-46944522, FAX 33-1-46944599.

330.9 FRA
PREVISIONS GLISSANTES DETAILLEES EN PERSPECTIVES SECTORIELLES (VOL.27): LOGEMENT. Text in French. 1959. irreg. charts; stat.
Supersedes in part: Economie Francaise en Perspectives Sectorielles (Vols.1-5); Which supersedes in part: Prevision a Un An de l'Economie Francaise
Published by: B I P E Conseil, L'Atrium - 6 Place Abel Gance, Boulogne-Billancourt, Cedex 92652, France. TEL 33-1-46944522, FAX 33-1-46944599.

330.9 690 FRA
PREVISIONS GLISSANTES DETAILLEES EN PERSPECTIVES SECTORIELLES (VOL.28): BATIMENTS D'ACTIVITE. Text in French. 1959. irreg. charts; stat.
Supersedes in part: Economie Francaise en Perspectives Sectorielles (Vols.1-5); Which supersedes in part: Prevision a Un An de l'Economie Francaise
Published by: B I P E Conseil, L'Atrium - 6 Place Abel Gance, Boulogne-Billancourt, Cedex 92652, France. TEL 33-1-46944522, FAX 33-1-46944599.

330.9 624 FRA
PREVISIONS GLISSANTES DETAILLEES EN PERSPECTIVES SECTORIELLES (VOL.29): TRAVAUX PUBLICS. Text in French. 1959. irreg. charts; stat.
Supersedes in part: Economie Francaise en Perspectives Sectorielles (Vols.1-5); Which supersedes in part: Prevision a Un An de l'Economie Francaise
Published by: B I P E Conseil, L'Atrium - 6 Place Abel Gance, Boulogne-Billancourt, Cedex 92652, France. TEL 33-1-46944522, FAX 33-1-46944599.

338 685 FRA
PREVISIONS GLISSANTES DETAILLEES EN PERSPECTIVES SECTORIELLES (VOL.3): TEXTILE - HABILLEMENT - CUIR. Text in French. 1959. irreg. (in 42 vols.). charts; stat.
Supersedes in part: Economie Francaise en Perspectives Sectorielles (Vols.1-5); Which supersedes in part: Prevision a Un An de l'Economie Francaise
Published by: B I P E Conseil, L'Atrium - 6 Place Abel Gance, Boulogne-Billancourt, Cedex 92652, France. TEL 33-1-46944522, FAX 33-1-46944599.

330.9 691 FRA
PREVISIONS GLISSANTES DETAILLEES EN PERSPECTIVES SECTORIELLES (VOL.30): MATERIAUX DE CONSTRUCTION I. Text in French. 1959. irreg. charts; stat.
Supersedes in part: Economie Francaise en Perspectives Sectorielles (Vols.1-5); Which supersedes in part: Prevision a Un An de l'Economie Francaise
Published by: B I P E Conseil, L'Atrium - 6 Place Abel Gance, Boulogne-Billancourt, Cedex 92652, France. TEL 33-1-46944522, FAX 33-1-46944599.

330.9 691 FRA
PREVISIONS GLISSANTES DETAILLEES EN PERSPECTIVES SECTORIELLES (VOL.31): MATERIAUX ET COMPOSANTS DE CONSTRUCTION II. Text in French. 1959. irreg. charts; stat.
Supersedes in part: Economie Francaise en Perspectives Sectorielles (Vols.1-5); Which supersedes in part: Prevision a Un An de l'Economie Francaise
Published by: B I P E Conseil, L'Atrium - 6 Place Abel Gance, Boulogne-Billancourt, Cedex 92652, France. TEL 33-1-46944522, FAX 33-1-46944599.

330.9 FRA
PREVISIONS GLISSANTES DETAILLEES EN PERSPECTIVES SECTORIELLES (VOL.32): INDUSTRIES DE LA COMMUNICATION. Text in French. 1959. irreg. charts; stat.
Supersedes in part: Economie Francaise en Perspectives Sectorielles (Vols.1-5); Which supersedes in part: Prevision a Un An de l'Economie Francaise
Published by: B I P E Conseil, L'Atrium - 6 Place Abel Gance, Boulogne-Billancourt, Cedex 92652, France. TEL 33-1-46944522, FAX 33-1-46944599.

330.9 332.1 FRA
PREVISIONS GLISSANTES DETAILLEES EN PERSPECTIVES SECTORIELLES (VOL.33): BANQUES. Text in French. 1959. irreg. charts; stat.
Supersedes in part: Economie Francaise en Perspectives Sectorielles (Vols.1-5); Which supersedes in part: Prevision a Un An de l'Economie Francaise
Published by: B I P E Conseil, L'Atrium - 6 Place Abel Gance, Boulogne-Billancourt, Cedex 92652, France. TEL 33-1-46944522, FAX 33-1-46944599.

330.9 FRA
PREVISIONS GLISSANTES DETAILLEES EN PERSPECTIVES SECTORIELLES (VOL.34): ASSURANCES. Text in French. 1959. irreg. charts; stat.
Supersedes in part: Economie Francaise en Perspectives Sectorielles (Vols.1-5); Which supersedes in part: Prevision a Un An de l'Economie Francaise
Published by: B I P E Conseil, L'Atrium - 6 Place Abel Gance, Boulogne-Billancourt, Cedex 92652, France. TEL 33-1-46944522, FAX 33-1-46944599.

330.9 FRA
PREVISIONS GLISSANTES DETAILLEES EN PERSPECTIVES SECTORIELLES (VOL.35): COMMERCE. Text in French. 1959. irreg. charts; stat.
Supersedes in part: Economie Francaise en Perspectives Sectorielles (Vols.1-5); Which supersedes in part: Prevision a Un An de l'Economie Francaise
Published by: B I P E Conseil, L'Atrium - 6 Place Abel Gance, Boulogne-Billancourt, Cedex 92652, France. TEL 33-1-46944522, FAX 33-1-46944599.

330.9 380.5 FRA
PREVISIONS GLISSANTES DETAILLEES EN PERSPECTIVES SECTORIELLES (VOL.36): TRANSPORTS. Text in French. 1959. irreg. charts; stat.
Supersedes in part: Economie Francaise en Perspectives Sectorielles (Vols.1-5); Which supersedes in part: Prevision a Un An de l'Economie Francaise
Published by: B I P E Conseil, L'Atrium - 6 Place Abel Gance, Boulogne-Billancourt, Cedex 92652, France. TEL 33-1-46944522, FAX 33-1-46944599.

330.9 900 FRA
PREVISIONS GLISSANTES DETAILLEES EN PERSPECTIVES SECTORIELLES (VOL.37): TOURISME, HOTELLERIE, RESTAURATION, LOISIRS. Text in French. 1959. irreg. charts; stat.
Supersedes in part: Economie Francaise en Perspectives Sectorielles (Vols.1-5); Which supersedes in part: Prevision a Un An de l'Economie Francaise
Published by: B I P E Conseil, L'Atrium - 6 Place Abel Gance, Boulogne-Billancourt, Cedex 92652, France. TEL 33-1-46944522, FAX 33-1-46944599.

330.9 610   FRA
PREVISIONS GLISSANTES DETAILLEES EN PERSPECTIVES SECTORIELLES (VOL.38): PHARMACIE - SANTE. Text in French. 1959. irreg. charts; stat.
Formerly: Previsions Glissantes Detaillees en Perspectives Sectorielles (Vol.35): Sante; Supersedes in part: Economie Francaise en Perspectives Sectorielles (Vols.1-5); Which supersedes in part: Prevision a Un An de l'Economie Francaise
Published by: B I P E Conseil, L'Atrium - 6 Place Abel Gance, Boulogne-Billancourt, Cedex 92652, France. TEL 33-1-46944522, FAX 33-1-46944599.

PREVISIONS GLISSANTES DETAILLEES EN PERSPECTIVES SECTORIELLES (VOL.39): SERVICES PUBLICS. see *PUBLIC ADMINISTRATION*

330.9 645   FRA
PREVISIONS GLISSANTES DETAILLEES EN PERSPECTIVES SECTORIELLES (VOL.4): INDUSTRIES DU BOIS ET DE L'AMEUBLEMENT. Text in French. 1959. irreg. charts; stat.
Supersedes in part: Economie Francaise en Perspectives Sectorielles (Vols.1-5); Which supersedes in part: Prevision a Un An de l'Economie Francaise
Published by: B I P E Conseil, L'Atrium - 6 Place Abel Gance, Boulogne-Billancourt, Cedex 92652, France. TEL 33-1-46944522, FAX 33-1-46944599.

330.9   FRA
PREVISIONS GLISSANTES DETAILLEES EN PERSPECTIVES SECTORIELLES (VOL.40): SERVICES AUX ENTREPRISES. Text in French. 1959. irreg. charts; stat.
Supersedes in part: Economie Francaise en Perspectives Sectorielles (Vols.1-5); Which supersedes in part: Prevision a Un An de l'Economie Francaise
Published by: B I P E Conseil, L'Atrium - 6 Place Abel Gance, Boulogne-Billancourt, Cedex 92652, France. TEL 33-1-46944522, FAX 33-1-46944599.

338 621.9   FRA
PREVISIONS GLISSANTES DETAILLEES EN PERSPECTIVES SECTORIELLES (VOL.5): CONSTRUCTION DE MACHINES. Text in French. 1959. irreg. charts; stat.
Supersedes in part: Economie Francaise en Perspectives Sectorielles (Vols.1-5); Which supersedes in part: Prevision a Un An de l'Economie Francaise
Published by: B I P E Conseil, L'Atrium - 6 Place Abel Gance, Boulogne-Billancourt, Cedex 92652, France. TEL 33-1-46944522, FAX 33-1-46944599.

330.9 621.9   FRA
PREVISIONS GLISSANTES DETAILLEES EN PERSPECTIVES SECTORIELLES (VOL.6): MACHINES - OUTILS. Text in French. 1959. irreg. charts; stat.
Supersedes in part: Economie Francaise en Perspectives Sectorielles (Vols.1-5); Which supersedes in part: Prevision a Un An de l'Economie Francaise
Published by: B I P E Conseil, Axe Seine 21, 12 rue Rouget de Lisle, Issy-les-Moulineaux, Cedex 92442, France. TEL 1-46-62-33-00, FAX 1-46-62-62-20.

330.9 621.9   FRA
PREVISIONS GLISSANTES DETAILLEES EN PERSPECTIVES SECTORIELLES (VOL.7): EQUIPEMENT INDUSTRIEL. Text in French. 1959. irreg. charts; stat.
Supersedes in part: Economie Francaise en Perspectives Sectorielles (Vols.1-5); Which supersedes in part: Prevision a Un An de l'Economie Francaise
Published by: B I P E Conseil, L'Atrium - 6 Place Abel Gance, Boulogne-Billancourt, Cedex 92652, France. TEL 33-1-46944522, FAX 33-1-46944599.

330.9 621.9   FRA
PREVISIONS GLISSANTES DETAILLEES EN PERSPECTIVES SECTORIELLES (VOL.8): MECANIQUE DE PRECISION. Text in French. 1959. irreg. charts; stat.
Supersedes in part: Economie Francaise en Perspectives Sectorielles (Vols.1-5); Which supersedes in part: Prevision a Un An de l'Economie Francaise
Published by: B I P E Conseil, L'Atrium - 6 Place Abel Gance, Boulogne-Billancourt, Cedex 92652, France. TEL 33-1-46944522, FAX 33-1-46944599.

330.9 669   FRA
PREVISIONS GLISSANTES DETAILLEES EN PERSPECTIVES SECTORIELLES (VOL.9): FONDERIE ET TRANSFORMATION DES METAUX. Text in French. 1959. irreg. charts; stat.
Supersedes in part: Economie Francaise en Perspectives Sectorielles (Vols.1-5); Which supersedes in part: Prevision a Un An de l'Economie Francaise
Published by: B I P E Conseil, L'Atrium - 6 Place Abel Gance, Boulogne-Billancourt, Cedex 92652, France. TEL 33-1-46944522, FAX 33-1-46944599.

PRICES OF AGRICULTURAL PRODUCTS AND SELECTED INPUTS IN EUROPE AND NORTH AMERICA. see *AGRICULTURE—Agricultural Economics*

330.9   IRL
PRIVATE RESEARCH. Text in English. 1991. m. EUR 583 (effective 2005). adv. index. back issues avail. **Document type:** *Bulletin.*
Related titles: Diskette ed.
Published by: Private Research Ltd., Coliemore House, Coliemore Rd., Dalkey, Co. Dublin, Ireland. TEL 353-1-2848911, FAX 353-1-2048177, info@privateresearch.ie, http://www.privateresearch.ie.

338.947   RUS
PROBLEMY PROGNOZIROVANIYA. Text in Russian. 1990. 6/yr.
Document type: *Journal, Academic/Scholarly.* **Description:** Provides up-to-date inside information on socioeconomic problems in Russia.
Related titles: ♦ English Translation: Studies on Russian Economic Development. ISSN 1075-7007.
Indexed: RASB, RefZh.
Published by: (Rossisskaya Akademiya Nauk), Izdatel'stvo Nauka, Profsoyuznaya ul 90, Moscow, 117864, Russian Federation. TEL 7-095-3347151, FAX 7-095-4202220, secret@naukaran.ru, http://www.maik.rssi.ru/journals/rusec.htm, http://www.naukaran.ru.

330.9   GBR   ISSN 1369-4057
PRODUCER PRICE INDICES. Text in English. 1996. m. GBP 230 (effective 1998). charts; stat. **Document type:** *Government.*
Description: Contains indices on UK manufactured products, together with the materials and fuel purchased and the home sales at both broad and detailed industry levels.
Former titles (until 1996): U K Economy: Producer Price Indices (1365-5930); Business Monitor: Producer Price Incides
—BLDSC (3659.530050).
Published by: (Great Britain. Office for National Statistics), Home Office, 50 Queen Anne's Gate, London, SW1 9AT, United Kingdom. book.orders@theso.co.uk, http://www.national-publishing.co.uk, http://www.open.gov.uk.

330.9   USA
PRODUCTIVITY BY INDUSTRY (YEAR). Text in English. a. **Document type:** *Government.*
Related titles: ♦ Series of: U.S. Bureau of Labor Statistics. National Office News Releases.
Published by: U.S. Department of Labor, Bureau of Labor Statistics, Postal Square Bldg., 2 Massachusetts Ave, NE, Washington, DC 20212-0001 . TEL 202-691-5200, http://www.bls.gov. **Subscr. to:** U.S. Government Printing Office, Superintendent of Documents.

330.9   USA
PRODUCTIVITY MEASURES FOR SELECTED INDUSTRIES. Text in English. a. price varies. **Document type:** *Government.*
Former titles: Productivity Indexes for Selected Industries; Indexes of Output per Man-Hour: Selected Industries
Related titles: CD-ROM ed.; Microform ed.
Published by: U.S. Department of Labor, Bureau of Labor Statistics, Postal Square Bldg., 2 Massachusetts Ave, NE, Washington, DC 20212-0001 . TEL 202-691-5200, FAX 202-691-6325, http://www.bls.gov. **Subscr. to:** U.S. Government Printing Office, Superintendent of Documents.

PROFESIA. see *OCCUPATIONS AND CAREERS*

333   AUS   ISSN 1035-1396
PROGRESS. Text in English. 1904. bi-m. AUD 15 domestic; AUD 36 foreign (effective 2000). bk.rev. **Document type:** *Newsletter.* **Description:** Discusses economics, prosperity, employment and the social philosophy of Henry George.
Published by: Tax Reform Australia, 31 Hardware Ln, Melbourne, VIC 3000, Australia. TEL 61-3-9670-2874, FAX 61-3-96703063, mhassed@lexicon.net.au, http://www.earthsharing.org.au. Ed., R&P Mark Hassed TEL 61-3-97005777. Pub. Geoff Forster. Circ: 200.

PROGRESS IN DEVELOPMENT STUDIES. see *SOCIOLOGY*

330.9   PRT   ISSN 0873-4410
HC391
PROSPECTIVA E PLANEAMENTO. Text in Portuguese. 1978. a. **Document type:** *Government.*
Formerly (until 1994): Planeamento (0870-3043)
Indexed: ELLIS, ILD, PAIS, RRTA, WAE&RSA.
—BLDSC (6927.725000).
Published by: Ministerio do Ambiente, do Ordenamento do Territorio e do Desenvolvimento Regional, Departamento de Prospectiva e Planeamento, Avda. D. Carlos I, 126, Lisbon, 1249-079, Portugal. TEL 351-21-3935200, FAX 351-21-3935209, nic@dpp.pt, http://www.dpp.pt/.

338   NGA   ISSN 0048-5608
PROSPERITY; Nigeria's business quarterly. Text in English. 1971. q. adv. **Document type:** *Trade.*
Related titles: Microfilm ed.: (from PQC).
Published by: People's Publishing Co. Ltd., PO Box 3121, Lagos, Nigeria. Ed. Olu Akinsanya. Circ: 5,000.

382   ITA   ISSN 0033-1902
PROVINCIA DI FORLI IN CIFRE. Text in Italian. 1959-1997; resumed 1999. w. charts; mkt.; stat. **Description:** Includes the wholesale prices of livestock, produce, eggs, grains, vegetable oils, and other agricultural commodities for Forli-Cesena province.

Published by: Camera di Commercio Industria Artigianato e Agricoltura di Forli-Cesena, Corso della Repubblica 5, Forli', FC 47100, Italy. Ed. Ettore Neri.

330   CAN   ISSN 0827-5785
PROVINCIAL OUTLOOK. Text in English. 1976. q. CND 3,000 to non-members.
Formerly: Conference Board of Canada. Quarterly Provincial Forecast (0381-0100)
Related titles: Online - full text ed.
Indexed: CSI.
—CISTI.
Published by: Conference Board of Canada, 255 Smyth Rd, Ste 100, Ottawa, ON K1H 8M7, Canada. TEL 613-526-3280, FAX 613-526-4857.

330.971   CAN   ISSN 0832-3542
PROVINCIAL OUTLOOK, EXECUTIVE SUMMARY. Text in English. 197?. q.
Formerly (until 1986): Quarterly Provincial Forecast. Executive Summary (0829-111X)
Published by: Conference Board of Canada, 255 Smyth Rd, Ste 100, Ottawa, ON K1H 8M7, Canada. TEL 613-526-3280, FAX 613-526-4857, corpcomm@conferenceboard.ca, http://www.conferenceboard.ca/.

330.9   USA
PRUDENTIAL INSURANCE COMPANY OF AMERICA. ECONOMIC FORECAST. Text in English. 1982 (vol.31). a. charts.
Published by: (Economic & Investment Research Dept.), Prudential Insurance Co. of America, Public Relations & Advertising Dept, 5 Plaza, Newark, NJ 07101. TEL 201-877-6000.

330 646.066   POL   ISSN 0137-5490
K16
PRZEGLAD USTAWODAWSTWA GOSPODARCZEGO/ ECONOMIC LEGISLATION REVIEW. Text in Polish. 1948. m. PLZ 32 per issue (effective 2003). bk.rev. bibl. 32 p./no.
Indexed: FLP, RASB.
Published by: Polskie Wydawnictwo Ekonomiczne, ul Canaletta 4, Warsaw, 00099, Poland. TEL 48-22-8278001, FAX 48-22-8275567, pug@pwe.com.pl, marketing@pwe.com.pl, http://www.pug.pl, http://www.pwe.com.pl. Ed. Kazimierz Strzyczkowski. Adv. contact Monika Kolodziejczyk TEL 48-22-8278001 ext 320.

330.9   CAN   ISSN 1187-8657
HJ13
PUBLIC ACCOUNTS OF BRITISH COLUMBIA. Text in English. a. (in 3 vols.). CND 46.90. back issues avail.
Published by: Ministry of Finance and Corporate Relations, Sta Prov Govt, P O Box 9410, Victoria, BC V8W 9V1, Canada. **Subscr. to:** Crown Publications Inc., 521 Fort St, Victoria, BC BC V8W 1E7, Canada. TEL 604-386-4636.

330.9   USA   ISSN 1066-7156
PUEBLO BUSINESS JOURNAL. Text in English. 1993. s-m. USD 19.50 (effective 2004). adv. charts; illus.; mkt.; stat. back issues avail. **Document type:** *Magazine, Trade.* **Description:** Provides local business news and feature articles of interest to the business and professional community.
Related titles: E-mail ed.; Microform ed.: (from PQC); Online - full text ed.: (from Gale Group, Newsbank, Inc., Northern Light Technology, Inc., O C L C Online Computer Library Center, Inc., ProQuest Information & Learning).
Indexed: ABIn, BusDate.
Address: 1541, Colorado Spgs, CO 80901-1541. thepbj@aol.com. Circ: 6,500 (paid and free).

PUERTO RICO ECONOMIC INDICATORS. see *BUSINESS AND ECONOMICS—Abstracting, Bibliographies, Statistics*

PUGET SOUND BUSINESS JOURNAL. see *BUSINESS AND ECONOMICS*

330.9   BOL   ISSN 1609-7076
PULSO ANALITICO. Text in Spanish. 1999. w.
Media: Online - full text. **Related titles:** E-mail ed.
Published by: (Centro de Estudios para el Desarrollo Laborar y Agrario), Pulso, Ave Mariscal Santa Cruz, Edif Esperanza, 3er Piso, Oficina 2, La Paz, Bolivia. TEL 591-2-313418, http://www.pulsobolivia.com/analitico/.

330.9   ITA   ISSN 0391-3082
PUNTO; rivista di economia di Como, Lecco, Varese, Alto Milanese e Canton Ticino. Text in Italian. 1980. bi-m. CHF 55 domestic; CHF 71 foreign (effective 2000). back issues avail.
Description: Provides a forum on the economy in Como, Lecce, and Varese, Italy and in Tessin Canton in Switzerland. Presents joint economical, industrial, cultural and social interests.
Published by: Fratelli Pini Editori s.r.l., Via L. Battista Alberti 10, Milan, MI 20149, Italy. TEL 39-02-33101836, FAX 39-02-3450749. Adv. contact Lilia Pini. Circ: 18,000.

330.9   PER
PUNTO INICIAL. Text in Spanish. q.

B

Published by: Asociacion Nacional de Periodistas del Peru, Jiron Huancavelica No 320, Ofic 501, Lima, Peru. TEL 51-14-270-687, FAX 51-14-278-8493, anp@amauta.rcp.net.pe, http://www.ekeko2.rcp.net.pe/anp.

330.9 FRA ISSN 1015-4639
PURCHASING POWER PARITIES AND REAL EXPENDITURES/PARITES DE POUVOIR D'ACHAT ET DEPENSES REELLES. Text in French. a. price varies.
Related titles: Online - full content ed.
Published by: Organization for Economic Cooperation and Development, 2 Rue Andre Pascal, Paris, 75775 Cedex 16, France. TEL 33-1-45248200, FAX 33-1-45248500, http://www.oecd.org. **Subscr. in U.S. to:** O E C D Turpin North America, PO Box 194, Downingtown, PA 19335-0194. TEL 610-524-5361, 800-456-6323, FAX 610-524-5417, bookscustomer@turpinna.com.

330 ITA ISSN 1121-9610
HC307.S3
QUADERNI DI ECONOMIA E FINANZA. Text in English, Italian. 1971. 3/yr. free. bk.rev. bibl.; stat. index.
Former titles (until 1992): Quaderni Sardi di Economia (0391-8394); (until 1978): Quaderni dell'Economia Sarda
Indexed: JEL, PAIS.
Published by: Banco di Sardegna SpA, Servizio Studi, Viale Umberto I, 36, Sassari, SS 07100, Italy. TEL 39-79-226572, FAX 39-79-226579. Ed. Lorenzo Idda. Circ: 2,000 (controlled).

338 USA
QUARTERLY BUSINESS FAILURES. Text in English. 1900. q. USD 40 (effective 2000). **Description:** Provides number of failures and liabilities by detailed lines of business. Includes data for all 2-digit, 3-digit and most 4-digit SIC codes.
Former titles: Quarterly Business Failures Report; Quarterly Analysis of Failures (0033-5290)
Indexed: SRI.
Published by: Dun & Bradstreet, Economic Analysis Department (Subsidiary of: Dun & Bradstreet Corporation), c/o Judy Webb, 3 Sylvan Way, Parsippany, NJ 07054. FAX 973-254-4063, http://www.dnb.com. R&P Judy Webb.

330.9 USA
QUARTERLY BUSINESS STARTS. Text in English. 1978. q. USD 40 (effective 2000). **Document type:** *Trade.* **Description:** Provides number of starts and total employees by detailed lines of business. Includes data for all 2-digit, 3-digit and most 4-digit SIC codes.
Formerly: Quarterly Business Starts Report
Published by: Dun & Bradstreet, Economic Analysis Department (Subsidiary of: Dun & Bradstreet Corporation), c/o Judy Webb, 3 Sylvan Way, Parsippany, NJ 07054. FAX 973-254-4063, http://www.dnb.com. R&P Judy Webb.

330.9 339 GBR ISSN 0952-0724
HC251
QUARTERLY ECONOMIC BULLETIN. Text in English. 1982. q. looseleaf. GBP 90 to individuals; GBP 325 to institutions; GBP 300 to corporations (effective 2001). charts; stat. 33 p./no. 2 cols./p.; **Document type:** *Bulletin, Trade.* **Description:** Provides forecasts and commentary on the state of the world and the British economy.
Indexed: IBSS.
Published by: (Liverpool Research Group in Macroeconomics), Liverpool Macroeconomic Research Ltd, 5 Cable Rd, Whiston, Liverpool, L35 5AN, United Kingdom. TELEX 627095-UNILPL-G, jfnw36652@cableinet.co.uk. Ed. Patrick Minford. **Subscr. to:** c/o Jane Francis, 131 Mount Pleasant, Liverpool, Merseyside L3 5TF, United Kingdom. TEL 44-151-709-2221.

330.9 IND
QUARTERLY REVIEW OF INDIAN ECONOMY. Text in English. 1990. q. USD 200. **Description:** An analytical report on current Indian economic situations in the fields of agriculture, infrastructure, industry, investment climate, banking and finance, price situation, foreign trade, and balance of payments positions.
Published by: Economic and Scientific Research Foundation, Federation House, New Delhi, 110 001, India. TEL 331-9251-61, TELEX 031-2546 & 62521. Ed. Jagdish Shettigar.

QUINZAINE AFRICAINE. see *POLITICAL SCIENCE—International Relations*

R B C LETTER. (Royal Bank of Canada) see *BUSINESS AND ECONOMICS—Banking And Finance*

330.9 PHL
THE R D C. Text in English. 1978. 2/school-academic yr. USD 6 (effective 2001). illus.; mkt.; stat. **Document type:** *Newsletter, Government.*
Formerly: Regional Development Communicator (0116-2551)
Published by: Regional Development Council of Western Mindanao, National Economic and Development Authority, R.T. Lim Blvd, Zamboanga City, Philippines. TEL 991-6741, 991-3615, FAX 991-1364, neda9@jetlink.com.ph, http://www.jetlink.com.ph/rdc9. Eds. Rustico Varela Jr., Susan C Valerio. Circ: 120.

330 SYR ISSN 0079-9696
HC497.S8
RAPPORT ANNUEL SUR L'ECONOMIE SYRIENNE. Text in English, French. 1963. a. USD 300 (effective 2001). Index. 300 p./no.; back issues avail. **Document type:** *Yearbook, Corporate.*
Published by: Office Arabe de Presse et de Documentation, 67, Place Chahbandar, PO Box 3550, Damascus, Syria. TEL 963-11-3318237, FAX 963-11-4426021, ofa@net.sy, http://www.ofa-holding.com. Ed., Pub. Raghda Bittar. Circ: 1,000 (paid).

330.9 ITA ISSN 0390-010X
HC301
RASSEGNA ECONOMICA. Text in Italian. 1931. 2/yr. free to qualified personnel. bk.rev. bibl.; charts; stat. index. reprints avail.
Indexed: IBSS, JEL, PAIS, RASB, RRTA, RefZh, WAE&RSA. —BLDSC (7294.137000).
Published by: Associazione Sudi e Ricerche per il Mezzogiorno, Via Cervantes 64, Naples, NA 80133, Italy. TEL 39-081-7917659, FAX 39-081-5529307, mariafederica.masturzo@sanpaoloimi.com, http://www.srmezzogiorno.it. Circ: 4,600 (controlled).

330.9 USA
REAL EARNINGS. Text in English. m. **Document type:** *Government.*
Related titles: ◆ Series of: U.S. Bureau of Labor Statistics. National Office News Releases.
Indexed: AmStI.
Published by: U.S. Department of Labor, Bureau of Labor Statistics, Postal Square Bldg., 2 Massachusetts Ave, NE, Washington, DC 20212-0001 . TEL 202-691-5200, http://www.bls.gov. **Subscr. to:** U.S. Government Printing Office, Superintendent of Documents.

REAL ESTATE ANALYSIS AND PLANNING SERVICE. see *REAL ESTATE*

330.9 ARG ISSN 0325-1926
HC121
REALIDAD ECONOMICA. Text in Spanish. 1970. every 45 days, latest vol.180. ARS 75 domestic; USD 130 foreign (effective 2005). adv. bk.rev. **Document type:** *Magazine, Trade.*
Related titles: Online - full text ed.
Indexed: AEA, AgBio, AltPI, DSA, HAPI, HortAb, IBSS, PAIS, RASB, RDA, RRTA, SIA, TriticAb, WAE&RSA.
Published by: Instituto Argentino para el Desarrollo Economico, Hipolito Yrigoyen, 1116 Piso 4, Capital Federal, Buenos Aires 1086, Argentina. TEL 54-11-43819337, FAX 54-11-43812158, iade@iade.com.ar, http://www.iade.org.ar. Ed. Juan Carlos Amigo.

338.9 PER
REALIDAD PERUANA. Text in Spanish. 1975 (no.3). irreg. price varies. charts; stat. **Document type:** *Monographic series.*
Published by: Editorial Horizonte, Casilla 2118, Ave. Nicolas De Pierola, 995, Lima, 1, Peru.

388 USA ISSN 0080-0449
REFERENCE BOOK - ARGENTINA. Text in Spanish. a.
Published by: Dun's Marketing Services (Subsidiary of: Dun & Bradstreet, Inc.), 3 Sylvan Way, Parsippany, NJ 07054-3896. TEL 201-455-0900.

380 USA ISSN 0080-0457
REFERENCE BOOK - REPUBLIC OF SOUTH AFRICA. (Published in 4 provincial editions: Sec. 1: Orange Free State, Sec. 2: Cape Province, Sec. 3: Natal, Sec. 4: Transvaal) Text in English. a.
Published by: Dun's Marketing Services (Subsidiary of: Dun & Bradstreet, Inc.), 3 Sylvan Way, Parsippany, NJ 07054-3896. TEL 201-455-0900.

REGION ET DEVELOPPEMENT. see *PUBLIC ADMINISTRATION*

330.9 USA ISSN 1093-1767
HC107.A13
REGION FOCUS. Text in English. 1997. q. free. charts; stat. back issues avail.; reprint service avail. from CIS. **Document type:** *Corporate.* **Description:** Review of business conditions and economic developments in the Fifth Federal Reserve District.
Formerly (until 1997): Cross Section (0747-5543)
Related titles: Microfiche ed.: (from CIS); Online - full text ed.: (from Northern Light Technology, Inc., ProQuest Information & Learning).
Indexed: AmStI, BLI, FiP.
Published by: Federal Reserve Bank of Richmond, Research Department, 701 E Byrd St, Richmond, VA 23219. TEL 804-697-8000, FAX 804-697-8287, regionfocus@rich.frb.org, http://www.rich.frb.org. Ed. Laura Fortunate. Circ: 20,000. **Subscr. to:** Public Affairs, PO Box 27622, Richmond, VA 23261. TEL 804-697-8111.

330 CAN
REGIONAL DEVELOPMENT CORPORATION. ANNUAL REPORT/SOCIETE D'AMENAGEMENT REGIONAL. RAPPORT ANNUEL. Text in English, French. 1967. a. free.
Formerly (until Nov. 1987): Community Improvement Corporation. Annual Report (0069-7842)
Published by: Regional Development Corporation, P O Box 428, Fredericton, NB E3B 5R4, Canada. TEL 506-453-2277. Ed. Celine Doucet Rousselle. Circ: 1,000 (controlled).

330.9 658.8 USA
HC101
REGIONAL ECONOMIES AND MARKETS; a quarterly analysis from the Conference Board. Text in English. 1986. q. USD 295 to non-members; USD 145 to members (effective 2003). **Document type:** *Newsletter.* **Description:** Examines trends and prospects in the nine major US regions.
Media: Online - full text.
Published by: Conference Board, Inc., 845 Third Ave, New York, NY 10022. TEL 212-759-0900, FAX 212-980-7014, http://www.conference-board.org. Circ: 9,000.

330.9 USA
REGIONAL ECONOMIST. Text in English. q. free. **Document type:** *Corporate.* **Description:** Addresses national and regional economic issues as they affect the Eighth Federal Reserve District.
Formerly: Pieces of Eight
Related titles: Online - full text ed.
Indexed: AmStI.
Published by: (Public Affairs), Federal Reserve Bank of St. Louis, PO Box 442, St. Louis, MO 63166. TEL 314-444-8808, http://www.stls.frb.org/fred.

330.9 SGP ISSN 0218-3056
DS520
REGIONAL OUTLOOK: SOUTHEAST ASIA. Text in English. 1992. a., latest 2003-04. USD 21.90, SGD 29.90 (effective 2005). **Document type:** *Academic/Scholarly.* **Description:** Covers the political and economic situations in Southeast Asia.
Related titles: Online - full text ed.: (from EBSCO Publishing, O C L C Online Computer Library Center, Inc., ProQuest Information & Learning).
Indexed: ABIn.
Published by: Institute of Southeast Asian Studies, 30 Heng Mui Keng Terrace, Pasir Panjang, Singapore, 119614, Singapore. TEL 65-6870-2447, FAX 65-6775-6259, pubsunit@iseas.edu.sg, http://www.iseas.edu.sg/. Eds. Rahul Sen, Russell H.K. Heng.

330.9 ITA
REGIONE ABRUZZO. Text in Italian. 1972. m. free. back issues avail.
Published by: Servizio Informazione Stampa e Pubbliche Relazioni, Via Michele Jacobucci, 4, L'Aquila, 67100, Italy. Circ: 8,500.

REGIONY ROSSII. SOTSIAL'NO-EKONOMICHESKIE POKAZATELI (YEAR). see *BUSINESS AND ECONOMICS—Abstracting, Bibliographies, Statistics*

REGULATION (WASHINGTON, 1977); the Cato review of business & government. see *POLITICAL SCIENCE*

330.9 USA ISSN 1075-7848
REIMBURSEMENT UPDATE. Text in English. 1984. q. USD 105. **Document type:** *Newsletter.*
Address: 355 Oak Trail Dr., Louisville, TX 75067. TEL 817-491-3593. Ed. Frederic R Curtiss.

330.9 PRT ISSN 0871-9365
RELATORIO MENSAL DE ECONOMIA. Text in Portuguese. 1998. m. adv. mkt.; stat.; tr.lit. back issues avail. **Document type:** *Corporate.* **Description:** Covers national and international economic evaluation.
Published by: Associacao Industrial Portuense, Praca das Industrias, Apdo 3200, Lisbon, 1301-965, Portugal. TEL 351-21-3601000, FAX 351-21-3641301, aip@aip.pt, http://www.aip.pt/. Pub. Angelo Ludgero Marques. Circ: 1,500.

RENKOU YU JINGJI/POPULATION & ECONOMICS. see *POPULATION STUDIES*

330.9 MAR ISSN 1113-738X
REPERES STATISTIQUES. Text in French. 1996. m. free. **Document type:** *Bulletin.*
Published by: Morocco. Direction de la Statistique, B P 178, Rabat, Morocco. TEL 212-7-77-36-06, FAX 212-7-773042.

REPORT OF THE (YEAR) BUSINESS TRADE AND SERVICES SURVEY. see *BUSINESS AND ECONOMICS—Abstracting, Bibliographies, Statistics*

REPORT OF THE (YEAR) INDUSTRIAL CENSUS. see *BUSINESS AND ECONOMICS—Abstracting, Bibliographies, Statistics*

REPORT OF THE (YEAR) SURVEY OF FERTILITY IN THAILAND. see *BUSINESS AND ECONOMICS—Abstracting, Bibliographies, Statistics*

REPORT OF THE LABOR FORCE SURVEY, WHOLE KINGDOM, ROUND FOUR (YEAR). see *BUSINESS AND ECONOMICS—Abstracting, Bibliographies, Statistics*

REPORT ON GUATEMALA. see *POLITICAL SCIENCE—International Relations*

330.9 MEX ISSN 1606-7819
REPORTE POLITICO POLICIACO. Text in Spanish. 1997. bi-m. back issues avail. **Document type:** *Magazine, Trade.*
Related titles: Online - full text ed.: ISSN 1606-7800. 2000.
Published by: Cu4tro.com, El Novillo 102 E2B 204, Aguascalientes, Aguascalientes, Mexico. TEL 52-4-9700435, reportepp@acnet.net, http://www.reporte.8m.com/, http://www.cu4tro.com/.

REPORTING ON GOVERNMENTS. see *BUSINESS AND ECONOMICS—Investments*

330 ARG ISSN 1515-5471
REPUBLIC OF ARGENTINA. MINISTRY OF ECONOMY AND PRODUCTION, SECRETARIAT OF ECONOMY POLICY. ECONOMIC REPORT. Text in Spanish. 1992. q. back issues avail.
Related titles: Print ed.: ISSN 1515-548X. 1994; ♦ Spanish ed.: Republica Argentina. Ministerio de Economia y Produccion. Secretaria de Politica Economica. Informe Economico Trimestral.
Published by: Argentina. Ministerio de Economia, Servicio de Prensa, 501, Balcarce, 136 Piso 5, Capital Federal, Buenos Aires 1064, Argentina. TEL 54-114-3495079, FAX 54-114-3495730, mpqonz@mecon.gov.ar, http://www.mecon.gov.ar/.

330 ARG
HC171
REPUBLICA ARGENTINA. MINISTERIO DE ECONOMIA Y PRODUCCION. SECRETARIA DE POLITICA ECONOMICA. INFORME ECONOMICO TRIMESTRAL. Text in Spanish. 1968. q. stat. **Document type:** *Government.*
Former titles: Argentina. Ministerio de Economia y Obras y Servicios Publicos. Informe Economico (0327-7275); (until 1992): Argentina. Ministerio de Economia. Informe Economico (0570-8672); (until 1968): Argentina. Ministerio de Hacienda y Finanzas. Informe Economico
Related titles: Online - full text ed.: ISSN 1515-5498; ♦ Spanish ed.: Republic of Argentina. Ministry of Economy and Production, Secretariat of Economy Policy. Economic Report. ISSN 1515-5471.
Published by: Republica Argentina. Ministerio de Economia y Produccion, Secretaria de Politica Economica/Republic of Argentina. Ministry of Economy and Production, Secretariat of Economy Policy, Av. Pte. Julio A. Roca 609-1067, Capital Federal, Buenos Aires, Argentina. TEL 54-1-43499646, FAX 54-1-43499621, asesores@mecon.gov.ar, http://www.mecon.gov.ar/peconomica/informe/informe45/indice.htm, http://www.mecon.gov.ar/peconomica/default.htm.

RESERVE BANK OF AUSTRALIA. OCCASIONAL PAPERS. see *BUSINESS AND ECONOMICS—Banking And Finance*

RESERVE BANK OF AUSTRALIA. RESEARCH DISCUSSION PAPER. see *BUSINESS AND ECONOMICS—Banking And Finance*

330.9 332 FJI
RESERVE BANK OF FIJI. ANNUAL REPORT. Text in English. 1975. a. USD 10. charts; stat. **Document type:** *Corporate.* **Description:** Covers a comprehensive review of the domestic economy and an overview of developments in the international economy as well as operations and accounts of the bank for the calendar year. Also contains financial and economic data.
Formerly (until 1984): Fiji. Central Monetary Authority. Annual Report
Published by: Reserve Bank of Fiji, Private Mail Bag, Suva, Fiji. TEL 679-313611, FAX 679-301688, TELEX 2164. Circ: 750.

330.9 332 FJI
RESERVE BANK OF FIJI. MONTHLY ECONOMIC BULLETIN. Text in English. 1994. m. USD 6 in United States. **Document type:** *Bulletin.* **Description:** Reviews Fiji economy.
Published by: Reserve Bank of Fiji, Private Mail Bag, Suva, Fiji. TEL 679-313611, FAX 679-301688. Circ: 300.

330.9 332 FJI
RESERVE BANK OF FIJI. NEWS REVIEW. Text in English. 1984. w. USD 10 in United States. **Document type:** *Newsletter.* **Description:** Provides edited highlights of the local and international financial as well as economic news. Also contains selected financial and economic data.
Published by: Reserve Bank of Fiji, Private Mail Bag, Suva, Fiji. TEL 679-313611, FAX 679-301688. Circ: 350.

330.9 332 FJI
RESERVE BANK OF FIJI. QUARTERLY REVIEW. Text in English. 1976. q. USD 46 in United States. stat. **Document type:** *Corporate.* **Description:** Provides a quarterly analysis of the Fiji economy together with time series of selected economic and financial statistics.
Formerly (until 1984): Fiji. Central Monetary Authority. Quarterly Review
Published by: Reserve Bank of Fiji, Private Mail Bag, Suva, Fiji. TEL 679-313611, FAX 679-301688. Circ: 500.

332 MWI ISSN 0376-5725
HC517.M3
RESERVE BANK OF MALAWI. FINANCIAL AND ECONOMIC REVIEW. Text in English. 1968. q. free. charts; stat. **Document type:** *Academic/Scholarly.* **Description:** Offers a quarterly assessment of developments in the major economic indicators. Contains sections on money and credit, public finance, balance of payments and the international economic situation, production and prices, as well as a statistical annex section.
Formerly: Reserve Bank of Malawi. Economic and Financial Review (0034-5520)
Indexed: KES, WBA.
—BLDSC (3926.941000).
Published by: (Research Department), Reserve Bank of Malawi, PO Box 30063, Lilongwe, Malawi. TEL 265-780600.

RESERVE BANK OF NEW ZEALAND BULLETIN. see *BUSINESS AND ECONOMICS—Banking And Finance*

330.9 NZL ISSN 1170-4829
RESERVE BANK OF NEW ZEALAND. MONETARY POLICY STATEMENT. Text in English. 1990. q. NZD 48 (effective 2005). back issues avail. **Document type:** *Corporate.*
Published by: Reserve Bank of New Zealand, Public Affairs & Information Service Section, 2 The Terrace, PO Box 2498, Wellington, New Zealand. TEL 64-4-4722029, FAX 64-4-4738554, rbnz-info@rbnz.govt.nz, http://www.rbnz.govt.nz/monpol/statements/index.html.

330.9 NZL ISSN 0110-523X
RESERVE BANK OF NEW ZEALAND. RESEARCH PAPERS. Text in English. 1971. irreg. free. bibl.; stat. **Document type:** *Academic/Scholarly.*
—BLDSC (7777.240400).
Published by: Reserve Bank of New Zealand, Public Affairs & Information Service Section, 2 The Terrace, PO Box 2498, Wellington, New Zealand. TEL 64-4-4722029, FAX 64-4-4738554, rbnz-info@rbnz.govt.nz, http://www.rbnz.govt.nz/research/econresearch/0093780.html. Circ: 1,000.

330.9 BGR ISSN 1013-1450
LA RESTRUCTURATION/RESTRUCTURING. Text in English, French, German, Russian, Spanish. 1987. m. looseleaf. USD 24. back issues avail. **Description:** Covers the process of restructuring in all spheres of life, promotes Bulgarian economy among its foreign partners.
Published by: Sofia Press Agency, 29 Slavianska ul, Sofia, 1040, Bulgaria. TEL 359-2-885831, FAX 359-2-883455, TELEX 22622. Ed. Ekaterina Licheva. Circ: 2,500.

330.9 USA
RETAIL FOOD PRICE INDEX: WASHINGTON, D.C. Text in English. m. **Document type:** *Government.*
Related titles: ♦ Series of: U.S. Bureau of Labor Statistics. National Office News Releases.
Published by: U.S. Department of Labor, Bureau of Labor Statistics, Postal Square Bldg., 2 Massachusetts Ave, NE, Washington, DC 20212-0001 . TEL 202-691-5200, http://www.bls.gov. **Subscr. to:** U.S. Government Printing Office, Superintendent of Documents.

330.9 USA ISSN 1094-2025
HB1 CODEN: REDEB7
REVIEW OF ECONOMIC DYNAMICS. Text in English. 1998. 4/yr. EUR 115 in Europe to individuals; JPY 12,300 in Japan to individuals; USD 99 to individuals except Europe and Japan; EUR 560 in Europe to institutions; JPY 58,400 in Japan to institutions; USD 486 to institutions except Europe and Japan; EUR 59 in Europe to students; JPY 6,300 in Japan to students; USD 51 to students except Europe and Japan (effective 2006). back issues avail. **Document type:** *Journal, Academic/Scholarly.* **Description:** Publishes original contributions to dynamic economics.
Related titles: Online - full text ed.: ISSN 1096-6099. 1998. USD 479 (effective 2002) (from EBSCO Publishing, Gale Group, IngentaConnect, O C L C Online Computer Library Center, Inc., ScienceDirect, Swets Information Services).
Indexed: ABIn, CurCont, IBSS, JEL, SSCI.
—BLDSC (7790.191500), IE, Infotrieve, ingenta. **CCC.**
Published by: Academic Press (Subsidiary of: Elsevier Science & Technology), 525 B St, Ste 1900, San Diego, CA 92101-4495. TEL 619-231-6616, 800-894-3434, FAX 619-699-6422, apsubs@acad.com, http://www.elsevier.com/locate/red, http://www.academicpress.com. Eds. G. D. Hansen, M Boldrin, N Kocherlakota.

330.9 GBR ISSN 0969-2290
HF1354 CODEN: RIPEFV
➤ **REVIEW OF INTERNATIONAL POLITICAL ECONOMY.** Text in English. 1994. 5/yr. GBP 331, USD 547 combined subscription to institutions print & online eds. (effective 2006). adv. reprint service avail. from PSC. **Document type:** *Journal, Academic/Scholarly.* **Description:** Encourages analytical synthesis and novel combinations between economics, politics, geography, sociology and cultural studies.
Related titles: Online - full text ed.: ISSN 1466-4526. GBP 314, USD 520 to institutions (effective 2006) (from EBSCO Publishing, Gale Group, IngentaConnect, O C L C Online Computer Library Center, Inc., Swets Information Services).
Indexed: ABIn, BrHumI, CJA, CurCont, DIP, IBR, IBSS, IBZ, IPSA, JEL, PSA, PhilInd, SOPODA, SSA, SSCI, SociolAb.
—BLDSC (7790.935000), IDS, IE, Infotrieve, ingenta. **CCC.**
Published by: Routledge (Subsidiary of: Taylor & Francis Group), 4 Park Sq, Milton Park, Abingdon, Oxon OX14 4RN, United Kingdom. TEL 44-1235-828600, FAX 44-1235-829000, journals@routledge.com, http://www.tandf.co.uk/journals/titles/09692290.asp, http://www.routledge.co.uk. Eds. Eric Helleiner, Henry Wai-Chung Yeung, Mark Blythe, Walden Bello. R&P Sally Sweet. adv.: page GBP 150; trim 205 x 135. **Subscr. to:** Taylor & Francis Ltd, Journals Customer Service, Rankine Rd, Basingstoke, Hants RG24 8PR, United Kingdom. TEL 44-1256-813000, FAX 44-1256-330245, enquiry@tandf.co.uk.

330.9 GBR ISSN 0962-2055
HB126.4
➤ **REVIEW OF ISLAMIC ECONOMICS.** Text in English. 1991. a. GBP 12 domestic to individuals; GBP 15 foreign to individuals; GBP 20 domestic to institutions; GBP 24 foreign to institutions (effective 2000). back issues avail. **Document type:** *Academic/Scholarly.* **Description:** Provides a forum for specialists wishing to contribute to the development of Islamic economics as a distinct branch of knowledge.
Indexed: IBSS.
—BLDSC (7791.110000), IE, ingenta.
Published by: (International Association for Islamic Economics), Islamic Foundation, Conference Centre, Ratby Ln, Markfield, Leics LE67 9SY, United Kingdom. TEL 01530-244944, FAX 01530-244946, i.foundation@islamic-foundation.org.uk. Ed. Munawar Iqbal. R&P, Adv. contact A K Chachi.

B

➤ **REVIEW OF POLITICAL ECONOMY.** see *POLITICAL SCIENCE*

➤ **REVIEW OF REGIONAL STUDIES;** the official journal of the Southern regional science association. see *HOUSING AND URBAN PLANNING*

330.9 371.42 GBR ISSN 0265-9387
REVIEW OF THE ECONOMY AND EMPLOYMENT. Text in English. 1981. irreg. (in 2 vols.). GBP 80 (effective 1999). **Document type:** *Monographic series, Academic/Scholarly.* **Description:** Provides a medium-term assessment of the U.K. labor market. Publication form varies, but all gather information on employment prospects according to industry, occupation, gender and employment status, distinguishing employees from the self employed and splitting employees into those who are working full-time and those working part-time.
—BLDSC (7790.257000).
Published by: Institute for Employment Research, University Of Warwick, Gibbet Hill Rd, Coventry, Warks CV4 7AL, United Kingdom. TEL 44-203-524127, FAX 44-203-524241. Ed., R&P Robert Wilson TEL 44-203-523530.

338 ARG ISSN 0034-6810
REVIEW OF THE RIVER PLATE; dealing with Argentine financial, economic, agricultural and shipping affairs. Text in English, Spanish. 1891. 2/m. USD 225. adv. charts; mkt.
Related titles: Microfilm ed.: (from PQC).
Indexed: KES, PAIS.
—CISTI.
Address: P.B."A", Bulnes, 44 A, Capital Federal, Buenos Aires 1176, Argentina. Ed. Archibald B Norman. Circ: 4,000.

330.9 ESP ISSN 1134-8291
REVISTA ASTURIANA DE ECONOMIA. Text in Spanish. 1994. 3/yr.
—CINDOC.
Published by: Asociacion Asturiana de Estudios Economicos, Apdo. de Correos 1693, Oviedo, 33080, Spain. TEL 34-929-867179, http://www.uniovi.es/rae/. Ed. Fernando Rubiera.

330.9 339 HND ISSN 0254-4210
HC141.A1
REVISTA CENTROAMERICANA DE ECONOMIA; postgrado centroamericana en economia y planificacion del desarrollo. Text in Spanish. 1979. 3/yr. USD 18.
Indexed: IBR, PAIS.
Published by: Universidad Nacional Autonoma de Honduras, Postgrado en Economia, Apdo. 1748, Ciudad Universitaria, Tegucigalpa DC, Honduras. TEL 504-31-3289. Circ: 600.
Co-sponsor: Consejo Superior Universitario Centroamericano.

330.9 CHL ISSN 0716-5927
HB1.A1
REVISTA DE ANALISIS ECONOMICO. Text in Spanish, English. 1987. s-a. CLP 12,000 domestic to individuals; USD 35 foreign to individuals; CLP 16,000 domestic to institutions; USD 40 foreign to institutions (effective 2005). abstr. **Document type:** *Journal, Academic/Scholarly.* **Description:** Stimulates production and intellectual exchange of theories related to developing economies. Includes coverage of literature in this area.
Related titles: Online - full text ed.: (from EBSCO Publishing).
Indexed: JEL.
—BLDSC (7840.863000).
Published by: Georgetown University, I L A D E S, Almirante Barroso 6, Santiago, Chile. TEL 56-2-6980046, FAX 56-2-6986873. Ed. Felipe Morande. **Co-sponsor:** Georgetown University, Postgraduate Program in Economics.

▼ *new title* ➤ *refereed* ✶ *unverified* ♦ *full entry avail.*

330.9 SLV
HC148.A1
➤ **REVISTA DE CIENCIAS SOCIALES Y HUMANIDADES.** Cover title: R E A L I D A D. Text in Spanish. 1987. bi-m. SVC 125 domestic; USD 35 in Central America; USD 60 in North America; USD 75 elsewhere (effective 2005). back issues avail. **Document type:** *Magazine, Academic/Scholarly.*
Formerly: Realidad Economico-Social (1012-5515)
Related titles: Online - full text ed.
Indexed: RASB.
Published by: Universidad Centroamericana Jose Simeon Canas, U C A Editores, Apartado Postal 01-168, San Salvador, El Salvador. TEL 503-210-6600, FAX 503-210-6650 ext 240, 241, 242, distpubli@ued.uca.edu.sv, http://www.uca.edu.sv/publica/ued/ucaeditores.html.

330.9 ESP ISSN 1576-0162
REVISTA DE ECONOMIA MUNDIAL. Text in Spanish, English. 1999. s-a. EUR 30 to individuals; EUR 50 to institutions (effective 2005).
Indexed: JEL.
—CINDOC.
Published by: Universidad de Huelva, Servicio de Publicaciones, Campus el Carmen, Ave. de las Fuerzas Armadas, s-n, Huelva, Andalucia 21071, Spain. TEL 34-95-9018000, publica@uhu.es, http://www.uhu.es/publicaciones/index.html. Ed. Manuela De Paz Banez.

REVISTA DE ECONOMIA POLITICA/BRAZILIAN JOURNAL OF POLITICAL ECONOMY. see *POLITICAL SCIENCE*

330.9 ESP ISSN 0212-6109
HC10
REVISTA DE HISTORIA ECONOMICA. Text in Spanish. 1943. 3/yr. USD 37.
Former titles (until 1983): Revista de Economia Politica (0034-8058); (until 1945): Revista de Estudios Politicos. Suplemento de Informacion Economica (1132-3159)
Indexed: AmH&L, BibInd, HistAb, IBR, IBSS, IBZ, JEL, PAIS, PCI, RASB.
—BLDSC (7858.534000), CINDOC, IE, Infotrieve, ingenta. **CCC.**
Published by: (Fundacion SEPI), Alianza Editorial, Juan Ignacio Luca de Tena 15, Madrid, 28027, Spain. TEL 34-91-3938888, FAX 34-91-7414343, alianza@anaya.es, http://www.alianzaeditorial.es.

330.9 CHL ISSN 0252-0257
REVISTA DE LA C E P A L. Text in Spanish. 1956. s-a.
Formerly (until 1975): Boletin Economico de America Latina (0520-4402)
Related titles: Online - full text ed.: ISSN 1682-0908. 199?; ♦ Spanish ed.: C E P A L Review. ISSN 0251-2920.
Indexed: RASB.
—CINDOC, IE.
Published by: Comision Economica para America Latina y el Caribe/Economic Commission for Latin America and the Caribbean, Ave Dag Hammarskjold 3477, Vitacura, Santiago de Chile, Chile. TEL 56-2-471-2000, FAX 56-2-208-0252, publications@eclac.cl, http://www.eclac.cl. Ed. Oscar Altimir.

330.9 ESP ISSN 1135-819X
LA REVISTA ECONOMICA DE CATALUNYA. Text in Spanish. 1975. 3/yr. back issues avail.
Formerly (until 1986): Revista Economica de Cataluna (1135-8181)
Related titles: Online - full text ed.
—CINDOC.
Published by: Col-legi d'Economistes de Catalunya/Colegio de Economistas de Cataluna, Ave. Diagonal, 512 pral., Barcelona, Spain. http://www.economistes.com/. Ed. Marti Parellada.

330 BRA ISSN 0100-4956
HC186 CODEN: RENOFN
REVISTA ECONOMICA DO NORDESTE. Abbreviated title: REN. Text in Portuguese; Summaries in English. 1969. q. BRL 40 domestic; USD 50 foreign (effective 2005). charts; illus. back issues avail. **Document type:** *Government.* **Description:** Includes articles on the economic situation of Brazil.
Formerly (until 1973): Revista Economica
Indexed: IBSS, PAIS.
Published by: Banco do Nordeste do Brasil, Av Paranjana 5.700 - Castelao, Fortaleza, CE 60740-000, Brazil. TEL 55-85-2993137, FAX 55-85-2993788, ren@banconordeste.gov.br. Ed. Ademir da Silva Costa. Circ: 1,200.

330.9 CUB ISSN 0259-8299
REVISTA ESTADISTICA. Text in Spanish. 1978. 3/yr. USD 24 in North America; USD 25 in South America; USD 26 in Europe.
Indexed: PAIS, RASB.
Published by: (Instituto de Investigaciones Estadisticas), Ediciones Cubanas, Obispo No. 527, Apdo. 605, Havana, Cuba. Ed. Ramon Sabadi Rodriguez. Circ: 2,500.

330.9 ESP ISSN 1132-2799
HC387.G3
➤ **REVISTA GALEGA DE ECONOMIA.** Text in Gallegan; Summaries in English. 1992. s-a. EUR 14.42 (effective 2003). bk.rev. bibl. back issues avail. **Document type:** *Magazine, Academic/Scholarly.*
Indexed: GEOBASE.
—CINDOC.
Published by: Universidad de Santiago de Compostela, Servicio de Publicacions, Campus Universitario Sur, Santiago de Compostela, 15782, Spain. TEL 34-981-593500, FAX 34-981-593963, spublic@usc.es, http://www.usc.es/spubl/reveconomia.htm. Pub. J A Diez de Castro. Circ: 500.

330.9 ESP ISSN 0212-7687
HD3525
REVISTA IBEROAMERICANA DE AUTOGESTION Y ACCION COMUNAL. Text in Spanish. 1983. 3/yr.
—CINDOC.
Published by: Universidad Autonoma de Madrid, Instituto Intercultural para la Autogestion y la Accion Comunal, Cantoblanco, Madrid, 28049, Spain. TEL 34-91-3978715, FAX 34-91-3974123, antoniocolomer@uv.es. Ed. Antonio Colomer.

330.9 338.91 BEL ISSN 1245-4060
HD72
REVUE D'ECONOMIE DU DEVELOPPEMENT. Text in French. 1993. q. EUR 75 (effective 2004). charts; stat. **Document type:** *Academic/Scholarly.*
Indexed: BAS, JEL.
Published by: De Boeck Universite, Fond Jean-Paques 4, Louvain-la-Neuve, 1348, Belgium. TEL 32-10-482511, FAX 32-10-482519, info@universite.deboeck.com, http://universite.deboeck.com. **Subscr. to:** Acces S.P.R.L., Fond Jean-Paques 4, Louvain-la-Neuve 1348, Belgium. acces+cde@deboeck.be.

REVUE D'ECONOMIE FINANCIERE. see *BUSINESS AND ECONOMICS—Banking And Finance*

330 FRA ISSN 0154-3229
HD30.22
REVUE D'ECONOMIE INDUSTRIELLE. Text in French. q. EUR 95 domestic; EUR 119.22 foreign (effective 2005).
Description: Theoretical economic analyses and evaluations of different aspects of the industrial production system.
Indexed: ELLIS, JEL, RASB, SCIMP.
—BLDSC (7898.745000), IE, Infotrieve, ingenta.
Published by: Editions Techniques et Economiques, 3 rue Soufflot, Paris, 75005, France. TEL 33-1-55426130, FAX 33-1-55426139, http://www.editecom.com/index_rei.htm.

330.9 FRA ISSN 0180-7307
HT388
➤ **REVUE D'ECONOMIE REGIONALE ET URBAINE.** Text in French; Summaries in English. 1978. 5/yr. EUR 73 domestic; EUR 84 in the European Union; EUR 93 elsewhere (effective 2003). bk.rev. bibl.; illus.; stat. 150 p./no.; back issues avail. **Document type:** *Proceedings, Academic/Scholarly.*
Indexed: IBSS, JEL, PAIS, SSA, SociolAb, WAE&RSA.
—BLDSC (7898.780000), IE, Infotrieve, ingenta.
Published by: Universite de Bordeaux IV (Montesquieu), Institut d'Economie Regionale du Sud-Ouest, Av. Leon Duguit, Bordeaux, 33608, France. TEL 33-5-56848552, FAX 33-5-56848647, lacour@montesquieu.u-bordeaux.fr, http://www.montesquieu-bordeaux.fr/reru. Ed. Claude Lacour. Circ: 1,000.

➤ **REVUE D'INTEGRATION EUROPEENNE/JOURNAL OF EUROPEAN INTEGRATION.** see *POLITICAL SCIENCE—International Relations*

338.9 CIV ISSN 1015-2628
HC1025.A1
REVUE ECONOMIQUE ET FINANCIERE IVOIRIENNE. Short title: R E F A. Text in French. 1978. q. XOF 5,000.
Supersedes (1969-1976): Ivory Coast. Ministere de l'Economie et des Finances. Etudes Economiques et Financieres
Indexed: PAIS.
Published by: (Ministere de l'Economie, des Finances et du Plan), Inter Afrique Presse, 01 BP 3901, Abidjan, Ivory Coast. Circ: 1,500.

330.9 CHN ISSN 1002-7874
RIBEN XUEKAN. Text in Chinese. 1985. bi-m. CNY 48 (effective 2004). **Document type:** *Journal, Academic/Scholarly.*
Formerly: Riben Wenti
Related titles: Online - full text ed.: (from East View Information Services).
Published by: Zhongguo Shehui Kexueyuan, Riben Yanjiusuo, 3, Zhangzizhong Lu, Dongyuan Ribensuo, Beijing, 100007, China. TEL 86-10-64039045, FAX 86-10-64014022, rbxk@isc.cass.net.cn, http://www.cass.net.cn/chinese/s30_rbs/files/xuekan/bjb.htm, http://www.cass.net.cn/chinese/s30_rbs/files/yjsindex.htm. **Dist. in US by:** China Books & Periodicals Inc, 360 Swift Ave., Ste. 48, S San Fran, CA 94080-6220. TEL 415-282-2994; **Dist. by:** China International Book Trading Corp, 35 Chegongzhuang Xilu, Haidian District, PO Box 399, Beijing 100044, China. TEL 86-10-68412045, FAX 86-10-68412023, cibtc@mail.cibtc.com.cn, http://www.cibtc.com.cn.

330 BRA ISSN 0103-3905
HC188.R4
➤ **RIO GRANDE DO SUL, BRAZIL. FUNDACAO DE ECONOMIA E ESTATISTICA. INDICADORES ECONOMICOS F E E.** Text in Portuguese. 1973. q. BRL 75 (effective 2005). charts; stat. back issues avail. **Document type:** *Journal, Academic/Scholarly.*
Formerly (until 1988): Rio Grande so Sul, Brazil. Fundacao de Economia e Estatistica. Indicadores Economicos R S (0102-020X)
Indexed: HAPI, IBSS, PAIS, PSA, SociolAb.
Published by: Fundacao de Economia e Estatistica, Rua Duque de Caxias, 1691, Andar 8, Centro, Porto Alegre, RS 90010-283, Brazil. TEL 55-51-3216-9008, FAX 55-51-3225-0006, revistas@fee.tche.br, diretoria@fee.tche.br, http://www.fee.tche.br. Ed. Maria Heloisa Lenz. Circ: 600.

➤ **RIVERLANDER NOTES.** see *CONSERVATION*

330 ITA
RIVISTA MILANESE DI ECONOMIA. Text in Italian. 1972 (vol.7). q. free. charts; stat.
Formerly (until 1982): Congiuntura Economica Lombarda (0045-8082)
Published by: Cassa di Risparmio delle Provincie Lombarde, Via Monte Di Pieta', 8, Milan, MI 20121, Italy. http://www.cariplo.it.

330.9 USA ISSN 0896-3274
ROCHESTER BUSINESS JOURNAL. Text in English. 1987. w. USD 72 (effective 2005). adv. 48 p./no. 4 cols./p.; back issues avail.; reprints avail. **Document type:** *Newspaper, Trade.* **Description:** Contains local business news.
Formerly (until 1987): Rochester Business Journal and Chamber of Commerce News (0884-0199)
Related titles: CD-ROM ed.; Online - full text ed.: (from O C L C Online Computer Library Center, Inc., ProQuest Information & Learning); Alternate Frequency ed(s).: d.
Indexed: ABIn, BusDate.
Address: 45 East Ave., Ste. 500, Rochester, NY 14604-2292. rbj@rbj.net, http://www.rbj.net. Ed. Paul Ericson. Pub., Adv. contact Susan R Holliday. R&P Suzanne Y Seldes. Circ: 10,000 (paid and free).

330.9 RUS
ROSSIISKAYA EKONOMIKA: PROGNOZY I TENDENTSII. Text in Russian. 1993. m. USD 100 domestic; USD 295 foreign (effective 2000). **Document type:** *Academic/Scholarly.* **Description:** Covers the general state, dynamics and forecasts of key economic indicators. Also chronicles major economic developments.
Indexed: RefZh.
Published by: Vysshaya Shkola Ekonomiki, Tsentr Analiza Dannykh, Myatnitskaya 20, Moscow, 101987, Russian Federation. TEL 7-095-9219192, 7-095-9280821, FAX 7-095-9288622, imiphse@glasnet.ru. Ed., R&P Yelena A Ivanova. Adv. contact Dmitry V Kornienko. Circ: 300 (paid and controlled). **US dist. addr.:** East View Information Services, 3020 Harbor Ln. N., Minneapolis, MN 55447. TEL 612-550-0961.

ROSSIISKII STATISTICHESKII YEZHEGODNIK/RUSSIAN STATISTICAL YEARBOOK. see *BUSINESS AND ECONOMICS—Abstracting, Bibliographies, Statistics*

ROSSIYA (YEAR). see *BUSINESS AND ECONOMICS—Abstracting, Bibliographies, Statistics*

ROSSIYA I STRANY S N G/RUSSIA AND C I S COUNTRIES. (Sodruzhestvo Nezavisimykh Gosudarstv) see *BUSINESS AND ECONOMICS—Abstracting, Bibliographies, Statistics*

ROSSIYA V TSIFRAKH (YEAR); kratkii statisticheskii zbornik. see *BUSINESS AND ECONOMICS—Abstracting, Bibliographies, Statistics*

338.952 GBR
ROUTLEDGE ADVANCES IN INTERNATIONAL POLITICAL ECONOMY. Text in English. 1996. irreg., latest 1999, Oct. price varies. bibl. Index. **Document type:** *Monographic series, Academic/Scholarly.* **Description:** Covers the latest arguments and research in this field including: Liberalist, Realist and Marxist thought the interaction of politics and economics in the global economy states versus transnational corporations.
—BLDSC (8026.466000), ingenta.
Published by: Routledge (Subsidiary of: Taylor & Francis Group), 4 Park Square, Milton Park, Abingdon, Oxon OX14 4RN, United Kingdom. TEL 44-1235-828600, FAX 44-1235-829000, info@routledge.co.uk, http://www.reference.routledge.com/research/polecon/ipe.html, http://www.routledge.co.uk.

RUNDT'S WORLD BUSINESS INTELLIGENCE. see *BUSINESS AND ECONOMICS—International Commerce*

RUSSIA (YEAR). see *BUSINESS AND ECONOMICS—Abstracting, Bibliographies, Statistics*

RUSSIA IN FIGURES (YEAR). see *BUSINESS AND ECONOMICS—Abstracting, Bibliographies, Statistics*

330.947 GBR ISSN 1470-7446
RUSSIA QUARTERLY FORECAST REPORT. Text in English. 1994. 3/yr. GBP 330, USD 495, EUR 450 (effective 2003). **Document type:** *Journal, Trade.* **Description:** Provides a comprehensive assessment of the Russian government, economy and business environment over the next 30 months. Identifies opportunities and reduce risk, and answers key questions facing executives at this time.
Formerly (until 2000): Annual Country Forecast Report. Russia (1353-4726)
Related titles: Online - full text ed.: (from EBSCO Publishing). —CCC.
Published by: Business Monitor International Ltd., Mermaid House, 2 Puddle Dock, Blackfriars, London, EC4V 3DS, United Kingdom. TEL 44-20-72480468, FAX 44-20-72480467, marketing@businessmonitor.com, http://www.businessmonitor.com/russiaforecast.html.

330.947 FIN
RUSSIAN AND BALTIC ECONOMIES; the week in review. Text in English. 1997. w. free. **Document type:** *Newsletter.*
Media: E-mail.
Published by: Bank of Finland, Institute for Economies in Transition (BOFIT), P O Box 160, Helsinki, 00101, Finland. TEL 358-9-183-2268, FAX 358-9-183-2294, bofit@bof.fi, http://www.bof.fi/bofit. Ed. Timo Harell.

330.9 RUS
RUSSIAN ECONOMIC DEVELOPMENTS. Text in English. m. USD 225 in United States. **Document type:** *Academic/Scholarly.*
Published by: Higher School of Economics, Institute of Macroeconomic Research and Forecasting, Pr. Akademiya Sakharova, 12, Moscow, 107078, Russian Federation. TEL 7-095-9236745. **US dist. addr.:** East View Information Services, 3020 Harbor Ln. N., Minneapolis, MN 55447. TEL 612-550-0961.

330.947 FIN ISSN 1455-7355
RUSSIAN ECONOMY; the month in review. Text in English. 1998. m. free. **Document type:** *Newsletter, Corporate.*
Related titles: ♦ Online - full text ed.: B O F I T Russia Review (Online Edition).
Published by: Bank of Finland, Institute for Economies in Transition (BOFIT), P O Box 160, Helsinki, 00101, Finland. TEL 358-9-183-2268, FAX 358-9-183-2294, bofit@bof.fi, http://www.bof.fi/bofit. Ed. Vesa Korhonen.

330.9 RWA
RWANDA. DIRECTION GENERALE DE LA STATISTIQUE. SITUATION ECONOMIQUE DE LA REPUBLIQUE RWANDAISE AU 31 DECEMBRE. Text in French. 1973. irreg.?. USD 26.
Formerly: Rwanda. Direction Generale de la Documentation et de la Statistique Generale. Situation Economique de la Republique Rwandaise au 31 Decembre
Published by: Direction Generale de la Statistique, BP 46, Kigali, Rwanda.

330.9 JPN ISSN 0916-3158
RYUGIN KEIZAI REPORT. Text in Japanese. 1951. q. free. stat.
Formerly (until Oct. 1989): Kin'yu Keizai (0023-1711)
Indexed: AmH&L, HistAb.
Published by: Bank of the Ryukyus Ltd., Research Dept., 1-7-1 Kumo-Ji, Naha-shi, Okinawa-ken 900-0015, Japan. FAX 098-861-5942. Ed. Hirotaka Makino. Circ: 1,700.

330 300 NLD ISSN 0920-4849
S E R BULLETIN. Key Title: SER-bulletin. Text in Dutch. 1960. m. EUR 24.95 (effective 2005). **Document type:** *Bulletin, Trade.* **Description:** News on labor and social and economic matters.
Former titles (until 1981): S E R Informatie- en Documentatiebulletin (0166-9125); Sociaal-Economisch Raad. Informatie- en Documentatie Bulletin (0037-7589)
Media: Duplicated (not offset).
Indexed: KES.
—IE, Infotrieve.
Published by: Sociaal-Economische Raad, Postbus 90405, The Hague, 2509 LK, Netherlands. TEL 31-70-3499499, FAX 31-70-3832535, ser.info@ser.nl, http://www.ser.nl/publicaties/default.asp?desc=publicaties_bulletins.

330.9 USA ISSN 8755-7282
S G P B ALERT. Text in English. irreg., latest vol.38, 1994. USD 7.50. **Document type:** *Bulletin.*
Published by: Southern Growth Policies Board, PO Box 12293, Research Triangle Park, NC 27709. TEL 919-941-5145, FAX 919-941-5594, info@southern.org, http://www.southern.org.

S N G V (YEAR). (Sodruzhestvo Nezavisimykh Gosudarst) see *BUSINESS AND ECONOMICS—Abstracting, Bibliographies, Statistics*

330.9 LCA
ST. LUCIA. STATISTICAL DEPARTMENT. ANNUAL BULLETIN ON C A R I C O M TRADE. (Caribbean Common Market) Text in English. 1984. a. XEC 6. **Document type:** *Bulletin.*
Published by: Statistical Department, New Government Bldg, Block C, 2nd Fl, Conway, Castries, St. Lucia. TEL 758-45-22697, FAX 758-45-31648, TELEX 6394 FORAFF. Ed. Bryan Boxill.

330.9 LCA
ST. LUCIA. STATISTICAL DEPARTMENT. MONTHLY CONSUMER PRICE INDEX. Text in English. 1960. m. free.
Published by: Statistical Department, New Government Bldg, Block C, 2nd Fl, Conway, Castries, St. Lucia. TEL 758-45-22697, FAX 758-45-31648, TELEX 6394 FORAFF. Ed. Bryan Boxill.

330.9 LCA
ST. LUCIA. STATISTICAL DEPARTMENT. QUARTERLY BULLETIN ON C A R I C O M TRADE. (Caribbean Common Market) Text in English. 1984. q. XEC 10. **Document type:** *Bulletin.*
Published by: Statistical Department, New Government Bldg, Block C, 2nd Fl, Conway, Castries, St. Lucia. TEL 758-45-22697, FAX 758-45-31648, TELEX 6394 FORAFF. Ed. Bryan Boxill.

330.9 658 USA
SALARY SURVEY (WASHINGTON). Text in English. 1964. biennial. USD 150 to non-members; free to members (effective 2004). cum.index. back issues avail. **Description:** Covers salaries of business economists and business analysts, including median salary data by industry, geographic area, area of responsibility, size of firm, number supervised, attained education and years of experience. Also provides information on additional gross compensation from primary employment and secondary professional income.
Formerly: Salary Characteristics
Published by: National Association for Business Economics, 1233 20th St, N W, Ste 505, Washington, DC 20036-2304. TEL 202-463-6223, FAX 202-463-6239, nabe@nabe.com, http://www.nabe.com.

SAMARITAN. see *RELIGIONS AND THEOLOGY*

330 IND ISSN 0036-3871
SAMPADA. Text in Hindi. 1952. m. INR 12. bk.rev. stat. index.
Published by: Ashok Prakashan Mandir, 28-11 Shaktinagar, New Delhi, 110 007, India. Ed. Sh Krishn Chander Vidyalankar. Circ: 5,500.

330.9 LKA
SAMVARDHANA. Text in English, Singhalese. irreg. LKR 3.75 per issue.
Address: 27-3 M Housing Scheme, Kiribathgoda, Kelaniya, Sri Lanka.

SAN DIEGO BUSINESS JOURNAL. see *BUSINESS AND ECONOMICS*

330.968 ZAF
SANLAM'S ECONOMIC SURVEY. Text in English. 1993. m.
Related titles: Afrikaans ed.: Sanlam se Ekonomiese Oorsig.
Indexed: ISAP.
Published by: Sanlam, Economic Research Department, PO Box 1, Sanlamhof, 7532, South Africa.

330.9 CAN ISSN 0558-6976
HC117.S3
SASKATCHEWAN ECONOMIC REVIEW. Text in English. 1951. a. free. **Document type:** *Bulletin.*
Related titles: Online - full text ed.
—CISTI.
Published by: Bureau of Statistics, 5th Fl, 2350 Albert St, Regina, SK S4P 4A6, Canada. TEL 306-787-6327, FAX 306-787-6311, http://www.gov.sk.ca/bureau.stats. Circ: 2,000.

330.9 LKA
SATAHANA. Text in Singhalese. m. LKR 70. **Document type:** *Bulletin.* **Description:** Contains articles on the economic and social issues of interest to the Sinhala reading public.
Published by: Central Bank of Sri Lanka, Janadhipathi Mawatha, P O Box 590, Colombo, 1, Sri Lanka. TEL 94-1-847243, FAX 94-1-867383.

330.9538 GBR ISSN 1470-7349
SAUDI ARABIA QUARTERLY FORECAST REPORT. Text in English. 1993. 3/yr. GBP 330, USD 495, EUR 450 (effective 2003). **Document type:** *Journal, Trade.* **Description:** Provides a comprehensive assessment of the Saudi Arabian government, economy and business environment over the next 30 months. Helps to identify opportunities and reduce risk, and answers key questions facing executives at this time.
Formerly (until 2000): Annual Country Forecast Report. Saudi Arabia (0966-8144)
Related titles: Online - full text ed.: (from EBSCO Publishing). —CCC.
Published by: Business Monitor International Ltd., Mermaid House, 2 Puddle Dock, Blackfriars, London, EC4V 3DS, United Kingdom. TEL 44-20-72480468, FAX 44-20-72480467, marketing@businessmonitor.com, http://www.businessmonitor.com/saudiarabiaforecast.html.

330 GBR ISSN 1468-4705
HC415.33.A1
SAUDI ARABIA REPORT. Text in English. 1991. q. GBP 290 (effective 2002). adv. **Document type:** *Newsletter, Trade.* **Description:** Provides an in-depth analysis of political and economic trends in Saudi Arabia.
Formerly (until 1999): Saudi Arabia Quarterly (0960-6483)
Published by: M E E D - Emap Communications (Subsidiary of: Emap Business Communications Ltd.), 33-39 Bowling Green Lane, London, EC1R 0DA, United Kingdom. TEL 44-20-7470-6200, FAX 44-20-7837-8271, customerservice@meed.com, http://www.meed.com. Ed., Pub., R&P Edmund O'Sullivan TEL 44-207-470-6200. Adv. contact Richard Baker.

330.9 DEU ISSN 0720-7018
SCHRIFTENREIHE ZUR INDUSTRIE- UND ENTWICKLUNGSPOLITIK. Text in German. 1970. irreg., latest vol.27, 1985. price varies. **Document type:** *Monographic series, Academic/Scholarly.*
Published by: Duncker und Humblot GmbH, Carl-Heinrich-Becker-Weg 9, Berlin, 12165, Germany. TEL 49-30-7900060, FAX 49-30-79000631, info@duncker-humblot.de, http://www.duncker-humblot.de.

330.9 GBR ISSN 0952-6498
HC257.S4
SCOTTISH ECONOMIC BULLETIN. Text in English. 1971. s-a. GBP 12.50 per issue. **Document type:** *Government.*
Indexed: CREJ, PAIS.
—BLDSC (8206.830000), ingenta.
Published by: (Great Britain. Scottish Office, Industry Department), Stationery Office, 51 Nine Elms Ln, London, SW8 5DA, United Kingdom. TEL 44-20-7873-0011, FAX 44-20-7873-8247, book.orders@theso.co.uk, http://www.national-publishing.co.uk. Ed. John Rigg.

B

330.9 IND
SEARCH; the industrial sourcebook. Text in English. 1998. m. adv. **Document type:** *Magazine, Trade.*
Published by: Tata Infomedia Ltd., 414, Veer Savarkar Marg, Prabhadevi, Mumbai, 400 025, India. TEL 91-22-56666665, FAX 91-22-24302707, tilho@tatainfomedia.com, http://www.tatainfomedia.com. adv.: B&W page INR 18,600, color page INR 23,000; bleed 201 x 281.

330.9 BGR
SECONDARY MARKET OF GOVERNMENT SECURITIES. Text in English. m. USD 84 foreign (effective 2002).
Published by: Bulgarska Narodna Banka/Bulgarian National Bank, 1 Alexander Batterberg Sq, Sofia, 1000, Bulgaria. TEL 359-2-91459, FAX 359-2-9802425, press_office@bnbank.org, http://www.bnb.bg. **Dist. by:** Sofia Books, ul Silivria 16, Sofia 1404, Bulgaria. TEL 359-2-9586257, info@sofiabooks-bg.com, http://www.sofiabooks-bg.com.

330.9 AUT
SELBSTAENDIG IN DER WIRTSCHAFT✶. Text in German. 1947. bi-m. **Document type:** *Journal, Trade.*
Published by: Wirtschaftsverband Oesterreich, Wiedner Hauptstr 57, Vienna, W 1040, Austria. TEL 43-1-501210, FAX 43-1-5012120, info@wirtschaftsverband.at, http://www.wirtschaftsverband.at. Ed. Wolfgang Slawik. Circ: 15,000.

330.9 UZB
SEL'SKOE KHOZYAISTVO UZBEKISTANA. Text in Uzbek. bi-m. USD 129 in United States.
Indexed: RASB.
Address: Ul Volgogradskoi 9-a, Tashkent, 700097, Uzbekistan. TEL 76-59-27, FAX 76-49-18. Ed. Z Uldashev. **US dist. addr.:** East View Information Services, 3020 Harbor Ln. N., Minneapolis, MN 55447. TEL 612-550-0961.

SENEGAL. MINISTERE DE L'ECONOMIE, DES FINANCES ET DU PLAN. BANQUE DE DONNEES ECONOMIQUES ET FINANCIERES. see *BUSINESS AND ECONOMICS—Abstracting, Bibliographies, Statistics*

SENEGAL. MINISTERE DE L'ECONOMIE, DES FINANCES ET DU PLAN. BULLETIN ECONOMIQUE ET STATISTIQUE. see *BUSINESS AND ECONOMICS—Abstracting, Bibliographies, Statistics*

330.21 SEN ISSN 0850-1009
SENEGAL. MINISTERE DE L'ECONOMIE, DES FINANCES ET DU PLAN. COMPTES ECONOMIQUES. Text in French. 1959. a. XOF 5,000; XOF 7,000 foreign (effective 1998). **Document type:** *Government.*
Formerly: Senegal. Ministere de l'Economie et des Finances. Comptes Economiques du Senegal
Published by: Ministere de l'Economie des Finances et du Plan, Direction de la Prevision et de la Statistique, BP 116, Dakar, Senegal. TEL 221-21-03-01. Pub. Ibrahima Sarr.

SENEGAL. MINISTERE DE L'ECONOMIE, DES FINANCES ET DU PLAN. DOSSIERS DOCUMENTAIRES. see *BUSINESS AND ECONOMICS—Abstracting, Bibliographies, Statistics*

SENEGAL. MINISTERE DE L'ECONOMIE, DES FINANCES ET DU PLAN. NOTE DE CONJONCTURE. see *BUSINESS AND ECONOMICS—Abstracting, Bibliographies, Statistics*

SENEGAL. MINISTERE DE L'ECONOMIE, DES FINANCES ET DU PLAN. RAPPORT SUR LES PERSPECTIVES ECONOMIQUES. see *BUSINESS AND ECONOMICS—Abstracting, Bibliographies, Statistics*

▼ new title ➤ refereed ✶ unverified ♦ full entry avail.

SENEGAL. MINISTERE DE L'ECONOMIE, DES FINANCES ET DU PLAN. SITUATION ECONOMIQUE REGIONALE. see *BUSINESS AND ECONOMICS—Abstracting, Bibliographies, Statistics*

SENEGAL. MINISTERE DE L'ECONOMIE, DES FINANCES ET DU PLAN. TABLEAU DE BORD DE L'ECONOMIE SENEGALAISE. see *BUSINESS AND ECONOMICS— Abstracting, Bibliographies, Statistics*

SENTINEL INVESTMENT LETTER. see *BUSINESS AND ECONOMICS—Investments*

381   GBR
➤ **SERIES IN INTERNATIONAL BUSINESS AND ECONOMICS.** Short title: S I B E. Text in English. 1994. irreg., latest vol.20, 2001. price varies. back issues avail. **Document type:** *Monographic series, Academic/Scholarly.* **Description:** Designed to encourage research and scholarly publications in this, one of the most rapidly growing areas of business studies.
Published by: Elsevier Ltd., Books Division (Subsidiary of: Elsevier Science & Technology), Kidlington, PO Box 800, Oxford, OX2 1DX, United Kingdom. TEL 44-1865-843000, FAX 44-1865-843410. Ed. Khosrow Fatemi TEL 760-768-5520. **Subscr. to:** Elsevier BV, PO Box 211, Amsterdam 1000 AE, Netherlands. TEL 31-20-485-3757, FAX 31-20-485-3432, nlinfo-f@elsevier.nl, http://www.elsevier.nl.

330.9   HKG
SHENZHEN TODAY. Text in English. 1990. irreg. HKD 30, USD 8 per issue. **Description:** Introduces the investment environment of Shenzhen Economic Special Zone, a gateway to China from Hong Kong.
Published by: Economic Information & Agency, 342 Hennessy Rd 10th Fl, 10 th Fl, Wanchai, Hong Kong. TEL 852-573-8217, FAX 852-838-8304. Ed. Li Yang.

SHIJIE JINGJI YANJIU/WORLD ECONOMY RESEARCH. see *BUSINESS AND ECONOMICS—Macroeconomics*

SHIJIE JINGJIXUE/WORLD ECONOMICS. see *BUSINESS AND ECONOMICS—Macroeconomics*

330.9   SLE
SIERRA LEONE OUTLOOK∗ . Text in English. 6/yr. adv. **Document type:** *Academic/Scholarly.*
Published by: United Methodist Church, c/o Council of Churches in Sierra Leone, 4A King Harman Rd, Brookfields, PO Box 404, Freetown, Sierra Leone. Ed. S A Warratie. Circ: 1,300.

388   USA   ISSN 0080-9756
SINOPSIS DUN - BRAZIL. Text in Portuguese. a.
Published by: Dun's Marketing Services (Subsidiary of: Dun & Bradstreet, Inc.), 3 Sylvan Way, Parsippany, NJ 07054-3896. TEL 201-455-0900.

332   ARG   ISSN 0037-5799
HC171
SINTESIS INFORMATIVA ECONOMICA Y FINANCIERA. Text in Spanish. 1964. m. free. charts; stat.
Related titles: Microform ed.
Published by: Banco de la Provincia de Buenos Aires, San Martin, 137, Capital Federal, Buenos Aires 1004, Argentina. Ed. Armando V Rey. Circ: 3,000.

330.1   CIV   ISSN 0080-9829
SITUATION ECONOMIQUE DE COTE D'IVOIRE∗ . Text in French. 1960. irreg.
Published by: Service de la Statistique, BP 222, Abidjan, Ivory Coast.

330.9   FRA
SITUATION ECONOMIQUE ET PERSPECTIVES D'AVENIR. Text in French. 1962. irreg.
Published by: Chambre de Commerce et d'Industrie de Pau, 21 rue Louis Barthou, Pau, 64000, France. Circ: 6,000.

SITUATION ECONOMIQUE ET SOCIALE DU SENEGAL. see *BUSINESS AND ECONOMICS—Abstracting, Bibliographies, Statistics*

330.9   USA
SKI TOUR OPERATORS ASSOCIATION ANNUAL BUSINESS SURVEY (YEAR). Text in English. a., latest 1988. USD 25 (effective 2001). **Document type:** *Trade.*
Published by: University of Colorado, Business Research Division, Campus Box 420, Boulder, CO 80309-0420. TEL 303-492-8227, FAX 303-492-3620.

338.6   USA   ISSN 1080-0816
SMALL BUSINESS ECONOMIC TRENDS. Text in English. 1974. q. USD 30. stat.
Former titles (until 1993): Quarterly Economic Report for Small Business (1080-0913); (until 1986): N F I B Quarterly Economic Report for Small Business (0362-3548); (until 1975): National Federation of Independent Business. Quarterly Economic Report (0094-7695).
Related titles: Online - full text ed.: (from O C L C Online Computer Library Center, Inc., ProQuest Information & Learning).

Indexed: ABIn, BPIA, SRI.
Published by: National Federation of Independent Business, 53 Century Blvd, Ste 205, Nashville, TN 37214. comments@nfibonline.com, http://www.nfibonline.com/.

330.9   CHL   ISSN 1020-5160
SOCIAL PANORAMA OF LATIN AMERICA (YEAR). Text in English. 1995. a.
Related titles: ◆ Spanish ed.: Panorama Social de America Latina (Year). ISSN 1020-5152.
Published by: Comision Economica para America Latina y el Chile/Economic Commission for Latin America and the Caribbean, Casilla 179-D, Santiago, Chile.

330.9   FRA   ISSN 1274-3356
SOCIETAL; analyse mensuelle des realites economiques et sociales. Text in French. 1996. 11/yr. EUR 43 domestic to individuals; EUR 57.18 foreign to individuals; EUR 50 domestic to institutions; EUR 61.26 foreign to institutions (effective 2005). charts. **Document type:** *Journal, Academic/Scholarly.* **Description:** Covers sociopolitical issues in Europe.
Formed by the merger of (1978-1996): Analyses de la S E D E I S (0399-1245); Chroniques Economiques (1251-0998); Which was formerly (until 1994): Chroniques de la S.E.D.E.I.S. (1164-8759); (until 1991): Chroniques d'Actualite de la S E D E I S (0396-437X); (until 1975): Chroniques d'Actualites (0009-613X); (until 1966): Bulletin Sedeis. Chroniques d'Actualite (1140-8642); (until 1959): Sedeis. Chroniques d'Actualite (1140-8634); (until 1955): Sedeis Notes et Informations (1140-8626)
Related titles: Online - full text ed.: (from ProQuest Information & Learning).
Indexed: ABIn, ELLIS, PAIS.
—CCC.
Published by: (Societe d'Etudes et de Documentation Economiques Industrielles et Sociales), Presses Universitaires de France, 6 Avenue Reille, Paris, 75685 Cedex 14, France. TEL 33-1-58103100, FAX 33-1-58103182, revues@puf.com, http://www.societal.fr, http://www.puf.com.

330.9 301   GBR   ISSN 1475-1461
▼ ➤ **SOCIO-ECONOMIC REVIEW.** Text in English. 2003 (Jan.). 3/yr. GBP 153, USD 275, EUR 230 to institutions; GBP 161, USD 290, EUR 242 combined subscription to institutions print & online eds. (effective 2006). **Document type:** *Journal, Academic/Scholarly.* **Description:** Aims to encourage work on the relationship between society, economy, institutions and markets, moral commitments and the rational pursuit of self-interest.
Related titles: Online - full text ed.: ISSN 1475-147X. 2003. GBP 128, USD 199 to institutions (effective 2004) (from EBSCO Publishing, Gale Group, HighWire Press, IngentaConnect, O C L C Online Computer Library Center, Inc., Oxford University Press Online Journals, Swets Information Services).
Indexed: IPSA, JEL, SociolAb.
—BLDSC (8319.559700), IE. CCC.
Published by: (Society for the Advancement of Socio-Economics USA), Oxford University Press, Great Clarendon St, Oxford, OX2 6DP, United Kingdom. TEL 44-1865-556767, FAX 44-1865-556646, jnl.orders@oup.co.uk, http:// ser.oxfordjournals.org/, http://www.oxfordjournals.org/. Eds. Alexander Hicks, David Marsden.

330.9   IND
SOCIO-ECONOMIC REVIEW OF PUNJAB. Text in English. a. stat.
Published by: Economic and Statistical Organisation, Chandigarh, Haryana, India.

330.9 338   GBR
SOMERSET BUSINESS; the magazine for the Somerset business community. Text in English. bi-m. GBP 2 newsstand/cover. bk.rev.; software rev. stat.; tr.lit. back issues avail. **Document type:** *Trade.* **Description:** Includes letters, appointments, and articles relevant to local business. Features updates on finance, personnel, the workplace, IT internet, business links, as well as a venue check.
Formerly: Somerset Business News
Published by: (Somerset Training & Enterprise Council), Somerset Business Community Business Services, East Reach House, Taunton, Somers TA1 3EN, United Kingdom. TEL 44-1823-321421, FAX 44-1823-335202, sbc@somerset.tec.org.uk. Ed., R&P Sandra Manser. Pub. Julie Spencer Cingor. Circ: 17,000 (controlled).

SOTSIAL'NO-EKONOMICHESKOE POLOZHENIE DAL'NEVOSTOCHNOGO FEDERAL'NOGO OKRUGA/SOCIO-ECONOMIC SITUATION OF THE FAR EASTERN FEDERAL REGION. see *BUSINESS AND ECONOMICS—Abstracting, Bibliographies, Statistics*

SOTSIAL'NO-EKONOMICHESKOE POLOZHENIE PRIVOLZHSKOGO FEDERAL'NOGO OKRUGA/SOCIO-ECONOMIC SITUATION OF THE VOLGA FEDERAL REGION. see *BUSINESS AND ECONOMICS—Abstracting, Bibliographies, Statistics*

SOTSIAL'NO-EKONOMICHESKOE POLOZHENIE ROSSII/SOCIAL AND ECONOMIC SITUATION IN RUSSIA; ekonomicheskii obzor. see *BUSINESS AND ECONOMICS—Abstracting, Bibliographies, Statistics*

SOTSIAL'NO-EKONOMICHESKOE POLOZHENIE SEVERO-ZAPADNOGO FEDERAL'NOGO OKRUGA/SOCIO-ECONOMIC SITUATION OF THE NORTH-WESTERN FEDERAL REGION. see *BUSINESS AND ECONOMICS—Abstracting, Bibliographies, Statistics*

SOTSIAL'NO-EKONOMICHESKOE POLOZHENIE SIBIRSKOGO FEDERAL'NOGO OKRUGA/SOCIO-ECONOMIC SITUATION OF THE SIBERIAN FEDERAL REGION. see *BUSINESS AND ECONOMICS—Abstracting, Bibliographies, Statistics*

SOTSIAL'NO-EKONOMICHESKOE POLOZHENIE TSENTRAL'NOGO FEDERAL'NOGO OKRUGA/SOCIO-ECONOMIC SITUATION OF THE CENTRAL FEDERAL REGION. see *BUSINESS AND ECONOMICS—Abstracting, Bibliographies, Statistics*

SOTSIAL'NO-EKONOMICHESKOE POLOZHENIE URAL'SKOGO FEDERAL'NOGO OKRUGA/SOCIO-ECONOMIC SITUATION OF THE URAL FEDERAL REGION. see *BUSINESS AND ECONOMICS—Abstracting, Bibliographies, Statistics*

SOTSIAL'NO-EKONOMICHESKOE POLOZHENIE YUZHNOGO FEDERAL'NOGO OKRUGA/SOCIO-ECONOMIC SITUATION OF THE SOUTHERN FEDERAL REGION. see *BUSINESS AND ECONOMICS—Abstracting, Bibliographies, Statistics*

330.9   USA
SOUND OF THE ECONOMY. Text in English. m. **Document type:** *Trade.*
Media: Audio cassette/tape.
Published by: D R I - McGraw-Hill, 24 Hartwell Ave, Lexington, MA 02173. TEL 617-863-5100, FAX 617-860-6332, TELEX 200 284. Ed. Cynthia Latta.

330.9   USA   ISSN 1054-8890
SOURCEMEX; economic and political news and analysis on Mexico. Text in English. 1990. w. USD 95 to individuals; USD 375 to institutions (effective 2005). back issues avail. **Document type:** *Bulletin, Consumer.* **Description:** Covers Mexican political and economic affairs, including private investment, public policy, petroleum, agriculture, trade, environment and social welfare.
Media: Online - full text (from Factiva, Gale Group, The Dialog Corporation). **Related titles:** CD-ROM ed.: (from National Information Services Corp. (N I S C)).
Published by: Latin America Database, University Of New Mexico, Latin American And Iberian Institute, MSC 02 1690, 1 University of New Mexico, Albuquerque, NM 87131-0001. TEL 505-277-6839, FAX 505-277-5989, info@ladb.unm.edu, http://ladb.unm.edu/sourcemex/.

330.9   ZAF
SOUTH AFRICA (YEAR). Text in English. 1969. a. ZAR 6 (effective 1994). stat.
Formerly: South Africa Foundation. Information Digest (Year)
Published by: South Africa Foundation, PO Box 7006, Johannesburg, 2000, South Africa. TEL 27-12-726-6105, FAX 27-12-726-4705. Circ: 40,000.

SOUTH AFRICA. COMMISSIONER FOR CUSTOMS AND EXCISE. FOREIGN TRADE STATISTICS. see *BUSINESS AND ECONOMICS—Abstracting, Bibliographies, Statistics*

SOUTH AFRICA. COMMISSIONER FOR CUSTOMS AND EXCISE. MONTHLY ABSTRACT OF TRADE STATISTICS. see *BUSINESS AND ECONOMICS—Abstracting, Bibliographies, Statistics*

320.9   ZAF   ISSN 1021-1780
SOUTH AFRICA FOUNDATION REVIEW. Text in English. bi-m. free. illus. **Description:** Attempts to foster a responsible and sophisticated reaction to the international pressures on South Africa by analyzing and then explaining the nature, sources and purposes of these pressures.
Formerly: South Africa Foundation News (1016-8486)
Published by: South Africa Foundation, PO Box 7006, Johannesburg, 2000, South Africa. TEL 27-12-726-6105, FAX 27-12-726-4705. Ed. G L M Lewis. Circ: 15,000.

330.968   GBR   ISSN 1474-1482
SOUTH AFRICA QUARTERLY FORECAST REPORT. Text in English. 1995. 3/yr. GBP 330, USD 495, EUR 450 (effective 2003). **Document type:** *Journal, Trade.* **Description:** Provides a comprehensive assessment of the South African government, economy and business environment. Helps to identify opportunities and reduce risk, and answers key questions facing executives at this time.
Formerly (until 2001): Annual Country Forecast Report. South Africa (1359-7167)
Related titles: CD-ROM ed.: GBP 410, USD 675 (effective 2000); Online - full text ed.: (from EBSCO Publishing).
—CCC.
Published by: Business Monitor International Ltd., Mermaid House, 2 Puddle Dock, Blackfriars, London, EC4V 3DS, United Kingdom. TEL 44-20-72480468, FAX 44-20-72480467, marketing@businessmonitor.com, http:// www.businessmonitor.com.

SOUTH AFRICA. STATISTICS SOUTH AFRICA. AGRICULTURAL SURVEY. see AGRICULTURE—Abstracting, Bibliographies, Statistics

SOUTH AFRICA. STATISTICS SOUTH AFRICA. BIRTHS. see POPULATION STUDIES—Abstracting, Bibliographies, Statistics

SOUTH AFRICA. STATISTICS SOUTH AFRICA. CENSUS OF MANUFACTURING - (YEAR) PRINCIPAL STATISTICS ON A REGIONAL BASIS. see BUSINESS AND ECONOMICS—Abstracting, Bibliographies, Statistics

SOUTH AFRICA. STATISTICS SOUTH AFRICA. CENSUS OF MANUFACTURING - MATERIALS PURCHASED AND MANUFACTURES SOLD. see BUSINESS AND ECONOMICS—Abstracting, Bibliographies, Statistics

SOUTH AFRICA. STATISTICS SOUTH AFRICA. CENSUS OF MANUFACTURING - PRINCIPAL STATISTICS ON A REGIONAL BASIS PART-I. see BUSINESS AND ECONOMICS—Abstracting, Bibliographies, Statistics

SOUTH AFRICA. STATISTICS SOUTH AFRICA. CENSUS OF SOCIAL, RECREATIONAL AND PERSONAL SERVICES - MOTION PICTURE AND VIDEO PRODUCTION. see MOTION PICTURES—Abstracting, Bibliographies, Statistics

SOUTH AFRICA. STATISTICS SOUTH AFRICA. CENSUS OF SOCIAL, RECREATIONAL AND PERSONAL SERVICES - WELFARE ORGANISATIONS. see SOCIAL SERVICES AND WELFARE—Abstracting, Bibliographies, Statistics

SOUTH AFRICA. STATISTICS SOUTH AFRICA. CENSUS OF TRANSPORT AND ALLIED SERVICES. see TRANSPORTATION—Abstracting, Bibliographies, Statistics

SOUTH AFRICA. STATISTICS SOUTH AFRICA. DEMOGRAPHIC STATISTICS. see POPULATION STUDIES—Abstracting, Bibliographies, Statistics

SOUTH AFRICA. STATISTICS SOUTH AFRICA. FINAL SOCIAL ACCOUNTING MATRIX FOR SOUTH AFRICA. see PUBLIC ADMINISTRATION—Abstracting, Bibliographies, Statistics

SOUTH AFRICA. STATISTICS SOUTH AFRICA. FINANCIAL STATISTICS OF LOCAL GOVERNMENTS. see PUBLIC ADMINISTRATION—Abstracting, Bibliographies, Statistics

SOUTH AFRICA. STATISTICS SOUTH AFRICA. INPUT OUTPUT TABLES. see BUSINESS AND ECONOMICS—Abstracting, Bibliographies, Statistics

SOUTH AFRICA. STATISTICS SOUTH AFRICA. LOCAL GOVERNMENT STATISTICS. see PUBLIC ADMINISTRATION—Abstracting, Bibliographies, Statistics

SOUTH AFRICA. STATISTICS SOUTH AFRICA. MANPOWER SURVEY (OCCUPATIONAL INFORMATION). see BUSINESS AND ECONOMICS—Abstracting, Bibliographies, Statistics

SOUTH AFRICA. STATISTICS SOUTH AFRICA. POPULATION CENSUS (YEAR). see POPULATION STUDIES—Abstracting, Bibliographies, Statistics

SOUTH AFRICA. STATISTICS SOUTH AFRICA. POPULATION CENSUS, (YEAR). ECONOMIC CHARACTERISTICS OF POPULATION. see POPULATION STUDIES—Abstracting, Bibliographies, Statistics

SOUTH AFRICA. STATISTICS SOUTH AFRICA. POPULATION CENSUS, (YEAR). SELECTED STATISTICAL REGIONS. see POPULATION STUDIES—Abstracting, Bibliographies, Statistics

SOUTH AFRICA. STATISTICS SOUTH AFRICA. POPULATION CENSUS, (YEAR). SUMMARISED RESULTS AFTER ADJUSTMENT FOR UNDERCOUNT. see POPULATION STUDIES—Abstracting, Bibliographies, Statistics

SOUTH AFRICA. STATISTICS SOUTH AFRICA. PROVINCIAL STATISTICS PART 1 - WESTERN CAPE. see STATISTICS

SOUTH AFRICA. STATISTICS SOUTH AFRICA. PROVINCIAL STATISTICS PART 10 - REPUBLIC OF SOUTH AFRICA. see STATISTICS

SOUTH AFRICA. STATISTICS SOUTH AFRICA. PROVINCIAL STATISTICS PART 2 - EASTERN CAPE. see STATISTICS

SOUTH AFRICA. STATISTICS SOUTH AFRICA. PROVINCIAL STATISTICS PART 3 - NORTHERN CAPE. see STATISTICS

SOUTH AFRICA. STATISTICS SOUTH AFRICA. PROVINCIAL STATISTICS PART 4 - ORANGE FREE STATE. see STATISTICS

SOUTH AFRICA. STATISTICS SOUTH AFRICA. PROVINCIAL STATISTICS PART 5 - KWAZULU - NATAL. see STATISTICS

SOUTH AFRICA. STATISTICS SOUTH AFRICA. PROVINCIAL STATISTICS PART 6 - NORTH-WEST. see STATISTICS

SOUTH AFRICA. STATISTICS SOUTH AFRICA. PROVINCIAL STATISTICS PART 7 - PRETORIA - WITWATERSRAND - VEREENIGING. see STATISTICS

SOUTH AFRICA. STATISTICS SOUTH AFRICA. PROVINCIAL STATISTICS PART 8 - EASTERN TRANSVAAL. see STATISTICS

SOUTH AFRICA. STATISTICS SOUTH AFRICA. PROVINCIAL STATISTICS PART 9 - NORTHERN TRANSVAAL. see STATISTICS

SOUTH AFRICA. STATISTICS SOUTH AFRICA. STATISTICAL RELEASE. see STATISTICS

SOUTH AFRICA. STATISTICS SOUTH AFRICA. STATISTICAL RELEASE. AGRICULTURAL SURVEY. see AGRICULTURE—Abstracting, Bibliographies, Statistics

SOUTH AFRICA. STATISTICS SOUTH AFRICA. STATISTICAL RELEASE. BUILDING INDUSTRY ADVISORY COUNCIL CONTRACT PRICE ADJUSTMENT PROVISIONS - WORKGROUP INDICES (HAYLETT). see BUILDING AND CONSTRUCTION—Abstracting, Bibliographies, Statistics

SOUTH AFRICA. STATISTICS SOUTH AFRICA. STATISTICAL RELEASE. BUILDING STATISTICS - PRIVATE SECTOR. see BUILDING AND CONSTRUCTION—Abstracting, Bibliographies, Statistics

SOUTH AFRICA. STATISTICS SOUTH AFRICA. STATISTICAL RELEASE. CENSUS OF CONSTRUCTION. see BUILDING AND CONSTRUCTION—Abstracting, Bibliographies, Statistics

SOUTH AFRICA. STATISTICS SOUTH AFRICA. STATISTICAL RELEASE. CENSUS OF ELECTRICITY, GAS AND STEAM. see ENERGY—Abstracting, Bibliographies, Statistics

SOUTH AFRICA. STATISTICS SOUTH AFRICA. STATISTICAL RELEASE. CENSUS OF LETTING OF OWN FIXED PROPERTY (YEAR). see REAL ESTATE—Abstracting, Bibliographies, Statistics

SOUTH AFRICA. STATISTICS SOUTH AFRICA. STATISTICAL RELEASE. CENSUS OF MINING. see MINES AND MINING INDUSTRY—Abstracting, Bibliographies, Statistics

SOUTH AFRICA. STATISTICS SOUTH AFRICA. STATISTICAL RELEASE. CENSUS OF TRANSPORT AND ALLIED SERVICES. see TRANSPORTATION—Abstracting, Bibliographies, Statistics

SOUTH AFRICA. STATISTICS SOUTH AFRICA. STATISTICAL RELEASE. CENTRAL GOVERNMENT: REVENUE OF THE STATE REVENUE AND OTHER REVENUE ACCOUNTS. see PUBLIC ADMINISTRATION—Abstracting, Bibliographies, Statistics

SOUTH AFRICA. STATISTICS SOUTH AFRICA. STATISTICAL RELEASE. CONSUMER PRICE INDEX. see BUSINESS AND ECONOMICS—Abstracting, Bibliographies, Statistics

SOUTH AFRICA. STATISTICS SOUTH AFRICA. STATISTICAL RELEASE. CONSUMER PRICE INDEX BASE. see BUSINESS AND ECONOMICS—Abstracting, Bibliographies, Statistics

SOUTH AFRICA. STATISTICS SOUTH AFRICA. STATISTICAL RELEASE. CONSUMER PRICE INDEX WEIGHTS. see BUSINESS AND ECONOMICS—Abstracting, Bibliographies, Statistics

SOUTH AFRICA. STATISTICS SOUTH AFRICA. STATISTICAL RELEASE. ELECTRICITY AVAILABLE FOR DISTRIBUTION. see ENERGY—Abstracting, Bibliographies, Statistics

SOUTH AFRICA. STATISTICS SOUTH AFRICA. STATISTICAL RELEASE. EXPENDITURE BY THE GENERAL GOVERNMENT. see PUBLIC ADMINISTRATION—Abstracting, Bibliographies, Statistics

SOUTH AFRICA. STATISTICS SOUTH AFRICA. STATISTICAL RELEASE. EXPENDITURE OF THE CENTRAL GOVERNMENT. see PUBLIC ADMINISTRATION—Abstracting, Bibliographies, Statistics

SOUTH AFRICA. STATISTICS SOUTH AFRICA. STATISTICAL RELEASE. FINANCIAL STATISTICS OF EXTRABUDGETARY ACCOUNTS AND FUNDS. see BUSINESS AND ECONOMICS—Abstracting, Bibliographies, Statistics

SOUTH AFRICA. STATISTICS SOUTH AFRICA. STATISTICAL RELEASE. FINANCIAL STATISTICS OF LOCAL AUTHORITIES AND REGIONAL SERVICES COUNCILS AND JOINT SERVICES BOARDS. see PUBLIC ADMINISTRATION—Abstracting, Bibliographies, Statistics

SOUTH AFRICA. STATISTICS SOUTH AFRICA. STATISTICAL RELEASE. FINANCIAL STATISTICS OF LOCAL GOVERNMENTS (YEAR). see PUBLIC ADMINISTRATION—Abstracting, Bibliographies, Statistics

SOUTH AFRICA. STATISTICS SOUTH AFRICA. STATISTICAL RELEASE. GROSS DOMESTIC PRODUCT AT CONSTANT PRICES. see BUSINESS AND ECONOMICS—Abstracting, Bibliographies, Statistics

SOUTH AFRICA. STATISTICS SOUTH AFRICA. STATISTICAL RELEASE. GROSS GEOGRAPHIC PRODUCT AT FACTOR INCOMES. see BUSINESS AND ECONOMICS—Abstracting, Bibliographies, Statistics

SOUTH AFRICA. STATISTICS SOUTH AFRICA. STATISTICAL RELEASE. HOUSEHOLD EXPENDITURE. see BUSINESS AND ECONOMICS—Abstracting, Bibliographies, Statistics

SOUTH AFRICA. STATISTICS SOUTH AFRICA. STATISTICAL RELEASE. MANUFACTURING - CAPITAL EXPENDITURE ON NEW ASSETS. see BUSINESS AND ECONOMICS—Abstracting, Bibliographies, Statistics

SOUTH AFRICA. STATISTICS SOUTH AFRICA. STATISTICAL RELEASE. MANUFACTURING - FINANCIAL STATISTICS. see BUSINESS AND ECONOMICS—Abstracting, Bibliographies, Statistics

SOUTH AFRICA. STATISTICS SOUTH AFRICA. STATISTICAL RELEASE. MANUFACTURING - FINANCIAL STATISTICS (QUARTERLY). see BUSINESS AND ECONOMICS—Abstracting, Bibliographies, Statistics

SOUTH AFRICA. STATISTICS SOUTH AFRICA. STATISTICAL RELEASE. MANUFACTURING PRODUCTION. see BUSINESS AND ECONOMICS—Abstracting, Bibliographies, Statistics

SOUTH AFRICA. STATISTICS SOUTH AFRICA. STATISTICAL RELEASE. MINING - FINANCIAL STATISTICS. see MINES AND MINING INDUSTRY—Abstracting, Bibliographies, Statistics

SOUTH AFRICA. STATISTICS SOUTH AFRICA. STATISTICAL RELEASE. MINING - PRODUCTION AND SALES. see MINES AND MINING INDUSTRY—Abstracting, Bibliographies, Statistics

SOUTH AFRICA. STATISTICS SOUTH AFRICA. STATISTICAL RELEASE. PRODUCTION PRICE INDEX. see BUSINESS AND ECONOMICS—Abstracting, Bibliographies, Statistics

SOUTH AFRICA. STATISTICS SOUTH AFRICA. STATISTICAL RELEASE. PRODUCTION PRICE INDEX BASE (YEAR). see BUSINESS AND ECONOMICS—Abstracting, Bibliographies, Statistics

SOUTH AFRICA. STATISTICS SOUTH AFRICA. STATISTICAL RELEASE. PUBLIC ROAD TRANSPORT (NON-GOVERNMENTAL INSTITUTIONS) OF PASSENGERS AND GOODS - FINANCIAL STATISTICS. see TRANSPORTATION—Abstracting, Bibliographies, Statistics

SOUTH AFRICA. STATISTICS SOUTH AFRICA. STATISTICAL RELEASE. REGIONAL MID-YEAR ESTIMATES - REPUBLIC OF SOUTH AFRICA. see POPULATION STUDIES—Abstracting, Bibliographies, Statistics

SOUTH AFRICA. STATISTICS SOUTH AFRICA. STATISTICAL RELEASE. RETAIL TRADE - FINANCIAL STATISTICS. see BUSINESS AND ECONOMICS—Abstracting, Bibliographies, Statistics

SOUTH AFRICA. STATISTICS SOUTH AFRICA. STATISTICAL RELEASE. RETAIL TRADE SALES. see BUSINESS AND ECONOMICS—Abstracting, Bibliographies, Statistics

SOUTH AFRICA. STATISTICS SOUTH AFRICA. STATISTICAL RELEASE. RETAIL TRADE SALES (FINAL). see BUSINESS AND ECONOMICS—Abstracting, Bibliographies, Statistics

SOUTH AFRICA. STATISTICS SOUTH AFRICA. STATISTICAL RELEASE. RETAIL TRADE SALES - PRELIMINARY. see BUSINESS AND ECONOMICS—Abstracting, Bibliographies, Statistics

SOUTH AFRICA. STATISTICS SOUTH AFRICA. STATISTICAL RELEASE. TOTAL VALUE OF WHOLESALE TRADE SALES - EXPECTED SALES. see BUSINESS AND ECONOMICS—Abstracting, Bibliographies, Statistics

SOUTH AFRICA. STATISTICS SOUTH AFRICA. STATISTICAL RELEASE. TOURISM AND IMMIGRATION. see POPULATION STUDIES—Abstracting, Bibliographies, Statistics

B

SOUTH AFRICA. STATISTICS SOUTH AFRICA. STATISTICAL RELEASE. TRANSPORT OF GOODS BY ROAD AND RAIL. see *TRANSPORTATION—Abstracting, Bibliographies, Statistics*

SOUTH AFRICA. STATISTICS SOUTH AFRICA. STATISTICAL RELEASE. WHOLESALE TRADE SALES. see *BUSINESS AND ECONOMICS—Abstracting, Bibliographies, Statistics*

SOUTH AFRICA. STATISTICS SOUTH AFRICA. TOURISM AND MIGRATION. see *POPULATION STUDIES—Abstracting, Bibliographies, Statistics*

SOUTH AFRICAN LABOUR STATISTICS. see *BUSINESS AND ECONOMICS—Abstracting, Bibliographies, Statistics*

332 ZAF ISSN 0081-2528
SOUTH AFRICAN RESERVE BANK. ANNUAL ECONOMIC REPORT/SUID-AFRIKAANSE RESERWEBANK. JAARLIKSE EKONOMIESE VERSLAG. Text in English. 1961. a. ZAR 25 (effective 1999). charts; stat. **Document type:** *Corporate.*
Related titles: Afrikaans ed.: Jaarlikse Ekonomiese Verslag - Suid-Afrikaanse Reserwebank. ISSN 1026-8731.
Published by: South African Reserve Bank/Suid-Afrikaanse Reserwebank, PO Box 427, Pretoria, 0001, South Africa. TEL 27-12-313-3911, FAX 27-12-313-3197, info@resbank.co.za, info@gwisel.resbank.co.za, http://www.resbank.co.za. Ed. B L de Jager. R&P B P Pretorius TEL 27-12-3133690. Circ: 2,000.

SOUTH AFRICAN STATISTICS. see *STATISTICS*

SOUTH AMERICA, CENTRAL AMERICA AND THE CARIBBEAN (YEAR). see *POLITICAL SCIENCE*

330.9 IND ISSN 1391-5614
HC430.6.A5
➤ **SOUTH ASIA ECONOMIC JOURNAL.** Text in English. 2000. s-a. USD 140, GBP 80 to institutions; USD 146, GBP 83 combined subscription to institutions print & online eds. (effective 2006). back issues avail. **Document type:** *Journal, Academic/Scholarly.* **Description:** Devoted to economic analysis and policy options aimed at promoting cooperation among the countries comprising South Asia.
Related titles: Online - full text ed.: USD 138, GBP 79 to institutions (effective 2006) (from EBSCO Publishing, Sage Publications, Inc.).
Indexed: JEL.
—BLDSC (8348.567000), IE.
Published by: Sage Publications India Pvt. Ltd. (Subsidiary of: Sage Publications, Inc.), M-32 Market, Greater Kailash-I, PO Box 4215, New Delhi, 110 048, India. TEL 91-11-6444958, FAX 91-11-6472426, editors@indiasage.com, http://www.sagepub.co.uk/journal.aspx?pid=105784, http://www.indiasage.com/. Eds. Nagesh Kumar, Saman Kelegama. **Subscr. to:** Sage Publications, Inc., 2455 Teller Rd, Thousand Oaks, CA 91320. TEL 805-499-0721, FAX 805-499-0871, journals@sagepub.com; Sage Publications Ltd., 1 Oliver's Yard, 55 City Rd, London EC1 1SP, United Kingdom. TEL 44-20-73740645, FAX 44-20-73748741, subscription@sagepub.co.uk.

330 USA ISSN 0038-304X
HC107.S7
SOUTH CAROLINA ECONOMIC INDICATORS. Text in English. 1968. m. free. charts; stat. **Document type:** *Academic/Scholarly.* **Description:** Surveys economic and labor trends and indicators for South Carolina.
Published by: (South Carolina. Division of Research), University of South Carolina, College of Business Administration, Division of Research, Columbia, SC 29208. TEL 803-777-2510, FAX 803-777-9344, woodward@darla.badm.sc.edu. Ed. Douglas P Woodward. Circ: 1,129.

330.9 USA ISSN 0145-3637
HC107.S7
SOUTH CAROLINA ECONOMIC REPORT. Text in English. a. USD 7 (effective 1999). **Document type:** *Government.*
Indexed: SRI.
Published by: Budget and Control Board, Board of Economic Advisors, Ste 442, Rembert Dennis Bldg, 1000 Assembly St, Columbia, SC 29201. TEL 803-734-3805, FAX 803-734-4719. R&P Robert W Martin.

330.9 BEL ISSN 1561-8439
SOUTH-EAST EUROPE. Text in English. 1999. m. (11/yr.). EUR 625 (effective 2000). **Document type:** *Bulletin.* **Description:** Focuses on the economic developments of the South-East European countries: Croatia, Bosnia and Herzegovina, Serbia, Montenegro, Macedonia, Slovenia and Albania.
Related titles: CD-ROM ed.; Online - full text ed.
Published by: Europe Information Service SA, Av Adolphe Lacomble 66-68, Brussels, 1030, Belgium. TEL 332-2-7377709, FAX 32-2-732-6757, eis@eis.be, http://www.eis.be. Pub. Eric Damiens.

330.947 GBR ISSN 1469-5286
SOUTH EAST EUROPE MONITOR. Key Title: Emerging Europe Monitor. South East Europe. Text in English. 2000. m. **Document type:** *Journal, Trade.* **Description:** Covers political risk, the business environment, and economic prospects in South East European countries.
Supersedes in part (1994-2000): Central and South East Europe Monitor (1466-3937); Which was formerly (until 1999): Eastern Europe Monitor (1353-4696)
Related titles: Online - full text ed.: (from EBSCO Publishing, Florida Center for Library Automation).
—IE. **CCC.**
Published by: Business Monitor International Ltd., Mermaid House, 2 Puddle Dock, Blackfriars, London, EC4V 3DS, United Kingdom. TEL 44-20-72480468, FAX 44-20-72480467, busmon@dial.pipex.com, http://www.businessmonitor.com.

SOUTH FLORIDA BUSINESS JOURNAL. see *BUSINESS AND ECONOMICS*

330.9 NCL ISSN 0377-452X
DU720.4
SOUTH PACIFIC COMMISSION. REPORT OF MEETINGS. Text in English. irreg. **Document type:** *Monographic series.*
Formerly: South Pacific Commission. Report of S P C Fisheries Technical Meetings (0081-2846)
Related titles: French ed.: Commission de Pacifique Sud. Rapport de Conference. ISSN 1017-9240.
Indexed: ASFA, ESPM.
Published by: Secretariat of the Pacific Community, PO Box D5, Noumea, Cedex 98848, New Caledonia. TEL 687-262000, FAX 687-263818, spc@spc.int, http://www.spc.int.

330.9 GBR
SOUTH WEST ECONOMY TRENDS AND PROSPECTS. Text in English. 1989. a. GBP 95. **Document type:** *Academic/Scholarly.*
—BLDSC (8352.181000).
Published by: University of Plymouth, South West Economic Research Centre, Drake Circus, Plymouth, Devon PL4 8AA, United Kingdom. TEL 44-1752-232827. Ed., R&P Peter Gripaios. Circ: 120.

SOUTHEAST ASIAN AFFAIRS. see *POLITICAL SCIENCE*

338.9 GBR ISSN 0143-5256
HC161
SOUTHERN CONE REPORT. Variant title: Latin American Regional Reports - Southern Cone Report. Text in English. 1967. 10/yr. looseleaf. GBP 150, USD 205 to institutions; GBP 85, USD 103 to libraries (effective 2001). 8 p./no.; back issues avail. **Document type:** *Newsletter.* **Description:** Covers in detail political, business, economic, and financial events in Argentina, Chile, Uruguay, and Paraguay.
Related titles: Online - full text ed.
Indexed: RASB.
—IE, Infotrieve.
Published by: Lettres (U.K.) Ltd., 61 Old St, London, EC1V 9HW, United Kingdom. TEL 44-20-7251-0012, FAX 44-20-7253-8193, subs@latinnews.com, http://www.latinnews.com. Ed. Colin Harding. R&P Alex McHallam.

330.9 USA
SOUTHERN GROWTH (RESEARCH TRIANGLE PARK). Text in English. q. **Document type:** *Newsletter.*
Formerly: Southern Growth Problems and Promises
Published by: Southern Growth Policies Board, PO Box 12293, Research Triangle Park, NC 27709. TEL 919-941-5145, FAX 919-941-5594, info@southern.org, http://www.southern.org. Ed. Robert Donnan.

330.9 DEU
SOZIALPRODUKT UND EINKOMMENSKREISLAUF. Text in German. 1973. q. EUR 55 (effective 2003). **Document type:** *Journal, Academic/Scholarly.*
Formerly (until 1997): Lange Reihen der Vierteljaehrlichen Volkswirtschaftlichen Gesamtrechnung
Related titles: E-mail ed.: EUR 840 (effective 2003).
Published by: Deutsches Institut fuer Wirtschaftsforschung, Koenigin-Luise-Str 5, Berlin, 14195, Germany. TEL 49-30-89789-0, FAX 49-30-89789200, postmaster@diw.de. Ed. Andreas Cors. Adv. contact Helmut Goepel TEL 49-30-89789404. Circ: 150.

330.9 ESP ISSN 1132-0052
SPAIN. MINISTERIO DE ECONOMIA Y HACIENDA. BOLETIN DE INFORMACION TRIMESTRAL. Text in Spanish. 1986. q. **Document type:** *Bulletin, Government.*
Published by: Ministerio de Economia y Hacienda, Direccion General de Seguros, Paseo Castellana, 44, Madrid, 28046, Spain. TEL 34-1-3397000, FAX 34-1-3397113. Circ: 550.

330.9 DEU ISSN 1435-5469
HC381
➤ **SPANISH ECONOMIC REVIEW/REVISTA ESPANOLA DE ECONOMIA.** Text in English. 1999. q. EUR 190 combined subscription to institutions print & online eds. (effective 2005). adv. back issues avail. **Document type:** *Journal, Academic/Scholarly.* **Description:** Publishes scientific articles in all fields of economics.
Related titles: Online - full text ed.: ISSN 1435-5477 (from EBSCO Publishing, Springer LINK, Swets Information Services).
Indexed: IBSS, JEL.
—BLDSC (8361.737520), IE, Infotrieve. **CCC.**
Published by: Springer-Verlag (Subsidiary of: Springer Science+Business Media), Tiergartenstr 17, Heidelberg, 69121, Germany. TEL 49-6221-3450, FAX 49-6221-345229, http://link.springer.de/link/service/journals/10108/index.htm. Ed. Jordi Caballe. Adv. contact Stephan Kroeck TEL 49-30-827875739. **Subscr. in the Americas to:** Springer-Verlag New York, Inc., Journal Fulfillment, PO Box 2485, Secaucus, NJ 07096-2485. TEL 800-777-4643, 201-348-4033, FAX 201-348-4505, journals@springer-ny.com, http://www.springer-ny.com; **Subscr. to:** Springer GmbH Auslieferungsgesellschaft, Haberstr 7, Heidelberg 69126, Germany. TEL 49-6221-345-0, FAX 49-6221-345-4229, subscriptions@springer.de.

330.9485 336.485 SWE ISSN 1101-4709
SPAROEVERSIKT. Text in Swedish. 1986. 7/yr. SEK 294; SEK 45 per issue (effective 2004). adv. **Document type:** *Magazine, Consumer.*
Formerly (until 1989): Sparformer i Sverige (1101-5101)
Published by: Svensk Fondstatistik AB, Kornhamnstorg 61, PO Box 2135, Stockholm, 10314, Sweden. TEL 46-8-4419160, FAX 46-8-214720, sparoversikt@westerco.se, http://www.sparoversikt.nu. Ed., Pub. Mats Wester. Adv. contact Chris Lindstrom TEL 46-8-6505657. color page SEK 17,500; trim 184 x 265. Circ: 11,600.

330.9 ITA
SPECCHIO ECONOMICO; mensile di economia, politica e attualita. Text in Italian. 1982. m. adv. **Document type:** *Magazine, Consumer.*
Published by: Ciuffa Editore Srl, Via Rasella 139, Rome, 00187, Italy. TEL 39-02-4851150, FAX 39-02-485964, specchioeconomico@iol.it, http://www.specchioeconomico.com. Ed. Victor Ciuffa. Adv. contact Anna Maria Ciuffa. Circ: 30,000.

330.9 LKA ISSN 1391-5894
SRI LANKA ECONOMIC JOURNAL. Text in English. 1986. s-a. USD 20. bk.rev. **Document type:** *Academic/Scholarly.*
Indexed: JEL.
Published by: Sri Lanka Economic Association, 61 Carmel Rd., Colombo, 3, Sri Lanka. Ed. N L Sirisena. Circ: 500.

330.9 LKA
SRI LANKA. MINISTRY OF PLANNING AND ECONOMIC AFFAIRS. DIVISION OF EXTERNAL RESOURCES. ECONOMIC INDICATORS. Text in English. a. charts; stat.
Published by: Ministry of Planning and Economic Affairs, Division of External Resources, Ceylingo House 2nd Fl., P O Box 277, Colombo, 1, Sri Lanka.

330.9 DEU
STANDORTE: JAHRBUCH RUHRGEBIET. Text in German. 1995. a. **Document type:** *Bulletin.*
Published by: (Kommunalverband Ruhrgebiet), Klartext Verlag GmbH, Dickmannstr 2-4, Essen, 45143, Germany. TEL 49-201-8620633, FAX 49-201-8620622.

START-UP; Windhover's review of emerging medical ventures. see *MEDICAL SCIENCES*

330.9 USA
STATE AND METROPOLITAN AREA EMPLOYMENT AND UNEMPLOYMENT. Text in English. m. **Document type:** *Government.*
Incorporates (in Feb. 1994): State Employment and Metropolitan Area Unemployment
Related titles: ♦ Series of: U.S. Bureau of Labor Statistics. National Office News Releases.
Indexed: AmStI.
Published by: U.S. Department of Labor, Bureau of Labor Statistics, Postal Square Bldg., 2 Massachusetts Ave, NE, Washington, DC 20212-0001 . TEL 202-691-5200, http://www.bls.gov. **Subscr. to:** U.S. Government Printing Office, Superintendent of Documents.

330.9 IND
STATE BANK OF INDIA. ECONOMIC NEWSLETTER. Text in English. w. free. **Document type:** *Newsletter.*
Published by: State Bank of India, Economic Research Department, New Administration Bldg., Backbay Reclamation, P O Box 12, Mumbai, Maharashtra 400 021, India.

330.9 IND
STATE BANK OF INDIA. INDIAN ECONOMIC NEWSLETTER. Text in English. bi-m. free. **Document type:** *Newsletter.*
Published by: State Bank of India, Economic Research Department, New Administration Bldg., Backbay Reclamation, P O Box 12, Mumbai, Maharashtra 400 021, India.

330.9 IND ISSN 0039-0003
STATE BANK OF INDIA. MONTHLY REVIEW. Text in English. 1961. m. free. charts; stat. **Description:** Covers current topics in banking and public finance in India. Includes legal decisions, parliamentary actions and empirical studies.
Formerly: State Bank of India. Economic Research Department. Studies
Indexed: AEA, AgBio, BAS, DSA, HortAb, IBSS, NutrAb, PHN&I, PoultAb, RDA, RRTA, SeedAb, WAE&RSA, WBA.
Published by: State Bank of India, Economic Research Department, New Administration Bldg., Backbay Reclamation, P O Box 12, Mumbai, Maharashtra 400 021, India. Ed. V R Gundannavar. Circ: 24,000.

330.9 658 GBR
THE STATE OF THE MARKET. Text in English. 1991. q. membership. **Document type:** *Corporate.*
Published by: Chartered Institute of Marketing, Moor Hall, Cookham, Maidenhead, Berks SL6 9QH, United Kingdom. TEL 44-1628-427500, FAX 44-1628-427499, corporatecommunications@cim.co.uk, http://www.cim.co.uk. Adv. contact Claire Forbes. Circ: 25,000 (controlled).

330.9 USA ISSN 1054-2159
HD8051
THE STATE OF WORKING AMERICA. Text in English. 1988. biennial. price varies. **Document type:** *Journal, Academic/Scholarly.*
Indexed: HortAb, SRI.
—BLDSC (8438.335530). **CCC.**
Published by: M.E. Sharpe, Inc., 80 Business Park Dr, Armonk, NY 10504. TEL 914-273-1800, 800-541-6563, FAX 914-273-2106, custserv@mesharpe.com, http://www.mesharpe.com.

STATISTICAL AND SOCIAL INQUIRY SOCIETY OF IRELAND. JOURNAL. see *STATISTICS*

STATISTICAL INDICATORS FOR ASIA AND THE PACIFIC. see *BUSINESS AND ECONOMICS—Abstracting, Bibliographies, Statistics*

330.9 USA ISSN 0251-0073
STATISTICAL INDICATORS OF SHORT TERM ECONOMIC CHANGES IN E.C.E. COUNTRIES. Text in English. m. price varies. **Description:** Provides an up-to-date overall picture of short-term economic trends in Europe and the U.S.
Indexed: RASB.
Published by: United Nations Publications, Rm DC2-853, United Nations Bldg, 2 United Nations Plaza, New York, NY 10017. TEL 212-963-8302, 800-253-9646, FAX 212-963-3489, publications@un.org, http://www.un.org/publications, http://www.un.org/Pubs. Circ: 1,650.

STATISTICAL REPORT OF REGION. see *BUSINESS AND ECONOMICS—Abstracting, Bibliographies, Statistics*

STATISTICAL YEARBOOK FOR ASIA AND THE PACIFIC/ANNUAIRE STATISTIQUE POUR L'ASIE ET LE PACIFIQUE. see *BUSINESS AND ECONOMICS—Abstracting, Bibliographies, Statistics*

338 AUT ISSN 0039-1107
STEIRISCHE WIRTSCHAFT; Mitteilungsblatt des Steirisch Wirtschaftsbundes. Text in German. 1964. m. membership. adv. bk.rev. stat. index.
Formerly: Steirischer Wirtschaftsbund
Published by: Oesterreichischer Wirtschaftsbund, Landesleitung Steiermark, Graz, St 8010, Austria. Ed. Fritz Kofler. Circ: 30,000.

330.9 USA ISSN 1051-9521
STRAIGHTTALK. Text in English. 1990. 10/yr. USD 395 to non-members; USD 195 to members (effective 2003). **Document type:** *Newsletter.* **Description:** Forecasts and commentary on the effect of domestic and international events on the economic outlook by the Conference Board's chief economist.
Formerly: Chief Economist's Letter
Related titles: Online - full text ed.
—CCC.
Published by: Conference Board, Inc., 845 Third Ave, New York, NY 10022. TEL 212-759-0900, FAX 212-980-7014, http://www.conference-board.org. Ed. Gail Fosler. Circ: 8,000.

STRATEGIC COMMENTARY. see *MEDICAL SCIENCES*

STREAMING MEDIA ADVERTISING FORECAST (YEAR). see *ADVERTISING AND PUBLIC RELATIONS*

330.9 JPN
STRUCTURE OF THE JAPANESE AUTO PARTS INDUSTRY. Text in English. irreg., latest 1993, Oct. USD 890. charts. **Document type:** *Directory.* **Description:** Covers the leading 500 Japanese auto parts and the 11 automobile manufacturers, their nearly 700 overseas subsidiaries and joint ventures, aftermarket overview and 39 major trade associations.
Published by: Dodwell Marketing Consultants, Kowa no 35 Bldg, 14-14 Akasaka 1-chome, Minato-ku, Tokyo, 107-0052, Japan. TEL 03-3589-0207, FAX 03-5570-7132.

330.9 DEU ISSN 0536-1621
STRUKTUR UND WACHSTUM. REIHE INDUSTRIE. Text in German. 1964. irreg., latest vol.48, 1996. price varies. **Document type:** *Monographic series, Academic/Scholarly.*
Published by: Duncker und Humblot GmbH, Carl-Heinrich-Becker-Weg 9, Berlin, 12165, Germany. TEL 49-30-7900060, FAX 49-30-79000631, info@duncker-humblot.de, http://www.duncker-humblot.de.

330.9 POL
STUDIA EKONOMICZNE. Text in Polish; Summaries in English, Russian. irreg., latest vol.28, 1992. price varies. **Document type:** *Monographic series.* **Description:** Papers on different items of economic systems, their reforms, legal aspects of economy and economical functions of state.
Published by: Polska Akademiya Nauk, Instytut Nauk Ekonomicznych/Polish Academy of Sciences, Institute of Economic Sciences, Ul Nowy Swiat 72, Warsaw, 00330, Poland. TEL 48-22-299146, FAX 48-22-295897. Ed. Mieczyslaw Mieszczankowski.

330.9 USA
STUDIES IN INCOME DISTRIBUTION SERIES. Short title: S I D Series. Text in English. irreg. stat. **Document type:** *Government.*
Published by: U.S. Social Security Administration, Office of Research, Evaluation and Statistics, 500 E St, S W, 8th Fl, Washington, DC 20254-0001. TEL 202-358-6274, FAX 202-358-6192, ores.publications@ssa.gov, http://www.ssa.gov. **Subscr. to:** U.S. Government Printing Office, Superintendent of Documents, PO Box 371954, Pittsburgh, PA 15250-7954. TEL 202-512-1800, FAX 202-512-2250.

330.9 NLD ISSN 0886-0416
➤ **STUDIES IN REGIONAL SCIENCE AND URBAN ECONOMICS.** Text in Dutch. 1977. irreg., latest vol.24, 1993. price varies. **Document type:** *Monographic series, Academic/Scholarly.* **Description:** Studies issues in city transit and other areas of urban economics.
Indexed: MathR.
—BLDSC (8491.421000).
Published by: Elsevier BV (Subsidiary of: Elsevier Science & Technology), Radarweg 29, Amsterdam, 1043 NX, Netherlands. TEL 31-20-4853911, FAX 31-20-4852457, nlinfo-f@elsevier.nl, http://www.elsevier.com/inca/tree/?key=B1SRSUE, http://www.elsevier.nl. Eds. Ake Andersson, Walter Isard.

338.947 RUS ISSN 1075-7007
HC331
STUDIES ON RUSSIAN ECONOMIC DEVELOPMENT. Text in English. 1990. 6/yr. USD 982 in North America; USD 1,127 elsewhere (effective 2004). **Document type:** *Journal, Academic/Scholarly.* **Description:** Provides up-to-date inside information on socioeconomic problems in Russia.
Formerly (until 1993): Studies on Soviet Economic Development (1054-6588)
Related titles: ♦ Translation of: Problemy Prognozirovaniya.
—IE, Infotrieve. **CCC.**
Published by: (Rossiiskaya Akademiya Nauk/Russian Academy of Sciences), M A I K Nauka - Interperiodica, Profsoyuznaya ul 90, Moscow, 117997, Russian Federation. TEL 7-095-3347420, FAX 7-095-3360666, compmg@maik.ru, http://www.maik.rssi.ru/journals/rusec.htm, http://www.maik.ru. Ed. Viktor V Ivanter. **Subscr. to:** Interperiodica, PO Box 1831, Birmingham, AL 35201-1831. TEL 205-995-1567, 800-633-4931, FAX 205-995-1588.

330.9 003.5 ROM ISSN 0585-7511
STUDII SI CERCETARI DE CALCUL ECONOMIC SI CIBERNETICE ECONOMICE. Text in Romanian. 1966. q.
Related titles: English ed.: Economic Computation and Economic Cybernetics Studies and Research. ISSN 0424-267X.
Published by: (Academia de Studii Economice), Editura A S E, Piata Romana 6, Sector 1, Bucharest, 70167, Romania. TEL 40-21-2112650, FAX 40-21-3129549, editura.ase@net.ase.ro, http://www.ase.ro.

SUDAN. ECONOMIC AND SOCIAL RESEARCH COUNCIL. OCCASIONAL PAPER. see *SOCIAL SCIENCES: COMPREHENSIVE WORKS*

330 SDN
SUDAN. MINISTRY OF FINANCE AND NATIONAL ECONOMY. ECONOMIC AND FINANCIAL RESEARCH SECTION. ECONOMIC SURVEY. Text in English. a.
Supersedes: Sudan. National Planning Commission. Economic Survey (0081-9050)
Published by: Ministry of Finance and National Economy, Economic and Financial Research Section, P O Box 2092, Khartoum, Sudan.

SUDAN. NATIONAL COUNCIL FOR RESEARCH. ECONOMIC AND SOCIAL RESEARCH COUNCIL. BULLETIN. see *SOCIAL SCIENCES: COMPREHENSIVE WORKS*

SUDAN. NATIONAL COUNCIL FOR RESEARCH. ECONOMIC AND SOCIAL RESEARCH COUNCIL. RESEARCH REPORT. see *SOCIAL SCIENCES: COMPREHENSIVE WORKS*

330.9 GBR
SUDAN TRADE DIRECTORY. Text in English. a. adv. **Document type:** *Directory.*
Published by: Arthur H. Thrower Ltd., 44-46 S Ealing Rd, London, W5, United Kingdom.

SUED-AFRIKA; Magazin fuer Reisen, Wirtschaft und Kultur im suedlichen Afrika. see *TRAVEL AND TOURISM*

330.9 URY ISSN 0797-0064
SUMA. Text in Spanish; Summaries in English. 1986. 2/yr. UYP 68,000, USD 23 in Latin America; USD 25 elsewhere. bk.rev. back issues avail. **Document type:** *Academic/Scholarly.* **Description:** Publishes research done by CINVE on an academic level.
Indexed: PAIS.
—CINDOC.
Published by: (Centro de Investigaciones Economicas), Ediciones Trilce, Guayabo, 1729 Ap 702, Montevideo, 11209, Uruguay. TEL 598-2-40-49-17, FAX 598-2-40-49-47. Circ: 700.

330.9 GBR ISSN 1350-8148
SUMMARY OF WORLD BROADCASTS. PART 1: FORMER SOVIET UNION (DAILY). Text in English. 1947. d. looseleaf. GBP 485 (effective 2000). back issues avail. **Document type:** *Newspaper.*
Related titles: Online - full text ed.: GBP 550 (effective 2000) (from The Dialog Corporation); ♦ Series: Summary of World Broadcasts. Part 1: Former Soviet Union (Weekly Economic Report); ♦ Summary of World Broadcasts. Part 2: Central Europe, the Balkans (Daily). ISSN 1352-1365; ♦ Summary of World Broadcasts. Part 2: Central Europe, the Balkans (Weekly Economic Report). ISSN 1352-1373; ♦ Summary of World Broadcasts. Part 3: Asia - Pacific (Daily). ISSN 1352-139X; ♦ Summary of World Broadcasts. Part 3: Asia - Pacific (Weekly Economic Report). ISSN 1352-1403; ♦ Summary of World Broadcasts. Part 4: Middle East (Daily). ISSN 1350-8199; ♦ Summary of World Broadcasts. Part 4: Middle East (Weekly Economic Report). ISSN 1350-8202; ♦ Summary of World Broadcasts. Part 5: Africa, Latin America and the Caribbean (Weekly Economic Report). ISSN 1350-8253; ♦ Summary of World Broadcasts. Part 5: Africa, Latin America and the Caribbean (Daily). ISSN 1350-8245.
Published by: B B C Monitoring, Caversham Park, Peppard Rd, Reading, Berks RG4 8TZ, United Kingdom. TEL 44-118-948-6289, FAX 44-118-946-3823, marketing@mon.bbc.co.uk, http://www.monitor.bbc.co.uk. Ed. Mike Elliott. R&P Rosy Wolfe.

330.9 GBR
SUMMARY OF WORLD BROADCASTS. PART 1: FORMER SOVIET UNION (WEEKLY ECONOMIC REPORT). Text in English. 1943. w. looseleaf. GBP 345 for print ed. (effective 2000). back issues avail. **Document type:** *Newspaper.*
Formerly: Summary of World Broadcasts. Part 1: Former U S S R (Weekly Economic Report) (1350-8156)
Related titles: Online - full text ed.: GBP 350 (effective 2000) (from The Dialog Corporation); ♦ Series: Summary of World Broadcasts. Part 1: Former Soviet Union (Daily). ISSN 1350-8148; ♦ Summary of World Broadcasts. Part 2: Central Europe, the Balkans (Daily). ISSN 1352-1365; ♦ Summary of World Broadcasts. Part 2: Central Europe, the Balkans (Weekly Economic Report). ISSN 1352-1373; ♦ Summary of World Broadcasts. Part 3: Asia - Pacific (Daily). ISSN 1352-139X; ♦ Summary of World Broadcasts. Part 3: Asia - Pacific (Weekly Economic Report). ISSN 1352-1403; ♦ Summary of World Broadcasts. Part 4: Middle East (Daily). ISSN 1350-8199; ♦ Summary of World Broadcasts. Part 4: Middle East (Weekly Economic Report). ISSN 1350-8202; ♦ Summary of World Broadcasts. Part 5: Africa, Latin America and the Caribbean (Weekly Economic Report). ISSN 1350-8253; ♦ Summary of World Broadcasts. Part 5: Africa, Latin America and the Caribbean (Daily). ISSN 1350-8245.
Published by: B B C Monitoring, Caversham Park, Peppard Rd, Reading, Berks RG4 8TZ, United Kingdom. TEL 44-118-948-6289, FAX 44-118-946-3823, marketing@mon.bbc.co.uk, http://www.monitor.bbc.co.uk. Ed. Mike Elliott. R&P Rosy Wolfe.

330.9 GBR ISSN 1352-1365
SUMMARY OF WORLD BROADCASTS. PART 2: CENTRAL EUROPE, THE BALKANS (DAILY). Text in English. 1947. d. looseleaf. GBP 485 print ed. (effective 2000). back issues avail. **Document type:** *Newspaper.*
Supersedes (in 1993): Summary of World Broadcasts. Part 2: Eastern Europe (Daily) (0960-0361)
Related titles: Online - full text ed.: GBP 550 online ed. (effective 2000) (from The Dialog Corporation); ♦ Series: Summary of World Broadcasts. Part 1: Former Soviet Union (Daily). ISSN 1350-8148; ♦ Summary of World Broadcasts. Part 1: Former Soviet Union (Weekly Economic Report); ♦ Summary of World Broadcasts. Part 2: Central Europe, the Balkans (Weekly Economic Report). ISSN 1352-1373; ♦ Summary of World Broadcasts. Part 3: Asia - Pacific (Daily). ISSN 1352-139X; ♦ Summary of World Broadcasts. Part 3: Asia - Pacific (Weekly Economic Report). ISSN 1352-1403; ♦ Summary of World Broadcasts. Part 4: Middle East (Daily). ISSN 1350-8199; ♦ Summary of World Broadcasts. Part 4: Middle East (Weekly Economic Report). ISSN 1350-8202; ♦ Summary of World Broadcasts. Part 5: Africa, Latin America and the Caribbean (Weekly Economic Report). ISSN 1350-8253; ♦ Summary of World Broadcasts. Part 5: Africa, Latin America and the Caribbean (Daily). ISSN 1350-8245.
Published by: B B C Monitoring, Caversham Park, Peppard Rd, Reading, Berks RG4 8TZ, United Kingdom. TEL 44-118-948-6289, FAX 44-118-946-3823, marketing@mon.bbc.co.uk, http://www.monitor.bbc.co.uk. Ed. Mike Elliott. R&P Rosy Wolfe.

B

▼ new title ➤ refereed ✶ unverified ♦ full entry avail.

330.9 GBR ISSN 1352-1373
SUMMARY OF WORLD BROADCASTS. PART 2: CENTRAL EUROPE, THE BALKANS (WEEKLY ECONOMIC REPORT). Text in English. 1943. w. looseleaf. GBP 345 print ed. (effective 2000). back issues avail. **Document type:** *Newspaper.*
Supersedes (in 1993): Summary of World Broadcasts. Part 2: Eastern Europe (Weekly Economic Report) (0960-037X)
Related titles: Online - full text ed.: GBP 350 online ed. (effective 2000) (from The Dialog Corporation); ♦ Series: Summary of World Broadcasts. Part 1: Former Soviet Union (Daily). ISSN 1350-8148; ♦ Summary of World Broadcasts. Part 1: Former Soviet Union (Weekly Economic Report); ♦ Summary of World Broadcasts. Part 2: Central Europe, the Balkans (Daily). ISSN 1352-1365; ♦ Summary of World Broadcasts. Part 3: Asia - Pacific (Daily). ISSN 1352-139X; ♦ Summary of World Broadcasts. Part 3: Asia - Pacific (Weekly Economic Report). ISSN 1352-1403; ♦ Summary of World Broadcasts. Part 4: Middle East (Daily). ISSN 1350-8199; ♦ Summary of World Broadcasts. Part 4: Middle East (Weekly Economic Report). ISSN 1350-8202; ♦ Summary of World Broadcasts. Part 5: Africa, Latin America and the Caribbean (Weekly Economic Report). ISSN 1350-8253; ♦ Summary of World Broadcasts. Part 5: Africa, Latin America and the Caribbean (Daily). ISSN 1350-8245.
Published by: B B C Monitoring, Caversham Park, Peppard Rd, Reading, Berks RG4 8TZ, United Kingdom. TEL 44-118-948-6289, FAX 44-118-946-3823, marketing@mon.bbc.co.ukcom, http://www.monitor.bbc.co.uk. Ed. Mike Elliott. R&P Rosy Wolfe.

330.9 GBR ISSN 1352-139X
SUMMARY OF WORLD BROADCASTS. PART 3: ASIA - PACIFIC (DAILY). Text in English. 1947. d. looseleaf. GBP 485 (effective 2000). back issues avail. **Document type:** *Newspaper.*
Supersedes (in 1993): Summary of World Broadcasts. Part 3: Far East (Daily) (0960-0388)
Related titles: Online - full text ed.: GBP 550 (effective 2000) (from The Dialog Corporation); ♦ Series: Summary of World Broadcasts. Part 1: Former Soviet Union (Daily). ISSN 1350-8148; ♦ Summary of World Broadcasts. Part 1: Former Soviet Union (Weekly Economic Report); ♦ Summary of World Broadcasts. Part 2: Central Europe, the Balkans (Daily). ISSN 1352-1365; ♦ Summary of World Broadcasts. Part 2: Central Europe, the Balkans (Weekly Economic Report). ISSN 1352-1373; ♦ Summary of World Broadcasts. Part 3: Asia - Pacific (Weekly Economic Report). ISSN 1352-1403; ♦ Summary of World Broadcasts. Part 4: Middle East (Daily). ISSN 1350-8199; ♦ Summary of World Broadcasts. Part 4: Middle East (Weekly Economic Report). ISSN 1350-8202; ♦ Summary of World Broadcasts. Part 5: Africa, Latin America and the Caribbean (Weekly Economic Report). ISSN 1350-8253; ♦ Summary of World Broadcasts. Part 5: Africa, Latin America and the Caribbean (Daily). ISSN 1350-8245.
Published by: B B C Monitoring, Caversham Park, Peppard Rd, Reading, Berks RG4 8TZ, United Kingdom. TEL 44-118-948-6289, FAX 44-118-946-3823, marketing@mon.bbc.co.uk, http://www.monitor.bbc.co.uk. Ed. Mike Elliott. R&P Rosy Wolfe.

330.9 GBR ISSN 1352-1403
SUMMARY OF WORLD BROADCASTS. PART 3: ASIA - PACIFIC (WEEKLY ECONOMIC REPORT). Text in English. 1943. w. looseleaf. GBP 345 (effective 2000). back issues avail. **Document type:** *Newspaper.*
Supersedes (in 1993): Summary of World Broadcasts. Part 3: Far East (Weekly Economic Report) (0960-0396)
Related titles: Online - full text ed.: GBP 350 (effective 2000) (from The Dialog Corporation); ♦ Series: Summary of World Broadcasts. Part 1: Former Soviet Union (Daily). ISSN 1350-8148; ♦ Summary of World Broadcasts. Part 1: Former Soviet Union (Weekly Economic Report); ♦ Summary of World Broadcasts. Part 2: Central Europe, the Balkans (Daily). ISSN 1352-1365; ♦ Summary of World Broadcasts. Part 2: Central Europe, the Balkans (Weekly Economic Report). ISSN 1352-1373; ♦ Summary of World Broadcasts. Part 3: Asia - Pacific (Daily). ISSN 1352-139X; ♦ Summary of World Broadcasts. Part 4: Middle East (Daily). ISSN 1350-8199; ♦ Summary of World Broadcasts. Part 4: Middle East (Weekly Economic Report). ISSN 1350-8202; ♦ Summary of World Broadcasts. Part 5: Africa, Latin America and the Caribbean (Weekly Economic Report). ISSN 1350-8253; ♦ Summary of World Broadcasts. Part 5: Africa, Latin America and the Caribbean (Daily). ISSN 1350-8245.
Published by: B B C Monitoring, Caversham Park, Peppard Rd, Reading, Berks RG4 8TZ, United Kingdom. TEL 44-118-948-6289, FAX 44-118-946-3823, marketing@monitor.bbc.co.uk, http://www.monitor.bbc.co.uk. Ed. Mike Elliott. R&P Rosy Wolfe.

330.9 GBR ISSN 1350-8199
SUMMARY OF WORLD BROADCASTS. PART 4: MIDDLE EAST (DAILY). Text in English. 1947. d. looseleaf. GBP 485 (effective 2000). back issues avail. **Document type:** *Newspaper.*
Supersedes in part (in 1993): Summary of World Broadcasts. Part 4: Middle East, Africa and Latin America (Daily) (0960-040X)
Related titles: Online - full text ed.: GBP 550 (effective 2000) (from The Dialog Corporation); ♦ Series: Summary of World Broadcasts. Part 1: Former Soviet Union (Daily). ISSN 1350-8148; ♦ Summary of World Broadcasts. Part 1: Former Soviet Union (Weekly Economic Report); ♦ Summary of World Broadcasts. Part 2: Central Europe, the Balkans (Daily). ISSN 1352-1365; ♦ Summary of World Broadcasts. Part 2: Central Europe, the Balkans (Weekly Economic Report). ISSN 1352-1373; ♦ Summary of World Broadcasts. Part 3: Asia - Pacific (Daily). ISSN 1352-139X; ♦ Summary of World Broadcasts. Part 3: Asia - Pacific (Weekly Economic Report). ISSN 1352-1403; ♦ Summary of World Broadcasts. Part 4: Middle East (Weekly Economic Report). ISSN 1350-8202; ♦ Summary of World Broadcasts. Part 5: Africa, Latin America and the Caribbean (Weekly Economic Report). ISSN 1350-8253; ♦ Summary of World Broadcasts. Part 5: Africa, Latin America and the Caribbean (Daily). ISSN 1350-8245.
Published by: B B C Monitoring, Caversham Park, Peppard Rd, Reading, Berks RG4 8TZ, United Kingdom. TEL 44-118-948-6289, FAX 44-118-946-3823, marketing@mon.bbc.co.uk, http://www.monitor.bbc.co.uk. Ed. Mike Elliott. R&P Rosy Wolfe.

330.9 GBR ISSN 1350-8202
SUMMARY OF WORLD BROADCASTS. PART 4: MIDDLE EAST (WEEKLY ECONOMIC REPORT). Text in English. 1943. w. looseleaf. GBP 34 (effective 2000). back issues avail. **Document type:** *Newspaper.*
Supersedes in part (in 1993): Summary of World Broadcasts. Part 4: Middle East, Africa and Latin America (Weekly Economic Report) (0960-0418)
Related titles: Online - full text ed.: GBP 350 (effective 2000) (from The Dialog Corporation); ♦ Series: Summary of World Broadcasts. Part 1: Former Soviet Union (Daily). ISSN 1350-8148; ♦ Summary of World Broadcasts. Part 1: Former Soviet Union (Weekly Economic Report); ♦ Summary of World Broadcasts. Part 2: Central Europe, the Balkans (Daily). ISSN 1352-1365; ♦ Summary of World Broadcasts. Part 2: Central Europe, the Balkans (Weekly Economic Report). ISSN 1352-1373; ♦ Summary of World Broadcasts. Part 3: Asia - Pacific (Daily). ISSN 1352-139X; ♦ Summary of World Broadcasts. Part 3: Asia - Pacific (Weekly Economic Report). ISSN 1352-1403; ♦ Summary of World Broadcasts. Part 4: Middle East (Daily). ISSN 1350-8199; ♦ Summary of World Broadcasts. Part 5: Africa, Latin America and the Caribbean (Weekly Economic Report). ISSN 1350-8253; ♦ Summary of World Broadcasts. Part 5: Africa, Latin America and the Caribbean (Daily). ISSN 1350-8245.
Published by: B B C Monitoring, Caversham Park, Peppard Rd, Reading, Berks RG4 8TZ, United Kingdom. TEL 44-118-948-6289, FAX 44-118-946-3823, marketing@mon.bbc.co.uk, http://www.monitor.bbc.co.uk. Ed. Mike Eliott. R&P Rosy Wolfe.

330.9 GBR ISSN 1350-8245
SUMMARY OF WORLD BROADCASTS. PART 5: AFRICA, LATIN AMERICA AND THE CARIBBEAN (DAILY). Text in English. 1993. d. looseleaf. GBP 485 (effective 2000). back issues avail. **Document type:** *Newspaper.*
Supersedes in part (in 1993): Summary of World Broadcasts. Part 4: Middle East, Africa and Latin America (Daily) (0960-040X)
Related titles: Online - full text ed.: GBP 550 (effective 2000) (from The Dialog Corporation); ♦ Series: Summary of World Broadcasts. Part 1: Former Soviet Union (Daily). ISSN 1350-8148; ♦ Summary of World Broadcasts. Part 1: Former Soviet Union (Weekly Economic Report); ♦ Summary of World Broadcasts. Part 2: Central Europe, the Balkans (Daily). ISSN 1352-1365; ♦ Summary of World Broadcasts. Part 2: Central Europe, the Balkans (Weekly Economic Report). ISSN 1352-1373; ♦ Summary of World Broadcasts. Part 3: Asia - Pacific (Daily). ISSN 1352-139X; ♦ Summary of World Broadcasts. Part 3: Asia - Pacific (Weekly Economic Report). ISSN 1352-1403; ♦ Summary of World Broadcasts. Part 4: Middle East (Daily). ISSN 1350-8199; ♦ Summary of World Broadcasts. Part 4: Middle East (Weekly Economic Report). ISSN 1350-8202; ♦ Summary of World Broadcasts. Part 5: Africa, Latin America and the Caribbean (Weekly Economic Report). ISSN 1350-8253.
Published by: B B C Monitoring, Caversham Park, Peppard Rd, Reading, Berks RG4 8TZ, United Kingdom. TEL 44-118-948-6289, FAX 44-118-946-3823, marketing@mon.bbc.co.uk, http://www.monitor.bbc.co.uk. R&P Rosy Wolfe.

330.9 GBR ISSN 1350-8253
SUMMARY OF WORLD BROADCASTS. PART 5: AFRICA, LATIN AMERICA AND THE CARIBBEAN (WEEKLY ECONOMIC REPORT). Text in English. 1993. w. looseleaf. GBP 345 (effective 2000). back issues avail. **Document type:** *Newspaper.*
Supersedes in part (in 1993): Summary of World Broadcasts. Part 4: Middle East, Africa and Latin America (Weekly Economic Report) (0960-0418)
Related titles: Online - full text ed.: GBP 350 (effective 2000) (from The Dialog Corporation); ♦ Series: Summary of World Broadcasts. Part 1: Former Soviet Union (Daily). ISSN 1350-8148; ♦ Summary of World Broadcasts. Part 1: Former Soviet Union (Weekly Economic Report); ♦ Summary of World Broadcasts. Part 2: Central Europe, the Balkans (Daily). ISSN 1352-1365; ♦ Summary of World Broadcasts. Part 2: Central Europe, the Balkans (Weekly Economic Report). ISSN 1352-1373; ♦ Summary of World Broadcasts. Part 3: Asia - Pacific (Daily). ISSN 1352-139X; ♦ Summary of World Broadcasts. Part 3: Asia - Pacific (Weekly Economic Report). ISSN 1352-1403; ♦ Summary of World Broadcasts. Part 4: Middle East (Daily). ISSN 1350-8199; ♦ Summary of World Broadcasts. Part 4: Middle East (Weekly Economic Report). ISSN 1350-8202; ♦ Summary of World Broadcasts. Part 5: Africa, Latin America and the Caribbean (Daily). ISSN 1350-8245.
Published by: B B C Monitoring, Caversham Park, Peppard Rd, Reading, Berks RG4 8TZ, United Kingdom. TEL 44-118-948-6289, FAX 44-118-946-3823, marketing@mon.bbc.co.uk, http://www.monitor.bbc.co.uk. Ed. Mike Elliott. R&P Rosy Wolfe.

338 USA ISSN 0039-6222
HC101 CODEN: SVCBAK
SURVEY OF CURRENT BUSINESS. Text in English. 1921. m. USD 63 domestic; USD 88.20 foreign; USD 25 per issue (effective 2004). charts; illus.; mkt.; stat. index, s-a. index. back issues avail.; reprint service avail. from CIS. **Document type:** *Government.* **Description:** Gives information on trends in industry, business, and the general economic outlook, as well as other points pertinent to the business world. Includes the Gross National Product, GDP, implicit price deflator and corporate profits.
Related titles: CD-ROM ed.; Microfiche ed.: (from CIS); Online - full text ed.: (from bigchalk, EBSCO Publishing, Florida Center for Library Automation, Gale Group, H.W. Wilson, Northern Light Technology, Inc., O C L C Online Computer Library Center, Inc., ProQuest Information & Learning, The Dialog Corporation).
Indexed: ABIn, AcaI, AmStI, BPI, BPIA, IUSGP, JEL, KES, PAIS, PROMT, RASB, T&II.
—BLDSC (8549.100000), IE, Infotrieve, ingenta.
Published by: U.S. Department of Commerce, Bureau of Economic Analysis, 1441 L St NW, Washington, DC 20230. TEL 202-606-9900, http://www.bea.doc.gov/bea/pubs.htm. Circ: 7,600 (paid). **Subscr. to:** U.S. Government Printing Office, Superintendent of Documents, PO Box 371954, Pittsburgh, PA 15250-7954. TEL 202-512-1800, FAX 202-512-2250, orders@gpo.gov, http://www.access.gpo.gov.

330.9 LKA
SURVEY OF HOUSEHOLD ECONOMIC ACTIVITIES (YEAR). Text in English. irreg., latest 1984-85, 2nd ed. LKR 65. **Document type:** *Government.*
Published by: Department of Census and Statistics, 15-12 Maitland Crescent, P O Box 563, Colombo, 07, Sri Lanka. TEL 94-682178. Ed. A G W Nanayakkara. Circ: 1,441. **Dist. by:** Superintendent, Government Publications Bureau, Colombo 1, Sri Lanka.

330.9 GBR
SURVEY OF SCOTTISH MANUFACTURING AND EXPORTS IN (YEAR). Text in English. a. **Document type:** *Bulletin.*
Formerly: Survey of Dunbartonshire Manufacturing and Exports in (Year)
Published by: Scottish Council Development and Industry, 23 Chester St, Edinburgh, EH3 7ET, United Kingdom. TEL 44-131-225-7911, FAX 44-131-220-2116.

330.9 GBR
SURVEY OF SCOTTISH PRIMARY EXPORTS. Text in English. a. **Document type:** *Bulletin.*
Published by: Scottish Council Development and Industry, 23 Chester St, Edinburgh, EH3 7ET, United Kingdom. TEL 44-131-225-7911, FAX 44-131-220-2116.

330.9 GBR
SURVEY OF SERVICE SECTOR EXPORTS. Text in English. a. membership. **Document type:** *Academic/Scholarly.*
Published by: Scottish Council Development and Industry, 23 Chester St, Edinburgh, EH3 7ET, United Kingdom. TEL 44-131-225-7911, FAX 44-131-225-7911, edinburgh@scdi.org.uk, http://www.scdi.org.uk.

330.9 USA ISSN 0085-3410
HC110.S3
SURVEYS OF CONSUMERS; contributions to behavioral economics. Text in English. 1947. irreg. USD 16.
Formerly (until 1970): Survey of Consumer Finances (0081-9727)
Indexed: SRI.
Published by: University of Michigan, Institute for Social Research, I S R Administration, Box 1248, Ann Arbor, MI 48106. TEL 313-763-8363, FAX 313-747-4575.

330.9 SWE ISSN 0345-2719
SVENSKA BANKFOERENINGEN. EKONOMISKA MEDDELANDEN. Text in Swedish. 1910. w.
Published by: Svenska Bankfoereningen/Swedish Bankers' Association, PO Box 7603, Stockholm, 10394, Sweden. TEL 46-8-4534400, FAX 46-8-7969395, info@bankforeningen.se, http://www.bankforeningen.se. Circ: 1,350.

330.9 SWZ
SWAZILAND. MINISTRY OF ECONOMIC PLANNING AND STATISTICS. ECONOMIC REVIEW. Text in English. 1970. a. SZL 4. illus. **Document type:** *Government.*
Former titles: Swaziland. Department of Economic Planning and Statistics. Economic Review; Swaziland. Economic Planning Office. Economic Review

B

Published by: Ministry of Economic Planning and Statistics, PO Box 602, Mbabane, Swaziland.

330.9 CHE ISSN 0255-9064
HC59
SWITZERLAND. KOMMISSION FUER KONJUNKTURFRAGEN. WIRTSCHAFTSLAGE. Text in German. 1932. q. stat. **Document type:** *Government.*
Incorporates (in 1989): Schweizerische Konjunktur und Vorausschau
Related titles: French ed.: Switzerland. Commission pour les Questions Conjoncturelles. Situation Economique. ISSN 1421-3907; ♦ Supplement to: Die Volkswirtschaft. ISSN 1011-386X.
Published by: State Secretariat for Economic Affairs, Kommission fuer Konjunkturfragen, Bundesgasse 8, Bern, 3003, Switzerland. TEL 41-31-3222138, FAX 41-31-3235001.

330.9 GBR ISSN 1462-6292
T E U B R G WORKING PAPER SERIES. Text in English. 1997. irreg. GBP 5 (effective 1999). **Document type:** *Monographic series, Academic/Scholarly.*
—BLDSC (9350.934000).
Published by: (Turkey - E U Business Research Group), University of Birmingham, Birmingham Business School, University Of Birmingham, Edgbaston, Birmingham B15 2TT, United Kingdom. TEL 44-121-414-3419, FAX 44-121-414-6707, m.r.oktemgil@bham.ac.uk. Ed. Ed M R Oktemgil.

330.9 REU ISSN 0994-415X
HC598.A1
TABLEAU ECONOMIQUE DE LA REUNION. Text in French. 1981. a. bk.rev. charts; illus.; maps; stat. **Document type:** *Yearbook.*
Formerly: Panorama de l'Economie de la Reunion
Published by: Institut National de la Statistique et des Etudes Economiques, Direction Regionale de la Reunion, 15 rue de L'Ecole, B P 13, St. Denis Messag, Cedex 9 97408, Reunion. TEL 02-62-488900, FAX 02-62-488989. Ed. Gaillard Jean. Circ: 4,000.

330.9 FRA ISSN 1635-0529
TABLEAUX ECONOMIQUES REGIONAUX. Text in French. 1979. biennial. adv. index. back issues avail.
Formerly (until 1999): Tableaux Economiques de l'Ile-de-France. Edition (Year) (0983-5733)
Published by: Institut National de la Statistique et des Etudes Economiques (INSEE), Direction Regionale d'Ile-de-France, 7 rue Stephenson, Saint-quentin-en-yvelines, Cedex 78188, France. TEL 33-1-30969000, FAX 33-1-30969001. Ed. Annie Etienne. Adv. contact Francoise Charbonnier. Circ: 2,300.

330.9 TWN ISSN 0255-5697
TAIWAN ECONOMY. Key Title: Taiwan Jingji. Text mainly in Chinese; Text occasionally in English. 1977. m. charts; stat.
Published by: Taiwan Provincial Government, Council for Economic Planning and Mobilization, 56 Chung-Hsing Hsin-Tsun Fu W. Rd, Nantou, Taiwan. TEL 049-333963. Ed. Hsu Lai Chun. **Overseas subscr. to:** Guoli Zhongyang Tushuguan, 20 Chung Shan S. Rd, Taipei 100-01, Taiwan.

TAIWAN, REPUBLIC OF CHINA. EXECUTIVE YUAN. DIRECTORATE-GENERAL OF BUDGET, ACCOUNTING & STATISTICS. NATIONAL INCOME IN TAIWAN AREA, R.O.C. see *BUSINESS AND ECONOMICS—Abstracting, Bibliographies, Statistics*

330.9 TWN ISSN 0257-5663
TAIWAN, REPUBLIC OF CHINA. EXECUTIVE YUAN. DIRECTORATE-GENERAL OF BUDGET, ACCOUNTING & STATISTICS. QUARTERLY NATIONAL ECONOMIC TRENDS, TAIWAN AREA. Key Title: Guomin Jingji Dongxiang Tongji Jibao - Zhonghua Minguo Taiwan Diqu. Text in Chinese, English. 1978. q. TWD 200 (effective 2000). charts; stat.
Published by: Executive Yuan, Directorate-General of Budget, Accounting & Statistics, 2 Kwangchow St, Taipei, Taiwan. TEL 886-2-2381-4910, http://www.dgbasey.gov.tw/, http://www.stat.gov.tw/main.htm/. Circ: 1,600. **Subscr. to:** Chen Chung Book Co., 3F, 20 Heng-Yang Rd, Taipei, Taiwan. TEL 886-2-2382-1394, FAX 886-2-2382-2805, http://www.ccbc.com.tw.

330.9 TJK
TAJIKISTAN ECONOMIC REVIEW. Text in English. 24/yr. USD 399 in United States.
Address: Bohtar 35-1, 8 etazh, Dushanbe, Tajikistan. TEL 21-78-63, FAX 21-72-20. Ed. Umed Babahanov. **US dist. addr.:** East View Information Services, 3020 Harbor Ln. N., Minneapolis, MN 55447. TEL 612-550-0961.

330.4 USA ISSN 1094-7612
HC106.7
TAKING SIDES: CLASHING VIEWS ON CONTROVERSIAL ECONOMIC ISSUES. Text in English. irreg., latest 2003, 11th ed. USD 22.50 per vol. (effective 2004). illus. **Document type:** *Academic/Scholarly.*
Published by: McGraw-Hill - Dushkin (Subsidiary of: McGraw-Hill Higher Education), 2460 Kerper Blvd, Dubuque, IA 52001. TEL 800-243-6532, customer.service@mcgraw-hill.com, http://www.dushkin.com/text-data/catalog/0072845139.mhtml. Eds. Frank J Bonello, Thomas R Swartz. Pub. David Dean. R&P Cheryl Greenleaf.

330.9 USA
▼ **TECHCONNECT.** Text in English. 2004. 3/yr. USD 20 domestic; USD 28 in Canada; USD 41 elsewhere (effective 2005). adv. **Document type:** *Journal, Trade.* **Description:** Showcases Arizona's technology assets through company profiles, feature stories, R&D analysis, entrepreneur spotlights and trend reports.
Published by: Arizona Technology Council, 1295 W Washington St, Ste 104, Tempe, AZ 85281. TEL 602-343-8324, FAX 602-343-8330, http://www.aztechcouncil.org/custom.cfm?name=c_TechConnect.cfm&nav=Resources. Ed., Pub. Kathy Sacks. adv.: color page USD 3,575; trim 8.375 x 10.875. Circ: 25,000 (paid and controlled).

330.9 RUS
TEKHNIKA, EKONOMIKA. SERIYA. EKONOMIKA ZA RUBEZHOM. Text in Russian. q. USD 85 in United States.
Indexed: RASB.
Published by: V.I.M.I., Volokolamskoe shosse 77, Moscow, 123584, Russian Federation. TEL 7-095-4911306, FAX 7-095-4916820. **US dist. addr.:** East View Information Services, 3020 Harbor Ln. N., Minneapolis, MN 55447. TEL 612-550-0961.

TEKUSHTA STOPANSKA KONIUNKTURA. see *STATISTICS*

TELEVISION IN ASIA PACIFIC TO THE YEAR... see *COMMUNICATIONS—Television And Cable*

TELEVISION IN EUROPE TO THE YEAR... see *COMMUNICATIONS—Television And Cable*

330.9 FRA ISSN 1290-0400
TENDANCES REGIONALES. Text in French. 1998. 11/yr. EUR 38; EUR 15 per issue (effective 2003). stat. **Document type:** *Academic/Scholarly.*
Formed by the merger of (1977-1998): Lettre Mensuelle Regionale (0180-8591); (1986-1997): Banque de France. Cahiers Regionaux (0767-6530); Which was formerly: Notes de Conjoncture Regionale
Indexed: PAIS.
Published by: Banque de France, Service Relations avec le Public, 48 rue Croix-des-Petits-Champs, Paris, 75049, France. TEL 33-1-42923908, FAX 33-1-42923940, http://www.banque-france.fr.

TENNESSEE'S BUSINESS. see *BUSINESS AND ECONOMICS—Small Business*

TEXAS LABOR MARKET REVIEW. see *BUSINESS AND ECONOMICS—Labor And Industrial Relations*

330 THA
THAILAND: ECONOMIC CONDITIONS IN AND OUTLOOK FOR. Text in Thai. 1978. a.
Published by: Bank of Thailand, Information & Public Relations Group, PO Box 154, Hua Lamphong BPC, 10331, Thailand. TEL 662-283-5619, FAX 662-280-4591. Circ: 5,000.

338 THA
THAILAND INVESTMENT; a directory of companies promoted by the Board of Investment. Text in Thai. a. USD 60. illus. **Document type:** *Directory.* **Description:** Lists about 4000 companies promoted by the Board of Investment of Thailand, and other useful contact addresses for doing business in Thailand.
Published by: Cosmic Group of Companies, 4th Fl Phyathai Bldg, Rajthevi, 31 Phyathai Rd, Bangkok, 10400, Thailand. adv.: color page USD 1,320.

330.9593 GBR ISSN 1474-1415
THAILAND QUARTERLY FORECAST REPORT. Text in English. 199?. 3/yr. GBP 330, USD 495, EUR 450 (effective 2003). **Document type:** *Journal, Trade.* **Description:** Provides a comprehensive assessment of the Thai government, economy and business environment over the next 30 months. Helps to identify opportunities and reduce risk, and answers key questions facing executives at this time.
Formerly (until 2001): Annual Country Forecast Report. Thailand (0966-8217)
Related titles: CD-ROM ed.: GBP 410, USD 675 (effective 2000); Online - full text ed.: (from EBSCO Publishing).
—CCC.
Published by: Business Monitor International Ltd., Mermaid House, 2 Puddle Dock, Blackfriars, London, EC4V 3DS, United Kingdom. TEL 44-20-72480468, FAX 44-20-72480467, subs@businessmonitor.com, http://www.businessmonitor.com/thailandforecast.html.

330.9 THA ISSN 0125-1074
THANAKHAN HAENG PRATHET THAI RAINGAN SETTHAKIT RAIDUAN/BANK OF THAILAND. MONTHLY BULLETIN. Text in Thai. 1961. m. USD 69; USD 87 in Asia; USD 99 in Europe, Africa & Oceania; USD 111 in the Americas; USD 5.75 per issue; USD 7.25 per issue in Asia; USD 8.25 per issue in Europe, Africa & Oceania; USD 9.25 per issue in the Americas (effective 2000). **Document type:** *Bulletin.*
Published by: Bank of Thailand, Information & Public Relations Group, PO Box 154, Hua Lamphong BPC, 10331, Thailand. TEL 662-283-5619, FAX 662-280-4591. Circ: 1,800.

330.9 DEU
THEMEN UND TENDENZEN; aus dem Wirtschaftsraum Mannheim. Text in German. q. **Document type:** *Magazine, Trade.*
Published by: Grunert Medien & Kommunikation GmbH, Am Paradeplatz 5-6, Mannheim, 68161, Germany. TEL 49-621-400404-0, FAX 49-621-40040488, info@grunert-medien.de, http://www.grunert-medien.de. Ed. Christian Deutsch. Circ: 6,500 (controlled).

338 MWI ISSN 0563-4784
THIS IS MALAWI. Text in English. 1964-1969; resumed 1971. m. MWK 5. adv. bk.rev. illus.; stat. back issues avail. **Document type:** *Government.*
Formerly: Vision of Malawi
Indexed: RASB.
Published by: Department of Information, PO Box 494, Blantyre, Malawi. TEL 265-620266, TELEX 44471. Ed. A Livuza. Circ: 3,000.

330.9 USA
THRIFT FINANCIAL REPORT. Text in English. q. USD 1,220 in North America; USD 2,440 elsewhere (effective 1999). **Description:** Data are available beginning March 1987 and are reported for the institution as a whole. For geographic reports, data are reported on the basis of home office location.
Media: Magnetic Tape.
Published by: (Federal Home Loan Bank Board), U.S. Department of Commerce, National Technical Information Service, 5285 Port Royal Rd, Springfield, VA 22161. TEL 703-605-6000, info@ntis.gov, http://www.ntis.gov.

TIMELY DISCLOSURE. see *BUSINESS AND ECONOMICS—Banking And Finance*

TIMER MAGAZINE. see *COMPUTERS—Internet*

330.9 LBN
TODAY'S OUTLOOK. Text in English. bi-m. USD 20 domestic to individuals; USD 50 foreign to individuals; USD 50 domestic to institutions; USD 70 foreign to institutions (effective 2003). adv. **Document type:** *Magazine, Consumer.* **Description:** Offers a unique blend of business coverage and reporting on a wide variety of topics including business reports, Middle Eastern regional issues and trends, and significant social and political events.
Address: PO Box 90792, Jdeidet el Metn, Beirut, Lebanon. TEL 961-4-714565, FAX 961-4-718566, info@todaysoutlook.com, outlook@inco.com.lb, http://www.todaysoutlook.com.

TOP 50 EUROPEAN MEDIA OWNERS. see *COMMUNICATIONS*

330.9 USA ISSN 1051-7197
TRACKING EASTERN EUROPE; executive business guide. Text in English. 1990. bi-w. USD 445; USD 465 in Canada; USD 475 in Europe. bk.rev. **Document type:** *Newsletter.* **Description:** Provides news, current trends, and listings from Eastern Europe and former Soviet marketplaces.
Published by: A M F International Consultants, 812 N Wood Ave, Ste 204, Linden, NJ 07036. TEL 908-486-3534, FAX 908-486-4084. Ed. Fred T Rossi. Pub., R&P Andrew M Findeisen.

330.9 USA
TRANSITION (WASHINGTON D.C.); the newsletter about reforming economies. Text in English. 1990. 8/yr. free. adv. bk.rev. **Document type:** *Newsletter.* **Description:** Covers transition economies, including Central and Eastern Europe, FSU, Asia, China and more.
Related titles: Online - full text ed.: Transition Newsletter; Russian ed.
Indexed: IIS.
Published by: World Bank Group, 1818 H St, NW, Washington, DC 20433. TEL 202-473-6982, jprochnow@worldbank.org, http://www.worldbank.org/transitionnewsletter. Ed. Richard Hirschler. Circ: 15,000. **Russian language ed. subscr. addr.:** International Centre for Policy Studies, International Centre for Policy Studies, 8-5 Voloska St, Kiev 250470, Ukraine. TEL 380-44-4636337, 380-44-462-4937.

330.9 USA ISSN 1020-5470
HD87
TRANSITION - WORLD BANK. Variant title: Transition Newsletter. Text in English. 1990. bi-m. **Document type:** *Newsletter.*
—CCC.
Published by: World Bank Group, 1818 H St, NW, Washington, DC 20433. TEL 202-473-1000, FAX 202-477-6391, books@worldbank.org, http://www.worldbank.org.

▼ new title ➤ refereed ✶ unverified ♦ full entry avail.

TRANSITIONS; ex-revue des pays de l'est. see *POLITICAL SCIENCE—International Relations*

TRAVAIL EMPLOI FORMATION. see *SOCIOLOGY*

TRAVEL BUSINESS ANALYST (ASIA PACIFIC EDITION). see *TRAVEL AND TOURISM*

TRAVEL BUSINESS ANALYST (EUROPEAN EDITION). see *TRAVEL AND TOURISM*

330.9 USA ISSN 1093-5428
HC10
TREND LETTER; your authoritative twice-monthly report on the forces transforming the economy, business, technology, society and the world. Text in English. 1982. fortn. USD 295 in North America; USD 535 elsewhere (effective 2005).
Document type: *Newsletter, Trade.*
Formerly (until 1997): John Naisbitt's Trend Letter (0883-136X)
—CCC.
Published by: Briefings Publishing Group (Subsidiary of: Douglas Publications, Inc.), 1101 King St, Ste 110, Alexandria, VA 22314. TEL 703-518-2343, 800-722-9221, FAX 703-684-2136, customerservice@briefings.com, http://www.trendletter.com, http://www.briefings.com. Circ: 20,000 (paid).

330 DEU ISSN 0942-1319
HC281
TRENDS (ENGLISH EDITION). Text in English. m.
Formerly (until 1988): Economic Quarterly (0174-0431)
Related titles: ♦ English ed.: Trends (Frankfurt). ISSN 0942-1300.
Published by: Dresdner Bank AG, Volkswirtschaftliche Abteilung, Frankfurt Am Main, 60301, Germany. TEL 49-69-2632153, FAX 49-69-2636973. Ed. Alfred Apholte.

330 DEU ISSN 0942-1300
TRENDS (FRANKFURT). Text in English, German. 1948. q. charts; stat. reprint service avail. from SCH. **Document type:** *Trade.*
Former titles (until 1988): Wirtschaftsberichte (0043-6259)
Related titles: ♦ English ed.: Trends (English Edition). ISSN 0942-1319.
Indexed: PAIS, RRTA, WAE&RSA.
Published by: Dresdner Bank AG, Volkswirtschaftliche Abteilung, Frankfurt Am Main, 60301, Germany. TEL 49-69-2632153, FAX 49-69-2636973. Ed. Alfred Apholte.

330 ROM ISSN 1222-7803
TRIBUNA ECONOMICA. Text in Romanian. 1974. w. ROL 3,130,400, USD 396 (effective 2000). adv. bk.rev.
Description: Provides information, analyses, studies, and economic and legal regulations.
Formerly (until Dec. 1989): Revista Economica
Indexed: RASB.
Published by: Tribuna Economica SA, Bd. Gh. Magheru 28-30, Bucharest, 70159, Romania. TEL 40-1-6595158, FAX 40-1-3102934, tribunae@tribunaeconomica.ro, tribunae@tribunaeconomica.ro. Ed. Bogdan Padure. Circ: 50,000. **Dist. by:** Rodipet S.A., Piata Presei Libere 1, sector 1, PO Box 33-57, Bucharest 3, Romania. TEL 40-21-2224126, 40-21-2226407, rodipet@rodipet.ro.

330.9 AZE
TURAN INFORMATION AGENCY. DAILY ECONOMIC BULLETIN. Text in English, Azerbaijani, Russian. d. (except Sun.). **Description:** Covers energy, finance, markets, transport, agriculture and other topics related to economics in Azerbaijan.
Related titles: Azerbaijani ed.; ♦ Russian ed.: Informatsionnoe Agentstvo Turan. Ekonomicheskii Byulleten'.
Published by: Turan Information Agency/Turna Informasiya Agentilyi, Khagani ul 33, Baku, 370000, Azerbaijan. TEL 994-12-984226, 994-12-935967, FAX 994-12-983817, root@turan.baku.az, http://www.turaninfo.com.

330 AZE
TURAN INFORMATION AGENCY. MACROECONOMIC INDEXES. Text in English. a.
Related titles: Russian ed.: Turan Informatsionnoe Agentstvo. Makroekonomicheskie Pokazateli.
Published by: Turan Information Agency/Turna Informasiya Agentilyi, Khagani ul 33, Baku, 370000, Azerbaijan. TEL 994-12-984226, 994-12-935967, FAX 994-12-983817, root@turan.baku.az, http://www.turaninfo.com.

330.9 AZE
TURAN INFORMATION AGENCY. MONTHLY ECONOMIC REVIEW. Text in English. m. **Description:** Covers privitization's progress in Azerbaijan, infrastructure development, formation of new markets, industry sector reviews, banking news, and other socio-economic developments.
Related titles: Ed.: Turan Informatsionnoe Agentstvo. Ezhemesyachnoe Ekonomicheskoe Obozrenie.
Published by: Turan Information Agency/Turna Informasiya Agentilyi, Khagani ul 33, Baku, 370000, Azerbaijan. TEL 994-12-984226, 994-12-935967, FAX 994-12-983817, root@turan.baku.az, http://www.turaninfo.com.

TURKEY. DEVLET ISTATISTIK ENSTITUSU. YAYINLAY VE ELEKTRONIK HIZMETLER KATALOGU/PUBLICATIONS AND ELECTRONIC SERVICES CATALOGUE. see *BUSINESS AND ECONOMICS—Abstracting, Bibliographies, Statistics*

330.9561 GBR ISSN 1470-7357
TURKEY QUARTERLY FORECAST REPORT. Text in English. 1994. 3/yr. GBP 330, USD 495, EUR 450 (effective 2003). **Document type:** *Journal, Trade.* **Description:** Provides a comprehensive assessment of the Turkish government, economy and business environment over the next 30 months. Helps to identify opportunities and reduce risk, and answers key questions facing executives at this time.
Formerly (until 2000): Annual Country Forecast Report. Turkey (1353-4718)
Related titles: Online - full text ed.: (from EBSCO Publishing).
—CCC.
Published by: Business Monitor International Ltd., Mermaid House, 2 Puddle Dock, Blackfriars, London, EC4V 3DS, United Kingdom. TEL 44-20-72480468, FAX 44-20-72480467, marketing@businessmonitor.com, http://www.businessmonitor.com/turkeyforecast.html.

330 TUR ISSN 0034-6500
HC491
TURKIYE IS BANKASI. REVIEW OF ECONOMIC CONDITIONS. Text in English. 1954. q. free. abstr.; charts; stat. **Document type:** *Bulletin.*
Related titles: Turkish ed.
Published by: (Economic Research and Planning Department), Turkiye Is Bankasi, Istiklal Caddesi 300, Beyoglu-Istanbul, Turkey. FAX 90-212-249-8298. Ed., R&P Kamil Sandikcioglu TEL 90-212-2927764. Circ: 1,850.

330.9 USA ISSN 1072-673X
CODEN: TCBMEW
TWIN CITIES BUSINESS MONTHLY. Text in English. 1993. m. free. **Document type:** *Magazine, Consumer.*
Published by: M S P Communications, Pillsbury Ctr, S Tower, 220 S Sixth St, Ste 500, Minneapolis, MN 55402. TEL 612-339-7571, FAX 612-339-5806, info@mspcommunications.com, http://mspcommunications.com/pubs/tcbm. Pub. Jay Novak.

330.9438 POL ISSN 0208-8045
TYGODNIK SOLIDARNOSC/SOLIDARITY WEEKLY. Text in Polish. 1981 (Aug.)-1981 (Dec.); resumed 1989 (Jun.). w. **Description:** Articles on the political and economic situation in Poland, with emphasis on the Solidarity labor movement.
Related titles: Microfilm ed.: (from PQC).
Indexed: AgrLib, RASB.
Published by: Wydawca Spolka "Tysol" Sp. z o.o, Ul. Franciszkanska 6, Warsaw, 00214, Poland. TEL 48-22-6352037 48-22-0-22 635-20-37, FAX 48-22-8317858, http://www.tygodniksolidarnosc.pol.pl/. Ed. Andrzej Gelberg.

330.9 GBR ISSN 0968-8196
U K ECONOMIC FORECASTS✶. Text in English. 1974. m. GBP 1,190, USD 1,785 (effective 1994). charts; stat. **Document type:** *Trade.* **Description:** Presents short- and medium-term views of the U.K. economy, providing detailed economic forecasts.
Formerly (until 1992): Framework Forecasts for the U K Economy (0305-5620)
Published by: Henley Centre for Forecasting Ltd., 9 Bridewell Pl, London, EC4Y 6AY, United Kingdom. TEL 0171-353-9961, FAX 0171-353-2899. Eds. Krishnan Sharma, Stephen Radley.

U K MEDIA YEARBOOK. see *COMMUNICATIONS*

U K TELEVISION FORECASTS. see *COMMUNICATIONS—Television And Cable*

THE U S A AND CANADA (YEAR). see *POLITICAL SCIENCE*

330.9021 USA ISSN 0095-926X
HB235.U6
U.S. BUREAU OF LABOR STATISTICS. C P I DETAILED REPORT. (Consumer Price Index) Text in English. 1919. m. USD 45 (effective 2001). stat. back issues avail.; reprint service avail. from CIS. **Document type:** *Government.*
Description: Compiles all current consumer price indices and measures consumer goods and services nationally and select metropolitan areas.
Formerly (1953-1974): U.S. Bureau of Labor Statistics. Consumer Price Index (0094-8616); Incorporates (1980-1985): News. Consumer Prices, Energy and Food (0737-1985)
Related titles: CD-ROM ed.; Microfiche ed.: (from CIS); Online - full text ed.: (from ProQuest Information & Learning).
Indexed: AmStI, PAIS, RASB.
—CISTI.
Published by: U.S. Department of Labor, Bureau of Labor Statistics, Postal Square Bldg., 2 Massachusetts Ave, NE, Washington, DC 20212-0001 . TEL 202-691-5200, http://www.bls.gov. **Subscr. to:** U.S. Government Printing Office, Superintendent of Documents, PO Box 371954, Pittsburgh, PA 15250-7954. TEL 202-512-1800, FAX 202-512-2250, orders@gpo.gov, http://www.access.gpo.gov.

U.S. BUREAU OF THE CENSUS. ANNUAL CAPITAL EXPENDITURES. see *BUSINESS AND ECONOMICS—Abstracting, Bibliographies, Statistics*

330.9 USA
U.S. DEPARTMENT OF STATE. QUARTERLY REPORT. Variant title: Living Costs Abroad, Quarters Allowances, and Hardship Differentials. Text in English. q. USD 10 (effective 2001).
Document type: *Government.* **Description:** Based on the difference between living costs in Washington, DC, and each of more than 160 foreign cities. Each issue also lists United States State Department housing (quarters) allowances for about half the cities and hardship differentials for all important posts. May be used to adjust the pay of American employees abroad.
Related titles: Online - full content ed.
Published by: U.S. Department of State, Bureau of Administration, Office of Allowances, Washington, DC 20522-0104. TEL 202-663-1121, AllowancesO@state.gov, http://www.state.gov/www/perdiems/quarterly_reports/, http://www.state.gov/www/perdiems/allowances_index.html.
Subscr. to: U.S. Government Printing Office, Superintendent of Documents, PO Box 371954, Pittsburgh, PA 15250-7954. TEL 202-512-1800, FAX 202-512-2250, orders@gpo.gov, http://www.access.gpo.gov.

330.9 332.6 USA
U.S. IMPORT AND EXPORT PRICE INDEXES. Text in English. m. **Document type:** *Government.*
Related titles: Diskette ed.; ♦ Series of: U.S. Bureau of Labor Statistics. National Office News Releases.
Indexed: AmStI.
Published by: U.S. Department of Labor, Bureau of Labor Statistics, Postal Square Bldg., 2 Massachusetts Ave, NE, Washington, DC 20212-0001 . TEL 202-691-5200, http://www.bls.gov. **Subscr. to:** U.S. Government Printing Office, Superintendent of Documents.

330.9 USA
U S MARKETS REVIEW. Text in English. q. (in 5 vols.).
Document type: *Trade.*
Formerly: Regional Information Service Review
Published by: D R I - McGraw-Hill, 24 Hartwell Ave, Lexington, MA 02173. TEL 617-863-5100, FAX 617-860-6332. Ed. Sara Johnson.

330.9 USA
UNEMPLOYMENT IN STATES. Text in English. m. **Document type:** *Government.*
Related titles: ♦ Series of: U.S. Bureau of Labor Statistics. National Office News Releases.
Published by: U.S. Department of Labor, Bureau of Labor Statistics, Postal Square Bldg., 2 Massachusetts Ave, NE, Washington, DC 20212-0001 . TEL 202-691-5200, http://www.bls.gov. **Subscr. to:** U.S. Government Printing Office, Superintendent of Documents.

330.9 332 HTI
UNITE DE PROGRAMMATION DU MINISTERE. BULLETIN DE CONJONCTURE. Text in French. 1956 (vol.8). q. free.
Formerly: Economie et Developpement
Published by: Unite de Programmation du Ministere, Economie des Finances et de l'Industrie, Port-au-Prince, Haiti. FAX 509-23-12-47.

330.95357 GBR ISSN 1470-7373
UNITED ARAB EMIRATES QUARTERLY FORECAST REPORT. Text in English. 1993. 3/yr. GBP 330, USD 495, EUR 450 (effective 2003). **Document type:** *Journal, Trade.*
Description: Provides a comprehensive assessment of the Emirates government, economy and business environment over the next 30 months. Helps to identify opportunities and reduce risk, and answers key questions facing executives at this time.
Formerly (until 2000): Annual Country Forecast Report. United Arab Emirates (0966-8160)
Related titles: Online - full text ed.: (from EBSCO Publishing).
—CCC.
Published by: Business Monitor International Ltd., Mermaid House, 2 Puddle Dock, Blackfriars, London, EC4V 3DS, United Kingdom. TEL 44-20-72480468, FAX 44-20-72480467, marketing@businessmonitor.com, http://www.businessmonitor.com/uaeforecast.html.

330 PAK
UNITED BANK LIMITED. ECONOMIC JOURNAL. Text in English. 1973 (vol.5). m. free. bk.rev. charts; stat.
Formerly (until Dec. 1981): United Bank Limited. Monthly Economic Newsletter
Published by: (Research Department), United Bank Limited, State Life Bldg., I.I. Chundrigar Rd., Karachi, Pakistan. TEL 224954. Ed. Jalees Ahmed Faruqui. Circ: 4,000.

338 CHE ISSN 1014-4994
UNITED NATIONS. ECONOMIC COMMISSION FOR EUROPE. ECONOMIC STUDIES. Text in English. 1949. irreg. (approx. a.). **Document type:** *Monographic series, Trade.*
Supersedes in part (in 1989): Economic Bulletin for Europe (Quarterly) (0041-638X)
Related titles: Microfiche ed.; Online - full text ed.: (from EBSCO Publishing).

Published by: United Nations, Economic Commission for Europe (ECE), Palais des Nations, Geneva 10, 1211, Switzerland. TEL 41-22-9174444, FAX 41-22-9170505, info.ece@unece.org, http://www.unece.org.

330.9 ECU
UNIVERSIDAD CENTRAL DEL ECUADOR. INSTITUTO DE INVESTIGACIONES ECONOMICAS. BOLETIN ECONOMIA. Text in Spanish. 4/yr. USD 12.50.
Indexed: PAIS.
Published by: Universidad Central del Ecuador, Instituto de Investigaciones Economicas, Ciudad Universitaria, Apdo 17 03 0724, Quito, Pichincha, Ecuador. TEL 593-2-525018, FAX 593-2-229481, secretar@iieuc.ecx.ec. Ed. Isaias Campana C.

330.9 COL ISSN 0120-3789
UNIVERSIDAD Y COOPERATIVISMO. Text in Spanish. 1975. q. COP 1,500.
Formerly: Cooperativismo y Desarrollo
Indexed: PAIS.
Published by: Cooperativa I N D E S C O, Ave. Caracas, 37-63, Bogota, CUND, Colombia. Ed. Armando Suescun.

330.96751 COD
UNIVERSITE NATIONALE DU ZAIRE, KINSHASA. INSTITUT DE RECHERCHES ECONOMIQUES ET SOCIALES. DOCUMENT DU MOIS. Text in French. 1974. q. USD 15.
Published by: Universite de Kinshasa, Institut de Recherches Economiques et Sociales, BP 257, Kinshasa, 11, Congo, Dem. Republic.

330.9 USA
UNIVERSITY OF COLORADO. BUSINESS RESEARCH DIVISION. ANNUAL BUSINESS - ECONOMIC OUTLOOK FORUM. Text in English. 1964. a. USD 25 to Colorado non-residents (effective 2001). **Document type:** *Proceedings.*
Published by: University of Colorado, Business Research Division, Campus Box 420, Boulder, CO 80309-0420. TEL 303-492-8227, FAX 303-492-3620.

338 NGA
UNIVERSITY OF JOS. CENTRE FOR DEVELOPMENT STUDIES. DEVELOPMENT STUDIES REVIEW. Text in English. irreg.
Indexed: PAIS.
Published by: University of Jos, Centre for Development Studies, Plateau State, Nigeria.

330.9 GBR
UNIVERSITY OF MANCHESTER. SCHOOL OF ECONOMIC STUDIES. DISCUSSION PAPER. Text in English. irreg. **Document type:** *Monographic series, Academic/Scholarly.*
Formerly (until 1994): University of Manchester. Department of Econometrics and Social Statistics. Discussion Paper
—BLDSC (3597.980300).
Published by: University of Manchester, School of Economic Studies, Oxford Rd, Manchester, Lancs M13 9PL, United Kingdom. TEL 44-161-275-4868, FAX 44-161-275-4812.

UNIVERSITY OF NAIROBI. INSTITUTE FOR DEVELOPMENT STUDIES. WORKING PAPER. see *HISTORY—History Of Africa*

330.968 ZAF ISSN 0259-4862
UNIVERSITY OF STELLENBOSCH. BUREAU FOR ECONOMIC RESEARCH. ECONOMIC PROSPECTS. Key Title: Economic Prospects (Stellenbosch). Text in English. 1957. q. ZAR 810 domestic includes updates; USD 165 foreign includes updates (effective 2003). Supplement avail. **Document type:** *Journal, Academic/Scholarly.* **Description:** Covers the entire South African economy, including consumer income considerations, the impact of political developments and international events. Reviews current economic trends and events and provides forecasts of inflation, exchange rates, interest rates and other factors.
Formerly (until 1986): University of Stellenbosch. Bureau for Economic Research. Survey of Contemporary Economic Conditions and Prospects (0081-5454)
Related titles: Online - full text ed.: (from International Network for the Availability of Scientific Publications, African Journals Online); ♦ Supplement(s): University of Stellenbosch. Bureau for Economic Research. Update.
Published by: Universiteit Stellenbosch, Bureau for Economic Research/Stellenbosch University, University, Private Bag 5050, Stellenbosch, 7599, South Africa. TEL 27-21-8872810, FAX 27-21-8899225, hhman@maties.sun.ac.za, http://www.journals.co.za/ej/ejour_epros.html, http://www.sun.ac.za/. Ed. P Laubscher. Circ: 800.

330.968 ZAF
UNIVERSITY OF STELLENBOSCH. BUREAU FOR ECONOMIC RESEARCH. UPDATE. Text in English. 1994. m. ZAR 830 worldwide to individuals (effective 2003).
Formed by the merger of (1983-1994): South African Business Cycle Indicators; (1989-1994): Economic Update
Related titles: ♦ Supplement to: University of Stellenbosch. Bureau for Economic Research. Economic Prospects. ISSN 0259-4862.
Indexed: ISAP.
Published by: Universiteit Stellenbosch, Bureau for Economic Research/Stellenbosch University, University, Private Bag 5050, Stellenbosch, 7599, South Africa. TEL 27-21-8872810, FAX 27-21-8899225, hhman@maties.sun.ac.za, http://www.sun.ac.za/.

UNIVERZITA KOMENSKEHO. USTAV MARXIZMU-LENINIZMU. ZBORNIK: POLITICKA EKONOMIA. see *BUSINESS AND ECONOMICS—Economic Systems And Theories, Economic History*

330.9 POL ISSN 1234-5369
UNIWERSYTET OPOLSKI. ZESZYTY NAUKOWE. EKONOMIA. Text in Polish; Summaries in English. 1965. irreg., latest vol.27, 2002. price varies; avail. on exchange basis. **Document type:** *Monographic series, Academic/Scholarly.*
Formerly (until 1994): Wyzsza Szkola Pedagogiczna, Opole. Zeszyty Naukowe. Seria A. Ekonomia (0474-2966)
Indexed: AgrLib, RASB.
Published by: Wydawnictwo Uniwersytetu Opolskiego, ul Sienkiewicza 33, Opole, 45037, Poland. TEL 48-77-4410878, wydawnictwo@uni.opole.pl. Ed. Janusz Slodczyk.

330.9 URY
URUGUAY SINTESIS ECONOMICA. Text in Spanish. s-a.
Published by: Banco Central del Uruguay, Departamento de Estadisticas Economicas, Casilla 1467, Paysando y Florida, Montevideo, Uruguay.

330.9 USA
USUAL WEEKLY EARNINGS OF WAGE AND SALARY WORKERS. Text in English. a. **Document type:** *Government.*
Related titles: ♦ Series of: U.S. Bureau of Labor Statistics. National Office News Releases.
Published by: U.S. Department of Labor, Bureau of Labor Statistics, Postal Square Bldg., 2 Massachusetts Ave, NE, Washington, DC 20212-0001 . TEL 202-691-5200, http://www.bls.gov. **Subscr. to:** U.S. Government Printing Office, Superintendent of Documents.

330.9 USA
UTAH LABOR MARKET REPORT. Text in English. 1950. m. free. **Document type:** *Newsletter, Government.* **Description:** Current labor market statistics and analysis for Utah.
Related titles: Microfiche ed.: (from CIS).
Indexed: SRI.
Published by: Workforce Services, Service Delivery Support, PO Box 45249, Salt Lake City, UT 84145-0249. TEL 801-526-9340, FAX 801-526-9238, http://www.dws.state.ut.us/wi/pubs/rm/ulmr/. Ed. Kenneth E Jensen. Circ: 4,100.

VADE MECUM: BEGROTING VAN DE SOCIALE BESCHERMING (YEAR)/SOCIAL PROTECTION BUDGET. see *PUBLIC ADMINISTRATION*

VADE MECUM: BEGROTINGSCONTROLE (YEAR)/BUDGET CONTROL. see *PUBLIC ADMINISTRATION*

VANTAGE POINT; developments in North Korea. see *POLITICAL SCIENCE*

VANUATU. STATISTICS OFFICE. STATISTICAL INDICATORS. see *BUSINESS AND ECONOMICS—Abstracting, Bibliographies, Statistics*

330.9 BRA
VENEZUELA COMPANY HANDBOOK. Text in English. a. USD 29.95. charts; stat. **Document type:** *Trade.* **Description:** Profiles the economy, recent developments in privatization and accounting rules, as well as the Caracas Stock Exchange.
Formerly: Company Handbook, Venezuela
Published by: I M F Editora Ltda., Av Almirante Barroso, 63, Grupo 409, Centro, Rio De Janeiro, RJ 20031-003, Brazil. TEL 55-21-240-4347, FAX 55-21-262-7570. **Dist. worldwide by:** Reference Press Inc.. TEL 512-454-7778, FAX 512-454-9401.

330.987 GBR ISSN 1474-1466
HC237
VENEZUELA QUARTERLY FORECAST REPORT. Text in English. 1985. 3/yr. GBP 330, USD 495, EUR 450 (effective 2003). **Document type:** *Journal, Trade.* **Description:** Provides a comprehensive assessment of the Venezuelan government, economy and business environment. Helps to identify opportunities and reduce risk, and answers key questions facing executives at this time.
Formerly (until 2001): Annual Country Forecast Report. Venezuela (0267-9957)
Related titles: CD-ROM ed.: GBP 410, USD 675 (effective 2000); Online - full text ed.: (from EBSCO Publishing).
—CCC.
Published by: Business Monitor International Ltd., Mermaid House, 2 Puddle Dock, Blackfriars, London, EC4V 3DS, United Kingdom. TEL 44-20-72480468, FAX 44-20-72480467, subs@businessmonitor.com, http://www.businessmonitor.com/venezuelaforecast.html.

330.1 DEU ISSN 0085-7661
VERBAENDE, BEHOERDEN, ORGANISATIONEN DER WIRTSCHAFT. Text in German. a. EUR 194.29 (effective 1999). **Document type:** *Directory.*
Related titles: CD-ROM ed.; Online - full text ed.: (from G B I).
Published by: Hoppenstedt Bonnier Zeitschriften GmbH, Havelstr. 9, Darmstadt, 64295, Germany. TEL 49-6151-380-0, FAX 49-6151-380-360, engelhardt@hopp.de, http://www.firmendatenbank.de. Circ: 35,800.

330.9 RUS
VESTNIK EKONOMIKI. Text in Russian. 1995. s-m. USD 764 foreign (effective 2004). **Document type:** *Journal, Trade.*
Indexed: RASB, RefZh.
Published by: (Ministerstvo Ekonomiki Rossiiskoi Federatsii), Rossiiskoe Agentstvo Mezhdunarodnoi Informatsii R I A Novosti, Zubovskii bulv 4, Moscow, 119021, Russian Federation. TEL 7-095-2012746, marketing@rian.ru, http://en.rian.ru. **US dist. addr.:** East View Information Services, 3020 Harbor Ln. N., Minneapolis, MN 55447. TEL 800-477-1005, FAX 800-800-3839, eastview@eastview.com, http://www.eastview.com.

330.9597 GBR ISSN 1474-1423
VIETNAM QUARTERLY FORECAST REPORT. Text in English. 199?. 3/yr. GBP 330, USD 495, EUR 450 (effective 2003). **Document type:** *Journal, Trade.* **Description:** Provides a comprehensive assessment of the Vietnamese government, economy and business environment over the next 30 months. Helps to identify opportunities and reduce risk, and answers key questions facing executives at this time.
Formerly (until 2001): Annual Country Forecast Report. Vietnam (0966-8187)
Related titles: CD-ROM ed.: GBP 410, USD 675 (effective 2000); Online - full text ed.: (from EBSCO Publishing).
—CCC.
Published by: Business Monitor International Ltd., Mermaid House, 2 Puddle Dock, Blackfriars, London, EC4V 3DS, United Kingdom. TEL 44-20-72480468, FAX 44-20-72480467, subs@businessmonitor.com, http://www.businessmonitor.com/vietnamforecast.html.

339 HUN ISSN 0042-6148
VILAGGAZDASAG. Text in Hungarian. 1969. d. HUF 52,080 (effective 2002). adv. **Document type:** *Newspaper, Trade.*
Related titles: Online - full text ed.: ISSN 1418-1525. 1996.
Published by: Axel Springer - Budapest Kft., Varosmajor u 11, Budapest, 1122, Hungary. TEL 36-1-4885700, FAX 36-1-2025332, vgterjesztes@vilaggazdasag.hu, bayerj@axels.hu, http://www.vilaggazdasag.hu.

330.9 VIR
VIRGIN ISLANDS BUSINESS JOURNAL; serving the business community of the US Virgin Islands. Text in English. 1985. s-m. USD 25. **Description:** Covers all areas of Virgin Islands business.
Published by: Media Ventures (V.I.) Inc., 40 CCC Taarenberg, P O Box 1208, St Thomas, 00804-1208, Virgin Isl., US. TEL 809-776-2874, FAX 809-774-3636. Ed. Christopher B Garrity. Circ: 8,000.

330 USA ISSN 0042-6490
HC107.V8
VIRGINIA ECONOMIC INDICATORS. Text in English. 1967. q. free. charts; stat. **Document type:** *Bulletin.* **Description:** Includes an article on a special topic of interest to Virginia's employers and workers.
Media: Duplicated (not offset). **Related titles:** Microfiche ed.: (from CIS).
Indexed: SRI.
Published by: Employment Commission, 703 E Main St, Box 1358, Richmond, VA 23218-1358. FAX 804-225-3923. Ed. William Mezger. Circ: 1,200.

330.9 USA ISSN 1528-2406
VIRGINIA ECONOMIC TRENDS. Text in English. 1999. q. USD 225 (effective 2004).
Related titles: Online - full text ed.
Published by: Chmura Economics & Analytics, 1309 E. Cary St., Richmond, VA 23219-4153. info@chmuraecon.com, http://www.chmuraecon.com/core.htm.

330.9 USA
VISTA (DALLAS); south Texas economic trends and issues. Text in English. 1998. s-a. free. charts. back issues avail. **Document type:** *Newsletter.* **Description:** Monitors economic trends and issues in southern Texas.
Published by: Federal Reserve Bank of Dallas, PO Box 655906, Dallas, TX 75265-5906. TEL 214-922-5254, FAX 214-922-5268, kay.champagne@dal.frb.org, http://www.dallasfed.org. R&P Kay Champagne. Circ: 2,000.

330.9 TZA
VIVA AFRICA; the magazine on trade, industry and development issues in Africa. Text in English. 1980. m. **Document type:** *Trade.*
Published by: Afro-Commercial and Industrial Services, PO Box 6924, Dar Es Salaam, Tanzania.

330.9 RUS
VNESHNEEKONOMICHESKAYA DEYATEL'NOST': SOVREMENNAYA PRAKTIKA, PROBLEMY, PERSPEKTIVY. Text in Russian. m. USD 210 in United States.
Indexed: RASB.

Published by: Vneshneekonomicheskaya Deyatel'nost': Sovremennaya Praktika Problemy Perspektivy, Ul T Frunze 8-5, Moscow, 119021, Russian Federation. TEL 7-095-2450213. **US dist. addr.:** East View Information Services, 3020 Harbor Ln. N., Minneapolis, MN 55447. TEL 612-550-0961.

330.9 RUS ISSN 0236-1426
VNESHNEEKONOMICHESKIE SVYAZI ROSSII. Text in Russian. 3/yr. USD 99.95 in United States.
Indexed: RASB.
—East View.
Address: Ul Kuusinena 21-b, Moscow, 125252, Russian Federation. TEL 7-095-1987210, FAX 7-095-9430089. **US dist. addr.:** East View Information Services, 3020 Harbor Ln. N., Minneapolis, MN 55447. TEL 612-550-0961.

330.9 RUS
VNESHNEEKONOMICHESKII BYULLETEN'. Text in Russian. m. USD 245 in United States.
Indexed: RASB, RefZh.
Published by: Biznes Shkola Intel-Sintez, Profsoyuznaya ul 3, ofis 620, Moscow, 117036, Russian Federation. TEL 7-095-1299555, FAX 7-095-1247055. Ed. V P Shalashov. **US dist. addr.:** East View Information Services, 3020 Harbor Ln. N., Minneapolis, MN 55447. TEL 612-550-0961.

330.9 DEU ISSN 1435-6880
VOLKSWIRTSCHAFTEN DER WELT. Text in German. 1988. irreg., latest vol.17, 2004. price varies. **Document type:** *Monographic series, Academic/Scholarly.*
Published by: Verlag Dr. Kovac, Arnoldstr 49, Hamburg, 22763, Germany. TEL 49-40-3988800, FAX 49-40-39888055, info@verlagdrkovac.de, http://www.verlagdrkovac.de/15-2.htm.

VORTEILHAFTE GELDANLAGEN; Handbuch fuer Anleger, Berater und Vermittler. see *BUSINESS AND ECONOMICS—Banking And Finance*

VOTE AND SURVEY; magazine of political, social and economic issues. see *POLITICAL SCIENCE*

W R F COMMENT. see *RELIGIONS AND THEOLOGY*

WALL STREET DIGEST. see *BUSINESS AND ECONOMICS—Banking And Finance*

338.9 BEL ISSN 0379-3753
WALLONIE. Text in French. 1948. q. EUR 30 (effective 2005). adv. bk.rev. abstr.; bibl.; charts; illus. **Document type:** *Government.* **Description:** Covers economic developments and social issues affecting the Walloon region.
Former titles (1952-1972): Revue du Conseil Economique Wallon; Chronique du Conseil Economique Wallon
Indexed: KES, PAIS, RASB, RRTA, WAE&RSA.
Published by: Conseil Economique et Social de la Region Wallonne, Rue du Vertbois 13C, Liege, 4000, Belgium. TEL 32-4-232-9811, FAX 32-4-232-9810, Info@cesrw.be, http://www.cesrw.be/pages/27_1.html. Ed. Natalie Blanchant. Circ: 2,500.

330.9 USA ISSN 1061-1622
WARFIELD'S BUSINESS RECORD. Text in English. 1986. w. USD 30. adv. bk.rev. back issues avail. **Description:** Features stories on companies, executives, and major trends in Maryland's business.
Formerly (until 1992): Warfield's (0892-7243)
Related titles: Online - full text ed.: (from ProQuest Information & Learning).
Indexed: BusDate.
Address: 11 E Saratoga St, Baltimore, MD 21202. TEL 410-752-3849, FAX 410-332-0698. Ed. Robert A Dawson. Circ: 10,500.

WASHINGTON (STATE). EMPLOYMENT SECURITY DEPARTMENT. AREA WAGE SURVEYS. see *BUSINESS AND ECONOMICS—Labor And Industrial Relations*

WASHINGTON (STATE). EMPLOYMENT SECURITY DEPARTMENT. COUNTY LABOR MARKET AND ECONOMIC PROFILES. see *BUSINESS AND ECONOMICS—Labor And Industrial Relations*

WASHINGTON (STATE). EMPLOYMENT SECURITY DEPARTMENT. STUDIES IN INDUSTRY AND EMPLOYMENT. see *BUSINESS AND ECONOMICS—Labor And Industrial Relations*

WASHINGTON REPORT ON AFRICA. see *POLITICAL SCIENCE*

WASHINGTON REPORT ON THE HEMISPHERE. see *POLITICAL SCIENCE—International Relations*

WATER & WASTE TREATMENT: LATIN AMERICAN INDUSTRIAL REPORT. see *ENGINEERING—Civil Engineering*

WATERLINE. see *TRANSPORTATION—Ships And Shipping*

320 ECU ISSN 0252-2659
WEEKLY ANALYSIS OF ECUADORIAN ISSUES. Text in English. 1971. w. USD 480 (effective 1999). bk.rev. index. **Document type:** *Newsletter.*
Related titles: ◆ Spanish ed.: Analisis Semanal.
Published by: Walter R. Spurrier Ed. & Pub., ELIZALDE, 119 10o, Apdo 4925, Guayaquil, Guayas, Ecuador. FAX 593-4326842. Circ: 1,000.

330.9 USA
WEEKLY BUSINESS FAILURES. Text in English. w. USD 45 (effective 2000). **Description:** Provides number of weekly failures, the year-to-date total and changes from previous periods. Includes a 13-week moving average of failures, plus comment and analysis.
Media: Online - full text.
Published by: Dun & Bradstreet, Economic Analysis Department (Subsidiary of: Dun & Bradstreet Corporation), c/o Judy Webb, 3 Sylvan Way, Parsippany, NJ 07054. FAX 973-254-4063, http://www.dnb.com. R&P Judy Webb.

330.9 ZAF
WEEKLY ECONOMIC MONITOR. Text in English. w.
Media: Online - full text.
Published by: Nedbank Ltd., 135 Rivonia Road, Sandown, Sandton, Johannesburg, 2196, South Africa. TEL 011-295-6435, dennisd@nedcor.com. Ed. Dennis Dykes.

338 MWI
WEEKLY NEWS. Text in English. 1996. w. MWK 5.50. **Document type:** *Government.*
Published by: Department of Information, PO Box 494, Blantyre, Malawi. TEL 265-620266. Circ: 3,000.

330.9 GBR ISSN 0963-0864
WELSH ECONOMIC REVIEW. Text in English. s-a.?.
Description: Reviews the economic and employment situation in Wales and offers forecasts.
Published by: Cardiff Business School, Cardiff University, Aberconway Bldg, Colum Drive, Cardiff, Wales CF10 3EU, United Kingdom. TEL 44-29-20874000, FAX 44-29-20874419, http://www.cf.ac.uk. Ed. Stephen Hill.

330.9 GBR ISSN 1479-6015
WEST CARIBBEAN QUARTERLY FORECAST REPORT. Text in English. q. GBP 330, EUR 475, USD 575 (effective 2004).
Related titles: Online - full text ed.: (from EBSCO Publishing).
Published by: Business Monitor International Ltd., Mermaid House, 2 Puddle Dock, Blackfriars, London, EC4V 3DS, United Kingdom. TEL 44-20-72480468, FAX 44-20-72480467, subs@businessmonitor.com, http://www.businessmonitor.com/caribbeanforecast.html.

338 USA ISSN 1057-686X
WESTCHESTER COUNTY BUSINESS JOURNAL. Text in English. 1967. w. (Wed.). USD 60 (effective 2004). adv. bk.rev. charts; illus.; mkt.; pat.; stat. 40 p./no. 4 cols./p.; **Document type:** *Newspaper, Trade.* **Description:** Deals with local business news and information especially economic forecasts and profiles for upper management executives, professionals, entrepreneurs and business owners.
Former titles (until 198?): Westchester Business Journal (0889-5317); (until 1988): Westchester Business (0887-2309)
Related titles: Online - full text ed.: (from bigchalk, EBSCO Publishing, Factiva, Florida Center for Library Automation, Gale Group, Northern Light Technology, Inc., O C L C Online Computer Library Center, Inc., ProQuest Information & Learning).
Indexed: ABIn, BusDate, T&II.
Published by: Westfair Communications, Inc., 3 Gannett Dr, White Plains, NY 10604-3407. TEL 914-694-3600, 914-694-3600, FAX 914-694-3699, 914-694-3699, mills@westfairinc.com, http://www.businessjrnls.com. Ed. Mills Korte. Pub. Dee Delbello. R&P Bruce Spring TEL 914-694-3003. Adv. contact Michael Carney. B&W page USD 2,240, color page USD 3,460. Circ: 14,000.

330.9 AUS ISSN 0706-2176
WESTERN AUSTRALIAN ECONOMIC REVIEW. Text in English. 1981. 2/yr. AUD 80. **Document type:** *Academic/Scholarly.* **Description:** Survey of current trends and prospects for the Western Australian and Australian economies.
Published by: Chamber of Commerce & Industry of Western Australia, Hay St., E., P.O. Box 6209, Perth, W.A. 6892, Australia. TEL 61-8-93657555. Ed. Nicky Cusworth.

330.9 USA ISSN 1042-6795
WESTERN BLUE CHIP ECONOMIC FORECAST; what blue chip economists are saying about the Western states. Text in English. 1987. 10/yr. USD 110 (effective 2005). illus. back issues avail. **Document type:** *Newsletter.* **Description:** Provides the latest economic forecasts for 10 Western states: AZ, CA, CO, ID, NM, OR, TX, UT, and WA. Forecasts are furnished by economists in each state representing major banks, companies, universities, and state agencies.
Indexed: SRI.
Published by: Arizona State University, Bank One Economic Outlook Center, PO Box 874406, Tempe, AZ 85287-4406. TEL 602-965-5543, 800-448-0432, FAX 602-965-5458. Circ: 405.

WESTERN CANADIAN AEROSPACE INDUSTRY CAPABILITIES GUIDE. see *AERONAUTICS AND SPACE FLIGHT*

330.9 USA
WESTERN ECONOMIC DEVELOPMENTS. Text in English. 8/yr. free. charts; stat. **Document type:** *Newsletter.*
Related titles: Online - full text ed.
Published by: Federal Reserve Bank of San Francisco, PO Box 7702, San Francisco, CA 94120. TEL 415-974-3230, FAX 415-974-3341, http://www.frbsf.org. R&P Anita Todd.

WESTERN EUROPE (YEAR); a political and economic survey. see *POLITICAL SCIENCE*

330 JPN
WHITE PAPER ON JAPANESE ECONOMY. Text in English. 1970. a. USD 67.
Published by: (Japan. Ministry of Finance/Okura-sho, Japan. Economic Planning Agency/Keizai Keikaku-kyoku), Business Intercommunication, Inc., C.P.O. Box 587, Tokyo, 100-02, Japan. TEL 03-3486-6966, FAX 03-3486-7266.

330.9 JPN
WHITE PAPER ON THE NATIONAL LIFESTYLE. Text in English. a. JPY 2,200 (effective 2000). back issues avail. **Document type:** *Government.*
Formerly: Japan. Annual Report on the National Life
Published by: (Japan. Economic Planning Agency/Keizai Keikaku-kyoku), Ministry of Finance, Printing Bureau, 2-2-4 Toranomon, Minato-ku, Tokyo, 105-0001, Japan.

330 THA
WHOLESALE PRICE INDEXES FOR THAILAND. Text in English, Thai. 1976. m. THB 60.
Published by: Department of Business Economics, Bangkok, Thailand.

WHO'S WHO IN ECONOMIC DEVELOPMENT. see *BIOGRAPHY*

WIEN IN ZAHLEN; Ausgabe (Year). see *BUSINESS AND ECONOMICS—Abstracting, Bibliographies, Statistics*

WINDHOVER'S IN VIVO; the business and medicine report. see *MEDICAL SCIENCES*

330.9 DEU ISSN 0433-7484
HC281
WIRTSCHAFTLICHE LAGE IN DER BUNDESREPUBLIK DEUTSCHLAND. Text in German. 1947. m. stat. **Document type:** *Government.*
Published by: Bundesministerium der Finanzen, Adenauerallee 99-103, Bonn, 53105, Germany. FAX 49-228-6824629.

330.9 DEU
WIRTSCHAFTSANALYSEN. Text in German. 1974. 3/yr. free. **Document type:** *Bulletin, Trade.* **Description:** Economic situation of the Hamburg area.
Published by: Hamburgische Landesbank, Volkswirtschaftliche Abteilung, Heidenkampsweg 99, Hamburg, 20079, Germany. TEL 49-40-33332345, FAX 49-40-3333-3047, volkswirtschaft@hamburglb.de, http://www.hamburglb.de. Ed. Konrad Kentmann. R&P Ulrich Kuske. Circ: 6,000.

330.9 DEU
WIRTSCHAFTSBERICHT BERLIN. Text in German. a. free. **Document type:** *Government.*
Published by: Senatsverwaltung fuer Wirtschaft und Technologie, Martin Luther Str 105, Berlin, 10820, Germany. TEL 49-30-90138309, FAX 49-30-90137597. Ed. David Weissert. Circ: 3,000.

382 DEU ISSN 1619-8867
WIRTSCHAFTSPOLITIK IN FORSCHUNG UND PRAXIS. Text in German. 2002. irreg., latest vol.14, 2005. price varies. **Document type:** *Monographic series, Academic/Scholarly.*
Published by: Verlag Dr. Kovac, Arnoldstr 49, Hamburg, 22763, Germany. TEL 49-40-3988800, FAX 49-40-39888055, info@verlagdrkovac.de, http://www.verlagdrkovac.de/15-6.htm.

330 DEU ISSN 0042-8582
WIRTSCHAFTSWOCHE; das Nachrichtenmagazin fuer die Wirtschaft. Text in German. 1926. w. EUR 139; EUR 2.80 newsstand/cover (effective 2005). adv. bk.rev. abstr.; illus.; stat. index. reprints avail. **Document type:** *Magazine, Trade.*
Incorporates (1987-1991): Profitravel (0932-4631); (1967-1974): Plus (0032-1702); Former titles: Wirtschaftswoche: Volkswirt; Volkswirt
Related titles: Microfilm ed.: (from ALP); Online - full text ed.: (from EBSCO Publishing).
Indexed: B&I, ELLIS, KES, PAIS, PROMT, RASB, RefZh.
—IE.
Published by: Verlagsgruppe Handelsblatt GmbH, Kasernenstr 67, Duesseldorf, 40213, Germany. TEL 49-211-8870, FAX 49-211-371792, wiwo@wiwo.de, leser-service@vhb.de, http://www.wirtschaftswoche.de, http://www.vhb.de. Ed. Stefan Baron. Adv. contact Gerlinde Volk. B&W page EUR 15,900, color page EUR 21,280. Circ: 191,965 (paid and controlled).

330.9   USA   ISSN 0740-4077
WORK AMERICA; the business voice on workforce development. Text in English. m. membership only. **Description:** Reports on and provides information about current workforce development practice, policy and legislation, with particular emphasis on education and training issues and joint initiatives between business and government in this area.
Published by: National Alliance of Business, 1025 Connecticut Ave NW, # 1025, Washington, DC 20036-5405. TEL 202-289-2888, FAX 202-289-1303, info@nab.com, http://www.nab.com.

WORKING PAPER. see *BUSINESS AND ECONOMICS—Banking And Finance*

WORKING PARTY REPORTS. see *POLITICAL SCIENCE—International Relations*

330.9   USA   ISSN 0258-6770
HC59.69
➤ **THE WORLD BANK ECONOMIC REVIEW.** Text in English. 1986. 3/yr. GBP 124, USD 196, EUR 186 to institutions; GBP 83, USD 131, EUR 125 academic; GBP 130, USD 205, EUR 195 combined subscription to institutions print & online eds.; GBP 87, USD 137, EUR 131 combined subscription academic; print & online eds. (effective 2006). charts; stat.; illus. back issues avail.; reprint service avail. from PSC. **Document type:** *Journal, Academic/Scholarly.* **Description:** For economists, social scientists in government, business, and international agencies. Focuses on policy relevance and operational aspects of economics.
Related titles: Microform ed.: (from PQC); Online - full text ed.: ISSN 1564-698X. GBP 117, USD 185, EUR 176 to institutions; GBP 78, USD 123, EUR 117 academic (effective 2006) (from EBSCO Publishing, Gale Group, HighWire Press, IngentaConnect, Northern Light Technology, Inc., O C L C Online Computer Library Center, Inc., Oxford University Press Online Journals, ProQuest Information & Learning, Swets Information Services).
Indexed: ABIn, APEL, ASCA, AbAn, BAS, CurCont, DIP, FPA, FamI, ForAb, GEOBASE, HortAb, I&DA, IBR, IBSS, IBZ, IIS, JEL, NutrAb, OrnHort, PAA&I, PAIS, PCI, PN&I, PRA, RASB, RDA, S&F, SSCI, SeedAb, TDB, TriticAb, WAE&RSA. —BLDSC (9352.926200), IDS, IE, Infotrieve, ingenta. **CCC.**
Published by: (World Bank Group), Oxford University Press (Subsidiary of: Oxford University Press), 2001 Evans Rd, Cary, NC 27513. TEL 919-677-0977, 800-852-7323, FAX 919-677-1714, jnkorders@oup-usa.org, http://wber.oxfordjournals.org/, http://www.us.oup.com. Ed. Francois Bourguignon. Pub. Eric Staib. Circ. 11,000.

330.9   CHE   ISSN 1026-2628
THE WORLD COMPETITIVENESS YEARBOOK. Short title: W C Y. Text in English. 1989. a., latest 2004. CHF 850 per vol. (effective 2004); includes CD-ROM. **Document type:** *Directory, Trade.* **Description:** Comprehensive annual report on the competitiveness of nations, ranking and analyzing how a nation's environment sustains the competitiveness of enterprises.
Supersedes in part (in 1995): The World Competitive Report (1015-5449)
—CISTI.
Published by: I M D International, Ch. de Bellerive 23, Lausanne, CH-1001, Switzerland. TEL 41-21-618-0111, FAX 41-21-618-0707, http://www02.imd.ch/wcy. **Subscr. to:** P O Box 915, Lausanne CH-1001, Switzerland. TEL 41-21-618-0251, FAX 41-21-618-0204.

330   USA
HC59
WORLD ECONOMIC AND SOCIAL SURVEY; current trends and policies in the world economy. Text in English. 1945. a. USD 55 (effective 1997).
Formerly: World Economic Survey (0084-1714)
Related titles: Microfiche ed.: (from CIS); French ed.; Spanish ed.
Indexed: IIS, ILD, RASB.
—CISTI. **CCC.**
Published by: United Nations Publications, Rm DC2-853, United Nations Bldg, 2 United Nations Plaza, New York, NY 10017. TEL 212-963-8302, 800-253-9646, FAX 212-963-3489, publications@un.org, http://www.un.org/publications, http://www.un.org/Pubs.

330.9   USA   ISSN 0891-4125
WORLD ECONOMIC DATA. Text in English. 1987. irreg.
Published by: A B C - C L I O, 130 Cremona Dr, Ste C, Santa Barbara, CA 93117. TEL 805-968-1911, http://www.abc-clio.com/.

330.9   GBR   ISSN 1461-9601
WORLD ECONOMIC PROSPECTS. Text in English. 199?. irreg., latest vol.3, 2002. GBP 295, EUR 490, USD 490 per vol. (effective 2003). **Document type:** *Directory, Trade.* **Description:** Provides detailed information on economic growth in 52 countries.
Published by: Euromonitor, 60-61 Britton St, London, EC1 5UX, United Kingdom. TEL 44-20-7251-8024, FAX 44-20-7608-3149, info@euromonitor, http://www.euromonitor.com.

WORLD GOLD. see *METALLURGY*

WORLD GOLD ANALYST. see *METALLURGY*

333.5029   GBR   ISSN 0264-0732
HD9999.L436
WORLD LEASING YEARBOOK (YEAR). Text in English. 1980. a., latest 2005, 26th Ed. GBP 160, EUR 240, USD 250 (effective 2005). back issues avail. **Document type:** *Directory, Trade.* **Description:** Lists 6,800 international leasing services companies. Includes glossary of leasing terminology. Aims to serve as a reference book for the asset financing and leasing industry.
Related titles: ♦ Supplement(s): Studies in Leasing Law & Tax. —BLDSC (9356.420000). **CCC.**
Published by: Euromoney Institutional Investor Plc., Nestor House, Playhouse Yard, London, EC4V 5EX, United Kingdom. TEL 44-20-7779-8888, information@euromoneyplc.com, http://www.euromoneyplc.com/. Circ: 7,000. **Dist in the USA by:** Institutional Investor, Inc., 225 Park Ave. S., 7th Fl., New York, NY 10003-1605. TEL 212-224-3800, FAX 212-224-3974; **Dist. by:** Portica, Portica House, 2 Lady Lane Industrial Estate, Hadleigh, Ipswich, Suffolk IP7 6BQ, United Kingdom. TEL 44-1473-825500, FAX 44-870-4430816.

THE WORLD MARKET FOR HOT DRINKS. see *BEVERAGES*

330.9 320   GBR   ISSN 1364-100X
WORLD OF INFORMATION BUSINESS INTELLIGENCE REPORTS. ALBANIA. Text in English. 1990. s-a. GBP 35, USD 70 (effective 2003).
Related titles: Online - full content ed.; Online - full text ed.: (from Gale Group, IngentaConnect).
Published by: World of Information, 2 Market St, Saffron Walden, Essex CB10 1HZ, United Kingdom. TEL 44-1799-521150, FAX 44-1799-524805, info@worldinformation.com, http://www.worldinformation.com. Ed., Pub. Anthony Axon. **Subscr. addr. in the US:** PO Box 830840, Birmingham, AL 35283-0430. TEL 800-633-4931, FAX 205-995-1588.

WORLD OF INFORMATION BUSINESS INTELLIGENCE REPORTS. ALGERIA. see *BUSINESS AND ECONOMICS—International Commerce*

330.9 320   GBR   ISSN 1364-2251
WORLD OF INFORMATION BUSINESS INTELLIGENCE REPORTS. ANGOLA. Text in English. 1990. s-a. GBP 35, USD 70 (effective 2003).
Related titles: Online - full content ed.; Online - full text ed.: (from Gale Group, IngentaConnect).
Published by: World of Information, 2 Market St, Saffron Walden, Essex CB10 1HZ, United Kingdom. TEL 44-1799-521150, FAX 44-1799-524805, info@worldinformation.com, http://www.worldinformation.com. Ed., Pub. Anthony Axon. **Subscr. to:** PO Box 830840, Birmingham, AL 35283-0430. TEL 800-633-4931, FAX 205-995-1588.

330.9 320   GBR   ISSN 1364-226X
WORLD OF INFORMATION BUSINESS INTELLIGENCE REPORTS. ARGENTINA. Text in English. 1990. s-a. USD 29.95 (effective 2003).
Related titles: Online - full content ed.; Online - full text ed.: (from Gale Group, IngentaConnect).
Published by: World of Information, 2 Market St, Saffron Walden, Essex CB10 1HZ, United Kingdom. TEL 44-1799-521150, FAX 44-1799-524805, info@worldinformation.com, http://www.worldinformation.com. Ed., Pub. Anthony Axon. **Subscr. to:** PO Box 830840, Birmingham, AL 35283-0430. TEL 800-633-4931, FAX 205-995-1588.

330.9 320   GBR   ISSN 1364-2278
WORLD OF INFORMATION BUSINESS INTELLIGENCE REPORTS. AUSTRALIA. Text in English. 1990. s-a. GBP 35, USD 70 (effective 2003).
Related titles: Online - full content ed.; Online - full text ed.: (from Gale Group, IngentaConnect).
Published by: World of Information, 2 Market St, Saffron Walden, Essex CB10 1HZ, United Kingdom. TEL 44-1799-521150, FAX 44-1799-524805, info@worldinformation.com, http://www.worldinformation.com. Ed., Pub. Anthony Axon. **Subscr. to:** PO Box 830840, Birmingham, AL 35283-0430. TEL 800-633-4931, FAX 205-995-1588.

330.9 320   GBR   ISSN 1364-2286
WORLD OF INFORMATION BUSINESS INTELLIGENCE REPORTS. AUSTRIA. Text in English. 1990. s-a. GBP 35, USD 70 (effective 2003).
Related titles: Online - full content ed.; Online - full text ed.: (from Gale Group, IngentaConnect).
Published by: World of Information, 2 Market St, Saffron Walden, Essex CB10 1HZ, United Kingdom. TEL 44-1799-521150, FAX 44-1799-524805, info@worldinformation.com, http://www.worldinformation.com. Ed., Pub. Anthony Axon. **Subscr. to:** PO Box 830840, Birmingham, AL 35283-0430. TEL 800-633-4931, FAX 205-995-1588.

330.9 320   GBR   ISSN 1364-1018
WORLD OF INFORMATION BUSINESS INTELLIGENCE REPORTS. AZERBAIJAN. Text in English. 1990. s-a. GBP 35, USD 70 (effective 2003).
Related titles: Online - full content ed.; Online - full text ed.: (from Gale Group, IngentaConnect).

Published by: World of Information, 2 Market St, Saffron Walden, Essex CB10 1HZ, United Kingdom. TEL 44-1799-521150, FAX 44-1799-524805, info@worldinformation.com, http://www.worldinformation.com. Ed., Pub. Anthony Axon. **Subscr. to:** PO Box 830840, Birmingham, AL 35283-0430. TEL 800-633-4931, FAX 205-995-1588.

330.9 320   GBR   ISSN 1364-2294
WORLD OF INFORMATION BUSINESS INTELLIGENCE REPORTS. BAHAMAS. Text in English. 1990. s-a. USD 29.95 (effective 2003).
Related titles: Online - full content ed.; Online - full text ed.: (from Gale Group, IngentaConnect).
Published by: World of Information, 2 Market St, Saffron Walden, Essex CB10 1HZ, United Kingdom. TEL 44-1799-521150, FAX 44-1799-524805, info@worldinformation.com, http://www.worldinformation.com. Ed., Pub. Anthony Axon. **Subscr. to:** PO Box 830840, Birmingham, AL 35283-0430. TEL 800-633-4931, FAX 205-995-1588.

330.9 320   GBR   ISSN 1364-2308
WORLD OF INFORMATION BUSINESS INTELLIGENCE REPORTS. BAHRAIN. Text in English. 1990. s-a. GBP 35, USD 70 (effective 2003).
Related titles: Online - full content ed.
Published by: World of Information, 2 Market St, Saffron Walden, Essex CB10 1HZ, United Kingdom. TEL 44-1799-521150, FAX 44-1799-524805, info@worldinformation.com, http://www.worldinformation.com. Ed., Pub. Anthony Axon. **Subscr. to:** PO Box 830840, Birmingham, AL 35283-0430. TEL 800-633-4931, FAX 205-995-1588.

330.9 320   GBR   ISSN 1364-2316
WORLD OF INFORMATION BUSINESS INTELLIGENCE REPORTS. BANGLADESH. Text in English. 1990. s-a. GBP 35, USD 70 (effective 2003).
Related titles: Online - full content ed.; Online - full text ed.: (from Gale Group, IngentaConnect).
Published by: World of Information, 2 Market St, Saffron Walden, Essex CB10 1HZ, United Kingdom. TEL 44-1799-521150, FAX 44-1799-524805, info@worldinformation.com, http://www.worldinformation.com. Ed., Pub. Anthony Axon. **Subscr. to:** PO Box 830840, Birmingham, AL 35283-0430. TEL 800-633-4931, FAX 205-995-1588.

330.9 320   GBR   ISSN 1364-1026
WORLD OF INFORMATION BUSINESS INTELLIGENCE REPORTS. BELARUS. Text in English. 1994. s-a. GBP 35, USD 70 (effective 2003).
Related titles: Online - full content ed.; Online - full text ed.: (from Gale Group, IngentaConnect).
Published by: World of Information, 2 Market St, Saffron Walden, Essex CB10 1HZ, United Kingdom. TEL 44-1799-521150, FAX 44-1799-524805, info@worldinformation.com, http://www.worldinformation.com. Ed., Pub. Anthony Axon. **Subscr. to:** PO Box 830840, Birmingham, AL 35283-0430. TEL 800-633-4931, FAX 205-995-1588.

330.9 320   GBR   ISSN 1364-2324
WORLD OF INFORMATION BUSINESS INTELLIGENCE REPORTS. BELGIUM. Text in English. 1990. s-a. GBP 35, USD 70 (effective 2003).
Related titles: Online - full content ed.; Online - full text ed.: (from Gale Group, IngentaConnect).
Published by: World of Information, 2 Market St, Saffron Walden, Essex CB10 1HZ, United Kingdom. TEL 44-1799-521150, FAX 44-1799-524805, info@worldinformation.com, http://www.worldinformation.com. Ed., Pub. Anthony Axon. **Subscr. to:** PO Box 830840, Birmingham, AL 35283-0430. TEL 800-633-4931, FAX 205-995-1588.

330.9 320   GBR   ISSN 1364-2332
WORLD OF INFORMATION BUSINESS INTELLIGENCE REPORTS. BOLIVIA. Text in English. 1990. s-a. USD 29.95 (effective 2003).
Related titles: Online - full content ed.; Online - full text ed.: (from Gale Group, IngentaConnect).
Published by: World of Information, 2 Market St, Saffron Walden, Essex CB10 1HZ, United Kingdom. TEL 44-1799-521150, FAX 44-1799-524805, info@worldinformation.com, http://www.worldinformation.com. Ed., Pub. Anthony Axon. **Subscr. to:** PO Box 830840, Birmingham, AL 35283-0430. TEL 800-633-4931, FAX 205-995-1588.

330.9 320   GBR   ISSN 1364-1034
WORLD OF INFORMATION BUSINESS INTELLIGENCE REPORTS. BOSNIA. Text in English. 1990. s-a. GBP 35, USD 70 (effective 2003).
Related titles: Online - full content ed.; Online - full text ed.: (from Gale Group, IngentaConnect).
Published by: World of Information, 2 Market St, Saffron Walden, Essex CB10 1HZ, United Kingdom. TEL 44-1799-521150, FAX 44-1799-524805, info@worldinformation.com, http://www.worldinformation.com. Ed., Pub. Anthony Axon. **Subscr. to:** PO Box 830840, Birmingham, AL 35283-0430. TEL 800-633-4931, FAX 205-995-1588.

330.9 320   GBR   ISSN 1364-2340
WORLD OF INFORMATION BUSINESS INTELLIGENCE REPORTS. BOTSWANA. Text in English. 1990. s-a. GBP 35, USD 70 (effective 2003).

B

Related titles: Online - full content ed.; Online - full text ed.: (from Gale Group, IngentaConnect).
Published by: World of Information, 2 Market St, Saffron Walden, Essex CB10 1HZ, United Kingdom. TEL 44-1799-521150, FAX 44-1799-524805, info@worldinformation.com, http://www.worldinformation.com. Ed., Pub. Anthony Axon.
Subscr. to: PO Box 830840, Birmingham, AL 35283-0430. TEL 800-633-4931, FAX 205-995-1588.

330.9 320   GBR   ISSN 1364-2359
WORLD OF INFORMATION BUSINESS INTELLIGENCE REPORTS. BRAZIL. Text in English. 1990. s-a. USD 29.95 (effective 2003).
Related titles: Online - full content ed.; Online - full text ed.: (from Gale Group, IngentaConnect).
Published by: World of Information, 2 Market St, Saffron Walden, Essex CB10 1HZ, United Kingdom. TEL 44-1799-521150, FAX 44-1799-524805, info@worldinformation.com, http://www.worldinformation.com. Ed., Pub. Anthony Axon.
Subscr. to: PO Box 830840, Birmingham, AL 35283-0430. TEL 800-633-4931, FAX 205-995-1588.

330.9 320   GBR   ISSN 1364-2367
WORLD OF INFORMATION BUSINESS INTELLIGENCE REPORTS. BRUNEI. Text in English. 1990. s-a. GBP 35, USD 70 (effective 2003).
Related titles: Online - full content ed.; Online - full text ed.: (from Gale Group, IngentaConnect).
Published by: World of Information, 2 Market St, Saffron Walden, Essex CB10 1HZ, United Kingdom. TEL 44-1799-521150, FAX 44-1799-524805, info@worldinformation.com, http://www.worldinformation.com. Ed., Pub. Anthony Axon.
Subscr. to: PO Box 830840, Birmingham, AL 35283-0430. TEL 800-633-4931, FAX 205-995-1588.

WORLD OF INFORMATION BUSINESS INTELLIGENCE REPORTS. BULGARIA. see BUSINESS AND ECONOMICS—International Commerce

330.9 320   GBR   ISSN 1364-2375
WORLD OF INFORMATION BUSINESS INTELLIGENCE REPORTS. CAMEROON. Text in English. 1990. s-a. GBP 35, USD 70 (effective 2003).
Related titles: Online - full content ed.; Online - full text ed.: (from Gale Group, IngentaConnect).
Published by: World of Information, 2 Market St, Saffron Walden, Essex CB10 1HZ, United Kingdom. TEL 44-1799-521150, FAX 44-1799-524805, info@worldinformation.com, http://www.worldinformation.com. Ed., Pub. Anthony Axon.
Subscr. to: PO Box 830840, Birmingham, AL 35283-0430. TEL 800-633-4931, FAX 205-995-1588.

330.9 320   GBR   ISSN 1364-2383
WORLD OF INFORMATION BUSINESS INTELLIGENCE REPORTS. CANADA. Text in English. 1990. s-a. USD 29.95 (effective 2003).
Related titles: Online - full content ed.; Online - full text ed.: (from Gale Group, IngentaConnect).
Published by: World of Information, 2 Market St, Saffron Walden, Essex CB10 1HZ, United Kingdom. TEL 44-1799-521150, FAX 44-1799-524805, info@worldinformation.com, http://www.worldinformation.com. Ed., Pub. Anthony Axon.
Subscr. to: PO Box 830840, Birmingham, AL 35283-0430. TEL 800-633-4931, FAX 205-995-1588.

330.9 320   GBR   ISSN 1364-2391
WORLD OF INFORMATION BUSINESS INTELLIGENCE REPORTS. CHILE. Text in English. 1990. s-a. USD 29.95 (effective 2003).
Related titles: Online - full content ed.; Online - full text ed.: (from Gale Group, IngentaConnect).
Published by: World of Information, 2 Market St, Saffron Walden, Essex CB10 1HZ, United Kingdom. TEL 44-1799-521150, FAX 44-1799-524805, info@worldinformation.com, http://www.worldinformation.com. Ed., Pub. Anthony Axon.
Subscr. to: PO Box 830840, Birmingham, AL 35283-0430. TEL 800-633-4931, FAX 205-995-1588.

330.9 320   GBR   ISSN 1364-2405
WORLD OF INFORMATION BUSINESS INTELLIGENCE REPORTS. CHINA. Text in English. 1990. s-a. BRL 35, USD 70 (effective 2003).
Related titles: Online - full content ed.; Online - full text ed.: (from Gale Group, IngentaConnect).
Published by: World of Information, 2 Market St, Saffron Walden, Essex CB10 1HZ, United Kingdom. TEL 44-1799-521150, FAX 44-1799-524805, info@worldinformation.com, http://www.worldinformation.com. Ed., Pub. Anthony Axon.
Subscr. to: PO Box 830840, Birmingham, AL 35283-0430. TEL 800-633-4931, FAX 205-995-1588.

330.9 320   GBR   ISSN 1364-2413
WORLD OF INFORMATION BUSINESS INTELLIGENCE REPORTS. COLOMBIA. Text in English. 1990. s-a. USD 29.95 (effective 2003).
Related titles: Online - full content ed.; Online - full text ed.: (from Gale Group, IngentaConnect).

Published by: World of Information, 2 Market St, Saffron Walden, Essex CB10 1HZ, United Kingdom. TEL 44-1799-521150, FAX 44-1799-524805, info@worldinformation.com, http://www.worldinformation.com. Ed., Pub. Anthony Axon.
Subscr. to: PO Box 830840, Birmingham, AL 35283-0430. TEL 800-633-4931, FAX 205-995-1588.

330.9 320   GBR   ISSN 1364-2421
WORLD OF INFORMATION BUSINESS INTELLIGENCE REPORTS. COSTA RICA. Text in English. 1990. s-a. GBP 35, USD 70 (effective 2003). **Description:** Provides an economic analysis, key facts and features of the country, and details regarding national population, labor market and public services.
Related titles: Online - full content ed.; Online - full text ed.: (from IngentaConnect).
Published by: World of Information, 2 Market St, Saffron Walden, Essex CB10 1HZ, United Kingdom. TEL 44-1799-521150, FAX 44-1799-524805, info@worldinformation.com, http://www.worldinformation.com. Ed., Pub. Anthony Axon.
Subscr. to: PO Box 830840, Birmingham, AL 35283-0430. TEL 800-633-4931, FAX 205-995-1588.

330.9 320   GBR   ISSN 1364-243X
WORLD OF INFORMATION BUSINESS INTELLIGENCE REPORTS. COTE D'IVOIRE. Text in English. 1990. s-a. GBP 35, USD 70 (effective 2003).
Related titles: Online - full content ed.; Online - full text ed.: (from Gale Group, IngentaConnect).
Published by: World of Information, 2 Market St, Saffron Walden, Essex CB10 1HZ, United Kingdom. TEL 44-1799-521150, FAX 44-1799-524805, info@worldinformation.com, http://www.worldinformation.com. Ed., Pub. Anthony Axon.
Subscr. to: PO Box 830840, Birmingham, AL 35283-0430. TEL 800-633-4931, FAX 205-995-1588.

330.9   GBR   ISSN 1363-9102
WORLD OF INFORMATION BUSINESS INTELLIGENCE REPORTS. CROATIA. Text in English. 1996. s-a. GBP 35, USD 70 (effective 2003). **Document type:** Trade.
Related titles: Online - full content ed.; Online - full text ed.: (from Gale Group, IngentaConnect).
Published by: World of Information, 2 Market St, Saffron Walden, Essex CB10 1HZ, United Kingdom. TEL 44-1799-521150, FAX 44-1799-524805, info@worldinformation.com, http://www.worldinformation.com. Ed., Pub. Anthony Axon.
Orders in N. America to: PO Box 830840, Birmingham, AL 35283-0430. TEL 800-633-4931, FAX 205-995-1588.

330.9 320   GBR   ISSN 1364-2448
WORLD OF INFORMATION BUSINESS INTELLIGENCE REPORTS. CUBA. Text in English. 1990. s-a. GBP 35, USD 70 (effective 2003).
Related titles: Online - full content ed.; Online - full text ed.: (from Gale Group, IngentaConnect).
Published by: World of Information, 2 Market St, Saffron Walden, Essex CB10 1HZ, United Kingdom. TEL 44-1799-521150, FAX 44-1799-524805, info@worldinformation.com, http://www.worldinformation.com. Ed., Pub. Anthony Axon.
Subscr. to: PO Box 830840, Birmingham, AL 35283-0430. TEL 800-633-4931, FAX 205-995-1588.

WORLD OF INFORMATION BUSINESS INTELLIGENCE REPORTS. CZECH REPUBLIC. see BUSINESS AND ECONOMICS—International Commerce

330.9   GBR   ISSN 1364-6397
WORLD OF INFORMATION BUSINESS INTELLIGENCE REPORTS. DEMOCRATIC REPUBLIC OF CONGO. Text in English. irreg.
Related titles: Online - full text ed.: (from Gale Group, IngentaConnect).
Published by: World of Information, 2 Market St, Saffron Walden, Essex CB10 1HZ, United Kingdom. TEL 44-1799-521150, FAX 44-1799-524805, waldenpub@easynet.co.uk, info@worldinformation.com, http://www.worldinformation.com.
Subscr. to: PO Box 830840, Birmingham, AL 35283-0430.

330.9 320   GBR   ISSN 1364-2456
WORLD OF INFORMATION BUSINESS INTELLIGENCE REPORTS. DENMARK. Text in English. 1990. s-a. GBP 35, USD 75 (effective 2003).
Related titles: Online - full content ed.; Online - full text ed.: (from Gale Group, IngentaConnect).
Published by: World of Information, 2 Market St, Saffron Walden, Essex CB10 1HZ, United Kingdom. TEL 44-1799-521150, FAX 44-1799-524805, info@worldinformation.com, http://www.worldinformation.com. Ed., Pub. Anthony Axon.
Subscr. to: PO Box 830840, Birmingham, AL 35283-0430. TEL 800-633-4931, FAX 205-995-1588.

330.9 320   GBR   ISSN 1364-2464
WORLD OF INFORMATION BUSINESS INTELLIGENCE REPORTS. ECUADOR. Text in English. 1990. s-a. GBP 35, USD 70 (effective 2003).
Related titles: Online - full content ed.; Online - full text ed.: (from Gale Group, IngentaConnect).

Published by: World of Information, 2 Market St, Saffron Walden, Essex CB10 1HZ, United Kingdom. TEL 44-1799-521150, FAX 44-1799-524805, info@worldinformation.com, http://www.worldinformation.com. Ed., Pub. Anthony Axon.
Subscr. to: PO Box 830840, Birmingham, AL 35283-0430. TEL 800-633-4931, FAX 205-995-1588.

330.9 320   GBR   ISSN 1364-2472
WORLD OF INFORMATION BUSINESS INTELLIGENCE REPORTS. EGYPT. Text in English. 1990. s-a. GBP 35, USD 70 (effective 2003).
Related titles: Online - full content ed.; Online - full text ed.: (from Gale Group, IngentaConnect).
Published by: World of Information, 2 Market St, Saffron Walden, Essex CB10 1HZ, United Kingdom. TEL 44-1799-521150, FAX 44-1799-524805, info@worldinformation.com, http://www.worldinformation.com. Ed., Pub. Anthony Axon.
Subscr. to: PO Box 830840, Birmingham, AL 35283-0430. TEL 800-633-4931, FAX 205-995-1588.

330.9 320   GBR   ISSN 1364-2480
WORLD OF INFORMATION BUSINESS INTELLIGENCE REPORTS. EL SALVADOR. Text in English. 1990. s-a. GBP 35, USD 70 (effective 2003).
Related titles: Online - full content ed.; Online - full text ed.: (from Gale Group, IngentaConnect).
Published by: World of Information, 2 Market St, Saffron Walden, Essex CB10 1HZ, United Kingdom. TEL 44-1799-521150, FAX 44-1799-524805, info@worldinformation.com, http://www.worldinformation.com. Ed., Pub. Anthony Axon.
Subscr. to: PO Box 830840, Birmingham, AL 35283-0430. TEL 800-633-4931, FAX 205-995-1588.

330.9 320   GBR   ISSN 1364-1042
WORLD OF INFORMATION BUSINESS INTELLIGENCE REPORTS. ESTONIA. Text in English. 1990. s-a. GBP 35, USD 70 (effective 2003).
Related titles: Online - full content ed.; Online - full text ed.: (from Gale Group, IngentaConnect).
Published by: World of Information, 2 Market St, Saffron Walden, Essex CB10 1HZ, United Kingdom. TEL 44-1799-521150, FAX 44-1799-524805, info@worldinformation.com, http://www.worldinformation.com. Ed., Pub. Anthony Axon.
Subscr. to: PO Box 830840, Birmingham, AL 35283-0430. TEL 800-633-4931, FAX 205-995-1588.

330.9 320   GBR   ISSN 1364-2499
WORLD OF INFORMATION BUSINESS INTELLIGENCE REPORTS. FINLAND. Text in English. 1990. s-a. GBP 35, USD 70 (effective 2003).
Related titles: Online - full content ed.; Online - full text ed.: (from Gale Group, IngentaConnect).
Published by: World of Information, 2 Market St, Saffron Walden, Essex CB10 1HZ, United Kingdom. TEL 44-1799-521150, FAX 44-1799-524805, info@worldinformation.com, http://www.worldinformation.com. Ed., Pub. Anthony Axon.
Subscr. to: PO Box 830840, Birmingham, AL 35283-0430. TEL 800-633-4931, FAX 205-995-1588.

330.9 320   GBR   ISSN 1364-3258
WORLD OF INFORMATION BUSINESS INTELLIGENCE REPORTS. FRANCE. Text in English. 1990. s-a. GBP 35, USD 70 (effective 2003).
Related titles: Online - full content ed.
Published by: World of Information, 2 Market St, Saffron Walden, Essex CB10 1HZ, United Kingdom. TEL 44-1799-521150, FAX 44-1799-524805, info@worldinformation.com, http://www.worldinformation.com. Ed., Pub. Anthony Axon.
Subscr. to: PO Box 830840, Birmingham, AL 35283-0430. TEL 800-633-4931, FAX 205-995-1588.

330.9 320   GBR   ISSN 1364-3266
WORLD OF INFORMATION BUSINESS INTELLIGENCE REPORTS. GABON. Text in English. 1990. s-a. GBP 35, USD 70 (effective 2003).
Related titles: Online - full content ed.; Online - full text ed.: (from Gale Group, IngentaConnect).
Published by: World of Information, 2 Market St, Saffron Walden, Essex CB10 1HZ, United Kingdom. TEL 44-1799-521150, FAX 44-1799-524805, info@worldinformation.com, http://www.worldinformation.com. Ed., Pub. Anthony Axon.
Subscr. addr. in the US: PO Box 830840, Birmingham, AL 35283-0430. TEL 800-633-4931, FAX 205-995-1588.

330.9 320   GBR   ISSN 1364-3274
WORLD OF INFORMATION BUSINESS INTELLIGENCE REPORTS. GERMANY. Text in English. 1990. s-a. GBP 35, USD 70 (effective 2003).
Related titles: Online - full content ed.; Online - full text ed.: (from Gale Group, IngentaConnect).
Published by: World of Information, 2 Market St, Saffron Walden, Essex CB10 1HZ, United Kingdom. TEL 44-1799-521150, FAX 44-1799-524805, info@worldinformation.com, http://www.worldinformation.com. Ed., Pub. Anthony Axon.
Subscr. to: PO Box 830840, Birmingham, AL 35283-0430. TEL 800-633-4931, FAX 205-995-1588.

330.9 320   GBR   ISSN 1364-3282
WORLD OF INFORMATION BUSINESS INTELLIGENCE REPORTS. GHANA. Text in English. 1990. s-a. GBP 35, USD 70 (effective 2003).

Related titles: Online - full content ed.; Online - full text ed.: (from Gale Group, IngentaConnect).
Published by: World of Information, 2 Market St, Saffron Walden, Essex CB10 1HZ, United Kingdom. TEL 44-1799-521150, FAX 44-1799-524805, info@worldinformation.com, http://www.worldinformation.com. Ed., Pub. Anthony Axon. **Subscr. to:** PO Box 830840, Birmingham, AL 35283-0430. TEL 800-633-4931, FAX 205-995-1588.

330.9 320 GBR ISSN 1364-3290
WORLD OF INFORMATION BUSINESS INTELLIGENCE REPORTS. GREECE. Text in English. 1990. s-a. GBP 35, USD 70 (effective 2003).
Related titles: Online - full content ed.; Online - full text ed.: (from Gale Group, IngentaConnect).
Published by: World of Information, 2 Market St, Saffron Walden, Essex CB10 1HZ, United Kingdom. TEL 44-1799-521150, FAX 44-1799-524805, info@worldinformation.com, http://www.worldinformation.com. Ed., Pub. Anthony Axon. **Subscr. to:** PO Box 830840, Birmingham, AL 35283-0430. TEL 800-633-4931, FAX 205-995-1588.

330.9 320 GBR ISSN 1364-3304
WORLD OF INFORMATION BUSINESS INTELLIGENCE REPORTS. GUATEMALA. Text in English. 1990. s-a. GBP 35, USD 70 (effective 2003).
Related titles: Online - full content ed.; Online - full text ed.: (from Gale Group, IngentaConnect).
Published by: World of Information, 2 Market St, Saffron Walden, Essex CB10 1HZ, United Kingdom. TEL 44-1799-521150, FAX 44-1799-524805, info@worldinformation.com, http://www.worldinformation.com. Ed., Pub. Anthony Axon. **Subscr. to:** PO Box 830840, Birmingham, AL 35283-0430. TEL 800-633-4931, FAX 205-995-1588.

330.9 320 GBR ISSN 1364-3312
WORLD OF INFORMATION BUSINESS INTELLIGENCE REPORTS. GUYANA. Text in English. 1990. s-a. GBP 35, USD 70 (effective 2003).
Related titles: Online - full content ed.; Online - full text ed.: (from Gale Group, IngentaConnect).
Published by: World of Information, 2 Market St, Saffron Walden, Essex CB10 1HZ, United Kingdom. TEL 44-1799-521150, FAX 44-1799-524805, info@worldinformation.com, http://www.worldinformation.com. Ed., Pub. Anthony Axon. **Subscr. to:** PO Box 830840, Birmingham, AL 35283-0430. TEL 800-633-4931, FAX 205-995-1588.

330.9 320 GBR ISSN 1364-3320
WORLD OF INFORMATION BUSINESS INTELLIGENCE REPORTS. HAITI. Text in English. 1990. s-a. GBP 35, USD 70 (effective 2003).
Related titles: Online - full content ed.; Online - full text ed.: (from Gale Group, IngentaConnect).
Published by: World of Information, 2 Market St, Saffron Walden, Essex CB10 1HZ, United Kingdom. TEL 44-1799-521150, FAX 44-1799-524805, info@worldinformation.com, http://www.worldinformation.com. Ed., Pub. Anthony Axon. **Subscr. to:** PO Box 830840, Birmingham, AL 35283-0430. TEL 800-633-4931, FAX 205-995-1588.

330.9 320 GBR ISSN 1364-3339
WORLD OF INFORMATION BUSINESS INTELLIGENCE REPORTS. HONDURAS. Text in English. 1990. s-a. GBP 35, USD 70 (effective 2003).
Related titles: Online - full content ed.
Published by: World of Information, 2 Market St, Saffron Walden, Essex CB10 1HZ, United Kingdom. TEL 44-1799-521150, FAX 44-1799-524805, info@worldinformation.com, http://www.worldinformation.com. Ed., Pub. Anthony Axon. **Subscr. to:** PO Box 830840, Birmingham, AL 35283-0430. TEL 800-633-4931, FAX 205-995-1588.

330.9 320 GBR ISSN 1364-3347
WORLD OF INFORMATION BUSINESS INTELLIGENCE REPORTS. HONG KONG. Text in English. 1990. s-a. GBP 35, USD 70 (effective 2003).
Related titles: Online - full content ed.; Online - full text ed.: (from Gale Group, IngentaConnect).
Published by: World of Information, 2 Market St, Saffron Walden, Essex CB10 1HZ, United Kingdom. TEL 44-1799-521150, FAX 44-1799-524805, info@worldinformation.com, http://www.worldinformation.com. Ed., Pub. Anthony Axon. **Subscr. to:** PO Box 830840, Birmingham, AL 35283-0430. TEL 800-633-4931, FAX 205-995-1588.

WORLD OF INFORMATION BUSINESS INTELLIGENCE REPORTS. HUNGARY. see *BUSINESS AND ECONOMICS—International Commerce*

330.9 320 GBR ISSN 1364-3355
WORLD OF INFORMATION BUSINESS INTELLIGENCE REPORTS. INDIA. Text in English. 1990. s-a. GBP 35, USD 70 (effective 2003).
Related titles: Online - full content ed.; Online - full text ed.: (from Gale Group, IngentaConnect).
Published by: World of Information, 2 Market St, Saffron Walden, Essex CB10 1HZ, United Kingdom. TEL 44-1799-521150, FAX 44-1799-524805, info@worldinformation.com, http://www.worldinformation.com. Ed., Pub. Anthony Axon. **Subscr. to:** PO Box 830840, Birmingham, AL 35283-0430. TEL 800-633-4931, FAX 205-995-1588.

330.9 320 GBR ISSN 1364-3363
WORLD OF INFORMATION BUSINESS INTELLIGENCE REPORTS. INDONESIA. Text in English. 1990. s-a. GBP 35, USD 70 (effective 2003).
Related titles: Online - full content ed.; Online - full text ed.: (from Gale Group, IngentaConnect).
Published by: World of Information, 2 Market St, Saffron Walden, Essex CB10 1HZ, United Kingdom. TEL 44-1799-521150, FAX 44-1799-524805, info@worldinformation.com, http://www.worldinformation.com. Ed., Pub. Anthony Axon. **Subscr. to:** PO Box 830840, Birmingham, AL 35283-0430. TEL 800-633-4931, FAX 205-995-1588.

330.9 320 GBR ISSN 1364-3371
WORLD OF INFORMATION BUSINESS INTELLIGENCE REPORTS. IRAN. Text in English. 1990. s-a. GBP 35, USD 70 (effective 2003).
Related titles: Online - full content ed.; Online - full text ed.: (from Gale Group, IngentaConnect).
Published by: World of Information, 2 Market St, Saffron Walden, Essex CB10 1HZ, United Kingdom. TEL 44-1799-521150, FAX 44-1799-524805, info@worldinformation.com, http://www.worldinformation.com. Ed., Pub. Anthony Axon. **Subscr. to:** PO Box 830840, Birmingham, AL 35283-0430. TEL 800-633-4931, FAX 205-995-1588.

330.9 320 GBR ISSN 1364-338X
WORLD OF INFORMATION BUSINESS INTELLIGENCE REPORTS. IRAQ. Text in English. 1990. s-a. GBP 35, USD 70 (effective 2003).
Related titles: Online - full content ed.; Online - full text ed.: (from Gale Group, IngentaConnect).
Published by: World of Information, 2 Market St, Saffron Walden, Essex CB10 1HZ, United Kingdom. TEL 44-1799-521150, FAX 44-1799-524805, info@worldinformation.com, http://www.worldinformation.com. Ed., Pub. Anthony Axon. **Subscr. to:** PO Box 830840, Birmingham, AL 35283-0430. TEL 800-633-4931, FAX 205-995-1588.

330.9 320 GBR ISSN 1364-3398
WORLD OF INFORMATION BUSINESS INTELLIGENCE REPORTS. IRELAND. Text in English. 1990. s-a. GBP 35, USD 70 (effective 2003).
Related titles: Online - full content ed.; Online - full text ed.: (from Gale Group, IngentaConnect).
Published by: World of Information, 2 Market St, Saffron Walden, Essex CB10 1HZ, United Kingdom. TEL 44-1799-521150, FAX 44-1799-524805, info@worldinformation.com, http://www.worldinformation.com. Ed., Pub. Anthony Axon. **Subscr. to:** PO Box 830840, Birmingham, AL 35283-0430. TEL 800-633-4931, FAX 205-995-1588.

330.9 320 GBR ISSN 1364-3401
WORLD OF INFORMATION BUSINESS INTELLIGENCE REPORTS. ISRAEL. Text in English. 1990. s-a. GBP 35, USD 70 (effective 2003).
Related titles: Online - full content ed.; Online - full text ed.: (from Gale Group, IngentaConnect).
Published by: World of Information, 2 Market St, Saffron Walden, Essex CB10 1HZ, United Kingdom. TEL 44-1799-521150, FAX 44-1799-524805, info@worldinformation.com, http://www.worldinformation.com. Ed., Pub. Anthony Axon. **Subscr. to:** PO Box 830840, Birmingham, AL 35283-0430. TEL 800-633-4931, FAX 205-995-1588.

330.9 320 GBR ISSN 1364-341X
WORLD OF INFORMATION BUSINESS INTELLIGENCE REPORTS. ITALY. Text in English. 1990. s-a. GBP 35, USD 70 (effective 2003).
Related titles: Online - full content ed.; Online - full text ed.: (from Gale Group, IngentaConnect).
Published by: World of Information, 2 Market St, Saffron Walden, Essex CB10 1HZ, United Kingdom. TEL 44-1799-521150, FAX 44-1799-524805, info@worldinformation.com, http://www.worldinformation.com. Ed., Pub. Anthony Axon. **Subscr. to:** PO Box 830840, Birmingham, AL 35283-0430. TEL 800-633-4931, FAX 205-995-1588.

330.9 320 GBR ISSN 1364-3428
WORLD OF INFORMATION BUSINESS INTELLIGENCE REPORTS. JAMAICA. Text in English. 1990. s-a. GBP 35, USD 70 (effective 2003).
Related titles: Online - full content ed.; Online - full text ed.: (from Gale Group, IngentaConnect).
Published by: World of Information, 2 Market St, Saffron Walden, Essex CB10 1HZ, United Kingdom. TEL 44-1799-521150, FAX 44-1799-524805, info@worldinformation.com, http://www.worldinformation.com. Ed., Pub. Anthony Axon. **Subscr. to:** PO Box 830840, Birmingham, AL 35283-0430. TEL 800-633-4931, FAX 205-995-1588.

330.9 320 GBR ISSN 1364-3436
WORLD OF INFORMATION BUSINESS INTELLIGENCE REPORTS. JAPAN. Text in English. 1990. s-a. GBP 35, USD 70 (effective 2003).
Related titles: Online - full content ed.; Online - full text ed.: (from Gale Group, IngentaConnect).
Published by: World of Information, 2 Market St, Saffron Walden, Essex CB10 1HZ, United Kingdom. TEL 44-1799-521150, FAX 44-1799-524805, k, info@worldinformation.com, http://www.worldinformation.com. Ed., Pub. Anthony Axon. **Subscr. to:** PO Box 830840, Birmingham, AL 35283-0430. TEL 800-633-4931, FAX 205-995-1588.

330.9 320 GBR ISSN 1364-3444
WORLD OF INFORMATION BUSINESS INTELLIGENCE REPORTS. JORDAN. Text in English. 1990. s-a. GBP 35, USD 70 (effective 2003).
Related titles: Online - full content ed.; Online - full text ed.: (from Gale Group, IngentaConnect).
Published by: World of Information, 2 Market St, Saffron Walden, Essex CB10 1HZ, United Kingdom. TEL 44-1799-521150, FAX 44-1799-524805, info@worldinformation.com, http://www.worldinformation.com. Ed., Pub. Anthony Axon. **Subscr. to:** PO Box 830840, Birmingham, AL 35283-0430. TEL 800-633-4931, FAX 205-995-1588.

330.9 320 GBR ISSN 1364-1050
WORLD OF INFORMATION BUSINESS INTELLIGENCE REPORTS. KAZAKHSTAN. Text in English. 1994. s-a. GBP 35, USD 70 (effective 2003).
Related titles: Online - full content ed.; Online - full text ed.: (from Gale Group, IngentaConnect).
Published by: World of Information, 2 Market St, Saffron Walden, Essex CB10 1HZ, United Kingdom. TEL 44-1799-521150, FAX 44-1799-524805, info@worldinformation.com, http://www.worldinformation.com. Ed., Pub. Anthony Axon. **Subscr. to:** PO Box 830840, Birmingham, AL 35283-0430. TEL 800-633-4931, FAX 205-995-1588.

330.9 320 GBR ISSN 1364-3452
WORLD OF INFORMATION BUSINESS INTELLIGENCE REPORTS. KENYA. Text in English. 1990. s-a. GBP 35, USD 70 (effective 2003).
Related titles: Online - full content ed.; Online - full text ed.: (from Gale Group, IngentaConnect).
Published by: World of Information, 2 Market St, Saffron Walden, Essex CB10 1HZ, United Kingdom. TEL 44-1799-521150, FAX 44-1799-524805, info@worldinformation.com, http://www.worldinformation.com. Ed., Pub. Anthony Axon. **Subscr. to:** PO Box 830840, Birmingham, AL 35283-0430. TEL 800-633-4931, FAX 205-995-1588.

330.9 320 GBR ISSN 1364-3460
WORLD OF INFORMATION BUSINESS INTELLIGENCE REPORTS. KOREA. Text in English. 1990. s-a. GBP 35, USD 70 (effective 2003).
Related titles: Online - full content ed.; Online - full text ed.: (from Gale Group, IngentaConnect).
Published by: World of Information, 2 Market St, Saffron Walden, Essex CB10 1HZ, United Kingdom. TEL 44-1799-521150, FAX 44-1799-524805, info@worldinformation.com, http://www.worldinformation.com. Ed., Pub. Anthony Axon. **Subscr. to:** PO Box 830840, Birmingham, AL 35283-0430. TEL 800-633-4931, FAX 205-995-1588.

330.9 320 GBR ISSN 1364-3479
WORLD OF INFORMATION BUSINESS INTELLIGENCE REPORTS. KUWAIT. Text in English. 1990. s-a. GBP 35, USD 70 (effective 2003).
Related titles: Online - full content ed.; Online - full text ed.: (from Gale Group, IngentaConnect).
Published by: World of Information, 2 Market St, Saffron Walden, Essex CB10 1HZ, United Kingdom. TEL 44-1799-521150, FAX 44-1799-524805, info@worldinformation.com, http://www.worldinformation.com. Ed., Pub. Anthony Axon. **Subscr. to:** PO Box 830840, Birmingham, AL 35283-0430. TEL 800-633-4931, FAX 205-995-1588.

330.9 320 GBR ISSN 1364-1069
WORLD OF INFORMATION BUSINESS INTELLIGENCE REPORTS. KYRGHYZSTAN. Text in English. 1990. s-a. GBP 35, USD 70 (effective 2003).
Related titles: Online - full content ed.; Online - full text ed.: (from Gale Group, IngentaConnect).
Published by: World of Information, 2 Market St, Saffron Walden, Essex CB10 1HZ, United Kingdom. TEL 44-1799-521150, FAX 44-1799-524805, info@worldinformation.com, http://www.worldinformation.com. Ed., Pub. Anthony Axon. **Subscr. to:** PO Box 830840, Birmingham, AL 35283-0430. TEL 800-633-4931, FAX 205-995-1588.

330.9 320 GBR ISSN 1364-1077
WORLD OF INFORMATION BUSINESS INTELLIGENCE REPORTS. LATVIA. Text in English. 1990. s-a. GBP 35, USD 70 (effective 2003).
Related titles: Online - full content ed.
Published by: World of Information, 2 Market St, Saffron Walden, Essex CB10 1HZ, United Kingdom. TEL 44-1799-521150, FAX 44-1799-524805, info@worldinformation.com, http://www.worldinformation.com. Ed., Pub. Anthony Axon. **Subscr. to:** PO Box 830840, Birmingham, AL 35283-0430. TEL 800-633-4931, FAX 205-995-1588.

330.9 320 GBR ISSN 1364-3487
WORLD OF INFORMATION BUSINESS INTELLIGENCE REPORTS. LEBANON. Text in English. 1990. s-a. GBP 35, USD 70 (effective 2003).

B

▼ *new title* ➤ *refereed* ✶ *unverified* ♦ *full entry avail.*

Related titles: Online - full content ed.; Online - full text ed.: (from Gale Group, IngentaConnect).
Published by: World of Information, 2 Market St, Saffron Walden, Essex CB10 1HZ, United Kingdom. TEL 44-1799-521150, FAX 44-1799-524805, info@worldinformation.com, http://www.worldinformation.com. Ed., Pub. Anthony Axon. **Subscr. to:** PO Box 830840, Birmingham, AL 35283-0430. TEL 800-633-4931, FAX 205-995-1588.

330.9 320 GBR ISSN 1364-3495
WORLD OF INFORMATION BUSINESS INTELLIGENCE REPORTS. LIBYA. Text in English. 1990. s-a. GBP 35, USD 70 (effective 2003).
Related titles: Online - full content ed.; Online - full text ed.: (from Gale Group, IngentaConnect).
Published by: World of Information, 2 Market St, Saffron Walden, Essex CB10 1HZ, United Kingdom. TEL 44-1799-521150, FAX 44-1799-524805, info@worldinformation.com, http://www.worldinformation.com. Ed., Pub. Anthony Axon. **Subscr. to:** PO Box 830840, Birmingham, AL 35283-0430. TEL 800-633-4931, FAX 205-995-1588.

330.9 320 GBR ISSN 1364-1085
WORLD OF INFORMATION BUSINESS INTELLIGENCE REPORTS. LITHUANIA. Text in English. 1990. s-a. GBP 35, USD 70 (effective 2003).
Related titles: Online - full content ed.; Online - full text ed.: (from Gale Group, IngentaConnect).
Published by: World of Information, 2 Market St, Saffron Walden, Essex CB10 1HZ, United Kingdom. TEL 44-1799-521150, FAX 44-1799-524805, info@worldinformation.com, http://www.worldinformation.com. Ed., Pub. Anthony Axon. **Subscr. to:** PO Box 830840, Birmingham, AL 35283-0430. TEL 800-633-4931, FAX 205-995-1588.

330.9 320 GBR ISSN 1364-4556
WORLD OF INFORMATION BUSINESS INTELLIGENCE REPORTS. LUXEMBOURG. Text in English. 1990. s-a. GBP 35, USD 70 (effective 2003).
Related titles: Online - full content ed.; Online - full text ed.: (from Gale Group, IngentaConnect).
Published by: World of Information, 2 Market St, Saffron Walden, Essex CB10 1HZ, United Kingdom. TEL 44-1799-521150, FAX 44-1799-524805, info@worldinformation.com, http://www.worldinformation.com. Ed., Pub. Anthony Axon. **Subscr. to:** PO Box 830840, Birmingham, AL 35283-0430. TEL 800-633-4931, FAX 205-995-1588.

330.9 382 GBR ISSN 1474-4368
WORLD OF INFORMATION BUSINESS INTELLIGENCE REPORTS. MACEDONIA. Text in English. 2001. irreg. GBP 35, USD 70 (effective 2003).
Related titles: Online - full text ed.: (from Gale Group, IngentaConnect).
Published by: World of Information, 2 Market St, Saffron Walden, Essex CB10 1HZ, United Kingdom. TEL 44-1799-521150, FAX 44-1799-524805, info@worldinformation.com, http://www.worldinformation.com. **Subscr. to:** PO Box 830840, Birmingham, AL 35283-0430. TEL 800-633-4931, FAX 205-995-1588.

330.9 320 GBR ISSN 1364-4564
WORLD OF INFORMATION BUSINESS INTELLIGENCE REPORTS. MALAYSIA. Text in English. 1990. s-a. GBP 35, USD 70 (effective 2003).
Related titles: Online - full content ed.; Online - full text ed.: (from Gale Group, IngentaConnect).
Published by: World of Information, 2 Market St, Saffron Walden, Essex CB10 1HZ, United Kingdom. TEL 44-1799-521150, FAX 44-1799-524805, info@worldinformation.com, http://www.worldinformation.com. Ed., Pub. Anthony Axon. **Subscr. to:** PO Box 830840, Birmingham, AL 35283-0430. TEL 800-633-4931, FAX 205-995-1588.

330.9 320 GBR ISSN 1364-4572
WORLD OF INFORMATION BUSINESS INTELLIGENCE REPORTS. MEXICO. Text in English. 1990. s-a. GBP 35, USD 70 (effective 2003).
Related titles: Online - full content ed.; Online - full text ed.: (from Gale Group, IngentaConnect).
Published by: World of Information, 2 Market St, Saffron Walden, Essex CB10 1HZ, United Kingdom. TEL 44-1799-521150, FAX 44-1799-524805, info@worldinformation.com, http://www.worldinformation.com. Ed., Pub. Anthony Axon. **Subscr. to:** PO Box 830840, Birmingham, AL 35283-0430. TEL 800-633-4931, FAX 205-995-1588.

330.9 320 GBR ISSN 1364-1093
WORLD OF INFORMATION BUSINESS INTELLIGENCE REPORTS. MOLDOVA. Text in English. 1990. s-a. GBP 35, USD 70 (effective 2003).
Related titles: Online - full content ed.; Online - full text ed.: (from Gale Group, IngentaConnect).
Published by: World of Information, 2 Market St, Saffron Walden, Essex CB10 1HZ, United Kingdom. TEL 44-1799-521150, FAX 44-1799-524805, info@worldinformation.com, http://www.worldinformation.com. Ed., Pub. Anthony Axon. **Subscr. to:** PO Box 830840, Birmingham, AL 35283-0430. TEL 800-633-4931, FAX 205-995-1588.

330.9 320 GBR ISSN 1364-4580
WORLD OF INFORMATION BUSINESS INTELLIGENCE REPORTS. MOROCCO. Text in English. 1990. s-a. GBP 35, USD 70 (effective 2003).
Related titles: Online - full content ed.; Online - full text ed.: (from Gale Group, IngentaConnect).
Published by: World of Information, 2 Market St, Saffron Walden, Essex CB10 1HZ, United Kingdom. TEL 44-1799-521150, FAX 44-1799-524805, info@worldinformation.com, http://www.worldinformation.com. Ed., Pub. Anthony Axon. **Subscr. to:** PO Box 830840, Birmingham, AL 35283-0430. TEL 800-633-4931, FAX 205-995-1588.

330.9 320 GBR ISSN 1364-4599
WORLD OF INFORMATION BUSINESS INTELLIGENCE REPORTS. MOZAMBIQUE. Text in English. 1990. s-a. GBP 35, USD 70 (effective 2003).
Related titles: Online - full content ed.; Online - full text ed.: (from Gale Group, IngentaConnect).
Published by: World of Information, 2 Market St, Saffron Walden, Essex CB10 1HZ, United Kingdom. TEL 44-1799-521150, FAX 44-1799-524805, info@worldinformation.com, http://www.worldinformation.com. Ed., Pub. Anthony Axon. **Subscr. to:** PO Box 830840, Birmingham, AL 35283-0430. TEL 800-633-4931, FAX 205-995-1588.

330.9 320 GBR ISSN 1364-4602
WORLD OF INFORMATION BUSINESS INTELLIGENCE REPORTS. NETHERLANDS. Text in English. 1990. s-a. GBP 35, USD 70 (effective 2003).
Related titles: Online - full content ed.; Online - full text ed.: (from Gale Group, IngentaConnect).
Published by: World of Information, 2 Market St, Saffron Walden, Essex CB10 1HZ, United Kingdom. TEL 44-1799-521150, FAX 44-1799-524805, info@worldinformation.com, http://www.worldinformation.com. Ed., Pub. Anthony Axon. **Subscr. to:** PO Box 830840, Birmingham, AL 35283-0430. TEL 800-633-4931, FAX 205-995-1588.

330.9 320 GBR ISSN 1364-4610
WORLD OF INFORMATION BUSINESS INTELLIGENCE REPORTS. NEW ZEALAND. Text in English. 1990. s-a. GBP 35, USD 70 (effective 2003).
Related titles: Online - full content ed.; Online - full text ed.: (from Gale Group, IngentaConnect).
Published by: World of Information, 2 Market St, Saffron Walden, Essex CB10 1HZ, United Kingdom. TEL 44-1799-521150, FAX 44-1799-524805, info@worldinformation.com, http://www.worldinformation.com. Ed., Pub. Anthony Axon. **Subscr. to:** PO Box 830840, Birmingham, AL 35283-0430. TEL 800-633-4931, FAX 205-995-1588.

330.9 320 GBR ISSN 1364-4629
WORLD OF INFORMATION BUSINESS INTELLIGENCE REPORTS. NICARAGUA. Text in English. 1990. s-a. GBP 35, USD 70 (effective 2003).
Related titles: Online - full content ed.
Published by: World of Information, 2 Market St, Saffron Walden, Essex CB10 1HZ, United Kingdom. TEL 44-1799-521150, FAX 44-1799-524805, info@worldinformation.com, http://www.worldinformation.com. Ed., Pub. Anthony Axon. **Subscr. to:** PO Box 830840, Birmingham, AL 35283-0430. TEL 800-633-4931, FAX 205-995-1588.

330.9 320 GBR ISSN 1364-4637
WORLD OF INFORMATION BUSINESS INTELLIGENCE REPORTS. NIGERIA. Text in English. 1990. s-a. GBP 35, USD 70 (effective 2003).
Related titles: Online - full content ed.; Online - full text ed.: (from Gale Group, IngentaConnect).
Published by: World of Information, 2 Market St, Saffron Walden, Essex CB10 1HZ, United Kingdom. TEL 44-1799-521150, FAX 44-1799-524805, info@worldinformation.com, http://www.worldinformation.com. Ed., Pub. Anthony Axon. **Subscr. to:** PO Box 830840, Birmingham, AL 35283-0430. TEL 800-633-4931, FAX 205-995-1588.

330.9 320 GBR ISSN 1364-4645
WORLD OF INFORMATION BUSINESS INTELLIGENCE REPORTS. NORWAY. Text in English. 1990. s-a. GBP 35, USD 70 (effective 2003).
Related titles: Online - full content ed.; Online - full text ed.: (from Gale Group, IngentaConnect).
Published by: World of Information, 2 Market St, Saffron Walden, Essex CB10 1HZ, United Kingdom. TEL 44-1799-521150, FAX 44-1799-524805, info@worldinformation.com, http://www.worldinformation.com. Ed., Pub. Anthony Axon. **Subscr. to:** PO Box 830840, Birmingham, AL 35283-0430. TEL 800-633-4931, FAX 205-995-1588.

330.9 320 GBR ISSN 1364-4653
WORLD OF INFORMATION BUSINESS INTELLIGENCE REPORTS. OMAN. Text in English. 1990. s-a. GBP 35, USD 70 (effective 2003).
Related titles: Online - full content ed.; Online - full text ed.: (from Gale Group, IngentaConnect).
Published by: World of Information, 2 Market St, Saffron Walden, Essex CB10 1HZ, United Kingdom. TEL 44-1799-521150, FAX 44-1799-524805, info@worldinformation.com, http://www.worldinformation.com. Ed., Pub. Anthony Axon. **Subscr. to:** PO Box 830840, Birmingham, AL 35283-0430. TEL 800-633-4931, FAX 205-995-1588.

330.9 320 GBR ISSN 1364-4661
WORLD OF INFORMATION BUSINESS INTELLIGENCE REPORTS. PAKISTAN. Text in English. 1990. s-a. GBP 35, USD 70 (effective 2003).
Related titles: Online - full content ed.; Online - full text ed.: (from Gale Group, IngentaConnect).
Published by: World of Information, 2 Market St, Saffron Walden, Essex CB10 1HZ, United Kingdom. TEL 44-1799-521150, FAX 44-1799-524805, info@worldinformation.com, http://www.worldinformation.com. Ed., Pub. Anthony Axon. **Subscr. to:** PO Box 830840, Birmingham, AL 35283-0430. TEL 800-633-4931, FAX 205-995-1588.

330.9 320 GBR ISSN 1364-467X
WORLD OF INFORMATION BUSINESS INTELLIGENCE REPORTS. PANAMA. Text in English. 1990. s-a. GBP 35, USD 70 (effective 2003).
Related titles: Online - full content ed.; Online - full text ed.: (from Gale Group, IngentaConnect).
Published by: World of Information, 2 Market St, Saffron Walden, Essex CB10 1HZ, United Kingdom. TEL 44-1799-521150, FAX 44-1799-524805, info@worldinformation.com, http://www.worldinformation.com. Ed., Pub. Anthony Axon. **Subscr. to:** PO Box 830840, Birmingham, AL 35283-0430. TEL 800-633-4931, FAX 205-995-1588.

330.9 320 GBR ISSN 1364-4688
WORLD OF INFORMATION BUSINESS INTELLIGENCE REPORTS. PAPUA NEW GUINEA. Text in English. 1990. s-a. GBP 35, USD 70 (effective 2003).
Related titles: Online - full content ed.; Online - full text ed.: (from Gale Group, IngentaConnect).
Published by: World of Information, 2 Market St, Saffron Walden, Essex CB10 1HZ, United Kingdom. TEL 44-1799-521150, FAX 44-1799-524805, info@worldinformation.com, http://www.worldinformation.com. Ed., Pub. Anthony Axon. **Subscr. to:** PO Box 830840, Birmingham, AL 35283-0430. TEL 800-633-4931, FAX 205-995-1588.

330.9 320 GBR ISSN 1364-4696
WORLD OF INFORMATION BUSINESS INTELLIGENCE REPORTS. PARAGUAY. Text in English. 1990. s-a. GBP 35, USD 70 (effective 2003).
Related titles: Online - full content ed.; Online - full text ed.: (from Gale Group, IngentaConnect).
Published by: World of Information, 2 Market St, Saffron Walden, Essex CB10 1HZ, United Kingdom. TEL 44-1799-521150, FAX 44-1799-524805, info@worldinformation.com, http://www.worldinformation.com. Ed., Pub. Anthony Axon. **Subscr. to:** PO Box 830840, Birmingham, AL 35283-0430. TEL 800-633-4931, FAX 205-995-1588.

330.9 320 GBR ISSN 1364-470X
WORLD OF INFORMATION BUSINESS INTELLIGENCE REPORTS. PERU. Text in English. 1990. s-a. GBP 35, USD 70 (effective 2003).
Related titles: Online - full content ed.; Online - full text ed.: (from Gale Group, IngentaConnect).
Published by: World of Information, 2 Market St, Saffron Walden, Essex CB10 1HZ, United Kingdom. TEL 44-1799-521150, FAX 44-1799-524805, info@worldinformation.com, http://www.worldinformation.com. Ed., Pub. Anthony Axon. **Subscr. to:** PO Box 830840, Birmingham, AL 35283-0430. TEL 800-633-4931, FAX 205-995-1588.

330.9 320 GBR ISSN 1364-4718
WORLD OF INFORMATION BUSINESS INTELLIGENCE REPORTS. PHILIPPINES. Text in English. 1990. s-a. GBP 35, USD 70 (effective 2003).
Related titles: Online - full content ed.; Online - full text ed.: (from Gale Group, IngentaConnect).
Published by: World of Information, 2 Market St, Saffron Walden, Essex CB10 1HZ, United Kingdom. TEL 44-1799-521150, FAX 44-1799-524805, info@worldinformation.com, http://www.worldinformation.com. Ed., Pub. Anthony Axon. **Subscr. to:** PO Box 830840, Birmingham, AL 35283-0430. TEL 800-633-4931, FAX 205-995-1588.

WORLD OF INFORMATION BUSINESS INTELLIGENCE REPORTS. POLAND. see *BUSINESS AND ECONOMICS—International Commerce*

330.9 320 GBR ISSN 1364-4726
WORLD OF INFORMATION BUSINESS INTELLIGENCE REPORTS. PORTUGAL. Text in English. 1990. s-a. GBP 35, USD 70 (effective 2003).
Related titles: Online - full content ed.; Online - full text ed.: (from Gale Group, IngentaConnect).
Published by: World of Information, 2 Market St, Saffron Walden, Essex CB10 1HZ, United Kingdom. TEL 44-1799-521150, FAX 44-1799-524805, info@worldinformation.com, http://www.worldinformation.com. Ed., Pub. Anthony Axon. **Subscr. to:** PO Box 830840, Birmingham, AL 35283-0430. TEL 800-633-4931, FAX 205-995-1588.

330.9 320 GBR ISSN 1364-4734
WORLD OF INFORMATION BUSINESS INTELLIGENCE REPORTS. PUERTO RICO. Text in English. 1990. s-a. GBP 35, USD 70 (effective 2003).
Related titles: Online - full content ed.

Published by: World of Information, 2 Market St, Saffron Walden, Essex CB10 1HZ, United Kingdom. TEL 44-1799-521150, FAX 44-1799-524805, info@worldinformation.com, http://www.worldinformation.com. Ed., Pub. Anthony Axon. **Subscr. to:** PO Box 830840, Birmingham, AL 35283-0430. TEL 800-633-4931, FAX 205-995-1588.

WORLD OF INFORMATION BUSINESS INTELLIGENCE REPORTS. ROMANIA. see *BUSINESS AND ECONOMICS—International Commerce*

330.9 320 GBR ISSN 1364-1107
WORLD OF INFORMATION BUSINESS INTELLIGENCE REPORTS. RUSSIA. Text in English. 1990. s-a. GBP 35, USD 70 (effective 2003).
Related titles: Online - full content ed.; Online - full text ed.: (from Gale Group, IngentaConnect).
Published by: World of Information, 2 Market St, Saffron Walden, Essex CB10 1HZ, United Kingdom. TEL 44-1799-521150, FAX 44-1799-524805, info@worldinformation.com, http://www.worldinformation.com. Ed., Pub. Anthony Axon. **Subscr. to:** PO Box 830840, Birmingham, AL 35283-0430. TEL 800-633-4931, FAX 205-995-1588.

330.9 320 GBR ISSN 1364-4742
WORLD OF INFORMATION BUSINESS INTELLIGENCE REPORTS. SAUDI ARABIA. Text in English. 1990. s-a. GBP 35, USD 70 (effective 2003).
Related titles: Online - full content ed.; Online - full text ed.: (from Gale Group, IngentaConnect).
Published by: World of Information, 2 Market St, Saffron Walden, Essex CB10 1HZ, United Kingdom. TEL 44-1799-521150, FAX 44-1799-524805, info@worldinformation.com, http://www.worldinformation.com. Ed., Pub. Anthony Axon. **Subscr. to:** PO Box 830840, Birmingham, AL 35283-0430. TEL 800-633-4931, FAX 205-995-1588.

330.9 320 GBR ISSN 1364-4750
WORLD OF INFORMATION BUSINESS INTELLIGENCE REPORTS. SENEGAL. Text in English. 1990. s-a. GBP 35, USD 70 (effective 2003).
Related titles: Online - full content ed.; Online - full text ed.: (from Gale Group, IngentaConnect).
Published by: World of Information, 2 Market St, Saffron Walden, Essex CB10 1HZ, United Kingdom. TEL 44-1799-521150, FAX 44-1799-524805, info@worldinformation.com, http://www.worldinformation.com. Ed., Pub. Anthony Axon. **Subscr. to:** PO Box 830840, Birmingham, AL 35283-0430. TEL 800-633-4931, FAX 205-995-1588.

330.9 320 GBR ISSN 1364-1115
WORLD OF INFORMATION BUSINESS INTELLIGENCE REPORTS. SERBIA. Text in English. 1990. s-a.
Related titles: Online - full content ed.; Online - full text ed.: (from Gale Group, IngentaConnect).
Published by: World of Information, 2 Market St, Saffron Walden, Essex CB10 1HZ, United Kingdom. TEL 44-1799-521150, FAX 44-1799-524805, info@worldinformation.com, http://www.worldinformation.com. Ed., Pub. Anthony Axon. **Subscr. to:** PO Box 830840, Birmingham, AL 35283-0430. TEL 800-633-4931, FAX 205-995-1588.

330.9 320 GBR ISSN 1364-4769
WORLD OF INFORMATION BUSINESS INTELLIGENCE REPORTS. SINGAPORE. Text in English. 1990. s-a. GBP 35, USD 70 (effective 2003).
Related titles: Online - full content ed.; Online - full text ed.: (from Gale Group, IngentaConnect).
Published by: World of Information, 2 Market St, Saffron Walden, Essex CB10 1HZ, United Kingdom. TEL 44-1799-521150, FAX 44-1799-524805, info@worldinformation.com, http://www.worldinformation.com. Ed., Pub. Anthony Axon. **Subscr. to:** PO Box 830840, Birmingham, AL 35283-0430. TEL 800-633-4931, FAX 205-995-1588.

330.9 320 GBR ISSN 1364-1123
WORLD OF INFORMATION BUSINESS INTELLIGENCE REPORTS. SLOVAKIA. Text in English. 1990. s-a. GBP 35, USD 70 (effective 2003).
Related titles: Online - full content ed.; Online - full text ed.: (from Gale Group, IngentaConnect).
Published by: World of Information, 2 Market St, Saffron Walden, Essex CB10 1HZ, United Kingdom. TEL 44-1799-521150, FAX 44-1799-524805, info@worldinformation.com, http://www.worldinformation.com. Ed., Pub. Anthony Axon. **Subscr. to:** PO Box 830840, Birmingham, AL 35283-0430. TEL 800-633-4931, FAX 205-995-1588.

330.9 320 GBR ISSN 1364-1131
WORLD OF INFORMATION BUSINESS INTELLIGENCE REPORTS. SLOVENIA. Text in English. 1994. s-a. GBP 35, USD 70 (effective 2003).
Related titles: Online - full content ed.; Online - full text ed.: (from Gale Group, IngentaConnect).
Published by: World of Information, 2 Market St, Saffron Walden, Essex CB10 1HZ, United Kingdom. TEL 44-1799-521150, FAX 44-1799-524805, info@worldinformation.com, http://www.worldinformation.com. Ed., Pub. Anthony Axon. **Subscr. to:** PO Box 830840, Birmingham, AL 35283-0430. TEL 800-633-4931, FAX 205-995-1588.

330.9 320 GBR ISSN 1364-4777
WORLD OF INFORMATION BUSINESS INTELLIGENCE REPORTS. SOUTH AFRICA. Text in English. 1990. s-a. GBP 35, USD 70 (effective 2003).
Related titles: Online - full content ed.; Online - full text ed.: (from Gale Group, IngentaConnect).
Published by: World of Information, 2 Market St, Saffron Walden, Essex CB10 1HZ, United Kingdom. TEL 44-1799-521150, FAX 44-1799-524805, info@worldinformation.com, http://www.worldinformation.com. Ed., Pub. Anthony Axon. **Subscr. to:** PO Box 830840, Birmingham, AL 35283-0430. TEL 800-633-4931, FAX 205-995-1588.

330.9 320 GBR ISSN 1364-4785
WORLD OF INFORMATION BUSINESS INTELLIGENCE REPORTS. SPAIN. Text in English. 1990. s-a. GBP 35, USD 70 (effective 2003).
Related titles: Online - full content ed.; Online - full text ed.: (from Gale Group, IngentaConnect).
Published by: World of Information, 2 Market St, Saffron Walden, Essex CB10 1HZ, United Kingdom. TEL 44-1799-521150, FAX 44-1799-524805, info@worldinformation.com, http://www.worldinformation.com. Ed., Pub. Anthony Axon. **Subscr. to:** PO Box 830840, Birmingham, AL 35283-0430. TEL 800-633-4931, FAX 205-995-1588.

330.9 320 GBR ISSN 1364-4793
WORLD OF INFORMATION BUSINESS INTELLIGENCE REPORTS. SRI LANKA. Text in English. 1990. s-a. GBP 35, USD 70 (effective 2003).
Related titles: Online - full content ed.; Online - full text ed.: (from Gale Group, IngentaConnect).
Published by: World of Information, 2 Market St, Saffron Walden, Essex CB10 1HZ, United Kingdom. TEL 44-1799-521150, FAX 44-1799-524805, info@worldinformation.com, http://www.worldinformation.com. Ed., Pub. Anthony Axon. **Subscr. to:** PO Box 830840, Birmingham, AL 35283-0430. TEL 800-633-4931, FAX 205-995-1588.

330.9 320 GBR ISSN 1364-6257
WORLD OF INFORMATION BUSINESS INTELLIGENCE REPORTS. SUDAN. Text in English. 1990. s-a. GBP 35, USD 70 (effective 2003).
Related titles: Online - full content ed.; Online - full text ed.: (from Gale Group, IngentaConnect).
Published by: World of Information, 2 Market St, Saffron Walden, Essex CB10 1HZ, United Kingdom. TEL 44-1799-521150, FAX 44-1799-524805, info@worldinformation.com, http://www.worldinformation.com. Ed., Pub. Anthony Axon. **Subscr. to:** PO Box 830840, Birmingham, AL 35283-0430. TEL 800-633-4931, FAX 205-995-1588.

330.9 320 GBR ISSN 1364-114X
WORLD OF INFORMATION BUSINESS INTELLIGENCE REPORTS. SWEDEN. Text in English. 1990. s-a. GBP 35, USD 70 (effective 2003).
Related titles: Online - full content ed.; Online - full text ed.: (from Gale Group, IngentaConnect).
Published by: World of Information, 2 Market St, Saffron Walden, Essex CB10 1HZ, United Kingdom. TEL 44-1799-521150, FAX 44-1799-524805, info@worldinformation.com, http://www.worldinformation.com. Ed., Pub. Anthony Axon. **Subscr. to:** PO Box 830840, Birmingham, AL 35283-0430. TEL 800-633-4931, FAX 205-995-1588.

330.9 320 GBR ISSN 1364-6265
WORLD OF INFORMATION BUSINESS INTELLIGENCE REPORTS. SWITZERLAND. Text in English. 1990. s-a. GBP 35, USD 70 (effective 2003).
Related titles: Online - full content ed.; Online - full text ed.: (from Gale Group, IngentaConnect).
Published by: World of Information, 2 Market St, Saffron Walden, Essex CB10 1HZ, United Kingdom. TEL 44-1799-521150, FAX 44-1799-524805, info@worldinformation.com, http://www.worldinformation.com. Ed., Pub. Anthony Axon. **Subscr. to:** PO Box 830840, Birmingham, AL 35283-0430. TEL 800-633-4931, FAX 205-995-1588.

330.9 320 GBR ISSN 1364-6273
WORLD OF INFORMATION BUSINESS INTELLIGENCE REPORTS. SYRIA. Text in English. 1990. s-a. GBP 35, USD 70 (effective 2003).
Related titles: Online - full content ed.; Online - full text ed.: (from Gale Group, IngentaConnect).
Published by: World of Information, 2 Market St, Saffron Walden, Essex CB10 1HZ, United Kingdom. TEL 44-1799-521150, FAX 44-1799-524805, info@worldinformation.com, http://www.worldinformation.com. Ed., Pub. Anthony Axon. **Subscr. to:** PO Box 830840, Birmingham, AL 35283-0430. TEL 800-633-4931, FAX 205-995-1588.

330.9 320 GBR ISSN 1364-6281
WORLD OF INFORMATION BUSINESS INTELLIGENCE REPORTS. TAIWAN. Text in English. 1990. s-a. GBP 35, USD 70 (effective 2003).
Related titles: Online - full content ed.; Online - full text ed.: (from Gale Group, IngentaConnect).
Published by: World of Information, 2 Market St, Saffron Walden, Essex CB10 1HZ, United Kingdom. TEL 44-1799-521150, FAX 44-1799-524805, info@worldinformation.com, http://www.worldinformation.com. Ed., Pub. Anthony Axon. **Subscr. to:** PO Box 830840, Birmingham, AL 35283-0430. TEL 800-633-4931, FAX 205-995-1588.

330.9 320 GBR ISSN 1364-1158
WORLD OF INFORMATION BUSINESS INTELLIGENCE REPORTS. TAJIKISTAN. Text in English. 1994. s-a. GBP 35, USD 70 (effective 2003).
Related titles: Online - full content ed.; Online - full text ed.: (from Gale Group, IngentaConnect).
Published by: World of Information, 2 Market St, Saffron Walden, Essex CB10 1HZ, United Kingdom. TEL 44-1799-521150, FAX 44-1799-524805, info@worldinformation.com, http://www.worldinformation.com. Ed., Pub. Anthony Axon. **Subscr. to:** PO Box 830840, Birmingham, AL 35283-0430. TEL 800-633-4931, FAX 205-995-1588.

330.9 320 GBR ISSN 1364-629X
WORLD OF INFORMATION BUSINESS INTELLIGENCE REPORTS. TANZANIA. Text in English. 1990. s-a. USD 29.95 (effective 2003).
Related titles: Online - full content ed.; Online - full text ed.: (from Gale Group, IngentaConnect).
Published by: World of Information, 2 Market St, Saffron Walden, Essex CB10 1HZ, United Kingdom. TEL 44-1799-521150, FAX 44-1799-524805, info@worldinformation.com, http://www.worldinformation.com. Ed., Pub. Anthony Axon. **Subscr. to:** PO Box 830840, Birmingham, AL 35283-0430. TEL 800-633-4931, FAX 205-995-1588.

330.9 320 GBR ISSN 1364-6303
WORLD OF INFORMATION BUSINESS INTELLIGENCE REPORTS. THAILAND. Text in English. 1990. s-a. GBP 35, USD 70 (effective 2003).
Related titles: Online - full content ed.; Online - full text ed.: (from Gale Group, IngentaConnect).
Published by: World of Information, 2 Market St, Saffron Walden, Essex CB10 1HZ, United Kingdom. TEL 44-1799-521150, FAX 44-1799-524805, info@worldinformation.com, http://www.worldinformation.com. Ed., Pub. Anthony Axon. **Subscr. to:** PO Box 830840, Birmingham, AL 35283-0430. TEL 800-633-4931, FAX 205-995-1588.

330.9 382 GBR ISSN 1474-4384
WORLD OF INFORMATION BUSINESS INTELLIGENCE REPORTS. TRINIDAD AND TOBAGO. Text in English. irreg. USD 75 (effective 2003).
Related titles: Online - full text ed.: (from Gale Group, IngentaConnect).
Published by: World of Information, 2 Market St, Saffron Walden, Essex CB10 1HZ, United Kingdom. TEL 44-1799-521150, FAX 44-1799-524805, info@worldinformation.com. **Subscr. to:** PO Box 830840, Birmingham, AL 35283-0430. TEL 800-633-4931, FAX 205-995-1588.

330.9 320 GBR ISSN 1364-6311
WORLD OF INFORMATION BUSINESS INTELLIGENCE REPORTS. TUNISIA. Text in English. 1990. s-a. USD 29.95 (effective 2003).
Related titles: Online - full content ed.; Online - full text ed.: (from Gale Group, IngentaConnect).
Published by: World of Information, 2 Market St, Saffron Walden, Essex CB10 1HZ, United Kingdom. TEL 44-1799-521150, FAX 44-1799-524805, info@worldinformation.com, http://www.worldinformation.com. Ed., Pub. Anthony Axon. **Subscr. to:** PO Box 830840, Birmingham, AL 35283-0430. TEL 800-633-4931, FAX 205-995-1588.

330.9 320 GBR ISSN 1364-632X
WORLD OF INFORMATION BUSINESS INTELLIGENCE REPORTS. TURKEY. Text in English. 1990. s-a. GBP 35, USD 70 (effective 2003).
Related titles: Online - full content ed.; Online - full text ed.: (from Gale Group, IngentaConnect).
Published by: World of Information, 2 Market St, Saffron Walden, Essex CB10 1HZ, United Kingdom. TEL 44-1799-521150, FAX 44-1799-524805, info@worldinformation.com, http://www.worldinformation.com. Ed., Pub. Anthony Axon. **Subscr. to:** PO Box 830840, Birmingham, AL 35283-0430. TEL 800-633-4931, FAX 205-995-1588.

330.9 320 GBR ISSN 1364-1166
WORLD OF INFORMATION BUSINESS INTELLIGENCE REPORTS. TURKMENISTAN. Text in English. 1990. s-a. GBP 35, USD 70 (effective 2003).
Related titles: Online - full content ed.; Online - full text ed.: (from Gale Group, IngentaConnect).
Published by: World of Information, 2 Market St, Saffron Walden, Essex CB10 1HZ, United Kingdom. TEL 44-1799-521150, FAX 44-1799-524805, info@worldinformation.com, http://www.worldinformation.com. Ed., Pub. Anthony Axon. **Subscr. to:** PO Box 830840, Birmingham, AL 35283-0430. TEL 800-633-4931, FAX 205-995-1588.

330.9 320 GBR ISSN 1364-6338
WORLD OF INFORMATION BUSINESS INTELLIGENCE REPORTS. UGANDA. Text in English. 1990. s-a. GBP 35, USD 70 (effective 2003).

B

▼ new title ➤ refereed ✶ unverified ♦ full entry avail.

Related titles: Online - full content ed.; Online - full text ed.: (from Gale Group, IngentaConnect).
Published by: World of Information, 2 Market St, Saffron Walden, Essex CB10 1HZ, United Kingdom. TEL 44-1799-521150, FAX 44-1799-524805, info@worldinformation.com, http://www.worldinformation.com. Ed., Pub. Anthony Axon. **Subscr. to:** PO Box 830840, Birmingham, AL 35283-0430. TEL 800-633-4931, FAX 205-995-1588.

330.9 320 GBR ISSN 1364-1174
WORLD OF INFORMATION BUSINESS INTELLIGENCE REPORTS. UKRAINE. Text in English. 1990. s-a. GBP 35, USD 70 (effective 2003).
Related titles: Online - full content ed.; Online - full text ed.: (from Gale Group, IngentaConnect).
Published by: World of Information, 2 Market St, Saffron Walden, Essex CB10 1HZ, United Kingdom. TEL 44-1799-521150, FAX 44-1799-524805, info@worldinformation.com, http://www.worldinformation.com. Ed., Pub. Anthony Axon. **Subscr. to:** PO Box 830840, Birmingham, AL 35283-0430. TEL 800-633-4931, FAX 205-995-1588.

330.9 320 GBR ISSN 1364-6354
WORLD OF INFORMATION BUSINESS INTELLIGENCE REPORTS. UNITED ARAB EMIRATES. Text in English. 1990. s-a. GBP 35, USD 70 (effective 2003).
Related titles: Online - full content ed.; Online - full text ed.: (from Gale Group, IngentaConnect).
Published by: World of Information, 2 Market St, Saffron Walden, Essex CB10 1HZ, United Kingdom. TEL 44-1799-521150, FAX 44-1799-524805, info@worldinformation.com, http://www.worldinformation.com. Ed., Pub. Anthony Axon. **Subscr. to:** PO Box 830840, Birmingham, AL 35283-0430. TEL 800-633-4931, FAX 205-995-1588.

330.9 320 GBR ISSN 1364-6346
WORLD OF INFORMATION BUSINESS INTELLIGENCE REPORTS. UNITED KINGDOM. Text in English. 1990. s-a. GBP 35, USD 70 (effective 2003).
Related titles: Online - full content ed.; Online - full text ed.: (from Gale Group, IngentaConnect).
Published by: World of Information, 2 Market St, Saffron Walden, Essex CB10 1HZ, United Kingdom. TEL 44-1799-521150, FAX 44-1799-524805, info@worldinformation.com, http://www.worldinformation.com. Ed., Pub. Anthony Axon. **Subscr. to:** PO Box 830840, Birmingham, AL 35283-0430. TEL 800-633-4931, FAX 205-995-1588.

330.9 320 GBR ISSN 1364-6370
WORLD OF INFORMATION BUSINESS INTELLIGENCE REPORTS. UNITED STATES. Text in English. 1990. s-a. GBP 35, USD 70 (effective 2003).
Related titles: Online - full content ed.; Online - full text ed.: (from Gale Group, IngentaConnect).
Published by: World of Information, 2 Market St, Saffron Walden, Essex CB10 1HZ, United Kingdom. TEL 44-1799-521150, FAX 44-1799-524805, info@worldinformation.com, http://www.worldinformation.com. Ed., Pub. Anthony Axon. **Subscr. to:** PO Box 830840, Birmingham, AL 35283-0430. TEL 800-633-4931, FAX 205-995-1588.

330.9 320 GBR ISSN 1364-6362
WORLD OF INFORMATION BUSINESS INTELLIGENCE REPORTS. URUGUAY. Text in English. 1990. s-a. GBP 35, USD 70 (effective 2003).
Related titles: Online - full content ed.; Online - full text ed.: (from Gale Group, IngentaConnect).
Published by: World of Information, 2 Market St, Saffron Walden, Essex CB10 1HZ, United Kingdom. TEL 44-1799-521150, FAX 44-1799-524805, info@worldinformation.com, http://www.worldinformation.com. Ed., Pub. Anthony Axon. **Subscr. to:** PO Box 830840, Birmingham, AL 35283-0430. TEL 800-633-4931, FAX 205-995-1588.

330.9 320 GBR ISSN 1364-1182
WORLD OF INFORMATION BUSINESS INTELLIGENCE REPORTS. UZBEKISTAN. Text in English. 1990. s-a. GBP 35, USD 70 (effective 2003).
Related titles: Online - full content ed.; Online - full text ed.: (from Gale Group, IngentaConnect).
Published by: World of Information, 2 Market St, Saffron Walden, Essex CB10 1HZ, United Kingdom. TEL 44-1799-521150, FAX 44-1799-524805, info@worldinformation.com, http://www.worldinformation.com. Ed., Pub. Anthony Axon. **Subscr. to:** PO Box 830840, Birmingham, AL 35283-0430. TEL 800-633-4931, FAX 205-995-1588.

330.9 320 GBR ISSN 1364-1190
WORLD OF INFORMATION BUSINESS INTELLIGENCE REPORTS. VENEZUELA. Text in English. 1990. s-a. GBP 35, USD 70 (effective 2003).
Related titles: Online - full content ed.; Online - full text ed.: (from Gale Group, IngentaConnect).
Published by: World of Information, 2 Market St, Saffron Walden, Essex CB10 1HZ, United Kingdom. TEL 44-1799-521150, FAX 44-1799-524805, info@worldinformation.com, http://www.worldinformation.com. Ed., Pub. Anthony Axon. **Subscr. to:** PO Box 830840, Birmingham, AL 35283-0430. TEL 800-633-4931, FAX 205-995-1588.

330.9 320 GBR ISSN 1364-6389
WORLD OF INFORMATION BUSINESS INTELLIGENCE REPORTS. VIETNAM. Text in English. 1990. s-a. GBP 35, USD 70 (effective 2003).
Related titles: Online - full content ed.; Online - full text ed.: (from Gale Group, IngentaConnect).
Published by: World of Information, 2 Market St, Saffron Walden, Essex CB10 1HZ, United Kingdom. TEL 44-1799-521150, FAX 44-1799-524805, info@worldinformation.com, http://www.worldinformation.com. Ed., Pub. Anthony Axon. **Subscr. to:** PO Box 830840, Birmingham, AL 35283-0430. TEL 800-633-4931, FAX 205-995-1588.

330.9 320 GBR
WORLD OF INFORMATION BUSINESS INTELLIGENCE REPORTS. ZAIRE. Text in English. 1990. s-a.
Related titles: Online - full content ed.
Published by: World of Information, 2 Market St, Saffron Walden, Essex CB10 1HZ, United Kingdom. TEL 44-1799-521150, FAX 44-1799-524805, info@worldinformation.com, http://www.worldinformation.com. Ed., Pub. Anthony Axon. **Subscr. to:** PO Box 830840, Birmingham, AL 35283-0430. TEL 800-633-4931, FAX 205-995-1588.

330.9 320 GBR ISSN 1364-6400
WORLD OF INFORMATION BUSINESS INTELLIGENCE REPORTS. ZAMBIA. Text in English. 1990. s-a. USD 29.95 (effective 2003).
Related titles: Online - full content ed.; Online - full text ed.: (from Gale Group, IngentaConnect).
Published by: World of Information, 2 Market St, Saffron Walden, Essex CB10 1HZ, United Kingdom. TEL 44-1799-521150, FAX 44-1799-524805, info@worldinformation.com, http://www.worldinformation.com. Ed., Pub. Anthony Axon. **Subscr. to:** PO Box 830840, Birmingham, AL 35283-0430. TEL 800-633-4931, FAX 205-995-1588.

330.9 320 GBR ISSN 1364-6419
WORLD OF INFORMATION BUSINESS INTELLIGENCE REPORTS. ZIMBABWE. Text in English. 1990. s-a. USD 29.95 (effective 2003).
Related titles: Online - full content ed.; Online - full text ed.: (from Gale Group, IngentaConnect).
Published by: World of Information, 2 Market St, Saffron Walden, Essex CB10 1HZ, United Kingdom. TEL 44-1799-521150, FAX 44-1799-524805, info@worldinformation.com, http://www.worldinformation.com. Ed., Pub. Anthony Axon. **Subscr. to:** PO Box 830840, Birmingham, AL 35283-0430. TEL 800-633-4931, FAX 205-995-1588.

330.9 320 GBR
WORLD OF INFORMATION REGIONAL DEVELOPMENT SERIES. Text in English. 1998. irreg. price varies.
Description: Published in association with major regional international organizations and development agencies. Looks at the activitities and achievements of each organization, its regional context, the challenges and problems that it faces.
Related titles: Online - full content ed.
Published by: World of Information, 2 Market St, Saffron Walden, Essex CB10 1HZ, United Kingdom. TEL 44-1799-521150, FAX 44-1799-524805, info@worldinformation.com, http://www.worldinformation.com.

330.9 CAN ISSN 0843-4328
WORLD OUTLOOK. Text in English. 1989. q. CND 2,700 (effective 2004). **Description:** Examines trends in the global economy and provides in-depth analysis of key issues affecting the world's economic performance.
—CISTI.
Published by: Conference Board of Canada, 255 Smyth Rd, Ste 100, Ottawa, ON K1H 8M7, Canada. TEL 613-526-3280, 866-711-2262, FAX 613-526-4857, http://www.conferenceboard.ca/.

WORLD TODAY SERIES: AFRICA. see *HISTORY—History Of Africa*

WORLD TODAY SERIES: CANADA. see *HISTORY—History Of North And South America*

WORLD TODAY SERIES: EAST, SOUTHEAST ASIA, AND THE WESTERN PACIFIC. see *HISTORY—History Of Asia*

WORLD TODAY SERIES: LATIN AMERICA. see *HISTORY—History Of North And South America*

WORLD TODAY SERIES: MIDDLE EAST AND SOUTH ASIA. see *HISTORY—History Of Asia*

WORLD TODAY SERIES: RUSSIA, EURASIAN STATES, AND EASTERN EUROPE. see *HISTORY—History Of Europe*

WORLD TODAY SERIES: WESTERN EUROPE. see *HISTORY—History Of Europe*

WOSTOK; Informationen aus dem Osten fuer den Westen. see *LITERARY AND POLITICAL REVIEWS*

XINCUN. see *AGRICULTURE*

330.9 USA
YALE UNIVERSITY. ECONOMIC GROWTH CENTER. CENTER DISCUSSION PAPER. Text in English. irreg., latest vol.499, 1985. USD 2 (effective 1999).
Indexed: PopulInd, RDA, WAE&RSA.
—BLDSC (3106.487700).
Published by: Yale University, Economic Growth Center, PO Box 208269, New Haven, CT 06520-8269. TEL 203-432-3610, FAX 203-432-3898.

330.9 KWT
YAQZA. Text in Arabic. 1979. w. adv.
Address: P O Box 6000, Safat, Kuwait. Ed. Ahmed Yousef Behbehani. Circ: 21,713.

YEARBOOK OF ASIA-PACIFIC TELECOMMUNICATIONS (YEAR). see *COMMUNICATIONS*

YEARBOOK OF LATIN AMERICAN TELECOMMUNICATIONS (YEAR). see *COMMUNICATIONS*

330.9 CHN
YUNNAN JINGJI RIBAO/YUNNAN ECONOMY DAILY. Text in Chinese. d. CNY 144 (effective 2004). adv. **Document type:** *Newspaper, Trade.*
Published by: Yunnan Ribao Baoye Jituan, 209, Dongfeng Donglu, Kunming, 650041, China. **Dist. by:** China International Book Trading Corp, 35 Chegongzhuang Xilu, Haidian District, PO Box 399, Beijing 100044, China. TEL 86-10-68412045, FAX 86-10-68412023, cibtc@mail.cibtc.com.cn, http://www.cibtc.com.cn.

330.9 COD
ZAIRE BUSINESS. Text in French. 1973. w. illus.
Address: 3986, rue Ex-Belgika, Bldg. Amasco, BP 9839, Kinshasa, Congo, Dem. Republic.

330.9 ZMB
ZAMBIA. NATIONAL COMMISSION FOR DEVELOPMENT PLANNING. ECONOMIC REPORT. Text in English. a. ZMK 450. **Document type:** *Government.*
Published by: National Commission for Development Planning, PO Box 50268, Lusaka, Zambia. FAX 260-1-222440, TELEX 40430. Circ: 1,500.

ZEITSCHRIFT FUER ENERGIEWIRTSCHAFT. see *ENERGY*

330.9 CHN
ZHONGGUO FAZHAN PINGLUN/CHINA DEVELOPMENT REVIEW. Text in Chinese. 1999. q. **Document type:** *Government.*
Published by: Guowuyuan, Fazhan Yanjiu Zhongxin/Development Research Center of the State Council, No.225, Chaonei Street, Beijing, 100010, China. TEL 86-10-65230262, FAX 86-10-65270099, zhangh@drc.gov.cn, drc@drc.gov.cn, http://www.drc.gov.cn/index.html.

330.9 CHN
ZHONGGUO JINGJI DAOBAO/CHINA ECONOMIC HERALD. Text in Chinese. 1995. 3/w. CNY 189 (effective 2004). **Document type:** *Newspaper.*
Address: Xuanwu-qu, 315, Guanganmennei Dajie, Xinxi Dasha B-ceng, Beijing, 100053, China. TEL 86-10-63691996, FAX 86-10-63691260, cehnews@sina.com, http://www.ceh.com.cn. **Dist. by:** China International Book Trading Corp, 35 Chegongzhuang Xilu, Haidian District, PO Box 399, Beijing 100044, China. TEL 86-10-68412045, FAX 86-10-68412023, cibtc@mail.cibtc.com.cn, http://www.cibtc.com.cn.

330.9 CHN ISSN 1005-703X
HC427.92
ZHONGGUO JINGJI TIZHI GAIGE NIANJIAN/CHINA ECONOMIC SYSTEMS REFORM YEARBOOK. Text in Chinese. 1993. a. **Document type:** *Journal, Academic/Scholarly.*
Related titles: Online - full text ed.: (from WanFang Data Corp.).
Published by: Zhongguo Caizheng Jingji Chubanshe, Haidian-qu, 28, Fucheng Lu Jia, Beijing, 100036, China. TEL 86-10-88190957, cfeph@cfeph.cn, http://zgjjtzggnj.periodicals.net.cn/, http://www.cfeph.cn/.

330.9 CHN ISSN 1000-9094
HF3831 CODEN: JMCPE6
ZHONGGUO JINGJI XINWEN/CHINA ECONOMIC NEWS. Text in Chinese. w. USD 430 (effective 2000). **Document type:** *Newspaper.*
Indexed: RASB.
Address: PO Box 8025, Beijing, China. TEL 201-6803. **Dist. in US by:** China Books & Periodicals Inc, 360 Swift Ave., Ste. 48, S San Fran, CA 94080-6220.

ZHONGGUO NONGCUN JINGJI/CHINESE RURAL ECONOMY. see *AGRICULTURE—Agricultural Economics*

330.9 ZWE
ZIMBABWE: A FIELD FOR INVESTMENT. Text in English. 1961. a. ZWD 105; ZWD 113.10 foreign (effective 1999). illus.; stat. **Document type:** *Trade.*
Published by: Thomson Publications Zimbabwe (Pvt) Ltd., Thomson House, PO Box 1683, Harare, Zimbabwe. TEL 263-4-736835, FAX 263-4-752390.

330.9 ZWE
HC910.A1
ZIMBABWE ECONOMIC REVIEW. Text in English. 1973. q. ZWD 120 domestic; USD 50 in Africa; USD 80 elsewhere (effective 2000). charts; stat. 12 p./no. 2 cols./p.; back issues avail. **Document type:** *Magazine, Trade.* **Description:** Covers the economic situation in Zimbabwe and international developments affecting Zimbabwe.
Formerly (until 1991): Economic Review (0256-1603)
Published by: Zimbabwe Financial Holdings Limited, PO Box 3198, Harare, Zimbabwe. TEL 263-4-756671, 263-4-700511, FAX 263-4-756674, 263-4-792385, drmuzulu@africaonline.co.zw, drmuzulu@africaonline.co.zur, http://www.finhold.co.zw. Ed. I J Muzulu. Circ: 3,500.

330.9 ZWE
ZIMBABWE IN FIGURES. Text in English. 1982. a. stat. back issues avail. **Document type:** *Bulletin, Trade.*
Published by: Zimbabwe Financial Holdings Limited, PO Box 3198, Harare, Zimbabwe. TEL 263-4-756671, 263-4-700511, FAX 263-4-756674, 263-4-792385, TELEX 24163 ZW, drmuzulu@africaonline.co.zw, http://www.finhold.co.zw. Ed. J Muzulu. Circ: 3,000.

ZONA LIBRE; periodismo sin frontera. see *POLITICAL SCIENCE*

BUSINESS AND ECONOMICS—Economic Systems And Theories, Economic History

330.1 DEU ISSN 0724-9756
ABHANDLUNGEN ZU DEN WIRTSCHAFTLICHEN STAATSWISSENSCHAFTEN. Text in German. 1968. irreg., latest vol.36, 1991. price varies. **Document type:** *Monographic series, Academic/Scholarly.*
Published by: Vandenhoeck und Ruprecht, Robert-Bosch-Breite 6, Goettingen, 37079, Germany. TEL 49-551-508440, FAX 49-551-5084422, info@v-r.de, http://www.vandenhoeck-ruprecht.de. Ed. Horst C Recktenwald.

330.9 HRV ISSN 1330-0024
CODEN: AHIUDI
ACTA HISTORICO-OECONOMICA. Text in Croatian; Summaries in English, German. 1974. a. USD 15. bk.rev. **Document type:** *Academic/Scholarly.*
Formerly (until 1991): Acta Historico-oeconomica Iugoslaviae (0350-3631)
Indexed: AmH&L, HistAb.
Published by: (Drustvo Povjesnicara Hrvatske, Komisija za Ekonomsku Povijest), Skolska Knjiga, Hanamanova ul 26, Zagreb, 10000, Croatia. Ed. Ivan Erceg. Circ: 1,000.

330.1 FIN ISSN 0355-2667
ACTA WASAENSIA. Text in Finnish. 1971. irreg., latest vol.60, 1998. price varies. adv. **Document type:** *Academic/Scholarly.*
Indexed: ZentMath.
Published by: Vaasan Yliopisto, Library/University of Vaasa, PL 331, Vaasa, 65101, Finland. TEL 358-6-3248151, FAX 358-6-3248200. Ed., R&P Antero Niemikorpi. Adv. contact Tarja Salo. Circ: 200.

ACTUEL MARX. see *POLITICAL SCIENCE*

330.1 519.5 NLD ISSN 1570-5811
➤ **ADVANCED STUDIES IN THEORETICAL AND APPLIED ECONOMETRICS.** Text in English. 1982. irreg., latest vol.42, 2005. price varies. back issues avail. **Document type:** *Monographic series, Academic/Scholarly.*
Indexed: ZentMath.
—BLDSC (0696.931000), ingenta.
Published by: Springer-Verlag Dordrecht (Subsidiary of: Springer Science+Business Media), Van Godewijckstraat 30, Dordrecht, 3311 GX, Netherlands. TEL 31-78-6576050, FAX 31-78-6576474, http://www.springeronline.com. Ed. J Marquez.

330.1 NLD ISSN 0169-5568
➤ **ADVANCED TEXTBOOKS IN ECONOMICS.** Text in Dutch. 1971. irreg., latest vol.37, 2000. price varies. **Document type:** *Monographic series, Academic/Scholarly.* **Description:** Covers topics in economics, mathematical economics, and econometrics at a graduate level.
Indexed: MathR, RASB, ZentMath.
—BLDSC (0696.935500), ingenta.
Published by: Elsevier BV, North-Holland (Subsidiary of: Elsevier Science & Technology), Sara Burgerhartstraat 25, Amsterdam, 1055 KV, Netherlands. TEL 31-20-485-3911, FAX 31-20-485-2457, nlinfo-f@elsevier.nl, http://www.elsevier.nl. Eds. C. Bliss, M Intriligator. **Subscr. to:** Elsevier BV, PO Box 211, Amsterdam 1000 AE, Netherlands. TEL 31-20-485-3757, FAX 31-20-485-3432, http://www.elsevier.nl.

330.1 USA ISSN 0278-0984
HB172
ADVANCES IN APPLIED MICROECONOMICS; a research annual. Text in English. 1981. a., latest vol.13, 2005. price varies. back issues avail. **Document type:** *Monographic series, Academic/Scholarly.* **Description:** Provides a forum in which researchers may disseminate frontier research in applied microeconomics to include both theoretical and empirical contributions in applied areas such as industrial organization, consumer and producer behavior, public economics, natural resources, and other applied microeconomic fields.
Related titles: Online - full text ed.: (from ScienceDirect).
—BLDSC (0699.113000). **CCC.**
Published by: J A I Press Inc. (Subsidiary of: Elsevier Science & Technology), 360 Park Ave S, New York, NY 10010-1710. TEL 212-989-5800, FAX 212-633-3990, usinfo-f@elsevier.com, http://www.elsevier.com/wps/find/bookdescription.cws_home/BS_AAME/description#description. Ed. M R Baye.

ADVANCES IN ECONOMETRICS. see *BUSINESS AND ECONOMICS—Economic Situation And Conditions*

330.1 USA ISSN 1538-0637
HB1
ADVANCES IN ECONOMIC ANALYSIS & POLICY. Text in English. 2001. a. Included with subscription to The B E Journals in Economic Analysis and Policy.. **Document type:** *Journal, Academic/Scholarly.*
Media: Online - full content. **Related titles:** Online - full text ed.: (from O C L C Online Computer Library Center, Inc., ProQuest Information & Learning); ♦ Series of: The B E Journals in Economic Analysis & Policy. ISSN 1555-0494.
Indexed: ABIn, IBSS, JEL, PAIS.
—**CCC.**
Published by: Berkeley Electronic Press, 2809 Telegraph Ave., Ste 202, Berkeley, CA 94705. FAX 510-665-1201, info@bepress.com, http://www.bepress.com/bejeap/advances/. Eds. Aaron S Edlin, Bruce D Myer, Don Fullerton, Hermalin E Benjamin, Kyle Bagwell.

ADVANCES IN THE STUDY OF ENTREPRENEURSHIP, INNOVATION, AND ECONOMIC GROWTH. see *BUSINESS AND ECONOMICS—Economic Situation And Conditions*

330.1 USA ISSN 1534-5963
HB1
ADVANCES IN THEORETICAL ECONOMICS. Text in English. 2001. irreg. Included with subscription to The B E Journals in Theoretical Economics. **Document type:** *Journal, Academic/Scholarly.*
Media: Online - full content. **Related titles:** Online - full text ed.: (from O C L C Online Computer Library Center, Inc., ProQuest Information & Learning); ♦ Series of: The B E Journals in Theoretical Economics. ISSN 1555-0478.
Indexed: ABIn, IBSS, JEL, MathR, MathSciNet.
Published by: Berkeley Electronic Press, 2809 Telegraph Ave., Ste 202, Berkeley, CA 94705. FAX 510-665-1201, info@bepress.com, http://www.bepress.com/bejte/advances/. Eds. Chris Shannon, Dilip Abreu, Ilya Segal, Patrick Bolton.

AFRICA DEVELOPMENT/AFRIQUE ET DEVELOPPEMENT. see *BUSINESS AND ECONOMICS—International Development And Assistance*

330.9 960 USA ISSN 0145-2258
HC501
➤ **AFRICAN ECONOMIC HISTORY.** Text in English, French. 1974. a., latest vol.29, 2001. USD 18 per issue to individuals; USD 36 per issue to institutions (effective 2003). adv. bk.rev. illus. back issues avail.; reprint service avail. from ISI,PSC. **Document type:** *Academic/Scholarly.*
Formerly (until 1976): African Economic History Review (0360-6333)
Indexed: ASCA, ASD, AbAn, AmH&L, ArtHuCI, CCA, CurCont, FamI, HistAb, IBSS, JEL, PAIS, PCI, RASB, SSCI.
—BLDSC (0732.423000), IDS.
Published by: University of Wisconsin at Madison, African Studies Program, 205 Ingraham Hall, 1155 Observatory Dr, Madison, WI 53706. TEL 608-262-2380, FAX 608-265-5851, publications@africa.wisc.edu, asp@africa.wisc.edu, http://africa.wisc.edu/publications/aeh/index.htm, http://www.africa/wisc.edu. Eds. Colleen Kriger, Donna Maier, Paul Lovejoy, Toyin Falola. Circ: 250.

➤ **AMERICAN ECONOMIC ASSOCIATION. PAPERS AND PROCEEDINGS OF THE ANNUAL MEETING.** see *BUSINESS AND ECONOMICS—Economic Situation And Conditions*

➤ **THE AMERICAN ECONOMIC REVIEW (ONLINE EDITION).** see *BUSINESS AND ECONOMICS—Economic Situation And Conditions*

➤ **THE AMERICAN ECONOMIC REVIEW (PRINT EDITION).** see *BUSINESS AND ECONOMICS—Economic Situation And Conditions*

330.1 USA ISSN 0741-2150
AMERICAN UNIVERSITY STUDIES. SERIES 16. ECONOMICS. Text in English. 1984. irreg., latest 1994. USD 38.95 per vol. (effective 2004). **Document type:** *Monographic series, Academic/Scholarly.* **Description:** Explores various issues of economics and their social and political implications.
Published by: Peter Lang Publishing, Inc., 275 Seventh Ave, 28th Fl, New York, NY 10001. TEL 212-647-7700, 212-647-7706, 800-770-5264, FAX 212-647-7707, customerservice@plang.com, http://www.peterlang.com. Ed. David Bergeron. Pub. Christopher Myers. R&P Stephanie Archer. Adv. contact Patricia Mulrane.

330.1 DEU ISSN 0720-8227
ANGEWANDTE STATISTIK UND OEKONOMETRIE. Text in English, German. 1975. irreg., latest vol.47, 2000. price varies. **Document type:** *Monographic series, Academic/Scholarly.*
Indexed: ZentMath.
—**CCC.**
Published by: Vandenhoeck und Ruprecht, Robert-Bosch-Breite 6, Goettingen, 37079, Germany. TEL 49-551-508440, FAX 49-551-5084422, info@v-r.de, http://www.vandenhoeck-ruprecht.de.

330.1 USA ISSN 1096-4258
HB172
➤ **ANNUAL EDITIONS: MICROECONOMICS.** Text in English. 1991. a., latest 2001, 6th ed. USD 19.38 per vol. (effective 2004). illus. **Document type:** *Academic/Scholarly.*
Published by: McGraw-Hill - Dushkin (Subsidiary of: McGraw-Hill Higher Education), 2460 Kerper Blvd, Dubuque, IA 52001. TEL 800-243-6532, customer.service@mcgraw-hill.com, http://www.dushkin.com/text-data/catalog/0072479949.mhtml. Ed. Don Cole. Pub. Ian Nielsen. R&P Cheryl Greenleaf.

330.1 LKA
ARTHIKA VIDYA NIBANDHANA ✶ . Text in Singhalese. 1977. q. LKR 30, USD 2. adv. charts. **Document type:** *Government.*
Address: c/o Sri Lanka Ministry of Cultural Affairs and Information, 34 Malay St., Colombo, 2, Sri Lanka. Circ: 3,000.

ASIA - PACIFIC FINANCIAL MARKETS. see *BUSINESS AND ECONOMICS—Banking And Finance—Computer Applications*

330.1 AUS ISSN 1351-3958
➤ **ASIAN ECONOMIC JOURNAL.** Text in English. 1994 (vol.8). q. USD 53 combined subscription in the Americas to individuals print & online eds.; EUR 51 combined subscription in Europe to individuals print & online eds.; GBP 34 combined subscription elsewhere to individuals print & online eds.; USD 210 combined subscription in the Americas to institutions print & online eds.; USD 109, GBP 67 combined subscription in developing nations to institutions print & online eds.; GBP 134 combined subscription elsewhere to institutions print & online eds. (effective 2006). back issues avail. **Document type:** *Journal, Academic/Scholarly.* **Description:** Provides detailed coverage of a wide range of topics in economics relating to East Asia, including investigation of current research, international comparisons and country studies.
Related titles: Online - full text ed.: ISSN 1467-8381. USD 200 in the Americas to institutions & Caribbean; USD 104 in developing nations to institutions in developing nations; GBP 64 in developing nations to institutions; GBP 127 elsewhere to institutions (effective 2006) (from Blackwell Synergy, EBSCO Publishing, Gale Group, IngentaConnect, O C L C Online Computer Library Center, Inc., Swets Information Services).
Indexed: ABIn, APEL, BAS, GEOBASE, IBSS, JEL.
—BLDSC (1742.410000), IE, Infotrieve, ingenta. **CCC.**
Published by: (East Asian Economic Association GBR), Blackwell Publishing Asia (Subsidiary of: Blackwell Publishing Ltd.), 550 Swanston St, Carlton South, VIC 3053, Australia. TEL 61-383591011, FAX 61-383591120, subs@blackwellpublishingasia.com, http://www.blackwellpublishing.com/journals/ASEJ. Eds. Akira Kohsaka, Yun-Wing Sung. **Subscr. to:** Blackwell Publishing Ltd., Journal Customer Services, 9600 Garsington Rd, PO Box 1354, Oxford OX4 2XG, United Kingdom. TEL 44-1865-778315, FAX 44-1865-471775.

330.1 IND ISSN 0970-7530
ASSAM ECONOMIC JOURNAL. Text in English. 1977 (vol.3). a. INR 10, USD 2.
Indexed: BAS.
Published by: Dibrugarh University, Department of Economics, Dibrugarh, 786 001, India.

B

▼ new title ➤ refereed ✶ unverified ♦ full entry avail.

330 AUS ISSN 0004-8992
HC601
➤ **AUSTRALIAN ECONOMIC HISTORY REVIEW**; an Asia-Pacific journal of economic, business & social history. Text in English. 1962. 3/yr. GBP 91 combined subscription in Australia & New Zealand to institutions print & online eds.; USD 200 combined subscription in the Americas to institutions print & online eds.; GBP 63, USD 90 combined subscription in developing nations to institutions print & online eds.; GBP 137 combined subscription elsewhere to institutions print & online eds.; AUD 35 combined subscription in Australia & New Zealand to students print & online eds.; USD 30 combined subscription in the Americas to students print & online eds.; EUR 30 combined subscription in Europe to students print & online eds.; GBP 20 combined subscription elsewhere to students print & online eds. (effective 2006). bk.rev. Index. reprint service avail. from PSC. **Document type:** *Journal, Academic/Scholarly.* **Description:** Covers the historical treatment of economic, social and business issues, particularly relating to the countries in the Asia-Pacific region, including Australia and New Zealand, and parts of the region.
Formerly: Business Archives and History
Related titles: Online - full text ed.: ISSN 1467-8446. GBP 87 in Australia & New Zealand to institutions; USD 188 in the Americas to institutions; GBP 130 elsewhere to institutions; GBP 60, USD 86 in developing nations to institutions (effective 2006) (from Blackwell Synergy, EBSCO Publishing, Gale Group, IngentaConnect, O C L C Online Computer Library Center, Inc., R M I T Publishing, Swets Information Services).
Indexed: ABIn, ASCA, AmH&L, AusPAIS, BibInd, CurCont, HistAb, IBSS, JEL, PAIS, PCI, PSA, RASB, SSCI, WBA, WMB.
—BLDSC (1798.650000), IDS, IE, Infotrieve, ingenta. **CCC.**
Published by: (Economic History Society of Australia and New Zealand), Blackwell Publishing Asia (Subsidiary of: Blackwell Publishing Ltd.), 550 Swanston St, Carlton South, VIC 3053, Australia. TEL 61-383591011, FAX 61-383591120, subs@blackwellpublishingasia.com, http://www.blackwellpublishing.com/journals/AEHR. Eds. Dr. Martin Shanahan, Dr. Pierre van der Eng. Circ: 500.

330.1 USA ISSN 1045-3288
HB98
AUSTRIAN ECONOMICS NEWSLETTER. Text in English. 1977. q. USD 15.95 (effective 2000). bk.rev. bibl.; illus.; tr.lit. back issues avail. **Document type:** *Newsletter.* **Description:** Provides interviews with prominent figures in the Austrian school of economics.
Published by: Ludwig von Mises Institute, 518 W Magnolia Ave, Auburn, AL 36832. TEL 334-321-2100, FAX 334-321-2119, mail@mises.org, http://www.mises.org. Ed., R&P Jeffrey Tucker TEL 334-321-2108. Circ: 3,000.

330.1 USA ISSN 1555-0494
THE B E JOURNALS IN ECONOMIC ANALYSIS & POLICY. Text in English. 200?. a. USD 35 to individuals; USD 450 to institutions (effective 2006); Subscription includes the four titles in series: Advances in Economic Analysis & Policy, Contributions to Economic Analysis & Policy, Frontiers of Economic Analysis & Policy and Topics in Economic Analysis & Policy.. **Document type:** *Journal, Academic/Scholarly.* **Description:** Covers issues in business and public policy with microeconomics analysis.
Media: Online - full content. **Related titles:** ♦ Series: Frontiers of Economic Analysis & Policy. ISSN 1538-0629; ♦ Advances in Economic Analysis & Policy. ISSN 1538-0637; ♦ Contributions on Economic Analysis & Policy. ISSN 1538-0645; ♦ Topics in Economic Analysis & Policy. ISSN 1538-0653.
Published by: Berkeley Electronic Press, 2809 Telegraph Ave., Ste 202, Berkeley, CA 94705. FAX 510-665-1201, info@bepress.com, http://www.bepress.com/bejeap/. Eds. Aaron S Edlin, Bruce D Myer, Don Fullerton, Hermalin E Benjamin, Kyle Bagwell.

330.1 USA ISSN 1555-0478
THE B E JOURNALS IN THEORETICAL ECONOMICS. Text in English. 2001. a. USD 35 to individuals; USD 300 to institutions (effective 2006); Subscription includes the four titles in series: Advances in Theoretical Economics, Contributions to Theoretical Economics, Frontiers of Theoretical Economics and Topics in Theoretical Economics.. **Document type:** *Journal, Academic/Scholarly.* **Description:** Covers all aspects of economic theory, including decision theory, game theory, general equilibrium theory, and the theory of economic mechanisms.
Media: Online - full content. **Related titles:** ♦ Series: Advances in Theoretical Economics. ISSN 1534-5963; ♦ Contributions to Theoretical Economics. ISSN 1534-5971; ♦ Topics in Theoretical Economics. ISSN 1534-598X; ♦ Frontiers of Theoretical Economics. ISSN 1534-5955.
Published by: Berkeley Electronic Press, 2809 Telegraph Ave., Ste 202, Berkeley, CA 94705. FAX 510-665-1201, info@bepress.com, http://www.bepress.com/bejte/. Ed. Aaron S Edlin.

330.1 ESP
BANCO DE ESPANA. ESTUDIOS DE HISTORIA ECONOMICA; serie roja. Text in Spanish. irreg., latest vol.18, 1989.
Published by: Banco de Espana, Alcala 50, Madrid, 28014, Spain. TEL 34-91-3385180, FAX 34-91-3385320, http://www.bde.es.

330.1 GRC ISSN 1108-2690
HG1200.5
BANK OF GREECE. MONETARY POLICY. Text in English, Greek. 1998. a. free.
Published by: Bank of Greece, Economic Research Division, 21 Panepistimiou St, Athens, 102 50, Greece. FAX 30-1-3233025, boglibr@ath.forthnet.gr.

330.1 DEU ISSN 1433-8645
BEITRAEGE ZUR UNTERNEHMENSGESCHICHTE. BEIHEFTE. Text in German. 1959. irreg., latest vol.8, 1999. price varies. **Document type:** *Monographic series, Academic/Scholarly.*
Former titles (until 1997): Zeitschrift fuer Unternehmensgeschichte. Beihefte (0342-3956); (until 1977): Beiheft der Tradition (0342-4189)
Published by: (Gesellschaft fuer Unternehmensgeschichte e.V., Koeln), Franz Steiner Verlag Stuttgart GmbH, Birkenwaldstr 44, Stuttgart, 70191, Germany. TEL 49-711-25820, FAX 49-711-2582390, franz.steiner.verlag@t-online.de, http://www.steiner-verlag.de. Ed. H Pohl. R&P Sabine Koerner.

330.1 CHE ISSN 0522-7216
➤ **BEITRAEGE ZUR WIRTSCHAFTSPOLITIK.** Text in German, English. 1965. irreg., latest vol.78, 2003. price varies. **Document type:** *Monographic series, Academic/Scholarly.*
—**CCC.**
Published by: Paul Haupt AG, Falkenplatz 14, Bern, 3001, Switzerland. TEL 41-31-3012425, FAX 41-31-3014669, verlag@haupt.ch, http://www.haupt.ch. Ed. E Tuchtfeldt.

330.1 CAN
BELL CANADA PAPERS SERIES. Text in English. 1993. a. CND 25 per issue (effective 2004). back issues avail. **Document type:** *Monographic series.*
Published by: John Deutsch Institute for the Study of Economic Policy, Dunning Hall Room 216C, Queen's University, Kingston, ON K7L 3N6, Canada. TEL 613-533-2294, FAX 613-533-6025. Ed. Charles M Beach. R&P Sharon Sullivan.

330 GNB ISSN 1017-1460
BOLETIM DE INFORMACAO SOCIO-ECONOMICA. Text in Portuguese. 1985. irreg.
Indexed: PAIS.
Published by: Instituto Nacional de Estudos e Pesquisa, Bairro Cobornel, C.P. 112, Bissau, Guinea-Bissau. TEL 245-251-867.

330.1 NLD
➤ **BOSTON STUDIES IN APPLIED ECONOMICS.** Text in English. 1981. irreg., latest vol.2, 1981. price varies. **Document type:** *Monographic series, Academic/Scholarly.*
Published by: Springer-Verlag Dordrecht (Subsidiary of: Springer Science+Business Media), Van Godewijckstraat 30, Dordrecht, 3311 GX, Netherlands. TEL 31-78-6576050, FAX 31-78-6576474, http://www.springeronline.com.

330.1 BRA
BRAZILIAN REVIEW OF ECONOMETRICS. Text in Portuguese, English. 1981. s-a.
Formerly (until 2003): Revista de Econometria (0101-7012)
Indexed: JEL.
Published by: Sociedade Brasileira de Econometria, Praia de Botafogo 190, 10 Andar, Sala 1032, Botafogo, Rio de Janeiro, RJ, Brazil. TEL 55-21-25514658, FAX 55-21-25524898, sbe@fgv.br, http://www.sbe.org.br/vol_ultimo.htm. Ed. Naercio A. Menezes Filho.

330 USA ISSN 0007-2303
HC101
➤ **BROOKINGS PAPERS ON ECONOMIC ACTIVITY.** Text in English. 1970. s-a. USD 50 domestic to individuals; USD 70 foreign to individuals; USD 65 domestic to institutions; USD 85 foreign to institutions; USD 25 per issue (effective 2005). illus. Index. reprint service avail. from PQC. **Document type:** *Journal, Academic/Scholarly.* **Description:** Provides academic and business economists, government officials, and members of the financial and business community with analyses of current economic developments.
Related titles: Microform ed.: (from PQC); Online - full text ed.: ISSN 1533-4465 (from EBSCO Publishing, Florida Center for Library Automation, Gale Group, H.W. Wilson, JSTOR (Web-based Journal Archive), Northern Light Technology, Inc., O C L C Online Computer Library Center, Inc., Project MUSE, ProQuest Information & Learning, Swets Information Services).
Indexed: ABIn, ABS&EES, APEL, ASCA, Acal, AgeL, BPI, BPIA, CPM, CREJ, CurCont, FamI, HRA, IBR, IBSS, IBZ, ILD, JEL, KES, PAIS, PROMT, RASB, SFSA, SSCI, SSI, T&II, WAE&RSA.
—BLDSC (2350.070000), CISTI, IDS, IE, Infotrieve, ingenta. **CCC.**
Published by: Brookings Institution Press, 1775 Massachusetts Ave, NW, Washington, DC 20036-2188. TEL 202-797-6255, FAX 202-797-6195, http://www.brookings.edu/es/commentary/journals/bpea_macro/bpea_macro.htm, http://www.brook.edu/press. Eds. George L Perry, William C Brainard.

330.1 GBR ISSN 0260-5171
BUSINESS HISTORY NEWSLETTER. Text in English. 1980. s-a. free. adv. bk.rev. reprint service avail. from SCH. **Document type:** *Newsletter.*
Published by: London School of Economics, Business History Unit, Houghton St, London, WC2A 2AE, United Kingdom. TEL 44-171-955-7109, FAX 44-171-955-6861, TELEX 24655 BLPES G. Circ: 1,500.

C E D R E S. REVUE ECONOMIQUE ET SOCIALE. see *AGRICULTURE—Agricultural Economics*

C E P S PAPERS. see *POLITICAL SCIENCE—International Relations*

C E P S WORKING DOCUMENTS. see *POLITICAL SCIENCE—International Relations*

330.1 HUN
➤ **C E U PRIVATIZATION REPORTS.** Text in Hungarian. 1993. irreg., latest vol.4, 1995. USD 15. **Document type:** *Monographic series, Academic/Scholarly.* **Description:** Provides essential data on the privatization process in Central and Eastern Europe.
—BLDSC (3123.940800).
Published by: (Central European University, Privatization Project), Central European University Press, Nador utca 9, Budapest, 1051, Hungary. TEL 36-1-1762333, FAX 36-1-1762778. Ed. Pauline Wickham. Pub. Frances Pinter.

330.1 320 FRA ISSN 1299-5606
CAHIERS D'ECONOMIE POLITIQUE. Variant title: Collection les Cahiers d"Economie Politique. Text in French. 1999. irreg. price varies. **Document type:** *Monographic series, Academic/Scholarly.*
Published by: L' Harmattan, 5 rue de l'Ecole Polytechnique, Paris, 75005, France. TEL 33-1-43257651, FAX 33-1-43258203, http://www.editions-harmattan.fr.

330.9 FRA ISSN 0298-7899
CAHIERS D'ETUDE ET DE RECHERCHE. Text in French. 1986. irreg. adv. bibl.; charts; illus.; stat. back issues avail. **Document type:** *Monographic series.* **Description:** Provides an educational tool for students, trade unionists and social activists, covering Europe, both East and West, the Americas, Asia, Africa and the major issues of socialist theory.
Related titles: ♦ English ed.: Notebooks for Study and Research. ISSN 0298-7902.
Published by: (International Institute for Research and Education/Institut International de Recherche et de Formation NLD), Editions Pierre Rousset, 2 rue Richard Lenoir, Montreuil, Cedex 93108, France. FAX 33-1-43792106, iire@antenna.nl. Ed., R&P Peter Drucker. Pub. Pierre Rousset. Circ: 1,500. **Subscr. to:** IIRE, Postbus 53290, Amsterdam 1007 RG, Netherlands. TEL 31-20-6717263, FAX 31-20-6732106.

330 BEL ISSN 0008-0195
HC311
➤ **CAHIERS ECONOMIQUES DE BRUXELLES.** Text in French, English, Dutch. 1958. q. EUR 35 domestic to individuals; EUR 50 foreign to individuals; EUR 85 domestic to institutions; EUR 100 foreign to institutions (effective 2005). adv. bibl.; charts; illus. index. back issues avail.; reprints avail. **Document type:** *Journal.*
Incorporating: Series Statistiques de Bruxelles
Indexed: ELLIS, ILD, JEL, KES, PAIS, SSCI.
Published by: (Universite Libre de Bruxelles, Department of Economics), Editions du Dulbea a.s.b.l, Av FD Roosevelt 50, Brussels, 1050, Belgium. TEL 32-2-650-4123, FAX 32-2-650-3825, imalacor@ulb.ac.be, http://homepages.vub.ac.be/~mcincera/BER/BER.html. Circ: 300.

330.1 ITA ISSN 1125-8306
CAMERA DI COMMERCIO, INDUSTRIA, E AGRICOLTURA DI GENOVA. REGESTI EMEROGRAFICI. Text in Italian. 1948. q.
Supersedes in part (until 1978): Bollettino Emerografico di Economia Internazionale (0006-680X)
Published by: (Camera di Commercio, Industria, e Agricoltura di Genova), Istituto di Economia Internazionale, Via Garibaldi, 4, Genoa, GE 16124, Italy. TEL 39-10-2704202, FAX 39-10-2704300.

CAMERA DI COMMERCIO, INDUSTRIA, E AGRICOLTURA DI GENOVA. SEGNALAZIONI BIBLIOGRAFICHE. see *BUSINESS AND ECONOMICS—Abstracting, Bibliographies, Statistics*

330 ITA ISSN 1125-8284
CAMERA DI COMMERCIO, INDUSTRIA, E AGRICOLTURA DI GENOVA. SEGNALAZIONI EMEROGRAFICHE. Text in Italian. 1948. q. abstr.; bibl. **Document type:** *Bulletin, Academic/Scholarly.* **Description:** Examines the fields of economic systems, theories and history.
Supersedes in part (until 1978): Bollettino Emerografico di Economia Internazionale (0006-680X)
Published by: (Camera di Commercio, Industria, e Agricoltura di Genova), Istituto di Economia Internazionale, Via Garibaldi, 4, Genoa, GE 16124, Italy. TEL 39-10-2704202, FAX 39-10-2704300. Circ: 20.

CANADA. STATISTICS CANADA. SERVICE INDUSTRIES IN THE CANADIAN INPUT - OUTPUT ACCOUNTS: CURRENT PRICES, SOURCES OF DATA AND METHODS OF ESTIMATION/CANADA. STATISTIQUE CANADA. INDUSTRIES DE SERVICES DANS LES COMPTES D'ENTREES - SORTIES DU CANADA: EN PRIX COURANTS, SOURCES DE DONNEES ET METHODES D'ESTIMATION. see *BUSINESS AND ECONOMICS—Abstracting, Bibliographies, Statistics*

330.1 CAN ISSN 0705-4580
HT395.C3
➤ **CANADIAN JOURNAL OF REGIONAL SCIENCE/REVUE CANADIENNE DES SCIENCES REGIONALES.** Text in English, French. 1978. 3/yr. CND 60 (effective 2005). bk.rev. back issues avail. **Document type:** *Academic/Scholarly.*
Related titles: Online - full text ed.: (from Florida Center for Library Automation, Gale Group).
Indexed: ASFA, AgeL, CBCARef, CBPI, CPerI, ESPM, JEL, RASB, SRRA, SSCI.
—BLDSC (3035.300000), CISTI, IE, Infotrieve, ingenta. **CCC.**
Published by: University of Montreal, Department of Geography, CP 6128, Succursale Centre Ville, Montreal, PQ H3C 3J7, Canada. TEL 514-343-8061, FAX 514-343-8008, cr_bryant@stratec.ca, http://www.lib.unb.ca/Texts/CJRS/, http://ultratext.hil.unbc.ca/texts/cjrs/. Ed. Christopher Bryant. R&P C R Bryant. Circ: 550. **Co-sponsor:** Canadian Association of Regional Science.

330.122 GBR ISSN 0309-8168
HB97.5
CAPITAL AND CLASS. Text in English. 1970. 3/yr. GBP 25 domestic to individuals; EUR 40, USD 45, GBP 28 foreign to individuals (effective 2005). adv. bk.rev. 200 p./no.; back issues avail. **Document type:** *Journal, Academic/Scholarly.* **Description:** Provides a critique of global capitalism in the Marxist tradition, reaching out into the labour, trade union and other radical movements, such as anti-racism, environmentalism and feminism.
Formerly: Conference of Socialist Economists. Bulletin
Related titles: Online - full text ed.: (from EBSCO Publishing, Gale Group, H.W. Wilson, O C L C Online Computer Library Center, Inc., ProQuest Information & Learning).
Indexed: AltPI, ChPerI, DIP, IBR, IBSS, IBZ, LRI, LeftInd, PCI, PSA, SOPODA, SRRA, SSA, SSI, SWA, SociolAb.
—BLDSC (3050.667200), IE, Infotrieve, ingenta. **CCC.**
Published by: Conference of Socialist Economists, 25 Horsell Rd, London, N5 1XL, United Kingdom. cseoffice@gn.apc.org, http://www.cseweb.org.uk/curr.shtml. Adv. contact Anna Melamed. Circ: 3,000.

338.9 GBR ISSN 0265-7996
HD72
CENTRE FOR ECONOMIC POLICY RESEARCH. BULLETIN. Text in English. 1983. q. free (effective 2005). 2 cols./p.; back issues avail. **Document type:** *Bulletin, Trade.* **Description:** Contains articles on CEPR reports, lunchtime meetings and Discussion Papers, and information on forthcoming meetings and publications.
Related titles: Online - full content ed.
—CCC.
Published by: Centre for Economic Policy Research, 90-98 Goswell Rd, London, EC1V 7RR, United Kingdom. TEL 44-20-78782900, FAX 44-20-78782999, cepr@cepr.org, http://www.cepr.org/pubs/Bulletin/. Ed. Niall Flynn. Circ: 10,000.

338.9 GBR ISSN 0265-8003
HD87
CENTRE FOR ECONOMIC POLICY RESEARCH. DISCUSSION PAPERS. Text in English. 1984. irreg. price varies. abstr. back issues avail. **Document type:** *Academic/Scholarly.*
Related titles: Online - full content ed.; Online - full text ed.: (from EBSCO Publishing).
Indexed: AbHyg, AgBio, PHN&I, RDA, WAE&RSA.
—BLDSC (3597.951200), IE, ingenta. **CCC.**
Published by: Centre for Economic Policy Research, 90-98 Goswell Rd, London, EC1V 7RR, United Kingdom. TEL 44-20-78782900, FAX 44-20-78782999, orders@cepr.org, cepr@cepr.org, http://www.cepr.org/pubs/new-dps/dp_papers.htm. R&P Mike Kelly TEL 44-20-78782906.

338.9 GBR
CENTRE FOR ECONOMIC POLICY RESEARCH. POLICY PAPERS. Text in English. irreg. GBP 39 (effective 2003). abstr. **Document type:** *Academic/Scholarly.*
Related titles: Online - full text ed.: GBP 29 (effective 2003).
Published by: Centre for Economic Policy Research, 90-98 Goswell Rd, London, EC1V 7RR, United Kingdom. TEL 44-20-78782900, FAX 44-20-78782999, cepr@cepr.org, http://www.cepr.org/pubs/PolicyPapers/.

330.1 AUS ISSN 0155-7386
CENTRE FOR INDEPENDENT STUDIES. OCCASIONAL PAPERS. Text in English. 1978. irreg. price varies. abstr.; bibl.; stat. back issues avail.
Indexed: WBA.
—BLDSC (3267.639070).
Published by: Centre for Independent Studies, PO Box 92, St Leonards, NSW 1590, Australia. TEL 61-2-94384377, FAX 61-2-94397310, cis@cis.org.au, http://www.cis.org.au. Circ: 1,500.

330.1 GBR ISSN 1362-3761
CENTREPIECE. Text in English. 3/yr. USD 17 to individuals; USD 55 to institutions (effective 2000). **Description:** Aimed at academics and policymakers concerned with various aspects of the English and European economy.
Published by: London School of Economics and Political Science, Centre for Economic Performance, Room H102, Freepost LON 14052, London, WC2A 2BR, United Kingdom.

CENTRUM VOOR BEDRIJFSGESCHIEDENIS. CAHIERS. see *HISTORY—History Of Europe*

CICLOS; en la historia, la economia y la sociedad. see *HISTORY—History Of North And South America*

330.1 CRI ISSN 0252-9521
HB9
CIENCIAS ECONOMICAS. Text in Spanish. 1980. s-a. USD 30 (effective 2000). adv. **Document type:** *Academic/Scholarly.*
Related titles: Online - full text ed.: (from Gale Group).
Indexed: IBR, RASB.
Published by: Editorial de la Universidad de Costa Rica, Apdo. 75-2060, Ciudad Universitaria Rodrigo Facio Brenes, San Pedro de Montes de Oca, San Jose, 2050, Costa Rica. TEL 506-207-4000, FAX 506-207-5535, cmmoreno@cariari.ucr.ac.cr, http://www.ucr.ac.cr/. Ed. Juan Rafael Vargas. R&P Mario Murillo TEL 506-2075003. Adv. contact Cristina Moreno Murillo.

CIVILISATIONS ET SOCIETES. see *HISTORY—History Of Europe*

330.1 ESP
COLECCION DE ECONOMIA. Text in Spanish. 1976. irreg. price varies. back issues avail. **Document type:** *Academic/Scholarly.*
Published by: (Universidad de Navarra, Instituto de Estudios Superiores de la Empresa), Ediciones Universidad de Navarra S.A., Pza. Los Sauces, 1-2, Baranain, (Navarra) 31010, Spain. TEL 34-948-256850, FAX 34-948-256854, eunsaedi@abc.ibernet.com, http://www.unav.es.

330 GBR ISSN 0888-7233
HC701
➤ **COMPARATIVE ECONOMIC STUDIES.** Text in English. 1961 (vol.17). q. GBP 70 combined subscription in Europe to individuals; USD 112 combined subscription elsewhere to individuals; GBP 165 combined subscription in Europe to institutions; USD 265 combined subscription elsewhere to institutions (effective 2005); combined subscr. includes print & online. bk.rev. back issues avail.; reprints avail. **Document type:** *Journal, Academic/Scholarly.* **Description:** Comparative studies of economic systems, planning and development.
Former titles (until 1984): A C E S Bulletin (0360-5930); (until 1971): A S T E Bulletin (0001-2645)
Related titles: Microform ed.; Online - full text ed.: ISSN 1478-3320. GBP 131 in Europe to institutions; USD 189 elsewhere to institutions (effective 2004) (from EBSCO Publishing, Florida Center for Library Automation, Gale Group, IngentaConnect, Northern Light Technology, Inc., O C L C Online Computer Library Center, Inc., ProQuest Information & Learning, Swets Information Services).
Indexed: ABIn, ABS&EES, BAS, CREJ, IBR, IBSS, IBZ, JEL, MEA&I, PAIS, RASB, T&II.
—BLDSC (3363.758000), CISTI, IE, Infotrieve, ingenta. **CCC.**
Published by: (Association for Comparative Economic Studies USA), Palgrave Macmillan Ltd. (Subsidiary of: Macmillan Publishers Ltd.), Houndmills, Basingstoke, Hants RG21 6XS, United Kingdom. TEL 44-1256-329242, FAX 44-1256-810526, journal-info@palgrave.com, http://www.palgrave-journals.com/ces/index.html. Ed. Jeffrey B Miller. Circ: 1,000 (paid).

330.1 USA ISSN 0084-9235
CONTRIBUTIONS IN ECONOMICS AND ECONOMIC HISTORY. Text in English. 1970. irreg., latest vol.230, 2003. price varies. **Document type:** *Monographic series, Academic/Scholarly.*
—BLDSC (3458.370000), IE, ingenta.
Published by: Greenwood Publishing Group Inc. (Subsidiary of: Harcourt International), 88 Post Rd W, PO Box 5007, Westport, CT 06881. TEL 203-226-3571, FAX 203-226-1502, webmaster@greenwood.com, http://www.greenwood.com. Ed. Robert Sobel.

330.1 USA ISSN 1538-0645
HB1
CONTRIBUTIONS ON ECONOMIC ANALYSIS & POLICY. Text in English. 2001. a. Included with subscription to The B E Journals in Economic Analysis and Policy.. **Document type:** *Journal, Academic/Scholarly.*
Media: Online - full content. **Related titles:** Online - full text ed.: (from O C L C Online Computer Library Center, Inc., ProQuest Information & Learning); ♦ Series of: The B E Journals in Economic Analysis & Policy. ISSN 1555-0494.
Indexed: ABIn, IBSS, JEL.
Published by: Berkeley Electronic Press, 2809 Telegraph Ave., Ste 202, Berkeley, CA 94705. FAX 510-665-1201, info@bepress.com, http://www.bepress.com/bejeap/contributions/. Eds. Aaron S Edlin, Bruce D Myer, Don Fullerton, Hermalin E Benjamin, Kyle Bagwell.

330 NLD ISSN 0573-8555
➤ **CONTRIBUTIONS TO ECONOMIC ANALYSIS.** Text in Dutch. 1952. irreg., latest vol.256, 2002. price. back issues avail. **Document type:** *Monographic series, Academic/Scholarly.* **Description:** Stimulates international debate of scientific information on economic analysis by publishing original research in applied economics.
Indexed: Inspec, MathR.
—BLDSC (3458.320000), CISTI, IE, ingenta, Linda Hall.
Published by: Elsevier BV, North-Holland (Subsidiary of: Elsevier Science & Technology), Sara Burgerhartstraat 25, Amsterdam, 1055 KV, Netherlands. TEL 31-20-485-3911, FAX 31-20-485-2457, nlinfo-f@elsevier.nl, http://www.elsevier.nl. Eds. J-J Laffont, R Blundell, T Persson. **Subscr. to:** Elsevier BV, PO Box 211, Amsterdam 1000 AE, Netherlands. TEL 31-20-485-3757, FAX 31-20-485-3432, http://www.elsevier.nl.

330.1 USA ISSN 1534-5971
HB1
CONTRIBUTIONS TO THEORETICAL ECONOMICS. Text in English. 2001. irreg. Included with subscription to The B E Journals in Theoretical Economics. **Document type:** *Journal, Academic/Scholarly.*
Media: Online - full content. **Related titles:** Online - full text ed.: (from O C L C Online Computer Library Center, Inc., ProQuest Information & Learning); ♦ Series of: The B E Journals in Theoretical Economics. ISSN 1555-0478.
Indexed: ABIn, IBSS, JEL, MathR, MathSciNet.
Published by: Berkeley Electronic Press, 2809 Telegraph Ave., Ste 202, Berkeley, CA 94705. FAX 510-665-1201, info@bepress.com, http://www.bepress.com/bejte/contributions/. Eds. Chris Shannon, Dilip Abreu, Ilya Segal, Patrick Bolton.

COUNTRY PROFILE. AFGHANISTAN; annual survey of political and economic background. see *POLITICAL SCIENCE*

COUNTRY PROFILE. ALBANIA; annual survey of political and economic background. see *POLITICAL SCIENCE*

COUNTRY PROFILE. ALGERIA; annual survey of political and economic background. see *POLITICAL SCIENCE*

COUNTRY PROFILE. ANGOLA; annual survey of political and economic background. see *POLITICAL SCIENCE*

COUNTRY PROFILE. ARGENTINA; annual survey of political and economic background. see *POLITICAL SCIENCE*

COUNTRY PROFILE. ARMENIA; annual survey of political and economic background. see *POLITICAL SCIENCE*

COUNTRY PROFILE. ARUBA; annual survey of political and economic background. see *POLITICAL SCIENCE*

COUNTRY PROFILE. AUSTRALIA; annual survey of political and economic background. see *POLITICAL SCIENCE*

COUNTRY PROFILE. AUSTRIA; annual survey of political and economic background. see *POLITICAL SCIENCE*

COUNTRY PROFILE. AZERBAIJAN; annual survey of political and economic background. see *POLITICAL SCIENCE*

COUNTRY PROFILE. BAHAMAS; annual survey of political and economic background. see *POLITICAL SCIENCE*

COUNTRY PROFILE. BAHRAIN; annual survey of political and economic background. see *POLITICAL SCIENCE*

COUNTRY PROFILE. BANGLADESH; annual survey of political and economic background. see *POLITICAL SCIENCE*

COUNTRY PROFILE. BELARUS; annual survey of political and economic background. see *POLITICAL SCIENCE*

COUNTRY PROFILE. BELGIUM; annual survey of political and economic background. see *POLITICAL SCIENCE*

COUNTRY PROFILE. BELIZE; annual survey of political and economic background. see *POLITICAL SCIENCE*

COUNTRY PROFILE. BENIN; annual survey of political and economic background. see *POLITICAL SCIENCE*

COUNTRY PROFILE. BERMUDA; annual survey of political and economic background. see *POLITICAL SCIENCE*

COUNTRY PROFILE. BOLIVIA; annual survey of political and economic background. see *POLITICAL SCIENCE*

COUNTRY PROFILE. BOSNIA-HERCEGOVINA; annual survey of political and economic background. see *POLITICAL SCIENCE*

COUNTRY PROFILE. BOTSWANA; annual survey of political and economic background. see *POLITICAL SCIENCE*

COUNTRY PROFILE. BRAZIL; annual survey of political and economic background. see *POLITICAL SCIENCE*

B

B

COUNTRY PROFILE. BULGARIA; annual survey of political and economic background. see *POLITICAL SCIENCE*

COUNTRY PROFILE. BURKINA FASO; annual survey of political and economic background. see *POLITICAL SCIENCE*

COUNTRY PROFILE. BURUNDI; annual survey of political and economic background. see *POLITICAL SCIENCE*

COUNTRY PROFILE. CAMBODIA; annual survey of political and economic background. see *POLITICAL SCIENCE*

COUNTRY PROFILE. CAMEROON; annual survey of political and economic background. see *POLITICAL SCIENCE*

COUNTRY PROFILE. CANADA; annual survey of political and economic background. see *POLITICAL SCIENCE*

COUNTRY PROFILE. CAPE VERDE; annual survey of political and economic background. see *POLITICAL SCIENCE*

COUNTRY PROFILE. CAYMAN ISLANDS; annual survey of political and economic background. see *POLITICAL SCIENCE*

COUNTRY PROFILE. CENTRAL AFRICAN REPUBLIC; annual survey of political and economic background. see *POLITICAL SCIENCE*

COUNTRY PROFILE. CHAD; annual survey of political and economic background. see *POLITICAL SCIENCE*

COUNTRY PROFILE. CHILE; annual survey of political and economic background. see *POLITICAL SCIENCE*

COUNTRY PROFILE. CHINA; annual survey of political and economic background. see *POLITICAL SCIENCE*

COUNTRY PROFILE. COLOMBIA; annual survey of political and economic background. see *POLITICAL SCIENCE*

COUNTRY PROFILE. COMOROS; annual survey of political and economic background. see *POLITICAL SCIENCE*

COUNTRY PROFILE. CONGO; annual survey of political and economic background. see *POLITICAL SCIENCE*

COUNTRY PROFILE. COSTA RICA; annual survey of political and economic background. see *POLITICAL SCIENCE*

COUNTRY PROFILE. COTE D'IVOIRE; annual survey of political and economic background. see *POLITICAL SCIENCE*

COUNTRY PROFILE. CROATIA; annual survey of political and economic background. see *POLITICAL SCIENCE*

COUNTRY PROFILE. CUBA; annual survey of political and economic background. see *POLITICAL SCIENCE*

COUNTRY PROFILE. CYPRUS; annual survey of political and economic background. see *POLITICAL SCIENCE*

COUNTRY PROFILE. CZECH REPUBLIC; annual survey of political and economic background. see *POLITICAL SCIENCE*

COUNTRY PROFILE. DEMOCRATIC REPUBLIC OF CONGO; annual survey of political and economic background. see *POLITICAL SCIENCE*

COUNTRY PROFILE. DENMARK; annual survey of political and economic background. see *POLITICAL SCIENCE*

COUNTRY PROFILE. DJIBOUTI; annual survey of political and economic background. see *POLITICAL SCIENCE*

COUNTRY PROFILE. DOMINICAN REPUBLIC; annual survey of political and economic background. see *POLITICAL SCIENCE*

COUNTRY PROFILE. ECUADOR; annual survey of political and economic background. see *POLITICAL SCIENCE*

COUNTRY PROFILE. EGYPT; annual survey of political and economic background. see *POLITICAL SCIENCE*

COUNTRY PROFILE. EL SALVADOR; annual survey of political and economic background. see *POLITICAL SCIENCE*

COUNTRY PROFILE. EQUATORIAL GUINEA; annual survey of political and economic background. see *POLITICAL SCIENCE*

COUNTRY PROFILE. ERITREA; annual survey of political and economic background. see *POLITICAL SCIENCE*

COUNTRY PROFILE. ESTONIA; annual survey of political and economic background. see *POLITICAL SCIENCE*

COUNTRY PROFILE. ETHIOPIA; annual survey of political and economic background. see *POLITICAL SCIENCE*

COUNTRY PROFILE. EUROPEAN UNION; annual survey of political and economic background. see *POLITICAL SCIENCE*

COUNTRY PROFILE. FINLAND; annual survey of political and economic background. see *POLITICAL SCIENCE*

COUNTRY PROFILE. FRANCE; annual survey of political and economic background. see *POLITICAL SCIENCE*

COUNTRY PROFILE. GABON; annual survey of political and economic background. see *POLITICAL SCIENCE*

COUNTRY PROFILE. GEORGIA; annual survey of political and economic background. see *POLITICAL SCIENCE*

COUNTRY PROFILE. GERMANY; annual survey of political and economic background. see *POLITICAL SCIENCE*

COUNTRY PROFILE. GHANA; annual survey of political and economic background. see *POLITICAL SCIENCE*

COUNTRY PROFILE. GREECE; annual survey of political and economic background. see *POLITICAL SCIENCE*

COUNTRY PROFILE. GUATEMALA; annual survey of political and economic background. see *POLITICAL SCIENCE*

COUNTRY PROFILE. GUINEA; annual survey of political and economic background. see *POLITICAL SCIENCE*

COUNTRY PROFILE. GUINEA-BISSAU; annual survey of political and economic background. see *POLITICAL SCIENCE*

COUNTRY PROFILE. GUYANA; annual survey of political and economic background. see *POLITICAL SCIENCE*

COUNTRY PROFILE. HAITI; annual survey of political and economic background. see *POLITICAL SCIENCE*

COUNTRY PROFILE. HONDURAS; annual survey of political and economic background. see *POLITICAL SCIENCE*

COUNTRY PROFILE. HONG KONG; annual survey of political and economic background. see *POLITICAL SCIENCE*

COUNTRY PROFILE. HUNGARY; annual survey of political and economic background. see *POLITICAL SCIENCE*

COUNTRY PROFILE. ICELAND; annual survey of political and economic background. see *POLITICAL SCIENCE*

COUNTRY PROFILE. INDIA; annual survey of political and economic background. see *POLITICAL SCIENCE*

COUNTRY PROFILE. INDONESIA; annual survey of political and economic background. see *POLITICAL SCIENCE*

COUNTRY PROFILE. IRAN; annual survey of political and economic background. see *POLITICAL SCIENCE*

COUNTRY PROFILE. IRAQ; annual survey of political and economic background. see *POLITICAL SCIENCE*

COUNTRY PROFILE. IRELAND; annual survey of political and economic background. see *POLITICAL SCIENCE*

COUNTRY PROFILE. ISRAEL, PALESTINIAN TERRITORIES. see *POLITICAL SCIENCE*

COUNTRY PROFILE. ITALY; annual survey of political and economic background. see *POLITICAL SCIENCE*

COUNTRY PROFILE. JAMAICA, BELIZE, ORGANISATION OF EASTERN CARIBBEAN STATES, WINDWARD AND LEEWARD ISLANDS. see *POLITICAL SCIENCE*

COUNTRY PROFILE. JAPAN; annual survey of political and economic background. see *POLITICAL SCIENCE*

COUNTRY PROFILE. JORDAN; annual survey of political and economic background. see *POLITICAL SCIENCE*

COUNTRY PROFILE. KAZAKHSTAN; annual survey of political and economic background. see *POLITICAL SCIENCE*

COUNTRY PROFILE. KENYA; annual survey of political and economic background. see *POLITICAL SCIENCE*

COUNTRY PROFILE. KUWAIT; annual survey of political and economic background. see *POLITICAL SCIENCE*

COUNTRY PROFILE. KYRGYZ REPUBLIC; annual survey of political and economic background. see *POLITICAL SCIENCE*

COUNTRY PROFILE. LAOS; annual survey of political and economic background. see *POLITICAL SCIENCE*

COUNTRY PROFILE. LEBANON; annual survey of political and economic background. see *POLITICAL SCIENCE*

COUNTRY PROFILE. LESOTHO; annual survey of political and economic background. see *POLITICAL SCIENCE*

COUNTRY PROFILE. LIBERIA; annual survey of political and economic background. see *POLITICAL SCIENCE*

COUNTRY PROFILE. LIBYA; annual survey of political and economic background. see *POLITICAL SCIENCE*

COUNTRY PROFILE. LITHUANIA; annual survey of political and economic background. see *POLITICAL SCIENCE*

COUNTRY PROFILE. LUXEMBOURG; annual survey of political and economic background. see *POLITICAL SCIENCE*

COUNTRY PROFILE. MACAU; annual survey of political and economic background. see *POLITICAL SCIENCE*

COUNTRY PROFILE. MACEDONIA; annual survey of political and economic background. see *POLITICAL SCIENCE*

COUNTRY PROFILE. MADAGASCAR; annual survey of political and economic background. see *POLITICAL SCIENCE*

COUNTRY PROFILE. MALAWI; annual survey of political and economic background. see *POLITICAL SCIENCE*

COUNTRY PROFILE. MALAYSIA; annual survey of political and economic background. see *POLITICAL SCIENCE*

COUNTRY PROFILE. MALI; annual survey of political and economic background. see *POLITICAL SCIENCE*

COUNTRY PROFILE. MALTA; annual survey of political and economic background. see *POLITICAL SCIENCE*

COUNTRY PROFILE. MAURITANIA; annual survey of political and economic background. see *POLITICAL SCIENCE*

COUNTRY PROFILE. MAURITIUS; annual survey of political and economic background. see *POLITICAL SCIENCE*

COUNTRY PROFILE. MEXICO; annual survey of political and economic background. see *POLITICAL SCIENCE*

COUNTRY PROFILE. MOLDOVA; annual survey of political and economic background. see *POLITICAL SCIENCE*

COUNTRY PROFILE. MONGOLIA; annual survey of political and economic background. see *POLITICAL SCIENCE*

COUNTRY PROFILE. MOROCCO; annual survey of political and economic background. see *POLITICAL SCIENCE*

COUNTRY PROFILE. MOZAMBIQUE; annual survey of political and economic background. see *POLITICAL SCIENCE*

COUNTRY PROFILE. MYANMAR; annual survey of political and economic background. see *POLITICAL SCIENCE*

COUNTRY PROFILE. NAMIBIA; annual survey of political and economic background. see *POLITICAL SCIENCE*

COUNTRY PROFILE. NEPAL; annual survey of political and economic background. see *POLITICAL SCIENCE*

COUNTRY PROFILE. NETHERLANDS; annual survey of political and economic background. see *POLITICAL SCIENCE*

COUNTRY PROFILE. NETHERLANDS ANTILLES; annual survey of political and economic background. see *POLITICAL SCIENCE*

COUNTRY PROFILE. NEW ZEALAND; annual survey of political and economic background. see *POLITICAL SCIENCE*

COUNTRY PROFILE. NICARAGUA; annual survey of political and economic background. see *POLITICAL SCIENCE*

COUNTRY PROFILE. NIGER; annual survey of political and economic background. see *POLITICAL SCIENCE*

COUNTRY PROFILE. NIGERIA; annual survey of political and economic background. see *POLITICAL SCIENCE*

COUNTRY PROFILE. NORTH KOREA; annual survey of political and economic background. see *POLITICAL SCIENCE*

COUNTRY PROFILE. NORWAY; annual survey of political and economic background. see *POLITICAL SCIENCE*

COUNTRY PROFILE. OMAN; annual survey of political and economic background. see *POLITICAL SCIENCE*

COUNTRY PROFILE. PACIFIC ISLANDS: FIJI, NEW CALEDONIA, SAMOA, SOLOMON ISLANDS, VANUATU, TONGA; annual survey of political and economic background. see *POLITICAL SCIENCE*

COUNTRY PROFILE. PAKISTAN; annual survey of political and economic background. see *POLITICAL SCIENCE*

COUNTRY PROFILE. PANAMA; annual survey of political and economic background. see *POLITICAL SCIENCE*

COUNTRY PROFILE. PAPUA NEW GUINEA; annual survey of political and economic background. see *POLITICAL SCIENCE*

COUNTRY PROFILE. PARAGUAY; annual survey of political and economic background. see *POLITICAL SCIENCE*

COUNTRY PROFILE. PERU; annual survey of political and economic background. see *POLITICAL SCIENCE*

COUNTRY PROFILE. PHILIPPINES; annual survey of political and economic background. see *POLITICAL SCIENCE*

COUNTRY PROFILE. POLAND; annual survey of political and economic background. see *POLITICAL SCIENCE*

COUNTRY PROFILE. PORTUGAL; annual survey of political and economic background. see *POLITICAL SCIENCE*

COUNTRY PROFILE. PUERTO RICO; annual survey of political and economic background. see *POLITICAL SCIENCE*

COUNTRY PROFILE. QATAR; annual survey of political and economic background. see *POLITICAL SCIENCE*

COUNTRY PROFILE. ROMANIA; annual survey of political and economic background. see *POLITICAL SCIENCE*

COUNTRY PROFILE. RUSSIA; annual survey of political and economic background. see *POLITICAL SCIENCE*

COUNTRY PROFILE. RWANDA; annual survey of political and economic background. see *POLITICAL SCIENCE*

COUNTRY PROFILE. SAO TOME AND PRINCIPE; annual survey of political and economic background. see *POLITICAL SCIENCE*

COUNTRY PROFILE. SAUDI ARABIA; annual survey of political and economic background. see *POLITICAL SCIENCE*

COUNTRY PROFILE. SENEGAL; annual survey of political and economic background. see *POLITICAL SCIENCE*

COUNTRY PROFILE. SERBIA-MONTENEGRO; annual survey of political and economic background. see *POLITICAL SCIENCE*

COUNTRY PROFILE. SEYCHELLES; annual survey of political and economic background. see *POLITICAL SCIENCE*

COUNTRY PROFILE. SIERRA LEONE; annual survey of political and economic background. see *POLITICAL SCIENCE*

COUNTRY PROFILE. SINGAPORE; annual survey of political and economic background. see *POLITICAL SCIENCE*

COUNTRY PROFILE. SLOVAKIA; annual survey of political and economic background. see *POLITICAL SCIENCE*

COUNTRY PROFILE. SLOVENIA; annual survey of political and economic background. see *POLITICAL SCIENCE*

COUNTRY PROFILE. SOMALIA; annual survey of political and economic background. see *POLITICAL SCIENCE*

COUNTRY PROFILE. SOUTH AFRICA; annual survey of political and economic background. see *POLITICAL SCIENCE*

COUNTRY PROFILE. SOUTH KOREA; annual survey of political and economic background. see *POLITICAL SCIENCE*

COUNTRY PROFILE. SPAIN; annual survey of political and economic background. see *POLITICAL SCIENCE*

COUNTRY PROFILE. SRI LANKA; annual survey of political and economic background. see *POLITICAL SCIENCE*

COUNTRY PROFILE. SUDAN; annual survey of political and economic background. see *POLITICAL SCIENCE*

COUNTRY PROFILE. SURINAME; annual survey of political and economic background. see *POLITICAL SCIENCE*

COUNTRY PROFILE. SWAZILAND; annual survey of political and economic background. see *POLITICAL SCIENCE*

COUNTRY PROFILE. SWEDEN; annual survey of political and economic background. see *POLITICAL SCIENCE*

COUNTRY PROFILE. SWITZERLAND; annual survey of political and economic background. see *POLITICAL SCIENCE*

COUNTRY PROFILE. SYRIA; annual survey of political and economic background. see *POLITICAL SCIENCE*

COUNTRY PROFILE. TAIWAN; annual survey of political and economic background. see *POLITICAL SCIENCE*

COUNTRY PROFILE. TAJIKISTAN; annual survey of political and economic background. see *POLITICAL SCIENCE*

COUNTRY PROFILE. TANZANIA; annual survey of political and economic background. see *POLITICAL SCIENCE*

COUNTRY PROFILE. THAILAND; annual survey of political and economic background. see *POLITICAL SCIENCE*

COUNTRY PROFILE. THE GAMBIA; annual survey of political and economic background. see *POLITICAL SCIENCE*

COUNTRY PROFILE. THE PALESTINIAN TERRITORIES; annual survey of political and economic background. see *POLITICAL SCIENCE*

COUNTRY PROFILE. TOGO; annual survey of political and economic background. see *POLITICAL SCIENCE*

COUNTRY PROFILE. TRINIDAD AND TOBAGO; annual survey of political and economic background. see *POLITICAL SCIENCE*

COUNTRY PROFILE. TUNISIA; annual survey of political and economic background. see *POLITICAL SCIENCE*

COUNTRY PROFILE. TURKEY; annual survey of political and economic background. see *POLITICAL SCIENCE*

COUNTRY PROFILE. TURKMENISTAN; annual survey of political and economic background. see *POLITICAL SCIENCE*

COUNTRY PROFILE. TURKS AND CAICOS ISLANDS; annual survey of political and economic background. see *POLITICAL SCIENCE*

COUNTRY PROFILE. UGANDA; annual survey of political and economic background. see *POLITICAL SCIENCE*

COUNTRY PROFILE. UKRAINE; annual survey of political and economic background. see *POLITICAL SCIENCE*

COUNTRY PROFILE. UNITED ARAB EMIRATES; annual survey of political and economic background. see *POLITICAL SCIENCE*

COUNTRY PROFILE. UNITED KINGDOM; annual survey of political and economic background. see *POLITICAL SCIENCE*

COUNTRY PROFILE. UNITED STATES OF AMERICA; annual survey of political and economic background. see *POLITICAL SCIENCE*

COUNTRY PROFILE. URUGUAY; annual survey of political and economic background. see *POLITICAL SCIENCE*

COUNTRY PROFILE. UZBEKISTAN; annual survey of political and economic background. see *POLITICAL SCIENCE*

COUNTRY PROFILE. VENEZUELA; annual survey of political and economic background. see *POLITICAL SCIENCE*

COUNTRY PROFILE. VIETNAM; annual survey of political and economic background. see *POLITICAL SCIENCE*

COUNTRY PROFILE. WINDWARD AND LEEWARD ISLANDS; annual survey of political and economic background. see *POLITICAL SCIENCE*

COUNTRY PROFILE. YEMEN; annual survey of political and economic background. see *POLITICAL SCIENCE*

COUNTRY PROFILE. ZAMBIA; annual survey of political and economic background. see *POLITICAL SCIENCE*

COUNTRY PROFILE. ZIMBABWE; annual survey of political and economic background. see *POLITICAL SCIENCE*

COUNTRY REPORT. AFGHANISTAN; analysis of economic and political trends every quarter. see *BUSINESS AND ECONOMICS—Economic Situation And Conditions*

COUNTRY REPORT. ALBANIA; analysis of economic and political trends every quarter. see *BUSINESS AND ECONOMICS—Economic Situation And Conditions*

COUNTRY REPORT. ALGERIA; analysis of economic and political trends every quarter. see *BUSINESS AND ECONOMICS—Economic Situation And Conditions*

COUNTRY REPORT. ANGOLA; analysis of economic and political trends every quarter. see *BUSINESS AND ECONOMICS—Economic Situation And Conditions*

COUNTRY REPORT. ARGENTINA; analysis of economic and political trends every quarter. see *BUSINESS AND ECONOMICS—Economic Situation And Conditions*

COUNTRY REPORT. ARMENIA; analysis of economic and political trends every quarter. see *BUSINESS AND ECONOMICS—Economic Situation And Conditions*

COUNTRY REPORT. ARUBA; analysis of economic and political trends every quarter. see *BUSINESS AND ECONOMICS—Economic Situation And Conditions*

COUNTRY REPORT. AUSTRALIA; analysis of economic and political trends every quarter. see *BUSINESS AND ECONOMICS—Economic Situation And Conditions*

COUNTRY REPORT. AUSTRIA; analysis of economic and political trends every quarter. see *BUSINESS AND ECONOMICS—Economic Situation And Conditions*

COUNTRY REPORT. AZERBAIJAN; analysis of economic and political trends every quarter. see *BUSINESS AND ECONOMICS—Economic Situation And Conditions*

COUNTRY REPORT. BAHAMAS; analysis of economic and political trends every quarter. see *BUSINESS AND ECONOMICS—Economic Situation And Conditions*

COUNTRY REPORT. BAHRAIN; analysis of economic and political trends every quarter. see *BUSINESS AND ECONOMICS—Economic Situation And Conditions*

COUNTRY REPORT. BANGLADESH; analysis of economic and political trends every quarter. see *BUSINESS AND ECONOMICS—Economic Situation And Conditions*

COUNTRY REPORT. BARBADOS; analysis of economic and political trends every quarter. see *BUSINESS AND ECONOMICS—Economic Situation And Conditions*

COUNTRY REPORT. BELARUS; analysis of economic and political trends every quarter. see *BUSINESS AND ECONOMICS—Economic Situation And Conditions*

COUNTRY REPORT. BELGIUM; analysis of economic and political trends every quarter. see *BUSINESS AND ECONOMICS—Economic Situation And Conditions*

COUNTRY REPORT. BELIZE; analysis of economic and political trends every quarter. see *BUSINESS AND ECONOMICS—Economic Situation And Conditions*

COUNTRY REPORT. BENIN. see *BUSINESS AND ECONOMICS—Economic Situation And Conditions*

COUNTRY REPORT. BERMUDA; analysis of economic and political trends every quarter. see *BUSINESS AND ECONOMICS—Economic Situation And Conditions*

COUNTRY REPORT. BOLIVIA; analysis of economic and political trends every quarter. see *BUSINESS AND ECONOMICS—Economic Situation And Conditions*

COUNTRY REPORT. BOSNIA-HERCEGOVINA; analysis of economic and political trends every quarter. see *BUSINESS AND ECONOMICS—Economic Situation And Conditions*

COUNTRY REPORT. BOTSWANA; analysis of economic and political trends every quarter. see *BUSINESS AND ECONOMICS—Economic Situation And Conditions*

COUNTRY REPORT. BRAZIL; analysis of economic and political trends every quarter. see *BUSINESS AND ECONOMICS—Economic Situation And Conditions*

COUNTRY REPORT. BRUNEI; analysis of economic and political trends every quarter. see *BUSINESS AND ECONOMICS—Economic Situation And Conditions*

COUNTRY REPORT. BULGARIA; analysis of economic and political trends every quarter. see *BUSINESS AND ECONOMICS—Economic Situation And Conditions*

COUNTRY REPORT. BURKINA FASO; analysis of economic and political trends every quarter. see *BUSINESS AND ECONOMICS—Economic Situation And Conditions*

COUNTRY REPORT. BURUNDI. see *BUSINESS AND ECONOMICS—Economic Situation And Conditions*

COUNTRY REPORT. CAMBODIA; analysis of economic and political trends every quarter. see *BUSINESS AND ECONOMICS—Economic Situation And Conditions*

▼ *new title*   ➤ *refereed*   ✷ *unverified*   ◆ *full entry avail.*

B

COUNTRY REPORT. CAMEROON; analysis of economic and political trends every quarter. see *BUSINESS AND ECONOMICS—Economic Situation And Conditions*

COUNTRY REPORT. CANADA; analysis of economic and political trends every quarter. see *BUSINESS AND ECONOMICS—Economic Situation And Conditions*

COUNTRY REPORT. CAPE VERDE; analysis of economic and political trends every quarter. see *BUSINESS AND ECONOMICS—Economic Situation And Conditions*

COUNTRY REPORT. CENTRAL AFRICAN REPUBLIC; analysis of economic and political trends every quarter. see *BUSINESS AND ECONOMICS—Economic Situation And Conditions*

COUNTRY REPORT. CHAD; analysis of economic and political trends every quarter. see *BUSINESS AND ECONOMICS—Economic Situation And Conditions*

COUNTRY REPORT. CHILE; analysis of economic and political trends every quarter. see *BUSINESS AND ECONOMICS—Economic Situation And Conditions*

COUNTRY REPORT. CHINA; analysis of economic and political trends every quarter. see *BUSINESS AND ECONOMICS—Economic Situation And Conditions*

COUNTRY REPORT. COLOMBIA; analysis of economic and political trends every quarter. see *BUSINESS AND ECONOMICS—Economic Situation And Conditions*

COUNTRY REPORT. COMOROS; analysis of economic and political trends every quarter. see *BUSINESS AND ECONOMICS—Economic Situation And Conditions*

COUNTRY REPORT. CONGO (BRAZZAVILLE); analysis of economic and political trends every quarter. see *BUSINESS AND ECONOMICS—Economic Situation And Conditions*

COUNTRY REPORT. COSTA RICA; analysis of economic and political trends every quarter. see *BUSINESS AND ECONOMICS—Economic Situation And Conditions*

COUNTRY REPORT. COTE D'IVOIRE; analysis of economic and political trends every quarter. see *BUSINESS AND ECONOMICS—Economic Situation And Conditions*

COUNTRY REPORT. CROATIA; analysis of economic and political trends every quarter. see *BUSINESS AND ECONOMICS—Economic Situation And Conditions*

COUNTRY REPORT. CUBA; analysis of economic and political trends every quarter. see *BUSINESS AND ECONOMICS—Economic Situation And Conditions*

COUNTRY REPORT. CYPRUS; analysis of economic and political trends every quarter. see *BUSINESS AND ECONOMICS—Economic Situation And Conditions*

COUNTRY REPORT. CZECH REPUBLIC; analysis of economic and political trends every quarter. see *BUSINESS AND ECONOMICS—Economic Situation And Conditions*

COUNTRY REPORT. DEMOCRATIC REPUBLIC OF CONGO; analysis of economic and political trends every quarter. see *BUSINESS AND ECONOMICS—Economic Situation And Conditions*

COUNTRY REPORT. DENMARK; analysis of economic and political trends every quarter. see *BUSINESS AND ECONOMICS—Economic Situation And Conditions*

COUNTRY REPORT. DJIBOUTI; analysis of economic and political trends every quarter. see *BUSINESS AND ECONOMICS—Economic Situation And Conditions*

COUNTRY REPORT. DOMINICAN REPUBLIC; analysis of economic and political trends every quarter. see *BUSINESS AND ECONOMICS—Economic Situation And Conditions*

COUNTRY REPORT. ECUADOR; analysis of economic and political trends every quarter. see *BUSINESS AND ECONOMICS—Economic Situation And Conditions*

COUNTRY REPORT. EGYPT; analysis of economic and political trends every quarter. see *BUSINESS AND ECONOMICS—Economic Situation And Conditions*

COUNTRY REPORT. EL SALVADOR; analysis of economic and political trends every quarter. see *BUSINESS AND ECONOMICS—Economic Situation And Conditions*

COUNTRY REPORT. EQUATORIAL GUINEA; analysis of economic and political trends every quarter. see *BUSINESS AND ECONOMICS—Economic Situation And Conditions*

COUNTRY REPORT. ERITREA; analysis of economic and political trends every quarter. see *BUSINESS AND ECONOMICS—Economic Situation And Conditions*

COUNTRY REPORT. ESTONIA; analysis of economic and political trends every quarter. see *BUSINESS AND ECONOMICS—Economic Situation And Conditions*

COUNTRY REPORT. ETHIOPIA; analysis of economic and political trends every quarter. see *BUSINESS AND ECONOMICS—Economic Situation And Conditions*

COUNTRY REPORT. EUROPEAN UNION. see *BUSINESS AND ECONOMICS—Economic Situation And Conditions*

COUNTRY REPORT. FIJI; analysis of economic and political trends every quarter. see *BUSINESS AND ECONOMICS—Economic Situation And Conditions*

COUNTRY REPORT. FINLAND; analysis of economic and political trends every quarter. see *BUSINESS AND ECONOMICS—Economic Situation And Conditions*

COUNTRY REPORT. FRANCE; analysis of economic and political trends every quarter. see *BUSINESS AND ECONOMICS—Economic Situation And Conditions*

COUNTRY REPORT. GABON; analysis of economic and political trends every quarter. see *BUSINESS AND ECONOMICS—Economic Situation And Conditions*

COUNTRY REPORT. GEORGIA; analysis of economic and political trends every quarter. see *BUSINESS AND ECONOMICS—Economic Situation And Conditions*

COUNTRY REPORT. GERMANY; analysis of economic and political trends every quarter. see *BUSINESS AND ECONOMICS—Economic Situation And Conditions*

COUNTRY REPORT. GHANA; analysis of economic and political trends every quarter. see *BUSINESS AND ECONOMICS—Economic Situation And Conditions*

COUNTRY REPORT. GREECE; analysis of economic and political trends every quarter. see *BUSINESS AND ECONOMICS—Economic Situation And Conditions*

COUNTRY REPORT. GUATEMALA; analysis of economic and political trends every quarter. see *BUSINESS AND ECONOMICS—Economic Situation And Conditions*

COUNTRY REPORT. GUINEA; analysis of economic and political trends every quarter. see *BUSINESS AND ECONOMICS—Economic Situation And Conditions*

COUNTRY REPORT. GUINEA-BISSAU; analysis of economic and political trends every quarter. see *BUSINESS AND ECONOMICS—Economic Situation And Conditions*

COUNTRY REPORT. GUYANA; analysis of economic and political trends every quarter. see *BUSINESS AND ECONOMICS—Economic Situation And Conditions*

COUNTRY REPORT. HAITI; analysis of economic and political trends every quarter. see *BUSINESS AND ECONOMICS—Economic Situation And Conditions*

COUNTRY REPORT. HONDURAS; analysis of economic and political trends every quarter. see *BUSINESS AND ECONOMICS—Economic Situation And Conditions*

COUNTRY REPORT. HONG KONG; analysis of economic and political trends every quarter. see *BUSINESS AND ECONOMICS—Economic Situation And Conditions*

COUNTRY REPORT. HUNGARY; analysis of economic and political trends every quarter. see *BUSINESS AND ECONOMICS—Economic Situation And Conditions*

COUNTRY REPORT. ICELAND; analysis of economic and political trends every quarter. see *BUSINESS AND ECONOMICS—Economic Situation And Conditions*

COUNTRY REPORT. INDIA. see *BUSINESS AND ECONOMICS—Economic Situation And Conditions*

COUNTRY REPORT. INDONESIA; analysis of economic and political trends every quarter. see *BUSINESS AND ECONOMICS—Economic Situation And Conditions*

COUNTRY REPORT. IRAN; analysis of economic and political trends every quarter. see *BUSINESS AND ECONOMICS—Economic Situation And Conditions*

COUNTRY REPORT. IRAQ; analysis of economic and political trends every quarter. see *BUSINESS AND ECONOMICS—Economic Situation And Conditions*

COUNTRY REPORT. IRELAND; analysis of economic and political trends every quarter. see *BUSINESS AND ECONOMICS—Economic Situation And Conditions*

COUNTRY REPORT. ISRAEL; analysis of economic and political trends every quarter. see *BUSINESS AND ECONOMICS—Economic Situation And Conditions*

COUNTRY REPORT. ITALY; analysis of economic and political trends every quarter. see *BUSINESS AND ECONOMICS—Economic Situation And Conditions*

COUNTRY REPORT. JAMAICA; analysis of economic and political trends every quarter. see *BUSINESS AND ECONOMICS—Economic Situation And Conditions*

COUNTRY REPORT. JAPAN; analysis of economic and political trends every quarter. see *BUSINESS AND ECONOMICS—Economic Situation And Conditions*

COUNTRY REPORT. JORDAN; analysis of economic and political trends every quarter. see *BUSINESS AND ECONOMICS—Economic Situation And Conditions*

COUNTRY REPORT. KAZAKHSTAN. see *BUSINESS AND ECONOMICS—Economic Situation And Conditions*

COUNTRY REPORT. KENYA; analysis of economic and political trends every quarter. see *BUSINESS AND ECONOMICS—Economic Situation And Conditions*

COUNTRY REPORT. KUWAIT; analysis of economic and political trends every quarter. see *BUSINESS AND ECONOMICS—Economic Situation And Conditions*

COUNTRY REPORT. KYRGYZ REPUBLIC; analysis of economic and political trends every quarter. see *BUSINESS AND ECONOMICS—Economic Situation And Conditions*

COUNTRY REPORT. LAOS; analysis of economic and political trends every quarter. see *BUSINESS AND ECONOMICS—Economic Situation And Conditions*

COUNTRY REPORT. LATVIA; analysis of economic and political trends every quarter. see *BUSINESS AND ECONOMICS—Economic Situation And Conditions*

COUNTRY REPORT. LEBANON; analysis of economic and political trends every quarter. see *BUSINESS AND ECONOMICS—Economic Situation And Conditions*

COUNTRY REPORT. LESOTHO; analysis of economic and political trends every quarter. see *BUSINESS AND ECONOMICS—Economic Situation And Conditions*

COUNTRY REPORT. LIBERIA; analysis of economic and political trends every quarter. see *BUSINESS AND ECONOMICS—Economic Situation And Conditions*

COUNTRY REPORT. LIBYA; analysis of economic and political trends every quarter. see *BUSINESS AND ECONOMICS—Economic Situation And Conditions*

COUNTRY REPORT. LITHUANIA; analysis of economic and political trends every quarter. see *BUSINESS AND ECONOMICS—Economic Situation And Conditions*

COUNTRY REPORT. LUXEMBOURG; analysis of economic and political trends every quarter. see *BUSINESS AND ECONOMICS—Economic Situation And Conditions*

COUNTRY REPORT. MACAU; analysis of economic and political trends every quarter. see *BUSINESS AND ECONOMICS—Economic Situation And Conditions*

COUNTRY REPORT. MACEDONIA; analysis of economic and political trends every quarter. see *BUSINESS AND ECONOMICS—Economic Situation And Conditions*

COUNTRY REPORT. MADAGASCAR; analysis of economic and political trends every quarter. see *BUSINESS AND ECONOMICS—Economic Situation And Conditions*

COUNTRY REPORT. MALAWI; analysis of economic and political trends every quarter. see *BUSINESS AND ECONOMICS—Economic Situation And Conditions*

COUNTRY REPORT. MALAYSIA; analysis of economic and political trends every quarter. see *BUSINESS AND ECONOMICS—Economic Situation And Conditions*

COUNTRY REPORT. MALI; analysis of economic and political trends every quarter. see *BUSINESS AND ECONOMICS—Economic Situation And Conditions*

COUNTRY REPORT. MALTA; analysis of economic and political trends every quarter. see *BUSINESS AND ECONOMICS—Economic Situation And Conditions*

COUNTRY REPORT. MAURITANIA; analysis of economic and political trends every quarter. see *BUSINESS AND ECONOMICS—Economic Situation And Conditions*

COUNTRY REPORT. MAURITIUS; analysis of economic and political trends every quarter. see *BUSINESS AND ECONOMICS—Economic Situation And Conditions*

COUNTRY REPORT. MEXICO; analysis of economic and political trends every quarter. see *BUSINESS AND ECONOMICS—Economic Situation And Conditions*

COUNTRY REPORT. MOLDOVA; analysis of economic and political trends every quarter. see *BUSINESS AND ECONOMICS—Economic Situation And Conditions*

COUNTRY REPORT. MONGOLIA; analysis of economic and political trends every quarter. see *BUSINESS AND ECONOMICS—Economic Situation And Conditions*

COUNTRY REPORT. MOROCCO; analysis of economic and political trends every quarter. see *BUSINESS AND ECONOMICS—Economic Situation And Conditions*

COUNTRY REPORT. MOZAMBIQUE; analysis of economic and political trends every quarter. see *BUSINESS AND ECONOMICS—Economic Situation And Conditions*

COUNTRY REPORT. MYANMAR; analysis of economic and political trends every quarter. see *BUSINESS AND ECONOMICS—Economic Situation And Conditions*

COUNTRY REPORT. NAMIBIA; analysis of economic and political trends every quarter. see *BUSINESS AND ECONOMICS—Economic Situation And Conditions*

COUNTRY REPORT. NEPAL; analysis of economic and political trends every quarter. see *BUSINESS AND ECONOMICS—Economic Situation And Conditions*

COUNTRY REPORT. NETHERLANDS; analysis of economic and political trends every quarter. see *BUSINESS AND ECONOMICS—Economic Situation And Conditions*

COUNTRY REPORT. NETHERLANDS ANTILLES; analysis of economic and political trends every quarter. see *BUSINESS AND ECONOMICS—Economic Situation And Conditions*

COUNTRY REPORT. NEW CALEDONIA; analysis of economic and political trends every quarter. see *BUSINESS AND ECONOMICS—Economic Situation And Conditions*

COUNTRY REPORT. NEW ZEALAND; analysis of economic and political trends every quarter. see *BUSINESS AND ECONOMICS—Economic Situation And Conditions*

COUNTRY REPORT. NICARAGUA; analysis of economic and political trends every quarter. see *BUSINESS AND ECONOMICS—Economic Situation And Conditions*

COUNTRY REPORT. NIGER; analysis of economic and political trends every quarter. see *BUSINESS AND ECONOMICS—Economic Situation And Conditions*

COUNTRY REPORT. NIGERIA; analysis of economic and political trends every quarter. see *BUSINESS AND ECONOMICS—Economic Situation And Conditions*

COUNTRY REPORT. NORTH KOREA; analysis of economic and political trends every quarter. see *BUSINESS AND ECONOMICS—Economic Situation And Conditions*

COUNTRY REPORT. NORWAY; analysis of economic and political trends every quarter. see *BUSINESS AND ECONOMICS—Economic Situation And Conditions*

COUNTRY REPORT. OMAN; analysis of economic and political trends every quarter. see *BUSINESS AND ECONOMICS—Economic Situation And Conditions*

COUNTRY REPORT. PAKISTAN; analysis of economic and political trends every quarter. see *BUSINESS AND ECONOMICS—Economic Situation And Conditions*

COUNTRY REPORT. PANAMA; analysis of economic and political trends every quarter. see *BUSINESS AND ECONOMICS—Economic Situation And Conditions*

COUNTRY REPORT. PAPUA NEW GUINEA; analysis of economic and political trends every quarter. see *BUSINESS AND ECONOMICS—Economic Situation And Conditions*

COUNTRY REPORT. PARAGUAY; analysis of economic and political trends every quarter. see *BUSINESS AND ECONOMICS—Economic Situation And Conditions*

COUNTRY REPORT. PERU; analysis of economic and political trends every quarter. see *BUSINESS AND ECONOMICS—Economic Situation And Conditions*

COUNTRY REPORT. PHILIPPINES; analysis of economic and political trends every quarter. see *BUSINESS AND ECONOMICS—Economic Situation And Conditions*

COUNTRY REPORT. POLAND; analysis of economic and political trends every quarter. see *BUSINESS AND ECONOMICS—Economic Situation And Conditions*

COUNTRY REPORT. PORTUGAL; analysis of economic and political trends every quarter. see *BUSINESS AND ECONOMICS—Economic Situation And Conditions*

COUNTRY REPORT. PUERTO RICO; analysis of economic and political trends every quarter. see *BUSINESS AND ECONOMICS—Economic Situation And Conditions*

COUNTRY REPORT. QATAR; analysis of economic and political trends every quarter. see *BUSINESS AND ECONOMICS—Economic Situation And Conditions*

COUNTRY REPORT. ROMANIA; analysis of economic and political trends every quarter. see *BUSINESS AND ECONOMICS—Economic Situation And Conditions*

COUNTRY REPORT. RUSSIA; analysis of economic and political trends every quarter. see *BUSINESS AND ECONOMICS—Economic Situation And Conditions*

COUNTRY REPORT. RWANDA; analysis of economic and political trends every quarter. see *BUSINESS AND ECONOMICS—Economic Situation And Conditions*

COUNTRY REPORT. SAMOA; analysis of economic and political trends every quarter. see *BUSINESS AND ECONOMICS—Economic Situation And Conditions*

COUNTRY REPORT. SAO TOME AND PRINCIPE; analysis of economic and political trends every quarter. see *BUSINESS AND ECONOMICS—Economic Situation And Conditions*

COUNTRY REPORT. SAUDI ARABIA; analysis of economic and political trends every quarter. see *BUSINESS AND ECONOMICS—Economic Situation And Conditions*

COUNTRY REPORT. SENEGAL; analysis of economic and political trends every quarter. see *BUSINESS AND ECONOMICS—Economic Situation And Conditions*

COUNTRY REPORT. SEYCHELLES; analysis of economic and political trends every quarter. see *BUSINESS AND ECONOMICS—Economic Situation And Conditions*

COUNTRY REPORT. SIERRA LEONE; analysis of economic and political trends every quarter. see *BUSINESS AND ECONOMICS—Economic Situation And Conditions*

COUNTRY REPORT. SINGAPORE; analysis of economic and political trends every quarter. see *BUSINESS AND ECONOMICS—Economic Situation And Conditions*

COUNTRY REPORT. SLOVAKIA; analysis of economic and political trends every quarter. see *BUSINESS AND ECONOMICS—Economic Situation And Conditions*

COUNTRY REPORT. SLOVENIA; analysis of economic and political trends every quarter. see *BUSINESS AND ECONOMICS—Economic Situation And Conditions*

COUNTRY REPORT. SOLOMON ISLANDS; analysis of economic and political trends every quarter. see *BUSINESS AND ECONOMICS—Economic Situation And Conditions*

COUNTRY REPORT. SOMALIA; analysis of economic and political trends every quarter. see *BUSINESS AND ECONOMICS—Economic Situation And Conditions*

COUNTRY REPORT. SOUTH AFRICA; analysis of economic and political trends every quarter. see *BUSINESS AND ECONOMICS—Economic Situation And Conditions*

COUNTRY REPORT. SOUTH KOREA; analysis of economic and political trends every quarter. see *BUSINESS AND ECONOMICS—Economic Situation And Conditions*

COUNTRY REPORT. SPAIN; analysis of economic and political trends every quarter. see *BUSINESS AND ECONOMICS—Economic Situation And Conditions*

COUNTRY REPORT. SRI LANKA; analysis of economic and political trends every quarter. see *BUSINESS AND ECONOMICS—Economic Situation And Conditions*

COUNTRY REPORT. SUDAN; analysis of economic and political trends every quarter. see *BUSINESS AND ECONOMICS—Economic Situation And Conditions*

COUNTRY REPORT. SURINAME; analysis of economic and political trends every quarter. see *BUSINESS AND ECONOMICS—Economic Situation And Conditions*

COUNTRY REPORT. SWAZILAND; analysis of economic and political trends every quarter. see *BUSINESS AND ECONOMICS—Economic Situation And Conditions*

COUNTRY REPORT. SWEDEN; analysis of economic and political trends every quarter. see *BUSINESS AND ECONOMICS—Economic Situation And Conditions*

COUNTRY REPORT. SWITZERLAND; analysis of economic and political trends every quarter. see *BUSINESS AND ECONOMICS—Economic Situation And Conditions*

COUNTRY REPORT. SYRIA; analysis of economic and political trends every quarter. see *BUSINESS AND ECONOMICS—Economic Situation And Conditions*

COUNTRY REPORT. TAIWAN; analysis of economic and political trends every quarter. see *BUSINESS AND ECONOMICS—Economic Situation And Conditions*

COUNTRY REPORT. TAJIKISTAN; analysis of economic and political trends every quarter. see *BUSINESS AND ECONOMICS—Economic Situation And Conditions*

COUNTRY REPORT. TANZANIA; analysis of economic and political trends every quarter. see *BUSINESS AND ECONOMICS—Economic Situation And Conditions*

COUNTRY REPORT. THAILAND; analysis of economic and political trends every quarter. see *BUSINESS AND ECONOMICS—Economic Situation And Conditions*

COUNTRY REPORT. THE GAMBIA; analysis of economic and political trends every quarter. see *BUSINESS AND ECONOMICS—Economic Situation And Conditions*

COUNTRY REPORT. THE PALESTINIAN TERRITORIES; analysis of economic and political trends every quarter. see *BUSINESS AND ECONOMICS—Economic Situation And Conditions*

COUNTRY REPORT. TOGO; analysis of economic and political trends every quarter. see *BUSINESS AND ECONOMICS—Economic Situation And Conditions*

COUNTRY REPORT. TONGA; analysis of economic and political trends every quarter. see *BUSINESS AND ECONOMICS—Economic Situation And Conditions*

COUNTRY REPORT. TRINIDAD & TOBAGO; analysis of economic and political trends every quarter. see *BUSINESS AND ECONOMICS—Economic Situation And Conditions*

COUNTRY REPORT. TUNISIA; analysis of economic and political trends every quarter. see *BUSINESS AND ECONOMICS—Economic Situation And Conditions*

COUNTRY REPORT. TURKEY; analysis of economic and political trends every quarter. see *BUSINESS AND ECONOMICS—Economic Situation And Conditions*

COUNTRY REPORT. TURKMENISTAN; analysis of economic and political trends every quarter. see *BUSINESS AND ECONOMICS—Economic Situation And Conditions*

COUNTRY REPORT. UGANDA; analysis of economic and political trends every quarter. see *BUSINESS AND ECONOMICS—Economic Situation And Conditions*

COUNTRY REPORT. UKRAINE; analysis of economic and political trends every quarter. see *BUSINESS AND ECONOMICS—Economic Situation And Conditions*

COUNTRY REPORT. UNITED ARAB EMIRATES; analysis of economic and political trends every quarter. see *BUSINESS AND ECONOMICS—Economic Situation And Conditions*

COUNTRY REPORT. UNITED KINGDOM; analysis of economic and political trends every quarter. see *BUSINESS AND ECONOMICS—Economic Situation And Conditions*

COUNTRY REPORT. UNITED STATES OF AMERICA; analysis of economic and political trends every quarter. see *BUSINESS AND ECONOMICS—Economic Situation And Conditions*

COUNTRY REPORT. URUGUAY; analysis of economic and political trends every quarter. see *BUSINESS AND ECONOMICS—Economic Situation And Conditions*

COUNTRY REPORT. UZBEKISTAN; analysis of economic and political trends every quarter. see *BUSINESS AND ECONOMICS—Economic Situation And Conditions*

COUNTRY REPORT. VANUATU; analysis of economic and political trends every quarter. see *BUSINESS AND ECONOMICS—Economic Situation And Conditions*

▼ *new title*   ➤ *refereed*   ✳ *unverified*   ◆ *full entry avail.*

COUNTRY REPORT. VENEZUELA; analysis of economic and political trends every quarter. see *BUSINESS AND ECONOMICS—Economic Situation And Conditions*

COUNTRY REPORT. VIETNAM; analysis of economic and political trends every quarter. see *BUSINESS AND ECONOMICS—Economic Situation And Conditions*

COUNTRY REPORT. WINDWARD & LEEWARD ISLANDS; analysis of economic and political trends every quarter. see *BUSINESS AND ECONOMICS—Economic Situation And Conditions*

COUNTRY REPORT. YEMEN; analysis of economic and political trends every quarter. see *BUSINESS AND ECONOMICS—Economic Situation And Conditions*

COUNTRY REPORT. YUGOSLAVIA (SERBIA-MONTENEGRO); analysis of economic and political trends every quarter. see *BUSINESS AND ECONOMICS—Economic Situation And Conditions*

COUNTRY REPORT. ZAMBIA; analysis of economic and political trends every quarter. see *BUSINESS AND ECONOMICS—Economic Situation And Conditions*

COUNTRY REPORT. ZIMBABWE; analysis of economic and political trends every quarter. see *BUSINESS AND ECONOMICS—Economic Situation And Conditions*

330.1 PER
CRITICA. Text in Spanish. 1976. q.
Published by: Universidad Nacional Mayor de San Marcos, Instituto de Investigaciones Economicas, Lima, 1, Peru.

330.1 COL ISSN 0121-4772
HC196
➤ **CUADERNOS DE ECONOMIA.** Text and summaries in Spanish. 1979. s-a. COP 28,000 domestic; USD 50 foreign (effective 2004). adv. Website rev. abstr.; charts; illus.; maps; stat. back issues avail.; reprints avail. **Document type:** *Journal, Academic/Scholarly.*
Indexed: JEL, PAIS.
Published by: Universidad Nacional de Colombia, Facultad de Ciencias Economicas, Escuela de Economia, Ciudad Universitaria, Edificio 310, Oficina 116, Bogota, Colombia. revcecon@bacata.usc.unal.edu.co, http://www.fce.unal.edu.co. Ed., R&P, Adv. contact Jose G Garcia. Pub. Homero Cuevas. B&W page USD 250; trim 13 x 23. Circ: 500 (paid); 500 (controlled).

330.1 CUB
CUADERNOS ECONOMICOS TRIMESTRALES. Text in Spanish. 1988. 4/yr.
Published by: Centro de Estudios sobre America, Ave. 3ra., No. 1805 (18 y 20), Zona 13, Municipio Playa, Ciudad de La Habana, Cuba.

CUBA: ECONOMIA PLANIFICADA. see *BUSINESS AND ECONOMICS—Macroeconomics*

330.1 CUB
CUESTIONES DE LA ECONOMIA PLANIFICADO. Text in Spanish. bi-m. USD 14. illus.
Published by: (El Salvador. Instituto de Investigaciones Economicas), Ediciones Cubanas, Obispo No. 527, Apdo. 605, Havana, Cuba.

CURRENT ECONOMICS. see *BUSINESS AND ECONOMICS—Macroeconomics*

DYNAMIC ECONOMETRIC MODELS. see *MATHEMATICS*

330.1 NLD ISSN 1566-0419
DYNAMIC MODELING AND ECONOMETRICS IN ECONOMICS AND FINANCE. Text in English. 1999. irreg., latest vol.7, 2005. price varies. **Document type:** *Monographic series, Academic/Scholarly.* **Description:** Designed to further the understanding of dynamic phenomena in economics and finance by bridging the gap between dynamic theory and empirics.
—BLDSC (3637.125000).
Published by: Springer-Verlag Dordrecht (Subsidiary of: Springer Science+Business Media), Van Godewijckstraat 30, Dordrecht, 3311 GX, Netherlands. TEL 31-78-6576050, FAX 31-78-6576474, http://www.springeronline.com. Eds. Stefan Mittnik, Willi Semmler.

E I U COUNTRY REPORTS ON DISC: ASIA-PACIFIC. (Economist Intelligence Unit) see *BUSINESS AND ECONOMICS—Economic Situation And Conditions*

E I U COUNTRY REPORTS ON DISC: EASTERN EUROPE. (Economist Intelligence Unit) see *BUSINESS AND ECONOMICS—Economic Situation And Conditions*

E I U COUNTRY REPORTS ON DISC: MIDDLE EAST - NORTH AFRICA. (Economist Intelligence Unit) see *BUSINESS AND ECONOMICS—Economic Situation And Conditions*

E I U COUNTRY REPORTS ON DISC: SUB-SAHARAN AFRICA. (Economist Intelligence Unit) see *BUSINESS AND ECONOMICS—Economic Situation And Conditions*

E I U COUNTRY REPORTS ON DISC: THE AMERICAS. (Economist Intelligence Unit) see *BUSINESS AND ECONOMICS—Economic Situation And Conditions*

ECOLOGICAL ECONOMICS. see *ENVIRONMENTAL STUDIES*

ECOLOGICAL ECONOMICS BULLETIN. see *ENVIRONMENTAL STUDIES*

ECOLOGY, ECONOMY & ENVIRONMENT. see *ENVIRONMENTAL STUDIES*

330.1 GBR ISSN 0266-4666
HB139
➤ **ECONOMETRIC THEORY.** Text in English. 1985. bi-m. USD 505 in North America to institutions; GBP 308 elsewhere to institutions; USD 559 combined subscription in North America to institutions print & online eds.; GBP 342 combined subscription elsewhere to institutions print & online eds. (effective 2006). adv. bk.rev. illus. back issues avail.; reprint service avail. from PSC. **Document type:** *Journal, Academic/Scholarly.* **Description:** Contains original theoretical contributions on all areas of econometrics.
Related titles: Microform ed.: (from PQC); Online - full text ed.: ISSN 1469-4360. USD 475 in North America to institutions; GBP 290 elsewhere to institutions (effective 2006) (from EBSCO Publishing, O C L C Online Computer Library Center, Inc., Swets Information Services).
Indexed: ABIn, ASCA, CCMJ, CIS, CMCI, CREJ, CurCont, IBSS, JCQM, JEL, MathR, MathSciNet, PCI, RefZh, SSCI, ST&MA.
—BLDSC (3650.096000), IDS, IE, Infotrieve, ingenta. **CCC.**
Published by: Cambridge University Press, The Edinburgh Bldg, Shaftesbury Rd, Cambridge, CB2 2RU, United Kingdom. TEL 44-1223-312393, FAX 44-1223-315052, journals@cambridge.org, http://uk.cambridge.org/journals/ect/. Ed. Peter C B Phillips. R&P Linda Nicol TEL 44-1223-325757. Adv. contact Rebecca Curtis TEL 44-1223-325757. **Subscr. addr. in N America:** Cambridge University Press, 100 Brook Hill Dr, West Nyack, NY 10994. TEL 845-353-7500, FAX 845-353-4141, journals_subscriptions@cup.org

330.1 AUS
ECONOMETRICS DISCUSSION PAPERS. Text in English. 1985. irreg. **Document type:** *Monographic series.*
—BLDSC (3650.112000).
Published by: University of Sydney, School of Economics and Political Sciences, Rm 384, Merewether Bldg, Corner City Rd and Butlin Ave, Sydney, NSW 2006, Australia. TEL 61-2-9351-6621, FAX 61-2-9351-4341.

330.1 ITA ISSN 1120-7019
ECONOMIA DELLE SCELTE PUBBLICHE/JOURNAL OF PUBLIC FINANCE AND PUBLIC CHOICE. Text and summaries in English, Italian. 1983. 3/yr. EUR 30 domestic; EUR 30 foreign to individuals; EUR 50 foreign to institutions (effective 2004). adv. bk.rev. **Document type:** *Journal, Academic/Scholarly.* **Description:** Deals with the analysis, both theoretical and empirical, of governmental action in economy, following the teachings of the Public Choice School.
Indexed: JEL, PAIS.
—BLDSC (3651.110000).
Published by: (Fondazione Luigi Einaudi), Gangemi Editore, Piazza San Pantaleo 4, Rome, Italy. TEL 39-06-6872774, FAX 39-06-68806189, gangemieditorerc@tin.it, http://www.gangemieditore.it.

ECONOMIA EM REVISTA. see *BUSINESS AND ECONOMICS—Economic Situation And Conditions*

330.1 USA ISSN 0891-2424
HC101
➤ **ECONOMIC DEVELOPMENT QUARTERLY**; the journal of American economic revitalization. Text in English. 1987. q. USD 520, GBP 336 to institutions; USD 541, GBP 350 combined subscription to institutions print & online eds. (effective 2006). adv. bk.rev. back issues avail.; reprints avail. **Document type:** *Journal, Academic/Scholarly.* **Description:** Disseminates information on the latest research, programs, policies, and trends in the field of economic development.
Related titles: Online - full text ed.: ISSN 1552-3543. USD 514, GBP 332 to institutions (effective 2006) (from C S A, EBSCO Publishing, Florida Center for Library Automation, Gale Group, O C L C Online Computer Library Center, Inc., Sage Publications, Inc., Swets Information Services).
Indexed: ABIn, ASCA, BPI, CurCont, GEOBASE, HRA, IBSS, JEL, PAIS, PRA, PSA, SOPODA, SPAA, SSA, SSCI, SSI, SUSA, SociolAb, V&AA.
—BLDSC (3652.727000), IDS, IE, Infotrieve, ingenta. **CCC.**
Published by: Sage Publications, Inc., 2455 Teller Rd, Thousand Oaks, CA 91320. TEL 805-499-0721, FAX 805-499-8096, info@sagepub.com, http://www.sagepub.com/journal.aspx?pid=19. Eds. George Erickcek, Richard D Bingham, Timothy J Bartik. Pub. Sara Miller McCune. R&P Tanya Udin TEL 805-499-0721 ext 7716. Adv. contact Kirsten Beaulieu TEL 805-499-0721 ext 7160. page USD 350. Circ: 800 (paid). **Subscr. overseas to:** Sage Publications Ltd., 1 Oliver's Yard, 55 City Rd, London EC1 1SP, United Kingdom. TEL 44-20-73740645, FAX 44-20-73748741, subscription@sagepub.co.uk.

330 GBR ISSN 0013-0117
HC10
➤ **ECONOMIC HISTORY REVIEW**; a journal of economic and social history. Text in English. 1927. q. GBP 158 combined subscription in Europe to institutions print & online eds.; USD 316 combined subscription in the Americas to institutions & Caribbean (print & online eds.); GBP 88, USD 125 combined subscription in developing nations to institutions print & online eds.; GBP 188 combined subscription elsewhere to institutions print & online eds. (effective 2006). adv. bk.rev. bibl.; charts; stat.; illus. index, cum.index. back issues avail.; reprint service avail. from PSC. **Document type:** *Journal, Academic/Scholarly.*
Related titles: Microfiche ed.: (from IDC); Microfilm ed.: (from PQC); Online - full text ed.: ISSN 1468-0289. GBP 150 in Europe to institutions; GBP 84, USD 119 in developing nations to institutions; USD 301 in the Americas to institutions & Caribbean; GBP 179 elsewhere to institutions (effective 2006) (from Blackwell Synergy, EBSCO Publishing, Gale Group, IngentaConnect, JSTOR (Web-based Journal Archive), O C L C Online Computer Library Center, Inc., Swets Information Services).
Indexed: ABIn, ASCA, AgeL, AmH&L, ArtHuCI, BrArAb, BrHumI, CurCont, DIP, GEOBASE, HistAb, IBR, IBSS, IBZ, IMMAb, IndIslam, JEL, MEA&I, NumL, PAIS, PCI, PSA, PopulInd, SSA, SSCI, SSI, SociolAb, WorkRelAb.
—BLDSC (3653.500000), IDS, IE, Infotrieve, ingenta. **CCC.**
Published by: (Economic History Society), Blackwell Publishing Ltd., 9600 Garsington Rd, Oxford, OX4 2ZG, United Kingdom. TEL 44-1865-776868, FAX 44-1865-714591, customerservices@oxon.blackwellpublishing.com, http://www.blackwellpublishing.com/journals/EHR. Ed. Jane Humphries. Circ: 5,000.

➤ **ECONOMIC INTELLIGENCE REVIEW.** see *POLITICAL SCIENCE*

330.1 330.9 GBR ISSN 1363-7029
HB1
ECONOMIC ISSUES. Text in English. 1977. 2/yr. adv. bk.rev. back issues avail. **Document type:** *Academic/Scholarly.*
Formerly (until 1996): British Review of Economic Issues (0141-4739)
Related titles: Online - full text ed.: (from EBSCO Publishing).
Indexed: CPM, IBSS, JEL, PAIS.
—BLDSC (3653.729000), IE, ingenta.
Published by: Association of Polytechnic Teachers in Economics, University, Business School, Leek Rd, Stoke-on-Trent, Staffs ST4 2DF, United Kingdom. TEL 44-1782-294000, FAX 44-1782-747006. Ed. P J Reynolds. Circ: 400.

ECONOMIC JOURNAL OF NEPAL. see *BUSINESS AND ECONOMICS—International Development And Assistance*

330.1 NLD ISSN 0264-9993
HB141
➤ **ECONOMIC MODELLING.** Text in English. 1984. 6/yr. EUR 52 in Europe to individuals; JPY 7,000 in Japan to individuals; USD 54 elsewhere to individuals; EUR 797 in Europe to institutions; JPY 105,800 in Japan to institutions; USD 890 elsewhere to institutions (effective 2006). adv. bk.rev. abstr.; illus. index. back issues avail. **Document type:** *Academic/Scholarly.* **Description:** Presents complete versions, developed for policy analysis, of large-scale models of industrially advanced economies.
Related titles: Microform ed.: (from PQC); Online - full text ed.: (from EBSCO Publishing, Gale Group, IngentaConnect, ScienceDirect, Swets Information Services).
Indexed: ABIn, APEL, ASCA, BAS, CIS, CREJ, CurCont, ESPM, IBSS, JCQM, JEL, PCI, RiskAb, SSCI.
—BLDSC (3653.913500), CISTI, IDS, IE, Infotrieve, ingenta. **CCC.**
Published by: Elsevier BV, North-Holland (Subsidiary of: Elsevier Science & Technology), Sara Burgerhartstraat 25, Amsterdam, 1055 KV, Netherlands. TEL 31-20-485-3911, FAX 31-20-485-2457, nlinfo-f@elsevier.nl, http://www.elsevier.com/locate/ecmod, http://www.elsevier.nl. Eds. P Pauly, S Hall. **Subscr. to:** Elsevier BV, PO Box 211, Amsterdam 1000 AE, Netherlands. TEL 31-20-485-3757, FAX 31-20-485-3432, http://www.elsevier.nl.

➤ **ECONOMIC NOTES.** see *BUSINESS AND ECONOMICS*

➤ **ECONOMIC SYSTEMS.** see *BUSINESS AND ECONOMICS—International Commerce*

330.1 GBR ISSN 0953-5314
HB142
➤ **ECONOMIC SYSTEMS RESEARCH.** Text in English. 1989. q. GBP 665, USD 1,098 combined subscription to institutions print & online eds. (effective 2006). adv. bk.rev. reprint service avail. from PSC. **Document type:** *Journal, Academic/Scholarly.* **Description:** Contains practical matter-of-fact tools and data for modeling, policy analysis, planning and decision making in macroeconomic contexts.
Related titles: Microfiche ed.; Online - full text ed.: ISSN 1469-5758. GBP 632, USD 1,043 to institutions (effective 2006) (from EBSCO Publishing, Gale Group, IngentaConnect, Northern Light Technology, Inc., O C L C Online Computer Library Center, Inc., ProQuest Information & Learning, Swets Information Services).
Indexed: ABIn, BAS, ESPM, GEOBASE, IBR, IBSS, IBZ, JEL, RefZh, RiskAb, WTA.
—BLDSC (3656.683000), IE, Infotrieve, ingenta. **CCC.**
Published by: (Input - Output Association), Routledge (Subsidiary of: Taylor & Francis Group), 4 Park Square, Milton Park, Abingdon, Oxon OX14 4RN, United Kingdom. TEL 44-1235-828600, FAX 44-1235-829000, journals@routledge.com, http://www.tandf.co.uk/journals/titles/09535314.asp, http://www.routledge.co.uk. Ed. Erik Dietzenbacher.

330.1 DEU ISSN 0938-2259
HB1.A1 CODEN: ECTHEA
➤ **ECONOMIC THEORY.** Text in English. 1991. 8/yr. EUR 1,118 combined subscription to institutions print & online eds. (effective 2005). adv. illus. reprints avail. **Document type:** *Journal, Academic/Scholarly.* **Description:** Presents research in all areas of economics based on theoretical reasoning and on specific topics in mathematics that are motivated by the analysis of economic problems.
Related titles: Online - full text ed.: ISSN 1432-0479 (from EBSCO Publishing, ProQuest Information & Learning, Springer LINK, Swets Information Services).
Indexed: ABIn, ASCA, AgeL, CCMJ, CurCont, IBSS, JEL, MathR, MathSciNet, RefZh, SSCI, ZentMath.
—BLDSC (3656.684200), IDS, IE, Infotrieve, ingenta. **CCC.**
Published by: Springer-Verlag (Subsidiary of: Springer Science+Business Media), Tiergartenstr 17, Heidelberg, 69121, Germany. TEL 49-6221-3450, FAX 49-6221-345229, ET@mgmt.purdue.edu, subscriptions@springer.de, http://link.springer.de/link/service/journals/00199/index.htm, http://www.springer.de. Ed. Charalambos D Aliprantis. Adv. contact Stephan Kroeck TEL 49-30-827875739. **Subscr. in the Americas to:** Springer-Verlag New York, Inc., Journal Fulfillment, PO Box 2485, Secaucus, NJ 07096-2485. TEL 212-460-1500, FAX 212-473-6272; **Subscr. to:** Springer GmbH Auslieferungsgesellschaft, Haberstr 7, Heidelberg 69126, Germany.

320.9 GBR ISSN 0954-1985
ECONOMICS & POLITICS. Text in English. 1988. 3/yr. USD 81 combined subscription in the Americas to individuals & Caribbean (print & online eds.); EUR 72 combined subscription in Europe to individuals print & online eds.; GBP 48 combined subscription elsewhere to individuals print & online eds.; USD 679 combined subscription in the Americas to institutions & Caribbean (print & online eds.); GBP 341 combined subscription in Europe to institutions print & online eds.; GBP 404 combined subscription elsewhere to institutions print & online eds. (effective 2006). adv. bk.rev. illus. index. back issues avail.; reprints avail. **Document type:** *Journal, Academic/Scholarly.* **Description:** Provides a forum for the dissemination of work in political economy with emphasis on analytical political economy.
Related titles: Online - full text ed.: ISSN 1468-0343. GBP 324 in Europe to institutions; USD 645 in the Americas to institutions & Caribbean; GBP 384 elsewhere to institutions (effective 2006) (from Blackwell Synergy, EBSCO Publishing, Gale Group, IngentaConnect, O C L C Online Computer Library Center, Inc., Swets Information Services).
Indexed: ABIn, BAS, ESPM, GEOBASE, IBSS, IPSA, JEL, PCI, PRA, PSA, RiskAb, SPAA, WAE&RSA.
—BLDSC (3656.930980), IE, Infotrieve, ingenta. **CCC.**
Published by: Blackwell Publishing Ltd., 9600 Garsington Rd, Oxford, OX4 2ZG, United Kingdom. TEL 44-1865-776868, FAX 44-1865-714591, customerservices@oxon.blackwellpublishing.com, http://www.blackwellpublishing.com/journals/ECPO. Eds. Jagdish Bhagwati, John McLaren. Circ: 300.

330.1 NLD ISSN 0165-1765
HB1 CODEN: ECLEDS
➤ **ECONOMICS LETTERS.** Text in English. 1978. 12/yr. EUR 310 in Europe to individuals; JPY 41,100 in Japan to individuals; USD 324 elsewhere to individuals; EUR 1,923 in Europe to institutions; JPY 255,200 in Japan to institutions; USD 2,150 elsewhere to institutions (effective 2006). adv. bk.rev. illus. index. back issues avail.; reprints avail. **Document type:** *Journal, Academic/Scholarly.* **Description:** Presents new results, models and methods in all fields of economic research.
Related titles: Microform ed.: (from PQC); Online - full text ed.: (from EBSCO Publishing, Gale Group, IngentaConnect, ScienceDirect, Swets Information Services).
Indexed: ASCA, AgeL, CCMJ, CJA, CREJ, CurCont, FamI, IBSS, JEL, MathR, MathSciNet, SSCI, WAE&RSA, ZentMath.
—BLDSC (3657.025000), IDS, IE, Infotrieve, ingenta. **CCC.**
Published by: Elsevier BV, North-Holland (Subsidiary of: Elsevier Science & Technology), Sara Burgerhartstraat 25, Amsterdam, 1055 KV, Netherlands. TEL 31-20-485-3911, FAX 31-20-485-2457, econlett@ias.edu, nlinfo-f@elsevier.nl, http://www.elsevier.com/locate/ecolet, http://www.elsevier.nl. Ed. Dr. Eric Maskin. **Subscr. to:** Elsevier BV, PO Box 211, Amsterdam 1000 AE, Netherlands. TEL 31-20-485-3757, FAX 31-20-485-3432, http://www.elsevier.nl.

330.1 GBR ISSN 0967-0750
HC244.A1
➤ **THE ECONOMICS OF TRANSITION.** Text in English. 1993. q. EUR 72 combined subscription in Europe to individuals print & online eds.; USD 81 combined subscription in the Americas to individuals & Caribbean (print & online eds.); GBP 48 combined subscription elsewhere to individuals print & online eds.; USD 451 combined subscription in the Americas to institutions & Caribbean (print & online eds.); GBP 67, USD 67 combined subscription in developing nations to institutions print & online eds.; GBP 269 combined subscription elsewhere to institutions print & online eds.; USD 724 combined subscription in the Americas to corporations & Caribbean (print & online eds.); GBP 431 combined subscription elsewhere to corporations print & online eds. (effective 2006). adv. bk.rev. reprint service avail. from PSC. **Document type:** *Journal, Academic/Scholarly.* **Description:** Provides information on the economics of transition from centrally planned to market economies, particularly in Eastern Europe and the CIS.
Related titles: Online - full text ed.: ISSN 1468-0351. USD 430 in the Americas to institutions & Caribbean; GBP 64, USD 64 in developing nations to institutions; GBP 256 elsewhere to institutions (effective 2006) (from Blackwell Synergy, EBSCO Publishing, Gale Group, IngentaConnect, O C L C Online Computer Library Center, Inc., Swets Information Services).
Indexed: ABIn, BAS, CurCont, GEOBASE, IBSS, JEL, PAIS, RDA, RefZh, SSCI, WAE&RSA.
—BLDSC (3657.183000), IDS, IE, Infotrieve, ingenta. **CCC.**
Published by: (European Bank for Reconstruction and Development), Blackwell Publishing Ltd., 9600 Garsington Rd, Oxford, OX4 2ZG, United Kingdom. TEL 44-1865-776868, FAX 44-1865-714591, customerservices@oxon.blackwellpublishing.com, http://www.blackwellpublishing.com/journals/ECOT. Ed. Erik Berglof. Pub. Martin Green. R&P Joolz Longley. Adv. contact Jane Parker. Circ: 1,150.

330.1 BGD
ECONOMICUS. Text in English. 1976 (Apr., vol.2). irreg. BDT 2.
Published by: Chittagong University, Department of Economics, Chittagong, Bangladesh.

330.1 320 FRA ISSN 1621-7063
L'ECONOMIE POLITIQUE. Text in French. 2000. q. EUR 34 domestic to individuals; EUR 40 in Europe to individuals; EUR 40 to individuals French speaking Africa; EUR 43 elsewhere to individuals; EUR 26 domestic to students; EUR 32 in Europe to students; EUR 32 to students French speaking Africa; EUR 35 elsewhere to students (effective 2002).
Published by: Alternatives Economiques, 28 rue du Sentier, Paris, 75002, France. TEL 33-01-44882890, FAX 33-01-40284358, http://www.alternatives-economiques.fr.

330.1 338.91 FRA ISSN 0068-4902
ECONOMIES ET SOCIETES. SERIE P. RELATIONS ECONOMIQUES INTERNATIONALES. Text in French. 1944. irreg. EUR 29.
—IE, Infotrieve.
Published by: Les Presses de l'I S M E A, BP 22, Paris, Cedex 13 75622, France. TEL 33-1-55489076, FAX 33-1-55489071, http://www.ismea.org. Ed. Gerard de Bernis. Circ: 1,600.

330.1 FRA
ECONOMIES ET SOCIETES. SERIE PE. RELATIONS ECONOMIQUES INTERNATIONALES. Text in French. irreg.
Published by: Les Presses de l'I S M E A, BP 22, Paris, Cedex 13 75622, France. TEL 33-1-55489076, FAX 33-1-55489071, http://www.ismea.org. Ed. Gerard de Bernis.

THE ECONOMIST. see *BUSINESS AND ECONOMICS—Economic Situation And Conditions*

330.1 USA ISSN 1553-3832
▼ **THE ECONOMISTS' VOICE.** Text in English. 2004. 3/yr. USD 20 to individuals; USD 300 to institutions (effective 2006). **Description:** It is a non-partisan forum for economists to present innovative policy ideas and engaging commentary on important policy issues of the day. Readers will include professional economists, lawyers, policy analysts, policy makers and students of economics.
Media: Online - full content (from O C L C Online Computer Library Center, Inc.).
Published by: Berkeley Electronic Press, 2809 Telegraph Ave., Ste 202, Berkeley, CA 94705. TEL 510-665-1200, FAX 510-665-1201, info@bepress.com, http://www.bepress.com/ev. Ed. Joseph Stiglitz.

330.1 GRC
ECONOMY AND THE FOREIGN POLICY. Text in Greek. 1991. a. adv.
Related titles: ♦ Supplement to: Epilogi. ISSN 1105-2503.
Published by: Electra Press, 4 Stadiou St, Athens, 105 64, Greece. TEL 323-3203, FAX 323-5160. Ed. Christos Papaioannou. Circ: 11,000.

330.1 CYP ISSN 1025-5508
➤ **EKONOMIA.** Text in English. s-a. USD 35 to individuals; USD 70 to institutions (effective 2000). adv. bk.rev. abstr.; stat. back issues avail. **Document type:** *Journal, Academic/Scholarly.* **Description:** Aims to cover a wide spectrum of areas including economic theory, policy, finance, development economics, applied econometrics, history of economic thought and political economy.
Supersedes (in 1997): Cyprus Journal of Economics (1013-3224)
Media: Microfiche.
Indexed: IBSS, JEL.
—BLDSC (3669.023030).
Published by: Cyprus Economic Society, PO Box 28724, Nicosia, Cyprus. p.kalaitzidakis@ucy.ac.cy. Ed. Panicos Demetriades. R&P Pantelis Kalaitzidakis TEL 357-2-394225. Adv. contact Chris Patsalides. Circ: 600.

330.1 UKR ISSN 0131-7741
HC337.UU5
➤ **EKONOMIKA UKRAINY/UKRAINE'S ECONOMY.** Text in Russian. 1958. m. USD 181 foreign (effective 2005). bk.rev. bibl.; charts; stat. index. **Document type:** *Journal, Academic/Scholarly.* **Description:** Political and economic magazine, which covers finance, taxes, credits, theory and practice of economic management, current problems of macroeconomics, agricultural development, economic and law, economic problems of use and preservation of the environment.
Formerly: Ekonomika Radyanskoi Ukrainy (0131-775X)
Related titles: Ukrainian ed.
Indexed: AmH&L, Djerelo, IBSS, JEL, RefZh.
—East View.
Published by: (Natsional'na Akademiya Nauk Ukrainy, Institut Ekonomiki), Vydavnytstvo Presa Ukrainy, pr-kt Peremohy, Kyiv 47, 03047, Ukraine. TEL 380-44-4548272, FAX 380-44-4548810. Ed. Ivan I Lukinov. Circ: 9,000. **Subscr. to:** Smoloskyp, Chkalova 52, kv 29, Kiev 252054, Ukraine. **Dist. by:** East View Information Services, 3020 Harbor Ln. N., Minneapolis, MN 55447. TEL 800-477-1005, FAX 800-800-3839, eastview@eastview.com, http://www.eastview.com.

➤ **ENERGY ECONOMICS.** see *ENERGY*

➤ **THE ENERGY JOURNAL.** see *ENERGY*

330.9 BRA ISSN 0101-1723
CODEN: AIRLEA
➤ **ENSAIOS F E E.** Text in Portuguese. 1980. s-a. BRL 40 (effective 2005). abstr.; charts; stat. back issues avail. **Document type:** *Journal, Academic/Scholarly.*
Indexed: JEL, PAIS, PSA, SociolAb.
Published by: Fundacao de Economia e Estatistica, Rua Duque de Caxias, 1691, Andar 8, Centro, Porto Alegre, RS 90010-283, Brazil. TEL 55-51-3216-9008, FAX 55-51-3225-0006, revistas@fee.tche.br, diretoria@fee.tche.br, http://www.fee.tche.br. Ed. Octavio A Conceicao. Circ: 600 (paid).

330.1 ESP
ESPECIAL DIRECTIVOS. Text in Spanish. 1985. 44/yr. EUR 307 Print & online eds. (effective 2004). adv. **Document type:** *Magazine, Consumer.*
Related titles: Online - full text ed.
Published by: Grupo Especial Directivos (Subsidiary of: Wolters Kluwer BV), Orense 16, Madrid, 28020, Spain. TEL 34-902-250520, FAX 34-902-250502, clientes@edirectivos.com, http://www.especialdirectivos.es, http://www.e-directivos.com. Ed. Fernando Serra. Adv. contact Francisco Romero.

330.1 USA ISSN 0896-226X
HC10
➤ **ESSAYS IN ECONOMIC AND BUSINESS HISTORY.** Text in English. 1979. a. price varies. back issues avail. **Document type:** *Proceedings, Academic/Scholarly.* **Description:** Selected papers delivered at annual meetings of the Economic and Business Historical Society.
Indexed: AmH&L, HistAb.
Published by: University of Mississippi, Department of History, 310 Bishop Hall, Oxford, MS 38677. TEL 662-915-7148, FAX 662-915-7033, www.ebhsoc.org/journal.html, http://www.olemiss.edu. Circ: 300. **Co-sponsor:** Economic and Business Historical Society.

330.1 339 MEX ISSN 0188-6916
ESTUDIOS ECONOMICOS. Text in English, Spanish. 1986. s-a. USD 64 (effective 1999). adv. bk.rev. abstr. back issues avail.
Indexed: HAPI, IBR, IBSS, JEL.
Published by: Colegio de Mexico, A.C., Departamento de Publicaciones, Camino al Ajusco 20, Col. Pedregal Santa Teresa, Mexico City, DF 10740, Mexico. TEL 52-5-4493077, FAX 52-5-4493083. Ed., R&P Francisco Gomez Rulz TEL 525-449-3080. Adv. contact Maria Cruz Mora. Circ: 1,000.

ESTUDOS ECONOMICOS. see *BUSINESS AND ECONOMICS*

B

▼ new title ➤ refereed ✶ unverified ♦ full entry avail.

B

330 BEL ISSN 0071-1977
ETUDES D'HISTOIRE ECONOMIQUE ET SOCIALE. Text in French. 1941. irreg., latest vol.10, 1993. price varies. **Document type:** *Monographic series.* **Description:** Studies on social and economic history, with emphasis on the relations between Belgium and the Southern Low Countries and Italy.
Published by: (Institut Historique Belge de Rome), Brepols Publishers, Begijnhof 67, Turnhout, 2300, Belgium. FAX 32-14-42-89-19, publishers@brepols.com, periodicals@brepols.net. Circ: (controlled).

ETUDES NORMANDES. see *GEOGRAPHY*

330.1 GBR ISSN 1351-7937
HC240
➤ **EUROPEAN ECONOMIC PERSPECTIVES.** Text in English. 1993. m. free (effective 2003). back issues avail. **Document type:** *Bulletin, Academic/Scholarly.* **Description:** Presents articles on economic issues ranging from open-economy macroeconomics to trade policy, from the economic transformation of Eastern Europe to European competition, with emphasis on aspects of European integration.
Media: Online - full content.
—IE, ingenta.
Published by: Centre for Economic Policy Research, 90-98 Goswell Rd, London, EC1V 7RR, United Kingdom. TEL 44-20-78782900, FAX 44-20-78782999, cepr@cepr.org, http://www.cepr.org/eep. Ed. Romesh Vaitilingam. R&P Jane Linekar TEL 44-20-7878-2909. Circ: 14,000.

330.1 FRA ISSN 1292-8895
Q295 CODEN: EJSYF4
EUROPEAN JOURNAL OF ECONOMIC AND SOCIAL SYSTEMS. Abbreviated title: E J E S S. Text in English, French. 1986. q. EUR 230 in the European Union; EUR 265 elsewhere (effective 2003). adv. **Document type:** *Academic/Scholarly.* **Description:** Provides a forum for the interdisciplinary approach of scientific, philosophical and technical problems raised by systems science.
Formerly (until 1998): Revue Internationale de Systemique (0980-1472)
Related titles: Online - full text ed.: ISSN 1292-8909 (from EBSCO Publishing, Swets Information Services).
Indexed: CurCont, DIP, IBR, IBZ, Inspec, ZentMath.
—BLDSC (3829.728350), AskIEEE, IE, ingenta. **CCC.**
Published by: (Association Francaise des Sciences et Technologies de l'Information et des Systemes), Lavoisier, 11 rue Lavoisier, Paris, 75008, France. TEL 33-1-42653995, FAX 33-1-42650246, info@lavoisier.fr, http://www.lavoisier.fr. Circ: 850. **Subscr. to:** Lavoisier - Dept Abonnements, 14 rue de Provigny, Cachan 94236, France. TEL 33-1-47406700, FAX 33-1-47406702, abo@lavoisier.fr.

330.1 GBR ISSN 0967-2567
HB1.A1
➤ **EUROPEAN JOURNAL OF THE HISTORY OF ECONOMIC THOUGHT.** Short title: E J H E T. Text in English. 1993. q. GBP 330, USD 541 combined subscription to institutions print & online eds. (effective 2006). adv. reprint service avail. from PSC. **Document type:** *Journal, Academic/Scholarly.* **Description:** Provides a pluralistic forum for the discussion of traditions in the history of economic thought.
Related titles: Online - full text ed.: ISSN 1469-5936. GBP 314, USD 514 to institutions (effective 2006) (from EBSCO Publishing, Gale Group, IngentaConnect, O C L C Online Computer Library Center, Inc., Swets Information Services).
Indexed: ABIn, AmH&L, BrHumI, DIP, HistAb, IBR, IBSS, IBZ, JEL.
—BLDSC (3829.729950), IE, Infotrieve. **CCC.**
Published by: Routledge (Subsidiary of: Taylor & Francis Group), 4 Park Square, Milton Park, Abingdon, Oxon OX14 4RN, United Kingdom. TEL 44-1235-828600, FAX 44-1235-829000, info@routledge-ny.com, http://www.tandf.co.uk/journals/titles/09672567.asp, http://www.routledge.co.uk. Eds. Antoin E Murphy, Gilbert Faccarello, Heinz D Kurz, Jose Luis Cardoso. R&P Sally Sweet. adv.: page GBP 150; trim 190 x 115. **Subscr. to:** Taylor & Francis Ltd, Journals Customer Service, Rankine Rd, Basingstoke, Hants RG24 8PR, United Kingdom. TEL 44-1256-813000, FAX 44-1256-330245, enquiry@tandf.co.uk.

330.1 GBR ISSN 1361-4916
HC240.A1
➤ **EUROPEAN REVIEW OF ECONOMIC HISTORY.** Text in English. 1997. 3/yr. GBP 102 to institutions; USD 166 in North America to institutions; GBP 107 combined subscription to institutions print & online eds.; USD 172 combined subscription in North America to institutions print & online eds. (effective 2006). adv. illus. **Document type:** *Journal, Academic/Scholarly.* **Description:** Aims to further research, scholarship, and understanding of economic structure, change, and economic development in Europe since early modern times.
Related titles: Online - full text ed.: ISSN 1474-0044. GBP 91 to institutions; USD 148 in North America to institutions (effective 2006) (from EBSCO Publishing, O C L C Online Computer Library Center, Inc., Swets Information Services).
Indexed: AmH&L, HistAb, JEL.
—BLDSC (3829.948000), IE, Infotrieve, ingenta. **CCC.**
Published by: (European Historical Economics Society), Cambridge University Press, The Edinburgh Bldg, Shaftesbury Rd, Cambridge, CB2 2RU, United Kingdom. TEL 44-1223-312393, FAX 44-1223-315052, journals@cambridge.org, http://uk.cambridge.org/journals/ere. Eds. Albrecht Ritschl, Giovanni Federico, Kevin O'Rourke. R&P Linda Nicol TEL 44-1223-325757. Adv. contact Rebecca Curtis TEL 44-1223-325757. **Subscr. to:** Cambridge University Press, 100 Brook Hill Dr, West Nyack, NY 10994. TEL 845-353-7500, FAX 845-353-4141, journals_subscriptions@cup.org

➤ **EUROSTAT STATISTICS IN FOCUS. GENERAL STATISTICS.** see *BUSINESS AND ECONOMICS—Abstracting, Bibliographies, Statistics*

330.1 USA ISSN 1386-4157
HB71 CODEN: EXECFY
EXPERIMENTAL ECONOMICS. Text in English. 1998. q. EUR 295, USD 295, GBP 192 combined subscription to institutions print & online eds. (effective 2005). adv. reprint service avail. from PSC. **Document type:** *Journal, Academic/Scholarly.* **Description:** Covers experimental research in the economics and related fields such as political science, and the psychology of decision making.
Related titles: Online - full text ed.: ISSN 1573-6938 (from EBSCO Publishing, Gale Group, IngentaConnect, Kluwer Online, O C L C Online Computer Library Center, Inc., ProQuest Information & Learning, Springer LINK, Swets Information Services).
Indexed: ABIn, BibLing, CurCont, IBSS, Inspec, JEL, RefZh, SSCI.
—BLDSC (3839.095000), IE, Infotrieve, ingenta. **CCC.**
Published by: Springer-Verlag New York, Inc. (Subsidiary of: Springer Science+Business Media), 233 Spring St, New York, NY 10013. TEL 212-460-1500, FAX 212-460-1575, service@springer-ny.com, http://springerlink.metapress.com/openurl.asp?genre=journal&issn=1386-4157, http://www.springer-ny.com. Eds. Arthur J H C Schram, Timothy Cason. **Subscr. to:** Journal Fulfillment, PO Box 2485, Secaucus, NJ 07096-2485. TEL 201-348-4033, FAX 201-348-4505, journals@springer-ny.com.

330 USA ISSN 0014-4983
HB615
➤ **EXPLORATIONS IN ECONOMIC HISTORY.** Text in English. 1963. 4/yr. EUR 307 in Europe to individuals; JPY 32,000 in Japan to individuals; USD 232 elsewhere to individuals; EUR 644 in Europe to institutions; JPY 67,300 in Japan to institutions; USD 486 elsewhere to institutions; EUR 58 in Europe to students; JPY 6,000 in Japan to students; USD 51 elsewhere to students (effective 2006). adv. bk.rev. charts; illus. index. back issues avail.; reprints avail. **Document type:** *Journal, Academic/Scholarly.* **Description:** Publishes original papers that provide broad coverage of the application of economic analysis to historical episodes.
Formerly: Explorations in Entrepreneurial History (0884-5425)
Related titles: Online - full text ed.: ISSN 1090-2457. USD 517 (effective 2002) (from Chadwyck-Healey Inc., EBSCO Publishing, Gale Group, IngentaConnect, O C L C Online Computer Library Center, Inc., ScienceDirect, Swets Information Services).
Indexed: ABIn, ABS&EES, ASCA, Agr, AmH&L, ArtHuCI, BAS, BibAg, CurCont, DIP, HistAb, IBR, IBSS, IBZ, JEL, MEA&I, PAIS, PCI, SSCI, SSI, SWA.
—BLDSC (3842.204000), IDS, IE, Infotrieve, ingenta. **CCC.**
Published by: Academic Press (Subsidiary of: Elsevier Science & Technology), 525 B St, Ste 1900, San Diego, CA 92101-4495. TEL 619-231-6616, 800-894-3434, apsubs@acad.com, http://www.elsevier.com/locate/eeh, http://www.academicpress.com. Ed. R A Margo.

330.1 DEU ISSN 0430-4977
FINANZWISSENSCHAFTLICHE FORSCHUNGSARBEITEN. Text in German. 1950. irreg., latest vol.72, 2001. price varies. **Document type:** *Monographic series, Academic/Scholarly.*
Published by: Duncker und Humblot GmbH, Carl-Heinrich-Becker-Weg 9, Berlin, 12165, Germany. TEL 49-30-7900060, FAX 49-30-79000631, info@duncker-humblot.de, http://www.duncker-humblot.de.

330.1 DEU ISSN 0170-8252
FINANZWISSENSCHAFTLICHE SCHRIFTEN. Text in German. 1976. irreg., latest vol.105, 2001. **Document type:** *Monographic series, Academic/Scholarly.*
Published by: Peter Lang GmbH Europaeischer Verlag der Wissenschaften, Eschborner Landstr 42-50, Frankfurt Am Main, 60489, Germany. TEL 49-69-7807050, FAX 49-69-78070543, zentrale.frankfurt@peterlang.com, http://www.peterlang.de. R&P Ruediger Brunsch. **Dist. by:** Verlag Peter Lang AG, Hochfeldstr. 32, Postfach 746, Bern 9 3000, Switzerland. FAX 41-32-3761727, customerservice@peterlang.com.

330.1 ISR
FOERDER INSTITUTE FOR ECONOMIC RESEARCH. WORKING PAPERS. Text in English. irreg. **Document type:** *Academic/Scholarly.*
Published by: Foerder Institute for Economic Research, Tel Aviv University, Eitan Berglas School of Economics, Ramat Aviv, Tel Aviv, 69978, Israel. TEL 972-3-640-9255, FAX 972-3-640-5815, foerder@post.tau.ac.il, http://econ.tau.ac.il. Ed. Stella Padeh. **Co-sponsor:** Sackler Institute for Economic Studies.

FOERETAGSMINNEN. see *HISTORY—History Of Europe*

FOLIA UNIVERSITATIS AGRICULTURAE STETINENSIS. OECONOMICA. see *SOCIAL SCIENCES: COMPREHENSIVE WORKS*

330.1 USA ISSN 0736-0932
HB1
➤ **FORUM FOR SOCIAL ECONOMICS.** Text in English. 1975. s-a. USD 5 to individuals; USD 7 to institutions (effective 2005); USD 13 to non-members (effective 2003). adv. bk.rev. back issues avail. **Document type:** *Journal, Academic/Scholarly.* **Description:** Presents timely topics reflecting areas of interest to social economists; scholarly research and essays on economic issues such as distribution of well-being, poverty, economic institutions. Deals with relation of economics to broader social questions.
Indexed: AmH&L, CPL, CREJ, HistAb, JEL, SSCI.
—BLDSC (4024.105500).
Published by: Association for Social Economics, Department of Economics, St. Louis University, Saint Louis, MO 63108. TEL 314-977-3814, FAX 314-977-1478, welchpj@slu.edu, http://www.socialeconomics.org/forum.htm. Ed., R&P, Adv. contact Patrick J Welch. Circ: 500 (paid).

330.1 USA ISSN 1551-3076
▼ ➤ **FOUNDATIONS AND TRENDS IN ECONOMETRICS.** Text in English. 2005. 4/yr. USD 300, EUR 300; USD 340, EUR 340 combined subscription print & online eds. (effective 2006). **Document type:** *Journal, Academic/Scholarly.*
Related titles: Online - full text ed.: ISSN 1551-3084. 2005. USD 300, EUR 300 (effective 2005).
Published by: Now Publishers Inc., PO Box 1024, Hanover, MA 02339. TEL 781-871-0245, FAX 781-871-6172, sales@nowpublishers.com, http://www.nowpublishers.com/eco. Ed. William H Greene. Pub. Zac Rolnik. R&P Mike Casey.

330.1 USA ISSN 1552-2245
▼ ➤ **FOUNDATIONS AND TRENDS IN ECONOMIC THEORY.** Text in English. 2005. 4/yr. USD 300, EUR 300; USD 340, EUR 340 combined subscription print & online eds. (effective 2006). **Document type:** *Journal, Academic/Scholarly.*
Related titles: Online - full text ed.: ISSN 1552-2253. 2005. USD 300 (effective 2005).
Published by: Now Publishers Inc., PO Box 1024, Hanover, MA 02339. TEL 781-871-0245, FAX 781-871-6172, sales@nowpublishers.com, http://www.nowpublisher.com/eth, http://www.nowpublishers.com. Ed. William Zame. Pub. Zac Rolnik. R&P Mike Casey.

330.1 USA ISSN 1547-9846
▼ ➤ **FOUNDATIONS AND TRENDS IN MICROECONOMICS.** Text in English. 2005. 4/yr. USD 300, EUR 300; USD 340, EUR 340 combined subscription print & online eds. (effective 2006). **Document type:** *Journal, Academic/Scholarly.*
Related titles: Online - full text ed.: ISSN 1547-9854. 2005. USD 300, EUR 300 (effective 2005).
Published by: Now Publishers Inc., PO Box 1024, Hanover, MA 02339. TEL 781-871-0245, FAX 781-871-6172, sales@nowpublishers.com, http://www.nowpublishers.com. Ed. Kip Viscusi. Pub. Zac Rolnik. R&P Mike Casey.

➤ **FRAGEN DER FREIHEIT**; Schriftenreihe fuer Ordnungsfragen der Wirtschaft des Staates und des kulturellen Lebens. see *POLITICAL SCIENCE—Civil Rights*

330.1 FRA ISSN 1259-4261
FRANCE. INSTITUT NATIONAL DE LA STATISTIQUE ET DES ETUDES ECONOMIQUES. RECUEIL D'ETUDES SOCIALES. Text in French. 3/yr. FRF 315; FRF 394 in Europe; FRF 421 elsewhere.
Published by: Institut National de la Statistique et des Etudes Economiques, 1 rue Vincent Auriol, Amiens, Cedex 1 80027, France. TEL 33-3-22927322, FAX 33-3-22979295, inseeactualites@insee.fr.

330.1 FRA ISSN 0249-4744
HC271
FRANCE. MINISTERE DE L'ECONOMIE, DES FINANCES ET DE L'INDUSTRIE. ECONOMIE ET PREVISION. Text in French. 1981. 5/yr. EUR 51 domestic; EUR 61.20 in the European Union; EUR 63.20 DOM-TOM; EUR 71.40 elsewhere (effective 2003). charts. **Document type:** *Government.*
Formerly (until 1980): France. Ministere de l'Economie et des Finances. Statistiques et Etudes Financieres. Serie Orange (0338-4217)
Related titles: Microfiche ed..
Indexed: JEL, PAIS, PHN&I, SIA, WAE&RSA.
—BLDSC (3657.810000), IE, Infotrieve, ingenta.
Published by: (France. Ministere de l'Economie, des Finances et de l'Industrie), Documentation Francaise, 29-31 quai Voltaire, Paris, Cedex 7 75344, France. FAX 33-1-40157230.

330.1 USA ISSN 1051-4333
THE FREE MARKET. Text in English. 1983. m. USD 35 donation (effective 2000). bk.rev. illus. back issues avail. **Document type:** *Newsletter.* **Description:** Features items on free-market economics.
Published by: Ludwig von Mises Institute, 518 W Magnolia Ave, Auburn, AL 36832. TEL 334-321-2100, FAX 334-321-2119, mail@mises.org, http://www.mises.org. Ed., R&P Jeffrey Tucker TEL 334-321-2108. Circ: 6,500.

330.1 USA ISSN 1538-0629
HB1
FRONTIERS OF ECONOMIC ANALYSIS & POLICY. Text in English. 2001. a. Included with subscription to The B E Journals in Economic Analysis and Policy.. **Document type:** *Journal, Academic/Scholarly.*
Media: Online - full content. **Related titles:** ♦ Series of: The B E Journals in Economic Analysis & Policy. ISSN 1555-0494.
Published by: Berkeley Electronic Press, 2809 Telegraph Ave., Ste 202, Berkeley, CA 94705. FAX 510-665-1201, info@bepress.com, http://www.bepress.com/bejeap/frontiers/. Eds. Aaron S Edlin, Bruce D Myer, Don Fullerton, Hermalin E Benjamin, Kyle Bagwell.

330.1 USA
➤ **FRONTIERS OF ECONOMIC RESESEARCH.** Text in English. 1993. irreg., latest 2002. price varies. charts; illus.; stat. back issues avail. **Document type:** *Monographic series, Academic/Scholarly.* **Description:** Examines issues and trends in economics from various perspectives.
Indexed: CCMJ.
Published by: Princeton University Press, 41 William St, Princeton, NJ 08540-5237. TEL 609-258-4900, 800-777-4726, FAX 609-258-6305, http://pup.princeton.edu/catalogs/series/fer.html. Eds. David M Kreps, Thomas J Sargent. **Subscr. addr. in US:** California - Princeton Fulfillment Services, 1445 Lower Ferry Rd, Ewing, NJ 08618. FAX 800-999-1958, orders@cpfs.pupress.princeton.edu. **Dist. addr. in Canada, Australia & New Zealand, and Latin America:** University Press Group, 164 Hillsdale Ave E, Toronto, ON M4S 1T5, Canada.; **Dist. addr. in Europe & Africa:** John Wiley & Sons Ltd., The Atrium, Southern Gate, Chichester, West Sussex PO19 8SQ, United Kingdom.

330.1 USA ISSN 1534-5955
HB1
FRONTIERS OF THEORETICAL ECONOMICS. Text in English. 2001. irreg. Included with subscription to The B E Journals in Theoretical Economics. **Document type:** *Journal, Academic/Scholarly.*
Media: Online - full content. **Related titles:** Online - full text ed.: (from O C L C Online Computer Library Center, Inc., ProQuest Information & Learning); ♦ Series of: The B E Journals in Theoretical Economics. ISSN 1555-0478.
Indexed: ABIn, IBSS, JEL, MathR, MathSciNet.
Published by: Berkeley Electronic Press, 2809 Telegraph Ave., Ste 202, Berkeley, CA 94705. FAX 510-665-1201, info@bepress.com, http://www.bepress.com/bejte/topics/. Eds. Chris Shannon, Dilip Abreu, Ilya Segal, Patrick Bolton.

330 CHN ISSN 1007-2195
GAIGE ZONGHENG/REFORM: AN OVERALL VIEW. Text in Chinese. 1991. m. CNY 60 (effective 2004). **Document type:** *Journal, Academic/Scholarly.* **Description:** Covers economic improvement, ideas and information on issues.
Published by: Hunan Sheng Jingji Tizhi Gaige Weiyuanhui, 69, 51 Zhonglu, Changsha, 410011, China. TEL 86-731-2212243. **Dist. by:** China International Book Trading Corp, 35 Chegongzhuang Xilu, Haidian District, PO Box 399, Beijing 100044, China. TEL 86-10-68412045, FAX 86-10-68412023, cibtc@mail.cibtc.com.cn, http://www.cibtc.com.cn.

330 USA ISSN 0887-6290
GEORGIST JOURNAL ✶; an international journal serving the movement for land value taxation and free trade based on the philosophy of Henry George. Text in English. 1973. q. USD 10. adv. bk.rev. 48 p./no. 1 cols./p.; back issues avail. **Document type:** *Trade.* **Description:** Commentary, essays, articles, historical accounts, and news about this political and economic movement, which aims to distribute the outcomes of the free enterprise system more equitably among taxpayers.
Media: Duplicated (not offset).
Published by: Henry George Institute, RR1 Box 1137, Drooks, MO 04921-9717. TEL 212-689-0075, lindy@henrygeorge.org. Ed., Adv. contact Lindrith Davies. Circ: 650.

330.1 DEU
GESELLSCHAFT FUER WESTFAELISCHE WIRTSCHAFTSGESCHICHTE. VORTRAGSREIHE. Text in German. 1954. irreg., latest vol.30, 1994. **Document type:** *Monographic series, Academic/Scholarly.*
Published by: (Gesellschaft fuer Westfaelische Wirtschaftsgeschichte), Ardey-Verlag Muenster, An den Speichern 6, Muenster, 48157, Germany. TEL 49-251-4132-0, FAX 49-251-413220, grabowsky@ardey-verlag.de, http://www.ardey-verlag.de.

330 SWE ISSN 0072-5080
GOETEBORGS UNIVERSITET. EKONOMISK-HISTORISKA INSTITUTIONEN. MEDDELANDEN. Text in Swedish; Text occasionally in English; Abstracts occasionally in English, French. 1958. irreg., latest vol.68, 1993. price varies. **Document type:** *Academic/Scholarly.*
Published by: Goeteborgs Universitet, Ekonomisk-Historiska Institutionen, PO Box 720, Goeteborg, 40530, Sweden. TEL 46-31-7734742, FAX 46-31-7734739, ekonomisk.historia@gu.se, http://www.econhist.gu.se. Ed. Sverker Jonsson. Circ: 600.

330.1 SWE ISSN 0434-2410
HB54
GOETEBORGS UNIVERSITET. NATIONALEKONOMISKA INSTITUTIONEN. EKONOMISKA STUDIER. Text in Swedish. 1978. irreg., latest vol.55, 1994. SEK 200 per issue. **Document type:** *Monographic series.*
Published by: Goeteborgs Universitet, Nationalekonomiska Institutionen/University of Goeteborg, Department of Economics, Vasagatan 1, Goeteborg, 41180, Sweden. FAX 31-773-13-26. Circ: 500.

330.9 AUS ISSN 0818-2493
GOOD GOVERNMENT; a journal of political, social & economic comment. Text in English. 1905. bi-m. AUD 18 (effective 2003). adv. bk.rev. 8 p./no.; back issues avail. **Document type:** *Journal, Academic/Scholarly.* **Description:** Promotes the cause of the Henry George philosophy in Australia.
Published by: Association for Good Government, PO Box 443, Enfield, NSW 2136, Australia. TEL 61-2-9744-8815, FAX 61-2-9744-3804, goodgov@oprusnet.com.au. Ed., R&P Richard Giles. Circ: 450.

330.01 GBR
THE GRAZ SCHUMPETER LECTURES. Text in English. 1998. irreg., latest vol.4, 2001, May. price varies. **Description:** Designed to inform the scientific community about advances in particularly dynamic fields of research.
—BLDSC (4214.338000).
Published by: Routledge (Subsidiary of: Taylor & Francis Group), 4 Park Square, Milton Park, Abingdon, Oxon OX14 4RN, United Kingdom. TEL 44-1235-828600, FAX 44-1235-829000, info@routledge.co.uk, http://www.reference.routledge.com/research/economics/gsl.html, http://www.tandf.co.uk, http://www.routledge.co.uk.

GROSS REPORT; a summary of key economic statistics. see *BUSINESS AND ECONOMICS—Abstracting, Bibliographies, Statistics*

330.1 HTI
HAITI. SECRETAIRE D'ETAT DU PLAN. PLAN ANNUEL ET BUDGET DE DEVELOPPEMENT. Text in French. a.
Formerly: Haiti. Conseil National de Developpement et de Planification. Plan Annuel et Budget de Developpement
Published by: Secretaire d'Etat du Plan, Port-au-Prince, Haiti.

330.1 USA
HANDBOOK OF AMERICAN BUSINESS HISTORY. Text in English. 1990. irreg. price varies. **Document type:** *Monographic series.*
Published by: Praeger Publishers (Subsidiary of: Greenwood Publishing Group Inc.), 88 Post Rd W, Box 5007, Westport, CT 06881-5007. TEL 203-226-3571, FAX 203-222-1502.

330.1 USA ISSN 1054-7681
HANDBOOK OF COMPARATIVE ECONOMIC POLICIES. Text in English. 1991. irreg. price varies. **Document type:** *Monographic series, Academic/Scholarly.*
Published by: Greenwood Publishing Group Inc. (Subsidiary of: Harcourt International), 88 Post Rd W, PO Box 5007, Westport, CT 06881. TEL 203-226-3571, FAX 203-226-1502, webmaster@greenwood.com, http://www.greenwood.com.

330.1 NLD ISSN 0169-7218
➤ **HANDBOOKS IN ECONOMICS.** Text in Dutch. 1981. irreg., latest 2002. price varies. back issues avail. **Document type:** *Monographic series, Academic/Scholarly.* **Description:** Provides researchers, advanced-level graduate students, and academics with comprehensive reference sources for each of the various branches of economics.
—BLDSC (4250.435200), IE, ingenta. **CCC.**
Published by: Elsevier BV, North-Holland (Subsidiary of: Elsevier Science & Technology), Sara Burgerhartstraat 25, Amsterdam, 1055 KV, Netherlands. TEL 31-20-485-3911, FAX 31-20-485-2457, nlinfo-f@elsevier.nl, http://www.elsevier.nl. Eds. K Arrow, M Intriligator. **Subscr. to:** Elsevier BV, PO Box 211, Amsterdam 1000 AE, Netherlands. TEL 31-20-485-3757, FAX 31-20-485-3432, http://www.elsevier.nl.

➤ **HARVARD COLLEGE ECONOMIST.** see *BUSINESS AND ECONOMICS—Macroeconomics*

650 USA ISSN 0073-067X
➤ **HARVARD STUDIES IN BUSINESS HISTORY.** Text in English. 1931. irreg., latest vol.42, 1994. price varies. adv. **Document type:** *Monographic series, Academic/Scholarly.*
Published by: (Harvard University Graduate School of Business Administration), Harvard University Press, 79 Garden St, Cambridge, MA 02138. TEL 617-495-2600, FAX 617-495-5898, http://www.hup.harvard.edu. Ed. Alfred D Chandler Jr. R&P Mindy Koyanis TEL 617-495-2619. Adv. contact Denise Waddington.

330 FRA ISSN 0752-5702
H3
HISTOIRE, ECONOMIE ET SOCIETE. Text in French. 1913. q. EUR 60 domestic to individuals; EUR 70 foreign to individuals; EUR 99 domestic to institutions; EUR 109 foreign to institutions (effective 2005). bk.rev. index. reprint service avail. from SCH. **Document type:** *Journal, Academic/Scholarly.* **Description:** Fosters economic and social studies of France and the world from the 16th century to the present day.
Formerly (until 1982): Revue d'Histoire Economique et Sociale (0035-239X)
Related titles: Online - full text ed.: (from EBSCO Publishing).
Indexed: AmH&L, BHA, DIP, HistAb, IBR, IBZ, PCI, RILM.
—BLDSC (4316.006850), IE, Infotrieve, ingenta.
Published by: Armand Colin Editeur (Subsidiary of: Masson), 21 Rue du Montparnasse, Paris, 75283 Cedex 06, France. TEL 33-1-44395447, FAX 33-1-44394343, infos@armand-colin.com, http://www.armand-colin.com. Circ: 700.

330.1 FRA ISSN 1248-6620
HISTOIRE ECONOMIQUE ET FINANCIERE DE LA FRANCE. ANIMATION DE LA RECHERCHE. Text in French. 1991. irreg. Price varies. **Document type:** *Monographic series.*
Published by: Ministere de l'Economie, des Finances et de l'Industrie, Comite pour l'Histoire Economique et Financiere de la France, 6 av. de l'Opera, 2eme Etage, Paris, 75001, France. TEL 33-1-44775264, FAX 33-1-44775298, http://www.minefi.gouv.fr/DICOM/cheff.

330.1 FRA ISSN 1241-3496
HC271
HISTOIRE ECONOMIQUE ET FINANCIERE DE LA FRANCE. ETUDES ET DOCUMENTS. Text in French. 1989. a. Price varies. **Document type:** *Monographic series, Academic/Scholarly.* **Description:** Compiles scientific articles and economic and financial historical documents from the Middle Ages until now.
Published by: Ministere de l'Economie, des Finances et de l'Industrie, Comite pour l'Histoire Economique et Financiere de la France, 6 av. de l'Opera, 2eme Etage, Paris, 75001, France. TEL 33-1-44775264, FAX 33-1-44775298, http://www.minefi.gouv.fr/DICOM/cheff.

330.1 FRA ISSN 1251-5140
HISTOIRE ECONOMIQUE ET FINANCIERE DE LA FRANCE. ETUDES GENERALES. Text in French. 1990. irreg. Price varies. **Document type:** *Monographic series.*
Published by: Ministere de l'Economie, des Finances et de l'Industrie, Comite pour l'Histoire Economique et Financiere de la France, 6 av. de l'Opera, 2eme Etage, Paris, 75001, France. TEL 33-1-44775264, FAX 33-1-44775298, http://www.minefi.gouv.fr/DICOM/cheff.

330.1 FRA ISSN 1151-9037
HC271
HISTOIRE ECONOMIQUE ET FINANCIERE DE LA FRANCE. RECUEILS DE DOCUMENTS. Text in French. 1993. irreg. Price varies. **Document type:** *Monographic series.*
Published by: Ministere de l'Economie, des Finances et de l'Industrie, Comite pour l'Histoire Economique et Financiere de la France, 6 av. de l'Opera, 2eme Etage, Paris, 75001, France. TEL 33-1-44775264, FAX 33-1-44775298, http://www.minefi.gouv.fr/DICOM/cheff.

330.1 FRA ISSN 1248-6221
HISTOIRE ECONOMIQUE ET FINANCIERE DE LA FRANCE. SOURCES. Text in French. 1993. irreg. Price varies. **Document type:** *Monographic series.*
Published by: Ministere de l'Economie, des Finances et de l'Industrie, Comite pour l'Histoire Economique et Financiere de la France, 6 av. de l'Opera, 2eme Etage, Paris, 75001, France. TEL 33-1-44775264, FAX 33-1-44775298, http://www.minefi.gouv.fr/DICOM/cheff.

335.4 NLD ISSN 1465-4466
D16.9
➤ **HISTORICAL MATERIALISM**; research in critical Marxist theory. Text in English. 1997. q. USD 56 in the Americas to individuals; EUR 45 elsewhere to individuals; USD 236 combined subscription in the Americas to institutions print & online eds.; EUR 189 combined subscription elsewhere to institutions print & online eds. (effective 2006). back issues avail. **Document type:** *Journal, Academic/Scholarly.* **Description:** An interdisciplinary journal dedicated to exploring and developing the critical and explanatory potential of Marxist theory.
Related titles: Online - full text ed.: ISSN 1569-206X. USD 212 in the Americas to institutions; EUR 170 elsewhere to institutions (effective 2006) (from EBSCO Publishing, Gale Group, IngentaConnect, Kluwer Online, O C L C Online Computer Library Center, Inc., Springer LINK, Swets Information Services).
Indexed: IPSA, LeftInd, PSA, SSA, SociolAb.
—BLDSC (4316.439000), IE, ingenta. **CCC.**

Published by: (London School of Economics and Political Science GBR), Brill Academic Publishers, PO Box 9000, Leiden, 2300 PA, Netherlands. TEL 31-71-53-53-500, FAX 31-71-53-17-532, cs@brill.nl, http://www.brill.nl/m_catalogue_sub6_id17936.htm. Eds. Paul Blackledge, Sam Ashman. **Subscr. in N. America to:** PO Box 605, Herndon, VA 20172. TEL 703-661-1585, 800-337-9255, FAX 703-661-1501, cs@brillusa.com. **Distr. outside N. America by:** c/o Turpin Distribution, Stratton Business Park, Pegasus Drive, Biggleswade, BEDFORDSHIRE SG 18 8TQ, United Kingdom. TEL 44-1767-604-954, FAX 44-1767-601-640, brill@turpin-distribution.com.

330.1 ITA ISSN 1122-8792
HISTORY OF ECONOMIC IDEAS. Text in Italian. 1982. 3/yr. EUR 85 domestic to individuals; EUR 155 foreign to individuals; EUR 155 domestic to institutions; EUR 295 foreign to institutions (effective 2004). **Document type:** *Academic/Scholarly.*
Formerly (until 1993): Quaderni di Storia dell'Economia Politica (1122-9411)
Indexed: AmH&L, HistAb, JEL.
—BLDSC (4317.985000), IE, ingenta.
Published by: Istituti Editoriali e Poligrafici Internazionali (Subsidiary of: Libra Web), Via Giosue' Carducci, 60, Ghezzano - La Fontina, PI 56010, Italy. TEL 39-050-878066, FAX 39-050-878732, iepi@iepi.it, http://www.iepi.it.

330 GBR ISSN 0440-9884
HB75
HISTORY OF ECONOMIC THOUGHT NEWSLETTER. Text in English. 1968. s-a. GBP 10 (effective 2000). adv. bk.rev. cum.index 1975-1979. reprint service avail. from PQC. **Document type:** *Academic/Scholarly.*
Related titles: Microfilm ed.: (from PQC).
—IE, Infotrieve.
Published by: Manchester Metropolitan University, Faculty of Humanities and Social Science, Mabel Tylecote Bldg, Cavendish St, Manchester, Lancs M15 6BG, United Kingdom. TEL 44-161-226-4799, FAX 44-161-226-6302. Ed. John Vint. Circ: 400.

330 USA ISSN 0018-2702
HB1
➤ **HISTORY OF POLITICAL ECONOMY.** Text in English. 1969. q. USD 70 to individuals; USD 315 to institutions; USD 350 combined subscription to institutions print & online eds. (effective 2006). adv. bk.rev. charts; illus. Index. Supplement avail.; back issues avail.; reprint service avail. from PQC,ISI,PSC. **Document type:** *Magazine, Academic/Scholarly.* **Description:** Focusing on the history of economic thought and analysis, History of Political Economy has made significant contributions to the history of political economics and remains the field's foremost means of communication. In addition to book reviews, each issue contains original research on the development of economic thought, the historical background behind major figures in the history of economics, the interpretation of economic theories, and the methodologies available to historians of economic theory.
Related titles: Microform ed.: (from MIM, PQC); Online - full text ed.: History of Political Economy Online. ISSN 1527-1919. 2000. USD 315 to institutions (effective 2006) (from bigchalk, EBSCO Publishing, Gale Group, IngentaConnect, Northern Light Technology, Inc., O C L C Online Computer Library Center, Inc., Project MUSE, ProQuest Information & Learning, Swets Information Services).
Indexed: ABIn, ASCA, AmH&L, ArtHuCI, BAS, CJA, CurCont, DIP, HistAb, IBR, IBSS, IBZ, JEL, KES, MEA&I, MathSciNet, PAIS, PSA, PhilInd, RASB, SSCI, SSI.
—BLDSC (4318.400000), IDS, IE, Infotrieve, ingenta. **CCC.**
Published by: Duke University Press, 905 W Main St, Ste 18 B, Durham, NC 27701. TEL 919-687-3600, FAX 919-688-3524, subscriptions@dukeupress.edu, http://dukeupress.edu/journals/j_titles.php3?user_id=5594026714, http://www.dukeupress.edu. Eds. Craufurd D W Goodwin, Neil De Marchi. R&P Kay Robin Alexander. Adv. contact Mandy Dailey-Berman TEL 919-687-3636. page USD 200; trim 4.125 x 7.375. Circ: 1,350 (paid).

➤ **HOBBES STUDIES.** see *PHILOSOPHY*

330.1 HKG ISSN 1018-6751
HONG KONG ECONOMIC JOURNAL/XINBAO CAIJING YUEKAN. Text in Chinese. 1973. m. HKD 5 newsstand/cover; USD 0.65 newsstand/cover in United States. adv. **Document type:** *Newspaper.*
Published by: Shun Po Co. Ltd., 22-F North Point International Bldg, 499 King's Rd, Hong Kong, Hong Kong. TEL 852-2856-7567, FAX 852-2811-1070, hkej@netvigator.com. Ed. Lian Yi Zheng. Pub. Lam Shan Muk. Adv. contact Hon Kowong Kwok. page HKD 38,800; trim 533 x 355. Circ: 70,000.

330.1 CZE ISSN 0231-7540
HC270.2
HOSPODARSKE DEJINY✱ /ECONOMIC HISTORY. Text in Czech, English, German, Russian, Slovak. 1978. 2/yr. per issue exchange basis only. bk.rev. bibl. **Document type:** *Academic/Scholarly.* **Description:** Economic history of Europe.
Indexed: AmH&L, HistAb, IBR, IBZ, RASB.
Published by: (Akademie Ved Ceske Republiky), Academia, Publishing House of the Czech Academy of Sciences, Vaclavske Namesti 34, Prague 1, 110 00, Czech Republic. Ed. Jan Hajek.

330.1 GBR ISSN 0828-8666
HB72 CODEN: HUMAEB
➤ **HUMANOMICS.** Text in English. 1984. q. EUR 899 in Europe; USD 969 in North America; AUD 599 in Australasia; GBP 599 in the UK & elsewhere (effective 2005). back issues avail. **Document type:** *Journal, Academic/Scholarly.* **Description:** Studies the theoretical foundations of ethico-economics and the nature of ethics and values in economic knowledge.
Related titles: Online - full text ed.: (from ProQuest Information & Learning).
Indexed: ABIn, JEL, PerIslam, SOPODA.
Published by: (Centre of Humanomics, University College of Cape Breton CAN), Barmarick Publications, Enholmes Hall, Patrington, Hull, East Yorkshire HU12 0PR, United Kingdom. TEL 44-1964-630033, FAX 44-1964-631716, http://www.emeraldinsight.com/h.htm. Ed. Masudul Alam Choudhury. Circ: 150. **Dist. by:** Emerald Group Publishing Limited, 60-62 Toller Ln, Bradford, W Yorks BD8 9BY, United Kingdom. TEL 44-1274-777700, FAX 44-1274-785200, infomation@emeraldinsight.com, http://www.emeraldinsight.com/.

330.1 FRA ISSN 1636-5690
IDEES - C N D P. Abbreviated title: D E E S. Text in French. 1970. 4/yr. **Description:** Offers a forum for economists and social scientists.
Formerly (until 2002): Documents pour l'Enseignement Economique et Social (0396-8898)
Published by: Centre National de Documentation Pedagogique, 29 rue de l'Ulm, Paris, Cedex 5 75230, France. TEL 33-1-46349000, FAX 33-1-46345544. Ed. Pascal Combemale. Circ: 2,000. **Subscr. to:** CNDP - Abonnement, B.P. 750, Sainte Genevieve Cedex 60732, France. FAX 33-3-44033013.

THE INDEPENDENT REVIEW; a journal of political economy. see *POLITICAL SCIENCE*

INDIAN ECONOMIC AND SOCIAL HISTORY REVIEW. see *SOCIAL SCIENCES: COMPREHENSIVE WORKS*

INDIAN JOURNAL OF MARKETING GEOGRAPHY. see *GEOGRAPHY*

330.1 GBR ISSN 0960-6491
HD2709
➤ **INDUSTRIAL AND CORPORATE CHANGE.** Text in English. 1991. bi-m. GBP 310, USD 558, EUR 465 to institutions; GBP 326, USD 587, EUR 489 combined subscription to institutions print & online eds. (effective 2006). adv. bk.rev. illus. index. back issues avail.; reprint service avail. from PSC. **Document type:** *Journal, Academic/Scholarly.* **Description:** Committed to present and interpret the evidence on corporate and industrial change, drawing from an interdisciplinary set of approaches and theories from economics, sociology of organizacion and social psychology.
Related titles: Online - full text ed.: ISSN 1464-3650. GBP 293, USD 527, EUR 440 to institutions (effective 2006) (from EBSCO Publishing, Gale Group, HighWire Press, IngentaConnect, O C L C Online Computer Library Center, Inc., Oxford University Press Online Journals, ProQuest Information & Learning, Swets Information Services).
Indexed: ABIn, BPI, CPM, CurCont, Emerald, GEOBASE, HRA, IBSS, JEL, PCI, SSCI.
—BLDSC (4444.973000), IE, Infotrieve, ingenta. **CCC.**
Published by: (Associazione I C C), Oxford University Press, Great Clarendon St, Oxford, OX2 6DP, United Kingdom. TEL 44-1865-556767, FAX 44-1865-556646, jnlorders@oup-usa.org, jnl.orders@oup.co.uk, http://icc.oxfordjournals.org/, http://www.oxfordjournals.org/. Ed. Adriana Mongelli. R&P Fiona Bennett. Adv. contact Helen Pearson. B&W page GBP 240, B&W page USD 400; 110 x 195. Circ: 950.

➤ **INSTITUT DER DEUTSCHEN WIRTSCHAFT. FORUM.** see *BUSINESS AND ECONOMICS—Management*

330.1 BOL
INSTITUTO DE INVESTIGACIONES ECONOMICAS. REVISTA. Text in Spanish. 1950. a.
Published by: Universidad Tecnica de Oruro, Facultad de Ciencias Economicas y Financieras, Casilla 264, Oruro, Bolivia. TEL 55503. Ed. Freddy Sanjines Montan.

330 GBR ISSN 1742-7355
▼ **INTERNATIONAL JOURNAL OF ECONOMIC THEORY.** Text in English. 2004. q. EUR 131 in Europe to individuals; USD 142 in the Americas to individuals; GBP 87 elsewhere to individuals; USD 398 in the Americas to institutions & Caribbean; GBP 245 elsewhere to institutions (effective 2006). **Description:** Publishes articles for international audiences in all fields of economic theory. Covers topics of micro- and macroeconomics, game theory, general equilibrium, welfare economics, public economics, industrial organization, development economics and mathematical methods for economics.
Related titles: Online - full text ed.: ISSN 1742-7363. USD 378 in the Americas to institutions; GBP 233 elsewhere to institutions (effective 2006) (from Blackwell Synergy, EBSCO Publishing, O C L C Online Computer Library Center, Inc., Swets Information Services).
—CCC.
Published by: Blackwell Publishing Ltd., 9600 Garsington Rd, Oxford, OX4 2ZG, United Kingdom. TEL 44-1865-776868, FAX 44-1865-714591, customerservices@oxon.blackwellpublishing.com, http://www.blackwellpublishing.com/journals/IJET.

INTERNATIONAL JOURNAL OF GAME THEORY. see *MATHEMATICS*

INTERNATIONAL JOURNAL OF INDUSTRIAL ORGANIZATION. see *BUSINESS AND ECONOMICS—Management*

INTERNATIONAL REVIEW OF LAW AND ECONOMICS. see *LAW*

INTERNATIONAL SERIES IN ECONOMIC MODELING. see *BUSINESS AND ECONOMICS—Computer Applications*

330.1 USA
▼ ➤ **THE INTERNET JOURNAL OF ECONOMICS.** Text in English. 2004. irreg. free to individuals; USD 500 to institutions (effective 2005). **Document type:** *Journal, Academic/Scholarly.*
Media: Online - full content.
Published by: Internet Scientific Publications, L.L.C., 23 Rippling Creek Dr, Sugar Land, TX 77479. TEL 832-443-1193, FAX 281-240-1533, wenker@ispub.com, http://www.ispub.com/ostia/index.php?xmlFilePath=journals/ijeco/front.xml.

330.1 MEX ISSN 0185-1667
HB9
INVESTIGACION ECONOMICA. Text in Spanish. 1941. q. MXP 110, USD 25 (effective 2000). **Description:** Publishes articles about Latin America economic affairs from the theoretical and methodological points of view.
Indexed: AmH&L, JEL, PAIS, PCI.
Published by: Universidad Nacional Autonoma de Mexico, Facultad de Economia, Departamento de Distribucion Editorial, Edificio Anexo a la Facultad, 2o Piso, Circuito Interior, Ciudad Universitaria, Mexico City, DF 04510, Mexico. TEL 52-5-6222137, http://herzog.economia.unam.mx/. Ed. Roberto Escalante.

330.1 UKR ISSN 0320-4421
HC337
ISTORIYA NARODNOHO HOSPODARSTVA TA EKONOMICHNOI DUMKY UKRAINY; mizhvidomchyi zbirnik naukovykh prac. Text in Ukrainian; Summaries in Russian. 1965. a. **Document type:** *Journal, Academic/Scholarly.*
Published by: Natsional'na Akademiya Nauk Ukrainy, Instytut Ekonomiky, vul P Myrnoho 26, Kyiv 11, 01011, Ukraine. TEL 380-44-2908444, FAX 380-44-2908663, instecon@ln.ua. Ed. T I Dereviankin.

330 USA ISSN 0021-3624
HB1 CODEN: JECIAR
➤ **J E I.** (Journal of Economic Issues) Text in English. 1967. q. USD 45 domestic to individuals; USD 50 foreign to individuals; USD 55 domestic to libraries; USD 65 foreign to libraries; USD 15 domestic to students; USD 20 foreign to students (effective 2005). adv. bk.rev. illus. Index. reprint service avail. from PQC,PSC. **Document type:** *Journal, Academic/Scholarly.*
Related titles: Microform ed.: (from PQC); Online - full text ed.: (from bigchalk, EBSCO Publishing, Florida Center for Library Automation, Gale Group, H.W. Wilson, O C L C Online Computer Library Center, Inc., ProQuest Information & Learning).
Indexed: ABIn, ABS&EES, APEL, ASCA, AgeL, BPI, BPIA, BusI, CJA, CLOSS, CPM, CREJ, CurCont, DIP, EIA, EnerInd, FamI, ForAb, IBR, IBSS, IBZ, ILD, JEL, LRI, MCR, MEA&I, PAIS, PCI, PSA, RASB, RDA, SOPODA, SRRA, SSA, SSCI, SSI, SociolAb, T&II, WAE&RSA.
—BLDSC (4973.052000), CISTI, IDS, IE, Infotrieve, ingenta.
Published by: Association for Evolutionary Economics, Department of Economics, University of Nevada, Reno, NV 89507. afee@bucknell.edu, http://www.orgs.bucknell.edu/afee/jei/. Ed., Adv. contact Glen Atkinson. R&P Janet Knoedler TEL 717-524-3447. Circ: 2,000 (paid).

330.1 DEU ISSN 0722-5369
HB5
JAHRBUCH FUER NEUE POLITISCHE OEKONOMIE. Text in German; Summaries in English. 1983. a. **Document type:** *Academic/Scholarly.* **Description:** Reports on developments in the theory of "new political economy.".
Indexed: DIP, IBR, IBZ, RASB.
—BLDSC (4631.830000).
Published by: Mohr Siebeck, Wilhelmstr 18, Tuebingen, 72074, Germany. TEL 49-7071-923-0, FAX 49-7071-51104, postmaster@mohr.de, info@mohr.de, http://www.mohr.de. R&P Jill Sopper.

B

330 DEU ISSN 0075-2800
HC281
JAHRBUCH FUER WIRTSCHAFTSGESCHICHTE. Text in German. 1960. a. (in two vols.). EUR 39.80 per vol. (effective 2002). reprint service avail. from SCH. **Document type:** *Journal, Academic/Scholarly.*
Indexed: AmH&L, HistAb, IBR, IBSS, IBZ, PAIS, RASB.
Published by: Akademie Verlag GmbH (Subsidiary of: Oldenbourg Wissenschaftsverlag GmbH), Palisadenstr 40, Berlin, 10243, Germany. TEL 49-30-4220060, FAX 49-30-42200657, info@akademie-verlag.de, http://www.akademie-verlag.de.

330.1 NLD ISSN 0922-1425
HF1601
➤ **JAPAN AND THE WORLD ECONOMY.** Text in English. 1988. 4/yr. EUR 458 in Europe to institutions; JPY 60,700 in Japan to institutions; USD 512 elsewhere to institutions (effective 2006). adv. illus. back issues avail.; reprints avail. **Document type:** *Journal, Academic/Scholarly.* **Description:** Provides a forum for examining issues and problems relevant to the economic interdependence between Japan and major trading partners throughout the world.
Related titles: Microform ed.: (from PQC); Online - full text ed.: (from EBSCO Publishing, Gale Group, IngentaConnect, ScienceDirect, Swets Information Services).
Indexed: APEL, ASCA, BAS, CurCont, Faml, IBSS, Inspec, JEL, PAIS, PCI, RASB, SSCI.
—BLDSC (4648.015000), IDS, IE, Infotrieve, ingenta. **CCC.**
Published by: (New York University, Leonard N. Stern School of Business, The Center for Japan-US Business and Economic Studies USA), Elsevier BV, North-Holland (Subsidiary of: Elsevier Science & Technology), Sara Burgerhartstraat 25, Amsterdam, 1055 KV, Netherlands. TEL 31-20-485-3911, FAX 31-20-485-2457, nlinfo-f@elsevier.nl, http://www.elsevier.com/locate/jwe, http://www.elsevier.nl. Eds. Robert Dekle, Yasushi Hamao. **Subscr. to:** Elsevier BV, PO Box 211, Amsterdam 1000 AE, Netherlands. TEL 31-20-485-3757, FAX 31-20-485-3432, http://www.elsevier.nl.

330.1 CHN
JIANGSU JINGJI TANTAO/JIANGSU ECONOMIC INQUIRY. Text in Chinese. m.
Published by: Jiangsu Academy of Social Sciences, Economic Research Institute, 12 Huju Beilu, Nanjing, Jiangsu 210013, China. TEL 635276. Ed. Gu Songnian.

JINGJI LILUN YU JINGJI GUANLI/ECONOMIC THEORY & BUSINESS MANAGEMENT. see *BUSINESS AND ECONOMICS—Management*

330.1 CHN ISSN 0577-9154
JINGJI YANJIU/ECONOMIC RESEARCH. Text in Chinese; Contents page in English. 1955. m. CNY 18, USD 61.20. charts; stat.
Related titles: Online - full text ed.: (from East View Information Services).
Indexed: AmH&L, HistAb, RASB.
Published by: Zhongguo Shehui Kexueyuan, Jingji Yanjiusuo/Chinese Academy of Social Sciences, Economic Research Institute, 2 Yuetan Beixiaojie, Beijing, 100836, China. TEL 895024. Ed. Zhao Renwei. **Dist. in US by:** China Books & Periodicals Inc, 360 Swift Ave., Ste. 48, S San Fran, CA 94080-6220. TEL 415-282-2994; **Dist. outside China by:** China International Book Trading Corp, 35 Chegongzhuang Xilu, Haidian District, PO Box 399, Beijing 100044, China. TEL 86-10-68412045, FAX 86-10-68412023, cibtc@mail.cibtc.com.cn, http://www.cibtc.com.cn.

330.1 HKG ISSN 1011-9108
HB9
JINGJI YU FALU/ECONOMY AND LAW. Text in Chinese, English. 1985. bi-m. HKD 180 domestic; HKD 196 in Taiwan; USD 55 elsewhere; HKD 30 newsstand/cover (effective 2001). adv. bk.rev. abstr. index. back issues avail. **Document type:** *Trade.* **Description:** For the academic exchange of studies in business, investment, economics, and law.
Related titles: Microfilm ed.
Published by: Economy and Law Press, PO Box 20763, Hennessy Rd Post Office, Hong Kong, Hong Kong. TEL 852-25197556, FAX 852-25073079, gz@economy-and-law.com, http://www.economy-and-law.com/. Ed. Chan Ying Liong. Pub. Ying Liong Chan. Adv. contact Chan See Wai. Circ: 10,000.

330.1 CAN ISSN 0840-5425
HD87
JOHN DEUTSCH INSTITUTE FOR THE STUDY OF ECONOMIC POLICY. DISCUSSION PAPER SERIES. Text in English. 1989. irreg., latest vol.17, 1994. CND 3 per issue in US & Canada; CND 3.50 per issue elsewhere (effective 2004). back issues avail. **Document type:** *Monographic series.*
Published by: John Deutsch Institute for the Study of Economic Policy, Dunning Hall Room 216C, Queen's University, Kingston, ON K7L 3N6, Canada. TEL 613-533-2294, FAX 613-533-6025. Ed. Charles M Beach. R&P Sharon Sullivan.

330.1 CAN
JOHN DEUTSCH INSTITUTE FOR THE STUDY OF ECONOMIC POLICY. POLICY FORUM SERIES. Text in English. 1983. irreg., latest vol.35, 1997. price varies. back issues avail. **Document type:** *Monographic series.*
Published by: John Deutsch Institute for the Study of Economic Policy, Dunning Hall Room 216C, Queen's University, Kingston, ON K7L 3N6, Canada. TEL 613-533-2294, FAX 613-533-6025. Ed. Thomas J Courchene. R&P Sharon Sullivan.

330.1 CAN
JOHN DEUTSCH INSTITUTE FOR THE STUDY OF ECONOMIC POLICY. ROUNDTABLE SERIES. Text in English. 1983. a. price varies. back issues avail. **Document type:** *Monographic series.*
Formerly: John Deutsch Roundtable on Economic Policy
Published by: John Deutsch Institute for the Study of Economic Policy, Dunning Hall Room 216C, Queen's University, Kingston, ON K7L 3N6, Canada. TEL 613-533-2294, FAX 613-533-6025. Ed. Thomas J Courchene. R&P Sharon Sullivan. Circ: 500.

330.1 ZAF ISSN 0379-6205
HB9
➤ **JOURNAL FOR STUDIES IN ECONOMICS AND ECONOMETRICS/TYDSKRIF VIR STUDIES IN EKONOMIE EN EKONOMETRIE.** Short title: S E E. Text in English. 1977. 3/yr. ZAR 180 domestic; USD 40 foreign (effective 2003). **Document type:** *Journal, Academic/Scholarly.* **Description:** Presents detailed studies of economic issues.
Related titles: Online - full text ed.: (from International Network for the Availability of Scientific Publications, African Journals Online).
Indexed: ISAP, JEL, PAIS.
—BLDSC (5066.897000), IE, ingenta.
Published by: Universiteit Stellenbosch, Bureau for Economic Research/Stellenbosch University, University, Private Bag 5050, Stellenbosch, 7599, South Africa. TEL 27-21-8872810, FAX 27-21-8899225, hhman@maties.sun.ac.za, http://www.inasp.info/ajol/journals/see/about.html, http://www.sun.ac.za/. Eds. E Smit, G M P Pellissier. Circ: 350.

330.1 GBR ISSN 0883-7252
HB139 CODEN: JAECET
➤ **JOURNAL OF APPLIED ECONOMETRICS.** Text in English. 1986. 8/yr. USD 1,285 to institutions; USD 1,414 combined subscription to institutions print & online eds. (effective 2006). adv. bk.rev. illus. Index. back issues avail.; reprint service avail. from PSC. **Document type:** *Journal, Academic/Scholarly.* **Description:** Provides articles dealing with the application of econometric techniques to a wide variety of problems in economics and related subjects: covering topics in measurement, estimation, testing, forecasting, and policy analysis.
Related titles: Microform ed.: (from PQC); Online - full text ed.: ISSN 1099-1255. USD 1,285 to institutions (effective 2006) (from EBSCO Publishing, JSTOR (Web-based Journal Archive), ProQuest Information & Learning, Swets Information Services, Wiley InterScience).
Indexed: ABIn, ASCA, AgeL, BAS, CIS, CurCont, ESPM, IBSS, Inspec, JEL, ORMS, PCI, QC&AS, RASB, RefZh, RiskAb, SSCI, ST&MA, WAE&RSA, ZentMath.
—BLDSC (4942.520000), CISTI, IDS, IE, Infotrieve, ingenta. **CCC.**
Published by: John Wiley & Sons Ltd. (Subsidiary of: John Wiley & Sons, Inc.), The Atrium, Southern Gate, Chichester, West Sussex PO19 8SQ, United Kingdom. TEL 44-1243-779777, FAX 44-1243-775878, customer@wiley.co.uk, http://jae.wiley.com, http://www.wiley.co.uk. Ed. M Hashem Pesaran. adv.: B&W page GBP 650, color page GBP 1,550; trim 200 x 260. Circ: 1,300. **Subscr. in the Americas to:** John Wiley & Sons, Inc., 111 River St, Hoboken, NJ 07030-5774. TEL 201-748-6645, 800-225-5945, subinfo@wiley.com.

➤ **JOURNAL OF AUSTRALIAN POLITICAL ECONOMY.** see *BUSINESS AND ECONOMICS—Economic Situation And Conditions*

➤ **JOURNAL OF BIOECONOMICS.** see *BIOLOGY*

➤ **JOURNAL OF BUSINESS RESEARCH.** see *BUSINESS AND ECONOMICS—Management*

330.1 USA ISSN 0885-2545
NX180.S6 CODEN: JCUEER
➤ **JOURNAL OF CULTURAL ECONOMICS.** Text in English. 1977. q. EUR 398, USD 408, GBP 248 combined subscription to institutions print & online eds. (effective 2005). adv. bk.rev. reprint service avail. from PSC. **Document type:** *Journal, Academic/Scholarly.* **Description:** Publishes papers applying economic analysis to the area of all creative and performing arts, and to the heritage and cultural industries, whether publicly or privately owned.
Related titles: Online - full text ed.: ISSN 1573-6997 (from EBSCO Publishing, Gale Group, IngentaConnect, Kluwer Online, O C L C Online Computer Library Center, Inc., ProQuest Information & Learning, Springer LINK, Swets Information Services).
Indexed: ABIn, BibInd, BibLing, IBSS, JEL, RASB, RRTA, SOPODA, WAE&RSA.
—BLDSC (4965.843000), IE, Infotrieve, ingenta. **CCC.**
Published by: (Association for Cultural Economics), Springer-Verlag New York, Inc. (Subsidiary of: Springer Science+Business Media), 233 Spring St, New York, NY 10013. TEL 212-460-1500, FAX 212-460-1575, service@springer-ny.com, http://springerlink.metapress.com/openurl.asp?genre=journal&issn=0885-2545, http://www.springer-ny.com. Eds. Guenther G Schulze, J Mark Schuster. **Subscr. to:** Journal Fulfillment, PO Box 2485, Secaucus, NJ 07096-2485. TEL 201-348-4033, FAX 201-348-4505, journals@springer-ny.com.

330.1 NPL ISSN 0259-0956
JOURNAL OF DEVELOPMENT AND ADMINISTRATIVE STUDIES. Text in English. 1978. s-a. NPR 30, USD 6.
Indexed: BAS.
Published by: Centre for Economic Development and Administration, Publications and Information Services Division, Kirtipur Campus, P O Box 797, Kathmandu, Nepal.

330.1 USA ISSN 1066-9868
HF4050 CODEN: JEBUFT
➤ **JOURNAL OF EAST - WEST BUSINESS.** Abbreviated title: J E B. Text in English. 1993. q. USD 330 combined subscription domestic to institutions print & online eds.; USD 445.50 combined subscription in Canada to institutions print & online eds.; USD 478.50 combined subscription elsewhere to institutions print & online eds. (effective 2006). adv. bk.rev. 120 p./no. 1 cols./p.; back issues avail.; reprint service avail. from HAW. **Document type:** *Journal, Academic/Scholarly.* **Description:** Deals with contemporary and emerging topics of business studies, strategies, development, and practice as they relate to the Russian Republic, the new Asian republics, the Eastern European republics, the Baltic republics, and other worldwide business relationships.
Related titles: Microfiche ed.: (from PQC); Microform ed.; Online - full text ed.: ISSN 1528-6959 (from EBSCO Publishing, O C L C Online Computer Library Center, Inc., Swets Information Services).
Indexed: ABIn, DIP, ESPM, GEOBASE, GSS&RPL, IBR, IBZ, JEL, M&MA, PerIslam, RefZh, RiskAb, SOPODA.
—BLDSC (4971.530000), Haworth, IE, Infotrieve, ingenta. **CCC.**
Published by: International Business Press (Subsidiary of: Haworth Press, Inc.), 10 Alice St, Binghamton, NY 13904. TEL 607-722-5857, 800-429-6784, FAX 607-771-0012, 800-895-0582, getinfo@haworthpress.com, http://www.haworthpress.com/web/JEB. Ed. Erdener Kaynak TEL 717-566-3054. Pub. William Cohen. R&P Ruth Ann Heath TEL 607-722-5857 ext 316. Adv. contact Rebecca Miller-Baum TEL 607-722-5857 ext 337. B&W page USD 315, color page USD 550; trim 4.375 x 7.125. Circ: 153 (paid).

330.01 519.5 NLD ISSN 0304-4076
HB139 CODEN: JECMB6
➤ **JOURNAL OF ECONOMETRICS.** Text in Dutch. 1973. 12/yr. EUR 165 in Europe to individuals; JPY 22,000 in Japan to individuals; USD 169 elsewhere to individuals; EUR 2,440 in Europe to institutions; JPY 324,300 in Japan to institutions; USD 2,728 elsewhere to institutions (effective 2006). adv. bk.rev. charts; illus. index. back issues avail.; reprints avail. **Document type:** *Journal, Academic/Scholarly.* **Description:** Deals with the application of statistical inference to economic data, as well as the application of econometric techniques to substantive areas of economics. Focuses on both theoretical and applied econometrics.
Related titles: Microform ed.: (from PQC); Online - full text ed.: (from EBSCO Publishing, Gale Group, IngentaConnect, ScienceDirect, Swets Information Services).
Indexed: ABIn, ASCA, AgeL, BAS, BPIA, BusI, CCMJ, CIS, CMCI, CPM, CREJ, CurCont, DIP, ESPM, EngInd, IBR, IBSS, IBZ, JCQM, JEL, MathR, MathSciNet, PCI, RASB, RRTA, RiskAb, SSCI, SSI, ST&MA, T&II, WAE&RSA, ZentMath.
—BLDSC (4972.400000), CISTI, IDS, IE, Infotrieve, ingenta. **CCC.**
Published by: Elsevier BV, North-Holland (Subsidiary of: Elsevier Science & Technology), Sara Burgerhartstraat 25, Amsterdam, 1055 KV, Netherlands. TEL 31-20-485-3911, FAX 31-20-485-2457, nlinfo-f@elsevier.nl, http://www.elsevier.com/locate/jeconom, http://www.elsevier.nl. Eds. A. R. Gallant, J F Geweke, T. Amemiya. **Subscr. to:** Elsevier BV, PO Box 211, Amsterdam 1000 AE, Netherlands. TEL 31-20-485-3757, FAX 31-20-485-3432, http://www.elsevier.nl.

330.1 300 TUR ISSN 1302-1060
HB1
JOURNAL OF ECONOMIC AND SOCIAL RESEARCH. Text in English. 1999. s-a. **Document type:** *Journal, Academic/Scholarly.* **Description:** Provides a platform for social-scientific studies of theoretical, practical and historical importance on economic, political, and social processes.
Related titles: Online - full text ed.: (from EBSCO Publishing).
Indexed: IndIslam, JEL, PSA, SSCI, SociolAb.
Published by: Fatih University, Department of Economics, 34500 Buyukcekmece, Istanbul, Turkey. TEL 90-212-8890810, FAX 90-212-8890912, info@fatih.edu.tr, http://jesr.journal.fatih.edu.tr/, http://www.fatih.edu.tr. Eds. Ahmet Kara, Ali S. Hadi.

330.1 NLD ISSN 0165-1889
HB1 CODEN: JEDCDH

➤ **JOURNAL OF ECONOMIC DYNAMICS AND CONTROL.** Text in English. 1979. 12/yr. EUR 78 in Europe to individuals; JPY 10,400 in Japan to individuals; USD 79 elsewhere to individuals; EUR 1,456 in Europe to institutions; JPY 193,300 in Japan to institutions; USD 1,628 elsewhere to institutions (effective 2006). adv. bk.rev. illus. Index. back issues avail.; reprints avail. **Document type:** *Journal, Academic/Scholarly.* **Description:** Publishes papers on economic dynamics, computing, control and decision support in economic systems.
Related titles: Microform ed.: (from PQC); Online - full text ed.: (from EBSCO Publishing, Gale Group, IngentaConnect, ScienceDirect, Swets Information Services).
Indexed: ABIn, AIT, ASCA, BPIA, BusI, CCMJ, CIS, CREJ, CurCont, ESPM, IBR, IBSS, IBZ, Inspec, JCQM, JEL, ManagCont, MathR, MathSciNet, RASB, RRTA, RiskAb, SSCI, T&II, WAE&RSA, ZentMath.
—BLDSC (4972.870000), AskIEEE, IDS, IE, Infotrieve, ingenta. **CCC.**
Published by: Elsevier BV, North-Holland (Subsidiary of: Elsevier Science & Technology), Sara Burgerhartstraat 25, Amsterdam, 1055 KV, Netherlands. TEL 31-20-485-3911, FAX 31-20-485-2457, nlinfo-f@elsevier.nl, http://www.elsevier.com/locate/jedc, http://www.elsevier.nl. Eds. C Chiarella, C. H. Hommes, W. J. Den Haan. **Subscr. to:** Elsevier BV, PO Box 211, Amsterdam 1000 AE, Netherlands. TEL 31-20-485-3757, FAX 31-20-485-3432, http://www.elsevier.nl.

330.1 USA ISSN 1381-4338
HD72 CODEN: JEGRFB

➤ **JOURNAL OF ECONOMIC GROWTH.** Text in English. 1996. q. EUR 518, USD 535, GBP 328 combined subscription to institutions print & online eds. (effective 2005). adv. back issues avail.; reprint service avail. from PSC. **Document type:** *Journal, Academic/Scholarly.* **Description:** Serve as the principal outlet for theoretical as well as empirical research in economic growth and dynamic macroeconomics. The editorial board consists of prominent researchers in the fields of economic growth, dynamic macroeconomics, international economics, urban economics, migration, and development.
Related titles: Online - full text ed.: ISSN 1573-7020 (from EBSCO Publishing, Gale Group, IngentaConnect, Kluwer Online, O C L C Online Computer Library Center, Inc., ProQuest Information & Learning, Springer LINK, Swets Information Services).
Indexed: ABIn, APEL, BAS, BibLing, CurCont, IBSS, JEL, RefZh, SSCI.
—BLDSC (4973.020000), IE, Infotrieve, ingenta. **CCC.**
Published by: Springer-Verlag New York, Inc. (Subsidiary of: Springer Science+Business Media), 233 Spring St, New York, NY 10013. TEL 212-460-1500, FAX 212-460-1575, service@springer-ny.com, http://springerlink.metapress.com/openurl.asp?genre=journal&issn=1381-4338, http://www.springer-ny.com. Ed. Oded Galor. **Subscr. to:** Journal Fulfillment, PO Box 2485, Secaucus, NJ 07096-2485. TEL 201-348-4033, FAX 201-348-4505, journals@springer-ny.com.

330 GBR ISSN 0022-0507
HC10

➤ **JOURNAL OF ECONOMIC HISTORY.** Text in English. 1941. q. GBP 110 to institutions; USD 170 in North America to institutions; GBP 120 combined subscription to institutions print & online eds.; USD 189 combined subscription in North America to institutions print & online eds. (effective 2006). adv. bk.rev. bibl.; illus. index. back issues avail.; reprints avail. **Document type:** *Journal, Academic/Scholarly.* **Description:** Examines a wide range of topics: agriculture, servitude, money and banking, trade, manufacturing, and technology.
Related titles: Microform ed.: (from MIM, PQC); Online - full text ed.: ISSN 1471-6372. GBP 102 to institutions; USD 160 in North America to institutions (effective 2006) (from EBSCO Publishing, JSTOR (Web-based Journal Archive), O C L C Online Computer Library Center, Inc., Swets Information Services).
Indexed: ABIn, ABS&EES, APEL, ASCA, Acal, AgeL, Agr, AmH&L, ArtHuCI, BAS, BRI, CBRI, ChPerI, CurCont, DIP, FamI, GEOBASE, HistAb, IBR, IBSS, IBZ, IndIslam, JEL, MEA&I, PAIS, PCI, PopulInd, RASB, SSCI, SSI, T&II, WAE&RSA, WorkRelAb.
—BLDSC (4973.050000), IDS, IE, Infotrieve, ingenta. **CCC.**
Published by: (Economic History Association SWE), Cambridge University Press, The Edinburgh Bldg, Shaftesbury Rd, Cambridge, CB2 2RU, United Kingdom. TEL 44-1223-312393, FAX 44-1223-315052, journals@cambridge.org, http://uk.cambridge.org/journals/jeh. Eds. C Knick Harley, Jeremy Atack. R&P Linda Nicol TEL 44-1223-325757. Adv. contact Rebecca Curtis TEL 44-1223-325757. **Subscr. to:** Cambridge University Press, 100 Brook Hill Dr, West Nyack, NY 10994. TEL 845-353-7500, FAX 845-353-4141, journals_subscriptions@cup.org

330.1 USA ISSN 0895-3309
HB1

➤ **JOURNAL OF ECONOMIC PERSPECTIVES.** Text in English. 1987. q. free to members (effective 2005). adv. illus. Index. reprints avail. **Document type:** *Journal, Academic/Scholarly.* **Description:** Provides economists with accessible articles that report on and critique recent research findings, and evaluate public policy initiatives.
Related titles: CD-ROM ed.; Online - full text ed.: (from EBSCO Publishing, Gale Group, IngentaConnect, JSTOR (Web-based Journal Archive), O C L C Online Computer Library Center, Inc., ProQuest Information & Learning).
Indexed: ABIn, ABS&EES, APEL, ASCA, AgeL, AmH&L, BAS, BPI, CIS, CJA, CurCont, Emerald, FamI, HistAb, IBR, IBSS, IBZ, JEL, MEDLINE, ORMS, PAA&I, PAIS, PCI, QC&AS, RASB, SSCI, SSI, WAE&RSA.
—BLDSC (4973.054000), CISTI, IDS, IE, Infotrieve, ingenta, Linda Hall. **CCC.**
Published by: American Economic Association, 2014 Broadway, Ste 305, Nashville, TN 37203. http://www.aeaweb.org/jep/, http://www.vanderbilt.edu/AEA/. Ed. Alan B Krueger. R&P Edda B Leithner.

330 USA ISSN 0022-0531
HB1 CODEN: JECTAQ

➤ **JOURNAL OF ECONOMIC THEORY.** Text in English. 1969. 6/yr. EUR 119 in Europe to individuals; JPY 12,800 in Japan to individuals; USD 99 elsewhere to individuals; EUR 3,188 in Europe to institutions; JPY 332,800 in Japan to institutions; USD 2,629 elsewhere to institutions; EUR 49 in Europe to students; JPY 5,200 in Japan to students; USD 44 elsewhere to students (effective 2006). adv. back issues avail.; reprints avail. **Document type:** *Academic/Scholarly.* **Description:** Publishes original research on economic theory and emphasizes the theoretical analysis of economic models, including the study of related mathematical techniques.
Related titles: Online - full text ed.: ISSN 1095-7235. USD 2,660 (effective 2002) (from EBSCO Publishing, Gale Group, IngentaConnect, O C L C Online Computer Library Center, Inc., ScienceDirect, Swets Information Services).
Indexed: ABIn, ASCA, AgeL, BPIA, BusI, CCMJ, CIS, CREJ, CurCont, ESPM, IBSS, JCQM, JEL, MathR, MathSciNet, PCI, PhilInd, RASB, RiskAb, SSCI, SSI, T&II, ZentMath.
—BLDSC (4973.070000), CISTI, IDS, IE, Infotrieve, ingenta, Linda Hall. **CCC.**
Published by: Academic Press (Subsidiary of: Elsevier Science & Technology), 525 B St, Ste 1900, San Diego, CA 92101-4495. TEL 619-231-6616, 800-894-3434, FAX 619-699-6422, apsubs@acad.com, http://www.elsevier.com/locate/jet, http://www.academicpress.com. Eds. A Lizzeri, Karl Shell.

330.1 KOR ISSN 1229-2893

JOURNAL OF ECONOMIC THEORY AND ECONOMETRICS. Text in English. s-a. **Document type:** *Journal, Academic/Scholarly.*
Related titles: Online - full content ed.
Indexed: JEL.
—BLDSC (4973.070300).
Published by: Han'gug Gye'lyang Gyeongje Haghoe/Korean Econometric Society, Seoul National University, School of Economics, Seoul, 151-742, Korea, S. chyunee@hanmail.net, http://dasan.snu.ac.kr/~kes/.

330.1 658 USA ISSN 1058-6407
HD28

➤ **JOURNAL OF ECONOMICS & MANAGEMENT STRATEGY.** Text in English. 1992. q. USD 53 combined subscription in the Americas to individuals & Caribbean (print & online eds.); EUR 78 combined subscription in Europe to individuals print & online eds.; GBP 52 combined subscription elsewhere to individuals print & online eds.; USD 271 combined subscription in the Americas to institutions & Caribbean (print & online eds.); GBP 213 combined subscription elsewhere to institutions print & online eds. (effective 2006). adv. back issues avail. **Document type:** *Academic/Scholarly.* **Description:** Provides a forum for the interaction and research on the competitive strategies of managers and the organizational structure of firms.
Related titles: Microform ed.: (from PQC); Online - full text ed.: ISSN 1530-9134. USD 50 in the Americas to individuals & Caribbean; EUR 74 in Europe to individuals; GBP 19 elsewhere to individuals; USD 257 in the Americas to institutions & Caribbean; GBP 202 elsewhere to institutions (effective 2006) (from Blackwell Synergy, EBSCO Publishing, Gale Group, IngentaConnect, O C L C Online Computer Library Center, Inc., Swets Information Services).
Indexed: ABIn, ASCA, CurCont, IBSS, JEL, SSCI, SWR&A.
—BLDSC (4973.095300), IDS, IE, Infotrieve, ingenta. **CCC.**
Published by: Blackwell Publishing, Inc. (Subsidiary of: Blackwell Publishing Ltd.), Commerce Place, 350 Main St, Malden, MA 02148. TEL 781-388-8206, FAX 781-388-8232, jems@nwu.edu, subscrip@blackwellpub.com, http://www.blackwellpublishing.com/journals/JEMS. Ed. Daniel Spulber.

➤ **JOURNAL OF EMPIRICAL FINANCE.** see *BUSINESS AND ECONOMICS—Banking And Finance*

330.1 DEU ISSN 0936-9937
HB1.A1 CODEN: JEECEN

➤ **JOURNAL OF EVOLUTIONARY ECONOMICS.** Text in English. 1991. 5/yr. EUR 428 combined subscription to institutions print & online eds. (effective 2005). adv. reprint service avail. from PSC. **Document type:** *Journal, Academic/Scholarly.* **Description:** Aims to provide an international forum for a new approach to economics, with an emphasis on dynamics, changing structures, and disequilibrium processes.
Related titles: Online - full text ed.: ISSN 1432-1386 (from EBSCO Publishing, ProQuest Information & Learning, Springer LINK, Swets Information Services).
Indexed: ABIn, CurCont, IBSS, JEL, RASB, SSCI.
—BLDSC (4979.642500), IDS, IE, Infotrieve, ingenta. **CCC.**
Published by: (International Joseph A. Schumpeter Society), Springer-Verlag (Subsidiary of: Springer Science+Business Media), Tiergartenstr 17, Heidelberg, 69121, Germany. TEL 49-6221-3450, FAX 49-6221-345229, http://link.springer.de/link/service/journals/00191/index.htm. Eds. Horst Hanusch, Uwe Cantner. **Subscr. in the Americas to:** Springer-Verlag New York, Inc., Journal Fulfillment, PO Box 2485, Secaucus, NJ 07096-2485. TEL 800-777-4643, 201-348-4033, FAX 201-348-4505, journals@springer-ny.com, http://www.springer-ny.com; **Subscr. to:** Springer GmbH Auslieferungsgesellschaft, Haberstr 7, Heidelberg 69126, Germany. TEL 49-6221-345-0, FAX 49-6221-345-4229, subscriptions@springer.de.

330.1 USA ISSN 1042-9573
HG4515.2 CODEN: JFIOAE

➤ **JOURNAL OF FINANCIAL INTERMEDIATION.** Text in English. 1990. 4/yr. EUR 69 in Europe to individuals; JPY 7,400 in Japan to individuals; USD 55 elsewhere to individuals; EUR 469 in Europe to institutions; JPY 49,100 in Japan to institutions; USD 365 elsewhere to institutions (effective 2006). illus. back issues avail.; reprints avail. **Document type:** *Academic/Scholarly.* **Description:** Collects and stimulates research in the design of financial contracts and institutions, stressing the use of contemporary analytical and empirical tools.
Related titles: Online - full text ed.: ISSN 1096-0473. USD 382 (effective 2002) (from EBSCO Publishing, Gale Group, IngentaConnect, O C L C Online Computer Library Center, Inc., ScienceDirect, Swets Information Services).
Indexed: ASCA, CurCont, IBSS, JEL, RASB, SSCI.
—BLDSC (4984.259500), IDS, IE, Infotrieve, ingenta. **CCC.**
Published by: Academic Press (Subsidiary of: Elsevier Science & Technology), 525 B St, Ste 1900, San Diego, CA 92101-4495. TEL 619-231-6616, 800-894-3434, FAX 619-699-6422, apsubs@acad.com, http://www.elsevier.com/locate/jfi, http://www.academicpress.com.

330.1 USA
K10

➤ **JOURNAL OF FORENSIC ECONOMICS.** Text in English. 1987. 3/yr. USD 165 to individuals; USD 110 libraries & institutions (effective 2005). adv. bk.rev. back issues avail. **Document type:** *Journal, Academic/Scholarly.* **Description:** Provides a forum for applications of economics in litigation. Articles include original economic research in areas of projection of loss earnings and services, vocational rehabilitation business valuation, medical economics and antitrust.
Related titles: Online - full text ed.: (from Florida Center for Library Automation).
Indexed: ABIn, CLI, FamI, IBR, IBSS, IBZ, JEL, LRI.
—BLDSC (4984.587000), IE, ingenta.
Published by: National Association of Forensic Economics, PO Box 30067, Kansas City, MO 64112. TEL 816-235-2833, FAX 816-235-5263, umkcnafe@umkc.edu, http://www.nafe.net. Eds. John O Ward, Michael J Piette. R&P, Adv. contact Nancy Eldredge TEL 816-235-2833. Circ: 800 (paid).

330.1 USA ISSN 0926-6437
HC79.I5

➤ **JOURNAL OF INCOME DISTRIBUTION**; an international journal of social economics. Text in English. 1991. q. USD 104 to individuals; USD 115 combined subscription to individuals print & online eds.; USD 312 to institutions; USD 359 combined subscription to institutions print & online eds. (effective 2005). adv. abstr. back issues avail. **Document type:** *Academic/Scholarly.* **Description:** Publishes original scholarly research in the field of social economics, and particularly in the sphere of the distribution of income and wealth.
Related titles: Online - full text ed.: USD 104 to individuals; USD 312 to institutions (effective 2005) (from EBSCO Publishing, Gale Group, IngentaConnect, O C L C Online Computer Library Center, Inc., ScienceDirect, Swets Information Services).
Indexed: ABIn, BAS, IBSS, JEL.
—BLDSC (5005.110000), IE, ingenta. **CCC.**
Published by: (International Centre for Social Economics NLD, Uiniversiteit Utrecht NLD), Transaction Publishers, 390 Campus Dr, Somerset, NJ 07830. TEL 888-999-6778, FAX 732-748-9801, trans@transactionpub.com, http://www.transactionpub.com. Ed. M C Sawyer. adv.: B&W page USD 300. Circ: 200. **Subscr. to:** Transaction Distribution Center, 390 Campus Dr., Somerset, NJ 08873. TEL 732-445-1245, orders@transactionpub.com.

➤ **JOURNAL OF INSTITUTIONAL AND THEORETICAL ECONOMICS.** see *POLITICAL SCIENCE*

➤ **JOURNAL OF LAW, ECONOMICS, AND ORGANIZATION.** see *LAW*

330.1 340.6 USA ISSN 1054-3023
K10 CODEN: JLECE4

➤ **JOURNAL OF LEGAL ECONOMICS.** Text in English. 1991. 3/yr. USD 60 domestic; USD 75 foreign (effective 2004). adv. bk.rev. reprint service avail. from WSH. **Document type:** *Journal, Academic/Scholarly.* **Description:** Devoted to legal economics, as well as related fields of finance, sociology, and vocational rehabilitation. Addresses areas of litigation, including personal injury, business valuation, antitrust, pension valuation, and divorce settlement.
Related titles: Microform ed.: (from PQC); Online - full text ed.: (from EBSCO Publishing, Factiva, LexisNexis, Northern Light Technology, Inc., O C L C Online Computer Library Center, Inc., ProQuest Information & Learning).
Indexed: ABIn, BLI, CLI, FamI, JEL, LRI, PAIS.
—BLDSC (5010.249000), IE, ingenta. **CCC.**
Published by: American Academy of Economic and Financial Experts, University of North Alabama, P O Box 5077, Florence, AL 35632. TEL 256-765-4144, FAX 256-765-4170, leglecon@unanov.una.edu, http://www.journaloflegaleconomics.com/, http://www.aaefe.org. Ed. Michael Butler. Pub., R&P, Adv. contact Toysan Reed. page USD 250. Circ: 500 (paid).

330.01 NLD ISSN 0304-4068
HB135 CODEN: JMECDA

➤ **JOURNAL OF MATHEMATICAL ECONOMICS.** Text in English. 1974. 8/yr. EUR 118 in Europe to individuals; JPY 15,800 in Japan to individuals; USD 122 elsewhere to individuals; EUR 1,478 in Europe to institutions; JPY 196,300 in Japan to institutions; USD 1,653 elsewhere to institutions (effective 2006). adv. bk.rev. abstr.; illus. index. back issues avail.; reprints avail. **Document type:** *Academic/Scholarly.* **Description:** Provides a forum for work in economic theory that expresses economic ideas, using formal mathematical reasoning.
Related titles: Microform ed.: (from PQC); Online - full text ed.: (from EBSCO Publishing, Gale Group, IngentaConnect, ScienceDirect, Swets Information Services).
Indexed: ABIn, ASCA, BPIA, BusI, CCMJ, CIS, CMCI, CREJ, CurCont, ESPM, IBSS, JCQM, JEL, MathR, MathSciNet, RASB, RiskAb, SSCI, T&II, ZentMath.
—BLDSC (5012.377000), IDS, IE, Infotrieve, ingenta. **CCC.**
Published by: Elsevier BV, North-Holland (Subsidiary of: Elsevier Science & Technology), Sara Burgerhartstraat 25, Amsterdam, 1055 KV, Netherlands. TEL 31-20-485-3911, FAX 31-20-485-2457, nlinfo-f@elsevier.nl, http://www.elsevier.com/locate/jmateco, http://www.elsevier.nl. Eds. Bernard Cornet, F. Delbaen, J. Geanakoplos. **Subscr. to:** Elsevier BV, PO Box 211, Amsterdam 1000 AE, Netherlands. TEL 31-20-485-3757, FAX 31-20-485-3432, http://www.elsevier.nl.

➤ **JOURNAL OF MONETARY ECONOMICS.** see *BUSINESS AND ECONOMICS—Banking And Finance*

330.1 USA ISSN 0160-3477
HB1

➤ **JOURNAL OF POST KEYNESIAN ECONOMICS.** Key Title: J P K E. Journal of Post Keynesian Economics. Text in English. 1978. q. USD 98 domestic to individuals; USD 126 foreign to individuals; USD 319 domestic to institutions print & online eds.; USD 379 foreign to institutions print & online eds. (effective 2006). adv. illus. Index. back issues avail.; reprint service avail. from PSC. **Document type:** *Journal, Academic/Scholarly.*
Related titles: Online - full text ed.: ISSN 1557-7821. 2002 (Sep.) (from EBSCO Publishing, Florida Center for Library Automation, Gale Group, H.W. Wilson, Northern Light Technology, Inc., O C L C Online Computer Library Center, Inc., ProQuest Information & Learning, Swets Information Services).
Indexed: ABIn, ASCA, BPIA, BusI, CREJ, CurCont, FutSurv, IBR, IBSS, IBZ, JEL, ManagCont, RASB, SRRA, SSCI, SSI, T&II.
—BLDSC (5041.149000), CISTI, IDS, IE, Infotrieve, ingenta. **CCC.**
Published by: M.E. Sharpe, Inc., 80 Business Park Dr, Armonk, NY 10504. TEL 914-273-1800, 800-541-6563, FAX 914-273-2106, custserv@mesharpe.com, http://www.mesharpe.com/mall/results1.asp. Ed. Sidney Weintraub. adv.: page USD 300; 8 x 5. Circ: 1,700.

240 USA ISSN 1097-3923
HD87

➤ **JOURNAL OF PUBLIC ECONOMIC THEORY.** Text in English. 1999. 5/yr. USD 28 combined subscription in the Americas to individuals print & online eds.; EUR 47 combined subscription in Europe to individuals print & online eds.; GBP 30 combined subscription elsewhere to individuals print & online eds.; USD 575 combined subscription in the Americas to institutions print & online eds.; GBP 425 combined subscription elsewhere to institutions print & online eds. (effective 2006). adv. reprint service avail. from PSC. **Document type:** *Journal, Academic/Scholarly.* **Description:** Publishes theoretical work in all areas of public economics.
Related titles: Online - full text ed.: ISSN 1467-9779. USD 546 in the Americas to institutions; GBP 403 elsewhere to institutions (effective 2006) (from Blackwell Synergy, EBSCO Publishing, Gale Group, IngentaConnect, O C L C Online Computer Library Center, Inc., Swets Information Services).
Indexed: ABIn, JEL.
—BLDSC (5043.493000), IE, Infotrieve, ingenta. **CCC.**
Published by: Blackwell Publishing, Inc. (Subsidiary of: Blackwell Publishing Ltd.), Commerce Place, 350 Main St, Malden, MA 02148. TEL 781-388-8206, FAX 781-388-8232, subscrip@blackwellpub.com, http://www.blackwellpublishing.com/journals/JPET. Eds. John P Conley TEL 615-322-2920, Myrna Holtz Wooden.

330.01 NLD ISSN 0047-2727
CODEN: JPBEBK

➤ **JOURNAL OF PUBLIC ECONOMICS.** Text in English. 1972. 12/yr. EUR 179 in Europe to individuals; JPY 24,600 in Japan to individuals; USD 187 to individuals except Europe and Japan; EUR 1,998 in Europe to institutions; JPY 265,300 in Japan to institutions; USD 2,234 to institutions except Europe and Japan (effective 2006). adv. bk.rev. charts; stat.; illus. index. back issues avail.; reprints avail. **Document type:** *Academic/Scholarly.* **Description:** Covers public economics, with emphasis on the application of modern economic theory and methods of quantitative analysis.
Related titles: Microform ed.: (from PQC); Online - full text ed.: (from EBSCO Publishing, Gale Group, IngentaConnect, ScienceDirect, Swets Information Services).
Indexed: ABIn, APEL, ASCA, ASG, AgeL, BPIA, BusI, CREJ, CurCont, EAA, ExcerpMed, FamI, HRA, IBR, IBSS, IBZ, JEL, LRI, MEA&I, PAIS, PRA, RASB, SPAA, SSCI, SUSA, T&II, WBA.
—BLDSC (5043.495000), IDS, IE, Infotrieve, ingenta. **CCC.**
Published by: Elsevier BV, North-Holland (Subsidiary of: Elsevier Science & Technology), Sara Burgerhartstraat 25, Amsterdam, 1055 KV, Netherlands. TEL 31-20-485-3911, FAX 31-20-485-2457, econbase-m@elsevier.nl, nlinfo-f@elsevier.nl, http://www.elsevier.com/locate/jpube, http://www.elsevier.nl. Eds. J. Poterba, R. Boadway. **Subscr. to:** Elsevier BV, PO Box 211, Amsterdam 1000 AE, Netherlands. TEL 31-20-485-3757, FAX 31-20-485-3432, http://www.elsevier.nl.

330.1 USA ISSN 0922-680X
HD3616.U45 CODEN: JRECEC

➤ **JOURNAL OF REGULATORY ECONOMICS.** Text in English. 1989. bi-m. EUR 698, USD 698, GBP 438 combined subscription to institutions print & online eds. (effective 2005). illus. Index. reprint service avail. from PSC. **Document type:** *Journal, Academic/Scholarly.* **Description:** Publishes articles on the analysis of regulatory theories and institutions and on the practical aspects of regulation, including natural monopoly, deregulation, and new policy instruments.
Related titles: Microform ed.: (from PQC); Online - full text ed.: ISSN 1573-0468 (from Chadwyck-Healey Inc., EBSCO Publishing, Gale Group, IngentaConnect, Kluwer Online, O C L C Online Computer Library Center, Inc., ProQuest Information & Learning, Springer LINK, Swets Information Services).
Indexed: ABIn, ASCA, BibLing, CurCont, IBSS, JEL, PCI, RASB, RefZh, SSCI.
—BLDSC (5048.800000), IDS, IE, Infotrieve, ingenta. **CCC.**
Published by: Springer-Verlag New York, Inc. (Subsidiary of: Springer Science+Business Media), 233 Spring St, New York, NY 10013. TEL 212-460-1500, FAX 212-460-1575, service@springer-ny.com, http://springerlink.metapress.com/openurl.asp?genre=journal&issn=0922-680X, http://www.springer-ny.com. Ed. Michael A Crew. **Subscr. to:** Journal Fulfillment, PO Box 2485, Secaucus, NJ 07096-2485. TEL 201-348-4033, FAX 201-348-4505, journals@springer-ny.com.

153.83 330 USA ISSN 0895-5646
HB615 CODEN: JRUNEN

➤ **JOURNAL OF RISK AND UNCERTAINTY.** Text in English. 1988. bi-m. EUR 688, USD 705, GBP 435 combined subscription to institutions print & online eds. (effective 2005). adv. reprint service avail. from PQC,PSC. **Document type:** *Journal, Academic/Scholarly.* **Description:** Publishes original theoretical and empirical contributions dealing with the analysis of risk-bearing behavior and decision making under uncertainty.
Related titles: Microform ed.: (from PQC); Online - full text ed.: ISSN 1573-0476 (from EBSCO Publishing, Gale Group, IngentaConnect, Kluwer Online, O C L C Online Computer Library Center, Inc., Ovid Technologies, Inc., ProQuest Information & Learning, Springer LINK, Swets Information Services).
Indexed: ABIn, ASCA, BibLing, CurCont, ESPM, FamI, IBSS, JEL, ORMS, QC&AS, RefZh, RiskAb, SOPODA, SSCI, ST&MA, ZentMath, e-psyche.
—BLDSC (5052.101000), IDS, IE, Infotrieve, ingenta. **CCC.**
Published by: Springer-Verlag New York, Inc. (Subsidiary of: Springer Science+Business Media), 233 Spring St, New York, NY 10013. TEL 212-460-1500, FAX 212-460-1575, service@springer-ny.com, http://springerlink.metapress.com/openurl.asp?genre=journal&issn=0895-5646, http://www.springer-ny.com. Ed. W Kip Viscusi. **Subscr. to:** Journal Fulfillment, PO Box 2485, Secaucus, NJ 07096-2485. TEL 201-348-4033, FAX 201-348-4505, journals@springer-ny.com.

330 NLD ISSN 1053-5357
HB1 CODEN: JSECFK

➤ **JOURNAL OF SOCIO-ECONOMICS.** Text in English. 1972. 6/yr. EUR 95 in Europe to individuals; JPY 13,100 in Japan to individuals; USD 99 to individuals except Europe and Japan; EUR 483 in Europe to institutions; JPY 64,000 in Japan to institutions; USD 540 to institutions except Europe and Japan (effective 2006). adv. bk.rev. bibl.; charts; stat.; abstr. back issues avail. **Document type:** *Academic/Scholarly.* **Description:** Promotes interdisciplinary dialogue about economic processes, institutions and policies.
Formerly: Journal of Behavioral Economics (0090-5720)
Related titles: Microform ed.: (from PQC); Online - full text ed.: (from EBSCO Publishing, Florida Center for Library Automation, Gale Group, IngentaConnect, Northern Light Technology, Inc., ScienceDirect, Swets Information Services).
Indexed: ABIn, BPIA, BusI, CJA, ESPM, JEL, ManagCont, PRA, PSA, PsycInfo, PsycholAb, RiskAb, SOPODA, SSA, SociolAb, T&II, e-psyche.
—BLDSC (5064.926000), IE, Infotrieve, ingenta. **CCC.**
Published by: Elsevier BV, North-Holland (Subsidiary of: Elsevier Science & Technology), Sara Burgerhartstraat 25, Amsterdam, 1055 KV, Netherlands. TEL 31-20-485-3911, FAX 31-20-485-2457, nlinfo-f@elsevier.nl, http://www.elsevier.com/locate/soceco, http://www.elsevier.nl. Eds. J. Tomer, M. Altman. Circ: 360. **Subscr. to:** Elsevier BV, PO Box 211, Amsterdam 1000 AE, Netherlands. TEL 31-20-485-3757, FAX 31-20-485-3432, http://www.elsevier.nl.

➤ **JOURNAL OF THE ECONOMIC AND SOCIAL HISTORY OF THE ORIENT/JOURNAL D'HISTOIRE ECONOMIQUE ET SOCIALE DE L'ORIENT.** see *HISTORY—History Of The Near East*

330 GBR ISSN 1053-8372
HB75

➤ **JOURNAL OF THE HISTORY OF ECONOMIC THOUGHT.** Text in English. 1979. q. GBP 238, USD 395 combined subscription to institutions print & online eds. (effective 2006). adv. bk.rev. illus. index. reprint service avail. from PSC. **Document type:** *Journal, Academic/Scholarly.* **Description:** Encourages and makes available research in the fields of history of economic thought and the history of economic methodology.
Formerly (until 1990): History of Economics Society Bulletin (1042-7716)
Related titles: Online - full text ed.: ISSN 1469-9656. GBP 226, USD 375 to institutions (effective 2006) (from EBSCO Publishing, Gale Group, IngentaConnect, O C L C Online Computer Library Center, Inc., Swets Information Services).
Indexed: AmH&L, DIP, HistAb, IBR, IBSS, IBZ, JEL.
—BLDSC (5000.780000), IE, Infotrieve, ingenta. **CCC.**
Published by: (History of Economics Society), Routledge (Subsidiary of: Taylor & Francis Group), 4 Park Sq, Milton Park, Abingdon, Oxon OX14 4RN, United Kingdom. TEL 44-1235-828600, FAX 44-1235-829000, info@routledge.co.uk, http://www.tandf.co.uk/journals/titles/10427716.asp, http://www.routledge.co.uk. Ed. Steven G Medema. **Subscr. to:** Taylor & Francis Ltd, Journals Customer Service, Rankine Rd, Basingstoke, Hants RG24 8PR, United Kingdom. TEL 44-1256-813000, FAX 44-1256-330245, enquiry@tandf.co.uk.

➤ **JOURNAL OF TRANSPORT ECONOMICS AND POLICY.** see *TRANSPORTATION*

➤ **JUSTICIA SOCIAL.** see *BUSINESS AND ECONOMICS—Labor And Industrial Relations*

➤ **KEIZAI RIRON/WAKAYAMA ECONOMIC REVIEW.** see *BUSINESS AND ECONOMICS—Management*

330.1 JPN ISSN 0453-4786
HB75

KEIZAIGAKUSHI GAKKAI NENPO/SOCIETY FOR THE HISTORY OF SOCIAL AND ECONOMIC THOUGHT. ANNUAL BULLETIN. Text in Japanese. 1963. a. **Document type:** *Bulletin, Academic/Scholarly.*
Indexed: AmH&L, JEL.
—BLDSC (1031.675000), IE, ingenta.
Published by: Keizaigakushi Gakkai/Society for the History of Social and Economic Thought, 4-4-25 Shibuya, Shibuya-ku, Aoyama Gakuin University, Tokyo, 150-8366, Japan. TEL 81-3-3409-8111, FAX 81-3-5485-0782.

330.1 ESP ISSN 1132-6123

KOIUNTURAZ; boletin de coyuntura economica vasca. Text in Spanish, Basque. 1992. q. charts; stat. **Document type:** *Magazine.*
Published by: Eusko Jaurlaritzaren Argitalpen-Zerbitzu Nagusia/Servicio Central de Publicaciones del Gobierno Vasco, Donostia-San Sebastian, 1, Vitoria-gasteiz, Alava 01010, Spain. TEL 34-945-018561, FAX 34-945-018709, hac-sabd@ej-gv.es, http://www.ej-gv.net/publicaciones.

LABOUR ECONOMICS. see *BUSINESS AND ECONOMICS—Labor And Industrial Relations*

330.1 GBR

➤ **LANCASTER WORKING PAPERS IN POLITICAL ECONOMY. POLITICAL ECONOMY OF LOCAL GOVERNANCE SERIES.** Text in English. 1978. irreg., latest vol.47, 1994. **Document type:** *Monographic series, Academic/Scholarly.*

B

Published by: Lancaster University, Department of Sociology, Lancaster, Lancs LA1 4YL, United Kingdom. TEL 44-1524-594178, FAX 44-1524-594256, http://www.comp.lancs.ac.uk/sociology.

➤ **LARRY ABRAHAM'S INSIDER REPORT.** see *BUSINESS AND ECONOMICS—Investments*

➤ **LECTURAS DE ECONOMIA.** see *BUSINESS AND ECONOMICS—Abstracting, Bibliographies, Statistics*

➤ **LIBERTY (PORT TOWNSEND).** see *LITERARY AND POLITICAL REVIEWS*

➤ **LIGHTHOUSE.** see *POLITICAL SCIENCE*

330.1 CHN ISSN 1005-4286
HB97.5
LILUN JINGJIXUE/THEORETICAL ECONOMICS. Text in Chinese. m. CNY 132 (effective 2004). 112 p./no.; **Document type:** *Journal, Academic/Scholarly.* **Description:** Covers Chinese and Western economic theories.
Indexed: RASB.
Published by: Zhongguo Renmin Daxue, Shubao Zilio Zhongxin/Renmin University of China, Information Center for Social Server, Dongcheng-qu, 3, Zhangzizhong Lu, Beijing, 100007, China. TEL 86-10-64039458, FAX 86-10-64015080, kyes@163.net, http://www.confucius.cn.net/bkdetail.asp?fzt=F11. **Dist. in US by:** China Publications Service, PO Box 49614, Chicago, IL 60649. TEL 312-288-3291, FAX 312-288-8570; **Dist. by:** China International Book Trading Corp, 35 Chegongzhuang Xilu, Haidian District, PO Box 399, Beijing 100044, China. TEL 86-10-68412045, FAX 86-10-68412023, cibtc@mail.cibtc.com.cn, http://www.cibtc.com.cn.

330.1 SWE ISSN 1400-4860
LUND STUDIES IN ECONOMIC HISTORY. Text in English, Swedish. 1995. a. price varies. **Document type:** *Academic/Scholarly.*
Published by: Lunds Universitet, Department of Economic History/Lund University, Box 7083, Lund, 22007, Sweden.

330 658 SWE ISSN 0284-5075
LUND STUDIES IN ECONOMICS AND MANAGEMENT. Text in English, Swedish. 1989. irreg., latest vol.36, 1997. price varies. **Document type:** *Academic/Scholarly.*
—BLDSC (5304.978000).
Published by: Institute of Economic Research, Box 7080, Lund, 22007, Sweden.

330.1 GBR ISSN 1460-4906
MANCHESTER METROPOLITAN UNIVERSITY. DEPARTMENT OF ECONOMICS. DISCUSSION PAPERS. Text in English. irreg. **Document type:** *Monographic series, Academic/Scholarly.*
Former titles: Manchester Metropolitan University. Department of Economics and Economic History. Discussion Papers (1360-5933); (until 1995): Manchester Metropolitan University. Department of Economics and Economic History. Papers.
—BLDSC (3597.919000).
Published by: Manchester Metropolitan University, Department of Economics, Mabel Tylecote Bldg, Cavendish St, Manchester, Lancs M15 6BG, United Kingdom. TEL 44-161-247-3912, FAX 44-161-247-6302, j.tomkins@mmu.ac.uk. Ed. Judith Tomkins.

330 300 GBR ISSN 1463-6786
HB1
➤ **THE MANCHESTER SCHOOL.** Text in English. 1930. bi-m. GBP 57, EUR 86 combined subscription in Europe to individuals print & online eds.; USD 109 combined subscription in the Americas to individuals & Caribbean, print & online eds.; GBP 65 combined subscription elsewhere to individuals print & online eds.; GBP 299 combined subscription in Europe to institutions print & online eds.; USD 623 combined subscription in the Americas to institutions & Caribbean, print & online eds.; GBP 371 combined subscription elsewhere to institutions print & online eds. (effective 2006). adv. bk.rev. bibl.; charts; stat.; illus. index. Supplement avail.; reprint service avail. from PSC. **Document type:** *Journal, Academic/Scholarly.*
Formerly: Manchester School of Economic and Social Studies (0025-2034)
Related titles: Microform ed.; Online - full text ed.: ISSN 1467-9957. GBP 284 in Europe to institutions; GBP 591 in the Americas to institutions & Caribbean; GBP 352 elsewhere to institutions (effective 2006) (from Blackwell Synergy, EBSCO Publishing, Gale Group, IngentaConnect, O C L C Online Computer Library Center, Inc., Swets Information Services).
Indexed: ABIn, ASCA, AmH&L, BrHumI, BusI, CPM, CREJ, CurCont, DIP, ESPM, HistAb, IBR, IBSS, IBZ, JEL, KES, MEA&I, PAIS, PCI, RASB, RRTA, RiskAb, SSCI, SSI, WAE&RSA, WorkRelAb.
—BLDSC (5359.645000), CISTI, IDS, IE, Infotrieve, ingenta. **CCC.**
Published by: Blackwell Publishing Ltd., 9600 Garsington Rd, Oxford, OX4 2ZG, United Kingdom. TEL 44-1865-776868, FAX 44-1865-714591, customerservices@oxon.blackwellpublishing.com, http://www.blackwellpublishing.com/journals/MANC. Eds. Eyal Winter, Keith Blackburn, Martyn Andrews. Circ: 1,300.

➤ **MARKET INDICATORS AND FORECASTS.** see *BUSINESS AND ECONOMICS—Economic Situation And Conditions*

330.1 USA
MISES REVIEW. Text in English. 1995. q. USD 15.95 domestic; USD 25 foreign (effective 2000). bk.rev. **Document type:** *Academic/Scholarly.* **Description:** Surveys and reviews books of interest in free-market and Austrian economics.
Published by: Ludwig von Mises Institute, 518 W Magnolia Ave, Auburn, AL 36832. TEL 334-321-2100, FAX 334-321-2119, mail@mises.org, http://www.mises.org. Ed., R&P Jeffrey Tucker TEL 334-321-2108.

330.1 FRA ISSN 0077-0434
MONNAIE, PRIX, CONJONCTURE. Text in French. 1952. irreg., latest vol.11, 1973. price varies.
Published by: Editions de l' Ecole des Hautes Etudes en Sciences Sociales, 131 bd. Saint-Michel, Paris, 75005, France. TEL 33-1-40467080, FAX 33-1-44070889, editions@ehess.fr, http://www.ehess.fr/editions, http://www.ehess.fr/editions/publications.html. **Dist. by:** Centre Interinstitutionnel pour la Diffusion de Publications en Sciences Humaines, 131 bd. Saint-Michel, Paris 75005, France. TEL 33-1-43544715, FAX 33-1-43548073.

330.1 USA ISSN 0276-119X
N B E R REPORTER. (National Bureau of Economic Research) Text in English. 1968. q. USD 20; free to qualified personnel (effective 2005). back issues avail. **Document type:** *Newsletter, Trade.* **Description:** Reviews broad areas of economic research and activity.
Formerly (until 1977): National Bureau Report (0547-4701)
Related titles: Online - full text ed.: N B E R Reporter OnLine (from EBSCO Publishing, Florida Center for Library Automation, Gale Group).
Indexed: RASB.
Published by: National Bureau of Economic Research, 1050 Massachusetts Ave, 3rd Fl, Cambridge, MA 02138-5398. TEL 617-868-3900, FAX 617-349-3955, http://www.nber.org/reporter. Circ: 10,000.

N W POSTHUMUS REEKS. see *HISTORY—History Of Europe*

330 CHL ISSN 0252-2209
NACIONES UNIDAS. COMISION ECONOMICA PARA AMERICA LATINA Y EL CARIBE. BOLETIN DE PLANIFICACION. Text in Spanish. 3/w.
Indexed: PAIS.
Published by: United Nations Economic Commission for Latin America and the Caribbean, Av. Dag Hammarskjold 3477, Vitacura, Casilla 179-D, Santiago de Chile, Chile. TEL 56-2-471-2000, FAX 56-2-208-0252.

330.1 USA ISSN 1058-8450
HC10
NATIONAL BUREAU OF ECONOMIC RESEARCH. WORKING PAPER SERIES ON HISTORICAL FACTORS IN LONG RUN GROWTH. Text in English. 1989. irreg. price varies. **Document type:** *Monographic series.*
Published by: National Bureau of Economic Research, 1050 Massachusetts Ave, 3rd Fl, Cambridge, MA 02138-5398. TEL 617-868-3900, FAX 617-349-3955, http://www.nber.org.

THE NEW AMERICAN (APPLETON). see *POLITICAL SCIENCE*

NEW FEDERALIST. see *BUSINESS AND ECONOMICS—Economic Situation And Conditions*

330 GBR ISSN 1356-3467
HB1
➤ **NEW POLITICAL ECONOMY.** Text in English. 1996. q. GBP 340, USD 559 combined subscription to institutions print & online eds. (effective 2006). reprint service avail. from PSC. **Document type:** *Journal, Academic/Scholarly.* **Description:** Seeks to bridge past empirical and conceptual divides.
Related titles: Online - full text ed.: ISSN 1469-9923. GBP 323, USD 531 to institutions (effective 2006) (from EBSCO Publishing, Gale Group, IngentaConnect, Northern Light Technology, Inc., O C L C Online Computer Library Center, Inc., ProQuest Information & Learning, Swets Information Services).
Indexed: ABIn, APEL, AltPI, CurCont, GEOBASE, IBR, IBSS, IBZ, IPSA, IndIslam, JEL, LeftInd, PSA, SSCI, SociolAb.
—BLDSC (6085.740000), IE, Infotrieve, ingenta. **CCC.**
Published by: (Political Economy Research Centre), Routledge (Subsidiary of: Taylor & Francis Group), 4 Park Sq, Milton Park, Abingdon, Oxon OX14 4RN, United Kingdom. info@routledge.co.uk, http://www.tandf.co.uk/journals/titles/13563467.asp, http://www.routledge.co.uk. **Subscr. to:** Taylor & Francis Ltd, Journals Customer Service, Rankine Rd, Basingstoke, Hants RG24 8PR, United Kingdom. TEL 44-1256-813000, FAX 44-1256-330245.

327.111 NOR ISSN 0801-9568
H8
NORSK OEKONOMISK TIDSSKRIFT. Text in Norwegian; Summaries in English. 1887. 2/yr. NOK 175 to individuals; NOK 100 to students (effective 1999). adv. bk.rev. charts. index. back issues avail. **Document type:** *Academic/Scholarly.*
Supersedes in part (in 1987): Statsoekonomisk Tidsskrift (0039-0720)
Indexed: IBSS, PAIS, RASB.
Published by: Sosialoekonomenes Forening, Youngstorget, Postboks 8872, Oslo, 0181, Norway. TEL 47-22-41-32-90, FAX 47-22-41-32-93. Ed. Jon Vislie. Circ: 1,600.

330 ITA
HC10
NUOVA ECONOMIA E STORIA; rivista italiana di storia economica e sociale. Text in Italian; Summaries in English, French. 1954. q. EUR 25 domestic to individuals; EUR 45 domestic to libraries; EUR 55 foreign (effective 2003). adv. bk.rev. abstr.; bibl.; charts; illus.; stat. index.
Formerly (until 1994): Economia e Storia (0012-9798)
Indexed: AmH&L, HistAb, NumL, PCI.
Published by: I.P.E.M. - C.I.S.P.E., Via di Fortezza 1, Pisa, 56125, Italy. TEL 39-050-571181, FAX 39-050-571198. Circ: 600.

330.1 658 TUR ISSN 1010-9935
HD72
➤ **O D T U GELISME DERGISI/M E T U STUDIES IN DEVELOPMENT.** (Orta Dogu Teknik Universitesi) Text in English, Turkish. 1970. q. USD 20 (effective 2001). adv. bk.rev. abstr. index, cum.index. back issues avail. **Document type:** *Journal, Academic/Scholarly.* **Description:** Publishes research articles in the field of economics and administrative sciences.
Formerly (until 1980): Gelisme Dergisi - Orta Dogu Teknik Universitesi (1010-9927)
Related titles: Online - full content ed.
Indexed: CIS, IndIslam, JEL, MathR, RASB, RDA, WAE&RSA, ZentMath.
—BLDSC (5750.365000), IE, ingenta.
Published by: Orta Dogu Teknik Universitesi, Iktisadi ve Idari Bilimler Fakultesi/Middle East Technical University, Faculty of Economic and Administrative Sciences, Department of Economics, Balgat, Ankara, 06531, Turkey. TEL 90-312-2102006, FAX 90-312-2101244, metusd@metu.edu.tr, http://www.econ.metu.edu.tr/metusd/gelisme.htm, http://www.feas.metu.edu.tr. Eds. Cem Somel TEL 90-312-2103043, Fatih Tayfur. Adv. contact Cem Somel TEL 90-312-2103043. Circ: 1,500. **Subscr. to:** METU Bookstore, Middle East Technical University, Ankara O6531, Turkey.

330.1 USA ISSN 1546-2803
HB1
OECONOMICUS. Text in English. 1998. a.
Published by: University of Missouri at Kansas City, Dept. of Economics, 211 Haag Hall, 5100 Rockhill Rd., Kansas City, MO 64110. TEL 816-235-1314, FAX 816-235-2834, economics@umkc.edu, http://iml.umkc.edu/econ.

330 USA ISSN 0923-7992
HB1 CODEN: OEREED
➤ **OPEN ECONOMIES REVIEW.** Text in English. 1990. q. EUR 428, USD 438, GBP 268 combined subscription to institutions print & online eds. (effective 2005). adv. back issues avail.; reprint service avail. from PSC. **Document type:** *Journal, Academic/Scholarly.* **Description:** Publishes original theoretical and empirical papers dealing with international economic issues or national economic issues that have transnational relevance, such as trade flows, commercial policies, exchange rate movements, external debt, alternative monetary regimes and monetary union.
Related titles: Microform ed.: (from PQC); Online - full text ed.: ISSN 1573-708X (from EBSCO Publishing, Gale Group, IngentaConnect, Kluwer Online, O C L C Online Computer Library Center, Inc., ProQuest Information & Learning, Springer LINK, Swets Information Services).
Indexed: ABIn, ASCA, BLI, BibLing, CurCont, GEOBASE, IBSS, JEL, RASB, RefZh, SSCI, ZentMath.
—BLDSC (6265.953750), IDS, IE, Infotrieve, ingenta. **CCC.**
Published by: (Italian International Economic Center ITA), Springer-Verlag New York, Inc. (Subsidiary of: Springer Science+Business Media), 233 Spring St, New York, NY 10013. TEL 212-460-1500, FAX 212-460-1575, service@springer-ny.com, http://springerlink.metapress.com/openurl.asp?genre=journal&issn=0923-7992, http://www.springer-ny.com. Eds. George Tavlas, Michele Fratianni. **Subscr. to:** Journal Fulfillment, PO Box 2485, Secaucus, NJ 07096-2485. TEL 201-348-4033, FAX 201-348-4505, journals@springer-ny.com.

330.1 IND
P S E ECONOMIC ANALYST. Text in English. 1980. s-a. INR 200 domestic to individuals; USD 40 foreign to individuals; GBP 300 domestic to institutions; USD 50 foreign to institutions (effective 2003). **Document type:** *Academic/Scholarly.* **Description:** Devotes to both theoretical and empirical research in economics at macro and micro levels.
Published by: Guru Nanak Dev University Press, Press & Publications Department, Amritsar, Punjab 143 005, India. TEL 91-183-258802, FAX 91-183-258819, dcse.gndu@yahoo.com. Ed. Satish Verma. Circ: 250.

330.1 ITA
➤ **IL PENSIERO ECONOMICO MODERNO.** Text in Italian. 1982. q. EUR 34 domestic; EUR 55 foreign (effective 2003). adv. **Document type:** *Academic/Scholarly.* **Description:** Covers topics in modern economic thought.
Published by: I.P.E.M. - C.I.S.P.E., Via di Fortezza 1, Pisa, 56125, Italy. TEL 39-050-571181, FAX 39-050-571198.

➤ **POLITECHNIKA KRAKOWSKA. MONOGRAFIE. SERIA: NAUKI SPOLECZNE I EKONOMICZNE.** see *SOCIAL SCIENCES: COMPREHENSIVE WORKS*

330.1 IND ISSN 0971-2097
HC431
POLITICAL ECONOMY JOURNAL OF INDIA. Text and summaries in English. 1992. 2/yr. INR 80 domestic to individuals; INR 120 domestic to institutions; USD 20 foreign; INR 40 newsstand/cover domestic (effective 2000). adv. bk.rev. bibl. **Document type:** *Academic/Scholarly.* **Description:** Covers Indian economic developments and their relations with the world economy.
Indexed: IBSS, PAA&I.
Published by: Centre for Indian Development Studies, 206 Sector 9-C, P O Box 130, Chandigarh, 160017, India. TEL 91-172-741362, FAX 91-172-747525. Ed., R&P, Adv. contact V S Mahajan. Circ: 800.

330.1 BRA ISSN 0104-1495
HC186
PONTIFICIA UNIVERSIDADE CATOLICA DE CAMPINAS. FACULDADE DE CIENCIAS ECONOMICAS CONTABEIS E ADMINISTRATIVAS. CADERNOS. Key Title: Cadernos da F C E C A. Variant title: Cadernos da F A C E C A. Summaries in Portuguese. 1992. 2/yr., latest vol.6, no.2, 1997. USD 30 (effective 1999). bibl. **Document type:** *Magazine, Academic/Scholarly.*
Published by: Pontificia Universidade Catolica de Campinas, Faculdade de Ciencias Economicas Contabeis e Administrativas, Campus 1, CP 317, Campinas, SP 13020-904, Brazil. TEL 55-19-7567099. Ed. Jose Geraldo Souza Carreira. Pub. Jose Homero Adabo. Circ: 1,500.

330.1 FRA ISSN 0079-4074
PORTS - ROUTES - TRAFICS. Text in French. 1951. irreg., latest vol.29, 1988. price varies.
Published by: Editions de l' Ecole des Hautes Etudes en Sciences Sociales, 131 bd. Saint-Michel, Paris, 75005, France. TEL 33-1-40467080, FAX 33-1-44070889, editions@ehess.fr, http://www.ehess.fr/editions, http://www.ehess.fr/editions/publications.html. **Dist. by:** Centre Interinstitutionnel pour la Diffusion de Publications en Sciences Humaines, 131 bd. Saint-Michel, Paris 75005, France. TEL 33-1-43544715, FAX 33-1-43548073.

320.5322 GBR ISSN 1463-1377
HC701 CODEN: PCECF8
➤ **POST-COMMUNIST ECONOMIES.** Text in English. 1989. q. GBP 479, USD 904 combined subscription to institutions print & online eds. (effective 2006). adv. bk.rev. illus. Index. reprint service avail. from PSC. **Document type:** *Journal, Academic/Scholarly.* **Description:** International journal concerned with the economies of communist countries, primarily, but not exclusively, the former U.S.S.R. and Eastern Europe.
Former titles (until 1998): Communist Economies and Economic Transformation (1351-4393); Communist Economies (0954-0113)
Related titles: Microfiche ed.; Online - full text ed.: ISSN 1465-3958. GBP 455, USD 859 to institutions (effective 2006) (from EBSCO Publishing, Gale Group, IngentaConnect, O C L C Online Computer Library Center, Inc., ProQuest Information & Learning, Swets Information Services).
Indexed: ABIn, APEL, ASCA, BAS, CurCont, ESPM, GEOBASE, IBR, IBSS, IBZ, JEL, LID&ISL, PRA, RASB, RiskAb, SSCI.
—BLDSC (6561.968850), IDS, IE, Infotrieve, ingenta. **CCC.**
Published by: (Centre for Research into Communist Economies), Routledge (Subsidiary of: Taylor & Francis Group), 4 Park Sq, Milton Park, Abingdon, Oxon OX14 4RN, United Kingdom. TEL 44-1235-828600, FAX 44-1235-829000, info@routledge.co.uk, http://www.tandf.co.uk/journals/titles/14631377.asp, http://www.routledge.co.uk. Ed. Roger Clarke. **Subscr. to:** Taylor & Francis Ltd, Journals Customer Service, Rankine Rd, Basingstoke, Hants RG24 8PR, United Kingdom. TEL 44-1256-813000, FAX 44-1256-330245, enquiry@tandf.co.uk.

330.1 USA ISSN 0885-6699
PRAGMATIST; a utilitarian approach. Text in English. 1983. bi-m. USD 12; USD 15 foreign. adv. bk.rev. charts; stat. index. back issues avail.; reprints avail. **Document type:** *Newsletter.* **Description:** Libertarian publication proposing the abolition of all forms of taxation.
Address: PO Box 392, Forest Grove, PA 18922. FAX 215-348-8006. Ed. Jorge E Amador. Pub. Hans G Schroeder. Circ: 1,050 (paid).

PRILOZI/CONTRIBUTIONS. see *ARCHAEOLOGY*

330.1 GBR ISSN 1744-5396
HN1
PUBLIC POLICY RESEARCH. Text in English. 1994. q. EUR 60 combined subscription in Europe to individuals print & online eds.; USD 67 combined subscription in the Americas to individuals & Caribbean, print & online eds.; GBP 40 combined subscription elsewhere to individuals print & online eds.; USD 452 combined subscription in the Americas to institutions & Caribbean, print & online eds.; GBP 269 combined subscription elsewhere to institutions print & online eds. (effective 2006). adv. bk.rev. back issues avail.; reprint service avail. from PSC. **Document type:** *Journal, Academic/Scholarly.* **Description:** Publishes articles which apply the latest economic theories and research to the policy issues of the day.
Formerly (until 2004): New Economy (1070-3535)
Related titles: Online - full text ed.: ISSN 1468-0041. USD 430 in the Americas to institutions & Caribbean; GBP 256 elsewhere to institutions (effective 2006) (from Blackwell Synergy, EBSCO Publishing, Gale Group, IngentaConnect, O C L C Online Computer Library Center, Inc., Swets Information Services).
Indexed: ABIn, GEOBASE, IBSS, JEL, PSA, SSA, SociolAb.
—BLDSC (6968.382750), IE, Infotrieve, ingenta. **CCC.**
Published by: (Institute for Public Policy Research), Blackwell Publishing Ltd., 9600 Garsington Rd, Oxford, OX4 2ZG, United Kingdom. TEL 44-1865-776868, FAX 44-1865-714591, customerservices@oxon.blackwellpublishing.com, http://www.blackwellpublishing.com/journals/NEWE. Ed. Peter Robinson TEL 44-1714-706117. R&P Catherine John. Adv. contact Nik Screen.

330.1 USA ISSN 1098-3708
HB98
➤ **QUARTERLY JOURNAL OF AUSTRIAN ECONOMICS.** Text in English. 1987. q. USD 100 to individuals; USD 110 combined subscription to individuals print & online eds.; USD 280 to institutions; USD 308 combined subscription to institutions print & online eds. (effective 2005). adv. bk.rev. back issues avail.; reprint service avail. from PSC. **Document type:** *Academic/Scholarly.* **Description:** Promotes the development and extension of Austrian economics, and encourages the analysis of contemporary issues in the mainstream of economics from an Austrian perspective.
Related titles: Online - full content ed.: USD 100 to individuals; USD 280 to institutions (effective 2005); Online - full text ed.: (from EBSCO Publishing, O C L C Online Computer Library Center, Inc., Swets Information Services).
Indexed: JEL.
—CCC.
Published by: (Ludwig von Mises Institute), Transaction Publishers, 390 Campus Dr, Somerset, NJ 07830. TEL 888-999-6778, FAX 732-748-9801, qjae@mises.org, trans@transactionpub.com, http://www.mises.org/store/product1.aspx?Product_ID=130, http://www.transactionpub.com. Ed. Joseph Salerno. Pub. Mary Curtis. R&P Marlena Davidian TEL 732-445-2280 ext 100. Adv. contact Alicja Garbie. B&W page USD 400; trim 5.25 x 8.5. Circ: 800. **Subscr. to:** Transaction Distribution Center. orders@transactionpub.com.

330.1 USA ISSN 0033-5533
HB1 CODEN: QJECAT
➤ **QUARTERLY JOURNAL OF ECONOMICS.** Text in English. 1886. q. USD 50 combined subscription in US & Canada to individuals print & online eds.; USD 74 combined subscription elsewhere to individuals print & online eds.; USD 310 combined subscription in US & Canada to institutions print & online eds.; USD 334 combined subscription elsewhere to institutions print & online eds. (effective 2006). charts; illus. index. back issues avail.; reprint service avail. from PQC,PSC. **Document type:** *Journal, Academic/Scholarly.* **Description:** Covers all aspects of the economics field, including theoretical and empirical macroeconomics. For professional and academic economists and students.
Related titles: Microform ed.: (from PQC); Online - full text ed.: ISSN 1531-4650. USD 45 to individuals; USD 279 to institutions (effective 2006) (from EBSCO Publishing, Florida Center for Library Automation, Gale Group, H.W. Wilson, IngentaConnect, JSTOR (Web-based Journal Archive), O C L C Online Computer Library Center, Inc., Swets Information Services).
Indexed: ABIn, ASCA, Acal, AgeL, AmH&L, BAS, BPI, BPIA, BusI, CIS, CJA, CPM, CREJ, CurCont, DIP, ESPM, Emerald, ExcerpMed, FamI, HRA, HistAb, IBR, IBSS, IBZ, ILD, IPARL, JEL, KES, MathR, ORMS, PAA&I, PCI, QC&AS, RRTA, RiskAb, SPAA, SSCI, SSI, SUSA, SWR&A, T&II, WAE&RSA, WBA, WorkRelAb, ZentMath.
—BLDSC (7188.400000), IDS, IE, Infotrieve, ingenta. **CCC.**
Published by: (Harvard University, Department of Economics), M I T Press, 55 Hayward St, Cambridge, MA 02142-1493. TEL 617-253-5646, FAX 617-258-6779, que@arrow.harvard.edu, journals-info@mit.edu, http://mitpress.mit.edu/QJE. Eds. Edward Glaeser, Robert J Barro. Adv. contact Michael Darden. Circ: 5,100 (paid).

➤ **REALIZM - NOWY USTROJ SPOLECZNO-POLITYCZNY:** miesiecznik IV Rzeczypospolitej. see *POLITICAL SCIENCE*

330.1 NLD ISSN 0924-199X
➤ **RECENT ECONOMIC THOUGHT.** Text in English. 1982. irreg., latest vol.76, 2003. price varies. back issues avail. **Document type:** *Monographic series, Academic/Scholarly.* **Description:** Publishes scholarly articles addressing theoretical and practical issues in contemporary economic research, including policy matters, and concerns from related disciplines.
Published by: Springer-Verlag Dordrecht (Subsidiary of: Springer Science+Business Media), Van Godewijckstraat 30, Dordrecht, 3311 GX, Netherlands. TEL 31-78-6576050, FAX 31-78-6576474, http://www.springeronline.com. Eds. James K Galbraith, William Alexander Darity Jr.

330 USA ISSN 0363-3268
HC1
RESEARCH IN ECONOMIC HISTORY. Text in English. 1976. irreg., latest vol.22, 2004. price varies. bibl.; charts; stat. back issues avail. **Document type:** *Monographic series, Academic/Scholarly.*
Related titles: Online - full text ed.: (from ScienceDirect).
Indexed: AmH&L, HistAb, PCI, SSCI.
—BLDSC (7738.920000), IE, ingenta. **CCC.**
Published by: J A I Press Inc. (Subsidiary of: Elsevier Science & Technology), 360 Park Ave S, New York, NY 10010-1710. TEL 212-989-5800, FAX 212-633-3990, usinfo-f@elsevier.com, http://www.elsevier.com/wps/find/bookdescription.cws_home/BS_REH/description#description. Eds. Alex J Field, G Clark, W Sundstrom.

330.1 USA ISSN 0193-2306
HB1
RESEARCH IN EXPERIMENTAL ECONOMICS. Text in English. 1979. irreg., latest vol.10, 2005. price varies. Supplement avail.; back issues avail. **Document type:** *Monographic series, Academic/Scholarly.* **Description:** Presents research utilizing laboratory experimental methods in economics.
Related titles: Online - full text ed.: (from ScienceDirect).
—BLDSC (7739.970000). **CCC.**
Published by: J A I Press Inc. (Subsidiary of: Elsevier Science & Technology), 360 Park Ave S, New York, NY 10010-1710. TEL 212-989-5800, FAX 212-633-3990, usinfo-f@elsevier.com, http://www.elsevier.com/wps/find/bookdescription.cws_home/BS_REE/description#description. Ed. R M Isaac.

330.9 USA ISSN 0161-7230
HC10
RESEARCH IN POLITICAL ECONOMY. Text in English. 1978. irreg., latest vol.22, 2005. price varies. back issues avail.; reprints avail. **Document type:** *Monographic series, Academic/Scholarly.* **Description:** Deals primarily with economic and political issues and the unity between them.
Related titles: Online - full text ed.: (from ScienceDirect).
Indexed: IBSS.
—BLDSC (7755.077300), IE, ingenta. **CCC.**
Published by: J A I Press Inc. (Subsidiary of: Elsevier Science & Technology), 360 Park Ave S, New York, NY 10010-1710. TEL 212-989-5800, FAX 212-633-3990, usinfo-f@elsevier.com, http://www.elsevier.com/wps/find/bookseriesdescription.cws_home/BS_RPE/description. Ed. Paul Zarembka.

330.1 USA ISSN 0743-4154
HB75
➤ **RESEARCH IN THE HISTORY OF ECONOMIC THOUGHT AND METHODOLOGY.** Text in English. 1983. a., latest vol.23, 2005. price varies. back issues avail. **Document type:** *Monographic series, Academic/Scholarly.*
Related titles: Online - full text ed.: (from ScienceDirect); ♦ Supplement(s): Research in the History of Economic Thought and Methodology. Archival Supplement. ISSN 1051-6751.
Indexed: AmH&L, HistAb.
—BLDSC (7741.308000), IE, ingenta. **CCC.**
Published by: J A I Press Inc. (Subsidiary of: Elsevier Science & Technology), 360 Park Ave S, New York, NY 10010-1710. TEL 212-989-5800, FAX 212-633-3990, usinfo-f@elsevier.com, http://www.elsevier.com/wps/find/bookdescription.cws_home/BS_RHE/description#description. Eds. J E Biddle, Warren J Samuels.

330.1 USA ISSN 1051-6751
HB75
RESEARCH IN THE HISTORY OF ECONOMIC THOUGHT AND METHODOLOGY. ARCHIVAL SUPPLEMENT. Text in English. 1990. irreg., latest vol.9, 1999. price varies. **Document type:** *Monographic series, Academic/Scholarly.*
Related titles: ♦ Supplement to: Research in the History of Economic Thought and Methodology. ISSN 0743-4154.
—BLDSC (7741.308500).
Published by: J A I Press Inc. (Subsidiary of: Elsevier Science & Technology), 360 Park Ave S, New York, NY 10010-1710. TEL 212-989-5800, FAX 212-633-3990, usinfo-f@elsevier.com, http://www.elsevier.com. Ed. Warren J Samuels.

330.07 SWE ISSN 0283-8974
HC371
RESEARCH INSTITUTE OF INDUSTRIAL ECONOMICS. YEARBOOK. Text in English. 1969. a., latest 2002. free. bk.rev. 50 p./no.; **Document type:** *Yearbook, Academic/Scholarly.*

B

▼ new title ➤ refereed ∗ unverified ♦ full entry avail.

Former titles (until 1983): Industrial Institute for Economic and Social Research. Research Program (0280-5626); (until 1979): Industrial Institute for Economic and Social Research. Current Research Projects (0348-8578)
Related titles: Online - full text ed.
Published by: Research Institute of Industrial Economics/Industriens Utredningsinstitut, Box 5501, Stockholm, 11485, Sweden. TEL 46-8-6654500, FAX 46-8-6654599, info@iui.se, http://www.iui.se. Ed. Lars Persson. Circ: 600.

330.1 900 USA ISSN 0147-9032
D1
➤ **REVIEW (BINGHAMTON).** Text in English. 1977. q. USD 28 domestic to individuals; USD 36 foreign to individuals; USD 98 domestic to institutions; USD 106 foreign to institutions (effective 2004). bk.rev. illus. index. back issues avail. **Document type:** *Journal, Academic/Scholarly.*
Indexed: AltPI, AmH&L, BibInd, CurCont, DIP, GEOBASE, HistAb, IBR, IBSS, IBZ, IPSA, LeftInd, PCI, PSA, RASB, SOPODA, SSA, SociolAb.
—BLDSC (7785.894000), IE, Infotrieve, ingenta.
Published by: Fernand Braudel Center for the Study of Economies, Historical Systems, and Civilizations, Binghamton University, P.O. Box 6000, Binghamton, NY 13902-6000. TEL 607-777-4924, FAX 607-777-4315, review@binghamton.edu, http://fbc.binghamton.edu/rev.htm. Ed. Immanuel Wallerstein. R&P Donna DeVoist. Circ: 1,100.

330.1 USA ISSN 0889-3047
HB98 CODEN: RAECFG
➤ **THE REVIEW OF AUSTRIAN ECONOMICS.** Text in English. 1986. 4/yr. EUR 380, USD 380, GBP 237 combined subscription to institutions print & online eds. (effective 2005). bk.rev. back issues avail. **Document type:** *Academic/Scholarly.* **Description:** Covers the promotion of the development and extension of Austrian economics and the analysis of contemporary issues in the mainstream of economics from an Australian perspective.
Related titles: Microform ed.: (from PQC); Online - full text ed.: ISSN 1573-7128 (from EBSCO Publishing, Gale Group, IngentaConnect, Kluwer Online, O C L C Online Computer Library Center, Inc., ProQuest Information & Learning, Springer LINK, Swets Information Services).
Indexed: ABIn, BibLing, DIP, IBR, IBSS, IBZ, JEL, PSA, RefZh, SOPODA.
—BLDSC (7788.170000), IE, Infotrieve, ingenta. **CCC.**
Published by: (Ludwig von Mises Institute), Springer-Verlag New York, Inc. (Subsidiary of: Springer Science+Business Media), 233 Spring St, New York, NY 10013. TEL 212-460-1500, FAX 212-460-1575, service@springer-ny.com, http://springerlink.metapress.com/openurl.asp?genre=journal&issn=0889-3047, http://www.springer-ny.com. Ed. Peter J Boettke. Circ: 2,000. **Subscr. to:** Journal Fulfillment, PO Box 2485, Secaucus, NJ 07096-2485. TEL 201-348-4033, FAX 201-348-4505, journals@springer-ny.com.

330.1 DEU ISSN 1434-4742
HB1 CODEN: EDESE9
➤ **REVIEW OF ECONOMIC DESIGN.** Text in English. 1994. q. EUR 247 combined subscription to institutions print & online eds. (effective 2005). adv. bk.rev. abstr.; bibl.; stat. index. back issues avail. **Document type:** *Journal, Academic/Scholarly.* **Description:** Provides an international forum for research in economic design, including game theory, and applications to the design and assembly of relevant mathematical techniques and comparative assessments of the performance of economic systems.
Formerly (until 1997): Economic Design (0928-5040)
Related titles: Microform ed.: (from PQC); Online - full text ed.: ISSN 1434-4750 (from EBSCO Publishing, ProQuest Information & Learning, Springer LINK, Swets Information Services).
Indexed: ABIn, IBZ, JEL.
—BLDSC (7790.191000), IE, Infotrieve, ingenta. **CCC.**
Published by: Springer-Verlag (Subsidiary of: Springer Science+Business Media), Tiergartenstr 17, Heidelberg, 69121, Germany. TEL 49-6221-3450, FAX 49-6221-345229, http://link.springer.de/link/service/journals/10058/index.htm. Ed. Murat R Sertel. Adv. contact Stephan Kroeck TEL 49-30-827875739. **Subscr. in the Americas to:** Springer-Verlag New York, Inc., Journal Fulfillment, PO Box 2485, Secaucus, NJ 07096-2485. TEL 800-777-4643, 201-348-4033, FAX 201-348-4505, journals@springer-ny.com, http://www.springer-ny.com; **Subscr. to:** Springer GmbH Auslieferungsgesellschaft, Haberstr 7, Heidelberg 69126, Germany. TEL 49-6221-345-0, FAX 49-6221-345-4229, subscriptions@springer.de.

330.1 GBR ISSN 1479-5663
▼ ➤ **THE REVIEW OF ECONOMIC THEORY.** Text in English. forthcoming 2006. q. GBP 450, EUR 700 combined subscription in Europe to corporations; USD 700 combined subscription in North America to corporations; GBP 225, EUR 350 combined subscription in Europe to libraries; USD 350 combined subscription in North America to libraries; free elsewhere to libraries; GBP 130, EUR 200 combined subscription in Europe to non-profit organizations; USD 200 combined subscription in North America to non-profit organizations (effective 2004); free elsewhere to non-profit organizations (effective 2004 - 2005). **Document type:** *Journal, Academic/Scholarly.* **Description:** Contains original papers on economic theories.
Related titles: Online - full content ed.: ISSN 1479-8727. forthcoming 2006.
Published by: Electronic Society for Social Scientists, University of St Andrews, Department of Economics, St. Andrews, Fife KY16 9AL, United Kingdom. TEL 44-1334-462434, RET@elsss.org, elsss@elsss.org, http://www.elsss.org/?current=Review+of+Economic+Theory. Pub., R&P, Adv. contact Dr. Manfredi La Manna TEL 44-1334-462434.

333 USA ISSN 1084-7480
REVIEW OF HETERODOX ECONOMICS. Text in English. 1995. q. **Description:** Contains articles on economics of interest to Marxists, feminists, institutionalists, post-Keynesians, and Sraffians.
Published by: California State University, San Bernadino, Department of Economics, 5500 University Parkway, San Bernadino, CA 92407. TEL 909-880-5511, FAX 909-880-7025, enilsson@csusb.edu, http://economics.csusb.edu/orgs/RHE/rhe.html. Ed. Eric Nilsson.

330.1 658 USA ISSN 0889-938X
HD2326 CODEN: RIOREU
➤ **REVIEW OF INDUSTRIAL ORGANIZATION.** Text in English. 1984. 8/yr. EUR 648, USD 665, GBP 408 combined subscription to institutions print & online eds. (effective 2005). adv. bk.rev. illus. Index. back issues avail.; reprint service avail. from PSC. **Document type:** *Journal, Academic/Scholarly.* **Description:** Publishes research papers on all aspects of industrial organization, with particular emphasis on ideas which can be verified by econometric evidence, case studies, and analysis of real conditions.
Related titles: Microform ed.: (from PQC); Online - full text ed.: ISSN 1573-7160 (from EBSCO Publishing, Gale Group, IngentaConnect, Kluwer Online, O C L C Online Computer Library Center, Inc., ProQuest Information & Learning, Springer LINK, Swets Information Services).
Indexed: ABIn, ASCA, BibLing, CurCont, GEOBASE, IBR, IBSS, IBZ, JEL, MaizeAb, PHN&I, RefZh, SIA, SOPODA, SSA, SSCI, WAE&RSA.
—BLDSC (7790.787000), IDS, IE, Infotrieve, ingenta. **CCC.**
Published by: (Industrial Organization Society NLD), Springer-Verlag New York, Inc. (Subsidiary of: Springer Science+Business Media), 233 Spring St, New York, NY 10013. TEL 212-460-1500, FAX 212-460-1575, service@springer-ny.com, http://springerlink.metapress.com/openurl.asp?genre=journal&issn=0889-938X, http://www.springer-ny.com. Ed. Lawrence J White. **Subscr. to:** Journal Fulfillment, PO Box 2485, Secaucus, NJ 07096-2485. TEL 201-348-4033, FAX 201-348-4505, journals@springer-ny.com.

➤ **REVIEW OF QUANTITATIVE FINANCE AND ACCOUNTING.** see *BUSINESS AND ECONOMICS—Accounting*

330 USA ISSN 0486-6134
HC101
REVIEW OF RADICAL POLITICAL ECONOMICS. Text in English. 1969. q. USD 343, GBP 222 to institutions; USD 357, GBP 231 combined subscription to institutions prin & online eds. (effective 2006). adv. bk.rev. abstr. cum.index 1969-1979. back issues avail.; reprint service avail. from PQC. **Document type:** *Journal, Academic/Scholarly.* **Description:** Presents articles on radical political economic theory and applied analysis from a wide source of theoretical traditions, including Marxian, institutional, feminist, and post-Keynesian.
Related titles: Microform ed.: (from PQC); Online - full text ed.: ISSN 1552-8502. USD 340, GBP 219 to institutions (effective 2006) (from C S A, EBSCO Publishing, Gale Group, IngentaConnect, O C L C Online Computer Library Center, Inc., Sage Publications, Inc., ScienceDirect, Swets Information Services).
Indexed: ABIn, ABS&EES, Acal, Agr, AltPI, AmH&L, DIP, ESPM, HistAb, IBR, IBSS, IBZ, IPSA, JEL, LeftInd, MEA, MEA&I, PAA&I, PAIS, PSA, Perlslam, RASB, RiskAb, SSCI, SWA.
—BLDSC (7794.185000), IE, Infotrieve, ingenta. **CCC.**
Published by: Sage Publications, Inc., 2455 Teller Rd, Thousand Oaks, CA 91320. TEL 805-499-0721, 800-818-7243, FAX 805-499-0871, 800-583-2665, info@sagepub.com, http://www.sagepub.com/journal.aspx?pid=9187. adv.: page USD 210; trim 7.5 x 4.25. Circ: 1,800. **Subscr. to:** Sage Publications Ltd., 1 Oliver's Yard, 55 City Rd, London EC1 1SP, United Kingdom. TEL 44-20-73740645, FAX 44-20-73748741, subscription@sagepub.co.uk.

REVISTA DE HISTORIA ECONOMICA. see *BUSINESS AND ECONOMICS—Economic Situation And Conditions*

REVISTA DE HISTORIA ECONOMICA E SOCIAL. see *HISTORY*

REVISTA DE HISTORIA ECONOMICA E SOCIAL. CADERNOS. see *HISTORY*

REVISTA INTERDISCIPLINARIA DE ESTUDIOS AGRARIOS. see *AGRICULTURE*

330.1 BEL ISSN 1376-0971
➤ **REVUE DE PHILOSOPHIE ECONOMIQUE.** Text in French. 1999. 2/yr. EUR 58 (effective 2003). bk.rev. abstr. back issues avail. **Document type:** *Monographic series, Academic/Scholarly.*
Indexed: JEL.
Published by: De Boeck Universite, Fond Jean-Paques 4, Louvain-la-Neuve, 1348, Belgium. TEL 32-10-482511, FAX 32-10-482519, info@universite.deboeck.com, http://universite.deboeck.com. Ed. Alain Leroux.

330 FRA ISSN 0338-0599
HC244.A1
➤ **REVUE D'ETUDES COMPARATIVES EST-OUEST**; economies et techniques de planification - droit et sciences sociales. Text in French; Summaries in English. 1970. q. EUR 65 domestic to individuals; EUR 75 foreign to individuals; EUR 99 domestic to institutions; EUR 115 foreign to institutions (effective 2005). bk.rev. abstr.; bibl.; illus. index. **Document type:** *Journal, Academic/Scholarly.* **Description:** Set up to fill the gaps in the information on socialist countries.
Formerly (until 1975): Revue de l'Est (0035-1415)
Indexed: ABCPolSci, ABS&EES, ASCA, AmH&L, ArtHuCI, BAS, CurCont, DIP, HistAb, IBR, IBSS, IBZ, ILD, IPSA, JEL, KES, PAIS, PSA, RASB, RefZh, SSCI, SociolAb, WAE&RSA.
—BLDSC (7900.158000), IE, Infotrieve, ingenta.
Published by: Armand Colin Editeur (Subsidiary of: Masson), 21 Rue du Montparnasse, Paris, 75283 Cedex 06, France. TEL 33-1-44395447, FAX 33-1-44394343, infos@armand-colin.com, http://www.armand-colin.com. Circ: 800.

330.1 FRA ISSN 0769-0479
HC271
REVUE FRANCAISE D'ECONOMIE. Text in French. 1986. q.
Indexed: JEL, PAIS, RASB.
—IE.
Address: 5 rue de Constantinople, Paris, 75008, France. TEL 33-1-42941488. Ed. Gilles Etrillard. Pub. Cecile Thiebault.

330.1 ITA ISSN 0393-3415
H7
RIVISTA DI STORIA ECONOMICA. Text in Italian. 1936. 3/yr. EUR 48 domestic to individuals; EUR 84 foreign to individuals; EUR 63 domestic to institutions; EUR 114 foreign to institutions (effective 2004). bk.rev. back issues avail.; reprint service avail. from SCH. **Document type:** *Academic/Scholarly.*
Indexed: AmH&L, HistAb, IBSS, JEL.
—IE, Infotrieve.
Published by: Societa Editrice Il Mulino, Strada Maggiore 37, Bologna, 40125, Italy. TEL 39-051-256011, FAX 39-051-256034, riviste@mulino.it, http://www.mulino.it. Circ: 1,200.

330.1 NLD ISSN 0924-6002
➤ **ROCHESTER STUDIES IN ECONOMICS AND POLICY ISSUES.** Text in English. 1979. irreg., latest vol.7, 1990. price varies. **Document type:** *Monographic series, Academic/Scholarly.*
Published by: Springer-Verlag Dordrecht (Subsidiary of: Springer Science+Business Media), Van Godewijckstraat 30, Dordrecht, 3311 GX, Netherlands. TEL 31-78-6576050, FAX 31-78-6576474, http://www.springeronline.com.

330.1 GBR ISSN 1359-7892
ROUTLEDGE EXPLORATIONS IN ECONOMIC HISTORY. Text in English. 1995. irreg., latest vol.23, 2003, Feb. price varies. **Document type:** *Monographic series, Academic/Scholarly.* **Description:** Provides a platform for books which break new ground in the understanding of the development of the modern world economy.
—BLDSC (8026.506000).
Published by: Routledge (Subsidiary of: Taylor & Francis Group), 4 Park Square, Milton Park, Abingdon, Oxon OX14 4RN, United Kingdom. TEL 44-1235-828600, FAX 44-1235-829000, info@routledge.co.uk, http://www.reference.routledge.com/research/economics/eeh.html, http://www.tandf.co.uk.

330.1 GBR
ROUTLEDGE INTERNATIONAL STUDIES IN BUSINESS HISTORY. Text in English. 1996. irreg., latest vol.10, 2001, Oct. price varies. **Document type:** *Monographic series, Academic/Scholarly.*
—BLDSC (8026.508500).
Published by: Routledge (Subsidiary of: Taylor & Francis Group), 4 Park Square, Milton Park, Abingdon, Oxon OX14 4RN, United Kingdom. TEL 44-1235-828600, FAX 44-1235-829000, info@routledge.co.uk, http://www.tandf.co.uk, http://www.routledge.co.uk. Eds. C W Nobes, T E Cooke.

330.1 GBR ISSN 1359-7957
ROUTLEDGE STUDIES IN THE EUROPEAN ECONOMY. Text in English. 1995. irreg., latest vol.11, 2000, Oct. price varies. back issues avail. **Document type:** *Monographic series, Academic/Scholarly.*
—BLDSC (8026.519420).

Published by: Routledge (Subsidiary of: Taylor & Francis Group), 4 Park Square, Milton Park, Abingdon, Oxon OX14 4RN, United Kingdom. TEL 44-1235-828600, FAX 44-1235-829000, info@routledge.co.uk, http://www.tandf.co.uk, http://www.routledge.co.uk. Eds. Noel Whiteside, Robert Salais.

330.1 GBR ISSN 1359-7906
ROUTLEDGE STUDIES IN THE HISTORY OF ECONOMICS. Text in English. 1995. irreg., latest vol.59, 2002, Dec. price varies. back issues avail. **Document type:** *Monographic series, Academic/Scholarly.* **Description:** Provides an arena for current debate in the study of the history of economics.
—BLDSC (8026.519500).
Published by: Routledge (Subsidiary of: Taylor & Francis Group), 4 Park Square, Milton Park, Abingdon, Oxon OX14 4RN, United Kingdom. TEL 44-1235-828600, FAX 44-1235-829000, info@routledge.co.uk, http://www.tandf.co.uk, http://www.routledge.co.uk.

338 339.5 DNK ISSN 0358-5522
SCANDINAVIAN ECONOMIC HISTORY REVIEW. Text in English. 1953. 3/yr., latest vol.53, no.1, 2005. DKK 300 to individuals; DKK 400 to institutions (effective 2006). adv. bk.rev. bibl.; charts; illus.; stat. cum.index: vols.1-20. back issues avail. **Document type:** *Journal, Academic/Scholarly.*
Indexed: AmH&L, GEOBASE, HistAb, IBR, IBSS, IBZ, JEL, NumL, PAIS, PCI, RASB, SWA.
—BLDSC (8087.475000), IE, Infotrieve, ingenta.
Published by: Syddansk Universitetsforlag/University Press of Southern Denmark, Campusvej 55, Odense M, 5230, Denmark. TEL 45-66-157999, FAX 45-66-158126, press@forlag.sdu.dk, http://www.valt.helsinki.fi/yhis/sehr/sehr.html, http://www.universitypress.dk. Ed. Jaakko Autio. Circ: 700.

330.1 339 300 ITA
➤ **SCIENZE REGIONALI**; Italian journal of regional science. Text in Italian, English. 2002. 3/yr. EUR 42 domestic; EUR 67.50 foreign (effective 2003). **Document type:** *Journal, Academic/Scholarly.*
Published by: Franco Angeli Edizioni, Viale Monza 106, Milan, 20127, Italy. TEL 39-02-2837141, FAX 39-02-26144793, redazioni@francoangeli.it, http://www.francoangeli.it.

330 DEU ISSN 0036-973X
HC10
SCRIPTA MERCATURAE; Zeitschrift fuer Wirtschafts- und Sozialgeschichte. Text in German. 1967. s-a. EUR 24; EUR 13 newsstand/cover (effective 2005). charts; illus. **Document type:** *Journal, Academic/Scholarly.*
Indexed: AmH&L, DIP, HistAb, IBR, IBZ.
—IE, Infotrieve. **CCC.**
Published by: Scripta Mercaturae Verlag, Am Roten Berg 5-9, St. Katharinen, 55595, Germany. TEL 49-6706-8800, FAX 49-6706-8859, info@scripta-mercaturae.de, http://www.scripta-mercaturae.de. Eds. F R Henning, H Winkel.

330.9 GBR ISSN 1359-7507
HC59.69
SMALL STATES; economic review and basic statistics. Text in English. a. GBP 12.99. stat.
Formerly (until 1995): Basic Statistical Data on Selected Countries
—BLDSC (8310.158000).
Published by: (Information and Public Affairs Division), Commonwealth Secretariat, Marlborough House, Pall Mall, London, SW1Y 5HX, United Kingdom. TEL 44-2078-393411, FAX 44-2079-300827, vale@valeltd.co.uk, http://www.thecommonwealth.org. **Subscr. to:** Vale Packaging Ltd., 420 Vale Rd, Tonbridge, Kent TN9 1TY, United Kingdom. TEL 44-1732-359387, FAX 44-1732-779620.

330.1 658 SWE ISSN 1402-5353
SMEDJAN (ONLINE EDITION). Text in Swedish. 1986. w.
Former titles (until 1997): Smedjan (Print edition) (1102-7304); (until 1991): Marknadsekonomisk Tidskrift (0283-7595)
Media: Online - full content.
Published by: Timbro, Grev Turegatan 19, PO Box 5234, Stockholm, 10245, Sweden. TEL 46-8-58789800, FAX 46-8-58789850, red@smedjan.com, http://www.smedjan.com, http://www.timbro.se. Ed. Carl Rudbeck TEL 46-8-78789841.

330.1 NLD ISSN 0924-6061
➤ **SOCIAL DIMENSIONS OF ECONOMICS.** Text in English. 1981. irreg., latest vol.3, 1981. price varies. **Document type:** *Monographic series, Academic/Scholarly.*
Published by: Springer-Verlag Dordrecht (Subsidiary of: Springer Science+Business Media), Van Godewijckstraat 30, Dordrecht, 3311 GX, Netherlands. TEL 31-78-6576050, FAX 31-78-6576474, http://www.springeronline.com.

330.1 GBR ISSN 1366-2546
SOCIAL SCIENCE WORKING PAPER. Text in English. irreg., latest vol.19, 1996. **Document type:** *Academic/Scholarly.*
—BLDSC (8318.182345).
Published by: Napier University, Department of Economics, Sighthill Ct, Edinburgh, Midlothian EH11 4BN, United Kingdom. FAX 44-131-447-3475. Ed. R W McQuaid.

330 JPN ISSN 0038-0113
HC51
SOCIO-ECONOMIC HISTORY/SHAKAI KEIZAI SHIGAKU. Text in Japanese. 1931. bi-m. JPY 1,390. adv. bk.rev.
Indexed: AmH&L, HistAb.
Published by: Socio-Economic History Society, c/o Economic Department, Sophia University, Chiyodaku, Tokyo, 102, Japan. TEL 03-3238-3090. Ed. Yasuo Okada. Circ: 1,600.

330.1 BGR ISSN 0861-8518
HB9
SOFIISKI UNIVERSITET SV. KLIMENT OHRIDSKI. KATEDRA OBSHA IKONOMICHESKA TEORIYA. GODISNIK. Text in Bulgarian; Summaries in English, Russian. 1978. irreg. price varies. reprint service avail. from IRC.
Formerly (until 1993): Sofiiski Universitet. Katedra po Politicheska Ikonomiya. Godisnik (0204-9627)
Indexed: BSLEcon, IBSS, RASB.
Published by: (Sofiiski Universitet Sv. Kliment Ohridski, Katedra Obsha Ikonomicheska Teoriya), Universitetsko Izdatelstvo Sv. Kliment Okhridski/Publishing House of the Sofia University St. Kliment Ohridski, Akad G Bonchev 6, Sofia, 1113, Bulgaria.

SOOCHOW JOURNAL OF ECONOMICS AND BUSINESS. see *BUSINESS AND ECONOMICS*

SOUNDVIEW EXECUTIVE BOOK SUMMARIES. see *BUSINESS AND ECONOMICS—Management*

320.1 ZAF ISSN 1011-3436
➤ **SOUTH AFRICAN JOURNAL OF ECONOMIC HISTORY.** Text in English. 1982. s-a. ZAR 50 domestic; ZAR 100 foreign (effective 2003). bk.rev. abstr.; charts. 150 p./no.; back issues avail. **Document type:** *Journal, Academic/Scholarly.*
Formerly (until 1986): Perspectives in Economic History (1012-036X)
Related titles: Online - full text ed.
Indexed: AmH&L, HistAb, IBSS, ISAP.
—BLDSC (8338.858000).
Published by: Economic History Society of Southern Africa, University of Witwatersrand, School of Economic and Business Sciences, Private Bag X3, Wits, 2050, South Africa. TEL 27-11-7178088, FAX 27-11-7178061, vivian@sebs.wits.ac.za, inggsej@unisa.ac.za, http://home.intekom.com/joni/ehsoc.htm. Ed., R&P Stuart Jones. Circ: 250.

330.1 AUT
SOZIAL- UND WIRTSCHAFTSHISTORISCHE STUDIEN. Text in German. 1972. irreg. price varies. **Document type:** *Academic/Scholarly.*
Indexed: PAIS.
Published by: Verlag fuer Geschichte und Politik, Neulinggasse 26, Vienna, W 1030, Austria. TEL 43-1-7126258-0, FAX 43-1-712625819.

STATO E MERCATO. see *POLITICAL SCIENCE*

330.1 NLD ISSN 0954-349X
HB135 CODEN: SCEDFA
➤ **STRUCTURAL CHANGE AND ECONOMIC DYNAMICS.** Text in Dutch. 1989. 4/yr. EUR 52 in Europe to individuals; JPY 7,000 in Japan to individuals; USD 54 to individuals except Europe and Japan; EUR 422 in Europe to institutions; JPY 56,000 in Japan to institutions; USD 474 to institutions except Europe and Japan (effective 2006). adv. bk.rev. abstr. back issues avail.; reprints avail. **Document type:** *Academic/Scholarly.* **Description:** Presents studies on the theoretical, applied and methodological aspects of structural change in economic systems.
Related titles: Microform ed.: (from PQC); Online - full text ed.: (from EBSCO Publishing, Gale Group, IngentaConnect, ScienceDirect, Swets Information Services).
Indexed: GEOBASE, Inspec, JEL, PerIslam, RefZh.
—BLDSC (8476.350000), AskIEEE, IE, Infotrieve, ingenta. **CCC.**
Published by: Elsevier BV, North-Holland (Subsidiary of: Elsevier Science & Technology), Sara Burgerhartstraat 25, Amsterdam, 1055 KV, Netherlands. TEL 31-20-485-3911, FAX 31-20-485-2457, nlinfo-f@elsevier.nl, http://www.elsevier.com/locate/sced, http://www.elsevier.nl/homepage/about/us/regional_sites.htt, http://www.elsevier.nl. **Subscr. to:** Elsevier BV, PO Box 211, Amsterdam 1000 AE, Netherlands. TEL 31-20-485-3757, FAX 31-20-485-3432.

330.1 POL ISSN 0081-6485
HB9
STUDIA HISTORIAE OECONOMICAE. Text in English, French, German. 1966. irreg., latest vol.22, 1997. price varies. **Document type:** *Monographic series, Academic/Scholarly.* **Description:** Contains papers and articles in the field of economic sciences written by A. Mickiewicz University economists, and other Polish specialists.
Indexed: AmH&L, HistAb, RASB.
Published by: (Uniwersytet im. Adama Mickiewicza w Poznaniu/Adam Mickiewicz University), Wydawnictwo Naukowe Uniwersytetu im. Adama Mickiewicza/Adam Mickiewicz University Press, Nowowiejskiego 55, Poznan, 61-734, Poland. TEL 48-61-527380, FAX 48-61-527701. Ed. Jerzy Topolski. Pub. Maria Jankowska. R&P Malgorzata Bis. Circ: 600.

330.1 SWE ISSN 0586-884X
STUDIA OECONOMIAE NEGOTIORUM. Text in Multiple languages. 1966. irreg., latest vol.49, 2002. price varies. back issues avail. **Document type:** *Monographic series, Academic/Scholarly.*
Related titles: ♦ Series of: Acta Universitatis Upsaliensis. ISSN 0346-5462.
—BLDSC (0586.600000), IE, ingenta.
Published by: (Uppsala Universitet), Uppsala Universitet, Acta Universitatis Upsaliensis/University Publications from Uppsala, PO Box 256, Uppsala, 75105, Sweden. TEL 46-18-4713922, http://www.ub.uu.se/upu/auu. Ed. Bengt Landgren. **Dist. by:** Almqvist & Wiksell International.

STUDIEN ZUR RECHTS-, WIRTSCHAFTS- UND KULTURGESCHICHTE. see *LAW*

330.1 BEL
STUDIES IN BELGIAN ECONOMIC HISTORY. Text in English. 1992. irreg., latest vol.5, 2000. price varies. back issues avail. **Document type:** *Monographic series.*
Published by: Koninklijke Vlaamse Academie van Belgie voor Wetenschappen en Kunsten/The Royal Flemish Academy of Belgium for Science and the Arts, Hertogsstraat 1, Brussels, 1000, Belgium. TEL 32-2-5502323, FAX 32-2-5502325, info@kvab.be, http://www.kvab.be. **Dist. by:** Brepols Publishers.

B

330 USA ISSN 0081-7643
STUDIES IN BUSINESS CYCLES. Text in English. 1927. irreg., latest vol.30, 1997. price varies. **Document type:** *Monographic series.*
Published by: (National Bureau of Economic Research), University of Chicago, 5801 S Ellis Ave, Chicago, IL 60637. sales@press.uchicago.edu, http://www.press.uchicago.edu.

330.1 NLD ISSN 0927-5460
➤ **STUDIES IN COMPARATIVE ECONOMIC POLICIES.** Text in English. 1991. irreg., latest vol.3, 1993. price varies. **Document type:** *Monographic series, Academic/Scholarly.* **Description:** Compares the economic policies of various countries or political systems and offers an in-depth analysis.
—BLDSC (8490.235000).
Published by: Elsevier BV (Subsidiary of: Elsevier Science & Technology), Radarweg 29, Amsterdam, 1043 NX, Netherlands. TEL 31-20-4853911, FAX 31-20-4852457, nlinfo-f@elsevier.nl, http://www.elsevier.com/inca/tree/?key=B1SCEP, http://www.elsevier.nl.

330.1 USA
STUDIES IN CONTEMPORARY ECONOMICS. Text in English. 1982. irreg., latest vol.6, 2004. price varies. **Document type:** *Monographic series, Academic/Scholarly.*
Published by: Springer-Verlag New York, Inc. (Subsidiary of: Springer Science+Business Media), 233 Spring St, New York, NY 10013. TEL 212-460-1500, 800-777-4643, FAX 212-473-6272, http://www.springer-ny.com.

330 GBR
STUDIES IN ECONOMIC HISTORY AND POLICY; the United States in the 20th Century. Text in English. irreg. price varies. **Document type:** *Monographic series.*
Formerly: Cambridge Studies in Economic History
Published by: Cambridge University Press, The Edinburgh Bldg, Shaftesbury Rd, Cambridge, CB2 2RU, United Kingdom. TEL 44-1223-312393, FAX 44-1223-315052, information@cambridge.org, http://www.cup.cam.ac.uk/. R&P Linda Nicol TEL 44-1223-325757.

330.1 USA
STUDIES IN HEALTH AND HUMAN VALUES. Text in English. 1989. irreg. price varies. **Document type:** *Monographic series.*
Published by: Praeger Publishers (Subsidiary of: Greenwood Publishing Group Inc.), 88 Post Rd W, Box 5007, Westport, CT 06881-5007. TEL 203-226-3571, FAX 203-222-1502.

330.1 NLD ISSN 0924-4646
➤ **STUDIES IN INDUSTRIAL ORGANIZATION.** Text in English. 1981. irreg., latest vol.25, 2005. price varies. back issues avail. **Document type:** *Monographic series, Academic/Scholarly.*
—BLDSC (8490.731000), ingenta.
Published by: Springer-Verlag Dordrecht (Subsidiary of: Springer Science+Business Media), Van Godewijckstraat 30, Dordrecht, 3311 GX, Netherlands. TEL 31-78-6576050, FAX 31-78-6576474, http://www.springeronline.com. Eds. Dennis C Mueller, Keith Cowling.

➤ **STUDIES IN NONLINEAR DYNAMICS AND ECONOMETRICS (ONLINE).** see *MATHEMATICS*

330.1 NLD ISSN 0924-4689
➤ **STUDIES IN OPERATIONAL REGIONAL SCIENCE.** Text in English. 1986. irreg., latest vol.10, 1992. price varies. back issues avail. **Document type:** *Monographic series, Academic/Scholarly.*
Published by: Springer-Verlag Dordrecht (Subsidiary of: Springer Science+Business Media), Van Godewijckstraat 30, Dordrecht, 3311 GX, Netherlands. TEL 31-78-6576050, FAX 31-78-6576474, http://www.springeronline.com.

➤ **STUDIES IN POLITICAL ECONOMY**; a socialist review. see *POLITICAL SCIENCE*

➤ **STUDIES IN PRODUCTIVITY ANALYSIS.** see *BUSINESS AND ECONOMICS—Management*

330.1 NLD ISSN 0924-4700
➤ **STUDIES IN PUBLIC CHOICE.** Text in English. 1978. irreg., latest vol.11, 1997. price varies. **Document type:** *Monographic series, Academic/Scholarly.*
Published by: Springer-Verlag Dordrecht (Subsidiary of: Springer Science+Business Media), Van Godewijckstraat 30, Dordrecht, 3311 GX, Netherlands. TEL 31-78-6576050, FAX 31-78-6576474, http://www.springeronline.com.

330.1 NLD ISSN 0926-972X
➤ **STUDIES IN RISK AND UNCERTAINTY.** Text in English. 1990. irreg., latest vol.15, 2004. price varies. back issues avail. **Document type:** *Monographic series, Academic/Scholarly.*
—BLDSC (8491.444300), IE, ingenta. **CCC.**
Published by: Springer-Verlag Dordrecht (Subsidiary of: Springer Science+Business Media), Van Godewijckstraat 30, Dordrecht, 3311 GX, Netherlands. TEL 31-78-6576050, FAX 31-78-6576474, http://www.springeronline.com.

330 BEL
STUDIES IN SOCIAL AND ECONOMIC HISTORY. Text mainly in English. 1988. irreg., latest vol.31, 1996. price varies. back issues avail. **Document type:** *Monographic series, Academic/Scholarly.* **Description:** Publishes scholarly research in all areas of social and economic history.
Published by: Leuven University Press, Blijde Inkomststraat 5, Leuven, 3000, Belgium. TEL 32-16-325345, FAX 32-16-325352, university.press@upers.kuleuven.ac.be, http://www.kuleuven.ac.be/upers.

SUMA. see *BUSINESS AND ECONOMICS—Economic Situation And Conditions*

330.1 DEU
TASHKENT LECTURE NOTES. Text in German. 1996. irreg., latest vol.6. **Document type:** *Monographic series.*
Published by: I F O Institut fuer Wirtschaftsforschung, Poschingerstr 5, Munich, 81679, Germany. TEL 49-89-9224-0, FAX 49-89-985369, ifo@ifo.de, http://www.ifo.de.

338.501 NLD ISSN 0924-6193
➤ **TECHNOLOGY, RISK AND SOCIETY**; an international series in risk analysis. Text in English. 1986. irreg., latest vol.13, 2000. price varies. back issues avail. **Document type:** *Monographic series, Academic/Scholarly.*
—BLDSC (8761.010000), ingenta.
Published by: Springer-Verlag Dordrecht (Subsidiary of: Springer Science+Business Media), Van Godewijckstraat 30, Dordrecht, 3311 GX, Netherlands. TEL 31-78-6576050, FAX 31-78-6576474, http://www.springeronline.com. Eds. Jeryl Mumpower, Ortwin Renn.

330 FRA ISSN 0987-710X
TERTIAIRE. Text in French. 1956. 5/yr. adv. mkt.
Former titles: Techniques Economiques (0040-1331); Enseignement Economique et Commercial
Published by: Centre National de Documentation Pedagogique, 29 rue de l'Ulm, Paris, Cedex 5 75230, France. TEL 33-1-46349000, FAX 33-1-46345544. Circ: 3,750. **Subscr. to:** CNDP - Abonnement, B.P. 750, Sainte Genevieve Cedex 60732, France. FAX 33-3-44033013.

▼ **TIJDSCHRIFT VOOR SOCIALE EN ECONOMISCHE GESCHIEDENIS.** see *SOCIOLOGY*

330.1 658 NLD ISSN 1566-3213
HBI.AI
TINBERGEN MAGAZINE. Text in English. 1989. s-a. adv. **Document type:** *Bulletin, Academic/Scholarly.* **Description:** Publishes original theoretical and applied research in progress, survey articles, reports of Institute workshops and reviews on topics covering the entire field of general and business economics.
Former titles (until 2000): Tinbergen Institute PhD Research Bulletin (1383-2042); (until 1994): Tinbergen Institute Research Bulletin (0924-056X)
Published by: Tinbergen Institute, Burg. Oudlaan 50, Rotterdam, 3062 PA, Netherlands. TEL 31-10-4088900, FAX 31-10-4089031, http://www.tinbergen.nl.

330.1 USA ISSN 1538-0653
TOPICS IN ECONOMIC ANALYSIS & POLICY. Text in English. 2001. a. Included with subscription to The B E Journals in Economic Analysis and Policy.. **Document type:** *Journal, Academic/Scholarly.*
Media: Online - full content. **Related titles:** Online - full text ed.: (from O C L C Online Computer Library Center, Inc., ProQuest Information & Learning); ♦ Series of: The B E Journals in Economic Analysis & Policy. ISSN 1555-0494.
Indexed: ABIn, IBSS, JEL, PAIS.
Published by: Berkeley Electronic Press, 2809 Telegraph Ave., Ste 202, Berkeley, CA 94705. FAX 510-665-1201, info@bepress.com, http://www.bepress.com/bejeap/topics/. Eds. Aaron S Edlin, Bruce D Myer, Don Fullerton, Hermalin E Benjamin, Kyle Bagwell.

330.1 USA ISSN 1534-598X
HB1
TOPICS IN THEORETICAL ECONOMICS. Text in English. 2001. irreg. Included with subscription to The B E Journals in Theoretical Economics. **Document type:** *Journal, Academic/Scholarly.*
Media: Online - full content. **Related titles:** Online - full text ed.: (from O C L C Online Computer Library Center, Inc., ProQuest Information & Learning); ♦ Series of: The B E Journals in Theoretical Economics. ISSN 1555-0478.
Indexed: ABIn, IBSS, JEL, MathR, MathSciNet.
Published by: Berkeley Electronic Press, 2809 Telegraph Ave., Ste 202, Berkeley, CA 94705. FAX 510-665-1201, info@bepress.com, http://www.bepress.com/bejte/topics/. Eds. Chris Shannon, Dilip Abreu, Ilya Segal, Patrick Bolton.

330.9 CHE ISSN 1020-5799
HA1107
TRENDS IN EUROPE AND NORTH AMERICA. Variant title: Economic Commission for Europe. Statistical Yearbook. Text in English. a. **Document type:** *Bulletin, Government.* **Description:** Covers trends in economic social life for 55 member states.
Published by: United Nations, Economic Commission for Europe (ECE), Palais des Nations, Geneva 10, 1211, Switzerland. TEL 41-22-9174444, FAX 41-22-9170505, info.ece@unece.org, http://www.unece.org.

330.1 338 ITA ISSN 0394-9605
UNIFICAZIONE & CERTIFICAZIONE. Short title: U & C. Text in Italian. 1955. m. free to members. adv. **Document type:** *Newsletter, Trade.* **Description:** Deals with normative matters, certification and standardization of industrial products, includes issues on the European unification.
Formerly (until 1986): L' Unificazione (0393-1234)
—CISTI.
Published by: Ente Nazionale Italiano di Unificazione, Via Battistotti Sassi 11b, Milan, 20133, Italy. TEL 39-02-70024, FAX 39-02-70106149, http://www.uni.com. adv.: B&W page ITL 1,850,000, color page ITL 2,960,000; trim 260 x 185. Circ: 9,266.

330.1 ITA
UNIVERSITA DEGLI STUDI DI MESSINA. FACOLTA DI ECONOMIA. ANNALI. Text in Multiple languages. 1963. irreg.
Formerly: Universita degli Studi di Messina. Facolta di Economia e Commercio. Annali (0543-5579)
—BLDSC (1006.074000).
Published by: Universita degli Studi di Messina, Facolta di Economia e Commercio, Via dei Verdi, Messina, 98100, Italy. TEL 39-090-6764632.

UNIVERSITATEA POLITEHNICA DIN TIMISOARA. BULETINUL STIINTIFIC. SERIA MANAGEMENT INGINERIE, ECONOMICA, INGINERIA, TRANSPORTURILOR. see *ENGINEERING*

378.10711 CHE
UNIVERSITE DE GENEVE. DEPARTEMENT D'HISTOIRE ECONOMIQUE. BULLETIN. Text in French. 1970. a. CHF 15. **Document type:** *Bulletin.*
Published by: Universite de Geneve, Departement d'Histoire Economique, Geneva 4, 1211, Switzerland. TEL 41-22-7058192. Circ: 350.

330.1 CMR
UNIVERSITE DE YAOUNDE. FACULTE DE DROIT ET DES SCIENCES ECONOMIQUES. ECONOMIE GENERALE. Text in French. irreg.
Published by: Universite de Yaounde, BP 337, Yaounde, Cameroon.

330.1 GBR
UNIVERSITY OF BIRMINGHAM. DEPARTMENT OF ECONOMICS. DISCUSSION PAPERS. Text in English. 1991. irreg. GBP 2 per issue. **Document type:** *Monographic series, Academic/Scholarly.*
—BLDSC (3553.800000), ingenta.
Published by: University of Birmingham, Department of Economics, University Of Birmingham, Edgbaston, Birmingham, Worcs B15 2TT, United Kingdom. FAX 0121-414-7377.

UNIVERSITY OF CALIFORNIA AT BERKELEY. INTERNATIONAL AND AREA STUDIES. RESEARCH SERIES. see *POLITICAL SCIENCE—International Relations*

330.1 ISL ISSN 1670-0090
UNIVERSITY OF ICELAND. INSTITUTE OF ECONOMIC STUDIES. WORKING PAPER SERIES. Text in English. 1987. irreg. price varies. back issues avail. **Document type:** *Monographic series, Academic/Scholarly.*
Formerly (until 1996): Iceland Economic Papers (1011-8888)
Published by: University of Iceland, Institute of Economic Studies., Aragata 14, University of Iceland, Reykjavik, 101, Iceland. TEL 354-525-4535, FAX 354-525-4096, ioes@hi.is, http://www.ioes.hi.is/rammi32.html. Ed. Tryggvi Thor Herbertson.

UNIVERSITY OF NEW ENGLAND. SCHOOL OF ECONOMIC STUDIES, ECONOMETRICS DISCIPLINE. WORKING PAPERS IN ECONOMETRICS AND APPLIED STATISTICS. see *STATISTICS*

330.1 FIN ISSN 0358-870X
HB9
UNIVERSITY OF VAASA. PROCEEDINGS. DISCUSSION PAPERS. Text in Finnish. 1979. irreg., latest vol.234, 1998. adv. **Document type:** *Academic/Scholarly.*
Formerly (until 1980): Vaasa School of Economics. Proceedings. Discussion Papers (0357-3486)
Indexed: BEL&L.
Published by: Vaasan Yliopisto, Library/University of Vaasa, PL 331, Vaasa, 65101, Finland. TEL 358-6-3248151, FAX 358-6-3248200. R&P Antero Niemikorpi. Adv. contact Tarja Salo.

330.1 330.9 SVK ISSN 0139-5521
UNIVERZITA KOMENSKEHO. USTAV MARXIZMU-LENINIZMU. ZBORNIK: POLITICKA EKONOMIA. Text in Slovak; Summaries in German, Russian. 1972. a. per issue exchange basis.
Published by: Univerzita Komenskeho, Ustav Marxizmu-Leninizmu, c/o Study and Information Center, Safarikovo nam 6, Bratislava, 81806, Slovakia. Ed. Jan Kukel. Circ: 400.

UNIVERZITET U ZAGREBU. PRAVNI FAKULTET. ZBORNIK. see *LAW*

330.1 DEU ISSN 0566-2710
DIE UNTERNEHMUNG IM MARKT. Text in German. 1955. irreg., latest vol.17, 1970. price varies. **Document type:** *Monographic series, Academic/Scholarly.*
Published by: Duncker und Humblot GmbH, Carl-Heinrich-Becker-Weg 9, Berlin, 12165, Germany. TEL 49-30-7900060, FAX 49-30-79000631, info@duncker-humblot.de, http://www.duncker-humblot.de.

330.1 SWE ISSN 0346-6493
UPPSALA STUDIES IN ECONOMIC HISTORY. Text in Swedish. 1974. irreg., latest vol.62, 2002. price varies. back issues avail. **Document type:** *Academic/Scholarly.*
Formerly: Ekonomisk-Historiska Studier
Related titles: ♦ Series of: Acta Universitatis Upsaliensis. ISSN 0346-5462.
—KNAW.
Published by: (Uppsala Universitet), Uppsala Universitet, Acta Universitatis Upsaliensis/University Publications from Uppsala, PO Box 256, Uppsala, 75105, Sweden. TEL 46-18-4713922, http://www.ub.uu.se/upu/auu. Ed. Bengt Landgren. **Dist. by:** Almqvist & Wiksell International.

V R FORECASTER; Mark Leibovit's annual forecast model. see *BUSINESS AND ECONOMICS—Investments*

V S W G - VIERTELJAHRSCHRIFT FUER SOZIAL- UND WIRTSCHAFTSGESCHICHTE. see *SOCIAL SCIENCES: COMPREHENSIVE WORKS*

330.1 FIN ISSN 1455-4321
VAASAN YLIOPISTO. JULKAISUJA. OPETUSJULKAISUJA/ UNIVERSITY OF VAASA. PROCEEDINGS. TEACHING AID SERIES. Text in Finnish. 1972. irreg., latest vol.50, 1994. adv. **Document type:** *Academic/Scholarly.*
Former titles (until 1994): Vaasan Yliopisto. Julkaisuja. Opetusmonisteita (0788-6659); (until 1990): Vaasan Korkeakoulu. Julkaisuja. Opetusmonisteita (0358-9110); (until 1980): Vaasan Kauppakorkeakoulu. Julkaisuja. Opetusmonisteita (0355-2624)
Indexed: BEL&L.
Published by: Vaasan Yliopisto, Library/University of Vaasa, PL 331, Vaasa, 65101, Finland. TEL 358-6-3248151, FAX 358-6-3248200. Ed., R&P Antero Niemikorpi. Adv. contact Tarja Salo.

330.1 FIN ISSN 0788-6667
VAASAN YLIOPISTO. JULKAISUJA. TUTKIMUKSIA/ UNIVERSITY OF VAASA. PROCEEDINGS. RESEARCH PAPERS. Text in Finnish. 1970. irreg., latest vol.220, 1998. price varies. adv. **Document type:** *Academic/Scholarly.*
Former titles (until 1990): Vaasan Korkeakoulu. Julkaisuja. Tutkimuksia (0358-9080); (until 1980): Vaasan Kauppakorkeakoulu. Julkaisuja. Tutkimuksia (0355-2632)
Indexed: BEL&L.
—BLDSC (9076.172840).
Published by: Vaasan Yliopisto, Library/University of Vaasa, PL 331, Vaasa, 65101, Finland. TEL 358-6-3248151, FAX 358-6-248200. R&P Antero Niemikorpi. Adv. contact Tarja Salo.

330 FIN ISSN 1238-7118
VAASAN YLIOPISTON JULKAISUJA. SELVITYKSIA JA RAPORTTEJA/PROCEEDINGS OF THE UNIVERSITY OF VAASA. REPORTS. Text in Multiple languages. 1995. irreg. price varies. **Document type:** *Proceedings, Academic/Scholarly.*
Published by: Vaasan Yliopisto, Library/University of Vaasa, PL 331, Vaasa, 65101, Finland. TEL 358-6-324-82-33, FAX 358-6-3248200, emm@uwasa.fi. Ed. Antero Niemikorpi.

VIERTELJAHRSCHRIFT FUER SOZIAL- UND WIRTSCHAFTSGESCHICHTE. BEIHEFTE. see *SOCIAL SCIENCES: COMPREHENSIVE WORKS*

330.1 NLD ISSN 0927-0132
VRIJE UNIVERSITEIT. FACULTEIT DER ECONOMISCHE WETENSCHAPPEN EN ECONOMETRIE. RESEARCH MEMORANDUM. Text in English. irreg., latest vol.42, 1988. free. **Document type:** *Academic/Scholarly.*
Related titles: Dutch ed.
Published by: Vrije Universiteit, Faculteit der Economische Wetenschappen en Econometrie, De Boelelaan 1105, Amsterdam, 1081 HV, Netherlands. FAX 20-6462645.

330.107 DEU ISSN 0174-6170
WIRTSCHAFT UND ERZIEHUNG. Text in German. 1949. m. **Document type:** *Trade.*
Indexed: DIP, IBR, IBZ.
—IE, Infotrieve. **CCC.**
Published by: Heckner Druck- und Verlagsgesellschaft mbH & Co. KG, Postfach 1559, Wolfenbuettel, 38285, Germany. FAX 05331-800858.

330.1 USA ISSN 0172-5963
WIRTSCHAFTSPOLITISCHE STUDIEN. Text in German. 1976. irreg. price varies. reprint service avail. from ISI. **Document type:** *Monographic series.*
Published by: Springer-Verlag New York, Inc. (Subsidiary of: Springer Science+Business Media), 233 Spring St, New York, NY 10013. TEL 212-460-1500, FAX 212-473-6272.

330.1 DEU ISSN 0170-3579
WISSENSCHAFTLICHE PAPERBACKS; Sozial- und Wirtschaftsgeschichte. Text in German. 1973. irreg., latest vol.25, 1996. price varies. **Document type:** *Monographic series, Academic/Scholarly.*
Published by: Franz Steiner Verlag Stuttgart GmbH, Birkenwaldstr 44, Stuttgart, 70191, Germany. TEL 49-711-25820, FAX 49-711-2582390, franz.steiner.verlag@t-online.de, http://www.steiner-verlag.de. Ed. Hans Pohl. R&P Sabine Koerner.

XUESHU YUEKAN/ACADEMIC MONTHLY. see *SOCIAL SCIENCES: COMPREHENSIVE WORKS*

ZEITSCHRIFT FUER OSTMITTELEUROPA-FORSCHUNG. see *HISTORY—History Of Europe*

330.1 CHN ISSN 1002-8005
HC427
ZHONGGUO JINGJISHI YANJIU/CHINESE ECONOMIC HISTORY RESEARCH. Text in Chinese. q. USD 31.50.
Related titles: Online - full text ed.: (from East View Information Services).
—BLDSC (7776.756000), IE, ingenta.
Published by: Zhongguo Shehui Kexueyuan, Jingji Yanjiusuo/Chinese Academy of Social Sciences, Economic Research Institute, 2 Yuetan Beixiaojie, Beijing, 100836, China. TEL 895191. Ed. Wei Jinyu. **Dist. in US by:** China Books & Periodicals Inc, 360 Swift Ave., Ste. 48, S San Fran, CA 94080-6220. TEL 415-282-2994.

ZHONGGUO SHEHUI JINGJISHI YANJIU/JOURNAL OF CHINESE SOCIAL AND ECONOMIC HISTORY. see *HISTORY—History Of Asia*

330 CHN ISSN 1003-5230
➤ **ZHONGNAN CAIJING DAXUE XUEBAO/CENTRAL-SOUTH UNIVERSITY OF FINANCE AND ECONOMICS. JOURNAL.** Text in Chinese. 1974. bi-m. CNY 30 (effective 1999). adv. bk.rev. **Document type:** *Academic/Scholarly.* **Description:** Researches contemporary applications and development of Marxist economic theory, explores theoretical problems of economic development and reform in China, and introduces academic developments in the field.
Related titles: Online - full text ed.: (from East View Information Services).
Published by: Zhongnan Caijing Daxue/Central-South University of Finance and Economics, 114 Wuluo Lu, Wuchang-qu, Wuhan, Hubei 430064, China. TEL 86-27-88045631, FAX 86-27-88044548. Ed. Qu Yanwen. Circ: 3,500. **Dist. outside China by:** China National Publishing Industry Trading Corporation, PO Box 782, Beijing 100011, China.

BUSINESS AND ECONOMICS—International Commerce

382 DEU ISSN 0944-5641
A B C EUROP PRODUCTION. Text in English, French, German, Italian, Spanish. 1960. a. adv. **Document type:** *Directory, Trade.* **Description:** Export-import guide covering 40 countries from Albania to the Ukraine.
Former titles (until 1993): Europ Production (0343-1592); (until 1964): A B C Edition Europ Production (0065-003X)
Related titles: CD-ROM ed.; Online - full text ed.: (from Data-Star, F I Z Technik).
Published by: A B C Publishing Group, Postfach 100262, Darmstadt, 64202, Germany. TEL 49-6151-3892-0, FAX 49-6151-33164, office@abc-europex.de, info@abconline.de, http://www.abc-europex.de, http://www.abconline.de. Pub. Margit Selka. Adv. contact Dieter Wozniak. Circ: 18,000. **Dist. in US by:** Western Hemisphere Publishing Corp., PO Box 847, Hillsboro, OR 97123. TEL 503-640-2748.

382 ESP ISSN 0001-1207
A F R E. (African Trade Review) Text and summaries in English, French. 1966. m. USD 45. adv. illus.
Indexed: KES.
Published by: Editorial Office, German Perez Carrasco, 63, Madrid, 28027, Spain. TEL 1-267-24-03, FAX 1-408-78-37, TELEX 43782 EDOF E. Ed. Arsenio Pardo Rodriguez. Circ: 30,000.

382 332.6 PHL
A F T A MONITOR. (ASEAN Free Trade Area) Text in English. m. USD 415. **Document type:** *Newsletter.* **Description:** Monthly guide to trade and investment news, developments and opportunities in ASEAN and the emerging economies of Asia.
Published by: Options Publishing Services, 10 Garcia Villa St, San Lorenzo Village, Makati City Mm, Philippines. TEL 63-2-818-3289, FAX 63-2-819-3752, opsi@mnl.sequel.net. Pub. Melva C Nath.

382 USA
A I B NEWSLETTER. Text in English. 1958. q. USD 68 to members (effective 2000). adv. back issues avail. **Document type:** *Newsletter.*
Published by: Academy of International Business, c/o James R Wills, Jr, Exec Sec, University of Hawaii at Manoa, CBA, 2404 Maile Way, Honolulu, HI 96822-2223. TEL 808-956-3665, FAX 808-956-3261, aib@cba.hawaii.edu, http://www.hawaii.edu/aib. Ed., R&P, Adv. contact Laurel King. Circ: 2,700.

A S A E INTERNATIONAL NEWS. see *BUSINESS AND ECONOMICS—Management*

332.6 DEU ISSN 0947-3017
A W PRAX - AUSSENWIRTSCHAFTLICHE PRAXIS; Zeitschrift fuer Aussenwirtschaft in Recht und Praxis. Text in German. 1995. m. EUR 241.60; EUR 19.40 newsstand/cover (effective 2004). adv. bk.rev. index. back issues avail. **Document type:** *Journal, Academic/Scholarly.*
Published by: (Europaeischen Forum fuer Aussenwirtschaft, Verbrauchsteuern und Zoll e.V.), Bundesanzeiger Verlagsgesellschaft mbH, Amsterdamer Str 192, Cologne, 50735, Germany. TEL 49-221-97668-0, FAX 49-221-97668278, vertrieb@bundesanzeiger.de, http://www.bundesanzeiger.de/old/zeitschri/awprax/awindex.htm. Ed. Hans Michael Wolffgang. Adv. contact Hans Brandl. B&W page EUR 948. Circ: 1,950 (controlled).

382 DNK
AARHUS HAVN. Text in Danish. 1963. m. DKK 18 per issue (effective 1999). adv. **Document type:** *Bulletin.*
Address: Mindet 2, PO Box 130, Aarhus C, 8100, Denmark. TEL 45-86-13-32-66, FAX 45-86-12-76-62, port@aarhus.dk, http://www.euroports.com/aarhus. Adv. contact K Bruun. B&W page DKK 3,300, color page DKK 6,900; trim 180 x 126. Circ: 4,100.

382 USA ISSN 1542-8710
HB1
▼ ➤ **ACADEMY OF BUSINESS AND ECONOMICS. JOURNAL**; JABE. Abbreviated title: J A B E(Journal of Academy of Business and Economics). Variant title: Journal of Academy of Business and Economics. Text in English. 2003 (Oct.). s-a. USD 100 (effective 2004). adv. back issues avail.; reprints avail. **Document type:** *Journal, Academic/Scholarly.* **Description:** Publishes research papers and articles on all aspects of business administration, economics, Internet/computers, E-business, public administration, health care administration, and related fields. Provides an international forum to exchange research, practice, and teaching in these fields to improve education and business understanding around the world.
Related titles: CD-ROM ed.; Online - full content ed.; Online - full text ed.: (from Gale Group).
Published by: International Academy of Business and Economics, 983 Woodland Dr, Turlock, CA 95382-7281. TEL 209-656-7084, AKhade@iabe.org, http://www.iabe.org/JABE-description.htm. Ed., R&P Dr. Alan S Khade TEL 209-656-7084. adv.: B&W page USD 500, color page USD 1,000. Circ: 150 (paid).

380 GBR ISSN 0001-4907
HC251
ACHIEVEMENT. Text in English. 1910. 4/yr. GBP 20; GBP 25 foreign. adv. bk.rev. illus. reprint service avail. from PQC. **Document type:** *Trade.*
Related titles: Microfilm ed.: (from PQC).
Indexed: CPM, RASB, RehabLit.
Published by: Response Publishing Group plc, 41-45 Goswell Rd, London, EC1V 7EH, United Kingdom. TEL 44-171-490-0550. Ed. Clive Branson. R&P Stewart McAlpine. Adv. contact James Straker. Circ: 10,220 (controlled).

382 FRA ISSN 0240-8236
ACTUALITES REGLEMENTAIRES. Text in French. 1975. m.
Related titles: ♦ Supplement to: M O C I. ISSN 0026-9719.
Published by: Societe d'Edition de Documentation Economique et Commerciale (SEDEC), 24 bd. de l'Hopital, Paris, 75005, France. TEL 33-1-40733925, FAX 33-1-43364798. Ed. Jean Marchand.

382 658 USA ISSN 1077-0097
➤ **ADVANCES IN COMPETITIVENESS RESEARCH**; ACR. Text in English. 1993. a. USD 30 per issue domestic to individuals; USD 50 per issue foreign to individuals; USD 60 per issue domestic to institutions; USD 80 per issue foreign to institutions (effective 2005). adv. bk.rev. back issues avail. **Document type:** *Journal, Academic/Scholarly.* **Description:** Provides a forum for advancing conceptual, theoretical, and empirical contributions in areas applicable to competitiveness and globalization.
Related titles: Microfilm ed.; Online - full text ed.: (from EBSCO Publishing, Florida Center for Library Automation, Gale Group, O C L C Online Computer Library Center, Inc., ProQuest Information & Learning).
Indexed: ABIn, BRI, CBRI, CPM.
Published by: Indiana University of Pennsylvania, International Academy of Business Disciplines, PO Box 1658, Indiana, PA 15705. TEL 754-357-5759, aaali@iup.edu, aaali@grove.iup.edu. Ed., R&P Abbas J Ali. adv.: page USD 120. Circ: 500 (paid).

658 GBR ISSN 1571-5027
HD30.55
ADVANCES IN INTERNATIONAL MANAGEMENT. Text in English. 1982. irreg., latest vol.15, 2003. price varies. back issues avail. **Document type:** *Monographic series, Academic/Scholarly.* **Description:** Devoted to advancing the cross-border study of organizations and management practices from a global, regional, or comparative perspective.
Formerly (until 2002, vol.14): Advances in International Comparative Management (0747-7929)
Related titles: Online - full text ed.: (from ScienceDirect).
Indexed: ABIn.
—BLDSC (0709.253350), IE, ingenta. **CCC.**
Published by: Elsevier Ltd. (Subsidiary of: Elsevier Science & Technology), The Boulevard, Langford Ln, Kidlington, Oxford, OX5 1GB, United Kingdom. TEL 44-1865-843000, FAX 44-1865-843010, nlinfo-f@elsevier.nl, http://www.elsevier.com/wps/find/bookdescription.cws_home/BS_ADVIM/description#description. Eds. Joseph L C Cheng, Michael A Hitt.

382 USA ISSN 1536-1454
HF3877
AFRICA (YEAR). Text in English. 2000. a., latest 2004. USD 28.95 per vol. (effective 2004).
Formerly (until 2002): Doing Business with Africa (1533-4538)
Published by: (The Corporate Council on Africa), Business Books International, 194 Putnam Rd, New Canaan, CT 06840. TEL 203-966-9645, FAX 203-966-6018.

382 ZAF ISSN 1019-0309
AFRICA PRODUCT DIGEST. Text in English, French, Portuguese. 1991. a. adv. tr.lit. **Document type:** *Directory.* **Description:** Information on South African products, services and technology available for export. Distributed into Africa, Indian Ocean islands, and the Gulf States.
Published by: Reed Business Information South Africa (Pty) Ltd (Subsidiary of: Reed Business Information International), PO Box 653207, Benmore, 2010, South Africa. TEL 27-11-886-2636, FAX 27-11-886-5424. Circ: 10,000 (controlled).

332.6 USA ISSN 1072-0812
AFRICAN BUSINESS HANDBOOK✶ ; a practical guide to business resources for U.S.-Africa trade and investment. Text in English. 1992. biennial.
Published by: (International Trade and Development Counsel), 21st Century Africa, Inc., PO Box. 7177, Silver Springs, MD 20907-7177. TEL 202-429-2083, FAX 202-429-9574. Ed. Michael E M Sudarkasa.

382 RUS
AFRIKANSKII RYNOK/AFRICAN MARKET; zhurnal delovoi informatsii. Text in Russian. 1992. m. **Description:** Publishes analytical reviews about economical conditions and markets of the countries of Africa; Russian-African economical and military-technical cooperation; current information on conjuncture of the markets of the various goods in the countries of Africa.
Published by: Rossiiskaya Akademiya Nauk, Institut Afriki, Spiridonovka, 30/1, Moscow, 103001, Russian Federation. TEL 7-095-2903034, FAX 7-095-2020786, abcc@inafr.rnsk.su. Ed. I. Borisov.

AIRSHOW AND DEFENSE EXPO INTERNATIONAL. see *AERONAUTICS AND SPACE FLIGHT*

ALMANAC OF CHINA'S FOREIGN ECONOMIC RELATIONS AND TRADE. see *BUSINESS AND ECONOMICS—International Development And Assistance*

ALTERNATIVE TRADING NEWS. see *BUSINESS AND ECONOMICS—International Development And Assistance*

AMERICAN FOOD AND AG EXPORTER DIRECTORY. see *AGRICULTURE—Agricultural Economics*

AMERICAN FOOD AND AG EXPORTER MAGAZINE. see *AGRICULTURE—Agricultural Economics*

382 IND
AMERICAN MARKET. Text in English. m. INR 140, USD 25.
Description: Devoted to promotion of Indo-American trade and economic relations through larger trade.
Published by: Trade Digest Publications, S-185 Greater Kailash-2, New Delhi, 110 048, India. TEL 6414185. Ed. C L Khanna. Circ: 7,500.

AMERICAN REVIEW OF INTERNATIONAL ARBITRATION. see *LAW—International Law*

AMERICAN SEAFOOD INSTITUTE. REPORT. see *FISH AND FISHERIES*

ANALISIS ANUAL DEL MERCADO DEL AZUCAR. see *BUSINESS AND ECONOMICS—Abstracting, Bibliographies, Statistics*

382.7 CHE
ANALYTICAL STUDIES ON TRADE, ENVIRONMENT AND DEVELOPMENT. Text in English. irreg., latest vol.6, 2000. **Document type:** *Monographic series, Academic/Scholarly.* **Description:** Reviews the relevance of trade and positive measures (such as access to and transfer of technology, finance and capacity building) in achieving the objectives of selected multilateral environmental agreements in light of their contribution to strengthening environmental policy while at the same time minimizing economic distortions.
Published by: United Nations Conference on Trade and Development, 8-14 Avenue de la Paix, Geneva 10, 1211, Switzerland. TEL 41-22-9174924, FAX 41-22-9070195, info@unctad.org, http://www.unctad.org.

382 341.57 USA ISSN 1554-4052
KF2976 .3
ANDREWS LITIGATION REPORTER: INTELLECTUAL PROPERTY. Text in English. bi-w. USD 1,024 (effective 2005). **Document type:** *Newsletter, Trade.* **Description:** Covers developments in state and federal intellectual property lawsuits, as well as legislation affecting intellectual property rights and important decisions by the U.S. Justice Department and the Patent and Trademark Office.
Formerly (until 200?): Intellectual Property Litigation Reporter (1078-2796)
Related titles: Online - full text ed.
—CCC.
Published by: Andrews Publications (Subsidiary of: Thomson West), 175 Strafford Ave, Ste 140, Wayne, PA 19087. TEL 610-255-0510, FAX 610-255-0501, http://west.thomson.com/product/40211146/product.asp?ref_id=40211185&event=sspdclk, http://www.andrewsonline.com.

382 GBR ISSN 1350-4819
ANGLO-NORDIC TIMES INTERNATIONAL. Text in English. 1976. 8/yr. GBP 24; GBP 43 foreign. adv. bk.rev. illus. back issues avail. **Document type:** *Trade.* **Description:** Specializes in in-depth corporate and product profiles, with special emphasis on companies trading between the U.K., Nordic countries, Baltic states and northern Germany.
Former titles: Anglo-Nordic Times (0964-5748); (until Sep. 1990): Nordic Times International (0951-0478); (until 1986): Anglo-Nordic Times; (until 1984): Anglo-Nordic Trade News
Related titles: Diskette ed.
Published by: Peregrine Publishing & Trojan Graphics Co. Ltd., Yorksville 86a, 86a Kingsley Park Terr, Northampton, NN2 7HJ, United Kingdom. TEL 44-1604-713777, FAX 44-1604-717999, nordica@wildnet.co.uk, http://www2.wildnet.co.uk/nordic-times/. Ed., R&P Geoffrey E Hamilton. Adv. contact Anna Maria Amato. Circ: 5,300 (controlled).

382 HTI
ANNUAIRE DU COMMERCE EXTERIEUR D'HAITI: IMPORTATIONS, EXPORTATIONS. Text in French. a. stat.
Published by: Administration Generale des Douanes, Port-au-Prince, Haiti.

382 USA ISSN 1074-8520
HF1351
➤ **ANNUAL EDITIONS: INTERNATIONAL BUSINESS.** Text in English. 1991. a., latest 2002, 12th ed. USD 20.31 per vol. (effective 2004). illus. **Document type:** *Academic/Scholarly.* **Description:** Contains public press articles from a cross section of periodicals and covers topics such as: the nature of international business; organizations and monetary systems in the international environment; foreign environments and dynamics; and how management deals with environmental forces.
Published by: McGraw-Hill - Dushkin (Subsidiary of: McGraw-Hill Higher Education), 2460 Kerper Blvd, Dubuque, IA 52001. TEL 800-243-6532, customer.service@mcgraw-hill.com, http://www.dushkin.com/text-data/catalog/0072548495.mhtml. Ed. Fred H Maidment. Pub. Ian Nielsen. R&P Cheryl Greenleaf.

332.6 DEU ISSN 0937-2423
ANSCHRIFTEN FUER DIE AUSSENWIRTSCHAFT. Text in German. 1953. 2 base vols. plus m. updates. looseleaf. EUR 99 (effective 2005). **Document type:** *Directory, Trade.*
Published by: Deutscher Wirtschaftsdienst (Subsidiary of: Wolters Kluwer Deutschland GmbH), Schoenhauser Str 64, Cologne, 50968, Germany. TEL 49-221-937630, FAX 49-221-9376399, box@dwd-verlag.de, http://www.dwd-verlag.de.

382 347.7 USA ISSN 0891-8546
KF1632
ANTITRUST FREEDOM OF INFORMATION LOG. Text in English. 1982. w. USD 451 (effective 2000). **Document type:** *Newsletter.* **Description:** Provides brief summaries of the Freedom of Information Act requests received at the Antitrust Division of the U.S. Department of Justice.
Media: Fax. **Related titles:** Online - full text ed.
—CCC.
Published by: Washington Regulatory Reporting Associates, PO Box 356, Basye, VA 22810. TEL 540-856-2216, FAX 202-478-0260. Ed. William Reuter. Pub. Arthur Amolsch.

ANUARIO DE IMPORTACION - EXPORTACION DEL URUGUAY. see *BUSINESS AND ECONOMICS—Abstracting, Bibliographies, Statistics*

APPAREL IMPORT DIGEST. see *CLOTHING TRADE*

ARBITRATION INTERNATIONAL. see *LAW—International Law*

ARGENTINA. JUNTA NACIONAL DE CARNES. EXPORTACIONES DE PRODUCTOS GANADEROS. see *AGRICULTURE—Poultry And Livestock*

382 USA
ARGENTINE-AMERICAN BUSINESS REVIEW DIRECTORY✶. Text in English. 1978. biennial. USD 25. adv. **Document type:** *Directory.*
Published by: Argentina American Chamber of Commerce, 630-5th Ave, New York, NY 10111. TEL 212-698-2238. Ed. Barry V Conforte. Circ: 15,000.

332.6 GBR
ASIA PACIFIC DUTY-FREE. Text in English. 1988. 7/yr. GBP 89 domestic; GBP 117 foreign. adv. **Document type:** *Trade.* **Description:** Reviews the duty-free industry for Asian and Pacific markets, including purchasing trends, infrastructure development and product previews.
Former titles (until 1997): Asia Pacific Duty-Free and Travel Retail World; Asia Pacific Duty-Free Marketing; (until 1992): Asia Pacific Duty-Free (0957-1817)
Published by: D M G World Media Ltd., International Trade Publications (Subsidiary of: Daily Mail and General Trust PLC), Queensway House, 2 Queensway, Redhill, Surrey RH1 1QS, United Kingdom. TEL 44-1737-768611, FAX 44-1737-855475, abain@dmg.co.uk, info@uk.dmgworldmedia.com, http://www.dmgworldmedia.com. Ed. Anthea Bain. Adv. contact Michael Lewis. B&W page GBP 1,390, color page GBP 1,950. Circ: 3,000.

ASIA PACIFIC JOURNAL OF FINANCE. see *BUSINESS AND ECONOMICS—Banking And Finance*

382.029 USA
HF54.52.A785
ASIA - PACIFIC MARKETS; a guide to company and industry information sources. Text in English. 1984. irreg., latest vol.4. USD 335 (effective 1999). **Document type:** *Directory.* **Description:** Informs executives how and where to obtain hard-to-find business information, from the U.S. and elsewhere, on the top 11 Asian nations.
Formerly: Asian Markets (1044-8713); Which incorporates (in 1991): How to Find Information about Japanese Companies and Industries
Published by: Washington Researchers, Ltd., 1655 Fort Myer Dr., Ste. 800, Arlington, VA 22209-3119. TEL 703-312-2863, FAX 703-527-4586, research@researchers.com, http://www.researchers.com, http://www.washingtonresearchers.com. Ed. M Newman. R&P Ellen O'Kane.

382 USA ISSN 1541-6135
HC411
ASIAN LONG-TERM OUTLOOK. Text in English. a.
Published by: W E F A, 800 Baldwin Tower, Eddystone, PA 19022. TEL 610-490-4000, FAX 610-490-2770, http://www.wefa.com.

ASIAN MANUFACTURERS JOURNAL. see *BUSINESS AND ECONOMICS—Production Of Goods And Services*

ASPIS; the classified Greek commercial directory. see *BUSINESS AND ECONOMICS—Trade And Industrial Directories*

382 CHE ISSN 0258-0756
ASSOCIATION EUROPEENNE DE LIBRE-ECHANGE. RAPPORT ANNUEL. Text in French. 1962. a.
Related titles: ♦ English ed.: European Free Trade Association. Annual Report. ISSN 0258-3844; ♦ German ed.: Europaeische Freihandelsassoziation. Jahresbericht. ISSN 0258-3852.
Published by: European Free Trade Association, 9-11 rue de Varembe, Geneva 20, 1211, Switzerland.

ASSOCIATION POUR L'ETUDE DES PROBLEMES D'OUTRE MER. DOCUMENTATION-DEVELOPPEMENT. see *POLITICAL SCIENCE—International Relations*

382 USA ISSN 1053-2404
ATLANTIC TRADE REPORT & GLOBAL DEFENSE INDUSTRY. Text in English. 1989. bi-w. USD 495 (effective 1998). bk.rev. index. back issues avail. **Document type:** *Trade.* **Description:** Reports on the economic conditions in Europe and their effect on the world economic community. Provides information on legal mechanisms, political responses from involved countries, and opinions from US executives. Examines the relationships between Europe and the United States in the area of high technology.
Formed by the 1990 merger of: Atlantic Trade Report (1047-0824); Global Military Industrialization (1049-4448)
Related titles: Online - full text ed.
Published by: Bergerac International Ltd., 4431 Broad Run Church Rd, Warrenton, VA 20187. TEL 703-349-2922, FAX 703-349-2922. Ed. J.L.R. Combemale. R&P J L R Combemale TEL 540-349-2922. Circ: 335.

AUSLAENDISCHES WIRTSCHAFTSRECHT; systematischer Arbeitskatalog fuer die Praxis. see *LAW—International Law*

330 DEU ISSN 0949-0396
AUSLANDSKURIER. Text in German. 1979. 10/yr. EUR 4.80 newsstand/cover (effective 2004). adv. **Document type:** *Magazine, Trade.*
Formerly (until 1992): Auslandskurier - Diplomatischer Kurier (0171-2624); Which was formed by the merger of (1952-1979): Diplomatischer Kurier (0415-8776); Which incorporated (19??-197?): Diplomatisches Bulletin (0170-4575); (1960-1979): Auslandskurier (0519-4644); Which was formerly (until 1961): Deutsche in der Welt (0174-9285)
Related titles: ♦ Supplement(s): Diplomatisches Magazin. ISSN 0949-040X.
Published by: Eppinger-Verlag OHG, Stauffenbergstr 18-20, Schwaebisch Hall, 74523, Germany. TEL 49-791-950610, FAX 49-791-9506141, info@eppinger-verlag.de, http://www.eppinger-verlag.de. adv.: B&W page EUR 2,800, color page EUR 3,800. Circ: 12,000 (controlled).

382 DEU
AUSSENHANDEL✶. Text in German. 1948. m. free. charts; stat. back issues avail. **Document type:** *Newsletter.*
Formerly: Vereinsbank Kundendienst
Indexed: RASB.
Published by: (Bayerische Vereinsbank AG, Zentralbereich Kommunikation und Volkswirtschaft), Metzler-Poeschel Verlag, Werastr 21-23, Stuttgart, 70182, Germany. TEL 49-711-2194-0, FAX 49-711-2194111. Ed. Manuela Fella. Circ: 42,000.

382 DEU ISSN 0171-8126
AUSSENHANDELSBLAETTER. Text in German. 1949. bi-m. free. **Document type:** *Bulletin, Trade.*
Published by: Commerzbank AG, Frankfurt Am Main, 60261, Germany. TEL 49-69-13622379, FAX 49-69-13622008, harry_schroeder@commerzbank.com, http://www.commerzbank.com. Ed., R&P Harry Schroeder TEL 49-69-13622538. Circ: 21,000.

382 CHE ISSN 0004-8216
HF35
AUSSENWIRTSCHAFT; Swiss review of international economic relations. Text in English, German. 1946. 4/yr. CHF 178 domestic; CHF 210 foreign; CHF 78 domestic to students; CHF 110 foreign to students (effective 2003). adv. bk.rev. index. 150 p./no. 1 cols./p.; back issues avail.; reprints avail. **Document type:** *Magazine, Academic/Scholarly.*
Related titles: Online - full text ed.: (from ProQuest Information & Learning).
Indexed: ABIn, BibInd, DIP, ELLIS, IBR, IBSS, IBZ, JEL, KES, PAIS, RASB.
—BLDSC (1792.965000), IE, Infotrieve, ingenta.
Published by: (Universitaet St. Gallen, Schweizerisches Institut fuer Aussenwirtschaft und Angewandte Wirtschaftsforschung), Verlag Ruegger, Postfach 1470, Zuerich, 8040, Switzerland. TEL 41-1-4912130, FAX 41-1-4931176, redaktion@journal-aussenwirtschaft.ch, info@rueggerverlag.ch, http://www.journal-aussenwirtschaft.ch, http://www.rueggerverlag.ch. Ed. Heinz Hauser. R&P Ingo Borchert. Circ: 1,500.

382 DEU ISSN 0936-5400
AUSSENWIRTSCHAFT. Text in German. 1959. m. adv. **Document type:** *Magazine, Trade.*
Published by: Deutscher Sparkassenverlag GmbH, Am Wallgraben 115, Stuttgart, 70565, Germany. TEL 49-711-7820, FAX 49-711-7821709, webredaktion@dsv-gruppe.de, http://www.dsv-gruppe.de. adv.: B&W page EUR 1,440, color page EUR 3,000; trim 180 x 250. Circ: 16,000 (controlled).

AUSSENWIRTSCHAFT AKTUELL. see *BUSINESS AND ECONOMICS—Chamber Of Commerce Publications*

382 DEU ISSN 0178-8876
AUSSENWIRTSCHAFTSBRIEF; Information fuer das Auslandsgeschaeft. Text in German. 1985. bi-m. EUR 44.10 (effective 2002). bk.rev. back issues avail. **Document type:** *Bulletin, Trade.*
Published by: Deutscher Wirtschaftsdienst (Subsidiary of: Wolters Kluwer Deutschland GmbH), Schoenhauser Str 64, Cologne, 50968, Germany. TEL 49-221-93763-0, FAX 49-221-9376399. Circ: 11,000.

332.6 DEU ISSN 0933-2723
AUSSENWIRTSCHAFTSRECHT; Ergaenzbare Sammlung der fuer die Aussenwirtschaft massgeblichen Bestimmungen der Bundesrepublik Deutschland und der Europaeischen Union. Text in German. 1961. irreg., latest 2003. price varies. **Document type:** *Monographic series, Trade.*
Published by: Erich Schmidt Verlag GmbH & Co. (Berlin), Genthiner Str 30G, Berlin, 10785, Germany. TEL 49-30-250085-0, FAX 49-30-25008511, esv@esvmedien.de, http://www.erich-schmidt-verlag.de.

332.6 DEU
AUSSENWIRTSCHAFTSRECHT (REGENSBURG). Text in German. base vol. plus bi-m. updates. looseleaf. EUR 45.50 (effective 2005). adv. **Document type:** *Journal, Government.*
Published by: Walhalla Fachverlag, Haus an der Eisernen Bruecke, Regensburg, 93042, Germany. TEL 49-941-56840, FAX 49-941-5684111, walhalla@walhalla.de, http://www.walhalla.de. Circ: 1,600.

382 DEU ISSN 0937-3438
AUSSENWIRTSCHAFTSRECHT (YEAR); Einfuehrung - Fundstellen - Vorschriftentexte. Text in German. 1970. base vol. plus q. updates. EUR 149 (effective 2005). adv. bk.rev. **Document type:** *Bulletin, Trade.*
Published by: Deutscher Wirtschaftsdienst (Subsidiary of: Wolters Kluwer Deutschland GmbH), Schoenhauser Str 64, Cologne, 50968, Germany. TEL 49-221-937630, FAX 49-221-9376399, box@dwd-verlag.de, http://www.dwd-verlag.de.

382 LUX ISSN 1027-6432
AUSSNHANDEL. WARENVERZEICHNIS/COMMERCE EXTERIEUR: NOMENCLATURE DES PAYS/EXTERNAL TRADE: NOMENCLATURE OF GOODS. Text in Multiple languages. irreg. (in 5 vols.). price varies.
Published by: European Commission, Office for Official Publications of the European Union, 2 Rue Mercier, Luxembourg, L-2985, Luxembourg. **Dist. in the U.S. by:** Bernan Associates, Bernan, 4611-F Assembly Dr., Lanham, MD 20706-4391. TEL 301-459-0056, 800-274-4447.

AUSTRALIA. BUREAU OF STATISTICS. AUSTRALIAN HARMONIZED EXPORT COMMODITY CLASSIFICATION. see *BUSINESS AND ECONOMICS—Abstracting, Bibliographies, Statistics*

AUSTRALIA. BUREAU OF STATISTICS. INFORMATION PAPER: INTERNATIONAL MERCHANDISE TRADE AND SHIPPING STATISTICS, AUSTRALIA: DATA CONFIDENTIALITY. see *BUSINESS AND ECONOMICS—Abstracting, Bibliographies, Statistics*

AUSTRALIA. BUREAU OF STATISTICS. INFORMATION PAPER: INTERNATIONAL MERCHANDISE TRADE STATISTICS, AUSTRALIA: DATA CONFIDENTIALITY. see *BUSINESS AND ECONOMICS—Abstracting, Bibliographies, Statistics*

AUSTRALIA. BUREAU OF STATISTICS. INFORMATION PAPER: MEASURING REGION OF ORIGIN MERCHANDISE EXPORTS. see *BUSINESS AND ECONOMICS—Abstracting, Bibliographies, Statistics*

AUSTRALIA. BUREAU OF STATISTICS. INTERNATIONAL MERCHANDISE EXPORTS, AUSTRALIA - ELECTRONIC DELIVERY. see *BUSINESS AND ECONOMICS—Abstracting, Bibliographies, Statistics*

AUSTRALIA. BUREAU OF STATISTICS. INTERNATIONAL MERCHANDISE IMPORTS, AUSTRALIA. see *BUSINESS AND ECONOMICS—Abstracting, Bibliographies, Statistics*

AUSTRALIA. BUREAU OF STATISTICS. INTERNATIONAL MERCHANDISE TRADE, AUSTRALIA. see *BUSINESS AND ECONOMICS—Abstracting, Bibliographies, Statistics*

AUSTRALIA. BUREAU OF STATISTICS. INTERNATIONAL MERCHANDISE TRADE, AUSTRALIA: CONCEPTS, SOURCES AND METHODS. see *BUSINESS AND ECONOMICS—Abstracting, Bibliographies, Statistics*

AUSTRALIA. BUREAU OF STATISTICS. INTERNATIONAL TRADE, AUSTRALIA - INFORMATION CONSULTANCY AD HOC SERVICE. see *BUSINESS AND ECONOMICS—Abstracting, Bibliographies, Statistics*

AUSTRALIA. BUREAU OF STATISTICS. INTERNATIONAL TRADE IN GOODS AND SERVICES, AUSTRALIA. see *BUSINESS AND ECONOMICS—Abstracting, Bibliographies, Statistics*

AUSTRALIA. BUREAU OF STATISTICS. INTERNATIONAL TRADE IN GOODS AND SERVICES, AUSTRALIA: MONTHLY FORWARD SEASONAL FACTORS. see *BUSINESS AND ECONOMICS—Abstracting, Bibliographies, Statistics*

AUSTRALIA. BUREAU OF STATISTICS. INTERNATIONAL TRADE IN GOODS AND SERVICES, MONTHLY FORWARD SEASONAL FACTORS SERVICE, AUSTRALIA. see *BUSINESS AND ECONOMICS—Abstracting, Bibliographies, Statistics*

AUSTRALIA. BUREAU OF STATISTICS. INTERNATIONAL TRADE IN SERVICES, AUSTRALIA. see *BUSINESS AND ECONOMICS—Abstracting, Bibliographies, Statistics*

AUSTRALIA IN BRITAIN. see *BUSINESS AND ECONOMICS—Chamber Of Commerce Publications*

AUSTRALIAN WOOL EXPORT QUARTERLY REVIEW. see *TEXTILE INDUSTRIES AND FABRICS*

382 AUT ISSN 0005-0490
AUSTRIA EXPORT. Text in English, French, German. 1954. 4/yr. free.
Published by: (Bundeskammer der Gewerblichen Wirtschaft), Internationale Werbegesellschaft m.b.H., Hoher Markt 12, Vienna, W 1010, Austria. Ed. Traute Franke. Circ: 5,000.

382 TUR ISSN 1301-4633
AUTOMOTIVE EXPORTS - TURKEY. Text in English. m. adv. 64 p./no. 5 cols./p.; **Document type:** *Magazine, Trade.*
Published by: Ihlas Magazine Group, Ihlas Holding Mrk. Binasi, 29 Ekim Cad. 23, Yenibosna - Istanbul, 34530, Turkey. TEL 90-212-4542530, FAX 90-212-4542555, bsensoz@img.com.tr, imga@img.com.tr, http://www.img.com.tr. Ed. Mehmet Soztutan. Pub. Dr. Enver Oren. R&P Muhsin Yilmaz. adv.: page USD 2,000; 25.5 x 37. Circ: 1,506 (paid); 21,178 (controlled).

AVANCE DE INFORMACION ECONOMICA. BALANZA COMERCIAL. see *BUSINESS AND ECONOMICS—Abstracting, Bibliographies, Statistics*

AVANCE DE INFORMACION ECONOMICA. INDUSTRIA MAQUILADORA DE EXPORTACION. see *BUSINESS AND ECONOMICS—Abstracting, Bibliographies, Statistics*

B B I N: MEDICAL DEVICE WEEK. (Biomedical Business International Newsletter) see *MEDICAL SCIENCES*

THE B B I NEWSLETTER. see *MEDICAL SCIENCES*

382 DEU
B D EX AUSSENWIRTSCHAFTSINFORMATIONEN. Text in German. fortn. free membership. adv. 16 p./no.; **Document type:** *Newsletter, Trade.* **Description:** Contains information on current events in international trade.
Published by: Bundesverband des Deutschen Exporthandels e.V., Am Weidendamm 1a, Berlin, 10117, Germany. TEL 49-30-72625790, FAX 49-30-72625799, contact@bdex.de, http://www.bdex.de. Ed. Hans-Juergen Mueller. Pub. Hans Juergen Mueller. Circ: 850 (paid); 1,000 (controlled).

382 DEU ISSN 0415-7508
T12.5.G3
B D I DEUTSCHLAND LIEFERT/B D I ALEMANIA SUMINISTRA/B D I GERMANY SUPPLIES/B D I L'ALLEMAGNE FOURNIT; official export register of the Federation of German Industries. Text in English, French, German, Spanish. 1952. a. EUR 116.57 per issue (effective 2000). adv. **Document type:** *Trade.*
Related titles: CD-ROM ed.; Online - full text ed.: (from Data-Star, F I Z Technik).
Published by: (Bundesverband der Deutschen Industrie), Verlag W. Sachon GmbH & Co., Schloss Mindelburg, Mindelheim, 87714, Germany. TEL 49-8261-9990, FAX 49-8261-999180, info@sachon.de, http://www.sachon.de. Ed. Werner Sachon. Circ: 15,122.

330 USA ISSN 1048-1583
CODEN: VORADB
B R I E WORKING PAPERS. (Berkeley Roundtable on the International Economy) Text in English. 1984. irreg.
Related titles: Online - full text ed.
—BLDSC (2283.928300).
Published by: University of California at Berkeley, Roundtable on the International Economy (BRIE), 2234 Piedmont Ave, Berkeley, CA 94720. TEL 510-642-3067, FAX 510-643-6617, brie@socrates.berkeley.edu, http://brie.berkeley.edu/~briewww/research/workingpapers.htm.

382.1 JAM ISSN 0259-6776
HG3883.J2
BALANCE OF PAYMENTS OF JAMAICA. Text in English. a. free. illus.; stat.
Published by: (Balance of Payments Department), Bank of Jamaica, Nethersole Place, P O Box 621, Kingston, Jamaica. TEL 809-922-0750, FAX 809-967-4265.

BALANCE OF PAYMENTS OF TRINIDAD AND TOBAGO. see *BUSINESS AND ECONOMICS—Abstracting, Bibliographies, Statistics*

BALANZA DE PAGOS DE ESPANA. see *BUSINESS AND ECONOMICS—Public Finance, Taxation*

380 NIC
BANCO CENTRAL DE NICARAGUA. COMERCIO EXTERIOR DE NICARAGUA POR PRODUCTOS Y PAISES✶. Text in Spanish. a. stat.
Published by: Ministerio de Comercio Exterior (MICE), Apdo 2412, Managua, Nicaragua. Circ: 3,000.

BANCO CENTRAL DE VENEZUELA. ANUARIO DE ESTADISTICAS INTERNACIONALES. see *BUSINESS AND ECONOMICS—Abstracting, Bibliographies, Statistics*

BANK OF JAPAN. BALANCE OF PAYMENTS MONTHLY. see *BUSINESS AND ECONOMICS—Public Finance, Taxation*

382 JPN
BANK OF JAPAN. COMMODITIES, WEIGHTS AND LINKED INDEXES OF (YEAR) BASE WHOLESALE PRICE INDEXES. Text in English, Japanese. every 5 yrs. JPY 1,700 (effective 1998). 260 p./no.; **Description:** Contains commodities, weights, and linked indexes for 1995 base wholesale prices.
Formerly: Bank of Japan. Price Indexes Annual (Appendix)
Published by: (Research and Statistics Department), Bank of Japan/Nippon Ginko, c/o Public Relations Department, 2-1-1 Hongoku-cho-Nihonbashi, Chuo-ku, Tokyo, 1030000, Japan. TEL 81-3-3299-1111, FAX 81-3-3510-1374, prd@info.boj.or.jp, http://www.boj.or.jp. **Dist. by:** Tokiwa Sohgoh Service Co. Ltd., Publication and Research Department, Kyodo Bldg, 2-4 Hongokucho, Nihonbashi 3-chome, Chuo-ku, Tokyo 103-0027, Japan. TEL 81-3-3270-5713, FAX 81-3-3270-5710; **Overseas dist. by:** Japan Publications Trading Co., Ltd., Book Export II Dept, PO Box 5030, Tokyo International, Tokyo 101-3191, Japan. TEL 81-3-32923753, FAX 81-3-32920410.

BANK OF LIBYA. BALANCE OF PAYMENTS. see *BUSINESS AND ECONOMICS—Public Finance, Taxation*

382 FRA ISSN 0184-9719
BANQUE AFRIQUE. Text in French. s-m. (22/yr.). GBP 40 in United Kingdom; EUR 80 in Europe eurozone; USD 90 in United States eurozone; GBP 55 elsewhere eurozone (effective 2005).
Related titles: ♦ Supplement(s): Fichier Banque Afrique. ISSN 1150-7608.
Indexed: RASB.
Published by: I C Publications, 10 rue Vineuse, Paris, 75784 Cedex 16, France. FAX 33-1-44308111, 33-1-44308100.

BANQUE NATIONALE DE BELGIQUE. INSTITUT DES COMPTES NATIONAUX. STATISTIQUES DES EXPORTATIONS BELGES: RESULTATS REGIONAUX. see *BUSINESS AND ECONOMICS—Abstracting, Bibliographies, Statistics*

382 NLD ISSN 0005-5956
BARID HOLLANDA. Text in Arabic, English, French. 1956. 3/yr. USD 12. adv. illus. **Description:** Promotes exports from the Netherlands to the Middle-East and Africa.
Indexed: KES.
Published by: Van Kouteren's Publishing Co., PO Box 4115, Rotterdam, 3006 AC, Netherlands. Circ: 4,000.

382 ESP
BAYARRI INTERNACIONAL; guia nacional de la exportacion and importacion. Text in Spanish. 1973; s-a. adv. abstr.; bibl.; charts; illus.; tr.lit.
Published by: Publicaciones Bayarri, Angel Guimera, 8, Valencia, 46008, Spain. Ed. Vicente Bayarri.

332.6 DEU
BEGLEITPAPIERE FUER AUSFUHRSENDUNGEN. Text in German. 1956. 10/yr. looseleaf. EUR 92 (effective 2001). **Document type:** *Trade.* **Description:** All necessary rules and regulations for exporting to foreign countries.
Related titles: CD-ROM ed.
Published by: Mendel Verlag, Robensstr 39, Aachen, 52070, Germany. TEL 49-241-154355, FAX 49-241-1570816, info@mendel-verlag.de, http://www.mendel-verlag.de.

338 DEU ISSN 0522-6449
BEITRAEGE ZUR FREMDENVERKEHRSFORSCHUNG. Text in German. 1954. irreg., latest vol.11, 1969. price varies. **Document type:** *Monographic series, Academic/Scholarly.*
Published by: Duncker und Humblot GmbH, Carl-Heinrich-Becker-Weg 9, Berlin, 12165, Germany. TEL 49-30-7900060, FAX 49-30-79000631, info@duncker-humblot.de, http://www.duncker-humblot.de.

382 SWE ISSN 1100-3006
BEST 'N' MOST IN D F S. (Duty Free Shopping) Text in English. 1980. a. adv. charts; stat. index. back issues avail. **Document type:** *Trade.*
Former titles: Duty and Tax-Free Shop World Guide Series (0349-2737); Duty and Tax-Free Shop World Review

Published by: Generation AB, Storgatan 3, Oernskoeldsvik, 89133, Sweden. TEL 46-660-10320, FAX 46-660-84811, best.n.most@generation.se. Ed. Yngve Bia.

382 IND ISSN 0006-0542
BHUSHAN'S WORLD TRADE ENQUIRIES. Text in English. 1961. bi-m. INR 30, USD 4.50. adv. tr.lit.
Published by: B. Bhushan Lal, Ed. & Pub., 738 Mammaran St., Jagadhri, Haryana, India. Circ: 1,000.

382 RUS ISSN 1606-1578
BIZNES ZA RUBEZHOM. Text in Russian. 2000. w. free (effective 2004). **Document type:** *Consumer.*
Media: Online - full text.
Published by: Al'yans Midiya, Bolotnaya ul 12, str 3, Moscow, 115035, Russian Federation. TEL 7-095-2345380, FAX 7-095-2345363, allmedia@allmedia.ru, http://www.businesspress.ru, http://allmedia.ru.

382 ITA
BOLLETTINO COMMERCIO ESTERO. Text in English. s-m. free.
Published by: Camera di Commercio Industria Artigianato e Agricoltura di Forli-Cesena, Corso della Repubblica 5, Forli', FC 47100, Italy. TEL 39-0547-21901, FAX 39-0547-23157, http://www.fo.camcom.it.

BOTSWANA. CENTRAL STATISTICS OFFICE. EXTERNAL TRADE STATISTICS. see *BUSINESS AND ECONOMICS—Abstracting, Bibliographies, Statistics*

BOUT DE PAPIER. see *BUSINESS AND ECONOMICS—International Development And Assistance*

BOYCOTT LAW BULLETIN. see *LAW—International Law*

BRASILIANS JOURNAL. see *ETHNIC INTERESTS*

382.029 BRA
BRAZILIAN EXPORT MARKET. Text in English, Portuguese, Spanish. 1982. a. USD 120. adv. back issues avail. **Description:** General information of use to business people interested in importing from Brazil. Lists Brazilian exporters.
Published by: (Brazilian Foreign Trade Association), Editora Pesquisa e Industria Ltda., Rua Martins Fontes, 230 Andar 1, Centro, Sao Paulo, SP 01050-000, Brazil. TEL 011-259-0333, FAX 011-256-8681. Ed. Hanibal Haddad. Circ: 30,000.

382 CAN ISSN 1480-8161
THE BRAZILIANIST. Text in English. 1996. q. adv. **Document type:** *Trade.* **Description:** Publishes stories and news about business, technology, people and ideas that are transforming Brazil.
Formerly: Brazilian Focus-Trade
Media: Online - full content.
Published by: Losango Electronic Publishing, 349 St Clair Ave, Ste 415, Toronto, ON M6P 1N3, Canada. TEL 416-826-1455, editor@brazilianist.com, brazilianist@usa.com, http://www.brazilianist.com.

382 GBR ISSN 0045-2866
BRITAIN AND OVERSEAS. Abbreviated title: B & O(Britain & Overseas). Text in English. 1971. q. GBP 15, USD 25 (effective 2003). adv. bk.rev. charts. 1 cols./p.; **Document type:** *Academic/Scholarly.*
Related titles: Microform ed.: (from RPI).
Published by: Economic Research Council, 7 St James's Sq, London, SW1Y 4JU, United Kingdom. TEL 44-20-74390271. Ed., Adv. contact Jim Bourlet. Circ: 500.

BRITISH EXPORTS/BRITISCHER EXPORT/EXPORTACIONES BRITANICAS/EXPORTATIONS BRITANNIQUES. see *BUSINESS AND ECONOMICS—Trade And Industrial Directories*

382 HKG
BRITISH INDUSTRY. Text in Chinese, English; Summaries in English. 1968. 3/yr. free.
Published by: (Sino-British Trade Council GBR), China Translation and Printing Services Ltd., GPO Box 4013, Hong Kong, Hong Kong. Circ: 10,000.

382 GBR
BRITISH INVISIBLE EXPORTS COUNCIL. ANNUAL REPORT. Text in English. 1968. a. free. illus.; stat. **Document type:** *Corporate.*
Formerly: Committee on Invisible Exports. Annual Report (0308-4892)
Published by: British Invisible Exports Council, Windsor House, 39 King St, London, EC2V 8DQ, United Kingdom. TEL 44-171-600-1198, FAX 44-171-606-4248, TELEX 941-3342-BIE-G. Circ: 3,500.

382 USA ISSN 1520-5479
HF1371
BROOKINGS TRADE FORUM. Text in English. 1998. a. USD 28.95; USD 40.53 combined subscription (effective 2004). back issues avail. **Document type:** *Monographic series, Academic/Scholarly.* **Description:** Analyzes international trade issues.
Related titles: Online - full content ed.: ISSN 1534-0635; Online - full text ed.: (from EBSCO Publishing, O C L C Online Computer Library Center, Inc., Project MUSE, Swets Information Services).
—BLDSC (2350.084000). **CCC.**
Published by: Brookings Institution Press, 1775 Massachusetts Ave, NW, Washington, DC 20036-2188. TEL 202-797-6252, 800-275-1447, FAX 202-797-6195, http://www.brook.edu/press/trade_forum/editors_summary2000.htm. Eds. Dani Rodrik, Susan M. Collins.

382 NLD ISSN 1380-6564
BUITENLANDSE MARKTEN. Text in Dutch. 1970. fortn. adv. bk.rev. **Document type:** *Magazine, Trade.* **Description:** Provides information on export and foreign markets. Includes listings of national and international events, and relevant new publications.
Former titles: Export Magazine (0168-7166); (until 1983): Wereldmarkt (0043-2741); Economische Voorlichting; Nieuws van Buitenlandse Markten
—IE, Infotrieve.
Published by: (Netherlands. Ministerie van Economische Zaken, Netherlands. Exportbevorderings- en Voorlichtendienst (EVD)), Samsom Bedrijfsinformatie BV (Subsidiary of: Wolters Kluwer N.V.), Postbus 4, Alphen aan den Rijn, 2400 MA, Netherlands. TEL 31-172-466800. Ed. Frans van Leeuwen.

382 FRA ISSN 1285-0888
BULLETIN JOLY SOCIETES; information des societes. Text in French. m. **Document type:** *Bulletin.*
Formerly (until 1997): Bulletin Joly (0997-5047)
Published by: Joly Editions, 31 rue Falguiere, Paris, 75015, France. TEL 33-1-56541600, FAX 33-1-56541647. Ed. Daniel Lepeltier.

382 FRA ISSN 0007-5264
BULLETIN QUOTIDIEN D'AFRIQUE. Text in French. 1965. d.
Formerly: Bulletin Quotidien d'Outre Mer
Indexed: RASB.
Published by: Agence France Presse, 1-13-15 place de la Bourse, B.P. 20, Paris, Cedex 2 75061, France. TEL 33-1-40414302, FAX 33-1-40414572, multimedia@afp.com.

382 665 GBR ISSN 0968-476X
BUNKER NEWS. Text in English. m. USD 595 in North America; GBP 375 elsewhere (effective 2002). **Description:** Covers all aspects of the international bunker market. It includes newsbreaking stories; technical, environmental and quality issues; key and legal cases; price risk management; credit insurance and financial issues; unique maps of bunkering regions, comprehensive listing of personnel changes and diary notes and port and company profiles.
Published by: Informa Maritime & Transport (Subsidiary of: T & F Informa plc), 69-77 Paul St, London, EC2A 4LQ, United Kingdom. TEL 44-20-7553-1000, FAX 44-20-7553-1105, http://www.bunkernews.com, http://www.informamaritime.com.

387 GBR
THE BUNKER NEWS DIRECTORY OF INTERNATIONAL BUNKER SUPPLIERS, TRADERS & BROKERS. Text in English. s-a. GBP 75 per issue domestic; USD 120 per issue foreign (effective 2003). 470 p./no.; **Document type:** *Directory, Trade.* **Description:** Lists every significant bunker supplier, trader and broker in the world—more than 800 companies and 2000 personnel, in over 75 countries.
Published by: Informa Maritime & Transport (Subsidiary of: T & F Informa plc), 69-77 Paul St, London, EC2A 4LQ, United Kingdom. TEL 44-20-7553-1000, FAX 44-20-7553-1105, info@bunkernews.com, http://www.bunkernews.com, http://www.informamaritime.com. Ed. Alisdair Pettigrew.

382 665 GBR
BUNKER NEWS SPECIAL SURVEYS. Text in English. 5/yr. GBP 125 domestic; USD 195 foreign; GBP 35 newsstand/cover domestic; USD 50 newsstand/cover foreign (effective 2002). **Description:** Focuses on one region: examining bunkering in all the major ports and offshore and covering the bunkering activities of the oil companies, suppliers, traders and barge operators. The surveys contain In-depth editorial, maps and comprehensive contract lists for the area's key players.
Published by: Informa Maritime & Transport (Subsidiary of: T & F Informa plc), 69-77 Paul St, London, EC2A 4LQ, United Kingdom. TEL 44-20-7553-1000, FAX 44-20-7553-1105, http://www.informamaritime.com.

BUSINESS AFRICA. see *BUSINESS AND ECONOMICS—Economic Situation And Conditions*

382 346 HKG
BUSINESS ALERT - US. Text in English. 1995. bi-w. looseleaf. USD 40 per issue foreign (effective 2000). back issues avail. **Document type:** *Newsletter, Trade.* **Description:** Provides information on the latest developments in US trade policy and trade regulations. Examines the foremost issue in US trade relations with Hong Kong and the Chinese mainland. Also covers US congressional events relevant to trade policy and trade relations.
Media: E-mail.
Published by: Hong Kong Trade Development Council, 38th Fl Office Tower, Convention Plaza, 1 Harbour Rd, Wanchai, Hong Kong. TEL 852-2584-4333, FAX 852-2824-0249, http://www.tdctrade.com/alert/us0509index.htm, http://www.tdc.org.hk. Circ: 2,800.

BUSINESS ASIA; fortnightly report to managers of Asia operations index. see *BUSINESS AND ECONOMICS—Economic Situation And Conditions*

332.6 341 AUS ISSN 1444-4062
HF1626.5.A8
BUSINESS ASIA (NORTH SYDNEY). Text in English. 1993. fortn. AUD 64.90 domestic; AUD 140.80 foreign (effective 2004). **Document type:** *Magazine, Trade.* **Description:** Covers the latest issues, news and trends concerning business and trade within the vitally important Asian market.
Former titles (until 1998): International Business Asia (1324-5414); (until 1995): Australian Business Asia (1320-9884); Incorporates (in 1997): Overseas Trading for Successful Exporters (1323-4161); Which was formerly (1947-199?): Overseas Trading (0030-7513)
Related titles: Online - full text ed.: (from Florida Center for Library Automation, Gale Group).
Indexed: CompD.
Published by: First Charlton Communications, Level 9, Tenix House, 100 Arthur St, North Sydney, NSW 2060, Australia. TEL 61-2-99576555, FAX 61-2-99571512, pctc@charlton.com.au, http://www.charlton.com.au/. Ed. Randolph Ramsay. Adv. contact Tony May TEL 61-2-99579809.

BUSINESS CHINA; fortnightly report to managers of China operations. see *BUSINESS AND ECONOMICS—Economic Situation And Conditions*

BUSINESS EASTERN EUROPE. see *BUSINESS AND ECONOMICS—Economic Situation And Conditions*

332.6 364 USA ISSN 1054-4216
HD38.7
BUSINESS ESPIONAGE REPORT; controls and countermeasures training for managers. Text in English. 1987. m. looseleaf. membership. bk.rev.; video rev.; software rev. illus. index every 3 yrs. back issues avail. **Document type:** *Newsletter.* **Description:** Contains training news, trends, and other information of business espionage as well as controls and countermeasures.
Published by: Business Espionage Controls & Countermeasures Association (BECCA), PO Box 44260, Ft. Washington, MD 20749. TEL 206-364-4672, FAX 301-292-4635, tsainc@erols.com. Ed. Glenn Whidden.

BUSINESS EUROPE. see *BUSINESS AND ECONOMICS—Economic Situation And Conditions*

332.6 GBR
BUSINESS EYE. Text in English. 1992. bi-m. free. adv. back issues avail. **Document type:** *Trade.* **Description:** Promotes U.K. trade and investment interests in South Asia.
Published by: (Great Britain. Department of Trade and Industry), Westoning House Ltd., 91-93 Charterhouse St, London, EC1M 6HR, United Kingdom. TEL 44-171-336-7212, FAX 44-171-336-7211. Ed., R&P Steve Hurst. Adv. contact David Chandler. Circ: 15,000.

BUSINESS LATIN AMERICA; weekly report to managers of Latin American operations. see *BUSINESS AND ECONOMICS—Economic Situation And Conditions*

BUSINESS MEXICO. see *BUSINESS AND ECONOMICS—Chamber Of Commerce Publications*

BUSINESS MIDDLE EAST. see *BUSINESS AND ECONOMICS—Economic Situation And Conditions*

BUSINESS MONITOR: GUIDE TO THE CLASSIFICATION OF OVERSEAS TRADE STATISTICS. see *BUSINESS AND ECONOMICS—Abstracting, Bibliographies, Statistics*

BUSINESS MONITOR: OVERSEAS DIRECT INVESTMENT. see *BUSINESS AND ECONOMICS—Abstracting, Bibliographies, Statistics*

BUSINESS MONITOR: OVERSEAS TRADE STATISTICS OF THE UNITED KINGDOM (QUARTERLY REVISION). see *BUSINESS AND ECONOMICS—Abstracting, Bibliographies, Statistics*

658 381 SGP ISSN 0129-4202
BUSINESS OPPORTUNITIES. Text in Spanish. 1977. m. SGD 130; USD 111 in Asia; USD 150 elsewhere. adv. **Document type:** *Trade.* **Description:** Contains hundreds of import and export opportunities throughout the world.
Published by: World-Wide Import-Export Promotion Centre, Marine Parade Post Office, Box 503, Singapore, 9144, Singapore. FAX 65-241-3982. Ed. E L Tay. Circ: 35,000.

332.6   HKG
BUSINESS P R C; an informative bridge between China and the world. Text in English. 1978. q. HKD 250, USD 90. adv. **Document type:** *Trade.*
Published by: Enterprise International, 1604 Eastern Commercial Centre, 393-407 Hennessy Rd, Hong Kong, Hong Kong. TEL 852-2573-4161, FAX 852-2838-3469, TELEX 66299-EIN-HX. Ed. C P Ho. Circ: 27,000.

382   NLD   ISSN 1023-9340
HF3321
BUSINESS T I P S ON CUBA. (Technological Information Promotion System) Text in English. 1992. m. USD 50 (effective 2001). **Document type:** *Magazine, Trade.*
Description: Covers business practices, trading policies, investment opportunities and economic development activities in Cuba.
Related titles: Online - full content ed.; Portuguese ed.: ISSN 1023-9359; French ed.: ISSN 1023-9367; German ed.: ISSN 1023-9375; Russian ed.: ISSN 1023-9383; Spanish ed.: ISSN 1023-1706.
Published by: Cuba T I P S International, Weena 290 NL-3012, Rotterdam, Netherlands. http://english.cubatips.com/, http://www.cubatips.com/. **Dist. by:** U S - Cuba Trade and Economic Council, Inc., c/o John S. Kavulich, II 30 Rockefeller Plaza, New York, NY 10112-1117. TEL 212-246-1444, FAX 212-246-2345, council@cubatrade.org, http://www.cubatrade.org.

BUSINESS VENEZUELA'S CORPORATE HANDBOOK. see *BUSINESS AND ECONOMICS—Investments*

BUSINESS WEEK (HUNGARIAN EDITION). see *BUSINESS AND ECONOMICS*

BUSINESS WEEK. ASIAN EDITION. see *BUSINESS AND ECONOMICS*

332.6   BGD
BUSINESSMAN. Text in Bengali. m. **Document type:** *Trade.*
Address: G.P.O. Box 2355, Dhaka, 2, Bangladesh. TEL 880-2-231345, FAX 880-2-833297, TELEX 642459 COMP BJ.

BUTTERWORTHS CUSTOM DUTIES HANDBOOK (YEAR). see *LAW—International Law*

382 341   GBR   ISSN 0142-6796
BUYER. Text in English. 1979. m. GBP 206; GBP 231, USD 462 foreign (effective 2000). back issues avail. **Document type:** *Newsletter.* **Description:** For specialists responsible for purchasing decisions in commerce, industry and public services. Covers new law, new regulations, statutory instruments and ministerial orders.
—BLDSC (2936.300000), IE.
Published by: Monitor Press Ltd. (Subsidiary of: T & F Informa plc), Suffolk House, Church Field Rd, Sudbury, Suffolk CO10 2YA, United Kingdom. TEL 44-1787-378607, FAX 44-1787-880201, http://www.monitorpress.co.uk. Pub. Zoe Turner.

382   ITA   ISSN 0007-7380
BUYERS' GUIDE. Text in Italian. 1962. m. illus.; mkt.; tr.lit.
Published by: Ente Italiano per lo Sviluppo dell'Esportazione, Piazzale Giotto, 8, Perugia, PG 06121, Italy. Circ: 9,500.

382   RUS   ISSN 0320-4529
BYULLETEN' INOSTRANNOI KOMMERCHESKOI INFORMATSII. Short title: B I K I. Text in Russian. 1948. 3/w. RUR 7,200 for 6 mos. domestic (effective 2004). adv. bk.rev. charts; stat. **Document type:** *Newspaper.*
Indexed: RASB.
Published by: Vserossiiskii Nauchno-Issledovatel'skii Kon'yukturnyi Institut (VNIKI)/All-Russia Market Research Institute, ul Pudovkina, 4, Moscow, 119285, Russian Federation. TEL 7-095-1430538, mrc@vniki.ru, http://www.vniki.ru/biki.nsf. Circ: 5,700. **Dist. by:** M K - Periodica, ul Gilyarovskogo 39, Moscow 129110, Russian Federation. TEL 7-095-2845008, FAX 7-095-2813798, info@periodicals.ru, http://www.mkniga.ru.

C G A - CANADA RESEARCH FOUNDATION. STUDY PAPERS. (Certified General Accountants) see *BUSINESS AND ECONOMICS—Accounting*

C I E S FOOD BUSINESS NEWS. (Comite International des Entreprises a Succursales) see *FOOD AND FOOD INDUSTRIES*

C I T B A NEWSLETTER. see *LAW—International Law*

C I T RULES. (Court of International Trade) see *LAW—International Law*

C I T TEST CASE RECORD. (Court of International Trade) see *LAW—International Law*

382   USA   ISSN 0263-3701
HC244
C O M E C O N DATA. (Council for Mutual Economic Assistance) Text in English. biennial (alternates with C O M E C O N Foreign Trade Data ,ISSN 0891-3404). price varies.

Related titles: ♦ Special ed(s).: C O M E C O N Foreign Trade Data.
Indexed: RASB.
Published by: (Vienna Institute for Comparative Economic Studies), Greenwood Publishing Group Inc. (Subsidiary of: Harcourt International), 88 Post Rd W, PO Box 5007, Westport, CT 06881. TEL 203-226-3571, FAX 203-226-1502, bookinfo@greenwood.com, http://www.greenwood.com.

382   USA
C O M E C O N FOREIGN TRADE DATA. (Council for Mutual Economic Assistance) Text in English. 1980. base vol. plus biennial updates. price varies. charts. back issues avail.
Related titles: ♦ Special ed. of: C O M E C O N Data. ISSN 0263-3701.
Published by: (Vienna Institute for Comparative Economic Studies), Greenwood Publishing Group Inc. (Subsidiary of: Harcourt International), 88 Post Rd W, PO Box 5007, Westport, CT 06881. TEL 203-226-3571, FAX 203-226-1502, bookinfo@greenwood.com, http://www.greenwood.com.

CAIMAO JINGJI/FINANCE AND TRADE ECONOMICS. see *BUSINESS AND ECONOMICS—Banking And Finance*

CALIFORNIA INTERNATIONAL TRADE REGISTER. see *BUSINESS AND ECONOMICS—Trade And Industrial Directories*

382   FRA   ISSN 0241-0257
CAMEROUN SELECTION. Text in French. s-m. (22/yr.).
Published by: I C Publications, 10 rue Vineuse, Paris, 75784 Cedex 16, France. FAX 33-1-44308111, 33-1-44308100.

382   CAN   ISSN 0847-0510
CANADA AND INTERNATIONAL RELATIONS. Text in English. irreg. price varies. adv. **Document type:** *Monographic series.*
Published by: University of British Columbia Press, 2029 West Mall, Vancouver, BC V6T 1Z2, Canada. TEL 604-822-5959, FAX 800-668-0821. Ed., R&P Jean Wilson TEL 604-822-6376. Adv. contact Berit Kraus.

382 614.7   CAN   ISSN 0846-5991
KE6096.A13
CANADA. CANADIAN INTERNATIONAL TRADE TRIBUNAL. ANNUAL REPORT. Text in English, French. 1969. a. free. adv. **Document type:** *Government.*
Former titles (until 1989): Canada. Canadian Import Tribunal. Annual Report (0846-6629); Canada. Anti-Dumping Tribunal. Annual Report
—CISTI.
Published by: Canadian International Trade Tribunal, 333 Laurier Ave W, Ottawa, ON K1A 0G7, Canada. TEL 613-993-7872, FAX 613-990-2439, secretary@citt.gc.ca, http://www.citt.gc.ca. Ed. Manon Carpentier. R&P, Adv. contact Michel Granger.

382   CAN   ISSN 0843-6509
CANADA. CANADIAN INTERNATIONAL TRADE TRIBUNAL. BULLETIN/CANADA. TRIBUNAL CANADIEN DU COMMERCE EXTERIEUR. BULLETIN. Text in English. q. free. adv. **Document type:** *Government.*
Published by: Canadian International Trade Tribunal, 333 Laurier Ave W, Ottawa, ON K1A 0G7, Canada. TEL 613-993-7872, FAX 613-990-2439, secretary@citt.gc.ca, http://www.citt.gc.ca. Ed. Manon Carpentier. Adv. contact Michel Granger.

CANADA. GRAIN COMMISSION. CORPORATE SERVICES. CANADIAN GRAIN EXPORTS. see *AGRICULTURE—Abstracting, Bibliographies, Statistics*

CANADA. STATISTICS CANADA. CANADA'S BALANCE OF INTERNATIONAL PAYMENTS/CANADA. STATISTIQUE CANADA. BALANCE DES PAIEMENTS INTERNATIONAUX DU CANADA. see *BUSINESS AND ECONOMICS—Abstracting, Bibliographies, Statistics*

332.6   CAN   ISSN 1499-1446
CANADA. STATISTICS CANADA. CANADA'S INTERNATIONAL TRADE IN SERVICES. Text in English. 1987. a. CND 40, USD 40 (effective 1999). adv. **Document type:** *Government.*
Description: Contains comprehensive source on international service transactions aggregate data from 1969. Major categories include travel, freight and shipping, business services and government transactions.
Formerly (until 1999): Canada. Statistics Canada. Canada's International Transactions in Services (0840-5859)
Related titles: Online - full text ed.: ISSN 1499-1454.
Published by: Statistics Canada, Operations and Integration Division, Circulation Management, Jean Talon Bldg, 2 C12, Tunney's Pasture, Ottawa, ON K1A 0T6, Canada. TEL 613-951-7277, 800-267-6677, FAX 613-951-1584, http://www.statcan.ca. Adv. contact Kathryn Bonner.

382.6   CAN   ISSN 0823-3330
CANADEXPORT (ENGLISH EDITION). Text in English. 1983. bi-w. free (effective 2004).
Incorporates (1974-1983): Canada. Department of Industry, Trade and Commerce. Trade News: Food and Agriculture (0700-2114)
Related titles: Online - full text ed.: ISSN 1493-7395.
—CISTI.

Published by: Canada. Department of Foreign Affairs and International Trade, 125 Sussex Dr, Ottawa, ON K1A OG2, Canada. TEL 613-996-2225, FAX 613-992-5791, canad.export@dfait-maeci.gc.ca, http://www.fac-aec.gc.ca/. Ed. Michaele Mancini.

382 322   CAN   ISSN 1206-2308
HC59.8
CANADIAN DEVELOPMENT REPORT. Text in English. 1997. a.
Published by: North-South Institute, 55 Murray St, Ste 200, Ottawa, ON K1N 5M3, Canada. TEL 613-241-3535, FAX 613-241-7435, nsi@nsi-ins.ca, http://www.nsi-ins.ca.

382   CAN   ISSN 0826-9815
HD9464.C19
CANADIAN FISHERIES. INTERNATIONAL TRADE/PECHES CANADIENNES. COMMERCE INTERNATIONAL. Text in English, French. 1985. q.
Formed by the 1985 merger of: Canadian Fisheries. Imports (0826-6549); (1981-1985): Canadian Fisheries. Exports (0826-6557)
Indexed: ESPM.
Published by: (Department of Fisheries and Oceans, Statistical Services), Department of Fisheries and Oceans, Communications Directorate, 200 Kent St, 13th Fl, Sta 13228, Ottawa, ON K1A 0E6, Canada. TEL 613-993-0999, FAX 613-990-1866, info@dfo-mpo.gc.ca, http://www.ncr.dfo.ca.

382   CAN   ISSN 0831-4527
CANADIAN FREE TRADER. Text in English. 1986. 10/yr. CND 145 (effective 2000). adv. back issues avail. **Document type:** *Newsletter.* **Description:** Covers Canada, the US and Mexico.
Incorporates: Canadian Free Trader International Supplement (1183-2088)
Published by: Intratech (Subsidiary of: E.L. LittleJohn and Associates), P O Box 56067, Minto Place Postal Outlet, Ottawa, ON K1R 7Z1, Canada. TEL 613-235-9183, FAX 613-594-3857. Ed. Edward L Littejohn. Adv. contact J Gillmore. Circ: 250.

CANADIAN INTERNATIONAL TRADE DIRECTORY. see *BUSINESS AND ECONOMICS—Trade And Industrial Directories*

CAPITAL FORMATION AND INVESTMENT INCENTIVES AROUND THE WORLD. see *BUSINESS AND ECONOMICS—Investments*

CARGOVISION. see *TRANSPORTATION—Air Transport*

338.0029   USA
CARIBBEAN GOLD COAST. Text in English. m.
Published by: Caribbean Publishing Co. Ltd., 815 NW 57th Ave., Ste. 125, Miami, FL 33126-2068. TEL 305-442-4505, FAX 305-442-8329.

338   GBR   ISSN 0142-4742
F2155
CARIBBEAN INSIGHT. Text in English. 1977. w. GBP 210, USD 400 (effective 2000). adv. bk.rev. **Document type:** *Newsletter.* **Description:** Covers economic and political developments in the Caribbean.
Incorporates: Caribbean and West Indies Chronicle (0143-1862); Which was formerly: West Indies Chronicle (0043-3152); West India Committee Chronicle
Indexed: PAIS, RASB.
Published by: West India Committee, One Birdcage Walk, London, SW1H 9JJ, United Kingdom. TEL 44-20-7976-1493, FAX 44-20-7304-6910, caribbean@compuserve.com. Ed., R&P Rod Prince. Adv. contact Geraldine Flower. Circ: 1,000.

CARIBBEAN STUDIES NEWSLETTER. see *POLITICAL SCIENCE—International Relations*

382 338.91 330.9   USA   ISSN 8756-324X
CARIBBEAN UPDATE. Text in English. 1985. m. USD 267 (effective 2005). bk.rev. back issues avail. **Document type:** *Newsletter, Consumer.* **Description:** Covers business, economic and political news in the Caribbean and Central America.
Related titles: Online - full text ed.: (from Factiva, Gale Group, Northern Light Technology, Inc., O C L C Online Computer Library Center, Inc., ProQuest Information & Learning).
Indexed: ABIn, B&I.
—CCC.
Published by: Caribbean Update Inc., 116 Myrtle Ave, Millburn, NJ 0704. TEL 973-376-2314, mexcarib@cs.com, http://www.caribbeanupdate.com. Ed., Pub. Kal Wagenheim.

382   BRA
CARTA INFORMATIVA. Text in Portuguese. 1976. m. free to qualified personnel. adv. bk.rev.
Formerly (until 1992): Arabe
Published by: Camara de Comercio Arabe Brasileira/Brazilian Arab Chamber of Commerce, Av. Paulista 326, 17 andar, CEP, Sao Paulo, SP 01310-902, Brazil. TEL 55-11-283-4066, FAX 55-11-288-8110, TELEX 011-34379 CCAB BR. Ed. Antonio Carlos D Greggio. Circ: 10,000.

▼ *new title*   ➤ *refereed*   ✶ *unverified*   ♦ *full entry avail.*

382   AUT
CASH. Text in German. 1984. m. adv. **Document type:** *Magazine, Trade.*
Published by: Manstein Zeitschriften Verlagsgesellschaft mbH, Brunner Feldstr 45, Perchtoldsdorf, N 2380, Austria. TEL 43-1-866480, FAX http://www.manstein.at, 43-1-86648100, cash@cash.at, office@manstein.at, http://www.cash.at. Ed. Sylvia Meissl. Adv. contact Petra Schimek. B&W page EUR 4,300, color page EUR 4,700; trim 210 x 297. Circ: 27,000 (paid and controlled).

382   ITA   ISSN 1594-0225
CATALOGO UNIFICATO. Text in Italian. 1974. a. EUR 28.50 (effective 2005). adv. **Document type:** *Catalog, Trade.*
Published by: Commercianti Italiani Filatelici, Via Privata Maria Teresa 11, Milan, MI 20123, Italy. TEL 39-02-877139, FAX 39-02-7202135, info@unificato.it, http://www.unificato.it. Ed. Igino Lottini. Adv. contact Paolo Deambrosi. Circ: 29,582.

332.6 336   DEU
CD-ROM DER AUSLANDSZOELLE. Text in German. 1956. bi-m. EUR 297 (effective 2001). **Document type:** *Trade.* **Description:** Provides complete information about all custom-tariffs in the world.
Formerly: Handbuch der Auslandszoelle
Media: CD-ROM.
Published by: Mendel Verlag, Robensstr 39, Aachen, 52070, Germany. TEL 49-241-154355, FAX 49-241-1570816, info@mendel-verlag.de, http://www.mendel-verlag.de.

382   USA   ISSN 1543-8864
HF3500.7
CENTRAL & EASTERN EUROPE COMMERCIAL UPDATE. Text in English. 2000. bi-m.
Published by: U.S. Department of Commerce, Central & Eastern Europe Business Information Center, Stop-R-CEEBIC, Washington, DC 20230. TEL 202-482-2645, FAX 202-482-3898, ceebic@ita.doc.gov, http://www.export.gov/ceebic. Eds. Leah Markowitz, Silvia Savich.

382   GBR
CENTRAL - EAST EUROPE BUSINESS ANALYST. Text in English. m. GBP 89, USD 175. **Description:** Analyzes economic conditions in the Commonwealth of Independent States, formerly U.S.S.R., and in central and eastern Europe. Monitors all international contracts involving the region. Provides detailed trade and production statistics.
Formerly: East - West Business Analyst
Published by: Debos Oxford Publications Ltd., 31 Warnborough Rd, Oxford, OX2 6JA, United Kingdom.

CENTRE FOR RESARCH IN ECONOMIC DEVELOPMENT AND INTERNATIONAL TRADE. RESEARCH PAPER. see *BUSINESS AND ECONOMICS*

332.6   AUT
CERCLE DIPLOMATIQUE INTERNATIONAL. Text in German. m.
Published by: Schmidt GmbH, Elisabethstrasse 13, Vienna, W 1010, Austria. TEL 01-5877707, FAX 01-5870752, TELEX 116036. Circ: 20,000.

332.6   CHE   ISSN 1420-0953
CH-D WIRTSCHAFT. Text in German. 1951. 11/yr. **Document type:** *Bulletin, Trade.*
Former titles (until 1985): Deutschland - Schweiz, Schweiz - Deutschland (1421-1300); (until 1952): Wirtschafts-Nachrichten Deutschland - Schweiz (1421-1297)
Published by: Handelskammer Deutschland - Schweiz, Toedistr 60, Zuerich, 8002, Switzerland. TEL 41-1-2836161, FAX 41-1-2836100. Ed. Martin Theurer. Circ: 5,200.

CHALLENGE EUROPE. see *BUSINESS AND ECONOMICS—Economic Situation And Conditions*

382   FRA
CHAMPAGNE - ARDENNE GUIDE DE L'EXPORTATEUR. Text in French. a.
Published by: Chambre Regionale de Commerce et d'Industrie Champagne - Ardenne, Direction de la Communication, 10 rue de Chastillon, B.P. 537, Chalons-sur-Marne, Cedex 51011, France. TEL 33-3-26693340, FAX 33-3-26693369.

382   IND   ISSN 0009-2207
CHEMEXCIL EXPORT BULLETIN. Text in English. 1967. m. INR 200, USD 6.06. adv.
Published by: Basic Chemicals Pharmaceuticals & Cosmetics Export Promotion Council, Jhansi Castle 4th Fl., 7 Cooperage Rd., Mumbai, Maharashtra 400 039, India. TEL 202-1288, FAX 202-6684, TELEX 011-4047. Ed. S Srinivasan. Circ: 5,500.

382   USA   ISSN 0884-4488
HC191
CHILE ECONOMIC REPORT✶. Text in English. 1967. m. free. **Document type:** *Newsletter.*
Related titles: Microform ed.: 1967 (from PQC).
Indexed: KES.
Published by: Corporacion de Fomento de la Produccion, Communications Department, 5900 N Andrews Ave, Ste 230, Fort Lauderdale, FL 33309-2366. TEL 212-938-0555, FAX 212-938-0568. Ed. Marco A Vallejo. Circ: 8,500.

332.6   CHL   ISSN 0716-288X
CHILE, EXPORTACIONES INVERSIONES ECONOMIA. Text in Spanish. 1982. bi-m.
Related titles: English ed.: Chile, Exports Investments Economy. ISSN 0716-3304.
Published by: Ministerio de Relaciones Exteriores, Direccion de Promocion de Exportaciones, Alameda Bernardo O Higgins, 1315 Piso 2, Santiago, Chile. TEL 696-0043. Ed. Carmen Marticorena. Circ: 16,500.

382   GBR
CHINA - BRITAIN BUSINESS REVIEW. Text in English. 1964. 10/yr. GBP 50 to individual members (effective 2005). adv. bk.rev. stat. **Document type:** *Magazine, Trade.* **Description:** Focuses on China's economic development and opportunities for foreign companies there.
Former titles (until Mar. 2005): China - Britain Trade Review (0952-9756); (until 1987): Sino-British Trade Review (0583-4279)
Related titles: Online - full text ed.
—BLDSC (3180.116500).
Published by: China - Britain Business Council, Abford House, 15 Wilton Rd, London, SW1V 1LT, United Kingdom. TEL 44-20-78285176, FAX 44-20-76305780, review@cbbc.org, http://www.cbbc.org/the_review/. Ed., R&P Janet Kealey. Adv. contact Olivia Browne. Circ: 6,000.

382   USA   ISSN 0731-7700
HF3831   CODEN: CHBTD2
CHINA BUSINESS AND TRADE✶. Text in English. 1979. s-m. looseleaf. USD 367.20 domestic to institutions; USD 377.20 in Canada & Mexico to institutions; USD 397.20 elsewhere to institutions; USD 459 domestic to corporations; USD 469 in Canada & Mexico to corporations; USD 489 elsewhere to corporations (effective 1999). adv. bk.rev. charts; stat.; tr.lit. back issues avail. **Document type:** *Newspaper.* **Description:** Provides news and analysis on business and economic developments throughout China and Hong Kong.
Supersedes in part: Business and Trade (0196-8602); Which was formerly: Soviet Business and Trade (0092-4695)
Indexed: CBNB, CIN, ChemAb, ChemTitl.
—CASDDS.
Published by: Welt Publishing Co., 1524 18th St, NW, Washington, DC 20036-1333. TEL 202-371-0555, 800-898-INTL, FAX 202-408-9369. Ed., Pub. Leo G.B. Welt. Adv. contact James Ford. Circ: 3,500.

382   USA   ISSN 1538-9596
CHINA BUSINESS INSIDER. Text in English. 2002. bi-m. (excpt. Feb.). USD 975 (effective 2002).
Related titles: Online - full text ed.: ISSN 1538-9650 (from EBSCO Publishing).
Published by: I O M A, 29 W 35th St, 5th Fl, New York, NY 10001-2299. TEL 212-244-0360, FAX 212-564-0465, http://www.ioma.com. Ed. Tian Hou. Pub. Lee Rath.

382   USA   ISSN 0163-7169
HF3128
CHINA BUSINESS REVIEW. Text in English. 1974. bi-m. USD 129 domestic; USD 169 foreign (effective 2005). adv. bk.rev. abstr.; charts; illus.; mkt.; maps; pat.; tr.lit. Index. back issues avail.; reprints avail. **Document type:** *Magazine, Trade.* **Description:** US business magazine of trade and investment in China and Hong Kong, focusing on opportunities for US and other foreign companies. Trends and issues in law, economics, and politics are analyzed for both immediate and long-term business implications.
Formerly (until 1977): U S China Business Review (0094-0089)
Related titles: Microform ed.: (from PQC); Online - full text ed.: ISSN 1542-5681. USD 100 (effective 2004) (from EBSCO Publishing, Gale Group, H.W. Wilson, Northern Light Technology, Inc., O C L C Online Computer Library Center, Inc., ProQuest Information & Learning, The Dialog Corporation).
Indexed: ABIn, APEL, B&I, BAS, BPI, BPIA, BusI, CPM, KES, LRI, ManagCont, PAIS, RASB, SRI, T&II.
—BLDSC (3180.125000), IE, Infotrieve, ingenta. **CCC.**
Published by: United States - China Business Council, 1818 N St, N W, Ste 200, Washington, DC 20036-2406. TEL 202-429-0340, FAX 202-833-9027, info@uschina.org, http://www.chinabusinessreview.com/. Ed. Catherine Gelb. R&P Gregory Heslin. Adv. contact Gregory S Heslin. B&W page USD 3,304, color page USD 4,721; trim 10.88 x 8.38. Circ: 3,000 (paid); 2,600 (controlled).

332.6   GBR   ISSN 1350-6390
CHINA ECONOMIC REVIEW (LONDON); the China international trade journal. Text in English. 1991. m. GBP 138, USD 240, EUR 250 (effective Oct. 2002). adv. back issues avail. **Document type:** *Journal, Trade.* **Description:** Provides business and financial news analysis for managers of organizations trading and investing in China.
Formerly (until 1992): Sdelano v Kitae - Made in China (0967-8182)
Related titles: Online - full text ed.
Indexed: APEL, JEL.
Published by: Alain Charles Publishing Ltd., Alain Charles House, 27 Wilfred St, London, SW1E 6PR, United Kingdom. TEL 44-20-78347676, FAX 44-20-79730076, post@alain.demon.co.uk, http://www.chinaeconomicreview.com, http://www.alaincharles.com. Ed. David Lammie. Adv. contact Marcus Langston. Circ: 8,614 (paid).

382   CHN
CHINA IMPORTERS & EXPORTERS. Text in Chinese, English. 1989. biennial. USD 385. **Document type:** *Directory.* **Description:** Provides information (names, addresses, products and services) on Chinese manufacturers and trade companies that are involved in the import and export business.
Published by: Han Consultants Inc., P.O. Box 71006, Wuhan, Hubei 430071, China. TEL 86-27-783-8532, FAX 86-27-787-8343. Circ: 6,000.

332.6   SGP   ISSN 0218-1517
HF41
CHINA MAIL/ZHONGGUO XINXUN. Text in English. 1988. q. SGD 30 domestic; SGD 42 in Malaysia; SGD 70 in Asia; SGD 76 in Australia & New Zealand; SGD 85 elsewhere (effective 2004). adv. **Document type:** *Trade.* **Description:** Emphasizes on rules & regulations, trade, market, economic, culture & tradition, and tourism pertaining to China.
Published by: T W L Publishing (Singapore) Pte. Ltd., Soon Seng Bldg, 25 Genting Rd 07-01, Singapore, 349482, Singapore. TEL 65-743-8606, FAX 65-743-6702, cic@pacific.net.sg, http://www.nihao.com/cic. Ed., Pub. Tang Kin Eng. R&P Angela Tang. Adv. contact Janet Wong. Circ: 51,650.

382.7   USA
CHINA MARKET✶; the businessman's guide to the China market. Text in English. 1982. bi-m. USD 50. adv. charts; stat.
Published by: East-West Trade Publications, P O Box 20564, New York, NY 10025-1521. Ed. Louis F Sharpe. Circ: 25,000.

382   USA   ISSN 1543-9356
HG5781
▼ **CHINA REPORT.** Text in English. 2003 (Mar.). bi-m. USD 125 (effective 2003).
Related titles: Online - full text ed.: ISSN 1543-9364.
Published by: Hartcourt Capital, Inc., 2500 E. Colorado Blvd. Ste. 301, Pasadena, CA 91107. TEL 626-844-2437, FAX 626-844-2442, http://www.hartcourt.com. Ed. Christian Giannini.

332.6   CHN
CHINA TRADE LINK. Text in Chinese, English. 1994. m. USD 345. **Document type:** *Newsletter.* **Description:** Provides information on import and export opportunities from and into China. Lists company name, address, telephone, fax and contact person.
Published by: Han Consultants Inc., P.O. Box 71006, Wuhan, Hubei 430071, China. TEL 86-27-783-8532, FAX 86-27-787-8343. Circ: 20,000.

382   HKG   ISSN 0009-448X
HF41   CODEN: CTRTAR
CHINA TRADE REPORT. Text in Chinese. 1963. m. USD 485 (effective 1999). stat. **Document type:** *Trade.* **Description:** Provides the latest information on trade and investment in China.
Indexed: KES, RASB.
—CASDDS, IE.
Published by: Review Publishing Co. Ltd. (Subsidiary of: Dow Jones Company), GPO Box 160, Hong Kong, Hong Kong. TEL 852-25737121, FAX 852-25031530, subscription@feer.com, http://www.feer.com. Ed. Paul Mooney.

382   DEU   ISSN 1439-2194
CHINACONTACT/CHUANG ZHI GUOZHONG; Das Wirtschaftsmagazin fuer Ihren Geschaeftserfolg in China. Key Title: China-Contact, Wirtschaftswelt China. Text in German. 1999. m. EUR 98 (effective 2004). adv. **Document type:** *Magazine, Trade.*
Formed by the merger of (199?-1999): China-Contact (1439-2186); (1994-1999): Wirtschaftswelt China (0947-2002)
Published by: Ost-West-Contact Verlags und Beratungs GmbH, Regenskamp 18, Muenster, 48157, Germany. TEL 49-251-261824, FAX 49-251-261373, info@owc.de, http://www.china-contact.cc, http://www.owc.de. Ed. Peter Tichauer. Adv. contact Horst Diedenhofen. B&W page EUR 2,250, color page EUR 3,100. Circ: 7,234 (paid and controlled).

382   CHN
CHINA'S EXPORTS. Text in Chinese. 1984. q. USD 42.
Published by: China Chamber of International Commerce (CCOIC), China Council for the Promotion of International Trade (CCPIT), 1 Fuxingmenwai St, Beijing, 100860, China. TEL 86-10-6857-2948, FAX 86-10-6851-0201, TELEX 22315 CCPIT CN, export@mx.cei.go.cn, http://www.ccpit.org/export. R&P Xinjiang Chen. Circ: 45,000.

382   CHN   ISSN 0009-4498
HF41
CHINA'S FOREIGN TRADE. Text in English. 1956. m. USD 123.20 (effective 2004). adv. illus. reprints avail. **Document type:** *Magazine, Trade.* **Description:** Contains articles on Chinese economic development and specialty products, as well as information on Chinese imports and exports, and related policies and regulations.
Related titles: Online - full text ed.: (from East View Information Services, LexisNexis); Chinese ed.: Zhongguo Duiwai Maoyi. USD 76.10 (effective 2000).
Indexed: BAS, KES, RASB.

Published by: (China Chamber of International Commerce (CCOIC), China Council for the Promotion of International Trade (CCPIT)), A S M Overseas Corp., Asian Games Garden, Bldg 2-6A,12 Xiaoying Lu, Chaoyang-qu, Beijing, 100101, China. TEL 86-1-64974451, FAX 86-1-64974872, cbwbj@cbwchina.com, icic@cbw.com, http://www.ccpit.org/publisher/ccpit24.html, http://www.cbw.com. Ed. Xinyi Li. Pub. Deyu Liu. Adv. contact Jiyong Chen. Circ: 70,000. **Subscr. to:** 227040, Los Angeles, CA 90022-0740. **Dist. by:** China International Book Trading Corp, 35 Chegongzhuang Xilu, Haidian District, PO Box 399, Beijing 100044, China.; **Dist. in US by:** China Books & Periodicals Inc, 360 Swift Ave., Ste. 48, S San Fran, CA 94080-6220. info@chinabooks.com, http://www.chinabooks.com/.

CINA NOTIZIE; rassegna informativa di attualita cinese. see *BUSINESS AND ECONOMICS*

382 330.9 CUB
COLABORACION INTERNACIONAL∗. Text in Spanish. 1979. q. USD 8 in North America; USD 10 in South America; USD 12 elsewhere. adv.
Published by: Ministerio de Cultura, Comite Estatal de Colaboracion Economica, Calle 2 No. 258 entre 11 y 13, Vedado, La Habana, Cuba. Ed. Eneida L Rodriquez Guanche. Circ: 4,000. **Dist. by:** Ediciones Cubanas, Obispo No. 527, Apdo. 605, Havana, Cuba.

382 COL ISSN 0120-6419
COLOMBIA. DEPARTAMENTO ADMINISTRATIVO NACIONAL DE ESTADISTICA. ANUARIO DE COMERCIO EXTERIOR. Text in Spanish. 1917. a. USD 160. **Document type:** *Government.*
Published by: Departamento Administrativo Nacional de Estadistica, Banco Nacional de Datos, Centro Administrativo Nacional (CAN), Avenida Eldorado, Apartado Aereo 80043, Bogota, CUND, Colombia. FAX 57-1-222-2305.

382 COL ISSN 0120-727X
COLOMBIA EXPORTA. Text in English, Spanish. 1982. a. charts; illus.; stat. **Description:** Covers Colombian trade and export industry.
Published by: Proexpo Fondo de Promocion de Exportaciones, Calle 28, 13-A-15 Piso 41, Bogota, CUND, Colombia. Ed. Amparo Jaramillo Sanin. Circ: 10,000.

332.6029 GBR
COMBINED INDEPENDENTS HOLDINGS DIRECTORY. Text in English. a. **Document type:** *Directory.*
Published by: D M G World Media Ltd. (Subsidiary of: Daily Mail and General Trust PLC), Queensway House, 2 Queensway, Redhill, Surrey RH1 1QS, United Kingdom. TEL 44-1737-768611, FAX 44-1737-760510.

382 MEX
COMERCIO. Text in Spanish. 1960. m. adv.
Published by: Alberto Barrauco Chavarria, Pub., Rio Tiber 87, 70, Mexico City, DF 06500, Mexico. TEL 5-514-0873, FAX 5-514-1169. Ed. Raul Horta. Circ: 40,000.

382 MEX ISSN 0185-0601
HF6
COMERCIO EXTERIOR. Text in Spanish; Abstracts in English. 1951. m. MXP 400 domestic; USD 70 foreign (effective 2005). adv. bk.rev. stat. index. **Document type:** *Trade.* **Description:** Presents socio-economic matters, especially those related to Mexico and Latin America.
Related titles: CD-ROM ed.; Online - full text ed.: ISSN 1563-7352. 1996.
Indexed: BAS, HAPI, IBR, IBSS, IBZ, ILD, JEL, PAIS, RASB, RRTA, WAE&RSA.
Published by: Banco Nacional de Comercio Exterior S.N.C., Camino a Santa Teresa #1679, Col. Jardines del Pedregal, Del. Alvaro Obregon, Mexico City, DF 01900, Mexico. TEL 52-555-4816000, bancomext@bancomext.gob.mx, http://www.bxt.gob.mx/esp/revista.html, http://www.bancomext.com/. Ed. Homero Urias Brambila. Pub., Adv. contact Sergio Hernandez Clark. Circ: 10,000. **Subscr. to:** Apdo. Postal 221258, Mexico City, DF 04100, Mexico.

382.025 ESP ISSN 1139-6318
HF5209.M2
COMERCIO EXTERIOR DE LA COMUNIDAD DE MADRID. Text in Spanish. 1990. a. EUR 12.02 (effective 2003).
Related titles: CD-ROM ed.: ISSN 1139-630X. 1998; Abridged ed.: ISSN 1579-3923. 2001.
Published by: Comunidad de Madrid, Consejeria de Economia e Innovacion Tecnologica. Instituto de Estadistica, Principe de Vergara, 108, Madrid, 28002, Spain. TEL 34-91-5802540, jestadis@madrid.org, http://www.madrid.org/iestadis/index.htm.

COMERTUL EXTERIOR AL ROMANIEI/FOREIGN TRADE OF ROMANIA. see *BUSINESS AND ECONOMICS—Abstracting, Bibliographies, Statistics*

COMISION DE LAS NACIONES UNIDAS PARA EL DERECHO MERCANTIL INTERNACIONAL. ANUARIO. see *LAW—International Law*

COMMERCE; English monthly. see *BUSINESS AND ECONOMICS—Domestic Commerce*

COMMERCE DU LEVANT. see *BUSINESS AND ECONOMICS—Domestic Commerce*

382 CIV
COMMERCE EXTERIEUR DE LA COTE D'IVOIRE: RESULTATS ET EVOLUTION∗. Text in French. irreg. stat.
Published by: Direction des Affaires Economiques et des Relations Economiques Exterieures, Imprimiere Nationale, 7 av Marchand, BP V87, Abidjan, Ivory Coast.

352 GBR ISSN 0962-5267
COMMERCE U S A. Text in English. 1978. bi-m. free. adv. back issues avail. **Description:** Contains information about United States export trade relations with regard to European investment and expansion.
Formerly: Commercial Newsletter
Published by: (U.S. Embassy (London)), Mediafine Ltd., Port of Liverpool Bldg, Liverpool, Merseyside L3 1BZ, United Kingdom. TEL 051-236-5757, FAX 051-227-29010. Ed. Mark Chivers. Circ: 7,500.

COMMERCIAL LAWS OF THE WORLD. see *LAW—International Law*

382 USA ISSN 0161-9772
HF1455
COMMERCIAL NEWS U S A. Abbreviated title: C N. Text in English. 1974. m. free. bk.rev. charts; illus. 30 p./no.; back issues avail. **Document type:** *Catalog, Government.* **Description:** Contains information about U.S. goods and services for 134,000 international sales representatives, distributors, purchasing officials, licensees, and end-users in more than 33 industry categories.
Formerly (until Jan.-Feb. 1978): Commercial News for the Foreign Service (0363-678X)
Related titles: Online - full text ed.
Published by: (U.S. and Foreign Commercial Service), U.S. Department of Commerce, International Trade Administration, 1401 Constitution Ave, N W, Room 3414, Washington, DC 20230. TEL 202-482-3251, FAX 202-482-5819, http://www.cnewsusa.com, http://www.ita.doc.gov. Circ: 134,000 (controlled).

332.6 ITA ISSN 1126-1617
COMMERCIO INTERNAZIONALE. Text in Italian. 1977. fortn. EUR 227 (effective 2005). adv. **Document type:** *Magazine, Consumer.*
Former titles (until 1989): Gazzetta Valutaria e del Commercio Internazionale (1125-9086); (until 1981): Gazzetta Valutaria (1125-9094)
Published by: IPSOA Editore (Subsidiary of: Wolters Kluwer Italia Srl), Strada 1, Palazzo F6, Milanofiori, Assago, MI 20090, Italy. TEL 39-02-82476888, FAX 39-02-82476436, http://www.ipsoa.it. Ed. Massimiliano Galioni. Adv. contact Luciano Alcaro Menichini. Circ: 10,500.

COMMISSION DES NATIONS UNIES POUR LE DROIT COMMERCIAL INTERNATIONAL. ANNUAIRE. see *LAW—International Law*

382 USA
COMMODITIES - U S A. Text in English, Spanish. 1998. m. free. adv. illus. **Document type:** *Trade.* **Description:** Brings the marketing news, regional trends, and new-product and marketing innovations of the United States to executives and other businesspersons throughout Central and South America.
Published by: Douglas Mayorga, Ed. & Pub., PO Box 720548, Miami, FL 33172. TEL 305-710-0671, FAX 305-260-0339, editor@commodities-usa.com, http://www.commodities-usa.com. Adv. contact Maria Loasiga. color page USD 1,795; trim 10.81 x 8. Circ: 35,000.

332.6 USA ISSN 1057-9966
HF1042
COMMODITY CLASSIFICATION UNDER THE HARMONIZED SYSTEM HANDBOOK. Text in English. m. USD 100; USD 125 foreign. back issues avail. **Document type:** *Government.*
Published by: U.S. Department of the Treasury, U.S. Customs Service, 1301 Constitution Ave, N W, Washington, DC 20229. TEL 202-566-5000. **Subscr. to:** U.S. Government Printing Office, Superintendent of Documents.

382 AUS ISSN 0813-8389
COMMONWEALTH OF AUSTRALIA GAZETTE. TARIFF CONCESSIONS. Text in English. 1990. w. AUD 115 (effective 1999 & 2000). **Document type:** *Government.* **Description:** Contains notices of the tariff concessions proposed, granted or revoked with the provisions of the Customs Act of 1901 (Australia).
Published by: Australia. Attorney-General's Department, Robert Garran Offices, National Circuit, Barton, ACT 2600, Australia. TEL 64-2-62506666, FAX 64-2-62505900, http://www.ausinfo.gov.au, http://www.ag.gov.au.

382 BEL
COMPAGNIE FINANCIERE EUROPEENNE ET D'OUTRE-MER. FINOUTREMER. RAPPORT ANNUEL. Text in French. 1972. a. free.
Former titles: Compagnie Europeenne et d'Outre-Mer. Rapports; Compagnie du Congo pour le Commerce et l'Industrie. Assemblee Generale. Rapports
Published by: Compagnie Financiere Europeene et d'Outre-Mer, Rue Royale 30, Brussels, 1000, Belgium.

382 340 USA
COMPETITION LAW OF THE EUROPEAN COMMUNITY. Text in English. 1988. 2 base vols. plus irreg. updates. looseleaf. USD 235 base vol(s). (effective 2003). Supplement avail. **Description:** Analysis of the competition policy of the EC. Provides thorough discussion of the founding treaty, organization, law and regulations of the EC, as well as examination of decisions and agreements affecting commerce and economic activity in such areas as pricing and distribution practices, mergers, joint ventures, monopolies, licensing, intellectual property rights and enforcement and remedies. Sets forth the text of the establishing treaty, and significant regulations, announcements, and protocols.
Published by: Matthew Bender & Co., Inc. (Subsidiary of: LexisNexis North America), 1275 Broadway, Albany, NY 12204. international@bender.com, http://bender.lexisnexis.com. Ed. Valentine Korah.

382.7 CHE
COMPETITION POLICY. Text in English. irreg., latest vol.18, 2000. back issues avail. **Document type:** *Monographic series, Academic/Scholarly.* **Description:** Addresses regulatory aspects, policies, practical measures and experiences gained by countries in the framework of competition law and policy.
Published by: United Nations Conference on Trade and Development, 8-14 Avenue de la Paix, Geneva 10, 1211, Switzerland. TEL 41-22-9174924, FAX 41-22-9070195, info@unctad.org, http://www.unctad.org.

B

332.6 658 USA ISSN 1059-5422
HB238 CODEN: COREFK
➤ **COMPETITIVENESS REVIEW**; an international business journal. Text in English. 1991. s-a. USD 60 domestic to individuals; USD 80 foreign to individuals; USD 120 domestic to institutions; USD 140 foreign to institutions (effective 2005). bk.rev. **Document type:** *Journal, Academic/Scholarly.* **Description:** Studies competitiveness issues around the globe. Devoted to the improvement and understanding of theory and application of issues related to competitiveness.
Related titles: Online - full text ed.: (from EBSCO Publishing, Florida Center for Library Automation, Gale Group, O C L C Online Computer Library Center, Inc., ProQuest Information & Learning).
Indexed: ABIn, CPM, ESPM, RiskAb, SOPODA.
—BLDSC (3363.993690), IE, ingenta.
Published by: Indiana University of Pennsylvania, International Academy of Business Disciplines, PO Box 1658, Indiana, PA 15705. TEL 754-357-5759, aaali@grove.iup.edu. Ed., R&P Abbas J Ali. Circ: 750.

382 MEX
CONACEX INFORMA. Text in Spanish. m. free. adv. **Document type:** *Bulletin.* **Description:** Keeps readers updated about international trade. Provides answers to members' problems in exporting-importing.
Supersedes (in Nov. 1997): Conacex Noreste Magazine; Formerly: Conacex Noreste Boletin Informativo
Published by: Consejo Nacional de Comercio Exterior del Noreste A.C./National Foreign Trade Council of the Northeast Region of Mexico, 95-E, Edf. Cintermex, Mexico, Ave. PARQUE FUNDIDORA 501, Col. Obrera, Monterrey, NL 64010, Mexico. TEL 528-3690292, FAX 528-3690293, conacex@technet.net.mx, http://www.technet.net.mx/conacex/. Adv. contact Ernesto Gonzalez. Circ: 2,000.

382.7 NZL ISSN 0113-3292
CONTRABAND; New Zealand Customs Service magazine. Text in English. 1968. bi-m. adv. Index. **Document type:** *Magazine, Trade.*
Supersedes: New Zealand. Customs Department. Customs Bulletin (0548-9962); New Zealand. Customs Department. Import Licensing Bulletin
—CCC.
Published by: New Zealand Customs Service, Private Bag 1928, Dunedin, New Zealand. TEL 64-3-4779251, FAX 64-3-4776773, feedback@customs.govt.nz, http://www.customs.govt.nz/default.htm. Ed. M B Anderton. Circ: 3,000.

CONTRACT OF SALE IN INTERNATIONAL TRADE LAW. see *LAW—International Law*

CORPORATE AIR TRAVEL SURVEY. see *TRANSPORTATION—Air Transport*

CORPORATE COMPASS. see *REAL ESTATE*

CORPORATE COUNSEL'S GUIDE TO BUSINESS-RELATED VISAS. see *LAW—Corporate Law*

382 346 USA
CORPORATE COUNSEL'S GUIDE TO DOING BUSINESS IN CHINA. Text in English. 1999. irreg. USD 185 (effective 2001).
Published by: Business Laws, Inc., 11630 Chillicothe Rd, Chesterland, OH 44026. TEL 440-729-7996, FAX 440-729-0645, http://www.businesslaws.com.

▼ new title ➤ refereed ∗ unverified ◆ full entry avail.

382 346   USA
CORPORATE COUNSEL'S GUIDE TO DOING BUSINESS IN INDIA. Text in English. 2001. irreg. USD 165 (effective 2001).
Published by: Business Laws, Inc., 11630 Chillicothe Rd, Chesterland, OH 44026. TEL 440-729-7996, FAX 440-729-0645, http://www.businesslaws.com.

CORPORATE COUNSEL'S GUIDE TO EXPORT CONTROLS.
see *BUSINESS AND ECONOMICS—Domestic Commerce*

382 341   USA   ISSN 0898-9907
K3943.A13
CORPORATE COUNSEL'S INTERNATIONAL ADVISER. Text in English. 1985. m. looseleaf. USD 365 (effective 2005). bk.rev. charts. cum.index. back issues avail. **Document type:** *Newsletter, Trade.* **Description:** Provides current information on international business topics.
—CCC.
Published by: Business Laws, Inc., 11630 Chillicothe Rd, Chesterland, OH 44026. TEL 440-729-7996, 800-759-0929, FAX 440-729-0645, custserv@businesslaws.com, http://www.businesslaws.com. Ed. William A Hancock.

382 346   USA   ISSN 1535-2285
K1005
CORPORATE COUNSEL'S INTERNATIONAL CONTRACT ADVISER. Text in English. 2001. m. USD 180 (effective 2001).
—CCC.
Published by: Business Laws, Inc., 11630 Chillicothe Rd, Chesterland, OH 44026. TEL 440-729-7996, FAX 440-729-0645, http://www.businesslaws.com.

382   FRA   ISSN 0221-5780
COTE-D'IVOIRE SELECTION. Text in French. s-m. (22/yr.).
Published by: I C Publications, 10 rue Vineuse, Paris, 75784 Cedex 16, France. FAX 33-1-44308111, 33-1-44308100.

COUNTERTRADE & OFFSET; weekly intelligence on unconventional & reciprocal international trade. see *BUSINESS AND ECONOMICS—Investments*

338.91   USA
COUNTRY COMMERCE. (55 separate country reports available.) Text in English. a. USD 395 subscr - carrier delivery (effective 2004). illus.; stat. back issues avail. **Document type:** *Trade.* **Description:** Provides a reference guide to the specific operating conditions, commercial laws and business regulations of 55 countries worldwide, including critical issues such as obtaining proper permits and registrations, protecting your intellectual property in the Internet age, complying with local tax laws, and e-commerce rules.
Published by: Economist Intelligence Unit, 111 W 57th St, New York, NY 10019. http://store.eiu.com/index.asp?layout= product_home_page&product_id=480000248&ref=av_search, http://www.eiu.com.

382   USA
COUNTRY COMMERCE. AMERICAS. Text in English. s-a. GBP 225, USD 345 (effective 2000). **Document type:** *Trade.* **Description:** Offers information on corporate tax rules, exchange and price controls, trade and licensing restrictions, labor conditions and investment rules.
Former titles (until 2000): Investing, Licensing and Trading. Americas; (until 1997): Investing, Licensing and Trading Conditions Abroad. Americas; Investing, Licensing and Trading Conditions Abroad. Latin America
Related titles: ♦ CD-ROM ed.: E I U Investing, Licensing and Trading; Online - full text ed.: (from SilverPlatter Information, Inc., The Dialog Corporation).
Published by: Economist Intelligence Unit, 111 W 57th St, New York, NY 10019. TEL 212-554-0600, 800-938-4685, FAX 212-586-1181, http://www.eiu.com.

332.6   USA
HG5311
COUNTRY COMMERCE. ARGENTINA. Text in English. a. GBP 225, USD 345 (effective 2000). **Document type:** *Trade.* **Description:** Provides information on corporate tax rules, exchange and price controls, trade and licensing restrictions, labor conditions and investment rules for Argentina.
Former titles (until 2000): Investing, Licensing and Trading. Argentina; (until 1997): Investing, Licensing and Trading Conditions Abroad. Argentina (1352-9838)
Related titles: ♦ CD-ROM ed.: E I U Investing, Licensing and Trading; Online - full text ed.: (from SilverPlatter Information, Inc., The Dialog Corporation).
Published by: Economist Intelligence Unit, 111 W 57th St, New York, NY 10019. TEL 212-554-0600, 800-938-4685, FAX 212-586-1181, http://www.eiu.com.

332.6   USA
COUNTRY COMMERCE. ASIA. Text in English. s-a. GBP 225, USD 345 (effective 2000). **Document type:** *Trade.* **Description:** Offers information on corporate tax rules, exchange and price controls, trade and licensing restrictions, labor conditions and investment rules.
Former titles (until 2000): Investing, Licensing and Trading. Asia; (until 1997): Investing, Licensing and Trading Conditions Abroad. Asia; Investing, Licensing and Trading Conditions Abroad. Asia - Pacific

Related titles: ♦ CD-ROM ed.: E I U Investing, Licensing and Trading; Online - full text ed.: (from SilverPlatter Information, Inc., The Dialog Corporation).
Published by: Economist Intelligence Unit, 111 W 57th St, New York, NY 10019. TEL 212-554-0600, 800-938-4685, FAX 212-586-1181, TELEX 175567, http://www.eiu.com.

332.6   USA
HG5891
COUNTRY COMMERCE. AUSTRALIA. Text in English. a. GBP 225, USD 345 (effective 2000). **Document type:** *Trade.* **Description:** Provides information on corporate tax rules, exchange and price controls, trade and licensing restrictions, labor conditions and investment rules.
Former titles (until 2000): Investing, Licensing and Trading. Australia; (until 1997): Investing, Licensing and Trading Conditions Abroad. Australia (1353-5889)
Related titles: ♦ CD-ROM ed.: E I U Investing, Licensing and Trading; Online - full text ed.: (from SilverPlatter Information, Inc., The Dialog Corporation).
Published by: Economist Intelligence Unit, 111 W 57th St, New York, NY 10019. TEL 212-554-0600, 800-938-4685, FAX 212-586-1181, http://www.eiu.com.

332.6   USA
HG5451
COUNTRY COMMERCE. AUSTRIA. Text in English. a. GBP 225, USD 345 (effective 2000). **Document type:** *Trade.* **Description:** Provides information on corporate tax rules, exchange and price controls, trade and licensing restrictions, labor conditions and investment rules.
Former titles (until 2000): Investing, Licensing and Trading. Austria; (until 1997): Investing, Licensing and Trading Conditions Abroad. Austria (1352-9943)
Related titles: ♦ CD-ROM ed.: E I U Investing, Licensing and Trading; Online - full text ed.: (from SilverPlatter Information, Inc., The Dialog Corporation).
Published by: Economist Intelligence Unit, 111 W 57th St, New York, NY 10019. TEL 212-554-0600, 800-938-4685, FAX 212-586-1181, http://www.eiu.com.

332.6   USA   ISSN 1553-6068
HG5551
COUNTRY COMMERCE. BELGIUM. Text in English. a. GBP 225, USD 345 (effective 2000). **Document type:** *Trade.* **Description:** Provides information on corporate tax rules, exchange and price controls, trade and licensing restrictions, labor conditions and investment rules.
Former titles (until 2000): Investing, Licensing and Trading. Belgium; (until 1997): Investing, Licensing and Trading Conditions Abroad. Belgium (1352-5913)
Related titles: ♦ CD-ROM ed.: E I U Investing, Licensing and Trading; Online - full text ed.: (from SilverPlatter Information, Inc., The Dialog Corporation).
Published by: Economist Intelligence Unit, 111 W 57th St, New York, NY 10019. TEL 212-554-0600, 800-938-4685, FAX 212-586-1181, http://www.eiu.com.

332.6   USA   ISSN 1547-920X
HG5331
COUNTRY COMMERCE. BRAZIL. Text in English. a. GBP 225, USD 345 (effective 2000). **Document type:** *Trade.* **Description:** Provides information on corporate tax rules, exchange and price controls, trade and licensing restrictions, labor conditions and investment rules.
Former titles (until 2001): Investing, Licensing and Trading. Brazil; (until 1997): Investing, Licensing and Trading Conditions Abroad. Brazil (1352-5921)
Related titles: ♦ CD-ROM ed.: E I U Investing, Licensing and Trading; Online - full text ed.: (from SilverPlatter Information, Inc., The Dialog Corporation).
Published by: Economist Intelligence Unit, 111 W 57th St, New York, NY 10019. TEL 212-554-0600, 800-938-4685, FAX 212-586-1181, http://www.eiu.com.

332.6   USA   ISSN 1547-9323
HG5151
COUNTRY COMMERCE. CANADA. Text in English. a. GBP 225, USD 345 (effective 2000). **Document type:** *Trade.* **Description:** Provides information on corporate tax rules, exchange and price controls, trade and licensing restrictions, labor conditions and investment rules.
Former titles (until 2000): Investing, Licensing and Trading. Canada; (until 1997): Investing, Licensing and Trading Conditions Abroad. Canada (1352-9811)
Related titles: ♦ CD-ROM ed.: E I U Investing, Licensing and Trading; Online - full text ed.: (from SilverPlatter Information, Inc., The Dialog Corporation).
—CCC.
Published by: Economist Intelligence Unit, 111 W 57th St, New York, NY 10019. TEL 212-554-0600, 800-938-4685, FAX 212-586-1181, http://www.eiu.com.

322.6   USA
HG5171
COUNTRY COMMERCE. CENTRAL AMERICA; including El Salvador, Guatemala, Honduras and Costa Rica. Text in English. a. GBP 225, USD 345 (effective 2000). **Document type:** *Trade.* **Description:** Provides information on corporate tax rules, exchange and price controls, trade and licensing restrictions, labor conditions and investment rules.

Former titles (until 2000): Investing, Licensing and Trading. Central America; (until 1997): Investing, Licensing and Trading Conditions Abroad. Central America (1353-6273); Which was formed by the merger of: Investing, Licensing and Trade Conditions Abroad. Honduras; Investing, Licensing and Trade Conditions Abroad. Guatemala; Investing, Licensing and Trade Conditions Abroad. El Salvador; Investing, Licensing and Trading Conditions Abroad. Costa Rica
Related titles: ♦ CD-ROM ed.: E I U Investing, Licensing and Trading; Online - full text ed.: (from SilverPlatter Information, Inc., The Dialog Corporation).
Published by: Economist Intelligence Unit, 111 W 57th St, New York, NY 10019. TEL 212-554-0600, 800-938-4685, FAX 212-586-1181, http://www.eiu.com.

322.6   USA
HG5341
COUNTRY COMMERCE. CHILE. Text in English. a. GBP 225, USD 345 (effective 2000). **Document type:** *Trade.* **Description:** Provides information on corporate tax rules, exchange and price controls, trade and licensing restrictions, labor conditions and investment rules.
Former titles (until 2001): Investing, Licensing and Trading. Chile; (until 1997): Investing, Licensing and Trading Conditions Abroad. Chile (1352-593X)
Related titles: ♦ CD-ROM ed.: E I U Investing, Licensing and Trading; Online - full text ed.: (from SilverPlatter Information, Inc., The Dialog Corporation).
Published by: Economist Intelligence Unit, 111 W 57th St, New York, NY 10019. TEL 212-554-0600, 800-938-4685, FAX 212-586-1181, http://www.eiu.com.

332.6   USA
HG5781
COUNTRY COMMERCE. CHINA. Text in English. a. GBP 225, USD 345 (effective 2000). **Document type:** *Trade.* **Description:** Provides information on corporate tax rules, exchange and price controls, trade and licensing restrictions, labor conditions and investment rules.
Former titles (until 2001): Investing, Licensing and Trading. China; (until 1997): Investing, Licensing and Trading Conditions Abroad. China (1353-6265)
Related titles: ♦ CD-ROM ed.: E I U Investing, Licensing and Trading; Online - full text ed.: (from SilverPlatter Information, Inc., The Dialog Corporation).
Published by: Economist Intelligence Unit, 111 W 57th St, New York, NY 10019. TEL 212-554-0600, 800-938-4685, FAX 212-586-1181, http://www.eiu.com.

332.6   USA   ISSN 1547-9218
HG5351
COUNTRY COMMERCE. COLOMBIA. Text in English. a. GBP 225, USD 345 (effective 2000). **Document type:** *Trade.* **Description:** Provides information on corporate tax rules, exchange and price controls, trade and licensing restrictions, labor conditions and investment rules.
Former titles (until 2001): Investing, Licensing and Trading. Colombia; (until 1997): Investing, Licensing and Trading Conditions Abroad. Colombia (1352-5948)
Related titles: ♦ CD-ROM ed.: E I U Investing, Licensing and Trading; Online - full text ed.: (from SilverPlatter Information, Inc., The Dialog Corporation).
Published by: Economist Intelligence Unit, 111 W 57th St, New York, NY 10019. TEL 212-554-0600, 800-938-4685, FAX 212-586-1181, http://www.eiu.com.

332.6   USA   ISSN 1549-5167
HG5470.3.A2
COUNTRY COMMERCE. CZECH REPUBLIC. Text in English. a. GBP 225, USD 345 (effective 2000). **Document type:** *Trade.* **Description:** Provides information on corporate tax rules, exchange and price controls, trade and licensing restrictions, labor conditions and investment rules.
Former titles (until 2000): Investing, Licensing and Trading. Czech Republic; (until 1997): Investing, Licensing and Trading Conditions Abroad. Czech Republic (1353-629X); Which superseded in part: Investing, Licensing and Trading Conditions. Czech Republic and Slovakia; Which was formerly (until 1993): Investing, Licensing and Trading Conditions Abroad. Czechoslovakia (1352-9951)
Related titles: ♦ CD-ROM ed.: E I U Investing, Licensing and Trading; Online - full text ed.: (from SilverPlatter Information, Inc., The Dialog Corporation).
Published by: Economist Intelligence Unit, 111 W 57th St, New York, NY 10019. TEL 212-554-0600, 800-938-4685, FAX 212-586-1181, http://www.eiu.com.

332.6   USA
HG5591
COUNTRY COMMERCE. DENMARK. Text in English. a. GBP 225, USD 345 (effective 2000). **Document type:** *Trade.* **Description:** Provides information on corporate tax rules, exchange and price controls, trade and licensing restrictions, labor conditions and investment rules.
Former titles (until 2001): Investing, Licensing and Trading. Denmark; (until 1997): Investing, Licensing and Trading Conditions Abroad. Denmark (1352-5956)
Related titles: ♦ CD-ROM ed.: E I U Investing, Licensing and Trading; Online - full text ed.: (from SilverPlatter Information, Inc., The Dialog Corporation).
Published by: Economist Intelligence Unit, 111 W 57th St, New York, NY 10019. TEL 212-554-0600, 800-938-4685, FAX 212-586-1181, http://www.eiu.com.

332.6 USA
HG5361
COUNTRY COMMERCE. ECUADOR. Text in English. a. GBP 225, USD 345 (effective 2000). **Document type:** *Trade.*
Description: Provides information on corporate tax rules, exchange and price controls, trade and licensing restrictions, labor conditions and investment rules.
Former titles (until 2000): Investing, Licensing and Trading. Ecuador; (until 1997): Investing, Licensing and Trading Conditions Abroad. Ecuador (1352-9846)
Related titles: ♦ CD-ROM ed.: E I U Investing, Licensing and Trading; Online - full text ed.: (from SilverPlatter Information, Inc., The Dialog Corporation).
Published by: Economist Intelligence Unit, 111 W 57th St, New York, NY 10019. TEL 212-554-0600, 800-938-4685, FAX 212-586-1181, http://www.eiu.com.

332.6 USA
HG5836.A2
COUNTRY COMMERCE. EGYPT. Text in English. a. GBP 225, USD 345 (effective 2000). **Document type:** *Trade.*
Description: Provides information on corporate tax rules, exchange and price controls, trade and licensing restrictions, labor conditions and investment rules.
Former titles (until 2000): Investing, Licensing and Trading. Egypt; (until 1997): Investing, Licensing and Trading Conditions Abroad. Egypt (1352-9781)
Related titles: ♦ CD-ROM ed.: E I U Investing, Licensing and Trading; Online - full text ed.: (from SilverPlatter Information, Inc., The Dialog Corporation).
Published by: Economist Intelligence Unit, 111 W 57th St, New York, NY 10019. TEL 212-554-0600, 800-938-4685, FAX 212-586-1181, http://www.eiu.com.

332.6 USA
HG5421
COUNTRY COMMERCE. EUROPEAN UNION. Text in English. a. GBP 225, USD 345 (effective 2000). **Description:** Provides information on corporate tax rules, exchange and price controls, trade and licensing restrictions, labor conditions and investment rules.
Former titles (until 2001): Investing, Licensing and Trading. European Union; (until 1997): Investing, Licensing and Trading Conditions Abroad. European Union
Related titles: ♦ CD-ROM ed.: E I U Investing, Licensing and Trading; Online - full text ed.: (from SilverPlatter Information, Inc., The Dialog Corporation).
Published by: Economist Intelligence Unit, 111 W 57th St, New York, NY 10019. TEL 212-554-0600, 800-938-4685, FAX 212-586-1181, http://www.eiu.com.

332.6 USA
HG5581
COUNTRY COMMERCE. FINLAND. Text in English. a. GBP 225, USD 345 (effective 2000). **Document type:** *Trade.*
Description: Provides information on corporate tax rules, exchange and price controls, trade and licensing restrictions, labor conditions and investment rules.
Former titles (until 2000): Investing, Licensing and Trading. Finland; (until 1997): Investing, Licensing and Trading Conditions Abroad. Finland
Related titles: ♦ CD-ROM ed.: E I U Investing, Licensing and Trading; Online - full text ed.: (from SilverPlatter Information, Inc., The Dialog Corporation).
Published by: Economist Intelligence Unit, 111 W 57th St, New York, NY 10019. TEL 212-554-0600, 800-938-4685, FAX 212-586-1181, http://www.eiu.com.

332.6 USA
HG5471
COUNTRY COMMERCE. FRANCE. Text in English. a. GBP 225, USD 345 (effective 2000). **Document type:** *Trade.*
Description: Provides information on corporate tax rules, exchange and price controls, trade and licensing restrictions, labor conditions and investment rules.
Former titles (until 2000): Investing, Licensing and Trading. France; (until 1997): Investing, Licensing and Trading Conditions Abroad. France (1352-9897)
Related titles: ♦ CD-ROM ed.: E I U Investing, Licensing and Trading; Online - full text ed.: (from SilverPlatter Information, Inc., The Dialog Corporation).
Published by: Economist Intelligence Unit, 111 W 57th St, New York, NY 10019. TEL 212-554-0600, 800-938-4685, FAX 212-586-1181, http://www.eiu.com.

332.6 USA ISSN 1547-9137
HG5491
COUNTRY COMMERCE. GERMANY. Text in English. a. GBP 225, USD 345 (effective 2000). **Document type:** *Trade.*
Description: Provides information on corporate tax rules, exchange and price controls, trade and licensing restrictions, labor conditions and investment rules.
Former titles (until 2000): Investing, Licensing and Trading. Germany; (until 1997): Investing, Licensing and Trading Conditions Abroad. Germany (1352-9900)
Related titles: ♦ CD-ROM ed.: E I U Investing, Licensing and Trading; Online - full text ed.: (from SilverPlatter Information, Inc., The Dialog Corporation).
Published by: Economist Intelligence Unit, 111 W 57th St, New York, NY 10019. TEL 212-554-0600, 800-938-4685, FAX 212-586-1181, http://www.eiu.com.

332.6 USA
HG5700.5.A2
COUNTRY COMMERCE. GREECE. Text in English. a. GBP 225, USD 345 (effective 2000). **Document type:** *Trade.*
Description: Provides information on corporate tax rules, exchange and price controls, trade and licensing restrictions, labor conditions and investment rules.
Former titles (until 2000): Investing, Licensing and Trading. Greece; (until 1997): Investing, Licensing and Trading Conditions Abroad. Greece (1352-9919)
Related titles: Online - full text ed.: (from The Dialog Corporation).
Published by: Economist Intelligence Unit, 111 W 57th St, New York, NY 10019. TEL 212-554-0600, 800-938-4685, FAX 212-586-1181, http://www.eiu.com.

332.6 USA ISSN 1547-9196
HG5801
COUNTRY COMMERCE. HONG KONG. Text in English. a. GBP 225, USD 345 (effective 2000). **Description:** Provides information on corporate tax rules, exchange and price controls, trade and licensing restrictions, labor conditions and investment rules.
Former titles (until 2000): Investing, Licensing and Trading. Hong Kong; (until 1997): Investing, Licensing and Trading Conditions Abroad. Hong Kong
Related titles: ♦ CD-ROM ed.: E I U Investing, Licensing and Trading; Online - full text ed.: (from SilverPlatter Information, Inc., The Dialog Corporation).
Published by: Economist Intelligence Unit, 111 W 57th St, New York, NY 10019. TEL 212-554-0600, 800-938-4685, FAX 212-586-1181, http://www.eiu.com.

332.6 USA ISSN 1547-9331
HG5470.5.A2
COUNTRY COMMERCE. HUNGARY. Text in English. a. GBP 225, USD 345 (effective 2000). **Document type:** *Trade.*
Description: Provides information on corporate tax rules, exchange and price controls, trade and licensing restrictions, labor conditions and investment rules.
Former titles (until 2000): Investing, Licensing and Trading. Hungary; (until 1997): Investing, Licensing and Trading Conditions Abroad. Hungary (1353-6281)
Related titles: ♦ CD-ROM ed.: E I U Investing, Licensing and Trading; Online - full text ed.: (from SilverPlatter Information, Inc., The Dialog Corporation).
Published by: Economist Intelligence Unit, The Economist Building, 111 W 57th St, New York, NY 10019. TEL 212-554-0600, 800-938-4685, FAX 212-586-1182, http://www.eiu.com.

332.6 USA
HG5731
COUNTRY COMMERCE. INDIA. Text in English. a. GBP 225, USD 345 (effective 2000). **Document type:** *Trade.*
Description: Provides information on corporate tax rules, exchange and price controls, trade and licensing restrictions, labor conditions and investment rules.
Former titles (until 2000): Investing, Licensing and Trading. India; (until 1997): Investing, Licensing and Trading Conditions Abroad. India
Related titles: ♦ CD-ROM ed.: E I U Investing, Licensing and Trading; Online - full text ed.: (from SilverPlatter Information, Inc., The Dialog Corporation).
Published by: Economist Intelligence Unit, 111 W 57th St, New York, NY 10019. TEL 212-554-0600, 800-938-4685, FAX 212-586-1181, http://www.eiu.com.

322.6 USA ISSN 1547-9234
HG5751
COUNTRY COMMERCE. INDONESIA. Text in English. a. GBP 225, USD 345 (effective 2000). **Document type:** *Trade.*
Description: Provides information on corporate tax rules, exchange and price controls, trade and licensing restrictions, labor conditions and investment rules.
Former titles (until 2001): Investing, Licensing and Trading. Indonesia; (until 1997): Investing, Licensing and Trading Conditions Abroad. Indonesia (1353-5749)
Related titles: ♦ CD-ROM ed.: E I U Investing, Licensing and Trading; Online - full text ed.: (from SilverPlatter Information, Inc., The Dialog Corporation).
Published by: Economist Intelligence Unit, 111 W 57th St, New York, NY 10019. TEL 212-554-0600, 800-938-4685, FAX 212-586-1181, http://www.eiu.com.

332.6 USA
HG5450.3.A2
COUNTRY COMMERCE. IRELAND. Text in English. a. GBP 225, USD 345 (effective 2000). **Document type:** *Trade.*
Description: Provides information on corporate tax rules, exchange and price controls, trade and licensing restrictions, labor conditions and investment rules.
Former titles (until 2000): Investing, Licensing and Trading. Ireland; (until 1997): Investing, Licensing and Trading Conditions Abroad. Ireland (1352-9927)
Related titles: ♦ CD-ROM ed.: E I U Investing, Licensing and Trading.
Published by: Economist Intelligence Unit, 111 W 57th St, New York, NY 10019. TEL 212-554-0600, 800-938-4685, FAX 212-586-1181, http://www.eiu.com. **Subscr. to:** Economist Intelligence Unit Ltd., Harold Hill, Romford, PO Box 200, Essex RM3 8UX, United Kingdom. TEL 44-1708-381444, FAX 44-1708-371850.

332.6 USA ISSN 1547-9250
HG5710.A2
COUNTRY COMMERCE. ISRAEL. Text in English. a. GBP 225, USD 345 (effective 2000). **Document type:** *Trade.*
Description: Provides information on corporate tax rules, exchange and price controls, trade and licensing restrictions, labor conditions and investment rules.
Former titles (until 2000): Investing, Licensing and Trading. Israel; (until 1997): Investing, Licensing and Trading Conditions Abroad. Israel (1352-979X)
Related titles: ♦ CD-ROM ed.: E I U Investing, Licensing and Trading; Online - full text ed.: (from SilverPlatter Information, Inc., The Dialog Corporation).
Published by: Economist Intelligence Unit, 111 W 57th St, New York, NY 10019. TEL 212-554-0600, 800-938-4685, FAX 212-586-1181, http://www.eiu.com.

332.6 USA
HG5521
COUNTRY COMMERCE. ITALY. Text in English. a. GBP 225, USD 345 (effective 2000). **Document type:** *Trade.*
Description: Provides information on corporate tax rules, exchange and price controls, trade and licensing restriction, labor conditions and investment rules.
Former titles (until 2000): Investing, Licensing and Trading. Italy; (until 1997): Investing, Licensing and Trading Conditions. Italy (1353-5803)
Related titles: ♦ CD-ROM ed.: E I U Investing, Licensing and Trading; Online - full text ed.: (from SilverPlatter Information, Inc., The Dialog Corporation).
Published by: Economist Intelligence Unit, 111 W 57th St, New York, NY 10019. TEL 212-554-0600, 800-938-4685, FAX 212-586-1181, http://www.eiu.com.

B

322.6 USA ISSN 1548-100X
HG5771
COUNTRY COMMERCE. JAPAN. Text in English. a. GBP 225, USD 345 (effective 2000). **Document type:** *Trade.*
Description: Provides information on corporate tax rules, exchange and price controls, trade and licensing restrictions, labor conditions and investment rules.
Former titles (until 2000): Investing, Licensing and Trading. Japan; (until 1997): Investing, Licensing and Trading Conditions Abroad. Japan (1353-579X)
Related titles: ♦ CD-ROM ed.: E I U Investing, Licensing and Trading; Online - full text ed.: (from SilverPlatter Information, Inc., The Dialog Corporation).
Published by: Economist Intelligence Unit, 111 W 57th St, New York, NY 10019. TEL 212-554-0600, 800-938-4685, FAX 212-586-1181, http://www.eiu.com.

332.6 USA ISSN 1548-1026
KSK971.5.A13
COUNTRY COMMERCE. KENYA. Text in English. a. GBP 225, USD 345 (effective 2000). **Document type:** *Trade.*
Description: Provides information on corporate tax rules, exchange and price controls, trade and licensing restrictions, labor conditions and investment rules.
Former titles (until 2001): Investing, Licensing and Trading. Kenya; (until 1997): Investing, Licensing and Trading Conditions Abroad. Kenya (1352-5964)
Related titles: ♦ CD-ROM ed.: E I U Investing, Licensing and Trading; Online - full text ed.: (from SilverPlatter Information, Inc., The Dialog Corporation).
Published by: Economist Intelligence Unit, 111 W 57th St, New York, NY 10019. TEL 212-554-0600, 800-938-4685, FAX 212-586-1181, http://www.eiu.com.

322.6 USA
HG5570.5.A2
COUNTRY COMMERCE. LUXEMBOURG. Text in English. a. GBP 225, USD 345 (effective 2000). **Document type:** *Trade.*
Description: Provides information on corporate tax rules, exchange and price controls, trade and licensing restrictions, labor conditions and investment rules.
Former titles (until 2000): Investing, Licensing and Trading. Luxembourg; (until 1997): Investing, Licensing and Trading Conditions Abroad. Luxembourg (1353-5781)
Related titles: ♦ CD-ROM ed.: E I U Investing, Licensing and Trading; Online - full text ed.: (from SilverPlatter Information, Inc., The Dialog Corporation).
Published by: Economist Intelligence Unit, 111 W 57th St, New York, NY 10019. TEL 212-554-0600, 800-938-4685, FAX 212-586-1181, http://www.eiu.com.

322.6 USA
HG5750.6.A2
COUNTRY COMMERCE. MALAYSIA. Text in English. a. GBP 225, USD 345 (effective 2000). **Document type:** *Trade.*
Description: Provides information on corporate tax rules, exchange and price controls, trade and licensing restrictions, labor conditions and investment rules.
Former titles (until 2000): Investing, Licensing and Trading. Malaysia; (until 1997): Investing, Licensing and Trading Conditions Abroad (1353-5765)
Related titles: ♦ CD-ROM ed.: E I U Investing, Licensing and Trading; Online - full text ed.: (from SilverPlatter Information, Inc., The Dialog Corporation).
Published by: Economist Intelligence Unit, 111 W 57th St, New York, NY 10019. TEL 212-554-0600, 800-938-4685, FAX 212-586-1181, http://www.eiu.com.

▼ *new title* ➤ *refereed* ✶ *unverified* ♦ *full entry avail.*

332.6 USA ISSN 1548-0984
HG5161
COUNTRY COMMERCE. MEXICO. Text in English. a. GBP 225, USD 345 (effective 2000). **Document type:** *Trade.*
Description: Provides information on corporate tax rules, exchange and price controls, trade and licensing restrictions, labor conditions and investment rules.
Former titles (until 2000): Investing, Licensing and Trading. Mexico; (until 1997): Investing, Licensing and Trading Conditions Abroad. Mexico (1352-9854)
Related titles: ♦ CD-ROM ed.: E I U Investing, Licensing and Trading; Online - full text ed.: (from SilverPlatter Information, Inc., The Dialog Corporation).
—CCC.
Published by: Economist Intelligence Unit, 111 W 57th St, New York, NY 10019. TEL 212-554-0600, 800-938-4685, FAX 212-586-1181, http://www.eiu.com.

332.6 USA
COUNTRY COMMERCE. MIDDLE EAST - AFRICA. Text in English. s-a. GBP 225, USD 345 (effective 2000). **Document type:** *Trade.* **Description:** Offers information on corporate tax rules, exchange and price controls, trade and licensing restrictions, labor conditions and investment rules.
Former titles (until 2000): Investing, Licensing and Trading. Middle East - Africa; (until 1997): Investing, Licensing and Trading Conditions Abroad. Middle East - Africa; Investing, Licensing and Trading Conditions Abroad. Europe - Middle East - Africa
Related titles: ♦ CD-ROM ed.: E I U Investing, Licensing and Trading; Online - full text ed.: (from SilverPlatter Information, Inc., The Dialog Corporation).
Published by: Economist Intelligence Unit, 111 W 57th St, New York, NY 10019. TEL 212-554-0600, 800-938-4685, FAX 212-586-1181, http://www.eiu.com.

332.6 USA
HG5561
COUNTRY COMMERCE. NETHERLANDS. Text in English. a. GBP 225, USD 345 (effective 2000). **Description:** Provides information on corporate tax rules, exchange and price controls, trade and licensing restrictions, labor conditions and investment rules.
Former titles (until 2000): Investing, Licensing and Trading. Netherlands; (until 1997): Investing, Licensing and Trading Conditions Abroad. Netherlands
Related titles: ♦ CD-ROM ed.: E I U Investing, Licensing and Trading; Online - full text ed.: (from SilverPlatter Information, Inc., The Dialog Corporation).
Published by: Economist Intelligence Unit, 111 W 57th St, New York, NY 10019. TEL 212-554-0600, 800-938-4685, FAX 212-586-1181, http://www.eiu.com.

332.6 USA
HG5980.5.A2
COUNTRY COMMERCE. NEW ZEALAND. Text in English. a. GBP 225, USD 345 (effective 2000). **Document type:** *Trade.*
Description: Provides information on corporate tax rules, exchange and price controls, trade and licensing restrictions, labor conditions and investment rules.
Former titles (until 2000): Investing, Licensing and Trading. New Zealand; (until 1997): Investing, Licensing and Trading Conditions Abroad. New Zealand (1353-5919)
Related titles: ♦ CD-ROM ed.: E I U Investing, Licensing and Trading; Online - full text ed.: (from SilverPlatter Information, Inc., The Dialog Corporation).
Published by: Economist Intelligence Unit, 111 W 57th St, New York, NY 10019. TEL 212-554-0600, 800-938-4685, FAX 212-586-1181, http://www.eiu.com.

332.6 USA ISSN 1548-1018
KTA78.B87
COUNTRY COMMERCE. NIGERIA. Text in English. a. GBP 225, USD 345 (effective 2000). **Document type:** *Trade.*
Description: Provides information on corporate tax rules, exchange and price controls, trade and licensing restrictions, labor conditions and investment rules.
Former titles (until 2001): Investing, Licensing and Trading. Nigeria; (until 1997): Investing, Licensing and Trading Conditions Abroad. Nigeria (1352-5972)
Related titles: ♦ CD-ROM ed.: E I U Investing, Licensing and Trading; Online - full text ed.: (from SilverPlatter Information, Inc., The Dialog Corporation).
Published by: Economist Intelligence Unit, 111 W 57th St, New York, NY 10019. TEL 212-554-0600, 800-938-4685, FAX 212-586-1181, http://www.eiu.com.

332.6 USA
HG5611
COUNTRY COMMERCE. NORWAY. Text in English. a. GBP 225, USD 345 (effective 2000). **Document type:** *Trade.*
Description: Provides information on corporate tax rules, exchange and price controls, trade and licensing restrictions, labor conditions and investment rules.
Former titles (until 2000): Investing, Licensing and Trading. Norway; (until 1997): Investing, Licensing and Trading Conditions Abroad. Norway (1352-996X)
Related titles: ♦ CD-ROM ed.: E I U Investing, Licensing and Trading; Online - full text ed.: (from SilverPlatter Information, Inc., The Dialog Corporation).
Published by: Economist Intelligence Unit, 111 W 57th St, New York, NY 10019. TEL 212-554-0600, 800-938-4685, FAX 212-586-1181, http://www.eiu.com.

332.6 USA ISSN 1548-095X
HG5740.5.A2
COUNTRY COMMERCE. PAKISTAN. Text in English. a. GBP 225, USD 345 (effective 2000). **Document type:** *Trade.*
Description: Provides information on corporate tax rules, exchange and price controls, trade and licensing restrictions, labor conditions and investment rules.
Former titles (until 2000): Investing, Licensing and Trading. Pakistan; (until 1997): Investing, Licensing and Trading Conditions Abroad. Pakistan (1353-5927)
Related titles: ♦ CD-ROM ed.: E I U Investing, Licensing and Trading; Online - full text ed.: (from SilverPlatter Information, Inc., The Dialog Corporation).
Published by: Economist Intelligence Unit, 111 W 57th St, New York, NY 10019. TEL 212-554-0600, 800-938-4685, FAX 212-586-1181, http://www.eiu.com.

332.6 USA
HG5221
COUNTRY COMMERCE. PANAMA. Text in English. a. GBP 225, USD 345 (effective 2000). **Document type:** *Trade.*
Description: Provides information on corporate tax rules, exchange and price controls, trade and licensing restrictions, labor conditions and investment rules.
Former titles (until 2000): Investing, Licensing and Trading. Panama; (until 1997): Investing, Licensing and Trading Conditions Abroad. Panama (1352-9862)
Related titles: ♦ CD-ROM ed.: E I U Investing, Licensing and Trading; Online - full text ed.: (from SilverPlatter Information, Inc., The Dialog Corporation).
Published by: Economist Intelligence Unit, 111 W 57th St, New York, NY 10019. TEL 212-554-0600, 800-938-4685, FAX 212-586-1181, http://www.eiu.com.

332.6 USA ISSN 1548-2529
HG5391
COUNTRY COMMERCE. PERU. Text in English. a. GBP 225, USD 345 (effective 2000). **Document type:** *Trade.*
Description: Provides information on corporate tax rules, exchange and price controls, trade and licensing restrictions, labor conditions and investment rules.
Former titles (until 2000): Investing, Licensing and Trading. Peru; (until 1997): Investing, Licensing and Trading Conditions Abroad. Peru (1352-9870)
Related titles: ♦ CD-ROM ed.: E I U Investing, Licensing and Trading; Online - full text ed.: (from SilverPlatter Information, Inc., The Dialog Corporation).
Published by: Economist Intelligence Unit, 111 W 57th St, New York, NY 10019. TEL 212-554-0600, 800-938-4685, FAX 212-586-1181, http://www.eiu.com.

332.6 USA ISSN 1548-2510
KPM971.5.A13
COUNTRY COMMERCE. PHILIPPINES. Text in English. a. GBP 225, USD 345 (effective 2000). **Document type:** *Trade.*
Description: Provides information on corporate tax rules, exchange and price controls, trade and licensing restrictions, labor conditions and investment rules.
Former titles (until 2001): Investing, Licensing and Trading. Philippines; (until 1997): Investing, Licensing and Trading Conditions Abroad. Philippines (1352-5980)
Related titles: ♦ CD-ROM ed.: E I U Investing, Licensing and Trading; Online - full text ed.: (from SilverPlatter Information, Inc., The Dialog Corporation).
Published by: Economist Intelligence Unit, 111 W 57th St, New York, NY 10019. TEL 212-554-0600, 800-938-4685, FAX 212-586-1181, http://www.eiu.com.

332.6 USA
HG5586
COUNTRY COMMERCE. POLAND. Text in English. a. GBP 225, USD 345 (effective 2000). **Document type:** *Trade.*
Description: Provides information on corporate tax rules, exchange and price controls, trade and licensing restrictions, labor conditions and investment rules.
Former titles (until 2000): Investing, Licensing and Trading. Poland (1554-625X); (until 1997): Investing, Licensing and Trading Conditions Abroad. Poland (1352-5999)
Related titles: ♦ CD-ROM ed.: E I U Investing, Licensing and Trading; Online - full text ed.: (from SilverPlatter Information, Inc., The Dialog Corporation).
Published by: Economist Intelligence Unit, 111 W 57th St, New York, NY 10019. TEL 212-554-0600, 800-938-4685, FAX 212-586-1181, http://www.eiu.com.

332.6 USA
HG5641
COUNTRY COMMERCE. PORTUGAL. Text in English. a. GBP 225, USD 345 (effective 2000). **Document type:** *Trade.*
Description: Provides information on corporate tax rules, exchange and price controls, trade and licensing restrictions, labor conditions and investment rules.
Former titles (until 2000): Investing, Licensing and Trading. Portugal; (until 1997): Investing, Licensing and Trading Conditions Abroad. Portugal (1352-9935)
Related titles: ♦ CD-ROM ed.: E I U Investing, Licensing and Trading; Online - full text ed.: (from SilverPlatter Information, Inc., The Dialog Corporation).
Published by: Economist Intelligence Unit, 111 W 57th St, New York, NY 10019. TEL 212-554-0600, 800-938-4685, FAX 212-586-1181, http://www.eiu.com.

332.6 USA
HF3351
COUNTRY COMMERCE. PUERTO RICO. Text in English. a. GBP 225, USD 345 (effective 2000). **Document type:** *Trade.*
Description: Provides information on corporate tax rules, exchange and price controls, trade and licensing restrictions, labor conditions and investment rules.
Former titles (until 2001): Investing, Licensing and Trading. Puerto Rico; (until 1997): Investing, Licensing and Trading Conditions Abroad. Puerto Rico (1352-6057)
Related titles: ♦ CD-ROM ed.: E I U Investing, Licensing and Trading; Online - full text ed.: (from SilverPlatter Information, Inc., The Dialog Corporation).
Published by: Economist Intelligence Unit, 111 W 57th St, New York, NY 10019. TEL 212-554-0600, 800-938-4685, FAX 212-586-1181, http://www.eiu.com.

332.6 USA
HG5571
COUNTRY COMMERCE. RUSSIA. Text in English. a. GBP 225, USD 345 (effective 2000). **Document type:** *Trade.*
Description: Provides information on corporate tax rules, exchange and price controls, trade and licensing restrictions, labor conditions and investment rules.
Former titles (until 2000): Investing, Licensing and Trading. Russia; (until 1997): Investing, Licensing and Trading Conditions Abroad. Russia (1352-9773)
Related titles: ♦ CD-ROM ed.: E I U Investing, Licensing and Trading; Online - full text ed.: (from SilverPlatter Information, Inc., The Dialog Corporation).
Published by: Economist Intelligence Unit, 111 W 57th St, New York, NY 10019. TEL 212-554-0600, 800-938-4685, FAX 212-586-1181, http://www.eiu.com.

332.6 USA
HG5713.A2
COUNTRY COMMERCE. SAUDI ARABIA. Text in English. a. GBP 225, USD 345 (effective 2000). **Document type:** *Trade.*
Description: Provides information on corporate tax rules, exchange and price controls, trade and licensing restrictions, labor conditions and investment rules.
Former titles (until 2000): Investing, Licensing and Trading. Saudi Arabia; (until 1997): Investing, Licensing and Trading Conditions Abroad. Saudi Arabia (1352-6065)
Related titles: ♦ CD-ROM ed.: E I U Investing, Licensing and Trading; Online - full text ed.: (from SilverPlatter Information, Inc., The Dialog Corporation).
—CCC.
Published by: Economist Intelligence Unit, 111 W 57th St, New York, NY 10019. TEL 212-554-0600, 800-938-4685, FAX 212-586-1181, http://www.eiu.com.

332.6 USA
HG5750.67.A2
COUNTRY COMMERCE. SINGAPORE. Text in English. a. GBP 225, USD 345 (effective 2000). **Document type:** *Trade.*
Description: Provides information on corporate tax rules, exchange and price controls, trade and licensing restrictions, labor conditions and investment rules.
Former titles (until 2000): Investing, Licensing and Trading. Singapore; (until 1997): Investing, Licensing and Trading Conditions Abroad. Singapore (1353-5994)
Related titles: ♦ CD-ROM ed.: E I U Investing, Licensing and Trading; Online - full text ed.: (from SilverPlatter Information, Inc., The Dialog Corporation).
Published by: Economist Intelligence Unit, 111 W 57th St, New York, NY 10019. TEL 212-554-0600, 800-938-4685, FAX 212-586-1181, http://www.eiu.com.

332.6 USA
HG5851.A2
COUNTRY COMMERCE. SOUTH AFRICA. Text in English. a. GBP 225, USD 345 (effective 2000). **Document type:** *Trade.*
Description: Provides information on corporate tax rules, exchange and price controls, trade and licensing restrictions, labor conditions and investment rules.
Former titles (until 2001): Investing, Licensing and Trading. South Africa; (until 1997): Investing, Licensing and Trading Conditions Abroad. South Africa (1352-6073)
Related titles: ♦ CD-ROM ed.: E I U Investing, Licensing and Trading; Online - full text ed.: (from SilverPlatter Information, Inc., The Dialog Corporation).
Published by: Economist Intelligence Unit, 111 W 57th St, New York, NY 10019. TEL 212-554-0600, 800-938-4685, FAX 212-586-1181, http://www.eiu.com.

332.6 USA ISSN 1553-5819
HG5780.5.A2
COUNTRY COMMERCE. SOUTH KOREA. Text in English. a. GBP 225, USD 345 (effective 2000). **Document type:** *Trade.*
Description: Provides information on corporate tax rules, exchange and price controls, trade and licensing restrictions, labor conditions and investment rules.
Former titles (until 2000): Investing, Licensing and Trading. South Korea; (until 1997): Investing, Licensing and Trading Conditions Abroad. South Korea (1353-6257)
Related titles: ♦ CD-ROM ed.: E I U Investing, Licensing and Trading; Online - full text ed.: (from SilverPlatter Information, Inc., The Dialog Corporation).
Published by: Economist Intelligence Unit, 111 W 57th St, New York, NY 10019. TEL 212-554-0600, 800-938-4685, FAX 212-586-1181, http://www.eiu.com.

B

332.6   USA   ISSN 1548-0968
HG5631
COUNTRY COMMERCE. SPAIN. Text in English. a. GBP 225,
USD 345 (effective 2000). **Document type:** *Trade.*
Description: Provides information on corporate tax rules,
exchange and price controls, trade and licensing restrictions,
labor conditions and investment rules.
Former titles (until 2001): Investing, Licensing and Trading.
Spain; (until 1997): Investing, Licensing and Trading
Conditions Abroad. Spain (1352-6081)
Related titles: ♦ CD-ROM ed.: E I U Investing, Licensing and
Trading; Online - full text ed.: (from SilverPlatter Information,
Inc., The Dialog Corporation).
Published by: Economist Intelligence Unit, 111 W 57th St, New
York, NY 10019. TEL 212-554-0600, 800-938-4685, FAX
212-586-1181, http://www.eiu.com.

332.6   USA
HG5621
COUNTRY COMMERCE. SWEDEN. Text in English. a. GBP 225,
USD 345 (effective 2000). **Document type:** *Trade.*
Description: Provides information on corporate tax rules,
exchange and price controls, trade and licensing restrictions,
labor conditions and investment rules.
Former titles (until 2001): Investing, Licensing and Trading.
Sweden; (until 1997): Investing, Licensing and Trading
Conditions Abroad. Sweden (1352-609X)
Related titles: ♦ CD-ROM ed.: E I U Investing, Licensing and
Trading; Online - full text ed.: (from SilverPlatter Information,
Inc., The Dialog Corporation).
Published by: Economist Intelligence Unit, 111 W 57th St, New
York, NY 10019. TEL 212-554-0600, 800-938-4685, FAX
212-586-1181, http://www.eiu.com.

332.6   USA
HG5651
COUNTRY COMMERCE. SWITZERLAND. Text in English. a.
GBP 225, USD 345 (effective 2000). **Document type:** *Trade.*
Description: Provides information on corporate tax rules,
exchange and price controls, trade and licensing restrictions,
labor conditions and investment rules.
Former titles (until 2000): Investing, Licensing and Trading.
Switzerland; (until 1997): Investing, Licensing and Trading
Conditions Abroad. Switzerland (1352-9757)
Related titles: ♦ CD-ROM ed.: E I U Investing, Licensing and
Trading; Online - full text ed.: (from SilverPlatter Information,
Inc., The Dialog Corporation).
Published by: Economist Intelligence Unit, 111 W 57th St, New
York, NY 10019. TEL 212-554-0600, FAX 212-586-1181,
http://www.eiu.com.

332.6   USA
HG5796
COUNTRY COMMERCE. TAIWAN. Text in English. a. GBP 225,
USD 345 (effective 2000). **Description:** Provides information
on corporate tax rules, exchange and price controls, trade and
licensing restrictions, labor conditions and investment rules.
Former titles (until 2000): Investing, Licensing and Trading.
Taiwan; (until 1997): Investing, Licensing and Trading
Conditions Abroad. Taiwan
Related titles: ♦ CD-ROM ed.: E I U Investing, Licensing and
Trading; Online - full text ed.: (from SilverPlatter Information,
Inc., The Dialog Corporation).
Published by: Economist Intelligence Unit, 111 W 57th St, New
York, NY 10019. TEL 212-554-0600, 800-938-4685, FAX
212-586-1181, http://www.eiu.com.

332.6   USA
HG5750.55.A2
COUNTRY COMMERCE. THAILAND. Text in English. a. GBP
225, USD 345 (effective 2000). **Description:** Provides
information on corporate tax rules, exchange and price
controls, trade and licensing restrictions, labor conditions and
investment rules.
Former titles (until 2000): Investing, Licensing and Trading.
Thailand; (until 1997): Investing, Licensing and Trading
Conditions Abroad. Thailand
Related titles: ♦ CD-ROM ed.: E I U Investing, Licensing and
Trading; Online - full text ed.: (from SilverPlatter Information,
Inc., The Dialog Corporation).
Published by: Economist Intelligence Unit, 111 W 57th St, New
York, NY 10019. TEL 212-554-0600, 800-938-4685, FAX
212-586-1181, http://www.eiu.com.

332.6   USA
HG5706.5.A2
COUNTRY COMMERCE. TURKEY. Text in English. a. GBP 225,
USD 345 (effective 2000). **Document type:** *Trade.*
Description: Provides information on corporate tax rules,
exchange and price controls, trade and licensing restrictions,
labor conditions and investment rules.
Former titles (until 2000): Investing, Licensing and Trading.
Turkey; (until 1997): Investing, Licensing and Trading
Conditions Abroad. Turkey (1352-9803)
Related titles: ♦ CD-ROM ed.: E I U Investing, Licensing and
Trading; Online - full text ed.: (from SilverPlatter Information,
Inc., The Dialog Corporation).
Published by: Economist Intelligence Unit, 111 W 57th St, New
York, NY 10019. TEL 212-554-0600, 800-938-4685, FAX
212-586-1181, http://www.eiu.com.

332.6   USA   ISSN 1548-0976
HG5431
COUNTRY COMMERCE. UNITED KINGDOM. Text in English. a.
GBP 225, USD 345 (effective 2000). **Document type:** *Trade.*
Description: Provides information on corporate tax rules,
exchange and price controls, trade and licensing restrictions,
labor conditions and investment rules.
Former titles (until 2000): Investing, Licensing and Trading.
United Kingdom; (until 1997): Investing, Licensing and Trading
Conditions Abroad. United Kingdom (1352-9765); (until 1995):
Investing, Licensing and Trading Conditions Abroad. Britain
Related titles: ♦ CD-ROM ed.: E I U Investing, Licensing and
Trading; Online - full text ed.: (from SilverPlatter Information,
Inc., The Dialog Corporation).
Published by: Economist Intelligence Unit, 111 W 57th St, New
York, NY 10019. TEL 212-554-0600, 800-938-4685, FAX
212-586-1181, http://www.eiu.com.

332.6   USA   ISSN 1553-6599
HG4501
COUNTRY COMMERCE. UNITED STATES OF AMERICA. Text in
English. a. GBP 225, USD 345 (effective 2000). **Document
type:** *Trade.* **Description:** Provides information on corporate
tax rules, exchange and price controls, trade and licensing
restrictions, labor conditions and investment rules.
Former titles (until 2000): Investing, Licensing and Trading.
United States of America; (until 1997): Investing, Licensing
and Trading Conditions Abroad. United States of America
(1352-982X)
Related titles: ♦ CD-ROM ed.: E I U Investing, Licensing and
Trading; Online - full text ed.: (from SilverPlatter Information,
Inc., The Dialog Corporation).
—CCC.
Published by: Economist Intelligence Unit, 111 W 57th St, New
York, NY 10019. TEL 212-554-0600, 800-938-4685, FAX
212-586-1181, http://www.eiu.com.

332.6   USA
HG5401
COUNTRY COMMERCE. URUGUAY. Text in English. a. GBP
225, USD 345 (effective 2000). **Document type:** *Trade.*
Description: Provides information on corporate tax rules,
exchange and price controls, trade and licensing restrictions,
labor conditions and investment rules.
Former titles (until 2000): Investing, Licensing and Trading.
Uruguay; (until 1997): Investing, Licensing and Trading
Conditions Abroad. Uruguay (1352-6103)
Related titles: ♦ CD-ROM ed.: E I U Investing, Licensing and
Trading; Online - full text ed.: (from SilverPlatter Information,
Inc., The Dialog Corporation).
Published by: Economist Intelligence Unit, 111 W 57th St, New
York, NY 10019. TEL 212-554-0600, 800-938-4685, FAX
212-586-1181, http://www.eiu.com.

322.6   USA   ISSN 1548-2502
HG5411
COUNTRY COMMERCE. VENEZUELA. Text in English. a. GBP
225, USD 345 (effective 2000). **Document type:** *Trade.*
Description: Provides information on corporate tax rules,
exchange and price controls, trade and licensing restrictions,
labor conditions and investment rules.
Former titles (until 2000): Investing, Licensing and Trading.
Venezuela; (until 1997): Investing, Licensing and Trading
Conditions Abroad. Venezuela (1352-9889)
Related titles: ♦ CD-ROM ed.: (from SilverPlatter Information, Inc.);
Online - full text ed.: (from SilverPlatter Information, Inc., The
Dialog Corporation).
—CCC.
Published by: Economist Intelligence Unit, 111 W 57th St, New
York, NY 10019. TEL 212-554-0600, 800-938-4685, FAX
212-586-1181, http://www.eiu.com.

322.6   USA
HG5750.5.A3
COUNTRY COMMERCE. VIETNAM. Text in English. a. GBP 225,
USD 345 (effective 2000). **Description:** Provides information
on corporate tax rules, exchange and price controls, trade and
licensing restrictions, labor conditions and investment rules.
Former titles (until 2000): Investing, Licensing and Trading.
Vietnam; (until 1997): Investing, Licensing and Trading
Conditions Abroad. Vietnam
Related titles: ♦ CD-ROM ed.: E I U Investing, Licensing and
Trading; Online - full text ed.: (from SilverPlatter Information,
Inc., The Dialog Corporation).
Published by: Economist Intelligence Unit, 111 W 57th St, New
York, NY 10019. TEL 212-554-0600, 800-938-4685, FAX
212-586-1181, http://www.eiu.com.

COUNTRY FINANCE. AFRICA. see *BUSINESS AND
ECONOMICS—Banking And Finance*

COUNTRY FINANCE. ARGENTINA. see *BUSINESS AND
ECONOMICS—Banking And Finance*

COUNTRY FINANCE. AUSTRALIA. see *BUSINESS AND
ECONOMICS—Banking And Finance*

COUNTRY FINANCE. BELGIUM. see *BUSINESS AND
ECONOMICS—Banking And Finance*

COUNTRY FINANCE. BRAZIL. see *BUSINESS AND
ECONOMICS—Banking And Finance*

COUNTRY FINANCE. CANADA. see *BUSINESS AND
ECONOMICS—Banking And Finance*

COUNTRY FINANCE. CENTRAL AMERICA. see *BUSINESS
AND ECONOMICS—Banking And Finance*

COUNTRY FINANCE. CHILE. see *BUSINESS AND
ECONOMICS—Banking And Finance*

COUNTRY FINANCE. CHINA. see *BUSINESS AND
ECONOMICS—Banking And Finance*

COUNTRY FINANCE. COLOMBIA. see *BUSINESS AND
ECONOMICS—Banking And Finance*

COUNTRY FINANCE. CZECH REPUBLIC. see *BUSINESS AND
ECONOMICS—Banking And Finance*

COUNTRY FINANCE. FRANCE. see *BUSINESS AND
ECONOMICS—Banking And Finance*

COUNTRY FINANCE. GERMANY. see *BUSINESS AND
ECONOMICS—Banking And Finance*

COUNTRY FINANCE. GREECE. see *BUSINESS AND
ECONOMICS—Banking And Finance*

COUNTRY FINANCE. HONG KONG. see *BUSINESS AND
ECONOMICS—Banking And Finance*

COUNTRY FINANCE. HUNGARY. see *BUSINESS AND
ECONOMICS—Banking And Finance*

COUNTRY FINANCE. INDIA. see *BUSINESS AND
ECONOMICS—Banking And Finance*

COUNTRY FINANCE. INDONESIA. see *BUSINESS AND
ECONOMICS—Banking And Finance*

COUNTRY FINANCE. ITALY. see *BUSINESS AND
ECONOMICS—Banking And Finance*

COUNTRY FINANCE. JAPAN. see *BUSINESS AND
ECONOMICS—Banking And Finance*

COUNTRY FINANCE. MALAYSIA. see *BUSINESS AND
ECONOMICS—Banking And Finance*

COUNTRY FINANCE. MEXICO. see *BUSINESS AND
ECONOMICS—Banking And Finance*

COUNTRY FINANCE. NETHERLANDS. see *BUSINESS AND
ECONOMICS—Banking And Finance*

COUNTRY FINANCE. NEW ZEALAND. see *BUSINESS AND
ECONOMICS—Banking And Finance*

COUNTRY FINANCE. NIGERIA. see *BUSINESS AND
ECONOMICS—Banking And Finance*

COUNTRY FINANCE. NORWAY. see *BUSINESS AND
ECONOMICS—Banking And Finance*

COUNTRY FINANCE. PANAMA. see *BUSINESS AND
ECONOMICS—Banking And Finance*

COUNTRY FINANCE. PHILIPPINES. see *BUSINESS AND
ECONOMICS—Banking And Finance*

COUNTRY FINANCE. POLAND. see *BUSINESS AND
ECONOMICS—Banking And Finance*

COUNTRY FINANCE. PORTUGAL. see *BUSINESS AND
ECONOMICS—Banking And Finance*

COUNTRY FINANCE. RUSSIA. see *BUSINESS AND
ECONOMICS—Banking And Finance*

COUNTRY FINANCE. SAUDI ARABIA. see *BUSINESS AND
ECONOMICS—Banking And Finance*

COUNTRY FINANCE. SINGAPORE. see *BUSINESS AND
ECONOMICS—Banking And Finance*

COUNTRY FINANCE. SOUTH AFRICA. see *BUSINESS AND
ECONOMICS—Banking And Finance*

COUNTRY FINANCE. SOUTH KOREA. see *BUSINESS AND
ECONOMICS—Banking And Finance*

COUNTRY FINANCE. SPAIN. see *BUSINESS AND
ECONOMICS—Banking And Finance*

COUNTRY FINANCE. SWEDEN. see *BUSINESS AND
ECONOMICS—Banking And Finance*

COUNTRY FINANCE. SWITZERLAND. see *BUSINESS AND
ECONOMICS—Banking And Finance*

B

▼ *new title*   ➤ *refereed*   ✳ *unverified*   ♦ *full entry avail.*

COUNTRY FINANCE. TAIWAN. see *BUSINESS AND ECONOMICS—Banking And Finance*

COUNTRY FINANCE. THAILAND. see *BUSINESS AND ECONOMICS—Banking And Finance*

COUNTRY FINANCE. TURKEY. see *BUSINESS AND ECONOMICS—Banking And Finance*

COUNTRY FINANCE. UNITED KINGDOM. see *BUSINESS AND ECONOMICS—Banking And Finance*

COUNTRY FINANCE. UNITED STATES OF AMERICA. see *BUSINESS AND ECONOMICS—Banking And Finance*

COUNTRY FINANCE. VENEZUELA. see *BUSINESS AND ECONOMICS—Banking And Finance*

COUNTRY FORECASTS (SYRACUSE). see *BUSINESS AND ECONOMICS*

COUNTRY MONITOR. see *BUSINESS AND ECONOMICS—Economic Situation And Conditions*

382 USA
COUNTRY RISK: GLOBAL PROSPECTS. Text in English. a. USD 565 print or online (effective 2004). illus.; stat. back issues avail. **Document type:** *Trade.* **Description:** Provides analysis of political, economic and financial market risks in some 100 emerging economies.
Related titles: Online - full content ed.
Published by: Economist Intelligence Unit, 111 W 57th St, New York, NY 10019. TEL 212-554-0600, FAX 212-586-1181, newyork@eiu.com, http://www.eiu.com.

COUNTRY RISK REVIEW. see *POLITICAL SCIENCE*

COW NEWS & BULL VIEWS. see *AGRICULTURE—Poultry And Livestock*

CRAIGHEAD'S COUNTRY REPORTS. see *TRAVEL AND TOURISM*

382 USA
CRICKET LETTER; The Newsletter for International Investment within the U.S. Text in English. 1972. m. USD 275 (effective 2000). bk.rev. **Document type:** *Newsletter.* **Description:** Aimed at multinationals interested in US taxation, financing strategies and regional site development.
Published by: Cricket Communications, Inc., PO Box 527, Ardmore, PA 19003. TEL 215-789-2480, crclstine@aol.com. Ed. Mark E Battersby. Circ: 3,150.

▼ **CRITICAL PERSPECTIVES ON INTERNATIONAL BUSINESS.** see *BUSINESS AND ECONOMICS*

332.6 GBR
CRONER'S EUROPE. Text in English. 1988. base vol. plus m. updates. GBP 393.72 (effective 1999). **Document type:** *Trade.*
Related titles: Diskette ed.; Online - full text ed.
—BLDSC (3487.818000).
Published by: Croner.C C H Group Ltd. (Subsidiary of: Wolters Kluwer N.V.), 145 London Rd, Kingston, Surrey KT2 6SR, United Kingdom. TEL 44-20-85473333, FAX 44-20-85472637, info@croner.co.uk, http://www.croner.co.uk. Ed. Jane Simmonds.

382 GBR ISSN 0070-1599
CRONER'S REFERENCE BOOK FOR EXPORTERS. Text in English. 1942. base vol. plus m. updates. looseleaf. GBP 362.42 (effective 1999). **Document type:** *Trade.* **Description:** Provides comprehensive, current information for exporters.
Related titles: Online - full text ed.
Published by: Croner.C C H Group Ltd. (Subsidiary of: Wolters Kluwer N.V.), 145 London Rd, Kingston, Surrey KT2 6SR, United Kingdom. TEL 44-20-85473333, FAX 44-20-85472637, info@croner.co.uk, http://www.croner.co.uk. Ed. David Wright.

382 GBR ISSN 0070-1602
CRONER'S REFERENCE BOOK FOR IMPORTERS. Text in English. 1959. base vol. plus m. updates. looseleaf. GBP 279.21 (effective 1999). **Description:** Provides comprehensive information on regulations governing imports to the United Kingdom.
—BLDSC (3487.831000).
Published by: Croner.C C H Group Ltd. (Subsidiary of: Wolters Kluwer N.V.), 145 London Rd, Kingston, Surrey KT2 6SR, United Kingdom. TEL 44-20-85473333, FAX 44-20-85472637, info@croner.co.uk, http://www.croner.co.uk. Ed. V Ganley.

382 URY ISSN 0797-8960
HC125
CUADERNOS DE NEGOCIOS INTERNACIONALES E INTEGRACION. Text in Spanish. 1995. s-m.
Published by: Universidad Catolica del Uruguay "Damaso Antonio Larranaga", 8 de Octubre 2738, Montevideo, 11600, Uruguay. TEL 598-2-472717, FAX 598-2-470323, http://www.ucu.edu.uy.

CUBA FOREIGN TRADE. see *BUSINESS AND ECONOMICS—Chamber Of Commerce Publications*

382 CUB
CUBA. MINISTERIO DEL COMERCIO EXTERIOR. BOLETIN SEMANAL DE PRECIOS DE LOS ALIMENTOS. Text in Spanish. 1984. w. CUP 14. **Document type:** *Bulletin, Government.* **Description:** Covers markets and prices information on food.
Published by: (Cuba. Ministerio del Comercio Exterior (MINCEX)), Empresa Alimport, Calle 23 No. 55,, Vedado, La Habana, Cuba. TEL 7-4971, TELEX 51-1454.

382 CUB
CUBA. MINISTERIO DEL COMERCIO EXTERIOR. REPORTE SEMANAL DEL AZUCAR. Text in Spanish. 1981. w. CUP 14. **Description:** Provides markets and prices information on sugar.
Published by: (Cuba. Ministerio del Comercio Exterior (MINCEX)), Empresa Cubazucar, Calle 23 No. 55,, Vedado, La Habana, Cuba. TEL 70-9742.

382 PAK ISSN 0011-4154
CUSTOMS IMPORTS AND EXPORTS JOURNAL. Text in English. 1967 (vol.5). m. PKR 55. charts; stat.
Published by: Taxation Publishers, 6 Liaqat Rd., Lahore 6, Pakistan. Ed. S M Raza Naqvi.

382 AUS
CUSTOMS OFFICER'S ASSOCIATION OF AUSTRALIA. FOURTH DIVISION. FOURTH DIVISION CUSTOMS OFFICER. Text in English. 1968. irreg. AUD 0.05 per issue.
Published by: (Customs Officer's Association of Australia, Fourth Division), Percival Publishing Co. Pty. Ltd., 862-870 Elizabeth St, Waterloo Dc, NSW 2017, Australia.

CYPRUS. DEPARTMENT OF STATISTICS AND RESEARCH. STATISTICS OF IMPORTS AND EXPORTS. see *BUSINESS AND ECONOMICS—Abstracting, Bibliographies, Statistics*

CYPRUS. TOURISM ORGANISATION. ANNUAL REPORT. see *TRAVEL AND TOURISM*

382 CZE ISSN 1211-2208
HF37.C9
CZECH BUSINESS AND TRADE. Text in English. m. USD 54 (effective 1999). adv. abstr.; illus.; stat. index. back issues avail. **Document type:** *Trade.* **Description:** Covers economic policy, international cooperation, Czech trading and manufacturing organizations, exhibitions and fairs, finance, joint ventures, legislation.
Former titles (until Feb. 1994): Czech Foreign Trade (1210-5546); (until 1993): Czechoslovak Foreign Trade (0011-460X)
Related titles: Online - full text ed.: (from EBSCO Publishing); Spanish ed.: Empresas y Negocios en la Republica Checa. ISSN 1211-3158. 1996; Russian ed.: Cheshkaya Torgovlya i Predprinimatel'stvo. ISSN 1211-6912; French ed.: Industrie et Commerce Tcheque. ISSN 1211-2224; German ed.: Wirtschaft und Handel in det Tschechischen. ISSN 1211-2216; Supplement(s): Czech Industry. ISSN 1212-7108. 1997.
Indexed: KES, MEA&I, PROMT.
Published by: (Israel. Ministry of Industry and Trade ISR), P.P. Agency, V Jircharich 150-8, Prague 1, 110 00, Czech Republic. TEL 420-2-24912185, FAX 420-2-24912355, journal@ppagency.cz, http://www.mpo.cz/english/g/gc/index.htm. Ed. Pavla Podskalska. R&P Vera Durinova. Adv. contact Libuse Teprtova. page USD 1,500. Circ: 13,500.

382 DNK ISSN 1397-7229
D D NEWSLETTER; informationen der Deutsch- Daenischen handelskammer. (Deutsch Daenischen) Text in Danish, German. 1996. irreg. **Document type:** *Newsletter.*
Supersedes in part (in 1996): Erhvervs-Bladet (0014-0155)
Media: Online - full content.
Published by: Det Tysk-Danske Handelskammer/Deutsch-Daenischen Handelskammer, Boersen, Copenhagen K, 1217, Denmark. TEL 45-33-913335, http://www.ddnewsletter.dk, ahk-daenemark.dk. Eds. Bodil Pedersen, Flemming Vestergaard.

382 USA
D M NEWS INTERNATIONAL. Text in English. w.
Related titles: Online - full text ed.; ◆ Supplement to: D M News. ISSN 0194-3588.
Published by: Courtenay Communications Corp., 100 Avenue of the Americas, 6th Fl, New York, NY 10013-1689. TEL 212-925-7300, FAX 212-925-8797, editor@dmnews.com, http://www.dmnews.com/.

DAGENS NAERINGSLIV. see *GENERAL INTEREST PERIODICALS—Norway*

332.6 KOR
DAILY TRADE NEWS. Text in Korean. 1949. d. (2/day). KRW 24,000 per month. adv. bk.rev. back issues avail. **Document type:** *Newspaper.*
Published by: Korea Foreign Trade Association, 159-1 Samsung dong, Dang-nam-ku, Seoul, 135729, Korea, S. TEL 02-551-5441, FAX 02-551-5400. Ed. Choi Jung Keun. Pub. Koo Pyong Hwoi. Adv. contact Yong Soo Chang. B&W page USD 1,840, color page USD 3,060; trim 24 x 35. Circ: 80,000 (paid); 20,000 (controlled).

382.029 IND
DALIL AL-MUSADDIRIN/DIRECTORY OF EXPORTERS. Text in Arabic, English. 1996. a. USD 30. **Document type:** *Directory.* **Description:** Carries classified listings and advertisements of exporters of goods and services to the Arab world.
Published by: Pharos Media & Publishing (P) Ltd., D-84 Abul Fazl Enclave, P O Box 9701, New Delhi, 110 025, India. TEL 91-11-692-7483, FAX 91-11-683-5825, zik.pharos@axcess.net.in. Ed. Zafarul Islam Khan. Adv. contact Asghar Ali. Circ: 20,000.

DANGDAI SHIJIE/CONTEMPORARY WORLD. see *POLITICAL SCIENCE—International Relations*

382 DNK ISSN 0109-2669
DANSK-FRANSK HANDELSUNION. BULLETIN/CHAMBRE DE COMMERCE FRANCO-DANOISE. BULLETIN. Text in Danish, French. 1983. q. free to members. adv. illus. **Document type:** *Bulletin.*
Published by: Dansk-Fransk Handelsunion, c/o P.R. Meurs-Gerken, Advokaterne, Amaliegade 42, Copenhagen K, 1256, Denmark. TEL 33-113399, FAX 33-32-46-25, TELEX 27223 AMALEX DK. Circ: 10,000.

332.6 USA
DEALER - DISTRIBUTOR MAGAZINE; the international business magazine. Text in English. 1975. q. USD 6. adv. **Description:** Covers income opportunities, wholesale sources, dealerships, franchises, distributorships, businesses for sale, businesses wanted, real estate, advertising services, import and export, MLM.
Published by: Interstate Publications, Drawer 19689, Houston, TX 77224. TEL 281-578-6993, FAX 281-578-6993, intpub@aol.com. Ed. Linda Graham. Circ: 10,000.

382 GBR ISSN 1351-9786
DERBY TRADER. Text in English. 1966. w. free. adv. bk.rev. —CCC.
Published by: Trader Group of Newspapers, Abbotshill Chambers, Gower St, Derby, United Kingdom. Ed. T Mather. Circ: 130,300.

382 USA
DEVELOPMENT BUSINESS (NEW YORK, 1985). Text in English. 1985. w. looseleaf. USD 295. **Description:** Geared towards civil works, contractors, subcontractors, suppliers, and consultants around the world by providing comprehensive information about the Bank's procurement opportunities and upcoming projects.
Formerly: International Business Opportunities Service
Published by: United Nations Publications, Rm DC2-853, United Nations Bldg, 2 United Nations Plaza, New York, NY 10017. TEL 212-963-1516, publications@un.org, http://www.un.org/publications, http://www.un.org/Pubs.

382 341 FRA ISSN 1244-443X
DICTIONNAIRE JOLY PRATIQUE DES CONTRATS INTERNATIONAUX. Text in French. 7 base vols. plus s-a. updates. looseleaf. **Document type:** *Trade.*
Published by: Joly Editions, 31 rue Falguiere, Paris, 75015, France. TEL 33-1-56541600, FAX 33-1-56541647. Ed. Vincent Heuze.

DIGEST OF COMMERCIAL LAWS OF THE WORLD. see *LAW—International Law*

382.029 GBR ISSN 0958-2347
DIRECTORY IN RUSSIAN OF BRITISH FIRMS INTERESTED IN TRADE WITH THE F S U. (Former Soviet Union) Text in Russian. 1903. a. adv. **Document type:** *Directory.* **Description:** Promotes British and other products and services through the former U.S.S.R.
Former titles (until 1990): Directory in Russian of British Firms Interested in Trade with the U S S R; (until 1946): Russian Buyers' Guide
Published by: Exact Communications Ltd., First Floor Chambers, 1101 Warwick Rd, Acocks Green, Birmingham, Worcs B27 6RA, United Kingdom. TEL 44-121-707-7272, FAX 44-121-707-2288. Ed. Jonathan Hunt. Pub. Vitek Aukstolis. Adv. contact Michael Burgess. Circ: (controlled).

382.029 USA ISSN 0070-5071
HG4538.A1
DIRECTORY OF AMERICAN FIRMS OPERATING IN FOREIGN COUNTRIES. Text in English. 1955. irreg., latest vol.16, 2001. USD 325 (effective 2001). 4100 p./no.; **Document type:** *Directory.* **Description:** Lists approximately 2,500 American companies with more than 34,500 subsidiaries and affiliates in 190 foreign countries.
Related titles: CD-ROM ed.: USD 975 domestic; USD 1,500 for 2 yrs. domestic (effective 2001); individual country/regions price available upon request.

Published by: Uniworld Business Publications, 257 Central Park West, New York, NY 10017-4110. TEL 212-496-2448, FAX 212-769-0413, uniworldbp@aol.com, http://www.uniworldbp.com. Ed., R&P Barbara Fiorito. Pub. Debra Lipian.

DIRECTORY OF ARIZONA EXPORTERS. see *BUSINESS AND ECONOMICS—Trade And Industrial Directories*

382 CHN
DIRECTORY OF CHINA'S FOREIGN TRADE. Text in Chinese. a. USD 90. **Document type:** *Directory.*
Related titles: English ed.
Published by: China Chamber of International Commerce (CCOIC), China Council for the Promotion of International Trade (CCPIT), 1 Fuxingmenwai St, Beijing, 100860, China. TEL 86-10-6851-9388, FAX 86-10-6851-0201, cft@public.gb.co.cn. Circ: 20,000. **Dist. overseas by:** China International Book Trading Corp, 35 Chegongzhuang Xilu, Haidian District, PO Box 399, Beijing 100044, China; **Dist. by:** Current Pacific Ltd., PO Box 36-536, Northcote, Auckland, New Zealand. TEL 64-9-480-1388, FAX 64-9-480-1387, info@cplnz.com, http://www.cplnz.com.

382 332.6 USA
DIRECTORY OF COUNTERTRADE & OFFSET SERVICES. Text in English. irreg., latest 1996/97. USD 160 domestic; USD 180 foreign (effective 2000). back issues avail.
Former titles: Directory of Countertrade Services; Index to Countertrade (Year)
Published by: C T O Data Services, 1512 Valley Run., Durham, NC 27707-3640. TEL 703-383-5816, FAX 703-383-5815.

382 PAK
DIRECTORY OF EXPORTERS (YEAR)✶. Text in English. 1966. a. PKR 200, USD 20. adv. **Document type:** *Directory.* **Description:** Contains profiles of Pakistani exporters with well-established businesses.
Former titles: Directory of Pakistan Exporters; Pakistan Export Directory (0078-8090)
Published by: Export Promotion Bureau, Export Information & Advisory Centre, Press Trust Bldg., Chundrigrar Rd., Karachi, Pakistan. FAX 21-213415, TELEX 23663-EXPOM-PK. Ed. G Naseeruddin. Circ: 2,000.

382 IND
DIRECTORY OF INDIAN EXPORTERS. Text in English. 1919. triennial. USD 129.60. adv. **Document type:** *Directory.*
Formerly: Indian Export Directory
Published by: (India. Ministry of Commerce, Directorate General of Commercial Intelligence and Statistics), Controller of Publications, Civil Lines, New Delhi, 110 006, India. Circ: 2,500.

382.029 USA ISSN 1057-6878
HF3011
DIRECTORY OF UNITED STATES EXPORTERS. Text in English. 1988. a. USD 475 includes electronic index; USD 675 combined subscription includes Directory of United States Importers & electronic index; USD 995 combined subscription includes Directory of United States Importers & reference CD-ROM (effective 2003). adv. **Document type:** *Directory, Trade.* **Description:** Lists U.S. export companies, including S.I.C. codes, air, land or sea indicator, executive names, phone and fax numbers.
Supersedes in part (in 1990): United States Importers and Exporters Directory (1057-512X); Which was formed by the merger of (1967-1988): Directory of United States Importers (0070-6531); (1978-1988): Exporters Directory - U S Buying Guide (0149-8479)
Related titles: CD-ROM ed.: (from The Dialog Corporation); Diskette ed.
—CCC.
Published by: Journal of Commerce, Inc. (Subsidiary of: Commonwealth Business Media, Inc.), 33 Washington St, 13th Fl, Newark, NJ 07102. TEL 973-848-7000, 800-215-6084, FAX 609-371-7883, customersvs@joc.com, http://www.pierspub.com/ImpExp.htm, http://www.joc.com. Ed., Pub. Richard Paige. Adv. contact Mitzi McCullough. Circ: 2,500.

382.029 USA ISSN 1057-5111
HF3012
DIRECTORY OF UNITED STATES IMPORTERS. Text in English. 1988. a. Contact publisher fpr prices.. adv. index. **Document type:** *Directory, Trade.* **Description:** Provides logistics professionals with active confirmed leads for over 60,000 U.S. companies involved in world trade.
Supersedes in part (in 1990): United States Importers and Exporters Directory (1057-512X); Which was formed by the merger of (1967-1988): Directory of United States Importers (0070-6531); (1978-1988): Exporters Directory - U S Buying Guide (0149-8479)
Related titles: CD-ROM ed.: ISSN 1555-2624 (from The Dialog Corporation).
—CCC.
Published by: Journal of Commerce, Inc. (Subsidiary of: Commonwealth Business Media, Inc.), 33 Washington St, 13th Fl, Newark, NJ 07102. TEL 973-848-7000, 800-215-6084, FAX 609-371-7883, customersvs@joc.com, http://www.cbizmedia.com/prodserv/products/?pub=DEI, http://www.joc.com. Ed., Pub. Richard Paige.

382 ITA ISSN 0391-6111
K4
DIRITTO COMUNITARIO E DEGLI SCAMBI INTERNAZIONALI. Text in Italian. 1962. s-a. EUR 65 (effective 2005). **Document type:** *Journal, Academic/Scholarly.*
Formerly (until 1975): Diritto negli Scambi Internazionali (0419-3938)
Indexed: ELLIS, FLP, WAE&RSA.
—IE, Infotrieve.
Published by: Editoriale Scientifica s.r.l., Via San Biagio dei Librai 39, Naples, NA 80138, Italy. TEL 39-081-5800459, FAX 39-081-4971006, es@editorialescientificasrl.it, http://www.editorialescientificasrl.it.

382 341 ITA ISSN 1593-2605
DIRITTO DEL COMMERCIO INTERNAZIONALE; practica internazionale e diritto interno. Text in Italian. 1987. q. EUR 72.30 in the European Union; EUR 108.46 elsewhere (effective 2002). **Description:** Contains any issues which may pertain to international law, including technology transfer, joint ventures, precontractual documents, and contracted services.
Related titles: CD-ROM ed.: ISSN 1593-2591.
Indexed: DIP, ELLIS, IBR, IBZ.
Published by: Casa Editrice Dott. A. Giuffre (Subsidiary of: LexisNexis Europe and Africa), Via Busto Arsizio, 40, Milan, MI 20151, Italy. TEL 39-02-28089200, FAX 39-02-38009582, giuffre@giuffre.it, http://www.giuffre.it. Ed. Franco Bonelli.

DOCUMENTARY CREDITS INSIGHT. see *BUSINESS AND ECONOMICS—Banking And Finance*

382 USA ISSN 1076-0164
DOING BUSINES IN FIJI. Text in English. 1977. a. USD 39.95 (effective 2005).
Published by: Price Waterhouse Coopers LLP, 1177 Ave of the Americas, New York, NY 10036. TEL 646-471-4000, FAX 646-471-3188, http://www.pwcglobal.com.

382 USA ISSN 1059-1273
DOING BUSINESS IN ARGENTINA. Text in English. 1975. a. USD 39.95 (effective 2005).
Published by: Price Waterhouse Coopers LLP, 1177 Ave of the Americas, New York, NY 10036. TEL 646-471-4000, FAX 646-471-3188, http://www.pwcglobal.com.

382 USA ISSN 1520-0124
DOING BUSINESS IN BAHRAIN. Text in English. 1975. a. USD 39.95 (effective 2005).
Published by: Price Waterhouse Coopers LLP, 1177 Ave of the Americas, New York, NY 10036. TEL 646-471-4000, FAX 646-471-3188, http://www.pwcglobal.com.

382 USA ISSN 1067-3016
DOING BUSINESS IN BOTSWANA. Text in English. 1990. a. USD 39.95 (effective 2005).
Published by: Price Waterhouse Coopers LLP, 1177 Ave of the Americas, New York, NY 10036. TEL 646-471-4000, FAX 646-471-3188, http://www.pwcglobal.com.

382 USA ISSN 1067-2990
DOING BUSINESS IN CHILE. Text in English. 1975. a. USD 39.95 (effective 2005).
Published by: Price Waterhouse Coopers LLP, 1177 Ave of the Americas, New York, NY 10036. TEL 646-471-4000, FAX 646-471-3188, http://www.pwcglobal.com.

382 USA ISSN 1059-1265
DOING BUSINESS IN CYPRUS. Text in English. 1980. a. USD 39.95 (effective 2005).
Published by: Price Waterhouse Coopers LLP, 1177 Ave of the Americas, New York, NY 10036. TEL 646-471-4000, FAX 646-471-3188, http://www.pwcglobal.com.

382 USA ISSN 1057-641X
KKF78.B86 b D65
DOING BUSINESS IN HUNGARY. Text in English. 1990. irreg. USD 39.95 (effective 2004).
Published by: Price Waterhouse Coopers LLP, 1177 Ave of the Americas, New York, NY 10036. TEL 646-471-4000, FAX 646-471-3188, http://www.pwcglobal.com.

382 USA ISSN 1071-9423
DOING BUSINESS IN INDONESIA. Text in English. 1978. a. USD 39.95 (effective 2005).
Published by: Price Waterhouse Coopers LLP, 1177 Ave of the Americas, New York, NY 10036. TEL 646-471-4000, FAX 646-471-3188, http://www.pwcglobal.com.

382 USA ISSN 1057-3879
DOING BUSINESS IN MALAYSIA. Text in English. 1977. a. USD 39.95 (effective 2005).
Published by: Price Waterhouse Coopers LLP, 1177 Ave of the Americas, New York, NY 10036. TEL 646-471-4000, FAX 646-471-3188, http://www.pwcglobal.com.

382 USA ISSN 1067-8778
DOING BUSINESS IN MALTA. Text in English. 1983. a. USD 39.95 (effective 2005).
Published by: Price Waterhouse Coopers LLP, 1177 Ave of the Americas, New York, NY 10036. TEL 646-471-4000, FAX 646-471-3188, http://www.pwcglobal.com.

382 USA ISSN 1067-8786
DOING BUSINESS IN NIGERIA. Text in English. 19??. a. USD 39.95 (effective 2005).
Published by: Price Waterhouse Coopers LLP, 1177 Ave of the Americas, New York, NY 10036. TEL 646-471-4000, FAX 646-471-3188, http://www.pwcglobal.com.

382 USA ISSN 1062-8029
DOING BUSINESS IN PARAGUAY. Text in English. 1976. a. USD 39.95 (effective 2005).
Published by: Price Waterhouse Coopers LLP, 1177 Ave of the Americas, New York, NY 10036. TEL 646-471-4000, FAX 646-471-3188, http://www.pwcglobal.com.

382 USA ISSN 1057-3909
DOING BUSINESS IN SINGAPORE. Text in English. 1975. a. USD 39.95 (effective 2005).
Published by: Price Waterhouse Coopers LLP, 1177 Ave of the Americas, New York, NY 10036. TEL 646-471-4000, FAX 646-471-3188, http://www.pwcglobal.com.

382 USA ISSN 1057-3801
KTL1051.A13
DOING BUSINESS IN SOUTH AFRICA. Text in English. 1977. irreg. USD 39.95 (effective 2005). **Document type:** *Monographic series, Consumer.*
Published by: Price Waterhouse Coopers LLP, 1177 Ave of the Americas, New York, NY 10036. TEL 646-471-4000, FAX 646-471-3188, http://www.pwcglobal.com.

382 USA ISSN 1067-3008
DOING BUSINESS IN SWITZERLAND. Text in English. 1976. a. USD 39.95 (effective 2005).
Published by: Price Waterhouse Coopers LLP, 1177 Ave of the Americas, New York, NY 10036. TEL 646-471-4000, FAX 646-471-3188, http://www.pwcglobal.com.

382 USA ISSN 1067-2974
DOING BUSINESS IN TAIWAN. Text in English. 1979. a. USD 39.95 (effective 2005).
Published by: Price Waterhouse Coopers LLP, 1177 Ave of the Americas, New York, NY 10036. TEL 646-471-4000, FAX 646-471-3188, http://www.pwcglobal.com.

382 USA ISSN 1081-8952
DOING BUSINESS IN THE BAHAMAS. Text in English. 1975. a. USD 39.95 (effective 2005).
Published by: Price Waterhouse Coopers LLP, 1177 Ave of the Americas, New York, NY 10036. TEL 646-471-4000, FAX 646-471-3188, http://www.pwcglobal.com.

DOING BUSINESS IN THE CZECH REPUBLIC. see *BUSINESS AND ECONOMICS—Economic Situation And Conditions*

382 USA ISSN 1057-381X
KTZ107.5.A13
DOING BUSINESS IN ZIMBABWE. Text in English. 1984. irreg. USD 39.95 (effective 2005).
Published by: Price Waterhouse Coopers LLP, 1177 Ave of the Americas, New York, NY 10036. TEL 646-471-4000, FAX 646-471-3188, http://www.pwcglobal.com.

DOMINICA. MINISTRY OF FINANCE. CENTRAL STATISTICAL OFFICE. ANNUAL OVERSEAS TRADE REPORT. see *BUSINESS AND ECONOMICS—Abstracting, Bibliographies, Statistics*

382 DOM
DOMINICAN REPUBLIC. CENTRO DOMINICANO DE PROMOCION DE EXPORTACIONES. BOLETIN ESTADISTICO. Text in Spanish. 1972. a. DOP 35, USD 10. illus. **Document type:** *Bulletin, Government.*
Published by: Centro Dominicano de Promocion de Exportaciones, Plaza de la Independencia, Apdo 199 2, Santo Domingo, Dominican Republic.

DOUANERECHTSPRAAK. see *BUSINESS AND ECONOMICS—Public Finance, Taxation*

382 CHN
DUIWAI JINGJI MAOYI/JOURNAL OF FOREIGN ECONOMICS AND TRADE. Text in Chinese. q.
Published by: Tianjin Shehui Kexueyuan, Duiwai Jingji Yanjiusuo/Tianjin Academy of Social Sciences, Institute of Foreign Economics, 34 Youyi Lu, Heping-qu, Tianjin 300061, China. TEL 344032. Ed. Hou Yigang.

382 CHN
DUIWAI JINGJI MAOYI DAXUE XUEBAO/UNIVERSITY OF INTERNATIONAL BUSINESS AND ECONOMICS. JOURNAL. Text in Chinese. bi-m.
Published by: Duiwai Jingji Maoyi Daxue/Foreign Economics and Trade University, Yinghua Dongjie Beikou, Andingmenwai, Beijing, 100029, China. TEL 86-10-4225522, FAX 96-10-4212022. Ed. Wang Linsheng.

382 CHN
DUIWAI JINGMAO/INTERNATIONAL ECONOMICS AND TRADE. Text in Chinese. bi-m.

B

Published by: Heilongjiang Sheng Duiwai Maoyi Jingji Yanjiusuo/Heilongjiang Institute of International Trade and Economics, 55, Heping Lu, Dongli-qu, Harbin, Heilongjiang 150001, China. TEL 226987. Ed. Wang Cheng.

382 CHN ISSN 1003-5559
DUIWAI JINGMAO SHIWU/PRACTICE IN FOREIGN ECONOMIC RELATIONS AND TRADE. Text in Chinese. 1983. m. CNY 48. adv. **Document type:** *Trade.*
Related titles: Online - full text ed.: (from East View Information Services).
Published by: Duiwai Jingji Maoyi Bu, Jiaoyu Ju/Ministry of Foreign Economics and Trade, Education Bureau, No 198, Zhuodaoquan Lu, Wuchang-qu, Wuhan, Hubei 430079, China. TEL 86-27-7800575. Ed. Yongyou Yuan. R&P Wangsheng Bai. Adv. contact Zheng Zhang. page CNY 3,800. Circ: 20,000.

E-COMMERCE MARKET REPORTER. see *COMPUTERS—Internet*

E-COMMERCE QUARTERLY. see *COMPUTERS—Internet*

382.63060489 DNK ISSN 0902-2236
E F R - AARSBERETNING. (Erhvervsfremme) Text in Danish. 1982. a. free. illus. **Document type:** *Government.*
Supersedes in part (in 1985): Eksportkredit, Eksportfremme. Aarsberetninger (0108-7509); Which was formed by the merger of: Eksportkreditraadet. Beretning (0108-755X); Eksportfremmeraadet. Beretning (0107-1890)
Published by: E F R - Erhvervsfremme Styrelsen, Tagensvej 137, Copenhagen N, 2200, Denmark. TEL 45-35-86-86-87, FAX 45-35-86-86-87.

382 BEL ISSN 0012-7655
HF1531
E F T A BULLETIN. Text in English, French, German, Norwegian, Swedish. 1960. q. free. reprint service avail. from PQC. **Document type:** *Bulletin.*
Indexed: ABIn, BPI, BPIA, BusI, ELLIS, IIS, KES, LRI, PAIS, RRTA, T&II, WAE&RSA, WBA, WTA.
Published by: European Free Trade Association, Rue de Treves 74, Brussels, B-1040, Belgium. TEL 41-22-7491111, FAX 41-22-7339291, TELEX EFTA-CH-414102, mailbox@efta.int, http://www.secretariat.efta.int. Ed. Glumur Baldvinsson. Circ: 26,000.

332.66 DEU ISSN 0937-2369
E G WIRTSCHAFTSRECHT AUSSENWIRTSCHAFT. Text in German. 12/yr. looseleaf. **Document type:** *Bulletin, Trade.*
Published by: Deutscher Wirtschaftsdienst (Subsidiary of: Wolters Kluwer Deutschland GmbH), Schoenhauser Str 64, Cologne, 50968, Germany. TEL 49-221-937630, FAX 49-221-9376399, box@dwd-verlag.de, http://www.dwd-verlag.de.

E I U INTERNATIONAL BUSINESS NEWSLETTERS ON DISC. (Economist Intelligence Unit) see *BUSINESS AND ECONOMICS—Economic Situation And Conditions*

322.6 USA
E I U INVESTING, LICENSING AND TRADING. (Economist Intelligence Unit) Text in English. 1995. m. **Document type:** *Trade.* **Description:** Provides a guide to the operating conditions, commercial laws, and business regulations business face in each of 60 nations.
Media: CD-ROM. **Related titles:** Online - full text ed.: (from SilverPlatter Information, Inc., The Dialog Corporation); ♦ Print ed.: Country Commerce. Middle East - Africa; ♦ Country Commerce. Americas; ♦ Country Commerce. European Union; ♦ Country Commerce. Asia; ♦ Investing, Licensing and Trading. Global Edition; ♦ Country Commerce. Kenya. ISSN 1548-1026; ♦ Country Commerce. Nigeria. ISSN 1548-1018; ♦ Country Commerce. South Africa; ♦ Country Commerce. Austria; ♦ Country Commerce. Belgium. ISSN 1553-6068; ♦ Country Commerce. Denmark; ♦ Country Commerce. Finland; ♦ Country Commerce. France; ♦ Country Commerce. Germany. ISSN 1547-9137; ♦ Country Commerce. United States of America. ISSN 1553-6599; ♦ Country Commerce. Canada. ISSN 1547-9323; ♦ Country Commerce. Saudi Arabia; ♦ Country Commerce. Israel. ISSN 1547-9250; ♦ Country Commerce. Egypt; ♦ Country Commerce. India; ♦ Country Commerce. Pakistan. ISSN 1548-095X; ♦ Country Commerce. Argentina; ♦ Country Commerce. Brazil. ISSN 1547-920X; ♦ Country Commerce. Chile; ♦ Country Commerce. Colombia. ISSN 1547-9218; ♦ Country Commerce. Central America; ♦ Country Commerce. Ecuador; ♦ Country Commerce. Mexico. ISSN 1548-0984; ♦ Country Commerce. Panama; ♦ Country Commerce. Peru. ISSN 1548-2529; ♦ Country Commerce. Puerto Rico; ♦ Country Commerce. Uruguay; ♦ Country Commerce. United Kingdom. ISSN 1548-0976; ♦ Country Commerce. Turkey; ♦ Country Commerce. Switzerland; ♦ Country Commerce. Ireland; ♦ Country Commerce. Italy; ♦ Country Commerce. Luxembourg; ♦ Country Commerce. Netherlands; ♦ Country Commerce. Norway; ♦ Country Commerce. Portugal; ♦ Country Commerce. Spain. ISSN 1548-0968; ♦ Country Commerce. Sweden; ♦ Country Commerce. Australia; ♦ Country Commerce. China; ♦ Country Commerce. Hong Kong. ISSN 1547-9196; ♦ Country Commerce. Indonesia. ISSN 1547-9234; ♦ Country Commerce. Japan. ISSN 1548-100X; ♦ Country Commerce. South Korea. ISSN 1553-5819; ♦ Country Commerce. Malaysia; ♦ Country Commerce. New Zealand; ♦ Country Commerce. Philippines. ISSN 1548-2510; ♦ Country Commerce. Singapore; ♦ Country Commerce. Taiwan; ♦ Country Commerce. Thailand; ♦ Country Commerce. Vietnam; ♦ Country Commerce. Russia; ♦ Country Commerce. Poland; ♦ Country Commerce. Hungary. ISSN 1547-9331; ♦ Country Commerce. Czech Republic. ISSN 1549-5167.
Published by: SilverPlatter Information, Incorporated (Subsidiary of: Ovid Technologies, Incorporated), 100 River Ridge Dr., Norwood, MA 02062. TEL 800-343-0064, FAX 781-769-87632, info@silverplatter.com, sales@ovid.com, http://www.silverplatter.com, http://www.ovid.com.

E M U - THE NEWS BULLETIN. (European Monetary Union) see *BUSINESS AND ECONOMICS*

382 PHL
E P Z A NEWS∗. Text in English. 12/yr.
Published by: Department of Trade & Industry, 361 Sen. Gil J. Puyat, Buendia, Makati, Philippines.

382 GBR ISSN 1368-907X
E U FOCUS. (European Focus) Text in English. 1982. bi-w. (22/yr.). GBP 340, EUR 511 in Europe; GBP 405, USD 736 elsewhere; GBP 170, EUR 256 in Europe to students; GBP 203, USD 368 elsewhere to students (effective 2006). back issues avail. **Document type:** *Newsletter, Trade.*
Formerly (until 1996): E C Update (0968-6290)
Published by: (United States Council for International Business USA), Sweet & Maxwell Ltd., 100 Avenue Road, London, NW3 3PF, United Kingdom. TEL 44-20-74491111, FAX 44-20-74491144, customer.services@sweetandmaxwell.co.uk, http://www.sweetandmaxwell.co.uk. Circ: 3,000.

382.9142 CAN ISSN 1488-2787
E U INFO. (European Union) Text in English. 1981. bi-m. **Document type:** *Newsletter, Government.*
Formerly (until 1999): European Union Newsletter (1196-6483); Which superseded in part (in 1993): Delegation of the Commission of the European Communities. E C Newsletter (0835-8451); Which was formerly (until 1987): Europe (0712-9874)
Related titles: French ed.: Info U E. ISSN 1488-2809. 1981.
—CISTI.
Published by: Delegation of the European Commission to Canada, 45 O'Connor St, Suite 1900, Ottawa, ON K1P 1A4, Canada. TEL 613-238-6464, FAX 613-238-5191, mailto@delcan.cec.eu.int, http://www.delcan.cec.eu.int/en/press_and_information/newsletter/2004/.

382 DEU ISSN 0014-3871
E W G - WARENHANDEL. Text in German. 1966. q. EUR 40 (effective 2001). adv. bk.rev. charts; stat.; tr.lit. **Document type:** *Magazine, Trade.*
Published by: Zeitungs- und Zeitschriftenverlag Heinrichs, Brueggekamp 1, Barsinghausen, 30890, Germany. TEL 49-5105-2289. Ed., Pub. Gerhard Heinrichs.

EAST AFRICAN FREIGHT FORWARDING. see *TRANSPORTATION*

382 USA ISSN 0888-580X
EAST ASIAN BUSINESS INTELLIGENCE. Text in English. 1986. bi-m. USD 355 (effective 2002). adv. **Document type:** *Newsletter.* **Description:** For business executives looking for sales and contracting opportunities in East Asia. Provides more than 1700 new business leads each year with a brief description of the business opportunity, the person to contact, and full address, phone and fax number.
Related titles: Online - full text ed.
—**CCC.**
Published by: International Executive Reports, Ltd., 717 D St, N W, Ste 300, Washington, DC 20004-2807. TEL 202-628-6900, FAX 202-628-6618, http://www.his.com/~ili/pubeabi.html. Ed. Anne Phelan. Pub., R&P William C Hearn. Adv. contact Lloyd Gibson. Circ: 300.

382 IND ISSN 0012-8457
EAST EUROPEAN TRADE. Text in English. 1963. m. INR 50, USD 10. adv. bk.rev. pat.; stat.
Published by: Gurdip Singh Ed. & Pub., B-3-69 Safdarjang Enclave, New Delhi, 110 029, India. Circ: 5,000.

382 SVN ISSN 0353-6874
ECHO∗; economy - finance - trade. Text in English. 1961. q. USD 10. adv. charts; illus.; stat.
Former titles (until 1989): Yugoslavia Echo (0352-6828); Economic Echo from Yugoslavia (0012-916X)
Published by: Gospodarski Vestnik/Economic Courier, Dunajska 5, Ljubljana, 1000, Slovenia. FAX 3861-311-871, TELEX 31255. Ed. Dusan Snoj. Circ: 6,000.

ECHO DES M.I.N.; mensuel de la filiere fruits et legumes. see *AGRICULTURE*

382 FRA ISSN 1148-1757
ECHOS DE L'EXPORTATION. Text in French. 1984. 48/yr.
Formerly (until 1991): Exportation Magazine (0761-2818)
Address: 46 rue la Boetie, Paris, Cedex 8 75381, France. TEL 49-53-65-65, FAX 45-62-43-44, TELEX 640 331 F. Ed. Roselyne de Clapiers. Circ: 25,000.

658.005 FRA ISSN 1760-1800
▼ **ECOFINANCE.** Text in French. 2003. m. EUR 29 (effective 2004). adv. **Document type:** *Magazine, Consumer.*
Published by: Groupe Jeune Afrique, 57 bis, rue d'Auteuil, Paris, 75016, France. TEL 33-1-44301960, FAX 33-1-44301930, redaction@jeuneafrique.com, http://www.jeuneafrique.com/ecofinance.htm. adv.: page EUR 8,500; trim 205 x 275. Circ: 52,000 (paid and controlled).

ECONOMIA INTERNAZIONALE. see *BUSINESS AND ECONOMICS—Chamber Of Commerce Publications*

382 330.1 NLD
HF1351
➤ **ECONOMIC SYSTEMS.** Text in German. 1992. q. EUR 286 in Europe to institutions; JPY 37,800 in Japan to institutions; USD 319 elsewhere to institutions (effective 2006). bk.rev. reprint service avail. from PSC. **Document type:** *Academic/Scholarly.* **Description:** Presents an analysis of market and non-market solutions to allocation and distribution problems.
Supersedes in part (in 1997): Economic Systems - J O I C E; Which was formed by the merger of (1992-1995): J O I C E (0940-4821); (1991-1995): Economic Systems (0939-3625); Which was formerly (1970-1990): Jahrbuch der Wirtschaft Osteuropas (0449-5225)
Related titles: Microform ed.: (from PQC); Online - full text ed.: (from EBSCO Publishing, Gale Group, IngentaConnect, ScienceDirect, Swets Information Services).
Indexed: BAS, IBSS, JEL, PAIS, RASB.
—BLDSC (3656.682500), IE, ingenta.
Published by: Elsevier BV, North-Holland (Subsidiary of: Elsevier Science & Technology), Sara Burgerhartstraat 25, Amsterdam, 1055 KV, Netherlands. TEL 31-20-485-3911, FAX 31-20-485-2457, nlinfo-f@elsevier.nl, http://www.elsevier.com/locate/ecosys, http://www.elsevier.nl. **Subscr. to:** Elsevier BV, PO Box 211, Amsterdam 1000 AE, Netherlands. TEL 31-20-485-3757, FAX 31-20-485-3432, http://www.elsevier.nl.

382 FRA ISSN 1240-8093
HC10
ECONOMIE INTERNATIONALE. Text in French; Summaries in English. 1979. q. EUR 66.70 domestic; EUR 69.80 in the European Union; EUR 70.80 DOM-TOM; EUR 73.80 elsewhere (effective 2003). **Document type:** *Government.*
Formerly (until 1993): Economie Prospective Internationale (0242-7818)
Related titles: Microfiche ed.
Indexed: ELLIS, IBSS, ILD, JEL, SCIMP.
Published by: (France. Centre d'Etudes Prospectives et d'Informations Internationales), Documentation Francaise, 29-31 quai Voltaire, Paris, Cedex 7 75344, France. FAX 33-1-40157230. Circ: 1,800.

382 GAB
ECONOMISTE GABONAIS. Text in French. q.
Published by: Centre Gabonais du Commerce Exterieur, BP 3906, Libreville, Gabon.

382 SLV
EL SALVADOR. MINISTERIO DE COMERCIO EXTERIOR. DIRECTORIO DE OFERTA EXPORTABLE (YEAR)/EL SALVADOR. MINISTRY OF FOREIGN COMMERCE. EXPORTABLE OFFER DIRECTORY. Text in English, Spanish. a. **Document type:** *Directory, Government.*
Published by: Ministerio de Comercio Exterior/Ministry of Foreign Trade of El Salvador, Alameda Juan Pablo II y Calle Guadalupe, Edificio C1-C2, San Salvador, El Salvador. TEL 503-281-1122, FAX 503-221-5446.

EL SALVADOR. MINISTERIO DE COMERCIO EXTERIOR. ESTADISTICAS. see *BUSINESS AND ECONOMICS—Abstracting, Bibliographies, Statistics*

382 USA ISSN 1540-496X
HF25
➤ **EMERGING MARKETS FINANCE & TRADE.** Text in English. 1965. bi-m. USD 149 domestic to individuals; USD 221 foreign to individuals; USD 1,150 domestic to institutions; USD 1,270 foreign to institutions (effective 2006). adv. charts; pat.; stat.; illus. index. back issues avail.; reprint service avail. from PSC. **Document type:** *Journal, Academic/Scholarly.* **Description:** Publishes English-language translations of Russian research articles on finance and international trade from Russia and the other former Soviet republics.
Former titles (until 2002): Russian and East European Finance and Trade (1061-2009); (until 1992): Soviet and Eastern European Foreign Trade (0038-5263); (until 1966): American Review of Soviet and Eastern European Foreign Trade (0886-1005)
Related titles: Online - full text ed.: 2004 (Feb.) (from EBSCO Publishing, O C L C Online Computer Library Center, Inc., ProQuest Information & Learning, Swets Information Services).
Indexed: ABIn, ASCA, CREJ, CurCont, JEL, MEA&I, PAIS, SSCI.
—BLDSC (3733.426840), IDS, IE, ingenta. **CCC.**
Published by: M.E. Sharpe, Inc., 80 Business Park Dr, Armonk, NY 10504. TEL 914-273-1800, 800-541-6563, FAX 914-273-2106, custserv@mesharpe.com, http://www.mesharpe.com/mall/results1.asp?ACR=REE. Ed. Ali M Kutan. Adv. contact Barbara Ladd TEL 914-273-1800 ext 121. page USD 300; trim 8 x 5.

▼ ➤ **ENCYCLOPEDIA OF E-COMMERCE LAW.** see
COMPUTERS—Internet

➤ **ENFORCEMENT OF FOREIGN JUDGEMENTS.** see
LAW—International Law

341.754   USA
ENFORCING INTERNATIONAL TRADE LAW; the evolution of
the modern GATT legal system. Text in English. base vol. plus
irreg. updates. USD 125.
Published by: LexisNexis (Subsidiary of: LexisNexis North
America), PO Box 7587, Charlottesville, VA 22906-7587. TEL
804-972-7600, 800-562-1197, FAX 804-972-7666,
llp.customer.support@lexis-nexis.com, http://
www.lexislawpublishing.com. Ed. Robert E Hudec.

ENVIRONMENT WATCH: EUROPE. see *ENVIRONMENTAL
STUDIES*

382   USA   ISSN 1544-6956
ENVIRONMENTAL EXPORT NEWS. Text in English. 1992. q.
Published by: U. S. Department of Commerce, International
Trade Administration, Office of Environmental Technologies
Industries, 1401 Constitution Ave., NW, Washington, DC
20230. http://environment.ita.doc.gov.

662.6   GRC
ERMIS. Text in Greek, Russian. 199?. s-a. adv. **Document type:**
Trade. **Description:** Discusses all aspects of trade between
Greece and Russia, including tourism.
Published by: Exodos Publicista (Subsidiary of: Publishing
Property Unitrade Ltd.), 5 Vironos St, Thessaloniki, 546 22,
Greece. TEL 30-31-261393, FAX 30-31-261636. Ed. Erofili
Pantelidou.

382   ITA   ISSN 0014-0740
ESPORTAZIONE; mensile per gli esportatori. Text in Italian. 1961.
11/yr. adv. bk.rev. bibl.; tr.lit.
Published by: Ente Italiano per lo Sviluppo dell'Esportazione,
Piazzale Giotto, 8, Perugia, PG 06121, Italy. Circ: 9,500.

**ESTADISTICA DE LA INDUSTRIA MAQUILADORA DE
EXPORTACION.** see *BUSINESS AND ECONOMICS—
Abstracting, Bibliographies, Statistics*

**ESTADISTICA PANAMENA. SITUACION ECONOMICA.
SECCION 331. COMERCIO. ANUARIO DE COMERCIO
EXTERIOR.** see *BUSINESS AND ECONOMICS—Abstracting,
Bibliographies, Statistics*

**ESTADISTICA PANAMENA. SITUACION ECONOMICA.
SECCION 341. BALANZA DE PAGOS.** see *BUSINESS AND
ECONOMICS—Abstracting, Bibliographies, Statistics*

382   CUB
ESTIMADO DE PRODUCCION Y CONSUMO DE AZUCAR. Text
in Spanish. 1981. q. CUP 13. **Description:** Lists production
and consumption estimates by countries and geographical
areas.
Published by: (Cuba. Ministerio del Comercio Exterior
(MINCEX)), Empresa Cubazucar, Calle 23 No. 55,, Vedado,
La Habana, Cuba. TEL 70-9742.

382   CUB
**ESTIMADOS SOBRE REQUERIMIENTOS DE IMPORTACION
DE AZUCAR.** Text in Spanish. 1981. q. CUP 10. **Description:**
Covers import requirements of principal sugar importing
countries.
Published by: (Cuba. Ministerio del Comercio Exterior
(MINCEX)), Empresa Cubazucar, Calle 23 No. 55,, Vedado,
La Habana, Cuba. TEL 70-9742.

ETAGE; Chef-Informationen. see *BUSINESS AND ECONOMICS*

382 327   CAN   ISSN 0712-1180
L'ETAT DU MONDE (YEAR); annuaire economique et
geopolitique mondial. Text in French. a. CND 27.95 per vol.
(effective 2004). **Description:** Essays and documents.
Published by: Les Editions du Boreal, 4447, rue Saint-Denis,
Montreal, PQ, Canada. info@editionsboreal.com,
http://www.editionsboreal.qc.ca.

382   USA
E*TRADE; the magazine. Text in English. 2000. q. adv.
Document type: *Consumer.*
Published by: Imagination Publishing, 2222 N. Elston Ave., 2nd
Fl., Chicago, IL 60614. TEL 312-627-1020, FAX 312-627-1105,
http://www.imaginepub.com. Ed. Rebecca Rolfes.

THE EURO. see *BUSINESS AND ECONOMICS—Banking And
Finance*

EURO-EAST. see *POLITICAL SCIENCE—International Relations*

382   DEU   ISSN 1435-6899
EURO-WIRTSCHAFT; Studien zur oekonomischen Entwicklung
Europas. Text in German. 1987. irreg., latest vol.22, 2005.
price varies. **Document type:** *Monographic series,
Academic/Scholarly.*

Published by: Verlag Dr. Kovac, Arnoldstr 49, Hamburg, 22763,
Germany. TEL 49-40-3988800, FAX 49-40-39888055,
info@verlagdrkovac.de, http://www.verlagdrkovac.de/15-3.htm.

EUROMONEY; the monthly journal of international money and
capital markets. see *BUSINESS AND ECONOMICS—Banking
And Finance*

**THE EUROMONEY FOREIGN EXCHANGE HANDBOOK
(YEAR).** see *BUSINESS AND ECONOMICS—Banking And
Finance*

337.1 327   NOR   ISSN 0803-8767
EUROPABREVET. NYHETSBREV; informasjon for norske ledere
om utviklingen av EFs indre marked. Text in Norwegian. 1988.
30/yr. NOK 2,460 in Nordic countries; USD 468 elsewhere.
Document type: *Newsletter.* **Description:** Focuses on the
development of the internal market of the European
Community, aimed at Norwegian public leaders and leaders of
private companies.
Formerly (until 1992): 1992 - Nyhetsbrev (0802-2607)
Published by: Alpha Beta Media, Postboks 1663, Vika, Oslo,
0120, Norway. TEL 47-22-831381, FAX 47-22-831319,
hans.chr.erlandsen@login.eunet.no. Ed. Hans Chr Erlandsen.

382   CHE   ISSN 0258-3852
**EUROPAEISCHE FREIHANDELSASSOZIATION.
JAHRESBERICHT.** Text in German. 1986. a.
Related titles: ◆ English ed.: European Free Trade Association.
Annual Report. ISSN 0258-3844; ◆ French ed.: Association
Europeenne de Libre-echange. Rapport Annuel. ISSN
0258-0756.
Published by: European Free Trade Association, 9-11 rue de
Varembe, Geneva 20, 1211, Switzerland.

EUROPE REVIEW. see *BUSINESS AND ECONOMICS—Trade
And Industrial Directories*

382   USA   ISSN 1542-4766
▼ ➤ **EUROPEAN ECONOMIC ASSOCIATION. JOURNAL.**
Variant title: Journal of the European Economic Association.
Text in English. 2003 (Apr.). bi-m. USD 400 combined
subscription in US & Canada to institutions print & online eds.;
USD 430 combined subscription elsewhere to institutions print
& online eds. (effective 2006). **Description:** Committed to
promoting the development and application of economics as a
science as well as the communication and exchange between
teachers, researchers, and students in economics.
Related titles: Online - full text ed.: ISSN 1542-4774. USD 360 to
institutions (effective 2006) (from EBSCO Publishing, Gale
Group, IngentaConnect, O C L C Online Computer Library
Center, Inc., Swets Information Services).
Indexed: IBSS, JEL.
—BLDSC (4741.633500), IE.
Published by: M I T Press, 55 Hayward St, Cambridge, MA
02142-1493. TEL 617-253-5646, FAX 617-258-6779,
journals-info@mit.edu, http://mitpress.mit.edu/jeea. Eds. Alan
Krueger, Patrick Bolton, Roberto Perotti.

382   BEL   ISSN 0379-3133
HC241.2
EUROPEAN FILE. Text in English. 1979. s-m. free. **Document
type:** *Corporate.*
Related titles: Danish ed.: Europa Noter. ISSN 0379-315X. 1979;
Greek ed.: Europaika Themata. ISSN 0258-8250; Spanish ed.:
Documentos Europeos. ISSN 0258-8269; Portuguese ed.:
O'Dossier da Europa. ISSN 0258-8277. 1979; Dutch ed.:
Notities over Europa. ISSN 0379-3117. 1979; Italian ed.:
Schede Europee. ISSN 0379-3125. 1979; German ed.:
Stichwort Europa. ISSN 0379-3141; French ed.: Dossier de
l'Europe. ISSN 0379-3109. 1979.
Indexed: BldManAb, BrCerAb, WBA, WSCA, WTA.
—CISTI.
Published by: European Commission, Directorate General -
Information Society, Rue de la Loi 200, Brussels, 1049,
Belgium. TEL 32-2-2968800, FAX 32-2-2994170,
http://europa.eu.int/information_society/.

EUROPEAN FOUNDATION. BRIEFING PAPER. see *POLITICAL
SCIENCE—International Relations*

382   CHE   ISSN 0258-3844
HF1531
EUROPEAN FREE TRADE ASSOCIATION. ANNUAL REPORT.
Text in English. 1960. a. free. **Document type:** *Corporate.*
Related titles: ◆ French ed.: Association Europeenne de
Libre-echange. Rapport Annuel. ISSN 0258-0756; ◆ German
ed.: Europaeische Freihandelsassoziation. Jahresbericht. ISSN
0258-3852.
Indexed: IIS.
—BLDSC (1245.460000).
Published by: European Free Trade Association, 9-11 rue de
Varembe, Geneva 20, 1211, Switzerland. TEL 41-22-7491111,
FAX 41-22-7339291, http://www.efta.int, http://
www.secretariat.efta.int. Ed. Glumur Baldvinsson.

332.6   GBR   ISSN 0964-6299
EUROPEAN GOVERNMENT. Text in English. q.
Address: The Publishing House, 3 Highbury Station Rd, London,
N1 1SE, United Kingdom. TEL 44-171-226-2222, FAX
44-171-226-1255. Ed. Alan Spence.

THE EUROPEAN JOURNAL. see *POLITICAL SCIENCE*

EUROPEAN JOURNAL OF INTERNATIONAL AFFAIRS. see
POLITICAL SCIENCE—International Relations

338.0029   USA   ISSN 1044-9280
HF3493
**EUROPEAN MARKETS: A GUIDE TO COMPANY AND
INDUSTRY INFORMATION SOURCES.** Text in English. 1983.
irreg., latest vol.6. USD 335 (effective 1999). **Document type:**
Directory. **Description:** Informs executives of the best sources
of business information for each European nation.
Published by: Washington Researchers, Ltd., 1655 Fort Myer Dr.,
Ste. 800, Arlington, VA 22209-3119. TEL 703-312-2863, FAX
703-527-4586, research@researchers.com,
http://www.researchers.com, http://
www.washingtonresearchers.com. Ed. M Newman. R&P Ellen
O'Kane.

EUROPEAN MONETARY UNION; the journal for business. see
BUSINESS AND ECONOMICS

382   GBR   ISSN 1473-7868
EUROPEAN NEWSLETTER. Text in English. 1987. 10/yr. GBP
175, EUR 260 in Europe; GBP 200, USD 365 elsewhere;
GBP 88, EUR 130 in Europe to students; GBP 100, USD 183
elsewhere to students; GBP 17.50, EUR 26, USD 37
newsstand/cover (effective 2005). **Description:** Focuses on
the tax regimes and laws affecting business transactions in
Europe.
Published by: Sweet & Maxwell Ltd., 100 Avenue Road, London,
NW3 3PF, United Kingdom. TEL 44-20-74491111, FAX
44-20-74491144, customer.services@sweetandmaxwell.co.uk,
http://www.sweetandmaxwell.co.uk. **Subscr. to:** Cheriton
House, North Way, Andover, Hants SP10 5BE, United
Kingdom. TEL 44-1264-342706.

EUROPEAN POLICY ANALYST. see *BUSINESS AND
ECONOMICS—Economic Situation And Conditions*

THE EUROPEAN POLICY CENTRE. ANNUAL REPORT. see
*BUSINESS AND ECONOMICS—Economic Situation And
Conditions*

THE EUROPEAN POLICY CENTRE. CONFERENCE REPORTS.
see *BUSINESS AND ECONOMICS—Economic Situation And
Conditions*

THE EUROPEAN POLICY CENTRE. NEWSLETTER. see
*BUSINESS AND ECONOMICS—Economic Situation And
Conditions*

THE EUROPEAN POLICY CENTRE. OCCASIONAL PAPERS.
see *BUSINESS AND ECONOMICS—Economic Situation And
Conditions*

THE EUROPEAN POLICY CENTRE. POSITION PAPERS. see
*BUSINESS AND ECONOMICS—Economic Situation And
Conditions*

382   BEL   ISSN 0777-5814
THE EUROPEAN PUBLIC AFFAIRS DIRECTORY (YEAR). Text
in English. 1990. a., latest vol.14, 2004. EUR 105 per issue
domestic; EUR 109 per issue in Europe; EUR 118 per issue
elsewhere (effective 2004). 504 p./no.; **Description:** Provides
a wealth of essential contacts such as key people in
corporations, EU institutions, trade associations and NGOs, as
well as law firms, consultancies and media. Various indexes
are included to facilitate a search for a given person,
organization, acronym or area of specialization. It also gives
information on the role of the EU institutions, maps to find
one's way around them and calendars of their events.
Published by: Landmarks, Avenue de Tervuren 402, Brussels,
1150, Belgium. TEL 32-2-7799549, FAX 32-2-7799563,
info@contacteu.com, http://www.landmarks.be.

669 338.47669142   GBR   ISSN 1369-8583
EUROPEAN STEEL REVIEW. Text in English. 1984. m. GBP 870
domestic; GBP 880 elsewhere (effective 2002). **Document
type:** *Newsletter, Trade.*
Related titles: Regional ed(s).: European Steel Review
Supplement. ISSN 1369-8591. GBP 420 domestic; GBP 430
foreign (effective 2002).
Indexed: BrCerAb, C&ISA, CerAb, CorrAb, E&CAJ, EMA, IAA,
M&TEA, MBF, METADEX, SolStAb, WAA.
—Linda Hall.
Published by: M E P S (International) Ltd, 263 Glossop Rd,
Sheffield, S10 2GZ, United Kingdom. TEL 44-114-2750570,
FAX 44-114-2759808, jmilnes@meps.co.uk,
http://www.meps.co.uk.

337.142   DNK   ISSN 0900-5323
EUROPEISK NYHEDSBREV. Text in Danish. 1984. s-m. DKK 50.
bk.rev. **Document type:** *Newsletter.*
Published by: Europa - Kommissionen, Repraesentation i
Danmark, Hoejbrohus, Oestergade 61, PO Box 144,
Copenhagen K, 1004, Denmark. TEL 45-33-14-41-40, FAX
45-33-11-12-03. Ed. Thomas A Christensen. Circ: 8,000.

B

EUROSTAT STATISTICS IN FOCUS. EXTERNAL TRADE. see *BUSINESS AND ECONOMICS—Abstracting, Bibliographies, Statistics*

382 IND
EX-IMP TIMES. Text in English. 1979. fortn. INR 500, USD 50. adv. bk.rev.
Published by: Anupam Publishers, R-98, Model Town III, New Delhi, 110 009, India. TEL 7127784. Ed. Anil Kumar. Circ: 2,000.

382.7 IND
EXCISE AND CUSTOMS REPORTER. Short title: E C R. Text in English. 1973. fortn. INR 1,200, USD 120 (effective 1995). adv. charts; stat. index. **Document type:** *Trade.* **Description:** Covers the technical fields of customs and excise. Provides information on import and export duties, policy and procedures, connected trade restrictions, government notifications, tariff advices and interpretation of international classification and valuation of goods in the import and export trade.
Formerly: C E N C U S: Central Excise and Customs Journal (0376-7809)
Published by: Cencus Publications, C-7 Main Market, Vasant Vihar, New Delhi, Bihar 110 057, India. TEL 91-11-673313, FAX 91-11-6883942. Ed. S K Kohli. Circ: 3,400.

382 FRA ISSN 1145-8836
EXPO-NEWS. Text in French. 1978. w. adv. bk.rev. Supplement avail. **Document type:** *Newsletter, Trade.* **Description:** Contains professional information about trade shows, conventions, congresses and business travel.
Formerly (until 1983): Infos-Expos
Published by: Groupe Expo News, 5 rue de Chazelles, Paris, 75017, France. TEL 33-1-44299740, FAX 33-1-47664164. Ed., Pub., Adv. contact Pierre Gougeon. Circ: 20,000.

382 330.9048 DNK ISSN 0900-3177
EXPORT; udenrigsministeriets tidsskrift. Text in Danish. 1920. w. DKK 732 (effective 1998). adv. index. **Document type:** *Trade.*
Former titles (until 1985): U T (0106-3952); Udenrigsministeriets Tidsskrift (0041-5685)
—CCC.
Published by: Udenrigsministeriet, Secretariat for Foreign Trade/Ministry of Foreign Affairs, Asiatisk Plads 2, Copenhagen K, 1448, Denmark. TEL 45-33920825, FAX 45-33920819. Ed., R&P Mogens Lange. Circ: 2,600.

382 USA ISSN 0014-519X
EXPORT. Text in English. 1877. 6/yr. USD 60; free to qualified personnel. adv. bk.rev. charts; illus.; tr.lit. back issues avail. **Description:** Serving importing distributors and retailers of consumer, commercial and light industrial goods in 183 countries and territories worldwide.
Formerly: Exportador Americano - American Exporter
Related titles: Spanish ed.: Export en Espanol. ISSN 1065-6677.
Indexed: KES.
Published by: Hunter Publishing Limited Partnership, 2101 S Arlington Heights Rd, Ste 150, Arlington, IL 60005. TEL 847-427-9512, FAX 847-427-2097. Ed. Ted P Eugenis. Circ: 29,489.

382 USA ISSN 1534-3588
HF3000
EXPORT AMERICA. Text in English. 1999. m. USD 58 domestic; USD 81.20 foreign; USD 6 newsstand/cover domestic; USD 8 newsstand/cover foreign (effective 2005). **Document type:** *Government.*
Related titles: Online - full text ed.: (from EBSCO Publishing, H.W. Wilson, O C L C Online Computer Library Center, Inc.).
Indexed: BPI.
Published by: U.S. Department of Commerce, International Trade Administration, 1401 Constitution Ave, N W, Room 3414, Washington, DC 20230. TEL 202-482-3251, FAX 202-482-5819, Export_America@ita.doc.gov, http://www.export.gov/exportamerica/, http://www.ita.doc.gov. **Subscr. to:** U.S. Government Printing Office, Superintendent of Documents, PO Box 371954, Pittsburgh, PA 15250-7954. TEL 202-512-1800, FAX 202-512-2250, orders@gpo.gov, http://www.access.gpo.gov.

382 GBR ISSN 0014-5122
EXPORT COURIER; product information for international buyers. Text in Arabic, English, French, German, Spanish. 1967. 3/yr. adv. illus. **Document type:** *Catalog, Trade.* **Description:** Details of British consumer products and manufacturers seeking trading partners and importers worldwide.
Published by: Stokes & Lindley-Jones Ltd., 36 Stonehills House, Welwyn Garden City, Herts AL8 6NA, United Kingdom. TEL 44-1707-326688, FAX 44-1707-323447, exporters@exportcourier.co.uk, http://www.exportcourier.co.uk. Ed. I Warren. Pub. L G Warren. Adv. contact L.G. Warren. page GBP 2,150; 168 x 240. Circ: 9,500 (controlled).

354.74 CAN ISSN 1707-4533
EXPORT DEVELOPMENT CANADA. ANNUAL REPORT. Text in English. 1944. a.
Former titles (until 2001): Export Development Corporation. Annual Report (0709-1605); (until 1969): Export Credits Insurance Corporation. Annual Report and Financial Statements (0709-1443)
—CISTI.
Published by: Export Development Canada/Exportation et Developpement, 151 O'Connor, Ottawa, ON K1A 1K3, Canada. TEL 613-598-2500, FAX 613-237-2690, http://www.edc.ca/corpinfo/pubs/index_e.htm.

382 GBR
EXPORT DIGEST. Text in English. 1947. q. GBP 362.42 (effective 1999); includes w. Personnel in Practice. adv. Supplement avail. **Document type:** *Trade.*
Related titles: Online - full text ed.
Published by: Croner.C C H Group Ltd. (Subsidiary of: Wolters Kluwer N.V.), 145 London Rd, Kingston, Surrey KT2 6SR, United Kingdom. TEL 44-20-85473333, FAX 44-20-85472637, info@croner.co.uk, http://www.croner.co.uk. Ed. D Wright. Adv. contact Louise Saunders.

EXPORT DIRECTORY; members and buyers guide. see *BUSINESS AND ECONOMICS—Trade And Industrial Directories*

EXPORT DIRECTORY, ISLAMIC REPUBLIC OF IRAN. see *BUSINESS AND ECONOMICS—Trade And Industrial Directories*

380.102 DNK ISSN 1397-5501
HF3643
EXPORT DIRECTORY OF DENMARK: DANISH EXPORTERS. Text in English, French, German, Spanish; Summaries in English. 1927. a. DKK 700 (effective 2001). adv. 1100 p./no.; **Document type:** *Directory, Trade.*
Former titles (until 1997): Kraks Export Directory of Denmark (1395-4067); Export Directory of Denmark (0905-9652)
Related titles: CD-ROM ed.
—CISTI.
Published by: Kraks Forlag AS, Virumgaardsvej 21, Virum, 2830, Denmark. TEL 45-45-95-65-00, FAX 45-45-95-65-65, export@krak.dk, http://www.danishexporters.dk. Ed. Per Engel Moeller. Circ: 25,000. **Dist. by:** Current Pacific Ltd., PO Box 36-536, Northcote, Auckland, New Zealand. TEL 64-9-480-1388, FAX 64-9-480-1387. **Co-publisher:** Udenrigsministeriet, Danmarks Exportraad/Royal Danish Ministry of Foreign Affairs. Danish Trade Council.

382 AUS
EXPORT EDGE. Text in English. 1977. irreg. free. **Document type:** *Newspaper.* **Description:** Discusses export finance and credit insurance business.
Supersedes in part (1977-1999): E F I C; Which was formerly (until 1991): Export Finance & Insurance Review; (until 1990): Export Finance and Insurance Quarterly; (until 1986): E F I C Quarterly (0314-7568)
Published by: Export Finance and Insurance Corporation, 22 Pitts St, Sydney, NSW 2000, Australia. TEL 800-685-109, FAX 61-2-9201-5222, info@efic.gov.au, http://www.efic.gov.au/pdfs/Export%20Edge.pdf. Circ: 5,000 (controlled).

382 332.1 JPN ISSN 0071-3503
EXPORT - IMPORT BANK OF JAPAN. ANNUAL REPORT. Text in English. 1951. a. free. **Document type:** *Corporate.*
Published by: Export - Import Bank of Japan, 1-4-1 Ote-Machi, Chiyoda-ku, Tokyo, 100-0004, Japan. TEL 3287-9101, FAX 3287-9539, TELEX 222-3728 YUGIN J. Ed. Seiichiro Shimamoto. Circ: 7,000.

332.1 KOR
EXPORT - IMPORT BANK OF KOREA. ANNUAL REPORT. Text in English. a. charts; illus.; stat. **Document type:** *Corporate.*
Published by: Export - Import Bank of Korea, PO Box 4009, Seoul, 100, Korea, S.

382 IND ISSN 0014-5149
EXPORT - IMPORT NEWS; a fortnightly journal about export-import trade. Text in English. 1969. fortn. INR 500, USD 100 (effective 1999).
Published by: (Exporters - Importers Club), India-International News Service, 12 India Exchange Place, Kolkata, West Bengal 700 001, India. Ed. H Kothari. Circ: (controlled).

382.6 IRL ISSN 1393-743X
EXPORT IRELAND SERVICES TO IRISH EXPORTERS GUIDE. Variant title: Services to Irish Exporters Guide. Text in English. 1998. a. **Document type:** *Directory, Trade.*
Published by: Setanta Editorial Services, 9 Morehampton Rd., Dublin, 4, Ireland. TEL 353-1-6683844, FAX 353-1-6683437, mail@setanta.ie, http://www.setanta.ie.

332.6 USA ISSN 1064-1513
EXPORT LEADS; worldwide export marketing opportunities monthly. Text in English. 1989. m. USD 95 domestic (effective 2005). adv. 32 p./no. 4 cols./p.; back issues avail. **Document type:** *Newspaper, Trade.* **Description:** Contains 800-1000 export/import offers each issue.
Related titles: Online - full content ed.: 1996. USD 95 (effective 2001).
Published by: Interdata, 1741 Kekamek, Poulsbo, WA 98370. TEL 360-779-1511, 800-818-0140, FAX 360-697-4696, helpdesk@export-leads.com, http://www.export-leads.com, http://www.importersnet.com. Ed., Pub. Tage M Blytmann. Circ: 2,500. **Dist. by:** Current Pacific Ltd., PO Box 36-536, Northcote, Auckland, New Zealand. TEL 64-9-480-1388, FAX 64-9-480-1387, info@cplnz.com, http://www.cplnz.com.

382.6 NZL ISSN 0113-1338
EXPORT NEWS. Text in English. 1957. bi-w. NZD 49; NZD 96.89 in North America and Asia; NZD 107.56 in Europe; NZD 128.89 elsewhere. adv. back issues avail. **Document type:** *Trade.* **Description:** Lists and promotes all companies that are sucessfully exporting goods and ideas from New Zealand.
Indexed: INZP.
Published by: Headliner Publishing Co. Ltd., Level 2 Age Concern Bldg., 64 Cashel St, Christchurch, 8001, New Zealand. TEL 64-3-3650-301, FAX 64-3-3654-255, headliner@xtra.co.nz. Ed. Robin Major. Pub. Warren Head. Adv. contact Rociney Laredo. B&W page NZD 1,595, color page NZD 1,975. Circ: 8,000. **Co-sponsor:** New Zealand Trade Development Board.

382 MWI
EXPORT NEWS BULLETIN. Text in English. q. **Document type:** *Bulletin, Trade.* **Description:** Covers market information and trade opportunities.
Formerly: Export Information
Published by: Malawi Export Promotion Council, Delamere House Fourth Floor, PO Box 1299, Blantyre, Malawi. TEL 265-620499, FAX 265-635429. Ed. Chatonda Mhone. Circ: 600.

382.6 382.029 USA ISSN 1528-0233
EXPORT REFERENCE GUIDE. Text in English. 1999. m. **Document type:** *Trade.*
Related titles: Online - full content ed.; Online - full text ed.: (from The Bureau of National Affairs, Inc.); Print ed.: Export Reference Guide on CD. ISSN 1097-2277. 1997.
—CCC.
Published by: B N A Inc. (Subsidiary of: The Bureau of National Affairs, Inc.), 1231 25th St, NW, Washington, DC 20037. TEL 202-452-4343, FAX 202-452-4997, customercare@bna.com, http://www.bna.com.

332.6 USA ISSN 1097-4482
HF1416.5
EXPORT SALES AND MARKETING MANUAL (YEAR). Text in English. 1988. a. USD 315 in United States; USD 395 in United States print and CD-ROM together; USD 335 elsewhere; USD 415 elsewhere print and CD-ROM together (effective 2001). bk.rev. charts; illus. **Document type:** *Trade.* **Description:** Contains comprehensive plan for entrepreneurs and companies to export their products and services, including locating foreign markets and agents, pricing, writing contracts, receiving payment, shipping and budgeting for export. Contains 1200 Internet addresses (URL's) (hyperlinked directly to the Internet on the CD-Rom) to conduct international market research and development.
Related titles: CD-ROM ed.
Published by: Export Institute, 6901 W. 84th St., Apt. 359, Minneapolis, MN 55438-3107. TEL 612-943-1505, FAX 612-943-1535, info@exportinstitute.com, http://www.exportinstitute.com. Ed. Agnes Brown. R&P John R Jagoe. Circ: 14,500 (paid).

382 JPN
EXPORT STATISTICAL SCHEDULE OF JAPAN (YEAR). Text in English, Japanese. 1965. a. JPY 9,515, USD 36. **Document type:** *Government.*
Supersedes in part: Commodity Classification for Foreign Trade Statistics: Japan (0546-0786)
Published by: Japan Tariff Association, c/o Jibiki Daini Bldg, 4-7-8 Koji-Machi, Chiyoda-ku, Tokyo, 102-0083, Japan.

382 GBR
EXPORT TIMES; newspaper for international business & travel. Text in English. 1969. 10/yr. free to qualified personnel. adv. **Document type:** *Newspaper, Trade.* **Description:** Provides industry news, interviews, case studies and in-depth features.
Indexed: IPackAb, M&MA.
Published by: Nexus Media Ltd. (Subsidiary of: Highbury House Communications PLC), Nexus House, Azalea Dr, Swanley, Kent BR8 8HU, United Kingdom. TEL 44-1322-660070, FAX 44-1322-616311, info@nexusmedia.com, http://www.hhc.co.uk/exporttimes. Ed. Russell Flanders TEL 44-1322-660070 ext 2445. Adv. contact Daniel Emmerson TEL 44-1322-660070 ext 2441. B&W page GBP 2,400, color page GBP 2,945; trim 379 x 273. Circ: 7,000.

382 GBR
EXPORT TODAY. Text in English. 1937. bi-m. GBP 22.50. adv. bk.rev. illus. **Document type:** *Trade.*
Incorporates: Export (0014-5084)
Indexed: KES.
Published by: (Institute of Export), Nexus Media Ltd. (Subsidiary of: Highbury House Communications PLC), Nexus House, Azalea Dr, Swanley, Kent BR8 8HU, United Kingdom. TEL 44-1322-660070, FAX 44-1322-666408. Ed. Laura McCaffrey. Adv. contact Gordon Russell. Circ: 10,000.

382 USA ISSN 1530-8472
HF1455
EXPORT TODAY'S GLOBAL BUSINESS. Text in English. 1985. m. USD 49. adv. index. back issues avail. **Document type:** *Trade.*
Formerly (until 1999): Export Today (0882-4711)
Related titles: Online - full text ed.: (from EBSCO Publishing).
—CCC.

Published by: Trade Communications Inc., 733 15th St N W, Ste 1100, Washington, DC 20005. TEL 202-737-1060, FAX 202-783-5966, Mjohn@interserv.com. Ed. Barry Lynn. Pub. John Mooney. R&P Julie Wallace. Adv. contact Patricia Steele. Circ: 68,656.

382   TUR
EXPORT TURKEY; ticaret. Text in Turkish. 1981. q. **Description:** Promotes Turkish exports in order to increase trade relations with foreign countries.
Published by: Nesriyat ve Matbaacilik Ltd. Sti., Gazi Bulvari 18, Izmir, Turkey. TEL 51-25-93-50. Ed. Ahmet S Tukel. Circ: 6,800.

332.6   GBR
EXPORT WALES. Text in English. m. **Document type:** Government.
—BLDSC (3842.863000).
Published by: Welsh Office, Export Branch, New Crown Bldg, Cathays Park, Cardiff, CF1 3NP, United Kingdom. TEL 0222-825414, FAX 0222-825350. Ed. Roy Chappell.

332.6   USA   ISSN 1055-8365
EXPORT YELLOW PAGES✳ . Text in English. 1990. a. free. **Document type:** Directory. **Description:** Source book of US companies exporting products and services covering all industries.
Published by: (U.S. Department of Commerce), U S West, c/o Scot Burgos, 198 Inverness Dr, 3rd Fl, Englewood, CO 80112-5306. Ed. Patricia Lingeman. Circ: 100,000.

382   ESP   ISSN 1137-6384
EL EXPORTADOR. Text in Spanish. 1984. 11/yr. USD 35 domestic; USD 75 foreign (effective 2005). bk.rev. index. **Document type:** Magazine, Trade. **Description:** Aimed at export companies or companies related to foreign trade. Contains information on economic conditions, buying trends, investment opportunities, and international issues.
Former titles (until 1997): Expansion Internacional (1133-8075); (until 1994): Expansion Comercial (0212-7350)
—CINDOC.
Published by: Instituto Espanol de Comercio Exterior, Paseo Castellana, 14, Madrid, 28046, Spain. TEL 34-1-3496237, FAX 34-1-4358876, TELEX 44838 IECE, http://www.el-exportador.com. Ed. Jose Antonio Garcia Rubio. Circ: 7,000.

382   DOM
EXPORTADOR DOMINICANO/EXPORT NEWS. Text in Spanish. 1973. bi-m. DOP 18, USD 10. stat.
Formerly: Dominican Republic. Centro Dominicano de Promocion de Exportaciones. Informes
Published by: Centro Dominicano de Promocion de Exportaciones, Plaza de la Independencia, Apdo 199 2, Santo Domingo, Dominican Republic.

382   COL
EXPORTADOR LATINOAMERICANO. Text in Spanish. 1973. 6/yr. USD 250 (effective 2000). **Document type:** Trade.
Address: Transversal 6 no. 51A-43, Apartado Aereo 54520 & 91391, Bogota, CUND, Colombia. TEL 57-1-2871005, FAX 57-1-2871005, expolati@cable.net.co. Ed. Jaime Villamil Leon. Circ: 55,000.

382   PRT   ISSN 0870-9173
EXPORTAR. Text in Portuguese. 1988. 6/yr. adv. bk.rev. **Document type:** Government.
Published by: ICEP, Av. 5 de Outubro 101, Lisbon, 1050-051, Portugal. TEL 351-21-7909500, FAX 351-21-7935028, icep@icep.pt, http://www.icep.pt/. Ed. Eurico Roseta. Adv. contact Joaquim Santos. Circ: 6,000.

332.6   GBR   ISSN 1366-2406
EXPORTER. Variant title: East Midlands Exporter. Text in English. 1991. q. adv. **Document type:** Trade.
Formerly (until 1994): D T I East Midlands Exporter (0969-3750)
—BLDSC (3842.944476).
Published by: T D A Marketing Communications, Apex House, Bank St, Lutterworth, Leics LE17 4AG, United Kingdom. TEL 44-1455-558377, FAX 44-1455-559845. Ed. Brian Drescher. Adv. contact Susan Darrall.

382   USA   ISSN 0736-9239
                                 CODEN: ATTDD4
THE EXPORTER; the magazine for the business of exporting. Text in English. 1980. m. USD 218 (effective 2004). adv. bk.rev. **Document type:** Magazine, Trade. **Description:** Provides a guide to exporting services and resources for people involved in the business who need to understand and meet foreign import or U.S. export requirements.
Formerly: Export Shipper
Related titles: Online - full text ed.
—CCC.
Published by: Trade Data Reports, Inc., 5 Hanover Sq #21, New York, NY 10004-2614. TEL 212-269-2016, FAX 212-587-1344, exporter@exporter.com, http://www.exporter.com. Ed., Pub. Leslie Stroh. R&P, Adv. contact Kathleen Bingham TEL 212-587-1340. B&W page USD 1,220. Circ: 5,000.

382.6   USA   ISSN 8755-013X
HF3011
EXPORTERS' ENCYCLOPAEDIA. Text in English. 1904. a. (plus s-m. updates). adv. index. **Document type:** Directory, Trade. **Description:** Provides essential exporting, travel, communications and research information for more than 170 world markets.
Former titles (until 1981): Exporters' Encyclopaedia. World Marketing Guide (0732-0159); (until 1980): Dun and Bradstreet Exporters' Encyclopaedia - World Marketing Guide (0149-8118); Exporters' Encyclopaedia-World Marketing Guide (0071-3546)
—CISTI. **CCC.**
Published by: Dun & Bradstreet (Subsidiary of: Dun & Bradstreet Corporation), c/o Ethan Chazin, Director, Reference Services, Murray Hill, NJ 07094-1218. TEL 973-605-6000. Ed. Joseph Douress. Circ: 5,100. **Dist. by:** Current Pacific Ltd., PO Box 36-536, Northcote, Auckland, New Zealand. TEL 64-9-480-1388, FAX 64-9-480-1387, info@cplnz.com, http://www.cplnz.com.

382.6   IRL   ISSN 1393-4384
EXPORTING TODAY. Text in English. 1997. irreg. **Document type:** Directory, Trade.
Published by: Setanta Editorial Services, 9 Morehampton Rd., Dublin, 4, Ireland. TEL 353-1-6683844, FAX 353-1-6683437, mail@setanta.ie, http://www.setanta.ie.

332.6   DEU
EXPORTPRAXIS. Text in German. 2000. 6/yr. EUR 297 (effective 2001). **Document type:** Trade. **Description:** Contains all necessary rules and regulations for exporting to foreign countries.
Media: CD-ROM.
Published by: Mendel Verlag, Robensstr 39, Aachen, 52070, Germany. TEL 49-241-154355, FAX 49-241-1570816, info@mendel-verlag.de, http://www.mendel-verlag.de.

EXPORTS BY COUNTRIES. see BUSINESS AND ECONOMICS—Abstracting, Bibliographies, Statistics

382   NLD   ISSN 1381-3587
HF5470
EXPOVISIE✳ . Text in Dutch. 1950. 6/yr. adv. illus. **Document type:** Trade.
Supersedes in part: Expo - Congresvisie (0927-7420); **Former titles** (until 1992): Expovisie (0014-5254); Beursklanken
Indexed: KES.
—IE, Infotrieve.
Published by: Hollandia Publishing BV, Postbus 70, Baarn, 3740 AB, Netherlands. Ed. H Klompenhouwer. Circ: 5,000.

382.5   LBR
EXTERNAL TRADE OF LIBERIA: IMPORT AND EXPORT✳ . Text in English. a. USD 5.
Published by: Ministry of Planning and Economic Affairs, PO Box 9016, Monrovia, Liberia.

EXTERNAL TRADE STATISTICS OF GAMBIA. see BUSINESS AND ECONOMICS—Abstracting, Bibliographies, Statistics

EXTERNAL TRADE STATISTICS OF GHANA (ANNUAL). see BUSINESS AND ECONOMICS—Abstracting, Bibliographies, Statistics

EXTERNAL TRADE STATISTICS OF GHANA (HALF-YEARLY). see BUSINESS AND ECONOMICS—Abstracting, Bibliographies, Statistics

EXTERNAL TRADE STATISTICS OF GHANA (QUARTERLY). see BUSINESS AND ECONOMICS—Abstracting, Bibliographies, Statistics

F A O YEARBOOK, TRADE. see AGRICULTURE—Agricultural Economics

382 332.7   USA
F C I B COUNTRY REPORT. Text in English. 1982. USD 125 to non-members; USD 100 to members.
Formerly: F C I B Country Credit Report
Published by: (Finance, Credit and International Business - National Association of Credit Management), F C I B - N A C M Corp., 8840 Columbia 100 Pkwy, Columbia, MD 21045-2158. TEL 410-423-1840, FAX 410-423-1845, fcib_info@nacm.org, fcib_info@fcibglobal.com, http://www.nacm.org, http://www.fcibglobal.com.

382   USA
F C I B CREDIT REPORTS. Text in English. irreg.
Published by: F C I B - N A C M Corp., 8840 Columbia 100 Pkwy, Columbia, MD 21045-2158. TEL 410-423-1840, FAX 410-423-1845, fcib_info@fcibglobal.com, http://www.fcibglobal.com.

382 332.7   USA
F C I B INTERNATIONAL BULLETIN. Text in English. 1919. q. free to members only.
Formerly: F C I B Bulletin (0014-5718)

Published by: (Finance, Credit and International Business - National Association of Credit Management), F C I B - N A C M Corp., 8840 Columbia 100 Pkwy, Columbia, MD 21045-2158. TEL 410-423-1840, FAX 410-423-1845, fcib_info@fcibglobal.com, http://www.fcibglobal.com.

332.7   USA
F C I B MINUTES OF ROUND TABLE CONFERENCE. (Finance, Credit and International Business) Text in English. free; Free only to members.
Formerly: F C I B - N A C M Minutes of Round Table Conference
Published by: (Finance, Credit and International Business - National Association of Credit Management), F C I B - N A C M Corp., 8840 Columbia 100 Pkwy, Columbia, MD 21045-2158. TEL 410-423-1840, FAX 410-423-1845, fcib_info@fcibglobal.com, http://www.fcibglobal.com.

382   PAN
F O B COLON FREE ZONE. (Free on Board) Text in English, Spanish. 1979. a. USD 15 (effective 1999). adv. **Document type:** Directory. **Description:** Directory of companies, products and trademarks incorporating full color product catalogue and information for potential investors.
Formerly: Colon Free Zone Directory
Published by: (Colon Free Zone Users Association), Focus Publications (Int.) S.A., Apdo. 6-3287, El Dorado, Panama City, Panama. TEL 507-225-6638, FAX 507-225-0466, focusint@sinfo.net, http://www.colonfreezone.com, http://focuspublicationsint.com. Ed. Kenneth J Jones. Circ: 35,000.

382 340   USA   ISSN 0161-7036
F T C FREEDOM OF INFORMATION LOG. (Federal Trade Commission) Text in English. 1980. w. USD 451 (effective 2000). **Document type:** Newsletter. **Description:** Provides summaries of the Freedom of Information Act requests received at the U.S. Federal Trade Commission.
Related titles: Fax ed.
—CCC.
Published by: Washington Regulatory Reporting Associates, PO Box 356, Basye, VA 22810. TEL 202-639-0581, FAX 202-478-0260. Ed. Genevieve McCarthy. Pub. Arthur Amolsch.

382   JPN
F T C - JAPAN VIEWS: INFORMATION & OPINION FROM THE FAIR TRADE COMMISSION OF JAPAN. Text in English. 1988. q. free. **Document type:** Government. **Description:** Contains the JFTC's materials on such subjects such as regulations for mergers and acquisitions, deregulation of industries, competition policy, fair trade, distribution practices, and recommendations for specific sectors or companies in Japan.
Media: Online - full text.
Published by: Fair Trade Commisssion, International Affairs Division, 1-1-1 Kasumigaseki, Chiyoda-ku, Tokyo, 100-0013, Japan. TEL 81-3-3581-4968, FAX 81-3-3581-1944, jftc@mxb.meshnet.or.jp, http://www.jftc.admix.go.jp/. Ed. Kazuyuki Funhashi. Pub., R&P Masaya Sakuma.

354.73   USA   ISSN 0196-0016
KF1602
F T C WATCH. (Federal Trade Commission) Text in English. 1976. fortn. looseleaf. USD 740 (effective 2000). bk.rev. **Document type:** Newsletter. **Description:** Provides information on the policies, personnel and law enforcement programs of the U.S. Federal Trade Commission, the Antitrust Division of the U.S. Department of Justice, and the multistate task force of the National Association of Attorneys General, including merger enforcement.
Related titles: Online - full text ed.: (from Florida Center for Library Automation, Gale Group).
—CCC.
Published by: Washington Regulatory Reporting Associates, PO Box 356, Basye, VA 22810. TEL 202-639-0581, http://www.ftcwatch.com. Ed., Pub. Arthur Amolsch.

382   GBR   ISSN 1050-0782
F X WEEK. (Foreign Exchange) Text in English. 1990. w. USD 1,745 (effective 2000). adv. **Document type:** Newsletter, Trade. **Description:** Delivers the latest insider news in the ever-changing business of foreign exchange and money markets.
Related titles: Online - full text ed.: (from Factiva).
—CCC.
Published by: Risk Waters Group (Subsidiary of: Incisive Media Plc.), Haymarket House, 28-29 Haymarket, London, SW1Y 4RX, United Kingdom. TEL 44-20-74849700, FAX 44-20-79302238, customerservices@incisivemedia.com, http://www.fxweek.com, http://www.incisivemedia.com/. Ed. Nikki Marmery TEL 44-20-74849700. Pub., Adv. contact Couling Stephen TEL 44-20-74849700. **Subscr. in US & Canada to:** Incisive Media Plc., 270 Lafayette St, Ste 700, New York, NY 10012. TEL 212-925-6990, FAX 212-925-7585, customerservices@incisivemedia.com.

FEDERAL REPUBLIC OF GERMANY - PARTNER OF THE WORLD; documentation of economy and export. see BUSINESS AND ECONOMICS—Economic Situation And Conditions

382 FRA ISSN 0992-7425
FEDERATION FRANCAISE DE LA FRANCHISE. LETTRE. Key Title: Lettre de la F F F. Text in French. 10/yr. bk.rev.
Document type: *Newsletter.*
Formerly: Franchise Actualites
Published by: Federation Francaise de la Franchise, 60 rue la Boetie, Paris, 75008, France. TEL 33-1-53752225, FAX 33-1-53752220, fff@club-internet.fr, http://www.franchiseline.com/fff.html. Ed. Chantal Zimmer.

382 NLD ISSN 1381-7647
FENENDEXPRESS. Text in Dutch. 1980. m.
Published by: Federatie voor de Nederlandse Export, Postbus 90409, The Hague, 2509 LK, Netherlands. TEL 31-70-3305600, FAX 31-70-3305656.

332 FRA ISSN 1150-7608
FICHIER BANQUE AFRIQUE. Text in French. 1990. m.
Related titles: ◆ Supplement to: Banque Afrique. ISSN 0184-9719.
Published by: I C Publications, 10 rue Vineuse, Paris, 75784 Cedex 16, France. FAX 33-1-44308111, 33-1-44308100.

FIJI. BUREAU OF STATISTICS. OVERSEAS TRADE (YEAR). see *BUSINESS AND ECONOMICS—Abstracting, Bibliographies, Statistics*

382 ZAF
FINAL INPUT - OUTPUT TABLES ADUSTED TO SHOW IMPORTS SEPARATELY. Text in English. 1989. irreg. stat.
Document type: *Government.*
Published by: Statistics South Africa/Statistieke Suid-Afrika, Private Bag X44, Pretoria, 0001, South Africa. TEL 27-12-310-8911, FAX 27-12-310-8500, info@statssa.pwv.gov.za, http://www.statssa.gov.za.

382 USA ISSN 1084-4244
FINANCIAL EXECUTIVE'S COUNTRY RISK ALERT. Text in English. 3/yr. USD 475 for print or diskette version; USD 550 for print and diskette versions (effective 1999). stat.
Document type: *Corporate.* **Description:** Provides surveys and forecast information on international trade and currency matters, with specific risk evaluations for all countries.
Related titles: Diskette ed.; Online - full text ed.
Published by: S.J. Rundt & Associates, Inc., 130 E 63rd St, New York, NY 10021-7334. TEL 212-838-0141, info@rundtsintelligence.com, http://www.rundtsintelligence.com. Ed., Pub. Hans P Belcsak. R&P J Wilfinger TEL 973-783-5206.

382 338 USA ISSN 0146-1958
HF1
THE FLAGSTAFF INSTITUTE. JOURNAL. Text in English. 1976. s-a. USD 50 to individuals; USD 150 to corporations & government agencies (effective 2003). index. back issues avail. **Document type:** *Journal, Academic/Scholarly.*
Description: Covers articles of interest on development of manufacturing in the Third World Countries to serve global export markets.
Published by: The Flagstaff Institute, PO Box 986, Flagstaff, AZ 86002. TEL 928-779-0052, FAX 928-774-8589, instflag@aol.com, http://www.wepza.org. Ed., Pub., R&P Richard L Bolin. Circ: 100.

382 NLD
FOCUS ON HOLLAND; tijdschrift t.b.v. de Nederlandse industrie, handel, landbouwen verkeer, ter bevordering van de Nederlandse export naar diverse landen. Text in Dutch. q. adv.
Indexed: KES.
Published by: Nederlands Centrum voor Handelsbevordering, Postbus 10, The Hague, 2501 CA, Netherlands. Circ: 5,000.

382.029 COL
FONDO DE PROMOCION DE EXPORTACIONES. DIRECTORIO DE EXPORTADORES/EXPORT DIRECTORY. Text in English, Spanish. 1969. a. free. adv. charts; illus.; stat. **Document type:** *Directory.*
Published by: Proexpo Fondo de Promocion de Exportaciones, Calle 28, 13-A-15 Piso 41, Bogota, CUND, Colombia. FAX 57-1-2825071, TELEX 45690-44452. Circ: 15,000.

FOOD AND AGRICULTURAL EXPORT DIRECTORY. see *AGRICULTURE—Agricultural Economics*

382 TUR
FOOD & PACKAGING EXPORTS - TURKEY. Text in English. q.
Published by: Ihlas Magazine Group, Ihlas Holding Mrk. Binasi, 29 Ekim Cad. 23, Yenibosna - Istanbul, 34530, Turkey. TEL 90-212-4542530, FAX 90-212-4542555, bsensoz@img.com.tr, http://www.img.com.tr.

382 USA
FOREIGN AGRICULTURAL TRADE OF THE UNITED STATES/U.S. AGRICULTURAL TRADE UPDATE. Text in English. 1995. m. USD 50 (effective 2001). **Document type:** *Government.* **Description:** Updates the quantity and value of U.S. farm exports and imports, plus price trends. Concise articles analyze specific aspects of the export/import picture. Keeps readers abreast of how U.S. trade stacks up in a global market.
Related titles: Online - full content ed.; Supplement(s): USD 46 newsstand/cover (effective 2001).
Published by: U.S. Department of Agriculture, Economic Research Service, 1800 M St. NW, Washington, DC 20036-5831. **Subscr. to:** U.S. Government Printing Office, Superintendent of Documents, PO Box 371954, Pittsburgh, PA 15250-7954. TEL 202-512-1800, FAX 202-512-2250, orders@gpo.gov, http://www.access.gpo.gov.

382 USA ISSN 0732-0418
HG4501
FOREIGN DIRECT INVESTMENT IN THE UNITED STATES; operations of U.S. affiliates of foreign companies. Text in English. 1977. a. **Document type:** *Government.* **Description:** Covers the financial structure and operations of the non-bank U.S. affiliates of foreign direct investors.
Published by: (International Investment Division), U.S. Department of Commerce, Bureau of Economic Analysis, 1441 L St NW, Washington, DC 20230. TEL 202-523-0640, FAX 202-523-7538.

FOREIGN INVESTMENT IN CHINA. see *BUSINESS AND ECONOMICS—Investments*

382 346 BRA
FOREIGN INVESTMENTS IN BRAZIL. LEGISLATION. Text in Portuguese. 1967. irreg., latest 1998, Dec. BRL 74 domestic; USD 66.11 foreign (effective 1999). **Document type:** *Directory.* **Description:** Covers current laws and other normatives concerning foreign capital in Brazil and Brazilian capital abroad.
Formerly: Foreign Investments in Brazil
Published by: Banco Central do Brasil/Central Bank of Brazil, Departamento de Capitais Estrangeiros - FIRCE, SBS, Ed. Sede Banco Central, 2 SS, Brasilia, DF 70074900, Brazil. TEL 55-61-414-1764. Circ: 250. **Subscr. to:** DEMAP - DISUP SIG - Quadra 8 - Lote 2025, Brasilia, DF 70610400, Brazil.

FOREIGN TAX AND TRADE BRIEFS. see *BUSINESS AND ECONOMICS—Public Finance, Taxation*

382 IND ISSN 0015-7317
HF41
FOREIGN TRADE BULLETIN. Text in English. 1970. m. INR 100; USD 25 foreign. adv. charts; stat. **Document type:** *Bulletin.*
Description: Provides commercial information and market intelligence on export opportunities and sales prospects of Indian products in foreign markets.
Published by: Indian Institute of Foreign Trade, B-21, Mehrauli Institutional Area, New Delhi, 110 016, India.

382 658 USA ISSN 0883-4687
FOREIGN TRADE FAIRS NEW PRODUCTS NEWSLETTER. Text in English. 1980. m. looseleaf. USD 45 (effective 2001). back issues avail. **Document type:** *Newsletter.* **Description:** Contains news about new products displayed at foreign trade fairs seeking U.S. importers and distributors.
Related titles: ◆ Supplement to: International Intertrade Index. ISSN 0020-7004.
Published by: International Intertrade Index, PO Box 636, Federal Sq, Newark, NJ 07101. TEL 973-686-2382, FAX 973-622-1740. Ed. John E Felber.

382 PRK
FOREIGN TRADE OF THE DEMOCRATIC PEOPLE'S REPUBLIC OF KOREA. Text in English. bi-m. USD 28. adv. illus.
Related titles: Arabic ed.; Chinese ed.; French ed.; Japanese ed.; Russian ed.; Spanish ed.
Indexed: RASB.
Published by: Foreign Trade Publishing House, Potonggang District, Pyongyang, Korea, N. TELEX 37018 EPB KP. Ed. Mun Sun Hui. **Dist. by:** Korean Publications Exchange Association, Export Section, P.O. Box 222, Pyongyang, Korea, N.. FAX 850-2-3814632.

382 USA
HF105
FOREIGN TRADE REPORTS. U.S. EXPORT AND IMPORT MERCHANDISE TRADE. Text in English. 1945. m. USD 120. reprint service avail. from CIS.
Former titles (until 1988): United States Foreign Trade. FT900, Summary Of U.S. Export and Import Merchandise Trade (0730-3270); (until 1976): Foreign Trade Reports. Summary of U.S. Export and Import Merchandise Trade (0361-0047)
Related titles: Microfiche ed.: (from CIS); Online - full text ed.: (from CompuServe Inc., The Dialog Corporation).
Indexed: AmStI.
Published by: U.S. Bureau of the Census (Subsidiary of: U.S. Department of Commerce), Foreign Trade Division, 4700 Silver Hill Rd, Rm 2179, Federal Office Building #3, Washington, DC 20233. http://www.census.gov. **Subscr. to:** U.S. Government Printing Office, Superintendent of Documents, PO Box 371954, Pittsburgh, PA 15250-7954. TEL 202-512-1800, FAX 202-512-2250, orders@gpo.gov, http://www.access.gpo.gov.

382 USA ISSN 0565-1204
HF3060
FOREIGN TRADE REPORTS. U.S. TRADE WITH PUERTO RICO AND U.S. POSSESSIONS. Text in English. 1943. a. price varies. reprint service avail. from CIS.
Related titles: Microfiche ed.: (from CIS).
Indexed: AmStI.
Published by: U.S. Bureau of the Census (Subsidiary of: U.S. Department of Commerce), Foreign Trade Division, 4700 Silver Hill Rd, Rm 2179, Federal Office Building #3, Washington, DC 20233. http://www.census.gov/prod/www/abs/ftdpr895.html. **Dist. by:** U.S. Government Printing Office, Superintendent of Documents, PO Box 371954, Pittsburgh, PA 15250-7954. TEL 202-512-1800, FAX 202-512-2250, orders@gpo.gov, http://www.access.gpo.gov.

382 USA
HF105
FOREIGN TRADE REPORTS. U.S. WATERBORNE EXPORTS AND GENERAL IMPORTS (ONLINE). Text in English. 1952. q. stat. reprint service avail. from CIS. **Document type:** *Government.*
Former titles (until 1998): Foreign Trade Reports. U.S. Waterborne Exports and General Imports (Print); (until 1976): U.S. Waterborne Exports and General Imports; Trade Area, District, Port, Type Service and U.S. Flag (0095-0890); U.S. Foreign Trade. Waterborne Exports and General Imports. Trade Area, District, Port, Type Service, U.S. Flag
Media: Online - full content. **Related titles:** CD-ROM ed.; Microfiche ed.: (from CIS).
Indexed: AmStI.
Published by: U.S. Maritime Administration, U.S. Department of Transportation, 400 7th St, S W, Washington, DC 20590. TEL 800-996-2723, Data.Marad@marad. dot.gov, http://www.marad.dot.gov.

382 IND ISSN 0015-7325
HF41
FOREIGN TRADE REVIEW. Text in English. 1966. q. INR 275; USD 30 foreign. adv. **Document type:** *Trade.* **Description:** Publishes papers and articles on foreign trade for trade and industry, government departments, research and academic institutions.
Indexed: BPIA, CREJ, IBSS, KES.
—BLDSC (3987.320000).
Published by: Indian Institute of Foreign Trade, B-21, Mehrauli Institutional Area, New Delhi, 110 016, India. TEL 91-11-6965124, FAX 91-11-6853956. Ed. R Jaikumar.

FOREIGN TRADE STATISTICS OF ASIA AND THE PACIFIC. see *BUSINESS AND ECONOMICS—Abstracting, Bibliographies, Statistics*

382 IND
FOREIGN TRADE - TRENDS & TIDINGS. Text in English. m. INR 215, USD 50.
Published by: Indian Institute of Foreign Trade, B-21, Mehrauli Institutional Area, New Delhi, 110 016, India. TEL 91-11-6965124, FAX 91-11-6853956.

382 USA ISSN 1544-2322
FOREIGN-TRADE ZONES BOARD. ANNUAL REPORT TO CONGRESS. Text in English. 1954. a. **Document type:** *Government.*
Formerly: Annual Report to Congress for the Fiscal Year Ended June 30...
Related titles: Online - full content ed.
Published by: U.S. Department of Commerce, Foreign-Trade Zones Board, FCB- Ste 4100W, 1401 Constitution Ave., NW, Washington, DC 20230. TEL 202-482-2862, FAX 202-482-0002, http://ia.ita.doc.gov/ftzpage/annual-report.html.

FORWARD MARKETS BULLETIN. see *BUSINESS AND ECONOMICS—Domestic Commerce*

382 USA
FORWARD THINKING. Text in English. 1994. s-a. USD 144; USD 18 newsstand/cover domestic; USD 24 newsstand/cover foreign (effective 2004). **Document type:** *Newsletter.*
Description: Provides information for public and corporate leaders who seek creative ideas to form the passenger and cargo mobility vision for their project needs.
Formerly: Outlook (San Jose)
Published by: Jakes Associates, Inc., Jakes Plaza, 1940 The Alameda, Ste 200, San Jose, CA 95126-1456. TEL 408-249-7200, FAX 408-249-7296, jai9330@aol.com, http://www.jakesassociates.com. Eds. Andrew S Jakes, Michael Ang. R&P Linda Rose. Circ: 1,000.

FRANCE. DIRECTION DE LA BALANCE DES PAIEMENTS. LA BALANCE DES PAIEMENTS ET LA POSITION EXTERIEURE DE LA FRANCE. see *BUSINESS AND ECONOMICS—Public Finance, Taxation*

382 FRA ISSN 0071-8645
FRANCE. DIRECTION GENERALE DES DOUANES ET DROITS INDIRECTS. RESULTATS ANNUELS DES STATISTIQUES DU COMMERCE EXTERIEUR. Text in French. a.
Formerly: France. Direction Generale des Douanes et Droits Indirects. Commentaires Annuels des Statistiques du Commerce Exterieur (0532-4416)
Published by: (France. Direction Generale des Douanes et Droits Indirects), Imprimerie Nationale, BP 514, Douai, Cedex 59505, France. TEL 27-93-70-70, FAX 27-93-70-96.

B

382   FRA   ISSN 0071-8726
FRANCE. DIRECTION NATIONALE DES DOUANES ET DROITS INDIRECTS. TABLEAU GENERAL DES TRANSPORTS. Text in French. 1964. a. price varies.
Published by: (France. Direction Generale des Douanes et Droits Indirects), Imprimerie Nationale, BP 514, Douai, Cedex 59505, France. TEL 27-93-70-90, FAX 27-93-70-96.

382   FRA   ISSN 0071-8718
FRANCE. DIRECTION NATIONALE DES DOUANES ET DROITS INDIRECTS. TRANSPORT DU COMMERCE EXTERIEUR. Text in French. a.
Published by: (France. Direction Generale des Douanes et Droits Indirects), Imprimerie Nationale, BP 514, Douai, Cedex 59505, France. TEL 27-93-70-90, FAX 27-93-70-96.

338.1   FRA
FRANCE. MINISTERE DE L'AGRICULTURE ET DE LA PECHE. CONJONCTURE COMMERCE EXTERIEUR AGRO-ALIMENTAIRE. Text in French. 1976. m. **Document type:** *Government.*
Former titles: France. Ministere de l'Agriculture, de la Peche et de l'Alimentation. Conjoncture Exterieur Agro-Alimentaire; France. Ministere de l'Agriculture et de la Foret. Conjoncture Commerce Exterieur Agro-Alimentaire; France. Ministere de l'Agriculture. Informations Rapides Commerce Exterieur Agro-Alimentaire (0153-1999)
Published by: Ministere de l'Agriculture et de la Peche, Service Central des Enquetes et Etudes Statistiques, 251 rue de Vaugirard, Paris, Cedex 15 75732, France. TEL 33-1-49558585, FAX 33-1-49558503, http://www.agriculture.gouv.fr.

FRANCE TELEXPORT. see *BUSINESS AND ECONOMICS— Trade And Industrial Directories*

FRANCHISE INTERNATIONAL. see *BUSINESS AND ECONOMICS—Marketing And Purchasing*

THE FRANCHISE MAGAZINE. see *BUSINESS AND ECONOMICS—Marketing And Purchasing*

FRANCO-BRITISH TRADE DIRECTORY. see *BUSINESS AND ECONOMICS—Trade And Industrial Directories*

382   PRT
FROM PORTUGAL. Text in English. 1975. m. free. adv. illus.; stat.
Published by: Interfil - Centro de Promocao de Informacao Tecnica Lda, Rua Heliodoro Salgado, 44-r-c, Lisbon, 1100, Portugal. Ed. Fernando Bravo. Circ. 7,500.

382   CAN   ISSN 1194-630X
FROM THE CENTRE. Text in English. 1989. s-a. free. back issues avail. **Document type:** *Newsletter.* **Description:** Reports student and faculty activities at the Centre.
Published by: Centre for International Business Studies, Dalhousie University, 6152 Coburg Rd, Halifax, NS B3H 1Z5, Canada. TEL 902-494-6553, FAX 902-494-1483, mlapp@mgmt.dal.ca, http://ttg.sba.dal.ca/sba/cibs. Ed. Mary Brooks. Circ. 1,200.

332.6 341   LUX   ISSN 1021-2353
HC241.2.A1
FRONTIER-FREE EUROPE. Text in English. 1993. m. free. charts; pat. **Document type:** *Newsletter, Government.* **Description:** Reports on the progress of internal market legislation.
Formerly (until 1993): Target 92 (0776-8508)
Related titles: French ed.: Europe sans Frontieres. ISSN 1021-237X. 1993; German ed.: Europa ohne Grenzen. ISSN 1021-2345. 1993; Spanish ed.: Europa sin Fronteras. ISSN 1021-2361. 1993; Danish ed.: Graenseloese Europa. ISSN 1021-2337. 1993; Dutch ed.: Europa zonder Grenzen. ISSN 1021-240X. 1993; Greek ed.: Europe horis Sunora. ISSN 1021-2388. 1993; Portuguese ed.: Europa sem Fronteiras. ISSN 1021-2418. 1993; Italian ed.: Europa Senza Frontiere. 1993.
Published by: (European Commission BEL, Directorate-General for Audiovisual Media, Information, Communication and Culture), European Commission, Office for Official Publications of the European Union, 2 Rue Mercier, Luxembourg, L-2985, Luxembourg. TEL 352-29291, FAX 352-2929-44637, publications@cec.eu.int, idea@opoce.cec.be, http://europa.eu.int/comm/dg10/publications/newsletters/esf/index_en.html, http://www.eurunion.org/publicat/index.htm.
Dist. in the U.S. by: Bernan Associates, Bernan, 4611-F Assembly Dr., Lanham, MD 20706-4391. TEL 301-459-0056, 800-274-4447.

382   GBR   ISSN 0964-1912
FRONTIERS (LONDON); planning for consumer change in Europe. Text in English, French. 1991. a. USD 40,000 (effective 1996). **Document type:** *Trade.* **Description:** Presents a pan-European forecast of consumer trends in the E.U. for companies with ambitions or operations in Europe.
Published by: Henley Centre for Forecasting Ltd., 9 Bridewell Pl, London, EC4Y 6AY, United Kingdom. TEL 44-171-353-9961, FAX 44-171-353-2899. Ed. James Murphy.

382   CHN
FUJIAN DUIWAI JINGMAO/FUJIAN FOREIGN TRADE. Text in Chinese. m.
Published by: Fujian Sheng Duiwai Jingji Maoyi Yanjiusuo/Fujian Institute of Foreign Trade, No17, Hualin Lu, 15th Fl, Fuzhou, Fujian 350003, China. TEL 572614. Ed. Gu Ming.

THE G-7 REPORT INVESTORS NEWSMAGAZINE. see *BUSINESS AND ECONOMICS—Investments*

G S R. (Gakki Shoho Review) see *MUSIC*

382   FRA   ISSN 0247-8315
GABON SELECTION. Text in French. s-m. (22/yr.).
Published by: I C Publications, 10 rue Vineuse, Paris, 75784 Cedex 16, France. FAX 33-1-44308111, 33-1-44308100.

GAMBIA. CENTRAL STATISTICS DEPARTMENT. MONTHLY SUMMARY OF EXTERNAL TRADE STATISTICS. see *BUSINESS AND ECONOMICS—Abstracting, Bibliographies, Statistics*

382   CHE   ISSN 0072-0623
K4602
GENERAL AGREEMENT ON TARIFFS AND TRADE. BASIC INSTRUMENTS AND SELECTED DOCUMENTS SERIES. SUPPLEMENT. Text in English. 1952. a. price varies. cum.index. **Document type:** *Trade.* **Description:** Presents the decisions, recommendations and reports adopted by the GATT Contracting Parties each year.
Related titles: Microfiche ed.: (from CIS); French ed.; Spanish ed.
Indexed: IIS.
Published by: General Agreement on Tariffs and Trade, Centre William Rappard, 154 rue de Lausanne, Geneva 21, 1211, Switzerland. TEL 41-22-739-5208, FAX 41-22-739-5458. R&P Nathalie Bourgoin. Circ. 4,700. **Dist. in U.S. by:** Bernan Associates, Bernan, 4611-F Assembly Dr., Lanham, MD 20706-4391.

382.0973   CAN   ISSN 1182-803X
HF3099
GERMAN AMERICAN TRADE. Text in English, German. 1949. 10/yr. USD 50. adv. bk.rev. illus.; tr.lit. reprint service avail. from PQC. **Document type:** *Trade.*
Supersedes (in 1990): German American Commerce; Which was formerly: German Business Weekly (0433-6305); G A T N (0192-0103); German American Trade News (0016-8718); (until 1952): United States German Chamber of Commerce. Monthly Bulletin (0733-3854)
Related titles: Microform ed.: (from PQC).
Indexed: PAIS, PROMT.
Published by: (German American Chamber of Commerce USA), Ruland Communications Inc., 12 Lawton Blvd, Toronto, ON M4V 1Z4, Canada. TEL 416-927-9129, FAX 416-927-9118. Ed. Ulrich Hoppe. Pubs. Joseph Ruland, Ulli Ruland. Circ. 6,000. **Subscr. in U.S. to:** GACC Publication Services, 40 W 57th St, 31st Fl, New York, NY 10019. TEL 212-874-8830, 212-974-8867.

GERMAN INVESTMENT WORLD. see *BUSINESS AND ECONOMICS—Economic Situation And Conditions*

382.7   DEU
GESCHAEFTSKONTAKTE. Text in German. w. EUR 209 (effective 2005). **Document type:** *Newsletter, Trade.*
Published by: Bundesagentur fuer Aussenwirtschaft, Agrippastr 87-93, Cologne, 50676, Germany. TEL 49-221-20570, FAX 49-221-2057212, info@bfai.de, http://www.bfai.com.

GLOBAL ASSET ALLOCATION. see *BUSINESS AND ECONOMICS—Investments*

332.6 332 658   USA   ISSN 1088-6931
HG3879   CODEN: GBFRFK
➤ **GLOBAL BUSINESS & FINANCE REVIEW.** Text in English. 1996. s-a. USD 50 to individuals; USD 100 to institutions; USD 30 to students (effective 2004). adv. bk.rev. index. back issues avail. **Document type:** *Journal, Academic/Scholarly.* **Description:** Provides a forum for the exchange of ideas, information, and analysis in this era of globalization. Applied research on domestic issues will also be included.
Related titles: Microfiche ed.
Indexed: SOPODA.
—BLDSC (4195.354400), IE, ingenta.
Published by: Global Business and Finance Review, Department of Economics and Finance, Montclair State University, 1 Normal Ave, Upper Montclair, NJ 07043. TEL 973-655-7013, FAX 973-655-7629, kims@mail.montclair.edu, http://www.montclair.edu/pages/econfin/GBFRmain.htm. Eds. Sang-Hoon Kim, T Chotigeat. adv.: page USD 200. Circ. 750.

382   USA
GLOBAL COMMERCE. Text in English. 1995. q. free. **Document type:** *Newsletter, Academic/Scholarly.* **Description:** Provides an analysis of current international trade relations in middle Tennessee.

Published by: Middle Tennessee State University, College of Business, 1301 E Main St, MTSU Box 102, Murfreesboro, TN 37132. TEL 615-898-5627, FAX 615-898-5045, slivings@mtsu.edu, http://www.mtsu/~berc/trade_database.html. Ed. Steven G Livingston. R&P Sally Govan. Circ. 3,600.

332.6 322   USA   ISSN 1060-8710
HG4009
GLOBAL COMPANY HANDBOOK∗ . Text in English. 1992. a. USD 495. **Description:** Analysis of the financial performance of the world's leading 10,000 companies.
Related titles: CD-ROM ed.: 1992; Magnetic Tape ed.: 1992; Online - full text ed.: 1992.
Published by: C I F A R Publications, Inc., PO Box 3228, Princeton, NJ 08543-3228. TEL 609-520-9333, FAX 609-520-0905. Ed. Vinod B Bavishi.

382   USA   ISSN 1090-3976
GLOBAL ECONOMIC TRENDS. Text in English. m. USD 149 domestic; USD 179 foreign. **Document type:** *Newsletter.* **Description:** Delivers timely analysis of current economic conditions around the world. Provides information needed to make profitable business and investment decisions.
Published by: Cornell Research Inc., PO Box 7055, Deerfield, IL 60015. FAX 847-948-7164, info@getrends.com, http://www.getrends.com.

GLOBAL FINANCE. see *BUSINESS AND ECONOMICS— Banking And Finance*

GLOBAL FINANCE JOURNAL. see *BUSINESS AND ECONOMICS—Banking And Finance*

382   USA
GLOBAL GLIMPSES∗ . Text in English. 1991. bi-w. USD 60. back issues avail. **Document type:** *Newsletter.* **Description:** Provides information on resources, events and tools available to the international business and education communities.
Published by: Assist International, 26 Broadway., Ste. 776, New York, NY 10004-1748. TEL 212-725-3311, FAX 212-725-3312. Circ. 1,000 (paid).

GLOBAL INVESTOR. see *BUSINESS AND ECONOMICS— Banking And Finance*

382.7   USA   ISSN 1525-4887
GLOBAL LOGISTICS & SUPPLY CHAIN STRATEGIES. Text in English. 1999. m. free to qualified personnel. **Document type:** *Magazine, Trade.*
Incorporates (in 2002): Supply Chain e-Business
Indexed: HRIS.
—CCC.
Published by: Keller International Publishing Corp., 150 Great Neck Rd, Great Neck, NY 11021. TEL 516-829-9210, FAX 516-824-5414, info@supplychainbrain.com, http://www.e-circ.net/gsl/cs/cs.htm, http://www.kellerpubs.com.

382 011   USA
GLOBAL PERSPECTIVES IN REAL ESTATE. Text in English. q. membership. adv. back issues avail. **Document type:** *Newsletter.* **Description:** Aimed at international real estate practitioners in more than forty nations.
Former titles: International Update; F I A B C I - U S A News
Published by: Certified International Property Specialist Network, 430 N Michigan Ave, Chicago, IL 60611. TEL 312-329-8389, FAX 312-329-8358. Ed. Carol Weinrich. Pub. Miriam Meyer Lowe. Circ. 2,000 (paid).

327   USA   ISSN 0739-4640
HG4538
➤ **GLOBAL RISK ASSESSMENTS;** issues, concepts and applications. Text in English. 1983. irreg., latest vol.5, 2004. price varies. bk.rev. **Document type:** *Monographic series, Academic/Scholarly.* **Description:** Contains manuscripts on international business environment assessment; country, investment and trade risk analysis; political risk assessment and management.
Indexed: CurCont, ManagCont, PAIS.
Published by: Global Risk Assessments, Inc., 3638 University Ave, Ste 215, Riverside, CA 92501. TEL 909-447-5690, FAX 909-788-0672, jrogers@grai.com, http://www.grai.com. Ed. Jerry Rogers. Circ. 1,000.

382 332.6   GBR
GLOBAL RISK TRENDS. Text in English. m. GBP 750; GBP 50 newsstand/cover (effective 2001). **Document type:** *Trade.* **Description:** Provides information on the changes in market economics and situations for 80 countries over the past year.
Related titles: E-mail ed.: GBP 600 (effective 2001).
Published by: Merchant International Group Ltd., 4A-5 William St, Knightsbridge, London, SW1X 9HL, United Kingdom. TEL 44-20-7259-5060, FAX 44-20-7259-5090, headoffice@merchantinternational.com, http://www.merchantinternational.com/.

B

▼ *new title*   ➤ *refereed*   ∗ *unverified*   ◆ *full entry avail.*

382   USA   ISSN 1056-3857
HJ6622
GLOBAL TRADE TALK. Text in English. 1991. bi-m. USD 12
(effective 1998). back issues avail. **Document type:**
Government. **Description:** Focuses on pertinent and timely
issues concerning international trade and the role of the U.S.
Customs Service in facilitating it while enforcing U.S. trade
law.
Published by: U.S. Customs Service, National Support Staff, Rm
B338, 1301 Constitution Ave, N W, Washington, DC 20229.
Subscr. to: U.S. Government Printing Office, Superintendent
of Documents.

**GOVERNO DA REGIAO ADMINISTRATIVA ESPECIAL DE
MACAU. DIRECCAO DOS SERVICOS DE ESTATISTICA E
CENSOS. ESTATISTICAS DO COMERCIO
EXTERNO/GOVERNMENT OF MACAO SPECIAL
ADMINISTRATIVE REGION. STATISTICS AND CENSUS
SERVICE EXTERNAL TRADE STATISTICS.** see *BUSINESS
AND ECONOMICS—Abstracting, Bibliographies, Statistics*

332.6   GBR
GREAT BRITAIN. OFFICE OF FAIR TRADING. REPORT. Text in
English. 1975. a. GBP 13.50. reprint service avail. from PQC.
Document type: *Government.*
Published by: Stationery Office, 51 Nine Elms Ln, London, SW8
5DA, United Kingdom. TEL 44-20-7873-0011, FAX
44-20-7873-8247, book.orders@theso.co.uk,
http://www.national-publishing.co.uk.

382   GRL   ISSN 1604-4959
GREENLAND. GROENLANDS STATISTIK. UDENRIGSHANDEL.
Text in Danish. 2000. q. stat. back issues avail. **Document
type:** *Magazine, Government.* **Description:** Updates in text
and statistics about Greenland's foreign trade.
Media: Online - full content.
Published by: Groenlands Statistik (GL)/Kalaallit Nunaanni
Naatsorsueqqissaartarfik, PO Box 1025, Nuuk, 3900,
Greenland. TEL 299-345000, FAX 299-322954, stat@gh.gl,
http://www.statgreen.gl/dk/publ/udenhand/
index_udenhand.html. Ed. Josef Kajangmat.

382   CHN
**GUANGDONG DUIWAI JINGMAO/GUANGDONG FOREIGN
ECONOMICS AND TRADE.** Text in Chinese. m.
Published by: Guangdong Sheng Duiwai Jingji Maoyi
Weiyuanhui, No 774, Dongfeng Donglu, Building No 11,
Guangzhou, Guangdong 510087, China. TEL 775090. Ed.
Ren Lao.

382   DOM
GUIA; del exportador de la Republica Dominicana. Text in
Spanish; Contents page in English. 1982. bi-m.
Published by: Editora Corripio C. Por A., Apdo 20374, Santo
Domingo, Dominican Republic. TEL 682-7092. Ed. Andres
Gomez Solis.

**GUIA DE COMERCIO EXTERIOR EXPORTADORES/GUIDE TO
FOREIGN TRADE EXPORTERS.** see *BUSINESS AND
ECONOMICS—Trade And Industrial Directories*

GUIDE - DANISH TEXTILE AND CLOTHING INDUSTRIES. see
TEXTILE INDUSTRIES AND FABRICS

382   GBR
THE GUIDE TO EXPORT FINANCE✳. Text in English. a.
Document type: *Trade.*
Published by: Euromoney Institutional Investor Plc., Nestor
House, Playhouse Yard, London, EC4V 5EX, United Kingdom.
TEL 44-20-7779-8673, FAX 44-20-7779-8541,
http://www.euromoney.com. Eds. James Ball, Martin Knight.

GUIDE TO FOREIGN TRADE STATISTICS. see *BUSINESS AND
ECONOMICS—Abstracting, Bibliographies, Statistics*

**GUIDE TO THE INTERNATIONAL SALE OF GOODS
CONVENTION.** see *LAW—Corporate Law*

382 665   GBR
GUIDE TO WORLDWIDE BUNKERING SERVICES. Text in
English. a. GBP 70 domestic; USD 119 foreign (effective
2002). **Document type:** *Directory.* **Description:** Provides a
country by country listing of oil companies, bunker suppliers,
traders and brokers with contact details, delivery methods and
rates. A review of the market and future prospects is also
included.
Related titles: ◆ Supplement to: Lloyd's Ship Manager. ISSN
0265-2455.
Published by: Informa Maritime & Transport (Subsidiary of: T & F
Informa plc), 69-77 Paul St, London, EC2A 4LQ, United
Kingdom. TEL 44-20-7553-1000, FAX 44-20-7553-1105,
http://www.informamaritime.com.

GULF MARKETING REVIEW. see *BUSINESS AND
ECONOMICS—Marketing And Purchasing*

382   CHN
GUOJI CHANYE JINGJI JISHU. Text in Chinese. bi-m.
Published by: Guangxi Kexue Jishu Weiyuanhui, 17 Xinghu Lu,
Nanning, Guangxi 530022, China. TEL 43817. Ed. Zhang
Zhengyou.

**GUOJI JINGJI HEZUO/INTERNATIONAL ECONOMIC
COOPERATION.** see *BUSINESS AND ECONOMICS—
International Development And Assistance*

382   CHN   ISSN 1002-0594
**GUOJI JINGMAO TANSUO/INTERNATIONAL ECONOMICS AND
TRADE RESEARCH.** Text in Chinese; Abstracts in English.
1990. q. CNY 24 (effective 2004). **Document type:** *Journal,
Academic/Scholarly.*
Related titles: Online - full text ed.: (from East View Information
Services).
—BLDSC (4539.814000), IE, ingenta.
Published by: (Guangdong Waiyu Waimao Daxue/Guangdong
University of Foreign Studies), China International Book
Trading Corp/Zhongguo Guoji Tushu Maoyi Zonggongsi, 35
Chegongzhuang Xilu, Haidian District, PO Box 399, Beijing,
100044, China. gpxb306@gdufs.edu.cn, http://
secwww.gdufs.edu.cn/gwxb/.

382   CHN   ISSN 1002-4999
HF3831
GUOJI MAOYI/INTERNATIONAL TRADE. Text in Chinese. 1982.
m. USD 49.50.
Related titles: Online - full text ed.: (from East View Information
Services).
Published by: (Guoji Maoyi Yanjiusuo), Duiwai Jingji Maoyi
Bu/Ministry of Foreign Economics and Trade, International
Economic Cooperation Research Institute, No 28
Andingmenwai Donghouxiang, Beijing, 100710, China. TEL
4212149. Ed. Qin Xuanren. **Dist. in US by:** China Books &
Periodicals Inc, 360 Swift Ave., Ste. 48, S San Fran, CA
94080-6220. TEL 415-282-2994.

382   CHN   ISSN 1002-4670
HF3831
GUOJI MAOYI WENTI/INTERNATIONAL TRADE JOURNAL. Text
in Chinese. 1975. m. USD 17.76 domestic; USD 41.30
foreign.
Related titles: Online - full text ed.: (from East View Information
Services).
Published by: Duiwai Jingji Maoyi Daxue/Foreign Economics and
Trade University, Yinghua Dongjie Beikou, Andingmenwai,
Beijing, 100029, China. TEL 4225522, FAX 86-1-4212022. Ed.
Li Kanghua. **Dist. in US by:** China Books & Periodicals Inc,
360 Swift Ave., Ste. 48, S San Fran, CA 94080-6220. TEL
415-282-2994; **Dist. overseas by:** China International Book
Trading Corp, 35 Chegongzhuang Xilu, Haidian District, PO
Box 399, Beijing 100044, China.

382   CHN   ISSN 1002-5170
HF3831
GUOJI SHANGBAO/INTERNATIONAL BUSINESS. Text in
Chinese. 1985 (Apr.). d. CNY 174. **Document type:**
Newspaper. **Description:** Contains economic and business
information by MOFTEC and an authoritative and
comprehensive newspaper in China's foreign economic and
trade field and also one of china's five financial and economic
newspapers.
Contact Dist.: China Books & Periodicals Inc, 360 Swift Ave.,
Ste. 48, S San Fran, CA 94080-6220. TEL 415-282-2994.
Dist. by: China International Book Trading Corp, 35
Chegongzhuang Xilu, Haidian District, PO Box 399, Beijing
100044, China. TEL 86-10-68412045, FAX 86-10-68412023,
cibtc@mail.cibtc.com.cn.

382   CHN
**GUOJI SHANGBAO YUEKAN/INTERNATIONAL BUSINESS
MONTHLY.** Text in Chinese. bi-m. adv. **Document type:**
Trade.
Related titles: English ed.
Published by: Ministry of Commerce of the People's Republic of
China/Zhonghua Renmin Gongheguo Shangfubu, Bldg 14, 3rd
District, Fang Xing Yuan, Fang Zhuang Lu, Fang Zhuang,
Beijing, 100078, China. TEL 86-1-7628822, 86-1-7629580,
FAX 86-1-7629153, 86-1-7626875, webmaster@moftec.gov.cn,
http://www.mofcom.gov.cn/.

382   CHN   ISSN 1001-5450
GUOJI SHICHANG/INTERNATIONAL MARKET. Text in Chinese.
m.
Related titles: Online - full text ed.: (from East View Information
Services).
Published by: Shanghai Guoji Jingji Maoyi Yanjiusuo/Shanghai
International Economics and Trade Institute, 33 Zhongshan
Dongyi Lu, Shanghai, 200002, China. TEL 3212659. Ed. Xu
Pengyuan.

382   CHN
GUOWEI SHANGQING/INTERNATIONAL TRADE NEWS. Text in
Chinese; Summaries in English. 1958. 5/w. CNY 100.80
(effective 2005). adv. stat. Supplement avail. **Document type:**
Newspaper, Government. **Description:** Aims to bridge China
with the world and promote trade development. Uses a
world-wide network to monitor global economic activities,
world economy, international trade, financial and commodities
markets, and economic cooperation.
Formerly: Guoji Jingmao Xiaoxi Bao
Related titles: ◆ Supplement(s): Shuangbian Jingmao Zhuankan.

Contact Dist.: China International Book Trading Corp/Zhongguo
Guoji Tushu Maoyi Zonggongsi, 35 Chegongzhuang Xilu,
Haidian District, PO Box 399, Beijing, 100044, China. TEL
86-10-68412045, FAX 86-10-68412023,
cibtc@mail.cibtc.com.cn, http://www.cibtc.com.cn. Circ:
960,000.

**GUYANA. STATISTICAL BUREAU. ANNUAL ACCOUNT
RELATING TO EXTERNAL TRADE.** see *BUSINESS AND
ECONOMICS—Abstracting, Bibliographies, Statistics*

382   DEU   ISSN 0017-6931
HAMBURGER EXPORT-WOCHE. Text in German. 1951. w. adv.
bk.rev. abstr.
Published by: Verlag Holger Stuenings, Inselstr 34, Hamburg,
22297, Germany. Ed. H Stuenings. Circ: 1,500.

338   DEU   ISSN 0017-6990
HAMBURGER VORSCHAU; Offizielles Veranstaltungsprogramm
der Freien und Hansestadt Hamburg. Text in German. 1948.
m. adv. **Document type:** *Magazine, Consumer.*
Published by: v. Wels & Schuetze - Mensing GmbH & Co. KG,
Marschnerstieg 2, Hamburg, 22081, Germany. TEL
49-40-2980030, FAX 49-40-29800390. adv.: B&W page EUR
940.78, color page EUR 1,175.97. Circ: 19,800 (paid and
controlled).

HANDBOOK OF W T O - G A T T DISPUTE SETTLEMENT.
(World Trade Organization - General Agreement of Tariffs and
Trade) see *LAW—International Law*

332.6   DEU
HANDBUCH DER EINFUHR-NEBENABGABEN. Text in German.
1956. bi-m. looseleaf. EUR 88 (effective 2001). **Document
type:** *Trade.* **Description:** Complete survey about VAT, import
taxes, and consumption taxes for countries throughout the
world.
Published by: Mendel Verlag, Robensstr 39, Aachen, 52070,
Germany. TEL 49-241-154355, FAX 49-241-1570816,
info@mendel-verlag.de, http://www.mendel-verlag.de. Ed.
Peter Kuessner.

332.6   DEU   ISSN 0947-5931
HANDBUCH FUER DAS ERFOLGREICHE OSTGESCHAEFT.
Text in German. irreg. (6-8/yr.). looseleaf. **Document type:**
Directory, Trade.
Formerly: Handbuch fuer den Osthandel (0937-2784)
Published by: Deutscher Wirtschaftsdienst (Subsidiary of: Wolters
Kluwer Deutschland GmbH), Schoenhauser Str 64, Cologne,
50968, Germany. TEL 49-221-937630, FAX 49-221-9376399,
box@dwd-verlag.de, http://www.dwd-verlag.de. Ed. Wolfgang
von Llingelsheim-Seibicke.

382   POL   ISSN 0017-7245
HANDEL ZAGRANICZNY/FOREIGN TRADE. Text in Polish.
1955. m. (plus special numbers). USD 84. adv. bk.rev. abstr.;
bibl.; charts; illus.; stat. index. reprint service avail. from PQC.
Related titles: Microform ed.: (from PQC).
Indexed: AESIS, RASB.
Published by: Krajowa Izba Gospodarcza, Ul Trebacka 4,
Warsaw, 00074, Poland. Ed. Maciej Deniszczuk. Circ: 3,000.
Dist. by: Ars Polona, Krakowskie Przedmiescie 7, Warsaw,
Poland.

**HANDEL ZAGRANICZNY PRODUKTAMI ROLNO-
SPOZYWCZYMI;** analizy rynkowe. see *AGRICULTURE—
Agricultural Economics*

HARVARD INTERNATIONAL REVIEW. see *POLITICAL
SCIENCE—International Relations*

**HARVESTING, MARKETING AND DISTRIBUTION COSTS FOR
AUSTRALIAN WOOL - SHEEP'S BACK TO OVERSEAS
MILL.** see *TEXTILE INDUSTRIES AND FABRICS*

**HAVEN GENT. JAARBOEK/GHENT PORT ANNUAL/HAFEN
VON GENT. JAHRBUCH/PORT DE GAND. ANNUAIRE.** see
TRANSPORTATION—Ships And Shipping

HAVEN VAN ANTWERPEN. INDEX/PORT D'ANVERS. INDEX.
see *TRANSPORTATION—Ships And Shipping*

**HAVENS ZEEBRUGGE EN OOSTENDE. JAARBOEK/HAVEN
VON ZEEBRUGGE UND OSTENDE. JAHRBUCH/PORTS DE
ZEEBRUGGE ET D'OSTENDE. ANNUAIRE/ZEEBRUGGE
AND OSTEND PORTS. ANNUAL.** see *TRANSPORTATION—
Ships And Shipping*

382   USA
HEDGE FUND NEWS. Text in English. 1994. q. USD 195
(effective 2000). **Document type:** *Newsletter.* **Description:**
Serves the hedge fund community, onshore and offshore.
Published by: Dome Capital Management, Inc., 405 Park Ave,
Ste 500, New York, NY 10022. TEL 212-371-5935, FAX
212-758-9032, abernehein@hedgefundnews.com,
http://www.hedgefundnews.com.

382 NLD ISSN 1380-846X
HF3613
HOLLAND EXPORTS. Text in English, French, German, Spanish. 1993. a. free. adv. **Document type:** *Directory, Trade.* **Description:** Provides information on more than 8000 exporting firms in the Netherlands.
Formed by the 1993 merger of: Industrial Products (0923-8077); Consumer goods - Non Food (0923-8069); Consumer Goods - Food (0923-8050); Commercial Gardening and Farming (0923-8042); Services (0923-8085)
Related titles: CD-ROM ed.; Online - full text ed.: (from Data-Star).
—BLDSC (4322.304000).
Published by: A B C voor Handel en Industrie C.V., PO Box 190, Haarlem, 2000 AD, Netherlands. TEL 31-23-5533533, FAX 31-23-5327033, info@abc-d.nl, http://www.hollandexports.com. Ed. F Droog. Adv. contact T Vlot. Circ: 14,000. **Dist. by:** Current Pacific Ltd., PO Box 36-536, Northcote, Auckland, New Zealand. TEL 64-9-480-1388, FAX 64-9-480-1387, info@cplnz.com, http://www.cplnz.com.

382.6 HKG
HONG KONG AWARDS FOR INDUSTRY: EXPORT MARKETING. Text in English. a., latest 1999. **Document type:** *Trade.* **Description:** Aims to recognise excellence in export marketing and to heighten awareness of the importance of effective marketing among Hong Kong's manufacturers and exporters.
Related titles: Online - full content ed.
Published by: Hong Kong Trade Development Council, 38th Fl Office Tower, Convention Plaza, 1 Harbour Rd, Wanchai, Hong Kong. TEL 852-2584-4333, publications@tdc.org.hk, hktdc@tdc.org.hk, http://www.tdc.org.hk/prodmag/export/export.htm. Adv. contact Wengi Yuen.

HONG KONG IMPORTERS' DIRECTORY (YEAR). see *BUSINESS AND ECONOMICS—Trade And Industrial Directories*

HONG KONG REVENUE LEGISLATION. see *LAW*

HONG KONG SPECIAL ADMINISTRATIVE REGION OF CHINA. CENSUS AND STATISTICS DEPARTMENT. HONG KONG TRADE STATISTICS. IMPORTS. see *BUSINESS AND ECONOMICS—Abstracting, Bibliographies, Statistics*

332.6 HKG
HONG KONG TRADER; a T D C newspaper. Text in English. 1976. m. free to qualified personnel. adv. illus.; stat. **Document type:** *Trade.*
Media: Online - full content.
Indexed: HongKongiana, TTI.
Published by: Hong Kong Trade Development Council, 38th Fl Office Tower, Convention Plaza, 1 Harbour Rd, Wanchai, Hong Kong. TEL 852-2584-4333, trader@tdc.org.hk, hktdc@tdc.org.hk, http://www.tdc.org.hk/hktrader/. Ed. Neil Colcloush. Circ: 52,000.

HOUSTON JOURNAL OF INTERNATIONAL LAW. see *LAW*

382 CHN
HUANQIU CAIJING/GLOBAL FINANCE. Text in Chinese. 1995. m. CNY 120 (effective 2004). **Document type:** *Journal, Academic/Scholarly.*
Formerly: Haiwai Gongshang/Overseas Industry and Commerce
Related titles: Online - full text ed.: (from WanFang Data Corp.).
Published by: Zhongguo Renmin Daxue, Shubao Zilio Zhongxin/Renmin University of China, Information Center for Social Server, Dongcheng-qu, 3, Zhangzizhong Lu, Beijing, 100007, China. TEL 86-10-64039458, FAX 86-10-64015080, bizworld2000@sina.com, kyes@163.net, http://www.confucius.cn.net/bkdetail.asp?fzt=X4. **Dist. by:** China International Book Trading Corp, 35 Chegongzhuang Xilu, Haidian District, PO Box 399, Beijing 100044, China. TEL 86-10-68412045, FAX 86-10-68412023, cibtc@mail.cibtc.com.cn, http://www.cibtc.com.cn.

382 338 HUN ISSN 1419-0540
HUNGARIAN EXPORT & PRODUCTION DATABASE ON CD-ROM. Text in Hungarian. 1998. a. HUF 15,000; USD 85 foreign (effective 2000). adv. stat.; tr.lit. **Document type:** *Directory.* **Description:** Provides detailed information on 3,500 Hungarian companies.
Media: CD-ROM.
Published by: Kopint - Datorg Plc, Csokonai u 3, Budapest, 1081, Hungary. TEL 36-1-303-9582, FAX 36-1-303-9582, nemeth@kopdat.hu, http://www.kopdat.hu. Ed. Ilona Nemeth.

382 USA
I G O REPORT. (Intergovernmental Organizations) Text in English. bi-m. **Document type:** *Newsletter.* **Description:** Reports on developments in the major intergovernmental organizations of interest to the business community.
Media: Online - full text.
Published by: United States Council for International Business, 1212 Ave of the Americas, New York, NY 10036. TEL 212-354-4480, FAX 212-575-0327, http://www.uscib.org. Ed. William J Stibravy.

382 IND ISSN 0019-4980
I I T C BULLETIN. Text in English. 1967. s-m. INR 50, USD 16. **Document type:** *Bulletin.*
Related titles: Record ed.
Published by: Indian International Trade Center, 59 Jolly Maker Chambers-1, Nariman Point, Mumbai, Maharashtra 400 020, India. Ed. S K Urval. Circ: 500.

382 IND ISSN 0073-6546
I I T C DIRECTORY. Text in English. 1969. a. free to qualified personnel.
Published by: Indian International Trade Center, 59 Jolly Maker Chambers-1, Nariman Point, Mumbai, Maharashtra 400 020, India.

382 USA ISSN 1553-0752
I O M A'S REPORT ON MANAGING EXPORTS & IMPORTS. Variant title: Managing Exports & Imports. Text in English. 1996. m. USD 311.95 in US & Canada print & online eds.; USD 323 elsewhere print & online eds. (effective 2006). **Document type:** *Newsletter, Trade.* **Description:** Shows how to increase international sales, find new distribution channels and reduce export costs and risks. Also covers discovering new markets, freight and credit terms, export controls, insurance, laws and licenses, and software.
Formerly (until Oct. 2004): I O M A's Report on Managing Exports (1090-9427)
Related titles: Diskette ed.; E-mail ed.; Online - full content ed.: (from Florida Center for Library Automation); Online - full text ed.: (from EBSCO Publishing, Gale Group, LexisNexis).
Published by: Institute of Management & Administration, Inc., 3 Park Ave, New York, NY 10016-5902. TEL 212-244-0360, FAX 212-564-0465, subserve@ioma.com, http://www.ioma.com/products/prod_detail.php?prodid=33. Ed. Chris Horner. R&P Sofie Kourkoutakis.

382 387 GBR
I S M SUPPLEMENT. Text in English. s-a. GBP 80 domestic; USD 136 foreign (effective 2002). **Document type:** *Directory.* **Description:** Provides the complete listing of every merchant vessel currently in possession of the ISM certificate, the start and end dates of the certificates and the issue and auditor involved in awarding the certification.
Published by: Informa Maritime & Transport (Subsidiary of: T & F Informa plc), 69-77 Paul St, London, EC2A 4LQ, United Kingdom. TEL 44-20-7553-1000, FAX 44-20-7553-1105, http://www.informamaritime.com.

IMPACT OF INTERNATIONAL VISITOR SPENDING ON STATE ECONOMICS. see *TRAVEL AND TOURISM*

382 USA
IMPORT - EXPORT CLUBLETTER*. Text in English. m. USD 36.
Formerly: Import - Export Newsletter
Published by: Keith Kittrell & Associates, Inc., 33831 Oldbridge Rd, Dana Point, CA 92629-2029. TEL 913-628-9466, FAX 714-859-9131.

382 IND ISSN 0536-9983
IMPORT TRADE CONTROL: HANDBOOK OF RULES AND PROCEDURES. Text in English. a.
Published by: Ministry of Commerce, New Delhi, India. **Order from:** Controller of Publications, Civil Lines, New Delhi 110 006, India.

382 IND ISSN 0536-9061
IMPORT TRADE CONTROL POLICY. Text in English. a. (in 2 vols.). price varies.
Published by: Ministry of Commerce, New Delhi, India. **Order from:** Controller of Publications, Civil Lines, New Delhi 110 006, India.

382 TWN ISSN 1028-110X
IMPORTERS AND EXPORTERS IN TAIWAN, R.O.C. Text in Chinese. 1992. a. USD 150. **Document type:** *Directory.* **Description:** Directory of select Taiwan import and export commodities and leading importers and exporters. Selection of entries is based on a set level of import - export value supplied by the ROC's customs office.
Formerly: Imports - Exports of the Republic of China; Formed by the merger of (1973-1992): Imports of the Republic of China; (1970-1992): Exports of the Republic of China (0301-9217)
Published by: China External Trade Development Council, 8th Fl, 333 Keelung Rd, Sec 1, Taipei, Taiwan. TEL 2-725-5200, FAX 2-2757-6828, http://www.tptaiwan.org.tw. Ed. Peter F H Chan. Pub. Ricky Y S Kao. Circ: 4,500. **Dist. by:** Current Pacific Ltd., PO Box 36-536, Northcote, Auckland, New Zealand. TEL 64-9-480-1388, FAX 64-9-480-1387, info@cplnz.com, http://www.cplnz.com.

382 GBR
IMPORTERS BULLETIN. Variant title: Croner's Importers Bulletin. Text in English. 1994. q.
—BLDSC (4371.462912).
Published by: Croner.C C H Group Ltd. (Subsidiary of: Wolters Kluwer N.V.), 145 London Rd, Kingston, Surrey KT2 6SR, United Kingdom. TEL 44-20-85473333, FAX 44-20-85472637, info@croner.co.uk, http://www.croner.cch.co.uk.

382 USA ISSN 1065-5158
HF3035
IMPORTERS MANUAL U S A. Text in English. 1993. a. USD 145 per issue (effective 2004).
Published by: World Trade Press, 1450 Grant Ave Ste 204, Novato, CA 94945. TEL 415-898-1124, 800-833-8586, FAX 415-898-1080, http://www.worldtradepress.com.

332.6 GBR
IMPORTING TODAY. Text in English. 6/yr. GBP 21. **Document type:** *Trade.* **Description:** Offers news and features on finance, legal matters, transportation, customs, and other aspects of overseas markets.
Indexed: M&MA.
Address: 32 Vauxhall Bridge Rd, London, SW1V 2SS, United Kingdom. Ed. Carol Debell. Circ: 12,000.

IMPORTS BY COMMODITIES. see *BUSINESS AND ECONOMICS—Abstracting, Bibliographies, Statistics*

IMPORTS BY COUNTRIES. see *BUSINESS AND ECONOMICS—Abstracting, Bibliographies, Statistics*

382 NLD ISSN 0019-3178
IN- EN UITVOER NIEUWS. Text in Dutch. 30/yr. bk.rev. index. **Document type:** *Trade.*
Related titles: ♦ Supplement(s): Douanerechtspraak. ISSN 1569-352X.
—IE, Infotrieve.
Published by: Kluwer B.V. (Subsidiary of: Wolters Kluwer N.V.), Postbus 23, Deventer, 7400 GA, Netherlands. TEL 31-570-673449, FAX 31-570-691555, juridisch@kluwer.nl, http://www.kluwer.nl. Circ: 1,300.

387 GBR ISSN 0308-7212
IN TOUCH (LONDON). Text in Dutch, English. m.
—BLDSC (4372.470000).
Published by: Netherlands-British Chamber of Commerce, Netherlands British Chamber Of Commerce, The Dutch House 307-308, High Holborn, London, WC1V 7LS, United Kingdom. Eds. Koenraad van Hasselt, Wim Kootstra.

382 COL ISSN 0121-604X
HF3421
INCOMEX SIN FRONTERAS. Text in Spanish. 1992. bi-m. **Document type:** *Magazine, Trade.* **Description:** Covers foreign commerce and related themes.
Published by: Instituto Colombiano de Comercio Exterior (INCOMEX), Oficina 225, Calle 28, 13-A-15, Bogota, CUND, Colombia. TEL 57-1-281-2200, FAX 57-1-284-9592. Ed. Patricia Tovar Alarcon. Circ: 5,000.

332.6 USA ISSN 1543-4842
HF5238
INDIA BUSINESS & INVESTMENT REPORT. Text in English. 1991. m. USD 510; USD 60 newsstand/cover (effective 2005). **Document type:** *Newsletter, Trade.* **Description:** Contains analyses of the impact of local developments firms, on international economic forecasts, political and economic outlooks, detailed analyses of key business and industry sectors, reports on business opportunities and trends, case studies of successful companies in India, recent cross-border deals, economic statistics, and expert opinions from business practitioners operating in India.
Formerly: India Business News (1064-0231)
Published by: P S I, Inc., PO Box 237191, Ansonia Sta, New York, NY 10023. TEL 212-331-0010, FAX 212-791-9509, contact@psi-world.com, http://www.psi-world.com/newsletter.htm. Ed. Tina Narang. R&P Manu Bammi.

382 IND ISSN 0019-4239
INDIA TODAY AND TOMORROW. Text in English. 1968. q. INR 450, USD 25. adv. bk.rev. illus. reprints avail. **Description:** Devoted to the country's economic development, industrial and agricultural growth and social progress.
Indexed: BAS.
Published by: V.J. Joseph Ed. & Pub., 2nd Fl., Orange House, 41 Hamam St., Mumbai, Maharashtra 400 001, India. TEL 91-22-265-3187, FAX 91-22-265-5691. Circ: 11,000.

382 IND
INDIAN EXPORT BULLETIN. Text in English. 1965. w. INR 25. adv. **Document type:** *Bulletin.*
Incorporates (1978-1992): Trade Intelligence Bulletin; Formerly: Indian Export Service Bulletin
Published by: India Trade Promotion Organisation, Pragati Maidan, New Delhi, 110 001, India. TEL 91-11-332-8239, FAX 91-11-331-8142, TELEX 031-61022-COMX-IN. Circ: 5,000.

382 IND
INDIAN EXPORT YEAR BOOK (YEAR). Text in Arabic, English. 1975. a. USD 80 (effective 1999). **Document type:** *Directory.* **Description:** Contains reference material on foreign trade of India. Contains product indices in Arabic and English.
Published by: Sales Overseas, D - 20 Green Park, New Delhi, 110 016, India. TEL 91-11-6516279, FAX 91-11-6862206, http://www.nctiindia.com/sales. Ed. H R Suri. adv.: B&W page USD 800, color page USD 2,000; trim 160 x 210. Circ: 10,000.

382 IND ISSN 0073-6473
INDIAN INSTITUTE OF FOREIGN TRADE. REPORT. Text in English. a. price varies.
Published by: Indian Institute of Foreign Trade, B-21, Mehrauli Institutional Area, New Delhi, 110 016, India.

B

382 633 IND ISSN 0019-6401
INDIAN SPICES. Text in English. 1964. q. INR 300, USD 30 (effective 2000). adv. abstr.; bibl.; charts; illus.; mkt.; stat. **Document type:** *Government.* **Description:** Export promotion on spices journal to different buying houses and spices consumers world wide.
Indexed: FS&TA.
—BLDSC (4429.757000).
Published by: Ministry of Commerce, Spices Board, N.H. Bypass, Palarivattom P.O., P O Box 2277, Cochin, Kerala 682 025, India. TEL 91-484-333610, FAX 91-484-331429, sbhochn@giasmdo1.vsnl.net.in, http://www.indianspices.com. Ed. P S Sreekantan Thampi. Circ: 4,500.

382 USA
INDIANA DIRECTORY OF INTERNATIONAL BUSINESS SERVICES. Text in English. a. free. **Document type:** *Directory.*
Formerly: Indiana International Trade Directory
Published by: Department of Commerce, International Trade Division, One N Capitol, Ste 700, Indianapolis, IN 46204-2288. TEL 317-233-3762, FAX 317-232-4146. Ed. Luana Leonard.

382 IND
INDIA'S PRODUCTION, EXPORTS, AND INTERNAL CONSUMPTION OF COIR. Text and summaries in English. 1967. a. INR 50. stat.
Formerly: India's Exports and Internal Consumption of Coir and Coir Goods
Published by: Coir Board, Cochin, Kerala 682 016, India. Circ: 300.

382 CHL ISSN 0716-2405
HF3411
INDICADORES DE COMERCIO EXTERIOR. Text in Spanish. 1978. m. CLP 55,000, USD 250 (effective 1999). charts; stat. index. back issues avail. **Document type:** *Government.* **Description:** Contains statistics of Chilean foreign trade.
Indexed: PAIS.
Published by: Banco Central de Chile, Casilla 967, Santiago, Chile. TEL 56-2-670-2000, FAX 56-2-698-4847. Circ: 650.

382.021 PRT ISSN 0871-9144
INDICE DO COMERCIO EXTERNO. Text in Portuguese. 1991. irreg.
Published by: Instituto Nacional de Estatistica, Ave. Antonio Jose de Almeida 2, Lisbon, 1000-043, Portugal. TEL 351-21-8426100, FAX 351-21-8426380, ine@ine.pt, http://www.ine.pt/.

382 IDN ISSN 0126-3714
HF3809.J35
INDONESIA. EXPORT BY COMMODITY, COUNTRY OF DESTINATION AND PORT OF EXPORT. Text in English. 1967. a. IDR 150,000, USD 65.21. **Document type:** *Government.*
Published by: Central Bureau of Statistics/Biro Pusat Statistik, Jalan Dr. Sutomo No. 8, PO Box 3, Jakarta Pusat, Indonesia. TEL 62-21-372808. Circ: 300.

382 IDN ISSN 0126-4419
HF247
INDONESIA. IMPORT BY COMMODITY AND COUNTRY OF ORIGIN. Text in English. 1963. a. IDR 150,000, USD 65.21. **Document type:** *Government.*
Published by: Central Bureau of Statistics/Biro Pusat Statistik, Jalan Dr. Sutomo No. 8, PO Box 3, Jakarta Pusat, Indonesia. TEL 62-21-372808. Circ: 300.

INDONESIAN IMPORTERS DIRECTORY. see *BUSINESS AND ECONOMICS—Trade And Industrial Directories*

382 BEL ISSN 0772-4942
INDUSTRIE MAGAZINE; magazine voor produktie, inkoop en techniek. Key Title: Industrie (Nederlandse Editie). Text in Dutch. 1984. m. back issues avail. **Document type:** *Magazine, Trade.*
Related titles: Microfiche ed.; French ed.: Industrie (Edition Francaise). ISSN 0772-4950.
Published by: Publindus N.V., de Jamblinne de Meuxplein 10, Brussel, 1030, Belgium. Ed. Wim Heirbaut. Circ: 27,000.

382 CAN ISSN 1496-1911
INDUSTRY CANADA. MICRO-ECONOMIC POLICY ANALYSIS BRANCH. MONTHLY TRADE BULLETIN. Text in English. 1999. m. **Description:** Provides a summary of recent developments in aggregate trade and priority trade sectors.
Related titles: Online - full content ed.: ISSN 1496-192X.
Published by: Industry Canada, Micro-Economic Policy Analysis Branch, C D Howe Bldg, 235 Queen St, Ottawa, ON K1A 0H5, Canada. TEL 613-952-3466, FAX 613-952-6927, mepa.apme@ic.gc.ca, http://strategis.ic.gc.ca/epic/internet/ineas-aes.nsf/en/h_ra01872e.html.

350.827 USA
INDUSTRY, TRADE, AND TECHNOLOGY REVIEW. Abbreviated title: I T T R. Text in English. 1992. q. free. **Document type:** *Journal, Trade.* **Description:** Analyzes important issues and provides insight into the global position of US industries, the technological competitiveness of the US, and implications of trade and policy developments.
Indexed: AmStI.
Published by: U.S. International Trade Commission, Office of Industries, 500 E St, S W, Washington, DC 20436. TEL 202-205-3296, FAX 202-205-3161, http://www.usitc.gov/ind_econ_ana/research_ana/ier_ittr/ittr/index.htm. Ed. Robert Hughes. R&P Larry Brookhart.

INFEURO (ENGLISH EDITION). see *LAW—International Law*

INFORMACION COMERCIAL ESPANOLA. SECTOR EXTERIOR (YEAR). see *BUSINESS AND ECONOMICS—Abstracting, Bibliographies, Statistics*

382 DEU
INFORMATIONSDIENST GROSS- UND AUSSENHANDEL. Text in German. 1947. s-m. adv. bk.rev. **Document type:** *Trade.* **Description:** Promotion of wholesale and international trade.
Published by: Wirtschaftsvereinigung Gross- und Aussenhandel Hamburg e.V., Gotenstr 21, Hamburg, 20097, Germany. TEL 49-40-236016-0, FAX 49-40-23601610, contact@wga-hh.de. Circ: 1,000.

382 GBR
INITIATIVE. Text in English. 1972. q. GBP 20 to non-members (effective 2005). adv. bk.rev. **Document type:** *Magazine, Trade.* **Description:** Contains topical articles on commercial issues and news and information from the Chamber, its members and other interested parties.
Formerly (until 1993): British German Trade
Published by: German British Chamber of Industry and Commerce, 16 Buckingham Gate, London, SW1E 6LB, United Kingdom. TEL 44-20-79764100, FAX 44-20-79764101, initiative@ahk-london.co.uk, mail@ahk-london.co.uk, http://www.ahk-london.co.uk/de/publ_initiative.php. Ed., R&P, Adv. contact Ian Wivell. B&W page GBP 1,150, color page GBP 1,300; trim 400 x 275. Circ: 12,000 (controlled).

INSIDE EXPORT; a guide to growing international markets for the U.S. publishing industry. see *PUBLISHING AND BOOK TRADE*

382 USA ISSN 0897-1676
HF3000
INSIDE U S TRADE. Text in English. 1983. w. USD 1,080 in US & Canada; USD 1,130 elsewhere (effective 2004). **Document type:** *Newsletter, Trade.*
Related titles: E-mail ed.; Online - full content ed.
—CISTI. **CCC.**
Published by: Inside Washington Publishers, PO Box 7176, Ben Franklin Sta, Washington, DC 20044-7176. TEL 703-416-8500, 800-424-9068, FAX 703-416-8543, custsvc@iwpnews.com, http://www.insidetrade.com, http://www.iwpnews.com. Ed. Jutta Hennig.

382 ARG ISSN 1027-1899
HC121
INTAL CARTA MENSUAL (ONLINE EDITION). Text in Spanish. 1996. m. free (effective 2003). bk.rev. abstr.; bibl.; charts; stat. Index. back issues avail. **Document type:** *Newsletter.* **Description:** Provides information on regional events, meetings, agreements and publications related to integration. Contains a bibliographical section with abstracts and information about Intal activities.
Formerly (until 2000): Intal Carta Mensual (Print Edition)
Related titles: English ed.: Intal Monthly Newsletter. ISSN 1027-2550; Portuguese ed.: Intal Carta Mensal. ISSN 1028-0464.
Published by: Banco Interamericano de Desarrollo, Instituto para la Integracion de America Latina y el Caribe/Inter-American Development Bank, Esmeralda 130 Piso 17, Buenos Aires, 1035, Argentina. TEL 54-11-43201850, FAX 54-11-43201865, pubintal@iadb.org, int/inl@iadb.org, http://www.iadb.org/intal/ingles/publicaciones/i-icm.htm. Ed. Alicia Pinotti.

INTEGRACION Y COMERCIO. see *BUSINESS AND ECONOMICS—International Development And Assistance*

382 341.57 GBR ISSN 0141-7584
INTELLECTUAL PROPERTY DECISIONS. Text in English. 1978. m. GBP 385 domestic; GBP 410 foreign (effective 1999). back issues avail. **Document type:** *Abstract/Index.* **Description:** Abstracts of significant UK and EU decisions in the field of industrial property.
Published by: Informa Law (Subsidiary of: Informa Publishing), Informa House, 30-32 Mortimer St, London, W1W 7RE, United Kingdom. TEL 44-207-5531000, FAX 44-207-5531593. Ed. Barry Stonelake. R&P Peter Plaistowe.

382 341.57 GBR ISSN 0141-9749
INTELLECTUAL PROPERTY NEWSLETTER. Text in English. m. GBP 236 domestic; GBP 261 foreign (effective 1999). back issues avail. **Document type:** *Newsletter.* **Description:** Reports on patents, trademarks, commercial secrets and the increasing trend toward legislation about all forms of unfair competition.
Indexed: LJI.
—BLDSC (4531.824500), IE.
Published by: Informa Law (Subsidiary of: Informa Publishing), Informa House, 30-32 Mortimer St, London, W1W 7RE, United Kingdom. TEL 44-207-5531000, FAX 44-207-5531593. R&P Peter Plaistowe.

382 341.57 USA ISSN 1521-7256
KF2972
INTELLECTUAL PROPERTY TODAY. Text in English. 1996. m. USD 96 domestic; USD 126 in Canada & Mexico; USD 156 elsewhere (effective 2004). **Document type:** *Magazine, Trade.*
Formerly: The Law Work
Related titles: Online - full text ed.: (from LexisNexis).
—**CCC.**
Published by: Omega Communications, 369 W Northwest Hwy, Palatine, IL 60067. TEL 800-232-8078, FAX 847-705-7112, http://www.iptoday.com/. Ed. Douglas Dean. Adv. contact Steve Barnes. Circ: 20,000.

382 332.6 GBR
THE INTELLIGENCE GAP. Text in English. a. **Document type:** *Trade.* **Description:** Contains case studies and clients surveys designed to highlight the 'real' experience of doing business compared to the perceived risk.
Published by: Merchant International Group Ltd., 4A-5 William St, Knightsbridge, London, SW1X 9HL, United Kingdom. TEL 44-20-7259-5060, FAX 44-20-7259-5090, headoffice@merchantinternational.com, http://www.merchantinternational.com/.

382 659 338 USA ISSN 1523-1631
INTERACTIVE GLOBAL NEWS. Text in English. 1995. m. USD 36 domestic; USD 48 foreign; USD 5 newsstand/cover (effective 2000). adv. back issues avail.
Related titles: E-mail ed.; Online - full text ed.
Published by: PANGAEA Communications, 630 Ninth Ave, Ste. 1000, New York, NY 10036. TEL 212-445-8580, FAX 212-445-2542, ign@pangaea.net, http://www.pangaea.net/ign/news.htm. Ed., Pub., R&P Beth Stone. adv.: page USD 100. Circ: 5,000.

382 MEX
INTERCAMBIO INTERNACIONAL. Text in Spanish. 1975. s-a. USD 12. adv. bk.rev.
Published by: Grupo Internacional Editores, S.A., Nicolas San Juan No. 1154, Mexico City 12, DF, Mexico. Ed. Arq Dolores Norma. Circ: 50,000.

330 382 DEU ISSN 0020-5346
HF1410
➤ **INTERECONOMICS**; review of European economic policy. Text in English. 1966. bi-m. EUR 99 combined subscription to institutions print & online eds. (effective 2005). adv. index. reprint service avail. from ISI. **Document type:** *Journal, Academic/Scholarly.* **Description:** Provides a European perspective on major issues in international trade and development. Examines the European Economic Community, monetary policy, resource trade, and overall economic trends as they affect the relationship between Europe, America, and the Third World.
Related titles: Online - full text ed.: ISSN 1613-964X (from Northern Light Technology, Inc., O C L C Online Computer Library Center, Inc., ProQuest Information & Learning, Springer LINK).
Indexed: ABIn, APEL, AgBio, BAS, CREJ, ELLIS, ForAb, IBR, IBSS, IBZ, ILD, IndVet, JEL, KES, PAIS, PROMT, RASB, RDA, RRTA, S&F, VetBull, WAE&RSA.
—BLDSC (4533.400000), CISTI, IE, Infotrieve, ingenta. **CCC.**
Published by: (H W W A - Hamburgisches Welt-Wirtschafts-Archiv), Springer-Verlag (Subsidiary of: Springer Science+Business Media), Tiergartenstr 17, Heidelberg, 69121, Germany. TEL 49-6221-3450, FAX 49-6221-345229. Ed. Klaus Kwasniewski. Adv. contact Stephan Kroeck TEL 49-30-827875739. **Subscr. in the Americas to:** Springer-Verlag New York, Inc., Journal Fulfillment, PO Box 2485, Secaucus, NJ 07096-2485. TEL 800-777-4643, 201-348-4033, FAX 201-348-4505, journals@springer-ny.com, http://www.springer-ny.com; **Subscr. to:** Springer GmbH Auslieferungsgesellschaft, Haberstr 7, Heidelberg 69126, Germany. TEL 49-6221-345-0, FAX 49-6221-345-4229, subscriptions@springer.de.

➤ **INTERFACE.** see *BUSINESS AND ECONOMICS—Chamber Of Commerce Publications*

382 USA ISSN 0748-4631
HF1371
INTERFLO; trade monitor of the former Soviet republics. Text in English. 1981. m. USD 172; USD 192 foreign. adv. abstr. index. back issues avail. **Document type:** *Abstract/Index.* **Description:** Covers comprehensive information on trade, investment, and joint ventures in the former Soviet republics, as well as information about technology and management.
Address: PO Box 42, Maplewood, NJ 07040. TEL 973-763-9493. Ed., Pub., R&P, Adv. contact Paul R Surovell. Circ: 400.

382 341 NLD ISSN 1570-3215
INTERNATIONAL BANKING, FINANCE AND ECONOMIC LAW. Variant title: International Banking, Finance and Economic Law Series. Text in English. 1994. irreg., latest 2002, Dec. price varies. **Document type:** *Monographic series, Academic/Scholarly.* **Description:** Designed to provide a broad foundation for comparative analysis of changes and reforms occurring worldwide in international banking regulation and practice.
—BLDSC (4536.535460).

Published by: Kluwer Law International (Subsidiary of: Aspen Publishers, Inc.), Laan van Meerdervoort 70, PO Box 85889, The Hague, 2508 CN, Netherlands. TEL 31-70-3081500, FAX 31-70-3081515, sales@kluwerlaw.com, http://www.kluwerlaw.com. Ed. Joseph J Norton.

382   USA   ISSN 1535-0754
HD30.4
➤ **INTERNATIONAL BUSINESS & ECONOMICS RESEARCH JOURNAL.** Text in English. 2002. m. USD 100 domestic to individuals; USD 200 foreign to individuals; USD 495 worldwide to libraries (effective 2005). bk.rev. abstr. 120 p./no. 1 cols./p.; back issues avail.; reprints avail. **Document type:** *Journal, Academic/Scholarly.*
—BLDSC (4538.275250), IE.
Published by: Western Academic Press, PO Box 620760, Littleton, CO 80162. TEL 303-904-4750, FAX 303-978-0413, cluter@wapress.com, http://www.wapress.com/IBERJMain.htm. Circ: 600 (paid and controlled).

➤ **INTERNATIONAL BUSINESS PLANNING: LAW AND TAXATION (US).** see *LAW—Corporate Law*

383   USA   ISSN 0278-5439
INTERNATIONAL BUSINESS REPORT. Text in English. irreg.
Published by: Praeger Publishers (Subsidiary of: Greenwood Publishing Group Inc.), 1800 K St, N W, Ste 400, Washington, DC 20006-2294. TEL 202-775-3119, FAX 202-775-3199, books@csis.org, http://www.csis.org.

INTERNATIONAL BUSINESS SERIES. VOLUME 1: LEGAL ASPECTS OF DOING BUSINESS IN EUROPE. see *LAW—International Law*

INTERNATIONAL BUSINESS SERIES. VOLUME 2: LEGAL ASPECTS OF DOING BUSINESS IN LATIN AMERICA. see *LAW—International Law*

INTERNATIONAL BUSINESS SERIES. VOLUME 3: LEGAL ASPECTS OF DOING BUSINESS IN ASIA AND THE PACIFIC. see *LAW—International Law*

INTERNATIONAL BUSINESS SERIES. VOLUME 4: LEGAL ASPECTS OF DOING BUSINESS IN AFRICA. see *LAW—International Law*

INTERNATIONAL BUSINESS SERIES. VOLUME 5: LEGAL ASPECTS OF DOING BUSINESS IN THE MIDDLE EAST. see *LAW—International Law*

INTERNATIONAL BUSINESS SERIES. VOLUME 6-7: LEGAL ASPECTS OF DOING BUSINESS IN NORTH AMERICA AND CANADA. see *LAW—International Law*

INTERNATIONAL BUSINESS TRANSACTIONS; commercial forms and documents including wordprocessing software. see *LAW—International Law*

INTERNATIONAL COAL. see *MINES AND MINING INDUSTRY*

INTERNATIONAL CONTRACT MANUAL. see *LAW—International Law*

INTERNATIONAL CUSTOMS JOURNAL/BULLETIN INTERNATIONAL DES DOUANES. see *BUSINESS AND ECONOMICS—Public Finance, Taxation*

380.1029   GBR
THE INTERNATIONAL DIRECTORY OF BUSINESS INFORMATION SOURCES & SERVICES. Text in English. irreg., latest vol.2, 1996. GBP 125, USD 195 (effective 2001). **Document type:** *Directory.* **Description:** Lists government and private-industry organizations that produce information on international commerce, along with business libraries, chambers of commerce, and research institutions.
Published by: Europa Publications Limited (Subsidiary of: Taylor & Francis Group), 11 New Fetter Ln, London, EC4P 4EE, United Kingdom. TEL 44-20-7822-4300, FAX 44-20-7842-2249, sales.europa@tandf.co.uk, http://www.europapublications.co.uk/titles/idbiss.html, http://www.europapublications.com.

INTERNATIONAL DIRECTORY OF IMPORTERS: AFRICA. see *BUSINESS AND ECONOMICS—Trade And Industrial Directories*

INTERNATIONAL DIRECTORY OF IMPORTERS: ASIA - PACIFIC. see *BUSINESS AND ECONOMICS—Trade And Industrial Directories*

INTERNATIONAL DIRECTORY OF IMPORTERS: EUROPE. see *BUSINESS AND ECONOMICS—Trade And Industrial Directories*

INTERNATIONAL DIRECTORY OF IMPORTERS: MIDDLE EAST. see *BUSINESS AND ECONOMICS—Trade And Industrial Directories*

INTERNATIONAL DIRECTORY OF IMPORTERS: NORTH AMERICA. see *BUSINESS AND ECONOMICS—Trade And Industrial Directories*

INTERNATIONAL DIRECTORY OF IMPORTERS: SOUTH - CENTRAL AMERICA. see *BUSINESS AND ECONOMICS—Trade And Industrial Directories*

382   DEU   ISSN 1612-4804
▼ ➤ **INTERNATIONAL ECONOMICS AND ECONOMIC POLICY.** Text in English. 2004. 4/yr. EUR 218 (effective 2005). **Document type:** *Journal, Academic/Scholarly.* **Description:** Focuses on comparative economic policy, international political economy, including international organizations and policy cooperation, monetary and real/technological dynamics in open economies, globalization and regional integration, trade, migration, international investment, internet commerce and regulation.
Related titles: Online - full text ed.: ISSN 1612-4812 (from EBSCO Publishing, ProQuest Information & Learning, Springer LINK, Swets Information Services).
Indexed: ABIn, JEL.
—BLDSC (4539.813000). CCC.
Published by: Springer-Verlag (Subsidiary of: Springer Science+Business Media), Tiergartenstr 17, Heidelberg, 69121, Germany. TEL 49-6221-3450, FAX 49-6221-345229, subscriptions@springer.de, http://www.springer.de. Eds. H C Wolf, J Wolters, P Welfens. Adv. contact Stephan Kroeck TEL 49-30-827875739.

330   USA   ISSN 0898-4336
HG3879
INTERNATIONAL ECONOMY; the magazine of International Economic Policy. Text in English. 1987. q. USD 72 (effective 2005). adv. bk.rev. illus.; charts. back issues avail.; reprints avail. **Document type:** *Magazine, Trade.* **Description:** Provides a forum for the emerging international financial and trade debate at the highest level; serves the world's top strategic decision makers.
Related titles: Online - full text ed.: (from EBSCO Publishing, Florida Center for Library Automation, Gale Group, Northern Light Technology, Inc., ProQuest Information & Learning).
Indexed: ABIn, ABS&EES, BPI, ESPM, JEL, PAIS, RiskAb.
—BLDSC (4539.827000), IE, Infotrieve, ingenta. CCC.
Published by: International Economy Publications, 888 16th St NW, Ste 740, Washington, DC 20006. TEL 202-861-0791, FAX 202-861-0790, internationaleconomy@att.net, http://www.international-economy.com. Ed. David M Smick. Circ: 5,000.

INTERNATIONAL EXPORTING AGREEMENTS. see *LAW*

INTERNATIONAL FINANCE. see *BUSINESS AND ECONOMICS—Banking And Finance*

INTERNATIONAL FINANCE & TREASURY. see *BUSINESS AND ECONOMICS—Banking And Finance*

INTERNATIONAL FINANCE: TAX & REGULATION ADVISOR. see *BUSINESS AND ECONOMICS—Public Finance, Taxation*

382   AUS
INTERNATIONAL FOCUS. Text in English. 1969. s-a. adv. **Document type:** *Newsletter.* **Description:** Details major international development that affect business opportunities in Australia.
Supersedes: M T I A's Engineering Exporter; Which was formerly: M T I A N E G's Export Note Pad; Australian Metal Trades Export Group's Export Note Pad
Published by: Australian Industry Group, 214 Northbourne Ave, Canberra, ACT 2601 , Australia. TEL 61-2-6217-0188, FAX 61-2-6217-9199. Circ: 1,000.

INTERNATIONAL GAME THEORY REVIEW. see *TECHNOLOGY: COMPREHENSIVE WORKS*

INTERNATIONAL GRAINS COUNCIL. WHEAT AND COARSE GRAIN SHIPMENTS. see *AGRICULTURE—Feed, Flour And Grain*

INTERNATIONAL H R JOURNAL. (Human Resources) see *BUSINESS AND ECONOMICS—Personnel Management*

INTERNATIONAL HUMAN RESOURCES GUIDE. see *BUSINESS AND ECONOMICS—Personnel Management*

INTERNATIONAL INTERTRADE INDEX; new foreign products - marketing techniques. see *BUSINESS AND ECONOMICS—Marketing And Purchasing*

INTERNATIONAL JOURNAL OF ADVERTISING; the quarterly review of marketing communications. see *ADVERTISING AND PUBLIC RELATIONS*

382 332 658   USA   ISSN 1083-4346
HF5001
➤ **INTERNATIONAL JOURNAL OF BUSINESS.** Text in English. 1992; N.S. 1996. q. USD 40 domestic to individuals; USD 50 foreign to individuals; USD 120 domestic to institutions; USD 130 foreign to institutions (effective 2004). adv. index. back issues avail. **Document type:** *Journal, Academic/Scholarly.* **Description:** Serves and provides a forum for exchange of ideas among business executives and academicians concerned with global business and economic issues.
Formerly (until 1996): Review of Business Studies (1047-4595)
Related titles: Microform ed.: N.S. (from PQC).
Indexed: JEL.
—IE, Infotrieve.
Published by: Premier Publishing, Inc., PO Box 27647, Fresno, CA 93729-7647. FAX 559-278-5220, premierijb@hotmail.com, http://www.craig.csufresno.edu/ijb. Ed., R&P K.C. Chen. Pub. Lingle Liao.

382 332 658   USA   ISSN 1555-7715
▼ ➤ **INTERNATIONAL JOURNAL OF BUSINESS STUDIES.** Abbreviated title: I J B S. Text in English. 2005 (May). s-a. USD 100 to individuals (effective 2005). **Document type:** *Journal, Academic/Scholarly.* **Description:** Contains original research papers in business, international business, economics and related subjects.
Published by: International Academy of Business and Economics, 983 Woodland Dr, Turlock, CA 95382-7281. TEL 209-667-3074, 209-656-7084, FAX 209-667-3210, Admin@iabe.com, http://www.iabe.com. R&P Dr. Bhavesh S Patel.

➤ **INTERNATIONAL JOURNAL OF COMMERCE AND MANAGEMENT.** see *BUSINESS AND ECONOMICS—Management*

382   GBR   ISSN 1746-8809
▼ ➤ **INTERNATIONAL JOURNAL OF EMERGING MARKETS.** Text in English. forthcoming 2006 (Feb.). q. EUR 303.41 in Europe; USD 359 in North America; AUD 479; GBP 216.41 in the UK & elsewhere (effective 2006). **Document type:** *Journal, Academic/Scholarly.* **Description:** Brings together the latest theoretical and empirical management research in emerging markets.
Related titles: Online - full content ed.: forthcoming.
Published by: Emerald Group Publishing Limited, 60-62 Toller Ln, Bradford, W Yorks BD8 9BY, United Kingdom. TEL 44-1274-777700, FAX 44-1274-785200, infomation@emeraldinsight.com, http://www.emeraldinsight.com/ijoem.htm. Ed. Dr. Yusaf Akbar. Pub. Ms. Kate Snowden. R&P Ms. Anne-Marie Thorslund.

▼ ➤ **INTERNATIONAL JOURNAL OF GLOBALISATION AND SMALL BUSINESS.** see *BUSINESS AND ECONOMICS—Small Business*

➤ **INTERNATIONAL MARKET INDEXES.** see *BUSINESS AND ECONOMICS—Investments*

382   HKG
INTERNATIONAL MARKET NEWS (ONLINE EDITION). Text in English. 1984. q. (4-5/yr.). adv. back issues avail. **Document type:** *Trade.* **Description:** Covers international market developments, consumer trends, business opportunities, and new technologies and product innovations. Includes features, a special section focusing on China, and a selection of queries from traders addressed to the HK Trade Council's research department accompanied by concise answers.
Formerly: International Market News (Print Edition)
Media: Online - full content.
Published by: Hong Kong Trade Development Council, 38th Fl Office Tower, Convention Plaza, 1 Harbour Rd, Wanchai, Hong Kong. hktdc@tdc.org.hk, http://www.tdctrade.com/imn/, http://www.tdc.org.hk. Circ: 7,800.

INTERNATIONAL MARKET REVIEW. see *BUSINESS AND ECONOMICS—Banking And Finance*

INTERNATIONAL MERGERS & ACQUISITIONS (YEARS). see *BUSINESS AND ECONOMICS*

INTERNATIONAL MONETARY FUND. BALANCE OF PAYMENTS STATISTICS YEARBOOK. see *BUSINESS AND ECONOMICS—Abstracting, Bibliographies, Statistics*

INTERNATIONAL MONETARY FUND. DIRECTION OF TRADE STATISTICS. see *BUSINESS AND ECONOMICS—Abstracting, Bibliographies, Statistics*

382.1   USA
INTERNATIONAL ONLINE MARKETS (YEAR): STRATEGIC OUTLOOK AND FORECASTS. Text in English. 1996. a., latest vol.3, 2000. USD 1,995 (effective 2000). **Document type:** *Trade.* **Description:** Surveys the international online landscape, offering historical perspectives and market forecasts to aid in strategic planning.
Published by: SIMBA Information (Subsidiary of: R.R. Bowker LLC), 60 Long Ridge Rd., Ste 300, Stamford, CT 06902. TEL 203-325-8193, 800-307-2529, 888-269-5372, FAX 203-325-8915, info@simbanet.com, http://www.simbanet.com.

B

382 IND ISSN 0047-0953
INTERNATIONAL PRESS CUTTING SERVICE: IMPORT - EXPORT - LICENSES; customs notifications. Text in English. 1967. w. INR 735, USD 85 (effective 1999). bk.rev. index.
Document type: *Newsletter.* **Description:** Covers topics about imports, exports and licenses in India.
Media: Duplicated (not offset).
Published by: International Press Cutting Service, PO Box 121, Allahabad, Uttar Pradesh 211 001, India. TEL 91-532-622392. Ed. Nandi Khanna. Circ: 1,200.

382 IND ISSN 0047-1127
INTERNATIONAL PRESS CUTTING SERVICE: TENDER NOTIFICATIONS (INDIAN & GLOBAL). Text in English. 1967. fortn. INR 750, USD 85 (effective 1999). bk.rev. index.
Document type: *Newsletter.* **Description:** Covers tender notifications in India.
Media: Duplicated (not offset).
Published by: International Press Cutting Service, PO Box 121, Allahabad, Uttar Pradesh 211 001, India. TEL 91-532-622392. Ed. Nandi Khanna. Circ: 1,200.

658 USA ISSN 1523-262X
INTERNATIONAL SECURITIZATION & STRUCTURED FINANCE REPORT. Text in English. 1998. 2/m. USD 1,333 (effective 2005). **Document type:** *Newsletter, Trade.* **Description:** Keeps readers informed of unique new structures for different regions including confusing regulations, stability of currency, capital controls, and international tax and accounting issues.
Published by: WorldTrade Executive, Inc., 2250 Main St, Ste 100, PO Box 761, Concord, MA 01742. TEL 978-287-0301, FAX 978-287-0302, info@wtexec.com, http://www.wtexec.com/Secur.html.

INTERNATIONAL SPACE INDUSTRY REPORT. see *AERONAUTICS AND SPACE FLIGHT*

INTERNATIONAL STEEL REVIEW. see *METALLURGY*

382.7 336 GBR ISSN 0958-7594
K4456.2
INTERNATIONAL TAX REVIEW. Text in English. 1989. 10/yr. GBP 492 combined subscription domestic print & online eds.; EUR 745 combined subscription in Europe print & online eds.; USD 861 combined subscription elsewhere print & online eds. (effective 2005). **Document type:** *Magazine, Trade.* **Description:** Covers the most recent developments in cross-border taxation. Analyzes all tax issues including new case law, opinions, treaties and statutes affecting corporations and financial institutions.
Related titles: Online - full text ed.: (from EBSCO Publishing, Florida Center for Library Automation, Gale Group, O C L C Online Computer Library Center, Inc., ProQuest Information & Learning).
Indexed: ABIn, ATI, ELJI, LJI.
—BLDSC (4550.399500). **CCC.**
Published by: Euromoney Institutional Investor Plc., Nestor House, Playhouse Yard, London, EC4V 5EX, United Kingdom. TEL 44-20-7779-8673, FAX 44-20-7779-8541, http://www.internationaltaxreview.com, http://www.euromoney.com. Eds. Ralph Cunningham TEL 44-20-77798308, Sed Crest TEL 44-20-77798789. **Subscr. to:** Eclipse, The In-house Fulfillment Bureau, PO Box 18083, London EC4V 5JS, United Kingdom. TEL 44-20-7779-8610, FAX 44-20-7779-8602, CustomerService@euromoneyplc.com. **Dist. in US by:** American Educational Systems, PO Box 246, New York, NY 10024-0246. TEL 800-431-1579.

382 USA ISSN 0744-5660
INTERNATIONAL TRADE ALERT✶. Text in English. w. looseleaf. membership. back issues avail. **Document type:** *Newsletter.* **Description:** Covers international trade and US Customs and other government regulations affecting imports and exports.
Formerly: Import Alert (0195-4458)
Published by: American Association of Exporters and Importers, 700 11th St NW, Ste. 110, Washington, DC 20001-4576. TEL 212-944-2606, FAX 212-382-2606. Ed. Elizabeth Stern Bayer. R&P Elizabeth Stern Bayer TEL 212-944-2230.

INTERNATIONAL TRADE AND BUSINESS ANNUAL. see *LAW—International Law*

382 GBR
INTERNATIONAL TRADE AND BUSINESS LAW ANNUAL. Text in English. 1996. a.
Published by: (Australian Institute of Foreign and Comparative Law AUS), Cavendish Publishing Ltd., The Glass House, Wharton St, London, WC1X 9PX, United Kingdom. TEL 44-20-72788000, FAX 44-20-72788080, info@cavendishpublishing.com, http://www.cavendishpublishing.com.

382 USA ISSN 0890-4251
INTERNATIONAL TRADE AND INVESTMENT LETTER; trends in US policies, trade finance, and trading operations. Text in English. 1979. m. USD 240. **Document type:** *Newsletter.*
Published by: International Business Affairs Corporation, 4938 Hampden Ln, Bethesda, MD 20814-2914. TEL 301-907-8647. Ed. Richard L Barovich.

382 GBR ISSN 1464-6080
THE INTERNATIONAL TRADE CORRUPTION MONITOR. Text in English. 1998. q. looseleaf. GBP 260, USD 425 (effective 1999). **Document type:** *Trade.* **Description:** Includes current legislation such as the OECD treaty, emerging international and national instruments, regular articles, essential documentation and upcoming events.
Published by: Cameron May Ltd., 69 Bondway, London, SW8 1SQ, United Kingdom. TEL 44-20-7582-7567, FAX 44-20-7793-8353, orders@cameronmay.com, http://www.cameronmay.com. Ed. Jeremy Pope.

382 USA ISSN 1533-1350
INTERNATIONAL TRADE DAILY. Text in English. 2000. d. USD 2,296 domestic (effective 2005 - 2006). back issues avail. **Document type:** *Newsletter, Trade.* **Description:** Reports on developments affecting U.S. trade and international business policy and the policies of major U.S. trading partners.
Media: Online - full text (from The Bureau of National Affairs, Inc.).
—CCC.
Published by: The Bureau of National Affairs, Inc., 1231 25th St., NW, Washington, DC 20037. TEL 800-372-1033, 800-452-7773, FAX 800-253-0332, customercare@bna.com, http://www.bna.com/products/corplaw/tdln.htm. **Subscr. to:** 9435 Key West Ave, Rockville, MD 20850.

382 CHE ISSN 0020-8957
HF1410 CODEN: ITFREV
INTERNATIONAL TRADE FORUM. Text in English. 1964. q. USD 20 in developing nations; USD 65 elsewhere (effective 2000). bk.rev. bibl.; charts; illus. index. reprint service avail. from PQC. **Document type:** *Journal, Trade.* **Description:** Focuses on trade promotion, export development and import methods, as part of its technical co-operation programme with developing countries and economics in transition.
Related titles: Microform ed.: (from PQC); Online - full text ed.: (from EBSCO Publishing, Florida Center for Library Automation, Gale Group, H.W. Wilson, Northern Light Technology, Inc., O C L C Online Computer Library Center, Inc., ProQuest Information & Learning); Spanish ed.: Forum de Comercio Internacional. ISSN 0251-009X; French ed.: Forum du Commerce International. ISSN 0591-2512.
Indexed: ABIn, ADPA, BPI, BPIA, BusI, Emerald, FS&TA, HortAb, KES, LRI, M&MA, ManagCont, PAIS, PHN&I, RA&MP, RASB, RDA, RRTA, RefZh, T&II, WAE&RSA, WBA, WMB.
—BLDSC (4551.280000), IE, ingenta.
Published by: International Trade Centre, Plais des Nations, Geneva 10, 1211, Switzerland. TEL 41-22-730-0111, FAX 41-22-733-4439, TELEX 414119 ITC, itcreg@intracen.org, http://www.intracen.org. Ed. Natalie Domeisen. Circ: 30,000.

382 AUS ISSN 1038-2267
INTERNATIONAL TRADE HANDBOOK FOR WESTERN AUSTRALIA. Text in English. 1992. a. AUD 55 domestic; USD 50 foreign (effective 2002). adv. stat.; tr.lit. **Document type:** *Trade.* **Description:** Provides a guide for exporters and importers.
Published by: Chamber of Commerce and Industry of Western Australia, 190 Hay St, East Perth, W.A. 6004, Australia. TEL 61-8-9365-7555, FAX 61-8-9365-7550, whitaker@cciwa.com, http://www.cciwa.com. Ed. Ian Whitaker. Adv. contact Glen Cocks. Circ: 1,500 (paid).

382 USA ISSN 0885-3908
HF1371 CODEN: ITRJEX
➤ **THE INTERNATIONAL TRADE JOURNAL.** Text in English. 1986. q. GBP 208, USD 342 combined subscription to institutions print & online eds. (effective 2006). adv. bk.rev. back issues avail.; reprint service avail. from PSC. **Document type:** *Journal, Academic/Scholarly.* **Description:** Provides a forum for ideas among academicians, government officials, and both macro- and microeconomic practitioners; covers both practical and theoretical contributions to the field of international trade.
Related titles: Online - full text ed.: ISSN 1521-0545. GBP 198, USD 325 (effective 2006) (from EBSCO Publishing, Gale Group, IngentaConnect, O C L C Online Computer Library Center, Inc., Swets Information Services).
Indexed: ABIn, BAS, JEL, WAE&RSA, WBA, WMB.
—BLDSC (4551.301000), IE, Infotrieve, ingenta. **CCC.**
Published by: (International Trade & Finance Association), Taylor & Francis Inc. (Subsidiary of: Taylor & Francis Group), 325 Chestnut St, Ste 800, Philadelphia, PA 19016. TEL 215-625-8900, 800-354-1420, FAX 215-625-8914, info@taylorandfrancis.com, http://www.tandf.co.uk/journals/titles/08853908.asp, http://www.taylorandfrancis.com. Ed. Antonio J Rodriguez. **Subscr. outside N. America to:** Taylor & Francis Ltd, Journals Customer Service, Rankine Rd, Basingstoke, Hants RG24 8PR, United Kingdom. TEL 44-1256-813000, FAX 44-1256-330245, enquiry@tandf.co.uk.

➤ **THE INTERNATIONAL TRADE LAW REPORTS.** see *LAW—International Law*

382.7 USA ISSN 1098-4240
HF3000
INTERNATIONAL TRADE REPORTER. Text in English. 1947. w. USD 1,744 domestic (effective 2005 - 2006). s-a. index. 32 p./no.; back issues avail. **Document type:** *Trade.* **Description:** Reports and analyzes legislative and regulatory developments as well as private sector activities affecting international trade (both export and import).
Former titles: B N A's International Trade Reporter (1098-4488); (until 1997): International Trade Reporter (1075-833X); (until 1995): International Trade Reporter Current Reporter (0748-0172); Which was formed by the merger of (1974-1984): International Trade Reporter's U.S. Export Weekly (0093-9633); (1979-1984): US Import Weekly (0195-7589); Which was formerly (until 1966): Interantional Trade Reporter's Survey and Analysis of Current Developments; (until 1950): International Trade Reporter Survey and Analysis of Current Developments
Related titles: CD-ROM ed.; Online - full text ed.: ISSN 1523-2816 (from The Bureau of National Affairs, Inc., Thomson West); ♦ Series: International Trade Reporter Export Reference Manual. ISSN 1043-5670; ♦ International Trade Reporter Decisions. ISSN 0748-0709; ♦ International Trade Reporter. Import Reference Manual. ISSN 1043-5662.
—CCC.
Published by: The Bureau of National Affairs, Inc., 1231 25th St., NW, Washington, DC 20037. TEL 202-452-4200, 800-372-1033, FAX 202-822-8092, customercare@bna.com, http://www.bna.com/products/corplaw/itr.htm. Pub. Greg C McCaffery.

382 341.57 USA ISSN 0748-0709
INTERNATIONAL TRADE REPORTER DECISIONS. Text in English. 1984. bi-w. looseleaf. USD 2,265 domestic (effective 2005 - 2006). back issues avail. **Description:** Digested, classified, and indexed judicial and administrative decisions dealing with legal issues arising from US trade law (mostly import cases).
Formerly (until 1984): International Trade Reporter's U S Import Weekly. Decisions
Related titles: Online - full text ed.: (from The Bureau of National Affairs, Inc.); ♦ Series of: International Trade Reporter. ISSN 1098-4240.
—CCC.
Published by: The Bureau of National Affairs, Inc., 1231 25th St., NW, Washington, DC 20037. TEL 202-452-4200, 800-372-1033, 800-452-7773, FAX 202-822-8092, customercare@bna.com, http://www.bna.com. Ed. Linda G Botsford. Pub. Greg C McCaffery.

382 USA ISSN 1043-5670
CODEN: ITRME8
INTERNATIONAL TRADE REPORTER EXPORT REFERENCE MANUAL. Text in English. 1947. bi-w. looseleaf. USD 873 (effective 2001). back issues avail. **Description:** Comprehensive source for foreign import regulations, US export controls, and related requirements for preparing US exports for shipment abroad.
Formerly (until 1989): Export Shipping Manual (0014-5181)
Related titles: Online - full text ed.: (from The Bureau of National Affairs, Inc.); ♦ Series of: International Trade Reporter. ISSN 1098-4240.
—CCC.
Published by: The Bureau of National Affairs, Inc., 1231 25th St., NW, Washington, DC 20037. TEL 202-452-4200, 800-372-1033, 800-452-7773, FAX 202-822-8092, customercare@bna.com, bnaplus@bna.com, http://www.bna.com/. Ed. Deanne E Neuman. Pub. Greg C McCaffery. **Subscr. to:** 9435 Key West Ave, Rockville, MD 20850.

382 USA ISSN 1043-5662
INTERNATIONAL TRADE REPORTER. IMPORT REFERENCE MANUAL. Text in English. 1980. 6/yr. looseleaf. USD 1,781 (effective 2005 - 2006). index. back issues avail. **Document type:** *Trade.* **Description:** Guide to the entire import process with analysis and full text of statutes, regulations, and executive orders on subjects such as custom house brokers, dumping, countervailing duties, escape clauses, and presidential retaliation.
Former titles (until 1989): International Trade Reporter's Reference File (0748-0695); (until 1984): International Trade Reporter's U S Import Weekly Reference File (1040-4058)
Related titles: Online - full text ed.: (from The Bureau of National Affairs, Inc.); ♦ Series of: International Trade Reporter. ISSN 1098-4240.
—CCC.
Published by: The Bureau of National Affairs, Inc., 1231 25th St., NW, Washington, DC 20037. TEL 202-452-4200, 800-372-1033, 800-452-7773, FAX 202-822-8092, customercare@bna.com, http://www.bna.com. Ed. Linda G Bosford. Pub. Greg C McCaffery.

INTERNATIONAL TRADE RESOURCES; an internet miniguide. see *BUSINESS AND ECONOMICS—Abstracting, Bibliographies, Statistics*

382 IND ISSN 0020-8981
INTERNATIONAL TRADE REVIEW. Text in English. 1969. m. INR 20, USD 5. adv. bk.rev. stat.; tr.lit.
Published by: (Indian Council of Foreign Trade), United Asia Publications Pvt. Ltd., 12 Rampart Row, Mumbai, Maharashtra 400 001, India. Ed. G S Pohekar.

382 GBR
INTERNATIONAL TRADE TODAY. Text in English. 2000. m. —BLDSC (4551.305825).
Published by: Hemming Information Services Ltd. (Subsidiary of: Hemming Group Ltd.), 32 Vauxhall Bridge Rd, London, SW1V 288, United Kingdom. TEL 44-20-79736402, FAX 44-20-72335057, h-info@hemming-group.co.uk, https://www.h-info.co.uk/.

382 USA ISSN 1091-3637
INTERNATIONAL WEALTH SUCCESS NEWSLETTER; the monthly newsletter of worldwide wealth opportunities. Text in English. 1967. m. USD 24 domestic; USD 48 foreign (effective 2000). adv. bk.rev. tr.lit. reprint service avail. from PQC. **Document type:** *Newsletter.* **Description:** Covers a variety of small-business topics including borrowing money, raising capital, mail order, real estate, and import-export.
Related titles: Microform ed.: (from PQC).
Published by: International Wealth Success, Inc., 24 Cantebury Rd, Rockville Centre, NY 11570-1310. TEL 516-766-5850, FAX 516-766-5919. Ed., Pub. Tyler G Hicks.

INTERNATIONAL WITHHOLDING TAX TREATY GUIDE. see *BUSINESS AND ECONOMICS—Public Finance, Taxation*

330 AUS ISSN 1033-6427
INTERNATIONAL WORKING PAPER. Text in English. 1973. irreg. —BLDSC (4552.177000).
Published by: University of Melbourne, Department of Economics, Melbourne, VIC 3010, Australia.

INTERNATIONAL YEARBOOK OF INDUSTRIAL STATISTICS (YEAR). see *BUSINESS AND ECONOMICS—Abstracting, Bibliographies, Statistics*

382.7 DEU ISSN 1617-5395
➤ **INTERNATIONALES HANDELSRECHT**; Zeitschrift fuer die wirtschaftsrechtliche Praxis. Abbreviated title: I H R. Text in German. 2001. bi-m. EUR 132; EUR 82 to students; EUR 25 newsstand/cover (effective 2003). **Document type:** *Journal, Academic/Scholarly.*
Published by: Sellier - European Law Publishers GmbH, Geibelstr. 8, Munich, 81679, Germany. TEL 49-89-476047, FAX 49-89-4704327, info@sellier-elp.de, http://www.sellier-elp.de. Ed. Rolf Herber.

382 USA
INTERNATIONALIST✶ ; the journal of international activity. Text in English. 1993. 3/yr. USD 15. adv. back issues avail. **Document type:** *Trade.* **Description:** Highlights international trade related events in the tri-state area and organizations supporting international trade.
Published by: Assist International, 26 Broadway., Ste. 776, New York, NY 10004-1748. TEL 212-725-3311, FAX 212-725-3312, info@assist-intl.com. Eds. Brooks Shumway, Juan C Heredia. Pub. Peter J Robinson Jr. Adv. contact Brooks Shumway. page USD 1,100. Circ: 20,000.

338.5 NLD ISSN 0165-2826
CODEN: INTXE9
➤ **INTERTAX**; international tax review. Text in English. m. EUR 729, USD 861, GBP 511 combined subscription print & online eds. (effective 2006); inludes EC Tax Review. adv. reprint service avail. from PSC. **Document type:** *Journal, Academic/Scholarly.* **Description:** Provides practical, up-to-date and high-level international tax information, including coverage of transnational tax issues.
Formerly: Fiscalite du Marche Commun (0015-282X).
Related titles: Online - full text ed.: (from EBSCO Publishing, Gale Group, Kluwer Online, O C L C Online Computer Library Center, Inc., Swets Information Services); ◆ Supplement(s): E C Tax Review. ISSN 0928-2750.
Indexed: ELLIS, FLP, IBR, IBZ, KES, LJI, PAIS. —BLDSC (4557.455000), IE, Infotrieve, ingenta. **CCC.**
Published by: Kluwer Law International (Subsidiary of: Aspen Publishers, Inc.), Laan van Meerdervoort 70, PO Box 85889, The Hague, 2508 CN, Netherlands. TEL 31-70-3081500, FAX 31-70-3081515, sales@kluwerlaw.com, http://www.kluwerlaw.com. Ed. Fred C de Hosson. Pub. Lukas Claerhout.

382 CHN
INTERTRADE. Text in Chinese, English. **Document type:** *Government.* **Description:** Contains forum, interview, foreign economic relations and trade, world economy, international trade, finance, laws, investment, market, study of work and translations of selected foreign articles.
Indexed: RASB.
Published by: Ministry of Commerce of the People's Republic of China/Zhonghua Renmin Gongheguo Shangfubu, 28 Dong Hou Ln, An Ding Men Wai, Beijing, 100710, China. TEL 86-1-4269332, FAX 86-1-4212149.

INTERTRAFFIC INTERNATIONAL DIRECTORY. see *BUSINESS AND ECONOMICS—Trade And Industrial Directories*

332.6 USA
INVESTING, LICENSING AND TRADING. GLOBAL EDITION. (Avail. in global, regional and individual country eds.) Text in English. 1965. s-a. GBP 225, USD 345 (effective 2000). **Document type:** *Trade.* **Description:** Reference service that advises on how to operate profitably in 60 countries.
Former titles (until 1997): Investing, Licensing and Trading Conditions Abroad. Global Edition (0021-003X); Investing, Licensing and Trading Conditions in 5 Countries
Related titles: ◆ CD-ROM ed.: E I U Investing, Licensing and Trading.
—**CCC.**
Published by: Economist Intelligence Unit, 111 W 57th St, New York, NY 10019. TEL 212-554-0600, 800-938-4685, FAX 212-586-1181, http://www.eiu.com. Ed. Bob Harris.

332.6 USA
INVESTING, LICENSING AND TRADING. SLOVAKIA. Text in English. a. GBP 225, USD 345 (effective 2000). **Document type:** *Trade.* **Description:** Provides information on corporate tax rules, exchange and price controls, trade and licensing restrictions, labor conditions and investment rules.
Formerly (until 1997): Investing, Licensing and Trading Conditions Abroad. Slovakia; Which superseded in part: Investing, Licensing and Trading Conditions. Czech Republic and Slovakia; Which was formerly (until 1993): Investing, Licensing and Trading Conditions Abroad. Czechoslovakia (1352-9951)
Related titles: CD-ROM ed.: (from SilverPlatter Information, Inc.); Online - full text ed.: (from SilverPlatter Information, Inc., The Dialog Corporation).
Published by: Economist Intelligence Unit, 111 W 57th St, New York, NY 10019. TEL 212-554-0600, 800-938-4685, FAX 212-586-1181, http://www.eiu.com.

INVESTORS' JOURNAL OF LEGISLATIVE IMPACT. see *BUSINESS AND ECONOMICS—Investments*

332 UAE
AL-IQTISAD WAL-TIJARAH/ECONOMY AND COMMERCE. Text in Arabic. 1972. s-m. free. **Description:** Covers the local economy of Abu Dhabi, the U.A.E., and economic relations with the Arab world and the international community.
Published by: Ministry of Economy and Commerce, PO Box 433, Abu Dhabi, United Arab Emirates. TEL 726000.

332.6 IRN ISSN 1016-8885
IRAN EXPORTS & IMPORTS. Key Title: Iran Exports. Text in English. 1987. bi-m. IRR 65,000 domestic (effective 2000). adv. illus. back issues avail. **Document type:** *Trade.* **Description:** Covers the production of goods and services, exports and imports, and Iranian economic issues, with the intent of promoting trade between Iran and other countries.
Related titles: Diskette ed.
Published by: Iran Exports Publication Co. Ltd., P O Box 14335 746, Tehran, 15956, Iran. TEL 98-21-8801800, 800-880-1999, FAX 98-21-8900547, http://www.neda.net/iranexports/. R&P M R Samimi. Adv. contact Fereidoun Sa'adat. Circ: 5,000.

382 USA
▼ **IRAQ RECONSTRUCTION REPORT.** Text in English. 2004. bi-w. USD 1,495 (effective 2005). **Document type:** *Newsletter, Trade.* **Description:** Provides up-to-the minute details on reconstruction contracts from various governments and international organizations including subcontractor and supplier opportunities.
Published by: WorldTrade Executive, Inc., 2250 Main St, Ste 100, PO Box 761, Concord, MA 01742. TEL 978-287-0301, FAX 978-287-0302, info@wtexec.com, http://www.wtexec.com.

IRELAND. CENTRAL STATISTICS OFFICE. EXTERNAL TRADE. see *BUSINESS AND ECONOMICS—Abstracting, Bibliographies, Statistics*

IRELAND. CENTRAL STATISTICS OFFICE. STATISTICS OF PORT TRAFFIC. see *TRANSPORTATION—Abstracting, Bibliographies, Statistics*

IRELAND. CENTRAL STATISTICS OFFICE. TRADE STATISTICS. see *BUSINESS AND ECONOMICS—Abstracting, Bibliographies, Statistics*

IRELAND. CENTRAL STATISTICS OFFICE. TRADE WITH NON - E U COUNTRIES. see *BUSINESS AND ECONOMICS—Abstracting, Bibliographies, Statistics*

382 IRL
IRISH FISH EXPORTS/IMPORTS. Text in English. a.
Published by: Irish Sea Fisheries Board/Bord Iascaigh Mhara, Crofton Rd., PO Box 12, Dun Laoghaire, Co. Dublin, Ireland. TEL 353-1-2144100, FAX 353-1-2841123, info@bim.ie, http://www.bim.ie.

ISRAEL CONVENTIONS, TRADE SHOWS, FESTIVALS & SPECIAL EVENTS. see *MEETINGS AND CONGRESSES*

382 ISR ISSN 0793-4939
ISRAEL EXPORT (YEAR). Text in English. 1993. a. adv. charts; illus.; stat.; tr.lit. back issues avail. **Document type:** *Trade.* **Description:** Profiles the leading companies, including high technology projects. Reports on prize-winning companies.
Related titles: ◆ Supplement to: Link. ISSN 0792-9765.
Published by: (Israel. Ministry of Industry and Trade), Pick Communications Ltd., P O Box 57500, Tel Aviv, 61574, Israel. TEL 972-3-5759790, FAX 972-3-5759791. Ed. Nicky Blackburn. Pub., R&P Amos Pick. Adv. contact Anna Schein.

382 ZAF
ISRAEL SOUTH AFRICA BUSINESS OPPORTUNITIES NEWSLETTER. Text in English. 1994. q. illus. **Document type:** *Newsletter.*
Published by: Israel Trade Centre, PO Box 542541, Saxonwold, Johannesburg 2132, South Africa.

382 338.95694 ISR ISSN 0793-4955
ISRAELI FORUM. Text in English. 1993. a. free. **Document type:** *Trade.* **Description:** Covers issues relating to business investment in Israel, including technological, scientific and banking developments.
Published by: Pick Communications Ltd., P O Box 57500, Tel Aviv, 61574, Israel. TEL 972-3-5759790, FAX 972-3-5759791. R&P Amos Pick.

382 USA ISSN 1056-3024
HD2755.5
ISSUES IN INTERNATIONAL BUSINESS. Text in English. 1984. s-a. abstr.; bibl.; charts. **Document type:** *Trade.*
Published by: Montclair State University, School of Business Administration, Upper, Montclair, NJ 07043. Circ: 2,000.

382 ITA
ISTITUTO DI COMMERCIO ESTERO. GIORNALE; settimanale di commercio estero. Text in Italian. 52/yr. **Document type:** *Newspaper.*
Published by: (Istituto di Commercio Estero/National Institute for Foreign Trade), Edizioni Sistema Italia SpA, Via Liszt, 21, Rome, RM 00144, Italy. TEL 06-5992-1, FAX 06-59926702. Ed. Stefano Sassi. Circ: 50,000.

ITALY. ISTITUTO NAZIONALE DI STATISTICA. STATISTICA ANNUALE DEL COMMERCIO CON L'ESTERO. TOMO 2: MERCI PER PAESI. see *BUSINESS AND ECONOMICS—Abstracting, Bibliographies, Statistics*

IZNOS I VNOS/EXPORT AND IMPORT. see *STATISTICS*

382 JPN ISSN 0386-3042
K2
J C A JOURNAL. Key Title: J C A Janaru. Text in Japanese. 1953. m. JPY 14,000 (effective 1999).
Formerly (until 1972): Boeki Kuremu to Chusai (0523-8153)
Published by: Japan Commercial Arbitration Association/Kokusai Shoji Chusai Kyokai, 9-1 Yuraku-cho 1-chome, Chiyoda-ku, Tokyo, 100-0006, Japan. TEL 81-3-3287-3061, FAX 81-3-3287-3064. Ed. Norihiko Maeda. Circ: 1,700.

332.6 DEU
JAHRBUCH ZUR AUSSENWIRTSCHAFTSPOLITIK. Text in German. 1992. a. index. back issues avail. **Document type:** *Academic/Scholarly.*
Published by: Lit Verlag, Grindelberg 15a, Hamburg, 20144, Germany. lit@lit-verlag.de, http://www.lit-verlag.de.

382 JAM
JAMAICAN EXPORTER. Text in English. 1972. a. free. adv.
Published by: Jamaica Exporters' Association, 13 Dominica Dr, Kingston, 5, Jamaica. TEL 876-92-91292. Ed. Puline Gray.

JAPAN AND THE WORLD ECONOMY. see *BUSINESS AND ECONOMICS—Economic Systems And Theories, Economic History*

382 JPN ISSN 0452-3385
KNX1829.A15
JAPAN COMMERCIAL ARBITRATION ASSOCIATION. QUARTERLY. Text in English. q.
Published by: Japan Commercial Arbitration Association/Kokusai Shoji Chusai Kyokai, 9-1 Yuraku-cho 1-chome, Chiyoda-ku, Tokyo, 100-0006, Japan. TEL 81-3-3287-3061, FAX 81-3-3287-3064. Ed. Norihiko Maeda. Circ: 300.

332.6 GBR ISSN 0957-1426
JAPAN CONTACT. Text in English, Japanese. 1989. 6/yr. GBP 12 domestic to individuals; GBP 18 foreign to individuals; GBP 18 domestic to institutions; GBP 24 foreign to institutions.
Published by: Brennan Publications, 148 Birchover Way, Allestree, Derby DE22 2RW, United Kingdom. TEL 0332-551884. Ed. James Brennan.

JAPAN ELECTRONICS ALMANAC. see *ELECTRONICS*

JAPAN EXPORTS & IMPORTS: COMMODITY BY COUNTRY. see *BUSINESS AND ECONOMICS—Abstracting, Bibliographies, Statistics*

382 DEU ISSN 0931-3230
JAPANINFO; Fernost Berichte: Deutscher Dienst fuer Wirtschaft, Politik, Technologie und Gesellschaft. Text in German. 1980. every 3 wks. adv. bk.rev. back issues avail. **Document type:** *Newsletter.*
Published by: Japaninfo Verlag, Bismarckring 40, Ulm, 89077, Germany. TEL 0731-68093, FAX 0731-68095. Ed. I Botskor. Circ: 550.

382 600 CHN ISSN 1002-1221
JINZHAN: GUOJI MAOYI YU KEJI JIAOLIU/PROGRESS: INTERNATIONAL EXCHANGE IN TRADE, SCIENCE AND TECHNOLOGY. Text in Chinese. 1988. bi-m. USD 20.

▼ new title ➤ refereed ✶ unverified ◆ full entry avail.

B

Published by: Zhongguo Keji Xinxisuo, Chongqing Fensuo/China Science and Technology Information Institute, Consultation Center, 132 Shengli Lu, Shizhong-qu, Chongqing, Sichuan, China. TEL 0811-3852750, FAX 0811-3852473, TELEX 62128 CBIST CN. Ed. Fred H Laughter. Circ: 10,000.

382 346.066 FRA ISSN 1286-9074
JOLY COMMUNAUTAIRE. Text in French. 6 base vols. plus a. updates. looseleaf. **Document type:** *Trade.*
Formerly: Dictionnaire du Marche Commun
Published by: Joly Editions, 31 rue Falguiere, Paris, 75015, France. TEL 33-1-56541600, FAX 33-1-56541647.

JOURNAL OF AMERICAN - EAST ASIAN RELATIONS. see *SOCIAL SCIENCES: COMPREHENSIVE WORKS*

332.6 USA ISSN 1059-9231
HD70.A7 CODEN: JAPBFE
➤ **JOURNAL OF ASIA - PACIFIC BUSINESS.** Abbreviated title: J A P B. Text in English. 1993. q. USD 230 combined subscription domestic to institutions print & online eds.; USD 310.50 combined subscription in Canada to institutions print & online eds.; USD 333.50 combined subscription elsewhere to institutions print & online eds. (effective 2006). adv. bk.rev. 120 p./no. 1 cols./p.; back issues avail.; reprint service avail. from HAW. **Document type:** *Journal, Academic/Scholarly.*
Description: Covers the gamut of marketing, management, finance, accounting, business law, manufacturing, service and other areas of business in Asia-Pacific region.
Related titles: Microfiche ed.: (from PQC); Microform ed.; Online - full text ed.: ISSN 1528-6940 (from EBSCO Publishing, O C L C Online Computer Library Center, Inc., Swets Information Services).
Indexed: ABIX, ABIn, APEL, BAS, CPM, DIP, ESPM, Emerald, GSS&RPL, IBR, IBZ, JEL, M&MA, RefZh, RevApplEntom, RiskAb, SOPODA.
—BLDSC (4947.219000), Haworth, IE, ingenta. **CCC.**
Published by: International Business Press (Subsidiary of: Haworth Press, Inc.), 10 Alice St, Binghamton, NY 13904. TEL 607-722-5857, 800-429-6784, FAX 607-771-0012, 800-895-0582, getinfo@haworthpress.com, http://www.haworthpress.com/web/JAPB. Ed. Riad A Ajami. Pub. William Cohen. R&P Ruth Ann Heath TEL 607-722-5857 ext 316. Adv. contact Rebecca Miller-Baum TEL 607-722-5857 ext 337. B&W page USD 315, color page USD 550; trim 4.375 x 7.125. Circ: 204 (paid).

➤ **JOURNAL OF BORDERLANDS STUDIES.** see *POLITICAL SCIENCE—International Relations*

382 USA ISSN 1542-4448
▼ ➤ **JOURNAL OF BUSINESS & ECONOMICS RESEARCH.** Text in English. 2003 (Jan.). m. USD 100 domestic to individuals; USD 200 foreign to individuals; USD 495 domestic to institutions; USD 595 foreign to institutions (effective 2005). bk.rev. abstr. 120 p./no. 1 cols./p.; back issues avail.; reprints avail. **Document type:** *Journal, Academic/Scholarly.*
—BLDSC (4954.660600).
Published by: Western Academic Press, PO Box 620760, Littleton, CO 80162. TEL 303-904-4750, FAX 303-978-0413, cluter@wapress.com, http://www.wapress.com/JBERMain.htm. Circ: 600 (paid and controlled).

➤ **THE JOURNAL OF COMMERCE.** see *BUSINESS AND ECONOMICS—Domestic Commerce*

➤ **JOURNAL OF COMMODITY SCIENCE.** see *BUSINESS AND ECONOMICS—Domestic Commerce*

➤ **THE JOURNAL OF CORPORATE CITIZENSHIP.** see *BUSINESS AND ECONOMICS—Management*

382 USA ISSN 1436-8811
HD28
JOURNAL OF CROSS-CULTURAL COMPETENCE & MANAGEMENT. Text in English. 1998. a. USD 38 per issue (effective 2003). **Document type:** *Magazine, Academic/Scholarly.*
—**CCC.**
Published by: Transaction Publishers, 390 Campus Dr, Somerset, NJ 07830. TEL 888-999-6778, FAX 732-748-9801, trans@transactionpub.com, http://www.transactionpub.com.

JOURNAL OF ELECTRONIC COMMERCE RESEARCH (ONLINE EDITION). see *ELECTRONICS*

JOURNAL OF EUROMARKETING. see *BUSINESS AND ECONOMICS—Marketing And Purchasing*

JOURNAL OF GLOBAL MARKETING. see *BUSINESS AND ECONOMICS—Marketing And Purchasing*

382 327 KOR ISSN 1226-8550
DS1
➤ **JOURNAL OF INTERNATIONAL AND AREA STUDIES.** Text in English. 1994. s-a. KRW 30,000 to individuals; KRW 60,000 to institutions (effective 2001). adv. illus. Index. **Document type:** *Journal, Academic/Scholarly.* **Description:** Covers international trade, international cooperation, area studies, Korean studies, and other related subjects.
Formerly (until 1997): Asia Journal (1225-8512)
Related titles: Online - full content ed.; Online - full text ed.: (from bigchalk, O C L C Online Computer Library Center, Inc., ProQuest Information & Learning).
Indexed: ABIn, IPSA, JEL, PAIS, PSA, SociolAb.
—BLDSC (5007.555000), IE.
Published by: Seoul National University, Graduate School of International Studies, 56-1, Shillim-dong, Gwanak-gu, Seoul, 151-742, Korea, S. http://sias.snu.ac.kr/publication/d-jias/d-jiasindex.htm. Ed. Geun Lee TEL 82-2-880-6993.

382 004.678 USA ISSN 1544-8037
▼ ➤ **JOURNAL OF INTERNATIONAL BUSINESS AND ECONOMICS.** Abbreviated title: J I B E(Journal of International Business and Economics). Text in English. 2004 (Oct.). s-a. USD 100 to individuals (effective 2004). adv. back issues avail. **Document type:** *Journal, Academic/Scholarly.*
Description: Publishes original research papers and articles in international business administration, economics, management, marketing, accounting, finance, operations management, information management, E-commerce, E-business, public administration, health care administration, business law, and related areas.
Published by: Academy of International Business and Economics, PO Box 2536, Ceres, CA 95307. TEL 209-656-7084, Review@aibe.org, http://www.AIBE.org. R&P Dr. Alan S Khade. adv.: B&W page USD 500, color page USD 750.

382 370 IRL
JOURNAL OF INTERNATIONAL BUSINESS EDUCATION. Text in English. 2002 (Summer). q. **Document type:** *Magazine, Academic/Scholarly.* **Description:** Covers all aspect of international business, including case studies and overviews of textbooks in specific sub fields. Also contains teaching strategies which have been proved to be successful and represent best practice in the teaching of international business. These may include reviews of new courses, e-learning, and new approaches by leading international business teaching institutions.
Published by: Senate Hall Academic Publishing, PO Box 8261, Shankill, Co. Dublin, Ireland. TEL 353-1-2005066, FAX 353-1-2823701, info@senatehall.com, http://www.senatehall.com/jibe/index.html. Eds. Haskel Benishay, John Kasarda, Joseph Lapalombara, Meinolf Dierkes.

382 USA ISSN 1544-0222
HF1
➤ **JOURNAL OF INTERNATIONAL BUSINESS RESEARCH.** Text in English. 2002. a. **Document type:** *Journal, Academic/Scholarly.*
Related titles: Online - full text ed.: ISSN 1544-0230.
Published by: (Academy for Studies in International Business), Allied Academies, 145 Travis Rd., P. O. Box 2689, Cullowhee, NC 28723. http://www.alliedacademies.org/international-business/asib.html. Ed. Nader Asgary.

382 658 USA ISSN 1552-2903
▼ ➤ **JOURNAL OF INTERNATIONAL BUSINESS STRATEGY.** Variant title: JIBStrategy. Text in English. 2004 (Oct.). s-a. USD 100 to individuals (effective 2005). **Document type:** *Journal, Academic/Scholarly.* **Description:** Contains original research papers in international business strategy, including management, finance, marketing, economics, e-business, and related subjects.
Related titles: Online - full text ed.
Published by: Academy of International Business and Economics, 983 Woodland Dr, Turlock, CA 95382-7281. TEL 209-656-7084, Review@aibe.org, AKhade@iabe.org, http://www.AIBE.org, http://www.aibe.org. R&P Dr. Alan S Khade.

➤ **JOURNAL OF INTERNATIONAL CONSUMER MARKETING.** see *BUSINESS AND ECONOMICS—Marketing And Purchasing*

382 USA ISSN 1570-7385
▼ **JOURNAL OF INTERNATIONAL ENTREPRENEURSHIP.** Text in English. 2003. q. EUR 315, USD 315, GBP 197 combined subscription to institutions print & online eds. (effective 2005). adv. reprint service avail. from PSC. **Document type:** *Journal, Academic/Scholarly.* **Description:** Offers an outlet for high-quality research addressing the opportunities and challenges intrinsic to internationalisation.
Related titles: Online - full text ed.: ISSN 1573-7349 (from EBSCO Publishing, Gale Group, IngentaConnect, Kluwer Online, O C L C Online Computer Library Center, Inc., Springer LINK, Swets Information Services).
Indexed: BibLing.
—BLDSC (5007.660200), IE. **CCC.**
Published by: Springer-Verlag New York, Inc. (Subsidiary of: Springer Science+Business Media), 233 Spring St, New York, NY 10013. TEL 212-460-1500, FAX 212-460-1575, service@springer-ny.com, http://springerlink.metapress.com/openurl.asp?genre=journal&issn=1570-7385, http://www.springer-ny.com. Eds. Hamid Etemad, Zoltan J Acs. **Subscr. to:** Journal Fulfillment, PO Box 2485, Secaucus, NJ 07096-2485. TEL 201-348-4033, FAX 201-348-4505, journals@springer-ny.com.

JOURNAL OF INTERNATIONAL MARKETING. see *BUSINESS AND ECONOMICS—Marketing And Purchasing*

JOURNAL OF INTERNATIONAL MARKETING AND EXPORTING. see *BUSINESS AND ECONOMICS—Marketing And Purchasing*

JOURNAL OF LANGUAGE FOR INTERNATIONAL BUSINESS. see *LINGUISTICS*

JOURNAL OF LAW & COMMERCE. see *LAW—Corporate Law*

JOURNAL OF MULTINATIONAL FINANCIAL MANAGEMENT. see *BUSINESS AND ECONOMICS—Management*

382 341.7 USA ISSN 1539-3712
K10
JOURNAL OF TAXATION OF GLOBAL TRANSACTIONS. Text in English. 2001 (Fall). q. USD 225 (effective 2004).
Description: Covers the evolving international tax landscape from the perspective of the U.S. tax laws. Addresses these tax issues with practical analysis of the latest developments written by leading international tax practitioners.
Published by: C C H Inc., 2700 Lake Cook Rd, Riverwoods, IL 60015. TEL 847-267-7000, cust_serv@cch.com, http://www.cch.com. Ed. Lowell D Yoder.

650.071 USA ISSN 0897-5930
HD62.4 CODEN: JTIBE9
➤ **JOURNAL OF TEACHING IN INTERNATIONAL BUSINESS.** Abbreviated title: J T I B. Text in English. 1989. q. USD 350 combined subscription domestic to institutions print & online eds.; USD 472.50 combined subscription in Canada to institutions print & online eds.; USD 507.50 combined subscription elsewhere to institutions print & online eds. (effective 2005 & 2006). adv. bk.rev. 120 p./no. 1 cols./p.; back issues avail.; reprint service avail. from HAW. **Document type:** *Journal, Academic/Scholarly.* **Description:** Aimed at practicing international business educators and curriculum developers. Focuses on successful methods and techniques for better business teaching.
Related titles: Microfiche ed.: (from PQC); Microform ed.; Online - full text ed.: ISSN 1528-6991. free to institutions (effective 2003); free with print subs. (from EBSCO Publishing, O C L C Online Computer Library Center, Inc., Swets Information Services).
Indexed: ABIn, BusEdI, CIJE, CPE, CPM, DIP, ERA, ETA, IBR, IBZ, IPARL, M&MA, MEA, RHEA, SEA, SENA, SOMA, SOPODA, TEA.
—BLDSC (5068.285600), Haworth, IE, Infotrieve, ingenta. **CCC.**
Published by: International Business Press (Subsidiary of: Haworth Press, Inc.), 10 Alice St, Binghamton, NY 13904. TEL 607-722-5857, 800-429-6784, FAX 607-771-0012, 800-895-0582, getinfo@haworthpress.com, http://www.haworthpress.com/web/JTIB. Ed. Erdener Kaynak TEL 717-566-3054. Pub. William Cohen. R&P Ruth Ann Heath TEL 607-722-5857 ext 316. Adv. contact Rebecca Miller-Baum TEL 607-722-5857 ext 337. B&W page USD 315, color page USD 550; trim 4.375 x 7.125. Circ: 242 (paid).

382 USA ISSN 0889-1583
HF1601 CODEN: JJIEBD
➤ **JOURNAL OF THE JAPANESE AND INTERNATIONAL ECONOMIES.** Text in English. 1987. 4/yr. EUR 69 in Europe to individuals; JPY 7,400 in Japan to individuals; USD 53 to individuals except Europe and Japan; EUR 660 in Europe to institutions; JPY 69,000 in Japan to institutions; USD 507 to institutions except Europe and Japan (effective 2006). back issues avail. **Document type:** *Academic/Scholarly.*
Description: Publishes original reports of research devoted to academic analyses of the Japanese economy and its interdependence with other national economies.
Related titles: Online - full text ed.: ISSN 1095-8681. USD 533 (effective 2002) (from EBSCO Publishing, Gale Group, IngentaConnect, O C L C Online Computer Library Center, Inc., ScienceDirect, Swets Information Services).
Indexed: APEL, ASCA, AgeL, BAS, CurCont, IBSS, JEL, RASB, SSCI.
—BLDSC (5008.650000), IDS, IE, Infotrieve, ingenta. **CCC.**
Published by: (Tokyo Center for Economic Research), Academic Press (Subsidiary of: Elsevier Science & Technology), 525 B St, Ste 1900, San Diego, CA 92101-4495. TEL 619-231-6616, 800-894-3434, FAX 619-699-6422, apsubs@acad.com, http://www.elsevier.com/locate/jjie, http://www.academicpress.com. Ed. T. Hoshi.

332.6 USA ISSN 1547-5778
HD62.4 CODEN: JTMDEZ
➤ **JOURNAL OF TRANSNATIONAL MANAGEMENT.** Abbreviated title: J T M D. Text in English. 1994. q. USD 400 combined subscription domestic to institutions print & online eds.; USD 540 combined subscription in Canada to institutions print & online eds.; USD 580 combined subscription elsewhere to institutions print & online eds. (effective academic year 2005 - 2006). adv. 120 p./no. 1 cols./p.; back issues avail.; reprint service avail. from HAW. **Document type:** *Journal, Academic/Scholarly.* **Description:** Offers transnational research across business and related disciplines and across geographies and levels of economic development.
Formerly (until 2004): Journal of Transnational Management Development (1068-6061)
Related titles: Microform ed.: (from PQC); Online - full text ed.: ISSN 1547-5786. free to institutions (effective 2003); free with print subs. (from EBSCO Publishing, O C L C Online Computer Library Center, Inc., Swets Information Services).

Indexed: ABIn, ESPM, GEOBASE, JEL, M&MA, ORMS, PerIslam, RefZh, RiskAb, SOPODA, WorkRelAb.
—BLDSC (5069.866000), Haworth, IE, ingenta. **CCC.**
Published by: (International Management Development Association), International Business Press (Subsidiary of: Haworth Press, Inc.), 10 Alice St, Binghamton, NY 13904. TEL 607-722-5857, 800-429-6784, FAX 607-771-0012, 800-895-0582, getinfo@haworthpress.com, http://www.haworthpress.com/web/JTMD. Eds. Kip Becker, Erdener Kaynak TEL 717-566-3054. Pub. William Cohen. R&P Ruth Ann Heath TEL 607-722-5857 ext 316. Adv. contact Rebecca Miller-Baum TEL 607-722-5857 ext 337. B&W page USD 315, color page USD 550; trim 4.375 x 7.125. Circ: 220 (paid).

650 GBR ISSN 1090-9516
HF5001
➤ **JOURNAL OF WORLD BUSINESS.** Text in English. 1965. 4/yr. EUR 128 in Europe to individuals; JPY 16,800 in Japan to individuals; USD 141 to individuals except Europe and Japan; EUR 312 in Europe to institutions; JPY 41,400 in Japan to institutions; USD 349 to institutions except Europe and Japan (effective 2006). adv. bk.rev. charts; illus. index. back issues avail.; reprint service avail. from PQC,ISI. **Document type:** *Academic/Scholarly.* **Description:** Aims at using sound theory and basic research findings as a point of departure for exciting new breakthrough in the development and practice of international management.
Formerly (until 1997): Columbia Journal of World Business (0022-5428)
Related titles: Microform ed.: (from PQC); Online - full text ed.: (from EBSCO Publishing, Florida Center for Library Automation, Gale Group, H.W. Wilson, IngentaConnect, O C L C Online Computer Library Center, Inc., ScienceDirect, Swets Information Services).
Indexed: AAR, ABIn, ABS&EES, ADPA, ASCA, ASEANManA, ATI, BLI, BPI, BPIA, BusI, CPM, CommAb, CurCont, DPD, ESPM, Emerald, IBSS, IPARL, JEL, KES, M&MA, MEA&I, ManagCont, PAIS, PRA, PsycInfo, PsycholAb, RASB, RRTA, RiskAb, SCIMP, SSCI, T&II, WAE&RSA, WBA, WMB, WorkRelAb.
—BLDSC (5072.640000), IE, Infotrieve, ingenta. **CCC.**
Published by: (Columbia University USA, Trustees of Columbia University), Pergamon (Subsidiary of: Elsevier Science & Technology), The Boulevard, Langford Ln, East Park, Kidlington, Oxford OX5 1GB, United Kingdom. TEL 44-1865-843000, FAX 44-1865-843010, http://www.elsevier.com/locate/jwb. Eds. F. Luthans, J W Slocum Jr. Circ: 3,500. **Subscr. to:** Elsevier BV, PO Box 211, Amsterdam 1000 AE, Netherlands. TEL 31-20-485-3757, FAX 31-20-485-3432, nlinfo-f@elsevier.nl, http://www.elsevier.nl.

➤ **JOURNAL OF WORLD TRADE.** see *LAW—International Law*

➤ **KANSAI UNIVERSITY REVIEW OF BUSINESS AND COMMERCE.** see *BUSINESS AND ECONOMICS—Domestic Commerce*

382 PAK
KARACHI. CHAMBER OF COMMERCE AND INDUSTRY. PATTERN OF FOREIGN TRADE OF PAKISTAN. Text in English. irreg. PKR 250.
Published by: Karachi Chamber of Commerce and Industry, Aiwan-e-Tijarat, Nicol Rd., P O Box 4258, Karachi 2, Pakistan.

382 KEN
KENYA. COMMISSIONER OF CUSTOMS AND EXCISE. ANNUAL TRADE REPORT. Text in English. a. KES 300. **Document type:** *Government.*
Supersedes in part: Annual Trade Report of Tanzania, Uganda and Kenya
Related titles: Magnetic Tape ed.
Published by: Customs and Excise Department, Statistical Branch, PO Box 40160, Nairobi, Kenya. TEL 254-2-715540. Ed. V Da Costa. Circ: 1,000.

382.029 KEN
KENYA EXPORT DIRECTORY. Text in English. 197?. irreg., latest 1985. KES 100. adv. stat. **Document type:** *Directory, Government.* **Description:** Covers general information about Kenya, special articles on the economy and management of the economy, and names of all exporters registered with the Central Bank of Kenya. It also contains useful names and addresses for the prospective investor who may be interested in setting up business in Kenya.
Published by: (Kenya. Ministry of Commerce and Industry, Kenya. Department of External Trade), News Publisher, PO Box 43137, Nairobi, Kenya. Ed. Joe Rodrigues. Circ: 4,000.

382 DEU ISSN 0340-6989
KIELER STUDIEN. Text in English, German. 1949. irreg., latest vol.316, 2002. price varies. **Document type:** *Monographic series, Academic/Scholarly.* **Description:** Studies in international economics.
Indexed: MLA, RASB, WAE&RSA.
—BLDSC (5095.100000), IE, ingenta.
Published by: (Institut fuer Weltwirtschaft, Universitaet Kiel), Mohr Siebeck, Wilhelmstr 18, Tuebingen, 72074, Germany. TEL 49-7071-923-0, FAX 49-7071-51104, info@mohr.de, http://www.uni-kiel.de:8080/ifw/pub/studien/. Ed. Horst Siebert. R&P Jill Sopper. Circ: 700.

382 SWE ISSN 1100-4959
KINA-NYTT. Text in Swedish. 1987. 8/yr.
Published by: Sweden-China Trade Council (SCTC), Fack 5513, Stockholm, 11485, Sweden.

KOMISSIYA ORGANIZATSII OB'EDINENNYKH NATSII PO PRAVU MEZHDUNARODNOI TORGOVLI. EZEGODNIK. see *LAW—International Law*

382 FIN ISSN 0786-7883
KOMPASS FINLAND/HANDBOK OVER FINLANDS INDUSTRI OCH NAERINGSLIV/INFORMATIONSWERK FUER DIE FINNISCHE WIRTSCHAFT/REGISTER OF FINNISH INDUSTRY AND COMMERCE/REPERTOIRE GENERAL DE L'ECONOMIE FINLANDAISE. Variant title: Kompass Suomi. Text in English, Finnish, French, German, Swedish. 1989. a. **Document type:** *Directory.*
Related titles: CD-ROM ed.; Online - full text ed.; Supplement(s): Euro Kompass. Sahko- ja Elektroniikkalaitteet, Tieteelliset ja Teolliset Instrumentit. ISSN 1237-797X. 1997; Euro Kompass. Rakentaminen, Puu- ja Huonekaluteollisuus. ISSN 1237-7937. 1997; Euro Kompass. Paperi- ja Graafinen Teollisuus, Palvelut, Kuljetus. ISSN 1237-7945. 1997; Euro Kompass. Muovi ja Kumi, Kemikaalit. ISSN 1237-7953. 1997; Euro Kompass. Metalli, Koneet, Kuljetusvalineet. ISSN 1237-7961. 1997; Euro Kompass. Elintarvikkeet ja Juomat, Tekstiili, Vaatetus ja Nahkatuotteet. ISSN 1237-7929. 1997.
Published by: Kompass Finland Oy, Bonnier Business Information, Vattuniemenkatu 21 A, Helsinki, 00210, Finland. TEL 358-9-5860260, FAX 358-9-58602626, info@kompass.fi, http://www.kompass.fi.

354.489 382 DNK ISSN 0108-4291
KONTAKTKALENDER; danske repraesentationer i udlandet. Text in Danish. 1973. a. adv. **Document type:** *Directory, Government.*
Published by: Udenrigsministeriet, Sekretariatet for Udenrigshandel/Ministry of Foreign Affairs, Asiatisk Plads 2, Copenhagen K, 1448, Denmark. TEL 45-33-92-08-25, FAX 45-33-92-08-19. Circ: 6,000.

KOREA INSTITUTE OF FINANCE. WEEKLY INTERNATIONAL FINANCIAL REVIEW. see *BUSINESS AND ECONOMICS—Banking And Finance*

382 KOR ISSN 0023-3943
KOREA TRADE. Text in English. 1973. 10/yr. free. adv. illus.; tr.lit.
Related titles: Arabic ed.: 1962; French ed.: 1962; Japanese ed.: 1962; Spanish ed.: 1962.
Indexed: PAIS.
Published by: Korea Trade Investment Promotion Corp., 300-9 Yomgok-dong, Seocho-gu, Seoul, Korea, S. TEL 82-2-3460-7114, FAX 82-2-3460-7777, 82-2-3460-7778, http://www.kotra.or.kr. Ed. Doo-Yun Hwang.

382 KOR
KOREA TRADE & INVESTMENT. Text in English. 1983. bi-m. USD 20; free (effective 2003). **Document type:** *Consumer.*
Formerly: Korea Trade & Business (1012-0742)
Related titles: Online - full text ed.
Published by: Korea Trade Investment Promotion Corp., 300-9 Yomgok-dong, Seocho-gu, Seoul, Korea, S. TEL 82-2-3460-7114, FAX 82-2-3460-7777, 82-2-3460-7778, http://www.kt-i.com, http://www.kotra.or.kr. Ed. Doo-Yun Hwang. Circ: 12,000.

382 341 FRA ISSN 0997-9662
LAMY CONTRATS INTERNATIONAUX. Text in French. 7 base vols. plus updates 2/yr. EUR 1,394.71 (effective 2004). Supplement avail. **Description:** Covers international contracts, construction and industrial contracts, the public sector market, sales, distribution, banking, and litigation.
Published by: Lamy S.A. (Subsidiary of: Wolters Kluwer France), 21/23 rue des Ardennes, Paris, 75935 Cedex 19, France. TEL 33-1-825080800, FAX 33-1-44721388, lamy@lamy.fr, http://www.lamy.fr.

LANDBRUGSEKSPORTEN. see *AGRICULTURE*

382 658 USA ISSN 1097-8526
HC121 CODEN: LABRCB
➤ **LATIN AMERICAN BUSINESS REVIEW;** published in cooperation and partnership with COPPEAD, EGADE, and USD. Abbreviated title: L A B R. Variant title: Business Review. Text in English. 1998. q. USD 235 combined subscription domestic to institutions print & online eds.; USD 317.25 combined subscription in Canada to institutions print & online eds.; USD 340.75 combined subscription elsewhere to institutions print & online eds. (effective 2006). adv. 120 p./no. 1 cols./p.; back issues avail.; reprint service avail. from HAW. **Document type:** *Journal, Academic/Scholarly.* **Description:** Facilitates the exchange of information and new ideas between the academic business practitioner, public policymaker, and those interested in the international development community.
Related titles: Microform ed.: (from PQC); Online - full text ed.: ISSN 1528-6932. free to institutions (effective 2003); free with print subs. (from EBSCO Publishing, O C L C Online Computer Library Center, Inc., Swets Information Services).
Indexed: DIP, ESPM, Emerald, HAPI, IBR, IBSS, IBZ, M&MA, RiskAb.
—Haworth. **CCC.**
Published by: (Monterrey Institute of Technology (ITESM), Graduate School of Business Administration and Leadership (EGADE), University of San Diego, Ahlers Center for International Business, Federal University of Rio de Janeiro, COPPEAD Graduate School of Business BRA, Business Association of Latin American Studies (BALAS)), International Business Press (Subsidiary of: Haworth Press, Inc.), 10 Alice St, Binghamton, NY 13904. TEL 607-722-5857, 800-429-6784, FAX 607-771-0012, 800-895-0582, getinfo@haworthpress.com, http://www.haworthpress.com/web/LABR. Eds. Dr. Angela da Rocha, Dr. Denise Dimon, Dr. Jamie Alonso Gomez, Dr. Ricardo Leal. Pub. William Cohen. R&P Ruth Ann Heath TEL 607-722-5857 ext 316. Adv. contact Rebecca Miller-Baum TEL 607-722-5857 ext 337. B&W page USD 315, color page USD 550; trim 4.375 x 7.125. Circ: 143 (paid).

382 GBR ISSN 0960-8702
HC121 CODEN: LAEBFF
LATIN AMERICAN ECONOMY AND BUSINESS. Text in English. 1989. 16/yr. GBP 550, USD 735 (effective 2001). back issues avail. **Document type:** *Newsletter.* **Description:** Monthly coverage of every economy in the region and the impact of world and local events on them.
Incorporates (in 1990): Latin America Commodities Report (0309-300X); Latin American Economic Report (0309-443X)
Related titles: Online - full text ed.
Indexed: CIN, ChemAb, ChemTitl, RASB.
—CASDDS, IE, Infotrieve.
Published by: Latin American Newsletters (Subsidiary of: Lettres (U.K.) Ltd.), 61 Old St, London, EC1V 9HW, United Kingdom. TEL 44-20-7251-0012, FAX 44-20-7253-8193, subs@latinnews.com, http://www.latinnews.com. Ed. Eduardo Crawley. R&P Alex McHallam TEL 44-20-7251-0012.

B

332.6 USA
LATIN AMERICAN MARKET PLANNING HANDBOOK; population - demography - household buying power - comparative market data. Text in English. a. USD 295. **Document type:** *Trade.*
Published by: Strategy Research Corporation, 100 N W 37th Ave, Miami, FL 33125. TEL 305-649-5400, FAX 305-649-6312.

332.6 020 USA ISSN 1067-0408
HF3230.5.A48
LATIN AMERICAN MARKETS: A GUIDE TO COMPANY AND INDUSTRY INFORMATION SOURCES. Text in English. 1994. irreg., latest vol.2. USD 335 (effective 1999). **Document type:** *Directory.* **Description:** Lists domestic and foreign information sources on each nation, including Mexico and the rest of Central America, South America, and the Caribbean.
Published by: Washington Researchers, Ltd., 1655 Fort Myer Dr., Ste. 800, Arlington, VA 22209-3119. TEL 703-312-2863, FAX 703-527-4586, research@researchers.com, http://www.researchers.com, http://www.washingtonresearchers.com. Ed. M Newman. R&P Ellen O'Kane.

LATIN AMERICAN POWER WATCH. see *ENERGY—Electrical Energy*

327 GBR ISSN 0265-0886
F1401
THE LATIN AMERICAN TIMES. Text in English. 1975. 10/yr. GBP 235 domestic; GBP 365 foreign (effective 2003). back issues avail. **Document type:** *Journal.* **Description:** Covers geostrategic, political, intelligence, financial, economic, and social developments in Central and South America, and the Caribbean.
Indexed: PAIS, RASB.
—**CCC.**
Published by: World Reports Ltd., 108 Horseferry Rd, London, SW1P 2EF, United Kingdom. TEL 44-20-72223836, FAX 44-20-72330185, subs@worldreports.org, http://www.worldreports.org. Ed. Christopher Story. **Subscr. in the US:** 280 Madison Ave, Ste 280, New York, NY 10016-0802. TEL 212-679-0095, FAX 212-679-1094.

382 USA
LATIN AMERICAN TRADE AGREEMENTS. Text in English. 1997. a. looseleaf. USD 185 (effective 2004). **Document type:** *Trade.* **Description:** Provides readers with hard-to-find information on the rules for exporting to or investing within the various major economic integration projects. Also suggests how foreign investors can benefit from the many opportunities provided by the new integration programs.
Published by: Transnational Publishers, Inc., 410 Saw Mill River Rd, Ardsley, NY 10502-2615. TEL 914-693-5100, 800-914-8186, FAX 914-693-4430, transbooks@aol.com, info@transnationalpubs.com, http://www.transnationalpubs.com.

382 USA ISSN 1087-0857
HF3230.5
LATIN TRADE; your business source for Latin America. Text in English. 1993. m. adv. bk.rev.; software rev. charts; illus.; mkt.; maps; stat.; tr.lit. back issues avail.; reprints avail. **Document type:** *Magazine, Trade.* **Description:** Provides buusiness reporting and analysis on Latin American commerce for corporate decision makers and government leaders.
Formerly (until 1996): U S - Latin Trade (1086-198X)

Related titles: Online - full text ed.: (from EBSCO Publishing, Factiva, Florida Center for Library Automation, Gale Group, LexisNexis, Northern Light Technology, Inc., O C L C Online Computer Library Center, Inc., ProQuest Information & Learning); Spanish ed.: Revista Latin Trade.
Indexed: ABIn, B&I, CurCont.
—IE, Infotrieve.
Published by: Freedom Publications, Inc. (Miami), 200 S Biscayne Blvd, Ste 1150, Miami, FL 33131. TEL 305-358-8373, 800-783-4903, FAX 305-358-9166, lattrade@aol.com, http://www.latintrade.com. Ed., Pub., Adv. contact Sabrina R Crow. B&W page USD 6,695, color page USD 8,700; trim 10 x 7. Circ: 74,000.

LATINAMERIKA. see *HISTORY—History Of North And South America*

382 341 USA
LAW REPRINTS: TRADE REGULATION SERIES. Text in English. 1967. irreg. USD 312 (effective 1999). index.
Document type: *Monographic series.* **Description:** Presents all antitrust and trade regulation briefs filed with the U.S. Supreme Court.
Former titles: B N A's Law Reprints: Trade Regulation Series (0275-6978); Law Reprints. Trade Regulation Series (0075-8256)
—CCC.
Published by: Law Reprints, c/o Bartlett Sigerson, Ed, 5442 30th St, N W, Washington, DC 20015. TEL 800-356-0671. Ed. Bartlett Sigerson. Circ: 150.

LAWS OF INTERNATIONAL TRADE. see *LAW—Corporate Law*

327 USA ISSN 0194-3510
LEADERS. Text in English. 1978. q. USD 100 (effective 2005). adv. **Document type:** *Magazine, Consumer.*
Published by: Leaders Magazine, Inc., 59 E 54th St, New York, NY 10022. TEL 212-758-0740, FAX 212-593-5194, info@leadersmag.com, http://www.leadersmag.com. Eds. Darrell J Brown, Henry O Dormann. Circ: 34,810 (controlled).

382 338.91 CHE ISSN 0257-7550
HC59.7
LEAST DEVELOPED COUNTRIES REPORT. Text in English, French; Summaries in Arabic, French, Russian, Spanish. 1984. a. USD 50 (effective 2001). back issues avail.
Document type: *Journal, Trade.* **Description:** Aims to focus the attention of the international community on development challenges facing the poorest countries in the world.
Related titles: Online - full text ed.
Indexed: IIS.
—CISTI.
Published by: United Nations Conference on Trade and Development, 8-14 Avenue de la Paix, Geneva 10, 1211, Switzerland. TEL 41-22-9172033, FAX 41-22-9070046, anna.tibaijuka@unctad.org, http://www.unctad.org. R&P Anna Kajumulo Tibaijuka.

LICENSING LAW HANDBOOK; the new companion to licensing negotiations. see *LAW*

382 338.95694 ISR ISSN 0792-9765
HF3760
LINK; Israel's international business magazine. Text in English. 1991. m. ILS 109; USD 54 in United States; USD 79 elsewhere. adv. bk.rev.; software rev. charts; illus.; stat.; tr.lit. back issues avail. **Document type:** *Consumer.* **Description:** Promotes investment in Israel, and covers technological and political developments affecting Israeli businesses and their activities inside Israel and in the global market.
Related titles: ♦ Supplement(s): Israel Export (Year). ISSN 0793-4939.
—IE.
Published by: Pick Communications Ltd., P O Box 57500, Tel Aviv, 61574, Israel. TEL 972-3-5628511, FAX 972-3-5628512, linkmrkt@link2link.co.il, http://link2link.co.il. Ed., R&P Michael Eilan. Pub. Tamara Genosar. Adv. contact Alan Klein. **Subscr. in US to:** Link Magazine, PO Box 3000, Denville, NJ 07834.

DE LLOYD (DUTCH EDITION); dagblad voor transporteconomie. see *TRANSPORTATION—Ships And Shipping*

LE LLOYD (FRENCH EDITION); l'economie des transports au quotodien. see *TRANSPORTATION—Ships And Shipping*

LLOYD'S LIST PORTS OF THE WORLD (YEAR). see *TRANSPORTATION—Ships And Shipping*

LLOYD'S LOADING LIST. see *TRANSPORTATION—Ships And Shipping*

332.6 GBR
LLOYD'S REGISTER. ANNUAL REVIEW OF THE L R GROUP. Text in English. a. **Document type:** *Corporate.*
Formerly: Lloyd's Register. Annual Report
—BLDSC (1520.265900).
Published by: Lloyd's Register - Fairplay Ltd., Lombard House, 3 Princess Way, Redhill, Surrey RH1 1UP, United Kingdom. TEL 44-1737-379000, FAX 44-1737-379001, info@lrfairplay.com, http://www.lrfairplay.com/.

LUXEMBOURG. SERVICE CENTRAL DE LA STATISTIQUE ET DES ETUDES ECONOMIQUES. INDICATEURS RAPIDES. SERIE H: COMMERCE EXTERIEUR DU LUXEMBOURG. see *BUSINESS AND ECONOMICS—Abstracting, Bibliographies, Statistics*

780.65 GBR
M B I EASTERN EUROPEAN REPORT. (Music Business International) Text in English. a. GBP 595, USD 965.
Document type: *Directory, Trade.* **Description:** Contains the music business information needed to effectively operate in Eastern Europe's eight major markets and smaller sales territories.
Related titles: CD-ROM ed.
Published by: (Market Tracking International Ltd.), C M P Information Ltd. (Subsidiary of: United Business Media), 8 Montague Close, 4th Fl, London, SE1 9UR, United Kingdom. TEL 44-20-7620-3636, FAX 44-20-7921-5984, mbi@dotmusic.com, http://www.marketfile.co.uk. **Subscr. in US to:** C M P Information, Inc., PO Box 0532, Baldwin, NY 11510. TEL 212-378-0406, FAX 212-378-2160.

780.65 GBR
M B I LATIN AMERICAN REPORT. (Music Business International) Text in English. a. GBP 595, USD 965 (effective 1997).
Document type: *Directory, Trade.* **Description:** Contains music business information on eleven separate music markets and territories in Latin America.
Related titles: CD-ROM ed.
Published by: (Market Tracking International Ltd.), C M P Information Ltd. (Subsidiary of: United Business Media), 8 Montague Close, 4th Fl, London, SE1 9UR, United Kingdom. TEL 44-20-7620-3636, FAX 44-20-7921-5984, mbi@dotmusic.com, http://www.marketfile.co.uk. **Subscr. in US to:** C M P Information, Inc., PO Box 0532, Baldwin, NY 11510. TEL 212-378-0406, FAX 212-378-2160.

781.64 GBR ISSN 1369-9520
M B I WORLD DIRECTORY. (Music Business International) Text in English. 1997. a. **Document type:** *Directory, Trade.*
Published by: C M P Information Ltd. (Subsidiary of: United Business Media), 8 Montague Close, 4th Fl, London, SE1 9UR, United Kingdom. TEL 44-20-7620-3636, FAX 44-20-7921-5984, enquiries@cmpinformation.com, http://www.cmpinformation.com. **Subscr. in US to:** C M P Information, Inc., PO Box 0532, Baldwin, NY 11510. TEL 212-378-0406, FAX 212-378-2160.

780.65 GBR ISSN 1361-746X
M B I WORLD REPORT. (Music Business International) Text in English. 1993. a. GBP 495, USD 795 (effective 1997).
Document type: *Directory, Trade.* **Description:** Provides up-to-date, comprehensive and practical information on the world music market.
Related titles: CD-ROM ed.
Published by: (Market Tracking International Ltd.), C M P Information Ltd. (Subsidiary of: United Business Media), 8 Montague Close, 4th Fl, London, SE1 9UR, United Kingdom. FAX 44-20-7921-5984, enquiries@cmpinformation.com, http://www.cmpinformation.com. **Subscr. in US to:** C M P Information, Inc., PO Box 0532, Baldwin, NY 11510. TEL 212-378-0406, FAX 212-378-2160.

332.6 GBR ISSN 1358-6874
HC415.15.A1
M E E D MONEY; the Middle East money weekly. (Middle East Economic Digest) Key Title: Meedmoney. Text in English. 1995. w. adv. bk.rev. **Document type:** *Trade.* **Description:** Covers the markets of the Middle East countries.
Indexed: RASB.
Published by: M E E D - Emap Communications (Subsidiary of: Emap Business Communications Ltd.), 33-39 Bowling Green Lane, London, EC1R 0DA, United Kingdom. TEL 44-20-7470-6200, FAX 44-20-7837-8271, customerservice@meed.com, http://www.emap.com, http://www.meed.com. Ed. Edmund O'Sullivan TEL 44-207-470-6200.

382 FRA ISSN 0026-9719
HF15
M O C I. (Moniteur du Commerce International) Text in French. 1883. w. EUR 305 (effective 2005). bk.rev. bibl.; illus.; stat. index. **Document type:** *Newspaper.* **Description:** Provides a selection of technical and strategic informations to develop sales abroad.
Former titles (until 1966): Moniteur Officiel du Commerce International (0991-7977); (until 1961): Moniteur Officiel du Commerce et de l'Industrie (0991-7993)
Related titles: Online - full text ed.; ♦ Supplement(s): M O C I. Hors Serie. ISSN 1253-0808; ♦ Actualites Reglementaires. ISSN 0240-8236; ♦ Savoir International. ISSN 1158-6826.
Indexed: ELLIS, PAIS, PROMT, RASB, TriticAb, WAE&RSA.
—BLDSC (5879.965000), IE, Infotrieve, ingenta.
Published by: Societe d'Edition de Documentation Economique et Commerciale (SEDEC), 24 bd. de l'Hopital, Paris, 75005, France. TEL 33-1-40733925, FAX 33-1-43364798, TELEX 206 811 F, http://www.lemoci.com/. Ed. Jean Marchand. Pub. Paul Rechter. R&P, Adv. contact Anton Keil. Circ: 15,000.

382 FRA ISSN 1253-0808
M O C I. HORS SERIE. (Moniteur du Commerce International) Text in French. 1996. q.
Related titles: ♦ Supplement to: M O C I. ISSN 0026-9719.
Published by: Societe d'Edition de Documentation Economique et Commerciale (SEDEC), 24 bd. de l'Hopital, Paris, 75005, France. TEL 33-1-40733925, FAX 33-1-43364798. Ed. Jean Marchand.

MACAO. DIRECCAO DOS SERVICOS DE ESTATISTICA E CENSOS. ESTATISTICAS DO COMERCIO EXTERNO/MACAO. CENSUS AND STATISTICS DEPARTMENT. STATISTICS ON EXTERNAL TRADE. see *BUSINESS AND ECONOMICS—Abstracting, Bibliographies, Statistics*

MACAO. DIRECCAO DOS SERVICOS DE ESTATISTICA E CENSOS. ESTATISTICAS DO COMERCIO EXTERNO/MACAO. CENSUS AND STATISTICS DEPARTMENT. EXTERNAL TRADE INDICATORS. see *BUSINESS AND ECONOMICS—Abstracting, Bibliographies, Statistics*

382 MAC
MACAU IMAGE; the trade and investment magazine of the Government of Macau. Text in English. 1982. s-a. free. adv.
Document type: *Government.* **Description:** Includes a directory of the main producers and exporters by product.
Published by: Macau Trade and Investment Promotion Institute, World Trade Centre 4 & 5 Andares, Amizade Av 918, Macau, Macau. TEL 853-710300, FAX 853-590309, ipim@ipim.gov.mo, http://www.ipim.gov.mo. adv.: page MOP 7,500. Circ: 35,000.

382 TUR
MACHINERY EXPORTS - TURKEY. Text in English. q.
Published by: Ihlas Magazine Group, Ihlas Holding Mrk. Binasi, 29 Ekim Cad. 23, Yenibosna - Istanbul, 34530, Turkey. TEL 90-212-4542530, FAX 90-212-4542555, bsensoz@img.com.tr, http://www.img.com.tr.

382 CHE
MADE FOR EXPORT & ELECTRONIC COMMERCE. Text in English. 1954. bi-m. adv. bk.rev. illus.; mkt. **Document type:** *Catalog, Trade.* **Description:** International purchasing system for importers, distributors, agents and traders all over the world.
Former titles: Made for Export. General Merchandise (0946-5197); (until 1998): Made in Europe. General Merchandise (0172-2182); Made in Europe (0024-9378)
Related titles: CD-ROM ed.; Online - full text ed.
Published by: Made in Europe Systems AG, Bruggacherstr 24, Faellanden, 8117, Switzerland. TEL 41-1-8062828, FAX 41-1-8062829, mie@novacom.ch, http://www.miesys.com. Ed., Pub., R&P Martin Romer. Adv. contact Franziska Bastanier. Circ: 18,000.

382 DEU
MADE FOR EXPORT CONSUMER GOODS. Text in English. 1954. bi-m. USD 60 (effective 2001). **Document type:** *Catalog, Trade.*
Published by: Made in Europe Marketing Organisation GmbH, Unterhainstr 50, Aschaffenburg, 63743, Germany. TEL 49-6021-391850, FAX 49-6021-3918525, mie@miesys.com, http://www.miesys.com.

382 BRA
MADE IN BRAZIL; Brazilian export market. Text in Portuguese. 1977 (no.6). a. adv. charts; illus.; stat.
Published by: Assessoria de Promocao e Cultura Editora Ltda., Av Brigadeiro Luis Antonio, 402, B Vista, PO Box 5390, Sao Paulo, SP 01318-000, Brazil. Ed. Jose L Ribeiro Leite.
Co-sponsors: Ministerio da Industria; Banco do Brasil S.A.

382 DEU
MADE IN EUROPE. INDUSTRIAL SUPPLY BUYER'S GUIDE. Text in English. 1966. q. USD 60 (effective 2001). adv. bk.rev.
Document type: *Catalog, Trade.* **Description:** Contains international purchasing information for importers, distributors, agents, and traders in 180 countries.
Former titles: Made in Europe. Technical and Industrial Supply Guide (0946-5170); Made in Europe. Technical Equipment and Industrial Supplies (0179-4663); (until 1984): Made in Europe. Technical Equipment Catalog (0047-5424)
Published by: Made in Europe Marketing Organisation GmbH, Unterhainstr 50, Aschaffenburg, 63743, Germany. TEL 49-6021-391850, FAX 49-6021-3918525, mie@miesys.com, http://www.miesys.com. Ed., Pub., R&P Martin Romer. Adv. contact Franziska Bastanier. Circ: 18,000.

382 DEU ISSN 0179-6291
MADE IN GERMANY; technology, products and services. Text in English. 1982. bi-m. EUR 51; EUR 10 newsstand/cover (effective 2003). adv. bk.rev. charts; illus.; tr.lit. back issues avail. **Document type:** *Magazine, Trade.* **Description:** Informs decision makers in business and industry of products and services made in Germany that are on the international market.
Published by: Made in Germany Publication GmbH, Siemensstr 18, Dreieich, 63303, Germany. TEL 49-6103-936597, FAX 49-6103-34175, info@made-in-germany-web.de, http://www.made-in-germany-web.de. Ed. Willoughby Ann Walshe. Pub., Adv. contact Armin Loescher. B&W page EUR 5,215, color page EUR 9,387; trim 180 x 246. Circ: 110,000 (controlled).

382 TUR
MADE IN TURKEY. Text in Russian. m.
Published by: Ihlas Magazine Group, Ihlas Holding Mrk. Binasi, 29 Ekim Cad. 23, Yenibosna - Istanbul, 34530, Turkey. TEL 90-212-4542530, FAX 90-212-4542555, bsensoz@img.com.tr, http://www.img.com.tr.

382.6 GTM
MAGAZINE BUSINESS GUATEMALA. Text in English. 1975. m. USD 48; USD 4 newsstand/cover (effective 2000). adv.
Related titles: Online - full text ed.
Published by: American Chamber of Commerce of Guatemala, Ave de la Americas 18-81 Z, 14 Edif Columbus Center, Nivel 8, Ciudad de Guatemala, Guatemala. TEL 502-363-1774, FAX 502-367-3414, amchamdirector@workmail.com, http://www.guatemalanamcham.com. Ed. Scott Robbertson. adv.: page USD 600. Circ: 2,000.

382 FRA ISSN 0153-4157
MAGHREB SELECTION. Text in French. 1975. w. (45/yr).
Published by: I C Publications, 10 rue Vineuse, Paris, 75784 Cedex 16, France. FAX 33-1-44308111, 33-1-44308100.

MAJOR COMPANIES OF CENTRAL & EASTERN EUROPE AND THE COMMONWEALTH OF INDEPENDENT STATES. see *BUSINESS AND ECONOMICS—Trade And Industrial Directories*

MALAWI. NATIONAL STATISTICAL OFFICE. BALANCE OF PAYMENTS. see *BUSINESS AND ECONOMICS—Abstracting, Bibliographies, Statistics*

382 MWI
MALAWI PRODUCTS HANDBOOK (YEAR). Text in English. 1976. biennial. USD 20. adv. bk.rev. **Description:** Serves as a reference for companies and individuals interested in doing business with Malawi.
Formerly: Malawi Buyers' Guide; Which supersedes (in 1982): Malawi Export
Published by: Malawi Export Promotion Council, Delamere House Fourth Floor, PO Box 1299, Blantyre, Malawi. TEL 265-620499, FAX 265-635429. Ed. Chatonda Mhone. Circ: 3,000.

MALAYSIA. DEPARTMENT OF STATISTICS. EXTERNAL TRADE STATISTICS, SABAH/MALAYSIA. JABATAN PERANGKAAN. PERANGKAAN PERDANGANGAN LUAR NEGERI. SABAH. see *BUSINESS AND ECONOMICS—Abstracting, Bibliographies, Statistics*

MALAYSIA. DEPARTMENT OF STATISTICS. EXTERNAL TRADE SUMMARY MALAYSIA. see *BUSINESS AND ECONOMICS—Abstracting, Bibliographies, Statistics*

MALAYSIA. DEPARTMENT OF STATISTICS. MONTHLY EXTERNAL TRADE STATISTICS, MALAYSIA/MALAYSIA. JABATAN PERANGKANN. PERANGKAAN PERDAGANGAN LUAR NEGERI BULANAN, MALAYSIA. see *BUSINESS AND ECONOMICS—Abstracting, Bibliographies, Statistics*

MALAYSIA. DEPARTMENT OF STATISTICS. STATISTICS OF EXTERNAL TRADE. SARAWAK/MALAYSIA. JABATAN PERANGKAAN. PERANGKAAN PERDAGANGAN LUAR NEGERI. SARAWAK. see *BUSINESS AND ECONOMICS—Abstracting, Bibliographies, Statistics*

382 MLT ISSN 0580-5260
HF234.5.M3
MALTA. CENTRAL OFFICE OF STATISTICS. TRADE STATISTICS. Text in English. 1966. s-a. MTL 8 per issue. **Document type:** *Government.*
Former titles: Malta Trade Statistics; Trade of the Maltese Islands (0041-0462)
Published by: Central Office of Statistics, Merchants' St., Valletta, Malta. FAX 356-248483, cos@magent.mt. **Subscr. to:** Publications Bookshop, Castille Place, Valletta, Malta.

382 FRA ISSN 0984-9521
MARCHES AFRICAINS. Text in French. w. (45/yr).
Formerly (until 1988): Afrique Informations (0753-0145)
Indexed: RASB.
Published by: I C Publications, 10 rue Vineuse, Paris, 75784 Cedex 16, France. FAX 33-1-44308111, 33-1-44308100.

382 FRA ISSN 1147-7717
MARCHES ARABES. Text in French. s-m. (22/yr.).
Formerly (until 1988): Marches Arabes, Moyen-Orient Selection (0986-6868); Which was formed by the 1987 merger of: Marches Arabes (0756-0486); Moyen-Orient Selection (0182-0176)
Published by: I C Publications, 10 rue Vineuse, Paris, 75784 Cedex 16, France. FAX 33-1-44308111, 33-1-44308100.

382 FRA ISSN 0989-8131
MARCHES LATINO-AMERICAINS. Text in French. 1977. s-m. (22/yr.). **Description:** Presents financial, industrial and commercial information and analyzes current events.
Formerly (until 1988): Amerique Latine (0151-9530)
Indexed: RASB.
Published by: I C Publications, 10 rue Vineuse, Paris, 75784 Cedex 16, France. FAX 33-1-44308111, 33-1-44308100.

382 FRA ISSN 0025-2859
HC10
MARCHES TROPICAUX ET MEDITERRANEENS. Text in French. 1945. w. adv. bk.rev. charts; illus.; stat. index. **Description:** African trade review.
Former titles (until 1958): Marches Tropicaux du Monde (0995-869X); (until 1956): Marches Coloniaux du Monde (0995-8681); (until 1947): Marches Coloniaux (0995-8673)
Related titles: Online - full text ed.: (from EBSCO Publishing).
Indexed: AEA, ASD, B&I, BAS, CTFA, ELLIS, HRIR, I&DA, ILD, KES, PAIS, PoultAb, RASB, RDA, S&F.
—CISTI, IE, Infotrieve.
Published by: Moreux S.A., 190 bd. Haussmann, Paris, 75008, France. TEL 33-1-44959992, FAX 33-1-49539016, TELEX NAVIM 651131F, moreux@club-internet.fr. Ed. Serge Marpaud. Circ: 18,000.

382 IND
MARINE PRODUCTS EXPORT DEVELOPMENT AUTHORITY. ANNUAL REPORT AND ACCOUNTS. Text in English, Hindi. a.
Published by: Marine Products Export Development Authority, MPEDA House, Panampilly Avenue Rd., Cochin, Kerala 682 036, India. http://www.mpeda.com.

MARITIME RESEARCH CHARTER NEWSLETTER. see *TRANSPORTATION—Ships And Shipping*

382 USA ISSN 1083-5512
HC800.A1
MARKET: AFRICA - MID-EAST. Text in English. 1995. 8/yr. USD 397 (effective 2001). charts; mkt.; stat. index. back issues avail. **Document type:** *Newsletter, Trade.* **Description:** Covers demographic and marketing trends in Africa and the Middle East.
Related titles: Online - full text ed.: (from CompuServe Inc., Data-Star, EBSCO Publishing, Florida Center for Library Automation, Gale Group, O C L C Online Computer Library Center, Inc., The Dialog Corporation).
Indexed: CWI.
Published by: The P R S Group, Inc., PO Box 248, East Syracuse, NY 13057-0248. TEL 315-431-0511, FAX 315-431-0200, custserv@prsgroup.com, http://www.prsgroup.com. R&P Patti Davis.

382 USA ISSN 1059-275X
MARKET: ASIA PACIFIC. Text in English. 1992. m. USD 397 (effective 2001). **Document type:** *Newsletter.* **Description:** Covers a wide variety of topics, including the demographics and life-styles of the Asia-Pacific consumers.
Related titles: Online - full text ed.: (from Data-Star, EBSCO Publishing, Factiva, Florida Center for Library Automation, Gale Group, O C L C Online Computer Library Center, Inc., The Dialog Corporation).
Indexed: CWI.
Published by: The P R S Group, Inc., PO Box 248, East Syracuse, NY 13057-0248. TEL 315-431-0511, FAX 315-431-0200, custserv@prsgroup.com, http://www.prsgroup.com. Ed., Pub. Doris Walsh. R&P Patti Davis.

382 USA ISSN 1050-9410
MARKET: EUROPE. Text in English. 1990. m. bk.rev. index. back issues avail. **Document type:** *Newsletter, Consumer.* **Description:** Covers a wide variety of subjects, including the demographics and life-styles of European consumers.
Related titles: Online - full text ed.: (from CompuServe Inc., Data-Star, EBSCO Publishing, Factiva, Florida Center for Library Automation, Gale Group, O C L C Online Computer Library Center, Inc., The Dialog Corporation).
Indexed: CWI.
Published by: The P R S Group, Inc., PO Box 248, East Syracuse, NY 13057-0248. TEL 315-431-0511, FAX 315-431-0200, custserv@prsgroup.com, http://www.prsgroup.com. Ed., Pub. Doris Walsh.

332.6 GBR ISSN 0959-2482
MARKET SOUTH EAST. Text in English. m.
Address: The Lodge, 37 Fairhazel Gardens, London, NW6 3QN, United Kingdom. TEL 071-624-8675, FAX 081-341-2750. Ed. Michael Griffin.

382 AUS
MARKET WATCH. Text in English. fortn. **Document type:** *Bulletin, Trade.* **Description:** Covers international payment risks that may impact export business.
Media: E-mail.
Published by: Export Finance and Insurance Corporation, 22 Pitts St, Sydney, NSW 2000, Australia. TEL 800-685-109, FAX 61-2-9201-5222, info@efic.gov.au, http://www.efic.gov.au.

382 NLD
MARKTGILDE GIDS; vakblad voor de ambulante handel. Text in Dutch. 1807. 5/yr. adv. **Document type:** *Trade.*
Formerly: Attent
Published by: R. Barbieri Pub., Postbus 427, Rijswijk (ZH), 2280 AK, Netherlands. TEL 31-70-393-7004, FAX 31-70-396-1576.

MAURITIUS. CENTRAL STATISTICAL OFFICE. DIGEST OF EXTERNAL TRADE STATISTICS. see *BUSINESS AND ECONOMICS—Abstracting, Bibliographies, Statistics*

382 336 CAN ISSN 1183-3246
MCGOLDRICK'S CANADIAN CUSTOMS GUIDE "HARMONIZED SYSTEM". Text in English. 1921. a. looseleaf. USD 225 (effective 2002). adv. bk.rev. **Document type:** *Trade.* **Description:** Covers rates of duty and general customs information.
Former titles: McGoldrick's Canadian Customs Tariff "Harmonized System"; McGoldrick's Handbook of Canadian Customs Tariff and Excise Duties (0076-1990)
—CCC.
Published by: McMullin Publishers Ltd., 417 St Pierre, Montreal, PQ H2Y 2M4, Canada. TEL 514-849-1424, FAX 514-849-9809, orders@mcmullinpublishers.com, http://www.mcmullinpublishers.com. Ed., Pub., Adv. contact Louise Ledoux. 1/4 page CND 190, 1/2 page CND 290, page CND 450. Circ: 10,000.

MEALEY'S INTERNATIONAL ARBITRATION QUARTERLY LAW REVIEW. see *LAW—Judicial Systems*

MEALEY'S INTERNATIONAL ARBITRATION REPORT. see *LAW—International Law*

382 DEU ISSN 0934-4217
MEDIA SELECTION; Nachrichten und Meinungen der internationalen Presse. Text in German. 1988. 26/yr. **Document type:** *Newsletter, Abstract/Index.* **Description:** Contains news and opinions of the International Press for executives.
Published by: Dr. Horst Kerlikowsky Verlag, Antonienstr 3, Munich, 80802, Germany. TEL 49-89-344012, FAX 49-89-390662, MediaSelection@t-online.de, Dr. Horst Kerlikowsky@t-online.de, http://www.etage-media-selection.de/Seiten/indexSelection.html. Ed., R&P Horst Kerlikowsky. Circ: 1,000.

382 DEU ISSN 0076-6208
MEIER-DUDY/MEIER'S DIRECTORY OF EXPORTERS AND IMPORTERS; Meier's Addressbuch der Exporteure und Importeure. Text in English, French, Italian, Spanish. 1903. a. adv. bk.rev.
Published by: Verlag von Meier's Adressbuch der Exporteure Rudolf Dudy KG, Neue Kirchgasse 10-12, Graevenwiesbach, 61279, Germany. FAX 069-731330, TELEX 411249-ATLAS-D. Ed. Christa Reichel. Circ: 5,000. **Dist. by:** Intl. Publications Service, 114 E. 32nd St., New York, NY 10016.

382 ESP ISSN 0539-3728
MERCADO MUNDIAL/WORLD MARKET. Text in English, Spanish. 1962. m. USD 45. back issues avail. **Document type:** *Newspaper.*
Published by: Editorial Ofice, German Perez Carrasco, 63, Madrid, 28027, Spain. TEL 1-267-24-03, FAX 1-408-78-37. Ed. Pilar Pardo. Circ: 30,000.

332.6 CAN
MERCHANDISE IMPORTS AMERICA DIRECTORY. Text in English. 1994. a. USD 110. bk.rev. charts; illus.; stat. **Document type:** *Directory.*
Published by: Global Traders Association, P O BOX 797, Sta A, Scarborough, ON M1K 5C8, Canada. TEL 416-650-9309, FAX 416-650-9280. Ed. K Bhattacharyya.

MEXICAN PRODUCT GUIDE. see *BUSINESS AND ECONOMICS—Trade And Industrial Directories*

382 GBR ISSN 1054-2663
HF3066
MEXICO BUSINESS MONTHLY✶. Text in English. 1991. m. USD 124 to academic institutions; USD 247 to institutions (effective 2000). adv. back issues avail. **Document type:** *Newsletter.* **Description:** Covers business, economic, and political news.
Formerly: Caribbean Update & Mexico Business Monthly
Related titles: Online - full text ed.: (from Factiva, Gale Group, Northern Light Technology, Inc., O C L C Online Computer Library Center, Inc., ProQuest Information & Learning).
Indexed: ABIn, B&I.
—CCC.
Published by: Business Monitor International Ltd., Mermaid House, 2 Puddle Dock, Blackfriars, London, EC4V 3DS, United Kingdom. TEL 44-20-72480468, FAX 44-20-72480467, mexcarib@compuserve.com, http://www.businessmonitor.com.

382 USA ISSN 0731-6305
MIDDLE EAST BUSINESS INTELLIGENCE. Text in English. 1982. bi-w. USD 355 (effective 2002). back issues avail.; reprints avail. **Document type:** *Newsletter.* **Description:** For business executives looking for sales and contracting opportunities in the Middle East or North Africa. Provides more than 1700 new business leads each year, with a brief description of the business opportunity, the person to contact, address, phone and fax number.
Related titles: Online - full text ed.: (from EBSCO Publishing).
—CCC.
Published by: International Executive Reports, Ltd., 717 D St, N W, Ste 300, Washington, DC 20004-2807. TEL 202-628-6900, FAX 202-628-6618, TELEX 440462 MEER UI, http://www.his.com/~ili/pubmebi.html. Ed. Mimi Mann. Pub. William Hearn. Circ: 400.

382 USA
MIDDLE EAST BUSINESS STRATEGIES. Text in English. s-m. USD 1,495 (effective 2005). adv. **Document type:** *Newsletter, Trade.* **Description:** Provides you with the in-depth coverage of the regulatory climate, business activity, and investment opportunities you need to successfully do business in this dynamic region.
Related titles: Online - full content ed.
Published by: WorldTrade Executive, Inc., 2250 Main St, Ste 100, PO Box 761, Concord, MA 01742. TEL 978-287-0301, FAX 978-287-0302, smahapatra@wtexec.com, info@wtexec.com, http://www.wtexecutive.com/cms/content.jsp?id=com.tms.cms.section.Section_1022_sub_options, http://www.wtexec.com. Pub. Gary A Brown. Adv. contact Jay Stanley.

330.9 USA ISSN 0271-0498
K13
MIDDLE EAST EXECUTIVE REPORTS. Text in English. 1978. m. USD 455 (effective 2004). **Document type:** *Magazine, Trade.* **Description:** Provides legal and practical information on the requirements for doing business in the Middle East and North Africa. Contains in-depth analysis of trade, contracting, marketing and investment.
Related titles: Online - full text ed.: (from Thomson West).
Indexed: ABIn, CLI, FLP, LRI, PAIS, RASB.
—BLDSC (5761.373950), IE, Infotrieve, ingenta. **CCC.**
Published by: International Executive Reports, Ltd., 717 D St, N W, Ste 300, Washington, DC 20004-2807. TEL 202-628-6900, FAX 202-628-6618, pub@ili.org, http://www.his.com/~ili/pubmeer.html, http://www.his.com/~ili/index.htm.

MIDDLE EAST FORUM. see *POLITICAL SCIENCE—International Relations*

MIDDLE EAST POLICY. see *POLITICAL SCIENCE—International Relations*

382 GBR ISSN 0026-3192
MIDDLE EAST TRADE/TIJJARAT ASH-SHARQ AL-'AWSSAT. Text in Arabic; Summaries in English. 1961. 10/yr. adv. illus.; tr.lit. **Document type:** *Trade.*
Published by: Middle East Trade Publications Ltd., 21 Newman St, London, W1P 3HB, United Kingdom. TEL 44-171-636-2911, FAX 44-171-637-5733. Ed. Armea I Bekheit. Circ: 15,320 (controlled).

MILANO FINANZA. see *BUSINESS AND ECONOMICS—Investments*

THE MILLENNIUM PROJECTS REVIEW. see *BUSINESS AND ECONOMICS—Economic Situation And Conditions*

382 USA
MINNESOTA JOURNAL OF GLOBAL TRADE. Text in English. 1991. s-a. USD 23 domestic; USD 26 outside contiguous US (effective 2005). back issues avail. **Document type:** *Journal, Academic/Scholarly.* **Description:** Developed as a joint effort between these students and various members of the law faculty who were keenly interested in the analysis of the legal issues involved in international trade. It is a scholarly publication that has been dedicated to the study of economic policy and international trade law from its inception.
Indexed: CLI, ILP.
—ingenta.
Published by: University of Minnesota, Law School, 220 Law Center, 229 Nineteenthe Ave S, Minneapolis, MN 55455. TEL 612-625-1000, FAX 612-625-2011, http://www.law.umn.edu/GlobalTrade/.

382 JPN
MONITOR. Text in English. 1987. m. free to qualified personnel. **Document type:** *Newsletter.* **Description:** Newsletter of Mitsubishi companies for overseas employees.
Published by: Mitsubishi Public Affairs Committee, Mitsubishi Shoji Bldg Annex (DK-M), 2-3-1 Marunochi, Chiyoda-ku, Tokyo, 100-0005, Japan. TEL 03-3210-2524, FAX 03-3210-2527. Ed. Hisashi Akazome. Circ: 10,000.

MONTHLY EXPORT TRENDS; monitor of Pakistan's export trade. see *BUSINESS AND ECONOMICS—Chamber Of Commerce Publications*

382 USA
MONTHLY IMPORT DETENTION LIST. Text in English. m. USD 350 in North America; USD 700 elsewhere. reprint service avail. from CIS. **Document type:** *Government.* **Description:** Detentions are arranged by: product code, sample number, the product, district and port of entry, manufacturer's and shipper's names, city and country of origin, the primary and secondary reasons for detention, unit type and quantity, and value.
Related titles: Microfiche ed.: (from CIS).
Indexed: AmStI.
Published by: U.S. Department of Health and Human Services, Food and Drug Administration, 5600 Fishers Ln, Rockville, MD 20857. TEL 301-443-3220. **Subscr. to:** National Technical Information Service, Government Research Center, 5285 Port Royal Rd, Springfield, VA 22161. TEL 703-605-6060, 800-363-2068, http://www.ntis.gov.

332.6 LUX ISSN 1561-6177
HC241.2
MONTHLY PANORAMA OF EUROPEAN BUSINESS. Text in English. irreg., latest 1997. USD 195. **Document type:** *Monographic series.*
Former titles (until 1999): Monthly Panorama of European Industry (1027-7315); (until 1997): Panorama of E U Industry. Short-Term Supplement (1021-349X); (until 1994): Panorama of E C Industry. Short-Term Supplement (1017-592X)
Indexed: IIS.
—BLDSC (6357.409800).
Published by: European Commission, Office for Official Publications of the European Union, 2 Rue Mercier, Luxembourg, L-2985, Luxembourg. TEL 352-49-92-81, FAX 352-48-85-73. **Dist. in the U.S. by:** Bernan Associates, Bernan, 4611-F Assembly Dr., Lanham, MD 20706-4391. TEL 301-459-0056, 800-274-4447.

382 USA
MONTHLY SUMMARY OF EXPORT CREDIT GUARANTEE PROGRAM ACTIVITY. Text in English. m. stat. back issues avail. **Document type:** *Government.*
Related titles: Online - full content ed.
Published by: U.S. Department of Agriculture, Foreign Agricultural Service, Deputy Administrator, Export Credits, 1400 Independence Avenue, SW, Washington, DC 20250-1031. TEL 202-720-6301, FAX 202-690-0727, askec@fas.usda.gov, info@fas.usda.gov, http://www.fas.usda.gov/excredits/Monthly/ecg.html.

MONTSERRAT. STATISTICS OFFICE. DIGEST OF STATISTICS. see *BUSINESS AND ECONOMICS—Abstracting, Bibliographies, Statistics*

382 332.96 RUS ISSN 1566-7472
DK510.76
THE MOSCOW TIMES BUSINESS REVIEW. Text in Russian. 1994. fortn. adv. **Document type:** *Magazine, Consumer.* **Description:** Targeted at people doing business or seeking to do business in Russia.
Former titles (until 1999): The Russia Businessreview (1566-1539); Russia Review (1385-1063); (until 1995): Moscow Times - International Weekly Edition (1381-0642)
Related titles: ♦ Supplement to: The Moscow Times.
Indexed: PAIS.
Published by: Independent Media (Moscow), ul Vyborgskaya dom 16, str 1, Moscow, 125212, Russian Federation. TEL 7-095-2323200, FAX 7-095-2329265, podpiska@imedia.ru, http://www.independent-media.ru. Ed. Ashleigh Morris. Pub. Charles Black. Adv. contact Yury Primich. Circ: 3,000 (paid).

MOTORCYCLES, PARTS & ACCESSORIES BUYERS' GUIDE. see *BUSINESS AND ECONOMICS—Trade And Industrial Directories*

382 ITA ISSN 1128-2835
MOVIMENTO VALUTARIO. Text in Italian. 1958. q.
Indexed: PAIS.
Published by: Istituto Nazionale per il Commercio Estero, Via Liszt 21, Rome, RM 00144, Italy. TEL 39-06-59921, ice@ice.it, http://www.ice.it.

MOZAMBIQUE. INSTITUTO NACIONAL DE ESTATISTICA. ESTATISTICAS DO COMERCIO EXTERNO. see *BUSINESS AND ECONOMICS—Abstracting, Bibliographies, Statistics*

332.6 USA ISSN 1525-383X
HD2755.5
➤ **MULTINATIONAL BUSINESS REVIEW.** Short title: M B R. Text in English. 1993. s-a. USD 30 in North America to individuals; USD 40 elsewhere to individuals; USD 60 in North America to institutions; USD 70 elsewhere to institutions; USD 15 in North America to students; USD 25 elsewhere to students. **Document type:** *Academic/Scholarly.* **Description:** Publishes application-oriented articles dealing with international aspects of accounting, management and information systems, finance, management, and marketing.
Related titles: CD-ROM ed.: (from ProQuest Information & Learning); Microform ed.: (from PQC); Online - full text ed.: (from EBSCO Publishing, H.W. Wilson, O C L C Online Computer Library Center, Inc., ProQuest Information & Learning).
Indexed: ABIn, BPI, Emerald, PAIS, SOPODA.
—BLDSC (5983.150500), ingenta.
Published by: University of Detroit Mercy, College of Business Administration, PO Box 19900, Detroit, MI 48219-0900. TEL 313-993-1264, FAX 313-993-1673, kimsuk@udmercy.edu, http://www.mich.lom/~kimsuk/. Ed. Suk H Kim. Circ: 375 (paid).

338.8 GBR ISSN 1469-3798
MULTINATIONAL CHEMICALS AND PETROCHEMICALS COMPANIES. Text in English. 1999. a. GBP 345, USD 500 (effective 2001). **Description:** Research and marketing directory of worldwide professionals in the field of chemicals and petrochemicals.
Published by: Business Monitor International Ltd., Commercial Intelligence Service, 179 Queen Victoria St, London, EC4V 4DU, United Kingdom. TEL 44-20-7248-0468, FAX 44-20-7248-0467, http://www.businessmonitor.com.

338.8 GBR ISSN 1469-3801
MULTINATIONAL CONSTRUCTION AND ENGINEERING COMPANIES. Text in English. 1999. a. GBP 345, USD 550 (effective 2001). **Description:** Research and marketing directory of worldwide professionals in the fields of construction and engineering.
Related titles: CD-ROM ed.: GBP 580, USD 930 (effective 2001).
Published by: Business Monitor International Ltd., Commercial Intelligence Service, 179 Queen Victoria St, London, EC4V 4DU, United Kingdom. TEL 44-20-7248-0468, FAX 44-20-7248-0467, http://www.businessmonitor.com.

338.8 GBR ISSN 1469-381X
MULTINATIONAL ENERGY AND MINING COMPANIES. Text in English. 1999. a. GBP 345, USD 550 (effective 2001). **Description:** Research and marketing directory of worldwide professionals in the fields of energy and mining.
Published by: Business Monitor International Ltd., Commercial Intelligence Service, 179 Queen Victoria St, London, EC4V 4DU, United Kingdom. TEL 44-20-7248-0468, FAX 44-20-7248-0467, http://www.businessmonitor.com.

338.8 GBR
MULTINATIONAL FINANCIAL SERVICES. Text in English. 1999. a. GBP 345, USD 550 (effective 2001). **Description:** Research and marketing directory of worldwide professionals in the financial services field.
Related titles: CD-ROM ed.: GBP 580, USD 930 (effective 2001).
Published by: Business Monitor International Ltd., Commercial Intelligence Service, 179 Queen Victoria St, London, EC4V 4DU, United Kingdom. TEL 44-20-7248-0468, FAX 44-20-7248-0467, http://www.businessmonitor.com.

MULTINATIONAL MANAGERS AND DEVELOPING COUNTRIES. see *BUSINESS AND ECONOMICS—Management*

382 USA ISSN 0197-4637
HD2755.5
➤ **MULTINATIONAL MONITOR.** Text in English. 1980. m. USD 25 to individuals; USD 30 to non-profit organizations; USD 40 to corporations (effective 2003). adv. bk.rev.; film rev. bibl.; charts; illus. index. reprints avail. **Document type:** *Journal, Academic/Scholarly.* **Description:** Provides current news and analysis on Third World development, the environment and the politics of business.
Supersedes: Elements
Related titles: Microfiche ed.: (from PQC); Online - full text ed.: (from EBSCO Publishing, Florida Center for Library Automation, Gale Group, Northern Light Technology, Inc., O C L C Online Computer Library Center, Inc., ProQuest Information & Learning); Talking Book ed.
Indexed: ABIn, AltPI, DIP, HRIR, IBR, IBZ, LeftInd, PAIS, RASB.
—BLDSC (5983.162000), IE, ingenta.
Published by: Essential Information, PO Box 19405, Washington, DC 20036. TEL 202-387-8034, FAX 202-234-5176, monitor@essential.org, http://www.multinationalmonitor.org. Ed. Robert Weissman. R&P Stephanie Donnie TEL 202-387-8030. Circ: 10,000.

338.8 GBR ISSN 1469-3836
MULTINATIONAL TELECOMMUNICATIONS COMPANIES. Text in English. 1999. a. GBP 345, USD 550 (effective 2001). **Description:** Research and marketing directory of worldwide professionals in the telecommunications field.
Related titles: CD-ROM ed.: GBP 580, USD 930 (effective 2001).
Published by: Business Monitor International Ltd., Commercial Intelligence Service, 179 Queen Victoria St, London, EC4V 4DU, United Kingdom. TEL 44-20-7248-0468, FAX 44-20-7248-0467, http://www.businessmonitor.com.

338.8 GBR
MULTINATIONAL TRANSPORT. Text in English. 1999. a. GBP 345, USD 550 (effective 2001). **Description:** Research and marketing directory of worldwide professionals in the field of transportation.
Related titles: CD-ROM ed.: GBP 580, USD 930 (effective 2001).
Published by: Business Monitor International Ltd., Commercial Intelligence Service, 179 Queen Victoria St, London, EC4V 4DU, United Kingdom. TEL 44-20-7248-0468, FAX 44-20-7248-0467, http://www.businessmonitor.com.

N A C L A REPORT ON THE AMERICAS. see *POLITICAL SCIENCE—International Relations*

N A F T A: LAW & BUSINESS REVIEW OF THE AMERICAS. (North American Free Trade Agreement) see *LAW—International Law*

N A F T A LAW AND POLICY SERIES. (North American Free Trade Agreement) see *LAW—International Law*

382 BEL
N A T O ANNUAL ECONOMIC COLLOQUIA. PROCEEDINGS/O T A N COLLOQUES ANNUELS. Text in English, French. 1975. a. free. **Document type:** *Proceedings, Academic/Scholarly.*
Formerly: North Atlantic Treaty Organization. Directorate of Economic Affairs. Colloquium. Series
Related titles: Microfiche ed.: (from CIS).
Indexed: IIS.

B

Published by: North Atlantic Treaty Organization, Office of Information and Press, Brussels, 1110, Belgium. TEL 32-2-7075009, FAX 32-2-7074579, natodocs@hq.nato.int, http://www.nato.int, http://www.nato.int. Circ: 2,500.

382 LBN ISSN 1564-7617
NASRAT AL-TIGARAT AL-HARIGIYYAT LI-MINTAQUAT AL-LAGNAT AL-IQTISADIYYAT WA-AL-IQTIMA'IYYAT LI-GARBI ASIYA/EXTERNAL TRADE BULLETIN OF THE ESCWA REGION. Text in English, Arabic. 1983. biennial, latest vol.11, 2002. USD 30 (effective 2004). **Description:** Provides summary tables on overall trade, trends and share of the region in total world trade, including data on direction of trade of ESCWA countries.
Formerly: Nasrat al-Tigarat al-Harigiyyat li-Mintaqat al-Lagnat al-Iqtisadiyyat li-Garbi Asiya (0258-4948)
Published by: United Nations, Economic and Social Commission for Western Asia, PO Box 11-8575, Beirut, Lebanon. TEL 961-1-981301, FAX 961-1-981510, http://www.escwa.org.lb/information/publications/division/sd.html.

NATIONAL ASSOCIATION OF BEVERAGE IMPORTERS. BULLETIN. see *BEVERAGES*

NATIONAL ASSOCIATION OF BEVERAGE IMPORTERS. IMPORT REPORT. see *BEVERAGES*

332.6 336 USA
NATIONAL CUSTOMS TARIFF GUIDEBOOK - ISRAEL. Text in English. 1994. a. looseleaf. USD 465. **Document type:** *Directory.*
Related titles: Diskette ed.
Published by: Worldtariff, 220 Montgomery St, Ste 448, San Francisco, CA 94104-3410. TEL 415-391-7501, FAX 415-391-7537, sales@worldtariff.com, http://www.worldtariff.com.

382 USA ISSN 0898-3887
NATIONAL TRADE ESTIMATE, REPORT ON FOREIGN TRADE BARRIERS. Text in English. 1986. a.
Published by: Office of the U. S. Trade Representative (Subsidiary of: Executive Office of the President), 600 17th St, N W, Washington, DC 20508. TEL 888-473-8787, contactustr@ustr.gov, http://www.ustr.gov/reports/nte/2004/index.htm.

382 GBR ISSN 0960-8710
NEGOCIOS AL DIA. Text in Spanish. 1990. 12/yr. GBP 158, USD 220 (effective 2001). back issues avail. **Document type:** *Newsletter.*
Published by: Latin American Newsletters (Subsidiary of: Lettres (U.K.) Ltd.), 61 Old St, London, EC1V 9HW, United Kingdom. TEL 44-20-7251-0012, FAX 44-20-7253-8193, subs@latinnews.com, http://www.latinnews.com. Ed. Miguel Angel Diez. R&P Alex McHallam TEL 44-20-7251-0012.

NELSON INFORMATION'S DIRECTORY OF INVESTMENT RESEARCH. see *BUSINESS AND ECONOMICS—Trade And Industrial Directories*

382 NPL
NEPAL FOREIGN TRADE ASSOCIATION. BULLETIN. Text in Nepali. irreg. (2-5/w.).
Published by: Nepal Foreign Trade Association, Meera Home, Khichapokhari, P O Box 541, Kathmandu, Nepal. TEL 223784, TELEX 2542 JTREDS NP.

382 CHE ISSN 0028-3339
NEUE PRODUKTE✶ ; Weltmarkt-Umschau fuer Industrie und Handel. Text in German. 1964. fortn. CHF 137. adv. pat.
Published by: G. Buechi Verlag, Schaffhauserstr 439, Postfach 236, Zuerich, 8052, Switzerland. Ed. Heinrich Roth. Circ: 5,000.

382 336 GBR
NEW IN DUTY FREE. Text in English. 1983. s-a. adv. **Document type:** *Trade.*
Published by: D M G World Media Ltd. (Subsidiary of: Daily Mail and General Trust PLC), Queensway House, 2 Queensway, Redhill, Surrey RH1 1QS, United Kingdom. TEL 44-1737-768611, FAX 44-1737-760510. Adv. contact Michael Lewis.

NEW YORK MERCANTILE EXCHANGE GUIDE. see *BUSINESS AND ECONOMICS—Economic Situation And Conditions*

NEW ZEALAND FOREIGN AFFAIRS AND TRADE RECORD. see *POLITICAL SCIENCE—International Relations*

382 310 NZL
NEW ZEALAND. STATISTICS NEW ZEALAND. CENSUS OF INTERNATIONAL TRADE IN SERVICES AND ROYALTIES. Text in English. stat. **Document type:** *Government.* **Description:** Measures the services transactions between New Zealand and the rest of the world.
Published by: Statistics New Zealand/Te Tari Tatau, PO Box 2922, Wellington, New Zealand. TEL 64-4-495-4600, FAX 64-4-473-2626, info@stats.govt.nz, http://www.stats.govt.nz.

382 310 NZL
NEW ZEALAND. STATISTICS NEW ZEALAND. INTERNATIONAL INVESTMENT POSITION. Text in English. a. stat. **Document type:** *Government.* **Description:** Shows New Zealand's stock of foreign assets and liabilities.
Published by: Statistics New Zealand/Te Tari Tatau, PO Box 2922, Wellington, New Zealand. TEL 64-4-495-4600, FAX 64-4-473-2626, info@stats.govt.nz, http://www.stats.govt.nz.

382 310 NZL
NEW ZEALAND. STATISTICS NEW ZEALAND. OVERSEAS CARGO STATISTICS (12 MONTHS). Text in English. a. stat. **Document type:** *Government.* **Description:** Measures the value and volume of cargo loaded and unloaded at New Zealand ports for 12 months.
Published by: Statistics New Zealand/Te Tari Tatau, PO Box 2922, Wellington, New Zealand. TEL 64-4-495-4600, FAX 64-4-473-2626, info@stats.govt.nz, http://www.stats.govt.nz.

382 310 NZL
NEW ZEALAND. STATISTICS NEW ZEALAND. OVERSEAS CARGO STATISTICS (6 MONTHS). Text in English. s-a. stat. **Document type:** *Government.*
Published by: Statistics New Zealand/Te Tari Tatau, PO Box 2922, Wellington, New Zealand. TEL 64-4-495-4600, FAX 64-4-473-2626, info@stats.govt.nz, http://www.stats.govt.nz.

382 310 NZL
NEW ZEALAND. STATISTICS NEW ZEALAND. OVERSEAS MERCHANDISE TRADE. Text in English. m. stat. **Document type:** *Government.* **Description:** Releases give statistics on the value of New Zealand's merchandise trade with the rest of the world. In addition to actual trade values, trend values and major country and commodity values are included.
Published by: Statistics New Zealand/Te Tari Tatau, PO Box 2922, Wellington, New Zealand. TEL 64-4-495-4600, FAX 64-4-473-2626, info@stats.govt.nz, http://www.stats.govt.nz.

382 310 NZL
NEW ZEALAND. STATISTICS NEW ZEALAND. OVERSEAS TRADE PRICE, VOLUME AND TERMS OF TRADE INDEXES (PROVISIONAL). Text in English. q. stat. **Document type:** *Government.*
Published by: Statistics New Zealand/Te Tari Tatau, PO Box 2922, Wellington, New Zealand. TEL 64-4-495-4600, FAX 64-4-473-2626, info@stats.govt.nz, http://www.stats.govt.nz.

382.7 BEL
NIEUWSBRIEF DOUANE. Text in Flemish. s-m. **Description:** Customs information.
Published by: C E D Samsom (Subsidiary of: Wolters Samsom Belgie n.v.), Kouterveld 14, Diegem, 1831, Belgium. TEL 32-2-7231111.

382 BEL
NIEUWSBRIEF TRANSPORT. Text in Flemish. s-m. **Description:** Transportation information.
Published by: C E D Samsom (Subsidiary of: Wolters Samsom Belgie n.v.), Kouterveld 14, Diegem, 1831, Belgium. TEL 32-2-7231111.

382 NGA ISSN 0029-0041
HF46
NIGERIA TRADE JOURNAL. Text in English. 1953. q. adv. charts; illus.; mkt.; stat. index. **Document type:** *Magazine, Trade.*
Published by: Department of Information, 15 Awolowo Rd., Ikoyi, Lagos State, Nigeria. Ed. Philip Ideh. Circ: 20,000.

382 NGA ISSN 0078-0650
NIGERIA TRADE SUMMARY. Text in English. 1964. a. bk.rev. **Document type:** *Government.*
Published by: National Integrated Survey of Households, PMB 12528, Lagos, Nigeria. TEL 234-1-630264. Circ: 3,000.

382 NGA ISSN 0189-0840
NIGERIAN INSTITUTE OF INTERNATIONAL AFFAIRS. DIALOGUES. Text in English. 1978. irreg., latest 1985. NGN 60, USD 6 (effective 2003). adv. **Document type:** *Monographic series.* **Description:** Establishes contact with other organizations with similar objectives.
Published by: (Nigerian Institute of International Affairs), N I I A Press, 13-15 Kofo Abayomi Rd., Victory Island, GPO Box 1727, Lagos, Nigeria. TEL 234-1-2615606, FAX 234-1-2611360, http://www.niianet.org. Ed., R&P, Adv. contact George A Obiozor.

382 USA ISSN 1556-0376
HF1746
NORTH AMERICAN FREE TRADE & INVESTMENT REPORT; biweekly news on trade, investment, and related trans-border issues. Text in English. 22/yr. USD 734 domestic; USD 784 foreign (effective 2005). adv. **Document type:** *Newsletter, Trade.* **Description:** Covers important North American Free Trade Agreement developments, plus the latest information on trade, investment and related trans-border issues in Mexico, the United States, and Canada.
Formerly: U S - Mexico Free Trade Reporter (1064-802X); Which incorporated (1979-1995): Direct Investment in North America (1352-6367); Which was formerly (until Jan. 1994): Foreign Investment in the U S (0958-3076); (until 1989): Investment - U S A (0142-6354)
—CCC.
Published by: WorldTrade Executive, Inc., 2250 Main St, Ste 100, PO Box 761, Concord, MA 01742. TEL 978-287-0301, FAX 978-287-0302, info@wtexec.com, http://www.wtexec.com/naftir.html. Ed. Kathryn Rosenblum. Pub., R&P Gary A Brown. Adv. contact Ken Parker. page USD 975; 7.5 x 9.5.

380 USA ISSN 1071-958X
HF1746
NORTH AMERICAN TRADE GUIDE. Text in English. 1994. biennial. USD 399 (effective 1996).
Published by: K-III Directory Corp., 155 Village Blvd., Princeton, NJ 08540-5765. TEL 609-371-7700.

382 USA ISSN 1092-6682
NORTHEAST EXPORT MAGAZINE. Text in English. 1997. bi-m. USD 18; USD 36 foreign (effective 1999). adv. **Document type:** *Trade.* **Description:** Deals with issues, trends and resources of interest to executive-level decision makers at New England based exporting companies.
Published by: Laurentian Business Publishing Inc., 670 N. Commercial St., Ste. 110, Manchester, NH 03101-1185. TEL 603-626-6354, FAX 603-626-6359, neexport@aol.com. Ed., R&P Hope Jordan. Pub. B J Eckardt. Adv. contact Kathy Morris. B&W page USD 2,363, color page USD 3,416; trim 10.88 x 8.13. Circ: 13,500.

382 GRC
NORTHERN GREECE - THESSALONIKI INTERNATIONAL TRADE FAIR (YEAR). Text in Greek. 1990. a. adv.
Related titles: ◆ Supplement to: Epilogi. ISSN 1105-2503.
Published by: Electra Press, 4 Stadiou St, Athens, 105 64, Greece. TEL 323-3203, FAX 323-5160. Ed. Christos Papaioannou. Circ: 9,000.

NORTHWESTERN JOURNAL OF INTERNATIONAL LAW & BUSINESS. see *LAW—International Law*

382 ESP ISSN 1133-6447
NOTICIARI DE COMERC EXTERIOR. Text in Spanish. 1960. 4/yr. adv.
Formerly (until 1993): Noticiario de Comercio Exterior (0210-8267)
Published by: Cambra Oficial de Comerc Industria i Navegacio de Barcelona, Avinguda Diagonal, 452, Barcelona, 08006, Spain. TEL 34-3-4169300, FAX 34-3-4169301. Ed. Carmen Miro. Adv. contact Oriol Prats. Circ: 6,000.

382 ITA
NOTIZIARIO COMMERCIALE QUINDICINALE DI COMMERCIO ESTERO. Text in Italian. 26/yr.
Address: Via Meravigli, 9 B, Milan, MI 20123, Italy.

NOTIZIARIO MOTORISTICO/MOTOR - NACHRICHTEN/MOTOR NEWS/NOUVELLES DE L'AUTOMOBILE; autoattrezzature-impiantistica-ricambi-accessori. see *TRANSPORTATION—Automobiles*

O E C D CODE OF LIBERALIZATION OF CAPITAL MOVEMENTS/O C D E CODE DE LA LIBERATION DES MOUVEMENTS DE CAPITAUX. see *BUSINESS AND ECONOMICS—Banking And Finance*

O E C D ECONOMIC OUTLOOK. see *BUSINESS AND ECONOMICS—Economic Situation And Conditions*

382 FRA ISSN 1021-5794
HG5521
O E C D REVIEWS OF FOREIGN DIRECT INVESTMENT. Text in English. 1993. q. price varies. **Description:** Reviews the policies adopted by the government of a specific country towards inward investment and commends the generally open environment in which foreign firms are allowed to operate in that country.
Related titles: Online - full content ed.; French ed.: Examens de l'O C D E sur l'Investissement Direct Etranger. ISSN 1021-5808.
Published by: Organization for Economic Cooperation and Development, 2 Rue Andre Pascal, Paris, 75775 Cedex 16, France. TEL 33-1-45248200, FAX 33-1-45248500, http://www.oecd.org. **Dist. by:** O E C D Turpin North America, PO Box 194, Downingtown, PA 19335-0194. TEL 610-524-5361, 800-456-6323, FAX 610-524-5417, bookscustomer@turpinna.com.

382 016 BEL ISSN 1371-0370
HF3601
OFFICE BELGE DU COMMERCE EXTERIEUR. COMMERCE EXTERIEUR/BUITENLANDSE HANDEL. Text in Dutch, French. 1963. s-m. adv. bk.rev. abstr.; bibl. index. Supplement avail. **Document type:** *Government.*
Former titles (until 1996): Informations du Commerce Exterieur. Serie A (0770-3058); (until 1996): Informations du Commerce Exterieur (0037-1416)
Published by: L' Agence pour le Commerce Exterieur, Bd Emile Jacqmain 162, World Trade Center, BP 36, Bruxelles, 1000, Belgium. TEL 32-2-2063511, FAX 32-2-2031812. Circ: 11,500.

B

382 USA ISSN 1531-0078
HF1416.5
OFFICIAL EXPORT GUIDE: COUNTRY TRADE SOURCEBOOK. Text in English. a. **Description:** Provides information about the export process: contains country profiles, air/ocean cargo carriers, international services index, and U.S. ports.
Supersedes in part (in 2001): Offical Export Guide (0278-6389)
Published by: Commonwealth Business Media, Inc., 400 Windsor Corporate Ctr, 50 Millstone Rd, Ste 200, East Windsor, NJ 08520-1415. TEL 609-371-7700, 800-221-5488, FAX 609-371-7883, http://www.cbizmedia.com. Eds. Michelle Scott, Amy Middlebrook. Pub. John G John III.

382 USA ISSN 1531-0094
KF1987.A29
OFFICIAL EXPORT GUIDE: U.S. EXPORT REGULATIONS. Text in English. a. USD 505 (effective 2000). adv. Supplement avail. **Document type:** *Directory.* **Description:** Provides information about the export process. Includes Schedule B; Schedules C, D, and K; Export Administration Regulations; and Hazardous Materials Regulations.
Supersedes in part (in 2001): Official Export Guide (0278-6389)
Related titles: CD-ROM ed.
Published by: Commonwealth Business Media, Inc., 400 Windsor Corporate Ctr, 50 Millstone Rd, Ste 200, East Windsor, NJ 08520-1415. TEL 609-371-7700, 800-221-5488, FAX 609-371-7883, http://www.officialexportguide.com, http://www.cbizmedia.com. Eds. Michelle Scott, Amy Middlebrook. Pub. John G John III. adv.: B&W page USD 3,930; 7 x 10.

382 665.5 GBR ISSN 0952-7125
OFFSHORE CENTRES REPORT. Text in English. 1989. 10/yr. GBP 150 domestic; GBP 235 foreign (effective 2003). **Document type:** *Newsletter.* **Description:** Provides comparative information on offshore centers worldwide, plus overviews of international measures to undermine offshore centers. Addresses issues such as back secrecy, money laundering and drug trafficking.
Published by: World Reports Ltd., 108 Horseferry Rd, London, SW1P 2EF, United Kingdom. TEL 44-20-72223836, FAX 44-20-72330185, subs@worldreports.org, http://www.worldreports.org. **Subscr. in US to:** 280 Madison Ave, Ste 280, New York, NY 10016-0802. TEL 212-679-0095, FAX 212-679-1094.

OPEN ECONOMIES REVIEW. see *BUSINESS AND ECONOMICS—Economic Systems And Theories, Economic History*

382.0971 CAN ISSN 1495-3773
OPENING DOORS TO THE WORLD, CANADA'S INTERNATIONAL MARKET ACCESS PRIORITIES. Text in English, French. 1998. a.
Related titles: Print ed.: ISSN 1495-3420. 1998.
Published by: Canada. Department of Foreign Affairs and International Trade, 125 Sussex Dr, Ottawa, ON K1A OG2, Canada. TEL 613-944-4000, FAX 613-996-9709, http://www.dfait-maeci.gc.ca/.

ORGANISATION OF EASTERN CARIBBEAN STATES. FISHERIES STATISTICAL DIGEST. see *FISH AND FISHERIES*

382 DEU ISSN 0948-1680
OST-WEST-CONTACT; das Wirtschaftsmagazin fuer Ost-West-Kooperation. Text in German. 1955. m. EUR 98; EUR 10 newsstand/cover (effective 2004). adv. back issues avail. **Document type:** *Magazine, Trade.*
Former titles (until 1994): Ost-West-Commerz (0341-8588); (until 1973): Informationen ueber den West-Ost-Handel (0020-0360); (until 1968): Informationen ueber den Innerdeutschen Handel und West-Ost-Handel (0446-1940)
Related titles: Online - full text ed.
Published by: Ost-West-Contact Verlags und Beratungs GmbH, Regenskamp 18, Muenster, 48157, Germany. TEL 49-251-261824, FAX 49-251-261373, info@owc.de, http://www.owc.de. Ed. Jutta Falkner. Pubs. Jutta Falkner, Klaus Leger. R&P Klaus Leger. adv.: B&W page EUR 2,800, color page EUR 3,950; trim 175 x 250. Circ: 8,389 (paid); 11,819 (controlled).

332.6 IND
OVERSEAS BUSINESS CONTACTS. Text in English. fortn. INR 1,250, USD 100.
Published by: Associated Chambers of Commerce and Industry of India, c/o Federation of Indian Chambers of Commerce and Industry, Federation H S C, Tansen Marg, New Delhi, 110 001, India. TEL 91-11-3360704, FAX 91-11-3342193, raghuraman@sansad.nic.in, http://www.assocham.org. Circ: 1,000.

382 CAN
OVERSEAS EXPORTERS. Text in English. 1994. m. USD 75. adv. bk.rev. charts; illus.; stat. **Document type:** *Newsletter.*
Published by: Global Traders Association, P O BOX 797, Sta A, Scarborough, ON M1K 5C8, Canada. TEL 416-650-9309, FAX 416-650-9280. Circ: 370.

OVERSEAS TRADE STATISTICS. UNITED KINGDOM TRADE WITH THE EUROPEAN COMMUNITY AND THE WORLD. see *BUSINESS AND ECONOMICS—Abstracting, Bibliographies, Statistics*

382 IND ISSN 0971-3239
P R I M E. (Price Indicator of Marine Products Export) Text in English. 1977. w.
Indexed: ESPM.
Published by: Marine Products Export Development Authority, MPEDA House, Panampilly Avenue Rd., Cochin, Kerala 682 036, India. http://www.mpeda.com.

THE P R S GROUP. COUNTRY REPORTS: WORLD SERVICE. (Political Risk Services) see *BUSINESS AND ECONOMICS—Economic Situation And Conditions*

382.09 AUS ISSN 0728-8409
PACIFIC ECONOMIC PAPERS. Text in English. 1973. m. AUD 66 per vol. domestic; AUD 60 per vol. foreign; AUD 110 per vol. domestic; AUD 100 per vol. foreign (effective 2005). **Document type:** *Monographic series, Academic/Scholarly.* **Description:** Covers various economics and political issues in the Asia Pacific region.
Former titles (until 1982): Australian National University. Australia-Japan Research Centre. Research Paper (0727-3029); (until 1980): Australian National University. Australia-Japan Economic Relations Research Project. Research Paper (0727-3002)
—BLDSC (6329.185000).
Published by: Australian National University, Australia-Japan Research Centre, Canberra, ACT 0200, Australia. TEL 61-2-61253780, FAX 61-2-61250767, ajrc@anu.edu.au, http://apseg.anu.edu.au/publish/pub_papers.php, http://apseg.anu.edu.au/ajrc/ajrc.php.

919.6 USA ISSN 0744-1754
PACIFIC MAGAZINE. Text in English. 1976. bi-m. USD 15 in Asia & the Pacific; USD 39 elsewhere. adv. bk.rev. illus. reprints avail. **Document type:** *Magazine, Consumer.*
Former titles: New Pacific (0192-2408); American Pacific
Indexed: SPPI.
—CCC.
Published by: Pacific Magazine Corporation, PO Box 25488, Honolulu, HI 96825. TEL 808-377-5335, FAX 808-373-3953. Ed. Bud Benedix. Pub. Bruce Jensen. Circ: 10,000.

332.6 ESP ISSN 1134-2145
PAISES DEL I C E. (Informacion Comercial Espanola) Text in Spanish. 15/yr. **Description:** Each issue pertains to a country which has business dealings with Spain.
Published by: Ministerio de Comercio y Turismo, Paseo Castellana, 162, pl. 16, Madrid, 28046, Spain. TEL 34-1-349-36-47, FAX 34-1-349-36-34.

332 382 PAK ISSN 0078-8058
PAKISTAN CUSTOMS TARIFF✶. Text in English. 1960. irreg. price varies. bk.rev. **Document type:** *Government.*
Published by: Manager of Publications, Government of Pakistan, 2nd Fl., Ahmad Chamber, Tariq Rd., P.E.C.H.S., Karachi 29, Pakistan. Ed. M I Said. Circ: 6,000.

382 PAK ISSN 0030-977X
HF41
PAKISTAN EXPORTS. Text in English. 1968 (vol.19). m. USD 45. charts; stat.; tr.lit.
Published by: (Pakistan. Export Promotion Bureau BGD), Publishers (Private) Ltd., Shafi Court Merewether Rd., P O Box 10449, Karachi 4, Pakistan. TEL 522032, TELEX 25737-PAGE-PK. Ed. Tahir Shaikh.

PAKISTAN'S BALANCE OF PAYMENTS (ANNUAL). see *BUSINESS AND ECONOMICS—Public Finance, Taxation*

PAKISTAN'S BALANCE OF PAYMENTS (QUARTERLY). see *BUSINESS AND ECONOMICS—Public Finance, Taxation*

PAPUA NEW GUINEA. NATIONAL STATISTICAL OFFICE. EXPORT PRICE INDEXES. see *BUSINESS AND ECONOMICS—Abstracting, Bibliographies, Statistics*

PAPUA NEW GUINEA. NATIONAL STATISTICAL OFFICE. IMPORT PRICE INDEXES. see *BUSINESS AND ECONOMICS—Abstracting, Bibliographies, Statistics*

PAPUA NEW GUINEA. NATIONAL STATISTICAL OFFICE. INTERNATIONAL TRADE - EXPORTS. see *BUSINESS AND ECONOMICS—Abstracting, Bibliographies, Statistics*

PAPUA NEW GUINEA. NATIONAL STATISTICAL OFFICE. INTERNATIONAL TRADE - IMPORTS. see *BUSINESS AND ECONOMICS—Abstracting, Bibliographies, Statistics*

382 PRY
PARAGUAY. CENTRO DE PROMOCION DE LAS EXPORTACIONES. DIRECTORIO DE EXPORTADORES - EXPORT DIRECTORY. Text in Spanish. a. USD 12.
Published by: (Paraguay. Centro de Promocion de las Exportaciones), Ministerio de Industria y Comercio, C.C. 1772, Ave. ESPANA, 374, Asuncion, Paraguay. TEL 204-880-44 231.

PERGAMENT. see *POLITICAL SCIENCE—International Relations*

382 381 PHL
PHILIPPINES. DEPARTMENT OF TRADE AND INDUSTRY. ANNUAL REPORT. Text in English. 1948. a. free. **Document type:** *Government.*
Former titles (until 1981): Philippines. Ministry of Trade. Annual Report; Philippines. Department of Commerce and Industry. Annual Report (0079-1539)
Published by: Department of Trade and Industry, Trade & Industry Information Center, 385 Industry and Investments Bldg., Sen. Gil Puyat Ave., Makati City, 1200, Philippines. TEL 02-895-3611, FAX 02-895-6487, TELEX 14830 MTI PS. Ed. Minerva R Fajardo. R&P Alfonso M Valenzuela.

PHILIPPINES. NATIONAL STATISTICS OFFICE. COMMODITY FLOW IN THE PHILIPPINES. see *BUSINESS AND ECONOMICS—Domestic Commerce*

382 USA
PLATT'S EXPORT / IMPORT REPORT✶. Text in English. m. USD 400; USD 485 foreign. **Document type:** *Trade.*
Published by: Platts (Subsidiary of: McGraw-Hill Companies, Inc.), 2 Penn Plaza, 25th Fl, New York, NY 10121-2298. TEL 212-904-3070, 800-752-8878, FAX 212-904-4209, http://www.platts.com.

POLISH ENGINEERING. see *ENGINEERING*

382 POL ISSN 0032-2881
POLISH FOREIGN TRADE. Text in English. 1949. 6/yr. USD 78. adv. bk.rev. charts; illus.; mkt.; pat.; tr.mk.
Incorporates (1959-1975): Polish Export-Import (0238-969X)
Related titles: French ed.: Commerce Exterieur Polonais. ISSN 0208-6565; German ed.: Polnischer Aussenhandel. ISSN 0239-2976; Russian ed.: Pol'skaya Vneshnyaya Torgovlya; Spanish ed.: Comercio Exterior Polonia. ISSN 0208-7936.
Indexed: MEA&I.
—BLDSC (6543.650000).
Published by: AGPOL - Polexportpress, Ul Kierbedzia 4, Warsaw, 00957, Poland. Ed. Danuta Gasiorowska. Circ: 20,000. **Dist. by:** Ars Polona, Krakowskie Przedmiescie 7, Warsaw, Poland.

382 POL ISSN 0239-989X
POLISH TRADE MAGAZINE. Text in Polish. 1952. q. USD 40. adv. illus. **Description:** Presents the offer of Poland's foreign trade in the line of consumer goods and services.
Supersedes (in 1982): Polish Fair Magazine
Related titles: German ed.: Polnisches Handelsmagazin; Russian ed.: Polskii Torgovyi Zhurnal; French ed.: Magazine Commercial Polonais.
Published by: AGPOL - Polexportpress, Ul Kierbedzia 4, Warsaw, 00957, Poland. Circ: 20,000. **Dist. by:** Ars Polona, Krakowskie Przedmiescie 7, Warsaw, Poland.

332 USA ISSN 0887-7629
POLITICAL RISK LETTER. Text in English. 1979. m. looseleaf. USD 395 (effective 2001). back issues avail. **Document type:** *Newsletter.* **Description:** Provides the latest evaluations in table format for 100 countries and territories, with expanded analysis for 20 countries each month; assessments cover categories including turmoil risk, transfer risk, direct investment risk, export risk, and regime stability for 18-month and 5-year forecast periods.
Related titles: Diskette ed.; Online - full text ed.
Published by: The P R S Group, Inc., PO Box 248, East Syracuse, NY 13057-0248. TEL 315-431-0511, FAX 315-431-0200, custserv@prsgroup.com, http://www.countrydata.com, http://www.prsgroup.com. Eds. Michael K O'Leary, William D Coplin.

POLITICAL RISK YEARBOOK (SET). see *BUSINESS AND ECONOMICS—Banking And Finance*

POLITICAL RISK YEARBOOK. VOLUME 1: NORTH & CENTRAL AMERICA. see *BUSINESS AND ECONOMICS—Banking And Finance*

POLITICAL RISK YEARBOOK. VOLUME 2: MIDDLE EAST & NORTH AFRICA. see *BUSINESS AND ECONOMICS—Banking And Finance*

POLITICAL RISK YEARBOOK. VOLUME 3: SOUTH AMERICA. see *BUSINESS AND ECONOMICS—Banking And Finance*

POLITICAL RISK YEARBOOK. VOLUME 4: SUB-SAHARAN AFRICA. see *BUSINESS AND ECONOMICS—Banking And Finance*

POLITICAL RISK YEARBOOK. VOLUME 5: EAST ASIA & THE PACIFIC. see *BUSINESS AND ECONOMICS—Banking And Finance*

POLITICAL RISK YEARBOOK. VOLUME 6: WEST EUROPE. see *BUSINESS AND ECONOMICS—Banking And Finance*

POLITICAL RISK YEARBOOK. VOLUME 7: EAST EUROPE. see *BUSINESS AND ECONOMICS—Banking And Finance*

POLITICAL RISK YEARBOOK. VOLUME 8: CENTRAL AND SOUTH AFRICA. see *BUSINESS AND ECONOMICS— Banking And Finance*

PORT OF ANTWERP YEARBOOK. see *TRANSPORTATION— Ships And Shipping*

POWER, FINANCE & RISK. see *BUSINESS AND ECONOMICS—Banking And Finance*

382 POL ISSN 0860-0023
POZNAN FAIR MAGAZINE. Text in English. 1982. 4/yr. USD 11.
Related titles: German ed.: Poznan Messemagazin. ISSN 0860-0031.
Published by: (Poznan International Fair), AGPOL - Polexportpress, Ul Kierbedzia 4, Warsaw, 00957, Poland. Ed. Lidia Neuman Gisnka. Circ: 4,000. **Dist. by:** Ars Polona, Krakowskie Przedmiescie 7, Warsaw, Poland.

PRACTICAL GUIDE TO FOREIGN DIRECT INVESTMENT IN THE EUROPEAN UNION - THE GREEN BOOK. see *BUSINESS AND ECONOMICS—Investments*

382.7 LUX
PRACTICAL GUIDE TO THE USE OF THE EUROPEAN COMMUNITIES' SCHEME OF GENERALIZED TARIFF PREFERENCES. Text in English. irreg., latest 1986. USD 12. charts; stat.
Published by: (European Commission BEL, Directorate-General for External Relations), European Commission, Office for Official Publications of the European Union, 2 Rue Mercier, Luxembourg, L-2985, Luxembourg. **Dist. in U.S. by:** Bernan Associates, Bernan, 4611-F Assembly Dr., Lanham, MD 20706-4391. TEL 301-459-0056, 800-274-4447.

382 USA
PRINCETON STUDIES IN INTERNATIONAL ECONOMICS. Text in English. irreg. **Description:** Covers commissioned works by leading scholars in international trade, international macroeconomics and international finance.
—BLDSC (6612.954000).
Published by: Princeton University, Department of Economics, International Economics Section, Fisher Hall, Princeton, NJ 08544-1021. TEL 609-258-4048, FAX 609-258-1374, ies@princeton.edu, http://www.princeton.edu/~ies/.
Co-publisher: Princeton University Press.

382 338.91 PHL
PRIVATE DEVELOPMENT CORPORATION OF THE PHILIPPINES. EXECUTIVE UPDATE; international markets report. Text in English. 1986. bi-m. USD 50.
Published by: Private Development Corporation of the Philippines/Pribadong Korporasyon sa Pagpapaunlad ng Pilipinas, P.O. Box 757, Makati, Manila, 3117, Philippines. TEL 02-8100231, FAX 02-8195376.

332.6 USA
PRODUCT CUSTOMS TARIFF GUIDEBOOKS. Text in English. a. **Document type:** *Directory*. **Description:** Focuses more precisely on the range of tariff and nontariff measures that affect trade of a particular product both at the border of the customs district and within it.
Published by: Worldtariff, 220 Montgomery St, Ste 448, San Francisco, CA 94104-3410. TEL 415-391-7501, FAX 415-391-7537.

PROJECT FINANCE. see *BUSINESS AND ECONOMICS— Banking And Finance*

382 COD
PROMOTEUR ZAIROIS. Text in French. 1979. bi-m. XAF 120.
Published by: Centre de Commerce International du Zaire, 119 av. Colonel Tshatshi, BP 13396, Kinshasa, 1, Congo, Dem. Republic.

PROVEN TRADE CONTACTS. see *MEDICAL SCIENCES*

382 JPN
PURCHASE GUIDE OF JAPAN. Text in English, Japanese. 1952. 8/yr. (plus 4 intl. nos.). JPY 1,200, USD 35. adv.
Published by: P.G.J. Press Inc., 20-3 Shonai-Nishi-Machi 4-chome, Toyonaka-shi, Osaka-fu 561-0832, Japan. Ed. Eiji Shibayama. Circ: 15,000.

QUALITY IN MEETINGS. see *MEETINGS AND CONGRESSES*

382 USA ISSN 0270-5435
HF3092
QUARTERLY REPORT TO THE CONGRESS AND THE TRADE POLICY COMMITTEE ON TRADE BETWEEN THE UNITED STATES AND CHINA, THE SUCCESSOR STATES TO THE FORMER SOVIET UNION, AND OTHER TITLE IV COUNTRIES. Text in English. 1975. q. stat. reprint service avail. from CIS. **Document type:** *Government*. **Description:** Contains information and analysis on U.S. trade with nonmarket economy countries.
Formerly (until 1980): Quarterly Report to the Congress and the East-West Foreign Trade Board on Trade between the United States and the Nonmarket Economy Countries During (Year) (0098-910X)

Related titles: Microfiche ed.: (from CIS); ◆ Series of: U S I T C Publication. ISSN 0196-9153.
Indexed: AmStI.
Published by: (Trade Reports Division), U.S. International Trade Commission, Office of Information Services, 500 E St, S W, Washington, DC 20436. TEL 202-205-2000. **Orders to:** U.S. Government Printing Office, Superintendent of Documents.

382 GBR ISSN 1462-9704
QUEEN'S AWARDS MAGAZINE. Text in English. 1992. a. GBP 4.50 per issue (effective 2003). back issues avail. **Document type:** *Trade*. **Description:** Provides a platform for the success stories of each year's award winners in British export, technology and environmental achievement.
Published by: Nexus Media Ltd. (Subsidiary of: Highbury House Communications PLC), Nexus House, Azalea Dr, Swanley, Kent BR8 8HU, United Kingdom. TEL 44-1322-660070, FAX 44-1322-616311, info@nexusmedia.com, http:// www.queensawards.org.uk/, http://www.hhc.co.uk/. Adv. contact Daniel Emerson. Circ: 10,000 (controlled).

RANDOM LENGTHS INTERNATIONAL REPORT; the report on global wood products markets. see *FORESTS AND FORESTRY—Lumber And Wood*

382 ITA ISSN 0483-9722
RASSEGNA DI DIRITTO E TECNICA DOGANALE E DELLE IMPOSTE DI FABBRICAZIONE. Text in Italian. 1952. m. adv.
Address: Via Conca D'Oro, 348, Rome, RM 00141, Italy. TEL 6-810-33-51. Ed. Efisio Serra. Circ: 2,800.

RECHT UND SCHADEN; Monatliche Informationsschrift fuer Schadenversicherung und Schadenersatz. see *LAW—International Law*

RECHT-WIRTSCHAFT-AUSSENHANDEL SCHRIFTENREIHE. see *LAW*

382 DEU
RECHTSFRAGEN DER GLOBALISIERUNG. Text in German. 2002. irreg., latest vol.7, 2003. price varies. **Document type:** *Monographic series, Academic/Scholarly*.
Published by: Duncker und Humblot GmbH, Carl-Heinrich-Becker-Weg 9, Berlin, 12165, Germany. TEL 49-30-7900060, FAX 49-30-79000631, info@duncker-humblot.de, http://www.duncker-humblot.de.

RECYCLING INTERNATIONAL. see *ENVIRONMENTAL STUDIES—Waste Management*

REFERATIVNYI ZHURNAL. MIROVAYA EKONOMIKA. SOTSYAL'NO-EKONOMICHESKOE RAZVITIE STRAN MIRA. see *BUSINESS AND ECONOMICS—Abstracting, Bibliographies, Statistics*

382 FRA ISSN 0080-1070
REPERTOIRE DES SOCIETES DE COMMERCE EXTERIEUR FRANCAISES. Text in French. 1969. biennial. **Document type:** *Directory*.
Published by: (Federation Francaise des Societes de Commerce International), Editions Techniques Professionnelles (E.T.P.), 31 av. Pierre I de Serbie, Paris, Cedex 16 75784, France. TEL 40-69-44-43, FAX 47-23-47-32. Circ: 3,000.

REPORT ON ELECTRONIC COMMERCE; online business, financial and consumer strategies and trends. see *COMPUTERS—Internet*

330 USA ISSN 0275-5319
HD2755.5
RESEARCH IN INTERNATIONAL BUSINESS AND FINANCE. Text in English. 1979. 3/yr. EUR 49 in Europe to individuals; JPY 6,400 in Japan to individuals; USD 54 to individuals except Europe and Japan; EUR 194 in Europe to institutions; JPY 25,800 in Japan to institutions; USD 217 to institutions except Europe and Japan (effective 2006). back issues avail. **Document type:** *Journal, Academic/Scholarly*. **Description:** Provides an outlet for high quality international finance related research. Each monograph in the series is devoted to a specific topic that is germane to international business and finance.
Related titles: Online - full text ed.: (from EBSCO Publishing, ScienceDirect, Swets Information Services).
—BLDSC (7741.554900), IE. **CCC.**
Published by: J A I Press Inc. (Subsidiary of: Elsevier Science & Technology), 360 Park Ave S, New York, NY 10010-1710. TEL 212-989-5800, FAX 212-633-3990, usinfo-f@elsevier.com, http://www.elsevier.com/locate/ribaf. Eds. J A Batten, T Fetherston.

RESUMENES ESTADISTICOS DE IMPORTACION. see *BUSINESS AND ECONOMICS—Abstracting, Bibliographies, Statistics*

382 USA ISSN 1546-2609
HF1
▼ ➤ **REVIEW OF BUSINESS RESEARCH.** Text in English. 2003. s-a. USD 100 (effective 2004). adv. back issues avail.
Document type: *Journal, Academic/Scholarly*. **Description:** Contains original research papers/articles in international business administration, economics, management, marketing, accounting, finance, operations management, information management, E-commerce, E-business, public administration, health care administration, business law, and related areas.
Related titles: Online - full content ed.
Published by: International Academy of Business and Economics, 983 Woodland Dr, Turlock, CA 95382-7281. TEL 209-656-7084, AKhade@iabe.com, http://www.iabe.org/RBR-description.htm, http://www.aibe.org. Ed. Dr. Bhavesh S Patel. R&P Dr. Alan S Khade TEL 209-656-7084. adv.: B&W page USD 500, color page USD 750. Circ: 100 (paid).

382 327 KOR
D16.25
➤ **REVIEW OF INTERNATIONAL AND AREA STUDIES/INTERNATIONAL AND AREA STUDIES.** Text in Korean; Abstracts in English. 1992 (Sept.). q. KRW 70,000 membership (effective 2004 - 2005). bk.rev. abstr.; bibl. 130 p./no.; back issues avail.; reprints avail. **Document type:** *Journal, Academic/Scholarly*.
Former titles: Gugje Jiyeog Yeon'gu - Seoul Daehag'gyo (1226-7317); (until 1997): Jiyeog Yeon'gu - Seoul Daehag'gyo / Area Studies - Center for Area Studies (1225-5165)
Related titles: Online - full content ed.
Indexed: IPSA, PSA, SocioAb.
Published by: Seoul National University, Graduate School of International Studies, 56-1, Shillim-dong, Gwanak-gu, Seoul, 151-742, Korea, S. TEL 82-2-880-8975, 82-2-884-9352, FAX 82-2-874-7368, rias@snu.ac.kr, public@snu.ac.kr, http://gsis.snu.ac.kr/publication/d-area/d-areaindex.htm, http://sias.snu.ac.kr/. Ed. Dr. Young-Rok Cheong. Pub. Dr. Yong-Deok Kim. Adv. contact Ms. Ji-Young Ha.

382.7 343.056 URY
REVISTA DE COMERCIO EXTERIOR Y ADUANA. Text in Spanish. 1995. a. USD 16 (effective 1999). **Document type:** *Government*.
Published by: Fundacion de Cultura Universitaria, Casilla de Correo Central, Veinticinco De Mayo, 568, Montevideo, 11003, Uruguay. TEL 598-2-9161152, FAX 598-2-9152549, fcuventa@multi.com.uy, http://www.fcu.com.uy.

338.7 ESP
➤ **REVISTA EUROPEA DE DIRECCION Y ECONOMIA DE LA EMPRESA/EUROPAISCHE ZEITSCHRIFT FUR UNTERNEHMENSFUHRUNG UND BETRIEBSWIRTSCHAFT/ EUROPEAN REVIEW OF MANAGEMENT AND BUSINESS ECONOMICS/REVISTA EUROPEIA DE DIRECCAO E ECONOMIA DA EMPRESA/REVUE EUROPEENE D'ADMINISTRATION ET ECONOMIE DE'ENTREPRISE/ RIVISTA EUROPEA DI RAGIONERIA E DI ECONOMIA AZIENDALE.** Text in Spanish. 1992. q. EUR 165 in Europe; USD 200 elsewhere (effective 2003). **Document type:** *Academic/Scholarly*. **Description:** Deals with works of investigation relating to the specialities of Business Management.
—CINDOC.
Published by: Asociacion de Direccion y Economia de Empresa/European Association of Management and Business Economics, Facultad C. Economicas y Empresariales, Avda Xoan XXIII, s/n, Santiago de Compostela, A Coruqa 15071, Spain. TEL 34-981-563100, 34-981-582500, FAX 34-981-563637, oejavg@usc.es. Ed. Jose Varela Gonzalez. Circ: 1,000.

382 BRA ISSN 0014-5203
REVISTA MENSAL DE EXPORTACAO/EXPORTATION MONTHLY REVIEW. Text in Portuguese. 1914. m. USD 280. adv.
Formerly (until 1968): Fernandes Bulletin
Published by: Revista Mensal de Exportacao Ltda., Rua General Camara, 77 Andar 5, Santos, SP 11010-121, Brazil. Ed. G S Fernandes. Circ: 7,800.

382 338.91 ROM ISSN 1220-2908
REVISTA ROMANA DE STUDII INTERNATIONALE/ROMANIAN JOURNAL OF INTERNATIONAL STUDIES. Text in Romanian. 6/yr. ROL 150, USD 50.
Related titles: ◆ English ed.: Revue Roumaine d'Etudes Internationales. ISSN 0048-8178.
Published by: Academia Romana, Asociatia de Drept International si Relatii Internationale N. Titulescu, Sos. Kiseleff 47, Bucharest, 71268, Romania. TEL 40-1-227462. Ed. A Pop.

REVUE DE DROIT DES AFFAIRES INTERNATIONALES/ INTERNATIONAL BUSINESS LAW JOURNAL. see *LAW—International Law*

327 FRA ISSN 1624-365X
HC241.A1
REVUE DU DROIT DE L'UNION EUROPEENNE. Text in French. 1991. q. bk.rev.
Formerly (until 2000): Revue du Marche Unique Europeen (1155-4274)
Indexed: PAIS.
—BLDSC (7898.557700), IE, ingenta. **CCC.**

B

Published by: Clement Juglar, 62 av. de Suffren, Paris, 75015, France. TEL 45-67-58-06, FAX 45-66-50-70.

338 FRA ISSN 0035-2616
HF1531
REVUE DU MARCHE COMMUN; et de l'Union Europeenne. Text in French. 1958. m. adv. bk.rev. charts. reprint service avail. from SCH. **Description:** For those who wish to understand the goals, difficulties, set-backs and achievements of European construction.
Indexed: AgBio, DSA, ELLIS, FLP, GEOBASE, HortAb, IBR, IBSS, IBZ, IPSA, MAB, NutrAb, PAIS, RASB, RDA, RRTA, RiceAb, TriticAb, WAE&RSA.
—BLDSC (7880.365000), IE, Infotrieve, ingenta. **CCC.**
Published by: Editions Techniques et Economiques, 3 rue Soufflot, Paris, 75005, France. TEL 33-1-55426130, FAX 33-1-55426139.

B

382 332.6 GBR ISSN 1467-3886
RISK UPDATE (LONDON, 1997). Text in English. 1997. s-m. GBP 300; GBP 25 newsstand/cover (effective 2001).
Document type: *Trade.* **Description:** Identifies risk trends and discusses and tracks their impact on the global business community.
Related titles: E-mail ed.: GBP 265; GBP 20 newsstand/cover (effective 2001).
Published by: Merchant International Group Ltd., 4A-5 William St, Knightsbridge, London, SW1X 9HL, United Kingdom. TEL 44-20-7259-5060, FAX 44-20-7259-5090, headoffice@merchantinternational.com, http://www.merchantinternational.com/.

382.7 DEU
RISTER ZOLLGESETZE; Sammlung von Vorschriften der Bundes Zollverwaltung. Text in German. 6/yr. looseleaf. adv.
Document type: *Trade.*
Published by: Walhalla Fachverlag, Haus an der Eisernen Bruecke, Regensburg, 93042, Germany. TEL 49-941-5684-0, FAX 49-941-5684111, walhalla@walhalla.de, http://www.walhalla.de. Circ: 7,100.

RIVISTA DI DIRITTO VALUTARIO E DI ECONOMIA INTERNAZIONALE/REVIEW OF CURRENCY LAW AND INTERNATIONAL ECONOMICS; legislazione internazionale - ricerche - giurisprudenza - documenti. see *LAW—International Law*

ROSSIYA I STRANY MIRA/RUSSIA AND COUNTRIES OF THE WORLD. see *BUSINESS AND ECONOMICS—Abstracting, Bibliographies, Statistics*

382 GBR ISSN 1359-7930
ROUTLEDGE STUDIES IN INTERNATIONAL BUSINESS AND THE WORLD ECONOMY. Text in English. 1995 (Nov.). irreg., latest vol.29, 2001, Jan. price varies. back issues avail.
Document type: *Monographic series, Academic/Scholarly.*
—BLDSC (8026.519700), IE, ingenta.
Published by: Routledge (Subsidiary of: Taylor & Francis Group), 4 Park Square, Milton Park, Abingdon, Oxon OX14 4RN, United Kingdom. TEL 44-1235-828600, FAX 44-1235-829000, info@routledge.co.uk, http://www.tandf.co.uk, http://www.routledge.co.uk. Eds. Dilip Ghosh, Edgar Ortiz.

RUMANIA. COMISIA NATIONALA PENTRU STATISTICA. BULETIN STATISTIC DE COMERT EXTERIOR/RUMANIA. NATIONAL COMMISSION FOR STATISTICS. FOREIGN TRADE STATISTICS. see *BUSINESS AND ECONOMICS—Abstracting, Bibliographies, Statistics*

330.9 USA ISSN 1540-1286
RUNDT'S WORLD BUSINESS INTELLIGENCE. Variant title: Rundt's New York Intelligence Briefs. Text in English. 1952. w. USD 695 (effective 1999). **Description:** Covers international trade, security risk evaluations, political, financial, export and currency exchange forecasting for all countries.
Formerly: Rundt's Weekly Intelligence (0485-6627)
Related titles: Diskette ed.; Online - full text ed.
Published by: S.J. Rundt & Associates, Inc., 130 E 63rd St, New York, NY 10021-7334. TEL 212-838-0141, FAX 973-744-3073, info@rundtsintelligence.com, http://www.rundtsintelligence.com. Ed. Hans Belcsak. Pub. Hans P Belcsak. R&P J Wilfinger TEL 973-783-5206.

RUSSIA AND CHINA TRAVEL NEWS; weekly news - travel - trade - tranportation - marketing - media. see *TRAVEL AND TOURISM*

RUSSIA AND THE REPUBLICS LEGAL MATERIALS. see *LAW—International Law*

382 340 USA ISSN 1551-157X
RUSSIA - EURASIA EXECUTIVE GUIDE. Text in English. 1999. s-m. USD 879 domestic; USD 979 foreign (effective 2005). adv. **Document type:** *Journal, Trade.* **Description:** Provides detailed advice, prepared by people facing legal and practical issues in the region every day, on how to do business in Russia, the CIS, and East-Central Europe.
Formerly (until 2003): Russia - Central Europe Executive Guide (1544-5852); Which was formed by the merger of (1992-1999): East-West Commersant (1081-8421); Which was formerly: East - West Business and Financial Alert; (1992-1999): East-West Executive Guide (1067-635X); Which incorporated (1990-1992): East-West Business Report (1053-7155); (198?-1999): Soviet and Eastern European Report (0963-7036)
Related titles: Online - full content ed.
Published by: WorldTrade Executive, Inc., 2250 Main St, Ste 100, PO Box 761, Concord, MA 01742. TEL 978-287-0301, FAX 978-287-0302, smahapatra@wtexec.com, info@wtexec.com, http://www.wtexecutive.com/cms/content.jsp?id=com.tms.cms.section.Section_1014, http://www.wtexec.com. Ed. Daniel Satinsky. Pub. Gary A Brown. Adv. contact Jay Stanley.

382 RUS
RUSSIA: FOREIGN ECONOMIC RELATIONS. TRENDS AND PROSPECTS. Text in English. q. **Document type:** *Journal, Academic/Scholarly.* **Description:** Presents the most up-to-date comprehensive review of early statistics, developments and legal position of Russia's foreign trade and investments, demonstrating business opportunities in this country on macro- and micro level.
Published by: Vserossiiskii Nauchno-Issledovatel'skii Kon'yukturnyi Institut (VNIKI)/All-Russia Market Research Institute, ul Pudovkina, 4, Moscow, 119285, Russian Federation. TEL 7-095-1430538, mrc@vniki.ru, http://www.rating.com.ru/VNIKI/ENG/Vol1/default.htm, http://www.vniki.ru.

382 GBR
RUSSIAN JOURNAL OF BRITISH INDUSTRY AND COMMERCE. Text in English. 1903. a. adv. **Document type:** *Directory.* **Description:** Promotes British and other products and services throughout the former Soviet Union.
Formerly: Russian Journal of British Machinery and Trade
Published by: Exact Communications Ltd., First Floor Chambers, 1101 Warwick Rd, Acocks Green, Birmingham, Worcs B27 6RA, United Kingdom. TEL 44-121-707-7272, FAX 44-121-707-2288. Ed. Jonathan Hunt. Pub. Vitek Aukstolis. Adv. contact Michael Burgess.

382 POL ISSN 0036-052X
RYNKI ZAGRANICZNE/FOREIGN MARKETS. Text in Polish. 1957. 156/yr. USD 234. adv. bk.rev. index. **Description:** Covers world economy, international business, Polish export-import.
Indexed: RASB.
Published by: Krajowa Izba Gospodarcza, Ul Trebacka 4, Warsaw, 00074, Poland. Ed. Andrzej Zielinski. Circ: 5,000.
Dist. by: Ars Polona, Krakowskie Przedmiescie 7, Warsaw, Poland.

382 ZAF ISSN 0081-2552
S A F T O ANNUAL REPORT/SUID-AFRIKAANSE BUITELANDSE HANDELSORGANISASIE JAARVERSLAG. Text in Afrikaans, English. a. free. **Document type:** *Corporate.*
Published by: (South African Foreign Trade Organisation), S A F T O, Safto House, No. 5 Esterhyzen Street, PO Box 782706, Sandton, Transvaal 2146, South Africa. TEL 27-11-883-3737, FAX 27-11-883-6569, emalstar@ide.co.za, http://www.safto.co za.

S A I S REVIEW; a journal of international affairs. see *POLITICAL SCIENCE—International Relations*

ST. LUCIA. STATISTICAL DEPARTMENT. ANNUAL OVERSEAS TRADE REPORT: PART 2. see *BUSINESS AND ECONOMICS—Abstracting, Bibliographies, Statistics*

ST. LUCIA. STATISTICAL DEPARTMENT. QUARTERLY OVERSEAS TRADE REPORTS. see *BUSINESS AND ECONOMICS—Abstracting, Bibliographies, Statistics*

SAUDI ARABIA. CENTRAL DEPARTMENT OF STATISTICS. QUARTERLY DIGEST OF FOREIGN TRADE STATISTICS. see *BUSINESS AND ECONOMICS—Abstracting, Bibliographies, Statistics*

382 FRA ISSN 1158-6826
SAVOIR INTERNATIONAL. Text in French. 1987. irreg.
Related titles: ♦ Supplement to: M O C I. ISSN 0026-9719.
Published by: Societe d'Edition de Documentation Economique et Commerciale (SEDEC), 24 bd. de l'Hopital, Paris, 75005, France. TEL 33-1-40733925, FAX 33-1-43364798. Ed. Jean Marchand.

382 DEU ISSN 0720-6984
SCHRIFTEN ZU INTERNATIONALEN WIRTSCHAFTSFRAGEN. Text in German. 1974. irreg., latest vol.33, 2002. price varies.
Document type: *Monographic series, Academic/Scholarly.*
Published by: Duncker und Humblot GmbH, Carl-Heinrich-Becker-Weg 9, Berlin, 12165, Germany. TEL 49-30-7900060, FAX 49-30-79000631, info@duncker-humblot.de, http://www.duncker-humblot.de.

338 DEU ISSN 0582-0170
SCHRIFTEN ZU REGIONAL- UND VERKEHRSPROBLEMEN IN INDUSTRIE- UND ENTWICKLUNGSLAENDERN. Text in German. 1969. irreg., latest vol.65, 1999. price varies.
Document type: *Monographic series, Academic/Scholarly.*
Published by: Duncker und Humblot GmbH, Carl-Heinrich-Becker-Weg 9, Berlin, 12165, Germany. TEL 49-30-7900060, FAX 49-30-79000631, info@duncker-humblot.de, http://www.duncker-humblot.de.

SEATRADE. see *TRANSPORTATION—Ships And Shipping*

SEATRADE WEEK NEWSFRONT. see *TRANSPORTATION—Ships And Shipping*

382 GTM
SECRETARIA PERMANENTE DEL TRATADO GENERAL DE INTEGRACION ECONOMICA CENTROAMERICANA. CUADERNOS. Text in Spanish. s-a. USD 8 per issue.
Published by: Secretaria Permanente del Tratado General de Integracion Economica Centroamericana, 4a Avda. 10-25, ZONA, 14, PO Box 1237, Guatemala City, 01901, Guatemala. TEL 502-3682151, FAX 502-3681071, TELEX 5676, sieca@pronet.net.gt.

332.6 USA
SECTOR CUSTOMS TARIFF GUIDEBOOKS. Text in English. a.
Document type: *Directory.*
Published by: Worldtariff, 220 Montgomery St, Ste 448, San Francisco, CA 94104-3410. TEL 415-391-7501, FAX 415-391-7537.

SENEGAL. MINISTERE DE L'ECONOMIE, DES FINANCES ET DU PLAN. NOTE D'ANALYSE DU COMMERCE EXTERIEUR. see *BUSINESS AND ECONOMICS—Abstracting, Bibliographies, Statistics*

SERIES IN INTERNATIONAL BUSINESS AND ECONOMICS. see *BUSINESS AND ECONOMICS—Economic Situation And Conditions*

382 ESP ISSN 0488-3721
SERVEX; el semanario del comercio exterior. Text in Spanish. w. free. charts; stat.
Published by: Banco de Bilbao, Servicio de Estudios, Apartado 21, Bilbao, Vizcaya 48070, Spain.

382 SYC
SEYCHELLES TRADE REPORT. Text in English. a., latest 1983. SCR 60.
Published by: (Seychelles. Statistics Division), President's Office, Department of Finance, Box 206, Victoria, Mahe, Seychelles.

332.6 CHN
SHENZHEN SHANGBAO/SHENZHEN COMMERCIAL NEWS. Text in Chinese. d. CNY 144.96. 16 p./no.; **Document type:** *Newspaper.* **Description:** Focuses on economic and trade news.
Published by: Shenzhen Shangbao She, Shangbao Lu, Jingtian Shenghuo-qu, 3 Xiao-qu, Futian-qu, Shenzhen, Guangdong 518034, China. TEL 3344736, FAX 3209410. **Dist. overseas by:** China International Book Trading Corp, 35 Chegongzhuang Xilu, Haidian District, PO Box 399, Beijing 100044, China. cibtc@mail.cibtc.com.cn, http://www.cibtc.com.cn.

SHIPPING AND TRADE LAW. see *LAW—International Law*

SHIPPING AND TRADE NEWS. see *TRANSPORTATION—Ships And Shipping*

382 CHN
SHUANGBIAN JINGMAO ZHUANKAN/INTERNATIONAL TRADE NEWS SUPPLEMENT. Text in Chinese; Summaries in English. 1980. 30/yr. adv. **Document type:** *Government.* **Description:** Each supplement covers a specific country or region. Focuses mainly on bilateral trade and mutual economic cooperation.
Related titles: ♦ Supplement to: Guowei Shangqing.
Published by: Ministry of Commerce of the People's Republic of China/Zhonghua Renmin Gongheguo Shangfubu, 28 Dong Hou Ln, An Ding Men Wai, Beijing, 100710, China. TEL 86-1-64248987, FAX 86-1-64211398, itna@public.bta.net.cn, http://www.itn.com.cn. Circ: 960,000.

SHUIWU YU JINGJI/TAXATION AND ECONOMY. see *BUSINESS AND ECONOMICS—Banking And Finance*

SILK EXPORT BULLETIN. see *TEXTILE INDUSTRIES AND FABRICS*

SINGAPORE EXPORTERS. see *BUSINESS AND ECONOMICS—Trade And Industrial Directories*

332.6 SGP
SINGAPORE TRADE CONNECTION✶; a powerful single source of statistical and company data. Text in English. m. USD 300. stat. **Description:** Analyses Singapore's trade performance, market trends and competition. Provides source for products and services.
Media: CD-ROM.

Published by: Singapore Trade Development Board, Office Tower, 230 Victoria Street, 07-00 Bugis Juction, Singapore, 188024, Singapore. TEL 279-0426, FAX 278-7073, TELEX RS 28617 TRADEV.

---

382   ESP   ISSN 0213-2273
HC381
SITUACION; review of the Spanish economy. Text in Spanish. 1973. q. free. charts; stat.
Related titles: English ed.: ISSN 0213-2303.
Indexed: IECT.
Published by: Banco de Bilbao - Vizcaya, Servicio de Estudios, Gran Via 1, Bilbao, 48001, Spain. TEL 447-6100. Ed. Roberto Alvarez Llano.

382   CUB
SITUACION DE LOS EDULCORANTES. Text in Spanish. 1981. a. CUP 10. **Description:** Covers the market development of sugar substitutes.
Published by: (Cuba. Ministerio del Comercio Exterior (MINCEX)), Empresa Cubazucar, Calle 23 No. 55,, Vedado, La Habana, Cuba. TEL 70-9742, TELEX 51-1147.

382   ESP   ISSN 0213-229X
HC381
SITUACION. SUPLEMENTO DE COYUNTURA. Text in Spanish. 1980. m. charts; stat.
Published by: Banco de Bilbao - Vizcaya, Servicio de Estudios, Gran Via 1, Bilbao, 48001, Spain.

SITUATION & OUTLOOK REPORT. OUTLOOK FOR U.S. AGRICULTURAL TRADE. see AGRICULTURE—Agricultural Economics

332.6   USA   ISSN 1084-4848
SITUATION AND OUTLOOK SERIES. INTERNATIONAL AGRICULTURE AND TRADE REPORTS NAFTA. Text in English. 1995. a.
Published by: U.S. Department of Agriculture, Economic Research Service, 1800 M St, N W, Rm 3100, Washington, DC 20036. http://www.econ.ag.gov.

SOCIAL AGENDA. see BUSINESS AND ECONOMICS—Labor And Industrial Relations

382   FRA   ISSN 1683-2353
SOURCE O C D E. INDUSTRIE, SERVICES ET ECHANGES. (Organisation de Cooperation et de Developpement Economiques) Text in French. irreg. EUR 1,700, USD 1,955, GBP 1,122, JPY 229,500 (effective 2005).
Related titles: Online - full content ed.: ISSN 1684-3002. EUR 1,190, USD 1,368, GBP 785, JPY 160,700 (effective 2005); Online - full text ed.: (from EBSCO Publishing, Gale Group, IngentaConnect, Swets Information Services); ◆ English ed.: Source O E C D. Industry, Services & Trade. ISSN 1608-0203.
Published by: Organization for Economic Cooperation and Development, 2 Rue Andre Pascal, Paris, 75775 Cedex 16, France. TEL 33-1-45248200, FAX 33-1-45248500, http://www.oecd.org. **Dist. by:** Extenza - Turpin, Pegasus Dr, Stratton Business Park, Biggleswade, Beds SG18 8TQ, United Kingdom. TEL 44-1462-687552, FAX 44-1462-480947, subscriptions@extenza-turpin.com; O E C D Turpin North America, PO Box 194, Downingtown, PA 19335-0194. TEL 610-524-5361, 800-456-6323, FAX 610-524-5417, journalscustomer@turpinna.com.

382   FRA   ISSN 1608-0203
SOURCE O E C D. INDUSTRY, SERVICES & TRADE. Text in English. irreg. EUR 1,700, USD 1,955, GBP 1,122, JPY 229,500 (effective 2005). **Description:** Studies on the private sector and international trade, including the OECD Science & Technology Outlook and Scoreboard.
Related titles: Online - full content ed.: ISSN 1681-1992. EUR 1,190, USD 1,368, JPY 160,700 (effective 2005); Online - full text ed.: 2000 (from EBSCO Publishing, Gale Group, IngentaConnect, Swets Information Services); ◆ French ed.: Source O C D E. Industrie, Services et Echanges. ISSN 1683-2353.
Published by: Organization for Economic Cooperation and Development, 2 Rue Andre Pascal, Paris, 75775 Cedex 16, France. TEL 33-1-45248200, FAX 33-1-45248500, http://www.oecd.org. **Dist. by:** Extenza - Turpin, Pegasus Dr, Stratton Business Park, Biggleswade, Beds SG18 8TQ, United Kingdom. TEL 44-1462-687552, FAX 44-1462-480947, subscriptions@extenza-turpin.com; O E C D Turpin North America, PO Box 194, Downingtown, PA 19335-0194. TEL 610-524-5361, 800-456-6323, FAX 610-524-5417, journalscustomer@turpinna.com.

SOUTH AFRICA. COMMISSIONER FOR CUSTOMS AND EXCISE. MONTHLY ABSTRACT OF TRADE STATISTICS. see BUSINESS AND ECONOMICS—Abstracting, Bibliographies, Statistics

---

381   ZAF   ISSN 0259-1855
SOUTH AFRICAN EXPORTERS/EXPORTADORES DE SUD AFRICA/EXPORTADORES SUL-AFRICANOS/EXPORTATEURS SUD-AFRICAINS/SUEDAFRIKANISCHE EXPORTEURE. Variant title: South African Exporters Directory. Text in English. 1978. a. ZAR 400 (effective 1999). stat. **Document type:** Directory. **Description:** Provides information on products and services available for export from South Africa, including detailed company listings, bankers and contact names. Provides an overview of South Africa, its infrastructure and economy.
Published by: Reed Business Information South Africa (Pty) Ltd (Subsidiary of: Reed Business Information International), PO Box 653207, Benmore, 2010, South Africa. TEL 27-11-886-2636, FAX 27-11-886-5424. Circ: 10,000 (controlled).

382   USA
SOUTH AFRICAN MARKET NEWS. Text in English. 1989. 4/yr. free. illus. **Document type:** Trade. **Description:** Provides information and news on South African trade, business, investment, products and services, trade exhibitions and conferences, and the economy.
Published by: South African Embassy, 3051 Massachusetts Ave NW, Washington, DC 20008. TEL 202-232-4400, FAX 202-966-5919, saedc@ix.netcom.com, http://www.southafrica.net. Ed., R&P, Adv. contact Jennifer Cheong. Circ: 15,000.

382.0918 332.6   USA   ISSN 1082-183X
HF3371
SOUTH AMERICA REPORT. Text in English. 1995. m. USD 395; USD 425 foreign (effective 1999). charts; tr.lit. back issues avail. **Document type:** Newsletter. **Description:** Covers Fortune 500 companies doing business in South America.
Related titles: E-mail ed.; Online - full text ed.: (from Northern Light Technology, Inc.).
Indexed: B&I.
—CCC.
Published by: Luxner News, Inc., 10454 Parthenon Court, Bethesda, MD 20817. TEL 301-365-1745, FAX 301-365-1829, ani@luxner.com. Ed. Larry Luxner. Pub. Ani Luxner. Circ: 300 (paid).

SOUTH CAROLINA PORT NEWS. see TRANSPORTATION— Ships And Shipping

SOVEREIGN ASSESSMENT MONTHLY. see BUSINESS AND ECONOMICS—Investments

SPACE NEWS (SPRINGFIELD). see AERONAUTICS AND SPACE FLIGHT

382.7   ESP
SPAIN. AGENCIA TRIBUTARIA. INFORMACION ESTADISTICA SOBRE EL COMERCIO EXTERIOR. Text in Spanish. 1965. m. free. **Document type:** Government. **Description:** Presents statistics on trade by commodity, country, economic area, CUCI and more.
Former titles (until 1980): Spain. Direccion General de Aduanas. Informe Mensual sobre el Comercio Exterior (0584-6544); (until 1966): Avance Mensual de la Estadistica del Comercio Exterior de Espana (0212-6834)
Published by: Agencia Tributaria, Departamento de Aduanas e Impuestos Especiales, C/ Infanta Mercedes 37, Madrid, 28020, Spain. TEL 34-91-5837000, intrasta@correo.aetat.es, http://www.aetat.es. Circ: 300.

382   USA
SPAIN: THE BUSINESS LINK. Text in English, Spanish. 1985. q. USD 32; USD 37 foreign. adv. charts; illus.; stat. **Description:** Includes articles on business, finance, economics, law, technology and tourism issues affecting business relations between Spanish and US firms.
Former titles: Business Link; Spain - U.S. Trade Bulletin (0561-5313)
Related titles: Microfiche ed.
Indexed: SRI.
Published by: Spain - U.S. Chamber of Commerce Inc., Empire State Building, 350 Fifth Ave, Ste 2029, New York, NY 10118. TEL 212-967-2170, FAX 212-564-1415. Ed. Edward N Chaves. Circ: 5,000,

SPORT PARTNER; magazine for the sports trade in the Bennelux. see SPORTS AND GAMES

SPORTS AND CHARACTER LICENSING. see SPORTS AND GAMES

382   LKA   ISSN 0069-2360
SRI LANKA EXPORT DIRECTORY. Text in English. a. free. adv. illus. **Document type:** Directory, Government. **Description:** Contains alphabetical listing of exports from Sri Lanka, exporting companies, products, and CCCN numbers. Includes cross-references and general information on Sri Lanka relevant to overseas customers.
Published by: (Sri Lanka. Trade Information Service), Export Development Board, Mawatha, 115 Sir Chittampalam A Gardiner, Colombo, 2, Sri Lanka. TEL 438523, FAX 438404, TELEX 21245-TRADINF-CE. Circ: 5,000.

STAINLESS STEEL REVIEW. see METALLURGY

STAT (BLAINE). see AGRICULTURE

382   PAK   ISSN 0585-1009
STATE BANK OF PAKISTAN. EXPORT RECEIPTS. Text in English. 1966. m. PKR 600, USD 84 (effective 2000). **Document type:** Government. **Description:** Discusses exports covered under the Barter Agreement.
Published by: State Bank of Pakistan, Central Directorate, Public Relations Department, I.I. Chundrigar Rd, PO Box 4456, Karachi, Pakistan. TEL 92-21-9212400, FAX 92-21-9217865, TELEX 21774 SBPK PK.

STATISTICS OF MARINE PRODUCTS EXPORTS. see BUSINESS AND ECONOMICS—Abstracting, Bibliographies, Statistics

338.476 669.142   AUS   ISSN 0726-0865
STEEL PROFILE. Text in English. 1981. q. **Document type:** Journal, Trade.
Published by: Broken Hill Proprietary Co. Ltd, 140 William St, Melbourne, VIC 3001, Australia.

382   FRA
STRATEGIC EUROPE. Text in French. w.
Published by: Lamy S.A. (Subsidiary of: Wolters Kluwer France), 21/23 rue des Ardennes, Paris, 75935 Cedex 19, France. TEL 33-1-825080800, FAX 33-1-44721388, lamy@lamy.fr, http://www.lamy.fr.

382   ITA
STUDI RICERCHE DOCUMENTAZIONE. Text in Italian. 1975. 3/yr. bk.rev. **Document type:** Trade.
Published by: Unione Regionale dfelle Camere di Commercio dell'Emilia-Romagna, Via Aldo Moro 62, Bologna, BO 40127, Italy. TEL 39-051-6377011, FAX 39-051-6377050, staff@rer.camcom.it, http://www.rer.camcom.it. Ed. Claudio Pasini. Circ: 1,000.

STUDIES IN INTERNATIONAL POLICY. see POLITICAL SCIENCE—International Relations

382   USA
SUCCESSFUL FRANCHISING. Text in English. 1996. m. USD 34.95. adv. bk.rev.; software rev.; video rev. bibl.; charts; illus.; stat.; tr.lit. back issues avail. **Document type:** Consumer. **Description:** Designed to help people who are looking to buy a franchise make wise investment decisions.
Related titles: Online - full text ed.
Published by: H I S Publishing, 1575 Lakeview Trl., Berne, IN 46711-1713. TEL 219-589-3997, sfmag@aol.com, http://www.entremkt.com/sf. Ed. John P Hayes. Pub. Brad Bentley. Adv. contact Kevin Miller. page USD 3,995; trim 10.75 x 8. Circ: 75,000. **Subscr. to:** 1105 Leighton Ave, Anniston, AL 36207.

382   JPN
SUMITOMO CORPORATION. ANNUAL REPORT. Text in Japanese. 1980. a. free. charts; stat. **Document type:** Corporate. **Description:** Reviews financial highlights of the Sumitomo Corporation, and its activities in the industrial, commercial, and consumer sectors worldwide.
Published by: Sumitomo Corporation, Corporate Communications Department, 2-2 Hitotsubashi 1-chome, Chiyoda-ku, Tokyo, 100-8601, Japan. TEL 81-3-3217-5114, FAX 81-3-3217-5128, TELEX 22202 SUMIT A J22202, info@sumitomocorp.co.jp, http://www.sumitomocorp.co.jp.

382   FIN   ISSN 0355-7820
SUOMEN TUKKUKAUPPA. Text in Finnish. 10/yr.
Published by: Suomen Tukkukauppiaiden Liitto, Mannerheimintie 76, Helsinki, 00250, Finland.

382   HKG
SUPERTRADER HONG KONG. Text in English. 1998. a. adv. **Document type:** Trade. **Description:** Covers international trade.
Published by: Hong Kong Trade Development Council, 38th Fl Office Tower, Convention Plaza, 1 Harbour Rd, Wanchai, Hong Kong. TEL 852-2584-4333, publications@tdc.org.hk, hktdc@tdc.org.hk, http://www.tdc.org.hk, http://www.tdc.org.hk/. Ed. K S Chan. Adv. contact Wengi Yuen.

382   CHE
SWISSEXPORT. Text in German. q. adv. **Document type:** Bulletin, Trade.
Published by: (Swissexport Association), Exim Index AG, Alderstr 49, Zuerich, 8034, Switzerland. TEL 41-1-4214151, FAX 41-1-4214161, exim@swisstrade.com, http://www.swisstrade.com. Ed. Claudia Moerker. Adv. contact Hans Fasnacht. B&W page CHF 2,850, color page CHF 3,700; trim 210 x 297. Circ: 13,500.

382   CHE
SWISSEXPORT MAGAZIN. Text in German. q. **Document type:** Magazine, Trade.
Formerly: Swissexport Extern
Published by: (Swissexport Association), Exim Index AG, Alderstr 49, Zuerich, 8034, Switzerland. TEL 41-1-4214151, FAX 41-1-4214161, exim@swisstrade.com, http://www.swisstrade.com.

B

382 CHE
SWISSTRADE; current business opportunities with Switzerland. Text in German. 1979. m. (10/yr.). CHF 25 (effective 2000).
Document type: *Magazine, Trade.*
Published by: (Swissexport Cooperation Alliance), Exim Index AG, Alderstr 49, Zuerich, 8034, Switzerland. TEL 41-1-4214151, FAX 41-1-4214161, exim@swisstrade.com, http://www.swisstrade.com.

382 658 CHE
SWITZERLAND. CENTER FOR TRADE FAIRS. Text in English. a. **Document type:** *Directory, Trade.*
Formerly: Swiss Fairs
Published by: Swiss Office for Trade Promotion, Stampfenbachstr 85, Zuerich, 8035, Switzerland. TEL 41-1-3655151, FAX 41-1-3655221, info.zurich@osec.ch, http://www.osec.ch.

SYNDICAT DES EXPORTATEURS ET NEGOCIANTS EN BOIS DE COTE D'IVOIRE. BULLETIN DE LIAISON ET D'INFORMATION. see *FORESTS AND FORESTRY*

SYRACUSE JOURNAL OF INTERNATIONAL LAW & COMMERCE. see *LAW—International Law*

382 ESP
T E T. (The East Trade) Text in English. 1968. m. USD 45. back issues avail. **Document type:** *Newspaper.*
Published by: German Perez Editore, Carrasco 63, Madrid 17, Spain. TEL 1-267-24-03, FAX 1-406-78-37, TELEX 43782 EDOF E. Ed. Arsenio Pardo Rodriquez.

382.7 CHE ISSN 1421-2773
T V A - M W S T - V A T JOURNAL✱. Text in English, French, German. 1996. q. CHF 102 (effective 2000). **Document type:** *Bulletin, Trade.*
Indexed: IBR, IBZ.
Published by: (Institut fuer Abgabe- und Wirtschaftsrecht), Staempfli Verlag AG (Subsidiary of: LexisNexis Europe and Africa), Woelflistr 1, Bern, 3001, Switzerland. TEL 41-31-3006666, FAX 41-31-3006688, verlag@staempfli.com, http://www.staempfli.com. Circ: 500 (paid).

TAIPAN. see *BUSINESS AND ECONOMICS—Investments*

382 TWN
TAIWAN EXPORT EXPRESS. Text in English. m. USD 40 in in Americas, Europe & Africa; USD 3,540 in Middle East & Asia (effective 2000). adv. **Document type:** *Trade.* **Description:** Contains information on products manufactured in Taiwan.
Published by: China Economic News Service, 555 Chunghsiao E. Rd Sec 4, Taipei, 110, Taiwan. TEL 886-2-2642-2629, FAX 886-2-2642-7422, webmaster@www.cens.com, http://www.cens.com. adv.: B&W page TWD 22,500, color page TWD 35,000.

382 TWN
TAIWAN EXPORTERS. Text in Chinese. 1980 (no.92). s-m. USD 12.
Published by: Nancy Yu Huang, 8 Fu Shun St, Taipei, 104, Taiwan.

382.6 TWN ISSN 0494-5336
TAIWAN EXPORTS. Text mainly in English. 1957. irreg. illus.
Published by: Board of Foreign Trade, 1 Hu Kou St, Taipei, Taiwan.

382.0951 TWN ISSN 0257-8158
TAIWAN INTERNATIONAL TRADE. Text in Chinese. 1971. m. USD 60 in Asia; USD 70 elsewhere. **Document type:** *Catalog.* **Description:** A detailed guide to general merchandise from Taiwan, including footwear, houseware, D.I.Y. products, hardware, and sporting goods.
Formerly: Trade Monthly
Published by: United Pacific International Inc., P.O. Box 81-417, Taipei, Taiwan. TEL 02-7150751, FAX 886-2-7125591, TELEX 28784-UNIPAINC.

382 TWN
TAIWAN MERCHANDISE. Text in English. 1977. bi-m. USD 35 in Asia; USD 40 elsewhere (effective 2000). adv.
Formerly: Taiwan Products
Related titles: Japanese ed.: Taiwan Merchandise Japanese Special. USD 40 in Americas, Europe & Africa; USD 35 in Middle East & Asia (effective 2000); Spanish ed.: Mercancia de Taiwan. USD 40 in Americas, Europe & Africa; USD 35 in Middle East & Asia (effective 2000).
Indexed: PST.
Published by: China Economic News Service, 561 Chunghsiao E. Rd Sec 4, Taipei, 10516, Taiwan. TEL 886-2-642-2629, FAX 886-2-2642-7422, TELEX 27710-CENSPC, webmaster@www.cens.com, http://www.cens.com. Ed. Steve Shen. adv.: B&W page TWD 35,000, color page TWD 40,000. Circ: 5,000. **Subscr. to:** P.O. Box 43-60, Taipei, Taiwan.

TAIWAN, REPUBLIC OF CHINA. MINISTRY OF FINANCE. DEPARTMENT OF STATISTICS. MONTHLY STATISTICS OF EXPORTS AND IMPORTS/CHIN CH'U K'OU MAO I T'UNG CHI YUEH PAO. see *BUSINESS AND ECONOMICS—Abstracting, Bibliographies, Statistics*

382 TWN ISSN 1028-1126
TAIWAN TRADE OPPORTUNITIES. Text in Chinese. 1973. m. TWD 900, USD 50. adv. **Document type:** *Trade.* **Description:** Provides information on sources of supply and demand in Taiwan. Also covers industry reports, company profiles and trade statistics.
Formerly (until 1993): Trade Opportunities in Taiwan
Indexed: KES.
Published by: China External Trade Development Council, 8th Fl, 333 Keelung Rd, Sec 1, Taipei, Taiwan. TEL 02-725-5200, FAX 02-2757-6828. Ed. Peter F H Chan. Pub. Ricky Y S Kao. Circ: 8,000.

382 RUS
TAMOZHENNYI VESTNIK; prilozhenie k gazete ekonomicheskie novosti. Text in Russian. bi-m. USD 239 foreign (effective 2005). **Document type:** *Newspaper, Trade.*
Published by: Ekonomicheskie Novosti/Economic News, Post Box 58, Moscow 9, 103050, Russian Federation. TEL 7-095-2993827, FAX 7-095-9210609, econews@econews.ru, http://www.econews.ru. Circ: 47,000. **US dist. addr.:** East View Information Services, 3020 Harbor Ln. N., Minneapolis, MN 55447. TEL 800-477-1005, FAX 763-559-2931, eastview@eastview.com, http://www.eastview.com.

382.029 TZA
TANZANIA IMPORT AND EXPORT DIRECTORY. Text in English. 1975. irreg. adv. illus. **Document type:** *Directory.*
Published by: (Directorate of International Operations), National Bank of Commerce, PO Box 1863, Dar Es Salaam, Tanzania. Circ: 3,000.

332.6 TZA ISSN 0856-2105
HF1612.9
TANZANIA TRADE CURRENTS. Text in English. 1983. bi-m. USD 25. **Document type:** *Newsletter.* **Description:** Publishes information on trade fairs, marketing research, trade and investment opportunities.
Formed by the 1987 merger of: Market Newsletter. Trade Brief (0856-0668); Market Newsletter. World Market Prices and Trends for Agricultural Commodities (0856-0544)
Published by: Board of External Trade, PO Box 5402, Dar Es Salaam, Tanzania. TEL 255-51-36303, FAX 255-51-46240, TELEX 41408 EXTRADE. Ed. R L Mkenda. Circ: 2,000.

382 FRA
TARGET INTERNATIONAL MAGAZINE; your best source of money making opportunities. Variant title: T I M. Text in French. 1975. q. USD 36. adv. **Document type:** *Trade.* **Description:** Contains information on new products, ideas, services and inventions from around the world. Gives tips on import - export and international trade.
Formerly (until 1995): Globe - Contact International (1018-1830)
Published by: Rendement - Plus, 32 rue de la Favorite, Lyon, Cedex 5 69246, France. TEL 78-36-36-38, FAX 78-25-55-00. Ed. Annabel Dubois. Pub., Adv. contact Thierry C Pradat. B&W page USD 1,260; 130 x 195. Circ: 15,000.

382 GBR ISSN 1367-4390
TARIFICA ALERT. Text in English. 1997. w. GBP 595 (effective 2004). **Document type:** *Newsletter.*
Media: E-mail. **Related titles:** Online - full text ed.: (from Gale Group).
Published by: Phillips Tarifica Ltd (Subsidiary of: Access Intelligence, LLC), 40/41 Furnival St, London, EC4A 1JQ, United Kingdom. TEL 44 171 440 6500, FAX 44 171 831 8552, consult@tarifica.com, http://www.tarifica.com/alerts.

382 GBR ISSN 1361-9519
TAX-FREE TRADER & TRAVEL RETAIL WORLD. Text in English. 1972. 10/yr. GBP 131 domestic; GBP 155 foreign; GBP 17 newsstand/cover (effective 1999 - 2000). adv. **Document type:** *Journal, Trade.*
Former titles (until 1995): International Tax-Free Trader (1354-0548); (until 1994): International Tax-Free Trader & Duty-Free World (0306-6045)
Related titles: Online - full text ed.: (from Gale Group).
Published by: D M G World Media Ltd. (Subsidiary of: Daily Mail and General Trust PLC), Queensway House, 2 Queensway, Redhill, Surrey RH1 1QS, United Kingdom. TEL 44-1737-855527, FAX 44-1737-855470, http://www.dmg.co.uk, http://www.dmgworldmedia.com. Ed. Peter Tipthorpe. Adv. contact Michael Lewis. Circ: 4,971.

TAX MANAGEMENT COUNTRY PORTFOLIOS. see *BUSINESS AND ECONOMICS—Public Finance, Taxation*

382 USA
TAXES AND TRADE INTERNATIONAL; trade without borders. Text in English. 1985. m. USD 425 (effective 2001). bk.rev.; software rev.; Website rev. stat. index. 16 p./no.; back issues avail. **Document type:** *Newsletter, Trade.*
Formerly (until 2001): Cricket Trade
Related titles: E-mail ed.; Fax ed.
Published by: Cricket Communications, Inc., PO Box 527, Ardmore, PA 19003. TEL 610-924-9158, FAX 610-924-9159, crcktinc@aol.com. Ed. Mark E Battensby. Circ: 2,615 (paid).

382 CAN ISSN 1704-1368
HF1479
TEAM CANADA INC. ANNUAL REPORT. Text in English, French. 2001. a.
Formed by the merger of (2000-2001): Team Canada Inc. Business Plan (1704-1341); (1997-2001): Team Canada Inc. Achievements Report (1704-1333)
Related titles: Online - full content ed.: ISSN 1702-6660.
Published by: Public Works and Government Services Canada, Place du Portage, Phase III, 11 Laurier St, Gatineau, PQ K1A 0S5, Canada. TEL 800-622-6232, Questions@pwgsc.gc.ca, http://www.pwgsc.gc.ca/text/home-e.html.

382 600 USA ISSN 0886-103X
TECHNOLOGY MANAGEMENT ACTION. Text in English. 1973. m. looseleaf. USD 218 domestic; USD 245 in Canada & Mexico; USD 286 elsewhere (effective 2005). bk.rev. charts; stat. index. back issues avail. **Document type:** *Newsletter.* **Description:** Shows how technology managers and executives worldwide improve competitiveness, productivity, and innovation through the wise use of technology tools and enlightened policies. Covers topics in engineering, research, finance, trade, technology transfer, and productivity.
Former titles: Technology Transfer Action; Overseas Business Action
Published by: Technology News Center, 6810 Butler Valley Rd, Korbel, CA 95550. tnc@humboldt1.com. Ed., Pub. Norman Lynn. R&P Shirley Annis. Circ: 6,200 (paid).

TECHNOLOGY TRANSFER SOCIETY. INTERNATIONAL SYMPOSIUM AND EXHIBIT. ANNUAL MEETING PROCEEDINGS. see *BUSINESS AND ECONOMICS—Management*

382 332 GBR ISSN 1352-6456
TELECOM FINANCE. Text in English. 1994. m. GBP 755, USD 1,090 (effective 2001). adv. mkt. back issues avail. **Document type:** *Journal, Trade.* **Description:** Worldwide primary source information on debt & equity funding in the telecommunications industry.
Related titles: CD-ROM ed.; Fax ed.; Online - full text ed.: GBP 375, USD 540 (effective 2001).
—CCC.
Published by: Thompson Stanley Publishers Ltd., Clerkenwell House, 45-47 Clerkenwell Green, London, EC1R 0EB, United Kingdom. TEL 44-20-7553-3919, FAX 44-20-7251-1833, http://www.telecomfinance.com. Ed. Carol Dean. R&P Chris Thompson. Adv. contact Jo Nhan. Circ: 5,000.

TELEMARKETER. see *BUSINESS AND ECONOMICS—Marketing And Purchasing*

TELEVISION BUSINESS INTERNATIONAL. see *COMMUNICATIONS—Television And Cable*

382 TUR ISSN 1301-4617
TEXTILE EXPORTS - TURKEY. Text in English. 1997. m. adv. **Document type:** *Government.*
Published by: Ihlas Magazine Group, Ihlas Holding Mrk. Binasi, 29 Ekim Cad. 23, Yenibosna - Istanbul, 34530, Turkey. TEL 90-212-4542530, FAX 90-212-4542555, bsensoz@img.com.tr, http://www.img.com.tr. Ed. Mehmet Soztutan. Pub. Dr. Enver Oren. R&P Muhsin Yilmaz. Adv. contact Ms. Bahar Sensoz. page USD 2,000; 25.5 x 37. Circ: 2,500 (paid); 25,588 (controlled).

332.6 THA ISSN 0857-6548
THAILAND EXIMPORT REVIEW. Text in English. 1987. m. **Document type:** *Academic/Scholarly.*
Published by: Eximport Publishing Co. Ltd., PO Box 11 1165, Nana Post Office, Bangkok, 10110, Thailand. TEL 662-234-7768, FAX 662-234-2567. Circ: 50,000.

332.6 THA
THAILAND SHOWCASE; a buyers' guide. Text in Thai. 1992. a. USD 40. adv. **Document type:** *Directory, Trade.* **Description:** Lists over 3,000 selected exporters broken down into 19 industrial sectors. Also provides an overview of the Thai economy.
Published by: (Thai Chamber of Commerce), Cosmic Group of Companies, 4th Fl Phyathai Bldg, Rajthevi, 31 Phyathai Rd, Bangkok, 10400, Thailand. TEL 245-3850, FAX 246-4737. Ed. Gordon E Fairclough. Adv. contact Porntip Petchsingh. color page USD 1,320. Circ: 10,000 (controlled). **Dist. by:** Current Pacific Ltd., PO Box 36-536, Northcote, Auckland, New Zealand. TEL 64-9-480-1388, FAX 64-9-480-1387, info@cplnz.com, http://www.cplnz.com.

382 THA
THAILAND TRADE INDEX. Text in English, Thai. 1976. a. adv. illus.; stat.
Published by: Interstate Publications, Pathumwan, P.O. Box 5-85, Bangkok 5, Thailand.

332.6 665.5 VNM ISSN 0866-7500
HF3800.5+
THUONGMAI/COMMERCIAL REVIEW. Text in Vietnamese. bi-m.
Published by: Vietnam National Petroleum Export - Import Corporation, 1 Kham Thien, Hanoi, Viet Nam. TEL 42-52603, FAX 84-42-59203, TELEX 411241 TCTXD VT.

332.6 SGP
TODAY WORLD TRADE OPPORTUNITIES DIGEST. Text in English. 1987. m. SGD 60; USD 50 in Asia; USD 66 in North America; USD 60 elsewhere. adv. **Document type:** *Trade.* **Description:** Covers world trade opportunities for importers, exporters, manufacturers, agents, trade associations, and chambers of commerce & industry worldwide.
Published by: Rightway Marketing & Trade Promotions, Toa Payoh Central, P.O. Box 221, Singapore, 9131, Singapore. TEL 065-4670083, FAX 065-4677372.

332.6 CHN
TOP 500 FOREIGN TRADE COMPANIES IN CHINA. Text in Chinese, English. 1991. a. USD 79.50. **Document type:** *Directory.* **Description:** Provides information on the top 500 import and export companies ranked by their annual turnover, company name, address, phone, fax, contact person and business activity.
Published by: Han Consultants Inc., P.O. Box 71006, Wuhan, Hubei 430071, China. TEL 86-27-787-8532, FAX 86-27-787-8343. Circ: 6,000.

TOTAL RATE-OF-RETURN INDEXES. see *BUSINESS AND ECONOMICS—Investments*

332.6 USA
TOWARD SEAMLESS BORDERS. Text in English. 1993. irreg., latest vol.3, 1994. **Document type:** *Monographic series.* **Description:** Deals with the major aspects of free trade in the Americas.
Published by: National Law Center for Inter-American Free Trade, 2 E Congress St, 500, Tucson, AZ 85701-1728. TEL 602-622-1200, FAX 602-622-0957, natlaw@natlaw.com, http://www.natlaw.com.

TOYS AND GAMES IMPORTS AMERICA DIRECTORY. see *GIFTWARE AND TOYS*

TRADE ACTION MONITORING SYSTEM. see *BUSINESS AND ECONOMICS—Domestic Commerce*

332.6 338.91 USA
TRADE & DEVELOPMENT✶ ; news and trade opportunities. Text in English. 1992. bi-w. looseleaf. USD 175 domestic; USD 270 foreign (effective 2000). back issues avail. **Description:** International trade and development clearinghouse.
Published by: Congressional Information Bureau, Inc., 146, Wachapreague, VA 23480-0146. TEL 703-516-4801, 703-516-4804. Ed., Pub. Robert Cazalas. Circ: 500.

382 338.91 USA
TRADE AND DEVELOPMENT AGENCY✶ **.** Text in English. bi-w. USD 175 in North America; USD 315 elsewhere (effective 2000); includes TDA Pipeline, World Bank, Export-Import Bank, Inter-American Development Bank, USAID, and others.
Published by: Congressional Information Bureau, Inc., 146, Wachapreague, VA 23480-0146. TEL 703-516-4804, cibaech@erols.com, http://www.cibpub.scom, http://www.cibpubs.com. Pub. Robert Cazalas.

382 338.91 CHE ISSN 0255-4607
HF1008
TRADE AND DEVELOPMENT REPORT. Abbreviated title: T D R. Text in English, French, Spanish. 1981. a. USD 39 developed countries; USD 19 developing countries (effective 2004). back issues avail. **Document type:** *Monographic series, Academic/Scholarly.* **Description:** Examines trends and prospects in the international economy with an emphasis on the policy implications for developing countries. Aimed at policy makers and academics.
Related titles: Microfiche ed.: (from CIS); Online - full text ed.; French ed.: Rapport sur le Commerce et le Developpement. ISSN 0256-0887; Spanish ed.: Informe Sobre el Comercio y el Desarrollo. ISSN 0257-8093.
Indexed: IIS, PAIS, RASB.
—BLDSC (8879.247000). **CCC.**
Published by: United Nations Conference on Trade and Development, Palais des Nations, 8-14 Av de la Paix, Geneva 10, 1211, Switzerland. TEL 41-22-907-1234, info@unctad.org, http://www.un.org/publications. Circ: 11,000.

382 USA
TRADE AND EMPLOYMENT EFFECTS OF THE ANDEAN TRADE PERFERENCE ACT; annual report to the Congress pursuant to Section 207 of the Andean Trade Preference Act. Text in English. a. **Document type:** *Government.*
Related titles: Online - full content ed.
Published by: U.S. Department of Labor, Bureau of International Labor Affairs, Frances Perkins Bldg, Rm C-4325, 200 Constitution Ave, NW, Washington, DC 20210. TEL 202-693-4770, FAX 202-693-4780, Contact-ILAB@dol.gov, http://www.dol.gov/ilab/.

382 GBR ISSN 1465-136X
TRADE & FORFAITING REVIEW. Text in English. 1997. 10/yr. GBP 195 domestic print or online; EUR 305 in Europe print or online; USD 350 elsewhere print or online; GBP 295 combined subscription domestic print & online; EUR 475 combined subscription in Europe print & online; USD 495 combined subscription elsewhere print & online (effective 2005). adv. **Document type:** *Magazine, Trade.*
Formerly (until 1998): Forfaiting Review (1460-1044)
Related titles: Online - full content ed.
—**CCC.**
Published by: Ark Group Ltd, 86-88 Upper Richmond Rd, London, SW15 2UR, United Kingdom. TEL 44-20-87852700, FAX 44-20-87859373, info@ark-group.com, http://www.tfreview.com, http://www.ark-group.com. Ed. Michele Martensen. Pub. Andreas Silbermann. Adv. contact Nick Rust.

382 NLD
TRADE CHANNEL (CONSUMER PRODUCTS EDITION). Text in Dutch. 1946. m. USD 88 (effective 1998 & 1999). adv. bk.rev. **Document type:** *Trade.* **Description:** Gives product offerings and business opportunities in housewares, hobbies, textiles and fashion, food, cosmetics and health, gifts and toys, luxuries, and office equipment.
Former titles (until 1996): Export Channel (Consumer Products Edition); Export Channel (Consumer Edition)
Indexed: KES.
Published by: Trade Channel Organisation B.V., Stolbergstraat 14, Haarlem, 2012 EP, Netherlands. TEL 31-23-5319022, FAX 31-23-5317974, tco_nl@compuserve.com, http://www.tradechannel.com. Ed. Henk van Capelle. Pub., R&P Paul Vroom. Adv. contact Fred van der Heyden. Circ: 30,000.

382 NLD
TRADE CHANNEL (TECHNICAL PRODUCTS EDITION). Text in Dutch. 1946. m. USD 88 (effective 1998 & 1999). adv. bk.rev. **Document type:** *Trade.* **Description:** Gives product offerings and business opportunities in metalworking, machinery, construction, electronics, transportation and industrial supplies.
Former titles (until 1996): Export Channel (Technical Products Edition); Export Channel (Technical Edition); Trade Channel (0041-0403)
Indexed: KES.
Published by: Trade Channel Organisation B.V., Stolbergstraat 14, Haarlem, 2012 EP, Netherlands. TEL 31-23-5319022, FAX 31-23-5317974, tco_nl@compuserve.com, http://www.tradechannel.com. Ed. Henk van Capelle. Pub., R&P Paul Vroom. Adv. contact Fred van der Heyden. Circ: 55,000.

332.6 USA
TRADE CONNECTIONS. Text in English. 1984. a. free to qualified personnel. tr.lit. 150 p./no.; **Document type:** *Directory, Trade.*
Related titles: Online - full content ed.
Published by: Federation of International Trade Associations, 11800 Sunrise Valley Dr, Ste 210, Reston, VA 20191-5302. TEL 703-620-1588, FAX 703-391-0159, info@fita.org, http://www.fita.org. Ed. N T Joyner. Circ: 5,000.

382.029 USA
TRADE DIRECTORY OF MEXICO. Text in English. a. USD 100. **Document type:** *Directory.* **Description:** Contains contact and business information for import and export companies located in Mexico.
Related titles: Diskette ed.: USD 195.
Published by: Mexican Foreign Trade Bank, c/o Walker's Research, 1650 Borel Pl, Ste 130, San Mateo, CA 94402. TEL 800-258-5737, FAX 650-341-2351.

TRADE FINANCE. see *BUSINESS AND ECONOMICS—Banking And Finance*

382 TWN
TRADE PAGES. Text in English. 4/yr. USD 40. **Description:** Emphasizes gifts, premiums, novelties, houseware, toys and games, electronic and electric appliances, personal care items, sporting goods.
Published by: Taiwan Trade Pages Corp., P.O. Box 72-50, Taipei, Taiwan. TEL 02-3050759, FAX 886-2-3071000, TELEX 24838TRADEPAG.

382.3 CAN ISSN 1702-5524
HF1410
TRADE POLICY RESEARCH. Text in English. 2001. a.
Related titles: Online - full text ed.: ISSN 1702-5540.
—CISTI.
Published by: Canada. Department of Foreign Affairs and International Trade, 125 Sussex Dr, Ottawa, ON K1A OG2, Canada. TEL 613-944-4000, FAX 613-996-9709, enqserv@dfait-maeci.gc.ca, http://www.dfait-maeci.gc.ca/.

382 CHE ISSN 1014-7411
HF1455
TRADE POLICY REVIEW. Text in English. 1990. a. price varies. charts. **Document type:** *Trade.* **Description:** Contains comprehensive trade policy analysis prepared by the country under review and the GATT secretariat.
Related titles: French ed.; Spanish ed.
Indexed: IIS.
—CISTI.
Published by: General Agreement on Tariffs and Trade, Centre William Rappard, 154 rue de Lausanne, Geneva 21, 1211, Switzerland. TEL 41-22-7395208, FAX 41-22-7395458, info@gatt.org.

382.9 CAN
TRADE ROUNDUP.COM. Text in English. irreg. USD 99. **Document type:** *Trade.* **Description:** Presents a summary of the week's top Nafta related stories.
Formerly: N A F T A Roundup
Media: Online - full text.
Published by: SmartSources.Com, 2030 Marine Dr, Ste 100, N. Vancouver, BC V7P 1V7, Canada. TEL 604-986-0889, FAX 604-986-0869, tmartin@smartsources.com, http://www.cluborigin.com. Ed. Todd Martin.

TRADE SECRETS LAW. see *LAW—Corporate Law*

382 USA ISSN 1531-006X
HF3035
TRADE SERVICES DIRECTORY & GUIDE. Text in English. 2001. a. USD 425 (effective 1996). adv. Supplement avail. **Document type:** *Trade.* **Description:** Provides service listings, information sources, a glossary of international trade terms, sample forms, and maps for the import and export processes.
Formed by the 2001 merger of part of: Official Export Guide (0278-6389); part of: U.S. Custom House Guide (1084-8681); Which was formerly (until 1988): Official U.S. Customs House Guide (0891-1517); (until 1987): U.S. Customs Guide (0890-6769); (until 1986): Custom House Guide (0070-2250)
—**CCC.**
Published by: Commonwealth Business Media, Inc., 400 Windsor Corporate Ctr, 50 Millstone Rd, Ste 200, East Windsor, NJ 08520-1415. TEL 609-371-7700, 800-221-5488, FAX 609-371-7883, amiddlebrook@cbizmedia.com, http://www.cbizmedia.com. Ed. Amy Middlebrook. Pub. John G John III. adv.: B&W page USD 3,930; 7 x 10. Circ: 5,600.

382 HKG
TRADE WATCH. Text in Chinese. m. **Document type:** *Trade.*
Indexed: HongKongiana.
Published by: (Research Department), Hong Kong Trade Development Council, 38th Fl Office Tower, Convention Plaza, 1 Harbour Rd, Wanchai, Hong Kong. TEL 852-2584-4333, hktdc@tdc.org.hk, http://www.tdc.org.hk/. Ed. Edward Leung.

382 TWN
TRADE WEEKLY. Text in Chinese. w. USD 120 in Hong Kong; USD 140 elsewhere.
Published by: Importers & Exporters Association of Taipei, 5th Fl, 350 Sungkiang Rd, Taipei, 104, Taiwan. TEL 02-581-3521, FAX 02-536-3328.

382 TWN ISSN 0259-9880
TRADE WINDS MONTHLY. Text in English. 1980. m. USD 90 in Asia & the Pacific (effective 2001); USD 110 elsewhere (effective 2000). adv. tr.lit. **Document type:** *Trade.* **Description:** Covers Taiwan's export industries and products, emphasizing consumer products.
Published by: Interface Global Taiwan Co., Ltd., PO Box 173-12, Taipei, 116, Taiwan. TEL 886-2-2393-2718, FAX 886-2-2395-2901, tradwind@ms2.hinet.net, http://www.asiatrademart.com. Ed. Daniel Foong. Pub. Herbert Chen. R&P Donald Shapiro. Adv. contact Melody Lin TEL 886-2-2351-3180. Circ: 10,000. **Subscr. in U.S. to:** Trade Winds Inc., PO Box 820519, Dallas, TX 75382. TEL 877-861-1188, FAX 972-699-1189, twinds8888@aol.com.

TRADELINK - CHINESE. see *BUSINESS AND ECONOMICS—Trade And Industrial Directories*

TRADELINK - ENGLISH. see *BUSINESS AND ECONOMICS—Trade And Industrial Directories*

332.6 GBR
TRADEWINDS - THE NETWORK FOR PORTUGAL. Text in English. 1980. 4/yr. membership. adv. bk.rev. **Document type:** *Newsletter, Trade.* **Description:** Contains bilateral business and membership news concerning Portugal and the U.K.
Former titles: Tradewinds; Tradewinds Newsletter (1352-1152)
Related titles: E-mail ed.: E-Tradewinds.
Published by: Portuguese UK Chamber of Commerce, 22-25a Sackville St, 4th Fl, London, W1X 1DE, United Kingdom. TEL 44-20-7494-1844, FAX 44-20-7494-1822, info@portuguese-chamber.org.uk, http://www.portuguese-chamber.org.uk. Ed., R&P Ronald Price. Circ: 2,000 (controlled).

382 GBR
TRADING LAW NEWSLETTER. Text in English. q. **Document type:** *Newsletter.*
Published by: Lovell White Durrant, 65 Holburn Viaduct, London, EC1A 2DY, United Kingdom. TEL 44-20-7236-0066, FAX 44-20-7248-4212, publications@lovellwhitedurrant.com, http://www.lovellwhitedurrant.com.

382 CHE ISSN 1014-9562
HD2755.5
➤ **TRANSNATIONAL CORPORATIONS.** Short title: T N Cs. Text in English. 1976. 3/yr. USD 45; USD 20 newsstand/cover; CND 4.95 newsstand/cover in Canada; GBP 2.95 newsstand/cover in United Kingdom (effective 2004). bk.rev. **Document type:** *Journal, Academic/Scholarly.* **Description:** Publishes articles and research notes that provide foreign direct investment in an increasingly global economy and the policy implications that arise therefrom.
Formerly (until 1992): C T C Reporter (0255-4216)
Related titles: Microfiche ed.: (from CIS); Online - full text ed.: (from Gale Group).
Indexed: ABIn, CREJ, IIS, IPSA, JEL, PAIS, RASB.
—BLDSC (9024.975220), IE, Infotrieve, ingenta. **CCC.**

Published by: (Division on Investment, Technology and Enterprise Development USA), United Nations Conference on Trade and Development, Palais des Nations, 8-14 Av de la Paix, Geneva 10, 1211, Switzerland. TEL 41-22-9175809, FAX 41-22-9170051, info@unctad.org, http://www.unctad.org/en/subsites/dite/1_itncs/1_tncs.htm. Ed., R&P Karl P Sauvant. Circ: 3,500. **Subscr. to:** United Nations Publications, Distribution and Sales Section, Palais des Nations, Geneva CH-1211, Switzerland. TEL 41-22-907-2612, publications@un.org. **Dist. by:** United Nations Publications.

382.029 AUS ISSN 0810-025X
TRAVELTRADE VISA GUIDE. Text in English. 1977. a. AUD 51.98 (effective 2001). adv. **Document type:** *Trade.* **Description:** Lists the names, addresses and telephone numbers of embassies, consulates, and high commissions in Australia and New Zealand.
Former titles (until 1982): Traveltrade Travel Guide (0159-7752); (until 1980): Traveltrade Visa Handbook (0156-1545)
Published by: Reed Business Information Pty Ltd (Subsidiary of: Reed Business Information International), Locked Bag 2999, Chatswood, NSW 2067, Australia. customerservice@reedbusiness.com.au, http://www.reedbusiness.com.au. Ed. Doug Kujovic. Pub. Barrie Parsons. Adv. contact John McGaulley. Circ: 2,200.

THE TREASURER; the official journal of the Association of Corporate Treasurers. see *BUSINESS AND ECONOMICS—Banking And Finance*

338 382 FRA ISSN 0041-2872
TRIBUNE LIBRE. Text in French. 1906. m. adv. bk.rev. charts; illus.; stat. index. **Document type:** *Newspaper.*
Published by: Chambre Syndicale Nationale des Forces de Vente, 2 rue d'Hauteville, Paris, Cedex 10 75480, France. TEL 33-1-48249759. Ed. Jean Pierre Broggi. Adv. contact Dominique Michaud. Circ: 30,000.

382 TTO
THE TRINIDAD AND TOBAGO EXPORTER. Text in English. 1996. 3/yr. **Document type:** *Magazine, Trade.* **Description:** Promotes Trinidad and Tobago exports.
Published by: Media & Editorial Projects Ltd., 6 Prospect Ave, Maraval, Port of Spain, Trinidad & Tobago. TEL 868-622-3821, FAX 868-628-0639, mep@wow.net, http://www.readcaribbean.com. Ed., Pub. Jeremy Taylor. Circ: 7,500 (controlled).

382.029 GBR ISSN 0082-657X
TRINIDAD AND TOBAGO TRADE DIRECTORY. Text in English. 1963. a. index.
Published by: Arthur H. Thrower Ltd., 44-46 S Ealing Rd, London, W5, United Kingdom. Ed. Arthur H Thrower.

382 TUR
TURKISH EXPORTERS CATALOGUE. Text in English. 1991. m. **Document type:** *Catalog.*
Published by: Ihlas Magazine Group, Ihlas Holding Mrk. Binasi, 29 Ekim Cad. 23, Yenibosna - Istanbul, 34530, Turkey. TEL 90-212-4542530, FAX 90-212-4542555, bsensoz@img.com.tr, imga@img.com.tr, http://www.img.com.tr. Ed. Mehmet Soztutan. Pub. Dr. Enver Oren. R&P Muhsin Yilmaz. Adv. contact Ms. Bahar Sensoz. Circ: 2,117 (paid); 18,000 (controlled).

382 USA ISSN 1046-9427
HD9734.M43
TWIN PLANT NEWS; the magazine of the maquiladora industry. Text in English. 1985. m. USD 85 domestic; USD 95 in Canada; USD 110 elsewhere. adv. bk.rev. **Document type:** *Trade.* **Description:** Provides information on doing business in Mexico.
—Linda Hall.
Published by: Nibbe, Hernandez & Associates, Inc., 725 S. Mesa Hills Dr., Ste. 1-2, El Paso, TX 79912-5557. TEL 915-532-1567, FAX 915-544-7556. Ed., R&P Mike Patten. Pub. Rosa Maria Nibbe. Adv. contact Chet Corey. Circ: 10,000.

U C L A JOURNAL OF INTERNATIONAL LAW AND FOREIGN AFFAIRS. (University of California at Los Angeles) see *LAW—International Law*

382 USA ISSN 0259-3181
U N C T A D BULLETIN. Text in English. 1966. m. bibl.
Formerly (until 1983): U N C T A D Monthly Bulletin (0252-5232)
Media: Duplicated (not offset). **Related titles:** French ed.: C N U C E D Bulletin. ISSN 1011-1131.
Indexed: BibInd, EnvAb.
Published by: (United Nations, Conference on Trade and Development), United Nations Publications, Rm DC2-853, United Nations Bldg, 2 United Nations Plaza, New York, NY 10017. TEL 212-963-8302, 800-253-9646, FAX 212-963-3489, publications@un.org, http://www.un.org/publications, http://www.un.org/Pubs.

382.7 CHE ISSN 1014-546X
U N C T A D DISCUSSION PAPERS SERIES. Text in English. 1983. irreg., latest vol.153, 2000. back issues avail. **Document type:** *Monographic series, Academic/Scholarly.*
Related titles: Online - full text ed.: ISSN 1564-9687.
Published by: United Nations Conference on Trade and Development, 8-14 Avenue de la Paix, Geneva 10, 1211, Switzerland. TEL 41-22-9174924, FAX 41-22-9070195, info@unctad.org, http://www.unctad.org.

U N C T A D HANDBOOK OF STATISTICS/MANUEL DE STATISTIQUES DE LA C N U C E D. (United Nations Conference on Trade and Development) see *BUSINESS AND ECONOMICS—Abstracting, Bibliographies, Statistics*

382 338.91 USA ISSN 1014-370X
HF1410
U N C T A D REVIEW. Text in English. 1979. s-a. USD 30. **Description:** International journal on trade, finance and development issues.
Formerly: Trade and Development: An U N C T A Review (0252-5216)
Related titles: Microfiche ed.: (from CIS).
Indexed: APEL, CREJ, IIS, JEL, PAIS, RASB.
—CISTI.
Published by: (United Nations, Conference on Trade and Development), United Nations Publications, Rm DC2-853, United Nations Bldg, 2 United Nations Plaza, New York, NY 10017. TEL 212-963-8302, 800-253-9646, FAX 212-963-3489, publications@un.org, http://www.un.org/publications, http://www.un.org/Pubs.

332.6 GBR ISSN 1351-1637
U S A AND EUROPE IN BUSINESS. Text in English. a. GBP 29.95 per issue; free to qualified personnel (effective 2003). adv. **Document type:** *Journal, Trade.* **Description:** Covers important facets of all key business sectors, including a country-by-country report on business tactics and projections.
Published by: S P G Media Ltd. (Subsidiary of: Sterling Publishing Group Plc.), Brunel House, 55-57 North Wharf Rd, London, W2 1LA, United Kingdom. TEL 44-20-79159600, FAX 44-20-77242089, info@sterlingpublications.com, http://www.usaeurope-business.com/, http://www.spgmedia.com/. Pub. Sarah Woddis. Circ: 17,000 (controlled).

382 DEU
U S A HANDEL. Text in German. 1963. bi-m. USD 18.75. **Document type:** *Trade.* **Description:** Covers import-export topics, new products and services, investment opportunities, trade policy issues and US Dept. of Commerce export promotion programs.
Published by: American Embassy, Foreign Commercial Service, Deichmanns Aue 29, Bonn, 53179, Germany. TEL 0228-339-2944, FAX 0228-334649. adv.: B&W page USD 620, color page USD 1,675; trim 265 x 185. Circ: 4,500.

382 USA
U.S. BUREAU OF THE CENSUS. SCHEDULE B: STATISTICAL CLASSIFICATION OF DOMESTIC AND FOREIGN COMMODITIES EXPORTED FROM THE UNITED STATES. (Base vol. updates are titled: Public Bulletins) Text in English. 2 base vols. plus irreg. updates. looseleaf. USD 121 for base vol. & updates for an indeterminate period (effective 2001). 1600 p./no.; **Document type:** *Government.* **Description:** Contains approximately 40,007 digit commodity classifications, based on the organization framework of the Tariff Schedules of the United States, Annotated, to be used by shippers in reporting export shipments from the United States and for use in compiling official statistics on exports of merchandise from the United States.
Related titles: CD-ROM ed.
Published by: U.S. Bureau of the Census (Subsidiary of: U.S. Department of Commerce), Foreign Trade Division, 4700 Silver Hill Rd, Rm 2179, Federal Office Building #3, Washington, DC 20233. http://www.census.gov/mp/www/pub/ftd/msftd08a.html. **Subscr. to:** U.S. Government Printing Office, Superintendent of Documents, PO Box 371954, Pittsburgh, PA 15250-7954. TEL 202-512-1800, FAX 202-512-2250, orders@gpo.gov, http://www.access.gpo.gov.

382 USA ISSN 1066-1778
U.S. CORPORATIONS DOING BUSINESS ABROAD. Text in English. 1972. a. USD 39.95 (effective 2005).
Published by: Price Waterhouse Coopers LLP, 1177 Ave of the Americas, New York, NY 10036. TEL 646-471-4000, FAX 646-471-3188, http://www.pwcglobal.com.

382 USA ISSN 0740-9540
KF6655.A2
U.S. COURT OF INTERNATIONAL TRADE. REPORTS. Text in English. 1938. a. price varies.
Formerly (until 1981): U.S. Customs Court. Reports
Published by: (U.S. Court of International Trade), U.S. Government Printing Office, 732 N Capitol St NW, Washington, DC 20401. TEL 202-512-1530, 888-293-6498, FAX 202-512-1262, gpoaccess@gpo.gov, http://www.gpo.gov.

382 USA ISSN 1531-0108
KF6680.99
U.S. CUSTOM HOUSE GUIDE: PORTS OF ENTRY AND U.S. IMPORT REGULATIONS. Text in English. a. **Description:** Includes information about the import process: includes Ports of Entry, Customs Regulations of the United States and Special & Administrative Provisions stage.
Supersedes in part (in 2001): U.S. Custom House Guide (1084-8681)
Published by: Commonwealth Business Media, Inc., 400 Windsor Corporate Ctr, 50 Millstone Rd, Ste 200, East Windsor, NJ 08520-1415. TEL 609-371-7700, 800-221-5488, FAX 609-371-7883, amiddlebrook@cbizmedia.com, http://www.cbizmedia.com. Ed. Amy Middlebrook. Pub. John G John III.

382 USA ISSN 1531-0086
KF6654.599
U.S. CUSTOM HOUSE GUIDE: U.S. HARMONIZED TARIFF SCHEDULE. Text in English. a. **Description:** Provides information about the import process: includes U.S. Harmonized Tariff Schedule, and Schedules C, D, and K.
Supersedes in part (in 2001): U.S. Custom House Guide (1084-8681)
Published by: Commonwealth Business Media, Inc., 400 Windsor Corporate Ctr, 50 Millstone Rd, Ste 200, East Windsor, NJ 08520-1415. TEL 609-371-7700, 800-221-5488, FAX 609-371-7883, amiddlebrook@cbizmedia.com, http://www.cbizmedia.com. Ed. Amy Middlebrook. Pub. John G John III.

U S CUSTOMS AND INTERNATIONAL TRADE GUIDE. see *LAW—International Law*

382 USA ISSN 0730-9848
HG4538
U.S. DIRECT INVESTMENT ABROAD. Text in English. a. **Document type:** *Government.*
Published by: U.S. Department of Commerce, Bureau of Economic Analysis, 1441 L St NW, Washington, DC 20230. TEL 202-606-9900, http://www.bea.doc.gov/bea/.

U.S. EXPORT ADMINISTRATION REGULATIONS. see *PUBLIC ADMINISTRATION*

382.029 USA ISSN 1080-9414
U.S. EXPORT DIRECTORY. Text in English. 1990. a. **Document type:** *Directory.* **Description:** Serves as an international buyer's guide for industrial products.
Formerly: U.S. Industrial Export Directory
Published by: Reed Information Services, 1350 E Touhy Ave, Box 5080, Des Plaines, IL 60017. TEL 800-347-8743, FAX 708-390-2850. Ed. Anne Brickley. Circ: 40,000. **Subscr. to:** 44 Cook St, Boulder, CO 80206.

382 USA ISSN 0145-0352
HF3003
U S EXPORT SALES REPORTS. Text in English. w. **Document type:** *Government.*
Published by: U.S. Department of Agriculture, Foreign Agricultural Service, 1400 Independence Ave SW, Washington, DC 20250-1000. TEL 202-720-7115, info@fas.usda.gov, http://www.fas.usda.gov.

382.7 DEU
U S - EXPORTBESTIMMUNGEN. Text in German. m. EUR 215 (effective 2003). **Document type:** *Bulletin, Government.*
Published by: Bundesanzeiger Verlagsgesellschaft mbH, Amsterdamer Str 192, Cologne, 50735, Germany. TEL 49-221-97668-0, FAX 49-221-07668278, vertrieb@bundesanzeiger.de, http://www.bundesanzeiger.de.

382 USA ISSN 1057-8773
HF3003
U S EXPORTS OF MERCHANDISE. Text in English. 1989. m. USD 1,200 domestic; USD 1,525 foreign (effective 2004). **Document type:** *Government.*
Media: CD-ROM. **Related titles:** Optical Disk - DVD ed.
Published by: U.S. Department of Commerce, Bureau of the Census, Economics and Statistics Administration, 14th St between Constitution & E Sts, Washington, DC 20230.

382 USA ISSN 0884-3171
U.S. FOREIGN TRADE HIGHLIGHTS. Text in English. a.
Published by: U.S. Department of Commerce, International Trade Administration, 1401 Constitution Ave, N W, Room 3414, Washington, DC 20230. TEL 202-482-3251, FAX 202-482-5819, http://www.ita.doc.gov/td/industry/otea/usfth/index.html.

350.827 USA ISSN 0196-9153
CODEN: USPUDA
U S I T C PUBLICATION. (U.S. International Trade Commission) Text in English. irreg. **Document type:** *Monographic series, Government.*
Former titles: I T C Publication (0196-9277); U.S. Tariff Commission. T C Publication (0502-5338)
Related titles: ♦ Series: Quarterly Report to the Congress and the Trade Policy Committee on Trade between the United States and China, the Successor States to the Former Soviet Union, and Other Title IV Countries. ISSN 0270-5435; ♦ Harmonized Tariff Schedule of the United States. ISSN 1066-0925; ♦ The Year in Trade (Year).
—BLDSC (9099.800000), CASDDS, CISTI.
Published by: U.S. International Trade Commission, Office of Information Services, 500 E St, S W, Washington, DC 20436. TEL 202-205-2000, http://www.usitc.gov.

U.S. IMPORT AND EXPORT PRICE INDEXES. see *BUSINESS AND ECONOMICS—Economic Situation And Conditions*

382 USA ISSN 1057-8765
HF3005
U S IMPORTS OF MERCHANDISE. Text in English. 1989. m. USD 1,200 domestic; USD 1,525 foreign (effective 2004). **Document type:** *Government.*
Media: CD-ROM. **Related titles:** Optical Disk - DVD ed.
Published by: U.S. Department of Commerce, Bureau of the Census, Economics and Statistics Administration, 14th St between Constitution & E Sts, Washington, DC 20230.

382 USA
U.S. INTERNATIONAL TRADE COMMISSION. INTERNATIONAL ECONOMIC REVIEW. Text in English. bi-m. **Description:** Features articles on developments in international economics and trade. Also reviews US economic performance relative to other major trade partners, US trade performance, and economic forecasts.
Published by: U.S. International Trade Commission, Office of External Relations, 500 E St SW, Washington, DC 20436. TEL 202-205-1819.

382 USA
HF1455
U.S. INTERNATIONAL TRADE COMMISSION. YEAR IN REVIEW. Text in English. 1917. a. USD 6. **Document type:** *Government.* **Description:** Describes the Commission's activities during the fiscal year with lists of investigations and studies conducted.
Former titles (until 2000): U.S. International Trade Commission. Annual Report (0147-5568); (until 1975): U.S. Tariff Commission. Annual Report (0083-3428)
Indexed: RASB.
Published by: U.S. International Trade Commission, Office of Information Services, 500 E St, S W, Washington, DC 20436. TEL 202-205-2000. Ed. Peg O'Laughlin. Circ: 3,000. **Orders to:** U.S. Government Printing Office, Superintendent of Documents.

382 USA
HF3001
U.S. MERCHANDISE TRADE: EXPORTS, GENERAL IMPORTS, AND IMPORTS FOR CONSUMPTION - STANDARD INTERNATIONAL TRADE CLASSIFICATION REVISION 3 - COMMODITY BY COUNTRY (ONLINE EDITION). Text in English. 1943. m. USD 136. reprint service avail. from CIS. **Document type:** *Government.*
Formerly (until 1996): U.S. Merchandise Trade: Exports, General Imports, and Imports for Consumption - Standard International Trade Classification Revision 3 - Commodity by Country (Print Edition) (1057-9680); Which was formed by the 1988 merger of: Foreign Trade Reports. U.S. Exports - Schedule E - Commodity by Country (0198-6759); Which was formerly: Foreign Trade Reports. U.S. Exports - Schedule E - Commodity Groupings Commodity by Country (0190-499X); Foreign Trade Reports. U.S. General Imports and Imports for Consumption. Schedule A - Commodity by Country (0736-234X); Which was formerly: Foreign Trade Reports. U.S. Exports - Schedule A - Commodity by Country (0095-5493)
Media: Online - full content.
Indexed: AmStI.
—CISTI.
Published by: U.S. Bureau of the Census (Subsidiary of: U.S. Department of Commerce), 4700 Silver Hill Rd., Washington, DC 20233. TEL 301-763-5140.

332.6 USA
HG4930
THE U S OFFSHORE FUNDS DIRECTORY. Text in English. 1990. a. USD 195 (effective 2000). adv. **Document type:** *Directory.*
Published by: Dome Capital Management, Inc., 405 Park Ave, Ste 500, New York, NY 10022. TEL 212-371-5935, FAX 212-758-9032, abernehein@hegdefundnews.com, http://www.hedgefundnews.com. R&P Antoine Bernheim Ed Pub.

UKERS' INTERNATIONAL TEA & COFFEE DIRECTORY & BUYERS' GUIDE. see *FOOD AND FOOD INDUSTRIES*

332.6 346.04 USA
UNFAIR COMPETITION AND THE I T C. Text in English. a. USD 320 per vol. (effective 2004). **Document type:** *Trade.* **Description:** Offers complete procedural guidance to prosecuting and defending unfair import trade practice cases.
Formerly: Federal Unfair Competition Actions
Published by: Thomson West (Subsidiary of: Thomson Corporation, The), 610 Opperman Dr, Eagan, MN 55123-1396. TEL 651-687-8000, 800-328-4880, FAX 651-687-7302, http://west.thomson.com/product/14512553/product.asp. Ed. Donald Knox Duvall.

UNFAIR TRADE PRACTICES LITIGATION. see *LAW—International Law*

UNITED NATIONS COMMISSION ON INTERNATIONAL TRADE LAW. YEARBOOK. see *LAW—International Law*

382 338.91 CHE
UNITED NATIONS CONFERENCE ON TRADE AND DEVELOPMENT: PROCEEDINGS. Text in Multiple languages. irreg., latest 2000, 10th, Bangkok. price varies. Website rev. **Document type:** *Proceedings, Trade.*
Related titles: Online - full text ed.
Published by: United Nations Conference on Trade and Development, Palais des Nations, 8-14 Av de la Paix, Geneva 10, 1211, Switzerland. TEL 41-22-9174924, FAX 41-22-9070195, http://www.unctad.org. **Subscr. to:** United Nations Publications, Distribution and Sales Section, Palais des Nations, Geneva CH-1211, Switzerland. TEL 41-22-907-2612, publications@un.org, unpubli@unog.ch.

UNITED NATIONS WEEKLY REPORT. see *POLITICAL SCIENCE—International Relations*

UNITED STATES - GERMAN ECONOMIC YEARBOOK (YEAR). see *BUSINESS AND ECONOMICS—Chamber Of Commerce Publications*

UNITED STATES IMPORT TRADE LAW. see *LAW—International Law*

UNITED STATES IMPORTERS PRODUCT GUIDE. see *BUSINESS AND ECONOMICS—Trade And Industrial Directories*

UNIWERSYTET SLASKI W KATOWICACH. PRACE NAUKOWE. PROBLEMY PRAWNE HANDLU ZAGRANICZNEGO. see *LAW—International Law*

382 URY
URUGUAY. DIRECCION GENERAL DE COMERCIO EXTERIOR. ESTADISTICAS DE COMERCIO EXTERIOR. Text in Spanish. 1977. a. **Document type:** *Government.*
Published by: Direccion General de Comercio Exterior, Colonia 1206, Montevideo, Uruguay. TEL 598-2-9020319, FAX 598-2-9021726, coexdin@tips.com.uy. Circ: 1,000.

382 CHE
V S I G - MITTEILUNGEN/INFORMATIONS V S I G. Text in German. 1942. m. membership. **Document type:** *Bulletin.*
Published by: Vereinigung des Schweizerischen Import- und Grosshandels, Gueterstr 78, Basel, 4010, Switzerland. TEL 41-61-2713385, FAX 41-61-2723039. Pub. J R Zeller.

382 DEU
V W D AUSSENHANDELSDIENST. Variant title: Vereinigte Wirtschaftsdienste Aussenhandelsdienst. Text in German. 1951. w. bk.rev. index. **Document type:** *Bulletin.*
Formerly: Aussenhandelsdienst der Industrie- und Handelskammern und Wirtschaftsverbaende (0001-1401); Which was formed by the merger of (1950-1956): Aussenhandelsdienst der Industrie- und Handelskammern und Wirtschaftsverbaende. Ausgabe A (0343-8031); (1950-1956): Aussenhandelsdienst der Industrie- und Handelskammern und Wirtschaftsverbaende. Ausgabe B (0343-804X)
Indexed: KES, PAIS.
Published by: Vereinigte Wirtschaftsdienste GmbH, Niederurseler Allee 8-10, Eschborn, 65760, Germany. feedback@vwd.de, http://www.vwd.de. Circ: 1,700.

V W D - EUROPA. see *BUSINESS AND ECONOMICS—Investments*

VANUATU. STATISTICS OFFICE. ANNUAL SUMMARY OF OVERSEAS TRADE. see *BUSINESS AND ECONOMICS—Abstracting, Bibliographies, Statistics*

382 DEU
VEREIN HAMBURGER EXPORTEURE. RUNDSCHREIBENDIENST FUER MITGLIEDSUNTERNEHMEN. Text in German. bi-m. adv. bk.rev. **Document type:** *Newsletter.*
Published by: Verein Hamburger Exporteure e.V., Gotenstr 21, Hamburg, 20097, Germany. TEL 49-40-23601625, FAX 49-40-23601610, vhe@wga-hh.de. Circ: 300.

382 332.6 VNM
VIETNAM BUSINESS. Text in English. 1991. s-m. VND 15,000; USD 5.95 in US & Canada; USD 5 in Europe; USD 4.50 in Asia; USD 5 in Africa (effective 2000). adv. **Document type:** *Trade.* **Description:** Provides information for foreign traders and investors.
Published by: Vietnam Trade Information Center, Ministry of Trade, 46 Ngo Nguyen St, Hanoi, Viet Nam. TEL 84-4-8259772, FAX 84-4-259542, vbmag@hcm.vnn.vn. Ed. Ho Hai Long. adv.: B&W page USD 400, color page USD 800. Circ: 6,000.

332.6 VNM
VIETNAM TRADE REVIEW. Text in Vietnamese; Summaries in English. 1961. s-m. VND 120,000; USD 24 foreign (effective 1999). adv. **Document type:** *Trade.* **Description:** Covers Vietnamese policies on foreign economic relations, foreign trade, economic situations and international economic ties.
Formerly (until 1990): Vietnam Trade and Tourism Review
Published by: (Vietnam. Vietnam Trade Review), Ministry of Trade, 46 Ngo Quyen, Hanoi, Viet Nam. TEL 84-4-8257558, FAX 84-4-8262311. Ed. Truong Duc Ngai. adv.: color page USD 800. Circ: 10,000.

382 FRA ISSN 1018-6735
VILLES ET PORTS/CITIES AND PORTS. Text in English, French, Spanish. 198?. **Document type:** *Newsletter.*
Published by: Association Internationale Villes & Ports, 45, rue Lord Kitchener, Le Havre, 76600, France. TEL 33-2-35427884, FAX 33-2-35422194, bureau@aivp.com, http://www.aivp.com.

382 RUS ISSN 0321-057X
VNESHNAYA TORGOVLYA. Text in Russian. 1931. m. USD 120 foreign (effective 1999). adv. bk.rev. bibl.; illus.; mkt.; stat. index. Supplement avail. **Description:** Covers Russia's foreign economic relations, including problems concerning Russian integration into the world economy; Russian relations with world trade organizations; recommendations of the world's leading economists; financial, legal and transport issues, etc.
Related titles: Microfiche ed.: (from EVP); English ed.: Foreign Trade. ISSN 0134-8469; French ed.: Commerce Exterieur. ISSN 0134-8272; German ed.: Aussenhandel. ISSN 0134-8280; Spanish ed.: Commercio Exterior. ISSN 0134-8299.
Indexed: KES, MEA&I, RASB, RefZh.
—East View.
Published by: (Russia. Ministerstvo Vneshnei Torgovli), Vneshnaya Torgovlya, Minskaya ul 11, Moscow, 121108, Russian Federation. TEL 7-095-1456894. Ed. V Dushenkin. Circ: 30,000. **Distr. in US by:** East View Information Services, 3020 Harbor Ln. N., Minneapolis, MN 55447. TEL 612-550-0961.

B

382 RUS ISSN 1606-1616
VNESHNEEKONOMICHESKOYE OBOZRENIYE; yezhenedel'nyi obzor vneshneekonomicheskoi informatsii. Text in Russian. 2000. w. free (effective 2004). **Document type:** *Consumer.*
Media: Online - full text.
Published by: Al'yans Midiya, Bolotnaya ul 12, str 3, Moscow, 115035, Russian Federation. TEL 7-095-2345380, FAX 7-095-2345363, allmedia@allmedia.ru, http://www.businesspress.ru, http://allmedia.ru.

VUNSHNA TURGOVIA NA REPUBLIKA BULGARIA/FOREIGN TRADE IN THE REPUBLIC OF BULGARIA. see *STATISTICS*

382 USA ISSN 0047-5068
W C N COMMERCIAL NEWS. Variant title: L.A. Commercial News. Text in English. 1912. w. USD 25. adv. Supplement avail. **Document type:** *Newspaper, Trade.*
Published by: C.A. Page Publishing Co., PO Box 530, Redondo Beach, CA 90277-0530. TEL 213-608-3350. Ed. Shay Ramos. Adv. contact Mark Wagner. Circ: 5,500.

382 338 USA ISSN 0887-9990
W E P Z A NEWSLETTER. (World Economic Processing Zones Association) Text in English. 1978. m. membership only. **Document type:** *Newsletter.* **Description:** Stimulates industrial development in export processing zones through exchange of information, research, and management training.
Published by: The Flagstaff Institute, PO Box 986, Flagstaff, AZ 86002. TEL 928-779-0052, FAX 928-774-8589, instflag@aol.com, http://www.wepza.org. Ed. Robert C Haywood. R&P Richard L Bolin. Circ: 100.

382 DEU ISSN 0042-966X
W G A GESCHAEFTSBERICHT. Text in German. 1947. a. free. adv. bk.rev. illus. **Document type:** *Bulletin.*
Published by: Wirtschaftsvereinigung Gross- und Aussenhandel Hamburg e.V., Gotenstr 21, Hamburg, 20097, Germany. TEL 49-40-236016-0, FAX 49-40-23601610, contact@wga-hh.de. Ed. Hans Juergen Mueller. Circ: 2,000.

W S S A GRAPEVINE. see *BEVERAGES*

382 CHE ISSN 1020-4997
HF1371
W T O ANNUAL REPORT. (World Trade Organisation) Text in English. 1953. a. CHF 50, EUR 32.90 (effective 2005). stat. **Document type:** *Journal, Trade.* **Description:** Analyzes main trends and developments in international trade. Contains comprehensive statistical information.
Formed by the 1998 merger of: G A T T Activities (0072-0615); General Agreement of Tariffs and Trade. International Trade (0589-5669)
Related titles: Microfiche ed.: (from CIS); French ed.: Organisation Mondiale du Commerce, Rapport Annuel. ISSN 1020-5004; Spanish ed.: Organizacion Mundial del Comercio, Informe Anual. ISSN 1020-5012.
Indexed: IIS.
—CISTI.
Published by: World Trade Organization/Accord General sur les Tarifs Douaniers et le Commerce, 154 rue de Lausanne, Geneva 21, 1211, Switzerland. TEL 41-22-7395111, FAX 41-22-7314206, enquiries@wto.org, http://www.wto.org. Circ: 7,200. **Dist. in U.S. by:** Bernan Associates, Bernan, 4611-F Assembly Dr., Lanham, MD 20706-4391.

330 CHE ISSN 1563-9088
HF1701
W T O FOCUS (ONLINE EDITION). Text in English. 1981. 10/yr. free. bk.rev. **Document type:** *Newsletter, Trade.* **Description:** Covers current events and issues in international trade, member countries' efforts to resolve trade problems, and the Uruguay Round multilateral trade negotiations.
Former titles (until 2001): W T O Focus (Print Edition) (1563-907X); (until 1994): G A T T Focus (0256-0119)
Related titles: French ed.: ISSN 0256-0127; Spanish ed.: ISSN 0256-0135.
—CISTI.
Published by: (Information and Media Relations Division), World Trade Organization/Accord General sur les Tarifs Douaniers et le Commerce, 154 rue de Lausanne, Geneva 21, 1211, Switzerland. TEL 41-22-7395111, FAX 41-22-7314206, TELEX 4122324-GATT-CH, enquiries@wto.org, http://www.wto.org. Ed. Luis Ople. R&P Nathalie Bourgoin. Circ: 5,000.

382.92 USA ISSN 1529-4153
W T O REPORTER. (World Trade Organization) Text in English. 2000. d. USD 835 (effective 2001). back issues avail. **Document type:** *Newsletter, Trade.* **Description:** Covers news from and about the World Trade Organization, including dispute settlements, multilateral trade negotiations, and WTO decisions on emerging trade issues.
Media: Online - full text (from The Bureau of National Affairs, Inc.). **Related titles:** E-mail ed.
—CCC.
Published by: The Bureau of National Affairs, Inc., 1231 25th St., NW, Washington, DC 20037. TEL 800-372-1033, 800-452-7773, FAX 800-253-0332, customercare@bna.com, bnaplus@bna.com, http://www.bna.com/products/corplaw/wtor.htm. Pub. Greg C McCaffery. **Subscr. to:** 9435 Key West Ave, Rockville, MD 20850.

382 CHN ISSN 1001-3407
HF1371
WAIMAO JINGJI, GUOJI MAOYI. Running title: Foreign Trade Economics and International Trade. Text in Chinese. 1980. m. CNY 96 (effective 2004). 96 p./no.; **Document type:** *Journal, Academic/Scholarly.* **Description:** Covers issues related to international commerce and international market management.
Indexed: RASB.
Published by: Zhongguo Renmin Daxue, Shubao Zilio Zhongxin/Renmin University of China, Information Center for Social Server, Dongcheng-qu, 3, Zhangzhizhong Lu, Beijing, 100007, China. TEL 86-10-64039458, FAX 86-10-64015080, kyes@163.net, http://www.confucius.cn.net/bkdetail.asp?fzt=F52. **Dist. in US by:** China Publications Service, PO Box 49614, Chicago, IL 60649. TEL 312-288-3291, FAX 312-288-8570; **Dist. by:** China International Book Trading Corp, 35 Chegongzhuang Xilu, Haidian District, PO Box 399, Beijing 100044, China. TEL 86-10-68412045, FAX 86-10-68412023, cibtc@mail.cibtc.com.cn, http://www.cibtc.com.cn.

332.6 346 DEU
WARENURSPRUNG UND PRAEFERENZEN IN DER TAEGLICHEN PRAXIS. Text in German. 1997. irreg. (3-5/yr.). looseleaf. EUR 76.60 (effective 2001). **Document type:** *Trade.* **Description:** Information on preferential and non-preferential origins in international trade.
Related titles: CD-ROM ed.
Published by: Mendel Verlag, Robensstr 39, Aachen, 52070, Germany. TEL 49-241-154355, FAX 49-241-1570816, info@mendel-verlag.de, http://www.mendel-verlag.de.

382 USA ISSN 0049-691X
WASHINGTON INTERNATIONAL BUSINESS REPORT. Text in English. 1972. m. USD 288 (effective 2000). reprints avail.
Media: Duplicated (not offset). **Related titles:** Online - full text ed.
Published by: International Business-Government Counsellors Inc., 818 Connecticut Ave N W, 12th Fl, Washington, DC 20006-2702. TEL 202-872-8181, FAX 202-872-8696, arobbins@ibgc.com, http://www.ibgc.com. Ed. Solveig B Spielmann. Circ: 800.

WASHINGTON TARIFF & TRADE LETTER; a weekly report for business executives on U.S. international trade policies, legislation, opportunities and restrictions. see *LAW—International Law*

382 USA ISSN 1522-3671
WASHINGTON TRADE DAILY. Text in English. 1988. d. USD 650 (effective 2005). **Document type:** *Newsletter.* **Description:** Includes detailed reporting and analyses of events in Washington and at the Geneva headquarters of the World Trade Organization as well as coverage from other parts of the world.
Formerly (until 1988): Washington Trade Week
Related titles: E-mail ed.; Fax ed.
Published by: Trade Reports International Group, PO Box 1802, Wheaton, MD 20915-1802. TEL 301-946-0817, FAX 301-946-2631, trigtrig@aol.com, http://washingtontradedaily.com. Eds. Jim Berger, Mary Berger. Pub., R&P Jim Berger.

332.6 DEU
WEINRECHT; der Europaeischen Gemeinschaft, der Bundesrepublik Deutschland und der Bundeslaender. Text in German. irreg. (4-5/yr.). looseleaf. adv. **Document type:** *Trade.*
Published by: Walhalla Fachverlag, Haus an der Eisernen Bruecke, Regensburg, 93042, Germany. TEL 49-941-5684-0, FAX 49-941-5684111, walhalla@walhalla.de, http://www.walhalla.de. Circ: 4,200.

382 DEU ISSN 0720-3683
WELTHANDEL/WORLD TRADE. Text in German. 1981. bi-m. EUR 6 newsstand/cover (effective 2005). adv. bk.rev. **Document type:** *Magazine, Trade.* **Description:** Economic news about world markets.
Incorporates (1985-1988): Reisemarkt (0178-2258); (1988-1998): Weltmarkt (0935-1582); Which was formerly (1986-1988): Trade Letter (1615-6633)
Published by: H P B Welthandel Verlag GmbH, Postfach 650909, Hamburg, 22369, Germany. TEL 49-40-6004670, FAX 49-40-6013114. Ed. Hiltrud Boeckmann. Adv. contact Peter Fox. B&W page EUR 3,500, color page EUR 6,125; trim 175 x 258. Circ: 19,765 (paid and controlled).

330 DEU ISSN 0043-2652
HC59.A15
➤ **DIE WELTWIRTSCHAFT.** Text in German. 1950. q. EUR 49.07 combined subscription to institutions print & online eds. (effective 2005). adv. charts. back issues avail.; reprints avail. **Document type:** *Journal, Academic/Scholarly.* **Description:** Current facts about the world economy.
Related titles: Online - full text ed.: ISSN 1613-9828 (from Springer LINK).
Indexed: ELLIS, IBR, IBSS, IBZ, KES, PAIS, RASB, RefZh, SCIMP, WAE&RSA.
—BLDSC (9295.040000), IE, Infotrieve, ingenta. **CCC.**
Published by: (Institut fuer Weltwirtschaft, Kiel), Springer-Verlag (Subsidiary of: Springer Science+Business Media), Tiergartenstr 17, Heidelberg, 69121, Germany. TEL 49-6221-3450, FAX 49-6221-345229. Ed. Horst Siebert. Adv. contact Stephan Kroeck TEL 49-30-827875739. Circ: 1,250. **Subscr. in the Americas to:** Springer-Verlag New York, Inc., Journal Fulfillment, PO Box 2485, Secaucus, NJ 07096-2485. TEL 800-777-4643, 201-348-4033, FAX 201-348-4505, journals@springer-ny.com, http://www.springer-ny.com; **Subscr. to:** Springer GmbH Auslieferungsgesellschaft, Haberstr 7, Heidelberg 69126, Germany. TEL 49-6221-345-0, FAX 49-6221-345-4229, subscriptions@springer.de.

382 AUS
WEST AUSTRALIAN BUSINESS NEWS. Text in English. 1992. fortn. AUD 159 domestic; AUD 259 foreign (effective 2003). adv. back issues avail. **Document type:** *Newspaper, Trade.* **Description:** Business publication aimed at small- to medium-sized business operators.
Former titles: Business News (1320-0801); (until 1992): W.A. Business World (0729-8374)
Address: Perth Business Centre, PO Box 8352, Perth, W.A. 6849, Australia. TEL 61-8-92279544, FAX 61-8-92276503, http://www.businessnews.com.au/. Ed. Mark Pownall. Pub., R&P Harry Kleyn. Adv. contact Bob Barnett. B&W page AUD 1,834, color page AUD 2,494; trim 26 x 40. Circ: 22,675.

WESTERN WOOD PRODUCTS ASSOCIATION. IMPORT REPORT. see *FORESTS AND FORESTRY—Lumber And Wood*

WHAT'S WORKING FOR AMERICAN COMPANIES IN INTERNATIONAL SALES & MARKETING. see *BUSINESS AND ECONOMICS—Marketing And Purchasing*

382 JPN ISSN 0921-8475
WHITE PAPER ON INTERNATIONAL TRADE, JAPAN (YEAR). Text in English. a. JPY 8,800 (effective 2001). **Description:** Analyzes the trend of world trade and economy in the past year, the development of international activity and a sophisticated system of international work sharing and the conditions of long-term world economic growth.
Published by: (Publications Department), Japan External Trade Organization, 2-5 Toranomom 2-chome, Minato-ku, Tokyo, 105-8466, Japan. TEL 03-3582-3518, FAX 03-3587-2485. Circ: 1,000.

WHO'S WHO IN INTERNATIONAL REAL ESTATE; certified international property specialists network membership directory. see *REAL ESTATE*

382 CAN
WISH TO IMPORT. Text in English. 1993. m. USD 100. bk.rev. charts; illus.; stat. **Document type:** *Newsletter.* **Description:** Lists consumer and commercial ventures wishing to import goods.
Published by: Global Traders Association, P O BOX 797, Sta A, Scarborough, ON M1K 5C8, Canada. TEL 416-650-9309, FAX 416-650-9280. Ed. K Bhattacharyya. Circ: 300 (paid).

WOOD PRODUCTS: INTERNATIONAL TRADE AND FOREIGN MARKETS. see *AGRICULTURE—Agricultural Economics*

382 AUS ISSN 0816-5181
HC59.69
WORKING PAPERS IN TRADE AND DEVELOPMENT. Text in English. 1986. irreg. **Description:** Provides a vehicle for preliminary circulation of research results in the fields of economic development and international trade.
Related titles: Online - full text ed.
Published by: Australian National University, Economics Division, Canberra, ACT 0200, Australia. TEL 61-2-6249-4705, FAX 61-2-6257-2886, seminars.economics@anu.edu.au, http://ecopnomics.anu.edu.au/publish/papers/. Ed. Ron Duncan.

382 UAE
WORLD ARAB TRADE. Text in Arabic. 1947. q. adv.
Published by: Mussad Bader Al Sayer Establishment, c/o Zabeel Printing Press, P O Box 5143, Dubai, United Arab Emirates. FAX 229504. Circ: 12,580.

363.7 USA ISSN 1025-6881
HC79.E5
THE WORLD BANK AND THE ENVIRONMENT SINCE THE RIO EARTH SUMMIT. Text in English. 1990. a. illus. reprints avail. **Document type:** *Consumer.*
Formerly (until 1995): The World Bank and the Environment (1014-8132)
Indexed: S&F.
—CCC.
Published by: (International Bank for Reconstruction and Development), World Bank Group, PO Box 960, Herndon, VA 20172-0960. TEL 703-661-1501, FAX 703-661-1501, books@worldbank.org, http://www-esd.worldbank.org/envmat.

382 CAN
WORLD BUSINESS CONFERENCE. Text in English. 1997. m. free. **Document type:** *Trade.* **Description:** Helps academic and professional business consultants increase awareness of their specialized services and provides the Internet community with valuable information on key areas of international business.
Media: Online - full text.
Published by: World Business Network, 326 Pennywell Rd, St. John's, NF, Canada. TEL 709-754-3989, FAX 709-754-3989, info@worldbusiness.net, http://worldbusiness.net/conference. Ed. Douglas Freake.

332.6 USA ISSN 1081-3284
WORLD BUSINESS REVIEW. Text in English; Summaries in Chinese. 1991. bi-m. USD 20.95; USD 39.95 foreign (effective 1998). adv. **Document type:** *Trade.* **Description:** Analyzes national and global business, along with political events affecting business for manufacturers, importers and exporters, bankers, and investors.
Published by: World Business Research Center, PO Box 11437, Baltimore, MD 21239. TEL 410-685-0032, FAX 410-661-0032. Ed., Pub., R&P Patrick Ngwolo TEL 410-685-5104. Adv. contact Eva N'ulia. Circ: 10,000.

382 USA
WORLD COMMODITY PROFILES. Text in English. m. USD 545 (effective 2003). **Document type:** *Trade.*
Published by: Economist Intelligence Unit, 111 W 57th St, New York, NY 10019. http://store.eiu.com/index.asp?layout=product_home_page&product_id=1000000300&country_id=&ref=product_detail_list_by_title_home_title, http://www.eiu.com.

382.7 CHE ISSN 1020-7813
WORLD COMMODITY SURVEY. Text in English. 1999. a. USD 85 (effective 2001). back issues avail. **Document type:** *Bulletin, Trade.* **Description:** Contains systematic analytical information on the world of commodities and raw materials.
—BLDSC (9353.254230), CISTI.
Published by: United Nations Conference on Trade and Development, 8-14 Avenue de la Paix, Geneva 10, 1211, Switzerland. TEL 41-22-9174924, FAX 41-22-9070195, info@unctad.org, http://www.unctad.org.

WORLD DIRECTORY OF LINER SHIPPING AGENTS. see *BUSINESS AND ECONOMICS—Trade And Industrial Directories*

WORLD DIRECTORY OF NON-OFFICIAL STATISTICAL SOURCES. see *BUSINESS AND ECONOMICS—Abstracting, Bibliographies, Statistics*

THE WORLD ECONOMY. see *BUSINESS AND ECONOMICS*

WORLD EXPORT CREDIT GUIDE. see *BUSINESS AND ECONOMICS—Banking And Finance*

WORLD LICENSING LAW REPORT. see *LAW*

330.9 GBR ISSN 1363-9099
WORLD OF INFORMATION BUSINESS INTELLIGENCE REPORTS. ALGERIA. Text in English. 1990. s-a. GBP 35, USD 70 (effective 2003). **Document type:** *Bulletin.*
Formerly (until 1996): Wiley Business Intelligence Reports. (1073-3213)
Related titles: Online - full content ed.; Online - full text ed.: (from Gale Group, IngentaConnect).

Published by: World of Information, 2 Market St, Saffron Walden, Essex CB10 1HZ, United Kingdom. TEL 44-1799-521150, FAX 44-1799-524805, info@worldinformation.com, http://www.worldinformation.com. Ed., Pub. Anthony Axon. **Orders in USA:** PO Box 830840, Birmingham, AL 35283-0430. TEL 800-633-4931, FAX 205-995-1588.

330.9 GBR ISSN 1363-7282
WORLD OF INFORMATION BUSINESS INTELLIGENCE REPORTS. BULGARIA. Text in English. 1990. irreg. GBP 35, USD 70 (effective 2003). **Document type:** *Trade.*
Formerly (until 1996): Wiley Business Intelligence Reports. Bulgaria (1073-3353)
Related titles: Online - full content ed.; Online - full text ed.: (from Gale Group, IngentaConnect).
Published by: World of Information, 2 Market St, Saffron Walden, Essex CB10 1HZ, United Kingdom. TEL 44-1799-521150, FAX 44-1799-524805, info@worldinformation.com, http://www.worldinformation.com. Ed., Pub. Anthony Axon. **Subscr. to:** PO Box 830840, Birmingham, AL 35283-0430. TEL 800-633-4931, FAX 205-995-1588.

330.9 GBR ISSN 1363-9110
WORLD OF INFORMATION BUSINESS INTELLIGENCE REPORTS. CZECH REPUBLIC. Text in English. 1994. s-a. GBP 35, USD 70 (effective 2003). **Document type:** *Trade.*
Formerly (until 1996): Wiley Business Intelligence Reports. Czech Republic (1073-3434)
Related titles: Online - full content ed.; Online - full text ed.: (from Gale Group, IngentaConnect).
Published by: World of Information, 2 Market St, Saffron Walden, Essex CB10 1HZ, United Kingdom. TEL 44-1799-521150, FAX 44-1799-524805, info@worldinformation.com, http://www.worldinformation.com. Ed., Pub. Anthony Axon. **Orders in US:** PO Box 830840, Birmingham, AL 35283-0430. TEL 800-633-4931, FAX 205-995-1588.

330.9 GBR ISSN 1363-9129
WORLD OF INFORMATION BUSINESS INTELLIGENCE REPORTS. HUNGARY. Text in English. 1994. s-a. GBP 35, USD 70 (effective 2003). **Document type:** *Trade.*
Formerly (until 1996): Wiley Business Intelligence Reports. Hungary (1073-3582)
Related titles: Online - full content ed.; Online - full text ed.: (from Gale Group, IngentaConnect).
Published by: World of Information, 2 Market St, Saffron Walden, Essex CB10 1HZ, United Kingdom. TEL 44-1799-521150, FAX 44-1799-524805, info@worldinformation.com, http://www.worldinformation.com. Ed., Pub. Anthony Axon. **Orders in USA:** PO Box 830840, Birmingham, AL 35283-0430. TEL 800-633-4931, FAX 205-995-1588.

WORLD OF INFORMATION BUSINESS INTELLIGENCE REPORTS. MACEDONIA. see *BUSINESS AND ECONOMICS—Economic Situation And Conditions*

330.9 GBR ISSN 1363-7290
WORLD OF INFORMATION BUSINESS INTELLIGENCE REPORTS. POLAND. Text in English. 1994. s-a. GBP 35, USD 70 (effective 2003). **Document type:** *Trade.*
Formerly (until 1996): Wiley Business Intelligence Reports. Poland (1073-3930)
Related titles: Online - full content ed.; Online - full text ed.: (from Gale Group, IngentaConnect).
Published by: World of Information, 2 Market St, Saffron Walden, Essex CB10 1HZ, United Kingdom. TEL 44-1799-521150, FAX 44-1799-524805, info@worldinformation.com, http://www.worldinformation.com. Ed., Pub. Anthony Axon. **Orders in USA:** PO Box 830840, Birmingham, AL 35283-0430. TEL 800-633-4931, FAX 205-995-1588.

330.9 GBR ISSN 1363-9137
WORLD OF INFORMATION BUSINESS INTELLIGENCE REPORTS. ROMANIA. Text in English. 1996. s-a. GBP 35, USD 70 (effective 2003). **Document type:** *Trade.*
Related titles: Online - full content ed.; Online - full text ed.: (from Gale Group, IngentaConnect).
Published by: World of Information, 2 Market St, Saffron Walden, Essex CB10 1HZ, United Kingdom. TEL 44-1799-521150, FAX 44-1799-524805, info@worldinformation.com, http://www.worldinformation.com. Ed., Pub. Anthony Axon. **Orders in USA:** PO Box 830840, Birmingham, AL 35283-0430. TEL 800-633-4931, FAX 205-995-1588.

WORLD OF INFORMATION BUSINESS INTELLIGENCE REPORTS. TRINIDAD AND TOBAGO. see *BUSINESS AND ECONOMICS—Economic Situation And Conditions*

WORLD OIL TRADE. see *PETROLEUM AND GAS*

382 USA
WORLD RISK ANALYSIS REPORTS. Text in English. a. USD 2,000 (effective 1999); includes 3 supplements. stat.
Description: Covers full country reports, external and internal accounts, foreign exchange regulations, international trade and currency concerns, providing specific country risk, historic data, and outlook and projections analyses for 56 countries.
Related titles: Diskette ed.
Published by: S.J. Rundt & Associates, Inc., 130 E 63rd St, New York, NY 10021-7334. TEL 212-838-0141, info@rundtsintelligence.com, http://www.rundtsintelligence.com. Ed. Hans P Belcsak.

WORLD STAINLESS STEEL STATISTICS. see *METALLURGY—Abstracting, Bibliographies, Statistics*

338.47669142 669 GBR ISSN 1369-8613
WORLD STEEL OUTLOOK. Text in English. 1990. q. GBP 760 domestic; GBP 770 foreign (effective 2002).
Indexed: BrCerAb, C&ISA, CerAb, CorrAb, E&CAJ, EMA, IAA, M&TEA, MBF, METADEX, WAA.
Published by: M E P S (International) Ltd, 263 Glossop Rd, Sheffield, S10 2GZ, United Kingdom. TEL 44-114-2750570, FAX 44-114-2759808, jmilnes@meps.co.uk, http://www.meps.co.uk.

382 USA ISSN 1054-8637
HF1371
WORLD TRADE. Text in English. 1987. m. adv. back issues avail.; reprints avail. **Document type:** *Magazine, Trade.*
Description: Directed to senior executives of U.S.-based international companies focusing on banking, transport, logistics, e-commerce, finance, computers and communications, insurance, and other business topics.
Related titles: Microform ed.: (from PQC); Online - full text ed.: (from bigchalk, EBSCO Publishing, Florida Center for Library Automation, Gale Group, O C L C Online Computer Library Center, Inc., ProQuest Information & Learning); Supplement(s): Global Online Supplement (from Northern Light Technology, Inc.).
Indexed: ABIn, ABS&EES, B&I, MASUSE.
—BLDSC (9360.151500), IE, ingenta. **CCC.**
Published by: B N P Media, 27130 Paseo Espada Ste A-1427, San Juan Capistrano, CA 92675-6712. TEL 949-234-1700, FAX 949-234-1701, info@worldtrademag.com, http://www.worldtrademag.com/, http://www.bnp.com/. Ed. Davis P Goodman TEL 949-661-4260. Pub. Brian Noto TEL 949-661-4262. R&Ps Brian Noto TEL 949-661-4262, Lisa Caso TEL 949-661-4268. Adv. contact Carol Eidson TEL 949-661-4270. Circ: 85,000.

382 IND ISSN 0043-9142
WORLD TRADE. Text in English. 1964. s-a. INR 3, USD 2.
Related titles: Online - full text ed.: (from Northern Light Technology, Inc.).
Published by: Onlooker Publications Pvt. Ltd., 20-G Sleater Rd., Mumbai, Maharashtra 400 007, India. Ed. N K Kanga. Circ: 5,000.

382 341.522 NLD ISSN 1022-6583
K27
WORLD TRADE AND ARBITRATION MATERIALS. Text in Dutch. bi-m. EUR 415, USD 489, GBP 291 combined subscription print & online eds. (effective 2006). back issues avail.; reprint service avail. from PSC. **Document type:** *Bulletin, Trade.* **Description:** Reports on the texts of current documents relating to international trade and arbitration.
Formed by the 1994 merger of: Arbitration Materials (1013-7432); World Trade Materials (1013-4514)
Related titles: Online - full text ed.: (from EBSCO Publishing, Gale Group, Kluwer Online, O C L C Online Computer Library Center, Inc., Swets Information Services).
Indexed: BAS.
—BLDSC (9360.151900), IE, Infotrieve, ingenta. **CCC.**
Published by: Kluwer Law International (Subsidiary of: Aspen Publishers, Inc.), Laan van Meerdervoort 70, PO Box 85889, The Hague, 2508 CN, Netherlands. TEL 31-70-3081500, FAX 31-70-3081515, sales@kluwerlaw.com, http://www.kluwerlaw.com. Ed. Jacques Werner. Pub. Lukas Claerhout.

WORLD TRADE ANNUAL. see *BUSINESS AND ECONOMICS—Abstracting, Bibliographies, Statistics*

WORLD TRADE ANNUAL SUPPLEMENT. see *BUSINESS AND ECONOMICS—Abstracting, Bibliographies, Statistics*

382 GBR ISSN 1474-7456
HF1371
WORLD TRADE REVIEW. Text in English. 3/yr. GBP 140 to institutions; USD 240 in North America to institutions; GBP 159 combined subscription to institutions print & online eds.; USD 273 combined subscription in North America to institutions print & online eds. (effective 2006). back issues avail. **Document type:** *Journal, Academic/Scholarly.*
Description: Includes articles written from economic, legal and inter-disciplinary perspectives on issues of relevance to the multilateral trading system.
Related titles: Online - full text ed.: ISSN 1475-3138. GBP 145 to institutions; USD 250 in North America to institutions (effective 2006) (from EBSCO Publishing, O C L C Online Computer Library Center, Inc., Swets Information Services).
Indexed: JEL.
—BLDSC (9360.152865), IE, Infotrieve, ingenta. **CCC.**
Published by: Cambridge University Press, The Edinburgh Bldg, Shaftesbury Rd, Cambridge, CB2 2RU, United Kingdom. TEL 44-1223-312393, FAX 44-1223-315052, journals@cambridge.org, http://uk.cambridge.org/journals/wtr/. Ed. Douglas A Irwin. **Subscr. to:** Cambridge University Press, 100 Brook Hill Dr, West Nyack, NY 10994. TEL 845-353-7500, FAX 845-353-4141, journals_subscriptions@cup.org

382 346.07 USA
WORLD TRADE WITHOUT BARRIERS: THE WORLD TRADE ORGANIZATION (W T O) AND DISPUTE RESOLUTION. Text in English. 1995. irreg. (w/ current supplement) (in 2 vols.). USD 210 base vol(s). (effective 2003). **Description:** Explains the new WTO and how it operates to resolve disputes in international trade through the Dispute Settlement Understanding (DSU).
Published by: Michie Company (Subsidiary of: LexisNexis North America), 701 E Water St, Charlottesville, VA 22902-5389. TEL 434-972-7600, 800-446-3410, FAX 434-972-7677, http://www.michie.com. Eds. Frank W Swacker, Kenneth R Redden.

382 IND
WORLDWIDE BUSINESS COLLABORATIONS - CONSULTANTS NEWS AND BUSINESS OPPORTUNITIES. Text in English. 1977. w. looseleaf. INR 715, USD 85 (effective 1999). **Document type:** *Newsletter.* **Description:** Contains news about business collaborations in India.
Formerly: World Business Opportunities - Consultants News
Published by: International Press Cutting Service, PO Box 121, Allahabad, Uttar Pradesh 211 001, India. Ed. Nandi Khanna.

382 USA
WORLDWIDE BUSINESS COST COMPARISONS. Text in English. m. USD 545 (effective 2003). **Document type:** *Trade.*
Media: Online - full content.
Published by: Economist Intelligence Unit, 111 W 57th St, New York, NY 10019. http://store.eiu.com/index.asp?layout=product_home_page&product_id=1524905152&country_id=&ref=product_detail_list_by_title_home_title, http://www.eiu.com.

382 USA ISSN 1069-4447
WORLDWIDE BUSINESS PRACTICES REPORT. Text in English. m. USD 195. **Document type:** *Newsletter.* **Description:** Dedicated to helping busy international executives conduct successful business abroad. Offers practical recommendations, international business customs and protocol.
Published by: International Cultural Enterprises, Inc., PO Box 514, Deerfield, IL 60015. TEL 800-626-2772, FAX 847-945-9614. Pub. Yuri Kovalenko.

382 USA
WORLDWIDE REGULATORY UPDATE. Text in English. q. USD 100 (effective 2003). charts. **Document type:** *Trade.*
Media: Online - full content.
Published by: Economist Intelligence Unit, 111 W 57th St, New York, NY 10019. TEL 800-586-4685, 800-938-4685, FAX 212-586-1181, newyork@eiu.com, http://store.eiu.com/index.asp?layout=product_home_page&product_id=1010000301&country_id=&ref=product_detail_list_by_title_home_title, http://www.eiu.com.

350.827 USA
HF1731.A32
THE YEAR IN TRADE (YEAR). Text in English. 1934. a. **Document type:** *Government.* **Description:** Highlights major American trade policy developments.
Formerly (until 1990): Operation of the Trade Agreements Program (0083-3444)
Related titles: Microfiche ed.; ♦ Series of: U S I T C Publication. ISSN 0196-9153.
Published by: U.S. International Trade Commission, Office of Information Services, 500 E St, S W, Washington, DC 20436. TEL 202-205-2000. **Orders to:** U.S. Government Printing Office, Superintendent of Documents.

YEARBOOK OF ISRAEL PORTS STATISTICS/SHENATON STATISTI: LE NEMLEI ISRAEL. see *BUSINESS AND ECONOMICS—Abstracting, Bibliographies, Statistics*

YEARBOOK OF WORLD ELECTRONICS DATA VOL. 3: EMERGING COUNTRIES. see *BUSINESS AND ECONOMICS—Production Of Goods And Services*

YINJIN YU ZIXUN/IMPORTING AND CONSULTING. see *BUSINESS AND ECONOMICS—Investments*

050 DEU ISSN 0938-7870
ZENTRALMARKT. Text in German. 1946. w. EUR 98 domestic; EUR 143 foreign; EUR 10 newsstand/cover (effective 2005). adv. **Document type:** *Journal, Trade.*
Published by: Max Schimmel Verlag GmbH & Co. KG (Subsidiary of: Rudolf Haufe Verlag GmbH & Co. KG), Im Kreuz 9, Wuerzburg, 97076, Germany. TEL 49-931-2791420, FAX 49-931-2791444, info@schimmelverlag.de, http://www.zentralmarkt.de, http://www.schimmelverlag.de. Ed. Martina Schimmel-Schloo. Pub. Annemarie Schimmel. Adv. contact Gudrun Schimmel Wanner. B&W page EUR 1,360, color page EUR 1,740. Circ: 29,625 (paid and controlled).

382.7 CHN ISSN 1001-0637
ZHONGGUO HAIGUAN/CHINA CUSTOMS. Text in Chinese. m. USD 41.30.
Related titles: Online - full text ed.: (from East View Information Services).

B

Published by: (Haiguan Zongshu/General Office of China Customs), Zhongguo Haiguan Bianjibu, 4 Taipingqiao Dajie, Beijing, 100810, China. TEL 6011155. Ed. Yang Bingyue. **Dist. in US by:** China Books & Periodicals Inc, 360 Swift Ave., Ste. 48, S San Fran, CA 94080-6220. TEL 415-282-2994.

382 CHN
ZHONGGUO MAOYI BAO/CHINA TRADE NEWS. Text in Chinese. 1988. 3/w. CNY 44.88. **Document type:** *Newspaper.* **Description:** Covers Chinese import and export as well as international market situation and trends.
Published by: (Zhongguo Guoji Maoyi Cujin Weiyuanhui), Zhongguo Maoyi Bao Bianjibu, 2 Building, Jing'an Xijie, Beisanhuan Donglu, Chaoyang-qu, Beijing, 100028, China. TEL 86-10-4667277. **Dist. overseas by:** China International Book Trading Corp, 35 Chegongzhuang Xilu, Haidian District, PO Box 399, Beijing 100044, China. **Co-sponsor:** Zhongguo Guoji Shanghui.

382 CHN
ZHONGGUO YINJIN BAO✶ /CHINA IMPORT NEWS. Text in English. 2/w. **Document type:** *Newspaper.* **Description:** Provides up-to-date information on Chinese import of technology, equipment, capital and management experiences as well as related policies and regulations.
Published by: (Guojia Waiguo Zhuanjia Ju), China International Book Trading Corp/Zhongguo Guoji Tushu Maoyi Zonggongsi, 35 Chegongzhuang Xilu, Haidian District, PO Box 399, Beijing, 100044, China. Ed. Wang Zuoli.

B

382 CHN
ZHONGHUA RENMIN GONGHEGUO. DUIWAI MAOYI JINGJI HEZUOBU. TONGBAO/PEOPLE'S REPUBLIC OF CHINA. MINISTRY OF FOREIGN TRADE & ECONOMIC COOPERATION. BULLETIN. Text in Chinese, English. 1993 (Oct.). **Document type:** *Government.* **Description:** Contains timely promulgation of foreign economic and trade laws and regulations approved by the state.
Published by: Ministry of Commerce of the People's Republic of China/Zhonghua Renmin Gongheguo Shangfubu, No.2 Dong Chang'an Ave, Beijing, 100731, China. TEL 86-1-5198306, 86-1-5198346, 86-1-5198316.

382 CHN ISSN 1004-7247
ZHONGHUA RENMIN GONGHEGUO. DUIWAI MAOYI JINGJI HEZUOBU. XINWEN GONGBAO/PEOPLE'S REPUBLIC OF CHINA. MINISTRY OF FOREIGN TRADE & ECONOMIC COOPERATION. BULLETIN. Text in Chinese, English. 1991. bi-m. **Document type:** *Government.* **Description:** Provides official information on China's foreign economic relations and gives brief introduction to the status quo of china's foreign economic and trade development, trend of future development and policy measures, administration methods and laws, regulations and rules.
Published by: Ministry of Commerce of the People's Republic of China/Zhonghua Renmin Gongheguo Shangfubu, No.2 Dong Chang'an Ave, Beijing, 100731, China. TEL 86-1-67081526, 86-1-67081527, FAX 86-1-67081513.

330 CHN ISSN 1005-4448
ZHONGWAI JINGMAO XINXI/INFORMATION ON CHINA AND FOREIGN TRADE. Text in Chinese. s-m. CNY 108 (effective 2004). **Document type:** *Journal, Academic/Scholarly.*
Related titles: Alternate Frequency ed(s).: s-a. USD 80.20 (effective 2002).
Published by: Zhongguo Renmin Daxue, Shubao Zilio Zhongxin/Renmin University of China, Information Center for Social Server, Dongcheng-qu, 3, Zhangzizhong Lu, Beijing, 100007, China. TEL 86-10-64039458, FAX 86-10-64015080, kyes@163.net, http://www.confucius.cn.net/bkdetail.asp?fzt=X7. **Dist. in the US by:** China Publications Service, PO Box 49614, Chicago, IL 60649. TEL 312-288-3291, FAX 312-288-8570; **Dist. outside of China by:** China International Book Trading Corp, 35 Chegongzhuang Xilu, Haidian District, PO Box 399, Beijing 100044, China. TEL 86-10-68412045, FAX 86-10-68412023, cibtc@mail.cibtc.com.cn, http://www.cibtc.com.cn/.

ZIMBABWE EXPORT DIRECTORY. see *BUSINESS AND ECONOMICS—Trade And Industrial Directories*

ZISE; told- og skattehistorisk tidsskrift. see *BUSINESS AND ECONOMICS—Public Finance, Taxation*

382.7 DEU
ZOLL SPEZIAL. Text in German. m. EUR 63 (effective 2004). **Document type:** *Journal, Trade.*
Published by: Bundesagentur fuer Aussenwirtschaft, Agrippastr 87-93, Cologne, 50676, Germany. TEL 49-221-20570, FAX 49-221-2057212, info@bfai.de, http://www.bfai.com.

332.6 DEU
DAS ZOLL- UND VERBRAUCHSSTEUERSTRAFRECHT. Text in German. irreg. (1-2/yr.). looseleaf. adv. **Document type:** *Government.*
Published by: Walhalla Fachverlag, Haus an der Eisernen Bruecke, Regensburg, 93042, Germany. TEL 49-941-5684-0, FAX 49-941-5684111, walhalla@walhalla.de, http://www.walhalla.de. Circ: 600.

332.6 DEU
ZOLLKODEX. Text in German. 2000. irreg. EUR 74.50 (effective 2001). **Document type:** *Trade.*
Media: CD-ROM. **Related titles:** Print ed.: 2001. EUR 77 (effective 2001).
Published by: Mendel Verlag, Robensstr 39, Aachen, 52070, Germany. TEL 49-241-154355, FAX 49-241-1570816, info@mendel-verlag.de, http://www.mendel-verlag.de.

332.6 AUT
ZOLLWACHT. Text in German. bi-m.
Address: Flossgasse 6, Postfach 6, Vienna, W 1025, Austria. TEL 01-332383. Ed. Herwig Jordan.

332.6 CHE
ZUELLNER. Text in German. 26/yr. **Document type:** *Bulletin.*
Published by: Postes Telephones et Telegraphes Suisses, Monbijoustr 130, Bern, 3007, Switzerland. TEL 031-452886, FAX 031-460592. Ed. Jean Marc Eggenberger. Circ: 4,000.

BUSINESS AND ECONOMICS—International Development And Assistance

338.9 LBY
A C A R T S O D MONOGRAPH SERIES. Variant title: African Social Challenges. Text in English. 1990. irreg., latest vol.4, 1991. **Document type:** *Monographic series, Trade.* **Description:** Scholarly research into social, labor, development issues and policies affecting Africa.
Published by: African Centre for Applied Research and Training in Social Development, P O Box 80606, Tripoli, Libya. TEL 218-21-833640. **N. American subscr. to:** K.G. Saur, Division of R R Bowker, 121 Chanlon Rd, New Providence, NJ 07974. **Dist. by:** Hans Zell Publishers (Subsidiary of, Hans Zell Publishers, (Subsidiary of: Bowker - Saur Ltd.), PO Box 56, Oxford OX1 2SJ, United Kingdom. TEL 44-856-511428.

360 LBY
A C A R T S O D NEWSLETTER. Text in Arabic, English, French. 1980. q. free. back issues avail. **Document type:** *Newsletter.*
Published by: African Centre for Applied Research and Training in Social Development, P O Box 80606, Tripoli, Libya. TEL 218-21-833640, TELEX 20803. Ed. Oscar Gasana. Circ: 1,500.

338.91 CAN ISSN 1192-1846
A C C C INTERNATIONAL. Text in English, French. 1990. q. **Document type:** *Newsletter.* **Description:** Provides a forum for the discussion of issues pertinent to international development. Features the perspective and experience of the college and institute personnel.
Published by: Association of Canadian Community Colleges, 1223 Michael St N, Ste 200, Ottawa, ON K1J 7T2, Canada. TEL 613-746-2222, FAX 613-746-6721, lmalcolmson@cccc.ca, http://www.accc.ca. Circ: 1,700.

338.91 CAN ISSN 1709-853X
A C D I MARCHES/C I D A CONTRACTS. (Agence Canadienne de Developpment International) Text in English, French. 1995. s-a. **Document type:** *Government.*
Formerly (until 2003): Agence Canadienne de Developpment International. Marches de Services et Lignes de Credit (1209-5281); Which was formed by the merger of (1987-1995): Canadian International Development Agency. Executing Agencies (1187-6921); Which was formerly (until 1991): Canadian International Development Agency. Business of Development, Executing Agencies (0835-2089); (198?-1995): Canadian International Development Agency. Service Contracts Bilateral Program (1187-693X); Which was formerly (until 1991): Business of Development. Active Contracts (0835-1651); (198?-1995): Canadian International Development Agency. Lines of Credit (1200-2097); Which was formerly (until 199?): Business of Development. Lines of Credit (0835-166X)
—CISTI.
Published by: Canadian International Development Agency, Communications Branch, 200 Promenade du Portage, Hull, PQ K1A 0G4, Canada. TEL 819-997-6100, FAX 819-953-6088, http://www.acdi-cida.gc.ca. Ed. Jim Holmes.

338.91 630 USA
A C D I - V O C A WORLD REPORT. Text in English. 1963. q. USD 10 (effective 1999). **Document type:** *Newsletter.* **Description:** Focuses on international development in the fields of agriculture, agribusiness, marketing, finance and natural resource management.
Formerly (until 1997): Cooperative News International
Published by: Agricultural Cooperative Development International, Volunteer in Overseas Cooperative Assistant, 50 F St, N W, Ste 1075, Washington, DC 20001. TEL 202-383-4961, FAX 202-783-7204, voca@mcimail.com, http:www.acdivoca.org. Ed. Nancy Long. Circ: 7,000; 7,000 (controlled).

338.91 AUS ISSN 0811-4692
A C F O A NEWS. Text in English. 1982. irreg. (approx. 6/yr). AUD 10; AUD 15 foreign (effective 1998). **Document type:** *Newsletter.*
Published by: Australian Council for Overseas Aid, Pravate Bag 3, Deakin, ACT 2600, Australia. TEL 61-6-2851816, FAX 61-2-2851720. Ed. Janet Hunt. Circ: 1,500.

338.91 LUX ISSN 1029-7065
HC241.25.A3
A C P - E C COUNCIL OF MINISTERS. ANNUAL REPORT (YEAR). Text in Danish, Dutch, English, French, German, Greek, Italian, Portuguese, Spanish. a., latest 1995. USD 10. **Description:** Covers civil services, international organizations, trade and professional bodies, research foundations. Also of concern to individuals interested in the problems of development and co-operation.
Formerly (until 1995): A C P - E E C Council of Ministers. Annual Report (Year) (1010-1446)
Indexed: IIS.
—BLDSC (1095.814000).
Published by: European Commission, Office for Official Publications of the European Union, 2 Rue Mercier, Luxembourg, L-2985, Luxembourg. http://europa.eu.int. **Subscr. to:** Bernan Associates, Bernan, 4611-F Assembly Dr., Lanham, MD 20706-4391. TEL 301-459-0056.

338 PHL
A D B REVIEW. (Asian Development Bank) Text in English. 1969. 6/yr. free. bk.rev. charts; illus.; stat. **Document type:** *Bulletin.* **Description:** Reports on social, education, economic, and political issues in the bank's member nations. Reviews A.D.B. symposia and meetings, and offers economic statistics.
Former titles: A D B Quarterly Review (0115-074X); (until 1976): A D B Quarterly Newsletter; Asian Development Bank. Newsletter (0044-9199)
Related titles: Microfiche ed.: (from CIS).
Indexed: AESIS, IIS, IPP, RRTA, WAE&RSA, WBA.
Published by: (Publications Unit), Asian Development Bank, Publications Unit, P.O. Box 789, Manila, 0980, Philippines. adbpub@adb.org, http://www.adb.org. Ed. Carolyn Dedolph.

A P O ANNUAL REPORT. see *BUSINESS AND ECONOMICS—Production Of Goods And Services*

A P O NEWS. see *BUSINESS AND ECONOMICS—Production Of Goods And Services*

338.91 IDN ISSN 0854-543X
HC441.A1
A S E A N ECONOMIC INFO VIEW. (Association of South East Asian Nations) Text in English. 1993. q. **Document type:** *Bulletin.*
Published by: Association of South East Asian Nations (ASEAN), ASEAN Secretariat, Jalan Sisingamangaraja 70 A, Jakarta, 12110, Indonesia. TEL 62-21-7262991, FAX 62-21-7398234, public@aseansec.org, http://www.aseansec.org.

338.91 IDN ISSN 0215-1103
A S E A N STANDING COMMITTEE. ANNUAL REPORT. Text in English. 1980. a.
Published by: Association of South East Asian Nations (ASEAN), ASEAN Secretariat, Jalan Sisingamangaraja 70 A, Jakarta, 12110, Indonesia. TEL 62-21-7262991, FAX 62-21-7398234, public@aseansec.org, http://www.aseansec.org.

600 338.91 CHE ISSN 1020-4199
A T A S INFORMATION TECHNOLOGY FOR DEVELOPMENT. Text in English. 1986. irreg. price varies. **Document type:** *Monographic series, Academic/Scholarly.*
—BLDSC (0696.932800).
Published by: (Advanced Technology Assesment System USA), United Nations Conference on Trade and Development, Palais des Nations, 8-14 Av de la Paix, Geneva 10, 1211, Switzerland. TEL 41-22-9175809, FAX 41-22-9170051, info@unctad.org, http://www.unctad.org.

A V R D C REPORT. see *AGRICULTURE*

ADVANCE (WASHINGTON). see *POLITICAL SCIENCE—International Relations*

338 SEN ISSN 0850-3907
HC501
➤ **AFRICA DEVELOPMENT/AFRIQUE ET DEVELOPPEMENT.** Text in English, French. 1976. q. USD 30 to individuals; USD 32 in Africa to institutions; USD 45 elsewhere to institutions (effective 2004). adv. bk.rev. illus.; bibl. index. back issues avail. **Document type:** *Journal, Academic/Scholarly.*
Related titles: Online - full text ed.: (from International Network for the Availability of Scientific Publications, African Journals Online).
Indexed: ASD, AbAn, CCA, IBR, IBSS, IBZ, ILD, PSA, Perlslam, RASB, RDA, RRTA, WAE&RSA.
—BLDSC (0732.154800), IE, Infotrieve, ingenta.
Published by: Council for the Development of Social Science Research in Africa, BP 3304, Dakar, Senegal. TEL 221-825-9822, FAX 221-824-1289, codesria@sentoo.sn, http://www.codesria.org. Ed., R&P, Adv. contact Felicia Oyekanmi. Circ: 600.

338 GBR ISSN 0141-3929
HC800.A1
AFRICAN BUSINESS. Text in English. 1966. 11/yr. GBP 40 domestic; EUR 80 in Europe Eurozone; USD 90 in United States; GBP 55 elsewhere (effective 2006). bk.rev. illus.; stat. Index. 64 p./no. 3 cols./p.; back issues avail.; reprints avail. **Document type:** *Magazine, Consumer.* **Description:** Provides pan-African coverage of business: economics, industry, marketing and commodities for executives living in and trading with Africa.
Related titles: Microfilm ed.: (from PQC); Online - full text ed.: (from bigchalk, EBSCO Publishing, Florida Center for Library Automation, Gale Group, H.W. Wilson, Northern Light Technology, Inc., O C L C Online Computer Library Center, Inc., ProQuest Information & Learning).
Indexed: ABIn, BPI, KES, PAIS, PROMT, RASB, RDA, RRTA.
—BLDSC (0732.370000), IE, Infotrieve, ingenta. **CCC.**
Published by: I C Publications Ltd., 7 Coldbath Sq, London, EC1R 4LQ, United Kingdom. TEL 44-20-7713-7711, FAX 44-20-7713-7898, icpubs@africasia.com, http://www.africasia.com/africanbusiness/index.php. Ed. Anver Versi. Pub. Afif Ben Yedder. R&P Carole Jones. Adv. contact Khalid Bazid. Circ: 18,961. **Subscr. to:** Tower House, Tower House, Sovereign Park, Market Harborough, Leics LE16 9EF, United Kingdom. TEL 44-1858-438792, FAX 44-1858-461739, subscriptions@africasia.com. **Dist. by:** Speedimpex U S A, Inc., 35-02 48th Ave, Long Island City, NY 11101. TEL 718-392-7477, FAX 718-361-0815, information@speedimpex.com, http://www.speedimpex.com.

AFRICAN DEVELOPMENT BANK. COMPENDIUM OF STATISTICS ON BANK GROUP OPERATIONS/BANQUE AFRICAINE DE DEVELOPPEMENT. COMPENDIUM DE STATISTIQUES SUR LES OPERATIONS DU GROUPE DE LA BANQUE. see *BUSINESS AND ECONOMICS—Abstracting, Bibliographies, Statistics*

AFRICAN DEVELOPMENT BANK. ECONOMIC RESEARCH PAPERS. see *BUSINESS AND ECONOMICS—Economic Situation And Conditions*

338.9 CIV ISSN 0568-1308
AFRICAN DEVELOPMENT BANK. REPORT BY THE BOARD OF DIRECTORS/BANQUE AFRICAINE DE DEVELOPPEMENT. RAPPORT ANNUEL/BANQUE AFRICAINE DE DEVELOPPEMENT. RAPPORT DU CONSEIL D'ADMINISTRATION. Cover title: African Development Bank. Annual Report. Text in French. 1966. a. **Document type:** *Corporate.*
Related titles: Microfiche ed.: (from CIS).
Indexed: IIS.
Published by: African Development Bank, 01 BP 1387, Abidjan, Ivory Coast. TEL 20-44-44, FAX 22-78-39, TELEX 23717.

AFRICAN DEVELOPMENT BANK. SELECTED STATISTICS ON AFRICAN COUNTRIES/BANQUE AFRICAINE DE DEVELOPPEMENT. STATISTIQUES CHOISIES SUR LES PAYS AFRICAINS. see *BUSINESS AND ECONOMICS—Abstracting, Bibliographies, Statistics*

338.91 CIV
AFRICAN DEVELOPMENT FUND. ANNUAL REPORT/FONDS AFRICAIN DE DEVELOPPEMENT. RAPPORT ANNUEL. Text in French. 1974. a. free. **Document type:** *Corporate.*
Published by: (African Development Fund), African Development Bank, 01 BP 1387, Abidjan, Ivory Coast. TEL 20-44-44, FAX 22-78-39. Circ: 5,000.

AFRICAN DEVELOPMENT INDICATORS. see *BUSINESS AND ECONOMICS—Economic Situation And Conditions*

338.96 GBR
AFRICAN DEVELOPMENT REPORT (YEAR)/RAPPORT SUR LE DEVELOPPEMENT EN AFRIQUE; rural development and poverty reduction in Africa. Text in English. a., latest 2004, May. GBP 16.99 per issue (effective 2004). charts; stat. **Document type:** *Corporate.* **Description:** Covers recent economic developments in Africa, provides in-depth analysis of a development policy issues of major importance to Africa and updated statistical information on the African economies.
—BLDSC (0732.410000).
Published by: (African Development Bank CIV, Development Research and Policy Department USA), Oxford University Press, Great Clarendon St, Oxford, OX2 6DP, United Kingdom. TEL 44-1865-556767, FAX 44-1865-556646, enquiry@oup.co.uk, http://www.oup.co.uk/isbn/0-19-927179-8, http://www.oxfordjournals.org/.

338.91 GBR ISSN 1017-6772
HC800.A1
➤ **AFRICAN DEVELOPMENT REVIEW/REVUE AFRICAINE DE DEVELOPPEMENT.** Text in English. 1989. 3/yr. EUR 65 combined subscription in Europe to individuals print & online eds.; USD 72 combined subscription in the Americas to individuals & the Caribbean (print & online eds.); GBP 43 combined subscription elsewhere to individuals print & online eds.; USD 227 combined subscription in the Americas to institutions & the Caribbean (print & online eds.); GBP 135 combined subscription elsewhere to institutions print & online eds. (effective 2006). bk.rev. charts; stat.; illus. back issues avail.; reprints avail. **Document type:** *Journal, Academic/Scholarly.* **Description:** Offers study and analysis of development issues in Africa.
Related titles: Online - full text ed.: ISSN 1467-8268. EUR 62 in Europe to individuals; USD 69 in the Americas to individuals & Caribbean; GBP 41 elsewhere to individuals; USD 215 in the Americas to institutions & Caribbean; GBP 128 elsewhere to institutions (effective 2006) (from Blackwell Synergy, EBSCO Publishing, Gale Group, IngentaConnect, O C L C Online Computer Library Center, Inc., Swets Information Services).
Indexed: ABIn, ASD, ASSIA, AgBio, CurCont, GEOBASE, HortAb, IBSS, IIS, JEL, NutrAb, PAIS, PCI, PHN&I, PSA, RDA, S&F, SSCI, SSI, TriticAb, WAE&RSA.
—BLDSC (0732.412000), IE, Infotrieve, ingenta. **CCC.**
Published by: (African Development Bank CIV), Blackwell Publishing Ltd., 9600 Garsington Rd, Oxford, OX4 2ZG, United Kingdom. TEL 44-1865-776868, FAX 44-1865-714591, customerservices@oxon.blackwellpublishing.com, http://www.blackwellpublishing.com/journals/AFDR. Ed. Mohammed N Hussain.

➤ **AFRICAN URBAN QUARTERLY.** see *HOUSING AND URBAN PLANNING*

338.91 DEU ISSN 0947-8353
DT737
AFRIKA SUED. Text in German. 1971. 6/yr. EUR 35 to individuals; EUR 50 to institutions; EUR 6 newsstand/cover (effective 2005). adv. bk.rev. 40 p./no. 3 cols./p.; back issues avail. **Document type:** *Bulletin, Trade.* **Description:** Covers political, social and economic development in southern Africa.
Formerly (until 1994): Informationsdienst Suedliches Afrika (0721-5088)
Indexed: DIP, IBR, IBZ.
Published by: Informationsstelle Suedliches Afrika (I.S.S.A.), Koenigswinterer Str 116, Bonn, 53227, Germany. TEL 49-228-464369, FAX 49-228-468177, issa@comlink.org, http://www.issa-bonn.org/afsued.htm. Ed. Hein Moellers. Circ: 2,500.

338.91 360 SEN
➤ **AFRIKA ZAMANI.** Text and summaries in English, French. 1973. a. USD 10 to individuals; USD 15 to institutions (effective 2002). adv. bk.rev. bibl.; illus.; maps. back issues avail. **Document type:** *Journal, Academic/Scholarly.* **Description:** Contains articles on world history in English and French for both African scholars and scholars elsewhere working on Africa.
Indexed: IBSS.
Published by: Council for the Development of Social Science Research in Africa, BP 3304, Dakar, Senegal. TEL 221-825-9823, FAX 221-824-1289, codesria@sonatel.senet.net, http://www.sas.upenn.edu/African_Studies/codesria/codes_Menu.html, http://www.codesria.org. Eds. Penda Mbow, Rokhaya Fall. Circ: 1,250.

338 EGY ISSN 0002-0613
AFRO ASIAN ECONOMIC REVIEW*. Text in English. 1959. bi-m. USD 7. adv. charts; illus.; stat.
Indexed: AmH&L, HistAb.
Published by: Afro-Asian Organization for Economic Co-Operation, Cairo Chamber of Commerce Bldg., Midan el Falaky, 4, Cairo, Egypt. Ed. Emad El Rashidi.

338.91 CAN ISSN 1482-6526
AGENCE CANADIENNE DE DEVELOPPEMENT INTERNATIONAL. RAPPORT ANNUEL. Text in French. a.
Supersedes in part (in 1991): Canadian International Development Agency. Annual Report (0839-2382); Which was formerly (until 1984): Canadians in the Third World (0715-8459); Canadians in the Third World. Statistical Annex (0715-8467); Which superseded in part (in 1981): Canada and Development Cooperation (0710-7064); Agence Canadienne de Developpement International. Rapport Annuel (0700-1711); Both of which superseded in part (in 1975): Canadian International Development Agency. Annual Review (0576-0216); Which was formerly (until 1967): External Aid Office. Annual Review (0700-1703); (until 1967): Canada's External Aid Programs. Report
—CISTI.
Published by: Canadian International Development Agency, 200 Promenade du Portage, Gatineau, PQ K1A 0G4, Canada. TEL 819-997-5006, 800-230-6349, FAX 819-953-6088, info@acdi-cida.gc.ca, http://www.acdi-cida.gc.ca.

338.91 630 GBR ISSN 0952-2468
AGRICULTURAL RESEARCH AND EXTENSION NETWORK. PAPERS. Text in English. s-a. back issues avail. **Document type:** *Academic/Scholarly.*
Indexed: MaizeAb, RDA, SeedAb, WAE&RSA.
Published by: Overseas Development Institute, Portland House, Stag Pl, London, SWIE 5DP, United Kingdom. TEL 44-171-393-1600, FAX 44-171-393-1699, rpeg@odi.org.uk, http://www.oneworld.org/odi/rpeg. Ed. Cate Turton.

338.91 CAN ISSN 0842-7038
AID TO DEVELOPING COUNTRIES. Text in English. 1985. irreg. **Document type:** *Government.*
Formerly (until 1987): External Aid, Canada's Program (0840-0563)
Related titles: Online - full content ed.: ISSN 1700-1935; ♦ French ed.: Aide aux Pays en Developpement. ISSN 0842-7046.
Published by: Library of Parliament, Parliamentary Research Branch, Information Service, Ottawa, ON K1A 0A9, Canada.

338.91 AUS ISSN 1322-4018
AID - WATCH. Text in English. 1993. q. AUD 35 to individuals. adv. **Document type:** *Bulletin.* **Description:** Reports on overseas development issues with a particular focus on the social and environmental impacts of World Bank, Asian Development Bank and AusAID activities in the Asia-Pacific region.
Related titles: Online - full text ed.
Published by: Aid - Watch Inc., PO Box 652, Woollahra, NSW 2025, Australia. TEL 61-2-9387-5210, FAX 61-2-9386-1497, aidwatch@peg.apc.org, http://www.peg.apc.org/~aidwatch. Ed. Lee Rhiannon. Adv. contact Liam Phelan. Circ: 500.

338.91 CAN ISSN 0842-7046
AIDE AUX PAYS EN DEVELOPPEMENT. Text in French. irreg. **Document type:** *Government.*
Related titles: Online - full content ed.: ISSN 1700-1943; ♦ English ed.: Aid to Developing Countries. ISSN 0842-7038.
Published by: Library of Parliament, Parliamentary Research Branch, Information Service, Ottawa, ON K1A 0A9, Canada.

338.91 DEU ISSN 1436-3100
ALASKA; Zeitschrift fuer Internationalismus. Text in German. 1979. 7/yr. EUR 3.50 newsstand/cover (effective 2005). bk.rev.; film rev.; music rev. back issues avail. **Document type:** *Journal, Trade.*
Formerly (until 1996): Forum (Bremen) (0932-285X)
Published by: IntKom - Verein fuer Internationalismus und Kommunikation e.V., Bernhardstr 12, Bremen, 28203, Germany. alaska@outofthisworld.de, intkom@outofthisworld.de, http://www.outofthisworld.de/alaska/, http://www.outofthisworld.de/intkom/impress.htm. Ed. Claudia Bernhard. Circ: 1,000.

338.91 CHN
ALMANAC OF CHINA'S FOREIGN ECONOMIC RELATIONS AND TRADE. Text in Chinese, English. 1984. a. HKD 855 domestic; USD 110 foreign. adv. stat. back issues avail. **Document type:** *Trade.* **Description:** Contains statistics and information on the PRC's imports and exports, utilization of foreign capital, contracted projects and labor service cooperation, foreign economic aid, and bilateral or multilateral economic and technical cooperation. Also covers relevant laws and regulations on foreign trade and investment, technology transfer, custom and taxation, finance and foreign exchange, commodity inspection and arbitration.
Related titles: Chinese ed.: Zhongguo Duiwai Jingji Maoyi Nianjian.
—BLDSC (0796.425600).
Published by: Ministry of Commerce of the People's Republic of China/Zhonghua Renmin Gongheguo Shangfubu, 28 Dong Hou Ln, An Ding Men Wai, Beijing, 100710, China. TEL 86-1-64246856, 86-1-64216661ext 1101, FAX 86-1-1-64212175, 86-1-64246856. Circ: 10,000.

ALTERCATIF. see *ENGINEERING*

327 USA ISSN 0892-2950
ALTERNATIVE TRADING NEWS. Text in English. 1975. q. looseleaf. USD 10 (effective 1999). bk.rev. bibl. **Document type:** *Newsletter.* **Description:** Publishes news and information pertaining to the projects, educational resources, activities, and members of the Friends of the Third World, which promotes building the product exportation capabilities of poverty-prone countries to raise their standard of living.
Formerly: Friends in Action
Published by: Friends of Third World, Inc., 611 W. Wayne St., Ft. Wayne, IN 46802-2167. TEL 219-422-6821, FAX 219-422-1650, http://www.parlorcity.com/scoop/fotw. Ed., R&P Jim Goetsch. Pub. Marian Waltz. Circ: 10,000 (paid).

AMERICAS UPDATE. see *POLITICAL SCIENCE—International Relations*

338.9 CHE ISSN 0256-5382
HF1573
ANNUAIRE SUISSE-TIERS MONDE. Text in French. 1981. a. CHF 42 (effective 2001). **Document type:** *Yearbook, Academic/Scholarly.*
Related titles: German ed.: Jahrbuch Schweiz-Dritte Welt. ISSN 1421-9581. 1982.
Published by: Institut Universitaire d'Etudes du Developpement, Case Postale 136, Geneva 21, 1211, Switzerland. TEL 41-22-9065940, FAX 41-22-9065953, publications@iued.unige.ch, http://www.iued.unige.ch.

ANNUAL EDITIONS: DEVELOPING WORLD. see *GEOGRAPHY*

338.91 MUS
ANNUAL REPORT ON DEVELOPMENT ASSISTANCE TO MAURITIUS. Text in English. a. free. **Document type:** *Government.*
Published by: United Nations Development Programme Mauritius and the Seychelles, PO Box 253, Port Louis, Mauritius. Ed. Robert J Utz. Circ: 175.

ANNUAL REPORT ON THE ENVIRONMENT AND NATURAL RESOURCES. see *ENVIRONMENTAL STUDIES*

338 USA ISSN 1520-9733
ANNUAL REVIEW OF DEVELOPMENT EFFECTIVENESS. Text in English. 1975. a.
Formerly (until 1987): Evaluation Results for... - World Bank (1019-4363)
Related titles: Online - full text ed.: ISSN 1564-6564.
Published by: World Bank, Operations Evaluation Department, 1818 H St NW, Washington, DC 20433g.

ANNUAL THIRD WORLD CONFERENCE PROCEEDINGS. see *HISTORY*

338.91 USA ISSN 1020-6140
ANNUAL WORLD BANK CONFERENCE ON DEVELOPMENT IN LATIN AMERICA AND THE CARIBBEAN. Text in English. 1997. a.
Indexed: GEOBASE.
Published by: World Bank Group, 1818 H St, NW, Washington, DC 20433. TEL 703-661-1580, FAX 703-661-1501, books@worldbank.org, http://www.worldbank.org.

ARAB BANK FOR ECONOMIC DEVELOPMENT IN AFRICA. ANNUAL REPORT. see *BUSINESS AND ECONOMICS—Banking And Finance*

338.9 KWT ISSN 0304-6729
HC498.A1
ARAB FUND FOR ECONOMIC AND SOCIAL DEVELOPMENT. ANNUAL REPORT. Text in Arabic, English. 1973. a. free. illus. **Document type:** *Corporate.*
Related titles: Microfiche ed.: (from CIS).
Indexed: IIS.
Published by: Arab Fund for Economic and Social Development/Al-Sandouq al-Arabi lil-Enma' al-Eqtissadi wa al-Ejtima'i, P O Box 21923, Safat, 13080, Kuwait. TEL 965-4815750, FAX 965-4844500, malkhubaizi@afesd.qualitynet.net.

ARISE; a women's developmental magazine. see *WOMEN'S INTERESTS*

ASIA MONITOR. CHINA & NORTH EAST ASIA. see *BUSINESS AND ECONOMICS—Economic Situation And Conditions*

ASIA MONITOR. SOUTH EAST ASIA. see *BUSINESS AND ECONOMICS—Economic Situation And Conditions*

338.91 AUS ISSN 1441-984X
HC59.69
ASIA PACIFIC SCHOOL OF ECONOMICS AND MANAGEMENT WORKING PAPERS. DEVELOPMENT ISSUES. Text in English. 1975. irreg., latest vol.12. AUD 10 (effective 2000). back issues avail. **Document type:** *Monographic series.* **Description:** Covers economics, trade, development and policy issues.
Former titles: Economics Division Working Papers. Development Issues (Online Edition) (1441-9475); (until 1996): Economics Division Working Papers. Development Issues (Print Edition) (1038-412X); Incorporates in part (in 1991): National Centre for Development Studies, Australian National University.Working Paper (0815-7596); (until 1985): Development Studies Centre. Working Paper (0814-1266); (until 1984): Development Studies Centre. Occasional Papers (0313-637X); (until 1983): Development Studies Centre. Working Paper
Media: Online - full content.
Indexed: RDA.
Published by: Australian National University, National Centre for Development Studies, Canberra, ACT 0200, Australia. TEL 61-2-6249-4705, FAX 61-2-6257-2886. Ed. Maree Tait. **Subscr. to:** Landmark Educational Supplies, PO Box 130, Drovin, VIC 3818, Australia.

338.91 AUS ISSN 1360-7456
AS741
➤ **ASIA PACIFIC VIEWPOINT**; specialises in the study of development, change and underdevelopment. Text in English. 1960. 3/yr., latest vol.43, no.3, 2002. GBP 54 combined subscription in New Zealand to individuals print & online eds.; EUR 60 combined subscription in Europe to individuals print & online eds.; USD 57 combined subscription in the Americas to individuals print & online eds.; GBP 40 combined subscription elsewhere to individuals print & online eds.; GBP 79 combined subscription in New Zealand to institutions print & online eds.; USD 171 combined subscription in the Americas to institutions & Caribbean (print & online eds.); GBP 120 combined subscription elsewhere to institutions print & online eds. (effective 2006). adv. bk.rev. charts; illus.; maps. back issues avail.; reprint service avail. from PSC. **Document type:** *Academic/Scholarly.*
Formerly (until 1996): Pacific Viewpoint (0030-8978)
Related titles: Microfilm ed.: (from PQC); Online - full text ed.: ISSN 1467-8373. USD 149 in the Americas to institutions & Caribbean; GBP 60 in New Zealand to institutions; GBP 105 elsewhere to institutions (effective 2005) (from Blackwell Synergy, EBSCO Publishing, Gale Group, IngentaConnect, O C L C Online Computer Library Center, Inc., Swets Information Services).
Indexed: ABIn, APEL, AmH&L, AnthLit, BAS, BibInd, GEOBASE, HistAb, IBR, IBSS, IBZ, INZP, IPSA, IndIslam, KES, PAIS, PSA, RDA, SPPI, SSA, SWA, SociolAb.
—BLDSC (1742.262450), IE, Infotrieve, ingenta. **CCC.**
Published by: (Victoria University of Wellington NZL, Department of Geography NZL), Blackwell Publishing Asia (Subsidiary of: Blackwell Publishing Ltd.), 550 Swanston St, Carlton South, VIC 3053, Australia. TEL 61-383591011, FAX 61-383591120, apv@vuw.ac.nz, subs@blackwellpublishingasia.com, http://www.blackwellpublishing.com/journals/APV. Ed. Dr. Warwick E Murray. Circ: 850.

338.91 BEL ISSN 1725-1370
ASIA URBS MAGAZINE. Text in English. 1999. s-a.
Published by: European Commission, EuropeAid Co-operation Office, Asia Urbs Programme, Loi 41 3/49, Brussels, B-1049, Belgium. TEL 32-2-298-4731, FAX 32-2-298-4863, europeaid-asia-urbs@cec.eu.int, http://europa.eu.int/comm/europeaid/projects/asia-urbs.

ASIAN DEVELOPMENT BANK. ANNUAL REPORT. see *BUSINESS AND ECONOMICS—Banking And Finance*

332.1 PHL ISSN 0066-8389
ASIAN DEVELOPMENT BANK. BOARD OF GOVERNORS. SUMMARY OF PROCEEDINGS. Text in English. 1968. a. **Description:** Records the bank's annual meeting.
Published by: Asian Development Bank, Publications Unit, P.O. Box 789, Manila, 0980, Philippines. adbpub@adb.org, http://www.adb.org.

ASIAN DEVELOPMENT BANK. KEY INDICATORS OF DEVELOPING ASIAN AND PACIFIC COUNTRIES. see *BUSINESS AND ECONOMICS—Banking And Finance*

338.91 PHL ISSN 0116-1105
HC411
➤ **ASIAN DEVELOPMENT REVIEW**; studies of Asian and Pacific economic issues. Text in English. 1983. s-a. USD 5 (effective 2004). adv. illus. back issues avail.; reprints avail. **Document type:** *Academic/Scholarly.* **Description:** Covers economic issues in the Asia-Pacific region. Focuses on questions of development.
Related titles: Online - full text ed.: free (effective 2005) (from CIS, ProQuest Information & Learning).
Indexed: ABIn, APEL, ARDT, BAS, DSA, GEOBASE, IBR, IBSS, IBZ, IIS, IPP, JEL, JOF, NutrAb, PAA&I, PAIS, RASB, RDA, SWA, TDB, WAE&RSA, WBA.
—BLDSC (1742.407750), IE, Infotrieve, ingenta.
Published by: (Information Office), Asian Development Bank, Publications Unit, P.O. Box 789, Manila, 0980, Philippines. adbpub@adb.org, http://www.adb.org/documents/periodicals/adr/default.asp. Ed. Satish C Jha.

➤ **ASIAN ECONOMIC AND SOCIAL REVIEW**; techno-economic quarterly of Asian co-operation. see *SOCIAL SCIENCES: COMPREHENSIVE WORKS*

338.9 JPN ISSN 0002-2942
HC411
➤ **ASIAN ECONOMIES/AJIA KEIZAI.** Text in Japanese. 1960. m. JPY 12,600 (effective 2003). adv. bk.rev. cum.index. back issues avail. **Document type:** *Academic/Scholarly.* **Description:** Reports on studies on development issues and related topics. Contains articles, theoretical and empirical notes, and occasionally, reports of surveys and conferences.
Indexed: APEL, AmH&L, HistAb, PAIS, PSA, RASB, SSCI, SociolAb.
—BLDSC (1742.416000).
Published by: Institute of Developing Economies/Ajia Keizai Kenkyusho, 3-2-2 Wakaba, Mihana-ku, Chiba-shi, Chiba 261-8545, Japan. TEL 81-43-299-9536, FAX 84-43-299-9724, info@ide.go.jp, http://www.ide.go.jp. Ed. Takshi Nohara. Circ: 750.

➤ **ASIAN - PACIFIC ECONOMIC LITERATURE.** see *BUSINESS AND ECONOMICS—Abstracting, Bibliographies, Statistics*

➤ **ASIAN VEGETABLE RESEARCH AND DEVELOPMENT CENTER. TECHNICAL BULLETIN.** see *AGRICULTURE*

338.91 AUS
AUSTRALIA AND THE ASIAN DEVELOPMENT BANK. Text in English. 199?. a. charts; stat. back issues avail. **Document type:** *Government.* **Description:** Reports on the Commonwealth of Australia's involvement in the Asian Development Bank.
Related titles: Online - full text ed.
Published by: (Australia. Department of the Treasury), AusInfo, GPO Box 1920, Canberra Mc, ACT 2610, Australia. TEL 61-2-6295-4512, http://www.ausinfo.gov.au, http://www.treasury.gov.au. **Orders to:** AusInfo Mail Order Sales, GPO Box 84, Canberra, ACT 2601, Australia. FAX 61-2-6295-4888.

338.91 AUS
HC605
AUSTRALIA AND THE I M F (YEAR). (International Monetary Fund) Text in English. a. price varies. back issues avail. **Document type:** *Government.* **Description:** Reports on the operations under the International Monetary Agreements Act of 1947, as they relate to Australia, the International Monetary Fund, and the International Bank for Reconstruction and Development.
Formerly (until 1990): International Monetary Agreements Act. Annual Report (0818-6316)
Related titles: Online - full text ed.
Published by: (Australia. Department of the Treasury), AusInfo, GPO Box 1920, Canberra Mc, ACT 2610, Australia. TEL 61-2-6295-4512, FAX 61-2-6295-4555, http://www.ausinfo.gov.au, http://www.treasury.gov.au. **Orders to:** AusInfo Mail Order Sales, GPO Box 84, Canberra, ACT 2601, Australia. FAX 61-2-6295-4888.

338.91 AUS ISSN 1038-409X
AUSTRALIA AND THE WORLD BANK. Text in English. 1989. a. price varies. charts; stat. back issues avail.; reprints avail. **Document type:** *Monographic series, Government.* **Description:** Reports on Australian Commonwealth Government operations as they relate to the World Bank and affect Australia.
Formerly (until 1990): International Bank for Reconstruction and Development (General Capital Increase) Act of 1989 Annual Report (1035-087X)
Related titles: Online - full text ed.
Published by: (Australia. Department of the Treasury), AusInfo, GPO Box 1920, Canberra Mc, ACT 2610, Australia. TEL 61-2-6295-4512, FAX 61-2-6295-4455, http://www.ausinfo.gov.au, http://www.treasury.gov.au. **Orders to:** AusInfo Mail Order Sales, GPO Box 84, Canberra, ACT 2601, Australia. FAX 61-2-6295-4888.

338.91 AUS ISSN 0818-0512
AUSTRALIAN NATIONAL UNIVERSITY. NATIONAL CENTRE FOR DEVELOPMENT STUDIES. ANNUAL REPORT (YEAR). Key Title: Annual Report - National Centre for Development Studies. Text in English. 1985. a. **Document type:** *Corporate.* **Description:** Summarizes the Centre's past year's activities, including programs sponsored, research results, graduate studies and scholarships.
Published by: Australian National University, National Centre for Development Studies, Canberra, ACT 0200, Australia. TEL 61-2-6249-4705, FAX 61-2-6257-2886, http://www.asiapacificpress.com. Ed. Maree Tait.

338.91 AUS ISSN 0815-6301
AUSTRALIAN NATIONAL UNIVERSITY. NATIONAL CENTRE FOR DEVELOPMENT STUDIES. HISTORY OF DEVELOPMENT STUDIES. Text in English. 1985. irreg. price varies. **Document type:** *Monographic series.* **Description:** A monograph series that details the life and work of prominent development economists.
—BLDSC (4317.972000).
Published by: Australian National University, National Centre for Development Studies, Canberra, ACT 0200, Australia. TEL 61-2-6249-4705, FAX 61-2-6257-2886, http://www.asiapacificpress.com. Ed. Maree Tait.

338.91 AUS ISSN 0817-0444
AUSTRALIAN NATIONAL UNIVERSITY. NATIONAL CENTRE FOR DEVELOPMENT STUDIES. PACIFIC POLICY PAPERS. Text in English. 1986. irreg., latest vol.32. price varies. **Document type:** *Monographic series.* **Description:** Covers economics, trade, development and policy issues.
Indexed: GEOBASE, NutrAb, RDA, RRTA, SIA, WAE&RSA.
Published by: Australian National University, National Centre for Development Studies, Canberra, ACT 0200, Australia. TEL 61-2-6249-4705, FAX 61-2-6257-2886, http://www.asiapacificpress.com. Ed. Maree Tait.

B I D S MONOGRAPH. see *SOCIOLOGY*

338.91 BGD
B I D S NEWSLETTER. Text in English. 1985. m. abstr.; bibl.; stat. **Document type:** *Newsletter.* **Description:** Presents research on development problems of Bangladesh and promotes dissemination of knowledge regarding these issues.

B

Published by: Bangladesh Unnayan Gobeshona Protishthan/Bangladesh Institute of Development Studies, E-17 Agargaon, Sher-e-Banglanagar, GPO Box 3854, Dhaka, 1207, Bangladesh. TEL 325041. Eds. Atiq Rahman, Trina Haque.

B I D S RESEARCH REPORTS. see *SOCIOLOGY*

B I D S WORKING PAPER. see *SOCIOLOGY*

338.9 DEU
B M Z - MATERIALIEN. Text in German. 1970. bi-m. free.
Document type: *Government.*
Published by: Bundesministerium fuer Wirtschaftliche Zusammenarbeit und Entwicklung, Friedrich-Ebert-Allee 114-116, Bonn, 53113, Germany.

330 GBR ISSN 1359-1398
B R I D G E REPORT. (Briefings on Development & Gender) Text in English. irreg. **Document type:** *Monographic series.*
—BLDSC (2283.926110).
Published by: University of Sussex, Institute of Development Studies, Brighton, Sussex BN1 9RE, United Kingdom. TEL 44-1273-606261, FAX 44-1273-621202, ids@ids.ac.uk, http://www.ids.ac.uk/ids.

338.91 079.517 MNG
BLUE SKY BULLETIN. Text in English. irreg., latest vol.9. free. illus. **Document type:** *Bulletin.* **Description:** Reports on the UNDPs efforts in Mongolia, along with items on that country's culture.
Media: Online - full text.
Published by: United Nations Development Programme Mongolia, Erhuu St 7, PO Box 49 207, Ulan Bator, Mongolia. TEL 976-1-327585, FAX 976-1-326221, registry@undp.org.mn, http://www.un-mongolia.mn/undp/.

338.91 360 305.4 USA
BORDER CONNECTIONS. Text in English. 1984. q. free.
Document type: *Bulletin.* **Description:** Covers long-term community development programs that empower women to help themselves and their communities.
Related titles: Online - full text ed.
Published by: Los Ninos, 287 G St, Chula Vista, CA 91910. TEL 619-426-9110, FAX 619-426-6664, losninos@electriciti.com, http://www.electriciti.com/~losninos. Ed. Liz Kownslar. Circ: 6,000.

BOSTON COLLEGE THIRD WORLD LAW JOURNAL. see *LAW—International Law*

338.91 CAN ISSN 0833-9864
F1034.2
BOUT DE PAPIER. Text in English. 1973. q. CND 16 domestic; CND 20 in United States; CND 22 elsewhere; CND 4.50 newsstand/cover (effective 2000). adv. back issues avail.
Description: Examines all aspects of Canadian foreign policy and life in the foreign service.
Indexed: CBCARef.
Published by: Professional Association of Foreign Service Officers, 47 Clarence St, Ste 412, Ottawa, ON K1N 9K1, Canada. TEL 613-241-1391, FAX 613-241-5911, boutdepapier@pafso.com, http://www.pafso.com. Ed. Kevin O'Shea. Adv. contact Debra Hulley. page CND 475; trim 11 x 8.5.

BULLETIN DE L'AFRIQUE NOIRE. see *POLITICAL SCIENCE*

338.91 USA
BUSINESS & LABOR DIALOGUE. Text in English. 1997. q.
Document type: *Newsletter.* **Description:** Explores public and private efforts at international development from the perspectives of business and labor.
Published by: National Policy Association, 3424 Porter St NW, Washington, DC 20016-3126. TEL 202-265-7685, FAX 202-797-5516, npa@npa1.org, http://www.npa1.org.

BUSINESS COUNCIL FOR THE U N BRIEFING. see *POLITICAL SCIENCE—International Relations*

BUSINESS P R C; an informative bridge between China and the world. see *BUSINESS AND ECONOMICS—International Commerce*

C A F O D MAGAZINE. see *RELIGIONS AND THEOLOGY—Roman Catholic*

338.91 FRA ISSN 1262-3857
C C E INTERNATIONAL. Text in French; Summaries in French. 1911. m. (10/yr.). adv. bk.rev. bibl.; illus. back issues avail.
Document type: *Bulletin, Trade.*
Formerly (until 1944): Conseiller du Commerce Exterieur (0294-8494)
Related titles: Online - full text ed.
Indexed: KES.
Published by: Comite National des Conseillers du Commerce Exterieur, 24 rue de Cronstadt, Paris, 75015, France. TEL 33-0-153-689000, FAX 33-0-153-689010. Ed. Madeleine Barbier Decrozes. Pub. J M Taupin. Adv. contact Luc Lehericy. Circ: 10,000.

C C S O WORKING PAPERS. (Centrum voor Conjunctuur en Structuuronderzoek) see *BUSINESS AND ECONOMICS—Public Finance, Taxation*

330 DNK ISSN 0904-4701
HD72
C D R WORKING PAPER. Text in English. 1969. irreg.
Document type: *Monographic series, Academic/Scholarly.*
Description: Explores Third World socio-economic development issues.
Indexed: ForAb, GEOBASE, HerbAb, HortAb, I&DA, PGegResA, PHN&I, RDA, RRTA, RiceAb, S&F, SeedAb, TDB, WAE&RSA.
Published by: Centre for Development Research, Gammel Kongevej 5, Copenhagen V, 1610, Denmark. TEL 45-33-25-12-00, FAX 45-33-25-81-10, cdr@cdr.dk.

C E D P A NETWORK. see *WOMEN'S INTERESTS*

338.9 CAN ISSN 0826-4228
C - F A R NEWSLETTER. Text in English. 1976. m. CND 16. bk.rev. **Document type:** *Newsletter.*
Formerly (until 1983): C - F A R (0711-5725)
Published by: Citizens for Foreign Aid Reform Inc., P O Box 332, Sta B, Etobicoke, ON M9W 5L3, Canada. TEL 905-897-7221, FAX 905-277-3914. Ed. Paul Fromm. Circ: 1,500 (controlled).

C O D E S R I A BULLETIN. see *HISTORY—History Of Africa*

338.91 GBR
C S - D R M S. (Commonwealth Secretariat - Debt Recording Management System) Text in English. s-a. **Document type:** *Newsletter.* **Description:** For users of the Commonwealth Secretariat - Debt Recording Management System.
Published by: Commonwealth Secretariat, Marlborough House, Pall Mall, London, SW1Y 5HX, United Kingdom. FAX 44-2079-300827, http://www.thecommonwealth.org.

338.91 CAN ISSN 0823-5740
C U S O FORUM. Text in English. 1969. 2/yr. free. **Document type:** *Newsletter.*
Published by: C U S O, 2255 Carling Ave, Ottawa, ON K2B 1A6, Canada. TEL 613-829-7445, FAX 613-829-7996, TELEX 053-4706. Circ: 5,000.

338.91 CMR
LES CAHIERS DE L' I P D/P A I D REPORTS. Text in English, French. 1981. s-a. XAF 9,000, USD 45. back issues avail.
Description: Reflections and information concerning training, research and support-consultancy activities for rural development in sub-Saharan Africa.
Formerly: I P D Cahier (0256-4912)
Published by: Institut Panafricain pour le Developpement/ Panafrican Institute for Development, PO Box 4056, Douala, Cameroon. TEL 237-42-10-61, FAX 237-42-43-35. Ed. Dr. Mbuki Mwamufiya. Circ: 2,000.

CANADIAN DEVELOPMENT REPORT. see *BUSINESS AND ECONOMICS—International Commerce*

338.91 CAN ISSN 1707-7168
CANADIAN INTERNATIONAL DEVELOPMENT AGENCY. MASS MEDIA INITIATIVE. DEVELOPMENT INFORMATION PROGRAM. GUIDELINES FOR SUBMITTING PROPOSALS. Text in English. 1995. a.
Formerly (until 2002): Canadian International Development Agency. Development Information Program. Guidelines for Submitting Proposals (1208-011X)
Published by: (Canadian International Development Agency, Development Information Program), Canadian International Development Agency, 200 Promenade du Portage, Gatineau, PQ K1A 0G4, Canada. TEL 819-997-5006, 800-230-6349, FAX 819-953-6088, info@acdi-cida.gc.ca, http://www.acdi-cida.gc.ca/dip.

338.91 CAN ISSN 1483-9687
CANADIAN INTERNATIONAL DEVELOPMENT AGENCY. PERFORMANCE REPORT. Text in English, French. 1997. a.
Related titles: Online - full text ed.: ISSN 1490-4829.
Published by: (Canadian International Development Agency), Treasury Board of Canada Secretariat, Corporate Communications, West Tower, Rm P-135, 300 Laurier Ave W, Ottawa, ON K1A 0R5, Canada. TEL 613-995-2855, FAX 613-996-0518, services-publications@tbs-sct.gc.ca, http://www.acdi-cida.gc.ca/publications-e.htm, http://www.tbs-sct.gc.ca.

CANADIAN JOURNAL OF REGIONAL SCIENCE/REVUE CANADIENNE DES SCIENCES REGIONALES. see *BUSINESS AND ECONOMICS—Economic Systems And Theories, Economic History*

CARIBBEAN UPDATE. see *BUSINESS AND ECONOMICS—International Commerce*

CATALOGUE OF STATISTICAL MATERIALS OF DEVELOPING COUNTRIES. see *BUSINESS AND ECONOMICS—Abstracting, Bibliographies, Statistics*

CENTERPOINT. see *AGRICULTURE*

338.91 BDI
CENTRE UNIVERSITAIRE DE RECHERCHE POUR LE DEVELOPPEMENT ECONOMIQUE ET SOCIAL. CAHIERS. Cover title: Cahiers du C U R D E S. Text in French. 1982. irreg., latest vol.7, 1989.
Indexed: PLESA.
Published by: Universite du Burundi, BP 1550, Bujumbura, Burundi.

338.91 URY
CENTRO INTERDISCIPLINARIO DE ESTUDIOS SOBRE EL DESARROLLO. INVESTIGACIONES. Text in Spanish. irreg.
Published by: Centro Interdisciplinario de Estudios sobre el Desarrollo, Av Americo Ricaldoni 2529, 602, Montevideo, 11600, Uruguay. ciedur@chasque.apc.org, http://www.chasque.apc.org/ciedur.

CHICAGO JOURNAL OF INTERNATIONAL LAW. see *LAW—International Law*

338.91 AUS
CHINESE ECONOMIC ASSOCIATION PROCEEDINGS. Text in English. 1989. irreg. price varies. **Document type:** *Proceedings.* **Description:** Papers presented at annual seminars held amongst Chinese doctoral students studying in Australia and New Zealand. Covers topics related to reform, trade and development.
Formerly: Chinese Students' Conference Proceedings
Published by: Australian National University, National Centre for Development Studies, Canberra, ACT 0200, Australia. Ed. Maree Tait. **Subscr. to:** Landmark Educational Supplies, PO Box 130, Drovin, VIC 3818, Australia.

338.91 JPN ISSN 0910-8882
JX1395
CHUBU UNIVERSITY. COLLEGE OF INTERNATIONAL STUDIES. JOURNAL. Text in English. 1985. a. exchange basis to libraries.
Related titles: Japanese ed.: Kokusai Kankei Gakubu. Kiyo.
Published by: Chubu University, College of International Studies, Kasugai, Aichi 487, Japan.

338 LKA
COLOMBO PLAN BUREAU. THE COLOMBO PLAN COUNCIL REPORT. Text in English. 1951. a. free. **Document type:** *Newsletter, Trade.*
Formerly: Colombo Plan Bureau. Technical Cooperation under the Colombo Plan. Report (0069-5947)
Published by: (Colombo Plan for Co-Operative Economic and Social Development in Asia and the Pacific), Colombo Plan Bureau, 12 Melbourne Ave., P O Box 596, Colombo, 4, Sri Lanka. TEL 94-1-581813, FAX 94-1-581754. Ed. J P Pathirana. Circ: 1,500.

338.9 LKA
COLOMBO PLAN FOR CO-OPERATIVE ECONOMIC AND SOCIAL DEVELOPMENT IN ASIA AND THE PACIFIC. CONSULTATIVE COMMITTEE. PROCEEDINGS AND CONCLUSIONS. Text in English. 1952. biennial. free. index, cum.index: 1952-1972. **Document type:** *Proceedings.*
Former titles: Colombo Plan for Co-operative Economic and Social Development in Asia and the Pacific. Consultative Committee. Report; Colombo Plan for Co-operative Economic Development in South and South-East Asia. Report of the Consultative Committee (0069-5963)
Published by: (Colombo Plan for Co-Operative Economic and Social Development in Asia and the Pacific), Colombo Plan Bureau, 12 Melbourne Ave., P O Box 596, Colombo, 4, Sri Lanka. TEL 94-1-581813, FAX 94-1-581754. Ed. J P Pathirana. Circ: 1,500.

338.9 LKA
COLOMBO PLAN FOR CO-OPERATIVE ECONOMIC AND SOCIAL DEVELOPMENT IN ASIA AND THE PACIFIC. DEVELOPMENT PERSPECTIVES. COUNTRY ISSUES PAPERS BY MEMBER GOVERNMENTS TO THE CONSULTATIVE COMMITTEE. Text in English. 1980. biennial. free. cum.index. **Document type:** *Proceedings.*
Formerly: Colombo Plan for Co-operative Economic Development in South and South East Asia. Country Issues Papers
Published by: (Colombo Plan for Co-Operative Economic and Social Development in Asia and the Pacific), Colombo Plan Bureau, 12 Melbourne Ave., P O Box 596, Colombo, 4, Sri Lanka. TEL 94-1-581813, FAX 94-1-581754. Ed. J P Pathirana. Circ: 1,500.

338.9 LKA ISSN 0010-1419
HC411
COLOMBO PLAN NEWSLETTER. Text in English. 1970. m. free. illus.; stat. **Document type:** *Newsletter.*
Published by: (Colombo Plan for Co-Operative Economic and Social Development in Asia and the Pacific), Colombo Plan Bureau, 12 Melbourne Ave., P O Box 596, Colombo, 4, Sri Lanka. TEL 94-1-581813, FAX 94-1-581754, TELEX 21537-METALIX-CE. Ed. J P Pathirana. Circ: 2,500 (controlled).

338.91 600 CHL ISSN 1020-5179
HC121
COMISION ECONOMICA PARA AMERICA LATINA Y EL CARIBE. SERIE DESARROLLO PRODUCTIVO. Key Title: Desarrollo Productivo. Text in Spanish. 1985. irreg.

Formerly (until 1996?): Industrializacion y Desarrollo Tecnologico (0259-2398)
Indexed: IIS.
Published by: Comision Economica para America Latina y el Caribe/Economic Commission for Latin America and the Caribbean, Ave Dag Hammarskjold 3477, Vitacura, Santiago de Chile, Chile. TEL 56-2-471-2000, FAX 56-2-208-0252, publications@eclac.cl, http://www.eclac.cl.

338.911   CHL
COMISION ECONOMICA PARA AMERICA LATINA Y EL CARIBE. SERIE FINANCIAMIENTO DEL DESARROLLO. Text in Chinese. irreg. price varies.
Indexed: IIS.
Published by: Comision Economica para America Latina y el Caribe/Economic Commission for Latin America and the Caribbean, Ave Dag Hammarskjold 3477, Vitacura, Santiago de Chile, Chile. TEL 56-2-471-2000, FAX 56-2-208-0252, publications@eclac.cl, http://www.eclac.cl.

338.91   CHL   ISSN 0259-0107
COMISION ECONOMICA PARA AMERICA LATINA Y EL CARIBE. SERIE INFOPLAN; temas especiales del desarrollo. Text in Spanish. 1986. irreg., latest vol.13, 1996. price varies.
Published by: Comision Economica para America Latina y el Caribe/Economic Commission for Latin America and the Caribbean, Ave Dag Hammarskjold 3477, Vitacura, Santiago de Chile, Chile. TEL 56-2-471-2000, FAX 56-2-208-0252, publications@eclac.cl, http://www.eclac.cl.

338.91   URY
COMISION SECTORIAL PARA EL MERCOSUR. BOLETIN. Text in Spanish. q.
Published by: Comision Sectorial para el Mercosur, Paysandu, 919, Montevideo, 11102, Uruguay. TEL 91-55-56, FAX 92-36-55.

338.9   GBR   ISSN 0967-0130
COMMON CAUSE; open the window on the developing world. Text in English. 1989. s-a. free (effective 2002). adv. charts; stat. index. 3 cols./p.; **Document type:** *Newsletter.*
Description: Serves as ActionAid's supporter magazine.
Related titles: Online - full text ed.: (from Northern Light Technology, Inc.).
Published by: ActionAid, Hamlyn House, Macdonald Rd, Archway, London, N19 5PG, United Kingdom. TEL 44-20-7561-7561, FAX 44-20-7281-0899, TELEX 266272 ACTAID G, commoncause@actionaid.org.uk, http://www.actionaid.org. Ed., R&P Nicola Peckett. Adv. contact Imelda McGuigan. Circ: 140,000.

338.9   LUX
COMMUNAUTE EUROPEENNE DU CHARBON ET DE L'ACIER. COMITE CONSULTATIF. ANNUAIRE. Text in French. a.
Related titles: ◆ German ed.: Europaeische Gemeinschaft fuer Kohle und Stahl. Beratender Ausschuss. Jahrbuch; Ed.: European Coal and Steel Community. Consultative Committee. Yearbook. ISSN 0423-6831. 1954. free.
Published by: European Coal and Steel Community, Consultative Committee, Secretariat, Luxembourg, L-2920, Luxembourg.

338.91   USA
COMMUNIQUE (TALLAHASSEE)∗ ; the newsletter of Florida's unique development partnership with the Caribbean and Central America. Text in English, French, Spanish. 1982. q. USD 35. adv. back issues avail. **Document type:** *Newsletter.*
Description: Covers the work of the Florida International Volunteer Corps, which conducts training and provides technical assistance by request to Caribbean and Central American nations.
Published by: Florida Association of Voluntary Agencies for Caribbean Action, 1310 N Paul Russell Rd, Tallahassee, FL 32301-4825. TEL 850-877-4705, favaca@worldnet.att.net, http://www.favaca.org. R&P Cy Brewer. Circ: 2,700.

COMMUNIQUE (WASHINGTON, 1971). see *BUSINESS AND ECONOMICS*

338.91   URY
CONEXION; revista latinoamericana de integracion. Text in Spanish. 1991. q.
Published by: Fundacion Banco de Boston, Bv. G Artigas, 934-902, Montevideo, 11311, Uruguay. TEL 986342. Ed. Claudio Trobo.

CONFLICT ASSESSMENTS. see *MILITARY*

338.91   DEU
CONTACTS. Text in German. 1965. q. bk.rev. **Document type:** *Magazine, Consumer.*
Published by: Arbeitsgemeinschaft fuer Entwicklungshilfe e.V., Ripuarenstr 8, Cologne, 50679, Germany. TEL 49-221-8896210, FAX 49-221-8896100, infoline@ageh.org, http://www.ageh.de/informationen/contacts.htm. Ed. Martin Fuchs. Circ: 7,000.

338.91   ARG   ISSN 0326-4068
HC121
➤ **CONTRIBUCIONES;** estudios interdisciplinarios sobre desarrollo y cooperacion internacional. Text in Spanish. 1984. q. USD 40 (effective 2000). bk.rev. stat. back issues avail. **Document type:** *Academic/Scholarly.*

Indexed: ASFA, DIP, IBR, IBZ, RASB.
Published by: (Konrad Adenauer Stiftung Asociacion Civil), Centro Interdisciplinario de Estudios sobre el Desarrollo Latinoamericano, Avda. Leandro N. Alem, 690 Piso 20 O, Capital Federal, Buenos Aires 1001, Argentina. TEL 54-114-3133522, FAX 54-114-3112902, konrad@datamarkets.com.ar, kas-ciedla@kas-ciedla.org.ar, http://www.kas-ciedla.org.ar. Ed. Dieter W Benecke. Circ: 4,000.

338.9   GTM   ISSN 0553-6863
CONVENIOS CENTROAMERICANOS DE INTEGRATION ECONOMICA. Text in Spanish. 1963. irreg., latest vol.11. USD 5.
Published by: Secretaria Permanente del Tratado General de Integracion Economica Centroamericana, 4a Avda. 10-25, ZONA, 14, PO Box 1237, Guatemala City, 01901, Guatemala. TEL 502-3682151, FAX 502-3681071, sieca@pronet.net.gt.

338.91   MEX
COOPERACION. Text in German, Spanish. 1966. bi-m. free. adv. bk.rev. **Document type:** *Trade.*
Published by: Camara Mexicano-Alemana de Comercio e Industria A.C., BOSQUE DE CIRUELOS 130-1202, Bosques de las Lomas, Mexico City, DF 11700, Mexico. TEL 525-2514022, FAX 525-5967695, TELEX 01771226 DEHAME. Ed. Johannes Hauser. Circ: 5,000.

338.91   ESP
COOPERACION ESPANOLA. Text in Spanish. 2000. q.
Document type: *Magazine.* **Description:** It is both a means to inform on the efforts of the Spanish Government to assist in the development of third world countries and a forum to discuss ways to improve such efforts.
Published by: Agencia Espanola de Cooperacion Internacional, Av Reyes Catolicos 4, Ciudad Universitaria, Madrid, 28040, Spain. TEL 34-91-5838105, FAX 34-91-5838310, http://www.aeci.es.

338.91   ESP
COOPERACION PUBLICA VASCA PARA EL DESARROLLO. MEMORIA (YEARS); ayudas al tercer mundo. Text in Spanish. 1991. irreg., latest 1988-97 ed. **Document type:** *Government.*
Published by: (Basque Region. Secretaria de la Presidencia, Basque Region. Secretaria General de Accion Exterior), Eusko Jaurlaritzaren Argitalpen-Zerbitzu Nagusia/Servicio Central de Publicaciones del Gobierno Vasco, Donostia-San Sebastian, 1, Vitoria-gasteiz, Alava 01010, Spain. TEL 34-945-018561, FAX 34-945-018709, hac-sabd@ej-gv.es, http://www.ej-gv.net/publicaciones. Circ: 1,000.

338.91   SDN
COOPERATION FOR DEVELOPMENT. Text in Arabic, English, French. 1979. 3/yr. free. **Document type:** *Newsletter, Trade.*
Description: Reflects bank's development activities and Arab assistance to non-Arab African countries.
Published by: Arab Bank for Economic Development in Africa, Abdulrahman el-Mahdi St., PO Box 2640, Khartoum, 1111, Sudan. TEL 249-11-773709, FAX 249-11-770498. Circ: 750.

CORDAID BULLETIN. see *SOCIAL SERVICES AND WELFARE*

338.91   USA
COUNCIL ON HEMISPHERIC AFFAIRS NEWS AND ANALYSIS. Text in English. s-w. USD 145 (effective 1999). back issues avail.
Published by: Council on Hemispheric Affairs, 1250 Connecticut Ave NW, # C1, Washington, DC 20036-2603. TEL 202-216-9261, FAX 202-216-9193. Ed. Laurence Birns. Circ: 1,500.

COUNTRYSIDE AGENGY. RESEARCH NOTES. see *HOUSING AND URBAN PLANNING*

COW NEWS & BULL VIEWS. see *AGRICULTURE—Poultry And Livestock*

338.91   FRA
CREDITOR REPORTING SYSTEM ON AID ACTIVITIES. Variant title: CRS Gazette. Text in English, French. bi-m. EUR 195, USD 224, GBP 126, JPY 26,300 (effective 2005). **Document type:** *Government.* **Description:** Records all the funding commitments reported by members of the OECD Development Assistance Committee and by multilateral institutions.
Formerly (until 2000): Creditor Reporting System Gazette (1023-8875)
Related titles: CD-ROM ed.; Online - full content ed.; Online - full text ed.: (from EBSCO Publishing, Gale Group, IngentaConnect, O C L C Online Computer Library Center, Inc., Swets Information Services).
Indexed: IIS.
—IE, Infotrieve.

Published by: Organization for Economic Cooperation and Development, 2 Rue Andre Pascal, Paris, 75775 Cedex 16, France. TEL 33-1-45248200, FAX 33-1-45248500, http://www.oecdbookshop.org/oecd/display.asp?TAG=X7YJ18XX5X3979286BAG5F&CID=&LANG=EN&SF1=DI&ST1=5LMQCR2KR2LR, http://www.oecd.org. **Dist. in N. America by:** O E C D Turpin North America, PO Box 194, Downingtown, PA 19335-0194. TEL 610-524-5361, 800-456-6323, FAX 610-524-5417, bookscustomer@turpinna.com, journalscustomer@turpinna.com.

338.91   FRA   ISSN 1563-3152
HC59.8
D A C JOURNAL. (Development Assistance Committee) Text in English. 1971. q. EUR 184, USD 211, GBP 120, JPY 24,800 (effective 2005). **Document type:** *Government.* **Description:** Provides overview and analysis of member countries' development co-operation programs.
Supersedes (in 2000): Development Co-operation (1016-541X); Which was formerly (until 1972): Development Assistance (1016-5401)
Related titles: Online - full content ed.: ISSN 1609-7645. USD 128 (effective 2004); Online - full text ed.: (from EBSCO Publishing, Gale Group, IngentaConnect, O C L C Online Computer Library Center, Inc., Swets Information Services); French ed.: Les Dossiers du C A D. ISSN 1563-3144.
Indexed: ABIn, PAIS.
—CISTI, IE.
Published by: Organization for Economic Cooperation and Development, 2 Rue Andre Pascal, Paris, 75775 Cedex 16, France. TEL 33-1-45248200, FAX 33-1-45248500, http://www.oecdwash.org/PUBS/PERIOD/per-dac.htm, http://www.oecd.org. **Dist. in N. America by:** O E C D Turpin North America, PO Box 194, Downingtown, PA 19335-0194. TEL 610-524-5361, 800-456-6323, FAX 610-524-5417, journalscustomer@turpinna.com.

338.91   DEU   ISSN 0723-7006
D & C - DESARROLLO Y COOPERACION. Text in Spanish. 1974. bi-m. **Document type:** *Bulletin, Trade.* **Description:** Reports new trends and tendencies in the development debate and the German contribution to the development efforts.
Published by: (Deutsche Stiftung fuer internationale Entwicklung/German Foundation for International Development), Frankfurter Societaets-Druckerei GmbH, Postfach 100801, Frankfurt Am Main, 60008, Germany. TEL 49-69-75014366, FAX 49-69-75014855, verlag@fsd.de, http://www.fsd.de. Ed. J Pablo Kummetz. Circ: 11,000.

338.91   DEU   ISSN 0723-6980
D & C - DEVELOPMENT AND COOPERATION. Text in English. 1974. bi-m. EUR 24 domestic; EUR 27 foreign (effective 2005). **Document type:** *Journal, Trade.* **Description:** Covers new trends and tendencies in the development debate and the German contribution to the development efforts.
Indexed: AEA, ExcerpMed, MEA&I, NutrAb, RASB, RDA, RRTA, RiceAb, S&F, TDB, WAE&RSA.
—BLDSC (3578.760000), IE, ingenta. **CCC.**
Published by: (Deutsche Stiftung fuer internationale Entwicklung/German Foundation for International Development), InWEnt - Internationale Weiterbildung und Entwicklung GmbH, Tulpenfeld 5, Bonn, 53113, Germany. TEL 49-228-24345, FAX 49-228-2434999, info@inwent.org, http://www.inwent.org/E+Z/index-eng.html. Ed. Hans Dembowski. Circ: 22,000.

338.91   DEU   ISSN 0723-6999
D & C - DEVELOPPEMENT ET COOPERATION. Text in French. 1974. bi-m. **Document type:** *Bulletin, Trade.* **Description:** New trends and tendencies in the development debate and the German contribution to the development efforts.
Indexed: IBZ.
Published by: (Deutsche Stiftung fuer internationale Entwicklung/German Foundation for International Development), Frankfurter Societaets-Druckerei GmbH, Postfach 100801, Frankfurt Am Main, 60008, Germany. TEL 49-69-75014366, FAX 49-69-75014855, verlag@fsd.de, http://www.fsd.de. Ed. Reinhold Meyer. Circ: 6,000.

338.91   DEU
D E D BRIEF. Text in German. 1964. q. free. bk.rev. **Document type:** *Magazine, Consumer.* **Description:** Experiences of DED development workers in different aspects of personal aid in Third World countries.
Published by: Deutscher Entwicklungsdienst, Heussallee 2-10, Bonn, 53113, Germany. TEL 49-228-2434-0, redaktion@ded.de, http://www.ded.de. Ed. Sabine Ludwig. Circ: 15,000.

338.91   DEU   ISSN 0935-1809
D E S W O S - BRIEF. Text in German. 1974. q. bk.rev. bibl.; illus.; stat. **Document type:** *Bulletin, Consumer.* **Description:** Project information on housing and development in Third World countries.
Published by: Deutsche Entwicklungshilfe fuer Soziales Wohnungs- und Siedlungswesen e.V., Gustav-Heinemann-Ufer 84-88, Cologne, 50968, Germany. TEL 49-221-57989-0, FAX 49-221-5798999, public@deswos.de, http://www.deswos.de. Ed. Dieter Baldeaux. Circ: 10,000.

338.91 DNK ISSN 1396-6588
HC60
DENMARK. UDENRIGSMINISTERIET. DANIDAS AARSBERETNING. Spine title: Danmarks Deltagelse i det Internationale Udviklingsarbejde. Text in Danish. 1973. a. free. illus.; stat. **Document type:** *Government.*
Formerly (until 1996): Danmarks Deltagelse i det Internationale Udviklingssamarbejde. Aarsrapport (0106-0090)
Related titles: Online - full content ed.; English ed.: ISSN 1397-8497. 1998.
Published by: Udenrigsministeriet, Dansk International Udviklingsbistand (Danida)/Royal Danish Ministry of Foreign Affairs. Danish International Development Assistance. (Danida), Asiatisk Plads 2, Copenhagen K, 1448, Denmark. TEL 45-33-920000, FAX 45-33-540533, um@um.dk, http://www.um.dk.

338.91 USA ISSN 0733-6594
HC121
DESARROLLO DE BASE. Text in Spanish. 1977. 2/yr. free. bk.rev. back issues avail. **Document type:** *Newsletter.* **Description:** Reports on how the poor in Latin America and the Caribbean organize and work to improve their lives.
Related titles: Microfilm ed.; ♦ English ed.: Grassroots Development. ISSN 0733-6608; Portuguese ed.: Desenvolvimento de Base.
Published by: Inter-American Foundation, 901 N Stuart St, 10th Fl, Arlington, VA 22203-1821. TEL 202-841-3800, FAX 703-841-0973. Circ: 10,200.

DESARROLLO Y ENERGIA. see *ENERGY*

338.91 UGA
THE DEVELOPER. Text in English. 1990. q. UGX 24,000 (effective 1993). bk.rev. bibl.; illus. **Document type:** *Academic/Scholarly.* **Description:** Sensitizes readers on development.
Indexed: PLESA.
Published by: Foundation for African Development, PO Box 16206, Kampala, Uganda. TEL 256-41-231824, FAX 256-41-251243. Ed. Syed A Abidi. Circ: 2,000 (controlled).
Co-sponsor: Konrad Adenauer.

338.9 JPN ISSN 0012-1533
HC59.7
➤ **DEVELOPING ECONOMIES.** Text in English. 1962. q. JPY 1,575 (effective 2004). adv. bk.rev. abstr.; bibl.; stat. Index. reprints avail. **Document type:** *Journal, Academic/Scholarly.* **Description:** An international and interdisciplinary forum on social studies of the developing countries. Aims to promote theoetical, empirical and comparative studies on the problems confronting developing countries.
Related titles: Microform ed.
Indexed: ABIn, APEL, ASCA, AgBio, BAS, CREJ, CurCont, EI, EIP, ExcerpMed, FamI, GEOBASE, HortAb, IBSS, ILD, IndIslam, JEL, KES, MEA&I, MaizeAb, PAA&I, PHN&I, PSA, RASB, RDA, RRTA, RiceAb, SPPI, SSCI, SociolAb, SoyAb, TriticAb, WAE&RSA.
—BLDSC (3578.545000), CISTI, IE, Infotrieve, ingenta.
Published by: Institute of Developing Economies/Ajia Keizai Kenkyusho, 3-2-2 Wakaba, Mihana-ku, Chiba-shi, Chiba 261-8545, Japan. TEL 81-43-299-9536, FAX 84-43-299-9724, info@ide.go.jp, http://www.ide.go.jp/Japanese/Publish/De/index.html. Ed. Shigeto Kawano. Circ: 1,650. **Subscr. to:** Maruzen Co., Ltd., Export Dept., PO Box 5050, Tokyo International 100-3191, Japan. FAX 81-3-3278-9256, journal@maruzen.co.jp, http://www.maruzen.co.jp.

327 GBR ISSN 1011-6370
HC60
➤ **DEVELOPMENT (BASINGSTOKE).** Text in English. 1959. q. GBP 30 combined subscription in Europe to individuals print & online; USD 46 combined subscription elsewhere to individuals print & online; GBP 280 combined subscription in Europe to institutions print & online; USD 455 combined subscription elsewhere to institutions print & online (effective 2005). adv. bk.rev. back issues avail.; reprint service avail. from PQC,SCH. **Document type:** *Journal, Academic/Scholarly.* **Description:** Explores the issues of human centred development. Covers alternative perspectives on civil society, development policy and community based strategies for livelihoods, gender and social justice.
Former titles (until 1977): Revista del Desarrollo Internacional (0095-7062); (until 1969): International Development Review (0020-6555)
Related titles: Microform ed.: (from PQC); Online - full text ed.: GBP 239 in Europe to institutions; USD 382 elsewhere to institutions (effective 2004) (from EBSCO Publishing, Gale Group, IngentaConnect, O C L C Online Computer Library Center, Inc., ProQuest Information & Learning, Swets Information Services); Ed.: Desarrollo. ISSN 0212-2448. 1998; Ed.
Indexed: ABCPolSci, ABIn, AbHyg, AgBio, AmH&L, AnBrAb, BioCN&I, BusI, CommAb, CurCont, DSA, FutSurv, GEOBASE, HRA, HRIR, HistAb, I&DA, IBSS, ILD, IPSA, JEL, MRD, NutrAb, PAA&I, PAIS, PBA, PGegResA, PRA, PSA, PerIslam, RDA, RRTA, S&F, SOPODA, SSA, SSCI, SSI, SeedAb, SociolAb, TDB, WAE&RSA.
—BLDSC (3578.680000), CISTI, IE, ingenta. **CCC.**
Published by: (Society for International Development ITA), Palgrave Macmillan Ltd. (Subsidiary of: Macmillan Publishers Ltd.), Houndmills, Basingstoke, Hants RG21 6XS, United Kingdom. TEL 44-1256-329242, FAX 44-1256-810526, journal-info@palgrave.com, http://www.palgrave-journals.com/development/index.html. Ed. Wendy Harcourt. adv.: page GBP 195; trim 200 x 154. Circ: 1,650. **Subscr. addr. in N. America:** Sage Publications, Inc., 2455 Teller Rd, Thousand Oaks, CA 91320. TEL 805-499-0721, FAX 805-499-0871.

327 GBR ISSN 0012-155X
HD82
➤ **DEVELOPMENT AND CHANGE.** Text in English. 1969. bi-m. USD 109 combined subscription in the Americas to individuals & the Caribbean (print & online eds.); EUR 98 combined subscription in Europe to individuals print & online eds.; GBP 65 combined subscription elsewhere to individuals print & online eds.; GBP 44 combined subscription in developing nations to individuals print & online eds.; USD 68 combined subscription in developing nations to institutions print & online eds.; USD 694 combined subscription in the Americas to institutions & the Caribbean (print & online eds.); GBP 413 combined subscription elsewhere to institutions print & online eds.; USD 212, GBP 120 combined subscription in developing nations to institutions print & online eds.; EUR 33 combined subscription in Europe to students print & online eds.; USD 36 combined subscription in the Americas to students print & online eds.; GBP 22 combined subscription elsewhere to students print & online eds. (effective 2006). bk.rev. charts. reprint service avail. from PSC. **Document type:** *Journal, Academic/Scholarly.* **Description:** Contributes to the understanding of Third World problems. Publishes critical analysis and articles from all disciplines of the social sciences discussing current development issues.
Related titles: Microform ed.: (from PQC); Online - full text ed.: ISSN 1467-7660. USD 558 in the Americas to institutions & Caribbean; GBP 114 in Eastern Europe to institutions; GBP 40 in India to institutions; USD 332 elsewhere to institutions (effective 2005) (from Blackwell Synergy, EBSCO Publishing, Gale Group, IngentaConnect, O C L C Online Computer Library Center, Inc., Swets Information Services).
Indexed: ABCPolSci, APEL, ARDT, ASCA, ASD, ASSIA, AgeL, AgrForAb, AmH&L, ArtHuCI, BAS, CommAb, CurCont, EI, EIA, EnerInd, FCA, FPA, FS&TA, FamI, ForAb, GEOBASE, HRIR, HerbAb, HistAb, HortAb, I&DA, IBR, IBSS, ILD, IPSA, IndVet, JEL, KES, MEA&I, MaizeAb, NutrAb, PAA&I, PAIS, PCI, PGegResA, PHN&I, PSA, PerIslam, RASB, RDA, REE&TA, RRTA, RiceAb, S&F, SFSA, SIA, SOPODA, SSCI, SUSA, SWA, SociolAb, TDB, TriticAb, VetBull, WAE&RSA.
—BLDSC (3578.750000), IDS, IE, Infotrieve, ingenta, KNAW. **CCC.**
Published by: (Institute of Social Studies, The Hague NLD), Blackwell Publishing Ltd., 9600 Garsington Rd, Oxford, OX4 2ZG, United Kingdom. TEL 44-1865-776868, FAX 44-1865-714591, customerservices@oxon.blackwellpublishing.com, http://www.blackwellpublishing.com/journals/DECH. Eds. Ashwani Saith, Ben White.

338.0968 ZAF
DEVELOPMENT BANK OF SOUTHERN AFRICA. DEVELOPMENT PAPERS. Text in English. 1993. irreg., latest vol.68, 1995. price varies. back issues avail. **Document type:** *Monographic series.* **Description:** Makes available the bank's work on policy, information, evaluation and related development issues.
Formerly: Development Bank of Southern Africa. Centre for Policy Analysis. Policy Working Paper (1022-0127)
Related titles: Series of: Construction & Development Series.
Indexed: NutrAb, RDA, RRTA.
Published by: Development Bank of Southern Africa, PO Box 1234, Halfway House, 1685, South Africa. TEL 27-11-3133911, FAX 27-11-3133086, TELEX 4-25546. Ed. Mrs. Anne E Wille.

338.91 USA ISSN 0259-5893
DEVELOPMENT BUSINESS (NEW YORK, 1978). Text in English, Spanish, French, Portuguese. 1978. fortn. USD 590 (effective 2004). adv. illus. 36 p./no. 3 cols./p.; **Document type:** *Newspaper.* **Description:** Lists procurement notices and bid invitations that alert readers to consulting, contracting, and supply opportunities as soon as projects are proposed.
Formerly (until 1984): Development Forum. Business Edition; Incorporates: U N D P Business Bulletin; Which superseded in part: Pre-Investment News (0032-7093)
Related titles: Online - full text ed.: USD 445 (effective 1999) (from Data-Star, The Dialog Corporation).
Indexed: CRIA, CRICC, KES.
Published by: United Nations, Division of Public Information, United Nations Plaza, DC1 574, New York, NY 10017. TEL 212-963-1516, FAX 212-963-1381, TELEX 422311 UNUI, dbusiness@un.org, http://www.devbusiness.com. Ed. Sawad Sommereyns. R&P Soad Sommereyns. Adv. contact Sherifa Kahn. Circ: 5,000. **Subscr. to:** PO Box 5850, Grand Central Sta, New York, NY 10163.

327 USA
DEVELOPMENT CONNECTIONS. Text in English. 1957. bi-m. USD 75 to members; USD 35 to students. adv. bk.rev. index. back issues avail. **Document type:** *Newsletter.*
Former titles (until 1987): Society for International Development. Newsletter; International Society for Community Development. Newsletter
Published by: (Society for International Development - Washington Chapter), Society for International Development, 1875 Connecticut Ave, N W, Ste 720, Washington, DC 20009. TEL 202-884-8590, FAX 202-884-8499, sid@aed.org. Ed. Andrea S Camoens. Circ: 1,000.

DEVELOPMENT DIALOGUE; a journal of international development cooperation. see *POLITICAL SCIENCE—International Relations*

338.9 AUS ISSN 0815-9424
DEVELOPMENT DOSSIER. Text in English. 1972. q. bk.rev. illus.
Incorporates (in 1980): Development News Digest (0155-0489)
Indexed: HRIR, PAIS, SPPI.
Published by: Australian Council for Overseas Aid, Pravate Bag 3, Deakin, ACT 2600, Australia. TEL 61-2-2851816, FAX 61-2-2851720. Ed. Kerrie Griffin. Circ: 2,000.

338.91 CAN
DEVELOPMENT EXPRESS. Text in English, French. 1995. irreg. back issues avail. **Document type:** *Newsletter.* **Description:** Provides access to consolidated information from significant works on critical topics and issues related to international development.
Related titles: Online - full text ed.
Published by: Canadian International Development Agency, International Development Information Center, 200 Promenade du Portage, 8 fl., Hull, PQ K1A 0G4, Canada. express@acdi-cida.gc.ca, http://www.acdi-cida.gc.ca/devexpress.

338.91 USA ISSN 0251-6632
HC59
DEVELOPMENT FORUM. Text in English. 1978. irreg. free.
Related titles: French ed.: Forum du Developpement. ISSN 0251-6640; German ed.: Forum. ISSN 0251-6659; Spanish ed.: Foro del Desarrollo. ISSN 0251-6667.
Indexed: EnvAb, IPARL.
Published by: Division for Economic and Social Information (DESI), Room S 0556, New York, NY 10017. TEL 212-963-8070. Ed. Paul Hoeffel.

338.91 GBR ISSN 0961-4524
HC59.8 CODEN: DEPRFO
➤ **DEVELOPMENT IN PRACTICE.** Text in English. 1991. bi-m. GBP 313, USD 517 combined subscription to institutions print & online eds. (effective 2006). bk.rev. back issues avail.; reprint service avail. from PSC. **Document type:** *Journal, Academic/Scholarly.* **Description:** Provides a forum for practitioners, policy makers, and academics to exchange information and analysis concerning the social dimensions of development and humanitarian action.
Related titles: Online - full text ed.: ISSN 1364-9213. GBP 297, USD 491 to institutions (effective 2006) (from EBSCO Publishing, Gale Group, IngentaConnect, O C L C Online Computer Library Center, Inc., Swets Information Services).
Indexed: AICP, ASD, ASSIA, AgrForAb, BrHumI, DIP, DSA, ERA, ForAb, GEOBASE, HerbAb, HortAb, I&DA, IBR, IBSS, IBZ, IPSA, IndIslam, IndVet, NutrAb, PAIS, PBA, PGegResA, PHN&I, PSA, PoultAb, ProtozoAb, RASB, RDA, S&F, SIA, SOPODA, SSA, SWA, SociolAb, TDB, WAE&RSA.
—BLDSC (3579.039930), IE, Infotrieve, ingenta. **CCC.**
Published by: (Oxfam International), Routledge (Subsidiary of: Taylor & Francis Group), 4 Park Sq, Milton Park, Abingdon, Oxon OX14 4RN, United Kingdom. TEL 44-1235-828600, FAX 44-1235-829000, info@routledge.co.uk, http://www.tandf.co.uk/journals/titles/09614524.asp, http://www.routledge.com. Ed. Deborah Eade. **Subscr. in N. America to:** Taylor & Francis Inc., Customer Services Dept, 325 Chestnut St, 8th Fl, Philadelphia, PA 19106. TEL 215-625-8900, 800-354-1420, FAX 215-625-8914, customerservice@taylorandfrancis.com; **Subscr. to:** Taylor & Francis Ltd, Journals Customer Service, Rankine Rd, Basingstoke, Hants RG24 8PR, United Kingdom. TEL 44-1256-813000, FAX 44-1256-330245.

➤ **DEVELOPMENT ORIENTED RESEARCH IN AGRICULTURE.** see *AGRICULTURE*

338 USA ISSN 1020-797X
HC59.8
DEVELOPMENT OUTREACH; promoting knowledge to work for development. Text in English. 1999. q. free Undeveloped countries; USD 18 Developed countries (effective 2005). **Document type:** *Magazine, Consumer.*
Related titles: Online - full text ed.
Indexed: RDA, RRTA, TDB, WAE&RSA.
—CCC.
Published by: World Bank Group, 1818 H St, NW, Washington, DC 20433. TEL 202-473-1000, FAX 202-477-6391, books@worldbank.org, http://www1.worldbank.org/devoutreach/, http://www.worldbank.org.

338.9 GBR ISSN 0950-6764
HC59.7 CODEN: DPORER
➤ **DEVELOPMENT POLICY REVIEW.** Text in English. 1974. bi-m. EUR 62 combined subscription in Europe to individuals print & online eds.; USD 69 combined subscription in the Americas to individuals & Caribbean, print & online eds.; GBP 41 combined subscription elsewhere to individuals print & online eds.; USD 507 combined subscription in the Americas to institutions & Caribbean, print & online eds.; GBP 302 combined subscription elsewhere to institutions print & online eds. (effective 2006). adv. bk.rev. reprint service avail. from PSC. **Document type:** *Journal, Academic/Scholarly.*
Description: Provides a forum for new research and information on social and economic issues in development among persons directly concerned with development in business, government, and other organizations.
Formerly: O D I Review (0078-7116)
Related titles: Online - full text ed.: ISSN 1467-7679. USD 482 in the Americas to institutions & Caribbean; GBP 287 elsewhere to institutions (effective 2006) (from Blackwell Synergy, EBSCO Publishing, Gale Group, IngentaConnect, O C L C Online Computer Library Center, Inc., Swets Information Services).
Indexed: ABIn, APEL, ASD, AgrForAb, CREJ, DSA, FPA, FS&TA, ForAb, GEOBASE, HortAb, IBSS, IPSA, IndVet, JEL, KES, MEA&I, PAIS, PBA, PGegResA, PHN&I, PSA, RASB, RDA, RRTA, RiceAb, SIA, SOPODA, SSA, SociolAb, TriticAb, WAE&RSA.
—BLDSC (3579.039850), IE, Infotrieve, ingenta. **CCC.**
Published by: (Overseas Development Institute), Blackwell Publishing Ltd., 9600 Garsington Rd, Oxford, OX4 2ZG, United Kingdom. TEL 44-1865-776868, FAX 44-1865-714591, customerservices@oxon.blackwellpublishing.com, http://www.blackwellpublishing.com/journals/DPR. Ed. David Booth TEL 44-20-79220300.

338.91 PHL ISSN 0115-9097
DEVELOPMENT RESEARCH NEWS. Short title: D R N. Text in English. 1983. bi-m. PHP 200 domestic; USD 20 foreign (effective 2005). back issues avail. **Document type:** *Newsletter, Academic/Scholarly.* **Description:** Covers questions of development, with an emphasis on the Asian Pacific perspective.
Related titles: CD-ROM ed.; Online - full text ed.
Indexed: IPP, JOF.
Published by: Philippine Institute for Development Studies, NEDA sa Makati Bldg, 106 Amorsolo St, Legaspi Village, Makati Mm, 1229, Philippines. TEL 632-893-5705, 632-893-9573, FAX 632-816-1091, 632-893-9589, publications@pidsnet.pids.gov.ph, http://publication.pids.gov.ph/devresnews.phtml, http://www.pids.gov.ph. Ed., R&P Jennifer P T Liguton. Circ: 2,500.

338.91 IRL ISSN 0790-9403
➤ **DEVELOPMENT REVIEW.** Text in English. 1985. a. adv. bk.rev. back issues avail. **Document type:** *Journal, Academic/Scholarly.* **Description:** Deals with development policy and human rights. Highlights injustice, identifies key policy issues espicially in relation to poverty.
Related titles: Online - full text ed.
Published by: Trocaire, Maynooth, Co. Kildare, Ireland. TEL 353-1-6293333, FAX 353-1-6290661, info@trocaire.ie, http://www.trocaire.org. Ed. Lorna Gold. R&P Fergus Mulligan. Circ: 500.

338.91 GBR ISSN 0376-835X
HC900.A1
➤ **DEVELOPMENT SOUTHERN AFRICA.** Text in English. 1974. 5/yr. GBP 229, USD 380 combined subscription to institutions print & online eds. (effective 2006). adv. bk.rev. bibl.; illus. reprint service avail. from PSC. **Document type:** *Journal, Academic/Scholarly.* **Description:** Promotes research and discussion on development issues relating to southern Africa.
Related titles: Online - full text ed.: ISSN 1470-3637 (from EBSCO Publishing, Gale Group, IngentaConnect, O C L C Online Computer Library Center, Inc., Swets Information Services).
Indexed: AgrForAb, DSA, FCA, FPA, ForAb, GEOBASE, HortAb, I&DA, IBR, IBSS, IBZ, ISAP, JEL, MaizeAb, NutrAb, PHN&I, PSA, PoultAb, RDA, RRTA, RiceAb, S&F, SeedAb, SociolAb, TDB, WAE&RSA.
—BLDSC (3579.042780), IE, Infotrieve, ingenta.
Published by: (Development Bank of Southern Africa ZAF), Routledge (Subsidiary of: Taylor & Francis Group), 4 Park Sq, Milton Park, Abingdon, Oxon OX14 4RN, United Kingdom. TEL 44-1235-828600, FAX 44-1235-829000, info@routledge.co.uk, http://www.tandf.co.uk/journals/titles/0376835x.asp, http://www.routledge.com. Ed. Caroline Kihato. adv.: B&W page ZAR 500. Circ: 2,000. **Subscr. to:** Taylor & Francis Ltd, Journals Customer Service, Rankine Rd, Basingstoke, Hants RG24 8PR, United Kingdom. TEL 44-1256-813000, FAX 44-1256-330245, enquiry@tandf.co.uk.

338.9 GBR ISSN 1461-474X
HN978
DEVELOPMENTS; the international development magazine. Text in English. 1966. 4/yr. free. adv. bk.rev. 40 p./no.; back issues avail. **Document type:** *Magazine, Government.*
Former titles (until 1999): British Overseas Development; (until Apr. 1988): Overseas Development (0030-7440)
Indexed: AEA, ASFA, ApicAb, ESPM, RASB.
—CCC.
Published by: Department for International Development, Information Department, Abercrombie Huse, Eaglesham Road, East Kilbride, Glasgow G7S 8EA, United Kingdom. TEL 44-20-7240-4700, FAX 44-20-7240-4771, enquiry@dfid.gov.uk, http://www.developments.org.uk. Ed. Clare Shaw TEL 44-1355-843417. R&Ps Carolyn Oxlee, Clare Shaw TEL 44-1355-843417. Circ: 40,000.

DIRECTORY OF THE NATIONAL PRODUCTIVITY ORGANIZATIONS IN A P O MEMBER COUNTRIES. see *BUSINESS AND ECONOMICS—Production Of Goods And Services*

338.91 GBR ISSN 0361-3666
HV553
➤ **DISASTERS;** the journal of disaster studies, policy and management. Text in English. 1977. q. USD 72 combined subscription in the Americas to individuals & Caribbean (print & online eds.); EUR 65 combined subscription in Europe to individuals print & online eds.; USD 43 combined subscription elsewhere to individuals print & online eds.; USD 437 combined subscription in the Americas to institutions & Caribbean (print & online eds.); GBP 123, USD 199 combined subscription in developing nations to institutions print & online eds.; GBP 200 combined subscription elsewhere to institutions print & online eds.; USD 39 combined subscription in the Americas to students print & online eds.; EUR 35 combined subscription in Europe to students print & online eds. (effective 2006). adv. bk.rev. charts; illus.; stat. index. reprint service avail. from PQC,PSC. **Document type:** *Journal, Academic/Scholarly.* **Description:** Reports on all aspects of disaster studies, policy and management. It aims to provide a forum for academics, policy-makers and practitioners for high-quality research and practice related to natural disasters and complex political emergencies around the world.
Related titles: Microform ed.: (from PQC); Online - full text ed.: ISSN 1467-7717. USD 415 in the Americas to institutions & Caribbean; GBP 117, USD 189 in developing nations to institutions; GBP 247 elsewhere to institutions (effective 2006) (from Blackwell Synergy, EBSCO Publishing, Gale Group, IngentaConnect, O C L C Online Computer Library Center, Inc., Swets Information Services).
Indexed: AJEE, APEL, API, ARDT, ASCA, ASFA, AbHyg, CivEngAb, CurCont, DIP, EEA, EPB, ESPM, EnvAb, ExcerpMed, GEOBASE, H&SSA, HRIR, IBR, IBSS, IBZ, ILD, IPSA, IndMed, M&GPA, MEDLINE, NutrAb, PAIS, PBA, PCI, PGegResA, PHN&I, PSA, ProtozoAb, RDA, RRTA, RefugAb, Repind, RevApplEntom, RiskAb, S&F, SOPODA, SSA, SSCI, SUSA, SWRA, SeedAb, SociolAb, TDB, WAE&RSA.
—BLDSC (3595.510000), IDS, IE, Infotrieve, ingenta. **CCC.**
Published by: (Overseas Development Institute), Blackwell Publishing Ltd., 9600 Garsington Rd, Oxford, OX4 2ZG, United Kingdom. TEL 44-1865-776868, FAX 44-1865-714591, customerservices@oxon.blackwellpublishing.com, http://www.blackwellpublishing.com/journals/DISA. Eds. David Alexander, Helen Young, Paul Harvey. Circ: 2,000.

➤ **DRITTE-WELT-KALENDER.** see *POLITICAL SCIENCE—International Relations*

338.91 GBR ISSN 1462-2181
E A D I BOOK SERIES. Text in English. 1990. irreg., latest 2004, Mar. price varies. back issues avail. **Document type:** *Monographic series, Academic/Scholarly.* **Description:** Covers matters of policy, theory and practice in all aspects of development studies.
—BLDSC (3642.455000), ingenta.
Published by: (European Association of Development Research and Training Institutes CHE), Routledge (Subsidiary of: Taylor & Francis Group), 2 Park Sq, Milton Park, Abingdon, Oxon OX14 4RN, United Kingdom. TEL 44-20-70176000, FAX 44-20-70176699, info@routledge.co.uk, http://www.routledge.co.uk.

338.91 DEU
E A D I NEWSLETTER. Text in English, French. s-a. CHF 16 (effective 2000). bk.rev. charts; illus. **Document type:** *Newsletter.* **Description:** Collects and disseminates information pertinent to EADI membership.
Published by: European Association of Development Research and Training Institutes, Kaiser-Friedrich-Str 11, Bonn, 53113, Germany. TEL 49-228-2618101, FAX 49-228-2618103, eadi@uni2a.unige.ch, http://www.eadi.org/.

338.91 BEL
E C H O NEWS. Text in English. q. free. **Document type:** *Newsletter.* **Description:** Discusses the organizations humanitarian and relief efforts in countries worldwide ravaged by war or natural disaster.
Related titles: French ed.
Published by: (European Community Humanitarian Office), European Commission, Rue de la Loi - Wetstraat 200, Brussels, 1049, Belgium. TEL 32-2-295-44-00, FAX 32-2-295-45-72. **Dist. in the U.S. by:** Bernan Associates, Bernan, 4611-F Assembly Dr., Lanham, MD 20706-4391. TEL 800-274-4447, FAX 800-865-3450.

338.91 CHL ISSN 1564-4235
E C L A C NOTES. Text in English. 1998. bi-m.
Related titles: Online - full text ed.: ISSN 1681-0279.
Published by: United Nations Economic Commission for Latin America and the Caribbean, Av. Dag Hammarskjold 3477, Vitacura, Casilla 179-D, Santiago de Chile, Chile. TEL 56-2-2102380, FAX 56-2-2102238, dpisantiago@eclac.cl, http://www.eclac.cl/prensa/noticias/notas/todas_notas.asp?idioma=IN.

▼ **EARLY WARNING: BULGARIA BEYOND THE FACTS (MONTHLY EDITION).** see *POLITICAL SCIENCE—International Relations*

EAST ASIAN BUSINESS INTELLIGENCE. see *BUSINESS AND ECONOMICS—International Commerce*

338.91 THA ISSN 0252-2284
HC411.U4
ECONOMIC AND SOCIAL COMMISSION FOR ASIA AND THE PACIFIC. ANNUAL REPORT. Text in English. 1947. a. USD 19 (effective 2005). back issues avail.
Formerly (until 1974): Economic Commission for Asia and the Far East. Report (1011-2731)
Related titles: French ed.: Nations Unies. Commission Economique et Sociale pour l'Asie et le Pacifique. Rapport Annuel. ISSN 0252-2276; Chinese ed.: Yazhou ji Taipingyang Jingji Shehui Weiyuanhui. Niandu Baogao. ISSN 0257-0343; Russian ed.: Ekonomicheskaya i Social'naya Komissiya Dlya Azii i Tikhogo Okeana. Godovoi Doklad. ISSN 0257-0335.
Published by: United Nations Economic and Social Commission for Asia and the Pacific, United Nations Bldg., Rajadamnern Ave., Bangkok, 10200, Thailand. TEL 66-2-2881234, FAX 66-2-2881000, unescap@unescap.org, http://www.unescap.org. **Orders to:** United Nations Publications, Distribution and Sales Section, Palais des Nations, Rm C-116, 8-14 av de la Paix, Geneva 1211, Switzerland; United Nations Publications, Rm DC2-853, United Nations Bldg, 2 United Nations Plaza, New York, NY 10017.

338.91 340 JPN
ECONOMIC COOPERATION SERIES/KEIZAI-KYORYOKU SERIES. Text in Japanese. 1970. irreg. (2-3/yr.). price varies. **Document type:** *Academic/Scholarly.* **Description:** Focuses on various aspects of economic development assistance. Includes information on legal systems, tax systems, and the investment circumstances of developing countries.
Published by: Institute of Developing Economies/Ajia Keizai Kenkyusho, 3-2-2 Wakaba, Mihama-ku, Chiba-shi, Chiba 261-8545, Japan. TEL 81-43-299-9536, FAX 84-43-299-9724, info@ide.go.jp, http://www.ide.go.jp. Circ: 650.

303.482 USA ISSN 0013-0079
CODEN: EDCCAF
➤ **ECONOMIC DEVELOPMENT AND CULTURAL CHANGE.** Text in English. 1952. q. USD 53 domestic to individuals; USD 63.71 in Canada to individuals; USD 63 elsewhere to individuals; USD 240 domestic to institutions; USD 263.80 in Canada to institutions; USD 250 elsewhere to institutions; USD 40 domestic to students; USD 49.80 in Canada to students; USD 50 elsewhere to students; USD 18.25 newsstand/cover to individuals; USD 65 newsstand/cover to institutions (effective 2005). adv. bk.rev. illus. index, cum.index: vols. 1-51. 224 p./no.; reprint service avail. from PQC,ISI,PSC. **Document type:** *Journal, Academic/Scholarly.*
Description: Searches for new theoretical approaches that integrate the concepts of social change with economic theories. Examines the social and economic forces that affect development and its effect on culture.
Related titles: Microform ed.: (from PMC, PQC); Online - full text ed.: ISSN 1539-2988. USD 216 to institutions (effective 2005) (from Chadwyck-Healey Inc., EBSCO Publishing, Florida Center for Library Automation, Gale Group, JSTOR (Web-based Journal Archive), ProQuest Information & Learning).
Indexed: ABCPolSci, ABIn, ABS&EES, AEA, AICP, APEL, ARDT, ASCA, ASFA, ASSIA, AbAn, AbHyg, AcaI, AgBio, AgeL, Agr, AgrForAb, AmH&L, BPI, BPIA, BusI, CREJ, CTFA, CurCont, DIP, DSA, EI, EIA, ESPM, EnerInd, FCA, FPA, FamI, ForAb, GEOBASE, HAPI, HRA, HRIS, HerbAb, HistAb, HortAb, I&DA, IBR, IBSS, IBZ, IMFL, IPSA, IndIslam, JEL, KES, MEA&I, MaizeAb, NutrAb, PAA&I, PAIS, PBA, PCI, PGegResA, PHN&I, PRA, PSA, PopulInd, RDA, REE&TA, RRTA, RiceAb, S&F, SFSA, SOPODA, SPPI, SSA, SSCI, SSI, SUSA, SWA, SociolAb, T&II, TDB, TriticAb, WAE&RSA, WBA, WTA.
—BLDSC (3652.700000), CISTI, IDS, IE, Infotrieve, ingenta, Linda Hall. **CCC.**
Published by: University of Chicago Press, Journals Division, 1111 E. 60th St, Chicago, IL 60637. subscriptions@press.uchicago.edu, http://www.journals.uchicago.edu/EDCC. Ed. John Strauss. Adv. contact Cheryl Jones. page USD 475; trim 6 x 9. Circ: 2,000 (paid).

338.91 330.1 NPL ISSN 1018-631X
ECONOMIC JOURNAL OF NEPAL. Text in English. 1977. q. NPR 280, USD 88. bk.rev. bibl.; charts; stat. **Document type:** *Academic/Scholarly.* **Description:** Contains research papers on the economic and social problems facing Nepal and other developing countries.
Formerly (until 1978): Economic Monthly
Indexed: RDA, REE&TA, S&F, TriticAb, WAE&RSA.
Published by: Tribhuvan University, Central Department of Economics, Kirtipur, P O Box 3821, Kathmandu, Nepal. TEL 977-1-213277. Ed. V P Sharma. Circ: 500.

338.91   AUS
ECONOMICS DIVISION WORKING PAPERS. EAST ASIA. Text in English. 1992. irreg. AUD 10 per issue. **Document type:** *Academic/Scholarly.* **Description:** Covers economics, trade, development and policy issues.
Incorporates: Australian National University. National Centre for Development Studies. Working Papers. Series: China Working Papers (1030-360X)
Indexed: RDA, WAE&RSA.
Published by: Australian National University, Economics Division, Canberra, ACT 0200, Australia. TEL 61-2-6249-4705, FAX 61-2-6257-2886. Ed. Maree Tait. **Subscr. to:** Bibliotech Anutech Pty. Ltd., GPO Box 4, Canberra, ACT 2601, Australia. FAX 61-2-6257-5088.

338.91   AUS
ECONOMICS DIVISION WORKING PAPERS. SOUTH ASIA. Text in English. irreg. AUD 10 per issue. **Description:** Covers economics, trade, development and policy issues.
Indexed: WAE&RSA.
Published by: Australian National University, Economics Division, Canberra, ACT 0200, Australia. TEL 61-2-6249-4705, FAX 61-2-6257-2886. Ed. Maree Tait. **Subscr. to:** Bibliotech Anutech Pty. Ltd., GPO Box 4, Canberra, ACT 2601, Australia.

338.91   AUS
ECONOMICS DIVISION WORKING PAPERS. SOUTH PACIFIC. Text in English. irreg. AUD 10 per issue. **Document type:** *Monographic series.* **Description:** Covers economics, trade, development and policy issues.
Incorporates: Australian National University. National Centre for Development Studies. Working Papers. Series: Islands - Australia Working Papers (0816-5165)
Indexed: WAE&RSA.
Published by: Australian National University, Economics Division, Canberra, ACT 0200, Australia. TEL 61-2-6249-4705, FAX 61-2-6257-2886. Ed. Maree Tait. **Subscr. to:** Bibliotech Anutech Pty. Ltd., GPO Box 4, Canberra, ACT 2601, Australia. FAX 61-2-6257-5088.

338.91   AUS
ECONOMICS DIVISION WORKING PAPERS. SOUTHEAST ASIA. Text in English. irreg. AUD 10 per issue. **Document type:** *Academic/Scholarly.* **Description:** Economics, trade, development and policy issues.
Incorporates in part: Australian National University. National Centre for Development Studies. Working Papers. Series: N C D S Working Papers (0815-7596)
Indexed: RDA, RRTA, TriticAb, WAE&RSA.
Published by: Australian National University, Economics Division, Canberra, ACT 0200, Australia. TEL 61-2-6249-4705, FAX 61-2-6257-2886. Ed. Maree Tait. **Subscr. to:** Bibliotech Anutech Pty. Ltd., GPO Box 4, Canberra, ACT 2601, Australia. FAX 61-2-6257-5088.

338.9   FRA   ISSN 0068-4813
ECONOMIES ET SOCIETES. SERIE F. DEVELOPPEMENT, CROISSANCE, PROGRES DES PAYS EN VOIE DE DEVELOPPEMENT. Text in French. 1955. irreg.
—IE.
Published by: Les Presses de l'I S M E A, BP 22, Paris, Cedex 13 75622, France. TEL 33-1-55489076, FAX 33-1-55489071, http://www.ismea.org. Ed. Gerard de Bernis. Circ: 1,600.

ECONOMIES ET SOCIETES. SERIE P. RELATIONS ECONOMIQUES INTERNATIONALES. see *BUSINESS AND ECONOMICS—Economic Systems And Theories, Economic History*

ENTWICKLUNGSLAENDER-STUDIEN; Bibliographie entwicklungslaenderbezogener Forschungsarbeiten. see *BUSINESS AND ECONOMICS—Abstracting, Bibliographies, Statistics*

ENVIRONMENT AND URBANIZATION. see *ENVIRONMENTAL STUDIES*

363.7   USA
ENVIRONMENTALLY SUSTAINABLE DEVELOPMENT PROCEEDINGS SERIES. Text in English. 1994. irreg. free to qualified personnel. **Document type:** *Monographic series.* **Description:** Discusses how World Bank policies can effect and affect ecologically sustainable development worldwide.
Related titles: French ed.
Indexed: RDA, WAE&RSA.
Published by: World Bank Group, PO Box 960, Herndon, VA 20172-0960. TEL 201-476-2192, FAX 201-476-2197, books@worldbank.org.

338.91   CHE
ERITREA-INFO∗ . Text in German. 1977. 3/yr. CHF 10.
Published by: Schweizerisches Unterstuetzungskomitee fuer Eritrea, Schwyzerstr 12, Wettingen, 5430, Switzerland. Ed. Toni Locher.

338.91   CHL   ISSN 0256-9795
ESTUDIOS E INFORMES DE LA C E P A L. Text in Spanish. 1980. irreg. latest vol.95, 1996. price varies. back issues avail. **Document type:** *Proceedings.*
Related titles: English ed.: C E P A L Studies and Reports.

Published by: Comision Economica para America Latina y el Caribe/Economic Commission for Latin America and the Caribbean, Ave Dag Hammarskjold 3477, Vitacura, Santiago de Chile, Chile. TEL 56-2-471-2000, FAX 56-2-208-0252, publications@eclac.cl, http://www.eclac.cl. **Subscr. to:** United Nations Publications, Distribution and Sales Section, Palais des Nations, Rm C-116, 8-14 av de la Paix, Geneva 1211, Switzerland; United Nations Publications, Rm DC2-853, United Nations Bldg, 2 United Nations Plaza, New York, NY 10017.

ETHIOPIAN JOURNAL OF DEVELOPMENT RESEARCH. see *BUSINESS AND ECONOMICS—Production Of Goods And Services*

338.9   LUX
EUROPAEISCHE GEMEINSCHAFT FUER KOHLE UND STAHL. BERATENDER AUSSCHUSS. JAHRBUCH. Text in German. a.
Related titles: ◆ French ed.: Communaute Europeenne du Charbon et de l'Acier. Comite Consultatif. Annuaire; Ed.: European Coal and Steel Community. Consultative Committee. Yearbook. ISSN 0423-6831. 1954. free.
Published by: European Coal and Steel Community, Consultative Committee, Secretariat, Luxembourg, L-2920, Luxembourg.

AZ EUROPAI UNIO AGRARGAZDASAGA. see *AGRICULTURE*

338.91   LUX   ISSN 1012-2184
EUROPE INFORMATION DEVELOPMENT. Text in English. m. free. **Document type:** *Newsletter.*
Related titles: French ed.: Europe Information Developpement. ISSN 1012-2192.
Indexed: IIS.
—BLDSC (3829.619440).
Published by: (European Commission BEL), European Commission, Office for Official Publications of the European Union, 2 Rue Mercier, Luxembourg, L-2985, Luxembourg.

338.91   DEU
EUROPEAN ASSOCIATION OF DEVELOPMENT RESEARCH AND TRAINING INSTITUTES. ANNUAL REPORT. Text in English. a. free. **Document type:** *Corporate.* **Description:** Discusses the association's activities and objectives both accomplished and planned.
Related titles: Online - full text ed.
Published by: European Association of Development Research and Training Institutes, Kaiser-Friedrich-Str 11, Bonn, 53113, Germany. TEL 49-228-2618101, FAX 49-228-2618103, eadi@uni2a.unige.ch, http://www.eadi.org.

338.91   GBR   ISSN 0969-8906
EUROPEAN BANK FOR RECONSTRUCTION AND DEVELOPMENT. WORKING PAPER. Text in English. 1993. irreg., latest no.85, 2003. free. back issues avail. **Document type:** *Monographic series.* **Description:** Produced to stimulate debate on the economic transformation of central and eastern Europe and the CIS.
—BLDSC (9349.228500).
Published by: European Bank for Reconstruction and Development, Publications Desk, One Exchange Sq, London, EC2A 2EH, United Kingdom. TEL 44-20-73387553, FAX 44-20-73386102, pubsdesk@ebrd.com, http://www.ebrd.com/pubs/index.htm.

338.91   LUX
EUROPEAN COMMISSION. TACIS PROGRAMME. CONTRACT INFORMATION UPDATE. Text in English. 1994. irreg.
Description: Outlines projects funded by the Tacis Programme to support initiatives among the nations of the former Soviet Union to foster the transition to market economies and to forge harmonious links between these countries.
Published by: European Commission, Office for Official Publications of the European Union, 2 Rue Mercier, Luxembourg, L-2985, Luxembourg. TEL 352-29291, FAX 352-2929-44637, info-info-opoce@cec.eu.int, http://europa.eu.int/comm/dg1a/tacis/index.htm.

338.91 360   BEL
EUROPEAN COMMUNITY HUMANITARIAN OFFICE. ANNUAL REPORT. Text in English. a. free. **Document type:** *Corporate.* **Description:** Shows the work of ECHO in terms of how and why humanitarian aid was distributed in the past year.
Published by: (European Community Humanitarian Office), European Commission, Rue de Geneve 3, Brussels, 1140, Belgium. TEL 32-2-295-44-00, FAX 32-2-295-45-72. **Dist. in the U.S. by:** Bernan Associates, Bernan, 4611-F Assembly Dr., Lanham, MD 20706-4391. TEL 301-459-0056, 800-274-4447.

338.91   GBR   ISSN 0957-8811
HC59.69   CODEN: EJDRE9
➤ **THE EUROPEAN JOURNAL OF DEVELOPMENT RESEARCH.** Text in English. 1989. q. GBP 272, USD 439 combined subscription to institutions print & online eds. (effective 2006). adv. bk.rev. index. back issues avail.; reprint service avail. from PSC. **Document type:** *Journal, Academic/Scholarly.* **Description:** Covers research articles on matters of policy, theory, and practice in all aspects of development studies.

Related titles: Online - full text ed.: ISSN 1743-9728. GBP 258, USD 417 to institutions (effective 2006) (from EBSCO Publishing, Gale Group, IngentaConnect, O C L C Online Computer Library Center, Inc., Swets Information Services).
Indexed: ABIn, ASSIA, BAS, BrHumI, GEOBASE, IBSS, IPSA, JEL, PRA, PSA, S&F, SSA, SWA, SociolAb, V&AA, WAE&RSA.
—BLDSC (3829.728280), IE, Infotrieve, ingenta. **CCC.**
Published by: (European Association of Development Research and Training Institutes CHE), Routledge (Subsidiary of: Taylor & Francis Group), 4 Park Sq, Milton Park, Abingdon, Oxon OX14 4RN, United Kingdom. TEL 44-1235-828600, FAX 44-1235-829000, info@routledge.co.uk, http://www.tandf.co.uk/journals/titles/09578811.asp, http://www.routledge.com. Eds. Andrew Mold, Claire Mainguy. adv.: B&W page GBP 195, B&W page USD 285; trim 110 x 178.

338.9   BEL   ISSN 0071-2884
EUROPEAN LEAGUE FOR ECONOMIC COOPERATION. PUBLICATIONS. Text in English, French. 1949. irreg. free.
Published by: European League for Economic Cooperation, Rue de Ligne 11, Brussels, 1000, Belgium.

336   BEL   ISSN 0531-7436
EUROPEAN LEAGUE FOR ECONOMIC COOPERATION. REPORT OF THE SECRETARY GENERAL ON THE ACTIVITIES OF E.L.E.C. Text in English, French. a. free.
Published by: European League for Economic Cooperation, Rue de Ligne 11, Brussels, 1000, Belgium.

EUROPEAN PERSPECTIVES ON RURAL DEVELOPMENT. see *AGRICULTURE*

EUROWATCH. see *POLITICAL SCIENCE—International Relations*

EXECUTIVE INTELLIGENCE REVIEW. see *POLITICAL SCIENCE*

F A O INVESTMENT CENTRE TECHNICAL PAPER. (Food and Agriculture Organization) see *AGRICULTURE—Agricultural Economics*

338.91 331   DNK   ISSN 1395-4911
F A U NYT. (Foreningen af Udviklingsforskere) Text in Danish. 1985. biennial. back issues avail. **Document type:** *Newsletter.*
Formerly (until 1994): Nyhedsbrev (FAU) (0903-563X)
Published by: Foreningen af Udviklingsforskere i Danmark/Association of Development Researchers in Denmark, c/o Tilde Narp, Gl. Kongevej 5, Copenhagen V, 1610, Denmark. TEL 45-33-854690, FAX 45-33-258110, fau@diis.dk, info@udviklingsforskning.dk, http://www.udviklingsforskning.dk.

FINANCE AND DEVELOPMENT (PRINT EDITION). see *BUSINESS AND ECONOMICS—Banking And Finance*

FINANCES ET DEVELOPPEMENT (PRINT EDITION). see *BUSINESS AND ECONOMICS—Banking And Finance*

338.91   USA
FLORIDA ASSOCIATION OF VOLUNTARY AGENCIES FOR CARIBBEAN ACTION. ANNUAL REPORT∗ . Text in English. a.
Published by: Florida Association of Voluntary Agencies for Caribbean Action, 1310 N Paul Russell Rd, Tallahassee, FL 32301-4825. TEL 850-877-4705, favaca@worldnet.att.net, http://www.favaca.org.

FOI ET DEVELOPPEMENT. see *SOCIAL SCIENCES: COMPREHENSIVE WORKS*

FONDS MONETAIRE INTERNATIONAL. ETUDES ECONOMIQUES ET FINANCIERES. see *BUSINESS AND ECONOMICS—Banking And Finance*

338.91   NOR   ISSN 0803-9410
D880
➤ **FORUM FOR DEVELOPMENT STUDIES.** Text in English. 2/yr. NOK 220 in Scandinavia; NOK 300 elsewhere (effective 2002). bk.rev. abstr. **Document type:** *Academic/Scholarly.* **Description:** Covers political, economical, ecological, technological dimensions of development in the Third World.
Formerly (until 1992): Forum for Utviklingsstudier (0332-8244)
Indexed: AgBio, AgrForAb, BAS, FPA, ForAb, GEOBASE, HerbAb, IBSS, IPSA, JEL, PAIS, PGegResA, PSA, RDA, RRTA, S&F, SociolAb, WAE&RSA.
—BLDSC (4024.085190), IE, Infotrieve, ingenta. **CCC.**
Published by: Norsk Utenrikspolitisk Institutt/Norwegian Institute of International Affairs, C. J. Hambros Pl. 2 D, PO Box 8159, Dep, Oslo, 0033, Norway. TEL 47-22-05-65-00, FAX 47-22-17-70-15, pub@nupi.no, http://www.nupi.no/pubnor/pub-set-no.htm. Ed. Olav Stokke. Circ: 600 (controlled).
Co-sponsor: Norwegian Association for Development Research.

338.91   ITA   ISSN 1121-2616
FORUM VALUTAZIONE. Text in Italian. 1991. s-a.
Published by: Comitato Internazionale per lo Sviluppo dei Popoli, Via Germanico 198, Rome, 00192, Italy. TEL 39-06-3216163, cisp@cisp-ngo.org, http://www.cisp-ngo.org.

▼ *new title*   ➤ *refereed*   ∗ *unverified*   ◆ *full entry avail.*

338.91 USA
FRONT LINES (WASHINGTON). Text in English. 1961. m. free.
Document type: *Newsletter, Government.* **Description:** Discusses agency projects and policy, and broader issues in international development.
Published by: U.S. Agency for International Development, Multimedia Communications Division, 1300 Pennsylvania Ave, N W, Rm 6 10, RRB, Washington, DC 20523-6100. TEL 202-712-4330, FAX 202-216-3035. Ed. Suzanne Chase. Circ: 10,000.

338.91 370.116 USA
FRONTLINE. Text in English. bi-m. free. illus.; maps; stat. back issues avail. **Document type:** *Newsletter, Academic/Scholarly.* **Description:** Discusses IREX field research and professional training exchanges between the United States and the former Soviet Union, Mongolia, and China, along with the organization's commitment to international education.
Formerly: New In Brief
Media: Online - full text.
Published by: International Research and Exchange Board, 2121 K St, NW, Ste 700, Washington, DC 20037. TEL 202-628-8188, FAX 202-628-8189, irex@irex.org, http://www.irex.org. Ed., R&P Dova Wilson. Circ: 11,000.

G-24 DISCUSSION PAPER SERIES. see *BUSINESS AND ECONOMICS—Banking And Finance*

338.91 GBR ISSN 1460-4175
G D I BOOK SERIES. Text in English. 1993. irreg., latest 2001. price varies. back issues avail. **Document type:** *Monographic series, Academic/Scholarly.* **Description:** Covers matters of policy, theory and practice in all aspects of development studies.
—BLDSC (4095.352500), ingenta.
Published by: (German Development Institute), Routledge (Subsidiary of: Taylor & Francis Group), 2 Park Sq, Milton Park, Abingdon, Oxon OX14 4RN, United Kingdom. TEL 44-20-70176000, FAX 44-20-70176699, info@routledge.co.uk, http://www.routledge.co.uk.

GENDER AND DEVELOPMENT. see *WOMEN'S STUDIES*

GENDER AND DEVELOPMENT DIRECTORY. AUSTRALIA. see *WOMEN'S STUDIES*

338.91 323.4 ITA ISSN 1564-3506
CODEN: NU014
GENDER NEWSLETTER. Text in English. 199?. q. free. illus.
Document type: *Newsletter.* **Description:** Examines issues of gender inequality in the context of international development aid.
Related titles: Online - full content ed.
Published by: World Food Programme, Gender Unit, Via Cesare Guilio Viola 68-70, Parco de Medici, Rome, 00148, Italy. TEL 39-06-6513-2221, FAX 39-06-6513-2817, elina.sana@wfp.org, http://www.wfp.org/genderweb. Ed. Elina Sana.

338.9 GTM ISSN 0553-6898
GENERAL TREATY FOR CENTRAL AMERICAN ECONOMIC INTEGRATION. PERMANENT SECRETARIAT. NEWSLETTER. Text in Spanish. 1963. irreg.
Published by: Secretaria Permanente del Tratado General de Integracion Economica Centroamericana, 4a Avda. 10-25, ZONA, 14, PO Box 1237, Guatemala City, 01901, Guatemala. TEL 502-3682151, FAX 502-3681071, sieca@pronet.net.gt.

338.9 FRA
HC60
GEOGRAPHICAL DISTRIBUTION OF FINANCIAL FLOWS TO AID RECIPIENTS/REPARTITION GEOGRAPHIQUE DES RESSOURCES FINANCIERES ALLOUEES AUX PAYS BENEFICIAIRES DE L'AIDE. VERSEMENTS - ENGAGEMENTS - INDICATEURS PAR PAYS. Text in English, French. 1966. a. EUR 90, USD 117, GBP 61, JPY 12,000 per issue (effective 2005). charts; stat. **Document type:** *Government.* **Description:** Provides comprehensive data on the volume, origin, and types of aid and other resource flows to more than 180 recipient nations, including new ones in Eastern Europe.
Former titles (until 2003): Geographical Distribution of Financial Flows to Aid Recipients. Disbursements - Commitments - Country Indicators (1026-1869); (until 1994): Geographical Distribution of Financial Flows to Developing Countries. Disbursements - Commitments - Economic Indicators (1015-3934); (until 1977): Geographical Distribution of Financial Flows to Less Developed Countries. (Disbursements) (0474-5434); Which superseded: Organization for Economic Cooperation and Development. Flow of Financial Resources to Less Developed Countries
Related titles: Online - full content ed.: EUR 63, USD 81, GBP 42, JPY 8,400 (effective 2005).
Indexed: IIS.
Published by: Organization for Economic Cooperation and Development, 2 Rue Andre Pascal, Paris, 75775 Cedex 16, France. TEL 33-1-45248200, FAX 33-1-45248500, http://www.oecd.org. **Subscr. in N. America to:** O E C D Turpin North America, PO Box 194, Downingtown, PA 19335-0194. TEL 610-524-5361, 800-456-6323, FAX 610-524-5417, bookscustomer@turpinna.com.

338.91 CAN ISSN 1492-4099
HC59.8
GLOBAL CITIZENSHIP IN ACTION. Text in Multiple languages. 2000. q.
Related titles: Online - full text ed.: ISSN 1497-3936. 2000.
Published by: Canadian International Development Agency, Communications Branch, 200 Promenade du Portage, Hull, PQ K1A 0G4, Canada. TEL 819-997-6100, FAX 819-953-6088, http://www.acdi-cida.gc.ca/publications-e.htm, http://www.acdi.cida.gc.ca.

338.91 658 USA ISSN 1071-0736
HF3000
➤ **GLOBAL COMPETITIVENESS.** Text in English. 1992. a. USD 40 per issue domestic to individuals; USD 60 per issue foreign to individuals; USD 60 per issue domestic to institutions; USD 80 per issue foreign to institutions (effective 2005). adv. tr.lit. back issues avail. **Document type:** *Journal, Academic/Scholarly.* **Description:** Provides knowledge related to international competitiveness, competition and economic integration and cooperation.
Related titles: Online - full text ed.: (from Florida Center for Library Automation, Gale Group, O C L C Online Computer Library Center, Inc.).
Published by: Indiana University of Pennsylvania, International Academy of Business Disciplines, PO Box 1658, Indiana, PA 15705. TEL 754-357-5759, aaali@grove.iup.edu, aaali@grove.iup.edu. Ed., R&P Abbas J Ali. adv.: page USD 30. Circ: 600 (paid).

338.91 USA ISSN 1020-5454
HJ8899
GLOBAL DEVELOPMENT FINANCE. Text in English. 197?. a. USD 400 (effective 2004). **Description:** Covers data on the external debt of 109 developing countries. Includes periodic updates.
Formerly (until 1996): World Debt Tables (0253-2859)
Related titles: CD-ROM ed.: USD 125; Diskette ed.: USD 125; Online - full text ed.: (from EBSCO Publishing).
Indexed: IIS.
—BLDSC (4195.388000), CISTI. **CCC.**
Published by: World Bank Group, 1818 H St, NW, Washington, DC 20433. TEL 202-473-1000, FAX 202-477-6391, books@worldbank.org, http://www.worldbank.org.

327 USA ISSN 1093-8281
H96 CODEN: CPOREG
GLOBAL DEVELOPMENT STUDIES. Text in English. s-a. USD 35 to individuals; USD 65 to institutions; USD 25 to students. adv.
Formerly: Twenty-First Century Policy Review (1055-3630)
Indexed: SOPODA, SSA.
Published by: International Development Options, PO Box 4871, Largo, MD 20775. TEL 301-350-3910.

338.91 332 USA ISSN 1014-8906
HC59.69
GLOBAL ECONOMICS PROSPECTS AND THE DEVELOPING COUNTRIES. Text in English. 1991. irreg. USD 25 (effective 2005). charts; illus.; stat. back issues avail. **Document type:** *Monographic series.* **Description:** Examines the economic linkages between industrial and developing countries.
Related titles: Online - full content ed.: ISSN 1564-7021. 1997; French ed.: Perspectives Economiques Mondiales et les Pays en Developpement. ISSN 1025-6237.
—BLDSC (4195.392000), IE, ingenta. **CCC.**
Published by: World Bank Group, 1818 H St, NW, Washington, DC 20433. TEL 202-473-1155, FAX 202-522-2627, books@worldbank.org, http://www.worldbank.org.

GLOBAL ENVIRONMENT OUTLOOK (YEAR). see *ENVIRONMENTAL STUDIES*

338.91 CAN ISSN 0383-6711
GLOBAL VILLAGE VOICE. Text in English. 1967. q. CND 10 (effective 1997). bk.rev. **Document type:** *Newsletter.*
Description: Focuses on international development, social justice, human rights, socio-economic development issues in Third World countries.
Published by: Canadian Catholic Organization for Development and Peace, 420 10 St Mary St, Toronto, ON M4Y 1P9, Canada. TEL 416-922-1592, 800-494-1401, FAX 416-922-0957, ccodp@web.net. Ed. Jack Panozzo. Circ: 45,000 (controlled).

338.91 USA ISSN 0733-6608
HC121
GRASSROOTS DEVELOPMENT. Text in English. 1977. 2/yr. free. bk.rev. bibl.; illus. Index. reprints avail. **Document type:** *Newsletter.* **Description:** Reports on how the poor in Latin America and the Caribbean organize and work to improve their lives.
Formerly: Inter-American Foundation. Journal
Related titles: Microfilm ed.: (from PQC); Online - full text ed.: (from Gale Group, Northern Light Technology, Inc., O C L C Online Computer Library Center, Inc.); ◆ Spanish ed.: Desarrollo de Base. ISSN 0733-6594; Portuguese ed.: Desenvolvimento de Base.
Indexed: AbAn, Agr, CIJE, CWI, GEOBASE, HAPI, IBSS, ILD, JOF, PAIS, RDA, REE&TA, RRTA, WAE&RSA.
—BLDSC (4213.580000), Infotrieve.
Published by: Inter-American Foundation, 901 N Stuart St, 10th Fl, Arlington, VA 22203-1821. TEL 703-841-3800, publications@iaf.gov, http://www.iaf.gov/publications/publications_text_en.asp?journal_id=1. Circ: 11,700.

GREAT BRITAIN. NATURAL RESOURCES INSTITUTE. BULLETIN. see *AGRICULTURE*

352.73 GBR ISSN 0952-1518
GUIDE TO EUROPEAN COMMUNITY GRANTS AND LOANS. Text in English. 1980. base vol. plus q. updates. looseleaf. GBP 170. Supplement avail. **Document type:** *Directory.* **Description:** Provides informations on European Community funding programs, indicating scheme objectives, legislative basis, eligibility, levels of award, deadlines, and contact points in the EC. Aimed at libraries, academic institutions, government bodies, business persons, and lawyers.
—BLDSC (4226.387000).
Published by: Eurofi Ltd., 44 Melville St, Edinburgh, EH3 7HF, United Kingdom. TEL 44-131-225-8451, FAX 44-131-220-1972, edinburgh.office@eurofi.co.uk, http://www.eurofi.co.uk. Ed. Pilar Martinez. Circ: 500 (paid).

338.91 CHN ISSN 1002-1515
HF3831
GUOJI JINGJI HEZUO/INTERNATIONAL ECONOMIC COOPERATION. Text in Chinese; Abstracts in English. 1986. m. USD 36.80. **Document type:** *Government.* **Description:** Reports on the major events in international economic and trade practices and establishing foreign-funded enterprises.
Related titles: Online - full text ed.: (from East View Information Services).
Indexed: RASB.
Contact Dist.: China Books & Periodicals Inc, 360 Swift Ave., Ste. 48, S San Fran, CA 94080-6220. info@chinabooks.com, http://www.chinabooks.com/. **Dist. by:** China International Book Trading Corp, 35 Chegongzhuang Xilu, Haidian District, PO Box 399, Beijing 100044, China. TEL 86-10-68412045, FAX 86-10-68412023, cibtc@mail.cibtc.com.cn, http://www.cibtc.com.cn.

338.91 NLD
H I V O S MAGAZINE. Text in Dutch. 1983. q. free. adv.
Document type: *Bulletin.*
Former titles: H I V O S - Projectbericht (0169-0337); H I V O S - Informatie Bulletin
Published by: Humanistisch Instituut voor Ontwikkelingssamenwerking/Humanist Institute for Development Cooperation, Raamweg 16, The Hague, 2596 HL, Netherlands. TEL 31-70-137-6550, FAX 31-70-362-4600, TELEX 34472 HIVOS NL, Hivos@hivos.nl. Ed. Jacqueline Schuiling. Circ: 10,000 (controlled).

327 USA ISSN 1062-578X
HAITI NEWS. Text in English. 1985. 3/yr. USD 16. bk.rev.; film rev. **Document type:** *Newsletter, Trade.* **Description:** Contains articles on development programs in Haiti, resources, classifieds and a directory with indices for geographical location and type of program.
Address: PO Box 2120, Brewster, MA 02631. TEL 508-896-5647, FAX 508-896-9790, tortora@meol.mass.edu. Ed. Patrick Tortora. Pub. Peter Kinney. Circ: 632. **Subscr. to:** 131 N Main St, Sharon, MA 02067.

HARAMATA - BULLETIN OF THE DRYLANDS. see *ENVIRONMENTAL STUDIES*

338.91 AUS ISSN 1038-5479
HORIZONS. Text in English. 1979. q. maps; stat. back issues avail. **Document type:** *Consumer.* **Description:** Contains brief accounts of CAA's development work with poor communities, mostly in 3rd world countries. Basic aim is to help impoverished communities to become more independent, through education, improved sanitation, access to clean water, etc. Also keeps CAA supporters/donors up to date with development issues being tackled by CAA.
Former titles (until 1992): Action - Australian Freedom from Hunger Campaign (0729-980X); (until 1982): Caring (Melbourne) (0159-9410)
Published by: Community Aid Abroad (Subsidiary of: Oxfam International), 156 George St, Fitzroy, VIC 3065, Australia. TEL 61-3-9289-9444, FAX 61-3-9419-5895, enquire@caa.org.au, http://www.caa.org.au. Ed. Sarah Lowe. Circ: 80,000.

338.91 USA ISSN 1542-250X
▼ ➤ **HORIZONS (HATTIESBURG);** the journal of global development in the 21st century. Text in English. forthcoming 2006. s-a. **Document type:** *Journal, Academic/Scholarly.*
Media: Online - full content.
Published by: University of Southern Mississippi, International Development Program, Box 5051, Hattiesburg, MS 39406-5051. TEL 601-266-6519, horizons@usm.edu, http://www.usm.edu/horizons, http://www.usm.edu/idv. Ed. David Butler.

338.91 MNG
HUMAN DEVELOPMENT REPORT (YEAR). Text in English. a. free. illus. **Document type:** *Corporate.*
Indexed: RDA.
—BLDSC (4336.054000).

Published by: United Nations Development Programme Mongolia, Erhuu St 7, PO Box 49 207, Ulan Bator, Mongolia. TEL 976-1-327585, FAX 976-1-326221, registry@undp.org.mn, http://www.un-mongolia.mn/undp/.

HUNGER NEWS & HOPE. see *SOCIAL SERVICES AND WELFARE*

I D B AMERICA. see *BUSINESS AND ECONOMICS—Banking And Finance*

I D B PROJECTS. see *BUSINESS AND ECONOMICS—Banking And Finance*

338.91   BRB
I D C IMPACT. (Industrial Development Corporation) Text in English. q.
Address: Pelican Industrial Pk., Bridgetown, Barbados.

I D E STATISTICAL DATA SERIES. see *BUSINESS AND ECONOMICS—Abstracting, Bibliographies, Statistics*

338.91   GBR
I D P M DISCUSSION AND WORKING PAPERS. Text in English. irreg. **Document type:** *Monographic series, Academic/Scholarly.* **Description:** Examines research in development and other areas of international developmental policy.
Formerly: I D P M Working Papers
Published by: University of Manchester, Institute for Development Policy and Management, Crawford House, Precinct Centre, Oxford Rd, Manchester, Lancs M13 9GH, United Kingdom. TEL 44-161-275-2800, FAX 44-161-273-8829, idpm@man.ac.uk, http://www.man.ac.uk/idpm.

338.9   CAN   ISSN 0315-9981
     CODEN: IDRIDJ
I D R C REPORTS. Text in English. 1972. w. free email ed.. back issues avail. **Document type:** *Academic/Scholarly.* **Description:** For researchers and educators interested in development issues and who can spread the knowledge of research results in their community; members of government bodies that formulate policies or help in the dissemination of technologies; libraries and information networks in Third World countries.
Media: Online - full text. **Related titles:** French ed.: C R D I Explore. ISSN 0380-1438; Spanish ed.: C I I D Informa. ISSN 0304-5544.
Indexed: ASFA, BAS, CBCARef, CBPI, CPerl, EIA, EPB, ESPM, EnvAb, FS&TA, JOF, MCR, PollutAb, RASB, RDA, Repind, SFSA, TOSA.
—CASDDS. **CCC.**
Published by: International Development Research Centre/Centre de Recherches pour le developpement international, P O Box 8500, Ottawa, ON K1G 3H9, Canada. TEL 613-236-6163, FAX 613-563-2476, order@idrc.ca, http://www.idrc.ca. Ed. Neale MacMillan. Circ: 34,300.

338.91   GBR   ISSN 0265-5012
HC59.7   CODEN: IDBUFB
➤ **I D S BULLETIN.** Text in English. 1969. q. GBP 14.95 per issue (effective 2005). bk.rev. bibl.; charts; stat. back issues avail. **Document type:** *Bulletin, Academic/Scholarly.* **Description:** Covers themes of topical importance to all working on development. Combines scholarly research with clear explanation.
Former titles (until 1984): Institute of Development Studies. Bulletin (0960-734X); (until 1980): I D S Bulletin (1975) (0308-5872); (until 1975): Institute of Development Studies Bulletin (0020-2835).
Related titles: Online - full text ed. (from EBSCO Publishing, Gale Group, IngentaConnect).
Indexed: APEL, ASCA, ASSIA, AbHyg, AgBio, AgrForAb, BAS, CTFA, CurCont, EI, FamI, ForAb, GEOBASE, HerbAb, HortAb, I&DA, IBSS, ILD, IndIslam, JOF, MEA, NutrAb, PAIS, PBA, PGegResA, PHN&I, PSA, RASB, RDA, REE&TA, RRTA, S&F, SIA, SOPODA, SSA, SSCI, SWA, SociolAb, TDB, TEA, WAE&RSA.
—BLDSC (4362.585000), IDS, IE, Infotrieve, ingenta. **CCC.**
Published by: Institute of Development Studies, University Of Sussex, Brighton, BN1 9RE, United Kingdom. TEL 44-1273-606261, FAX 44-1273-621202, 44-1273-691647, ids@ids.ac.uk, http://www.ntd.co.uk/idsbookshop/details.asp?id=853, http://www.ids.ac.uk/ids/. Ed. Katherine Henry. Circ: 2,500.

338   GBR   ISSN 0308-5864
HD72
I D S DISCUSSION PAPER. Text in English. 1972. irreg. (8-12/yr.). **Document type:** *Academic/Scholarly.* **Description:** Contains preliminary field and theoretical research findings circulated to stimulate feedback.
Indexed: ForAb, RASB, RDA, RRTA, SWA, WAE&RSA.
—BLDSC (4362.594000). **CCC.**
Published by: Institute of Development Studies, University Of Sussex, Brighton, BN1 9RE, United Kingdom. TEL 44-1273-606261, FAX 44-1273-621202, ids.subs@sussex.ac.uk, ids@ids.ac.uk. Ed. Katherine Henry. Circ: 600.

338   GBR   ISSN 1360-4724
I D S POLICY BRIEFING. (Institute of Development Studies) Text in English. 1994. irreg.
Formerly (until 1995): University of Sussex. Institute of Development Studies. Policy Briefing Paper (1353-8772)
Indexed: WAE&RSA.
—BLDSC (4362.610500), CISTI.
Published by: University of Sussex, Institute of Development Studies, Brighton, Sussex BN1 9RE, United Kingdom. TEL 44-1273-606261, FAX 44-1273-621202, ids@ids.ac.uk, http://www.ids.ac.uk/ids.

338.91   GBR   ISSN 0141-1314
I D S RESEARCH REPORTS. Text in English. 1978. irreg. (1-3/yr). **Document type:** *Monographic series, Academic/Scholarly.* **Description:** Contains the final results of major research projects regarding a range of development themes.
Indexed: RRTA, WAE&RSA.
—BLDSC (7762.352700).
Published by: Institute of Development Studies, University Of Sussex, Brighton, BN1 9RE, United Kingdom. TEL 44-1273-606261, FAX 44-1273-6210202. Ed. Katherine Henry. Circ: 500.

338.91 630   ITA
I F A D UPDATE. Text in English. q. free. **Document type:** *Newsletter.* **Description:** Studies the fight to combat hunger and rural poverty in the low-income food deficit regions of the world.
Related titles: Arabic ed.; French ed.; Spanish ed.
Published by: (Information and Communications Division), International Fund for Agricultural Development/Fonds International de Developpement Agricole, Via Del Serafico, 107, Rome, RM 00142, Italy. TEL 39-6-54591, FAX 39-6-5043463, TELEX 620330 IFAD. Ed. Maria Elisa Pinzon. Circ: 14,000.

338.91 332.6   USA   ISSN 1012-8069
I F C DISCUSSION PAPER. Text in English. 1989. a. **Document type:** *Monographic series, Trade.* **Description:** Reports on private-sector economic and finance issues worldwide.
Related titles: Online - full text ed. ISSN 1564-5568. 1998; ◆ Series: Trends in Private Investment in Developing Countries. ISSN 1018-208X.
Indexed: IIS, RDA, WAE&RSA.
—BLDSC (3597.364500). **CCC.**
Published by: International Finance Corporation, 1818 H St N W, Washington, DC 20433. TEL 202-473-1155, FAX 202-676-0581.

339   DEU
I F O MITTEILUNGEN DER ABTEILUNG ENTWICKLUNGSLAENDER. Text in German. 1965. a. free. adv. bk.rev. abstr.; charts; illus. **Document type:** *Academic/Scholarly.* **Description:** Compilation of research in developing countries.
Former titles: I F O Mitteilungen: Entwicklungslaender - Afrika Studienstelle; Informationen der Afrika-Studienstelle (0046-9394)
Published by: I F O Institut fuer Wirtschaftsforschung, Poschingerstr 5, Munich, 81679, Germany. TEL 49-89-9224-0, FAX 49-89-985369, ifo@ifo.de, http://www.ifo.de. Ed. Axel J Halbach. Circ: 400.

338.91   DEU   ISSN 0170-5709
I F O STUDIEN ZUR ENTWICKLUNGSFORSCHUNG. Text in German. 1976. irreg., latest vol.33, 1998. price varies. **Document type:** *Monographic series.*
Related titles: ◆ Supplement(s): I F O Studien zur Entwicklungsforschung. Sonderreihe Information und Dokumentation. ISSN 0723-8975.
Indexed: RASB.
Published by: I F O Institut fuer Wirtschaftsforschung, Poschingerstr 5, Munich, 81679, Germany. TEL 49-89-9224-0, FAX 49-89-985369, ifo@ifo.de, http://www.ifo.de. Circ: 400.

338.91   DEU   ISSN 0723-8975
I F O STUDIEN ZUR ENTWICKLUNGSFORSCHUNG. SONDERREIHE INFORMATION UND DOKUMENTATION. Text in German. 1980. irreg., latest vol.34, 1999. price varies. **Document type:** *Monographic series.*
Related titles: ◆ Supplement to: I F O Studien zur Entwicklungsforschung. ISSN 0170-5709.
Published by: I F O Institut fuer Wirtschaftsforschung), Weltforum Verlag, Hohenzollernplatz 3, Bonn, 53173, Germany. TEL 49-228-368243-0, FAX 49-228-3682439, ifo@ifo.de.

338.91489   DNK   ISSN 0901-6171
HC59.7
I F U ANNUAL REPORT. Text in Danish. 1970. a. free. **Document type:** *Corporate.* **Description:** Focuses on all aspects of economic activity in developing countries in order to promote investments in these countries in collaboration with Danish trades and industries.
Formerly: I F U's Participation in Joint Ventures (0108-1969)
Published by: Industrialiseringsfonden for Udviklingslandene/ Industrialization Fund for Developing Countries, Bremerholm 4, PO Box 2155, Copenhagen K, 1016, Denmark. TEL 45-33637500, FAX 45-33322524, ifu@ifu.dk, http://www.ifu.dk. Circ: 13,000.

I I C ANNUAL REPORT. see *BUSINESS AND ECONOMICS—Banking And Finance*

338.9   USA   ISSN 1011-8721
I I R R REPORT. Text in English. 1960. s-a. free. **Description:** Carries out research and training in rural development in the Third World.
Published by: International Institute of Rural Reconstruction, 475 Riverside Dr, New York, NY 10115. TEL 212-870-2992. Ed. Eric Blitz. Circ: 2,500.

338.91   SWE   ISSN 0345-5165
I M. Text in Swedish. 1944. 10/yr. SEK 100 (effective 1998).
Related titles: Audio cassette/tape ed.
Published by: Bistaandsorganisationen IM Individuell Maenniskohjaelp, Fack 45, Lund, 22100, Sweden. TEL 46-46-32-99-530, FAX 46-46-15-83-09, anna.persson@manniskohjalp.se, http://www.individuell.manniskohjalp.se.

338.91   USA
I M F HEAVILY INDEBTED POOR COUNTRIES COUNTRY DOCUMENTS. (International Monetary Fund) Text in English. s-m. back issues avail.
Published by: International Monetary Fund, Publication Services, 700 19th St, N W, Ste 12-607, Washington, DC 20431. TEL 202-623-7430, FAX 202-623-7201, publications@imf.org, http://www.imf.org.

338.91   USA
I M F POVERTY REDUCTION STRATEGY PAPERS. (International Monetary Fund) Text in English. 3/m.
Formerly: I M F Poverty Reduction Strategies
Published by: International Monetary Fund, Publication Services, 700 19th St, N W, Ste 12-607, Washington, DC 20431. TEL 202-623-7430, FAX 202-623-7201, publications@imf.org, http://www.imf.org.

338.9   ARG
I N T A L DOCUMENTOS DE DIVULGACION. (Instituto para la Integracion de America Latina y el Caribe) Text in Spanish, English, Portuguese. 1997. irreg., latest vol.3. USD 15 per vol. (effective 2000). bibl.; stat.; charts; tr.lit. back issues avail. **Document type:** *Monographic series, Academic/Scholarly.*
Related titles: Online - full text ed.
Published by: Banco Interamericano de Desarrollo, Instituto para la Integracion de America Latina y el Caribe/Inter-American Development Bank, Esmeralda 130 Piso 17, Buenos Aires, 1035, Argentina. TEL 54-11-43201850, FAX 54-11-43201865, pubintal@iadb.org, int/inl@iadb.org, http://www.iadb.org/intal/publicaciones/docdivul.htm. Eds. Mariela Marchiaio, Susana Filippa.

338.91   ARG
➤ **I N T A L DOCUMENTOS DE TRABAJO.** (Instituto para la Integracion de America Latina y el Caribe) Text in Spanish, English, Portuguese. 1997. irreg., latest vol.3. USD 15 per issue (effective 2003). bibl.; charts; stat.; tr.lit. back issues avail. **Document type:** *Monographic series, Academic/Scholarly.* **Description:** Presents technical contributions by authorities in international cooperation and development.
Related titles: Online - full text ed.
Published by: Banco Interamericano de Desarrollo, Instituto para la Integracion de America Latina y el Caribe/Inter-American Development Bank, Esmeralda 130 Piso 17, Buenos Aires, 1035, Argentina. TEL 54-11-43201850, FAX 54-11-43201865, pubintal@iadb.org, int/inl@iadb.org, http://www.iadb.org/intal/publicaciones/irabserie.htm.

332.673489   DNK   ISSN 0906-3560
I OE ANNUAL REPORT. Text in Danish. 1991. a. **Document type:** *Corporate.* **Description:** Promotes Danish investment in Central and Eastern Europe, as well as increased economic cooperation between Denmark and the developing countries of Central and Eastern Europe.
Published by: I OE Investment Fund for Central and Eastern Europe - Denmark, Bremerholm 4, PO Box 2155, Copenhagen K, 1016, Denmark. TEL 45-33-63-75-00, FAX 45-33-322524, io-cph@inet.unil.dk, io-cph@inet.uni2.dk.

338.91   ITA   ISSN 0390-6272
HC301
I R I GRUPPO YEARBOOK. Text in Italian. a.
Published by: Istituto per la Ricostruzione Industriale, Via Vittorio Veneto, 89, Rome, RM 00187, Italy. TEL 06-47271, FAX 06-47272308.

338.91   FRA   ISSN 1271-4046
I S T E D. LETTRE. Text in French, English. 1996. q. free. bk.rev. **Document type:** *Newsletter.* **Description:** Provides a forum for ideas, information, and action at the service of members in the private and public sectors of public works, development, and the environment. Promotes French expertise at the international level and disseminates scientific and technical information.
Related titles: Online - full text ed.; English ed.: ISSN 1270-8348.
Indexed: RefZh.

Published by: Institut des Sciences et des Techniques de L'Equipement et de l'Environnement pour le Developpement, La Grande Arche, Paroi Sud, Paris La Defense, Cedex 92055, France. TEL 33-1-40812406, FAX 33-1-40812331. Ed. Xavier Crepin. Pub., R&P Jean Smagghe. Circ: 3,500.

338.91 362.5   USA
IMPACT! (SEATTLE). Text in English. 1999. irreg. free. **Document type:** *Newsletter, Bulletin, Consumer.* **Description:** Informs interested persons of activities of the The Hunger Site, a Web portal that enables individuals to make a daily donation to the United Nations World Food Programme paid for by corporate sponsors who place button advertisements on this visually prominent Web site. Also contains news of Greatergood.com, an organization with a prominent Web portal that offers users access to online merchants who pledge to donate a percentage of their profits to a charitable organization chosen by the customer.
Media: E-mail.
Published by: The Hunger Site, One Union Sq, 600 University St, Ste 1000, Seattle, WA 98101. TEL 206-344-5154, 888-509-7676, sponsor@thehungersite.com, info@greatergood.com, http://www.thehungersite.com, http://www.greatergood.com. **Co-sponsor:** World Food Programme.

▼ 330   IND
INDIAN DEVELOPMENT REVIEW; an international journal of development economics. Text in English. 2003. s-a. USD 125 to institutions (effective 2006).
Published by: Scientific Publishers, 5-A New Pali Rd., Near Hotel Taj Hari Mahal, PO Box 91, Jodhpur, Rajasthan 342 003, India. TEL 91-291-2433323, FAX 91-291-2512580, journals@scientificpub.com, http://www.scientificpub.com/bookdetails.php?booktransid=479&bookid=475.

338.91   IND   ISSN 0970-1532
HB1
INDIAN JOURNAL OF QUANTITATIVE ECONOMICS; an international journal of development economics. Text in English. 1985. s-a. INR 60 newsstand/cover domestic to individuals; GBP 15 newsstand/cover foreign to individuals; INR 100 newsstand/cover domestic to institutions; USD 20 newsstand/cover foreign to institutions (effective 2003). adv. bk.rev. **Document type:** *Academic/Scholarly.*
Indexed: JEL, PAIS, RDA, SSI.
Published by: Guru Nanak Dev University Press, Punjab School of Economics, Amritsar, 143 005, India. dcse.gndu@yahoo.com. Circ: 200.

INDIAN JOURNAL OF RURAL TECHNOLOGY. see *TECHNOLOGY: COMPREHENSIVE WORKS*

333.72   NLD   ISSN 1570-0291
S494.5.I5
INDIGENOUS KNOWLEDGE WORLDWIDE; linking global and indigenous knowledge. Text in English. 1993. 4/yr. free (effective 2003). bk.rev. abstr. 8 p./no.; **Document type:** *Newsletter, Newspaper-distributed.* **Description:** Disseminates research and information relating to the study and application of indigenous knowledge. Encourages international cooperation in matters relating to sustainable development in policy and practice.
Formerly (until 2001): Indigenous Knowledge and Development Monitor (0928-1460)
Indexed: AICP, IndVet, PGegResA, RA&MP, RDA, RiceAb, SeedAb, WAE&RSA.
—BLDSC (4437.084000), KNAW.
Published by: NUFFIC (OS/IK Unit), PO Box 29777, The Hague, 2502 LT, Netherlands. TEL 31-70-4260260, FAX 31-70-4260329, ik@nuffic.nl, http://www.nuffic.nl/ik-pages. Ed. Anna van Marrewijk. Circ: 2,800.

338   THA
HC411
INDUSTRIAL AND TECHNOLOGICAL DEVELOPMENT NEWS FOR ASIA AND THE PACIFIC. Text in English. 1962. irreg., latest vol.27, 2001. USD 20 (effective 2003). back issues avail.; reprints avail. **Document type:** *Bulletin.*
Former titles: Industrial and Technological Development; (until 1993): Industrial Development News for Asia and The Pacific; Industry and Technology Development News - Asia and the Pacific (1010-514X); (until 1983): Industrial Development News - Asia and the Pacific (0252-4481); (until 1977): Asian Industrial Development News (0572-4171)
Indexed: PAIS.
Published by: United Nations Economic and Social Commission for Asia and the Pacific, United Nations Bldg., Rajadamnern Ave., Bangkok, 10200, Thailand. TEL 662-2881174, FAX 662-2883022, unescap@unescap.org, http://www.unescap.org. **Dist. by:** United Nations Publications, Distribution and Sales Section, Palais des Nations, Rm C-116, 8-14 av de la Paix, Geneva 1211, Switzerland; United Nations, Conference Services Unit, ESCAP, Bangkok, Thailand; United Nations Publications, Rm DC2-853, United Nations Bldg, 2 United Nations Plaza, New York, NY 10017.

INDUSTRIAL DEVELOPMENT POLICY DISCUSSION PAPER. see *BUSINESS AND ECONOMICS—Economic Situation And Conditions*

338.91   LUX
INFO PHARE. Text in French. 1994. bi-m. free. illus. **Document type:** *Newsletter.* **Description:** Provides information on developments of Phare to provide financial aid for the social and economic conversion of Central and Eastern Europe's economies.
Published by: European Commission, Office for Official Publications of the European Union, 2 Rue Mercier, Luxembourg, L-2985, Luxembourg. TEL 352-29291, FAX 352-292942027, http://www.cec.lu, http://europa.eu.int. Circ: 20,000.

▼ **INFORMATION TECHNOLOGIES AND INTERNATIONAL DEVELOPMENT.** see *COMPUTERS—Information Science And Information Theory*

338.91 004   USA   ISSN 0268-1102
HC59.72.I55
➤ **INFORMATION TECHNOLOGY FOR DEVELOPMENT.** Text in English. 1986-1990; resumed 1995. q. USD 248 domestic; USD 288 in Canada & Mexico; USD 322 elsewhere; USD 273 combined subscription domestic print & online eds.; USD 313 combined subscription in Canada & Mexico print & online eds.; USD 347 combined subscription elsewhere print & online eds. (effective 2006). adv. **Document type:** *Journal, Academic/Scholarly.* **Description:** Encourages critical debate on the role of information technology in the development process.
Related titles: Online - full text ed.: ISSN 1554-0170. USD 248 to institutions (effective 2006) (from EBSCO Publishing, Northern Light Technology, Inc., O C L C Online Computer Library Center, Inc., ProQuest Information & Learning, Swets Information Services, Wiley InterScience).
Indexed: ABIn, BrCerAb, C&ISA, CerAb, CompLI, CompR, CorrAb, E&CAJ, EMA, IAA, IBR, IBZ, InfoSAb, Inspec, LISA, M&TEA, MBF, METADEX, RASB, RDA, WAA, WAE&RSA. —BLDSC (4496.368810), AskIEEE, IE, Infotrieve, ingenta. **CCC.**
Published by: (National Centre for Software Technology IND), John Wiley & Sons, Inc., 605 Third Ave, New York, NY 10158-0012. TEL 212-850-6000, FAX 212-850-6088, uscs-wis@wiley.com, http://www.wiley.com. Circ: 500.

338.91   ARG
INFORME MERCOSUR. Text in Spanish, Portuguese, English. 1996. a., latest vol.7, 2001. USD 25 (effective 2003). bibl.; stat.; charts; tr.lit. back issues avail. **Document type:** *Monographic series, Trade.*
Related titles: Online - full text ed.
Published by: Banco Interamericano de Desarrollo, Instituto para la Integracion de America Latina y el Caribe/Inter-American Development Bank, Esmeralda 130 Piso 17, Buenos Aires, 1035, Argentina. TEL 54-11-43201850, FAX 54-11-43201865, pubintal@iadb.org, int/inl@iadb.org, http://www.iadb.org/intal/publicaciones/i-informes_subregionales.htm.

INSIDE INDONESIA. see *POLITICAL SCIENCE—International Relations*

330   FRA   ISSN 1635-2262
INSTITUT D'EMISSION D'OUTRE MER, PARIS. RAPPORT ANNUEL. Text in French. 1967. a.
Formerly (until 1989): Institut d'Emission d'Outre Mer, Paris. Rapport d'Activite (0073-8247)
Published by: Institut d'Emission d'Outre Mer Paris, 5 rue Roland Barthes, Paris, 75598, France. TEL 33-1-53444141, FAX 33-1-43475134.

338.91 658   CMR
INSTITUT PANAFRICAIN POUR LE DEVELOPPEMENT. CENTRE DE FORMATION AU MANAGEMENT DES PROJETS. BILAN DES ACTIVITES. Text in French. irreg.
Published by: Institut Panafricain pour le Developpement, Centre de Documentation/Pan African Institute for Development, BP 4078, Douala, Cameroon. TEL 237-403770, FAX 237-403068, ipdac@sprynet.com, sgpaidafr@camfido.gn.apc.org.

338.91 658   CMR
INSTITUT PANAFRICAIN POUR LE DEVELOPPEMENT. CENTRE D'ETUDES ET DE RECHERCHES APPLIQUEES. EVALUATION DU SEMINAIRE SUR LA METHODOLOGIE DU MANAGEMENT DES PROJETS. Text in French. a. USD 25. bk.rev.
Published by: Institut Panafricain pour le Developpement, Centre de Documentation/Pan African Institute for Development, BP 4078, Douala, Cameroon. TEL 237-403770, FAX 237-403068, ipdac@sprynet.com, sgpaidafr@camfido.gn.apc.org. Ed. Adovi John Bosco. Circ: 1,500.

338   CMR
INSTITUT PANAFRICAIN POUR LE DEVELOPPEMENT. TRAVAUX D'ETUDIANTS. BULLETIN ANALYTIQUE. Text in French. 1967. q. bk.rev. **Document type:** *Bulletin.*
Formerly: Institut Panafricain pour le Developpement. Annuaire des Anciens Etudiants (0046-9734)
Published by: Institut Panafricain pour le Developpement, Centre de Documentation/Pan African Institute for Development, BP 4078, Douala, Cameroon. TEL 237-403770, FAX 237-403068, ipdac@sprynet.com, sgpaidafr@camfido.gn.apc.org.

INSTITUT PANAFRICAIN POUR LE DEVELOPPEMENT. TRAVAUX MANUSCRITS. see *AGRICULTURE—Agricultural Economics*

338.9   CHE   ISSN 1260-8971
INSTITUT UNIVERSITAIRE D'ETUDES DU DEVELOPPEMENT. LES NOUVEAUX CAHIERS. Text in French. 1975. irreg. price varies. reprints avail. **Document type:** *Monographic series, Academic/Scholarly.*
Former titles (until 1993): Institut Universitaire d'Etudes du Developpement. Cahiers (1421-4172); (until 1977): Institut d'Etudes du Developpement. Cahiers (0378-9470)
Published by: Institut Universitaire d'Etudes du Developpement, Case Postale 136, Geneva 21, 1211, Switzerland. TEL 41-22-9065940, FAX 41-22-9065953, publications@iued.unige.ch, http://www.iued.unige.ch.

330.06   JPN
INSTITUTE OF DEVELOPING ECONOMICS. ANNUAL REPORT. Text in English. 1968. a. **Document type:** *Corporate.*
Related titles: Japanese ed.
Published by: Institute of Developing Economies/Ajia Keizai Kenkyusho, 3-2-2 Wakaba, Mihana-ku, Chiba-shi, Chiba 261-8545, Japan. TEL 81-43-299-9536, FAX 84-43-299-9724, info@ide.go.jp, http://www.ide.go.jp. Circ: 2,500.

338.9   GBR
INSTITUTE OF DEVELOPMENT STUDIES. ANNUAL REPORT. Text in English. a. **Document type:** *Corporate.* **Description:** Provides a full account of the year's activities and a listing of current staff and research interests. Includes a teaching schedule.
Published by: Institute of Development Studies, University Of Sussex, Brighton, BN1 9RE, United Kingdom. TEL 44-1273-606261, FAX 44-1273-691647, ids.subs@sussex.ac.uk, ids@ids.ac.uk, http://www.ids.ac.uk/ids/publicat/. Ed. Katherine Henry.

INSTITUTO DO DESENVOLVIMENTO ECONOMICO-SOCIAL DO PARA. PARA DESENVOLVIMENTO. see *BUSINESS AND ECONOMICS—Economic Situation And Conditions*

INTAL CARTA MENSUAL (ONLINE EDITION). see *BUSINESS AND ECONOMICS—International Commerce*

338.9   ARG   ISSN 1026-0463
HC121
INTEGRACION Y COMERCIO. Text in Spanish, English. 1976-1995; resumed 1996. 2/yr. USD 30 domestic; USD 35 in the Americas; USD 45 elsewhere (effective 2003). adv. bk.rev. abstr.; charts; stat.; bibl.; tr.lit. back issues avail. **Document type:** *Journal, Trade.* **Description:** Discusses issues in international banking and commerce in Latin America and the Caribbean.
Formerly: Integracion Latinoamericana - Latin American Integration (0325-1675); Which was formed by the merger of: Boletin de la Integracion (0047-0007); Revista de la Integracion (0034-8422)
Related titles: Online - full text ed.; English ed.: Integration and Trade. ISSN 1027-5703.
Indexed: ELLIS, FLP, HAPI, IBR, IBSS, JEL, PAIS, RASB, RILM.
Published by: Banco Interamericano de Desarrollo, Instituto para la Integracion de America Latina y el Caribe/Inter-American Development Bank, Esmeralda 130 Piso 17, Buenos Aires, 1035, Argentina. TEL 54-11-43201850, FAX 54-11-43201865, pubintal@iadb.org, int/inl@iadb.org, http://www.iadb.org/intal/ingles/publicaciones/i-i&c.htm. Circ: 700.

INTEGRATED RURAL DEVELOPMENT. PUBLICATIONS. see *POPULATION STUDIES*

L'INTELLIGENT. see *POLITICAL SCIENCE—International Relations*

380 338   URY   ISSN 0538-3048
INTER-AMERICAN COUNCIL OF COMMERCE AND PRODUCTION. URUGUAYAN SECTION. PUBLICACIONES. Text in Spanish. 1951. irreg.
Published by: Inter-American Council of Commerce and Production, Misiones, 1400, Montevideo, 11006, Uruguay.

INTER-AMERICAN DEVELOPMENT BANK. ANNUAL REPORT. see *BUSINESS AND ECONOMICS—Banking And Finance*

INTER-AMERICAN DEVELOPMENT BANK. BOARD OF GOVERNORS. PROCEEDINGS OF THE MEETING. see *BUSINESS AND ECONOMICS—Banking And Finance*

INTER-AMERICAN DEVELOPMENT BANK. OCCASIONAL PAPERS. see *BUSINESS AND ECONOMICS—Banking And Finance*

INTER-AMERICAN DEVELOPMENT BANK. WORKING PAPERS SERIES. see *BUSINESS AND ECONOMICS—Banking And Finance*

330   USA
INTER-AMERICAN FOUNDATION. YEAR IN REVIEW. Text in English. a. free. back issues avail. **Document type:** *Corporate.*
Formerly: Inter-American Foundation. Annual Report
Related titles: Spanish ed.: Fundacion Interamericana. Anuario; Portuguese ed.

Published by: Inter-American Foundation, 901 N Stuart St, 10th Fl, Arlington, VA 22203-1821. TEL 703-841-3800, FAX 703-527-3529. Circ: 11,700.

INTERNATIONAL DEVELOPMENT PLANNING REVIEW. see *HOUSING AND URBAN PLANNING*

338.91 GBR ISSN 0964-699X
INTERNATIONAL DEVELOPMENT POLICIES; review of the activities of international organisations. Text in English. q. GBP 40 (effective 2000). back issues avail. **Document type:** *Bulletin.* **Description:** Reviews the main developments in the evolution of international development policies and related economic topics at various international organizations.
Indexed: IBSS.
Published by: Commonwealth Secretariat, Marlborough House, Pall Mall, London, SW1Y 5HX, United Kingdom. TEL 44-2078-393411, FAX 44-2079-300827, http://www.thecommonwealth.org. Ed. Ian Thomas. Circ: 350 (controlled).

INTERNATIONAL DIRECTORY OF SOURCES. INFOTERRA. see *ENVIRONMENTAL STUDIES*

INTERNATIONAL ECONOMIC DEVELOPMENT LAW. see *LAW—International Law*

338.91 USA ISSN 1020-7856
INTERNATIONAL ECONOMIC POLICY REVIEW. Text in English. 1999. a., latest vol.2, 2000. **Document type:** *Monographic series.*
Related titles: Online - full text ed.: ISSN 1607-9574.
Published by: International Monetary Fund, Publication Services, 700 19th St, N W, Ste 12-607, Washington, DC 20431. TEL 202-623-7430, FAX 202-623-7201, publications@imf.org, http://www.imf.org.

338.91 GBR
INTERNATIONAL GRAINS COUNCIL. FOOD AID SHIPMENTS. Text in English. 1980. a., latest 2000. GBP 50, USD 80 (effective 2000). charts; stat. **Document type:** *Bulletin.* **Description:** Contains statistical information about shipments of cereals food aid by members of the Food Aid Convention.
Former titles: International Wheat Council. Food Aid Shipments; International Wheat Council. Food Aid Convention
Published by: International Grains Council, One Canada Sq, Canary Wharf, London, E14 5AE, United Kingdom. TEL 44-20-7513-1122, FAX 44-20-7513-0630, publications@igc.org.uk, igc-fac@igc.org.uk.

INTERNATIONAL INSTITUTE FOR ENVIRONMENT AND DEVELOPMENT. DISCUSSION PAPER. see *AGRICULTURE*

INTERNATIONAL INSTITUTE FOR ENVIRONMENT AND DEVELOPMENT. DRYLANDS PAPER. see *ENVIRONMENTAL STUDIES*

INTERNATIONAL INSTITUTE FOR ENVIRONMENT AND DEVELOPMENT. PASTORAL LAND TENURE SERIES. see *ENVIRONMENTAL STUDIES*

338.91 IND ISSN 0970-1044
HG1505
INTERNATIONAL JOURNAL OF DEVELOPMENT BANKING. Short title: I J D B. Text in English. 1983. s-a. INR 100, USD 40. bk.rev. bibl. back issues avail. **Description:** Studies the role of finance and related areas in the development of Third World countries from an international perspective.
Published by: Industrial Credit and Investment Corporation of India Limited, 163 Backbay Reclamation, Mumbai, Maharashtra 400 020, India. TEL 22-2022535, FAX 22-2046582, TELEX 11-83062 ICIC IN. Ed. N J Jhaveri. Circ: 500.

338.91 GBR ISSN 1463-371X
➤ **INTERNATIONAL JOURNAL OF PUBLIC - PRIVATE PARTNERSHIPS.** Text in English. 1998. q. GBP 25 to individuals; GBP 55 to institutions (effective 1999 - 2000). adv. bk.rev. back issues avail. **Document type:** *Journal, Academic/Scholarly.* **Description:** Serves academics, executives, practitioners, researchers and policy makers in the national and international fields by providing the professional community with quality information to support each other's work in making a positive contribution to knowledge.
Indexed: BrEdI.
—BLDSC (4542.509150), IE, ingenta.
Published by: Sheffield Hallam University Press, c/o Mrs. Monica Moseley, Pub., Sheffield Hallam University Press, Learning Centre, Sheffield, S Yorks S1 1WB, United Kingdom. TEL 44-114-2254702, FAX 44-114-2254478, m.mosely@shu.ac.uk, http://www.shu.ac.uk/schools/sbs/prc/ppsr/publications.htm. Ed. Luiz Montanheiro TEL 44-114-225-5260. R&P, Adv. contact Mrs. Monica Moseley. Circ: 250 (paid and controlled).

➤ **INTERNATIONAL MONETARY FUND. GLOBAL FINANCIAL STABILITY REPORT.** see *BUSINESS AND ECONOMICS—Banking And Finance*

➤ **INTERNATIONAL MONETARY FUND. WORLD ECONOMIC AND FINANCIAL SURVEYS.** see *BUSINESS AND ECONOMICS—Banking And Finance*

➤ **INTERNATIONAL POLITICAL ECONOMY YEARBOOK.** see *POLITICAL SCIENCE—International Relations*

338.91 327 IND ISSN 0972-8864
INTERNATIONAL RELATIONS IN A GLOBALISING WORLD. Text in English. s-a. GBP 146, USD 256 to institutions; GBP 152, USD 266 combined subscription to institutions print & online eds. (effective 2006). **Document type:** *Journal, Academic/Scholarly.* **Description:** Devoted to the promotion of greater understanding between the developed and the developing nations of the world. Aims to promote mutual understanding by means of dialogue. It will promote the concept of meaningful globalisation in order to minimise the gap between the developed and developing nations and encourage world peace and stability.
Related titles: Online - full text ed.: GBP 145, USD 253 to institutions (effective 2006).
—CCC.
Published by: (Bandranaike Centre for International Studies LKA), Sage Publications India Pvt. Ltd. (Subsidiary of: Sage Publications, Inc.), M-32 Market, Greater Kailash-I, PO Box 4215, New Delhi, 110 048, India. TEL 91-11-6444958, FAX 91-11-6472426, http://www.sagepub.co.uk/journal.aspx?pid=106131, http://www.indiasage.com/, http://www.sagepub.com. Eds. Lakshman Kadirgamar, Tissa Jayatilaka. **Subscr. in Europe, Middle East & Australasia to:** Sage Publications Ltd., 1 Oliver's Yard, 55 City Rd, London EC1 1SP, United Kingdom. TEL 44-20-73740645, FAX 44-20-73748741, subscription@sagepub.co.uk; **Subscr. in the Americas to:** Sage Publications, Inc., 2455 Teller Rd, Thousand Oaks, CA 91320. TEL 805-499-0721, FAX 805-499-0871, journals@sagepub.com.

INTERNATIONAL RESEARCH CENTER FOR ENERGY AND ECONOMIC DEVELOPMENT. ANNUAL CONFERENCE. PROCEEDINGS. see *ENERGY*

INTERNATIONAL RESEARCH CENTER FOR ENERGY AND ECONOMIC DEVELOPMENT. OCCASIONAL PAPERS; Occasional papers nos. 33 and 34. see *ENERGY*

INTERNATIONAL REVIEW OF FINANCE. see *BUSINESS AND ECONOMICS—Banking And Finance*

338.91 USA ISSN 1011-8713
INTERNATIONAL SHARING. Text in English. 1986. 3/yr. **Description:** Covers issues, resources and practical methods for implementing rural development programs in the Third World.
Published by: International Institute of Rural Reconstruction, 475 Riverside Dr, New York, NY 10115. TEL 212-870-2992. Circ: 1,000.

338.91 USA
INTERNATIONAL SURVEY OF BUSINESS EXPECTATIONS. Text in English. q. USD 40 (effective 2000). **Description:** International survey of business executives worldwide, regarding their expectations for sales, profits, prices, inventories, and employment in the upcoming quarter. Results are provided by country.
Related titles: Online - full text ed.: free.
Published by: Dun & Bradstreet, Economic Analysis Department (Subsidiary of: Dun & Bradstreet Corporation), c/o Judy Webb, 3 Sylvan Way, Parsippany, NJ 07054. FAX 973-254-4063, http://www.dnb.com. R&P Judy Webb.

338.91 361 USA
INTERNATIONAL WORKCAMP LISTING (YEAR). Text in English. 1982. a. USD 5. **Document type:** *Directory.* **Description:** Provides description of voluntary, community-based, service workcamps available in the U.S. and throughout Europe.
Published by: Service Civil International - International Voluntary Service, 5474 Walnut Level Rd, Crozet, VA 22932. TEL 804-823-1826, sciivsusa@igc.apc.org, http://wworks.com/~sciivs/. Eds. Claire Andrews, Dave Axtell. Circ: 1,000.

INTERNATIONALE POLITIK UND GESELLSCHAFT. see *POLITICAL SCIENCE—International Relations*

INTERNATIONALE SPECTATOR; maandblad voor internationale politiek. see *LAW—International Law*

INTLEC CD-ROM. see *BUSINESS AND ECONOMICS—Economic Situation And Conditions*

338.91 CHL ISSN 1020-5144
INVERSION EXTRANJERA EN AMERICA LATINA Y EL CARIBE; La Inversion Extranjera en America Latina y el Caribe. Text in Spanish. a. USD 15 (effective 1999). back issues avail.
Indexed: IIS.
Published by: Comision Economica para America Latina y el Caribe/Economic Commission for Latin America and the Caribbean, Ave Dag Hammarskjold 3477, Vitacura, Santiago de Chile, Chile. TEL 56-2-471-2000, FAX 56-2-208-0252, publications@eclac.cl, http://www.eclac.cl. **Subscr. to:** United Nations Publications, Distribution and Sales Section, Palais des Nations, Rm C-116, 8-14 av de la Paix, Geneva 1211, Switzerland; United Nations Publications, Rm DC2-853, United Nations Bldg, 2 United Nations Plaza, New York, NY 10017.

INVESTMENT POLICY REVIEW SERIES. see *BUSINESS AND ECONOMICS—Investments*

338.91 NLD ISSN 1385-7363
INZET MAGAZINE. Text in Dutch. 1992. 5/yr. adv. bk.rev. back issues avail.
Formerly (until 1997): Inzet (0927-5770); Which was formed by the merger of (1981-1992): CON-Tekst (0168-8421); (1988-1992): Veldwerk (0922-2782); (1988-1992): KNV-Kortom (0922-355X); (1979-1992): NIO-Kroniek (0927-5657); (1985-1992): Stand van Zaken (0927-5894)
Published by: Inzet, Keizersgracht 132, Amsterdam, 1015 CW, Netherlands. TEL 31-20-627-3339, FAX 31-20-627-3839, admin@inzet.nl, http://www.inzet.nl. Eds. Mark van Kollenburg, Nies Medema. Circ: 1,750.

338.91 IRL
IRISH AID ANNUAL REPORT; food - human rights - health - water - education. Text in English. a. illus.; stat. **Document type:** *Government, Corporate.* **Description:** Reports on the efforts of Irish Aid (with and without the cooperation of international organizations) to administer development and emergency relief. Discusses water and sanitation, food security, health, education, and human rights in the recipient countries.
Related titles: Online - full text ed.
Published by: Department of Foreign Affairs, Development Co-operation Division, Irish Aid, 76-78 Harcourt St., Dublin, 2, Ireland. TEL 353-1-478-0822, http://www.irlgov.ie/iveagh/foreignaffairs/irishaid/.

IRISH STUDIES IN INTERNATIONAL AFFAIRS. see *POLITICAL SCIENCE—International Relations*

331 CHE ISSN 1020-3877
ISSUES IN DEVELOPMENT. DISCUSSION PAPER. Text in English. 1995. irreg., latest vol.22, 1998. **Document type:** *Monographic series, Academic/Scholarly.*
—BLDSC (4584.225000).
Published by: (International Labour Office), I L O Publications, PO Box 6, Geneva 22, 1211, Switzerland. TEL 41-22-799-6111, FAX 41-22-798-6358, http://www.ilo.org, http://www.ilo.org/publns.

338.91 JPN
J B I C TODAY. (Japan Bank for International Cooperation) Text in English. 1999. irreg. free.
Published by: Japan Bank for International Cooperation, Research Institute for Development and Finance, 4-1 Ohtemachi 1-chome, Chiyoda-ku, Tokyo, 100-8144, Japan. TEL 81-3-52183101, FAX 81-3-52183955.

338.9 JPN
JAPAN BANK FOR INTERNATIONAL COOPERATION. ANNUAL REPORT. Text in English, French, Japanese, Spanish. 1982. a. free.
Formerly (until 1999): Overseas Economic Cooperation Fund. Annual Report/Kaigai Keizai Kyoryoku Kikin Nenpo
Published by: Japan Bank for International Cooperation, Research Institute for Development and Finance, 4-1 Ohtemachi 1-chome, Chiyoda-ku, Tokyo, 100-8144, Japan. TEL 81-3-52183101, FAX 81-3-52183955.

338.91 JPN
JAPAN BANK FOR INTERNATIONAL COOPERATION. RESEARCH PAPER. Text in Japanese. 1999. irreg.
Published by: Japan Bank for International Cooperation, Research Institute for Development and Finance, 4-1 Ohtemachi 1-chome, Chiyoda-ku, Tokyo, 100-8144, Japan. TEL 81-3-52183101, FAX 81-3-52183955.

338.91 JPN ISSN 0914-5427
HC60
JAPAN INTERNATIONAL COOPERATION AGENCY. ANNUAL REPORT. Variant title: J I C A Annual Report. Text in English. 1975. a.
Published by: Japan International Cooperation Agency/Kokusai Kyoryoku Jigyodan, 6-13F, Shinjuku Maynds Tower, 1-1, Yoyogi 2-chome, Shibuya-ku, Tokyo, 151-8558, Japan. TEL 81-3-5352-5311, http://www.jica.go.jp/english/publication/index.html.

338.91 JPN
JAPAN INTERNATIONAL COOPERATION AGENCY. ORGANIZATION AND FUNCTIONS. Text in English, French, Japanese, Spanish. 1975. a. free. **Document type:** *Journal, Academic/Scholarly.*
Published by: Japan International Cooperation Agency/Kokusai Kyoryoku Jigyodan, 6-13F, Shinjuku Maynds Tower, 1-1, Yoyogi 2-chome, Shibuya-ku, Tokyo, 151-8558, Japan. TEL 81-3-5352-5311, matuyama@ific.or.jp, http://www.jica.go.jp/. Circ: 2,000.

▼ new title ➤ refereed ✶ unverified ♦ full entry avail.

338.91 JPN
JAPAN JOURNAL (ENGLISH EDITION). Text in English. 1953; N.S. 2004 (May). m. USD 83 Southeast Asia; USD 83 East Asia (execpt Japan); USD 88 Oceania; USD 94 in Europe; USD 94 in Africa; USD 94 in the Middle East; USD 94 in North America; USD 94 in South America; USD 94 in Central America; SGD 132 in Singapore; SGD 136 in Malaysia; SGD 136 in Brunei Darussalam (effective Sep. 2004). adv. bk.rev. illus. Index. back issues avail.; reprints avail. **Document type:** *Magazine, Consumer.* **Description:** Covers Japanese business and economic trends, politics and culture.
Formerly (until 2004): Look Japan (0456-5339)
Related titles: Online - full text ed.: (from Gale Group); Spanish ed.: Japan Journal (Edicion Espanola). 1990. JPY 10,000; Chinese ed.: Japan Journal (Chinese Edition). 1995. JPY 10,000.
Indexed: BAS, PAIS, RASB.
Published by: The Japan Journal, Ltd., Kosei Bldg. (4F), 2-2-5 Uchikanda, Chiyoda-ku, Tokyo, 101-0047, Japan. TEL 81-3-52982111, FAX 81-3-52982112, contact_tjj@japanjournal.jp, http://www.japanjournal.jp/tjje/. Ed. Kasuya Kazuki. Circ: 75,000.

JEUNESSE DU QUART MONDE/FOURTH WORLD YOUTH JOURNAL. see *CHILDREN AND YOUTH—For*

JOINT VENTURES WITH THE SOVIET REPUBLICS; law and practice. see *LAW—International Law*

338.91 DEU ISSN 0258-2384
HC60
JOURNAL FUER ENTWICKLUNGSPOLITIK. Text and summaries in English, German. 1984. q. EUR 41; EUR 8.80 newsstand/cover (effective 2004). bk.rev. **Document type:** *Journal, Academic/Scholarly.*
Indexed: DIP, GEOBASE, IBR, IBSS, IBZ, PSA, RDA, SOPODA, SSA, SociolAb.
—BLDSC (4979.355000), IE.
Published by: (Mattersburger Kreis fuer Entwicklungspolitik), Brandes und Apsel Verlag GmbH, Scheidswaldstr 33, Frankfurt Am Main, 60389, Germany. TEL 49-69-95730186, FAX 49-69-95730187, brandes-apsel@doodees.de, http://www.brandes-apsel-verlag.de.

338.91 USA ISSN 1551-4080
➤ **JOURNAL OF BUSINESS IN DEVELOPING NATIONS.** Text in English. 1997. q. free. **Document type:** *Academic/Scholarly.* **Description:** Contains reports on research concerning business advances as they relate to the developing world.
Media: Online - full content.
Published by: Golden Gate University, School of Business, 536 Mission St, San Francisco, CA 94105. TEL 415-442-6523, dkent@ggu.edu, http://www.rh.edu/jbdn/, http://internet.ggu/edu/jbdn/. Ed., R&P David H Kent.

382 ISSN 1533-9114
THE JOURNAL OF COMPARATIVE ASIAN DEVELOPMENT. Text in English. 2002 (Spring). s-a. USD 40 domestic to individuals; USD 50 foreign to individuals; USD 90 domestic to institutions; USD 100 foreign to institutions (effective 2002).
Published by: Imprint Publications, 230 E. Ohio St., Ste. 300, Chicago, IL 60611-3201. TEL 312-337-9268, FAX 312-337-9622, imppub@aol.com. Ed. Joseph Y.S. Cheng.

307.1412 USA ISSN 0022-037X
HC59.7 CODEN: JDARB4
➤ **JOURNAL OF DEVELOPING AREAS.** Text in English. 1966. s-a. USD 34 to institutions print or online; USD 47.60 combined subscription to institutions print or online (effective 2004). adv. bk.rev. bibl.; charts; illus. index. back issues avail.; reprints avail. **Document type:** *Journal, Academic/Scholarly.* **Description:** Focuses on development issues affecting Third World countries and less-developed regions of other nations.
Related titles: Online - full text ed.: ISSN 1548-2278 (from O C L C Online Computer Library Center, Inc., Project MUSE, Swets Information Services).
Indexed: ABCPolSci, ABIn, AEA, APEL, ARDT, ASCA, ASD, ASFA, AbAn, AgeL, Agr, AmH&L, BAS, BPI, BPIA, BusI, CurCont, DIP, ESPM, FPA, HAPI, HRA, HistAb, IBR, IBSS, IBZ, ILD, IPSA, IndIslam, JEL, KES, MAB, MEA&I, PAA&I, PAIS, PRA, PerIslam, RASB, RDA, REE&TA, RRTA, RefZh, S&F, SOPODA, SPPI, SSA, SSCI, SUSA, SociolAb, T&II, TriticAb, WAE&RSA.
—BLDSC (4969.200000), IDS, IE, Infotrieve, ingenta.
Address: College of Business, Tennessee State University, 330 10th Ave N, Nashville, TN 37203-3401. TEL 615-963-7152, FAX 615-963-7139, jda@tnstate.edu, http://www.tnstate.edu/oibp/journal.htm, http://www.cob.tnstate.edu/. Ed. Abu Wahid. Circ: 1,264.

338.9 NLD ISSN 0304-3878
HC59.7 CODEN: JDECDF
➤ **JOURNAL OF DEVELOPMENT ECONOMICS.** Text in English. 1974. 6/yr. EUR 135 in Europe to individuals; JPY 18,500 in Japan to individuals; USD 140 elsewhere to individuals; EUR 1,613 in Europe to institutions; JPY 214,500 in Japan to institutions; USD 1,805 elsewhere to institutions (effective 2006). adv. bk.rev. illus. Index. back issues avail.; reprints avail. **Document type:** *Journal, Academic/Scholarly.* **Description:** Publishes papers relating to all aspects of economic development - from immediate policy concerns to structural problems of underdevelopment.
Related titles: Microform ed.: (from PQC); Online - full text ed.: (from EBSCO Publishing, Gale Group, IngentaConnect, ScienceDirect, Swets Information Services).
Indexed: ABIn, APEL, ARDT, ASCA, BAS, BPIA, BusI, CJA, CLOSS, CREJ, CurCont, ESPM, FamI, GEOBASE, H&SSA, IBR, IBSS, IBZ, ILD, Inspec, JEL, MEA&I, PAIS, PCI, PollutAb, PopulInd, RASB, RDA, RRTA, RiceAb, RiskAb, SSCI, SSI, WAE&RSA.
—BLDSC (4969.220000), IDS, IE, Infotrieve, ingenta. **CCC.**
Published by: Elsevier BV, North-Holland (Subsidiary of: Elsevier Science & Technology), Sara Burgerhartstraat 25, Amsterdam, 1055 KV, Netherlands. TEL 31-20-485-3911, FAX 31-20-485-2457, jde@econ.berkeley.edu, nlinfo-f@elsevier.nl, http://www.elsevier.com/locate/devec, http://www.elsevier.nl. Ed. Mark R Rosenzweig. **Subscr. to:** Elsevier BV, PO Box 211, Amsterdam 1000 AE, Netherlands. TEL 31-20-485-3757, FAX 31-20-485-3432, http://www.elsevier.nl.

307.14 GBR ISSN 0022-0388
HC10
➤ **THE JOURNAL OF DEVELOPMENT STUDIES.** Text in English. 1964. 8/yr. GBP 536, USD 810 combined subscription to institutions print & online eds. (effective 2006). adv. bk.rev. abstr. index. back issues avail.; reprint service avail. from PSC. **Document type:** *Journal, Academic/Scholarly.* **Description:** Covers development studies and the concept of development: economic, political, and social.
Related titles: CD-ROM ed.; Microfilm ed.: (from PQC); Online - full text ed.: ISSN 1743-9140. GBP 509, USD 770 to institutions (effective 2006) (from EBSCO Publishing, Florida Center for Library Automation, Gale Group, IngentaConnect, Northern Light Technology, Inc., O C L C Online Computer Library Center, Inc., ProQuest Information & Learning, Swets Information Services).
Indexed: ABCPolSci, ABIn, APEL, ARDT, ASCA, ASD, ASSIA, AmH&L, BAS, BPIA, BrHumI, BusI, CREJ, CurCont, DIP, EI, ERA, GEOBASE, HRA, HistAb, I&DA, IBR, IBSS, IBZ, ILD, IPSA, IndIslam, JEL, KES, MEA&I, PAIS, PCI, PRA, PSA, RASB, RDA, RRTA, RefZh, RiceAb, SOPODA, SPAA, SSA, SSCI, SSI, SUSA, SWA, SociolAb, T&II, WAE&RSA, WBA, WTA, WorkRelAb.
—BLDSC (4969.250000), IDS, IE, Infotrieve, ingenta. **CCC.**
Published by: Routledge (Subsidiary of: Taylor & Francis Group), 4 Park Sq, Milton Park, Abingdon, Oxon OX14 4RN, United Kingdom. TEL 44-1235-828600, FAX 44-1235-829000, info@routledge.co.uk, http://www.tandf.co.uk/journals/titles/00220388.asp, http://www.routledge.co.uk. Eds. Chris Milner, Howard White, John Harriss. adv.: B&W page GBP 195, B&W page USD 285; trim 110 x 178.

➤ **JOURNAL OF EASTERN AFRICAN RESEARCH & DEVELOPMENT.** see *SOCIAL SCIENCES: COMPREHENSIVE WORKS*

331 KOR ISSN 0254-8372
JOURNAL OF ECONOMIC DEVELOPMENT. Text in English. 1976. s-a. USD 20 to individuals; USD 40 to institutions (effective 2005). **Document type:** *Journal, Academic/Scholarly.* **Description:** Promotes research in international economic development, growth, and trade and finance. Explores analysis of economic development throughout the world. Includes theoretical and empirical papers.
Related titles: Online - full text ed.
Indexed: JEL.
—BLDSC (4972.830000), IE, ingenta.
Published by: Chung-Ang University, Economic Research Institute, Heukseok-Dong, Dongjak-Ku, Seoul, 156-756, Korea, S. TEL 82-2-8206356, FAX 82-2-8129718, kgsuic21@ms.cau.ac.kr, http://jed.econ.cau.ac.kr.

JOURNAL OF ECONOMIC INTEGRATION. see *BUSINESS AND ECONOMICS*

JOURNAL OF ENERGY AND DEVELOPMENT. see *ENERGY*

JOURNAL OF HIMALAYAN STUDIES AND REGIONAL DEVELOPMENT. see *ENVIRONMENTAL STUDIES*

JOURNAL OF INTERNATIONAL COMMUNICATION. see *SOCIOLOGY*

338.91 GBR ISSN 0954-1748
HC59.72.E44 CODEN: JINDEV
➤ **JOURNAL OF INTERNATIONAL DEVELOPMENT.** Text in English. 1981. 8/yr. USD 1,125 to institutions; USD 1,238 combined subscription to institutions print & online eds. (effective 2006). adv. bk.rev. back issues avail.; reprint service avail. from PSC. **Document type:** *Journal, Academic/Scholarly.* **Description:** Presents scholarly research articles on international development from the broad field of economic, political, and social development.
Formerly (until 1989): Manchester Papers on Development (0260-8235)
Related titles: Microform ed.: (from PQC); Online - full text ed.: ISSN 1099-1328. 1996. USD 1,125 to institutions (effective 2006) (from EBSCO Publishing, ProQuest Information & Learning, Swets Information Services, Wiley InterScience).
Indexed: ABIn, AEA, APEL, ARDT, AbHyg, AgBio, BAS, DIP, ERA, ETA, FPA, ForAb, GEOBASE, HortAb, I&DA, IBR, IBSS, IBZ, ILD, IndVet, JEL, MEA, MaizeAb, NutrAb, PAIS, PBA, PCI, PGegResA, PHN&I, PSA, RDA, RHEA, RRTA, RiceAb, S&F, SEA, SENA, SOMA, SOPODA, SSA, SWA, SeedAb, SociolAb, TDB, TEA, TriticAb, VetBull, WAE&RSA.
—BLDSC (5007.635000), GNLM, IE, Infotrieve, ingenta. **CCC.**
Published by: (Development Studies Association), John Wiley & Sons Ltd. (Subsidiary of: John Wiley & Sons, Inc.), The Atrium, Southern Gate, Chichester, West Sussex PO19 8SQ, United Kingdom. TEL 44-1243-779777, FAX 44-1243-775878, customer@wiley.co.uk, http://www.interscience.com/journal/jid, http://www.wiley.co.uk. Eds. Dr. Hazel Johnson, Dr. Paul Mosley. adv.: B&W page GBP 650, color page GBP 1,550; trim 165 x 248. Circ: 700. **Subscr. in the Americas to:** John Wiley & Sons, Inc., 111 River St, Hoboken, NJ 07030-5774. TEL 201-748-6645, FAX 201-748-6088, subinfo@wiley.com.

338.91 GBR ISSN 0963-8199
HF1371
➤ **THE JOURNAL OF INTERNATIONAL TRADE AND ECONOMIC DEVELOPMENT;** an international and comparative review. Short title: J I T E D. Text in English. 1992. q. GBP 489, USD 807 combined subscription to institutions print & online eds. (effective 2006). adv. reprint service avail. from PSC. **Document type:** *Journal, Academic/Scholarly.* **Description:** Covers international economics, economic development, and the interface between trade and development.
Related titles: Online - full text ed.: ISSN 1469-9559. GBP 465, USD 767 to institutions (effective 2006) (from EBSCO Publishing, Gale Group, IngentaConnect, O C L C Online Computer Library Center, Inc., Swets Information Services).
Indexed: ABIn, APEL, BAS, GEOBASE, IBR, IBSS, IBZ, JEL, RDA, WAE&RSA.
—BLDSC (5007.686900), IE, Infotrieve, ingenta. **CCC.**
Published by: Routledge (Subsidiary of: Taylor & Francis Group), 4 Park Square, Milton Park, Abingdon, Oxon OX14 4RN, United Kingdom. TEL 44-1235-828600, FAX 44-1235-829000, info@routledge.co.uk, info@routledge-ny.com, http://www.tandf.co.uk/journals/routledge/09638199.html. Eds. Bharat R Hazari, David E A Giles, Pasquale M Sgro. R&P Sally Sweet. adv.: page GBP 150; trim 190 x 115. Circ: 500. **Subscr. to:** Taylor & Francis Ltd, Journals Customer Service, Rankine Rd, Basingstoke, Hants RG24 8PR, United Kingdom. TEL 44-1256-813000, FAX 44-1256-330245, enquiry@tandf.co.uk.

➤ **THE JOURNAL OF PEASANT STUDIES.** see *SOCIOLOGY*

338.91 USA ISSN 1070-521X
JOURNAL OF PUBLIC AND INTERNATIONAL AFFAIRS (PRINCETON). Text in English. 1990. a. **Document type:** *Journal, Academic/Scholarly.*
Indexed: IPSA, JEL, PAIS, SSCI.
—BLDSC (5043.490800), IE.
Published by: (Association of Professional Schools in International Affairs), Princeton University, Woodrow Wilson School of Public and International Affairs, Robertson Hall, Princeton, NJ 08544-1013. TEL 609-258-4800, jpia@princeton.edu, wwswww@princeton.edu, http://www.princeton.edu/~jpia/, http://www.wws.princeton.edu. Eds. Barbara Feinstein, Jordan Tama.

338.91 IND ISSN 0972-5792
➤ **JOURNAL OF SOCIAL AND ECONOMIC DEVELOPMENT.** Text in English. 1998. s-a. INR 120 SAARC to individuals; USD 25 elsewhere to individuals; INR 200 SAARC to institutions; USD 50 elsewhere to institutions (effective 2004). **Document type:** *Journal, Academic/Scholarly.*
Indexed: JEL, SSCI.
Published by: Institute for Social and Economic Change, Prof. VKRV Rao Ave., Nagarabhavi PO, Bangalore, 560 072, India. TEL 91-80-3215468, FAX 91-80-3217008, mascanil@isec.ac.in, http://www.isec.ac.in/journal.htm. Ed. Gopal K. Kadekodi. Circ: 150.

338.91 GBR ISSN 0973-1741
▼ **JOURNAL OF SOUTH ASIAN DEVELOPMENT.** Text in English. forthcoming 2006. s-a. GBP 125, USD 219 to institutions; GBP 130, USD 228 combined subscription to institutions print & online eds. (effective 2006). **Document type:** *Journal, Academic/Scholarly.*
Related titles: Online - full text ed.: ISSN 0973-1733. forthcoming. GBP 124, USD 217 to institutions (effective 2006).

Published by: Sage Publications Ltd. (Subsidiary of: Sage Publications, Inc.), 1 Oliver's Yard, 55 City Rd, London, EC1 1SP, United Kingdom. TEL 44-20-73248500, FAX 44-20-73248600, info@sagepub.co.uk, http://www.sagepub.co.uk/journal.aspx?pid=107339. **Subscr. to:** Sage Publications, Inc., 2455 Teller Rd, Thousand Oaks, CA 91320. TEL 805-499-0721, FAX 805-499-0871, journals@sagepub.com.

338.91 DEU
JOURNALISTENHANDBUCH ENTWICKLUNGSPOLITIK. Text in German. 1974. a. **Document type:** *Government.*
Published by: Bundesministerium fuer Wirtschaftliche Zusammenarbeit und Entwicklung, Friedrich-Ebert-Allee 114-116, Bonn, 53113, Germany.

338.91 NLD ISSN 1380-1643
G905
K I T NEWSLETTER. Text in English. 1991. s-a. illus. **Document type:** *Newsletter.* **Description:** Discusses the activities and projects of the KIT in the areas of agriculture, health, and culture.
Published by: (Koninklijk Instituut voor de Tropen/Royal Tropical Institute), K I T Publishers, Mauritskade 63, PO Box 95001, Amsterdam, 1090 HA, Netherlands. TEL 31-20-568-8272, FAX 31-20-568-8286, pr@kit.nl, http://www.kit.nl. Pub. Ron Smit.

338.91 JPN ISSN 1345-238X
KAIHATSU KIN'YU KENKYUJOHO/RESEARCH INSTITUTE FOR DEVELOPMENT AND FINANCE. JOURNAL. Text in Japanese. 1999. q.
Formed by the merger of (1975-1999): Kaigai Toshi Kenkyushoho (0914-546X); (1994-1999): Kaihatsu Enjo Kenkyu (1340-7198); Which was formerly (1964-1994): Kikin Chosa Kiho (0910-9668)
Published by: Japan Bank for International Cooperation, Research Institute for Development and Finance, 4-1 Ohtemachi 1-chome, Chiyoda-ku, Tokyo, 100-8144, Japan. TEL 81-3-52183101, FAX 81-3-52183955.

KAIHATSU RONSHU/JOURNAL OF DEVELOPMENT POLICY STUDIES. see *BUSINESS AND ECONOMICS—Economic Situation And Conditions*

646.70099305 NZL ISSN 1173-8340
KOKIRI PAETAE. Text in English, Maori. 1996. bi-m. **Document type:** *Newsletter.*
Published by: New Zealand. Te Puni Kokiri/New Zealand. Ministry of Maori Development, PO Box 3943, Wellington, New Zealand. TEL 64-6-9226000, FAX 64-6-9226299, http://www.tpk.govt.nz/publications/paetae/default.htm.

338.91 IND
KRISHI SAMEEKSHA. Text in Hindi. m. INR 100, USD 36. **Document type:** *Government.*
Published by: Ministry of Agriculture, Directorate of Economics and Statistics, A-2E-3 Kasturba Gandhi Marg Barracks, New Delhi, 110 001, India.

L A W G LETTER. see *POLITICAL SCIENCE—International Relations*

304.6 USA ISSN 0253-4517
L S M S WORKING PAPER. (Living Standards Measurement Study) Text in English. 1980. irreg., latest vol.135. price varies. back issues avail. **Document type:** *Monographic series.* **Description:** Covers demographic and socioeconomic issues in the context of World Bank international monetary aid.
Indexed: RDA.
—BLDSC (5283.240000), IE, ingenta. **CCC.**
Published by: World Bank Group, 1818 H St, NW, Washington, DC 20433. TEL 703-661-1580, FAX 703-661-1501, 202-522-1153, lsms@worldbank.org, books@worldbank.org, http://www.worldbank.org/lsms/research/wp/wp_title.html.

338.91 331 CAN ISSN 0706-1706
➤ **LABOUR, CAPITAL AND SOCIETY/TRAVAIL, CAPITAL ET SOCIETE**; a journal on the Third World. Text in English, French. 1968. s-a., latest vol.34, 2001. CND 30 to individuals; CND 40 to institutions; CND 20 in developing nations (effective 2005). adv. bk.rev. abstr. back issues avail. **Document type:** *Journal, Academic/Scholarly.*
Former titles (until vol.12, 1979): Manpower and Unemployment Research (0702-7605); (until 1976): Manpower and Unemployment Research in Africa. Newsletter (0025-2417)
Related titles: Online - full text ed.: (from EBSCO Publishing, ProQuest Information & Learning, SoftLine Information).
Indexed: ARDT, ASD, AltPI, CBCARef, EI, GEOBASE, HRA, IBSS, ILD, IndIslam, LeftInd, PAIS, PRA, PSA, RASB, RDA, REE&TA, RRTA, SOPODA, SSA, SSCI, SSI, SociolAb, WAE&RSA.
—BLDSC (5142.065000), IE, Infotrieve, ingenta. **CCC.**
Published by: McGill University, Centre for Developing-Area Studies, 3715 Peel St, Montreal, PQ H3A 1X1, Canada. TEL 514-398-3507, FAX 514-398-8432, pub.cdas@mcgill.ca, adm.cdas@mcgill.ca, http://www.mcgill.ca/cdas/labour, http://www.arts.mcgill.ca. Ed., R&P Rosalind Boyd. Circ: 800.

338.91 DEU ISSN 0174-6324
LATEINAMERIKA NACHRICHTEN. Text in German. 1973. m. adv. bk.rev. index. back issues avail. **Document type:** *Journal, Academic/Scholarly.*
Indexed: HAPI, I&DA, IBR, IBZ, RASB, RDA.
Published by: Lateinamerika Nachrichten GbR, Gneisenaustr 2, Berlin, 10961, Germany. TEL 49-30-6946100, FAX 49-30-6926590, ln@inn.de, http://www.lateinamerikanachrichten.de/?/aktuell/index.html. Circ: 2,500.

LEAST DEVELOPED COUNTRIES REPORT. see *BUSINESS AND ECONOMICS—International Commerce*

338.9 PAK
LECTURES IN DEVELOPMENT ECONOMICS. Text in English. 1982. irreg., latest vol.10, 1999. price varies. bibl.; charts; stat. back issues avail. **Document type:** *Academic/Scholarly.*
Supersedes (1970-1982): Readings in Development Economics (0557-8280)
Published by: Pakistan Institute of Development Economics, P O Box 1091, Islamabad, 44000, Pakistan. TEL 92-51-9206610, FAX 92-51-9210886, pide@isb.paknet.com.pk, pide@appollo.net.pk, http://www.pide.org.pk. Ed. A R Kemal. Circ: 1,000.

LETTRE DE LA FRANCOPHONIE. see *BUSINESS AND ECONOMICS—Cooperatives*

LIBRARY OF PEASANT STUDIES. see *SOCIOLOGY*

338.91 ETH ISSN 0255-5182
LIST OF E C A DOCUMENTS ISSUED/LISTE DES DOCUMENTS PUBLIES PAR LA C E A. Text in English. q. free.
Published by: (Documents & Publishing Services Unit), United Nations, Economic Commission for Africa/Commission Economique pour l'Afrique, PO Box 3001, Addis Ababa, Ethiopia.

338.91 GBR
LONDON SCHOOL OF ECONOMICS AND POLITICAL SCIENCE. DEVELOPMENT STUDIES INSTITUTE. WORKING PAPERS. Text in English. irreg., latest no.5. GBP 5 newsstand/cover (effective 2002). back issues avail. **Document type:** *Monographic series, Academic/Scholarly.*
Published by: London School of Economics and Politcal Science, Development Studies Institute, Houghton St, London, WC2A 2AE, United Kingdom. TEL 44-20-79557425, FAX 44-20-79556844, http://www.lse.ac.uk/.

M A P NEWS. see *SOCIAL SERVICES AND WELFARE*

338.91 341 BEL
HC59.7
MAGAZINE OF A C P - E U DEVELOPMENT CO-OPERATION. Text in English. 1975. bi-m. free. **Document type:** *Newsletter.* **Description:** Profiles a country in Africa, the Caribbean, Oceania and the European Union and analyzes its social, economic, and political issues.
Former titles (until 2000): The Courier. Africa - Caribbean - Pacific - European Union (1606-2000); (until 1993): The Courier. Africa - Caribbean - Pacific - European Communities (1013-7335)
Related titles: French ed.: Le Courrier: Afrique - Caraibes - Pacifique - Union Europeenne. ISSN 1026-2350. 1963.
Indexed: ASFA, AgBio, ESPM, FPA, IIS, PAIS, RDA, RRTA, SPPI, WAE&RSA.
—BLDSC (3482.563500), IE, ingenta.
Published by: European Commission, Directorate General for Development, 200 Rue de la Loi, Brussels, 1049, Belgium. **Dist. in the U.S. by:** Bernan Associates.

338.91 FRA
MARINE SCIENCE COUNTRY PROFILES. Text in English. irreg. price varies. **Description:** Provides an overview of the infrastructure in terms of facilities, training and education, which may be required to support proposed programs allocating funds to marine science programs.
Published by: (Western Indian Ocean Marine Science Association TZA, Intergovernmental Oceanographic Commission USA), UNESCO Publishing, 7 place de Fontenoy, Paris, 75352, France. FAX 33-1-45685737, http://www.unesco.org/publishing.

338.91 361.75 NLD ISSN 1568-3478
MENSEN IN NOOD NIEUWS. Text in Dutch. bi-m. contribution. bk.rev. **Document type:** *Newsletter, Consumer.* **Description:** Covers Dutch aid to Third World countries and Eastern Europe. Includes lists of projects and expenditures in different countries.
Formerly (until 2000): Clamavi (0166-3488)
Published by: Stichting Mensen in Nood - Cordaid, Postbus 16436, Den Haag, 2500 BK, Netherlands. TEL 31-70-3136200, FAX 31-70-3136201, info@menseninnood.nl. Ed. Gerda Kranendonk. Circ: 250,000 (controlled).

338.2 GBR ISSN 1404-1049
HF1051 CODEN: MERRFV
➤ **MINERALS & ENERGY**; raw materials report. Text in English. 1981. q. GBP 151, USD 249 combined subscription to institutions print & online eds. (effective 2006). adv. bk.rev. illus.; bibl.; charts; stat. index. back issues avail.; reprint service avail. from PQC,PSC. **Document type:** *Journal, Academic/Scholarly.* **Description:** Covers the development of the mining and energy industries worldwide.
Formerly (until 1999): Journal of Mineral Policy, Business and Environment. Raw Materials Report (0349-6287)
Related titles: CD-ROM ed.; Microform ed.: (from PQC); Online - full text ed.: ISSN 1651-2286. GBP 143, USD 237 to institutions (effective 2006) (from EBSCO Publishing, Gale Group, IngentaConnect, O C L C Online Computer Library Center, Inc., Swets Information Services).
Indexed: AESIS, AltPI, BrCerAb, C&ISA, CerAb, CivEngAb, CorrAb, E&CAJ, EMA, EnvAb, GEOBASE, IAA, IMMAb, M&TEA, MBF, METADEX, PAIS, PerIslam, RASB, RefZh, SolStAb, WAA.
—BLDSC (5790.497000), IE, Infotrieve, ingenta, Linda Hall. **CCC.**
Published by: (Raavarugruppen Ekonomisk Foerening/Raw Materials Group, Sweden SWE), Routledge (Subsidiary of: Taylor & Francis Group), 4 Park Sq, Milton Park, Abingdon, Oxon OX14 4RN, United Kingdom. TEL 44-1235-828600, FAX 44-1235-829000, info@routledge.co.uk, http://www.tandf.co.uk/journals/titles/14041049.asp, http://www.routledge.co.uk. Ed. Dr. Mats Nilsson TEL 46-16-5442140. Circ: 500. **Subscr. to:** Taylor & Francis Ltd, Journals Customer Service, Rankine Rd, Basingstoke, Hants RG24 8PR, United Kingdom. TEL 44-1256-813000, FAX 44-1256-330245, enquiry@tandf.co.uk. **Co-sponsor:** University of Dundee, Centre for Mineral and Petroleum Law and Policy.

338.91 DEU ISSN 0942-2269
MISEREOR AKTUELL. Text in German. 1968. q. bk.rev.
Published by: (Bischoefliches Hilfswerk Misereor e.V.), Misereor Vertriebsgesellschaft mbH, Mozartstr 9, Aachen, 52064, Germany. TEL 49-241-4420, FAX 49-241-442524, postmaster@misereor.de, http://www.misereor.de. Ed. Walter Schaefer. Circ: 11,000.

MONDAY DEVELOPMENTS. see *SOCIAL SERVICES AND WELFARE*

338.9 BEL ISSN 0302-3052
HD83
MONDES EN DEVELOPPEMENT/SPREADING WORLDS. Text in English, French, Spanish. 1973. q. EUR 145 (effective 2004). adv. bk.rev. index. back issues avail.; reprints avail. **Document type:** *Academic/Scholarly.*
Indexed: ARDT, BAS, CurCont, GEOBASE, IBSS, IPSA, IndIslam, PAIS, RRTA, WAE&RSA.
—BLDSC (5908.055000), CISTI, IE, Infotrieve, ingenta.
Published by: (Institut de Sciences Mathematiques et Economiques Appliquees FRA), I.S.M.E.A. - CECOEDUC, Av des Naiades 11, Brussels, 1170, Belgium. TEL 32-2-6758563, FAX 32-2-6758563. Eds. Andre Philippart, Rene Gendarme. Circ: 800. **Subscr. to:** Acces S.P.R.L., Fond Jean-Paques 4, Louvain-la-Neuve 1348, Belgium. acces+cde@deboeck.be.

615.1 GBR ISSN 1469-3828
MULTINATIONAL PHARMACEUTICAL COMPANIES. Text in English. 1999. a. GBP 345, USD 550 (effective 2001). **Description:** Research and marketing directory of worldwide professionals in the pharmaceutical field.
Related titles: CD-ROM ed.: GBP 580, USD 930 (effective 2001).
Published by: Business Monitor International Ltd., Commercial Intelligence Service, 179 Queen Victoria St, London, EC4V 4DU, United Kingdom. TEL 44-20-7248-0468, FAX 44-20-7248-0467, http://www.businessmonitor.com.

338.91 622 NAM ISSN 1012-2818
NAMIBIA BRIEF. Text in English. 1991 (no.13). m. ZAR 6 per issue. adv. charts; illus. **Description:** Covers economic, social, and political issues relating to development in independent Namibia, including government policy, education and training projects, mining, and famine relief.
Published by: Namibia Foundation, PO Box 2123, Windhoek, Namibia. TEL 061-37250, FAX 061-37251. Ed. Cathy Blatt.

338.91 NAM ISSN 0963-8229
HC940.A1
NAMIBIA DEVELOPMENT BRIEFING; the voice of the Namibian non-governmental forum. Text in English. 1991. bi-m. film rev. back issues avail. **Description:** Informs the international community of development issues facing Namibia.
Published by: Bricks Community Project, 4 Katatura Community Centre, PO Box 20642, Windhoek, 9000, Namibia. TEL 264-61-62726, FAX 264-61-63510. Circ: 1,000.

NATIONAL HUMAN DEVELOPMENT REPORTS. see *SOCIAL SCIENCES: COMPREHENSIVE WORKS*

338.91 GBR ISSN 1356-9228
NATURAL RESOURCE PERSPECTIVES. Text in English. 1994. 5/yr. back issues avail. **Document type:** *Academic/Scholarly.* **Description:** Presents accessible information on development issues.
Related titles: Online - full text ed.

Indexed: AgBio, AgrForAb, DSA, FPA, ForAb, HortAb, I&DA, PBA, PGegResA, PHN&I, RDA, RRTA, S&F, SeedAb, TDB, WAE&RSA.
—CISTI.
Published by: Overseas Development Institute, 111 Westminster Bridge Rd, London, SE1 7JD, United Kingdom. TEL 44-171-393-1600, FAX 44-171-393-1699, rpeg@odi.org.uk, http://www.oneworld.org/odi/rpeg. Ed. John Farrington. Circ: 6,000 (controlled).

327 USA
NEAR EAST FOUNDATION. ANNUAL REPORT. Text in English. 1930. a. **Document type:** *Corporate.*
Published by: Near East Foundation, 90 Broad St., Rm. 1506, New York, NY 10004-2291. TEL 212-867-0064, FAX 212-867-0169, TELEX 226000 ETLX-UR-NEF. Circ: 5,000.

NETHERLANDS INVESTMENT BANK FOR DEVELOPING COUNTRIES. REPORT/NEDERLANDSE INVESTERINGSBANK VOOR ONTWIKKELINGSLANDEN. VERSLAG. see *BUSINESS AND ECONOMICS—Banking And Finance*

NETZ. see *SOCIAL SERVICES AND WELFARE*

338 GBR ISSN 0142-9345
HC511
NEW AFRICAN. Text in English. 1966. 11/yr. GBP 40 domestic; EUR 80 in Europe eurozone; USD 90 in United States; GBP 55 elsewhere (effective 2006). adv. bk.rev. charts; illus. 64 p./no. 3 cols./p.; back issues avail.; reprint service avail. from PQC. **Document type:** *Consumer.* **Description:** Contains a balanced mix of political reporting and commentary, economic and financial analysis, and features on social and cultural affairs.
Former titles (until 1978): New African Development (0140-833X); (until 1977): African Development (0001-9984)
Related titles: Microfilm ed.: (from PQC); Online - full text ed.: (from Chadwyck-Healey Inc., EBSCO Publishing, Florida Center for Library Automation, Gale Group, Northern Light Technology, Inc., ProQuest Information & Learning).
Indexed: IIBP, KES, MEA&I, PAIS, PCI, PROMT, RASB, RRTA, WAE&RSA.
—BLDSC (6081.750500), IE, Infotrieve, ingenta. **CCC.**
Published by: I C Publications Ltd., 7 Coldbath Sq, London, EC1R 4LQ, United Kingdom. TEL 44-20-7713-7711, FAX 44-20-7713-7898, icpubs@africasia.com, http://www.africasia.com/newafrican/index.php. Ed. Baffour Ankomah. Pub. Afif Ben Yedder. R&P Carole Jones. Adv. contact Khalid Bazid. Circ: 28,853. **Subscr. to:** Tower House, Tower House, Sovereign Park, Market Harborough, Leics LE16 9EF, United Kingdom. TEL 44-1858-438792, FAX 44-1858-461739, subscriptions@africasia.com.

330.9 CHE
NEW HORIZONS. Text in English, Spanish. 2/yr. bk.rev. 24 p./no. 3 cols./p.; **Document type:** *Newsletter, Consumer.* **Description:** Provides general information concerning internal development and assistance for an ecumenical micro-credit institution.
Former titles (until 1992): Horizons; W C C Horizons
Related titles: Online - full text ed.
Published by: Ecumenical Church Loan Fund, 150 route de Ferney, PO Box 2100, Geneva 2, 1211, Switzerland. TEL 41-22-7916312, FAX 41-22-7102005, TELEX 415730-OIK-CH, eclof@eclof.org, http://www.eclof.org. R&P Muhungi Kanyoro. Circ: 1,500.

338.91 NZL ISSN 1172-1901
NEW ZEALAND OFFICIAL DEVELOPMENT ASSISTANCE PROGRAMME. ANNUAL REVIEW. Text in English. 1991. a. **Document type:** *Government.*
Published by: (New Zealand. Development Cooperation Division), Ministry of Foreign Affairs and Trade, c/o Publication Officer, Private Bag 18-901, Wellington, New Zealand. TEL 64-4-4948500, FAX 64-4-4948514.

354.93068 NZL ISSN 1171-6673
NEW ZEALAND. TE PUNI KOKIRI. NEWSLETTER. Text in English, Maori. 1992. irreg. **Document type:** *Newsletter.*
Published by: New Zealand. Te Puni Kokiri/New Zealand. Ministry of Maori Development, PO Box 3943, Wellington, New Zealand. TEL 64-6-9226000, FAX 64-6-9226299, http://www.tpk.govt.nz.

338.91 USA
NICARAGUA MONITOR. Text mainly in English; Text occasionally in Spanish; Text in English. 1986. m. USD 20 (effective 2005). adv. bk.rev.; film rev. back issues avail. **Document type:** *Newsletter, Consumer.* **Description:** News and analysis of the effects of U.S. policy on the people of Nicaragua. Seeks to establish ties of peace and friendship between the people of the U.S. and Nicaragua.
Formerly: Nicaragua Network News
Published by: Nicaragua Network, 1247 E St, S E, Washington, DC 20003-2221. TEL 202-544-9355, FAX 202-544-9359, nizanet@igc.org. Ed. Katherine Hoyt. Circ: 5,000 (paid and controlled).

NIGERIAN FORUM. see *POLITICAL SCIENCE—International Relations*

338.91 SWE ISSN 1104-8417
➤ **NORDISKA AFRIKAINSTITUTET. DISCUSSION PAPERS.** Text in English. 1988. irreg., latest vol.23, 2003. SEK 100 (effective 2003). back issues avail.; reprints avail. **Document type:** *Monographic series, Academic/Scholarly.*
Formerly (until 1990): Scandinavian Institute of African Studies - Discussion Paper (1100-2131)
Related titles: Online - full text ed.
Indexed: RDA, WAE&RSA.
Published by: Nordiska Afrikainstitutet/Nordic Africa Institute, PO Box 1703, Uppsala, 75147, Sweden. TEL 46-18-562200, FAX 46-18-562290, orders@nai.uu.se, nai@nai.uu.se, http://www.nai.uu.se. Circ: 1,500.

338.91 DNK ISSN 0902-9206
NOTAT C U F. Variant title: C U F Notat. Text in Danish. 1987. irreg. **Document type:** *Monographic series.* **Description:** Explores Third World socio-economic development issues.
Published by: Centre for Development Research, Gammel Kongevej 5, Copenhagen V, 1610, Denmark. TEL 45-33-25-12-00, FAX 45-33-25-81-10, cdr@cdr.dk. Circ: 500.

NOTICEN; Central American & Caribbean political and economic affairs, including Cuba. see *BUSINESS AND ECONOMICS—Economic Situation And Conditions*

330.91724 DNK ISSN 0029-6775
AP42
DEN NY VERDEN. Text in Danish. 1964. q. DKK 195 (effective 1997). **Description:** Explores social science development in the Third World.
Published by: Centre for Development Research, Gammel Kongevej 5, Copenhagen V, 1610, Denmark. TEL 45-33-25-12-00, FAX 45-33-25-81-10, cdr@cdr.dk. Circ: 1,000.

338.91 JPN
O D A LOAN REPORT. Text in English. 2000. a. free.
Published by: Japan Bank for International Cooperation, Research Institute for Development and Finance, 4-1 Ohtemachi 1-chome, Chiyoda-ku, Tokyo, 100-8144, Japan. TEL 81-3-52183101, FAX 81-3-52183955.

338.91 GBR ISSN 1465-2617
➤ **O D I POVERTY BRIEFINGS.** Text in English. 1998. irreg. looseleaf. free (effective 2005). back issues avail. **Document type:** *Academic/Scholarly.* **Description:** Summarizes contemporary debate, insights and experience on ways of more effectively reaching and benefiting the poor. Covers new thinking on and recent experience of poverty reduction measures and emerging approaches to poverty alleviation by donor agencies as well as natural resource, finance and trade aspects.
—BLDSC (6571.560000). **CCC.**
Published by: Overseas Development Institute, 111 Westminster Bridge Rd, London, SE1 7JD, United Kingdom. TEL 44-20-79220300, FAX 44-20-79220399, publications@odi.org.uk, http://www.odi.org.uk/publications/briefing/poverty/index..html. Ed. John Healey. R&P Peter Gee.

➤ **O D T U GELISME DERGISI/M E T U STUDIES IN DEVELOPMENT.** (Orta Dogu Teknik Universitesi) see *BUSINESS AND ECONOMICS—Economic Systems And Theories, Economic History*

➤ **O E C D CATALOGUE OF PUBLICATIONS.** see *BIBLIOGRAPHIES*

➤ **O E C D CODE OF LIBERALIZATION OF CAPITAL MOVEMENTS/O C D E CODE DE LA LIBERATION DES MOUVEMENTS DE CAPITAUX.** see *BUSINESS AND ECONOMICS—Banking And Finance*

338.91 FRA ISSN 1563-4329
O E C D DEVELOPMENT CENTRE SEMINARS. Text in French. irreg., latest 2003. price varies. **Document type:** *Monographic series.*
Related titles: French ed.: Seminaires du Centre de Developpement. ISSN 1563-4337.
Published by: Organization for Economic Cooperation and Development, 2 Rue Andre Pascal, Paris, 75775 Cedex 16, France. TEL 33-1-45248200, FAX 33-1-45248500, http://www.oecd.org. **U.S. orders to:** O E C D Turpin North America, PO Box 194, Downingtown, PA 19335-0194. TEL 610-524-5361, 800-456-6323, FAX 610-524-5417, bookscustomer@turpinna.com.

338.91 FRA ISSN 1563-4302
O E C D DEVELOPMENT CENTRE STUDIES. (Some issues avail. in multiple langauges) Text in English. irreg. price varies. **Document type:** *Monographic series.* **Description:** Covers the politic, social and historical aspects of world economic studies, including poverty, trade, privatization, corporate governance, education, and more.
Related titles: French ed.: Etudes du Centre de Developpement. ISSN 1563-4310.
Indexed: ARDT.
—ingenta.
Published by: Organization for Economic Cooperation and Development, 2 Rue Andre Pascal, Paris, 75775 Cedex 16, France. TEL 33-1-45248200, FAX 33-1-45248500, http://www.oecd.org. **Dist. in N. America by:** O E C D Turpin North America, PO Box 194, Downingtown, PA 19335-0194. TEL 610-524-5361, 800-456-6323, FAX 610-524-5417, bookscustomer@turpinna.com.

338.9 FRA ISSN 0474-5663
O E C D DEVELOPMENT CO-OPERATION; efforts and policies of the members of the Development Assistance Committee. Text in English. a.
Related titles: Online - full text ed.; French ed.
Indexed: IIS.
—**CCC.**
Published by: Organization for Economic Cooperation and Development, 2 Rue Andre Pascal, Paris, 75775 Cedex 16, France. TEL 33-1-45248200, FAX 33-1-45248500, http://www.oecd.org.

338.91 GBR ISSN 1351-8569
OASIS (LONDON, 1986). Text in English. 1986. s-a. free. **Document type:** *Newsletter.* **Description:** Reports on technology for drinking water supply and sanitation projects funded by WaterAid throughout Africa and Asia.
Published by: WaterAid, Wateraid, Prince Consort House, 27-29, Albert Embankment, London, SE1 7UB, United Kingdom. TEL 44-171-793-4500, FAX 44-171-793-4545, wateraid@compuserve.com, http://www.wateraid.org.uk. Ed., R&P Michelle Bell. Circ: 85,000 (controlled).

338.91 AUT
OESTERREICHISCHE ENTWICKLUNGSPOLITIK; Berichte, Analysen, Informationen. Text in German. 1997. a. **Document type:** *Journal, Government.*
Published by: Oesterreichische Forschungsstiftung fuer Entwicklungshilfe/Austrian Foundation for Development Research, Berggasse 7, Vienna, W 1090, Austria. TEL 43-1-3174010, FAX 43-1-3174015, office@oefse.at, http://www.oefse.at/publikationen/oeepol.htm.

OESTERREICHISCHE FORSCHUNGSSTIFTUNG FUER ENTWICKLUNGSHILFE. ANNOTIERTE BIBLIOGRAPHIE; ausgewaehlte neue Literatur zur Entwicklungspolitik. see *BUSINESS AND ECONOMICS—Abstracting, Bibliographies, Statistics*

338.91 AUT
OESTERREICHISCHE FORSCHUNGSSTIFTUNG FUER ENTWICKLUNGSHILFE. EDITION. Cover title: Oe F S E Edition. Text mainly in German; Text occasionally in English. 1992. irreg., latest vol.12, 2004. ATS 180 per vol.; price varies. back issues avail. **Document type:** *Monographic series, Academic/Scholarly.* **Description:** Discusses issues relevant to international development assistance.
Published by: Oesterreichische Forschungsstiftung fuer Entwicklungshilfe/Austrian Foundation for Development Research, Berggasse 7, Vienna, W 1090, Austria. TEL 43-1-3174010, FAX 43-1-3174015, office@oefse.at, http://www.oefse.at/publikationen/edition.htm.

338.91 AUT
OESTERREICHISCHE FORSCHUNGSSTIFTUNG FUER ENTWICKLUNGSHILFE. FORUM. Cover title: Oe F S E Forum. Text in German. 1996. irreg., latest vol.25, 2004. price varies. back issues avail. **Document type:** *Monographic series, Academic/Scholarly.* **Description:** Publishes theses and dissertations relevant to the topic of international development assistance and politics.
Published by: Oesterreichische Forschungsstiftung fuer Entwicklungshilfe/Austrian Foundation for Development Research, Berggasse 7, Vienna, W 1090, Austria. TEL 43-1-3174010, FAX 43-1-3174015, office@oefse.at, http://www.oefse.at/publikationen/forum.htm.

338.9 AUT ISSN 0078-3536
OESTERREICHISCHE SCHRIFTEN ZUR ENTWICKLUNGSHILFE. Text in German. 1963. irreg., latest vol.12, 1985. price varies. **Document type:** *Monographic series, Academic/Scholarly.*
Published by: Verlag Ferdinand Berger und Soehne GmbH, Wienerstr 80, Horn, N 3580, Austria. TEL 43-2982-4161332, FAX 43-2982-4161382, office@berger.at, http://www.berger.at. Ed. Leopold Scheidl.

338.91 SWE ISSN 1400-4569
HC60
OMVAERLDEN. Variant title: Om Vaerlden. Text in Swedish. 1970. 8/yr. SEK 250; SEK 120 to students (effective 2004).
Former titles (until 1995): S I D A Rapport (0282-6011); (until 1985): Rapport fraan S I D A (0345-9705)
Related titles: Online - full text ed.
Published by: Styrelsen foer Internationel Utvecklingssamarbete/Swedish International Development Cooperation Agency (SIDA), Sveavaegen 20, Stockholm, 10525, Sweden. TEL 46-8-6985000, FAX 46-8-208864, omvarlden@sida.se, sida@sida.se, http://www.omvarlden.nu, http://www.sida.se. Ed., Pub. Joeran Hoek TEL 46-8-6985065. **Subscr. to:** Datarutin, kundtjaenst, Fack 30044, Stockholm 10425, Sweden. TEL 46-8-6195541, FAX 46-8-6193535.

338.91 351 LUX ISSN 1683-3457
ON THE IMPLEMENTATION OF THE EUROPEAN COMMISSION'S EXTERNAL ASSISTANCE (YEAR). ANNUAL REPORT. Text in English. 2001. a.
Related titles: Ed.: Sur la Mise en Oeuvre de l'Aide Exterieure de la Commission Europeenne. Situation au (Annee). Rapport Annuel. ISSN 1683-3473.
Published by: European Commission, Office for Official Publications of the European Union, 2 Rue Mercier, Luxembourg, L-2985, Luxembourg. TEL 352-29291, FAX 352-2929-44637, http://europa.eu.int/comm/development/body/publications/descript/pub1_5_en.cfm.

OPEN ECONOMIES REVIEW. see *BUSINESS AND ECONOMICS—Economic Systems And Theories, Economic History*

330 FRA
ORGANIZATION FOR ECONOMIC COOPERATION AND DEVELOPMENT. ACTIVITIES: REPORT BY THE SECRETARY GENERAL. Text in French. 1971. a. free.
Related titles: Microfiche ed.: (from WSH).
Indexed: RASB.
Published by: Organization for Economic Cooperation and Development, 2 Rue Andre Pascal, Paris, 75775 Cedex 16, France. TEL 33-1-45248200, FAX 33-1-45248500, http://www.oecd.org.

338.91 USA ISSN 0092-7643
HD82
OVERSEAS DEVELOPMENT COUNCIL. ANNUAL REPORT. Key Title: Annual Report - Overseas Development Council. Text in English. 1971. a. free. illus. **Document type:** *Corporate.*
—CCC.
Published by: Overseas Development Council, 1875 Connecticut Ave, N W, Ste 1012, Washington, DC 20009. TEL 202-234-8701, FAX 202-745-0067, http://www.odc.org. Ed. Jacqueline Edlund Braun. R&P Jacqueline Edlund-Braun.

338.91 GBR ISSN 0140-8682
HC59.8
OVERSEAS DEVELOPMENT INSTITUTE. BRIEFING PAPER. Variant title: O D I Briefing Paper. Text in English. 1976. 4/yr. free (effective 2005). back issues avail. **Document type:** *Academic/Scholarly.*
Related titles: Online - full text ed.
Indexed: NutrAb, RDA, WAE&RSA.
—BLDSC (2283.958270). **CCC.**
Published by: Overseas Development Institute, 111 Westminster Bridge Rd, London, SE1 7JD, United Kingdom. TEL 44-20-79220300, FAX 44-20-79220399, publications@odi.org.uk, http://www.odi.org.uk/publications/briefing/briefing_papers/index.html. Ed. Simon Maxwell. Circ: 7,000.

338.91 362.5 GBR
OXFAM INTERNATIONAL. POLICY PAPERS. Text in English. irreg. free. back issues avail. **Document type:** *Monographic series.* **Description:** Discusses economics issues affecting developing-nation populations.
Related titles: Online - full text ed.
Published by: Oxfam International, Oxfam House, 274 Banbury Rd, Oxford, Oxon OX2 7DZ, United Kingdom. TEL 44-1865-313600, FAX 44-1865-313925, publish@oxfam.org.uk, http://www.oxfam.org.uk/policy.html. **Orders in N. America to:** Stylus Publishing, PO Box 605, Herndon, VA 20172-0605. TEL 703-661-1581, 703-661-1501; **Orders to:** BEBC Distribution Ltd.. TEL 44-1202-715555, FAX 44-1202-715556.

338.1 GBR ISSN 1360-0818
HD1401
➤ **OXFORD DEVELOPMENT STUDIES.** Text in English. 1933. q. GBP 516, USD 856 combined subscription to institutions print & online eds. (effective 2006). bibl.; charts; stat. index. reprint service avail. from PSC. **Document type:** *Journal, Academic/Scholarly.* **Description:** Presents articles in agricultural economics and development issues worldwide.
Former titles (until vol.24): Oxford Agrarian Studies (0264-5491); Farm Economist (0014-7931)
Related titles: Online - full text ed.: ISSN 1469-9966. GBP 490, USD 813 to institutions (effective 2006) (from EBSCO Publishing, Gale Group, IngentaConnect, O C L C Online Computer Library Center, Inc., Swets Information Services).
Indexed: AEA, APEL, BAS, CREJ, CurCont, DIP, DSA, FPA, FS&TA, ForAb, GEOBASE, HortAb, I&DA, IAOP, IBR, IBSS, IBZ, JEL, MaizeAb, NutrAb, PSA, RASB, RDA, REE&TA, RRTA, RiceAb, S&F, SWA, SociolAb, TDB, TriticAb, WAE&RSA.
—BLDSC (6320.696300), CISTI, IE, Infotrieve, ingenta. **CCC.**
Published by: (Agricultural Economics Unit), Routledge (Subsidiary of: Taylor & Francis Group), 4 Park Sq, Milton Park, Abingdon, Oxon OX14 4RN, United Kingdom. TEL 44-1235-828600, FAX 44-1235-829000, info@routledge.co.uk, http://www.tandf.co.uk/journals/titles/13600818.asp, http://www.routledge.co.uk. Eds. Nandini Gooptu, Raufu Mustapha, Sanjaya Lall. **Subscr. to:** Taylor & Francis Ltd, Journals Customer Service, Rankine Rd, Basingstoke, Hants RG24 8PR, United Kingdom. TEL 44-1256-813000, FAX 44-1256-330245.

338.9 USA ISSN 8755-3848
P A D F NEWS. Text in English. 2/yr. **Description:** News of the foundation's activities, including environmental programs and corporate in-kind donations.
Formerly: Action (Washington)
Published by: Pan American Development Foundation, 1889 F St, N W, Washington, DC 20006. TEL 202-458-3969. Ed. Jeanine Hess. Circ: 9,000.

338.91 PHL
➤ **P I D S RESEARCH PAPER SERIES.** Text in English. 1979. irreg., latest 1994. price varies. back issues avail. **Document type:** *Monographic series, Academic/Scholarly.*
Formerly (until 1994): P I D S Working Paper Series; Which superseded (in 1987): P I D S Staff Paper Series
Published by: Philippine Institute for Development Studies, NEDA sa Makati Bldg, 106 Amorsolo St, Legaspi Village, Makati Mm, 1229, Philippines. TEL 632-893-5705, 632-893-9573, FAX 632-816-1091, 632-893-9589, publications@pidsnet.pids.gov.ph, http://publication.pids.gov.ph/rps.phtml, http://www.pids.gov.ph. Ed. Jennifer P T Liguton.

➤ **P L A NOTES.** (Participatory Learning and Action) see *AGRICULTURE*

➤ **PACIFIC ECONOMIC BULLETIN.** see *BUSINESS AND ECONOMICS—Economic Situation And Conditions*

➤ **PACIFIC MAGAZINE.** see *BUSINESS AND ECONOMICS—International Commerce*

➤ **PAKISTAN DEVELOPMENT REVIEW**; international journal of development economics. see *BUSINESS AND ECONOMICS*

338.91 PAK ISSN 1011-002X
HC440.5.A1
➤ **PAKISTAN ECONOMIC AND SOCIAL REVIEW.** Text in English. 1952. 2/yr. PKR 150, USD 52 (effective 1999). adv. bk.rev. index, cum.index: 1952-1983. **Document type:** *Academic/Scholarly.* **Description:** Publishes articles concerned with the economic and social problems facing Pakistan and other emerging nations.
Formerly (until 1971): Punjab University Economist (0031-0794)
Indexed: BAS, IBSS, ILD, JEL, MEA&I, PAIS, PerIslam, RRTA, WAE&RSA.
—BLDSC (6340.683000).
Published by: University of the Punjab, Department of Economics, New Campus, Lahore, 54590, Pakistan. TEL 92-42-5863997, FAX 92-42-5868313. Ed. Rafiq Ahmad. Circ: 650.

➤ **PAKISTAN INSTITUTE OF DEVELOPMENT ECONOMICS. REPORT.** see *BUSINESS AND ECONOMICS*

➤ **PAKISTAN INSTITUTE OF DEVELOPMENT ECONOMICS. RESEARCH REPORTS.** see *BUSINESS AND ECONOMICS*

980 USA ISSN 0552-9913
PAN AMERICAN DEVELOPMENT FOUNDATION. ANNUAL REPORT. Text in English. 1964. a. free.
Published by: Pan American Development Foundation, 1889 F St, N W, Washington, DC 20006. TEL 202-458-3969. Ed. Jeanine Hess. Circ: 3,000.

338.91 CHL
PANORAMA DE LA INSERCION INTERNATIONAL DE AMERICA LATINA Y EL CARIBE. Text in Spanish. 1996. a. USD 15 (effective 1999). back issues avail.
Published by: Comision Economica para America Latina y el Caribe/Economic Commission for Latin America and the Caribbean, Ave Dag Hammarskjold 3477, Vitacura, Santiago de Chile, Chile. TEL 56-2-471-2000, FAX 56-2-208-0252, publications@eclac.cl, http://www.eclac.cl. **Subscr. to:** United Nations Publications, Distribution and Sales Section, Palais des Nations, Rm C-116, 8-14 av de la Paix, Geneva 1211, Switzerland; United Nations Publications, Rm DC2-853, United Nations Bldg, 2 United Nations Plaza, New York, NY 10017.

338.91 GBR ISSN 0268-4020
PAPERS IN THE ADMINISTRATION OF DEVELOPMENT. Text in English. irreg. (2-3/yr.). price varies. back issues avail. **Document type:** *Monographic series.*
—BLDSC (6393.420000).
Published by: (Development and Administration Group), University of Birmingham, Institute of Local and Government Studies, Univ. of Birmingham, University Of Birmingham, Edgbaston, Birmingham, Worcs B15 2TT, United Kingdom.

338.91 DEU ISSN 0173-184X
PERIPHERIE; Zeitschrift fuer Politik und Oekonomie in der dritten Welt. Text in German; Summaries in English. 1980. q. EUR 30.10 to individuals; EUR 55.20 to institutions; EUR 9.10 newsstand/cover (effective 2003). adv. bk.rev. back issues avail. **Document type:** *Magazine, Academic/Scholarly.* **Description:** Interdisciplinary studies of the problems of underdevelopment and development, and liberation movements in the Third World.
Indexed: ARDT, DIP, IBR, IBSS, IBZ, SOPODA, SSA, SociolAb.
—CCC.
Published by: (Wissenschaftliche Vereinigung fuer Entwicklungstheorie und Entwicklungspolitik e.V.), Verlag Westfaelisches Dampfboot, Hafenweg 26a, Muenster, 48155, Germany. TEL 49-251-3900480, FAX 49-251-3900480, info@zeitschrift-peripherie.de, info@dampfboot-verlag.de, http://www.zeitschrift-peripherie.de, http://www.dampfboot-verlag.de. Circ: 1,000.

338.91 RWA
PERSONNEL DES NATIONS UNIES ET DES AGENCES SPECIALISEES EN REPUBLIQUE DE RWANDA. Text in French. a.
Published by: United Nations Development Programme Rwanda, BP 445, Kigali, Rwanda.

PERSPECTIVES (MADISON). see *BUSINESS AND ECONOMICS—Banking And Finance*

338.91 ITA ISSN 1720-2809
PIROGA. Text in Italian. 1999. bi-m.
Related titles: Online - full text ed.: ISSN 1720-3635.
Published by: Comitato Internazionale per lo Sviluppo dei Popoli, Via Germanico 198, Rome, 00192, Italy. TEL 39-06-3216163, cisp@cisp-ngo.org, http://www.cisp-ngo.org.

338.1 613 USA
PLENTY BULLETIN. Text in English. 1974. q. USD 10 donation. bk.rev. 4 p./no. 2 cols./p.; back issues avail. **Document type:** *Bulletin.* **Description:** Covers agricultural relief and development activities of Plenty.
Formerly: Plenty News
Related titles: Online - full content ed.: 1998.
Published by: Plenty International, PO Box 394, Summertown, TN 38483-0394. plenty@plenty.org, http://www.plenty.org. Ed., R&P Peter Schweitzer. Circ: 4,500.

338.91 USA
PRAXIS (MEDFORD); the Fletcher journal of development studies. Text in English. 3/yr. **Description:** Focuses on international development.
Published by: Fletcher School of Law and Diplomacy, Tufts University, Medford, MA 02155. TEL 617-627-5564.

PRIVATE DEVELOPMENT CORPORATION OF THE PHILIPPINES. EXECUTIVE UPDATE; international markets report. see *BUSINESS AND ECONOMICS—International Commerce*

338.91 PHL
PRIVATE DEVELOPMENT CORPORATION OF THE PHILIPPINES. POLICY ANALYSIS. Text in English. 1986. bi-m. USD 35.
Published by: Private Development Corporation of the Philippines/Pribadong Korporasyon sa Pagpapaunlad ng Pilipinas, P.O. Box 757, Makati, Manila, 3117, Philippines. TEL 02-8100231, FAX 02-8195376.

338.91 ZAF
PRODDER - NEWSLETTER. Text in English. w. free. **Document type:** *Newsletter.* **Description:** Publishes articles on development trends, current and completed research, and reports on conferences of interest to the development community.
Formerly: Prodder Mail
Published by: (Environmental Management Division), Human Sciences Research Council, Programme for Development Research, Private Bag X41, Pretoria, 0001, South Africa. TEL 27-12-302-2999, FAX 27-12-302-2445, yzettet@beauty.hsrc.ac.za, http://www.prodder.co.za, http://www.hsrc.ac.za/. Ed. David Bernard. Circ: 4,000. **Co-sponsor:** Sasol.

338.91 ZAF
PRODDER: THE SOUTHERN AFRICAN DEVELOPMENT DIRECTORY (YEARS)✶. Text in English. 1987. biennial. ZAR 200; USD 80 foreign. **Document type:** *Directory.* **Description:** Includes information on development roleplayers in the Southern Africa region.
Published by: Human Sciences Research Council, Programme for Development Research, Private Bag X41, Pretoria, 0001, South Africa. TEL 27-12-302-2999, FAX 27-12-302-2445, yzettet@beauty.hsrc.ac.za, http://www.web.co.za/prodder/.

338.91 GBR ISSN 0271-2075
JF60 CODEN: PADEDR
➤ **PUBLIC ADMINISTRATION AND DEVELOPMENT**; the international journal of management research and practice. Text in English. 1981. 5/yr. USD 1,230 to institutions; USD 1,353 combined subscription to institutions print & online eds. (effective 2006). adv. bk.rev. back issues avail.; reprint service avail. from PQC,PSC. **Document type:** *Journal, Academic/Scholarly.* **Description:** Focuses on administrative practice at the local, regional and national levels.
Supersedes: Journal of Administration Overseas (0021-8472)
Related titles: Microform ed.: (from PQC); Online - full text ed.: ISSN 1099-162X. USD 1,230 to institutions (effective 2006) (from EBSCO Publishing, ProQuest Information & Learning, Swets Information Services, Wiley InterScience).

B

Indexed: ABCPolSci, ABIn, AICP, ASCA, ASD, ASSIA, BAS, BPIA, CCA, CurCont, EI, ERA, Emerald, ForAb, GEOBASE, HRA, HortAb, I&DA, IBSS, ILD, IPSA, MAB, MEA, MEA&I, PAA&I, PAIS, PCI, PRA, PSA, RASB, RDA, RRTA, S&F, SOPODA, SPAA, SPPI, SSA, SSCI, SUSA, SWA, SociolAb, TDB, TEA, WAE&RSA.
—BLDSC (6962.560800), CISTI, IDS, IE, Infotrieve, ingenta. CCC.
Published by: (Royal Institute of Public Administration), John Wiley & Sons Ltd. (Subsidiary of: John Wiley & Sons, Inc.), The Atrium, Southern Gate, Chichester, West Sussex PO19 8SQ, United Kingdom. TEL 44-1243-779777, FAX 44-1243-775878, customer@wiley.co.uk, http://www.interscience.wiley.com/journal/pad, http://www.wiley.co.uk. Ed. Paul Collins. Pub. Lesley Valentine. R&P Diane Southern TEL 44-1243-770347. adv.: B&W page GBP 650, color page GBP 1,550; trim 165 x 248. Circ: 1,800. **Subscr. in the Americas to:** John Wiley & Sons, Inc., 111 River St, Hoboken, NJ 07030-5774. TEL 201-748-6645, FAX 201-748-6088, subinfo@wiley.com.

338.91   NZL   ISSN 1175-3099
DU423.A1
HE PUNA KORERO/JOURNAL OF MAORI AND PACIFIC DEVELOPMENT. Text in English, Maori. 2000. s-a.
Published by: University of Waikato, School of Maori and Pacific Development, Private Bag 3105, Hamilton, New Zealand. TEL 9-647-838-4466, http://www.waikato.ac.nz/smpd/journal/.

338.91   USA
RAPPORT ANNUEL SUR LA COOPERATION AU DEVELOPPEMENT - BURUNDI. Text in French. a.
Formerly (until 1984): Rapport Annuel sur l'Assistance au Developpement: Burundi
Published by: United Nations Development Programme, Division of Information, 345 E 46th St, Rm CN 315, New York, NY 10017. Circ: (controlled).

338.91   RWA
RAPPORT ANNUEL SUR L'ASSISTANCE AU DEVELOPPEMENT: RWANDA. Text in French. a.
Published by: United Nations Development Programme Rwanda, BP 445, Kigali, Rwanda.

338.91   USA   ISSN 0271-1710
RAPPORT SUR LE DEVELOPPEMENT DANS LE MONDE. Text in French. 1978. a.
Related titles: ◆ English ed.: World Development Report. ISSN 0163-5085.
—CCC.
Published by: World Bank Group, 1818 H St, NW, Washington, DC 20433. TEL 202-477-1234, FAX 202-477-6391, http://www.worldbank.org.

338.91   GBR
THE REALITY OF AID (YEAR). Text in English. 1993. irreg., latest vol.2, 1997-98. GBP 14.95. **Document type:** Bulletin. **Description:** Provides an independent evaluation of the aid policies of major donors and their effectiveness in fulfilling their official purpose of relieving poverty and assisting development.
—BLDSC (7303.504200).
Published by: Earthscan Publications Ltd. (Subsidiary of: Kogan Page Ltd.), 120 Pentonville Rd, London, N1 9JN, United Kingdom. TEL 44-20-7278-0433, FAX 44-207-278-1142, TELEX 266272 ACTAID G, earthinfo@earthscan.co.uk, http://www.earthscan.co.uk.

REENCUENTRO/REUNION. see POLITICAL SCIENCE—Civil Rights

307.1   JPN   ISSN 0250-6505
HT390
REGIONAL DEVELOPMENT DIALOGUE; an international journal focusing on Third World development problems. Text in English. 1980. s-a. USD 30 in developing nations; USD 40 elsewhere (effective 2005). adv. charts. reprints avail. **Document type:** Journal, Academic/Scholarly. **Description:** Provides a forum for critical discussion of regional development problems, policies, and perspectives among academicians and practitioners.
Related titles: Microfiche ed.: (from CIS).
Indexed: APEL, AgBio, AgrForAb, BAS, DSA, EIP, ESPM, FPA, ForAb, GEOBASE, I&DA, IBR, IBZ, IIS, ILD, PAA&I, PAIS, PGegResA, PN&I, PRA, PSA, RDA, RRTA, RiskAb, S&F, SIA, SOPODA, SPAA, SSA, SUSA, SociolAb, TDB, WAE&RSA.
—BLDSC (7336.595400), CISTI, IE, Infotrieve, ingenta.
Published by: United Nations Centre for Regional Development, 1-47-1 Nagono, Nakamura-ku, Nagoya, Aichi 450-0001, Japan. TEL 81-52-5619379, FAX 81-52-5619375, info@uncrd.or.jp, http://www.uncrd.or.jp. Ed. Yo Kimura. Circ: 1,000.

307.1   JPN   ISSN 1020-3060
HT390   CODEN: RRDSF8
➤ **REGIONAL DEVELOPMENT STUDIES.** Text in English. 1995. a. USD 20; USD 15 in developing nations (effective 2001). charts; illus. **Document type:** Academic/Scholarly. **Description:** Covers various issues in international development assistance for regional development.
Indexed: APEL, PAIS, PSA, SOPODA, SSA, SociolAb.

Published by: United Nations Centre for Regional Development, 1-47-1 Nagono, Nakamura-ku, Nagoya, Aichi 450-0001, Japan. TEL 81-52-5619377, FAX 81-52-5619375, info@uncrd.or.jp, http://www.uncrd.or.jp. Circ: 500.

338.9   SEN   ISSN 0850-4008
REGISTER DEVELOPMENT RESEARCH PROJECTS AFRICA. Text in English, French. 1973. a. USD 35 (effective 2000). bibl. **Document type:** Bulletin, Academic/Scholarly.
Formerly (until 1983): Africa Development Research Annual-Annuaire des Recherches Africaines sur les Problemes de Developpement
Published by: Council for the Development of Social Science Research in Africa, BP 3304, Dakar, Senegal. TEL 221-825-9822, FAX 221-824-1289, codesria@sonatel.senet.net, http://www.sas.upenn.edu/African_Studies/codesria/codes_menu.html. Ed. Tade Akin Aina.

338.91   GBR
RELIEF AND REHABILITATION NETWORK PAPERS AND NEWSLETTER. Text in English, French. s-a. back issues avail. **Document type:** Academic/Scholarly.
Formerly: Relief and Rehabilitation Network Papers (1353-8691)
Related titles: Online - full text ed.
Published by: Overseas Development Institute, 111 Westminster Bridge Rd, London, SE1 7JD, United Kingdom. TEL 44-171-393-1699, FAX 44-171-393-1699, rrn@odi.org.uk, http://www.oneworld.org/odi/hpg. Ed. Koenraad Van Brabant.

RELIEFWEB; a global information system to support the delivery of humanitarian assistance. see SOCIAL SERVICES AND WELFARE

338.9   ETH
REPORT ON DEVELOPMENT ASSISTANCE TO ETHIOPIA. Text in English. a.
Published by: United Nations Development Programme Ethiopia, PO Box 5580, Addis Ababa, Ethiopia.

338.91   SDN
REPORT ON DEVELOPMENT COOPERATION TO THE DEMOCRATIC REPUBLIC OF THE SUDAN. Text in English. a.
Formerly: Development Assistance to the Democratic Republic of the Sudan
Published by: United Nations Development Programme Sudan, P O Box 913, Khartoum, Sudan.

338.91   GBR   ISSN 1363-6669
HD72
➤ **REVIEW OF DEVELOPMENT ECONOMICS.** Text in English. q. EUR 111 combined subscription in Europe to individuals print & online eds.; USD 89 combined subscription in the Americas to individuals & Caribbean, print & online eds.; GBP 74 combined subscription elsewhere to individuals print & online eds.; USD 612 combined subscription in the Americas to institutions & Caribbean, print & online eds.; GBP 415 combined subscription elsewhere to institutions print & online eds. (effective 2006). reprint service avail. from PSC. **Document type:** Journal, Academic/Scholarly. **Description:** Publishes rigorous analytical papers, theoretical and empirical, which deal with contemporary growth problems of developing countries, including the transition economies.
Related titles: Online - full text ed.: ISSN 1467-9361. USD 581 in the Americas to institutions & Caribbean; GBP 394 elsewhere to institutions (effective 2006) (from Blackwell Synergy, EBSCO Publishing, Gale Group, IngentaConnect, O C L C Online Computer Library Center, Inc., Swets Information Services).
Indexed: ABIn, ESPM, GEOBASE, JEL, PSA, RiskAb, SociolAb.
—BLDSC (7790.161750), IE, Infotrieve, ingenta. CCC.
Published by: Blackwell Publishing Ltd., 9600 Garsington Rd, Oxford, OX4 2ZG, United Kingdom. TEL 44-1865-776868, FAX 44-1865-714591, customerservices@oxon.blackwellpublishing.com, http://www.blackwellpublishing.com/journals/RDE. Ed. E Kwan Choi TEL 515-294-5999.

333.38 351   AUS   ISSN 0917-0553
HT390   CODEN: RURDEJ
➤ **REVIEW OF URBAN & REGIONAL DEVELOPMENT STUDIES.** Key Title: RURDS. Review of Urban and Regional Development Studies. Text in English. 1989. 3/yr. GBP 110 combined subscription in Japan to individuals print & online eds.; USD 79 combined subscription in the Americas to individuals & Caribbean, print & online eds.; GBP 56 combined subscription elsewhere to individuals print & online eds.; GBP 93 combined subscription in Japan to institutions print & online eds.; USD 234 combined subscription in the Americas to institutions & Caribbean (print & online eds.); GBP 164 combined subscription elsewhere to institutions print & online eds.; USD 36 combined subscription in the Americas to students & Caribbean, print & online eds.; EUR 38 combined subscription in Europe to students print & online eds.; GBP 24 combined subscription elsewhere to students print & online eds. (effective 2006). illus.; maps. **Document type:** Journal, Academic/Scholarly. **Description:** Emphasizes policy relevance and the operational aspects of academic disciplines, rather than primarily theoretical and methodological issues. For scholars, planners, engineers and managers in government, business, and international agencies.
Related titles: Online - full text ed.: ISSN 1467-940X. GBP 88 in Japan to institutions; USD 222 in the Americas to institutions & Caribbean; GBP 156 elsewhere to institutions (effective 2006) (from Blackwell Synergy, EBSCO Publishing, Gale Group, IngentaConnect, O C L C Online Computer Library Center, Inc., Swets Information Services).
Indexed: ABIn, GEOBASE, IBSS, JEL, RDA, RRTA, S&F, SOPODA, SSA, SUSA, SociolAb, TDB, V&AA, WAE&RSA.
—BLDSC (8052.642750), IE, Infotrieve, ingenta.
Published by: (Applied Regional Science Conference JPN), Blackwell Publishing Asia (Subsidiary of: Blackwell Publishing Ltd.), 550 Swanston St, Carlton South, VIC 3053, Australia. TEL 61-383591011, FAX 61-383591120, subs@blackwellpublishingasia.com, http://www.blackwellpublishing.com/journals/RURDS. **Co-sponsor:** Tokyo International University, Showa Foundation for Economic Research.

338   HND   ISSN 0252-8762
HC141.A1
REVISTA DE LA INTEGRACION Y EL DESARROLLO DE CENTROAMERICA. Text in Spanish. 1976. s-a. adv. **Document type:** Academic/Scholarly.
Formerly: Revista de la Integracion Centroamericana
Indexed: PAIS.
Published by: Banco Centroamericano de Integracion Economica, Apdo. Postal 772, Tegucigalpa D.C, Honduras. TEL 504-222230. Ed. Carlos Guillermo Herrera. Pub. Alejandro Arpenal. Adv. contact Carlos Imendia.

338.91   ECU
REVISTA INTERAMERICANA DE PLANIFICACION. CORREO INFORMATIVO. Text in Spanish. 1967. q. USD 30 in the Americas; USD 40 in Europe; USD 42 elsewhere. adv. bk.rev. stat. cum.index every 2 yrs. **Document type:** Academic/Scholarly.
Formerly: Sociedad Interamericana de Planificacion. Correo Informativo (0579-3718)
Published by: Sociedad Interamericana de Planificacion, Casilla 01-05-1978, Cuenca, Azuay, Ecuador. TEL 593-7-823860, FAX 593-7-823949, siap1@siap.org.ec. Ed. Luis E Camacho. Circ: 2,000 (paid).

REVISTA ROMANA DE STUDII INTERNATIONALE/ROMANIAN JOURNAL OF INTERNATIONAL STUDIES. see BUSINESS AND ECONOMICS—International Commerce

REVUE D'ECONOMIE DU DEVELOPPEMENT. see BUSINESS AND ECONOMICS—Economic Situation And Conditions

338   FRA   ISSN 1293-8882
HC59.7
REVUE TIERS MONDE. Text in French. 1960. q. EUR 74 domestic; EUR 84 foreign (effective 2005). bk.rev. abstr. index. reprint service avail. from SCH. **Document type:** Journal, Abstract/Index. **Description:** Studies the economic and social problems of Third World countries.
Formerly (until 1996): Tiers Monde (0040-7356)
Indexed: BAS, DIP, DSA, EI, HAPI, HortAb, IBR, IBSS, IBZ, ILD, IPSA, IndIslam, JEL, NutrAb, PAIS, PSA, RASB, RDA, SSA, SociolAb, WAE&RSA.
—BLDSC (7956.190000), CISTI, IE, Infotrieve, ingenta. CCC.
Published by: (Institut d'Etude du Developpement Economique et Social), Presses Universitaires de France, 6 Avenue Reille, Paris, 75685 Cedex 14, France. TEL 33-1-58103100, FAX 33-1-58103182, tiermond@univ-paris1.fr, revues@puf.com, http://www.puf.com. Ed. Maxine Haubert.

338.91   DNK   ISSN 0907-2829
ROSKILDE UNIVERSITSCENTER. INTERNATIONAL DEVELOPMENT STUDIES. OCCASIONAL PAPER. Text in Danish. 1990. irreg., latest vol.21, 2001. **Document type:** Monographic series.
Indexed: GEOBASE.

Published by: Roskilde Universitetscenter, Institut for Geografi og Internationale Udviklingsstudier/Roskilde University, Department of Geography and International Development Studies, PO Box 260, Roskilde, 4000, Denmark. TEL 45-4-6742000, FAX 45-4-6743000, inge@ruc.dk, ruc@ruc.dk, http://www.ruc.dk/inst3/IDS/Public/occasional/.

338.91 360   SEN
ROSTER OF AFRICA SOCIAL SCIENTISTS. Text in English, French. 1981. a. USD 35 (effective 2000). **Document type:** *Bulletin, Academic/Scholarly.*
Published by: Council for the Development of Social Science Research in Africa, BP 3304, Dakar, Senegal. TEL 221-825-9823, FAX 221-824-1289, codesria@sonatel.senet.net, http://www.sas.upenn.edu/African_Studies/codesria/codes_Menu.html. Ed. Tade Akin Aina.

338.91   GBR   ISSN 1359-7884
ROUTLEDGE STUDIES IN DEVELOPMENT ECONOMICS. Text in English. 1995. irreg., latest vol.29, 2002, Dec. price varies. back issues avail. **Document type:** *Monographic series, Academic/Scholarly.* **Description:** Presents accounts of the present position of, and future prospects for, the developing countries.
—BLDSC (8026.519400).
Published by: Routledge (Subsidiary of: Taylor & Francis Group), 4 Park Square, Milton Park, Abingdon, Oxon OX14 4RN, United Kingdom. TEL 44-1235-828600, FAX 44-1235-829000, info@routledge.co.uk, http://www.reference.routledge.com/research/development/de.html, http://www.tandf.co.uk, http://www.routledge.co.uk.

ROYAL TROPICAL INSTITUTE. BULLETIN. see *ANTHROPOLOGY*

338.91 634.9   GBR
RURAL DEVELOPMENT FORESTRY NETWORK PAPERS AND NEWSLETTER. Text in English, French, Spanish. s-a. back issues avail. **Document type:** *Academic/Scholarly.*
Formerly: Rural Development Forestry Network Papers (0968-2627)
Indexed: AgrForAb, FPA, ForAb, HortAb, RDA, RRTA, S&F, WAE&RSA.
Published by: Overseas Development Institute, 111 Westminster Bridge Rd, London, SE1 7JD, United Kingdom. TEL 44-171-393-1600, FAX 44-171-393-1699, fpeg@odi.org.uk, http://www.oneworld.org/odi/fpeg. Ed. Kate Schreckenberg. Circ: 2,500.

338.91   USA   ISSN 1011-873X
HN981.C6
RURAL RECONSTRUCTION REVIEW. Text in English. 1979. a. adv. bk.rev. **Description:** Action research on rural development in the Third World.
Indexed: ILD, RDA, REE&TA.
Published by: International Institute of Rural Reconstruction, 475 Riverside Dr, New York, NY 10115. TEL 212-870-2992. Ed. Jaime P Ronquillo. Circ: 2,000.

338.91   USA
RUSSIAN DEFENSE BUSINESS DIRECTORY (YEAR). Text in English. 1992. a. **Document type:** *Directory, Government.* **Description:** Discusses the U.S. government's program to encourage American private investment in Russian companies that are converting from military to commercial goods or services.
Related titles: Online - full text ed.
Published by: U.S. Department of Commerce, U.S.-Russia Defense Conversion Subcommittee, 14th St between Constitution & E Sts NW, Washington, DC 20230. TEL 202-482-4695. Ed. Daniel C. Hurley, Jr.

338.91   SWE   ISSN 1401-0402
S I D A EVALUATION. (Swedish International Development Cooperation Agency) Key Title: Sida Evaluation. Text in English. 1995. irreg. back issues avail. **Document type:** *Monographic series.*
Formed by the merger of (1986-1995): S I D A Evaluation Report (0283-0736); (1990-1995): Evaluations
Related titles: Online - full text ed.
Indexed: RDA.
—BLDSC (8271.710300).
Published by: Styrelsen foer Internationel Utvecklingssamarbete/Swedish International Development Cooperation Agency (SIDA), Sveavaegen 20, Stockholm, 10525, Sweden. TEL 46-8-6985000, FAX 46-8-208864, sida@sida.se, http://www.sida.se/Sida/jsp/polopoly.jsp?d=2269&a=17840.

338.91   SWE   ISSN 1403-1922
S I D A EVALUATIONS NEWSLETTER. (Swedish International Development Cooperation Agency) Variant title: Sida Evaluation Newsletter. Text in English. 1996. irreg. free. **Document type:** *Newsletter, Government.* **Description:** Contains summaries of selected evaluation reports and backlisting of all Sida evaluation reports.
Related titles: Diskette ed.; Online - full text ed.
—BLDSC (8271.710520).

Published by: Styrelsen foer Internationel Utvecklingssamarbete/Swedish International Development Cooperation Agency (SIDA), Sveavaegen 20, Stockholm, 10525, Sweden. TEL 46-8-6985000, FAX 46-8-208864, sida@sida.se, http://www.sida.se/Sida/jsp/polopoly.jsp?d=2548&a=17846. Circ: 2,000.

338.41   SWE   ISSN 1404-9562
S I D A STUDIES. Text mainly in English; Text occasionally in Swedish. 2000. irreg., latest vol.10, 2003. back issues avail. **Document type:** *Monographic series.*
Published by: Styrelsen foer Internationel Utvecklingssamarbete/Swedish International Development Cooperation Agency (SIDA), Sveavaegen 20, Stockholm, 10525, Sweden. TEL 46-8-6985000, FAX 46-8-208864, sida@sida.se, http://www.sida.se.

338.41   SWE   ISSN 1402-215X
S I D A STUDIES IN EVALUATION. Text in English. 1996. irreg., latest 2003. back issues avail. **Document type:** *Monographic series.*
Published by: Styrelsen foer Internationel Utvecklingssamarbete/Swedish International Development Cooperation Agency (SIDA), Sveavaegen 20, Stockholm, 10525, Sweden. TEL 46-8-6985000, FAX 46-8-208864, sida@sida.se, http://www.sida.se.

338.91   UAE
SANDUQ ABU DHABI LIL-INMA' AL-IQTISADI AL-ARABI. AL-TAQRIR AL-SANAWI/ABU DHABI FUND FOR ARAB ECONOMIC DEVELOPMENT. ANNUAL REPORT. Text in Arabic. 1984. a. stat. **Document type:** *Corporate.* **Description:** Provides an overview of domestic and international development projects under the administration of the fund, including loans and technical assistance.
Published by: Abu Dhabi Fund for Arab Economic Development/Sanduq Abu Dhabi lil-Inma' al-Iqtisadi al-Arabi, PO Box 814, Abu Dhabi, United Arab Emirates. TEL 971-2-725800, FAX 971-2-728890, TELEX 22287 FUND EM, opadfdmn@emirates.net.ae. Circ: 1,000 (controlled).

338.91   TCD
SECOURS CATHOLIQUE ET DEVELOPPEMENT. RAPPORT D'ACTIVITES ET COMPTE-RENDU FINANCIER (YEAR). Text in French. a.
Published by: Secours Catholique et Developpement, BP 1166, N'djamena, Chad. TEL 54-44-53, FAX 51-40-60.

338.9   GTM
SECRETARIA PERMANENTE DEL TRATADO GENERAL DE INTEGRACION ECONOMICA CENTROAMERICANA. BOLETIN INFORMATIVO. Text in Spanish. 1961. m. USD 25. bk.rev.
Formerly: Secretaria Permanente del Tratado General de Integracion Economica Centroamericana. Carta Informativa (0553-6855)
Published by: Secretaria Permanente del Tratado General de Integracion Economica Centroamericana, 4a Avda. 10-25, ZONA, 14, PO Box 1237, Guatemala City, 01901, Guatemala. TEL 502-3682151, FAX 502-3681071. Ed. Eduardo Bolanos. Circ: 6,000.

338.91   BRA
SELECOES ECONOMICAS/JITSUGYO NO BURAJIRU. Text in Japanese. m. BRL 1,200. illus.
Address: Av Paulista, 807, B Vista, Sao Paulo, SP 01311-100, Brazil.

SHALOM; magazine for alumni of Mashav training courses. see *EDUCATION—Adult Education*

SHARE INTERNATIONAL. see *NEW AGE PUBLICATIONS*

338.91   FRA   ISSN 1683-2396
SOURCE O C D E. DEVELOPPEMENT. (Organisation de Cooperation et de Developpement Economiques) Variant title: Source O C D E. Developpement International. Text in French. irreg. EUR 693, USD 796, GBP 457, JPY 93,600 (effective 2005).
Related titles: Online - full text ed.: ISSN 1684-3045. EUR 485, USD 557, GBP 320, JPY 65,500 (effective 2005) (from EBSCO Publishing, Gale Group, IngentaConnect, Swets Information Services); ◆ English ed.: Source O E C D. Development. ISSN 1608-0254.
Published by: Organization for Economic Cooperation and Development, 2 Rue Andre Pascal, Paris, 75775 Cedex 16, France. TEL 33-1-45248200, FAX 33-1-45248500, http://www.oecd.org. **Dist. by:** Extenza - Turpin, Pegasus Dr, Stratton Business Park, Biggleswade, Beds SG18 8TQ, United Kingdom. TEL 44-1462-687552, FAX 44-1462-480947, subscriptions@extenza-turpin.com; O E C D Turpin North America, PO Box 194, Downingtown, PA 19335-0194. TEL 610-524-5361, 800-456-6323, FAX 610-524-5417, journalscustomer@turpinna.com.

338.91   FRA   ISSN 1608-0254
SOURCE O E C D. DEVELOPMENT. Variant title: SourceOECD. Development. Text in English. irreg. EUR 693, USD 796, GBP 457, JPY 93,600 (effective 2005). **Document type:** *Government.*

Related titles: Online - full content ed.: ISSN 1681-1984. EUR 485, USD 557, GBP 320, JPY 65,500 (effective 2005); Online - full text ed.: 2000 (from EBSCO Publishing, Gale Group, IngentaConnect, Swets Information Services); ◆ French ed.: Source O C D E. Developpement. ISSN 1683-2396.
Published by: Organization for Economic Cooperation and Development, 2 Rue Andre Pascal, Paris, 75775 Cedex 16, France. TEL 33-1-45248200, FAX 33-1-45248500, http://www.oecd.org. **Dist. by:** Extenza - Turpin, Pegasus Dr, Stratton Business Park, Biggleswade, Beds SG18 8TQ, United Kingdom. TEL 44-1462-687552, FAX 44-1462-480947, subscriptions@extenza-turpin.com; O E C D Turpin North America, PO Box 194, Downingtown, PA 19335-0194. TEL 610-524-5361, 800-456-6323, FAX 610-524-5417, journalscustomer@turpinna.com.

338.91   NCL   ISSN 0081-2811
                             CODEN: SPHAD3
SOUTH PACIFIC COMMISSION. HANDBOOK. Text in English. 1968. irreg., latest vol.32, 1993.
Related titles: French ed.: Commission de Pacifique Sud. Manuel. ISSN 0377-9955.
Indexed: ASFA, ESPM.
Published by: Secretariat of the Pacific Community, PO Box D5, Noumea, Cedex 98848, New Caledonia. TEL 687-262000, FAX 687-263818, spc@spc.int, http://www.spc.int.

338.9   MYS
SOUTHEAST ASIA DEVELOPMENT CORPORATION BERHAD. REPORTS AND ACCOUNTS. Text in English. a. charts; stat.
Published by: Southeast Asia Development Corporation Berhad, G.P.O. Box 2171, Kuala Lumpur, 01-20, Malaysia.

STATECO. see *BUSINESS AND ECONOMICS—Abstracting, Bibliographies, Statistics*

STATISTICS ON INTERNATIONAL DEVELOPMENT; statistics of U.K. economic assistance to developing countries and countries of transition. see *BUSINESS AND ECONOMICS—Abstracting, Bibliographies, Statistics*

631   DEU   ISSN 0177-0160
STUDIES IN APPLIED ECONOMICS AND RURAL INSTITUTIONS. Text in English. 1972. irreg. price varies. **Document type:** *Monographic series, Academic/Scholarly.*
Formerly (until 1984): Forschungsstelle fuer Internationale Agrarentwicklung. Publikationen (0302-8704)
Indexed: IBR, IBZ, WAE&RSA.
—BLDSC (4283.925000).
Published by: Forschungsstelle fuer Internationale Agrar- und Wirtschaftsentwicklung e.V./Research Centre for International Agrarian & Economic Development, Ringstr 19, Heidelberg, 69115, Germany. TEL 49-6221-183056, FAX 49-6221-167482, fia@urz.uni-heidelberg.de, http://www.rzuser.uni-heidelberg.de/~t08.

338.9   NLD   ISSN 0924-607X
➤ **STUDIES IN DEVELOPMENT AND PLANNING.** Text in English. 1973. irreg., latest vol.11, 1980. price varies. **Document type:** *Monographic series, Academic/Scholarly.*
Published by: (Erasmus Universiteit Rotterdam, Centre for Development and Planning, Erasmus Universiteit Rotterdam), Springer-Verlag Dordrecht (Subsidiary of: Springer Science+Business Media), Van Godewijckstraat 30, Dordrecht, 3311 GX, Netherlands. TEL 31-78-6576050, FAX 31-78-6576474, http://www.springeronline.com.

➤ **SUARA SAM;** Malaysia's leading environmental newspaper. see *ENVIRONMENTAL STUDIES*

338.91   SDN
SUDAN DEVELOPMENT STUDIES REVIEW. Text in English. s-a.
Published by: University of Khartoum, Development Studies and Research Centre, P O Box 321, Khartoum, Sudan.

SUDAN. NATIONAL COUNCIL FOR RESEARCH. ECONOMIC AND SOCIAL RESEARCH COUNCIL. RESEARCH METHODS. see *SOCIAL SCIENCES: COMPREHENSIVE WORKS*

338.91   DEU   ISSN 1438-2814
SUEDZEIT. Text in German. 1999. q. EUR 10 (effective 2005). **Document type:** *Newsletter, Trade.*
Published by: Dachverband Entwicklungspolitischer Aktionsgruppen in Baden-Wuerttemberg e.V., Weissenburgstr 13, Stuttgart, 70180, Germany. TEL 49-711-6453120, FAX 49-711-6453136, suedzeit@deab.de, info@deab.de, http://www.deab.de.

338.91   ETH   ISSN 0252-5712
SURVEY OF ECONOMIC AND SOCIAL CONDITIONS IN AFRICA. Text in English. irreg., latest 1996.
Formerly: Survey of Economic Conditions in Africa
Related titles: French ed.: Etude des Conditions Economiques et Sociales en Afrique.
Published by: (Documents & Publishing Services Unit), United Nations, Economic Commission for Africa/Commission Economique pour l'Afrique, PO Box 3001, Addis Ababa, Ethiopia.

B

338.91 HRV
SVETSKO GOSPODARSTVO. Text in Croatian. m. **Document type:** *Magazine, Trade.*
Published by: Institut za Razvoj i Medunarodne Odnose (IRMO)/Institute for Development and International Relations, Ljudevita F Vukotinovica 2, Zagreb, 10000, Croatia. TEL 385-1-4826522, FAX 385-1-4828361. Ed. Mladen Stancic.

T R A C ANNUAL REPORT. (Transvaal Rural Action Committee) see *POLITICAL SCIENCE—Civil Rights*

T R A C NEWSLETTER. (Transvaal Rural Action Committee) see *POLITICAL SCIENCE—Civil Rights*

338.91 JPN ISSN 0914-918X
TECHNOLOGY AND DEVELOPMENT. Text in English. 1988. a.
Description: Covers the natural, socioeconomic, and cultural environment of developing countries.
Indexed: IBSS.
—BLDSC (8758.607000), IE.
Published by: Japan International Cooperation Agency, Institute for International Cooperation, 10-5, Ichigaya Honmura-cho, Shinjuku-ku, Tokyo, 162-8433, Japan. TEL 81-3-32692911, http://www.jica.go.jp/english/publication/studyreport/index.html.

THIRD WORLD LEGAL STUDIES (YEAR). see *LAW—International Law*

338.9 GBR ISSN 0143-6597
HC59.7
➤ **THIRD WORLD QUARTERLY;** journal of emerging areas. Text in English. 1979. 8/yr. GBP 688, USD 1,135 combined subscription to institutions print & online eds. (effective 2006). adv. bk.rev. illus. Index. reprint service avail. from PSC. **Document type:** *Journal, Academic/Scholarly.* **Description:** Covers social, economic and political studies relating to the Third World.
Related titles: Microfiche ed.; Microform ed.; Online - full text ed.: ISSN 1360-2241. GBP 654, USD 1,078 to institutions (effective 2006) (from bigchalk, EBSCO Publishing, Gale Group, IngentaConnect, Northern Light Technology, Inc., O C L C Online Computer Library Center, Inc., ProQuest Information & Learning, Swets Information Services).
Indexed: ABC, APEL, ASCA, AbHyg, AltPI, AmH&L, BAS, BrHumI, CurCont, DIP, EI, ForAb, GEOBASE, HistAb, I&DA, IBR, IBSS, IBZ, ILD, IPSA, IndIslam, KES, LID&ISL, LeftInd, MAB, MaizeAb, PAA&I, PAIS, PBA, PCI, PGegResA, PRA, PSA, PerIslam, PhilInd, RASB, RDA, RRTA, RefugAb, S&F, SOPODA, SPAA, SPPI, SSA, SSCI, SSI, SWA, SeedAb, SociolAb, TDB, WAE&RSA.
—BLDSC (8820.145300), IDS, IE, Infotrieve, ingenta. **CCC.**
Published by: Routledge (Subsidiary of: Taylor & Francis Group), 4 Park Sq, Milton Park, Abingdon, Oxon OX14 4RN, United Kingdom. TEL 44-1235-828600, FAX 44-1235-829000, journals@routledge.com, http://www.tandf.co.uk/journals/titles/01436597.asp, http://www.routledge.co.uk. Ed. Shahid Qadir. Circ: 6,000. **Subscr. to:** Taylor & Francis Ltd, Journals Customer Service, Rankine Rd, Basingstoke, Hants RG24 8PR, United Kingdom. TEL 44-1256-813000, FAX 44-1256-330245.

382 PAK ISSN 1018-8991
HC59.7
THIRDWORLD. Text in English. 1977. m. USD 45. adv. bk.rev. illus. **Document type:** *Academic/Scholarly.* **Description:** Covers all aspects of developing countries' affairs, including political and economic analysis, international assistance programs, human rights issues, the environment, education, law, with business surveys, interviews, and more.
Former titles (until 1988): Third World International (0253-9527); Third World Quarterly
Published by: Corporate & Marketing Communications (Pvt) Ltd., 47-A-2 Block 6, Pechs, Karachi, 75400, Pakistan. TEL 92-21-448569, FAX 92-21-437656, TELEX 23531-INDMN-PK. Ed. Syed Jawaid Iqbal. Circ: 45,000.

TRADE & DEVELOPMENT; news and trade opportunities. see *BUSINESS AND ECONOMICS—International Commerce*

TRADE AND DEVELOPMENT AGENCY. see *BUSINESS AND ECONOMICS—International Commerce*

TRADE AND DEVELOPMENT REPORT. see *BUSINESS AND ECONOMICS—International Commerce*

338.91 341.242 GBR ISSN 1356-3424
HC331
TRANSITION REPORT (YEAR). Text in English. 1992. a., latest 2004. GBP 30, EUR 45.71, USD 59.57 per issue; GBP 40, EUR 60.94, USD 79.42 combined subscription per issue print & online (effective 2005). back issues avail. **Document type:** *Trade.* **Description:** Source of information on developments in central and eastern Europe and the Commonwealth of Independent States (CIS). Offers comprehensive analysis of the transition to market economies and macroeconomic performance. Country-by-country assessments comprise macroeconomic tables, including output and expenditure and foreign direct investment. Also provides key data on liberalization, stabilization, privatization, enterprise reform, infrastructure, financial institutions and social reform.
Former titles (until 1994): E B R D. Economic Report (1351-8259); (until 1993): European Bank for Reconstruction and Development. Quarterly Economic Review (0967-9634)
Related titles: Online - full text ed.: GBP 20, EUR 30.47, USD 39.71 (effective 2005) (from Gale Group, IngentaConnect).
—BLDSC (9020.863000). **CCC.**
Published by: European Bank for Reconstruction and Development, Publications Desk, One Exchange Sq, London, EC2A 2EH, United Kingdom. TEL 44-20-73387553, FAX 44-20-73386102, pubsdesk@ebrd.com, http://www.ebrd.com/pubs/tr/index.htm.

338.91 USA ISSN 1018-208X
HG5993
TRENDS IN PRIVATE INVESTMENT IN DEVELOPING COUNTRIES. Text in English. 1990. a.
Related titles: ◆ Series of: I F C Discussion Paper. ISSN 1012-8069.
Indexed: IIS.
—CCC.
Published by: International Finance Corporation, 1818 H St N W, Washington, DC 20433. TEL 202-473-1155, FAX 202-676-0581.

TURKISH POLICY QUARTERLY. see *POLITICAL SCIENCE—International Relations*

U I E STUDIES IN EDUCATION. see *EDUCATION*

307.14 JPN ISSN 1020-3478
U N C R D ANNUAL REPORT (ENGLISH EDITION). Text in English. 1993. a. free. charts; illus. **Document type:** *Corporate.*
Related titles: Japanese ed.: U N C R D Annual Report (Nihonban). ISSN 1020-3486.
Published by: United Nations Centre for Regional Development, 1-47-1 Nagono, Nakamura-ku, Nagoya, Aichi 450-0001, Japan. TEL 81-52-5619377, FAX 81-52-5619375, info@uncrd.or.jp, http://www.uncrd.or.jp. Circ: 1,000.

307.1 JPN ISSN 0379-0347
HT390
U N C R D NEWSLETTER. Text in English. 1975. s-a. free. illus. **Document type:** *Newsletter.*
Published by: United Nations Centre for Regional Development, 1-47-1 Nagono, Nakamura-ku, Nagoya, Aichi 450-0001, Japan. TEL 81-52-5619377, FAX 81-52-5619375, info@uncrd.or.jp, http://www.uncrd.or.jp. Circ: 3,500.

U N C T A D BULLETIN. see *BUSINESS AND ECONOMICS—International Commerce*

338.91 CHE
U N C T A D OCCASIONAL PAPERS. Text in English. 2000. irreg., latest vol.136, 2001. back issues avail. **Document type:** *Monographic series, Academic/Scholarly.*
Published by: United Nations Conference on Trade and Development, 8-14 Avenue de la Paix, Geneva 10, 1211, Switzerland. TEL 41-22-9174924, FAX 41-22-9070195, info@unctad.org, http://www.unctad.org.

U N C T A D REVIEW. see *BUSINESS AND ECONOMICS—International Commerce*

U N C T A D SERIES ON ISSUES IN INTERNATIONAL INVESTMENT AGREEMENTS. see *BUSINESS AND ECONOMICS—Investments*

338.91 MNG
U N D P QUARTERLY REPORT. Text in English. q. free. back issues avail. **Document type:** *Corporate.*
Related titles: Online - full text ed.
Published by: United Nations Development Programme Mongolia, Erhuu St 7, PO Box 49 207, Ulan Bator, Mongolia. TEL 976-1-327585, FAX 973-1-326221, registry@undp.org.htm, http://www.un-mongolia.mn/undp/.

338 AUT ISSN 0258-8137
U N I D O ANNUAL REPORT. (United Nations Industrial Development Organization) Text in English. a.
Related titles: Online - full text ed.
Published by: United Nations Industrial Development Organization, Postfach 300, Vienna, W 1400, Austria. http://www.unido.org/doc/3480.

338 AUT ISSN 1020-2781
HD72 CODEN: UNINAI
U N I D O LINKS. Text in English. 1967. m. free. **Document type:** *Newsletter.* **Description:** Features expertise and other resources sought by developing countries' firms, resources available to them, recent publications and information products from UNIDO and forthcoming UNIDO events.
Formerly (until 1994): U N I D O Newsletter (0049-5387)
Media: Online - full text. **Related titles:** Arabic ed.: U N I D O Links. Al-Tab'at al-'Arabiyyat. ISSN 1020-2838; Chinese ed.: U N I D O Links. Zhongguohua. ISSN 1020-282X; French ed.: U N I D O Links. Ed. Francaise. ISSN 1020-279X; Russian ed.: U N I D O Links. Russkoe Izd.. ISSN 1020-2811; Spanish ed.: U N I D O Links. Ed. Espanola. ISSN 1020-2803.
Indexed: ABIPC, CRIA, CRICC, FLUIDEX, KES, RAPRA, RASB, WSCA.
Published by: United Nations Industrial Development Organization, Postfach 300, Vienna, W 1400, Austria. TEL 43-1-211-31-5538, FAX 43-1-209-2669, http://www.unido.org. Ed. Peter Ellwood. Circ: 12,000 (controlled).

338.91 DEU ISSN 1564-8184
U N VOLUNTEER NEWS. Text in English, French, Spanish. q. **Document type:** *Newsletter, Consumer.* **Description:** Concerns contributions of UN Volunteer specialists to international assistance for development, humanitarian relief, promotion of human rights and peace building.
Formed by the merger of (1975-19??): Bulletin V N U (0251-5318); (1975-19??): Boletin V N U (0251-5326); (1975-19??): U N V News (1016-0531); Which was formerly (until 1988): U N V Newsletter (0251-5334)
Related titles: Online - full text ed.: ISSN 1564-8176.
Published by: United Nations Volunteers, Martin-Luther-King-Str 8, Bonn, 53153, Germany. TEL 49-228-815-2000, FAX 49-228-815-2001, hq@unv.org, http://www.unv.org. Ed. Nanette Braun. R&P Fabienne Copin. Circ: 20,000 (controlled).

327 USA
U S A I D DEVELOPMENTS. Text in English. 1984. q. free. **Document type:** *Newsletter, Government.*
Former titles (until 1994): U S A I D Highlights (0899-6016); (until 1987): A I D Highlights (0743-5436)
Indexed: CWI.
Published by: U.S. Agency for International Development, Multimedia Communications Division, 1300 Pennsylvania Ave, N W, Rm 6 10, RRB, Washington, DC 20523-6100. TEL 202-712-4330, FAX 202-216-3035. Ed. Suzanne Chase. Circ: 15,000.

338.91 USA
U.S. AGENCY FOR INTERNATIONAL DEVELOPMENT. ANNUAL REPORT. Text in English. a. free. **Document type:** *Government.* **Description:** Summarizes the programs supported by U.S.A.I.D.
Published by: U.S. Agency for International Development, Office of Housing and Urban Developments, Bureau for Global Programs, Field Support and Research, Rm. 401, State Annex 2, Washington, DC 20523-0214. TEL 202-663-2530.

338.91 USA ISSN 0276-6469
HC60
U.S. AGENCY FOR INTERNATIONAL DEVELOPMENT. CONGRESSIONAL PRESENTATION, FISCAL YEAR. Text in English. 1961. a. free to qualified personnel. **Document type:** *Government.*
Published by: U.S. Agency for International Development, Office of Public Affairs, Washington, DC 20523. TEL 202-647-4330.

338.91 USA
U.S. DEPARTMENT OF COMMERCE. LATIN AMERICAN - CARIBBEAN BUSINESS DEPARTMENT CENTER. BULLETIN. Text in English. m. free. **Document type:** *Government.* **Description:** Offers trade and investment leads and news for businesses interested in opportunities in Latin America and the Caribbean (excluding Mexico). Also features a calendar of events.
Published by: U.S. Department of Commerce, Latin American - Caribbean Business Department Center, Rm H 3203, Washington, DC 20230. TEL 202-482-0841, FAX 202-482-2218. Circ: 10,500.

338.91 327.1 DNK ISSN 0106-3014
U-VEJVISER (YEAR); U-landsaktiviteter i Danmark. Text in Danish. 1979. a. DKK 125 domestic (effective 2000).
Description: Registers and describes 280 Danish organizations and groups concerned with developing countries.
Published by: Mellemfolkeligt Samvirke/Danish Association for International Co-operation, Borgergade 14, Copenhagen K, 1300, Denmark. FAX 45-77-31-01-01, ms@ms.dk. Ed. Hanne Palludan. Circ: 1,700.

338.91 AUS ISSN 1033-1891
AS4.U825
UNESCO AUSTRALIA. Text in English. 1991. s-a. free to approved institutions. **Document type:** *Newsletter, Government.* **Description:** Thematic issues on subjects related to education, science and culture in UNESCO, and Australian National Commission activities.
Formed by the merger of (1985-1991): Australian National Commission for UNESCO Newsletter (0725-5756); (1979-1991): UNESCO Review (0158-779X)
Indexed: GdIns, SPPI.
Published by: (Australia. Department of Foreign Affairs Trade), Australian National Commission for UNESCO, International Organisations Branch, Parkes, ACT 2600, Australia. TEL 06-261-2289, FAX 06-261-3424. Circ: 3,000.

UNITED NATIONS CONFERENCE ON TRADE AND DEVELOPMENT: PROCEEDINGS. see *BUSINESS AND ECONOMICS—International Commerce*

338.9 USA ISSN 0503-4108
UNITED NATIONS. CONFERENCE ON TRADE AND DEVELOPMENT. TRADE AND DEVELOPMENT BOARD. OFFICIAL RECORDS. Text in English. 1965. irreg. price varies. Supplement avail.

Formerly: United Nations. Trade and Development Board. Official Records (0082-8475)
Published by: (United Nations, Conference on Trade and Development (UNCTAD), Trade and Development Board), United Nations Publications, Rm DC2-853, United Nations Bldg, 2 United Nations Plaza, New York, NY 10017. TEL 212-963-8302, 800-253-9646, FAX 212-963-3489.

338.91 USA ISSN 0379-8119
JX1977
UNITED NATIONS DEVELOPMENT PROGRAMME. COMPENDIUM OF APPROVED PROJECTS✶. Text in English. 1972. a. USD 20.
Published by: United Publications, Inc., One U N Plaza, Rm DC2 0853, New York, NY 10017.

338.91 ETH
UNITED NATIONS ECONOMIC COMMISSION FOR AFRICA. ANNUAL REPORT. Text in English. irreg., latest 1997.
Published by: (Documents & Publishing Services Unit), United Nations, Economic Commission for Africa/Commission Economique pour l'Afrique, PO Box 3001, Addis Ababa, Ethiopia.

338.91 ETH ISSN 0252-2128
UNITED NATIONS ECONOMIC COMMISSION FOR AFRICA. BIENNIAL REPORT OF THE EXECUTIVE SECRETARY. Text in English. irreg., latest 1994.
Related titles: Microfiche ed.: (from CIS).
Indexed: IIS.
Published by: (Documents & Publishing Services Unit), United Nations, Economic Commission for Africa/Commission Economique pour l'Afrique, PO Box 3001, Addis Ababa, Ethiopia.

338.91 JPN ISSN 0259-4285
UNITED NATIONS UNIVERSITY. WORK IN PROGRESS. Text in English. 1976. 3/yr. free. bk.rev. charts; illus. **Document type:** *Newsletter.* **Description:** Covers peace and governance issues, environment and sustainable development, etc.
Related titles: French ed.; Japanese ed.; Spanish ed.
—BLDSC (9348.205000).
Published by: United Nations University, Public Affairs Section, 53-70 Jingu-Mae 5-chome, Shibuya-ku, Tokyo, 150-8925, Japan. TEL 03-3499-2811, FAX 03-3499-2828, TELEX J25442 UNATUNIV, mbox@hq.unu.edu, http://www.unu.edu/hq/ginfo/wip/wipindex.html. Circ: 35,000.

UNITED NATIONS WEEKLY REPORT. see *POLITICAL SCIENCE—International Relations*

338.91 GBR
➤ **UNIVERSITY OF BRADFORD. DEVELOPMENT AND PROJECT PLANNING CENTRE. BRADFORD DEVELOPMENT PAPERS.** Text in English. N.S. 1989. irreg. adv. **Document type:** *Academic/Scholarly.* **Description:** Discusses practical aspects of international development planning and management.
Former titles (until 1997): University of Bradford. Development and Project Planning Centre. New Series Discussion Papers (0957-6479); University of Bradford. Development and Project Centre. Occasional Paper Series
Published by: University of Bradford, Development and Project Planning Centre, The Library, Bradford, W Yorks BD7 1DP, United Kingdom. dppc-library@bradford.ac.uk, http://www.brad.ac.uk/acad/dppc/dppclib/publist.htm. Ed. Frances Cleaver. R&P John Weiss. Adv. contact Lesley Knight.

338.91 300 SDN
UNIVERSITY OF KHARTOUM. DEVELOPMENT STUDIES AND RESEARCH CENTRE. DISCUSSION PAPERS. Text in English. irreg.
Published by: University of Khartoum, Development Studies and Research Centre, Faculty of Economic & Social Studies, Khartoum, Sudan.

338.91 SDN
UNIVERSITY OF KHARTOUM. DEVELOPMENT STUDIES AND RESEARCH CENTRE. MONOGRAPH SERIES. Text in English. irreg. **Document type:** *Monographic series.*
Published by: University of Khartoum, Development Studies and Research Centre, P O Box 321, Khartoum, Sudan. Ed. Sadig Rasheed.

338.91 SDN
UNIVERSITY OF KHARTOUM. DEVELOPMENT STUDIES AND RESEARCH CENTRE. OCCASIONAL PAPERS. Text in English. 1979. irreg.
Published by: University of Khartoum, Development Studies and Research Centre, P O Box 321, Khartoum, Sudan. Ed. Sadig Rasheed.

338.91 KEN
UNIVERSITY OF NAIROBI. INSTITUTE FOR DEVELOPMENT STUDIES. CONSULTANCY REPORTS. Text in English. 1979. irreg., latest vol.16. price varies. charts; stat. back issues avail. **Document type:** *Monographic series, Academic/Scholarly.* **Description:** Researches social and economic issues affecting development in Kenya.
Published by: University of Nairobi, Institute for Development Studies, PO Box 30197, Nairobi, Kenya. TEL 254-2-332986, FAX 254-2-222036, TELEX 22095, ids.uon@elci.sasa.unon.org. Ed. Kibisu Kabatesi.

960 338.91 KEN ISSN 0547-1788
UNIVERSITY OF NAIROBI. INSTITUTE FOR DEVELOPMENT STUDIES. DISCUSSION PAPER. Text in English. 1965. irreg., latest vol.297, 1997. price varies. back issues avail. **Document type:** *Monographic series, Academic/Scholarly.* **Description:** Examines social and economic development issues in Kenya.
Indexed: ARDT, RRTA, WAE&RSA.
Published by: University of Nairobi, Institute for Development Studies, PO Box 30197, Nairobi, Kenya. TEL 254-2-332986, FAX 254-2-222036, TELEX 22095, ids.uon@elci.sasa.unon.org. Ed. Kibisu Kabatesi.

338.41 KEN
UNIVERSITY OF NAIROBI. INSTITUTE FOR DEVELOPMENT STUDIES. OCCASIONAL PAPER. Text in English. 1967. irreg., latest vol.63, 1996. price varies. bibl.; illus.; stat. back issues avail. **Document type:** *Monographic series, Academic/Scholarly.* **Description:** Discusses economic issues in Kenya.
Formerly: University College, Nairobi. Institute for Development Studies. Occasional Papers
Published by: University of Nairobi, Institute for Development Studies, PO Box 30197, Nairobi, Kenya. TEL 254-2-332986, FAX 254-2-222036, TELEX 22095, ids.uon@elci.sasa.unon.org. Ed. Kibisu Kabatesi.

338.91 GBR ISSN 0956-0742
UPFRONT. Text in English. 1989. q. USD 15 (effective 2000). adv. bk.rev. **Document type:** *Newsletter.* **Description:** Provides information on matters and issues causing poverty in Third World countries.
Indexed: RILM.
Published by: War on Want, Fenner Brockway House, 37-39 Great Guildford St, London, SE1 0ES, United Kingdom. TEL 44-20-7620-1111, FAX 44-20-7261-9291, wow@gn.apc.org, http://www.waronwant.org. Ed. Rob Cartridge. Adv. contact Steve Tibbett. Circ: 10,000.

338.91 USA ISSN 1560-0483
URBAN AGE. Text in Arabic, English, French, Spanish. 1977. q. USD 19.95 domestic; USD 29.95 in Canada; USD 34.95 elsewhere (effective 2005). adv. **Document type:** *Newsletter.* **Description:** Focuses on timely and relevant urban issues, such as violence in the cities, transportation, immigration, and infrastructure.
Formerly (until 1992): Urban Edge (0163-6510)
Indexed: AIAP, EIP, JOF, PAA&I.
—**CCC.**
Published by: Urban Age Institute, 870 Estancia, 11th Fl, San Francisco, CA 94903. http://www.urbanage.org/magazine.php.

URBAN ANTHROPOLOGY AND STUDIES OF CULTURAL SYSTEMS AND WORLD ECONOMIC DEVELOPMENT. see *ANTHROPOLOGY*

338.91 USA ISSN 1020-0215
URBAN MANAGEMENT PROGRAM. Text in English. irreg.
—BLDSC (9123.688704). **CCC.**
Published by: (International Bank for Reconstruction and Development), World Bank Group, PO Box 960, Herndon, VA 20172-0960. TEL 703-660-1580, FAX 703-661-1501, books@worldbank.org, http://www.worldbank.org. **Subscr. to:** Urban Management, PO Box 30030, Nairobi, Kenya. TEL 245-2-623536, 254-2-623218.

VIETNAM INVESTMENT REVIEW. see *BUSINESS AND ECONOMICS*

338.91 GBR
W D M IN ACTION. Text in English. 1972. q. GBP 16 to individuals; GBP 30 to institutions (effective 2002). adv. charts; illus. index. back issues avail. **Document type:** *Newsletter.* **Description:** Presents news and features on Third World debt and trade issues.
Formerly (until 1997): Spur (0306-5367)
Published by: World Development Movement, 25 Beehive Pl, London, SW9 7QR, United Kingdom. TEL 44-20-7737-6215, FAX 44-20-7274-8232, wdm@wdm.org.uk, http://www.wdm.org.uk. Ed., R&P Dave Timms. Adv. contact Anna Zohra Tikly. Circ: 12,500 (paid).

W I D BULLETIN. see *POLITICAL SCIENCE—Civil Rights*

330.9 FIN ISSN 1238-9544
W I D E R ANGLE. Text in English. 1990. s-a. **Document type:** *Newsletter.*
Related titles: Online - full content ed.
Published by: United Nations University, World Institute for Development Economics Research, UNU/WIDER Publications, Katajanokanlaituri 6 B, Helsinki, 00160, Finland. TEL 358-9-61599228, FAX 358-9-61599333, http://www.wider.unu.edu/welcome.htm. Ed. Adam Swallow.

W I D FORUM. see *POLITICAL SCIENCE—Civil Rights*

338.9 AUT
W I I W CURRENT ANALYSES AND COUNTRY PROFILES. Text in English. 1991. irreg., latest vol.11, 1998. **Document type:** *Monographic series, Academic/Scholarly.*
Formerly: W I I W Current Analyses
Published by: Wiener Institut fuer Internationale Wirtschaftsvergleiche/Vienna Institute for International Economic Studies, Oppolzergasse 6, Vienna, W 1010, Austria. TEL 43-1-53366100, FAX 43-1-533661050, wiiw@wsr.ac.at, http://www.wllw.ac.at.

338.9 AUT ISSN 1025-8930
➤ **W I I W FORSCHUNGSBERICHTE/W I I W RESEARCH REPORTS.** Text in German. 1972. irreg., latest vol.294, 2003. price varies. **Document type:** *Monographic series, Academic/Scholarly.* **Description:** Studies on the economies of the countries of Eastern Europe and the Commonwealth of Independent States and China, major issues of East-West trade, and Eastern enlargement for the European Union.
—BLDSC (4011.470000), IE.
Published by: Wiener Institut fuer Internationale Wirtschaftsvergleiche/Vienna Institute for International Economic Studies, Oppolzergasse 6, Vienna, W 1010, Austria. TEL 43-1-53366100, FAX 43-1-533661050, wiiw@wsr.ac.at, http://www.wiiw.ac.at. Ed. Michael Landesmann. R&P Ingrid Gazzari.

338.9 AUT
W I I W MONOGRAPHS/W I I W MONOGRAPHIEN. Text in English, German. irreg. **Document type:** *Monographic series, Academic/Scholarly.*
Published by: Wiener Institut fuer Internationale Wirtschaftsvergleiche/Vienna Institute for International Economic Studies, Oppolzergasse 6, Vienna, W 1010, Austria. TEL 43-1-53366100, FAX 43-1-533661050, wiiw@wsr.ac.at, http://www.wiiw.ac.at.

338.9 AUT
W I I W WORKING PAPERS. Text in English. irreg., latest vol.10, 1999. **Document type:** *Monographic series.*
Published by: Wiener Institut fuer Internationale Wirtschaftsvergleiche/Vienna Institute for International Economic Studies, Oppolzergasse 6, Vienna, W 1010, Austria. TEL 43-1-53366100, FAX 43-1-533661050, wiiw@wsr.ac.at, http://www.wiiw.ac.at.

THE WASHINGTON PACIFIC REPORT; the insider's newsletter highlighting the latest developments of interest involving the insular Pacific. see *POLITICAL SCIENCE*

338.91 USA ISSN 1069-5958
WASHINGTON WEEKLY REPORT (WASHINGTON)✶; a review of Congressional action affecting multilateral issues and institutions. Text in English. 1974. w. USD 60 to individuals; USD 100 to institutions.
Published by: United Nations Association of the United States of America, 801 Second Ave, 2nd Fl, New York, NY 10017. Ed. Steven A Dimoff. Circ: 400.

338.91 GBR
WELSH DEVELOPMENT AGENCY. ANNUAL REPORT/AWDURDOD DATBLYGU CYMRU. ADRODDIAD BLYNYDDOL. Text in English. a. free (effective 2005). **Document type:** *Corporate.*
Formerly (until 1996): Welsh Development Agency. Reports and Accounts
—BLDSC (1492.837000).
Published by: Welsh Development Agency/Awdurdod Datblygu Cymru, Principality House, The Friary, Cardiff, CF10 3FE, United Kingdom. TEL 44-1443-845500, FAX 44-1443-845589, enquires@wda.co.uk, http://www.wda.co.uk.

338.91 BEL ISSN 1370-2378
DE WERELD MORGEN. Text in Dutch. 1967. m. (11/yr.). EUR 19.83 domestic; EUR 29.74 in the European Union; EUR 39.66 elsewhere (effective 2002). bk.rev. charts; illus.; maps; stat. 40 p./no.; back issues avail. **Document type:** *Magazine.*
Published by: Flemish North South Movement, Vlasfabriekstraat 11, Brussels, 1060, Belgium. TEL 32-02-5361145, FAX 32-02-5361905, info@11.be, http://www.11.be/dewereldmorgen. Ed., R&P Stef Boogaerts. Pub. Jozef De Witte. Adv. contact Corine Van Kelecom TEL 32-02-5361117. Circ: 7,000 (paid).

338.91 JPN
WHAT IS ASIA SERIES/AJIA O MIRUME SERIES. Text in Japanese. 1966. irreg. (1-2/yr.). price varies. **Document type:** *Academic/Scholarly.* **Description:** Consists of introductory books for the study of development issues, "written in plain language." In spite of its title, it deals with all regions under development and issues concerning development.
Published by: Institute of Developing Economies/Ajia Keizai Kenkyusho, 3-2-2 Wakaba, Mihana-ku, Chiba-shi, Chiba 261-8545, Japan. TEL 81-43-299-9536, FAX 84-43-299-9724, info@ide.go.jp, http://www.ide.go.jp. Circ: 1,500.

338.91 CAN ISSN 1203-3634
WHO'S WHO IN INTERNATIONAL DEVELOPMENT. Text in English. 1986. biennial.
Formerly (until 1995): I D Profile (0832-8102)
Related titles: French ed.: Qui Fait Quoi en Developpement International. ISSN 1203-3642.

B

Published by: Canadian Council for International Cooperation, 1 Nicholas St, Ste 300, Ottawa, ON K1N 7B7, Canada. TEL 613-241-7007, FAX 613-241-5302, http://www.ccic.ca.

338.91 USA ISSN 1045-893X
HQ1240
THE WOMEN AND INTERNATIONAL DEVELOPMENT ANNUAL. Text in English. 1989. a. price varies. bibl.; charts. index. **Document type:** *Monographic series, Academic/Scholarly.*
Published by: (Michigan State University, Women & International Development Program), Westview Press (Subsidiary of: Perseus Books Group), 5500 Central Ave, Boulder, CO 80301. TEL 303-444-3541, FAX 303-449-3356. Eds. Anne Ferguson, Rita Gallin. Circ: 650.

WOMEN'S ENVIRONMENT AND DEVELOPMENT ORGANIZATION NEWS & VIEWS. see *WOMEN'S INTERESTS*

305.42 USA ISSN 0888-5354
HD6223
WORKING PAPERS ON WOMEN IN INTERNATIONAL DEVELOPMENT. Text in English. 1981. irreg., latest vol.265, 1998. price varies. adv. bk.rev. **Document type:** *Monographic series.* **Description:** Features journal-length articles based on original research or analytical summaries of relevant research, theoretical analyses, and evaluations of development programming and policy.
Formerly: W I D Working Papers
Indexed: PAIS, PopulInd, RDA.
Published by: Michigan State University, Women and International Development Program, 202 International Center, E. Lansing, MI 48824-1035. TEL 517-353-5040, FAX 517-432-4845, wid@msu.edu, http://www.isp.msu.edu/wid/. Circ: 1,000.

338.9 USA ISSN 0252-2942
HG3881
WORLD BANK. ANNUAL REPORT. Text in Arabic, Chinese, English, French, German, Japanese, Spanish. 1947. a. free to qualified personnel. charts; stat. reprint service avail. from SCH. **Document type:** *Corporate.*
Related titles: Online - full text ed.: (from EBSCO Publishing).
Indexed: IIS, RDA, WBA.
—BLDSC (1497.370000). **CCC.**
Published by: World Bank Group, 1818 H St, NW, Washington, DC 20433. TEL 202-473-1000, FAX 202-477-6391, books@worldbank.org, http://www.worldbank.org.

332.1 912 USA ISSN 0085-8293
WORLD BANK ATLAS. Text in English. 1967. a. USD 20 (effective 2005).
Related titles: Microfiche ed.: (from CIS).
Indexed: IIS, RASB.
—CISTI.
Published by: World Bank Group, PO Box 960, Herndon, VA 20172-0960. TEL 703-661-1580, FAX 703-661-1501, books@worldbank.org, http://www.worldbank.org.

320 USA ISSN 0253-2123
WORLD BANK COUNTRY STUDY. Text in English. irreg. price varies. back issues avail. **Document type:** *Monographic series, Consumer.* **Description:** Covers, in detail, a sociopolitical issue of a nation in the context of World Bank international development assistance.
Indexed: GEOBASE, IIS.
—**CCC.**
Published by: World Bank Group, 1818 H St, NW, Washington, DC 20433. TEL 202-473-1000, FAX 202-477-6391, books@worldbank.org, http://www.worldbank.org.

338.91 USA ISSN 0259-210X
WORLD BANK DISCUSSION PAPER. Text in English. 1986. irreg. price varies. back issues avail. **Document type:** *Monographic series, Consumer.* **Description:** Discusses topics of regional and global importance affected by World Bank loans.
Related titles: Online - full text ed.: (from Gale Group, O C L C Online Computer Library Center, Inc.).
Indexed: ASFA, AbAn, AgBio, ESPM, FPA, ForAb, GEOBASE, HortAb, IIS, NutrAb, OceAb, PGegResA, ProtozoAb, RDA, RRTA, RiceAb, SFA, SoyAb, WAE&RSA.
—BLDSC (9352.926100), IE, ingenta. **CCC.**
Published by: World Bank Group, 1818 H St, NW, Washington, DC 20433. TEL 202-473-1000, FAX 202-477-6391, books@worldbank.org, http://www.worldbank.org.

338.91 332 USA ISSN 1020-105X
WORLD BANK. E D I DEVELOPMENT STUDY. Text in English. 1991. irreg. price varies. back issues avail. **Document type:** *Monographic series.* **Description:** Discusses worldwide economic issues affecting and affected by E.D.I.
—**CCC.**
Published by: (Economic Development Institute), World Bank Group, 1818 H St, NW, Washington, DC 20433. TEL 202-473-1155, FAX 202-522-2627, books@worldbank.org, http://www.worldbank.org.

338.91 USA ISSN 1026-115X
WORLD BANK ENVIRONMENT PAPER. Text in English. irreg. price varies. back issues avail. **Document type:** *Monographic series.* **Description:** Treats, within the context of World Bank assistance, various environmental issues worldwide.
Indexed: GEOBASE, WAE&RSA.
—BLDSC (9352.926300).
Published by: World Bank Group, PO Box 960, Herndon, VA 20172-0960. TEL 703-661-1580, FAX 703-661-1501, books@worldbank.org.

363.7 USA ISSN 1020-0894
WORLD BANK. GLOBAL ENVIRONMENT FACILITY PAPER. Text in French. 1993. irreg., latest vol.12, 1994. price varies. back issues avail. **Description:** Discusses global issues affecting and affected by the World Bank Global Environment Facility.
Indexed: I&DA, PGegResA, RDA, S&F, WAE&RSA.
Published by: (Global Environment Facility), World Bank Group, 1818 H St, NW, Washington, DC 20433. TEL 202-473-1155, FAX 202-522-2627, books@worldbank.org, http://www.worldbank.org.

338.91 USA ISSN 0379-8674
HG3881.5.W57
WORLD BANK. MONTHLY OPERATIONAL SUMMARY. Text in English. 1978. m. USD 295 (effective 2004). **Description:** Updates the international business community about World Bank projects at all stages of development, from inception to approval, noting possible bank loans or IDA credits.
Formerly (until 1979): World Bank. Operational Summary of Proposed Projects (0161-9659)
Indexed: IIS.
—BLDSC (5944.310000). **CCC.**
Published by: World Bank Group, 1818 H St, NW, Washington, DC 20433. TEL 202-473-1155, FAX 202-522-2627. **Subscr. to:** The Johns Hopkins University Press, Journals Publishing Division, PO Box 19966, Baltimore, MD 21211.

338.91 USA ISSN 0258-2120
WORLD BANK POLICY PAPER. Text mainly in English. 1986. irreg. price varies. back issues avail. **Description:** Discusses worldwide issues of importance affecting World Bank loans.
Indexed: FPA, TDB.
—**CCC.**
Published by: (International Bank for Reconstruction and Development), World Bank Group, 1818 H St, NW, Washington, DC 20433. TEL 202-473-1155, FAX 202-522-2627, books@worldbank.org, http://www.worldbank.org.

332.1 016 USA
Z7164.F5
WORLD BANK. PUBLICATIONS UPDATE. Text in English. 1973. bi-m. free to qualified personnel. index. **Description:** Lists of new World Bank titles with brief descriptions and ordering information.
Former titles: World Bank Publications. Index (0095-5434); Catalog of World Bank Publications; (1973-1974): World Bank Catalog. Accession List
Published by: World Bank Group, PO Box 960, Herndon, VA 20172-0960. TEL 703-661-1580, FAX 703-661-1501, books@worldbank.org.

320 USA
WORLD BANK REGIONAL AND SECTORAL STUDIES. Text in English. irreg., latest 1994, Feb. price varies. back issues avail. **Document type:** *Monographic series.* **Description:** Discusses various social and political issues in the context of World Bank aid.
Published by: World Bank Group, PO Box 960, Herndon, VA 20172-0960. TEL 703-661-1580, FAX 703-661-1501, books@worldbank.org.

338.91 USA
WORLD BANK SERIES ON EVALUATION AND DEVELOPMENT. Text in English. 1998. s-a. USD 49.95 cloth ed.; USD 29.95 paper ed. (effective 2003). **Document type:** *Academic/Scholarly.* **Description:** Explores how to assess the proper relationship between institutions and development challenges through evaluative techniques.
Published by: Transaction Publishers, 390 Campus Dr, Somerset, NJ 07830. TEL 888-999-6778, FAX 732-748-9801, trans@transactionpub.com, http://www.transactionpub.com. Ed. Uma J Lele. Pub. Mary Curtis. R&P Marlena Davidian TEL 732-445-2280 ext 100. Adv. contact Alicja Garbie. **Subscr. to:** Transaction Distribution Center, 390 Campus Dr., Somerset, NJ 08873. TEL 732-445-1245, 888-999-6778, FAX 732-748-9801, orders@transactionpub.com.

338.91 USA ISSN 1726-5878
CODEN: WBTPEL
WORLD BANK WORKING PAPER. Text mainly in English. 1982. irreg. price varies. back issues avail. **Document type:** *Monographic series.* **Description:** Covers environmental, energy, or sociopolitical topics worldwide.
Formerly (until 2003): World Bank Technical Paper (0253-7494)
Related titles: Online - full text ed.: (from Gale Group, O C L C Online Computer Library Center, Inc.).

Indexed: ASFA, AbHyg, AgrForAb, BIOSIS Prev, ESPM, FPA, FS&TA, ForAb, GEOBASE, HortAb, I&DA, IIS, NutrAb, OceAb, OrnHort, PGegResA, PHN&I, RA&MP, RDA, RRTA, S&F, SFA, SoyAb, WAE&RSA.
—BLDSC (9352.934900), IE, ingenta. **CCC.**
Published by: World Bank Group, 1818 H St, NW, Washington, DC 20433. TEL 703-661-1580, FAX 703-661-1501, books@worldbank.org.

942 GBR ISSN 0305-750X
HC4 CODEN: WODEDW
➤ **WORLD DEVELOPMENT.** Text in English. 1973. 12/yr. EUR 1,869 in Europe to institutions; JPY 248,200 in Japan to institutions; USD 2,090 elsewhere to institutions; EUR 277 in Europe to qualified personnel; JPY 36,800 in Japan to qualified personnel; USD 309 elsewhere to qualified personnel; EUR 81 in Europe to students; JPY 10,700 in Japan to students; USD 90 elsewhere to students (effective 2006). adv. bk.rev. charts; illus. back issues avail. **Document type:** *Academic/Scholarly.* **Description:** Multidisciplinary journal publishing research and review articles on the social, economic and political consequences of development, focusing on reforms and cooperative efforts to eliminate disease, poverty, and illiteracy.
Incorporates: New Commonwealth (0028-4475)
Related titles: Microfilm ed.: (from PQC); Online - full text ed.: (from EBSCO Publishing, Gale Group, IngentaConnect, ScienceDirect, Swets Information Services).
Indexed: ABCPolSci, ABIn, ABS&EES, APEL, ARDT, ASCA, ASD, AbHyg, AgBio, Agr, AgrForAb, AnBrAb, BAS, BPIA, BrHumI, BusI, CREJ, CurCont, DIP, DSA, EI, ESPM, EnvEAb, FCA, FPA, FS&TA, FamI, ForAb, FutSurv, GEOBASE, HerbAb, HortAb, I&DA, IBR, IBSS, IBZ, ILD, IPSA, JEL, JOF, KES, MaizeAb, NutrAb, PAIS, PBA, PGegResA, PHN&I, PRA, PSA, PotatoAb, ProtozoAb, RASB, RDA, RRTA, RefZh, RevApplEntom, RiceAb, RiskAb, S&F, SOPODA, SPPI, SSA, SSCI, SSI, SWA, SeedAb, SociolAb, SoyAb, T&II, TDB, TriticAb, WAE&RSA, WTA.
—BLDSC (9354.150000), CISTI, IDS, IE, Infotrieve, ingenta. **CCC.**
Published by: (McGill University, Department of Geography CAN), Pergamon (Subsidiary of: Elsevier Science & Technology), The Boulevard, Langford Ln, East Park, Kidlington, Oxford OX5 1GB, United Kingdom. TEL 44-1865-843000, FAX 44-1865-843010, nlinfo-f@elsevier.nl, http://www.elsevier.com/locate/worlddev, http://www.elsevier.nl. Ed. Oliver T. Coomes. adv.: B&W page USD 550, color page USD 1,350. Circ: 1,600. **Subscr. to:** Elsevier BV, PO Box 211, Amsterdam 1000 AE, Netherlands. TEL 31-20-485-3757, FAX 31-20-485-3432, http://www.elsevier.nl.

338.91 USA ISSN 0163-5085
HC59.7
WORLD DEVELOPMENT REPORT. (Translations avail. in: Arabic, Chinese, French, German, Japanese, Portuguese, Russian, Spanish) Text in English. 1978. a. USD 26 softcover edition (effective 2005). stat. **Description:** Provides a summary of the state of economic development in developing countries. Includes a current overview of the world economy, statistics on social and economic development, and a special theme of current importance.
Related titles: CD-ROM ed.: USD 375 for single-user version; USD 750 for network version (effective 2000); Microfiche ed.: (from CIS); ♦ French ed.: Rapport sur le Developpement dans le Monde. ISSN 0271-1710.
Indexed: IIS, RASB, RiceAb.
—BLDSC (9354.170000), CISTI, IE, Infotrieve, ingenta. **CCC.**
Published by: World Bank Group, 1818 H St, NW, Washington, DC 20433. TEL 202-473-1000, FAX 202-477-6391, books@worldbank.org, http://www.worldbank.org.

338.91 USA
WORLD FOOD AID NEEDS AND AVAILABILITIES. FOOD AID NEEDS ASSESSMENT. Text in English. a. USD 20 (effective 2001). **Document type:** *Government.* **Description:** Examines the near- and long-term prospects for global food aid needs and for food aid availabilities from donor countries. Factors considered include supply and demand, prices, trade, food production, crop yields, fertilizer use, land constraints, water and irrigation, population growth, food consumption and nutrition, domestic policies and foreign exchange availablilities.
Published by: U.S. Department of Agriculture, Economic Research Service, 1800 M St. NW, Washington, DC 20036-5831. ersinfo@ers.usda.gov, ersinfo@ers.usda.gov, http://www.ers.usda.gov/publications/so/view.asp?f=international/gfa/. **Dist. by:** ERS-NASS, 5285 Port Royal Rd, Springfield, VA 22161. TEL 800-999-6779, 202-694-5050.

338.91 USA
WORLD FOOD AID NEEDS AND AVAILABILITIES. FOOD SECURITY ASSESSMENT. Text in English. a. **Document type:** *Government.* **Description:** Examines the near- and long-term prospects for global food aid needs and for food aid availabilities from donor countries. Factors considered include supply and demand, prices, trade, food production, crop yields, fertilizer use, land constraints, water and irrigation, population growth, food consumption and nutrition, domestic policies and foreign exchange availablilities.
Formerly: Food Aid Needs Assessment Report
Related titles: Online - full text ed.

Published by: U.S. Department of Agriculture, Economic Research Service, 1800 M St. NW, Washington, DC 20036-5831. TEL 202-694-5050, ersinfo@ers.usda.gov, http://www.ers.usda.gov/publications/so/view.asp?f=international/gfa/. **Dist. by:** ERS-NASS, 5285 Port Royal Rd, Springfield, VA 22161. TEL 800-999-6779.

338.91 ITA
WORLD FOOD PROGRAMME. ANNUAL REPORT✶. Text in Italian. 1987. a.
Formerly (until 1994): Food Aid Review (1014-8574); Which supersedes (in 1990): World Food Programme. Annual Report (1014-8515); Which was formerly (until 1988): World Food Programme. In Review (1014-1596)
Indexed: NutrAb, RDA, WAE&RSA.
Published by: World Food Programme, Public Affairs Service, Via C G Viola 68, Parco dei Medici, Rome, RM 00148, Italy. TEL 396-522821, FAX 396-5228240, TELEX 626675 WFP 1. Ed. Sylvana Foa. Circ: 24,000.

WORLD LIBRARIES; an international journal focusing on libraries and socio-economic development in Africa, Asia, and Latin America. see *LIBRARY AND INFORMATION SCIENCES*

WORLD TODAY SERIES: LATIN AMERICA. see *HISTORY—History Of North And South America*

WORLDWATCH READER. see *ENVIRONMENTAL STUDIES*

ZAMBIA NIEUWSBRIEF. see *HISTORY—History Of Africa*

338.91 DNK ISSN 0906-2408
ZIGZAG; en verden i bevaegelse. Text in Danish. 1991. q. DKK 200 membership (effective 2004). **Document type:** *Journal, Consumer.*
Formed by the merger of (1986-1991): Cikaden (0901-5418); (1980-1991): W U S Nyhedsbrev (0107-3710); Incorporates (1991-1992): Nyhedsbrev fra Ibis (0907-4872); Which was formerly (until 1992): W U S - Nyt (0906-3595)
Related titles: Online - full text ed.
Published by: W U S - Solidaritet og Bistand, c/o Ibis, Noerrebrogade 68B, Copenhagen N, 2200, Denmark. TEL 45-35-358788, FAX 45-35-350696, ibis@ibis.dk, http://www.ibis.dk/presse.php?dbt=zigzag&mode=list. Ed. Anders Tybjerg.

BUSINESS AND ECONOMICS—Investments

332.6 GBR
A A A INVESTMENT GUIDE. Text in English. 1982. a. GBP 29.99 (effective 2000). **Document type:** *Consumer.*
Former titles: Savers and Investors Guide; (until 1986): Money Mail Savers Guide (0265-2579)
Related titles: Diskette ed.
Published by: Wisebuy Publications, 25 West Cottages, West End Ln, London, NW6 1RJ, United Kingdom. TEL 44-20-7433-1121, http://www.wisebuy.co.uk. Ed. David Lewis.

332.6 USA ISSN 0192-3315
HG4501
A A I I JOURNAL. Text in English. 1979. 10/yr. USD 49 domestic; USD 64 foreign (effective 2005). adv. bk.rev. illus. Index. back issues avail.; reprints avail. **Document type:** *Magazine, Trade.* **Description:** Provides investment information and research to enable individual investors to become more effective managers of their own assets.
Indexed: BPI.
Published by: American Association of Individual Investors, 625 N Michigan Ave, Ste 1900, Chicago, IL 60611. TEL 312-280-0170, FAX 312-280-9883, members@aaii.com, http://www.aaii.com. Ed., R&P Maria Crawford Scott. Circ: 150,000 (paid).

A F T A MONITOR. (ASEAN Free Trade Area) see *BUSINESS AND ECONOMICS—International Commerce*

332.6 USA
A I C INVESTMENT BULLETIN✶. Text in English. 1934. s-m. looseleaf. USD 48. bk.rev. charts; stat. index.
Formerly: Investment Bulletin (0021-0072)
Published by: A I C Investment Advisors, Inc., 30 Stockbridge Rd, Great Barrington, MA 01230-1226. TEL 413-499-1111. Ed. Richard F Maloney.

332.6 ESP
A I F REVISTA. Text in Spanish. 6/yr.
Published by: Association of Professional Financial and Investment Consultants, Gran Via 594, 4o, Barcelona, 108007, Spain.

332.6 USA ISSN 1535-0207
A I M R CONFERENCE PROCEEDINGS. Text in English. q. **Document type:** *Proceedings, Academic/Scholarly.*
Formerly: I F C A Continuing Education (1086-5055)
—CCC.
Published by: Association for Investment Management and Research, 560 Ray C Hunt Drive, Charlottesville, VA 22903. TEL 434-951-5442, FAX 434-951-5370, http://www.aimr.org.

332.6 GBR
A I T C INVESTMENT TRUST DIRECTORY✶. Text in English. a. **Document type:** *Directory.*
Published by: Association of Investment Trust Companies, Durrant House, 3rd Fl, 8-13 Chiswell St, London, EC1Y 4YY, United Kingdom.

332 USA
A P P A DIGEST. Text in English. 1963. s-a. membership. adv. bk.rev. charts; illus. **Document type:** *Newsletter.*
Published by: American Professional Practice Association, 350 Fairway Dr, Ste 200, Deerfield Beach, FL 33441-1834. TEL 954-571-1877, membership@assnservices.com, http://www.appa-assn.com. Ed. B Lydia Young. Adv. contact Joe Santoli. Circ: 20,000.

ACCOUNTANTS S E C PRACTICE MANUAL. see *BUSINESS AND ECONOMICS—Accounting*

ACCOUNTING RESEARCH JOURNAL. see *BUSINESS AND ECONOMICS—Accounting*

332.6 GBR ISSN 0952-3618
HD2746.5 CODEN: AQMNED
ACQUISITIONS MONTHLY; the internationa m&a and buyouts magazine. Text in English. 1984. m. GBP 295 domestic; GBP 320 foreign (effective 1999). adv. index. back issues avail. **Document type:** *Trade.* **Description:** Global mergers and acquisitions. Analyzes latest bids, successes and stalled attempts.
Related titles: CD-ROM ed.; Online - full text ed.: (from Florida Center for Library Automation, Gale Group).
—BLDSC (0578.882300), IE, Infotrieve, ingenta.
Published by: Thompson Financial Services, Aldgate House, 33 Aldgate High St, London, EC3N 1DL, United Kingdom. TEL 44-171-369-7000, FAX 44-171-369-7766, editor@acquisitions-monthly.com, http://www.acquisitions-monthly.com. Ed. David Rothnie. Pub. Francesca Carnvale. R&P Martin McNulty. Adv. contact Lucy Hawthorne.

332.6 USA ISSN 1542-9466
HG4515.95
ACTIVE TRADER. Text in English. 2000. m. USD 59.40; USD 4.95 newsstand/cover domestic; USD 6.95 newsstand/cover in Canada (effective 2002). adv. **Document type:** *Magazine, Consumer.*
Published by: Tech Info, Inc., 150 S. Wacker Dr., Ste 880, Chicago, IL 60606. TEL 800-341-9384, FAX 312-775-5423, http://www.activetradermag.com. Ed. Mark Etzkorn. Pub. Bob Dorman.

332 URY ISSN 1688-0706
ACTIVIDAD DE FONDOS DE INVERSION. Cover title: Boletin Mensual de Fondos de Inversion. Text in Spanish. 1999. m. free (effective 2004). back issues avail.
Media: Online - full text.
Published by: Banco Central del Uruguay, Diagonal Fabini 777, Montevideo, Uruguay. info@bcu.gub.uy, http://www.bcu.gub.uy/a5454.html.

ACTUALIDAD EN SEGUROS Y FIANZAS. see *INSURANCE*

332.6 CUB
ACTUALIZACION DE LAS INVERSIONES AZUCARERAS. Text in Spanish. 1981. a. CUP 10. **Description:** Provides information on the relations of new plants and modernizations for the world sugar industry.
Published by: (Cuba. Ministerio del Comercio Exterior (MINCEX)), Empresa Cubazucar, Calle 23 No. 55,, Vedado, La Habana, Cuba. TEL 70-9742.

332.6 USA
ADDISON REPORT. Text in English. 1980. every 3 wks. USD 250. charts. back issues avail. **Document type:** *Newsletter.* **Description:** Advisory service utilizing "market integration." Analyzes the interaction of stocks, bonds and commodities. Provides specific mutual fund switch advice for gold, stock and Fidelity Select investors.
Published by: Addison Investment Management Co., 17 Robin Rd., Norfolk, MA 02056-1707. TEL 508-528-8678. Ed., Pub. Andrew L Addison. Circ: 1,000.

332 NLD ISSN 1384-6140
➤ **ADVANCES IN FINANCE, INVESTMENT AND BANKING.** Text in English. 1995. irreg., latest vol.7, 1998. price varies. bibl. back issues avail. **Document type:** *Monographic series, Academic/Scholarly.* **Description:** Presents unpublished studies on a variety of financial themes.
—BLDSC (0706.578000), ingenta.
Published by: Elsevier BV, North-Holland (Subsidiary of: Elsevier Science & Technology), Sara Burgerhartstraat 25, Amsterdam, 1055 KV, Netherlands. TEL 31-20-485-3911, FAX 31-20-485-2457, nlinfo-f@elsevier.nl, http://www.elsevier.nl/homepage/about/us/regional_sites.htt. **Subscr. to:** Elsevier BV, PO Box 211, Amsterdam 1000 AE, Netherlands. TEL 31-20-485-3757, FAX 31-20-485-3432.

332.6 USA ISSN 1555-5658
▼ **ADVISING BOOMERS**; the financial and lifestyle resource for trusted advisors. Text in English. 2005. q. USD 99 domestic; USD 129 in Canada; USD 159 elsewhere (effective 2005).
Published by: Highline Media, 33-41 Newark St, Fl 2, Hoboken, NJ 07030. TEL 201-526-1230, agoodenough@highlinemedia.com, http://www.advisingboomers.com.

332.6 336.2 368 CAN ISSN 1490-814X
ADVISOR'S EDGE; canada's magazine for the financial professional. Text in English. 1998. m. free domestic to qualified personnel; CND 68.95 domestic; CND 146.10 foreign (effective 2005). adv. **Document type:** *Magazine, Trade.* **Description:** Provides monthly information on trends, strategies, profiles and ideas of interest to financial advisors.
Related titles: Online - full text ed.: (from Micromedia ProQuest, ProQuest Information & Learning); ♦ Supplement(s): Advisor's Edge Report.
Indexed: ABIn.
Published by: Rogers Media Publishing Ltd, One Mount Pleasant Rd, 11th Fl, Toronto, ON M4Y 2Y5, Canada. TEL 416-764-2000, FAX 416-764-3941, http://www.advisor.ca/edge, http://www.rogers.com. Ed. Deanne Gage.

B

332.6 336.2 368 CAN
▼ **ADVISOR'S EDGE REPORT.** Text in English. 2005. m. **Document type:** *Newsletter.* **Description:** Targeted to financial planners, investment advisors and insurance specialists. Focuses on business building and planning issues and tax, investment and insurance trends.
Related titles: ♦ Supplement to: Advisor's Edge. ISSN 1490-814X.
Published by: Rogers Media Publishing Ltd, One Mount Pleasant Rd, 11th Fl, Toronto, ON M4Y 2Y5, Canada. TEL 416-764-2000, 416-764-1593, http://www.rogers.com. Ed. John Craig.

332.6 SWE ISSN 0345-3766
HC371
AFFAERSVAERLDEN. Text in Swedish. 1967. w. (43/yr.). SEK 1,460 in Sweden; SEK 2,132 in Europe; SEK 2,008 elsewhere;). adv. bk.rev. charts; stat. index. **Document type:** *Magazine, Trade.* **Description:** In-depth coverage, analyses and commentary of important developments and trends of Swedish companies and the international economy.
Formerly (until 1975): Affaersvaerlden - Finanstidningen (0001-9658); Which was formed by the merger of (1901-1967): Affaersvaerlden; (1936-1967): Finanstidningen
Related titles: Microform ed.: (from PQC); Online - full content ed.; ♦ Series: Placeringsguiden. ISSN 1651-4084.
Indexed: RASB.
Published by: Ekonomi och Teknik Foerlag, Maester Samuelsgatan 56, Stockholm, 10612, Sweden. TEL 46-8-7966650, FAX 46-8-202157, info@affarsvarlsen.se, info@et.se, http://www.affarsvarlden.se, http://www.et.se. Ed. Thomas Petersson. Adv. contact Fredrik Stockenstrand TEL 46-8-7966520. B&W page SEK 29,200, color page SEK 32,500; 210 x 297. Circ: 19,200.

AFRICA FINANCING REVIEW. see *BUSINESS AND ECONOMICS—Banking And Finance*

AFRICAN BUSINESS HANDBOOK; a practical guide to business resources for U.S.-Africa trade and investment. see *BUSINESS AND ECONOMICS—International Commerce*

332.6 ZAF ISSN 1606-8793
AFRICAN MARKETS OVERVIEW. Text in English. 2000. m. ZAR 150, USD 20 (effective 2004).
Related titles: Online - full text ed.
Published by: Univeristy of Stellenbosch, Business School. African Centre for Investment and Analysis, Belville, 7535, South Africa. TEL 27-21-9184254, FAX 27-21-9184262, mzorun@acia.sun.ac.za, http://www.acia.sun.ac.za/projects/research/AMOt.htm.

332.6 ITA
AGENDA DEL REDDITO FISSO. Text in Italian; Prefatory materials in English. 1990. a. USD 90. index. **Document type:** *Trade.* **Description:** Contains information on all fixed interest securities listed on the Italian stock exchanges having circulating amounts in excess of 10 billion lire.
Published by: Databank SpA, SASIP Division, Via Spartaco, 19, Milan, MI 20135, Italy. FAX 39-02-55183152. Ed. Carlo Colombi. Circ: 2,000.

332.6 DEU ISSN 0944-7598
AKTIEN ANALYZE. Text in German. 1993. m. looseleaf. **Document type:** *Bulletin.* **Description:** Information on stocks and the stock market.
Published by: V N R Verlag fuer die Deutsche Wirtschaft AG, Theodor-Heuss-Str 2-4, Bonn, 53095, Germany. TEL 49-228-8205-0, FAX 49-228-364411. Ed. Hans Joachim Oberhettinger.

332.62 DEU
AKTIEN & CO.; Alles ueber Boersen, Renten, Steuern, Zinsen. Text in German. 2000. w. adv. **Document type:** *Magazine, Consumer.* **Description:** Provides advice and information on investing in the stock market.
Formerly (until 2001): Aktienresearch (1615-3251)

Published by: Axel Springer Verlag AG, Axel-Springer-Platz 1, Hamburg, 20350, Germany. TEL 49-40-34727848, FAX 49-40-34727711, aktienresearch@finanzen.net, http://www.aktienundco.net, http://www.asv.de. Ed. Marc Reisner. Adv. contact Concetta Herion TEL 49-89-27264363. color page EUR 4,800; trim 188 x 252. Circ: 75,000 (paid). **Dist. by:** ASV Vertriebs GmbH, Suederstr 77, Hamburg 20097, Germany. TEL 49-40-34724857, FAX 49-40-23786715.

332.6 SWE ISSN 0345-049X
AKTIESPARAREN/SHAREHOLDER; foer aktivt aegande. Text in Swedish. 1967. 11/yr. SEK 405 to non-members; SEK 48 newsstand/cover to non-members (effective 2002). adv. bk.rev. **Document type:** *Magazine, Consumer.*
Related titles: Online - full text ed.
Published by: Sveriges Aktiesparares Riksfoerbund/Swedish Shareholders' Association, Radmansgatan 70A, Stockholm, 11389, Sweden. TEL 46-8-50651500, FAX 46-8-50651573, aktiespararen@aktiespararna.se, http://www.aktiespararna.se. Ed. Gunnar Johansson. Adv. contact Bjarne Kristiansen. B&W page SEK 38,000, color page SEK 47,000; trim 185 x 269. Circ: 84,400.

330 DEU ISSN 1432-4911
DER AKTIONAER. Text in German. 1996. m. EUR 3 newsstand/cover (effective 2004). adv. **Document type:** *Magazine, Trade.*
Published by: Boersenmedien AG, Hofer Str 20, Kulmbach, 95326, Germany. TEL 49-9221-90510, FAX 49-9221-877288, aktionaer@boersenmedien.de, http://www.deraktionaer.de. adv.: B&W page EUR 4,950, color page EUR 5,950. Circ: 37,645 (paid).

332.6 USA ISSN 0736-007X
AL HANSON'S ECONOMIC NEWSLETTER; the professional trader. Text in English. 1972. m. USD 120 (effective 2001). **Document type:** *Newsletter.*
Published by: Al Hanson, Ed. & Pub., PO Box 9, Ottertail, MN 56571. TEL 218-367-2404. R&P Al Hanson. Circ: 100,000.

332.6 USA ISSN 0095-2931
ALAN SHAWN FEINSTEIN INSIDERS REPORT. Variant title: Alan Shawn Feinstein's International Insiders Report. Text in English. 1973. m. USD 45. bk.rev. charts; stat.
Formerly: Insiders Report
Published by: Alan Shawn Feinstein & Associates, 41 Alhambra Circle, Cranston, RI 02905. TEL 401-467-5155. Ed. Alan Shawn Feinstein. Circ: 10,000.

332.6 350 USA ISSN 0092-6736
HJ3835.A4
ALASKA. DEPARTMENT OF REVENUE. STATE INVESTMENT PORTFOLIO. Key Title: State Investment Portfolio. (Juneau). Text in English. a. stat. **Document type:** *Government.*
Published by: Department of Revenue, PO Box SB, Juneau, AK 99811. TEL 907-465-2173.

332.6 GBR
ALLIED DUNBAR INVESTMENT AND SAVINGS HANDBOOK. Text in English. a. **Document type:** *Corporate.*
Former titles (until 1994): Allied Dunbar Investment and Savings Guide; (until 1990): Allied Dunbar Investment Guide
Published by: Longman Group Ltd., Law Tax and Finance Division, 21-27 Lambs Conduit St, London, WC1N 3NJ, United Kingdom. TEL 44-171-242-2548, FAX 44-171-831-8119.

ALMANAC OF BUSINESS AND INDUSTRIAL FINANCIAL RATIOS. see *BUSINESS AND ECONOMICS—Banking And Finance*

332.6 RUS
ALMAZY ROSSII SAKHA. VESTNIK. Abbreviated title: Vestnik ALROSA. Text in Russian. s-m. USD 105 in United States.
Published by: Almazy Rossii Sakha, Kazachii per 10-12, Moscow, 109017, Russian Federation. TEL 7-095-2306685.

332.6 USA ISSN 1544-7596
ALTERNATIVE INVESTMENT NEWS. Text in English. m. USD 2,395 combined subscription domestic print & online eds.; USD 2,470 combined subscription foreign print & online eds. (effective 2005). **Document type:** *Newsletter, Trade.* **Description:** Contains news and analysis on the fast growing institutional market for alternative investments - specifically the use of hedge funds and similar entities by public and corporate pension funds.
Related titles: Online - full text ed.: (from Gale Group).
—CCC.
Published by: Institutional Investor News (Subsidiary of: Euromoney Institutional Investor Plc.), 225 Park Ave S, 7th Fl, New York, NY 10003-1605. TEL 212-224-3570, FAX 212-224-3491, info@iiplatinum.com, http://www.iinews.com. Pub. Nanzeen Kanga TEL 212-224-3005.

332.6 USA
AMERICAN STOCK EXCHANGE WEEKLY BULLETIN. Text in English. 1927. w. looseleaf. USD 20 (effective 1999). **Document type:** *Bulletin.*
Published by: Nasdaq - AMEX Market Group, 86 Trinity Pl, New York, NY 10006-1872. TEL 212-306-1442.

332.6 658 338 USA
AMERICAN VENTURE; for entrepreneurs and accredited investors. Text in English. 1997. q. USD 15; USD 4.95 newsstand/cover. adv. bk.rev. back issues avail. **Document type:** *Consumer.* **Description:** Lists summaries of business plans and articles on venture investment, raising financing, and running a start-up venture.
Related titles: Online - full text ed.
Published by: Fusion International Inc., 8442 Limerick Ave., Winnetka, CA 91306-1521. TEL 503-221-9981, avce@aol.com, http://www.avce.com. Ed. Darlene Rominger. Pub. Douglas Clements. Adv. contact Warren Ledecky. page USD 1,700. Circ: 26,000.

332.6 USA ISSN 1088-0194
AMERNICK MARKET REPORT. Text in English. 1995. w. USD 249 (effective 2001). charts; stat. back issues avail. **Document type:** *Newsletter, Consumer.* **Description:** International stock market news for the general public, academicians, and new and experienced investors.
Related titles: Online - full text ed.: 1995.
Published by: Amernick Publishing Co., PO Box 10065, Berkeley, CA 94709-1065. amernick@attbi.com. Ed., Pub., R&P Larry Amernick. Adv. contact Ruth Amernick.

332.6 NLD
AMSTERDAM STOCK EXCHANGE. Text in English. 1969. a. charts; illus.; stat. **Description:** Covers issues, stocks, indices, trading activity, and bond market. Includes general information, statistics, and list of members.
Address: Beursplein 5, Amsterdam, 1001, Netherlands. Circ: 5,000.

332.6 340 USA ISSN 0887-1337
KF1439
ANALYSIS OF KEY S E C NO-ACTION LETTERS. Text in English. 1985. a., latest 2003-2004. USD 290 (effective 2004). 1136 p./no.; **Document type:** *Trade.* **Description:** Focuses on what currently constitutes the "common law" of the SEC, and its implications for today's securities practice.
Published by: Thomson West (Subsidiary of: Thomson Corporation, The), 610 Opperman Dr, Eagan, MN 55123-1396. TEL 651-687-8000, 800-328-4880, FAX 651-687-7302, http://west.thomson.com/product/14942868/product.asp. Ed. Robert J Haft.

332.6 USA ISSN 0884-6936
HG4905
ANALYST'S HANDBOOK. Text in English. 1964. a. (plus m. updates). USD 795. stat. **Document type:** *Trade.* **Description:** Enables anyone concerned with company or industry performance to compare the most important financial and per-share data for the S&P Industrial and the Index's 88 industry groups.
Published by: Standard & Poor's (Subsidiary of: McGraw-Hill Companies, Inc.), 55 Water St, New York, NY 10041. TEL 212-208-8000. Ed. C Levine.

ANDREWS LITIGATION REPORTER: BANK & LENDER LIABILITY. see *LAW*

332.6 USA ISSN 1532-3552
HG4961
ANGEL ADVISOR; the magazine for early stage investing. Text in English. 2000 (Dec). bi-m. USD 24.95 domestic; USD 39.95 foreign (effective 2001). adv. **Document type:** *Magazine, Trade.* **Description:** Informs, educates and inspires early-stage angel investors. Through its hands-on reporting, insightful editorial and up-to-the-minute market coverage. Serves as a guide to the most exciting and enriching sector of private investing. Coverage includes leads, start-up trends, tools on how to improve productivity, events calendar, case studies and more.
Published by: AngelSociety, 11 Broadway, 17th Fl, New York, NY 10004. TEL 212-248-5580, FAX 212-248-5581, info@angelsociety.com, http://www.angelsociety.com/advisor.html. Ed. Christine Miles. Adv. contact Stacy Kelly. **Co-publisher:** Bloomberg L.P.

332.96 ITA
ANNUARIO DELL'INVESTITORE; tutti i numeri dell'anno finanziario. Text in Italian. 1994. a. **Document type:** *Directory.*
Published by: Editrice Il Sole 24 Ore SpA, Via Paolo Lomazzo 52, Milan, 20154, Italy. TEL 39-02-30221, FAX 39-02-312055, info@ilsole24ore.com, http://www.ilsole24ore.com.

332.6 USA ISSN 1525-2221
ANNUITY MARKET NEWS. Text in English. 1994. m. USD 1,100 domestic; USD 1,200 elsewhere (effective 2005). adv. **Document type:** *Newsletter, Trade.*
Formerly (until 1999): Variable Annuity Market News (1077-9922)
Related titles: Online - full text ed.: (from EBSCO Publishing, Florida Center for Library Automation, Gale Group, O C L C Online Computer Library Center, Inc.).
Indexed: B&I.
—CCC.
Published by: Source Media, Inc., One State St Plaza, 27th Fl, New York, NY 10004. TEL 607-257-8997, 800-221-1809, Elizabeth.Barney@sourcemedia.com, custserv@sourcemedia.com, http://www.annuitymarketnews.com, http://www.sourcemedia.com. Ed. Lee Barney TEL 212-803-8751. adv.: B&W page USD 3,225.

ANNUITY SHOPPER. see *INSURANCE*

332.6 USA
ARGUS WEEKLY STAFF REPORT. Text in English. w. adv.
Published by: Argus Research, 61 Broadway Suite 1700, New York, NY 10006. TEL 212-425-7500. Ed. Jim Kelleher. Adv. contact Karena Bernard.

332.6 700 DEU
ARTINVESTOR. Text in German. 2001. 4/yr. EUR 34.50; EUR 24.50 to students; EUR 7.50 newsstand/cover (effective 2004). adv. **Document type:** *Magazine, Trade.* **Description:** Provides insight and analysis on the investment and financial aspects of the art world.
Published by: Finanzen Verlagsgesellschaft mbH (Subsidiary of: Axel Springer Verlag AG), Augustenstr 10, Munich, 80333, Germany. TEL 49-89-27264262, FAX 49-89-27264328, artinvestor@art-investor.de, redaktion@finanzen.net, http://www.artinvestor.de, http://www.finanzen.net. Ed., Pub. Edgar Quadt. Adv. contact Axel Zoerkendoerfer. page EUR 8,900. Circ: 44,000 (paid and controlled).

332.6 330.9 CAN
AS A MATTER OF FACT. Text in English. a. CND 5. index. **Description:** Information on the structure and services of the Toronto Stock Exchange.
Former titles: Everything You Ever Wanted to Know about the Toronto Stock Exchange; Toronto Stock Exchange Fact Book
Published by: Toronto Stock Exchange, 2 First Canadian Pl, Toronto, ON M5X 1J2, Canada. TEL 416-947-4222.

332.6 GBR ISSN 0966-0453
ASIA PACIFIC HANDBOOK. Text in English. 1991. s-a. **Description:** Covers the financial data of 1800 leading companies in Southeast Asia and Australia.
Published by: Financial Times Information Ltd., Fitzroy House, 13-17 Epworth St, London, EC2A 4DL, United Kingdom. TEL 44-20-7825-8000, FAX 44-20-7608-2032, justine.dye@ft.com, http://www.ft.com.

ASIA RISK. see *BUSINESS AND ECONOMICS—Banking And Finance*

ASIA TODAY INTERNATIONAL. see *BUSINESS AND ECONOMICS*

332.6 IRL ISSN 0332-4567
ASPECT. Text in English. 1982. 11/yr. **Description:** An investors' business magazine.
Address: P.O. Box 15, New Road, Greystones, Co. Dublin, Ireland. TEL 875514, FAX 875118. Ed. John O'Neill. Circ: 10,512.

ASSET. see *BUSINESS AND ECONOMICS—Banking And Finance*

332.63 USA ISSN 1520-3700
ASSET-BACKED ALERT. Text in English. 1995. 47/yr. USD 1,997 (effective 2005). adv. **Document type:** *Newsletter, Trade.* **Description:** Covers the global asset-backed securities (ABS) and mortgage-backed securities (MBS) markets, including the securitization of consumer debt, home mortgages and corporate receivables.
Related titles: Fax ed.; Online - full text ed.: (from Factiva, ProQuest Information & Learning).
Indexed: ATI.
Published by: Harrison Scott Publications, Inc., 5 Marine View Plaza, Ste 301, Hoboken, NJ 07030-5795. TEL 201-659-1700, FAX 201-659-4141, blebowitz@hspnews.com, info@hspnews.com, http://www.abalert.com/, http://www.hspnewsletters.com. Ed. Daniel Cowles TEL 201-234-3963. Adv. contact Mary E Romano TEL 201-234-3968. B&W page USD 3,100, color page USD 5,100.

332.6 330.9 GBR ISSN 1367-8086
ASSET FINANCE INTERNATIONAL. Text in English. 1976. 11/yr. GBP 695 combined subscription domestic print & online eds.; EUR 1,110 combined subscription in Europe print & online eds.; USD 1,140 combined subscription elsewhere print & online eds. (effective 2005). adv. back issues avail. **Document type:** *Trade.* **Description:** Supplies information on asset-based finance and leasing, domestic and international.
Former titles (until 1996): Asset Finance and Leasing Digest; Leasing Digest (0309-5258)
Related titles: Online - full text ed.: (from EBSCO Publishing, Gale Group, O C L C Online Computer Library Center, Inc.).
Indexed: ABIn, ATI, B&I.
—CCC.
Published by: Euromoney Institutional Investor Plc., Nestor House, Playhouse Yard, London, EC4V 5EX, United Kingdom. TEL 44-20-7779-8673, FAX 44-20-7779-8541, http://www.assetfinance.com, http://www.euromoney.com. Ed. Alasdaiz Whyte. Adv. contact Marc Lapeyre TEL 44-20-7779-8324. page GBP 6,150, page USD 9,500; 185 x

272. Circ: 7,500. **Subscr. to:** Eclipse, The In-house Fulfillment Bureau, PO Box 18083, London EC4V 5JS, United Kingdom. TEL 44-20-7779-8610, FAX 44-20-7779-8602, CustomerService@euromoneyplc.com. **Dist. in US by:** American Educational Systems, PO Box 246, New York, NY 10024-0246. TEL 800-431-1579, aesbooks@aol.com.

332.6   USA   ISSN 1553-4634
HG4028.A84
ASSET SECURITIZATION DIRECTORY. Text in English. 1992. a. **Document type:** *Directory, Trade.* **Description:** Contains updated listings and contact information for companies and personnel in the asset-backed securities industry, including credit enhancers, investors, issuers, rating agencies, software/information services, trustees and underwriters.
Formerly (until 1994): Securitization Directory & Handbook (1062-5135)
Related titles: Online - full text ed.: (from Gale Group).
—CCC.
Published by: Thomson Financial, Investment Banking/Capital Markets, 22 Thomson Pl., 11F4, Boston, MA 02210. TEL 800-607-4463.

332.6   USA   ISSN 1547-3422
ASSET SECURITIZATION REPORT. Text in English. 2001. 48/yr. USD 2,195 in US & Canada (effective 2005). adv. **Document type:** *Newsletter, Trade.* **Description:** Covers the field of loan sales and asset securitization, including reports on industry developments and trends, the volume of commercial loans sold by 10 of North America's largest banks, closing prices, and yield on activity traded asset-backed securities, and interviews with market leaders.
Formed by the merger of (1987-2001): Asset Sales Report (0894-6175); (199?-2001): Asset Sales Report International (1097-0762); (1986-2001): Mortgage Backed Securities Letter (1097-9204)
Related titles: Online - full text ed.: (from Data-Star, EBSCO Publishing, Gale Group, Northern Light Technology, Inc., O C L C Online Computer Library Center, Inc., ProQuest Information & Learning, The Dialog Corporation).
Indexed: ATI, B&I.
—CCC.
Published by: Source Media, Inc., One State St Plaza, 27th Fl, New York, NY 10004. TEL 212-803-6077, 800-221-1809, FAX 212-747-1154, custserv@sourcemedia.com, http://www.asreport.com, http://www.sourcemedia.com. Ed. Ronald Cooper TEL 212-803-8722.

332.6   FRA   ISSN 0066-9008
ASSOCIATION DES SOCIETES ET FONDS FRANCAIS D'INVESTISSEMENT. ANNUAIRE. Text in French. 1963. a. abstr.; stat. cum.index. **Document type:** *Directory.*
Published by: Association des Societes et Fonds Francais d'Investissement, 31 rue de Miromesnil, Paris, 75008, France. TEL 42-65-75-26, FAX 42-65-16-31. Ed. Pierre Boeglin. Circ: 2,500.

332.6 658   USA   ISSN 1056-6074
HG4928.5
ASSOCIATION FOR INVESTMENT MANAGEMENT AND RESEARCH. MEMBERSHIP DIRECTORY. Text in English. a. USD 150 (effective 2000). **Document type:** *Directory.* **Description:** Lists financial analysts and other investment professionals worldwide.
Formerly (until 1990): Institute of Chartered Financial Analysts. Joint Membership Directory (0897-3040); Which incorporates (in 1987): Financial Analysts Federation. Membership Directory (0430-4756)
Published by: Association for Investment Management and Research, 560 Ray C Hunt Drive, Charlottesville, VA 22903. TEL 804-951-5499, FAX 804-951-5262, http://www.aimr.org. Circ: 40,000.

133.5 332.6   USA
THE ASTRO-INVESTOR; a newsletter for investors. Text in English. 1986. m. looseleaf. USD 45 (effective 2000). bk.rev. charts; tr.lit. back issues avail. **Document type:** *Newsletter.* **Description:** Predicts the Dow Jones Industrial Average via Gann and Elliott Wave theories, Fibonacci ratios and astrology. One industry is reviewed each month.
Former titles (until 1991): Carol Mull's Market Forecast; (until 1990): Wall Street Astrologer
Published by: Mull Publications, PO Box 11133, Indianapolis, IN 46201-0133. TEL 317-357-6855, FAX 317-353-6246. Ed., R&P Carol S Mull. Circ: 250 (paid).

332.6   USA   ISSN 0736-7643
ASTUTE INVESTOR. Text in English. 1982. m. USD 48 (effective 2005). bk.rev. stat. 8 p./no.; back issues avail. **Document type:** *Newsletter, Trade.* **Description:** Benjamin-Graham stock screens service for value-oriented investors. Reviews investment strategies.
Published by: Charles E. Cardwell, Ed.& Pub., 135 Beechwood Ln, Kingston, TN 37763. TEL 865-376-2732, astute_investor@compuserve.com. Ed., Pub. Charles E Cardwell. Circ: 1,000 (paid and controlled).

332.6   DEU   ISSN 0949-0175
AUKTIONEN UND INVESTMENT. Text in German. 1995. m. **Document type:** *Trade.*
Formerly (until 1995): Immobilien-Informant (0947-6695)

Published by: Arbinger Verlags GmbH, Ludwig Ebner Str 9, Deggendorf, 94469, Germany. TEL 49-991-29029-0, FAX 49-991-2902990.

AURA WEALTH NEWSLETTER; economic survival in perilous times. see *BUSINESS AND ECONOMICS—Economic Situation And Conditions*

AUSTRALIA. BUREAU OF STATISTICS. HOUSEHOLD INVESTORS IN RENTAL DWELLINGS, AUSTRALIA. see *BUSINESS AND ECONOMICS—Abstracting, Bibliographies, Statistics*

AUSTRALIA. BUREAU OF STATISTICS. INFORMATION PAPER: UPGRADED BALANCE OF PAYMENTS AND INTERNATIONAL INVESTMENT POSITION STATISTICS. see *BUSINESS AND ECONOMICS—Abstracting, Bibliographies, Statistics*

AUSTRALIA. BUREAU OF STATISTICS. INTERNATIONAL INVESTMENT POSITION. AUSTRALIA: AUSTRALIAN SECURITIES HELD BY NOMINEES ON BEHALF OF NON-RESIDENTS. see *BUSINESS AND ECONOMICS—Abstracting, Bibliographies, Statistics*

AUSTRALIA. BUREAU OF STATISTICS. INTERNATIONAL INVESTMENT POSITION, AUSTRALIA: SUPPLEMENTARY COUNTRY STATISTICS. see *BUSINESS AND ECONOMICS—Abstracting, Bibliographies, Statistics*

332.6   AUS   ISSN 0155-0802
HG5891
AUSTRALIA. DEPARTMENT OF THE TREASURY. FOREIGN INVESTMENT REVIEW BOARD. REPORT. Key Title: Foreign Investment Review Board Report. Text in English. 1977-1994; resumed. a. price varies. back issues avail. **Document type:** *Government.* **Description:** Reports on the Board's examination of proposals by foreign interests to undertake direct investment in Australia and evaluates whether these proposals are suitable for approval under Australian Commonwealth Goverment policy.
Published by: (Australia. Department of the Treasury, Australia. Foreign Investment Review Board), AusInfo, GPO Box 1920, Canberra Mc, ACT 2610, Australia. TEL 61-2-6295-4512, FAX 61-2-6295-4455, http://www.ausinfo.gov.au, http://www.treasury.gov.au. **Orders to:** AusInfo Mail Order Sales, GPO Box 84, Canberra, ACT 2601, Australia. FAX 61-2-6295-4888.

338.0029   USA   ISSN 0067-1959
AUSTRALIAN MARKET GUIDE. Text in English. biennial.
Published by: Dun's Marketing Services (Subsidiary of: Dun & Bradstreet, Inc.), 3 Sylvan Way, Parsippany, NJ 07054-3896. TEL 201-455-0900.

332.6   AUS
AUSTRALIAN SHAREMARKET INVESTOR. Text in English. 1993. bi-m. AUD 150. **Description:** Presents research, analysis and comments on the top 100 companies on the Australian stock market.
Related titles: Online - full text ed.
Published by: Australian Equities Research P.L., Level 20, 90 Collins St, Melbourne, VIC 3000, Australia. TEL 61-3-965501442, FAX 61-3-96501592, research@aer.com.au, http://www.aer.com.au. Ed., Pub. Michael Gordon.

AVANTAGES. see *BUSINESS AND ECONOMICS—Labor And Industrial Relations*

332.6   CAN   ISSN 0849-1364
HG226   CODEN: BIRFE3
B C A INTEREST RATE FORECAST; a monthly analysis and forecast of U.S. bond and money market trends. Text in English. 1979. m. USD 695. **Description:** Analyzes bond and money market trends in the US based on a continuous appraisal of money and credit flows, economic developments, currency movements, budget and monetary policy.
Formerly (until 1990): Bank Credit Analyst. Interest Rate Forecast (0821-7858)
—CCC.
Published by: B C A Research, 1002 Sherbrooke St W, Ste 1600, Montreal, PQ H3A 3L6, Canada. TEL 514-499-9706, 800-724-2942, FAX 514-499-9709, http://www.bcaresearch.com. Ed. J Anthony Boeckh.

332.6 340   USA
B D WEEK. Text in English. bi-w. (48/yr.). USD 1,195 (effective 2005). back issues avail. **Document type:** *Newsletter, Trade.* **Description:** Keeps compliance and continuing education professionals informed about federal and state regulatory and enforcement activity affecting their organizations and operations.
Published by: Argosy Group (Subsidiary of: United Communications Group), 11300 Rockville Pike, Ste 1100, Rockville, MD 20852. TEL 888-287-2223, FAX 301-816-8945, http://www.bdweek.com/bdwjsp/index.jsp, http://www.ucg.com/argosy.html. Ed. Darrell Delamaide TEL 301-287-2654.

332.6   USA
B I RESEARCH. Text in English. 1980. every 6 wks. USD 110 domestic; USD 120 foreign (effective 2000). back issues avail. **Document type:** *Newsletter.* **Description:** Features market commentaries and detailed updates on recommended stocks.
Related titles: E-mail ed.: USD 156 (effective 2000).
Published by: B I Research, Inc., PO Box 133, Redding, CT 06875. TEL 203-270-9244, birstocks@aol.com, http://www.biresearch.com. Ed. Thomas C Bishop. Circ: 4,000 (paid).

332.6 910.202   USA   ISSN 0749-5714
BAHAMAS DATELINE. Text in English. 1976. m. USD 46 (effective 2000). adv. back issues avail. **Document type:** *Newsletter, Consumer.* **Description:** Reports on real estate, economic and political news and conditions, business, investment, banking laws and regulations, vacation living and other pertinent information for the foreign investor.
Incorporates: Bahamas Journal
Published by: Caribbean Dateline Publications, PO Box 41599, Arlington, VA 22204-8599. TEL 703-404-0894, pday@bahamasdateline.com, http://www.bahamasdateline.com. Ed., Pub., R&P N Poteat Day. Adv. contact Kathy Richards. Circ: 1,250.

332.6   BHS
BAHAMAS FINANCIAL DIGEST & BUSINESS TODAY. Text in English. 1973. bi-m. USD 60; USD 75 foreign. adv. bk.rev. back issues avail. **Document type:** *Trade.* **Description:** Contains business and financial information.
Published by: Symonette's Communication of the Bahamas Ltd., PO Box N 4824, Nassau, Bahamas. TEL 242-3562981, FAX 242-3565050. Ed. Michael A J Symonette. Adv. contact Rhonda Lighthouse. B&W page USD 495, color page USD 1,864. Circ: 17,500. **Subscr. to:** PO Box N 4271, Nassau, Bahamas.

332.66   BRA   ISSN 0100-767X
BALANCO FINANCEIRO. Text in Portuguese. 1978. m.
Published by: Gazetta Mercantil, Rua da Consolacao 247, 5 andar, Sao Paulo, SP CEP 01301, Brazil. TELEX 391-113-2871. Ed. Klaus Kleber. Circ: 32,000.

332.6   ESP   ISSN 0213-2648
BANCO DE BILBAO. INFORMACION SEMANAL DE VALORES. Text in Spanish. 1985 (no.2227). w. stat. **Description:** Lists the latest financial news concerned with the stock market.
Published by: (Servicio de Estudios), Banco de Bilbao, Gran via, 12, Bilbao, Spain.

332.6   ESP   ISSN 0005-4992
BANIF'S INVESTMENT BULLETIN. Text in Spanish. 1969. m. charts; stat.
Published by: Publibanif S.A., Juan Bravo, 2, Madrid, 28006, Spain. Ed. Jose Luis Sanchez Fernandez Valderrama. Circ: 5,000.

332.6   CAN   ISSN 0821-7866
BANK CREDIT ANALYST. Text in English. 1949. m. USD 695. charts; stat. **Description:** Provides a forecast of trends in major US investment markets, with particular emphasis on equities, business conditions, inflationary trends, interest rates, gold and the dollar.
—IE.
Published by: B C A Research, 1002 Sherbrooke St W, Ste 1600, Montreal, PQ H3A 3L6, Canada. TEL 514-499-9706, 800-724-2942, FAX 514-499-9709, http://www.bcaresearch.com. Ed. J Anthony Boeckh. Circ: (controlled).

368.854   USA   ISSN 1543-2068
HG1616.I5
BANK INVESTMENT CONSULTANT; insights and analysis for bank securities and insurance professionals. Text in English. 1993. m. free to qualified personnel; USD 89; USD 10 newsstand/cover (effective 2005). adv. reprints avail. **Document type:** *Magazine, Trade.*
Former titles (until 200?): Bank Investment Marketing (1088-730X); (until 1996): Financial Planning's Bank Investment Marketing (1074-2220); Incorporates (1991-1995): Bank Investment Representative (1055-3193)
Related titles: Online - full text ed.: (from EBSCO Publishing, Gale Group, LexisNexis, Northern Light Technology, Inc., O C L C Online Computer Library Center, Inc.).
Indexed: B&I.
—CCC.
Published by: Source Media, Inc., One State St Plaza, 27th Fl, New York, NY 10004. TEL 212-803-6077, 800-221-1809, FAX 212-747-1154, custserv@sourcemedia.com, http://www.bankinvestmentmktg.com, http://www.sourcemedia.com. Ed. Robert Hertzberg TEL 212-803-8695. Circ: 40,000 (controlled).

332.6   USA
BANK INVESTMENT PRODUCT NEWS. Text in English. w. USD 1,195; USD 1,225 in Canada; USD 1,270 elsewhere. **Document type:** *Newsletter.* **Description:** Provides information on mutual fund, brokerage and insurance product sales through bank channels.
Related titles: Online - full text ed.

B

Published by: Institutional Investor News (Subsidiary of: Euromoney Institutional Investor Plc.), 225 Park Ave S, 7th Fl, New York, NY 10003-1605. TEL 212-224-3800, FAX 212-224-3491.

BANK INVESTOR. see *BUSINESS AND ECONOMICS—Banking And Finance*

332.6 USA ISSN 1522-1318
BANK MERGERS & ACQUSITIONS WEEKLY. Text in English. w. USD 1,700 (effective 2002).
Published by: S N L Financial LC, 212 7th St NE, Charlottesvle, VA 22902-5307. TEL 434-977-1600, FAX 434-293-0407, http://www.snl.com.

332.6 USA
BANXQUOTE ONLINE✶. Text in English. 1985. w. USD 390. **Document type:** *Bulletin, Trade.* **Description:** Shows the highest-yielding jumbo and savings CDs and money market accounts quoted by federally-insured banks and S&Ls nationwide.
Media: Online - full text.
Published by: Masterfund Inc., 305 Madison Ave 5240, New York, NY 10165-0006. TEL 800-666-2000. Ed. Norbert Mehl.

B

332.6 USA
BARCLAY MANAGED FUNDS REPORT. Text in English. 1990. q. USD 150 domestic; USD 165 foreign (effective 2005). adv. 22 p./no.; back issues avail. **Document type:** *Newsletter, Trade.* **Description:** Provides an overview of performance of money managers specializing in equity, fixed income and derivatives markets. Includes interviews with money managers on current issues facing investors.
Formerly (until 2000): Barclay Managed Futures Report (1060-3158)
Published by: Barclay Trading Group, Ltd., 2094 185th St., Ste. 1B, Fairfield, IA 52556-8758. info@barclaygrp.com, http://www.barclaygrp.com. Ed., Pub., R&P, Adv. contact Sol Waksman. page USD 2,400. Circ: 2,000 (paid and controlled).

332.6 USA ISSN 1077-8039
HG1
BARRON'S; the Dow Jones business and financial weekly. Text in English. 1921. w. USD 149; USD 4 newsstand/cover (effective 2005). adv. bk.rev. illus. reprint service avail. from PQC. **Document type:** *Magazine, Consumer.* **Description:** Analyzes the impact of capital markets on the future of business and government. Discusses industrial developments and investment opportunities affecting the businessperson, money manager, investor, advocate, and consumer.
Former titles (until vol.74, no.13, 1994): Barron's National Business and Financial Weekly (0005-6073); (until 1942): Barron's
Related titles: Microfilm ed.: (from BHP, PQC); Microform ed.: (from PQC); Online - full text ed.: USD 29 (effective 2000) (from bigchalk, O C L C Online Computer Library Center, Inc., ProQuest Information & Learning).
Indexed: ABIn, ATI, BPI, BPIA, BRI, BusI, CBRI, EIA, EnvAb, LRI, MEDLINE, MagInd, NewsAb, PMR, RASB, T&II.
—BLDSC (1863.825000), IE, Infotrieve. **CCC.**
Published by: Dow Jones Company, 200 Liberty St, New York, NY 10281. TEL 212-416-2700, 800-223-2274, FAX 212-416-2829, http://www.barrons.com, http://www.dowjones.com/. Ed. Edwin A Finn Jr. Adv. contact Gary Holland. B&W page USD 30,088, color page USD 33,774. Circ: 301,230 (paid).

332.6 USA
BARRON'S ONLINE. Text in English. w. USD 29 (effective 1998). back issues avail. **Description:** Delivers a panoramic market view, investment ideas and insights from the experts, and the most complete statistical review of the preceding week's trading and financial activity.
Media: Online - full text.
Address: inquiries@interactive.wsj.com, http://www.barrons.com.

332.6 USA
BARTLETT LETTERS. Text in English. 1953. m. looseleaf. USD 25. back issues avail. **Document type:** *Newsletter.* **Description:** Investment advisory service recommending conservative stocks.
Address: 151 S Evanslawn, Box 465, Aurora, IL 60507. TEL 708-896-3143. Ed. John W Bartlett.

BAXTER; a world economic and investment service. see *BUSINESS AND ECONOMICS—Production Of Goods And Services*

332.6 DEU ISSN 0005-7029
BAYERISCHE BOERSE IN MUENCHEN. AMTLICHES KURSBLATT. Text in German. 1869. 5/w. **Document type:** *Journal, Trade.* **Description:** Contains news and information on traded papers and stock prices from the Bavaria stock exchange.
Published by: Muenchner Handelsverein e.V., Lenbachplatz 2A, Munich, 80333, Germany. TEL 49-89-549045-0, FAX 49-89-54904532, info@bayerische-boerse.de, http://www.bayerische-boerse.de. Circ: 500.

332.6 NLD
BELEGGEN MET VAN LANSCHOT. Text in Dutch. 1980. fortn. free. adv. charts.
Published by: F. van Lanschot Bankiers, Postbus 1021, 's Hertogenbosch, 5200 HC, Netherlands. TEL 073-153911, FAX 070-153151. Ed. R Verdam. Circ: 15,000.

BENEFITS & COMPENSATION INTERNATIONAL. see *INSURANCE*

BENEFITS CANADA; pension investment and employee benefits. see *BUSINESS AND ECONOMICS—Labor And Industrial Relations*

332.6 SCG
BEOGRADSKA BERZA. BILTEN. Text in Serbian, English. 1995. m. looseleaf. tr.lit.; charts; stat. 28 p./no. 3 cols./p.; back issues avail. **Document type:** *Bulletin.* **Description:** Includes statistical data on Belgrade Stock Exchange trading and other BSE news. Covers trading, listing, clearing, public and international relations, education, conferences and seminars, cooperation with financial institutions and other participants, plus news from other world stock exchanges.
Related titles: Online - full content ed.
Published by: Beogradska Berza, Omladinskih brigada 1, Novi Beograd, 11070. TEL 381-11-3115360, 381-11-3117410, FAX 381-11-138242, 381-11-3224967, http://www.belex.co.yu. Ed., R&P, Adv. contact Svetlana Cerovic. Circ: 3,000.

BERLINER BANK. BOERSENBRIEF. see *BUSINESS AND ECONOMICS—Banking And Finance*

332.6 DEU
BERLINER WERTPAPIERBOERSE AKTUELL. Text in German. 1994. q. **Document type:** *Newsletter.*
Published by: Boerse Berlin - Bremen, Fasanenstr 85, Berlin, 10623, Germany. info@boerse-berlin-bremen.de, http://www.berlinerboerse.de. Ed. Eva Klose.

332.6 CHE
BERNER BOERSENVEREIN. JAHRESBERICHT. Text in German. a. membership. **Document type:** *Yearbook, Corporate.*
Published by: Berner Boersenverein/Berne Stock Exchange, Aarbergergasse 36, Bern, 3011, Switzerland. TEL 41-31-3114042, FAX 41-31-3115309, http://www.bernerboerse.ch.

332.96 USA
BERT DOHMEN'S MUTUAL FUND STRATEGY. Text in English. m. USD 149.
Published by: Phillips International, Inc., 1201 Seven Locks Rd, Potomac, MD 20854. TEL 301-340-1520, 800-777-5005, FAX 301-424-4297. Ed. Bert Dohmen.

332.6 USA
BERT DOHMEN'S WELLINGTON LETTER✶. Text in English. 1977. m. USD 350; includes irreg. supplement. **Document type:** *Newsletter.* **Description:** Provides analysis and forecasts of the economy, Federal Reserve policy, and the global scene.
Published by: Dohmen Capital Research Institute, Inc., 1132 Bishop St, 1500, Honolulu, HI 96813-2807. TEL 808-545-2243, 800-992-9989, FAX 808-545-2243, dohmcap@aol.com. Ed. Bert Dohmen. Circ: 8,000.

332.109497 SCG ISSN 0354-1975
HG186.Y8
BERZA (BELGRADE). Text in Serbian. 1991. m. **Document type:** *Magazine, Trade.* **Description:** Provides latest information on the Yugoslav financial market, both by Yugoslav and foreign experts.
Published by: Trziste Novca a.d., Vojvode Milenka 40, Belgrade, 11000. TEL 381-11-3612430, info@tn.co.yu, http://www.tn.co.yu. Circ: 500.

332.64 DEU
BETAFAKTOR.INFO; der Boersen-Infodienst fuer Ihre Aktien. Text in German. 2002 (Feb.). 2/w. EUR 49 (effective 2002). adv. **Document type:** *Newsletter, Trade.* **Description:** Provides coverage of the latest prices, news, rumors and trends involving German and NASDAQ stocks.
Media: E-mail.
Published by: Creatix Medien GmbH, Arnulfstr 27, Munich, 80335, Germany. TEL 49-89-85631661, FAX 49-89-85631669, redaktion@betafaktor.info, http://www.betafaktor.info. Ed., Pub. Engelbert Hoermannsdorfer. Adv. contact Florian Kraenzle TEL 49-89-85631662. Circ: 500 (paid and controlled).

332.6 USA ISSN 0006-016X
BETTER INVESTING. Text in English. 1951. m. USD 29 domestic; USD 64 foreign (effective 2004). adv. bk.rev. illus.; charts. Index. 100 p./no.; reprint service avail. from PQC. **Document type:** *Magazine, Consumer.*
Related titles: Microform ed.: (from PQC); Online - full content ed.: membership only (effective 2001); Online - full text ed.: (from bigchalk, ProQuest Information & Learning).
Indexed: ABIn, ARG.
Published by: Betterinvesting, 711 W Thirteen Mile Rd, Madison Heights, MI 48071. TEL 248-583-6242, FAX 248-583-4880, bi@betterinvesting.org, http://www.betterinvesting.org. Adv. contact Maureen Feder TEL 248-583-6242 ext 366. B&W page USD 16,492, color page USD 24,950. Circ: 220,074 (paid).

346.092 USA
BEYOND ARBITRATION: DESIGNING ALTERNATIVES TO SECURITIES LITIGATION. Text in English. 1992. base vol. plus a. updates. USD 105.
Published by: LexisNexis (Subsidiary of: LexisNexis North America), PO Box 7587, Charlottesville, VA 22906-7587. TEL 804-972-7600, 800-562-1197, FAX 804-972-7666, llp.customer.support@lexis-nexis.com, http://www.lexislawpublishing.com. Eds. Danny Ertel, Ralph C Ferrara.

380.141 USA ISSN 1529-6199
BILL GARY'S PRICE PERCEPTIONS. Variant title: Price Perceptions. Text in English. 1970. bi-m. USD 360 (effective 2005). adv. charts; illus.; stat. back issues avail. **Document type:** *Newsletter, Trade.* **Description:** Commodity market research and analysis.
Incorporates (in Jan. 1997): Timing; Formerly: Commodity Investment Analyst
Published by: Commodity Information Systems, Inc., 3030 NW Expressway St., Ste 725, Oklahoma City, OK 73112-5434. TEL 405-604-8726, FAX 405-604-9696, info@cis-okc.com, http://www.cis-okc.com. Ed. William K Gary. R&P, Adv. contact Robert Howard. Circ: 1,000 (paid and controlled).

338 USA
BIOCENTURY QUARTERLY STOCK REPORTS. Text in English. q. USD 2,195 combined subscription for BioCentury: The Bernstein Report on BioBusiness, BioCentury Extra, BioCentury Part II, BioCentury Quarterly Stock Reports (effective 2004). **Document type:** *Trade.* **Description:** Provides a complete overview stock performance for nearly 500 public biotech companies in the US, Europe, Canada and Australia, plus the performance of 44 industry subgroups and benchmark indices.
Published by: BioCentury Publicattions Inc., PO Box 1246, San Carlos, CA 94070. http://www.biocentury.com/.

BIONICS. see *MEDICAL SCIENCES—Experimental Medicine, Laboratory Technique*

332.6322 USA ISSN 1092-8995
BIOTECH NAVIGATOR. Text in English. 1997. m. USD 199 in US & Canada; USD 235 elsewhere (effective 2000). back issues avail. **Document type:** *Newsletter.* **Description:** Gives detailed rationale explaining the logic behind each biotechnology stock evaluation, whether positive or negative.
Media: Online - full text.
Address: PO Box 7274, Beaverton, OR 97007-7274. TEL 503-649-1355, FAX 503-649-4490, info@biotechnav.com, nwong@biotechnav.com, http://www.biotechnav.com. Ed. Nadine Wong.

330 DEU ISSN 1619-5965
BIOTECH-REPORT. Text in German. 1999. m. **Document type:** *Newsletter, Trade.*
Published by: Boersenmedien AG, Hofer Str 20, Kulmbach, 95326, Germany. TEL 49-9221-90510, FAX 49-9221-877288, http://www.deraktionaer.de/AboInfoBiotechReport.phtml.

338.47660605 GBR ISSN 1471-583X
BIOTECHNOLOGY INVESTOR'S FORUM. Text in English. 2001. 2/yr. GBP 99 (effective 2003). **Document type:** *Magazine, Trade.*
Related titles: Online - full text ed.: (from Gale Group).
Published by: Euromoney Institutional Investor Plc., Nestor House, Playhouse Yard, London, EC4V 5EX, United Kingdom. TEL 44-20-7779-8714, FAX 44-20-7779-8760, information@euromoneyplc.com, http://www.biotechnology-investor.com, http://www.euromoneyplc.com.

332.6 RUS ISSN 0869-7124
BIZNES I INVESTITSII V S N G. Text in English, Russian. q. **Document type:** *Trade.*
Published by: Joint Ventures Ltd., Kutuzovskii pr-t 4-6, Moscow, 121170, Russian Federation. TEL 7-095-1486523, FAX 7-095-1481563. **US dist. addr.:** East View Information Services, 3020 Harbor Ln. N., Minneapolis, MN 55447. TEL 612-550-0961.

332 USA ISSN 1531-5061
BLOOMBERG MARKETS. Text in English. 1992. m. **Document type:** *Trade.* **Description:** Complements Bloomberg financial services with insight on everything from financial products and markets to industry analysis and career management.
Formerly (until 2000): Bloomberg (1063-2123)
Indexed: ASIP.
—**CCC.**
Published by: Bloomberg L.P., 499 Park Ave, New York, NY 10022. TEL 212-318-2200, FAX 212-980-4585, magazine@bloomberg.com, http://www.bloomberg.com. Ed. Ronald Henkoff. Pub. Michael Bloomberg.

332.6 GBR ISSN 1461-3638
BLOOMBERG MONEY. Text in English. 1998. m. GBP 29.40 domestic; GBP 68 foreign (effective 2005). adv. **Document type:** *Magazine, Consumer.* **Description:** Covers a wide range of personal finance issues including news and comment on Isas, unit trusts, investment trusts, property investment, equities, pensions and tax planning.

Published by: Incisive Media Plc., Haymarket House, 28-29 Haymarket, London, SW1Y 4RX, United Kingdom. TEL 44-20-74849700, FAX 44-20-79302238, customerservices@incisivemedia.com, http://www.masteringmoney.com/, http://www.incisivemedia.com/. Ed. Julian Marr TEL 44-20-74849771. Pub. Rod Boulogne TEL 44-20-79684513. Adv. contact Lisa Lloyd TEL 44-20-74849542.

332 USA ISSN 1522-6565
HG4529.5
BLOOMBERG WEALTH MANAGER. Text in English. 1999. bi-m. free to qualified personnel. adv. **Document type:** *Magazine, Trade.* **Description:** Targets the needs of financial planners and investment advisers who counsel the affluent.
—CCC.
Published by: Bloomberg L.P., 499 Park Ave, New York, NY 10022. TEL 212-318-4585, magazine@bloomberg.com, http://www.bloomberg.com/wealth. Ed. Robert Casey.

332.6 CAN
BLUE BOOK OF STOCK REPORTS. Text in English. fortn. looseleaf. CND 279 (effective 1999). charts; stat. back issues avail. **Document type:** *Newsletter.* **Description:** Contains information about over 250 Canadian companies.
Formerly: Blue Book of C B S Stock Reports (0384-7802)
Indexed: AgeL.
Published by: M P L Communications Inc., 133 Richmond St W, Ste 700, Toronto, ON M5H 3M8, Canada. TEL 416-869-1177, FAX 416-869-0456. Ed. Jon Chaplin. Pubs. Barrie Martland, Steven Pepper.

332.6 USA ISSN 0741-8345
BLUE CHIP FINANCIAL FORECASTS. Text in English. 1982. m. USD 695 (effective 2005). **Document type:** *Newsletter.* **Description:** Covers addresses what top analysts are saying about interest rates and monetary policy.
Related titles: E-mail ed.: USD 399.
Published by: Aspen Publishers, Inc. (Subsidiary of: Wolters Kluwer N.V.), 5301 Buckeystown Pike, Ste. 400, Frederick, MD 21704-8319. customer.service@aspenpubl.com, http://www.aspenpublishers.com. Ed. Randell Moore. **Dist. by:** Customer Care, 7201 McKinney Circle, Frederick, MD 21704. TEL 800-234-1660, FAX 800-901-9075.

332.6 USA ISSN 0896-4904
BLUE CHIP STOCKS. Text in English. 1974. a. looseleaf. USD 59.95 (effective 2005). index. back issues avail. **Document type:** *Newsletter, Trade.*
Published by: Elton Stephens Investments, PO Box 476, South Bend, IN 46624-0746. TEL 800-553-5866, http://www.eltonstephens.com. Ed., R&P Elton Stephens. Circ: 2,500 (paid).

332.6 USA
BLUE LIST OF CURRENT MUNICIPAL AND CORPORATE OFFERINGS. Text in English. 1935. d. (5/w.). USD 940. adv. back issues avail. **Document type:** *Trade.* **Description:** Gives municipal bond listings for municipal bond dealers.
Related titles: Online - full text ed.
Published by: Standard & Poor's (Subsidiary of: McGraw-Hill Companies, Inc.), 55 Water St, New York, NY 10041. TEL 212-208-8000. Ed. Marjorie Schmidt. Adv. contact Dominick Didiorgio. Circ: 4,700 (paid).

332.6 USA
BLUE SKY PRACTICE; for public and private direct participation offerings. Text in English. latest 2003-2004 Edition, base vol. plus a. updates. USD 325 base vol(s). (effective 2003). **Document type:** *Trade.* **Description:** Designed to provide a general introduction to state regulation of public and private offerings of securities of direct participation programs, as well as provide an examination of the requirements relating to the various types of programs.
Published by: Thomson West (Subsidiary of: Thomson Corporation, The), 610 Opperman Dr, Eagan, MN 55123-1396. TEL 651-687-8000, 800-328-4880, FAX 651-687-7302, http://west.thomson.com/product/13405326/product.asp. Eds. Derek A Wittner, Peter M Fass.

332.6 USA
THE BLUE STAR LIST. Text in English. 1996. w. free. **Document type:** *Newsletter, Trade.* **Description:** Constitutes a financial publication that specializes in uncovering under and overvaluations in fundamentally sound companies. Contains critical information crucial for making intelligent investing decisions.
Media: Online - full text.
Published by: Buttonwood Financial Resources, 135 Crow Hill Rd, Ste 2H, Mount Kisco, NY 10549. bfr@buttonwood.net, http://www.buttonwood.net/. Ed. Justin Dangler.

332.6 USA
BOB BRINKER'S MARKETIMER. Text in English. 1986. m. USD 185 (effective 2001). **Document type:** *Newsletter.* **Description:** An investment advisory newsletter providing stock market and interest rate timing forecasts, no-load mutual fund recommendations, model portfolios, and discussions on the factors leading to conclusions.
Address: 2023 N Atlantic Ave, Ste 301, Cocoa, FL 32931. Ed., Pub. Bob Brinker.

332.6 DEU
BOERSE BERLIN - BREMEN. AMTLICHES KURSBLATT. Text in German. 5/w. mkt. **Document type:** *Newspaper, Trade.*
Formerly: Berliner Wertpapierboerse. Amtliches Kursblatt (0003-214X)
Published by: Boerse Berlin - Bremen, Fasanenstr 85, Berlin, 10623, Germany. TEL 49-30-3110910, FAX 49-30-31109178, info@boerse-berlin-bremen.de, http://www.berlinerboerse.de. Ed. Eva Klose. Circ: 500.

332.6 DEU ISSN 0934-8441
BOERSE ONLINE; das Anlegermagazin. Text in German. 1987. w. EUR 140.40; EUR 3 newsstand/cover (effective 2003). adv. bk.rev. back issues avail. **Document type:** *Magazine, Consumer.* **Description:** Presents tips and advice on the stock markets for investors.
Published by: Boerse Online Verlag GmbH, Weihenstephaner Str 7, Munich, 81673, Germany. TEL 49-89-415206, FAX 49-89-4152310, info@boerse-online.de, http://www.boerse-online.de. Ed. Thomas Schumm. Adv. contact Carl-Joachim Rantz. page EUR 10,500. Circ: 109,687 (paid and controlled).

332.6 DEU
BOERSE STUTTGART. AMTLICHES KURSBLATT. Text in German. 1861. 5/w. **Document type:** *Bulletin, Trade.* **Description:** Lists stocks and their prices from the local stock exchange.
Former titles: Baden-Wuerttembergische Wertpapierboerse zu Stuttgart. Amtliches Kursblatt; Wertpapierboerse in Stuttgart. Amtliches Kursblatt (0003-2158)
Published by: Boerse Stuttgart AG, Schlossstr 20, Stuttgart, 70174, Germany. anfrage@boerse-stuttgart.de, http://www.boerse-stuttgart.de. Circ: 200.

332.6 AUT
BOERSEN-KURIER. Text in German. 1922. w. EUR 79.90 (effective 2005); ATS 1,400 foreign; EUR 2.50 newsstand/cover (effective 2005). adv. bk.rev. **Document type:** *Newspaper, Trade.* **Description:** Reports on all areas of investment, including stock markets, options and futures, antiques, investor relations, related software, etc.
Formerly: Wiener Boersen-Kurier
Published by: Observer GmbH, Lessinggasse 21, Vienna, W 1020, Austria. TEL 43-1-213220, FAX 43-1-21322810, redaktion@boersen-kurier.at, http://www.boersen-kurier.at. Ed. Marius Perger. Pub. Herbert Laszlo. adv.: B&W page EUR 5,700; trim 272 x 420. Circ: 11,500 (paid and controlled).

336.764 DEU ISSN 0942-5861
BOERSENBERATER. Text in German. 1989. m. EUR 3.58 newsstand/cover (effective 2004). adv. **Document type:** *Magazine, Trade.*
Published by: S V Corporate Media GmbH (Subsidiary of: Sueddeutscher Verlag GmbH), Emmy-Noether-Str 2, Munich, 80992, Germany. TEL 49-89-5485201, FAX 49-89-54852192, info@sv-medien-service.de, http://www.sv-medien-service.de/svcm/. adv.: B&W page EUR 1,440, color page EUR 3,000; trim 178 x 246. Circ: 11,867 (controlled).

332.6 SWE ISSN 0281-3149
BOERSGUIDE. Text in Swedish. 1966. s-a. SEK 195 (effective 1993).
Formerly (until 1975): Investment Guide (0579-4013)
Published by: Oehman, Fack 7415, Stockholm, 10391, Sweden. **Dist. by:** Sveriges Aktiesparares Riksfoerbund, Fack 21194, Stockholm 10031, Sweden.

332.6 SWE ISSN 0284-0162
BOERSINSIKT. Text in Swedish. 1982. 30/yr. SEK 1,795 (effective 1993).
Former titles (until 1985): Insikt - Placeringsraadgivning; (until 1983): Insikt i Aktier, Raavaror, Valutor, Obligationer, Skatter, Privatekonomi
Address: Fack 6044, Sollentuna, 19106, Sweden. TEL 46-8-754-92-00, FAX 46-8-754-89-40. Ed. Mab Jonnerhag.

332.6 SWE ISSN 1100-1275
BOERSVECKAN. Text in Swedish. 1986. 43/yr. SEK 2,390 combined subscription print & online eds (effective 2004). adv. **Document type:** *Newsletter.*
Related titles: Online - full text ed.
Address: PO Box 7465, Stockholm, 10392, Sweden. TEL 46-8-103350, FAX 46-8-201400, redaktionen@borsvekan.se, http://www.borsveckan.se. Eds. Bjoern Davegaardh, Per Forsberg. Adv. contact Christian Danielsson TEL 46-70-5716588.

332.6 PER
BOLETIN BURSATIL. Text in Spanish. 1978. m. free. **Document type:** *Bulletin.*
Published by: Bolsa de Valores de Lima, Miro Quesada 265, Casilla Postal 1538, Lima, 100, Peru.

332.6 ESP ISSN 0214-2368
BOLETIN DE BOLSA EN DISKETTE. Text in Spanish. 1988. 52/yr. EUR 42 (effective 2000). back issues avail. **Document type:** *Bulletin, Trade.*
Media: CD-ROM. **Related titles:** E-mail ed.; Fax ed.
Published by: San Niceforo S.L., C. Xavier Cabello 10, S.I. Escorial, 28200, Spain. TEL 34-1-8903998, juanca@tinn.net, sanniceforo@retemail.es. Ed. Juan Ignacio Callejo Rio.

070.5 USA
BOLITHO - CRIBB REPORT✶; a broker's report on the free newspaper, shopper, and specialty paper industry. Text in English. m. **Document type:** *Newsletter, Trade.*
Formerly: Cribb Report
Published by: Bolitho - Cribb & Associates, 89 Columbine CT, Bozeman, MT 59715. TEL 406-586-6621, FAX 406-586-6774, jcribb@imt.net, http://www.cribb.comjcribb/bcreport.html.

332.64 ESP ISSN 1132-3337
BOLSA DE BARCELONA. INFORME ANUAL. Text in Spanish, Catalan, English. 1978. a. stat. **Document type:** *Yearbook, Corporate.*
Former titles (until 1990): Bolsa de Barcelona. Memoria (1132-1377); Bolsa de Barcelona. Estadisticas
Published by: Sociedad Rectora de la Bolsa de Valores de Barcelona, S.A./Barcelona Stock Exchange, Paseo de Gracia 19, Barcelona, 08007, Spain. TEL 34-93-1013555, FAX 34-93-4013650, informacion@borsaben.es, http://www.borsaben.es. Circ: 2,000.

332.64 ARG
BOLSA DE COMERCIO DE ROSARIO. INFORMATIVO SEMANAL. Text in Spanish. 1983. w. ARS 66 domestic; USD 140 foreign. adv. charts; stat. **Document type:** *Newsletter, Trade.*
Formerly: Bolsa de Comercio de Rosario. Boletin Informativo
Published by: (Direccion de Informaciones y Estudios Economicos), Bolsa de Comercio de Rosario, Cordoba, 1402, Rosario, Santa Fe 2000, Argentina. TEL 54-341-4213437, FAX 54-341-4241019, dyiee@bcr.com.ar, http://www.bolsarosario.com. R&P Rogelio Tomas Ponton. Adv. contact Patricia Bergero.

332.6 VEN
BOLSA DE VALORES DE CARACAS. ANUARIO BURSATIL✶ /CARACAS STOCK EXCHANGE. ANNUAL REPORT. Text in Spanish. 1979. a. USD 65. **Document type:** *Corporate.*
Published by: Bolsa de Valores de Caracas C.A., Ed. Atrium Nivel P, C. Sorocaima e Avdas. Tamanaco y Venezuela, Caracas, DF 1080, Venezuela. TEL 81 51 11. Ed. Ariel Viale.

332.6 VEN
BOLSA DE VALORES DE CARACAS. MONTHLY BULLETIN✶ . Text in Spanish. 1976. m. USD 25. **Document type:** *Bulletin.*
Published by: Bolsa de Valores de Caracas C.A., Ed. Atrium Nivel P, C. Sorocaima e Avdas. Tamanaco y Venezuela, Caracas, DF 1080, Venezuela. TEL 81 51 11. Ed. Ariel Viale.

332.6 VEN
BOLSA DE VALORES DE CARACAS. REVISTA TRIMESTRAL✶ /CARACAS STOCK EXCHANGE. QUARTERLY BULLETIN. Text in Spanish. 1947. irreg. USD 60. **Document type:** *Bulletin.*
Published by: Bolsa de Valores de Caracas C.A., Ed. Atrium Nivel P, C. Sorocaima e Avdas. Tamanaco y Venezuela, Caracas, DF 1080, Venezuela. TEL 81-51-11, TELEX BOLVA 26536. Ed. Ariel Viale.

332.6 VEN
BOLSA DE VALORES DE CARACAS. WEEKLY BULLETIN✶ . Text in Spanish. 1988. w. USD 50. **Document type:** *Bulletin.*
Published by: Bolsa de Valores de Caracas C.A., Ed. Atrium Nivel P, C. Sorocaima e Avdas. Tamanaco y Venezuela, Caracas, DF 1080, Venezuela. TEL 81 51 41. Ed. Ariel Viale.

332.6 PER ISSN 1682-430X
BOLSA DE VALORES DE LIMA. BOLETIN DIARIO. Text in Spanish. 1999. d.
Media: Online - full text.
Published by: Bolsa de Valores de Lima, Miro Quesada 265, Casilla Postal 1538, Lima, 100, Peru. TEL 51-1-4260714, FAX 51-1-4267650, http://www.bvl.com.pe/pubdif/publica_boletin.htm.

332.64 PER
BOLSA DE VALORES DE LIMA. MEMORIA. Text in Spanish. 1975. a. free.
Published by: Bolsa de Valores de Lima, Miro Quesada 265, Casilla Postal 1538, Lima, 100, Peru.

332.6 PRT
BOLSA DE VALORES DE LISBOA. BOLETIM DE COTACOES. Text in Portuguese. 250/yr. **Document type:** *Bulletin.*
Related titles: E-mail ed.
Published by: Bolsa de Valores de Lisboa, Editora da Bolsa, Rua Soeiro Pereira Gomes, Lisbon, 1649-017, Portugal. TEL 351-1-7900000, FAX 351-1-7952024, TELEX 44751 BVLISB P, infomktg@bvl.pt, bdp.marketing@bvl.pt, http://www.bvlp.pt. Circ: 1,000.

332.64 URY ISSN 0797-5198
BOLSA DE VALORES DE MONTEVIDEO. BOLETIN MENSUAL. Text in Spanish. 1981. m. USD 7.
Published by: Bolsa de Valores de Montevideo, Misiones, 1400, Montevideo, 11006, Uruguay.

332.6 URY
BOLSA DE VALORES DE MONTEVIDEO. ESTUDIO ESTADISTICOS. BOLETIN TRIMESTRAL. Text in Spanish. q.
Published by: Bolsa de Valores de Montevideo, Misiones, 1400, Montevideo, 11006, Uruguay.

B

▼ new title ➤ refereed ✶ unverified ◆ full entry avail.

BOLSA DE VALORES DE QUITO. BOLETIN DE OPERACIONES. see *BUSINESS AND ECONOMICS—Abstracting, Bibliographies, Statistics*

332.64 ECU
BOLSA DE VALORES DE QUITO. INFORMES Y MEMORIA ANUAL. Text in Spanish. a. **Document type:** *Corporate.* **Description:** Reports exchange transactions. Includes statistics of floor and electronic trading, fixed and variable income securities, and the performance of various market sectors.
Published by: Bolsa de Valores de Quito, Amazonas 540 y Carrion, Apartado 17-01-3772, Quito, Ecuador. TEL 593-2-526805, FAX 593-2-500942, information@ccbvq.com, http://www.ccbvq.com.

332.6 BRA ISSN 0557-0506
BOLSA DE VALORES DO RIO DE JANEIRO. RESUMO ANUAL. Text in Portuguese. 1964. a. BRL 1,500, USD 20.
Published by: Bolsa de Valores do Rio de Janeiro/Rio de Janeiro Stock Exchange, Praca 15 de Novembro, 20, Rio de Janeiro, RJ, Brazil. FAX 5521-221-2151. Circ: 500.

B

332.64 MEX
BOLSA MEXICANA DE VALORES. BOLETIN BURSATIL CAPITALES/MEXICAN STOCK EXCHANGE. CAPITAL MARKET BULLETIN. Text in Spanish. d. MXP 7,750 (effective 1999). **Document type:** *Bulletin.* **Description:** Provides daily market operation in this market. Includes an analysis and capital market instruments valuation section, news and methodological notes.
Published by: Bolsa Mexicana de Valores, S.A. de C.V./Mexican Stock Exchange, Paseo de la Reforma 255, Mexico City, DF 06500, Mexico. TEL 52-5-7266794, FAX 52-5-7266836, cinvforma@bmv.com.mx, http://www.bmv.com.mx/bmv/suscripciones.html.

332.64 MEX
HG5710.M48
BOLSA MEXICANA DE VALORES. BOLETIN BURSATIL DINERO Y METALES/MEXICAN STOCK EXCHANGE. MONEY & METAL MARKET BULLETIN. Text in Spanish. d. MXP 8,000 (effective 1999). **Document type:** *Bulletin.* **Description:** Provides information related to rates, news of interest and Banco de Mexico information.
Formerly: Bolsa Mexicana de Valores. Boletin Bursatil Dinero (0188-3887)
Published by: Bolsa Mexicana de Valores, S.A. de C.V./Mexican Stock Exchange, Paseo de la Reforma 255, Mexico City, DF 06500, Mexico. TEL 525-726-67-91, FAX 52-5-5910634, cinforma@bmv.com.mx, http://www.bmv.com.mx/suscriptions.html.

332 MEX
BOLSA MEXICANA DE VALORES. INFORMACION FINANCIERA ANUAL SOBRE ASAMBLEAS/MEXICAN STOCK EXCHANGE. GENERAL STOCKHOLDERS' MEETINGS INFORMATION. Text in Spanish. a. MXP 1,750 (effective 1999). **Description:** Contains information on the main financial data of companies registered on the stock exchange.
Published by: Bolsa Mexicana de Valores, S.A. de C.V./Mexican Stock Exchange, Paseo de la Reforma 255, Mexico City, DF 06500, Mexico. TEL 52-5-7266794, FAX 52-5-7266836, cinforma@bmv.com.mx, http://www.bmv.com.mx/bmv/suscripciones.html.

332.6 MEX
BOLSA MEXICANA DE VALORES. INFORMACION FINANCIERA MENSUAL/MEXICAN STOCK EXCHANGE. MONTHLY FINANCIAL INFORMATION. Text in Spanish. m. MXP 13,000 (effective 1999). **Description:** Publishes financial reports on the mutual funds listed on the stock exchange.
Published by: Bolsa Mexicana de Valores, S.A. de C.V./Mexican Stock Exchange, Paseo de la Reforma 255, Mexico City, DF 06500, Mexico. TEL 525-726-67-91, FAX 525-591-0534, cinfoma@bmv.com.mx, http://www.bmv.com.mx/suscripciones.html.

332.6 MEX
BOLSA MEXICANA DE VALORES. PROGRAMA EXTRAORDINARIO DE DIVULGACION DE INFORMACION FINANCIERA. Text in Spanish. irreg. USD 30. **Description:** Contains preliminary information on the foreign currency position trade balance and cash flow information for companies registered on the exchange.
Published by: Bolsa Mexicana de Valores, S.A. de C.V./Mexican Stock Exchange, Paseo de la Reforma 255, Mexico City, DF 06500, Mexico. TEL 525-726-67-91, FAX 525-591-0534.

BOLSA MEXICANA DE VALORES. RESUMEN BURSATIL/MEXICAN STOCK EXCHANGE. STATISTICS SUMMARY. see *BUSINESS AND ECONOMICS—Abstracting, Bibliographies, Statistics*

332.6 USA ISSN 0732-0469
HG4501
THE BOND BUYER. Text in English. 1891. d. (Mon.-Fri.). USD 2,197 print or online; USD 2,627 combined (effective 2005). adv. **Document type:** *Newspaper, Trade.*
Formerly (until 1982): Daily Bond Buyer (0884-3937)
Related titles: Microfilm ed.: 1891 (from PMC); Online - full text ed.: 1891 (from EBSCO Publishing, Florida Center for Library Automation, Gale Group, Northern Light Technology, Inc., O C L C Online Computer Library Center, Inc., ProQuest Information & Learning).
Indexed: ABIn, B&I, T&II.
—CCC.
Published by: Source Media, Inc., One State St Plaza, 27th Fl, New York, NY 10004. TEL 212-803-6077, 800-221-1809, FAX 212-747-1154, custserv@sourcemedia.com, http://www.bondbuyer.com, http://www.sourcemedia.com. Circ: 40,000. **Co-publisher:** Deutsche Bank.

THE BOND BUYER'S MUNICIPAL MARKETPLACE. see *BUSINESS AND ECONOMICS—Trade And Industrial Directories*

332.6 USA ISSN 0738-5579
BOND FUND SURVEY✶. Text in English. 1983. m. looseleaf. USD 450. charts; stat. back issues avail. **Description:** Performance and descriptive reports on over 300 corporate, municipal, government, closed-end funds and unit trusts.
Published by: Survey Publications Co., 23 E 81 St, Apt 2, New York, NY 10028-0224. TEL 212-988-2498. Ed. Judith C Lack.

332.63 USA
BOND MARKET: ANALYSIS AND OUTLOOK. Text in English. a.
Published by: Salomon Brothers, Inc., Marketing Department, 7 World Trade Center, New York, NY 10048. TEL 212-783-7000.

332.6 DEU ISSN 0931-119X
BOND UND SHARE; der Wertpapiersammler. Text in German. 1985. q. adv. bk.rev. back issues avail. **Document type:** *Magazine, Trade.* **Description:** Reports on bonds and sharecertificates for collecting, as gift items and investment.
Published by: Aktien Galerie GmbH, Spetzgarter Weg 1, Ueberlingen, 88662, Germany. TEL 49-7551-9445714, FAX 49-7551-9445715, w.k@aktien-galerie.de, http://www.geburtstagsaktie.de. Ed. Wilhelm Kuhlmann. Circ: 3,300.

332.6 GBR ISSN 0961-8171
HG4502
THE BONDHOLDER; with Euro shares coverage. Text in English. 1872. w. (plus d. online updates). GBP 2,750. adv. stat. q. index. Supplement avail. **Document type:** *Newsletter.* **Description:** Covers corporate action on worldwide bonds, warrants, and European equities and funds.
Formerly: Bondholder's Register (0006-7075)
Published by: Valorinform, Aldgate House, 33 Aldgate High St, 2nd. Fl, London, EC3N 1DL, United Kingdom. TEL 44-171-369-7059, FAX 44-171-369-7065, bassfeldr@tfseur.co.uk. Ed., Adv. contact Ralph Bassfeld. page GBP 990; 175 x 261.

332.6 USA ISSN 1089-8794
HF5429.235.U5
BOND'S FRANCHISE GUIDE. Text in English. 1985. a. USD 35.
Formerly (until 1995): Source Book of Franchise Opportunities (1056-8654)
Published by: Irwin Professional Publishing, 1333 Burr Ridge Pkwy., Burr Ridge, IL 60521-6489. Eds. Christopher E Bond, Robert E Bond.

332 USA ISSN 0278-8896
HG1
BONDWEEK (NEW YORK, 1981); the newsweekly of fixed income and credit markets. Text in English. 1981. w. (51x/yr). USD 2,245 combined subscription for print & online eds. (effective 2005). adv. reprint service avail. from PQC. **Document type:** *Newsletter, Trade.* **Description:** Covers the major taxable debt markets - treasuries and foreign sovereigns, mortgage and asset-backed, and investment-grade and high-yield corporates.
Related titles: Online - full text ed.: (from Florida Center for Library Automation, Gale Group, ProQuest Information & Learning).
Indexed: ABIn.
—CCC.
Published by: Institutional Investor News (Subsidiary of: Euromoney Institutional Investor Plc.), 225 Park Ave S, 7th Fl, New York, NY 10003-1605. TEL 212-224-3800, FAX 212-224-3491, info@iiplatinum.com, http://www.bondweek.com, http://www.iinews.com. Pub. Elayne Glick. Circ: 5,000 (paid).

332.6 USA
BOSTON STOCK EXCHANGE GUIDE. Text in English. 1970. base vol. plus q. updates. USD 505 base vol(s). (effective 2004). **Description:** It is the official publication of the directory, constitution, rules and policies of the Exchange and the Boston Stock Exchange Clearing Corporation. Information concerning all stocks and bonds listed on the Exchange are listed in alphabetical order by corporation.
Related titles: CD-ROM ed.: USD 355 (effective 2004); Online - full content ed.: USD 355 (effective 2004).
Published by: C C H Inc., 2700 Lake Cook Rd, Riverwoods, IL 60015. TEL 847-267-7000, 800-449-6439, cust_serv@cch.com, http://www.cch.com.

338.7 BWA
BOTSWANA DEVELOPMENT CORPORATION. ANNUAL REPORT. Text in English. 1971. a. **Description:** Reports on BDC's role in identifying investment opportunities in Botswana for exploitation by both local and foreign investors.
Published by: Botswana Development Corporation, Private Bag 160, Gaborone, Botswana. TEL 267-351151, FAX 267-373539, TELEX 2251-BD. Circ: 2,500.

332.6 BWA
BOTSWANA DEVELOPMENT CORPORATION. NEWSLETTER. Text in English. 1971. q. free. illus. **Description:** Informs the public of ongoing activities within BDC.
Published by: (Public Relations Unit), Botswana Development Corporation, Private Bag 160, Gaborone, Botswana. TEL 267-351151, FAX 267-0373539, TELEX 2251 BD. Circ: 1,500.

332.6 FRA ISSN 1168-3155
BOURSE DE PARIS. ACTIONS. Text in French. 1967. m. charts; mkt.; stat. **Description:** Studies the French stock market evolution.
Former titles (until 1992): Bourse de France. Revue Mensuelle de Statistiques (0995-1164); (until 1988): Bourse de Paris. Statistiques Mensuelles (0039-0623)
Published by: Bourse de Paris, 39 rue Cambon, Paris, 75001, France. TEL 49-27-1000, FAX 33-49-271433, TELEX 215 561 F. Circ: 900.

BOWNE DIGEST FOR CORPORATE & SECURITIES LAWYERS; abstracts of current articles from more than 280 legal periodicals. see *LAW—Abstracting, Bibliographies, Statistics*

332.6 USA ISSN 1053-0908
BOWSER DIRECTORY OF SMALL STOCKS. Text in English. 1990. m. USD 89 (effective 2004). back issues avail. **Document type:** *Directory.* **Description:** Covers 14 fields of information on over 700 low-priced stocks for the do-it-yourself researchers.
Published by: Bowser Report, PO Box 6278, Newport News, VA 23606. TEL 757-877-5979, FAX 757-595-0622, ministocks@aol.com, http://stock-information.com/stocks/small-stocks-directory.shtml. Ed. Cindy Bowser.

332.6 USA ISSN 0738-7288
BOWSER REPORT; a newsletter for minipriced stocks. Text in English. 1976. m. USD 54 domestic; USD 63 foreign (effective 2005). back issues avail. **Document type:** *Newsletter, Consumer.* **Description:** Features up-to-date information on stocks selling for $3 a share or less.
Address: PO Box 6278, Newport News, VA 23606. TEL 757-877-5979, FAX 757-595-0622, ministocks@aol.com, http://stock-information.com/stocks/bowser-report.shtml, http://www.thebowserreport.com. Ed. R Max Bowser. Circ: 10,000 (paid).

332.62 USA
BRADFORD NETWORK NEWS. Text in English. bi-m. **Document type:** *Newsletter, Trade.* **Description:** Provides a communications link between J.C. Bradford & Co.'s corporate offices and its employees.
Published by: (J.C. Bradford & Co.), Hammock Publishing, Inc., 3322 W End Ave, Ste 700, Nashville, TN 37203. TEL 615-690-3400, FAX 615-690-3401, info@hammock.com, http://www.hammock.com.

332.6 GBR
BRIEFING ON BRITAIN. Text in English. 1985. 3/yr. free. **Document type:** *Government.* **Description:** Designed to meet the needs of the U.S. corporate investor and executive thinking of locating their business in the U.K.
—BLDSC (2283.957990).
Published by: Invest in Britain Bureau, 1 Victoria St, 66-74 Victoria St, London, SW1H 0ET, United Kingdom. TEL 44-171-215-5638, FAX 44-171-215-5651, http://www.dti.gov.uk/ibb. Ed. Lynnette Falk. adv.: B&W page GBP 1,350. Circ: 13,750 (controlled). **Dist. in U.S. by:** British Trade & Investment Office, British Consulate General, 11th Fl, 845 Third Ave, New York, NY 10022.

BRIEFINGS IN REAL ESTATE FINANCE. see *REAL ESTATE*

332.6 GBR
BRITAIN THE PREFERRED LOCATION. Text in English. 1987. a. free. charts; illus.; stat. **Document type:** *Government.* **Description:** Informs corporate executives on the advantages of investing in the U.K. rather than other European nations.
Related titles: Chinese ed.; Japanese ed.; Korean ed.
Published by: Invest in Britain Bureau, 1 Victoria St, 66-74 Victoria St, London, SW1H 0ET, United Kingdom. TEL 44-171-215-5638, FAX 44-171-215-5651, http://www.dti.gov.uk/ibb. Ed. Michael White. Circ: 11,500 (controlled).

384.55 USA ISSN 0146-0110
BROADCAST INVESTOR; newsletter on radio-TV station finance. Text in English. 1975. m. USD 1,295; USD 1,690 combined subscription print & e-mail eds. (effective 2005). adv. charts. index. **Document type:** *Newsletter, Trade.* **Description:** Covers investments in private radio and TV stations plus public broadcast companies. Gives analysis of cash flow multiples, valuations of stations and companies.
Related titles: E-mail ed.: USD 1,195 (effective 2005); Fax ed.: USD 925 (effective 2001).

Published by: Kagan Research, LLC, One Lower Ragsdale Dr, Bldg One, Ste 130, Monterey, CA 93940. TEL 831-624-1536, FAX 831-625-3225, info@kagan.com, http://www.kagan.com/cgi-bin/pkcat/bdf.html?id=BT92E4g3. adv.: page USD 3,670.

BROADCAST INVESTOR CHARTS; monthly service showing price movements of broadcast stocks over two-year spans. see *COMMUNICATIONS—Television And Cable*

332.6 346.065 USA ISSN 1527-2672
BROKER / DEALER COMPLIANCE REPORT (ONLINE EDITION). Text in English. 1999 (Sept.). w. USD 1,271 (effective 2005 & 2006). back issues avail. **Document type:** *Newsletter, Trade.* **Description:** Reports on changes in federal and state securities laws, Securities and Exchange Commission and other federal agency regulations, and National Associations of Securities Dealers, Inc. and other self-regulatory organizations' policies that affect broker/dealers compliance responsibilities.
Media: Online - full text (from The Bureau of National Affairs, Inc.).
—CCC.
Published by: The Bureau of National Affairs, Inc., 1231 25th St., NW, Washington, DC 20037. TEL 800-372-1033, 800-452-7773, FAX 800-253-0332, customercare@bna.com, bnaplus@bna.com, http://www.bna.com/products/corplaw/bdcr.htm. Pub. Greg C McCaffery. **Subscr. to:** 9435 Key West Ave, Rockville, MD 20850.

332.6029 GBR
THE (YEAR) BROKERS 1000. Text in English. a. GBP 170, USD 295. **Document type:** *Directory.* **Description:** Profiles more than 54 markets worldwide, giving an economic overview of each country, including the structure, operation, and performance of the equity and debt markets, along with trading, settlement, and clearing details.
Published by: Euromoney Publications plc, Nestor House, Playhouse Yard, London, EC4V 5EX, United Kingdom. TEL 44-207-7798673, FAX 44-20-77798541. **Orders to:** Plymbridge Distributors Ltd, Plymbridge House, Estover Rd, Plymouth, Devon PL6 7PY, United Kingdom. TEL 44-1752-202300, FAX 44-1752-202330.

BROWNING NEWSLETTER. see *METEOROLOGY*

332.6 USA
BRUCE GOULD ON COMMODITIES. Text in English. 1976. bi-w. looseleaf. USD 285 (effective 2000). back issues avail. **Document type:** *Newsletter.*
Published by: Bruce Gould Publications, PO Box 16, Seattle, WA 98111. FAX 509-422-5109. Ed. Bruce Gould.

332.6 BEL
BRUSSELS EXCHANGES. MONTHLY STATISTICS. Text in English. 1943. m. charts; stat. **Document type:** *Bulletin.*
Former titles: Societe de la Bourse de Valeurs Mobilieres de Bruxelles. Bulletin Mensuel; Commission de la Bourse de Bruxelles. Indices et Statistiques. Bulletin Mensuel
Published by: Brussels Exchanges, Palais de la Bourse, Brussels, 1000, Belgium. FAX 32-2-5091375, http://www.bxs.be. Ed. Olivier Lefebvre. Circ: 200.

332.6 USA ISSN 0319-1362
BULL & BEAR FINANCIAL NEWSPAPER. Text in English. 1974. m. USD 36 (effective 2000). adv. bk.rev. back issues avail. **Document type:** *Newspaper.* **Description:** Presents articles on precious metals, stocks, mutual funds, coins, real estate, and economic trends.
Address: PO Box 917179, Longwood, FL 32791. TEL 407-682-6170, http://www.thebullandbear.com. Ed. David J Robinson. Adv. contact Valerie Waters. Circ: 45,000 (paid); 10,000 (controlled).

332.6 FRA ISSN 1166-5785
BULLETIN BOURSE ET PRODUITS FINANCIERS. Text in French. bi-m. **Document type:** *Bulletin.*
Published by: Joly Editions, 31 rue Falguiere, Paris, 75015, France. TEL 33-1-56541600, FAX 33-1-56541647.

332.645 USA
BULLION ADVISORY✶ . Text in English. m. USD 36.
Description: Specializes in gold, silver and platinum.
Published by: Moneypower, 1304 Edgewood Ave, Ann Arbor, MI 48103-5522. TEL 612-537-8096. Ed. James H Moore.

336.76 HRV ISSN 1330-495X
BURZA. Text in Croatian. 1990. w. **Document type:** *Magazine, Trade.*
Formerly (until 1992): Ri Telefaks (0353-8621)
Related titles: Online - full text ed.
Published by: Ri Telefax, Trg Rijecke Rezolucije 4, Rijeka, 51000, Croatia. TEL 385-51-212005, FAX 385-51-214908, info@ritelefax.hr, http://www.ritelefax.hr. Ed. Josip Povrzenic.

332.6 USA ISSN 1082-2054
HG4501
BUSINESS AND INVESTMENT CYCLES. Text in English. m. USD 295. **Document type:** *Newsletter.* **Description:** Presents an analysis of major investment opportunities. Demonstrates the practical application of cycles to investment strategies.
Formerly (until 1995): Investment Cycles (1080-1073)
Published by: Cycles Research Institute, 214 Carnegie Ctr, Ste 204, Princeton, NJ 08540-6237. TEL 610-995-2120, FAX 610-995-2130, cycles@cycles.org, http://www.cycles.org/~cycles, http://www.cyclesresearchinstitute.org. Ed. Chester Joy.

BUSINESS AND THE ENVIRONMENT; monthly global news and analysis. see *ENVIRONMENTAL STUDIES*

BUSINESS MONEY. see *BUSINESS AND ECONOMICS—Banking And Finance*

332.6 USA
BUSINESS OPPORTUNITIES JOURNAL. Text in English. 1969. m. free. adv. bk.rev. **Document type:** *Journal, Trade.* **Description:** Specializes in franchising and business opportunities in the U.S.
Formerly: Business Opportunities Journal (Print Edition) (0193-3221); Incorporates (1989-1993): Business Ventures
Media: Online - full text.
Published by: Business Service Corporation, PO Box 60762, San Diego, CA 92166. TEL 619-223-5661, boj@boj.com, BussOppJrnl@aol.com, http://www.boj.com. Ed. John R Brocker TEL 619-688-1954. Pub. Wayne Wakefield. Adv. contact Maria Constantine. Circ: 102,000 (controlled).

336.74 NLD ISSN 0927-8370
BUSINESS SUPPORTER. Key Title: A B N Amro Business Supporter. Text in Dutch. 1991. s-m.
Published by: A B N Amro Bank N.V., PO Box 283, Amsterdam, 1000 EA, Netherlands.

332.6 VEN
BUSINESS VENEZUELA'S CORPORATE HANDBOOK. Text in Spanish. a. USD 30. **Document type:** *Directory.* **Description:** Guide to Venezuela's political, economic and legal environment for foreign investors.
Formerly: Investing in Venezuela
Published by: Venezuelan - American Chamber of Commerce and Industry/Camara Venezolano-Americana de Comercio e Industria, Apdo 5181, Caracas, DF 1010-A, Venezuela. TEL 58-2-2630833, FAX 58-2-2631829.

332.63 USA
▼ **BUSINESS VIEW**; the H P magazine of business and technology. (Hewlett-Packard) Text in English. 2003. q. adv. **Document type:** *Magazine, Trade.* **Description:** Webzine created for business and IT executives who demand more.
Media: Online - full content.
Published by: (Hewlett-Packard Co. (Palo Alto)), Imagination Publishing, 2222 N. Elston Ave., 2nd Fl., Chicago, IL 60614. TEL 312-627-1020, FAX 312-627-1105, http://www.hp.com/large/globalsolutions/ae/hpbusinessview/, http://www.imaginepub.com. adv.: B&W page USD 8,500, color page USD 10,000; trim 8 x 10.5. Circ: 50,000.

332.6 USA ISSN 1040-0990
HD2746.5
BUYOUTS. Text in English. 1987. bi-w. USD 1,725 in US & Canada; USD 1,750 elsewhere (effective 2005). **Document type:** *Newsletter, Trade.* **Description:** Source of news, data analysis and interpretation of trends in the buyout industry.
Related titles: Online - full text ed.: (from EBSCO Publishing, Florida Center for Library Automation, Gale Group, LexisNexis, O C L C Online Computer Library Center, Inc., ProQuest Information & Learning).
Indexed: ABIn.
—CCC.
Published by: Venture Economics, Inc. (Subsidiary of: Source Media, Inc.), 395 Hudson St, 3rd Fl, New York, NY 10014. TEL 888-605-3385, FAX 917-408-5276, http://www.buyoutsnewsletter.com, http://www.ventureeconomics.com/. Pub. Adam Reinebach TEL 917-408-5268.

332.6 USA
BUYOUTS YEARBOOK. Text in English. a. USD 285 (effective 1998). **Document type:** *Directory.* **Description:** Provides a year-end summary of the LBO industry's key events and essential data.
Published by: Securities Data Publishing (Subsidiary of: Thomson Financial / I M G Media), 195 Broadway, New York, NY 10007. TEL 212-765-5311, FAX 212-765-6123.

332.6 USA ISSN 1543-5563
BUYSIDE; ideas for today's institutional investors. Text in English. m. USD 35 domestic; free to qualified personnel (effective 2005). **Document type:** *Magazine, Trade.* **Description:** Covers investment ideas from every sector of the global market.
Related titles: Online - full content ed.; Online - full text ed.: (from Gale Group).
Published by: Adams Business Media, PO Box 320, Sonoma, CA 95476. TEL 707-933-2800, FAX 707-933-2820, http://www.buyside.com/. Eds. Megan Leerskov, Sandy Serva. Pub. Jim Patrick.

332.6 USA ISSN 1074-0139
HG1
C D A INVESTNET INSIDERS' CHRONICLE✶ . Text in English. 1896. w. USD 445. adv. reprint service avail. from PQC. **Document type:** *Newsletter.* **Description:** Reports on the buy-sell stock transactions of corporate officers, directors and beneficial owners, providing a gauge of corporate confidence levels and expectations.
Formed by the 1993 merger of: Invest/Net Inside; (1976-1992): Insiders' Chronicle (0162-5152); Which superseded in part (in 1976): Commercial and Financial Chronicle (0010-2903)
Related titles: Microform ed.: 1896 (from PQC); Online - full text ed.: 1896 (from Florida Center for Library Automation, Gale Group).
Indexed: BusI, RASB, T&II.
Published by: C D A Investment Technologies, Inc., 1455 Research Blvd, Rockville, MD 20850-3194. TEL 800-232-6362, FAX 301-590-1329. Ed. Bob Gabele.

332.6 USA
C D RATE SHOPPER. (Certificate of Deposit) Text in English. w. **Document type:** *Newsletter, Consumer.* **Description:** Contains current information and trends involving CD rates.
Media: E-mail.
Published by: Bankrate Inc., 11811 US Hwy 1, North Palm Beach, FL 33408. TEL 561-630-2400, FAX 561-625-4540, webmaster@bankrate.com, http://bankrate.process9.com/bankrate/subscribe.html, http://www.bankrate.com.

332.6 GBR
C G T CAPITAL LOSSES. (Capital Gains Tax) Text in English. s-a. GBP 65. **Document type:** *Directory.* **Description:** Covers securities declared valueless by Inland Revenue, as well as companies in liquidation or receivership, where a final distribution or negligible value announcement has not yet been issued.
Published by: Financial Times Information Ltd., Extel, Fitzroy House, 13-17 Epworth St, London, EC2A 4DL, United Kingdom. TEL 44-20-7825-8000, FAX 44-20-7608-2032, eic@ft.com.

C M B S WORLD. (Commerical Mortgage Backed Securities) see *BUSINESS AND ECONOMICS—Banking And Finance*

332.6 USA
C R B COMMODITY INDEX REPORT. Text in English. w. USD 295 (effective 1999). adv. charts; stat. **Document type:** *Trade.* **Description:** Provides CRB price index data, including technical analysis, and a daily recorded statistical hotline that provides closing prices on all CRB indices.
Published by: Commodity Research Bureau, 330 S. Wells St., Ste. 612, Chicago, IL 60606-7112. TEL 312-454-1801, 800-621-5271, FAX 312-454-0239, crbinfo@bridge.com, info@crbtrader.com, http://www.crbindex.com, http://www.crbtrader.com. Ed., Adv. contact Bob Hafer. R&P Jennifer Ehrich.

338 USA ISSN 1076-2906
HF1041
C R B COMMODITY YEARBOOK. Text in English. 1939. a. USD 299 with CD (effective 2005). charts; stat. index. reprints avail. **Document type:** *Trade.* **Description:** Covers previous year's activity for over 100 commodities. Includes approximately 1,000 charts, tables, supply-and-demand data, and background information on each market.
Former titles: Knight-Ridder C R B Commodity Year Book (1074-1933); (until 1993): C R B Commodity Yearbook (1046-8226); (until 1985): Commodity Year Book (0069-6862)
Related titles: CD-ROM ed.: ISSN 1555-1695.
Indexed: SRI.
—CISTI.
Published by: Commodity Research Bureau, 330 S. Wells St., Ste. 612, Chicago, IL 60606-7112. TEL 312-554-8456, 800-621-5271, FAX 312-939-4135, info@crbtrader.com, http://www.crbtrader.com/pubs/yb.asp. Eds. Bob Hafer, Chris Lown. R&P Jennifer Ehrich.

332.6 USA ISSN 1057-4883
HD9001
C R B FUTURES MARKET SERVICE. Text in English. 1934. w. USD 150 (effective 1999). mkt. **Document type:** *Trade.* **Description:** Provides a synopsis update for about 36 major markets. Analyzes the week's most active commodity or futures-related conditions.
Media: Duplicated (not offset). **Related titles:** Online - full text ed.
Published by: Commodity Research Bureau, 330 S. Wells St., Ste. 612, Chicago, IL 60606-7112. TEL 312-454-1801, 800-621-5271, FAX 312-454-0239, cribinfo@bridge.com, info@crbtrader.com, http://www.crbindex.com, http://www.crbtrader.com. Ed. Bob Hafer. R&P Jennifer Ehrich. Circ: 8,000.

332.63 USA
C R B FUTURES PERSPECTIVE - AGRICULTURAL EDITION. Text in English. 1972. w. (bi-w., and m. eds. avail.). USD 230 domestic for w. ed.; USD 490 in Europe for w. ed.; USD 155 domestic for bi-w. ed.; USD 285 in Europe for bi-w. ed.; USD 95 domestic for m. ed.; USD 155 in Europe for m. ed..
Document type: *Trade.*

Published by: Commodity Research Bureau, 330 S. Wells St., Ste. 612, Chicago, IL 60606-7112. TEL 312-454-1801, 800-621-5271, FAX 312-454-0239, info@crbtrader.com, http://www.crbtrader.com. Ed. Steve Lown. Pub. Robert Hafer. R&P Jennifer Ehrich.

332.63 USA
C R B FUTURES PERSPECTIVE - FINANCIAL EDITION. Text in English. 1972. w. (bi-w., and m. eds. avail.). USD 275 domestic for w. ed.; USD 535 in Europe for w. ed.; USD 175 domestic for bi-w. ed.; USD 305 in Europe for bi-w. ed.; USD 105 domestic for m. ed.; USD 165 in Europe for m. ed.. **Document type:** *Trade.*
Published by: Commodity Research Bureau, 330 S. Wells St., Ste. 612, Chicago, IL 60606-7112. TEL 312-454-1801, 800-621-5271, FAX 312-454-0239, info@crbtrader.com, http://www.crbtrader.com. Ed. Steve Lown. Pub. Robert Hafer. R&P Jennifer Ehrich.

332.63 USA
HG6046
C R B FUTURES PERSPECTIVE - FULL EDITION. Text in English. w. (bi-w., and m. eds. avail.). USD 425 w. ed.; USD 685 in Europe w. ed.; USD 685 in Asia w. ed.; USD 265 bi-w ed.; USD 395 in Europe bi-w ed.; USD 395 in Asia bi-w ed.; USD 175 m. ed.; USD 235 in Europe m. ed.; USD 235 in Asia m. ed. (effective 1999). charts; mkt.; stat. **Document type:** *Trade.* **Description:** Charting service on 87 major international (US, Canadian, European, Asian) futures markets displaying over 425 daily price charts for futures, cash, spreads, moving averages, momentum oscillators, RSI, and CFTC commitment of Traders Report.
Former titles (until 1996): Commodity Perspective (0730-7217); K R - C R B Futures Perspective; C R B Futures Chart Service; Commodity Chart Service (0010-3225)
Published by: Commodity Research Bureau, 330 S. Wells St., Ste. 612, Chicago, IL 60606-7112. TEL 312-554-8456, 800-621-5271, FAX 312-939-4135, info@crbtrader.com, http://www.crbtrader.com. Ed. Steven Lowan. Pub. Robert Hafer. R&P Jennifer Ehrich.

332.6 USA
C T A OUTPUT. Text in English. 1976. m. **Document type:** *Newsletter.* **Description:** Contains articles of interest to securities transfer industry.
Published by: Corporate Transfer Agents Association, c/o Mobil Corporation, 3225 Gallows Rd, Fairfax, VA 22037-0001.

332.6 USA ISSN 0569-2954
C U S I P MASTER DIRECTORY. (Committee on Uniform Security Identification Procedures) Text in English. 1969. a. USD 2,400. **Document type:** *Directory.*
Formerly: C U S I P Directory (0091-2212)
Related titles: CD-ROM ed.; Magnetic Tape ed.
Published by: (American Bankers Association, Committee on Uniform Security Identification Procedures), Standard & Poor's (Subsidiary of: McGraw-Hill Companies, Inc.), 55 Water St, New York, NY 10041. TEL 212-208-8052. R&P Harry Lopez.

CABLE T V INVESTOR; newsletter on investments in cable T V systems and publicly held cable T V stocks. see *COMMUNICATIONS—Television And Cable*

332.6 USA ISSN 0733-8554
CABOT MARKET LETTER. Text in English. 1970. 24/yr. USD 335 (effective 2005). **Document type:** *Newsletter, Trade.*
Published by: Cabot Heritage Corporation, 176 North St, PO Box 2049, Salem, MA 01970. TEL 978-745-5532, 800-777-2658, FAX 978-745-1283, office@cabot.net, http://www.cabot.net. Eds. Timothy W Lutts, Carlton G Lutts. Circ: 25,000 (paid).

332.6 USA
CADENCE INVESTMENT ADVISORS PERFORMANCE SURVEY. Text in English. q. USD 650. **Description:** Performance statistics for equity, fixed income and balanced accounts. Over 850 investment advisors disclosed by name.
Media: Magnetic Tape.
Published by: C D A - Cadence, 1455 Research Blvd, Rockville, MD 20850-3194. TEL 301-975-9600, FAX 301-590-1350. Circ: 700.

332.6 USA
CADENCE UNIVERSE PERFORMANCE REPORT. Text in English. q. USD 850. **Description:** Provides return, comparative performance and risk statistics of individual bank pooled funds, mutual funds, insurance company funds and investment advisors, as well as market and specialized indices.
Related titles: Magnetic Tape ed.; Online - full text ed.
Published by: C D A - Cadence, 1455 Research Blvd, Rockville, MD 20850-3194. TEL 301-975-9600, FAX 301-590-1350. Circ: 300.

332.6 USA ISSN 0749-2375
CALIFORNIA MUNICIPAL BOND ADVISOR. Text in English. 1984. m. USD 125 (effective 2003). **Document type:** *Newsletter.* **Description:** Monetary, economic, investment analysis for tax-exempt bond investors.
Address: 3155 E. Ramon Rd., Apt. 601, Palm Springs, CA 92264-7974. TEL 760-320-7997. Ed. Dennis Walters. Pub. Zane B Mann.

332.6 USA ISSN 8756-2154
CALIFORNIA TECHNOLOGY STOCK LETTER; authoritative independent advice for high-technology investing. Text in English. 1982. s-m. USD 295 domestic; USD 345 foreign (effective 2000). back issues avail. **Document type:** *Newsletter.* **Description:** Analyzes computer, electronics, biotechnology and medical companies and their stocks offerings.
Published by: C T S L Publishing Partners, PO Box 308, Half Moon Bay, CA 94019. TEL 650-726-8495, http://batnet.com/ctsl/CTSLNewsletterInfo.html. Ed., Pub. Michael Murphy. R&P Pamela Floquet.

CALLAHAN'S CREDIT UNION REPORT. see *BUSINESS AND ECONOMICS—Banking And Finance*

332.6 USA
CALLAHAN'S FUND ADVISOR*. Text in English. 1986. m. USD 135. **Description:** Provides model portfolios, investment timing signals, and market analysis for sector funds, single premium variable life funds, and closed-end international funds.
Formerly: Sectorfund Advisor
Published by: Asset Control Services, Inc., 9101 E Kenyon Ave Ste 3000, Denver, CO 80237-1855. TEL 303-751-6661. Ed. Craig Callahan. Circ: 400.

332.6 USA
CALLED BOND SERVICE. Text in English. w. USD 12,000 (effective 1999). **Description:** Provides daily electronic updates of all announcements on US Corporate and Municipal securities and preferred stoks. Cover issue description, series, maturity date and list of serial numbers called.
Published by: Mergent, 5250 77 Center Dr, Ste 150, Charlotte, NC 28217. customerservice@mergent.com, http://www.mergent.com.

344.71023 CAN ISSN 1486-6188
CANADA PENSION PLAN. ANNUAL REPORT. Text in English. 1995. a., latest 2002. **Document type:** *Government.*
Related titles: Online - full content ed.: ISSN 1494-4987; ♦ French ed.: Regime de Pensions du Canada. Rapport Annuel. ISSN 1486-6196.
Published by: Human Resources Development Canada, Public Enquiries Centre, 140 Promenade du Portage, Hull, PQ K1A 0J9, Canada. FAX 819-953-7260, http://www.hrsdc.gc.ca/.

368.4300971 CAN ISSN 0319-7247
CANADA PENSION PLAN CONTRIBUTORS. Text in English. a., latest 2002. **Document type:** *Government.*
Related titles: Online - full content ed.
Published by: Social Development Canada, Forecasting, Information & Analysis, Income Security Programs Branch, 19th Fl, Tower B Pl Vanier, 355 N River Rd, Ottawa, ON K1A 0L1, Canada. http://www.sdc.gc.ca/en/isp/statistics/statmain.shtml.

332.6 CAN ISSN 1701-0039
CANADA PENSION PLAN INVESTMENT BOARD. ANNUAL REPORT. Text in English. 1999. a. **Document type:** *Government.*
Published by: Canada Pension Plan Investment Board, 1 Queen St E, Ste 2700, Toronto, ON M5C 2W5, Canada. TEL 416-868-4075, 866-557-9510, FAX 416-868-4083, http://www.cppib.ca/info/annual/ar_2004.pdf.

332.6 CAN
CANADA STOCKWATCH. EASTERN EDITION. Text in English. 1987. d. USD 395. **Document type:** *Trade.* **Description:** Covers daily-issued news by every company listed on the Toronto and Montreal Stock Exchanges.
Formerly: Toronto Stockwatch
Related titles: Online - full text ed.
Published by: Canjex Publishing, 700 W Georgia St, P O Box 10371, Vancouver, BC V7Y 1J6, Canada. TEL 604-687-1500, FAX 604-687-2304. Ed. John Woods.

332.6 CAN
CANADA STOCKWATCH. WESTERN EDITION. Text in English. 1984. d. USD 395. **Document type:** *Trade.* **Description:** Covers news issued that day or week by every company listed on the Vancouver and Alberta stock exchanges.
Formerly: Vancouver Stockwatch
Related titles: Online - full text ed.
Published by: Canjex Publishing, 700 W Georgia St, P O Box 10371, Vancouver, BC V7Y 1J6, Canada. TEL 604-687-1500, FAX 604-687-2304. Ed. John Woods.

CANADIAN CAPITAL PROJECTS. see *BUSINESS AND ECONOMICS—Domestic Commerce*

332.6 CAN
THE CANADIAN CREDIT AND COLLECTION GUIDE. Text in English. 1989. a. looseleaf. CND 265 per issue domestic; USD 224.58 per issue foreign (effective 2005). charts; illus. cum.index. **Description:** Provides practical guidance on secured credit transactions, evaluating and monitoring customer accounts, writing collection letters and training collection staff, etc.
Published by: Carswell (Subsidiary of: Thomson Corporation), One Corporate Plaza, 2075 Kennedy Rd, Toronto, ON M1T 3V4, Canada. TEL 416-609-8000, 800-387-5164, FAX 416-298-5094, carswell.customerrelations@thomson.com, http://www.carswell.com. Ed. Ross Edmunds. Circ: 900.

332.6 CAN ISSN 0840-6863
HG5152
➤ **CANADIAN INVESTMENT REVIEW.** Text in English. 1988. q. free to qualified personnel (effective 2005). adv. bk.rev. back issues avail. **Document type:** *Magazine, Academic/Scholarly.* **Description:** Provides a forum for academics, institutional investors and industry practitioners to exchange ideas on the capital markets, investment and economic theory, and the related sociology and demographics.
Related titles: Microfiche ed.: (from MML); Microform ed.: (from MML); Online - full text ed.: (from EBSCO Publishing, Micromedia ProQuest, O C L C Online Computer Library Center, Inc., ProQuest Information & Learning).
Indexed: ABIn, CBCABus, CBCARef.
—CCC.
Published by: Rogers Media Publishing Ltd, One Mount Pleasant Rd, 11th Fl, Toronto, ON M4Y 2Y5, Canada. TEL 416-764-2000, FAX 416-764-3941, http://www.investmentreview.com. Pub. Lori Bak. Circ: 8,500.

332.6 CAN ISSN 0713-3286
CANADIAN MONEYSAVER; your personal finance guide. Text in English. 1981. m. (11/yr.). CND 21.35 domestic; USD 36 foreign (effective 2000 - 2001). bk.rev. **Document type:** *Consumer.* **Description:** Offers independent personal finance advice on tax, investments and financial planning.
Related titles: Microfiche ed.: (from MML); Microform ed.: (from MML).
Indexed: CBCARef, CBPI, CPerI.
Published by: Canadian Money Saver Inc., P O Box 370, Bath, ON K0H 1G0, Canada. TEL 613-352-7448, FAX 613-352-7700, moneyinfo@canadianmoneysaver.ca, http://www.canadianmoneysaver.ca. Ed., Pub., R&P Dale Ennis. Circ: 30,000 (paid).

332.6 CAN ISSN 1182-1590
CANADIAN RESOURCES AND PENNYMINES ANALYST. Text in English. 1986. m. CND 157 (effective 1999). **Document type:** *Trade.* **Description:** Covers resource, penny and junior mining stocks from a geological point of view, with emphasis on minimizing risk.
Formerly (until 1990): Canadian PennyMines Analyst (0836-6357)
Published by: M P L Communications Inc., 133 Richmond St W, Ste 700, Toronto, ON M5H 3M8, Canada. TEL 416-869-1177, FAX 416-869-0456.

CANADIAN SECURITIES LAW REPORTER. see *LAW*

332.6 CAN
CANADIAN STOCK EXCHANGES MANUAL. Text in English. m. looseleaf. CND 510 (effective 2005). **Document type:** *Trade.* **Description:** Contains policies, charters, by-laws and regulations of Investment Dealers Association, Investment Funds Institute, Toronto Futures Exchange, Winnipeg Commodity Exchanges and all stock exchanges in Canada.
Published by: C C H Canadian Ltd., 90 Sheppard Ave E, Ste 300, North York, ON M2N 6X1, Canada. TEL 416-224-2248, 800-268-4522, FAX 416-224-2243, cservice@cch.ca, http://www.cch.ca.

CANADIAN TREASURY MANAGEMENT REVIEW. see *BUSINESS AND ECONOMICS—Banking And Finance*

CAPITAL CHANGES REPORTS. see *BUSINESS AND ECONOMICS—Public Finance, Taxation*

332.6 382 USA
CAPITAL FORMATION AND INVESTMENT INCENTIVES AROUND THE WORLD. Text in English. irreg. (in 2 vols.). looseleaf. USD 830 (effective 1999).
Published by: Matthew Bender & Co., Inc. (Subsidiary of: LexisNexis North America), 1275 Broadway, Albany, NY 12204. international@bender.com, http://bender.lexisnexis.com. Eds. Dorothy Diamond, Walter Diamond.

332.6 USA ISSN 1093-5630
CAPITAL GROWTH INTERACTIVE. Text in English. m. USD 265 domestic (effective 2001). adv. back issues avail. **Document type:** *Newsletter, Corporate.* **Description:** Covers private capital and growth company financing for investors and entrepreneurs.
Related titles: Online - full text ed.: 1996. USD 199 (effective 2001); Supplement(s): Guide to Entrepreneurial Venture Financing. 1998. USD 99 (effective 2001).
Published by: Capital Growth Inc., Ste 200, 817 Cedar Grove Rd, Baltimore, MD 21221-2006. TEL 410-238-1742, FAX 410-238-1744, info@capitalgrowth.com, http://www.capitalgrowth.com.

332.6 HKG
CAPITAL MAGAZINE*. Text in Chinese. m. adv. **Document type:** *Consumer.*

B

Published by: Capital Communications Corp. Ltd., Westlands Centre 24F, 20 Westlands Rd, Quarry Bay, Hong Kong. TEL 852-28112006, FAX 852-25650722. adv.: B&W page HKD 235,000, color page HKD 32,000; trim 210 x 286. Circ: 25,000.

332.6 RUS ISSN 1562-9163
CAPITAL MARKETS EURASIA. Text in English. 1996. w. back issues avail. **Document type:** *Newsletter, Trade.* **Description:** Provides the latest statistics and market comparisons on the Russian, FSU and CEE economies and financial markets.
Related titles: Online - full text ed.: ISSN 1562-9171.
Published by: Skate, Inc., Nikoloyamskaya 13, Bld 2, Moscow, 109240, Russian Federation. TEL 7-095-3636090, FAX 7-095-3636099, info@skatefn.com, http://www.skatefn.com/cme.html. Ed. Michael Androssov. **Dist. by:** Skate, Inc. (U S A), c/o Pavel Prybolovsky, Ste 3100, 140 Broadway, New York, NY 10005-9998. TEL 212-973-8142, FAX 212-972-8798, pribyl@skatefn.com.

332.6 910.202 USA
CARIBBEAN DATELINE. Text in English. 1980. m. USD 95 (effective 2000). adv. back issues avail. **Document type:** *Newsletter, Consumer.* **Description:** Reports on tax haven activities, real estate, banking, incorporation, trust formation, tax free businesses, vacation living, retirement, direct investments, stocks and other securities. Covers news, trends, opinions and opportunities in the Caribbean and Central America.
Incorporates: Caribbean and Central American Letter
Published by: Caribbean Dateline Publications, PO Box 41599, Arlington, VA 22204-8599. TEL 703-404-0894, pday@bahamasdateline.com, http://www.bahamasdateline.com. Ed., Pub., R&P N Poteat Day. Adv. contact Kathy Richards. Circ: 1,100.

332.6 USA
CAROLAN'S SPIRAL CALENDAR RESEARCH. Text in English. 1993. m. USD 279; USD 299 foreign (effective 1999). **Document type:** *Newsletter.* **Description:** Covers the U.S. stock market, bonds, precious metals, major foreign stock markets and currencies. Forecasts market movements that are related to exact time relationships.
Published by: (Calendar Research, Inc.), Elliott Wave International, PO Box 1618, Gainesville, GA 30503. TEL 770-536-0309. Ed. Christopher Carolan.

CASH; die Wirtschaftszeitung der Schweiz. see *BUSINESS AND ECONOMICS—Banking And Finance*

332.6 DEU ISSN 0178-5125
CASH. Text in German. 1983. bi-m. EUR 38.50; EUR 4.50 newsstand/cover (effective 2005). adv. reprints avail. **Document type:** *Magazine, Consumer.*
Published by: Cash Print GmbH, Brabandstr 1, Hamburg, 22297, Germany. TEL 49-40-5144402, FAX 49-40-51444120, info@cash-online.de, http://www.cash-online.de. Ed. Wilhelm Furler. Pub. Dieter Jansen. Adv. contact Alexander Mandenge. B&W page EUR 6,040, color page EUR 6,880; trim 175 x 275. Circ: 56,489 (paid).

336.7 BEL ISSN 1371-0508
CASH!. Text in French. 1994. w. EUR 192 (effective 2004). adv. **Document type:** *Magazine, Consumer.* **Description:** Provides a practical guide to personal finances and investments.
Related titles: Dutch ed.: ISSN 1371-0516.
Published by: Roularta Media Group, Research Park, Zellik, 1731, Belgium. TEL 32-2-4675611, FAX 32-2-4675757, communication@roularta.be, http://www.roularta.be.

332.6 USA ISSN 0742-6534
HG4528
CATALYST (MONTPELIER)✶ ; economics for the living earth. Text in English. 1984. q. USD 25. bk.rev. bibl.; illus.; stat. back issues avail. **Document type:** *Newsletter.* **Description:** Profiles of and articles on social investing: small businesses, revolving loan funds, co-ops, land trusts, and other organizations to support positive economic change for disadvantaged populations and to save and regenerate existing farm and forestland. Focuses on small-scale, grass roots enterprises seeking some form of capital: loans, partnerships, equity, and grants.
Published by: Catalyst Press, RR 1 Box 84, Fryeburg, ME 04037-9709. Eds. Susan Meeker Lowry, Susan Meeker-Lowry. Circ: 1,000.

332.6 POL ISSN 1231-9511
CEDULA GIELDY WARSZAWSKIEJ; oficjalny biuletyn. Text in English, Polish. 1991. 5/w. PLZ 200, USD 148. back issues avail. **Document type:** *Bulletin.* **Description:** Provides results of the Warsaw Stock Exchange daily sessions.
Published by: Gielda Papierow Wartosciowych w Warszawie S.A./Warsaw Stock Exchange, Nowy Swiat 6-12, Warsaw, 00400, Poland. TEL 48-22-6283232, FAX 48-22-6282754. Ed. Arkadiusz W Szymanek.

332.6 BEL
CENTRE FOR EUROPEAN POLICY STUDIES. TASK FORCE REPORTS. Variant title: C E P S Task Force Reports. Text in English. irreg., latest 2003, Oct. price varies. **Document type:** *Monographic series.*
Published by: Centre for European Policy Studies, Pl du Congres 1, Brussels, 1000, Belgium. TEL 32-2-2293911, FAX 32-2-2194151, http://www.ceps.be/Default.php.

332.6 ITA
CENTRO STUDI CONFINDUSTRIA. NOTE. Key Title: Note dal C S C. Text in Italian. irreg.
Published by: Centro Studi Confindustria, Viale Pasteur 6, Rome, 00144, Italy. TEL 06-5920509, FAX 06-5924819, http://www.confindustria.it.

332.6 ITA
CENTRO STUDI CONFINDUSTRIA. RICERCHE. Key Title: C S C Ricerche. Text in Italian. irreg.
Published by: Centro Studi Confindustria, Viale Pasteur 6, Rome, 00144, Italy. TEL 06-5920509, FAX 06-5924819, http://www.confindustria.it.

332.6 ITA
CENTRO STUDI CONFINDUSTRIA. WORKING PAPERS. Key Title: C S C Working Papers. Text in Italian, English. irreg.
Published by: Centro Studi Confindustria, Viale Pasteur 6, Rome, 00144, Italy. TEL 06-5920509, FAX 06-5924819, http://www.confindustria.it.

332.6 GBR
CHANGES OF NAMES. Text in English. a. GBP 75. **Description:** Lists changes of names for all companies quoted on the London and Republic of Ireland Stock Exchanges.
Published by: Financial Times Information Ltd., Extel, Fitzroy House, 13-17 Epworth St, London, EC2A 4DL, United Kingdom. TEL 44-20-7825-8000, FAX 44-20-7608-2032, eic@ft.com, http://www.info.ft.com.

332.6 GBR
CHARITY FINANCE YEARBOOK. Text in English. 1996. a. GBP 25 (effective 1999). adv. **Document type:** *Trade.* **Description:** Provides full coverage of all aspects of managing the finances of a charity.
Published by: Plaza Publishing Ltd, 3 Rectory Grove, London, SW4 0DX, United Kingdom. TEL 44-171-819-1200, FAX 44-171-819-1210. Ed. Daniel Phelan. Adv. contact Alice Frackelton. page GBP 795.

332.6 USA
CHARTCRAFT COMMODITY SERVICE. Text in English. 1958. w. USD 256 (effective 1998).
Published by: Chartcraft, Inc., 30 Church St, Box 2046, New Rochelle, NY 10801. TEL 914-632-0422, FAX 914-632-0335. Ed. John E Gray.

332.6 USA
CHARTCRAFT MONTHLY N Y S E AND A S E CHARTBOOK. Text in English. m. USD 402 (effective 1998).
Published by: Chartcraft, Inc., 30 Church St, Box 2046, New Rochelle, NY 10801. TEL 914-632-0422, FAX 914-632-0335. Ed. Mike Burke.

332.6 USA
CHARTCRAFT OVER-THE-COUNTER CHARTBOOK. Text in English. q. USD 114 (effective 1998).
Published by: Chartcraft, Inc., 30 Church St, Box 2046, New Rochelle, NY 10801. TEL 914-632-0422, FAX 914-632-0335. Ed. Michael Burke.

332.6 USA
CHARTCRAFT QUARTERLY OPTION CHARTBOOK. Text in English. q. USD 160 (effective 1998).
Published by: Chartcraft, Inc., 30 Church St, Box 2046, New Rochelle, NY 10801. TEL 914-632-0422, FAX 914-632-0335. Ed. Michael Burke.

332.6 USA
CHARTCRAFT WEEKLY FUTURES SERVICE. Text in English. w. USD 256 (effective 1998). **Description:** Illustrates more than 40 different futures through point and figure charts.
Formerly: Chartcraft Weekly Commodity Service
Published by: Chartcraft, Inc., 30 Church St, Box 2046, New Rochelle, NY 10801. TEL 914-632-0422, FAX 914-632-0335. Ed. John E Gray.

332.6 USA
CHARTCRAFT WEEKLY N Y S E. Text in English. w. USD 256 (effective 1998).
Published by: Chartcraft, Inc., 30 Church St, Box 2046, New Rochelle, NY 10801. TEL 914-632-0422, FAX 914-632-0335. Ed. Michael Burke.

332.6 USA
CHARTCRAFT WEEKLY OPTIONS SERVICE. Text in English. w. USD 186 (effective 1998). **Description:** Covers the technical needs of options traders.
Published by: Chartcraft, Inc., 30 Church St, Box 2046, New Rochelle, NY 10801. TEL 914-632-0422, FAX 914-632-0335. Ed. Michael Burke.

332.6 USA
CHARTIST. Text in English. 18/yr. USD 150. **Document type:** *Newsletter.*
Address: PO Box 758, Seal Beach, CA 90740. TEL 310-596-2385. Ed., Pub. Dan Sullivan.

CHART'S; la lettre des previsions boursieres. see *BUSINESS AND ECONOMICS—Banking And Finance*

332.96 USA ISSN 1048-2717
HG4501
CHASE INVESTMENT PERFORMANCE DIGEST✶. Text in English. 1988. a. USD 23.95 (effective 1996). adv. illus. **Document type:** *Trade.* **Description:** Includes performance, returns and rankings on the world's major investments.
Formerly (until 1990): Chase Global Investment Almanac (1041-8636)
Published by: Chase Global Data & Research, Inc., 22 Thomson Pl No MS512F2, Boston, MA 02210-1212. TEL 508-371-9100, FAX 508-371-9105. Ed. C David Chase. Adv. contact Herb Benjamin.

332.6 USA ISSN 0747-7236
THE CHEAP INVESTOR; the investor's guide to microcap and turn around stocks under $5 per share. Text in English. 1981. m. USD 145 (effective 2005). 12 p./no.; **Document type:** *Newsletter, Trade.* **Description:** Recommends profitable investments for its subscribers. Each issue contains 3 to 4 recommendations along with updates on some previous recommendations.
Published by: Mathews and Associates, Inc., 2549 W Golf Rd, Ste 350, Hoffman Estates, IL 60194-1165. TEL 847-697-5666, FAX 847-697-5699, http://www.investmentnewsletters.net. Ed. Bill Mathews. Circ: 6,000.

B

332.6 USA
CHICAGO BOARD OPTIONS EXCHANGE GUIDE. Text in English. 1973. base vol. plus m. updates. looseleaf. USD 670 base vol(s). (effective 2004). **Description:** Provides the complete exchange constitution, including all the rules, by-laws and policies governing the day-to-day, as well as the regulatory, activities of the exchange and it's members.
Related titles: CD-ROM ed.: USD 635 (effective 2004); Online - full text ed.: USD 635 (effective 2004).
Published by: C C H Inc., 2700 Lake Cook Rd, Riverwoods, IL 60015. TEL 847-267-7000, 800-449-6439, cust_serv@cch.com, http://www.cch.com. Pub. Stacey Caywood.

332.6 USA
CHICAGO STOCK EXCHANGE GUIDE. Text in English. 1967. base vol. plus m. updates. looseleaf. USD 625 base vol(s). (effective 2004). **Description:** Provides the Directory Certificate of Incorporation, Constitution, Rules and Policies of the Chicago Stock Exchange, and the By-Laws and Rules of the Midwest Securities Trust Company.
Formerly (until 1993): Midwest Stock Exchange Guide
Related titles: CD-ROM ed.: USD 400 (effective 2004); Online - full text ed.: USD 400 (effective 2004).
Published by: C C H Inc., 2700 Lake Cook Rd, Riverwoods, IL 60015. TEL 847-267-7000, 800-449-6439, cust_serv@cch.com, http://www.cch.com. Pub. Stacey Caywood.

332.96 HKG
CHINA INVESTMENT GUIDE. Text in English. irreg., latest vol.5. HKD 1,500. **Description:** Covers joint-venture negotiations, rules and regulations, and the investment environment.
Published by: (Ministry of Foreign Trade and Economic Co-operation, Department of Foreign Investment), Pearson Professional (HK) Ltd., Ste. 1808 Asian House, 1 Hennessy Rd, Wanchai, Hong Kong, Hong Kong. TEL 852-2863-2659, FAX 852-2520-6954, pphkg@hk.super.net. **Co-publisher:** CITIC Publishing House.

346.092 USA
CHINA'S INVESTMENT LAWS: NEWS DIRECTIONS. Text in English. 1988. irreg. USD 75.
Published by: LexisNexis (Subsidiary of: LexisNexis North America), PO Box 7587, Charlottesville, VA 22906-7587. TEL 804-972-7600, FAX 804-972-7666, llp.customer.support@lexis-nexis.com, http://www.lexislawpublishing.com. Ed. Guiguo Wang.

CHINESE BUSINESS JOURNAL. see *BUSINESS AND ECONOMICS—Economic Situation And Conditions*

332.6 MEX
CIRCULARES DE FIANZAS. Text in Spanish. a. **Document type:** *Government.* **Description:** Official communications on surety bond law reforms.
Published by: Comision Nacional de Seguros y Fianzas, Ave. DE LOS INSURGENTES SUR 1971 Piso 3, Col Guadalupe Inn, Mexico City, DF 01020, Mexico. TEL 52-5-6618053, FAX 52-5-7247602, cnsfdgdi@mail.internet.com.mx.

332.6 USA
CLICK ON MONEY✶. Text in English. w.
Media: Online - full content.
Address: metz211@aol.com, http://www.clickonmoney.com.

332.63 USA ISSN 1067-6279
CLOSED-END FUND SOURCEBOOK. Text in English. 1992. a. USD 195 in United States; USD 105 in Canada; USD 125 elsewhere. **Description:** Provides performance data, star ratings, and portfolio information for 500 closed-end funds.

▼ new title ➤ refereed ✶ unverified ◆ full entry avail.

Published by: Morningstar, Inc., 225 W Wacker Dr, Ste 400, Chicago, IL 60606. TEL 312-696-6000, FAX 312-696-6001. Ed. Catherine Gillis. Circ: 400.

332.6   USA
COASTLINES (SAN FRANCISCO); quarterly newsletter published by the Pacific Stock Exchange. Text in English. 1990. q. free. back issues avail. **Document type:** *Newsletter.* **Description:** Presents news and activities of the Pacific Stock Exchange, the securities industry, trading highlights, and related topics.
Formed by the 1990 merger of: Final Quotes; Pacific Stock Exchange Highlights
Published by: Pacific Stock Exchange, Inc., 115 Sansome St., Ste. 315, San Francisco, CA 94104-3330. TEL 415-393-4253, FAX 415-393-4108. Ed. Genie W Williams. Circ: 4,000.

332.6   USA
COGENT COMMENTS. Text in English. w. **Document type:** *Newsletter.* **Description:** Contains pertinent selections from more than 120 market letters surveyed weekly by the Bullish Consensus.
Published by: Market Vane Corporation, PO Box 90490, Pasadena, CA 91109-0490. TEL 818-395-7436, FAX 818-795-7654. Ed. Richard Ishida.

COIN PREVIEWER; numismatic investment newsletter. see *NUMISMATICS*

COIN WORLD ANNUAL PRICE GUIDE. see *NUMISMATICS*

THE COINFIDENTIAL REPORT. see *NUMISMATICS*

332.6   GBR
COLLECTIVE INVESTMENT SCHEMES. Text in English. 1989. 2 base vols. plus updates 2/yr. looseleaf. GBP 767 (effective 2006). **Document type:** *Journal, Trade.*
Published by: Sweet & Maxwell Ltd., 100 Avenue Road, London, NW3 3PF, United Kingdom. TEL 44-20-74491111, FAX 44-20-74491144, customer.services@sweetandmaxwell.co.uk, http://www.sweetandmaxwell.co.uk. **Subscr. to:** Cheriton House, North Way, Andover, Hants SP10 5BE, United Kingdom.

COMICS VALUES MONTHLY. see *ART*

COMMERCIAL INVESTMENT REAL ESTATE. see *REAL ESTATE*

COMMERCIAL MORTGAGE ALERT. see *REAL ESTATE*

332.6   USA   ISSN 0279-0939
COMMODEX SYSTEM. Text in English. 1959. d. USD 575. back issues avail. **Document type:** *Newsletter.*
Published by: Equidex, Derlein's Susan M, 275 W El Nopal, Green Valley, AZ 85614-3815. TEL 201-868-2600, commodex@commodex.com, http://www.commodex.com. Circ: 5,000.

332.63   GBR   ISSN 1365-6953
COMMODITIES NOW. Text in English. 1997. q. GBP 45 domestic (effective 2001). adv. **Document type:** *Magazine, Trade.* **Description:** Covers power & energy, base & precious metals, agriculture, softs, exchanges, and technology as well as a host of related issues.
Published by: Isherwood Production Ltd., Ste 16, Imperial Studios, London, SW6 2AG, United Kingdom. TEL 44-20-77360774, FAX 44-20-77316405, info@commodities-now.com, http://www.commodities-now.com/. Ed. Guy Isherwood. Adv. contact Charlotte James. color page GBP 3,950, B&W page GBP 3,634.

332.63   GBR
COMMODITIES ONLINE DAILY. Variant title: Daily Online Prices. The Public Ledger Commodities Online. Text in English. d. (Mon.-Fri.). GBP 433 domestic; GBP 456 in Europe; GBP 479 elsewhere (effective 2004); included with subscription to The Public Ledger. **Description:** Contains updates of over 700 commodity prices including grains, vegetables oils, food ingredients and softs as well as fibres, forest products and metals.
Related titles: Online - full content ed.
Published by: Agra Europe (London) Ltd. (Subsidiary of: T & F Informa plc), 80 Calverley Rd, Tunbridge Wells, Kent TN1 2UN, United Kingdom. TEL 44-1892-533813, FAX 44-1892-544895, marketing@agra-net.com, http://www.public-ledger.com/cod.html, http://www.agra-net.com.

332.6 630   USA   ISSN 0279-0947
COMMODITY FUTURES FORECAST SERVICE. Text in English. 1956. w. USD 350. back issues avail. **Document type:** *Newsletter.*
Published by: Equidex, Derlein's Susan M, 275 W El Nopal, Green Valley, AZ 85614-3815. TEL 201-868-2600, commodex@commodex.com, http://www.commodex.com. Ed. Philip Gotthelf.

COMMODITY FUTURES LAW REPORTER. see *LAW*

332.63   USA   ISSN 0148-9283
COMMODITY FUTURES TRADING COMMISSION. ANNUAL REPORT. Text in English. 1976. a.
Published by: U.S. Commodity Futures Trading Commission, 2033 K St, N W, Washington, DC 20581. TEL 202-254-6387.

332.6   USA
COMMODITY PRICE CHARTS. Text in English. 1976. w. USD 435.
Address: 833 W. Jackson Blvd., Flr. 7, Chicago, IL 60607-3015. TEL 312-977-0999. Ed. Karla Kelley.

332.63 332.678   USA
COMMODITY TRADERS CONSUMER REPORT. Text in English. 1983. m. USD 225 (effective 1999). bk.rev.; software rev. charts; stat.; tr.lit. back issues avail. **Document type:** *Newsletter, Trade.* **Description:** Covers the futures investment industry and rates newsletter, hot lines, and fax lines that give investment signals; includes an advisory newsletter.
Related titles: E-mail ed.; Fax ed.; Online - full text ed.
Address: 67 E 11th St, Ste 5145, New York, NY 10003. TEL 973-744-0388, 800-832-6065, courtney@investors.net, http://ctcr.investors.net. Ed. Courtney Smith. Circ: 1,000. **Dist. by:** CTCR, 79 Valley Rd, No B, Montclair, NJ 07042. TEL 800-832-6065, FAX 973-744-0388.

COMMONWEALTH LETTERS; for investors in single family homes. see *REAL ESTATE*

COMMUNITY ECONOMICS. see *BUSINESS AND ECONOMICS—Cooperatives*

363.5   USA
COMMUNITY INVESTMENT AND AFFORDABLE HOUSING. Text in English. 1990. q. free.
Published by: Federal Home Loan Bank of Des Moines, 907 Walnut St, Des Moines, IA 50309. TEL 515-281-1101, FAX 515-281-1022.

COMPANY R E F S (MONTHLY). (Really Essential Financial Statistics) see *BUSINESS AND ECONOMICS—Banking And Finance*

THE (YEAR) COMPETITIVENESS REPORT ON ARGENTINA: FINANCIALS RETURNS, LABOR PRODUCTIVITY AND INTERNATIONAL GAPS. see *BUSINESS AND ECONOMICS*

332.6   USA
THE (YEAR) COMPETITIVENESS REPORT ON BEAUPORT, CANADA: FINANCIALS RETURNS, LABOR PRODUCTIVITY, BENCHMARKS AND INTERNATIONAL GAPS. Text in English. a., latest 2000. USD 210 (effective 2001). **Description:** Aims to assist managers in gauging the competitive performance of Canada at the global level, including the deployment and productivity from regional and global benchmarks.
Published by: Icon Group International, Inc., 4370 La Jolla Village Dr. 4o. Fl., San Diego, CA 92122. TEL 858-546-4340, FAX 858-546-4341, http://www.icongrouponline.com/. Ed. Stephanie Winters.

332.6   USA
THE (YEAR) COMPETITIVENESS REPORT ON BOLTON, CANADA: FINANCIALS RETURNS, LABOR PRODUCTIVITY, BENCHMARKS AND INTERNATIONAL GAPS. Text in English. a., latest 2000. USD 210 (effective 2001). **Description:** Aims to assist managers in gauging the competitive performance of Canada at the global level, including the deployment and productivity from regional and global benchmarks.
Published by: Icon Group International, Inc., 4370 La Jolla Village Dr. 4o. Fl., San Diego, CA 92122. TEL 858-546-4340, FAX 858-546-4341, http://www.icongrouponline.com/. Ed. Stephanie Winters.

332.6   USA
THE (YEAR) COMPETITIVENESS REPORT ON BRAMPTON, CANADA: FINANCIALS RETURNS, LABOR PRODUCTIVITY, BENCHMARKS AND INTERNATIONAL GAPS. Text in English. a., latest 2000. USD 210 (effective 2001). **Description:** Aims to assist managers in gauging the competitive performance of Canada at the global level, including the deployment and productivity from regional and global benchmarks.
Published by: Icon Group International, Inc., 4370 La Jolla Village Dr. 4o. Fl., San Diego, CA 92122. TEL 858-546-4340, FAX 858-546-4341, http://www.icongrouponline.com/. Ed. Stephanie Winters.

332.6   USA
THE (YEAR) COMPETITIVENESS REPORT ON BRANTFORD, CANADA: FINANCIAL RETURNS, LABOR PRODUCTIVITY, BENCHMARKS AND INTERNATIONAL GAPS. Text in English. a., latest 2000. USD 210 (effective 2001). **Description:** Aims to assist managers in gauging the competitive performance of Canada at the global level, including the deployment and productivity from regional and global benchmarks.
Published by: Icon Group International, Inc., 4370 La Jolla Village Dr. 4o. Fl., San Diego, CA 92122. TEL 858-546-4340, FAX 858-546-4341, http://www.icongrouponline.com/. Ed. Stephanie Winters.

THE (YEAR) COMPETITIVENESS REPORT ON BRAZIL: FINANCIALS RETURNS, LABOR PRODUCTIVITY AND INTERNATIONAL GAPS. see *BUSINESS AND ECONOMICS*

332.6   USA
THE (YEAR) COMPETITIVENESS REPORT ON CALGARY, CANADA: FINANCIAL RETURNS, LABOR PRODUCTIVITY, BENCHMARKS AND INTERNATIONAL GAPS. Text in English. a., latest 2000. USD 210 (effective 2001). **Description:** Aims to assist managers in gauging the competitive performance of Canada at the global level, including the deployment and productivity from regional and global benchmarks.
Published by: Icon Group International, Inc., 4370 La Jolla Village Dr. 4o. Fl., San Diego, CA 92122. TEL 858-546-4340, FAX 858-546-4341, http://www.icongrouponline.com/. Ed. Stephanie Winters.

THE (YEAR) COMPETITIVENESS REPORT ON CANADA: FINANCIALS RETURNS, LABOR PRODUCTIVITY AND INTERNATIONAL GAPS. see *BUSINESS AND ECONOMICS*

332.6   USA
THE (YEAR) COMPETITIVENESS REPORT ON CHARLOTTETOWN, CANADA: FINANCIAL RETURNS, LABOR PRODUCTIVITY, BENCHMARKS AND INTERNATIONAL GAPS. Text in Spanish. a. USD 210 (effective 2001). **Description:** Aims to assist managers in gauging the competitive performance of Canada at the global level, including the deployment and productivity from regional and global benchmarks.
Published by: Icon Group International, Inc., 4370 La Jolla Village Dr. 4o. Fl., San Diego, CA 92122. TEL 858-546-4340, FAX 858-546-4341, http://www.icongrouponline.com/. Ed. Stephanie Winters.

THE (YEAR) COMPETITIVENESS REPORT ON CHILE: FINANCIALS RETURNS, LABOR PRODUCTIVITY AND INTERNATIONAL GAPS. see *BUSINESS AND ECONOMICS*

THE (YEAR) COMPETITIVENESS REPORT ON COLOMBIA: FINANCIALS RETURNS, LABOR PRODUCTIVITY AND INTERNATIONAL GAPS. see *BUSINESS AND ECONOMICS*

332.6   USA
THE (YEAR) COMPETITIVENESS REPORT ON DON MILLS, CANADA: FINANCIAL RETURNS, LABOR PRODUCTIVITY, BENCHMARKS AND INTERNATIONAL GAPS. Text in English. a., latest 2000. USD 210 (effective 2001). **Description:** Aims to assist managers in gauging the competitive performance of Canada at the global level, including the deployment and productivity from regional and global benchmarks.
Published by: Icon Group International, Inc., 4370 La Jolla Village Dr. 4o. Fl., San Diego, CA 92122. TEL 858-546-4340, FAX 858-546-4341, http://www.icongrouponline.com/. Ed. Stephanie Winters.

332.6   USA
THE (YEAR) COMPETITIVENESS REPORT ON DORVAL, CANADA: FINANCIAL RETURNS, LABOR PRODUCTIVITY, BENCHMARKS AND INTERNATIONAL GAPS. Text in English. a., latest 2000. USD 210 (effective 2001). **Description:** Aims to assist managers in gauging the competitive performance of Canada at the global level, including the deployment and productivity from regional and global benchmarks.
Published by: Icon Group International, Inc., 4370 La Jolla Village Dr. 4o. Fl., San Diego, CA 92122. TEL 858-546-4340, FAX 858-546-4341, http://www.icongrouponline.com/. Ed. Stephanie Winters.

332.6   USA
THE (YEAR) COMPETITIVENESS REPORT ON EDMONTON, CANADA: FINANCIAL RETURNS, LABOR PRODUCTIVITY, BENCHMARKS AND INTERNATIONAL GAPS. Text in English. a., latest 2000. USD 210 (effective 2001). **Description:** Aims to assist managers in gauging the competitive performance of Canada at the global level, including the deployment and productivity from regional and global benchmarks.
Published by: Icon Group International, Inc., 4370 La Jolla Village Dr. 4o. Fl., San Diego, CA 92122. TEL 858-546-4340, FAX 858-546-4341, http://www.icongrouponline.com/. Ed. Stephanie Winters.

332.6   USA
THE (YEAR) COMPETITIVENESS REPORT ON ETOBICOKE, CANADA: FINANCIAL RETURNS, LABOR PRODUCTIVITY, BENCHMARKS AND INTERNATIONAL GAPS. Text in English. a., latest 2000. USD 210 (effective 2001). **Description:** Aims to assist managers in gauging the competitive performance of Canada at the global level, including the deployment and productivity from regional and global benchmarks.
Published by: Icon Group International, Inc., 4370 La Jolla Village Dr. 4o. Fl., San Diego, CA 92122. TEL 858-546-4340, FAX 858-546-4341, http://www.icongrouponline.com/. Ed. Stephanie Winters.

332.6 USA
THE (YEAR) COMPETITIVENESS REPORT ON GRANBY, CANADA: FINANCIAL RETURNS, LABOR PRODUCTIVITY, BENCHMARKS AND INTERNATIONAL GAPS. Text in English. a., latest 2000. USD 210 (effective 2001).
Description: Aims to assist managers in gauging the competitive performance of Canada at the global level, including the deployment and productivity from regional and global benchmarks.
Published by: Icon Group International, Inc., 4370 La Jolla Village Dr. 4o. Fl., San Diego, CA 92122. TEL 858-546-4340, FAX 858-546-4341, http://www.icongrouponline.com/. Ed. Stephanie Winters.

332.6 USA
THE (YEAR) COMPETITIVENESS REPORT ON GUELPH, CANADA: FINANCIAL RETURNS, LABOR PRODUCTIVITY, BENCHMARKS AND INTERNATIONAL GAPS. Text in English. a., latest 2000. USD 210 (effective 2001).
Description: Aims to assist managers in gauging the competitive performance of Canada at the global level, including the deployment and productivity from regional and global benchmarks.
Published by: Icon Group International, Inc., 4370 La Jolla Village Dr. 4o. Fl., San Diego, CA 92122. TEL 858-546-4340, FAX 858-546-4341, http://www.icongrouponline.com/. Ed. Stephanie Winters.

332.6 USA
THE (YEAR) COMPETITIVENESS REPORT ON HALEY, CANADA: FINANCIAL RETURNS, LABOR PRODUCTIVITY, BENCHMARKS AND INTERNATIONAL GAPS. Text in English. a., latest 2000. USD 210 (effective 2001).
Description: Aims to assist managers in gauging the competitive performance of Canada at the global level, including the deployment and productivity from regional and global benchmarks.
Published by: Icon Group International, Inc., 4370 La Jolla Village Dr. 4o. Fl., San Diego, CA 92122. TEL 858-546-4340, FAX 858-546-4341, http://www.icongrouponline.com/. Ed. Stephanie Winters.

332.6 USA
THE (YEAR) COMPETITIVENESS REPORT ON HALIFAX, CANADA: FINANCIAL RETURNS, LABOR PRODUCTIVITY, BENCHMARKS AND INTERNATIONAL GAPS. Text in English. a., latest 2000. USD 210 (effective 2001).
Description: Aims to assist managers in gauging the competitive performance of Canada at the global level, including the deployment and productivity from regional and global benchmarks.
Published by: Icon Group International, Inc., 4370 La Jolla Village Dr. 4o. Fl., San Diego, CA 92122. TEL 858-546-4340, FAX 858-546-4341, http://www.icongrouponline.com/. Ed. Stephanie Winters.

332.6 USA
THE (YEAR) COMPETITIVENESS REPORT ON KANATA, CANADA: FINANCIAL RETURNS, LABOR PRODUCTIVITY, BENCHMARKS AND INTERNATIONAL GAPS. Text in English. a., latest 2000. USD 210 (effective 2001).
Description: Aims to assist managers in gauging the competitive performance of Canada at the global level, including the deployment and productivity from regional and global benchmarks.
Published by: Icon Group International, Inc., 4370 La Jolla Village Dr. 4o. Fl., San Diego, CA 92122. TEL 858-546-4340, FAX 858-546-4341, http://www.icongrouponline.com/. Ed. Stephanie Winters.

332.6 USA
THE (YEAR) COMPETITIVENESS REPORT ON KELOWNA, CANADA: FINANCIAL RETURNS, LABOR PRODUCTIVITY, BENCHMARKS AND INTERNATIONAL GAPS. Text in English. a., latest 2000. USD 210 (effective 2001).
Description: Aims to assist managers in gauging the competitive performance of Canada at the global level, including the deployment and productivity from regional and global benchmarks.
Published by: Icon Group International, Inc., 4370 La Jolla Village Dr. 4o. Fl., San Diego, CA 92122. TEL 858-546-4340, FAX 858-546-4341, http://www.icongrouponline.com/. Ed. Stephanie Winters.

332.6 USA
THE (YEAR) COMPETITIVENESS REPORT ON KINGSEY FALLS, CANADA: FINANCIAL RETURNS, LABOR PRODUCTIVITY, BENCHMARKS AND INTERNATIONAL GAPS. Text in English. a., latest 2000. USD 210 (effective 2001). **Description:** Aims to assist managers in gauging the competitive performance of Canada at the global level, including the deployment and productivity from regional and global benchmarks.
Published by: Icon Group International, Inc., 4370 La Jolla Village Dr. 4o. Fl., San Diego, CA 92122. TEL 858-546-4340, FAX 858-546-4341, http://www.icongrouponline.com/. Ed. Stephanie Winters.

332.6 USA
THE (YEAR) COMPETITIVENESS REPORT ON KITCHENER, CANADA: FINANCIAL RETURNS, LABOR PRODUCTIVITY, BENCHMARKS AND INTERNATIONAL GAPS. Text in English. a., latest 2000. USD 210 (effective 2001).
Description: Aims to assist managers in gauging the competitive performance of Canada at the global level, including the deployment and productivity from regional and global benchmarks.
Published by: Icon Group International, Inc., 4370 La Jolla Village Dr. 4o. Fl., San Diego, CA 92122. TEL 858-546-4340, FAX 858-546-4341, http://www.icongrouponline.com/. Ed. Stephanie Winters.

THE (YEAR) COMPETITIVENESS REPORT ON LATIN AMERICA: FINANCIALS RETURNS, LABOR PRODUCTIVITY AND INTERNATIONAL GAPS. see *BUSINESS AND ECONOMICS*

332.6 USA
THE (YEAR) COMPETITIVENESS REPORT ON LAVAL, CANADA: FINANCIAL RETURNS, LABOR PRODUCTIVITY, BENCHMARKS AND INTERNATIONAL GAPS. Text in English. a., latest 2000. USD 210 (effective 2001).
Description: Aims to assist managers in gauging the competitive performance of Canada at the global level, including the deployment and productivity from regional and global benchmarks.
Published by: Icon Group International, Inc., 4370 La Jolla Village Dr. 4o. Fl., San Diego, CA 92122. TEL 858-546-4340, FAX 858-546-4341, http://www.icongrouponline.com/. Ed. Stephanie Winters.

332.6 USA
THE (YEAR) COMPETITIVENESS REPORT ON LETHBRIDGE, CANADA: FINANCIAL RETURNS, LABOR PRODUCTIVITY, BENCHMARKS AND INTERNATIONAL GAPS. Text in English. a., latest 2000. USD 210 (effective 2001).
Description: Aims to assist managers in gauging the competitive performance of Canada at the global level, including the deployment and productivity from regional and global benchmarks.
Published by: Icon Group International, Inc., 4370 La Jolla Village Dr. 4o. Fl., San Diego, CA 92122. TEL 858-546-4340, FAX 858-546-4341, http://www.icongrouponline.com/. Ed. Stephanie Winters.

332.6 USA
THE (YEAR) COMPETITIVENESS REPORT ON LEVIS, CANADA: FINANCIAL RETURNS, LABOR PRODUCTIVITY, BENCHMARKS AND INTERNATIONAL GAPS. Text in English. a., latest 2000. USD 210 (effective 2001).
Description: Aims to assist managers in gauging the competitive performance of Canada at the global level, including the deployment and productivity from regional and global benchmarks.
Published by: Icon Group International, Inc., 4370 La Jolla Village Dr. 4o. Fl., San Diego, CA 92122. TEL 858-546-4340, FAX 858-546-4341, http://www.icongrouponline.com/. Ed. Stephanie Winters.

332.6 USA
THE (YEAR) COMPETITIVENESS REPORT ON LONGUEUIL, CANADA: FINANCIAL RETURNS, LABOR PRODUCTIVITY, BENCHMARKS AND INTERNATIONAL GAPS. Text in English. a., latest 2000. USD 210 (effective 2001).
Description: Aims to assist managers in gauging the competitive performance of Canada at the global level, including the deployment and productivity from regional and global benchmarks.
Published by: Icon Group International, Inc., 4370 La Jolla Village Dr. 4o. Fl., San Diego, CA 92122. TEL 858-546-4340, FAX 858-546-4341, http://www.icongrouponline.com/. Ed. Stephanie Winters.

332.6 USA
THE (YEAR) COMPETITIVENESS REPORT ON LUNENBURG, CANADA: FINANCIAL RETURNS, LABOR PRODUCTIVITY, BENCHMARKS AND INTERNATIONAL GAPS. Text in English. a., latest 2000. USD 210 (effective 2001).
Description: Aims to assist managers in gauging the competitive performance of Canada at the global level, including the deployment and productivity from regional and global benchmarks.
Published by: Icon Group International, Inc., 4370 La Jolla Village Dr. 4o. Fl., San Diego, CA 92122. TEL 858-546-4340, FAX 858-546-4341, http://www.icongrouponline.com/. Ed. Stephanie Winters.

332.6 USA
THE (YEAR) COMPETITIVENESS REPORT ON MARKHAM, CANADA: FINANCIAL RETURNS, LABOR PRODUCTIVITY, BENCHMARKS AND INTERNATIONAL GAPS. Text in English. a., latest 2000. USD 210 (effective 2001).
Description: Aims to assist managers in gauging the competitive performance of Canada at the global level, including the deployment and productivity from regional and global benchmarks.
Published by: Icon Group International, Inc., 4370 La Jolla Village Dr. 4o. Fl., San Diego, CA 92122. TEL 858-546-4340, FAX 858-546-4341, http://www.icongrouponline.com/. Ed. Stephanie Winters.

THE (YEAR) COMPETITIVENESS REPORT ON MEXICO: FINANCIALS RETURNS, LABOR PRODUCTIVITY AND INTERNATIONAL GAPS. see *BUSINESS AND ECONOMICS*

332.6 USA
THE (YEAR) COMPETITIVENESS REPORT ON MISSISSAUGA, CANADA: FINANCIAL RETURNS, LABOR PRODUCTIVITY, BENCHMARKS AND INTERNATIONAL GAPS. Text in English. a., latest 2000. USD 210 (effective 2001).
Description: Aims to assist managers in gauging the competitive performance of Canada at the global level, including the deployment and productivity from regional and global benchmarks.
Published by: Icon Group International, Inc., 4370 La Jolla Village Dr. 4o. Fl., San Diego, CA 92122. TEL 858-546-4340, FAX 858-546-4341, http://www.icongrouponline.com/. Ed. Stephanie Winters.

332.6 USA
THE (YEAR) COMPETITIVENESS REPORT ON MONTREAL, CANADA: FINANCIAL RETURNS, LABOR PRODUCTIVITY, BENCHMARKS AND INTERNATIONAL GAPS. Text in English. a., latest 2000. USD 210 (effective 2001).
Description: Aims to assist managers in gauging the competitive performance of Canada at the global level, including the deployment and productivity from regional and global benchmarks.
Published by: Icon Group International, Inc., 4370 La Jolla Village Dr. 4o. Fl., San Diego, CA 92122. TEL 858-546-4340, FAX 858-546-4341, http://www.icongrouponline.com/. Ed. Stephanie Winters.

332.6 USA
THE (YEAR) COMPETITIVENESS REPORT ON MOUNT ROYAL, CANADA: FINANCIAL RETURNS, LABOR PRODUCTIVITY, BENCHMARKS AND INTERNATIONAL GAPS. Text in English. a., latest 2000. USD 210 (effective 2001).
Description: Aims to assist managers in gauging the competitive performance of Canada at the global level, including the deployment and productivity from regional and global benchmarks.
Published by: Icon Group International, Inc., 4370 La Jolla Village Dr. 4o. Fl., San Diego, CA 92122. TEL 858-546-4340, FAX 858-546-4341, http://www.icongrouponline.com/. Ed. Stephanie Winters.

332.6 USA
THE (YEAR) COMPETITIVENESS REPORT ON NEPEAN, CANADA: FINANCIAL RETURNS, LABOR PRODUCTIVITY, BENCHMARKS AND INTERNATIONAL GAPS. Text in English. a., latest 2000. USD 210 (effective 2001).
Description: Aims to assist managers in gauging the competitive performance of Canada at the global level, including the deployment and productivity from regional and global benchmarks.
Published by: Icon Group International, Inc., 4370 La Jolla Village Dr. 4o. Fl., San Diego, CA 92122. TEL 858-546-4340, FAX 858-546-4341, http://www.icongrouponline.com/. Ed. Stephanie Winters.

THE (YEAR) COMPETITIVENESS REPORT ON PERU: FINANCIALS RETURNS, LABOR PRODUCTIVITY AND INTERNATIONAL GAPS. see *BUSINESS AND ECONOMICS*

332.6 USA
THE (YEAR) COMPETITIVENESS REPORT ON QUEBEC CITY, CANADA: FINANCIAL RETURNS, LABOR PRODUCTIVITY, BENCHMARKS AND INTERNATIONAL GAPS. Text in English. a., latest 2000. USD 210 (effective 2001).
Description: Aims to assist managers in gauging the competitive performance of Canada at the global level, including the deployment and productivity from regional and global benchmarks.
Published by: Icon Group International, Inc., 4370 La Jolla Village Dr. 4o. Fl., San Diego, CA 92122. TEL 858-546-4340, FAX 858-546-4341, http://www.icongrouponline.com/. Ed. Stephanie Winters.

332.6 USA
THE (YEAR) COMPETITIVENESS REPORT ON REGINA, CANADA: FINANCIAL RETURNS, LABOR PRODUCTIVITY, BENCHMARKS AND INTERNATIONAL GAPS. Text in English. a., latest 2000. USD 210 (effective 2001).
Description: Aims to assist managers in gauging the competitive performance of Canada at the global level, including the deployment and productivity from regional and global benchmarks.
Published by: Icon Group International, Inc., 4370 La Jolla Village Dr. 4o. Fl., San Diego, CA 92122. TEL 858-546-4340, FAX 858-546-4341, http://www.icongrouponline.com/. Ed. Stephanie Winters.

332.6 USA
THE (YEAR) COMPETITIVENESS REPORT ON SAINT-DAMIEN REGINA, CANADA: FINANCIAL RETURNS, LABOR PRODUCTIVITY, BENCHMARKS AND INTERNATIONAL GAPS. Text in English. a., latest 2000. USD 210 (effective 2001). **Description:** Aims to assist managers in gauging the competitive performance of Canada at the global level, including the deployment and productivity from regional and global benchmarks.

B

▼ new title ➤ refereed ✶ unverified ♦ full entry avail.

Published by: Icon Group International, Inc., 4370 La Jolla Village Dr. 4o. Fl., San Diego, CA 92122. TEL 858-546-4340, FAX 858-546-4341, http://www.icongrouponline.com/. Ed. Stephanie Winters.

332.6 USA
THE (YEAR) COMPETITIVENESS REPORT ON SAINT-LAURENT, CANADA: FINANCIAL RETURNS, LABOR PRODUCTIVITY, BENCHMARKS AND INTERNATIONAL GAPS. Text in English. a., latest 2000. USD 210 (effective 2001). **Description:** Aims to assist managers in gauging the competitive performance of Canada at the global level, including the deployment and productivity from regional and global benchmarks.
Published by: Icon Group International, Inc., 4370 La Jolla Village Dr. 4o. Fl., San Diego, CA 92122. TEL 858-546-4340, FAX 858-546-4341, http://www.icongrouponline.com/. Ed. Stephanie Winters.

332.6 USA
THE (YEAR) COMPETITIVENESS REPORT ON SAINT-LEONARD, CANADA: FINANCIAL RETURNS, LABOR PRODUCTIVITY, BENCHMARKS AND INTERNATIONAL GAPS. Text in English. a., latest 2000. USD 210 (effective 2001). **Description:** Aims to assist managers in gauging the competitive performance of Canada at the global level, including the deployment and productivity from regional and global benchmarks.
Published by: Icon Group International, Inc., 4370 La Jolla Village Dr. 4o. Fl., San Diego, CA 92122. TEL 858-546-4340, FAX 858-546-4341, http://www.icongrouponline.com/. Ed. Stephanie Winters.

332.6 USA
THE (YEAR) COMPETITIVENESS REPORT ON SAINTE-MARIE-DE-BEAUCE, CANADA: FINANCIAL RETURNS, LABOR PRODUCTIVITY, BENCHMARKS AND INTERNATIONAL GAPS. Text in English. a. USD 210 (effective 2001). **Description:** Aims to assist managers in gauging the competitive performance of Canada at the global level, including the deployment and productivity from regional and global benchmarks.
Published by: Icon Group International, Inc., 4370 La Jolla Village Dr. 4o. Fl., San Diego, CA 92122. TEL 858-546-4340, FAX 858-546-4341, http://www.icongrouponline.com/. Ed. Stephanie Winters.

332.6 USA
THE (YEAR) COMPETITIVENESS REPORT ON SASKATOON, CANADA: FINANCIAL RETURNS, LABOR PRODUCTIVITY, BENCHMARKS AND INTERNATIONAL GAPS. Text in English. a., latest 2000. USD 210 (effective 2001). **Description:** Aims to assist managers in gauging the competitive performance of Canada at the global level, including the deployment and productivity from regional and global benchmarks.
Published by: Icon Group International, Inc., 4370 La Jolla Village Dr. 4o. Fl., San Diego, CA 92122. TEL 858-546-4340, FAX 858-546-4341, http://www.icongrouponline.com/. Ed. Stephanie Winters.

332.6 USA
THE (YEAR) COMPETITIVENESS REPORT ON SHERBROOKE, CANADA: FINANCIAL RETURNS, LABOR PRODUCTIVITY, BENCHMARKS AND INTERNATIONAL GAPS. Text in English. a., latest 2000. USD 210 (effective 2001). **Description:** Aims to assist managers in gauging the competitive performance of Canada at the global level, including the deployment and productivity from regional and global benchmarks.
Published by: Icon Group International, Inc., 4370 La Jolla Village Dr. 4o. Fl., San Diego, CA 92122. TEL 858-546-4340, FAX 858-546-4341, http://www.icongrouponline.com/. Ed. Stephanie Winters.

332.6 USA
THE (YEAR) COMPETITIVENESS REPORT ON ST. JEROME, CANADA: FINANCIAL RETURNS, LABOR PRODUCTIVITY, BENCHMARKS AND INTERNATIONAL GAPS. Text in English. a., latest 2000. USD 210 (effective 2001). **Description:** Aims to assist managers in gauging the competitive performance of Canada at the global level, including the deployment and productivity from regional and global benchmarks.
Published by: Icon Group International, Inc., 4370 La Jolla Village Dr. 4o. Fl., San Diego, CA 92122. TEL 858-546-4340, FAX 858-546-4341, http://www.icongrouponline.com/. Ed. Stephanie Winters.

332.6 USA
THE (YEAR) COMPETITIVENESS REPORT ON ST. JOHN'S, CANADA: FINANCIAL RETURNS, LABOR PRODUCTIVITY, BENCHMARKS AND INTERNATIONAL GAPS. Text in English. a., latest 2000. USD 210 (effective 2001). **Description:** Aims to assist managers in gauging the competitive performance of Canada at the global level, including the deployment and productivity from regional and global benchmarks.
Published by: Icon Group International, Inc., 4370 La Jolla Village Dr. 4o. Fl., San Diego, CA 92122. TEL 858-546-4340, FAX 858-546-4341, http://www.icongrouponline.com/. Ed. Stephanie Winters.

332.6 USA
THE (YEAR) COMPETITIVENESS REPORT ON ST. LAURENT, CANADA: FINANCIAL RETURNS, LABOR PRODUCTIVITY, BENCHMARKS AND INTERNATIONAL GAPS. Text in English. a., latest 2000. USD 210 (effective 2001). **Description:** Aims to assist managers in gauging the competitive performance of Canada at the global level, including the deployment and productivity from regional and global benchmarks.
Published by: Icon Group International, Inc., 4370 La Jolla Village Dr. 4o. Fl., San Diego, CA 92122. TEL 858-546-4340, FAX 858-546-4341, http://www.icongrouponline.com/. Ed. Stephanie Winters.

332.6 USA
THE (YEAR) COMPETITIVENESS REPORT ON STELLARTON, CANADA: FINANCIAL RETURNS, LABOR PRODUCTIVITY, BENCHMARKS AND INTERNATIONAL GAPS. Text in English. a., latest 2000. USD 210 (effective 2001). **Description:** Aims to assist managers in gauging the competitive performance of Canada at the global level, including the deployment and productivity from regional and global benchmarks.
Published by: Icon Group International, Inc., 4370 La Jolla Village Dr. 4o. Fl., San Diego, CA 92122. TEL 858-546-4340, FAX 858-546-4341, http://www.icongrouponline.com/. Ed. Stephanie Winters.

332.6 USA
THE (YEAR) COMPETITIVENESS REPORT ON THORNHILL, CANADA: FINANCIAL RETURNS, LABOR PRODUCTIVITY, BENCHMARKS AND INTERNATIONAL GAPS. Text in English. a., latest 2000. USD 210 (effective 2001). **Description:** Aims to assist managers in gauging the competitive performance of Canada at the global level, including the deployment and productivity from regional and global benchmarks.
Published by: Icon Group International, Inc., 4370 La Jolla Village Dr. 4o. Fl., San Diego, CA 92122. TEL 858-546-4340, FAX 858-546-4341, http://www.icongrouponline.com/. Ed. Stephanie Winters.

THE (YEAR) COMPETITIVENESS REPORT ON VENEZUELA: FINANCIALS RETURNS, LABOR PRODUCTIVITY AND INTERNATIONAL GAPS. see *BUSINESS AND ECONOMICS*

332.6 USA
THE (YEAR) COMPETITIVENESS REPORT ON VILLE DE SAINT-GEORGES, CANADA: FINANCIAL RETURNS, LABOR PRODUCTIVITY, BENCHMARKS AND INTERNATIONAL GAPS. Text in English. a., latest 2000. USD 210 (effective 2001). **Description:** Aims to assist managers in gauging the competitive performance of Canada at the global level, including the deployment and productivity from regional and global benchmarks.
Published by: Icon Group International, Inc., 4370 La Jolla Village Dr. 4o. Fl., San Diego, CA 92122. TEL 858-546-4340, FAX 858-546-4341, http://www.icongrouponline.com/. Ed. Stephanie Winters.

332.6 USA
THE (YEAR) COMPETITIVENESS REPORT ON VILLE DE SAINT-LAURENT, CANADA: FINANCIAL RETURNS, LABOR PRODUCTIVITY, BENCHMARKS AND INTERNATIONAL GAPS. Text in English. a., latest 2000. USD 210 (effective 2001). **Description:** Aims to assist managers in gauging the competitive performance of Canada at the global level, including the deployment and productivity from regional and global benchmarks.
Published by: Icon Group International, Inc., 4370 La Jolla Village Dr. 4o. Fl., San Diego, CA 92122. TEL 858-546-4340, FAX 858-546-4341, http://www.icongrouponline.com/. Ed. Stephanie Winters.

332.6 USA
THE (YEAR) COMPETITIVENESS REPORT ON WESTMOUNT, CANADA: FINANCIAL RETURNS, LABOR PRODUCTIVITY, BENCHMARKS AND INTERNATIONAL GAPS. Text in English. a., latest 2000. USD 210 (effective 2001). **Description:** Aims to assist managers in gauging the competitive performance of Canada at the global level, including the deployment and productivity from regional and global benchmarks.
Published by: Icon Group International, Inc., 4370 La Jolla Village Dr. 4o. Fl., San Diego, CA 92122. TEL 858-546-4340, FAX 858-546-4341, http://www.icongrouponline.com/. Ed. Stephanie Winters.

332.6 USA
THE (YEAR) COMPETITIVENESS REPORT ON WILLOWDALE, CANADA: FINANCIAL RETURNS, LABOR PRODUCTIVITY, BENCHMARKS AND INTERNATIONAL GAPS. Text in English. a., latest 2000. USD 210 (effective 2001). **Description:** Aims to assist managers in gauging the competitive performance of Canada at the global level, including the deployment and productivity from regional and global benchmarks.
Published by: Icon Group International, Inc., 4370 La Jolla Village Dr. 4o. Fl., San Diego, CA 92122. TEL 858-546-4340, FAX 858-546-4341, http://www.icongrouponline.com/. Ed. Stephanie Winters.

332.6 USA
THE (YEAR) COMPETITIVENESS REPORT ON WINNIPEG, CANADA: FINANCIAL RETURNS, LABOR PRODUCTIVITY, BENCHMARKS AND INTERNATIONAL GAPS. Text in English. a., latest 2000. USD 210 (effective 2001). **Description:** Aims to assist managers in gauging the competitive performance of Canada at the global level, including the deployment and productivity from regional and global benchmarks.
Published by: Icon Group International, Inc., 4370 La Jolla Village Dr. 4o. Fl., San Diego, CA 92122. TEL 858-546-4340, FAX 858-546-4341, http://www.icongrouponline.com/. Ed. Stephanie Winters.

COMPLETE COMMODITY FUTURES DIRECTORY. see *BUSINESS AND ECONOMICS—Trade And Industrial Directories*

332.6 USA ISSN 1546-0134
▼ **THE COMPLETE INVESTOR.** Text in English. 2003 (Sept.). m. USD 99 domestic; USD 137.50 foreign (effective 2003).
Published by: T C I Enterprises, LLC, 500 5th Ave. 57th Fl., New York, NY 10110. TEL 212-653-1504. Ed. Stephen Leeb.

332.6 AUS ISSN 1442-0422
COMPLETE RETIREMENT PLANNER. Text in English. 1990. s-a.
Formerly (until 1999): Complete Retirement Guide (1039-9585); Which was superseded: Complete Retirement Guide (N.S.W. ed.) (1030-7524)
Published by: Universal Magazines Pty. Ltd., Unite 5, 6-8 Byfield St, North Ryde, NSW 2113, Australia. TEL 61-2-98870399, FAX 61-2-98050714, info@universalmagazines.com.au, http://www.universalmagazines.com.au/.

332.6 MEX
COMPORTAMIENTO DEL SISTEMA ASEGURADOR Y AFIANZADOR MEXICANO. Text in Spanish. a. **Document type:** *Government.* **Description:** Contains information on the historical development of the insurance and surety bond market during the previous five years.
Formed by the merger of: Comportamiento del Sistema Asegurador Mexicano; Comportamiento del Sistema Afianzador Mexicano
Published by: Comision Nacional de Seguros y Fianzas, Ave. DE LOS INSURGENTES SUR 1971 Piso 3, Col Guadalupe Inn, Mexico City, DF 01020, Mexico. TEL 52-5-6618053, FAX 52-5-7247602, cnsfdgdi@mail.internet.com.mx.

004.16 USA ISSN 0734-4597
COMPUTERIZED INVESTING. Text in English. 1982. bi-m. USD 40 (effective 2000).
Published by: American Association of Individual Investors, 625 N Michigan Ave, Ste 1900, Chicago, IL 60611. members@aaii.com, http://www.aaii.com. R&P Alyna Johnson.

332.6 CAN
CONFERENCE BOARD OF CANADA. INDEX OF BUSINESS CONFIDENCE. Text in English. q. membership. charts. **Document type:** *Trade.*
Former titles: Conference Board of Canada. Business Attitudes and Investment Spending Intentions (0827-6277); (until 1986): Conference Board of Canada. Survey of Business Attitudes and Investment Spending Intentions (0703-1920)
Indexed: CSI.
—CISTI.
Published by: Conference Board of Canada, 255 Smyth Rd, Ste 100, Ottawa, ON K1H 8M7, Canada. TEL 613-526-3280, FAX 613-526-4857.

332.6 ITA ISSN 1129-6283
CONGIUNTURA FLASH. Text in Italian. 1986. m.
Formerly (until 1993): Rassegna Congiunturale (0394-2236)
Related titles: ♦ Supplement(s): I Settori Industriali.
Indexed: PAIS.
Published by: Centro Studi Confindustria, Viale Pasteur 6, Rome, 00144, Italy. TEL 06-5920509, FAX 06-5924819, http://www.confindustria.it.

332.6 USA ISSN 1056-9766
CONSENSUS (KANSAS CITY); national futures and financial weekly. Text in English. 1970. w. USD 365 domestic; USD 395 in Canada; USD 595 elsewhere (effective 2003). adv. charts; stat. 40 p./no. 3 cols./p.; **Document type:** *Newspaper, Consumer.* **Description:** Investment newspaper for the futures industry used by most brokers and traders. Market letters, special reports, and buy/sell advise from over 100 top national and international sources. Covers all stock and financial markets, metals, agricultural markets, livestock, grains and oilseeds.
Related titles: Online - full text ed.: USD 295 (effective 2003).
Published by: Consensus, Inc. (Kansas City), PO Box 520526, Independence, MO 64052-0526. TEL 816-373-3700, FAX 816-373-3701, rsalva@aol.com, http://www.consensus-inc.com. Ed., Pub., R&P Robert E Salva TEL 816-373-3700. Adv. contact Sharon Buchko.

332.645 USA
CONSERVATIVE SPECULATOR; emerging growth stocks/special situations. Text in English. 1988. q. free. bk.rev.; software rev. tr.lit.; stat. 14 p./no.; back issues avail. **Document type:** *Newsletter, Consumer.* **Description:** Helps readers make more with the 10 percent they put into special situations than they make with the 90 percent put into everything else. Includes 1-2 special situations, sneak previews, update briefs and Dow 30 timing.
Related titles: Online - full text ed.: USD 39.
Published by: Wall Street Corner.com, Inc., 103 Ft Beauregard Ln, Bluffton, SC 29909. up415@aol.com, http://www.wallstreetcorner.com. Ed., R&P Lawrence C Oakley. Pub. Rosanne C Oakley. Circ: 13,000 (free).

332.6 DEU
CONSULT. Text in German. q. **Document type:** *Magazine, Trade.* **Description:** Contains information and advice for investment and financial advisors and professionals.
Published by: (Skandia Lebensversicherung AG), BurdaYukom Publishing GmbH (Subsidiary of: Hubert Burda Media Holding GmbH & Co. KG), Schleissheimer Str 141, Munich, 80797, Germany. TEL 49-89-306200, FAX 49-89-30620100, info@burdayukom.de, http://www.yukom.de. Circ: 5,000 (controlled).

332.6 USA
THE CONTRARIAN'S VIEW. Text in English. 1986. m. USD 39 domestic; USD 54 foreign (effective 2000). back issues avail. **Document type:** *Newsletter.* **Description:** Stock market advisory service.
Related titles: Online - full text ed.
Published by: Contrarian's View, 132 Moreland St, Worcester, MA 01609. TEL 508-757-2881, nick15@eve.assumption.edu, http://fennel.assumption.edu. Ed. Nick Chase. Circ: 50 (paid).

332.6 USA ISSN 0015-6019
CONTRARY INVESTOR FOLLOW-UP SERVICE. Text in English. ceased; resumed 1965. m. USD 75 (effective 2002). mkt. **Document type:** *Newsletter.* **Description:** Analyses and regular reports on all Contrary Investor selections until closed out with a definite selling price.
Media: Duplicated (not offset).
Published by: Fraser Management Associates, Inc., 309 S Willard St, Box 494, Burlington, VT 05402. TEL 802-658-0322, FAX 802-658-0260, ellen@fraser.com, http://www.fraser.com. Ed. James L Fraser.

332.6 USA
CONTRARY OPINION LIBRARY. Text in English. 1969. a. free. adv. **Document type:** *Catalog.*
Published by: Fraser Publishing Co. (Subsidiary of: Fraser Management Associates, Inc.), 309 S Willard St, Box 494, Burlington, VT 05402. TEL 802-658-0324, 877-996-3336, FAX 802-658-0260, info@fraserbooks.com, http://www.fraserbooks.com. Ed., Pub., R&P, Adv. contact Jeanne R Smith. Circ: 30,000.

332.6 USA
CONTROL PREMIUM STUDY. Text in English. q. USD 395 (effective 2000). **Document type:** *Journal, Trade.* **Description:** Tracks acquisition premiums for completed transactions involving publicly traded target companies where a controlling interest was acquired.
Published by: Houlihan, Lokey, Howard & Zukin, 1930 Century Park W, Los Angeles, CA 90067. TEL 800-788-5300, FAX 310-553-2173, http://www.hlhz.com.

332.6 USA
CORPORATE BOND MARKET MONTHLY. Text in English. m. stat.
Related titles: Series of: Global Corporate Bond Research.
Published by: Salomon Brothers, Inc., 7 World Trade Center, New York, NY 10048. TEL 212-783-7000.

332.6 340 USA ISSN 1547-7584
KF1477.A15M2
CORPORATE DEALMAKER. Text in English. 1989-1994; resumed 2003. bi-m. looseleaf. USD 10 per issue (effective 2005). adv. **Document type:** *Magazine, Trade.* **Description:** Lists vital statistics of the people involved in ongoing deals: lawyers and law firms, investment banks, bankers, accountants, proxy solicitation firms, PR firms and more.
Formerly: M & A Dealmaker (1041-7907)
Published by: The Deal, LLC (Subsidiary of: A L M), 105 Madison Ave, 5th Fl, New York, NY 10016. TEL 212-313-9238, 888-667-3325, FAX 212-313-9293, http://www.thedeal.com/corporatedealmaker. Ed. Robert Teitelman. adv.: color page USD 17,500; trim 8 x 10.75.

332.6 USA ISSN 1059-7964
HG4057
CORPORATE DIRECTORY OF US PUBLIC COMPANIES. Text in English. 1988. a. USD 360 per issue (effective 2003). 2600 p./no.; **Document type:** *Directory, Corporate.* **Description:** Profiles the business activities and finances of more than 10,000 publicly traded companies. Includes officers' and directors' names, subsidiaries and ownership information, as well as stock data and financial information.
Formerly (until 1991): Corporate Directory (1044-3525)
Published by: Walker's Research, LLC, 1650 Borel Pl, Ste 130, San Mateo, CA 94402. TEL 650-341-1110, 800-258-5737, FAX 650-341-2351, walkersres@aol.com, http://www.walkersresearch.com. Ed. Elizabeth Walsh. **Dist. in U.K. by:** Graham & Whiteside Ltd, Tuition House, 5-6 Francis Grove, London SW19 4DT, United Kingdom. TEL 44-20-8947-1011.

CORPORATE FINANCING WEEK; the newsweekly of corporate finance, investment banking and M & A. see *BUSINESS AND ECONOMICS—Banking And Finance*

332.6 GBR
CORPORATE GOVERNANCE - MEETING INSTITUTIONAL INVESTORS. Text in English. a. GBP 195.
Published by: Financial Times Information Ltd., Extel, Fitzroy House, 13-17 Epworth St, London, EC2A 4DL, United Kingdom. TEL 44-20-7825-8000, FAX 44-20-7608-2032, eic@ft.com, http://www.info.ft.com.

346 USA ISSN 1050-320X
HG4028.M4
CORPORATE GROWTH REPORT. Text in English. 1981. 50/yr. USD 495; USD 595 combined subscription plus database access (effective 2005). adv. **Document type:** *Newsletter.* **Description:** Provides legal and financial details on current mergers and acquisitions, as well as joint ventures, restructurings and methods of increasing shareholder value.
Formed by the 1992 merger of: Acquisition - Divestiture Weekly Report (0279-4160); Corporate Growth Magazine (0898-8390); Which was formerly: Buyouts and Acquisitions Magazine; Journal of Buyouts and Acquisitions (0736-5527)
Related titles: Microform ed.: (from PQC); Online - full text ed.: USD 1,150 (effective 2001) (from EBSCO Publishing, O C L C Online Computer Library Center, Inc., ProQuest Information & Learning).
Indexed: ABIn, BPIA, PAIS.
—BLDSC (3472.066300).
Published by: N V S T.com, Inc., 14450 N E 29th Pl., Ste.108, Bellevue, WA 98007. TEL 425-702-9733, 800-910-6878, FAX 425-702-9753, http://www.nvst.com/pubs/cgr-pub.asp. Circ: 1,000 (paid).

332.67 USA
CORPORATE SHAREHOLDER✶ ; first in financial-investor-shareholder relations. Text in English. 1974. s-m. USD 225. bk.rev.
Published by: Market Value, Inc., 2166 Broadway Apt 18E, New York, NY 10024-6672. TEL 212-662-0877. Ed. Edward Kulkosky. Circ: 1,000.

332.67 USA ISSN 1090-0829
HD60.5.U5
CORPORATE SOCIAL ISSUES REPORTER. Text in English. 1974. m. (11/yr.). USD 275 (effective 1999 & 2000). bk.rev. **Document type:** *Newsletter.* **Description:** Updates readers on developments affecting corporate social responsibility in such areas as investment in South Africa, Northern Ireland, military production, tobacco, labor laws and practices, energy, the environment and equal employment opportunity.
Formerly (until 1996): News for Investors (1053-5470)
Published by: Investor Responsibility Research Center, Inc., 1350 Connecticut Ave, N W, Ste 700, Washington, DC 20036. TEL 202-833-0700, FAX 202-833-3555, Heidi.Salkeld@irrc.org, http://www.irrc.org. Ed. Meg Voorhes. R&P Heidi Salkeld. Circ: 1,200.

332.62 USA
CORPORATE VENTURING REPORT. Text in English. m. USD 895 domestic; USD 970 foreign (effective 2002).
Published by: Alternative Investor, 170 Linden St, 2nd Fl, Wellesley, MA 02482. TEL 781-304-1400, FAX 781-304-1440, info@assetnews.com, http://www.assetnews.com/products/news/cvr.htm.

CORPORATION AND SECURITIES. see *LAW—Corporate Law*

332.6 CRI
COSTA RICAN BEACON. Text in Spanish. 1982. m. USD 48 (effective 2004). bk.rev. **Document type:** *Newsletter.* **Description:** Offers information on international finance, living and investing in Costa Rica. Covers tourism and news analysis.
Published by: Consorcio de Comunicaciones Interamericanas S.A., c/o Daniel Langlois, Apdo 196, San Jose, 2120, Costa Rica. TEL 506-2236833. Ed. Edwin L Lowery. R&P Jaime Vargas. Circ: 5,400.

332.6 FRA ISSN 0220-6358
HG4503
COTE OFFICIELLE. Text in French. d. **Document type:** *Newspaper.* **Description:** Daily stock exchange price list.
Published by: Bourse de Paris, 39 rue Cambon, Paris, 75001, France. TEL 49-27-1000, FAX 33-49-271433.

332.6 GBR
COUNTERTRADE. Text in English. irreg., latest vol.3, 1997. GBP 95, USD 170.
Published by: Euromoney Publications plc, Nestor House, Playhouse Yard, London, EC4V 5EX, United Kingdom. TEL 44-207-7798673, FAX 44-20-77798541.

332.6 USA ISSN 1087-4151
HF1414.3.C68
COUNTERTRADE & OFFSET; weekly intelligence on unconventional & reciprocal international trade. Text in English. 1983. 24/yr. USD 688 domestic includes Directory of Countertrade Services; USD 748 foreign includes Directory of Countertrade Services (effective 2000). **Document type:** *Newsletter.*
Formerly: Countertrade Outlook (0743-0396)
Published by: C T O Data Services, 1512 Valley Run., Durham, NC 27707-3640. TEL 703-383-5816, FAX 703-383-5815. Ed. James Thomas. Pub. Jayne Casillas.

COUNTRY FORECASTS (SYRACUSE). see *BUSINESS AND ECONOMICS*

COUNTRY RISK REVIEW. see *POLITICAL SCIENCE*

332.6 USA
COURAGEOUS CONTRARIAN✶ . Text in English. 1985. m. USD 75. **Description:** Features stock selection reports complete with five years of financial data.
Formerly (until 1987): Bond Market Manager
Published by: Mann Consultants, 3065 Branch Dr, Clearwater, FL 34620-1741. Ed. David Cheesman.

B

332.6 USA
CRAWFORD PERSPECTIVES. Text in English. 1977. m. USD 250; USD 275 foreign (effective 1999). bk.rev. **Document type:** *Newsletter.* **Description:** Presents stock market forecasting methods which focus on astronomic cycles and technical analysis.
Published by: Arch Crawford, Ed. & Pub., 6890 E Sunrise, 70, Tucson, AZ 85750-0840. TEL 520-577-1158, astromoney@worldnet.att.net, http://www.astromoney.com. Circ: 2,000 (controlled).

CREDIT. see *BUSINESS AND ECONOMICS—Banking And Finance*

332.6 USA ISSN 0731-1974
HG4501
CREDITWEEK. Text in English. 1973. w. price varies. **Document type:** *Directory, Trade.*
Former titles (until 1981): Standard & Poor's Fixed Income Investor (0193-9335); Fixed Income Investor (0091-8415); Standard & Poor's Bond Outlook (0006-7067)
Related titles: Online - full text ed.
—CCC.
Published by: Standard & Poor's (Subsidiary of: McGraw-Hill Companies, Inc.), 55 Water St, New York, NY 10041. TEL 212-208-8000. Ed. Matthew Korten.

332.6 USA ISSN 1058-6679
HJ9103
CREDITWEEK (MUNICIPAL EDITION). Text in English. 1991. w. **Document type:** *Trade.*
Published by: Standard & Poor's (Subsidiary of: McGraw-Hill Companies, Inc.), 55 Water St, New York, NY 10041. TEL 212-208-8000.

332.6 USA ISSN 1084-8053
CRIMINAL POLITICS. Text in English. 1975. m. USD 187.50. adv. bk.rev. index. back issues avail. **Description:** Covers offshore investment news, current and pending legislation relevant to financial management, with conservative analysis of political news and issues.
Former titles (until 1989): Monthly Lesson in Criminal Politics; Patterson Strategy Letter
Related titles: Microform ed.: (from PQC).
Published by: Patterson Strategy Organization, PO Box 37812, Cincinnati, OH 45222. TEL 513-475-0100, FAX 513-475-6014, TELEX 466053 LT PATSN SLCI, crimpol@eos.net. Ed., Pub. Lawrence T Patterson. R&P Judy Pieper. Adv. contact Nita Kennedy. Circ: 30,000.

332.678 USA
CRISIS INVESTING. Text in English. 1979. m. USD 145. **Description:** Information on precious metals, gold mining, commodities, start-up companies and technologically innovative firms.
Formerly: Investing in Crisis (0740-3666)
Published by: Agora, Inc., 105 W Monument St, Baltimore, MD 21201. TEL 410-223-2611, FAX 410-223-2696. Ed. Douglas R Casey.

332.63 USA
CRITTENDEN'S SURETY BOND NEWS. Text in English. 1993. s-m. looseleaf. USD 307 (effective 1998). back issues avail.
Published by: Crittenden Newsletters, Inc., 250 Bel Marin Keys, Bldg A, PO Box 1150, Novato, CA 94949. TEL 415-382-2456, 800-421-3483, FAX 415-382-2476. Ed. Sarah Gardner. Pub. Robert Fink.

332 USA ISSN 0499-6453
CUMULATIVE LIST OF ORGANIZATIONS DESCRIBED IN SECTION 170C OF THE INTERNATL REVENUE CODE OF 1954. Text in English. a.
Published by: U.S. Internal Revenue Service, 1111 Constitution Ave, N W, Washington, DC 20224. TEL 800-829-1040, 800-829-1040, http://www.irs.gov.

▼ new title ➤ refereed ✶ unverified ♦ full entry avail.

332.6 USA
CURRENT DEVELOPMENTS. Text in English. 1972. m. USD 10,000. **Description:** Investment policy report describing capital markets, asset allocation, industry ratings and buy and sell decisions.
Formerly: Expectations Monitor
Published by: Callard, Madden & Associates, Inc., 11 S La Salle St, Ste 820, Chicago, IL 60603-1205. TEL 312-263-0027, FAX 312-260-0007. Ed. Charles G Callard. Circ: 200.

CZERWENSKY INTERN. see *BUSINESS AND ECONOMICS—Banking And Finance*

332.6 340 USA
D & O LIABILITY HANDBOOK: LAW, SAMPLE DOCUMENTS, FORMS. Text in English. a. price varies. **Document type:** *Monographic series, Trade.* **Description:** Provides a concise guide to the director and officer liability landscape through a collection of legal commentary, statutory provisions, and sample documents and forms.
Published by: Thomson West (Subsidiary of: Thomson Corporation, The), 610 Opperman Dr, Eagan, MN 55123-1396. TEL 651-687-8000, 800-328-4880, FAX 651-687-7302, customer.service@westgroup.com, http://west.thomson.com. Ed. Mark A Sargent.

332.64 CAN ISSN 0838-9365
THE DAILIES. Text in English. w. CND 753.60 domestic; CND 857.60 in United States; CND 1,190.40 elsewhere (effective 2000). **Description:** For the short-term trader who needs a closer view of what is currently happening in the market.
Formerly (until 1988): Canadian Daily Stock Charts (0045-4656)
Published by: Canadian Analyst Ltd., 21 Squires Ave, Toronto, ON M4B 2R2, Canada. TEL 416-285-9134, FAX 416-285-0554, 1-877-919-6999.

332.6 USA
DAILY GRAPHS. LONG TERM VALUES. Text in English. 1981. 48/yr. USD 256 (effective 1999). **Document type:** *Consumer.*
Published by: Daily Graphs Inc., PO Box 66919, Los Angeles, CA 90066-0919. TEL 310-448-6843, 800-472-7479. Ed. William O'Neil. Pub. G Mansourian. R&P Garo Mansourian.

332.6 USA
HG4916
DAILY GRAPHS. N A S D A Q O.T.C. - AMERICAN STOCK EXCHANGE - O.T.C. Text in English. w. USD 363 (effective 1999). charts. **Document type:** *Consumer.*
Formerly: Daily Graphs. American Stock Exchange - O.T.C. (1055-0658)
Published by: Daily Graphs Inc., PO Box 66919, Los Angeles, CA 90066-0919. TEL 310-448-6843, 800-472-7479. Ed. William O'Neil. R&P Garo Mansourian.

332.6 USA
DAILY GRAPHS. N.Y.S.E. Text in English. 1972. w. USD 363 (effective 1999). charts. **Document type:** *Consumer.*
Formerly: Daily Graphs. N.Y.S.E.-O.T.C.
Published by: Daily Graphs Inc., PO Box 66919, Los Angeles, CA 90066-0919. TEL 310-448-6843, 800-472-7479. Ed. William O'Neil. R&P Garo Mansourian. Circ: 5,000.

332.6 USA
DAILY GRAPHS. OPTION GUIDE. Text in English. w. USD 300 (effective 1999).
Formerly: Daily Graphs. Stock Option Guide (0195-2021)
Published by: Daily Graphs Inc., PO Box 66919, Los Angeles, CA 90066-0919. TEL 310-448-6843, 800-472-7479. Ed. William O'Neil. R&P Garo Mansourian.

DAILY INSURANCE REPORTER. see *INSURANCE*

332.6 USA
DAILY MARKET REPORT. Text in English. d. USD 110. **Description:** Discusses trading and spot prices, open interest, volume and warehouse stocks.
Published by: Coffee, Sugar & Cocoa Exchange, Inc., Four World Trade Center, New York, NY 10048. TEL 212-938-2800, FAX 212-524-9863.

332 USA
THE DAILY SWING TRADE. Text in English. d. USD 999.95 (effective 2003). **Description:** Explains how you can follow predictable market patterns to look for potential new profits each week.
Media: Online - full text.
Published by: TheStreet.com, 14 Wall St, New York, NY 10005. TEL 212-321-5000, FAX 212-321-5016, http://www.thestreet.com. Ed. Alan Farley.

DAILY TENDER BULLETIN. see *BUSINESS AND ECONOMICS—Banking And Finance*

DAVID HALL'S INSIDE VIEW. see *NUMISMATICS*

332.6 USA ISSN 1057-7521
DEFAULTED BONDS NEWSLETTER. Text in English. 1987. m. USD 365 (effective 2000). charts. **Document type:** *Newsletter, Trade.*
Related titles: Online - full text ed.
Published by: Income Securities Advisors Inc, 6175 NW 153rd St, Ste 201, Miami, FL 33014-2435. TEL 305-557-1832.

332.6 USA ISSN 1556-3774
▼ **DEFINED CONTRIBUTION & SAVINGS PLAN ALERT.** Text in English. 2005. w. **Document type:** *Newsletter, Trade.*
Published by: Institutional Investor, Inc. (Subsidiary of: Euromoney Institutional Investor Plc.), 225 Park Ave. S., New York, NY 10003. TEL 212-224-3800, http://www.definedsavingsalert.com/, http://www.institutionalinvestor.com.

332.6 USA ISSN 1529-5729
DEFINED CONTRIBUTION NEWS. Text in English. 1993. bi-w. USD 2,365 combined subscription domestic for print & online eds.; USD 2,440 combined subscription foreign for print & online eds. (effective 2005). **Document type:** *Newsletter, Trade.* **Description:** Provides information on who's hiring managers, recordkeepers or consultants and why. Includes news on new educational products, alliances and plan sponsor profiles.
Related titles: Online - full text ed.: (from EBSCO Publishing).
Indexed: ATI.
—CCC.
Published by: Institutional Investor News (Subsidiary of: Euromoney Institutional Investor Plc.), 225 Park Ave S, 7th Fl, New York, NY 10003-1605. TEL 212-224-3800, FAX 212-224-3491, info@iiplatinum.com, http://www.dcnews.com, http://www.iinews.com. Pub. Nanzeen Kanga TEL 212-224-3005.

332.6 USA
DELIBERATIONS ON WORLD MARKETS. Text in English. 1972. 18/yr. USD 225. **Document type:** *Newsletter.*
Formerly (until 1991): Deliberations (Tucson)
Address: P O Box 40097, Tucson, AZ 85717-0097. TEL 416-964-1359. Ed. Ian McAvity.

DELUXE; ideas for the business of living. see *BUSINESS AND ECONOMICS—Banking And Finance*

332.6 RUS
DEN'GI BEZ DENEG. Text in Russian. m.
Indexed: RASB.
Address: Khvostov per 11-a, Moscow, 109180, Russian Federation. TEL 7-095-2361011. **US dist. addr.:** East View Information Services, 3020 Harbor Ln. N., Minneapolis, MN 55447. TEL 612-550-0961.

332.6 GBR
THE DENISON SCHEME TRUST. Text in English. 1985. m. GBP 278; USD 556 foreign (effective 2000). adv. back issues avail. **Document type:** *Newsletter, Trade.* **Description:** Covers legislation, investment news, legal issues, and surveys and updates.
Published by: Monitor Press Ltd. (Subsidiary of: T & F Informa plc), Suffolk House, Church Field Rd, Sudbury, Suffolk CO10 2YA, United Kingdom. TEL 44-1787-467206, FAX 44-1787-881147. Ed. Ian Kossick. Pub. Zoe Turner. Adv. contact Caroline Gasking.

332.6 DNK ISSN 0907-3752
HG5594.5
DENMARK. FINANSTILSYNET. STATISTISK MATERIALE: INVESTERINGSFORENINGER. Text in Danish. 1989. a. DKK 40. **Document type:** *Government.*
Formerly (until 1991): Denmark. Finanstilsynet. Beretning. Bilag 5: Investeringsforeninger
Published by: Finanstilsynet, Gl Kongevej 74 A, Frederiksberg C, 1850, Denmark. TEL 45-31-23-11-88, FAX 45-31-23-04-41. **Dist. by:** D B K Bogdistribution, Siljangade 2-8, Copenhagen S 2300, Denmark.

332.6 DNK ISSN 0907-3701
DENMARK. FINANSTILSYNET. STATISTISK MATERIALE. LIVSFORSIKRINGSSELSKABER M.V. Text in Danish. 1989. a. DKK 75. **Document type:** *Government.*
Formerly (until 1991): Denmark. Finanstilsynet. Beretning. Bilag 2: Livsforsikringsselskaber m.v.
Published by: Finanstilsynet, Gl Kongevej 74 A, Frederiksberg C, 1850, Denmark. TEL 45-33-55-82-82, FAX 45-33-55-82-00. **Dist. by:** D B K Bogdistribution, Siljangade 2-8, Copenhagen S 2300, Denmark.

THE DENTAL PRACTICE ACQUISITION REPORT. see *MEDICAL SCIENCES—Dentistry*

332.64 336.2 NLD ISSN 1389-1863
K4527.A15
DERIVATIVES & FINANCIAL INSTRUMENTS. Text in English. 1999. bi-m. USD 420 (effective 2002). **Document type:** *Academic/Scholarly.* **Description:** Covers major issues in the taxation of derivatives and financial instruments. Discusses the taxation of trades, swaps, futures, options, forward contracts, credit derivatives, index-linked and unit-linked contracts, and forward rate agreements.
Related titles: Online - full text ed.: (from Swets Information Services).
—IE.
Published by: (International Bureau of Fiscal Documentation), I B F D Publications BV, H J E Wenckebachweg 210, PO Box 20237, Amsterdam, 1000 HE, Netherlands. TEL 31-20-554-0100, FAX 31-20-620-8626, info@ibfd.nl, http://www.ibfd.nl.

332.6 USA
DERIVATIVES: TAX, REGULATION, FINANCE. Text in English. m. USD 183.75. **Description:** Aims to provide comprehensive coverage of developments in the derivative industry.
Published by: W G & L Financial Reporting & Management Research (Subsidiary of: R I A), 90 Fifth Ave, New York, NY 10011. TEL 212-645-4800, FAX 212-337-4280, http://www.riatax.com/journals/jourhom.html.

332.6 GBR ISSN 1357-0927
DERIVATIVES USE, TRADING & REGULATION; the official journal of the Futures and Options Association. Text in English. 1994. q. GBP 285 in Europe to institutions; USD 450 in North America to institutions; GBP 300 elsewhere to institutions (effective 2004). bk.rev. back issues avail.; reprint service avail. from PSC. **Document type:** *Journal, Trade.* **Description:** Publishes papers which educate in the use, trading and regulation of all forms of derivatives.
Related titles: Online - full text ed.: (from EBSCO Publishing, Gale Group, IngentaConnect, O C L C Online Computer Library Center, Inc., ProQuest Information & Learning).
Indexed: ABIn, CPM.
—BLDSC (3554.967300), IE. **CCC.**
Published by: Palgrave Macmillan Ltd. (Subsidiary of: Macmillan Publishers Ltd.), Houndmills, Basingstoke, Hants RG21 6XS, United Kingdom. TEL 44-1256-329242, FAX 44-1256-810526, journal-info@palgrave.com, http://www.palgrave-journals.com/. Eds. Dr. Emmanuel Acar, Dr. Stephen Satchell. Circ: 600 (paid).

332.6 USA ISSN 1075-2412
HG6024.A3
DERIVATIVES WEEK; the newsweekly on derivatives worldwide. Text in English. 1992. w. (51x/yr). USD 2,245 combined subscription for print & online eds. (effective 2005). adv. **Document type:** *Newsletter, Trade.* **Description:** Tells who's using derivatives and how. Includes coverage of instruments linked to equities, interest rates, commodities and currencies worldwide.
Related titles: Online - full text ed.: (from Florida Center for Library Automation, Gale Group, O C L C Online Computer Library Center, Inc., ProQuest Information & Learning).
Indexed: ABIn.
—CCC.
Published by: Institutional Investor News (Subsidiary of: Euromoney Institutional Investor Plc.), 225 Park Ave S, 7th Fl, New York, NY 10003-1605. TEL 212-224-3800, FAX 212-224-3491, info@iiplatinum.com, http://www.derivativesweek.com, http://www.iinews.com. Pub. Elayne Glick.

332.6 JPN
DIAMOND REPORT. Text in Japanese. 1916. w. JPY 60,000.
Published by: Diamond Inc., 4-2 Kasumigaseki 1-chome, Chiyoda-ku, Tokyo, 100-0013, Japan. Ed. Kiichi Sakai.

332.6 JPN
DIAMOND, STOCK INVESTMENT EDITION/DAIYAMONDO KABUSHIKI-TOSHI-BAN. Text in Japanese. 1977. bi-m. JPY 5,700.
Published by: Diamond Inc., 4-2 Kasumigaseki 1-chome, Chiyoda-ku, Tokyo, 100-0013, Japan. Ed. Toshikazu Yatsu.

332.6 USA ISSN 0890-0957
DICK DAVIS DIGEST. Text in English. 1982. s-m. USD 145 domestic; USD 175 foreign (effective 2001). s-a. index. back issues avail. **Document type:** *Newsletter.* **Description:** Features the latest opinions of the nation's top-performing market letter writers, as well as specific stock recommendations.
Related titles: E-mail ed.: USD 145 (effective 2001).
Published by: Dick Davis Publishing Inc., P O 8128, Ft. Lauderdale, FL 33310. TEL 800-654-1514, FAX 654-567-0630, http://www.dickdavis.com. Ed. Steven Halpern. Pub., R&P Steven Lord. Circ: 33,000 (paid).

332.6 USA ISSN 0012-2971
DINES LETTER; advice and information for traders and investors. Text in English. 1960. 20/yr. looseleaf. USD 365 (effective 2005). bk.rev. charts; mkt.; stat. index. **Document type:** *Newsletter.* **Description:** Contains buy and sell advice based on mass psychology, technical analysis, and fundamental considerations for stocks, options and the economy.
Published by: James Dines & Co., Inc., PO Box 22, Belvedere, CA 94920. TEL 402-925-5230, 800-845-8259, production@dinesletter.com, http://www.dinesletter.com. Ed. James Dines.

332.6029 USA
DIRECTORY OF ALTERNATIVE INVESTMENT PROGRAMS. Text in English. 1996. a. USD 1,295 combined subscription domestic print & CD-ROM eds.; USD 1,365 combined subscription foreign print & CD-ROM eds. (effective 2003). adv. stat. **Document type:** *Directory, Trade.* **Description:** Identifies active institutional investors and includes the criteria they use to select alternative investment partnerships.

B

Related titles: CD-ROM ed.
Published by: Alternative Investor, 170 Linden St, 2nd Fl, Wellesley, MA 02482. TEL 781-304-1400, FAX 781-304-1440, info@assetnews.com, http://www.assetnews.com. Ed., Pub. David Toll. R&P, Adv. contact Doreen C Purvis. B&W page USD 1,950, color page USD 2,250; trim 10.5 x 7.75. Circ: 800 (paid).

332.6   USA   ISSN 1528-1388
HG4907
DIRECTORY OF BOND AGENTS. Short title: Directory of Bond Agents. Text in English. 1975. bi-m. USD 1,075. Supplement avail. **Document type:** Directory.
Formerly (until 1998): Standard and Poor's Directory of Bond Agents (1088-8888)
Published by: Standard & Poor's (Subsidiary of: McGraw-Hill Companies, Inc.), 55 Water St, New York, NY 10041. TEL 212-208-8000. Ed. Vito Calbi.

DIRECTORY OF BUYOUT FINANCING SOURCES. see BUSINESS AND ECONOMICS—Trade And Industrial Directories

DIRECTORY OF COMPANIES OFFERING DIVIDEND REINVESTMENT PLANS. see BUSINESS AND ECONOMICS—Trade And Industrial Directories

DIRECTORY OF COUNTERTRADE & OFFSET SERVICES. see BUSINESS AND ECONOMICS—International Commerce

332.6   USA   ISSN 1547-1071
▼ **DIRECTORY OF INDEPENDENT INVESTMENT RESEARCH.** Variant title: Thomson Financial Directory of Independent Investment Research. Text in English. 2004. a. **Document type:** Directory, Trade.
Published by: Thomson Financial Media, One State St Plaza, 27th Fl, New York, NY 10004-1549. custserv@thomsonmedia.com, http://www.thomsonmedia.com.

DIRECTORY OF INSTITUTIONAL INVESTMENT FUNDS. see BUSINESS AND ECONOMICS—Trade And Industrial Directories

332.6   GBR   ISSN 0967-9626
DIRECTORY OF NOMINEES. Text in English. 1974. a. GBP 75.
Document type: Directory.
Published by: Tertiary Publications, Brook House, Eriswell Crescent, Walton-on-thames, Surrey, United Kingdom. TEL 01932-248358, FAX 01932-245569.

332.6   USA   ISSN 0085-0551
HG4961
DIRECTORY OF OBSOLETE SECURITIES. Text in English. 1927. a., latest 2001. USD 655 (effective 2001). **Document type:** Directory.
Related titles: Online - full text ed.
Published by: Financial Information Incorporated, 30 Montgomery St, Jersey City, NJ 07302. TEL 800-367-3441, FAX 800-344-3292, http://www.fiinet.com. Ed. Charles Page. R&P Don Hardie TEL 201-369-3651.

658.0029   USA   ISSN 0196-8262
HF6146.P7
DIRECTORY OF PREMIUM, INCENTIVE & TRAVEL BUYERS. Text in English. 1970. a. USD 275 (effective 2000). **Document type:** Directory, Trade. **Description:** Profiles 20,000 buyers of premiums, incentives, and travel programs at more than 12,000 companies.
Former titles (until 1992): Nationwide Directory of Premium, Incentive and Travel Buyers; Directory of Premium and Incentive Buyers (0070-6124)
Media: Magnetic Tape. **Related titles:** Diskette ed.
Published by: Douglas Publications, Inc., Salesman's Guide, 2807 N Parham Rd, Ste 210, Richmond, VA 23294. TEL 804-762-4455, FAX 804-935-0271, http://www.douglaspublications.com. Ed. Travis Parrish.

332.6   USA
DIRECTORY OF PRIVATE EQUITY INVESTORS. Text in English. 1996. a. USD 630 (effective 1998). **Document type:** Directory. **Description:** Includes listings of 450 capital sources.
Published by: Securities Data Publishing (Subsidiary of: Thomson Financial / I M G Media), 195 Broadway, New York, NY 10007. TEL 212-765-5311, FAX 212-765-6123. Ed. Kathleen Devlin.

DIRECTORY OF PROPERTY INVESTORS AND DEVELOPERS. see BUSINESS AND ECONOMICS—Trade And Industrial Directories

332.6   USA   ISSN 0094-2561
DISCLOSURE RECORD∗ . Text in English. 1973. w. USD 50. adv. tr.lit. **Description:** Full text of corporate news releases.
Published by: Newsfeatures, Inc., 8511 249th St, Jamaica, NY 11426-2105. Ed. Lori Link. Circ: 10,000.

382   GBR
DISCUSSION PAPERS IN INTERNATIONAL INVESTMENT AND MANAGEMENT. Text in English. 1988. irreg., latest vol.10, no.243, 1997-98.

Formerly: Discussion Papers in International Investment and Business Studies (1369-3891)
—BLDSC (3597.948030).
Published by: University of Reading, Department of Economics, Whiteknights, PO Box 218, Reading, RG6 6AA, United Kingdom.

DISTRESSED PROPERTY INVESTOR'S MONTHLY. see REAL ESTATE

332.67   USA
DOLLAR-WISE INVESTOR∗ . Text in English. 1991 (vol.6). q.
Published by: Gentsch Financial, 8035 E R L Thornton Hwy, Ste 400A, Dallas, TX 75228-7021. TEL 214-480-8237.

332.6   USA   ISSN 1553-5967
▼ **DOUG FABIAN'S HIGH MONTHLY INCOME**; the Fabian way to your richer retirement. Text in English. 2004 (Sept). m. USD 1,995 (effective 2005). **Document type:** Newsletter, Consumer.
Published by: Phillips Investment Resources, LLC (Subsidiary of: Phillips International Inc.), 7811 Montrose Rd., Potomac, MD 20854-3394. TEL 301-424-3700, 800-219-8592, http://www.fabian.com/highmonthlyincome, income@fabian.com, http://www.phillips.com/pir/. Ed. Doug Fabian.

332.6   USA
DOW JONES CHARTING MONEY. Variant title: Charting Money. Text in English. w. (every Fri.). **Document type:** Provides technical analysis of major global markets.
Media: E-mail.
Published by: Dow Jones Company, 200 Liberty St, New York, NY 10281. TEL 800-223-2274, newswires@dowjones.com, http://www.djnewswires.com/charting/charting.html.

332.6   USA
DOW JONES DISCOUNT AND DISTRESSED TECHNOLOGY ALERT. Variant title: Discount and Distressed Technology Alert. Text in English. w. (Thur.). **Document type:** Newsletter, Trade. **Description:** Helps institutional investors spot the risks and opportunities in technology companies; and features the week's top stories, market statistics, and a recap of major corporate events for distressed technology firms.
Media: E-mail.
Published by: Dow Jones Company, 200 Liberty St, New York, NY 10281. TEL 800-223-2274, newswires@dowjones.com, http://www.djnewswires.com/fin-pro/dta.html.

332.6   USA   ISSN 1094-6438
THE DOW JONES GUIDE TO THE WORLD STOCK MARKET. Text in English. irreg.
Published by: Dow Jones Company, PO Box 300, Princeton, NJ 08540.

DOW JONES MICROCHIP REPORT. see ELECTRONICS

332.6   USA   ISSN 0300-7324
DOW THEORY FORECASTS; business and stock market. Text in English. 1946. w. USD 233.
Related titles: Online - full text ed.: (from EBSCO Publishing).
Published by: Dow Theory Forecasts, Inc., 7412 Calumet Ave, Hammond, IN 46324-2692. TEL 219-931-6480, FAX 219-931-6487. Ed. Richard J Moroney. Circ: 20,000.

332.6   USA
DOW THEORY LETTERS. Text in English. 1958. 17/yr. USD 250 (effective 2000). bk.rev. charts. 6 p./no. 2 cols./p.; back issues avail.; reprints avail. **Document type:** Newsletter.
Related titles: Microfiche ed.
Published by: Dow Theory Letters, Inc., PO Box 1759, La Jolla, CA 92038. TEL 619-454-0481, dowtheory@hotmail.com, http://www.dowtheoryletters.com. Ed. Richard Russell. Circ: 7,000.

332.6   USA
DOWBEATERS. Text in English. 1977. m. USD 100.
Published by: Dow Beaters Inc., PO Box 284, Ironia, NJ 07845. TEL 201-273-0120. Ed. P Deangelis.

332.6   USA   ISSN 1093-2518
DRIP INVESTOR. Text in English. 1992. m. USD 89 (effective 1999). **Document type:** Trade.
Related titles: Online - full text ed.: (from EBSCO Publishing).
Published by: Horizon Publishing Co., L L C, 7412 Calumet Ave, Ste 200, Hammond, IN 46324-2692. TEL 219-852-3220, FAX 219-931-6487. Ed., R&P Charles B Carlson. Circ: 34,000.

332.6   USA
DRISCOLL INSIDER∗ . Text in English. s-m. USD 95.
Description: Provides a complete listing of all initial public stock offerings.
Published by: Driscoll Industrial, P O Box 2806, Carmel, CA 93921-2806. TEL 408-625-9026. Ed. Joseph L Driscoll Jr.

332.6   USA   ISSN 1526-5919
HG4905
DUNNAN'S GUIDE TO YOUR INVESTMENTS. Text in English. 1973. a. USD 17.95 paperback; USD 35 hardcover.

Former titles (until 1999): Dun & Bradstreet's Guide to Your Investments (Year) (0098-2466); Your Investments: How to Increase Your Capital and Income
Published by: HarperCollins Publishers, Inc., 10 E 53rd St, New York, NY 10022. TEL 800-242-7737.

E C U - E U R O EUROBOND MARKET. (European Currency Unit) see BUSINESS AND ECONOMICS—Abstracting, Bibliographies, Statistics

332.6   USA
E N C REPORTER. (Engineering and Construction) Text in English. q. **Document type:** Journal, Trade. **Description:** Designed to assist management and investors in engineering and construction (ENC) companies in understanding the market pricing and investor sentiment of the industry, as well as comprehending the valuation implication of the current economic environment and industry-specific issues.
Published by: Houlihan, Lokey, Howard & Zukin, 1930 Century Park W, Los Angeles, CA 90067. TEL 800-788-5300, FAX 310-553-2173, http://www.hlhz.com.

332.6   USA
E S O A A OPTIONS ALERT. Text in English. 2000. irreg. back issues avail. **Document type:** Bulletin.
Media: E-mail.
Published by: E S O A A, LLC, 1265 S Bascom Ave, 106, San Jose, CA 95128. http://www.stockoptionadvisors.com/optionalert. R&P Michael Gray. Circ: 800 (free).

E S O P REPORT. (Employee Stock Ownership Plan) see BUSINESS AND ECONOMICS—Management

332.6   USA
E-ZINE MAGAZINE. Text in English. 2001. q. **Document type:** Magazine, Trade. **Description:** Contains relevant information on funding solutions and how to attract investors for particular projects.
Published by: B.A. Enterprises, LLC, PO Box 1015, LaPlace, LA 70069. TEL 504-653-7676, FAX 504-653-9256, info@ba-enterprises.com, http://www.ba-enterprises.com/magazine, http://ba-enterprises.com. Pubs. Alfred E Adams, Patrick J Babin Sr.

332.6   USA   ISSN 1064-7678
HG4915
EARNINGS GUIDE. Text in English. 1991. m. USD 153. stat. back issues avail. **Document type:** Trade. **Description:** Provides quarterly and yearly estimates of corporate stock earnings.
Published by: Standard & Poor's (Subsidiary of: McGraw-Hill Companies, Inc.), 55 Water St, New York, NY 10041. TEL 212-208-8000, FAX 212-208-0040. Ed. Frank Lovaglio. Circ: 4,000.

332.6   USA   ISSN 1063-5262
HG5430.7.A2
EAST EUROPEAN INVESTMENT MONTHLY∗ . Text in English. m. USD 290.
Published by: Dixon & Co., 124 E 19th St, New York, NY 10003-2404. TEL 212-388-1500, FAX 212-254-3386. Ed. Mark Dixon.

EASTERN BLOC JOINT VENTURES. see LAW—Corporate Law

EASTERN EUROPEAN TELECOM MONTHLY. see COMMUNICATIONS

332.6   USA
ECONOMIC LOGIC. Text in English. 1981. bi-m. USD 12 (effective 1996 & 1997). **Document type:** Newsletter. **Description:** Presents concise, logical analyses of current economic issues and a stock market forecast.
Address: 23031 Britner Ct., Bingham Farms, MI 48025. TEL 313-642-6373. Ed., R&P Richard K Greene. Circ: 500.

ECONOMIE PAPETIERE. see PAPER AND PULP

332.6   FRA
ECONOMIES ET SOCIETES. SERIE ME. MONNAIE. Text in French. irreg.
Published by: Les Presses de l'I S M E A, BP 22, Paris, Cedex 13 75622, France. TEL 33-1-55489076, FAX 33-1-55489071, http://www.ismea.org. Ed. Gerard de Bernis.

332.6   NLD   ISSN 1567-4703
EFFECTENGIDS. Text in Dutch. 1894. a. **Document type:** Trade. **Description:** Covers stocks and bonds at the Amsterdam Stock Exchange.
Formerly (until 1996): Gids bij de Officiele Prijscourant van de Amsterdamse Effectenbeurs (0922-7822)
Published by: Kluwer B.V. (Subsidiary of: Wolters Kluwer N.V.), Postbus 23, Deventer, 7400 GA, Netherlands. TEL 31-570-673449, FAX 31-570-691555, juridisch@kluwer.nl, http://www.kluwer.nl. Ed. O Blikslager. Circ: 1,600.

332.6   USA
EFFICIENT FRONTIER. Text in English. 1996. q. free. **Description:** Investing-portfolio theory for sophisticated investors.

Published by: William J. Bernstein, 3333 East Bay Dr, North Bend, OR 97459. wbern@mail.coos.or.us, http://www.coos.or.us/~wbern.

EKSPERT. see *BUSINESS AND ECONOMICS—Banking And Finance*

ELECTRONICS INDUSTRY OUTLOOK. see *ELECTRONICS*

332.6 USA ISSN 0742-5252
ELLIOTT WAVE THEORIST. Text in English. 1979. m. USD 240 (effective 2005). **Document type:** *Newsletter.* **Description:** Each issue thoroughly analyzes Elliott waves, Fibonacci relationships, fixed time cycles, momentum, sentiment and supply-demand factors in a comprehensive approach covering stocks, precious metals, interest rates, and the economy.
Indexed: M&MA.
Published by: Elliott Wave International, PO Box 1618, Gainesville, GA 30503. TEL 770-536-0309. Ed. Robert Prechter.

332.6 USA
ELTON STEPHENS - INVESTMENT ADVISOR. Variant title: Elton Stephens-Investment Advisor. Text in English. 1991. w. looseleaf. USD 59.95 (effective 2004). index. back issues avail. **Document type:** *Newsletter.*
Formerly: N Y S E Weekly Stock Buys (1060-6629)
Published by: Elton Stephens Investments, 4016 S Michigan St, South Bend, IN 46614. elton@eltonspephens.com, http://www.eltonstephens.com. Ed. Elton Stephens. Circ: 7,500 (paid and controlled).

332.6 330.9 POL ISSN 1644-5198
EMERGING EUROPE MARKET REVIEW. Text in English. 2002. q. EUR 325 foreign (effective 2005). **Document type:** *Newsletter, Trade.* **Description:** Designed for senior managers interested in investment opportunities, it comments on the economic situation in the Czech Republic, Hungary, Poland, Russia and Slovakia.
Published by: Polish Market Review Ltd., ul Supniewskiego 9, Krakow, 31527, Poland. TEL 48-12-4280360, FAX 48-12-4134012, pmr@pmrpublications.com, http://www.pmrpublications.com.

332.6 POL
EMERGING EUROPE NEWS. Text in English. w. EUR 380 foreign (effective 2005). **Document type:** *Newsletter, Trade.* **Description:** Offers the latest on the investment climate in the Czech Republic, Poland, Russia, Slovakia and Hungary.
Media: E-mail.
Published by: Polish Market Review Ltd., ul Supniewskiego 9, Krakow, 31527, Poland. TEL 48-12-4280360, FAX 48-12-4134012, pmr@pmrpublications.com, http://www.pmrpublications.com.

332.63 DEU
EMERGING MARKETS. Text in German. w. **Document type:** *Trade.* **Description:** Contains information and advice on investment opportunities in new and emerging markets.
Media: Online - full text.
Published by: Verlag Aktuelle Information GmbH (Subsidiary of: Springer Science+Business Media), Postfach 111926, Frankfurt Am Main, 60054, Germany. TEL 49-69-2426390, FAX 49-69-236909, info.platow@bertelsmann.de, http://www.platow.de.

332.6 GBR ISSN 1354-8549
EMERGING MARKETS INVESTOR. Text in English. 1994. m. GBP 375, USD 579, EUR 666 (effective 2001). adv. **Document type:** *Bulletin.* **Description:** Coverage includes debt and equity markets in all emerging economies.
Related titles: Online - full text ed.
—CCC.
Published by: Risk Waters Group (Subsidiary of: Incisive Media Plc.), Haymarket House, 28-29 Haymarket, London, SW1Y 4RX, United Kingdom. TEL 44-20-74849700, FAX 44-20-79302238, http://www.riskwaters.com/emi/, http://www.incisivemedia.com. Eds. Guy Norton, Oonagh Leighton, Sudip Roy. Pub. Brid Hayes. Adv. contacts Adrian Tapping, Milena Harrison. B&W page GBP 5,350, color page GBP 6,590; trim 297 x 230. **Affiliate:** Risk Waters Group.

332.65 GBR ISSN 1359-0006
THE EMERGING MARKETS MONITOR; the weekly brief for global investors. Text in English. 1995. 48/yr. GBP 1,250 domestic; USD 1,985, EUR 1,750 foreign (effective 2005). back issues avail. **Document type:** *Newsletter, Trade.* **Description:** Briefs on debt, bonds, equities and money in emerging markets worldwide. Offers financial professionals operating in emerging capital markets, current news, analysis and startegy on more than 50 emerging markets worldwide.
Related titles: CD-ROM ed.; Online - full text ed.: (from EBSCO Publishing).
Indexed: RASB.
—CCC.
Published by: Business Monitor International Ltd., Mermaid House, 2 Puddle Dock, Blackfriars, London, EC4V 3DS, United Kingdom. TEL 44-20-72480468, FAX 44-20-72480467, subs@businessmonitor.com, marketing@businessmonitor.com, https://www.businessmonitor.com/bmi/emm_order.html, http://www.businessmonitor.com. Ed. William Kemble Diaz. Circ: 500 (paid).

332.6 USA ISSN 1093-2666
EMERGING MARKETS QUARTERLY. Text in English. 1993. q. USD 335 domestic; USD 410 foreign (effective 2005). **Document type:** *Journal, Trade.* **Description:** Provides the latest financing plans and investment strategies from Latin America, Southeast Asia, Africa and Eastern Europe.
Formerly: Emerging Markets Week (1529-6628)
Related titles: Online - full text ed.: (from EBSCO Publishing, ProQuest Information & Learning).
Indexed: ABIn, ATI.
—BLDSC (3733.426942). **CCC.**
Published by: Institutional Investor, Journals (Subsidiary of: Euromoney Institutional Investor Plc.), 225 Park Ave S, 7th Fl., New York, NY 10003-1605. TEL 212-224-3800, FAX 212-224-3491, info@iijournals.com, http://www.investmentresearch.org/emq.htm, http://www.iijournals.com.

332.6 340 USA ISSN 1049-3808
KF1439
EMERGING TRENDS IN SECURITIES LAW. Text in English. a. price varies. **Document type:** *Monographic series, Trade.* **Description:** Features detailed coverage of the latest developments in securities regulation.
Published by: Thomson West (Subsidiary of: Thomson Corporation, The), 610 Opperman Dr, Eagan, MN 55123-1396. TEL 651-687-8000, 800-328-4880, FAX 651-687-7302, customer.service@westgroup.com, http://www.westgroup.com/store/product.asp?product%5Fid=15315603&catalog%5Fname=wgstore, http://west.thomson.com.

332.6 USA
ENCYCLOPEDIA OF STOCK MARKET TECHNIQUES. Text in English. base vol. plus irreg. updates. looseleaf. USD 65.
Published by: Investors Intelligence, 30 Church St, Box 2046, New Rochelle, NY 10801. TEL 914-632-0422, FAX 914-632-0335.

ENTREPRENEUR'S BE YOUR OWN BOSS. see *BUSINESS AND ECONOMICS—Small Business*

332.6 USA
ENVEST*; the business and investment newsletter for energy and the environment. Text in English. bi-w. USD 225.
Published by: Energy Investment Research, PO Box 73, Glenville Sta, Greenwich, CT 06830. TEL 914-937-6939.

332.6 USA
EQUIDATA INVESTOR; a monthly stock market newsletter. Text in English. q. USD 195 (effective 2005). **Document type:** *Newsletter, Trade.* **Description:** Provides investors with investment strategies.
Published by: Equidata1, Inc., 1540 Clearglades Dr, Wesley Chapel, FL 33543. TEL 813-929-6136, equidata@yahoo.com, http://www.equidata1.com. Ed., Pub. A. David Coles.

332.6 USA ISSN 1053-2544
HG4501
EQUITIES. Text in English. 1951. q. USD 12 (effective 2004). adv. bk.rev. illus. reprints avail. **Document type:** *Magazine, Consumer.* **Description:** Covers the security trading markets and the public companies that do business in them.
Former titles (until Sep. 1990): O T C Review (0161-0694); (until Feb. 1977): Over-the-Counter Securities Review (0030-736X)
Related titles: Online - full text ed.: (from EBSCO Publishing, Florida Center for Library Automation, Gale Group).
Indexed: PAIS, PROMT.
—CCC.
Published by: Equities Magazine LLC, Box 130 H, Scarsdale, NY 10583. TEL 914-723-6702, FAX 914-723-0176, equitymag@aol.com, http://www.equitiesmagazine.com. Ed. Robert J Flaherty. Pub. Brian Flaherty. adv.: B&W page USD 2,640, color page USD 3,540. Circ: 5,000 (paid).

332.6 USA
EQUITY ANALYST*. Text in English. m. USD 110.
Address: 1163 Perrot St, Green Bay, WI 54302-1623. TEL 414-437-9474. Ed. Louie Nejedlo.

332.64 HUN ISSN 1418-9496
HG5430.7.A2
EQUITY CENTRAL EUROPE. Text in Hungarian. 1994. irreg. USD 19.95 (effective 1999). **Document type:** *Consumer.* **Description:** Covers a comprehensive overview of central Europe's equity markets with detailed information on the region's most important publicly traded companies and stock exchanges.
Former titles (until 1998): Taking Stock Central Europe (1417-4812); (until 1996): Taking Stock (1219-4158)
Related titles: ◆ Supplement to: Budapest Business Journal. ISSN 1216-7304; ◆ Supplement to: Prague Business Journal. ISSN 1211-3514; ◆ Supplement to: Warsaw Business Journal. ISSN 1233-7889.
Published by: New World Publishing Inc., Szent Istvan Korut 11, III emelet, Budapest, 1055, Hungary. TEL 36-1-374-3344, FAX 361-374-3345, editor@bbj.hu, http://www.ceebiz.com.

332.6 USA
EQUITY INVESTMENT STRATEGY REPORT. Text in English. w.?.
Published by: Salomon Brothers, Inc., Marketing Department, 7 World Trade Center, New York, NY 10048.

332.6 336 USA
ERNST & YOUNG FINANCIAL PLANNING REPORTER*. Text in English. 1975. m. USD 96. back issues avail. **Description:** For the professional entrepreneur, investor, CPA, attorney or high, net-worth individual.
Formerly (until 1988): Brennan Reports on Sophisticated Tax and Investment Planning
Published by: Ernst Young Ken Mitchell, 1225 Connecticut Ave, N W, Washington, DC 20036-2604. TEL 202-663-9756.

332.6 PER ISSN 1682-4326
ESTADOS FINANCIEROS COMPARADOS. Text in Spanish. 2000. 3/yr.
Media: Online - full text.
Published by: Bolsa de Valores de Lima, Miro Quesada 265, Casilla Postal 1538, Lima, 100, Peru. TEL 51-1-4260714, FAX 51-1-4267650, http://www.bvl.com.pe/pubdif/publica_estados.htm.

ESTATE PLANNER'S ALERT. see *LAW—Estate Planning*

THE EURO. see *BUSINESS AND ECONOMICS—Banking And Finance*

EURO AM SONNTAG. see *BUSINESS AND ECONOMICS—Banking And Finance*

332.6 GBR ISSN 1467-0046
EUROMARKET DECISIONS. Text in English. 1999. s-a. GBP 19.95 per issue; free to qualified personnel (effective 2003). adv. **Document type:** *Journal, Trade.* **Description:** Provides unique, well-informed analysis for the benefit of top institutional investors, senior bankers and brokers, and finance ministers.
—CCC.
Published by: S P G Media Ltd. (Subsidiary of: Sterling Publishing Group Plc.), Brunel House, 55-57 North Wharf Rd, London, W2 1LA, United Kingdom. TEL 44-20-79159600, FAX 44-20-77242089, info@sterlingpublications.com, http://www.sterlingpublications.com/pub/euromarket.html, http://www.spgmedia.com/. Pub. Sarah Woddis. Circ: 12,000 (controlled).

EUROMONEY BANK REGISTER (YEAR). see *BUSINESS AND ECONOMICS—Banking And Finance*

332.6 GBR
EUROMONEY DERIVATIVES HANDBOOK (YEAR). Text in English. a. GBP 140, USD 250. **Description:** For derivatives users at both an operational and strategic level, portfolio managers and corporate treasurers, traders and analysts.
Published by: Euromoney Publications plc, Nestor House, Playhouse Yard, London, EC4V 5EX, United Kingdom. TEL 44-20-77798673, FAX 44-20-77798541.

332.6 GBR
THE EUROMONEY INTERNATIONAL EQUITY CAPITAL MARKETS HANDBOOK (YEAR). Text in English. a. GBP 115, USD 195 (effective 2001). **Document type:** *Yearbook, Trade.*
Former titles: The World Guide to World Equity Markets; Salomon Smith Barney Guide to World Equity Markets (1464-1992); (until 1998): L G T Guide to World Equity Markets (1365-7895); (until 1992): G T Guide to World Equity Markets (0957-2503)
Published by: (G T Management plc.), Euromoney Institutional Investor Plc., Nestor House, Playhouse Yard, London, EC4V 5EX, United Kingdom. TEL 44-20-7779-8673, FAX 44-20-7779-8541, http://www.euromoney.com. Eds. Selina O'Connor, Stuart Allen. Adv. contact Alister Hughes TEL 44-20-7779-8535.

EUROPEAN BROADBAND. see *COMMUNICATIONS—Television And Cable*

332.6 GBR ISSN 0966-4858
EUROPEAN HANDBOOK. Text in English. 1991. s-a. **Description:** Provides detailed financial information on 2,100 leading European companies.
Published by: Financial Times Information Ltd., Fitzroy House, 13-17 Epworth St, London, EC2A 4DL, United Kingdom. TEL 44-20-7825-8000, FAX 44-20-7608-2032, justine.dye@ft.com, http://www.ft.com.

332.66 LUX ISSN 0250-3891
EUROPEAN INVESTMENT BANK. INFORMATION. Variant title: E I B - Information. Text in English. 1975. 4/yr. free. charts. **Description:** Features topical articles on European Investment Bank activities. Available in all EU official languages. Produced quarterly.

Related titles: Finnish ed.: Euroopan Investointipankki. Tiedote; Danish ed.: Europaeiske Investeringsbank. Information. ISSN 0250-3875; German ed.: Europaeische Investitionsbank. Informationen. ISSN 0250-3883; Italian ed.: Banca Europea per gli Investimenti. Informazioni. ISSN 0250-3905; Dutch ed.: Europese Investeringsbank. Mededelingen. ISSN 0250-3913; Greek ed.: Europaike Trapeza Ependuseon. Plerofories. ISSN 0251-0677; Spanish ed.: B E I - Informaciones. ISSN 0258-2139; French ed.: Banque Europeenne d'Investissement. Informations. ISSN 0250-3867; Swedish ed.: Europeiska Investeringsbanken. Information.
Indexed: IIS, WBA.
—BLDSC (3664.770000).
Published by: European Investment Bank/Banque Europeenne d'Investissement, 100 bd. Konrad Adenauer, Luxembourg, L-2950, Luxembourg. TEL 352-4379-3122, FAX 352-4379-3189, http://www.eib.org. **Dist. in U.S. by:** European Community Information Service, 2100 M St, NW Ste 707, Washington, DC 20037.

EUROPEAN REAL ESTATE QUARTERLY. see *REAL ESTATE*

332.6   USA   ISSN 1092-0854
EUROPEAN SECURITIES TRADING. Text in English. 1996. m.
Related titles: Online - full text ed.: (from ProQuest Information & Learning).
Published by: Securities Data Publishing (Subsidiary of: Thomson Financial / I M G Media), 195 Broadway, New York, NY 10007. TEL 212-333-9202, sdp@tfn.com, http://www.thomsonfinancial.com.

332.6   BEL   ISSN 1368-8340
EUROPEAN VENTURE CAPITAL ASSOCIATION. YEARBOOK. Text in English. 1986. a.
Formerly (until 1992): Venture Capital in Europe (0964-1688)
—BLDSC (3830.765720).
Published by: European Venture Capital Association, Minervastraat 4, Zaventem, 1930, Belgium. TEL 32-2-7150020, FAX 32-2-7250704, evca@evca.com, http://www.evca.com.

332.6   USA   ISSN 0954-1675
HG4751
EUROPEAN VENTURE CAPITAL JOURNAL. Text in English. 1989. bi-m. adv. **Document type:** *Journal, Trade.*
Description: Provides news and analysis on leading private equity firms and their portfolios.
Related titles: Online - full text ed.: (from EBSCO Publishing, Florida Center for Library Automation, Gale Group, LexisNexis, O C L C Online Computer Library Center, Inc., ProQuest Information & Learning).
Indexed: ABIn, B&I.
—IE. **CCC.**
Published by: Securities Data Publishing (Subsidiary of: Thomson Financial / I M G Media), 195 Broadway, New York, NY 10007. TEL 212-765-5311, FAX 212-765-6123. Ed. Jennifer Reed. adv.: B&W page GBP 500; trim 11.75 x 8.38. Circ: 123.

332.6 333.33   GBR   ISSN 0961-9712
EUROPROPERTY (LONDON, 1991). Text in English. 1991. m. GBP 225; GBP 235 in Europe; GBP 245 in United States; GBP 255 elsewhere. adv. **Document type:** *Trade.*
Indexed: RICS.
—IE.
Published by: I F R Publishing (Subsidiary of: Thomson Financial Services Ltd.), Aldgate House, 33 Aldgate High St, London, EC3N 1DL, United Kingdom. TEL 44-207-396-7000, FAX 44-207-396-7525. Ed. Adrienne Margolis. Adv. contact Jonathan Holmes.

332.6   USA   ISSN 0014-4436
HG1
THE EXCHANGE. Text in English. 1939. m. USD 8. adv. bk.rev. illus. **Document type:** *Newsletter.*
Related titles: Online - full content ed.; Online - full text ed.: (from Factiva, Gale Group).
Indexed: PAIS, RI-1.
Published by: New York Stock Exchange, Communications Division, 11 Wall St, New York, NY 10005. TEL 212-656-4964, nysenewsletter@nyse.com, http://www.nyse.com/about/publication/1105214472043.html. Ed. Edward Kulkosky. Circ: 80,000.

332.6   USA   ISSN 0195-0746
          CODEN: EWADE9
EXECUTIVE WEALTH ADVISORY. Text in English. 1978. m. USD 96 (effective 2001). **Document type:** *Newsletter.* **Description:** Provides financial planning advice designed to build personbal wealth rapidly and safely.
—CCC.
Published by: National Institute of Business Management, PO Box 9266, Mclean, VA 22102-0266. TEL 703-905-8000. Ed. Morey Stettner. Pub. Philip W Clark. R&P Carolyn Frazier. Circ: 5,000.

EXEMPT ORGANIZATIONS REPORTS LIBRARY. see *BUSINESS AND ECONOMICS—Public Finance, Taxation*

332.6   GBR
EXEMPTIONS FROM CAPITAL GAINS TAX. Text in English. s-a. GBP 120. **Document type:** *Trade.* **Description:** Covers fixed interest and floating rate securities quoted on the London and Republic of Ireland Stock Exchanges, separating those exempt from CGT from those that are not.
Published by: Financial Times Information Ltd., Extel, Fitzroy House, 13-17 Epworth St, London, EC2A 4DL, United Kingdom. TEL 44-20-7825-8000, FAX 44-20-7608-2032, eic@ft.com, http://www.info.ft.com.

332.6029   GBR   ISSN 1366-4603
EXTEL ANNUAL REGISTRARS SERVICE. Text in English. 1953. a. GBP 100; GBP 145 with s-a supplement (effective 1999). Supplement avail. **Description:** Provides information on registrars for UK quoted companies. Provides details on types of stocks and shares issues and the nominal value on each entry. Includes registration amendments occurring during the previous year, including name changes, liquidations, and new companies.
Former titles (until 1996): Annual Registrars Service (1361-7842); (until 1995): Extel Financial Annual Registrars Service (1351-444X); (until 1993): Register of Registrars (0482-1319)
Related titles: CD-ROM ed.; ♦ Supplement(s): Extel Annual Registrars Service Supplement. ISSN 1366-4611.
Published by: Financial Times Information Ltd., Extel, Fitzroy House, 13-17 Epworth St, London, EC2A 4DL, United Kingdom. TEL 44-20-7825-8000, FAX 44-20-7608-2032, justine.dye@ft.com, http://www.info.ft.com.

332.6029   GBR   ISSN 1366-4611
EXTEL ANNUAL REGISTRARS SERVICE SUPPLEMENT. Text in English. 1996. a.
Formerly: Annual Registrars Service Supplement (1361-7850)
Related titles: ♦ Supplement to: Extel Annual Registrars Service. ISSN 1366-4603.
Published by: Financial Times Information Ltd., Extel, Fitzroy House, 13-17 Epworth St, London, EC2A 4DL, United Kingdom. TEL 44-20-7608-8000, FAX 44-20-7825-8000, eic@ft.com, http://www.info.ft.com.

332.6   USA
F I I ANNUAL GUIDE TO BONDS. Text in English. 1972. a., latest 2001. USD 2,046 (effective 2001). Supplement avail. **Document type:** *Directory.*
Former titles: Financial Corporate - Municipal Bond Transfer Service; Financial Corporate Bond Transfer Service (0360-5825)
Related titles: Online - full text ed.
Published by: Financial Information Incorporated, 30 Montgomery St, Jersey City, NJ 07302. TEL 800-367-3441, FAX 800-344-3292, http://www.fiinet.com. Ed. Camille Doria. R&P Don Hardie TEL 201-369-3651.

332.678   USA
HG4512
F I I ANNUAL GUIDE TO STOCKS. Text in English. a. USD 2,250 (effective 1997). Supplement avail. **Document type:** *Directory.*
Formerly: Financial Stock Guide Service. Directory of Active Stocks (0364-0752)
Related titles: Online - full text ed.
Published by: Financial Information Incorporated, 30 Montgomery St, Jersey City, NJ 07302. TEL 800-367-3441, FAX 800-344-3292. Ed. Charles Page. R&P Don Hardie TEL 201-369-3651.

332.6   CAN   ISSN 1486-7273
F P BONDS, GOVERNMENT. (Financial Post) Text in English. 1972. a. CND 59.95 (effective 1998).
Former titles (until 1998): Government Bond Record (0833-9430); (until 1985): Bond Record (0317-607X); Investment Dealers' Association of Canada. Canada and Canad: Funded Debts Outstanding (0075-028X)
Published by: Financial Post Datagroup, 300-1450 Don Mills Rd, Don Mills, ON M3B 3R5, Canada. TEL 416-350-6501. Circ: 4,000.

332.6   CAN   ISSN 1492-5338
F P EQUITIES, PREFERREDS & DERIVATIVES. (Financial Post) Text in English. 2000. a.
Published by: Financial Post Datagroup, 300-1450 Don Mills Rd, Don Mills, ON M3B 3R5, Canada. TEL 416-350-6176, FAX 416-350-6171.

332.6   CAN   ISSN 1481-4919
HG4090.Z65
F P SURVEY, INDUSTRIALS. Text in English. 1927. a. CND 119.95. adv. **Document type:** *Journal, Trade.* **Description:** Gives investment and statistical data on public Canadian securities.
Former titles (until 1998): Survey of Industrials (0833-9597); (until 1985): Financial Post Survey of Industrials (0071-5050); (until 1949): Financial Post Survey of Corporate Securities (0316-8115)
—CISTI.
Published by: Financial Post Datagroup, 300-1450 Don Mills Rd, Don Mills, ON M3B 3R5, Canada. TEL 416-350-6477, FAX 416-350-6501, fpdg@fpdata.finpost.com. Ed. Steven Pattison. Circ: 4,000.

F X C NEWSLETTER. see *BUSINESS AND ECONOMICS—Economic Situation And Conditions*

332.63   USA
FAMENT STOCK SERVICE ADVISORY. (37+ Years Stock Market, 21+ Years Ted Warrgn, 31+ Years Publishing) Text in English. 1980. bi-m. looseleaf. USD 180 (effective 2001). adv. Website rev. mkt. Bi-Monthly. 4 p./no.; back issues avail.; reprints avail. **Document type:** *Newsletter, Consumer.* **Description:** Uses methods developed by Ted Warren to recommend buy, sell, and hold positions on various stocks.
Related titles: E-mail ed.; Online - full content ed.
Published by: Fament Stock Advisory Service, 9157 Trujillo Way, Sacramento, CA 95826-4155. TEL 916-363-2138, FAX 916-366-7326, fament1@prodigy.net, http://fament.anthill.com. Ed., Pub., Adv. contact Gordon D Mors. Circ: 20,000.

332.63   USA
FANNIE MAE INVESTOR ANALYST REPORT. Text in English. q.
Published by: (Fannie Mae, Office of Investor Relations), Federal National Mortgage Association, 3900 Wisconsin Ave, N W, Washington, DC 20016. TEL 202-752-4422, FAX 202-752-4933.

FAST COMPANY. see *BUSINESS AND ECONOMICS—Management*

FASTCOMPANY.COM. see *BUSINESS AND ECONOMICS—Management*

332.6   USA   ISSN 8756-4769
FAVORABLY POSITIONED STOCKS∗ . Text in English. 1984. m. USD 117; free to qualified personnel. **Description:** Provides data on growth stocks currently undervalued according to fundamental and technical criteria.
Published by: Barrow Investment Management, Inc., 3800 W Bay To Bay Blvd, Ste 21, Tampa, FL 33629-6826. Ed. Alston Marc Barrow. Circ: 5,000. **Subscr. to:** PO Box 1260, Tampa, FL 33601.

332.6 346.066   USA
FEDERAL SECURITIES ACT OF 1933. Text in English. 1965. irreg. (in 2 vols.). looseleaf. USD 693 (effective 2003).
Formerly: Federal Securities Act of 1933: Treatise and Primary Source Manual
Related titles: CD-ROM ed.
Published by: Matthew Bender & Co., Inc. (Subsidiary of: LexisNexis North America), 1275 Broadway, Albany, NY 12204. international@bender.com, http://bookstore.lexis.com/bookstore/catalog?action=product&prod_id=10510&cat_id=J&pcat_id=65&pub_id=1, http://bender.lexisnexis.com. Ed. A A Sommer Jr.

FEDERAL SECURITIES LAW REPORTS. see *LAW*

FELL'S U S COINS QUARTERLY INVESTMENT GUIDE. see *NUMISMATICS*

332.6   USA   ISSN 1097-8372
FIDELITY INVESTOR. Text in English. 1998. m. USD 99.95 (effective 2004). **Document type:** *Newsletter, Trade.*
Published by: Phillips International, Inc., 1201 Seven Locks Rd., Potomac, MD 20854. TEL 301-340-2100, FAX 301-738-8453, http://www.fidelityinvestor.com. Ed. Jim Lowell. Circ: 19,000 (paid).

FIDELITY LAW JOURNAL. see *LAW*

332.6   USA
FIDELITY MAGAZINE; the magazine for Fidelity's investors. Text in English. q. free domestic to customers. charts; illus.
Document type: *Magazine, Consumer.* **Description:** Offers views on trends in the stock and bond markets in the US and overseas; profiles key portfolio managers.
Formerly: Fidelity Focus
Published by: Fidelity Investments, 82 Devonshire St, R20E, Boston, MA 02109. TEL 617-563-4200, FAX 617-476-5979, http://www.fidelity.com. Ed. Bob Barrett. Pub. Clair Haung. Circ: (controlled).

332.6327   USA
FIDELITY MONITOR; the independent newsletter for Fidelity Investors. Text in English. 1986. m. USD 116 (effective 2000). **Document type:** *Newsletter.* **Description:** Covers buy, sell, and hold recommendations for most Fidelity funds.
Published by: Independent Fidelity Investors, Inc., PO Box 1270, Rocklin, CA 95677. TEL 800-397-3094. Ed., Pub., R&P Jack Bowers.

332.6   USA
FIDELITY OUTLOOK. Text in English. q. **Document type:** *Magazine, Consumer.*
Published by: (Fidelity Investments), Pohly & Partners Inc., 27 Melcher St., 2nd Fl., Boston, MA 02210. TEL 617-451-1700, 877-687-6459, FAX 617-338-7767, ginnyf@pohlypartners.com, http://www.pohlypartners.com. Circ: 800,000 (controlled).

332.6   USA
FINANCIAL ADVICE & COMMUNITY. Text in English. w.
Document type: *Newsletter, Consumer.* **Description:** Contains practical, everyday advice for real people.

▼ *new title*   ➤ *refereed*   ∗ *unverified*   ♦ *full entry avail.*

B

Media: E-mail.
Published by: Bankrate Inc., 11811 US Hwy 1, North Palm Beach, FL 33408. TEL 561-630-2400, FAX 561-625-4540, webmaster@bankrate.com, http://bankrate.process9.com/bankrate/subscribe.html, http://www.bankrate.com.

332.6 GBR ISSN 0953-5276
FINANCIAL ADVISER (LONDON). Text in English. w. (50/yr.). GBP 90; GBP 140 foreign. stat. **Document type:** *Newspaper, Trade.* **Description:** Covers the financial intermediary market, from new products to new legislation.
Related titles: Online - full text ed.: (from Gale Group).
Published by: Financial Times Business Information, Magazines (Subsidiary of: Financial Times Group), Tabernacle Court, 16-28 Tabernacle St, London, EC2A 4DD, United Kingdom. TEL 44-20-7405-6969, FAX 44-20-7405-5276, http://www.iii.co.uk/ftmags/fa/., http://www.ftbusiness.com. Circ: (controlled).

332 USA ISSN 0015-198X
HG4501 CODEN: FIAJA4
FINANCIAL ANALYSTS JOURNAL. Text in English. 1945. bi-m. USD 235 domestic print & online eds. (effective 2005). adv. bk.rev. charts; stat.; illus. cum.index: vols. 1-51 (1945-1995). back issues avail.; reprint service avail. from PQC. **Document type:** *Magazine, Trade.*
Related titles: Microform ed.: (from PQC); Online - full text ed.: (from EBSCO Publishing, Northern Light Technology, Inc., O C L C Online Computer Library Center, Inc., ProQuest Information & Learning).
Indexed: ABIn, ATI, BPI, BPIA, BusI, CPM, CurCont, Emerald, IBSS, Inspec, MEA&I, ManagCont, PAIS, PROMT, RASB, RefZh, SCIMP, SSCI, WBA.
—BLDSC (3926.938000), AskIEEE, IE, Infotrieve, ingenta. **CCC.**
Published by: Association for Investment Management and Research, 560 Ray C Hunt Drive, Charlottesville, VA 22903. TEL 434-951-5442, FAX 434-951-5370, faj@aimr.org, http://www.aimrpubs.org/faj/home.html, http://www.aimr.org. Ed. Robert Arnott. Circ: 40,000.

FINANCIAL CRIME REVIEW. see *BUSINESS AND ECONOMICS—Banking And Finance*

FINANCIAL CYCLES; wealth creation & investment success through person-centered financial astrology. see *ASTROLOGY*

332.6 ISR ISSN 0334-6595
FINANCIAL DATA OF T A - 100 COMPANIES - QUARTERLY. Text in English. 1985. q. free. **Document type:** *Bulletin, Trade.* **Description:** Provides a reliable source for obtaining updated perspectives on the performance of the TASE's largest companies.
Published by: Tel Aviv Stock Exchange, 54 Ahad Ha am St, Tel Aviv, 65202, Israel. TEL 972-3-5677411, FAX 972-3-5105379, http://www.tase.co.il.

330
FINANCIAL EDGE. Text in English. 1993. bi-m. USD 15 (effective 1994). adv. bk.rev. **Document type:** *Consumer.* **Description:** Publishes articles on financial planning, investing and money management.
Published by: Institute for Financial Integrity, Inc., 4150 123rd Trl N, Royal, Palm Beach, FL 33411. TEL 407-845-2867. Ed. Frank A Provenzano. Circ: 50,000.

332.6 USA ISSN 1092-6380
FINANCIAL ENGINEERING NEWS. Text in English. 1997. bi-m. free to qualified personnel (effective 2004). adv. **Document type:** *Magazine, Trade.*
Published by: Cusp Communications Group, Inc., 185 Haynes Rd., Sudbury, MA 01776-1393. TEL 978-443-4428, FAX 978-440-4025, editor@fenews.com, http://www.fenews.com/. Ed. Jim Finnegan. Adv. contact Ms. Carol Breitman TEL 212-744-6142. B&W page USD 3,335, color page USD 4,170; trim 10.75 x 17. Circ: 25,259.

332.6 336.2 USA ISSN 1522-9882
FINANCIAL FOCUS; wealth producer and protector. Text in English. 1980. m. USD 39.97 (effective 2000). bk.rev. back issues avail. **Document type:** *Newsletter, Consumer.* **Description:** Contains practical information for the average investor and taxpayer.
Published by: Financial and Tax Planning Center, 2140 Professional Dr, 105, Roseville, CA 95661. TEL 916-791-1447, 800-678-3872, FAX 916-791-3444, jeverett@quiknet.com. Ed., Pub., R&P Jack W Everett. Circ: 3,000.

332.6 658.8 GBR ISSN 1460-2288
FINANCIAL MARKETING (LONDON). Text in English. 1997. 10/yr. GBP 495 (effective 2005). adv. **Document type:** *Magazine, Trade.* **Description:** Reports on the latest marketing strategies of financial services organisations, providing need-to-know information on issues including, customer attitudes, brand management, government regulation and product development. Each issue delivers the news, features and case studies required to make the best strategic decisions.
Former titles (until 1997): Insurance Marketing Review (1364-6664); (until 1991): Insurance Marketing (0966-2944); (1983-1997): Financial Marketing Update (0962-1474); Which was formerly (until 1988): Financial Marketing News (0265-7465)
Related titles: Online - full content ed.
Published by: Incisive Media Plc., Haymarket House, 28-29 Haymarket, London, SW1Y 4RX, United Kingdom. TEL 44-20-74849700, FAX 44-20-79302238, customerservices@incisivemedia.com, http://www.financialmarketingonline.com/, http://www.incisivemedia.com/. Ed. Jonathan Boyd TEL 44-20-74849769. Pub., Adv. contact Mike Jones TEL 44-20-79684530.

332.6 USA ISSN 0816-6897
FINANCIAL MONITOR. Text in English. bi-m. **Document type:** *Newsletter, Trade.* **Description:** Aimed at consumers interested in money management and financial and retirement planning.
Published by: (Society of Financial Service Professionals), Liberty Publishing, 85 Sam Fonzo Dr, Beverly, MA 01915-1000.

332.6 GBR ISSN 1461-1260
FINANCIAL NEWS. Text in English. 1996. w. GBP 199 domestic; GBP 5 newsstand/cover; GBP 245 overseas (effective 2000). adv. bk.rev. **Document type:** *Newspaper, Trade.* **Description:** Focuses on the investment banking, fund management and securities industry. Provides in depth coverage of the firms, personalities and issues facing the industry in Europe and internationally.
Formerly (until 1998): London Financial News (1362-3222)
Related titles: Online - full text ed.: GBP 57 (effective 2000) (from Gale Group, O C L C Online Computer Library Center, Inc.).
Address: 29-33 Scrutton St, 2nd Fl, London, EC2A 4HU, United Kingdom. TEL 44-20-7426-3333, FAX 44-20-7377-8927, info@financialnews.co.uk, http://www.financialnews.co.uk. Ed. Peter Wilson-Smith. R&P Lydia Braithwaite. Adv. contact Nicola Gilmour. Circ: 10,088. **Dist. by:** Seymour Distribution Ltd, 86 Newman St, London W1T 3EX, United Kingdom. enquiries@seymour.co.uk, http://www.seymour.co.uk.

332.6 628.1 GBR
FINANCIAL PERFORMANCE AND EXPENDITURE OF THE WATER COMPANIES IN ENGLAND AND WALES. Text in English. 1991. a., latest 1999-2000. free. **Document type:** *Monographic series.*
Former titles: Report on Capital Investment and Financial Performance of the Water Companies in England and Wales; Report on Capital Investment by the Water Companies in England and Wales
Published by: Office of Water Services, Centre City Tower, 7 Hill St, Birmingham, Warks B5 4UA, United Kingdom. TEL 44-121-625-1373, FAX 44-121-625-1362, http://www.ofwat.gov.uk. Circ: 2,000.

332.6 CAN ISSN 0829-1640
HG4090
FINANCIAL POST 500. Text in English. a. adv.
Formerly (until 1978): Financial Post 300 (0829-1632)
Related titles: ◆ Supplement to: The Financial Post. ISSN 0015-2021.
Indexed: CBCABus, CBCARef, CBPI, CPerI.
Published by: Financial Post Datagroup, 300-1450 Don Mills Rd, Don Mills, ON M3B 3R5, Canada. TEL 416-350-6176, FAX 416-350-6171. Ed. Wayne Gooding. Adv. contact Victoria Petrolo. Circ: 190,000.

332.63 CAN ISSN 1486-7168
FINANCIAL POST BONDS - CORPORATE. Text in English. 1978. a. CND 79.95 (effective 1999). **Description:** Contains detailed information on Canadian corporate debt issues. Lists public offerings and private placements; coupon rates and maturity dates; DBRS, S & P ratings and more.
Former titles: Corporate Bond Record (0831-9774); (until 1985): BondRecord 2 (0709-5066)
Published by: Financial Post Datagroup, 300-1450 Don Mills Rd, Don Mills, ON M3B 3R5, Canada. TEL 416-350-6507, 800-661-7678, FAX 416-350-6501.

332.63 CAN
FINANCIAL POST - CANADIAN PRICES. Text in English. 1983. a. CND 199.95 (effective 1999). **Description:** Lists monthly closing bid prices and yields for outstanding Canadian federal, provincial, corporate and municipal debt issues.
Formerly: Canadian Bond Prices (0828-170X)
Published by: Financial Post Datagroup, 300-1450 Don Mills Rd, Don Mills, ON M3B 3R5, Canada. TEL 416-350-6507, 800-661-7678, FAX 416-350-6501.

FINANCIAL POST DIVIDENDS, ANNUAL RECORD & 10 YEAR PRICE RANGE. see *BUSINESS AND ECONOMICS—Banking And Finance*

332.6 CAN ISSN 1196-8281
FINANCIAL POST INVESTMENT REPORTS. Text in English. 1993. a. price varies.
—**CCC.**
Published by: Financial Post Datagroup, 300-1450 Don Mills Rd, Don Mills, ON M3B 3R5, Canada. TEL 416-350-6507, 800-661-7678, FAX 416-350-6501.

332.6 USA ISSN 1099-4343
FINANCIAL SENTINEL. Text in English. m. USD 29.95; USD 3.50 newsstand/cover (effective 1999). adv.
Published by: Gulf Atlantic Publishing, Inc., 1947 Lee Rd, Winter Park, FL 32789-1834. TEL 407-628-5700, FAX 407-628-0807. Ed. Robert T Jordan. Adv. contact Sean P Jordan. Circ: 100,000.

FINANCIAL SURVEY. METAL STOCKHOLDERS. see *BUSINESS AND ECONOMICS—Trade And Industrial Directories*

332.6 GBR ISSN 1466-2469
FINANCIAL TIMES MANDATE. Text in German. fortn. GBP 375, EUR 593, USD 581 (effective 2003). adv. **Document type:** *Magazine, Trade.* **Description:** Provides comprehensive coverage of mandate wins and losses, comparative analysis of fund management performance plus new business opportunities, authoritative comment and in-depth supplements and surveys covering both geographic regions and market sectors.
Related titles: Online - full text ed.: (from Gale Group).
Published by: Financial Times Business Information, Magazines (Subsidiary of: Financial Times Group), Tabernacle Court, 16-28 Tabernacle St, London, EC2A 4DD, United Kingdom. TEL 44-20-73828000, FAX 44-20-73828099, http://www.ftbusiness.com. Ed. Henry Smith. Pub. Angus Cushley. Adv. contact Angus Maclaine. B&W page EUR 5,720, color page EUR 7,128. Circ: 12,469 (controlled).

332.6 USA
▼ **FINANCING MARKET FORECAST.** Text in English. 2003. q. USD 695 (effective 2004). **Document type:** *Newsletter, Trade.* **Description:** Provides practical forecasts on the future of the financial services industry.
Media: E-mail.
Published by: Royal Media Group, 1359 Broadway, Ste 1512, New York, NY 10018. TEL 800-320-4418, FAX 212-564-8973, info@royalmedia.com, http://www.royalmedia.com/.

332.6 DNK ISSN 0106-1798
FINANS - INVEST. Text in Danish. 10/yr. adv.
Published by: Fabtidskriftet Finans - Invest, Holmstrupaardvej 140, Aarhus V, 8210, Denmark. TEL 38-33-80-00, FAX 38-33-82-80. Circ: 3,300.

332.6 CHE ISSN 0015-220X
FINANZ UND WIRTSCHAFT. Text in German. 1928. 2/w. CHF 280 domestic (effective 2005). adv. bk.rev. **Document type:** *Newspaper, Trade.* **Description:** Covers the national and international markets, stock markets, banking, art and automobile markets.
Published by: Verlag Finanz und Wirtschaft AG, Hallwylstr 71, Postfach, Zuerich, 8021, Switzerland. TEL 49-44-2983535, FAX 49-44-2983500, redaktion@fuw.ch, verlag@fuw.ch, http://www.finanzinfo.ch. Ed. Peter Bohnenblust. Pub. Gerhart Isler. adv.: B&W page CHF 9,900, color page CHF 13,440; trim 297 x 440. Circ: 50,397 (paid).

FINANZEN; Boerse & Wirtschaft fuer Anleger. see *BUSINESS AND ECONOMICS—Banking And Finance*

332.6 DEU
FINANZEN INVESTMENTFONDS; die Wochenzeitung fuer erfolgreiche Fondsanleger. Text in German. 1994. w. (Mon.). EUR 198 (effective 2003). adv. charts; stat. 44 p./no.; reprints avail. **Document type:** *Newspaper, Trade.*
Related titles: Online - full text ed.
Published by: Finanzen Verlagsgesellschaft mbH (Subsidiary of: Axel Springer Verlag AG), Isabellastr 32, Munich, 80796, Germany. TEL 49-89-272640, FAX 49-89-27264199, joern.kraenicke@finanzen.de, http://www.finanzen.net. Adv. contact Belinda Lohse. B&W page EUR 971, color page EUR 1,278; trim 187 x 255. Circ: 2,100 (paid). **Subscr. to:** Finanzen Leserservice, Hauptstr 42 a, Herzberg Am Harz 37412, Germany.

332.65 DEU ISSN 1619-2923
FINANZWOCHE. Text in German. 1974. w. EUR 600 (effective 2005). back issues avail. **Document type:** *Newspaper, Trade.*
Published by: Finanzwoche GmbH, Georg Kalb Str 9, Pullach, 82049, Germany. TEL 49-89-790453-0, FAX 49-89-7911653, info@finanzwoche.de, http://www.finanzwoche.de.

FINLAND. TILASTOKESKUS. SIJOITUSPALVELUYRITTYKSET/FINLAND. STATISTICS FINLAND. INVESTMENT FIRMS/FINLAND. STATISTIKCENTRALEN. VAERDEPAPPERSFOERETAG. see *BUSINESS AND ECONOMICS—Abstracting, Bibliographies, Statistics*

332.6 USA
FINVESTOR REPORT - STOCKS AROUND FIVE DOLLARS✶. Text in English. 1985. m. USD 50. **Description:** Provides information on inexpensive stocks that are typically not followed by Wall Street brokerage houses.
Published by: Nils G. Peterson, Ed. & Pub., 6666 Van Winkle Dr, Falls Church, VA 22044-1010.

332.6 USA
FIVE PERCENT OWNERSHIP PORTFOLIOS✶. Text in English. m. USD 495. back issues avail.
Former titles: Spectrum 5: Five Percent Ownership Based on 13D, 13G, and 14D-1 Filings; (until 1980): Spectrum Five: Five per Cent Beneficial Ownership
Related titles: Magnetic Tape ed.; Online - full text ed.

Published by: C D A Investment Technologies, Inc., 1455 Research Blvd, Rockville, MD 20850-3194. TEL 800-232-6362, FAX 301-590-1350. Circ: 200.

332.6327   USA   ISSN 1065-3414
HG4501
FIVE STAR INVESTOR. Text in English. 1992. m. USD 65 in United States; USD 80 in Canada & Mexico; USD 105 elsewhere. **Description:** Provides performance data and ratings on 500 select open- and closed-end funds, in a format geared towards the individual investor. Features commentaries on various fund-related subjects.
Published by: Morningstar, Inc., 225 W Wacker Dr, Ste 400, Chicago, IL 60606. TEL 312-696-6000, FAX 312-696-6001. Ed. Kylelane Purcell. Circ: 45,000.

332.6   USA   ISSN 1073-6727
HG4650
THE FIXED INCOME ALMANAC∗ . Text in English. 1993. a. **Document type:** *Directory.*
Published by: Probus Publishing Co., 1333 Burr Ridge Pkwy., Burr Ridge, IL 60521-6489. TEL 312-868-1100, FAX 312-868-6250. Ed. Livingston Douglas.

332.6   GBR   ISSN 0300-4228
FLEET STREET LETTER∗ . Text in English. 1939. fortn. GBP 96. index.
Incorporating: Investment Advisory Service
—CCC.
Published by: Fleet Street Publications Ltd., 271 Regent St, London, WIR 7PAU, United Kingdom. TEL 44-20-7447-4040, FAX 44-20-7447-4041. Ed. Nigel Wray. Circ: 20,000.

332.6   USA
FLEXO MARKET NEWS. Text in English. 1999. bi-w. USD 70 in US & Canada; USD 90 in Europe (effective 2005). adv. **Document type:** *Newsletter, Trade.*
Published by: N.V. Business Publishers Corp., 43 Main St, Avon By The Sea, NJ 07717. TEL 732-502-0500, FAX 732-502-9606, jcurley@nvpublications.com, http://www.nvpublications.com/flexo.htm. Eds. Greg Kishbaum, Jim Curley. Pubs. Greg Kishbaum, Tom Vilardi. adv.: B&W page USD 800, color page USD 995; trim 7.5 x 10.

332.6   DEU   ISSN 1615-4576
FOCUS MONEY. Text in German. 2000. w. EUR 132.60; EUR 2.80 newsstand/cover (effective 2003). adv. **Document type:** *Magazine, Consumer.* **Description:** Contains articles and advice on how to invest intelligently in the Internet economy.
Published by: Focus Magazin Verlag GmbH, Arabellastr 23, Munich, 81925, Germany. TEL 49-89-9250-0, FAX 49-89-92502026, leserbriefe@focus-money.de, http://www.focus-money.de. Eds. Frank Poepsel, Kai Stepp. adv.: B&W page EUR 9,500, color page EUR 12,500. Circ: 140,662 (paid). **Subscr. to:** Burda Medien Abo-Service, Postfach 1351, Lindau 88103, Germany. TEL 49-8382-963180, FAX 49-8382-963119.

332   BGR
FONDOV PAZAR/STOCK MARKET; sedmichen obzor za investitsii i finansi. Text in Bulgarian; Section in English. 1994. w. BGL 65; BGL 1.30 newsstand/cover (effective 2001). back issues avail. **Document type:** *Newspaper, Trade.*
Description: Contains news, analysis, and comments on the stock market. Includes developments on listed companies.
Formerly (until May 1998): Capital Market
Published by: Roubicon ITK PARI AD, 47A Tsarigradsko Shaussee Blvd, Sofia, 1504, Bulgaria. TEL 359-2-9433646, 359-2-9433651, FAX 359-2-9433646, zago@pari.bg, http://www.pari.bg. Pub. Valentin Panayotov. Circ: 1,300 (paid).

330   DEU   ISSN 1439-3344
DER FONDS; Deutschlands groesstes unabhaengiges Fondsmagazin. Text in German. 1999. m. EUR 32; EUR 3.50 newsstand/cover (effective 2003). adv. **Document type:** *Magazine, Consumer.*
Published by: Fonds & Friends Verlagsgesellschaft mbH, Mittelweg 22-24, Hamburg, 20148, Germany. TEL 49-40-40199950, FAX 49-40-40199960, info@derfonds.com, http://www.derfonds.net. Ed. Thorsten Geil. Adv. contact Juergen Heins. B&W page EUR 4,472, color page EUR 5,952. Circ: 31,052 (paid).

330   DEU   ISSN 1434-0259
FONDSMAGAZIN. Text in German. 1996. bi-m. EUR 2.50 newsstand/cover (effective 2003). adv. **Document type:** *Magazine, Consumer.*
Published by: W D V Gesellschaft fuer Medien & Kommunikation mbH & Co. oHG, Siemensstr 6, Bad Homburg, 61352, Germany. TEL 49-6172-6700, FAX 49-6172-670144, info@wdv.de, http://www.wdv.de. Adv. contact Sabine Nieth. B&W page EUR 12,000, color page EUR 13,800; trim 182 x 237. Circ: 901,016 (paid and controlled).

332.6 664   USA
FOOD & BEVERAGE MONITOR. Text in English. w. free to qualified personnel. **Description:** Provides updates on industry performance for investment research purposes.
Published by: Donaldson, Lufkin & Jenrette, 277 Park Ave, New York, NY 10172. TEL 212-892-3000. Ed. Bill Leach. Circ: (controlled).

332.6 664   USA
FOOD & BEVERAGE SPOTLIGHT. Text in English. m. free to qualified personnel. stat. **Description:** Provides comprehensive information on industry performance for investment research purposes.
Published by: Donaldson, Lufkin & Jenrette, 277 Park Ave, New York, NY 10172. TEL 212-892-3000. Ed. Bill Leach. Circ: (controlled).

332.6   USA
FORBES - LEHMANN INCOME SECURITIES INVESTOR; building your wealth with bonds, convertibles & preferreds. Text in English. m. USD 195 (effective 2004). Supplement avail. **Document type:** *Newsletter, Trade.*
Former titles: Income Securities Newsletter; (until 1999): Income Securities Advisor (1086-3079); (until 1995): Bond Investors Association Newsletter (1057-7513); Which incorporated (1992-199?): High Yield Securities Journal (1065-089X); Preferred Stock Journal
Related titles: Online - full text ed.
Published by: Income Securities Advisors Inc, 6175 NW 153rd St, Ste 201, Miami, FL 33014-2435. TEL 800-472-2680, FAX 305-557-1454, http://www.incomesecurities.com/login.cfm. Ed. Jack Colombo.

332.6   USA
FORD DATA BASE REPORT. Text in English. 1982. w. USD 1,800. **Description:** Contains all the information from the Ford Data Base, a computerized database covering 2,680 common stocks, with 93 data items per stock.
Published by: Ford Investor Services, 11722 Sorrento Valley Rd, Ste 1, San Diego, CA 92121. TEL 619-755-1327. Ed. David C Morse.

332.6   USA
FORD INVESTMENT MANAGEMENT REPORT. Text in English. 1974. m. USD 240. back issues avail. **Description:** Financial data on common stocks plus proprietary inputs.
Related titles: Diskette ed.; Magnetic Tape ed.; Online - full text ed.
Published by: Ford Investor Services, 11722 Sorrento Valley Rd, Ste 1, San Diego, CA 92121. TEL 619-755-1327. Ed. David C Morse.

332.6   USA
FORD VALUE REPORT. Text in English. 1970. m. USD 120. back issues avail. **Description:** Financial data on common stocks.
Related titles: Diskette ed.; Magnetic Tape ed.; Online - full text ed.
Published by: Ford Investor Services, 11722 Sorrento Valley Rd, Ste 1, San Diego, CA 92121. TEL 619-755-1327. Ed. David C Morse.

332.6   USA
FOREIGN ACTIVITY REPORT. Text in English. q. USD 75 to non-members; USD 50 to members. back issues avail. **Document type:** *Trade.* **Description:** Tracks purchases and sales of U.S. securities by foreign investors.
Indexed: SRI.
Published by: Securities Industry Association, 120 Broadway, 35th Fl, New York, NY 10271. TEL 212-608-1500. Ed. David G Strongin.

332.6   USA
FOREIGN EXCHANGE LETTER. Text in English. w. USD 1,595; USD 1,625 in Canada; USD 1,670 elsewhere. **Document type:** *Newsletter.* **Description:** Covers foreign investment and currency plans of funds and corporations worldwide.
Published by: Institutional Investor News (Subsidiary of: Euromoney Institutional Investor Plc.), 225 Park Ave S, 7th Fl, New York, NY 10003-1605. TEL 212-224-3800, FAX 212-224-3491.

332.6   AUS
FOREIGN INVESTMENT IN AUSTRALIA. Text in English. 1994. 2-4 updates/yr.), base vol. plus s-a. updates. looseleaf. AUD 909 (effective 2004). **Document type:** *Trade.* **Description:** Covers the regulation of foreign investment in Australia.
Published by: Lawbook Co. (Subsidiary of: Thomson Legal & Regulatory Ltd.), PO Box 3502, Rozelle, NSW 2039, Australia. LRA.Service@thomson.com, http://onlineecom01.thomson.com.au/thomson/Catalog.asp?EES_CMD=SI&EES_ID=100216, http://www.lawbookco.com.au/. Eds. A Millhouse, W D Duncan.

332.6   CHN
FOREIGN INVESTMENT IN CHINA. Text in Chinese, English. m. **Document type:** *Government.* **Description:** Covers the utilization of foreign investment and foreign-funded enterprises in China.
Published by: Ministry of Commerce of the People's Republic of China/Zhonghua Renmin Gongheguo Shangfubu, 6th Fl, South Bldg 1, Da Ya Bao Lu, Dong Cheng District, Beijing, 100730, China. TEL 86-1-5231281, FAX 86-1-5231281, webmaster@moftec.gov.cn, http://www.mofcom.gov.cn/.

332.6   PAK   ISSN 0071-7339
FOREIGN LIABILITIES, ASSETS AND FOREIGN INVESTMENTS IN PAKISTAN. Text in English. a. PKR 30, USD 6 (effective 2000). **Document type:** *Government.*

Published by: State Bank of Pakistan, Central Directorate, Public Relations Department, I.I. Chundrigar Rd, PO Box 4456, Karachi, Pakistan. TEL 92-21-9212400, FAX 92-21-9212436, TELEX 21774 SBPK PK.

332.6   IND
FORTUNE INDIA; premier business, finance and investment magazine. Text in English. 1982. fortn. INR 15 newsstand/cover. adv. **Document type:** *Trade.* **Description:** Covers economic, business, and corporate affairs and investment.
Published by: Fortune Publications Pvt. Ltd., Karachiwala Bldg., 98 Mody St., Mumbai, Maharashtra 400 001, India. TEL 22-2671009. Ed., Pub. Deven Malkan. R&P Bhupendra Shah. Adv. contact Leon Anthony. B&W page INR 35,000, color page INR 60,000; trim 180 x 240. Circ: 21,000.

FORUM (HEIDELBERG). see *BUSINESS AND ECONOMICS—Banking And Finance*

FORUM (NEW YORK, 1986). see *BUSINESS AND ECONOMICS*

332.6   USA   ISSN 1529-2355
FOUNDATION & ENDOWMENT MONEY MANAGEMENT; exclusive news on nonprofits' investment management. Text in English. 1998. m. USD 2,245 combined subscription domestic print & online eds.; USD 2,565 combined subscription foreign print & online eds. (effective 2005). **Document type:** *Newsletter, Trade.* **Description:** Provides search leads and inside intelligence on the investment strategies of nonprofits.
Related titles: Online - full text ed.: (from Florida Center for Library Automation, Gale Group).
—CCC.
Published by: Institutional Investor News (Subsidiary of: Euromoney Institutional Investor Plc.), 225 Park Ave S, 7th Fl, New York, NY 10003-1605. TEL 212-224-3800, FAX 212-224-3491, info@iiplatinum.com, http://www.foundationendowment.com, http://www.iinews.com. Pub. Mark Fortune. **Subscr. to:** New Orders, PO Box 5063, Brentwood, TN 37024. TEL 615-377-3322, 800-945-2034, 800-715-9197, FAX 615-337-0525, vlockridge@sunbeltfs.com.

332.6   FRA   ISSN 0533-0742
FRANCE. COMMISSION DES OPERATIONS DE BOURSE. RAPPORT AU PRESIDENT DE LA REPUBLIQUE. Text in French. irreg.
Published by: (France. Commission des Operations de Bourse), Imprimerie Nationale, BP 514, Douai, Cedex 59505, France. FAX 27-93-70-96.

332.67   USA   ISSN 1085-6765
FRANKLIN RESEARCH'S INSIGHT; the advisory letter for concerned investors. Text in English. 1983. m. looseleaf. USD 225. adv. bk.rev. charts; stat. index. back issues avail. **Document type:** *Newsletter.* **Description:** News and research pertaining to capital investment, with analyses of the social and financial performance of selected companies and quarterly profiles on specific industries.
Former titles (until 1993): Franklin's Insight; (until 1987): Insight (0742-5244)
Indexed: HECAB.
Published by: Franklin Research and Development Corporation, 711 Atlantic Ave, 4th Fl, Boston, MA 02111. TEL 800-548-5684. Ed. Eric Becker. Adv. contact A Brosco. Circ: 800.

332.6   USA   ISSN 1073-0796
FREEMARKET GOLD & MONEY REPORT. Text in English. 1987. 20/yr. USD 260 in US & Canada; USD 285 elsewhere (effective 2005). charts; mkt. back issues avail. **Document type:** *Newsletter, Trade.* **Description:** Provides specific advice on monetary and investment matters.
Published by: Greenfield Associates, PO Box 5002-240, North Conway, NH 03860-5002. TEL 603-323-8182, FAX 603-323-8161, contact@fgmr.com, http://www.fgmr.com. Ed., Pub. James Turk.

FREQUENTLY ASKED QUESTIONS ABOUT R E I TS. see *REAL ESTATE*

332.63   DEU
FUCHS-16. Text in German. 5/w. **Document type:** *Newsletter, Trade.* **Description:** Provides a daily listing of the top 16 stocks.
Media: E-mail.
Published by: Verlag Fuchsbriefe (Subsidiary of: Springer Science+Business Media), Albrechtstr 22, Berlin, 10117, Germany. TEL 49-30-28881720, FAX 49-30-28045576, http://www.fuchsbriefe.de.

332.63   DEU
FUCHS-32. Text in German. 5/w. **Document type:** *Newsletter, Trade.* **Description:** Contains daily updates of the latest prices and quotes for stocks.
Media: E-mail.
Published by: Verlag Fuchsbriefe (Subsidiary of: Springer Science+Business Media), Albrechtstr 22, Berlin, 10117, Germany. TEL 49-30-28881720, FAX 49-30-28045576, britta.rossbach@bertelsmann.de, http://www.fuchsbriefe.de.

332.6 DEU
FUCHS-HITECH. Text in German. w. adv. **Document type:** *Newsletter, Trade.* **Description:** Contains news and information on the latest technology-related stocks and companies.
Related titles: E-mail ed.
Published by: Verlag Fuchsbriefe (Subsidiary of: Springer Science+Business Media), Albrechtstr 22, Berlin, 10117, Germany. TEL 49-30-28881720, FAX 49-30-28045576, http://www.fuchsbriefe.de. Ed., Pub. Ralf Vielhaber.

332.6 DEU
FUCHS-KAPITALANLAGEN. Text in German. w. adv. **Document type:** *Newsletter, Trade.* **Description:** Covers the latest tips and trends in the various stock exchanges.
Related titles: E-mail ed.
Published by: Verlag Fuchsbriefe (Subsidiary of: Springer Science+Business Media), Albrechtstr 22, Berlin, 10117, Germany. TEL 49-30-28881720, FAX 49-30-28045576, http://www.fuchsbriefe.de. Ed., Pub. Ralf Vielhaber.

332.6 USA
FUND DECODER. Text in English. w. USD 1,295; USD 1,325 in Canada; USD 1,370 elsewhere. **Document type:** *Newsletter.* **Description:** Covers trends in mutual fund marketing and analysis of new fund filings.
Published by: Institutional Investor News (Subsidiary of: Euromoney Institutional Investor Plc.), 225 Park Ave S, 7th Fl, New York, NY 10003-1605. TEL 212-224-3800, FAX 212-224-3491.

332.6 USA ISSN 1076-4135
HG4930
FUND DIRECTIONS. Text in English. m. **Document type:** *Newsletter, Trade.* **Description:** Identifies trends in the rapidly-changing fund environment and presents analyses of issues in fund governance for fund trustee.
Related titles: Online - full text ed.: (from Florida Center for Library Automation, Gale Group, O C L C Online Computer Library Center, Inc.).
—CCC.
Published by: Institutional Investor News (Subsidiary of: Euromoney Institutional Investor Plc.), 225 Park Ave S, 7th Fl, New York, NY 10003-1605. TEL 212-224-3800, FAX 212-224-3491, info@iiplatinum.com, http://www.funddirections.com, http://www.iinews.com. Pub. Nanzeen Kanga TEL 212-224-3005.

332.6 USA
FUND PROFIT ALERT. Text in English. 1991. 12/yr. USD 200. **Document type:** *Newsletter.* **Description:** Utilizes a contrarian approach to provide strategic, carefully researched recommendations, sector analysis, market timing indicators and specific advice aimed to generate high profits in short time periods.
Published by: Investment Research Institute Inc., 1259 Kemper Meadow Dr, Ste 100, Cincinnati, OH 45240. TEL 513-589-3800, 800-448-2080, FAX 513-589-3810, bernieIRI@aol.com, http://www.options-iri.com. Ed. Bernard G Schaeffer. Pub. Robert D Bergen.

332.6 GBR
FUND STRATEGY. Text in English. w. **Document type:** *Trade.* **Description:** Publishes news and analysis for retail investment professionals.
Published by: Centaur Publishing, St Giles House, 50 Poland St, London, W1V 4AX, United Kingdom. TEL 44-20-7970-4000, http://www.centaur.co.uk/. Ed. Roger Anderson.

332.6 USA ISSN 1057-6703
FUND WATCH✶; the official guide to high-performance mutual funds. Text in English. 1991. m. USD 80. charts; stat. back issues avail. **Document type:** *Newsletter.* **Description:** Charts of the price performance of leading equity mutual funds.
Published by: Institute for Econometric Research, 6454 NW 5th Way, Fort Lauderdale, FL 33309-6112. TEL 954-421-1000, 800-442-9000, FAX 954-570-8200, http://www.mfmag.com. Ed. Norman G Fosback. Circ: 30,000 (paid).

332.6 USA
FUNDADVICE.COM. Text in English. 1983. m. USD 125 (effective 2000). **Description:** Mutual fund market timing service.
Former titles: Fund Exchange; Fund Exchange Report
Related titles: Online - full text ed.: free.
Published by: Merriman Capital Management, Inc, 1200 Westlake Ave N Ste 700, Seattle, WA 98109. TEL 206-285-8877, http://www.fundadvice.com. Ed., Pub. Paul A Merriman. R&P, Adv. contact Paul A Merriam.

332.6 CAN ISSN 1202-9262
THE FUNDLETTER. Text in English. 1994. m. CND 89 (effective 1999). **Document type:** *Newsletter.* **Description:** Investment advice and recommendations on investing in mutual funds.
Published by: Hume Publishing Company Ltd., 604 2200 Yonge St, Toronto, ON M4S 2C6, Canada. TEL 800-733-4863, FAX 416-440-8268, customerservice@humepublishing.com, humenewsletters@mindspring.com, http://www.humepublishing.com. Ed. A Michael Keerma.

332.6 USA
FUNDS FOCUS. Text in English. q. **Document type:** *Newsletter.* **Description:** Offers views on the stock and bond markets, reports on how Neuberger & Bermann is responding, and profiles fund managers.
Published by: Neuberger & Bermann Management Inc., 605 Third Ave, New York, NY 10158.

332.6 USA
FUTUREDEX. Text in English. 2002. m. USD 195 membership (effective 2002). **Document type:** *Magazine, Consumer.* **Description:** Provides venture capital intelligence, editorial, and data and analysis. Each month's content include: feature stories, companies of the future, investors of the month, money watch.
Published by: Futuredex, Inc., 1067 Folsom St, Ste 400, San Francisco, CA 94103. TEL 415-558-8068, 800-810-2194, info@futuredex.com, http://www.futuredex.com/mag/. Ed. Damir Perge. Circ: 345,000.

332.63 USA ISSN 0746-2468
HG6046 CODEN: FUTSEA
FUTURES (CHICAGO); news, analysis and strategies for futures, options and derivatives traders. Variant title: Futures Source Book. Text in English. 1972. m. USD 49 in North America print & online eds.; USD 102 elsewhere print & online eds. (effective 2004). adv. bk.rev. charts; illus.; stat. Index. back issues avail.; reprints avail. **Document type:** *Magazine, Consumer.*
Formerly (until 1984): Commodities (0279-5590); Incorporates (in 199?): Trends in Futures; Which was formerly: Commodity Closeup
Related titles: Microform ed.: (from PQC); Online - full text ed.: (from EBSCO Publishing, Florida Center for Library Automation, Gale Group, H.W. Wilson, O C L C Online Computer Library Center, Inc., ProQuest Information & Learning).
Indexed: ABIn, BPI, BPIA, CLOSS, EAA, PAIS, SoftBase, T&II. —BLDSC (4060.642000), CISTI, IE, ingenta.
Address: 250 S Wacker Dr, Ste 1150, Chicago, IL 60606. TEL 312-977-0999, FAX 312-977-1042, futuresm@aol.com., jbecker@futuresmag.com, http://www.futuresmag.com. Ed., Pub. Ginger Szala. adv.: B&W page USD 9,950, color page USD 12,200; trim 10.75 x 7.13. Circ: 62,000 (controlled). **Subscr. to:** Futures Magazine, PO Box 832, Winchester, MA 01890. TEL 888-898-5514.

332.6 GBR ISSN 1462-9658
HG6024.A3
FUTURES & O T C WORLD. (Over the Counter) Text in English. 1982. m. USD 435 (effective 2001). adv. **Document type:** *Trade.* **Description:** Contains articles and analysis of the investment and trade activities of the risk management market, with survey research findings, announcements of conferences and seminars, industry profiles, and news briefs.
Former titles (until 1998): Futures and Options World (0953-6620); Futures World (0262-8376)
Related titles: ◆ Supplement(s): I T Directory. ISSN 1463-3922. —IE. **CCC.**
Published by: Metal Bulletin plc, Park House, 3 Park Terr, Worcester Park, Surrey KT4 7HY, United Kingdom. TEL 44-20-78279977, FAX 44-20-78275290, subscriptions@metalbulletin.plc.uk, http://www.metalbulletin.com. Ed. Emma Davey. Circ: 11,000.

332.64 CAN ISSN 1183-4242
FUTURES AND OPTIONS. Text in French, English. 1985. q. looseleaf. free. charts; stat. **Document type:** *Newsletter.* **Description:** Covers new products' development in the derivatives market, trading and hedging strategies using interest rates, derivative products targeted towards institutional and corporate end-users.
Formerly: Montreal Options Monthly Strategies
Published by: Montreal Exchange, Derivative Products Department, Stock Exchange Tower, 800 Victoria Sq, P O Box 61, Montreal, PQ H4Z 1A9, Canada. TEL 514-871-3585, FAX 514-871-3531. Ed. Jose Slobodrian. Pub. Jean Laflamme. Circ: 2,400 (paid).

332.6 USA ISSN 0892-0869
FUTURES & OPTIONS FACTORS; the futures portfolio advisor. Variant title: Russel R. Wasendorf's Futures & Options Factors. Text in English, Spanish. 1980. w. looseleaf. USD 228 (effective 2005). bk.rev. back issues avail. **Document type:** *Newsletter, Trade.* **Description:** Contains comments, recommendations and charts of proprietary Wasendorf composite and group indexes.
Formerly: Futures Portfolio Advisor
Published by: Wasendorf & Associates, P O Box 849, Cedar, IA 50613. TEL 319-268-0441, FAX 319-277-0880, Russ-Wasendorf@msn.com, http://www.flight2quality.com. Ed., Pub., R&P Russell R Wasendorf Sr. TEL 312-648-3800. Circ: 2,000 (paid).

332.644 GBR ISSN 1361-8571
FUTURES AND OPTIONS WEEK. Text in English. 1992. w. USD 1,233 (effective 2001). adv. stat. back issues avail. **Document type:** *Newsletter.* **Description:** Covers the world futures and options industry.
Formerly (until 1995): Futures and Options Plus (0966-7296)
Media: E-mail. **Related titles:** Online - full text ed.
—CCC.
Published by: Metal Bulletin plc, Park House, 3 Park Terr, Worcester Park, Surrey KT4 7HY, United Kingdom. TEL 44-20-78279977, FAX 44-20-78275290, subscriptions@metalbulletin.plc.uk, http://www.metalbulletin.com. Ed. Neil Wilson. Pub. David Setters. Adv. contact Michael Popay.

332.6 USA
FUTURESCOPE. Text in English. 1983. m. USD 1,500. **Description:** Executive portfolio that focuses on tomorrow's technologies, products and markets, as well as trends and emerging ideas.
Related titles: Online - full text ed.
Published by: Decision Resources, Inc., Bay Colony Corporate Center, 1100 Winter St, Waltham, MA 02154-1238. TEL 781-487-3737, FAX 781-487-3735, drreports@dresources.com. Ed. Jean Carbone.

332.6 CAN ISSN 1485-8193
THE G-7 REPORT INVESTORS NEWSMAGAZINE. Text in English. 1992. 8/yr. USD 35.95. **Document type:** *Magazine, Trade.* **Description:** Covers issues concerning foreign direct investment, cross border mergers/acquisitions, and global portfolio allocation.
Former titles: The G-7 Report: Money Trade & Investment (1485-8185); The G-7 Report (1188-505X)
Published by: G7 Report Investors' Newsmagazine, PO Box 824, Posta Sta Q, Toronto, ON M4T 2N7, Canada. TEL 416-699-3530, FAX 416-699-5683, mailroom@g7report.com, http://www.g7report.com. Ed., Pub. William Vukson.

332.6 BEL ISSN 0778-7170
G - INVEST; nouvelles des fonds. Text in French. 1991. q. charts; stat. **Document type:** *Newsletter.*
Published by: Generale Bank, Montagne du Parc 3, Brussels, 1000, Belgium. TEL 32-2-5162266, FAX 32-2-5653474. Ed. P Y Goemans.

332.6 USA
G T S ADVISOR. (Government Technical Services) Text in English. q. **Document type:** *Trade.* **Description:** Provides stock pricing, financial performance, industry trends, and related information to managers, investors, and advisors in the government contracting industry.
Published by: Houlihan, Lokey, Howard & Zukin, 1930 Century Park W, Los Angeles, CA 90067. TEL 800-788-5300, FAX 310-553-2173, mergerstat@hlhz.com, http://www.hlhz.com.

332.6 USA
HG4961
GALANTE'S VENTURE CAPITAL AND PRIVATE EQUITY DIRECTORY. Text in English. 1994. a. USD 395 domestic; USD 490 foreign (effective 2000). adv. stat. **Document type:** *Directory.* **Description:** Features more than 2,000 venture capital, buyout and mezzanine firms. Provides profiles of domestic and international capital resources.
Former titles: Galante's Complete Venture Capital and Private Equity Directory (1088-6052); (until 1996): Vankirk's Venture Capital Directory (1078-0041)
Related titles: CD-ROM ed.; Online - full text ed.
Published by: Alternative Investor, 170 Linden St, 2nd Fl, Wellesley, MA 02482. TEL 781-304-1400, FAX 781-304-1440, info@assetnews.com, http://www.assetnews.com. Ed., Pub. David Toll. Adv. contact Barbara Bissonnette. page USD 1,600; 7.75 x 10.5. Circ: 950 (paid).

332.6 DEU ISSN 0939-4966
GELDANLAGE BERATER. Text in German. 1991. bi-m. looseleaf. **Document type:** *Bulletin.*
Published by: V N R Verlag fuer die Deutsche Wirtschaft AG, Theodor-Heuss-Str 2-4, Bonn, 53095, Germany. TEL 49-228-8205-0, FAX 49-228-364411. Ed. Hans Joachim Oberhettinger.

GENERIC LINE. see *PHARMACY AND PHARMACOLOGY*

332.62 USA ISSN 1535-2420
GENOMICS INVESTING. Text in English. m. USD 1,095 domestic; USD 1,170 foreign (effective 2002). adv. back issues avail.; reprints avail. **Document type:** *Newsletter.*
Published by: Alternative Investor, 170 Linden St, 2nd Fl, Wellesley, MA 02482. TEL 781-304-1400, FAX 781-304-1440, info@assetnews.com, http://www.assetnews.com/products/news/gen.htm.

332.6 658 USA ISSN 1044-7121
GEORGESON REPORT. Text in English. 1952. q. free. bk.rev. **Document type:** *Newsletter.*
Formerly: Trends in Management - Stockholder Relations (0041-2406)
Published by: Georgeson & Company Inc., 88 Pine St, New York, NY 10005. FAX 212-440-9014. Ed. Ernest Sando. Circ: 4,000 (controlled).

332.678 GBR
GERMAN FINANCIAL MARKETS YEARBOOK (YEAR). Text in English. 2001 (Nov). a., latest 2002. GBP 115, USD 195 per issue (effective 2002). **Document type:** *Yearbook, Trade.* **Description:** Contains policy statements from both the Central Bank and the Ministry of Finance, along with in-depth editorial, provides essential advice and information for all professionals either active in, or considering investment in the German marketplace.
Published by: Euromoney Institutional Investor Plc., Nestor House, Playhouse Yard, London, EC4V 5EX, United Kingdom. TEL 44-20-7779-8888, information@euromoneyplc.com, http://www.euromoneyplc.com/. **Dist. addr:** Portica, Portica House, 2 Lady Lane Industrial Estate, Hadleigh, Ipswich, Suffolk IP7 6BQ, United Kingdom. TEL 44-1473-825500, FAX 44-870-4430816; **Dist. addr. in the USA:** Institutional Investor, Inc., 225 Park Ave. S., 7th Fl., New York, NY 10003-1605. TEL 212-224-3800, FAX 212-224-3974.

GERMAN INVESTMENT WORLD. see *BUSINESS AND ECONOMICS—Economic Situation And Conditions*

GESTION DE FORTUNE; le journal de la gestion de patrimoine. see *BUSINESS AND ECONOMICS—Banking And Finance*

332.6 POL ISSN 1426-1553
GIELDA PAPIEROW WARTOSCIOWYCH. BIULETYN MIESIECZNY/W S E MONTHLY BULLETIN. Cover title: Biuletyn Miesieczny G P W. Text in Polish, English. m. PLZ 42 domestic; USD 25 foreign.
Published by: Gielda Papierow Wartosciowych w Warszawie S.A./Warsaw Stock Exchange, Nowy Swiat 6-12, Warsaw, 00400, Poland. TEL 48-22-6283232, FAX 48-22-6282754. Ed. Arkadiusz W Szymanek.

340 USA
GILBERT LAW SUMMARIES. SECURITIES REGULATION. Text in English. irreg., latest vol.5. USD 22.95 (effective 2000). **Document type:** *Trade.* **Description:** Reviews all aspects of the regulation of securities.
Published by: Gilbert Law Summaries (Subsidiary of: B A R / B R I Group), 111 W Jackson, 7th Fl, Chicago, IL 60604. TEL 312-853-3662, 800-787-8717, FAX 312-853-3622, http://www.gilbertlaw.com. Eds. David H Barber, Niels B Schaumann.

GILIBERTO-LEVY MONITOR. see *REAL ESTATE*

332.6 CAN
THE GLOBAL ADVISOR; offshore news for prudent investors. Text in English. m. USD 126 (effective 2000).
Published by: The Corporate Group, 357 Bay Street, Ste. 900, Toronto, ON, Ontario M5H 2T7, Canada. TEL 416-362-9949, FAX 416-369-0129, smonteith@thecorpgroup.com.

332 USA
GLOBAL ASSET ALLOCATION. Text in English. m. charts; stat. **Description:** Covers both equity and bond markets including the impact of fiscal conditions on these markets.
Published by: Salomon Brothers, Inc., 7 World Trade Center, New York, NY 10048. TEL 212-783-7000.

332.6 USA ISSN 1047-8736
HG3810
GLOBAL CUSTODIAN. Text in English. 1989. 5/yr. USD 165 domestic; USD 215 foreign (effective 2005). adv. back issues avail. **Document type:** *Trade.* **Description:** For investors, custodial and operational decision-makers in the international investment industry.
—BLDSC (4195.385000), IE. **CCC.**
Published by: Asset International, Inc., 125 Greenwich Ave, Greenwich, CT 06830. TEL 203-629 5014, FAX 203-629 5024, http://www.globalcustodian.com. Circ: 17,000.

332.6 USA ISSN 1529-5710
GLOBAL FUND NEWS. Text in English. 1997. m. USD 1,935 combined subscription domestic print & online eds.; USD 2,010 combined subscription foreign print & online eds. (effective 2005). **Document type:** *Newsletter, Trade.* **Description:** Targeted at investment fund executives that breaks news worldwide on the fund industry. Delivers market intelligence, which is a valuable tool for fund companies.
Related titles: Online - full text ed.: (from Florida Center for Library Automation, Gale Group, O C L C Online Computer Library Center, Inc.).
Indexed: B&I.
—CCC.
Published by: Institutional Investor News (Subsidiary of: Euromoney Institutional Investor Plc.), 225 Park Ave S, 7th Fl, New York, NY 10003-1605. TEL 212-224-3800, FAX 212-224-3491, info@iiplatinum.com, http://www.globalfundnews.com, http://www.iinews.com. Pub. Nanzeen Kanga TEL 212-224-3005. **Subscr. to:** New Orders, PO Box 5063, Brentwood, TN 37024. TEL 615-377-3322, 800-945-2034, 800-715-9197, FAX 615-337-0525, vlockridge@sunbeltfs.com.

332.6 GBR
GLOBAL INVESTMENT SERVICES. Text in English. 1991. 10/yr. USD 379 (effective 2001). **Document type:** *Trade.* **Description:** Looks at the financial operations sector of the cash and derivatives markets.
Formerly (until 1999): Clearing and Settlement (0964-671X)
—CCC.
Published by: Metal Bulletin plc, Park House, 3 Park Terr, Worcester Park, Surrey KT4 7HY, United Kingdom. TEL 44-20-78279977, FAX 44-20-78275290, subscriptions@metalbulletin.plc.uk, http://www.metalbulletin.com. Pub. David Setters.

GLOBAL INVESTMENT TECHNOLOGY. see *BUSINESS AND ECONOMICS—Banking And Finance*

GLOBAL INVESTOR. see *BUSINESS AND ECONOMICS—Banking And Finance*

332.6 USA ISSN 1055-9671
HG1
GLOBAL MARKET PERSPECTIVE. Text in English. 1991. m. USD 599 domestic; USD 645 in Europe; USD 899 elsewhere (effective 1999). **Document type:** *Newsletter.* **Description:** Provides the intermediate to longer-term technical outlook for all major world stock, bond and currency markets, as well as the outlook for precious metals, and economic and social trends.
Published by: Elliott Wave International, PO Box 1618, Gainesville, GA 30503. TEL 770-536-0309. Ed. Robert R Prechter Jr.

332.6 USA ISSN 1529-6679
GLOBAL MONEY MANAGEMENT. Text in English. 1990. bi-w. USD 2,380 combined subscription domestic print & online eds.; USD 2,455 combined subscription foreign print & online eds. (effective 2005). adv. back issues avail. **Document type:** *Newsletter, Trade.* **Description:** Covers the international fund management industry.
Related titles: Online - full text ed.: (from Florida Center for Library Automation, Gale Group).
—CCC.
Published by: Institutional Investor News (Subsidiary of: Euromoney Institutional Investor Plc.), 225 Park Ave S, 7th Fl, New York, NY 10003-1605. TEL 212-224-3800, FAX 212-224-3491, info@iiplatinum.com, http://www.globalmoneymanagement.com, http://www.iinews.com. Pub. Nanzeen Kanga TEL 212-224-3005. **Subscr. to:** New Orders, PO Box 5063, Brentwood, TN 37024. TEL 615-377-3322, 800-945-2034, 800-715-9197, FAX 615-337-0525, vlockridge@sunbeltfs.com.

GLOBAL RISK TRENDS. see *BUSINESS AND ECONOMICS—International Commerce*

▼ **GLOBAL S T M MARKET ANALYSIS & FORECAST (YEAR).** see *BUSINESS AND ECONOMICS—Economic Situation And Conditions*

332.6 GBR
GLOBAL TRENDS✶. Text in English. 1980. m. GBP 445.
Former titles (until 1990): World Markets Service (0961-0472); International Investment Guide (0144-5324)
Published by: Investment Research of Cambridge Ltd., 2 Hills Rd, Cambridge, CB2 1DH, United Kingdom. TEL 44-1223-356251, FAX 44-1223-329806, enquiries@investresearch.u-net.com, http://www.investresearch.u-net.com/. Circ: 200.

332.645 USA ISSN 0743-8508
GOLD MINING STOCK REPORT. Text in English. 1983. m. looseleaf. USD 159. stat. **Description:** Specializes in gold and precious metals mining shares. Includes specific recommendations and follow-ups.
Formerly (until Mar. 1989): Penny Mining Stock Report
Address: PO Box 1217, Lafayette, CA 94549. TEL 510-283-4848, FAX 510-283-8901. Ed. Robert Bishop. Circ: 5,000.

330 DEU ISSN 1610-0247
DER GOLD-REPORT; Edelmetall-Aktien. Text in German. 2002. m. EUR 184 (effective 2003). **Document type:** *Newsletter, Trade.*
Published by: Boersenmedien AG, Hofer Str 20, Kulmbach, 95326, Germany. TEL 49-9221-90510, FAX 49-9221-877288.

332 USA ISSN 1041-8407
GOLD SHEETS. Text in English. 1987. w. **Document type:** *Newsletter, Trade.* **Description:** Provides a weekly analysis of market trends in the global syndicated loan and high-yield bond markets, including coverage of pricing, structure, tenor and industry segments.
Published by: Loan Pricing Corporation, 500 Seventh Ave, 12th Fl, New York, NY 10018. TEL 212-833-9200, FAX 212-833-9285, americas@loanpricing.com, http://www.loanpricing.com.

332.6 USA ISSN 0891-2351
GOLD STOCKS ADVISORY. Text in English. 1987. m. USD 150; USD 15 newsstand/cover (effective 1997). back issues avail. **Document type:** *Newsletter.* **Description:** Carries analysis and recommendation of gold mining stocks on a global basis.
Published by: (Agora, Inc.), Marketing and Publishing Associates, Ltd., 749 Rivenwood Rd., Franklin Lks, NJ 07417-1443. TEL 201-794-8886, FAX 201-794-1221. Ed. Paul Sarnoff. Pub. N S Hayden.

332.6 USA ISSN 0742-4515
HG4528
GOOD MONEY; the newsletter for socially concerned investors. Text in English. 1982. bi-m. USD 75; subscr. includes Netback. abstr.; bibl.; charts; stat. back issues avail.
Published by: Good Money Publications, Inc., 370A Granite Rd, Ossipee, NH 03864. TEL 603-539-3852, FAX 603-539-3852, goodmoney2@aol.com, http://www.goodmoney.com. Ed. Ritchie P Lowry.

332.6327 USA
GOOD MONEY'S SOCIAL FUNDS GUIDE. Text in English. a. USD 30. **Description:** Guide to socially screened mutual funds. Includes an analysis of the holdings of social and environmental funds.
Published by: Good Money Publications, Inc., 370A Granite Rd, Ossipee, NH 03864. TEL 603-539-3852, FAX 603-539-3852, goodmoney2@aol.com, http://www.goodmoney.com.

332.6 USA ISSN 0748-8424
HG1623.U5
GRANT'S INTEREST RATE OBSERVER. Text in English. 1983. bi-w. USD 760 domestic; USD 815 foreign; USD 50 newsstand/cover (effective 2004). back issues avail. **Document type:** *Newsletter, Trade.* **Description:** Reports on issues concerning credit, interest rates, the bond markets, commodities, real estate and monetary trends.
Related titles: Online - full text ed.
Published by: Grant's Financial Publishing Inc., 2 Wall St, New York, NY 10005. TEL 212-809-7994, FAX 212-809-8426, subscriptions@grantspub.com, http://www.grantspub.com. Ed., Pub. James Grant.

332.6 USA
GRANT'S INVESTOR. Text in English. **Document type:** *Trade.* **Description:** Reports on investment ideas and topics for individual and professional investors.
Media: Online - full content.
Published by: Grant's Financial Publishing Inc., 2 Wall St, New York, NY 10005. TEL 212-809-7994, 888-947-2687, FAX 212-809-8492, help@grantsinvestor.com, subscriptions@grantspub.com, http://www.grantsinvestor.com, http://www.grantspub.com.

332.6 USA
GRANVILLE MARKET LETTER✶. Text in English. 46/yr. USD 250.
Address: PO Box 413006, Kansas City, MO 64141. TEL 800-876-5388. Ed. Joseph E Granville.

332.6327 USA
GRAPHIC FUND FORECASTER. Text in English. 1984. w. (m. versions avail.). USD 35 for monthly letter; USD 129 for weekly letter (effective 2000). **Document type:** *Newsletter.* **Description:** Uses the market-timing approach for Fidelity, Invesco, and Rydex funds. Offers hotline and exchange management service.
Formerly (until Dec. 1988): T Y S Fund Letter
Published by: Time Your Switch Management Services, 6 Pioneer Circle, Andover, MA 01810. TEL 508-470-3511, 800-532-2322, tysfred@aol.com, http://people.ne.mediaone.net/tysfred. Ed., R&P Fred W Hohn.

332.6 CAN ISSN 0046-631X
GRAPHOSCOPE. Text in English. bi-m. CND 272.70 domestic (effective 2000); CND 49 newsstand/cover; CND 295.80 in United States; CND 288 elsewhere (effective 2000). **Document type:** *Trade.* **Description:** Compilation of vital statistics to aid decision-making in the stock market.
Related titles: Online - full text ed.
Published by: Canadian Analyst Ltd., 21 Squires Ave, Toronto, ON M4B 2R2, Canada. TEL 416-285-9134, FAX 416-285-0554, 1-877-919-6999, call@graposcope.com, http://www.graphoscope.com.

GREEN MONEY JOURNAL. see *BUSINESS AND ECONOMICS—Banking And Finance*

332.6 USA
GREENMAGAZINE.COM; this website is about money. Text in English. d. adv. **Document type:** *Consumer.* **Description:** Contains stories, tools and daily market commentaries with an underlying philosophy that personal finance could be compelling, cool, intriguing and intelligent.
Media: Online - full content.
Published by: ilife.com, 11 E 44th St, Ste 1200, New York, NY 10017. TEL 917-368-8650, FAX 917-368-8611, johnp@greenmagazine.com, http://www.greenmagazine.com. Ed. Ken Kurson. Pub., R&P, Adv. contact John Packel.

332.6 USA
GROUND FLOOR. Text in English. 1981. m. free (effective 2004). illus. **Document type:** *Trade.* **Description:** Focuses on dynamic companies with fast growth potential, but still young enough to have most of their growth ahead of them. Each issue includes our performance records, as well as current advice, stock recommendations and follow-ups.
Published by: Hirsch Organization Inc., 79 Main St., # 3, Nyack, NY 10960-3109. TEL 201-767-4100, FAX 201-767-7337, http://www.hirschorganization.com. Ed. Jeffrey A Hirsch. Circ: 5,000.

B

▼ new title ➤ refereed ✶ unverified ♦ full entry avail.

332.6 BEL
GROUPE BRUXELLES LAMBERT. ANNUAL REPORTS. Text in English. 1979. a. **Document type:** *Corporate.*
Published by: Groupe Bruxelles Lambert, Av Marnix 24, Brussels, 1000, Belgium. TEL 32-2-5472352, FAX 32-2-5472285.

332.6 BEL
GROUPE BRUXELLES LAMBERT. INTERIM REPORTS. Text in French. 1988. a. **Document type:** *Corporate.*
Indexed: AnthLit.
Published by: Groupe Bruxelles Lambert, Av Marnix 24, Brussels, 1000, Belgium. TEL 32-2-5472352, FAX 32-2-5472285.

332.678 USA ISSN 0017-4831
GROWTH FUND GUIDE; the investors guide to dynamic growth funds. Text in English. 1968. m. USD 159 in United States (effective 2004 & 2005). charts; stat. **Document type:** *Newsletter.* **Description:** Includes several portfolios, data pages, barometers, commentary, free telephone hot line.
Published by: Growth Fund Research, Inc., PO Box 6600, Rapid City, SD 57709. TEL 605-341-1971, http://www.growthfundguide.com. Ed. Walter J Rouleau.

332.6 USA ISSN 1073-7626
HG4501
GROWTH STOCK OUTLOOK. Text in English. 1965. s-m. USD 235 domestic; USD 270 foreign (effective 2001); subscr. includes Junior Growth Stocks, New Issue Digest, Bank Stock Analyst. charts; stat. **Document type:** *Newsletter.* **Description:** Provides data on stock earnings, sales, price-earnings ratios, dividends, book values, return on shareholder equity, and institutional holdings. Recommends specific companies for long-term investment.
Related titles: ♦ Supplement to: Junior Growth Stocks. ISSN 1073-7634.
Published by: Growth Stock Outlook, Inc., 4405 East West Hwy, Ste 305, Bethesda, MD 20814. TEL 301-654-5205. Ed. Charles Allmon.

GRUNDLAGEN UND PRAXIS DES BANK- UND BOERSENWESENS. see *BUSINESS AND ECONOMICS—Banking And Finance*

332.6 ITA
GUIDA DEL MERCATO RISTRETTO; the unlisted market guide. Text in Italian. 1962. a. USD 130. **Description:** Lists 80 companies quoted on the official Italian second market and traded over-the-counter.
Published by: Databank SpA, SASIP Division, Via Spartaco, 19, Milan, MI 20135, Italy. FAX 392-55183152, TELEX 24217 DTBK I.

GUIDE TO LIFE, HEALTH AND ANNUITY INSURERS. see *INSURANCE*

332.64 HKG
H K EX CASH AND DERIVATIVES MARKETS QUARTERLY REPORT. (Hong Kong Exchange) Text in Chinese, English. 2001. q. **Document type:** *Trade.*
Media: Online - full content.
Published by: Hong Kong Exchanges and Clearing Ltd., Corporate Communications, 12/F, One International Finance Centre, 1 Harbour View St, Hong Kong, Hong Kong. TEL 852-2522-1122, FAX 852-2845-3554, info@hkex.com.hk, http://www.hkex.com.hk.

332.64 HKG
H K EX FACT BOOK (YEAR). (Hong Kong Exchange) Text in Chinese, English. a. Free. **Document type:** *Trade.*
Media: Online - full content.
Published by: Hong Kong Exchanges and Clearing Ltd., Corporate Communications, 12/F, One International Finance Centre, 1 Harbour View St, Hong Kong, Hong Kong. TEL 852-2522-1122, FAX 852-2845-3554, info@hkex.com.hk, http://www.hkex.com.hk.

HAMBROS DEALERS DIRECTORY (YEAR); foreign exchange treasury and bullion. see *BUSINESS AND ECONOMICS—Trade And Industrial Directories*

332.6 USA ISSN 0736-6264
HG4501
HANDBOOK FOR NO-LOAD FUND INVESTORS. Text in English. 1981. a. USD 45; USD 159 with No-Load Fund Investor (effective 2000). charts; stat. **Description:** Covers no-load and low-load funds.
Published by: No-Load Fund Investor, Inc., 44 Mountainview Dr., Cold Spring, NY 10516-4129. TEL 914-693-7420, 800-252-2042. Ed. Sheldon Jacobs.

332.6 USA ISSN 1061-7094
HG4936
HANDBOOK OF U S GOVERNMENT AND FEDERAL AGENCY & RELATED MONEY MARKET INSTRUMENTS✶ . Text in English. 1922. biennial. USD 29.95.
Formerly: Handbook of Securities of the United States Government and Federal Agencies and Related Money Market Instruments (0072-9892)
Published by: Probus Publishing Co., 1333 Burr Ridge Pkwy., Burr Ridge, IL 60521-6489. TEL 312-868-1100, FAX 312-868-6250. Ed. Zwen A Goy. Circ: 60,000.

HAUS & INVEST. see *REAL ESTATE*

332.6 USA ISSN 0745-7073
HAWAII INVESTOR. Text in English. m. USD 15.
Formerly: Hawaii Real Estate Investor (0273-5806)
Related titles: Online - full text ed.
Published by: Honolulu Publishing Company, Ltd., 707 Richards St., Ste. 525, Honolulu, HI 96813-4623. TEL 808-524-7400, FAX 808-531-2306. Ed. Lucy Jokiel.

332.6 NZL ISSN 0110-9790
HEADLINER; investment newsletter. Text in English. 1979. fortn. NZD 81, USD 50. adv. back issues avail. **Description:** Covers domestic and international areas of investment, including New Zealand, Australian, Asian, US, and European stockmarkets, managed funds and bonds.
Published by: Headliner Publishing Co. Ltd., Level 2 Age Concern Bldg., 64 Cashel St, Christchurch, 8001, New Zealand. TEL 64-3-3650-301, FAX 64-3-3654-255. Ed. W P Head. Circ: 10,000.

THE HEALTH CARE M & A MONTHLY. see *BUSINESS AND ECONOMICS*

THE HEALTH CARE SERVICES ACQUISITION REPORT. see *BUSINESS AND ECONOMICS*

HEALTHCARE CORPORATE FINANCE NEWS; market intelligence on healthcare venture capital, M&A and IPOs. see *HEALTH FACILITIES AND ADMINISTRATION*

332.6 USA ISSN 1531-0256
HG4530
HEDGE. Text in English. 1994. m. USD 995 in US & Canada; USD 1,125 elsewhere (effective 2005). **Description:** A source of qualitative and quantitative information on the global hedge fund marketplace.
—CCC.
Published by: Managed Account Reports LLC, 1250 Broadway, 26th Fl, New York, NY 10001. TEL 212-213-6202, FAX 212-213-1870, http://www.marhedge.com/publications/hedgebio.htm.

332.63 USA ISSN 1530-7832
HEDGE FUND ALERT. Text in English. 2000. w. USD 1,397 domestic (effective 2001). adv. **Document type:** *Newsletter, Trade.* **Description:** Covers news about hedge funds and the alternative-investment community.
Related titles: E-mail ed.; Fax ed.
Published by: Harrison Scott Publications, Inc., 5 Marine View Plaza, Ste 301, Hoboken, NJ 07030-5795. TEL 201-659-1700, FAX 201-659-4141, swood@hspnews.com, info@hspnews.com, http://www.hfalert.com/hfa/index.htm, http://www.hspnewsletters.com. Ed. Daniel Cowles TEL 201-234-3963. Adv. contact Mary E Romano TEL 201-234-3968. B&W page USD 2,300, color page USD 3,300.

332.64 GRC
HELLENIC INDUSTRIAL DEVELOPMENT BANK. INVESTMENT GUIDE. Spine title: E T B A Investment Guide. Text in English, Greek. 1961. irreg. USD 5. Supplement avail. **Description:** Provides information on the Greek economy and the country's infrastructure. Presents a concise picture of the legal and economic framework of business activity in Greece.
Published by: Hellenic Industrial Development Bank S.A., 18 Panepistimiou St, Athens, 106 72, Greece. TEL 3237-981, FAX 3621023, TELEX 215203 ETVA GR. Circ: 3,000.

332.6 USA
HERZFELD'S GUIDE TO CLOSED-END FUNDS. Text in English. biennial. USD 25.95 (effective 2000). adv. stat. **Document type:** *Newsletter.* **Description:** Provides a complete guide from the basics of every risk level, including chapters on takeovers, hedging, and arbitrage. Also offers a complete statistical section comparing each fund by performance, expense ratio, income ratio, size, and management.
Published by: Thomas J. Herzfeld Advisors, Inc., PO Box 161465, Miami, FL 33116. TEL 305-271-1900, 800-854-3863, FAX 305-270-7040. Ed. Cecilia L Gondor. Adv. contact Thomas Herzfeld.

332.6 USA
HIGH-NET-WORTH INVESTMENT MANAGER SURVEY. Text in English. 1997. a. USD 100 (effective 1998). **Document type:** *Trade.*
Published by: Institutional Investor News (Subsidiary of: Euromoney Institutional Investor Plc.), 225 Park Ave S, 7th Fl, New York, NY 10003-1605.

332.6 USA
HIGH RETURN, LOW RISK INVESTMENTS; using stock selection and market timing. Text in English. 1993. biennial. USD 25.95 (effective 2000). **Description:** Insider's perspective on playing the stock market.
Published by: Thomas J. Herzfeld Advisors, Inc., PO Box 161465, Miami, FL 33116. TEL 305-271-1900, 800-854-3863, FAX 305-270-1040, http://www.herzfeld.com. Eds. Robert F Drach, Thomas J Herzfeld.

332.6 USA
HIGH TECH GROWTH FORECASTER✶ . Text in English. 1985. m. USD 195. **Document type:** *Newsletter.* **Description:** Advisory report featuring high-tech and growth stock selections.
Address: 8 Tidy Island Blvd, Bradenton, FL 34210-3301. Ed., Pub. Robert S Morrow. Circ: 400.

332.6 330 USA
HIGH TECHNOLOGY AND OTHER GROWTH STOCKS. Text in English. 1981. m. USD 175. **Description:** Covers investments in fast growing companies.
Published by: High Technology Growth Stocks, 402 Border Rd, Concord, MA 01742. TEL 508-371-0096. Ed. Bud Anderson.

332.6 USA ISSN 1055-9337
KF1477.Z9
HIGH-YIELD BONDS. Text in English. a.
Published by: Practising Law Institute, 810 Seventh Ave, New York, NY 10019.

332.6 332.75 USA
HIGH YIELD WEEKLY. Text in English. w. (Mon.). **Document type:** *Newsletter, Trade.* **Description:** Features news on high yield issuers and events in the junk bond market.
Media: E-mail.
Published by: Dow Jones Company, 200 Liberty St, New York, NY 10281. TEL 800-223-2274, newswires@dowjones.com, http://www.djnewswires.com/fin-pro/hyw.html.

THE HOME HEALTH CARE ACQUISITION REPORT. see *MEDICAL SCIENCES—Nurses And Nursing*

332.6 USA
HONE REPORT. Text in English. 1980. m. USD 95 (effective 2001). **Document type:** *Consumer.*
Formerly: Money School Monitor
Published by: Money School, PO Box 473, Williamsburg, VA 23187. TEL 804-725-2234. Ed., Pub., R&P Harry Hone. Circ: 7,000.

HONG KONG EXCHANGES AND CLEARING LTD. MONTHLY MARKET DATA (MAIN BOARD AND STOCK OPTIONS MARKET). see *BUSINESS AND ECONOMICS—Banking And Finance*

332.64 HKG
HONG KONG EXCHANGES AND CLEARING LTD. MONTHLY MARKET STATISTICS. Text in Chinese, English. m. Free. **Document type:** *Trade.*
Media: Online - full content.
Published by: Hong Kong Exchanges and Clearing Ltd., Corporate Communications, 12/F, One International Finance Centre, 1 Harbour View St, Hong Kong, Hong Kong. TEL 852-2522-1122, FAX 852-2845-3554, info@hkex.com.hk, http://www.hkex.com.hk.

332.64 HKG
HONG KONG EXCHANGES AND CLEARING LTD. WEEKLY QUOTATIONS. Text in Chinese, English. w. Free. **Document type:** *Trade.*
Media: Online - full content.
Published by: Hong Kong Exchanges and Clearing Ltd., Corporate Communications, 12/F, One International Finance Centre, 1 Harbour View St, Hong Kong, Hong Kong. TEL 852-2522-1122, FAX 852-2845-3554, info@hkex.com.hk, http://www.hkex.com.hk.

332.6 HKG
HONG KONG - THE PROFITABLE OPPORTUNITY. Text in English. 1978. biennial. free to qualified personnel. illus.; stat. **Document type:** *Government.* **Description:** Promotes industrial investment in Hong Kong.
Formerly: Industrial Investment Hong Kong
Related titles: Chinese ed.; French ed.; German ed.; Japanese ed.
Published by: Special Administrative Region, 14-Fl Ocean Centre, 5, Canton Rd, Tsim Sha Tsui, Kowloon, Hong Kong. TEL 852-2737-2434, FAX 852-2730-4633, TELEX 50151-INDHK-HX, invest@id.gcn.gov.hk. Circ: 15,000.

HOOVER'S HANDBOOK OF EMERGING COMPANIES; profiles of America's most exciting grown enterprises. see *BUSINESS AND ECONOMICS—Trade And Industrial Directories*

332.6 DEU
HOPPENSTEDT AKTIENFUEHRER. Text in German. 1868. a. EUR 122.20 (effective 1999). adv. **Document type:** *Trade.*
Formerly: Saling Aktienfuehrer (0080-5572)
Related titles: CD-ROM ed.
Published by: Hoppenstedt Bonnier Zeitschriften GmbH, Havelstr. 9, Darmstadt, 64295, Germany. TEL 49-6151-380-0, FAX 49-6151-380-360.

HOPPENSTEDT CHARTS. see *BUSINESS AND ECONOMICS—Banking And Finance*

332.6 DEU ISSN 1433-8238
HOPPENSTEDT FONDSFUEHRER. Text in German. 1961. a. EUR 168.73 (effective 1999). adv. bk.rev. **Document type:** *Directory.*
Formerly (until 1997): Hoppenstedt Vademecum der Investmentfonds (0073-3342)
Related titles: CD-ROM ed.: EUR 193.78 (effective 1999).
Published by: Hoppenstedt Bonnier Zeitschriften GmbH, Havelstr. 9, Darmstadt, 64295, Germany. TEL 49-6151-380-0, FAX 49-6151-380-360. Ed. Marlie Prell. R&P, Adv. contact Judith Kuehnert TEL 49-6151-380290.

332.6 DEU ISSN 0174-1284
HOPPENSTEDT KURSTABELLEN - KURSANALYSEN. Text in German. 1947. m. EUR 138.02 (effective 1999). adv. stat. **Document type:** *Trade.*
Formerly: Hoppenstedt-Monatskurstabellen (0018-4896)
Published by: Hoppenstedt Bonnier Zeitschriften GmbH, Havelstr. 9, Darmstadt, 64295, Germany. TEL 49-6151-380-0, FAX 49-6151-380-360. Ed. Thomas Thelen. R&P, Adv. contact Judith Kuehnert TEL 49-6151-380290.

332.6 DEU ISSN 0933-3169
HOPPENSTEDT STOCK GUIDE GERMANY. Text in English, German. 1987. q. EUR 193.78. adv. **Document type:** *Trade.* **Description:** Current and historical characteristics in terms of financial analysis for the purpose of stock evaluation of the most important listed German stock corporations.
Published by: Hoppenstedt Bonnier Zeitschriften GmbH, Havelstr. 9, Darmstadt, 64295, Germany. TEL 49-6151-380-0, FAX 49-6151-380-360. Ed. Friederike Mueller. R&P, Adv. contact Judith Kuehnert TEL 49-6151-380290.

HORSE OWNERS AND BREEDERS TAX HANDBOOK. see *SPORTS AND GAMES—Horses And Horsemanship*

HOTELS' INVESTMENT OUTLOOK. see *HOTELS AND RESTAURANTS*

332.6 BRA
HOW TO INVEST IN BRAZIL. Text in English. a. USD 100. Supplement avail.
Published by: E S T E P E, Publishing Department, ZC-06, Rua Senador Dantas, 19 Grupo 707, Centro, Rio De Janeiro, RJ 20031-200, Brazil.

332.6 USA ISSN 1042-4261
HG4515.9
THE HULBERT FINANCIAL DIGEST✶. Text in English. 1980. m. USD 135 (effective 2001). back issues avail. **Document type:** *Newsletter, Consumer.* **Description:** Includes in-depth analyses of the investment approaches of financial newsletters.
Published by: Hulbert Financial Digest, Inc., 5051B Backlick Rd, Annandale, VA 22003-6045. TEL 888-485-2378, hfd@hulbertdigest.com, http://www.hulbertdigest.com. Ed. Mark Hulbert. Circ: 5,000.

332.6 USA
I A WEEK. Variant title: Investment Advisers Week. Text in English. 1998. bi-w. (48/yr.). USD 1,195 (effective 2005). back issues avail. **Document type:** *Newsletter, Trade.* **Description:** Covers regulatory and compliance issues for SEC-registered investment advisers.
Published by: Argosy Group (Subsidiary of: United Communications Group), 11300 Rockville Pike, Ste 1100, Rockville, MD 20852. TEL 888-287-2223, FAX 301-816-8945, http://www.iaweek.com/iajsp/index.jsp, http://www.ucg.com/argosy.html.

332.6 USA ISSN 1082-2569
I B C'S RATED MONEY FUND REPORT✶. Text in English. 1995. m. looseleaf. USD 1,095 (effective 1999). **Document type:** *Newsletter.* **Description:** Dedicated to improving cash management decisions by focusing on the performance, trends and composition of rated money market mutual funds.
Published by: iMoneyNet Inc. (Subsidiary of: Informa U K Limited), One Research Dr, Westborough, MA 01581. TEL 508-616-6600, FAX 508-616-5511, http://www.ibcdata.com, http://www.imoneynet.com. Ed. Peter G Crane. Pub. Kenneth B Bohlin. R&P Marie Albin. Circ: 130.

332.63 GBR ISSN 1355-8455
I C B SETTLEMENTS REPORT. (International Correspondent Banker) Text in English. q. GBP 245 in United Kingdom; GBP 255 in Europe; USD 460 elsewhere (effective 2001). **Document type:** *Newsletter.* **Description:** Monitor of worldwide transaction standards devoted to international securities clearing and settlement.
Published by: Euromoney Institutional Investor Plc., Nestor House, Playhouse Yard, London, EC4V 5EX, United Kingdom. TEL 44-20-7779-8673, FAX 44-20-7779-8541, meuer@euromoneyplc.com, http://www.euromoney.com. **Dist. in US by:** American Educational Systems, PO Box 246, New York, NY 10024-0246. TEL 800-431-1579, aesbooks@aol.com.

332.6 340 USA ISSN 0258-3690
K9
I C S I D REVIEW: FOREIGN INVESTMENT LAW JOURNAL. Text in English. 1986. s-a. USD 78 (effective 2006). adv. bk.rev. bibl. reprint service avail. from WSH. **Document type:** *Magazine, Academic/Scholarly.* **Description:** Consists of articles, comments, cases, and documents pertinent to investment law and international business transactions.
Indexed: APEL, FLP, IBR, IBZ, ILP, LRI, PAIS.
—BLDSC (4362.091525), IE, Infotrieve, ingenta.
Published by: (International Centre for Settlement of Investment Disputes), The Johns Hopkins University Press, Journals Publishing Division, 2715 N Charles St, Baltimore, MD 21218-4363. TEL 410-516-6984, 410-516-6987, FAX 410-516-6968, jlorder@jhupress.jhu.edu, http://www.press.jhu.edu/journals/icsid_review/index.html. Ed. Antonio R Parra. Adv. contact Monica Queen TEL 410-516-6984. page USD 225; 5.5 x 9. Circ: 440. **Subscr. to:** PO Box 19966, Baltimore, MD 21211. TEL 800-548-1784, jlorder@jhunix.hcf.jhu.edu.

332.6 GBR
I D E A S BULLETIN. (Investment Diversification & Economic Analysis) Text in English. 1986. 3/yr. GBP 45. **Document type:** *Bulletin.*
Published by: Headline Promotions, Wellington House, 6 Ashford Rd, Maidstone, Kent ME14 5BH, United Kingdom. TEL 01-248-1404, FAX 01-353-0612. Ed. R Hill.

I F C DISCUSSION PAPER. see *BUSINESS AND ECONOMICS—International Development And Assistance*

332.6 GBR ISSN 1362-1157
I F R C - LLOYDS BANK PLC FRANCHISING IN BRITAIN REPORT. Variant title: Franchising in Britain Report. Text in English. 1995. q. GBP 20. **Document type:** *Trade.*
Published by: University of Westminster, International Franchise Research Centre, 35 Marylebone Rd, London, NW1 5LS, United Kingdom. TEL 44-171-911-5000, FAX 44-171-911-5059, http://www.wmin.ac.uk/~purdyd/. **Co-sponsor:** Lloyds Bank Plc.

332.6 BEL
I N G BELGIQUE. BULLETIN FINANCIER. Text in French. 1928. m. free. charts; stat.; illus. **Document type:** *Bulletin, Consumer.*
Formerly: Banque Bruxelles Lambert. Bulletin Financier (0771-6273)
Related titles: Dutch ed.
Indexed: ELLIS, PAIS.
Published by: I N G Belgique, Av Marnix 24, Brussels, 1000, Belgium. TEL 32-2-5472111, FAX 32-2-5473844, http://www.ing.be. Circ: 20,000.

332.6 USA
I P O OUTLOOK. Text in English. w. USD 99 (effective 2003). **Document type:** *Newsletter, Trade.*
Media: E-mail.
Published by: 123Jump.com, 407 Lincoln Rd Ste 12D, Miami Beach, FL 33139. TEL 305-673-6339, FAX 305-673-6386, editorial@123jump.com, http://www.123jump.com/.

332.6 USA ISSN 0739-2168
THE I R A REPORTER. (Individual Retirement Account) Text in English. m. looseleaf. USD 115 (effective 2000). charts. yes. 8 p./no. 2 cols./p.; back issues avail.; reprints avail. **Document type:** *Newsletter, Corporate.*
Indexed: BLI.
Published by: Universal Pensions, Inc.,a Bisys Company (Subsidiary of: Bisys), PO Box 979, Brainerd, MN 56401-9965. TEL 800-825-5000, 800-346-3860, FAX 218-825-5010. Ed. Jennifer Olsen.

332.6 USA ISSN 1098-5220
I R UPDATE. Variant title: Investor Relations Update. Text in English. m. USD 175 (effective 2001). **Document type:** *Newsletter.* **Description:** Covers investor relations practitioners who maintain contact with the financial community on behalf of their companies or clients.
Published by: National Investor Relations Institute, 8020 Towers Crescent Dr., # 250, Vienna, VA 22182-6224. TEL 703-506-3570. Ed. Laura F Bernstein. Adv. contact Melissa Jones. Circ: 5,500.

332.6 GBR ISSN 1463-3922
I T DIRECTORY. (Information Technology) Text in English. a.
Related titles: ♦ Supplement to: Futures & O T C World. ISSN 1462-9658.
Published by: Metal Bulletin plc, Park House, 3 Park Terr, Worcester Park, Surrey KT4 7HY, United Kingdom. TEL 44-20-78279977, FAX 44-20-78275290.

332.63 USA
THE I T R REPORT; quarterly trading advisor performance report. Text in English. 1989. q. USD 575 (effective 1999). **Document type:** *Trade.*
Formerly: Stark Report (1094-8139)
Related titles: Online - full text ed.
Published by: International Traders Research, 1020 Prospect St, Ste 405, La Jolla, CA 92037. TEL 619-459-0818, FAX 619-459-0819, info@managedfutures.com, http://www.managedfutures.com. Ed. John F Maginnis. Circ: 250 (controlled).

332.6 HUN
IDEAS FOR JOINT VENTURES. Text in English. 1988. irreg. (2-3/yr.). USD 10 per issue (effective 1992). **Description:** Covers investments in 4 areas: Agricultural & Food industries; Travel & Trade, Service; Industry; and, Real Estate for rent or sale.
Published by: Magyar Kereskedelmi Kamara, Kossuth Lajos ter 608, Budapest, 1055, Hungary. TEL 36-1-1531225, FAX 36-1-1531285. Circ: 2,500.

332.6 USA
IMPACT (WASHINGTON, 1997); the I F C review of private investment in developing countries. Text in English. 1997. q. free. **Document type:** *Journal, Trade.*
Indexed: RRTA.
Published by: International Finance Corporation, 2121 Pennsylvania Ave, N W, Washington, DC 20433. FAX 202-974-4384, Impact@ifc.org, http://www.ifc.org. Ed., R&P Rob Wright. Circ: 20,000 (controlled).

332.6 USA
IN THE VANGUARD; investment views from the Vanguard Group. Text in English. q. free. bk.rev. charts; illus. **Document type:** *Newsletter, Consumer.* **Description:** Informs Vanguard shareholders of investment opportunities and offers general advice.
Published by: Vanguard Group, PO Box 2600, Valley Forge, PA 19482. TEL 610-669-1000, FAX 610-503-1499, online@vanguard.com, http://www.vanguard.com. Ed. Brian S Mattes.

332.6 USA
INCOME DIGEST. Text in English. m. USD 99 domestic; USD 114 foreign (effective 2005). **Document type:** *Newsletter, Consumer.* **Description:** Concentrates on income-oriented investment ideas.
Related titles: E-mail ed.: USD 99 (effective 2001).
Published by: Dick Davis Publishing Inc., P O 8128, Ft. Lauderdale, FL 33310. TEL 954-733-3996, FAX 954-733-8559, http://www.Dickdavis.com, http://www.dickdavis.com. Eds. Denise Saari, Nancy Zambell.

332.6 USA ISSN 0890-0515
INCOME INVESTOR PERSPECTIVES✶. Text in English. 1985. fortn. USD 119. **Description:** Overview of events and trends that have an impact on credit and stock markets.
Published by: Uniplan, Inc., 839 Jefferson St, Ste 200, Milwaukee, WI 53202-3733. TEL 414-529-0675. Ed. Richard Imperiale.

332.6 ITA
INDAGINE CONGIUNTURALE RAPIDA. Text in Italian. m.
Published by: Centro Studi Confindustria, Viale Pasteur 6, Rome, 00144, Italy. TEL 06-5920509, FAX 06-5924819, http://www.confindustria.it.

332.6 USA ISSN 1093-4200
INDEPENDENT ADVISER FOR VANGUARD INVESTORS. Text in English. m. USD 199 (effective 2005). **Document type:** *Newsletter, Trade.*
Published by: Phillips International, Inc., 1201 Seven Locks Rd., Potomac, MD 20854. TEL 301-340-2100, http://www.adviseronline.com. Ed. Dan Wiener. Circ: 50,000 (paid).

332.6 USA
INDEPENDENT THINKER. Text in English. 1985. m. USD 65. **Description:** Covers portfolios of common stocks for long-term gains.
Address: PO Box 40325, Rochester, NY 14604. TEL 716-427-0350. Ed. Rama S Marda.

332.6 IND
INDIA INVESTMENT OPPORTUNITIES. Text in English. 1987. w. INR 4 newsstand/cover.
Published by: Regent Publishers Pvt. Ltd., 1st Fl., Bank Bldg., 17-B Horniman Circle, Fort, Mumbai, Maharashtra 400 023, India. TEL 2664075. Pub. Rusi J Daruwala. Circ: 55,000.

004.16 USA ISSN 1097-2862
HG4515.5
INDIVIDUAL INVESTOR'S GUIDE TO COMPUTERIZED INVESTING. Text in English. 1980. a. USD 40 (effective 2000). **Document type:** *Newsletter.* **Description:** Publishes articles on using computers to assist in investment analysis and valuation. Reviews investment software and information services. Compares similar investment-related products and reviews of investing-related Internet sites.
Formerly (Until 1990): Individual Investor's Microcomputer Resource Guide
Published by: American Association of Individual Investors, 625 N Michigan Ave, Ste 1900, Chicago, IL 60611. TEL 312-280-0170, FAX 312-280-1625, members@aaii.com, http://www.aaii.com. R&P Alyna Johnson. Circ: 51,000 (paid).

▼ *new title* ➤ *refereed* ✶ *unverified* ♦ *full entry avail.*

332.6327 USA ISSN 1079-1841
HG4930
THE INDIVIDUAL INVESTOR'S GUIDE TO LOW-LOAD MUTUAL FUNDS. Text in English. 1980. a. USD 24.95 (effective 2000). charts; stat. **Document type:** *Consumer.* **Description:** Provides ten-year fund data on more than 1000 mutual funds.
Formerly (until 1994): Individual Investor's Guide to No-Load Mutual Funds
Indexed: ATI.
Published by: American Association of Individual Investors, 625 N Michigan Ave, Ste 1900, Chicago, IL 60611. TEL 312-280-0170, FAX 312-280-1625, members@aaii.com, http://www.aaii.com. R&P Anna Chan. Circ: 175,000 (paid).

332.6 IDN
INDONESIAN INVESTMENT HIGHLIGHTS. Text in English. m. IDR 275,000 domestic; USD 225 in ASEAN countries; USD 245 in Asia; USD 290 in Europe; USD 310 in US & Canada (effective 2004). **Document type:** *Trade.* **Description:** Contains a review of current investment which is illustrated by number and value of investment projects both under domestic Investment and Foreign Investment schemes.
Published by: PT Data Consult Inc., Jalan Kramat Raya No. 5-L, Jakarta Pusat, Indonesia. TEL 62-21-3904711, FAX 62-21-3901878, datacon@idola.net.id, http://www.datacon.co.id/.

332.6 CAN ISSN 1700-2001
INDUSTRY CANADA RESEARCH SERIES. Text in English. 1991. irreg. price varies. adv. **Document type:** *Academic/Scholarly.* **Description:** Provides a forum for the analysis of key microeconomic challenges facing the Canadian economy, with the intent of aiding constructive public policy determination in the area.
Formerly (until 1994): Investment Canada Research Series (1188-0988)
Related titles: French ed.: Documents de Recherche d'Industrie Canada. ISSN 1700-201X. 1991.
Published by: (Canada. Industry Canada/Industrie Canada), University of Calgary Press, University of Calgary, Faculty of Education ETD 722, 2500 University Dr N W, Calgary, AB T2N 1N4, Canada. TEL 403-220-7578, FAX 403-282-7269, http://www.ucalgary.ca/ucpress, http://www.uofcpress.com. Ed. Shirley A Onn. R&P Wendy Stephens TEL 403-220-3721. Adv. contact Sharon Boyle. **Subscr. to:** Raincoast Books in Vancouver, 8680 Cambie St, Vancouver, BC V6P 6M9, Canada. TEL 800-663-5714, FAX 800-565-3770.

332.6 PER ISSN 1682-4318
INFORME BURSATIL. Text in Spanish. 1999. m.
Media: Online - full text.
Published by: Bolsa de Valores de Lima, Miro Quesada 265, Casilla Postal 1538, Lima, 100, Peru. TEL 51-1-4260714, FAX 51-1-4267650, http://www.bvl.com.pe/pubdif/publica_informes.htm.

332.6 CAN
THE INFORMED INVESTOR. Text in English. m. CND 89 (effective 1999). **Document type:** *Trade.* **Description:** Provides timely, concise and unbiased opinions on Canadian mutual funds.
Published by: Canadian Analyst Ltd., 21 Squires Ave, Toronto, ON M4B 2R2, Canada. TEL 416-971-6543, 800-348-6661, FAX 416-598-0049.

332.6 CHE
INKASSO-PRAXIS. Text in German. q.
Published by: Verband Schweizerischer Inkasso- und Treuhandinstitut, Seeburgstr. 20, Lucerne, 6002, Switzerland. TEL 041-311055.

332.66021 PRT ISSN 0870-4376
INQUERITO DE CONJUNTURA AO INVESTIMENTO. Text in Portuguese. 1987. 6/m. **Description:** Provides estimates and variations about investments made by companies in the financial sector.
Published by: Instituto Nacional de Estatistica, Ave. Antonio Jose de Almeida 2, Lisbon, 1000-043, Portugal. TEL 351-21-8426100, FAX 351-21-8426380, ine@ine.pt, http://www.ine.pt/.

332.6 GBR ISSN 0969-2436
INSIDE EYE. Text in English. 1993. m. **Document type:** *Newsletter.* **Description:** Aimed at those who work at and/or invest in the Lloyds of London insurance market.
Published by: (Lloyds of London), Centaur Publishing, St Giles House, 50 Poland St, London, W1V 4AX, United Kingdom. TEL 44-161-970-4000, FAX 44-20-7970-4009.

INSIDE M B S & A B S. see *BUSINESS AND ECONOMICS—Banking And Finance*

332.6 USA ISSN 1523-0902
INSIDE PERSONAL FINANCE WITH RIC EDELMAN. Text in English. 1995. m. USD 39.95 (effective 2001). 12 p./no.; back issues avail. **Document type:** *Newsletter.* **Description:** Offers readers the latest information on taxes, insurance, estate planning, retirement and elder care, retirement plans, savings and debt management, and teaching children good money-management practices and habits.
Former titles: Your Money with Ric Edelman; Best of Your Money Matters
Published by: Edelman Financial Services, Inc., 12450 Fair Lakes Circle, Ste 200, Fairfax, VA 22033. http://www.ricedelman.com. Ed., Pub. Ric Edelman. R&P Lisa Korhnak. Circ: 9,500 (paid).

332.67 USA
INSIDER HOLDINGS∗ . Text in English. s-a. USD 250.
Formerly: Spectrum 6: Insider Ownership
Related titles: Magnetic Tape ed.; Online - full text ed.
Published by: C D A Investment Technologies, Inc., 1455 Research Blvd, Rockville, MD 20850-3194. TEL 800-232-6362, FAX 301-590-1329. Circ: 200.

332.678 USA ISSN 0730-2908
THE INSIDERS∗ ; America's most knowledgeable investors. Text in English. 1980. s-m. USD 100. charts; stat. **Document type:** *Newsletter.* **Description:** Summary of insider trading activity over the past 12 months for more than 1000 listed and over-the-counter stocks, with specific buy and sell recommendations.
Published by: Institute for Econometric Research, 6454 NW 5th Way, Fort Lauderdale, FL 33309-6112. TEL 954-421-1000, 800-442-9000, FAX 954-570-8200. Ed. Norman G Fosback. Circ: 7,000.

332.62 USA
INSIGHT. Text in English. q. **Document type:** *Newsletter, Trade.* **Description:** Provides news and information to clients of the J.C. Bradford brokerage firm.
Published by: (J.C. Bradford & Co.), Hammock Publishing, Inc., 3322 W End Ave, Ste 700, Nashville, TN 37203. TEL 615-690-3400, FAX 615-690-3401, info@hammock.com, http://www.hammock.com.

INSOLVENCY BULLETIN. see *BUSINESS AND ECONOMICS*

332.6 USA
INSTITUTIONAL HOLDINGS OF OIL STOCKS. Text in English. 1984. m.
Published by: (Argus Research Group), Vickers Stock Research Corp., 98 Pratt Oval., Glen Cove, NY 11542-1413. TEL 800-645-5043, FAX 516-423-7715.

332.63 GBR
INSTITUTIONAL INVESTMENT REVIEW (YEAR). Text in English. a., latest 2002. GBP 115, USD 195 per issue (effective 2002). **Document type:** *Trade.* **Description:** Provides a unique and invaluable guide to international capital markets and investment opportunities.
Published by: Euromoney Institutional Investor Plc., Nestor House, Playhouse Yard, London, EC4V 5EX, United Kingdom. TEL 44-20-7779-8888, information@euromoneyplc.com, http://www.euromoneyplc.com/. **Dist. by:** Portica, Portica House, 2 Lady Lane Industrial Estate, Hadleigh, Ipswich, Suffolk IP7 6BQ, United Kingdom. TEL 44-1473-825500, FAX 44-870-4430816; **Dist. in the USA by:** Institutional Investor, Inc., 225 Park Ave. S., 7th Fl., New York, NY 10003-1605. TEL 212-224-3800, FAX 212-224-3974.

332.6 USA ISSN 0020-3580
HG4501 CODEN: ITIVAK
INSTITUTIONAL INVESTOR; the premier magazine of professional finance. Text in English. 1967. m. USD 445 combined subscription print & online eds. (effective 2005). adv. bk.rev. charts; illus. Index. back issues avail.; reprint service avail. from PQC. **Document type:** *Magazine, Trade.*
Incorporates (1970-1973): Corporate Financing (0010-8960)
Related titles: CD-ROM ed.; Microform ed.: (from PQC); Online - full text ed.: Institutional Investor Platinum (from EBSCO Publishing, Florida Center for Library Automation, Gale Group, H.W. Wilson, Northern Light Technology, Inc., O C L C Online Computer Library Center, Inc., ProQuest Information & Learning); ♦ International ed.: Institutional Investor International Edition. ISSN 0192-5660.
Indexed: ABIn, ATI, AgeL, B&I, BLI, BPI, BPIA, BusI, CADCAM, EnvAb, KES, ManagCont, PAIS, SSCI, T&II, WBA.
—BLDSC (4523.345000), IE, Infotrieve, ingenta. **CCC.**
Published by: Institutional Investor, Inc. (Subsidiary of: Euromoney Institutional Investor Plc.), 225 Park Ave. S., 7th Fl., New York, NY 10003-1605. TEL 212-224-3800, FAX 212-224-3369, customerservice@iinews.com, http://www.institutionalinvestor.com/default.asp?page=12&pub=62, http://www.iiplatinum.com. Ed. Michael Carroll. adv.: B&W page USD 30,900, color page USD 43,525; bleed. Circ: 101,615 (paid and controlled).

332.6 USA ISSN 0192-5660
HG4501
INSTITUTIONAL INVESTOR INTERNATIONAL EDITION; the magazine for international finance and investment. Text in English. 1976. m. USD 475 (effective 2005). reprint service avail. from PQC. **Document type:** *Magazine, Trade.*
Related titles: CD-ROM ed.; Microform ed.: (from PQC); Online - full text ed.: (from EBSCO Publishing, Factiva, Florida Center for Library Automation, Gale Group, H.W. Wilson, O C L C Online Computer Library Center, Inc., ProQuest Information & Learning); ♦ International ed. of: Institutional Investor. ISSN 0020-3580.
Indexed: B&I, BPI, BPIA, BusI, T&II.
—BLDSC (4523.345100), IE, Infotrieve, ingenta. **CCC.**
Published by: Institutional Investor, Inc. (Subsidiary of: Euromoney Institutional Investor Plc.), 225 Park Ave. S., 7th Fl., New York, NY 10003-1605. TEL 212-224-3800, FAX 212-224-3369, info@iimagazine.com, customerservice@iinews.com, http://www.iimagazine.com. Ed. David Cudaback.

THE INSTITUTIONAL PHARMACY ACQUISITION REPORT. see *PHARMACY AND PHARMACOLOGY*

INSTITUTIONAL REAL ESTATE NEWSLINE. see *REAL ESTATE*

INSTITUTIONAL TRADING TECHNOLOGY. see *BUSINESS AND ECONOMICS—Banking And Finance—Computer Applications*

332 USA ISSN 1525-450X
INSURANCE INVESTOR. Text in English. m. **Document type:** *Trade.*
Media: Online - full content.
Published by: S N L Financial LC, 212 7th St NE, Charlottesvle, VA 22902-5307. TEL 434-977-1600, FAX 434-293-0407, http://www.snl.com/Interactive/InsuranceInvestor/. Eds. Dail Willis, Michael Crittenden, Tim Zawacki. Pub. Alan Zimmerman. Adv. contact Mark Outlaw.

INSURANCE M & A WEEKLY. (Mergers and Acquisitions) see *INSURANCE*

332 368 USA ISSN 1095-3329
INSURANCE MERGERS AND ACQUISITIONS. Text in English. s-m. USD 998 (effective 2004). **Document type:** *Newsletter, Trade.* **Description:** Analyzes and reports on consolidation in the insurance industry.
Media: E-mail. **Related titles:** Fax ed.
Published by: S N L Financial LC, 212 7th St NE, Charlottesvle, VA 22902-5307. TEL 434-977-1600, customerservice@snl.com, http://www.snl.com/products/insurance/ima.asp?PID=IMA.

THE INTELLIGENCE GAP. see *BUSINESS AND ECONOMICS—International Commerce*

INTER-AMERICAN TRADE REPORT. see *LAW—International Law*

INTERACTIVE T V INVESTOR. see *COMMUNICATIONS*

332.6 FRA ISSN 0153-9884
INTERETS PRIVES. Text in French. m. **Document type:** *Consumer.* **Description:** Gives its readers practical information to make better decisions in real estate, finance, and other personal interests.
Published by: Groupe Revue Fiduciaire, 100 rue La Fayette, Paris, Cedex 10 75485, France. TEL 33-1-41835252, FAX 33-1-41835253, http://www.grouperf.com. Ed. Francoise Lagre.

332.6 USA ISSN 1096-312X
INTERFAX. INVESTMENT REPORT. Text in English. w. **Document type:** *Trade.*
Related titles: E-mail ed.; Fax ed.; Online - full content ed.
Contact Dist.: Interfax America, Inc. (Subsidiary of: Interfax Ltd.), 3025 S Parker Rd, Ste 737, Aurora, CO 80014-2925. TEL 852-2537-2262, FAX 852-2537-2264. **Dist. in Germany Austria and Switzerland by:** Interfax Deutschland GmbH, IndustriestraBe 6, Kronberg/Tx 61476 , Germany. TEL 49-61-7361369, FAX 49-61-7361206; **Dist. in Western Europe by:** Interfax Europe Ltd., 1st Fl, 50 Hans Crescent, Knightsbridge, London SW1X 0N, United Kingdom. TEL 44-20-7581-5550, FAX 44-20-7581-4490.

332.6 USA
INTERINVEST REVIEW AND OUTLOOK. Text in English. 1976. m. USD 125. **Document type:** *Newsletter.* **Description:** Discusses international markets, provides a US stock market analysis, a bond market commentary, a discussion concerning precious metals markets, a currency comment, portfolio review, and an international political overview.
Published by: Interinvest Corporation, 84 State St, 7th Fl, Boston, MA 02109-2200. TEL 617-723-7870, FAX 617-723-1966. Ed. Hans Black. Circ: 1,100.

332.2 USA
INTERMARKET GLOBAL CHARTBOOK∗ . Text in English. ceased. m. USD 195 in US & Canada; USD 240 elsewhere. **Document type:** *Trade.* **Description:** Contains over 150 charts featuring a variety of momentum indicators and moving averages. Most charts have a monthly (12 years) and a weekly (5 year) chart. Global index coverage including world stock, bond and commodity indexes. U.S. stock and debt markets, commodities, international stock and bond markets, emerging market indexes, currencies, precious metals, and stock, bond, money market and commodity barometers.
Published by: International Institute for Economic Research, Inc., 1539 S Orange Ave, Sarasota, FL 34239-2035. TEL 804-694-0415, FAX 804-694-0028, infrp@pring.com, http://www.pring.com. Ed. Martin J Pring.

332.6 GBR
THE INTERNATIONAL (LONDON, 1988). Text in English. 1988. m. GBP 75 in Europe; GBP 90 elsewhere. adv. **Document type:** *Trade.* **Description:** Offers investors outside the U.K. and U.S. tips and information on currency-exchange markets, U.K. domestic equities, offshore deposits, bonds, mutual funds, unit trusts, and international equities.
Related titles: Microform ed.: (from PQC).
Published by: Financial Times Business Information, Magazines (Subsidiary of: Financial Times Group), Tabernacle Court, 16-28 Tabernacle St, London, EC2A 4DD, United Kingdom. TEL 44-20-7405-6969, FAX 44-20-7405-5276. Ed. Bruce Wraight. Adv. contact Ian Prickett. Circ: 35,000 (controlled).

332.6 341 USA ISSN 0074-2163
INTERNATIONAL CENTRE FOR SETTLEMENT OF INVESTMENT DISPUTES. ANNUAL REPORT. Text in English. 1966. a. free. **Document type:** *Corporate.*
Related titles: French ed.; Spanish ed.
Published by: International Centre for Settlement of Investment Disputes, 1818 H St, N W, Washington, DC 20433. TEL 202-458-1535, FAX 202-522-2615, TELEX ITT 440098 WORLDBANK. Ed. Antonio R Parra. Circ: 5,000.

332.6 GBR ISSN 1460-9037
INTERNATIONAL COMMODITIES REVIEW (YEAR). Text in English. a., latest 2002, 5th Ed. GBP 115, USD 195 per issue (effective 2002). **Description:** Provides a guide for the commodities market featuring contributions from experts within the field and a comprehensive glossary and index of commodity exchanges.
Published by: Euromoney Institutional Investor Plc., Nestor House, Playhouse Yard, London, EC4V 5EX, United Kingdom. TEL 44-20-7779-8673, FAX 44-20-7779-8541, http://www.euromoney.com.

332.6 GBR ISSN 1360-4953
INTERNATIONAL EQUITY REVIEW. Text in English. 1995. q. GBP 475 domestic; USD 750 elsewhere (effective 2003). adv. charts; mkt.; stat.; tr.lit. back issues avail. **Document type:** *Journal, Trade.* **Description:** Addresses institutional and corporate investors, government privatization agencies and investment banks.
Related titles: E-mail ed.; Online - full text ed.: (from Gale Group).
Published by: Euromoney Institutional Investor Plc., Nestor House, Playhouse Yard, London, EC4V 5EX, United Kingdom. TEL 44-20-7779-8673, FAX 44-20-7779-8541, http://www.euromoney.com. Ed. Michael Hoare TEL 44-20-77798655. Pub. Dennis Millard. Adv. contact Anjali Menon TEL 44-20-77798804. page GBP 4,950; trim 297 x 210. Circ: 7,500. **Subscr. to:** Eclipse, The In-house Fulfillment Bureau, PO Box 18083, London EC4V 5JS, United Kingdom. TEL 44-20-7779-8610, FAX 44-20-7779-8602, CustomerService@euromoneyplc.com.

332.6 GBR ISSN 1475-0376
INTERNATIONAL FINANCIAL ADVISER. Text in English. 1987. m. GBP 75; GBP 125 foreign. stat. **Document type:** *Journal, Trade.* **Description:** Covers industry changes and fund performance for financial advisors whose clients have offshore businesses.
Former titles (until 2001): International Wealth Management (1468-7399); (until 2000): Offshore Financial Review (1352-030X); (until 1991): Offshore Adviser (0953-7937)
Related titles: Microform ed.: (from PQC); Online - full text ed.: (from Gale Group, ProQuest Information & Learning).
Indexed: ABIn, BLI.
Published by: Financial Times Business Information, Magazines (Subsidiary of: Financial Times Group), Tabernacle Court, 16-28 Tabernacle St, London, EC2A 4DD, United Kingdom. TEL 44-20-7405-6969, FAX 44-20-7405-5726. Circ: (controlled).

INTERNATIONAL FINANCIER. see *BUSINESS AND ECONOMICS—Banking And Finance*

THE INTERNATIONAL GUIDE TO TAXATION OF LIFE ASSURANCE AND MUTUAL FUNDS. see *BUSINESS AND ECONOMICS—Public Finance, Taxation*

332.6 GBR ISSN 0953-2714
INTERNATIONAL INSIDER. Text in English. 1973. w. **Document type:** *Trade.*
Published by: International Insider Publishing Company Ltd., I B C Business Publishing (Subsidiary of: I B C Group Plc), Ludgate House, 107 Fleet St, London, EC4A 2AB, United Kingdom. TEL 44-171-535-7314, FAX 44-171-353-0017.

332.6 GBR ISSN 1475-844X
INTERNATIONAL INVESTMENT. Text in English. 1997. m. free to qualified personnel (effective 2005). adv. stat. **Document type:** *Magazine, Trade.* **Description:** Designed to meet the needs of the adviser worldwide, covers offshore investment, offshore products, fund administration, global custody, offshore business centers and company formation.
Related titles: Online - full content ed.
Published by: Incisive Media Plc., Haymarket House, 28-29 Haymarket, London, SW1Y 4RX, United Kingdom. TEL 44-20-74849700, FAX 44-20-79302238, customerservices@incisivemedia.com, http://www.intinv.com/, http://www.incisivemedia.com/. Ed. Dylan Emery TEL 44-20-79684558. Pub. Rod Boulogne TEL 44-20-79684513. adv.: B&W page GBP 3,390, color page GBP 4,950. Circ: 14,907 (controlled).

INTERNATIONAL INVESTOR'S DIRECTORY; sourcebook for international investor. see *BUSINESS AND ECONOMICS—Trade And Industrial Directories*

332.6 USA
INTERNATIONAL JOINT VENTURES. Text in English. 1996. 2 base vols. plus a. updates. looseleaf. USD 433 base vol(s). (effective 2002). **Description:** Covers legal aspects of joint ventures in 37 countries plus the European Union, including alternate business structures, financing, restrictions, drafting of agreements and protections from foreign investors.
Published by: (Center for International Legal Studies AUT), Matthew Bender & Co., Inc. (Subsidiary of: LexisNexis North America), 1275 Broadway, Albany, NY 12204. international@bender.com, http://bender.lexisnexis.com. Ed. Dennis Campbell.

▼ **INTERNATIONAL JOURNAL OF EMERGING MARKETS.** see *BUSINESS AND ECONOMICS—International Commerce*

332.6 USA ISSN 1051-8061
INTERNATIONAL MARKET ALERT✱. Text in English. d. price varies. **Description:** Provides in-depth coverage of developments in the world economy as well as forecasts for foreign exchange and U.S. interest rates.
Related titles: Online - full text ed.: (from Factiva).
—CCC.
Published by: International Reports, Inc. (Subsidiary of: I B C U.S.A.), 11300 Rockville Pike, Ste 1100, Rockville, MD 20852-3035. TELEX 233139 RPTUR.

332.6 USA
INTERNATIONAL MARKET INDEXES. Text in English. m. charts; stat.
Related titles: Series of: Global Index Group.
Published by: Salomon Brothers, Inc., 7 World Trade Center, New York, NY 10048. TEL 212-783-7000.

331.252 GBR ISSN 1470-5680
HD7105.4
INTERNATIONAL PENSION FUNDS AND THEIR ADVISORS. Abbreviated title: IPFA. Text in English. 2000. a. (quarterly updates). GBP 565 (effective 2005). adv. stat. 1000 p./no. 2 cols./p.; **Document type:** *Directory, Trade.* **Description:** Provides details of the major corporate, industry-wide and public authority pension funds, pension fund associations and government departments in over 47 countries world-wide covering Europe, North America and Australasia.
Related titles: CD-ROM ed.
Published by: A P Information Services, Marlborough House, 298 Regents Park Rd, London, N3 2UU, United Kingdom. TEL 44-20-83499988, FAX 44-20-83499797, pfa@ap-info.co.uk, info@apinfo.co.uk, http://www.apinfo.co.uk/ipfa/ipfa.htm, http://www.ap-info.co.uk. Eds. Derek Kelly, Fennel Betson. Pubs. Alan Philipp, Piers Diacre. Adv. contact Ed Gorman. **Co-publisher:** I P E International Publishers Ltd.

332.6 GBR
INTERNATIONAL SECURITIES SERVICE - CAPITAL EVENT FILE. Text in English. w. GBP 1,740; GBP 1,940 foreign. **Document type:** *Trade.* **Description:** Provides a record of capital events on international securities.
Published by: Financial Times Information Ltd., Extel, Fitzroy House, 13-17 Epworth St, London, EC2A 4DL, United Kingdom. TEL 44-20-7825-8000, FAX 44-20-7608-2032, eic@ft.com, http://www.info.ft.com.

332.6 GBR
INTERNATIONAL SECURITIES SERVICE - CODING AND PRICES FILE. Text in English. m. looseleaf. GBP 3,180; GBP 3,400 foreign. **Document type:** *Newsletter.* **Description:** Provides a source of cross-reference coding and month-end pricing data for international securities from 80 stock exchanges around the world.
Published by: Financial Times Information Ltd., Extel, Fitzroy House, 13-17 Epworth St, London, EC2A 4DL, United Kingdom. TEL 44-20-7825-8000, FAX 44-20-7608-2032, eic@ft.com, http://www.info.ft.com.

332.3 GBR
INTERNATIONAL SECURITIES SERVICE - DIVIDEND FILE. Text in English. w. GBP 1,740; GBP 1,940 foreign. **Document type:** *Newsletter.* **Description:** Provides a record of dividend announcements on securities worldwide.
Published by: Financial Times Information Ltd., Extel, Fitzroy House, 13-17 Epworth St, London, EC2A 4DL, United Kingdom. TEL 44-20-7825-8000, FAX 44-20-7608-2032, eic@ft.com, http://www.info.ft.com.

INTERNATIONAL TRADE AND INVESTMENT LETTER; trends in US policies, trade finance, and trading operations. see *BUSINESS AND ECONOMICS—International Commerce*

332.6 USA ISSN 1082-6998
HG181
THE INTERNATIONAL WHO'S WHO OF INSTITUTIONS & MUTUAL FUNDS. Text in English. a. USD 499. **Document type:** *Directory.*
Published by: Carson Publications, 1790 Broadway, New York, NY 10019.

332.6 USA
INTERNET - STOCK WATCH. Text in English. m. USD 199 domestic; USD 214 foreign (effective 2000). **Description:** Investigates hundreds of internet companies each month.
Related titles: E-mail ed.; Fax ed.
Published by: O T C Research Corporation, 300 Chestnut St., Ste. 200, Needham, MA 02492-2427. TEL 781-444-6100. Pub. Geoffrey Eiten.

332.6 IDN ISSN 0535-4900
AP95.I5
INTISARI/DIGEST. Text in Indonesian. 1962. m. adv. **Document type:** *Magazine, Consumer.*
Indexed: EngInd.
Published by: P T Gramedia, Jalan Palmerah Selatan 22-26, Jakarta, 10270, Indonesia. intisari@gramedia-majalah.com, ulj@gramedia-majalah.com, http://www.intisari-online.com, http://www.gramedia.com. Ed. Rudy Badil. Pub. Yayasan Intisari. Adv. contact Panji Indra. Circ: 141,000.

332 KOR
INTRODUCTION TO THE KOREAN SECURITIES MARKET. Text in English. irreg. free. illus.
Formerly: Securities Market in Korea
Published by: Korea Stock Exchange, 33 Yoido dong, Youngdeungpo-gu, Seoul, 150010, Korea, S. TEL 783-2271, FAX 786-0263, TELEX K28384 KOSTEX. Circ: 1,500.

332.6 MEX ISSN 1405-0595
INVERSION Y FINANZAS/FINANCE AND INVESTMENT. Text in Spanish. s-a. USD 20. **Description:** Covers issues about the securities industry.
Published by: Bolsa Mexicana de Valores, S.A. de C.V./Mexican Stock Exchange, Paseo de la Reforma 255, Mexico City, DF 06500, Mexico. TEL 525-726-67-91, FAX 525-591-0534.

332.6 VEN
INVERSIONES, VENEZUELA. Text in Spanish. 1988. m. VEB 3,648, USD 150. adv. back issues avail. **Description:** Informs the investment community, both private and institutional, on trends, opportunities and dangers. Gives rates and information on all capital market instruments, national and international.
Published by: Edipress C.A., Parque Cristal Of. Local 5 Mezz.2, Ave. Francisco de Miranda, Los Palos Grandes,, 1000, Venezuela. TEL 582-285-4833, FAX 582-285-2513. Ed. Arlene Shapiro. adv.: B&W page USD 2,500, color page USD 3,300; trim 288 x 218. Circ: 25,000. **Subscr. to:** Jet Cargo Int'l, Casella M 675, Box 020010, Miami, FL 33102.

332.6 MEX ISSN 1405-0811
INVERSIONISTA MEXICANO. Text in Spanish. 1969. s-m. (22/yr.). USD 465 in US & Canada; USD 495 elsewhere. adv. bk.rev. **Document type:** *Newsletter.* **Description:** Investment business newsletter for company policy makers and money managers.
Published by: Inversionista Mexicano S.A. de C.V., FELIX CUEVAS 301-204, Col Del Valle, Deleg. Benito Juarez, Mexico City, DF 03100, Mexico. TEL 905-524-3131, FAX 905-524-3794. Ed., R&P Hugo Ortiz Dietz. Pub. Ruben Sanchez Crespo. Circ: 3,000.

332.6 ROM ISSN 1224-810X
INVEST ROMANIA MAGAZINE. Text in English. 1996. q. USD 17 domestic; USD 24 in Europe; USD 27 in North America; USD 27 in Asia; USD 5 newsstand/cover (effective 2001). adv. 64 p./no.; back issues avail. **Document type:** *Magazine, Trade.* **Description:** Provides information on the current Romanian business and investment markets, financial and legal systems, and international trade developments.
Published by: Media On S R L Romania, Str. Viesparilor nr. 19, sector 2, Bucharest, Romania. TEL 40-21-2102934, FAX 40-21-2102935, editor@investromania.ro, sales@investromania.ro, http://www.investromania.ro/magazine/index.shtml. R&P Cristian Pavel. Adv. contact Cristian Vilcinscki. color page USD 2,999. Circ: 4,000 (paid); 6,000 (controlled).

332.6 ROM
INVEST ROMANIA NEWSLETTER. Text in English. 2000. m. Distributed free to selected venues.. adv. back issues avail. **Document type:** *Newsletter, Trade.* **Description:** Covers economic news, statistical data and current business opportunities in Romania.
Published by: Media On S R L Romania, Str. Viesparilor nr. 19, sector 2, Bucharest, Romania. TEL 40-21-2102934, FAX 40-21-2102935, sales@investromania.ro, http://www.investromania.ro. Ed. Isabela Tarcomnicu. R&P Isabella Hurezan. Adv. contact Cristian Vilcinscki. color page USD 999. Circ: 3,000 (controlled).

332.6 USA ISSN 0896-4157
INVESTECH MARKET ANALYST. Text in English. 1981. every 3 wks. USD 190 (effective 2000). adv. **Document type:** *Newsletter.* **Description:** Technical and monetary analysis.

B

▼ *new title* ➤ *refereed* ✱ *unverified* ♦ *full entry avail.*

Published by: InvesTech Research, 2472 Birch Glen, Whitefish, MT 59937. TEL 406-862-7777, 800-955-8500, FAX 406-862-7707, http://www.investech.com. Ed. James B Stack. Adv. contact Stacy Tandy.

332.6 USA ISSN 0896-4165
INVESTECH MUTUAL FUND ADVISOR; professional portfolio allocation. Text in English. 1987. every 3 wks. USD 190 (effective 2000). adv. **Document type:** *Newsletter.*
Published by: InvesTech Research, 2472 Birch Glen, Whitefish, MT 59937. TEL 406-862-7777, 800-955-8500, FAX 406-862-7707, http://www.investech.com. Ed. James B Stack. Adv. contact Stacy Tandy.

332.6 PRT ISSN 0870-4805
INVESTIMENTO E TECNOLOGIA. Text in Portuguese. 1980. q.
Indexed: PAIS.
Published by: Instituto do Investimento Estrangeiro, Rua D Francisco Manuel de Melo, no.1, 2 Dto, Lisboa, 1070, Portugal. TEL 21-3812780, FAX 21-3877219.

332.6 GBR
INVESTING FOR GROWTH. Text in English. m. GBP 200 (effective 2001).
Published by: Investors News Ltd. (Subsidiary of: Hemmington Scott Publishing Ltd.), City Innovation Centre, 26-31 Wiskin St, London, EC1R 0JD, United Kingdom. TEL 44-20-7278-7769, FAX 44-20-7278-9808, http://www.hemscott.net/. Ed., Adv. contact Nigel Milton TEL 44-20-7278-7769. Pub. James Ranft.

332 700 USA ISSN 1053-4857
N8670
INVESTING IN ART✶. Text in English. 1990. a.
Published by: Beacon Publishing, 22 Bethany Rd, Monson, MA 01057-1104.

332.6 330.968 ZAF
INVESTING IN KWAZULU NATAL. Text in English. 1994. a. free. maps. **Document type:** *Journal, Trade.* **Description:** Covers aspects of investment in the KwaZulu-Natal province, with the foreign investor in mind.
Published by: KwaNatal Marketing Initiative, PO Box 1105, Durban, KwaZulu-Natal 4000, South Africa. TEL 27-31-9078700, FAX 27-31-9075685, kmi@neptune.infolink.co.za, http://www.lia.ca.za/users/kmi. Ed. J A Griesel. R&P C W Rudman. Circ: 25,000.

332.7 USA
INVESTING NEWS. Text in English. w. **Document type:** *Newsletter, Consumer.* **Description:** Presents basic information on stocks and other investments.
Media: E-mail.
Published by: Bankrate Inc., 11811 US Hwy 1, North Palm Beach, FL 33408. TEL 561-630-2400, FAX 561-625-4540, webmaster@bankrate.com, http://bankrate.process9.com/bankrate/subscribe.html, http://www.bankrate.com.

332.6 RUS
INVESTITSII V ROSSII. Text in Russian. 1993. m. USD 175 in North America (effective 2000).
Indexed: RefZh.
Published by: Sisteminvest, E-37, Moscow, 105037, Russian Federation. TEL 7-095-1656047, FAX 7-095-1660818. Ed. R P Vcherashnii. **Dist. by:** East View Information Services, 3020 Harbor Ln. N., Minneapolis, MN 55447. TEL 763-550-0961, FAX 763-559-2931.

INVESTITSIONNAYA DEYATEL'NOST' V ROSSII: USLOVIYA, FAKTORY, TENDENTSII (YEAR)/INVESTMENT ACTIVITY IN RUSSIA: CONDITIONS, FACTORS AND TENDENCIES. see *BUSINESS AND ECONOMICS—Abstracting, Bibliographies, Statistics*

332.6 RUS
INVESTITSIONNYE PROEKTY PREDPRIYATII ROSSII. Text in Russian. q. USD 125 in North America (effective 2000).
Published by: Izdatel'stvo VIMI, Volokolamskoe shosse 77, Moscow, 123584, Russian Federation. TEL 7-095-4911306, FAX 7-095-4916820. **Dist. by:** East View Information Services, 3020 Harbor Ln. N., Minneapolis, MN 55447. TEL 763-550-0961, FAX 763-559-2931.

332.6 RUS
INVESTITSIONNYI EKSPERT. Text in Russian. m. USD 95 in North America (effective 2000).
Published by: Finvest Ltd., 1-i Khvostov 11a, Moscow, 109180, Russian Federation. TEL 7-095-2383833, FAX 7-095-2303859. Ed. A D Paskal'. **Dist. by:** East View Information Services, 3020 Harbor Ln. N., Minneapolis, MN 55447. TEL 763-550-0961, FAX 763-559-2931.

332.6 DEU
INVESTMENT (AARBERGEN). Text in German. 1999. bi-m. EUR 5.06 newsstand/cover (effective 2003). adv. **Document type:** *Magazine, Consumer.*
Published by: Pulch Publishing GmbH, Kirchstr 9, Aarbergen, 65326, Germany. TEL 49-1805-785728, FAX 49-1805-785723, http://www.investment-on.com. Ed., Pub. Bernd M. Pulch. adv.: color page EUR 6,980; trim 185 x 250. Circ: 149,000 (paid and controlled).

332.6 DEU ISSN 0935-1744
INVESTMENT (BERLIN); Ergaenzbares Handbuch fuer das gesamte Investmentwesen. Text in German. 1970. irreg. looseleaf. **Document type:** *Monographic series, Trade.*
Published by: Erich Schmidt Verlag GmbH & Co. (Berlin), Genthiner Str 30G, Berlin, 10785, Germany. TEL 49-30-250085-0, FAX 49-30-25008521, vertrieb@esvmedien.de, http://www.erich-schmidt-verlag.de.

332.6 JPN
INVESTMENT ADVICE/TOSHI SODAN. Text in Japanese. 1953. m. JPY 7,300.
Formerly: Investment Consultation
Published by: Jitsugyo no Nihon Sha Ltd., 3-9 Ginza 1-chome, Chuo-ku, Tokyo, 104-0061, Japan. TEL 81-3-3562-1967, FAX 81-3-3562-3200, lebo2234@niftyserve.or.jp. Ed. Shinichi Nemoto.

332.6 GBR ISSN 1361-1593
INVESTMENT ADVISER. Text in English. 1995. w. GBP 90 domestic; GBP 140 foreign; GBP 1.80 newsstand/cover. **Document type:** *Trade.*
Related titles: Online - full text ed.: (from Gale Group).
Published by: Financial Times Business Information, Magazines (Subsidiary of: Financial Times Group), Tabernacle Court, 16-28 Tabernacle St, London, EC2A 4DD, United Kingdom. TEL 44-20-7405-6969, FAX 44-20-7405-5276.

332 USA ISSN 1069-1731
INVESTMENT ADVISOR. Text in English. 1985. m. USD 79 domestic; USD 89 in Canada; USD 109 elsewhere; free to qualified personnel (effective 2005). adv. back issues avail. **Document type:** *Newsletter, Trade.*
Former titles (until 1992): Stanger's Investment Advisor (1062-5186); Which incorporated (1985-19??): Financial Product News (1044-9604); (until 1990): The Stanger Register (0747-1548)
Related titles: Online - full text ed.
Published by: Investment Advisor Group (Subsidiary of: Wicks Business Information LLC), 1161 Broad St, Ste 200, Shrewsbury, NJ 07702. TEL 732-389-8700, FAX 732-389-6065, http://www.investmentadvisor.com/. Eds. James L Green, William Glasgall. adv.: B&W page USD 9,000.

332.67 USA
INVESTMENT ADVISORS EQUITY CHARACTERISTICS. Text in English. q. USD 525. **Description:** Portrays the management style of over 500 investment advisors. Portfolios are evaluated in terms of P-E ratio, dividend yield, volatility, market capital of the underlying stockholdings, and commitment to major economic sectors.
Formerly: Investment Advisors Equity Performance
Related titles: Magnetic Tape ed.; Online - full text ed.
Published by: C D A - Cadence, 1455 Research Blvd, Rockville, MD 20850-3194. TEL 301-975-9600, FAX 301-590-1350.

332.6 ZAF ISSN 1029-3523
INVESTMENT ANALYSTS JOURNAL✶ / BELEGGINGSONTLEDERS TYDSKRIF. Text in Afrikaans, English. 1972. s-a. ZAR 30. adv.
Indexed: ISAP.
Published by: Investment Analysts Society of S.A., PO Box 4229, Honeydew, 2040, South Africa. TEL 27-11-7910105, FAX 27-11-7910107, http://www.journals.co.za/ej/ejour_invest.html, http://www.iassa.co.za/. Ed. R W Bethlehem. Circ: 1,000.

INVESTMENT & MARKETING. see *BUSINESS AND ECONOMICS—Marketing And Purchasing*

332.6 PHL
INVESTMENT AND OPERATING COST IN THE PHILIPPINES. Text in English. 1990. a.
Published by: Board of Investments, Ortigas Bldg, Ortigas Ave, PO Box 676, Rizal, Philippines. TEL 63-2-8953666, FAX 63-2-18953521.

332.6 GBR
INVESTMENT AND PENSIONS EUROPE MAGAZINE. Abbreviated title: I P E. Text in English. m. adv. back issues avail. **Document type:** *Trade.* **Description:** Presents investment and pension indicators. Reports daily changes in equities, bonds and currency exchange rates.
Media: Online - full text.
Published by: I P E International Publishers Ltd., 320 Great Guildford House, 30 Great Guildford St, London, SE1 0HS, United Kingdom. TEL 44-20-72610666, FAX 44-20-79283332, info@ipeurope.co.uk, http://www.ipeurope.co.uk. Ed. Fennell Betson. Pub. Piers Diacre. Adv. contact Tony Hay. Circ: 8,800.

INVESTMENT BULLETIN; survey of mortgage commitments on commercial properties. see *INSURANCE*

332.6 GBR ISSN 0951-3736
THE INVESTMENT CALENDAR. Text in English. 1980. a. GBP 13.99 (effective 1999). adv. bk.rev. **Document type:** *Bulletin.* **Description:** Contains vital market information on UK stocks and shares.
Published by: Square Mile Publications Ltd., Park House, 3 Park Terr, Worcester Park, Surrey KT4 7HY, United Kingdom. TEL 44-171-827-9977, FAX 44-181-337-8943. Ed. Emma Davey. R&P, Adv. contact Emma Dawson. Circ: 35,000 (paid).

332.6 USA ISSN 0739-6449
INVESTMENT COLUMN QUARTERLY. Text in English. 1983. q. USD 375 (effective 2000). bk.rev. charts. **Document type:** *Newsletter.* **Description:** Provides investment guidance for long-term investors (not traders).
Published by: N A R Publications, PO Box 233, Barryville, NY 12719. TEL 914-557-8713, FAX 914-557-6770. Ed., R&P Nicholas A Roes.

332.63 CAN
INVESTMENT.COM. Text in English. d. adv. **Document type:** *Consumer.* **Description:** Provides a one-stop global financial community and infomediary that enables individuals to research, track and purchase a broad range of investments.
Media: Online - full text. **Related titles:** ◆ Print ed.: Planning for Profits Magazine. ISSN 1702-1626.
Indexed: CBCARef.
Published by: Global Financial Group Inc., 2844 Bainbridge Ave, PO Box 84028, Burnaby, BC V5A 4T9, Canada. TEL 604-681-7210, 800-370-4412, FAX 604-681-7213, editor@investment.com, http://www.investment.com.

332.6 USA
INVESTMENT COMPANY PORTFOLIOS✶. Text in English. 1973. q. USD 275.
Former titles: Spectrum 2: U S and European Investment Company Portfolios; Spectrum Two: Investment Company Portfolios (0091-6862)
Related titles: Magnetic Tape ed.: 1973; Online - full text ed.: 1973.
Published by: C D A Investment Technologies, Inc., 1455 Research Blvd, Rockville, MD 20850-3194. TEL 800-232-6362, FAX 301-590-1329. Circ: 200.

332.6 USA
INVESTMENT COMPANY STOCK HOLDINGS✶. Text in English. 1973. q. USD 250.
Former titles: Spectrum 1: U S and European Investment Company Stock Holdings Survey; Spectrum One: Stock Holdings Survey (0091-6854)
Related titles: Magnetic Tape ed.: 1973; Online - full text ed.: 1973.
Published by: C D A Investment Technologies, Inc., 1455 Research Blvd, Rockville, MD 20850-3194. TEL 800-232-6362, FAX 301-590-1329. Circ: 275.

332.6 USA ISSN 0021-0080
HG4501
INVESTMENT DEALERS' DIGEST; news magazine of the financial community. Text in English. 1935. w. USD 1,095 (effective 2005). adv. illus. Index. reprints avail. **Document type:** *Magazine, Trade.*
Formerly (until 1997): I D D
Related titles: Online - full text ed.: (from bigchalk, EBSCO Publishing, Florida Center for Library Automation, Gale Group, LexisNexis, O C L C Online Computer Library Center, Inc., ProQuest Information & Learning).
Indexed: ABIn, B&I, PAIS, PROMT.
—BLDSC (4560.950000), IE, ingenta. **CCC.**
Published by: Source Media, Inc., One State St Plaza, 27th Fl, New York, NY 10004. TEL 212-803-6077, 800-221-1809, FAX 212-747-1154, custserv@sourcemedia.com, http://www.iddmagazine.com, http://www.sourcemedia.com. Ed. Ronald Cooper TEL 212-803-8722. adv.: B&W page USD 9,000. Circ: 50,000 (paid).

332.6 JPN
INVESTMENT ECONOMICS/TOSHI KEIZAI. Text in Japanese. 1933. fortn. adv.
Published by: Toshi-Keizai-Sha, 2-14-9 Nihonbashi, Chuo-ku, Tokyo, 103-0027, Japan. Ed. Koichi Takei. Circ: 35,000.

332.6 CAN ISSN 0840-9137
INVESTMENT EXECUTIVE; Canadian's newspaper for financial advisors. Text in English. 1989. m. CND 60 (effective 2003). adv. bk.rev. **Description:** For stockbrokers, mutual fund salespeople, financial advisors and investment industry executives.
Related titles: Online - full text ed.
Indexed: CBCARef.
Address: 90 Richmond St E, Ste 400, Toronto, ON M5C 1P1, Canada. TEL 416-366-4200, FAX 416-366-7846, adsales@iemoney.com, http://www.investmentexecutive.com/client/en/accueil.asp. Ed. Tessa Wilmott. Pub. Barbara Hyland. R&P, Adv. contact Ozy Camacho. Circ: 30,373.

332.6 GBR ISSN 0954-2485
HG5436
INVESTMENT FUND INDEX - INVESTMENT TRUSTS. Text in English. 1988. s-a. GBP 15 (effective 1998). **Document type:** *Trade.*
Published by: (Association of Investment Trust Companies), Centaur Publishing, St Giles House, 50 Poland St, London, W1V 4AX, United Kingdom. TEL 44—20-7970-4000, FAX 44-20-7970-4009. Circ: 10,000.

332.6 USA ISSN 0736-2919
INVESTMENT HORIZONS✶. Text in English. 1983. s-m. USD 250. adv. **Document type:** *Newsletter.* **Description:** Provides information for investing in small emerging growth stocks.

Published by: Investment Information Services, Inc., 10 S Riverside Plz, Ste 1520, Chicago, IL 60606-3802. TEL 312-649-6940, 800-326-6941. Ed. Gerald W Perritt. Adv. contact Michael Corbett. Circ: 2,000.

332 GBR ISSN 0950-6195
INVESTMENT INTERNATIONAL. Text in English. 1986. m. GBP 50 (effective 1998). **Description:** Provides investment information for people living outside the U.K. and seeks to make them aware of the services available to them.
Related titles: Online - full text ed.: (from Gale Group).
—CCC.
Published by: Charterhouse Communications Group Ltd., Arnold House, 36-41 Holywell Ln, London, EC2A 3ET, United Kingdom. TEL 44-20-7827-5454. Ed. Andrew Coyne. Circ: 20,000.

332.6 346.052 USA ISSN 1075-4512
KF1066.A3
THE INVESTMENT LAWYER; covering legal and regulatory issues of asset management. Text in English. 1994. m. USD 375 (effective 2004). **Document type:** *Journal.* **Description:** This is a legal publication devoted exclusively to investment management.
Related titles: Online - full text ed.: (from EBSCO Publishing, Florida Center for Library Automation, Gale Group, ProQuest Information & Learning).
Indexed: ABIn.
—CCC.
Published by: Aspen Publishers, Inc. (Subsidiary of: Wolters Kluwer N.V.), 111Eighth Ave., 7th Fl, New York, NY 10011. TEL 212-771-0600, FAX 212-771-0885, http://www.aspenpublishers.com. Ed. Stephanie Djinis.

INVESTMENT MANAGEMENT. see *BUSINESS AND ECONOMICS—Banking And Finance*

332.6 UKR ISSN 1810-4967
▼ ➤ **INVESTMENT MANAGEMENT & FINANCIAL INNOVATIONS.** Text in English, Ukrainian. 2004. q. USD 300 foreign (effective 2005). adv. back issues avail. **Document type:** *Journal, Academic/Scholarly.* **Description:** Exposes problems in investment management and financial innovations and finds the solutions of their improvement with the further dissemination of research results, by enabling both renowned and emerging researchers and scholars to present their findings to a global audience of peers.
Related titles: CD-ROM ed.: ISSN 1813-4998; Online - full content ed.: ISSN 1812-9358; Online - full text ed.: (from EBSCO Publishing).
Published by: Dilovi Perspektyvy, Karbysheva lane 138, office 4, Sumy, 40018, Ukraine. TEL 380-542-345455, FAX 380-542-345455, head@businessperspectives.sumy.ua, http://www.businessperspectives.org. Ed. Serhiy Kozmenko. Adv. contact Natalia Ivakhnenko. B&W page USD 200.

332.6 USA ISSN 0896-8500
INVESTMENT MANAGEMENT WEEKLY. Text in English. 1988. w. USD 1,750 domestic; USD 1,850 foreign (effective 2005). adv. back issues avail. **Document type:** *Newsletter, Consumer.* **Description:** Reports on the activities of institutional investors, primarily U.S. and Canadian plan sponsors, and the investment management business worldwide.
Related titles: Online - full text ed.: (from bigchalk, EBSCO Publishing, Florida Center for Library Automation, Gale Group, LexisNexis, ProQuest Information & Learning).
Indexed: ABIn, ATI, B&I.
—CCC.
Published by: Source Media, Inc., One State St Plaza, 27th Fl, New York, NY 10004. TEL 212-803-6077, 800-221-1809, FAX 212-747-1154, custserv@sourcemedia.com, http://www.imweekly.com, http://www.sourcemedia.com. Pub. John Toth TEL 212-803-6565. adv.: B&W page USD 1,700, color page USD 2,895. Circ: 1,200 (paid).

332.6 330 KEN
INVESTMENT NEWS. Text in English. 1985. w. USD 460. adv. bk.rev.
Published by: New Press Publications, PO Box 8454, Nairobi, Kenya. Ed. Muli Wa Kyendo. Circ: 18,580.

332.6 USA ISSN 1098-1837
INVESTMENT NEWS. Text in English. 1997. bi-w. USD 29 domestic; USD 103 in Canada & Mexico; USD 183 elsewhere (effective 2003). charts; illus.; stat. **Document type:** *Trade.* **Description:** Provides news vital to the businesses of financial advisors including news affecting their clients' investments and reports about the growing financial planning industry and the companies that serve it.
Related titles: Online - full text ed.: (from Florida Center for Library Automation, Gale Group, O C L C Online Computer Library Center, Inc.).
Published by: Crain Communications, Inc., 711 Third Ave, New York, NY 10017-4036. TEL 212-210-0280, http://www.investmentnews.com/, http://www.crain.com. Ed. James Pavia. Pub. William Bisson. Circ: 60,426 (paid).

332.6 GBR ISSN 0262-4257
INVESTMENT OPPORTUNITIES✶; an independent monthly guide to investment alternatives. Text in English. 1980. m. GBP 40.
Published by: Leasing Report Ltd., 73 Mill Ln, London, NW6, United Kingdom.

INVESTMENT PLANNING AND PROJECT EVALUATION BIBLIOGRAPHY. see *BIBLIOGRAPHIES*

338.91 CHE
INVESTMENT POLICY REVIEW SERIES. Text in English. irreg. back issues avail. **Document type:** *Monographic series, Trade.* **Description:** Aims to familiarize government and international private sectors with an individuals country's investment environment and policies.
Published by: United Nations Conference on Trade and Development, 8-14 Avenue de la Paix, Geneva 10, 1211, Switzerland. TEL 41-22-9174924, FAX 41-22-9070195, info@unctad.org, http://www.unctad.org.

332.96 USA ISSN 0883-1661
INVESTMENT PORTFOLIO GUIDE. Text in English. m. USD 235. back issues avail. **Description:** Includes economic and market outlook, interest rate forecasts, bond valuation analysis, technical trends, industry ratings and analysis.
Related titles: Online - full text ed.
Published by: Argus Research, 61 Broadway Suite 1700, New York, NY 10006. TEL 212-425-7500, FAX 212-809-2975. Ed. Matthew Kovary.

332.6 AUS ISSN 0725-3850
INVESTMENT PROJECTS IN THE HUNTER REGION. Text in English. 1980. q. stat. back issues avail.
Published by: Hunter Valley Research Foundation, DC, PO Box 302, Hamilton, NSW 2303, Australia. TEL 61-49-69-4566, FAX 61-49-614981, oukhvrf@cc.newcastle.edu.au, http://www.hvrf.com.au. Circ: 750.

INVESTMENT PROPERTY. see *REAL ESTATE*

332.6 USA ISSN 0021-0110
INVESTMENT QUALITY TRENDS; for the enlightened investor. Text in English. 1966. bi-m. looseleaf. USD 310 (effective 2005). adv. bk.rev. charts; stat. 12 p./no.; back issues avail. **Document type:** *Newsletter, Consumer.*
Related titles: Online - full text ed.: USD 265 (effective 2004).
Published by: Investment Quality Trends, INc., 6450 Lusk Blvd., Ste. D104, San Diego, CA 92121-2762. TEL 619-459-3818, FAX 619-459-3819, IQTrends@aol.com, http://www.IQTrends.com. Pub. Geraldine Weiss. Circ: 5,000.

332.6 USA ISSN 1062-4678
THE INVESTMENT REPORTER. Text in English. 1989. m. USD 38. adv. bk.rev. **Document type:** *Newspaper.* **Description:** Contains editorial material on mid- and small-captstocks, for stockbrokers, analysts, fund managers, corporate executives and individual investors.
Published by: Share Holder Communication Systems, PO Box 8049-300, Newport Beach, CA 92658. TEL 949-335-0087, FAX 949-335-0100, investrptr@aol.com. Ed. Peggy Powell. Pub., R&P, Adv. contact John Robbins. Circ: 50,000 (paid and controlled).

332.6 CAN ISSN 0700-5539
INVESTMENT REPORTER. Text in English. 1941. w. looseleaf. CND 279. charts; stat. index. **Description:** Stock market news and recommendations.
Incorporates (in 1990): Personal Wealth Reporter; (in 1989): Low-Priced Stock Analyst
Related titles: Supplement(s): Investment Planning Guide.
Indexed: PROMT.
Published by: M P L Communications Inc., 133 Richmond St W, Ste 700, Toronto, ON M5H 3M8, Canada. TEL 416-869-1177, FAX 416-869-0456. Ed. James Kedzierski.

332.6 USA
INVESTMENT STRATEGY. Text in English. 1970. m. free to qualified personnel.
Published by: Crosby-Ware Trusts, 201 Squire Row, San Antonio, TX 78213. TEL 512-344-7211. Ed. Stephen H Crosby Jr. Circ: 300.

332.64 USA
INVESTMENT STRATEGY QUARTERLY. Text in English. q. **Document type:** *Newsletter.* **Description:** Contains timely and educational investment information.
Media: Online - full text.
Published by: Green Mountain Asset Management Corp., 139 Bank St., Bulrington, VT 05401. bobbose@stockresearch.com, http://www.stockresearch.com/. Ed. Bob Bose.

332.6 GBR
INVESTMENT TRUST HANDBOOK. Text in English. s-a. **Document type:** *Trade.* **Description:** Provides financial information on all investment trusts quoted on the London Stock Exchange.
Published by: Financial Times Information Ltd., Extel, Fitzroy House, 13-17 Epworth St, London, EC2A 4DL, United Kingdom. TEL 44-20-7608-2032, FAX 44-20-7608-2032, eic@ft.com, http://www.info.ft.com.

332.6 GBR ISSN 0959-9568
INVESTMENT TRUSTS. Text in English. 1986. q. GBP 14 domestic; GBP 24 in Europe; GBP 30 elsewhere (effective 2004). adv. index. back issues avail. **Document type:** *Consumer.* **Description:** Contains comprehensive information about UK investment, or closed-end, trusts.
Published by: Flaxdale Printers Ltd., PO Box 326, Sittingbourne, Kent ME9 8FB, United Kingdom. TEL 44-179-5414894, FAX 44-179-5414555, http://www.investment-trusts-magazine.co.uk/index.html. Ed., Pub. John Davis. Adv. contact Rupert Simmons TEL 44-1435-813481. B&W page GBP 1,450, color page GBP 1,750; trim 182 x 264. Circ: 25,000.

332.6 GBR ISSN 1469-1876
INVESTMENT WEEK. Text in English. 1994. w. free to qualified personnel (effective 2005). **Document type:** *Newspaper, Trade.* **Description:** Provides news, market sector coverage, stats and product information that is authoritative, objective and independent.
Related titles: Online - full content ed.
Published by: Incisive Media Plc., Haymarket House, 28-29 Haymarket, London, SW1Y 4RX, United Kingdom. TEL 44-20-74849700, FAX 44-20-79302238, customerservices@incisivemedia.com, http://www.investmentweek.co.uk/, http://www.incisivemedia.com/. Eds. Mark Colegate TEL 44-20-79684565, Lawrence Gosling TEL 44-20-79684569. Pub. Nicky Cooper TEL 44-20-79684522. Adv. contact Ben Bonney-James TEL 44-20-79684523.

INVESTMENTS IN EMERGING MARKETS. see *FOOD AND FOOD INDUSTRIES*

332.6 GBR ISSN 1358-6440
THE INVESTOR✶. Text in English. 1995. m. GBP 35; GBP 2.95 newsstand/cover. adv. **Document type:** *Magazine, Trade.*
—CCC.
Published by: P B I Publishing Ltd., 12-18 Paul St, London, EC2A 4NX, United Kingdom. TEL 44-171-377-9977, FAX 44-171-377-8099, pbi@ndirect.co.uk. Ed. Keiron Root. Pub. Geoff Gamble. Adv. contact Ramesh Sharma. **Dist. by:** Seymour Distribution Ltd, 86 Newman St, London W1T 3EX, United Kingdom. FAX 44-207-396-8002, enquiries@seymour.co.uk.

332.6 THA ISSN 0021-0153
INVESTOR. Text in English; Summaries in Thai. 1968. m. THB 95, USD 6.50. adv. bk.rev. bibl.; charts; illus.; stat. index.
Supersedes: Investment Newsletter
Indexed: PAIS.
Address: Pansak Bldg 4th Fl, 138-1 Petchburi Rd, Bangkok, 10400, Thailand. Ed. Tos Patumsen.

332.96 IND
THE INVESTOR. Text in English. a. INR 25 per issue.
Published by: (Securities Analysis Pvt. Ltd.), Mid-Day Publications Ltd., 156 D.J. Dadajee Rd., Tardeo, Mumbai, Maharashtra 400 034, India. TEL 4942586, FAX 3054536. Ed. Rajasjekar Iyer.

332.62 659.2 GBR ISSN 0958-6679
HG4538
INVESTOR RELATIONS MAGAZINE. Variant title: I R - Investor Relations. Text in English. 1993. m. (11/yr.). free (effective 2005). adv. charts; illus.; mkt.; stat.; tr.lit. back issues avail. **Document type:** *Magazine, Trade.* **Description:** Covers investor relations for investor relations officers and financial communicators.
Related titles: Online - full text ed.
Published by: Cross Border Publishing Ltd., 111-113 Great Titchfield St, London, W1P 7FQ, United Kingdom. TEL 44-20-76373579, FAX 44-20-76373594, mail@irmag.com, http://www.irmag.com. Ed. Janet Dignan. Pub. Ian Richman. R&P Rebecca Bawcutt. Adv. contacts Andrew Thomas, Ian Richman. Circ: 10,000.

659.2 332.6 USA ISSN 1535-5802
INVESTOR RELATIONS NEWSLETTER. Text in English. 1964. m. looseleaf. USD 295 in US & Canada; USD 345 elsewhere (effective 2005). charts; illus. index. **Document type:** *Newsletter, Consumer.* **Description:** Provides practical hands-on strategy and tactics for the investor relations professional.
Related titles: Online - full text ed.
Published by: Kennedy Information Inc., One Phoenix Mill Ln., 5th Fl., Peterborough, NH 03458. TEL 603-924-1006, FAX 603-924-4034, ir-editor@kennedyinfo.com, http://www.kennedyinfo.com/ir/irn.html. Ed. Gerald Murray. Pub. David Beck.

332.67 USA
INVESTOR RESPONSIBILITY RESEARCH CENTER. ANNUAL REPORT. Text in English. 1973. a. free. **Document type:** *Corporate.*
Published by: Investor Responsibility Research Center, Inc., 1350 Connecticut Ave, N W, Ste 700, Washington, DC 20036. TEL 202-833-0700, FAX 202-833-3555, http://www.irrc.org. Ed. Scott Fenn. R&P Sharon Easley.

332.6 USA ISSN 1061-2890
HF5001
INVESTOR'S BUSINESS DAILY. Text in English. 1984. d. (Mon.-Fri.). USD 295 (effective 2005). adv. illus. reprints avail. **Document type:** *Newspaper, Trade.* **Description:** For the upper echelon of corporate America. Covers business and finance and provides decision-making information.
Formerly (until 1991): Investor's Daily (0743-9423)
Related titles: Online - full text ed.: ISSN 1553-6580 (from Gale Group, LexisNexis, Newsbank, Inc.).
—CCC.
Published by: Investor's Business Daily, Inc., 12655 Beatrice St, Los Angeles, CA 90066. TEL 310-448-6700, custcare@investors.com, http://www.investors.com. Ed. Wesley Mann. adv.: page USD 28,267.78. Circ: 264,699. Wire service: AP, RN.

332.6 JAM
THE INVESTOR'S CHOICE. Text in English. 1989. m. JMD 100, USD 2.50 per issue. adv.
Published by: Financial & Economic Resources Ltd., 12 Merrick Ave, Kingston, 10, Jamaica. TEL 809-929-2993, FAX 809-968-1188. Ed. John Jackson. Adv. contact Paul Anderson. Circ: 10,000.

332.6 GBR ISSN 0261-3115
HG4502
INVESTORS CHRONICLE (LONDON, 1860). Text in English. 1860. w. GBP 125 domestic; GBP 4.95 newsstand/cover domestic; GBP 164 in Europe; GBP 195 elsewhere (effective 2003). adv. bk.rev. charts; illus.; stat. index. reprints avail. **Document type:** *Trade.* **Description:** Provides private and professional investors with analysis and comment on the U.K. investment scene.
Formerly: Investors Chronicle and Stock Exchange Gazette (0021-0161); Incorporates: Stock Exchange Gazette; Financial World
Related titles: Microfilm ed.: (from RPI); Microform ed.: (from PQC); Online - full text ed.: (from Gale Group, LexisNexis, O C L C Online Computer Library Center, Inc., ProQuest Information & Learning).
Indexed: ABIn, B&I, BLI, BldManAb, IndBusRep, PAIS, RICS, WBA.
—BLDSC (4562.520000), IE, Infotrieve.
Published by: Financial Times Business Ltd. (Subsidiary of: Financial Times Group), Maple House, 149 Tottenham Court Rd, London, W1P 9LL, United Kingdom. TEL 44-20-7896-2525, FAX 44-20-7896-2054, TELEX 296926 BUSINF G, ceri.jones@ft.com, http://www.investorschronicle.co.uk, http://www.ft.com. Ed. Matthew Vincent. Circ: 44,770. **Subscr. to:** PO Box 387, Haywards Heath, W Sussex RH16 3GS, United Kingdom. **Dist. by:** Seymour Distribution Ltd, 86 Newman St, London W1T 3EX, United Kingdom. TEL 44-20-73968000, FAX 44-20-73968002.

332.6 USA
INVESTOR'S DAILY✶ ; America's business newspaper. Text in English. 1984. d. USD 94. adv. index. **Document type:** *Newspaper.*
Related titles: Microfiche ed.: 1984; Online - full text ed.: 1984.
Indexed: TelAb, Telegen.
Published by: Investor's Business Daily, Inc., 92057, Los Angeles, CA 90009-2057. Ed. Stephen P Fox. Circ: 110,000.

332.6 USA ISSN 1057-6711
INVESTOR'S DIGEST✶ . Text in English. 1989. m. USD 60. charts; stat. back issues avail. **Document type:** *Newsletter.* **Description:** A digest of stock market advice and recommendations condensed from hundreds of Wall Street analysts.
Related titles: Online - full text ed.
Indexed: CPerI.
Published by: Institute for Econometric Research, 6454 NW 5th Way, Fort Lauderdale, FL 33309-6112. TEL 954-421-1000, 800-442-9000, FAX 954-570-8200. Ed. Norman G Fosback. Circ: 80,000 (paid).

332.6 CAN ISSN 0047-1356
INVESTOR'S DIGEST OF CANADA. Text in English. 1969. s-m. CND 137. adv. **Document type:** *Trade.* **Description:** Covers current digests and news on the stock market.
Indexed: CBCARef, CBPI, CPerI.
Published by: M P L Communications Inc., 133 Richmond St W, Ste 700, Toronto, ON M5H 3M8, Canada. TEL 416-869-1177, FAX 416-869-0456. Ed. Joseph Chrysdale. Circ: 32,000.

332.6 ZAF ISSN 0250-1732
HG5851.A2
THE INVESTORS' GUIDE. Text in English. 1971. 4/yr., latest no.100. ZAR 70. adv. Website rev. 550 p./no.; back issues avail. **Document type:** *Magazine, Corporate.* **Description:** Provides investors and business people with relevant, current data on every company listed on the Johannesburg stock exchange.
Former titles: Facts Investors Guide; Investor's Guide
Related titles: CD-ROM ed.: USD 126 (effective 2001) (from National Information Services Corp. (N I S C)); Online - full text ed.: (from National Information Services Corp. (N I S C)).
Published by: The Investors' Group (Pty) Ltd., PO Box 62000, Marshalltown, 2107, South Africa. TEL 27-11-836-9321, FAX 27-11-836-9328, tig@pixie.co.za, http://www.investorsguide.co.za. Ed. Shanee Smart. Adv. contact T Kuiper. B&W page ZAR 1,840, color page ZAR 2,620; trim 205 x 270. Circ: 4,300.

332.6 CAN
INVESTOR'S GUIDE. Text in English. 1990. a. adv.
Published by: Financial Post Datagroup, 300-1450 Don Mills Rd, Don Mills, ON M3B 3R5, Canada. TEL 416-350-6176, FAX 416-350-6171. Ed. Wayne Gooding.

332.6 USA
THE INVESTOR'S GUIDE TO CLOSED-END FUNDS. Text in English. m. looseleaf. USD 475 (effective 2000). charts. **Description:** Offers comprehensive timely information on closed-end funds, including editor's recommendations.
Published by: Thomas J. Herzfeld Advisors, Inc., PO Box 161465, Miami, FL 33116. TEL 305-271-1900, FAX 305-270-7040, http://www.herzfeld.com. Ed. Thomas J Herzfeld.

332.6 HUN ISSN 0865-6746
INVESTORS' GUIDE TO HUNGARY. Text in English, German. 1989. a. USD 30 (effective 1992).
Published by: Magyar Kereskedelmi Kamara, Kossuth Lajos ter 608, Budapest, 1055, Hungary. TEL 36-1-153333, FAX 36-1-1531285.

332.6 USA
INVESTOR'S GUIDE TO LOW-COST MUTUAL FUNDS. Text in English. 1976. a. USD 15 per issue. **Document type:** *Directory.* **Description:** Provides educational information on the use of mutual funds to achieve financial goals, and performance listings of low and no-load funds.
Published by: Mutual Fund Education Alliance, 100 NW Englewood Rd, Ste 130, Box 419263, Kansas City, MO 64118. TEL 816-464-2213, FAX 816-454-9322, mfeamail@mfea.com, http://www.mfea.com. Ed., R&P Michelle Smith.

332.6 NPL
INVESTORS' GUIDE TO NEPAL. Text in English. 1975. irreg. adv.
Published by: Industrial Services Centre, Documentation & Publication Branch, Balaju Industrial Districts, Balaju, Kathmandu, Nepal. Circ: 3,000.

332.6 SGP ISSN 0129-5276
HG5750.6.S5
INVESTOR'S GUIDE TO SINGAPORE. Text in English. 1973. a. SGD 32 per issue. **Description:** Explains in detail the investment requirements and opportunities in Singapore.
Formerly: Investor's Guide to the Economic Climate of Singapore
Published by: Singapore International Chamber of Commerce, John Hancock Tower, 6 Raffles Quay 10-01, Singapore, 048580, Singapore. TEL 65-2241255, FAX 65-2242785, singicc@asianconnect.com, http://www.sicc.com.sg. Circ: 4,500.

332.63 USA
INVESTORS INTELLIGENCE. Text in English. 1957. fortn. USD 184 (effective 2001). **Document type:** *Newsletter, Trade.*
Published by: Chartcraft, Inc., 30 Church St, Box 2046, New Rochelle, NY 10801. TEL 914-632-0422, FAX 914-632-0335, usinfo@chartcraft.com, http://www.chartcraft.com. Ed. Michael Burke.

346.092 332.6 GBR
INVESTORS' JOURNAL OF LEGISLATIVE IMPACT✶ . Text in English. 1997. q. GBP 495 (effective 1999). adv. back issues avail. **Document type:** *Journal, Trade.*
Related titles: CD-ROM ed.; E-mail ed.
Published by: World Markets Research Centre, Cardinal Tower, 12 Farringdon Rd, London, EC1M 3NN, United Kingdom. TEL 44-20-74525000, FAX 44-20-74525035, info@wmrc.com, http://www.wmrc.com. Ed., Pub., R&P, Adv. contact Toby Curthoys. Circ: 3,500.

332.6 USA
INVESTORS UPDATE; real news report. Text in English. 1956. q. USD 25. **Document type:** *Newsletter.* **Description:** Reviews of precious metals and economic - financial - political commentary.
Published by: (California Numismatic Investments, Inc.), C N I Newsletter, 525 W Manchester Blvd, Inglewood, CA 90301. TEL 213-674-3330, FAX 213-330-3766. Ed. Richard Schwary. Circ: 12,000.

332.6 ECU
INVIERTA EN EL ECUADOR. Text in Spanish. a. free.
Related titles: French ed.; German ed.; English ed.: Invest in Ecuador.
Published by: Banco Central del Ecuador, Avenida 10 de Agosto y Briceno, Quito, Ecuador. TEL 593-2-2580158, uweb@uio.bce.fin.ec, http://www.bce.fin.ec. Circ: 5,000.

332.6 POL ISSN 1641-5280
INWESTOR FINANSOWY. Text in Polish. 2000. m. free (effective 2005).
Published by: Warszawska Grupa Inwestycyjna, Dom Maklerski SA, ul Chlodna 51, 28 pietro, Warsaw, 00867, Poland. TEL 48-22-5283100, FAX 48-22-5283105, info@wgi.pl, http://www.wgi.pl.

332.63 USA ISSN 1535-5810
IRA, 401(K), T S A & PENSION DISTRIBUTION ADVISOR. Variant title: Distribution Advisor. Text in English. 2001. m. USD 195 to individuals; USD 20 newsstand/cover (effective 2002). **Document type:** *Newsletter.* **Description:** Delivers timesly, comprehensive analysis of distribution issues related to pension plans.
Related titles: Online - full text ed.: (from Florida Center for Library Automation, Gale Group).
Published by: Aspen Publishers, Inc. (Subsidiary of: Wolters Kluwer N.V.), 111Eighth Ave., 7th Fl, New York, NY 10011. TEL 212-771-0600, FAX 212-771-0885, http://www.aspenpublishers.com.

IREIZINE. see *REAL ESTATE*

IRELAND. CENTRAL STATISTICS OFFICE. CAPITAL ASSETS IN INDUSTRY. see *BUSINESS AND ECONOMICS—Abstracting, Bibliographies, Statistics*

IRELAND. CENTRAL STATISTICS OFFICE. INDUSTRIAL STOCKS. see *BUSINESS AND ECONOMICS—Abstracting, Bibliographies, Statistics*

332.6 IRL
IRISH STOCK MARKET ANNUAL. Text in English. 1987. a. EUR 21.99, GBP 15.99 (effective 2005). adv. back issues avail. **Document type:** *Corporate.*
Related titles: Diskette ed.
Published by: Private Research Ltd., Coliemore House, Coliemore Rd., Dalkey, Co. Dublin, Ireland. TEL 353-1-2848911, FAX 353-1-2048177, stockmarket@eircom.net, info@privateresearch.ie, http://www.privateresearch.ie. Adv. contact Mark O'Neill. B&W page EUR 1,644, color page EUR 1,771. Circ: 7,000.

332.6 USA ISSN 1080-3912
HG4921
THE IRWIN INVESTOR'S HANDBOOK. Text in English. 1982. a. USD 25.
Former titles (until 1994): Business One Investor's Handbook (1062-0028); (until 1991): Dow Jones Investor's Handbook (0748-2140)
Indexed: ATI.
Published by: Irwin Professional Publishing, 1333 Burr Ridge Pkwy., Burr Ridge, IL 60521-6489. Ed. Phyllis Pierce.

ISRAEL HIGH-TECH & INVESTMENT REPORT. see *TECHNOLOGY: COMPREHENSIVE WORKS*

332.6 GBR
IT'S OUR BUSINESS; news magazine of the Employee Share Ownership Centre. Text in English. 1980. m. USD 250 to members (effective 2000). adv. back issues avail. **Document type:** *Newsletter.* **Description:** Covers news items, including IPOs, MBOs, corporate flotation news, and ESOP (Employee Share/Stock Ownership Plans) transactions, both in the UK and worldwide.
Related titles: E-mail ed.
Published by: ESOP Centre Ltd., 2 Ridgmount St, London, WC1E 7AA, United Kingdom. TEL 44-20-7436-9936, FAX 44-20-7580-0016, esop@mhcc.co.uk. Ed., Adv. contact Fred Hackworth. B&W page GBP 750.

332.6 332 AUS ISSN 0313-5934
➤ **J A S S A.** Variant title: Journal of the Securities Institute of Australia. Text in English. 1966. q. AUD 106 to non-members; free to members (effective 2005). bk.rev. **Document type:** *Magazine, Trade.* **Description:** This is the journal of the Securities Institute; it contains articles on topics of current interest to the professional investment community and provides a venue for views and information on matters effecting the finance and investment industry.
Related titles: Online - full text ed.
Indexed: ABIX, AusPAIS, RevApplEntom.
Published by: (Securities Institute of Australia), Hardie Grant Magazines, 85 High St, Prahran, VIC 3181, Australia. TEL 61-3-85206444, FAX 61-3-85206422, info@hardiegrant.com.au, http://www.hardiegrant.com.au. Ed. John Hoffmann. Circ: 10,100 (paid and controlled).

332.6 USA
J. MICHAEL PINSON'S INVESTMENT DIGEST. Text in English. 1983. m. USD 99 membership (effective 2002); incls. Investment Digest Hotline, Pinson's Guide to Mutual Funds and Charles Schwab's How to be Your Own Stockbroker.. **Description:** Contains reviews of mutual funds, individual stocks as well as market predictions.
Formerly: Investment Digest
Published by: Pinson Communications, Inc., 2653 McCormick Dr, Clearwater, FL 34620. TEL 727-799-6138, 800-229-2005, FAX 727-796-1087, pinson@tfc.com, http://www.investmentdigest.com/, http://www.pinsoncommunications.com/. Circ: 8,000.

332.6   USA
J TAYLOR'S GOLD & TECHNOLOGY STOCKS. Text in English. 1981. m. USD 99 (effective 2000). **Document type:** *Newsletter.* **Description:** Deals with mining, energy and environmental stocks.
Former titles: J Taylor's Gold Resources & Environmental Stocks; J Taylor's Gold and Gold Stocks; North American Gold Mining Stocks
Published by: Taylor Hard Money Advisors, Inc., 33-42 61st St., Woodside, NY 11377. TEL 718-457-1426, http://www.miningstocks.com. Ed. Jay L Taylor. Circ. 400 (paid).

332.6327   USA   ISSN 1555-564X
THE JACKSON LETTER; the financial newsletter for dentists. Text in English. 1984. m. USD 95 (effective 2005). **Description:** Covers all aspects of investing.
Former titles (until 1990): Jackson Financial Letter; Jackson Letter
Published by: Jackson Publishing Company, P O Box 1008, Mount Pleasant, SC 29465. TEL 843-881-3434, FAX 843-881-1557, http://www.thejacksonletter.com. Ed. James B Jackson. Circ. 2,000.

332.6327   USA
JAY SCHABACKER'S MUTUAL FUND BUYING GUIDE. Text in English. q. USD 88.85.
Formerly: Mutual Fund Quarterly Performance Review
Published by: Phillips International, Inc., 1 Massachusetts Ave., NW, Washington, DC 20001. TEL 301-340-2100, FAX 301-309-3847. Ed. Jay Schabacker.

332.6327   USA
JIM HIGHLAND'S FUND SWITCH ✳ . Text in English. 1985. m. USD 140. **Description:** Provides commentary on stocks, bonds, metals, and international markets, with recommendations on the strongest markets. Examines specific funds within those markets.
Published by: Highland Associates, Inc., 24001 W Rockwood Creek Ln, Rhododendron, OR 97049-9750. TEL 503-622-4990. Ed. Jim Highland.

332.63   AUS
HG5891
JOBSON'S YEAR BOOK OF PUBLIC COMPANIES. Text in English. 1920. a. AUD 295. adv. illus. **Document type:** *Directory.* **Description:** Covers the industrial and second board listed companies on Australian and New Zealand stock exchanges.
Former titles: Jobson's Year Book of Australian Companies (1038-2194); (until 1980): Jobson's Year Book (0075-3785)
Published by: Dun & Bradstreet Marketing Pty. Ltd., 19 Havilah St, Chatswood, NSW 2067, Australia. TEL 61-2-9352700, FAX 61-2-9352777, http://www.dbmarketing.com.au. R&P Sue Francis. Circ. 5,000.

332.6   ZAF   ISSN 0021-7182
JOHANNESBURG STOCK EXCHANGE MONTHLY BULLETIN. Text in English. 1969. m. ZAR 221; ZAR 296 in Africa; ZAR 296 in Australasia; ZAR 437 in the Americas; ZAR 445 in Europe; ZAR 516 in the Middle East. adv. charts; stat. **Document type:** *Bulletin.* **Description:** Publishes information on markets, JSE Actuaries Index movement, securities, and notes on companies, including rights and capitalization issues, changes in capital, and special situations.
Published by: Johannesburg Stock Exchange, PO Box 1174, Johannesburg, South Africa. TEL 27-11-377-2206, FAX 27-11-834-7402. Circ. 3,400.

332.6   USA   ISSN 1557-1254
JOHN BOLLINGER'S CAPITAL GROWTH LETTER. Text in English. 1987. m. USD 300 (effective 2006). bk.rev.; software rev.; Website rev. 12 p./no. 2 cols./p.; back issues avail. **Document type:** *Newsletter.* **Description:** Provides investors with specific investment advice on stocks, bonds, precious metals, energy, the dollar and the international markets.
Related titles: Online - full text ed.: ISSN 1557-1262.
Published by: Bollinger Capital Management, PO Box 3358, Manhattan Beach, CA 90266. TEL 310-798-8855, bbands@bollingerbands.com, http://www.bollingerbands.com. Ed. John Bollinger. Pub., R&P Dorit Kehr.

JOHN LINER REVIEW. see *INSURANCE*

JOHN T. REED'S REAL ESTATE INVESTOR'S MONTHLY. see *REAL ESTATE*

332.67   USA   ISSN 0735-7672
HG4530
JOHNSON'S INVESTMENT COMPANY CHARTS. Text in English. 1949. a. USD 469; includes 4 performance reports. film rev. charts; illus.; stat. **Document type:** *Trade.* **Description:** Chartbook on mutual funds, interest rates, inflation, market indexes, stocks, bonds, and financial planning.
Published by: Johnson's Charts, Inc., 175 Bridle Path, Buffalo, NY 14221-4537. TEL 716-626-0845, FAX 716-626-4899. Ed., R&P Fred C Cohn. Circ. 1,000.

338.7 346.068   USA
JOINT VENTURES WITH INTERNATIONAL PARTNERS. Text in English. 1989. 3 base vols. plus a. updates. looseleaf. USD 270. Supplement avail.

Published by: LexisNexis (Subsidiary of: LexisNexis North America), PO Box 7587, Charlottesville, VA 22906-7587. TEL 804-972-7600, 800-562-1197, FAX 804-972-7666, llp.customer.support@lexis-nexis.com, http://www.lexislawpublishing.com. Eds. James A Dobkin, Jeffrey A Burt.

332.6   USA   ISSN 1520-3255
HG4501
JOURNAL OF ALTERNATIVE INVESTMENTS. Text in English. 1998. q. USD 540 combined subscription domestic print & online eds.; USD 615 combined subscription foreign print & online eds. (effective 2005). back issues avail. **Document type:** *Magazine, Trade.*
Related titles: Online - full text ed.: (from EBSCO Publishing, Florida Center for Library Automation, Gale Group, O C L C Online Computer Library Center, Inc.).
Indexed: ABIn, BLI.
—BLDSC (4927.202600), IE. CCC.
Published by: Institutional Investor, Journals (Subsidiary of: Euromoney Institutional Investor Plc.), 225 Park Ave S, 7th Fl., New York, NY 10003-1605. TEL 212-224-3800, FAX 212-224-3563, info@iijournals.com, http://www.iijournals.com. Ed. Thomas Schneeweis. Pub. Allison Adams TEL 212-224-3584.

332.63   GBR   ISSN 1470-8272
➤ **THE JOURNAL OF ASSET MANAGEMENT.** Text in English. 2000. q. GBP 245 in Europe; USD 360 in North America; GBP 260 elsewhere (effective 2004). adv. reprint service avail. from PSC. **Document type:** *Journal, Academic/Scholarly.* **Description:** Offers an international forum for latest thinking, new developments and cutting-edge techniques in the industry, and provides a bridge between academic work, commercial best practice and regulatory interests globally.
Related titles: Online - full text ed.: ISSN 1479-179X (from EBSCO Publishing, Gale Group, IngentaConnect, O C L C Online Computer Library Center, Inc., ProQuest Information & Learning, Swets Information Services).
Indexed: ABIn.
—BLDSC (4947.283200), IE, ingenta.
Published by: Palgrave Macmillan Ltd. (Subsidiary of: Macmillan Publishers Ltd.), Houndmills, Basingstoke, Hants RG21 6XS, United Kingdom. TEL 44-1256-329242, FAX 44-1256-810526, journal-info@palgrave.com, http://www.palgrave-journals.com/. Eds. Kenneth F Kroner, Dr. Stephen Satchell. Circ. 600 (paid).

332.6   GBR   ISSN 1476-1688
JOURNAL OF BOND TRADING AND MANAGEMENT. Text in English. 2002. q. GBP 80 in Europe to individuals full-time academic teaching, research, or study; USD 115 in North America to individuals full-time academic teaching, research, or study; GBP 95 elsewhere to individuals full-time academic teaching, research, or study; GBP 200 in Europe to institutions; USD 290 in North America to institutions; GBP 215 elsewhere to institutions (effective 2004). **Document type:** *Journal, Academic/Scholarly.* **Description:** Brings together the work and interests of both academic researchers and practitioners in the field of debt capital markets; and provides an authoritative forum for the dissemination of the latest research, product development and leading edge practice in every area of the global bond markets.
Related titles: Online - full text ed.: ISSN 1479-1781 (from Gale Group, IngentaConnect, O C L C Online Computer Library Center, Inc., Swets Information Services).
Published by: Henry Stewart Publications, Russell House, 28-30 Little Russell St, London, WC1A 2HN, United Kingdom. TEL 44-20-74043040, FAX 44-20-74042081, enquiries@hspublications.co.uk, qweny@henrystewart.co.uk, http://www.henrystewart.com/journals/bt/index.html. Ed. Moorad Choudhry. **Subscr. addr. in US & Canada to:** Henry Stewart Publications, Subscriptions Office, PO Box 10812, Birmingham, AL 35202-1588. TEL 800-633-4931, FAX 205-955-1588, hsp@ebsco.com; **Subscr. outside N America to:** Museum House, 25 Museum St, London WC1A 1JT, United Kingdom. TEL 44-20-73232916, FAX 44-20-73232918, subscriptions@hspublications.co.uk.

THE JOURNAL OF CORPORATE CITIZENSHIP. see *BUSINESS AND ECONOMICS—Management*

JOURNAL OF DERIVATIVES. see *BUSINESS AND ECONOMICS—Banking And Finance*

332.6   IND   ISSN 0972-6527
➤ **JOURNAL OF EMERGING MARKET FINANCE.** Text in English. 2002. 3/yr. GBP 128, USD 224 to institutions; GBP 133, USD 233 combined subscription to institutions print & online eds. (effective 2006). **Document type:** *Journal, Academic/Scholarly.* **Description:** Provides a forum for debate and discussion on the theory and practice of finance in emerging markets.
Related titles: Online - full text ed.: GBP 127, USD 222 to institutions (effective 2006) (from EBSCO Publishing, Sage Publications, Inc.).
—BLDSC (4977.453000), IE.
Published by: Sage Publications India Pvt. Ltd. (Subsidiary of: Sage Publications, Inc.), M-32 Market, Greater Kailash-I, PO Box 4215, New Delhi, 110 048, India. TEL 91-11-6444958, FAX 91-11-6472426, editors@indiasage.com, http://www.sagepub.co.uk/journal.aspx?pid=105637, http://www.indiasage.com/, http://www.sagepub.com. Ed.

Shubhashis Gangopadhyay. **Subscr. to:** Sage Publications, Inc., 2455 Teller Rd, Thousand Oaks, CA 91320. TEL 805-499-0721, FAX 805-499-0871, journals@sagepub.com; Sage Publications Ltd., 1 Oliver's Yard, 55 City Rd, London EC1 1SP, United Kingdom. TEL 44-20-73740645, FAX 44-20-73748741, subscription@sagepub.co.uk.

➤ **JOURNAL OF EMERGING MARKETS.** see *BUSINESS AND ECONOMICS—Banking And Finance*

➤ **JOURNAL OF FINANCIAL INTERMEDIATION.** see *BUSINESS AND ECONOMICS—Economic Systems And Theories, Economic History*

332.6   USA   ISSN 1040-3981
HG179
JOURNAL OF FINANCIAL PLANNING. Text in English. 1979. 12/yr. USD 109 domestic to non-members; USD 134 in Canada to non-members; USD 144 elsewhere to non-members (effective 2005). adv. bk.rev. tr.lit.; illus.; abstr.; charts. index. 116 p./no. 3 cols./p.; reprints avail. **Document type:** *Journal, Trade.* **Description:** Acts as a forum for the free exchange of ideas, facts, and information relevant to the financial planning profession.
Formerly (until 1988): Institute of Certified Financial Planners. Journal (0746-1984)
Related titles: Online - full text ed.: (from bigchalk, EBSCO Publishing, H.W. Wilson, O C L C Online Computer Library Center, Inc., ProQuest Information & Learning).
Indexed: ABIn, ATI, AgeL, BPI, ESPM, PAIS, RiskAb.
—BLDSC (4984.260500), IE, ingenta. CCC.
Published by: Financial Planning Association, 4100 E Mississippi Ave Ste 400, Denver, CO 80246. TEL 800-322-4237 ext 7146, FAX 303-759-0749, journal@fpanet.org, http://www.fpanet.org/journal/index.cfm. Ed., Pub. Ian W. MacKenzie. R&P Suzie Black. Adv. contacts Bob Haddad, Dave Jeans. B&W page USD 4,940; bleed 8.5 x 11.12. Circ. 27,000 (paid); 23,000 (controlled).

JOURNAL OF FINANCIAL SERVICES RESEARCH. see *BUSINESS AND ECONOMICS—Banking And Finance*

332.6   USA   ISSN 1059-8596
HG4961
JOURNAL OF FIXED INCOME. Text in English. 1991. q. USD 370 combined subscription domestic print & online eds.; USD 445 combined subscription foreign print & online eds. (effective 2005). adv. illus. Index. back issues avail.; reprints avail. **Document type:** *Journal, Trade.* **Description:** Offers original works of applied research in the field of fixed income, covering topics such as mortgage-backed securities, corporate bonds, asset-backed securities, international bond markets, and more.
Related titles: Online - full text ed.: (from EBSCO Publishing, Florida Center for Library Automation, Gale Group, H.W. Wilson, O C L C Online Computer Library Center, Inc., ProQuest Information & Learning).
Indexed: ABIn, ATI, BPI.
—BLDSC (4984.380000), IE, Infotrieve, ingenta. CCC.
Published by: Institutional Investor, Journals (Subsidiary of: Euromoney Institutional Investor Plc.), 225 Park Ave S, 7th Fl., New York, NY 10003-1605. TEL 212-224-3800, FAX 212-224-3563, info@iijournals.com, http://www.iijournals.com. Ed. Stanley J Kon. Pub. Allison Adams TEL 212-224-3584. adv.: B&W page USD 4,500, color page USD 7,700.

332.63   USA   ISSN 0270-7314
HG6001   CODEN: JFMADT
➤ **THE JOURNAL OF FUTURES MARKETS.** Text in English. 1981. m. USD 1,664 domestic to institutions; USD 1,784 in Canada & Mexico to institutions; USD 1,886 elsewhere to institutions; USD 1,831 combined subscription domestic to institutions print & online eds.; USD 1,951 combined subscription in Canada & Mexico to institutions print & online eds.; USD 2,053 combined subscription elsewhere to institutions print & online eds. (effective 2006). adv. illus. Index. back issues avail.; reprint service avail. from PSC. **Document type:** *Journal, Academic/Scholarly.* **Description:** Topics include financial futures, commodity forecasting techniques, corporate hedging strategies, tax and accounting implications of hedging, analysis of commodity trading systems.
Related titles: Microform ed.: (from PQC); Online - full text ed.: ISSN 1096-9934. 1996. USD 1,664 to institutions (effective 2006) (from EBSCO Publishing, ProQuest Information & Learning, Swets Information Services, Wiley InterScience).
Indexed: ABIn, ASCA, ATI, BLI, BPI, BPIA, BusI, CPM, CurCont, ESPM, IBSS, JEL, ManagCont, PAIS, PSI, RiskAb, SSCI, T&II.
—BLDSC (4986.910000), CISTI, IDS, IE, Infotrieve, ingenta. CCC.
Published by: John Wiley & Sons, Inc., 111 River St, Hoboken, NJ 07030-5774. TEL 201-748-6000, FAX 201-748-5915, uscs-wis@wiley.com, http://www.interscience.wiley.com/jpages/0270-7314/, http://www.wiley.com. Ed. Robert I Webb. adv.: B&W page GBP 640, color page GBP 1,515; trim 172 x 254. Circ. 1,100. **Subscr. outside the Americas to:** John Wiley & Sons Ltd., The Atrium, Southern Gate, Chichester, West Sussex PO19 8SQ, United Kingdom. TEL 44-1243-843335, 0800-243407, FAX 44-1243-843232, cs-journals@wiley.co.uk.

332.6 USA ISSN 1068-0896
HG4501
JOURNAL OF INVESTING. Text in English. 1992. q. USD 360 combined subscription domestic print & online eds.; USD 435 combined subscription foreign print & online eds. (effective 2005). adv. illus. back issues avail.; reprints avail. **Document type:** *Magazine, Trade.* **Description:** Provides articles on the latest developments affecting financial and investment decisions.
Related titles: Online - full text ed.: (from EBSCO Publishing, Florida Center for Library Automation, Gale Group, H.W. Wilson, O C L C Online Computer Library Center, Inc., ProQuest Information & Learning).
Indexed: ABIn, BPI.
—BLDSC (5008.050000), IE, ingenta. **CCC.**
Published by: Institutional Investor, Journals (Subsidiary of: Euromoney Institutional Investor Plc.), 225 Park Ave S, 7th Fl., New York, NY 10003-1605. TEL 212-224-3800, FAX 212-224-3563, info@iijournals.com, http://www.iijoi.com, http://www.iijournals.com. Ed. Brian Bruce. Pub. Allison Adams TEL 212-224-3584. adv.: B&W page USD 4,500, color page USD 7,700. Circ: 2,500 (paid).

332.6 GBR ISSN 1528-5812
K10
JOURNAL OF INVESTMENT COMPLIANCE. Text in English. 2000. q. USD 629 combined subscription print & online eds. (effective 2006). back issues avail. **Document type:** *Journal, Trade.* **Description:** Contains analysis and advice on the regulation of institutional investment funds as it relates to their trading, management, custody, transfers and investor rules.
Related titles: Online - full text ed.: (from EBSCO Publishing, Florida Center for Library Automation, Gale Group, O C L C Online Computer Library Center, Inc.).
Indexed: ABIn, BLI.
—**CCC.**
Published by: Emerald Group Publishing Limited, 60-62 Toller Ln, Bradford, W Yorks BD8 9BY, United Kingdom. TEL 44-1274-777700, FAX 44-1274-785200, infomation@emeraldinsight.com, http://www.emeraldinsight.com/joic.htm. R&P Ms. Anne-Marie Thorslund.

332.6 USA ISSN 1524-6035
HG4529
THE JOURNAL OF INVESTMENT CONSULTING. Text in English. s-a. USD 160 (effective 2005). **Document type:** *Magazine, Trade.*
Indexed: ABIn.
Published by: Investment Management Consultants Association, 5619 Dtc Pkwy., Ste. 500, Greenwood Vlg, CO 80111-3044. http://www.imca.org. Ed. Tricia Fleming.

▼ **JOURNAL OF INVESTMENT MANAGEMENT.** see *BUSINESS AND ECONOMICS—Banking And Finance*

332.6 USA ISSN 0095-4918
HG4501
➤ **JOURNAL OF PORTFOLIO MANAGEMENT**; the journal for investment professionals. Text in English. 1975. q. USD 430 combined subscription domestic print & online eds.; USD 505 combined subscription foreign print & online eds. (effective 2005). adv. bk.rev. bibl.; charts; illus. Index. back issues avail.; reprint service avail. from PQC. **Document type:** *Journal, Trade.* **Description:** Reports and explores the development and application of theoretical concepts dominating the investment scene.
Related titles: CD-ROM ed.; Microform ed.: (from PQC); Online - full text ed.: (from EBSCO Publishing, Florida Center for Library Automation, Gale Group, H.W. Wilson, O C L C Online Computer Library Center, Inc., ProQuest Information & Learning).
Indexed: ABIn, ASCA, ATI, BLI, BPI, BPIA, BusI, CurCont, Emerald, JEL, ManagCont, PAIS, SSCI, T&II.
—BLDSC (5041.147000), IDS, IE, Infotrieve, ingenta. **CCC.**
Published by: Institutional Investor, Journals (Subsidiary of: Euromoney Institutional Investor Plc.), 225 Park Ave S, 7th Fl., New York, NY 10003-1605. TEL 212-224-3800, FAX 212-224-3563, info@iijournals.com, http://www.iijournals.com. Eds. Frank Fabozzi, Peter Bernstein. adv.: B&W page USD 4,500, color page USD 7,700.

332 USA ISSN 1096-5572
HG4961
THE JOURNAL OF PRIVATE EQUITY. Text in English. 1997. q. USD 450 combined subscription domestic print & online eds.; USD 525 combined subscription foreign print & online eds. (effective 2005). back issues avail.; reprints avail. **Document type:** *Magazine, Trade.* **Description:** Contains in-depth analysis of today's most innovative strategies and effective techniques in venture capital and private equity.
Related titles: Online - full text ed.: (from EBSCO Publishing, Florida Center for Library Automation, Gale Group, H.W. Wilson, O C L C Online Computer Library Center, Inc.).
Indexed: ABIn, BLI, BPI.
—BLDSC (5042.470000), IE. **CCC.**
Published by: Institutional Investor, Journals (Subsidiary of: Euromoney Institutional Investor Plc.), 225 Park Ave S, 7th Fl., New York, NY 10003-1605. TEL 212-224-3800, FAX 212-224-3563, info@iijournals.com, http://www.iijournals.com. Pub. Allison Adams TEL 212-224-3584. Adv. contact Trisha Gorman.

THE JOURNAL OF RISK. see *BUSINESS AND ECONOMICS—Banking And Finance*

332.6 GBR ISSN 1526-5943
HD61
➤ **THE JOURNAL OF RISK FINANCE**; incorporating Balance Sheet. Text in English. 2000. 5/yr. EUR 1,336.54 in Europe; USD 1,429 in North America; AUD 2,129 in Australasia; GBP 934.16 in the UK & elsewhere (effective 2006). reprint service avail. from PSC. **Document type:** *Journal, Academic/Scholarly.* **Description:** Creates an advice resource for corporate users of insurance and financial products whilst supporting those institutions who supply them, discussing pricing, allocation and distribution.
Incorporates (in 2004): Balance Sheet (0965-7967)
Related titles: Online - full text ed.: (from EBSCO Publishing, Emerald Group Publishing Limited, Florida Center for Library Automation, Gale Group, O C L C Online Computer Library Center, Inc., ProQuest Information & Learning).
Indexed: ABIn, ESPM, RiskAb.
—BLDSC (5052.101200), IE. **CCC.**
Published by: Emerald Group Publishing Limited, 60-62 Toller Ln, Bradford, W Yorks BD8 9BY, United Kingdom. TEL 44-1274-777700, FAX 44-1274-785200, infomation@emeraldinsight.com, http://www.emeraldinsight.com/jrf.htm. Ed. Michael Powers. Pub. Anna Torrance. R&P Ms. Anne-Marie Thorslund. Circ: 10,700 (controlled and free).

332.6 USA ISSN 1538-7461
HD259
JOURNAL OF TAX CREDIT INVESTING; analysis and data on tax-advantaged investing and leasing. Text in English. 2002. q. adv.
Published by: Alexander and Edwards Publishing, Inc., 111 Sutter St, Ste 975, San Francisco, CA 94104-4547. TEL 415-315-1241, FAX 415-315-1248, http://www.housingfinance.com. Ed., Pub. Andre Shashaty.

JOURNAL OF TAXATION OF INVESTMENTS. see *BUSINESS AND ECONOMICS—Public Finance, Taxation*

332.6 USA ISSN 1534-7524
THE JOURNAL OF WEALTH MANAGEMENT. Text in English. 1998. q. USD 410 combined subscription domestic print & online eds.; USD 485 combined subscription foreign print & online eds. (effective 2005). back issues avail. **Document type:** *Journal, Trade.* **Description:** Provides analysis on investment strategies for high-net worth, taxable portfolios.
Formerly (until 2000): The Journal of Private Portfolio Management (1520-4154)
Related titles: Online - full text ed.: (from EBSCO Publishing, Gale Group, O C L C Online Computer Library Center, Inc.).
Indexed: ABIn, BLI.
—BLDSC (5072.550000). **CCC.**
Published by: Institutional Investor, Journals (Subsidiary of: Euromoney Institutional Investor Plc.), 225 Park Ave S, 7th Fl., New York, NY 10003-1605. TEL 212-224-3800, FAX 212-224-3563, info@iijournals.com, http://www.iijournals.com. Ed. Jean L P Brunel. Pub. Allison Adams TEL 212-224-3584. Adv. contact David Blide TEL 212-224-3187.

332.6 CHE ISSN 1660-7112
K10
THE JOURNAL OF WORLD INVESTMENT & TRADE. Text in English. 2000. 6/yr. CHF 610; CHF 110 newsstand/cover (effective 2004). 190 p./no.; back issues avail. **Document type:** *Journal, Trade.* **Description:** Contains information and articles on the arbitration of investment disputes and the regulation of investment flows.
Formerly (until 2004): The Journal of World Investment (1424-1196)
—BLDSC (5072.682500). **CCC.**
Published by: Werner Publishing Company, 13 rue du Rhone, PO Box 5134, Geneva 11, 1211, Switzerland. TEL 41-22-3103422, FAX 41-22-3114592, wernerp@iprolink.ch, http://www.wernerpubl.com. Ed., Pub., R&P Jacques Werner.

JUDGE'S RETIREMENT SYSTEM. ANNUAL FINANCIAL REPORT AND REPORT OF OPERATIONS. see *BUSINESS AND ECONOMICS—Economic Situation And Conditions*

332.6 USA
JUMBO FLASH REPORT✶. Text in English. 1989. w. looseleaf. USD 245 (effective 2000). charts; mkt.; stat. **Document type:** *Newsletter.* **Description:** Covers high yielding jumbo CDs and money markets offered by federally-insured institutions nationwide.
Published by: Bankrate, Inc., 11760 US Highway One, Ste 500, N Palm Beach, FL 33408. TEL 561-630-2400, FAX 561-625-4540, www.bankrate.com. Ed. Linda Green. Circ: 50 (paid).

JUMBO RATE NEWS. see *BUSINESS AND ECONOMICS—Banking And Finance*

332.6 USA ISSN 1073-7634
JUNIOR GROWTH STOCKS. Text in English. 1971. q. USD 50 per issue. **Document type:** *Newsletter.* **Description:** Provides investors with data on more than 300 growth companies, most of which are "emerging growth" companies. Includes data on earnings, sales, shares outstanding, compound growth rates, book values, and price-earnings ratio.
Related titles: ◆ Supplement(s): Growth Stock Outlook. ISSN 1073-7626; ◆ New Issue Digest. ISSN 1073-7642.
Published by: Growth Stock Outlook, Inc., 4405 East West Hwy, Ste 305, Bethesda, MD 20814. TEL 301-654-5205. Ed. Charles Allmon.

332.6 FRA ISSN 1764-0563
JURI-DICTIONNAIRE JOLY. BOURSE ET PRODUITS FINANCIERS. Text in French. 5 base vols. plus s-a. updates. looseleaf. FRF 4,250 (effective 1998). **Document type:** *Trade.*
Formerly: Dictionnaire Joly Bourse et Produits Financiers (1244-4448)
Published by: Joly Editions, 31 rue Falguiere, Paris, 75015, France. TEL 33-1-56541600, FAX 33-1-56541647. Ed. Thierry Bonneau.

K-GELD. see *BUSINESS AND ECONOMICS—Banking And Finance*

332.63 JPN
KABUSHIKI NIPPON. Text in Japanese. 3/m. adv. **Description:** For businessmen interested in the securities market.
Published by: Shijo Shimbun Sha, 5-6 Shinkawa 2-chome, Chuo-ku, Tokyo, 104-0033, Japan. TEL 81-3-5566-1805, FAX 81-3-5566-1811. Adv. contact Hiroshi Yasuzawa. Circ: 30,800.

332.6 USA ISSN 1536-7886
KAGAN MEDIA MONEY. Text in English. 1999. 48/yr. USD 1,245; USD 1,640 combined subscription print & e-mail eds. (effective 2005). adv. **Document type:** *Newsletter, Trade.*
Formerly (until 2001): Kagan Media Investor (1528-5332)
Related titles: E-mail ed.: USD 1,145 (effective 2005).
Published by: Kagan Research, LLC, One Lower Ragsdale Dr, Bldg One, Ste 130, Monterey, CA 93940. TEL 831-624-1536, FAX 831-625-3225, info@kagan.com, http://research.kagan.com/keo/subscriptionsDetailPage.aspx?SubscriptionID=17, http://www.kagan.com. adv.: page USD 3,670.

332.6 DEU ISSN 0948-5163
KAPITALMARKTRECHT. Text in German. 1995. irreg. price varies. **Document type:** *Monographic series, Trade.*
Published by: Erich Schmidt Verlag GmbH & Co. (Berlin), Genthiner Str 30G, Berlin, 10785, Germany. TEL 49-30-250085-0, FAX 49-30-25008511, esv@esvmedien.de, http://www.erich-schmidt-verlag.de.

332.678 PAK
KARACHI. CHAMBER OF COMMERCE AND INDUSTRY. GUIDE FOR INDUSTRIAL INVESTMENT IN PAKISTAN. Text in English. irreg. PKR 100.
Published by: Karachi Chamber of Commerce and Industry, Aiwan-e-Tijarat, Nicol Rd., P O Box 4258, Karachi 2, Pakistan.

380 332.6 KEN
KENYA: THE GATEWAY TO AFRICA; guidelines to investors. Text in English. irreg. free. **Document type:** *Government.*
Formerly: Guidelines for Industrial Investors in Kenya
Published by: Ministry of Industry, Industrial Promotion Department, PO Box 30418, Nairobi, Kenya.

332.6 NLD ISSN 0927-4340
KERNGETALLEN NEDERLANDSE BEURSFONDSEN. Text in Dutch. 1962. 3/yr. stat.
Formerly (until 1991): Kerngetallen van Nederlandse Effecten (0023-0669)
Related titles: English ed.: Dutch Company Profiles. ISSN 0927-4790.
Indexed: KES.
Published by: A B N Amro Bank N.V., PO Box 283, Amsterdam, 1000 EA, Netherlands. Ed. Wim Sprey. Circ: 14,000. **Subscr. to:** Amro Effecten Centrum, Postbus 3200, Breda 4800 DE, Netherlands.

332.6 GBR ISSN 1364-8004
KEY NOTE MARKET REPORT: PENSIONS. Variant title: Pensions. Text in English. 1996. irreg. (2nd Edition), latest 1998, Jan. GBP 340 per issue (effective 2002). **Document type:** *Trade.* **Description:** Provides an overview of a specific UK market segment and includes executive summary, market definition, market size, industry background, competitor analysis, current issues, forecasts, company profiles, and more.
Published by: Key Note Ltd., Field House, 72 Oldfield Rd, Hampton, Mddx TW12 2HQ, United Kingdom. TEL 44-20-8481-8750, FAX 44-20-8783-0049, info@keynote.co.uk, http://www.keynote.co.uk. Ed. Richard Caines.

332.64 GBR ISSN 1363-3260
KEY NOTE MARKET REPORT: STOCKBROKING. Variant title: Stockbroking. Text in English. 1993. irreg. (4th Edition), latest 1996, Jan. GBP 340 per issue (effective 2002). **Document type:** *Trade.* **Description:** Provides an overview of a specific UK market segment and includes executive summary, market definition, market size, industry background, competitor analysis, current issues, forecasts, company profiles, and more.
Published by: Key Note Ltd., Field House, 72 Oldfield Rd, Hampton, Mddx TW12 2HQ, United Kingdom. TEL 44-20-8481-8750, FAX 44-20-8783-0049, info@keynote.co.uk, http://www.keynote.co.uk. Ed. Richard Caines.

332.63 AUS
KEYNOTE. Text in English. s-a. adv. **Document type:** *Magazine, Consumer.* **Description:** Provides educative, yet interesting and entertaining information on various types of financial services.
Published by: Pacific Client Publishing, 35-51 Mitchell St., McMahons Point, NSW 2060, Australia. TEL 61-2-9464-3300, FAX 61-2-9464-3488, http://www.clientpublishing.com.au. Adv. contact Alison Owen. Circ: 623,000 (controlled).

332.6 USA ISSN 0453-9249
KIPLINGER CALIFORNIA LETTER. Text in English. 1965. s-m. USD 73 (effective 2004). charts; stat. **Document type:** *Newsletter, Consumer.* **Description:** Contains special analysis on the outlook for business in California.
Related titles: Online - full text ed.: (from bigchalk, Florida Center for Library Automation, Gale Group, H.W. Wilson, LexisNexis, ProQuest Information & Learning).
Indexed: BPI.
—CCC.
Published by: Kiplinger Washington Editors, Inc., 1729 H St, N W, Washington, DC 20006. TEL 888-419-0424, FAX 202-778-8976, 202-331-1206, letterresponse@kiplinger.com, http://www.kiplinger.com/clients/. Ed., Pub. Knight A Kiplinger.

332.6 USA ISSN 1528-7130
HC101
THE KIPLINGER LETTER. Text in English. 1923. w. USD 84 (effective 2004). illus. reprints avail. **Document type:** *Newsletter, Consumer.* **Description:** Contains weekly news, information, analyses, and forecasts affecting personal lives and finances.
Formerly (until 1999): Kiplinger Washington Letter (0023-1770)
Related titles: Online - full text ed.: ISSN 1528-7122 (from EBSCO Publishing, H.W. Wilson, LexisNexis, ProQuest Information & Learning).
Indexed: BPI, CCR.
—CASDDS. CCC.
Published by: Kiplinger Washington Editors, Inc., 1729 H St, N W, Washington, DC 20006. TEL 202-887-6400, FAX 202-331-1206, letterresponse@kiplinger.com, http://www.kiplinger.com/clients/. Eds. Melissa Bristow, Knight A Kiplinger. Pub. Knight A Kiplinger. Circ: 350,000 (paid).

646.79 USA ISSN 1529-6245
KIPLINGER'S PERSONAL FINANCE MUTUAL FUNDS. Text in English. 1994. a. USD 5.95 newsstand/cover (effective 2003). **Document type:** *Magazine, Consumer.* **Description:** Provides information on mutual fund portfolios for every investing goal - very-long-term, long-term, medium-term, and short-term.
Formerly (until 199?): Kiplinger's Mutual Funds (1081-8901)
Related titles: Online - full text ed.: (from Gale Group, H.W. Wilson, ProQuest Information & Learning).
Indexed: ABIn, RGPR.
Published by: Kiplinger Washington Editors, Inc., 1729 H St, N W, Washington, DC 20006. TEL 202-887-6400, FAX 202-331-1206, letterresponse@kiplinger.com, https://www.kiplinger.com/annual/mutualfund2001.html, http://www.kiplinger.com.

646.79 USA ISSN 1528-9753
KIPLINGER'S PERSONAL FINANCE RETIREMENT PLANNING. Text in English. irreg.
Related titles: Online - full text ed.: (from H.W. Wilson, ProQuest Information & Learning).
Indexed: ABIn, RGPR.
Published by: Kiplinger Washington Editors, Inc., 1729 H St, N W, Washington, DC 20006. TEL 202-887-6400, FAX 202-778-8976, http://www.kiplinger.com.

646.79 USA
KIPLINGER'S RETIREMENT PLANNING. Text in English. q. USD 5.95 newsstand/cover (effective 2004).
Published by: Kiplinger Washington Editors, Inc., 1729 H St, N W, Washington, DC 20006. TEL 888-419-0424, FAX 202-331-1206, http://www.kiplinger.com. Ed. Knight A Kiplinger.

646.79 USA ISSN 1529-4293
KIPLINGER'S RETIREMENT PLANNING GUIDE. Text in English. a. USD 5.95 newsstand/cover (effective 2001). adv. **Document type:** *Magazine, Consumer.* **Description:** Provides information and guidance on how to retire with more wealth and less worries.
Related titles: Online - full text ed.: (from Gale Group).
Published by: Kiplinger Washington Editors, Inc., 1729 H St, N W, Washington, DC 20006. TEL 202-887-6400, FAX 202-331-1206, letterresponse@kiplinger.com, https://www.kiplinger.com/annual/retire.html, http://www.kiplinger.com.

646.79 USA ISSN 1075-6671
KIPLINGER'S RETIREMENT REPORT. Text in English. 1994. m. USD 59.95 (effective 2005). **Document type:** *Newsletter, Consumer.* **Description:** Articles on finances, investments, health, household management and travel, as well as taxes, Social Security and pensions.
Related titles: Online - full text ed.: (from bigchalk, Florida Center for Library Automation, Gale Group, H.W. Wilson, LexisNexis, O C L C Online Computer Library Center, Inc., ProQuest Information & Learning).
Indexed: RGPR.
—CCC.
Published by: Kiplinger Washington Editors, Inc., 1729 H St, N W, Washington, DC 20006. FAX 202-331-1206, http://www.kiplinger.com/retreport/, http://www.kiplinger.com/clients. Eds. Priscilla Brandon, Knight A Kiplinger. Pub. Knight A Kiplinger.

646.79 USA ISSN 1529-0778
HG4661
KIPLINGER'S STOCKS. Text in English. 2000. a. USD 5.95 newsstand/cover (effective 2001). **Document type:** *Magazine, Consumer.* **Description:** Provides information and investing advice on how to pick the stocks that will build and protect wealth.
Related titles: Online - full text ed.: (from Gale Group).
Published by: Kiplinger Washington Editors, Inc., 1729 H St, N W, Washington, DC 20006. TEL 202-887-6400, FAX 202-331-1206, letterresponse@kiplinger.com, http://www.kiplinger.com/service/annuals.html.

332.642 DNK ISSN 0907-1016
KOEBENHAVNS FONDSBOERS. AARSRAPPORT/ COPENHAGEN STOCK EXCHANGE. ANNUAL REPORT. Text in Danish. 1963. a. DKK 50. stat.
Published by: Koebenhavns Fondsboers/Copenhagen Stock Exchange, Nikolaj Plads 6, Copenhagen K, 1067, Denmark. TEL 01-933366, FAX 45-33-128613, TELEX +4533. Circ: 2,000.

332.6 USA
THE KON-LIN LETTER. Text in English. m. USD 95 (effective 2000). charts. 5 p./no.; **Document type:** *Newsletter, Trade.* **Description:** Covers low-priced stocks under $10, with emphasis on emerging growth and special situations for price appreciation potential.
Published by: KonLin, 5 Water Rd, Rocky Point, NY 11778. TEL 631-744-8536, FAX 631-744-3096. Ed. Konrad J Kuhn.

332.63 USA
THE KONLIN LETTER. Text in English. 1979. m. USD 95 (effective 2005). **Document type:** *Newsletter, Trade.* **Description:** Contains technical and fundamental information and analysis on low-priced stocks and the market.
Published by: KonLin, 5 Water Rd, Rocky Point, NY 11778. TEL 631-744-8536, FAX 631-744-3096, newsletter@konlin.com, kon-lin@msn.com, http://www.konlin.com.

332.64 KOR
KOREA STOCK EXCHANGE. FACT BOOK. Text in English. 1979. a. free.
Published by: Korea Stock Exchange, 33 Yoido dong, Youngdeungpo-gu, Seoul, 150010, Korea, S. TEL 783-2271, FAX 786-0263. Ed. Se Yeal Yang. Pub. Byung Woo Koh. Circ: 1,000.

KOTHARI'S INDUSTRIAL DIRECTORY OF INDIA. see *BUSINESS AND ECONOMICS—Trade And Industrial Directories*

332.6 AUT
KURSBLATT DER WIENER BOERSE. Text in German. 1948. d. (5/w.). **Document type:** *Bulletin, Trade.*
Former titles: Kursblatt der Wiener Wertpapierboerse; Kursblatt der Wiener Wertpapierboerse - Geregelter Freiverkehr; Kursblatt der Amtlich Nicht Notierten Wertpapiere - Geregelter Freiverkehr an der Wiener Boerse (0003-2093)
Published by: Boersedruck GmbH, Liesinger Flurgasse 8, Vienna, W 1230, Austria. TEL 43-1-86978810, FAX 43-1-869788149, office@boersedruck.at, http://www.boersedruck.at.

332.6 USA
▼ **L B O WIRE.** Text in English. 2005. d. USD 1,195 (effective 2005). **Document type:** *Newsletter, Trade.* **Description:** Brings news, scoops and analysis of all of the companies in play, deals, deal closures, fund-raising activity, deal finance, and exits.
Published by: Dow Jones Company, 1155 Ave of the Americas, New York, NY 11104. newswires@dowjones.com, http://www.djnewsletters.com/Product.aspx?fp=NMII, http://www.djnewswires.com/.

THE L T C ANCILLARY SERVICES ACQUISITION REPORT. see *MEDICAL SCIENCES*

332.6 USA
LALOGGIA'S SUPERSTOCK INVESTOR. Text in English. 1974. every 3 wks. USD 395 (effective 2000). charts; illus. **Document type:** *Newsletter.*
Formerly: LaLoggia's Special Situation Report & Stock Investor (0890-8079)
Published by: C M L Market Letter, Inc., PO Box 30547, Rochester, NY 14603-0547. TEL 800-450-0551, ssinvestor@aol.com. Ed. Charles M Laloggia. Circ: 3,000.

332.678 USA
LAMBDA FINANCIAL ADVISOR. Text in English. 1984. m. USD 36. charts; stat. back issues avail. **Document type:** *Newsletter.*
Published by: Lambda Publishing Co., PO Box 3569, Jersey City, NJ 07303-3569. TEL 201-963-1357. Ed., Pub. Julius J Spohn.

332.67 USA
LANCZ LETTER. Text in English. 1981. irreg. (every 3-4 wks.). USD 250 (effective 2000). back issues avail. **Document type:** *Newsletter.* **Description:** Presents analyses of contemporary issues in stock market investment, including specific recommendations in addition to general strategies and investment tips.
Published by: Alan B. Lancz & Associates,Inc., 2400 N Reynolds Rd, Toledo, OH 43615-2818. TEL 419-536-5200, FAX 419-536-5401. Ed. Alan B Lancz. R&P Ron Pawlicki. Circ: 1,200.

B

332.6 330.1 USA
LARRY ABRAHAM'S INSIDER REPORT. Text in English. 1983. m. USD 199. bk.rev. back issues avail. **Document type:** *Newsletter.*
Published by: Soundview Communications, PO Box 467939, Atlanta, GA 30346. TEL 800-728-2288. Ed. Larry Abraham. Circ: 10,000.

332.6 330.9 USA ISSN 1551-1588
HG5160.5.A2
LATIN AMERICAN FINANCE EXECUTIVE REPORT. Text in English. 22/yr. USD 656 domestic; USD 706 foreign (effective 2005). adv. **Document type:** *Newsletter, Trade.* **Description:** Covers opportunities, hazards, and important developments for the treasury manager or investor involved in Latin American markets. Includes risk-management techniques, economic performance, and financial sector developments in the area.
Formerly (until 2004): Latin American Finance & Capital Markets (1523-2646)
Published by: WorldTrade Executive, Inc., 2250 Main St, Ste 100, PO Box 761, Concord, MA 01742. TEL 978-287-0301, FAX 978-287-0302, info@wtexec.com, http://www.wtexec.com/lafer.html. adv.: page USD 975; 7.5 x 9.5.

332.6 GBR ISSN 0266-2914
LATIN AMERICAN INFORMES ESPECIALES. Variant title: Informes Especiales. Text in Spanish. 1983. bi-m. GBP 194, USD 268 (effective 2001). back issues avail. **Document type:** *Newsletter.* **Description:** Covers six areas of topical interest in Latin America.
Related titles: Online - full text ed.
Published by: Latin American Newsletters (Subsidiary of: Lettres (U.K.) Ltd.), 61 Old St, London, EC1V 9HW, United Kingdom. TEL 44-20-7251-0012, FAX 44-20-7253-8193, subs@latinnews.com, http://www.latinnews.com. Ed. Eduardo Crawley. R&P Alex McHallam TEL 44-20-7251-0012.

332.62 USA ISSN 1095-9475
LATIN AMERICAN PRIVATE EQUITY ANALYST. Text in English. 1997. m. USD 795 domestic; USD 855 foreign (effective 2000). adv. charts; stat.; tr.lit. back issues avail. **Document type:** *Newsletter.* **Description:** Covers private equity markets in Mexico and South and Central America. Includes profiles of key Latin American industries that are ripe for private equity investments.
Published by: Alternative Investor, 170 Linden St, 2nd Fl, Wellesley, MA 02482. TEL 781-304-1400, FAX 781-304-1440, info@assetnews.com, http://www.assetnews.com. Ed., Pub. David Toll. Adv. contact Doreen C Purvis. B&W page USD 1,000, color page USD 1,200; trim 11 x 8.5. Circ: 300 (paid).

332.6 340 USA ISSN 1069-2312
KF313.A15
LIABILITY OF ATTORNEYS AND ACCOUNTANTS FOR SECURITIES TRANSACTIONS. Text in English. a., latest 2004-2005 ed. USD 371.50 per vol. (effective 2004). **Document type:** *Trade.* **Description:** Explores potential attorney liability for disclosure advise to clients, preparation of disclosure documents, agreements, and closing documents, and creation of formal legal opinions.
Published by: Thomson West (Subsidiary of: Thomson Corporation, The), 610 Opperman Dr, Eagan, MN 55123-1396. TEL 651-687-8000, 800-328-4880, FAX 651-687-7302, customer.service@westgroup.com, http://west.thomson.com/product/13515109/product.asp. Ed. Robert J Haft.

LIFESTYLE AND LONDON LIVING. see *REAL ESTATE*

332.6 USA
LINDQUIST - LEPIC MARKET LETTER. Text in English. 1979. m. USD 139 (effective 2000). **Document type:** *Newsletter, Trade.* **Description:** Reviews stocks and commodity markets.
Published by: Elkton Street Managers Inc, 3011 S Josephine St, Denver, CO 80210. TEL 303-759-8471, http://www.fination.com, http://www.dickdavis.com. Ed. Larry E Lindquist. Circ: 300.

332.63 330.9 ITA
LIST OF ITALIAN STOCKS. Text in Italian. 1950. m. free. stat.
Published by: Banca Commerciale Italiana, Piazza Della Scala, 6, Milan, MI 20121, Italy. Ed. Franco Pedriali. Circ: 2,000.

332 USA ISSN 0196-0628
LIST OF O T C MARGIN STOCKS. Text in English. q. free. **Document type:** *Government.*
Published by: U.S. Federal Reserve System, Board of Governors, Publications Services, Rm MS 138, Washington, DC 20551. TEL 202-452-3244, FAX 202-728-5886.

332.64 HKG
LIST OF STOCK EXCHANGE PARTICIPANTS. Text in Chinese, English. irreg. Free.
Media: Online - full content.
Published by: Hong Kong Exchanges and Clearing Ltd., Corporate Communications, 12/F, One International Finance Centre, 1 Harbour View St, Hong Kong, Hong Kong. TEL 852-2522-1122, FAX 852-2845-3554, info@hkex.com.hk, http://www.hkex.com.hk.

339 332.6 GBR ISSN 0951-9262
LIVERPOOL INVESTMENT LETTER. Text in English. 1986. m. GBP 300 (effective 2001). charts. **Document type:** *Bulletin, Academic/Scholarly.* **Description:** Provides information to investors and investment managers acting on their own initiative.
Related titles: E-mail ed.
Published by: (University of Liverpool, Department of Economics and Accounting), Liverpool Macroeconomic Research Ltd, 5 Cable Rd, Whiston, Liverpool, L35 5AN, United Kingdom. TELEX 627095-UNILPL-G, jfnw36652@cableinet.co.uk, http://www.euro-know.org/lmr.html. Eds. John Wilmot, Patrick Minford. **Subscr. to:** c/o Jane Francis, 131 Mount Pleasant, Liverpool, Merseyside L3 5TF, United Kingdom. TEL 44-151-709-2221.

332.6 GBR
LONDON STOCK EXCHANGE. FACT SHEET MONTHLY. Text in English. 1980. m. charts; stat. **Document type:** *Bulletin.*
Former titles: International Stock Exchange Fact Sheet Monthly; Stock Exchange Fact Sheet Monthly (0265-1513); Supersedes in part: London. Stock Exchange. Stock Exchange Fact Service
Published by: London Stock Exchange, Public Information, T-19, London, EC2N 1HP, United Kingdom. TEL 44-171-797-1372, FAX 44-17-410-6861. Circ: 2,500.

332.6 GBR ISSN 0965-4356
LONDON STOCK EXCHANGE. MEMBER FIRMS. Cover title: Member Firms. Text in English. 1802. a. GBP 10. **Document type:** *Directory.*
Former titles: I S E Firms and Members; Stock Exchange, London. Members and Firms of the Stock Exchange (0305-1129)
—CCC.
Published by: London Stock Exchange, Public Information, T-19, London, EC2N 1HP, United Kingdom. TEL 44-171-797-1372, FAX 44-171-410-6861. Circ: 6,000.

332.645 USA
LONG TERM INVESTING. Text in English. 1967. m. USD 98 (effective 1999). charts. index. **Description:** General information on investing, estate planning, and tax planning for sophisticated investors.
Published by: Concept Publishing, PO Box 500, York, NY 14592. TEL 716-243-4214, FAX 716-243-3148. Ed. David Coleman. Circ: 400.

332.6 USA
LONG-TERM SCORE. Text in English. 1987. m. USD 900. **Description:** Provides signals (buy, short, hedge, neutral) on market momentum based on a proprietary model that uses internal market data and economic analysis.
Published by: Financial Market Models, PO Box 308, Williamsport, PA 17703-0663. TEL 717-433-4236. Eds. David Chessman, Gregory P Breon.

332.6 USA ISSN 1545-1135
▼ **THE LOU DOBBS MONEY LETTER.** Text in English. 2003 (May). m. USD 199 (effective 2003).
Published by: Phillips Investment Resources, LLC (Subsidiary of: Phillips International Inc.), 7811 Montrose Rd., Potomac, MD 20854-3394. TEL 301-424-3700, 800-219-8592, service@dobbsmoneyletter.com, http://www.dobbsmoneyletter.com, http://www.phillips.com/pir/. Eds. Lou Dobbs, H P Newquist.

332.6 USA ISSN 1096-1461
LOUIS NAVELLIER'S BLUE CHIP GROWTH LETTER. Text in English. 1996. m. USD 149 (effective 2005). **Document type:** *Newsletter, Trade.*
Formerly (until 1997): The Garzarelli Outlook (1090-4239)
Contact: Phillips Investment Resources, LLC (Subsidiary of: Phillips International Inc.), 7811 Montrose Rd., Potomac, MD 20854-3394. TEL 301-424-3700, 800-219-8592, FAX 301-424-5059, http://www.bluechipgrowth.com/, http://www.phillips.com/pir/.

332.6 USA
LOUIS RUKEYSER'S MUTUAL FUNDS. Text in English. m. USD 39 (effective 2005). **Document type:** *Newsletter, Abstract/Index.*
Related titles: Online - full text ed.
Published by: Louis Rukeyser's Wall Street Club, 1750 Old Meadow Rd., Ste. 300, Mclean, VA 22102-4304. TEL 800-892-9702, FAX 703-905-8040, customer-service@rukeyser.com, http://www.rukeyser.com. Ed. Louis Rukeyser.

332.6 USA ISSN 1060-9903
HG4501
LOUIS RUKEYSER'S WALL STREET. Text in English. 1992. m. USD 33.50 (effective 2005). **Document type:** *Newsletter, Trade.* **Description:** Provides tips on how the personal investor can make money on Wall Street.
Related titles: Online - full text ed.
Published by: Louis Rukeyser's Wall Street Club, 1750 Old Meadow Rd., Ste. 300, Mclean, VA 22102-4304. TEL 800-892-9702, FAX 703-905-8040, customer-service@rukeyser.com, http://www.rukeyser.com. Ed. Louis Rukeyser. Circ: 400,000.

332.64 USA ISSN 0273-7752
LOW PRICED STOCK SURVEY. Text in English. 1980. m. looseleaf. USD 129 (effective 1999). back issues avail.
Published by: Horizon Publishing Co., L L C, 7412 Calumet Ave, Ste 200, Hammond, IN 46324-2692. TEL 219-852-3210. Ed. Richard J Moroney. Circ: 8,000.

332.6 USA
LYNCH INTERNATIONAL INVESTMENT SURVEY✶. Text in English. 1971. w. USD 175. charts; stat. **Document type:** *Newsletter.*
Published by: Lynch-Bowes, Inc., 431 Beach 136th St, Far Rockaway, NY 11694-1325. TEL 516-883-7094, FAX 516-883-4338. Ed. Walter A Lynch. Circ: 3,000.

332.6 USA
LYNCH MUNICIPAL BOND ADVISORY. Text in English. 1986. m. USD 250. **Document type:** *Newspaper.*
Published by: Lynch Municipal Bond Advisory, Inc., 2840 Broadway, 201, New York, NY 10025. TEL 212-663-5552. Ed. James F Lynch.

M A R PERFORMANCE & EVALUATION DIRECTORY. see *BUSINESS AND ECONOMICS—Economic Situation And Conditions*

M & A REVIEW. (Mergers & Acquisitions) see *BUSINESS AND ECONOMICS—Banking And Finance*

332.6 USA
M B H NEWSLETTER. Text in English. 1972. q. USD 895 (effective 2005). **Document type:** *Newsletter.*
Formerly (until 2005): Jake Bernstein's Letter of Long Term Trends
Published by: M B H Commodity Advisors, Inc., PO Box 353, Winnetka, IL 60093-0353. TEL 847-446-0800, FAX 847-831-2637, jbtrend@mcs.com, http://www.trade-futures.com. Ed. Jacob Bernstein.

332.6 USA
M B H WEEKLY FUTURES TRADING LETTER. Text in English. w. USD 895 (effective 1999). **Document type:** *Newsletter.*
Formerly: M B H Weekly Commodity Letter
Published by: M B H Commodity Advisors, Inc., PO Box 353, Winnetka, IL 60093-0353. TEL 847-291-1870, FAX 847-291-9435, marilyn@trade-futures.com, jake@trade-futures.com. Ed. Jacob Bernstein.

332.6 USA
M F S PERSPECTIVE. Text in English. q. illus. **Document type:** *Newsletter.* **Description:** Provides shareholders and their advisers with investment tips and retirement planning. Covers new funds and profiles managers.
Published by: M F S Investment Management, 500 Boylston St, Boston, MA 02116-3741. TEL 800-637-2929, jluiz@mfs.com. Ed. John Luiz.

332.6 USA
M J F GROWTH STOCK ADVISORY✶. Text in English. 1986. m. USD 78.
Published by: Kephart Communications, Inc., 1750 Old Meadow Rd., 3rd Fl., Mclean, VA 22102-4304. TEL 703-548-2400, FAX 703-683-6974. Ed. Michael J Funke. Circ: 15,000.

332.678 USA
M P T REVIEW; specializing in modern portfolio theory. (Modern Portfolio Theory) Text in English. 1980. m. looseleaf. USD 275; USD 300 foreign. charts; illus.; stat. index. back issues avail. **Document type:** *Newsletter.* **Description:** Provides quantitative analysis of stocks and model portfolios.
Formerly (until 1987): O T C Insight
Related titles: Online - full text ed.
Published by: Navellier and Associates, Inc., 1 E Liberty St, Reno, NV 89501-2110. TEL 800-454-1395, FAX 775-785-2323, info@navellier.com, http://www.mptreview.com. Ed., Pub. Louis G Navellier. R&P Jerry Rushing TEL 775-785-9426. Circ: 10,000.

332.6 CAN ISSN 1187-0176
MAGAZINE AFFAIRES PLUS. Text in French. 1978. m. CND 48.45 (effective 2005). adv. back issues avail. **Description:** Personal business magazine for professionals, entrepreneurs and other business people.
Former titles (until 1991): A Plus (0836-6942); (until 1986): Magazine Affaires (0229-9992)
Indexed: CBCARef, CBPI, CPerI, PAIS, PdeR.
—CISTI. CCC.
Published by: Transcontinental Media, Inc. (Subsidiary of: Transcontinental, Inc.), 1100 Blvd Rene Levesque W, 24th Fl, Montreal, PQ H3B 4X9, Canada. TEL 514-392-9000, FAX 514-392-1489, info@transcontinental.ca, http://www.lesaffaires.com/fr/Aujourdhui/AccueilBis.asp, http://www.transcontinental-gtc.com/en/home.html. Ed. Pierre Duhamel. Circ: 95,845 (paid).

332.6 CAN ISSN 1488-3244
MAGAZINE FINANCE. Text in French. 1998. m. CND 18.50 domestic; CND 39.50 foreign; CND 2.95 newsstand/cover (effective 2002). **Document type:** *Magazine, Consumer.*
Published by: Editions du Journal de l'Assurance Inc., 353 St Nicholas, Ste 102, Montreal, PQ H2Y 2P1, Canada. TEL 514-289-9595, FAX 514-289-9527. Ed. Claude Breton. Pub. Serge Therrien.

332 HUN ISSN 1216-0229
MAGYAR ELEKTRONIKUS TOZSDE/HUNGARIAN ELECTRONIC EXCHANGE. Text in English, Hungarian. 1990. w. free. adv. Website rev. back issues avail. **Document type:** *Newsletter.* **Description:** Provides news of the stock exchange and House of Parliament.
Media: Online - full text. **Related titles:** CD-ROM ed.
Address: PF 311, Budapest, 1536, Hungary. TEL 36-1-2526697, FAX 36-1-3420887, orczanz@mars.iif.hu, http://www.metpress.hu. Ed. Csaba Orczan. Pub., Adv. contact Zsolt Orczan.

332.64 GBR ISSN 1355-7939
MAJOR U K COMPANIES HANDBOOK. Text in English. 1976. s-a. GBP 195 domestic; GBP 220 foreign (effective 1999). stat. back issues avail. **Description:** Provides background and financial information on all UK quoted companies contained in the FTSE All Share Index. Includes market capitalisation, share price, business summary, performance ratios, dividend details, and more.
Supersedes: Extel Handbook of Market Leaders (0308-9673)
Published by: Financial Times Information Ltd., Fitzroy House, 13-17 Epworth St, London, EC2A 4DL, United Kingdom. TEL 44-20-7825-8000, FAX 44-20-7608-2032, justine.dye@ft.com, http://www.ft.com.

292 USA
MAKING BREAD; the magazine for women who need dough. Text in English. 2002 (Sept.). bi-m. USD 20 (effective 2004). adv. **Document type:** *Magazine, Consumer.* **Description:** Contains financial information and advice specifically tailored to women's perspectives, attitudes, and realities.
Media: Online - full content. **Related titles:** CD-ROM ed.
Address: 1528 Walnut St, Ste 1925, Philadelphia, PA 19102. TEL 215-670-2470, FAX 215-670-2077, gail@makingbreadmagazine.com, http://www.makingbreadmagazine.com. Ed., R&P Gail Harlow. Pub. Reginald Owens. Adv. contact Andre Vanterpool.

332.6 USA ISSN 0197-5382
MANAGED ACCOUNTS REPORTS; the clearing house for commodity money management. Text in English. 1979. m. USD 775 in US & Canada; USD 995 elsewhere (effective 2004). charts; stat. back issues avail. **Description:** Features, analysis, and indexes on money management, and performance data for individual accounts, private pools, and publicly offered futures funds.
Incorporates: Futures Industry (0197-5390)
—CCC.
Published by: Managed Account Reports LLC, 1250 Broadway, 26th Fl, New York, NY 10001. TEL 212-213-6202, FAX 212-213-1870, http://www.marhedge.com/publications/marbio.htm.

THE MANAGED CARE ACQUISITION REPORT. see *BUSINESS AND ECONOMICS*

332.6 USA
MANSFIELD STOCK CHART SERVICE. Text in English. 1938. w. price varies. stat. **Document type:** *Newsletter.* **Description:** Provides charts with technical indicators and market commentary to assist investors and market professionals with stock selections.
Published by: R.W. Mansfield Co., Inc., 2973 Kennedy Blvd, Jersey City, NJ 07306. TEL 201-795-0630, 877-626-7353, FAX 201-795-5476. Ed. R W Mansfield.

332.65　　　　　　　USA
MANUAL OF FOREIGN INVESTMENT IN THE UNITED STATES. Text in English. 1986. base vol. plus a. updates. USD 190.
Document type: *Trade.* **Description:** Provides analyses and practical commentary on antitrust restrictions on foreign direct investment, taxation of foreign investors, federal securities laws, U.S. acquisitions by foreign investors and foreign investment in real property.
Published by: Shepard's (Subsidiary of: LexisNexis North America), 555 Middle Creek Pkwy, Colorado Springs, CO 80921. TEL 800-743-7393, customer_service@shepards.com, http://www.shepards.com, http://www.lexisnexis.com/shepards/.

LE MARCHE DES EMPRUNTS OBLIGATAIRES EN FRANCS LUXEMBOURGEOIS/BOND MARKET IN LUXEMBOURG FRANCS. see *BUSINESS AND ECONOMICS—Abstracting, Bibliographies, Statistics*

332.642　　　　　　USA　　　　　　ISSN 1071-1740
MARKET CHARTS. Text in English. 1962. m. (& s-m.). USD 555 domestic includes online ed.; USD 595 foreign includes online ed.; USD 38.20 per issue for s-m edition (effective 2001). back issues avail. **Document type:** *Consumer.* **Description:** Publishes 1 pt. reversal point & figure charts on all stocks on ASE & NYSE and 200 NASDAQ.
Published by: Market Charts, Inc., 250 Hudson St., New York, NY 10013-1413. TEL 212-243-0829, mktchts@aol.com, http://www.marketchartsonline.com. Ed. Dirk J Vandenheuvel. **Subscr. to:** PO Box 824, Village Sta, New York, NY 10014-0824.

332.6　　　　　　　USA　　　　　　ISSN 0892-3272
MARKET CYCLE INVESTING✳ ; my bucks report. Text in English. 1974. 12/yr. looseleaf. USD 98.50. back issues avail. **Document type:** *Newsletter.* **Description:** Growth stocks for long-term investors.
Formerly (until 1983): Andrews Market Cycle Investing
Published by: Andrews Publications (Templeton), 156 Shadow Creek Ln, Paso Robles, CA 93446-1922. TEL 408-778-2925. Ed. R Earl Andrews.

332.6 640.73　　　　　USA　　　　　ISSN 1046-2171
THE MARKET GUIDE. Text in English. 1983. q. USD 345.
Document type: *Directory.* **Description:** Covers 800 research reports on NASDAQ companies demonstrating high growth, financial strength and underlying value.
Formerly (until 1989): Unlisted Market Guide (0882-0775)
Published by: Market Guide Inc., 2001 Marcus Ave., Lake Success, NY 11042. TEL 516-327-2400, FAX 516-327-2425. Circ: 500.

332.6　　　　　　　USA　　　　　　ISSN 0162-6817
MARKET LOGIC✳ . Text in English. 1975. s-m. looseleaf. USD 200. charts; stat. **Document type:** *Newsletter.* **Description:** Forecasts of average market price levels in 3, 6, and 12 months and of the major market trend.
Published by: Institute for Econometric Research, 6454 NW 5th Way, Fort Lauderdale, FL 33309-6112. TEL 954-421-1000, 800-442-9000, FAX 954-570-8200. Ed. Norman G Fosback. Circ: 13,000.

332.6　　　　　　　USA　　　　　　ISSN 0890-023X
MARKET MONTH; Standard & Poor's investment review and forecast. Text in English. m. USD 59. adv. **Document type:** *Newsletter.* **Description:** Offers discount brokerage customers third-party investment advice and recommendations.
Published by: Standard & Poor's (Subsidiary of: McGraw-Hill Companies, Inc.), 55 Water St, New York, NY 10041. TEL 212-281-8000. Ed. Jean Kozlowski.

332.64　　　　　　ECU
MARKET NEWS. Text in English, Spanish. m. ECS 390,000.
Description: Contains information regarding changes in the companies listed on the exchange.
Published by: Bolsa de Valores de Quito, Amazonas 540 y Carrion, Apartado 17-01-3772, Quito, Ecuador. TEL 593-2-526805, FAX 593-2-500942, information@ccbvq.com, http://www.ccbvq.com.

332.6　　　　　　　CAN　　　　　　ISSN 1194-2339
MARKET PROGRESS EXECUTIVE REPORT. Text in English. m. CND 133.75; CND 132.10 in United States; CND 137.45 elsewhere. **Description:** Regional and international analysis including equities, options, futures, interlisted stocks, 5 Canadian exchanges and market quality analysis.
Published by: Toronto Stock Exchange, 2 First Canadian Pl, Toronto, ON M5X 1J2, Canada. TEL 416-947-4655, FAX 416-947-4585.

332.6　　　　　　　USA
MARKET PULSE JOURNAL. Text in English. 1997. q. USD 10 (effective 2000). adv. back issues avail. **Document type:** *Trade.* **Description:** Dedicated to profiling publicly traded companies, micro-cap stocks, IPOs and undervalued securities from around the world.
Related titles: Online - full text ed.
Address: 1100 University Ave, Ste 214, Rochester, NY 14607. TEL 800-290-8935, FAX 716-256-6226, http://www.market-pulse.com, http://www.marketpulsenavigator.com. Ed. Meg Cowles TEL 716-256-6505 ext 207. R&P Lindsay Colombo TEL 716-256-6505 ext 101. Adv. contact Bernard Schmitt TEL 404-252-3710.

332.6　　　　　　　USA
MARKET SCREEN. Text in English. 1985. w. price varies.
Description: An investment analysis program that allows the user to screen all 6,600 publicly traded companies in the Market Guide electronic database, or a selected subset of the user's choice.
Related titles: Online - full text ed.
Published by: Market Guide Inc., 49 Glen Head Rd, Glen Head, NY 11545. TEL 516-759-1253, FAX 516-676-9240. Circ: 1,000.

MARKET SURVEY CUM DETAILED TECHNO ECONOMIC FEASIBILITY REPORTS. see *BUSINESS AND ECONOMICS—Marketing And Purchasing*

332.6　　　　　　　USA
MARKET SYSTEMS NEWSLETTER. Text in English. 1987. m. (plus special reports). USD 366 (effective 1999). adv.
Document type: *Newsletter.* **Description:** Stockmarket timing newsletter with short-term and long-term recommendations on the Dow Jones Average and Mutual Funds.
Formerly: Market Watch
Published by: Market Timing Systems, Inc., 4451 E Cheyenne Mountain Blvd, Ste 318, Colorado Springs, CO 80906. TEL 719-226-1782, FAX 719-226-1535, mtsi@mastertimex.com, http://mastertimer.com. Ed., R&P, Adv. contact Greg Meadors.

332.6　　　　　　　USA　　　　　　ISSN 0889-7840
MARKET VANE'S BULLISH CONSENSUS. Text in English. 1964. w. looseleaf. USD 395. abstr.; charts; illus.; stat. **Description:** Futures market advisory service for traders and professionals.
Former titles: Bullish Consensus; Market Vane
Published by: Market Vane Corporation, PO Box 90490, Pasadena, CA 91109-0490. TEL 818-395-7436, FAX 818-795-7654. Ed. R Earl Hadady.

332.6　　　　　　　USA　　　　　　ISSN 0898-0799
MARKETBRIEF. Text in English. 1982. m. USD 195 (effective 2001). back issues avail. **Document type:** *Newsletter.* **Description:** Provides buy, sell, hold, avoid ratings on optionable stocks and client stocks.
Published by: Lovejoy Corporation, Box 1442, Palmer Square, Princeton, NJ 08542. TEL 609-989-9484, FAX 609-989-8455. Ed. David P Luciano. Pub. Marie Paladry.

MARTIN WEISS' SAFE MONEY REPORT. see *BUSINESS AND ECONOMICS—Economic Situation And Conditions*

332.6　　　　　　　USA　　　　　　ISSN 0047-6188
MASTER INDICATOR OF THE STOCK MARKET✳ . Text in English. 1966. 24/yr. USD 100. charts.
Address: 11371 Torchwood Ct, West Palm Beach, FL 33414-6040. Ed. John T Goddess. Circ: 3,700.

332.6　　　　　　　DEU
MAXIMIZE; das Anlegermagazin von maxblue. Text in German. q.
Document type: *Magazine, Consumer.*
Published by: (maxblue Deutsche Bank AG), corps - Corporate Publishing Services GmbH, Schanzenstr. 56, Duesseldorf, 40549, Germany. TEL 49-211-9541613, FAX 49-211-9541606, info@corps-verlag.de, http://www.corps-verlag.de. Circ: 425,000 (controlled).

330　　　　　　　DEU　　　　　　ISSN 1611-1400
MAYDORN-REPORT; der Boersenbrief fuer Technologie- und Wachstumsaktien. Text in German. 199?. m. **Document type:** *Newsletter, Trade.*
Formerly (until 2002): Infotech-Report (1619-5981)
Published by: Boersenmedien AG, Hofer Str 20, Kulmbach, 95326, Germany. TEL 49-9221-90510, FAX 49-9221-877288.

332.6　　　　　　　USA
MCALVANY INTELLIGENCE ADVISOR. Text in English. 1975. m. USD 115. **Document type:** *Newsletter.* **Description:** Provides current analysis of market trends and geopolitical developments.
Published by: International Collectors Associates, PO Box 84904, Phoenix, AZ 85071. TEL 970-259-4100, 800-528-0559. Ed., R&P Donald S McAlvany. Circ: 13,000.

MCGREGOR'S WHO OWNS WHOM; in South Africa. see *BUSINESS AND ECONOMICS—Trade And Industrial Directories*

332.6　　　　　　　USA　　　　　　ISSN 1065-996X
MEDICAL TECHNOLOGY STOCK LETTER. Text in English. 1983. bi-w. looseleaf. USD 350 combined subscription Print & Email; USD 65 3-mos. trial (effective 2004). back issues avail. **Document type:** *Newsletter.* **Description:** Investment advisory providing specific buy and sell recommendations on medical and biotechnology stocks.
Related titles: E-mail ed. USD 320 (effective 2004).
Published by: Piedmont Venture Group, PO Box 40460, Berkeley, CA 94704. TEL 510-843-1857, FAX 510-843-0901, mtsl@bioinvest.com, http://www.bioinvest.com. Ed. John McCamant.

332.6　　　　　　　GBR
MEESPIERSON INTERNATIONAL COMMODITIES HANDBOOK (YEAR). Text in English. 1997. irreg. GBP 90, USD 160.
Document type: *Trade.* **Description:** Aims to inform the reader of the changes in the trading world and new products being traded, as well as offering a directory of commodity and commodity-related business contacts.
Published by: Euromoney Publications plc, Nestor House, Playhouse Yard, London, EC4V 5EX, United Kingdom. TEL 44-207-7798673, FAX 44-20-77798541.

332.6　　　　　　　DEU　　　　　　ISSN 0947-4102
MEIN GELD. Text in German. 1992. bi-m. EUR 17.50; EUR 3.50 newsstand/cover (effective 2005). adv. **Document type:** *Magazine, Consumer.* **Description:** Provides information and content on the latest investment trends and strategies.
Formerly (until 1994): Mein Geld Anlegen (0940-9696)
Published by: B E O Group AG, Potsdamer Platz 1, Berlin, 10785, Germany. TEL 49-30-59008410, FAX 49-30-59008422, redaktion@meingeld-web.de, http://www.meingeld-magazin.de. Ed. Gian Hessami. Adv. contact Sylvia Matzkowiak. page EUR 4,920; trim 210 x 280.

332.6　　　　　　　MEX　　　　　　ISSN 0185-1268
HG4503
MERCADO DE VALORES. Text in Spanish. 1940. m. bk.rev. bibl.; charts; mkt. index, cum.index: 1946-1995. **Document type:** *Government.*
Related titles: CD-ROM ed.: MXP 920.
Indexed: PAIS, RASB.
Published by: Nacional Financiera S.N.C., Subdireccion de Informacion Tecnica y Publicaciones, INSURGENTES SUR 1971, Nivel Fuente, Col Guadalupe Inn, Mexico City, DF 01020, Mexico. TEL 52-5-3256047. Ed. Dauno Totoro Nieto. Circ: 10,000.

332.6　　　　　　　MEX
MERCADO DE VALORES (ENGLISH EDITION); an update on Mexico's economy and finance. Text in Spanish. 1994. bi-m. free. bk.rev. bibl.; charts; mkt. index. **Document type:** *Government.*
Published by: Nacional Financiera S.N.C., Subdireccion de Informacion Tecnica y Publicaciones, INSURGENTES SUR 1971, Nivel Fuente, Col Guadalupe Inn, Mexico City, DF 01020, Mexico. TEL 52-5-3256047. Ed. Dauno Totoro Nieto. Circ: 2,000.

332.6　　　　　　　AUT　　　　　　ISSN 0025-9926
MERCUR; authentischer Verlosungsanzeiger mit Anzeiger aufgebotener Wertpapiere. Text in German. m. adv. index.
Document type: *Bulletin, Trade.*
Published by: Oesterreichische Kontrollbank AG, Am Hof 4, Vienna, 1011, Austria. TEL 43-1-531270, FAX 43-1-531275698, oeffentlichkeitsarbeit@oekb.at, http://www.oekb.at. Circ: 2,000 (paid and controlled).

332.6　　　　　　　USA
HG4651
MERGENT ANNUAL BOND RECORD. Text in English. 1931. a.
Former titles (until 1999): Moody's Bond Record (1050-0820); (until 1936): Moody's Bond Ratings and Quotations; (until 1934): Moody's Bond Ratings
—CCC.
Published by: Mergent, 5250 77 Center Dr, Ste 150, Charlotte, NC 28217. TEL 704-559-7601, 800-342-5647, FAX 704-559-6945, customerservice@mergent.com, http://www.mergent.com.

332.6　　　　　　　USA　　　　　　ISSN 1532-5997
HG4905
MERGENT BOND RECORD. Text in English. 1936. m. USD 425 (effective 1999). **Description:** Comprehensive, fact-filled guide to 68,000 fixed-income issues.
Formerly (until 1999): Moody's Bond Record (0148-1878)
Related titles: Microform ed.: (from MIS).
—CCC.
Published by: Mergent, 5250 77 Center Dr, Ste 150, Charlotte, NC 28217. TEL 704-559-7601, 800-342-5647, FAX 704-559-6945, customerservice@mergent.com, http://www.mergent.com.

332.6　　　　　　　USA　　　　　　ISSN 0545-0217
MERGENT INDUSTRIAL MANUAL AND NEWS REPORTS. Text in English. 1914. a. price varies. stat. index. reprints avail.
Document type: *Directory, Trade.* **Description:** Provides business and financial information on nearly 2,000 top industrial corporations.
Formerly (until 1998): Moody's Industrial Manual
Related titles: Microfiche ed.
—CCC.
Published by: Mergent, 5250 77 Center Dr, Ste 150, Charlotte, NC 28217. TEL 704-559-7601, 800-342-5647, FAX 704-559-6945, customerservice@mergent.com, http://www.mergent.com.

332.678　　　　　　USA　　　　　　ISSN 0278-3509
MERGENT INTERNATIONAL MANUAL AND NEWS REPORTS. Text in English. 1981. a. price varies. reprints avail.
Document type: *Directory, Trade.* **Description:** Financial and business data on over 9,000 companies in nearly 100 countries.
Formerly (until 1998): Moody's International Manual

▼ *new title*　　➤ *refereed*　　✳ *unverified*　　◆ *full entry avail.*

—CCC.
Published by: Mergent, 5250 77 Center Dr, Ste 150, Charlotte, NC 28217. TEL 704-559-7601, 800-342-5647, FAX 704-559-6945, customerservice@mergent.com, http://www.mergent.com.

332.6 USA
MERGENT O T C INDUSTRIAL MANUAL AND NEWS REPORTS. (Over-the-Counter) Text in English. 1970. a. price varies. reprints avail. **Document type:** *Directory, Trade.* **Description:** Covers more than 2,000 industrial companies traded on NASDAQ over-the-counter and regional exchanges.
Formerly (until 1998): Moody's O T C Industrial Manual (0192-7167)
Related titles: Microfiche ed.
—CCC.
Published by: Mergent, 5250 77 Center Dr, Ste 150, Charlotte, NC 28217. TEL 704-559-7601, 800-342-5647, FAX 704-559-6945, customerservice@mergent.com, http://www.mergent.com.

332.6 USA ISSN 1546-6159
MERGENT O T C UNLISTED MANUAL. (Over-the-Counter) Text in English. 1986. a. USD 2,345 per issue to corporations; USD 985 per issue to libraries (effective 2005). stat. index. reprints avail. **Description:** Covers financial facts and corporate data on more than 2,200 companies not listed on the national or regional exchange systems.
Formerly (until 2001): Moody's O T C Unlisted Manual (0890-5282)
Related titles: Microfiche ed.; ♦ Supplement(s): Moody's O T C Industrial News Reports. ISSN 0027-0865.
—CCC.
Published by: Mergent, 5250 77 Center Dr, Ste 150, Charlotte, NC 28217. TEL 704-559-7601, 800-342-5647, FAX 704-559-6945, customerservice@mergent.com, http://www.mergent.com/publish/news%5Freports.asp.

332.6 USA
HG4907
MERGENT O T C UNLISTED NEWS REPORTS. (Over the Counter) Text in English. 1986. w.
Former titles (until 2001): Moody's O T C Unlisted News Reports (Online); (until 1999): Moody's O T C Unlisted News Reports (Print) (0895-3252)
Media: Online - full content.
—CCC.
Published by: Mergent, 5250 77 Center Dr, Ste 150, Charlotte, NC 28217. TEL 704-559-7601, 800-342-5647, FAX 704-559-6945, customerservice@mergent.com, http://www.mergent.com/publish/uploadedFiles/UNL_NEWS[94].pdf.

332.6 USA ISSN 1540-1316
HG4961
MERGENT PUBLIC UTILITY MANUAL. Text in English. 1913. a. USD 1,625 (effective 1999); includes bi-w. Moody's Public Utility News Reports. reprints avail. **Description:** Covers financial and operating data on all U.S. public and privately-held utilities.
Formerly (until 2001): Moody's Public Utility Manual (0545-0241)
Related titles: Microfiche ed.
—CCC.
Published by: Mergent, 5250 77 Center Dr, Ste 150, Charlotte, NC 28217. customerservice@mergent.com, http://www.mergent.com.

332.6 USA ISSN 1546-6000
HG4971
MERGENT TRANSPORTATION MANUAL. Text in English. 1909. a. USD 1,495 (effective 1999); includes w. Moody's Transportation News Reports. reprints avail. **Description:** Covers financial and operating data on all major public and private air, rail, bus, trucking, vehicle leasing and rental, and shipping companies.
Formerly (until 2001): Moody's Transportation Manual (0545-025X)
Related titles: Microfiche ed.
—CCC.
Published by: Mergent, 5250 77 Center Dr, Ste 150, Charlotte, NC 28217. customerservice@mergent.com, http://www.mergent.com.

332.6 USA ISSN 1527-4675
MERGENT UNIT INVESTMENT TRUSTS. Text in English. 1999. w.
Published by: Mergent, 5250 77 Center Dr, Ste 150, Charlotte, NC 28217. TEL 704-559-7601, 800-342-5647, FAX 704-559-6945, customerservice@mergent.com, http://www.mergent.com.

332.678 USA ISSN 1547-8335
HG4050
MERGENT'S DIVIDEND ACHIEVERS. Text in English. q. USD 189 domestic to institutions; USD 229 in Canada & Mexico to institutions; USD 263 elsewhere to institutions; USD 208 combined subscription domestic to institutions print & online eds.; USD 248 combined subscription in Canada & Mexico to institutions print & online eds.; USD 282 combined subscription elsewhere to institutions print & online eds. (effective 2006). **Document type:** *Journal, Trade.*
Former titles (until 2001): Handbook of Dividend Achievers (1541-1583); (until 2000): Moody's Handbook of Dividend Achievers (0737-1586)
Related titles: Online - full text ed.: ISSN 1548-2839. USD 189 to institutions (effective 2006) (from EBSCO Publishing, Wiley InterScience).
Published by: John Wiley & Sons, Inc., 111 River St, Hoboken, NJ 07030-5774. TEL 201-748-6000, FAX 201-748-5915, http://www3.interscience.wiley.com/cgi-bin/jhome/107642576, http://www.wiley.com.

332.6 USA ISSN 1547-8343
HG4501
MERGENT'S HANDBOOK OF COMMON STOCKS. Text in English. 1955; N.S. 2004. a. USD 405 domestic; USD 445 in Canada & Mexico; USD 479 elsewhere (effective 2006). adv. charts; stat. reprints avail. **Document type:** *Journal, Trade.* **Description:** Covers performing trends and financial summaries of 1,000 NYSE and AMEX companies, and financial listings of 1,150 additional companies.
Former titles (until 2002): Handbook of Common Stocks (1537-1980); (until 1999): Moody's Handbook of Common Stocks (0027-0830)
Related titles: Online - full text ed.: ISSN 1548-2723 (from Wiley InterScience).
—CCC.
Published by: John Wiley & Sons, Inc., 111 River St, Hoboken, NJ 07030-5774. TEL 201-748-6000, FAX 201-748-5915, http://www.wiley.com/WileyCDA/WileyTitle/productCd-COM.html. Ed. Stacy M Cleeland. Pub. Jonathan Worrall.

332.6 USA ISSN 1542-9326
HG4501
MERGENT'S HANDBOOK OF N A S D A Q STOCKS. (National Association of Securities Dealers Automated Quotations) Text in English. 1981; N.S. 2004. q. USD 365 domestic; USD 405 in Canada & Mexico; USD 439 elsewhere (effective 2006). **Document type:** *Journal, Trade.* **Description:** Reference for fast facts, performance trends and financial summaries of over 600 NASDAQ companies.
Former titles (until 2002): Handbook of N A S D A Q Stocks (1543-897X); (until 1999): Moody's Handbook of N A S D A Q Stocks (1059-8057); (until 1992): Moody's Handbook of O T C Stocks (0276-3516)
Related titles: Online - full text ed.: ISSN 1548-2847 (from Wiley InterScience).
—CCC.
Published by: John Wiley & Sons, Inc., 111 River St, Hoboken, NJ 07030-5774. TEL 201-748-6000, FAX 201-748-5915, http://www.wiley.com/WileyCDA/WileyTitle/productCd-NAS.html. Ed. Stacy M Cleeland. Pub. Jonathan Worrall.

MERGENT'S INDUSTRY REVIEW. see *BUSINESS AND ECONOMICS—Abstracting, Bibliographies, Statistics*

338.83 GBR
MERGERS & ACQUISITIONS YEARBOOK. Text in English. a. **Document type:** *Yearbook, Trade.*
Related titles: ♦ Supplement to: International Financial Law Review. ISSN 0262-6969.
—BLDSC (5680.782100).
Published by: Euromoney Institutional Investor Plc., Nestor House, Playhouse Yard, London, EC4V 5EX, United Kingdom. TEL 44-20-7779-8673, 44-20-77798888, information@euromoneyplc.com, http://www.euromoneyplc.com.

332.6 USA ISSN 1071-4065
HD2746.5
MERGERSTAT REVIEW. Text in English. 1981. a. USD 299 (effective Apr. 2002). **Document type:** *Journal, Trade.* **Description:** In-depth research & analysis of United States and cross-border mergers and acquisitions activity and multi-year trends.
Related titles: Online - full text ed.: USD 395 (effective Feb. 2002) (from LexisNexis).
Published by: Mergerstat, 1933 Pontius Ave, Los Angeles, CA 90025. TEL 800-455-8871, FAX 310-966-9462, mergerstat@hlhz.com, http://www.mergerstat.com.

332.6 USA
MERRILL LYNCH MARKET LETTER. Text in English. s-m. USD 49.
Published by: Merrill Lynch, Pierce, Fenner & Smith, Inc., 1 Liberty Plaza, New York, NY 10006. **Subscr. to:** Subscription Processing Center, New Brunswick, NJ 08988-0009.

332.6 BRA
MEU DINHEIRO. Text in Portuguese. m. BRL 58; BRL 5.90 newsstand/cover. **Document type:** *Magazine, Consumer.*
Published by: Editora Abril, S.A., Av. das Nacoes Unidas, 7221, 11 andar Pinheiros, Sao Paulo, SP 05425-902, Brazil. TEL 55-011-30372000, FAX 55-011-30375638, relacoes.corporativas@abril.com.br, http://www.abril.com.br/.

332.6 MEX
MEXICAN STOCK EXCHANGE. QUARTERLY FINANCIAL INFORMATION. Text in Spanish. q. USD 895. **Description:** Focuses on the main financial data of all the companies listed on the stock exchange. Includes notes on each company's operational performance and significant issues.
Published by: Bolsa Mexicana de Valores, S.A. de C.V./Mexican Stock Exchange, Paseo de la Reforma 255, Mexico City, DF 06500, Mexico. TEL 525-726-67-91, FAX 525-591-0534.

332.6 USA ISSN 1044-6303
HC131
MEXICO SERVICE. Text in English. fortn. USD 695. **Document type:** *Bulletin.* **Description:** Reports on economic, financial and political developments in Mexico.
Related titles: Online - full text ed.: (from Factiva).
—CCC.
Published by: International Reports, Inc. (Subsidiary of: I B C U.S.A.), 11300 Rockville Pike, Ste 1100, Rockville, MD 20852-3035. TEL 301-816-8950, FAX 301-816-8945. Ed. Robert G Taylor.

332.6 FRA ISSN 1145-623X
MIEUX VIVRE VOTRE ARGENT. Text in French. m. EUR 33 (effective 2005). **Document type:** *Magazine, Consumer.*
Published by: Groupe Mieux Vivre, 32 rue Notre Dame de Victoire, Paris, 75002, France. TEL 33-1-53002000, FAX 33-1-42334498, http://www.votreargent.fr. Ed. Francois de Witt. Pub. Jean-Antoine Bouchez. Circ: 350,000 (paid).

332.6 382 ITA ISSN 1594-6770
MILANO FINANZA. Variant title: M F. Text in Italian. 1986. w. **Document type:** *Magazine, Consumer.*
Related titles: Online - full text ed.: ISSN 1723-3801. 199?.
Indexed: PAIS.
Published by: Class Editori, Via Marco Burigozzo 5, Milan, MI 20122, Italy. TEL 39-02-582191, http://www.milanofinanza.it, http://www.classeditori.com. Circ: 90,000.

332.6 USA ISSN 0734-3957
MODERN SECURITIES TRANSFERS (SUPPLEMENT). Key Title: Israels and Guttman's Modern Securities Transfers. Cumulative Supplement. Text in English. base vol. plus irreg. updates. USD 115; USD 166.95 foreign. **Document type:** *Trade.*
Published by: W G & L Financial Reporting & Management Research (Subsidiary of: R I A), 395 Hudson St, New York, NY 10014. TEL 212-367-6300, FAX 212-367-6718. **Subscr. to:** The Park Square Bldg., 31 St James Ave, Boston, MA 02116-4112. TEL 800-950-1207.

332.6 USA
MONETARY DIGEST. Text in English. 1974. q. USD 36 to members. adv. bk.rev. reprints avail. **Document type:** *Newsletter, Consumer.* **Description:** Covers political, economic and social issues affecting the price of precious metals.
Published by: Certified Mint, Inc., 3550 N. Central Ave., Ste. 1407, Phoenix, AZ 85012-2112. Pub., R&P, Adv. contact Bill Haynes. Circ: 3,000.

332.6 CAN
MONEY DIGEST. Text in English. m.
Media: Online - full content. **Related titles:** Online - full text ed.: (from Micromedia ProQuest).
Published by: Investors Association of Canada, 1 Dundas St West, Ste 2500, Toronto, ON M5G 1Z3, Canada. contact@iac.ca, http://www.iac.ca. Ed. Dr. Chuck Chakrapani.

332.6 USA
MONEY - FORECAST LETTER. Text in English. 1980. m. USD 200 (effective 2001). **Document type:** *Newsletter.*
Formerly: Financial Forecast Letter
Published by: Financial Research Center, PO Box 6170, Holliston, MA 01746-2234. TEL 508-429-1920. Ed. Adrian Van Eck. Pub. David C Jennett. Circ: 5,000.

332.6 USA ISSN 1097-3443
HG201
MONEY FUND REPORT. Text in English. 1975. w. looseleaf. USD 3,375 (effective 2005). charts. back issues avail. **Document type:** *Newsletter, Trade.* **Description:** For investment professionals and bankers who compete with money funds. Reports on money fund portfolio holdings, 7-day and 30-day yields, and average maturities. Covers 1300-plus taxable and tax-free money funds registered in the U.S. and digests summary data for distinct groups of funds, from no-risk U.S. Treasury funds to more aggressive funds that buy second-tier paper.
Former titles: I B C - Donoghue's Money Fund Report; (until 1989): Donoghue's Money Fund Report (0197-7091); (until 197?): Butler's Money Fund Report (0363-5716)
Related titles: Online - full text ed.
Published by: iMoneyNet Inc. (Subsidiary of: Informa U K Limited), One Research Dr, Westborough, MA 01581. TEL 508-616-6600, FAX 508-616-5511, info@imoneynet.com, http://www.imoneynet.com/proddocs/imMfrProd.htm. Ed. Connie Bugbee. Circ: 500 (controlled and free).

MONEY MAGAZINE. see *BUSINESS AND ECONOMICS—Banking And Finance*

332.6 USA ISSN 1549-9111
HG4530
MONEY MANAGEMENT EXECUTIVE. Abbreviated title: M M E. Text in English. w. USD 1,750 domestic; USD 1,850 foreign (effective 2005). adv. back issues avail. **Document type:** *Newsletter, Trade.*

Former titles (until 2003): Mutual Fund Market News (1070-3373); (until 1993): F A C S of the Week (1056-2540)
Related titles: Online - full text ed.: (from EBSCO Publishing, Florida Center for Library Automation, Gale Group, O C L C Online Computer Library Center, Inc., ProQuest Information & Learning).
Indexed: B&I.
—CCC.
Published by: Source Media, Inc., One State St Plaza, 27th Fl, New York, NY 10004. TEL 212-803-6077, 800-221-1809, FAX 212-747-1154, custserv@sourcemedia.com, http://www.mmexecutive.com, http://www.sourcemedia.com. Ed. Lee Barney TEL 212-803-8751. Pub. John Toth TEL 212-803-6565. adv.: B&W page USD 3,275, color page USD 4,595. Circ: 930 (paid and free).

332.6 332 USA ISSN 1529-2347
MONEY MANAGEMENT LETTER; bi-weekly newsletter covering the pensions & money management industry. Text in English. 1980. bi-w. USD 2,440 combined subscription domestic print & online eds.; USD 2,515 combined subscription foreign print & online eds. (effective 2005). adv. reprint service avail. from PQC. **Document type:** *Newsletter, Trade.* **Description:** Covers the business of U.S. pension fund investment managers. Reports on which funds are hiring new money managers and why, what new strategies and products are being used, personnel changes that shift market power, and trends in master trust and custodial services.
Incorporates: Trust News
Related titles: CD-ROM ed.; Microfiche ed.; Online - full text ed.: (from Florida Center for Library Automation, Gale Group, O C L C Online Computer Library Center, Inc.).
Indexed: ATI.
—CCC.
Published by: Institutional Investor News (Subsidiary of: Euromoney Institutional Investor Plc.), 225 Park Ave S, 7th Fl, New York, NY 10003-1605. TEL 212-224-3800, FAX 212-224-3491, info@iiplatinum.com, http://www.moneymanagementletter.com, http://www.iinews.com. Pub. Nanzeen Kanga TEL 212-224-3005. **Subscr. to:** New Orders, PO Box 5063, Brentwood, TN 37024. TEL 615-377-3322, 800-945-2034, 800-715-9197, FAX 615-337-0525, vlockridge@sunbeltfs.com.

332.6 USA ISSN 0271-7751
MONEY MARKET FUND SURVEY✶. Text in English. 1980. m. looseleaf. USD 450. charts; stat. back issues avail.
Published by: Survey Publications Co., 23 E 81 St, Apt 2, New York, NY 10028-0224. TEL 212-988-2498. Ed. Judith C Lack.

332.6 USA
MONEY MARKET INSIGHT. Text in English. 1989. m. looseleaf. USD 1,225 (effective 2002). adv. charts; stat. 28 p./no.; back issues avail.; reprints avail. **Document type:** *Newsletter, Trade.* **Description:** Provides the investment professional with statistical summary on nearly 1,700 taxable and tax-free money funds and reports on trends in short term investing with in-depth analysis of the fixed income market.
Formerly: I B C's Money Market Insight (1043-285X)
Related titles: Online - full text ed.
Published by: iMoneyNet Inc. (Subsidiary of: Informa U K Limited), One Research Dr, Westborough, MA 01581. FAX 508-616-5511, http://www.imoneynet.com. Ed. Peter G Crane. Pub. Kenneth B Bohlin. Adv. contact Perry Leardi. Circ: 1,000.

MONEY MARKETING. see *BUSINESS AND ECONOMICS—Banking And Finance*

332.6 GBR ISSN 0263-7669
MONEY OBSERVER; 20 years of invaluable advice. Text in English. 1979. m. GBP 33 domestic; GBP 39.50 in Europe; GBP 42 elsewhere; GBP 3.25 newsstand/cover. adv. **Document type:** *Consumer.* **Description:** Advises on how to maximize investment returns without taking undue risks.
Published by: Guardian Newspapers Ltd. (Subsidiary of: Guardian Media Group plc), 119 Farringdon Rd, London, EC1R 3ER, United Kingdom. TEL 44-171-278-2332. Ed. Andrew Pitts. Adv. contact Chris Willis. Circ: 35,198 (paid). **Subscr. to:** Garrard House, Garrard House 2-6, Homesdale Rd, Bromley, Dorset BR2 9WL, United Kingdom. TEL 44-181-289-7960. **Dist. by:** M M C Ltd., Octagon House, White Hart Meadows, Ripley, Woking, Surrey GU23 6HR, United Kingdom. TEL 44-1483-211222, FAX 44-1483-224541.

332.6 CAN ISSN 0709-0579
MONEY REPORTER; the insider's letter for investors whose interest is more interest. Text in English. 1978. bi-w. CND 197. **Document type:** *Newsletter.* **Description:** Financial news about interest.
Related titles: Supplement(s): Monthly Key Investment.
Published by: M P L Communications Inc., 133 Richmond St W, Ste 700, Toronto, ON M5H 3M8, Canada. TEL 416-869-1177, FAX 416-869-0456.

332.6 USA ISSN 0899-1391
THE MONEYCHANGER. Text in English. 1981. m. USD 95; USD 107 foreign (effective 1999). bk.rev. back issues avail. **Document type:** *Bulletin.*
Published by: Little Mountain Corp., PO Box 236, Cordova, TN 38088-0236. TEL 901-853-6136, FAX 901-854-5138, moneychanger@compuserve.com, http://www.the-moneychanger.com. Ed., R&P Franklin Sanders.

332.6 GBR
MONEYEXTRA. Text in English. 1995. d. adv. **Document type:** *Magazine, Consumer.* **Description:** Provides up-to-date information and quotes for personal finance investors.
Formerly: MoneyWorld
Media: Online - full text.
Address: Cambridge House South, Henry St, Bath, BA1 1JS, United Kingdom. TEL 44-845-0777085, FAX 44-1225-402070, customer.services@moneyextra.com, http://www.moneyworld.co.uk.

332.6 CAN ISSN 0703-7163
THE MONEYLETTER. Text in English. 1976. s-m. CND 97 (effective 1999). adv. **Document type:** *Newsletter.* **Description:** Stock market advice with how-to tips on personal investment planning and strategy.
Published by: Hume Publishing Company Ltd., 604 2200 Yonge St, Toronto, ON M4S 2C6, Canada. TEL 800-733-4863, FAX 416-440-8268, customerservice@humepublishing.com, humenewsletters@mindspring.com, http://www.humepublishing.com. Ed. A Micheal Keerma. Adv. contact Barbara Ritchie.

332.6 USA
MONEYLETTER (ASHLAND)✶. Text in English. 1980. s-m. looseleaf. USD 109. charts; stat. **Document type:** *Newsletter.* **Description:** Information on no- and low-load mutual funds.
Formerly: Donoghue's Moneyletter (0197-7083); Butler's Moneyletter
Related titles: Online - full text ed.
Published by: IBC - Donoghue, Inc., PO Box 5193, Westborough, MA 01581-5193. TEL 508-881-2800, 800-343-5413, FAX 508-881-0982. Ed. Peter Crane. Circ: 30,000.

332.6 USA ISSN 0745-9858
MONEYPAPER. Text in English. 1982. m. USD 81 (effective 1999). **Document type:** *Newsletter.* **Description:** Publishes financial advise for the small investor, focusing on the benefits of direct investing plans.
Published by: (Temper of the Times Communications, Inc.), Vita Nelson, Ed. & Pub., 1010 Mamaroneck Ave, Mamaroneck, NY 10543. TEL 914-381-5400, FAX 914-381-7206. R&P Harriet Hanlon.

MONEYWISE; Britain's best-selling personal finance magazine. see *BUSINESS AND ECONOMICS*

332.6 USA
MONEYWORLD MAGAZINE. Text in English. 1987. m. USD 29.95. adv. bk.rev. **Description:** Offers new information, insights and specific recommendations for investors and professional financial planners.
Published by: Gulf Atlantic Publishing, Inc., 1947 Lee Rd, Winter Park, FL 32789-1834. TEL 407-628-5700, FAX 407-628-0807, money-world@money-world.net, http://www.money-world.net. Ed. Jessica Klarp. Circ: 350,000.

332.6 330.9 AUS
MONITOR MONEY REVIEW. Text in English. 1996. q. free to clients. charts; mkt. back issues avail. **Document type:** *Newsletter, Trade.* **Description:** Aimed at personal investors and retirees. Provides broad economic and legislative update to clients of a national, financial planing organization.
Formerly (until 2000): Midas Australian Mastersignal; Which was formed by the merger of (1961-1996): Australian Mastersignal; (1983-1996): Midas; Which was formerly (until 1995): Monitor Money Review (1442-0538); Which incorporated (in 1988): Monitor Money-Watch; Which was formerly (until 1987): Monitor Money Marketwatch; (until 1986): Midas Newsletter; Forecast; Monitor Money Review was formerly (until 1986): Australian Money (0812-6836)
Published by: Monitor Money Corp., PO Box 5216, Chatswood, NSW 2067, Australia. TEL 61-2-94138199, FAX 61-2-94131181, monitor@monmoney.com.au, contactmonitor@monitormoney.com.au, http://www.monitormoney.com.au/. Ed., Pub. Tim Titheradge. Circ: 4,000.

332.6 CAN ISSN 0828-8178
MONTHLY STOCK CHARTS - CANADIAN COMPANIES. Text in English. 1984. q. CND 111.28 (effective 2000 - 2001). adv. **Document type:** *Bulletin.* **Description:** Charts 12 years of monthly share price and volume for 1200 Canadian resource and industrial companies.
Published by: Independent Survey Co., ChartSmart Software, P O Box 29062, V6J 120, Vancouver, BC, Canada. TEL 604-731-5777, 604-737-1492, 800-665-3389, FAX 604-737-1475, info@chartsmart.com, bobstran@helix.net, http://www.chartsmart.com. Ed., Pub., Adv. contact Bob Stranks.

332.6 USA
MOODY'S DIVIDEND RECORD AND ANNUAL DIVIDEND RECORD. Text in English. 1930. s-w. USD 775 (effective 1999). Supplement avail. **Description:** Reports on current dividend data of 22,000 securities.
Formerly (until 1999): Moody's Dividend Record (0192-7019)
—CCC.
Published by: Mergent, 5250 77 Center Dr, Ste 150, Charlotte, NC 28217. customerservice@mergent.com, http://www.mergent.com.

332.6 USA ISSN 0027-0849
HG4961
MOODY'S INDUSTRIAL NEWS REPORTS. Text in English. 1928. 2/w. included in subscr. to Moody's Industrial Manual. stat. index, cum.index. **Description:** Informs readers of mergers and acquisitions, interim earnings, new products and any other financial developments.
Formerly (until 1970): Moody's Industrials
Related titles: Microfiche ed.
—CISTI. **CCC.**
Published by: Mergent, 5250 77 Center Dr, Ste 150, Charlotte, NC 28217. customerservice@mergent.com, http://www.mergent.com.

332.6 USA
MOODY'S INTERNATIONAL COMPANY DATA. Text in English. q. (plus m. updates). USD 7,000 (effective 1999). **Document type:** *Directory, Trade.* **Description:** Provides business and financial information on over 11,000 non-US based companies in more than 90 countries.
Formerly: Moody's International Plus
Published by: Mergent, 5250 77 Center Dr, Ste 150, Charlotte, NC 28217. customerservice@mergent.com, http://www.mergent.com.

332.678 USA ISSN 0278-3517
MOODY'S INTERNATIONAL NEWS REPORTS. Text in English. 1981. w. included in subscr. to Moody's International Manual. **Description:** Keeps readers on top of mergers and acquisitions, new companies, joint ventures, interim earnings, revised Moody's ratings and any other news and developments affecting companies in this manual.
Related titles: Microfiche ed.
—CCC.
Published by: Mergent, 5250 77 Center Dr, Ste 150, Charlotte, NC 28217. customerservice@mergent.com, http://www.mergent.com.

332.6 USA ISSN 0545-0233
MOODY'S MUNICIPAL AND GOVERNMENT MANUAL. Text in English. 1918. a. USD 2,495 (effective 1999); includes s-w. news report. stat. index. reprints avail. **Description:** Covers over 8,840 bond-issuing municipalities and government agencies.
Related titles: Microfiche ed.
—CCC.
Published by: Mergent, 5250 77 Center Dr, Ste 150, Charlotte, NC 28217. customerservice@mergent.com, http://www.mergent.com.

332.6 USA ISSN 0027-0857
HG4931
MOODY'S MUNICIPAL AND GOVERNMENT NEWS REPORTS. Text in English. 1928. s-w. incl. in subscr. to Moody's Municipal and Government Manual. stat. index, cum.index. **Description:** Updates changes in Moody's ratings and new bond descriptions, financial statistics and audit reports, plus news affecting issues rated and covered in the manual.
Formerly: Moody's Municipals and Government
Related titles: Microfiche ed.
—CCC.
Published by: Mergent, 5250 77 Center Dr, Ste 150, Charlotte, NC 28217. customerservice@mergent.com, http://www.mergent.com.

332.6 USA ISSN 0027-0865
HG4965
MOODY'S O T C INDUSTRIAL NEWS REPORTS. (Over-the-Counter) Text in English. 1970. s-w. included in subscr. to Moody's OTC Industrial Manual. stat. index, cum.index.
Formerly: Moody's O T C Industrials
Related titles: Microfiche ed.; ♦ Supplement to: Mergent O T C Unlisted Manual. ISSN 1546-6159.
—CCC.
Published by: Mergent, 5250 77 Center Dr, Ste 150, Charlotte, NC 28217. customerservice@mergent.com, http://www.mergent.com.

332.6 USA ISSN 0027-0873
MOODY'S PUBLIC UTILITY NEWS REPORTS. Text in English. 1928. s-w. included in subscr. to Moody's Public Utility Manual. stat. index, cum.index. **Description:** Informs readers of news affecting companies listed in the Public Utility Manual.
Related titles: Microfiche ed.
—CCC.
Published by: Mergent, 5250 77 Center Dr, Ste 150, Charlotte, NC 28217. customerservice@mergent.com, http://www.mergent.com.

332.6 USA ISSN 0027-089X
MOODY'S TRANSPORTATION NEWS REPORTS; railroads, airlines, shipping, bus, pipe and truck lines. Text in English. 1928. w. included in subscr. to Moody's Transportation Manual. **Description:** Informs readers of news affecting companies listed in the manual.
Formerly: Moody's Transportation
Related titles: Microfiche ed.
—CCC.
Published by: Mergent, 5250 77 Center Dr, Ste 150, Charlotte, NC 28217. customerservice@mergent.com, http://www.mergent.com.

332.6   USA   ISSN 1081-2598
MORE THAN MONEY; exploring the personal, political, and spiritual impact of wealth in our lives. Text in English. 1993. q. USD 45 (effective 2005). adv. bk.rev. illus. back issues avail. **Document type:** *Journal, Trade.* **Description:** Includes interviews, articles and personal stories of people who are thinking about-and acting on-ground breaking questions about money.
Address: 1430 Massachusetts Ave, PO Box 1094, Cambridge, MA 02138. TEL 617-864-8200, FAX 617-864-2044, impact@efn.org, info@morethanmoney.org, http://www.morethanmoney.org. Ed. Pamela Gerloff. Adv. contact Mara Peluso. Circ: 1,500 (controlled).

332.6   USA   ISSN 1059-1419
HG4530
MORNINGSTAR CLOSED-END FUNDS. Text in English. 1991. bi-w. USD 195 in United States; USD 225 in Canada & Mexico; USD 275 elsewhere. charts; stat. back issues avail. **Document type:** *Newsletter.* **Description:** Provides performance data, rankings, portfolio information and written analysis for over 280 closed-ends funds.
Published by: Morningstar, Inc., 225 W Wacker Dr, Ste 400, Chicago, IL 60606. TEL 312-696-6000, FAX 312-696-6001. Ed. Catherine Gillis. Circ: 7,000.

332.6   USA   ISSN 1557-2099
▼ **MORNINGSTAR DIVIDENDINVESTOR.** Text in English. 2005. m. USD 99 (effective 2006). **Document type:** *Newsletter, Consumer.*
Published by: Morningstar, Inc., 225 W Wacker Dr, Ste 400, Chicago, IL 60606. TEL 312 384-4000, 312 696-6311, FAX 312-696-6009, productinfo@morningstar.com, http://www.morningstar.com.

332.6   USA   ISSN 1099-0402
MORNINGSTAR FUNDINVESTOR. Text in English. 1998. m. USD 89 to individuals (effective 2005). **Document type:** *Newsletter, Consumer.*
Formerly: Five Star Investor
Published by: Morningstar, Inc., 225 W Wacker Dr, Ste 400, Chicago, IL 60606. TEL 312 384-4000, FAX 312-696-6009, http://www.morningstar.com/products/ymfi.html. Ed. Russel Kinnel. Circ: 40,000 (paid).

332.6   USA   ISSN 1556-7389
▼ **MORNINGSTAR GROWTHINVESTOR.** Text in English. 2005 (July). m. USD 99 (effective 2006). **Document type:** *Newsletter, Consumer.*
Published by: Morningstar, Inc., 225 W Wacker Dr, Ste 400, Chicago, IL 60606. TEL 312 384-4000, 312 696-6311, FAX 312-696-6009, http://www.morningstar.com.

332.6327   USA   ISSN 1059-1443
HG4530
MORNINGSTAR MUTUAL FUNDS. Text in English. 1986. bi-w. looseleaf. USD 549 to individuals; USD 795 to institutions (effective 2005). charts; stat. back issues avail. **Document type:** *Newsletter, Consumer.* **Description:** Provides comprehensive information, including performance data, ratings, portfolio listings, and written analyses on 1240 mutual funds. Features commentaries on various fund-related subjects.
Formerly: Mutual Fund Values (0890-7153)
Published by: Morningstar, Inc., 225 W Wacker Dr, Ste 400, Chicago, IL 60606. TEL 312 384-4000, FAX 312-696-6009, http://www.morningstar.com. Circ: 9,515 (controlled).

332.6   USA   ISSN 1059-1427
HG4530
MORNINGSTAR MUTUAL FUNDS ONDISC. Text in English. 1991. m. (plus q. and a. updates). price varies. **Description:** Compares, analyzes and tracks over 3,200 mutual funds and produces customized reports and graphs.
Media: CD-ROM.
Published by: Morningstar, Inc., 225 W Wacker Dr, Ste 400, Chicago, IL 60606. TEL 312-696-6000, FAX 312-696-6001. Ed. Michael Van Dam. Circ: 2,000.

332.6   USA   ISSN 1098-819X
HG4501
MORNINGSTAR STOCKINVESTOR. Text in English. 1998. m. USD 99 domestic; USD 129 in Canada & Mexico; USD 149 elsewhere (effective 2005). **Document type:** *Newsletter.*
Published by: Morningstar, 225 W Wacker Dr, Chicago, IL 60606. TEL 312-696-6383, FAX 312-696-6009, http://www.morningstar.com. Ed. Mark Sellers. Pub. Catherine Gillis Odelbo.

MORTGAGE AND REAL ESTATE EXECUTIVES REPORT. see *REAL ESTATE*

THE MOSCOW TIMES BUSINESS REVIEW. see *BUSINESS AND ECONOMICS—International Commerce*

332.6   USA   ISSN 1550-7955
▼ **MOTLEY FOOL CHAMPION FUNDS.** Text in English. 2004 (Apr.). m. USD 149 (effective 2004).
Media: Online - full content.

Published by: The Motley Fool, Inc., 123 N. Pitt St., Alexandria, VA 22314. TEL 703-838-3665, FAX 703-254-1999, http://www.championfunds.fool.com, http://www.fool.com. Ed. Paul Elliott.

332.6   USA   ISSN 1545-3286
▼ **MOTLEY FOOL HIDDEN GEMS.** Text in English. 2003 (Jun.). m. USD 149 (effective 2003).
Related titles: Online - full text ed.: ISSN 1545-3294.
Published by: The Motley Fool, Inc., 123 N. Pitt St., Alexandria, VA 22314. TEL 703-838-3665, FAX 703-254-1999, http://www.hiddengems.fool.com, http://www.fool.com.

332.6   USA   ISSN 1546-5047
▼ **MOTLEY FOOL INCOME INVESTOR.** Variant title: Mathew Emmert's Motley Fool Income Investor. Text in English. 2003 (Sept.). m. USD 149 (effective 2003).
Related titles: Online - full text ed.: ISSN 1546-5055.
Published by: The Motley Fool, Inc., 123 N. Pitt St., Alexandria, VA 22314. TEL 703-838-3665, FAX 703-254-1999, http://www.incomeinvestor.fool.com, http://www.fool.com. Ed. Mathew Emmert.

332.6   USA   ISSN 1551-9902
▼ **MOTLEY FOOL INSIDE VALUE.** Text in English. 2004 (Sept). m. USD 199 (effective 2005). **Document type:** *Newsletter, Consumer.*
Related titles: Online - full content ed.: ISSN 1553-0884.
Published by: The Motley Fool, Inc., 123 N. Pitt St., Alexandria, VA 22314. TEL 703-838-3665, FAX 703-254-1999, http://insidevalue.fool.com, http://www.fool.com.

332.6   USA   ISSN 1553-7625
▼ **MOTLEY FOOL RULE BREAKERS.** Text in English. 2004 (Oct). m. USD 299 (effective 2005). **Document type:** *Newsletter.*
Related titles: Online - full text ed.: ISSN 1553-8796.
Published by: The Motley Fool, Inc., 123 N. Pitt St., Alexandria, VA 22314. TEL 703-838-3665, FAX 703-254-1999, http://www.rulebreakers.com, http://www.fool.com. Ed. Bob Bobala.

332.6   USA   ISSN 1552-8073
▼ **MOTLEY FOOL RULE YOUR RETIREMENT.** Text in English. 2004 (Jul.). m. USD 149 (effective 2004). **Document type:** *Newsletter.*
Related titles: Online - full content ed.: ISSN 1551-7748.
Published by: The Motley Fool, Inc., 123 N. Pitt St., Alexandria, VA 22314. TEL 703-838-3665, FAX 703-254-1999, http://www.fool.com. Ed. Robert Brokamp.

332.6   USA   ISSN 1076-8491
HG4951
MUNICIPAL ISSUERS REGISTRY. Text in English. m. USD 1,994. adv. **Document type:** *Trade.*
Published by: Thomson Financial Services Company, 4709 W Golf Rd, Skokie, IL 60076-1256. TEL 847-676-9600, 800-321-3373, FAX 847-933-8101. Ed. Rene Reynaldo.

332.63   USA   ISSN 1067-6228
HG4530
MUTUAL FUND 500. Text in English. 1993. a., latest 2005. USD 35 (effective 2005). **Description:** Provides performance data, star ratings, and portfolio information for 500 select open- and closed-end funds.
Published by: Morningstar, Inc., 225 W Wacker Dr, Ste 400, Chicago, IL 60606. TEL 312 384-4000, 312 696-6311, FAX 312-696-6009, http://www.morningstar.com. Eds. Christine Benz, Russel Kinnel. Circ: 5,000.

332.6327   USA
MUTUAL FUND ADVANCE. Text in English. s-w. (Tues. & Fri.). **Document type:** *Newsletter, Trade.* **Description:** Acts as a surveillance tool for the mutual fund industry.
Media: Fax. **Related titles:** E-mail ed.
Published by: Dow Jones Company, 200 Liberty St, New York, NY 10281. TEL 800-223-2274, newswires@dowjones.com, http://www.djnewswires.com/fin-pro/mfa.html.

332.63   USA   ISSN 1050-656X
HG4930
MUTUAL FUND ADVISOR. Text in English. 1989. m. back issues avail. **Document type:** *Newsletter.*
Published by: Mutual Fund Advisor, Inc., One Sarasota Tower, 2N Tamiami Trail, Sarasota, FL 34236. TEL 813-954-5500, FAX 813-364-8447. Ed. Donald H Rowe. Circ: 19,000 (paid).

332.6   USA   ISSN 1067-1358
MUTUAL FUND BUYER'S GUIDE∗ . Text in English. 1992. m. USD 80. charts; stat. back issues avail. **Document type:** *Newsletter.* **Description:** Comprehensive array of ratings, statistics, past performance data and basic information on more than 1,500 mutual funds, covering all major stock funds, bond funds and tax-free funds.
Published by: Institute for Econometric Research, 6454 NW 5th Way, Fort Lauderdale, FL 33309-6112. TEL 954-421-1000, 800-442-9000, FAX 954-570-8200. Ed. Norman G Fosback. Circ: 45,000 (paid).

332.6327   USA   ISSN 0742-9657
CODEN: RCCMEF
MUTUAL FUND LETTER∗ . Text in English. 1984. m. USD 125. adv. **Document type:** *Newsletter.*
Published by: Investment Information Services, Inc., 10 S Riverside Plz, Ste 1520, Chicago, IL 60606-3802. TEL 312-649-6940, 800-326-6941. Ed. Gerald W Perritt. Adv. contact Michael Corbett. Circ: 4,000.

332.6327   USA   ISSN 0897-5108
HG4930
MUTUAL FUND PROFILES. Key Title: Standard & Poor's - Lipper Mutual Fund Profiles. Text in English. 1987. q. USD 158. reprints avail. **Document type:** *Trade.* **Description:** Profiles more than 3,500 mutual funds, categorized by investment objective, offering year-to-date and 5-year performance data.
Published by: Standard & Poor's (Subsidiary of: McGraw-Hill Companies, Inc.), 55 Water St, New York, NY 10041. TEL 212-208-8000. Ed. Joseph Spiers. R&P James Branscome.

332.63   CAN   ISSN 1497-6269
MUTUAL FUND REVIEW. Text in English. 1997. 4/yr. CND 8.50 (effective 2003). adv. **Document type:** *Magazine, Consumer.* **Description:** Aimed specifically at mutual fund professionals or those with a close interest in the mutual fund industry.
Published by: Global Financial Group Inc., 2844 Bainbridge Ave, PO Box 84028, Burnaby, BC V5A 4T9, Canada. TEL 604-681-7210, 800-370-4412, FAX 604-681-7213, info@investment.com, http://www.investment.com.

332.6327   USA
THE MUTUAL FUND SERVICE GUIDES. Text in English. 1986. a. USD 725 (effective 2005). adv. **Document type:** *Trade.*
Published by: Source Media, Inc., 22 Thomson Pl, Boston, MA 02210. TEL 617-856-2000, FAX 617-856-7236, http://www.sourcemedia.com. Ed. Lee Barney TEL 212-803-8751. Pub. John Toth TEL 212-803-6565. adv.: B&W page USD 3,725, color page USD 5,125.

332.6   USA   ISSN 0741-1278
MUTUAL FUND SPECIALIST∗ . Text in English. 1978. m. looseleaf. USD 95. back issues avail. **Document type:** *Newsletter.* **Description:** Provides analyses of equity markets and mutual fund trends. Focus on family of funds concept to mutual funds investing.
Published by: Royal R. Lemier & Co., S7720 State Rd 37, Eau Claire, WI 54701-9075. TEL 715-834-7425. Ed. Royal R Lemier.

332.6327   USA
MUTUAL FUND STRATEGIES. Text in English. 1982. m. USD 127. **Description:** Focuses on the top-performing Fidelity, Vanguard, and Charles Schwab mutual funds.
Published by: Progressive Investing, Inc., PO Box 446, Burlington, VT 05402. TEL 802-658-3515. Ed. Charlie Hooper.

332.6327   USA   ISSN 0889-0064
MUTUAL FUND TRENDS. Text in English. 1985. m. USD 139 (effective 2000). charts. **Document type:** *Newsletter.* **Description:** Provides charts and database for top-performing mutual funds. Includes weekly telephone hotline.
Formerly: Mutual Fund Chartist; Incorporates: Strongest Funds (0889-0870)
Published by: Growth Fund Research, Inc., PO Box 6600, Rapid City, SD 57709. TEL 607-341-1971. Ed. Cheryl R Johnson.

332.64   USA
MUTUAL FUND WEEKLY UPDATE. Text in English. 1998. w. free. **Document type:** *Newsletter.* **Description:** Keeps investors in touch with developments in the mutual fund industry.
Media: Online - full text.
Published by: The Mining Company, PO Box 6572, New York, NY 10128-0006. TEL 212-876-3512, FAX 212-876-3512, mutualfunds.guide@miningco.com, http://mutualfunds.miningco.com/gi/pages/mmail.htm. Ed. Marlene Dziegeleski.

332.6   USA   ISSN 1060-8524
HG4930
MUTUAL FUNDS ALMANAC∗ . Text in English. 1969. a. USD 39.95 softcover ed.. adv. **Description:** Provides names, addresses, telephone numbers and past ten year performance history.
Formerly: Manual of Mutual Funds (0076-4175)
Indexed: SRI.
Published by: IBC - Donoghue, Inc., PO Box 5193, Westborough, MA 01581-5193. TEL 508-881-2800, 800-343-5413, FAX 508-881-0982. Ed. Peter Crane. Adv. contact Randy Wood. Circ: 10,000.

332.6   USA   ISSN 0027-5182
MUTUAL FUNDS GUIDE. Text in English. 1969. 2 base vols. plus m. updates. looseleaf. USD 1,110 base vol(s). (effective 2005). cum.index. **Description:** Provides the legal requirements, key contacts and ongoing developments that affect mutual funds and their operations.
—CCC.
Published by: C C H Inc., 2700 Lake Cook Rd, Riverwoods, IL 60015. TEL 847-267-7000, 800-449-6439, cust_serv@cch.com, http://www.cch.com. Pub. Stacey Caywood.

332.6327 USA
MUTUAL FUNDS REPORT*. Text in English. m. USD 275 (effective 1999). **Document type:** *Trade.* **Description:** Analyzes the performance, risk posture, and percentile rankings of more than 9,800 open-end mutual funds.
Published by: (Wiesenberger Services, Inc.), Wiesenberger (Subsidiary of: Thomson Financial Services Company), 1455 Research Blvd, Rockville, MD 20850-3194. TEL 800-232-2285, FAX 301-545-6400, wies@cda.com. Ed. Stephanie M Kendall. Circ: 1,300.

332.6 USA ISSN 1066-9264
HG4930
MUTUAL FUNDS UPDATE*. Text in English. m. USD 295 (effective 1999). **Document type:** *Trade.* **Description:** Provides performance review, commentary and analysis on more than 9,800 open-end mutual funds. Includes the top-performing funds each month, as well as top-yielding funds.
Formerly (until 1991): Wiesenberger Mutual Funds Investment Report (0894-5977)
Published by: (Wiesenberger Services, Inc.), Wiesenberger (Subsidiary of: Thomson Financial Services Company), 1455 Research Blvd, Rockville, MD 20850-3194. TEL 800-232-2285, FAX 301-548-5105, wies@cda.com. Ed. Stephanie M Kendall. Circ: 2,500.

332 USA
N A R I STETHOSCOPE. Text in English. 1961. s-a. membership. adv. charts; illus. **Document type:** *Newsletter.*
Published by: National Association of Residents and Interns, 350 Fairway Dr, Ste 200, Deerfield Beach, FL 33441-1834. TEL 954-571-1877, http://www.nari-assn.com. Ed. B Lydia Young. Adv. contact Joe Santoli. Circ: 15,000.

332.6 338.642 USA ISSN 1089-7321
N A S B I C NEWS. Text in English. 1959. bi-m. USD 125 (effective 1999). **Document type:** *Newsletter.*
Published by: National Association of Small Business Investment Companies, 666 11th St, N W, Ste 750, Washington, DC 20001. nasbic@nasbic.org, http://www.nasbic.org. Ed. Jeanette D Paschal. Circ: 1,500.

332.6 USA
N A S D A Q - AMEX MARKET GROUP. ANNUAL REPORT. Text in English. a. **Document type:** *Corporate.*
Formerly: American Stock Exchange. Annual Report (0066-0779)
Published by: Nasdaq - AMEX Market Group, NASD MediaSource, PO Box 9403, Gaithersburg, MD 20898-9403. TEL 301-590-6142.

332.6 USA
HG4575.1
N A S D A Q - AMEX MARKET GROUP. FACT BOOK. Text in English. 1968. a. USD 20 (effective 1999).
Former titles: American Stock Exchange. Amex Fact Book (1075-1637); Amex Fact Book (1075-167X); (until 1983): American Stock Exchange. AMEX Databook (0066-0760); American Stock Exchange. AMEX Statistical Review
Published by: Nasdaq - AMEX Market Group, NASD MediaSource, PO Box 9403, Gaithersburg, MD 20898-9403. TEL 301-590-6142. Circ: 9,000.

332.6 332 USA ISSN 0741-0921
HG4905
N A S D A Q FACT BOOK. (National Association of Securities Dealers Automated Quotations) Text in English. a. USD 20. **Document type:** *Directory.* **Description:** Provides extensive data on the performance of Nasdaq securities in the preceding year, and on an historical basis.
Incorporates: N A S D A Q Company Directory
Indexed: SRI.
Published by: National Association of Securities Dealers, Inc., 1735 K St, N W, Washington, DC 20006. TEL 202-728-6900, FAX 202-728-8882. Ed. Laura Duerr. **Dist. by:** Reference Press Inc., TEL 512-454-7778, FAX 512-454-9401.

332.6 USA
N A S D A Q SUBSCRIBER BULLETIN. (National Association of Securities Dealers Automated Quotations) Text in English. q. USD 80. **Document type:** *Newsletter.* **Description:** Provides information on developments in and enhancements to the Nasdaq system of interest to the trading community.
Published by: National Association of Securities Dealers, Inc., 1735 K St, N W, Washington, DC 20006. TEL 202-728-8474, FAX 202-728-8882. Ed. David Casserly.

332.6 332 USA
N A S D ANNUAL REPORT. Text in English. a. **Document type:** *Corporate.*
Published by: National Association of Securities Dealers, Inc., 1735 K St, N W, Washington, DC 20006. TEL 202-728-6900, FAX 202-728-8882.

332.6 USA ISSN 0274-7340
N A S D MANUAL. Text in English. 1967. base vol. plus q. updates. USD 545 base vol(s). (effective 2004). **Description:** Provides pertinent information on the administration, organization, rules and regulations of the NASD.
Related titles: CD-ROM ed.: USD 550 (effective 2004); Online - full text ed.: USD 550 (effective 2004).
—CCC.
Published by: (National Association of Securities Dealers, Inc.), C C H Inc., 2700 Lake Cook Rd, Riverwoods, IL 60015. TEL 847-267-7000, 800-449-6439, cust_serv@cch.com, http://www.cch.com. Pub. Stacey Caywood.

332.6 USA
N A S D NOTICES TO MEMBERS. Text in English. m. USD 225 (effective 1998). **Document type:** *Newsletter.* **Description:** Provides updates on NASD regulations and legal topics, and summaries of actions taken at NASD board meetings.
Supersedes in part: N A S D Executive Digest
Published by: National Association of Securities Dealers, Inc., 1735 K St, N W, Washington, DC 20006. TEL 202-728-6900, FAX 202-728-8882. Ed. Claire McIntyre.

332.6 USA
N A S D REGULATORY AND COMPLIANCE ALERT. Text in English. q. USD 80. **Document type:** *Newsletter.* **Description:** Provides updates on regulatory developments and disciplinary actions affecting securities trading firms.
Published by: National Association of Securities Dealers, Inc., 1735 K St, N W, Washington, DC 20006. TEL 202-728-6000, FAX 202-728-8882. Ed. Rosa A Maymi.

332.6 NZL ISSN 1173-5384
N B R PERSONAL INVESTOR. (National Business Review) Text in English. 1993. 11/yr. (1st Friday of each month). NZD 76.45 (effective 2001). adv.
Formerly (until 1995): Personal Investor (1172-6652)
Related titles: ♦ Supplement to: National Business Review. ISSN 0110-6813.
Published by: Liberty Holdings, PO Box 1734, Auckland 1, New Zealand. TEL 64-9-307-1629, 64-9-307-5129, FAX 64-9-373-3997, http://www.nbr.co.nz.

332.6 GBR ISSN 0963-0295
N G O FINANCE; professional information for non-governmental organisations. (Non-Governmental Organization) Text in English. 1991. 10/yr. GBP 59 to charities; GBP 99 others (effective 1999). adv. **Document type:** *Trade.* **Description:** Offers essential information and analysis on all matters relating to the financial and legal management of charitable non-governmental organizations.
Incorporates (in Feb. 1998): Charity (1363-7614); Which was formerly (until 1995): Charity Magazine (1363-7606); (1983-1992): Charity (0265-5209)
Published by: Plaza Publishing Ltd, 3 Rectory Grove, London, SW4 0DX, United Kingdom. TEL 44-171-819-1210, FAX 44-171-819-1200. Ed. Heather Lamont. Pub. Daniel Phelan. Adv. contact Alice Frackelton. B&W page GBP 1,995, color page GBP 2,195. Circ: 5,500.

332.65 USA
N Y S E MAGAZINE; at the center of global business. Text in English. bi-m. adv. **Document type:** *Magazine, Trade.*
Published by: (New York Stock Exchange), Time Inc. Custom Publishing, Time & Life Bldg, Ste 2841A, Rockefeller Center, 1271 Ave of the Americas, New York, NY 10020-1393. TEL 212-522-1212, nyse@timeinc.com, http://www.nyse.com/about/publication/MagazineTOC_CurrentIssue.html, http://www.sony.com. Ed. Steven Mintz. Adv. contact George J Baer III.

332.63 DEU ISSN 0027-741X
NACHRICHTEN FUER AUSSENHANDEL. Short title: N F A. Text in German. 1947. d. (5/w.). **Document type:** *Trade.*
Former titles: V W D - Nachrichten fuer Aussenhandel; V W D - Informationen
Indexed: CBNB, RASB.
Published by: Vereinigte Wirtschaftsdienste GmbH, Niederurseler Allee 8-10, Eschborn, 65760, Germany. TEL 49-6196-4050, FAX 49-6196-405303.

330 DEU
▼ **NANOTECH-REPORT**; Deutschlands erster Boersenbrief ueber Nanotechnologie. Text in German. 2003. m. EUR 180 domestic; EUR 195 foreign (effective 2003). **Document type:** *Newsletter, Trade.*
Published by: Boersenmedien AG, Hofer Str 20, Kulmbach, 95326, Germany. TEL 49-9221-90510, FAX 49-9221-877288. Ed. Marco Beckmann. Pub. Bernd Foertsch.

332.6 658 UKR ISSN 1681-6102
NASHA SPRAVA. Text in Ukrainian. 1996. m. **Document type:** *Journal.*
Related titles: Online - full text ed.: ISSN 1681-6110.
Published by: Kyivs'kyi Instytut Investytsiinoho Menedzhmentu, bul'var Shevchenko 54/1, 8-i povetkh, Kyiv, 01032, Ukraine. TEL 380-44-4906791, kimi@kimi.kiev.ua, http://srv.kimi.kiev.ua/publication/publication.shtml, http://www.kimi.edu.

NATIONAL AGENCY OF INDUSTRY AND TRADE. ANNUAL REPORTS (YEAR)/AARSBERETNINGER. see *BUSINESS AND ECONOMICS—Production Of Goods And Services*

332.6 346.066 USA ISSN 0737-4062
NATIONAL FUTURES ASSOCIATION MANUAL. Text in English. 1983. q. looseleaf.
Published by: National Futures Association, 200 W Madison St, Ste 1600, Chicago, IL 60606. TEL 312-781-1300, FAX 312-781-1467, publicaffairs@nfa.futures.org, http://www.nfa.futures.org.

332.6 USA
NATIONAL INVESTOR RELATIONS INSTITUTE. ANNUAL REPORT. Text in English. a. **Document type:** *Corporate.*
Published by: National Investor Relations Institute, 8020 Towers Crescent Dr., # 250, Vienna, VA 22182-6224. TEL 703-506-3570.

NATIONAL POST BUSINESS. see *BUSINESS AND ECONOMICS—Banking And Finance*

330 DEU ISSN 1435-456X
NEBENWERTE-JOURNAL; das Magazin fuer aktive Aktionaere. Text in German. 1993. m. EUR 60 domestic; EUR 72 in Europe; EUR 96 elsewhere; EUR 5.50 newsstand/cover (effective 2003). adv. **Document type:** *Magazine, Trade.*
Published by: Nebenwerte-Journal AG, Haferweg 13, Bochum, 44797, Germany. TEL 49-234-797578, FAX 49-234-795172, redaktion@nebenwerte-journal.de, verlag@nebenwerte-journal.de, http://www.nebenwerte-journal.de. Ed., Pub. Klaus Hellwig. adv.: B&W page EUR 1,900, color page EUR 2,400. Circ: 3,000 (paid and controlled).

NELSON INFORMATION'S DIRECTORY OF INVESTMENT RESEARCH. see *BUSINESS AND ECONOMICS—Trade And Industrial Directories*

NELSON INFORMATION'S DIRECTORY OF PENSION FUND CONSULTANTS. see *BUSINESS AND ECONOMICS—Trade And Industrial Directories*

NELSON'S DIRECTORY OF INSTITUTIONAL REAL ESTATE. see *BUSINESS AND ECONOMICS—Trade And Industrial Directories*

NELSON'S DIRECTORY OF INVESTMENT MANAGERS. see *BUSINESS AND ECONOMICS—Trade And Industrial Directories*

NELSON'S DIRECTORY OF PLAN SPONSORS. see *BUSINESS AND ECONOMICS—Trade And Industrial Directories*

332.6 USA
NET PROFIT MONTHLY. Text in English. m. USD 120 newsstand/cover (effective 2003). charts. back issues avail. **Document type:** *Newsletter, Trade.*
Media: Online - full content.
Published by: Economist Intelligence Unit, 111 W 57th St, New York, NY 10019. http://www.eiu.com.

332.6 USA ISSN 0742-4507
HG4528
NETBACK. Text in English. 1982. bi-m. USD 75; included in subscr. to Good Money. bk.rev. abstr.; stat.; tr.lit. back issues avail.
Formerly (until 1985): Netbacking
Published by: Good Money Publications, Inc., 370A Granite Rd, Ossipee, NH 03864. TEL 603-539-3852, FAX 603-539-3852, goodmoney2@aol.com, http://www.goodmoney.com. Ed. Lisa M Syverson.

NEW & EMERGING TECHNOLOGY; executive newsreport and forecast on industrial innovation. see *TECHNOLOGY: COMPREHENSIVE WORKS*

332.6 USA ISSN 1073-7642
NEW ISSUE DIGEST. Text in English. 1971. q. USD 50 per issue. charts. **Document type:** *Newsletter.* **Description:** Monitors the new issue market; refers to the more attractive new issues before the public offering.
Related titles: ♦ Supplement to: Junior Growth Stocks. ISSN 1073-7634.
Published by: Growth Stock Outlook, Inc., 4405 East West Hwy, Ste 305, Bethesda, MD 20814. TEL 301-654-5205. Ed. Charles Allmon.

332.678 USA ISSN 0162-9050
HG4501
NEW ISSUES*; the investor's guide to initial public offerings. Text in English. 1978. m. USD 200. charts; stat. back issues avail. **Document type:** *Newsletter.* **Description:** In-depth analyses of attractive forthcoming initial public offerings, including fundamental and earnings data and details on the offerings and their underwriters.
Published by: Institute for Econometric Research, 6454 NW 5th Way, Fort Lauderdale, FL 33309-6112. TEL 954-421-1000, 800-442-9000, FAX 954-570-8200. Ed. Norman G Fosback.

332.6 384.33 GBR ISSN 1462-8856
NEW MEDIA INVESTOR. Text in English. 1998. bi-w. GBP 245 domestic; GBP 255 in Europe; GBP 265 elsewhere (effective 2001). **Document type:** *Magazine, Trade.* **Description:** Targets analysts, venture capitalists and entrepreneurs involved in funding and advising Internet companies.
Formed by the merger of (1997-1998): New Media Finance (1460-8367); (1994-1998): Digital Media Investor (1368-9436); Which was formerly (until 1997): Multimedia Business Analyst (1357-0080); Which incorporated (1984-1996): Business Computing Brief (1350-5092); Which was formerly (until 1993): FinTech 2 Electronic Office (0266-7797)
Related titles: Online - full text ed.: (from Gale Group, O C L C Online Computer Library Center, Inc.).

—IE.
Published by: Centaur Publishing, St Giles House, 50 Poland St, London, W1V 4AX, United Kingdom. TEL 44-20-7970-4000, http://www.centaur.co.uk.

332.63 332.678 GBR
THE NEW MINERVA REPORT. Text in English. 1992. m. GBP 90 (effective 2000). bk.rev. stat. **Description:** To assist investors in unit trusts.
Formery (until 1999): The Minerva Report (0969-4986); Which incorporated (1982-1992): Unit Trust Newsletter (0961-9488)
Published by: Minerva Fund Managers Ltd., Kelston View, Corston, Bath BA2 9AH, United Kingdom. TEL 44-1225-872300. Ed., R&P Paul Warner.

332.6 USA
NEW YORK STOCK EXCHANGE. FACT BOOK ONLINE. Text in English. d.
Formerly: New York Stock Exchange. Fact Book (8756-6788)
Media: Online - full content.
Published by: New York Stock Exchange, Communications Division, 11 Wall St, New York, NY 10005. TEL 212-623-3000, http://www.nysedata.com/factbook/main.asp.

332.6 USA ISSN 0271-0714
NEW YORK STOCK EXCHANGE GUIDE. Text in English. 1957. 3 base vols. plus m. updates. USD 855 base vol(s). (effective 2005). **Description:** Provides members, allied members and registered representatives of the Exchange with complete, up-to-date information concerning all the various facets of exchange operations.
Related titles: CD-ROM ed.: USD 885 (effective 2005); Online - full text ed.: USD 875 (effective 2005).
—CCC.
Published by: C C H Inc., 2700 Lake Cook Rd, Riverwoods, IL 60015. TEL 847-267-7000, 800-449-6439, cust_serv@cch.com, http://www.cch.com. Pub. Stacey Caywood.

332.6 NZL ISSN 1173-3748
THE NEW ZEALAND INVESTMENT JOURNAL. Text in English. 1994. 11/yr. NZD 32 domestic; NZD 64 foreign (effective 2001). back issues avail. **Document type:** *Journal, Trade.* **Description:** Covers the latest investment news concerning the New Zealand market.
Related titles: Online - full text ed.
Published by: New Zealand Investment Journal, Ground Floor Tower Bldg, 1 Brandon St, P O Box 5398, Wellington, New Zealand. TEL 64-4-4993592, FAX 64-4-4993590, invest@nzij.co.nz, http://nzij.co.nz/index.php, http://www.nzij.co.nz/.

382 USA
NEWS, FACTS, ACTIONS. Text in English. 1983. bi-m. free. **Document type:** *Newsletter.* **Description:** Covers the activities of the self-regulatory organization of the commodity futures industry.
Formerly: N F A News, Facts, Actions
Published by: National Futures Association, 200 W Madison St, Ste 1600, Chicago, IL 60606. TEL 312-781-1373, FAX 312-781-1467, publicaffairs@nfa.futures.org, www.nfa.futures.org. Ed. Larry Dyekman. Circ: 4,500.

332.6 USA ISSN 1015-0188
K3826.2
NEWS FROM I C S I D. Text in English. 1984. 2/yr. free. **Document type:** *Newsletter, Trade.*
Related titles: Online - full content ed.: ISSN 1564-6548. 1998.
Published by: International Centre for Settlement of Investment Disputes, 1818 H St, N W, Washington, DC 20433. TEL 202-458-1535, FAX 202-522-2615, http://www.worldbank.org/icsid/news/news.htm. Circ: 3,000.

NEWSLETTER DIGEST. see *BUSINESS AND ECONOMICS—Abstracting, Bibliographies, Statistics*

NEWSPAPER INVESTOR. see *JOURNALISM*

NIKKEI NET TRADING. see *BUSINESS AND ECONOMICS—Computer Applications*

332 USA ISSN 0736-6256
NO-LOAD FUND INVESTOR. Text in English. 1979. m. USD 139; USD 159 with Handbook (effective May. 2000). **Description:** Provides coverage of no-load funds available to the public, as well as direct-marketed low-loads. Includes specific fund recommendations, market timing advice, and fund news.
Published by: No-Load Fund Investor, Inc., 44 Mountainview Dr., Cold Spring, NY 10516-4129. TEL 914-693-7420, 800-252-2042. Ed. Sheldon Jacobs.

332.64 USA
NO-LOAD STOCK INSIDER. Text in English. 1996. bi-m. USD 58 (effective 1999).
Published by: Horizon Publishing Co., L L C, 7412 Calumet Ave, Ste 200, Hammond, IN 46324-2692. TEL 219-852-3220. Ed. Charles B Carlson. Circ: 4,500.

332.6 USA ISSN 0194-0104
NOLOAD FUND X; a monitoring system for the enterprising inverstor. Text in English. 1976. m. USD 149 (effective 2005). stat. back issues avail. **Document type:** *Newsletter, Consumer.* **Description:** Provides performance data on over 720 noload and loload mutual funds, including advice on which funds to buy, when to move your money and predictions on future top performers. Featuresinclude letters to the editor, summary of leading indexes, market commentary, fund news and analysis.
Related titles: E-mail ed.; Fax ed.
Published by: Dal Investment Co., Russ Bldg, Ste 662, 235 Montgomery St, San Francisco, CA 94104-2994. TEL 415-986-7979, 800-763-8639, FAX 415-986-1595, fundx@fundx.com, http://www.fundx.com. Circ: 79,250 (paid and controlled).

332.6 USA ISSN 0549-8333
NORTH DAKOTA SECURITIES BULLETIN. Text in English. a. free. **Document type:** *Bulletin.*
Published by: Commissioner of Securities, 600 East Boulevard, Dept 414, Bismarck, ND 58505. TEL 701-328-2910. Ed. Cal Hoovestol. Circ: 225.

NORTHERN NEW ENGLAND REAL ESTATE JOURNAL. see *REAL ESTATE*

332.6 GBR
NOTES. Text in English. q. **Document type:** *Consumer.* **Description:** Covers financial developments that directly affect customers of Alliance and Leicester services and products. Also includes a wide range of lifestyle features.
Published by: (Alliance & Leicester), T P D Ltd, 1-4 Long Island House Block A, Westpoint 33-34, Warple Way, London, W3 0RG, United Kingdom. TEL 44-208-600-9104, FAX 44-208-600-9101, karen.geary@tpd.co.uk, lucy.ryan@tpd.co.uk, http://www.tpd.co.uk.

332.6 USA ISSN 0892-2632
O T C GROWTH STOCK WATCH. (Over the Counter) Text in English. 1979. m. USD 199 domestic; USD 214 foreign (effective 2000). adv. back issues avail. **Document type:** *Newsletter.* **Description:** Features one in-depth company report in each issue.
Published by: O T C Research Corporation, 300 Chestnut St., Ste. 200, Needham, MA 02492-2427. TEL 781-444-6100, http://www.otcgsw.com. Ed., R&P, Adv. contact Piret Madar. Pub. Geoffrey Eiten. Circ: 1,000.

332.643 USA ISSN 0733-026X
HG4009
O T C HANDBOOK. (Over the Counter) Text in English. 1981. s-a. USD 74.
Published by: Standard & Poor's (Subsidiary of: McGraw-Hill Companies, Inc.), 55 Water St, New York, NY 10041. TEL 212-208-8000. Ed. Ronald Oliver.

OFFSHORE INVESTMENT. see *BUSINESS AND ECONOMICS—Banking And Finance*

▼ **OIL & GAS FINANCIAL JOURNAL.** see *PETROLEUM AND GAS*

332 USA ISSN 1523-5327
HG179
ON INVESTING. Text in English. 1999. q.
Published by: Bloomberg L.P., 499 Park Ave, New York, NY 10022. TEL 212-318-2200, FAX 212-980-4585, http://www.bloomberg.com. Pub. Michael Bloomberg.

332.6 USA ISSN 1092-1370
HG4501
ON WALL STREET. Text in English. 1991. m. USD 46 (effective 2005). adv. **Document type:** *Magazine, Trade.* **Description:** Dedicated to providing a blend of news, opinion, expert advice and practical feature coverage that helps brokers attract and retain clients.
Formerly (until Apr. 1996): Financial Planning on Wall Street (1074-4282)
Related titles: Online - full text ed.: (from EBSCO Publishing, Florida Center for Library Automation, Gale Group, LexisNexis, O C L C Online Computer Library Center, Inc., ProQuest Information & Learning).
Indexed: ABIn, B&I.
—CCC.
Published by: Source Media, Inc., One State St Plaza, 27th Fl, New York, NY 10004. TEL 212-803-6077, 800-221-1809, FAX 212-747-1154, custserv@sourcemedia.com, http://www.onwallstreet.com, http://www.sourcemedia.com. adv.: B&W page USD 4,850. Circ: 90,000 (controlled).

332.6 USA ISSN 1070-1117
ONLINE INVESTOR. Text in English. bi-m. USD 14.95; USD 20.95 in Canada; USD 26.95 elsewhere. adv. **Document type:** *Consumer.* **Description:** Provides investment advice and reports. Presents the latest news in the online investing market for individual investors.
Related titles: Online - full text ed.
Address: postings@onlineinvestor.com, http://www.onlineinvestor.com.

332.6 USA ISSN 1529-5648
OPERATIONS MANAGEMENT. Text in English. 1995. w. (51x/yr). USD 2,105 combined subscription domestic print & online eds.; USD 2,180 combined subscription foreign print & online eds. (effective 2005). **Document type:** *Newsletter, Trade.* **Description:** Provides information on securities clearance, settlement and processing for money managers, brokers-dealers and custodians.
Related titles: Online - full text ed.: (from EBSCO Publishing, Florida Center for Library Automation).
Published by: Institutional Investor News (Subsidiary of: Euromoney Institutional Investor Plc.), 225 Park Ave S, 7th Fl, New York, NY 10003-1605. TEL 212-224-3800, FAX 212-224-3294, customerservice@iinews.com, info@iiplatinum.com, http://www.operationsmanagement.com, http://www.iinews.com. Pub. Aaron Finkel TEL 212-224-3268.

332.6 USA
OPPORTUNIST; tomorrow's opportunity today. Text in English. 1993. q. USD 10; USD 3.99 newsstand/cover (effective 2000). adv. mkt. **Document type:** *Magazine, Consumer.* **Description:** Provides profiles of small companies and emerging markets for independent investors and brokers.
Related titles: Online - full text ed.
Published by: Grant Douglas Publishing, 2101 W State Rte 434, Ste 221, Longwood, FL 32779. TEL 407-949-9300, FAX 407-926-9208, philgdp@hotmail.com, http://www.grantdouglas.com. Ed., Adv. contact Phil Robertson. Pub. Roy Meadows. R&P Leslie Stone. color page USD 6,000; trim 8.325 x 10.825. Circ: 250,000.

332.6 USA
OPPORTUNITIES IN OPTIONS. Text in English. 1984. m. USD 119; includes hotline service. adv. bk.rev. **Document type:** *Newsletter.* **Description:** Specializes in using option strategies on all financial markets worldwide for investment, trading, and hedging. Shows how to recognize and use option-premium disparity (under- and over-valued options). Includes professional option traders' manual, notebook, and personal strategy service.
Address: 1208 Swansea, Ventura, CA 93004. TEL 800-456-9699, FAX 310-456-3840, http://www.oio.com. Ed., Pub. David L Caplan. R&P, Adv. contact Wayne Gordon TEL 800-926-0926. Circ: 5,000 (paid); 5,000 (controlled).

332.6 USA
OPTION ADVISOR. Text in English. 1981. 12/yr. USD 200. **Document type:** *Newsletter.* **Description:** Provides both aggressive and conservative recommendations on listed stock options.
Published by: Investment Research Institute Inc., 1259 Kemper Meadow Dr, Ste 100, Cincinnati, OH 45240. TEL 513-589-3800, 800-448-2080, FAX 513-589-3810, bernieIRI@aol.com, http://www.options-iri.com. Ed. Bernard G Schaeffer. Pub. Robert D Bergen.

332.6 USA
OPTION STRATEGIST. Text in English. 1990. s-m. USD 250 domestic; USD 280 foreign (effective 2000). **Document type:** *Newsletter.* **Description:** Publishes news and information on equity, index and futures option strategies.
Published by: McMillan Analysis Corp, 39 Meadowbrook Rd, Randolph, NJ 07869. TEL 973-328-1674, 800-724-1817, FAX 973-328-1303, mac19@ix.netcom.com, http://www.optionstrategist.com. Ed., Pub. Lawrence G McMillan. Circ: 500 (paid).

332.6 USA
OPTIONS ALERT. Text in English. 1977. w. USD 175.
Published by: Merrill Lynch, Pierce, Fenner & Smith, Inc., 1 Liberty Plaza, New York, NY 10006. Ed. Anthony H Scholl.

ORIENTACION ECONOMICA Y FINANCIERA. see *BUSINESS AND ECONOMICS—Chamber Of Commerce Publications*

THE ORIENTALIA JOURNAL. see *ANTIQUES*

332.6 NOR ISSN 0085-4565
HG5620.O75
OSLO BOERS. BERETNING/OSLO STOCK EXCHANGE. ANNUAL REPORT. Text in Norwegian. 1896. a. free. **Document type:** *Corporate.*
Former titles (until 1970): Oekonomisk Beretning - Oslo Boers, Oslo Handelskammer (0800-4528); (until 1948): Beretning om Oslo Handel, Industri og Skibsfart (0800-451X)
Published by: Oslo Boers/Oslo Stock Exchange, Tollbugata 2, Oslo, 0152, Norway. FAX 47-22-416-590. Ed. Bernt Bangstad. Circ: 5,000.

OSNOVNYE POKAZATELI INVESTITSIONNOI I STROITEL'NOI DEYATEL'NOSTI V ROSSIISKOI FEDERATSII/MAIN INDICATORS OF CONSTRUCTION AND INVESTMENT ACTIVITIES IN THE RUSSIAN FEDERATION. see *BUSINESS AND ECONOMICS—Abstracting, Bibliographies, Statistics*

332.6 USA ISSN 0030-7246
HG4501
THE OUTLOOK (NEW YORK). Text in English. 1937. w. USD 298. adv. charts; illus.; mkt.; stat. **Document type:** *Newsletter.* **Description:** Identifies developments that affect stock performance, and makes recommendations on when to buy, hold, and sell.
Published by: Standard & Poor's (Subsidiary of: McGraw-Hill Companies, Inc.), 55 Water St, New York, NY 10041. TEL 212-208-8000. Ed., R&P Arnold Kaufman. Adv. contact Betty Connor.

332.678 USA
OVERPRICED STOCK SERVICE; authoritative independent advice for short selling. Text in English. 1983. m. USD 495 (effective 2000). back issues avail. **Document type:** *Newsletter.* **Description:** Contains recommendations of stocks to sell short.
Published by: C T S L Publishing Partners, PO Box 308, Half Moon Bay, CA 94019. TEL 650-726-8495. Ed., Pub. Michael Murphy. R&P Pamela Floquet.

332.6 PAK ISSN 0078-8198
P I C I C ANNUAL REPORT. Text in English. 1962. a. charts; stat.
Published by: Pakistan Industrial Credit and Investment Corporation Ltd., Economic and Research Department, State Life Bldg., No. 1, I.I. Chundrigar Rd., P O Box 5080, Karachi 2, Pakistan. Ed. Abdul Hafeez Khan.

332.6 PAK ISSN 0030-8005
P I C I C NEWS. Text in English. 1962. q. free. charts; illus.
Published by: Pakistan Industrial Credit and Investment Corporation Ltd., Economic and Research Department, State Life Bldg., No. 1, I.I. Chundrigar Rd., P O Box 5080, Karachi 2, Pakistan. TELEX 2710 PICIC PK. Circ: 2,000.

368.37 USA ISSN 0164-176X
HG4905
P I P E R. (Pensions & Investments Performance Evaluation Reports) Variant title: ePiper. Text in English. 1977. q. USD 879 (effective 2003). adv. charts; illus.; stat. back issues avail.; reprints avail. **Document type:** *Trade.*
Related titles: Online - full text ed.
—CCC.
Published by: Crain Communications, Inc., 711 Third Ave, New York, NY 10017-4036. TEL 212-210-0280, info@crain.com, http://www.pionline.com/epiper, http://www.crain.com. Ed. James Pavia. Pub. William Bisson. Adv. contact Christopher Battaglia TEL 212-210-0100. Circ: 300.

332.6327 USA
P I P S' - INVESTMENT ADVISORY MONTHLY NEWSLETTER. Text in English. 1983. m. USD 60. **Document type:** *Newsletter.* **Description:** Recommends four diversified investment portfolios comprised of no-load and low load mutual and money market funds for long-term growth of investment savings. Provides non-technical investment advice.
Formerly: P I P S' - Monthly Newsletter
Published by: Personal Investment Portfolio Service, 374 Venus Dr, Prescott, AZ 86301. TEL 602-776-0660. Circ: 1,000.

332.6 USA
THE P Q WALL FORECAST. Text in English. 1980. m. looseleaf. USD 198; USD 20 newsstand/cover (effective 1999). back issues avail. **Document type:** *Newsletter.* **Description:** Covers market timing of the stock, bond, financial, and commodity markets. Aimed at cycle analysts, stock brokers, private investors, and students of the financial markets.
Related titles: Fax ed.; Online - full text ed.
Published by: P Q Wall Forecast, Inc., PO Box 15558, New Orleans, LA 70175. TEL 504-895-4901, 800-259-0088, FAX 504-895-4852, ectwall@msn.com. Eds. Ellen C Wall, P Q Wall. Pub. P.Q. Wall. R&P Ellen Wall TEL 504-895-4891. Circ: 4,000 (paid).

332.6 USA
PACIFIC STOCK EXCHANGE. ANNUAL REPORT. Text in English. a. free. **Document type:** *Corporate.*
Published by: Pacific Stock Exchange, Inc., 115 Sansome St., Ste. 315, San Francisco, CA 94104-3330. TEL 415-393-4000, FAX 415-393-4202, TELEX 203025 PSE UR (RCA). Ed. Genie W Williams.

332.6 USA
PACIFIC STOCK EXCHANGE GUIDE. Text in English. 1967. base vol. plus m. updates. USD 595 base vol(s). (effective 2004). **Description:** Includes full-text version of the Constitution, the Rules of the Board of Governors and the complete policies of the Pacific Stock Exchange.
Related titles: CD-ROM ed.: USD 355 (effective 2004); Online - full text ed.: USD 355 (effective 2004).
Published by: C C H Inc., 2700 Lake Cook Rd, Riverwoods, IL 60015. TEL 847-267-7000, 800-449-6439, cust_serv@cch.com, http://www.cch.com. Pub. Stacey Caywood.

332.6327 PRY
PARAGUAY. MINISTRY OF INDUSTRY AND TRADE. INVESTMENT GUIDE. Text in Spanish. 1986. irreg. free. **Document type:** *Government.* **Description:** Contains information useful to those who are considering investing in the country.
Published by: Ministerio de Industria y Comercio, C.C. 1772, Ave. ESPANA, 374, Asuncion, Paraguay. TEL 204-795, FAX 21-210-570, TELEX 259 PY MIC.

332.6 GBR ISSN 1353-6907
PARIBAS DERIVATIVES HANDBOOK (YEAR). Text in English. 1993. a. GBP 140, USD 250. **Document type:** *Directory, Trade.* **Description:** Combines a detailed analysis of derivative products and practices with a worldwide directory of derivative instruments and intermediaries. Lists more than 2,000 institutions active in the world derivatives markets, along with key personnel.
Published by: Euromoney Publications plc, Nestor House, Playhouse Yard, London, EC4V 5EX, United Kingdom. TEL 44-207-7798673, FAX 44-20-77798541. **Orders to:** Plymbridge Distributors Ltd, Plymbridge House, Estover Rd, Plymouth, Devon PL6 7PY, United Kingdom. TEL 44-1752-202300, FAX 44-1752-202330.

PARKER'S (YEAR) TEXAS BUSINESS STATUTES AND SECURITIES RULES. see *LAW—Corporate Law*

336 USA
PARTNERSHIP AND S CORPORATION COORDINATOR. Text in English. 1987. m. looseleaf. USD 250. **Description:** Provides tax analysis, planning guidance and practice aids for partnerships and S corporations.
Indexed: ATI.
Published by: R I A (Subsidiary of: Thomson Corporation), 395 Hudson St, New York, NY 10014. TEL 212-367- 6300, 212-367-6300.

332.6 USA
PAST, PRESENT, FUTURES. Text in English. 1990. m. USD 269; USD 289 foreign. **Document type:** *Newsletter.* **Description:** Analyzes stock market trends and tracks time cycles and their relation to stock prices, using W.D. Gann's master time factor.
Formerly: Investor's Edge
Published by: National Institute of Investment Research, 1821 Wilshire Blvd, Ste 415, Santa Monica, CA 60403-5679. TEL 310-829-4146, 800-545-9331. Ed. James Flanagan. R&P Forrest James.

332.6 USA
PAX CONNECTION. Text in English. q. **Description:** Discusses the fund's investments to promote social reforms.
Published by: Pax World Fund, 224 State St, Portsmouth, NH 03801. Eds. Randy Bernard, Rian Fried.

PAZAR I PRAVO. see *BUSINESS AND ECONOMICS—Domestic Commerce*

332.6 USA
PEARSON INVESTMENT LETTER. Text in English. 1982. m. USD 150. **Document type:** *Newsletter.* **Description:** Includes outlines of several stocks each month which seem ready for growth and advancement at that particular time, plus items of financial, political and economic interest. Also includes stocks recommended the previous year and their present status, as well as the past 12 months' featured stocks and progress, and lists special changes (dividend increases, splits, etc.) of recommended stocks.
Address: 1628 White Arrow Dr, Dover, FL 33527. TEL 813-659-2560. Ed. Elsa Pearson. Pub. Walter Pearson. Circ: 450 (paid).

332.6 GBR ISSN 0144-0160
PENNY SHARE GUIDE. Text in English. 1978. m. **Document type:** *Newsletter.* **Description:** Provides a guide to picking stocks which are quoted on the London Stock Exchange, and valued at GBP 1.00 or under.
Formerly (until 1979): Penny Punter (0141-5662)
—CCC.
Published by: Fleet Street Publications Ltd., 271 Regent St, London, WIR 7PAU, United Kingdom. TEL 44-20-7447-4040, FAX 44-20-7447-4041. Ed. John Campbell. Pub. David Gibson. Circ: 30,000 (paid).

332.6 NLD ISSN 0925-496X
PENSIOEN ADVIES; onafhankelijk vakblad voor de adviespratijk. Text in Dutch. 1990. 10/yr. adv. **Document type:** *Trade.*
—IE.
Published by: Wolters Kluwer N.V., Leewunburg 101, Deventer, 7411 TH, Netherlands. TEL 31-5700-48999, FAX 31-5700-11504. **Subscr. to:** Intermedia bv, Postbus 4, Alphen aan den Rijn 2400 MA, Netherlands. TEL 31-172-466321, FAX 31-172-435527.

332.6 USA
PENSION INVESTMENT REPORT. Text in English. 1986. irreg. looseleaf. USD 1,500 includes EBRI Issue Briefs and EBRI Notes; USD 500 newsstand/cover (effective 2000). charts; stat. 50 p./no.; **Document type:** *Monographic series, Academic/Scholarly.* **Description:** Data on assets in the private and public pension system and the performance of pension investments.
Formerly: E B R I Quarterly Pension Investment Report (0889-4396)
Related titles: Online - full content ed.
Indexed: SRI.
—CCC.
Published by: Employee Benefit Research Institute, 2121 K St, N W, Ste 600, Washington, DC 20037-1896. TEL 202-659-0670, FAX 202-775-6312, info@ebri.org, http://www.ebri.org. R&P Stephen Blakely TEL 202-775-6341. Circ: 350.

332.67 USA ISSN 1050-4974
HD7106.U5
PENSIONS & INVESTMENTS; the newspaper of corporate and institutional investing. Text in English. 1973. bi-w. USD 239 domestic; USD 255 in Canada; USD 325 elsewhere (effective 2005). adv. illus. Index. 40 p./no. 5 cols./p.; back issues avail.; reprint service avail. from PQC. **Document type:** *Newspaper, Trade.* **Description:** Delivers critical financial news to executives responsible for the investment of large institutioanl assets such as pension funds, endowments and foundations. It reaches top corporate executives and government leaders, pension fund managers, investment advisers, consultants, and financial institutions.
Former titles: Pensions and Investment Age (0273-5466); Pensions and Investments (0095-4772)
Related titles: Fax ed.: P & I Daily. USD 595 (effective 2002); Microfiche ed.: (from CIS); Microform ed.: (from PQC); Online - full text ed.: P & I Online. USD 695 (effective 2001) (from EBSCO Publishing, Florida Center for Library Automation, Gale Group, H.W. Wilson, LexisNexis, Northern Light Technology, Inc., O C L C Online Computer Library Center, Inc., ProQuest Information & Learning).
Indexed: ABIn, ATI, B&I, BLI, BPI, BPIA, LRI, PAIS, PROMT, SRI, T&II.
—BLDSC (6422.720100), IE, Infotrieve. **CCC.**
Published by: Crain Communications, Inc., 1155 Gratiot Ave, Detroit, MI 48207-2997. TEL 313-446-6000, FAX 313-446-1687, http://www.pionline.com, http://www.crain.com. Eds. Nancy Webman, Michael J. Clowes. Pub. William Bisson. adv.: B&W page USD 16,800. Circ: 50,000 (paid and controlled).

331.252 GBR ISSN 0140-8526
PENSIONS TODAY. Text in English. 1979. m. GBP 261; GBP 286, USD 572 foreign (effective 2000). back issues avail. **Document type:** *Newsletter.* **Description:** For pension-fund managers, trustees, company secretaries, pensions specialists in broking and insurance companies.
Indexed: ELJI, LJI.
Published by: Monitor Press Ltd. (Subsidiary of: T & F Informa plc), Suffolk House, Church Field Rd, Sudbury, Suffolk CO10 2YA, United Kingdom. TEL 44-1787-378607, FAX 44-1787-880201, http://www.monitorpress.co.uk.

PENSIONS WORLD. see *INSURANCE*

PERSONAL FINANCE. see *BUSINESS AND ECONOMICS—Banking And Finance*

332.6 USA
PERSONAL FINANCE✶. Text in English. 1974. 24/yr. USD 118. adv. bk.rev. charts; stat. index. back issues avail. **Description:** Stock market investment advice.
Former titles: Personal Finance: The Inflation Survival Letter (0164-7768); Inflation Survival Letter
Indexed: CPerI.
Published by: Kephart Communications, Inc., 1750 Old Meadow Rd., 3rd Fl., Mclean, VA 22102-4304. TEL 703-548-2400, FAX 703-683-6974, TELEX 901806 KEPCOM. Ed. Richard E Band. Circ: 100,000. **Subscr. to:** PO Box 1462, Alexandria, VA 22313.

332.6 USA ISSN 1044-4343
HG179
PERSONAL FINANCIAL PLANNING. Text in English. 1988. bi-m. USD 145 (effective 1999). adv. **Document type:** *Trade.* **Description:** Provides investment advisors, CPAs, and financial planners with articles, case studies, and interviews about investment strategies and portfolio management, insurance planning, tax strategies and tax shelters, and regulatory and legal issues.
Related titles: Microform ed.: (from PQC).
Indexed: ATI, BLI.
—CCC.
Published by: W G & L Financial Reporting & Management Research (Subsidiary of: R I A), 90 Fifth Ave, New York, NY 10011. TEL 212-645-4800, FAX 212-337-4280, http://www.riatax.xom/journals/jourhom.html. Ed. Jack Rubinson. Pub. Larry Selby. R&P Sarah Rutledge TEL 212-367-6536. Adv. contact Meg Chornicz.

332.6 GBR ISSN 1460-9746
PERSONAL INVESTMENT AUTHORITY. CONSULTATIVE PAPER. Text in English. 1994. irreg. **Document type:** *Monographic series.*
—BLDSC (3423.785500).
Published by: The Financial Services Authority, 25 The North Colonnade, Canary Wharf, London, E14 5HS, United Kingdom. TEL 44-20-76761000, FAX 44-20-76761099, http://www.fsa.gov.uk.

B

332.6 AUS
HG4503
PERSONAL INVESTOR. Text in English. 1972. m. AUD 66 (effective 2004). adv. index. back issues avail. **Document type:** *Magazine, Consumer.* **Description:** How-to magazine about investing, spending and making money. Directed to the average person.
Former titles: Personal Investment (0813-2992); (until 1983): Australian Stock Exchange Journal (0045-0901)
Related titles: Online - full text ed.; ◆ Supplement(s): Shares (Sydney). ISSN 1327-5798.
Indexed: ABIX, PAIS, WBA, WMB.
Published by: Fairfax Business Media (Subsidiary of: John Fairfax Holdings Ltd.), 201 Sussex St, Sydney, NSW 2000, Australia. TEL 61-2-9282-2822, http://www.personalinvestor.com.au, http://www.fxj.com.au/. adv.: B&W page USD 3,460, color page USD 4,945; bleed 213 x 282. Circ: 59,000.

332.6 ZAF
PERSPECTIVE/PERSPEKTIEF; economic, investment & portfolio review for employee benefit funds. Text in Afrikaans, English. 1993. q.
Published by: Southern Life Association, Investments Division, Great Westerford, Rondebosch, Cape Town 7700, South Africa.

332.6 USA
PETER ELIADES' STOCKMARKET CYCLES. Text in English. 1972. 3/w. looseleaf. USD 252 domestic with periodic telephone updates; USD 267 foreign with periodic telephone updates; USD 480 domestic with daily updates; USD 495 foreign with daily updates (effective 2000). charts; mkt. back issues avail. **Document type:** *Newsletter.* **Description:** Aids investors and traders in identifying market tops and bottoms.
Formerly: Stockmarket Cycles
Related titles: Online - full text ed.
Address: PO Box 6873, Santa Rosa, CA 95406-0873. TEL 707-579-8444, 800-888-4351, FAX 707-579-0274, info@stockmarketcycles.com, http://www.stockmarketcycles.com. Ed., Pub. Peter G Eliades. R&P Kerry Thompson. Circ: 2,000.

332.6 615.1 USA ISSN 1076-9382
PHARMACEUTICAL VENTURES. Text in English. 1991. 48/yr. looseleaf. USD 415 (effective 1999). back issues avail. **Document type:** *Newsletter.* **Description:** For sophisticated investors. Covers the financial markets of the pharmaceutical manufacturers and researchers.
Indexed: ABC, Inpharma, Reac.
Published by: Scitec Services, PO Box 261641, Columbus, OH 43226-1641. TEL 614-433-0648, FAX 614-433-0432. Ed., Pub. Frank McKim.

332.6 PHL
PHILIPPINE COMMERCIAL AND INDUSTRIAL BANK. INVESTMENT INFORMATION FOLIO* . Text in English. 1973. m. USD 100. charts; illus.; stat.
Published by: Equitable P C I Bank, Twr. Mkt Ave., cor. H.V. dela Costa Sts., Mkt. City, Philippines.

332.63 PHL
PHILIPPINE STANDARD COMMODITY CLASSIFICATION. Text in English. irreg., latest 1993. USD 205 in Asia; USD 211 in Australia & New Zealand; USD 227 in US & Canada; USD 230 in Europe; USD 265 in Latin America; USD 285 elsewhere. **Document type:** *Government.* **Description:** Represents the latest reclassification of commodities, particularly those that enter Philippine trade.
Published by: National Statistical Coordination Board, c/o National Statistical Information Center, Midland-Buendia Bldg, 403 Sen. Gil Puyat Ave., Makati City, Philippines. TEL 63-2-890-9405, FAX 63-2-890-9408, nscb_nsic@mozcom.com.

332.6 PHL ISSN 0079-1504
PHILIPPINES. BOARD OF INVESTMENTS. ANNUAL REPORT. Text in English. 1968. a. free.
Published by: Board of Investments, Ortigas Bldg, Ortigas Ave, PO Box 676, Rizal, Philippines. TEL 63-2-8953666, FAX 63-2-8953521. Circ: 3,000.

332.6 PHL
PHILIPPINES. BOARD OF INVESTMENTS. INDIVIDUAL SUMMARY OF WEEKLY APPROVED PROJECTS. Text in English. 1983. w.
Published by: Board of Investments, Industry & Investment Bldg, 385 Sen. Gil J. Puyat Ave, P.O. Box 676, Makati Mm, 3117, Philippines. TEL 818-1831, FAX 815-0702.

PHOTOGRAPH COLLECTOR; for collectors, curators and dealers. see *PHOTOGRAPHY*

THE PHYSICIAN MEDICAL GROUP ACQUISITION REPORT. see *BUSINESS AND ECONOMICS*

332.6 338.476 USA ISSN 1097-7139
PHYSICIAN'S MONEY DIGEST; the practical guide to personal finance. Text in English. 199?. 16/yr. USD 65 domestic to individuals; USD 115 domestic to institutions; USD 135 in Canada; USD 145 elsewhere (effective 2005). adv. **Document type:** *Magazine, Trade.* **Description:** Helps physicians improve their money-management and investment skills, protect their growing net worth, and avoid common financial mistakes.
—CCC.
Published by: Ascend Media, Medical Division (Subsidiary of: Ascend Media), 241 Forsgate Dr, Jamesburg, NJ 08831. TEL 732-656-1140, FAX 732-656-1142, http://www.pmdnet.com, http://www.mwc.com. Ed. Gregory Kelly. Pub. Susan Levy. Adv. contact Jennifer Greenstein. B&W page USD 13,210; trim 10.875 x 14.125.

THE PHYSICIAN'S PERSONAL ADVISORY. see *HEALTH FACILITIES AND ADMINISTRATION*

331.6 USA
PICKY PROFITS. Text in English. 1984. irreg. (6-12/yr.). USD 19 per issue.
Published by: Financial Guidance, Inc., PO Box 3831, Albany, GA 31706. TEL 912-883-7774. Ed. Price Howard.

332.6 SWE ISSN 1651-4084
PLACERINGSGUIDEN. Text in Swedish. 1978. a. SEK 250. adv. **Document type:** *Journal, Trade.*
Former titles (until 2001): Affaersvaerldens Aarsbok (0281-7586); (until 1983): Ekonomin (0348-1131)
Related titles: ◆ Series: Affaersvaerlden. ISSN 0345-3766.
Indexed: RASB.
Published by: Affaersvaerlden Foerlag AB, Klara Soedra Kyrkogata 1, Stockholm, 10612, Sweden. TEL 46-8-7966540, FAX 46-8-202157. Circ: 22,000.

PLANNER. see *BUSINESS AND ECONOMICS—Accounting*

332.63 CAN ISSN 1702-1626
PLANNING FOR PROFITS MAGAZINE. Text in English. 2000. 3/yr. CND 9.95; CND 3.95 per issue (effective 2005). **Document type:** *Magazine, Trade.* **Description:** Offers compelling news, views and informative articles to help plan and implement personalized investment strategies.
Formerly (until 2001): Investment.com Magazine (1497-6285)
Related titles: ◆ Online - full text ed.: Investment.com.
Published by: Global Financial Group Inc., 2844 Bainbridge Ave, PO Box 84028, Burnaby, BC V5A 4T9, Canada. TEL 604-681-7210, 800-370-4412, FAX 604-681-7213, info@investment.com, http://www.investment.com.

332.63 DEU ISSN 1439-7684
PLATOW BOERSE. Text in German. 3/w. EUR 423.50 (effective 2005). **Document type:** *Newsletter, Trade.* **Description:** Covers all aspects of the local and international stock markets.
Related titles: Online - full text ed.: EUR 368 (effective 2005).
Published by: Verlag Aktuelle Information GmbH (Subsidiary of: Springer Science+Business Media), Postfach 111926, Frankfurt Am Main, 60054, Germany. TEL 49-69-2426390, FAX 49-69-236909, info.platow@bertelsmann.de, http://www.platow.de. Ed. Frank Mahlmeister. Pub. Albrecht Schirmacher.

PLATT'S OIL PRICE HANDBOOK & OILMANAC. see *PETROLEUM AND GAS*

332.6 USA
PLATT'S PRICE REPORT* . Text in English. d. USD 1,347. **Document type:** *Trade.*
Published by: Platts (Subsidiary of: McGraw-Hill Companies, Inc.), 2 Penn Plaza, 25th Fl, New York, NY 10121-2298. TEL 212-904-3070, 800-752-8878, FAX 212-904-4209, http://www.platts.com.

PLUNKETT'S ON-LINE TRADING, FINANCE & INVESTMENT WEB SITES ALMANAC. see *BUSINESS AND ECONOMICS—Public Finance, Taxation*

332.6 POL
POLAND NEWS. Text in English. 1992. q. EUR 224 foreign (effective 2005). **Document type:** *Newsletter, Trade.* **Description:** Contains news on the key sectors of the Polish market and the overall state of the country's economy (chiefly through macroeconomic indicators).
Formerly: Executive News Briefing - Poland
Media: E-mail.
Published by: Polish Market Review Ltd., ul Supniewskiego 9, Krakow, 31527, Poland. TEL 48-12-4280360, FAX 48-12-4134012, pmr@pmrpublications.com, http://www.pmrpublications.com.

332.6 690 POL ISSN 1642-9249
POLISH CONSTRUCTION REVIEW. Text in English. 2001. m. EUR 420 foreign (effective 2005). 20 p./no.; **Document type:** *Newsletter, Trade.* **Description:** Serves the needs of foreign investors who wish to keep up-to-date on the changes affecting the Polish construction market.
Published by: Polish Market Review Ltd., ul Supniewskiego 9, Krakow, 31527, Poland. TEL 48-12-4280360, FAX 48-12-4134012, pmr@pmrpublications.com, http://www.pmrpublications.com.

332.6 658 POL ISSN 1426-434X
HF3636
POLISH MARKET REVIEW. Text in English. 1995. m. EUR 450 (effective 2005). **Document type:** *Newsletter, Trade.* **Description:** Reports for business professionals who are investing, managing investments, or marketing products on the Polish market.
Related titles: Online - full content ed.
Published by: Polish Market Review Ltd., ul Supniewskiego 9, Krakow, 31527, Poland. TEL 48-12-4280360, FAX 48-12-4134012, pmr@pmrpublications.com, http://www.pmrpublications.com.

POLITICAL RISK LETTER. see *BUSINESS AND ECONOMICS—International Commerce*

POLITICAL RISK YEARBOOK (SET). see *BUSINESS AND ECONOMICS—Banking And Finance*

POLITICAL RISK YEARBOOK. VOLUME 1: NORTH & CENTRAL AMERICA. see *BUSINESS AND ECONOMICS—Banking And Finance*

POLITICAL RISK YEARBOOK. VOLUME 2: MIDDLE EAST & NORTH AFRICA. see *BUSINESS AND ECONOMICS—Banking And Finance*

POLITICAL RISK YEARBOOK. VOLUME 3: SOUTH AMERICA. see *BUSINESS AND ECONOMICS—Banking And Finance*

POLITICAL RISK YEARBOOK. VOLUME 4: SUB-SAHARAN AFRICA. see *BUSINESS AND ECONOMICS—Banking And Finance*

POLITICAL RISK YEARBOOK. VOLUME 5: EAST ASIA & THE PACIFIC. see *BUSINESS AND ECONOMICS—Banking And Finance*

POLITICAL RISK YEARBOOK. VOLUME 6: WEST EUROPE. see *BUSINESS AND ECONOMICS—Banking And Finance*

POLITICAL RISK YEARBOOK. VOLUME 7: EAST EUROPE. see *BUSINESS AND ECONOMICS—Banking And Finance*

POLITICAL RISK YEARBOOK. VOLUME 8: CENTRAL AND SOUTH AFRICA. see *BUSINESS AND ECONOMICS—Banking And Finance*

332.6 CAN ISSN 0822-6970
POLYMETRIC REPORT. CANADIAN EDITION. Text in English. 1968. m. CND 210.28 (effective 1999). **Document type:** *Trade.* **Description:** Fundamental and technical rating service covering Canadian securities.
Formerly (until 1981): Polymetric Report. Canadian Stocks (0229-222X)
Published by: Canadian Analyst Ltd., 21 Squires Ave, Toronto, ON M4B 2R2, Canada. TEL 416-971-6543, 800-348-6661, FAX 416-598-0049.

332.6 CAN ISSN 0711-7965
POLYMETRIC REPORT. N Y S E EDITION. Text in English. m. CND 210.28 (effective 1999). **Document type:** *Trade.* **Description:** Fundamental and technical rating service covering American securities.
Formerly (until 1981): Polymetric Report. N Y S E Stocks (0822-6989)
Published by: Canadian Analyst Ltd., 21 Squires Ave, Toronto, ON M4B 2R2, Canada. TEL 416-971-6543, 800-348-6661, FAX 416-598-0049.

PONDICHERRY INDUSTRIAL PROMOTION, DEVELOPMENT AND INVESTMENT CORPORATION. ANNUAL REPORTS AND ACCOUNTS. see *BUSINESS AND ECONOMICS—Domestic Commerce*

PORTFOLIO INTERNATIONAL. see *BUSINESS AND ECONOMICS—Banking And Finance*

332.67 USA
PORTFOLIO LETTER; newsweekly covering the US equity markets. Text in English. 1979. w. USD 1,595 domestic; USD 1,625 in Canada; USD 1,670 elsewhere. adv. reprint service avail. from PQC. **Document type:** *Newsletter.* **Description:** Focuses on the equity markets worldwide by breaking news on issues that affect both the broad market and its industry groups, and by covering developments in specific stocks.
Related titles: CD-ROM ed.; Microfiche ed.
Published by: Institutional Investor News (Subsidiary of: Euromoney Institutional Investor Plc.), 225 Park Ave S, 7th Fl, New York, NY 10003-1605. TEL 212-224-3800, FAX 212-224-3491. Ed. Tom Lamont.

332.678 382 BEL ISSN 1029-4139
PRACTICAL GUIDE TO FOREIGN DIRECT INVESTMENT IN THE EUROPEAN UNION - THE GREEN BOOK. Text in English. 1997. irreg., latest vol.2, 1999. GBP 150 (effective 2000). charts. **Document type:** *Directory.* **Description:** Offers coverage of national and EU financial incentives, while drawing a comparative profile for each member state.
—CCC.
Published by: Euroconfidentiel s.a., Rue de Rixensart 18, Genval, 1332, Belgium. TEL 32-2-6520284, FAX 32-2-6530180, nigel.hunt @infoboard.be. **Dist. by:** Current Pacific Ltd., PO Box 36-536, Northcote, Auckland, New Zealand. TEL 64-9-480-1388, FAX 64-9-480-1387, info@cplnz.com, http://www.cplnz.com.

332.6 IND
PRACTICAL PROJECT EXECUTION KNOW HOW REPORTS. Text in English. irreg. INR 7,900, USD 250 per issue (effective 1999). charts. **Document type:** *Proceedings.* **Description:** Provides information on how to implement a practical project, including market survey, process of manufacture, raw materials, plant and machinery, land and building, and project economics.
Published by: Small Industry Research Institute, 4-43 Roop Nagar, P O Box 2106, New Delhi, 110 007, India. TEL 91-11-2910805, FAX 91-11-2923955.

332.678 USA
PRACTICAL STOCK PICKER. Text in English. 1983. m. USD 95 (effective 1993). **Document type:** *Newsletter.*
Address: 8 W. Parish Ct., Havenhill, MA 01832-1166. Ed. William J Fallon.

PRACTICE UNDER THE CALIFORNIA CORPORATION SECURITIES LAWS. see *LAW—Corporate Law*

332.6 USA
PRATT'S GUIDE CD-ROM. Text in English. a. USD 895 (effective 1998). bibl. **Description:** Lists 1,175 venture capital financing sources, all accessible by key word. Includes roughly 100 pages of articles by industry experts.
Media: CD-ROM.
Published by: Securities Data Publishing (Subsidiary of: Thomson Financial / I M G Media), 195 Broadway, New York, NY 10007. TEL 212-765-5311, FAX 212-765-6123. Ed. Daniel Bokser.

332.6 USA ISSN 1547-2213
HG65
PRATT'S GUIDE TO PRIVATE EQUITY SOURCES. Text in English. 1970. a., latest 2004. USD 645 per issue; USD 795 per issue with online access (effective 2005). bibl. **Document type:** *Directory, Trade.* **Description:** Provides detailed profiles of more than 950 active U.S. and Canadian venture capital firms, with addresses, telephone and fax numbers, contact names, investment amounts, industry and project preferences, and capital under management.
Former titles (until 2003): Pratt's Guide to Venture Capital Sources (0884-1616); (until 1984): Guide to Venture Capital Sources (0749-6893)
—BLDSC (6603.023510). **CCC.**
Published by: Securities Data Publishing (Subsidiary of: Thomson Financial / I M G Media), 195 Broadway, New York, NY 10007. TEL 212-333-9202, http://www.thomsonfinancial.com. Ed. Daniel Bokser.

PRAXISHANDBUCH AELDAULAGE. see *BUSINESS AND ECONOMICS—Banking And Finance*

332.6 USA
PRECIOUS METALS DATA BASE✶. Text in English. 1985. m. USD 36. **Description:** Features decision-data for precious metals investors.
Published by: Moneypower, 1304 Edgewood Ave, Ann Arbor, MI 48103-5522. TEL 612-537-8096. Ed. James H Moore.

332.6 CAN ISSN 0829-383X
PREFERRED SHARES & WARRANTS. Text in English. 1982. a. CND 64.95 (effective 1998).
Published by: Financial Post Datagroup, 300-1450 Don Mills Rd, Don Mills, ON M3B 3R5, Canada. TEL 416-350-6507, 800-661-7678.

332.6 ITA ISSN 0394-5367
PREVISIONI DELL'ECONOMIA ITALIANA. Text in Italian. 1987. s-a.
Published by: Centro Studi Confindustria, Viale Pasteur 6, Rome, 00144, Italy. TEL 06-5920509, FAX 06-5924819, http://www.confindustria.it.

332.63 USA ISSN 1013-7440
PRICE PROSPECTS FOR MAJOR PRIMARY COMMODITIES. Text in English. 1989. biennial.
—CCC.
Published by: World Bank Group, 1818 H St, NW, Washington, DC 20433.

332.6 USA
PRIMARY TREND. Text in English. 1979. s-m. USD 80; USD 100 foreign (effective 1998). back issues avail. **Document type:** *Newsletter.*
Published by: Arnold Investment Counsel, Inc., First Financial Center, 700 N Water St, Milwaukee, WI 53202. TEL 414-271-2726. Ed. Barry S Arnold. Circ: 2,000.

330 DEU ISSN 1611-2741
PRIME REPORT; Deutschlands erster Boersenbrief fuer den Prime Standard. Text in German. 1998. w. EUR 184 domestic; EUR 194 foreign (effective 2003). **Document type:** *Newsletter, Trade.*
Formerly: Neuer Markt Inside (1435-7291)
Published by: Boersenmedien AG, Hofer Str 20, Kulmbach, 95326, Germany. TEL 49-9221-90510, FAX 49-9221-877288. Ed. Thomas Bergmann. Pub. Bernd Foertsch.

332.6 USA ISSN 1529-5702
PRIVATE ASSET MANAGEMENT. Text in English. 199?. bi-w. USD 2,095 (effective 2005). **Document type:** *Newsletter, Trade.* **Description:** Covers how to find, service and retain high-net-worth clients. Includes new investment products, services and fee structures.
Related titles: Online - full text ed.: (from Florida Center for Library Automation, Gale Group, O C L C Online Computer Library Center, Inc.).
—CCC.
Published by: Institutional Investor News (Subsidiary of: Euromoney Institutional Investor Plc.), 225 Park Ave S, 7th Fl, New York, NY 10003-1605. TEL 212-224-3800, FAX 212-224-3491, info@iiplatinum.com, http://www.iiwealthmanagement.com, http://www.iinews.com. Pub. Aaron Finkel TEL 212-224-3268. **Subscr. to:** New Orders, PO Box 5063, Brentwood, TN 37024. TEL 615-377-3322, 800-945-2034, 800-715-9197, FAX 615-337-0525, vlockridge@sunbeltfs.com.

332.6 PHL
PRIVATE DEVELOPMENT CORPORATION OF THE PHILIPPINES. ANNUAL P D C P SURVEY ON BUSINESS PERFORMANCE. Text in English. 1977. a. USD 40.
Published by: Private Development Corporation of the Philippines/Pribadong Korporasyon sa Pagpapaunlad ng Pilipinas, P.O. Box 757, Makati, Manila, 3117, Philippines. TEL 02-8100231, FAX 02-8195376. Ed. Lucia C Laquindanum.

332.62 USA ISSN 1057-526X
HG4501
PRIVATE EQUITY ANALYST. Text in English. 1991. m. USD 1,195 domestic; USD 1,275 foreign (effective 2005). adv. charts; stat. back issues avail. **Document type:** *Newsletter.* **Description:** Covers the private equity market and its investment specialties, such as venture capital, buyouts, mezzanine and turnaround funds. Also tracks the fund-raising activities of private limited partnerships and institutional investors' participation in the market.
Related titles: Online - full text ed.; ◆ Alternate Frequency ed(s).: Private Equity Analyst Weekly. w.
—IE. **CCC.**
Published by: Alternative Investor, 170 Linden St, 2nd Fl, Wellesley, MA 02482. TEL 781-304-1400, FAX 781-304-1440, info@assetnews.com, http://www.assetnews.com. Ed., Pub. David Toll. Adv. contact Doreen C Purvis. page USD 1,890; trim 11 x 8.5. Circ: 1,968 (paid).

332.62 USA
PRIVATE EQUITY ANALYST WEEKLY. Text in English. w.
Media: Fax. **Related titles:** ◆ Alternate Frequency ed(s).: Private Equity Analyst. ISSN 1057-526X. m.
Published by: Alternative Investor, 170 Linden St, 2nd Fl, Wellesley, MA 02482.

332.6 USA ISSN 1551-093X
▼ **PRIVATE EQUITY INSIDER.** Text in English. 2004. w. (47/yr.). USD 1,897 print or email ed. (effective 2005). adv. **Document type:** *Magazine, Trade.*
Related titles: E-mail ed.; Online - full text ed.: ISSN 1551-0948.
Published by: Harrison Scott Publications, Inc., 5 Marine View Plaza, Ste 301, Hoboken, NJ 07030-5795. TEL 201-659-1700, FAX 201-659-4141, info@hspnews.com, http://www.peinsider.com/. Ed. Thomas Ferris TEL 201-234-3972. Pub. Andrew Albert TEL 201-234-3960. Adv. contact Mary E Romano TEL 201-234-3968. B&W page USD 2,900; trim 8.5 x 11.

332.67 341 USA ISSN 0090-9742
K3829.6
PRIVATE INVESTMENTS ABROAD; problems and solutions in international business. Text in English. 1967. a. USD 153 (effective 1999).
Related titles: Microfilm ed.: (from WSH); Online - full text ed.
Indexed: CLI, ILP, LRI.
—BLDSC (6617.068920). **CCC.**
Published by: (Southwestern Legal Foundation, International and Comparative Law Center), Matthew Bender & Co., Inc. (Subsidiary of: LexisNexis North America), 1275 Broadway, Albany, NY 12204. international@bender.com, http://www.bender.com, http://bender.lexisnexis.com.

332.6 USA ISSN 1053-6434
KF1428.A15
PRIVATE PLACEMENT ALERT. Key Title: Faulkner & Gray's Private Placement Alert. Text in English. 1990. m. USD 295 domestic; USD 395 foreign (effective 2005). **Document type:** *Magazine, Trade.* **Description:** Provides investment guidance on turnarounds, LBOs, bailouts, and licensing agreements.
Formerly: Faulkner and Gray's Corporate Financing Stategist (1047-1510)
Published by: Source Media, Inc., One State St Plaza, 27th Fl, New York, NY 10004. TEL 212-803-6077, FAX 212-747-1154, custserv@sourcemedia.com, http://www.sourcemedia.com.

PROBE DIRECTORY OF FOREIGN DIRECT INVESTMENT IN THE UNITED STATES. see *BUSINESS AND ECONOMICS—Trade And Industrial Directories*

332.678 USA
PROFESSIONAL TIMING SERVICE. Text in English. 3/w. USD 185.
Published by: Curtis J. Hesler, Pub., PO Box 7483, Missoula, MT 59807. TEL 406-543-4131.

B

332.6 ZAF ISSN 1025-1081
PROFILE'S (YEAR) UNIT TRUSTS HANDBOOK. Text in English. 1994. s-a. ZAR 89.90 domestic; USD 25 foreign (effective 2003). adv. 288 p./no.; **Document type:** *Journal, Trade.* **Description:** Provides a complete reference to unit trusts and unit trust management companies operating in South Africa.
Formerly (until 1999): Unit Trusts Handbook (1025-0506)
Published by: Profile Media, PO Box 87254, Houghton, Johannesburg 2041, South Africa. TEL 27-11-7285510, FAX 27-11-7285845, info@profile.co.za, ernie@profile.co.za, http://www.profile.co.za/books/unitbook.html. Ed. Nic Oldert. R&P, Adv. contact Ernie Alexander. B&W page ZAR 9,775, color page ZAR 12,500; trim 148 x 210. Circ: 13,000.

332.6 ZAF
PROFILE'S (YEARS) AFRICAN STOCK EXCHANGE HANDBOOK. Text in English. irreg., latest 1999. ZAR 89.90, USD 40 (effective 2003). adv. **Document type:** *Trade.* **Description:** Includes information on all stock exchanges in Africa.
Incorporates (1934-199?): The J S E Handbook; Formerly: African Exchanges Handbook
Published by: Profile Media, PO Box 87254, Houghton, Johannesburg 2041, South Africa. TEL 27-11-7285510, FAX 27-11-7285845, ernie@profile.co.za, http://www.profile.co.za/books/ashbook.html. R&P, Adv. contact Ernie Alexander. B&W page ZAR 9,775, color page ZAR 12,500; trim 148 x 210. Circ: 6,000.

332.6 ZAF
PROFILE'S (YEAR) FINANCIAL MARKETS HANDBOOK. Text in English. 1991. a., latest 2003. ZAR 99, USD 25 (effective 2003). adv. **Document type:** *Journal, Trade.* **Description:** Covers all major financial institutions in South Africa.
Formerly: Financial Markets Handbook (1018-0796)
Published by: Profile Media, PO Box 87254, Houghton, Johannesburg 2041, South Africa. TEL 27-11-7285510, FAX 27-11-7285845, ernie@profile.co.za, http://www.profile.co.za/books/finmbook.html. Ed., R&P, Adv. contact Ernie Alexander. B&W page ZAR 9,775, color page ZAR 12,506; trim 148 x 210. Circ: 3,000.

332.6 ZAF
PROFILE'S INVESTING OFFSHORE. Text in English. 2/yr. ZAR 89.90 domestic; USD 25 foreign (effective 2003). 352 p./no.; **Document type:** *Journal, Trade.* **Description:** Provides offshore investing information for brokers, agents, and other financial intermediaries.
Formerly: Profile's Offshore Unit Trusts (1608-2028)
Published by: Profile Media, PO Box 87254, Houghton, Johannesburg 2041, South Africa. TEL 27-11-7285510, FAX 27-11-7285845, ernie@profile.co.za, http://www.profile.co.za/books/offunitbook.html. Ed. Nic Oldert. Adv. contact Cynthia Price.

332.6 ZAF
PROFILE'S RESULTS & EARNINGS. Text in English. q. ZAR 135 domestic; USD 25 foreign (effective 2003). **Document type:** *Trade.* **Description:** Contains "results-as-published" for South Africa's top companies plus consensus forecast earnings.
Formerly: Profile's J S E Results & Earnings (1606-0962)
Published by: Profile Media, PO Box 87254, Houghton, Johannesburg 2041, South Africa. TEL 27-11-7285510, FAX 27-11-7285845, ernie@profile.co.za, http://www.profile.co.za/books/R&Ebook.html. Ed. Nic Oldert. Adv. contacts Cynthia Price, Ernie Alexander.

332.6 ZAF
PROFILE'S STOCK EXCHANGE HANDBOOK. Text in English. 1992. s-a. ZAR 49.90, USD 25 per issue (effective 2003). adv. **Document type:** *Trade.* **Description:** Includes fundamental information on companies listed on the Johannesburg Stock Exchange.
Formerly: Stock Exchange Handbook

Published by: Profile Media, PO Box 87254, Houghton, Johannesburg 2041, South Africa. TEL 27-11-7285510, FAX 27-11-7285845, ernie@profile.co.za, http://www.profile.co.za/books/stockbook.html. R&P, Adv. contact Ernie Alexander. B&W page ZAR 10,500, color page ZAR 13,500; trim 168 x 241. Circ: 25,710.

332.6 051 USA
PROFIT (RANCHO MIRAGE); the magazine, the investment, the lifestyle. Text in English. 1995. bi-m. USD 29.95; USD 4.95 newsstand/cover (effective 1999). adv. bk.rev. charts; stat. back issues avail. **Document type:** *Consumer.* **Description:** Investment strategies and health issues are covered.
Related titles: Online - full text ed.
Published by: Profit Publications, 69730 Highway 111, Ste 102, Rancho Mirage, CA 92270. TEL 760-202-1545, FAX 760-202-1549, ProfitMag@aol.com, http://www.promagazine.net. Ed. Marvin Bryan. Pub. Jayne Lanza. R&P, Adv. contact Lorena Estrada. B&W page USD 2,000, color page USD 5,000. Circ: 50,000.

344.01 USA ISSN 0033-0280
PROFIT SHARING. Text in English. 1970 (vol.18). bi-m. membership. adv. **Document type:** *Trade.* **Description:** Covers legislative and regulatory activity affecting defined contribution plans and provides information on profit-sharing and 401(k) plan design, compliance, administration, investment and communication. Geared toward plan administrators, benefits managers and benefits communicators.
Published by: Profit Sharing - 401(K) Council of America, 10 S Riverside Plaza, Ste 1610, Chicago, IL 60606-3802. TEL 312-441-8550, FAX 312-441-8559. Ed. Debra Schloesslin. Pub. David L Wray. R&P Charlie Seten. Circ: 3,000.

332.6 IND
PROJECT FEASIBILITY CUM MARKET SURVEY REPORT. Text in English. irreg. INR 1,050, USD 60 per issue (effective 1999). **Document type:** *Proceedings.* **Description:** Contains all information necessary for entrepreneurs looking for new investment opportunities.
Published by: Small Industry Research Institute, 4-43 Roop Nagar, P O Box 2106, New Delhi, 110 007, India. TEL 91-11-2910805, FAX 91-11-2923955, TELEX 031-61028 SIRI IN. Ed. D C Gupta.

332.6 AUS
PROJECTS QUEENSLAND. Text in English. 1980. a. AUD 25 (effective 2000). **Document type:** *Government.* **Description:** Major manufacturing, minerals processing, mining, infrastructure and energy project proposals in Queensland.
Formerly (until 1995): Major Development Projects and Proposals in Queensland (0728-4438)
Published by: Department of State Development, Level 22, 111 George St, Brisbane, QLD 4000, Australia. TEL 61-7-3234-1653, FAX 61-7-3234-1520, bron.mcclain@sd.qld.gov.au. Circ: 10,000.

332.6 GBR
PROTECTED INVESTMENT PLANS. Text in English. bi-m. adv. **Document type:** *Magazine, Trade.* **Description:** Contains: structured products news and developments; debate and comment from key players in the structured products market; details of structured investment product launches; a guide to maturing products with underlying indices and performance statistics; innovative ideas for enhancing client portfolios; and product construction techniques and terminology to explain risk/reward scenarios.
Published by: Incisive Media Plc., Haymarket House, 28-29 Haymarket, London, SW1Y 4RX, United Kingdom. TEL 44-20-74849700, FAX 44-20-79302238, pips@incisive,edia.com, customerservices@incisivemedia.com, http://www.incisivemedia.com/. Eds. Isobel McCalman TEL 44-20-74326950, Lawrence Gosling TEL 44-20-79684569. Pub. Rod Boulogne TEL 44-20-79684513. Adv. contact Rachel Calvert TEL 44-20-74326957.

332.6 CAN
PRUDENT INVESTORS MAGAZINE. Text in English. q. USD 36 (effective 2000).
Published by: The Corporate Group, 357 Bay Street, Ste. 900, Toronto, ON, Ontario M5H 2T7, Canada. TEL 416-362-9949, FAX 416-369-0129, smonteith@thecorpgroup.com.

332.6 USA ISSN 0743-0809
THE PRUDENT SPECULATOR. Text in English. 1977. m. looseleaf. USD 295 (effective 2005). bk.rev. back issues avail. **Document type:** *Newsletter, Consumer.* **Description:** Stock advisory letter showing investors what to consider in buying and selling stocks, managing a portfolio and adjusting to significant market-wide changes.
Published by: Al Frank Asset Management, Inc., PO Box 1438, Laguna Beach, CA 92652. TEL 949-499-3215, FAX 949-499-3218, info@alfrank.com, http://www.prudentspeculator.com, https://www.alfrank.com. Ed. Al Frank. R&P Vitoria Baldwin TEL 505-983-1579. Circ: 6,000 (paid and controlled).

332.6 USA
PUBLIC INVESTOR. Text in English. 1982. m. USD 85 to non-members; USD 55 to members. bk.rev. charts. cum.index. **Document type:** *Newsletter.* **Description:** Reports and analyzes major economic, political and market events affecting public-sector investment officers.
Published by: Government Finance Officers Association, 203 N LaSalle St, Ste 2700, Chicago, IL 60601-1210. Subscriptions@gfoa.org, http://www.gfoa.org. Ed. M Corinne Larson. Circ: 1,700.

PUBLIC LEDGER. see *AGRICULTURE—Agricultural Economics*

PUBLIC TREASURER. see *BUSINESS AND ECONOMICS—Public Finance, Taxation*

332.6 ESP
PULSO BURSATIL. Text in Spanish. m. free. charts; stat.
Published by: Banco Hispano Americano, Division de Banca Corporativa y Mercado de Capitales, Plaza Canalejas, 1, Madrid, 28014, Spain. TEL 531-18-36.

332.6 USA ISSN 1066-0631
HG6024.U6
PUT BOND HANDBOOK. Text in English. 1992. q. USD 435. charts; stat. **Document type:** *Trade.*
Published by: Standard & Poor's (Subsidiary of: McGraw-Hill Companies, Inc.), 55 Water St, New York, NY 10041. TEL 212-208-1146.

THE Q D R O REPORT; an insider's guide to QDROs and present values. (Qualified Domestic Relations Orders) see *BUSINESS AND ECONOMICS—Labor And Industrial Relations*

332.64 ECU
QOMPENDIUM. Text in Spanish. a. ECS 70,000. **Description:** Presents information on companies listed on the exchange.
Published by: Bolsa de Valores de Quito, Amazonas 540 y Carrion, Apartado 17-01-3772, Quito, Ecuador. TEL 593-2-526805, FAX 593-2-500942, information@ccbvq.com, http://www.ccbvq.com.

QUARTERLY BANK DIGEST. see *BUSINESS AND ECONOMICS—Banking And Finance*

332.6 IND ISSN 0033-5312
QUARTERLY BLUE BOOK ON JOINT STOCK COMPANIES IN INDIA✶. Text in English. 1966. q. INR 14, USD 5.04.
Published by: (India. Research and Statistics Division), Department of Company Affairs, Shastri Bhawan, Dr. Rajendraprasad Rd., New Delhi, India. Circ: 220. **Subscr. to:** Controller of Publications.

332.6 USA
QUARTERLY REPORT ON MONEY FUND PERFORMANCE✶. Text in English. 1988. q. USD 525. **Description:** Provides expense ratios and other information for a comparative analysis of money fund performance.
Former titles: I B C's Quarterly Report on Money Fund Performance; Quarterly Report on Money Fund Expense Ratios (0897-2044)
Published by: IBC - Donoghue, Inc., PO Box 5193, Westborough, MA 01581-5193. TEL 508-881-2800, FAX 508-881-0982. Ed. Tracy Burke. Circ: 1,000.

332.6 CAN
QUEBEC (PROVINCE). COMMISSION DES VALEURS MOBILIERES DU QUEBEC. BULLETIN HEBDOMADAIRE. Text in French. w. CND 475; CND 950 foreign. **Description:** Report activities in the real estate sector of the province of Quebec.
Published by: (Quebec (Province). Commission des Valeurs Mobilieres du Quebec), Publications du Quebec, P O Box 1005, Quebec, PQ G1K 7B5, Canada. TEL 418-643-5150, FAX 418-643-6177. **Subscr. to:** Service Abonnements, 4380 av Garand, St Laurent, PQ H4R 2A3, Canada.

332.6 USA
QUOTE AMERICAN✶. Text in English. 1962. w. USD 279. **Description:** Shows weekly price range, close, and volume on a semi-log scale.
Published by: Lankford-Quote Digest, 7 Rock Rd, Marion, KS 66861-9305. TEL 316-262-2111. Ed. Theresa Hogan. Circ: 200.

332.6 USA
QUOTE NEW YORK✶. Text in English. 1961. w. USD 338.
Published by: Lankford-Quote Digest, 7 Rock Rd, Marion, KS 66861-9305. TEL 316-262-2111. Ed. Theresa Hogan. Circ: 460.

332.6 USA
QUOTE O-T-C✶. (Over-the-Counter) Text in English. 1968. w. USD 293.
Published by: Lankford-Quote Digest, 7 Rock Rd, Marion, KS 66861-9305. TEL 316-262-2111. Ed. Theresa Hogan. Circ: 260.

332.6 ZAF ISSN 1023-9286
R D P MONITOR. (Reconstruction and Development Programme) Text in English. 1994. m. ZAR 550, USD 199 (effective 1998 & 1999). **Description:** Reports on national and international media coverage of the RDP.
Published by: Stock Information Service, PO Box 938, Pinegowrie, Transvaal 2123, South Africa. TEL 27-11-7871000, FAX 27-11-7895273, stock@iafrica.com. Ed. Gavin Lewis. Circ: 400 (paid).

332.63 USA
THE R E I T INVESTOR. (Real Estate Investment Trust) Text in English. w. (every Mon.). **Document type:** *Newsletter, Trade.* **Description:** Contains the latest on deals, mergers and transactions in the REIT marketplace.
Media: E-mail.
Published by: Dow Jones Company, 200 Liberty St, New York, NY 10281. TEL 800-223-2274, newswires@dowjones.com, http://www.djnewswires.com/fin-pro/reit.html.

R E I T STREET. (Real Estate Investment Trust) see *REAL ESTATE*

R E I T WEEK. (Real Estate Investment Trust) see *REAL ESTATE*

336.7 FIN ISSN 1457-3679
RAHASTOSAASTAJA. Text in Finnish. 2000. 2/yr. **Document type:** *Magazine, Trade.*
Published by: Sanoma Magazines Finland Corporation, Hoylaamotie 1 D, P.O. Box 100, Helsinki, 00040, Finland. TEL 358-9-1201, FAX 358-9-1205171, info@sanomamagazines.fi, http://www.sanomamagazines.fi.

332.6 GBR
RANKING OF INVESTMENT ANALYSTS. Text in English. a. GBP 340. **Document type:** *Trade.*
Published by: Financial Times Information Ltd., Extel, Fitzroy House, 13-17 Epworth St, London, EC2A 4DL, United Kingdom. TEL 44-20-7825-8000, FAX 44-20-7608-2032, eic@ft.com, http://www.info.ft.com.

332.6 ITA
I RAPPORTI MONOGRAFICI DEL C S C. Text in Italian. irreg.
Published by: Centro Studi Confindustria, Viale Pasteur 6, Rome, 00144, Italy. TEL 06-5920509, FAX 06-5924819, http://www.confindustria.it.

332.6 ITA ISSN 1592-663X
RAPPORTO SULL'INDUSTRIA ITALIANA. Text in Italian. 1995. a.
Published by: Centro Studi Confindustria, Viale Pasteur 6, Rome, 00144, Italy. TEL 06-5920509, FAX 06-5924819, http://www.confindustria.it.

332.6 TZA ISSN 0856-0382
RASILIMALI; Tanzania investment outlook. Text in English. 1972. irreg., latest vol.10, 1983.
Published by: Tanzania Investment Bank, PO Box 9373, Dar Es Salaam, Tanzania.

332.6 USA ISSN 1553-8818
THE RATIONAL INVESTOR. Text in English. 2002. m. USD 199 (effective 2005).
Published by: Phillips Investment Resources, LLC (Subsidiary of: Phillips International Inc.), 7811 Montrose Rd., Potomac, MD 20854-3394. TEL 301-424-3700, 800-219-8592, http://www.therationalinvestor.com/, http://www.phillips.com/pir/.

REAL ESTATE ALERT. see *REAL ESTATE*

REAL ESTATE PORTFOLIO. see *REAL ESTATE*

REAL ESTATE/PORTFOLIO STRATEGIST. see *REAL ESTATE*

332.6 GBR ISSN 1468-5612
REAL MONEY. Text in English. 1999. m. GBP 24; GBP 2.50 newsstand/cover (effective 2000). adv. **Document type:** *Magazine, Consumer.* **Description:** Provides articles and features on all aspects of personal financial investing.
Published by: Perspective Publishing Ltd., 408 Fruit & Wool Exchange, Brushfield St, London, E1 6EP, United Kingdom. TEL 44-20-74260636, FAX 44-20-74260123, muir@perspectivepublishing.com, http://www.perspectivepublishing.com/.

332.6 GBR
REALADVISER; for advisers outsourcing investment, life and pension decisions. Variant title: Real Adviser. Text in English. m. free to qualified personnel (effective 2005). **Document type:** *Magazine, Trade.* **Description:** Keeps IFAs informed of developments, the companies that are providing the best solutions and the business impact of outsourcing, it will help the IFA run a better business and make better investment decisions for their clients.
Incorporates: MultiManager
Related titles: Online - full content ed.

Published by: Incisive Media Plc., Haymarket House, 28-29 Haymarket, London, SW1Y 4RX, United Kingdom. TEL 44-20-74849700, FAX 44-20-79302238, customerservices@incisivemedia.com, http://www.realadviser.co.uk/, http://www.incisivemedia.com/. Ed. Cherry Reynard TEL 44-20-74849937. Pub. Nicky Cooper TEL 44-20-79684522. Adv. contact Gareth Wilde TEL 44-20-79684579.

332.6 USA
REALTY STOCK DIGEST; news summary of public REITs and real estate companies. Text in English. 1987. m. looseleaf. USD 265. index. back issues avail.
Published by: M J H Research Associates, 92 Kennedy Rd, Box 7, Tranquility, NJ 07879-0007. TEL 908-850-1155. Ed. Michael J Houston. Circ: 200.

332.6 USA ISSN 1075-7554
REALTY STOCK REVIEW; market analysis of securities of reits and real estate companies. Text in English. 1970. s-m. looseleaf. USD 325. index. back issues avail.
Formerly: Realty Trust Review
Address: 92 Kennedy Rd, Box 7, Tranquility, NJ 07879-0007. TEL 908-850-1155. Ed. Michael J Houston. Circ: 400.

RECAP. see *BUSINESS AND ECONOMICS—Banking And Finance*

332.6 USA
RECOMMENDED LENDING STANCE. Text in English. 1987. m. USD 300. **Description:** Review of the mortgage market with emphasis on a propriety FHLMC forecast model.
Published by: Quantum Group, Ltd., 1501 Oakes, Williamsport, PA 17701. TEL 717-433-4236. Eds. David Cheesman, Gregory P Breon.

332.6 CAN ISSN 0832-0748
RECORD OF NEW ISSUES. Text in English. 1951. a. CND 310 (effective 1998).
Published by: Financial Post Datagroup, 300-1450 Don Mills Rd, Don Mills, ON M3B 3R5, Canada. TEL 416-350-6507, 800-661-7678, FAX 416-350-6501.

344.71023 CAN ISSN 1486-6196
REGIME DE PENSIONS DU CANADA. RAPPORT ANNUEL. Text in French. 1996. a. **Document type:** *Government.*
Related titles: Online - full content ed.: ISSN 1494-4995; ♦ English ed.: Canada Pension Plan. Annual Report. ISSN 1486-6188.
Published by: Human Resources Development Canada, Public Enquiries Centre, 140 Promenade du Portage, Hull, PQ K1A 0J9, Canada. FAX 819-953-7260, http://www.hrsdc.gc.ca/.

332.6 USA ISSN 1539-7149
HG4621
REGISTERED REP. Text in English. 1976. m. free in US & Canada to qualified personnel; USD 59 elsewhere (effective 2005). adv. bk.rev. back issues avail.; reprints avail. **Document type:** *Magazine, Trade.* **Description:** Provides sales, marketing, management and product ideas for retail stockbrokers.
Formerly (until 2001): Registered Representative (0193-1865)
Related titles: Online - full text ed.: (from H.W. Wilson, LexisNexis, O C L C Online Computer Library Center, Inc., ProQuest Information & Learning).
Indexed: BPI.
—CCC.
Published by: Primedia Business Magazines & Media, Inc. (Subsidiary of: Primedia, Inc.), 249 W 17th St, New York, NY 10011. TEL 212-462-3600, FAX 212-206-3622, inquiries@primediabusiness.com, http://www.registeredrep.com/, http://www.primediabusiness.com. Ed. David A Geracioti TEL 212-462-3591. Pub. Rich Santos. adv.: color page USD 16,648. Circ: 115,000 (controlled).

332.6 340.066 USA
REGULATION OF INVESTMENT COMPANIES. Text in English. 1995. 3 base vols. plus irreg. updates. looseleaf. USD 466 base vol(s). (effective 2005). **Description:** covers section-by-section analysis of the investment company Act of 1940, comprehensive discussion of Mutual Fund Advertisement Requirements, practical advice on understanding the most critical compliance issues, coverage of current "Hot" topics and full text of the 1940 Act and rules promulgated thereunder.
Related titles: CD-ROM ed.: USD 380 (effective 2002).
Indexed: ATI.
Published by: Matthew Bender & Co., Inc. (Subsidiary of: LexisNexis North America), 1275 Broadway, Albany, NY 12204. TEL 518-487-3575, 800-252-9257, FAX 518-462-3788, international@bender.com, http://bender.lexisnexis.com. Ed. Thomas P. Lemke.

REGULATION OF THE COMMODITIES FUTURES AND OPTIONS MARKETS. see *LAW*

332.6 ESP ISSN 0486-3518
RELACIONES FINANCIERAS. Text in Spanish. 12/yr.
Address: Madonado 55, 1o, Ofc. 116, Madrid, 28001, Spain. TEL 1-411-0653, FAX 1-411-07-52. Ed. Miriam Dias Aroca.

332.6 USA
RELEASE TO THE MEMBERSHIP. Text in English. d. USD 60. **Description:** Covers all coffee, sugar and cocoa exchange releases. Also discusses rule and margin changes, warehouse information and notice days.
Published by: Coffee, Sugar & Cocoa Exchange, Inc., Four World Trade Center, New York, NY 10048. TEL 212-938-2800, FAX 212-524-9863.

332.6 LUX
RELEVE DES SOCIETES DONT LES ACTIONS, PARTS ET CERTIFICATS SONT COTES EN BOURSE DE LUXEMBOURG/LIST OF COMPANIES OF WHICH SHARES, PARTS AND FOREIGN SHARE CERTIFICATES ARE LISTED ON THE LUXEMBOURG STOCK EXCHANGE. Text in English, French. 1988. q. free.
Published by: Societe de la Bourse de Luxembourg/Luxembourg Stock Exchange, 11 av. de la Porte Neuve, BP 165, Luxembourg, L-2011, Luxembourg. TEL 352-4779361, FAX 352-473298, info@bourse.lu, http://www.bourse.lu. Circ: 220.

332.6 USA ISSN 0034-4834
REPORTING ON GOVERNMENTS✶. Text in English. 1944. w. USD 250. **Description:** Analysis of highest-grade bond and money markets, monetary and fiscal policies, the economic outlook and interest-rate trends.
Media: Duplicated (not offset).
Published by: Reporting on Governments, Inc., 38 Brite Ave, Scarsdale, NY 10583-2309. Ed. Ben Weberman.

332.6 USA ISSN 0192-172X
RESEARCH (SAN FRANCISCO); all an advisor needs to succeed. Text in English. 197?. m. free to qualified personnel. adv. **Document type:** *Magazine, Trade.*
Related titles: Online - full text ed.: (from Factiva, Florida Center for Library Automation, Gale Group).
Published by: Adams Business Media, 585 Fifth St., West, Sonoma, CA 95476. TEL 707-938-1082, FAX 707-935-6585, http://www.researchmag.com, http://www.adamsbusinessmedia.com/. Ed. Gil Weinreich. Pub. Robert R. Tyndall. adv.: B&W page USD 9,890, color page USD 11,603; trim 8 x 10.75. Circ: 95,800.

332.63 AUS ISSN 1441-9750
RESOURCESTOCKS. Text in English. 1999. q. adv. back issues avail. **Document type:** *Magazine, Consumer.* **Description:** Provides investment news for the resources sector, including analyses trends, issues, and barriers to investing in the resources market.
Published by: Aspermont Ltd., PO Box 78, Leederville, W.A. 6092, Australia. TEL 61-8-62639100, FAX 61-8-62639148, contact@aspermont.com, http://www.miningnews.net/companypages/rs/rs.html, http://www.aspermont.com. Ed. James Hamilton.

332.678 USA
▼ **RETIREMENT PLAN ADVISOR**; interactive edition. Text in English. 2005. m. **Document type:** *Newsletter.* **Description:** Focuses on needs of readers who offer 401 (k) and other qualified retirement plans to their clients.
Media: E-mail.
Published by: Investment Advisor Group (Subsidiary of: Wicks Business Information LLC), 1161 Broad St, Ste 200, Shrewsbury, NJ 07702. TEL 732-389-8700, FAX 732-389-6065, http://www.investmentadvisor.com.

646.79 USA
RETIREMENT PLANNING ADVISOR. Text in English. 1958. q. **Document type:** *Newsletter.* **Description:** Information on retirement planning issues for persons approaching retirement.
Published by: Hearst Business Communications, Inc., R A I division, 50 Charles Lindbergh Blvd., Ste. 100, Uniondale, NY 11553-3600. TEL 516-227-1300, FAX 516-229-3636. Ed. Beth Helfont. Pub. W Boyd Griffin. R&P Miriam Nacmanie TEL 516-229-3614.

332.6 USA
RETIREMENT PLANS BULLETIN. Text in English. 1994. m. USD 99 (effective 2000). charts; stat. yes. 10 p./no. 2 cols./p.; back issues avail.; reprints avail. **Document type:** *Newsletter, Corporate.*
Formed by the 1994 merger of: I R A Bulletin (1062-7499); Qualified Plan Update (1062-7480)
Related titles: Online - full text ed.
Indexed: ATI.
Published by: Universal Pensions, Inc.,a Bisys Company (Subsidiary of: Bisys), PO Box 979, Brainerd, MN 56401-9965. TEL 218-829-4781, 800-346-3860, FAX 218-829-2106. Ed., R&P Jennifer Olsen.

332 USA ISSN 1077-9493
HG226
RETURN ON INVESTMENT. Variant title: R O I. Text in English. 1994. bi-m. USD 150. 60 p./no. 2 cols./p.; back issues avail.; reprints avail. **Document type:** *Newsletter, Trade.* **Description:** Reports exclusively on the business of investment management worldwide for money management professionals and others involved in this rapidly growing global business.
Published by: Investment Management Publications, Inc., One Liberty Sq, 12th Fl, Boston, MA 02109. TEL 617-422-5450, 617-426-5450, FAX 617-422-0162, impubs@aol.com. Ed. Richard Chimberg. Pub. Melanie Decarolis. Circ: 30,000.

332.6 FRA ISSN 1293-4259
LE REVENU. Text in French. w. (45/yr.). illus. **Document type:** *Magazine, Consumer.*
Formerly (until 1999): Revenu Francais (0180-8389)
Published by: Groupe Revenu Francais, 1 bis av. de la Republique, Paris, 75011, France. TEL 33-1-43553999, FAX 33-1-43558282, boutique@lerevenu.com, http://www.lerevenu.com. Ed. Jean Dennis Errard. Circ: 190,000 (paid). **Subscr. to:** BP 520, Sainte Genevieve Cedex 60732, France.

REVIEW OF DERIVATIVES RESEARCH. see *BUSINESS AND ECONOMICS—Banking And Finance*

332.6 340 USA ISSN 0884-2426
KF1432
THE REVIEW OF SECURITIES & COMMODITIES REGULATION; an analysis of current laws, regulations affecting the securities and futures industries. Text in English. 1967. s-m. (22/yr.). looseleaf. price varies. index. back issues avail. **Document type:** *Newsletter.* **Description:** Emphasizes coverage of new rulings and case decisions as they affect an attorney's clients and practice.
Formerly (until 1985): Standard and Poor's Review of Securities Regulation (0034-6756)
Related titles: Online - full text ed.: (from LexisNexis).
Indexed: CLI, LRI.
—CCC.
Published by: Standard & Poor's (Subsidiary of: McGraw-Hill Companies, Inc.), 55 Water St, New York, NY 10041. TEL 212-208-8650, FAX 212-412-0240. Ed. Michael Finkelstein. R&P Joseph Tigue.

REVISTA BRASILEIRA DE MERCADO DE CAPITAIS. see *BUSINESS AND ECONOMICS*

REVISTA GALEGA DE ECONOMIA. see *BUSINESS AND ECONOMICS—Economic Situation And Conditions*

REVUE CANADIENNE DE GESTION DE TRESORERIE. see *BUSINESS AND ECONOMICS—Banking And Finance*

332.6 FRA ISSN 0223-4718
LA REVUE FIDUCIAIRE. Text in French. w. **Description:** Explores the different fields of the tax system with comments and analyses.
Published by: Groupe Revue Fiduciaire, 100 rue La Fayette, Paris, Cedex 10 75485, France. TEL 33-1-41835252, FAX 33-1-41835253, http://www.grouperf.com. Ed. Henry Gruson.

332.6 FRA ISSN 0396-3640
REVUE FIDUCIAIRE - COMPTABLE. Text in French. m. index. back issues avail. **Description:** Covers the management of business in terms of law, finance, computers and accounting.
—CCC.
Published by: Groupe Revue Fiduciaire, 100 rue La Fayette, Paris, Cedex 10 75485, France. TEL 33-1-41835252, FAX 33-1-41835253, http://www.grouperf.com. Ed. Monique Henrard.

332.6 DEU ISSN 0035-4457
RHEINISCH - WESTFAELISCHE BOERSE ZU DUESSELDORF. AMTLICHES KURSBLATT. Text in German. 1935. d. (Mon.-Fri.). adv. **Document type:** *Bulletin.*
Published by: Rheinisch - Westfaelische Boerse zu Duesseldorf, Ernst-Schneider-Platz 1, Duesseldorf, 40212, Germany. TEL 49-211-13890, FAX 49-211-133287. Adv. contact Dirk Elberskirch. Circ: 250.

332.6 USA ISSN 0884-3031
RICHARD C. YOUNG'S INTELLIGENCE REPORT. Text in English. 1986. m. USD 99.95 (effective 2005). **Document type:** *Newsletter.* **Description:** Provides investment strategies for all types of securities and mutual funds.
—CCC.
Published by: Phillips International, Inc., 1 Massachusetts Ave., NW, Washington, DC 20001. TEL 202-216-0600, 800-930-6801, http://www.intelligencereport.com/. Ed. Richard C Young.

332.6 USA ISSN 0895-1306
RICHARD C. YOUNG'S INTERNATIONAL GOLD REPORT. Text in English. 1978. m. USD 99. **Description:** Looks at a variety of investment strategies within the gold market.
—CCC.
Published by: Phillips International, Inc., 1 Massachusetts Ave., NW, Washington, DC 20001. TEL 301-340-2100, FAX 301-424-7034.

332 USA ISSN 1048-3667
RICHARD E. BAND'S PROFITABLE INVESTING. Text in English. 1990. m. USD 99.95 (effective 2005). **Document type:** *Newsletter, Trade.* **Description:** Covers ways to ensure the safety of investment strategies.
—CCC.

B

Published by: Phillips International, Inc., 1 Massachusetts Ave., NW, Washington, DC 20001. TEL 202-216-0600, 800-930-6801, FAX 202-216-0611. Ed. Richard E Band.

332.6   USA
RICHLAND REPORT. Text in English. 1976. s-m. USD 197 (effective 2001). adv. charts; illus.; mkt.; stat. back issues avail. **Document type:** *Newsletter.*
Published by: Richland Company, PO Box 222, La Jolla, CA 92038. TEL 858-459-2611, FAX 858-459-2612. Ed., Pub., R&P, Adv. contact Kennedy Gammage.

332.6   USA
RISK FACTOR METHOD OF INVESTING. Text in English. 1977. w. charts. back issues avail. **Document type:** *Newsletter.*
Related titles: E-mail ed.
Published by: INVEST-O-Registered Investment Advisors, PO Box 5996, Bend, OR 97708-5996. TEL 541-389-3676. Ed. M Leigh Cruden. R&P William Kuhn. Circ: 150.

332.6   GBR   ISSN 1367-9368
RISK FINANCIER. Text in English. 1997. m. **Document type:** *Trade.*
Published by: Emap Finance (Subsidiary of: Emap Business Communications Ltd.), 33-39 Bowling Green Ln, London, EC1R 0DA, United Kingdom. TEL 44-171-505-8000, FAX 44-171-505-8185, http://www.emap.com.

RISK MANAGEMENT; an international journal. see *INSURANCE*

RISK MANAGEMENT. see *INSURANCE*

RISK MEASUREMENT SERVICE. see *BUSINESS AND ECONOMICS—Banking And Finance*

332.6   USA
RISK RATINGS REVIEW. Text in English. q. USD 995 (effective 2003). **Document type:** *Trade.* **Description:** Provides a summary of risk ratings for all 100 key emerging and highly indebted countries monitored by the Country Risk Service.
Related titles: Online - full content ed.
Published by: Economist Intelligence Unit, 111 W 57th St, New York, NY 10019. http://www.eiu.com.

332.6   AUS
THE RISK REPORT. Text in English. 1996. fortn. AUD 425 (effective 1999). **Document type:** *Newsletter.* **Description:** Covers all aspects of risk management and includes news, analysis, and case studies.
Published by: Newsletter Information Services, PO Box 2095, Manly, NSW 2095, Australia. TEL 61-2-9977-7500, FAX 61-2-9977-3310, customer.support@newsinfo.com.au, http://www.newsinfo.com.au. Ed. Helen Jones.

RISK UPDATE (LONDON, 1997). see *BUSINESS AND ECONOMICS—International Commerce*

332.6   USA   ISSN 1547-6502
HG4501
ROBB REPORT WORTH. Text in English. 1986-2003 (Apr.); resumed 2003 (Fall). m. USD 65 domestic; USD 75 in Canada; USD 94.95 elsewhere (effective 2005). adv. illus. **Document type:** *Magazine, Consumer.* **Description:** For personal investors, discusses new investment opportunities, finance strategies and tax updates, emphasizing diversification of assets.
Former titles (until 2003): Worth (1060-5967); (until Jan.1992): Investment Vision (1055-2375); Which incorporated (1985-1991): Personal Investor (0747-3044)
Related titles: Online - full text ed.
Indexed: ASIP, AgeL.
Published by: CurtCo Media Labs, 29160 Heathercliff Rd, Ste 200, Malibu, CA 90265. TEL 310-589-7700, 800-229-7622, FAX 310-589-7701, info@worth.com, http://www.worth.com, http://www.curtco.com/. Ed. Dwight Cass. adv.: B&W page USD 32,800, color page USD 45,900. Circ: 500,000; 534,653 (paid).

332.6   USA
ROBBINS REPORT ∗ . Text in English. 1966. s-m. USD 125.
Published by: William Spencer Educational Foundation, 2323 Kelso, San Antonio, TX 78248-0952. TEL 512-733-0051. Ed. Richard S Robbins. Circ: 1,600.

332.6   USA
ROESCH MARKET MEMO ∗ . Text in English. 1981. m. USD 42. **Document type:** *Newsletter.* **Description:** Covers all technical and fundamental data pertinent to the market, with buy and sell recommendations.
Address: 6511 W 80th St, Overland, Park, KS 66204-3811. TEL 913-381-0857. Ed. Larry E Roesch.

332.64   ECU
RUEDA. Text in English, Spanish. m. ECS 205,000. **Description:** Contains information regarding the past month's market transactions.
Published by: Bolsa de Valores de Quito, Amazonas 540 y Carrion, Apartado 17-01-3772, Quito, Ecuador. TEL 593-2-526805, FAX 593-2-500942, information@ccbvq.com, http://www.ccbvq.com.

338 332.6   USA   ISSN 0891-5547
RUFF TIMES. Text in English. 1975. every 3 wks. USD 149. adv. bk.rev. charts; stat.
Former titles (until 1986): Howard Ruff's Financial Success Report (0747-0541); Howard Ruff's Financial Survival Report (0745-0672); (until 1984): Ruff Times (0279-2303)
Published by: Phoenix Ink, PO Box 31, Springville, UT 84663-0031. TEL 801-489-8681, FAX 801-489-9290. Ed. Howard J Ruff. Circ: 150,000.

332.6   USA
RUMINATIONS OF THE CONTRARY INVESTOR. Text in English. 1963. m. USD 125 (effective 2003). charts; illus. 6 p./no.; **Document type:** *Newsletter.* **Description:** Ponders the fields of investment and financial speculation. Lists specific securities, with contrarian speculative possibilities most likely to succeed.
Formerly: Contrary Investor (0010-793X)
Media: Duplicated (not offset).
Published by: Fraser Management Associates, Inc., 309 S Willard St, Box 494, Burlington, VT 05402. TEL 802-658-0322, FAX 802-658-0260, ellen@fraser.com, http://www.fraser.com. Ed. James L Fraser.

RUSSIA - NIS TELECOM WEEKLY. see *COMMUNICATIONS*

RUSSIAN TELECOMMUNICATIONS INVESTOR'S GUIDE. see *COMMUNICATIONS*

332.6   POL   ISSN 1231-9546
RYNEK GIELDOWY; biuletyn kwartalny. Text in Polish. 1992. q.
Published by: Gielda Papierow Wartosciowych w Warszawie S.A./Warsaw Stock Exchange, Nowy Swiat 6-12, Warsaw, 00400, Poland. Ed. Arkadiusz W Szymanek.

332   RUS
RYNOK. Text in Russian. w. USD 145 in United States.
Indexed: RASB.
Published by: Rabota dlya Vas, Krasnokholmskaya nab 13-15, Moscow, 109172, Russian Federation. TEL 7-095-9111360, FAX 7-095-9111360. Ed. E D Lapshina. **US dist. addr.:** East View Information Services, 3020 Harbor Ln. N., Minneapolis, MN 55447. TEL 612-550-0961.

332   RUS   ISSN 0869-6608
HG5580.2.A2
RYNOK TSENNYKH BUMAG/SECURITIES MARKET; analiticheskii zhurnal. Text in Russian; Summaries in English. 1992. s-m. USD 276 in United States. adv. abstr.; charts; illus. back issues avail. **Document type:** *Trade.* **Description:** Provides analytical information on the state and prospects of Russia's financial and stock market.
Related titles: Diskette ed.
Indexed: RASB, RefZh.
—East View.
Address: Raspletina ul 3, A-Ya 90, Moscow, 123060, Russian Federation. TEL 7-095-9469820, FAX 7-095-9469822, root@smmag.msk.su. Ed. Valery Kolankov. Adv. contact Vladimir Kadysev. page USD 3,900; trim 282 x 205. Circ: 25,000. **Dist. by:** M K - Periodica, ul Gilyarovskogo 39, Moscow 129110, Russian Federation. TEL 7-095-2845008, FAX 7-095-2813798, info@periodicals.ru, http://www.mkniga.ru; **US dist. addr.:** East View Information Services, 3020 Harbor Ln. N., Minneapolis, MN 55447. TEL 612-550-0961.

332 340   USA   ISSN 1526-2588
S A C AWARD REPORTER. (Securities Arbitration Commentator, Inc.) Text in English. 1990. m. USD 98; USD 200 with subscr. to Award Database Service. back issues avail. **Document type:** *Newsletter.* **Description:** Tracks, records, and reports on arbitration awards in the securities and commodities industry.
Former titles (until 1997): S A C Award Review; (until 1994): S A C Reporter
Published by: Securities Arbitration Commentator, Inc., PO Box 112, Maplewood, NJ 07040. TEL 973-761-5880, FAX 973-761-1504. R&P Richard P Ryder.

332.6   USA   ISSN 1088-8381
HG4915
S & P 100 INFORMATION BULLETIN. Text in English. m. USD 235. stat. back issues avail. **Document type:** *Bulletin.* **Description:** Provides a monthly statistical summary of stock prices of the Standard and Poor's 100 index component companies.
Published by: Standard & Poor's (Subsidiary of: McGraw-Hill Companies, Inc.), 55 Water St, New York, NY 10041. TEL 212-208-8275, FAX 212-208-8624.

332.6   USA   ISSN 1088-8926
HG4907
S & P 500 DIRECTORY. Text in English. a. charts; stat. **Document type:** *Directory.* **Description:** Lists and profiles all companies included in the Standard and Poor's 500 Index.
Published by: Standard & Poor's (Subsidiary of: McGraw-Hill Companies, Inc.), 55 Water St, New York, NY 10041. TEL 212-208-8000.

332.9   USA   ISSN 1088-8861
HG4907
S & P MIDCAP 400 DIRECTORY. Text in English. a. charts; stat. **Document type:** *Directory.* **Description:** Lists and profiles companies in the Standard and Poor's MidCap 400 Index.
Published by: Standard & Poor's (Subsidiary of: McGraw-Hill Companies, Inc.), 55 Water St, New York, NY 10041. TEL 212-208-8000.

332   USA   ISSN 1074-6498
S C O R REPORT; capital formation alternatives for small companies. (Small Corporate Offering Registration) Text in English. 1994. 14/yr. USD 280 (effective 2000). **Document type:** *Consumer.*
Related titles: Online - full text ed.: (from EBSCO Publishing, O C L C Online Computer Library Center, Inc., ProQuest Information & Learning).
—CCC.
Published by: Stewart-Gordon Associates, PO Box 781992, Dallas, TX 75378. TEL 972-620-2489, FAX 972-406-0213, http://www.scor-report.com. Ed., Pub., R&P Tom Stewart Gordon.

332.6 657   USA   ISSN 0277-3953
S E C ACCOUNTING RULES. (Securities and Exchange Commission) Text in English. 1968. base vol. plus m. updates. looseleaf. USD 475 base vol(s). (effective 2004). **Description:** Covers the federal requirements for filing financial statements with the SEC, as well as the SEC accounting rules for the registration of securities and periodic reports of issuers.
Related titles: CD-ROM ed.: USD 510 (effective 2004); Online - full text ed.: USD 510 (effective 2004).
—CCC.
Published by: C C H Inc., 2700 Lake Cook Rd, Riverwoods, IL 60015. TEL 847-267-7000, 800-449-6439, cust_serv@cch.com, http://www.cch.com. Pub. Stacey Caywood.

332.6 340   USA
S E C COMPLIANCE: FINANCIAL REPORTING AND FORMS. (Securities Exchange Commission) Text in English. 5 base vols. plus m. updates. looseleaf. USD 1,100 (effective 1998). **Document type:** *Trade.* **Description:** Contains the official text of the rules and forms required by the Securities and Exchange Commission along with explanations of periodic reporting forms, and coverage of other related developments.
Published by: W G & L Financial Reporting & Management Research (Subsidiary of: R I A), 395 Hudson St, New York, NY 10014. TEL 212-367-6300, FAX 212-367-6817. Eds. Daniel Schechtman, Michael A Walker. **Orders to:** The Park Square Bldg., 31 St James Ave, Boston, MA 02116-4112. TEL 800-950-1207.

332.6   USA   ISSN 0091-4061
KF1436.A2
S E C DOCKET. Text in English. 1973. w. looseleaf. back issues avail.; reprint service avail. from PQC. **Document type:** *Government.*
Related titles: Online - full text ed.: (from Thomson West).
Published by: U.S. Securities and Exchange Commission, 450 Fifth St, N W, MISC 11, Washington, DC 20549. TEL 202-942-7040, 202-942-8088, 800-732-0330, help@sec.gov, http://www.sec.gov/rules.shtml. Circ: 12,500 (controlled). **Orders to:** C C H Inc., 2700 Lake Cook Rd, Riverwoods, IL 60015.

332.6 657   USA
S E C FINANCIAL REPORTING: ANNUAL REPORTS TO SHAREHOLDERS, FORM 10-K, QUARTERLY FINANCIAL REPORTING. Text in English. 1977. base vol. plus irreg. updates. looseleaf. USD 230 base vol(s). (effective 2002). Supplement avail. **Description:** Comprehensive coverage of every aspect of financial reporting and disclosure under regulations S-X and S-K, with emphasis on common problem areas. Attempts to keep readers abreast of current developments in the field.
Published by: Matthew Bender & Co., Inc. (Subsidiary of: LexisNexis North America), 1275 Broadway, Albany, NY 12204. TEL 518-487-3575, 800-252-9257, FAX 518-462-3788, international@bender.com, http://bender.lexisnexis.com.

332.6 346.066   USA
S E C GUIDELINES: RULES AND REGULATIONS. Text in English. a. USD 99; USD 138.60 foreign (effective 1998). **Document type:** *Trade.*
Published by: W G & L Financial Reporting & Management Research (Subsidiary of: R I A), 395 Hudson St, New York, NY 10014. TEL 212-367-6300, FAX 212-367-6718. **Orders to:** The Park Square Bldg., 31 St James Ave, Boston, MA 02116-4112. TEL 800-950-1207.

332.6   USA   ISSN 0364-6718
HG4905
S E C NEWS DIGEST. Text in English. d. USD 100. reprint service avail. from PQC.
Related titles: Online - full text ed.: (from Thomson West).
Published by: U.S. Securities and Exchange Commission, 450 Fifth St, N W, MISC 11, Washington, DC 20549. TEL 202-272-7460, FAX 202-272-7050. Circ: (controlled). **Dist. by:** Washington Service Bureau, Inc., 1225 Connecticut Ave, N W, Washington, DC 20036.

332.6   THA   ISSN 0859-709X
S E T JOURNAL. Text in English. 1996. m.
Media: Online - full text.
Published by: Stock Exchange of Thailand, 62 Rachadapisek Rd,
Klongtoey, Bangkok, 10110, Thailand. TEL 662-229-2000, FAX
662-654-5649, webmaster@setinter1.set.or.th,
http://www.set.or.th.

332.6   THA
S E T NEWSLETTER. Text in English. 1998. m. THB 400; USD
25 in Asia; USD 30 elsewhere. Document type: Newsletter.
Published by: Stock Exchange of Thailand, 62 Rachadapisek Rd,
Klongtoey, Bangkok, 10110, Thailand. TEL 662-229-2000, FAX
662-654-5649, webmaster@setinter1.set.or.th,
http://www.set.or.th.

S I A DIRECTORY & GUIDE. see BUSINESS AND
ECONOMICS—Trade And Industrial Directories

332.029   USA
S I E INVESTMENT ADVISORY GUIDE. Text in English. 1966. q.
USD 2 (effective 2001). adv. bk.rev. bibl. Document type:
Directory. Description: Describes, analyzes, prices and
categorizes investment publications indexed by subject.
Former titles: S I E Guide to Investment Services; S I E
Sophisticated Investor; Investment Sources and Ideas
(0085-6355); Sources and Ideas; Which incorporates:
Sophisticated Investor
Published by: Select Information Exchange, 244 W 54th St, 6th
Fl, New York, NY 10024. TEL 212-247-7123, 800-743-9346,
FAX 212-247-7326, phyllis@stockfocus.com,
http://www.stockfocus.com. Ed. Matt Wein. Pub., Adv. contact
George Wein. page USD 4,995; trim 10 x 8. Circ: 135,000
(paid and controlled).

332.6   USA
S M R COMMODITY CHARTS. Text in English. 1967. w. USD
575; d. fax update service $250; d. fax comments and
recommendations $1500; free via web site. adv. Document
type: Newsletter. Description: Provides a technical charting
service wherein short-term signals are used as indicators to
direct market investments.
Formerly: S M R Commodity Service
Related titles: Online - full text ed.
Published by: Security Market Research, PO Box 7476, Boulder,
CO 80306-7476. TEL 303-494-8035, FAX 303-494-5474,
http://www.smr.com. Ed., Pub., R&P, Adv. contact Brad
Crotzer. Circ: 150.

332.6   USA
S M R STOCK CHARTS. Text in English. 1964. w. USD 575;
USD 150 d. fax update service; USD 1,500 d. fax comments
and recommendations. Document type: Newsletter.
Description: Provides a technical charting service wherein
short-term signals are used as indicators to direct market
investments.
Formerly: Wall Street's Top 50
Related titles: Online - full text ed.: free.
Published by: Security Market Research, PO Box 7476, Boulder,
CO 80306-7476. TEL 303-494-8035, FAX 303-494-5474,
http://www.smr.com. R&P Brad Crotzer. Circ: 300.

332.6   RUS
S.N.G.: OBSHCHII RYNOK. Text in Russian. irreg.
Address: Goncharnaya 1, Moscow, 109240, Russian Federation.
TEL 7-095-9157078, FAX 7-095-9157078. US dist. addr.:
East View Information Services, 3020 Harbor Ln. N.,
Minneapolis, MN 55447. TEL 612-550-0961.

332.6   USA   ISSN 1535-850X
S N L DAILY ENERGYWATCH. Text in English. d. price varies.
Media: Online - full content.
Published by: S N L Financial LC, 212 7th St NE, Charlottesvle,
VA 22902-5307. TEL 434-977-1600, FAX 434-293-0407,
http://www.snl.com.

332   USA   ISSN 1074-6595
S N L DAILY THRIFTWATCH. Text in English. d.
Published by: S N L Financial LC, 212 7th St NE, Charlottesvle,
VA 22902-5307. TEL 434-977-1600, FAX 434-293-0407,
http://www.snl.com.

332.6   USA   ISSN 1074-6609
THE S N L FINANCIAL SERVICES DAILY. Text in English. 1993.
d. USD 4,500.
Published by: S N L Financial LC, 212 7th St NE, Charlottesvle,
VA 22902-5307. TEL 434-977-1600, FAX 434-293-0407,
http://www.snl.com. Ed. Debra Davenport. Pub. Reid Nagle.

332.6   USA   ISSN 1074-5912
HG181
THE S N L FINANCIAL SERVICES QUARTERLY. Text in English.
1992. q. USD 696. Description: Provides financial analysts,
executives, investors and other members of the investment
community with detailed, financial and investment information.
Published by: S N L Financial LC, 212 7th St NE, Charlottesvle,
VA 22902-5307. TEL 434-977-1600, FAX 434-293-0407,
http://www.snl.com. Ed. Pamela Askea. Pub. Reid Nagle.

332 368   USA   ISSN 1090-4204
S N L INSURANCE DAILY. Text in English. d. price varies.
Media: E-mail. Related titles: Fax ed.

Published by: S N L Financial LC, 212 7th St NE, Charlottesvle,
VA 22902-5307. TEL 434-977-1600, FAX 434-293-0407,
http://www.snl.com.

332.6 368   USA   ISSN 1099-3215
HG8076
S N L INSURANCE MERGERS & ACQUISITIONS YEARBOOK.
Variant title: Insurance Mergers & Acquisitions Yearbook. Text
in English. 1998. a. Document type: Yearbook.
Published by: S N L Financial LC, 212 7th St NE, Charlottesvle,
VA 22902-5307. TEL 434-977-1600, FAX 434-293-0407,
http://www.snl.com.

368 332   USA   ISSN 1097-9832
HG8501
S N L INSURANCE QUARTERLY. Text in English. 1997. q. USD
799 (effective 2002).
Published by: S N L Financial LC, 212 7th St NE, Charlottesvle,
VA 22902-5307. TEL 434-977-1600, FAX 434-293-0407,
http://www.snl.com.

S N L INSURANCE WEEKLY. see INSURANCE

332.6   USA
S N L REAL ESTATE SECURITIES DAILY. Text in English. d.
price varies.
Media: E-mail. Related titles: Fax ed.: ISSN 1528-1566.
Published by: S N L Financial LC, 212 7th St NE, Charlottesvle,
VA 22902-5307. TEL 434-977-1600, FAX 434-293-0407,
http://www.snl.com.

332.6   USA   ISSN 1528-1574
HG5095
S N L REAL ESTATE SECURITIES MONTHLY. Text in English.
1995. m. USD 496 (effective 2002).
Formerly (until 2000): R E I T Securities Monthly (1090-0861)
Published by: S N L Financial LC, 212 7th St NE, Charlottesvle,
VA 22902-5307. TEL 434-977-1600, FAX 434-293-0407,
http://www.snl.com.

332   USA   ISSN 1528-1582
HG5095
S N L REAL ESTATE SECURITIES QUARTERLY. Text in
English. 1995. q. USD 696 (effective 2002).
Formerly (until 2000): S N L R E I T Quarterly (1082-1228)
Published by: S N L Financial LC, 212 7th St NE, Charlottesvle,
VA 22902-5307. TEL 434-977-1600, FAX 434-293-0407,
http://www.snl.com.

332.6   USA
S N L REAL ESTATE SECURITIES WEEKLY. Text in English. w.
USD 396 (effective 2002).
Media: E-mail. Related titles: Fax ed.: ISSN 1528-1604.
Published by: S N L Financial LC, 212 7th St NE, Charlottesvle,
VA 22902-5307. TEL 434-977-1600, FAX 434-293-0407,
http://www.snl.com.

332.6   USA   ISSN 8750-2356
HG4501
S R C BLUE BOOK OF 5-TREND CYCLI-GRAPHS; 12 years of
prices, earnings, dividends, relative performance, volume. Text
in English. q. USD 200 (effective 2001). adv. Document type:
Directory. Description: Explores price ranges, relative
performance, volume, quarterly earnings and dividends.
Published by: Securities Research Company (Subsidiary of:
Babson-United, Inc.), Babson-United Inc., 400 Talcott Ave.,
Watertown, MA 02472-2700. TEL 781-235-0900,
http://www.babson.com. Ed., Pub., R&P Donald S Jones. Adv.
contact Patricia Palmer.

332.6   USA   ISSN 0884-8475
HG4916
S R C GREEN BOOK OF 5-TREND 35-YEAR CHARTS. Text in
English. 1981. a. USD 150 (effective 2001). Description:
Covers 400 stocks, 39 industry groups, and 11 stock market
averages.
Published by: Securities Research Company (Subsidiary of:
Babson-United, Inc.), Babson-United Inc., 400 Talcott Ave.,
Watertown, MA 02472-2700. TEL 781-235-0900,
http://www.babson.com. Ed., Pub. Donald S Jones. Circ:
2,000.

332.6   USA   ISSN 1063-5173
HG4916
S R C ORANGE BOOK OF 5-TREND LONG-TERM O T C
CHARTS; 12 years of prices, earnings, dividends, relative
performance, volume. Text in English. 1992. q. USD 200
(effective 2001). adv. Description: Provides 1,012 stock
charts that include 12-year monthly price ranges, relative
market action, moving average and volume, as well as
capitalization data, earnings on a 12-month basis and
dividends on an annual rate basis.
Published by: Securities Research Company (Subsidiary of:
Babson-United, Inc.), Babson-United Inc., 400 Talcott Ave.,
Watertown, MA 02472-2700. TEL 781-235-0900,
http://www.babson.com. Ed., Pub., R&P Donald S Jones. Adv.
contact Patricia Palmer.

332.6327   USA   ISSN 1552-1249
HG4936
▼ SAVINGS BOND ALERT. Text in English. 2004. 2/yr. USD 28;
USD 14.95 newsstand/cover (effective 2005). Document
type: Journal, Trade. Description: Advises U.S. Savings
Bonds investors of the latest news about low-risk investments.
Published by: Alert Media, 501 W 120th St, Ste 8W, New York,
NY 10027. TEL 646-205-0579, periodical-sales@alert-
media.com, http://www.alert-media.com. Ed. Tom Adams. Pub.,
R&P Tom Weishaar.

332.6 368   USA   ISSN 1526-3126
HG8501
SCHIFF'S INSURANCE OBSERVER. Text in English. s-m.
Document type: Newsletter.
Media: E-mail. Related titles: Fax ed.
Published by: S N L Financial LC, 212 7th St NE, Charlottesvle,
VA 22902-5307. TEL 434-977-1600, FAX 434-293-0407,
subscriptions@InsuranceObserver.com, http://
www.insuranceobserver.com, http://www.snl.com. Ed. David
Schiff. Adv. contact Mark Outlaw.

SCIENCE STATISTICS. see SCIENCES: COMPREHENSIVE
WORKS—Abstracting, Bibliographies, Statistics

SCOTTISH BUSINESS INSIDER. see BUSINESS AND
ECONOMICS—Banking And Finance

332.6   USA
SCUDDER PERSPECTIVES; a world of investment for Scudder
shareholders. Text in English. 1985. q. free to shareholders of
Scudder funds (includes prospectus). charts; illus.; stat.
Document type: Newsletter. Description: Provides
investment information about mutual funds, financial markets,
the economy, retirement and college planning, as well as
Scudder products and services.
Formerly (until 1998): At the Helm
Published by: Scudder Funds, 2 International Pl, 16th Fl, Boston,
MA 02110. TEL 617-295-1000, 800-225-2470,
http://www.scudder.com. Circ: (controlled).

332.6 333.33   CYM
SEALES CAYMAN LETTER; an investment, economic and real
estate review of the tax-free Cayman Islands. Text in English.
bi-m. KYD 60, USD 180.
Published by: Seales & Company Ltd., Cayman Falls W. Bay
Rd., P.O. Box 1103, Grand Cayman, Cayman Isl. TEL
809-94-74325, FAX 809-94-74230.

332.6   USA
SEASONAL TRADER. Text in English. 48/yr. USD 349.
Published by: Steiner & Co., PO Box 4872, Manchester, NH
03108.

332.6   USA
SECURE MAGAZINE. Text in English. q.
Published by: Security Service Federal Credit Union, 7323 Hwy
90 W, San Antonio, TX 78227. TEL 512-670-4490. Ed. Mary
Glenewinkel.

332.6   USA
SECURED TRANSACTIONS GUIDE. Text in English. 1969. 5
base vols. plus bi-w. updates. USD 1,675 base vol(s).
(effective 2004). Description: This guide insures coverage of
all the latest developments and provides the guidance and
information sellers or secured lenders need in using security
instruments to protect their interests.
Related titles: CD-ROM ed.: USD 1,630 (effective 2004); Online -
full text ed.: USD 1,750 (effective 2004).
Published by: C C H Inc., 2700 Lake Cook Rd, Riverwoods, IL
60015. TEL 847-267-7000, 800-449-6439,
cust_serv@cch.com, http://www.cch.com. Pub. Stacey
Caywood.

332.6   HKG
SECURITIES (DISCLOSURE OF INTERESTS) NOTIFICATION
SUMMARIES. Text in English. d. HKD 200 domestic; HKD
350 in Asia; HKD 400 elsewhere (effective 2001).
Formerly: Stock Exchange of Hong Kong. Securities (Disclosure
of Interests) Notification Summaries
Published by: Hong Kong Exchanges and Clearing Ltd.,
Corporate Communications, 12/F, One International Finance
Centre, 1 Harbour View St, Hong Kong, Hong Kong. TEL
852-2522-1122, FAX 852-2845-3554, info@sehk.com.hk,
info@hkex.com.hk, http://www.sehk.com.hk,
http://www.hkex.com.hk.

332.6   GBR   ISSN 1369-3859
SECURITIES AND INVESTMENTS BOARD. CONSULTATIVE
PAPER. Text in English. 1987. irreg. Document type:
Monographic series.
—BLDSC (3423.786000).
Published by: The Financial Services Authority, 25 The North
Colonnade, Canary Wharf, London, E14 5HS, United
Kingdom. TEL 44-20-76761000, FAX 44-20-76761099,
http://www.fsa.gov.uk.

332.66   USA   ISSN 1099-3223
SECURITIES AND INVESTMENTS, MERGERS AND
ACQUISITIONS. Text in English. s-m. USD 695 (effective
2002).

Published by: S N L Financial LC, 212 7th St NE, Charlottesvle, VA 22902-5307. TEL 434-977-1600, FAX 434-293-0407, http://www.snl.com.

332.6 USA ISSN 1525-4445
HG4621
SECURITIES AND INVESTMETS QUARTERLY. Text in English. 1999. q. USD 696 (effective 2002).
Published by: S N L Financial LC, 212 7th St NE, Charlottesvle, VA 22902-5307. TEL 434-977-1600, FAX 434-293-0407, http://www.snl.com.

332.6 USA
SECURITIES AND INVESTMENTS WEEKLY. Text in English. w. USD 396 (effective 2002).
Media: E-mail. **Related titles:** Fax ed.: ISSN 1525-4518.
Published by: S N L Financial LC, 212 7th St NE, Charlottesvle, VA 22902-5307. TEL 434-977-1600, FAX 434-293-0407, http://www.snl.com.

332.6 USA ISSN 0739-8689
SECURITIES & SYNDICATION REVIEW. Text in English. 1983. bi-m. USD 75. back issues avail. **Description:** Covers the securities industry and financial planning.
Published by: Securities Sources, Inc., PO Box 85600, University Sta, Seattle, WA 98145-1600. TEL 206-284-5249. Ed. Robert E Frey. Circ: 500.

332.6 340 USA ISSN 1041-3057
KF9085.A59
SECURITIES ARBITRATION COMMENTATOR; covering significant issues & events in securities - commodities arbitration. Variant title: Commentator. Text in English. 1988. m. USD 290 (effective 2005). index. back issues avail. **Document type:** *Newsletter, Trade.*
Published by: Securities Arbitration Commentator, Inc., PO Box 112, Maplewood, NJ 07040. TEL 973-761-5880, FAX 973-761-1504, help@sacarbitration.com, http://www.sacarbitration.com/framecomm.htm. R&P Richard P Ryder. Circ: 800 (paid).

346.092 332.63 USA
SECURITIES ARBITRATION: PRACTICE AND FORMS. Text in English. 1991. irreg. looseleaf. USD 115 (effective 1999).
Formerly: Securities Arbitration
Published by: Matthew Bender & Co., Inc. (Subsidiary of: LexisNexis North America), 1275 Broadway, Albany, NY 12204. international@bender.com, http://www.bender.com, http://bender.lexisnexis.com. Eds. Anthony Djinis, Joseph Post.

332.6 USA ISSN 1045-9715
SECURITIES CLASS ACTION ALERT. Text in English. 1988. m. looseleaf. USD 645 domestic; USD 715 foreign (effective 2001). back issues avail. **Document type:** *Newsletter.*
Formerly (until 1989): Investors Class Action Monitor
Published by: Securities Class Action Services, 61 Broadway, 2610, New York, NY 10006. TEL 212-480-6383, FAX 212-785-1548, info@classactionalert.com, jnewman@classactionalert.com, http://www.classactionalert.com. Ed. James Newman.

332.63 346 USA ISSN 1543-1010
▼ **SECURITIES CLASS ACTION REPORTER.** Text in English. 2003 (Jan. 15). s-m. USD 1,467 (effective 2005). **Document type:** *Newsletter, Trade.*
Related titles: Online - full text ed.: (from LexisNexis).
Published by: Strafford Publications, Inc., 590 Dutch Valley Rd, N E, Postal Drawer 13729, Atlanta, GA 30324-0729. TEL 404-881-1141, FAX 404-881-0074, editors@straffordpub.com, http://www.straffordpub.com. Pub. Richard M Ossoff.

332.6 THA
SECURITIES EXCHANGE OF THAILAND. HANDBOOK. Text in Thai. 1975. irreg.
Media: Diskette. **Related titles:** Online - full text ed.
Published by: Securities Exchange of Thailand, Sinthom Bldg 2nd Fl, 132 Wireless Rd, Bangkok, 10500, Thailand.

SECURITIES FRAUD AND COMMODITIES FRAUD. see *LAW*

SECURITIES FRAUD: LITIGATING UNDER RULE 10B-5. see *LAW*

SECURITIES HANDBOOK SERIES. MORTGAGE-BACKED SECURITIES; developments and trends in the secondary mortgage market. see *BUSINESS AND ECONOMICS—Banking And Finance*

332.6 USA
SECURITIES HANDBOOK SERIES. PROXY RULES HANDBOOK. Text in English. a., latest 2004. USD 290 per vol. (effective 2004). **Document type:** *Trade.* **Description:** Focuses on the issues involved in electing and proposing a proxy contest.
Formerly: Proxy Contests Handbook
Published by: Thomson West (Subsidiary of: Thomson Corporation, The), 610 Opperman Dr, Eagan, MN 55123-1396. TEL 651-687-8000, 800-328-4880, FAX 651-687-7302, http://west.thomson.com/product/13516156/product.asp. Ed. Mark A Sargent.

332.6 340 USA ISSN 1076-2337
KF1072
SECURITIES HANDBOOK SERIES. REGULATION OF INVESTMENT ADVISERS. Text in English. base vol. plus a. updates. USD 346 base vol(s). (effective 2004). **Document type:** *Trade.* **Description:** Provides detailed explanations of SEC regulation requirements and procedures to help investment advisers avoid SEC violations.
Published by: Thomson West (Subsidiary of: Thomson Corporation, The), 610 Opperman Dr, Eagan, MN 55123-1396. TEL 651-687-8000, 800-328-4880, FAX 651-687-7302, http://west.thomson.com/product/14739686/product.asp. Eds. Gerald T Lins, Thomas P Lemke.

332.6 USA ISSN 1049-7110
KF1439.A1
SECURITIES HANDBOOK SERIES. RESALES OF RESTRICTED SECURITIES. Text in English. base vol. plus a. updates. USD 332 base vol(s). (effective 2003). **Document type:** *Trade.* **Description:** Contains analysis of the latest case law, SEC no-action letters, and regulatory changes.
Published by: Thomson West (Subsidiary of: Thomson Corporation, The), 610 Opperman Dr, Eagan, MN 55123-1396. TEL 651-687-8000, 800-328-4880, FAX 651-687-7302, http://www.westgroup.com/store/product.asp?product%5Fid=14552717&catalog%5Fname=wgstore, http://west.thomson.com. Ed. J William Hicks.

332.6 340 USA ISSN 0731-5805
KF1439
SECURITIES HANDBOOK SERIES. SECURITIES LAW HANDBOOK. Text in English. 1978. a. (in 2 vols.), latest 2004, Dec. USD 326 vols. 1 & 2 (effective 2005). **Document type:** *Trade.* **Description:** Covers developments in the field of securities law.
Indexed: ATI.
Published by: Thomson West (Subsidiary of: Thomson Corporation, The), 610 Opperman Dr, Eagan, MN 55123-1396. TEL 651-687-8000, 800-328-4880, FAX 651-687-7302, customer.service@westgroup.com, http://west.thomson.com/product/13517107/product.asp. Eds. Gary Roberts, Harold Bloomenthal.

336 340 USA
KF6415.A152
SECURITIES HANDBOOK SERIES. TAX-ADVANTAGED SECURITIES HANDBOOK. Text in English. a. (in 2 vols.), latest 2003. USD 334 vols. 1 & 2; USD 167 per vol. vol. 1 or 2 (effective 2004). **Document type:** *Trade.* **Description:** It offers insights into the latest tax, regulatory and business issues involved in this constantly changing area.
Former titles: Investment Limited Partnerships Handbook (0893-3944); Tax Sheltered Investments Handbook (0731-5821)
Published by: Thomson West (Subsidiary of: Thomson Corporation, The), 610 Opperman Dr, Eagan, MN 55123-1396. TEL 651-687-8000, 800-328-4880, FAX 651-687-7302, http://west.thomson.com/product/14633105/product.asp.

332.6 USA
SECURITIES INDUSTRY FACT BOOK. Text in English. a. **Document type:** *Trade.*
Published by: Securities Industry Association, 120 Broadway, 35th Fl, New York, NY 10271. TEL 212-608-1500. Eds. George Monahan, Grace Toto.

332.6 USA ISSN 1089-6333
SECURITIES INDUSTRY NEWS. Text in English. 198?. w. USD 575 combined subscription domestic print & online eds.; USD 699 combined subscription foreign print & online eds. (effective 2005). back issues avail. **Document type:** *Newspaper, Consumer.* **Description:** Reports on developments, ever-evolving technology and key events revolutionizing how securities are traded worldwide.
Former titles (until 199?): Redemption Digest and Securities Industry Daily (1075-9743); (until 1994): Redemption Digest and Corporate Actions (1056-506X)
Related titles: Online - full text ed.: USD 575 (effective 2005) (from EBSCO Publishing, Factiva, Gale Group, O C L C Online Computer Library Center, Inc.).
Indexed: B&I.
—CCC.
Published by: Source Media, Inc., One State St Plaza, 27th Fl, New York, NY 10004. TEL 212-803-6077, FAX 212-747-1154, custserv@sourcemedia.com, http://www.securitiesindustry.com, http://www.sourcemedia.com. Ed. Randall S Devere. Pub. Scott Dattoli.

332.6 USA
SECURITIES INDUSTRY TRENDS. Text in English. irreg. USD 125 to non-members; USD 75 to members. back issues avail. **Document type:** *Trade.* **Description:** Provides information on economic developments affecting securities firms. Includes profitability and financial statements of the securities industry.
Indexed: SRI.
Published by: Securities Industry Association, 120 Broadway, 35th Fl, New York, NY 10271. TEL 212-608-1500. Eds. George Monahan, Jeffrey M Schaeffer.

332.6 USA ISSN 0730-5796
HG4907
SECURITIES INDUSTRY YEARBOOK. Text in English. 1980. a. USD 125 to non-members; USD 85 to members. adv. stat. **Document type:** *Trade.* **Description:** Lists association members and capital statistics.
Formerly: Security Industry Yearbook
Related titles: Microfiche ed.: (from CIS).
Indexed: ATI, SRI.
Published by: Securities Industry Association, 120 Broadway, 35th Fl, New York, NY 10271. TEL 212-608-1500. Ed. Rosalie Pepe. Circ: 3,500.

332.6 340 USA ISSN 1524-7902
SECURITIES LAW DAILY. Text in English. 1999. d. back issues avail. **Document type:** *Newsletter, Trade.* **Description:** Reports on developments in the regulation of securities and futures trading and accounting, with coverage of the Securities and Exchange Commission, Commodities Futures Trading Commission, industry, federal and state courts, and Congress.
Media: Online - full text (from The Bureau of National Affairs, Inc.).
—CCC.
Published by: The Bureau of National Affairs, Inc., 1231 25th St., NW, Washington, DC 20037. TEL 800-372-1033, 800-452-7773, FAX 800-253-0332, customercare@bna.com, http://www.bna.com/products/corplaw/srld.htm. **Subscr. to:** 9435 Key West Ave, Rockville, MD 20850.

346.092 332.6 USA
SECURITIES LAW TECHNIQUES. Text in English. 1985. irreg. (in 7 vols.). looseleaf. USD 1,145 (effective 2002). **Description:** Contributions from over 50 leading practitioners in the field. The experts provide thorough treatment of securities registration and requirements exemptions therefrom, public reporting and recordkeeping requirements, common transactions (including the specific tasks of counsel, underwriters, accountants and company officers and directors), corporate charges and business combinations, as well as complete guidance for representing a client in securities litigation.
Related titles: CD-ROM ed.: USD 1,145 (effective 2002).
Published by: Matthew Bender & Co., Inc. (Subsidiary of: LexisNexis North America), 1275 Broadway, Albany, NY 12204. international@bender.com, http://bender.lexisnexis.com. Ed. A A Sommer Jr.

▼ **SECURITIES LITIGATION REPORTER.** see *LAW*

332.6 JPN
SECURITIES MARKET IN JAPAN. Text in English. 1973. biennial. JPY 3,045 domestic; JPY 5,600 foreign (effective 1999). charts. back issues avail.
Published by: Japan Securities Research Institute, Shokenkaikan, 1-5-8 Nihonbashikayaba-cho, Chuo-ku, Tokyo, 103-0025, Japan. TEL 81-3-3669-0737, FAX 81-3-3662-8294, jsri@ma4.justnet.ne.jp. Ed. Shozo Koyama.

SECURITIES PRO NEWSLETTER; the authority on African Americans in finance. see *ETHNIC INTERESTS*

332.6 340 USA ISSN 1066-0844
SECURITIES REGULATION. Text in English. 1990. 6 base vols. plus m. updates. looseleaf. USD 1,250 (effective 1998). **Description:** Covers U.S. legislation and other topics affecting the securities trading industries.
Published by: W G & L Financial Reporting & Management Research (Subsidiary of: R I A), 395 Hudson St, New York, NY 10014. TEL 212-367-6300, FAX 212-367-6718. **Orders to:** The Park Square Bldg., 31 St James Ave, Boston, MA 02116-4112. TEL 800-950-1207.

332.6 340 USA ISSN 0097-9554
➤ **SECURITIES REGULATION LAW JOURNAL.** Text in English. 1973. q. USD 425 (effective 2005). bk.rev. reprint service avail. from WSH,PQC. **Document type:** *Journal, Academic/Scholarly.* **Description:** Offers analysis and advice through articles and features by noted practitioners and scholars to help readers keep up with the constant changes in the law, rules, and regulations.
Related titles: Microform ed.: (from PQC); Online - full text ed.
Indexed: ABIn, ABRCLP, ASCA, ATI, BLI, BPIA, BusI, CLI, CurCont, ILP, LRI, LegCont, ManagCont, SSCI, T&II.
—BLDSC (8217.140000), IDS, IE, Infotrieve, ingenta. **CCC.**
Published by: Thomson West (Subsidiary of: Thomson Corporation, The), 610 Opperman Dr, Eagan, MN 55123-1396. TEL 800-328-4880, http://west.thomson.com/product/14938712/product.asp. Circ: 1,659.

332.6 USA ISSN 0149-3582
SECURITIES WEEK. Text in English. 1973. w. USD 2,000 (effective 2005). back issues avail.; reprint service avail. from PQC. **Document type:** *Newsletter, Trade.* **Description:** Contains news and analysis of the securities industry, futures and options industries.
Related titles: Online - full text ed.: (from Northern Light Technology, Inc.).
—CCC.
Published by: Standard & Poor's (Subsidiary of: McGraw-Hill Companies, Inc.), 55 Water St, New York, NY 10041. TEL 212-438-3897, 800-852-1641, FAX 212-438-3898.

332.6 USA ISSN 1544-4872
▼ **SECURITIZATION NEWS.** Text in English. 2003 (Mar.). w. (51X/yr). USD 1,695 combined subscription domestic print & online eds.; USD 1,770 combined subscription foreign print & online eds. (effective 2005).
—CCC.
Published by: Institutional Investor News (Subsidiary of: Euromoney Institutional Investor Plc.), 225 Park Ave S, 7th Fl, New York, NY 10003-1605. TEL 212-224-3800, FAX 212-224-3491, info@iiplatinum.com, http://www.securitizationnews.com, http://www.iinews.com. Ed. Tom Lamont. **Subscr. to:** New Orders, PO Box 5063, Brentwood, TN 37024. TEL 615-377-3322, 800-945-2034, 800-715-9197, FAX 615-337-0525, vlockridge@sunbeltfs.com.

332 USA
SECURITY DEALERS OF NORTH AMERICA. Text in English. 1923. s-a. USD 590. adv. Supplement avail. **Document type:** *Directory.* **Description:** Lists approximately 5,000 main offices and more than 8,500 branch offices of security dealers in North America; includes the names and addresses of more than 45,000 key executives, trade organizations, stock exchanges, and state securities administrators.
Related titles: Diskette ed.; Magnetic Tape ed.
Published by: Standard & Poor's (Subsidiary of: McGraw-Hill Companies, Inc.), 55 Water St, New York, NY 10041. TEL 212-208-8280, FAX 212-208-0305. Ed. Lilyan Deangelis. Pub. Tom Lupo. R&P Peggy Smith. Adv. contact Ellen Hartery.

332.6 365.34 USA
SECURITY INVESTING. Text in English. 1994. m. USD 195 (effective 2000). charts; mkt.; stat. back issues avail. **Document type:** *Newsletter.* **Description:** Provides information for investors on public companies in the global security and crime control industry.
Published by: (Security Investing, Inc.), Jack Mallon Ed.& Pub., 555 Fifth Ave, 17th fl, New York, NY 10017. TEL 212-697-0028, FAX 212-697-1576, jmallon@mallonassociates.com.

THE SENIOR CARE ACQUISITION REPORT. see *BUSINESS AND ECONOMICS*

THE SENIORCARE INVESTOR. see *BUSINESS AND ECONOMICS*

332.6 381 USA
SENTINEL INVESTMENT LETTER. Text in English. 1978. m. USD 150 (effective 1999). mkt.; stat. **Document type:** *Newsletter.*
Published by: Hanover Investment Management Corp., 1022 Neshaminy Valley Rd, Bensalem, PA 19020. TEL 215-891-8141.

332.6029 JPN
SETTING UP ENTERPRISES IN JAPAN. Text in Japanese. irreg., latest 2000, Nov., 5th ed. JPY 5,000 (effective 2001). **Document type:** *Directory.* **Description:** Provides the latest information on institutions and firms offering assistance required during the several stages of setting up a business in Japan.
Formerly: Investment Japan (Year)
Published by: (Publications Department), Japan External Trade Organization, 2-5 Toranomom 2-chome, Minato-ku, Tokyo, 105-8466, Japan. TEL 03-3582-3518, FAX 03-3587-2485.

332.6 CHN ISSN 1005-7552
SHANGHAI TOUZI/SHANGHAI INVESTMENT. Text in Chinese. 1985. m. CNY 72 (effective 2004). **Document type:** *Magazine, Trade.*
Published by: Shanghai Shi Touzi Xuehui, Pudongxin District, 201, Yinchengdong Road, 21st Floor, Shanghai, 200120, China. TEL 86-21-68490111, shiv@china.com. **Dist. outside of China by:** China International Book Trading Corp, 35 Chegongzhuang Xilu, Haidian District, PO Box 399, Beijing 100044, China. TEL 86-10-68412045, FAX 86-10-68412023, cibtc@mail.cibtc.com.cn, http://www.cibtc.com.cn/.

332.6327 CHN
SHANGHAI ZHENGQUAN BAO/SHANGHAI SECURITIES NEWS. Text in Chinese. d. CNY 396 (effective 2004). **Document type:** *Newspaper, Consumer.*
Related titles: Online - full content ed.
Address: 1100, Yanggao Nanlu, Shanghai, 200127, China. TEL 86-21-58391111, FAX 86-21-58396501, http://www.cnstock.com/ssnews/default.htm. **Dist. by:** China International Book Trading Corp, 35 Chegongzhuang Xilu, Haidian District, PO Box 399, Beijing 100044, China. TEL 86-10-68412045, FAX 86-10-68412023, cibtc@mail.cibtc.com.cn, http://www.cibtc.com.cn.

332.6 340 CAN
SHAREHOLDER REMEDIES IN CANADA. Text in English. q. looseleaf. CND 300 (effective 2001). **Document type:** *Trade.* **Description:** Provides a comprehensive examination of statutory provisions and common-law principles governing the remedies of shareholders.
Published by: LexisNexis Butterworths Canada Inc. (Subsidiary of: LexisNexis North America), 123 Commerce Valley Dr E, Ste 700, Markham, ON L3T 7W8, Canada. TEL 905-479-2665, FAX 905-479-2826, http://www.lexisnexis.ca/shareholderremediesincanada.htm. Ed. Dennis H Peterson.

332.6 USA ISSN 1535-3052
HG4028.V3
SHAREHOLDER VALUE. Text in English. 2000. bi-m. USD 99 (effective 2001).
Published by: Kennedy Information Inc., One Kennedy Place, Rte 12 S, Fitzwilliam, NH 03447. http://www.kennedyinfo.com. Pub. Marshall Cooper.

332.6 CAN ISSN 1704-1082
SHAREOWNER. Text in English. 1987. bi-m. CND 88 domestic; USD 108 foreign; CND 8 newsstand/cover (effective 2001). adv. bk.rev. charts. back issues avail. **Description:** Education about stock-market investment.
Formerly (until 2001): Canadian Shareowner (0836-0960)
Related titles: Microfiche ed.: (from MML); Microform ed.: (from MML); Online - full text ed.: (from Micromedia ProQuest, Northern Light Technology, Inc., O C L C Online Computer Library Center, Inc., ProQuest Information & Learning).
Indexed: ABIn, CBCARef, CBPI, CPerI.
Published by: Canadian Shareowner, 121 Richmond St W 7th Fl, Toronto, ON M5H 2K1, Canada. TEL 416-595-9600, FAX 416-595-0400, magazine@shareowner.com, http://www.shareowner.com. Ed. John T Bart. Adv. contact Oliver Sutherns. Circ: 20,000.

332.6327 GBR ISSN 1468-1102
SHARES. Text in English. 1999. w. GBP 99; GBP 2.95 newsstand/cover (effective 2004). adv. **Document type:** *Magazine, Consumer.* **Description:** Contains the latest information and advice on investments in the stock markets.
Published by: M S M Magazines Ltd., Thames House, 18 Park St, London, SE1 9ER, United Kingdom. TEL 44-171-378-7131, FAX 44-171-403-4682, support@moneyam.com, http://www.moneyam.com/sharesmag/edition50/. Ed. Ross Greenwood.

332.6 AUS ISSN 1327-5798
HG4503
SHARES (SYDNEY). Text in English. 1972. m. AUD 3.66. adv. bk.rev. charts; illus.; stat. **Document type:** *Trade.*
Supersedes (in Nov. 1996): Stock Exchange Journal (1036-840X); Which was formerly (until 1990): Australian Stock Exchange Journal (1033-288X); (until 1988): Sydney Stock Exchange Limited Gazette (0039-7598)
Related titles: Alternate Frequency ed(s).: Shares Weekly with Trendex. 48/yr. AUD 319 Includes subscription to Shares magazine; ♦ Supplement to: Personal Investor.
Indexed: ABIX, PAIS.
—IE.
Published by: Fairfax Business Media (Subsidiary of: John Fairfax Holdings Ltd.), 201 Sussex St, Sydney, NSW 2000, Australia. TEL 61-2-9282-2822, http://www.sharesdaily.com.au/, http://www.fxj.com.au/.

332.6 SGP ISSN 0218-8716
SHARES INVESTMENT; facts & figures. Text in English. 1995. bi-w. SGD 117; SGD 5 newsstand/cover (effective 1999). adv. charts; stat. **Document type:** *Trade.* **Description:** For investors, shareholders, CEOs, and businessmen. Covers market movements, including daily and weekly price charts, corporate profiles, results and earnings record.
Related titles: Chinese ed.: ISSN 0218-883X.
Published by: Pioneers & Leaders (Publishers) Pte. Ltd., Pioneers & Leaders Centre, 4 Ubi View (off Ubi Rd 3), Singapore, 408557, Singapore. TEL 65-68485481, FAX 65-745-8213, http://www.winner21.com/winner/Mainpage#. Ed. Ts Phan. Adv. contact Ho Keat. B&W page SGD 500, color page SGD 1,450; trim 215 x 148. Circ: 30,000.

332.6 USA
SHELBURNE SECURITIES FORECAST. Text in English. 1976. bi-w. USD 49. back issues avail. **Description:** Specializes in the stocks of companies involved in natural resources and electric utilities.
Address: 1017 N Quintana St, Box 5566, Arlington, VA 22205. Ed. Robert W Shelburne.

332.6 346.066 USA
SHEPARD'S FEDERAL SECURITIES LAW CITATIONS. Text in English. 1991. base vol. plus q. updates. USD 360.
Published by: Shepard's (Subsidiary of: LexisNexis North America), 555 Middle Creek Pkwy, Colorado Springs, CO 80921. TEL 719-488-3000, 800-833-9844, FAX 719-481-7621, customer_service@shepards.com, http://www.lexisnexis.com/shepards/.

332.6 CHN
SICHUAN JINRONG TOUZI BAO. Text in Chinese. 1980. d. (Mon.-Fri.). **Document type:** *Newspaper, Consumer.*
Related titles: Online - full content ed.
Published by: Sichuan Ribao Baoye Jituan, Hongxin Road, Section 2, no.70, Chengdu, 610012, China. TEL 86-28-86757777, FAX 86-28-86968633, stock@scol.com.cn, http://www.stocknews.sc.cn/. **Dist. by:** China International Book Trading Corp, 35 Chegongzhuang Xilu, Haidian District, PO Box 399, Beijing 100044, China. TEL 86-10-68412045, FAX 86-10-68412023, cibtc@mail.cibtc.com.cn, http://www.cibtc.com.cn.

332.6 USA ISSN 1083-6721
SID CATO'S NEWSLETTER ON ANNUAL REPORTS. Text in English. 1983 (Sept.). m. USD 197 (effective 2005). **Document type:** *Newsletter, Consumer.* **Description:** Provides analysis and commentary on annual reports to shareholders of publicly held companies.
Published by: Cato Communications, Inc., PO Box 817, Marshall, MI 49068-0817. TEL 269-781-6266, FAX 815-333-0136, sidcato@sidcato.com, http://www.sidcato.com. Ed., Pub., R&P Mr. Sid Cato.

332.6 USA
SILVER BARON'S MONEY FEVER. Text in English. 1984. m. USD 120 (effective 2000). adv. **Document type:** *Newsletter.* **Description:** Picks huge winners with as little risk as possible under the circumstances.
Former titles: Silver Baron - Stocks U S A; Silver Baron
Published by: S B Stocks U S A, 21 E. San Miguel Ave., Phoenix, AZ 85012-1336. TEL 602-265-4245, FAX 602-265-2806, slvrbaron@aol.com. Ed., Pub., R&P, Adv. contact Elliott R Pearson. Circ: 1,900 (controlled).

332.6 SGP ISSN 0217-3476
SINGAPORE STOCK EXCHANGE JOURNAL✶. Text in English. m. SGD 39 domestic; SGD 99 in Asia; SGD 111 elsewhere. adv. **Description:** Summarizes trading in all listed stocks. Provides stock market data, information on half-yearly reports, annual accounts, and chairmen's statements. Includes financial articles and reviews of activities in listed companies.
Published by: Stock Exchange of Singapore Ltd., Robinson Rd, P.O. Box 2306, Singapore, 9043, Singapore. TEL 535-3788, FAX 532-4476. Circ: 18,000.

332.6 RUS ISSN 1562-9147
SKATE EXTENSION. Key Title: Extension. Text in English. 1996. m. **Document type:** *Bulletin, Trade.* **Description:** Covers the performance of the region's technology stock index (SXTI), which includes select telecom operators and Internet companies in Central/Eastern Europe and Russia.
Related titles: Online - full text ed.
Published by: Skate, Inc., Nikoloyamskaya 13, Bld 2, Moscow, 109240, Russian Federation. TEL 7-095-3636090, FAX 7-095-3636099, info@skatefn.com, http://www.skatefn.com/sxt/index.html. Ed. Michael Androssov. **Dist. by:** Skate, Inc. (U S A), c/o Pavel Prybolovsky, Ste 3100, 140 Broadway, New York, NY 10005-9998. TEL 212-973-8142, FAX 212-972-8798, pribyl@skatefn.com.

332.6 USA
THE SLANKER REPORT. Text in English. 1992. m. USD 129 (effective 2005). **Document type:** *Newsletter, Trade.* **Description:** Hard money letter for conservative and aggressive investors.
Published by: The Slanker Report, R R 2, Box 175, Powderly, TX 75473-9740. TEL 903-732-4653, FAX 903-732-4151, slanker@neto.com, http://www.slanker.com/report/. Ed., Pub. Ted E Slanker Jr.

SMALL BUSINESS WORLD MAGAZINE. see *BUSINESS AND ECONOMICS—Small Business*

332.6 GBR ISSN 1356-2894
SMALLER U K COMPANIES HANDBOOK. Text in English. 1994. a. (in 2 vols.). GBP 200. charts; stat. **Description:** Covers 1,500 smaller companies quoted on the London Stock Exchange, including the USM and AIM. Includes a ranking of all companies by market capitalisation as well as indexes by industry sector and registrars.
Published by: Financial Times Information Ltd., Fitzroy House, 13-17 Epworth St, London, EC2A 4DL, United Kingdom. TEL 44-20-7825-8000, FAX 44-20-7608-2032, justine.dye@ft.com, http://www.ft.com.

332.6 USA
SMART MONEY (RIVER VALE). Text in English. 1973. m. USD 120; USD 150 foreign (effective 1999). **Document type:** *Trade.* **Description:** Provides both market advice and stock recommendations. A regular features is "America's Most Undiscovered Companies.".
Incorporates (in 1997): Higher Returns
Indexed: ASIP.
Published by: Hirsch Organization Inc., 79 Main St., # 3, Nyack, NY 10960-3109. TEL 201-767-4100, FAX 201-767-7337, http://www.hirschorganization.com. Ed. Jeffrey A Hirsch. Circ: 10,000.

332.6 ESP
SOCIEDADES COTIZADAS EN BOLSA. Text in Spanish. 1991 (no.152). w. free. charts; stat.
Published by: Banco Hispano Americano, Division de Banca Corporativa y Mercado de Capitales, Plaza Canalejas, 1, Madrid, 28014, Spain. TEL 531-18-36, FAX 522-18-23.

332.6 LUX
SOCIETE DE LA BOURSE DE LUXEMBOURG. COTE OFFICIELLE DE LA BOURSE DE LUXEMBOURG (BI-MONTHLY)/LUXEMBOURG STOCK EXCHANGE. OFFICIAL PRICE LIST. Text in French. 1929. bi-m. EUR 185.25 in Europe; EUR 285 elsewhere. **Description:** Contains latest updates for active securities.

B

Published by: Societe de la Bourse de Luxembourg/Luxembourg Stock Exchange, 11 av. de la Porte Neuve, BP 165, Luxembourg, L-2011, Luxembourg. TEL 352-4779361, FAX 352-473298, info@bourse.lu, http://www.bourse.lu. Circ: 480.

332.6 LUX
SOCIETE DE LA BOURSE DE LUXEMBOURG. COTE OFFICIELLE DE LA BOURSE DE LUXEMBOURG (DAILY)/LUXEMBOURG STOCK EXCHANGE. OFFICIAL PRICE LIST. Text in English. 1929. d. EUR 863.75 in Europe; EUR 1,555.50 elsewhere. **Description:** Contains latest updates for active securities.
Published by: Societe de la Bourse de Luxembourg/Luxembourg Stock Exchange, 11 av. de la Porte Neuve, BP 165, Luxembourg, L-2011, Luxembourg. TEL 352-4779361, FAX 352-473298, info@bourse.lu, http://www.bourse.lu. Circ: 380.

332.6 LUX
SOCIETE DE LA BOURSE DE LUXEMBOURG. COTE OFFICIELLE DE LA BOURSE DE LUXEMBOURG (MONTHLY)/LUXEMBOURG STOCK EXCHANGE. OFFICIAL PRICE LIST. Text in French. 1929. m. EUR 119.50 in Europe; EUR 152.50 elsewhere. **Description:** Contains all 13,000 listed securities, gives information about prices, yields of debt securities, and highest and lowest prices of listed securities.
Published by: Societe de la Bourse de Luxembourg/Luxembourg Stock Exchange, 11 av. de la Porte Neuve, BP 165, Luxembourg, L-2011, Luxembourg. TEL 352-4779361, FAX 352-473298, info@bourse.lu, http://www.bourse.lu. Circ: 900.

332.6 LUX
SOCIETE DE LA BOURSE DE LUXEMBOURG. COTE OFFICIELLE DE LA BOURSE DE LUXEMBOURG (WEEKLY)/LUXEMBOURG STOCK EXCHANGE. OFFICIAL PRICE LIST. Text in French. 1929. w. EUR 273.75 in Europe; EUR 450 elsewhere. **Description:** Contains latest updates for active securities.
Published by: Societe de la Bourse de Luxembourg/Luxembourg Stock Exchange, 11 av. de la Porte Neuve, BP 165, Luxembourg, L-2011, Luxembourg. TEL 352-4779361, FAX 352-473298, info@bourse.lu, http://www.bourse.lu. Circ: 480.

332.6 LUX
SOCIETE DE LA BOURSE DE LUXEMBOURG. FACT BOOK. Text in English. 1997. a. free. **Description:** Gives information on the activities of the Luxembourg Stock Exchange.
Published by: Societe de la Bourse de Luxembourg/Luxembourg Stock Exchange, 11 av. de la Porte Neuve, BP 165, Luxembourg, L-2011, Luxembourg. TEL 352-4779361, FAX 352-473298, info@bourse.lu, http://www.bourse.lu. Circ: 4,500.

SOCIETE DE LA BOURSE DE LUXEMBOURG. FAITS ET CHIFFRES/LUXEMBOURG STOCK EXCHANGE. FACTS AND FIGURES. see *BUSINESS AND ECONOMICS—Abstracting, Bibliographies, Statistics*

332.6 LUX
SOCIETE DE LA BOURSE DE LUXEMBOURG. RAPPORT ANNUEL/LUXEMBOURG STOCK EXCHANGE. ANNUAL REPORT. Text in English, French. 1929. a. free. **Description:** Covers fixed-income and variable-income securities, the gold market, warrants, etc.
Published by: Societe de la Bourse de Luxembourg/Luxembourg Stock Exchange, 11 av. de la Porte Neuve, BP 165, Luxembourg, L-2011, Luxembourg. TEL 352-4779361, FAX 352-473298, TELEX 2559-STOEX-LU, info@bourse.lu, http://www.bourse.lu. Circ: 1,000.

SOCIETE DE LA BOURSE DES VALEURS DE CASABLANCA. STATISTIQUES MENSUELLES. see *BUSINESS AND ECONOMICS—Abstracting, Bibliographies, Statistics*

332.6 RUS
SOFT MARKET✶. Text in Russian. w. USD 189.95 in United States.
Media: Online - full content.
Published by: R.I.A. Grant, Universitetskii pr-t 9, Moscow, 117296, Russian Federation. TEL 7-095-2091897, FAX 7-095-2094904, http://www.softmarket.ru. **US dist. addr.:** East View Information Services, 3020 Harbor Ln. N., Minneapolis, MN 55447. TEL 612-550-0961.

332.6 RUS
SOFT MARKET REVIEW✶. Text in Russian. m.
Published by: R.I.A. Grant, Universitetskii pr-t 9, Moscow, 117296, Russian Federation. TEL 7-095-2091897, FAX 7-095-2094904. **US dist. addr.:** East View Information Services, 3020 Harbor Ln. N., Minneapolis, MN 55447. TEL 612-550-0961.

SOFTWARE ECONOMICS LETTER; maximizing your return on corporate software. see *COMPUTERS—Software*

332.6 USA ISSN 1053-5845
SOLID VALUE; financially sound bargain-priced stocks. Text in English. 1986. s-m. looseleaf. USD 276 (effective 1998). adv. bk.rev. back issues avail. **Document type:** *Newsletter.* **Description:** Lists the market's most under-priced stocks; includes commentaries and updates on recommendations and market analysis.
Published by: Happy Man Corporation, 4410 S W Pt Robinson Rd, Vashon, WA 98070-7399. TEL 206-463-9399, FAX 206-463-9255. Ed. Irving Scott Wolfe. Pub. Leona V Troese.

332.67 USA
SOUND INVESTING BASICS. Text in English. 1995. q. USD 100 (effective 2000). **Document type:** *Newsletter.*
Published by: Alan B. Lancz & Associates,Inc., 2400 N Reynolds Rd, Toledo, OH 43615-2818. TEL 419-536-5200, FAX 419-536-5401. Ed. Alan B Lancz. R&P Ron Pawlicki. Circ: 55.

SOUTH AMERICA REPORT. see *BUSINESS AND ECONOMICS—International Commerce*

332.6 USA
SOUTH FLORIDA MONEY WATCH. Text in English. 2000. 10/yr. USD 3.95 newsstand/cover (effective 2001). adv. **Document type:** *Consumer.*
Published by: Radio Group, 2406 S Congress Ave, West Palm Beach, FL 33406. TEL 561-432-5100, FAX 561-432-5111. Ed., Pub. Steve Lapa.

SOUTHERN ILLINOIS UNIVERSITY AT EDWARDSVILLE. REGIONAL RESEARCH AND DEVELOPMENT SERVICES. REPORT: PRIVATE SECTOR INVESTMENTS. see *HOUSING AND URBAN PLANNING*

332 USA
SOVEREIGN ASSESSMENT MONTHLY. Text in English. m. **Document type:** *Trade.* **Description:** Includes assessments of foreign bonds, fiscal policies, and credit outlook.
Related titles: Series of: Global Corporate Bond Research.
Published by: Salomon Brothers, Inc., 7 World Trade Center, New York, NY 10048. TEL 212-783-7000.

332.6 USA ISSN 0038-6499
SPARE TIME; the magazine of money-making opportunities. Text in English. 1955. 11/yr. USD 23.95 (effective 2005). adv. bk.rev.; software rev. illus. **Document type:** *Magazine, Consumer.* **Description:** Deals with money-making opportunities, business start-up and small business "how-to" advice for those starting or growing their own part-time or full-time business.
Related titles: Online - full text ed.
Published by: Kipen Publishing Corporation, 2400 S Commerce Dr, Milwaukee, WI 53151-2718. TEL 262-780-1070, FAX 262-780-1071, publisher@spare-time.com, http://www.spare-time.com. Ed. Deborah Roan. Pub. Dennis Wilk. adv.: B&W page USD 4,635, color page USD 5,265; trim 10.63 x 7.75. Circ: 302,000 (controlled).

332.678 USA ISSN 1535-7309
THE SPEAR REPORT; consensus of leading analysts. Text in English. 1995. w. USD 197 (effective 1999). bk.rev. mkt.; stat. back issues avail. **Document type:** *Newsletter, Trade.* **Description:** Includes market editorial and recommendation list.
Formerly (until 1999): Independent Investor Digest (1094-8155)
Related titles: E-mail ed.; Fax ed.; Online - full text ed.
Published by: Spear Report, PO Box 271030, W Hartford, CT 06127-1030. TEL 800-491-7119, FAX 860-313-0242, info@spearreport.com, http://www.spearreport.com. Ed., R&P Gregory Spear TEL 860-313-0204. Circ: 3,640 (paid).

332.6 USA
SPECIAL INVESTMENT SITUATIONS. Text in English. 1979. m. USD 120. **Description:** Recommends stocks under $20 possessing 100-300 per cent upside potential.
Address: PO Box 4254, Chattanooga, TN 37405. TEL 615-886-1628. Ed. George W Southerland. Circ: 800.

332.6 USA ISSN 1081-129X
SPECIAL SITUATIONS NEWSLETTER; in-depth survey of under-valued stocks. Text in English. 1977. 12/yr. USD 75 (effective 1997). back issues avail. **Document type:** *Newsletter.* **Description:** Researches undervalued asset plays, neglected stocks, takeover candidates and turnaround situations. Emphasis is on small-cap stocks traded on NASDAQ and the NYSE.
Published by: Charles Howard Kaplan, Ed. & Pub., 26 Broadway, Ste 200, New York, NY 10004-1703. TEL 201-418-4411, 800-756-1811, FAX 201-418-5085.

332.67 USA
SPECTRUM CONVERTIBLES✶; 13(F) institutional convertible holdings survey. Text in English. q. USD 450.
Related titles: Magnetic Tape ed.; Online - full text ed.
Published by: C D A Investment Technologies, Inc., 1455 Research Blvd, Rockville, MD 20850-3194. TEL 800-232-6362, FAX 301-590-1329. Circ: 100.

332.6 USA
SPECTRUM INTERNATIONAL✶. Text in English. 1990. s-a. (in 2 vols.). USD 1,000. **Description:** Institutional holdings and ownership information on worldwide securities. Covers over 9,200 equities domiciled in 51 countries outside the US, and over 2,200 institutional trusts and funds in 14 countries worldwide.
Media: Magnetic Tape. **Related titles:** Online - full text ed.: 1990.
Published by: C D A Investment Technologies, Inc., 1455 Research Blvd, Rockville, MD 20850-3194. TEL 800-232-6362, FAX 301-590-1329.

332.6 USA
SPECULATOR; investment advisory service specializing in listed stocks under $20. Text in English. 1966. s-m. looseleaf. USD 175. charts.
Formerly: Penny Speculator
Published by: Growth-in-Funds, 77 So Palm Ave, Sarasota, FL 34236. TEL 201-792-0801, FAX 813-954-0647. Ed. Byron Sanders. Circ: 2,500.

332.6 USA ISSN 1088-8373
HG4915
STANDARD & POOR'S 500 INDEXES OF THE SECURITIES MARKETS - FLASH REPORT. Text in English. w. USD 615. charts. **Document type:** *Trade.* **Description:** Contains the current week's reading of more than 100 industry group stock price indexes.
Published by: Standard & Poor's (Subsidiary of: McGraw-Hill Companies, Inc.), 55 Water St, New York, NY 10041. TEL 212-208-8000.

332.6 USA ISSN 1088-839X
HG4915
STANDARD & POOR'S 500 INFORMATION BULLETIN. Text in English. m. USD 235. stat. back issues avail. **Document type:** *Bulletin.* **Description:** Provides a monthly statistical summary of stock prices of the Standard & Poor's 500 companies.
Published by: Standard & Poor's (Subsidiary of: McGraw-Hill Companies, Inc.), 55 Water St, New York, NY 10041. TEL 212-208-8725, FAX 212-208-8624.

332.6 USA ISSN 0277-3988
HG4905
STANDARD & POOR'S BOND GUIDE. Cover title: Bond Guide. Text in English. 1938. m. price varies. stat. **Document type:** *Directory, Trade.* **Description:** Covers domestic and international corporate bonds and their issuing companies.
Related titles: Online - full text ed.
Published by: Standard & Poor's (Subsidiary of: McGraw-Hill Companies, Inc.), 55 Water St, New York, NY 10041. TEL 212-208-8000, FAX 212-208-0040. Ed. Frank Lovaglio.

332.6 USA ISSN 1076-0318
STANDARD & POOR'S CANADIAN FOCUS. Text in English. 1994. m.
Published by: Standard & Poor's (Subsidiary of: McGraw-Hill Companies, Inc.), 55 Water St, New York, NY 10041. TEL 212-208-1146, FAX 212-208-0040.

332.6 USA
STANDARD & POOR'S CORPORATE REGISTERED BOND INTEREST RECORD. Text in English. 1967. a. (plus w. updates). looseleaf. USD 2,600.
Related titles: CD-ROM ed.; Magnetic Tape ed.
Published by: Standard & Poor's (Subsidiary of: McGraw-Hill Companies, Inc.), 55 Water St, New York, NY 10041. TEL 212-208-8000. Ed. V Calbi.

332.6 USA ISSN 0277-500X
HG4501
STANDARD & POOR'S CORPORATION RECORDS; with daily news. Key Title: Standard Corporation Descriptions. Text in English. 1915. s-m. (in 6 vols., plus 5/wk. Daily News Section). looseleaf. USD 3,400. stat. **Document type:** *Trade.* **Description:** Provides financial and descriptive information on more than 12,000 publicly held U.S. companies.
Related titles: CD-ROM ed.; Microfiche ed.; Online - full text ed.; ◆ Supplement to: Standard & Poor's Corporation Records. Current News Edition. ISSN 0196-4674.
Published by: Standard & Poor's (Subsidiary of: McGraw-Hill Companies, Inc.), 55 Water St, New York, NY 10041. TEL 212-208-8000, FAX 212-412-0459. Pub. Michael Antinoro. Circ: (controlled).

332.6 USA ISSN 0737-4127
HG4915
STANDARD & POOR'S DAILY STOCK PRICE RECORD. AMERICAN STOCK EXCHANGE. Key Title: Daily Stock Price Record. American Stock Exchange. Text in English. 1962. q. looseleaf. USD 441. mkt.; stat. **Document type:** *Trade.* **Description:** Reports on the high, low, and close of stocks traded on the American Stock Exchange, along with bid and asked prices for nontraded securities, daily and weekly volumes, shares outstanding, dividend information, and earnings reported most recently for the past four quarters.
Supersedes: Standard and Poor's I S L Daily Stock Price Index. American Stock Exchange (0019-0640)
Related titles: Microfiche ed.
Published by: Standard & Poor's (Subsidiary of: McGraw-Hill Companies, Inc.), 55 Water St, New York, NY 10041. TEL 212-208-8000. Ed. Carol Levine.

332.6 USA ISSN 1072-3846
HG4915
STANDARD & POOR'S. DAILY STOCK PRICE RECORD. NASDAQ. Key Title: Daily Stock Price Record: NASDAQ. Text in English. 1968. q. USD 530. mkt.; stat. back issues avail. **Document type:** *Trade.* **Description:** Gives the daily prices for all stocks traded on the NASDAQ and compiles their averages.

Formerly (until 1992): Daily Stock Price Record. Over the Counter (0737-4100); **Supersedes:** Standard and Poor's Over-the-Counter (0030-7351)
Related titles: Microfiche ed.
Published by: Standard & Poor's (Subsidiary of: McGraw-Hill Companies, Inc.), 55 Water St, New York, NY 10041. TEL 212-208-8000.

332.6   USA   ISSN 0737-4119
HG4915
STANDARD & POOR'S DAILY STOCK PRICE RECORD. NEW YORK STOCK EXCHANGE∗. Key Title: Daily Stock Price Record. New York Stock Exchange. Text in English. 1962. q. USD 420. mkt.; stat. reprints avail. **Document type:** *Trade.* **Description:** Covers the high, low, and close of stocks traded on the New York Stock Exchange, along with bid and asking prices for nontraded securities, daily and weekly volumes, number of shares outstanding, dividends distributed, and earnings most recently reported for the past four quarters.
Supersedes: Standard and Poor's I S L Daily Stock Price Index. New York Stock Exchange (0019-0659)
Related titles: Microfiche ed.
Published by: Standard & Poor's (Subsidiary of: McGraw-Hill Companies, Inc.), 55 Water St, New York, NY 10041. TEL 212-208-8000. Ed. Teresa Kowalski.

332.6   USA   ISSN 1062-5607
HG4028.D5
STANDARD & POOR'S DIRECTORY OF DIVIDEND REINVESTMENT PLANS. Text in English. 1991. a. USD 39.95. charts. **Document type:** *Directory.* **Description:** Helps investors locate more than 800 stocks of companies that feature asset-building dividend reinvestment plans and shows what $1,000 invested 10 years ago would be worth today, as well as other data, including S & P quality rankings.
Published by: Standard & Poor's (Subsidiary of: McGraw-Hill Companies, Inc.), 55 Water St, New York, NY 10041. TEL 212-208-8000, 800-852-1641, FAX 212-412-0240. Ed. Joseph Tigue.

332.6   USA   ISSN 0196-4658
HG4908
STANDARD & POOR'S DIVIDEND RECORD (DAILY). Text in English. d. looseleaf. USD 825. stat. **Document type:** *Trade.*
Related titles: Magnetic Tape ed.; Online - full text ed.
Published by: Standard & Poor's (Subsidiary of: McGraw-Hill Companies, Inc.), 55 Water St, New York, NY 10041. TEL 212-208-8000. Ed. Anthony Onofrio.

332.6   USA
STANDARD & POOR'S DIVIDEND RECORD (QUARTERLY). Text in English. 1925. q. looseleaf. USD 160. stat. **Document type:** *Trade.*
Published by: Standard & Poor's (Subsidiary of: McGraw-Hill Companies, Inc.), 55 Water St, New York, NY 10041. TEL 212-208-8000. Ed. Anthony Onofrio.

332.6   USA
STANDARD & POOR'S DIVIDEND RECORD (WEEKLY). Text in English. w. looseleaf. USD 420. stat. **Document type:** *Trade.*
Related titles: Magnetic Tape ed.
Published by: Standard & Poor's (Subsidiary of: McGraw-Hill Companies, Inc.), 55 Water St, New York, NY 10041. TEL 212-208-8000. Ed. Anthony Onofrio.

332.1   USA   ISSN 1055-0070
HG1501
STANDARD & POOR'S FINANCIAL INSTITUTIONS RATINGS. EUROPE, ASIA, OCEANIA. Text in English. a. charts; stat. **Document type:** *Trade.*
Supersedes in part (in 1990): S and P's Bank Book, C D Ratings (0899-5931)
Published by: Standard & Poor's (Subsidiary of: McGraw-Hill Companies, Inc.), 55 Water St, New York, NY 10041. TEL 212-280-8000.

332.1   USA   ISSN 1060-3468
HG1660.U5
STANDARD & POOR'S FINANCIAL INSTITUTIONS RATINGS. NORTH AMERICA. Text in English. 1988. a. charts; stat. **Document type:** *Trade.*
Supersedes in part (in 1990): S and P's Bank Book, C D Ratings (0899-5931)
Published by: Standard & Poor's (Subsidiary of: McGraw-Hill Companies, Inc.), 55 Water St, New York, NY 10041. TEL 212-208-8000.

332.6   USA
STANDARD & POOR'S INDUSTRY REPORTS. Text in English. m. looseleaf. charts; stat. **Document type:** *Trade.*
Description: Provides timely and topical economic, market, and industry reviews and forecasts.
Published by: Standard & Poor's (Subsidiary of: McGraw-Hill Companies, Inc.), 55 Water St, New York, NY 10041. TEL 212-208-8000.

332.6   USA   ISSN 0196-4666
HC106.6
STANDARD & POOR'S INDUSTRY SURVEYS. Text in English. 1973. s-a. looseleaf. price varies. charts; illus.; stat. Supplement avail. **Document type:** *Directory, Trade.*
Description: Provides a broad picture of major U.S. industries, including financial data on more than 1,000 companies. Report on 52 industry segments semi-annually and provides monthly investment outlooks on 120 industries.
Related titles: Diskette ed.; Online - full text ed.
Published by: Standard & Poor's (Subsidiary of: McGraw-Hill Companies, Inc.), 55 Water St, New York, NY 10041. TEL 212-208-8000. Ed. Eileen Martines.

332.6   USA   ISSN 1090-3933
STANDARD & POOR'S INSTITUTIONAL EQUITY RESEARCH. Text in English. m. (plus q. updates). charts; stat. **Document type:** *Trade.* **Description:** Thoroughly researches initial public offerings that show promising investment potential.
Published by: Standard & Poor's (Subsidiary of: McGraw-Hill Companies, Inc.), 55 Water St, New York, NY 10041. TEL 212-208-8000. Ed. Robert S Natale.

332.6   USA
STANDARD & POOR'S NEW ISSUES RESEARCH. Text in English. irreg. (120-150/yr.). **Document type:** *Trade.*
Description: Offers asset managers descriptions of promising initial public offerings, supplying investment appraisals, covering first-day investment factors, and providing buy-flip-avoid opinions.
Related titles: Fax ed.
Published by: Standard & Poor's (Subsidiary of: McGraw-Hill Companies, Inc.), 55 Water St, New York, NY 10041. TEL 212-208-8000. Ed. Robert S Natale.

332.6   USA   ISSN 0737-299X
STANDARD & POOR'S SEMI-WEEKLY CALLED BOND RECORD. Text in English. 1941. s-w. looseleaf. USD 1,173. stat. **Document type:** *Trade.*
Published by: Standard & Poor's (Subsidiary of: McGraw-Hill Companies, Inc.), 55 Water St, New York, NY 10041. TEL 212-208-8000. Ed. V Calbi.

332.6   USA   ISSN 1085-6927
HG4915
STANDARD & POOR'S SMALLCAP 600 GUIDE. Abbreviated title: S & P's Smallcap 600 Guide. Text in English. 1995. irreg.
Published by: McGraw-Hill Companies, Inc., 1221 Ave of the Americas, New York, NY 10020. TEL 212-512-2000, customer.service@mcgraw-hill.com, http://www.mcgraw-hill.com.

332.6   USA   ISSN 0147-636X
HC101
STANDARD & POOR'S STATISTICAL SERVICE. CURRENT STATISTICS. Text in English. m. USD 688. **Document type:** *Trade.* **Description:** Provides the performance history of particular stock groups during economic ups and downs, stock and bond prices during periods of inflation, and more.
Related titles: ◆ Supplement(s): Standard & Poor's Statistical Service. Security Price Index. ISSN 0272-0914.
Published by: Standard & Poor's (Subsidiary of: McGraw-Hill Companies, Inc.), 55 Water St, New York, NY 10041. TEL 212-208-8000. Ed. Karen Each.

332.63   USA   ISSN 0272-0914
HG4915
STANDARD & POOR'S STATISTICAL SERVICE. SECURITY PRICE INDEX. Text in English. 1978. biennial. looseleaf. charts; stat. **Document type:** *Trade.* **Description:** Provides the performance history of particular stock groups during economic ups and downs, along with data on stock and bond prices during inflationary periods.
Related titles: ◆ Supplement to: Standard & Poor's Statistical Service. Current Statistics. ISSN 0147-636X.
Published by: Standard & Poor's (Subsidiary of: McGraw-Hill Companies, Inc.), 55 Water St, New York, NY 10041. TEL 212-208-8000.

332.6   USA   ISSN 0737-4135
STANDARD & POOR'S STOCK GUIDE. Text in English. 1943. m. price varies. charts; stat. **Document type:** *Directory, Trade.*
Formerly: Standard and Poor's Security Owner's Stock Guide (0038-9412)
Related titles: Online - full text ed.
Published by: Standard & Poor's (Subsidiary of: McGraw-Hill Companies, Inc.), 55 Water St, New York, NY 10041. TEL 212-438-3897, FAX 212-438-3898. Ed. Frank Lovaglio. Circ: 300,000.

332.6   USA   ISSN 1097-4490
HG4905
STANDARD & POOR'S STOCK REPORTS; New York Stock Exchange, American Stock Exchange, Nasdaq Stock Market and regional exchanges. Text in English. 1933. irreg. (approx. 4/yr.). looseleaf. USD 1,295. stat.; charts. index. **Document type:** *Trade.* **Description:** Provides current and 10-year historical profiles on the stocks of companies actively traded on the New York Stock Exchange.
Formerly (until 1997): Standard & Poor's Stock Reports. New York Stock Exchange (0160-4899)
Related titles: CD-ROM ed.

Published by: Standard & Poor's (Subsidiary of: McGraw-Hill Companies, Inc.), 55 Water St, New York, NY 10041. TEL 212-208-8000. Ed. Joseph Spiers.

332.6   USA
HG4905
STANDARD & POOR'S STOCK REPORTS BOUND QUARTERLY. Variant title: American Stock Exchange Reports. Text in English. irreg. (approx. 4/yr.). looseleaf. USD 1,035. stat. **Document type:** *Trade.* **Description:** Provides current and 10-year historical data on the stocks publicly traded on the American Stock Exchange.
Formerly (until 1998): Standard & Poor's Stock Reports. American Stock Exchange (0191-1112)
Related titles: CD-ROM ed.
Published by: Standard & Poor's (Subsidiary of: McGraw-Hill Companies, Inc.), 55 Water St, New York, NY 10041. TEL 212-208-8000.

332.6   USA
STANDARD & POOR'S STOCK REPORTS. N A S D A Q AND REGIONAL EXCHANGES. Text in English. 1934. irreg. (approx. 4/yr.). looseleaf. USD 1,100. stat. index. **Document type:** *Trade.* **Description:** Reports on more than 1,500 of the most active companies whose securities are traded over the counter.
Formerly (until 1994): Standard and Poor's Stock Reports. Over the Counter (0163-1993)
Related titles: CD-ROM ed.
Published by: Standard & Poor's (Subsidiary of: McGraw-Hill Companies, Inc.), 55 Water St, New York, NY 10041. TEL 212-208-8000. Ed. Stephen Vallance.

332.6   USA   ISSN 1088-890X
HG4916
STANDARD & POOR'S TRENDLINE CURRENT MARKET PERSPECTIVES. Text in English. 1962. m. USD 290. charts; stat. **Document type:** *Trade.* **Description:** Presents almost 4 years of weekly price-volume data on over 2350 stocks from the NYSE, ASE and NASDAQ.
Former titles: Trendline Current Market Perspectives; Standard & Poor's Trendline Current Market Perspectives (0041-2333)
Published by: Standard & Poor's (Subsidiary of: McGraw-Hill Companies, Inc.), 55 Water St, New York, NY 10041. TEL 212-208-8000, FAX 212-208-0040. Ed. Frank Lovaglio. R&P James G Branscome.

332.6   USA   ISSN 0195-6620
STANGER REPORT. Text in English. 1979. q. USD 447. adv. charts; mkt.; stat. **Document type:** *Newsletter.* **Description:** Covers the limited partnership and REIT markets, including current offerings, secondary-market activity, and performance.
Published by: Robert A. Stanger & Co., Inc., 1129 Broad St, 2nd Fl, Shrewsbury, NJ 07702-4314. TEL 732-389-3600, FAX 732-389-1751, info@rastanger.com, http://www.rastanger.com. Ed. Nancy Schabel Mahon.

STATE BANK OF PAKISTAN. EQUITY YIELDS ON ORDINARY SHARES. see *BUSINESS AND ECONOMICS—Abstracting, Bibliographies, Statistics*

STATE BANK OF PAKISTAN. INDEX NUMBERS OF STOCK EXCHANGE SECURITIES. see *BUSINESS AND ECONOMICS—Abstracting, Bibliographies, Statistics*

STATE EXPEDITURE ON SCIENCE & TECHNOLOGY. see *SCIENCES: COMPREHENSIVE WORKS*

STATE INVESTMENT IN SCIENCE & TECHNOLOGY (YEAR). see *SCIENCES: COMPREHENSIVE WORKS*

332.6   USA
STATON INSTITUTE ADVISORY. Text in English. 1986. w. USD 49 (effective 2001). back issues avail. **Document type:** *Newsletter, Trade.* **Description:** Helps people cut risk and taxes to virtually zero, and double their money in 5 years.
Former titles: Bill Staton's Money Advisory; (until June 1990): Staton's Stock Market Advisory (0886-5078)
Related titles: E-mail ed.; Bill Staton's E-Money Digest. USD 99 (effective 2001).
Published by: Staton Institute Inc., 2431 Hartmill Ct, Charlotte, NC 28226-6463. TEL 704-365-2122, FAX 704-365-1910, bill@statoninstitute.com, bill@billstaton.com, http://www.billstaton.com, http://www.statoninstitute.com. Ed. Bill Staton. Circ: 105,000.

332.6   GBR
STOCK EXCHANGE DAILY OFFICIAL LIST. Text in English. d. (w., m., q., a. versions avail.). GBP 1,260; GBP 1,960 foreign. stat. back issues avail. **Document type:** *Trade.* **Description:** Summarizes trading activity carried out through the London Stock Exchange.
Related titles: Microfiche ed.
Published by: Financial Times Information Ltd., Extel, Fitzroy House, 13-17 Epworth St, London, EC2A 4DL, United Kingdom. TEL 44-20-7825-8000, FAX 44-20-7608-2032, eic@ft.com, http://www.info.ft.com.

332.6   SGP
STOCK EXCHANGE OF SINGAPORE. HANDBOOK∗. Text in English. 1966. q. SGD 99 domestic; SGD 185 in Asia; SGD 255 elsewhere. adv.

Published by: Stock Exchange of Singapore Ltd., Robinson Rd, P.O. Box 2306, Singapore, 9043, Singapore. TEL 535-3788, FAX 532-4476, TELEX RS-21853. Circ: 2,500.

332.6 THA
STOCK EXCHANGE OF THAILAND. FACT BOOK. Text in Thai. 1979. a. THB 220; USD 16 in Asia; USD 24 elsewhere.
Published by: Stock Exchange of Thailand, 62 Rachadapisek Rd, Klongtoey, Bangkok, 10110, Thailand. TEL 662-229-2000, FAX 662-654-5649, webmaster@setinter1.set.or.th, http://www.set.or.th.

332.6 THA ISSN 0125-1139
STOCK EXCHANGE OF THAILAND. MONTHLY REVIEW. Text in English. 1975. m. THB 700; USD 62.50 in Asia; USD 74.50 elsewhere.
Published by: Stock Exchange of Thailand, 62 Rachadapisek Rd, Klongtoey, Bangkok, 10110, Thailand. TEL 662-229-2000, FAX 662-654-5649, webmaster@setinter1.set.or.th, http://www.set.or.th.

STOCK EXCHANGE OFFICIAL DIRECTORY. see *BUSINESS AND ECONOMICS—Trade And Industrial Directories*

B

332.6 GBR
STOCK EXCHANGE WEEKLY OFFICIAL INTELLIGENCE. Text in English. w. GBP 466; GBP 600 foreign. **Document type:** *Trade.* **Description:** Provides an overview of all Stock Exchange announcements, including news and dividends.
Published by: Financial Times Information Ltd., Extel, Fitzroy House, 13-17 Epworth St, London, EC2A 4DL, United Kingdom. TEL 44-20-7825-8000, FAX 44-20-7608-2032, eic@ft.com, http://www.info.ft.com.

332.6 USA ISSN 0882-5467
HG4057
STOCK MARKET ENCYCLOPEDIA. Text in English. 1962. q. USD 124. **Document type:** *Trade.* **Description:** Researches 750 of the most actively traded stocks. Includes net quarterly sales for four years, dividends paid, price per share, and 10-year balance sheet data for each company covered.
Former titles (until 1985): S and P Stock Market Encyclopedia (0737-5026); (until 1983): Standard and Poor's Stock Market Encyclopedia of the S and P "500." Annual Report Edition (0730-9740)
Published by: Standard & Poor's (Subsidiary of: McGraw-Hill Companies, Inc.), 55 Water St, New York, NY 10041. TEL 212-208-8000. Ed. Ronald Oliver.

332.6 USA
STOCK SELECTOR. Text in English. 1986. m. USD 120. **Description:** Identifies the most attractive stocks each month based on momentum, relative strength, and valuations (PEs).
Published by: High Technology Growth Stocks, 402 Border Rd, Concord, MA 01742. TEL 617-371-0096. Ed. Bud Anderson.

332.6 USA ISSN 1080-3157
HG4905
STOCK SUMMARY (MONTHLY EDITION). Text in English. 1913. m. (q., and s-a). USD 528 for m. ed.; USD 330 for q. ed.; USD 220 for s-a. ed. (effective 2000). adv. **Document type:** *Directory.* **Description:** Contains information about corporate, partnership, and mutual fund issuers of securities traded on the NYSE, AMEX, and over-the-counter.
Formerly: National Monthly Stock Summary (0275-8326)
Related titles: Alternate Frequency ed(s).: Stock Summary (Semi-annual Edition). ISSN 1080-3165.
Published by: National Quotation Bureau, LLC, 11 Penn Plaza, 15th Fl, New York, NY 10001. TEL 212-868-7100, FAX 212-868-3848, allen@nqb.com. Ed., Pub. Allen C Swartz. R&P Evelyn Walsh TEL 212-896-4436.

332.6 USA ISSN 1553-4812
STOCK TRADER'S ALMANAC. Text in English. 1967. a. USD 34.95. **Document type:** *Trade.* **Description:** Summarizes years of research into patterns that help both traders and investors.
Published by: Hirsch Organization Inc., 79 Main St., # 3, Nyack, NY 10960-3109. TEL 201-767-4100, FAX 201-767-7337, http://www.hirschorganization.com. Ed. Jeffrey A Hirsch. Circ: 30,000.

332.6 SWE
STOCKHOLM STOCK EXCHANGE. ANNUAL REPORT. Text in Swedish. 1864. a.
Formerly: Stockholm Stock Exchange and the Stock Market. (Year)
Published by: Stockholm Stock Exchange, Fack 1256, Stockholm, 11182, Sweden. FAX 8-108110, TELEX 13551-BOURSE-S.

332.6 CAN
STOCKHOUSE ONLINE. Text in English. 1995. d. free (effective 2004). **Description:** Provides news, information and commentary on North American growth stocks.
Media: Online - full text.
Published by: StockHouse Online Journal, 500 - 750 W Pender St, Vancouver, BC V6C 2T7, Canada. TEL 604-331-0995, FAX 604-331-1194, http://www.stockhouse.com. Ed. Jeffrey D Berwick.

332.6 GBR ISSN 0263-9831
STOCKMARKET CONFIDENTIAL✶. Text in English. 1980. w. GBP 75.
Formerly (until 1981): YF: Yours Financially (0144-7165)
—CCC.
Published by: Fleet Street Publications Ltd., 271 Regent St, London, WIR 7PAU, United Kingdom. TEL 44-20-7447-4040, FAX 44-20-7447-4041. Ed. Malcolm Craig.

332.64 CHE ISSN 1424-7739
STOCKS. Text in German. 2000. w. adv. **Document type:** *Magazine, Trade.*
Published by: HandelsZeitung Fachverlag AG, Seestr 344, Zuerich, 8027, Switzerland. TEL 41-1-2889414, FAX 41-1-2889301, verlag@handelszeitung.ch, http://www.handelszeitung.ch.

332.6 USA ISSN 1047-2436
HG4501
STOCKS, BONDS, BILLS AND INFLATION (YEAR) YEARBOOK. Text in English. 1984. a. USD 110 (effective 2004). adv. charts; stat. Index. back issues avail. **Document type:** *Yearbook, Corporate.* **Description:** Covers the history of U.S. capital markets. Contains monthly returns from 1926 to the present.
Related titles: Online - full text ed.
Published by: Ibbotson Associates, 225 N Michigan Ave, Ste 700, Chicago, IL 60601. TEL 312-616-1620, 800-758-3557, FAX 312-616-0404, http://www.ibbotson.com. Circ: 5,000.

332.6 USA ISSN 1523-343X
STOCKS, BONDS, BILLS AND INFLATION YEARBOOK (VALUATION EDITION). Variant title: S B B I Valuation Edition. Text in English. 1999. a. USD 110 (effective 2004).
Published by: Ibbotson Associates, 225 N Michigan Ave, Ste 700, Chicago, IL 60601. TEL 312-616-1620, 800-758-3557, FAX 312-616-0404, http://www.ibbotson.com.

332.6 USA ISSN 0163-6235
HG4501
STOCKS IN THE S & P 500. OFFICIAL SERIES. Text in English. m. USD 880. **Document type:** *Trade.* **Description:** Details price performance and the precise composition of the Standard & Poor's 500 Index.
Published by: Standard & Poor's (Subsidiary of: McGraw-Hill Companies, Inc.), 55 Water St, New York, NY 10041. TEL 212-208-8000.

332.6 USA
THE STREET.COM. Text in English. 1996. w. USD 229.95 (effective 2003). **Document type:** *Trade.*
Media: Online - full content.
Published by: TheStreet.com, Inc. (Subsidiary of: New York Times Company), 14 Wall St, New York, NY 10005. TEL 212-321-5000, FAX 212-321-5016, twocents@thestreet.com, http://www.thestreet.com. Ed. Dave Kansas. Adv. contact Jason Young.

332.6 USA
SUCCESS FROM FAILURE. Text in English. bi-m. USD 119 domestic; USD 129 in Canada; USD 139 elsewhere (effective 2003).
Published by: Vision Quest Publishing, Inc., PO Box 27963, Prescott Valley, AZ 86312. TEL 928-772-4165, FAX 928-772-4074, mergers@firstlist.com, http://www.firstlist.com/newsletter.html.

332.6 USA ISSN 0277-2450
HG1
SUMMARY OF INSIDER TRANSACTIONS✶. Text in English. 1980. q. USD 250. reprint service avail. from PQC.
Formerly: Encyclopedia of Insider Trading
Published by: Thomson Financial Services Company, One State St Plaza, New York, NY 10004. TEL 301-654-5580, FAX 301-654-1678.

332.6 FIN ISSN 0781-4437
SUOMEN PANKKI. SUOMEN JOUKKOVELKAKIRJALAINAT/FINLANDSKA MASSKULDEBREVSLAAN/FINNISH BOND ISSUES; statistical bulletin. Text in English, Finnish, Swedish. 1945. a. free. **Document type:** *Trade.*
Formerly (until 1983): Suomen Obligaatiokirja (0585-9581)
Related titles: Online - full text ed.: ISSN 1456-5854. 2000.
Published by: Suomen Pankki/Bank of Finland, P O Box 160, Helsinki, 00101, Finland. TEL 358-9-183-2566, FAX 358-9-174-872, publications@bof.fi, http://www.bof.fi/env/rhinden.htm. Circ: 700.

SUPERMARKEDSHAANDBOGEN (YEAR)/SUPERMARKETS AND OTHER LARGE GROCERY STORES. see *BUSINESS AND ECONOMICS—Small Business*

332.6 GBR
SURVEY - SMALLER COMPANIES SECTOR. Text in English. a. GBP 245. **Document type:** *Trade.* **Description:** Reflects the views of UK fund managers on the quality of investment research in the smaller companies sector.
Published by: (City Group for Smaller Companies), Financial Times Information Ltd., Extel, Fitzroy House, 13-17 Epworth St, London, EC2A 4DL, United Kingdom. TEL 44-20-7825-8000, FAX 44-20-7608-2032, eic@ft.com, http://www.info.ft.com.

658.408 GBR ISSN 1472-0019
SUSTAINABLE BUSINESS INVESTOR - AMERICA. Text in English. 2000. 2/yr. USD 140 (effective 2003). **Document type:** *Journal, Trade.* **Description:** Examines corporate sustainability in practice and as an investment philosophy.
Related titles: Online - full text ed.: (from Gale Group).
Published by: Euromoney Institutional Investor Plc., Nestor House, Playhouse Yard, London, EC4V 5EX, United Kingdom. TEL 44-20-7779-8714, FAX 44-20-7779-8760, information@euromoneyplc.com, http://www.sbi-w.com/sbi-a/, http://www.euromoneyplc.com.

332.6 DEU ISSN 0178-9945
SWINGTREND. Text in German. 1968. w. EUR 500 (effective 2003). **Document type:** *Newsletter, Consumer.* **Description:** Covers European and U.S. stockmarkets, options, futures in currencies and commodities, gold, silver, etc.
Published by: Swingtrend GmbH, Georg-Kalb-Str 9, Pullach, 82049, Germany. TEL 49-89-7904530, FAX 49-89-7911076, info@swingtrend.de, http://www.swingtrend.de. Ed., R&P Albrecht Pfeiffer. Circ: 5,000.

332.6 BEL ISSN 0772-4799
SWINGTREND; beleggersbrief. Text in Dutch. 1970. s-w. **Document type:** *Newsletter.*
Related titles: Microfiche ed.; French ed.: Swingtrend (Edition Francaise). ISSN 0772-4780.
Published by: Biblo N.V., Brasschaatsteenweg 308, Kalmthout, 2920, Belgium. Ed. L van den Borre. Circ: 15,000.

332.6 CHE
SWISS BUSINESS. Text in English. bi-m. CHF 52; CHF 65 foreign. **Document type:** *Trade.*
Related titles: Online - full text ed.
Published by: S H Z Fachverlag AG, Seestr 37, Zuerich, 8027, Switzerland. TEL 41-1-2022046, FAX 41-1-2811970. Ed. John Wicks. Circ: 50,000.

332.6 CHE
SWX SWISS EXCHANGE. MONTHLY REPORT. Text in English, French, German. m. free. **Document type:** *Bulletin, Trade.* **Description:** Contains current information on listings, indices, trading volume and market capitalization, as well as details on price trends of listed securities and international comparative statistics.
Published by: SWX Swiss Exchange, Selnaustr 30, Postfach, Zuerich, 8021, Switzerland. TEL 41-1-2292111, FAX 41-1-2292233, swx@swx.com, http://www.swx.com.

332.6 CHE
SWX SWISS EXHANGE. ANNUAL REPORT. Text in English, French, German. a. free. **Document type:** *Yearbook, Trade.* **Description:** Supplies statistics on important data including market capitalization and listings, national and international index values and securities turnover as well as a wide variety of key figures relating to securities markets.
Published by: SWX Swiss Exchange, Selnaustr 30, Postfach, Zuerich, 8021, Switzerland. TEL 41-1-2292111, FAX 41-1-2292233, swx@swx.com, http://www.swx.com.

SYMPOSIUM ON PRIVATE INVESTMENTS ABROAD. see *LAW—International Law*

332.6 USA
SYSTEMS AND FORECASTS. Text in English. 1973. fortn. USD 225. bk.rev. charts; stat. **Document type:** *Newsletter.*
Published by: Signalert Corporation, 150 Great Neck Rd, Rm 301, Great Neck, NY 11021-3309. TEL 516-829-6444, FAX 516-829-9366. Ed. Gerald Appel. Circ: 2,500.

332.6 ISR
T A S E REVIEW - ANNUAL AND MID-YEAR. Text in English. s-a. free. **Description:** Reviews the TASE activity and includes main statistical indicators.
Published by: Tel Aviv Stock Exchange, 54 Ahad Ha am St, Tel Aviv, 65202, Israel. TEL 972-3-5677411, FAX 972-3-5105379, http://www.tase.co.il.

T V PROGRAM INVESTOR. see *COMMUNICATIONS—Television And Cable*

332.6 ITA ISSN 0082-1446
TACCUINO DELL'AZIONISTA. Text in Italian. 1935. a. USD 300. index. **Description:** Detailed profiles for each of the 240 companies listed on the Italian stock exchange.
Published by: Databank SpA, SASIP Division, Via Spartaco, 19, Milan, MI 20135, Italy. FAX 392-55183152. Ed. Carlo Colombi. Circ: 5,000.

332.6 GBR
TAIEI TOSHI NEWS. Text in Japanese. 1987. 3/yr. free. charts; illus.; stat. back issues avail. **Document type:** *Government.* **Description:** Serves Japanese corporate investors and executives planning to locate in the U.K.
Formerly: Eikoku Toshi News
Published by: Invest in Britain Bureau, 1 Victoria St, 66-74 Victoria St, London, SW1H 0ET, United Kingdom. TEL 44-171-215-5638, FAX 44-171-215-5651, http://www.dti.gov.uk/ibb. Ed. Stefano Hoyland. adv.: B&W page GBP 1,350. Circ: 11,300 (controlled). **Dist. by:** Burrups Japan Ltd., Ishinara Bldg, 3-3-12 Iida-Bashi, Chiyoda-ku, Tokyo 102-0072, Japan.

332.6 332.6 USA ISSN 1062-1016
TAIPAN. Text in English. 1988. m. USD 129. adv. back issues avail. **Document type:** *Newsletter.* **Description:** Covers international investment and business opportunity for open-minded, globally thinking investors.
Published by: Agora, Inc., 105 W Monument St, Baltimore, MD 21201. TEL 410-223-2611, 800-851-7100, FAX 410-223-2696. Ed. J Christoph Amberger. Adv. contact Doug Cooke. Circ: 70,000.

332.6 DEU ISSN 0949-7420
TAIPAN; Prognosen - Unternehmergeist - Gewinne. Text in German. 1995. m. EUR 14.80 newsstand/cover (effective 2005). back issues avail. **Document type:** *Magazine, Consumer.*
Related titles: Online - full text ed.
Published by: F I D Verlag GmbH, Koblenzer Str 99, Bonn, 53177, Germany. TEL 49-228-9550333, FAX 49-228-82055756, info@fid-verlag.de, http://www.fid-verlag.de. Ed. Volkmar Michler. **Subscr. to:** Leser-Service, Postfach 1327, Neckarsulm 74150, Germany. TEL 49-7132-959205, FAX 49-7132-959209.

332.6 USA
THE TAKEOVER STOCK REPORT. Text in English. 1996. w. USD 10,000 (effective 2005). **Document type:** *Newsletter, Trade.*
Published by: Source Media, Inc., One State St Plaza, 27th Fl, New York, NY 10004. TEL 212-803-6077, 800-221-1809, FAX 212-747-1154, custserv@sourcemedia.com, http://takeoverstockreport.com, http://www.sourcemedia.com. Ed., Pub. Lee Anne Washington.

332.6 USA
THE TAKEOVER STOCK REPORT EUROPE. Text in English. w. USD 5,000 (effective 2005). **Document type:** *Newsletter, Trade.*
Published by: Source Media, Inc., One State St Plaza, 27th Fl, New York, NY 10004. TEL 212-803-6077, 800-221-1809, FAX 212-747-1154, custserv@sourcemedia.com, http://takeoverstockreport.com, http://www.sourcemedia.com.

332.6 USA ISSN 1527-4446
HG4501
TAKING STOCK. Text in English. 1983. q. GBP 5 newsstand/cover (effective 2003). **Document type:** *Trade.* **Description:** Identifies and describes stocks selling for less than intrinsic value.
Published by: Highbury House Communications, Inc. (Subsidiary of: Highbury House Communications PLC), Barrett Court, Ste 23, 1925 Vaughn Rd, NW, Kennesaw, GA 30144. TEL 770-422-3225, 877-378-4732, FAX 770-422-7973, http://www.hhc.co.uk. Ed. David Pritchard TEL 770-422-3225 ext 229. Circ: 53,000.

TALOUSSANOMAT. see *BUSINESS AND ECONOMICS—Banking And Finance*

332.6 USA
TAURUS TOP 16. Text in English. 1976. w. USD 750; includes nightly hotline and fax service. adv. bk.rev. **Description:** Offers specific recommendations covering 16 commodity futures markets.
Former titles: Taurus (Winchester); Taurus and Optimum Trades
Published by: Taurus Corporation, 133 W Boscawen St, Winchester, VA 22601. TEL 540-667-4827, FAX 540-667-7484. Ed. Michael P Chisholm. Adv. contact Rachel Chisholm. Circ: 1,000.

TAX-ADVANTAGED SECURITIES LAW REPORT. see *LAW—Corporate Law*

332.6 USA ISSN 0739-6619
KF6415.A15
TAX FACTS 2; taxation on investments. Text in English. a. USD 23. **Description:** Provides answers to tax questions about investments in stocks, bonds and mutual funds, commodities futures, and more.
Published by: The National Underwriter Company (Subsidiary of: Highline Media), 5081 Olympic Blvd, Erlanger, KY 41018. TEL 859-692-2100, FAX 859-692-2293, http://www.nationalunderwriter.com.

TAX HAVEN REPORTER NEWSLETTER. see *BUSINESS AND ECONOMICS—Public Finance, Taxation*

TAX HAVENS OF THE WORLD. see *BUSINESS AND ECONOMICS—Public Finance, Taxation*

332.6 USA ISSN 0886-3547
KF6571.A15
TAX MANAGEMENT ESTATES, GIFTS AND TRUSTS JOURNAL. Text in English. 1976. bi-m. USD 371 (effective 2005). bk.rev. index. back issues avail. **Document type:** *Trade.* **Description:** Practical guidance and current review of developments in estates, gifts and trusts.
Formerly: Estates, Gifts and Trusts Journal (0364-9253)
Related titles: Online - full text ed.: ISSN 1543-9852 (from O C L C Online Computer Library Center, Inc., ProQuest Information & Learning, The Bureau of National Affairs, Inc., Thomson West).
Indexed: ABIn, ATI, BPIA, BusI, CLI, FamI, LII, LRI.
—CCC.
Published by: Tax Management Inc. (Subsidiary of: The Bureau of National Affairs, Inc.), 1231 25th St, N W, Washington, DC 20037. TEL 202-452-4200, 800-372-1033, FAX 202-785-7195, http://www.bnatax.com. Ed. Glenn B Davis.

TAXATION & INVESTMENT IN CANADA. see *BUSINESS AND ECONOMICS—Public Finance, Taxation*

TAXATION & INVESTMENT IN THE CARIBBEAN. see *BUSINESS AND ECONOMICS—Public Finance, Taxation*

TAXATION & INVESTMENT IN THE PEOPLE'S REPUBLIC OF CHINA. see *BUSINESS AND ECONOMICS—Public Finance, Taxation*

TAXATION OF SECURITIES TRANSACTIONS. see *BUSINESS AND ECONOMICS—Public Finance, Taxation*

343 USA ISSN 1048-2121
TAXLINE. Text in English. 1989. m.
Indexed: ATI.
Published by: The National Underwriter Company (Subsidiary of: Highline Media), 5081 Olympic Blvd, Erlanger, KY 41018. TEL 859-692-2100, FAX 859-692-2293, http://www.nationalunderwriter.com.

▼ **TECH CONFIDENTIAL.** see *BUSINESS AND ECONOMICS—Banking And Finance*

332 USA
THE TECH EDGE. Text in English. d. USD 199.95 (effective 2003). **Description:** Provides insights into the often confusing and volatile market of technology stocks.
Media: Online - full text.
Published by: TheStreet.com, 14 Wall St, New York, NY 10005. TEL 212-321-5000, FAX 212-321-5016, http://www.thestreet.com. Ed. Scott Moritz.

332.6 USA
TECHMANTRA; Asian Indian technology and business magazine. Text in English. 1998. d. **Description:** Covers topics such as venture capital, investments, and business analysis.
Published by: Neptune Technologies, 1594 Bittern Dr, Sunnyvale, CA 94087. TEL 408-739-6164, editor@techmantra.com, http://www.techmantra.com. Ed. Venkatesh Gautaman. Pub. Bhanu Gautaman.

332.6 USA ISSN 0738-3355
HG6001
TECHNICAL ANALYSIS OF STOCKS & COMMODITIES; the traders magazine. Text in English. 1982. 13/yr. USD 64.95 (effective 2005). adv. bk.rev.; software rev.; Website rev. charts; illus.; stat. index. 108 p./no.; back issues avail. **Document type:** *Magazine, Consumer.* **Description:** Covers computerized investing and charting techniques. Explains methods of trading publicly held stocks, bonds, mutual funds, options, commodities (futures), cash and hard money.
Related titles: CD-ROM ed.: S & C on CD; Microform ed.: (from PQC); Online - full text ed.; ♦ Supplement(s): Working Money (Online).
—BLDSC (8615.362500), IE, ingenta. **CCC.**
Published by: Technical Analysis, Inc., 4757 California Ave S W, Seattle, WA 98116-4499. TEL 206-938-0570, 800-832-4642, FAX 206-938-1307, TELEX 4993678-TECHANALYSIS, mail@Traders.com, http://www.Traders.com. Ed. Jayanthi Gopalakrishnan. Pub. Jack K Hutson. R&P Karen E Wasserman. Adv. contact Ed Schramm. B&W page USD 5,395, color page USD 7,595; trim 875 x 375. Circ: 65,000 (paid).

332.63 USA ISSN 1060-328X
TECHNICAL ANALYSIS OF STOCKS & COMMODITIES (YEAR). Text in English. 1986. a. USD 69.95 (effective 2005). **Description:** Teaches investors how to improve their trading in stocks, bonds, options, mutual funds, and futures.
—CCC.
Published by: Technical Analysis, Inc., 4757 California Ave S W, Seattle, WA 98116-4499. TEL 206-938-0570, 800-832-4642, FAX 206-938-1307, http://www.Traders.com.

332.6 USA ISSN 0889-9525
TECHNICAL TRENDS; the indicator accuracy service. Text in English. 1960. 40/yr. USD 147; USD 180 foreign. adv. charts; stat. **Document type:** *Newsletter.* **Description:** Provides data and charts on the most accurate, publicly available stock market indicators.
Published by: Technical Trends, Inc., 55 Liberty St., Wilton, CT 06897-3218. TEL 203-762-0229, 800-736-0229, FAX 203-761-1504, http://www.capecod.net/techtrends. Ed. John R McGinley. Pub., R&P, Adv. contact John McGinley.

332.6 USA ISSN 1522-483X
TECHNOLOGY INVESTING. Variant title: Michael Murphy's Technology Investing. Text in English. m. USD 195; USD 375 for 2 yrs. (effective 2005). **Document type:** *Newsletter.*
Related titles: Online - full content ed.
Published by: Phillips Investment Resources, LLC (Subsidiary of: Phillips International Inc.), 7811 Montrose Rd., Potomac, MD 20854-3394. TEL 301-424-3700, 800-219-8592, http://www.techinvestingonline.com/, http://www.phillips.com/pir/. Ed. Michael Murphy.

332.6 USA ISSN 1527-1471
HC79.H53
TECHNOLOGY INVESTOR. Text in English. 2000. m. USD 39.95; USD 4.95 newsstand/cover (effective 2001). adv. **Document type:** *Consumer.*
Address: 270 Madison Ave, 13th Fl, New York, NY 10016. TEL 212-685-4271, FAX 212-685-4265, Harry_Newton@TechnologyInvestor.com, http://www.TechnologyInvestor.com. Ed. Aaron Brenner. Pub. Harry Newton.

332.6 ISR
TEL AVIV CONTINUOUS TRADING SYSTEM. Short title: T A C T. Text in English. q. free. **Description:** Describes the TACT system.
Published by: Tel Aviv Stock Exchange, 54 Ahad Ha am St, Tel Aviv, 65202, Israel. TEL 972-3-5677411, FAX 972-3-5105379, http://www.tase.co.il.

B

332 USA
THE TELECOM CONNECTION. Text in Spanish. d. USD 799.95 (effective 2003). **Description:** Offers an insider's scoop on developments in the telecommunications industry.
Media: Online - full text.
Published by: TheStreet.com, 14 Wall St, New York, NY 10005. Ed. Cody Willard.

332.6 THA
THAILAND UPDATE. Text in English. m.
Published by: Office of the Board of Investment, Jatuchuck, 555 Vipavadee Rangsit Rd, Bangkok, 10900, Thailand. TEL 537-8111, FAX 537-8177. Circ: 10,000.

332.6 THA ISSN 0857-8702
THAILAND'S INVESTMENT PROMOTION JOURNAL. Text in Thai. m.
Published by: Office of the Board of Investment, Jatuchuck, 555 Vipavadee Rangsit Rd, Bangkok, 10900, Thailand. TEL 537-8111, FAX 537-8177. Circ: 6,000.

332.62 USA ISSN 1055-9035
HG4530
THE THOMAS J. HERZFELD ENCYCLOPEDIA OF CLOSED-END FUNDS. Text in English. 1990. a., latest 1997/1998. USD 135 (effective 2000). adv. **Document type:** *Trade.* **Description:** Analyzes approximately 300 closed-end funds.
Published by: Thomas J. Herzfeld Advisors, Inc., PO Box 161465, Miami, FL 33116. TEL 305-271-1900, 800-854-3863, FAX 305-270-1040, http://www.herzfeld.com. Ed. Thomas J Hezfeld. Adv. contact Thomas Herzfeld.

332 USA ISSN 1095-3655
HG1921
THRIFT INVESTOR. Text in English. 1986. m. USD 495 (effective 2003). adv. charts; mkt.; stat. back issues avail. **Document type:** *Trade.* **Description:** Combines articles on industry trends and management strategies with complete financial, market and conversion data on all publicly traded thrifts.
Formerly: Monthly Market Reports (1074-6579)
Related titles: Online - full text ed.
Published by: S N L Financial LC, 212 7th St NE, Charlottesvle, VA 22902-5307. TEL 434-977-1600, FAX 434-293-0407, subscriptions@snlnet.com, http://www.snl.com/products/bank/tmo.asp?PID=TMO. Ed. Christopher Smith. Pub. Reid Nagle. Adv. contact Mark Outlaw.

332.6 USA ISSN 1091-1936
HG4621
TICKER (NEW YORK, 1996). Text in English. 1996. m. USD 25 (effective 2004). adv. bk.rev. back issues avail. **Document type:** *Magazine, Trade.* **Description:** Features industry trends, personalities behind industry frontlines, columnist Maria Bartiromon's reprts from Wall Street, economic outlook, stock fund and bond stories, international investment opportunities, analyst spotlights, research spotlights, and more.
Related titles: Online - full content ed.: USD 29 (effective 2004).
Published by: Ticker Magazine, 407 Linclon Rd, Ste 12D, Miami Beach, FL 33139. TEL 305-673-6339, FAX 305-673-6386, ticker@ticker.com, subscribe@ticker.com, http://www.ticker.com/. Adv. contact Glen Sundin TEL 973-984-2432. B&W page USD 9,450, color page USD 13,230; trim 8.375 x 10.75. Circ: 78,936 (controlled).

TIMELY DISCLOSURE. see *BUSINESS AND ECONOMICS—Banking And Finance*

332.6 USA
TIMELY INVESTMENT INFORMATION. Text in English. 1996. w. **Document type:** *Newsletter.* **Description:** Provides timely investment information for serious do-it-yourself investors.
Media: Online - full text.
Published by: Green Mountain Asset Management Corp., 139 Bank St, Burlington, VT 05401. TEL 802-658-7806, 800-385-2673, bobbose@stockresearch.com, http://www.stockresearch.com. Ed. Bob Bose.

332.6 THA
TISNET TRADE AND INVESTMENT INFORMATION BULLETIN. Text in Thai. 1982. m. USD 75 (effective 2000). **Document type:** *Bulletin.*
Former titles (until 1995): Tisnet Trade Information Bulletin; (until 1993): Tisnet Trade Information Sheet; (until 1984): Trade Information Sheet
Published by: United Nations Economic and Social Commission for Asia and the Pacific, International Trade and Economic Cooperation Division, United Nations Bldg., Rajadamnern Ave., Bangkok, 10200, Thailand. TEL 662-288-1799, FAX 662-288-1026, Trade-inf.unescap@un.org, http://www.unescap.org.

332.6 USA ISSN 1042-8127
TODAY'S INVESTOR. Text in English. 1980. m. USD 59 domestic; USD 89 in Canada; USD 109 elsewhere. adv. bk.rev. illus. reprints avail. **Description:** Covers the emerging growth stocks of the securities markets.
Formerly (until 1989): Penny Stock News (0745-4600)
Published by: Forte Communications, Inc., 3272 37th St., Astoria, NY 11103-4004. TEL 212-785-6300, FAX 212-608-0315. Ed. Edward Taxin. Circ: 45,000.

332.6 USA ISSN 1068-090X
TODAY'S PAWNBROKER. Text in English. 1988. q. USD 25 (effective 2001). adv. software rev. 56 p./no. 3 cols./p.; back issues avail. **Document type:** *Magazine, Trade.* **Description:** Helps executives in the pawnbroking industry manage their business for continued growth. Includes general news, feature articles, legislative updates, reports on trends, marketing tips, product information and news of state and national association activities.
Published by: B K B Publications Inc, 98 Greenwich Ave, 1st Fl, New York, NY 10011-7743. TEL 212-807-7933, 212-807-6558, FAX 212-807-1821, bkbpub1@ix.netcom.com. Ed. Charlene Komar Storey. Pub., R&P, Adv. contact Brian K Burkart TEL 212-807-7933. B&W page USD 1,480, color page USD 2,185; trim 10.88 x 8.25. Circ: 12,000 (paid and controlled).

332.6 USA
TODAY'S VALUE INVESTOR. Text in English. m. USD 125 (effective 1999).
Published by: Horizon Publishing Co., L L C, 7412 Calumet Ave, Ste 200, Hammond, IN 46324-2692. TEL 219-852-3200, FAX 219-931-6487.

TOLLEY'S CAPITAL GAINS TAX. see *BUSINESS AND ECONOMICS—Public Finance, Taxation*

332.6 CAN ISSN 0705-2170
TORONTO STOCK EXCHANGE DAILY RECORD. Text in English. 1934. d. CND 731.78; USD 1,046.28 foreign. adv. **Description:** Complete record of each day's trading in all listed stocks, stock options and futures.
Related titles: Microfiche ed.; Microfilm ed.: (from MML); Microform ed.: (from MML).
Published by: T.S.E. Publications, 2 First Canadian Place, Toronto, ON M5X 1J2, Canada. TEL 416-947-4681, FAX 416-814-8811. Ed., R&P Catherine McGravey. Adv. contact Daniel Strong. Circ: 2,500.

332.6 CAN
TORONTO STOCK EXCHANGE. NOTICE TO MEMBERS. Text in English. 1957. irreg. CND 187.25, USD 175. **Description:** Relates changes in by-laws, listings, members, committees, events, holidays.
Published by: Toronto Stock Exchange, 2 First Canadian Pl, Toronto, ON M5X 1J2, Canada. TEL 416-947-4223, FAX 416-947-4662. Circ: 500.

332.64 CAN ISSN 0049-4216
HG5160.T6
TORONTO STOCK EXCHANGE REVIEW. Text in English. 1949. m. CND 156.22 domestic; USD 155 in United States; CND 225.93 elsewhere. **Description:** Summary of all equity trading on the Toronto Stock Exchange for each month.
Related titles: Microfiche ed.: (from MML); Microfilm ed.: (from MML); Microform ed.: (from MML).
Indexed: CBCARef, CBPI, CPerl.
Published by: Toronto Stock Exchange, 2 First Canadian Pl, Toronto, ON M5X 1J2, Canada. TEL 416-947-4222, FAX 416-947-4585. Ed. Catherine McGravey. Circ: 2,200 (paid); 1,150 (controlled).

232 USA
TOTAL RATE-OF-RETURN INDEXES. Text in English. m. charts; stat.
Related titles: Series of: Global Index Group.
Published by: Salomon Brothers, Inc., 7 World Trade Center, New York, NY 10048. TEL 212-783-7000.

332.6 CHN
TOUZI GUANLI YU YANJIU/INVESTMENT MANAGEMENT AND STUDY. Text in Chinese. bi-m.
Published by: Zhongguo Renmin Yinhang, Guangxi Fenhang/China People's Bank, Guangxi Branch, Taoyuan Lu, Nanning, Guangxi 530021, China. TEL 26731.

332.6 CHN ISSN 1003-7624
TOUZI YANJIU/INVESTMENT RESEARCH. Text in Chinese. 1982. m. USD 54 (effective 2004).
Related titles: Online - full text ed.: (from East View Information Services, WanFang Data Corp.).
Address: Xuanwu-qu, 68, Zaolinqian Jie, Beijing, 100053, China. TEL 86-10-63569126, FAX 86-10-63566042, http://swyj.periodicals.net.cn/default.html. **Dist. in US by:** China Books & Periodicals Inc, 360 Swift Ave., Ste. 48, S San Fran, CA 94080-6220. TEL 415-282-2994; **Dist. by:** China International Book Trading Corp, 35 Chegongzhuang Xilu, Haidian District, PO Box 399, Beijing 100044, China. TEL 86-10-68412045, FAX 86-10-68412023, cibtc@mail.cibtc.com.cn, http://www.cibtc.com.cn.

332.6 CHN ISSN 1009-1858
TOUZI YU LICAI/INVESTMENT AND MANAGEMENT OF FINANCIAL TRANSACTIONS. Text in Chinese. 2000. s-m. CNY 72 (effective 2004). **Document type:** *Journal, Academic/Scholarly.*
Related titles: Print ed.: USD 87 (effective 2001).
Published by: Zhongguo Renmin Daxue, Shubao Zilio Zhongxin/Renmin University of China, Information Center for Social Server, Dongcheng-qu, 3, Zhangzizhong Lu, Beijing, 100007, China. TEL 86-10-64039458, FAX 86-10-64015080, kyes@163.net, http://www.confucius.cn.net/bkdetail.asp?fzt=X2. **Dist. in the US by:** China Publications Service, PO Box 49614, Chicago, IL 60649. TEL 312-288-3291, FAX 312-288-8570; **Dist. outside of China by:** China International Book Trading Corp, 35 Chegongzhuang Xilu, Haidian District, PO Box 399, Beijing 100044, China. TEL 86-10-68412045, FAX 86-10-68412023, cibtc@mail.cibtc.com.cn, http://www.cibtc.com.cn/.

332.6 CHN ISSN 1007-6670
TOUZI YU ZHENGQUAN/INVESTMENT AND SECURITIES. Text in Chinese. 1998. m. CNY 144 (effective 2004). **Document type:** *Journal, Academic/Scholarly.*
Related titles: Alternate Frequency ed(s).: s-a. USD 70.60 (effective 2002).
Published by: Zhongguo Renmin Daxue, Shubao Zilio Zhongxin/Renmin University of China, Information Center for Social Server, Dongcheng-qu, 3, Zhangzizhong Lu, Beijing, 100007, China. TEL 86-10-64039458, FAX 86-10-64015080, kyes@163.net, http://www.confucius.cn.net/bkdetail.asp?fzt=F63. **Dist. in the US by:** China Publications Service, PO Box 49614, Chicago, IL 60649. TEL 312-288-3291, FAX 312-288-8570; **Dist. outside of China by:** China International Book Trading Corp, 35 Chegongzhuang Xilu, Haidian District, PO Box 399, Beijing 100044, China. TEL 86-10-68412045, FAX 86-10-68412023, cibtc@mail.cibtc.com.cn, http://www.cibtc.com.cn/.

TOWER INVESTOR. see *COMMUNICATIONS*

TRADE FINANCE. see *BUSINESS AND ECONOMICS—Banking And Finance*

292 USA ISSN 1556-1992
▼ **TRADER-SOURCE.** Text in English. 2004. bi-m. adv. **Document type:** *Magazine, Trade.*
Published by: Oster Communications, LLC, 219 Main St, Ste 200, Cedar Falls, IA 50613. TEL 800-635-3936, http://www.traderssource.net. Ed. Jim Kharouf. Adv. contact Sarah Haase.

TRADERS MAGAZINE; the magazine for the professional securities trader. see *BUSINESS AND ECONOMICS—Banking And Finance*

332.6 USA
TRADER'S OPTION. Text in English. 1985. m. USD 217. back issues avail.
Address: PO Box 727, Quincy, IL 62306. TEL 217-222-4827. Ed. Thomas J Lavery.

332.6 USA ISSN 1045-7690
TRADER'S WORLD MAGAZINE. Text in English. 1989. q. USD 19.95 in United States; USD 27.95 in Canada (effective 2002). adv. bk.rev.; software rev. **Document type:** *Trade.* **Description:** Covers both classical and modern methods of technical analysis. Subjects covered are cycles, trend analysis, studies of oscillators and more.
Published by: Halliker's Inc., 2508 Grayrock, Springfield, MO 65810-2114. TEL 417-882-9697, FAX 417-886-5180, publisher@tradersworld.com, http://www.tradersworld.com. Ed., R&P Larry Jacobs. Adv. contact Zachary David. Circ: 11,000 (paid).

332.6 USA ISSN 0892-3280
TRADING CYCLES★. Text in English. 1974. 12/yr. looseleaf. USD 97.99. back issues avail. **Document type:** *Newsletter.* **Description:** Market timing service for stocks, bonds, precious metals; currencies, options, computer generated decisions.
Formerly: Andrews Trading Cycles
Published by: Andrews Publications (Templeton), 156 Shadow Creek Ln, Paso Robles, CA 93446-1922. TEL 408-778-2925. Ed. R Earl Andrews.

332.6 658 USA ISSN 1067-0432
HG4028.C45 CODEN: TRMAFL
TREASURY & RISK MANAGEMENT. Text in English. 1991. 10/yr. USD 64 domestic; USD 80 foreign; free to qualified personnel (effective 2005). adv. illus. Index. back issues avail.; reprints avail. **Document type:** *Magazine, Trade.* **Description:** Provides specific solutions to day-to-day problems faced by corporate risk managers.
Incorporates (in 1996): Corporate Cashflow (1040-0311); Which was formerly (1980-1988): Cashflow (0196-6227); Formerly (until no.2, 1992): Treasury; Incorporates (1989-1992): Corporate Risk Management (1046-5626)
Related titles: Online - full text ed.: (from EBSCO Publishing, Gale Group, O C L C Online Computer Library Center, Inc.).
Indexed: ABIn, BLI.
—CCC.
Published by: Wicks Business Information LLC, 1375 Kings Hwy., Ste. 450, Fairfield, CT 06824-5398. info@wicksbusinessinfo.com, http://www.treasuryandrisk.com, http://www.wicksbusinessinfo.com. Eds. Kevin Reardon, Pat Wechsler. Pub. Steven Schwarzkopf. adv.: B&W page USD 11,755, color page USD 14,863. Circ: 46,000 (controlled).

332.63 LBN
TREASURY BILLS MARKET. Text in Arabic, English. bi-w.
Published by: Association of Banks in Lebanon, DORA Centre Moucarri, P O Box 80536, Beirut, Lebanon.

332.6 ITA
TREND & MARKET. Text in Italian. 11/yr.
Published by: Trend & Market Editrice s.r.l., Via Nino Bixio, 30, Milan, MI 20129, Italy. TEL 2-204-66-87, FAX 2-204-65-07. Ed. Anna Righini. Circ: 16,000.

332.63 AUT
TREND INVEST. Text in German. 5/yr. adv. **Document type:** *Magazine, Consumer.*
Published by: Verlagsgruppe News Gesellschaft mbH (Subsidiary of: Gruner und Jahr AG & Co.), Lindengasse 52, Vienna, 1070, Austria. TEL 43-1-53470-0, FAX 43-1-5353250, http://www.news.at.

332.6 AUS
TRENDEX. Text in English. 1975. fortn. AUD 200. adv. back issues avail. **Document type:** *Newsletter.* **Description:** In-depth analysis of and comment on stockmarket trents. Advice given on what stock to hold, sell or buy now and in the future.
Incorporates (1977-1990): Investment Action Newsletter (0819-3320)
Published by: B R W Media, Level 2, 469 La Trobe St, Melbourne, VIC 3000, Australia. TEL 61-3-9603-3888, FAX 61-3-9670-4328. Ed. Merril Armstrong. Adv. contact John Briggs. Circ: 3,050.

332.6 USA ISSN 1061-7477
HG4916
TRENDLINE CHART GUIDE. Text in English. 1991. m. USD 185. charts; stat. **Document type:** *Trade.* **Description:** Offers one-year price data, detailing weekly high, low, and closing prices and volume, along with 30-week moving averages, for each of more than 4,400 stocks.
Published by: Standard & Poor's (Subsidiary of: McGraw-Hill Companies, Inc.), 55 Water St, New York, NY 10041. TEL 212-208-8000, FAX 212-208-0040. Ed. Frank Lovaglio. R&P James G Branscome.

332.6 USA ISSN 0277-4968
TRENDLINE DAILY ACTION STOCK CHARTS (WEEKLY). Text in English. 1959. w. looseleaf. USD 650. charts; stat. **Document type:** *Trade.* **Description:** Covers 52 weeks of daily price-volume performance on more than 720 stocks, and compares past performance against the Standard and Poor's 500 index.
Formerly (until 1980): Trendline Daily Basis Stock Charts (0564-1896)
Published by: Standard & Poor's (Subsidiary of: McGraw-Hill Companies, Inc.), 55 Water St, New York, NY 10041. TEL 212-208-8000, FAX 212-208-0040. Ed. Frank Lovaglio. R&P James G Branscome.

TRENDS IN PRIVATE INVESTMENT IN DEVELOPING COUNTRIES. see *BUSINESS AND ECONOMICS—International Development And Assistance*

332.6 USA ISSN 0041-3682
CODEN: TRUSB9
TRUSTS & ESTATES. Text in English. 1904. m. USD 199 domestic; USD 212 in Canada; USD 231 elsewhere (effective 2005). adv. bk.rev. charts; illus. index, cum.index: 1945-1964. reprint service avail. from PQC,WSH. **Document type:** *Magazine, Trade.* **Description:** Serves the field of estate planning, trust administration and related areas of investment in the U.S. Covers investments, law, taxes, life insurance, accounting, property appraisal and liquidation, and employee benefits.
Related titles: Microfiche ed.: (from CIS); Microform ed.: (from PQC); Online - full text ed.: (from Florida Center for Library Automation, Gale Group, H.W. Wilson, O C L C Online Computer Library Center, Inc., ProQuest Information & Learning).

Indexed: ABIn, ATI, AgeL, BLI, BPI, BPIA, BusI, CLI, DPD, FamI, ILP, LII, LRI, LegCont, ManagCont, PAIS, PSI, SRI, T&II.
—BLDSC (9066.600000), IE, Infotrieve, ingenta. **CCC.**
Published by: Primedia Business Magazines & Media, Inc. (Subsidiary of: Primedia, Inc.), 249 W 17th St, New York, NY 10011. TEL 212-462-3600, FAX 212-206-3622, rsherman@primediabusiness.com, inquiries@primediabusiness.com, http://www.trustsandestates.com/, http://www.primediabusiness.com. Eds. Rorie Sherman, Geoffrey C. Lewis TEL 212-462-3588. Adv. contact Claire Cavaliere. B&W page USD 4,665, color page USD 6,165; trim 7 x 10. Circ: 14,597 (paid).

332.6 USA ISSN 1056-0173
TURNAROUND LETTER. Text in English. 1986. m. looseleaf. USD 195 (effective 2005). back issues avail. **Document type:** *Newsletter.* **Description:** Covers turnaround investing opportunities.
Published by: New Generation Research, Inc., 225 Friend St, Ste 801, Boston, MA 02114. TEL 617-573-9550, FAX 617-573-9554, http://www.turnarounds.com. Ed., Pub. George Putnam III. R&P Stacey Viveiros. Circ: 2,000.

332.63 USA ISSN 0274-8894
TURNING POINTS. Text in English. 1979. s-m. USD 200 (effective 1999). **Description:** Specific timing service for the stock market short term, stock market long term and bonds.
Indexed: CINAHL, RehabLit.
Published by: Concept Publishing, PO Box 500, York, NY 14592. TEL 716-243-4214, FAX 716-243-3148. Ed. David Coleman. Pub. Jim Dovan. Circ: 400.

332.6 USA
TWENTY-FIRST CENTURY RETIREMENT. Text in English. 1946. bi-m. USD 63 (effective 2001). **Document type:** *Newsletter, Trade.*
Former titles: Retirement in the Twenty-first Century; Query (Bryn Mawr) (0033-6270)
Published by: (Society of Financial Service Professionals), Liberty Publishing, 85 Sam Fonzo Dr, Beverly, MA 01915-1000.

332.6 332 UGA
U C B INVESTOR'S HANDBOOK. Text in English. 1983. biennial. **Description:** Investment opportunities and addresses of exporters and importers from commercial and industrial sectors in Uganda.
Published by: Uganda Commercial Bank, PO Box 973, Kampala, Uganda. Circ: 1,500.

332.65 GBR ISSN 1461-6785
U K INVESTMENT BULLETIN. Text in English. 1997. q.
—BLDSC (9082.657870).
Published by: Invest in Britain Bureau, 1 Victoria St, 66-74 Victoria St, London, SW1H 0ET, United Kingdom. TEL 44-171-215-2552, FAX 44-171-215-5681, invest.britain@iibb.dti.gov.uk, http://www.dti.gov.uk/ibb.

332.66 GBR
U K ONLINE INVESTING NEWS. Text in English. m. GBP 15 (effective 1999). adv. **Document type:** *Newsletter.* **Description:** Provides online investors with a collection of relevant information sources and annotated links on how and where to access information on UK quoted companies.
Media: Online - full text.
Published by: E M A R Publishers, 26 Cholmeley Park, London, N6 5EU, United Kingdom. sjd@emarp.freeserve.co.uk, http://www.ukonlineinvesting.com/. Ed. Steven Dotsch.

332.66 GBR
U K ONLINE INVESTING REPORT. Text in English. a. free. adv. **Document type:** *Newsletter.*
Media: Online - full text.
Published by: E M A R Publishers, 26 Cholmeley Park, London, N6 5EU, United Kingdom. sjd@emarp.freeserve.co.uk, http://www.ukonlineinvesting.com/. Ed. Steven Dotsch.

332.6 USA ISSN 0265-8364
HG5431
U K VENTURE CAPITAL JOURNAL. Text in English. 1983. bi-m. adv. charts. s-a. index. **Document type:** *Journal, Trade.* **Description:** Contains news, analysis and insights about the UK venture capital industry.
Related titles: Online - full text ed.: (from EBSCO Publishing, Gale Group, O C L C Online Computer Library Center, Inc., ProQuest Information & Learning).
Indexed: ABIn, B&I.
—**CCC.**
Published by: Securities Data Publishing (Subsidiary of: Thomson Financial / I M G Media), 195 Broadway, New York, NY 10007. TEL 212-765-5311, FAX 212-765-6123. Ed. Jennifer Reed. adv.: B&W page GBP 500; trim 11.75 x 8.38. Circ: 140.

338.91 CHE
U N C T A D SERIES ON ISSUES IN INTERNATIONAL INVESTMENT AGREEMENTS. Text in English. irreg., latest vol.22, 2001. USD 12 per vol.. back issues avail. **Document type:** *Monographic series, Trade.* **Description:** Provides balanced analyses of issues that may arise in discussions about international investment agreements.
Published by: United Nations Conference on Trade and Development, 8-14 Avenue de la Paix, Geneva 10, 1211, Switzerland. TEL 41-22-9174924, FAX 41-22-9070195, info@unctad.org, http://www.unctad.org.

332.6 USA
U S A FINANCIAL NEWS. Text in English. m. USD 69. **Document type:** *Newsletter.*
Formerly: Bonanza (0888-4889)
Address: 5160 S Valley View, Ste 106, Las Vegas, NV 89118. Ed. James Bartel. Pub. Mitchell Milgaten. R&P Mitchel Milgaten TEL 702-739-6552. Circ: 11,000.

332 USA ISSN 0148-8848
HG1 CODEN: USBAEH
U S BANKER. Variant title: United States Banker. Text in English. 1891. m. USD 89 domestic; USD 95 foreign (effective 2005). adv. illus. index. back issues avail.; reprint service avail. from PQC. **Document type:** *Magazine, Trade.*
Incorporates (1997-2002): FutureBanker (1092-9061); Incorporates (1886-1997): Bankers Magazine (0005-545X); Former titles (until 1977): United States Investor - Eastern Banker (0362-6741); (until 1971): United States Investor (0041-7718)
Related titles: Microform ed.: (from PQC); Online - full text ed.: (from EBSCO Publishing, Factiva, Gale Group, H.W. Wilson, LexisNexis, O C L C Online Computer Library Center, Inc., ProQuest Information & Learning).
Indexed: ABIn, B&I, BLI, BPI, BPIA, BusI, Inspec, LRI, PAIS, PSI, T&II.
—BLDSC (9124.741800), AskIEEE, IE, ingenta. **CCC.**
Published by: Source Media, Inc., One State St Plaza, 27th Fl, New York, NY 10004. TEL 212-803-6077, FAX 212-747-1154, http://www.us-banker.com. Ed. Holly Sraeel. Pub., Adv. contact David Cleworth TEL 813-977-5771. B&W page USD 7,510. Circ: 39,000 (controlled).

658.1526 USA
U.S. DEPARTMENT OF THE TREASURY. BUREAU OF PUBLIC DEBT. TABLES OF REDEMPTION VALUES FOR UNITED STATES SERIES E E SAVINGS BOND AND SERIES I SAVINGS BONDS. Text in English. s-a. USD 5 (effective 2001). **Document type:** *Government.*
Published by: U.S. Department of the Treasury, Bureau of Public Debt, 999 E St Ste 501, Washington, DC 20239-0001. TEL 304-480-6112, FAX 304-480-7959, OAdmin@bpd.treas.gov, http://www.publicdebt.treas.gov/. **Subscr. to:** U.S. Government Printing Office, Superintendent of Documents, PO Box 371954, Pittsburgh, PA 15250-7954. TEL 202-512-1800, FAX 202-512-2250, orders@gpo.gov, http://www.access.gpo.gov.

332.63 USA ISSN 0083-3215
HG4556.U5
U.S. SECURITIES AND EXCHANGE COMMISSION. ANNUAL REPORT. Text in English. 1935. a. price varies. reprint service avail. from WSH,PQC. **Description:** Based on a company's annual report on Form 10-K. All reports are different.
Published by: U.S. Securities and Exchange Commission, Directorate of Economic and Policy Research, 500 N Capitol St, Washington, DC 20549. TEL 202-655-4000. **Orders to:** U.S. Government Printing Office, Superintendent of Documents, PO Box 371954, Pittsburgh, PA 15250-7954. TEL 202-512-1800, FAX 202-512-2250, orders@gpo.gov, http://www.access.gpo.gov.

332.63 USA ISSN 0083-3223
KF1444
U.S. SECURITIES AND EXCHANGE COMMISSION. DECISIONS AND REPORTS. Text in English. 1934. irreg. price varies. reprint service avail. from PQC.
Related titles: Microfilm ed.: (from BHP); Microform ed.: (from BHP, PQC).
Published by: U.S. Securities and Exchange Commission, 450 Fifth St, N W, MISC 11, Washington, DC 20549. TEL 202-655-4000. **Orders to:** U.S. Government Printing Office, Superintendent of Documents, PO Box 371954, Pittsburgh, PA 15250-7954. TEL 202-512-1800, FAX 202-512-2250, orders@gpo.gov, http://www.access.gpo.gov.

332.63 USA ISSN 0083-3231
U.S. SECURITIES AND EXCHANGE COMMISSION. JUDICIAL DECISIONS. Text in English. 1934. irreg. price varies. reprint service avail. from PQC.
Published by: U.S. Securities and Exchange Commission, 450 Fifth St, N W, MISC 11, Washington, DC 20549. TEL 202-655-4000. **Orders to:** U.S. Government Printing Office, Superintendent of Documents, PO Box 371954, Pittsburgh, PA 15250-7954. TEL 202-512-1800, FAX 202-512-2250, orders@gpo.gov, http://www.access.gpo.gov.

332.6 USA ISSN 0364-2267
HG4556.U5
U.S. SECURITIES AND EXCHANGE COMMISSION. OFFICIAL SUMMARY OF SECURITY TRANSACTIONS AND HOLDINGS. Text in English. 1935. m. USD 166 (effective 2001). reprint service avail. from CIS,PQC. **Description:** Contains securities holdings figures showing owners, relationships to issues, amounts of securities bought or sold by each owner, their individual holdings at the end of the reported month, and types of securities.
Related titles: Microfiche ed.: (from CIS).
Indexed: AmStI.
Published by: U.S. Securities and Exchange Commission, 450 Fifth St, N W, MISC 11, Washington, DC 20549. TEL 202-655-4000. Circ: 7,000. **Orders to:** U.S. Government Printing Office, Superintendent of Documents, PO Box 371954, Pittsburgh, PA 15250-7954. TEL 202-512-1800, FAX 202-512-2250, orders@gpo.gov, http://www.access.gpo.gov.

332.6 300 USA ISSN 1095-6395
HD60.5.U5
U S SOCIAL POLICY SHAREHOLDER RESOLUTIONS IN (YEAR). Text in English. a. USD 55 (effective 1999 & 2000). back issues avail. **Document type:** *Trade.*
Former titles (until 1995): How Institutions Voted on Social Responsibility Shareholder Resolutions (1048-1443); (until 1985): How Institutions Voted on Shareholder Resolutions (8755-2264); (until 1980): Proxy Season: How Institutions Voted on Shareholder Resolutions and Management Proposals (0197-2642)
Published by: Investor Responsibility Research Center, Inc., 1350 Connecticut Ave, N W, Ste 700, Washington, DC 20036. TEL 202-833-0700, FAX 202-833-3555, Heidi.Salkeld@irrc.org, http://www.irrc.org. Ed. Meg Voorhes. R&P Heidi Salkeld.

332.6 NLD ISSN 0041-5936
UITLOTINGS-ARCHIEF. Text in Dutch. 1912. 3/w. looseleaf. stat.
Published by: Internationale Uitlotingsdienst/International Service of Drawings of Bonds, Postbus 1071, Amsterdam, 1000 BB, Netherlands. Circ: (controlled).

332.6 UKR ISSN 1816-1464
▼ ➤ **THE UKRAINIAN TIMES UPDATE.** Text in English. 2005. 2/w. adv. mkt. back issues avail. **Description:** Covers investment and business opportunities, privatization efforts, reprints of laws and decrees, articles on current political and economic events designed for investors and market researchers.
Related titles: Fax ed.; Online - full text ed.
Published by: Ukrainian Times, PO Box 127, Kyiv, 04211, Ukraine. ukrtimes@ukr.net. Ed. Vladimir Sytin. adv.: B&W page USD 670, color page USD 1,330. Circ: 5,000 (paid).

330.9 UKR
UKRAINS'KA INVESTITSIINA HAZETA. Text in Ukrainian. w. USD 275 in United States.
Published by: Ukrains'ka Investytsiina Hazeta, Ul Kutuzova 18-7, Kiev, Ukraine. TEL 380-44-294-4157, FAX 380-44-294-7373. **US dist. addr.:** East View Information Services, 3020 Harbor Ln. N., Minneapolis, MN 55447. TEL 612-550-0961.

332 USA ISSN 1550-3682
▼ **UNDER THE RADAR NEWSLETTER.** Text in English. 2003. m. **Document type:** *Newsletter, Trade.* **Description:** Focuses on small-cap stocks and is marketed towards institutional investors, buy-side and sell-side analysts, venture capitalists, hedge funds, investment banking firms, financial advisors, and registered representatives.
Published by: Under the Radar, Inc., 362 Davis Ave, Ste 4, 4th Fl, Greenwich, CT 06830. TEL 203-552-1600, FAX 203-625-9555, editor@utrnewsletter.com, http://www.utrnewsletter.com.

332.6 ZAF ISSN 1561-2767
UNDERSTANDING UNIT TRUSTS. Text in English. 1999. a., latest 2003. ZAR 45 domestic; USD 25 foreign (effective 2003). adv. 232 p./no.; **Document type:** *Trade.* **Description:** Informs investors interested in learning about unit trust investments.
Published by: Profile Media, PO Box 87254, Houghton, Johannesburg 2041, South Africa. TEL 27-11-7285510, FAX 27-11-7285845, ernie@profile.co.za, http://www.profile.co.za/books/underunitbook.html. Ed. Nic Oldert. Adv. contact Ernie Alexander. B&W page ZAR 9,775, color page ZAR 12,500; trim 148 x 210.

332.6 USA ISSN 1088-0208
UNDISCOVERED STOCKS. Text in English. m. USD 179. 8 p./no.; **Document type:** *Newsletter.* **Description:** Provides tips on how to invest in quality, undiscovered stocks that are ignored by Wall Street.
Published by: Weiss Research, Inc., 4176 Burns Rd, Palm Beach, FL 33410-4606. TEL 561-627-3311, FAX 561-625-6685, clara@weissinc.com, smr@weissinc.com, http://www.weissinc.com. Ed. Nancy Zambell. Pub. Martin Weiss. R&P Leslie Underwood.

UNEMPLOYMENT INSURANCE STATISTICS. see *BUSINESS AND ECONOMICS—Labor And Industrial Relations*

332.6 USA
UNIT INVESTMENT TRUSTS SERVICE MANUALS. Text in English. a. USD 1,275 (effective 1999). **Description:** Provides information on over 19,000 unit investment trusts, including multi-state series.
Related titles: Microfiche ed.
Published by: Mergent, 5250 77 Center Dr, Ste 150, Charlotte, NC 28217. customerservice@mergent.com, http://www.mergent.com.

332.6 USA
UNIT INVESTMENT TRUSTS WEEKLY REPORTS. Text in English. w. USD 595 (effective 1999); Bank and Finance Manual Subs.. **Description:** Provides current interest-principal payment data on over 19,000 series.
Published by: Mergent, 5250 77 Center Dr, Ste 150, Charlotte, NC 28217. customerservice@mergent.com, http://www.mergent.com.

332.6 USA ISSN 1064-5373
UTILITY FORECASTER✶. Text in English. 1992. m. USD 109.
Published by: Kephart Communications, Inc., 1750 Old Meadow Rd., 3rd Fl., Mclean, VA 22102-4304. TEL 800-832-2330. Ed. Roger S Conrad.

V A R D S REPORT. (Variable Annuity Research & Data Service) see *INSURANCE*

332.6 384.558 USA
V O D & I T V INVESTOR. (Video on Demand and Interactive Television) Text in English. 1998. m. USD 1,045; USD 1,440 combined subscription print & e-mail eds. (effective 2005). adv. **Document type:** *Newsletter, Trade.* **Description:** Covers all facets of the convergence of computers, consumer electronics, communications, cable TV, and content providers in Europe. Features exclusive growth projections, economic modeling, and analysis of new technologies.
Formerly: V O D Investor (1521-8694)
Related titles: E-mail ed.: USD 945 (effective 2005); Fax ed.: USD 945 (effective 2001).
Published by: Kagan Research, LLC, One Lower Ragsdale Dr, Bldg One, Ste 130, Monterey, CA 93940. TEL 831-624-1536, FAX 831-625-3225, info@kagan.com, http://research.kagan.com/keo/subscriptionsDetailPage.aspx?SubscriptionID=27, http://www.kagan.com. Pub. Paul Kagan. adv.: B&W page USD 3,670.

332.6 330.1 USA
V R FORECASTER; Mark Leibovit's annual forecast model. Text in English. 1979. a. USD 1,800 (effective 2003). charts; illus. **Document type:** *Newsletter, Trade.*
Former titles: Volume Reversal Survey Forecaster; Volume Reversal Survey (8755-3406)
Related titles: Fax ed.
—CCC.
Published by: V R Trader.Com, Inc., PO Box 1451, Sedona, AZ 86339. TEL 928-282-1275, FAX 928-282-6364, http://www.vrtrader.com/vr_forecaster/index.asp, http://www.vrsurvey.com. Ed., R&P Mark Leibovit. Circ: 500 (paid).

332.63 690 DEU ISSN 0723-564X
V W D - BAUWIRTSCHAFT. Text in German. d. (5/w.). **Document type:** *Trade.*
Published by: Vereinigte Wirtschaftsdienste GmbH, Niederurseler Allee 8-10, Eschborn, 65760, Germany. TEL 49-6196-4050, FAX 49-6196-405303.

332.63 540 DEU
V W D - CHEMIE: KAUTSCHUK. Text in German. d. (5/w.). **Document type:** *Trade.*
Formerly: V W D - Chemie
Published by: Vereinigte Wirtschaftsdienste GmbH, Niederurseler Allee 8-10, Eschborn, 65760, Germany. TEL 49-6196-4050, FAX 49-6196-405303.

332.63 621.3 DEU ISSN 0722-222X
V W D - ELEKTRO. Text in German. d. (5/w.). **Document type:** *Trade.*
Formerly (until 1981): Elektro (0344-7383)
Published by: Vereinigte Wirtschaftsdienste GmbH, Niederurseler Allee 8-10, Eschborn, 65760, Germany. TEL 49-6196-4050, FAX 49-6196-405303.

332.63 333.79 DEU
V W D - ENERGIE. Text in German. d. (5/w.). **Document type:** *Trade.*
Published by: Vereinigte Wirtschaftsdienste GmbH, Niederurseler Allee 8-10, Eschborn, 65760, Germany. TEL 49-6196-4050, FAX 49-6196-405303.

332.63 382 DEU ISSN 0344-7391
V W D - EUROPA. Text in German. d. (5/w.). **Document type:** *Trade.*
Published by: Vereinigte Wirtschaftsdienste GmbH, Niederurseler Allee 8-10, Eschborn, 65760, Germany. TEL 49-6196-4050, FAX 49-6196-405303.

332.63 DEU ISSN 0723-2993
V W D - FINANZ- UND WIRTSCHAFTSSPIEGEL. Text in German. d. (5/w.). **Document type:** *Trade.*
Formerly: V W D - Finanz
Published by: Vereinigte Wirtschaftsdienste GmbH, Niederurseler Allee 8-10, Eschborn, 65760, Germany. TEL 49-6196-4050, FAX 49-6196-405303.

332.63 663.1 DEU
V W D - GETRAENKE. Text in German. d. (5/w.). **Document type:** *Trade.*
Published by: Vereinigte Wirtschaftsdienste GmbH, Niederurseler Allee 8-10, Eschborn, 65760, Germany. TEL 49-6196-4050, FAX 49-6196-405303.

332.63 633.1 DEU ISSN 0944-5447
V W D - GETREIDE, FUTTERMITTEL, OELE. Text in German. d. (5/w.). **Document type:** *Trade.*
Formerly: V W D - Getreide und Futtermittel (0723-6344)
Published by: Vereinigte Wirtschaftsdienste GmbH, Niederurseler Allee 8-10, Eschborn, 65760, Germany. TEL 49-6196-4050, FAX 49-6196-405303.

332.63 663.94 DEU ISSN 0175-1662
V W D - KAFFEE, KAKAO, TEE, SUESSWAREN. Text in German. d. (5/w.). **Document type:** *Trade.*
Formerly: V W D - Kaffee, Kakao, Tee, Gewuerze
Published by: Vereinigte Wirtschaftsdienste GmbH, Niederurseler Allee 8-10, Eschborn, 65760, Germany. TEL 49-6196-4050, FAX 49-6196-405303.

332.63 677 DEU ISSN 0723-628X
V W D - LANDWIRTSCHAFT UND ERNAEHRUNG. Text in German. 1982. d. (5/w.). **Document type:** *Journal, Trade.*
Formed by the merger of (19??-1982): Kartoffeln (0344-7480); (19??-1982): Milch und Milchprodukte (0720-5368); (19??-1982): Gefluegel und Eier (0720-5376); (19??-1982): Landwirtschaft und Ernaehrung (0023-8120)
Published by: Vereinigte Wirtschaftsdienste GmbH, Niederurseler Allee 8-10, Eschborn, 65760, Germany. TEL 49-6196-4050, FAX 49-6196-405303, feedback@vwd.de, http://www.vwd.de.

332.63 681 DEU
V W D - MASCHINEN. Text in German. d. (5/w.). **Document type:** *Trade.*
Formerly: V W D - Maschinenbau
Published by: Vereinigte Wirtschaftsdienste GmbH, Niederurseler Allee 8-10, Eschborn, 65760, Germany. TEL 49-6196-4050, FAX 49-6196-405303.

332.63 622 DEU ISSN 0723-4937
V W D - MONTAN. Text in German. d. (5/w.). **Document type:** *Newspaper.*
Published by: Vereinigte Wirtschaftsdienste GmbH, Niederurseler Allee 8-10, Eschborn, 65760, Germany. TEL 49-6196-4050, FAX 49-6196-405303. **Subscr. to:** Postfach 6105, Eschborn 65735, Germany.

332.63 669 DEU ISSN 0723-5755
V W D - N E - METALLE. Text in German. d. (5/w.). **Document type:** *Newspaper.*
Published by: Vereinigte Wirtschaftsdienste GmbH, Niederurseler Allee 8-10, Eschborn, 65760, Germany. TEL 49-6196-4050, FAX 49-6196-405303.

332.63 669.142 DEU
V W D - STAHL. Text in German. d. (5/w.). **Document type:** *Trade.*
Published by: Vereinigte Wirtschaftsdienste GmbH, Niederurseler Allee 8-10, Eschborn, 65760, Germany. TEL 49-6196-4050, FAX 49-6196-405303.

332.63 685 DEU ISSN 0944-2839
V W D - TEXTIL, BEKLEIDUNG, LEDER. Text in German. d. (5/w.). **Document type:** *Trade.*
Formed by the 1991 merger of: V W D - Textil (0175-1719); V W D - Haeute und Leder (0722-7957); Which was formerly (until 1982): V W D - Haeute, Leder, Rauchwaren (0344-760X)
Published by: Vereinigte Wirtschaftsdienste GmbH, Niederurseler Allee 8-10, Eschborn, 65760, Germany. TEL 49-6196-4050, FAX 49-6196-405303.

332.63 636 DEU ISSN 0723-8037
V W D - VIEH UND FLEISCH. Text in German. d. (5/w.). **Document type:** *Trade.*
Published by: Vereinigte Wirtschaftsdienste GmbH, Niederurseler Allee 8-10, Eschborn, 65760, Germany. TEL 49-6196-4050, FAX 49-6196-405303.

332.63 664.1 DEU ISSN 0723-6301
V W D - ZUCKER. Text in German. d. (5/w.). **Document type:** *Trade.*
Published by: Vereinigte Wirtschaftsdienste GmbH, Niederurseler Allee 8-10, Eschborn, 65760, Germany. TEL 49-6196-4050, FAX 49-6196-405303.

332.6 PER
VADEMECUM BURSATIL. Text in Spanish. 1979. a.
Related titles: Online - full text ed.: ISSN 1682-4334. 1999.
Published by: Bolsa de Valores de Lima, Miro Quesada 265, Casilla Postal 1538, Lima, 100, Peru. TEL 51-1-4260714, FAX 51-1-4267650, http://www.bvl.com.pe/pubdif/publica_vandemecum.htm. Circ: 1,000. **Co-sponsor:** Banco Continental.

332.6 USA ISSN 0737-0717
HG4501
THE VALUE LINE CONVERTIBLES SURVEY. Text in English. 1970. w. (48/yr.). USD 625. **Document type:** *Newsletter.* **Description:** Contains general articles about convertible securities, lists purchase recommendations, and provides current information about those securities evaluated. Evaluates 585 convertible securities, along with 100 warrants and SCOREs.
Related titles: Online - full text ed.: Electronic Convertible. USD 175.
Published by: Value Line Publishing, Inc., 220 E 42nd St, 6th Fl, New York, NY 10017-5891. TEL 212-907-1500, FAX 212-818-9474. Ed. Anthony Cichocki.

332.6 USA ISSN 1541-3969
VALUE LINE INDUSTRY WATCH; tracking and reporting on timely stocks in timely industries. Text in English. 2002 (Aug.). m.
Published by: Value Line Publishing, Inc., 220 E 42nd St, 6th Fl, New York, NY 10017-5891. TEL 212-907-1500, vlcr@valueline.com, http://www.valueline.com.

332.6 USA ISSN 1537-5951
VALUE LINE INSIGHT. Text in English. 2002 (Jan.). m. USD 298 domestic (effective 2002).
Published by: Value Line Publishing, Inc., 220 E 42nd St, 6th Fl, New York, NY 10017-5891. TEL 212-907-1500, http://www.valueline.com. Ed. Reuben Gregg Brewer.

332.6 USA ISSN 0042-2401
THE VALUE LINE INVESTMENT SURVEY. Text in English. 1931. w. looseleaf. USD 598 (effective 2004). reprints avail. **Document type:** *Newsletter, Trade.* **Description:** Comprehensive reference source, including investment advice, on the 1,700 most widely traded stocks.
Related titles: CD-ROM ed.: USD 595; Diskette ed.; Online - full text ed.: (from EBSCO Publishing).
Indexed: PROMT.
Published by: Value Line Publishing, Inc., 220 E 42nd St, 6th Fl, New York, NY 10017-5891. TEL 212-907-1500, FAX 212-818-9474, http://www.ec-server.valueline.com/products/print1.html, http://www.valueline.com.

332.6327 USA ISSN 1070-4337
HG4530
THE VALUE LINE MUTUAL FUND SURVEY. Text in English. 1993. every 3 wks. USD 345 (effective 2004). **Document type:** *Newsletter, Trade.* **Description:** Provides current Value Line rankings and performance figures on more than 2,000 funds, articles on mutual funds, financial planning, and investment strategies.
Published by: Value Line Publishing, Inc., 220 E 42nd St, 6th Fl, New York, NY 10017-5891. TEL 212-907-1500, vlcr@valueline.com, http://www.ec-server.valueline.com/products/print3.html, http://www.valueline.com.

332.6 USA ISSN 0361-2589
HG4050
VALUE LINE O-T-C SPECIAL SITUATIONS SERVICE. Text in English. 1951. bi-m. USD 429. **Document type:** *Newsletter.* **Description:** Focuses on fast-growing, smaller companies.
Published by: Value Line Publishing, Inc., 220 E 42nd St, 6th Fl, New York, NY 10017-5891. TEL 212-907-1500, FAX 212-818-9747. Ed. Peter Shraga.

332.6 USA ISSN 0737-0709
HG4501
VALUE LINE OPTIONS; the all in one service for listed options. Text in English. 1970. 4/m. USD 445. charts; stat. back issues avail. **Document type:** *Newsletter.* **Description:** Divided in two parts: Part A - The Strategist contains feature articles, news briefs, option statistics and specific options recommendations; Part B - The Evaluation Section lists "Value Line's" evaluation and rank for future performance on over 15,000 options, along with deltas, volatilities, theoretical prices, and tickers.
Former titles: Value Line Option and Convertible Survey (0146-7581); Value Line Convertible Survey (0042-2398); Formed by the merger of: Value Line Convertible Bond Service & Value Line Convertible Preferred Stock Service; Formerly: Value Line Merger Evaluation Service; Value Line Warrant Service.
Published by: Value Line Publishing, Inc., 220 E 42nd St, 6th Fl, New York, NY 10017-5891. TEL 212-907-1500, FAX 212-818-9747, vloptions@valueline.com. Ed. Jean Bernhard Butler.

332.6 USA ISSN 1541-5694
HC110.H53
VENTURE (CAMBRIDGE). Text in English. 2002. q. USD 20 (effective 2002). adv.
Related titles: Online - full text ed.
Published by: Harvard University, Technology and Entrepreneurship Center, Pierce Hall 410, 29 Oxford St., Cambridge, MA 02138. TEL 617-496-3423, FAX 617-496-5264, tech@deas.harvard.edu, http://www.venturemag.org, http://deas.harvard.edu/tech/. Ed. David A. Vivero.

332.6 USA ISSN 1535-0711
VENTURE (HONOLULU); the magazine of risk and reward. Text in English. 2001 (Jun.). bi-m. USD 36; USD 6 per issue (effective 2003). adv. **Document type:** *Magazine, Trade.*
Published by: Media Venture Partners, Inc., 1000 Bishop St. Ste. 605, Honolulu, HI 96813. TEL 808-548-0400, FAX 808-548-0500, http://www.venturepublication.com, http://www.mvphonolulu.com. Ed. Jeanette Tscha. Pub. Kevin L. Halloran. adv.: color page USD 3,600; trim 9 x 10.8125. Circ: 25,000.

332.62 USA ISSN 1550-3224
THE VENTURE CAPITAL ANALYST: HEALTH CARE EDITION. Text in English. 1997. m. USD 995 (effective 2004). adv. charts; stat. back issues avail. **Document type:** *Newsletter.* **Description:** Explores the business of private equity investment in the trillion dollar health care market. For venture capitalists, private investors, investment banks, health care companies and entrepreneurs.
Formerly (until 2002): Venture Capital and Health Care (1092-9711)
—CCC.
Published by: Alternative Investor, 170 Linden St, 2nd Fl, Wellesley, MA 02482. TEL 781-304-1400, FAX 781-304-1440, info@assetnews.com, http://www.assetnews.com. Ed., Pub. David Toll. R&P, Adv. contact Doreen C Purvis. B&W page USD 1,000, color page USD 1,200; trim 11 x 8.5. Circ: 612 (paid).

332.645 GBR
VENTURE CAPITAL & PRIVATE EQUITY YEARBOOK (YEARS). Text in English. a., latest 2001. GBP 95, USD 170 (effective 2001). **Description:** Covers the rapid development of the venture capital and private equity industry and offers insight into buying and investing in new technology.
Published by: Euromoney Institutional Investor Plc., Nestor House, Playhouse Yard, London, EC4V 5EX, United Kingdom. TEL 44-20-7779-8673, FAX 44-20-7779-8541, http://www.euromoneyplc.com. **Dist. by:** Portica, Portica House, Addison Road, Sudbury, Suffolk CO10 2YW, United Kingdom. TEL 44-1787-319-933, FAX 44-870-242-9430.

332.6 USA ISSN 0883-2773
HG4961
VENTURE CAPITAL JOURNAL; the only financial analyst of small business investment companies and venture capital companies. Text in English. 1961. m. USD 1,625 in US & Canada; USD 1,680 elsewhere (effective 2005). adv. charts; stat. s-a. index. **Document type:** *Journal, Trade.* **Description:** Features stories on new capital sources, fund formations, key executive moves, recent deals, and profiles of leading firms.
Former titles: Venture Capital; S B I C - Venture Capital (0036-1046); S B I C-Venture Capital Service
Related titles: Online - full text ed.: (from bigchalk, EBSCO Publishing, Florida Center for Library Automation, Gale Group, LexisNexis, O C L C Online Computer Library Center, Inc., ProQuest Information & Learning); ♦ Supplement(s): Venture Capital Yearbook. ISSN 8756-8896.
Indexed: ABIn, B&I, LRI.
—IE. CCC.
Published by: Thomson Financial Media, 195 Broadway, 10th Fl, New York, NY 10007. lawrence.aragon@tfn.com, http://www.venturecapitaljournal.net. Ed. Lawrence Aragon. Pub. Adam Reinebach.

VENTURE CAPITAL REPORT. see *BUSINESS AND ECONOMICS—Small Business*

332.62 USA
VENTURE CAPITAL: WHERE TO FIND IT. Text in English. a. USD 25 (effective 1999). **Document type:** *Directory.*
Former titles: N A S B I C Membership Directory (1076-2159); National Association of Small Business Investment Companies. Membership Directory (0277-5018)
Published by: National Association of Small Business Investment Companies, 666 11th St, N W, Ste 750, Washington, DC 20001. nasbic@asbic.org, http://www.nasbic.org.

332.6 USA ISSN 8756-8896
VENTURE CAPITAL YEARBOOK. Text in English. 1983. a. USD 285 (effective 1998). **Document type:** *Directory.* **Description:** Annual overview of the year's most important venture activity, including venture capital industry resources, venture-backed initial public offerings, and capital commitments.
Related titles: ♦ Supplement to: Venture Capital Journal. ISSN 0883-2773.
—CCC.
Published by: Securities Data Publishing (Subsidiary of: Thomson Financial / I M G Media), 195 Broadway, New York, NY 10007. TEL 212-765-5311, FAX 212-765-6123.

332 USA ISSN 1540-1111
VENTURE EQUITY LATIN AMERICA. Text in English. 2002. s-m. USD 919 (effective 2005). adv. **Document type:** *Newsletter, Trade.* **Description:** Provides timely, accurate and comprehensive information on the Latin American private equity and venture capital industry.
Published by: WorldTrade Executive, Inc., 2250 Main St, Ste 100, PO Box 761, Concord, MA 01742. TEL 978-287-0301, FAX 978-287-0302, smahapatra@wtexec.com, info@wtexec.com, http://www.wtexecutive.com/cms/content.jsp?id=com.tms.cms.section.Section_1002, http://www.wtexec.com. Ed. Judy S Kuan. Pub. Gary A Brown. Adv. contact Jay Stanley.

332.6 USA
VENTURE REPORTER. Text in English. 2001. irreg. (15-20 E-mails daily). free (effective 2001). **Document type:** *Magazine, Trade.* **Description:** Provides instant alerts to the latest information major business deals, transactions and other investment related information. Daily edition provides a summary and wrap-up of the day's activity. Weekly edition provides a week-end summary of 75-125 deals of the week.
Media: E-mail. **Related titles:** Alternate Frequency ed(s).: w.
Published by: Rising Tide Studios, 307 W 36th St, 10th Fl, New York, NY 10018-6403. TEL 646-473-2222, FAX 646-473-2223, editor@venturereporter.net, http://www.venturereporter.net/. Ed. Jason McCabe Calacanis.

332.6 USA
VENTUREFINANCE. Text in English. m. USD 795; USD 100 newsstand/cover (effective 2002). **Document type:** *Trade.*
Media: Online - full content.
Published by: Dow Jones Newsletters (Subsidiary of: Dow Jones Newswires), 1155 Av of the Americas, New York, NY 10036. TEL 212-597-5716, VentureFinance@technologicp.com, http://venturefinance.venturewire.com/.

332.6 USA ISSN 1046-5340
HG4509
VICKERS DIRECTORY OF INSTITUTIONAL INVESTORS. Text in English. 1982. s-a. USD 195 (effective 1999). **Document type:** *Directory.*
Formerly: Directory of Institutional Investors (8755-0318)
Published by: Vickers Stock Research Corp., 98 Pratt Oval., Glen Cove, NY 11542-1413. TEL 800-645-5043, FAX 516-423-7715.

332 USA ISSN 1044-6850
HG4915
VICKERS STOCK TRADERS GUIDE. Text in English. 1982. q. USD 935 (effective 1999). **Document type:** *Trade.*
Formerly (until 1989): Stock Traders Guide (0882-6226)
Published by: Vickers Stock Research Corp., 98 Pratt Oval., Glen Cove, NY 11542-1413. TEL 800-645-5043, FAX 516-423-7715.

VIDEO INVESTOR. see *COMMUNICATIONS—Video*

VIETNAM BUSINESS. see *BUSINESS AND ECONOMICS—International Commerce*

332 USA ISSN 1523-5513
K26
➤ **VILLANOVA JOURNAL OF LAW AND INVESTMENT MANAGEMENT.** Text in English. 1999. a., latest vol.3, no.1, 2002. **Document type:** *Journal, Academic/Scholarly.*
Indexed: CLI, ILP, LRI.
Published by: Villanova University Law School, 299 N Spring Mill Rd, Villanova, PA 19085. astalone@law.villanova.edu, http://vls.law.villanova.edu/academics/vjlim. Ed. Mark Sargent.

➤ **VIRGINIA AGRICULTURE COMMODITY NEWSLETTER.** see *AGRICULTURE*

➤ **VORTEIL.** see *BUSINESS AND ECONOMICS—Banking And Finance*

➤ **VORTEILHAFTE GELDANLAGEN**; Handbuch fuer Anleger, Berater und Vermittler. see *BUSINESS AND ECONOMICS—Banking And Finance*

332.63 USA
THE WALKER MARKET LETTER. Text in English. 1996. 2/m. **Document type:** *Bulletin, Trade.* **Description:** Focuses on the stock market and investing in mutual funds.
Media: Online - full text.
Published by: Walker Market Letter TEL 303-980-1168, jwalker@lowrisk.com, http://www.lowrisk.com. Ed. Jeff Walker.

WALL STREET DIGEST. see *BUSINESS AND ECONOMICS—Banking And Finance*

THE WALL STREET JOURNAL INDEX. see *BUSINESS AND ECONOMICS—Banking And Finance*

332 USA ISSN 0277-4992
WALL STREET LETTER; newsweekly for investment banking and brokerage community. Text in English. 1969. w. (51x/yr). USD 2,665 combined subscription domestic print & online eds.; USD 2,740 combined subscription foreign print & online eds. (effective 2005). adv. reprint service avail. from PQC. **Document type:** *Newsletter, Trade.* **Description:** Coverage includes the big firms as well as a number of smaller regional brokerage, mutual fund companies and firms providing services to the brokerage industry.
Related titles: CD-ROM ed.; Microfiche ed.; Online - full text ed.: (from Factiva, Florida Center for Library Automation, Gale Group, Northern Light Technology, Inc., O C L C Online Computer Library Center, Inc., ProQuest Information & Learning).
Indexed: ATI.
—CCC.
Published by: Institutional Investor News (Subsidiary of: Euromoney Institutional Investor Plc.), 225 Park Ave S, 7th Fl, New York, NY 10003-1605. TEL 212-224-3800, FAX 212-224-3491, info@iiplatinum.com, http://www.wallstreetletter.com/, http://www.iinews.com. Pub. Nanzeen Kanga TEL 212-224-3005. **Subscr. to:** New Orders, PO Box 5063, Brentwood, TN 37024. TEL 615-377-3322, 800-945-2034, 800-715-9197, FAX 615-337-0525, vlockridge@sunbeltfs.com.

332.6 USA
WALL STREET RESEARCH MAGAZINE. Text in English. 2001 (Jun.). m. **Document type:** *Trade.* **Description:** Provides news & information for professional investors.
Published by: Banta Publications Group, 2215 York Rd., Ste. 400, Oak Brook, IL 60523-2378. http://www.wsrmag.com/, http://www.banta.com/.

332.6 USA
WALL STREET RESEARCH REPORTS ✶ . Text in English. irreg.
Published by: Frost & Sullivan, 7550 IH 10 W., Ste 400, San Antonio, TX 78229-5811. TEL 212-233-1080.

332 330 USA ISSN 0043-0102
HG4501
WALL STREET TRANSCRIPT; a professional publication for the business and financial community. Text in English. 1963. w. (Mon.). USD 2,290 (effective 2005). adv. **Document type:** *Newspaper, Trade.* **Description:** Aims to provide insight into companies and markets. Contains interviews with financial market leaders, including analysts, money managers and CEO's.
Related titles: Online - full text ed.: (from EBSCO Publishing, Gale Group, Swets Information Services).
Indexed: PROMT, T&II.
—CCC.
Published by: Wall Street Transcript Corp., 67 Wall St., New York, NY 10005. TEL 212-952-7400, FAX 212-668-9842, transcript@twst.com, http://www.twst.com. Ed. Paul Smith. Pub. Andrew Pickup. Circ: 8,000 (paid).

332.6 333.91 USA ISSN 1049-443X
WATER INVESTMENT NEWSLETTER. Text in English. 1987. m. looseleaf. USD 59 (effective 2005). back issues avail. **Document type:** *Newsletter.* **Description:** Covers water stocks and investments.
Published by: U.S. Water News, Inc., 230 Main St, Halstead, KS 67056. TEL 316-835-2222, FAX 316-835-2223, inquiries@uswaternews.com, http://www.uswaternews.com. Pub. Thomas C Bell.

WATERS. see *BUSINESS AND ECONOMICS—Banking And Finance—Computer Applications*

332.678 GBR
THE WEALTH CONNECTION. Text in English. s-a. GBP 19.95 per issue; free to qualified personnel (effective 2005). adv. **Document type:** *Magazine, Consumer.* **Description:** Offers a comprehensive to the risks and rewards of managing a substantial personal fortune, complimented by a connisseur's passion for the very best that life has to offer. Encompasses all aspects of luxurious living, from charitable giving, property and personal finance to major purchase decisions and an appreciation of the finer things in life.
Published by: S P G Media Ltd. (Subsidiary of: Sterling Publishing Group Plc.), Brunel House, 55-57 North Wharf Rd, London, W2 1LA, United Kingdom. TEL 44-20-79159600, FAX 44-20-77242089, info@sterlingpublications.com, http://www.wealthcollection.com/, http://www.spgmedia.com/. Ed. Geraldine Lip TEL 44-20-79159695. Pub. Mr. Sam Raingill TEL 44-20-79159729. Adv. contact Mr. Patrick Cadore TEL 44-20-79159908. B&W page GBP 5,800.

332.6 USA
WEEKLY ANALYSIS FOR INVESTORS. Text in English. w. back issues avail. **Document type:** *Newsletter.* **Description:** Presents suggestions on stocks and mutual fund investments.
Media: Online - full text.
Address: http://members.aol.com/LXiSebring/select.htm. Ed. David L Debertin.

332.6 GBR
WEEKLY CAPITAL EVENTS DIARY. (Consists of 3 sections: Forthcoming Events Diary, Forward Planning Diary, Capital Events Diary) Text in English. w. GBP 2,070. **Document type:** *Trade.* **Description:** Monitors capital events on all securities quoted on the London and Republic of Ireland Stock Exchanges.
Published by: Financial Times Information Ltd., Fitzroy House, 13-17 Epworth St, London, EC2A 4DL, United Kingdom. TEL 44-20-7825-8000, FAX 44-20-7608-2032, eic@ft.com, http://www.ft.com.

WEEKLY COTTON TRADE REPORT. see *AGRICULTURE—Agricultural Economics*

332.64 USA
WEEKLY ECONOMIC UPDATE. Text in English. w. **Description:** Contains timely investment information.
Media: Online - full text.
Published by: Green Mountain Asset Management Corp., 139 Bank St., Bulrington, VT 05401. TEL 802-658-7806, FAX 802-658-9409, bobbose@stockresearch.com, http://www.stockresearch.com/weekecon.html. Ed. Bob Bose.

332.6 USA
WEEKLY INSIDER REPORT. Text in English. 1971. w. USD 137 (effective 1999). bk.rev. **Description:** Contains all open market trades of corporate insiders, rates all stocks, commentary suggested portfolio, indicative ratios.

Published by: (Argus Research Group), Vickers Stock Research Corp., 98 Pratt Oval., Glen Cove, NY 11542-1413. TEL 800-645-5043, FAX 516-423-7715. Ed. Edwin A Buck Jr. Circ: 2,000.

332.6 USA
WEEKLY MARKET UPDATE. Text in English. w. **Document type:** *Journal, Trade.* **Description:** Provides the latest activity in the market, including updates on leading market indicators such as interest rates, equity indices, currency exchange rates, and swap spreads. Also lists the latest IPO, M&A, and bankruptcy information of the week.
Published by: Houlihan, Lokey, Howard & Zukin, 1930 Century Park W, Los Angeles, CA 90067. TEL 800-788-5300, FAX 310-553-2173, mergerstat@hlhz.com, http://www.hlhz.com.

332.6 USA
WEEKLY REVIEW OF THE MARKET. Text in English. w. USD 20; USD 55 foreign. **Description:** Synopsis of market activity in each commodity trade on the Coffee, Sugar & Cocoa Exchange.
Published by: Coffee, Sugar & Cocoa Exchange, Inc., Four World Trade Center, New York, NY 10048. TEL 212-938-2800, FAX 212-524-9863.

B

332.6 CAN ISSN 1196-4685
WEEKLY STOCK CHARTS - CANADIAN INDUSTRIAL COMPANIES. Text in English. 1965. m. CND 299.17 (effective 2000 - 2001). charts. back issues avail. **Document type:** *Bulletin.* **Description:** Charts a two year record of weekly share price and volume for 1800 Canadian industrial companies.
Former titles: Weekly Stock Charts - Canadian and U S Industrial Companies (0830-1972); (until 1985): Weekly Stock Charts - Canadian Industrial Companies (0829-3120); Canadian Weekly Stock Charts: Industrials (0383-2945); Industrials: Four Hundred and Twenty Five Canadian Weekly Stock Charts (0019-8935)
Published by: Independent Survey Co., ChartSmart Software, P O Box 29062, V6J 120, Vancouver, BC, Canada. TEL 604-737-1492, 800-665-3389, FAX 604-737-1475, info@chartsmart.com, bobstran@helix.net, http://www.chartsmart.com. Ed., Pub. Bob Stranks.

332.6 CAN ISSN 0829-3139
WEEKLY STOCK CHARTS - CANADIAN RESOURCE COMPANIES. Text in English. 1965. m. CND 299.17 (effective 2000 & 2001). charts. back issues avail. **Document type:** *Bulletin.* **Description:** Charts a year record of weekly share price and volume for 1800 Canadian resource companies.
Former titles: Canadian Weekly Stock Charts: Mines and Oils (0383-2953); Mines and Oils; Four Hundred and Fifty Canadian Weekly Stock Charts (0026-5039)
Published by: Independent Survey Co., ChartSmart Software, P O Box 29062, V6J 120, Vancouver, BC, Canada. TEL 604-737-1492, 800-665-3389, FAX 604-737-1475, info@chartsmart.com, bobstran@helix.net, http://www.chartsmart.com. Ed., Pub. Bob Stranks.

332.6 USA
WEEKLY UPDATE SERVICE✶ . Text in English. w. USD 75. **Document type:** *Trade.* **Description:** Provides commentary and charts on U.S. stock and bond markets, currencies and gold. Fax and e-mail commentaries include a two to three page layout with at least four charts. Special updates are sent when market conditions demand them.
Related titles: E-mail ed.: USD 99; Fax ed.
Published by: International Institute for Economic Research, Inc., 1539 S Orange Ave, Sarasota, FL 34239-2035. TEL 804-694-0415, FAX 804-694-0028. Ed. Martin J Pring.

332.63 USA ISSN 1522-3809
HG4930
WEISS GUIDE TO STOCK MUTUAL FUNDS. Variant title: Guide to Mutual Funds. Text in English. 1999. q. USD 438. Website rev. charts; stat. 577 p./no.; back issues avail. **Document type:** *Directory, Consumer.* **Description:** Analyzes and rates more than 5,000 mutual funds, including balanced and asset allocation funds.
Formerly: Weiss Guide to Mutual Funds
Published by: Weiss Ratings, Inc., 4176 Burns Rd, Palm Beach, FL 33410. TEL 561-627-3300, 800-289-9222, FAX 561-625-6885, wr@weissinc.com, http://www.weissratings.com. Pub. Martin Weiss. R&P Shelley Klovsky.

332.6 USA ISSN 1532-1835
HG4907
WEISS RATINGS' GUIDE TO BROKERAGE FIRMS. Variant title: Guide to Brokerage Firms. Text in English. 1992. q. USD 438 (effective 2001). Website rev. charts; stat. 461 p./no.; **Document type:** *Directory, Consumer.* **Description:** Presents current commission rates, services and the financial strength offered by U.S. brokerage firms and brokers.
Former titles: Weiss Ratings' Brokerage Firm Safety Directory; Weiss Research's Brokerage Firm Safety Directory (1074-2123); Brokerage Firm Safety Directory (1067-8794)
Published by: Weiss Ratings, Inc., 4176 Burns Rd, Palm Beach, FL 33410. TEL 561-627-3300, FAX 561-625-6685, wr@weissinc.com, http://www.weissratings.com. Pub. Martin Weiss. R&P Shelley Klovsky.

332.6 USA ISSN 1544-9327
HG4530
▼ **WEISS RATINGS' GUIDE TO CLOSED-END MUTUAL FUNDS.** Text in English. 2003 (Sum.). q. USD 438 (effective 2003).
Published by: Weiss Ratings, Inc., 4176 Burns Rd, Palm Beach, FL 33410. TEL 561-627-3300, FAX 561-625-6685, http://www.weissratings.com.

332.6 CHE
WELT KONJUNKTUR. Text in German. 24/yr.
Address: Postfach, Ebmatingen, 8123, Switzerland. TEL 01-9803622. Ed. Ueli Vonau. Circ: 4,000.

332.6 DEU ISSN 0049-7169
WERTPAPIER; das Boersen-Journal. Text in German. 1953. fortn. looseleaf. EUR 72; EUR 3.50 newsstand/cover (effective 2005). adv. charts. reprints avail. **Document type:** *Magazine, Trade.* **Description:** Provides timely information and analysis of stock markets and other investment opportunities.
Published by: Deutsche Schutzvereinigung fuer Wertpapierbesitz e.V., Postfach 350163, Duesseldorf, 40443, Germany. TEL 49-211-669701, FAX 49-211-669750, redaktion@wertpapier.de, http://www.das-wertpapier.de. Ed. Christian Faelschle. Adv. contact Arne Sill. page EUR 5,100. Circ: 18,783 (paid and controlled).

332.6 CAN
WESTCOAST SPECULATOR. Text in English. w.
Published by: Gert Investment Corporation, P O Box 23, Kelowna, BC V1Y 7N3, Canada. TEL 604-763-8773. Ed. George Simone.

332.6 AUS ISSN 1037-4590
WESTERN AUSTRALIAN PROSPECT. Text in English. 1978. q. AUD 12. adv. **Document type:** *Government.* **Description:** Showcases the diverse range of economic activity and investment opportunities in Western Australia - from a huge resources mining sector to manufacturing.
Former titles: Prospect (Perth) (1033-5196); (until 1988): Prospect Western Australia (1033-5188)
Indexed: AESIS, BrCerAb, C&ISA, CerAb, CivEngAb, CorrAb, E&CAJ, EMA, IAA, M&TEA, MBF, METADEX, S&F, SolStAb, WAA.
—Linda Hall.
Published by: Department of Resources Development, S.G.I.O. Atrium, 168 St George' s Terr, Perth, W.A. 6000, Australia. TEL 61-09-3275555, FAX 61-09-3275500, enquiries@drd.wa.gov.au, http://www.drd.wa.gov.au. Ed. Matthew Coomber. Adv. contact Alizabeth Petrich. B&W page AUD 1,375, color page AUD 1,955. Circ: 8,500.

THE WESTERN INVESTOR; commercial real estate & business opportunities in Western Canada. see *REAL ESTATE*

332.6 USA ISSN 0300-662X
WESTERN MINING NEWS✶ . Text in English. 1968. bi-w. USD 55. charts; stat. **Description:** Provides quotes on North American penny mining stocks.
Published by: Western Mining News, Inc., 2716 N Center Rd, Spokane, WA 99212-2226. TEL 509-922-4184. Ed. Roger Rutcosky. Circ: 9,000.

WESTERN REAL ESTATE NEWS. see *REAL ESTATE*

332.6 GBR ISSN 0263-953X
WHAT INVESTMENT. Text in English. 1982. m. GBP 26 in United Kingdom; GBP 37 in Europe; GBP 45 rest of world; GBP 2.75 newsstand/cover (effective 2001). adv. bk.rev. **Document type:** *Magazine, Consumer.*
Related titles: Online - full text ed.: (from Gale Group).
—CCC.
Published by: Charterhouse Communications Group Ltd., Arnold House, 36-41 Holywell Ln, London, EC2A 3ET, United Kingdom. TEL 44-20-7827-5454, FAX 44-20-7827-0567, info@themoneypages.com, http://www.charterhouse-communications.co.uk. Ed. Iain Yule. Pub. Geoff Gamble. Adv. contact Adam Braggs. Circ: 39,000. **Dist. by:** Seymour Distribution Ltd, 86 Newman St, London W1T 3EX, United Kingdom. TEL 44-20-73968000, FAX 44-20-73968002.

332.6 USA
WHISPER ON WALL STREET. Text in English. 1982. irreg. (5-8/yr.). USD 128 (effective 2000). **Document type:** *Newsletter.* **Description:** Analysis of stock market, stock selection; focuses on smaller issues.
Published by: G.H. Brooks Associates, Inc., 7925 Looking Glass Ct., Raleigh, NC 27612-7346. TEL 203-656-0261. Ed. George H Brooks.

332.6 USA
WHITE'S TAX EXEMPT BOND MARKET RATINGS✶ . Text in English. 1954. a. USD 300.
Published by: Delta Press, 2219, 41st Ave., #3, Long Island City, NY 11101-4803. TEL 212-285-6400. Ed. Wilson White Jr.

WHO'S BUYING WHOM. see *PUBLISHING AND BOOK TRADE*

332.6 AUT ISSN 0003-2166
WIENER WARENBOERSE. AMTLICHES KURSBLATT. HOLZ. Text in German. 1949. m. looseleaf. EUR 7.50 (effective 2000). **Document type:** *Bulletin.*
Published by: Wiener Boerse AG, Strauchgasse 1-3, Vienna, W 1014, Austria. TEL 43-1-53165257, FAX 43-1-53165270, info@wbag.at, http://www.wbag.at. R&P Margit Scozzari.

332.6 AUT ISSN 0003-2174
WIENER WARENBOERSE. AMTLICHES KURSBLATT. ROHHAEUTE UND FELLE, LEDER TREIBRIEMEN UND TECHNISCHE LEDERARTIKEL. Text in German. 1951. m. EUR 15 (effective 2000). **Document type:** *Bulletin.*
Published by: Wiener Boerse AG, Strauchgasse 1-3, Vienna, W 1014, Austria. TEL 43-1-53165257, FAX 43-1-53165270, info@wbag.at, http://www.wbag.at. R&P Margit Scozzari.

WIRELESS TELECOM INVESTOR. see *COMMUNICATIONS—Telephone And Telegraph*

332.6 USA
WISCONSIN. DEPARTMENT OF FINANCIAL INSTITUTIONS. ANNUAL REPORT. Text in English. 1924. a. free. **Description:** Includes information regarding the Divisions of Corporate and Consumer Services, Banking, Savings Institutions, Securities, and the Office of Credit Unions.
Former titles (until 1997): Wisconsin. Commissioner of Securities. Biennial Report; Wisconsin. Commisioner of Securities. Annual Report (0084-0548)
Published by: Department of Financial Institutions, 345 W Washington Ave, Madison, WI 53703. TEL 608-266-3431, http://www.wdfi.org. Circ: 2,000.

332.6 USA
WISCONSIN. DEPARTMENT OF FINANCIAL INSTITUTIONS. DIVISION OF SECURITIES. SECURITIES BULLETIN. Text in English. 1939. q. USD 15 (effective 1999). index. **Document type:** *Bulletin, Government.*
Formerly: Wisconsin Securities Bulletin
Published by: Department of Financial Institutions, Division of Securities, PO Box 1768, Madison, WI 53701. TEL 608-266-3431, http://www.wdfi.org. Circ: 4,250.

332.6 USA
WORKING MONEY (ONLINE). Text in English. irreg. USD 24.99 foreign (effective 2004). adv. back issues avail. **Document type:** *Magazine, Consumer.* **Description:** Covers investment issues of interest to people with discretionary funds.
Formerly (until Aug. 2001): Working Money (Print)
Media: Online - full content. **Related titles:** ♦ Supplement to: Technical Analysis of Stocks & Commodities. ISSN 0738-3355.
Published by: Technical Analysis, Inc., 4757 California Ave S W, Seattle, WA 98116-4499. TEL 206-938-0570, 800-832-4642, FAX 206-938-1307, mail@Traders.com, http://www.working-money.com, http://www.Traders.com. Ed. Jayanthi Gopalakrishnan. Pub. Jack K Hutson. R&P Karen E Wasserman. Adv. contact Ed Schramm. B&W page USD 7,447, color page USD 8,192.

332.6 USA
WORLD COMMODITY PERSPECTIVE. Text in English. 1983. m. USD 225; USD 255 foreign (effective 1999). **Document type:** *Newsletter.* **Description:** Designed for professionals and institutions. Analyzes agricultural and industrial commodities, using the wave principle, Fibonacci calculations and supporting technical methods.
Former titles (until 1996): Elliott Wave Currency and Commodity Forecast; Elliott Wave Commodity Forecast; Elliott Wave Commodity Letter
Published by: Elliott Wave International, PO Box 1618, Gainesville, GA 30503. TEL 770-536-0309. Ed. Jim Martens.

WORLD FINE ART. see *ART*

332.6 USA
WORLD INVESTMENT PROSPECTS. Text in English. a. USD 595 (effective 2003). **Document type:** *Trade.*
Published by: Economist Intelligence Unit, 111 W 57th St, New York, NY 10019. http://store.eiu.com/index.asp?layout=product_home_page&product_id=460000246&country_id=&ref=product_detail_list_by_title_home_title, http://www.eiu.com.

332.6 CHE ISSN 1020-2218
WORLD INVESTMENT REPORT. Text in English. 1991. a. USD 45 (effective 2001). **Document type:** *Monographic series, Trade.*
Indexed: ATI, IIS.
—BLDSC (9356.071487).
Published by: (Division on Investment, Technology and Enterprise Development USA), United Nations Conference on Trade and Development, Palais des Nations, 8-14 Av de la Paix, Geneva 10, 1211, Switzerland. TEL 41-22-9175809, FAX 41-22-9170051, info@unctad.org, http://www.unctad.org/en/pub/. Ed., R&P Karl P Sauvant. Circ: 15,475. **Subscr. to:** UN Publications, Distribution and Sales Section, Palais des Nations, Geneva 10 1211, Switzerland. TEL 41-22-907-2612, unpubli@unog.ch.

332.6 USA ISSN 1080-9201

WORLD INVESTOR. Text in English. 1987. m. USD 94. adv. **Document type:** *Newsletter.* **Description:** Includes commentary on US and foreign financial markets, outlook, and specific recommendations for two model portfolios: the income, and the long-term growth.
Former titles: Czeschin's World Investor; (until 1994): Czescin's Mutual Fund Outlook and Recommendations
Published by: Agora, Inc., 105 W Monument St, Baltimore, MD 21201. TEL 410-223-2611, 800-851-7100, FAX 410-223-2696. Ed. Eric Roseman. Pub. Ruth Lyons. Adv. contact Ruth Zeller. Circ: 11,500.

WORLD RISK ANALYSIS REPORTS. see *BUSINESS AND ECONOMICS—International Commerce*

332.63 346 GBR ISSN 1357-0889
K1114.A13

WORLD SECURITIES LAW REPORT. Text in English. 1995. m. EUR 1,275 in the eurozone; USD 1,295 in US & Canada; GBP 795 elsewhere (effective 2005). **Document type:** *Newsletter, Trade.* **Description:** Comprehensive coverage of the international regulation of securities. Provides news from around the world on moves made by national stock exchanges; analysis of issues such as the regulation of derivatives trading, and full-text of important documents.
Related titles: Online - full text ed.: (from The Bureau of National Affairs, Inc.).
—CCC.
Published by: B N A International Inc. (Subsidiary of: The Bureau of National Affairs, Inc.), 29th Fl, Millbank Tower, 21-24 Millbank, London, SW1P 4QP, United Kingdom. TEL 44-20-75594800, FAX 44-20-75594848, bnai@bna.com, http://www.bnai.com/templates/products.aspx?cat=10&obj=150&country=1. Ed. Basco Eszeki.

332.64 USA ISSN 1087-500X
HG4551

WORLD STOCK EXCHANGE FACT BOOK. Text in English. 1995. a. USD 595 (effective 2004).
Published by: Meridian Securities Markets, 2220 All Saints Ln., Plano, TX 75025-5534. info@meridiansecurities.com, http://www.meridiansecurities.com.

338.91 USA

WORLD STOCK MARKET ROUNDUP. Text in English. m. charts; stat. **Document type:** *Trade.*
Published by: Salomon Brothers, Inc., Marketing Department, 7 World Trade Center, New York, NY 10048. TEL 212-783-7000.

332.6 USA ISSN 1081-2539
HG4907

WORLD'S BEST MONEY MANAGERS. Text in English. 1991. q. USD 245 (effective 1999). **Document type:** *Trade.* **Description:** Ranks investment managers by performance results in each of 200 investment categories.
Formerly (until 1993): America's Best Money Managers (1061-7051)
Related titles: Online - full text ed.
Published by: Nelson Information, 195 Broadway, New York, NY 10007-3100. TEL 914-937-8400, 800-333-6357, FAX 914-937-8590, info@nelnet.com, jorrico@nelnet.com, http://www.nelnet.com. Ed. Joe Matera. Pub. J T Orrico.

332.645 GBR ISSN 1356-8930

THE WORLDWIDE DIRECTORY OF SECURITIES LENDING AND REPO (YEAR). Text in English. 1994. a., latest 2000/2001. GBP 195 per vol. in United Kingdom; USD 290 per vol. elsewhere (effective 2001).
Published by: Euromoney Institutional Investor Plc., Nestor House, Playhouse Yard, London, EC4V 5EX, United Kingdom. TEL 44-20-7779-8673, FAX 44-20-7779-8541, meuer@euromoneyplc.com, http://www.euromoneyplc.com. Ed. Margaret A Elliott. Adv. contact Catherine Nicholson. **Dist. in US by:** American Educational Systems, PO Box 246, New York, NY 10024-0246. TEL 800-431-1579, aesbooks@aol.com.

332.6 USA

YAMAMOTO FORECAST. Text in English. 1983. m. USD 350 (effective 2005). adv. **Document type:** *Newsletter, Trade.* **Description:** Analyzes and reports on undervalued stocks, selling at bargain prices and ready to emerge.
Address: PO Box 573, Kahului, HI 96733. TEL 808-877-2690. Ed., Pub. Irwin T Yamamoto.

332.6 LBN ISSN 0075-8361

YEAR-BOOK OF THE LEBANESE JOINT-STOCK COMPANIES/ANNUAIRE DES SOCIETES LIBANAISES PAR ACTION. Text in French. 1964. biennial. USD 45. adv. **Document type:** *Trade.*
Published by: Middle East Commercial Information Center, P O Box 6466, Beirut, Lebanon. Ed. Charles G Gedeon. Circ: 2,000. **Dist. by:** Bernan Associates, Bernan, 4611-F Assembly Dr., Lanham, MD 20706-4391.

332.6 LBN

YEAR-BOOK OF THE LEBANESE LIMITED LIABILITY COMPANIES/ANNUAIRE DES SOCIETES LIBANAISES A RESPONSABILITE LIMITEE. Text in French. 1973. a. USD 45. adv. index.
Published by: Middle East Commercial Information Center, P O Box 6466, Beirut, Lebanon. Ed. Charles C Gadeon. Circ: 2,000. **Dist. by:** Bernan Associates, Bernan, 4611-F Assembly Dr., Lanham, MD 20706-4391.

332.6 382 CHN

YINJIN YU ZIXUN/IMPORTING AND CONSULTING. Text in Chinese. q. CNY 4. **Description:** Provides consulting services to such issues as technology importing, financial loaning and international cooperation in technology and economics.
Published by: Fujian Sheng Keji Zixun Zhongxin/Fujian Science and Technology Consultation Center, Gaoqiao Dasha, 7th Fl, Wuyi Zhonglu, Fuzhou, Fujian 350005, China. TEL 537795. Ed. Fang Yue. **Dist. overseas by:** Jiangsu Publications Import & Export Corp., 56 Gao Yun Ling, Nanjing, Jiangsu, China.

332.6 305.235 USA ISSN 1098-8300

YOUNG MONEY. Text in English. 1998. bi-m. USD 15.95 domestic; USD 25.95 in Canada; USD 35.95 elsewhere (effective 2004). adv. **Document type:** *Magazine, Consumer.* **Description:** Resource for young adults in pursuit of earning, investing, and spending money.
Published by: InCharge Institute of America, Inc., 2101 Park Center Dr Ste 310, Orlando, FL 32835. TEL 407-291-7770, 888-436-8765, http://www.youngmoney.com/home/default.asp, http://www.incharge.org. Ed. Rebecca Stiehl. adv.: color page USD 4,500; trim 7.3 x 10.88. Circ: 50,000 (paid and controlled).

332.6 USA

YOUR FINANCIAL FUTURE; Standard & Poor's guide to retirement planning. Text in English. q. charts; stat. **Document type:** *Newsletter.* **Description:** Enables corporations to help their employees make financially sound investment decisions regarding their retirement plans.
Related titles: Online - full text ed.
Published by: Standard & Poor's (Subsidiary of: McGraw-Hill Companies, Inc.), 55 Water St, New York, NY 10041. TEL 212-208-8000, pneal@penn.com, http://users.penn.com/~pneal/index.html.

332.6 AUS ISSN 0158-2836

YOUR MONEY WEEKLY. Text in English. 1979. w. AUD 387. back issues avail.
Published by: Ian Huntley Pty. Ltd., PO Box 90, Cremorne, NSW 2090, Australia. TEL 61-2-9953-5788, FAX 61-2-9953-2280. Ed. Ian Huntley.

332.6327 USA

YOUR WINDOW INTO THE FUTURE∗. Text in English. 1982. m. USD 99. **Description:** Specializes in accurate prediction of future interest and inflation rates. Analyzes mutual fund bonds, utility and goldfund portfolios.
Published by: Moneypower, 1304 Edgewood Ave, Ann Arbor, MI 48103-5522. TEL 612-537-8096. Ed. James H Moore.

341 DEU ISSN 1611-6925

▼ **Z ST - ZEITSCHRIFT ZUM STIFTUNGSWESEN.** Text in German. 2003. 10/yr. EUR 138; EUR 15 newsstand/cover (effective 2004). **Document type:** *Journal, Academic/Scholarly.*
Published by: B W V - Berliner Wissenschafts Verlag GmbH, Axel-Springer-Str 54b, Berlin, 10117, Germany. TEL 49-30-8417700, FAX 49-30-84177021, bwv@bwv-verlag.de, http://www.bwv-verlag.de/files/katalog/zeitschr/zst/zst.htm. Ed. Ulrike Kilian.

332.6 DEU ISSN 1617-7223

ZEITSCHRIFT FUER BANK- UND KAPITALMARKTRECHT. Abbreviated title: B K R. Text in German. 2001. m. EUR 298 domestic; EUR 318.50 foreign; EUR 28 newsstand/cover (effective 2005). adv. **Document type:** *Journal, Trade.*
Indexed: DIP, IBR, IBZ.
Published by: Verlag C.H. Beck oHG, Wilhelmstr 9, Munich, 80801, Germany. TEL 49-89-38189338, FAX 49-89-38189398, bkr@beck.de, abo.service@beck.de, http://www.bkr.beck.de, http://www.beck.de. adv.: B&W page EUR 1,340, color page EUR 2,330. Circ: 624 (paid and controlled).

332.6 CHN

ZHENGQUAN RIBAO. Abbreviated title: Securities Daily. Text in Chinese. 2000. d. CNY 381 (effective 2004). **Document type:** *Journal, Trade.*
Related titles: Online - full content ed.
Published by: Jingji Ribao Baoye Jituan/Economic Daily Newspaper Group, 36, Guanganmen Nanjie, Yuangongyu B-zuo 20-ceng, Beijing, 100054, China. TEL 86-10-83524728, FAX 86-10-83510038, http://bkdy.ce.cn/fenlei/t20031120_213245.shtml. **Dist. by:** China International Book Trading Corp, 35 Chegongzhuang Xilu, Haidian District, PO Box 399, Beijing 100044, China. TEL 86-10-68412045, FAX 86-10-68412023, cibtc@mail.cibtc.com.cn, http://www.cibtc.com.cn.

332.6327 CHN

ZHONGGUO ZHENGQUAN BAO/CHINA SECURITIES. Text in Chinese. d. (6/week). CNY 396 (effective 2004). **Document type:** *Newspaper, Trade.*
Published by: Xinhua Tongxunshe/Xinhua News Agency, 57 Xuanwumen Xidajie, Beijing, 100803, China. TEL 86-10-63071114, http://www.cs.com.cn, http://www.xinhuanet.com/xhsjj/baokan.htm. **Dist. by:** China International Book Trading Corp, 35 Chegongzhuang Xilu, Haidian District, PO Box 399, Beijing 100044, China. TEL 86-10-68412045, FAX 86-10-68412023, cibtc@mail.cibtc.com.cn, http://www.cibtc.com.cn.

332.6 CHE

ZUERCHER BOERSE. JAHRESBERICHT. Text in German. 1877. a. free. charts; illus.; stat. **Document type:** *Trade.*
Published by: (Zuercher Boerse/Zurich Stock Exchange), Effektenboersenverein Zuerich, Selnaustr 32, Zuerich, 8021, Switzerland. FAX 01-2292233. Circ: 12,000.

332.6 CHE

ZUERCHER EFFEKTENBOERSE. KURSBLATT. Text in German. d. CHF 958.80; CHF 1,063 in Europe. **Document type:** *Newspaper, Consumer.*
Published by: (Zuercher Effektenboerse), Zuerichsee Medien AG, Seestr 86, Staefa, 8712, Switzerland. TEL 01-9285611, FAX 01-9285600.

332.605 DEU ISSN 1435-0920

ZUERICH CLUB COMMUNIQUE. Text in German. 1997. m. back issues avail. **Document type:** *Newsletter, Consumer.*
Published by: F I D Verlag GmbH, Koblenzer Str 99, Bonn, 53177, Germany. TEL 49-228-359585, FAX 49-228-361992. Ed. Friedrich Lange. **Subscr. to:** Leser-Service, Postfach 1327, Neckarsulm 74150, Germany. TEL 49-7132-959205, FAX 49-7132-959209.

332.66 USA

13(F) INSTITUTIONAL PORTFOLIOS∗. Text in English. 1978. q. USD 725.
Formerly: Spectrum 4: 13(F) Institutional Portfolios
Related titles: Magnetic Tape ed.: 1978; Online - full text ed.: 1978.
Published by: C D A Investment Technologies, Inc., 1455 Research Blvd, Rockville, MD 20850-3194. TEL 800-232-6362, FAX 301-590-1329. Circ: 230.

332.66 USA

13(F) INSTITUTIONAL STOCK HOLDINGS∗. Text in English. 1975. q. USD 725.
Former titles: Spectrum 3: 13(F) Institutional Stock Holdings Survey; (until 1978): Spectrum Three: Institutional Stock Holdings Survey
Related titles: Magnetic Tape ed.: 1975; Online - full text ed.: 1975.
Published by: C D A Investment Technologies, Inc., 1455 Research Blvd, Rockville, MD 20850-3194. TEL 800-232-6362, FAX 301-590-1329. Circ: 400.

332.6 USA

20-20 INSIGHT. Text in English. 1995. m. USD 98 (effective 2000). **Description:** Contains articles, commentary and fundamentals related to the stock market.
Related titles: E-mail ed.: USD 55 (effective 2000); Online - full text ed.
Published by: Mercury Capital Management, 510 King St, Ste 315A, Alexandria, VA 22314, VA 22314. TEL 703-683-8488, FAX 703-683-1494, mercury@2020insight.com, http://www.glbgroup.com. Ed. Robert Black.

343 USA ISSN 1080-2142

401(K) ADVISOR; the insider's guide to plan design, administration, and funding. Text in English. 1994. m. USD 313 (effective 2004). **Document type:** *Newsletter, Trade.* **Description:** Reports on every aspect of the ever-changing 401(k) field. Provides the latest developments in plan design, communication, investment and expenses, distribution, and much more.
Related titles: Online - full text ed.: (from EBSCO Publishing, Florida Center for Library Automation, Gale Group, ProQuest Information & Learning).
—CCC.
Published by: Panel Publishers, Inc. (Subsidiary of: Aspen Publishers, Inc.), 1185 Ave of the Americas, 37th Fl, New York, NY 10036. TEL 212-597-0200, 800-638-8437, FAX 212-597-0331, customer.service@aspenpubl.com, http://www.aspenpublishers.com. Ed. Gregory E Matthews. **Dist. by:** Aspen Publishers, Inc., Distribution Center, 7201 McKinney Circle, Frederick, MD 21701. TEL 301-698-7100, FAX 301-417-7550.

332.63 USA ISSN 1098-7169
KF3517.Z9

401(K) ANSWER BOOK. Text in English. 1992. a., latest 2003. USD 195 (effective 2003). **Document type:** *Trade.* **Description:** Provides guidance on implementation, administration, termination, and every other aspect of 401(k) plans.
Indexed: ATI.
Published by: Panel Publishers, Inc. (Subsidiary of: Aspen Publishers, Inc.), 1185 Ave of the Americas, 37th Fl, New York, NY 10036. TEL 212-597-0200, 800-638-8437, FAX 212-597-0331, customer.service@aspenpubl.com, http://www.aspenpublishers.com. **Dist. by:** Aspen Publishers, Inc., Distribution Center, 7201 McKinney Circle, Frederick, MD 21701. TEL 301-698-7100, FAX 301-417-7550.

B

332.63 USA ISSN 1523-1828
KF3517.Z9
401(K) ANSWER BOOK. FORMS & WORKSHEETS. Text in English. 1994. a., latest 2003. USD 225 (effective 2003). **Document type:** *Trade.* **Description:** Provides hundreds of ready-to-use aids, tax forms, and compliance guidelines, along with detailed instructions for their use.
Published by: Panel Publishers, Inc. (Subsidiary of: Aspen Publishers, Inc.), 1185 Ave of the Americas, 37th Fl, New York, NY 10036. TEL 212-597-0200, 800-638-8437, FAX 212-597-0331, customer.service@aspenpubl.com, http://www.aspenpublishers.com. Ed. John Michael Maier. **Dist. by:** Aspen Publishers, Inc., Distribution Center, 7201 McKinney Circle, Frederick, MD 21701. TEL 301-698-7100, FAX 301-417-7550.

BUSINESS AND ECONOMICS—Labor And Industrial Relations

see also LABOR UNIONS

331.1251378 USA
A A E E CONNECTIONS. Text in English. q. USD 10 to non-members (effective 1999). **Document type:** *Newsletter.*
Former titles: A A E E Staffer; A S C U S Staffer
Published by: American Association for Employment in Education, 3040 Riverside Dr., Ste. 125, Columbus, OH 43221-2575. TEL 847-864-1999, FAX 847-864-8303, aaee@nwu.edu, http://www.aaee.org.

A C J S TODAY. see *CRIMINOLOGY AND LAW ENFORCEMENT*

344.01 DEU ISSN 1619-6600
A E - ARBEITSRECHTLICHE ENTSCHEIDUNGEN. Text in German. 1991. q. EUR 88 domestic; EUR 92 foreign; EUR 20 newsstand/cover (effective 2003). adv. **Document type:** *Magazine, Trade.*
Published by: C.F. Mueller Verlag Huethig GmbH & Co. KG, Im Weiher 10, Heidelberg, 69121, Germany. TEL 49-6221-4890, FAX 49-6221-489529, Info@HJR-Verlag.de, http://www.arbeitsrechtliche-entscheidungen.de, http://www.huethig-jehle-rehm.de/content/cfmueller.html. Ed. Hans-Georg Meier TEL 49-30-25459155. adv.: B&W page EUR 515; trim 210 x 297.

A F C O M'S ANNUAL SURVEY OF DATA PROCESSING OPERATIONS SALARIES. see *BUSINESS AND ECONOMICS—Abstracting, Bibliographies, Statistics*

331 DEU
A G P MITTEILUNGEN; Zeitschrift fuer Partnerschaft in der Wirtschaft. Text in German. 1953. q. looseleaf. EUR 4 newsstand/cover (effective 2004). adv. bk.rev. charts; illus.; stat. index, cum.index. **Document type:** *Journal, Trade.*
Former titles (until 1995): Neue Unternehmen (0723-2500); A G P Mitteilungen (0001-1347)
Published by: Arbeitsgemeinschaft Partnerschaft in der Wirtschaft e.V., Landgraf-Karl-Str 2, Kassel, 34131, Germany. TEL 49-561-36044, FAX 49-561-33850, info@agpev.de, http://www.agpev.de/zeitung. Ed. Helge Walz. Adv. contact Michael Lezius. B&W page EUR 480, color page EUR 1,300; trim 186 x 258. Circ: 4,000.

A I D - AUSLAENDER IN DEUTSCHLAND; Informationsdienst zu aktuellen Fragen der Auslaenderarbeit. see *POPULATION STUDIES*

331.2598 RUS
A I F. RABOTA-EKSPRESS. (Argumenty i Fakty) Text in Russian. s-m. **Document type:** *Newspaper, Consumer.*
Related titles: Online - full content ed.
Published by: Redaktsiya Argumenty i Fakty, Myasnitskaya ul 42, Moscow, 101000, Russian Federation. TEL 7-095-9286862, info@aif.ru, http://www.aif.ru/online/rabota/.

331 IND ISSN 0001-1630
A I O E LABOUR NEWS. Text in English. 1966. m. USD 30. adv. bk.rev.
Media: Duplicated (not offset).
Published by: All India Organisation of Employers, Federation House, Tansen Marg, New Delhi, 110 001, India. TEL 11-3319251, FAX 11-3320714, TELEX 031-61768. Ed. R C Pande. Circ: 1,000.

344.01 USA
A K O O EMPLOYMENT LAW INSIDER. Text in English. q. free. **Document type:** *Newsletter.* **Description:** Informs clients, friends and fellow professionals of developments in labor and employment law.
Published by: Anderson Kill Olick LLP, 2100 M St NW, Ste. 650, Washington, DC 20037-1234. TEL 202-962-3999, http://www.andersonkill.com. Eds., Adv. contacts Bennett Pine, Pablo Quinones.

331 DNK ISSN 0909-2242
A - KASSE NYT. Text in Danish. 1985. q. membership. bk.rev. illus. 20 p./no.; back issues avail. **Document type:** *Magazine, Trade.*
Formerly (until 1994): A - Kasse Information (0109-9167)
Published by: Kristelig Arbejdsloeshedskasse, PO Box 239, Randers, 8900, Denmark. FAX 45-86-11-22-01, http://www.krifa.dk. Ed. Poul Langagergaard. Circ: 83,000.

331 DNK ISSN 0903-8876
A M I - RAPPORT. Text in Danish. 1978. irreg. DKK 25. illus.
Formerly (until 1987): Denmark. Arbejdstilsynet. Rapport (0106-6838)
Published by: Arbejdstilsynet, Tryksagsafdelningen, Landskronagade 33-35, Copenhagen Oe, 2100, Denmark. **Co-sponsor:** Arbejdsmiljoeinstituttet/National Institute of Occupational Health.

A Q P REPORT. see *BUSINESS AND ECONOMICS—Management*

331 FRA ISSN 0335-136X
ACTION SOCIALE ET SANTE. Text in French. 1974. bi-m. (plus 2 special nos.). adv.
Published by: Association Paritaire d'Action Sociale du Batiment, 113-115 av. de Choisy, Paris, 75013, France. TEL 40-77-51-23. Ed. J Brillouet.

342 ESP ISSN 1130-9946
ACTUALIDAD ADMINISTRATIVA (EDICION SEMANAL). Text in Spanish. 1985. w.
Related titles: ◆ Alternate Frequency ed(s).: Actualidad Administrativa (Edicion Cuatrimestral). ISSN 1139-8167. q.; ◆ Supplement(s): Actualidad Administrativa. Tribunales Superiores de Justicia. ISSN 1133-2549; ◆ Actualidad Administrativa. Legislacion. ISSN 1137-7631.
Published by: La Ley, Calle Collado Mediano, No. 9, Las Rozas (Madrid), 28230, Spain. TEL 34-902-420010, FAX 34-902-420012, clientes@laley.net, http://www.laley.net/.

344.01 ESP ISSN 1139-8396
ACTUALIDAD LABORAL (EDICION CUATRIMESTRAL). Text in Spanish. 1986. q.
Related titles: ◆ Alternate Frequency ed(s).: Actualidad Laboral (Edicion Semanal). ISSN 0213-7097. w.
Published by: La Ley, Calle Collado Mediano, No. 9, Las Rozas (Madrid), 28230, Spain. TEL 34-902-420010, FAX 34-902-420012, clientes@laley.net, http://www.laley.net/.

344.01 ESP ISSN 0213-7097
ACTUALIDAD LABORAL (EDICION SEMANAL). Text in Spanish. 1984. w.
Related titles: ◆ Alternate Frequency ed(s).: Actualidad Laboral (Edicion Cuatrimestral). ISSN 1139-8396. q.; ◆ Supplement(s): Actualidad Laboral. Legislacion, Convenios Colectivos. ISSN 1133-2603; ◆ Legislacion Laboral y de Seguridad Social. ISSN 1578-1992.
Published by: La Ley, Calle Collado Mediano, No. 9, Las Rozas (Madrid), 28230, Spain. TEL 34-902-420010, FAX 34-902-420012, clientes@laley.net, http://www.laley.net/.

344.01 ESP ISSN 1133-2603
ACTUALIDAD LABORAL. LEGISLACION, CONVENIOS COLECTIVOS. Text in Spanish. 1990. m.
Related titles: ◆ Supplement to: Actualidad Laboral (Edicion Semanal). ISSN 0213-7097.
Published by: La Ley, Calle Collado Mediano, No. 9, Las Rozas (Madrid), 28230, Spain. TEL 34-902-420010, FAX 34-902-420012, clientes@laley.net, http://www.laley.net/.

331.125 JPN
ADAPT JAPAN: EMPLOYMENT OPPORTUNITIES FOR YOU. Text in Japanese. q. **Description:** Ads and articles aimed at those who would like to work in Japan.
Published by: Selnate Publishing Co. Ltd., Fujibo Bldg 2F, 10-28 Fujimi 2-chome, Chiyoda-ku, Tokyo, 102-0071, Japan. TEL 03-2347717, FAX 03-2347716. Ed. Judith Yarrow.

352.63 USA
ADMINISTRATIVE AND OFFICE SUPPORT SURVEY. Text in English. a. USD 450. **Description:** Provides comparative salary information and compensation practices for 86 administrative and office support positions, representing 6,350 employees among 264 businesses throughout PA, NJ, MD, and DE.
Published by: MidAtlantic Employers' Association, PO Box 770, Valley Forge, PA 19482. TEL 215-666-7330, FAX 215-666-7866.

ADMINISTRATIVE ASSISTANTS ASSOCIATION OF THE U.S. HOUSE OF REPRESENTATIVES. NEWSLETTER. see *PUBLIC ADMINISTRATION*

331.281378 USA
ADMINISTRATIVE COMPENSATION SURVEY. Text in English. a. USD 310 to non-members Non-participants; USD 185 to non-members Survey participants; USD 140 to members Non-participants; USD 85 to members Survey participants (effective 2000). **Description:** Offers salary data on 174 positions at 1,433 public and private institutions.
Indexed: SRI.
Published by: College and University Personnel Association, 1233 20th St, N W, Ste 301, Washington, DC 20036. TEL 202-429-0311, FAX 202-429-0149, http://www.cupa.org. Ed. Melissa Edeburn. R&P Audrey Rothstein.

331.1 USA ISSN 0742-6186
HD6958.5
ADVANCES IN INDUSTRIAL AND LABOR RELATIONS. Text in English. 1983. irreg., latest vol.13, 2004. price varies. back issues avail. **Document type:** *Monographic series, Academic/Scholarly.* **Description:** Offers articles that provide longer and deeper analyses of contemporary and historical issues in industrial relations and human resources than appear in typical leading journals.
Related titles: Online - full text ed.: (from ScienceDirect).
—BLDSC (0709.115000), IE, ingenta. **CCC.**
Published by: J A I Press Inc. (Subsidiary of: Elsevier Science & Technology), 360 Park Ave S, New York, NY 10010-1710. TEL 212-989-5800, FAX 212-633-3990, usinfo-f@elsevier.com, http://www.elsevier.com/wps/find/bookdescription.cws_home/BS_AILR/description#description. Ed. D Lewin.

330 USA ISSN 0885-3339
ADVANCES IN THE ECONOMIC ANALYSIS OF PARTICIPATORY AND LABOR-MANAGED FIRMS. Text in English. 1985. irreg., latest vol.8, 2004. price varies. back issues avail. **Document type:** *Monographic series, Academic/Scholarly.*
Related titles: Online - full text ed.: (from ScienceDirect).
—BLDSC (0704.545000). **CCC.**
Published by: J A I Press Inc. (Subsidiary of: Elsevier Science & Technology), 360 Park Ave S, New York, NY 10010-1710. TEL 212-989-5800, FAX 212-633-3990, usinfo-f@elsevier.com, http://www.elsevier.com/wps/find/bookseriesdescription.cws_home/BS_PLMF/description. Ed. D C Jones.

331 ISL ISSN 1029-1253
AF VETTVANGI. Text in Icelandic. 1988. bi-m. free. **Document type:** *Newsletter.* **Description:** Deals with business and economics, labor and industrial relations from the view of Icelandic employers.
Published by: Vinnuveitendasamband Islands/Confederation of Icelandic Employers, Gardastraeti 41, PO Box 520, Reykjavik, 121, Iceland. TEL 354-511-5000, FAX 354-511-5050, skrifstofa@vsi.is, david.stefansson@vsi.is, http://www.vsi.is. Ed. David Stefansson. Circ: 5,400.

331 USA ISSN 0148-8147
AFFIRMATIVE ACTION COMPLIANCE MANUAL FOR FEDERAL CONTRACTORS. Text in English. 1975 (Oct.). m. looseleaf. USD 611 (effective 2005 - 2006). index. back issues avail. **Description:** Contains the official text of the Office of Federal Contract Compliance Programs Manual and reports on related developments.
Related titles: Online - full text ed.: (from The Bureau of National Affairs, Inc.).
—**CCC.**
Published by: The Bureau of National Affairs, Inc., 1231 25th St., NW, Washington, DC 20037. TEL 202-452-4200, FAX 202-822-8092, http://www.bna.com/products/labor/aacm.htm.

AFFIRMATIVE ACTION REGISTER; for effective equal opportuniy recruitment. see *OCCUPATIONS AND CAREERS*

AFFIRMATIVE EMPLOYMENT STATISTICS. see *BUSINESS AND ECONOMICS—Abstracting, Bibliographies, Statistics*

331 NOR ISSN 1502-7112
AGENDA. Text in Norwegian. 1916. bi-m. adv.
Incorporates (1993-2000): Nordsjoen (0805-0090); Former titles (until 1998): Arbeidslederen (0802-7676); (until 1925): Industri-Tidende (0802-7714); Which incorporated (1924-1989): Norsk Faktortidende (0029-1919)
Indexed: ABM.
Published by: Lederne, Drammensveien 40, Postboks 2523, Solli, Oslo, 0202, Norway. TEL 47-22-54-51-50, FAX 47-22-54-65-48. Ed. Gunnar J Larsen.

AGENDA; a journal of policy analysis and reform. see *BUSINESS AND ECONOMICS—Public Finance, Taxation*

331 DEU ISSN 0941-9888
AGPLAN-HANDBUCH ZUR UNTERNEHMENSPLANUNG. GESAMTAUSGABE. Text in German. 1970. irreg., latest 2004. price varies. **Document type:** *Monographic series, Trade.*
Published by: Erich Schmidt Verlag GmbH & Co. (Berlin), Genthiner Str 30G, Berlin, 10785, Germany. TEL 49-30-250085-0, FAX 49-30-25008511, esv@esvmedien.de, http://www.erich-schmidt-verlag.de.

331 DEU ISSN 0941-9837
AGPLAN-HANDBUCH ZUR UNTERNEHMENSPLANUNG. KURZAUSGABE. Text in German. 1985. irreg. price varies. **Document type:** *Monographic series, Trade.*
Published by: Erich Schmidt Verlag GmbH & Co. (Berlin), Genthiner Str 30G, Berlin, 10785, Germany. TEL 49-30-250085-0, FAX 49-30-25008511, esv@esvmedien.de, http://www.erich-schmidt-verlag.de.

AGRICULTURAL WAGES IN INDIA. see *AGRICULTURE—Agricultural Economics*

AL DIA. see *POLITICAL SCIENCE—International Relations*

ALABAMA EMPLOYMENT LAW LETTER. see *LAW*

ALASKA EMPLOYMENT LAW LETTER. see *LAW*

331.21 USA ISSN 1063-3758
ALASKA WAGE RATES (YEAR). Text in English. a. free.
Document type: *Government.* **Description:** Presents the results of a wage survey of nearly 1,500 employers for 160 occupations. Data are provided for Alaska statewide and by economic region.
Media: Online - full text.
Published by: Department of Labor, Research and Analysis Section, PO Box 22201, Juneau, AK 99802-5501. TEL 907-465-4508, FAX 907-465-2101, http://www.labor.state.ak.us/research/wage/menu.htm.

331.21 CAN ISSN 1489-4084
ALBERTA. WORKERS' COMPENSATION BOARD. ANNUAL REPORT. Text in English. a. **Document type:** *Government.*
Former titles (until 1996): Alberta. Workers' Compensation Board. Report on Objectives (1483-8176); (until 1995): Alberta. Workers' Compensation Board. Annual Report (0703-2307); (until 1973): Alberta. Workmen's Compensation Board. Annual Report (0703-2315)
Related titles: Online - full content ed.
Published by: Workers' Compensation Board Alberta, PO Box 2415, Edmonton, AB T5J 2S5, Canada. TEL 780-498-8680, http://www.wcb.ab.ca/publications/corporate_plans.asp.

352.63 USA ISSN 1088-3150
HF5382.75.U6
THE ALMANAC OF AMERICAN EMPLOYERS. Text in English. 1985. a. USD 199.99 combined subscription print & CD-ROM eds. (effective 2003). **Document type:** *Trade.* **Description:** Complete reference guide to America's 500 largest, fastest-growing employers.
Related titles: CD-ROM ed.: ISSN 1548-7369; ♦ Supplement(s): Plunkett's Companion to the Almanac of American Employers: Mid-Size Firms. ISSN 1544-2691.
Published by: Plunkett Research, Ltd, PO Drawer 541737, Houston, TX 77254-1737. TEL 713-932-0000, FAX 713-932-7080, info@plunkettresearch.com, http://www.plunkettresearch.com. Ed., Pub. Jack W Plunkett.

352.63 USA
ALMANAC OF AMERICAN EMPLOYERS (YEAR). Text in English. a. USD 199.99 (effective 2005). **Description:** Fully updated for the job seeker and researcher. Includes salaries, benefits, corporate culture, special hiring/training programs, women and minorities in top posts, contacts.
Published by: Plunkett Research, Ltd, PO Drawer 541737, Houston, TX 77254-1737. TEL 713-932-0000, FAX 713-932-7080, info@plunkettresearch.com, http://www.plunkettresearch.com.

AMERICAN ASSOCIATION OF ENGINEERING SOCIETIES. ENGINEERING WORKFORCE COMMISSION. ENGINEERING AND TECHNOLOGY ENROLLMENTS (YEAR). see *ENGINEERING*

AMERICAN ASSOCIATION OF ENGINEERING SOCIETIES. ENGINEERING WORKFORCE COMMISSION. PROFESSIONAL INCOME OF ENGINEERS (YEAR). see *ENGINEERING*

AMERICANS WITH DISABILITIES ACT: EMPLOYEE RIGHTS AND EMPLOYER OBLIGATIONS. see *HANDICAPPED*

331 DEU
AMTLICHE BEKANNTMACHUNG ZUM ARBEITSSCHUTZ. Text in German. m. EUR 62.40, CHF 122; EUR 8.20, CHF 16 newsstand/cover (effective 2002). **Document type:** *Journal, Government.*
Related titles: ♦ Supplement to: Bundesarbeitsblatt. ISSN 0007-5868.
Published by: (Germany. Bundesminister fuer Arbeit und Sozialordnung), W. Kohlhammer GmbH, Hessbruehlstr 69, Stuttgart, 70565, Germany. TEL 49-711-7863290, FAX 49-711-7863430, info@kohlhammer-katalog.de, http://www.kohlhammer.de.

331 PER
ANALISIS LABORAL. Text in Spanish. 1977. m. USD 75.
Published by: Asesoramiento y Analisis Laborales S.A., Mariano Odicio, 334, Miraflores, Lima 18, Peru. TEL 469477.

344.01
ANARCHO-SYNDICALIST REVIEW; anarchosyndicalist ideas and discussion. Text in English. 1986. q. USD 15 domestic; USD 17 foreign; USD 4 newsstand/cover (effective 2003). adv. bk.rev.; video rev. illus.; tr.lit. cum.index 1986-99. 44 p./no.; back issues avail. **Document type:** *Journal, Consumer.* **Description:** Features news of syndicalist unions around the world, documents, articles on anarchist economics and labor history and analysis.
Formerly: Libertarian Labor Review (1069-1995)
Related titles: Microfilm ed.; Online - full text ed.: (from ProQuest Information & Learning).
Indexed: AltPI.
Address: PO Box 2824, Champaign, IL 61825-2824. TEL 617-537-8142, asr@labourstart.zzn.com, http://www.syndicalist.org. Ed., Adv. contact Jon Bekken. Circ: 1,100 (paid).

ANDERMAN: THE LAW OF UNFAIR DISMISSAL. see *LAW*

331.21 USA ISSN 1093-1856
KFO342.A29
ANDERSON'S OHIO WORKERS' COMPENSATION LAW HANDBOOK. Variant title: Ohio Workers' Compensation Law Handbook. Text in English. 1995. a. USD 85 (effective 2005). **Document type:** *Trade.* **Description:** Compiles primary-source material for Ohio workers' compensation legislation going beyond mere rules and regulations.
Published by: Anderson Publishing Co (Subsidiary of: LexisNexis North America), 9443 Springboro Pike, Miamisburg, OH 45342-4425. TEL 513-421-4142, 800-833-9844, FAX 513-562-8116, mail@andersonpublishing.com, http://www.andersonpublishing.com. Ed. Philip J Fulton.

ANDREWS LITIGATION REPORTER: EMPLOYMENT. see *LAW*

331 DEU ISSN 0341-0900
ANGEWANDTE ARBEITSWISSENSCHAFT. Text in German. 1975. q. EUR 16.50 (effective 2003). index. **Document type:** *Journal, Academic/Scholarly.*
Indexed: DIP, IBR, IBZ.
—CCC.
Published by: (Institut fuer Angewandte Arbeitswissenschaft e.V.), Wirtschaftsverlag Bachem GmbH, Ursulaplatz 1, Cologne, 50668, Germany. TEL 49-221-1619149, FAX 49-221-1619231, jschauer@m-e.org, bachem-verlagsgruppe@netcologne.de, http://www.bachem-verlagsgruppe.de. Ed. Joachim Schauer. Circ: 4,000.

ANNOTATED BRITISH COLUMBIA LABOUR RELATIONS CODE. see *LAW*

ANNUAL EMPLOYMENT SURVEY (YEAR). see *BUSINESS AND ECONOMICS—Abstracting, Bibliographies, Statistics*

344.01 USA ISSN 0743-4146
KF3464.Z9
ANNUAL INSTITUTE ON EMPLOYMENT LAW. Text in English. 1972. a.
Formerly (until 1983): Annual Institute on Equal Employment Opportunity Compliance (0198-9022)
Published by: Practising Law Institute, 810 Seventh Ave, New York, NY 10019. TEL 212-824-5700, 800-260-4754, FAX 800-321-0093, info@pli.edu, http://www.pli.edu.

331.21 CAN ISSN 1185-3581
ANNUAL SALARY SURVEYS. ENGINEERING & TECHNICAL REPORT. Text in English. a. CND 240. **Description:** Covers draftspersons, engineering assistants, technologists-technicians and chief engineers; union and non-union comparison, bonus data, pay indices.
Formerly (until 1990): Salary Survey. Engineering and Technical Report (0711-317X); Which supersedes in part: Salary Survey (0711-3153); Which was formerly: Stevenson and Kellogg Salary Survey. An Annual Study of Compensation Across Canada (0706-6945)
Published by: K P M G, Pacific Centre, 500 777 Dunsmuir St, P O Box 10427, Vancouver, BC V7Y 1K5, Canada. TEL 604-691-3407, FAX 604-691-3456.

331.21 CAN ISSN 1185-3565
ANNUAL SALARY SURVEYS. EXECUTIVE COMPENSATION REPORT. Text in English. a. CND 695. **Description:** Covers general management, corporate staff, finance, administration, sales, marketing, manufacturing, distribution, engineering and human resources, and board of directors.
Former titles (until 1990): Salary Survey. Executive Compensation Report (0842-5280); (until 1987): Executive Salary Survey (0830-9876); (until 1985): Salary Survey. Executive Report (0711-3161)
Published by: K P M G, Pacific Centre, 500 777 Dunsmuir St, P O Box 10427, Vancouver, BC V7Y 1K5, Canada. TEL 604-691-3407, FAX 604-691-3456.

331.21 CAN ISSN 1185-3573
ANNUAL SALARY SURVEYS. PRODUCTION & DISTRIBUTION REPORT. Text in English. a. CND 350. **Description:** Covers lead hand, foreman, superintendents, maintenance, shipping, warehouse, production and distribution management.
Former titles (until 1990): Salary Survey. Production and Distribution Report (0830-9868); (until 1982): Salary Survey. Production Report (0711-3188)
Published by: K P M G, Pacific Centre, 500 777 Dunsmuir St, P O Box 10427, Vancouver, BC V7Y 1K5, Canada. TEL 604-691-3407, FAX 604-691-3456.

331.21 CAN ISSN 1185-3557
ANNUAL SALARY SURVEYS. SALES & MARKETING REPORT. Text in English. a. CND 425. **Description:** Covers junior and senior sales representatives, supervisor, and sales and marketing management.
Former titles (until 1990): Salary Survey. Sales and Marketing Report (0830-985X); (until 1985): Salary Survey. Sales Report (0826-0362); (until 1981): Salary Survey. Marketing Report (0711-320X)
Published by: K P M G, Pacific Centre, 500 777 Dunsmuir St, P O Box 10427, Vancouver, BC V7Y 1K5, Canada. TEL 604-691-3407, FAX 604-691-3456.

331 NOR ISSN 0908-3731
➤ **ARBEIDSLIV I NORDEN.** Variant title: Arbetsliv i Norden. Text in Danish, Finnish, Norwegian, Swedish. 1987. 3/yr. **Document type:** *Academic/Scholarly.*
Formerly (until 1993): Nordisk Arbetsmarknad (0902-9192)
Related titles: Online - full text ed.
Published by: (Nordisk Ministerraad, Embedsmandskomite for Arbejdsmarkeds- og Arbejdsmiljoepolitik/Nordic Council of Ministers. Committee for Labour Markets and Working Environment Policy DNK), Arbeidsforskningsinstituttet/Work Research Institute, St. Olavs Plass, PO Box 6954, Oslo, 0130, Norway. TEL 47-23-369200, FAX 47-22-568918, afi@afi-wri.no, http://www.norden.org/arb/ain/sk, http://www.afi-wri.no. Ed. Berit Kvam. Circ: 4,300.

344.01 NLD ISSN 0929-9289
ARBEIDSRECHT; maandblad voor de praktijk. Text in Dutch. 1994. 11/yr. EUR 121 (effective 2003). adv. back issues avail. **Document type:** *Trade.*
—IE.
Published by: Kluwer B.V. (Subsidiary of: Wolters Kluwer N.V.), Postbus 23, Deventer, 7400 GA, Netherlands. TEL 31-570-673449, FAX 31-570-691555, juridisch@kluwer.nl, http://www.kluwer.nl. Ed. P F van der Heijden.

331 AUT ISSN 0003-7605
HC261
DIE ARBEIT. Text in German. 1946. m. charts. index. **Document type:** *Magazine, Consumer.* **Description:** Socialist publication covering labor and economic conditions in Austria and abroad. Includes reports of events.
Indexed: RASB.
Published by: Gewerkschaftlicher Linksblock im OeGB, Apostelgasse 36/12, Vienna, W 1030, Austria. TEL 43-1-71826230, FAX 43-1-718262330, sekretariat@glb.at, http://www.glb.at. Ed. Helmuth Zink.

334.01 DEU
K1
▼ **ARBEIT UND ARBEITSRECHT FUER DEN PERSONAL-PROFI**; Zeitschrift fuer die betriebliche Praxis. Text in German. 2003. m. EUR 109 domestic; EUR 11 newsstand/cover (effective 2004). adv. bk.rev. index. 45 p./no.; **Document type:** *Newspaper, Trade.* **Description:** Articles cover labor relations, production, safety, health protection, automation, unemployment, rationalization, education and training, labor law, and court decisions. Includes questions and answers.
Formed by the merger of (1946-2003): Arbeit und Arbeitsrecht (0323-4568); (2000-2003): Personal-Profi (1439-6955)
Indexed: AcoustA, CISA, DIP, IBR, IBZ, RASB.
Published by: Huss-Medien GmbH, Am Friedrichshain 22, Berlin, 10407, Germany. TEL 49-30-421510, FAX 49-30-42151232, verlag.wirtschaft@hussberlin.de, http://www.arbeit-und-arbeitsrecht.de, http://www.huss-medien.de. Ed. Brigitte Udke. Adv. contact Kathrin Pobering TEL 49-30-42151343. B&W page EUR 1,990, color page EUR 3,160; trim 185 x 260. Circ: 9,261 (paid).

331 DEU ISSN 0343-1886
ARBEIT UND BERUF; Fachzeitschrift fuer die Aufgaben der Bundesanstalt fuer Arbeit. Text in German. 1950. m. EUR 60 domestic to qualified personnel; EUR 71 foreign to qualified personnel (effective 2005). adv. bk.rev. bibl. **Document type:** *Magazine, Trade.*
Formerly (until 1975): Arbeit, Beruf, und Arbeitslosenhilfe (0003-7621)
Indexed: IBR, IBZ, WBSS.
Published by: Verlag Arbeit und Beruf, Mendelstr 8, Erlangen, 91058, Germany. FAX 49-9131-604787, arbeitundberuf@t-online.de. Ed. Kurt Berlinger. Pub., R&P, Adv. contact Anne Zoellinger. Circ: 5,000.

ARBEIT UND RECHT; Zeitschrift fuer Arbeitsrechtspraxis. see *LAW*

331 AUT ISSN 0003-7656
HD4809
ARBEIT UND WIRTSCHAFT. Text in German. 1923. m. EUR 18.17 domestic; EUR 28.34 foreign (effective 2005). adv. bk.rev. charts; illus. index. **Document type:** *Magazine, Trade.*
Indexed: CISA, ELLIS, ILD, PAIS, RASB.
Published by: Oesterreichischer Gewerkschaftsbund, Hohenstaufengasse 10-12, Vienna, W 1010, Austria. TEL 43-1-534440, FAX 43-1-53444204, aw@oegb.or.at, oegb@oegb.at, http://www.arbeit-wirtschaft.at, http://www.oegb.at. Ed. Siegfried Sorz. Adv. contact Fritz Fadler. Circ: 30,000.

331 DEU
ARBEITERPOLITIK; Informationsbriefe der Gruppe Arbeiterpolitik. Text in German. 1960. q. EUR 15; EUR 1.50 newsstand/cover (effective 2005). bk.rev. bibl. **Document type:** *Newspaper, Consumer.*
Published by: Gesellschaft zur Foerderung des Studiums der Arbeiterbewegung e.V., Postfach 106426, Hamburg, 20043, Germany. arpo.berlin@gmx.de, http://www.arbeiterpolitik.de. Ed., Pub. W Mueller.

B

331   DEU   ISSN 0402-7787
HD4809
ARBEITGEBER. Text in German. 1948. m. EUR 132; EUR 66 to students; EUR 14.50 newsstand/cover (effective 2004). adv. reprints avail. **Document type:** *Magazine, Trade.*
Indexed: CISA, DIP, IBR, IBZ, ILD, WBSS.
—IE, Infotrieve.
Published by: (Bundesvereinigung der Deutschen Arbeitgeberverbaende e.V.), Verlagsgruppe Handelsblatt GmbH, Kasernenstr 67, Duesseldorf, 40213, Germany. TEL 49-211-8870, FAX 49-211-371792, red.arbeitgeber@bda-online.de, fachverlag@vhb.de, http://www.fachverlag-online.de/cap_muh/arbeitgeber.asp, http://www.vhb.de. Ed. Joerg Swane. adv.: B&W page EUR 3,375, color page EUR 4,388; trim 210 x 297. Circ: 10,000.

344.01   DEU
DER ARBEITS-RECHT-BERATER. Text in German. m. EUR 114; EUR 11.40 newsstand/cover (effective 2005). adv. **Document type:** *Journal, Trade.*
Published by: Verlag Dr. Otto Schmidt KG, Gustav-Heinemann-Ufer 58, Cologne, 50968, Germany. TEL 49-221-9373801, FAX 49-221-93738943, arbeitsrechtsberater@otto-schmidt.de, info@otto-schmidt.de, http://www.arbrb.de, http://www.otto-schmidt.de. Ed. Markus Bauer. Adv. contact Renate Becker. B&W page EUR 555, color page EUR 971. Circ: 1,687 (paid and controlled).

331   DEU   ISSN 0933-1344
ARBEITSGERICHTSGESETZ. Text in German. 1965. irreg. price varies. **Document type:** *Monographic series, Trade.*
Published by: Erich Schmidt Verlag GmbH & Co. (Berlin), Genthiner Str 30G, Berlin, 10785, Germany. TEL 49-30-250085-0, FAX 49-30-25008511, esv@esvmedien.de, http://www.erich-schmidt-verlag.de.

331.21   AUT
ARBEITSKOSTEN IN DER INDUSTRIE OESTERREICHS. Text in German. 1960. triennial. free. stat. **Document type:** *Monographic series, Government.*
Published by: Wirtschaftskammer Oesterreich, Wiedner Hauptstr 63, Vienna, 1045, Austria. TEL 43-1-590900, FAX 43-1-590900250, TELEX 111871-BUKA. Ed. Guenther Herget. Circ: 2,000.

331   DEU   ISSN 0172-2751
ARBEITSMARKT IN HESSEN; Monatsbericht zur Arbeitsmarktlage. Text in German. 1952. m. **Document type:** *Government.*
Published by: Landesarbeitsamt Hessen, Referat Statistik, Saonestr 2-4, Frankfurt Am Main, 60528, Germany. TEL 069-66701, FAX 069-6670459.

331   DEU   ISSN 0933-2243
ARBEITSPLATZSCHUTZGESETZ. Text in German. 1971. irreg., latest 2000. price varies. **Document type:** *Monographic series, Trade.*
Published by: Erich Schmidt Verlag GmbH & Co. (Berlin), Genthiner Str 30G, Berlin, 10785, Germany. TEL 49-30-250085-0, FAX 49-30-25008511, esv@esvmedien.de, http://www.erich-schmidt-verlag.de.

331   CHE
ARBEITSRECHT/DROIT DU TRAVAIL. Text in French, German, Italian. 1953. irreg. (3-4/yr.). CHF 72 (effective 2001). adv. index. **Document type:** *Journal, Government.*
Formerly: Arbeitsrecht und Arbeitslosenversicherung (0003-777X).
Published by: (Switzerland. Bundesamt fuer Industrie, Gewerbe und Arbeit), Schulthess Juristische Medien AG, Zwingliplatz 2, Zuerich, 8022, Switzerland. TEL 41-1-2519336, FAX 41-1-2616394, zs.verlag@schulthess.com, http://www.schulthess.com. Circ: 1,400 (paid and controlled).

331   DEU   ISSN 1611-3489
▼ **ARBEITSRECHT AKTIV.** Text in German. 2003. m. EUR 138 (effective 2004). adv. **Document type:** *Journal, Trade.*
Published by: Vogel Verlag und Druck GmbH & Co. KG, Max-Planck-Str 7-9, Wuerzburg, 97064, Germany. TEL 49-931-4180, FAX 49-931-4182100, marliese_bernhardt@vogel-medien.de, http://www.iww.de/rechtsanwaelte/arbeitsrechtakt/infoindex.php, http://www.vogel-medien.de.

ARBEITSRECHT IM BETRIEB. see *LAW*

344.01   DEU   ISSN 0003-7761
ARBEITSRECHT IN STICHWORTEN; Arbeitsrechtliche Entscheidungssammlung. Variant title: A R S T. Text in German. 1946. m. EUR 116 domestic; EUR 122 foreign; EUR 12 newsstand/cover (effective 2004). adv. bk.rev. index. reprints avail. **Document type:** *Magazine, Trade.*
—CCC.
Published by: Forkel Verlag GmbH (Subsidiary of: Huethig GmbH & Co. KG), Im Weiher 10, Heidelberg, 69121, Germany. TEL 49-6221-489441, FAX 49-6221-489529, hsv_zeitschrift@huethig.de, http://www.huethig.de. adv.: B&W page EUR 620, color page EUR 992. Circ: 1,400.

331   DEU   ISSN 1435-6848
ARBEITSRECHTLICHE FORSCHUNGSERGEBNISSE. Variant title: Studienreihe Arbeitsrechtliche Forschungsergebnisse. Text in German. 1996. irreg., latest vol.66, 2005. price varies. **Document type:** *Monographic series, Academic/Scholarly.*
Published by: Verlag Dr. Kovac, Arnoldstr 49, Hamburg, 22763, Germany. TEL 49-40-39888800, FAX 49-40-39888055, info@verlagdrkovac.de, http://www.verlagdrkovac.de/12-3.htm.

344.01   DEU   ISSN 0938-5800
ARBEITSRECHTLICHE PRAXIS AUF CD-ROM (DOS VERSION). Text in German. base vol. plus q. updates. EUR 298 base vol(s). per vol.; EUR 432 updates (effective 2003). **Document type:** *Abstract/Index.* **Description:** Covers the practice of labor law. Contains full text of important cases.
Media: CD-ROM.
Published by: Verlag C.H. Beck oHG, Wilhelmstr 9, Munich, 80801, Germany. TEL 49-89-38189338, FAX 49-89-38189398, abo.service@beck.de, http://www.beck.de.

344.01   DEU   ISSN 1436-5510
ARBEITSRECHTLICHE PRAXIS AUF CD-ROM (WINDOWS VERSION). Text in German. 1999. q. EUR 298 base vol(s). per vol.; EUR 432 updates (effective 2005). **Document type:** *Trade.*
Media: CD-ROM. **Related titles:** ✦ Print ed.: Nachschlagewerk des Bundesarbeitsgerichts - Arbeitsrechtliche Praxis. ISSN 0469-4333.
Published by: Verlag C.H. Beck oHG, Wilhelmstr 9, Munich, 80801, Germany. TEL 49-89-38189338, FAX 49-89-38189398, http://www.beck.de.

331   DEU
ARBEITSSCHUTZ UND ARBEITSSICHERHEIT. Text in German. 1989. irreg., latest 2003. looseleaf. price varies. **Document type:** *Monographic series, Trade.*
Formerly: Arbeitssicherheitsgesetz (0936-8574)
Published by: Erich Schmidt Verlag GmbH & Co. (Berlin), Genthiner Str 30G, Berlin, 10785, Germany. TEL 49-30-250085-0, FAX 49-30-25008521, vertrieb@esvmedien.de, http://www.erich-schmidt-verlag.de.

331   DEU   ISSN 0933-2448
ARBEITSSTAETTEN. Text in German. 1984. irreg., latest 2003. looseleaf. price varies. **Document type:** *Monographic series, Trade.*
Published by: Erich Schmidt Verlag GmbH & Co. (Berlin), Genthiner Str 30G, Berlin, 10785, Germany. TEL 49-30-250085-0, FAX 49-30-25008521, vertrieb@esvmedien.de, http://www.erich-schmidt-verlag.de.

331   DEU
ARBEITSZEITVORSCHRIFTEN. Text in German. irreg. price varies. **Document type:** *Monographic series, Trade.*
Published by: Erich Schmidt Verlag GmbH & Co. (Berlin), Genthiner Str 30G, Berlin, 10785, Germany. TEL 49-30-250085-0, FAX 49-30-25008511, esv@esvmedien.de, http://www.erich-schmidt-verlag.de.

ARBEJDERBEVAEGELSENS BIBLIOTEK OG ARKIV. AARSSKRIFT. see *POLITICAL SCIENCE*

331   DNK   ISSN 0108-9625
ARBEJDERBEVAEGELSENS ERHVERVSRAAD. BERETNING. Text in Danish. 1982. a. free. illus. **Document type:** *Trade.*
Published by: Arbejderbevaegelsens Erhvervsraad/Economic Council of the Labour Movement, Reventlowsgade 14-2, Copenhagen V, 1651, Denmark. TEL 45-33-557710, FAX 45-33-313041, ae@aeraadet.dk, http://www.aeraadet.dk. Circ: 2,500.

331.137   DNK   ISSN 0908-6072
ARBEJDSMARKEDETS ANKENAEVN. AARSBERETNING. Key Title: Aarsberetning fra Ankenaevnet for Arbejdsloeshedsforsikringen. Text in Danish. 1972. a. free.
Formerly: (until 1993): Ankenaevnet for Arbejdsloeshedsforsikringen. Beretning (0109-1107)
Published by: Arbejdsmarkedets Ankenaevn, Nytorv 11-13, Copenhagen K, 1450, Denmark. TEL 45 33 92 66 00, FAX 45 33 13 52 47, http://www.ama.dk/ama.publikationer.html. Circ: 3,600.

658   DNK   ISSN 0909-9077
ARBEJDSMARKEDSPOLITISK AGENDA. Text in Danish. 1994. s-m. **Document type:** *Trade.*
Related titles: Online - full text ed.: ISSN 1600-5341.
Published by: Dansk Arbejdsgiverforening/Danish Employers Confederation, Vester Voldgade 113, Copenhagen V, 1790, Denmark. TEL 45-33-389000, FAX 45-33-122976, da@da.dk, http://www.da.dk. Ed. Flemming Andersen. Circ: 4,500 (controlled).

344.01   DNK   ISSN 0108-7150
ARBEJDSRETLIGT TIDSSKRIFT; arbejdsrettens domme, arbejdsretlige kendelser. Text in Danish. 1980. a. price varies. back issues avail. **Document type:** *Academic/Scholarly.* **Description:** Reports on decisions by the Danish Labor Court and other collective labor law awards.
Formed by the merger of: Arbejdsretlige Domme; Arbejdsretlige Kendelser

Published by: Jurist- og Oekonomforbundets Forlag, Lyngbyvej 17, PO Box 2702, Copenhagen OE, 2100, Denmark. TEL 45-39-315500, FAX 45-39-135555, http://www.djoef.dk. Ed. Joern Andersen. Circ: 800.

331   SWE   ISSN 1400-9692
ARBETSMARKNAD & ARBETSLIV. Text in Swedish. 1995. q. SEK 300; SEK 150 per issue (effective 2004). back issues avail. **Document type:** *Journal, Government.*
Related titles: Online - full text ed.
Published by: (Arbetslivsinstitutet/The National Institute for Working Life), Arbetsmarknadsstyrelsen/National Labour Market Board, Kungstensgatan 5, Stockholm, 11399, Sweden. TEL 46-8-58606000, FAX 46-8-58606499, arbetsmarknadsstyrelsen@ams.smv.se, http://www.arbetslivsinstitutet.se/publikationer/aa/aa.asp, http://www.ams.amv.se. Ed. Ulla Arnell Gustafsson.
Co-publisher: Arbetslivsinstitutet/The National Institute for Working Life.

331   SWE   ISSN 1104-800X
ARBETSMARKNADEN. Text in Swedish. 1968. 9/yr. SEK 305 (effective 2003). adv. abstr.; charts; illus.
Former titles (until 1994): Nyhetsbladet Arbetsmarknaden (0283-3514); Which incorporates (1987-1988): Yrkesjournalen (0284-8902); (1986-1988): Nya Grepp; (until 1982): Arbetsmarknaden (0003-7850); Platsjournalen
Published by: Arbetsmarknadsstyrelsen/National Labour Market Board, Kungstensgatan 5, Stockholm, 11399, Sweden. TEL 46-8-58606000, FAX 46-8-58606499, arbetsmarknadsstyrelsen@ams.smv.se, http://www.ams.se/RDFS.asp?L=66, http://www.ams.amv.se. Eds. Anders Linden, Sara Bjoerkqvist. Circ: 30,000.

344.01   SWE   ISSN 1400-9706
ARBETSRAETT OCH ARBETSMARKNAD; foerfattningssamling foer Svenskt och europeisk arbetsliv. Text in Swedish. 1988. a., latest 2004. **Document type:** *Government.*
Formerly (until 1994): Lagbok foer Arbetsmarknaden (1100-0325)
Published by: Norstedts Juridik AB (Subsidiary of: Wolters Kluwer N.V.), Stockholm, 10647, Sweden. TEL 46-8-6909190, FAX 46-8-6909191, kundservice@nj.se, http://www.nj.se.

371.2   USA   ISSN 0003-7885
ARBITRATION IN THE SCHOOLS. Text in English. 1970. m. looseleaf. USD 120 (effective 2006). s-a. cum.index. reprints avail. **Document type:** *Newsletter, Trade.* **Description:** Summarizes decisions on disputes between teachers and their employers.
Related titles: Microfiche ed.
Published by: (American Arbitration Association), L R P Publications, 747 Dresher Rd, PO Box 980, Horsham, PA 19044. TEL 215-784-0860, FAX 215-784-9639, custserve@lrp.com, http://www.shoplrp.com/product/p-6302.N.html, http://www.lrp.com. Circ: 3,500.

331.09   AUT   ISSN 0003-8849
ARCHIV; Jahrbuch des Vereins fuer Geschichte der Arbeiterbewegung. Text in German. 1961. a. bk.rev. bibl.; illus. index. **Document type:** *Journal, Academic/Scholarly.*
Published by: Verein fuer Geschichte der Arbeiterbewegung, Rechte Wienzeile 97, Vienna, W 1050, Austria. TEL 43-1-5457870, FAX 43-1-5440734, vga@vienna.at, http://www.wien.gv.at/ma08/vga/. Ed. Wolfgang Maderthaner. Circ: 1,000.

ARIZONA EMPLOYMENT LAW LETTER. see *LAW*

331   USA
ARIZONA'S WORKFORCE. Text in English. 1977. m. free. charts; stat. **Document type:** *Newsletter, Government.*
Former titles: Arizona Labor Market Information Newsletter; Arizona Labor Market Newsletter (0743-5657)
Related titles: Microfiche ed.: (from CIS).
Indexed: SRI.
Published by: Arizona Department of Economic Security, 1789 W. Jefferson, Box 6123, SC-733A, Phoenix, AZ 85005. TEL 602-542-3871, FAX 602-542-6474. Circ: 5,000.

331.125   USA
ARKANSAS COVERED EMPLOYMENT AND EARNINGS. Text in English. 1948. irreg. free.
Formerly: Arkansas Average Covered Employment and Earnings by County and Industry (0092-2889)
Published by: (Arkansas. U I Research Section), Employment Security Department, PO Box 2981, Little Rock, AR 72203-2981. TEL 501-682-3197. Circ: 300.

ARKANSAS EMPLOYMENT LAW LETTER. see *LAW*

331   HKG   ISSN 0258-0268
ASIAN LABOUR UPDATE. Key Title: Asia Labour Monitor. Text in English. 1983. bi-m. USD 20 (effective 2000). **Document type:** *Bulletin, Trade.*
Indexed: AltPI.
Published by: Asia Monitor Research Center, 444 Nathan Rd 8 B, Kowloon, Hong Kong. TEL 852-2332-1346, FAX 852-2385-5319, amrc@hk.super.net. Ed. Ed Shepherd. R&P Ed Shpherd.

ASSOCIATION FOR QUALITY AND PARTICIPATION. ANNUAL CONFERENCE AND RESOURCE MART TRANSACTIONS. see *BUSINESS AND ECONOMICS—Management*

331.11   IDN
ATMA JAYA RESEARCH CENTRE. INTERNATIONAL CONTRACT LABOUR. Text in English. 1983. irreg.
Published by: Atma Jaya Research Centre/Pusat Penelitian Atma Jaya, Jalan Jenderal Sudirman 51, PO Box 2639, Jakarta, 10001, Indonesia.

▼ AUSTRALIA. BUREAU OF STATISTICS. AUSTRALIAN LABOUR MARKET STATISTICS. see *BUSINESS AND ECONOMICS—Abstracting, Bibliographies, Statistics*

AUSTRALIA. BUREAU OF STATISTICS. AVERAGE WEEKLY EARNINGS, AUSTRALIA. see *BUSINESS AND ECONOMICS—Abstracting, Bibliographies, Statistics*

AUSTRALIA. BUREAU OF STATISTICS. AVERAGE WEEKLY EARNINGS, AUSTRALIA, PRELIMINARY. see *BUSINESS AND ECONOMICS—Abstracting, Bibliographies, Statistics*

AUSTRALIA. BUREAU OF STATISTICS. BUSINESS EVENTS VENUES INDUSTRY, AUSTRALIA. see *BUSINESS AND ECONOMICS—Abstracting, Bibliographies, Statistics*

AUSTRALIA. BUREAU OF STATISTICS. DIRECTORY OF INDUSTRIAL RELATIONS STATISTICS. see *BUSINESS AND ECONOMICS—Abstracting, Bibliographies, Statistics*

AUSTRALIA. BUREAU OF STATISTICS. DIRECTORY OF LABOUR MARKET AND SOCIAL SURVEY DATA. see *BUSINESS AND ECONOMICS—Abstracting, Bibliographies, Statistics*

AUSTRALIA. BUREAU OF STATISTICS. DIRECTORY OF SUPERANNUATION RELATED STATISTICS. see *BUSINESS AND ECONOMICS—Abstracting, Bibliographies, Statistics*

AUSTRALIA. BUREAU OF STATISTICS. EDUCATION AND TRAINING EXPERIENCE, AUSTRALIA. see *BUSINESS AND ECONOMICS—Abstracting, Bibliographies, Statistics*

AUSTRALIA. BUREAU OF STATISTICS. EMPLOYEE EARNINGS AND HOURS, STATES AND AUSTRALIA - DATA SERVICE. see *BUSINESS AND ECONOMICS— Abstracting, Bibliographies, Statistics*

AUSTRALIA. BUREAU OF STATISTICS. EMPLOYER TRAINING EXPENDITURE AND PRACTICES, AUSTRALIA. see *BUSINESS AND ECONOMICS—Abstracting, Bibliographies, Statistics*

AUSTRALIA. BUREAU OF STATISTICS. EMPLOYMENT ARRANGEMENTS AND SUPERANNUATION, AUSTRALIA. see *BUSINESS AND ECONOMICS—Abstracting, Bibliographies, Statistics*

AUSTRALIA. BUREAU OF STATISTICS. EMPLOYMENT IN SELECTED CULTURE-LEISURE OCCUPATIONS, AUSTRALIA. see *BUSINESS AND ECONOMICS— Abstracting, Bibliographies, Statistics*

AUSTRALIA. BUREAU OF STATISTICS. EMPLOYMENT IN SELECTED SPORT AND RECREATION OCCUPATIONS, AUSTRALIA. see *BUSINESS AND ECONOMICS— Abstracting, Bibliographies, Statistics*

AUSTRALIA. BUREAU OF STATISTICS. EMPLOYMENT SERVICES, AUSTRALIA. see *BUSINESS AND ECONOMICS—Abstracting, Bibliographies, Statistics*

AUSTRALIA. BUREAU OF STATISTICS. EXPERIMENTAL ESTIMATES, REGIONAL SMALL BUSINESS STATISTICS, AUSTRALIA. see *BUSINESS AND ECONOMICS— Abstracting, Bibliographies, Statistics*

AUSTRALIA. BUREAU OF STATISTICS. EXPERIMENTAL ESTIMATES, REGIONAL WAGE AND SALARY EARNER STATISTICS, AUSTRALIA. see *BUSINESS AND ECONOMICS—Abstracting, Bibliographies, Statistics*

AUSTRALIA. BUREAU OF STATISTICS. FORMS OF EMPLOYMENT, AUSTRALIA. see *BUSINESS AND ECONOMICS—Abstracting, Bibliographies, Statistics*

AUSTRALIA. BUREAU OF STATISTICS. HEALTH AND COMMUNITY SERVICES LABOUR FORCE. see *BUSINESS AND ECONOMICS—Abstracting, Bibliographies, Statistics*

AUSTRALIA. BUREAU OF STATISTICS. HIRE INDUSTRIES, AUSTRALIA. see *BUSINESS AND ECONOMICS— Abstracting, Bibliographies, Statistics*

AUSTRALIA. BUREAU OF STATISTICS. HIRE INDUSTRIES, AUSTRALIA, PRELIMINARY. see *BUSINESS AND ECONOMICS—Abstracting, Bibliographies, Statistics*

AUSTRALIA. BUREAU OF STATISTICS. HUMAN RESOURCES IN SCIENCE AND TECHNOLOGY (HRST), AUSTRALIA. see *BUSINESS AND ECONOMICS—Abstracting, Bibliographies, Statistics*

AUSTRALIA. BUREAU OF STATISTICS. INDUSTRIAL DISPUTES, AUSTRALIA (MONTHLY). see *BUSINESS AND ECONOMICS—Abstracting, Bibliographies, Statistics*

AUSTRALIA. BUREAU OF STATISTICS. INFORMATION PAPER: CHANGES TO LABOUR FORCE STATISTICS PRODUCTS. see *BUSINESS AND ECONOMICS— Abstracting, Bibliographies, Statistics*

AUSTRALIA. BUREAU OF STATISTICS. INFORMATION PAPER: IMPLEMENTING THE REDESIGNED LABOUR FORCE SURVEY QUESTIONNAIRE. see *BUSINESS AND ECONOMICS—Abstracting, Bibliographies, Statistics*

AUSTRALIA. BUREAU OF STATISTICS. INFORMATION PAPER: LABOUR FORCE SURVEY, AUSTRALIA: REVISIONS TO HISTORICAL ANZSIC INDUSTRY DATA. see *BUSINESS AND ECONOMICS—Abstracting, Bibliographies, Statistics*

AUSTRALIA. BUREAU OF STATISTICS. INFORMATION PAPER: LABOUR FORCE SURVEY QUESTIONNAIRE REDESIGN. see *BUSINESS AND ECONOMICS—Abstracting, Bibliographies, Statistics*

AUSTRALIA. BUREAU OF STATISTICS. INFORMATION PAPER: LABOUR FORCE SURVEY SAMPLE DESIGN. see *BUSINESS AND ECONOMICS—Abstracting, Bibliographies, Statistics*

▼ AUSTRALIA. BUREAU OF STATISTICS. INFORMATION PAPER: LABOUR FORCE SURVEY STANDARD ERRORS. see *BUSINESS AND ECONOMICS—Abstracting, Bibliographies, Statistics*

AUSTRALIA. BUREAU OF STATISTICS. INFORMATION PAPER: MEASURING EMPLOYMENT AND UNEMPLOYMENT. see *BUSINESS AND ECONOMICS— Abstracting, Bibliographies, Statistics*

AUSTRALIA. BUREAU OF STATISTICS. INFORMATION PAPER: QUESTIONNAIRES IN THE LABOUR FORCE. see *BUSINESS AND ECONOMICS—Abstracting, Bibliographies, Statistics*

AUSTRALIA. BUREAU OF STATISTICS. INFORMATION PAPER: REGIONAL LABOUR FORCE STATISTICS. see *BUSINESS AND ECONOMICS—Abstracting, Bibliographies, Statistics*

AUSTRALIA. BUREAU OF STATISTICS. INFORMATION PAPER: USING THE A S G C REMOTENESS STRUCTURE TO ANALYSE CHARACTERISTICS OF WAGE AND SALARY EARNERS OF AUSTRALIA. see *BUSINESS AND ECONOMICS—Abstracting, Bibliographies, Statistics*

AUSTRALIA. BUREAU OF STATISTICS. INFORMATION PAPER: WAGE COST INDEX, AUSTRALIA. see *BUSINESS AND ECONOMICS—Abstracting, Bibliographies, Statistics*

AUSTRALIA. BUREAU OF STATISTICS. INVOLVEMENT IN ORGANIZED SPORT AND PHYSICAL ACTIVITY, AUSTRALIA. see *BUSINESS AND ECONOMICS— Abstracting, Bibliographies, Statistics*

AUSTRALIA. BUREAU OF STATISTICS. INVOLVEMENT IN SPORT, AUSTRALIA. see *BUSINESS AND ECONOMICS—Abstracting, Bibliographies, Statistics*

AUSTRALIA. BUREAU OF STATISTICS. JOB SEARCH EXPERIENCE, AUSTRALIA. see *BUSINESS AND ECONOMICS—Abstracting, Bibliographies, Statistics*

AUSTRALIA. BUREAU OF STATISTICS. LABOUR COSTS, AUSTRALIA. see *BUSINESS AND ECONOMICS— Abstracting, Bibliographies, Statistics*

AUSTRALIA. BUREAU OF STATISTICS. LABOUR FORCE, AUSTRALIA. see *BUSINESS AND ECONOMICS— Abstracting, Bibliographies, Statistics*

AUSTRALIA. BUREAU OF STATISTICS. LABOUR FORCE, AUSTRALIA, PRELIMINARY. see *BUSINESS AND ECONOMICS—Abstracting, Bibliographies, Statistics*

AUSTRALIA. BUREAU OF STATISTICS. LABOUR FORCE, AUSTRALIA - SEASONAL FACTORS. see *BUSINESS AND ECONOMICS—Abstracting, Bibliographies, Statistics*

AUSTRALIA. BUREAU OF STATISTICS. LABOUR FORCE, AUSTRALIA - STANDARD TABLES ON MICROFICHE. see *BUSINESS AND ECONOMICS—Abstracting, Bibliographies, Statistics*

AUSTRALIA. BUREAU OF STATISTICS. LABOUR FORCE EXPERIENCE, AUSTRALIA. see *BUSINESS AND ECONOMICS—Abstracting, Bibliographies, Statistics*

AUSTRALIA. BUREAU OF STATISTICS. LABOUR FORCE PROJECTIONS, AUSTRALIA. see *BUSINESS AND ECONOMICS—Abstracting, Bibliographies, Statistics*

AUSTRALIA. BUREAU OF STATISTICS. LABOUR FORCE, SELECTED SUMMARY TABLES, AUSTRALIA. see *BUSINESS AND ECONOMICS—Abstracting, Bibliographies, Statistics*

AUSTRALIA. BUREAU OF STATISTICS. LABOUR FORCE STATUS AND OTHER CHARACTERISTICS OF FAMILIES, AUSTRALIA. see *BUSINESS AND ECONOMICS— Abstracting, Bibliographies, Statistics*

AUSTRALIA. BUREAU OF STATISTICS. LABOUR FORCE STATUS AND OTHER CHARACTERISTICS OF MIGRANTS, AUSTRALIA. see *BUSINESS AND ECONOMICS— Abstracting, Bibliographies, Statistics*

AUSTRALIA. BUREAU OF STATISTICS. LABOUR MOBILITY, AUSTRALIA. see *BUSINESS AND ECONOMICS— Abstracting, Bibliographies, Statistics*

AUSTRALIA. BUREAU OF STATISTICS. LABOUR STATISTICS: CONCEPTS, SOURCES AND METHODS. see *BUSINESS AND ECONOMICS—Abstracting, Bibliographies, Statistics*

AUSTRALIA. BUREAU OF STATISTICS. LABOUR STATISTICS IN BRIEF, AUSTRALIA. see *BUSINESS AND ECONOMICS—Abstracting, Bibliographies, Statistics*

AUSTRALIA. BUREAU OF STATISTICS. LOCATIONS OF WORK, AUSTRALIA. see *BUSINESS AND ECONOMICS—Abstracting, Bibliographies, Statistics*

AUSTRALIA. BUREAU OF STATISTICS. MULTIPLE JOBHOLDING, AUSTRALIA. see *BUSINESS AND ECONOMICS—Abstracting, Bibliographies, Statistics*

AUSTRALIA. BUREAU OF STATISTICS. OCCASIONAL PAPER: A RISK INDEX APPROACH TO UNEMPLOYMENT - AN APPLICATION USING THE SURVEY OF EMPLOYMENT AND UNEMPLOYMENT PATTERNS. see *BUSINESS AND ECONOMICS—Abstracting, Bibliographies, Statistics*

AUSTRALIA. BUREAU OF STATISTICS. OCCASIONAL PAPER: DYNAMICS OF EARNED INCOME - AN APPLICATION USING THE SURVEY OF EMPLOYMENT AND UNEMPLOYMENT PATTERNS. see *BUSINESS AND ECONOMICS—Abstracting, Bibliographies, Statistics*

AUSTRALIA. BUREAU OF STATISTICS. OCCASIONAL PAPER: JOB QUALITY AND CHURNING OF THE POOL OF THE UNEMPLOYED. see *BUSINESS AND ECONOMICS— Abstracting, Bibliographies, Statistics*

AUSTRALIA. BUREAU OF STATISTICS. OCCASIONAL PAPER: LABOUR FORCE CHARACTERISTICS, INDIGENOUS AUSTRALIANS. see *BUSINESS AND ECONOMICS— Abstracting, Bibliographies, Statistics*

AUSTRALIA. BUREAU OF STATISTICS. OCCASIONAL PAPER: LABOUR MARKET DYNAMICS IN AUSTRALIA - AN APPLICATION USING THE SURVEY OF EMPLOYMENT AND UNEMPLOYMENT PATTERNS. see *BUSINESS AND ECONOMICS—Abstracting, Bibliographies, Statistics*

AUSTRALIA. BUREAU OF STATISTICS. OCCASIONAL PAPER: LABOUR MARKET OUTCOMES OF LOW PAID ADULT WORKERS. see *BUSINESS AND ECONOMICS—Abstracting, Bibliographies, Statistics*

AUSTRALIA. BUREAU OF STATISTICS. OCCASIONAL PAPER: LABOUR MARKET PROGRAMS, UNEMPLOYMENT AND EMPLOYMENT HAZARDS. see *BUSINESS AND ECONOMICS—Abstracting, Bibliographies, Statistics*

AUSTRALIA. BUREAU OF STATISTICS. OCCASIONAL PAPER: THE DYNAMICS OF WELFARE RECEIPT AND LABOUR MARKET STATUS. see *BUSINESS AND ECONOMICS— Abstracting, Bibliographies, Statistics*

AUSTRALIA. BUREAU OF STATISTICS. PERSONS NOT IN THE LABOUR FORCE, AUSTRALIA. see *BUSINESS AND ECONOMICS—Abstracting, Bibliographies, Statistics*

AUSTRALIA. BUREAU OF STATISTICS. QUEENSLAND OFFICE. WORKING HOURS OF WAGE AND SALARY EARNERS, QUEENSLAND. see *BUSINESS AND ECONOMICS—Abstracting, Bibliographies, Statistics*

AUSTRALIA. BUREAU OF STATISTICS. RETIREMENT AND RETIREMENT INTENTIONS, AUSTRALIA. see *BUSINESS AND ECONOMICS—Abstracting, Bibliographies, Statistics*

AUSTRALIA. BUREAU OF STATISTICS. RETRENCHMENT AND REDUNDANCY, AUSTRALIA. see *BUSINESS AND ECONOMICS—Abstracting, Bibliographies, Statistics*

AUSTRALIA. BUREAU OF STATISTICS. STANDARD AUSTRALIAN CLASSIFICATION OF COUNTRIES. see *POPULATION STUDIES—Abstracting, Bibliographies, Statistics*

AUSTRALIA. BUREAU OF STATISTICS. STANDARDS FOR LABOUR FORCE STATISTICS. see *BUSINESS AND ECONOMICS—Abstracting, Bibliographies, Statistics*

AUSTRALIA. BUREAU OF STATISTICS. SUCCESSFUL AND UNSUCCESSFUL JOB SEARCH EXPERIENCE, AUSTRALIA. see *BUSINESS AND ECONOMICS— Abstracting, Bibliographies, Statistics*

AUSTRALIA. BUREAU OF STATISTICS. SUPERANNUATION: COVERAGE AND FINANCIAL CHARACTERISTICS, AUSTRALIA. see *BUSINESS AND ECONOMICS— Abstracting, Bibliographies, Statistics*

AUSTRALIA. BUREAU OF STATISTICS. TASMANIAN OFFICE. BALANCING WORK AND CARING RESPONSIBILITIES, TASMANIA. see *BUSINESS AND ECONOMICS—Abstracting, Bibliographies, Statistics*

AUSTRALIA. BUREAU OF STATISTICS. UNDEREMPLOYED WORKERS, AUSTRALIA. see *BUSINESS AND ECONOMICS—Abstracting, Bibliographies, Statistics*

AUSTRALIA. BUREAU OF STATISTICS. VIDEO HIRE INDUSTRY, AUSTRALIA. see *BUSINESS AND ECONOMICS—Abstracting, Bibliographies, Statistics*

AUSTRALIA. BUREAU OF STATISTICS. WORK IN SELECTED CULTURE AND LEISURE ACTIVITIES, AUSTRALIA. see *BUSINESS AND ECONOMICS—Abstracting, Bibliographies, Statistics*

AUSTRALIA. BUREAU OF STATISTICS. WORK-RELATED INJURIES, AUSTRALIA. see *BUSINESS AND ECONOMICS—Abstracting, Bibliographies, Statistics*

AUSTRALIA. BUREAU OF STATISTICS. WORKING ARRANGEMENTS, AUSTRALIA. see *BUSINESS AND ECONOMICS—Abstracting, Bibliographies, Statistics*

331.259   AUS
L750
AUSTRALIA. DEPARTMENT OF EDUCATION, TRAINING AND YOUTH AFFAIRS. ANNUAL REPORT. Text in English. 1987. a. free. **Document type:** *Government.* **Description:** Reports on the activities of the department for the previous financial year (July to June).
Supersedes (in 1999): Australia. Department of Employment, Education, Training and Youth Affairs. Annual Report (1327-726X); (in 1995): Australia. Department of Employment, Education and Training. Annual Report (1032-4623); Which was formed by the merger of (1968-1987): Australia. Commonwealth Department of Education. Annual Report (1030-8229); And in part (1982-1987): Australia. Department of Employment and Industry Relations. Annual Report (0729-1213); Which was formed by the merger of (1979-1981): Australia. Department of Employment and Youth Affairs. Annual Report (0159-5695); And (1980-1981): Australia. Department of Industrial Relations. Report for the Period (0725-4016).
Related titles: Online - full text ed.
Published by: Department of Education Training and Youth Affairs, GPO Box 9880, Canberra, ACT 2601, Australia. TEL 61-2-62408556, FAX 61-2-62407442, publications@detya.gov.au, http://www.detya.gov.au. Ed. Elizabeth Smith. R&Ps Roger Edwards, Roger Edwards TEL 61-2-62753534. Circ: 5,000.

352.63   AUS   ISSN 1447-5758
AUSTRALIA. DEPARTMENT OF EMPLOYMENT AND WORKPLACE RELATIONS. ANNUAL REPORT. Text in English. 1982. a. free. **Document type:** *Government.* **Description:** Reports on the operations of the department and its performance in relation to government programs for employment, workplace relations, and small business.
Former titles: Australia. Department of Employment, Workplace Relations and Small Business. Annual Report (1442-9950); Australia. Department of Workplace Relations and Small Business. Annual Report (1440-9445); (until 1997): Australia. Department of Industrial Relations. Annual Report (1032-7266); Which superseded in part (in 1988): Australia. Department of the Special Minister of State. Annual Report (0812-2113); (in 1988): Australia. Department of Employment and Industrial Relations. Annual Report (0729-1213); Which was formed by the merger of (1979-1982): Australia. Department of Employment and Youth Affairs. Annual Report (0159-5695); (1982-1982): Australia. Department of Industrial Relations. Report for Period (0725-4016).
Related titles: Online - full text ed.

Published by: Department of Employment and Workplace Relations, GPO Box 9879, Canberra, ACT 2601, Australia. TEL 61-2-61216000, FAX 61-2-61217542, helen.connor@dewrsb.gov.au, http://www.dewrsb.gov.au/publications/annualReports/default.asp. Circ: 1,500.

331   AUS   ISSN 0311-6336
AUSTRALIAN BULLETIN OF LABOUR. Text in English. 1974. q. AUD 82.50; AUD 22 newsstand/cover (effective 2003). adv. bibl.; charts; stat. back issues avail. **Document type:** *Bulletin.* **Description:** Provides a forum for the discussion of issues, policies and developments as they affect the Australian labour market.
Related titles: Online - full text ed.: (from Gale Group, Northern Light Technology, Inc., O C L C Online Computer Library Center, Inc., ProQuest Information & Learning, R M I T Publishing).
Indexed: ABIn, AusPAIS, CIJE, ILD, JEL, PCI, RASB. —BLDSC (1798.093500), IE, Infotrieve, ingenta.
Published by: National Institute of Labour Studies Inc., c/o Flinders University, GPO Box 2100, Adelaide, SA 5001, Australia. TEL 61-8-8201-2642, 61-8-82012265, FAX 61-8-8276-9060, TELEX AA 89624 FLINDU, sofia.tassis@flinders.edu.au, http://www.ssn.flinders.edu.au/nils/. Ed. Keith Hancock. R&P, Adv. contact Diane Ovens. Circ: 400.

344.01   AUS   ISSN 1321-5957
AUSTRALIAN EMPLOYMENT LAW JOURNAL. Text in English. 1994. q. AUD 99. bk.rev. back issues avail. **Document type:** *Academic/Scholarly.* **Description:** Provides analysis of the law relating to employment for academics, professionals and consumers.
Published by: Australian Law Publishers Pty. Ltd., 254 Hawken Dr, St Lucia, QLD 4067, Australia. TEL 61-7-38709111, FAX 61-7-38702222, la510737@student.uq.edu.au. Ed. Russell Mathews. Circ: 20.

331   AUS   ISSN 1328-1143
HD8841
➤ **AUSTRALIAN JOURNAL OF LABOUR ECONOMICS**; a journal of labour economics and labour relations. Abbreviated title: A J L E. Text in English. 1989. q. AUD 55 domestic membership; AUD 65 foreign membership (effective 2003). bk.rev. back issues avail.; reprints avail. **Document type:** *Journal, Academic/Scholarly.* **Description:** Presents articles concerning contemporary issues of labor economics, vocational education and training.
Formerly (Mar. 1997): Labour Economics and Productivity (1033-4882)
Related titles: Online - full text ed.: (from R M I T Publishing).
Indexed: AusPAIS, JEL.
Published by: Centre for Labour Market Research, University of Western Australia, Crawley, W.A. 6009, Australia. TEL 61-8-93808672, FAX 61-8-93808671, pmadden@ecel.uwa.edu.au, http://www.clmr.ecel.uwa.edu.au. Ed. Paul Flatau. R&P Charles Mulvey. Circ: 300.

➤ **AUSTRALIAN JOURNAL OF LABOUR LAW.** see *LAW—Corporate Law*

➤ **AUSTRALIAN JOURNAL OF MANAGEMENT AND ORGANISATIONAL BEHAVIOUR.** see *PSYCHOLOGY*

➤ **AVANCE DE INFORMACION ECONOMICA. EMPLEO.** see *BUSINESS AND ECONOMICS—Abstracting, Bibliographies, Statistics*

331.2   CAN   ISSN 1196-8915
AVANTAGES. Text in French. 198?. bi-m. adv. **Document type:** *Magazine, Trade.*
Formerly (until 1994): Benefits Canada pour le Quebec (1196-8907)
Related titles: Online - full text ed.: (from Micromedia ProQuest).
Published by: Rogers Media Publishing Ltd, One Mount Pleasant Rd, 11th Fl, Toronto, ON M4Y 2Y5, Canada. TEL 416-764-2000, FAX 416-764-3941, http://www.rogers.com.

AVERAGE ANNUAL PAY BY STATE AND INDUSTRY. see *BUSINESS AND ECONOMICS—Abstracting, Bibliographies, Statistics*

331.1029   CAN   ISSN 0715-2574
HD6523
B C LABOUR DIRECTORY. Text in English. 1973; N.S. 1983. a. CND 9.25. **Document type:** *Directory, Government.* **Description:** Compiles information on membership and officials of collective bargaining organizations in British Columbia.
Formerly: Labour Directory (Victoria) (0702-0759)
Published by: Ministry of Labour, Parliament Bldgs, Victoria, BC V8V 1X4, Canada. TEL 604-387-1757. Ed. Patrick Stanton. Circ: 600. **Subscr. to:** Crown Publications Inc., 521 Fort St, Victoria, BC BC V8W 1E7, Canada. TEL 604-386-4636.

331.255   USA
B L S REPORTS ON EMPLOYEE BENEFITS IN THE UNITED STATES. Text in English. biennial?. **Document type:** *Government.*
Related titles: ◆ Series of: U.S. Bureau of Labor Statistics. Reports.

Published by: U.S. Department of Labor, Bureau of Labor Statistics, Postal Square Bldg., 2 Massachusetts Ave, NE, Washington, DC 20212-0001 . TEL 202-655-4000. **Subscr. to:** U.S. Government Printing Office, Superintendent of Documents.

B L S UPDATE. see *BUSINESS AND ECONOMICS—Abstracting, Bibliographies, Statistics*

331.21   USA
B N A POLICY AND PRACTICE SERIES. COMPENSATION. Text in English. w.
Media: Online - full text. **Related titles:** CD-ROM ed.
Published by: The Bureau of National Affairs, Inc., 1231 25th St., NW, Washington, DC 20037. TEL 202-452-4200, 800-372-1033, FAX 202-785-7167, customercare@bna.com, http://www.bna.com. **Subscr. to:** 9435 Key West Ave, Rockville, MD 20850.

331   USA   ISSN 0149-2683
B N A POLICY AND PRACTICE SERIES. FAIR EMPLOYMENT PRACTICES. Text in English. 1965. bi-w. looseleaf. USD 1,094 (effective 2005). back issues avail. **Document type:** *Newsletter, Trade.* **Description:** Provides a notification and reference covering developments affecting fair employment practices. Includes federal laws, orders and regulations; policy guides and discussions of federal court decisions; and state and local fair employment practice laws.
Related titles: Online - full text ed.: (from The Dialog Corporation); ◆ Series of: B N A Policy and Practice Series. ISSN 0005-3228.
—CCC.
Published by: The Bureau of National Affairs, Inc., 1231 25th St., NW, Washington, DC 20037. TEL 202-452-4200, 800-372-1033, FAX 202-785-7167, customercare@bna.com, http://www.bna.com/. Ed. Bill L Manville. Pub. Greg C McCaffery.

331.21   USA   ISSN 0149-2691
KF3315
B N A POLICY AND PRACTICE SERIES. WAGES AND HOURS. Text in English. 1938. w. looseleaf. USD 1,064 (effective 2004). back issues avail. **Document type:** *Newsletter.* **Description:** Contains full text, summaries, and explanations of federal exemptions, wage-hour division inspections, minimum wages, equal pay, overtime, and child labor. Cover enforcement policies, procedures, and precedent-setting decisions.
Formerly: Wage Hour Report
Related titles: ◆ Series of: B N A Policy and Practice Series. ISSN 0005-3228.
—CCC.
Published by: The Bureau of National Affairs, Inc., 1231 25th St., NW, Washington, DC 20037. TEL 202-452-4200, 800-372-1033, FAX 202-785-7167, customercare@bna.com, http://www.bna.com/. Ed. Bill L Manville. Pub. Greg C McCaffery.

331.255   USA   ISSN 1094-7809
KF3509
B N A'S EMPLOYEE BENEFITS LIBRARY ON CD. Text in English. 1995. m. USD 3,035 (effective 2005 - 2006). **Description:** Contains tax management's compensation planning portfolios, BNA's employee benefits cases, the ABA-BNA employee benefits law treatise, BNA's compensation and benefits guide, IRS and treasury regulations, federal statutes, IRS documents, federal agency opinion letters, and more than 150 IRS, DOL, SEC, SSA and PBGC interactive forms and instructions.
Media: CD-ROM. **Related titles:** Online - full text ed.: (from The Bureau of National Affairs, Inc.); ◆ Print ed.: Benefits & Compensation Management Update. ISSN 1526-3932.
—CCC.
Published by: The Bureau of National Affairs, Inc., 1231 25th St., NW, Washington, DC 20037. TEL 202-452-4200, FAX 202-822-8092, http://www.bna.com/. Ed. Chris Cosby.

331.21   USA   ISSN 1051-4775
KF3611.A3
B N A'S WORKERS' COMPENSATION REPORT. Text in English. 1990. s-m. USD 604 (effective 2006). Index. back issues avail. **Document type:** *Newsletter, Trade.* **Description:** Provides comprehensive coverage of national and state workers' compensation developments. Includes information on legal, legislative, and industry developments, actions, and trends related to workers' compensation.
Related titles: Online - full text ed.: ISSN 1521-4680 (from The Bureau of National Affairs, Inc.).
—CCC.
Published by: L R P Publications, 747 Dresher Rd, PO Box 980, Horsham, PA 19044. TEL 215-784-0941, 800-341-7874, FAX 215-784-9639, custserve@lrp.com, http://www.shoplrp.com/product/p-8001,WCR.html, http://www.lrp.com. Ed. Dalana Bewley.

331.8   USA
B W C FOCUS; Ohio workers' Compensation safety and risk magazine. Text in English. q.

Published by: Ohio Bureau of Workers' Compensation, Communications Department, 30 W Spring St, 3rd Fl, Columbus, OH 43266-0581. deborah.katterheinrich@bwc.state.oh.us, http://www.ohiobwc.com/.

B W C NEWS. see *INSURANCE*

BELGIUM. HOGE RAAD VOOR DE MIDDENSTAND. JAARVERSLAG. see *PUBLIC ADMINISTRATION*

331.11 BEL
BELGIUM. OFFICE NATIONAL DE L'EMPLOI. BULLETIN MENSUEL. Text in French. 1970. m. EUR 96.70; EUR 8.10 per issue (effective 2004). charts; stat. 70 p./no.; **Document type:** *Journal, Government.*
Indexed: PAIS.
Published by: (Belgium. Direction Statistiques-Etudes-Information), Office National de l'Emploi, Bd de l'Empereur 7, Brussels, 1000, Belgium. TEL 32-2-5154860, FAX 32-2-5141106, http://www.onem.fgov.be. Ed. Karel Baeck. R&P Dirk Debie. Circ: 2,000.

331 BEL ISSN 1375-7881
BELGIUM. OFFICE NATIONAL DE L'EMPLOI. COMMUNIQUE MENSUEL. Text in French. m. EUR 9.40; EUR 0.80 per issue (effective 2004). 19 p./no.; **Document type:** *Journal, Government.*
Formerly (until 2000): Belgium. Office National de l'Emploi. Communique Bimensuel
Related titles: Dutch ed.: Belgium. Rijksdienst voor Arbeidsvoorziening. Maandelijks Mededeling. ISSN 1375-789X. 2000.
Published by: Office National de l'Emploi, Bd de l'Empereur 7, Brussels, 1000, Belgium. TEL 32-2-5154860, FAX 32-2-5141106, http://www.onem.fgov.be. Ed. Karel Baeck. R&P Dirk Debie.

331 BEL
BELGIUM. OFFICE NATIONAL DE L'EMPLOI. ETUDES ECONOMIQUES ET SOCIALES. Text in French. 1935. a. **Document type:** *Journal, Government.*
Incorporates: Belgium. Office National de l'Emploi. Rapport Annuel (0067-5644)
Related titles: Dutch ed.: Belgium. Rijksdienst voor Arbeidsvoorziening. Jaarverslag. ISSN 0378-3146.
Published by: Office National de l'Emploi, Bd de l'Empereur 7, Brussels, 1000, Belgium. TEL 32-2-5154860, FAX 32-2-5141106, http://www.onem.fgov.be. Ed. Karel Baeck. R&P Dirk Debie. Circ: 3,000.

(YEAR) BELIZE LABOUR FORCE INDICATORS. see *BUSINESS AND ECONOMICS—Abstracting, Bibliographies, Statistics*

344.01 USA ISSN 1550-7610
KFC556
BENDER'S CALIFORNIA LABOR & EMPLOYMENT BULLETIN. Text in English. 1990. m. USD 538 (effective 2004).
Description: covers equal employment opportunity laws, wrongful termination and discipline, employee privacy issue, wages, hours and working conditions, trade secrets and unfair competition in the employment seting, california occupational safety and health law, employer liability to third parties for employee conduct and public sector labor relations.
Formerly (until 2004): California Employment Law Reporter (1062-5054)
—**CCC.**
Published by: Matthew Bender & Co., Inc. (Subsidiary of: LexisNexis North America), 1275 Broadway, Albany, NY 12204. international@bender.com, http://bender.lexisnexis.com. Eds. Brad Seligman, Mark S. Rudy.

331.2550973 USA ISSN 1550-4190
BENEFITS AND COMPENSATION DIGEST. Text in English. m. USD 100 combined subscription including Legal-Legislative Reporter (effective 2004). **Document type:** *Magazine, Trade.*
Description: Covers employee benefits issues and trends, including information on Foundation activities and a review of current employee benefits and compensation articles.
Formed by the 2004 merger of: Employee Benefits Journal (0361-4050); Employee Benefits Digest; Which was formerly: International Foundation of Employee Benefit Plans. Digest (0146-1141); N F Digest (National Foundation of Health, Welfare and Pension Plans)
Related titles: Online - full content ed.: ISSN 1550-4212; Online - full text ed.: (from H.W. Wilson, O C L C Online Computer Library Center, Inc.).
Indexed: ABIn, BPI.
—BLDSC (1891.466600). **CCC.**
Published by: International Foundation of Employee Benefit Plans, 18700 W Bluemound Rd, Box 69, Brookfield, WI 53008-0069. TEL 262-786-6700, FAX 262-786-8780, books@ifebp.org, http://www.ifebp.org/bookstore/periodicals/bcsum.asp.

331.255 USA ISSN 1526-3932
BENEFITS & COMPENSATION MANAGEMENT UPDATE. Text in English. 1993. bi-w. USD 287 in United States (effective 2005 - 2006).
Formerly (until 1999): Compensation and Benefits Guide (1071-0051)
Related titles: ♦ CD-ROM ed.: B N A's Employee Benefits Library on CD. ISSN 1094-7809; Online - full text ed.: (from The Bureau of National Affairs, Inc.).
—**CCC.**
Published by: The Bureau of National Affairs, Inc., 1231 25th St., NW, Washington, DC 20037. TEL 202-452-4132, 202-452-4200, http://www.bna.com/products/eb/cbgd.htm.

331.2 CAN ISSN 0703-7732
BENEFITS CANADA; pension investment and employee benefits. Text in English. 1977. 12/yr. free to qualified personnel (effective 2005). adv. **Document type:** *Magazine, Trade.*
Description: Provides information on news and trends in Canada's pension fund investment and employee benefits industry.
Related titles: Microfiche ed.: (from MML); Microform ed.: (from MML); Online - full text ed.: (from EBSCO Publishing, Micromedia ProQuest, O C L C Online Computer Library Center, Inc., ProQuest Information & Learning).
Indexed: ABIn, CBCABus, CBCARef, CBPI, CPerI.
—BLDSC (1891.469000), IE, ingenta. **CCC.**
Published by: Rogers Media Publishing Ltd, One Mount Pleasant Rd, 11th Fl, Toronto, ON M4Y 2Y5, Canada. TEL 416-764-2000, FAX 416-764-3941, http://www.benefitscanada.com, http://www.rogers.com. Ed. Kevin Press. Pub. Charles Lee. Adv. contact Peter Greenhough. Circ: 16,000.

331.2 GBR
BENEFITS FOR YOU; the benefits magazine for employees. Text in English. bi-m. adv. **Document type:** *Magazine, Consumer.*
Description: Provides benefits and lifestyle information for local government and council employees.
Published by: C & B Communications, 40 Marsh Wall, Docklands, London, E14 9TP, United Kingdom. TEL 44-20-7308-8500, FAX 44-20-7308-8555, info@cbcomm.co.uk, http://www.cbcomm.co.uk. Adv. contact Mark Toland. Circ: 400,000 (controlled and free).

344.01 USA ISSN 1067-7666
K9
➤ **BERKELEY JOURNAL OF EMPLOYMENT AND LABOR LAW.** Text in English. 1976. biennial. USD 36 domestic to individuals; USD 51 foreign to individuals; USD 47 domestic to institutions; USD 62 foreign to institutions (effective 2005). adv. bk.rev. illus. index. back issues avail.; reprint service avail. from PQC,WSH. **Document type:** *Journal, Academic/Scholarly.* **Description:** Covers the full range of employment and labor law.
Formerly (until 1993): Industrial Relations Law Journal (0145-188X)
Related titles: Microfiche ed.: (from WSH); Microfilm ed.: (from WSH); Microform ed.: (from PQC, WSH); Online - full text ed.: (from EBSCO Publishing, Florida Center for Library Automation, LexisNexis).
Indexed: ABIn, ABRCLP, BPIA, BusI, CJA, CLI, CurCont, ILP, LRI, LegCont, PAIS, SSCI.
—BLDSC (1940.348000), IE, ingenta. **CCC.**
Published by: University of California at Berkeley, School of Law, Publications Coordinator, Boalt Hall School of Law, 421 North Addition, Berkeley, CA 94720-7200. TEL 510-643-6600, FAX 510-643-6816, bjell@law.berkeley.edu, http://www.boalt.org/BJELL/. Eds. Heather Horne, Bridget Smith. adv.: B&W page USD 275. Circ: 650 (paid).

331 DEU ISSN 0934-5094
BESOLDUNGSRECHT. Text in German. 1975. irreg. price varies. **Document type:** *Monographic series, Trade.*
Published by: Erich Schmidt Verlag GmbH & Co. (Berlin), Genthiner Str 30G, Berlin, 10785, Germany. TEL 49-30-250085-0, FAX 49-30-25008511, esv@esvmedien.de, http://www.erich-schmidt-verlag.de.

BIBLIOGRAFIA DE POLITICA INDUSTRIAL. see *BUSINESS AND ECONOMICS—Abstracting, Bibliographies, Statistics*

BIBLIOGRAPHIE ZUR GESCHICHTE DER DEUTSCHEN ARBEITERBEWEGUNG. see *BUSINESS AND ECONOMICS—Abstracting, Bibliographies, Statistics*

331.125 USA
BIG AL RECRUITING NEWSLETTER. Text in English. irreg. **Document type:** *Newsletter.* **Description:** Presents tips on sponsoring and building a downline, resources on recruiting strategies and essays on employment.
Media: E-mail.
Address: bigalnews@tntmag.com, Maryelle@tntmag.com, http://www.fortunenow.com/. Ed. Maryelle Huber.

331 USA ISSN 1053-704X
BLACK EMPLOYMENT AND EDUCATION. Text in English. 1990. q. USD 15. adv. bk.rev. **Document type:** *Trade.* **Description:** Addresses career opportunities here and abroad and includes people and company profiles. Specializes in careers in business and healthcare administration.
Published by: Hamdani, Inc., 2625 Piedmont Rd, Ste 56 282, Atlanta, GA 30324. TEL 404-469-5891. Ed. S Barry Hamdani. Circ: 30,000 (paid); 120,000 (controlled).

BLACK PERSPECTIVE. see *OCCUPATIONS AND CAREERS*

BLACKSTONE'S STATUTES ON EMPLOYMENT LAW (YEAR). see *LAW*

331.125 PRT ISSN 0870-4821
BOLETIM DO TRABALHO E EMPREGO 1A SERIE. Text in Portuguese. 1933. w. EUR 198; EUR 289 combined subscription Series 1 and 2 (effective 2005).
Supersedes in part (in 1976): Ministerio do Trabalho. Boletim (0871-181X); Which was formerly (until 1974): Instituto Nacional do Trabajo e Previdencia. Boletim (0301-519X)
Published by: (Portugal. Servico de Informacao Cientifica e Tecnica), Ministerio do Trabalho, Praca de Londres, 2 - 16o, Lisbon, 1049-056, Portugal. TEL 351-21-8424100, FAX 351-21-8424108, gmtss@mtss.gov.pt, http://www.dgeep.mtss.gov.pt/edicoes/bte/indices.php, http://www.mtss.gov.pt/.

331 PRT ISSN 0870-516X
BOLETIM DO TRABALHO E EMPREGO. 2A SERIE. Text in Portuguese. 1933. q. EUR 127; EUR 289 combined subscription Series 1 and 2 (effective 2005).
Supersedes in part (in 1976): Ministerio do Trabalho. Boletim (0871-181X); Which was formerly (until 1974): Instituto Nacional do Trabalho e Previdencia. Boletim (0301-519X)
Published by: Ministerio do Trabalho, Praca de Londres, 2 - 16o, Lisbon, 1049-056, Portugal. TEL 351-21-8424100, FAX 351-21-8424108, gmtss@mtss.gov.pt, http://www.dgeep.mtss.gov.pt/edicoes/bte/bte2anteriores.php, http://www.mtss.gov.pt/.

331 IND ISSN 0067-9917
BOMBAY LABOUR JOURNAL✱. Text in English. 1960. a. free.
Published by: Bombay Labour Institute, Dadabhai Chamarbaugwala Rd., Parel, Mumbai, Maharashtra 400 012, India. Ed. S A Vaidya.

BOTSWANA. CENTRAL STATISTICS OFFICE. LABOUR STATISTICS. see *BUSINESS AND ECONOMICS—Abstracting, Bibliographies, Statistics*

331 DEU
BRENNPUNKTE DES ARBEITSRECHTS (YEAR). Text in German. a. **Document type:** *Bulletin, Trade.*
Published by: (Deutscher Anwaltsinstitut e.V.), Z A P - Verlag fuer die Rechts- und Anwaltspraxis GmbH und Co., Postfach 101953, Recklinghausen, 45619, Germany. FAX 49-2323-141123, hotline@zap-verlag.de, http://www.zap-verlag.de.

344.01 CAN
BRITISH COLUMBIA DECISIONS - LABOUR ARBITRATION: CUMULATIVE INDEX. Text in English. base vol. plus s-a. updates. looseleaf. **Document type:** *Trade.* **Description:** Provides the only cumulative listing of all British Columbia Labour Arbitration Awards from 1974 to the present.
Published by: Canada Law Book Inc., 240 Edward St, Aurora, ON L4G 3S9, Canada. TEL 905-841-6472, 800-263-3269, FAX 905-841-5085, b.loney@canadalawbook.ca, http://www.canadalawbook.ca/catalogue.cfm?DSP=Detail&ProductID=531. R&P Nancy Nesbitt.

331.11 CAN ISSN 1192-1099
BRITISH COLUMBIA. JOB PROTECTION COMMISSION. ANNUAL REPORT. Text in English. 1991. a.
Published by: British Columbia, Job Protection Commission, 1675 Douglas St 4th Fl, Victoria, BC V8V 1X4, Canada. TEL 250-387-5629, FAX 250-387-1696.

331 CAN ISSN 1205-0245
BRITISH COLUMBIA. LABOUR RELATIONS BOARD. ANNUAL REPORT. Text in English. 1974. a. CND 6. stat. **Document type:** *Government.* **Description:** Covers the structure of the Board, biographies of OICs, and statistics of all applications received.
Former titles (until 1993): British Columbia. Industrial Relations Council. Annual Report (0838-0899); (until 1987): British Columbia. Labour Relations Board. Annual Report (0319-0404)
Published by: Labour Relations Board, 900 360 W Georgia St, Vancouver, BC V6B 6B2, Canada. TEL 604-660-1300, FAX 604-660-1892. Ed. C Lyte. Circ: 500.

344.01 CAN
BRITISH COLUMBIA LABOUR RELATIONS BOARD DECISIONS - CUMULATIVE INDEX. Text in English. 2 base vols. plus s-a. updates. looseleaf. price avail. on request. **Document type:** *Trade.* **Description:** Provides the only cumulative listing of all British Columbia Labour Relations Board and Industrial Relations Council decisions from 1974 to the present.
Published by: Canada Law Book Inc., 240 Edward St, Aurora, ON L4G 3S9, Canada. TEL 905-841-6472, 800-263-3269, FAX 905-841-5085, b.loney@canadalawbook.ca, http://www.canadalawbook.ca/catalogue.cfm?DSP=Detail&ProductID=532. R&P Nancy Nesbitt.

B

344.01 CAN ISSN 0715-5808
BRITISH COLUMBIA LABOUR RELATIONS BOARD DECISIONS - DIGEST. Text in English. 1979. m. looseleaf. CND 436 (effective 2005). s-a. index; cum.index. **Document type:** *Trade.* **Description:** Provides full summaries of all written and letter decisions of the Industrial Relations Council of British Columbia.
Related titles: ◆ CD-ROM ed.: Dart: British Columbia Labour Decisions. ISSN 1480-5065; Online - full text ed.
Published by: Canada Law Book Inc., 240 Edward St, Aurora, ON L4G 3S9, Canada. TEL 905-841-6472, 800-263-3269, FAX 905-841-5085, b.loney@canadalawbook.ca, http://www.canadalawbook.ca. R&P Nancy Nesbitt.

331 CAN ISSN 1499-724X
HD8109.B7
BRITISH COLUMBIA. MINISTRY OF LABOUR. ANNUAL PERFORMANCE REPORT. Text in English. 1918. a. free. illus. **Document type:** *Government.*
Former titles (until 2001): British Columbia. Ministry of Labour. Annual Report (1206-9116); (until 1996): British Columbia. Ministry of Skills, Training and Labour. Annual Report (1201-7884); Which superseded in part (in 1994): British Columbia. Ministry of Labour and Consumer Services. Annual Report (0836-1126); Which was formerly (until 1986): British Columbia. Ministry of Labour. Annual Report (0705-9698); (until 1976): British Columbia. Department of Labour. Annual Report (0381-2898)
Published by: Ministry of Labour, Parliament Bldgs, Victoria, BC V8V 1X4, Canada. TEL 604-387-3169, FAX 604-356-8102. Ed. Ed Wall. Circ: 3,000.

331.1 GBR ISSN 0007-1080
HD6951 CODEN: BJIRAV
➤ **BRITISH JOURNAL OF INDUSTRIAL RELATIONS.** Text in English. 1963. q. GBP 66, EUR 99 combined subscription in Europe to individuals print & online eds.; USD 151 combined subscription in the Americas to individuals & Caribbean, print & online eds.; GBP 90 combined subscription elsewhere to individuals print & online eds.; GBP 290 combined subscription in Europe to institutions print & online eds.; USD 591 combined subscription in the Americas to institutions & Caribbean, print & online eds.; GBP 352 combined subscription elsewhere to institutions print & online eds.; GBP 47, EUR 71 combined subscription in Europe to students print & online eds.; USD 96 combined subscription in the Americas to students & Caribbean, print & online eds.; GBP 57 combined subscription elsewhere to students print & online eds. (effective 2006). adv. bk.rev. bibl.; charts; stat.; illus. index. back issues avail.; reprint service avail. from PQC,PSC. **Document type:** *Journal, Academic/Scholarly.* **Description:** Publishes articles covering both the theory and practice of industrial relations.
Related titles: Online - full text ed.: ISSN 1467-8543. GBP 276 in Europe to institutions; USD 561 in the Americas to institutions & Caribbean; GBP 334 elsewhere to institutions (effective 2006) (from Blackwell Synergy, EBSCO Publishing, Gale Group, IngentaConnect, O C L C Online Computer Library Center, Inc., Swets Information Services).
Indexed: ABIn, ASCA, ArtHuCI, BAS, BPI, BPIA, BrHumI, BusI, CPM, CREJ, CurCont, DIP, EI, ESPM, Emerald, ErgAb, H&SSA, HRA, IBR, IBSS, IBZ, ILD, IPSA, Inspec, JEL, M&MA, MEA&I, ManagCont, PAIS, PCI, PSA, RASB, RiskAb, SCIMP, SSA, SSCI, SociolAb, WBA, WorkRelAb.
—BLDSC (2310.500000), IDS, IE, Infotrieve, ingenta. **CCC.**
Published by: (London School of Economics and Political Science), Blackwell Publishing Ltd., 9600 Garsington Rd, Oxford, OX4 2ZG, United Kingdom. TEL 44-1865-776868, FAX 44-1865-714591, customerservices@oxon.blackwellpublishing.com, http://www.blackwellpublishing.com/journals/BJIR. Ed. Edmund Heery TEL 44-1222-874000. Circ: 2,000.

➤ **BUILDING COST INFORMATION SERVICE. LABOUR, HOURS & WAGES.** see *BUILDING AND CONSTRUCTION*

331 NLD ISSN 0770-3724
K2
BULLETIN OF COMPARATIVE LABOUR RELATIONS. Text in English. 1975. irreg. (1-2/yr.), latest vol.48, 2003. price varies. **Document type:** *Bulletin, Academic/Scholarly.* **Description:** Discusses labor relations in various countries at an international level, as well as specific topical issues in labor law and labor relations.
Indexed: BPIA, IBSS, ILD, PAIS.
—BLDSC (2839.080000), IE, ingenta.
Published by: (Institute for Labour Relations BEL), Kluwer Law International (Subsidiary of: Aspen Publishers, Inc.), Laan van Meerdervoort 70, PO Box 85889, The Hague, 2508 CN, Netherlands. TEL 31-70-3081500, FAX 31-70-3081515, sales@kluwerlaw.com, http://www.kluwerlaw.com. Ed. R Blanpain. Pub. Mr. Karel van der Linde.

331 FRA ISSN 0242-5874
BULLETIN SOCIAL. Text in French. 1977 (vol.9). m. EUR 82 (effective 2005). **Document type:** *Bulletin, Trade.*
Formerly: Bulletin de Documentation Pratique de Securite Sociale et de Legislation du Travail
Published by: Editions Francis Lefebvre, 42 rue de Villiers, Levallois-Perret, 92300, France. TEL 33-1-41052222, http://www.efl.fr.

331 CAN ISSN 0704-0865
BULLETIN SUR LES RELATIONS DU TRAVAIL. Text in French. 1969. m. CND 30 to non-members. **Document type:** *Bulletin.*
Related titles: English ed.: ISSN 0704-0873.
Published by: Conseil du Patronat du Quebec, 2075 rue University, Ste 606, Montreal, PQ H3A 2L1, Canada. TEL 514-288-5161, FAX 514-288-5165. Circ: 1,500.

331 DEU ISSN 0007-5868
BUNDESARBEITSBLATT. Text in German. 1949. m. EUR 114.30; EUR 12.60 newsstand/cover (effective 2004). adv. bk.rev. bibl.; charts; stat. index. reprints avail. **Document type:** *Journal, Government.*
Incorporates (1949-1979): Arbeitsschutz (0003-7788); (1950-1979): Arbeits- und Sozialstatistik (0341-7883); Which was formerly (until 1976): Arbeits- und Sozialstatistische Mitteilungen (0003-7672); Formerly (until 1950): Arbeitsblatt (0723-4139)
Related titles: ◆ Supplement(s): Amtliche Bekanntmachung zum Arbeitsschutz; ◆ Bundesversorgungsblatt. ISSN 0407-9132.
Indexed: CEABA, CISA, ILD, PAIS, RASB, WBSS.
—BLDSC (2930.105000), IE. **CCC.**
Published by: (Germany. Bundesministerium fuer Arbeit und Sozialordnung), W. Kohlhammer GmbH, Hessbruehlstr 69, Stuttgart, 70565, Germany. TEL 49-711-7863-1, FAX 49-711-7863263, bundesarbeitsblatt@bmwa.bund.de, info@kohlhammer-katalog.de, http://www.bundesarbeitsblatt.de, http://www.kohlhammer.de. Ed. Claus J Schmidt. adv.: B&W page EUR 1,350, color page EUR 2,362.50. Circ: 4,228 (paid).

331 DEU ISSN 0407-9132
BUNDESVERSORGUNGSBLATT. Text in German. 1951. 5/yr. **Document type:** *Government.*
Related titles: ◆ Supplement to: Bundesarbeitsblatt. ISSN 0007-5868.
Published by: (Germany. Bundesminister fuer Arbeit und Sozialordnung), W. Kohlhammer GmbH, Hessbruehlstr 69, Stuttgart, 70565, Germany. TEL 49-711-7863290, FAX 49-711-7863430.

331 AUS
BUSINESS ADVOCATE. Text in English. 1979. m. AUD 30. adv. bk.rev. **Document type:** *Trade.* **Description:** Information on latest developments in Western Australian business and industry.
Former titles (until 1997): Chamber of Commerce and Industry of Western Australia Business Report (1038-0515); (until 1992): Confederation of Western Australian Industry. Confederation Report (0810-1442); (until 1978): Industrial News
Published by: Chamber of Commerce & Industry of Western Australia, Hay St., E., P.O. Box 6209, Perth, W.A. 6892, Australia. TEL 61-8-93657555. Ed. R Pride. Circ: 7,000.

BUSINESS & LABOR DIALOGUE. see *BUSINESS AND ECONOMICS—International Development And Assistance*

344.01 USA
BUSINESS ORGANIZATIONS: LABOR LAW. Text in English. 1973. irreg. (in 1 vol.). looseleaf. USD 1,270 (effective 1999).
Published by: Matthew Bender & Co., Inc. (Subsidiary of: LexisNexis North America), 1275 Broadway, Albany, NY 12204. international@bender.com, http://bender.lexisnexis.com. Ed. T W Kheel.

BUTTERWORTHS EMPLOYMENT LAW BULLETIN. see *LAW—Corporate Law*

C B I A NEWS. see *BUSINESS AND ECONOMICS—Economic Situation And Conditions*

331.11 GBR ISSN 1362-4482
C B I. HUMAN RESOURCES REPORT. Key Title: Human Resources Report. Text in English. 1985. bi-m. GBP 160 to non-members; GBP 100 to members (effective 1999). adv. **Document type:** *Bulletin, Corporate.* **Description:** Covers major employment issues facing companies. Includes features and news articles on legislative change, new research, employment trends, and lobbying in areas such as employee relations, pay and benefits, and training.
Formerly (until 1996): Employment Affairs Report (0267-5374)
Published by: Confederation of British Industry, Centre Point, 103 New Oxford St, London, WC1A 1DU, United Kingdom. TEL 44-171-395-8154, FAX 44-171-240-1578. Ed. Nick Page. R&P Wendy Hay TEL 44-171-395-8036. Adv. contact Frances Hughes.

C I R NEWS. see *MEDICAL SCIENCES*

331.11 CAN ISSN 0045-5113
C L V REPORTS. (Canada Labour Views) Text in English. 1956. w. CND 500 domestic; USD 423.73 foreign (effective 2005). charts; stat. back issues avail. **Document type:** *Newsletter.* **Description:** Provides a summary of collective agreement renewal terms, industrial relations news, digests of labor law cases, and trend analyses for human resources, industrial relations, and union professionals.
Related titles: CD-ROM ed.
Published by: Carswell (Subsidiary of: Thomson Corporation), One Corporate Plaza, 2075 Kennedy Rd, Toronto, ON M1T 3V4, Canada. TEL 416-609-8000, 800-387-5164, FAX 416-298-5094, carswell.customerrelations@thomson.com, http://www.carswell.com. Ed. Gordon Sova.

352.63 USA ISSN 0194-3073
JK8755
C P E R. (California Public Employee Relations) Text in English. 1969. bi-m. USD 250 (effective 2004). bk.rev. index, cum.index. **Document type:** *Magazine, Trade.* **Description:** Contains comprehensive information on public sector employment relations at all levels of California government.
Indexed: PAIS.
Published by: (University of California at Berkeley, Institute of Industrial Relations), Berkeley Electronic Press, 2809 Telegraph Ave., Ste 202, Berkeley, CA 94705. TEL 510-665-1200, FAX 510-665-1201, info@bepress.com, http://services.bepress.com/cper/, http://www.bepress.com. Eds. Carol Vendrillo, Carol Vendrillo TEL 510-643-7096, Whitney Gabriel. R&P Sharon Melnyk TEL 510-643-7093. Circ: 1,000 (paid).

C S G STATE DIRECTORY. DIRECTORY III, ADMINISTRATIVE OFFICIALS. see *PUBLIC ADMINISTRATION*

CALIFORNIA COMPENSATION CASES. see *LAW*

331.1 USA
CALIFORNIA. DEPARTMENT OF INDUSTRIAL RELATIONS. BIENNIAL REPORT. Key Title: Biennial Report for the Department of Industrial Relations. Text in English. 1883. biennial. illus. **Document type:** *Government.*
Formerly: California. Department of Industrial Relations. Annual Report (0362-4129)
Published by: Department of Industrial Relations, Division of Labor Statistics and Research, PO Box 420603, San Francisco, CA 94132-0603. TEL 415-703-4981. Ed. Richard Stephens.

331.1 USA ISSN 0362-4110
HD6274.C3
CALIFORNIA. DEPARTMENT OF THE YOUTH AUTHORITY. AFFIRMATIVE ACTION STATISTICS; report. Key Title: Affirmative Action Statistics. Text in English. 1974. s-a. free. illus.
Published by: Department of the Youth Authority, 4241 Williamsbourgh Dr, Sacramento, CA 95823. TEL 916-445-9962.

331 USA ISSN 0098-1435
HD5725.C2
CALIFORNIA EMPLOYER. Text in English. 1937. q. free (effective 2005). illus. **Document type:** *Newsletter, Government.*
Former titles (until 1974): Employment News; (until 1969): H R D Newsletter to Employers; H R D News (0017-6214)
Indexed: BldManAb, BrCerAb, CalPI, M&MA.
Published by: Employment Development Department, 800 Capitol Mall, MIC 84, Sacramento, CA 95814. TEL 916-654-7079, FAX 916-654-5843, http://www.edd.ca.gov/. Ed., R&P Kevin Callori. Circ: 825,000.

344.01 USA ISSN 1058-4293
CALIFORNIA EMPLOYER ADVISOR. Text in English. 1991. m. USD 167 (effective 1999). index. back issues avail. **Document type:** *Newsletter.* **Description:** Award-winning guide to employment law and employee relations.
Published by: Employer Resource Institute, Inc., 98 Main St., Ste. 700, Tiburon, CA 94920. TEL 415-332-4747. Ed. Larry J Shapiro.

331 USA
CALIFORNIA EMPLOYERS' GUIDE TO EMPLOYEE HANDBOOKS AND PERSONNEL POLICY MANUALS. Text in English. 1989. base vol. plus a. updates. looseleaf. USD 141 base vol(s). (effective 2003). **Description:** Complete guide to writing, revising and updating employee handbooks and personnel policy manuals. Includes checklists, sample clauses, authority and cross references to California Employment Law.
Related titles: CD-ROM ed.
Published by: (Morrison & Foerster), Matthew Bender & Co., Inc. (Subsidiary of: LexisNexis North America), 1275 Broadway, Albany, NY 12204. international@bender.com, http://bender.lexisnexis.com.

344.01 USA
KFC556
CALIFORNIA EMPLOYMENT LAW. Text in English. 1989. 4 base vols. plus irreg. updates. looseleaf. USD 653 (effective 2003). Supplement avail. **Description:** Provides a comprehensive treatment of California law governing employer-employee relations in the private sector. Includes in-depth discussion of the law, practice tips from experienced employment law practitioners, factual illustrations, sample employment documents, and litigation forms.
Related titles: CD-ROM ed.: USD 1,637 (effective 2002).
Published by: Matthew Bender & Co., Inc. (Subsidiary of: LexisNexis North America), 1275 Broadway, Albany, NY 12204. international@bender.com, http://bender.lexisnexis.com. Ed. Kirby Wilcox.

CALIFORNIA EMPLOYMENT LAW LETTER. see *LAW*

344.01 USA
KFC557.A15C3
CALIFORNIA LABOR AND EMPLOYMENT ALERT NEWSLETTER. Text in English. 1982. bi-m. looseleaf. USD 75. adv. index. **Document type:** *Newsletter.* **Description:** Provides summaries of significant developments in labor, employment and benefits laws.
Formerly: California Labor and Employment Alert for All California Employers
Published by: Castle Publications Ltd., PO Box 580, Van Nuys, CA 91408. TEL 818-708-3208. Ed. Richard Simmons. Adv. contact Elliot Berk.

CALIFORNIA LABOR MARKET BULLETIN. see *BUSINESS AND ECONOMICS—Economic Situation And Conditions*

CALIFORNIA LAW OF EMPLOYEE INJURIES AND WORKERS' COMPENSATION. see *LAW*

331.21 USA ISSN 1529-2282
CALIFORNIA PAYROLL COMPLIANCE REPORT. Text in English. m.
Published by: ProPub Inc., PO Box 102, Wyckoff, NJ 07481-0102. TEL 201-447-6485, FAX 201-447-9356.

344.01 USA
CALIFORNIA PUBLIC EMPLOYEES' RETIREMENT LAW. Text in English. a. USD 28. 570 p./no.
Published by: LexisNexis (Subsidiary of: LexisNexis North America), PO Box 7587, Charlottesville, VA 22906-7587. TEL 804-972-7566, 800-562-1197, FAX 800-643-1280, llp.customer.support@lexis-nexis.com, http://www.lexislawpublishing.com. Ed. George Harley.

344.01 USA
CALIFORNIA PUBLIC SECTOR LABOR RELATIONS. Text in English. 1989. base vol. plus irreg. updates. looseleaf. USD 175 base vol(s). (effective 2003). Supplement avail.
Description: It is written specifically for California employment litigators, public sector human resource specialists, state and local public agency managers, and public sector employee organizations. This journal comprehensively discusses the statutes governing public sector labor relations, imprtant court cases, and the Public Employment Relations Board decisions interpreting those statutes.
Related titles: CD-ROM ed.
Published by: Matthew Bender & Co., Inc. (Subsidiary of: LexisNexis North America), 1275 Broadway, Albany, NY 12204. international@bender.com, http://bender.lexisnexis.com. Ed. Kristen L Zerger.

331.2529137 USA
LB2842.2
CALIFORNIA. TEACHERS' RETIREMENT BOARD. STATE TEACHERS' RETIREMENT SYSTEM; COMPREHENSIVE ANNUAL FINANCIAL REPORT TO THE GOVERNOR AND THE LEGISLATURE. Text in English. 1963. a. free. **Document type:** *Government.*
Formerly: California. Teachers' Retirement Board. State Teachers' Retirement System; Annual Report to the Governor and the Legislature (0090-5593)
Published by: Teachers' Retirement Board, PO Box 15275, Sacramento, CA 95851-0275. TEL 916-229-3700, http://www.calstrs.ca.gov, http://www.strs.ca.gov. Ed. James D Mosman. R&P Bill Rogers. Circ: 1,500 (controlled).

CALIFORNIA UNEMPLOYMENT AND DISABILITY COMPENSATION PROGRAMS. see *INSURANCE*

331.21 368.4 USA ISSN 1548-9647
▼ **CALIFORNIA WORKERS' COMP ALERT.** Text in English. 2004 (May). m. USD 187 (effective 2005). **Document type:** *Newsletter, Trade.* **Description:** Provides a month-by-month analysis of workers' compensation developments in California.
Published by: M. Lee Smith Publishers LLC, PO Box 5094, Brentwood, TN 37024. TEL 615-373-7517, 800-274-6774, FAX 615-373-5183, custserv@mleesmith.com, http://www.hrhero.com/wc/cawc.shtml, http://www.mleesmith.com.

▼ **CALIFORNIA WORKERS' COMP LAW BULLETIN.** see *LAW*

CALIFORNIA WORKERS' COMPENSATION CLAIMS AND BENEFITS. see *INSURANCE*

CALIFORNIA WORKERS' COMPENSATION HANDBOOK. see *INSURANCE*

CALIFORNIA WORKERS' COMPENSATION REPORTER; A Monthly Bulletin of Key Developments in Workers' Compensation Law. see *LAW*

331 GBR
CAMBRIDGE STUDIES IN WORK AND SOCIAL INEQUALITY. Text in English. irreg. adv. **Document type:** *Monographic series.*
Published by: U C L Press Ltd. (Subsidiary of: Cavendish Publishing Ltd.), 1 Gunpowder Sq, London, EC4A 3DE, United Kingdom. TEL 44-171-380-7707, FAX 44-171-413-8392. Adv. contact Tina Jeavons.

331 CAN ISSN 1198-2381
HD5710.5
CANADA EMPLOYMENT WEEKLY; the weekly survey of new job opportunities in 61 fields. Text in English. 1993. w. CND 310.20 domestic; CND 407.62 in United States; CND 558.19 elsewhere (effective 2005). adv. abstr.; stat. cum. index: 1998-2000. back issues avail.; reprints avail. **Document type:** *Newspaper, Consumer.* **Description:** Brings readers over 1000 new job opportunities in 16 major occupational categories every week.
Related titles: Online - full content ed.: C E W Express. CND 227.42 (effective 2005).
Published by: Mediacorp Canada Inc., 21 New St, Toronto, ON M5R 1P7, Canada. TEL 416-964-6069, FAX 416-964-3202, info@mediacorp2.com, http://www.mediacorp2.com. Ed. Karen Chow. Pub., R&P, Adv. contact Anthony Meehan. B&W page CND 3,026.40, color page CND 65,774.

331.11 CAN
CANADA. LABOUR CANADA. ANNUAL REPORT ON PROCEEDINGS UNDER THE CANADA LABOUR CODE, PART 3 (LABOUR STANDARDS)/CANADA. LABOUR CANADA. RAPPORT ANNUEL SUR LES MESURES PRISES EN VERTU DU CODE CANADIEN DU TRAVAIL, PARTIE 3 (LES NORMES DU TRAVAIL). Text in English. 1972. a. free.
Published by: Labour Canada, Publications Distribution, Ottawa, ON K1A 0J2, Canada. TEL 819-994-0543, FAX 819-997-1664. Circ: 700.

331.3021 CAN ISSN 1492-1480
CANADA. STATISTICS CANADA. INCOME IN CANADA. Text in English. 1998. a.
Formed by the merger of (1967-1998): Canada. Statistics Canada. Family Incomes, Census Families (0703-7368); (1968-1998): Canada. Statistics Canada. Household Facilities by Income and Other Characteristics (0226-4560); (1984-1998): Canada. Statistics Canada. Earnings of Men and Women (0829-6235); (1989-1998): Canada. Statistics Canada. Characteristics of Dual-Earner Families (1188-1879); (1990-1998): Canada. Statistics Canada. Low Income Persons (1201-4958); (1991-1998): Canada. Statistics Canada. Income after Tax, Distributions by Size in Canada (0319-0374); (1994-1998): Canada. Statistics Canada. Low Income after Tax (1209-1839); (1996-1998): Canada. Statistics Canada. Low Income Measure, Low Income after Tax Cut-Offs and Low Income after Tax Measures (1208-3542); (199?-1998): Canada. Statistics Canada. Low Income Cut-Offs (1201-494X); (19??-1998): Canada. Statistics Canada. Low Income Measure; (1965-1998): Canada. Statistics Canada. Income Distributions by Size in Canada (0575-8750); Which was formerly (1951-1961): Canada. Dominion Bureau of Statistics. Distribution of Non-Farm Incomes in Canada by Size (0837-4317)
Related titles: Online - full text ed.: ISSN 1492-1499. 1998; French ed.: Revenu au Canada. ISSN 1492-1804. 1998.
—CISTI.
Published by: Statistics Canada, Publications Sales and Services, Ottawa, ON K1A 0T6, Canada. TEL 613-951-7277, FAX 613-951-1582, http://www.statcan.ca/english/IPS/Data/75-202-XIE.htm.

CANADA. STATISTICS CANADA. PUBLIC SECTOR STATISTICS. see *BUSINESS AND ECONOMICS—Abstracting, Bibliographies, Statistics*

344.01 CAN
CANADA. STATISTICS CANADA. WOMEN'S LABOUR BUREAU. WOMEN IN THE LABOUR FORCE. Text in English. 1964. irreg. CND 40 domestic; USD 40 foreign (effective 1999). **Description:** Describes trends related to women's participation in the labour force.
Former titles: Canada. Women's Bureau. Women in the Labour Force. Facts and Figures (0382-2192); (until 1979): Canada. Women's Bureau. Facts and Figures. Women in the Labour Force (0068-7448)
Related titles: Microform ed.: (from MML); French ed.: Bureau de la Main-d'Oeuvre Feminine. Les Femmes dans la Population Active.
—CISTI.
Published by: Statistics Canada, Operations and Integration Division, Circulation Management, Jean Talon Bldg, 2 C12, Tunney's Pasture, Ottawa, ON K1A 0T6, Canada. TEL 613-951-7277, 800-267-6677, FAX 613-951-1584, http://www.statcan.ca.

331 CAN
CANADA'S TOP 100 EMPLOYERS. Text in English. a. CND 21.95 (effective 2003). **Document type:** *Monographic series, Consumer.* **Description:** Profiles industry leading employee benefits, working conditions and interesting perks, including business developments, benefits offered, work environment, employee feedback and community involvement. Also contains contact information, telephone & fax numbers, addresses, email addresses and websites.
Published by: Mediacorp Canada Inc., 21 New St, Toronto, ON M5R 1P7, Canada. TEL 416-964-6069, FAX 416-964-3202, info@mediacorp2.com, http://www.mediacorp2.com.

CANADIAN CONSTRUCTION LABOUR AND EMPLOYMENT LAW. see *LAW—Civil Law*

331.1 CAN ISSN 0045-4966
CANADIAN INDUSTRIAL RELATIONS AND PERSONNEL DEVELOPMENTS GUIDE. Text in English. 1969. m. looseleaf. CND 780 (effective 2005). bk.rev. abstr.; bibl.; charts; stat. index. **Document type:** *Trade.* **Description:** Reports major developments in industrial relations and personnel management. Presents Canadian economic indicators of the labor market.
Related titles: CD-ROM ed.: CND 730 (effective 2003); Online - full text ed.: CND 730 (effective 2003).
Published by: C C H Canadian Ltd., 90 Sheppard Ave E, Ste 300, North York, ON M2N 6X1, Canada. TEL 416-224-2248, 800-268-4522, FAX 416-224-2243, cservice@cch.ca, http://www.cch.ca.

344.01 CAN ISSN 0008-4328
CANADIAN LABOUR LAW REPORTER. Text in English. 1946. bi-w. looseleaf. CND 1,260 (effective 2005). back issues avail. **Document type:** *Trade.* **Description:** Federal and provincial laws on employer-employee relations, fair wages, vacations, statutory holidays, hours of work, industrial standards, fair employment practices. Outlines unemployment insurance and worker's compensation law.
Related titles: CD-ROM ed.: CND 1,260 (effective 2005); Online - full text ed.: CND 1,260 (effective 2005).
—CCC.
Published by: C C H Canadian Ltd., 90 Sheppard Ave E, Ste 300, North York, ON M2N 6X1, Canada. TEL 416-224-2248, 800-268-4522, FAX 416-224-2243, cservice@cch.ca, http://www.cch.ca.

B

331 CAN ISSN 0317-0535
KE3146.4
CANADIAN LABOUR RELATIONS BOARD REPORTS. Text in English. a. (in 9 parts and 9 vols.). CND 210 per vol. (effective 2001). **Description:** Presents the decisions of the federal and various provincial labour relations boards, as well as court decisions of appeals from the boards.
Published by: LexisNexis Butterworths Canada Inc. (Subsidiary of: LexisNexis North America), 123 Commerce Valley Dr E, Ste 700, Markham, ON L3T 7W8, Canada. TEL 905-479-2665, FAX 905-479-2826, http://www.lexisnexis.ca/canadianlabourrelationsboardreports.htm.

331 CAN ISSN 0846-3514
THE CAREER DIRECTORY. Text in English. 1991. a., latest 2001. CND 31.95 (effective 2003). **Document type:** *Directory, Consumer.* **Description:** Provides a listing of over 1,000 Canadian employers that cross reference job qualifications with degrees or diplomas.
Published by: Mediacorp Canada Inc., 21 New St, Toronto, ON M5R 1P7, Canada. TEL 416-964-6069, FAX 416-964-3202, info@mediacorp2.com, http://www.mediacorp2.com.

331.125 USA
CAREER EXPOSURE'S WHAT'S NEWS E-ZINE. Text in English. irreg. **Description:** Includes the latest career news, job placement tips, and employment issues.
Media: Online - full text.
Address: feedback@careerexposure.com, http://www.careerexposure.com/ezine.html.

CATHOLIC WORKER. see *RELIGIONS AND THEOLOGY—Roman Catholic*

331.21 GBR
CENTRAL LONDON SALARY SURVEY. Text in English. 2/yr. GBP 260 per vol. (effective 2001). **Document type:** *Bulletin.* **Description:** Pay and benefit salary survey for Central London.
Published by: The Reward Group Ltd., Reward House, Diamond Way, Stone Business Park, Stone, Staffs ST15 0SD, United Kingdom. TEL 44-1785-813566, FAX 44-1785-817007, enquiries@reward-group.co.uk, http://www.reward-group.co.uk.

331.21 GBR
CENTRAL SCOTLAND SALARY SURVEY. Text in English. 2/yr. GBP 280 per vol. (effective 2001). **Document type:** *Bulletin.* **Description:** Pay and benefit survey for Central Scotland covering the Tayside, Central Fife, Lothian and Strathclyde areas.
Published by: The Reward Group Ltd., Reward House, Diamond Way, Stone Business Park, Stone, Staffs ST15 0SD, United Kingdom. TEL 44-1785-813566, FAX 44-1785-817007, enquiries@reward-group.co.uk, http://www.reward-group.co.uk.

331 DNK ISSN 0908-8962
CENTRE FOR LABOUR MARKET AND SOCIAL RESEARCH. WORKING PAPERS. Text in Danish. 1981. irreg. price varies. illus.
Former titles (until 1994): Aarhus School of Business. Centre for Labour Economics. Working Papers (0905-6955); (until 1989): Studies in Labor Market Dynamics (0108-2469)
Published by: Centre for Labour Market and Social Research, Building 350, University of Aarhus, Aarhus C, 8000, Denmark. TEL 45-89-42-23-66, FAX 45-89-42-23-66, hbunzel@cls.dk, http://www.cls.dk/~hbunzel. Ed. Peder J Pedersen. Circ: 400.

331.12 AUS ISSN 1329-2676
CENTRE FOR LABOUR MARKET RESEARCH. DISCUSSION PAPER SERIES. Text in English. 1985. irreg. AUD 10 newsstand/cover domestic; AUD 15 newsstand/cover foreign (effective 2000). back issues avail. **Document type:** *Monographic series, Academic/Scholarly.* **Description:** Explores various aspects of the labor market and labor conditions.
Formerly (until l996): Western Australian Labour Market Research Centre. Discussion Paper (0819-6834)
Published by: Centre for Labour Market Research, University of Western Australia, Crawley, W.A. 6009, Australia. TEL 61-8-9380-8672, FAX 61-8-9380-8671, pmadden@ecel.uwa.edu.au, http://www.clmr.ecel.uwa.edu.au. Ed. Charles Mulvey.

331.11 PRY ISSN 1017-6055
CENTRO DE DOCUMENTACION Y ESTUDIOS. INFORMATIVO LABORAL. Text in Spanish. 1987. m. USD 72.
Published by: Centro de Documentacion y Estudios, PAI PEREZ, 737, Casilla de Correos 2558, Asuncion, Paraguay. TEL 595-21-23591, FAX 595-21-213246. Ed. Roberto Villalba. Circ: 800. **Dist. by:** D.I.P.P., PO Box 2507, Asuncion, Paraguay.

B

331.255 GBR ISSN 1357-7921
CHARITIES REWARDS. Text in English. 1990. a. GBP 280 per edition (effective 2001). **Document type:** *Bulletin.* **Description:** Provides pay and benefits information for the voluntary sector.
Formerly (until 1994): Charity Salary Survey (0962-6158)
Published by: The Reward Group Ltd., Reward House, Diamond Way, Stone Business Park, Stone, Staffs ST15 0SD, United Kingdom. TEL 44-1785-813566, FAX 44-1785-817007, enquiries@reward-group.co.uk, http://www.reward-group.co.uk.

331 USA
CHECKOFF (TALLAHASSEE). Text in English. irreg. (3-4/yr.). membership. **Document type:** *Newsletter.*
Published by: (Labor and Employment Law Section), The Florida Bar, 651 E Jefferson St, Tallahassee, FL 32399-2300. TEL 850-561-5631. Circ: 1,900.

331 658.3 331.1 TWN ISSN 1607-7016
CHEERS; Kuaile Gongzouren Zazhi. Text in Chinese. 2000. m. TWD 1,600 (effective 2002). **Document type:** *Magazine, Consumer.*
Related titles: Online - full content ed.
Published by: Tianxia Zazahi/Common Wealth Magazine Co., 104 Songjiang Road, no.87, 4F, Taipei, Taiwan. TEL 886-2-2662-0332, FAX 886-2-2662-6048, http://www.cheers.com.tw/default.asp.

331 340 RUS ISSN 0132-1552
CHELOVEK I TRUD. Text in Russian. m.
Related titles: Microfiche ed.: (from EVP).
Indexed: IBSS, RASB, RefZh.
—East View.
Published by: Ministerstvo Truda, Ul Elizarovoi 6, str 3, Moscow, 103064, Russian Federation. TEL 7-095-9161000, FAX 7-095-916100. Ed. G L Podvoiskii. **US dist. addr.:** East View Information Services, 3020 Harbor Ln. N., Minneapolis, MN 55447. TEL 612-550-0961. **Co-sponsor:** Federal'naya Sluzhba Zanyatosti Rossii.

331 340 RUS ISSN 0132-0831
K3
CHELOVEK I ZAKON. Text in Russian. m.
Related titles: Microfiche ed.: (from EVP).
Indexed: RASB.
—East View.
Address: Olimpiiskii pr-t 22, Moscow, 129850, Russian Federation. TEL 7-095-2816812, FAX 7-095-2813821. Ed. A E Yuferev. **US dist. addr.:** East View Information Services, 3020 Harbor Ln. N., Minneapolis, MN 55447. TEL 612-550-0961.

331 AUT
CHEMIEARBEITER. Text in German. m.
Indexed: RefZh.
Published by: Gewerkschaft der Chemiearbeiter, Stumpergasse 60, Vienna, W 1060, Austria. TEL 571501.

331.281378 USA
CHIEF EXECUTIVE COMPENSATION AND BENEFITS SURVEY. Text in English. biennial. USD 485 to non-members; USD 225 to members (effective 2000). **Description:** Provides data on chief executive officers, their institutions, salary and other cash compensation, employment policies and practices, and executive benefits and other perquisites.
Former titles: Compensation, Benefits and Conditions of Employment for College and University Chief Executive Officers; Compensation and Benefits Survey of College and University Chief Executive Officers
Indexed: SRI.
Published by: College and University Personnel Association, 1233 20th St, N W, Ste 301, Washington, DC 20036. TEL 202-429-0311, FAX 202-429-0149, http://www.cupa.org. Ed. Melissa Edeburn. R&P Audrey Rothstein.

331.21 GBR ISSN 1464-7354
CITIZEN'S INCOME NEWSLETTER. Text in English. 1984. biennial. GBP 25; GBP 27 foreign. adv. bk.rev. **Document type:** *Bulletin.* **Description:** Presents research and viewpoints on alternatives to the current welfare state that would guarantee everyone at least a small income.
Former titles (until 1998): C I R G Bulletin (1353-6729); (until 1993): B I R G Citizens Income (0954-8246)
Published by: Citizens Income Trust, Citizens Income Study Centre, St Philips Bldg., Sheffield St, London, WC2A 3EX, United Kingdom. TEL 44-20-7955-7453, FAX 44-20-7955-7534, citizens-income@rse.ac-uk, http://www.citizensincome.org/. Ed. Hermione Parker. R&P, Adv. contact Carolyn Armstrong. Circ: 1,000.

CIVIL SERVICE NEWS. see *PUBLIC ADMINISTRATION*

331 CAN
CLARKE'S CANADA INDUSTRIAL RELATIONS BOARD. Text in English. base vol. plus s-a. updates. looseleaf. CND 249 (effective 2005). **Document type:** *Trade.*
Formerly (until 1998): Canada Labour Relations Board
Published by: Canada Law Book Inc., 240 Edward St, Aurora, ON L4G 3S9, Canada. TEL 905-841-6472, 800-263-3269, FAX 905-841-5085, b.loney@canadalawbook.ca, http://www.canadalawbook.ca. Ed. Graham J Clarke. Adv. contact Mary Powell.

CLASSIFIED INDEX OF N.L.R.B. AND RELATED COURT DECISIONS. see *BUSINESS AND ECONOMICS—Abstracting, Bibliographies, Statistics*

331.21 GBR
CLERICAL AND OPERATIVE REWARDS. Text in English. 2/yr. GBP 280 per edition (effective 2001). **Document type:** *Bulletin.* **Description:** Provides salary data on a wide range of clerical and operative positions.
Published by: The Reward Group Ltd., Reward House, Diamond Way, Stone Business Park, Stone, Staffs ST15 0SD, United Kingdom. TEL 44-1785-813566, FAX 44-1785-817007, enquiries@reward-group.co.uk, http://www.reward-group.co.uk.

331.12 USA ISSN 0094-0372
COCKSHAW'S CONSTRUCTION LABOR NEWS & OPINION. Text in English. 1971. m. looseleaf. USD 247 (effective 2000 - 2001). bk.rev. back issues avail. **Document type:** *Newsletter.* **Description:** Analyzes labor relations trends in construction (i.e. bargaining, pay practices, union vs. non-union issues, productivity, skilled worker supply), as well as legal and legislative developments.
Former titles: Cockshaw's Construction Capsules; Cockshaw's Open Shop News and Trends; Open Shop News and Trends; Dual Shop News and Trends
Published by: Communications Counselors, Inc., PO Box 427, Newtown, PA 19073. TEL 610-353-0123, FAX 610-353-0111. Ed., Pub., R&P Peter A Cockshaw. Circ: 19,125 (paid).

331.89 CAN ISSN 1480-6908
HD6521
COLLECTIVE BARGAINING BULLETIN. Text in English. 1998. m. CND 65 (effective 2004). **Description:** Publishes information based on recently signed major collective agreements in Canada, summaries of changes to wages and benefits in selected settlements, status of key negotiations, and data on work stoppages.
Published by: Human Resources and Skills Development Canada, Workplace Information Directorate Labour Program, Ottawa, ON K1A 0J2, Canada. TEL 819-997-3117, 800-567-6866, FAX 819-953-9582, http://www.hrsdc.gc.ca/asp/gateway.asp?hr=en/lp/wid/pub/05collective_bargaining_bulletin.shtml&hs=axe. **Subscr. to:** Canadian Government Publishing Centre, Communication Canada, Ottawa, ON K1A 0S9, Canada. TEL 613-941-5995, 800-635-7943, FAX 613-954-5779, 800-565-7757, publications@communication.gc.ca, http://publications.gc.ca.

368.4 COL
COLOMBIA. MINISTERIO DE TRABAJO Y SEGURIDAD SOCIAL. CARTA INFORMATIVA. Text in Spanish. m. illus. **Document type:** *Newsletter, Government.*
Published by: Ministerio de Trabajo y Seguridad Social, Seccion de Biblioteca & Publicaciones, Av. 19 No. 6-68 Of. 806 y 809, Bogota, CUND, Colombia. TEL 57-1-282-9769, FAX 57-1-282-9709.

368.4 COL
COLOMBIA. MINISTERIO DE TRABAJO Y SEGURIDAD SOCIAL. MEMORIA AL CONGRESO NACIONAL. Text in Spanish. 1967. a.
Supersedes: Colombia. Ministerio de Trabajo, Higiene y Prevision Social. Memoria
Published by: Ministerio de Trabajo y Seguridad Social, Seccion de Biblioteca & Publicaciones, Av. 19 No. 6-68 Of. 806 y 809, Bogota, CUND, Colombia. Ed. Maria Teresa Forero de Saade.

COLORADO EMPLOYMENT LAW LETTER. see *LAW*

331.1 USA
COLORADO LABOR FORCE REVIEW. Text in English. 1964. m. free. charts; stat. **Document type:** *Government.*
Former titles: Colorado Manpower Review (0010-1656); Labor Area Highlights
Related titles: Microfiche ed.: (from CIS).
Indexed: SRI.
Published by: Department of Labor and Employment, 251 E 12th Ave, Denver, CO 80203. TEL 303-620-4856. Ed. David L Larson. Circ: 2,600.

331 331.8 USA ISSN 0745-6514
THE COMMUNICATOR (ALBANY). Text in English. 1978. 10/yr. membership. adv. 28 p./no. 3 cols./p.; back issues avail. **Document type:** *Newspaper, Trade.* **Description:** Publishes news and commentary of interest to employees in NY state service.
Published by: New York State Public Employees Federation, 1168 70 Troy Schenectady Rd, Box 12414, Albany, NY 12212-2414. TEL 518-785-1900, FAX 518-785-8174, http://www.nyspef.org. Ed., R&P Sherry Halbrook. Adv. contact Martha Ekstrom. Circ: 63,000.

COMMUNICATOR (ST. JOHN'S). see *PUBLIC ADMINISTRATION*

331 CAN ISSN 1198-6131
HD6958.5
COMPARATIVE INDUSTRIAL RELATIONS NEWSLETTER. Text in English. 1991. s-a. CND 25, USD 20 to individuals; CND 43, USD 35 to institutions. bk.rev. **Document type:** *Newsletter.* **Description:** Intended to foster cross-disciplinary communication among those interested in comparative and international labor issues.
Address: c/o DeGroote School of Business, McMaster University, Hamilton, ON L8S 4M4, Canada. TEL 905-525-9140, FAX 905-521-8995, adamsr@mcmail.cis.mcmaster.ca. Ed., Pub., R&P Roy Adams. Circ: 600 (paid).

344.01 USA ISSN 1095-6654
K3
➤ **COMPARATIVE LABOR LAW & POLICY JOURNAL.** Text in English. 1976. q. USD 30 domestic; USD 40 foreign; USD 10 newsstand/cover (effective 2005). bk.rev. abstr. index. 150 p./no.; back issues avail.; reprint service avail. from WSH. **Document type:** *Journal, Academic/Scholarly.* **Description:** Presents comparative studies of various aspects of labor, employment, and labor-related matters.
Former titles (until 1997): Comparative Labor Law Journal (1043-5255); (until 1986): Comparative Labor Law (0147-9202); (until 1975): U.S. National Committee. International Society for Labor Law and Social Legislation. Bulletin (0146-0234)
Related titles: Microfiche ed.: (from WSH); Microform ed.: (from WSH); Online - full text ed.: (from H.W. Wilson, LexisNexis, O C L C Online Computer Library Center, Inc.).
Indexed: ABRCLP, ABS&EES, BPIA, CLI, FamI, ILD, ILP, LRI, PAIS, WBSS.
—BLDSC (3363.784100), IE, Infotrieve, ingenta.
Published by: University of Illinois, College of Law, 116 Law Bldg, 504 E Pennsylvania Ave, Champaign, IL 61820. TEL 217-333-3884, FAX 217-244-1478, ballmes@law.uiuc.edu, mfinkin@law.uiuc.edu, http://www.law.uiuc.edu/publications/cll&pj. Ed. Matthew W Finkin. R&P, Adv. contact Stacey Ballmes TEL 217-33-9852. Circ: 876 (paid and free).
Co-sponsor: International Society for Labor Law and Social Security/Societe Internationale de Droit du Travail et de la Securite Sociale.

➤ **COMPARISON OF STATE UNEMPLOYMENT INSURANCE LAWS.** see *INSURANCE*

➤ **COMPENSATION (WASHINGTON, 1982);** an annual report on local government executive salaries and fringe benefits. see *BUSINESS AND ECONOMICS—Personnel Management*

331.21 USA
COMPENSATION & BENEFITS IN CONSULTING ENGINEERING FIRMS. Text in English. 1995. a. USD 1,200 (effective 2005). **Document type:** *Trade.*
Published by: (National Society of Professional Engineers), Abbott, Langer & Associates, 548 First St, Crete, IL 60417-9987. TEL 708-672-4200, FAX 708-672-4674, slanger@abbott-langer.com, http://www.abbott-langer.com. Ed. Steven Langer.

331.255 USA ISSN 1074-634X
TA157
COMPENSATION AND BENEFITS IN ENGINEERING FIRMS IN THE GEOTECHNICAL FIELD. Text in English. 1989. biennial. USD 650 (effective 2005). **Document type:** *Trade.*
Published by: (Association of Engineering Firms Practicing in the Geosciences), Abbott, Langer & Associates, 548 First St, Crete, IL 60417-9987. TEL 708-672-4200, FAX 708-672-4674, slanger@abbott-langer.com, http://www.abbott-langer.com. Ed. Steven Langer.

COMPENSATION & BENEFITS LIBRARY ON C D. see *BUSINESS AND ECONOMICS—Personnel Management*

331.21 USA
COMPENSATION & BENEFITS MANAGER'S MONTHLY. Text in English. 1989. m. looseleaf. USD 155.40. back issues avail. **Document type:** *Newsletter.*
Formerly: Employee Benefits Consultant
Published by: ProPub Inc., PO Box 102, Wyckoff, NJ 07481-0102. TEL 201-447-6485, FAX 201-447-9356. Ed. James A Seidel. Pub. Randy Cochran.

331.2   USA   ISSN 0738-1034
HV85
COMPENSATION & BENEFITS REPORT (WASHINGTON). Text in English. biennial.
Related titles: Online - full text ed.: (from ProQuest Information & Learning).
Indexed: ABIn.
Published by: Council on Foundations, Inc., 1828 L St, NW, Ste 300, Washington, DC 20036. TEL 202-466-6512, 800-771-8187, FAX 202-785-3926, http://www.cof.org/.

331.21   USA   ISSN 0886-3687
COMPENSATION AND BENEFITS REVIEW; the journal of total compensation strategies. Text in English. 1969. bi-m. USD 416, GBP 269 to institutions; USD 433, GBP 280 combined subscription to institutions print & online eds. (effective 2006). adv. bk.rev. abstr.; charts; illus. index. 2 cols./p.; back issues avail.; reprint service avail. from SCH. **Document type:** Journal, Trade. **Description:** Provides information on the strategic use of compensation and benefits, plus reports from other business and professional publications.
Formerly (until 1985): Compensation Review (0010-4248)
Related titles: Microform ed.: (from PQC); Online - full text ed.: ISSN 1552-3837. USD 412, GBP 266 to institutions (effective 2006) (from C S A, EBSCO Publishing, Gale Group, H.W. Wilson, O C L C Online Computer Library Center, Inc., ProQuest Information & Learning, Sage Publications, Inc., Swets Information Services, The Dialog Group).
Indexed: ABIn, ABS&EES, ADPA, ASEANManA, AgeL, BPI, BPIA, BusI, CurCont, EmerIntel, Emerald, HlthInd, MEDLINE, ManagCont, PAIS, PMA, PersLit, SSCI, T&II, WorkRelAb. —BLDSC (3363.985000), CASDDS, IE, Infotrieve, ingenta. CCC.
Published by: Sage Publications, Inc., 2455 Teller Rd, Thousand Oaks, CA 91320. TEL 805-499-0721, FAX 805-499-8096, fayhansen@optonline.net, info@sagepub.com, http://www.sagepub.com/journal.aspx?pid=68. Ed. Fay Hansen. Pub. Sara Miller McCune. Adv. contact Kirsten Beaulieu TEL 805-499-0721 ext 7160. B&W page USD 830, color page USD 1,275; bleed 8.375 x 11.25. Circ: 1,027 (paid). **Subscr. overseas to:** Sage Publications Ltd., 1 Oliver's Yard, 55 City Rd, London EC1 1SP, United Kingdom. TEL 44-20-73740645, FAX 44-20-73748741, subscription@sagepub.co.uk.

COMPENSATION & BENEFITS UPDATE. see BUSINESS AND ECONOMICS—Personnel Management

COMPENSATION COURT MONTHLY SUMMARIES. see LAW—Corporate Law

COMPENSATION GUIDE. see BUSINESS AND ECONOMICS—Personnel Management

331.21   USA   ISSN 1529-708X
HD8039.F7
COMPENSATION IN FOOD & BEVERAGE PROCESSING. Text in English. 1995. a. USD 750 (effective 2005). **Document type:** Trade.
Published by: Abbott, Langer & Associates, 548 First St, Crete, IL 60417-9987. TEL 708-672-4200, FAX 708-672-4674, slanger@abbott-langer.com, http://www.abbott-langer.com. Ed. Steven Langer.

331.21 551.49   USA   ISSN 1547-4658
TC23
COMPENSATION IN GROUND WATER SCIENCE AND ENGINEERING ORGANIZATIONS. Text in English. 1997. a. USD 650 (effective 2004).
Formerly (until 2002): Compensation & Benefits in Ground Water Science and Engineering Organizations
Published by: Abbott, Langer & Associates, 548 First St, Crete, IL 60417-9987. TEL 708-672-4200, FAX 708-672-4674, slanger@abbott-langer.com, http://www.abbott-langer.com. Ed. Steven Langer.

331.21 616   USA
COMPENSATION IN INDEPENDENT LABORATORY, TESTING AND INSPECTION FIRMS. Text in English. 1995. biennial. USD 650 (effective 2005).
Published by: Abbott, Langer & Associates, 548 First St, Crete, IL 60417-9987. TEL 708-672-4200, FAX 708-672-4674, slanger@abbott-langer.com, http://www.abbott-langer.com. Ed. Steven Langer.

331.21   USA   ISSN 1047-0344
T56.3
COMPENSATION IN MANUFACTURING. Text in English. 1976. a. USD 1,250 (effective 2005). **Document type:** Academic/Scholarly.
Formerly (until 1988): Compensation in Manufacturing - Engineers and Managers (0278-0992)
Published by: Abbott, Langer & Associates, 548 First St, Crete, IL 60417-9987. TEL 708-672-4200, FAX 708-672-4674, slanger@abbott-langer.com, http://www.abbott-langer.com. Ed. Steven Langer.

331.21   USA
COMPENSATION IN MECHANICAL ENGINEERING. Text in English. 2002. a. USD 395 (effective 2005).

331.21   USA   ISSN 1080-8558
HD4966.N652
COMPENSATION IN NONPROFIT ORGANIZATIONS. Text in English. 1988. a. USD 325 (effective 2005). **Document type:** Trade.
Indexed: ATI.
Published by: Abbott, Langer & Associates, 548 First St, Crete, IL 60417-9987. TEL 708-672-4200, FAX 708-672-4674, slanger@abbott-langer.com, http://www.abbott-langer.com. Ed. Steven Langer.

331.2 621.3   USA
▼ **COMPENSATION IN POWER GENERATION.** Text in English. 2003. biennial. USD 395 (effective 2005).
Published by: Abbott, Langer & Associates, 548 First St, Crete, IL 60417-9987. TEL 708-672-4200, FAX 708-672-4674, slanger@abbott-langer.com, http://www.abbott-langer.com. Ed. Steven Langer.

331.21   USA
COMPENSATION IN RESEARCH & DEVELOPMENT. Text in English. 1986. a. USD 1,100 (effective 2005). **Document type:** Trade.
Published by: Abbott, Langer & Associates, 548 First St, Crete, IL 60417-9987. TEL 708-672-4200, FAX 708-672-4674, slanger@abbott-langer.com, http://www.abbott-langer.com. Ed. Steven Langer.

331.21   USA
COMPENSATION IN SMALLER MANUFACTURING FIRMS. Text in English. 2000. a. USD 595 (effective 2005).
Published by: Abbott, Langer & Associates, 548 First St, Crete, IL 60417-9987. TEL 708-672-4200, FAX 708-672-4674, slanger@abbott-langer.com, http://www.abbott-langer.com. Ed. Steven Langer.

COMPENSATION LEGISLATION SERVICE. see LAW

344.01   USA
COMPENSATION OF LEGAL AND RELATED JOBS (NON-LAW FIRMS). Text in English. 1979. a. USD 995 (effective 2005). **Document type:** Trade.
Formerly: Compensation of Attorneys (Non-Law Firms)
Published by: Abbott, Langer & Associates, 548 First St, Crete, IL 60417-9987. TEL 708-672-4200, FAX 708-672-4674, slanger@abbott-langer.com, http://www.abbott-langer.com. Ed. Steven Langer.

331.2 500   USA
COMPENSATION OF LIFE SCIENTISTS. Text in English. 2001. a. USD 395 (effective 2005).
Published by: Abbott, Langer & Associates, 548 First St, Crete, IL 60417-9987. TEL 708-672-4200, FAX 708-672-4674, slanger@abbott-langer.com, http://www.abbott-langer.com. Ed. Steven Langer.

331.21   USA   ISSN 1546-5659
T56.3
COMPENSATION OF PLANT - FACILITIES MAINTENANCE - ENGINEERING MANAGERS & ENGINEERS. Text in English. 1993. a. USD 395 (effective 2005). **Document type:** Trade.
Published by: (American Institute of Plant Engineers Foundation and Plant Engineering), Abbott, Langer & Associates, 548 First St, Crete, IL 60417-9987. TEL 708-672-4200, FAX 708-672-4674, slanger@abbott-langer.com, http://www.abbott-langer.com. Ed. Steven Langer.

THE (YEAR) COMPETITIVENESS REPORT ON ARGENTINA: FINANCIALS RETURNS, LABOR PRODUCTIVITY AND INTERNATIONAL GAPS. see BUSINESS AND ECONOMICS

THE (YEAR) COMPETITIVENESS REPORT ON BEAUPORT, CANADA: FINANCIALS RETURNS, LABOR PRODUCTIVITY, BENCHMARKS AND INTERNATIONAL GAPS. see BUSINESS AND ECONOMICS—Investments

THE (YEAR) COMPETITIVENESS REPORT ON BOLTON, CANADA: FINANCIALS RETURNS, LABOR PRODUCTIVITY, BENCHMARKS AND INTERNATIONAL GAPS. see BUSINESS AND ECONOMICS—Investments

THE (YEAR) COMPETITIVENESS REPORT ON BRAMPTON, CANADA: FINANCIALS RETURNS, LABOR PRODUCTIVITY, BENCHMARKS AND INTERNATIONAL GAPS. see BUSINESS AND ECONOMICS—Investments

THE (YEAR) COMPETITIVENESS REPORT ON BRANTFORD, CANADA: FINANCIAL RETURNS, LABOR PRODUCTIVITY, BENCHMARKS AND INTERNATIONAL GAPS. see BUSINESS AND ECONOMICS—Investments

THE (YEAR) COMPETITIVENESS REPORT ON BRAZIL: FINANCIALS RETURNS, LABOR PRODUCTIVITY AND INTERNATIONAL GAPS. see BUSINESS AND ECONOMICS

THE (YEAR) COMPETITIVENESS REPORT ON CALGARY, CANADA: FINANCIAL RETURNS, LABOR PRODUCTIVITY, BENCHMARKS AND INTERNATIONAL GAPS. see BUSINESS AND ECONOMICS—Investments

THE (YEAR) COMPETITIVENESS REPORT ON CANADA: FINANCIALS RETURNS, LABOR PRODUCTIVITY AND INTERNATIONAL GAPS. see BUSINESS AND ECONOMICS

THE (YEAR) COMPETITIVENESS REPORT ON CHARLOTTETOWN, CANADA: FINANCIAL RETURNS, LABOR PRODUCTIVITY, BENCHMARKS AND INTERNATIONAL GAPS. see BUSINESS AND ECONOMICS—Investments

THE (YEAR) COMPETITIVENESS REPORT ON CHILE: FINANCIALS RETURNS, LABOR PRODUCTIVITY AND INTERNATIONAL GAPS. see BUSINESS AND ECONOMICS

THE (YEAR) COMPETITIVENESS REPORT ON COLOMBIA: FINANCIALS RETURNS, LABOR PRODUCTIVITY AND INTERNATIONAL GAPS. see BUSINESS AND ECONOMICS

THE (YEAR) COMPETITIVENESS REPORT ON DON MILLS, CANADA: FINANCIAL RETURNS, LABOR PRODUCTIVITY, BENCHMARKS AND INTERNATIONAL GAPS. see BUSINESS AND ECONOMICS—Investments

THE (YEAR) COMPETITIVENESS REPORT ON DORVAL, CANADA: FINANCIAL RETURNS, LABOR PRODUCTIVITY, BENCHMARKS AND INTERNATIONAL GAPS. see BUSINESS AND ECONOMICS—Investments

THE (YEAR) COMPETITIVENESS REPORT ON EDMONTON, CANADA: FINANCIAL RETURNS, LABOR PRODUCTIVITY, BENCHMARKS AND INTERNATIONAL GAPS. see BUSINESS AND ECONOMICS—Investments

THE (YEAR) COMPETITIVENESS REPORT ON ETOBICOKE, CANADA: FINANCIAL RETURNS, LABOR PRODUCTIVITY, BENCHMARKS AND INTERNATIONAL GAPS. see BUSINESS AND ECONOMICS—Investments

THE (YEAR) COMPETITIVENESS REPORT ON GRANBY, CANADA: FINANCIAL RETURNS, LABOR PRODUCTIVITY, BENCHMARKS AND INTERNATIONAL GAPS. see BUSINESS AND ECONOMICS—Investments

THE (YEAR) COMPETITIVENESS REPORT ON GUELPH, CANADA: FINANCIAL RETURNS, LABOR PRODUCTIVITY, BENCHMARKS AND INTERNATIONAL GAPS. see BUSINESS AND ECONOMICS—Investments

THE (YEAR) COMPETITIVENESS REPORT ON HALEY, CANADA: FINANCIAL RETURNS, LABOR PRODUCTIVITY, BENCHMARKS AND INTERNATIONAL GAPS. see BUSINESS AND ECONOMICS—Investments

THE (YEAR) COMPETITIVENESS REPORT ON HALIFAX, CANADA: FINANCIAL RETURNS, LABOR PRODUCTIVITY, BENCHMARKS AND INTERNATIONAL GAPS. see BUSINESS AND ECONOMICS—Investments

THE (YEAR) COMPETITIVENESS REPORT ON KANATA, CANADA: FINANCIAL RETURNS, LABOR PRODUCTIVITY, BENCHMARKS AND INTERNATIONAL GAPS. see BUSINESS AND ECONOMICS—Investments

THE (YEAR) COMPETITIVENESS REPORT ON KELOWNA, CANADA: FINANCIAL RETURNS, LABOR PRODUCTIVITY, BENCHMARKS AND INTERNATIONAL GAPS. see BUSINESS AND ECONOMICS—Investments

THE (YEAR) COMPETITIVENESS REPORT ON KINGSEY FALLS, CANADA: FINANCIAL RETURNS, LABOR PRODUCTIVITY, BENCHMARKS AND INTERNATIONAL GAPS. see BUSINESS AND ECONOMICS—Investments

THE (YEAR) COMPETITIVENESS REPORT ON KITCHENER, CANADA: FINANCIAL RETURNS, LABOR PRODUCTIVITY, BENCHMARKS AND INTERNATIONAL GAPS. see BUSINESS AND ECONOMICS—Investments

THE (YEAR) COMPETITIVENESS REPORT ON LATIN AMERICA: FINANCIALS RETURNS, LABOR PRODUCTIVITY AND INTERNATIONAL GAPS. see BUSINESS AND ECONOMICS

THE (YEAR) COMPETITIVENESS REPORT ON LAVAL, CANADA: FINANCIAL RETURNS, LABOR PRODUCTIVITY, BENCHMARKS AND INTERNATIONAL GAPS. see BUSINESS AND ECONOMICS—Investments

THE (YEAR) COMPETITIVENESS REPORT ON LETHBRIDGE, CANADA: FINANCIAL RETURNS, LABOR PRODUCTIVITY, BENCHMARKS AND INTERNATIONAL GAPS. see BUSINESS AND ECONOMICS—Investments

B

THE (YEAR) COMPETITIVENESS REPORT ON LEVIS, CANADA: FINANCIAL RETURNS, LABOR PRODUCTIVITY, BENCHMARKS AND INTERNATIONAL GAPS. see *BUSINESS AND ECONOMICS—Investments*

THE (YEAR) COMPETITIVENESS REPORT ON LONGUEUIL, CANADA: FINANCIAL RETURNS, LABOR PRODUCTIVITY, BENCHMARKS AND INTERNATIONAL GAPS. see *BUSINESS AND ECONOMICS—Investments*

THE (YEAR) COMPETITIVENESS REPORT ON LUNENBURG, CANADA: FINANCIAL RETURNS, LABOR PRODUCTIVITY, BENCHMARKS AND INTERNATIONAL GAPS. see *BUSINESS AND ECONOMICS—Investments*

THE (YEAR) COMPETITIVENESS REPORT ON MARKHAM, CANADA: FINANCIAL RETURNS, LABOR PRODUCTIVITY, BENCHMARKS AND INTERNATIONAL GAPS. see *BUSINESS AND ECONOMICS—Investments*

THE (YEAR) COMPETITIVENESS REPORT ON MEXICO: FINANCIALS RETURNS, LABOR PRODUCTIVITY AND INTERNATIONAL GAPS. see *BUSINESS AND ECONOMICS*

THE (YEAR) COMPETITIVENESS REPORT ON MISSISSAUGA, CANADA: FINANCIAL RETURNS, LABOR PRODUCTIVITY, BENCHMARKS AND INTERNATIONAL GAPS. see *BUSINESS AND ECONOMICS—Investments*

THE (YEAR) COMPETITIVENESS REPORT ON MONTREAL, CANADA: FINANCIAL RETURNS, LABOR PRODUCTIVITY, BENCHMARKS AND INTERNATIONAL GAPS. see *BUSINESS AND ECONOMICS—Investments*

THE (YEAR) COMPETITIVENESS REPORT ON MOUNT ROYAL, CANADA: FINANCIAL RETURNS, LABOR PRODUCTIVITY, BENCHMARKS AND INTERNATIONAL GAPS. see *BUSINESS AND ECONOMICS—Investments*

THE (YEAR) COMPETITIVENESS REPORT ON NEPEAN, CANADA: FINANCIAL RETURNS, LABOR PRODUCTIVITY, BENCHMARKS AND INTERNATIONAL GAPS. see *BUSINESS AND ECONOMICS—Investments*

THE (YEAR) COMPETITIVENESS REPORT ON PERU: FINANCIALS RETURNS, LABOR PRODUCTIVITY AND INTERNATIONAL GAPS. see *BUSINESS AND ECONOMICS*

THE (YEAR) COMPETITIVENESS REPORT ON QUEBEC CITY, CANADA: FINANCIAL RETURNS, LABOR PRODUCTIVITY, BENCHMARKS AND INTERNATIONAL GAPS. see *BUSINESS AND ECONOMICS—Investments*

THE (YEAR) COMPETITIVENESS REPORT ON REGINA, CANADA: FINANCIAL RETURNS, LABOR PRODUCTIVITY, BENCHMARKS AND INTERNATIONAL GAPS. see *BUSINESS AND ECONOMICS—Investments*

THE (YEAR) COMPETITIVENESS REPORT ON SAINT-DAMIEN REGINA, CANADA: FINANCIAL RETURNS, LABOR PRODUCTIVITY, BENCHMARKS AND INTERNATIONAL GAPS. see *BUSINESS AND ECONOMICS—Investments*

THE (YEAR) COMPETITIVENESS REPORT ON SAINT-LAURENT, CANADA: FINANCIAL RETURNS, LABOR PRODUCTIVITY, BENCHMARKS AND INTERNATIONAL GAPS. see *BUSINESS AND ECONOMICS—Investments*

THE (YEAR) COMPETITIVENESS REPORT ON SAINT-LEONARD, CANADA: FINANCIAL RETURNS, LABOR PRODUCTIVITY, BENCHMARKS AND INTERNATIONAL GAPS. see *BUSINESS AND ECONOMICS—Investments*

THE (YEAR) COMPETITIVENESS REPORT ON SAINTE-MARIE-DE-BEAUCE, CANADA: FINANCIAL RETURNS, LABOR PRODUCTIVITY, BENCHMARKS AND INTERNATIONAL GAPS. see *BUSINESS AND ECONOMICS—Investments*

THE (YEAR) COMPETITIVENESS REPORT ON SASKATOON, CANADA: FINANCIAL RETURNS, LABOR PRODUCTIVITY, BENCHMARKS AND INTERNATIONAL GAPS. see *BUSINESS AND ECONOMICS—Investments*

THE (YEAR) COMPETITIVENESS REPORT ON SHERBROOKE, CANADA: FINANCIAL RETURNS, LABOR PRODUCTIVITY, BENCHMARKS AND INTERNATIONAL GAPS. see *BUSINESS AND ECONOMICS—Investments*

THE (YEAR) COMPETITIVENESS REPORT ON ST. JEROME, CANADA: FINANCIAL RETURNS, LABOR PRODUCTIVITY, BENCHMARKS AND INTERNATIONAL GAPS. see *BUSINESS AND ECONOMICS—Investments*

THE (YEAR) COMPETITIVENESS REPORT ON ST. JOHN'S, CANADA: FINANCIAL RETURNS, LABOR PRODUCTIVITY, BENCHMARKS AND INTERNATIONAL GAPS. see *BUSINESS AND ECONOMICS—Investments*

THE (YEAR) COMPETITIVENESS REPORT ON ST. LAURENT, CANADA: FINANCIAL RETURNS, LABOR PRODUCTIVITY, BENCHMARKS AND INTERNATIONAL GAPS. see *BUSINESS AND ECONOMICS—Investments*

THE (YEAR) COMPETITIVENESS REPORT ON STELLARTON, CANADA: FINANCIAL RETURNS, LABOR PRODUCTIVITY, BENCHMARKS AND INTERNATIONAL GAPS. see *BUSINESS AND ECONOMICS—Investments*

THE (YEAR) COMPETITIVENESS REPORT ON THORNHILL, CANADA: FINANCIAL RETURNS, LABOR PRODUCTIVITY, BENCHMARKS AND INTERNATIONAL GAPS. see *BUSINESS AND ECONOMICS—Investments*

THE (YEAR) COMPETITIVENESS REPORT ON VENEZUELA: FINANCIALS RETURNS, LABOR PRODUCTIVITY AND INTERNATIONAL GAPS. see *BUSINESS AND ECONOMICS*

THE (YEAR) COMPETITIVENESS REPORT ON VILLE DE SAINT-GEORGES, CANADA: FINANCIAL RETURNS, LABOR PRODUCTIVITY, BENCHMARKS AND INTERNATIONAL GAPS. see *BUSINESS AND ECONOMICS—Investments*

THE (YEAR) COMPETITIVENESS REPORT ON VILLE DE SAINT-LAURENT, CANADA: FINANCIAL RETURNS, LABOR PRODUCTIVITY, BENCHMARKS AND INTERNATIONAL GAPS. see *BUSINESS AND ECONOMICS—Investments*

THE (YEAR) COMPETITIVENESS REPORT ON WESTMOUNT, CANADA: FINANCIAL RETURNS, LABOR PRODUCTIVITY, BENCHMARKS AND INTERNATIONAL GAPS. see *BUSINESS AND ECONOMICS—Investments*

THE (YEAR) COMPETITIVENESS REPORT ON WILLOWDALE, CANADA: FINANCIAL RETURNS, LABOR PRODUCTIVITY, BENCHMARKS AND INTERNATIONAL GAPS. see *BUSINESS AND ECONOMICS—Investments*

THE (YEAR) COMPETITIVENESS REPORT ON WINNIPEG, CANADA: FINANCIAL RETURNS, LABOR PRODUCTIVITY, BENCHMARKS AND INTERNATIONAL GAPS. see *BUSINESS AND ECONOMICS—Investments*

331.21   USA   ISSN 1554-141X
HD7103.65.U62
COMPSCOPE BENCHMARKS FOR CALIFORNIA. Text in English. a., latest 5th ed. USD 75 per issue to members; USD 135 per issue to non-members. **Document type:** *Trade.* **Description:** Comprehensive tool to help manage change. Provides the most meaningful comparisons currently available for more than 60 system performance measures for twelve large states including California, Connecticut, Florida, Illinois, Indiana, Louisiana, Massachusetts, North Carolina, Pennsylvania, Tennessee, Texas, and Wisconsin. **Related titles:** Online - full text ed.: ISSN 1554-1428. USD 45 per issue to members; USD 95 per issue to non-members (effective 2005). **Published by:** Workers Compensation Research Institute, 955 Massachusetts Ave, Cambridge, MA 02139. TEL 617-661-9274, FAX 617-661-9284, wcri@wcrinet.org, http://www.wcrinet.org/.

331.21   USA   ISSN 1554-1436
HD7103.65.U62
COMPSCOPE BENCHMARKS FOR FLORIDA. Text in English. a., latest 5th ed. USD 75 per issue to members; USD 135 per issue to non-members (effective 2005). **Document type:** *Trade.* **Description:** Comprehensive tool to help manage change. Provides the most meaningful comparisons currently available for more than 60 system performance measures for twelve large states including California, Connecticut, Florida, Illinois, Indiana, Louisiana, Massachusetts, North Carolina, Pennsylvania, Tennessee, Texas, and Wisconsin. **Related titles:** Online - full text ed.: ISSN 1554-1444. USD 45 per issue to members; USD 95 per issue to non-members (effective 2005). **Published by:** Workers Compensation Research Institute, 955 Massachusetts Ave, Cambridge, MA 02139. TEL 617-661-9274, FAX 617-661-9284, wcri@wcrinet.org, http://www.wcrinet.org/.

331.21   USA   ISSN 1554-1452
HD7103.65.U62
COMPSCOPE BENCHMARKS FOR LOUISIANA. Text in English. a., latest 5th ed. USD 75 per issue to members; USD 135 per issue to non-members (effective 2005). **Document type:** *Trade.* **Description:** Comprehensive tool to help manage change. Provides the most meaningful comparisons currently available for more than 60 system performance measures for twelve large states including California, Connecticut, Florida, Illinois, Indiana, Louisiana, Massachusetts, North Carolina, Pennsylvania, Tennessee, Texas, and Wisconsin. **Related titles:** Online - full text ed.: ISSN 1554-1460. USD 45 per issue to members; USD 95 per issue to non-members (effective 2005). **Published by:** Workers Compensation Research Institute, 955 Massachusetts Ave, Cambridge, MA 02139. TEL 617-661-9274, FAX 617-661-9284, wcri@wcrinet.org, http://www.wcrinet.org/.

331.21   USA   ISSN 1554-1479
HD7103.65.U62
COMPSCOPE BENCHMARKS FOR MASSACHUSETTS. Text in English. a., latest 5th ed. USD 75 per issue to members; USD 135 per issue to non-members (effective 2005). **Document type:** *Trade.* **Description:** Comprehensive tool to help manage change. Provides the most meaningful comparisons currently available for more than 60 system performance measures for twelve large states including California, Connecticut, Florida, Illinois, Indiana, Louisiana, Massachusetts, North Carolina, Pennsylvania, Tennessee, Texas, and Wisconsin. **Related titles:** Online - full text ed.: ISSN 1554-1487. USD 45 per issue to members; USD 95 per issue to non-members (effective 2005). **Published by:** Workers Compensation Research Institute, 955 Massachusetts Ave, Cambridge, MA 02139. TEL 617-661-9274, FAX 617-661-9284, wcri@wcrinet.org, http://www.wcrinet.org/.

331.21   USA   ISSN 1554-1495
HD7103.65.U62
COMPSCOPE BENCHMARKS FOR NORTH CAROLINA. Text in English. a., latest 5th ed. USD 75 per issue to members; USD 135 per issue to non-members (effective 2005). **Document type:** *Trade.* **Description:** Comprehensive tool to help manage change. Provides the most meaningful comparisons currently available for more than 60 system performance measures for twelve large states including California, Connecticut, Florida, Illinois, Indiana, Louisiana, Massachusetts, North Carolina, Pennsylvania, Tennessee, Texas, and Wisconsin. **Related titles:** Online - full text ed.: ISSN 1554-1509. USD 45 per issue to members; USD 95 per issue to non-members (effective 2005). **Published by:** Workers Compensation Research Institute, 955 Massachusetts Ave, Cambridge, MA 02139. TEL 617-661-9274, FAX 617-661-9284, wcri@wcrinet.org, http://www.wcrinet.org/.

331.21   USA   ISSN 1554-1517
HD7103.65.U62
COMPSCOPE BENCHMARKS FOR PENNSYLVANIA. Text in English. a., latest 5th ed. USD 75 per issue to members; USD 135 per issue to non-members (effective 2005). **Document type:** *Trade.* **Description:** Comprehensive tool to help manage change. Provides the most meaningful comparisons currently available for more than 60 system performance measures for twelve large states including California, Connecticut, Florida, Illinois, Indiana, Louisiana, Massachusetts, North Carolina, Pennsylvania, Tennessee, Texas, and Wisconsin. **Related titles:** Online - full text ed.: ISSN 1554-1525. USD 45 per issue to members; USD 95 per issue to non-members (effective 2005). **Published by:** Workers Compensation Research Institute, 955 Massachusetts Ave, Cambridge, MA 02139. TEL 617-661-9274, FAX 617-661-9284, wcri@wcrinet.org, http://www.wcrinet.org/.

331.21   USA   ISSN 1554-1533
HD7103.65.U62
COMPSCOPE BENCHMARKS FOR TENNESSEE. Text in English. a., latest 5th ed. USD 75 per issue to members; USD 135 per issue to non-members (effective 2005). **Document type:** *Trade.* **Description:** Comprehensive tool to help manage change. Provides the most meaningful comparisons currently available for more than 60 system performance measures for twelve large states including California, Connecticut, Florida, Illinois, Indiana, Louisiana, Massachusetts, North Carolina, Pennsylvania, Tennessee, Texas, and Wisconsin. **Related titles:** Online - full text ed.: ISSN 1554-1541. USD 45 per issue to members; USD 95 per issue to non-members (effective 2005). **Published by:** Workers Compensation Research Institute, 955 Massachusetts Ave, Cambridge, MA 02139. TEL 617-661-9274, FAX 617-661-9284, wcri@wcrinet.org, http://www.wcrinet.org/.

331.21   USA   ISSN 1554-155X
HD7103.65.U62
COMPSCOPE BENCHMARKS FOR TEXAS. Text in English. a., latest 5th ed. USD 75 per issue to members; USD 135 per issue to non-members (effective 2005). **Document type:** *Trade.* **Description:** Comprehensive tool to help manage change. Provides the most meaningful comparisons currently available for more than 60 system performance measures for twelve large states including California, Connecticut, Florida, Illinois, Indiana, Louisiana, Massachusetts, North Carolina, Pennsylvania, Tennessee, Texas, and Wisconsin. **Related titles:** Online - full text ed.: ISSN 1554-1568. USD 45 per issue to members; USD 95 per issue to non-members (effective 2005). **Published by:** Workers Compensation Research Institute, 955 Massachusetts Ave, Cambridge, MA 02139. TEL 617-661-9274, FAX 617-661-9284, wcri@wcrinet.org, http://www.wcrinet.org/.

331.21   USA   ISSN 1554-1576
HD7103.65.U62
COMPSCOPE BENCHMARKS FOR WISCONSIN. Text in English. a. USD 75 per issue to members; USD 135 per issue to non-members (effective 2005). **Document type:** *Trade.* **Description:** Comprehensive tool to help manage change. Provides the most meaningful comparisons currently available for more than 60 system performance measures for twelve large states including California, Connecticut, Florida, Illinois, Indiana, Louisiana, Massachusetts, North Carolina, Pennsylvania, Tennessee, Texas, and Wisconsin.
Related titles: Online - full text ed.: ISSN 1554-1584. USD 45 per issue to members; USD 95 per issue to non-members (effective 2005).
Published by: Workers Compensation Research Institute, 955 Massachusetts Ave, Cambridge, MA 02139. TEL 617-661-9274, FAX 617-661-9284, wcri@wcrinet.org, http://www.wcrinet.org/.

CONCEPTS AND TRANSFORMATION; international journal of action research and organizational renewal. see *BUSINESS AND ECONOMICS—Personnel Management*

CONNECTICUT EMPLOYMENT LAW LETTER. see *LAW*

CONNECTICUT WORKERS' COMPENSATION REVIEW OPINIONS. see *INSURANCE*

331   USA   ISSN 0161-990X
CONSTRUCTION LABOR NEWS. Text in English. 1978. s-m. USD 48. adv. tr.lit. back issues avail. **Document type:** *Newspaper.*
Published by: Construction Labor News, Inc., 2102 Almaden Rd, Ste 303, San Jose, CA 95125. TEL 408-265-6280, FAX 408-265-7371, mindyzmac@aol.com. Ed. Mindy Dravis Gonzales. Circ: 17,000.

331.1   USA   ISSN 0010-6836
HD8039.B892
CONSTRUCTION LABOR REPORT. Text in English. 1955. w. looseleaf. USD 1,543 (effective 2005 - 2006). bk.rev. charts; stat. cum.index. 52 p./no.; back issues avail. **Document type:** *Newsletter.* **Description:** Covers union-management relations in the construction industry, reporting on significant legislative, judicial, economic, management and union developments.
Related titles: Online - full text ed.: ISSN 1523-5688 (from The Bureau of National Affairs, Inc.).
—CCC.
Published by: The Bureau of National Affairs, Inc., 1231 25th St., NW, Washington, DC 20037. TEL 202-452-4200, 800-372-1033, 800-452-7773, FAX 202-822-8092, customercare@bna.com, bnaplus@bna.com, http://www.bna.com/. Ed. Anthony A Harris.

CONSUMER EXPENDITURE SURVEY. see *BUSINESS AND ECONOMICS—Economic Situation And Conditions*

331   USA   ISSN 1083-3781
➤ **CONTRACTING PROFITS.** Text in English. 1995. 10/yr. free domestic to qualified personnel (effective 2005). adv. **Document type:** *Magazine, Trade.* **Description:** Contains contractor industry news, updates, human resource issues, safety and other related issues.
Published by: Trade Press Publishing Corp., 2100 W Florist Ave, Milwaukee, WI 53209. TEL 414-228-7701, FAX 414-228-1134, stacie.whitacre@tradepress.com, dianna.b@tradepress.com, http://www.tradepress.com/publicat/cp/index.html, http://www.cleanlink.com/cp. Eds. Stacie Whitacre, Dick Yake. Pub. Robert Geissler. adv.: B&W page USD 3,935, color page USD 5,385. Circ: 32,000 (controlled).

331   USA   ISSN 0886-8239
CONTRIBUTIONS IN LABOR STUDIES. Text in English. 1977. irreg., latest vol.59, 2003. price varies. **Document type:** *Monographic series, Academic/Scholarly.*
Formerly: Contributions in Labor History (0146-3608)
Published by: Greenwood Publishing Group Inc. (Subsidiary of: Harcourt International), 88 Post Rd W, PO Box 5007, Westport, CT 06881. TEL 203-226-3571, FAX 203-226-1502, webmaster@greenwood.com, http://www.greenwood.com. Eds. Bruce Laurie, Milton Cantor.

331.1   USA   ISSN 0070-0029
CORNELL INTERNATIONAL INDUSTRIAL AND LABOR RELATIONS REPORTS. Text in English. 1954. irreg., latest vol.35, 1999. price varies. adv. **Document type:** *Monographic series.*
—BLDSC (3470.949000), ingenta.
Published by: (New York State School of Industrial and Labor Relations), I L R Press, Cornell University Press, 512 E State St, Ithaca, NY 14850. TEL 607-277-2338, 800-666-2211. Ed. Frances Benson. R&P Tonya Cook. Adv. contact Elizabeth Larsen.

331.1   USA   ISSN 0070-0053
CORNELL STUDIES IN INDUSTRIAL AND LABOR RELATIONS. Text in English. 1951. irreg., latest vol.32, 1999. price varies. adv. **Document type:** *Monographic series.*
—BLDSC (3470.964500), ingenta.

Published by: (New York State School of Industrial and Labor Relations), I L R Press, Cornell University Press, 512 E State St, Ithaca, NY 14850. TEL 607-277-2338, 800-666-2211. Ed. Frances Benson. R&P Tonya Cook. Adv. contact Elizabeth Larsen.

COST OF LIVING REPORT. REGIONAL COMPARISONS. see *BUSINESS AND ECONOMICS—Abstracting, Bibliographies, Statistics*

COUNTRY COMMERCE. AMERICAS. see *BUSINESS AND ECONOMICS—International Commerce*

COUNTRY COMMERCE. ARGENTINA. see *BUSINESS AND ECONOMICS—International Commerce*

COUNTRY COMMERCE. ASIA. see *BUSINESS AND ECONOMICS—International Commerce*

COUNTRY COMMERCE. AUSTRALIA. see *BUSINESS AND ECONOMICS—International Commerce*

COUNTRY COMMERCE. AUSTRIA. see *BUSINESS AND ECONOMICS—International Commerce*

COUNTRY COMMERCE. BELGIUM. see *BUSINESS AND ECONOMICS—International Commerce*

COUNTRY COMMERCE. BRAZIL. see *BUSINESS AND ECONOMICS—International Commerce*

COUNTRY COMMERCE. CANADA. see *BUSINESS AND ECONOMICS—International Commerce*

COUNTRY COMMERCE. CENTRAL AMERICA; including El Salvador, Guatemala, Honduras and Costa Rica. see *BUSINESS AND ECONOMICS—International Commerce*

COUNTRY COMMERCE. CHILE. see *BUSINESS AND ECONOMICS—International Commerce*

COUNTRY COMMERCE. CHINA. see *BUSINESS AND ECONOMICS—International Commerce*

COUNTRY COMMERCE. COLOMBIA. see *BUSINESS AND ECONOMICS—International Commerce*

COUNTRY COMMERCE. CZECH REPUBLIC. see *BUSINESS AND ECONOMICS—International Commerce*

COUNTRY COMMERCE. DENMARK. see *BUSINESS AND ECONOMICS—International Commerce*

COUNTRY COMMERCE. ECUADOR. see *BUSINESS AND ECONOMICS—International Commerce*

COUNTRY COMMERCE. EGYPT. see *BUSINESS AND ECONOMICS—International Commerce*

COUNTRY COMMERCE. EUROPEAN UNION. see *BUSINESS AND ECONOMICS—International Commerce*

COUNTRY COMMERCE. FINLAND. see *BUSINESS AND ECONOMICS—International Commerce*

COUNTRY COMMERCE. FRANCE. see *BUSINESS AND ECONOMICS—International Commerce*

COUNTRY COMMERCE. GERMANY. see *BUSINESS AND ECONOMICS—International Commerce*

COUNTRY COMMERCE. GREECE. see *BUSINESS AND ECONOMICS—International Commerce*

COUNTRY COMMERCE. HONG KONG. see *BUSINESS AND ECONOMICS—International Commerce*

COUNTRY COMMERCE. HUNGARY. see *BUSINESS AND ECONOMICS—International Commerce*

COUNTRY COMMERCE. INDIA. see *BUSINESS AND ECONOMICS—International Commerce*

COUNTRY COMMERCE. INDONESIA. see *BUSINESS AND ECONOMICS—International Commerce*

COUNTRY COMMERCE. IRELAND. see *BUSINESS AND ECONOMICS—International Commerce*

COUNTRY COMMERCE. ISRAEL. see *BUSINESS AND ECONOMICS—International Commerce*

COUNTRY COMMERCE. ITALY. see *BUSINESS AND ECONOMICS—International Commerce*

COUNTRY COMMERCE. JAPAN. see *BUSINESS AND ECONOMICS—International Commerce*

COUNTRY COMMERCE. KENYA. see *BUSINESS AND ECONOMICS—International Commerce*

COUNTRY COMMERCE. LUXEMBOURG. see *BUSINESS AND ECONOMICS—International Commerce*

COUNTRY COMMERCE. MALAYSIA. see *BUSINESS AND ECONOMICS—International Commerce*

COUNTRY COMMERCE. MEXICO. see *BUSINESS AND ECONOMICS—International Commerce*

COUNTRY COMMERCE. MIDDLE EAST - AFRICA. see *BUSINESS AND ECONOMICS—International Commerce*

COUNTRY COMMERCE. NETHERLANDS. see *BUSINESS AND ECONOMICS—International Commerce*

COUNTRY COMMERCE. NEW ZEALAND. see *BUSINESS AND ECONOMICS—International Commerce*

COUNTRY COMMERCE. NIGERIA. see *BUSINESS AND ECONOMICS—International Commerce*

COUNTRY COMMERCE. NORWAY. see *BUSINESS AND ECONOMICS—International Commerce*

COUNTRY COMMERCE. PAKISTAN. see *BUSINESS AND ECONOMICS—International Commerce*

COUNTRY COMMERCE. PANAMA. see *BUSINESS AND ECONOMICS—International Commerce*

COUNTRY COMMERCE. PERU. see *BUSINESS AND ECONOMICS—International Commerce*

COUNTRY COMMERCE. PHILIPPINES. see *BUSINESS AND ECONOMICS—International Commerce*

COUNTRY COMMERCE. POLAND. see *BUSINESS AND ECONOMICS—International Commerce*

COUNTRY COMMERCE. PORTUGAL. see *BUSINESS AND ECONOMICS—International Commerce*

COUNTRY COMMERCE. PUERTO RICO. see *BUSINESS AND ECONOMICS—International Commerce*

COUNTRY COMMERCE. RUSSIA. see *BUSINESS AND ECONOMICS—International Commerce*

COUNTRY COMMERCE. SAUDI ARABIA. see *BUSINESS AND ECONOMICS—International Commerce*

COUNTRY COMMERCE. SINGAPORE. see *BUSINESS AND ECONOMICS—International Commerce*

COUNTRY COMMERCE. SOUTH AFRICA. see *BUSINESS AND ECONOMICS—International Commerce*

COUNTRY COMMERCE. SOUTH KOREA. see *BUSINESS AND ECONOMICS—International Commerce*

COUNTRY COMMERCE. SPAIN. see *BUSINESS AND ECONOMICS—International Commerce*

COUNTRY COMMERCE. SWEDEN. see *BUSINESS AND ECONOMICS—International Commerce*

COUNTRY COMMERCE. SWITZERLAND. see *BUSINESS AND ECONOMICS—International Commerce*

COUNTRY COMMERCE. TAIWAN. see *BUSINESS AND ECONOMICS—International Commerce*

COUNTRY COMMERCE. THAILAND. see *BUSINESS AND ECONOMICS—International Commerce*

COUNTRY COMMERCE. TURKEY. see *BUSINESS AND ECONOMICS—International Commerce*

COUNTRY COMMERCE. UNITED KINGDOM. see *BUSINESS AND ECONOMICS—International Commerce*

COUNTRY COMMERCE. UNITED STATES OF AMERICA. see *BUSINESS AND ECONOMICS—International Commerce*

COUNTRY COMMERCE. URUGUAY. see *BUSINESS AND ECONOMICS—International Commerce*

COUNTRY COMMERCE. VENEZUELA. see *BUSINESS AND ECONOMICS—International Commerce*

COUNTRY COMMERCE. VIETNAM. see *BUSINESS AND ECONOMICS—International Commerce*

B

▼ *new title*   ➤ *refereed*   ✱ *unverified*   ◆ *full entry avail.*

331 USA
COUNTRY REFERENCE MANUALS. Text in English. 1969. base vol. plus q. updates. USD 2,000 base vol(s). includes q. updates for 1 year; USD 500 updates (effective 2005).
Document type: *Trade.* **Description:** Provides detailed information on social security, employee sponsored pension plans and private plans in each country.
Formerly: International Benefits Information Service (0018-8611)
Indexed: SCI, WBSS.
Published by: I B I S Communications, Inc., 5410 Wilshire Blvd, Ste 707, Los Angeles, CA 90036. TEL 323-297-4247, FAX 323-954-7009, info@ibisnews.org, http://www.ibisnews.org/. **Subscr. to:** PO Box 830409, Birmingham, AL 35283. TEL 800-633-4931, 205-995-1567.

331 GBR
CRONER AT C C H EMPLOYMENT CASE DIGEST. Text in English. 1977. q. GBP 379.08 (effective 1999). Supplement avail. **Document type:** *Trade.* **Description:** Provides current information on employment legislation, with analysis of prospective changes.
Former titles (until 2000): Croner Employment Case Digest; Employment Digest (0309-4995)
Related titles: Online - full text ed.; ♦ Supplement to: Personnel in Practice.
Indexed: M&MA.
—CCC.
Published by: Croner.C C H Group Ltd. (Subsidiary of: Wolters Kluwer N.V.), 145 London Rd, Kingston, Surrey KT2 6SR, United Kingdom. TEL 44-20-85473333, FAX 44-20-85472637, info@croner.co.uk, http://www.croner.co.uk. Ed. Lorna Brown.

344.01 GBR ISSN 1359-9127
CRONER'S EMPLOYMENT CASE LAW INDEX. Text in English. 1993. base vol. plus m. updates. looseleaf. GBP 288.57 (effective 1999). **Document type:** *Trade.*
Formerly: Employment Case Law Bulletin (0969-255X)
Related titles: Online - full text ed.
Published by: Croner.C C H Group Ltd. (Subsidiary of: Wolters Kluwer N.V.), 145 London Rd, Kingston, Surrey KT2 6SR, United Kingdom. TEL 44-20-85473333, FAX 44-20-85472637, info@croner.co.uk, http://www.croner.co.uk.

CRONER'S REFERENCE BOOK FOR EMPLOYERS. see *BUSINESS AND ECONOMICS—Personnel Management*

CRONER'S REFERENCE BOOK FOR EMPLOYERS - MAGAZINE. see *BUSINESS AND ECONOMICS—Personnel Management*

331 ARG
CUADERNOS DE INVESTIGACION - ACCION. Text in Spanish. 1992. s-a. USD 20; ARS 5 newsstand/cover.
Published by: Centro de Estudios Laborales, San Mauro, 444, Quilmes, Buenos Aires 1878, Argentina. Ed. Daniel Cieza.

331 ESP ISSN 1131-8635
HD8581
CUADERNOS DE RELACIONES LABORALES. Text in Spanish. 1992. s-a. EUR 27 in the European Union; EUR 40 elsewhere (effective 2003). back issues avail. **Document type:** *Journal, Academic/Scholarly.* **Description:** Presents studies on working conditions in Spanish institutions.
Related titles: CD-ROM ed.: EUR 38 to individuals; EUR 50 to institutions (effective 2003).
Indexed: PSA, SociolAb.
—CINDOC.
Published by: (Universidad Complutense de Madrid, Escuela de Relaciones Laborales), Universidad Complutense de Madrid, Servicio de Publicaciones, C Isaac Peral s/n, Ciudad Universitaria, Madrid, 28040, Spain. TEL 34-91-3946934, FAX 34-91-3946978, ites04@erl.ucm.es, servicio@publicaciones.ucm.es, http://www.ucm.es/publicaciones. Ed. Javier Zornoza Boy.

CURRENT GOVERNMENTS REPORTS: FINANCES OF EMPLOYEE RETIREMENT SYSTEMS OF STATE AND LOCAL GOVERNMENTS. see *PUBLIC ADMINISTRATION*

352.63 USA ISSN 0196-4437
HD8011.A1
CURRENT GOVERNMENTS REPORTS: PUBLIC EMPLOYMENT. Text in English. 1940. a. price varies. **Document type:** *Government.*
Related titles: Microfiche ed.; Online - full text ed.: (from CompuServe Inc., The Dialog Corporation).
Published by: U.S. Bureau of the Census (Subsidiary of: U.S. Department of Commerce), c/o Donna Hirsch, Governments Division, 4700 Silver Hill Rd., Washington, DC 20233. TEL 800-242-2184, http://www.census.gov. **Subscr. to:** U.S. Government Printing Office, Superintendent of Documents. TEL 202-783-3238, FAX 202-512-2233.

344.01 ZAF
CURRENT LABOUR LAW; a review of recent developments in key areas of labour law. Text in English. 1990. a. ZAR 185 (effective 2001). **Document type:** *Proceedings.*
Published by: Juta & Company Ltd., Law and Professional Publishing Division, PO Box 14373, Kenwyn, 7790, South Africa. TEL 27-21-7975101, FAX 27-21-7970121, cserv@juta.co.za, http://www.juta.co.za.

368.4 CYP ISSN 0070-2390
CYPRUS. MINISTRY OF LABOUR AND SOCIAL INSURANCE. ANNUAL REPORT. Text in Greek; Summaries in English. 1943. a. free. **Document type:** *Government.*
Published by: Ministry of Labour and Social Insurance, Editor, Nicosia, Cyprus. TEL 357-2-303481, FAX 357-2-670993.

331.11 170 DEU ISSN 0948-9533
D N W E SCHRIFTENREIHE. Text in German. 1995. irreg., latest vol.9, 2002. price varies. **Document type:** *Monographic series, Academic/Scholarly.*
Published by: (Deutsche Netzwerk Wirtschaftsethik - EBEN e.V.), Rainer Hampp Verlag, Meringerzellerstr 10, Mering, 86415, Germany. TEL 49-8233-4783, FAX 49-8233-30755, Rainer_Hampp_Verlag@t-online.de, http://www.hampp-verlag.de.

331 USA ISSN 0418-2693
HD4802
DAILY LABOR REPORT. Text in English. 1941. d. looseleaf. USD 9,264 in United States (effective 2005 & 2006). m. index. 30 p./no.; back issues avail. **Description:** Notification service that comprehensively covers labor developments in Congress, the courts, federal agencies, unions, management, and the NLRB.
Former titles: Daily Economic Reports on Current Trends Affecting Management and Labor; Washington Daily Reporter: Labor Section; Washington Daily Reporter System: Daily Labor Report
Related titles: Microform ed.; Online - full text ed.: ISSN 1522-5968 (from The Bureau of National Affairs, Inc., Thomson West).
—CCC.
Published by: The Bureau of National Affairs, Inc., 1231 25th St., NW, Washington, DC 20037. TEL 202-452-4200, 800-372-1033, 800-452-7773, FAX 202-822-8092, customercare@bna.com, bnaplus@bna.com, http://www.bna.com/products/labor/dlr.htm. Pub. Greg C McCaffery.

344.01 340.56 CAN ISSN 1480-5065
DART: BRITISH COLUMBIA LABOUR DECISIONS. Text in English. 1998. base vol. plus q. updates. CND 530 (effective 2005). **Document type:** *Trade.* **Description:** Presents court decisions originating in British Columbia regarding provincial and federal labor arbitration and Labour Relations Board outcomes.
Media: CD-ROM. **Related titles:** Online - full text ed.; ♦ Print ed.: British Columbia Labour Relations Board Decisions - Digest. ISSN 0715-5808.
Published by: Canada Law Book Inc., 240 Edward St, Aurora, ON L4G 3S9, Canada. TEL 905-841-6472, 800-263-3269, FAX 905-841-5085, b.loney@canadalawbook.ca, http://www.canadalawbook.com/catalogue.cfm?DSP=Detail&ProductID=502, http://www.canadalawbook.ca. R&P Nancy Nesbitt.

331 USA
DATA PROCESSING SURVEY. Text in English. a. USD 450. **Description:** Offers comparative information on compensation practices for 81 data processing positions among 136 businesses, representing 835 employees, in PA, NJ, MD, and DE.
Published by: MidAtlantic Employers' Association, PO Box 770, Valley Forge, PA 19482. TEL 215-666-7330.

331 CRI ISSN 1121-6573
DEBATE LABORAL; revista americana e italiana de derecho del trabajo. Text in Spanish. 1988. 3/yr.
Published by: I S C O S, c/o Daniel Lara S., Apdo 1119, San Jose, 1002, Costa Rica.

331.154 USA ISSN 0083-2227
KF3362.A2
DECISIONS AND ORDERS OF THE NATIONAL LABOR RELATIONS BOARD. Text in English. 1936. irreg., latest vol.344, 2005. reprint service avail. from WSH. **Document type:** *Government.*
Related titles: Microfiche ed.: (from WSH); Online - full text ed.
Indexed: RASB.
Published by: U.S. National Labor Relations Board, 1099 14th St, N W, Washington, DC 20570-0001. TEL 202-273-1000, 866-667-6572, http://www.nlrb.gov/nlrb/legal/decisions. **Subscr. to:** U.S. Government Printing Office, Superintendent of Documents, PO Box 371954, Pittsburgh, PA 15250-7954. TEL 202-512-1800, FAX 202-512-2250, orders@gpo.gov, http://www.access.gpo.gov.

344.01 331.795 USA ISSN 0278-7695
DECISIONS OF THE FEDERAL LABOR RELATIONS AUTHORITY. Text in English. 1973. irreg. **Document type:** *Government.*
Formerly (until 1979): Decisions and Interpretations of the Federal Labor Relations Council (0145-1529)
Published by: U.S. Federal Labor Relations Authority, 607 Fourteenth St, N W, Washington, DC 20424-0001. TEL 202-218-7770, 800-331-3572, http://www.flra.gov/.

331.4 USA
DEFENSE OF EQUAL EMPLOYMENT CLAIMS. Text in English. 1982. base vol. plus a. updates. USD 105. Supplement avail. **Document type:** *Trade.* **Description:** Provides analysis of the Equal Pay Act, Title VII of the Civil Rights Act of 1965, Sections 1981, 1983 and 1985, Executive Order 11,246 and the Age Discrimination in Employment Act.
Published by: Shepard's (Subsidiary of: LexisNexis North America), 555 Middle Creek Pkwy, Colorado Springs, CO 80921. TEL 800-743-7393, customer_service@shepards.com, http://www.shepards.com, http://www.lexisnexis.com/shepards/. Eds. William L Diedrich Jr., William Gaus.

DELAWARE EMPLOYMENT LAW LETTER. see *LAW*

331.21 USA
DELAWARE VALLEY EXECUTIVE COMPENSATION SURVEY. Text in English. a. USD 450. **Description:** Provides comparative information regarding 29 executive position compensation practices among companies in PA, NJ, MD, and DE.
Published by: MidAtlantic Employers' Association, PO Box 770, Valley Forge, PA 19482. TEL 215-666-7330, FAX 215-666-7866.

331 SVN ISSN 1408-3760
DELO + VARNOST; revija za varstvo pri delu. Text in Slovenian. 1956. bi-m. SIT 19,800 domestic (effective 1999). adv. bk.rev. 52 p./no.; back issues avail. **Document type:** *Journal.*
Indexed: CISA.
Published by: Zavod za Varstvo Pri Delu, Bohoriceva 22-a, Ljubljana, 61000, Slovenia. TEL 386-1-4320253, FAX 386-1-2312562, inof@zvd.si, info@zvd.si, http://www.zvd.si. Ed. Tatjana Srol. Circ: 1,000.

331 DNK ISSN 0900-6885
DENMARK. DIREKTORATET FOR ARBEJDSTILSYNET. ARBEJDSTILSYNETS AARSBERETNING. Text in Danish; Summaries in English. a. **Document type:** *Catalog.*
Published by: Arbejdstilsynet, Tryksagsafdelningen, Landskronagade 33-35, Copenhagen Oe, 2100, Denmark. TEL 01-180088.

THE DEPARTMENT OF LABOR'S (YEAR) FINDINGS ON THE WORST FORMS OF CHILD LABOR. see *CHILDREN AND YOUTH—About*

344.01 ARG ISSN 0325-3627
K4
DERECHO DEL TRABAJO; revista critica mensual de jurisprudencia, doctrina y legislacion. Text in Spanish. 1941. m. (plus 2 a. vols.). USD 600 (effective 1996). bk.rev. abstr.; bibl. Supplement avail. **Description:** Critical review of labor jurisprudence and legislation.
Indexed: WBSS.
Published by: Ediciones la Ley S.A., Tucuman, 1471, Capital Federal, Buenos Aires 1050, Argentina. TEL 54-114-495481, FAX 54-114-4760953. Ed. Juan J Etala.

344.01 USA
DESKBOOK ENCYCLOPEDIA OF EMPLOYMENT LAW✶. Text in English. 1993. a., latest 9th ed. USD 139 per vol. (effective 2003). **Document type:** *Trade.* **Description:** Provides an up-to-date compilation of summarized federal and state appellate court decisions that affect employment.
Published by: Oakstone Legal and Business Publishing, PO Box 381205, Birmingham, AL 35238-9950. TEL 800-365-4900, http://www.oakstonelegal.com/. Ed. Steven McEllistrem.

DESKBOOK ENCYCLOPEDIA OF PUBLIC EMPLOYMENT LAW. see *PUBLIC ADMINISTRATION—Municipal Government*

331 USA
DETROIT LABOR MARKET REVIEW. Text in English. 1946. m. free. charts; stat.
Formerly (until 1975): Detroit Manpower Review
Published by: (Michigan. Bureau of Research and Statistics), Employment Security Commission, 7310 Woodward Ave, Detroit, MI 48202. TEL 313-876-5000. Ed. James Astalos Jr. Circ: 1,800.

331 DEU ISSN 0178-6717
DEUTSCHE ANGESTELLTEN ZEITUNG. Text in German. 1894. bi-m. EUR 2 newsstand/cover (effective 2004). adv. **Document type:** *Magazine, Trade.*
Formerly (until 1985): Deutsche Handelswacht (0178-6407)
Published by: D H V Dienstleistungs GmbH, Postfach 600629, Hamburg, 22206, Germany. TEL 49-40-63280, FAX 49-40-63280225, dhv@dhv-cgb.de, http://www.dhv-cgb.de. adv.: B&W page EUR 2,900, color page EUR 5,800. Circ: 80,000 (controlled).

331 DEU ISSN 0942-3745
DEUTSCHE HANDWERKS ZEITUNG. AUSGABE HANDWERKSKAMMER RHEIN-MAIN. Text in German. 1947. 22/yr. EUR 22; EUR 1.30 newsstand/cover (effective 2004). adv. **Document type:** *Newspaper, Trade.*
Former titles (until 1990): Deutsche Handwerks Zeitung. Ausgabe Frankfurt (0343-4443); (until 1970): Frankfurter Handwerk (0015-9972); Incorporates (1950-1978): Wirtschaftszeitung fuer Handwerk und Gewerbe

Published by: Hans Holzmann Verlag GmbH, Gewerbestr 2, Bad Woerishofen, 86825, Germany. TEL 49-8247-35401, FAX 49-8247-354170, reddhz@holzmannverlag.de, http://www.deutsche-handwerks-zeitung.de/121761.html, http://www.holzmannverlag.de. Ed. Roman Leuthner. Adv. contact Eva-Maria Hammer. B&W page EUR 25,536, color page EUR 47,208. Circ: 436,590 (paid).

DIALOGUES ON WORK AND INNOVATION. see *BUSINESS AND ECONOMICS—Personnel Management*

331 FRA ISSN 0767-2187
DICTIONNAIRE PERMANENT: SECURITE ET CONDITIONS DE TRAVAIL. Text in French. 2 base vols. plus m. updates. looseleaf. EUR 303 base vol(s). (effective 2004). **Description:** Focuses on working conditions, on-site safety and hygiene.
Related titles: CD-ROM ed.; Online - full text ed.
Published by: Editions Legislatives, 80 Avenue de la Marne, Montrouge, Cedex 92546, France. TEL 33-1-40923636, FAX 33-1-40923663, infocom@editions-legislatives.fr, http://www.editions-legislatives.fr. Pub. Michel Vaillant.

344.01 FRA ISSN 0012-2513
DICTIONNAIRE PERMANENT: SOCIAL. Text in French. 1950. 3 base vols. plus bi-m. updates. looseleaf. EUR 330 base vol(s). (effective 2004). bibl. index, cum.index. **Description:** Provides information on labor laws and social security.
Related titles: CD-ROM ed.: ISSN 1635-7620; Online - full text ed.
Published by: Editions Legislatives, 80 Avenue de la Marne, Montrouge, Cedex 92546, France. TEL 33-1-40923636, FAX 33-1-40923663, infocom@editions-legislatives.fr, http://www.editions-legislatives.fr. Ed. Franck Lahellec. Pub. Michel Vaillant. Circ: 14,000.

331 GBR ISSN 0954-8165
DIRECTORS REWARDS. Text in English. 1980. a. GBP 295 per edition (effective 2001). **Document type:** *Bulletin.* **Description:** Details the pay and benefits for Chairman, Managing Director, Director and other management positions.
Published by: The Reward Group Ltd., Reward House, Diamond Way, Stone Business Park, Stone, Staffs ST15 0SD, United Kingdom. TEL 44-1785-813566, FAX 44-1785-817007, enquiries@reward-group.co.uk, http://www.reward-group.co.uk.

331.133 USA
DIRECTORY OF CAREER RESOURCES FOR MINORITIES; a guide to career resources and opportunities for minorities. Text in English. 1980. a. USD 37.50.
Published by: Ready Reference Press, PO Box 5169, Santa Monica, CA 90405. Ed. Alvin Renetzky.

331.025 GBR ISSN 1360-6255
DIRECTORY OF EMPLOYERS ASSOCIATIONS, TRADE UNIONS, AND OTHER EMPLOYEES' ASSOCIATIONS. Text in English. irreg. GBP 14.50. **Document type:** *Directory, Government.*
Formerly: Directory of Employers Associations, Trade Unions, Joint Organizations Etc. (0965-9633)
Published by: Stationery Office, 51 Nine Elms Ln, London, SW8 5DA, United Kingdom. TEL 44-20-7873-0011, FAX 44-20-7873-8247, book.orders@theso.co.uk, http://www.national-publishing.co.uk. Circ: 1,325.

331 USA
HF5549.5.D55
DIRECTORY OF OUTPLACEMENT FIRMS & CAREER MANAGEMENT FIRMS. Text in English. 1980. a., latest 2001. USD 129.95 (effective 2001). adv. **Document type:** *Directory.*
Formerly: Directory of Outplacement Firms (0735-3707)
Published by: Kennedy Information Inc., One Kennedy Place, Rte 12 S, Fitzwilliam, NH 03447. TEL 212-972-3793, FAX 212-972-1002, http://www.kennedyinfo.com/hr/dof.html. Adv. contact Carolyn D Edwards.

331.1251378 USA
LB2335.875.U6
DIRECTORY OF STAFF BARGAINING AGENTS IN INSTITUTIONS OF HIGHER EDUCATION. Text in English. 1991. irreg., latest 1995. USD 25 (effective 1999). **Document type:** *Directory.* **Description:** Lists all institutions of higher education in the U.S. which have collective bargaining contracts for staff members other than faculty. Includes names of agents.
Formerly: Directory of Non-Faculty Bargaining Agents in Institutions of Higher Education (1054-7568)
Published by: National Center for the Study of Collective Bargaining in Higher Education and the Professions, Bernard M Baruch College, City University of New York, 17 Lexington Ave, Box F 1228, New York, NY 10010. TEL 212-802-6751, FAX 212-802-5903. Ed. Richard W Hurd. R&P Beth Johnson.

344.01 ITA ISSN 1121-8762
DIRITTO DELLE RELAZIONI INDUSTRIALI. Text in Italian. 1991. q. EUR 46.48 in the European Union; EUR 69.72 elsewhere (effective 2002). **Description:** Adresses the complex issues surrounding industrial relations by offering a common ground for both academic and professional discourse.
Published by: (Associazione Lavoro e Ricerche), Casa Editrice Dott. A. Giuffre (Subsidiary of: LexisNexis Europe and Africa), Via Busto Arsizio, 40, Milan, MI 20151, Italy. TEL 39-02-28089200, FAX 39-02-38009582, giuffre@giuffre.it, http://www.giuffre.it. Eds. Luciano Spagnuolo Vigorita, Marco Biagi.

331 USA ISSN 1093-2836
KF3531.A15
DISABILITY LEAVE & ABSENCE REPORTER. Text in English. 1997. m. USD 245 to individuals; USD 25 newsstand/cover (effective 2002). index. **Document type:** *Newsletter.* **Description:** Balancing company responsibilities under workers compensation laws, FMLA, and ADA can be logistical nightmare. This newsletter gives hands-on tips in complying with these overlapping laws, news, and court rulings, expert advice, sample policies.
Incorporates (in 1999): Leave & Disability Compliance Alert (1527-6899)
Related titles: Online - full text ed.: (from Florida Center for Library Automation).
Published by: Bureau of Business Practice (Subsidiary of: Aspen Publishers, Inc.), 1185 Avenue of the Americas, 37th Fl, New York, NY 10036. TEL 860-442-4365, 800-243-0876, FAX 860-437-3150, customer.service@aspenpubl.com, http://www.bbpnews.com. Ed. Mary Lou Devine. Pub. Peter Garabedian. R&P Kathryn Mennone.

331.133 AUS ISSN 1324-9681
DISCRIMINATION ALERT; the national independent newsletter on equal opportunity & workforce diversity. Text in English. fortn. AUD 365 (effective 1999). **Document type:** *Newsletter.*
Published by: Newsletter Information Services, PO Box 2095, Manly, NSW 2095, Australia. TEL 61-2-9977-7500, FAX 61-2-9977-3310, customer.support@newsinfo.com.au, http://www.newsinfo.com.au. Ed. Peter Schwab.

331.133 GBR
DISCRIMINATION CASE LAW DIGEST. Text in English. q. GBP 90; GBP 95 foreign. **Document type:** *Bulletin.* **Description:** Reports on every significant development in case law involving discrimination in the workplace.
Published by: I R S (Subsidiary of: LexisNexis UK (Scottish Office)), 18-20 Highbury Pl, London, N5 1QP, United Kingdom. TEL 44-20-7354-5858, FAX 44-207-226-8618.

344.01 CAN ISSN 0831-2516
DISMISSAL AND EMPLOYMENT LAW DIGEST. Text in English. 1986. 9/yr. CND 207 (effective 2005). **Document type:** *Trade.*
Published by: Canada Law Book Inc., 240 Edward St, Aurora, ON L4G 3S9, Canada. TEL 905-841-6472, 800-263-3269, FAX 905-841-5085, b.loney@canadalawbook.ca, http://www.canadalawbook.com/catalogue.cfm?DSP=Detail&ProductID=336, http://www.canadalawbook.ca. Ed. Howard A Levitt.

DISPLACED WORKERS. see *BUSINESS AND ECONOMICS—Abstracting, Bibliographies, Statistics*

344.01 USA ISSN 1074-8105
K1
DISPUTE RESOLUTION JOURNAL. Text in English. 1937. q. USD 125 (effective 2004). bk.rev. bibl.; illus. index. 96 p./no.; reprint service avail. from WSH. **Document type:** *Magazine, Trade.* **Description:** Covers the spectrum of the dispute resolution field. Articles by practitioners and scholars analyze current trends in commercial dispute settlement, construction, accident claims, international arbitration, and labor relations.
Formerly (until 1993): Arbitration Journal (0003-7893)
Related titles: Microform ed.: (from PQC); Online - full text ed.: (from EBSCO Publishing, H.W. Wilson, Northern Light Technology, Inc., O C L C Online Computer Library Center, Inc., ProQuest Information & Learning).
Indexed: ABIn, ABRCLP, AmH&L, BPI, BPIA, BusI, CLI, CurCont, ESPM, FamI, HistAb, ILP, LRI, LegCont, PersLit, RiskAb, SSCI, T&II.
—BLDSC (3598.785000), IDS, IE, Infotrieve, ingenta. **CCC.**
Published by: American Arbitration Association, 335 Madison Ave, New York, NY 10017. TEL 212-484-4011, FAX 212-541-4841, http://www.adr.org/index2.1.jsp?JSPssid=15770&JSPsrc=upload LIVESITE NewsAndEvents Publications Updated%20Publications%20Files DRJ.htm. Ed. Susan Zuckerman. Circ: 10,000.

331.255 GBR
DISTRIBUTION REWARDS. Text in English. 2/yr. GBP 250 per edition (effective 2001). **Document type:** *Bulletin.* **Description:** Information on pay and benefits in distribution jobs from director to warehouse laborer.
Published by: The Reward Group Ltd., Reward House, Diamond Way, Stone Business Park, Stone, Staffs ST15 0SD, United Kingdom. TEL 44-1785-813566, FAX 44-1785-817007, enquiries@reward-group.co.uk, http://www.reward-group.co.uk.

DIVERSITY/CAREERS IN ENGINEERING & INFORMATION TECHNOLOGY. see *OCCUPATIONS AND CAREERS*

331 SGP ISSN 0219-8711
▼ **DIVISION OF LABOR AND TRANSACTION COSTS.** Text in English. 2005 (June). s-a. SGD 150, USD 85, EUR 84 to individuals; SGD 422, USD 240, EUR 238 combined subscription to institutions print & online eds. (effective 2006). **Document type:** *Journal, Academic/Scholarly.* **Description:** Covers the network effects of division of labor and general equilibrium mechanisms that simultaneously determine interdependent benefits of specialization and number of participants in the network of division of labor (extent of the market) in a modern body of inframarginal economics.
Related titles: Online - full content ed.
Published by: World Scientific Publishing Co. Pte. Ltd., 5 Toh Tuck Link, Singapore, 596224, Singapore. TEL 65-466-5775, FAX 65-467-7667, wspc@wspc.com.sg, http://www.worldscinet.com/dltc/dltc.shtml, http://www.worldscientific.com. Ed. N G Yew-Kwang. **Dist. by:** World Scientific Publishing Co., Inc., 1060 Main St, River Edge, NJ 07661. TEL 201-487-9655, FAX 201-487-9656, 888-977-2665, wspc@wspc.com; World Scientific Publishing Ltd., 57 Shelton St, London WC2H 9HE, United Kingdom. TEL 44-20-78360888, FAX 44-20-78362020, sales@wspc.co.uk.

331 ESP ISSN 0211-8556
DOCUMENTACION LABORAL. Text in Spanish. 1981. m.
—CINDOC.
Published by: Asociacion de Cajas de Ahorros para Relaciones Laborales, C. Principe, 5-4o, Madrid, 28012, Spain. TEL 34-91-4296596, FAX 34-91-4291026, http://www.acarl.es/. Ed. Francisco De la Rosa Moreno.

DOCUMENTING EMPLOYEE DISCIPLINE. see *BUSINESS AND ECONOMICS—Personnel Management*

344.01 FRA ISSN 0222-4194
KJV3392
LE DROIT OUVRIER. Text in French. 1920. m. EUR 100 domestic; EUR 137 foreign (effective 2004).
—IE.
Published by: (Confederation Generale du Travail), Droit Ouvrier, 263, rue de Paris, Montreuil, 93516, France. http://www.cgt.fr/04presse/05publi/froitouv1.htm.

DRUG DETECTION REPORT; the newsletter on drug testing in the workplace. see *BUSINESS AND ECONOMICS—Personnel Management*

331 USA ISSN 0012-6918
DUBUQUE LEADER. Text in English. 1906. w. (Fri.). USD 18 (effective 2005). **Document type:** *Newspaper, Consumer.*
Address: P O Box 817, Dubuque, IA 52004-0817. Ed., Pub. William R Winders. Circ: 5,100.

331 USA ISSN 1085-4452
HD4928.N62
E B R I NOTES. Text in English. 1980. m. USD 199 (effective 2005). stat. cum. index. back issues avail. **Document type:** *Newsletter.* **Description:** Covers employee benefits, with emphasis on legislative and regulatory actions, statistical findings, and research studies and publications.
Formerly (until 1993): Employee Benefit Notes (0887-1388)
Related titles: E-mail ed.: USD 49 (effective 2001); Microform ed.: (from PQC).
Indexed: AgeL, PAIS.
—**CCC.**
Published by: Employee Benefit Research Institute, 2121 K St, N W, Ste 600, Washington, DC 20037-1896. TEL 202-659-0670, FAX 202-775-6312, info@ebri.org, http://www.ebri.org. Ed., R&P Stephen Blakely TEL 202-775-6341. Circ: 3,500.

331.1 USA
E E O C COMPLIANCE MANUAL. (Equal Employment Opportunity Commission) Text in English. 1975. irreg. looseleaf. USD 316 (effective 2001). back issues avail. **Description:** Contains the complete text of the EEOC Compliance Manual, as issued by the EEOC, with monthly notification of related developments.
Published by: The Bureau of National Affairs, Inc., 1231 25th St., NW, Washington, DC 20037. TEL 202-452-4200, 800-372-1033, 800-452-7773, FAX 202-822-8092, customercare@bna.com, bnaplus@bna.com, http://www.bna.com/. Pub. Greg C McCaffery.

E I R E C KENKYU HOKOKUSHU. see *MEDICAL SCIENCES—Physical Medicine And Rehabilitation*

E I U INVESTING, LICENSING AND TRADING. (Economist Intelligence Unit) see *BUSINESS AND ECONOMICS—International Commerce*

331.125 USA
E M A REPORTER. Text in English. 1969. bi-m. membership only. adv. **Description:** Forum for the exchange of ideas and information on employment issues.
Published by: Employment Management Association, 1800 Duke St, Alexandria, VA 22314-3499. TEL 703-548-3440, FAX 703-836-0367, http://www.shrm.org/ema. R&P Rebecca Hastings. Adv. contact Christine Klein. Circ: 5,600.

B

331.21 331.255 USA
E R I S A COMPLIANCE & ENFORCEMENT LIBRARY✶. (Employee Retirement Income Security Act) Text in English. irreg.
Published by: B N A Inc. (Subsidiary of: The Bureau of National Affairs, Inc.), 1231 25th St, NW, Washington, DC 20037. TEL 202-452-4343, FAX 202-452-4997, customercare@bna.com, http://www.bna.com/products/eb/eclw.htm.

344 USA ISSN 1083-6268
KF3512.A15
E R I S A LITIGATION ALERT. (Employee Retirement Income Security Act) Text in English. 1995. m. USD 225; USD 23 newsstand/cover (effective 2002). **Document type:** *Newsletter, Trade.* **Description:** Provides insights and practical analysis on important ERISA decisions from courts throughout the country.
Related titles: Online - full text ed.: (from EBSCO Publishing, Gale Group, ProQuest Information & Learning).
Indexed: ABIn.
Published by: Aspen Publishers, Inc. (Subsidiary of: Wolters Kluwer N.V.), 5301 Buckeystown Pike, Ste. 400, Frederick, MD 21704-8319. TEL 800-638-8437, customer.service@aspenpubl.com, http://www.aspenpub.com, http://www.aspenpublishers.com. **Dist. by:** Distribution Center, 7201 McKinney Circle, Frederick, MD 21701. TEL 301-698-7100, FAX 301-695-7931.

B

331.252 USA ISSN 8755-5379
E R I S A NEWSLETTER. (Employee Retirement Income Security Act) Text in English. m. USD 89. back issues avail. **Document type:** *Newsletter.*
Published by: Two Crows, 11 Pleasant St, Berlin, MA 01503. Ed. Joanne Bergen. Circ: 2,000.

344.01 USA ISSN 1050-4230
KF3512.A29
E R I S A: THE LAW AND THE CODE. (Employee Retirement Income Security Act) Text in English. a., latest 2003. USD 105 per issue (effective 2003).
Indexed: ATI.
Published by: B N A Inc. (Subsidiary of: The Bureau of National Affairs, Inc.), 1231 25th St, NW, Washington, DC 20037. TEL 202-452-4343, FAX 202-452-4997, books@bna.com, http://www.bnabooks.com. Ed. Michael Kushner. **Subscr. to:** BNA Books, PO Box 7814, Edison, NJ 08818-7814. TEL 800-960-1220, FAX 732-346-1624.

331.21 GBR
EAST ANGLIA SALARY SURVEY. Text in English. 2/yr. GBP 280 per edition (effective 2001). **Document type:** *Bulletin.* **Description:** Pay and benefit survey for East Anglia covering the Norfolk, Suffolk and Cambridgeshire areas.
Published by: The Reward Group Ltd., Reward House, Diamond Way, Stone Business Park, Stone, Staffs ST15 0SD, United Kingdom. TEL 44-1785-813566, FAX 44-1785-817007, enquiries@reward-group.co.uk, http://www.reward-group.co.uk.

344.01 PAK ISSN 0012-8953
EASTERN WORKER; bi-monthly journal on labour laws, labour-management relations & socio-economic affairs. Text in English. 1950. bi-m. USD 70. adv. bk.rev. charts; illus.; stat. index. **Document type:** *Academic/Scholarly.*
Published by: Bureau of Labour Publications, 8, Business Centre Mumtaz Hasan Rd., P O Box 5833, Karachi, 74000, Pakistan. TEL 92-21-2414975. Ed. P Shafi. Circ: 1,000.

331 ITA ISSN 0012-978X
ECONOMIA & LAVORO. Text in Italian. 1967. q. bk.rev. illus.
Indexed: IBSS, ILD, JEL, PAIS.
—BLDSC (3650.450000).
Published by: Donzelli Editori, Via Mentana 2, Rome, 00185, Italy. TEL 39-06-4440600, FAX 39-06-4440607, editore@donzelli.it, http://www.donzelli.it. Circ: 4,000.

ECONOMIA EM REVISTA. see *BUSINESS AND ECONOMICS—Economic Situation And Conditions*

331 AUS ISSN 1035-3046
HC601
➤ **ECONOMIC AND LABOUR RELATIONS REVIEW.** Text in English. 1977. 3/yr. AUD 40 domestic to individuals; AUD 60 foreign to individuals; AUD 80 domestic to institutions; AUD 100 foreign to institutions (effective 2003). adv. bk.rev. back issues avail. **Document type:** *Academic/Scholarly.* **Description:** Focuses on contemporary issues, developments and policy making in the fields of economics and labor relations.
Formerly (until 1990): University of New South Wales. Centre for Applied Economic Research. Paper (0314-853X)
Indexed: AusPAIS, BAS, JEL.
—BLDSC (3651.467200).
Published by: Centre for Applied Economic Research, School of Economics, The University of New South Wales, Sydney, NSW 2052, Australia. TEL 61-293853371, FAX 61-2-93136337, irrc@unsw.edu.au, j.nevile@unsw.edu.au, http://www.economics.unsw.edu.au/research/caer/caerelrr.htm. Ed. M Quinlan. R&P, Adv. contact M Kwok TEL 61-2-93857156. Circ: 1,000 (controlled).

➤ **ECONOMIC RESTRUCTURING AND THE JOB MARKET**; a series on labor trends and their policy implications. see *PUBLIC ADMINISTRATION*

➤ **ECONOMIES ET SOCIETES. SERIE AB. ECONOMIE DU TRAVAIL.** see *BUSINESS AND ECONOMICS*

331.4 ECU
ECUADOR. INSTITUTO NACIONAL DE ESTADISTICA Y CENSOS. INDICE DE EMPLEO Y REMUNERACIONES. Text in Spanish. q. USD 6.84 per issue (effective 2001). **Document type:** *Government.*
Related titles: Diskette ed.
Published by: Instituto Nacional de Estadistica y Censos, Juan Larrea N15-36 y Jose Riofrio, Quito, Ecuador. TEL 593-2-529858, FAX 593-2-509836, inec1@ecnet.ec, http://www.inec.gov.ec.

EFFECTIVE TELEPHONE TECHNIQUES. see *BUSINESS AND ECONOMICS—Management*

EKISTIC INDEX OF PERIODICALS. see *HOUSING AND URBAN PLANNING—Abstracting, Bibliographies, Statistics*

EKSPRESS - ZAKON. see *BUSINESS AND ECONOMICS—Public Finance, Taxation*

331.21 GBR
ELECTRONICS INDUSTRY REWARDS. Text in English. a. GBP 250 per edition (effective 2001). **Document type:** *Bulletin.* **Description:** Provides detailed pay information on the electronics industry, from large international to small specialized companies.
Published by: The Reward Group Ltd., Reward House, Diamond Way, Stone Business Park, Stone, Staffs ST15 0SD, United Kingdom. TEL 44-1785-813566, FAX 44-1785-817007, enquiries@reward-group.co.uk, http://www.reward-group.co.uk.

331 ITA
ELENCO UFFICIALE PROTESTI. Text in Italian. s-m.
Published by: Camera di Commercio Industria Artigianato e Agricoltura di Forli-Cesena, Corso della Repubblica 5, Forli', FC 47100, Italy. TEL 39-0547-21901, FAX 39-0547-23157, http://www.fo.camcom.it.

331.125 PRI ISSN 0555-6635
EMPLEO Y DESEMPLEO EN PUERTO RICO/EMPLOYMENT AND UNEMPLOYMENT IN PUERTO RICO. Text in English, Spanish. 1967. a. free. **Document type:** *Government.*
Published by: Department of Labor & Human Resources, 505 Munoz Rivera Ave., Hato Rey, 00918, Puerto Rico.

331 USA ISSN 0896-0941
EMPLOYEE ASSISTANCE PROGRAM MANAGEMENT LETTER. Text in English. 1987. 12/yr. USD 247 (effective 2005). index. back issues avail. **Document type:** *Newsletter.* **Description:** Monitors the trends in the employee assistance field to give EA professionals the best strategies for managing their EAPs more effectively.
—CCC.
Published by: Health Resources Publishing, 1913 Atlantic Ave, Ste F4, Manasquan, NJ 08736. TEL 732-292-1100, FAX 732-292-1111, info@wellnessjunction.com, info@healthrespubs.com, http://www.wellnessjunction.com, http://www.healthrespubs.com. Ed. Beth-Ann Kerber. Pub. Robert K Jenkins.

331 USA ISSN 0273-236X
KF3509
EMPLOYEE BENEFIT CASES. Text in English. 1981. w. looseleaf. USD 1,582 in United States (effective 2005 - 2006). index. 30 p./no.; back issues avail. **Description:** Decisional service that reports the full text of federal and state court decisions and selected decisions of arbitrators and the NLRB employee benefits issues.
Related titles: Online - full text ed.: (from The Bureau of National Affairs, Inc.).
—CCC.
Published by: The Bureau of National Affairs, Inc., 1231 25th St., NW, Washington, DC 20037. TEL 202-452-4200, 800-372-1033, 800-452-7773, FAX 202-822-8092, customercare@bna.com, bnaplus@bna.com, http://www.bna.com/products/eb/ebcs.htm. Ed. David A Sayre. Pub. Greg C McCaffery.

331.255 USA ISSN 1044-6265
HD4928.N62
EMPLOYEE BENEFIT NEWS. Text in English. 1987. 18/yr. USD 94 domestic; USD 105 in Canada & Mexico; USD 150 elsewhere (effective 2005). adv. charts; illus.; stat.; tr.lit. back issues avail. **Document type:** *Newsletter, Trade.* **Description:** Covers news and trends, healthcare, retirement plans, insurance, legislation, and day care for employee benefits managers.
Incorporates (1988-1990): Pension Fund News
Related titles: Online - full text ed.: (from EBSCO Publishing, Florida Center for Library Automation, Gale Group, LexisNexis, O C L C Online Computer Library Center, Inc., ProQuest Information & Learning).
—CCC.
Published by: Source Media, Inc., 1325 G Street, N W, Ste 900, Washington, DC 20005. TEL 202-504-1122, FAX 202-772-1448, custserv@sourcemedia.com, http://www.benefitnews.com, http://www.sourcemedia.com. Ed. Lynn Gresham. Pub. James Callan. adv.: B&W page USD 9,090, color page USD 10,685. Circ: 61,000.

331.255 USA
KFI1534.5.P4A134
EMPLOYEE BENEFITS. Text in English. 1982. q. looseleaf. USD 68; USD 38 to non-profit organizations (effective 2006). back issues avail. **Document type:** *Newsletter, Trade.*
Published by: (Section on Employee Benefits), Illinois State Bar Association, Illinois Bar Center, 424 S Second St, Springfield, IL 62701. TEL 217-525-1760, 800-252-8908, sanderson@isba.org, http://www.isba.org. Eds. Brian Wydajewski, Kathryn Kennedy. Circ: 550.

331.255 USA ISSN 1090-4220
KF3509.A15
EMPLOYEE BENEFITS AND EXECUTIVE COMPENSATION COUNSELOR. Text in English. 1993. m. looseleaf. USD 295 (effective 1999). bk.rev. index, cum.index. back issues avail. **Document type:** *Newsletter.* **Description:** Discusses current ERISA and employee benefit issues.
Formerly: Employee Benefits Counselor (1068-4204)
—CCC.
Published by: Business Laws, Inc., 11630 Chillicothe Rd, Chesterland, OH 44026. TEL 440-729-7996, FAX 440-729-0645, hancock@counsel.com, custserv@businesslaws.com, http://www.businesslaws.com. Ed. William A Hancock.

331.255 USA
EMPLOYEE BENEFITS GUIDE. Text in English. 1991. 2 base vols. plus irreg. updates. looseleaf. USD 282 base vol(s). (effective 2002). Supplement avail. **Description:** Covers detailed analysis of statutes, regulations, opinion letters and case law, Employee Benefits.
Related titles: CD-ROM ed.
Published by: Matthew Bender & Co., Inc. (Subsidiary of: LexisNexis North America), 1275 Broadway, Albany, NY 12204. international@bender.com, http://bender.lexisnexis.com. Ed. David L Bacon.

331.255 USA ISSN 1048-2814
HD7106.U5
EMPLOYEE BENEFITS ISSUES: THE MULTIEMPLOYER PERSPECTIVE; proceedings of the annual employee benefits conference with papers from other multi-employer conferences. Text in English. 1957. a. price varies. 2 cols./p.; back issues avail. **Document type:** *Proceedings, Trade.*
Formerly: Employee Benefits Annual (Year)
—BLDSC (3737.032430). CCC.
Published by: International Foundation of Employee Benefit Plans, 18700 W Bluemound Rd, Box 69, Brookfield, WI 53008-0069. TEL 262-786-6700, FAX 262-786-8780, books@ifebp.org, http://www.ifebp.org. Ed. Judith A. Sankey.

331.255 GBR
EMPLOYEE BENEFITS REPORT. Text in English. a. GBP 280 per edition (effective 2001). **Document type:** *Bulletin.* **Description:** Overview of the current practices and trends in employee benefits.
Formerly: Employee Benefits 1
Published by: The Reward Group Ltd., Reward House, Diamond Way, Stone Business Park, Stone, Staffs ST15 0SD, United Kingdom. TEL 44-1785-813566, FAX 44-1785-817007, enquiries@reward-group.co.uk, http://www.reward-group.co.uk.

331.255 USA ISSN 1061-2556
KF3512
EMPLOYEE FRINGE AND WELFARE BENEFIT PLANS. Text in English. 1990. a., latest 2002. price varies. **Document type:** *Monographic series, Trade.* **Description:** Covers the major types of employee fringe and welfare benefit plans available under the Employee Retirement Income Security Act.
Published by: Thomson West (Subsidiary of: Thomson Corporation, The), 610 Opperman Dr, Eagan, MN 55123-1396. TEL 651-687-8000, 800-328-9352, FAX 651-687-7302, http://west.thomson.com.

331 GBR ISSN 0142-5455
CODEN: EMREDQ
➤ **EMPLOYEE RELATIONS.** Text in English. 1979. bi-m. EUR 13,364.29 in Europe; USD 13,109 in North America; AUD 15,899 in Australasia; GBP 8,927.29 in UK & elsewhere (effective 2006). bk.rev. charts; illus. reprint service avail. from PSC. **Document type:** *Journal, Academic/Scholarly.* **Description:** Aims to help all those involved in the management of organizations to find and compare alternative strategies for improving employment conditions. Covers developments in collective bargaining, management of industrial relations, and more.
Related titles: Online - full text ed.: (from EBSCO Publishing, Emerald Group Publishing Limited, Florida Center for Library Automation, Gale Group, IngentaConnect, O C L C Online Computer Library Center, Inc., ProQuest Information & Learning, Swets Information Services).

Indexed: ABIn, ADPA, ASEANManA, ASG, AgeL, BPIA, BusI, CIJE, CPM, CurCont, ERA, EmerIntel, Emerald, HRA, IBSS, ILD, KES, M&MA, ManagCont, PRA, PsycInfo, PsycholAb, TEA.
—BLDSC (3737.040000), IE, Infotrieve, ingenta. **CCC.**
Published by: Emerald Group Publishing Limited, 60-62 Toller Ln, Bradford, W Yorks BD8 9BY, United Kingdom. TEL 44-1274-777700, FAX 44-1274-785200, infomation@emeraldinsight.com, http://www.emeraldinsight.com/er.htm. Ed. John Gennard.

331.255 USA ISSN 1080-1871
EMPLOYEE RELATIONS BULLETIN. Text in English. 1963. s-m. USD 199 (effective 1999). bk.rev. charts. index. **Document type:** *Newsletter.* **Description:** Keeps managers informed of cutting-edge trends, ways to effectively manage staff, legislation affecting their organization, and methods to stay competitive in the ever-changing business world. For top decision-makers (CEO, CFO, COO, CIO, VPs, HR managers).
Former titles (until 1990): Employee Relations and Human Resources Bulletin (0744-7779); (until 1982): Employee Relations Bulletin (0013-6816)
Published by: Bureau of Business Practice (Subsidiary of: Aspen Publishers, Inc.), 1185 Avenue of the Americas, 37th Fl, New York, NY 10036. TEL 860-442-4365, 800-243-0876, FAX 860-437-3555, rebecca_armitage@prenhall.com. Ed. Christine Kotrba. Pub. Peter Garabedian. R&P Kathryn Mennone.

352.63 AUS
EMPLOYEE RELATIONS COMMISSION OF VICTORIA. MONTHLY NEWSLETTER. Text in English. m. looseleaf. AUD 80. **Document type:** *Newsletter.*
Published by: (Employee Relations Commission of Victoria), Law Press (Victoria), 52-58 Chetwynd St, West Melbourne, VIC 3003, Australia. TEL 61-3-93208686, FAX 61-3-93208699.

344.01 USA
EMPLOYEE RELATIONS GUIDE TO FEDERAL LAWS AND REGULATIONS. Text in English. a. USD 150. **Description:** Offers employers a reference source to assure compliance with all federal or state laws and regulations regarding employee relations.
Published by: MidAtlantic Employers' Association, PO Box 770, Valley Forge, PA 19482. TEL 215-666-7330, FAX 215-666-7866.

EMPLOYEE RELATIONS LAW JOURNAL. see *LAW*

331 USA ISSN 0892-7545
HD6958.5 CODEN: ERRJE9
➤ **EMPLOYEE RESPONSIBILITIES AND RIGHTS JOURNAL.** Text in English. 1988. q. EUR 372, USD 373, GBP 228 combined subscription to institutions print & online eds. (effective 2005). adv. bk.rev. illus. back issues avail.; reprint service avail. from PSC. **Document type:** *Journal, Academic/Scholarly.* **Description:** Focuses on the shifting rights and responsibilities between employer and employee.
Related titles: Microfilm ed.: (from PQC); Online - full text ed.: ISSN 1573-3378 (from EBSCO Publishing, Gale Group, IngentaConnect, Kluwer Online, O C L C Online Computer Library Center, Inc., ProQuest Information & Learning), Springer LINK, Swets Information Services).
Indexed: ABIn, BibLing, IMFL, IPSA, PAIS, PsycInfo, PsycholAb, SOPODA, SSA, e-psyche.
—BLDSC (3737.053500), IE, Infotrieve, ingenta. **CCC.**
Published by: (Council on Employee Responsibilities and Rights), Plenum US (Subsidiary of: Springer Science+Business Media), 233 Spring St, New York, NY 10013. TEL 212-460-1500, FAX 212-460-1575, service@springer-ny.com, http://springerlink.metapress.com/openurl.asp?genre=journal&issn=0892-7545, http://www.springeronline.com. Ed. John P Keenan.

331 USA ISSN 1522-2225
K5
EMPLOYEE RIGHTS AND EMPLOYMENT POLICY JOURNAL. Text in English. 1997. s-a. USD 60; USD 30 newsstand/cover (effective 2005). back issues avail. **Document type:** *Journal, Academic/Scholarly.* **Description:** Publishes articles containing diverse perspectives on legal and law related issues focused on the well-being of employees in the workplace.
Related titles: Online - full text ed.: (from LexisNexis).
Indexed: FamI, ILP.
Published by: Illinois Institute of Technology, Chicago - Kent College of Law, 565 W Adams St, Chicago, IL 60661-3691. TEL 312-906-5190, FAX 312-906-5189, lawrev@kentlaw.edu, http://www.kentlaw.edu/ilw/erepj/index.html.

344.01 USA
EMPLOYEE RIGHTS LITIGATION: PLEADING AND PRACTICE. Text in English. 1991. 3 base vols. plus irreg. updates. looseleaf. USD 503 base vol(s). (effective 2003). **Description:** Advocates for employee rights. Covers legal standards for statutory and common law claims raised on behalf of employees.
Published by: (National Employment Lawyers Association), Matthew Bender & Co., Inc. (Subsidiary of: LexisNexis North America), 1275 Broadway, Albany, NY 12204. international@bender.com, http://bender.lexisnexis.com. Ed. Janice Goodman.

344.01 USA ISSN 1063-097X
KF3471.A59
EMPLOYEE TERMINATIONS LAW BULLETIN. Text in English. 1982. m. looseleaf. USD 147 (effective 2005). Index. back issues avail. **Document type:** *Newsletter, Trade.* **Description:** Publishes case law summaries and prevention ideas om harassment, whistle blowing, discrimination, constructive discharge, employment contacts and more.
Former titles (until 1991): Employee Terminations Bulletin (1049-0914); National Report on Employee Terminations (1042-4407); Employee Terminations Law Bulletin (1986) (0898-5057); (until 1986): Discharged Worker (8755-822X)
Related titles: Online - full text ed.: ISSN 1545-9241.
—CCC.
Published by: Quinlan Publishing Group, Marine Industrial Park, 23 Drydock Ave, 6th Fl, Boston, MA 02210-2387. TEL 617-542-0048, 800-229-2084, FAX 617-507-1079, info@quinlan.com, http://www.quinlan.com. Ed. Laura Starczewski. Pub. Dennis Hofmaier.

EMPLOYER. see *BUSINESS AND ECONOMICS—Management*

EMPLOYER COSTS FOR EMPLOYEE COMPENSATION. see *BUSINESS AND ECONOMICS—Abstracting, Bibliographies, Statistics*

331 USA
EMPLOYER RESOURCES NEWSLETTER. Text in English. bi-m. USD 350 to non-members; USD 175 to members. **Description:** Discusses current events in industrial relations.
Published by: Graphic Arts Employers of America, 100 Daingerfield Rd, Alexandria, VA 22314. TEL 703-519-8150, FAX 703-548-4165. Ed. William Solomon. Circ: 325.

EMPLOYER'S BRIEFING. see *LAW—Corporate Law*

331.4 GBR
EMPLOYER'S GUIDE TO MATERNITY ONLINE. Text in English. irreg. **Document type:** *Trade.*
Media: Online - full content. **Related titles:** ♦ Series of: Croner's Reference Book for Employers. ISSN 0070-1580.
Published by: Croner.C C H Group Ltd. (Subsidiary of: Wolters Kluwer N.V.), 145 London Rd, Kingston, Surrey KT2 6SR, United Kingdom. TEL 44-20-85473333, FAX 44-20-85472637, info@croner.co.uk, http://www.croner.cch.co.uk.

344.012 USA
EMPLOYER'S WAGE MANUAL (FEDERAL). Text in English. latest 1999, base vol. plus irreg. updates. USD 85 (effective 2003). **Description:** A reference for employers who implement the Fair Labor Standards Act. This book helps employers avoid unnecessary lawsuits and additional wage and salary costs not required by the law. It specifies alternative methods of complying with the Act.
Published by: Michie Company (Subsidiary of: LexisNexis North America), 701 E Water St, Charlottesville, VA 22902-5389. TEL 434-972-7600, 800-446-3410, FAX 434-972-7677, http://www.michie.com. Ed. Lee T Paterson.

331.125 CAN
EMPLOYMENT AND BUSINESS JOURNAL. Text in English. m.
Formerly: Employment Journal
Media: Online - full text.
Published by: Cynthia Wilson, 1275 Kensington Pkwy, Ste 257, Brockville, ON K6V 7E6, Canada. FAX 613-345-5627, MicroLine@brocknet.com, publisher@employmentandbusiness.com, http://www.brocknet.com/employment-journal/. Pub. Cynthia Wilson.

331.21 USA ISSN 0013-6840
HD5723
EMPLOYMENT AND EARNINGS. Abbreviated title: E E. Text in English. m. USD 53 domestic; USD 74.20 foreign (effective 2005). reprint service avail. from CIS,PQC. **Document type:** *Government.* **Description:** Compiles national, state, and local data on unemployment, hours, and earnings. Includes data from the Census Bureau's Current Population Surveys.
Formerly (until 1969): Employment and Earnings and Monthly Report on the Labor Force
Related titles: Microfiche ed.: (from CIS); Microform ed.: (from PQC); Online - full text ed.: (from bigchalk, EBSCO Publishing, Florida Center for Library Automation, Gale Group, H.W. Wilson, O C L C Online Computer Library Center, Inc., ProQuest Information & Learning); Cumulative ed(s).: Employment and Earnings (Annual).
Indexed: AmStI, BPI, IUSGP, PAIS, PROMT.
Published by: U.S. Department of Labor, Bureau of Labor Statistics, Postal Square Bldg., 2 Massachusetts Ave, NE, Washington, DC 20212-0001 . TEL 202-691-5200, FAX 202-691-7890, 202-691-6325, blsdata_staff@bls.gov, http://www.bls.gov. **Subscr. to:** U.S. Government Printing Office, Superintendent of Documents, PO Box 371954, Pittsburgh, PA 15250-7954. TEL 202-512-1800, FAX 202-512-2250, orders@gpo.gov, http://www.access.gpo.gov.

331.125 CAN ISSN 0707-901X
HD5727
EMPLOYMENT AND IMMIGRATION CANADA. ANNUAL REPORT/EMPLOI ET IMMIGRATION CANADA. RAPPORT ANNUEL. Text in English, French. 1978. a. free. charts; stat. **Document type:** *Corporate.*
Incorporates: Employment and Immigration Commission. Annual Report; Unemployment Insurance Canada. Annual Report (0576-4157)
—CISTI.
Published by: Public Enquiries Centre, Employment and Immigration, Ottawa, ON K1A 0J9, Canada. Circ: 10,000.

344.01 CAN ISSN 1183-7152
EMPLOYMENT AND LABOUR LAW REPORTER. Text in English. 1989. m. CND 295 (effective 2001). back issues avail. **Document type:** *Newsletter.* **Description:** Covers employment and labor issues in Canada. For labor, management and human resources professionals and legal practitioners.
Formerly: British Columbia Employment and Labour Law Reporter
Published by: LexisNexis Butterworths Canada Inc. (Subsidiary of: LexisNexis North America), 123 Commerce Valley Dr E, Ste 700, Markham, ON L3T 7W8, Canada. TEL 905-479-2665, FAX 905-479-2826, http://www.lexisnexis.ca/employmentandlabourlawreporter.htm.

EMPLOYMENT AND THE ECONOMY. ATLANTIC COASTAL REGION. see *BUSINESS AND ECONOMICS—Economic Situation And Conditions*

B

331.259 USA ISSN 0146-9673
HD5724
EMPLOYMENT AND TRAINING REPORTER. Text in English. 1969. w. looseleaf. USD 747 e-mail ed.; USD 897 print ed. (effective 2004). adv. bk.rev. charts; maps; stat. q. index. back issues avail. **Document type:** *Newsletter, Trade.* **Description:** Provides coverage of government-sponsored employment and training programs for the unemployed, including youth, laid-off workers, and the economically disadvantaged.
Formerly (until 1976): Manpower Information Service (0542-5794)
Related titles: E-mail ed.
Published by: M I I Publications, Inc., 773 15th St NW Ste 900, Washington, DC 20005-2112. TEL 202-347-4822, 800-524-8960, FAX 202-347-4893, service@miipublications.com, http://www.miipublications.com. Eds. Ryan Hess, Cecilio J Morales. Pub. Cecilio J Morales. R&P David Barrows TEL 202-347-4822 ext 101. Adv. contact Lucy Scott.

EMPLOYMENT AND WAGES ANNUAL AVERAGES. see *BUSINESS AND ECONOMICS—Abstracting, Bibliographies, Statistics*

344.01 USA
EMPLOYMENT AT WILL REPORTER✶ . Text in English. 1993 (vol.11). m. USD 510. **Description:** Digests of decisions from all federal and state jurisdictions concerning non-unionized employment law, including wrongful discharge, non-competition, invasion of privacy, and related issues.
Published by: Landlaw Inc., 675 VFW Parkway, No. 354, Chestnut Hill, MA 02467. TEL 614-277-4455, 800-637-6330, FAX 617-277-7375.

331.255 USA
▼ **EMPLOYMENT BENEFIT NEWS CANADA.** Text in English. 2004 (Apr.). q. **Document type:** *Magazine, Trade.* **Description:** Covers employment trends, benefit finance and distribution, and legal and regulatory developments affecting both the United States and Canada.
Published by: Thomson Financial Services Company, 1325 G St, N W, Ste 970, Washington, DC 20005. TEL 202-504-1122, 888-280-4820, FAX 202-772-1448, editorial@benefitnews.com. Ed. David Albertson. Pub., Adv. contact Jim Callan.

THE EMPLOYMENT BULLETIN; legal issues in the workplace. see *LAW*

EMPLOYMENT CASE DIGEST. see *BUSINESS AND ECONOMICS—Personnel Management*

EMPLOYMENT COST INDEXES AND LEVELS. see *BUSINESS AND ECONOMICS—Economic Situation And Conditions*

344.01 USA
EMPLOYMENT DISCRIMINATION (VIRGINIA). Text in English. 1992. latest 1999, 3rd ed., 2 base vols. plus irreg. updates. looseleaf. USD 230 (effective 2003). **Description:** Covers law of employment discrimination for legal and business professionals on both sides of the discrimination issues.
Published by: Michie Company (Subsidiary of: LexisNexis North America), 701 E Water St, Charlottesville, VA 22902-5389. TEL 434-972-7600, 800-446-3410, FAX 434-972-7677, http://www.michie.com. Ed. Paul N Cox.

331.133 331.125 344.01 USA ISSN 1529-7926
EMPLOYMENT DISCRIMINATION VERDICTS AND SETTLEMENTS. Text in English. 1997. w. price varies per number of users. **Document type:** *Trade.* **Description:** Searchable database that contains thousands of employment discrimination verdicts and settlements reported in Employment Discrimination Report.
Media: Online - full content. **Related titles:** Online - full text ed.: (from The Bureau of National Affairs, Inc.).
—CCC.

Published by: B N A Inc. (Subsidiary of: The Bureau of National Affairs, Inc.), 1231 25th St, NW, Washington, DC 20037. TEL 202-452-4343, FAX 202-452-4997, customercare@bna.com, http://www.bna.com/products/labor/vsln.htm. Ed. Gregory C McCafferty.

331.133   CAN   ISSN 1189-9719
HD4903.5.C2
EMPLOYMENT EQUITY ACT. ANNUAL REPORT. Text in English, French. 1988. a.
Formerly (until 1990): Employment Equity Act. Annual Report to Parliament (0842-6422)
Published by: Canadian Human Rights Commission/Commission Canadienne des Droits de la Personne, 344 Slater St, 8th Flr, Ottawa, ON K1A 1E1, Canada. TEL 613-995-1151, 888-214-1090, FAX 613-996-9661, info.com@chrc-ccdp.ca, http://www.chrc-ccdp.ca/publications/reports-en.asp.

331.125   USA   ISSN 0896-3452
EMPLOYMENT GUIDE. Text in English. 1986. m. looseleaf. USD 590 (effective 2001). index. back issues avail. **Document type:** *Newsletter.* **Description:** Easy-to-read, practical reference guide to a broad range of employment topics, designed for the small to medium-sized organization.
Related titles: Online - full text ed.: (from The Bureau of National Affairs, Inc.).
Published by: The Bureau of National Affairs, Inc., 1231 25th St., NW, Washington, DC 20037. TEL 202-452-4200, 800-372-1033, 800-452-7773, FAX 202-822-8092, customercare@bna.com, bnaplus@bna.com, http://www.bna.com/. Ed. Bill L Manville. Pub. Greg C McCaffery.

331.125   USA
EMPLOYMENT, HOURS, AND EARNINGS: STATES AND AREAS. Text in English. 1939. a. charts; stat. **Document type:** *Government.*
Former titles: Employment and Earnings: States and Areas; Employment and Earnings Statistics for States and Areas
Related titles: ◆ Series of: U.S. Bureau of Labor Statistics. Bulletin. ISSN 0082-9021; Supplement(s): Supplement to Employment, Hours, and Earnings: States and Areas. ISSN 8755-4712.
Published by: U.S. Department of Labor, Bureau of Labor Statistics, Postal Square Bldg, 2 Massachusetts Ave, NE, Washington, DC 20212-0001 . TEL 202-691-5200, FAX 202-691-6325, http://www.bls.gov. **Subscr. to:** U.S. Government Printing Office, Superintendent of Documents, PO Box 371954, Pittsburgh, PA 15250-7954. TEL 202-512-1800, FAX 202-512-2250, orders@gpo.gov, http://www.access.gpo.gov.

EMPLOYMENT IN ALBERTA; a guide to conditions of work and employee benefits. see *LAW*

EMPLOYMENT IN BRITISH COLUMBIA; a guide to conditions of work and employee benefits. see *LAW*

331.125   LUX   ISSN 1016-5444
HD8380.5
EMPLOYMENT IN EUROPE. Text in English. irreg., latest 1997. USD 20. stat.
Indexed: IIS.
—BLDSC (3737.226500).
Published by: (European Commission BEL, Directorate-General Employment, Industrial Relations and Social Affairs), European Commission, Office for Official Publications of the European Union, 2 Rue Mercier, Luxembourg, L-2985, Luxembourg. TEL 352-49-92-81, FAX 352-48-85-73. **Dist. in the U.S. by:** Bernan Associates, Bernan, 4611-F Assembly Dr., Lanham, MD 20706-4391. TEL 301-459-0056, 800-274-4447.

344.01   USA
EMPLOYMENT IN FLORIDA; guide to employment laws, regulations and practices. Text in English. 1992. latest 2000, 2nd ed., base vol. plus irreg. updates. looseleaf. USD 105 (effective 2003). **Description:** Covers issues such as hiring and firing, worker safety and health, labor relations, dispute resolution, workers' compensation, record-keeping, AIDS in the workplace, employment of illegal aliens, and more.
Published by: Michie Company (Subsidiary of: LexisNexis North America), 701 E Water St, Charlottesville, VA 22902-5389. TEL 434-972-7600, 800-446-3410, FAX 434-972-7677, http://www.michie.com.

344.01   USA
EMPLOYMENT IN ILLINOIS; a guide to employment laws, regulations and practices. Text in English. 1983. w/ current supplement), latest 1997, base vol. plus irreg. updates. looseleaf. USD 105 (effective 2003). Supplement avail.
Published by: Michie Company (Subsidiary of: LexisNexis North America), 701 E Water St, Charlottesville, VA 22902-5389. TEL 434-972-7600, 800-446-3410, FAX 434-972-7677, http://www.michie.com. Ed. Maynard G. Sautter.

344.01   USA
EMPLOYMENT IN IOWA; a guide to employment laws, regulations and practices. Text in English. 1984. w/ current supplement), latest 1997, 3rd ed., base vol. plus irreg. updates. looseleaf. USD 105 (effective 2003). Supplement avail. **Description:** Provides explanation of applicable federal and state law regarding employment questions. Coverage includes: hiring, hours of work and payment of wages, health and safety standards, civil rights, union organizing, collective bargaining and strikes, employer liability for employees' acts, private health care and life insurance, disability or death of employee, employee retirement benefits, termination of employment, and advisors and information sources.
Published by: Michie Company (Subsidiary of: LexisNexis North America), 701 E Water St, Charlottesville, VA 22902-5389. TEL 434-972-7600, 800-446-3410, FAX 434-972-7677, http://www.michie.com. Ed. Maynard G. Sautter.

344.01   USA
EMPLOYMENT IN MICHIGAN; a guide to employment laws, regulations, and practices. Text in English. 1994. base vol. plus irreg. updates. looseleaf. USD 95.
Published by: LexisNexis (Subsidiary of: LexisNexis North America), PO Box 7587, Charlottesville, VA 22906-7587. TEL 804-972-7600, 800-562-1197, FAX 804-972-7666, llp.customer.support@lexis-nexis.com, http://www.lexislawpublishing.com.

344.01   USA
EMPLOYMENT IN MINNESOTA; a guide to employment laws, regulations and practices. Text in English. 1982. w/ current supplement), latest 1997, 3rd ed., base vol. plus irreg. updates. looseleaf. USD 115 (effective 2003). **Description:** Covers the entire employment relationship from hiring through termination or retirement; includes both Minnesota and federal law.
Published by: Michie Company (Subsidiary of: LexisNexis North America), 701 E Water St, Charlottesville, VA 22902-5389. TEL 434-972-7600, 800-446-3410, FAX 434-972-7677, http://www.michie.com. Ed. Maynard G. Sautter.

344.01   USA
EMPLOYMENT IN MISSOURI; a guide to employment practice and regulations. Text in English. base vol. plus a. updates. looseleaf. USD 95. Supplement avail. **Description:** Covers all aspects of employer-employee relations from interviewing to termination.
Published by: LexisNexis (Subsidiary of: LexisNexis North America), PO Box 7587, Charlottesville, VA 22906-7587. TEL 804-972-7600, 800-562-1197, FAX 804-972-7666, llp.customer.support@lexis-nexis.com, http://www.lexislawpublishing.com. Ed. Mark S Summers.

331.125   USA
EMPLOYMENT IN NEW YORK STATE. Text in English. 1991. m. free. 4 p./no. 3 cols./p.; back issues avail. **Document type:** *Newsletter, Government.*
Related titles: Online - full content ed.
Published by: Department of Labor, W Averell Harriman Office Bldg, Rm 480, Albany, NY 12240. TEL 518-457-7425, http://www.labor.state.ny.us/html/newsletr/current/index.htm. Ed. Vincent De Santis.

344.01   USA
EMPLOYMENT IN OHIO; guide to employment laws, regulations and practices. Text in English. 1984. latest 3rd ed., base vol. plus irreg. updates. looseleaf. USD 105 (effective 2003). Supplement avail. **Description:** Provides basic information concerning the laws, regulations, and policies affecting labor and employment in Ohio.
Published by: Michie Company (Subsidiary of: LexisNexis North America), 701 E Water St, Charlottesville, VA 22902-5389. TEL 434-972-7600, 800-446-3410, FAX 434-972-7677, custserv@michie.com, http://bookstore.lexis.com/bookstore/catalog?action=product&prod_id=6715, http://www.michie.com. Ed. Maynard G. Sautter.

EMPLOYMENT IN ONTARIO; a guide to conditions of work and employee benefits. see *LAW*

344.01   USA
EMPLOYMENT IN OREGON; guide to employment laws, regulations and practices. Text in English. 1982. w/ current supplement), latest 1998, 3rd ed., base vol. plus irreg. updates. looseleaf. USD 115 (effective 2003). Supplement avail. **Description:** Provides overviews and explanations of complex labor and employment law issues facing today's employers. It covers issues ranging from hiring to termination, helping one to keep pace with the rapid evolution of labor and employment law on the state and federal level.
Published by: Michie Company (Subsidiary of: LexisNexis North America), 701 E Water St, Charlottesville, VA 22902-5389. TEL 434-972-7600, 800-446-3410, FAX 434-972-7677, http://www.michie.com. Ed. Pamela S Knowles.

EMPLOYMENT IN PERSPECTIVE: MINORITY WORKERS. see *BUSINESS AND ECONOMICS—Abstracting, Bibliographies, Statistics*

331.4   USA
EMPLOYMENT IN PERSPECTIVE: WOMEN IN THE LABOR FORCE. Text in English. q. **Document type:** *Government.* **Description:** Summarizes data about the labor force activity of older women.
Related titles: ◆ Series of: U.S. Bureau of Labor Statistics. Reports.
Indexed: CWI.
Published by: U.S. Department of Labor, Bureau of Labor Statistics, Postal Square Bldg., 2 Massachusetts Ave, NE, Washington, DC 20212-0001 . TEL 202-655-4000. **Subscr. to:** U.S. Government Printing Office, Superintendent of Documents.

344.01   USA
EMPLOYMENT IN TEXAS; guide to employment laws, regulations and practices. Text in English. 1984. w/ current supplement), latest 1998, 5th ed., base vol. plus irreg. updates. USD 120 (effective 2003). Supplement avail. **Description:** A guidebook for business owners, personnel directors, general managers, and human resources staff who manage Texas employees daily.
Published by: Michie Company (Subsidiary of: LexisNexis North America), 701 E Water St, Charlottesville, VA 22902-5389. TEL 434-972-7600, 800-446-3410, FAX 434-972-7677, http://www.michie.com. Ed. Mark S Summers.

344.01   USA
EMPLOYMENT IN WASHINGTON; guide to employment laws, regulations and practices. Text in English. 1987. w/ current supplement), latest 1998, base vol. plus irreg. updates. looseleaf. USD 115 (effective 2003). Supplement avail. **Description:** Provides overviews and explanations of labor and employment law issues facing. It covers issues ranging from hiring to termination, helping one to keep pace with the rapid evolution of labor and employment law on the state and federal level.
Formerly (until 1999): Employment in Washington State
Published by: Michie Company (Subsidiary of: LexisNexis North America), 701 E Water St, Charlottesville, VA 22902-5389. TEL 434-972-7600, 800-446-3410, FAX 434-972-7677, http://www.michie.com. Ed. Michael J Killeen.

344.01   USA
EMPLOYMENT IN WISCONSIN; guide to employment laws, regulations and practices. Text in English. 1983. w/ current supplement), latest 1997, 3rd ed., base vol. plus irreg. updates. looseleaf. USD 105 (effective 2003). Supplement avail. **Description:** Offers an explanation of applicable federal and state laws and is especially popular with lawyers who want quick answers to employment questions - their clients' and their own.
Published by: Michie Company (Subsidiary of: LexisNexis North America), 701 E Water St, Charlottesville, VA 22902-5389. TEL 434-972-7600, 800-446-3410, FAX 434-972-7677, http://www.michie.com. Ed. Maynard G. Sautter.

EMPLOYMENT LAW. see *LAW—Corporate Law*

344.01   USA
EMPLOYMENT LAW BRIEFING. Text in English. 1986. q. looseleaf. free. **Document type:** *Newsletter.*
Published by: Sachnoff & Weaver, Ltd., 30 S Wacker Dr, Ste 2900, Chicago, IL 60606. TEL 312-207-1000, FAX 312-207-6400.

EMPLOYMENT LAW BULLETIN. see *LAW—Corporate Law*

344.01   USA   ISSN 1052-2964
KF3302
EMPLOYMENT LAW COUNSELOR. Text in English. 1990. m. looseleaf. USD 365 (effective 2005). bk.rev. index, cum.index. back issues avail. **Document type:** *Newsletter.* **Description:** Covers developments in all areas of employment relations law.
—CCC.
Published by: Business Laws, Inc., 11630 Chillicothe Rd, Chesterland, OH 44026. TEL 440-729-7996, 800-759-0929, FAX 440-729-0645, custserv@businesslaws.com, http://www.businesslaws.com. Ed. William A Hancock.

EMPLOYMENT LAW DESK BOOK FOR TENNESSEE EMPLOYERS. see *LAW*

344.01   USA
EMPLOYMENT LAW DESKBOOK. Text in English. 1989. base vol. plus a. updates. looseleaf. USD 170 base vol(s). (effective 2003). **Description:** Covers issues arising in employer-employee relationship and provides federal and state employment law analysis for human resources professionals, employers and attorneys.
Related titles: CD-ROM ed.
Published by: Matthew Bender & Co., Inc. (Subsidiary of: LexisNexis North America), 1275 Broadway, Albany, NY 12204. international@bender.com, http://bender.lexisnexis.com.

EMPLOYMENT LAW GUIDE (YEAR). see *LAW*

EMPLOYMENT LAW MANUAL. see *BUSINESS AND ECONOMICS—Personnel Management*

344.01 USA
KF3457.A15E45
EMPLOYMENT LAW NEWS✶. Text in English. 1979. 6/yr. USD 30. bk.rev. back issues avail. **Document type:** *Newsletter.*
Published by: National Employment Law Project, 55 John St, 7th Fl, New York, NY 10038-3712. TEL 212-870-2121, FAX 212-870-2197. Circ: 1,400.

344.01 USA ISSN 1058-1308
KF3457
EMPLOYMENT LAW REPORT. Text in English. 1991. m. looseleaf. USD 164 (effective 2004). cum.index. back issues avail. **Document type:** *Newsletter, Consumer.* **Description:** Covers the latest court cases and late-breaking legislation, along with the most recent law review articles affecting employment.
Published by: Oakstone Legal and Business Publishing, PO Box 381205, Birmingham, AL 35238-9950. TEL 800-365-4900, http://www.oakstonelegal.com/. Ed. Laurel Kasler.

▼ **EMPLOYMENT LAW REVIEW.** see *LAW—Corporate Law*

344.01 USA ISSN 1069-7829
EMPLOYMENT LAW STRATEGIST. Text in English. 1993. m. looseleaf. USD 279; USD 349 combined subscription print & online eds. (effective 2005). back issues avail. **Document type:** *Newsletter.*
Related titles: Online - full text ed.
—CCC.
Published by: A L M, 345 Park Ave., S, New York, NY 10010. TEL 212-313-9000, 800-888-8300, FAX 212-481-8255, apress@amlaw.com, http://www.ljnonline.com/pub/ljn_emplaw/, http://www.alm.com.

EMPLOYMENT LAW UPDATE (EVANSVILLE). see *LAW*

EMPLOYMENT LAW UPDATE (NEW YORK). see *LAW*

331 BEL ISSN 1019-4304
HD5764
EMPLOYMENT OBSERVATORY. POLICIES. Text in English. 1992. irreg.
Formerly (until 1991): InforMISEP (1024-9095)
Indexed: PAIS.
—BLDSC (3737.238400), IE, ingenta.
Published by: European Commission, Employment and Social Affairs, Rue de la Loi 200, Brussels, 1049, Belgium. TEL 32-2-2954988, FAX 32-2-2962393.

331 USA ISSN 0737-9633
EMPLOYMENT OUTLOOK SURVEY. Text in English. 1976. q. free to qualified personnel. **Description:** Measurement of hiring intentions of more than 16,000 employers in 487 cities on whether to increase, decrease or maintain the size of their present workforce for the upcoming 3-month period.
Indexed: SRI.
Published by: Manpower Temporary Services, International Headquarters, 5301 N Ironwood Rd, Milwaukee, WI 53217. TEL 414-961-1000, FAX 414-961-2124, http://www.manpower.com. Ed. Mary B Stewart. Circ: 40,000 (controlled).

331.125 USA
THE EMPLOYMENT PAPER (PITTSBURGH). Text in English. 1994. w. free.
Published by: American City Business Journals, Inc. (Austin), 505 Powell St, Austin, TX 78703-5121. adv.: B&W page USD 850. Circ: 31,000. **Subscr. to:** Pittsburgh Business Times, 2313 E Carson St, Ste 200, Pittsburgh, PA 15203-2109. TEL 412-481-5627, FAX 412-481-9956.

331.133 USA ISSN 1525-2736
EMPLOYMENT PRACTICE LIABILITY VERDICTS AND SETTLEMENTS. Text in English. 1999. m. USD 285 (effective 2006). **Document type:** *Newsletter, Trade.* **Description:** Contains consice summaries of the most recent employment-practice liability verdicts and settlements with the latest outcomes and gauge more accurate values for the cases.
—CCC.
Published by: L R P Publications, 747 Dresher Rd, PO Box 980, Horsham, PA 19044. TEL 215-784-0860, 800-341-7874, FAX 215-784-9639, custserve@lrp.com, http://www.shoplrp.com/product/p-2110.EPLV.html, http://www.lrp.com.

331 USA ISSN 0149-6255
EMPLOYMENT PRACTICES DECISIONS. Text in English. 1971. s-a.
—CCC.
Published by: C C H Inc., 2700 Lake Cook Rd, Riverwoods, IL 60015. TEL 800-449-6439, FAX 800-224-8299, cust_serv@cch.com, http://www.cch.com.

331.133 USA ISSN 1529-840X
KF1316.A15
EMPLOYMENT PRACTICES LIABILITY CONSULTANT. Text in English. 4/yr. USD 130 (effective 2003). **Document type:** *Journal, Trade.*
Related titles: CD-ROM ed.; Online - full text ed.: ISSN 1537-3495.
Published by: International Risk Management Institute, Inc., 12222 Merit Dr, Ste 1450, Dallas, TX 75251-2276. TEL 972-960-7693, FAX 972-371-5120, info@irmi.com, http://www.irmi.com.

331.133 USA
KF3464.A15
EMPLOYMENT PRACTICES UPDATE. Text in English. m. looseleaf. USD 375 (effective 2004). **Document type:** *Newsletter, Trade.* **Description:** Contains current interpretations of EEO laws and regulations, including recent court cases.
Former titles: Equal Employment Compliance Update (0160-435X); (until 1977): Equal Employment Compliance Special Report (0160-4368)
Published by: Thomson West (Subsidiary of: Thomson Corporation, The), 610 Opperman Dr, Eagan, MN 55123-1396. TEL 651-687-8000, 800-328-4880, FAX 651-687-7302, customer.service@westgroup.com, http://www.westgroup.com/store/product.asp?product%5Fid=13972968&catalog%5Fname=wgstore, http://west.thomson.com. Eds. Andrew J Ruzicho, Louis A Jacobs.

331.1142 CAN ISSN 1492-045X
EMPLOYMENT PROFILE: SUMMARY OF THE EMPLOYMENT EXPERIENCE OF COLLEGE GRADUATES SIX MONTHS AFTER GRADUATION. Text in English. 1989. a.
Formerly (until 1998): Employment Profile of Graduates of Ontario Colleges of Applied Arts and Technology (1192-7100)
Published by: Ontario. Ministry of Training Colleges and Universities, Mowat Block, 900 Bay St, Toronto, ON M7A 1L2, Canada. TEL 416-325-2929, FAX 416-325-6348, info@edu.gov.cn.ca, http://www.edu.gov.on.ca/eng/welcome.html.

331 USA ISSN 0746-9683
EMPLOYMENT RELATIONS BULLETIN. Text in English. 10/yr. **Document type:** *Bulletin.*
Published by: Florida State University, College of Law, 425 W Jefferson St, Tallahassee, FL 32306-1601. TEL 850-644-4240, FAX 850-644-7484, ewilliam@law.fsu.edu, http://www.law.fsu.edu. Ed. Brittany Alam.

331.1 USA ISSN 0745-7790
HD4903.5.U58 CODEN: EEOTDY
EMPLOYMENT RELATIONS TODAY. Text in English. 1973. q. USD 565 in North America; USD 589 elsewhere; USD 622 combined subscription in North America print & online eds.; USD 646 combined subscription elsewhere print & online eds. (effective 2006). adv. reprint service avail. from PQC. **Document type:** *Magazine, Trade.* **Description:** For senior human resources specialists. Covers the significance of changes in the workplace.
Formerly (until 1983): E E O Today (0362-5818)
Related titles: Microform ed.: (from PQC); Online - full text ed.: ISSN 1520-6459. USD 565 (effective 2006) (from EBSCO Publishing, Gale Group, Northern Light Technology, Inc., ProQuest Information & Learning, Swets Information Services, Wiley InterScience).
Indexed: ABIn, AgeL, BPI, BPIA, BusI, MEDLINE, ManagCont, PAIS, T&DA.
—BLDSC (3737.510000), IE, Infotrieve, ingenta. **CCC.**
Published by: John Wiley & Sons, Inc., 111 River St, Hoboken, NJ 07030-5774. TEL 800-825-7550, FAX 201-748-5915, uscs-wis@wiley.com, http://www3.interscience.wiley.com/cgi-bin/jhome/60500168, http://www.wiley.com. Ed. Carol Di Paola. adv.: B&W page USD 1,080, color page USD 2,420; trim 8.25 x 11. **Subscr. to:** John Wiley & Sons Ltd., The Atrium, Southern Gate, Chichester, West Sussex PO19 8SQ, United Kingdom. TEL 44-1243-779777, FAX 44-1243-775878, cs-journals@wiley.co.uk.

331.125 HKG ISSN 1022-4238
THE EMPLOYMENT REPORT. Text in English. 1993. 10/yr. HKD 1,595. **Description:** Provides up-to-date coverage of human resources issues in Hong Kong.
Published by: Pearson Professional (HK) Ltd., Ste. 1808 Asian House, 1 Hennessy Rd, Wanchai, Hong Kong, Hong Kong. TEL 852-2863-2659, FAX 852-2520-6954, pphkg@hk.super.net.

331.125 USA ISSN 1075-8445
EMPLOYMENT RESEARCH. Text in English. 1994. q. back issues avail. **Document type:** *Newsletter.*
Related titles: Online - full text ed.
—CCC.
Published by: W.E. Upjohn Institute for Employment Research, 300 S Westnedge Ave, Kalamazoo, MI 49007. TEL 616-343-5541, FAX 616-343-7310, http://www.upjohninst.org/publications/empres.htmll. Ed. Richard Wyrwa.

331.1 USA ISSN 0013-6883
HD5725.N7
EMPLOYMENT REVIEW. Text in English. 1942. m. free (effective 2004). charts; stat. **Document type:** *Government.*
Indexed: BPIA, BusI, RefZh, SRI.
Published by: Department of Labor, Division of Research and Statistics, Room 490, State Campus, Albany, NY 12240. TEL 518-457-1313, rspubs@labor.state.ny.us, http://www.labor.state.ny.us/labor_market/lmi_business/er/index.html. Ed. Tom Nespeco.

EMPLOYMENT SCREENING. see *LAW*

THE EMPLOYMENT SITUATION. see *BUSINESS AND ECONOMICS—Economic Situation And Conditions*

EMPLOYMENT STANDARDS HANDBOOK AND DIGEST. see *LAW*

344.01 CAN ISSN 1185-2429
KE3244.A72
EMPLOYMENT STANDARDS LEGISLATION IN CANADA. Text in English. 1951. a. free. reprints avail. **Document type:** *Government.* **Description:** Reports on minimum labor standards, such as hours of work, overtime pay, minimum wage and leave provisions in federal, provincial and territorial jurisdictions.
Formerly (until 1989): Labour Standards in Canada - Normes du Travail au Canada (0576-1123)
Related titles: Microform ed.: (from MML); French ed.: Legislation en Matiere d'Emploi.
—CISTI.
Published by: Government of Canada Publications, Publishing and Depository Services, Public Works and Government Services Canada, Ottawa, ON K1A 0S9, Canada. Circ: 2,150.

EMPLOYMENT TESTING; law and policy reporter. see *LAW*

ENCUESTA NACIONAL DEL EMPLEO TOTAL PAIS. see *BUSINESS AND ECONOMICS—Abstracting, Bibliographies, Statistics*

331 USA
ENGINEERING, SCIENTIFIC AND TECHNICAL SURVEY. Text in English. a. USD 450. **Description:** Provides comparative information for 78 engineering, scientific and technical position compensation practices among 160 companies, representing 4,100 employees in PA, NJ, MD, and DE.
Published by: MidAtlantic Employers' Association, PO Box 770, Valley Forge, PA 19482. TEL 215-666-7330, FAX 215-666-7866.

331.119179143 USA ISSN 1067-3970
ENTERTAINMENT EMPLOYMENT JOURNAL. Text in English. 1992. m. USD 75 domestic (effective 2004). adv. bk.rev. **Document type:** *Trade.* **Description:** Covers career issues for professionals in the entertainment industry.
Related titles: Online - full content ed.: EntertainmentJobs.com.
Published by: Studiolot Publishing, PO Box 72599, Corpus Christi, TX 78472-2599. TEL 800-335-4335, sales@studiolot.com, http://www.eejonline.com, http://www.eej.com. Ed. Lawrence Haberman. Pub. Greg Carbajal. R&P, Adv. contact Aaron Groves.

331 DEU ISSN 1432-6426
ENTGELTFORTZAHLUNG - KRANKENGELD - MUTTERSCHAFTSGELD. Text in German. 1970. irreg. looseleaf. price varies. **Document type:** *Monographic series, Trade.*
Formerly: Verguetung der Arbeitnehmer bei Krankheit und Mutterschaft (0936-224X)
Published by: Erich Schmidt Verlag GmbH & Co. (Berlin), Genthiner Str 30G, Berlin, 10785, Germany. TEL 49-30-250085-0, FAX 49-30-25008521, esv@esvmedien.de, http://www.erich-schmidt-verlag.de.

331 IRN
EQTESAD-E-MELLI. Text in Persian, Modern. 1979. m. IRR 150, USD 5. adv. bk.rev.
Published by: Eqtesade of Iran, 47 Gaffary St., 2nd Fl., Miadan Haft Tir, Tehran 15, Iran. Ed. Bejan Yazamadhie. Circ: 280.

331.133 LUX ISSN 1680-2381
EQUAL OPPORTUNITIES FOR WOMEN AND MEN IN THE EUROPEAN UNION. Text in English. 1996. a.
Related titles: French ed.: L' Egalite des Chances pour les Femmes et les Hommes dans l'Union Europeenne. ISSN 1562-8582; Spanish ed.: Igualdad de Oportunidades entre Mujeres y Hombres en la Union Europea. ISSN 1680-5038; Italian ed.: Pari Opportunita tra Donne e Uomini nell'Unione Europea. ISSN 1680-5054; Portuguese ed.: Igualdade de Oportunidades entre Mulheres e Homens na Uniao Europeia. ISSN 1680-5135; Greek ed.: Ises Eukairies gia tis Gunaikes kai tous Andres oten Europaike Enose. ISSN 1680-5089; Danish ed.: Ligestilling Mellem Maend og Kvinder i den Europaiske Union. ISSN 1680-5011; German ed.: Chancengleichheit fuer Frauen und Manner in der Europaischen Union. ISSN 1680-502X; Finnish ed.: Naisten ja Miesten Yhtalaiset Mahdollisuuet Euroopan Unionissa. ISSN 1680-5046; Dutch ed.: Gelijke Kansen voor Vrouwen en Mannen in de Europese Unie. ISSN 1680-5062; Swedish ed.: Lika Mojligheter for Kvinnor och Man i Euopeiska Unionen. ISSN 1680-5070.
—BLDSC (3794.504970).
Published by: European Commission, Office for Official Publications of the European Union, 2 Rue Mercier, Luxembourg, L-2985, Luxembourg. FAX 352-2929-1, opoce-info-info@cec.eu.int, http://publications.eu.int.

B

331.133 GBR ISSN 0268-7143
KD3102.A13
EQUAL OPPORTUNITIES REVIEW. Text in English. 1985. m. GBP 397.15 combined subscription domestic print & online; GBP 448.85 combined subscription foreign print & online (effective 2005). illus. index. 32 p./no.; back issues avail.; reprints avail. **Document type:** *Journal, Trade.* **Description:** Covers equal-opportunity law and employment practice: sex, race, disability, religion, and age.
Related titles: Microform ed.: (from PQC); Online - full text ed.: (from O C L C Online Computer Library Center, Inc.); Supplement(s): Discrimination: A Guide to the Relevant Case Law on Sex, Race and Disability Discrimination and Equal Pay.
Indexed: ABIn, ELJI, ERA, Emerald, LJI, M&MA, MEA, SWA.
—BLDSC (3794.504800), IE, ingenta. **CCC.**
Published by: I R S (Subsidiary of: LexisNexis UK (Scottish Office)), 18-20 Highbury Pl, London, N5 1QP, United Kingdom. TEL 44-20-7354-6742, 44-20-7354-5858, FAX 44-20-7226-8618, 44-20-7359-4000, publications@irseclipse.co.uk, http://www.irsonline.co.uk/pub_subjects/index_pub_equal.htm, http://www.irseclipse.co.uk. Eds. Michael Rubenstein, Sue Johnstone.

331 CYP
ERGATIKI PHONI/WORKER'S VOICE. Text in Greek. 1946. w.
Published by: S E K, SEK Bldg, 23 Alkeon St, PO Box 5018, Egnomi, Nicosia, Cyprus. TEL 357-2-441142, FAX 357-2-476360, TELEX 6180. Ed. Gregoris Gregoriades. Circ: 8,850.

331 CYP
ERGATIKO VIMA/WORKER'S HERALD. Text in Greek. 1956. w.
Published by: Pan-Cyprian Federation of Labor, 31-35 Archemos St, PO Box 1885, Nicosia, Cyprus. TEL 357-2-472192. Ed. Pantlis Varnavas. Circ: 15,850.

▼ **ERHVERVNORD**; profilavis. see *BUSINESS AND ECONOMICS—Economic Situation And Conditions*

ESSEX COUNTY COUNCIL. PLANNING. SUBJECT MONITORING REPORTS. EMPLOYMENT. see *PUBLIC ADMINISTRATION—Municipal Government*

ESTADISTICA PANAMENA. SITUACION SOCIAL. SECCION 441. ESTADISTICAS DEL TRABAJO. see *BUSINESS AND ECONOMICS—Abstracting, Bibliographies, Statistics*

331 ARG ISSN 0327-5744
HD8261
➤ **ESTUDIOS DEL TRABAJO.** Text in Spanish. 1991. s-a. USD 58 domestic; USD 64 in the Americas; USD 66 in Europe; USD 70 elsewhere. bk.rev. **Document type:** *Academic/Scholarly.* **Description:** Devoted to social sciences related to labor: labor economics, labor sociology and industrial relations. Publishes theoretical and empirical articles.
Published by: Asociacion Argentina de Especialistas en Estudios del Trabajo, Araoz, 2838, Capital Federal, Buenos Aires 1425, Argentina. TEL 54-114-8044949, FAX 54-114-8045856. Ed., R&P Silvio Feldman. Circ: 500.

344.01 ESP ISSN 1138-9532
ESTUDIOS FINANCIEROS. REVISTA DE TRABAJO Y SEGURIDAD SOCIAL. COMENTARIOS, CASOS PRACTICOS. Text in Spanish. 1995. m.
Supersedes in part (1988-1995): Estudios Financieros. Revista de Trabajo y Seguridad Social (1138-9583); Which superseded in part (1981-1988): Estudios Financieros (1138-9524)
Published by: Centro de Estudios Financieros, C. Viriato, 52 5o., Madrid, 28010, Spain. TEL 34-91-4444920, FAX 34-91-5938861, director@cef.es, http://www.cef.es/.

344.01 ESP ISSN 1138-9605
ESTUDIOS FINANCIEROS. REVISTA DE TRABAJO Y SEGURIDAD SOCIAL. LEGISLACION, JURISPRUDENCIA. Text in Spanish. 1995. m.
Supersedes in part (1988-1995): Estudios Financieros. Revista de Trabajo y Seguridad Social (1138-9583); Which superseded in part (1981-1988): Estudios Financieros (1138-9524)
Published by: Centro de Estudios Financieros, C. Viriato, 52 5o., Madrid, 28010, Spain. TEL 34-91-4444920, FAX 34-91-5938861, director@cef.es, http://www.cef.es/.

EUROPAEISCHER INFORMATIONSBRIEF BILDUNG UND BESCHAEFTIGUNG. see *BUSINESS AND ECONOMICS*

344.01 NLD ISSN 1385-1748
EUROPEAN EMPLOYMENT LAW REVIEW. Text in Dutch. 1993. 3/yr. charts. back issues avail. **Document type:** *Journal, Academic/Scholarly.* **Description:** Informs readers of EU employment law developments and new projects.
Published by: Global Law Association, PO Box 9001, Tilburg, 5000 HA, Netherlands. TEL 31-13-544-3135, FAX 31-24-355-4827, globallaw@writeme.com, http://web.inter.nl.net/global.wolf/empl.htm, http://www.globallaw.org. **Subscr. to:** PO Box 30151, Nijmegen 6503 CB, Netherlands. **Dist. in N. America by:** Wm. W. Gaunt & Sons Inc., Gaunt Bldg, 3011 Gulf Dr, Holmes Beach, FL 34217-2199. TEL 941-778-5211, 941-778-5252. **Co-sponsor:** Association for the Study of International Relations.

331 IRL
EUROPEAN FOUNDATION FOR THE IMPROVEMENT OF LIVING AND WORKING CONDITIONS. ANNUAL REPORT. Text in English. a.
—BLDSC (1245.455000).
Published by: European Foundation for the Improvement of Living and Working Conditions/Fondation Europeenne pour l'Amelioration des Conditions de Vie et de Travail, Wyattville Rd., Loughlinstown, Co. Dublin, Ireland. TEL 353-1-2043100, FAX 353-1-2826456.

EUROPEAN FOUNDATION FOR THE IMPROVEMENT OF LIVING AND WORKING CONDITIONS. COMMUNIQUE/ FONDATION EUROPEENNE POUR L'AMELIORATION DES CONDITIONS DE VIE ET DE TRAVAIL. COMMUNIQUE. see *PUBLIC HEALTH AND SAFETY*

331 LUX
EUROPEAN FOUNDATION FOR THE IMPROVEMENT OF LIVING AND WORKING CONDITIONS. INFORMATION BOOKLET SERIES. Text in English. irreg.
—BLDSC (4481.952500).
Published by: (European Foundation for the Improvement of Living and Working Conditions/Fondation Europeenne pour l'Amelioration des Conditions de Vie et de Travail IRL), European Commission, Office for Official Publications of the European Union, 2 Rue Mercier, Luxembourg, L-2985, Luxembourg. FAX 352-2929-1, http://publications.eu.int.

331 LUX ISSN 1562-8639
HD8371
EUROPEAN INDUSTRIAL RELATIONS OBSERVATORY. ANNUAL REVIEW. Text in English. 1998. a.
Published by: (European Foundation for the Improvement of Living and Working Conditions/Fondation Europeenne pour l'Amelioration des Conditions de Vie et de Travail IRL), European Commission, Office for Official Publications of the European Union, 2 Rue Mercier, Luxembourg, L-2985, Luxembourg. FAX 352-2929-1, http://publications.eu.int.

331 IRL ISSN 1028-0588
HD8371
EUROPEAN INDUSTRIAL RELATIONS OBSERVATORY OBSERVER. Key Title: EIRObserver. Text in English. 1997. m.
—BLDSC (3666.757200).
Published by: European Foundation for the Improvement of Living and Working Conditions/Fondation Europeenne pour l'Amelioration des Conditions de Vie et de Travail, Wyattville Rd., Loughlinstown, Co. Dublin, Ireland. TEL 353-1-2043100, FAX 353-1-2826456, postmaster@eurofound.ie, http://www.eiro.eurofound.ie.

331.1 GBR ISSN 0309-7234
HD8380.5.A5
EUROPEAN INDUSTRIAL RELATIONS REVIEW. Abbreviated title: E I R R. Text in English. 1974. m. GBP 358.20 domestic; GBP 398.70 foreign (effective 2005). reprint service avail. from PQC,SCH. **Document type:** *Journal, Trade.* **Description:** Reviews developments in all major European nations and relevant EC institutions.
Related titles: Microform ed.: (from PQC); Online - full text ed.: (from EBSCO Publishing, O C L C Online Computer Library Center, Inc.).
Indexed: ABIn, AgeL, BPIA, ELJI, ELLIS, ILD, KES, M&MA, RefZh, WBSS.
—BLDSC (3829.720500), IE, Infotrieve, ingenta. **CCC.**
Published by: I R S (Subsidiary of: LexisNexis UK (Scottish Office)), 18-20 Highbury Pl, London, N5 1QP, United Kingdom. TEL 44-20-7354-6742, 44-20-7354-5858, FAX 44-20-7226-8618, 44-20-7359-4000, publications@irseclipse.co.uk, http://www.irsonline.co.uk/pub_subjects/index_pub_human.htm, http://www.irseclipse.co.uk. Ed. Andrea Broughton.

331 GBR ISSN 0959-6801
HD8371 CODEN: EJIRFZ
➤ **EUROPEAN JOURNAL OF INDUSTRIAL RELATIONS.** Text in English. 1995. 3/yr. GBP 317, USD 555 to institutions; GBP 330, USD 578 combined subscription to institutions print & online eds. (effective 2006). adv. bk.rev. **Document type:** *Journal, Academic/Scholarly.* **Description:** Provides a forum for advancing understanding of the key developments in industrial relations in Europe and their practical and theoretical implications.
Related titles: Online - full text ed.: ISSN 1461-7129. GBP 314, USD 549 to institutions (effective 2006) (from C S A, EBSCO Publishing, O C L C Online Computer Library Center, Inc., Sage Publications, Inc., Swets Information Services).
Indexed: CurCont, ESPM, Emerald, HRA, IBSS, Inspec, JEL, PRA, PSA, RiskAb, SOPODA, SSA, SSCI, SociolAb, V&AA.
—BLDSC (3829.730300), IDS, IE, Infotrieve, ingenta. **CCC.**
Published by: Sage Publications Ltd. (Subsidiary of: Sage Publications, Inc.), 1 Oliver's Yard, 55 City Rd, London, EC1 1SP, United Kingdom. TEL 44-20-73248500, FAX 44-20-73248600, info@sagepub.co.uk, http://www.sagepub.co.uk/journal.aspx?pid=105539. Ed. Richard Hyman. Adv. contact Jenny Kirby. page GBP 220; trim 190 x 114. Circ: 900. **Subscr. in the Americas to:** Sage Publications, Inc., 2455 Teller Rd, Thousand Oaks, CA 91320. TEL 805-499-0721, FAX 805-499-0871, journals@sagepub.com.

331.11 GBR ISSN 1361-312X
HD5660.E9
EUROPEAN WORKS COUNCILS BULLETIN. Text in English. 1995. bi-m. GBP 256 domestic; USD 512 in United States (effective 2004). 16 p./no.; **Document type:** *Journal, Trade.* **Description:** Reports on European Works Council developments, negotiations, and agreements and contains the full text of important documents.
—BLDSC (3830.371080). **CCC.**
Published by: (University of Warwick. Business School. Industrial Relations Research Unit), I R S (Subsidiary of: LexisNexis UK (Scottish Office)), 18-20 Highbury Pl, London, N5 1QP, United Kingdom. TEL 44-20-7354-6742, 44-20-7354-5858, FAX 44-20-7226-8618, 44-20-7359-4000, publications@irseclipse.co.uk, http://www.irsonline.co.uk/pub_subjects/index_pub_human.htm, http://www.irseclipse.co.uk. Eds. Mark Carley, Mark Hall.

EVALUATING YOUR FIRM'S INJURY & ILLNESS RECORD. CONSTRUCTION INDUSTRIES. see *OCCUPATIONAL HEALTH AND SAFETY*

EVALUATING YOUR FIRM'S INJURY & ILLNESS RECORD. SERVICE INDUSTRIES. see *OCCUPATIONAL HEALTH AND SAFETY*

EVALUATING YOUR FIRM'S INJURY & ILLNESS RECORD. TRANSPORTATION & PUBLIC UTILITIES INDUSTRIES. see *OCCUPATIONAL HEALTH AND SAFETY*

EVALUATING YOUR FIRM'S INJURY & ILLNESS RECORD. WHOLESALE & RETAIL TRADE INDUSTRIES. see *OCCUPATIONAL HEALTH AND SAFETY*

331 TGO
EVEIL DU TRAVAILLEUR TOGOLAIS. q.
Published by: Confederation Nationale des Travailleurs du Togo, BP 163, Lome, Togo. TEL 21-57-39. Ed. M K Agbeka. Circ: 5,000.

331.2 USA ISSN 1541-3977
HD4965.5.U6
EXECUTIVE COMPENSATION (BRYN MAWR). Text in English. 1996. a.
Published by: American College, 270 S Bryn Mawr Ave., Bryn Mawr, PA 19010. TEL 610-526-1000, http://www.amercoll.edu. Ed. John Jay McFadden.

331.21 USA
EXECUTIVE COMPENSATION SURVEY REPORT. Text in English. a. USD 400. **Description:** Provides comparative information about executive compensation practices among businesses in the Mid-Atlantic states.
Published by: MidAtlantic Employers' Association, PO Box 770, Valley Forge, PA 19482. TEL 215-666-7330, FAX 215-666-7866.

F A U NYT. (Foreningen af Udviklingsforskere) see *BUSINESS AND ECONOMICS—International Development And Assistance*

FACHANWALT ARBEITSRECHT; Zeitschrift fuer die beratende und die gerichtliche Praxis. see *LAW*

331 USA ISSN 0885-7172
FAIR EMPLOYMENT COMPLIANCE✶; a confidential letter to management. Text in English. 1975. s-m. USD 245 (effective 2000). bk.rev. **Document type:** *Newsletter.*
Related titles: ◆ Supplement(s): In Depth (New York). ISSN 0885-7229.
Published by: Management Resources, Inc., 380 Ocean Rd., Unit 2, Portsmouth, NH 03801-6051. Ed. Kenneth Swann. Circ: 2,000.

331 USA ISSN 0525-552X
KF3315
FAIR EMPLOYMENT PRACTICE CASES. Text in English. 1969. 3/yr. USD 1,480 (effective 2004); only with Manual.
Related titles: Online - full text ed.: (from The Bureau of National Affairs, Inc.).
—**CCC.**
Published by: The Bureau of National Affairs, Inc., 1231 25th St., NW, Washington, DC 20037. TEL 202-452-4200, 800-372-1033, FAX 202-785-7167, customercare@bna.com, http://www.bna.com.

331 USA ISSN 1545-4460
FAIR EMPLOYMENT PRACTICES SUMMARY OF LATEST DEVELOPMENTS. Text in English. 1965. bi-w. USD 167 (effective 2001). 6 p./no.; back issues avail. **Document type:** *Newsletter.* **Description:** Covers developments affecting equal employment opportunities, fair employment practice policies, and affirmative action programs, from trends to relevant regulations, rules and guidelines to federal and state court decisions.
Related titles: Online - full text ed.; ◆ Series of: B N A Policy and Practice Series. ISSN 0005-3228.
—**CCC.**

B

Published by: The Bureau of National Affairs, Inc., 1231 25th St., NW, Washington, DC 20037. TEL 202-452-4200, 800-372-1033, 800-452-7773, FAX 202-822-8092, customercare@bna.com, bnaplus@bna.com, http://www.bna.com/. Ed. Bill L Manville. Pub. Greg C McCaffery.

331 SWE ISSN 1404-1227
FAKTA OM LOENER & ARBETSTIDER. Text in Swedish. 1996. a.
Formerly (until 1999): Fakta om Loener (1402-991X)
Published by: Svenskt Naeringsliv/Confederation of Swedish Enterprise, Storgatan 19, Stockholm, 11482, Sweden. TEL 46-8-55343000, FAX 46-8-55343099, info@svensktnaringsliv.se, http://www.svensktnaringsliv.se.

FEDERAL CIVILIAN WORKFORCE STATISTICS. AFFIRMATIVE EMPLOYMENT STATISTICS. see *BUSINESS AND ECONOMICS—Abstracting, Bibliographies, Statistics*

FEDERAL CIVILIAN WORKFORCE STATISTICS. PAY STRUCTURE OF THE FEDERAL CIVIL SERVICE. see *BUSINESS AND ECONOMICS—Abstracting, Bibliographies, Statistics*

FEDERAL CIVILIAN WORKFORCE STATISTICS. WORK YEARS AND PERSONNEL COSTS. EXECUTIVE BRANCH, UNITED STATES GOVERNMENT. see *BUSINESS AND ECONOMICS—Abstracting, Bibliographies, Statistics*

331.133 USA ISSN 1043-7274
KF3464
FEDERAL EQUAL OPPORTUNITY REPORTER. Text in English. 1982. bi-w. (22/yr.). looseleaf. USD 1,155 (effective 2006). index. back issues avail. **Description:** Provides complete coverage of the most significant decisions rendered by the Equal Employment Opportunity Commission and related federal courts.
—CCC.
Published by: L R P Publications, 747 Dresher Rd, PO Box 980, Horsham, PA 19044. TEL 215-784-0860, 800-341-7874, FAX 215-784-9639, custserve@lrp.com, http://www.shoplrp.com/product/p-4070.html, http://www.lrp.com.

331.133 USA
FEDERAL EQUAL OPPORTUNITY YEAR BOOK. Text in English. 1992. a. USD 66 (effective 2006). **Document type:** *Yearbook.* **Description:** Highlights the significant decision of the EEOC and federal courts regarding workplace discrimination.
Formerly: Federal Equal Opportunity Desk Book (1066-8764)
Published by: L R P Publications, 747 Dresher Rd, PO Box 980, Horsham, PA 19044. TEL 215-784-0860, 800-341-7874, FAX 215-784-9639, custserve@lrp.com, http://www.lrp.com.

352.63 USA ISSN 1075-6574
FEDERAL HUMAN RESOURCES WEEK; news, strategies and best practices for the H R professional. Text in English. 1994. 48/yr. USD 365 (effective 2006). Index. back issues avail. **Document type:** *Newsletter, Trade.* **Description:** Focuses on the latest trends and news in the federal sector.
Related titles: E-mail ed.; Online - full text ed.: (from LexisNexis).
—CCC.
Published by: L R P Publications, 747 Dresher Rd, PO Box 980, Horsham, PA 19044. TEL 215-784-0860, 800-341-7874, FAX 215-784-9639, custserve@lrp.com, http://www.shoplrp.com/product/p-4085.html, http://www.lrp.com.

FEDERAL LABOR LAWS. see *LAW*

331.1 USA ISSN 0885-3061
KF5365.A59
THE FEDERAL LABOR - MANAGEMENT AND EMPLOYEE RELATIONS CONSULTANT. Text in English. 1971. 24/yr. USD 39; USD 48.75 foreign. bk.rev. **Document type:** *Government.* **Description:** Reports on developments in Federal sector labor-management and employee relations.
Formerly: Federal Labor - Management Consultant (0046-3418)
Indexed: PersLit.
Published by: U.S. Office of Personnel Management, Office of Labor Relations and Workforce Performance, Rm 7429, Washington, DC 20415. TEL 202-606-2930. Ed. Mary L Hennessy. Circ: 10,000. **Subscr. to:** U.S. Government Printing Office, Superintendent of Documents, PO Box 371954, Pittsburgh, PA 15250-7954. TEL 202-512-1800, FAX 202-512-2250, orders@gpo.gov, http://www.access.gpo.gov.

334.01 347 USA ISSN 1525-2418
HD8005.2.U5
FEDERAL LABOR RELATIONS ADVISOR. Text in English. m. USD 220 (effective 2006). **Document type:** *Newsletter, Trade.* **Description:** It is designed for federal labor-relations professionals. It provides summaries of, and commentary on, the latest decisions by the FLRA, FSIP, labor arbitrators and federal courts. It includes the details on events and trends in the federal labor-relations community, along with timely analyses of labor-management related techniques and principles.
Related titles: E-mail ed.
—CCC.
Published by: L R P Publications, 747 Dresher Rd, PO Box 980, Horsham, PA 19044. TEL 800-341-7874, FAX 215-784-9639, custserve@lrp.com, http://www.shoplrp.com/product/p-4018.FLA.html, http://www.lrp.com.

344.01 USA ISSN 0199-4883
KF5365.A57
FEDERAL LABOR RELATIONS REPORTER. Text in English. 1978. 3 base vols. plus updates 48/yr. looseleaf. USD 995 (effective 2006). q. index. back issues avail. **Document type:** *Trade.* **Description:** Covers decisions by the Federal Labor Relations Authority, the Federal Service Impasses Panel, administrative law judges, labor arbitrators and the federal court.
—CCC.
Published by: L R P Publications, 747 Dresher Rd, PO Box 980, Horsham, PA 19044. TEL 215-784-0860, 800-341-7874, FAX 215-784-9639, custserve@lrp.com, http://www.shoplrp.com/product/p-4010.html, http://www.lrp.com.

344.01 USA
FEDERAL LABOR RELATIONS YEAR BOOK. Text in English. 1992. a. USD 64.50 (effective 2006). **Document type:** *Yearbook.* **Description:** Covers the most important decision from the Federal Labor Relations Authority and related courts from the past fiscal year.
Formerly: Federal Labor Relations Desk Book (1065-8238)
Published by: L R P Publications, 747 Dresher Rd, PO Box 980, Horsham, PA 19044. TEL 215-784-0860, 800-341-7874, FAX 215-784-9639, custserve@lrp.com, http://www.lrp.com.

352.63 USA
FEDERAL MERIT SYSTEMS (YEAR) YEARBOOK. Text in English. a. USD 65 (effective 2006). **Document type:** *Yearbook, Trade.* **Description:** Presents an overview of Merit Systems Protection Board (MSPB) decisions that have shaped the year in review.
Formerly: Federal Merit Systems (Year) Desk Book (1075-6590)
Published by: L R P Publications, 747 Dresher Rd, PO Box 980, Horsham, PA 19044. TEL 215-784-0860, 800-341-7874, FAX 215-784-9639, custserve@lrp.com, http://www.lrp.com.

344.01 USA ISSN 0746-035X
KF5336
FEDERAL MERIT SYSTEMS REPORTER. Text in English. 1979. w. (48/yr.). looseleaf. USD 995 (effective 2006). q. index. back issues avail. **Document type:** *Trade.* **Description:** Covers all decisions by the Merit Systems Protection Board and related federal courts as soon as they are rendered.
—CCC.
Published by: L R P Publications, 747 Dresher Rd, PO Box 980, Horsham, PA 19044. TEL 215-784-0860, 800-341-7874, FAX 215-784-9639, custserve@lrp.com, http://www.shoplrp.com/product/p-4050.html, http://www.lrp.com.

331.21 USA ISSN 0888-269X
KF5370
FEDERAL PAY AND BENEFITS REPORTER. Text in English. 2 base vols. plus m. updates. looseleaf. USD 725 (effective 2006). q. index. back issues avail. **Document type:** *Trade.* **Description:** Covers personnel cases concerning legal entitlement issues, and provides decisions of the Comptroller General, General Services Board of Contract Appeals, Office of Personnel Management, and related pay and benefits cases.
—CCC.
Published by: L R P Publications, 747 Dresher Rd, PO Box 980, Horsham, PA 19044. TEL 215-784-0860, 800-341-7874, FAX 215-784-9639, custserve@lrp.com, http://www.shoplrp.com/product/p-4060.html, http://www.lrp.com.

FEDERAL STAFF DIRECTORY. see *PUBLIC ADMINISTRATION*

FEDERAL YELLOW BOOK; who's who in the federal departments and agencies. see *PUBLIC ADMINISTRATION*

331 FRA ISSN 0753-5732
FEUILLET RAPIDE SOCIAL. Text in French. 1983. 3/m. EUR 107 combined subscription print & online eds. (effective 2005). **Document type:** *Magazine, Trade.*
Related titles: Online - full text ed.
Published by: Editions Francis Lefebvre, 42 rue de Villiers, Levallois-Perret, 92300, France. TEL 33-1-41052222, http://www.efl.fr.

FIJI. BUREAU OF STATISTICS. EMPLOYMENT SURVEY OF FIJI. see *BUSINESS AND ECONOMICS—Abstracting, Bibliographies, Statistics*

FIJI. BUREAU OF STATISTICS. NATIONWIDE UNEMPLOYMENT SURVEY. see *BUSINESS AND ECONOMICS—Abstracting, Bibliographies, Statistics*

331.1029 FJI
FIJI CLASSIFICATION & DICTIONARY OF OCCUPATIONS. Text in English. 1975. irreg., latest 1994. USD 5 per issue (effective 2000). **Document type:** *Government.*
Published by: Bureau of Statistics, c/o Librarian, Govt. Bldg. 5, PO Box 2221, Suva, Fiji. TEL 679-315-822, FAX 679-303-656.

FINLAND. TILASTOKESKUS. ANSIOTASOINDEKSI/FINLAND. STATISTICS FINLAND. INDEX OF WAGE AND SALARY EARNINGS. see *BUSINESS AND ECONOMICS—Abstracting, Bibliographies, Statistics*

FIREFIGHTERS EMPLOYMENT LAW. see *LAW*

331.346 CAN ISSN 1494-3409
FIRST NATIONS AND INUIT YOUTH EMPLOYMENT STRATEGY. ANNUAL REPORT/STRATEGIE D'EMPLOI POUR LES JEUNES INUITS ET DES PREMIERES NATIONS. RAPPORT ANNUEL. Text in English, French. 1998. a.
Related titles: Online - full text ed.: ISSN 1702-1138.
Published by: (First Nations and Inuit Youth Employment Strategy), Indian and Northern Affairs Canada/Affaires Indiennes et du Nord Canada, Terrasses de la Chaudiere, 10 Wellington, North Tower, Hull, PQ K1A 0H4, Canada. TEL 800-567-9604, infopubs@ainc-inac.gc.ca, http://www.ainc-inac.gc.ca/ps/ys/rep/index_e.html.

FLORIDA EMPLOYMENT LAW LETTER. see *LAW*

FLORIDA EMPLOYMENT LAW MANUAL. see *LAW*

340 331 331.8 USA ISSN 1042-0592
KFF332.8.P77
FLORIDA PUBLIC EMPLOYEE REPORTER. Text in English. base vol. plus updates 23/yr. looseleaf. USD 710 (effective 2006). back issues avail. **Document type:** *Trade.* **Description:** Reports on all significant Florida Public Employees Relations Commission decisions and veterans preference decisions, comprehensively indexed and headnoted. Contains the full text of the acts, rules and regulations, reported with amendments.
Related titles: CD-ROM ed.: Florida Public Employment Library on CD-ROM.
Published by: L R P Publications, 747 Dresher Rd, PO Box 980, Horsham, PA 19044. TEL 215-784-0860, 800-341-7874, FAX 215-784-9639, custserve@lrp.com, http://www.shoplrp.com/product/p-3030.html, http://www.lrp.com.

331 USA ISSN 1081-5341
FLORIDA WORKERS' COMPENSATION LAW BULLETIN. Text in English. 1994. s-m. (23/yr.). USD 275 (effective 2006). cum.index. **Document type:** *Bulletin, Trade.*
Related titles: Online - full text ed.: (from LexisNexis).
—CCC.
Published by: L R P Publications, 747 Dresher Rd, PO Box 980, Horsham, PA 19044. TEL 800-341-7874, custserve@lrp.com, http://www.shoplrp.com/product/p-8000.FLW.html, http://www.lrp.com.

331.21 USA
FLORIDA WORKERS' COMPENSATION MANUAL. Text in English. 1979. (2-3 updates/yr)), 2 base vols. plus irreg. updates. looseleaf. USD 160.
Published by: LexisNexis (Subsidiary of: LexisNexis North America), PO Box 7587, Charlottesville, VA 22906-7587. TEL 804-972-7600, 800-562-1197, FAX 804-972-7666, llp.customer.support@lexis-nexis.com, http://www.lexislawpublishing.com. Ed. Cathy Paris.

331.21 368.4 USA ISSN 1078-7003
FLORIDA WORKERS' COMPENSATION REPORTER. Text in English. 1994. m. USD 247 (effective 2005). **Document type:** *Newsletter, Trade.* **Description:** Reports on workers' compensation issues in Florida.
Published by: (Florida Workers' Compensation Institute), M. Lee Smith Publishers LLC, PO Box 5094, Brentwood, TN 37024. TEL 615-373-7517, 800-274-6774, FAX 615-373-5183, custserv@mleesmith.com, http://www.hrhero.com/wc/flwc.shtml, http://www.mleesmith.com. Ed. Michael Adams. Pub. M Lee Smith.

FOCUS ON CANADIAN EMPLOYMENT AND EQUALITY RIGHTS. see *BUSINESS AND ECONOMICS—Personnel Management*

352.63 SWE ISSN 0015-5306
FOERSVARSTJAENSTEMANNEN/CIVIL SERVANT IN THE DEFENCE FORCES. Variant title: Nya Foersvarstjaenstemannen. Text in Swedish. 1938. 9/yr. membership only. adv. bk.rev. illus. index. **Document type:** *Newspaper.*
Formerly (until 1959): Civila Foersvarstjaenstemannen
Published by: Foersvarets Civila Tjaenstemannafoerbund/Union of Civilian Employees in the Defence Forces, Sturegatan 15, Fack 5328, Stockholm, 10247, Sweden. TEL 46-8-790-52-00, FAX -46-8-20-56-92. Ed. Olle Forsberg. Circ: 12,500.

FOOD SHOP. see *FOOD AND FOOD INDUSTRIES*

331 USA ISSN 0046-4538
FORD WORLD. Text in English. 1964. 11/yr. free. adv. charts; illus. **Document type:** *Newspaper.* **Description:** For Ford employees and retirees, keeping them informed of company news.
Indexed: CLT&T, HRIS.

Published by: Ford Motor Co. (Dearborn), The American Rd, Rm 956, Dearborn, MI 48121. TEL 313-322-2738. Ed. Nancy Carollo. Adv. contact Bev Boyer. Circ: 250,000.

331.120715 DEU ISSN 0340-8973
FORSCHUNGSDOKUMENTATION ZUR ARBEITSMARKT- UND BERUFSFORSCHUNG. Text in German. 1970. 3/yr. EUR 15 per issue (effective 2005). back issues avail. **Document type:** *Bibliography.* **Description:** Lists ongoing and completed research projects on labor market and occupations.
—KNAW.
Published by: Bundesanstalt fuer Arbeit, Institut fuer Arbeitsmarkt- und Berufsforschung, Regensburger Str 104, Nuernberg, 90478, Germany. TEL 49-911-1790, FAX 49-911-1793258, iab.anfragen@iab.de, http://iab.de. Circ: 3,000.

331 SWE ISSN 1651-8578
▼ **FORSKNING OCH RESULTAT**; med stoed fraan F A S. Text in Swedish. 2003. q. **Document type:** *Journal, Academic/Scholarly.* **Description:** Research results from the Swedish Council for Working life and Social Research.
Related titles: Online - full text ed.
Published by: Forskningsraadet foer Arbetsliv och Socialvetenskap/Swedish Council for Working Life and Social Research, PO Box 2220, Stockholm, 10315, Sweden. TEL 46-8-7754070, FAX 46-8-7754075, fas@fas.forskning.se, http://www.fas.forskning.se/for/. Ed. Jan Jerring.

331.125 FRA ISSN 0249-5562
FRANCE. CENTRE D'ETUDES DE L'EMPLOI. CAHIERS. Text in French. 1972. a. price varies. **Document type:** *Monographic series.*
Indexed: PAIS, RASB.
Published by: Centre d'Etudes de l'Emploi, Le Descartes I, 29 promenade Michel Simon, Noisy-le-Grand, Cedex 93166, France. TEL 33-1-45926800, FAX 33-1-49310244, cee@mail.enpc.fr, http://www.cee-recherche.fr. Ed. Mr. J F Germe. R&P P Boisard TEL 33-1-45926845.

331.125 FRA
FRANCE. CENTRE D'ETUDES DE L'EMPLOI. DOSSIERS. Text in French. 1980. 3/yr. **Document type:** *Monographic series, Academic/Scholarly.*
Formerly: France. Centre d'Etudes de l'Emploi. Dossiers de Recherche (0291-9249)
Published by: Centre d'Etudes de l'Emploi, Le Descartes I, 29 promenade Michel Simon, Noisy-le-Grand, Cedex 93166, France. TEL 33-1-45926817, FAX 33-1-49310244, cee@mail.enpc.fr. Ed. Francoise Laroche.

331 FRA ISSN 1251-8107
FRANCE. CENTRE D'ETUDES DE L'EMPLOI. QUATRE PAGES. Key Title: 4 Pages. Text in French. 1994. 6/yr. free. **Document type:** *Bulletin.*
Published by: Centre d'Etudes de l'Emploi, Le Descartes I, 29 promenade Michel Simon, Noisy-le-Grand, Cedex 93166, France. TEL 33-1-45926854, FAX 33-1-49310244, cee@mail.enpc.fr. Ed. Jean Claude Barbier. R&P P Boisard TEL 33-1-45926845.

FRANCE. MINISTERE DES AFFAIRES SOCIALES ET DE LA SOLIDARITE NATIONALE. MINISTERE CHARGE DE L'EMPLOI. CONVENTIONS COLLECTIVES. see *PUBLIC ADMINISTRATION*

331 HND
FRENTE. Text in Spanish. 1981. q.
Published by: Universidad Nacional Autonoma de Honduras, Sindicato de Trabajadores, Tegucigalpa DC, Honduras. Circ: 1,000.

331.255 USA ISSN 1520-4936
HD4928.N62
FRINGE BENEFITS AND WORKING CONDITIONS IN NONPROFIT ORGANIZATIONS. Text in English. 1992. triennial. USD 295 (effective 2005). **Document type:** *Trade.*
Published by: Abbott, Langer & Associates, 548 First St, Crete, IL 60417-9987. TEL 708-672-4200, FAX 708-672-4674, slanger@abbott-langer.com, http://www.abbott-langer.com. Ed. Steven Langer.

331 DEU
G D E D INFORM. Text in German. 1897. m. membership. adv. bk.rev. **Document type:** *Trade.*
Formerly (until 1995): Deutsche Eisenbahner (0343-7108)
Published by: Gewerkschaft der Eisenbahner Deutschlands, Postfach 190369, Frankfurt Am Main, 60090, Germany. TEL 49-69-7536318, FAX 49-69-7536444, redaktion@gded.de, http://www.gded.de. Ed. Reinhard Sauer. Pub. Norbert Hansen. Circ: 350,000.

331 ESP ISSN 1133-035X
GACETA SINDICAL. Text in Spanish. 1980. m.
Related titles: Online - full text ed.
—CINDOC.
Published by: Confederacion Sindical de Comisiones Obreras, C. Fernandez de la Hoz, 12, 3a. planta, Madrid, 28010, Spain. TEL 34-91-7028105, FAX 34-91-3104804, http://www.ccoo.es/.

GAMBIA. CENTRAL STATISTICS DEPARTMENT. QUARTERLY SURVEY OF EMPLOYMENT AND EARNINGS. see *BUSINESS AND ECONOMICS—Abstracting, Bibliographies, Statistics*

344.01 POL ISSN 1231-8345
GAZETA PRACY. Text in Polish. 1994. m. PLZ 9.60. adv. back issues avail. **Description:** Describes labor law regulations, unemployment and labor problems. Contains labor offers.
Published by: Fundacja na Rzecz Restrukturyzacji Regionu Lodzkiego, Ul Tuwima 22-26, Lodz, 90002, Poland. TEL 48-42-322651, FAX 48-42-301741.

331.21 USA
GENERAL WAGE DETERMINATIONS ISSUED UNDER THE DAVIS-BACON AND RELATED ACTS: VOLUME 1. Text in English. base vol. plus w. updates. USD 1,235 (effective 2001). **Description:** Presents current wage decisions for laborers and mechanics engaged in Federal construction projects. Vol.1 covers: Connecticut, Maine, Massachusetts, New Hampshire, New Jersey, New York, Rhode Island, and Vermont, including Puerto Rico, Guam and Virgin Islands.
Published by: U.S. Department of Labor, Employment Standards Administration, Wage Hour Division, New York City District Office, 26 Federal Plaza, Rm 3838, New York, NY 10278. http://www.dol.gov/dol/esa/public/whd_org.htm. **Subscr. to:** U.S. Government Printing Office, Superintendent of Documents, PO Box 371954, Pittsburgh, PA 15250-7954. TEL 202-512-1800, FAX 202-512-2250, orders@gpo.gov, http://www.access.gpo.gov.

331.21 USA
GENERAL WAGE DETERMINATIONS ISSUED UNDER THE DAVIS-BACON AND RELATED ACTS: VOLUME 2. Text in English. base vol. plus w. updates. looseleaf. USD 1,130 (effective 2001). **Document type:** *Government.* **Description:** Presents current wage decisions for laborers and mechanics engaged in Federal construction projects. Vol.2 covers: Delaware, Maryland, Pennsylvania, Virginia, and West Virginia, including the District of Columbia.
Published by: U.S. Department of Labor, Employment Standards Administration, Wage Hour Division, New York City District Office, 26 Federal Plaza, Rm 3838, New York, NY 10278. http://www.dol.gov/dol/esa/public/whd_org.htm. **Subscr. to:** U.S. Government Printing Office, Superintendent of Documents, PO Box 371954, Pittsburgh, PA 15250-7954. TEL 202-512-1800, FAX 202-512-2250, orders@gpo.gov, http://www.access.gpo.gov.

331.21 USA
GENERAL WAGE DETERMINATIONS ISSUED UNDER THE DAVIS-BACON AND RELATED ACTS: VOLUME 3. Text in English. base vol. plus w. updates. looseleaf. USD 1,105 (effective 2001). **Document type:** *Government.* **Description:** Presents current wage decisions for laborers and mechanics engaged in Federal construction projects. Vol.3 covers: Alabama, Florida, Georgia, Kentucky, Mississippi, North Carolina, South Carolina, and Tennessee.
Published by: U.S. Department of Labor, Employment Standards Administration, Wage Hour Division, New York City District Office, 26 Federal Plaza, Rm 3838, New York, NY 10278. http://www.dol.gov/dol/esa/public/whd_org.htm. **Subscr. to:** U.S. Government Printing Office, Superintendent of Documents, PO Box 371954, Pittsburgh, PA 15250-7954. TEL 202-512-1800, FAX 202-512-2250, orders@gpo.gov, http://www.access.gpo.gov.

331.21 USA
GENERAL WAGE DETERMINATIONS ISSUED UNDER THE DAVIS-BACON AND RELATED ACTS: VOLUME 4. Text in English. base vol. plus w. updates. looseleaf. USD 1,625 (effective 2001). **Document type:** *Government.* **Description:** Presents current wage decisions for laborers and mechanics engaged in Federal construction projects. Vol.4 covers: Illinois, Indiana, Michigan, Minnesota, Ohio, and Wisconsin.
Published by: U.S. Department of Labor, Employment Standards Administration, Wage Hour Division, New York City District Office, 26 Federal Plaza, Rm 3838, New York, NY 10278. **Subscr. to:** U.S. Government Printing Office, Superintendent of Documents, PO Box 371954, Pittsburgh, PA 15250-7954. TEL 202-512-1800, FAX 202-512-2250, orders@gpo.gov, http://www.access.gpo.gov.

331.21 USA
GENERAL WAGE DETERMINATIONS ISSUED UNDER THE DAVIS-BACON AND RELATED ACTS: VOLUME 5. Text in English. base vol. plus w. updates. looseleaf. USD 1,295 (effective 2001). **Document type:** *Government.* **Description:** Presents current wage decisions for laborers and mechanics engaged in Federal construction projects. Vol.5 covers: Arkansas, Iowa, Kansas, Louisiana, Missouri, Nebraska, New Mexico, Oklahoma, and Texas.
Published by: U.S. Department of Labor, Employment Standards Administration, Wage Hour Division, New York City District Office, 26 Federal Plaza, Rm 3838, New York, NY 10278. http://www.dol.gov/dol/esa/public/whd_org.htm. **Subscr. to:** U.S. Government Printing Office, Superintendent of Documents, PO Box 371954, Pittsburgh, PA 15250-7954. TEL 202-512-1800, FAX 202-512-2250, orders@gpo.gov, http://www.access.gpo.gov.

331.21 USA
GENERAL WAGE DETERMINATIONS ISSUED UNDER THE DAVIS-BACON AND RELATED ACTS: VOLUME 6. Text in English. base vol. plus w. updates. looseleaf. **Document type:** *Government.* **Description:** Presents current wage decisions for laborers and mechanics engaged in Federal construction projects. Vol.6 covers: Alaska, Colorado, Idaho, Montana, North Dakota, Oregon, South Dakota, Utah, Washington, and Wyoming.
Published by: U.S. Department of Labor, Employment Standards Administration, Wage Hour Division, New York City District Office, 26 Federal Plaza, Rm 3838, New York, NY 10278. http://www.dol.gov/dol/esa/public/whd_org.htm. **Subscr. to:** U.S. Government Printing Office, Superintendent of Documents, PO Box 371954, Pittsburgh, PA 15250-7954. TEL 202-512-1800, FAX 202-512-2250, orders@gpo.gov, http://www.access.gpo.gov.

331.21 USA
GENERAL WAGE DETERMINATIONS ISSUED UNDER THE DAVIS-BACON AND RELATED ACTS: VOLUME 7. Text in English. base vol. plus w. updates. looseleaf. USD 1,300 (effective 2001). **Document type:** *Consumer.* **Description:** Presents current wage decisions for laborers and mechanics engaged in Federal construction projects. Vol.7 covers: Arizona, California, Hawaii, and Nevada.
Published by: U.S. Department of Labor, Employment Standards Administration, Wage Hour Division, New York City District Office, 26 Federal Plaza, Rm 3838, New York, NY 10278. http://www.dol.gov/dol/esa/public/whd_org.htm. **Subscr. to:** U.S. Government Printing Office, Superintendent of Documents, PO Box 371954, Pittsburgh, PA 15250-7954. TEL 202-512-1800, FAX 202-512-2250, orders@gpo.gov, http://www.access.gpo.gov.

331 USA ISSN 0145-7330
HD8051
GEOGRAPHIC PROFILE OF EMPLOYMENT AND UNEMPLOYMENT. Text in English. a. USD 16 (effective 2000). **Document type:** *Bulletin, Government.* **Description:** Profiles each state, 50 metropolitan areas, and 17 cities for employment and unemployment, using U.S. Census Current Population Survey data.
Related titles: ♦ Series of: U.S. Bureau of Labor Statistics. Bulletin. ISSN 0082-9021.
Published by: U.S. Department of Labor, Bureau of Labor Statistics, Postal Square Bldg., 2 Massachusetts Ave, NE, Washington, DC 20212-0001 . TEL 202-691-5200, http://www.bls.gov. **Subscr. to:** U.S. Government Printing Office, Superintendent of Documents.

GEORGIA EMPLOYMENT LAW LETTER. see *LAW*

331.12 USA ISSN 0147-9865
HD5725.G4
GEORGIA LABOR MARKET TRENDS. Text in English. 1975. m. free. stat. **Document type:** *Government.*
Incorporates (in 1978): Georgia Labor Force Newsletter; Formerly: Georgia Manpower Trends (0091-3464)
Indexed: SRI.
Published by: Department of Labor, Labor Information System, Sussex Pl, 148 International Blvd, N E, Atlanta, GA 30303. TEL 404-656-3177. Circ: 4,000.

344.01 USA
GEORGIA WORKERS' COMPENSATION LAWS, RULES AND REGULATIONS ANNOTATED. Text in English. a. (w/ CD ROM), latest 2002. USD 32 (effective 2003). 331 p./no.; **Description:** Contains case notes and annotations.
Related titles: Diskette ed.
Published by: Michie Company (Subsidiary of: LexisNexis North America), 701 E Water St, Charlottesville, VA 22902-5389. TEL 434-972-7600, 800-446-3410, FAX 434-972-7677, http://www.michie.com.

331.1 DEU ISSN 1613-9429
CODEN: AGDEE7
GERMANY. BUNDESAGENTUR FUER ARBEIT. AMTLICHE NACHRICHTEN. Text in German. 1953. m. charts; illus.; stat. index. **Document type:** *Journal, Government.*
Former titles (until 2004): Germany. Bundesanstalt fuer Arbeit. Amtliche Nachrichten (0007-585X); (until 1969): Bundesanstalt fuer Arbeitsvermittlung und Arbeitslosenversicherung. Amtliche Nachrichten (0407-8896)
Related titles: ♦ Supplement(s): Germany. Bundesanstalt fuer Arbeit. Foerderung der Beruflichen Weiterbildung. ISSN 1439-9350.
—IE, Infotrieve.
Published by: Bundesanstalt fuer Arbeit, Regensburger Str 104, Nuernberg, 90478, Germany. TEL 49-911-1790, FAX 49-911-1792123, zentrale@arbeitsagentur.de, http://www.arbeitsagentur.de. Circ: 5,000.

331 DEU ISSN 0943-8289
GESAMTE OEFFENTLICHE DIENSTRECHT. Text in German. 1972. irreg. looseleaf. price varies. **Document type:** *Monographic series, Trade.*
Published by: Erich Schmidt Verlag GmbH & Co. (Berlin), Genthiner Str 30G, Berlin, 10785, Germany. TEL 49-30-250085-0, FAX 49-30-25008521, vertrieb@esvmedien.de, http://www.erich-schmidt-verlag.de.

GESTION SOCIALE DU PERSONNEL DE CONDUITE. see *TRANSPORTATION*

331   DEU   ISSN 1611-5821
➤ **GESUNDHEITS- UND SOZIALPOLITIK.** Text in German. 1946. bi-m. EUR 104; EUR 24 newsstand/cover (effective 2004). adv. reprint service avail. from SCH. **Document type:** *Magazine, Academic/Scholarly.*
Formerly: Arbeit und Sozialpolitik (0340-8434)
Indexed: DIP, IBR, IBZ, PAIS, RASB, SCIMP, WBSS.
—IE. **CCC.**
Published by: Nomos Verlagsgesellschaft mbH und Co. KG, Waldseestr 3-5, Baden-Baden, 76530, Germany. TEL 49-7221-20140, FAX 49-7221-210427, nomos@nomos.de, http://www.nomos.de. Ed. Heinz Debold. Adv. contact Bettina Kohler. B&W page EUR 1,490; color page EUR 2,615; trim 190 x 255. Circ: 2,000 (paid and controlled).

➤ **GIDS VOOR SOCIALE REGLEMENTERING IN ONDERNEMINGEN.** see *LAW—Civil Law*

331   ITA
GIORNALE DI DIRITTO DEL LAVORO E DI RELAZIONI INDUSTRIALI. Text in Italian. 1979. q. EUR 68 domestic; EUR 89 foreign (effective 2003).
Indexed: ELLIS, PAIS.
Published by: Franco Angeli Edizioni, Viale Monza 106, Milan, 20127, Italy. TEL 39-02-2837141, FAX 39-02-26144793, redazioni@francoangeli.it, http://www.francoangeli.it. Ed. Gino Giugni.

331   USA
GOLDEN LODGE NEWS. Text in English. 1954. m. free domestic to members. **Document type:** *Newspaper, Trade.*
Published by: United Steel Workers of America, Local Union 1123, 1234 Harrison Ave, S. W., Canton, OH 44706. TEL 330-454-6137, FAX 330-454-3461, golden@neo.rr.com. Ed. Tom Sponhour. Circ: 7,500 (controlled).

GOVERNMENT CONTRACTS REPORTER (ONLINE EDITION). see *LAW*

352.63   USA   ISSN 0017-260X
HD8008.A1
GOVERNMENT EMPLOYEE RELATIONS REPORT. Text in English. 1963. w. looseleaf. USD 1,479 (effective 2005 - 2006). bk.rev. charts; stat. cum.index. 32 p./no.; back issues avail. **Description:** Notification and reference service covering federal, state and municipal government employee relations.
Related titles: Microfilm ed.; Online - full text ed.: ISSN 1523-3952 (from The Bureau of National Affairs, Inc., Thomson West).
—BLDSC (4204.100000), IE, ingenta. **CCC.**
Published by: The Bureau of National Affairs, Inc., 1231 25th St., NW, Washington, DC 20037. TEL 202-452-4200, 800-372-1033, 800-452-7773, FAX 202-822-8092, customercare@bna.com, bnaplus@bna.com, http://www.bna.com/products/labor/gerr.htm. Ed. Anthony A Harris. Pub. Greg C McCaffery.

352.63   USA
HD8008.A1
GOVERNMENT UNION REVIEW AND PUBLIC POLICY DIGEST; quarterly journal on public sector labor relations. Text in English. 1980. q. USD 20 (effective 2003). illus. back issues avail.; reprint service avail. from PQC,WSH. **Document type:** *Academic/Scholarly.* **Description:** Academic journal covering the labor relations field.
Formerly (until 2001): Government Union Review (0270-2487)
Related titles: Microform ed.: 1980 (from PQC); Online - full text ed.: (from Northern Light Technology, Inc., O C L C Online Computer Library Center, Inc., ProQuest Information & Learning).
Indexed: ABIn, BPIA, CIJE, CLI, IPARL, LRI, PAIS, PSA, PersLit, SOPODA, SPAA.
—BLDSC (4206.078000), IE.
Published by: Public Service Research Foundation, 320 Maple Ave E, Ste 4, Vienna, VA 22180-4742. TEL 703-242-3575, FAX 703-242-3579, info@psrf.org, http://www.psrf.org. Ed. David Y Denholm. Circ: 5,000.

331.21   GBR
GRAMPIAN SALARY SURVEY. Text in English. 2/yr. GBP 280 per edition (effective 2001). **Document type:** *Bulletin.*
Published by: The Reward Group Ltd., Reward House, Diamond Way, Stone Business Park, Stone, Staffs ST15 0SD, United Kingdom. TEL 44-1785-813566, FAX 44-1785-817007, enquiries@reward-group.co.uk, http://www.reward-group.co.uk.

331.125   GBR
GREAT BRITAIN. DEPARTMENT OF EMPLOYMENT. RESEARCH. Text in English. 1972. a. free. **Document type:** *Government.* **Description:** Provides details of research projects carried out for the department by external researchers and contractors.
Published by: Employment Department, Research Management, Moorfoot, Sheffield, London, S1 4PQ, United Kingdom. TEL 071-273-4875, FAX 071-273-5364. Circ: 2,000. **Dist. by:** H.M.S.O., 49 High Holborn, London WC1V 6HB, United Kingdom.

GREAT BRITAIN. DEPARTMENT OF TRADE AND INDUSTRY. ASSESSMENT PAPER. see *BUSINESS AND ECONOMICS—Management*

331   ITA   ISSN 1590-0304
KKH3190.A13
GUIDA NORMATIVA. IL SOLE 24 ORE. Text in Italian. 1991. d.
Published by: Editrice Il Sole 24 Ore SpA, Via Paolo Lomazzo 52, Milan, 20154, Italy. TEL 39-02-30221, FAX 39-02-312055, info@ilsole24ore.com, http://www.guidanormativa.ilsole24ore.com/, http://www.ilsole24ore.com.

331   ITA   ISSN 1590-0088
GUIDA PRATICA DEL LAVORO. Text in Italian. 1996. s-a. **Document type:** *Magazine, Consumer.*
Related titles: Online - full text ed.
Published by: Editrice Il Sole 24 Ore SpA, Via Paolo Lomazzo 52, Milan, 20154, Italy. TEL 39-02-30221, FAX 39-02-312055, info@ilsole24ore.com, http://www.ilsole24ore.com.

331.252 338.642   USA   ISSN 1530-4604
HD7105.35.U6
GUIDE TO CHOOSING RETIREMENT PLANS FOR SMALL BUSINESSES. Text in English. 1999. a. USD 104 newsstand/cover (effective 2003).
Published by: Practitioners Publishing Co., PO Box 966, Fort Worth, TX 76101-0966. TEL 817-332-3709, 800-323-8724, FAX 817-877-3694, http://www.ppcnet.com.

GUIDE TO EQUAL EMPLOYMENT PRACTICES. see *BUSINESS AND ECONOMICS—Personnel Management*

GUIDE TO MANAGING FAIR DISMISSAL. see *LAW—Corporate Law*

332.6   ZAF
GUIDE TO THE 1995 LABOUR RELATIONS ACT. Text in English. 1995. irreg. ZAR 185 (effective 2000). **Document type:** *Trade.* **Description:** Provides a guide to the South African Labour Relations Act of 1995 and informs of amendments to the legislation.
Related titles: Online - full text ed.
Published by: Van Zyl, Rudd and Associates, Centrahil, PO Box 12758, Port Elizabeth, 6006, South Africa. TEL 27-41-373-4322, FAX 27-41-373-4323, info@vanzylrudd.co.za, http://www.vanzylrudd.co.za. Eds. Brian van Zyl, Carol Rudd.

331   IND   ISSN 0017-5501
GUJARAT LABOUR GAZETTE. Text in English. 1967 (vol.7). m. INR 10. charts; stat. index.
Published by: Office of the Commissioner of Labour, Ahmedabad, Gujarat, India.

331   CHN   ISSN 1002-7823
GUOJI LAOGONG TONGXUN/INTERNATIONAL LABOR BULLETIN. Text in Chinese. 1990. 5/yr.
Published by: Laodong Renshi Chubanshe, 12 Hepingli Zhongjie, Beijing, 100013, China. TEL 4665588. Ed. Wang Jianxin.

H C E P. see *LAW—Corporate Law*

331   USA
H R C D: GENERAL SCHEDULE POSITION CLASSIFICATION AND FEDERAL WAGE SYSTEM JOB GRADING STANDARDS. (Human Resources Compact Disk) (Compatible with Windows & Macintosh) Text in English. s-a. USD 25 (effective 2001). **Document type:** *Government.* **Description:** Contains GS Classification Standards; FWS Job Grading Standards; GS Qualifications Standards; and Significant Classification Appeal Decisions.
Media: CD-ROM.
Published by: U.S. Office of Personnel Management, 1900 E. St. N.W., Washington, DC 20415. **Subscr. to:** U.S. Government Printing Office, Superintendent of Documents, PO Box 371954, Pittsburgh, PA 15250-7954. TEL 202-512-1800, FAX 202-512-2250, orders@gpo.gov, http://www.access.gpo.gov.

H R D ALERT. (Human Resource Development) see *BUSINESS AND ECONOMICS—Personnel Management*

H R O TODAY. see *BUSINESS AND ECONOMICS—Personnel Management*

H R PRACTITIONERS GUIDE. see *BUSINESS AND ECONOMICS—Personnel Management*

HADSHOT KUPPOT HOLIM. see *INSURANCE*

331.11   USA
HANDBOOK OF LABOR FORCE DATA FOR SELECTED AREAS OF OKLAHOMA. Text in English. 1966. a. free. stat. **Document type:** *Government.*
Published by: Employment Security Commission, Research Department, Will Rogers Bldg, 2401 N Lincoln Blvd, Oklahoma City, OK 73105. Ed. Brenda Beed. Circ: 300.

331   NLD
HANDBOOK ON EUROPEAN EMPLOYEE INVOLVEMENT. Text in English. 1987. 2 base vols. plus a. updates. looseleaf. price varies. **Description:** Covers contractual and other regulations governing employee participation in management at the shop floor and boardroom level for countries in Europe (including non-EC countries). Includes regulations drawn up by international organizations such as the ILO and OECD, and comparisons with relevant US law and practice.
Formerly: Handbook on European Employee Co-Management —BLDSC (4250.439400).
Published by: Kluwer Law International (Subsidiary of: Aspen Publishers, Inc.), Laan van Meerdervoort 70, PO Box 85889, The Hague, 2508 CN, Netherlands. TEL 31-70-3081500, FAX 31-70-3081515, sales@kluwerlaw.com, http://www.kluwerlaw.com. Eds. Peter Hanau, Walter Kolvenbach. **Dist. by:** Libresso Distribution Centre, PO Box 23, Deventer 7400 GA, Netherlands. TEL 31-570-633155, FAX 31-570-633834.

331.4   USA
(YEAR) HANDBOOK ON WOMEN WORKERS: TRENDS & ISSUES. Text in English. 1948. irreg. price varies. **Description:** Offers a comprehensive view of the labor force activity of women and describes a range of legal and socioeconomic developments that have impacted upon women's participation and progress in the work force.
Former titles: Trends and Issues: Handbook on Women Workers (Year); Time of Change: Handbook on Women Workers; Handbook of Women Workers (0083-3622); Time of Change
Related titles: Series of: Women's Bureau Bulletin. ISSN 0083-3606. 1919.
Indexed: CWI.
Published by: U.S. Department of Labor, Women's Bureau, Frances Perkins Bldg, 200 Constitution Ave, N W, Washington, DC 20210. TEL 202-219-6652, FAX 202-219-5529. Ed. Bernia Friedlander. **Orders to:** U.S. Government Printing Office, Superintendent of Documents, PO Box 371954, Pittsburgh, PA 15250-7954. TEL 202-512-1800, FAX 202-512-2250, orders@gpo.gov, http://www.access.gpo.gov.

331   DNK   ISSN 1397-6117
HANDELSHOEJSKOLEN I KOEBENHAVN. INSTITUT FOR ORGANISATION OG ARBEJDSSOCIOLOGI. H D STUDIET I ORGANISATION OG LEDELSE. Text in Danish. 1981 (vol.15). a. price varies. **Document type:** *Academic/Scholarly.*
Former titles (until 1997): Handelshoejskolen i Koebenhavn. Institut for Organisation og Arbejdssociologi. H D Studiet i Organisation (0107-4458); (until 1981): Haandbog for Studerende ved H D Studiet i Organisation (0900-0046)
Published by: Handelshoejskolen i Koebenhavn, Institut for Organisation og Arbejdssociologi/Copenhagen Business School. Department of Organization and Industrial Sociology, Solbjerg Plads 3, Frederiksberg, 2000, Denmark. TEL 45-38-152815, FAX 45-38-152828. **Subscr. to:** Danske Boghandleres Kommissionsanstalt, Siljangade 6-8, Copenhagen S 2300, Denmark.

331.11   USA
HARD HAT MAGAZINE. Text in English. q. USD 12 (effective 2001). **Document type:** *Magazine, Trade.* **Description:** Devoted to the best interests of construction workers in the US.
Address: PO Box 40668, San Francisco, CA 94140. hardhatsf@aol.com, http://members.tripod.com/~hard_hat/. Ed. Mike Orrfelt.

331   GBR
HARVEY ON INDUSTRIAL RELATIONS & EMPLOYMENT LAW. Text in English. 5 base vols. plus updates 6/yr. looseleaf. GBP 450 (effective 2000). **Document type:** *Trade.* **Description:** Provides a complete compendium of industrial relations and employment law and practice. Gives narrative guidance, analyzing the law, clarifying obscure passages and filling in the practical background.
Related titles: CD-ROM ed.
Published by: Butterworths Tolley (Subsidiary of: LexisNexis UK (Scottish Office)), Halsbury House, 35 Chancery Ln, London, Mddx WC2A 1EL, United Kingdom. TEL 44-20-74002500, FAX 44-20-7400-2842, order.line@butterworths.co.uk, http://www.butterworths.co.uk, http://www.butterworths.co.uk/. Ed. Bryn Perrins.

331   IND   ISSN 0046-6921
HARYANA LABOUR JOURNAL. Text in English, Hindi. 1970. q. INR 20. adv. charts; illus.
Published by: Department of Labour, Chandigarh, Haryana, India.

331   AUT
HAUSNACHRICHTEN. Text in German. irreg. (2-4/yr.). free. abstr.; illus. **Document type:** *Bulletin.*
Formerly: Shell Hausnachrichten (0037-3540)
Published by: Shell Austria AG, Rennweg 12, Vienna, W 1030, Austria. TEL 43-1-797972206, FAX 43-1-797972201. Ed. H Bieber. Circ: 1,500.

HAWAII EMPLOYMENT LAW LETTER. see *LAW—Corporate Law*

B

HEALTH CARE LABOR MANUAL. see *HEALTH FACILITIES AND ADMINISTRATION*

344.01 USA ISSN 0890-9245
KF3580.H4
HEALTH EMPLOYMENT LAW UPDATE. Text in English. 1985. 12/yr. looseleaf. USD 125 (effective 2001). index. 8 p./no.; back issues avail. **Document type:** *Newsletter.* **Description:** Presents advice covering current legislation and legal decisions, issues and trends, policy concerns and authoritative legal analysis for human resource executives.
Published by: Rutkowski & Associates Inc., PO Box 15250, Evansville, IN 47716-0250. TEL 812-476-4520. R&P Barbara Lang Rutkowski.

331.21 GBR
HERTFORDSHIRE - ESSEX SALARY SURVEY. Text in English. 2/yr. GBP 280 per edition (effective 2001). **Document type:** *Bulletin.* **Description:** Pay and benefit salary survey for the Hertfordshire and Essex areas.
Published by: The Reward Group Ltd., Reward House, Diamond Way, Stone Business Park, Stone, Staffs ST15 0SD, United Kingdom. TEL 44-1785-813566, FAX 44-1785-817007, enquiries@reward-group.co.uk, http://www.reward-group.co.uk.

331.11 CAN ISSN 1196-2488
HIGHLIGHTS OF MAJOR DEVELOPMENTS IN LABOUR LEGISLATION. Text in English. 1992. a.
Published by: Labour Canada, Publications Distribution, Ottawa, ON K1A 0J2, Canada. TEL 819-994-0543, FAX 819-997-1664.

331 GBR ISSN 1362-1572
HD6958.5
➤ **HISTORICAL STUDIES IN INDUSTRIAL RELATIONS.** Text in English. 1996. s-a. GBP 18 domestic to individuals; GBP 25 foreign to individuals; GBP 36 domestic to institutions; GBP 44 foreign to institutions. adv. bk.rev. **Document type:** *Academic/Scholarly.*
—BLDSC (4317.057000), IE, ingenta.
Published by: Centre for Industrial Relations, Keele University, Keele, Staffs ST5 5BG, United Kingdom. TEL 44-1782-583099, FAX 44-1782-584120, ida09@keele.ac.uk. Ed. Dave Lyddon. Adv. contact Margaret Yates. Circ: 400.

➤ **HOFSTRA LABOR & EMPLOYMENT LAW JOURNAL.** see *LAW*

331 CUB
HOMBRE Y TRABAJO; informacion especializada. Text in Spanish. 1979. q. USD 2.
Formerly: Economia del Trabajo (0864-0130)
Published by: Comite Estatal de Trabajo y Seguridad Social, 23 Calle O y P,, Vedado, Plaza, La Habana, Cuba. Circ: 2,000.

331 ITA ISSN 0439-4291
HOMO FABER; rassegna internazionale de lavoro e dell'istruzione. Text in Italian. 1950. m. bk.rev.
Published by: Mario Pantaleo Ed. & Pub., Via Dei Gracchi, 181-185, Rome, RM 00192, Italy.

HONG KONG SPECIAL ADMINISTRATIVE REGION OF CHINA. CENSUS AND STATISTICS DEPARTMENT. AVERAGE DAILY WAGES OF WORKERS ENGAGED IN GOVERNMENT BUILDING AND CONSTRUCTION PROJECTS. see *BUSINESS AND ECONOMICS—Abstracting, Bibliographies, Statistics*

HONG KONG SPECIAL ADMINISTRATIVE REGION OF CHINA. CENSUS AND STATISTICS DEPARTMENT. EMPLOYMENT AND VACANCIES STATISTICS (DETAILED TABLES) SERIES D. IMPORT/EXPORT TRADES. see *BUSINESS AND ECONOMICS*

HONG KONG SPECIAL ADMINISTRATIVE REGION OF CHINA. CENSUS AND STATISTICS DEPARTMENT. QUARTERLY REPORT OF EMPLOYMENT AND VACANCIES STATISTICS. see *BUSINESS AND ECONOMICS—Abstracting, Bibliographies, Statistics*

HONG KONG. STANDING COMMISSION ON CIVIL SERVICE SALARIES AND CONDITIONS OF SERVICE. CIVIL SERVICE PAY. see *PUBLIC ADMINISTRATION*

352.63 USA
HONOLULU EMPLOYEE JOURNAL. Text in English. 1971 (vol.9). bi-m. free. bk.rev. charts; illus. **Document type:** *Newsletter.* **Description:** For and about city workers.
Published by: Office of Information & Complaint, City Hall, Honolulu, HI 96813. TEL 808-527-5782, FAX 808-523-4386. Ed. Mng Ed Bill Brauker. Circ: 10,000.

HORECA INFO; vakblad voor werknemers. see *HOTELS AND RESTAURANTS*

HOSPITAL EMPLOYEE HEALTH. see *HEALTH FACILITIES AND ADMINISTRATION*

331.21 USA
HOURLY EARNINGS SURVEY. Text in English. a. USD 225.
Description: Summarizes data on employment, hours worked and earnings of hourly paid production workers from 148 companies, representing 9,800 employees in PA, NJ, MD, and DE.
Published by: MidAtlantic Employers' Association, PO Box 770, Valley Forge, PA 19482. TEL 215-666-7330, FAX 215-666-7866.

331 USA ISSN 1040-0443
HUMAN RESOURCE EXECUTIVE. Text in English. 1987. 16/yr. USD 94.95; free to qualified personnel (effective 2005). **Document type:** *Magazine, Trade.* **Description:** Covers key human resource issues facing organizations today.
Related titles: Online - full text ed.
Indexed: QAb, T&DA.
—CCC.
Published by: L R P Publications, 747 Dresher Rd, PO Box 980, Horsham, PA 19044. TEL 215-784-0910, FAX 215-784-0870, custserve@lrp.com, http://www.workindex.com/hrexecutive/, http://www.lrp.com. Ed., Pub., R&P David Shadovitz. Circ: 75,000 (paid and controlled).

HUMAN RESOURCE MANAGEMENT NEWS; the weekly newsletter for the human resource management field. see *BUSINESS AND ECONOMICS—Personnel Management*

331 HKG
THE HUMAN RESOURCES DIRECTORY. Text in English. a. HKD 500, USD 65 (effective 2001). **Document type:** *Directory, Trade.* **Description:** Covers the latest HR issues in Hong Kong, including information on a wide variety of human resources service providers.
Published by: Euromoney Publications plc., 5/F Printing House, 6 Duddell Street, Central, Hong Kong. TEL 852-2842-6906, FAX 852-2810-8417, enquiries@alphk.com, http://www.euromoney.com.

HUMAN RESOURCES GUIDE. see *BUSINESS AND ECONOMICS—Personnel Management*

HUMAN RESOURCES MANAGEMENT - COMPENSATION. see *BUSINESS AND ECONOMICS—Personnel Management*

HUMAN RESOURCES MANAGEMENT - EMPLOYMENT RELATIONS. see *BUSINESS AND ECONOMICS—Personnel Management*

331.133 USA ISSN 0745-2187
HUMAN RESOURCES MANAGEMENT - EQUAL EMPLOYMENT OPPORTUNITY. Text in English. 2 base vols. plus m. updates. looseleaf. USD 529 base vol(s). print or online or CD-ROM ed. (effective 2004). **Description:** Shows what companies and government contractors can do, can't do, and should do to comply with federal and state fair employment, affirmative action and equal pay rules.
Related titles: CD-ROM ed.; Online - full text ed.; Series of: Human Resources Management Library.
Published by: C C H Inc., 2700 Lake Cook Rd, Riverwoods, IL 60015. TEL 847-267-7000, 800-449-6439, cust_serv@cch.com, http://www.cch.com. Pub. Catherine Wolfe.

331.11 USA ISSN 1095-6239
HD8051
HUMAN RESOURCES REPORT. Text in English. 1983. w. looseleaf. USD 1,140 (effective 2005 - 2006). 32 p./no.; back issues avail. **Description:** Gives an overview of the developments influencing employee relations in both private and public sectors, with information on EEO policy, federal and state legislative and regulatory actions, NLRB actions, federal and state court decisions, and the impact of foreign competition.
Formerly: B N A's Employee Relations Weekly (0739-3016)
Related titles: Online - full content ed.: ISSN 1523-2832. USD 1,284 up to 5 users (effective 2004) (from The Bureau of National Affairs, Inc.); Online - full text ed.: (from The Bureau of National Affairs, Inc.).
—CCC.
Published by: The Bureau of National Affairs, Inc., 1231 25th St., NW, Washington, DC 20037. TEL 202-452-4200, 800-372-1033, FAX 202-785-7167, customercare@bna.com, http://www.bna.com/products/hr/hrr.htm. Pub. Greg C McCaffery.

650 FRA ISSN 0018-7372
HUMANISME ET ENTREPRISE; revue informant des problemes humains, sociaux et economiques dans l'entreprise. Text in French. 1959. bi-m. adv. bk.rev. mkt.; stat.; tr.lit.; tr.mk. back issues avail.
Formerly: Cahiers du Centre d'Etudes et de Recherches
Indexed: ELLIS.
—BLDSC (4336.499000).
Published by: Association des Anciens Eleves de Lettres et Sciences Humaines des Universites de Paris, 183-185, Bd. Bineau, Neuilly-sur-Seine, 92200, France. TEL 33-1-46244521, FAX 33-1-46245912. Ed. Charles Pierre Guillebeau. Circ: 1,750.

331 POL ISSN 1643-7446
HD6955 CODEN: HUMPEM
HUMANIZACJA PRACY/HUMANIZATION OF WORK. Text in Polish; Summaries in English, Russian. 1968. bi-m. bk.rev. bibl.
Supersedes in part (in 2001): Humanizacja Pracy. Zarzadzanie Zasobami Ludzkimi (1640-6737); Which was formerly (until 1999): Humanizacja Pracy (0137-3013); (until 1974): Humanizm Pracy (0137-3021)
Indexed: RASB.
Published by: Szkola Wyzsza im. Pawla Wlodkowica, al Kilinskiego 12, Plock, 09402, Poland. TEL 48-24-3664100, FAX 48-24-3664148, rekrutacja@wlodkowic.pl, http://www.wlodkowic.edu.pl. **Dist. by:** Ars Polona, Krakowskie Przedmiescie 7, Warsaw, Poland. TEL 48-22-9263914, FAX 48-22-9265334, arspolona@arspolona.com.pl, http://www.arspolona.com.pl.

HUNGARY. KOZPONTI STATISZTIKAI HIVATAL. FOGLALKOZTATOTTSAG ES KERESETI ARANYOK. see *BUSINESS AND ECONOMICS—Abstracting, Bibliographies, Statistics*

331 IND
I A M R WORKING PAPER. Text in English. 1963. irreg. price varies.
Published by: Institute of Applied Manpower Research, Indraprastha Estate, Mahatma Gandhi Marg, New Delhi, 110 002, India. TEL 91-11-3317849, FAX 91-11-3319909.

331.255 USA
I B I S NEWS. (International Benefits Information Service) Text in English. irreg. USD 1,350 (effective 2005). **Document type:** *Trade.* **Description:** Reports on developments affecting employee benefits in all parts of the world.
Media: Online - full content.
Published by: I B I S Communications, Inc., 5410 Wilshire Blvd, Ste 707, Los Angeles, CA 90036. TEL 323-297-4247, FAX 323-954-7009, info@ibisnews.org, http://www.ibisnews.org/. **Subscr. to:** PO Box 830409, Birmingham, AL 35283. TEL 800-633-4931, 205-995-1567.

331.255 USA
I B I S REPORT. Text in English. irreg. USD 300 (effective 2005). **Document type:** *Trade.* **Description:** Focuses on the important new trends and developments in international employee benefit programs, including pensions, stock options, severance pay, health, life, and disability insurance.
Media: Online - full content.
Published by: I B I S Communications, Inc., 5410 Wilshire Blvd, Ste 707, Los Angeles, CA 90036. TEL 323-297-4247, FAX 323-954-7009, info@ibisnews.org, http://www.ibisnews.org/. **Subscr. to:** PO Box 830409, Birmingham, AL 35283. TEL 800-633-4931, 205-995-1567.

331.2 GBR ISSN 0308-9312
I D S BRIEF; the legal side of employee relations. (Includes special section: Employment Law Problems) Text in English. 1972. fortn. GBP 375 (effective 2005). **Document type:** *Trade.* **Description:** Keeps subscribers up-to-date on the legal side of industrial relations.
Incorporates in part: Employment Law Cases
Related titles: Online - full text ed.
Indexed: ELJI, LJI, RDA.
—BLDSC (4362.571500), IE, ingenta.
Published by: Incomes Data Services Ltd., 77 Bastwick St, London, EC1V 3TT, United Kingdom. TEL 44-20-72503434, FAX 44-20-73242510, ids@incomesdata.co.uk, http://www.idsbrief.co.uk, http://www.incomesdata.co.uk.

331.2 GBR ISSN 1746-1847
I D S EXECUTIVE COMPENSATION REVIEW; monitoring executive and professional pay. Variant title: Management Pay Review. Text in English. m. GBP 338 (effective 2005). **Document type:** *Trade.* **Description:** Designed to provide HR specialists with ongoing information on the who, what and when of pay practice for managers and professionals and a guide to the range of pay benchmark data available.
Former titles (no.279, 2004): I D S Management Pay Review (1351-4954); (until 1993): I D S Monthly Review of Salaries and Benefits (0262-7361); (until 1981): Incomes Data Top Pay Unit Review
Related titles: Supplement(s): Research File.
—BLDSC (4362.589550), IE, ingenta.
Published by: Incomes Data Services Ltd., 77 Bastwick St, London, EC1V 3TT, United Kingdom. TEL 44-20-72503434, FAX 44-20-73242510, ids@incomesdata.co.uk, http://www.incomesdata.co.uk.

331.2 GBR
I D S HR STUDIES; benchmarking personnel policies and practice. Text in English. 1971. bi-m. GBP 340 (effective 2005). **Document type:** *Journal, Trade.* **Description:** Covers pay, terms, and conditions; working patterns and practices; and topical personnel issues for the personnel manager.
Incorporates in part: Guides to Suppliers; Formerly: I D S Studies (0308-9339)
—BLDSC (4362.605000), IE, ingenta.
Published by: Incomes Data Services Ltd., 77 Bastwick St, London, EC1V 3TT, United Kingdom. TEL 44-20-72503434, FAX 44-20-73242510, ids@incomesdata.co.uk, http://www.incomesdata.co.uk.

331.21 GBR ISSN 1474-1792
I D S PAY BENCHMARK. Variant title: Pay Directory. Text in English. 1982. 3/yr. GBP 165 per issue (effective 2005). 350 p./no.; **Document type:** *Directory, Trade.* **Description:** Compiles salary data by profession; also includes data on benefits and work conditions.
Formerly (until 2001): I D S Pay Directory (0265-6019)
Related titles: Online - full text ed.: (from EBSCO Publishing).
—IE.
Published by: Incomes Data Services Ltd., 77 Bastwick St, London, EC1V 3TT, United Kingdom. TEL 44-20-72503434, FAX 44-20-73242510, ids@incomesdata.co.uk, http://www.idspaybenchmark.co.uk, http://www.incomesdata.co.uk.

331.2 GBR
I D S PAY REPORT; authority on pay and the labour market. Key Title: Incomes Data Report. Text in English. 1966. s-m. GBP 396 (effective 2005). **Document type:** *Trade.* **Description:** Provides a factual record of all the latest news on pay bargaining and developments in pay.
Formerly: I D S Report (0019-3461)
Indexed: CPM.
—BLDSC (4362.610300).
Published by: Incomes Data Services Ltd., 77 Bastwick St, London, EC1V 3TT, United Kingdom. TEL 44-20-72503434, FAX 44-20-73242510, ids@incomesdata.co.uk, http://www.incomesdata.co.uk.

344.01 GBR ISSN 0959-8014
I D S PENSIONS LAW REPORTS; the key pensions cases without delay. Text in English. 1989. irreg. GBP 384 (effective 2005). **Description:** Provides the full text of legal decisions affecting pensions, along with a summary and commentary on the significance of each case.
Published by: Incomes Data Services Ltd., 77 Bastwick St, London, EC1V 3TT, United Kingdom. TEL 44-20-72503434, FAX 44-20-73242510, ids@incomesdata.co.uk, http://www.incomesdata.co.uk.

344.01 GBR ISSN 1353-1573
I D S PENSIONS SERVICE; guidance through the law and company practice. Text in English. a. (plus news bulletin 10/yr.). GBP 260 (effective 2005). **Document type:** *Bulletin, Trade.* **Description:** Covers the legal aspects of employee retirement-benefit packages.
Related titles: Regional ed(s).: IDS Pensions Service News Bulletin.
Published by: Incomes Data Services Ltd., 77 Bastwick St, London, EC1V 3TT, United Kingdom. TEL 44-20-72503434, FAX 44-20-73242510, ids@incomesdata.co.uk, http://www.incomesdata.co.uk.

331 DEU ISSN 0175-2944
I F O STUDIEN ZUR ARBEITSMARKTFORSCHUNG. Text in German. 1983. irreg., latest vol.10, 1998. price varies. **Document type:** *Monographic series.*
Published by: I F O Institut fuer Wirtschaftsforschung, Poschingerstr 5, Munich, 81679, Germany. TEL 49-89-9224-0, FAX 49-89-985369, ifo@ifo.de, http://www.ifo.de.

331 USA ISSN 0745-2098
I F P T E OUTLOOK✶. Text in English. 1943. bi-m. illus.
Formerly (until 1976?): Engineer's Outlook
Published by: International Federation of Professional and Technical Engineers, 8630 Fenton St, Ste 400, Silver Spring, MD 20910-3803. FAX 301-565-0018.

331 CHE
I I R A BULLETIN. Text in English. 1975. 3/yr. USD 25 (effective 2000). back issues avail. **Document type:** *Newsletter, Trade.*
Related titles: French ed.: Bulletin de l'A I R P; Spanish ed.: Boletin de la A I R T.
Published by: International Industrial Relations Association, Geneva 22, 1211, Switzerland. TEL 41-22-7996841, FAX 41-22-7998541, mennie@ilo.org. Ed. Kate Mennie Cecconi. Circ: 1,200.

331 CHE ISSN 0251-3803
HD4964
I L O COMMITTEE ON SALARIED EMPLOYEES AND PROFESSIONAL WORKERS. REPORT. Text in English. 1949. irreg. CHF 20. **Document type:** *Monographic series.*
Related titles: French ed.: B I T Commission des Employes et des Travailleurs Intellectuels. Rapport. ISSN 0251-379X; Spanish ed.: O I T Comision de Empleados y de Trabajadores Intelectuales. Informe. ISSN 1014-6784.
—CCC.
Published by: (International Labour Office), I L O Publications, 4 route des Morillons, Geneva 22, 1211, Switzerland. TEL 41-22-799-6111, FAX 41-22-799-6358. **Dist. in US by:** I L O Publications Center, 9 Jay Gould Court, Ste. CT, PO Box 753, Waldorf, MD 20604. TEL 301-638-3152, FAX 301-843-0159, ilopubs@tasco1.com.

352.63 CHE ISSN 0253-7834
I L O JOINT COMMITTEE ON THE PUBLIC SERVICE. REPORT. Text in English. irreg. CHF 20, USD 16. **Document type:** *Monographic series.*
Related titles: French ed.: B I T Commission Paritaire de la Fonction Publique. Rapport. ISSN 0253-7826; Spanish ed.: O I T Comision Paritaria del Servicio Publico. Informe. ISSN 0253-7818.
Published by: (International Labour Office), I L O Publications, 4 route des Morillons, Geneva 22, 1211, Switzerland. TEL 41-22-799-6111, FAX 41-22-799-6358. **Dist. in US by:** I L O Publications Center, 9 Jay Gould Court, Ste. CT, PO Box 753, Waldorf, MD 20604. TEL 301-638-3152, FAX 301-843-0159, ilopubs@tasco1.com.

344.01 NLD
I L O LEX CD-ROM. (International Labour Organization) Text in English, French, Spanish. 1992. latest 2002, base vol. plus a. updates. USD 140, EUR 117, GBP 87, CHF 192 (effective 2003). back issues avail. **Document type:** *Academic/Scholarly.* **Description:** Contains the ILO database relating to international labor standards.
Media: CD-ROM.
Published by: (International Labour Office CHE), Kluwer Law International (Subsidiary of: Aspen Publishers, Inc.), Laan van Meerdervoort 70, PO Box 85889, The Hague, 2508 CN, Netherlands. TEL 31-70-3081500, FAX 31-70-3081515, sales@kluwerlaw.com, http://www.wkap.nl/prod/c/90-411-1483-1, http://www.kluwerlaw.com.

331 CHE ISSN 1010-2388
I L O METAL TRADES COMMITTEE. REPORT. Text in English. irreg. CHF 25, USD 20. **Document type:** *Monographic series.*
Related titles: French ed.: B I T Commission des Industries Mecaniques. Rapport. ISSN 0259-3300; Spanish ed.: O I T Comision de Industrias Mecanicas. Informe. ISSN 1011-8543.
Published by: (International Labour Office), I L O Publications, PO Box 6, Geneva 22, 1211, Switzerland. TEL 41-22-799-6111, FAX 41-22-799-6358. **Dist. in US by:** I L O Publications Center, 9 Jay Gould Court, Ste. CT, PO Box 753, Waldorf, MD 20604. TEL 301-638-3152, FAX 301-843-0159, ilopubs@tasco1.com.

I L O MULTINATIONAL ENTERPRISES PROGRAMME. WORKING PAPER. see *BUSINESS AND ECONOMICS—Economic Situation And Conditions*

331 CHE ISSN 1014-9287
I L O TRAINING PAPERS IN POPULATION AND FAMILY WELFARE EDUCATION IN THE WORKSETTING. Text in English. 1993. irreg., latest vol.2, 1994. CHF 15, USD 12. **Document type:** *Monographic series.*
Published by: (International Labour Office), I L O Publications, 4 route des Morillons, Geneva 22, 1211, Switzerland. TEL 41-22-799-6111, FAX 41-22-799-6358. Ed. Judi Aubel. **Dist. in US by:** I L O Publications Center, 9 Jay Gould Court, Ste. CT, PO Box 753, Waldorf, MD 20604. TEL 301-638-3152, FAX 301-843-0159, ilopubs@tasco1.com.

331 GBR
I M I MONITOR. Text in English. 1962. q. free. back issues avail.
Formerly (until no.233, 1992): Metals Monitor
Published by: I M I plc., Witton, PO Box 216, Birmingham, W Mids B6 7BA, United Kingdom. TEL 44-121-356-4848, FAX 44-121-356-3526. Ed. Alan Deeley. Circ: 10,200.

I M P A C T NEWS. see *PUBLIC ADMINISTRATION*

I O M A'S REPORT ON SALARY SURVEYS. see *BUSINESS AND ECONOMICS—Personnel Management*

331 GBR ISSN 1363-6952
I P A MAGAZINE. Text in English. 1894. q. GBP 38 (effective 1998). adv. bk.rev. abstr. reprint service avail. from PQC.
Former titles: Involvement of Participation; Industrial Participation; Co-Partnership (0009-9864)
Related titles: Microfilm ed.: (from PQC).
Indexed: ADPA, Emerald, ILD, M&MA.
Published by: Involvement of Participation Association, 42 Colebrooke Row, London, N1 8AF, United Kingdom. FAX 44-171-3548040. Ed. Anthony Barry. Circ: 1,500.

331 DEU
I-PUNKT. Text in German. a. **Document type:** *Newsletter.*
Published by: Echter Wuerzburg Fraenkische Gesellschaftsdruckerei und Verlag GmbH, Postfach 5560, Wuerzburg, 97005, Germany. TEL 49-931-6671-171. Circ: (controlled).

I R M I WORKERS COMP; a complete guide to coverage, laws and cost containment. (International Risk Management Institute) see *INSURANCE*

331 USA
I R R A MEMBERSHIP DIRECTORY. Text in English. 1949. quadrennial. USD 25. **Document type:** *Directory.*
Published by: Industrial Relations Research Association, 4233 Social Science Bldg, University of Wisconsin, Madison, WI 53706. TEL 608-262-2762, FAX 608-265-4591. R&P Kay B Hutchinson.

331.1 USA
HD6958.5
I R R A NEWSLETTER. Text in English. 1958. q. USD 75 membership; USD 87 foreign membership (effective 1999). **Document type:** *Newsletter.*
Former titles (until 1996): Industrial Relations Research Association Series Newsletter (0749-2162); (until 1983): I R R A Newsletter (0019-0500)
—BLDSC (4580.600000).
Published by: Industrial Relations Research Association, 4233 Social Science Bldg, University of Wisconsin, Madison, WI 53706. TEL 608-262-2762, FAX 608-265-4591.

331.1 GBR ISSN 1358-2216
CODEN: MOQUF3
I R S EMPLOYMENT REVIEW; policy, practice and law in the workplace. Text in English. 1971. fortn. GBP 649 domestic; GBP 700 foreign (effective 2003); includes online access. stat. 60 p./no.; reprint service avail. from PQC. **Document type:** *Journal, Trade.* **Description:** Discusses topics in labor relations, labor law, personnel management, and occupational health and safety.
Formerly (until Jan. 1995): Industrial Relations Review and Report (0309-7269)
Related titles: Microform ed.: (from PQC); Online - full text ed.: (from EBSCO Publishing, O C L C Online Computer Library Center, Inc.); ◆ Supplement to: Industrial Relations Law Bulletin. ISSN 0969-3637.
Indexed: ABIn, CLI, CPM, Faml, LRI, M&MA.
—BLDSC (4581.695800), IE, Infotrieve, ingenta. **CCC.**
Published by: I R S (Subsidiary of: LexisNexis UK (Scottish Office)), 18-20 Highbury Pl, London, N5 1QP, United Kingdom. TEL 44-20-7354-6742, 44-20-7354-5858, FAX 44-20-7226-8618, 44-20-7359-4000, publications@irseclipse.co.uk, http://www.irsonline.co.uk/pub_subjects/index_pub_human.htm, http://www.irseclipse.co.uk. Eds. David Carr, Neil Rankin, Sarah Silcox.

331.1 GBR ISSN 1358-2194
I R S EMPLOYMENT TRENDS. Text in English. 197?. s-m.
Indexed: Faml, LRI.
—CCC.
Published by: Industrial Relations Services, 5 Church Farm Close, Dibden, Southampton, SO45 5TF, United Kingdom. TEL 020 7354 5858, FAX 020 7359 4000.

331.21 USA
I T A A SALARY STUDY. Text in English. a.
Formerly: A D A S P O Salary Study
Published by: Information Technology Association of America, 1401 Wilson Blvd., Ste. 1100, Arlington, VA 22209-2318. TEL 703-522-5055, FAX 703-522-2779.

331.11 USA
IDAHO. DEPARTMENT OF LABOR. IDAHO DEMOGRAPHIC PROFILE. Text in English. 1972. a. free. **Document type:** *Government.*
Former titles: Idaho. Department of Employment. Idaho Demographic Profile; Idaho. Department of Employment. Annual Planning Report
Related titles: Microfiche ed.: (from CIS).
Indexed: SRI.
Published by: Idaho Department of Labor, Public Affairs, 317 W Main St, Boise, ID 83735. TEL 208-334-6168. Ed. Janell Hyer. Circ: 1,200.

331 USA ISSN 0536-2733
IDAHO EMPLOYMENT. Text in English. m. stat. **Document type:** *Government.*
Published by: Idaho Department of Labor, Public Affairs, 317 W Main St, Boise, ID 83735. TEL 208-334-6168, http://www.labor.state.id.us. Ed. Katie Lamm.

IDAHO EMPLOYMENT LAW LETTER. see *LAW*

331.21 USA
IDAHO OCCUPATION WAGE SURVEY. Text in English. 1979. a. **Document type:** *Government.*
Published by: Department of Labor, Bureau of Research and Analysis, 317 Main St, Boise, ID 83735. TEL 208-334-6168, http://www.labor.state.id.us. Circ: 2,000.

ILLINOIS EMPLOYMENT LAW LETTER. see *LAW—Corporate Law*

331.09 USA ISSN 0085-1728
ILLINOIS LABOR HISTORY SOCIETY REPORTER. Text in English. 1970. irreg. (approx. 2/yr.). USD 10 (effective 1998). bk.rev. **Document type:** *Newsletter.* **Description:** Labor history.
Published by: Illinois Labor History Society, 28 E Jackson Blvd, Chicago, IL 60604. TEL 312-663-4107. Ed. Leslie F Orear. Circ: 500.

IMMIGRATION EMPLOYMENT COMPLIANCE HANDBOOK. see *LAW*

B

344.01 CAN
IMPACT (AURORA); labour law & management practices. Text in English. 10/yr. CND 218 includes binder (effective 2005). 4 p./no. 2 cols./p.; back issues avail. **Document type:** *Newsletter.* **Description:** Links managers at all levels to the law which relates to the labor force.
Published by: Canada Law Book Inc., 240 Edward St, Aurora, ON L4G 3S9, Canada. TEL 905-841-6472, 800-263-3269, FAX 905-841-5085, b.loney@canadalawbook.ca, http://www.canadalawbook.com/catalogue.cfm?DSP=Detail&ProductID=352, http://www.canadalawbook.ca. Ed. Jorge Talbott.

331 CHE ISSN 1020-0584
IMPROVE YOUR CONSTRUCTION BUSINESS SERIES. Text in English. 1994. irreg. CHF 27.50, USD 22. **Document type:** *Monographic series.*
Published by: (International Labour Office), I L O Publications, 4 route des Morillons, Geneva 22, 1211, Switzerland. TEL 41-22-799-6111, FAX 41-22-799-6358. **Dist. in US by:** I L O Publications Center, 9 Jay Gould Court, Ste. CT, PO Box 753, Waldorf, MD 20604. TEL 301-638-3152, FAX 301-843-0159, ilopubs@tasco1.com.

331 USA ISSN 0885-7229
IN DEPTH (NEW YORK)✶ ; report to management. Text in English. 1975. s-m. looseleaf. USD 195 (effective 2000). bk.rev. back issues avail.
Related titles: ♦ Supplement to: Fair Employment Compliance. ISSN 0885-7172.
Published by: Management Resources, Inc., 380 Ocean Rd., Unit 2, Portsmouth, NH 03801-6051. Ed. Ken Swann.

331.255 USA
IN FOCUS (BROOKFIELD). Text in English. 1986. q. USD 190 (effective 2003). back issues avail. **Document type:** *Newsletter, Trade.* **Description:** Provides an in-depth study of a single employee benefit-related topic.
Formerly (until 2001): Employee Benefits Practices (0896-0127)
—CCC.
Published by: International Foundation of Employee Benefit Plans, 18700 W Bluemound Rd, Box 69, Brookfield, WI 53008-0069. TEL 262-786-6700, FAX 262-786-8780, books@ifebp.org. Ed. Mary Jo Brzezinski.

331.1 IND ISSN 0019-5286
HD8682 CODEN: IPPYA2
➤ **INDIAN JOURNAL OF INDUSTRIAL RELATIONS.** Text in English. 1964. q. INR 300; USD 65 foreign (effective 1999). bk.rev. charts; stat. index. back issues avail. **Document type:** *Academic/Scholarly.* **Description:** Dissemination of knowledge in the fields of industrial and human resources including relevant aspects of labor and personal management. Audience: management, universities, colleges and other academic institutes.
Indexed: BAS, ESPM, H&SSA, IBSS, IIPL, ILD, IPsyAb, IndIndia, PAA&I, PsycholAb, RRTA, SSCI, WAE&RSA.
—BLDSC (4415.400000), IE, Infotrieve, ingenta.
Published by: Shri Ram Centre for Industrial Relations and Human Resources, 4-E 16 Jhandewalan Extention, New Delhi, 110 055, India. TEL 91-11-7519064, FAX 91-11-7526036, TELEX 031-62310 CCS IN, src@cna-india.com. Ed., R&P Rama J Joshi. Circ: 865 (paid); 100 (controlled).

331 IND ISSN 0019-5308
HD4811
INDIAN JOURNAL OF LABOUR ECONOMICS. Text in English. 1958. q. USD 100 to institutions (effective 2006). bk.rev. charts. index.
Indexed: BAS, CREJ, IBSS, ILD, JEL, RASB, RDA, SWA, WAE&RSA, WTA.
Published by: University of Lucknow, Indian Society of Labour Economics, Badshaw Bagh, Lucknow, Uttar Pradesh, India. http://www.scientificpub.com/bookdetails.php?booktransid=438&bookid=434. Ed. Dr. R S Mathur. Circ: 481. **Subscr. to:** Scientific Publishers, 5-A New Pali Rd., Near Hotel Taj Hari Mahal, PO Box 91, Jodhpur, Rajasthan 342 003, India. info@scientificpub.com, http://www.scientificpub.com.

331 IND ISSN 0019-5723
HD8681
INDIAN LABOUR JOURNAL. Text in English. 1960. m. USD 123 to institutions (effective 2006). adv. bk.rev. charts; stat. index. **Document type:** *Journal, Government.*
Indexed: BAS, IBSS, ILD.
Published by: Government of India, Department of Publications, Civil Lines, New Delhi, 110 054, India. TEL 11-2512527, http://www.scientificpub.com/bookdetails.php?booktransid=451&bookid=447. Circ: 1,250. **Subscr. to:** Scientific Publishers, 5-A New Pali Rd., Near Hotel Taj Hari Mahal, PO Box 91, Jodhpur, Rajasthan 342 003, India. info@scientificpub.com, http://www.scientificpub.com.

331.125 USA
INDIANA. DEPARTMENT OF EMPLOYMENT AND TRAINING SERVICES. COUNTY EMPLOYMENT PATTERNS. Text in English. a. free. **Document type:** *Government.* **Description:** Covers employment monthly and annual averages by county and selected industry divisions by county.
Published by: Department of Employment and Training Services, Labor Market Information, 10 N Senate Ave, Rm 101, Indianapolis, IN 46204. TEL 317-232-7716.

331.21 USA
INDIANA. DEPARTMENT OF EMPLOYMENT AND TRAINING SERVICES. COVERED EMPLOYMENT AND PAYROLLS. Text in English. q. free. **Description:** Based on employment and payroll reports from establishments covered by the Indiana Employment and Training Services Act.
Published by: Department of Employment and Training Services, Labor Market Statistics, 10 Senate Ave, Rm 101, Indianapolis, IN 46204. TEL 317-232-7716, FAX 317-232-6950, http://www.dwd.state.in.us.

331.11 USA
INDIANA. DEPARTMENT OF EMPLOYMENT AND TRAINING SERVICES. LABOR FORCE ESTIMATES. Text in English. m. free. Supplement avail. **Description:** Provides labor force, employment, and unemployment rates prepared under the Local Area Unemployment Statistics Program (LAUS).
Published by: Department of Employment and Training Services, Labor Market Information, 10 N Senate Ave, Rm 101, Indianapolis, IN 46204. TEL 317-232-8546, FAX 317-232-6950.

331.125 USA
INDIANA. DEPARTMENT OF EMPLOYMENT AND TRAINING SERVICES. NON - M S A ESTABLISHMENT EMPLOYMENT. (Metropolitan Statistical Area) Text in English. a. free. **Description:** Covers individual counties that are not part of an area. Provides annual average wages and salaried employment in county establishments.
Published by: Department of Employment and Training Services, Labor Market Information, 10 N Senate Ave, Rm 101, Indianapolis, IN 46204. TEL 317-232-8546, FAX 317-232-6950.

INDIANA. DEPARTMENT OF EMPLOYMENT AND TRAINING SERVICES. UNEMPLOYMENT INSURANCE CLAIMS BY AREA. see *INSURANCE*

INDIANA. DEPARTMENT OF EMPLOYMENT AND TRAINING SERVICES. UNEMPLOYMENT INSURANCE PAYMENTS BY INDUSTRY. see *INSURANCE—Abstracting, Bibliographies, Statistics*

INDIANA EMPLOYMENT LAW. see *LAW—Corporate Law*

INDIANA EMPLOYMENT LAW LETTER. see *LAW*

331.125 USA
INDIANA EMPLOYMENT REVIEW. Text in English. m. free. **Description:** Provides current establishment employment by industry for Indiana and its MSAs; includes hours and gross earnings for manufacturing.
Published by: Department of Employment and Training Services, Labor Market Statistics, 10 Senate Ave, Rm 101, Indianapolis, IN 46204. TEL 317-232-7716, FAX 317-232-6950, http://www.dwd.state.in.us.

344.01 USA
INDIANA WORKERS' COMPENSATION LAWS AND RULES ANNOTATED. Text in English. a., latest 1995. USD 42.50. Supplement avail.
Published by: LexisNexis (Subsidiary of: LexisNexis North America), PO Box 7587, Charlottesville, VA 22906-7587. TEL 804-972-7566, 800-562-1197, FAX 800-643-1280, llp.customer.support@lexis-nexis.com, http://www.lexislawpublishing.com. Ed. George Harley.

331 USA ISSN 1085-0058
INDIVIDUAL EMPLOYMENT RIGHTS. Text in English. 1986. irreg. looseleaf. USD 976 (effective 2001). back issues avail. **Document type:** *Newsletter.* **Description:** Presents case reference and notification on individual employment rights issues, including employment at will, privacy, polygraph testing, and other issues outside the traditional labor-management relations context.
Related titles: Online - full text ed.: (from Thomson West); ♦ Series of: Labor Relations Reporter. ISSN 0148-7981.
—CCC.
Published by: The Bureau of National Affairs, Inc., 1231 25th St., NW, Washington, DC 20037. TEL 202-452-4200, 800-372-1033, 800-452-7773, FAX 202-822-8092, customercare@bna.com, bnaplus@bna.com, http://www.bna.com/. Pub. Greg C McCaffery.

331.1 USA ISSN 0019-7939
HD4802 CODEN: ILREA
➤ **INDUSTRIAL AND LABOR RELATIONS REVIEW.** Short title: I L R Review. Text in English. 1947. q. USD 32 domestic to individuals; USD 38 foreign to individuals; USD 52 domestic to institutions; USD 62 foreign to institutions; USD 16 domestic to students; USD 24 foreign to students (effective 2005). adv. bk.rev. bibl.; charts; illus.; abstr. index, cum.index: vols.1-50 (1947-1997). 192 p./no. 2 cols./p.; back issues avail.; reprint service avail. from PQC,WSH. **Document type:** *Journal, Academic/Scholarly.* **Description:** Explores all aspects of the employment relationship from an interdisciplinary perspective.
Related titles: Microfilm ed.: (from PQC, WSH); Online - full text ed.: (from bigchalk, Chadwyck-Healey Inc., EBSCO Publishing, Florida Center for Library Automation, Gale Group, H.W. Wilson, JSTOR (Web-based Journal Archive), LexisNexis, O C L C Online Computer Library Center, Inc., ProQuest Information & Learning, The Dialog Corporation, Thomson West).
Indexed: ABCPolSci, ABIn, ABS&EES, APEL, ASCA, ASG, AgeL, AmH&L, ArtHuCI, BAS, BPI, BPIA, BRD, BRI, BusI, CBRI, CIJE, CJA, CLI, CPM, CREJ, ChPerI, CurCont, DIP, EAA, Emerald, FamI, HRA, HistAb, IBR, IBSS, IBZ, IBibSS, ILD, ILP, IPARL, IPSA, JEL, KES, LRI, MEA&I, MEDLINE, ManagAb, ManagCont, PAIS, PMA, PRA, PSA, PsycholAb, RASB, RefZh, SCIMP, SOPODA, SPAA, SRRA, SSA, SSCI, SSI, SUSA, SociolAb, T&II, V&AA, WBSS, WSA, WorkRelAb.
—BLDSC (4445.225000), IDS, IE, Infotrieve, ingenta. **CCC.**
Published by: Cornell University, New York State School of Industrial and Labor Relations, 158 Ives Hall, Ithaca, NY 14853-3901. TEL 607-255-3295, FAX 607-255-8016, ilrr@cornell.edu, blk5@cornell.edu, http://www.ilr.cornell.edu/ilrreview/, http://www.ilr.cornell.edu/depts/ilrrev/. Ed. Tove Hammer. R&P, Adv. contact Brian Keeling TEL 607-255-2732. page USD 250; trim 5.25 x 8. Circ: 2,500; 2,300 (paid); 400 (controlled).

➤ **INDUSTRIAL CASES REPORTS.** see *LAW—Corporate Law*

344.01 IND ISSN 0019-8102
INDUSTRIAL COURT REPORTER. Text in English. 1948. m. INR 50. adv. index.
Published by: Commissioner of Labour, Commerce Centre, Tardeo, Mumbai, Maharashtra 400 034, India. Ed. Shri R R Karosiya. Circ: 750.

344.01 GBR ISSN 0305-9332
K9
➤ **INDUSTRIAL LAW JOURNAL.** Text in English. 1972. q. GBP 81, USD 146, EUR 122 to institutions; GBP 85, USD 153, EUR 128 combined subscription to institutions print & online eds. (effective 2006). adv. bk.rev. bibl. back issues avail.; reprint service avail. from WSH,PSC. **Document type:** *Journal, Academic/Scholarly.* **Description:** Comment, in-depth analysis and information for academics, practicing lawyers and lay industrial relations experts on all aspects of UK labor law and unemployment law in USA.
Related titles: Online - full text ed.: ISSN 1464-3669. GBP 77, USD 139, EUR 116 to institutions (effective 2006) (from EBSCO Publishing, Gale Group, HighWire Press, IngentaConnect, O C L C Online Computer Library Center, Inc., Oxford University Press Online Journals, ProQuest Information & Learning, Swets Information Services).
Indexed: ABIn, CLI, CPM, DIP, ELJI, ERA, ESPM, Emerald, FamI, H&SSA, IBR, IBZ, ILD, ILP, ISAP, LJI, LRI, RiskAb, SWA.
—BLDSC (4457.535000), IE, Infotrieve, ingenta. **CCC.**
Published by: (Industrial Law Society), Oxford University Press, Great Clarendon St, Oxford, OX2 6DP, United Kingdom. TEL 44-1865-556767, FAX 44-1865-556646, jnl.orders@oup.co.uk, http://ilj.oxfordjournals.org/, http://www.oxfordjournals.org/. Ed. Paul L. Davies. Pub. Nina Curtis. R&P Fiona Bennett. Adv. contact Helen Pearson. B&W page GBP 255, B&W page USD 425; 135 x 210. Circ: 1,650.

➤ **INDUSTRIAL LAW - NEW SOUTH WALES.** see *LAW*

331.1 USA ISSN 0019-8676
HD6951 CODEN: IDRLAP
➤ **INDUSTRIAL RELATIONS**; a journal of economy and society. Text in English. 1961. q. USD 57 combined subscription in the Americas to individuals & Caribbean, print & online eds.; EUR 89 combined subscription in Europe to individuals print & online eds.; GBP 59 combined subscription elsewhere to individuals print & online eds.; USD 219 combined subscription in the Americas to institutions & Caribbean, print & online eds.; GBP 192 combined subscription elsewhere to institutions print & online eds.; USD 29 combined subscription in the Americas to students & Caribbean, print & online eds.; EUR 62 combined subscription in Europe to students print & online eds.; GBP 41 combined subscription elsewhere to students print & online eds. (effective 2006). adv. bk.rev. charts; illus. index. back issues avail.; reprints avail. **Document type:** *Journal, Academic/Scholarly.* **Description:** Offers a valuable international perspective on current topics in labor and employment.
Related titles: Microform ed.: (from PQC); Online - full text ed.: ISSN 1468-232X. USD 208 in the Americas to institutions & Caribbean; GBP 182 elsewhere to institutions (effective 2006) (from Blackwell Synergy, EBSCO Publishing, Gale Group, IngentaConnect, O C L C Online Computer Library Center, Inc., Swets Information Services).
Indexed: ABIn, ADPA, AcaI, AgeL, AltPI, BPI, BPIA, BusI, CBCARef, CJA, CLI, CPM, ChPerI, CurCont, EI, ESPM, Emerald, ErgAb, FamI, GEOBASE, H&SSA, HRA, IBR, IBSS, IBZ, ILD, IPSA, JEL, LRI, MEA&I, ManagCont, PAIS, PMA, PSA, PsycInfo, PsycholAb, RASB, RiskAb, SOPODA, SSA, SSCI, SWR&A, SociolAb, T&II, WorkRelAb.
—BLDSC (4461.080000), IDS, IE, Infotrieve, ingenta. **CCC.**

Published by: (University of California at Berkeley), Blackwell Publishing, Inc. (Subsidiary of: Blackwell Publishing Ltd.), Commerce Place, 350 Main St, Malden, MA 02148. TEL 781-388-8206, FAX 781-388-8232, irjrnl@socrates.berkeley.edu, subscrip@blackwellpub.com, http://www.blackwellpublishing.com/journals/IREL. Eds. Daniel J B Mitchell, David I Levine. Circ: 2,300.

331 AUS
INDUSTRIAL RELATIONS AND MANAGEMENT LETTER. Text in English. m. AUD 287. back issues avail. **Document type:** *Trade.* **Description:** Reports on trends and current actions of labor unions and on labor-management relations.
Published by: Ian Huntley Pty. Ltd., PO Box 99, Cremorne, NSW 2090, Australia. TEL 61-2-9953-5788, FAX 61-2-9953-2280. Ed. Pat Huntley.

331 GBR ISSN 0770-0148
INDUSTRIAL RELATIONS EUROPE. Text in English. 1973. m. bk.rev. **Document type:** *Newsletter.*
—IE, Infotrieve.
Published by: Wyatt Co., c/o Mike Groushko, Ed, 49 Bushey Grove Rd, Bushey, Herts, United Kingdom. TEL 0293-252440, FAX 0923-818271. Circ: 1,000.

331.1 GBR ISSN 0019-8692
HD4805
➤ **INDUSTRIAL RELATIONS JOURNAL.** Text in English. 1970. bi-m. GBP 79, EUR 119 combined subscription in Europe to individuals print & online eds.; USD 176 combined subscription in the Americas to individuals & Caribbean, print & online eds.; GBP 105 combined subscription elsewhere to individuals print & online eds.; GBP 490 combined subscription in Europe to institutions print & online eds.; USD 1,037 combined subscription in the Americas to institutions & Caribbean, print & online eds.; GBP 617 combined subscription elsewhere to institutions print & online eds.; EUR 60 combined subscription in Europe to students print & online eds.; USD 67 combined subscription in the Americas to students & Caribbean, print & online eds.; GBP 40 combined subscription elsewhere to students print & online eds. (effective 2006); includes subscr. to New Technology, Work and Employment & the European Annual Review. adv. bk.rev. abstr.; charts; stat.; illus. Index. reprint service avail. from PQC,PSC. **Document type:** *Journal, Academic/Scholarly.*
Incorporates: European Annual Review
Related titles: Microform ed.: (from PQC); Online - full text ed.: ISSN 1468-2338. GBP 466 in Europe to institutions; USD 984 in the Americas to institutions & Caribbean; GBP 586 elsewhere to institutions (effective 2006) (from Blackwell Synergy, EBSCO Publishing, Gale Group, IngentaConnect, O C L C Online Computer Library Center, Inc., Swets Information Services).
Indexed: ABIn, ADPA, AESIS, BMT, BPI, BPIA, BusI, CPM, CREJ, ELLIS, Emerald, IBR, IBSS, ILD, M&MA, ORMS, PAIS, PSA, QC&AS, SCIMP, SWA, SociolAb, T&II, TEA, WorkRelAb.
—BLDSC (4461.140000), IE, Infotrieve, ingenta. **CCC.**
Published by: Blackwell Publishing Ltd., 9600 Garsington Rd, Oxford, OX4 2ZG, United Kingdom. TEL 44-1865-776868, FAX 44-1865-714591, customerservices@oxon.blackwellpublishing.com, http://www.blackwellpublishing.com/journals/IRJ. Ed. Nicholas Bacon. Circ: 1,100.

331.1 GBR ISSN 0969-3637
INDUSTRIAL RELATIONS LAW BULLETIN. Abbreviated title: I R L B. Text in English. 1974. fortn. GBP 295 in United Kingdom; GBP 335 elsewhere (effective 2001). reprint service avail. from PQC. **Document type:** *Bulletin, Trade.* **Description:** Presents labor law news and case notes covering unfair dismissal, discrimination, layoffs, strikes, employment contracts, and business transfers.
Formerly (until 1994): Industrial Relations Legal Information Bulletin (0307-5540)
Related titles: Online - full text ed.: (from EBSCO Publishing, Gale Group, IngentaConnect); ♦ Supplement(s): I R S Employment Review. ISSN 1358-2216.
Indexed: BrCerAb, CLI, FamI, LRI.
Published by: I R S (Subsidiary of: LexisNexis UK (Scottish Office)), 18-20 Highbury Pl, London, N5 1QP, United Kingdom. TEL 44-20-7354-5858, FAX 44-207-226-8618. Ed. Marian Bell.

344.01 GBR ISSN 0307-5591
INDUSTRIAL RELATIONS LAW REPORTS. Abbreviated title: I R L R. Text in English. 1972. m. GBP 435; GBP 490 foreign (effective 1999). reprint service avail. from PQC. **Document type:** *Trade.* **Description:** Keeps readers informed of developments in employment case law, analyzing the implications of key decisions.
Related titles: Microform ed.: (from PQC); Online - full text ed.
—BLDSC (4461.147000), IE, Infotrieve.
Published by: I R S (Subsidiary of: LexisNexis UK (Scottish Office)), 18-20 Highbury Pl, London, N5 1QP, United Kingdom. TEL 44-20-7354-5858, FAX 44-207-226-8618. Ed. Michael Rubenstein.

331 CAN ISSN 1192-7283
KE3142
INDUSTRIAL RELATIONS LEGISLATION IN CANADA. Text in English. 1989. a. CND 24.95 domestic; CND 29.95 foreign. **Document type:** *Government.* **Description:** Reports on collective bargaining and related legislation in federal, provincial and territorial jurisdictions.
Related titles: French ed.: Relations Industrielles au Canada.
Indexed: HistAb.
Published by: Supply and Services Canada, Printing and Publishing, 270 Albert St, Ottawa, ON K1A 0S9, Canada. TEL 819-965-4802. Circ: 2,000.

331 IRL ISSN 0791-3788
INDUSTRIAL RELATIONS NEWS. Text in English. 1979. w. (48/yr.). EUR 600 (effective 2005). **Document type:** *Magazine, Trade.* **Description:** Provides comprehensive coverage of all industrial and employee relations issues.
Formerly (until 1987): I R N Report (0790-0732)
Related titles: Online - full content ed.
Published by: IRN Publishing, 123 Ranelagh, Dublin, 6, Ireland. TEL 353-1-4972711, FAX 353-1-4972779, irn@irn.ie, http://www.irn.ie. Ed. Brian Sheehan. Pub. Martin Macdonnell.

331.1 USA
INDUSTRIAL RELATIONS RESEARCH ASSOCIATION. ANNUAL RESEARCH VOLUME. Text in English. 1947. a. price varies. **Document type:** *Academic/Scholarly.*
Published by: Industrial Relations Research Association, 4233 Social Science Bldg, University of Wisconsin, Madison, WI 53706. TEL 608-262-2762, FAX 608-265-4591.

331 USA
INDUSTRIAL RELATIONS RESEARCH ASSOCIATION. PROCEEDINGS OF THE ANNUAL MEETING. Text in English. a. price varies. **Document type:** *Proceedings.*
Former titles: Industrial Relations Research Association. Proceedings of the Annual Winter Meeting (0277-7347); (until 1977): Industrial Relations Research Association. Proceedings of Annual Winter Meeting (0275-3081); Incorporates (in 1998): Industrial Relations Research Association. Proceedings of the Spring Meeting (0733-0898); Which was formerly (until 1978): Industrial Relations Research Association. Proceedings of the Annual Spring Meeting (0537-5428)
Indexed: BPIA, BusI, PCI.
—BLDSC (6841.483000), IE, ingenta.
Published by: Industrial Relations Research Association, 4233 Social Science Bldg, University of Wisconsin, Madison, WI 53706. TEL 608-262-2762, FAX 608-265-4591.

331 USA ISSN 0019-8870
HD8055.I4
INDUSTRIAL WORKER✶. Text in English. 1909. m. USD 15 to individuals; USD 20 to institutions (effective 2003). bk.rev.; film rev. illus. Alternative press index. 16 p./no. 4 cols./p.; back issues avail.; reprint service avail. from PQC. **Document type:** *Newspaper, Consumer.* **Description:** Provides rank and file labor news from the leading edge of the North American and world labor movement.
Related titles: Microfilm ed.: (from BHP, PQC); Online - full text ed.: (from ProQuest Information & Learning).
Indexed: AltPI.
Published by: Industrial Workers of the World, PO Box 13476, Philadelphia, PA 19101-3476. TEL 215-222-1905, 215-763-1274, iw@iww.org, http://iww.org. Ed. Jon Bekken. Circ: 4,300 (paid).

331 DEU ISSN 0943-2779
INDUSTRIELLE BEZIEHUNGEN; Zeitschrift fuer Arbeit, Organisation und Management. Text in German; Text occasionally in English. 1994. q. EUR 60 domestic; EUR 68 foreign (effective 2005). **Document type:** *Journal, Trade.* **Description:** Forum for up-to-date analysis and discussion for those with an interest in industrial relations.
Related titles: Online - full text ed.: (from EBSCO Publishing, ProQuest Information & Learning).
Indexed: ABIn, DIP, IBR, IBSS, IBZ.
—BLDSC (4474.809000).
Published by: Rainer Hampp Verlag, Meringerzellerstr 10, Mering, 86415, Germany. TEL 49-8233-4783, FAX 49-8233-30755, Rainer_Hampp_Verlag@t-online.de, http://www.hampp-verlag.de/hampp_ZS01.htm. **Dist. by:** Brockhaus Commission, Kreidlerstr 9, Kornwestheim 70806, Germany. TEL 49-7154-132739, FAX 49-7154-132713.

INDUSTRY REPORT. see *BUSINESS AND ECONOMICS—Economic Situation And Conditions*

331.125 USA ISSN 0148-9208
INDUSTRY WAGE SURVEYS. CORRUGATED AND SOLID FIBER BOXES. Text in English. irreg. **Document type:** *Bulletin, Government.*
Related titles: ♦ Series of: U.S. Bureau of Labor Statistics. Bulletin. ISSN 0082-9021.
Indexed: RASB.
Published by: U.S. Department of Labor, Bureau of Labor Statistics, Postal Square Bldg., 2 Massachusetts Ave, NE, Washington, DC 20212-0001 . TEL 202-691-5200, FAX 202-691-6325, http://www.bls.gov. **Subscr. to:** U.S. Government Printing Office, Superintendent of Documents.

331 CUB
INFORMACION LABORAL. Text in Spanish. q. USD 22.
Published by: (Comite Estatal de Trabajo y Seguridad Social), Ediciones Cubanas, Obispo No. 527, Apdo. 605, Havana, Cuba. TEL 32-5556-60.

INFORME P E D. (Pesquisa de Emprego e Desemprego) see *STATISTICS*

344.01 USA ISSN 1088-9922
INSIDE EMPLOYEE RIGHTS LITIGATION. Text in English. 1996. m. USD 149; USD 221 foreign (effective 1999). **Document type:** *Trade.* **Description:** Contains articles and information on the changing field of employee rights litigation.
—CCC.
Published by: Aspen Law & Business (Subsidiary of: Wolters Kluwer N.V.), 1185 Ave of the Americas, 37th Fl, New York, NY 10036. TEL 212-597-0210, 800-638-8437, FAX 212-597-0336, customer.service@aspenpubl.com, http://www.aspenpub.com. Ed. Sarah Magee. **Dist. by:** Aspen Publishers, Inc., Distribution Center, 7201 McKinney Circle, Frederick, MD 21701. TEL 301-698-7100, FAX 301-417-7550.

B

331 USA
INSIDE NEGOTIATIONS✶. Text in English. 1965. m. USD 98. bk.rev.
Formerly: Negotiations Management (0047-9292)
Published by: E F R Corp., PO Box 15236, Colorado Spring, CO 80935-5236. Ed. Dr. Eric Rhodes. Circ: 1,200.

INSIGHT. see *JOURNALISM*

331 CHE ISSN 1022-5625
INSTITUT FUER SCHWEIZERISCHES ARBEITSRECHT. MITTEILUNGEN. Text in German. 1982. a. CHF 37 (effective 2003). **Document type:** *Bulletin, Academic/Scholarly.*
Indexed: DIP, IBR, IBZ.
Published by: (Institut fuer Schweizerisches Arbeitsrecht), Staempfli Verlag AG (Subsidiary of: LexisNexis Europe and Africa), Woelflistr 1, Bern, 3001, Switzerland. TEL 41-31-3006666, FAX 41-31-3006688, verlag@staempfli.com, http://www.staempfli.com. Ed. Manfred Rehbinder. Circ: 400 (controlled).

331 COD
INSTITUT NATIONAL DE PREPARATION PROFESSIONNELLE. CAHIER✶. Text in French. irreg. illus.
Published by: Institut National de Preparation Professionnelle, BP 7248, Kinshasa, 1, Congo, Dem. Republic.

331.11 GBR ISSN 1369-409X
INSTITUTE FOR EMPLOYMENT STUDIES. ANNUAL REPORT (YEAR). Text in English. a.
Former titles: Institute for Employment Studies. Annual Review; (until 1995): Institute of Manpower Studies. Annual Review
—BLDSC (1302.901000), ingenta.
Published by: Institute for Employment Studies, Mantell Bldg, Falmer, Brighton, E Sussex BN1 9RF, United Kingdom. TEL 44-1273-686751, FAX 44-1273-690430, http://www.employment-studies.co.uk.

331 PHL
INSTITUTE FOR LABOR STUDIES. ANNUAL REPORT. Text in English. a., latest 2002. **Document type:** *Yearbook, Government.* **Description:** Provides a glimpse of the economic performance of the Philippines as well as developments in the labor and employment fronts.
Published by: Institute for Labor Studies, 5-F DOLE Bldg, General Luna St, Intramuros, Manila, Philippines. TEL 527-3490, http://www.sequel.net/~ilsdole/ilsdole.htm. Ed. Mitchell P Duran.

331.1 PHL ISSN 0118-3877
INSTITUTE FOR LABOR STUDIES. MONOGRAPH SERIES. Text in English. 1994 (Nov.). irreg., latest no.1. charts. **Document type:** *Monographic series.*
Published by: Institute for Labor Studies, 5-F DOLE Bldg, General Luna St, Intramuros, Manila, Philippines. TEL 527-3490, http://www.sequel.net/~ilsdole/ilsdole.htm. Ed. Mitchell P Duran.

INSTITUTE ON LABOR LAW DEVELOPMENTS. ANNUAL PROCEEDINGS. see *LAW*

INSTITUTO DE ESTUDIOS PERUANOS. DOCUMENTOS DE TRABAJO. SERIE TALLERES. see *BUSINESS AND ECONOMICS—Production Of Goods And Services*

331.11 BRA
INSTITUTO DO DESENVOLVIMENTO ECONOMICO-SOCIAL DO PARA. BOLETIM DE PESQUISA EMPREGO E DESEMPREGO NA REGIAO METROPOLITANA DE BELEM. Text in Portuguese. 1989. m. donation. **Document type:** *Government.* **Description:** Covers the employment situation in the regional area of Belem.
Published by: Instituto do Desenvolvimento Economico Social do Para, Av Nazare, 871, Nazare, Belem, Para 66035170, Brazil. TEL 55-91-2244411, FAX 55-91-2253414.

331 NER ISSN 0538-2807
INTER-AFRICAN LABOUR CONFERENCE REPORTS, RECOMMENDATIONS AND CONCLUSIONS*. Text in English, French. irreg. **Document type:** *Proceedings.*
Published by: (Commission for Technical Co-Operation in Africa South of the Sahara), Maison de l'Afrique, BP 878, Niamey, Niger.

INTERNATIONAL CAREER EMPLOYMENT WEEKLY. see *OCCUPATIONS AND CAREERS*

331.21 USA
INTERNATIONAL COMPARISONS OF MANUFACTURING PRODUCTIVITY AND UNIT LABOR COST TRENDS (YEAR). Text in English. a. **Document type:** *Government.*
Related titles: ♦ Series of: U.S. Bureau of Labor Statistics. National Office News Releases.
Published by: U.S. Department of Labor, Bureau of Labor Statistics, Postal Square Bldg., 2 Massachusetts Ave, NE, Washington, DC 20212-0001 . TEL 202-655-4000. **Subscr. to:** U.S. Government Printing Office, Superintendent of Documents.

INTERNATIONAL CONVENTION ON THE ELIMINATION OF ALL FORMS OF RACIAL DISCRIMINATION. REPORT OF CANADA. see *POLITICAL SCIENCE—Civil Rights*

331.125 USA ISSN 1058-0506
INTERNATIONAL EMPLOYMENT GAZETTE. Text in English. 1990. bi-w. USD 95 domestic; USD 135 foreign (effective 2004). adv. **Document type:** *Newspaper.* **Description:** Lists current employment openings worldwide, along with organizations under various geographic areas, and under various occupations within each area.
Related titles: Online - full text ed.
Address: 423 Townes St, Greenville, SC 29601-1619. TEL 864-235-4444, 800-882-9188, FAX 864-235-3369, editor@intemployment.com, http://www.intemployment.com. Ed. Kimberly Mertz. Pubs. Dee Dee Hindman, Dee Dee McCaleb. R&P Dee Dee McCaleb. Adv. contact Chandra Hale.

INTERNATIONAL EMPLOYMENT LAW. see *LAW—International Law*

331.125 AUS ISSN 1324-1125
INTERNATIONAL EMPLOYMENT RELATIONS REVIEW. Text in English. 1995. s-a. membership. **Document type:** *Academic/Scholarly.* **Description:** Publishes articles, reviews and book reviews in the field of employment relations.
Published by: (University of Wollongong, School pf Management, Marketing and Employment Relations), International Employment Relations Association, School of Business and Electronic Commerce, Monash University, Switchback Rd, Churchill, VIC 3842, Australia. TEL 61-3-9902-6380. Eds. Ray Markey, Terri Mylett. **Subscr. to:** University of Western Sydney, School of Management, Locked Bag 1797, Penrith South, NSW 1797, Australia. TEL 61-2-96859696, s.bond@uws.edu.au.

331.125 NLD
INTERNATIONAL HANDBOOK ON CONTRACTS OF EMPLOYMENT. Text in English. 1988. 2 base vols. plus s-a. updates. looseleaf. USD 367 (effective 2004). **Description:** Comprehensive coverage of labor laws in force in individual countries throughout the world.
Published by: Kluwer Law International (Subsidiary of: Aspen Publishers, Inc.), Laan van Meerdervoort 70, PO Box 85889, The Hague, 2508 CN, Netherlands. TEL 31-70-3081500, FAX 31-70-3081515, sales@kluwerlaw.com, http://www.kluwerlaw.com. Eds. A Williamson, R Jeffers, Tim Cox.

331 DNK ISSN 0109-2650
INTERNATIONAL HORISONT. Text in Danish. 1982. q. DKK 100 (effective 2000). adv. bk.rev. **Document type:** *Bulletin.*
Formerly (until 1984): Horisont (0108-8440)
Indexed: RASB.
Published by: Arbejderbevaegelsens Internationale Forum, Nyropsgade 14, 1, Copenhagen V, 1602, Denmark. TEL 45-33-69-11-40, FAX 45-33-69-11-41, aif@aif.dk. Ed. Michael Jagd. Pub. Ib Wistisen. Adv. contact Bent Christensen. Circ: 2,500.

INTERNATIONAL INSTITUTE FOR LABOUR STUDIES. BIBLIOGRAPHY SERIES. see *SOCIOLOGY*

331 CHE
INTERNATIONAL INSTITUTE FOR LABOUR STUDIES. RESEARCH SERIES. Text in English. 1976. irreg., latest vol.111, 1998. price varies. back issues avail. **Document type:** *Monographic series.* **Description:** Monographs reflecting the results and findings of research projects carried out by the institute.
—BLDSC (7769.987000), ingenta.
Published by: International Institute for Labour Studies, PO Box 6, Geneva 22, 1211, Switzerland. TEL 41-22-799-6128, FAX 41-22-788-0950.

THE INTERNATIONAL JOURNAL OF COMPARATIVE LABOUR LAW AND INDUSTRIAL RELATIONS. see *LAW*

331.1 AUS ISSN 1039-6993
INTERNATIONAL JOURNAL OF EMPLOYMENT STUDIES. Text in English. 1993. s-a.
—BLDSC (4542.233000), IE.
Published by: Group Researching Organisations, Work, Employment and Skills, University of Western Sydney, Parramatta Campus, Bldg EI, Locked Bag 1797, Penrith South DC, NSW 1797, Australia. TEL 61-2-96859657, s.bond@uws.edu.au. Ed. Sue Bond.

331 GBR ISSN 1741-8437
INTERNATIONAL JOURNAL OF ENVIRONMENT, WORKPLACE AND EMPLOYMENT. Text in English. q. USD 450 to institutions; USD 545 combined subscription to institutions print & online eds. (effective 2005).
Related titles: Online - full text ed.: ISSN 1741-8445. USD 450 to institutions (effective 2005) (from EBSCO Publishing).
Indexed: C&ISA, E&CAJ, IAA, Inspec.
—BLDSC (4542.240950).
Published by: Inderscience Publishers, IEL Editorial Office, PO Box 735, Olney, Bucks MK46 5WB, United Kingdom. TEL 44-1234-240519, FAX 44-1234-240515, ijewe@inderscience.com, info@inderscience.com, http://www.inderscience.com/ijewe. **Subscr. to:** World Trade Centre Bldg, 29 route de Pre-Bois, Case Postale 896, Geneva 15 1215, Switzerland. FAX 41-22-7910885, subs@inderscience.com.

331 GBR ISSN 0143-7720
HD4805
➤ **INTERNATIONAL JOURNAL OF MANPOWER.** Text in English. 1980. 8/yr. EUR 13,364.29 in Europe; USD 13,109 in North America; AUD 15,669 in Australasia; GBP 8,927.29 in UK & elsewhere (effective 2006). bk.rev. charts; illus. index. back issues avail.; reprint service avail. from PSC. **Document type:** *Journal, Academic/Scholarly.* **Description:** Aims to cover all key issues in the development of manpower planning and economics and their practical applications.
Related titles: Online - full text ed.: (from EBSCO Publishing, Emerald Group Publishing Limited, Florida Center for Library Automation, Gale Group, IngentaConnect, O C L C Online Computer Library Center, Inc., ProQuest Information & Learning, Swets Information Services).
Indexed: ABIn, ADPA, ASCA, AgeL, BAS, BPIA, BusI, CIJE, CJA, CurCont, ERA, ETA, EmerIntel, Emerald, ErgAb, FamI, HRA, IBSS, ILD, JEL, KES, M&MA, MEA, ManagCont, RHEA, SEA, SENA, SOMA, SPAA, SSCI, SWA, TEA.
—BLDSC (4542.329000), IDS, IE, Infotrieve, ingenta. **CCC.**
Published by: Emerald Group Publishing Limited, 60-62 Toller Ln, Bradford, W Yorks BD8 9BY, United Kingdom. TEL 44-1274-777700, FAX 44-1274-785200, infomation@emeraldinsight.com, http://www.emeraldinsight.com/ijm.htm. Ed. Adrian Ziderman.

➤ **INTERNATIONAL JOURNAL OF ORGANISATIONAL BEHAVIOUR.** see *PSYCHOLOGY*

331 GBR ISSN 0147-5479
HD4802 CODEN: ILWHFV
➤ **INTERNATIONAL LABOR AND WORKING-CLASS HISTORY.** Text in English. 1972. s-a. GBP 52 to institutions; USD 83 in North America to institutions; GBP 59 combined subscription to institutions print & online eds.; USD 92 combined subscription in North America to institutions print & online eds. (effective 2006). adv. bk.rev. bibl.; illus. Index. back issues avail.; reprints avail. **Document type:** *Journal, Academic/Scholarly.* **Description:** Links historians throughout the world and presents new scholarship on important issues and controversies in the field.
Formerly (until 1976): European Labor and Working Class History Newsletter (0097-8523)
Related titles: Online - full text ed.: ISSN 1471-6445. GBP 50 to institutions; USD 78 in North America to institutions (effective 2006) (from EBSCO Publishing, O C L C Online Computer Library Center, Inc., Swets Information Services).
Indexed: ABS&EES, ASCA, AltPI, AmH&L, ArtHuCI, BAS, CurCont, DIP, HistAb, IBR, IBZ, LeftInd, MEA&I, PSA, RASB, SOPODA, SSA, SociolAb.
—BLDSC (4542.702900), IDS, IE, Infotrieve, ingenta. **CCC.**
Published by: Cambridge University Press, The Edinburgh Bldg, Shaftesbury Rd, Cambridge, CB2 2RU, United Kingdom. TEL 44-1223-312393, FAX 44-1223-315052, journals@cambridge.org, http://uk.cambridge.org/journals/journal_catalogue.asp?historylinks=ALPHA&mnemonic=ILW. Eds. Geoffrey Fields, Peter Winn, Victoria Hattam. R&P Linda Nicol TEL 44-1223-325757. Adv. contact Rebecca Curtis TEL 44-1223-325757. Circ: 1,000. **Subscr. to:** Cambridge University Press, 100 Brook Hill Dr, West Nyack, NY 10994. TEL 845-353-7500, FAX 845-353-4141, journals_subscriptions@cup.org

331 CHE ISSN 0376-8678
INTERNATIONAL LABOUR CONFERENCE. DRAFT PROGRAMME AND BUDGET AND OTHER FINANCIAL QUESTIONS. Text in English. a.
Published by: International Labour Office, Publications Sales Service, 4, route des Morillons, Geneva, 1211, Switzerland. FAX 41-22-7996938, pubvente@ilo.org, http://www.ilo.org.

331 CHE ISSN 0074-6673
INTERNATIONAL LABOUR CONFERENCE. RECORD OF PROCEEDINGS. Text in English. 1919. a.
Published by: International Labour Office, Publications Sales Service, 4, route des Morillons, Geneva, 1211, Switzerland. FAX 41-22-7996938, pubvente@ilo.org, http://www.ilo.org.

331 CHE ISSN 0074-6681
HD4813
INTERNATIONAL LABOUR CONFERENCE. REPORTS. Text in English. 1919. a. CHF 430, USD 344 (effective 2001). back issues avail. **Document type:** *Proceedings, Trade.*
Related titles: Microform ed.: (from CIS, ILO); Arabic ed.; Chinese ed.; Russian ed.; French ed.: Conference Internationale du Travail. Compte Rendu des Travaux. ISSN 0251-3218; Spanish ed.: Conferencia Internacional del Trabajo. Actas. ISSN 0251-3226; German ed.: I A O Internationale Arbeitskonferenz. Bericht. ISSN 0251-4095.
Indexed: IIS.
—BLDSC (7326.082000).
Published by: (International Labour Office), I L O Publications, PO Box 6, Geneva 22, 1211, Switzerland. TEL 41-22-799-6111, FAX 41-22-798-6358, publns@ilo.org, http://www.ilo.org/publns. **Dist. in US by:** I L O Publications Center, 9 Jay Gould Court, Ste. CT, PO Box 753, Waldorf, MD 20604. TEL 301-638-3152, FAX 301-843-0159, ilopubs@tasco1.com.

INTERNATIONAL LABOUR LAW REPORTS. see *LAW*

331 CHE ISSN 0378-5882
HD7801
INTERNATIONAL LABOUR OFFICE. OFFICIAL BULLETIN. SERIES A. Text in English. 1920. 3/yr. CHF 150, USD 120 (effective 2001); both series. bibl. index. **Document type:** *Bulletin, Trade.*
Superseded in part: International Labour Office. Official Bulletin (0020-7772)
Related titles: Microfiche ed.: (from ILO); French ed.: Bureau International du Travail. Bulletin Officiel. Serie A. ISSN 0378-5432; Spanish ed.: Oficina Internacional del Trabajo. Boletin Oficial. Serie A. ISSN 0378-5513.
Indexed: CISA, RASB.
—CCC.
Published by: (International Labour Office), I L O Publications, PO Box 6, Geneva 22, 1211, Switzerland. TEL 41-22-799-6111, FAX 41-22-798-6358, publns@ilo.org, http://www.ilo.org/publns. Circ: 2,300. **Dist. in US by:** I L O Publications Center, 9 Jay Gould Court, Ste. CT, PO Box 753, Waldorf, MD 20604. TEL 301-638-3152, FAX 301-843-0159, ilopubs@tasco1.com.

331 CHE ISSN 0378-5890
HD7801
INTERNATIONAL LABOUR OFFICE. OFFICIAL BULLETIN. SERIES B. Text in English. 1920. 3/yr. CHF 150, USD 120 (effective 2001). bibl. index. **Document type:** *Bulletin, Trade.*
Superseded in part: International Labour Office. Official Bulletin (0020-7772)
Related titles: Microfiche ed.: (from ILO); Microform ed.; French ed.: Bureau International du Travail. Bulletin Officiel. Serie B; Spanish ed.: Oficina Internacional del Trabajo. Boletin Oficial. Serie B. ISSN 0378-5521.
Indexed: RASB.
Published by: (International Labour Office), I L O Publications, PO Box 6, Geneva 22, 1211, Switzerland. TEL 41-22-799-6111, FAX 41-22-798-6358, publns@ilo.org, http://www.ilo.org/publns. Circ: 2,300. **Dist. in US by:** I L O Publications Center, 9 Jay Gould Court, Ste. CT, PO Box 753, Waldorf, MD 20604. TEL 301-638-3152, FAX 301-843-0159, ilopubs@tasco1.com.

331 CHE ISSN 0020-7780
HD4811 CODEN: ILREDT
➤ **INTERNATIONAL LABOUR REVIEW.** Text in English. 1921. q. CHF 70 domestic to individuals; GBP 30, EUR 45 in Europe to individuals; USD 55 elsewhere to individuals (effective 2005). adv. bk.rev. bibl.; stat.; illus.; abstr. s-a. index. back issues avail.; reprint service avail. from SCH. **Document type:** *Bulletin, Academic/Scholarly.* **Description:** Contains articles based on present I.L.O. and other research into economic and social topics of international interest affecting labor.
Related titles: Microfiche ed.: (from CIS, ILO); Microform ed.: (from PMC, PQC); Online - full text ed.: International Labour Review Online. ISSN 1564-913X. 1999. CHF 75, GBP 40, EUR 50, USD 60 (effective 2005) (from EBSCO Publishing, Florida Center for Library Automation, Gale Group, H.W. Wilson, IngentaConnect, Northern Light Technology, Inc., O C L C Online Computer Library Center, Inc., ProQuest Information & Learning, Swets Information Services); ♦ French ed.: Revue Internationale du Travail. ISSN 0378-5599; ♦ Spanish ed.: Revista Internacional del Trabajo. ISSN 0378-5548.
Indexed: ABIn, APEL, ASCA, ASG, ASSIA, AbHyg, AgeL, BAS, BPI, BPIA, BRI, BusI, CBRI, CIJE, CISA, CLOSS, CPM, CREJ, CurCont, DIP, EIP, ELLIS, ERA, ESPM, Emerald, ErgAb, FLP, FutSurv, GEOBASE, HRA, HRIR, IBR, IBSS, IBZ, IIS, ILD, JEL, KES, M&MA, MCR, MEA, MEA&I, ManagCont, PAIS, PCI, PMA, PRA, PSA, PersLit, PopulInd, RASB, RDA, REE&TA, RRTA, RehabLit, RiceAb, RiskAb, SCIMP, SENA, SFSA, SOPODA, SSA, SSCI, SSI, SWA, SociolAb, TDB, TEA, V&AA, WAE&RSA, WBA, WorkRelAb.
—BLDSC (4542.780000), CISTI, IDS, IE, Infotrieve, ingenta. **CCC.**

Published by: (International Labour Office), I L O Publications, PO Box 6, Geneva 22, 1211, Switzerland. TEL 41-22-799-6111, FAX 41-22-798-6358, revue@ilo.org, publns@ilo.org, http://www.ilo.org/public/english/support/publ/revue/, http://www.ilo.org/publns. Ed. Iftikhar Ahmed. Circ: 5,300. **Dist. in US by:** I L O Publications Center, 9 Jay Gould Court, Ste. CT, PO Box 753, Waldorf, MD 20604. TEL 301-638-3152, FAX 301-843-0159, ilopubs@tasco1.com.

344.01   IND   ISSN 0047-097X
INTERNATIONAL PRESS CUTTING SERVICE: LABOUR WELFARE - INDUSTRIAL LEGISLATION AND PERSONNEL MANAGEMENT. Text in English. 1967. w. INR 735, USD 85 (effective 1999). bk.rev. index. **Document type:** *Newsletter.*
Media: Duplicated (not offset).
Published by: International Press Cutting Service, PO Box 121, Allahabad, Uttar Pradesh 211 001, India. TEL 91-532-622392. Ed. Nandi Khanna. Circ: 1,200.

368.4   CHE
INTERNATIONAL SOCIETY FOR LABOR LAW AND SOCIAL SECURITY. BULLETIN. Text in English, French, Spanish, German. 1976. irreg. membership. **Document type:** *Bulletin.*
Published by: International Society for Labor Law and Social Security/Societe Internationale de Droit du Travail et de la Securite Sociale, c/o Jean-Michel Servais, Sec.-Gen., 4 route des Morillons, Geneva 22, 1211, Switzerland. TEL 41-22-7996343, FAX 41-22-7998542, servaisjm@ilo.org.

INTERNATIONAL SOCIETY FOR OCCUPATIONAL ERGONOMICS AND SAFETY. NEWSLETTER. see *OCCUPATIONAL HEALTH AND SAFETY*

331.21   SWE   ISSN 1650-2280
INTERNATIONAL UTBLICK. LOENER OCH ARBETSKRAFTSKOSTNADER/INTERNATIONAL OUTLOOK. WAGES, SALARIES, LABOUR COSTS. Text in English, Swedish. 1969. a. **Document type:** *Journal, Trade.*
Supersedes in part (in 1996): Wages and Total Labour Costs for Workers: International Survey (0280-4743); Which was formerly (until 1975): Direct and Total Wage Costs for Workers
Published by: Svenskt Naeringsliv/Confederation of Swedish Enterprise, Storgatan 19, Stockholm, 11482, Sweden. TEL 46-8-55343000, FAX 46-8-55343099, info@svensktnaringsliv.se, http://www.svensktnaringsliv.se. Circ: 1,000.

331.11   DEU   ISSN 1430-5437
INTERNATIONAL VERGLEICHENDE SCHRIFTEN ZUR PERSONALOEKONOMIE UND ARBEITSPOLITIK. Text in German. irreg., latest vol.15, 2002. price varies. **Document type:** *Monographic series, Academic/Scholarly.*
Published by: Rainer Hampp Verlag, Meringerzellerstr 10, Mering, 86415, Germany. TEL 49-8233-4783, FAX 49-8233-30755, Rainer_Hampp_Verlag@t-online.de, http://www.hampp-verlag.de.

INVESTING, LICENSING AND TRADING. GLOBAL EDITION. see *BUSINESS AND ECONOMICS—International Commerce*

INVESTING, LICENSING AND TRADING. SLOVAKIA. see *BUSINESS AND ECONOMICS—International Commerce*

331.125   USA
HD7096.U6
IOWA. DEPARTMENT OF EMPLOYMENT SERVICES. ANNUAL REPORT. Text in English. 1938. a. free. **Document type:** *Government.*
Formerly: Iowa. Department of Job Service. Annual Report (0149-449X); Iowa. Employment Security Commission. Annual Report
Published by: Department of Employment Services, 1000 E Grand Ave, Des Moines, IA 50319. TEL 515-281-3201. Circ: 2,000 (controlled).

IOWA EMPLOYMENT LAW LETTER. see *LAW*

368.41   USA
IOWA LEGAL FORMS: WORKERS' COMPENSATION. Text in English. 1983. 2-3/yr.), base vol. plus irreg. updates. looseleaf. USD 60.
Related titles: Diskette ed.: USD 85.
Published by: LexisNexis (Subsidiary of: LexisNexis North America), PO Box 7587, Charlottesville, VA 22906-7587. TEL 804-972-7600, 800-562-1197, FAX 804-972-7666, llp.customer.support@lexis-nexis.com, http://www.lexislawpublishing.com. Ed. Dennis L Hanssen.

IRELAND. CENTRAL STATISTICS OFFICE. INDUSTRIAL DISPUTES. see *BUSINESS AND ECONOMICS—Abstracting, Bibliographies, Statistics*

IRELAND. CENTRAL STATISTICS OFFICE. LABOUR COSTS SURVEY - IN INDUSTRY, DISTRIBUTION, CREDIT AND INSURANCE. see *BUSINESS AND ECONOMICS—Abstracting, Bibliographies, Statistics*

ISSUES AND LETTERS. see *SOCIAL SCIENCES: COMPREHENSIVE WORKS*

ISSUES IN DEVELOPMENT. DISCUSSION PAPER. see *BUSINESS AND ECONOMICS—International Development And Assistance*

331.21   USA
ISSUES IN LABOR STATISTICS. Text in English. irreg.
Published by: U.S. Department of Labor, Bureau of Labor Statistics, Postal Square Bldg., 2 Massachusetts Ave, NE, Washington, DC 20212-0001 . TEL 202-691-5200, FAX 202-691-6325, blsdata_staff@bls.gov, http://stats.bls.gov/opub/ils/opbilshm.htm, http://www.bls.gov.

JAGIELLONIAN UNIVERSITY. YEARBOOK OF LABOUR LAW. see *LAW*

344.01   DEU
JAHRBUCH DES ARBEITSRECHTS. Text in German. 1963. a. price varies. adv. bk.rev. reprints avail. **Document type:** *Journal, Academic/Scholarly.*
Formerly (until 1999): Arbeitsrecht der Gegenwart (0066-586X)
Indexed: IBR, IBZ.
Published by: Erich Schmidt Verlag GmbH & Co. (Bielefeld), Viktoriastr 44A, Bielefeld, 33602, Germany. TEL 49-521-58308-0, esv@esvmedien.de, http://www.erich-schmidt-verlag.de. Ed. Thomas Dietrich.

331   DEU   ISSN 1610-093X
JAHRBUCH FUER FORSCHUNGEN ZUR GESCHICHTE DER ARBEITERBEWEGUNG. Text in German. 3/yr. EUR 25 domestic; EUR 35 foreign; EUR 10 newsstand/cover (effective 2003). **Document type:** *Journal, Academic/Scholarly.*
Description: Covers the history of various labor movements and organizations.
Indexed: AmH&L, HistAb.
Published by: N D Z - Neue Zeitungsverwaltung GmbH, Weydingerstr 14-16, Berlin, 10178, Germany. TEL 49-30-24009560.

331   LUX   ISSN 1018-3183
JANUS. Text in English. 1989. q.
Related titles: French ed.: ISSN 1018-3140; German ed.: ISSN 1018-3124; Italian ed.: ISSN 1018-3159; Danish ed.: ISSN 1017-7647; Spanish ed.: ISSN 1018-3132; Greek ed.: ISSN 1018-3175; Portuguese ed.: ISSN 1018-3167; Dutch ed.: ISSN 1018-3191.
Indexed: RAPRA.
—BLDSC (4647.507500), IE, ingenta.
Published by: (European Commission BEL), European Commission, Office for Official Publications of the European Union, 2 Rue Mercier, Luxembourg, L-2985, Luxembourg. **Dist. in the U.S. by:** Bernan Associates, Bernan, 4611-F Assembly Dr., Lanham, MD 20706-4391. TEL 301-459-0056, 800-274-4447.

331   JPN   ISSN 1348-9364
HD8721
▼ **JAPAN LABOR REVIEW.** Text in English. 2004. q. free. **Document type:** *Journal, Academic/Scholarly.*
Related titles: Online - full content ed.
—BLDSC (4648.345100), IE.
Published by: Japan Institute for Labour Policy and Training, International Affairs Department, 8-23, Kamishakujii 4-chome, Nerima-ku, Tokyo, 177-8502, Japan. TEL 81-3-59036111, FAX 81-3-35941113, jlr@jil.go.jp, http://www.jil.go.jp/english/JLR.htm.

331   JPN   ISSN 0021-4469
HD8721
JAPAN LABOUR BULLETIN. Text in English. 1962. m. JPY 4,320 domestic (effective 2000). stat.; illus. index, cum.index. 8 p./no.; reprints avail. **Document type:** *Bulletin.* **Description:** Introduces and analyzes current developments in Japanese industrial relations to overseas readers.
Indexed: ILD, RASB, WBSS.
Published by: Japan Institute of Labour/Nihon Rodo Kenkyu Kiko, Shinjuku Monolith, P.O. Box 7040, Tokyo, 163-0926, Japan. http://www.mol.go.jp/jil/index-e.htm, http://www.jil.go.jp. Ed. H. Sakashita. Circ: 3,100.

JAPAN. STATISTICS BUREAU. MANAGEMENT AND COORDINATION AGENCY. ANNUAL REPORT ON THE LABOUR FORCE SURVEY/NIHON TOKEI KYOKAI. RODORYOKU CHOSA NENPO. see *BUSINESS AND ECONOMICS—Abstracting, Bibliographies, Statistics*

JAPAN. STATISTICS BUREAU. MANAGEMENT AND COORDINATION AGENCY. MONTHLY REPORT ON THE LABOUR FORCE SURVEY. see *BUSINESS AND ECONOMICS—Abstracting, Bibliographies, Statistics*

331   JPN
JAPANESE ECONOMY & LABOR SERIES. Text in English. 1966. irreg., latest vol.17, 1990. JPY 1,500 for no.2 (effective 2000). **Document type:** *Trade.* **Description:** Provides information to the persons abroad on the various labor issues in Japan.
Incorporates (1988-1990): Japanese Industrial Relations Series
Published by: Japan Institute of Labour/Nihon Rodo Kenkyu Kiko, Shinjuku Monolith, P.O. Box 7040, Tokyo, 163-0926, Japan. TEL 03-5991-5165, FAX 03-3594-1112. Ed. Akira Takanashi.

JEWISH LABOR COMMITTEE REVIEW. see *ETHNIC INTERESTS*

JINGJIFAXUE, LAODONGFAXUE/STUDIES OF ECONOMIC LAW, STUDIES OF LABOR LAW. see *LAW—Corporate Law*

331.7   CAN   ISSN 0833-7195
JOB FUTURES. Text in English. 1987. irreg.
Related titles: CD-ROM ed.: ISSN 1205-4216. 1996; Diskette ed.: ISSN 1205-416X. 1989; Online - full text ed.: ISSN 1497-1704; Supplement(s): Job Futures Companion. ISSN 1497-0961, 1998.
—CISTI.
Published by: Employment and Immigration Canada, Public Affairs, 1441 St Urbaine St, 8th Fl, Montreal, PQ H2X 2M6, Canada. TEL 514-283-4695, http://jobfutures.ca/en/home.shtml.

331   FRA   ISSN 0751-4794
JOB PRATIQUE MAGAZINE. Text in French. 1981. 6/yr. adv. bk.rev. video rev. **Document type:** *Magazine, Trade.*
Related titles: Online - full text ed.
Address: 23 rue des Apennins, Paris, 75017, France. TEL 33-1-42285900, FAX 33-1-42282458, redaction@jobpratique.com, http://www.jobpratique.com, http://www.alma-inter.fr/jobpratique/. Ed. John Martial. R&P Myoux Laurent. Adv. contact Christiane Garnieri. Circ: 75,000 (paid); 11,000 (controlled).

331.125137   USA
THE JOB SEARCH HANDBOOK FOR EDUCATORS. Text in English. 1966. a. USD 8 to non-members (effective 2003). **Document type:** *Academic/Scholarly.*
Former titles: A S C U S Annual - A Job Search Handbook for Educators; (until 1980): A S C U S Annual - Teaching Opportunities for You (0066-9156)
Published by: American Association for Employment in Education, 3040 Riverside Dr., Ste. 125, Columbus, OH 43221-2575. TEL 847-864-1999, FAX 847-864-8303, aaee@nwu.edu, http://www.ub-careers.buffalo.edu/aaee/cand_pubs.shtml, http://www.aaee.org. Circ: 140,000.

331.11   USA
JOB SERVICE NORTH DAKOTA. ANNUAL REPORT. Text in English. 1937. a. free. **Document type:** *Government.*
Formerly: North Dakota. Employment Security Bureau. Annual Report (0078-155X)
Published by: Job Service North Dakota, 1000 E Divide Ave, Box 5507, Bismarck, ND 58506-5507. TEL 701-328-2868. Ed. Tom Pederson. Circ: 200.

331.11   USA
JOB SERVICE NORTH DAKOTA. BIENNIAL REPORT TO THE GOVERNOR. Text in English. 1964. biennial. free. **Document type:** *Government.*
Formerly: North Dakota. Employment Security Bureau. Biennial Report to the Governor (0078-1568)
Published by: Job Service North Dakota, 1000 E Divide Ave, Box 5507, Bismarck, ND 58506-5507. TEL 701-328-2825, FAX 701-328-4193, www.state.nd.us/jsnd. Circ: 75.

331.1251378   USA   ISSN 1074-5475
JOBS IN HIGHER EDUCATION✻ . Text in English. 1990. m. USD 48. adv. **Document type:** *Newsletter, Trade.* **Description:** Serves as a forum for universities and colleges seeking employees as well as persons looking for employment.
Formerly (until 1994): Minority Review (1053-4229)
Address: P O Box 9053, Colorado Springs, CO 80932-0053. TEL 719-475-9797, FAX 719-475-9693. Ed. Charles G Clute. Circ: 2,000.

JOHN LINER LETTER. see *INSURANCE*

352.63   USA
JOINT GOVERNMENTAL SALARY AND BENEFITS SURVEY: ARIZONA. Text in English. 1974. a. USD 75 (effective 1999). charts. **Document type:** *Government.*
Formerly: Joint Governmental Salary Survey: Arizona; **Supersedes:** Survey of Salaries and Employee Benefits of Private and Public Employers in Arizona. (0091-5599)
Published by: Department of Administration, Personnel Division, 1831 W Jefferson, Phoenix, AZ 85007-3204. TEL 602-542-5250. Ed. Joan Toner. Circ: (controlled).

JORDAN. DEPARTMENT OF STATISTICS. EMPLOYMENT SURVEY FOR ESTABLISHMENTS ENGAGING FIVE PERSONS OR MORE. see *BUSINESS AND ECONOMICS—Abstracting, Bibliographies, Statistics*

JOURNAL DES TRIBUNAUX DU TRAVAIL. see *LAW*

344.7301   USA   ISSN 1083-6276
K10
JOURNAL OF DEFERRED COMPENSATION; nonqualified plans and executive compensation. Text in English. 1995. q. USD 235 (effective 2005). **Document type:** *Journal, Trade.* **Description:** Provides timely analysis, innovative strategies, and practical advice to anyone involved in executive retirement and compensation planning.

Related titles: Online - full text ed.: (from EBSCO Publishing, Florida Center for Library Automation, Gale Group, ProQuest Information & Learning).
Indexed: ABIn, CLI, LRI.
—CCC.
Published by: Aspen Publishers, Inc. (Subsidiary of: Wolters Kluwer N.V.), 5301 Buckeystown Pike, Ste. 400, Frederick, MD 21704-8319. TEL 800-638-8437, customer.service@aspenpubl.com, http://www.aspenpublishers.com/Product.asp?catalog%5Fname=Aspen&category%5Fname=&product%5Fid=SS10836276&Mode=SEARCH&ProductType=J, http://www.aspenpub.com. Ed. Bruce J McNeil. **Dist. by:** Distribution Center, 7201 McKinney Circle, Frederick, MD 21701. TEL 301-698-7100, FAX 301-417-7550.

▼ **THE JOURNAL OF ECONOMIC INEQUALITY.** see *BUSINESS AND ECONOMICS—Economic Situation And Conditions*

JOURNAL OF HUMAN RESOURCES; education, manpower and welfare economics. see *BUSINESS AND ECONOMICS—Personnel Management*

331 USA ISSN 1055-7512
K10
➤ **JOURNAL OF INDIVIDUAL EMPLOYMENT RIGHTS.** Text in English. 1991. q. USD 67 to individuals; USD 237 domestic to institutions; USD 245 foreign to institutions (effective 2005). back issues avail.; reprints avail. **Document type:** *Journal, Academic/Scholarly.* **Description:** Researches and addresses the areas of individual employee rights as they are debated and developed by courts, academicians, legal practitioners, and personnel managers.
Related titles: Online - full text ed.: ISSN 1541-3799 (from EBSCO Publishing).
Indexed: CLI, HRA, LRI, PRA, RefZh, SPAA, V&AA.
—CCC.
Published by: Baywood Publishing Co., Inc., 26 Austin Ave, PO Box 337, Amityville, NY 11701-0337. TEL 631-691-1270, FAX 631-691-1770, info@baywood.com, http://www.baywood.com/Journals/PreviewJournal.asp?Id=1055-7512. Ed. Dr. Charles Coleman. R&P Julie Krempa. Adv. contact Rochelle Grant.

331.1 AUS ISSN 0022-1856
HD4811
➤ **JOURNAL OF INDUSTRIAL RELATIONS.** Text in English. 1959. 5/yr. GBP 269, USD 471 to institutions; GBP 280, USD 490 combined subscription to institutions print & online eds. (effective 2006). adv. bk.rev. charts; stat. Index. back issues avail. **Document type:** *Journal, Academic/Scholarly.* **Description:** Publishes articles on Australian and international industrial relations.
Related titles: Online - full text ed.: ISSN 1472-9296. GBP 266, USD 466 to institutions (effective 2006) (from Blackwell Synergy, EBSCO Publishing, Gale Group, IngentaConnect, O C L C Online Computer Library Center, Inc., Swets Information Services).
Indexed: ABIn, APEL, AusPAIS, BAS, BrHumI, CJA, CREJ, Emerald, HRA, IBSS, ILD, Inspec, PCI, RASB, SOPODA, SSA, SociolAb, WAE&RSA, WorkRelAb.
—BLDSC (5006.380000), IE, Infotrieve, ingenta. **CCC.**
Published by: (Industrial Relations Society of Australia), Sage Publications Ltd. (Subsidiary of: Sage Publications, Inc.), 1 Oliver's Yard, 55 City Rd, London, EC1 1SP, United Kingdom. TEL 44-20-73248500, FAX 44-20-73248600, info@sagepub.co.uk, http://www.sagepub.co.uk/journal.aspx?pid=107338. Eds. Ron Callus, Russell D Lansbury. Circ: 4,200 (paid). **Subscr. to:** Sage Publications, Inc., 2455 Teller Rd, Thousand Oaks, CA 91320. TEL 805-499-0721, FAX 805-499-0871, journals@sagepub.com.

331.11 USA ISSN 0734-306X
HD4802
➤ **JOURNAL OF LABOR ECONOMICS.** Text in English. 1983. q. USD 59 combined subscription to individuals print & online eds.; USD 278 combined subscription to institutions print & online eds.; USD 19 per issue to individuals; USD 76 per issue to institutions (effective 2006). adv. bk.rev. stat.; illus. Index. 198 p./no.; reprint service avail. from PSC. **Document type:** *Journal, Academic/Scholarly.* **Description:** Presents theoretical and empirical articles pertaining to labor economics, very broadly defined.
Related titles: Microform ed.: (from PQC); Online - full text ed.: ISSN 1537-5307. USD 250 to institutions (effective 2006) (from EBSCO Publishing, Florida Center for Library Automation, Gale Group, JSTOR (Web-based Journal Archive), O C L C Online Computer Library Center, Inc., ProQuest Information & Learning).
Indexed: ABIn, ASCA, AgeL, BPI, BPIA, CREJ, CurCont, ESPM, FamI, H&SSA, IBSS, JEL, PCI, RASB, RiskAb, SSCI, SSI.
—BLDSC (5009.940000), IDS, IE, Infotrieve, ingenta. **CCC.**
Published by: (National Opinion Research Center), University of Chicago Press, Journals Division, Journals Division, PO Box 37005, Chicago, IL 60637. TEL 773-753-3347, 877-705-1878, FAX 773-753-0811, 877-705-1879, subscriptions@press.uchicago.edu, http://www.journals.uchicago.edu/JOLE. Ed. Derek A Neal. adv.: page USD 475; trim 6 x 9. Circ: 2,000. **Co-sponsor:** Society of Labor Economists.

331.1 USA ISSN 0195-3613
HD4802
➤ **JOURNAL OF LABOR RESEARCH.** Text in English. 1979. q. USD 56 to individuals print or online; USD 200 to institutions print or online; USD 62 combined subscription to individuals print & online; USD 240 combined subscription to institutions print & online (effective 2004). adv. bk.rev. illus. Index. reprints avail. **Document type:** *Journal, Academic/Scholarly.* **Description:** Focuses on policy issues in the work place, including unions and their political and economic activities.
Related titles: Online - full text ed.: (from EBSCO Publishing, Florida Center for Library Automation, Gale Group, H.W. Wilson, Northern Light Technology, Inc., O C L C Online Computer Library Center, Inc., Swets Information Services).
Indexed: ABIn, ABRCLP, ASCA, AgeL, BPIA, BusI, CJA, CommAb, CurCont, ESPM, H&SSA, HRA, IBSS, JEL, ManagCont, PAIS, PCI, PRA, PSA, RiskAb, SFSA, SOPODA, SPAA, SSA, SSCI, SSI, SociolAb, T&II.
—BLDSC (5009.960000), IDS, IE, Infotrieve, ingenta. **CCC.**
Published by: (George Mason University, John M. Olin Institute), Transaction Publishers, 390 Campus Dr, Somerset, NJ 07830. TEL 888-999-6778, FAX 732-748-9801, trans@transactionpub.com, http://www.transactionpub.com. Ed. James T Bennett. Circ: 600.

331.252 USA ISSN 1069-4064
HD7105.45.U6
JOURNAL OF PENSION BENEFITS. Text in English. 1993. q. USD 207 (effective 2004). reprint service avail. from WSH. **Document type:** *Journal, Trade.* **Description:** Provides pension professionals with new ideas, fresh insights, and expert views on key topics affecting plan design, compliance, and administration.
Related titles: Microfiche ed.: (from WSH); Microform ed.: (from WSH); Online - full text ed.: (from EBSCO Publishing, Florida Center for Library Automation, Gale Group, ProQuest Information & Learning).
Indexed: ABIn.
—BLDSC (5030.510000), IE, ingenta. **CCC.**
Published by: Panel Publishers, Inc. (Subsidiary of: Aspen Publishers, Inc.), 1185 Ave of the Americas, 37th Fl, New York, NY 10036. TEL 212-597-0200, 800-638-8437, FAX 212-597-0331, customer.service@aspenpubl.com, http://www.aspenpublishers.com. Ed. Joan Gucciardi. **Dist. by:** Aspen Publishers, Inc., Distribution Center, 7201 McKinney Circle, Frederick, MD 21701. TEL 301-698-7100, FAX 301-417-7550.

JOURNAL OF PENSION PLANNING AND COMPLIANCE. see *BUSINESS AND ECONOMICS—Public Finance, Taxation*

JOURNAL OF WORKERS COMPENSATION. see *INSURANCE*

344.01 331 LUX ISSN 1814-036X
▼ **JURISNEWS, REGARD SUR LE DROIT DU TRAVAIL.** Text in French. 2005. 10/yr. EUR 52.80 in Europe to individuals (effective 2005). **Document type:** *Trade.*
Published by: Editions Promoculture, PO Box 1142, Luxembourg, L-1011, Luxembourg. TEL 352-480691, FAX 352-400950, info@promoculture.lu, http://www.promoculture.lu. Ed. Mr. Marc Feyereisen.

331 ARG ISSN 0327-1404
JUSTICIA SOCIAL. Text in Spanish. 1985. 3/yr. USD 15. bk.rev.
Published by: Centro de Estudios Laborales, San Mauro, 444, Quilmes, Buenos Aires 1878, Argentina. TEL 54-114-114886. Ed. Hector Roberto Roudil. Circ: 1,250.

331.137 NLD
K A B A M. (Krant voor Aktieve Baanlozen in Amsterdam) Text in Dutch. 1987. m. bk.rev. **Document type:** *Bulletin, Consumer.* **Description:** For unemployed people in the Netherlands.
Formerly: Baanbreker (0925-6075)
Published by: Werklozen Belangen Vereniging Amsterdam (WBVA), Postbus 2419, Amsterdam, 100 CK, Netherlands. TEL 31-20-6834423.

331 DEU
K H AKTUELL. (Kreishandwerkerschaft) Text in German. q. adv. **Document type:** *Magazine, Trade.*
Published by: (Kreishandwerkerschaft Emscher-Lippe-West), R D N Verlags GmbH & Co. KG, Barkhausstr 52, Marl, 45768, Germany. TEL 49-2365-13086, FAX 49-2365-13089, info@rdn-online.de, http://www.rdn-online.de. adv.: B&W page EUR 1,260.33; trim 183 x 250.

331 USA
K M U CORRESPONDENCE. Text in English. 1984. bi-m. USD 20 to individuals; USD 25 to institutions (effective 2000). adv. bk.rev. back issues avail. **Document type:** *Newsletter.* **Description:** Provides news and analysis of the Philippine workers' movement. Seeks to foster solidarity between workers' and unions around the globe and their counterparts in the Philippines.
Formerly: Philippine Labor Alert
Indexed: IPP.
Published by: (Kilusang Mayo Uno, Philipppines), Philippine Workers Support Committee, c/o John Witeck, 2252 Puna St, Honolulu, HI 96817. TEL 808-595-7362. R&P Norma Binas. Circ: 500.

331 JPN ISSN 0285-3094
KAIGAI RODO JIHO/INTERNATIONAL LABOR INFORMATION. Text in Japanese. 1977. m. JPY 6,840 domestic (effective 2000).
Published by: Japan Institute of Labour/Nihon Rodo Kenkyu Kiko, Shinjuku Monolith, P.O. Box 7040, Tokyo, 163-0926, Japan. TEL 03-5321-3074, FAX 03-5321-3015.

KANO (STATE) MANPOWER STATISTICS. see *BUSINESS AND ECONOMICS—Abstracting, Bibliographies, Statistics*

KANSAS EMPLOYMENT LAW LETTER. see *LAW*

331.125 IND ISSN 0971-7765
KARMAKSHETRA. Text in Bengali. 1980. w. INR 110 (effective 1999). adv. bk.rev. **Document type:** *Newspaper.* **Description:** Contains news of employment and self-employment opportunities and carrer guidence.
Published by: Swarnakshar Prakasani Pvt. Ltd., 29-1A Old Ballygunge, 2nd Ln., Kolkata, West Bengal 700 019, India. TEL 91-33-2472782, FAX 91-33-2476448, swarna@cal2.vsnl.net.in. Ed. Asoke Chakraborty. Pub., R&P Amarendra Chakravorty. Adv. contact B P Sarkar. Circ: 79,758 (paid).

KENTUCKY EMPLOYMENT LAW LETTER. see *LAW*

368.44 USA
KENTUCKY UNEMPLOYMENT COMPENSATION LAWS AND REGULATIONS. Text in English. irreg., latest 2000. USD 18 (effective 2003). 122 p./no.
Published by: Michie Company (Subsidiary of: LexisNexis North America), 701 E Water St, Charlottesville, VA 22902-5389. TEL 434-972-7600, 800-446-3410, FAX 434-972-7677, http://www.michie.com.

KEY NOTE MARKET ASSESSMENT. WORKING WOMEN. see *WOMEN'S INTERESTS*

331.259 GBR ISSN 1368-5988
KEY NOTE MARKET REPORT: TRAINING. Variant title: Training Market Assessment. Text in English. 1991. irreg., latest 2001, Nov. GBP 340 per issue (effective 2002). **Document type:** *Trade.* **Description:** Provides an overview of a specific UK market segment and includes executive summary, market definition, market size, industry background, competitor analysis, current issues, forecasts, company profiles, and more.
Formerly (until 1995): Key Note Report: Training (1352-7177)
Related titles: CD-ROM ed.; Online - full text ed.
Published by: Key Note Ltd., Field House, 72 Oldfield Rd, Hampton, Mddx TW12 2HQ, United Kingdom. TEL 44-20-8481-8750, FAX 44-20-8783-0049, info@keynote.co.uk, http://www.keynote.co.uk. Ed. Emily Pattullo.

331.252 USA
KING OF PENSION FUNDS CD-ROM. (Also avail. in 8 regional eds.: Western, Mountain, Southwest, Midwest, Southeast, Mid-Atlantic-North, Mid-Atlantic-South, New England) Text in English. 1990. s-a. USD 795 (effective 2000). adv. **Document type:** *Directory, Trade.* **Description:** Contains detailed 400 field per record listings of 800,000 US qualified pension funds.
Supersedes (in 1999): Data Base of Defined Contribution and Defined Benefit Plans (1062-6123)
Media: CD-ROM.
Published by: Judy Diamond Associates, Inc., 1155 15th St NW, Ste. 410, Washington, DC 20005-2748. TEL 202-728-0840, 800-231-0669, FAX 202-728-0845, info@judydiamond.com, http://judydiamond.com. Ed. Jeffrey Mathuran. Pub., Adv. contact Judy Diamond.

KIRCHLICHER DIENST IN DER ARBEITSWELT; Zeitschrift fuer evangelische Arbeitnehmer und evangelische Industrie- und Sozialarbeit. see *RELIGIONS AND THEOLOGY—Protestant*

331 SWE ISSN 0345-6307
KOMMUNALARBETAREN. Text in Swedish. 1911. 22/yr. SEK 300 (effective 2005). adv. **Document type:** *Magazine, Consumer.*
Related titles: Audio cassette/tape ed.
Published by: Svenska Kommunalarbetarefoerbundet/Union of Municipal Workers, PO Box 19034, Stockholm, 10432, Sweden. TEL 46-8-7282800, FAX 46-8-306142, kommunalarbetaren@kommunal.se, http://www.kommunalarbetaren.com. Eds. Susanne Hullstroem TEL 46-8-7283051, Liv Beckstroem TEL 46-8-7282957. Pub. Liv Beckstroem TEL 46-8-7282957. Adv. contact Agnete Kempe Erneberg TEL 46-8-7860321. B&W page SEK 31,800, color page SEK 44,200; trim 194 x 256. Circ: 643,000.

331 DEU ISSN 0176-246X
KONTAKT. Text in German. 1955. q. free. bk.rev. charts; stat. back issues avail. **Document type:** *Newspaper.*
Indexed: Inspec.
Published by: Richard Hirschmann GmbH, Stuttgarterstr 45-51, Neckartenzlingen, 72654, Germany. TEL 49-7127-141289, FAX 49-7127-141835, wdommers@nt.hirschmann.de, http://www.hirschmann.de. Ed. Wolfgang Dommershausen. Circ: 4,200.

KOREA (REPUBLIC). NATIONAL STATISTICAL OFFICE. ANNUAL REPORT ON THE ECONOMICALLY ACTIVE POPULATION SURVEY. see *BUSINESS AND ECONOMICS—Abstracting, Bibliographies, Statistics*

KWARTALNIK HISTORII I TEORII RUCHU ZAWODOWEGO. see *HISTORY—History Of Europe*

331.11   USA
L M I REVIEW; a quarterly review of Washington State labor market information. (Labor Market Information) Text in English. 1984. q. free. charts; stat. **Document type:** *Government.*
Description: Examines the labor market and economic conditions of the state of Washington and contains articles on the labor market, occupations, the economy, and demographics.
Published by: Employment Security Department, Labor Market and Economic Analysis Branch, PO Box 9046, Olympia, WA 98507-9046. TEL 360-438-3155, FAX 360-438-4846. Ed. Robert Baker. Circ: 2,400.

331   USA   ISSN 0895-5220
HC101
L R A'S ECONOMIC NOTES. Text in English. 1933. m. (except Aug.). USD 30 to individuals; USD 50 to institutions. adv. bk.rev. index. back issues avail. **Document type:** *Newsletter.*
Description: Publishes news and analysis for the trade unionist.
Formerly: Economic Notes (0013-0184)
Indexed: AltPI, CREJ.
Published by: Labor Research Association, 145 W 28th St, 6th Fl, New York, NY 10001-6191. TEL 212-714-1677, FAX 212-714-1674, info@LRA-NY.com. Ed. Gregory Tarpinian. Circ: 3,000.

331   USA
L S A - ZIP; federal contract coding guide. (Labor Surplus Areas) Text in English. 1990. a. USD 95 (effective 2000). **Document type:** *Directory.* **Description:** Lists all federally designated areas of high employment, FPDC federal contract updating information, and SBA business size standards. Organized by zip code, city, county, and state.
Related titles: Diskette ed.
Published by: Business Research Services, Inc., 4701 Sangamore Rd., Ste. S155, Bethesda, MD 20816-2532. TEL 202-364-6473, FAX 202-686-3228. Pub. Thomas D Johnson.

L S E - CENTRE FOR CIVIL SOCIETY. INTERNATIONAL WORKING PAPER. (London School of Economics and Political Science) see *SOCIOLOGY*

331   ITA   ISSN 0023-6489
DG401
LABOR. Text in Italian. 1960. q. bk.rev. abstr. index.
Address: Via Tunisi, 4, Palermo, PA 90138, Italy. TEL 39-91-580091. Ed. Cosmo Crifo. Circ: 700.

331   TGO
HD8772
LABOR AND DEVELOPMENT; a monthly review of African socio-economic events of interest to trade union leaders. Text in English. m.
Supersedes in part: Labor in Perspective (0377-0737)
Indexed: HRIR.
Published by: Regional Economic Research and Documentation Center, BP 7138, Lome, Togo.

344.01   USA
LABOR AND EMPLOYMENT IN CALIFORNIA. Text in English. 1992. w/ current supplement), latest 1997, base vol. plus irreg. updates. looseleaf. USD 115 (effective 2003).
Description: Provides practical reference guide to California and federal labor and employment related laws.
Published by: Michie Company (Subsidiary of: LexisNexis North America), 701 E Water St, Charlottesville, VA 22902-5389. TEL 434-972-7600, 800-446-3410, FAX 434-972-7677, http://www.michie.com. Eds. Bernadette M O'Brien, Steven B Eggleston.

344.01   USA
LABOR AND EMPLOYMENT IN CONNECTICUT; a guide to employment laws, regulations & practices. Text in English. 1991. latest 2000, 2nd ed., base vol. plus irreg. updates. looseleaf. USD 125 (effective 2003). **Description:** Provides a comprehensive analysis and explanation of state and federal laws and regulations governing all aspects of employer-employee relationships.
Published by: Michie Company (Subsidiary of: LexisNexis North America), 701 E Water St, Charlottesville, VA 22902-5389. TEL 434-972-7600, 800-446-3410, FAX 434-972-7677, http://www.michie.com. Ed. Jeffrey L Hirsch.

344.01   USA
LABOR AND EMPLOYMENT IN GEORGIA; a guide to employment laws, regulations & practices. Text in English. 1993. w/ current supplement), latest 1993, base vol. plus irreg. updates. looseleaf. USD 95 (effective 2003). Supplement avail. **Description:** Covers all the basic information concerning the laws, regulations and policies affecting labor and employment in Georgia.

Published by: Michie Company (Subsidiary of: LexisNexis North America), 701 E Water St, Charlottesville, VA 22902-5389. TEL 434-972-7600, 800-446-3410, FAX 434-972-7677, http://www.michie.com. Ed. Jeffrey L Hirsch.

344.01   USA
LABOR AND EMPLOYMENT IN LOUISIANA; a guide to employment laws, regulations & practices. Text in English. 1993. latest 1998, base vol. plus irreg. updates. looseleaf. USD 115 (effective 2003). Supplement avail.
Published by: Michie Company (Subsidiary of: LexisNexis North America), 701 E Water St, Charlottesville, VA 22902-5389. TEL 434-972-7600, 800-446-3410, FAX 434-972-7677, http://www.michie.com. Eds. David M Korn, M Nan Alessandra, Maureen F Moore.

344.01   USA
LABOR AND EMPLOYMENT IN MASSACHUSETTS; a guide to employment laws, regulations & practices. Text in English. 1990. w/ current supplement), latest 1998, base vol. plus irreg. updates. looseleaf. USD 125 (effective 2003).
Description: Provides private employers with information on state and federal laws and regulations governing employer-employee relationships.
Published by: Michie Company (Subsidiary of: LexisNexis North America), 701 E Water St, Charlottesville, VA 22902-5389. TEL 434-972-7600, 800-446-3410, FAX 434-972-7677, http://www.michie.com. Ed. Jeffrey L Hirsch.

344.01   USA
LABOR AND EMPLOYMENT IN NEBRASKA; a guide to employment laws, regulations & practices. Text in English. 1992. w/ current supplement), latest 1992, base vol. plus irreg. updates. looseleaf. USD 105 (effective 2003). Supplement avail. **Description:** Guide to state and federal laws and regulations governing all aspects of the employer-employee relationship.
Published by: Michie Company (Subsidiary of: LexisNexis North America), 701 E Water St, Charlottesville, VA 22902-5389. TEL 434-972-7600, 800-446-3410, FAX 434-972-7677, http://www.michie.com. Eds. Jeffrey L Hirsch, Lisa Druliner DeBuse.

344.01   USA
LABOR AND EMPLOYMENT IN NEW HAMPSHIRE; guide to employment in laws, regulations, & practices. Text in English. 1992. w/ current supplement), latest 1999, base vol. plus irreg. updates. looseleaf. USD 125 (effective 2003). Supplement avail. **Description:** Guide to state and federal laws and regulations governing all aspects of the employer-employee relationship, from hiring to termination or retirement.
Published by: Michie Company (Subsidiary of: LexisNexis North America), 701 E Water St, Charlottesville, VA 22902-5389. TEL 434-972-7600, 800-446-3410, FAX 434-972-7677, http://www.michie.com. Eds. Andrea K Johnstone, Jeffrey L Hirsch.

344.01   USA
LABOR AND EMPLOYMENT IN NEW JERSEY; a guide to employment laws, regulations, and practices. Text in English. 1992. base vol. plus a. updates. looseleaf. USD 95. Supplement avail. **Description:** A guide to the entire range of employment laws and regulations affecting employers in New Jersey.
Published by: LexisNexis (Subsidiary of: LexisNexis North America), PO Box 7587, Charlottesville, VA 22906-7587. TEL 804-972-7600, 800-562-1197, FAX 804-972-7666, llp.customer.support@lexis-nexis.com, http://www.lexislawpublishing.com. Ed. Roger B Jacobs.

344.01   USA
LABOR AND EMPLOYMENT IN NEW MEXICO; guide to employment laws, regulations & practices. Text in English. 1994. base vol. plus a. updates. USD 65. 400 p./no.; Supplement avail.
Published by: LexisNexis (Subsidiary of: LexisNexis North America), PO Box 7587, Charlottesville, VA 22906-7587. TEL 804-972-7600, 800-562-1197, FAX 804-972-7666, llp.customer.support@lexis-nexis.com, http://www.lexislawpublishing.com. Ed. Eric Sirotkin.

344.01   USA
LABOR AND EMPLOYMENT IN NEW YORK; guide to New York Laws, Regulations & Practices. Text in English. 1988. latest 1992, 2nd ed., base vol. plus a. updates. looseleaf. USD 95. 450 p./no.; Supplement avail.
Published by: LexisNexis (Subsidiary of: LexisNexis North America), PO Box 7587, Charlottesville, VA 22906-7587. TEL 804-972-7600, 800-562-1197, FAX 804-972-7666, llp.customer.support@lexis-nexis.com, http://www.lexislawpublishing.com. Eds. Jeffrey L Liddle, Michael F Marino.

344.01   USA
LABOR AND EMPLOYMENT IN PENNSYLVANIA; guide to employment laws, regulations, & practices. Text in English. 1994. base vol. plus a. updates. looseleaf. USD 95. Supplement avail. **Description:** Helps human resource professionals, small business owners, and general practice attorneys handle day-to-day employment law questions.

Published by: LexisNexis (Subsidiary of: LexisNexis North America), PO Box 7587, Charlottesville, VA 22906-7587. TEL 804-972-7600, 800-562-1197, FAX 804-972-7666, llp.customer.support@lexis-nexis.com, http://www.lexislawpublishing.com. Eds. John C Unkovic, Michael F Marino.

344.01   USA
LABOR AND EMPLOYMENT IN RHODE ISLAND; a guide to employment laws, regulations and practices. Text in English. 1992. w/ current supplement), latest 1992, base vol. plus irreg. updates. looseleaf. USD 105 (effective 2003). Supplement avail. **Description:** Provides private employers with the most current information on state and federal laws and regulations governing all aspects of the employer-employee relationship, from hiring to termination or retirement.
Published by: Michie Company (Subsidiary of: LexisNexis North America), 701 E Water St, Charlottesville, VA 22902-5389. TEL 434-972-7600, 800-446-3410, FAX 434-972-7677, custserv@michie.com. Eds. Catherine E Reuben, Jeffrey L Hirsch.

344.01   USA
LABOR AND EMPLOYMENT IN VERMONT. Text in English. 1994. base vol. plus a. updates. USD 65. Supplement avail. **Description:** Provides information on both state and federal laws and regulations that affect all aspects of the employment relationship, from hiring to termination or retirement.
Published by: LexisNexis (Subsidiary of: LexisNexis North America), PO Box 7587, Charlottesville, VA 22906-7587. TEL 804-972-7600, 800-562-1197, FAX 804-972-7666, llp.customer.support@lexis-nexis.com, http://www.lexislawpublishing.com. Ed. Kimberly B Cheney.

344.01   USA   ISSN 0193-5739
KF325.15
LABOR & EMPLOYMENT LAW. Text in English. 4/yr. membership only. reprint service avail. from WSH.
Description: News items and developments in the field of labor law.
Former titles: Labor Relations and Employment (0163-5077); Labor Relations Law Letter
Indexed: CLI, LRI.
Published by: American Bar Association, Labor and Employment Law Section, 321 N. Clark St., Ste. 1400, Chicago, IL 60610-7656. abasveetr@abanet.org, http://www.lexis-nexis.com.

331.125   USA   ISSN 8756-792X
KF3302
LABOR AND EMPLOYMENT LAW NEWSLETTER. Text in English. 1984. irreg. looseleaf. USD 268 (effective 2002). **Description:** covers the full spectrum of issues inportant to labor and employee practtioners.
—CCC.
Published by: Matthew Bender & Co., Inc. (Subsidiary of: LexisNexis North America), 1275 Broadway, Albany, NY 12204. international@bender.com, http://bender.lexisnexis.com.

LABOR ARBITRATION INFORMATION SYSTEM. see *LAW—Corporate Law*

331.11   AUS
LABOR COUNCIL OF NEW SOUTH WALES. ANNUAL REPORT. Text in English. 1998. a.
Media: Online - full text.
Published by: Labor Council of New South Wales, 10th Fl., 377-383 Sussex St, Sydney, NSW 2000, Australia. TEL 61-2-9264-1691, FAX 61-2-9261-3505, workers@lists.labor.net.au, http://workers.labor.net.au/. Ed. Peter Lewis.

LABOR FORCE AND NONAGRICULTURAL EMPLOYMENT ESTIMATES. see *BUSINESS AND ECONOMICS— Abstracting, Bibliographies, Statistics*

331.11   USA
LABOR FORCE IN IDAHO. Text in English. a. free. stat.
Document type: *Government.*
Supersedes in part: Labor Force in Idaho and Basic Economic Data for Idaho; Formerly: Labor Force in Idaho
Related titles: Microfiche ed.: (from CIS).
Indexed: SRI.
Published by: Idaho Department of Labor, Bureau of Research and Analysis, 317 W Main St, Boise, ID 83735. TEL 208-334-6168, http://www.labor.state.id.us.

331.09   GBR   ISSN 0023-656X
HD4802
➤ LABOR HISTORY. Text in English. 1960. q. GBP 191, USD 316 combined subscription to institutions print & online eds. (effective 2006). bk.rev. charts; pat.; tr.mk.; illus. index. reprint service avail. from PSC. **Document type:** *Journal, Academic/Scholarly.* **Description:** Seeks to contribute to a critical literacy encompassing trans-national and even global historical transformations.
Formerly: Labor Historian's Bulletin

Related titles: Microform ed.; Online - full text ed.: ISSN 1469-9702. GBP 181, USD 300 to institutions (effective 2006) (from bigchalk, EBSCO Publishing, Florida Center for Library Automation, Gale Group, IngentaConnect, Northern Light Technology, Inc., O C L C Online Computer Library Center, Inc., ProQuest Information & Learning, Swets Information Services).
Indexed: ABIn, ABS&EES, ASCA, AcaI, AltPI, AmH&L, ArtHuCI, BPI, CERDIC, ChPerI, CurCont, DIP, HRA, HistAb, HumInd, IBR, IBZ, JEL, LRI, LeftInd, PRA, PSA, RASB, RI-1, RI-2, RILM, SRRA, SSA, SSCI, SociolAb, V&AA, WorkRelAb.
—BLDSC (5137.907000), IDS, IE, Infotrieve, ingenta. **CCC.**
Published by: Routledge (Subsidiary of: Taylor & Francis Group), 4 Park Sq, Milton Park, Abingdon, Oxon OX14 4RN, United Kingdom. TEL 44-1235-828600, FAX 44-1235-829000, info@routledge.co.uk, 0023-656X, http://www.tandf.co.uk/journals, http://www.routledge.co.uk. Eds. Craig Phelan, Gerald Friedman. Circ: 1,800 (paid). **Subscr. to:** Taylor & Francis Ltd, Journals Customer Service, Rankine Rd, Basingstoke, Hants RG24 8PR, United Kingdom. TEL 44-1256-813000, FAX 44-1256-330245, enquiry@tandf.co.uk.

344.01 USA
LABOR LAW IN CHINA; choice and responsibility. Text in English. 1990. base vol. plus a. updates. USD 125. Supplement avail.
Published by: LexisNexis (Subsidiary of: LexisNexis North America), PO Box 7587, Charlottesville, VA 22906-7587. TEL 804-972-7600, 800-562-1197, FAX 804-972-7666, llp.customer.support@lexis-nexis.com, http://www.lexislawpublishing.com. Ed. Hilary K Josephs.

LABOR LAW INSTITUTE. see *LAW*

LABOR LAW JOURNAL; to promote sound thinking on labor law problems. see *LAW*

344.01 USA
LABOR LAW REPORTS: SUMMARY. Text in English. w. USD 159 (effective 2004). **Document type:** *Newsletter.* **Description:** Highlights current news and the latest developments in the labor law area. You'll see summaries of recent court cases, NLRB decisions, wage hour opinions and legislation on the federal and state levels. Commentary on current industry news and late-breaking developments is also included.
Published by: C C H Inc., 2700 Lake Cook Rd, Riverwoods, IL 60015. TEL 847-267-7000, 800-449-6439, cust_serv@cch.com, http://www.cch.com. Pub. Catherine Wolfe.

344.012 USA
LABOR LAWS OF VIRGINIA. Text in English. irreg., latest 1996. USD 15 (effective 2003). 140 p./no.
Published by: Michie Company (Subsidiary of: LexisNexis North America), 701 E Water St, Charlottesville, VA 22902-5389. TEL 434-972-7600, 800-446-3410, FAX 434-972-7677, http://www.michie.com.

331 USA
LABOR NEWS, INC. Text in English. 1965. m. USD 12 domestic to members; USD 24 domestic to non-members (effective 2004). **Document type:** *Newspaper, Trade.*
Address: 2620 E Tenth St, Indianapolis, IN 46201. TEL 317-264-4288, FAX 317-264-4280, webmaster@labornews.com, http://www.labornews.com. Ed. Sandra L Robinson. Pub. Fred W Levin. Circ: 40,000 (paid).

331 USA ISSN 0275-4452
LABOR NOTES. Text in English. 1979. m. USD 24 domestic to individuals; USD 30 foreign to individuals; USD 35 domestic to institutions; USD 40 foreign to institutions (effective 2004). bk.rev. illus. reprint service avail. from PQC. **Document type:** *Newsletter.* **Description:** Newsletter covering union issues and activities.
Related titles: Online - full text ed.: (from ProQuest Information & Learning, SoftLine Information).
Indexed: AltPI.
Published by: Labor Education & Research Project, 7435 Michigan Ave, Detroit, MI 48210. TEL 313-842-6262, FAX 313-842-0227, labornotes@labornotes.org, http://www.labornotes.org. Ed. Chris Kutalik. Circ: 11,000.

LABOR PARTY PRESS. see *POLITICAL SCIENCE*

344.01 USA ISSN 0149-2713
KF3315
LABOR RELATIONS (WASHINGTON, DC). Text in English. 1969. w. looseleaf. USD 938 (effective 2001). back issues avail. **Document type:** *Newsletter.* **Description:** Covers federal and state labor laws, including explanations of arbitration, NLRB and court decisions, and state board rulings. Reference materials cover many labor relations concerns: layoffs, strikes, grievances, and collective bargaining.
Related titles: Online - full text ed.; ◆ Series of: B N A Policy and Practice Series. ISSN 0005-3228.
—CCC.
Published by: The Bureau of National Affairs, Inc., 1231 25th St., NW, Washington, DC 20037. TEL 202-452-4200, 800-372-1033, 800-452-7773, FAX 202-822-8092, customercare@bna.com, bnaplus@bna.com, http://www.bna.com/. Ed. Bill L Manville. Pub. Greg C McCaffery.

344.01 USA ISSN 1080-3211
LABOR RELATIONS BULLETIN. Text in English. 1950. m. USD 219 to individuals; USD 21 newsstand/cover (effective 2003). illus. index. reprints avail. **Document type:** *Newsletter.* **Description:** Reports on the most current and relevant developments in labor law and labor relations; includes discipline and grievance cases and discusses the implications of the ruling.
Former titles (until 1994): Discipline and Grievances. White Collar Edition (0271-3462); (until 1993): Discipline and Grievances (0012-351X)
Related titles: Online - full text ed.: (from EBSCO Publishing, Florida Center for Library Automation, Gale Group).
Published by: Aspen Law & Business (Subsidiary of: Wolters Kluwer N.V.), 1185 Ave of the Americas, 37th Fl, New York, NY 10036. TEL 212-597-0210, 800-638-8437, FAX 212-597-0336, customer.service@aspenpubl.com, http://www.bbpnews.com, http://www.aspenpub.com. Ed. Robert Halprin.

344.01 USA
LABOR RELATIONS CIRCULAR. Text in English. bi-m. USD 150. back issues avail. **Document type:** *Abstract/Index.* **Description:** Contains arbitration awards and decisions of the courts and government agencies.
Published by: R.C. Simpson Co., 5950 Fairview Rd, 604, Charlotte, NC 28210. TEL 704-553-0716, FAX 704-553-0734.

331 USA
LABOR RELATIONS EXPEDITER. Text in English. 1937. bi-w. USD 798 (effective 2001).
Formerly: Labor Relations Reporter. Analysis and Expediter
Related titles: ◆ Series of: Labor Relations Reporter. ISSN 0148-7981.
Published by: The Bureau of National Affairs, Inc., 1231 25th St., NW, Washington, DC 20037. TEL 202-452-4200, 800-372-1033, 800-452-7773, FAX 202-822-8092, customercare@bna.com, bnaplus@bna.com, http://www.bna.com/. Pub. Greg C McCaffery.

344.01 USA ISSN 1046-3682
KF3352.L3
LABOR RELATIONS LAW. Text in English. 1964. q. USD 68; USD 38 to non-profit organizations (effective 2006). back issues avail. **Document type:** *Newsletter, Trade.*
Published by: (Section on Labor Law), Illinois State Bar Association, Illinois Bar Center, 424 S Second St, Springfield, IL 62701. TEL 217-525-1760, 800-252-8908, sanderson@isba.org, http://www.isba.org. Ed. Michael R Lied. Circ: 1,200.

331 USA ISSN 1043-5506
KF3315
LABOR RELATIONS REFERENCE MANUAL. Text in English. 1937. 3/yr. Available only as a part of "Labor Relations Reporter". back issues avail. **Description:** Contains a table of cases, summaries of all published NLRB decisions, and full-text of opinions of the U S Supreme Court, U S Courts of Appeals, and other courts.
Related titles: Online - full text ed.: (from The Bureau of National Affairs, Inc., Thomson West); ◆ Series of: Labor Relations Reporter. ISSN 0148-7981.
—CCC.
Published by: The Bureau of National Affairs, Inc., 1231 25th St., NW, Washington, DC 20037. TEL 202-452-4200, 800-372-1033, FAX 202-785-7167, customercare@bna.com, http://www.bna.com/products/labor/lelw.htm. Pub. Greg C McCaffery.

331.1 USA ISSN 0148-7981
KF3315
LABOR RELATIONS REPORTER. Variant title: B N A Labor Relations Reporter. Text in English. 1937. w. looseleaf. USD 6,175 domestic (effective 2005 - 2006). back issues avail. **Document type:** *Newsletter, Trade.* **Description:** Multi-part notification and reference service covering labor-management relations, wages and hours, labor arbitration, fair employment practices, and individual employment rights.
Related titles: Online - full text ed.: (from The Bureau of National Affairs, Inc., Thomson West); ◆ Series: Labor Relations Reporter. Labor Arbitration and Dispute Settlements; ◆ Individual Employment Rights. ISSN 1085-0058; ◆ Labor Relations Reporter. Fair Employment Practices; ◆ Labor Relations Reference Manual. ISSN 1043-5506; ◆ Labor Relations Reporter. State Labor Laws; ◆ Labor Relations Reporter. Wage and Hour Manual; ◆ Labor Relations Reporter. Labor - Management Relations Analysis - News and Background Information; ◆ Labor Relations Expediter; ◆ Americans with Disabilities Cases. ISSN 1076-2531; ◆ Labor Relations Reporter. Wage and Hour Cases. ISSN 1043-5689.
—CCC.
Published by: The Bureau of National Affairs, Inc., 1231 25th St., NW, Washington, DC 20037. TEL 202-452-4200, 800-372-1033, 800-452-7773, FAX 202-822-8092, customercare@bna.com, http://www.bna.com/products/labor/lelw.htm. Pub. Greg C McCaffery.

344.01 USA
LABOR RELATIONS REPORTER. FAIR EMPLOYMENT PRACTICES. Text in English. 1965. w. looseleaf. USD 1,343 (effective 2001). back issues avail. **Description:** Guide to the regulation of fair employment practices. Includes federal laws, orders, and regulations, policy guides and ground rules, and state and local fair employment practice laws.
Related titles: Microfiche ed.; Online - full text ed.: (from The Dialog Corporation, Thomson West); ◆ Series of: Labor Relations Reporter. ISSN 0148-7981.
Published by: The Bureau of National Affairs, Inc., 1231 25th St., NW, Washington, DC 20037. TEL 202-452-4200, 800-372-1033, 800-452-7773, FAX 202-822-8092, customercare@bna.com, bnaplus@bna.com, http://www.bna.com/. Pub. Greg C McCaffery.

331.1 USA
LABOR RELATIONS REPORTER. LABOR ARBITRATION AND DISPUTE SETTLEMENTS. Text in English. 1937. w. looseleaf. USD 1,333 (effective 2001). back issues avail. **Description:** Contains full-text arbitration cases and digests of court decisions involving arbitration.
Former titles: Labor Relations Reporter. Labor Arbitration; War Labor Reports
Related titles: Online - full text ed.: (from Thomson West); Cumulative ed(s).: Labor Arbitration Reports. ISSN 1043-5514; ◆ Series of: Labor Relations Reporter. ISSN 0148-7981.
Published by: The Bureau of National Affairs, Inc., 1231 25th St., NW, Washington, DC 20037. TEL 202-452-4200, 800-372-1033, 800-452-7773, FAX 202-822-8092, customercare@bna.com, bnaplus@bna.com, http://www.bna.com/. Pub. Greg C McCaffery.

331 USA
LABOR RELATIONS REPORTER. LABOR - MANAGEMENT RELATIONS. Text in English. 1937. w. looseleaf. USD 1,367 (effective 2001). **Description:** Contains digest, summaries of all published decisions of the NLRB, plus full text of federal and state court decisions. Federal laws covered are the Wagner Act, the Taft-Hartley Act, and the Landrum-Griffin Act.
Published by: The Bureau of National Affairs, Inc., 1231 25th St., NW, Washington, DC 20037. TEL 800-372-1033, 800-452-7773, customercare@bna.com, bnaplus@bna.com. Pub. Greg C McCaffery.

331 USA
LABOR RELATIONS REPORTER. LABOR - MANAGEMENT RELATIONS ANALYSIS - NEWS AND BACKGROUND INFORMATION. Text in English. w. looseleaf. USD 416 (effective 2001). 32 p./no.; back issues avail. **Description:** Summarizes developments and rulings in the field of labor law, covers major non-decisional developments and recent significant arbitration awards, and provides in-depth analysis and evaluation of the weeks labor news.
Related titles: Online - full text ed.: (from Thomson West); ◆ Series of: Labor Relations Reporter. ISSN 0148-7981.
Published by: The Bureau of National Affairs, Inc., 1231 25th St., NW, Washington, DC 20037. TEL 202-452-4200, 800-372-1033, 800-452-7773, FAX 202-822-8092, customercare@bna.com, bnaplus@bna.com, http://www.bna.com/. Pub. Greg C McCaffery.

344.01 USA
LABOR RELATIONS REPORTER. STATE LABOR LAWS. Text in English. 1954. bi-w. looseleaf. USD 1,379 (effective 2001). back issues avail. **Description:** Provides text and digest of state labor laws, covering their scope, jurisdiction, administration, and enforcement. Also discusses how state labor law relates to federal laws affecting labor relations and employment regulation, and provides directories of state agencies that administer and enforce these laws.
Related titles: ◆ Series of: Labor Relations Reporter. ISSN 0148-7981.
Published by: The Bureau of National Affairs, Inc., 1231 25th St., NW, Washington, DC 20037. TEL 202-452-4200, 800-372-1033, 800-452-7773, FAX 202-822-8092, customercare@bna.com, bnaplus@bna.com, http://www.bna.com/. Ed. Roberto Federigan. Pub. Greg C McCaffery.

331.21 344.01 USA ISSN 1043-5689
KF3315
LABOR RELATIONS REPORTER. WAGE AND HOUR CASES. Variant title: B N A Labor Relations Reporter. Wage and Hour Cases. Text in English. 1941. irreg. Available as a part of the set..
Related titles: Online - full text ed.: (from The Bureau of National Affairs, Inc.); ◆ Series of: Labor Relations Reporter. ISSN 0148-7981.
—CCC.
Published by: The Bureau of National Affairs, Inc., 1231 25th St., NW, Washington, DC 20037. TEL 202-452-4200, 800-372-1033, FAX 202-785-7167, customercare@bna.com, http://www.bna.com.

331.21 USA
LABOR RELATIONS REPORTER. WAGE AND HOUR MANUAL. Text in English. 1938. bi-w. looseleaf. USD 907 (effective 2001). back issues avail. **Description:** Full text, summaries, and explanations of federal laws and regulations in such areas as reporting, exemptions, wage-hour division inspection, minimum wages, equal pay, overtime, and child labor. Includes enforcement policies, procedures, and precedent-setting decisions.
Formerly: Labor Relations Reporter. Wages and Hours
Related titles: Online - full text ed.: (from The Dialog Corporation, Thomson West); ♦ Series of: Labor Relations Reporter. ISSN 0148-7981.
Published by: The Bureau of National Affairs, Inc., 1231 25th St., NW, Washington, DC 20037. TEL 202-452-4200, 800-372-1033, 800-452-7773, FAX 202-822-8092, customercare@bna.com, bnaplus@bna.com, http://www.bna.com/. Pub. Greg C McCaffery.

331 USA ISSN 0891-4141
KF3352
LABOR RELATIONS WEEK. Text in English. 1957. w. looseleaf. USD 1,472 domestic (effective 2005 - 2006). charts; stat. cum.index. back issues avail. **Document type:** *Trade.*
Description: Reporting service providing an overview of developments influencing labor relations in the private sector.
Formerly: White Collar Report (0043-4892); Incorporates: Retail - Services Labor Report (0148-7930); Which was formerly titled: Retail Labor Report (0034-6071)
Related titles: Online - full text ed.: ISSN 1522-8819 (from The Bureau of National Affairs, Inc.).
—CCC.
Published by: The Bureau of National Affairs, Inc., 1231 25th St., NW, Washington, DC 20037. TEL 202-452-4200, 800-372-1033, 800-452-7773, FAX 202-822-8092, customercare@bna.com, http://www.bna.com/products/labor/lrwk.htm. Ed., Pub. Greg C McCaffery.

331 USA ISSN 1547-6715
HD4854
▼ ➤ **LABOR: STUDIES IN WORKING-CLASS HISTORY OF THE AMERICAS.** Text in English. 2004. q. USD 40 to individuals; USD 210 to institutions; USD 233 combined subscription to institutions print &online eds. (effective 2006). adv. **Document type:** *Journal, Academic/Scholarly.*
Related titles: Online - full text ed.: USD 210 to institutions (effective 2006) (from EBSCO Publishing, Gale Group, IngentaConnect).
Indexed: AmH&L, HistAb, SociolAb.
—BLDSC (5137.905030).
Published by: (Campaign for Labor Rights), Duke University Press, 905 W Main St, Ste 18 B, Durham, NC 27701. TEL 919-687-3600, FAX 919-688-4574, labor@uic.edu, dukepress@duke.edu, http://dukeupress.edu/journals/j_titles.php3?user_id=
, http://www.dukeupress.edu. Ed. Leon Fink. Adv. contact Mandy Dailey-Berman TEL 919-687-3636. page USD 400.

331 USA ISSN 0160-449X
HD4802
➤ **LABOR STUDIES JOURNAL.** Text in English. 1976. q. USD 45 domestic to individuals; USD 83 foreign to individuals; USD 120 domestic to institutions; USD 158 elsewhere to institutions (effective 2004). adv. bk.rev. illus. reprint service avail. from PQC,PSC. **Document type:** *Journal, Academic/Scholarly.*
Description: Explores the role of the trade union movement in forging U.S. economic and social policy.
Related titles: Microfilm ed.: (from PQC); Online - full text ed.: ISSN 1538-9758 (from EBSCO Publishing, Florida Center for Library Automation, Gale Group, O C L C Online Computer Library Center, Inc., Project MUSE, Swets Information Services).
Indexed: ABIn, ABS&EES, AmH&L, BPI, BPIA, CISA, CJA, DIP, HistAb, IBR, IBZ, IPARL, IPSA, LRI, PAIS, PSA, RILM, SSA, SociolAb, T&II.
—BLDSC (5137.934000), IE, Infotrieve, ingenta. **CCC.**
Published by: (United Association for Labor Education), West Virginia University Press, PO Box 6295, Morgantown, WV 26506. TEL 304-293-8400, FAX 304-293-5380, press@wvu.edu, http://www.uale.org/lsj/lsj.shtml, http://www.as.wvu.edu/press. Eds. Bruce Nissan, Paul Jarley. adv.: page USD 400; 4.5 x 6.625. Circ: 800.

331 USA ISSN 1041-5904
HD8051
➤ **LABOR'S HERITAGE.** Text in English. 1989. q. USD 24 domestic; USD 32 in Canada; USD 40 elsewhere (effective 2004). illus. Index. reprints avail. **Document type:** *Journal, Academic/Scholarly.* **Description:** Scholarly-based articles written by historians, archivists, museum curators, folklorists and other writers for the general reader interested in the history of the American workplace.
Indexed: ABM, AmH&L, HistAb.
Published by: (George Meany Memorial Archives), George Meany Center for Labor Studies, 10000 New Hampshire Ave, Silver Spring, MD 20903. TEL 301-431-5451, FAX 301-431-5455, breynolds@georgemeany.org, http://www.georgemeany.org/archives/lh.html. Ed., R&P Robert Reynolds TEL 301-431-5443. Circ: 8,000 (paid).

344.01 USA ISSN 1084-2160
LABORWATCH. Text in English. 1984. m. USD 177 (effective 2000). index. back issues avail. **Document type:** *Newsletter.*
Description: Contains practical analysis of recent developments in labor law, updates in human resources management, and managing employees.
Published by: Berens & Tate, P.C., 10050 Regency Circle, Ste 400, Omaha, NE 68114. TEL 402-391-1991, 800-729-1441, FAX 402-391-7363, berens@berenstate.com. Ed., R&P Cristi L Robb. Pub. Kelvin C Berens. Circ: 3,000.

331 GBR ISSN 1121-7081
HD4811
➤ **LABOUR**; review of labour economics and industrial relations. Text in English. 1987. q. USD 381 combined subscription in the Americas to institutions & Caribbean (print & online eds.); GBP 227 combined subscription elsewhere to institutions print & online eds. (effective 2005). reprints avail. **Document type:** *Academic/Scholarly.* **Description:** Publishes work which combine both theoretical and analytical originality in the analysis of behaviour, institutions and policies relevant to the labour market.
Related titles: Online - full text ed.: ISSN 1467-9914. USD 363 in the Americas to institutions & Caribbean; GBP 216 elsewhere to institutions (effective 2005) (from Blackwell Synergy, EBSCO Publishing, Gale Group, IngentaConnect, O C L C Online Computer Library Center, Inc., Swets Information Services).
Indexed: ABIn, GEOBASE, IBSS, Inspec, JEL, SOPODA, SSA, SWA, SociolAb.
—BLDSC (5141.950530), IE, Infotrieve, ingenta. **CCC.**
Published by: Blackwell Publishing Ltd., 9600 Garsington Rd, Oxford, OX4 2ZG, United Kingdom. TEL 44-1865-776868, FAX 44-1865-714591, customerservices@oxon.blackwellpublishing.com, http://www.blackwellpublishing.com/journals/LABOUR. Ed. Renato Brunetta TEL 3-9-64746552.

331 EGY
LABOUR✶. Text in English. 1974 (no.10). s-a. bibl.; illus.
Indexed: ArtHuCI.
Published by: Alamal Magazine, 42 Elgomhoriah St., P O Box 1862, Cairo, Egypt. Ed. Abdel M Said.

331 CAN ISSN 0700-3862
CODEN: LATREZ
➤ **LABOUR/TRAVAIL**; journal of Canadian labour studies - revue d'etudes ouvrieres Canadiennes. Text in English, French. 1976. s-a. CND 25 domestic to individuals; CND 30 foreign to individuals; CND 35 domestic to institutions; CND 50 foreign to institutions; CND 15 domestic to students; CND 25 foreign to students; CND 20 per issue (effective 2005). adv. bk.rev. bibl.; illus. Index. back issues avail.; reprints avail. **Document type:** *Journal, Academic/Scholarly.* **Description:** An interdisciplinary journal of Canadian labor history. Aims to foster imaginative approaches to both teaching and research in labor studies through an open exchange of viewpoints.
Related titles: Online - full text ed.: (from Florida Center for Library Automation, Gale Group, Micromedia ProQuest).
Indexed: ASCA, AltPI, AmH&L, ArtHuCI, BibInd, CBCABus, CBPI, CPerI, CurCont, HRA, HistAb, IBSS, LeftInd, PAIS, PRA, RASB, SFSA, SPAA, SSCI, SociolAb, V&AA.
—IDS. **CCC.**
Published by: Canadian Committee on Labour History/Comite Canadien sur l'Histoire du Travail (CCHT), Faculty of Arts Publications, FM 2005, Memorial University of Newfoundland, St. John's, NF A1C 5S7, Canada. TEL 709-737-2144, FAX 709-737-4342, cclh@mun.ca, http://www.mun.ca/cclh/. Ed. Bryan D Palmer. R&P, Adv. contact Irene Whitfield. Circ: 1,200.

331 IND
LABOUR AND INDUSTRIAL CASES. Text in English. 1968. m. INR 1,320, USD 80 (effective 2000). adv. bk.rev. bibl.; charts. index.
Published by: All India Reporter Ltd., Congress Nagar, P O Box 209, Nagpur, Maharastra 440 012, India. TEL 91-712-534321, FAX 91-712-526283. Ed. V R Manohar. Circ: 4,000.

344.01 IND
LABOUR AND INDUSTRIAL LAW REPORTER. Text in English. 1975. m. USD 100 (effective 1998). **Description:** Reports all judgments of the Supreme Court and important judgments of high courts under the Industrial Disputes Act, Minimum Wages Act, Provident Fund Act, and more.
Published by: International Law Book Co., Nijhawan Bldg., Kashmere Gate, 1562 Church Rd., New Delhi, 110 006, India. TEL 91-11-296-7810, lakshmin@giasdla.vsnl.net.in.

331 AUS ISSN 1030-1763
➤ **LABOUR & INDUSTRY**; a journal of the social and economic relations of work. Text in English. 1987. 3/yr., latest vol.11, 2000. AUD 70 in Australia to individuals; AUD 80 overseas to individuals; AUD 94 in Australia to institutions; AUD 104 overseas to institutions (effective 2000). adv. bk.rev. back issues avail. **Document type:** *Academic/Scholarly.*
Description: Covers industrial relations, industrial sociology, labor economics, labor law, labor history, organization studies, labor process studies, political economy, management, public policy, and administration.
Related titles: Online - full text ed.: (from Gale Group).
Indexed: APEL, AusPAIS, PSA, SSA, SociolAb.
—BLDSC (5141.955300), IE, ingenta.
Published by: Royal Melbourne Institute of Technology, Centre for Workplace Culture Change, 2/356 Collins St, Melbourne, VIC 8007, Australia. TEL 61-3-9642-1269, FAX 61-3-9642-1326, mail@labourandindustry.com.au, http://www.labourandindustry.com.au. Ed. Ray Jureidini. R&P, Adv. contact David Clarke. **Co-sponsor:** Association of Industrial Relations Academics of Australia and New Zealand.

331 AUS
LABOUR AND MANAGEMENT IN DEVELOPMENT. Text in English. 2000. irreg. free (effective 2003). **Document type:** *Trade.* **Description:** Focuses on key factors in development frequently neglected in academic and policy debate and practice.
Media: Online - full content.
Published by: (National Centre for Development Studies), Asia Pacific Press, The Crawford Bldg, Ellery Circuit, The Australian National University, Canberra, ACT 0200, Australia. TEL 61-2-61250178, FAX 61-2-62572886, http://labour-management.anu.edu.au, http://www.asiapacificpress.com/. Ed. Michael Hess.

331 ISR ISSN 0005-2299
HD8761.P3
LABOUR AND NATIONAL INSURANCE/AVODA UBITUACH LEUMI. Text in English. 1949. m. charts; stat. cum.index every 2 yrs.
Indexed: IHP.
Published by: Ministry of Labour and Social Affairs, 10 Yad Harutzim St., Talpiod, P O Box 1260, Jerusalem, Israel. Ed. Zalman Heyn. Circ: 2,500.

331.155 CAN ISSN 0023-690X
LABOUR ARBITRATION CASES. Text in English. 1948. bi-w. (4th Series). CND 185 per vol. (effective 2005). adv. index, cum.index. 448 p./no.; **Document type:** *Trade.*
Related titles: Online - full text ed.
Published by: Canada Law Book Inc., 240 Edward St, Aurora, ON L4G 3S9, Canada. TEL 905-841-6472, 800-263-3269, FAX 905-841-5085, b.loney@canadalawbook.ca, http://www.canadalawbook.com/catalogue.cfm?DSP=Detail&ProductID=488, http://www.canadalawbook.ca. Ed. C G Simmons. Adv. contact Colleen Austin TEL 905-841-6472.

331.1 IND
LABOUR BULLETIN. Text in English. 1940. m. INR 24. adv. bk.rev.
Published by: Labour Department, Office of the Labour Commissioner, P O Box 220, Kanpur, Uttar Pradesh 208 002, India. Eds. C S Saxena, Hemant K Pant. Circ: 500.

LABOUR, CAPITAL AND SOCIETY/TRAVAIL, CAPITAL ET SOCIETE; a journal on the Third World. see *BUSINESS AND ECONOMICS—International Development And Assistance*

331 IND
LABOUR CHRONICLE. Text in English. 1968. m. INR 15. adv. bk.rev. bibl.
Related titles: Microfilm ed.: (from PQC).
Published by: Institute of Workers Education, A-30-37, Chittaranjan, Mumbai, Maharashtra 400 077, India. Ed. R Muthuswamy. Circ: 26,000.

331 PAK
LABOUR CODE OF PAKISTAN. Text in English. 1953. irreg., latest 1993. USD 250.
Published by: Bureau of Labour Publications, 8, Business Centre Mumtaz Hasan Rd., P O Box 5833, Karachi, 74000, Pakistan. TEL 92-21-2414975. Ed. P Shafi.

331 NLD ISSN 0927-5371
HD4811 CODEN: LECOE3
➤ **LABOUR ECONOMICS.** Text in English. 1993. 6/yr. EUR 60 in Europe to individuals; JPY 7,000 in Japan to individuals; USD 62 elsewhere to individuals; EUR 443 in Europe to institutions; JPY 58,800 in Japan to institutions; USD 495 elsewhere to institutions (effective 2006). bk.rev. back issues avail.
Document type: *Academic/Scholarly.* **Description:** Publishes research in the field of labor economics both on the microeconomic and macroeconomic level, covering theory, empirical testing and policy applications and analysis.
Related titles: Microform ed.: (from PQC); Online - full text ed.: (from EBSCO Publishing, Gale Group, IngentaConnect, ScienceDirect, Swets Information Services).
Indexed: CurCont, DIP, IBR, IBZ, JEL, SSCI.
—BLDSC (5142.086000), IE, Infotrieve, ingenta. **CCC.**
Published by: Elsevier BV, North-Holland (Subsidiary of: Elsevier Science & Technology), Sara Burgerhartstraat 25, Amsterdam, 1055 KV, Netherlands. TEL 31-20-485-3911, FAX 31-20-485-2457, labecon@essex.ac.uk, nlinfo-f@elsevier.nl, http://www.elsevier.com/locate/labeco, http://www.elsevier.nl. Ed. A Ichino. **Subscr. to:** Elsevier BV, PO Box 211, Amsterdam 1000 AE, Netherlands. TEL 31-20-485-3757, FAX 31-20-485-3432, http://www.elsevier.nl.

331.0715 CHE ISSN 0378-5467
LC5001
LABOUR EDUCATION. Text in English. 1964. q. CHF 55, USD 44 (effective 2002). bk.rev. bibl.; illus. reprint service avail. from PQC. **Document type:** *Bulletin, Trade.* **Description:** Articles of interest to trade union organizations, public authorities and individuals concerned with labor education. Includes activities of the ILO, methods and techniques, and history.
Related titles: Microform ed.: (from ILO); French ed.: Education Ouvriere. ISSN 0378-5572; Spanish ed.: Educacion Obrera. ISSN 0378-5564.
Indexed: CIJE, CPE, ERA, ETA, ILD, MEA, RASB, RHEA, SEA, SENA, SOMA, TEA.
—CCC.
Published by: (International Labour Office), I L O Publications, PO Box 6, Geneva 22, 1211, Switzerland. TEL 41-22-799-6111, FAX 41-22-798-6350, TELEX 425647-ILO-CH, publns@ilo.org, http://www.ilo.org/publns. Ed. Clara Foucault Mohammed. Circ: 2,500. **Dist. in US by:** I L O Publications Center, 9 Jay Gould Court, Ste. CT, PO Box 753, Waldorf, MD 20604. TEL 301-638-3152, FAX 301-843-0159, ilopubs@tasco1.com.

331.11 CAN ISSN 1480-5502
LABOUR FORCE HISTORICAL REVIEW. Text in English, French. a. CND 209 (effective 2004).
Media: CD-ROM.
Published by: Statistics Canada, Publications Sales and Services, Ottawa, ON K1A 0T6, Canada. infostats@statcan.ca, http://www.statcan.ca.

LABOUR FORCE SURVEY. see *BUSINESS AND ECONOMICS—Abstracting, Bibliographies, Statistics*

331.1 CAN ISSN 1206-6400
LABOUR FORCE UPDATE. Text in Multiple languages. 1997. q.
—CISTI.
Published by: Statistics Canada, Communications Division, 3rd Fl, R H Coats Bldg, Ottawa, ON K1A 0A6, Canada. TEL 613-951-7277, FAX 613-951-1584, infostats@statcan.ca, http://www.statcan.ca.

331 IND ISSN 0023-6934
LABOUR GAZETTE. Text in English. 1921. m. INR 100. adv. bk.rev. bibl.; charts; stat. index.
Related titles: Microfiche ed.: (from BHP).
Indexed: PAIS, RASB.
Published by: Commissioner of Labour, Commerce Centre, Tardeo, Mumbai, Maharashtra 400 034, India. Ed. Shri R R Korosiya. Circ: 700.

331.09 AUS ISSN 0023-6942
HD6891.A13
➤ **LABOUR HISTORY;** a journal of labour and social history. Text in English. 1962 (Jan.). s-a. (May & Nov.). AUD 50 domestic to individuals; AUD 65 in New Zealand to individuals; AUD 70 elsewhere to individuals; AUD 75 domestic to institutions; AUD 90 in New Zealand to institutions; AUD 105 elsewhere to institutions; AUD 110 domestic to libraries; AUD 130 in New Zealand to libraries; AUD 150 elsewhere to libraries (effective 2005). bk.rev. charts; illus. back issues avail. **Document type:** *Journal, Academic/Scholarly.* **Description:** Publishes essays, reviews, and memoirs that reflect the involvement of labour historians in the making of history.
Formerly (until Nov. 1962): Australian Society for the Study of Labour History. Bulletin
Related titles: Online - full text ed.: (from R M I T Publishing).
Indexed: AESIS, AmH&L, AusPAIS, HistAb, IBSS, PCI, RASB, SRRA, WorkRelAb.
—BLDSC (5142.160000), IE, Infotrieve, ingenta.
Published by: Australian Society for the Study of Labour History, c/o Margaret Walters, Rm 519, Level 5, Economics & Business Bldg H69, University of Sydney, Sydney, NSW 2006, Australia. TEL 61-2-93513786, FAX 61-2-93516755, m.walters@econ.usyd.edu.au, http://www.asslh.com/. Ed. Greg Patmore TEL 61-2-93514264. Circ: 1,000.

331.09 GBR ISSN 0961-5652
HD4805
➤ **LABOUR HISTORY REVIEW.** Text in English. 1960. 3/yr. USD 44 in North America to individuals; GBP 24 elsewhere to individuals; USD 158 in North America to institutions; GBP 89 elsewhere to institutions (effective 2005). bk.rev. bibl. cum.index. reprint service avail. from SCH. **Document type:** *Journal, Academic/Scholarly.* **Description:** Explores the working lives and politics of "ordinary" people. The emphasis is on British labour history, though comparative and international studies are not neglected.
Formerly (until 1989): Society for the Study of Labour History. Bulletin (0049-1179)
Related titles: Microfiche ed.; Online - full text ed.: ISSN 1745-8188 (from EBSCO Publishing, Gale Group, IngentaConnect).
Indexed: ABIn, AmH&L, HistAb, MEA&I, PCI, PSA, RASB.
—CCC.
Published by: (Society for the Study of Labour History - North West Labour History Group), Maney Publishing, Hudson Rd, Leeds, W Yorks LS9 7DL, United Kingdom. TEL 44-113-2497481, FAX 44-113-2486983, maney@maney.co.uk, http://www.maney.co.uk/search?fwaction=show&fwid=181. Eds. June Hannam, Tony Adams. Adv. contact Mary Starkey TEL 44-113-2846124. Circ: 1,000. **US Subscr. addr.:** Maney Publishing North America, 875 Massachusetts Ave, 7th Fl., Cambridge, MA 02139. TEL 866-297-5154, FAX 617-354-6875, maney@maneyusa.com.

344.01 ZAF ISSN 1026-6593
LABOUR LAW DIGEST. Text in English. 1992. m. ZAR 380 (effective 2001). **Document type:** *Journal, Abstract/Index.* **Description:** Contains a table of cases, index, highlights and case summaries of labout law cases. For lawyers and human resource managers.
Formerly (until 1996): Labour Court Digest (1019-9268)
Published by: Juta & Company Ltd., Law and Professional Publishing Division, PO Box 14373, Kenwyn, 7790, South Africa. TEL 27-21-7975101, FAX 27-21-7970121, cserv@juta.co.za, http://www.juta.co.za.

LABOUR LAW JOURNAL. see *LAW*

344.01 IND
LABOUR LAW REPORTER; a journal for human resources development. Text in English. 1970. m. USD 60 in United States. adv. bk.rev. **Description:** Covers appointment letters to the employees appointed in various activities, model agreements with contractor's employees, charge-sheets for various misconducts, model settlements with various unions and workmen, model service rules, standing orders, leave rules etc., Notices for dismissal, discharge, suspension, retirement, closure of establishment, transfer of employee etc.
Address: A-43, Lajpat Nagar-II, New Delhi, 110 024, India. TEL 91-11-6847174, FAX 91-11-2934694, hlkumar@vsnl.com. Ed., R&P Gaurav Kumar TEL 91-11-6847175. Pub. H L Kumar. Circ: 9,000 (paid).

344.01 ZAF ISSN 1023-3806
LABOUR LAW REPORTS. Text in English. m. back issues avail.
Formerly (until 1994): Labour Law Compendium
Published by: LexisNexis Butterworths South Africa (Subsidiary of: LexisNexis Europe and Africa), PO Box 792, Durban, KwaZulu-Natal 4000, South Africa. TEL 27-31-294247, FAX 27-31-283255.

332.6 ZAF
LABOUR LAW THROUGH THE CASES. Text in English. s-a. ZAR 475 (effective 2000). **Document type:** *Newsletter.* **Description:** Publishes cases and commentary on the most important labor law cases from the South African Labour Law Reports.
Media: Online - full text.
Published by: Van Zyl, Rudd and Associates, Centrahil, PO Box 12758, Port Elizabeth, 6006, South Africa. TEL 27-41-373-4322, FAX 41-27-373-4323, info@vanzylrudd.co.za, http://www.vanzylrudd.co.za. Ed. Carol Rudd.

344.01 NLD ISSN 1387-0777
LABOUR LAWS OF EUROPE. Text in Dutch. 1998. irreg. looseleaf. **Document type:** *Journal, Academic/Scholarly.* **Description:** Provides an overview of labor laws within the EU, covering national and European regulations and developments.
Published by: Global Law Association, PO Box 9001, Tilburg, 5000 HA, Netherlands. TEL 31-13-544-3135, FAX 31-24-355-4827, globallaw@writeme.com, http://web.inter.nl.net/hcc/global.wolf/, http://www.globallaw.org. Ed. Jim Johnsson. **Subscr. to:** PO Box 30151, Nijmegen 6503 CB, Netherlands. **Dist. in N. America by:** Wm. W. Gaunt & Sons Inc., Gaunt Bldg, 3011 Gulf Dr, Holmes Beach, FL 34217-2199. TEL 941-778-5211, 941-778-5252.

344.01 CAN ISSN 0383-3372
KEN7799.A72
LABOUR LEGISLATION IN NOVA SCOTIA. Text in English. irreg. **Document type:** *Government.* **Description:** Summary of legislative provisions applicable to labor in Nova Scotia.
Published by: Department of Labour, Research Division, P O Box 697, Halifax, NS B3J 2T8, Canada. TEL 902-424-8474, http://www.gov.ns.ca/labr/.

331 CHE ISSN 0538-8325
HD6961.A1
LABOUR-MANAGEMENT RELATIONS SERIES. Text in English. irreg. price varies. **Document type:** *Monographic series.*
Related titles: Microform ed.: (from ILO).
Indexed: RASB.
Published by: (International Labour Office), I L O Publications, PO Box 6, Geneva 22, 1211, Switzerland. TEL 41-22-799-6111, FAX 41-22-798-6358. **Dist. in US by:** I L O Publications Center, 9 Jay Gould Court, Ste. CT, PO Box 753, Waldorf, MD 20604. TEL 301-638-3152, FAX 301-843-0159, ilopubs@tasco1.com.

331.1 GBR ISSN 1361-4819
HD8381
LABOUR MARKET TRENDS. Text in English. 1893. m. GBP 85 domestic; GBP 116 foreign; GBP 9 newsstand/cover (effective 2000). charts; stat. index. reprint service avail. from PQC. **Document type:** *Government.* **Description:** Contains a comprehensive selection of labor market statistics, earnings, employment, labor disputes, redundancies, Retail Price Index, government training and enterprise programs, unemployment and vacancies.
Former titles (until 1995): Employment Gazette (0264-7052); (until 1980): Great Britain. Department of Employment. Employment Gazette (0013-6859)
Related titles: Microform ed.: (from PQC); Online - full text ed.: (from EBSCO Publishing, O C L C Online Computer Library Center, Inc., ProQuest Information & Learning).
Indexed: ABIn, M&MA, PAIS, WTA.
—BLDSC (5142.264740), IE, Infotrieve, ingenta. **CCC.**
Published by: Office for National Statistics, c/o Phil Lewin, Room B110, Pimlico, London, SW1V 2QQ, United Kingdom. TEL 44-20-7533-6165, FAX 44-20-7533-6185, http://www.statistics.gov.uk/nsbase/themes/labour_market/. Ed. David Bradbury. Circ: 5,000. **Subscr. to:** Stationery Office Publications Center, PO Box 276, London SW8 5DT, United Kingdom.

331.072 GBR ISSN 0023-7000
LABOUR RESEARCH. Text in English. 1917. m. GBP 27.50; GBP 28 foreign. adv. bk.rev. stat. index. **Document type:** *Trade.* **Description:** Covers political and industrial issues from a trade union perspective.
Related titles: Microfilm ed.: (from WMP).
Indexed: CSNB, LHB, PAIS, RASB.
—BLDSC (5142.500000), IE, Infotrieve, ingenta. **CCC.**
Published by: Labour Research Department, 78 Blackfriars Rd, London, SE1 8HF, United Kingdom. Ed. Clare Ruhemann. Adv. contact Ali Brown. Circ: 6,000.

331 GBR ISSN 1360-2020
LABOUR STUDIES WORKING PAPERS. Text in English. 1995. irreg. GBP 3. **Document type:** *Monographic series, Academic/Scholarly.*
—BLDSC (9348.714600).
Published by: University of Warwick, Centre for Comparative Labour Studies, University Of Warwick, Gibbet Hill Rd, Coventry, Warks CV4 7AL, United Kingdom.

331 ZAF
LABOUR UPDATE. Text in English. irreg. free.
Related titles: Online - full text ed.
Published by: Deneys Reitz Attorneys, PO Box 61334, Marshalltown, Johannesburg 2107, South Africa. TEL 27-11-8335600, FAX 27-11-8387444, jhb@deneysreitz.co.za, http://www.deneysreitz.co.za. Ed. Patrick Bracher. R&P Jacqui Hampton.

331 IND ISSN 0023-7035
HD4811
LABOUR WORLD✶. Text in English. 1969. m. adv. charts; illus.; stat.
Published by: Labour World Publications, 36-4 Ganya Ram Hospital, New Delhi, 100 005, India. Ed. E X Joseph.

331 GBR
LABOURSTART. Text in English. d.
Media: Online - full content.
Published by: Labour and Society International, ITF Bldg, Third Fl, 49-60 Borough Rd, London, SE1 1DS, United Kingdom. ecotton@isi.org.uk, http://www.labourstart.org. Ed. Eric Lee.

LABSTAT UPDATES. see *BUSINESS AND ECONOMICS—Abstracting, Bibliographies, Statistics*

331.11 SWE ISSN 0349-7143
LAG & AVTAL; tidningen om arbetsraett i praktiken. Text in Swedish. 1978. 10/yr. SEK 1,076 print edition; SEK 2,200 print & online eds.; SEK 538 to students print & online eds.; SEK 150 per issue (effective 2003). adv. bk.rev. index. Supplement avail.; back issues avail. **Document type:** *Magazine, Trade.* **Description:** News and features on Swedish labor law and industrial relations and legal questions that affect labor.
Related titles: Audio cassette/tape ed.; Online - full content ed.
Published by: (Stiftelsen Arbetsraettslig Tidskrift), Ekonomi och Teknik Foerlag, Maester Samuelsgatan 56, Stockholm, 10612, Sweden. TEL 46-8-7966650, FAX 46-8-202157, redaktionen@lag-avtal.nu, info@et.se, http://www.lag-avtal.nu, http://www.et.se. Ed. Johanna Kronlid. Adv. contact Peter Lithander TEL 46-8-7966637. B&W page SEK 12,600, color page SEK 23,000; trim 180 x 265. Circ: 9,000.

LAMY NEGOCIATION COLLECTIVE. see *LAW—Corporate Law*

LAMY PAYE. see *LAW—Corporate Law*

LAMY REMUNERATIONS COMPLEMENTAIRES. see *LAW—Corporate Law*

331 344.01 ESP ISSN 1575-7048
HD8589.P35
LAN HARREMANAK; revista de relaciones laborales. Text in Spanish. 1999. s-a. EUR 20 to individuals; EUR 40 to institutions (effective 2004). 250 p./no.; back issues avail. **Document type:** *Journal, Academic/Scholarly.* **Description:** Covers organizational and legal work issues.
Related titles: Online - full text ed.
Published by: (Universidad del Pais Vasco, Escuela Universitaria de Relaciones Laborales), Universidad del Pais Vasco, Servicio Editorial, Apartado 1397, Bilbao, 48080, Spain. TEL 34-94-6015126, FAX 34-94-4801314, luxedito@lg.ehu.es, http://www.ehu.es/servicios/se_az/pags/p40.htm. Ed. Mr. Juan Hernandez. R&P, Adv. contact Mr. Juan J Rodriguez.

LANCASTER'S EDUCATION EMPLOYMENT LAW NEWS. see *LAW*

LANCASTER'S LABOUR ARBITRATION NEWS. see *LAW*

LANCASTER'S LABOUR LAW NEWS. see *LAW*

331.152 DEU ISSN 0943-0865
LANDESPERSONALVERTRETUNGSGESETZ FUER DEN FREISTAAT SACHSEN. Text in German. 1992. irreg. price varies. **Document type:** *Monographic series, Trade.*
Published by: Erich Schmidt Verlag GmbH & Co. (Berlin), Genthiner Str 30G, Berlin, 10785, Germany. TEL 49-30-250085-0, FAX 49-30-25008511, esv@esvmedien.de, http://www.erich-schmidt-verlag.de.

331.152 DEU ISSN 0943-2124
LANDESPERSONALVERTRETUNGSGESETZ MECKLENBURG - VORPOMMERN. Text in German. 1992. irreg. price varies. **Document type:** *Monographic series, Trade.*
Published by: Erich Schmidt Verlag GmbH & Co. (Berlin), Genthiner Str 30G, Berlin, 10785, Germany. TEL 49-30-250085-0, FAX 49-30-25008511, esv@esvmedien.de, http://www.erich-schmidt-verlag.de.

331.152 DEU ISSN 0943-349X
LANDESPERSONALVERTRETUNGSGESETZ SACHSEN-ANHALT. Text in German. 1992. irreg. price varies. **Document type:** *Monographic series, Trade.*
Published by: Erich Schmidt Verlag GmbH & Co. (Berlin), Genthiner Str 30G, Berlin, 10785, Germany. TEL 49-30-250085-0, FAX 49-30-25008511, esv@esvmedien.de, http://www.erich-schmidt-verlag.de.

331.152 DEU ISSN 0943-0873
LANDESPERSONALVERTRETUNGSGESETZ THUERINGEN. Text in German. 1992. irreg. price varies. **Document type:** *Monographic series, Trade.*
Published by: Erich Schmidt Verlag GmbH & Co. (Berlin), Genthiner Str 30G, Berlin, 10785, Germany. TEL 49-30-250085-0, FAX 49-30-25008511, esv@esvmedien.de, http://www.erich-schmidt-verlag.de.

331 VNM ISSN 0866-7950
LAO DONG/LABOR. Text in Vietnamese. 1929. d. VND 2,000 newsstand/cover (effective until 2004). adv. Website rev. 8 p./no.; **Document type:** *Newspaper, Consumer.* **Description:** Covers domestic and foreign politics, external relations, economics, and culture, as well as issues relating to Vietnamese working class.
Related titles: Online - full text ed.
Published by: Lao Dong Newspaper (Subsidiary of: Vietnam General Confederation of Labour), 51 Hang Bo, Hanoi, Viet Nam. TEL 84-4-8252441, FAX 84-4-8288658, laodong@fpt.vn, http://www.laodong.com.vn. Ed., Pub., R&P Pham Huy Hoan TEL 84-4-8286744. Adv. contact Truong Loc TEL 84-8-9303023. B&W page VND 17,600,000, color page VND 23,100,000; trim 37.5 x 52. Circ: 80,000 (paid). **Dist. by:** Xunlasaba. TEL 84-4-8260382, xunhasaba@hn.vnn.vn.

331.11 CHN ISSN 1671-346X
LAODONG JINGJI YU LAODONG GUANXI/LABOUR ECONOMICS AND LABOR RELATIONS. Text in Chinese. 1980. q. CNY 36 (effective 2004). 96 p./no.; **Description:** Contains labor force studies.
Former titles: Laodong Jingji/Labor Economics; (until 199?): Laodong Jingji yu Renli Ziyuan Guanli (1005-4324); (until 1993): Laodong Jingji yu Renshi Guanli (1001-3164)
Indexed: RASB.
Published by: Zhongguo Renmin Daxue, Shubao Zilio Zhongxin/Renmin University of China, Information Center for Social Server, Dongcheng-qu, 3, Zhangzizhong Lu, Beijing, 100007, China. TEL 86-10-64039458, FAX 86-10-64015080, kyes@163.net, http://www.confucius.cn.net/bkdetail.asp?fzt=F103. **Dist. in US by:** China Publications Service, PO Box 49614, Chicago, IL 60649. TEL 312-288-3291, FAX 312-288-8570.

LARSON'S WORKERS' COMPENSATION: DESK EDITION. see *INSURANCE*

331 DNK ISSN 0909-6418
LEDERNE. Text in Danish. 1908. m. membership. adv. bk.rev. stat. index. **Document type:** *Newsletter.*
Formerly (until 1994): Arbejdslederen (0003-7826); Which incorporates (1910-1948): Staalet (0038-8831)
Related titles: Online - full text ed.
Published by: Ledernes Hovedorganisation/Danish Association of Managers and Executives, Vermlandsgade 63, Copenhagen S, 2300, Denmark. TEL 45-32-833283, FAX 45-32-833284, lh@lederne.dk, http://www.lederne.dk. Ed. Finn Poulsen. Circ: 78,532.

LEGAL ADVICE ON PENSIONS. see *LAW—Civil Law*

344.01 USA ISSN 0458-9599
KF3512.A16
LEGAL - LEGISLATIVE REPORTER. NEWS BULLETIN. Text in English. 1966. m. USD 190 (effective 2003). Index. 12 p./no. 3 cols./p.; back issues avail.; reprints avail. **Document type:** *Bulletin, Trade.* **Description:** Summaries of legal, legislative and regulatory developments related to employee benefits.
Former titles: N F Legal Legislative Reporter News Bulletin (National Foundation of Health, Welfare and Pension Plans) (0027-6510); Legal Legislative Reports. News Bulletin
Related titles: Microform ed.: (from PQC).
Indexed: LII.
—CCC.
Published by: International Foundation of Employee Benefit Plans, 18700 W Bluemound Rd, Box 69, Brookfield, WI 53008-0069. TEL 262-786-6700, FAX 262-786-8780, books@ifebp.org, http://www.ifebp.org. Ed. Harry W Burton. Circ: 36,000.

344.01 USA
LEGALINES: LABOR LAW KEYED TO THE COX CASEBOOK. Text in English. irreg., latest vol.12. USD 18.95 per vol.. **Document type:** *Trade.*
Published by: Gilbert Law Summaries (Subsidiary of: B A R / B R I Group), 111 W Jackson, 7th Fl, Chicago, IL 60604. TEL 312-853-3662, 800-787-8717, FAX 312-853-3622, http://www.gilbertlaw.com.

344.01 USA
LEGALINES: LABOR LAW KEYED TO THE MERRIFIELD CASEBOOK. Text in English. irreg., latest vol.9. USD 20.95 per vol.. **Document type:** *Trade.*
Published by: Gilbert Law Summaries (Subsidiary of: B A R / B R I Group), 111 W Jackson, 7th Fl, Chicago, IL 60604. TEL 312-853-3662, 800-787-8717, FAX 312-853-3622, http://www.gilbertlaw.com.

344.01 ESP ISSN 1578-1992
LEGISLACION LABORAL Y DE SEGURIDAD SOCIAL. Text in Spanish. 1988. w. **Document type:** *Journal, Trade.*
Formerly (until 2000): Actualidad Laboral. Legislacion (1133-2611)
Related titles: ♦ Supplement to: Actualidad Laboral (Edicion Semanal). ISSN 0213-7097.
Published by: La Ley, Calle Collado Mediano, No. 9, Las Rozas (Madrid), 28230, Spain. TEL 34-902-420010, FAX 34-902-420012, clientes@laley.net, http://www.laley.net/.

331 CHE
LEGISLATIVE INFORMATION. Text in English. m. back issues avail. **Document type:** *Bulletin, Academic/Scholarly.* **Description:** Provides bibliographic records for the most recent and important legislation that has been added to the NATLEX database.
Media: Online - full content. **Related titles:** Esperanto ed.; French ed.
Published by: International Labour Organization, 4, route des Morillons, Geneva 22, CH-1211, Switzerland. TEL 41-22-799-6111, FAX 41-22-798-8685, ilo@ilo.org, http://natlex.ilo.org/leginf/english/index.htm, http://www.ilo.org/.

331.2 GBR
LEISURE MAGAZINE; the benefits magazine for royal mail employees & pensioners. Text in English. bi-m. adv. **Document type:** *Magazine, Consumer.* **Description:** Covers all aspects of benefits and leisure activities for Royal Mail employees.
Published by: (Great Britain. Royal Mail), C & B Communications, 40 Marsh Wall, Docklands, London, E14 9TP, United Kingdom. TEL 44-20-7308-8500, FAX 44-20-7308-8555, info@cbcomm.co.uk, http://www.cbcomm.co.uk. Adv. contact Caroline Hales. Circ: 390,000 (controlled and free).

331 DEU
DER LETRONER. Text in German. 1985. s-a. **Description:** News for employees of the Letron company and neighbors of its plant.
Published by: Letron GmbH, Dorfstr 2, Aschaffenburg, 63741, Germany. TEL 06021-406350. Ed. Jochen E Kamenik.

331 FRA ISSN 0024-1725
LIAISONS SOCIALES. Text in French. 1946. d. FRF 3,400 (effective 1998). adv. bk.rev. stat. index.
Indexed: CISA, ILD, RASB, WBSS.
Published by: Groupe Liaisons S.A. (Subsidiary of: Wolters Kluwer BV), 1 Avenue Edouard Belin, Rueil Malmaison, Cedex 92856, France. TEL 33-1-41299696, FAX 33-1-41299880, http://www.liaisons-sociales.presse.fr/. Circ: 35,000.

331 GBR ISSN 0262-1452
LINCOLNSHIRE INFORMATION. EMPLOYMENT. Text in English. 1981. a. charts; illus.
Published by: Lincolnshire County Council, County Planning Office, Lincolnshire County Council, Newland, Lincoln, LN1 1YG, United Kingdom.

LITERATURE OF AMERICAN LABOR SERIES. see *BUSINESS AND ECONOMICS—Abstracting, Bibliographies, Statistics*

LITIGATION ECONOMICS DIGEST. see *BUSINESS AND ECONOMICS—Domestic Commerce*

331 GBR ISSN 0306-0837
HD8399.W3
LLAFUR. Text in English. 1972. a. GBP 10 domestic; GBP 15 foreign (effective 2000). adv. bk.rev. back issues avail. **Document type:** *Academic/Scholarly.*
Indexed: AmH&L, HistAb.
—BLDSC (5285.560000), IE, ingenta.
Published by: Welsh Labour History Society, c/o Robert V Smith, University of Wales, Centre for Advanced Welsh and Celtic Studies, Aberystwyth, Ceredigion, SY23 3HH, United Kingdom. Eds. Mari Williams, Neil Evans. R&P Dr. Robert V Smith TEL 44-1970-626717. Circ: 1,200.

331.11 GBR ISSN 0950-3080
LOCAL WORK. Text in English. 1986. 10/yr. GBP 40 (effective 2001). back issues avail. **Document type:** *Bulletin, Trade.* **Description:** Each issue looks at a topic of interest in the field of economic regeneration. Writers are experts in that area or are academics.
—BLDSC (5290.048960).
Published by: Centre for Local Economic Strategies, Barclay House Ground Fl, W, 35 Whitworth St, Manchester, Lancs M1 3QW, United Kingdom. TEL 44-161-236-7036, FAX 44-161-236-1891, info@cles.org.uk, http://www.cles.org.uk. Ed. Pauline Sturges.

331 SWE ISSN 1651-050X
LOENEBILDNINGEN; samhaellsekonomiska foerutsaettningar i Sverige. Text in Swedish. 2002. a. free (effective 2005).
Related titles: Online - full text ed.; ♦ English ed.: Wage Formation. ISSN 1651-4750.
Published by: Konjunkturinstitutet/National Institute of Economic Research, Kungsgatan 12-14, PO Box 3116, Stockholm, 10362, Sweden. TEL 46-8-4535900, FAX 46-8-4535980, ki@konj.se, http://www.konj.se.

331 SWE ISSN 1103-3878
HD5051
LOENNER I SVERIGE/WAGES AND SALARIES IN SWEDEN; en redovisning av loener och loeneutveckling for olika loentagargrupper. Text in Swedish. 1991. biennial. SEK 230 (effective 1993).
Published by: (Statiska Centralybraan), S C B Foerlag, Orebro, 70189, Sweden.

331.21 GBR
LONDON EXCLUDING CENTRAL SALARY SURVEY. Text in English. 2/yr. GBP 280 per edition (effective 2001). **Document type:** *Bulletin.* **Description:** Pay and benefit salary survey for the outer circle of London.
Published by: The Reward Group Ltd., Reward House, Diamond Way, Stone Business Park, Stone, Staffs ST15 0SD, United Kingdom. TEL 44-1785-813566, FAX 44-1785-817007, enquiries@reward-group.co.uk, http://www.reward-group.co.uk.

331.21 GBR
LONDON SECRETARIAL AND CLERICAL REWARDS. Text in English. 2/yr. GBP 280 per edition (effective 2001). **Document type:** *Bulletin.* **Description:** Salary survey providing information on secretarial jobs based in London.
Formerly (until 2000): Secretarial Staff in London
Published by: The Reward Group Ltd., Reward House, Diamond Way, Stone Business Park, Stone, Staffs ST15 0SD, United Kingdom. TEL 44-1785-813566, FAX 44-1785-817007, enquiries@reward-group.co.uk, http://www.reward-group.co.uk.

LONE STAR SOCIALIST; voice of the Socialist Party of Texas. see *POLITICAL SCIENCE*

331 USA ISSN 0024-6484
LORAIN LABOR LEADER. Text in English. m. membership. **Document type:** *Newspaper.*
Address: 2501 Broadway, Lorain, OH 44052. TEL 216-244-1358, FAX 216-244-3795. Ed. John Koscho. Circ: 3,000.

331.11 GBR
LOTHIAN & EDINBURGH LABOUR MARKET ASSESSMENT. Text in English. a. free. **Document type:** *Government.* **Description:** Provides an insight into industrial, employment, occupational, skill, and travel-to-work trends in the Lothian labor market.
Published by: City of Edinburgh Council, City Development Department, 1 Cockburn St, Edinburgh, EH1 1BJ, United Kingdom. TEL 44-131-5294849, FAX 44-131-5293215. Ed. Martin Wight.

LOUISIANA EMPLOYMENT LAW LETTER. see *LAW*

B

331.12 USA
LOUISIANA LABOR MARKET INFORMATION. Text in English. m. illus. **Document type:** *Government.* **Description:** Articles and statistics of employment and payroll trends and other labor information.
Formerly: Louisiana Labor Market (0091-4711)
Related titles: Microfiche ed.: (from CIS).
Indexed: SRI.
Published by: Department of Labor, PO Box 44094, Baton Rouge, LA 70804-9094. TEL 504-342-3141. Circ: 2,500.

331.255 USA
THE (YEAR) M T A S SALARY AND FRINGE BENEFIT SURVEY. Text in English. a. USD 2 (effective 1999). charts; stat. **Description:** Monitors the salaries and benefits earned by Tennessee municipal employees.
Formerly (until 1994): Salary and Fringe Benefits Survey of Tennessee Municipalities
Published by: University of Tennessee at Knoxville, Municipal Technical Advisory Service, 600 Henley, Ste 120, Knoxville, TN 37996-4105. TEL 423-974-0411, FAX 423-974-0423.

MACAO. DIRECCAO DOS SERVICOS DE ESTATISTICA E CENSOS. INDICES E SALARIOS NA CONSTRUCAO CIVIL/MACAO. CENSUS AND STATISTICS DEPARTMENT. INDEXES AND WAGES IN CIVIL CONTRUCTION. see *BUSINESS AND ECONOMICS—Abstracting, Bibliographies, Statistics*

331.255 USA
MAINE CONSTRUCTION WAGE RATES. Text in English. a. free. **Document type:** *Government.* **Description:** Contains results of the annual construction wage rate survey.
Related titles: Series of: Maine. Department of Labor. Bureau of Labor Standards. BLS Bulletin.
Published by: (Maine. Technical Services Division), Department of Labor, Bureau of Labor Standards, 45 State House Station, Augusta, ME 04333-0045. TEL 207-624-6440, FAX 207-624-6449, webmaster_bls@state.me.us. Ed., R&P Ruth A Ladd. Circ: 1,463.

MAINE. DEPARTMENT OF LABOR. BUREAU OF LABOR STANDARDS. SUBSTANCE ABUSE TESTING REPORT. see *DRUG ABUSE AND ALCOHOLISM*

MAINE EMPLOYMENT LAW LETTER. see *LAW*

331.1 USA
MAINE LABOR MARKET DIGEST. Text in English. 1962. m. free. charts. **Document type:** *Newsletter, Government.* **Description:** Updates on labor force, employment, unemployment and other related economic data.
Formerly: Maine Manpower (0025-0686)
Related titles: Microfiche ed.: (from CIS).
Indexed: SRI.
Published by: Department of Labor, Division of Labor Market Information Services, 20 Union St, Augusta, ME 04330-6826. TEL 207-287-2271. Ed., R&P Ray A Fongemie. Circ: 3,600.

MAJOR PROGRAMS. see *BUSINESS AND ECONOMICS—Economic Situation And Conditions*

352.63 MYS
MALAYSIAN EMPLOYERS FEDERATION ANNUAL REPORT. Text in English. 1962. a. membership only. **Document type:** *Corporate.*
Published by: Malaysian Employers Federation/Persekutuan Majikan Malaysia, PO Box 11026, Kuala Lumpur, 50732, Malaysia. TEL 60-3-755-7778, FAX 60-3-755-6808, 60-3-755-9008, TELEX MEF MA 31862. Ed. Shamsuddin Bardan. Circ: 2,100.

331 IND ISSN 0258-042X
HD28
MANAGEMENT AND LABOUR STUDIES. Text in English. 1975. q. INR 100, USD 25. adv. bk.rev. reprints avail. **Document type:** *Academic/Scholarly.*
Indexed: HRA, ManagAb, PAA&I, PsycholAb, SPAA, SUSA.
—BLDSC (5359.008500), IE, ingenta.
Published by: Xavier Labour Relations Institute, Jamshedpur, Bihar 831 001, India. FAX 91-657-7814, TELEX 626 240 XLRI IN. Ed. T A Mathias. R&P T.A. Mathias. Circ: 1,500.

331 USA ISSN 0745-4880
MANAGEMENT REPORT; for nonunion organizations. Text in English. 1978. m. USD 995 in North America; USD 1,067 elsewhere; USD 1,095 combined subscription in North America print & online eds.; USD 1,167 combined subscription elsewhere print & online eds. (effective 2005). adv. **Document type:** *Magazine, Trade.* **Description:** Discusses non-union alternatives for organization management.
Formerly (until 1983): Hughes Report (0732-7919)
Related titles: Online - full text ed.: ISSN 1530-8286. USD 995 (effective 2005) (from EBSCO Publishing, ProQuest Information & Learning, Swets Information Services, Wiley InterScience).
Indexed: ABIn.
—IE. **CCC.**
Published by: John Wiley & Sons, Inc., 111 River St, Hoboken, NJ 07030-5774. TEL 800-825-7550, FAX 201-748-5915, uscs-wis@wiley.com, http://www3.interscience.wiley.com/cgi-bin/jhome/73505326, http://www.wiley.com. Eds. Alfred T Demaria, Sarah Magee. adv.: B&W page USD 1,080, color page USD 2,420; trim 8.25 x 11. **Subscr. to:** John Wiley & Sons Ltd., The Atrium, Southern Gate, Chichester, West Sussex PO19 8SQ, United Kingdom. TEL 44-1243-779777, FAX 44-1243-775878, cs-journals@wiley.co.uk.

344.01 GBR ISSN 0309-0558
KD3006.A2
MANAGERIAL LAW. Text in English. 1966. bi-m. EUR 6,850.16 in Europe; USD 4,199 in North America; AUD 4,199 in Australasia; GBP 4,566.41 in the UK & elsewhere (effective 2005). back issues avail. **Document type:** *Journal, Academic/Scholarly.* **Description:** Provides details on the latest legislation, tribunal hearings, government orders and consultative documents. Focuses on labor relations, employment conditions, training, marketing, consumer sales, and credit transactions.
Incorporates: Knight's Industrial Reports (0023-2270)
Related titles: Online - full text ed.: (from EBSCO Publishing, Emerald Group Publishing Limited, Gale Group, IngentaConnect, O C L C Online Computer Library Center, Inc., ProQuest Information & Learning, Swets Information Services).
Indexed: ABIn, EmerIntel, RASB.
—BLDSC (5359.245000), IE, Infotrieve, ingenta. **CCC.**
Published by: Barmarick Publications, Enholmes Hall, Patrington, Hull, East Yorkshire HU12 0PR, United Kingdom. TEL 44-1964-630033, FAX 44-1964-631716, hr24@dial.pipex.com, http://www.emeraldinsight.com/ml.htm. Ed., Pub. Barrie O Pettman. Circ: 150. **Dist. by:** Emerald Group Publishing Limited, 60-62 Toller Ln, Bradford, W Yorks BD8 9BY, United Kingdom. TEL 44-1274-777700, FAX 44-1274-785200, infomation@emeraldinsight.com, http:// www.emeraldinsight.com/; **Dist. in US:** Emerald Group Publishing Ltd., 44 Brattle St, 4th Fl, Cambridge, MA 02138. TEL 617-497-2175, 888-622-0075, FAX 617-354-6875, america@emeraldinsight.com.

344.01 USA
MANAGERS GUIDE TO THE AMERICANS WITH DISABILITIES ACT. Text in English. irreg. USD 195. **Description:** Features a detailed and easily understandable explanation of the provisions of the law and offers practical tips and a checklist of steps employers should take to assure compliance.
Published by: MidAtlantic Employers' Association, PO Box 770, Valley Forge, PA 19482. TEL 215-666-7330, FAX 215-666-7866.

331.1 CAN ISSN 0076-3853
HD8109.M3
MANITOBA LABOUR - MANAGEMENT REVIEW COMMITTEE. ANNUAL REPORT. Text in English. 1965. a. free.
Published by: Department of Labour, Rm 606, Norquay Bldg, Winnipeg, MB R3C 0V8, Canada. TEL 204-944-3411.

352.63 CAN ISSN 0706-3792
JS1721.M3
MANITOBA. MUNICIPAL EMPLOYEES BENEFITS BOARD. ANNUAL REPORT. Text in English. 1977. a. **Document type:** *Government.*
Published by: Municipal Employees Benefits Board, 1200 444 St Mary Ave, Winnipeg, MB R3C 3T1, Canada. TEL 204-947-6574, FAX 204-948-3316. Ed. Rose Neufeld. Circ: 4,500.

MANNESMANN MAGAZIN. see *BUSINESS AND ECONOMICS—Domestic Commerce*

331.11 IND ISSN 0542-5808
HD5701
MANPOWER JOURNAL. Text in English. 1965. q. INR 400, USD 60 (effective 2000). bk.rev. bibl.
Indexed: ABIn, ADPA, IndIndia, ManagAb, PAA&I, PAIS, RDA, RRTA, WAE&RSA.
Published by: Institute of Applied Manpower Research, Indraprastha Estate, Mahatma Gandhi Marg, New Delhi, 110 002, India. TEL 91-11-3317849, FAX 91-11-3319909. Ed. T V Ramamurthy. Circ: 500. **Dist. by:** New Age International Pvt. Ltd., Journals Division, 4835-24 Ansari Rd., Darya Ganj, New Delhi 110 002, India. TEL 91-11-3267996, FAX 91-11-3267437.

331 PAK
MANPOWER REVIEW. Text in English. 1975. q. PKR 5 per issue. bk.rev.
Published by: Manpower Division, Islamabad, Pakistan. Circ: 500.

MANUAL OF RULES, CLASSIFICATIONS AND INTERPRETATIONS FOR WORKERS COMPENSATION INSURANCE. see *INSURANCE*

MARYLAND EMPLOYMENT LAW. see *LAW*

MARYLAND EMPLOYMENT LAW LETTER. see *LAW*

331.1 USA
MARYLAND MONTHLY LABOR REVIEW. Text in English. 1970 (vol.16). m. free. charts; stat. **Document type:** *Newsletter, Government.*
Former titles: Maryland Labor Market Dimensions; Employment Report for Maryland and Metropolitan Baltimore; Manpower Trends (0025-2433)
Indexed: SRI.
Published by: Department of Labor, Licensing and Regulation, Office of Labor Market Analysis and Information, 1100 N Eutaw St, Rm 601, Baltimore, MD 21201. TEL 410-767-2250, http://www.dllr.state.md.us/lmi/index.htm. Circ: 1,000.

MARYLAND WORKERS' COMPENSATION HANDBOOK. see *INSURANCE*

MASHABEI ENOSH/HUMAN RESOURCES; human resources magazine. see *BUSINESS AND ECONOMICS—Personnel Management*

MASSACHUSETTS. DEPARTMENT OF EMPLOYMENT AND TRAINING. EMPLOYMENT AND WAGES STATE SUMMARY. see *BUSINESS AND ECONOMICS—Abstracting, Bibliographies, Statistics*

MASSACHUSETTS EMPLOYMENT LAW LETTER. see *LAW*

344.01 USA ISSN 1051-6123
MASSACHUSETTS LABOR CASES. Text in English. 1975. m. USD 425 (effective 2001). **Description:** Full text of all decisions issued by the Massachusetts Labor Relations Commission.
Published by: Landlaw Inc., 675 VFW Parkway, No. 354, Chestnut Hill, MA 02467. TEL 800-637-6330, FAX 617-277-7375, http://www.landlaw.com.

344.01 USA ISSN 1522-6670
MASSACHUSETTS LABOR RELATIONS REPORTER. Text in English. 1975. m. USD 425 (effective 2001). **Description:** Digest of all decisions of the Massachusetts Labor Relations Commission and relevant court decisions.
Published by: Landlaw Inc., 675 VFW Parkway, No. 354, Chestnut Hill, MA 02467. TEL 800-637-6330, FAX 617-277-7375, http://www.landlaw.com.

344.021 USA
MASSACHUSETTS PRACTICE SERIES. WORKMEN'S COMPENSATION. Text in English. latest 2002, 2nd Ed., base vol. plus a. updates. USD 218 base vol(s). (effective 2004). **Document type:** *Monographic series, Academic/Scholarly.* **Description:** Covers the substantive and procedural law governing work-related injuries and provides checklists, charts, forms, benefit schedules, full-text statutes and rules and other information.
Related titles: ♦ Series of: Massachusetts Practice Series.
Published by: Thomson West (Subsidiary of: Thomson Corporation, The), 610 Opperman Dr, Eagan, MN 55123-1396. TEL 651-687-7000, 800-328-4880, http://west.thomson.com/product/22077785/product.asp.

MASSACHUSETTS WORKERS' COMPENSATION REPORTS. see *INSURANCE*

331 USA
MATCHING GIFT NOTES NEWSLETTER✱. Text in English. q. USD 49. back issues avail. **Document type:** *Newsletter.* **Description:** Contains articles about corporate matching gift trends and issues, and matching gift program changes.
Published by: Council for Advancement and Support of Education, 1307 New York Ave, N W, Ste 1000, Washington, DC 20005. Circ: 1,200.

MAURITIUS. CENTRAL STATISTICAL OFFICE. DIGEST OF LABOUR STATISTICS. see *BUSINESS AND ECONOMICS—Abstracting, Bibliographies, Statistics*

MAURITIUS. CENTRAL STATISTICS OFFICE. LABOUR FORCE SAMPLE SURVEY (YEAR). see *STATISTICS*

MAZENGARB'S EMPLOYMENT LAW SERVICE. see *LAW*

MEALEY'S LITIGATION REPORT: E R I S A. (Employee Retirement Income Security Act) see *LAW—Civil Law*

MEANS LABOR RATES FOR THE CONSTRUCTION INDUSTRY. see *BUILDING AND CONSTRUCTION*

MEDICAL PRACTICES COMMITTEE. RECRUITMENT SURVEY (YEAR). see *MEDICAL SCIENCES*

331 SCG ISSN 1450-9911
MENADZMENT. Text in Serbian; Summaries in English. 1951. bi-m. USD 150, YUN 9,000 (effective 2002).
Formerly: Organizacija Rada (0471-9506)
Related titles: ♦ Supplement to: Masinstvo. ISSN 0461-2531.
Indexed: ErgAb.
Published by: Savez Inzenjera i Tehnicara Srbije, Kneza Milosa 7, Belgrade, 11000. TEL 381-11-3237363, sits@yuonline.net, http://www.sits.org.yu. Ed. Dr. Milorad Terzic TEL 381-11-3243653. Adv. contact Ivanka Vuletic. Circ: 780 (controlled); 1,000 (paid).

331   AUT
MENSCH UND ARBEIT; internationale Zeitschrift fuer Arbeitspaedagogik, Arbeitspsychologie, Arbeitstechnik und Betriebswirtschaft. Text in German. 1947. irreg. bk.rev. **Document type:** *Journal, Trade.*
Indexed: CISA.
Published by: (Arbeitsgemeinschaft fuer Psychotechnik in Oesterreich), Psychotechnisches Institut, Augasse 9, Langenzersdorf, W 2103, Austria. TEL 43-2244-309960, FAX 43-2244-3099622, psychotech@utanet.at, http://www.psychotech.at. Ed. Dr. Susanne Hackl-Gruemm. Circ: 2,000.

331   NLD   ISSN 1388-3135
MENSENWERK. Text in Dutch. 1991. m. **Document type:** *Bulletin.*
Former titles (until 1998): Arboscoop (0929-5267); (until 1994): Nieuwsbrief Publikaties Albeidsinspectie (1380-6823); (until 1993): V G W Aktueel (0927-4049)
—Infotrieve.
Published by: Sdu Uitgevers bv, Postbus 20014, The Hague, 2500 EA, Netherlands.

331.252   CAN
MERCER PENSION MANUAL. Text in English. 1988. 6/yr. looseleaf. CND 825 domestic; USD 699.15 foreign (effective 2005). charts; illus. back issues avail. **Description:** Provides solutions to the problems of meeting payroll reporting requirements, plan costs, surplus withdrawals, employee termination, corporate restructuring or winding up a plan.
Published by: Carswell (Subsidiary of: Thomson Corporation), One Corporate Plaza, 2075 Kennedy Rd, Toronto, ON M1T 3V4, Canada. TEL 416-609-8000, 800-387-5164, FAX 416-298-5094, carswell.customerrelations@thomson.com, http://www.carswell.com. Ed. William M Mercer. Circ: 1,500.

331   USA
MERIT SYSTEMS PROTECTION BOARD SERVICE. Variant title: M S P B Digest Service. Text in English. 1984. m. looseleaf. USD 360 (effective 1998). back issues avail. **Document type:** *Abstract/Index.*
Published by: Hawkins Publishing Co., Inc., PO Box 480, Mayo, MD 21106-0480. TEL 410-798-1677. Ed. Carl R Eyler. Circ: 100.

331   USA
METROPOLITAN WASHINGTON D.C. AREA LABOR SUMMARY. Text in English. 1969. m. free. charts; stat. **Document type:** *Government.*
Formerly: Greater Washington Area Labor Summary
Related titles: Microfiche ed.: (from CIS).
Indexed: SRI.
Published by: Department of Employment Services, 500 C St, N W, Ste 201, Washington, DC 20001-2187. TEL 202-724-7213, FAX 202-724-7216. Ed. Eileen Dent. Circ: 1,500.

331.1   MEX
MEXICO. CENTRO DE INFORMACION TECNICA Y DOCUMENTACION. INDICE DE ARTICULOS SOBRE SEGURIDAD E HIGIENE INDUSTRIAL. Text in Spanish. 1979. 3/yr. MXP 140, USD 13.
Published by: Servicio Nacional de Adiestramiento Rapido de la Mano de Obra en la Industria, Centro de Informacion Tecnica y Documentacion, Calzada Atzcapotzalco-la Villa 209, Apdo. 16-099, Mexico City, DF, Mexico. Ed. Javier Pedraza Garcia. Circ: 2,000.

MEXICO. INSTITUTO NACIONAL DE ESTADISTICA, GEOGRAFIA E INFORMATICA. ENCUESTA NACIONAL DE EDUCACION CAPACITACION Y EMPLEO. see *EDUCATION—Abstracting, Bibliographies, Statistics*

331   MEX   ISSN 0302-5004
MEXICO. SECRETARIA DEL TRABAJO Y PREVISION SOCIAL. SUBDIRECCION DE DOCUMENTACION. RESENA LABORAL ✳. Text in Spanish. 2/yr. MXP 70. illus.
Published by: Secretaria del Trabajo y Prevision Social, PERIFERICO SUR 4271 Ed A 4o, Fuentes del Pedregal, Mexico City, DF 14140, Mexico. Ed. Javier Patino. Circ: 5,000.

352.63   USA
MICHIGAN. CIVIL SERVICE DEPARTMENT. ANNUAL WORK FORCE REPORT. Text in English. 1980. a. free. **Document type:** *Government.* **Description:** Provides statistics on Michigan's Classified Workforce. Includes average age, average pay rate, bargaining unit representation, insurance enrollment leave usage, turnover rate, etc.
Published by: Civil Service Department, Capitol Commons Center, 400 S Pine St, Box 30002, Lansing, MI 48909. TEL 517-335-0318, FAX 517-335-3867, http://www.state.mi.us/mdcs/index.html. Ed., R&P Linda S Coe.

MICHIGAN EMPLOYMENT LAW LETTER. see *LAW*

331.125   USA
MICHIGAN. EMPLOYMENT SECURITY COMMISSION. ANNUAL PLANNING REPORT. Variant title: Annual Planning Information Report. Text in English. 1972. a. free. illus.; stat.
Formerly: Michigan. Employment Security Commission. Labor Market Analysis Section. Annual Manpower Planning Report: Detroit Labor Market Area (0090-8401)

Published by: Employment Security Commission, 7310 Woodward Ave, Detroit, MI 48202. TEL 313-876-5427. Circ: 1,000.

331.1   USA
HD5725.M5
MICHIGAN LABOR MARKET NEWS. Text in English. 1946. m. free. charts; stat. **Document type:** *Government.*
Former titles (until 1992): Michigan Labor Market Review (0098-0307); Michigan Manpower Review; Michigan's Labor Market
Related titles: Microfiche ed.: (from CIS).
Indexed: SRI.
Published by: (Michigan. Bureau of Research and Statistics), Employment Security Commission, 7310 Woodward Ave, Detroit, MI 48202. TEL 313-876-5000. Ed. James Astalos Jr. Circ: 2,800.

MICHIGAN PUBLIC EMPLOYEE REPORTER. see *LAW*

331.252   USA   ISSN 0092-9212
JK5860.P4
MICHIGAN STATE EMPLOYEES' RETIREMENT SYSTEM FINANCIAL AND STATISTICAL REPORT. Key Title: Michigan State Employees' Retirement System. Text in English. 1953. a. free. stat.
Published by: State Employees Retirement System, Office of Retirement Services, 3rd Fl, General Office Bldg, P O Box 30171, Lansing, MI 48909. TEL 517-322-5103, 800-381-5111, http://www.state.mi.us/dmb.ors/. Circ: 1,100.

331   USA   ISSN 0036-6706
MICHIGAN STATE UNIVERSITY. SCHOOL OF LABOR AND INDUSTRIAL RELATIONS. NEWSLETTER. Text in English. 1962. 2/yr. free. bk.rev. **Document type:** *Newsletter.* **Description:** Contains information on school activities, its faculty, students and alumni.
Media: Duplicated (not offset).
Published by: Michigan State University, School of Labor and Industrial Relations, South Kedzie Hall, East Lansing, MI 48824. TEL 517-355-1801, FAX 517-355-7656. Ed. Michael L Moore. Circ: 1,800.

MICHIGAN WORKERS' COMP REPORTER. see *INSURANCE*

331.11   USA
MICRO O L M. (Occupations in the Labor Market) Text in English. irreg. USD 8. charts; stat. **Document type:** *Government.* **Description:** Comprises the most recent information on occupations, including supply and demand, characteristics, and wages.
Media: Diskette.
Published by: Employment Security Department, Labor Market and Economic Analysis Branch, PO Box 9046, Olympia, WA 98507-9046. TEL 360-438-4813.

331   RUS
MINISTERSTVO TRUDA I SOTSIAL'NOGO RAZVITIYA ROSSIISKOI FEDERATSII. BYULLETEN'. Text in Russian. 1966. m. USD 120.
Formerly: Gosudarstvennyi Komitet Soveta Ministrov S.S.S.R. po Voprosam Truda i Zarabotnoi Platy. Byulleten' (0007-7666)
Indexed: RASB.
Address: Zemlyanoi Val 34, Moscow, 103064, Russian Federation. TEL 7-095-9162988. Ed. Z S Bogatyrenko. **US dist. addr.:** East View Information Services, 3020 Harbor Ln. N., Minneapolis, MN 55447. TEL 612-550-0961.

331.259   USA
MINNESOTA. DEPARTMENT OF ECONOMIC SECURITY. ANNUAL REPORT ✳. Text in English. 1936. a. free.
Former titles: Minnesota. Department of Jobs and Training; (until 1979): Minnesota. Department of Employment Services. Annual Report (0364-717X); (until 1974): Minnesota. Department of Manpower Services. Annual Report (0076-9126); (until 1969): Minnesota. Department of Employment Security. Annual Report
Published by: Department Economic Security, Communications Team (CommTeam) Office, 390 N. Robert St., St. Paul, MN 55101. TEL 651-296-3340, FAX 651-296-0994, http://www.workforcecenter.org. Ed. Heidi Stennes. Circ: 1,500.

MINNESOTA EMPLOYMENT LAW LETTER. see *LAW*

331.125   USA
MINNESOTA EMPLOYMENT REVIEW. Text in English. m. free. **Document type:** *Newsletter, Government.*
Former titles: Minnesota Labor Market Review; Incorporates(1974-1993): Current Minnesota Labor Conditions
Indexed: SRI.
Published by: Minnesota Department of Economic Security, Research and Statistics Office, 390 N. Robert St., St. Paul, MN 55101. TEL 612-296-6545, FAX 612-282-5429, lmi@ng.wmail.des.state.mnus, http://www.des.state.mn.us/lmi/review/other.htm. Ed. Judith Trent. R&P Debbie Morrison TEL 651-296-6756. Circ: 5,200.

MISSISSIPPI EMPLOYMENT LAW LETTER. see *LAW*

331.1   USA   ISSN 0148-4214
HD5725.M8
MISSOURI AREA LABOR TRENDS. Text in English. 1977. m. free. illus. **Document type:** *Newsletter.*
Formerly: Missouri State and Area Labor Trends
Indexed: SRI.
Published by: (Missouri. Division of Employment Security), Department of Labor and Industry, PO Box 59, Jefferson City, MO 65101. TEL 314-751-3602. Ed. Linda J Rackers. Circ: 1,700.

MISSOURI EMPLOYMENT LAW LETTER. see *LAW*

331   AUT   ISSN 1561-2341
MITBESTIMMUNG; Zeitschrift fuer Demokratisierung der Arbeitswelt. Text in German. 1972. bi-m. EUR 23 domestic to individuals; EUR 27 foreign to individuals (effective 2005). bk.rev. index. back issues avail. **Document type:** *Bulletin, Trade.* **Description:** Contains and deals with questions concerning working life, relations between work and capital, trade unions, marxism and socialism.
Indexed: IBR, IBZ.
Published by: Arbeitsgemeinschaft zur Demokratisierung der Arbeitswelt, Postfach 220, Vienna, W 1172, Austria. TEL 43-1-4807793, FAX 43-1-48077934, mi.pul@chello.at. Ed. Mr. Peter Ulrich Lehner. Adv. contact Mr. Paul Habr. Circ: 1,200.

331   DEU   ISSN 0340-3254
HD4824
MITTEILUNGEN AUS DER ARBEITSMARKT- UND BERUFSFORSCHUNG. Text in German; Summaries in English, German. 1909. q. EUR 52, CHF 101.70; EUR 14, CHF 27.20 newsstand/cover (effective 2002), adv. bk.rev. back issues avail. **Document type:** *Journal, Government.*
Indexed: DIP, IBR, IBZ, ILD, JEL, RefZh.
—BLDSC (5876.388000); IE; Infotrieve. CCC.
Published by: (Germany. Bundesanstalt fuer Arbeit, Germany. Institut fuer Arbeitsmarkt- und Berufsforschung (Stuttgart)), W. Kohlhammer GmbH, Hessbruehlstr 69, Stuttgart, 70565, Germany. TEL 49-711-7863-1, FAX 49-711-7863263, info@kohlhammer-katalog.de, http://www.kohlhammer.de. Circ: 5,000.

MONOGRAFIEEN SOCIAAL RECHT. see *LAW—Civil Law*

MONTANA EMPLOYMENT LAW LETTER. see *LAW*

331   BRA
MULHER E TRABALHO. Text in Portuguese. a. free (effective 2001). charts. **Document type:** *Bulletin, Academic/Scholarly.*
Related titles: Online - full text ed.
Published by: Fundacao de Economia e Estatistica, Rua Duque de Caxias, 1691, Andar 8, Centro, Porto Alegre, RS 90010-283, Brazil. TEL 55-51-3216-9008, FAX 55-51-3225-0006, diretoria@fee.tche.br, http://www.fee.tche.br.

331.1251378   USA   ISSN 1542-2046
LB2343.5
N A C E JOURNAL; the international magazine of placement and recruitment. Text in English. 1940. q. USD 72 domestic to non-members; USD 97 foreign to non-members; USD 8.50 per issue to non-members; free to members (effective 2005); includes Spotlight newsletter. adv. bk.rev. charts; illus. index. reprint service avail. from PQC. **Document type:** *Magazine, Consumer.*
Former titles (until 2002): Journal of Career Planning & Employment (0884-5352); (until 1985): Journal of College Placement (0021-9770); (until 1951): School and College Placement (0363-6879)
Related titles: Microform ed.: (from PQC); Online - full text ed.: (from O C L C Online Computer Library Center, Inc., ProQuest Information & Learning).
Indexed: ABIn, ATI, BRI, CBRI, CIJE, EduInd, HEA, HECAB, PAIS, PMA, PersLit, WorkRelAb.
—BLDSC (6001.784070), IE, ingenta.
Published by: National Association of Colleges and Employers, 62 Highland Ave, Bethlehem, PA 18017-9085. TEL 610-868-1421, 800-544-5272, FAX 610-868-0208, info@naceweb.org, http://www.naceweb.org/. Ed. Jerry Bohovich. Pub. Mimi Collins. adv.: B&W page USD 790, color page USD 1,340. Circ: 4,314 (paid).

N A S D A STATE ECONOMIC DEVELOPMENT EXPENDITURES AND SALARY SURVEY. see *PUBLIC ADMINISTRATION*

N L R B ADVICE MEMORANDUM REPORTER. see *LAW*

N L R B CASE HANDLING MANUAL. see *LAW*

331   USA   ISSN 0270-9732
N L R B ELECTION REPORT. CASES CLOSED. Text in English. 1961. m. USD 31; USD 38.75 foreign; USD 4, USD 5 newsstand/cover (effective 1999). **Document type:** *Government.* **Description:** Lists the outcome of secret ballot voting by employees in NLRB-conducted representation elections in cases closed for each month. Election tallies are listed by unions involved.
Related titles: Online - full text ed.
Indexed: AmStI.

Published by: U.S. National Labor Relations Board, 1099 14th St, N W, Washington, DC 20570-0001. TEL 202-273-1991, FAX 202-273-1789, http://www.nlrb.gov/nlrb/shared_files/brochures/election_reports.asp. **Subscr. to:** U.S. Government Printing Office, Superintendent of Documents, PO Box 371954, Pittsburgh, PA 15250-7954. TEL 202-512-1800, FAX 202-512-2250, orders@gpo.gov, http://www.access.gpo.gov.

344.01 USA
N T S A REPORTER. Text in English. 1966. m. membership. adv. bk.rev. index. back issues avail.
Published by: National Technical Services Association, 2121 Eisenhower Ave, Alexandria, VA 22314-3501. TEL 703-684-4722, FAX 703-684-7627. Ed. Laura Mackail. Circ: 800.

331 FRA ISSN 1633-3284
N V O ESPACE ELUS. Text in French. 1960. 5/yr. FRF 110. adv. charts; illus.
Former titles (until 2001): R C E: Revue des Comites d'Entreprise et Equivalents (0984-1725); (until 1986): Revue des Comites d'Enterprise (0249-9142); (until 1980): V C O (0249-9134); (until 1966): Vie des Collectivites Ouvrieres (0399-1156)
Related titles: Supplement(s): La Lettre R C E C G T. ISSN 1168-996X. 1992.
Published by: Confederation Generale du Travail, 263 rue de Paris, Montreuil, 93516 Cedex, France. TEL 33-1-48188000, FAX 33-1-48188460.

331.11 CAN ISSN 0830-1611
N W T LABOUR FORCE SURVEY (YEAR); overall results & community detail. (Northwest Territories) Text in English. 1989. irreg.
Published by: Bureau of Statistics, Northwest Territories, Box 1320, Yellowknife, NT X1A 2L9, Canada. TEL 867-873-7147, FAX 867-873-0275, info@stats.gov.nt.ca, http://www.stats.gov.nt.ca/Statinfo/Labour/99LFS/99LFS.html.

344.01 DEU ISSN 0949-7137
N Z A RECHTSPRECHUNGS REPORT ARBEITSRECHT. (Neue Zeitschrift fuer Arbeitsrecht) Abbreviated title: N Z A - R R. Text in German. 1996. m. EUR 148 domestic; EUR 168.50 foreign; EUR 13.80 newsstand/cover (effective 2005). reprint service avail. from SCH. **Document type:** *Abstract/Index.*
Published by: Verlag C.H. Beck oHG, Wilhelmstr 9, Munich, 80801, Germany. TEL 49-89-38189338, FAX 49-89-38189398, abo.service@beck.de, http://www.beck.de.

344.01 DEU ISSN 0469-4333
NACHSCHLAGEWERK DES BUNDESARBEITSGERICHTS - ARBEITSRECHTLICHE PRAXIS. Text in German. 1954. m. EUR 440 domestic; EUR 471.40 foreign (effective 2005). **Document type:** *Journal, Academic/Scholarly.*
Related titles: ◆ CD-ROM ed.: Arbeitsrechtliche Praxis auf CD-ROM (Windows Version). ISSN 1436-5510.
Published by: Verlag C.H. Beck oHG, Wilhelmstr 9, Munich, 80801, Germany. TEL 49-89-38189340, FAX 49-89-38189398, abo.service@beck.de, http://www.beck.de.

331.2041378 USA ISSN 1520-8648
NATIONAL ASSOCIATION OF COLLEGES AND EMPLOYERS. SALARY SURVEY; a study of beginning salary offers. Text in English. 1974. 4/yr. price varies.
Formerly (until 1995): C P C Salary Survey (0196-1004)
Related titles: Microfiche ed.: (from CIS).
Indexed: SRI.
Published by: National Association of Colleges and Employers, 62 Highland Ave, Bethlehem, PA 18017-9085. TEL 610-868-1421, 800-544-5272, FAX 610-868-0208, info@naceweb.org, http://www.naceweb.org. Ed. Camille Luckenbaugh. Circ: 4,000.

331 USA
NATIONAL COMPENSATION SURVEY: EMPLOYEE BENEFITS IN PRIVATE INDUSTRY IN THE UNITED STATES. Text in English. a. **Document type:** *Government.*
Formed by the merger of: Employee Benefits in Small Private Establishments; Employee Benefits in Medium and Large Private Establishments; Employee Benefits in State and Local Governments
Related titles: Online - full content ed.
Published by: U.S. Department of Labor, Bureau of Labor Statistics, Division of Compensation Data Analysis & Planning, Postal Square Bldg., 2 Massachusetts Ave., NE, Rm 4175, Washington, DC 20212-0001. TEL 202-691-6199, OCLTINFO@bls.gov, http://www.bls.gov.

352.63 USA
NATIONAL CONFERENCE ON PUBLIC RETIREMENT SYSTEMS. PROCEEDINGS RECORD. Text in English. a. **Description:** Concerned with promoting and safeguarding the rights and benefits of government employees participating in retirement plans.
Published by: National Conference on Public Retirement Systems, c/o Carlos Resendez, Exec Admin, 4414 Centerview Dr, Ste 226, San Antonio, TX 78228. TEL 210-732-8600, FAX 210-732-8684, resendez@ncpers.org. Circ: 1,000.

331.125137 USA
NATIONAL DIRECTORY FOR EMPLOYMENT IN EDUCATION. Text in English. a. USD 20 to non-members; USD 10 to members (effective 2003). **Document type:** *Directory.*
Formerly: A S C U S Directory of Membership and Subject Field Index (0066-9164)
Published by: American Association for Employment in Education, 3040 Riverside Dr., Ste. 125, Columbus, OH 43221-2575. TEL 847-864-1999, FAX 847-864-8303, aaee@nwu.edu, http://www.aaee.org. Circ: 1,500.

NATIONAL ECONOMIC AND SOCIAL FORUM. NEWSLETTER. see *POLITICAL SCIENCE—Civil Rights*

THE NATIONAL EMPLOYER. see *LAW*

331 USA
NATIONAL EXECUTIVE COMPENSATION SURVEY. Text in English. a. USD 450. **Description:** Provides comparative information about 29 executive position compensation practices among 1,800 businesses, representing 16,500 executives throughout the country. All information is broken down by geographic region.
Published by: MidAtlantic Employers' Association, PO Box 770, Valley Forge, PA 19482. TEL 215-666-7330, FAX 215-666-7866.

331.281378 USA
NATIONAL FACULTY SALARY SURVEY BY DISCIPLINE AND RANK IN PRIVATE COLLEGES AND UNIVERSITIES. Text in English. a. USD 105 to non-members Non-participants; USD 80 to members Non-participants; USD 55 to survey participants (effective 2000). **Description:** Provides salary data on faculty members at nearly 500 private institutions.
Indexed: SRI.
Published by: College and University Personnel Association, 1233 20th St, N W, Ste 301, Washington, DC 20036. TEL 202-429-0311, FAX 202-429-0149, http://www.cupa.org. Ed. Melissa Edeburn. R&P Audrey Rothstein.

344.01 USA
NATIONAL LABOR RELATIONS ACT: LAW AND PRACTICE. Text in English. 1991. 3 base vols. plus s-a. updates. looseleaf. USD 353 base vol(s). (effective 2002). **Description:** Covers all aspects of the law and practice under the NLRA.
Related titles: CD-ROM ed.
Published by: Matthew Bender & Co., Inc. (Subsidiary of: LexisNexis North America), 1275 Broadway, Albany, NY 12204. international@bender.com, http://bender.lexisnexis.com. Ed. N Peter Lareau.

352.63 USA ISSN 1094-4079
NATIONAL PUBLIC EMPLOYMENT REPORTER. Text in English. 1979; N.S. 1997. m. USD 175 (effective 2006). back issues avail. **Document type:** *Newsletter, Trade.* **Description:** Provides state-by-state reporting of the indexed summaries of all public-sector labor decisions issued by every state and local labor board.
Related titles: Microfiche ed.; Online - full text ed.
Published by: L R P Publications, 747 Dresher Rd, PO Box 980, Horsham, PA 19044. TEL 215-784-0860, 800-341-7874, FAX 215-784-9639, custserve@lrp.com, http://www.shoplrp.com/product/p-3000.N.html, http://www.lrp.com.

331 USA ISSN 0197-7032
NATIONAL RIGHT TO WORK NEWSLETTER. Text in English. 1955. m. free. illus. back issues avail.; reprints avail. **Document type:** *Newsletter.*
Published by: National Right to Work Committee, 8001 Braddock Rd, Ste 500, Springfield, VA 22160. TEL 703-321-9820, FAX 703-321-7342, members@nrtw.org, http://www.nrtwc.org. Ed., R&P Stanley Greer. Circ: 150,000.

NATIONS IN TRANSIT. see *SOCIOLOGY*

331 DEU ISSN 0172-276X
NEBELHORN; Regionalmagazin fuer Politik und Kultur. Text in German. 1980. m. adv. bk.rev.
Published by: S & N Verlags GmbH, Schottenstr 3, Konstanz, 78462, Germany. Circ: 2,500.

NEBRASKA EMPLOYMENT LAW LETTER. see *LAW*

368.41 USA
NEBRASKA LEGAL FORMS: WORKERS' COMPENSATION. Text in English. 1988. supplemented through 1994 w/ diskette), base vol. plus irreg. updates. looseleaf. USD 75 (effective 2003). **Description:** Covers Nebraska workers' compensation benefits, procedure, and forms, which include petition, motions, applications, interrogatories, orders, and satisfactions.
Related titles: Diskette ed.
Published by: Michie Company (Subsidiary of: LexisNexis North America), 701 E Water St, Charlottesville, VA 22902-5389. TEL 434-972-7600, 800-446-3410, FAX 434-972-7677, http://www.michie.com. Ed. Michael P Cavel.

NEUE B S. (Betriebs Sicherheit) see *OCCUPATIONAL HEALTH AND SAFETY*

NEVADA EMPLOYMENT LAW LETTER. see *LAW*

331.125 USA
NEVADA WAGE SURVEY. Variant title: Nevada Statewide Wage Survey. Text in English. 1973. a. **Document type:** *Government.*
Formerly: State of Nevada Wage Report (0081-4563)
Related titles: Online - full text ed.
Published by: Employment, Training and Rehabilitation Department, Employment Security Division, 500 E Third St, Carson City, NV 89713. TEL 702-687-4550. Circ: 2,500.

331 CAN
NEW BRUNSWICK. DEPARTMENT OF ADVANCED EDUCATION AND LABOUR. ANNUAL REPORT. Text in English, French. 1944. a. free. **Document type:** *Government.*
Former titles: New Brunswick. Department of Labour. Annual Report; New Brunswick. Department of Labour and Human Resources. Annual Report; New Brunswick. Department of Labour and Manpower. Annual Report; New Brunswick. Department of Labour. Annual Report (0077-8052)
Published by: Department of Advanced Education and Labour, P O Box 6000, Fredericton, NB E3B 5H1, Canada. TEL 506-453-2568, FAX 506-453-3806, http://www.gov.nb.ca/ael/index.htm. Ed. Margot Brewer. Circ: 700 (controlled).

331.21 GBR ISSN 0262-0502
NEW EARNINGS SURVEY. PART A: REPORT AND KEY RESULTS. Text in English. 1970. a. **Document type:** *Government.* **Description:** Reports on earnings and work hours in Great Britain.
Supersedes in part (1970-1975): Great Britain. Department of Employment. New Earnings Survey (0308-1419)
Published by: Office for National Statistics, Government Offices, Rm 65c-3, Great George St, London, SW1P 3AQ, United Kingdom. TEL 44-171-270-6081, FAX 44-171-270-6019. **Dist. by:** Her Majesty's Stationery Office Publications Centre. TEL 44-171-873-9090, FAX 44-171-873-8200.

NEW EARNINGS SURVEY. PART B: ANALYSES BY AGREEMENT. see *BUSINESS AND ECONOMICS—Abstracting, Bibliographies, Statistics*

331 GBR ISSN 0262-0529
NEW EARNINGS SURVEY. PART C: ANALYSES BY INDUSTRY. Text in English. a. **Document type:** *Government.*
Supersedes in part (1970-1975): Great Britain. Department of Employment. New Earning Survey (0308-1419)
Published by: Office for National Statistics, Government Offices, Rm 65c-3, Great George St, London, SW1P 3AQ, United Kingdom. TEL 44-171-270-6081, FAX 44-171-270-6019. **Dist. by:** Her Majesty's Stationery Office Publications Centre. TEL 44-171-873-9090, FAX 44-171-873-8200.

NEW EARNINGS SURVEY. PART D: ANALYSES BY OCCUPATION. see *BUSINESS AND ECONOMICS—Abstracting, Bibliographies, Statistics*

NEW EARNINGS SURVEY. PART E: ANALYSES BY REGION AND AGE GROUP. see *BUSINESS AND ECONOMICS—Abstracting, Bibliographies, Statistics*

NEW EARNINGS SURVEY. PART F: HOURS, EARNINGS AND HOURS OF PART-TIME WOMEN WORKERS. see *BUSINESS AND ECONOMICS—Abstracting, Bibliographies, Statistics*

NEW GROUND. see *POLITICAL SCIENCE*

NEW HAMPSHIRE EMPLOYMENT LAW LETTER. see *LAW*

NEW JERSEY ECONOMIC INDICATORS. see *BUSINESS AND ECONOMICS—Economic Situation And Conditions*

NEW JERSEY EMPLOYMENT LAW LETTER. see *LAW*

NEW JERSEY LABOR AND EMPLOYMENT LAW QUARTERLY. see *LAW*

NEW JERSEY PUBLIC EMPLOYEE REPORTER. see *LAW*

331 USA
NEW LABOR REVIEW. Text in English. 1978. irreg., latest vol.4, 1981. free. adv. bk.rev.
Related titles: Microform ed.: (from PQC).
Published by: San Francisco State University, Labor Studies Forum, Division of Cross Disciplinary Programs in the Behavioral and Social Sciences, 1600 Holloway Ave, San Francisco, CA 94132. TEL 415-469-2055. Circ: 1,000.

331.125 USA
NEW MEXICO. DEPARTMENT OF LABOR. COVERED EMPLOYMENT AND WAGES. QUARTERLY REPORT. Text in English. 1948. q. free. **Document type:** *Government.*
Formerly: New Mexico. Employment Security Department. Covered Employment and Wages. Quarterly Report
Published by: Department of Labor, Box 1928, Albuquerque, NM 87103. TEL 505-841-8509. Eds. Ann Armijo, Steven Pazand. Circ: 250.

NEW MEXICO EMPLOYMENT LAW LETTER. see *LAW*

B

331.12 USA
NEW MEXICO LABOR MARKET REVIEW. Text in English. 1974 (vol.2). m. free. stat. **Document type:** *Government.*
Former titles: New Mexico Manpower Review; New Mexico Labor Market Trends (0550-9483)
Related titles: Microfiche ed.: (from CIS).
Indexed: SRI.
Published by: Department of Labor, Bureau of Economic Research & Analysis, PO Box 1928, Albuquerque, NM 87103. TEL 505-841-8645. Ed. Gerard P Bradley. Circ: 4,000.

331.1 AUS ISSN 0028-677X
HD8849.N48
NEW SOUTH WALES INDUSTRIAL GAZETTE. Text in English. 1912. w. AUD 584 (effective 2000). charts; stat. index. **Document type:** *Government.*
Published by: Department of Industrial Relations, 50 Phillip St, Sydney, NSW 2000, Australia. Ed. G K Robertson. Circ: 630. **Subscr. to:** 1 Oxford St, Darlinghurst, NSW 2010, Australia.

331.125 GBR ISSN 0268-1072
HD6331 CODEN: NWEMEJ
➤ **NEW TECHNOLOGY, WORK & EMPLOYMENT.** Text in English. 1986. q. GBP 70, EUR 105 combined subscription in Europe to individuals print & online eds.; USD 156 combined subscription in the Americas to individuals & Caribbean, print & online eds.; GBP 93 combined subscription elsewhere to individuals print & online eds.; GBP 227 combined subscription in Europe to institutions print & online eds.; USD 480 combined subscription in the Americas to institutions & Caribbean (print & online eds.); GBP 286 combined subscription elsewhere to institutions print & online eds.; GBP 30, EUR 45 combined subscription in Europe to students print & online eds.; USD 69 combined subscription in the Americas to students & Caribbean, print & online eds.; GBP 41 combined subscription elsewhere to students print & online eds. (effective 2006). adv. bk.rev. reprint service avail. from PSC. **Document type:** *Journal, Academic/Scholarly.* **Description:** Presents analysis of the changing contours of technological and organizational systems and processes, to encourage an enhanced understanding of the many dimensions of technological change in the work place.
Related titles: Microform ed.; Online - full text ed.: ISSN 1468-005X. GBP 216 in Europe to institutions; USD 457 in the Americas to institutions & Caribbean; GBP 272 elsewhere to institutions (effective 2006) (from Blackwell Synergy, EBSCO Publishing, Gale Group, IngentaConnect, O C L C Online Computer Library Center, Inc., Swets Information Services).
Indexed: ABIn, ASCA, ASSIA, CMCI, CPM, CompLI, CurCont, ERA, Emerald, ErgAb, GEOBASE, HRA, IBR, IBSS, Inspec, PAIS, RASB, SENA, SSA, SSCI, SociolAb, TEA, WTA.
—BLDSC (6088.840800), AskIEEE, IDS, IE, Infotrieve, ingenta. **CCC.**
Published by: Blackwell Publishing Ltd., 9600 Garsington Rd, Oxford, OX4 2ZG, United Kingdom. TEL 44-1865-776868, FAX 44-1865-714591, customerservices@oxon.blackwellpublishing.com, http://www.blackwellpublishing.com/journals/NTWE. Ed. Christopher Baldry.

331.133 USA
NEW YORK (CITY). HUMAN RESOURCES ADMINISTRATION. EQUAL EMPLOYMENT OPPORTUNITY QUARTERLY REPORT. Text in English. q.
Published by: Human Resources Administration, Office of Equal Employment Opportunity, 250 Church St, New York, NY 10013. TEL 212-553-5883.

344.01 USA
NEW YORK EMPLOYMENT LAW. Text in English. 1992. irreg. (in 5 vols.). looseleaf. USD 428 (effective 2002). **Description:** covers interviewing and employment applications, pre-employment testing and background checks, current issues associated with "truth-in-hiring" claims, privacy issues in the workplace from eavesdropping and monitoring of employment communications to employee access to personnel records.
Related titles: CD-ROM ed.: USD 621 (effective 2002).
Published by: Matthew Bender & Co., Inc. (Subsidiary of: LexisNexis North America), 1275 Broadway, Albany, NY 12204. international@bender.com, http://bender.lexisnexis.com. Ed. Jonathan L. Sulds.

NEW YORK EMPLOYMENT LAW LETTER. see *LAW*

334.01 USA
NEW YORK PRACTICE SERIES. EMPLOYMENT LITIGATION IN NEW YORK. Text in English. base vol. plus a. updates. USD 125 base vol(s). print & diskette eds. (effective 2004). **Document type:** *Monographic series, Academic/Scholarly.* **Description:** Covers all stages of employment litigation applicable in the state of New York.
Related titles: Diskette ed.; Series of: New York Practice Series.
Published by: Thomson West (Subsidiary of: Thomson Corporation, The), 610 Opperman Dr, Eagan, MN 55123-1396. TEL 651-687-7000, 800-328-4880, http://west.thomson.com/product/12448068/product.asp.

344.01 USA
NEW YORK STATE BAR ASSOCIATION. LABOR AND EMPLOYMENT LAW SECTION. NEWSLETTER. Key Title: Labor and Employment Law Section Newsletter. Text in English. 1975. 4/yr. USD 30 to libraries. bk.rev. back issues avail. **Document type:** *Newsletter.*
Formerly (until 1980): New York State Bar Association. Labor Law Section Newsletter (0160-5186)
Published by: (Labor and Employment Law Section), New York State Bar Association, 1 Elk St, Albany, NY 12207. TEL 518-463-3200, FAX 518-463-8844. Ed. Judith Lamanna. R&P Daniel J McMahon. Circ: 2,000 (controlled).

331 USA ISSN 0070-0134
NEW YORK STATE SCHOOL OF INDUSTRIAL AND LABOR RELATIONS. BULLETIN. Text in English. 1951. irreg., latest vol.70, 1995. price varies. adv. **Document type:** *Monographic series, Trade.*
Supersedes in part: Extension Bulletin; Research Bulletin
—CCC.
Published by: (New York State School of Industrial and Labor Relations), I L R Press, Cornell University Press, 512 E State St, Ithaca, NY 14850. TEL 607-277-2338, 800-666-2211. Ed. Frances Benson. R&P Tonya Cook. Adv. contact Elizabeth Larsen.

NEW YORK WORKERS' COMPENSATION LAW HANDBOOK. see *LAW*

331 NZL ISSN 0110-0637
HD8930.5
➤ **NEW ZEALAND JOURNAL OF INDUSTRIAL RELATIONS.** Text in English. 1976. 3/yr. NZD 75 to individuals; NZD 100 to institutions; NZD 40 newsstand/cover (effective 2003). adv. bk.rev. back issues avail. **Document type:** *Journal, Academic/Scholarly.* **Description:** Publishes articles on industrial relations and labor law with an emphasis on New Zealand and the Asia-Pacific region.
Related titles: Online - full text ed.: (from Northern Light Technology, Inc.).
Indexed: ABIn, AusPAIS, BrHumI, INZP, PAIS.
—BLDSC (6094.540000), IE, ingenta. **CCC.**
Published by: Foundation for Industrial Relations Research and Education (New Zealand), P.O. Box 6088, Dunedin, New Zealand. FAX 64-3-479-8173, ageare@business.otago.ac.nz, http://telperion.otago.ac.nz/mgmt/nzjir/main.html. Ed. Alan Geare. Adv. contact V Smaill TEL 64-3-479-8129. Circ: 350.

331.11 NZL ISSN 0113-1222
NEW ZEALAND LABOUR FORCE. Text in English. 1986. q. USD 75.
—CCC.
Published by: Statistics New Zealand/Te Tari Tatau, P.O. Box 2922, Wellington, New Zealand.

NEW ZEALAND RETAIL; New Zealand's leading retail magazine. see *BUSINESS AND ECONOMICS—Marketing And Purchasing*

331 310 NZL
NEW ZEALAND. STATISTICS NEW ZEALAND. HOUSEHOLD LABOUR FORCE SURVEY. Text in English. quadrennial. stat. **Document type:** *Government.* **Description:** Provides New Zealand's official employment and unemployment statistics.
Published by: Statistics New Zealand/Te Tari Tatau, PO Box 2922, Wellington, New Zealand. TEL 64-4-495-4600, FAX 64-4-473-2626, info@stats.govt.nz, http://www.stats.govt.nz.

331 310 NZL
NEW ZEALAND. STATISTICS NEW ZEALAND. LABOUR COST INDEX (ALL LABOUR COSTS). Text in English. q. stat. **Document type:** *Government.*
Published by: Statistics New Zealand/Te Tari Tatau, PO Box 2922, Wellington, New Zealand. TEL 64-4-495-4600, FAX 64-4-473-2626, info@stats.govt.nz, http://www.stats.govt.nz.

331 310 NZL
NEW ZEALAND. STATISTICS NEW ZEALAND. LABOUR COST INDEX (SALARY AND WAGE RATES). Text in English. q. stat. **Document type:** *Government.*
Published by: Statistics New Zealand/Te Tari Tatau, PO Box 2922, Wellington, New Zealand. TEL 64-4-495-4600, FAX 64-4-473-2626, info@stats.govt.nz, http://www.stats.govt.nz.

NEWSMONTH. see *LABOR UNIONS*

344.01 NLD ISSN 0923-8646
NIEUWSBRIEF WERK. Text in Dutch. 1989. bi-w. **Document type:** *Newsletter.*
Published by: Samsom H.D. Tjeenk Willink B.V. (Subsidiary of: Wolters Kluwer N.V.), Postbus 316, Alphen aan den Rijn, 2400 AH, Netherlands. TEL 31-1720-66822, FAX 31-1720-66639.

331 NGA
NIGERIA. FEDERAL MINISTRY OF LABOUR AND PRODUCTIVITY. ANNUAL REPORT. Text in English. 1958. a. free. stat. **Document type:** *Government.*
Formerly: Nigeria. Federal Ministry of Labour. Quarterly Review (0549-2351)
Media: Duplicated (not offset).
Published by: (Nigeria. Federal Secretariat, Phase I), Federal Ministry of Labour and Productivity, Planning, Research and Statistics Department, PMB 12576, Lagos, Ikoyi, Nigeria. Circ: 1,000.

NIGERIA. FEDERAL MINISTRY OF LABOUR AND PRODUCTIVITY. QUARTERLY BULLETIN OF LABOUR STATISTICS. see *BUSINESS AND ECONOMICS—Abstracting, Bibliographies, Statistics*

331.11 NGA
NIGERIA. NATIONAL MANPOWER BOARD. MANPOWER STUDIES. Text in English. 1963. irreg. (1-2/yr.). price varies. stat. **Document type:** *Government.*
Published by: National Manpower Board, PMB 12558, Ikoyi, Lagos State, Nigeria. Ed. C C Mmereole. Circ: 1,000.

331 JPN ISSN 0917-1843
HD4811
NIHON RODO KENKYU KIKO KENKYU KIYO/JAPAN INSTITUTE OF LABOUR. STUDIES. Text in English, Japanese. 1991. s-a.
Indexed: IBSS.
Published by: Japan Institute of Labour/Nihon Rodo Kenkyu Kiko, Shinjuku Monolith, P.O. Box 7040, Tokyo, 163-0926, Japan. TEL 03-5321-3074, FAX 03-5321-3015.

331 JPN ISSN 0916-3808
HD4811
NIHON RODO KENKYU ZASSHI/JAPAN INSTITUTE OF LABOUR. JOURNAL. Text in Japanese. 1959. m. JPY 10,740 domestic (effective 2000). bk.rev. bibl.; charts; stat. s-a. cum.index. **Document type:** *Academic/Scholarly.* **Description:** Information on industrial relations in Japan.
Formerly (until 1990): Nihon Rodo Kyokai Zasshi (0029-0378)
Indexed: AmH&L, HistAb, RASB.
Published by: Japan Institute of Labour/Nihon Rodo Kenkyu Kiko, Shinjuku Monolith, P.O. Box 7040, Tokyo, 163-0926, Japan. TEL 03-5321-3074, FAX 03-5321-3015. Ed. Akira Takanashi. Circ: 4,000.

331 150 JPN ISSN 0549-4974
NINGEN KOGAKU/JAPANESE JOURNAL OF ERGONOMICS. Text in English, Japanese. 1965. bi-m.
Indexed: ErgAb, Inspec.
—BLDSC (4651.820000), CISTI.
Published by: Nihon Ningen Kogakkai/Japan Ergonomics Society, 2-10-9 Akasaka, Tokyo, 1077, Japan. TEL 81-3-3587-0278, FAX 81-3-3587-0284, jes@cb.mbn.or.jp, http://plaza8.mbn.or.jp/~jes/.

331 NOR ISSN 1398-3458
NORDIC LABOUR JOURNAL; the labour market, the working environment and related issues. Text in English. 1996. s-a.
Related titles: Online - full text ed.
Published by: Arbeidsforskningsinstituttet/Work Research Institute, St. Olavs Plass, PO Box 6954, Oslo, 0130, Norway. TEL 47-23-369200, FAX 47-22-568918, afi@afi-wri.no, http://www.norden.org/arb/ain/arkiv/uk/index.asp?lang=1, http://www.afi-wri.no.

NORTH CAROLINA EMPLOYMENT LAW LETTER. see *LAW*

346.086 USA
NORTH CAROLINA WORKERS' COMPENSATION LAW ANNOTATED. Text in English. irreg. (w/ CD ROM), latest 2002. USD 45 base vol(s).; USD 60 base vol(s). Hardcover (effective 2003). 746 p./no.; **Description:** A compendium of relevant laws and cases in use by the North Carolina Industrial Commission.
Published by: Michie Company (Subsidiary of: LexisNexis North America), 701 E Water St, Charlottesville, VA 22902-5389. TEL 434-972-7600, 800-446-3410, FAX 434-972-7677, http://www.michie.com.

NORTH DAKOTA EMPLOYMENT LAW LETTER. see *LAW*

368.41 USA
NORTH DAKOTA WORKERS' COMPENSATION LAW. Text in English. irreg., latest 2001. USD 25 (effective 2003). 185 p./no.; **Description:** Contains the full text of the Title 65 of the North Dakota Century Code as well as a complete index, fully annotated with case notes and other research references.
Published by: Michie Company (Subsidiary of: LexisNexis North America), 701 E Water St, Charlottesville, VA 22902-5389. TEL 434-972-7600, 800-446-3410, FAX 434-972-7677, http://www.michie.com.

331.21 GBR
NORTH EAST MIDLANDS SALARY SURVEY. Text in English. 2/yr. GBP 280 per edition (effective 2001). **Document type:** *Bulletin.* **Description:** Salary survey covering the Derbyshire, Burton-upon-Trent, Nottinghamshire, Leicestershire and Lincolnshire areas.
Published by: The Reward Group Ltd., Reward House, Diamond Way, Stone Business Park, Stone, Staffs ST15 0SD, United Kingdom. TEL 44-1785-813566, FAX 44-1785-817007, enquiries@reward-group.co.uk, http://www.reward-group.co.uk.

NORTH WEST LABOUR HISTORY. see *HISTORY—History Of Europe*

331.21 GBR
NORTH WEST SALARY SURVEY. Text in English. 2/yr. GBP 280 per edition (effective 2001). **Document type:** *Bulletin.* **Description:** Salary survey for the North West covering the Lancashire, Greater Manchester, Merseyside, Cheshire and Clwyd areas.
Published by: The Reward Group Ltd., Reward House, Diamond Way, Stone Business Park, Stone, Staffs ST15 0SD, United Kingdom. TEL 44-1785-813566, FAX 44-1785-817007, enquiries@reward-group.co.uk, http://www.reward-group.co.uk.

331.21 GBR
NORTHERN IRELAND SALARY SURVEY. Text in English. 2/yr. GBP 280 per edition (effective 2001). **Document type:** *Bulletin.* **Description:** Pay and benefit salary survey covering Northern Ireland.
Published by: The Reward Group Ltd., Reward House, Diamond Way, Stone Business Park, Stone, Staffs ST15 0SD, United Kingdom. TEL 44-1785-813566, FAX 44-1785-817007, enquiries@reward-group.co.uk, http://www.reward-group.co.uk.

B

331 USA ISSN 0894-444X
NORTHWEST LABOR PRESS. Text in English. 1900. s-m. USD 14 (effective 2000). adv. **Document type:** *Newspaper, Trade.* **Description:** Covers issues of interest to labor.
Related titles: Microfilm ed.
Published by: Oregon Labor Press Publishing Co., 4313 N E Tillamook, Ste 206, Box 13150, Portland, OR 97213. TEL 503-288-3311, FAX 503-288-3320. Ed., R&P, Adv. contact Michael Gutwig. Circ: 52,000.

331 NOR ISSN 0801-1621
NORWAY. ARBEIDSDIREKTORATET. AARSMELDING. Text in English. 1917. a. free. **Document type:** *Government.* **Description:** Provides descriptions of the situation in the labor market and performance by the Public Employment Service.
Related titles: Norwegian ed.
Published by: Arbeidsdirektoratet, Postboks 8127, Oslo, 0032, Norway. TEL 47-22-94-24-00, FAX 47-22-94-27-63, adir@aetat.no, euroguidance@adir.aetat.no, http://www.aetat.no. Ed. Heidi Wiggen. Circ: 15,000.

NOTIZIARIO DEL LAVORO E PREVIDENZA. see *LAW—Corporate Law*

331 CAN ISSN 0380-5689
HD8101.N6
NOVA SCOTIA. DEPARTMENT OF LABOUR. ANNUAL REPORT. Text in English. 1935. a. **Document type:** *Government.* **Description:** Summary report of the year's activities of the Nova Scotia Department of Labour.
—CISTI.
Published by: Department of Labour, Research Division, P O Box 697, Halifax, NS B3J 2T8, Canada. TEL 902-424-4313, http://www.gov.ns.ca/labr/.

O E C D LABOUR FORCE STATISTICS/O C D E STATISTIQUES DE LA POPULATION ACTIVE. see *BUSINESS AND ECONOMICS—Abstracting, Bibliographies, Statistics*

O E C D SOCIAL, EMPLOYMENT AND MIGRATION WORKING PAPERS. see *SOCIAL SERVICES AND WELFARE*

331 NLD ISSN 0165-0823
O R INFORMATIE. (Ondernemingsraad) Text in Dutch. 1975. m. EUR 129; EUR 12.50 newsstand/cover (effective 2005). adv. **Document type:** *Trade.*
—IE, Infotrieve, KNAW.
Published by: Kluwer B.V. (Subsidiary of: Wolters Kluwer N.V.), Postbus 23, Deventer, 7400 GA, Netherlands. TEL 31-570-673449, FAX 31-570-691555, or-informatie@kluwer.nl, http://www.kluwer.nl/statics/or/oronline/index.html. Ed. Frank Robroek. Pub. Jeroen Hoogerwerf. Adv. contact Ria Consten. Circ: 12,100.

OBSLEDOVANIE NASELENIYA PO PROBLEMAM ZANYATOSTI/SURVEY ON EMPLOYMENT OF POPULATION. see *BUSINESS AND ECONOMICS—Abstracting, Bibliographies, Statistics*

OCCUPATIONAL COMPENSATION SUMMARIES. see *BUSINESS AND ECONOMICS—Abstracting, Bibliographies, Statistics*

331 USA
OCCUPATIONAL COMPENSATION SURVEYS. Text in English. a. price varies. **Document type:** *Government.* **Description:** Analyzes regions for pay levels and occupational descriptions.
Related titles: Diskette ed.; ♦ Series of: U.S. Bureau of Labor Statistics. Bulletin. ISSN 0082-9021.
Published by: U.S. Department of Labor, Bureau of Labor Statistics, Postal Square Bldg., 2 Massachusetts Ave, NE, Washington, DC 20212-0001 . TEL 202-691-5200, http://www.bls.gov. **Subscr. to:** U.S. Government Printing Office, Superintendent of Documents.

OCCUPATIONAL ERGONOMICS; the journal of the International Society for Occupational Ergonomics and Safety. see *OCCUPATIONAL HEALTH AND SAFETY*

OCCUPATIONAL PENSIONS. see *INSURANCE*

OCCUPATIONAL PENSIONS LAW REPORTS. see *INSURANCE*

331.11 CHL ISSN 0716-4521
OCUPACION Y DESOCUPACION EN EL GRAN SANTIAGO. Text in Spanish. q. charts; stat.
Published by: Universidad de Chile, Facultad de Ciencias Economicas y Administrativas, Ave. Ranacagua, 257, Santiago, Chile. TEL 2228521.

OFFICIAL DISABILITY GUIDELINES. see *OCCUPATIONAL HEALTH AND SAFETY*

OHIO EMPLOYMENT LAW LETTER. see *LAW*

331 USA ISSN 1063-9853
THE OHIO LABOR CITIZEN. Text in English. 1988. m. USD 7.50 subscr - mailed (effective 2005). back issues avail. **Document type:** *Newspaper, Trade.* **Description:** Contains news of interest to union members in the building and construction trades.
Published by: Cleveland Building & Construction Trades Council, 3250 Euclid Ave., Cleveland, OH 44115. TEL 216-361-8077, citizenpub@sbcglobal.net. Ed. William G. Obbagy. Adv. contact Terri A. Andrisin. Circ: 15,000 (controlled and free).

331.11 USA
OHIO LABOR MARKET INFORMATION: LABOR MARKET REVIEW. Text in English. 1983. m. free. **Document type:** *Government.*
Indexed: SRI.
Published by: Ohio Bureau of Employment Services, Labor Market Information Division, PO Box 1618, Columbus, OH 43216. TEL 614-752-9494, FAX 614-752-9621. Ed. Keith Ewald. Circ: 3,000.

OHIO PUBLIC EMPLOYEE REPORTER. see *LAW*

OKHRANA TRUDA I SOTSIAL'NOE STRAKHOVANIE. see *INSURANCE*

OKLAHOMA EMPLOYMENT LAW LETTER. see *LAW*

331 USA
OKLAHOMA. EMPLOYMENT SECURITY COMMISSION. RESEARCH DIVISION. ANNUAL REPORT TO THE GOVERNOR. Text in English. 1939. a. free. charts; stat. **Document type:** *Government.*
Formerly: Oklahoma. Employment Security Commission. Research and Planning Division. Annual Report to the Governor
Published by: Employment Security Commission, Research Department, Will Rogers Bldg, 2401 N Lincoln Blvd, Oklahoma City, OK 73105. Ed. Arthur Jordan. Circ: 1,200.

320.57 USA
ON THE LINE (NEW YORK). Text in English. 1978. 6/yr. USD 5 domestic to individuals; USD 10 foreign to individuals; USD 15 Libraries & Institutions (effective 2000). bk.rev. back issues avail. **Document type:** *Newsletter.* **Description:** Covers labor and anarchist issues.
Former titles (until 1994): East European News; (until 1989): On the Line (New York)
Published by: Workers Solidarity Alliance, New York Area Group, 339 Lafayette St, Rm 202, New York, NY 10012. TEL 212-979-8353. Ed. Mike Harris. Circ: 200.

331 CAN
OUR ONTARIO. Text in English. 1966. 5/yr. free. bk.rev. **Description:** News, feature articles, columns and letters by and about public sector workers in Ontario and the problems they face in a labour relations context.
Former titles (until Oct. 1997): O P S E U News (0229-8104); (until Feb. 1993): Voices (0838-7176); (until June 1987): O P S E U News
Published by: Ontario Public Service Employees Union, 100 Lesmill Rd, North York, ON M3B 3P8, Canada. TEL 416-443-8888, FAX 416-443-1762. Circ: 80,000 (controlled).

331.1 CAN ISSN 1195-0196
ONTARIO LABOUR AND EMPLOYMENT LEGISLATION. Text in English. 1993. a. CND 86 per vol. (effective 2005).
Published by: Canada Law Book Inc., 240 Edward St, Aurora, ON L4G 3S9, Canada. TEL 905-841-6472, 800-263-3269, FAX 905-841-5085, b.loney@canadalawbook.ca, http://www.canadalawbook.com/catalogue.cfm?DSP=Detail&ProductID=365, http://www.canadalawbook.ca.

331 CAN ISSN 0711-849X
KEO641.A72
ONTARIO. LABOUR RELATIONS BOARD. ANNUAL REPORT. Text in English. 1980. a. free. **Document type:** *Government.*
Published by: Labour Relations Board, 505 University Ave, Toronto, ON M5G 2P1, Canada. TEL 416-326-7500, FAX 416-326-0384. Circ: 1,150.

331 CAN
KEO636.4
ONTARIO. LABOUR RELATIONS BOARD. REPORT. Text in English. 1944. bi-m. CND 67.50. **Document type:** *Government.*
Former titles: Ontario. Labour Relations Board. Reports. A Monthly Series of Decisions (0383-4778); Ontario. Labour Relations Board. Decisions (0472-9986)
Related titles: Microfiche ed.; Online - full text ed.: (from QuickLaw Inc.).
Published by: Labour Relations Board, 505 University Ave, Toronto, ON M5G 2P1, Canada. TEL 416-326-7500, FAX 416-326-0384. Ed. Ron Lebi. Circ: 1,200.

331.11 CAN ISSN 1183-9341
ONTARIO. WORKPLACE HEALTH AND SAFETY AGENCY. ANNUAL REPORT. Text in English. 1990. a.
Published by: Ontario. Workpalce Health and Safety Agency, 200 Front St 19 Fl, Toronto, ON M5V 3J1, Canada.

ONTSLAGZAKBOEKJE. see *LAW—Civil Law*

331.4 BEL ISSN 0078-5164
OPEN DOOR INTERNATIONAL FOR THE EMANCIPATION OF THE WOMAN WORKER. REPORT OF CONGRESS. Text in Multiple languages. 1929. irreg., latest 1966, 13th, London. free. **Document type:** *Proceedings.*
Related titles: Microfilm ed.: (from AMP).
Published by: Open Door International, Rue Americaine 16, Brussels, 1060, Belgium. Ed. Adele Hauwel.

331.125122 USA
OPENINGS ONLINE✶ . Text in English. bi-m. avail. only with subscr. to Religious Studies News (ISSN 0885-0372). back issues avail. **Document type:** *Newsletter, Academic/Scholarly.* **Description:** Announces academic job openings in the fields of religion, comparative religion, Biblical studies, philosophy and oriental studies.
Formerly (until 1998): Openings
Media: Online - full text.
Published by: Scholars Press, PO Box 15299, Atlanta, GA 30333-0399. TEL 404-727-2345, 888-747-2354, FAX 404-727-2348, scholars@emory.edu.

OREGON EMPLOYMENT LAW LETTER. see *LAW*

P E R B NEWS. see *PUBLIC ADMINISTRATION*

P S ACTUA. (Periodiek voor Sociale Verzekering Documenta) see *INSURANCE*

P S DOCUMENTA. (Periodiek voor Sociale Verzekering Documenta) see *INSURANCE*

PAKISTAN LABOUR CASES; a monthly law journal containing cases on service laws and labour laws. see *LAW*

344.01 USA ISSN 1534-5300
KFC30.5.P35
PARKER'S CALIFORNIA LABOR CODE. Text in English. a. (w/ CD ROM), latest 2003. USD 45 (effective 2003).
Related titles: Diskette ed.: USD 45.
Published by: Michie Company (Subsidiary of: LexisNexis North America), 701 E Water St, Charlottesville, VA 22902-5389. TEL 434-972-7600, 800-446-3410, FAX 434-972-7677, http://www.michie.com.

PAY AND BENEFITS BULLETIN. see *BUSINESS AND ECONOMICS—Personnel Management*

331.21 USA
PAYROLL ADMINISTRATION GUIDE. Text in English. 1990. bi-w. looseleaf. USD 672 (effective 2001). **Document type:** *Newsletter.* **Description:** Notification and reference service for payroll managers. Covers federal and state employment tax, wage-hour, and wage-payment laws.
Related titles: E-mail ed.; Online - full text ed.
Indexed: ATI.
Published by: The Bureau of National Affairs, Inc., 1231 25th St., NW, Washington, DC 20037. TEL 202-452-4200, 800-372-1033, 800-452-7773, FAX 202-822-8092, customercare@bna.com, bnaplus@bna.com, http://www.bna.com/. Ed. Roslyn Rosenberg. Pub. Greg C McCaffery.

331.21 USA ISSN 1524-1580
KF6436.A15
PAYROLL ADMINISTRATION GUIDE NEWSLETTER. Text in English. 1990. bi-w. USD 258 (effective 2004). back issues avail. **Document type:** *Newsletter.* **Description:** For payroll professionals. Covers federal and state employment tax, wage-hour, and wage-payment laws.
Formerly (until 1999): Payroll Administration Guide (1524-1599)
Related titles: Online - full text ed.: (from The Bureau of National Affairs, Inc.).
—CCC.

Published by: The Bureau of National Affairs, Inc., 1231 25th St., NW, Washington, DC 20037. TEL 202-452-4200, 800-372-1033, FAX 202-785-7167, customercare@bna.com, http://www.bna.com. Ed. Roslyn Rosenberg. Pub. Greg C McCaffery. **Subscr. to:** 9435 Key West Ave, Rockville, MD 20850.

331.21 USA
THE PAYROLL ADVISOR. Text in English. m. USD 144; USD 17 newsstand/cover (effective 2001). **Document type:** *Trade.* **Description:** Helps payroll administrators keep up with developments in the law, regulations, and reporting requirements.
Published by: Aspen Publishers, Inc. (Subsidiary of: Wolters Kluwer N.V.), 5301 Buckeystown Pike, Ste. 400, Frederick, MD 21704-8319. TEL 800-638-8437, customer.service@aspenpubl.com, http://www.aspenpub.com. Ed. Vicki Lambert. **Dist. by:** Distribution Center, 7201 McKinney Circle, Frederick, MD 21701. TEL 301-698-7100, FAX 301-417-7550.

331.21 USA ISSN 1063-9047
PAYTECH. Text in English. 1982. m. USD 155 membership. adv. charts. 64 p./no.; back issues avail.; reprints avail. **Document type:** *Magazine, Trade.* **Description:** Provides professionals in the payroll and human resource industries with current information on tax legislation and innovations in payroll systems and processing procedures.
Formerly (until 1992): Payroll Exchange (0194-6196)
Indexed: SoftBase.
Published by: American Payroll Association, 660 N Main, San Antonio, TX 78205. TEL 210-226-4600. Eds. Eileen Gaughran, Monty Montgomery. Pub. Daniel Maddux. Circ: 16,000.

331.0715 MEX
PEDAGOGIA PARA EL ADIESTRAMIENTO. Text in Spanish. 1971. q. MXP 80, USD 5. abstr.; bibl. index, cum.index.
Related titles: Microfilm ed.
Published by: Servicio Nacional de Adiestramiento Rapido de la Mano de Obra en la Industria, Centro de Informacion Tecnica y Documentacion, Calzada Atzcapotzalco-la Villa 209, Apdo. 16-099, Mexico City, DF, Mexico. Ed. Marsella Cruz. Circ: 4,000.

PEDAGOGIKA PRACY. see *EDUCATION—Adult Education*

PENNSYLVANIA EMPLOYMENT LAW LETTER. see *LAW*

331 USA ISSN 1546-4229
PENNSYLVANIA LABOR HISTORY JOURNAL. Text in English. 1974. a.
Formerly (until 1997): Pennsylvania Labor History Notes
Published by: Pennsylvania Labor History Society, Labor Center IUP, 1 Keith Hall, 390 Pratt Dr., Pittsburgh, PA 15238. http://www.hhs.iup.edu/laborcenter/PartnerOrganizations/PALaborHistorySociety/. Ed. Russell W. Gibbons.

331 USA
PENNSYLVANIA. LABOR RELATIONS BOARD. ANNUAL REPORT. Text in English. 1937. a. free. charts; stat. **Document type:** *Government.* **Description:** Provides statistical information on the Board's case load and case processing activities, a summary of Board final orders and court decisions.
Formerly: Pennsylvania. Labor Relations Board. Report
Published by: Department of Labor and Industry, 102 CAB Building, 901 N 7th Street, Harrisburg, PA 17102. TEL 717-787-1091. Ed., R&P Patricia A Crawford TEL 717-783-6018. Circ: 1,000.

PENNSYLVANIA PUBLIC EMPLOYEE REPORTER. see *LAW*

PENSIOEN BULLETIN. see *INSURANCE*

331.252 NLD ISSN 1382-4015
PENSIOEN JURISPRUDENTIE. Text in Dutch. 1995. 10/yr. back issues avail. **Document type:** *Trade.* **Description:** Covers developments affecting pension management and administration, including recent jurisprudence, civil, social and tax law issues.
Published by: Uitgeverij Fed bv (Subsidiary of: Wolters Kluwer N.V.), Postbus 23, Deventer, 7400 GA, Netherlands. TEL 31-570-633155, FAX 31-570-633834. Eds. E Lutjens, J Th L Brouwer.

331.252 NLD
PENSIOEN MONOGRAFIEEN. Text in Dutch. 1995. irreg., latest vol.3, 1995. price varies. back issues avail. **Document type:** *Monographic series.*
Published by: Uitgeverij Fed bv (Subsidiary of: Wolters Kluwer N.V.), Postbus 23, Deventer, 7400 GA, Netherlands. TEL 31-570-633155, FAX 31-570-633834.

331.252 NLD ISSN 0929-8681
PENSIOENBRIEF. Text in Dutch. 1993. every 3 wks. back issues avail. **Document type:** *Newsletter.*
Published by: Uitgeverij Fed bv (Subsidiary of: Wolters Kluwer N.V.), Postbus 23, Deventer, 7400 GA, Netherlands. TEL 31-570-633155, FAX 31-570-633834. Ed. P Kavelaars.

331.252 NLD ISSN 1383-617X
PENSIOENGIDS. Text in Dutch. 1995. a. **Document type:** *Trade.*
Published by: Uitgeverij Fed bv (Subsidiary of: Wolters Kluwer N.V.), Postbus 23, Deventer, 7400 GA, Netherlands. TEL 31-570-633155, FAX 31-570-633834. Eds. G J B Dietvorst, L G M Stevens.

331.252 USA ISSN 1523-5718
PENSION & BENEFITS DAILY. Text in English. 1997. d. back issues avail. **Document type:** *Newsletter, Trade.* **Description:** Reports on industry news, developments, and emerging trends about pensions and benefits.
Media: Online - full text (from The Bureau of National Affairs, Inc.).
—CCC.
Published by: The Bureau of National Affairs, Inc., 1231 25th St., NW, Washington, DC 20037. TEL 800-372-1033, 800-452-7773, FAX 800-253-0332, customercare@bna.com, http://www.bna.com/products/eb/pend.htm. **Subscr. to:** 9435 Key West Ave, Rockville, MD 20850.

331.252 USA ISSN 1069-5117
HD7106.U5
PENSION & BENEFITS REPORTER. Text in English. 1974. w. looseleaf. back issues avail. **Document type:** *Trade.* **Description:** Covers latest pension developments stemming from the passage of ERISA and its amendments, plus pension and welfare benefit regulations, standards, enforcement actions, court decisions, legislative and administrative actions, agency options, and employee benefit trust fund requirements.
Formerly (until vol.20, no.20, 1993): B N A Pension Reporter (0095-7100)
Related titles: Microform ed.: (from PQC); Online - full text ed.: ISSN 1522-5976 (from The Bureau of National Affairs, Inc., Thomson West).
Indexed: LII, PLII.
—CCC.
Published by: The Bureau of National Affairs, Inc., 1231 25th St., NW, Washington, DC 20037. TEL 202-452-4200, FAX 202-822-8092, http://www.bna.com/products/eb/pen.htm. Ed. David A Sayer.

331.252 USA ISSN 1063-2476
PENSION BENEFITS. Text in English. 1992. m. USD 243 (effective 2004). **Document type:** *Newsletter, Trade.* **Description:** Focuses on cutting-edge trends and provides early warning of the issues that will affect pensions tomorrow.
Related titles: Online - full text ed.: (from EBSCO Publishing, Florida Center for Library Automation, Gale Group, ProQuest Information & Learning).
Indexed: ABIn.
—CCC.
Published by: Panel Publishers, Inc. (Subsidiary of: Aspen Publishers, Inc.), 1185 Ave of the Americas, 37th Fl, New York, NY 10036. TEL 212-597-0200, 800-638-8437, FAX 212-597-0331, customer.service@aspenpubl.com, http://www.aspenpublishers.com. **Dist. by:** Aspen Publishers, Inc., Distribution Center, 7201 McKinney Circle, Frederick, MD 21701. TEL 301-698-7100, FAX 301-417-7550.

331.252 USA ISSN 1076-030X
PENSION PLAN ADMINISTRATOR; a national network of ideas and solutions. Text in English. 1994. m. USD 180 (effective 2002). **Document type:** *Newsletter, Trade.* **Description:** Provides practical solutions to tough pension issues relating to 401(k) Plans, legislation and regulations, investments and funding, industry competition, fiduciary responsibilities, and more.
Related titles: Online - full text ed.: (from ProQuest Information & Learning).
Indexed: ABIn.
Published by: Aspen Publishers, Inc. (Subsidiary of: Wolters Kluwer N.V.), 5301 Buckeystown Pike, Ste. 400, Frederick, MD 21704-8319. customer.service@aspenpubl.com, http://www.aspenpub.com, http://www.aspenpublishers.com. **Dist. by:** Distribution Center, 7201 McKinney Circle, Frederick, MD 21701. TEL 301-698-7100, FAX 301-417-7550.

PENSION PLAN GUIDE. see *INSURANCE*

344.01 GBR
PENSIONS LAW AND PRACTICE WITH PRECEDENTS. Text in English. 1988. 4 base vols. plus updates 2/yr. looseleaf. GBP 525 base vol(s).; GBP 460, EUR 692 updates in Europe; GBP 470, USD 854 updates elsewhere (effective 2006). **Document type:** *Trade.*
Published by: Sweet & Maxwell Ltd., 100 Avenue Road, London, NW3 3PF, United Kingdom. TEL 44-20-74491111, FAX 44-20-74491144, customer.services@sweetandmaxwell.co.uk, http://www.sweetandmaxwell.co.uk. **Subscr. to:** Cheriton House, North Way, Andover, Hants SP10 5BE, United Kingdom.

331.252 GBR ISSN 0965-5409
PENSIONS POCKET BOOK. Text in English. 1989. a. GBP 22 per issue (effective 2000). charts; stat. **Document type:** *Trade.* **Description:** Contains latest budget requirements, statistical tables, charts, checklists and summaries to help in dealing with pension schemes and current pensions issues.
—CCC.
Published by: (Bacon & Woodrow), N T C Publications Ltd. (Subsidiary of: World Advertising Research Center Ltd.), Farm Rd, Henley-on-Thames, Oxon RG9 1EJ, United Kingdom. TEL 44-1491-411000, FAX 44-1491-571188, info@ntc.co.uk.

658.3 USA ISSN 0145-2932
PEOPLE (RALEIGH). Text in English. 1973. q. **Document type:** *Government.*
Published by: North Carolina Department of Health and Human Services, Division of Human Resources, 2003 Mail Service Center, Raleigh, NC 27699-2003. TEL 919-733-2940, FAX 919-733-6087, DHHS.HR.division@ncmail.net, http://www.dhhs.state.nc.us/humanresources/.

331.1 DEU ISSN 0031-5605
HD28
PERSONAL; Zeitschrift fuer Human Resource Management. Text in German. 1949. m. EUR 198; EUR 17 newsstand/cover (effective 2005). adv. bk.rev. bibl.; charts; illus.; mkt. index, cum.index. reprint service avail. from SCH. **Document type:** *Magazine, Trade.*
Formerly: Mensch und Arbeit
Indexed: CISA, DIP, IBR, IBZ, KES, ManagAb, RASB.
—IE, Infotrieve. **CCC.**
Published by: Verlagsgruppe Handelsblatt GmbH, Kasernenstr 67, Duesseldorf, 40213, Germany. TEL 49-211-8870, FAX 49-211-371792, personal-redaktion@vhb.de, fachverlag@vhb.de, http://www.vhb.de/personal/aktuelles.html. Ed. Ruth Lemmer. R&P Johanne Hoefer. Adv. contact Rolf Kluthausen. B&W page EUR 1,400, color page EUR 1,800; trim 166 x 271. Circ: 3,817 (paid).

B

PERSONAL INJURY DAMAGE ASSESSMENTS IN ALBERTA. see *LAW*

PERSONAL INJURY DAMAGE ASSESSMENTS IN BRITISH COLUMBIA. see *LAW*

331.152 658.3 DEU ISSN 0934-5744
PERSONALVERTRETUNGSRECHT DES BUNDES UND DER LAENDER. Text in German. 1974. irreg., latest vol.5, 2004. price varies. **Document type:** *Monographic series, Trade.*
Published by: Erich Schmidt Verlag GmbH & Co. (Berlin), Genthiner Str 30G, Berlin, 10785, Germany. TEL 49-30-250085-0, FAX 49-30-25008511, esv@esvmedien.de, http://www.erich-schmidt-verlag.de.

331.152 DEU ISSN 1435-8964
DAS PERSONALVERTRETUNGSRECHT IN NIEDERSACHSEN. Text in German. 1996. irreg. price varies. **Document type:** *Monographic series, Trade.*
Published by: Erich Schmidt Verlag GmbH & Co. (Berlin), Genthiner Str 30G, Berlin, 10785, Germany. TEL 49-30-250085-0, FAX 49-30-25008511, esv@esvmedien.de, http://www.erich-schmidt-verlag.de.

PERSONNEL IN PRACTICE. see *BUSINESS AND ECONOMICS—Personnel Management*

THE PERSONNEL LEGAL ALERT. see *BUSINESS AND ECONOMICS—Personnel Management*

PERSONNEL MANAGER'S ENCYCLOPEDIA OF PREWRITTEN PERSONNEL POLICIES. see *BUSINESS AND ECONOMICS—Personnel Management*

331.21 GBR ISSN 0964-2668
PERSONNEL REWARDS. Text in English. 1991. a. GBP 2 per edition (effective 2001). **Document type:** *Bulletin.* **Description:** Salary survey for personnel departments based on over 8,500 job recordings.
Published by: The Reward Group Ltd., Reward House, Diamond Way, Stone Business Park, Stone, Staffs ST15 0SD, United Kingdom. TEL 44-1785-813566, FAX 44-1785-817007, enquiries@reward-group.co.uk, http://www.reward-group.co.uk.

PERSONNEL TODAY. see *BUSINESS AND ECONOMICS—Personnel Management*

331 USA ISSN 1534-9276
HD6958.5
PERSPECTIVES ON WORK. Text mainly in English. 1997. s-a. looseleaf. USD 95 domestic; USD 110 foreign; USD 175 domestic; USD 190 foreign (effective 2005). adv. bk.rev. charts; illus. 48 p./no.; back issues avail. **Document type:** *Magazine, Trade.* **Description:** Covers issues about industrial relations and human resources.
Published by: (Industrial Relations Research Association), University of Illinois Press, 1325 S Oak St, Champaign, IL 61820-6903. TEL 866-244-0626, FAX 217-244-9910, journals@uillinois.edu, http://www.press.uillinois.edu/journals/pow.html. Ed. Charles Whalen. R&P Paula D. Wells TEL 217-333-1485. Adv. contact Clydette Wantland TEL 217-244-6496. B&W page USD 500; trim 7.375 x 9.75. Circ: 3,800 (paid).

331 SWE ISSN 1402-8603
PERSPEKTIV PAA ARBETSLIVET. Text in Swedish. 1990. 7/yr. **Document type:** *Newsletter, Consumer.*
Formerly (until 1997): Forskning Paagaar (1101-2455)
Related titles: Online - full text ed.: ISSN 1402-8956.

B

Published by: Arbetslivsinstitutet/The National Institute for Working Life, Vanadisvaegen 9, Stockholm, SE 11391, Sweden. TEL 46-8-6196700, FAX 46-8-6563025, registrator@arbetslivsinstitutet.se, http://www.arbetslivsinstitutet.se/perspektiv/default.asp. Ed. Ingemar Karlsson Gadea.

331.21   PER
PERU. ASOCIACION LABORAL PARA EL DESAROLLO. CUADERNOS LABORALES. Text in Spanish. m.
Indexed: PAIS.
Published by: Asociacion Laboral Para el Desarollo, Apdo Postal 4073, Lima, 100, Peru.

331   PHL
HD6958.5
PHILIPPINE JOURNAL OF LABOR AND INDUSTRIAL RELATIONS. Text in English. 1978. s-a. PHP 200; USD 24 foreign. adv. bk.rev. index. **Description:** Promotes discussion and research on labor and industrial relations using a multidisciplinary approach.
Supersedes: Philippine Journal of Industrial Relations (0115-6373); A L E C Report (0001-1762); Asian Labor Education Center. Labor Review
Indexed: BAS, IPP.
Published by: University of the Philippines, School of Labor and Industrial Relations, Diliman, Quezon City Mm, 1128, Philippines. TEL 99-63-96, FAX 632-98-83-40. Ed. Marie E Aganon. Circ: 200.

331   PHL   ISSN 0115-2629
HD8712
➤ **PHILIPPINE LABOR REVIEW.** Text in English. 1976. s-a. USD 25 (effective 2003). bk.rev. abstr. back issues avail. **Document type:** Journal, Academic/Scholarly. **Description:** Contains papers on labor and employment, the economy, industry, and other labor-related topics.
Indexed: BAS, IPP.
Published by: Department of Labor and Employment, Institute for Labor Studies, 5th Fl. DOLE Bldg, General Luna St, Intramuros, Manila, 1002, Philippines. TEL 6-32-5273490, FAX 6-32-5273491, mpduran@ilsdole.gov.ph, http://www.ilsdole.gov.ph. Ed., R&P Mitchell P Duran. Circ: 1,500.

➤ **PHILIPPINES. BUREAU OF LABOR AND EMPLOYMENT STATISTICS. CURRENT LABOR STATISTICS.** see BUSINESS AND ECONOMICS—Abstracting, Bibliographies, Statistics

➤ **PHILIPPINES. BUREAU OF LABOR AND EMPLOYMENT STATISTICS. LABOR AND EMPLOYMENT STATISTICAL REPORT.** see BUSINESS AND ECONOMICS—Abstracting, Bibliographies, Statistics

➤ **PHILIPPINES. BUREAU OF LABOR AND EMPLOYMENT STATISTICS. OCCUPATIONAL WAGES SURVEY.** see BUSINESS AND ECONOMICS—Abstracting, Bibliographies, Statistics

331.1   PHL   ISSN 0031-787X
K16
PHILIPPINES LABOR RELATIONS JOURNAL∗. Text in English. 1970 (vol.3). m. PHP 36, USD 36.
Address: 40 Gasan St, Quezon City, D-502, Philippines. Ed. Samson S Alcantara.

331   USA
PIERCE MEMORIAL LECTURESHIP AND CONFERENCE SERIES. Text in English. 1963. irreg. price varies. adv. **Document type:** Academic/Scholarly.
Published by: (New York State School of Industrial and Labor Relations), I L R Press, Cornell University Press, 512 E State St, Ithaca, NY 14850. TEL 607-277-2338, 800-666-2211. Ed. Frances Benson. R&P Tonya Cook. Adv. contact Elizabeth Larsen.

▼ **PINK**; a beautiful career, a beautiful life. see WOMEN'S INTERESTS

PLAN; tidsskrift for samfunnsplanlegging, byplan og regional utvikling. see BUSINESS AND ECONOMICS—Economic Situation And Conditions

331   USA   ISSN 1077-1816
HD7105.45.U6
PLAN SPONSOR. Text in English. 1993. m. USD 215 domestic; USD 363 elsewhere; free to qualified personnel (effective 2005). adv. **Document type:** Trade. **Description:** Edited for institutional investors focusing on the role of public and corporate pension funds, insurance companies, bank trust departments, and other large institutions.
—CCC.
Published by: Asset International, Inc., 125 Greenwich Ave, Greenwich, CT 06830. TEL 203-629 5014, FAX 203-629 5024, http://www.plansponsor.com/hp_type2/?page_id=4818. Adv. contact Charles Ruffel. B&W page USD 7,810, color page USD 10,580; trim 10.88 x 8.25. Circ: 30,000.

PLANNING GUIDE: ECONOMIC DATA - CLIENT DATA. see BUSINESS AND ECONOMICS—Economic Situation And Conditions

352.63   USA   ISSN 1544-2691
HF5382.75.U6
PLUNKETT'S COMPANION TO THE ALMANAC OF AMERICAN EMPLOYERS: MID-SIZE FIRMS. Text in English. 1999. a. USD 199.99 (effective 2005); includes CD-ROM. **Document type:** Directory.
Related titles: CD-ROM ed.: ISSN 1555-1733; Online - full text ed.: (from Gale Group); ♦ Supplement to: The Almanac of American Employers. ISSN 1088-3150.
Published by: Plunkett Research, Ltd, PO Drawer 541737, Houston, TX 77254-1737. TEL 713-932-0000, FAX 713-932-7080, info@plunkettresearch.com, http://www.plunkettresearch.com. Ed., Pub. Jack W Plunkett.

352.63   USA
HF5382.75.U6
PLUNKETT'S EMPLOYERS' INTERNET SITES WITH CAREERS INFORMATION. Text in English. 1999. a. USD 229.99 (effective 2005); includes CD-ROM. **Document type:** Directory, Trade. **Description:** Offers a comprehensive reference to employer's Internet sites and the career information they provide.
Related titles: CD-ROM ed.
Published by: Plunkett Research, Ltd, PO Drawer 541737, Houston, TX 77254-1737. TEL 713-932-0000, FAX 713-932-7080, info@plunkettresearch.com, http://www.plunkettresearch.com. Ed., Pub. Jack W Plunkett.

POLICE DEPARTMENT DISCIPLINARY BULLETIN. see CRIMINOLOGY AND LAW ENFORCEMENT

POLICE OFFICER GRIEVANCES BULLETIN. see CRIMINOLOGY AND LAW ENFORCEMENT

331.255   USA
POLICIES, PRACTICES, AND EMPLOYEE BENEFITS SURVEY. Text in English. a. USD 550. **Description:** Provides information regarding more than 400 personnel practices and benefits policies of 350 companies in PA, NJ, MD, and DE.
Published by: MidAtlantic Employers' Association, PO Box 770, Valley Forge, PA 19482. FAX 215-666-7866.

PRACA I ZABEZPIECZENIA SPOLECZNE. see LAW

331   CZE   ISSN 0032-6208
PRACE A MZDA∗. Text in Czech. 1953. 13/yr. USD 27.90. bk.rev. charts; stat. index.
Published by: Vydavatelstvi a Nakladatelstvi Prace s r.o., Vaclavske nam 17, Prague, 11258, Czech Republic. Ed. Sandze Stepanov.

PRAKTIJK SOCIAAL RECHT. see LAW—Civil Law

344.01 368.382   POL   ISSN 1509-6602
PRAWO PRACY I PRAWO SOCJALNE. PRZEGLAD ORZECZNICTWA. Text in Polish. 2000. m. PLZ 275 (effective 2003).
Published by: Wydawnictwo Prawnicze LexisNexis Sp. z o.o. (Subsidiary of: LexisNexis Europe and Africa), ul Gen K Sosnkowskiego 1, Warsaw, 02-495, Poland. TEL 48-22-6677543, FAX 48-22-7230739, biuro@LexisNexis.pl, http://sklep.lexpolonica.pl.

331.125   CAN
HD8101.5.P75
PRINCE EDWARD ISLAND. DEPARTMENT OF PROVINCIAL AFFAIRS. ANNUAL REPORT. Text in English. 1967. a. free. **Document type:** Government. **Description:** Provides annual reporting of the activities of the department; includes list of employees, organization chart, acts administered.
Supersedes in part (in 1985): Prince Edward Island. Department of Fisheries and Labor. Annual Report (0833-5869); Which was formed by the 1984 merger of: Prince Edward Island. Department of Fisheries. Annual Report (0079-5143); Prince Edward Island. Labour Division. Annual Report (0833-5850); Formerly (until 1982): Prince Edward Island. Department of Labor. Annual Report (0085-512X); Supersedes in part (in 1971): Prince Edward Island. Department of Labour, Industry and Commerce. Annual Report (0380-3007); Which was formerly (until 1970): Prince Edward Island. Department of Labour and Manpower Resources. Annual Report —CISTI.
Published by: Department of Provincial Affairs, P O Box 2000, Charlottetown, PE C1A 7N8, Canada. Ed. Douglas Carr. Circ: 250.

331.1   USA   ISSN 0079-5305
PRINCETON UNIVERSITY. INDUSTRIAL RELATIONS SECTION. RESEARCH REPORT. Text in English. 1926. irreg., latest vol.124, 1984. price varies. **Document type:** Academic/Scholarly.
Formerly: Princeton University. Industrial Relations Section. Research Series —ingenta.
Published by: Princeton University, Industrial Relations Section, Firestone Library, Princeton, NJ 08544. TEL 609-258-4040. Circ: 1,000.

331.252   USA
PRIVATE PENSION PLAN BULLETIN. Text in English. irreg., latest vol.4, 1995. **Document type:** Bulletin, Government. **Description:** Abstract of Form 5500 annual reports.
Published by: U.S. Department of Labor, Pension and Welfare Benefits Administration, 200 Constitution Ave, N W, Washington, DC 20216. TEL 202-523-8921.

PRODUCER PRICE INDICES. see BUSINESS AND ECONOMICS—Economic Situation And Conditions

331   USA
PRODUCTION, MAINTENANCE AND SERVICE SURVEY. Text in English. a. USD 405. **Description:** Offers comparative information about 86 production, maintenance and service position compensation practices, including salary information among 205 companies, representing 10,100 employees throughout PA, NJ, MD, and DE.
Published by: MidAtlantic Employers' Association, PO Box 770, Valley Forge, PA 19482. TEL 215-666-7330, FAX 215-666-7866.

PRODUCTIVITY BY INDUSTRY (YEAR). see BUSINESS AND ECONOMICS—Economic Situation And Conditions

PRODUCTIVITY MEASURES FOR SELECTED INDUSTRIES. see BUSINESS AND ECONOMICS—Economic Situation And Conditions

PROFESSIONAL LIABILITY REPORTER; recent decisions of national significance. see LAW

PROFESSIONAL NEGLIGENCE AND LIABILITY REPORTS. see LAW

331.21   USA   ISSN 1042-4482
HD4965.C2
PROFESSIONAL, SALES & TECHNICAL REMUNERATION, CANADA. Text in English. 1986. a. **Document type:** Trade.
Published by: (Executive Compensation Service (ECS)), Wyatt Data Services, 218 Rte 17 N, Rochelle Park, NJ 07622-9832. TEL 201-843-1177, FAX 201-843-0101.

331.21   CAN   ISSN 0709-5597
HD4965.C2
PROFESSIONAL, SCIENTIFIC, TECHNICAL REMUNERATION, CANADA∗. Text in English. 1978. a. CND 225.
Published by: Canadian Management Centre, 150 York St, Toronto, ON M5H 3S5, Canada. TEL 416-593-4600.

331.1   CAN   ISSN 1497-7222
HD6276.C29
PROFILE OF CANADIAN YOUTH IN THE LABOUR MARKET. Text in English. 1999. a.
Published by: Human Resources Development Canada, Applied Research Branch, 165 Hotel de Ville St, Phase II, 7th Fl, Hull, PQ K1A OJ2, Canada. FAX 819-953-8868, http://www.hrsdc.gc.ca.

PROFIT SHARING. see BUSINESS AND ECONOMICS—Investments

PSICOLOGIA E LAVORO. see PSYCHOLOGY

331   USA
PUBLIC EMPLOYEE REPORTER FOR CALIFORNIA. Text in English. base vol. plus updates 23/yr. looseleaf. USD 710 (effective 2006). **Document type:** Trade. **Description:** It is the only full-text reporting service available containing California public-sector labor law decisions. Every two weeks, PERC provides you with the full-text of all decisions issued by the California Public Employment Relations Board and related public-sector court decisions.
Published by: L R P Publications, 747 Dresher Rd, PO Box 980, Horsham, PA 19044. TEL 800-341-7874, custserve@lrp.com, http://www.shoplrp.com/product/p-3050.html, http://www.lrp.com.

PUBLIC EMPLOYEE REPORTER FOR ILLINOIS. see LAW

352.63   USA   ISSN 1071-1732
PUBLIC EMPLOYMENT LAW NOTES. Text in English. 1988. m. USD 345 (effective 2004). 24 p./no.; **Document type:** Newsletter, Trade. **Description:** Summarizes court and administrative decisions concerning public employment.
Incorporates (1988-2001): Discrimination Law Update (1522-4023); Which was formerly (until 1998): Affirmative Action - E E O Personnel Update (1094-4702); (until 199?): Affirmative Action - E E O Personnel Notes (1071-7390); (1985-2001): New York Civil Service Update (1094-4621); Which was formerly (until 1995): Civil Service Personnel Notes (1071-7439); (1985-2001): New York Education Personnel Update (1094-4591); Which was formerly (until 1997): Educational Personnel Notes (1071-7420); (1988-2001): New York Taylor Law Update (1094-4605); Which was formerly (until 1995): Labor Law Personnel Notes (1071-7404)
Related titles: Online - full text ed.: (from Thomson West).

Published by: Nyper Publications, 150 Capitol St, Augusta, ME 04330. TEL 207-621-0029, FAX 207-621-0069, nyper@capital.net, http://www.geocities.com/nyper/NYPER.html. Ed. Nancy Provencal.

352.63 USA ISSN 1043-8211
KF5336.A15
PUBLIC EMPLOYMENT LAW REPORT✶. Text in English. 1989. m. looseleaf. USD 159 (effective 2003). cum.index. back issues avail. **Document type:** *Newsletter.* **Description:** Reports the latest court cases and late-breaking legislation, along with the most recent law review articles affecting public employment.
Published by: Oakstone Legal and Business Publishing, PO Box 381205, Birmingham, AL 35238-9950. TEL 800-365-4900, http://www.oakstonelegal.com/. Ed. Laurel Kasler.

331 AUS
PUBLIC RELATIONS HANDBOOK FOR MANAGERS AND EXECUTIVES. Text in English. 1984. biennial. AUD 19.50 (effective 2000).
Published by: Crown Content, Level 1, 141 Capel St, Nth Melbourne, VIC 3051, Australia. Ed. Jim Macnamara.

PUBLIC SECTOR. see *ETHNIC INTERESTS*

PUBLIC SERVICE ASSOCIATION JOURNAL. see *PUBLIC ADMINISTRATION*

344.01 USA
THE PUNCH LIST. Text in English. q. USD 300 (effective 2000). **Description:** Addresses the concerns of the construction industry, and features insightful, practical articles for those involved in resolving disputes.
Published by: American Arbitration Association, 335 Madison Ave, New York, NY 10017. TEL 212-716-5800, FAX 212-716-5906. Ed. Ted Pons. Circ: 14,000.

331.11 USA
PURDUE UNIVERSITY. OFFICE OF MANPOWER STUDIES. MANPOWER & TECHNICAL EDUCATION REQUIREMENTS REPORTS. Text in English. 1965. irreg. USD 5 (effective 2000).
Formerly: Purdue University. Office of Manpower Studies. Manpower Report (0079-8134)
Indexed: CIJE.
Published by: Purdue University, Office of Manpower Studies, Knoy Hall, W, Lafayette, IN 47907. TEL 765-494-2559, FAX 765-494-0486. Ed. Kevin D Shell. Circ: (controlled).

331.252 USA ISSN 1523-3391
THE Q D R O REPORT; an insider's guide to QDROs and present values. (Qualified Domestic Relations Orders) Text in English. m. USD 164 (effective 1999). **Document type:** *Newsletter, Trade.* **Description:** Explains the complexities of present values, pension division strategies, and QDROs; and emphasizes ERISA and IRC regulatory topics.
Published by: Panel Publishers, Inc. (Subsidiary of: Aspen Publishers, Inc.), 1185 Ave of the Americas, 37th Fl, New York, NY 10036. TEL 212-597-0200, 800-638-8437, FAX 212-597-0331, customer.service@aspenpubl.com, http://www.aspenpublishers.com. Eds. David I Kelley, Gary A Shulman. **Dist. by:** Aspen Publishers, Inc., Distribution Center, 7201 McKinney Circle, Frederick, MD 21701. TEL 301-698-7100, FAX 301-417-7550.

331 ITA ISSN 0390-105X
QUADERNI DI ECONOMIA DEL LAVORO. Text in Italian. 197?. 3/yr.
Related titles: ♦ Includes: Tendenze della Occupazione. ISSN 0391-7940.
Published by: Franco Angeli Edizioni, Viale Monza 106, Milan, 20127, Italy. TEL 39-02-2837141, FAX 39-02-26144793, redazioni@francoangeli.it, http://www.francoangeli.it. Ed. Luigi Frey.

331 374 ITA
QUADERNI DI TECNOSTRUTTURA; tecnostruttura delle regioni per il Fondo Sociale Europeo. Short title: Q T. Text in Italian. 2000. q. EUR 54 domestic; EUR 84 foreign (effective 2003). **Document type:** *Magazine, Trade.*
Published by: Franco Angeli Edizioni, Viale Monza 106, Milan, 20127, Italy. TEL 39-02-2837141, FAX 39-02-26144793, redazioni@francoangeli.it, http://www.francoangeli.it.

331.11 USA ISSN 1049-8699
HD66 CODEN: QUDIFM
QUALITY DIGEST; the monthly magazine for and about participation . Text in English. 1981. m. free in US & Canada to qualified personnel (effective 2005). adv. bk.rev. illus. index. back issues avail.; reprints avail. **Document type:** *Magazine, Trade.* **Description:** Covers news, tips, techniques and provocative articles.
Formerly: Quality Circle Digest (0278-2642)
Related titles: Online - full text ed.: free (effective 2005).
Indexed: BPIA, CIS, Emerald, ORMS, QAb, QC&AS.
—BLDSC (7168.151800), IE, Infotrieve, ingenta, Linda Hall. CCC.
Published by: Q C I International, 40 Declaration Dr, Ste 100, Chico, CA 95973. TEL 530-893-4095, FAX 530-893-0395, editorial@qualitydigest.com, http://www.qualitydigest.com. Pub. Scott Paton. Adv. contact Tia Cronin. B&W page USD 3,560. Circ: 65,000.

332.6 ZAF
THE QUANTUM YEARBOOK. Text in English. 1992. a. ZAR 120 (effective 2000). **Document type:** *Academic/Scholarly.* **Description:** Publishes the amounts in Rands that can be claimed in personal-injury cases.
Published by: Van Zyl, Rudd and Associates, Centrahil, PO Box 12758, Port Elizabeth, 6006, South Africa. TEL 27-41-373-4322, FAX 27-41-373-4323, info@vanzylrudd.co.za, http://www.vanzylrudd.co.za. Ed. Carol Rudd.

331.11 FRA ISSN 0255-3627
HD5701
QUARTERLY LABOUR FORCE STATISTICS/O C D E STATISTIQUES TRIMESTRIELLES DE LA POPULATION ACTIVE. Text in French. 1983. q. EUR 105, USD 120, GBP 70, JPY 14,200 (effective 2005). stat. **Document type:** *Government.* **Description:** Provides data for the short-term evolution of the major labor force components and employment by sector.
Formerly: Organization for Economic Cooperation and Development. Labour Statistics (0304-3312)
Related titles: CD-ROM ed.: ISSN 1606-4542. 2002; Diskette ed.; Magnetic Tape ed.; Online - full text ed.: ISSN 1609-7602. USD 68 (effective 2004) (from EBSCO Publishing, Gale Group, IngentaConnect, O C L C Online Computer Library Center, Inc., Swets Information Services).
Indexed: IIS.
—CISTI, Infotrieve.
Published by: Organization for Economic Cooperation and Development, 2 Rue Andre Pascal, Paris, 75775 Cedex 16, France. TEL 33-1-45248200, FAX 33-1-45248500, http://www.oecd.org. **Subscr. in N. America to:** O E C D Turpin North America, PO Box 194, Downingtown, PA 19335-0194. TEL 610-524-5361, 800-456-6323, FAX 610-524-5417, journalscustomer@turpinna.com.

331.11 351 CAN ISSN 1709-3678
HD8109.Q4
QUEBEC. MINISTERE DU TRAVAIL. RAPPORT ANNUEL DE GESTION (YEAR). Text in French. a.
Former titles (until 2001): Quebec. Ministere du Travail. Rapport Annuel (1205-9048); (until 1995): Quebec. Ministere de l'Emploi. Rapport Annuel (1190-8815); (until 1993): Ministere du Travail. Rapport Annuel (0823-4442); (until 1982): Ministere du Travail, de la Main-d'oeuvre et de la Securite du Revenu. Rapport Annuel (0821-9648); (until 1981): Ministere du Travail et de la Main-d'oeuvre. Rapport Annuel (0701-6638); (until 1968): Ministere du Travail. Rapport Annuel (0481-2719); (until 1963): Ministre du Travail de la Province de Quebec. Rapport General (0701-662X); Minister of Labour of the Province of Quebec. General Report
Published by: Canada. Ministere du Travail, 200, chemin Sainte-Foy, Quebec, PQ G1R 5S1, Canada. TEL 418-643-4817, 800-643-4817, http://www.travail.gouv.qc.ca/publications/rapports.

331 CAN ISSN 0838-6609
HD8101
QUEEN'S UNIVERSITY. INDUSTRIAL RELATIONS CENTRE. QUEEN'S PAPERS IN INDUSTRIAL RELATIONS SERIES. Text in English. 1987. irreg., latest 1995, no.95-2. CND 10. **Document type:** *Monographic series, Academic/Scholarly.*
Published by: Queen's University, Industrial Relations Centre, 99 University Ave, Kingston, ON K7L 3N6, Canada. TEL 613-545-6709, FAX 613-545-6812.

344.01 USA ISSN 1553-8958
QUINLAN'S H R COMPLIANCE LAW BULLETIN. (Human Resources) Text in English. 1995. bi-w. USD 147 (effective 2005). **Document type:** *Newsletter, Trade.*
Former titles (until Sep. 2004): H R Manager's Advisor (1551-8736); (until May 2004): H R Compliance Law Bulletin (1542-4979); (until 1999): Employer Liability Prevention Bulletin (1083-7329)
Related titles: Online - full text ed.: ISSN 1553-894X.
Published by: Quinlan Publishing Group, Marine Industrial Park, 23 Drydock Ave, 6th Fl, Boston, MA 02210-2387. TEL 617-542-0048, 800-229-2084, FAX 617-345-9646, info@quinlan.com, http://www.quinlan.com. Ed. Laura Starczewski. Pub. Dennis Hofmaier.

331 DEU ISSN 0033-6874
HD28 CODEN: REFNA9
R E F A NACHRICHTEN. Text in German. 1948. bi-m. adv. bk.rev. charts. **Document type:** *Trade.* **Description:** Technical articles and reports on the REFA organization for the study of work.
Indexed: ABIn, CISA, DIP, ExcerpMed, IBR, IBZ, PAIS, RASB. —CCC.
Published by: R E F A - Verband fuer Arbeitsstudien und Betriebsorganisation e.V., Wittichstr 2, Darmstadt, 64295, Germany. TEL 06151-8801-0. Circ: 50,000. **Dist. by:** Beuth Verlag GmbH, Burggrafenstr 6, Berlin 10787, Germany. TEL 030-2601-0, FAX 030-26011260.

R W I : MATERIALIEN. see *SOCIAL SCIENCES: COMPREHENSIVE WORKS*

331 RUS
RABOTA & ZARPLATA. Text in Russian. 1999. w. **Document type:** *Magazine, Consumer.*
Published by: Servis Delovogo Mira, Khoroshevskoe shosse 32a, Moscow, 123007, Russian Federation. TEL 7-095-9401897, rabota@d-mir.ru, http://www.zarplata.ru/. Circ: 110,000.

RACE, POVERTY AND THE ENVIRONMENT. see *ENVIRONMENTAL STUDIES*

RAGGED EDGE. see *HANDICAPPED—Visually Impaired*

331.21 USA
RATE RANGE SURVEY. Text in English. a. USD 225. **Description:** Summarizes rate range information of companies in PA, NJ, MD, and DE.
Published by: MidAtlantic Employers' Association, PO Box 770, Valley Forge, PA 19482. TEL 215-666-7330, FAX 215-666-7866.

B

331 DEU ISSN 0934-6198
RECHT DER ARBEITER UND ANGESTELLTEN IM OEFFENTLICHEN DIENST. Text in German. 1976. irreg., latest vol.4, 2004. price varies. **Document type:** *Monographic series, Trade.*
Published by: Erich Schmidt Verlag GmbH & Co. (Berlin), Genthiner Str 30G, Berlin, 10785, Germany. TEL 49-30-250085-0, FAX 49-30-25008511, esv@esvmedien.de, http://www.erich-schmidt-verlag.de.

331 658 USA ISSN 0034-1827
HF5549.5.R44
RECRUITING TRENDS; the monthly newsletter for the recruiting executive. Text in English. 1962. m. looseleaf. USD 249 in US & Canada; USD 289 elsewhere (effective 2004). charts; stat. Index. back issues avail. **Document type:** *Newsletter, Trade.* **Description:** Contains strategies and tactics for creating and maintaining a competitive workforce.
Incorporates: Recruiting Engineers and Computer Professionals
Related titles: Online - full text ed.
Indexed: PersLit.
Published by: Kennedy Information Inc., One Kennedy Place, Rte 12 S, Fitzwilliam, NH 03447. rt-editor@kennedyinfo.com, http://www.kennedyinfo.com/rt/rectrends.html. Ed. Joseph Daniel McCool. Pub. David Beck.

331 USA ISSN 1540-8426
REGIONAL LABOR REVIEW. Text in English. 1998. s-a. USD 12 domestic to individuals; USD 15 foreign to individuals; USD 30 domestic to institutions; USD 33 foreign to institutions; USD 6 newsstand/cover (effective 2002).
Published by: Hofstra University, Center for the Study of Labor and Democracy, 200 Barnard Hall, 104 Hofstra University, Hempstead, NY 11549. TEL 516-463-5040, FAX 516-463-6519, laborstudies@hofstra.edu, http://www.hofstra.edu/cld. Ed. Gregory DeFreitas.

331.1 VEN
RELACIONES DE TRABAJO. Text in Spanish. 1982. irreg., latest vol.13. price varies. **Document type:** *Monographic series.*
Supersedes: Revista Relaciones de Trabajo
Published by: Asociacion de Relaciones de Trabajo (ART), Apdo. 5110, Naguanagua, Carabobo 2005, Venezuela. TEL 58-41-234780, FAX 58-41-670676. Ed. Hector Lucena. Circ: 1,000.

331 DEU
RELACIONES INDUSTRIALES. Text in German. 2002. irreg. price varies. **Document type:** *Monographic series, Academic/Scholarly.*
Published by: Bochumer Universitaetsverlag GmbH, Querenburger Hoehe 281, Bochum, 44801, Germany. TEL 49-234-9719780, FAX 49-234-9719786, bou@bou.de, http://bou.de.

344.01 ESP ISSN 0213-0556
RELACIONES LABORALES; revista critica de teoria y practica. Text in Spanish. 1984. bi-m.
Related titles: ♦ Supplement(s): Relaciones Laborales. Normativa Laboral y de Seguridad Social. ISSN 1137-8611. —CINDOC.
Published by: La Ley, Calle Collado Mediano, No. 9, Las Rozas (Madrid), 28230, Spain. TEL 34-902-420010, FAX 34-902-420012, clientes@laley.net, http://www.laley.net/.

344.01 ESP ISSN 1137-8611
RELACIONES LABORALES. NORMATIVA LABORAL Y DE SEGURIDAD SOCIAL. Text in Spanish. 1997. m.
Related titles: ♦ Supplement to: Relaciones Laborales. ISSN 0213-0556.
Published by: La Ley, Calle Collado Mediano, No. 9, Las Rozas (Madrid), 28230, Spain. TEL 34-902-420010, FAX 34-902-420012, clientes@laley.net, http://www.laley.net/.

331.1 CAN ISSN 0034-379X
HD8109.Q4 CODEN: RLINE9
➤ **RELATIONS INDUSTRIELLES/INDUSTRIAL RELATIONS.** Text in English, French. 1945. q. CND 50 domestic to individuals; USD 50 foreign to individuals; CND 100 domestic to institutions; USD 100 foreign to institutions (effective 2005). adv. bk.rev. bibl.; charts; illus. index, cum.index. 200 p./no.; reprint service avail. from PQC. **Document type:** *Journal, Academic/Scholarly.*
Related titles: Microform ed.: (from BNQ, PQC); Online - full text ed.: ISSN 1703-8138 (from EBSCO Publishing, Florida Center for Library Automation, Gale Group, Micromedia ProQuest, O C L C Online Computer Library Center, Inc., ProQuest Information & Learning).
Indexed: ABIn, ASCA, AgeL, AmH&L, BPIA, BibInd, CBCABus, CBPI, CLI, CPerI, CWPI, CurCont, DIP, HRA, HistAb, IBR, IBSS, IBZ, ICLPL, ILD, LRI, MAB, ManagCont, PAIS, PRA, PdeR, SFSA, SOPODA, SPAA, SSA, SSCI, SUSA, SocioIAb, T&II, V&AA, WBSS.
—BLDSC (4461.120000), CISTI, IDS, IE, Infotrieve, ingenta. **CCC.**
Published by: Universite Laval, Department of Industrial Relations, Pavillon DeSeve, bureau 3129, Quebec, PQ G1K 7P4, Canada. TEL 418-656-2468, FAX 418-656-3175, relat.ind@rlt.ulaval.ca, http://www.rlt.ulaval.ca/ri-ir/. Ed., R&P Sylvie Montreuil TEL 418-656-2800. Circ: 1,200.

➤ **REPORT OF THE LABOR FORCE SURVEY, WHOLE KINGDOM, ROUND FOUR (YEAR).** see *BUSINESS AND ECONOMICS—Abstracting, Bibliographies, Statistics*

➤ **REPORT ON SALARY SURVEYS YEARBOOK.** see *BUSINESS AND ECONOMICS—Personnel Management*

352.63 CAN ISSN 0828-4547
HD7096.C2
REPORT ON THE ADMINISTRATION OF THE LABOUR ADJUSTMENT BENEFITS ACT/RAPPORT SUR L'APPLICATION DE LA LOI SUR LES PRESTATIONS D'ADAPTATION POUR LES TRAVAILLEURS. Text in English. 1983. q. free. **Document type:** *Government.* **Description:** Reports on disbursement of income support payments to eligible workers in designated industries and regions.
Published by: Labour Canada, Publications Distribution, Ottawa, ON K1A 0J2, Canada. TEL 819-994-0543, FAX 819-997-1664. Circ: 1,000.

331 GBR
RESEARCH AND DEVELOPMENT REWARDS. Text in English. 1982. a. GBP 280 per edition (effective 2001). **Document type:** *Bulletin.* **Description:** Provides information on over 100 research, development and scientific jobs from research associations and research and development departments in the UK.
Formerly (until 1993): Research and Development Survey (0954-8173)
Published by: The Reward Group Ltd., Reward House, Diamond Way, Stone Business Park, Stone, Staffs ST15 0SD, United Kingdom. TEL 44-1785-813566, FAX 44-1785-817007, enquiries@reward-group.co.uk, http://www.reward-group.co.uk.

331 USA ISSN 0147-9121
HD4802
RESEARCH IN LABOR ECONOMICS. Text in English. 1977. irreg., latest vol.23, 2004. price varies. back issues avail. **Document type:** *Monographic series, Academic/Scholarly.*
Related titles: Online - full text ed.: (from ScienceDirect).
—BLDSC (7741.648000). **CCC.**
Published by: J A I Press Inc. (Subsidiary of: Elsevier Science & Technology), 360 Park Ave S, New York, NY 10010-1710. TEL 212-989-5800, FAX 212-633-3990, usinfo-f@elsevier.com, http://www.elsevier.com/wps/find/bookdescription.cws_home/BS_RLE/description#description. Ed. Solomon W Polachek.

331.125 GBR ISSN 0969-4080
REVIEW OF EMPLOYMENT TOPICS. Text in English. 1993. a., latest vol.6, 2003. GBP 17 per vol. (effective 2003). **Document type:** *Bulletin.* **Description:** Covers all issues relating to employment, with special interest in regional influences on industrial relations systems and comparative studies of Northern Ireland with other regions of Europe.
Published by: Labour Relations Agency, Labour Relations Agency, 2-8, Gordon St, Belfast, BT1 2LG, United Kingdom. TEL 44-1232-321442, FAX 44-1232-330827, info@lra.org.uk, LRA@dnet.co.uk. Ed. Mary O'Brien.

352.63 USA
REVIEW - S W A P✶. (Sharing with a Purpose) Text in English. 1972. bi-m. free. bk.rev. abstr. **Document type:** *Abstract/Index.* **Description:** Abstracts of civil service literature relating to personnel selection research.
Formerly: S W A P
Published by: (Section on Personnel Administration and Labor Relations), American Society for Public Administration, 1120 G St, N W, Ste 700, Washington, DC 20005. Ed. Jack Rabin. Circ: 2,200.

331.11 FRA ISSN 0473-6788
REVIEWS OF MANPOWER AND SOCIAL POLICIES. Text in French. 1963. irreg.
Published by: Organization for Economic Cooperation and Development, 2 Rue Andre Pascal, Paris, 75775 Cedex 16, France. TEL 33-1-45248200, FAX 33-1-45248500, http://www.oecd.org.

REVISTA DE DERECHO LABORAL. see *LAW*

REVISTA DE DIREITO DO TRABALHO (SAO PAULO). see *LAW*

349.2 ESP ISSN 1576-169X
REVISTA DE JUSTICIA LABORAL. Key Title: Justicia Laboral. Text in Spanish. 2000. q. EUR 95.64 (effective 2003).
Published by: Lex Nova, General Solchaga, 3, Valladolid, 47008, Spain. TEL 34-902-457038, FAX 34-902-457224, redac@lexnova.es, http://www.lexnova.es/.

REVISTA DE PSICOLOGIA DEL TRABAJO Y DE LAS ORGANIZACIONES. see *PSYCHOLOGY*

331.1 URY ISSN 1020-1319
K18
REVISTA DE RELACIONES LABORALES EN AMERICAN LATINA, CONO SUR. Short title: ReLaSur. Text in Spanish. 1993. s-a. USD 14 per issue (effective 1999). **Document type:** *Academic/Scholarly.*
Published by: (Organizacion Internacional del Trabajo), Fundacion de Cultura Universitaria, Casilla de Correo Central, Veinticinco De Mayo, 568, Montevideo, 11003, Uruguay. TEL 598-2-9161152, FAX 598-2-9152549, fcuventa@multi.com.uy, http://www.fcu.com.uy.

331 VEN ISSN 0034-8988
K19
REVISTA DE TRABAJO. Text in Spanish. 1950-1963; resumed 1965. q. stat.
Published by: Ministerio del Trabajo, Servicio de Publicaciones, Torre Sur Centro S, Bolivar, Caracas, DF 1060, Venezuela. FAX 582-4838914.

331 CHE ISSN 0378-5548
REVISTA INTERNACIONAL DEL TRABAJO. Text in Spanish. q.
Related titles: Online - full text ed.: ISSN 1564-9148 (from EBSCO Publishing, Gale Group, IngentaConnect, Swets Information Services); ♦ English ed.: International Labour Review. ISSN 0020-7780; ♦ French ed.: Revue Internationale du Travail. ISSN 0378-5599.
Indexed: DIP, ELLIS, IBR, IBZ, JEL, PAIS, PMA.
—CINDOC, IE, Infotrieve.
Published by: (International Labour Organisation), I L O Publications, PO Box 6, Geneva 22, 1211, Switzerland. TEL 41-22-799-6111, FAX 41-22-798-6358. Ed. T Lines. **Dist. in US by:** I L O Publications Center, 9 Jay Gould Court, Ste. CT, PO Box 753, Waldorf, MD 20604. TEL 301-638-3152, FAX 301-843-0159, ilopubs@tasco1.com.

331 VEN ISSN 0798-197X
REVISTA SOBRE RELACIONES INDUSTRIALES Y LABORALES. Text in Spanish. 1979. s-a. **Document type:** *Journal, Academic/Scholarly.*
Published by: Universidad Catolica Andres Bello, Departamento de Investigaciones Sobre Relaciones Industriales Y Laborales, Final Prolongacion Av Paez, Montalban, Caracas, 1020, Venezuela.

331 MTQ ISSN 0755-2742
REVOLUTION SOCIALISTE ANTILLES. Text in Creoles and Pidgins, French. 1973. w.
Formerly (until 1976): Revolution Socialiste (0755-2734)
Published by: Groupe Revolution Socialiste, B.P. 1031, Fort-de-France, Martinique 97200, Martinique. TEL 703649. Circ: 2,500.

344.01 FRA ISSN 0997-7422
REVUE DE JURISPRUDENCE SOCIALE. Text in French. 1989. m. EUR 235 combined subscription print & CD ROM eds. (effective 2005). **Document type:** *Magazine, Trade.*
Related titles: CD-ROM ed.
Published by: Editions Francis Lefebvre, 42 rue de Villiers, Levallois-Perret, 92300, France. TEL 33-1-41052222, http://www.efl.fr.

331 BEL ISSN 0035-2705
REVUE DU TRAVAIL. Text in French. 1896. q. free. bk.rev. bibl.; charts; stat. index. **Description:** Examines labour situation, laws and regulations.
Related titles: Dutch ed.: Arbeidsblad. ISSN 0772-1226. 1896.
Indexed: CISA, IBR, IBSS, IBZ, ILD, PAIS, RASB.
—BLDSC (7956.450000).
Published by: Ministere de l'Emploi et du Travail, 51 Rue Belliard, Brussels, 1040, Belgium. Circ: 1,250.

331 HTI ISSN 0482-8062
REVUE DU TRAVAIL. Text in French. 1951. a. stat.
Indexed: PAIS.
Published by: Departement du Travail et du Bien-Etre Social, Port-au-Prince, Haiti.

331 CHE ISSN 0378-5599
REVUE INTERNATIONALE DU TRAVAIL. Text in French. q.
Related titles: Online - full text ed.: ISSN 1564-9121 (from EBSCO Publishing, Gale Group, IngentaConnect, Swets Information Services); ♦ English ed.: International Labour Review. ISSN 0020-7780; ♦ Spanish ed.: Revista Internacional del Trabajo. ISSN 0378-5548.
Indexed: DIP, ELLIS, IBR, IBZ, IPSA, JEL, PdeR.
—IE, Infotrieve.
Published by: (Bureau International du Travail/International Labour Organisation), I L O Publications, 4 route des Morillons, Geneva 22, 1211, Switzerland. TEL 41-22-799-6111, FAX 41-22-798-6358, TELEX 415-647-ILOCH. Ed. T Lines. **Dist. in US by:** I L O Publications Center, 9 Jay Gould Court, Ste. CT, PO Box 753, Waldorf, MD 20604. TEL 301-638-3152, FAX 301-843-0159, ilopubs@tasco1.com.

331 GBR
REWARD MANAGEMENT REWARDS. Text in English. 2/yr. GBP 280 per edition (effective 2001). **Document type:** *Bulletin.* **Description:** Comprehensive salary survey containing data on over 180 management, administrative and technical jobs within the private and public sectors.
Formerly: Reward: The Management Survey
Published by: The Reward Group Ltd., Reward House, Diamond Way, Stone Business Park, Stone, Staffs ST15 0SD, United Kingdom. TEL 44-1785-813566, FAX 44-1785-817007, enquiries@reward-group.co.uk, http://www.reward-group.co.uk.

331.12 USA
RHODE ISLAND. DEPARTMENT OF LABOR & TRAINING. CHARACTERISTICS OF THE INSURED UNEMPLOYED IN RHODE ISLAND. Text in English. m. free. **Description:** Includes demographic data (age, gender, occupation, industry, and length of unemployment) for persons who qualify for unemployment compensation.
Related titles: Online - full text ed.
Published by: Rhode Island Department of Labor & Training, Labor Market Information Division, John O. Pastore Center, 1511 Pontiac Ave, Bldg 73, 2nd Fl, Cranston, RI 02929. TEL 401-462-8740, FAX 401-462-8766, dmurray@dlt.state.ri.us, http://www.dlt.state.ri.us.

331.12 USA
RHODE ISLAND. DEPARTMENT OF LABOR & TRAINING. COVERED EMPLOYMENT & WAGES IN RHODE ISLAND. Text in English. q. free. stat. **Description:** Includes employment and wage data by industry, by city and town.
Related titles: Online - full text ed.
Published by: Rhode Island Department of Labor & Training, Labor Market Information Division, John O. Pastore Center, 1511 Pontiac Ave, Bldg 73, 2nd Fl, Cranston, RI 02929. TEL 401-462-8740, FAX 401-462-8766, dmurray@dlt.state.ri.us, http://www.dlt.state.ri.us.

331.12 USA
RHODE ISLAND. DEPARTMENT OF LABOR & TRAINING. DIRECTORY OF LABOR INFORMATION. Text in English. irreg. free. stat. **Description:** Contains source information on products prepared by DLT and other state, federal, and private agencies.
Related titles: Online - full text ed.
Published by: Rhode Island Department of Labor & Training, Labor Market Information Division, John O. Pastore Center, 1511 Pontiac Ave, Bldg 73, 2nd Fl, Cranston, RI 02929. TEL 401-462-8740, FAX 401-462-8766, mferreira@dlt.state.ri.us, http://www.dlt.state.ri.us.

331.259 USA
RHODE ISLAND. DEPARTMENT OF LABOR AND TRAINING. EMPLOYMENT BULLETIN. Text in English. 1954. m. free (effective 2005). charts; stat. back issues avail. **Document type:** *Newsletter, Consumer.*
Former titles: Rhode Island. Department of Employment Security. Employment Bulletin; Rhode Island. Department of Labor and Employment Security. Employment Bulletin (0035-4600)
Indexed: SRI.
Published by: Department of Labor and Training, Labor Market Information, 1511 Pontiac Ave, Cranston, RI 02920-4407. TEL 401-462-8740, FAX 401-462-8766, lmi@dlt.state.ri.us, http://www.dlt.ri.gov/lmi/publications/bulletin.htm. Eds. Joyce D'Orsi, Maria Ferrira. Circ: 4,000.

331.12 USA
RHODE ISLAND. DEPARTMENT OF LABOR & TRAINING. ESTABLISHMENT EMPLOYMENT IN RHODE ISLAND. Text in English. m. free. stat. **Description:** Contains establishment employment data grouped by major industry from the Current Employment Statistics survey.
Related titles: Online - full text ed.
Published by: Rhode Island Department of Labor & Training, Labor Market Information Division, John O. Pastore Center, 1511 Pontiac Ave, Bldg 73, 2nd Fl, Cranston, RI 02929. TEL 401-462-8740, FAX 401-462-8766, gglover@dlt.state.ri.us, http://www.dlt.state.ri.us.

331.12 USA
RHODE ISLAND. DEPARTMENT OF LABOR & TRAINING. LOCAL AREA UNEMPLOYMENT STATISTICS. Text in English. m. free. stat. **Description:** Includes statistics on the labor force, employment, unemployment, and unemployment rate for the state of Rhode Island, sub-state areas, and city and towns, based on place of residence.
Related titles: Online - full text ed.

Published by: Rhode Island Department of Labor & Training, Labor Market Information Division, John O. Pastore Center, 1511 Pontiac Ave, Bldg 73, 2nd Fl, Cranston, RI 02929. TEL 401-462-8740, FAX 401-462-8766, ldutilly@dlt.state.ri.us, http://www.dlt.state.ri.us.

331.125 USA
RHODE ISLAND. DEPARTMENT OF LABOR & TRAINING. NONFARM EMPLOYMENT, HOUR, AND EARNINGS. Text in English. m. free. stat. **Description:** Includes monthly nonfarm employment and average weekly earnings and hours, and average hourly earnings for production workers, based on place-of-work.
Related titles: Online - full text ed.
Published by: Rhode Island Department of Labor & Training, Labor Market Information Division, John O. Pastore Center, 1511 Pontiac Ave, Bldg 73, 2nd Fl, Cranston, RI 02929. TEL 401-462-8740, FAX 401-462-8766, gglover@dlt.state.ri.us, http://www.dlt.state.ri.us.

331.21 USA
RHODE ISLAND. DEPARTMENT OF LABOR & TRAINING. OCCUPATIONAL EMPLOYMENT STATISTICS. Text in English. irreg. free. **Description:** Includes wages for over 500 Rhode Island occupations, both statewide and on an MSA level.
Formerly: Rhode Island. Department of Labor & Training. Occupational Wages
Related titles: Online - full text ed.
Published by: Rhode Island Department of Labor & Training, Labor Market Information Division, John O. Pastore Center, 1511 Pontiac Ave, Bldg 73, 2nd Fl, Cranston, RI 02929. TEL 401-462-8740, FAX 401-462-8766, ghellewell@dlt.state.ri.us, http://www.dlt.state.ri.us.

331.12 USA
RHODE ISLAND. DEPARTMENT OF LABOR & TRAINING. RHODE ISLAND 2006 - A POSITIVE OUTLOOK ON TOMORROW'S WORKFORCE. Text in English. biennial. free. stat. **Description:** Contains projected employment, growth, and total openings for over 600 occupations in Rhode Island.
Related titles: Online - full text ed.
Published by: Rhode Island Department of Labor & Training, Labor Market Information Division, John O. Pastore Center, 1511 Pontiac Ave, Bldg 73, 2nd Fl, Cranston, RI 02929. TEL 401-462-8740, FAX 401-462-8766, dmurray@dlt.state.ri.us, http://www.dlt.state.ri.us.

331.125 USA
RHODE ISLAND. DEPARTMENT OF LABOR & TRAINING. RHODE ISLAND EMPLOYMENT BULLETIN. Text in English. 1954. m. free. stat. **Document type:** *Newsletter.* **Description:** Provides information on the civilian labor force, employment by industry, manufacturing hours and earnings and other DLT information.
Related titles: Online - full text ed.
Published by: Rhode Island Department of Labor & Training, Labor Market Information Division, John O. Pastore Center, 1511 Pontiac Ave, Bldg 73, 2nd Fl, Cranston, RI 02929. TEL 401-462-8740, FAX 401-462-8766, ldutilly@dlt.state.ri.us, http://www.dlt.state.ri.us.

331 USA
RHODE ISLAND. DEPARTMENT OF LABOR & TRAINING. RHODE ISLAND STATISTICAL & FISCAL DIGEST. Text in English. a. free. stat. **Description:** Contains statistical summaries of funding sources, expenditures, employment and training activities, and labor force data. Also includes detailed activity reports for DLT programs such as Unemployment Insurance, Temporary Disability Insurance, and Workers' Compensation.
Related titles: Online - full text ed.
Published by: Rhode Island Department of Labor & Training, Labor Market Information Division, John O. Pastore Center, 1511 Pontiac Ave, Bldg 73, 2nd Fl, Cranston, RI 02929. TEL 401-462-8740, FAX 401-462-8766, dmurray@dlt.state.ri.us, http://www.dlt.state.ri.us.

RHODE ISLAND EMPLOYMENT LAW LETTER. see *LAW*

368.41 USA
RHODE ISLAND WORKERS' COMPENSATION LAW. Text in English. a. (w/ CD ROM), latest 2002-03 ed. USD 42 base vol(s). (effective 2003). 328 p./no.; **Description:** A reference for selected laws in the workers' compensation arena.
Published by: Michie Company (Subsidiary of: LexisNexis North America), 701 E Water St, Charlottesville, VA 22902-5389. TEL 434-972-7600, 800-446-3410, FAX 434-972-7677, http://www.michie.com.

331 ITA ISSN 0483-142X
RIVISTA DEL LAVORO. Text in Italian. 1951. m.
Published by: (Istituto de Studi Sul Lavoro), Edizioni del Lavoro s.r.l., Via Giovanni Battista Martini, 6, Rome, RM 00198, Italy.

344.01 ITA ISSN 1122-0147
K22
RIVISTA DELL'ARBITRATO. Text in Italian. 1991. q. EUR 67.14 in the European Union; EUR 100.71 elsewhere (effective 2002). bk.rev. index. **Description:** Dedicated to doctrinal law and legislation.
Formerly (until 1990): Rassegna dell'Arbitrato (0033-9415)
Related titles: CD-ROM ed.
Published by: (Associazione Italiana per l'Arbitrato), Casa Editrice Dott. A. Giuffre (Subsidiary of: LexisNexis Europe and Africa), Via Busto Arsizio, 40, Milan, MI 20151, Italy. TEL 39-02-28089200, FAX 39-02-38009582, giuffre@giuffre.it, http://www.giuffre.it. Ed. Elio Fazzalari. Circ: 1,500 (controlled).

RIVISTA ITALIANA DI DIRITTO DEL LAVORO. see *LAW*

344.01 JPN ISSN 0386-0639
RODO HO/JOURNAL OF LABOR LAW. Text in Japanese. 1951. s-a.
Published by: Japan Labour Law Association/Nihon Rodoho Gakkai, University, Hongo, Bunkyo-ku, Tokyo, 113-0033, Japan.

331.11 GBR ISSN 1359-8058
ROUTLEDGE STUDIES IN BUSINESS ORGANIZATION AND NETWORKS. Text in English. 1996. irreg., latest vol.21, 2003, April. price varies. back issues avail. **Document type:** *Monographic series, Academic/Scholarly.* **Description:** Presents titles which look at the dynamics of organizations and the particular effects of different types of business networks.
—BLDSC (8026.519200).
Published by: Routledge (Subsidiary of: Taylor & Francis Group), 4 Park Square, Milton Park, Abingdon, Oxon OX14 4RN, United Kingdom. TEL 44-1235-828600, FAX 44-1235-829000, info@routledge.co.uk, http://www.routledge.co.uk.

331 USA
RULES AND REGULATIONS AND STATEMENTS OF PROCEDURE OF THE NATIONAL LABOR RELATIONS BOARD. Text in English. base vol. plus irreg. updates. looseleaf. USD 52; USD 65 foreign (effective 1999). **Document type:** *Government.*
Related titles: Online - full text ed.
Published by: U.S. National Labor Relations Board, 1099 14th St, N W, Washington, DC 20570-0001. TEL 202-273-1991, FAX 202-273-1789, http://www.nlrb.gov. **Subscr. to:** U.S. Government Printing Office, Superintendent of Documents, PO Box 371954, Pittsburgh, PA 15250-7954. TEL 202-512-1800, FAX 202-512-2250, orders@gpo.gov, http://www.access.gpo.gov.

331 GBR ISSN 0261-5649
RUSKIN COLLEGE, OXFORD. LIBRARY. OCCASIONAL PUBLICATION. Text in English. 1979. irreg. price varies. **Document type:** *Monographic series.*
—BLDSC (8052.647700).
Published by: Ruskin College, Library, Ruskin College, Walton St, Oxford, OX1 2HE, United Kingdom. TEL 44-1865-554331. Ed. David Horsfield.

331 ISR
R'VACHA VA'AVEDA. Text in Hebrew. q.
Published by: Havaad Hapoel, Hagaf Le'igud Miktzo'i, 93 Arlozov St, Tel Aviv, 61002, Israel. TEL 03-210322.

344.01 DEU ISSN 0048-9069
K2
S A E. (Sammlung Arbeitsrechtlicher Entscheidungen) Text in German. 1948. 8/yr. bk.rev. index. **Document type:** *Magazine, Trade.*
Indexed: Englnd.
—CCC.
Published by: (Bundesvereinigung der Deutschen Arbeitgeberverbaende e.V.), Verlagsgruppe Handelsblatt GmbH, Kasernenstr 67, Duesseldorf, 40213, Germany. TEL 49-211-8870, FAX 49-211-371792, c.finke-hollweg@bda-online.de, leser-service@vhb.de, http://www.vhb.de/sae. Eds. Reinhard Goehner, Roland Wolf. Adv. contact Rolf Kluthausen. Circ: 2,000.

S & M ENCYCLOPEDIA OF EMPLOYMENT LAW. see *LAW—Corporate Law*

S K T FITIDNINGEN. see *PUBLIC ADMINISTRATION—Municipal Government*

352.63 SWE ISSN 1652-3075
S T PRESS. Text in Swedish. 1907. m. SEK 250 (effective 2001). adv. **Document type:** *Magazine, Trade.*
Former titles (until 2004): Statstjaenstemannen (0346-1815); (until 1945): Tidskrift foer den Centrala Statsfoervaltningens Tjaenstemaen; (until 1933): Medlemsblad foer Statsfoervaltningens Tjaenstemannafoerening; (until 1930): Fraan Svenska Statsfoervaltningen
Related titles: Audio cassette/tape ed.
Published by: (Statstjaenstemannafoerbundet/Union of Civil Servants), S T Press, Sturegatan 15, PO Box 5044, Stockholm, 10241, Sweden. TEL 46-8-7905100, http://www.stpress.se. Ed. Jan-Aake Porseryd TEL 46-8-7906280. adv.: B&W page SEK 21,000, color page SEK 30,000; trim 220 x 284. Circ: 91,000.

331 NLD ISSN 0165-8131
S W JOURNAAL. (Sociale Werkvoorziening) Text in Dutch. 1971. 10/yr. EUR 37.50 (effective 2005). adv. **Document type:** *Bulletin.*
Related titles: Audio cassette/tape ed.; Braille ed.
—IE, Infotrieve.
Published by: (Nationaal Overlegorgaan Sociale Werkvoorziening), Y-Publicaties, Postbus 10208, Amsterdam, 1001 EE, Netherlands. TEL 31-20-5206060, FAX 31-20-5206061, sw-journaal@y-publicaties.nl, info@y-publicaties.nl, http://www.y-publicaties.nl/html/sw-journaal.html. Circ: 9,000.

331.21 USA
SALARIES AND WAGES FOR MICHIGAN MUNICIPALITIES OVER 1,000 POPULATION. Text in English. 1942. a. USD 50 (effective 1997).
Formed by the merger of: Salaries and Wages for Michigan Municipalities over 4,000 Population; Which was formerly: Salaries, Wages, and Fringe Benefits in Michigan Municipalities over 4,000 Population (0080-5548); And: Salaries and Wages for Michigan Municipalities under 4,000 Population; Which was formerly: Salaries and Wages for Michigan Villages and Cities 1,000-4,000 Population; Salaries, Wages and Fringe Benefits for Michigan Villages and Cities 1,000-4,000 Population (0077-216X)
Published by: Michigan Municipal League, 1675 Green Rd, Box 1487, Ann Arbor, MI 48106. TEL 313-662-3246.

SALARY INCREASE SURVEY REPORT. see *OCCUPATIONS AND CAREERS*

331.1251378 USA
SALARY SURVEY (YEARS) (ST. LOUIS). Text in English. a. USD 25 domestic; USD 30 foreign (effective 2001). **Description:** Lists aggregate salary data of business school administrators and faculty by rank within discipline, with further breakdowns by school status, such as accredited and non-accredited, public and private.
Indexed: SRI.
Published by: The Association to Advance Collegiate Schools of Business, 600 Emerson Rd., Ste. 300, St. Louis, MO 63141-6762. TEL 314-872-8481, FAX 314-872-8495, http://www.aacsb.edu. Ed. Rosemarie Kroscher. R&P Howard Hoskins TEL 314-872-8507. Circ: 1,000.

331.21 GBR
SALES MARKETING REWARDS. Text in English. a. GBP 200 (effective 2001). **Document type:** *Bulletin.* **Description:** Salary surveys for sales and marketing departments covering jobs from director level to telesales jobs.
Formerly (until 2000): Sales and Marketing Salary Survey
Published by: (Chartered Institute of Marketing), The Reward Group Ltd., Reward House, Diamond Way, Stone Business Park, Stone, Staffs ST15 0SD, United Kingdom. TEL 44-1785-813566, FAX 44-1785-817007, enquiries@reward-group.co.uk, http://www.reward-group.co.uk.

331 CAN ISSN 0826-953X
SASKATCHEWAN HUMAN RIGHTS COMMISSION. ANNUAL REPORT. Text in English. 1981. a.
Published by: Saskatchewan Human Rights Commission, Sturdy Stone Bldg, 8th Flr, 122 Third Ave N, Saskatoon, SK S7K 2H6, Canada. TEL 306-933-5952, 800-667-9249, FAX 306-933-7863, shrc@justice.gov.sk.ca, http://www.gov.sk.ca/shrc/publications.html.

331.11 DEU ISSN 0937-6445
SCHRIFTENREIHE INDUSTRIELLE BEZIEHUNGEN. Text in German. 1990. irreg., latest vol.17, 2002. price varies. **Document type:** *Monographic series, Academic/Scholarly.*
Published by: Rainer Hampp Verlag, Meringerzellerstr 10, Mering, 86415, Germany. TEL 49-8233-4783, FAX 49-8233-30755, Rainer_Hampp_Verlag@t-online.de, http://www.hampp-verlag.de.

331.11 CHE
SCHWEIZER ARBEITGEBER/EMPLOYEUR SUISSE/ IMPRENDITORE SVIZZERO. Text in French, German, Italian. 1906. 2/m. CHF 110 domestic; CHF 152 foreign (effective 2001). adv. bk.rev. abstr.; charts; illus.; stat. index. **Document type:** *Bulletin.* **Description:** Reports on the various positions taken by Swiss employers on various major social, economic and political matters.
Formerly (until 1994): Schweizerische Arbeitgeber-Zeitung (0036-7516)
Indexed: CISA, KES.
Published by: Union Patronale Suisse/Confederation of Swiss Employers, Hegibachstrasse 47, Zurich, 8082, Switzerland. TEL 41-1-421-1717, FAX 41-1-4211718, zeitung@arbeitgeber.ch, employeur@arbeitgeber.ch, http://www.arbeitgeber.ch/deutsch/6-d_arbeitg-publ.htm. Eds. Alexandre Plassard, Hans Reis. Circ: 6,000.

331.12 USA ISSN 0278-9620
SCIENCE AND ENGINEERING PERSONNEL. Text in English. 1980. biennial.
—Linda Hall.
Published by: National Science Foundation, 1800 G St N W, Washington, DC 20550.

331 GBR
HD8399.S3
SCOTTISH LABOUR HISTORY. Text in English. 1969. a. reprints avail.
Formerly (until 1998): Scottish Labour History Society. Journal (0586-7762)

B

Indexed: AmH&L, HistAb.
—BLDSC (8210.647500).
Published by: Aberdeen Scottish Labour History Society, c/o Department of History, University of Strathclyde, McCance Bldg, 16 Richmond St, Glasgow, G1 1XQ, United Kingdom. Ed. Ian S Wood.

331 THA ISSN 0857-1163
SECRETARIES YEAR BOOK. Text in English. 1976. a.
Published by: Advertising and Media Consultants Ltd., Silom Condominium 12th Fl, 52-38 Soi Saladaeng 2, Bangkok, 10500, Thailand. TEL 266-9040, FAX 236-6764. Circ: 20,000.

331 BEL
SECURITE AU TRAVAIL. Text in French. 1982. 24/yr.
Published by: C E D Samsom (Subsidiary of: Wolters Samsom Belgie n.v.), Kouterveld 14, Diegem, 1831, Belgium. TEL 32-2-7231111.

SENNACIECA REVUO. see *POLITICAL SCIENCE—International Relations*

344.01 CUB
SERIE LEGISLACION LABORAL. Text in Spanish. m.
Published by: Comite Estatal de Trabajo y Seguridad Social, 23 Calle O y P,, Vedado, Plaza, La Habana, Cuba.

331.21 GBR
SEVERNSIDE - SOUTH WALES SALARY SURVEY. Text in English. 2/yr. GBP 280 per edition (effective 2001). **Document type:** *Bulletin.* **Description:** Salary survey covering the mid Glamorgan, Gwent, South Glamorgan, Avon, Gloucestershire and North Wiltshire areas.
Published by: The Reward Group Ltd., Reward House, Diamond Way, Stone Business Park, Stone, Staffs ST15 0SD, United Kingdom. TEL 44-1785-813566, FAX 44-1785-817007, enquiries@reward-group.co.uk, http://www.reward-group.co.uk.

SHEPARD'S LABOR ARBITRATION CITATIONS. see *LAW—Judicial Systems*

344.01 USA ISSN 1086-976X
SHEPARD'S LABOR LAW CITATIONS. Text in English. 1959. m. USD 910 (effective 2000). **Document type:** *Trade.* **Description:** Contains citations to Labor Court decisions, statutes and other legal sources.
Formerly (until 1995): Shepard's Federal Labor Law Citations (0559-779X)
Related titles: CD-ROM ed.: ISSN 1525-8289; Online - full text ed.
Published by: Shepard's (Subsidiary of: LexisNexis North America), 555 Middle Creek Pkwy, Colorado Springs, CO 80921. TEL 719-488-3000, customer_service@shepards.com, http://www.lexis.com.

331 IND
SHRAM PATRIKA. Text in English. 1974 (vol.4). q. INR 8. charts; stat.
Published by: Labour Commissioner, 15 Rajpur Rd., New Delhi, India.

331.1 IND
SHRAMJIVI. Text in Hindi. m. INR 18.
Published by: Labour Department, Office of the Labour Commissioner, P O Box 220, Kanpur, Uttar Pradesh 208 002, India. Eds. C S Saxena, Hemant K Pant.

331 DEU ISSN 0300-3337
SICHERHEITSBEAUFTRAGTER; Zeitschrift fuer Unfallverhuetung und Arbeitssicherheit. Text in German. 1966. m. EUR 34.88 domestic; EUR 54.32 foreign; EUR 3.32 newsstand/cover (effective 2002). adv. bk.rev. abstr.; illus. **Document type:** *Magazine, Trade.*
Indexed: CEABA.
—IE, Infotrieve. **CCC.**
Published by: Dr. Curt Haefner Verlag GmbH, Bachstr 14-16, Heidelberg, 69121, Germany. TEL 49-6221-6446-0, FAX 49-6221-644640, info@haefner-verlag.de, http://www.haefner-verlag.de. Circ: 41,400.

331 DEU ISSN 0300-3329
T55.A1
SICHERHEITSINGENIEUR; Zeitschrift fuer Arbeitssicherheit. Text in German. 1970. m. adv. bk.rev. abstr.; illus. **Document type:** *Magazine, Trade.*
Indexed: CISA, ErgAb.
—IE, Infotrieve. **CCC.**
Published by: Dr. Curt Haefner Verlag GmbH, Bachstr 14-16, Heidelberg, 69121, Germany. TEL 49-6221-6446-0, FAX 49-6221-644640, info@haefner-verlag.de, http://www.haefner-verlag.de. adv.: B&W page EUR 818, color page EUR 1,473; trim 172 x 250. Circ: 4,993 (paid).

331 SGP ISSN 0129-6310
SINGAPORE. MINISTRY OF LABOUR. ANNUAL REPORT. Text in English. 1946. a. price varies. charts; stat. **Document type:** *Government.*
Published by: Ministry of Labour, Havelock Rd, Singapore, 0105, Singapore. FAX 5344840, TELEX RS34364-LABOUR. Circ: 1,100.

331.88 NOR ISSN 0805-7656
SJOEOFFISEREN. Text in Norwegian. 1995. m.
Formerly (until 1995): Norsk Skibsfoerertidende, Norsk Maskin-Tidende, Norsk Styrmandsblad (0801-8715)
Published by: Norsk Sjoeoffisersforbund, PO Box 7153, Majorstua, Oslo, 7153, Norway. TEL 46-22-06-61-00, FAX 46-22-06-60-90.

344.01 BEL
SOCIAAL COMPENDIUM ARBEIDSRECHT; arbeidsrecht met fiscale notities. Text in Dutch. 1991. biennial. EUR 532.15 (effective 2003). **Document type:** *Trade.*
Supersedes in part: Sociaal Compendium (0778-5763)
Published by: Kluwer Uitgevers (Subsidiary of: Wolters Kluwer Belgique), Ragheno Business Park, Motstraat 30, Mechelen, B-2800, Belgium. TEL 32-15-800-94571, info@kluwer.be, http://www.kluwer.be. Ed. Willy van Eeckhoutte.

331.1 NLD ISSN 0037-7600
SOCIAAL MAANDBLAD ARBEID; tijdschrift voor sociaal recht en sociaal beleid. Text in Dutch. 1946. m. adv. bk.rev. charts; stat. index.
Indexed: ELLIS, IBR, IBZ, KES.
—IE, Infotrieve, KNAW.
Published by: Samsom H.D. Tjeenk Willink B.V. (Subsidiary of: Wolters Kluwer N.V.), Postbus 316, Alphen aan den Rijn, 2400 AH, Netherlands. TEL 31-1720-66822, FAX 31-1720-66639. Circ: 930.

SOCIAAL ZAKBOEKJE. see *LAW—Civil Law*

SOCIAALRECHTELIJKE KRONIEKEN/CHRONIQUE DE DROIT SOCIAL. see *LAW—Civil Law*

331 382 BEL ISSN 1682-7783
HC240.A1
SOCIAL AGENDA. Text in English. 2002. q.
Related titles: French ed.: Agenda Social. ISSN 1682-7791; German ed.: Sozial Agenda. ISSN 1682-7805.
Published by: European Commission, Employment and Social Affairs, Rue de la Loi 200, Brussels, 1049, Belgium. TEL 32-2-2954988, FAX 32-2-2962393, empl-info@cec.eu.int, http://europa.eu.int/comm/employment_social/soc_agenda_en.html.

SOCIAL POLICY. see *POLITICAL SCIENCE*

SOCIOLOGIA DEL TRABAJO. see *SOCIOLOGY*

306.36 FRA ISSN 0038-0296
HD4807
➤ **SOCIOLOGIE DU TRAVAIL.** Text in French. 1959. 4/yr. EUR 77.38 in France to individuals; EUR 99 in Europe to individuals; JPY 13,100 in Japan to individuals; USD 99 to individuals except Europe and Japan; EUR 128.31 in France to institutions; EUR 161 in Europe to institutions; JPY 17,200 in Japan to institutions; USD 196 to institutions except Europe and Japan (effective 2006). bibl.; charts; stat. back issues avail.; reprint service avail. from PQC,SCH. **Document type:** *Academic/Scholarly.* **Description:** Addresses all major problems of our industrial societies, including growth, urbanization, health, justice, education, and new social moves.
Related titles: Microform ed.: (from PQC); Online - full text ed.: (from EBSCO Publishing, Gale Group, IngentaConnect, ScienceDirect, Swets Information Services).
Indexed: ASCA, ArtHuCI, BAS, CJA, CurCont, DIP, ExcerpMed, IBR, IBSS, IBZ, ILD, IPSA, PAIS, PSA, RASB, SCIMP, SOPODA, SSA, SSCI, SociolAb.
—BLDSC (8319.651000), IDS, IE, Infotrieve, ingenta. **CCC.**
Published by: Elsevier France, Editions Scientifiques et Medicales (Subsidiary of: Elsevier Science & Technology), 23 Rue Linois, Paris, 75724, France. TEL 33-1-45589110, FAX 33-1-45589419, academic@elsevier-fr.com, http://www.elsevier.com/locate/soctra. Ed. A Borzeix.

331 AUT
SOLIDARITAET; die Illustrierte des Oe G B. Text in German. 11/yr. free. **Document type:** *Magazine, Consumer.*
Published by: Oesterreichischer Gewerkschaftsbund, Hohenstaufengasse 10-12, Vienna, W 1010, Austria. TEL 43-1-534440, FAX 43-1-53444204, soli@oegb.or.at, oegb@oegb.at, http://www.soli.at, http://www.oegb.at. Ed. Annemarie Kramser. Circ: 1,700,000.

331 RUS
SOTSIAL'NOE PARTNERSTVO. Text in Russian. q. **Document type:** *Magazine, Trade.*
Published by: Lukoil Inform, Sretenskii b-r 11, Moscow, 101000, Russian Federation. TEL 7-095-9271691, FAX 7-095-9271692, socpart@oilru.com, subscribe@oilru.com, http://www.oilru.com/sp. Circ: 3,000.

331 FRA ISSN 1683-2337
SOURCE O C D E. EMPLOI. (Organisation de Cooperation et de Developpement Economiques) Text in French. irreg. EUR 690, USD 793, GBP 456, JPY 93,200 (effective 2005).
Related titles: Online - full content ed.: ISSN 1684-2987. EUR 485, USD 557, GBP 320, GBP 65,500 (effective 2005); Online - full text ed.: (from EBSCO Publishing, Gale Group, IngentaConnect, Swets Information Services); ♦ English ed.: Source O E C D. Employment. ISSN 1608-0181.
Published by: Organization for Economic Cooperation and Development, 2 Rue Andre Pascal, Paris, 75775 Cedex 16, France. TEL 33-1-45248200, FAX 33-1-45248500, http://www.oecd.org. **Dist. by:** Extenza - Turpin, Pegasus Dr, Stratton Business Park, Biggleswade, Beds SG18 8TQ, United Kingdom. TEL 44-1462-687552, FAX 44-1462-480947, subscriptions@extenza-turpin.com; O E C D Turpin North America, PO Box 194, Downingtown, PA 19335-0194. TEL 610-524-5361, 800-456-6323, FAX 610-524-5417, journalscustomer@turpinna.com.

331 FRA ISSN 1608-0181
SOURCE O E C D. EMPLOYMENT. Text in English. irreg. EUR 690, USD 793, GBP 456, JPY 93,200 (effective 2005). stat. **Document type:** *Government.*
Related titles: Online - full content ed.: ISSN 1681-5343. EUR 485, USD 557, GBP 320, JPY 65,500 (effective 2005); Online - full text ed.: 2000 (from Gale Group, IngentaConnect, Swets Information Services); ♦ French ed.: Source O C D E. Emploi. ISSN 1683-2337.
Published by: Organization for Economic Cooperation and Development, 2 Rue Andre Pascal, Paris, 75775 Cedex 16, France. TEL 33-1-45248200, FAX 33-1-45248500, http://www.oecd.org. **Dist. by:** Extenza - Turpin, Pegasus Dr, Stratton Business Park, Biggleswade, Beds SG18 8TQ, United Kingdom. TEL 44-1462-687552, FAX 44-1462-480947, subscriptions@extenza-turpin.com; O E C D Turpin North America, PO Box 194, Downingtown, PA 19335-0194. TEL 610-524-5361, 800-456-6323, FAX 610-524-5417, journalscustomer@turpinna.com.

332.6 ZAF
SOUTH AFRICA. COMMISSION FOR CONCILIATION, MEDIATION, AND ARBITRATION (CCMA). AWARDS. Text in English. 1997. bi-w. ZAR 596.22 (effective 2000). **Document type:** *Trade.* **Description:** Publishes the full text of the labor awards handed down by South Africa's Commission for Conciliation, Mediation, and Arbitration.
Media: Online - full text.
Published by: (South Africa. Commission for Conciliation, Mediation, and Arbitration (CCMA)), Van Zyl, Rudd and Associates, Centrahil, PO Box 12758, Port Elizabeth, 6006, South Africa. TEL 27-41-373-4322, FAX 27-41-373-4323, info@vanzylrudd.co.za, http://www.vanzylrudd.co.za. Ed. Carol Rudd.

331 ZAF ISSN 0379-8410
HD8801.A5
➤ **SOUTH AFRICAN JOURNAL OF LABOUR RELATIONS.** Text in English, Afrikaans. 1977. q. ZAR 146 domestic to individuals; ZAR 311 foreign to individuals; ZAR 194 domestic to institutions; ZAR 311 foreign to institutions (effective 2002). back issues avail. **Document type:** *Academic/Scholarly.* **Description:** Features labor - industrial relations and related issues of interest to academics and practitioners.
Indexed: ISAP.
Published by: University of South Africa, Graduate School Business Leadership, P O Box 392, Pretoria, 0003, South Africa. TEL 27-11-6520335, FAX 27-11-6520299, delpomed@unisa.ac.za, http://www.journals.co.za/ej/ejour_labour.html. Ed. B Swanepoel. Circ: 400.

331.096 ZAF ISSN 0377-5429
HD8799.S72
SOUTH AFRICAN LABOUR BULLETIN. Text in English. 1974. 6/yr. ZAR 95, USD 70; to individuals; institutions ZAR 220 to institutions, USD 120 to institutions; ZAR 540 to corporations (effective 1997). adv. bk.rev. reprints avail. **Document type:** *Bulletin.* **Description:** Analyzes current developments in the South African labor movement. Attempts to reflect the constantly changing face of industrial relations in South Africa. Includes workplace issues, the political interface with unions, and international unionism.
Related titles: Microfiche ed.
Indexed: ASD, HRIR, IBSS, ISAP, PAIS, RASB.
—BLDSC (8340.400000), IE, Infotrieve, ingenta.
Published by: Umanyano Publications c.c., PO Box 3851, Johannesburg, 2000, South Africa. TEL 27-11-4871603, FAX 27-11-4871508. Ed. Deanne Collins. Circ: 6,000 (paid).

344.01 ZAF ISSN 1017-0618
SOUTH AFRICAN LABOUR LAW REPORTS. Text in English. 1990. m. ZAR 798. back issues avail. **Document type:** *Academic/Scholarly.* **Description:** Publishes judgments of and commentary on cases from South Africa's Labour Court, Labour Appeal Court, and selected cases from the Commission for Conciliation, Mediation and Arbitration (CCMA).
Related titles: Online - full text ed.
Published by: Van Zyl, Rudd and Associates, Centrahil, PO Box 12758, Port Elizabeth, 6000, South Africa. TEL 27-41-373-4322, FAX 27-41-373-4323, vzylrudd@cis.co.za, http://www.vanzylrudd.co.za. Ed. Carol Rudd.

344.01 ZAF ISSN 1022-8349
SOUTH AFRICAN LABOUR LIBRARY; cases, legislation and reference works. Text in English. 1994. q. ZAR 660.
Media: CD-ROM.
Published by: Juta & Company Ltd., Law and Professional Publishing Division, PO Box 14373, Kenwyn, 7790, South Africa. TEL 27-21-7975101, FAX 27-21-7970121, law@juta.co.za, http://www/juta.co.za, http://www.juta.co.za.

331 USA
SOUTH CAROLINA. DEPARTMENT OF LABOR. ANNUAL REPORT. Text in English. 1936. a. free. **Document type:** *Government.*
Published by: Department of Labor, 3600 Forest Dr, PO Box 11329, Columbia, SC 29211. TEL 803-734-9600. Ed. James Knight.

SOUTH CAROLINA EMPLOYMENT LAW LETTER. see *LAW*

331.21 GBR
SOUTH COAST SALARY SURVEY. Text in English. 2/yr. GBP 280 per edition (effective 2001). **Document type:** *Bulletin.* **Description:** Salary survey covering the West Sussex, East Sussex, Hampshire and East Kent areas.
Published by: The Reward Group Ltd., Reward House, Diamond Way, Stone Business Park, Stone, Staffs ST15 0SD, United Kingdom. TEL 44-1785-813566, FAX 44-1785-817007, enquiries@reward-group.co.uk, http://www.reward-group.co.uk.

331 USA
SOUTH DAKOTA. DEPARTMENT OF LABOR. LABOR BULLETIN. Text in English. 1949. m. free. charts; stat. back issues avail. **Document type:** *Bulletin, Government.*
Formerly: South Dakota. Department of Labor. Manpower Bulletin; Which superseded (in 1975): South Dakota Labor Bulletin
Indexed: SRI.
Published by: Department of Labor, Labor Market Information Center, 420 S Roosevelt, Box 4730, Aberdeen, SD 57402-4730. TEL 605-626-2314. Eds. Lisa Cooper, Melodee Lane. R&P Melodee Lane. Circ: 1,200.

SOUTH DAKOTA EMPLOYMENT LAW LETTER. see *LAW*

331.21 GBR
SOUTH EAST MIDLANDS SALARY SURVEY. Text in English. 2/yr. GBP 280 per edition (effective 2001). **Document type:** *Bulletin.* **Description:** Salary survey covering the Bedfordshire, North Oxfordshire and North Buckinghamshire areas.
Published by: The Reward Group Ltd., Reward House, Diamond Way, Stone Business Park, Stone, Staffs ST15 0SD, United Kingdom. TEL 44-1785-813566, FAX 44-1785-817007, enquiries@reward-group.co.uk, http://www.reward-group.co.uk.

331.21 GBR
SOUTH WEST SALARY SURVEY. Text in English. 2/yr. GBP 280 per edition (effective 2001). **Document type:** *Bulletin.* **Description:** Salary survey covering the Cornwall, Devon, Somerset, Dorset and South Wiltshire areas.
Published by: The Reward Group Ltd., Reward House, Diamond Way, Stone Business Park, Stone, Staffs ST15 0SD, United Kingdom. TEL 44-1785-813566, FAX 44-1785-817007, enquiries@reward-group.co.uk, http://www.reward-group.co.uk.

SOUTHERN COMMUNITIES. see *HOUSING AND URBAN PLANNING*

SOZIALES SEMINAR INFORMATIONEN; politisch-soziale Bildung in katholischer Traegerschaft. see *RELIGIONS AND THEOLOGY—Roman Catholic*

SOZIALGESETZBUCH: ARBEITSFOERDERUNG. see *LAW—Civil Law*

331 ESP
SPAIN. MINISTERIO DE TRABAJO Y ASUNTOS SOCIALES. REVISTA. (In 5 series: Derecho del Trabajo, Seguridad Social, Legislacion Internal y U.E., Economia y Sociologia del Trabajo, Asuntos Sociales) Text in Spanish. m. (10/yr.). **Document type:** *Government.*
Formerly (until 1997): Economia y Sociologia del Trabajo (0214-6029)
—CINDOC.
Published by: Ministerio de Trabajo y Seguridad Social, Centro de Publicaciones, Agustin de Bethencourt, 11, Madrid, 28003, Spain. TEL 34-1-5543400, FAX 34-1-915333847, sgpublic@mtas.es, http://www.ntas.es/. **Subscr. to:** Mundi-Prensa Libros, S.A., Castello, 37, Madrid 28001, Spain. TEL 34-1-4313222, FAX 34-1-5753998.

SPARTACO. see *POLITICAL SCIENCE*

331.21 USA
SPORTING GOODS MANUFACTURERS ASSOCIATION. EXECUTIVE COMPENSATION STUDY. Text in English. a. **Document type:** *Trade.*
Published by: Sporting Goods Manufacturers Association, 6650 W. Indiantown Rd., Ste. 220, Jupiter, FL 33458-4629. TEL 561-842-4100. Ed. Sebastian Dicasoli.

331 USA
SPORTING GOODS MANUFACTURERS ASSOCIATION. FINANCIAL PERFORMANCE STUDY. Text in English. a. membership. **Document type:** *Trade.*
Published by: Sporting Goods Manufacturers Association, 6650 W. Indiantown Rd., Ste. 220, Jupiter, FL 33458-4629. TEL 561-842-4100. Ed. Sebastian Dicasoli.

331 LKA ISSN 0379-3737
HD8670.8.A5
SRI LANKA LABOUR GAZETTE. Text in English. 1950. q. LKR 200, USD 4. adv. bk.rev. stat. index.
Formerly: Ceylon Labour Gazette (0009-0859)
Related titles: Singhalese ed.
Indexed: BAS, PAIS, SLSI.
Published by: Ministry of Labour and Vocational Training, Labour Secretariat, Colombo, 5, Sri Lanka. Ed. Sumanasiri Hulugalle. Circ: 1,500.

STAFFING MANAGEMENT. see *BUSINESS AND ECONOMICS—Personnel Management*

352.63 NOR ISSN 0800-658X
STAFO-NYTT. Text in Norwegian. 1925. m. (8/yr.). adv.
Formerly: Statstjenestemannen
—CCC.
Published by: Statstjenestemannsforbundet, Postboks 9038, Oslo, 0133, Norway. Ed. Tryque Christensen. Circ: 15,000.

331.21 USA
STATE & FEDERAL WAGE HOUR COMPLIANCE GUIDE. Text in English. base vol. plus s-a. updates. looseleaf. **Document type:** *Trade.* **Description:** Provides information on the federal Fair Labor Standards Act (FLSA) and related state laws, including minimum wage and overtime requirements and their implications.
Published by: W G & L Financial Reporting & Management Research (Subsidiary of: R I A), 395 Hudson St, New York, NY 10014. TEL 212-367-6300, FAX 212-367-6718, http://www.InsideHR.com. Ed. Tina Fritz. **Subscr. to:** The Park Square Bldg., 31 St James Ave, Boston, MA 02116-4112. TEL 800-950-1207.

331.1 USA ISSN 1541-9037
HD8083.C2
THE STATE OF CALIFORNIA LABOR. Text in English. 2001. a. USD 28 per issue to individuals; USD 75 per issue to institutions (effective 2005 & 2006). adv. **Document type:** *Journal, Academic/Scholarly.* **Description:** Includes extensive discussion of recent trends in employment and labor relations and serves as a resource for labor scholars, policy makers, union organizers, and others.
Related titles: Online - full text ed.: ISSN 1541-9045. USD 65 to institutions (effective 2005 & 2006) (from Swets Information Services).
—CCC.
Published by: (University of California, Institute for Labor and Employment), University of California Press, Journals Division, 2000 Center St, Ste 303, Berkeley, CA 94704-1223. TEL 510-643-7154, FAX 510-642-9917, journals@ucpress.edu, www.ucpress.edu/journals/scl, http://www.ucpress.edu/journals. Eds. Christopher Erickson, Margaret Weir, Michael Reich, Ruth Milkman. adv.: page USD 325; 5.5 x 8. Circ: 2,500.

STATUS. see *MUSIC*

344.01 USA
STATUTES, REGULATIONS AND CASE LAW PROTECTING INDIVIDUALS WITH DISABILITIES. Text in English. 1994. a., latest 7th ed. USD 149 per issue (effective 2003). **Document type:** *Trade.* **Description:** Compiles federal statutes and regulations that affect the rights Americans with disabilities.
Published by: Oakstone Legal and Business Publishing, 11975 Portland Ave Ste 110, Burnsville, MN 55337-1530. TEL 800-365-4900, http://www.oakstonelegal.com/. Ed. Steven McEllistrem.

331 DEU
STICHWORT: BAYER; fuer mehr Umweltschutz und sichere Arbeitsplaetze. Text in German. 1983. bi-m. EUR 30 (effective 2005). bk.rev. back issues avail. **Document type:** *Magazine, Trade.*
Published by: Coordination gegen Bayer Gefahren e.V., Postfach 150418, Duesseldorf, 40081, Germany. TEL 49-211-333911, FAX 49-211-333940, CBGnetwork@aol.com, http://www.cbgnetwork.org/Ubersicht/Zeitschrift_SWB/zeitschrift_swb.html. Ed. Hubert Ostendorf. Circ: 3,000.

331.125 USA
STRIPES JOBS. Text in English. 2001. m. **Document type:** *Magazine, Consumer.* **Description:** Contains articles & advise on civilian employment opportunities for ex-military personnel, including company profiles & job search tips.
Published by: Stars & Stripes Omnimedia, 100 First Avenue, Ste 1100, Pittsburgh, PA 15222. TEL 412-552-1350, info@stripes.com.

331 DNK ISSN 1601-717X
STRUKTURSTATISTIK. Text in Danish. 1994. a.
Related titles: ◆ Series of: Dansk Arbejdsgiverforening. D A Loenstatistik. ISSN 0909-0347.
Published by: Dansk Arbejdsgiverforening/Danish Employers Confederation, Vester Voldgade 113, Copenhagen V, 1790, Denmark. TEL 45-33-389000, FAX 45-33-122976, da@da.dk, http://www.da.dk. Ed. Ulla Stroeger.

334.01 USA ISSN 1082-9210
SUCCESSFUL JOB ACCOMMODATION STRATEGIES. Text in English. 1995. m. USD 185 (effective 2005). **Document type:** *Newsletter, Trade.* **Description:** Provides quick tips, new accommodation ideas and innovative workplace solutions to bring your injured or disabled employees back to work. Includes the outcomes of the latest legal cases involving workplace accommodations so you can avoid the mistakes that landed others in court.
Related titles: Online - full text ed.
—CCC.
Published by: L R P Publications, 747 Dresher Rd, PO Box 980, Horsham, PA 19044. TEL 800-341-7874, custserve@lrp.com, http://www.lrp.com.

SUMA. see *BUSINESS AND ECONOMICS—Economic Situation And Conditions*

331.1 DEU ISSN 1431-7168
SUPERVISION; Mensch - Arbeit - Organisation. Text in German. 1982. q. EUR 40; EUR 12.50 newsstand/cover (effective 2005). adv. **Document type:** *Magazine, Trade.* **Description:** Covers all aspects of management and employer-employee relationships at businesses and corporations in German-speaking countries.
Related titles: Online - full text ed.: (from Northern Light Technology, Inc.).
—CCC.
Published by: Julius Beltz GmbH & Co. KG, Werderstr 10, Weinheim, 69469, Germany. TEL 49-6201-6007200, FAX 49-6201-6007201, info@agentur-supervison.de, info@beltz.de, http://www.beltz.de/supervision/. Ed. Winfried Muench. Adv. contact Brigitte Bell. page EUR 820; trim 174 x 230. Circ: 2,800 (paid and controlled).

331.1 USA ISSN 0039-5854
TS155.A1 CODEN: SUPRAO
SUPERVISION; the magazine of industrial relations and operating management. Text in English. 1939. m. USD 64.05 domestic (effective 2005). adv. Index. reprint service avail. from PQC. **Document type:** *Magazine, Trade.* **Description:** Publishes relations information covering human relations, supervisory training, office and personnel, health and safety, training and self-development for the factory and /or office firstline supervisor.
Supersedes: Foreman
Related titles: Microform ed.: (from PQC); Online - full text ed.: (from bigchalk, EBSCO Publishing, Florida Center for Library Automation, Gale Group, H.W. Wilson, Northern Light Technology, Inc., O C L C Online Computer Library Center, Inc., ProQuest Information & Learning).
Indexed: ABIn, AgeL, BPI, BPIA, BusI, ExcerpMed, PersLit, T&II, WorkRelAb.
—BLDSC (8547.130000), Ei, IDS, IE, Infotrieve, ingenta. **CCC.**
Published by: National Research Bureau, 320 Valley St, Burlington, IA 52601-5513. TEL 319-752-5415, FAX 319-752-3421, national@willinet.net. Ed. Teresa Levinson. Pub. Michael Darnall. Circ: 1,100 (paid).

331.21 USA
SUPERVISORY AND MANAGEMENT SURVEY. Text in English. a. USD 450. **Description:** Offers salary information for 90 supervisory and management positions among 220 companies, representing 2,950 employees in PA, NJ, MD, and DE.
Published by: MidAtlantic Employers' Association, PO Box 770, Valley Forge, PA 19482. TEL 215-666-7330, FAX 215-666-7866.

331.21 GBR
SURREY - WEST KENT SALARY SURVEY. Text in English. 2/yr. GBP 280 per edition (effective 2001). **Document type:** *Bulletin.* **Description:** Pay and benefits salary survey for the Surrey, West Kent, Maidstone, Gillingham, Dartford, Severnoaks and Turnbridge areas.
Published by: The Reward Group Ltd., Reward House, Diamond Way, Stone Business Park, Stone, Staffs ST15 0SD, United Kingdom. TEL 44-1785-813566, FAX 44-1785-817007, enquiries@reward-group.co.uk, http://www.reward-group.co.uk.

331.252 USA
SURVEY OF STATE RETIREMENT SYSTEMS. Text in English. biennial. stat. **Description:** Reviews pension and retirement programs of state government employees.
Published by: National Association of State Retirement Administrators, 540 E 2005, Salt Lake City, UT 84102. TEL 801-355-3884.

363.7 CAN ISSN 1201-8384
THE SUSTAINABLE TIMES. Text in English. 1993. 4/yr. CND 9.95 domestic; USD 9.95 foreign; CND 2.95 newsstand/cover (effective 2000). **Description:** Discusses alternatives to the country's problems with employment and the environment.
Indexed: CBCARef.
Published by: Sustainable Times, 1657 Barrington St, Ste 508, Halifax, NS B3J 2A1, Canada. TEL 902-423-6709, FAX 902-423-9736, times@web.net.

SVENSKA JAERNVAEGSTIDNINGEN. see *TRANSPORTATION—Railroads*

SWAZILAND. CENTRAL STATISTICAL OFFICE. EMPLOYMENT AND WAGES. see *BUSINESS AND ECONOMICS—Abstracting, Bibliographies, Statistics*

T A A NEWS & VIEWS. (Texas Apartment Association) see *HOUSING AND URBAN PLANNING*

331   NLD   ISSN 1388-1558
T A P. TIJDSCHRIFT VOOR ARBEID EN PARTICIPATIE. Text in Dutch. 1977. q. EUR 34 to individuals; EUR 54.50 to institutions; EUR 18 to students (effective 2005).
Formerly (until 1998): T A B. Tijdschrift voor Arbeid en Bewustzijn (0166-6088)
Indexed: PSA, SSA, SociolAb.
—IE.
Published by: (Universiteit Utrecht, Faculteit Sociale Wetenschappen), Arkel, Uitgeverij Jan van, Postbus 13094, Utrecht, 3507, Netherlands. FAX 31-30-2711090, tap@fss.uu.nl. Ed. H Coenen.

331   SWE
T C O STYRELSE- OCH REVISIONS; berettelse. Text in Swedish. 1944. a.
Former titles: Aaret som Gaatt
Published by: Tjaenstemaennens Central Organisation/Swedish Confederation of Salaried Employees, Linnegatan 14, Stockholm, 11447, Sweden. FAX 46-8-663-75-20, TELEX 19104 TCO S. Circ: 15,000.

331   SWE   ISSN 0346-2935
T C O - TIDNINGEN. Text in Swedish. 1946. 20/yr. SEK 350 (effective 2001). adv. 16 p./no. 5 cols./p.; **Document type:** *Newspaper, Trade.*
Published by: Tjaenstemaennens Centralorganisation, Stockholm, 11494, Sweden. TEL 46-8-782-91-00, FAX 46-8-662-48-22, tco.tidningen@tco.se, http://www.tco.se/tco-tidningen. Ed., Pub. Anna-Britt Benjour. Adv. contact Hakan Fridell. B&W page SEK 35,000, color page SEK 43,500; trim 250 x 360. Circ: 59,500 (paid and controlled).

T+ D. see *BUSINESS AND ECONOMICS—Personnel Management*

331   PHL
TALA INDUSTRIAL RELATIONS BULLETIN. Text in English. 1976. m. PHP 240, USD 60. bk.rev. illus. index. back issues avail. **Document type:** *Bulletin.*
Published by: Tala Publishing Corporation, University of the Philippines, PO Box 95, Quezon City, Philippines. Ed. Perfecto V Fernandez. Circ: 1,000.

331   IND
TAMIL NADU LABOUR JOURNAL. Text in English, Tamil. 1972 (vol.15, no.12). m. INR 16. bk.rev. bibl.; charts; stat.
Formerly: Madras Labour Gazette. (0024-9610)
Published by: Commissioner of Labour, Chepauk, Chennai, Tamil Nadu 600 005, India.

TANZANIA. NATIONAL BUREAU OF STATISTICS. SURVEY OF EMPLOYMENT. see *BUSINESS AND ECONOMICS—Abstracting, Bibliographies, Statistics*

344.01   DEU   ISSN 0937-0951
TASCHENLEXIKON ARBEITSRECHTLICHER ENTSCHEIDUNGEN. Text in German. 1961. 3 base vols. plus irreg. updates. looseleaf. price varies. **Document type:** *Monographic series, Trade.*
Published by: Erich Schmidt Verlag GmbH & Co. (Berlin), Genthiner Str 30G, Berlin, 10785, Germany. TEL 49-30-250085-0, FAX 49-30-25008521, vertrieb@esvmedien.de, http://www.erich-schmidt-verlag.de.

331   USA   ISSN 0746-0384
TAX UPDATE FOR BUSINESS OWNERS; tax saving strategies for savvy business owners. Text in English. m. USD 125 (effective 1999). **Document type:** *Newsletter.* **Description:** Delivers information on the latest laws, trends, and loopholes, as well as summaries of the latest IRS rulings that effect your business.
Published by: Aspen Publishers, Inc. (Subsidiary of: Wolters Kluwer N.V.), 111 Eighth Ave., 7th Fl, New York, NY 10011. TEL 212-771-0600, FAX 212-771-0885, customer.service@aspenpubl.com, http://www.aspenpublishers.com.

344.01   USA
THE TEACHER RETIREMENT LAWS OF THE STATE OF ARKANSAS. Text in English. irreg., latest 2001. USD 32 base vol(s). (effective 2003). 198 p./no.
Published by: Michie Company (Subsidiary of: LexisNexis North America), 701 E Water St, Charlottesville, VA 22902-5389. TEL 434-972-7600, 800-446-3410, FAX 434-972-7677, http://www.michie.com.

TEACHERS' MONEY MATTERS. see *EDUCATION—School Organization And Administration*

331   USA
                    TA158
TECHNICAL & SKILLED TRADE PERSONNEL REPORT. Text in English. 1973. a. USD 470. **Document type:** *Trade.*

Formerly (until 1980): Executive Compensation Service. Technician Report (0093-8750)
Published by: (Executive Compensation Service (ECS)), Wyatt Data Services, 218 Rte 17 N, Rochelle Park, NJ 07622-9832. TEL 201-843-1177, FAX 201-843-0101. Ed. Michael D Marvin.

331.255   USA   ISSN 1529-3017
TELECOMMUTING TODAY. Text in English. 1998. 3/w. USD 4.50 per issue (effective 2000). **Description:** Provides information about telecommuting and to view current telecommuting positions in the United States.
Related titles: E-mail ed.
Address: 241 Worthington Lane, Warner Robins, GA 31088. TEL 912-971-1384, FAX 954-827-0895, http://www.telecommute-now.org. Pub. Michelle McCullers. Circ: 72,000.

331   ESP   ISSN 0213-0750
TEMAS LABORALES; revista andaluza de trabajo y bienestar social. Text in Spanish. 1984. q. **Description:** Covers social welfare, employee-employer relationships and all work related issues.
—CINDOC.
Published by: Junta de Andalucia, Consejeria de Trabajo e Industria, c/o Secretaria General Tecnica, Av. Heroes de Toledo s-n, Edificio Junta de Andalucia, Sevilla, 41006, Spain.
Dist. by: Mailing Andalucia, Almirante Topete, S/N, Sevilla 41013, Spain. TEL 34-54-236863, FAX 34-54-239749.

TEMPORARY DISABILITY INSURANCE AND UNEMPLOYMENT INSURANCE LAWS OF RHODE ISLAND. see *INSURANCE*

TENNESSEE EMPLOYMENT LAW LETTER. see *LAW*

331.11   USA   ISSN 0749-9930
                    HD5701.85
TENNESSEE. LABOR MARKET INFORMATION DIRECTORY. Text in English. a. **Document type:** *Directory, Government.*
Published by: (Tennessee. Research and Statistics Division); Department of Employment Security, 500 James Robertson Pkwy, 11th Fl, Nashville, TN 37245-1040. TEL 615-741-1729.

331   USA
TENNESSEE. THE LABOR MARKET REPORT. Text in English. m. free. charts; stat. **Document type:** *Newsletter, Government.*
Related titles: Microfiche ed.: (from CIS).
Indexed: SRI.
Published by: (Tennessee. Research and Statistics Division), Department of Employment Security, 500 James Robertson Pkwy, 11th Fl, Nashville, TN 37245-1040. TEL 615-741-1729.

TENNESSEE WORKERS' COMP REPORTER. see *INSURANCE*

368.41   USA
TENNESSEE WORKERS' COMPENSATION LAWS. Text in English. irreg., latest 2002. USD 29 base vol(s). (effective 2003). 376 p./no.; **Description:** Provides access to workers' compensation law and many related statutes, comprehensively annotated and indexed.
Published by: Michie Company (Subsidiary of: LexisNexis North America), 701 E Water St, Charlottesville, VA 22902-5389. TEL 434-972-7600, 800-446-3410, FAX 434-972-7677, http://www.michie.com.

TEXAS EMPLOYMENT LAW LETTER. see *LAW*

331.1   USA
TEXAS LABOR MARKET REVIEW. Text in English. 1945. m. free. charts; stat. **Document type:** *Newsletter, Government.*
Formerly: Texas Manpower Trends (0040-4462)
Related titles: Microfiche ed.: (from CIS); Online - full text ed.
Indexed: SRI.
Published by: Texas Workforce Commission, Labor Market Information Department, 101 E 15th St, Rm 252T, Austin, TX 78778. TEL 512-463-2843, FAX 512-475-1701, cgriffis@twc.state.tx.us, http://www.twc.state.tx.us. Ed. Clayton Griffis. Circ: 5,500.

331.21   USA   ISSN 1527-1439
TEXAS WORKERS' COMP ADVISOR. Text in English. 199?. m. **Document type:** *Trade.*
Published by: Providence Publications, LLC, PO Box 1100, Grass Valley, CA 95945-1100 . TEL 530-470-7500, FAX 530-470-7600.

▼ **TEXAS WORKERS' COMP REPORTER.** see *LAW—Corporate Law*

TEXTILE LABOUR COST COMPARISON - INTERNATIONAL. see *TEXTILE INDUSTRIES AND FABRICS*

THAILAND. NATIONAL STATISTICAL OFFICE. REPORT OF THE LABOR FORCE SURVEY, WHOLE KINGDOM (YEAR). see *BUSINESS AND ECONOMICS—Abstracting, Bibliographies, Statistics*

331   THA
THAILAND STANDARD INDUSTRIAL CLASSIFICATION. Text in English, Thai. 1972. irreg.
Published by: Department of Labour, Bangkok, Thailand.

331.21   GBR
THAMES VALLEY SALARY SURVEY. Text in English. 2/yr. GBP 280 per edition (effective 2001). **Document type:** *Bulletin.*
Description: Pay and benefit salary survey covering the Berkshire, Swindon, South Oxfordshire and South Buckinghamshire areas.
Published by: The Reward Group Ltd., Reward House, Diamond Way, Stone Business Park, Stone, Staffs ST15 0SD, United Kingdom. TEL 44-1785-813566, FAX 44-1785-817007, enquiries@reward-group.co.uk, http://www.reward-group.co.uk.

331 363.7 360   DNK   ISSN 1399-1442
▶ **TIDSSKRIFT FOR ARBEJDSLIV.** Text in Danish; Summaries in English. 1999. q. DKK 450 to individuals; DKK 675 to institutions; DKK 225 to students; DKK 170 per issue (effective 2006). bk.rev. abstr.; bibl. 128 p./no. 2 cols./p.; back issues avail. **Document type:** *Journal, Academic/Scholarly.*
Description: Multidisciplinary studies of the labor market, working life and working environment.
Formerly (until 1999): Nyt om Arbejdsliv (0909-1203)
Related titles: Online - full text ed.
Indexed: DIP, IBR, IBZ, PSA, SSA, SociolAb.
Published by: (Roskilde Universitetscenter, Center for Studier i Arbejdsliv), Syddansk Universitetsforlag/University Press of Southern Denmark, Campusvej 55, Odense M, 5230, Denmark. TEL 45-66-157999, FAX 45-66-158126, press@forlag.sdu.dk, http://www.nyt-om-arbejdsliv.dk, http://www.universitypress.dk. Ed. Joergen Burchardt. Circ: 800.

331   NLD   ISSN 0169-2216
TIJDSCHRIFT VOOR ARBEIDSVRAAGSTUKKEN. Text in Dutch. 1985. q. EUR 95 domestic to individuals; EUR 133 foreign to individuals; EUR 131 to institutions; EUR 65 to students; EUR 31.50 newsstand/cover (effective 2005). **Document type:** *Trade.* **Description:** Offers information for professionals involved with problems in labor relations, the labor market, and labor organization.
—IE, Infotrieve, KNAW.
Published by: (Stichting Interuniversitair Instituut voor Sociaal-Wetenschappelijk Onderzoek), Reed Business Information bv (Subsidiary of: Reed Business), Postbus 16500, Den Haag, 2500 BM, Netherlands. TEL 31-70-4415000, FAX 31-70-4415927, http://www.elsevierhr.nl. Ed. J J van Hoof.

TIME OUT. see *SPORTS AND GAMES—Ball Games*

352.63   NOR
TJENESTEMANNSBLADET. Text in Norwegian. 10/yr. adv.
Published by: Norsk Tjenestemannslag, Mollergata 10, Oslo, 0179, Norway. Ed. Anne Grete Lossius. Circ: 34,561.

331   USA
TOMORROW. Text in English. bi-m. membership. **Document type:** *Newsletter, Internal.*
Published by: (U A W, D C's National Training Center), Pohly & Partners Inc., 27 Melcher St., 2nd Fl., Boston, MA 02210. TEL 617-451-1700, 877-687-6459, FAX 617-338-7767, ginnyf@pohlypartners.com, http://www.pohlypartners.com. Circ: 85,000 (controlled).

658.3   GBR   ISSN 0262-2548
▶ **TOPICS (CAMBRIDGE).** Text in English. 1979. q. GBP 50; GBP 60 foreign. bk.rev. **Document type:** *Academic/Scholarly.* **Description:** Covers all aspects of human resource issues; aimed at senior and middle managers as well as personnel managers.
Indexed: M&MA.
—BLDSC (8867.415500), IE, ingenta.
Published by: E R Consultants, Compass House, 80 Newmarket Rd, Cambridge, CB5 8DZ, United Kingdom. TEL 44-1223-315944, FAX 44-1223-322565, sales@erconsultants.co.uk, http://www.erconsultants.co.uk/change. Ed., R&P Mark Goodridge. Circ: 2,500 (paid).

▶ **TOTAL SALARY INCREASE BUDGET SURVEY.** see *BUSINESS AND ECONOMICS—Personnel Management*

331   CUB   ISSN 0864-0432
TRABAJADORES. Text in Spanish. 1970. w. USD 40.
Related titles: Online - full text ed.: Trabajadores Digital. ISSN 1563-8367.
Published by: Central de Trabajadores de Cuba, Palacio de los Trabajadores, San Carlos y Penalver, Ciudad de La Habana, Cuba. http://www.trabajadores.cubaweb.cu/. Ed. Jorge Luis Canela Ciurana. Circ: 250,000. Dist. by: Ediciones Cubanas, Obispo No. 461, Apdo. 605, Havana, Cuba.

331   DOM   ISSN 0564-0334
TRABAJO. Text in Spanish. 1966. q.
Published by: Secretaria de Estado de Trabajo, Departamento de Relaciones Publicas y Prensa, Santo Domingo, Dominican Republic. Ed. Rafael A Grullon.

331   COL
TRABAJO. Text in Spanish. 1950. irreg.
Published by: Ministerio del Trabajo y Seguridad Social, Av. 19 No. 6-68 Of. 806-809, Santa Fe de Bogota, CUND, Colombia. Ed. I Reyes Rosada.

331 ARG ISSN 1514-6871
TRABAJO Y SOCIEDAD. Text in Spanish. 1999. q.
Media: Online - full text.
Published by: Universidad Nacional de Santiago del Estero, Programa de Investigaciones sobre Trabajo y Sociedad, Ave. Belgrano, 1912, Santiago del Estero, 4200, Argentina. TEL 54-385-4509506, FAX 54-385-4509529, http://www.geocities.com/athens/foreum/4113. Ed. Carlos Zurita.

331 AGO ISSN 0564-0342
TRABALHO. Text in Portuguese; Summaries in English, French, Portuguese. 1963. q. charts.
Published by: Instituto do Trabalho Previdencia e Accao Social de Angola, Avenida Alvaro Ferreira 5, Luanda, Angola.

331.259 AUS ISSN 0310-4664
TRAINING AND DEVELOPMENT IN AUSTRALIA. Text in English. 1971. bi-m. AUD 236.50 membership (effective 2005). adv. bk.rev. charts; illus.; stat. back issues avail. **Document type:** *Magazine, Trade.* **Description:** Covers the latest training tools, technology and related topics, including editorials and organizational information.
Indexed: AEI.
—BLDSC (88883.500950).
Published by: Australian Institute of Training and Development, Ste. 111, 410 Elizabeth St., Surry Hills, NSW 2010, Australia. TEL 61-2-92119414, FAX 61-2-92118784, journal@aitd.com.au, http://www.aitd.com.au. Ed. Rebecca Campbell. Adv. contact Vanessa Fink TEL 61-2-92119414. B&W page AUD 900, color page AUD 1,125. Circ: 38,000.

331 BEL ISSN 1024-2589
HD8371
TRANSFER; European review of labour and research. Text in English; Abstracts in English, French, German. 1995. q.
Description: Contains information on European trade union policy, labor, and industrial relations.
Indexed: IBSS.
—BLDSC (9020.583280), IE, ingenta.
Published by: Institut Syndical Europeen/European Trade Union Institute, Bd du Roi Albert II, 6, Boite 4, Brussels, 1210, Belgium. TEL 32-2-2240470, FAX 32-2-2240502.

331.21 GBR ISSN 0041-1531
TRANSPORT SALARIED STAFF JOURNAL. Text in English. 1904. m. GBP 6; GBP 8.50 foreign. adv. bk.rev. illus.
Document type: *Newsletter.*
Published by: Transport Salaried Staffs' Association, Transport Salaried Staffs Association, Walkden House 3-10, 10 Melton St, London, NW1 2EJ, United Kingdom. FAX 44-171-383-0656. Ed. Neil Tester. Circ: 40,000.

331 CHE ISSN 1020-0002
TRAVAIL. Text in French. q.
Formerly (until 1992): Informations O I T (0379-1750)
Related titles: Online - full text ed.: ISSN 1564-4596; ♦ English ed.: World of Work. ISSN 1020-0010; Arabic ed.; Chinese ed.; Czech ed.; Danish ed.; Finnish ed.; German ed.; Hungarian ed.; Japanese ed.; Norwegian ed.; Russian ed.; Spanish ed.; Swedish ed.
Published by: International Labour Office, Department of Communication, 4 Route des Morillons, Geneva 22 22, CH-1211, Switzerland. TEL 41-22-7997912, FAX 41-22-7998577, communication@ilo.org, http://www.ilo.org/public/french/bureau/inf/magazine/index.htm, http://www.ilo.org/communication.

TRAVAIL EMPLOI FORMATION. see *SOCIOLOGY*

331 614.85 FRA ISSN 1287-9290
TRAVAIL & CHANGEMENT. Text in French. 1975. m. EUR 53.36 (effective 2004).
Former titles (until 1996): Le Mensuel e l'A N A C T (1251-9200); (until 1992): Agence Nationale pour l'Amelioration des Conditions de Travail. Lettre d'Information (0399-449X)
Indexed: ErgAb.
Published by: Agence Nationale pour l'Amelioration des Conditions de Travail, 4, quai des Etroits, Lyon, 69321 Cedex 05, France. TEL 33-4-72561313, http://www.anact.fr/publications/tc/tc.html. Ed. Beatrice Sarazin.

331 FRA ISSN 0224-4365
HD8421
TRAVAIL ET EMPLOI. Text in French. 4/yr. EUR 52.30 domestic; EUR 56.40 in the European Union; EUR 58.40 DOM-TOM; EUR 59.40 elsewhere (effective 2003). abstr. reprint service avail. from SCH. **Document type:** *Government.*
Former titles (until 1979): Formation-Emploi; Emploi et Formation
Related titles: Microfiche ed.; Online - full text ed.
Indexed: JEL, PAIS, PSA, RASB, SCIMP, SociolAb.
—BLDSC (9026.859500), IE, Infotrieve.
Published by: (France. Ministere de l'Emploi et de la Solidarite), Documentation Francaise, 29-31 quai Voltaire, Paris, Cedex 7 75344, France. FAX 33-1-40157230.

331 305.3 FRA ISSN 1294-6303
HD4807
TRAVAIL, GENRE ET SOCIETES; la revue du M A G E. Text in French. 1995. s-a. EUR 45 domestic to individuals; EUR 50 foreign to individuals; EUR 55 domestic to institutions; EUR 60 foreign to institutions (effective 2005). **Document type:** *Journal, Academic/Scholarly.*
Formerly (until 1999): Les Cahiers du M A G E (1269-0236)
Indexed: IBSS.
Published by: Armand Colin Editeur (Subsidiary of: Masson), 21 Rue du Montparnasse, Paris, 75283 Cedex 06, France. TEL 33-1-44395447, FAX 33-1-44394343, infos@armand-colin.com, http://www.iresco.fr/revues/tgs, http://www.armand-colin.com.

LE TRAVAIL HUMAIN. see *PSYCHOLOGY*

331.21 USA
TRENDS IN EMPLOYMENT AND WAGES COVERED BY UNEMPLOYMENT INSURANCE. Text in English. 1944. a. USD 10 (effective 1999). **Document type:** *Government.*
Former titles: Covered Employment Trends in New Jersey; Covered Employment Trends in New Jersey by Geographical Areas of the State; New Jersey Covered Employment Trends by Geographical Areas of the State (0092-1459)
Published by: Department of Labor, Division of Labor Market and Demographic Research, PO Box 934, Trenton, NJ 08625. TEL 609-984-5586, http://www.state.nj.us/labor/ira. Ed. William Saley. Circ: 1,100.

331 RUS
TRUD I PRAVO. Text in Russian. bi-m. USD 115 in United States.
Published by: Izdatel'stvo Profizdat, Myasnitskaya ul 13, str 18, Moscow, 103006, Russian Federation. TEL 7-095-9240786, FAX 7-095-9752329. Ed. N N Raskova. **US dist. addr.:** East View Information Services, 3020 Harbor Ln. N., Minneapolis, MN 55447. TEL 612-550-0961.

340.56 331 BGR
TRUD I PRAVO. Text in Bulgarian. m. BGL 88.80 (effective 2002).
Description: Covers labour law, salaries and incomes, social insurance, pensions, health insurance, employment.
Related titles: CD-ROM ed.
Published by: Izdatelski Kompleks Trud i Pravo/Labour and Law Publishing House, Pl. Makedonia 1, Fl. 7, Sofia, 1040, Bulgaria. TEL 359-2-9875110, FAX 359-2-9870612, office@trudipravo.bg, http://www.trudipravo.bg.

TRUD I ZANYATOST' V ROSSII (YEAR). see *BUSINESS AND ECONOMICS—Abstracting, Bibliographies, Statistics*

331 RUS
TRUD. SUBBOTNII VYPUSK. Text in Russian. w. USD 145 in United States.
Indexed: RASB.
Published by: Trud, Nastas'inskii per 4, Moscow, 103792, Russian Federation. letter@trud.ru. **US dist. addr.:** East View Information Services, 3020 Harbor Ln. N., Minneapolis, MN 55447. TEL 612-550-0961.

TRUDOVI OTNOSHENIA. see *LAW—Civil Law*

331 RUS
TRUDOVOE PRAVO. Text in Russian. q. USD 75 in United States.
Indexed: RefZh.
Published by: Biznes Shkola Intel-Sintez, Profsoyuznaya ul 3, ofis 620, Moscow, 117036, Russian Federation. TEL 7-095-1299212, FAX 7-095-1246809. Ed. A I Stavtseva. **US dist. addr.:** East View Information Services, 3020 Harbor Ln. N., Minneapolis, MN 55447. TEL 612-550-0961.

TURKISH FORESTRY, LAND IRRIGATION, AGRICULTURE AND AGRICULTURAL INDUSTRY WORKERS' UNION. TARIM-IS/TURKIYE ORMAN, TOPRAKSU, TARIM VE TARIM SANAYII ISCILERI SENDIKASI. TARIM-IS. see *LABOR UNIONS*

331.125 USA
TWIN CITIES EMPLOYMENT WEEKLY. Text in English. 1993. w.
Published by: American City Business Journals, Inc. (Austin), 505 Powell St, Austin, TX 78703-5121. adv.: B&W page USD 1,250. Circ: 25,500.

U C GUIDE (YEAR). (Unemployment Compensation) see *LAW—Corporate Law*

331 FRA
U F C V. Text in French. 1910. m. (9/yr.). adv. bk.rev.
Published by: Union Francaise des Centres de Vacances Loisirs, 10 quai de Charente, Paris, 750019, France. TEL 33-01-44721414. Ed. D Mascolo. Circ: 7,500.

U.S. BUREAU OF LABOR STATISTICS. BULLETIN. see *BUSINESS AND ECONOMICS—Abstracting, Bibliographies, Statistics*

331.11 USA ISSN 0098-1818
HD8051
U.S. BUREAU OF LABOR STATISTICS. MONTHLY LABOR REVIEW. Text in English. 1915. m. USD 49 domestic; USD 68.60 foreign (effective 2005). bk.rev. illus. index, cum.index every 12 yrs. back issues avail.; reprint service avail. from CIS,WSH. **Document type:** *Journal, Government.*
Description: Contains articles on the labor force, including wage and benefit changes and trends, current labor statistics, and collective bargaining. Includes articles on worker satisfaction, social indicators, and labor developments abroad.
Supersedes: U.S. Bureau of Labor Statistics. Monthly Review (0027-044X)
Related titles: CD-ROM ed.; Microfiche ed.: (from CIS); Microform ed.: (from PMC); Online - full text ed.: Monthly Labor Review Online. free (effective 2005) (from EBSCO Publishing, Florida Center for Library Automation, Gale Group, H.W. Wilson, Northern Light Technology, Inc., O C L C Online Computer Library Center, Inc., ProQuest Information & Learning, The Dialog Corporation).
Indexed: ABIn, AHCMS, ASCA, ASG, ATI, Acal, AgeL, AmH&L, AmStI, B&I, BPI, BPIA, BRD, BRI, CBRI, CIJE, CLI, ChPerI, CurCont, ERA, FamI, HistAb, ILD, IUSGP, JEL, LRI, MASUSE, MEDLINE, MagInd, PAIS, PCI, PopulInd, PoultAb, RASB, RGAb, RGPR, SSCI, SSI, SWA, SWR&A, T&II, TEA, WAE&RSA, WorkRelAb.
—BLDSC (5938.700000), IDS, IE, Infotrieve, ingenta.
Published by: U.S. Department of Labor, Bureau of Labor Statistics, Postal Square Bldg., 2 Massachusetts Ave, NE, Washington, DC 20212-0001 . TEL 202-691-5900, FAX 202-691-5899, http://www.bls.gov/opub/mlr/mlrhome.htm. Ed. Deborah Klein. Circ: 9,000. **Subscr. to:** U.S. Government Printing Office, Superintendent of Documents, PO Box 371954, Pittsburgh, PA 15250-7954. TEL 202-512-1800, FAX 202-512-2250, orders@gpo.gov, http://www.access.gpo.gov.

U.S. BUREAU OF LABOR STATISTICS. NATIONAL COMPENSATION SURVEY. see *BUSINESS AND ECONOMICS—Abstracting, Bibliographies, Statistics*

U.S. BUREAU OF LABOR STATISTICS. NATIONAL OFFICE NEWS RELEASES. see *BUSINESS AND ECONOMICS—Abstracting, Bibliographies, Statistics*

331 USA ISSN 1543-3145
U.S. BUREAU OF LABOR STATISTICS. P P I DETAILED REPORT. Text in English. a. USD 55 (effective 2001). stat.
Document type: *Government.* **Description:** Reports on price movements at the primary market level, arranged by stage of processing and by commodity. Supplement contains changes in the relative importance of components of the indexes, revisions in coverage, and annual averages.
Related titles: ♦ Abridged ed. of: Producer Price Indexes. ISSN 1099-2863.
Published by: U.S. Department of Labor, Bureau of Labor Statistics, Postal Square Bldg., 2 Massachusetts Ave, NE, Washington, DC 20212-0001 . TEL 202-691-5200, FAX 202-691-6325, http://www.bls.gov. **Subscr. to:** U.S. Government Printing Office, Superintendent of Documents, PO Box 371954, Pittsburgh, PA 15250-7954. TEL 202-512-1800, FAX 202-512-2250, orders@gpo.gov, http://www.access.gpo.gov.

U.S. BUREAU OF LABOR STATISTICS. REPORTS. see *BUSINESS AND ECONOMICS—Abstracting, Bibliographies, Statistics*

U.S. BUREAU OF LABOR STATISTICS. REPRINT SERIES. see *BUSINESS AND ECONOMICS—Abstracting, Bibliographies, Statistics*

344.01 USA ISSN 0191-118X
KF3612.5
U.S. CHAMBER OF COMMERCE. ANALYSIS OF WORKERS' COMPENSATION LAWS (YEAR). Key Title: Analysis of Workers' Compensation Laws. Text and summaries in English. 1954. a., latest 2005. USD 63 to non-members; USD 28 to members (effective 2005). charts; bibl. 120 p./no.; back issues avail. **Document type:** *Journal, Trade.* **Description:** Offers an overview of workers' Compensation statutes for 50 United States, the District of Columbia, Guam, Puerto Rico, the U.S. Virgin Islands and the provinces and territories of Canada. It is intended to provide an improved understanding of the various laws. Sixteen detailed charts are presented to aid employers, insurance firms, agents brokers, attorneys, and others.
Formerly (until 1976): U.S. Chamber of Commerce. Analysis of Workmen's Compensation Laws (0577-5183)
Indexed: SRI.
Published by: U.S. Chamber of Commerce, Business Information and Development Dept., 1615 H St N W, Washington, DC 20062-2000. TEL 202-659-6000, 800-638-6582, statinfo@uschamber.com, statcenter@uschamber.com, http://www.uschamber.com/research/workercomp.htm. Ed., Pub. Chamain O'mahony.

U.S. DEPARTMENT OF AGRICULTURE. NATIONAL AGRICULTURAL STATISTICS SERVICE. FARM LABOR. see *AGRICULTURE—Abstracting, Bibliographies, Statistics*

344.73 USA ISSN 0271-1567
KF3512
U.S. DEPARTMENT OF LABOR. EMPLOYEE RETIREMENT INCOME SECURITY ACT. REPORT TO CONGRESS. Key Title: Employee Retirement Income Security Act. Report to Congress. Text in English. 1975. a. free. **Document type:** *Government.*
Formerly: Administration of the Employee Retirement Income Security Act (0146-7352)
Published by: U.S. Department of Labor, Pension and Welfare Benefits Administration, 200 Constitution Ave, N W, Washington, DC 20216. TEL 202-523-8921. Ed. William C Russell. Circ: 3,000.

331.1   USA
HD5723
U.S. DEPARTMENT OF LABOR. EMPLOYMENT & TRAINING ADMINISTRATION. TRAINING AND EMPLOYMENT REPORT OF THE SECRETARY OF LABOR. Text in English. 1963. a. **Document type:** *Government.*
Former titles (until 1985): U.S President. Employment and Training Report of the President (0145-2444); (unitl 1976): U.S. President. Manpower Report of the President (0502-4544)
Published by: U.S. Department of Labor, Employment & Training Administration, 200 Constitution Ave N W, Washington, DC 20210. http://www.doleta.gov/.

U.S. DEPARTMENT OF STATE INDEXES OF LIVING COSTS ABROAD, QUARTERS ALLOWANCES, AND HARDSHIP DIFFERENTIALS. see *BUSINESS AND ECONOMICS— Abstracting, Bibliographies, Statistics*

U.S. DEPARTMENT OF TRANSPORTATION. NATIONAL HIGHWAY TRAFFIC SAFETY ADMINISTRATION. EQUAL EMPLOYMENT OPPORTUNITY AND AFFIRMATIVE EMPLOYMENT FOR MINORITIES, WOMEN, AND PEOPLE WITH DISABILITIES; accomplishment report and updates. see *POLITICAL SCIENCE—Civil Rights*

331.87   USA   ISSN 0565-4688
U.S. EQUAL EMPLOYMENT OPPORTUNITY COMMISSION. ANNUAL REPORT. Variant title: Equal Employment Opportunity Report. Text in English. 1968. a. free. **Document type:** *Government.*
Published by: U.S. Equal Employment Opportunity Commission, 1801 L St, N W, Washington, DC 20507. TEL 800-669-3362,

331   USA   ISSN 0196-9927
U.S. FEDERAL MEDIATION AND CONCILIATION SERVICE. ANNUAL REPORT. Text in English. 1948. a. free. **Document type:** *Government.*
Published by: U.S. Federal Mediation and Conciliation Service., 2100 K St, N W, Washington, DC 20427. TEL 202-606-8100, FAX 202-606-4251, http:/www.fmcs.gov. Ed. David Helfert. R&P Jane Lorber.

331.11   USA   ISSN 0083-2200
KF3372
U.S. NATIONAL LABOR RELATIONS BOARD. ANNUAL REPORT. Variant title: Annual Report of the National Labor Relations Board for Fiscal Year (Year). Text in English. 1936. a. price varies. reprint service avail. from WSH. **Document type:** *Government.*
Published by: U.S. National Labor Relations Board, 1099 14th St, N W, Washington, DC 20570-0001. TEL 202-273-1991, FAX 202-273-1789, http://www.nlrb.gov. **Subscr. to:** U.S. Government Printing Office, Superintendent of Documents, PO Box 371954, Pittsburgh, PA 15250-7954. TEL 202-512-1800, FAX 202-512-2250, orders@gpo.gov, http:// www.access.gpo.gov.

331   USA   ISSN 0083-2219
KF3360.A2
U.S. NATIONAL LABOR RELATIONS BOARD. COURT DECISIONS RELATING TO THE NATIONAL LABOR RELATIONS ACT. Text in English. 1939. irreg., latest vol.38. USD 38 (effective 1999). reprints avail. **Document type:** *Government.*
Related titles: Microfiche ed.: (from WSH).
Published by: U.S. National Labor Relations Board, 1099 14th St, N W, Washington, DC 20570-0001. TEL 202-273-1991, FAX 202-273-1789, http://www.nlrb.gov. **Subscr. to:** U.S. Government Printing Office, Superintendent of Documents, PO Box 371954, Pittsburgh, PA 15250-7954. TEL 202-512-1800, FAX 202-512-2250, orders@gpo.gov, http:// www.access.gpo.gov.

331   USA
U.S. NATIONAL LABOR RELATIONS BOARD. ELECTION REPORT. Text in English. m. USD 39 (effective 2001). **Document type:** *Government.* **Description:** Lists the outcome of secret-ballot voting by employees in NLRB conducted representation elections as officially certified following resolution of post-election objections and/or challenges.
Published by: U.S. National Labor Relations Board, 1099 14th St, N W, Washington, DC 20570-0001. **Subscr. to:** U.S. Government Printing Office, Superintendent of Documents, PO Box 371954, Pittsburgh, PA 15250-7954. TEL 202-512-1800, FAX 202-512-2250, orders@gpo.gov, http:// www.access.gpo.gov.

331.11   USA
U.S. NATIONAL LABOR RELATIONS BOARD. OFFICE OF THE GENERAL COUNSEL. QUARTERLY REPORT. Text in English. q. **Document type:** *Government.*
Published by: U.S. National Labor Relations Board, Office of the General Counsel, 1717 Pennsylvania Ave, N W, Washington, DC 20570. TEL 202-275-2091. **Subscr. to:** U.S. Government Printing Office, Superintendent of Documents. TEL 202-783-3238, FAX 202-512-2233.

331.11   USA   ISSN 0364-8109
KF3364
U.S. NATIONAL LABOR RELATIONS BOARD. WEEKLY SUMMARY OF THE NATIONAL LABOR RELATIONS BOARD CASES. Text in English. 1983 (no.W-1869). w. USD 174 (effective 2001). back issues avail. **Document type:** *Government.* **Description:** Contains a synopsis of each published decision of the N.R.L.B. in unfair labor practices and representative election cases; lists decisions of N.L.R.B. administrative law judges and directions of elections by regional directors; carries guideline memoranda of the N.L.R.B. general counsel to field offices on important case-handling subjects; and carries notices of publication of volumes of N.L.R.B. decisions and orders, the Annual Report, and other agency informational literature.
Related titles: Microfiche ed.: (from WSH); Online - full text ed.: ISSN 1554-9909.
Published by: U.S. National Labor Relations Board, 1099 14th St, N W, Washington, DC 20570-0001. TEL 202-273-1991, FAX 202-273-1789, http://www.nlrb.gov. **Subscr. to:** U.S. Government Printing Office, Superintendent of Documents, PO Box 371954, Pittsburgh, PA 15250-7954. TEL 202-512-1800, FAX 202-512-2250, orders@gpo.gov, http:// www.access.gpo.gov.

331   USA   ISSN 0083-2278
U.S. NATIONAL MEDIATION BOARD. (REPORTS OF EMERGENCY BOARDS). Text in English. irreg. (3-4/yr.). USD 175; includes Annual Reports, Emergency Board Reports, Certifications and Dismissals, Determinations of Craft or Class, Findings upon Investigation, other N.M.B. information releases. **Document type:** *Government.*
Published by: U.S. National Mediation Board, 1301 K St, N W, Ste 250E, Washington, DC 20572. TEL 202-523-5335. **Orders to:** U.S. Government Printing Office, Superintendent of Documents.

331   USA   ISSN 0083-2286
HD5503
U.S. NATIONAL MEDIATION BOARD. ANNUAL REPORT. Text in English. 1935. a. price varies. **Document type:** *Government.*
Published by: U.S. National Mediation Board, 1301 K St, N W, Ste 250E, Washington, DC 20572. TEL 202-523-5920, FAX 202-523-1494. **Orders to:** U.S. Government Printing Office, Superintendent of Documents.

331   USA   ISSN 0270-4196
U.S. NATIONAL MEDIATION BOARD. DETERMINATIONS. Text in English. 1948. a. USD 18.75. **Document type:** *Government.*
Formerly (until 1976): U.S. National Mediation Board. Determination of Craft or Class (0891-9410)
Published by: U.S. National Mediation Board, 1301 K St, N W, Ste 250E, Washington, DC 20572. **Orders to:** U.S. Government Printing Office, Superintendent of Documents.

352.63   USA
U.S. OFFICE OF PERSONNEL MANAGEMENT. NEGOTIABILITY DETERMINATIONS BY THE FEDERAL LABOR RELATIONS AUTHORITY. Text in English. biennial. **Document type:** *Government.* **Description:** Summarizes negotiability determinations issued by F.L.R.A. over the previous two years.
Published by: U.S. Office of Personnel Management, Office of Labor Relations and Workforce Performance, Labor-Management Relations Division, Personnel Systems and Oversight Group, Theodore Roosevelt Bldg, 1900 E St NW, Washington, DC 20415. TEL 202-606-2930, **Dist by:** U.S. Government Printing Office, Superintendent of Documents, PO Box 371954, Pittsburgh, PA 15250-7954. TEL 202-512-1800, FAX 202-512-2250, orders@gpo.gov, http://www.access.gpo.gov.

U.S. OFFICE OF PERSONNEL MANAGEMENT. PERSONNEL SYSTEMS AND OVERSIGHT GROUP. FEDERAL CIVILIAN WORKFORCE STATISTICS. OCCUPATIONS OF FEDERAL WHITE-COLLAR AND BLUE-COLLAR WORKERS. see *BUSINESS AND ECONOMICS—Abstracting, Bibliographies, Statistics*

331.21   USA   ISSN 0891-8066
HD7116.R12
U.S. RAILROAD RETIREMENT BOARD. ANNUAL REPORT. Text in English. 1936. a. **Document type:** *Government.*
Published by: U.S. Railroad Retirement Board, 844 N Rush St, Chicago, IL 60611. TEL 312-751-4776. Ed. William Poulos. Circ: 1,700. **Subscr. to:** U.S. Government Printing Office, Superintendent of Documents.

U.S. RAILROAD RETIREMENT BOARD. QUARTERLY BENEFIT STATISTICS. see *BUSINESS AND ECONOMICS— Abstracting, Bibliographies, Statistics*

344.01   USA
U.S. SUPREME COURT EMPLOYMENT CASES∗. Text in English. 1993. a. USD 94.95. **Document type:** *Trade.* **Description:** Compiles summarized U.S. Supreme Court decisions that affect employment.
Published by: Oakstone Business and Legal Publishing, 11975 Portland Ave Ste 110, Burnsville, MN 55337-1530. TEL 651-452-8267, FAX 651-452-8694. Ed., R&P Steve McEllistrem. Pub. Joanne E Fiore.

331   DNK   ISSN 1602-1630
UGEBREVET A4; arbejdsmarked, politik, velfaerd og vaerdier. Variant title: Ugebrevet A Fire. Text in Danish. 2002. 44/yr. DKK 900 (effective 2004). **Document type:** *Newsletter.*
Formed by the merger of (1997-2002): Udspil (1397-9930); (1998-2001): L O Magasinet (1398-389X)
Related titles: Online - full text ed.: ISSN 1602-2203.
Published by: Landsorganisationen i Danmark (L O)/Danish Federation of Trade Unions, Islands Brygge 32D, Copenhagen S, 2300, Denmark. TEL 45-35-246000, FAX 45-35-246300, ugebrevetA4@lo.dk, lo@lo.dk, http://www.ugebreveta4.dk/ view.asp?ID=1, http://www.lo.dk. Eds. Bent Winther, Hans Jensen.

331   UKR
UKRAINS'KE PRAVO. Text in English, Ukrainian. q. USD 95 in United States.
Published by: Izdatel'stvo Pravo, Ul M Raskovoi 23, Kiev, Ukraine. TEL 517-55-77, FAX 517-52-36. **US dist. addr.:** East View Information Services, 3020 Harbor Ln. N., Minneapolis, MN 55447. TEL 612-550-0961.

331   ZAF
UNEMPLOYMENT & EMPLOYMENT. Text in English. irreg. Free. stat. **Document type:** *Government.*
Published by: Statistics South Africa/Statistieke Suid-Afrika, Private Bag X44, Pretoria, 0001, South Africa. TEL 27-12-310-8911, FAX 27-12-310-8500, info@statssa.pwv.gov.za, http://www.statssa.gov.za.

368.44   USA   ISSN 1063-3812
HD7096.U6
UNEMPLOYMENT INSURANCE ACTUARIAL STUDY & FINANCIAL HANDBOOK (YEAR). Text in English. a. free. **Document type:** *Government.* **Description:** Report of Alaska's unemployment insurance (UI) system focusing on the benefit and tax structures. Includes an overview of the current UI system and an analysis of fund adequacy with respect to potential future benefit obligations.
Related titles: Online - full text ed.
Published by: Department of Labor, Research and Analysis Section, PO Box 25501, Juneau, AK 99802-5501. TEL 907-465-4507, FAX 907-465-2101, http:// www.labor.state.ak.us/research/ui/ui.htm. Ed. JoAnn Erskine.

UNEMPLOYMENT INSURANCE REPORTER WITH SOCIAL SECURITY - FEDERAL ONLY. see *INSURANCE*

368.44021   CAN   ISSN 0829-1098
UNEMPLOYMENT INSURANCE STATISTICS. Text in Multiple languages. 1942. m.
Formerly (until 1985): Statistical Report on the Operation of the Unemployment Insurance Act (0382-4098)
Related titles: ♦ Supplement(s): Canada. Statistics Canada. Unemployment Insurance Statistics. Annual Supplement. ISSN 0828-3176.
Published by: (Statistics Canada, Unemployment Insurance Statistics Section), Statistics Canada, Publications Sales and Services, Ottawa, ON K1A 0T6, Canada. TEL 613-951-8116, 800-267-6677, infostats@statcan.ca, http://www.statcan.ca.

331   USA
UNFAIR LABOR PRACTICE CASE HANDLING MANUAL. Text in English. base vol. plus irreg. updates. looseleaf. USD 112 (effective 2001). **Document type:** *Government.*
Related titles: Online - full content ed.
Published by: U.S. Federal Labor Relations Authority, Office of the General Counsel, Tech World Plaza, 800 K St, NW, Ste 910, Washington, DC 20001-1206. TEL 202-482-6702, FAX 202-482-6724, http://www.flra.gov/gc/manuals/ulp/ch-manual.html, http://www.flra.gov/index.html. **Subscr. to:** U.S. Government Printing Office, Superintendent of Documents, PO Box 371954, Pittsburgh, PA 15250-7954. TEL 202-512-1800, FAX 202-512-2250, orders@gpo.gov, http:// www.access.gpo.gov.

344.01   USA   ISSN 1085-8296
UNFAIR LABOR PRACTICES BULLETIN. Text in English. 1987. m. looseleaf. USD 119 (effective 2005). index. back issues avail. **Document type:** *Newsletter.* **Description:** Covers the latest decisions in lawsuits brought against employers and unions for unfair labor practices, including anti-union activities by employers, unfair union representation, unsafe workplaces, election pressure tactics, strikes and wage disputes.
Formerly (until 1995): Unfair Labor Practices Law Bulletin (0895-8904)
—CCC.
Published by: E D M Publishers, 1528 Tremont St. - Unit 2B, Duxbury, MA 02332. TEL 781-934-6660, FAX 781-934-6644, info@edmpublishers.com, http://www.edmpublishers.com/ #ULP. Ed., Pub. E Michael Quinlan.

344.01   USA   ISSN 1096-3995
KF3407.A75
UNION CONTRACT LAW BULLETIN. Text in English. 1977. m. USD 147 (effective 2005). Index. back issues avail. **Document type:** *Newsletter, Trade.* **Description:** Covers legal decisions concerning labor contract disputes. Covers decisions from the National Labor Relations Board and the Federal Labor Relations Association.
Formerly (until 1997): Labor Contract Law Bulletin (8755-7886)
Related titles: Online - full text ed.: ISSN 1545-9268.

—CCC.
Published by: Quinlan Publishing Group, Marine Industrial Park, 23 Drydock Ave, 6th Fl, Boston, MA 02210-2387. TEL 617-542-0048, 800-229-2084, FAX 617-345-9646, info@quinlan.com, http://www.quinlan.com. Ed. Leslie Rosenbloom. Pub. Dennis Hofmaier.

UNION DEMOCRACY REVIEW. see *LABOR UNIONS*

344.73   USA   ISSN 0091-5459
KF3365
UNION LABOR REPORT. Text in English. 1947. bi-w. looseleaf. USD 1,125 (effective 2004). bk.rev. index. 8 p./no.; back issues avail. **Document type:** *Newsletter.* **Description:** Notification and reference service that provides practical guidance on day-to-day labor relations questions. Includes current reports on employee relations and union developments.
Related titles: Online - full content ed.: USD 283 up to 5 users (effective 2004); Online - full text ed.: (from The Bureau of National Affairs, Inc.).
—CCC.
Published by: The Bureau of National Affairs, Inc., 1231 25th St., NW, Washington, DC 20037. TEL 202-452-4200, 800-372-1033, FAX 202-785-7167, customercare@bna.com, http://www.bna.com. Ed. Bill L Manville. Pub. Greg C McCaffery.

331   USA
UNITED STATES N L R B ONLINE. Text in English. w.
Document type: *Journal.* **Description:** Expedites the process for users wanting to access the many resources and service of this federal agency that is central to labor and industrial relations in the United States. NLRB created in 1935 to enforce the National Labor Relations Act, this independent federal agency holds secret-ballot elections to determine whether employees want union representation and investigates and remedies unfair labor practices by employers and unions.
Media: Online - full text.
Published by: U.S. National Labor Relations Board, 1099 14th St, N W, Washington, DC 20570-0001. TEL 202-273-1991, FAX 202-273-1789, http://www.nlrb.gov.

331   CAN   ISSN 0842-2788
UNIVERSITIES ACACDEMIC PENSION PLAN (YEAR) ANNUAL REPORT. Text in English. 1979. a.
Former titles (until 1985): Universities Academic Pension Board Pursuant to Universities Academic Pension Act. Final Report (0842-277X); (until 1985): Universities Academic Pension Board Pursuant to the Universities Academic Pension Act. Annual Report (0842-2761); (until 1981): Proceedings of the Universities Academic Pension Board Pursuant to The Universities Academic Pension Act. Annual Report (0709-8731)
Published by: Universities Academic Pension Plan, 5th Fl, Park Plaza, 10611 - 98 Ave, Edmonton, AB T5K 2P7, Canada. FAX 780-415-8871, board@uapp.ca.

331   USA   ISSN 0739-439X
UNIVERSITY OF CALIFORNIA AT LOS ANGELES. INSTITUTE OF INDUSTRIAL RELATIONS. MONOGRAPH AND RESEARCH SERIES. Text in English. 1953. irreg., latest vol.58, 1994. price varies. back issues avail. **Document type:** *Monographic series, Academic/Scholarly.*
Formerly: University of California at Los Angeles. Institute of Industrial Relations. Monograph Series (0068-6255)
Published by: (Institute of Industrial Relations), University of California at Los Angeles, School of Public Policy and Social Research, 6350B Public Policy Building, Box 951478, Los Angeles, CA 90095-1478. TEL 310-794-5955, FAX 310-794-6410. Ed. Pat Kracow. R&P Carli Rogers TEL 310-825-0759. Circ: 500 (paid). **Orders to:** Book Masters, PO Box 388, Ashland, OH 44805-0388. TEL 800-247-6553.

331   USA   ISSN 0073-1226
UNIVERSITY OF HAWAII. INDUSTRIAL RELATIONS CENTER. OCCASIONAL PUBLICATIONS. Text in English. 1948. irreg., latest vol.180, 2003. price varies. **Document type:** *Monographic series, Academic/Scholarly.*
Published by: University of Hawaii, Industrial Relations Center, 2425 Campus Rd, Honolulu, HI 96822. TEL 808-956-8132, FAX 808-956-3609, uhirc@hawaii.edu. Ed. Joyce M Najita.

UNIVERSITY OF PENNSYLVANIA JOURNAL OF LABOR AND EMPLOYMENT LAW. see *LAW*

331   TTO
UNIVERSITY OF THE WEST INDIES, TRINIDAD. INSTITUTE OF SOCIAL & ECONOMIC RESEARCH. OCCASIONAL PAPERS: HUMAN RESOURCES SERIES. Text in English. 1977. irreg. price varies. charts; stat. back issues avail.
Published by: University of the West Indies, Institute of Social and Economic Research, St. Augustine, WI, Trinidad & Tobago. Ed. Jack Harewood. Circ: 220.

331   USA
UNJUST DISMISSAL. Text in English. 1985. 3 base vols. plus irreg. updates. looseleaf. USD 625 base vol(s). (effective 2005). **Description:** covers employee handbooks and personel manuals, free speech and privacy in the workplace, sexual morals, whistleblowing, refusal to participate in criminal activity and drug and alcohol screening.
Related titles: CD-ROM ed.
Published by: Matthew Bender & Co., Inc. (Subsidiary of: LexisNexis North America), 1275 Broadway, Albany, NY 12204. TEL 518-487-3575, 800-252-9257, FAX 518-462-3788, international@bender.com, http://bender.lexisnexis.com. Eds. Lex Larson, Philip Borowsky.

UNSUNG HEROES. see *OCCUPATIONS AND CAREERS*

331.11   RUS
URAL'SKII RABOCHII. Text in Russian. 260/yr. USD 459 in United States.
Related titles: Microfilm ed.: (from EVP).
Address: Ul Turgeneva 13, etazh 7-9, Ekaterinburg, 620219, Russian Federation. TEL 3432-51-51-40, FAX 3432-51-64-51. Ed. G M Kaeta. **US dist. addr.:** East View Information Services, 3020 Harbor Ln. N., Minneapolis, MN 55447. TEL 612-550-0961.

UTAH EMPLOYMENT LAW LETTER. see *LAW*

331.125   IND
UTTAR PRADESH ROZGAR DIGEST; an employment oriented & consultative Hindi fortnightly. Text in Hindi. 1978. fortn. adv.
Published by: Disha Publications Pvt. Ltd., Bazar Gunj, P O Box 205, Moradabad, 244 001, India. TEL 28925. Ed. Vishwapati Sharma. Pub. Vikas Sharma. Adv. contact Umesh Chandra Vaish. Circ: 36,439.

331   DEU
V W-AUTOGRAMM. Text in German. 1971. m. free. bk.rev. back issues avail. **Document type:** *Newsletter, Trade.*
Published by: Volkswagen AG, John-F.-Kennedy-Allee 64, Wolfsburg, 38444, Germany. TEL 49-5361-3085-0, FAX 49-5361-3085200, vwclub@dialogservice.com, http://www.vw-club.de. Ed. Hansjuergen Meisert. Circ: 100,000.

332.6   ZAF
VAN ZYL, RUDD INDUSTRIAL RELATIONS AND HUMAN RESOURCES DIARY. Text in English. 1997. a. ZAR 200 (effective 2000). **Document type:** *Directory.* **Description:** Provides a substantial listing of contact details of relevant companies in South Africa for business persons, laywers, industrial relations practitioners, and human resources managers.
Related titles: Online - full text ed.: Human Resources and Industrial Relations Directory.
Published by: Van Zyl, Rudd and Associates, Centrahil, PO Box 12758, Port Elizabeth, 6006, South Africa. TEL 27-41-373-4322, FAX 27-41-373-4323, info@vanzylrudd.co.za, http://www.vanzylrudd.co.za.

VANUATU. STATISTICS OFFICE. MANPOWER AND EMPLOYMENT SURVEYS. see *BUSINESS AND ECONOMICS—Abstracting, Bibliographies, Statistics*

344.01   USA
VERDICTSEARCH EMPLOYMENT LAW. Text in English. m. USD 345 (effective 2004). **Document type:** *Newsletter, Trade.* **Description:** Covers employment-related litigation nationwide.
Formerly: California Employment Law Monthly
Published by: VerdictSearch (Subsidiary of: A L M), 128 Carleton Ave, East Islip, NY 11730. TEL 212-313-9093, 800-832-1900, FAX 516-581-8937, info@verdictsearch.com, http://www.verdictsearch.com.

VERMONT EMPLOYMENT LAW LETTER. see *LAW*

331.12   USA
VERMONT LABOR MARKET. Text in English. 1964. m. free. charts; stat. **Document type:** *Government.* **Description:** Contains information on the labor market, economic conditions, and the department's programs.
Formerly: Vermont Labor Force (0506-7472)
Published by: Department of Employment & Training, PO Box 488, Montpelier, VT 05601-0488. TEL 802-828-4321, FAX 802-828-4022. Circ: 2,500.

VINNUMARKADUR/LABOR MARKET STATISTICS. see *BUSINESS AND ECONOMICS—Abstracting, Bibliographies, Statistics*

331.11   VIR
VIRGIN ISLANDS (U.S.). DEPARTMENT OF LABOR. ANNUAL REPORT. FISCAL YEAR. Text in English. a. **Document type:** *Government.*
Published by: Department of Labor, Bureau of Labor Statistics, P O Box 3359, Charlotte Amalie, St Thomas, 00803, Virgin Isl., US.

VIRGIN ISLANDS (U.S.). DEPARTMENT OF LABOR. BUREAU OF LABOR STATISTICS. LABOR MARKET REVIEW. see *BUSINESS AND ECONOMICS—Abstracting, Bibliographies, Statistics*

VIRGINIA EMPLOYMENT LAW LETTER. see *LAW*

368.41   USA
VIRGINIA WORKERS' COMPENSATION; law and practice. Text in English. 1993. latest 2000, 3rd ed., base vol. plus irreg. updates. USD 95 base vol(s). (effective 2003). Supplement avail. **Description:** Examines the legal relationships between employers, employees, and insurance carriers.
Published by: Matthew Bender & Co., Inc. (Subsidiary of: LexisNexis North America), 1275 Broadway, Albany, NY 12204. TEL 518-487-3575, 800-252-9257, FAX 518-462-3788, http://bender.lexisnexis.com. Ed. Lawrence J Pascal.

368.41   USA
THE VIRGINIA WORKERS' COMPENSATION ACT ANNOTATED. Text in English. irreg., latest 2002. USD 42 base vol(s). (effective 2003). 680 p./no.; **Description:** This annotated, indexed edition compiled from Michie's Code of Virginia contains Title 65.2, Workers' Compensation, Related Statutes, Selected Rules of the Supreme Court of Virginia, Rules of the Virginia Workers' Compensation Commission, Peer Review Regulations, and Procedure and Regulations for Filing.First Reports.
Published by: Michie Company (Subsidiary of: LexisNexis North America), 701 E Water St, Charlottesville, VA 22902-5389. TEL 434-972-7600, 800-446-3410, FAX 434-972-7677, http://www.michie.com.

344.01   USA
VIRGINIA WORKERS' COMPENSATION CASE FINDER. Text in English. 1990. latest 2003, 3rd ed., base vol. plus a. updates. USD 75. **Description:** A source book that integrates the workers' compensation opinions of the Virginia Supreme Court, Court of Appeals, and Workers' Compensation Commission.
Published by: Matthew Bender & Co., Inc. (Subsidiary of: LexisNexis North America), 1275 Broadway, Albany, NY 12204. TEL 518-487-3575, 800-252-9257, FAX 518-462-3788, http://bender.lexisnexis.com. Ed. Peter M Sweeny.

331.21   CAN   ISSN 1183-7780
VISION. Text in English. 1991. q. free. **Description:** Reports on pay equity for employers in the federal jurisdiction.
Published by: Labour Canada, Publications Distribution, Ottawa, ON K1A 0J2, Canada. TEL 819-994-0543, FAX 819-997-1664. Circ: 3,000.

331   HRV   ISSN 0042-7632
VJESNIK RADA; casopis za pitanja rada, radnih odnosa, zaposljavanja i socijalnog osiguranja. Text in Serbo-Croatian. 1970 (vol.13). m. **Document type:** *Magazine, Trade.*
Published by: Narodne Novine d.d., Trg Sv Marka 2, Zagreb, 10000, Croatia. TEL 385-1-4569244, FAX 385-1-4611824. Ed. Ivica Kranzelic.

323.092   USA
W D L NEWS. Text in English. 1972. 3/yr. USD 10; or membership. bk.rev. bibl.
Supersedes: Workers Defense Bulletin
Published by: Workers Defense League, Inc., 275 Seventh Ave, 15th fl, New York, NY 10001. TEL 212-627-1931, FAX 212-627-4628. Ed. Jon Bloom. Circ: 5,000.

331.125   USA
W.E. UPJOHN INSTITUTE FOR EMPLOYMENT RESEARCH. STAFF WORKING PAPERS. Text in English. 1990. irreg. abstr. back issues avail.
Related titles: Online - full text ed.
Published by: W.E. Upjohn Institute for Employment Research, 300 S Westnedge Ave, Kalamazoo, MI 49007. TEL 616-343-5541, FAX 616-343-7310, http://www.upjohninst.org/.

331.125   USA
W.E. UPJOHN INSTITUTE FOR EMPLOYMENT RESEARCH. TECHNICAL REPORTS. Text in English. 1993. irreg. back issues avail.
Related titles: Online - full text ed.
Published by: W.E. Upjohn Institute for Employment Research, 300 S Westnedge Ave, Kalamazoo, MI 49007. TEL 616-343-5541, FAX 616-343-7310, http://www.upjohninst.org/.

340 368.4   CAN   ISSN 1480-5731
W S I A T IN FOCUS. (Workplace Safety and Insurance Appeals Tribunal) Text in English. 1990. q.
Formerly (until 1998): W C A T in Focus (1180-2588)
Published by: Workplace Safety and Insurance Appeals Tribunal, 505 University Ave, 7th Fl., Toronto, ON M5G 2P2, Canada.

331   SWE   ISSN 1651-4750
WAGE FORMATION; economic conditions in Sweden. Text in English. 2002. a. free (effective 2005).
Related titles: Online - full text ed.; ◆ Swedish ed.: Loenebildningen. ISSN 1651-050X.
Published by: Konjunkturinstitutet/National Institute of Economic Research, Kungsgatan 12-14, PO Box 3116, Stockholm, 10362, Sweden. TEL 46-8-4535900, FAX 46-8-4535980, ki@konj.se, http://www.konj.se.

▼ *new title*   ➤ *refereed*   ✳ *unverified*   ◆ *full entry avail.*

B

331 658   USA
WAGE - HOUR ALERT. Text in English. 1990. m. USD 199
(effective 2002). **Document type:** *Newsletter.* **Description:**
Advice for employers seeking to fully comply with federal and
state wage-hour laws.
Published by: Aspen Publishers, Inc. (Subsidiary of: Wolters
Kluwer N.V.), 111 Eighth Ave., 7th Fl, New York, NY 10011.
TEL 212-771-0600, FAX 212-771-0885, http://
www.aspenpub.com. Eds. Michael Levin-Epstein, Robert
Halprin.

331.2   USA   ISSN 1537-6389
KF3482
WAGE, HOUR & LEAVE REPORT. Text in English. 2002. bi-w.
USD 695 (effective 2003).
—CCC.
Published by: The Bureau of National Affairs, Inc., 1231 25th St.,
NW, Washington, DC 20037. TEL 202-452-4200,
800-372-1033, http://www.bna.com. Pub. Greg C McCaffery.

331.21   CAN   ISSN 1186-6640
WAGE SETTLEMENTS BULLETIN. Text in English, French.
1990. m. CND 220 (effective 2004). **Document type:** *Bulletin,
Government.* **Description:** Information and analysis of major
wage developments.
Related titles: French ed.: Bulletins des Reglements Salariaux.
ISSN 1186-6632.
Published by: Human Resources and Skills Development
Canada, Workplace Information Directorate Labour Program,
Ottawa, ON K1A 0J2, Canada. TEL 819-997-3117,
800-567-6866, FAX 819-953-9582, wid-imt@hrdc-drhc.gc.ca,
http://labour.hrdc-drhc.gc.ca/., http://www.hrsdc.gc.ca.

331.21   USA
WAGES AND BENEFITS∗ . Text in English. 1965. m. USD 95.
bk.rev.
Formed by the merger of: Salary and Merit (0048-9026);
Personnel News for School Systems (0048-3478)
Published by: Employee Futures Research, PO Box 15236,
Colorado Springs, CO 80935-5236. Ed. Eric Rhodes. Circ:
700 (controlled).

331.21   USA
WAGES AND HOURS: LAW & PRACTICE. Text in English. 1990.
base vol. plus a. updates. looseleaf. USD 150 base vol(s).
(effective 2002). Supplement avail. **Description:** Describes
federal and state laws governing minimum wage, overtime
and child labor standards. Includes both state and federal
wage-hour provisions.
Related titles: CD-ROM ed.
Published by: Matthew Bender & Co., Inc. (Subsidiary of:
LexisNexis North America), 1275 Broadway, Albany, NY
12204. international@bender.com, http://bender.lexisnexis.com.
Ed. Laurie Leader.

331   USA
WALTER REUTHER LIBRARY NEWSLETTER. Text in English.
1971. irreg. free. bibl. back issues avail. **Document type:**
Newsletter.
Former titles: Archives of Labor and Urban Affairs Newsletter;
Archives of Labor History and Urban Affairs Newsletter
(0044-8729)
Published by: (Archives of Labor and Urban Affairs), Wayne
State University, Walter Reuther Library, 5401 Cass Ave,
Detroit, MI 48202. TEL 313-577-4024, FAX 313-577-4300,
M.O.Smith@wayne.edu, http://www.reuther.wayne.edu. Ed.,
R&P Mike Smith. Circ: 3,000.

**WASHINGTON (STATE). EMPLOYMENT SECURITY
DEPARTMENT. AFFIRMATIVE ACTION INFORMATION.** see
*BUSINESS AND ECONOMICS—Abstracting, Bibliographies,
Statistics*

331.21   USA
**WASHINGTON (STATE). EMPLOYMENT SECURITY
DEPARTMENT. AREA WAGE SURVEYS.** Text in English.
biennial (in 15 vols.). USD 1 per vol.. charts; stat. **Document
type:** *Government.* **Description:** Supplies data on
occupational salaries and wages for selected managerial,
technical, clerical, and general professions in each of 15
urban or rural areas of Washington State.
Published by: Employment Security Department, Labor Market
and Economic Analysis Branch, PO Box 9046, Olympia, WA
98507-9046.

331.11   USA
**WASHINGTON (STATE). EMPLOYMENT SECURITY
DEPARTMENT. COUNTY LABOR MARKET AND
ECONOMIC PROFILES.** (Issued in 39 separate editions for
each county.) Text in English. a. charts; stat. **Document type:**
Government. **Description:** Highlights labor market and
economic conditions in each county.
Published by: Employment Security Department, Labor Market
and Economic Analysis Branch, PO Box 9046, Olympia, WA
98507-9046. TEL 360-438-4818.

331.11   USA
**WASHINGTON (STATE). EMPLOYMENT SECURITY
DEPARTMENT. OCCUPATIONAL PROJECTIONS.** Text in
English. a. **Document type:** *Government.* **Description:** Lists
annual job openings and five-year projections on the basis of
Occupational Employment Statistics surveys.

Related titles: Micro Opaque ed.
Published by: Employment Security Department, Labor Market
and Economic Analysis Branch, PO Box 9046, Olympia, WA
98507-9046.

331.125   USA
**WASHINGTON (STATE). EMPLOYMENT SECURITY
DEPARTMENT. STUDIES IN INDUSTRY AND
EMPLOYMENT.** Text in English. 1994. irreg., latest vol.2. price
varies. charts; stat. **Document type:** *Government.*
Description: Profiles and analyzes a specific industry, along
with employment trends and prospects.
Published by: Employment Security Department, Labor Market
and Economic Analysis Branch, PO Box 9046, Olympia, WA
98507-9046.

**WASHINGTON (STATE). EMPLOYMENT SECURITY
DEPARTMENT. WEEKLY INSURED UNEMPLOYMENT
REPORT.** see *INSURANCE—Abstracting, Bibliographies,
Statistics*

WASHINGTON EMPLOYMENT LAW LETTER. see *LAW*

331.11   USA
**WASHINGTON STATE LABOR MARKET AND ECONOMIC
REPORT (YEAR).** Text in English. a. USD 7.50. charts; stat.
Document type: *Government.* **Description:** Supplies the
Governor and state legislators with Washington state labor
market data and information.
Published by: Employment Security Department, Labor Market
and Economic Analysis Branch, PO Box 9046, Olympia, WA
98507-9046.

331.255   USA
WELFARE BENEFITS GUIDE; health plans and other employer
sponsored benefits. Text in English. a., latest 2004 ed. USD
244 (effective 2004). **Document type:** *Trade.* **Description:**
Provides step-by-step guidance for properly structuring and
managing non-pension benefit plans, while detailing federal
tax law and the methods that ensure compliance.
Published by: Thomson West (Subsidiary of: Thomson
Corporation, The), 610 Opperman Dr, Eagan, MN
55123-1396. TEL 651-687-8000, 800-328-4880, FAX
651-687-7302, http://www.westgroup.com/store/product.asp?
product%5Fid=13517787&catalog%5Fname=wgstore,
http://west.thomson.com. Ed. Paul J Routh.

WELFARE TO WORK; a review of developments in the welfare
job training and placement field. see *SOCIAL SERVICES AND
WELFARE*

331.1   NZL
**WELLINGTON REGIONAL EMPLOYERS ASSOCIATION
NEWSLETTER.** Text in English. 1966. m. membership.
Document type: *Newsletter.*
Published by: Wellington Regional Employers Association (Inc.),
Federation House, 6th Floor, Box 1087, 95-99 Molesworth St,
Wellington, New Zealand. TEL 64-4-737224, FAX 374501,
TELEX NZ 30270. Circ: (controlled).

331   DEU   ISSN 0508-3133
WERDEN; Jahrbuch fuer die Deutschen Gewerkschaften. Text in
German. 1958. a. **Document type:** *Journal, Trade.*
Published by: F M S Fach Media Service Verlagsgesellschaft
mbH, Siemensstr 6, Bad Homburg, 61352, Germany. TEL
49-6172-670492, FAX 49-6172-670536.

WERKGELEGENHEID IN DE NEDERLANDSE ZEEHAVENS. see
*BUSINESS AND ECONOMICS—Abstracting, Bibliographies,
Statistics*

331   USA
➤ **WERTHEIM PUBLICATIONS IN INDUSTRIAL RELATIONS.**
Text in English. irreg. **Document type:** *Monographic series,
Academic/Scholarly.*
Published by: Harvard University, John F. Kennedy School of
Government, 79 John F Kennedy St, Cambridge, MA 02138.
TEL 617-495-4157, FAX 617-495-5898.

331   IND   ISSN 0043-3071
WEST BENGAL LABOUR GAZETTE. Text in English. 1957. irreg.
stat.
Published by: (West Bengal. Department of Labour), Government
Press, Publication Branch, 38 Gopal Nagar Rd., Alipore,
Kolkata, West Bengal 700 027, India.

331.21   GBR
WEST MIDLANDS SALARY SURVEY. Text in English. 2/yr. GBP
280 per edition (effective 2001). **Document type:** *Bulletin.*
Description: Salary survey covering the Shropshire,
Staffordshire, West Midlands, Warwickshire, Hereford and
Worcester areas.
Published by: The Reward Group Ltd., Reward House, Diamond
Way, Stone Business Park, Stone, Staffs ST15 0SD, United
Kingdom. TEL 44-1785-813566, FAX 44-1785-817007,
enquiries@reward-group.co.uk, http://www.reward-group.co.uk.

331   USA
WEST VIRGINIA ECONOMIC SUMMARY. Text in English. 1977
(vol.3). m. free. charts; stat. **Document type:** *Newsletter,
Government.*

Former titles: West Virginia. Department of Employment Security.
Labor Market Trends; West Virginia. Department of
Employment Security. Area Manpower Summary
Indexed: SRI.
Published by: Bureau of Employment Programs, Office of Labor
and Market Information, 112 California Ave, Charleston, WV
25305-0112. TEL 304-558-2660. Circ: 3,000.

331.125   USA
**WEST VIRGINIA EMPLOYMENT AND EARNINGS TRENDS:
ANNUAL SUMMARY.** Text in English. 1968. a. free.
Document type: *Government.*
Published by: Bureau of Employment Programs, Labor and
Economic Research, 112 California Ave, Charleston, WV
25305-0112. TEL 304-558-2660. Circ: 400.

WEST VIRGINIA EMPLOYMENT LAW LETTER. see *LAW*

344.01   BEL
WETBOEK ARBEIDSRECHT. Text in Dutch. 6 base vols. plus
updates 3/yr. looseleaf. EUR 590 (effective 2003). **Document
type:** *Trade.* **Description:** Covers individual, collective,
international and European labor law.
Published by: Kluwer Uitgevers (Subsidiary of: Wolters Kluwer
Belgique), Ragheno Business Park, Motstraat 30, Mechelen,
B-2800, Belgium. TEL 32-15-800-94571, info@kluwer.be,
http://www.kluwer.be.

WHAT'S NEW IN BENEFITS & COMPENSATION. see
BUSINESS AND ECONOMICS—Personnel Management

331   CAN   ISSN 1486-2239
WHO'S HIRING. Text in English. 1998. a. CND 39.95 (effective
2003). **Document type:** *Directory, Consumer.* **Description:**
Ranks over 5,000 Canadian employers in 60 major
occupations.
Published by: Mediacorp Canada Inc., 21 New St, Toronto, ON
M5R 1P7, Canada. TEL 416-964-6069, FAX 416-964-3202,
info@mediacorp2.com, http://www.mediacorp2.com.

WIENER BEITRAEGE ZUM ARBEITS- UND SOZIALRECHT. see
LAW

WISCONSIN EMPLOYMENT LAW LETTER. see *LAW*

331   AUS   ISSN 0311-5119
WOMEN & WORK. Text in English. 1977. q. free. bk.rev.; film rev.
Document type: *Government.*
Formerly: Victoria, Australia. Women's Bureau. Women and Work
Newsletter (0314-7134)
Media: Online - full text.
Contact Corp. Auth.: Department of Employment, Education,
Training and Youth Affairs, GPO Box 9880, Canberra, ACT
2601, Australia. TEL 61-2-6240-8111. Ed. Susan Munter. Circ:
10,000.

331.4   USA   ISSN 0882-0910
HD6050
WOMEN AND WORK (NEWBURY PARK); a research and policy
series. Text in English. 1985. irreg., latest vol.6, 1997, June.
USD 53.95 per issue (effective 2005). back issues avail.
Document type: *Monographic series.*
Related titles: Online - full text ed.
Indexed: PCI.
—BLDSC (9343.276200). **CCC.**
Published by: Sage Publications, Inc., Books, 2455 Teller Rd,
Thousand Oaks, CA 91320. TEL 805-499-0721,
800-818-7243, FAX 805-499-0871, journals@sagepub.com,
order@sagepub.com, http://www.sagepub.com/book.aspx?pid=
2836.

352.63   USA
WORD FROM WASHINGTON (SAN ANTONIO). Text in English.
m. **Description:** Concerned with promoting and safeguarding
the rights and benefits of government employees in retirement
plans.
Published by: National Conference on Public Employee
Retirement Systems, Attn: Carlos Resendez, 4414 Centerview
Dr, Ste 226, San Antonio, TX 78228. TEL 210-732-8600, FAX
210-732-8684.

331.11   USA
THE WORK DOCTOR MAGAZINE. Text in English. m. index.
back issues avail. **Document type:** *Trade.* **Description:**
Provides advice, education, support, news and educational
programs to prevent and combat harassment and abuse at
work.
Media: Online - full text.
Published by: Work Doctor, PO Box 29915, Bellingham, WA
98228-1915. TEL 707-745-6630, twd@workdoctor.com,
http://www.workdoctor.com. Ed. Gary Namie.

344.01   USA   ISSN 1054-7819
WORKERS' COMP ADVISOR (CALIFORNIA ED.)∗ ; helping
doctors, lawyers, and employers cope with the workers' comp
system. Text in English. 1987. m. USD 197. adv. bk.rev. back
issues avail. **Document type:** *Newsletter.* **Description:**
Covers the workers compensation industry.
Former titles (until 19??): California Workers' Comp Advisor
(1046-2775); (until 1989): Medical Legal Reporter (1044-0291)
—CCC.

Published by: Genesis Publishing, 7600 York Rd., Towson, MD 21204-7508. TEL 619-453-0858. Ed. Donna Buys Hawkins.

WORKERS' COMP. ADVISOR (NEW YORK). see *INSURANCE*

WORKERS' COMP BOTTOM LINE. see *INSURANCE*

344.021   USA   ISSN 1074-0988
WORKERS' COMP EXECUTIVE. Text in English. 1991. 22/yr. USD 395 (effective 2002). **Document type:** *Journal, Academic/Scholarly.*
Related titles: Online - full text ed.
Published by: Providence Publications, LLC, PO Box 1100, Grass Valley, CA 95945-1100 . TEL 530-470-7500, FAX 530-470-7600, http://www.naic.com/. Pub. Douglas D Moore.

WORKERS' COMP MANAGED CARE. see *INSURANCE*

WORKER'S COMP QUARTERLY. see *INSURANCE*

WORKERS COMPENSATION; exposures, coverage, claims. see *INSURANCE*

WORKERS' COMPENSATION BOARD OF NOVA SCOTIA. ANNUAL REPORT. see *INSURANCE*

WORKERS' COMPENSATION INSURANCE; the survival guide for business. see *INSURANCE*

331.121   USA   ISSN 0748-7878
KF3613.36
WORKERS' COMPENSATION LAW BULLETIN. Text in English. 1978. bi-w. USD 147 (effective 2005). Index. back issues avail. **Document type:** *Newsletter, Trade.* **Description:** Covers court decisions on when and how compensation is awarded in workers' compensation cases, including stress-related injuries, equipment malfunctions, travel-related injuries, employee negligence, toxic exposure and more.
Formerly: Worker's Compensation
Related titles: Online - full text ed.: ISSN 1544-5844.
—CCC.
Published by: Quinlan Publishing Group, Marine Industrial Park, 23 Drydock Ave, 6th Fl, Boston, MA 02210-2387. TEL 617-542-0048, 800-229-2084, FAX 617-345-9646, info@quinlan.com, http://www.quinlan.com. Ed. Carol Johnson Perkins. Pub. Dennis Hofmaier.

WORKERS COMPENSATION LAW MANUAL N S W. see *INSURANCE*

331   USA
WORKERS' COMPENSATION LAW OF MARYLAND ANNOTATED. Text in English. base vol. plus a. updates. USD 40.
Published by: LexisNexis (Subsidiary of: LexisNexis North America), PO Box 7587, Charlottesville, VA 22906-7587. TEL 804-972-7566, 800-562-1197, FAX 800-643-1280, llp.customer.support@lexis-nexis.com, http://www.lexislawpublishing.com. Ed. George Harley.

WORKERS' COMPENSATION LAWS OF CALIFORNIA. see *LAW*

WORKERS' COMPENSATION MONITOR. see *INSURANCE*

331.21   AUS
WORKERS COMPENSATION N S W. Text in English. base vol. plus updates 6/yr. looseleaf. AUD 675 (effective 2000). adv.
Related titles: CD-ROM ed.; Online - full text ed.
Published by: LexisNexis Butterworths (Subsidiary of: LexisNexis Asia Pacific), Tower 2, 475-495 Victoria Ave, Chatswood, NSW 2067, Australia. TEL 61-2-94222189, FAX 61-2-94222406, http://www.lexisnexis.com.au/aus/default.asp. Ed. C P Mills. R&P Deanne Castellino. Adv. contact Mary Greenfield.

331.21   USA
WORKERS' COMPENSATION NEWS AND FOUR-FORTY REPORT. Text in English. q. USD 27.50 to non-members. **Document type:** *Newsletter.*
Published by: (Workers' Compensation Section), The Florida Bar, 651 E Jefferson St, Tallahassee, FL 32399-2300. TEL 850-561-5621. Circ: 1,430.

WORKERS' COMPENSATION OUTLOOK. see *INSURANCE*

331.21   AUS   ISSN 0816-2107
WORKERS COMPENSATION REPORT. Text in English. 1984. fortn. AUD 390 (effective 1999). **Document type:** *Newsletter.* **Description:** Provides information for people involved in the field of workers compensation. Analyzes judgments from tribunals in each state. Explains the implications of legal and government developments and changing requirements on employers and unions.
Published by: Newsletter Information Services, PO Box 2095, Manly, NSW 2095, Australia. TEL 61-2-9977-7500, FAX 61-2-9977-3310, customer.support@newsinfo.com.au, http://www.newsinfo.com.au. Ed. Sheena Frost.

331.0715   IND
WORKERS EDUCATION JOURNAL. Text in English. 1966. q. free. adv. bk.rev. illus. **Description:** Textual and pictorial booklets on trade unionism, industrial relations, labor economics and tools and techniques.
Indexed: CPE.
Published by: Central Board for Workers Education, 1400 West High Court, Gokulpeth, Nagpur, Maharashtra 440 010, India. Ed. K R Khamborkar. Circ: 2,000 (controlled).

331   GBR
WORKERS PRESS. Text in English. 1986. w. GBP 27.50; GBP 63.50 foreign. **Document type:** *Newspaper.*
Address: PO Box 735, London, SW8 1YB, United Kingdom. TEL 44-171-387-0564, FAX 44-171-387-0569, s0gp@exnet.co.uk. Ed. M Cooke.

331   USA
WORKERS SOLIDARITY; newsletter of the Workers Solidarity Alliance. Text in English. bi-m. looseleaf. **Description:** Analyzes worker struggles, both in the US and abroad. Also covers such issues as racism, civil rights, etc. from a working class perspective.
Published by: Workers Solidarity Alliance, 339 Lafayette St, No 202, New York, NY 10012. TEL 212-979-8353, wsany@hotmail.com, http://flag.blackened.net/agony/wsa.html. Circ: 500.

331.11   AUS   ISSN 0811-9023
WORKFORCE. Text in English. 1974. w. AUD 540 (effective 1999). adv. Supplement avail. **Document type:** *Newsletter.* **Description:** Provides coverage of all industrial relations issues: dispute outcomes, tribunal judgements, settlements, latest enterprise agreements, award changes, interpretations and predictions and industrial trends.
Related titles: Online - full text ed.: (from Northern Light Technology, Inc.).
Published by: Newsletter Information Services, PO Box 2095, Manly, NSW 2095, Australia. TEL 61-2-9977-7500, FAX 61-2-9977-3310, customer.support@newsinfo.com.au, http://www.newsinfo.com.au. Eds. Bernadette McBride, David Vincent.

WORKFORCE MANAGEMENT. see *BUSINESS AND ECONOMICS—Personnel Management*

331   USA   ISSN 1524-1033
WORKFORCE PROFESSIONAL. Text in English. 1997. 8/yr. USD 25 to non-members; free to members (effective 2004). charts; illus. **Document type:** *Magazine.* **Description:** Provides news, updates and policies of employment programs.
Formerly (until 1998): Workforce (Louisville) (1094-5385); Which was formed by the merger of (1941-1997): International Association of Personnel in Employment Security. News (0020-6008); (1992-1997): Workforce (1063-4363); Which was formerly (1985-1992): Perspective (0887-798X)
—CCC.
Published by: International Association of Personnel in Employment Security, 1801 Louisville Rd, Frankfort, KY 40601-3922. TEL 502-223-4459, FAX 502-223-4127, iapes@iapes.org, http://www.iapes.org. Ed. Wanda A. Watts. Circ: 16,400 (paid and controlled).

331   USA
WORKINDEX. Text in English. 1997. d. illus.
Media: Online - full content.
Published by: Human Resources Executive, 747 Dresher Rd, Horsham, PA 19044. http://www.workindex.com/. Ed. Michelle Liberatore.

331   SWE   ISSN 1650-9781
WORKING LIFE; research and development news. Text in English. 199?. 6/yr. **Document type:** *Newsletter, Academic/Scholarly.*
Formerly (until 1997): Arbetsmiljoeinstitutet. Research News (1102-6537)
Media: Online - full content.
Published by: Arbetslivsinstitutet/The National Institute for Working Life, Vanadisvaegen 9, Stockholm, SE 11391, Sweden. TEL 46-8-6196700, FAX 46-8-6563025, registrator@arbetslivsinstitutet.se, http://www.arbetslivsinstitutet.se/workinglife/04-3/. Ed. Ingemar Karlsson Gadea.

331   SWE   ISSN 1404-790X
WORKING LIFE RESEARCH IN EUROPE. REPORT. Text in English. 2000. irreg. price varies. back issues avail.
Document type: *Monographic series, Academic/Scholarly.*
Published by: (Sveriges Akademikers Centralorganisation (SACO), Tjaenstemaennens Centralorganisation, Landsorganisationen), Arbetslivsinstitutet, Joint Programme for Working Life Research in Europe (SALTSA)/The National Institute for Working Life, Vanadisvaegen 9, Stockholm, Sweden. TEL 46-8-6563025, FAX 46-8-6196700, http://www.arbetslivsinstitutet.se/publikationer/saltsa/saltsa.asp, http://www.arbetslivsinstitutet.se/saltsa

331   USA   ISSN 1089-7011
HD8051   CODEN: WOUSFP
➤ **WORKING U S A;** the journal of labor and society. Variant title: WorkingUSA. Text in English. 1997. bi-m. USD 45 combined subscription in the Americas to individuals & Caribbean, print & online eds.; EUR 50 combined subscription in Europe to individuals print & online eds.; GBP 33 combined subscription elsewhere to individuals print & online eds.; USD 233 combined subscription in the Americas to institutions & Caribbean, print & online eds.; GBP 144 combined subscription elsewhere to institutions print & online eds. (effective 2006). adv. bk.rev. reprint service avail. from PSC. **Document type:** *Journal, Academic/Scholarly.* **Description:** Reports on and analyzes all aspects of the US labor movement and related policy in a manner that supports the interests of working people.
Related titles: Online - full text ed.: ISSN 1743-4580. USD 221 in the Americas to institutions & Caribbean; GBP 137 elsewhere to institutions (effective 2006) (from Blackwell Synergy, EBSCO Publishing, Gale Group, H.W. Wilson, IngentaConnect, O C L C Online Computer Library Center, Inc., ProQuest Information & Learning, SoftLine Information, Swets Information Services).
Indexed: AltPI, CIJE, JEL, LeftInd, PAIS, SSI.
—CCC.
Published by: Blackwell Publishing, Inc. (Subsidiary of: Blackwell Publishing Ltd.), Commerce Place, 350 Main St, Malden, MA 02148. TEL 781-388-8206, FAX 781-388-8232, subscrip@blackwellpub.com, http://www.blackwellpublishing.com/journals/WUSA. Ed. Immanuel Ness. adv.: page USD 750; 10 x 7.

331   CAN   ISSN 0700-3102
WORKLIFE (KINGSTON). Text in English. 1981. bi-m. CND 35; CND 39 foreign. bk.rev. reprint service avail. from PQC. **Description:** Aims to promote awareness of research, issues and trends in labor relations, personnel, and other work-related areas.
Formerly: Worklife Report (0834-292X)
Related titles: Online - full text ed.: (from EBSCO Publishing, Gale Group, Micromedia ProQuest, Northern Light Technology, Inc., O C L C Online Computer Library Center, Inc., ProQuest Information & Learning).
Indexed: ABIn, CBCABus, CBCARef, PAIS.
—BLDSC (9351.222000), IE, ingenta. CCC.
Published by: I R Research Services, P O Box 1092, Kingston, ON K7L 4Y5, Canada. TEL 613-542-5596. Ed. L A Kelly. Circ: 1,500.

331   AUS   ISSN 1327-6468
WORKPLACE CHANGE. Text in English. 1992. m. AUD 245 (effective 1999). **Document type:** *Newsletter.* **Description:** Covers issues such as penalty rates, performance pay, productivity targets, demarcations, work teams, dispute resolution. Analyzes how selected organizations negotiated specific enterprise bargaining matters and discusses many aspects of change in the workplace.
Formerly (until 1996): Inside Enterprise Bargaining (1320-1506)
Published by: Newsletter Information Services, PO Box 2095, Manly, NSW 2095, Australia. TEL 61-2-9977-7500, FAX 61-2-9977-3310, customer.support@newsinfo.com.au, http://www.newsinfo.com.au. Ed. David Vincent.

331.21   CAN
WORKPLACE EQUITY GUIDE. Text in English. q. looseleaf. CND 550 (effective 2005). **Document type:** *Trade.* **Description:** Designed to ensure smooth implementation and maintenance of both pay and employment equity in the workplace. It supplies full and up to date text of all relevant law, regulations, forms, guidelines and case law from across Canada.
Formerly (until June 2001): Ontario Pay & Employment Equity Guide
Related titles: CD-ROM ed.: CND 550 (effective 2005); Online - full text ed.: CND 550 (effective 2005).
Indexed: CBCABus.
Published by: C C H Canadian Ltd., 90 Sheppard Ave E, Ste 300, North York, ON M2N 6X1, Canada. TEL 416-224-2248, 800-268-4522, FAX 416-224-2243, cservice@cch.ca, http://www.cch.ca.

331.89   CAN   ISSN 1480-6886
HD8101
WORKPLACE GAZETTE. Text in English. 1998. q. CND 140 (effective 2004). back issues avail. **Document type:** *Government.*
Formed by the merger of (1965-1998): Collective Bargaining Review (0010-0803); (1996-1998): Revue de la Negociation Collective (0705-5072); (1984-1998): Major Wage Settlements (0848-6433); Which was formerly (1976-1984): Labour Data (0228-1678)
Related titles: French ed.: Gazette du Travail (Hull). ISSN 1480-6894.
Indexed: CPerI, CSI.
—CISTI.
Published by: Human Resources and Skills Development Canada, Workplace Information Directorate Labour Program, Ottawa, ON K1A 0J2, Canada. TEL 819-997-3117, 800-567-6866, FAX 819-953-9582, http://labour.hrdc-drhc.gc.ca, http://www.hrsdc.gc.ca.

344.01 ZAF
WORKPLACE LAW. Text in English. irreg., latest 2000, 6th ed. ZAR 192.50 (effective 2001). **Document type:** *Academic/Scholarly.* **Description:** Deal with every legal issue likely to arise on the shop floor or in the court room.
Published by: Juta & Company Ltd., Law and Professional Publishing Division, PO Box 14373, Kenwyn, 7790, South Africa. TEL 27-21-7975101, FAX 27-21-7970121, cserv@juta.co.za, http://www.juta.co.za.

331 GBR ISSN 1740-6307
WORKPLACE REPORT. Text in English. 1979. 11/yr. GBP 49 (effective 2003). back issues avail. **Document type:** *Journal, Academic/Scholarly.* **Description:** Covers the latest developments on pay and conditions, best practice, news on pay deals and employment law.
Formerly (until Feb. 2003): Bargaining Report (0143-2680); Which incorporated (1981-1983): L R D Book of Wage Rates, Hours and Holidays (0262-3447)
Related titles: Online - full text ed.
Indexed: CISA, CSNB.
—BLDSC (9351.298370).
Published by: (Labour Research Department), L R D Publications Ltd., 78 Blackfriars Rd, London, SE1 8HF, United Kingdom. TEL 44-20-79283649, FAX 44-20-79280621, info@lrd.org.uk, http://www.lrd.org.uk/coll.php3?pagid=44. Ed. S Peck. Circ: 2,500.

331 USA ISSN 1529-9465
HF5549.5.C67
WORKSPAN. Text in English. m. USD 195 domestic membership; CND 260 in Canada membership; USD 235 elsewhere membership (effective 2003). **Document type:** *Trade.*
Related titles: Online - full text ed.: (from ProQuest Information & Learning).
Indexed: ABIn, ATI.
Published by: WorldatWork, 14040 N Northsight Blvd, Scottsdale, AZ 85260. TEL 480-951-9191, 877-951-9191, FAX 480-483-8352, 866-816-2962, customerrelations@worldatwork.org, http://www.worldatwork.org/.

WORLD COST OF LIVING SURVEY. see *BUSINESS AND ECONOMICS*

331.125 CHE ISSN 1020-3079
HD5701
WORLD EMPLOYMENT (YEAR). Text in English. 1995. a. CHF 25. **Document type:** *Bulletin.* **Description:** Provides a comprehensive review of the worldwide employment crisis.
Published by: (International Labour Office), I L O Publications, PO Box 6, Geneva 22, 1211, Switzerland. TEL 022-799-6111, FAX 022-798-6358.

331 CHE ISSN 0255-5514
HD4802
WORLD LABOUR REPORT. Text in English. 1984. irreg., latest vol.8, 1995. price varies. **Document type:** *Monographic series.* **Description:** A round-up of developments, trends and major indicators in areas of interest to the ILO.
Related titles: Microfiche ed.: (from CIS); Spanish ed.: Trabajo en el Mundo. ISSN 0255-5522; French ed.: Travail dans le Monde. ISSN 0255-5506.
Indexed: IIS.
—BLDSC (9356.120000), ingenta. **CCC.**
Published by: (International Labour Office), I L O Publications, PO Box 6, Geneva 22, 1211, Switzerland. TEL 41-22-799-6111, FAX 41-22-798-6358. **Dist. in US by:** I L O Publications Center, 9 Jay Gould Court, Ste. CT, PO Box 753, Waldorf, MD 20604. TEL 301-638-3152, FAX 301-843-0159, ilopubs@tasco1.com.

WORLDATWORK JOURNAL. see *BUSINESS AND ECONOMICS—Personnel Management*

WRONGFUL DISMISSAL LAW. see *LAW*

WRONGFUL DISMISSAL PRACTICE MANUAL. see *LAW*

331 DEU
WUESTENROT - JOURNAL; Zeitschrift fuer Mitarbeiter der Wuestenrot-Gruppe. Text in German. 1973. q. membership. **Document type:** *Corporate.*
Published by: Wuestenrot Holding GmbH, Hohenzollernstr 46, Ludwigsburg, 71630, Germany. FAX 49-7141-163867. Ed. Katja Baecker Wittke. Circ: 10,000.

WYNAGRODZENIA. see *LAW*

WYOMING EMPLOYMENT LAW LETTER. see *LAW*

331.125 USA
WYOMING. EMPLOYMENT SECURITY COMMISSION. ANNUAL REPORT. Text in English. 1973. a. **Document type:** *Government.*
Published by: Employment Security Commission, PO Box 2760, Casper, WY 82602. TEL 307-335-3200. Ed. Philip J McAulay. Circ: 150.

331 USA ISSN 0512-4409
WYOMING LABOR FORCE TRENDS. Text in English. 1963. m. free. **Document type:** *Government.* **Description:** Features articles on issues relating to Wyoming's labor force including wages, occupational and industrial projections, unemployment insurance, non-agricultural employment, and civilian labor force and employment statistics.
Formerly: Wyoming. Employment Security Commission. Research and Analysis Section. Labor Force Trends
Related titles: Microfiche ed.: (from CIS); Online - full text ed.
Indexed: SRI.
Published by: Wyoming Department of Employment, Research & Planning Division, PO Box 2760, Casper, WY 82602. TEL 307-473-3808, FAX 307-473-3834, kshink@state.wy.us, http://lmi.state.wy.us/. Ed. Krista C Shinkle. R&P Tom Gallagher TEL 307-473-3801. Circ: 1,200.

331.21 GBR
YORKSHIRE AND NORTH EAST SALARY SURVEY. Text in English. 2/yr. GBP 280 per edition (effective 2001). **Document type:** *Bulletin.* **Description:** Pay and benefit salary survey for Yorkshire and the North East.
Published by: The Reward Group Ltd., Reward House, Diamond Way, Stone Business Park, Stone, Staffs ST15 0SD, United Kingdom. TEL 44-1785-813566, FAX 44-1785-817007, enquiries@reward-group.co.uk, http://www.reward-group.co.uk.

344.01 DEU ISSN 0342-328X
K30
Z F A. (Zeitschrift fuer Arbeitsrecht) Text in German. q. EUR 92; EUR 28.50 newsstand/cover (effective 2004). adv. reprint service avail. from SCH. **Document type:** *Journal, Academic/Scholarly.*
Indexed: ELLIS, IBR, IBZ.
—IE, Infotrieve.
Published by: Carl Heymanns Verlag KG, Luxemburger Str 449, Cologne, 50939, Germany. TEL 49-221-943730, FAX 49-221-94373901, marketing@heymanns.com, http://www.heymanns.com. Ed. E G Mager. adv.: B&W page EUR 721. Circ: 1,100 (paid and controlled).

331 ZMB ISSN 0084-4632
ZAMBIA. DEPARTMENT OF LABOUR. REPORT. Text in English. a. ZMK 200. **Document type:** *Government.* **Description:** Paper covering all aspects of labor matters.
Published by: (Zambia. Department of Labour), Government Printing Department, PO Box 30136, Lusaka, Zambia.

331.1 SVN
ZAPOSLENI PO OBCINAH. Text in Slovenian. irreg. SIT 20.
Published by: Zavod SR Slovenije za Statistiko, Vozarski pot 12, Ljubljana, Slovenia. Ed. Mlinar Branko.

ZEITSCHRIFT: BEHINDERTE IM BERUF. see *SOCIAL SERVICES AND WELFARE*

ZEITSCHRIFT FUER ARBEITSRECHT UND SOZIALRECHT. see *LAW*

331 DEU ISSN 0340-2444
HD4809
ZEITSCHRIFT FUER ARBEITSWISSENSCHAFT; Zentralblatt fuer Arbeitswissenschaft und soziale Betriebspraxis. Text in German. 1946. q. EUR 70; EUR 37 to students (effective 2005). adv. bk.rev. charts; illus. index. reprints avail. **Document type:** *Journal, Trade.*
Formerly (until 1975): Arbeit und Leistung (0003-763X)
Indexed: AEA, CISA, DIP, ErgAb, ExcerpMed, GJP, IBR, IBZ, KES, PAIS, RASB, RILM.
—BLDSC (9452.040000), IE, Infotrieve, ingenta. **CCC.**
Published by: (Gesellschaft fuer Arbeitswissenschaft e.V.), Ergonomia Verlag OHG, Bruno-Jacoby-Weg 11, Stuttgart, 70579, Germany. TEL 49-711-7280473, FAX 49-711-7280492, zfa-redaktion@arbeitswissenschaft.de, info@ergonomia.de, http://www.zfa-online.de, http://www.ergonomia.de. Ed. Kurt Landau. Adv. contact Regina Brauchler. B&W page EUR 1,200; trim 180 x 260. Circ: 899 (paid and controlled).

ZEITSCHRIFT FUER AUSLAENDISCHES UND INTERNATIONALES ARBEITS- UND SOZIALRECHT. see *LAW*

330 DEU ISSN 1439-2127
ZEITSCHRIFT FUER KONFLIKT-MANAGEMENT. Text in German. 1998. bi-m. EUR 19.80 newsstand/cover (effective 2005). adv. **Document type:** *Journal, Trade.*
Formerly (until 2000): Kon:sens (1434-8160)
Published by: Verlag Dr. Otto Schmidt KG, Gustav-Heinemann-Ufer 58, Cologne, 50968, Germany. TEL 49-221-93738460, FAX 49-221-93738943, info@otto-schmidt.de, http://www.otto-schmidt.de. adv.: B&W page EUR 720, color page EUR 1,260. Circ: 1,500 (paid and controlled).

331 CHN ISSN 1000-6230
ZHONGGUO LAODONG KEXUE/LABOR SCIENCE OF CHINA. Text in Chinese. 1986. m. CNY 14.40. back issues avail.
Published by: (Laodong Renshibu, Laodong Kexue Yanjiusuo), Laodong Renshi Chubanshe, 12 Hepingli Zhongjie, Beijing, 100013, China. TEL 4214015. Ed. Sun Zhen. **Co-sponsor:** Zhongguo Laodong Xuehui.

331.4 USA
9 TO 5 NATIONAL ASSOCIATION OF WORKING WOMEN. Text in English. 1973. 5/yr. USD 25 to individuals; USD 40 to institutions. bk.rev. back issues avail. **Document type:** *Newsletter.*
Former titles: Milwaukee 9 to 5; 9 to 5 Newsletter
Address: 152 W. Wisconsin Ave., Ste. 408, Milwaukee, WI 53203-2508. Circ: 13,000.

BUSINESS AND ECONOMICS— Macroeconomics

339 USA ISSN 1534-6013
HB172.5
ADVANCES IN MACROECONOMICS. Text in English. 2001. irreg. Included with subscription to The B E Journals in Macroeconomics.. **Document type:** *Journal, Academic/Scholarly.*
Media: Online - full content. **Related titles:** Online - full text ed.: (from O C L C Online Computer Library Center, Inc., ProQuest Information & Learning); ♦ Series of: The B E Journals in Macroeconomics. ISSN 1555-0486.
Indexed: ABIn, IBSS, JEL.
Published by: Berkeley Electronic Press, 2809 Telegraph Ave., Ste 202, Berkeley, CA 94705. FAX 510-665-1201, info@bepress.com, http://www.bepress.com/bejm/advances/. Eds. Charles I Jones, David Romer, Per Kursell, Robert Shimer.

ADVERTISING EXPENDITURE FORECASTS. see *ADVERTISING AND PUBLIC RELATIONS*

339 330.9 SWE ISSN 0345-0236
AKTUELL EKONOMI. Text in Swedish. 1973. 10/yr. **Document type:** *Newsletter.*
Published by: Svenska Handelsbanken, Markets Research, Kungstraedgaardsgatan 2, Stockholm, 10670, Sweden. http://www.handelsbanken.se. Ed. Christofer Halldin.

337 USA ISSN 1096-424X
► **ANNUAL EDITIONS: MACROECONOMICS.** Text in English. 1975. a., latest 2001, 14th ed. USD 20.31 per vol. (effective 2004). illus. **Document type:** *Academic/Scholarly.*
Published by: McGraw-Hill - Dushkin (Subsidiary of: McGraw-Hill Higher Education), 2460 Kerper Blvd, Dubuque, IA 52001. TEL 800-243-6532, customer.service@mcgraw-hill.com, http://www.dushkin.com/text-data/catalog/0072479922.mhtml. Ed. Don Cole. Pub. Ian Nielsen. R&P Cheryl Greenleaf.

► **AUSTRALIA. BUREAU OF STATISTICS. A GUIDE TO THE CONSUMER INDEX.** see *BUSINESS AND ECONOMICS—Abstracting, Bibliographies, Statistics*

► **AUSTRALIA. BUREAU OF STATISTICS. A GUIDE TO THE CONSUMER PRICE INDEX.** see *BUSINESS AND ECONOMICS—Abstracting, Bibliographies, Statistics*

► **AUSTRALIA. BUREAU OF STATISTICS. A PROVISIONAL FRAMEWORK FOR HOUSEHOLD INCOME, CONSUMPTION, SAVING AND WEALTH.** see *BUSINESS AND ECONOMICS—Abstracting, Bibliographies, Statistics*

► **AUSTRALIA. BUREAU OF STATISTICS. APPARENT CONSUMPTION OF FOODSTUFFS, AUSTRALIA.** see *BUSINESS AND ECONOMICS—Abstracting, Bibliographies, Statistics*

► **AUSTRALIA. BUREAU OF STATISTICS. AUSPEND.** see *BUSINESS AND ECONOMICS—Abstracting, Bibliographies, Statistics*

► **AUSTRALIA. BUREAU OF STATISTICS. AUSTRALIAN SYSTEM OF NATIONAL ACCOUNTS: CONCEPTS, SOURCES AND METHODS.** see *BUSINESS AND ECONOMICS—Abstracting, Bibliographies, Statistics*

► **AUSTRALIA. BUREAU OF STATISTICS. BALANCE OF PAYMENTS, AUSTRALIA - QUARTERLY FORWARD SEASONAL FACTORS SERVICE.** see *BUSINESS AND ECONOMICS—Abstracting, Bibliographies, Statistics*

► **AUSTRALIA. BUREAU OF STATISTICS. BALANCE OF PAYMENTS, AUSTRALIA - REGIONAL SERIES.** see *BUSINESS AND ECONOMICS—Abstracting, Bibliographies, Statistics*

► **AUSTRALIA. BUREAU OF STATISTICS. CONSUMER PRICE INDEX: CONCORDANCE WITH HOUSEHOLD EXPENDITURE CLASSIFICATION, AUSTRALIA.** see *BUSINESS AND ECONOMICS—Abstracting, Bibliographies, Statistics*

► **AUSTRALIA. BUREAU OF STATISTICS. CONSUMER PRICE INDEX STANDARD DATA REPORT: CAPITAL CITIES INDEX NUMBERS BY EXPENDITURE CLASS.** see *BUSINESS AND ECONOMICS—Abstracting, Bibliographies, Statistics*

➤ AUSTRALIA. BUREAU OF STATISTICS. GOVERNMENT BENEFITS, TAXES AND HOUSEHOLD INCOME, AUSTRALIA. see *BUSINESS AND ECONOMICS—Abstracting, Bibliographies, Statistics*

➤ AUSTRALIA. BUREAU OF STATISTICS. HOUSEHOLD EXPENDITURE SURVEY, AUSTRALIA: CONFIDENTIALISED UNIT RECORD FILE ON CD-ROM. see *BUSINESS AND ECONOMICS—Abstracting, Bibliographies, Statistics*

➤ AUSTRALIA. BUREAU OF STATISTICS. HOUSEHOLD EXPENDITURE SURVEY, AUSTRALIA: CONFIDENTIALISED UNIT RECORD FILE ON FLOPPY DISK. see *BUSINESS AND ECONOMICS—Abstracting, Bibliographies, Statistics*

➤ AUSTRALIA. BUREAU OF STATISTICS. HOUSEHOLD EXPENDITURE SURVEY, AUSTRALIA: DETAILED EXPENDITURE ITEMS. see *BUSINESS AND ECONOMICS—Abstracting, Bibliographies, Statistics*

➤ AUSTRALIA. BUREAU OF STATISTICS. HOUSEHOLD EXPENDITURE SURVEY, AUSTRALIA: HOUSEHOLD CHARACTERISTICS. see *BUSINESS AND ECONOMICS—Abstracting, Bibliographies, Statistics*

➤ AUSTRALIA. BUREAU OF STATISTICS. HOUSEHOLD EXPENDITURE SURVEY, AUSTRALIA: SUMMARY OF RESULTS. see *BUSINESS AND ECONOMICS—Abstracting, Bibliographies, Statistics*

➤ AUSTRALIA. BUREAU OF STATISTICS. HOUSEHOLD EXPENDITURE SURVEY, AUSTRALIA: USER GUIDE. see *BUSINESS AND ECONOMICS—Abstracting, Bibliographies, Statistics*

➤ AUSTRALIA. BUREAU OF STATISTICS. INCOME AND HOUSING COSTS SURVEY, AUSTRALIA: CONFIDENTIALISED UNIT RECORD FILE ON CD-ROM. see *BUSINESS AND ECONOMICS—Abstracting, Bibliographies, Statistics*

➤ AUSTRALIA. BUREAU OF STATISTICS. INFORMATION PAPER: AUSTRALIAN CONSUMER PRICE INDEX 13TH SERIES REVIEW. see *BUSINESS AND ECONOMICS—Abstracting, Bibliographies, Statistics*

➤ AUSTRALIA. BUREAU OF STATISTICS. INFORMATION PAPER: AUSTRALIAN NATIONAL ACCOUNTS, INTRODUCTION OF CHAIN VOLUME AND PRICE INDEXES. see *BUSINESS AND ECONOMICS—Abstracting, Bibliographies, Statistics*

➤ AUSTRALIA. BUREAU OF STATISTICS. INFORMATION PAPER: AUSTRALIAN NATIONAL ACCOUNTS: INTRODUCTION TO INPUT - OUTPUT MULTIPLIERS. see *BUSINESS AND ECONOMICS—Abstracting, Bibliographies, Statistics*

➤ AUSTRALIA. BUREAU OF STATISTICS. INFORMATION PAPER: IMPACT OF REVISED INTERNATIONAL STANDARDS ON THE AUSTRALIAN NATIONAL ACCOUNTS. see *BUSINESS AND ECONOMICS—Abstracting, Bibliographies, Statistics*

➤ AUSTRALIA. BUREAU OF STATISTICS. INFORMATION PAPER: IMPLEMENTATION OF REVISED INTERNATIONAL STANDARDS IN THE AUSTRALIAN NATIONAL ACCOUNTS. see *BUSINESS AND ECONOMICS—Abstracting, Bibliographies, Statistics*

➤ AUSTRALIA. BUREAU OF STATISTICS. INFORMATION PAPER: INTRODUCTION OF THE 13TH SERIES AUSTRALIAN CONSUMER PRICE INDEX. see *BUSINESS AND ECONOMICS—Abstracting, Bibliographies, Statistics*

➤ AUSTRALIA. BUREAU OF STATISTICS. INFORMATION PAPER: ISSUES TO BE CONSIDERED DURING THE 13TH SERIES AUSTRALIAN CONSUMER PRICE INDEX REVIEW. see *BUSINESS AND ECONOMICS—Abstracting, Bibliographies, Statistics*

➤ AUSTRALIA. BUREAU OF STATISTICS. INFORMATION PAPER: OUTCOME OF THE 13TH SERIES AUSTRALIAN CONSUMER PRICE INDEX REVIEW. see *BUSINESS AND ECONOMICS—Abstracting, Bibliographies, Statistics*

➤ AUSTRALIA. BUREAU OF STATISTICS. INFORMATION PAPER: PRICE INDEXES AND THE NEW TAX SYSTEM. see *BUSINESS AND ECONOMICS—Abstracting, Bibliographies, Statistics*

➤ AUSTRALIA. BUREAU OF STATISTICS. INFORMATION PAPER: PRODUCER PRICE INDEX DEVELOPMENTS. see *BUSINESS AND ECONOMICS—Abstracting, Bibliographies, Statistics*

➤ AUSTRALIA. BUREAU OF STATISTICS. INFORMATION PAPER: QUALITY OF AUSTRALIAN BALANCE OF PAYMENTS STATISTICS. see *BUSINESS AND ECONOMICS—Abstracting, Bibliographies, Statistics*

➤ AUSTRALIA. BUREAU OF STATISTICS. INFORMATION PAPER: REVIEW OF THE IMPORT PRICE INDEX AND EXPORT PRICE INDEX, AUSTRALIA. see *BUSINESS AND ECONOMICS—Abstracting, Bibliographies, Statistics*

➤ AUSTRALIA. BUREAU OF STATISTICS. INFORMATION PAPER: UPGRADED AUSTRALIAN NATIONAL ACCOUNTS. see *BUSINESS AND ECONOMICS—Abstracting, Bibliographies, Statistics*

➤ AUSTRALIA. BUREAU OF STATISTICS. INFORMATION PAPER: UPGRADED AUSTRALIAN NATIONAL ACCOUNTS: FINANCIAL ACCOUNTS. see *BUSINESS AND ECONOMICS—Abstracting, Bibliographies, Statistics*

➤ AUSTRALIA. BUREAU OF STATISTICS. INTERNATIONAL TRADE PRICE INDEXES, AUSTRALIA. see *BUSINESS AND ECONOMICS—Abstracting, Bibliographies, Statistics*

➤ AUSTRALIA. BUREAU OF STATISTICS. N I F - 10S MODEL DATA BASE MANUAL. (National Income Forecasting) see *BUSINESS AND ECONOMICS—Abstracting, Bibliographies, Statistics*

➤ AUSTRALIA. BUREAU OF STATISTICS. PRODUCER PRICE INDEXES, AUSTRALIA. see *BUSINESS AND ECONOMICS—Abstracting, Bibliographies, Statistics*

➤ AUSTRALIA. BUREAU OF STATISTICS. SURVEY OF INCOME AND HOUSING COSTS, AUSTRALIA: USER GUIDE. see *BUSINESS AND ECONOMICS—Abstracting, Bibliographies, Statistics*

339   USA   ISSN 1555-0486
THE B E JOURNALS IN MACROECONOMICS. Text in English. 2007. a. USD 35 to individuals; USD 500 to institutions (effective 2006); Subscription includes the four titles in series: Advances in Macroeconomics, Contributions to Macroeconomics, Frontiers of Macroeconomics and Topics in Macroeconomics.. **Document type:** *Journal, Academic/Scholarly.* **Description:** Publishes articles on significant research and scholarship in both theoretical and applied macroeconomics.
Media: Online - full content. **Related titles:** ◆ Series: Frontiers of Macroeconomics. ISSN 1534-6021; ◆ Advances in Macroeconomics. ISSN 1534-6013; ◆ Contributions to Macroeconomics. ISSN 1534-6005; ◆ Topics in Macroeconomics. ISSN 1534-5998.
Published by: Berkeley Electronic Press, 2809 Telegraph Ave., Ste 202, Berkeley, CA 94705. FAX 510-665-1201, info@bepress.com, http://www.bepress.com/bejm/. Eds. Charles I Jones, David Romer, Per Kursell, Robert Shimer.

B E R L FORECASTS. see *BUSINESS AND ECONOMICS—Economic Situation And Conditions*

339   URY
BANCO CENTRAL DEL URUGUAY. DEPARTAMENTO DE ESTADISTICAS ECONOMICAS. PRODUCTO E INGRESO NACIONALES. Text in Spanish. irreg. charts.
Formerly: Banco Central del Uruguay. Division Asesoria Economica y Estudios. Producto e Ingreso Nacionales. Actualizacion de las Principales Variables
Published by: Banco Central del Uruguay, Departamento de Estadisticas Economicas, Casilla 1467, Paysando y Florida, Montevideo, Uruguay. FAX 598-2-921782.

BULGARIAN ECONOMIC REVIEW (ONLINE EDITION). see *BUSINESS AND ECONOMICS—Banking And Finance*

CHINA MONTHLY STATISTICS. see *BUSINESS AND ECONOMICS—Abstracting, Bibliographies, Statistics*

339   COL
COLOMBIAN ECONOMY. Text in English. 1978. m. USD 75 (effective 2001). adv. charts. **Document type:** *Trade.*
Published by: Camara de Comercio Colombo-Americana, Calle 98 No. 22-64 Ofic. 1209, Apartado Aereo 8008, Bogota, CUND, Colombia. TEL 57-1-6237088, FAX 57-1-6216838, publicaciones@amchamcolombia.com.co, http://www.amchamcolombia.com.co. Ed. Alexandra Obolensky. Circ: 1,000.

CONSUMER POLICY REVIEW. see *CONSUMER EDUCATION AND PROTECTION*

339   IRN
CONSUMER PRICE INDEX IN URBAN AREAS OF IRAN. Text in Persian, Modern. m.
Published by: (Iran. Economic Statistics Department), Bank Markazi Jomhouri Islami Iran/Central Bank of the Islamic Republic of Iran, P O Box 11365-8531, Tehran, Iran. FAX 98-21-390323.

339.47   GBR   ISSN 1025-3866
CONSUMPTION, MARKETS & CULTURE. Text in English. 1997. q. GBP 206, USD 255 combined subscription to institutions print & online eds. (effective 2006). reprint service avail. from PSC. **Document type:** *Journal, Academic/Scholarly.*
Description: Focuses on consumerism and the markets as the site of social behaviour and discourse.

Related titles: Online - full text ed.: ISSN 1477-223X. 2002. GBP 196, USD 242 to institutions (effective 2006) (from EBSCO Publishing, Gale Group, IngentaConnect, O C L C Online Computer Library Center, Inc., Swets Information Services).
Indexed: IBSS.
—BLDSC (3424.764500), IE, Infotrieve, ingenta. **CCC.**
Published by: Routledge (Subsidiary of: Taylor & Francis Group), 4 Park Sq, Milton Park, Abingdon, Oxon OX14 4RN, United Kingdom. TEL 44-1235-828600, FAX 44-1235-829000, http://www.tandf.co.uk/journals/titles/10253866.asp, http://www.routledge.co.uk. Eds. A Fuat Firat, Alladi Venkatesh.
Subscr. to: Taylor & Francis Ltd, Journals Customer Service, Rankine Rd, Basingstoke, Hants RG24 8PR, United Kingdom. TEL 44-1256-813000, FAX 44-1256-330245, enquiry@tandf.co.uk.

339.021   PRT   ISSN 0872-1602
HC394.5.I5
CONTAS NACIONAIS TRIMESTRAIS. Text in Portuguese. 1992. q. EUR 12 (effective 2005).
Published by: Instituto Nacional de Estatistica, Ave. Antonio Jose de Almeida 2, Lisbon, 1000-043, Portugal. TEL 351-21-8426100, FAX 351-21-8426380, ine@ine.pt, http://www.ine.pt/.

CONTI DEGLI ITALIANI. see *BUSINESS AND ECONOMICS—Abstracting, Bibliographies, Statistics*

339   USA   ISSN 1534-6005
HB172.5
CONTRIBUTIONS TO MACROECONOMICS. Text in English. 1999. irreg. Included with subscription to The B E Journals in Macroeconomics.. **Document type:** *Journal, Academic/Scholarly.*
Media: Online - full content. **Related titles:** Online - full text ed.: (from O C L C Online Computer Library Center, Inc., ProQuest Information & Learning); ◆ Series of: The B E Journals in Macroeconomics. ISSN 1555-0486.
Indexed: ABIn, IBSS, JEL.
Published by: Berkeley Electronic Press, 2809 Telegraph Ave., Ste 202, Berkeley, CA 94705. FAX 510-665-1201, info@bepress.com, http://www.bepress.com/bejm/contributions/. Eds. Charles I Jones, David Romer, Per Kursell, Robert Shimer.

CROATIAN INTERNATIONAL RELATIONS REVIEW. see *POLITICAL SCIENCE—International Relations*

330.9   CUB   ISSN 0864-1420
HC152.5.A1
CUBA: ECONOMIA PLANIFICADA. Text in Spanish. 1986. q. USD 14 in North America; USD 16 in Europe; USD 18 elsewhere. charts; illus.; stat.
Published by: Junta Central de Planificacion (JUCEPLAN), 11 y C, Vedado, La Habana, Cuba. TEL 809 79-8661, TELEX 1158 Y 1170. Ed. Fernando Jimenez Gomez. Circ: 2,000. **Dist. by:** Ediciones Cubanas, Obispo No. 527, Apdo. 605, Havana, Cuba.

339   GBR   ISSN 0964-8518
CURRENT ECONOMICS. Text in English. m. GBP 195, USD 320 (effective 2003). 28 p./no.; back issues avail. **Document type:** *Journal, Academic/Scholarly.* **Description:** Reviews the research produced by international economists from the world's leading firms. Covers the economic outlook for a selection of countries, analysis of topical issues and, periodically, the outlook for exchange rates and interest rates.
—BLDSC (3496.456000), IE, ingenta.
Published by: Consensus Economics Inc., 53 Upper Brook St, London, W1K 2LT, United Kingdom. TEL 44-20-7491-3211, FAX 44-20-7409-2331, editors@consensuseconomics.com, http://www.consensuseconomics.com. Ed. Che-wing Pang. Pub. Philip M Hubbard.

D R I - MCGRAW-HILL COUNTRY REPORTS. see *BUSINESS AND ECONOMICS—Economic Situation And Conditions*

D R I - MCGRAW-HILL GLOBAL RISK REPORT. see *BUSINESS AND ECONOMICS—Economic Situation And Conditions*

D R I - MCGRAW-HILL REVIEW OF THE U S ECONOMY. see *BUSINESS AND ECONOMICS—Economic Situation And Conditions*

D R I - MCGRAW-HILL REVIEW OF THE U S ECONOMY: LONG RANGE FOCUS. see *BUSINESS AND ECONOMICS—Economic Situation And Conditions*

D R I - MCGRAW-HILL U S FORECAST SUMMARY. see *BUSINESS AND ECONOMICS—Economic Situation And Conditions*

ECONOMIA EM REVISTA. see *BUSINESS AND ECONOMICS—Economic Situation And Conditions*

339   ESP   ISSN 1137-4772
ECONOMIA EXTERIOR. Text in Spanish. 1997. q. EUR 40.50 domestic; EUR 69 foreign (effective 2002).
Indexed: PAIS.

Published by: Estudios de Politica Exterior S.A., Padilla 6, Madrid, 28006, Spain. TEL 34-91-4312711, FAX 34-91-5777252, revista@politicaexterior.com, http://www.politicaexterior.com.

ECONOMIC INDICATORS. see *BUSINESS AND ECONOMICS—Abstracting, Bibliographies, Statistics*

339 TUR ISSN 1300-9265
ECONOMIC INDICATORS OF TURKEY. Text in English. a. free. stat. **Document type:** *Bulletin.*
Related titles: Turkish ed.
Published by: (Economic Research and Planning Department), Turkiye Is Bankasi, Istiklal Caddesi 300, Beyoglu-Istanbul, Turkey. FAX 90-212-249-8298. Ed., R&P Kamil Sandikcioglu TEL 90-212-2927764. Circ: 2,000.

339 SWE
ECONOMIC OUTLOOK. Text in English. 1976. 4/yr. USD 65 (effective 2000). **Document type:** *Newsletter, Trade.*
Formerly: Outlook on the Swedish Economy (0349-5671)
Published by: Merita Nordbanken, Ekonomiska Sekretariatet, Stockholm, 10571, Sweden. Ed. Thomas Pousette. Pub. Nils Lundgren.

339 SWE
EKONOMISKA UTSIKTER. Text in Swedish. 1981. 4/yr. SEK 500 (effective 2000). **Document type:** *Newsletter, Trade.*
Formerly: Ekonomisk Information (0349-7860)
Published by: Merita Nordbanken, Ekonomiska Sekretariatet, Stockholm, 10571, Sweden. Ed. Olle Djerf. Pub. Nils Lundgren.

339 URY ISSN 0797-6291
ENCUESTA DE HOGARES: OCUPACION Y DESOCUPACION. Text in Spanish. 1968. s-a. stat.
Published by: Direccion General de Estadistica y Censos, Montevideo, Uruguay.

ESTADISTICA PANAMENA. SITUACION ECONOMICA. SECCION 342. CUENTAS NACIONALES. see *BUSINESS AND ECONOMICS—Abstracting, Bibliographies, Statistics*

ESTADISTICAS MACROECONOMICAS DE CENTROAMERICA. see *BUSINESS AND ECONOMICS—Abstracting, Bibliographies, Statistics*

339 SWE ISSN 0280-3364
HC371
FAKTA OM SVERIGES EKONOMI. Text in Swedish. 1978. a.
Incorporates (1949-1981): Det Ekonomiska Laeget (0013-3175)
Related titles: Online - full text ed.
Published by: Svenskt Naeringsliv/Confederation of Swedish Enterprise, Storgatan 19, Stockholm, 11482, Sweden. TEL 46-8-55343000, FAX 46-8-55343099, info@svensktnaringsliv.se, http://www.svensktnaringsliv.se/.

339 HRV ISSN 1332-3970
➤ **FINANCIJSKA TEORIJA I PRAKSA.** Text in Croatian; Summaries in English. 1977. 4/yr. HRK 400 domestic; USD 80 foreign (effective 2001). 100 p./no.; back issues avail. **Document type:** *Journal, Academic/Scholarly.* **Description:** Covers theory and practice of public finance, macro and micro finance, fiscal and monetary policy, local finance.
Formerly (until 2000): Financijska Praksa (0350-5669)
Indexed: JEL, RefZh.
—BLDSC (3927.240000).
Published by: Institut za Javne Financije/Institute of Public Finance, Katanciceva 5, Zagreb, 10000, Croatia. TEL 385-1-4819363, FAX 385-1-4819365, office@ijf.hr, http://www.ijf.hr/finproiksa. Ed. Katarina Ott. Circ: 800.

339 USA ISSN 1534-6021
HB172.5
FRONTIERS OF MACROECONOMICS. Text in English. 2001. irreg. Included with subscription to The B E Journals in Macroeconomics.. **Document type:** *Journal, Academic/Scholarly.* **Description:** Publishes research and scholarship in both theoretical and applied macroeconomics.
Media: Online - full content. **Related titles:** Online - full text ed.: (from O C L C Online Computer Library Center, Inc., ProQuest Information & Learning); ◆ Series of: The B E Journals in Macroeconomics. ISSN 1555-0486.
Indexed: ABIn, IBSS.
Published by: Berkeley Electronic Press, 2809 Telegraph Ave., Ste 202, Berkeley, CA 94705. FAX 510-665-1201, info@bepress.com, http://www.bepress.com/bejm/frontiers/. Eds. Charles I Jones, David Romer, Per Kursell, Robert Shimer.

339 GMB
GAMBIA. CENTRAL STATISTICS DEPARTMENT. MONTHLY BULLETIN OF PRICES. Text in English. m. GMD 12.
Published by: Central Statistics Department, Wellington St., Banjul, Gambia.

339 USA ISSN 1553-5304
HF1351
➤ **GLOBAL ECONOMY JOURNAL.** Text in English. 2000. q. free to members; USD 35 to individuals; USD 200 to institutions (effective 2006). adv. bk.rev. back issues avail.; reprints avail. **Document type:** *Journal, Academic/Scholarly.* **Description:** Provides an international forum for scholarly information and ideas regarding all aspects of the global economy, covering public policy, managerial, and macroeconomic considerations on a global scale.
Formerly (until 2002): Global Economy Quarterly (1524-5861)
Media: Online - full content.
Indexed: JEL.
—BLDSC (4195.392600).
Published by: (International Trade & Finance Association), Berkeley Electronic Press, 2809 Telegraph Ave., Ste 202, Berkeley, CA 94705. TEL 510-665-1200, FAX 510-665-1201, info@bepress.com, http://www.bepress.com/gej/. Eds. Alfred E Eckes, Khosrow Fatemi TEL 760-768-5520. adv.: B&W page USD 210; trim 4.75 x 8. Circ: 300 (controlled); 100 (paid).

➤ **GREAT BRITAIN. BOARD OF INLAND REVENUE. SURVEY OF PERSONAL INCOMES.** see *BUSINESS AND ECONOMICS—Public Finance, Taxation*

339 GBR ISSN 0965-1403
HD7023
GREAT BRITAIN. CENTRAL STATISTICAL OFFICE. FAMILY SPENDING. Text in English. 1957. a. GBP 20.50. stat. **Document type:** *Government.* **Description:** Contains macroeconomics research focusing on private households and how they spend their money, following a representative sampling of U.K. families.
Formerly (until 1991): Great Britain. Central Statistical Office. Family Expenditure Survey (0072-5927)
Related titles: Microfiche ed.: (from PQC).
—BLDSC (3865.576206). **CCC.**
Published by: Office for National Statistics, Government Buildings, Cardiff Rd, Newport, Gwent NP9 1XG, United Kingdom. TEL 44-1633-812973, FAX 44-1633-812599. **Orders to:** Stationery Office, PO Box 276, London SW8 5DT, United Kingdom. TEL 44-20-7873-9090, FAX 44-207-873-8200.

339 332 USA ISSN 0197-7636
HARVARD COLLEGE ECONOMIST. Text in English. 1976. s-a. USD 10 to individuals; USD 15 foreign to individuals; USD 15 to institutions; USD 20 foreign to institutions. adv. bk.rev. back issues avail. **Document type:** *Academic/Scholarly.* **Description:** Presents interviews with economists, articles on economic policy and theory, papers in economics by Harvard undergraduates.
Formerly: Harvard Undergraduate Journal of Economics
Published by: Harvard Economics Association, 200 Littauer Center, Dept of Economics, Harvard University, Cambridge, MA 02138. TEL 617-495-2145, FAX 617-495-7730, econ@hcs.harvard.edu, http://hcs.harvard.edu/~econ. Ed., R&P Carlo N Forcione. Adv. contact Jared Beck. Circ: 2,000.

339 HKG
HONG KONG. GOVERNMENT PUBLICATION CENTRE. ECONOMIC BACKGROUND. Text in English. a. HKD 28.
Related titles: Chinese ed.
Published by: Government Publications Centre, G.P.O. Bldg, Ground Fl, Connaught Pl, Hong Kong, Hong Kong. TEL 5-8428801. **Subscr. to:** Director of Information Services, Information Services Dept., 1 Battery Path G-F, Central, Hong Kong, Hong Kong.

339 HKG
HONG KONG. GOVERNMENT PUBLICATION CENTRE. ECONOMIC PROSPECTS. Text in English. a. HKD 10.
Related titles: Chinese ed.
Published by: Government Publications Centre, G.P.O. Bldg, Ground Fl, Connaught Pl, Hong Kong, Hong Kong. TEL 5-8428801. **Subscr. to:** Director of Information Services, Information Services Dept., 1 Battery Path G-F, Central, Hong Kong, Hong Kong.

339 HKG
HONG KONG. GOVERNMENT PUBLICATION CENTRE. ECONOMIC REPORT. Text in English. q. HKD 60.
Related titles: Chinese ed.
Published by: Government Publications Centre, G.P.O. Bldg, Ground Fl, Connaught Pl, Hong Kong, Hong Kong. TEL 5-8428801. **Subscr. to:** Director of Information Services, Information Services Dept., 1 Battery Path G-F, Central, Hong Kong, Hong Kong.

339 CHL ISSN 0020-4080
HC121
I L P E S CUADERNOS. Text in Spanish. 1967. irreg., latest vol.38, 1993. price varies. Supplement avail.
Published by: Instituto Latinoamericano y del Caribe de Planificacion Economica y Social/Latin American and Caribbean Institute for Economic and Social Planning, Casilla 179-D, Santiago, Chile. FAX 562480252. **Dist. in U.S. by:** Economic Commission for Latin America, 1801 K St N W, Suite 1261, Washington, DC 20006.

IKONOMIKA I FINANSI. see *STATISTICS*

INDIA. CENTRAL STATISTICAL ORGANIZATION. NATIONAL ACCOUNTS STATISTICS: SOURCES AND METHODS. see *BUSINESS AND ECONOMICS—Abstracting, Bibliographies, Statistics*

INDONESIA. CENTRAL BUREAU OF STATISTICS. ECONOMIC INDICATOR BULLETIN. see *BUSINESS AND ECONOMICS—Abstracting, Bibliographies, Statistics*

INTERNATIONAL FINANCE. see *BUSINESS AND ECONOMICS—Banking And Finance*

INTERNATIONAL MONETARY FUND. BALANCE OF PAYMENTS STATISTICS YEARBOOK. see *BUSINESS AND ECONOMICS—Abstracting, Bibliographies, Statistics*

IRELAND. CENTRAL STATISTICS OFFICE. NATIONAL INCOME AND EXPENDITURE. see *BUSINESS AND ECONOMICS—Abstracting, Bibliographies, Statistics*

IRELAND. CENTRAL STATISTICS OFFICE. RETAIL SALES INDEX. see *BUSINESS AND ECONOMICS—Abstracting, Bibliographies, Statistics*

IRELAND. CENTRAL STATISTICS OFFICE. SUPPLY AND USE AND INPUT-OUTPUT TABLES. see *BUSINESS AND ECONOMICS—Abstracting, Bibliographies, Statistics*

JAPAN AND THE WORLD ECONOMY. see *BUSINESS AND ECONOMICS—Economic Systems And Theories, Economic History*

JAPAN. STATISTICS BUREAU. MANAGEMENT AND COORDINATION AGENCY. MONTHLY REPORT ON THE FAMILY INCOME AND EXPENDITURE SURVEY/NIHON TOKEI KYOKAI. KAKEI CHOSA HOKOKU. see *BUSINESS AND ECONOMICS—Abstracting, Bibliographies, Statistics*

339 CHN
JINGJI TIZHI GAIGE/REFORMATION OF ECONOMIC SYSTEM. Text in Chinese; Summaries in Chinese, English. bi-m. CNY 12.
Indexed: RASB.
Published by: Sichuan Sheng Shehui Kexueyuan/Sichuan Academy of Social Science, Qingyang Gong, Chengdu, Sichuan 610072, China. TEL 669347. Ed. Lin Ling. **Dist. outside China by:** China Publication Foreign Trade Company, PO Box 782, Beijing 100011, China.

JOURNAL OF CONSUMER POLICY; consumer issues in law, economics and behavioral sciences. see *CONSUMER EDUCATION AND PROTECTION*

339 NLD ISSN 0164-0704
HB1
➤ **JOURNAL OF MACROECONOMICS.** Text in English. 1979. 4/yr. EUR 52 in Europe to individuals; JPY 7,200 in Japan to individuals; USD 54 to individuals except Europe and Japan; EUR 277 in Europe to institutions; JPY 36,600 in Japan to institutions; USD 277 to institutions except Europe and Japan (effective 2006). adv. bk.rev. illus. index. reprint service avail. from PQC. **Document type:** *Academic/Scholarly.* **Description:** Publishes theoretical and empirical articles that span the entire range of macroeconomics and monetary economics, including economic growth, economic fluctuations, the effects of monetary and fiscal policy, the political aspects of macroeconomics, exchange rate determination and other elements of open economy macroeconomics, the macroeconomics of income inequality, and macroeconomic forecasting.
Related titles: Microform ed.: (from PQC); Online - full text ed.: (from EBSCO Publishing, Gale Group, IngentaConnect, Northern Light Technology, Inc., ScienceDirect, Swets Information Services).
Indexed: ABIn, ASCA, CREJ, CurCont, FamI, IBR, IBSS, IBZ, JEL, RASB, SPAA, SSCI.
—BLDSC (5010.730000), IDS, IE, Infotrieve, ingenta. **CCC.**
Published by: Elsevier BV, North-Holland (Subsidiary of: Elsevier Science & Technology), Sara Burgerhartstraat 25, Amsterdam, 1055 KV, Netherlands. TEL 31-20-485-3911, FAX 31-20-485-2457, jmacro@lsu.edu, nlinfo-f@elsevier.nl, http://www.elsevier.com/locate/jmacro, http://www.elsevier.nl/homepage/about/us/regional_sites.htt, http://www.elsevier.nl. Eds. Douglas McMillin, Theodore Palivos. Circ: 950. **Subscr. to:** Elsevier BV, PO Box 211, Amsterdam 1000 AE, Netherlands. TEL 31-20-485-3757, FAX 31-20-485-3432.

➤ **K D B REPORT.** see *BUSINESS AND ECONOMICS*

339 KOR
KOREA ECONOMIC RESEARCH INSTITUTE. RESEARCH PAPER. MACROECONOMIC STUDIES. Text in Korean. 1995. irreg. (3-7/yr.).
Published by: Korea Economic Research Institute, Yeongdungpo-ku, 28-1 Yoido dong, Seoul, 150756, Korea, S. TEL 82-2-3771-0001, FAX 82-2-785-0270, http://www.keri.org.

KUWAIT. CENTRAL STATISTICAL OFFICE. MONTHLY CONSUMER PRICE INDEX NUMBERS. see *BUSINESS AND ECONOMICS—Abstracting, Bibliographies, Statistics*

LIVERPOOL INVESTMENT LETTER. see *BUSINESS AND ECONOMICS—Investments*

339 MEX
MACROECONOMIA. Text in Spanish. 199?. m. MXP 90 (effective 1999). back issues avail. **Description:** Presents articles about Mexican macroeconomics and its political situation.
Related titles: Online - full text ed.
Published by: Comunicacion y Medios Masivos S.A. de C.V., DR DURAN 4 Desp. 306,, Col Doctores, Mexico City, DF 06720, Mexico. TEL 52-5-588-0548, macro@planet.com, http://www.planet.com.mx/macroeconomia.

339 GBR ISSN 1365-1005
HB172.5
➤ **MACROECONOMIC DYNAMICS.** Text in English. 1997. 5/yr. GBP 203 to institutions; USD 333 in North America to institutions; GBP 224 combined subscription to institutions print & online eds.; USD 362 combined subscription in North America to institutions print & online eds. (effective 2006). adv. bk.rev.; software rev. back issues avail.; reprint service avail. from PSC. **Document type:** *Journal, Academic/Scholarly.* **Description:** Provides original peer-reviewed research of theoretical, empirical or quantitative sophistication from all areas of advanced macroeconomics and allied fields.
Related titles: Online - full text ed.: ISSN 1469-8056. GBP 190 to institutions; USD 303 in North America to institutions (effective 2006) (from EBSCO Publishing, O C L C Online Computer Library Center, Inc., Swets Information Services).
Indexed: ABIn, CurCont, JEL, SSCI.
—BLDSC (5330.394920), IDS, IE, Infotrieve, ingenta. **CCC.**
Published by: Cambridge University Press, The Edinburgh Bldg, Shaftesbury Rd, Cambridge, CB2 2RU, United Kingdom. TEL 44-1223-312393, FAX 44-1223-315052, journals@cambridge.org, http://uk.cambridge.org/journals/mdy. Ed. William A Barnett. Adv. contact Rebecca Curtis TEL 44-1223-325757. **Subscr. to:** Cambridge University Press, 100 Brook Hill Dr, West Nyack, NY 10994. TEL 845-353-7500, FAX 845-353-4141, journals_subscriptions@cup.org

339 USA ISSN 0889-3365
HB172.5
➤ **MACROECONOMICS ANNUAL.** Text in English. 1986. a. price varies. back issues avail.; reprint service avail. from PQC. **Document type:** *Monographic series, Academic/Scholarly.* **Description:** Links theoretical and empirical developments in economics with real-world examples and problems.
Related titles: Online - full text ed.: ISSN 1537-2642 (from EBSCO Publishing, Gale Group, IngentaConnect, O C L C Online Computer Library Center, Inc., Swets Information Services).
Indexed: ABIn, ASCA, JEL, SSCI.
—BLDSC (6067.717700), IE, Infotrieve. **CCC.**
Published by: (National Bureau of Economic Research), M I T Press, 55 Hayward St, Cambridge, MA 02142-1493. TEL 617-253-5646, FAX 617-258-6779, journals-info@mit.edu, http://mitpress.mit.edu/catalog/item/default.asp?sid=4C32A6F1-3916-4647-8D68-BF8D7B51096D&ttype=4&tid=47. Eds. Ben S Bernanke, Kenneth Rogoff. R&P Paul Dzus.

➤ **MERSEYSIDE BUSINESS PROSPECT.** see *BUSINESS AND ECONOMICS—Economic Situation And Conditions*

339 CAN ISSN 0712-4791
MONTHLY ECONOMIC REVIEW. Text in English. 1974. m. CND 375 (effective 2000). index. back issues avail. **Description:** Provides economic forecasts and analysis for the professional advisor or executive, and objective appraisal of economic conditions and policy for senior officials in government and business.
Published by: Informetrica Limited, P O Box 828, Sta B, Ottawa, ON K1P 5P9, Canada. TEL 613-238-4831, FAX 613-238-7698. Ed. Carl Sonnen. Circ: 500.

N A B E INDUSTRY SURVEY. see *BUSINESS AND ECONOMICS—Economic Situation And Conditions*

N A B E NEWS. see *BUSINESS AND ECONOMICS—Economic Situation And Conditions*

N A B E OUTLOOK & POLICY SURVEY. see *BUSINESS AND ECONOMICS—Economic Situation And Conditions*

339.368 BWA ISSN 0302-2056
HC517.B63
NATIONAL ACCOUNTS OF BOTSWANA. Text in English. a. BWP 10. charts. back issues avail. **Document type:** *Government.* **Description:** Contains data on Botswana from a macroeconomic perspective.
Related titles: E-mail ed.; Fax ed.
Published by: Central Statistics Office, c/o Government Statistician, Private Bag 0024, Gaborone, Botswana. TEL 267-31-352200, FAX 267-31-352201, csobots@gov.bw. Ed. G M Charumbira. Pub. J G Segwe. **Orders to:** Government Printer, Private Bag 0081, Gaborone, Botswana. TEL 267-353202, FAX 267-312001, http://www.gov.bw.

339 TWN ISSN 0256-4122
NATIONAL CONDITIONS OF THE REPUBLIC OF CHINA. Text in English. irreg.
Indexed: PAIS.
Published by: Executive Yuan, Directorate-General of Budget, Accounting & Statistics, 2 Kwangchow St, Taipei, Taiwan. TEL 886-2-2371-1521, FAX 886-2-2381-8246.

339 PHL
NATIONAL INCOME ACCOUNTS OF THE PHILIPPINES. Text in English. q. USD 163 in Asia; USD 187 in Australia & New Zealand; USD 203 in US & Canada; USD 243 in Europe; USD 255 elsewhere. illus. **Document type:** *Government.* **Description:** Presents measures of the aggregate or sum of factor incomes-payments arising from the production activities of the country. Valuates total final goods and services produced in a given period, and records flows from production to consumption, accumulation, and foreign trade.
Formerly: Philippines. National Economic and Development Authority. National Income Series
Media: Duplicated (not offset).
Published by: National Statistical Coordination Board, c/o National Statistical Information Center, Midland-Buendia Bldg, 403 Sen. Gil Puyat Ave., Makati City, Philippines. TEL 63-2-890-9405, FAX 63-2-890-9408, nscb_nsic@mozcom.com.

339 ARG ISSN 0326-5730
HC171
NUEVA ECONOMIA. Text in Spanish. 1984. bi-m. ARS 20, USD 24. adv. bk.rev.; film rev. bibl.; tr.lit. back issues avail.
Indexed: B&I, PAIS.
Published by: Zarco S.C.A. (Schwartzman y Asociados), Avda. Pueyrredon, 480 Piso 11 Of 71, Caixa Postal 1032, Capital Federal, Buenos Aires 1032, Argentina. Eds. Daniel M Schwartzman, Leon S Schwartzman. Circ: 7,500.

OUZHOU/EUROPE. see *SOCIAL SCIENCES: COMPREHENSIVE WORKS*

339 COL ISSN 0121-9782
PANORAMA MACROECONOMICO Y FINANCIERO. Text in Spanish. m. USD 70 (effective 1998). **Description:** Provides analyses on current national and international macroeconomic subjects.
Published by: Asociacion Bancaria y de Entidades Financieras, Apartado Aereo 13994, Bogota, CUND, Colombia. TEL 57-1-2114811, FAX 57-1-2119915, info@asobancaria.com, http://ww.asobancaria.com.

PARI; businessdaily. see *BUSINESS AND ECONOMICS—Banking And Finance*

339.2 USA
PERSONAL INCOME IN AREAS AND COUNTIES OF NEW YORK STATE. Text in English. 1961. a. free. **Document type:** *Government.* **Description:** Detailed estimates of income by type and source.
Formerly: Personal Income in Counties of New York State (0079-0907)
Published by: Department of Economic Development, One Commerce Plaza, Albany, NY 12245. www.empirestate.ny.us/nysdc/ftp.com. Ed. William Grainger. Circ: 1,500.

PERU. INSTITUTO NACIONAL DE ESTADISTICA. BOLETIN ANUAL. see *BUSINESS AND ECONOMICS—Abstracting, Bibliographies, Statistics*

339.021 PRT ISSN 0870-2659
HC394.5.I5
PORTUGAL. INSTITUTO NACIONAL DE ESTATISTICA. CONTAS NACIONAIS. Text in Portuguese. 1972. a. EUR 15 (effective 2005). **Document type:** *Government.* **Description:** Includes the Portuguese macroeconomic aggregates for the year under review.
Related titles: CD-ROM ed.; ♦ Supplement to: Anuario Estatistico de Portugal. ISSN 0871-8741.
Published by: Instituto Nacional de Estatistica, Ave. Antonio Jose de Almeida 2, Lisbon, 1000-043, Portugal. TEL 351-21-8426100, FAX 351-21-8426380, ine@ine.pt, http://www.ine.pt/.

339 CHE
PRICES AND EARNINGS AROUND THE GLOBE. Text in English. 1970. triennial. free. **Document type:** *Bulletin.* **Description:** Survey of prices and earnings in 53 cities. Includes a comparison of purchasing power.
Related titles: French ed.; German ed.; Italian ed.
Published by: Union Bank of Switzerland, Bahnhofstr 45, Zurich, 8021, Switzerland. TEL 41-1-2341111, FAX 41-1-2343245, TELEX 813811. Circ: 36,000.

PRIVATE DEVELOPMENT CORPORATION OF THE PHILIPPINES. POLICY ANALYSIS. see *BUSINESS AND ECONOMICS—International Development And Assistance*

QUARTERLY ECONOMIC BULLETIN. see *BUSINESS AND ECONOMICS—Economic Situation And Conditions*

339 NZL ISSN 0113-1680
HC670.I5
QUARTERLY PREDICTIONS. Text in English. 1964. q. membership. charts; stat. **Document type:** *Journal, Academic/Scholarly.* **Description:** Provides forecast of the New Zealand economy up to two years ahead.
Formerly (until 1984): Quarterly Predictions of National Income and Expenditure (0033-5711); Incorporates (1997-2003): New Zealand Industries and Regions (1175-8384); Which was formerly (until 2002): New Zealand Industry Outlook (1174-4065); (1983-1987): New Zealand Institute of Economic Research. Medium Term Review (0112-1170)
Indexed: KES, PAIS.
—**CCC.**
Published by: New Zealand Institute of Economic Research, PO Box 3479, Wellington 1, New Zealand. TEL 64-4-4721880, FAX 64-4-4721211, econ@nzier.org.nz, http://www.nzier.org.nz. Ed. M Hassan.

339 POL ISSN 1640-0747
HG1086
RAPORT O INFLACJI. Text in Polish. 1998. q.
Related titles: ♦ English ed.: National Bank of Poland. Inflation Report. ISSN 1640-0755.
Published by: Narodowy Bank Polski, ul Swietokrzyska 11-21, Warsaw, 00919, Poland. TEL 48-22-6532571, FAX 48-22-6531321, nbp@nbp.pl, http://www.nbp.pl.

RENKOU YU JINGJI/POPULATION & ECONOMICS. see *POPULATION STUDIES*

339 USA ISSN 0194-3960
HD82
RESEARCH IN HUMAN CAPITAL AND DEVELOPMENT. Text in English. 1979. irreg., latest vol.15, 2004. price varies. back issues avail. **Document type:** *Monographic series, Academic/Scholarly.*
Related titles: Online - full text ed.: (from ScienceDirect).
—BLDSC (7741.314000), IE, Infotrieve, ingenta. **CCC.**
Published by: J A I Press Inc. (Subsidiary of: Elsevier Science & Technology), 360 Park Ave S, New York, NY 10010-1710. TEL 212-989-5800, FAX 212-633-3990, usinfo-f@elsevier.com, http://www.elsevier.com/wps/find/bookdescription.cws_home/BS_RHCD/description#description. Ed. Alan Sorkin.

RESERVE BANK OF AUSTRALIA. RESEARCH DISCUSSION PAPER. see *BUSINESS AND ECONOMICS—Banking And Finance*

339 GBR ISSN 0034-6586
HC79.I5
➤ **REVIEW OF INCOME AND WEALTH.** Text in English. 1966. q. USD 250 combined subscription in the Americas to institutions & Caribbean (print & online eds.); GBP 156 combined subscription elsewhere to institutions print & online eds. (effective 2006). bk.rev. charts; stat. reprint service avail. from PSC. **Document type:** *Journal, Academic/Scholarly.* **Description:** Covers national and social accounting; microdata analysis of issues related to income and wealth; development and integration of micro and macro systems of economic, financial and social statistics; international comparisons of productivity, income and wealth; and related problems of measurement and statistical methodology.
Supersedes: Income and Wealth Series
Related titles: Online - full text ed.: ISSN 1475-4991. USD 238 in the Americas to institutions & Caribbean; GBP 148 elsewhere to institutions (effective 2006) (from Blackwell Synergy, EBSCO Publishing, Gale Group, IngentaConnect, O C L C Online Computer Library Center, Inc., Swets Information Services).
Indexed: ABIn, APEL, ASCA, AgeL, BAS, BPIA, CREJ, CurCont, ESPM, FamI, IBR, IBSS, ILD, JEL, MEA&I, PAIS, RASB, RiskAb, SSCI, WBA, WBSS.
—BLDSC (7790.770000), IE, Infotrieve, ingenta. **CCC.**
Published by: (International Association for Research in Income and Wealth USA), Blackwell Publishing Ltd., 9600 Garsington Rd, Oxford, OX4 2ZG, United Kingdom. TEL 44-1865-776868, FAX 44-1865-714591, customerservices@oxon.blackwellpublishing.com, http://www.blackwellpublishing.com/journals/ROIW. Ed. Edward N Wolff. Circ: 2,000.

➤ **REVISTA CENTROAMERICANA DE ECONOMIA**; postgrado centroamericana en economia y planificacion del desarrollo. see *BUSINESS AND ECONOMICS—Economic Situation And Conditions*

➤ **RIO GRANDE DO SUL, BRAZIL. FUNDACAO DE ECONOMIA E ESTATISTICA. INDICADORES ECONOMICOS F E E.** see *BUSINESS AND ECONOMICS—Economic Situation And Conditions*

➤ **RYNOK TSENNYKH BUMAG/SECURITIES MARKET**; analiticheskii zhurnal. see *BUSINESS AND ECONOMICS—Investments*

➤ **SCIENZE REGIONALI**; Italian journal of regional science. see *BUSINESS AND ECONOMICS—Economic Systems And Theories, Economic History*

➤ **SEYCHELLES. DEPARTMENT OF FINANCE. NATIONAL ACCOUNTS.** see *BUSINESS AND ECONOMICS—Abstracting, Bibliographies, Statistics*

B

▼ new title ➤ refereed ✱ unverified ♦ full entry avail.

339 CHN ISSN 1003-9589
SHANDONG JINGJI ZHANLUE YANJIU/STRATEGIC STUDY OF SHANDONG ECONOMICS. Text in Chinese. 1984. bi-m. USD 5. adv. bk.rev.
Related titles: Online - full text ed.: (from East View Information Services).
Published by: Shandong Sheng Jingji Yanjiu Zhongxin/Shandong Economic Research Center, No 1 Shengfu Qianjie, Jinan, Shandong, 250011, China. TEL 0531-612828. Ed. Guan Shenglan. Circ: 5,000.

339 330.1 CHN
SHIJIE JINGJI YANJIU/WORLD ECONOMY RESEARCH. Text in Chinese. 1985. bi-m. CNY 30.50 (effective 2004). **Document type:** *Journal, Academic/Scholarly.*
Related titles: Online - full content ed.
Published by: Shanghai Shehui Kexueyuan/Shanghai Academy of Social Sciences, No 7 Alley 622 Huaihai Zhonglu, Shanghai, 200020, China. TEL 86-21-53060606, http://www.sass.stc.sh.cn/link/xs/sjjjzyj6.asp. **Dist. in US by:** China Books & Periodicals Inc, 360 Swift Ave., Ste. 48, S San Fran, CA 94080-6220. TEL 415-282-2994; **Dist. by:** China International Book Trading Corp, 35 Chegongzhuang Xilu, Haidian District, PO Box 399, Beijing 100044, China. TEL 86-10-68412045, FAX 86-10-68412023, cibtc@mail.cibtc.com.cn, http://www.cibtc.com.cn.

B

339 330.9 CHN ISSN 1009-7511
SHIJIE JINGJIXUE/WORLD ECONOMICS. Text in Chinese. 1978. m. **Document type:** *Journal, Academic/Scholarly.*
Former titles (until 2001): Shijie Jingji (1008-3278); (until 1998): Guoji Jingji (1009-184X); (until 1994): Shijie Jingji (1001-3377)
Published by: Zhongguo Renmin Daxue, Shubao Zilio Zhongxin/Renmin University of China, Information Center for Social Server, Dongcheng-qu, 3, Zhangzizhong Lu, Beijing, 100007, China. TEL 86-10-64039458, FAX 86-10-64015080, kyes@163.net, http://www.confucius.cn.net/. **Dist. in US by:** China Publications Service, PO Box 49614, Chicago, IL 60649. TEL 312-288-3291, FAX 312-288-8570; **Dist. outside China by:** China International Book Trading Corp, 35 Chegongzhuang Xilu, Haidian District, PO Box 399, Beijing 100044, China. TEL 86-10-68412045, FAX 86-10-68412023, cibtc@mail.cibtc.com.cn, http://www.cibtc.com.cn/.

SOOCHOW JOURNAL OF ECONOMICS AND BUSINESS. see *BUSINESS AND ECONOMICS*

STATISTICHESKOE OBOZRENIE/CURRENT STATISTICAL SURVEY. see *BUSINESS AND ECONOMICS—Abstracting, Bibliographies, Statistics*

339 GBR ISSN 0081-864X
STUDIES IN THE NATIONAL INCOME AND EXPENDITURE OF THE UNITED KINGDOM. Text in English. 1966. irreg. price varies. **Document type:** *Monographic series.*
Published by: (National Institute of Economic and Social Research), Cambridge University Press, The Edinburgh Bldg, Shaftesbury Rd, Cambridge, CB2 2RU, United Kingdom. TEL 44-1223-312393, FAX 44-1223-315052, information@cambridge.org, http://www.cup.cam.ac.uk/. Ed. Richard Stone. R&P Linda Nicol TEL 44-1223-325757.
Co-sponsor: University of Cambridge, Department of Applied Economics.

339.2 SDN ISSN 0377-1652
HC591.S83
SUDAN. DEPARTMENT OF STATISTICS. NATIONAL INCOME ACCOUNTS AND SUPPORTING TABLES. Text in Arabic, English. a. illus.; stat. **Document type:** *Government.*
Published by: (Sudan. National Income Division), Department of Statistics, P O Box 700, Khartoum, Sudan.

339 SWE ISSN 0284-4974
SWEDEN'S ECONOMY. Text in English. 1986. s-a. SEK 190 (effective 1990). **Document type:** *Government.*
Published by: Ministry of Finance, Roedbodgatan 6, Stockholm, 10333, Sweden. **Dist. by:** Allmaenna Foerlaget AB, Stockholm 10647, Sweden.

339 TWN ISSN 1011-694X
HC430.5.Z9
TAIWAN, REPUBLIC OF CHINA. EXECUTIVE YUAN. DIRECTORATE-GENERAL OF BUDGET, ACCOUNTING & STATISTICS. REPORT ON THE SURVEY OF FAMILY INCOME & EXPENDITURE IN TAIWAN AREA. Key Title: Report on the Survey of Family Income & Expenditure in Taiwan Area. Text in English, Chinese. 1966. a. TWD 400 (effective 2000). charts; illus.; stat.
Formerly: China, Republic. Executive Yuan. Directorate-General of Budget, Accounting and Statistics. Report on the Survey of Personal Income Distribution in Taiwan Area (0257-5752)
Published by: Executive Yuan, Directorate-General of Budget, Accounting & Statistics, 2 Kwangchow St, Taipei, Taiwan. TEL 886-2-2381-4910, http://www.dgbasey.gov.tw/, http://www.stat.gov.tw/main.htm/. **Subscr. to:** Chen Chung Book Co., 3F, 20 Heng-Yang Rd, Taipei, Taiwan. TEL 886-2-2382-1394, FAX 886-2-2382-2805, http://www.ccbc.com.tw.

TELEVISION IN ASIA PACIFIC TO THE YEAR... see *COMMUNICATIONS—Television And Cable*

TELEVISION IN EUROPE TO THE YEAR... see *COMMUNICATIONS—Television And Cable*

TOP 50 EUROPEAN MEDIA OWNERS. see *COMMUNICATIONS*

339 USA ISSN 1534-5998
HB172.5
TOPICS IN MACROECONOMICS. Text in English. 2001. irreg. Included with subscription to The B E Journals in Macroeconomics.. **Document type:** *Journal, Academic/Scholarly.*
Media: Online - full content. **Related titles:** Online - full text ed.: (from O C L C Online Computer Library Center, Inc., ProQuest Information & Learning); ♦ Series of: The B E Journals in Macroeconomics. ISSN 1555-0486.
Indexed: ABIn, IBSS, JEL.
Published by: Berkeley Electronic Press, 2809 Telegraph Ave., Ste 202, Berkeley, CA 94705. FAX 510-665-1201, info@bepress.com, http://www.bepress.com/bejm/topics/. Eds. Charles I Jones, David Romer, Per Kursell, Robert Shimer.

U K MEDIA YEARBOOK. see *COMMUNICATIONS*

U K TELEVISION FORECASTS. see *COMMUNICATIONS—Television And Cable*

339.5 USA ISSN 0361-6665
HC101
WAGE-PRICE LAW & ECONOMICS REVIEW. Text in English. q. USD 129.50 (effective 2000).
Indexed: PAIS.
Published by: Antitrust Law and Economics Review, Inc., P O Box 3532, Vero Beach, FL 32964-3532. TEL 772-461-6007, http://home.mpinet.net. Ed. Charles E Mueller.

WASHINGTON C E O; connecting the ceo community. (Chief Executive Officer) see *BUSINESS AND ECONOMICS—Management*

WHOLESALE PRICE INDEX IN IRAN. see *BUSINESS AND ECONOMICS—Abstracting, Bibliographies, Statistics*

XI'OU YANJIU/WESTERN EUROPEAN STUDIES. see *SOCIAL SCIENCES: COMPREHENSIVE WORKS*

339 CHN ISSN 1005-2100
HC427.92
ZHONGGUO GAIGE/CHINA'S ECONOMIC STRUCTURE REFORM. Text in Chinese. m. CNY 22.20, USD 45.80. adv.
Formerly (until 1994): Zhongguo Jingji Tizhi Gaige (1002-865X)
Related titles: Online - full text ed.: (from East View Information Services).
Indexed: RASB.
Published by: (Guojia Jingji Tizhi Gaige Weiyuanhui/State Commission for Restructuring Economic Systems), Zhongguo Jingji Tizhi Gaige Zazhishe/China's Economic Structure Reform Magazine House, 22 Xi anmen Dajie, Beijing, 100017, China. TEL 3097726. Ed. Xiao Yingzhi. **Dist. in US by:** China Books & Periodicals Inc, 360 Swift Ave., Ste. 48, S San Fran, CA 94080-6220. TEL 415-282-2994; **Dist. outside China by:** China International Book Trading Corp, 35 Chegongzhuang Xilu, Haidian District, PO Box 399, Beijing 100044, China.

339 CHN ISSN 1006-480X
ZHONGGUO GONGYE JINGJI/CHINA INDUSTRIAL ECONOMY. Text in Chinese. 1984. m. CNY 18. bk.rev. **Document type:** *Academic/Scholarly.* **Description:** Covers theories and policies of Chinese industrial economics.
Formerly (until 1994): Zhongguo Gongye Jingji Yanjiu/China Industrial Economics Research (1002-5928)
Related titles: Online - full text ed.: (from East View Information Services, WanFang Data Corp.).
Indexed: RASB.
Published by: Zhongguo Shehui Kexueyuan, Gongye Jingji Yanjiusuo/Chinese Academy of Social Sciences, Institute of Industrial Economics, Xicheng-qu, 2, Fuwai Yuetan Beixiaojie, Beijing, 100836, China. TEL 86-10-68032678, FAX 86-10-68047499, gjbjb@sina.com.cn, http://zggyjj.periodicals.net.cn/. Circ: 10,000. **Dist. in US by:** China Books & Periodicals Inc, 360 Swift Ave., Ste. 48, S San Fran, CA 94080-6220. TEL 415-282-2994; **Dist. outside China by:** China International Book Trading Corp, 35 Chegongzhuang Xilu, Haidian District, PO Box 399, Beijing 100044, China. TEL 86-10-68412045, FAX 86-10-68412023, cibtc@mail.cibtc.com.cn, http://www.cibtc.com.cn.

339 CHN ISSN 1000-4181
HC427.92
ZHONGGUO JINGJI WENTI. Text in Chinese. 1959. bi-m. CNY 15, USD 21.58. bk.rev. **Document type:** *Academic/Scholarly.* **Description:** Examines Chinese economic problems.
Indexed: RASB.
Published by: (Jingji Yanjiusuo), Xiamen Daxue/Xiamen University, c/o Xiamen Daxue Tushuguan, Xiamen, Fujian 361005, China. TEL 86-592-218-6144, FAX 86-592-218-6227, xiaodh@xmu.edu.cn, http://www.xmu.edu.cn/library.html, http://www.xmu.edu.cn/library.html/. Ed. Hu Peizhao. Circ: 10,000. **Dist. in US by:** China Books & Periodicals Inc, 360 Swift Ave., Ste. 48, S San Fran, CA 94080-6220. TEL 415-282-2994; **Dist. outside China by:** China International Book Trading Corp, 35 Chegongzhuang Xilu, Haidian District, PO Box 399, Beijing 100044, China. TEL 86-10-68412045, FAX 86-10-68412023, cibtc@mail.cibtc.com.cn, http://www.cibtc.com.cn.

ZHONGGUO JINGJI XINWEN/CHINA ECONOMIC NEWS. see *BUSINESS AND ECONOMICS—Economic Situation And Conditions*

ZIMBABWE. CENTRAL STATISTICAL OFFICE. FACTS AND FIGURES. see *BUSINESS AND ECONOMICS—Abstracting, Bibliographies, Statistics*

ZIMBABWE. CENTRAL STATISTICAL OFFICE. NATIONAL ACCOUNTS. see *BUSINESS AND ECONOMICS—Abstracting, Bibliographies, Statistics*

ZIMBABWE. CENTRAL STATISTICAL OFFICE. STATISTICAL YEARBOOK. see *BUSINESS AND ECONOMICS—Abstracting, Bibliographies, Statistics*

BUSINESS AND ECONOMICS—Management

A B A TRUST & INVESTMENTS. see *BUSINESS AND ECONOMICS—Banking And Finance*

A B L O NYT; andels- og ejerboligbladet. (Andelsbolighavernes Lands-Organisation) see *BUILDING AND CONSTRUCTION*

658 011 USA
A C O M MODATE QUARTERLY✶. Text in English. q. **Document type:** *Newsletter.*
Published by: Association for Convention Operations Management, 2965 Flowers Rd S, Ste 105, Atlanta, GA 30341-5520. TEL 404-351-3220, FAX 404-351-3348.

A F M EXPLANATORY SERIES (NO.). see *BUSINESS AND ECONOMICS—Accounting*

A G P MITTEILUNGEN; Zeitschrift fuer Partnerschaft in der Wirtschaft. see *BUSINESS AND ECONOMICS—Labor And Industrial Relations*

A I M - R NEWS. see *BUSINESS AND ECONOMICS—Production Of Goods And Services*

650 USA
A M A MANAGEMENT BRIEFINGS. Text in English. 1971. irreg. (approx. 2/yr.). price varies. charts; illus.
Published by: American Management Association, 1610 Broadway, New York, NY 10019. TEL 212-586-8100, http://www.amanet.org. Circ: (controlled).

650 USA
A M A SURVEY REPORTS. Text in English. 1973. irreg. price varies. charts; illus.; stat.
Related titles: Online - full text ed.
Published by: American Management Association, 1610 Broadway, New York, NY 10019. TEL 212-586-8100, http://www.amanet.org.

658 USA
TS157.A1
A P I C S CONFERENCE PROCEEDINGS. Text in English. 1960. a. USD 35 to non-members. back issues avail. **Document type:** *Proceedings.*
Former titles: American Production and Inventory Control Society. International Conference Proceedings (1064-1939); (until 1989): American Producation and Inventory Control Society. Annual International Conference Proceedings (0895-6367); American Production and Inventory Control Society. Annual Conference Proceedings (0191-1783); A P I C S Annual Conference Proceedings (0065-9819); A P I C S International Technical Conference Proceedings (0190-8340)
Indexed: Englnd.
—BLDSC (4538.847100).
Published by: A P I C S - The Educational Society for Resource Management, 301 Shawnee Rd, Alexandria, VA 22312-2317. TEL 703-354-8851, 800-444-2742, FAX 703-354-8106, http://www.apics.org. Circ: 72,000.

658.5 338 USA ISSN 1056-0017
TS155.A1
A P I C S - THE PERFORMANCE ADVANTAGE. Variant title: The Performance Advantage. Text in English. 1991. 10/yr. USD 65 domestic to non-members; USD 77 in Canada & Mexico to non-members; USD 93 elsewhere to non-members (effective 2005). adv. bk.rev.; software rev. charts; mkt.; illus. Index. Supplement avail.; back issues avail.; reprints avail. **Document type:** *Magazine, Trade.* **Description:** For professionals in all phases of resource management, manufacturing, production and inventory control.
Related titles: Online - full text ed.
Indexed: Emerald, LogistBibl.
—BLDSC (1568.356000), IE, Infotrieve, ingenta, Linda Hall.

Published by: A P I C S - The Educational Society for Resource Management, 5301 Shawnee Rd, Alexandria, VA 22312-2317. TEL 703-354-8851, FAX 703-354-8768, editorial@apicshq.org, service@apicshq.org, http://www.apics.org/resources/magazine/default.htm. Ed. Doug Kelly. Adv. contact Gene Schuyler. B&W page USD 6,150, color page USD 7,335; trim 8.13 x 10.88. Circ: 72,153.

658 USA ISSN 1050-8813
A Q P REPORT✶. Text in English. 1983. bi-m. USD 45. bk.rev. back issues avail. **Document type:** *Newsletter.* **Description:** Quality and productivity improvement through team problem solving.
Formerly: I A Q C Circle Report
—CCC.
Published by: American Society for Quality, 600 N Plankinton Ave, Milwaukee, WI 53203. TEL 513-381-1959, FAX 513-381-0070. Ed. Ned Hamson. Circ: 9,500.

658 USA
A S A E ASSOCIATE MEMBER UPDATE. Variant title: A S A E Update. Text in English. q. membership. **Description:** Includes association news, marketing strategies, and new services available to those who exhibit or market products or services to associations.
Published by: American Society of Association Executives, 1575 Eye St, N W, Washington, DC 20005-1168. TEL 202-626-2739, FAX 202-408-9635, http://www.asaenet.org. Circ: 3,500.

658 USA
A S A E ASSOCIATION LAW AND POLICY. Text in English. 1987. bi-w. membership. **Description:** Includes relevant case reviews of non-profit organizations.
Published by: (Legal Section), American Society of Association Executives, 1575 Eye St, N W, Washington, DC 20005-1168. TEL 202-626-2739, FAX 202-408-9635, http://www.asaenet.org. Circ: 1,950.

658 USA
A S A E INTERNATIONAL NEWS. Text in English. bi-m. membership. adv. **Document type:** *Newsletter.* **Description:** Includes trade and tourism statistics; association management, meetings and marketing information; resources; and calendar of events.
Published by: (International Section), American Society of Association Executives, 1575 Eye St, N W, Washington, DC 20005-1168. TEL 202-626-2739, FAX 202-408-9635, http://www.asaenet.org. Ed. Joseph S Cavarretta. Circ: 1,000.

658 IND ISSN 0257-8069
HD20.15.I4
A S C I JOURNAL OF MANAGEMENT. Text in English. 1971. s-a. INR 120 domestic to non-members; INR 110 domestic to members; USD 30 (effective 2005). **Document type:** *Academic/Scholarly.* **Description:** Devoted to discussion on policy and management issues concerning various sectors of the national life, including business, industry, government, economic planning, science and technology, population, education, etc.
Indexed: ABIn, BPIA, BusI, CurCont, ManagCont, PAA&I, PAIS, T&II.
Published by: Administrative Staff College of India, Bella Vista, Raj Bhavan Road, Khairatabad, P O Box 4, Hyderabad, Andhra Pradesh 500 082, India. TEL 91-40-23324365, FAX 91-40-23312954, rrmathur@asci.org.in, http://www.asci.org.in/web/publications.aspx?id=9. Ed. Dr. Rohit Raj Mathur.

003 AUS ISSN 0812-860X
➤ **A S O R BULLETIN.** Text in English. 1981. q. AUD 24 (effective 2002). adv. bk.rev. 32 p./no.; back issues avail. **Document type:** *Bulletin, Academic/Scholarly.* **Description:** Covers the area of operations research, dissemination of information from other OR organizations. For persons in the business community, and academics.
Indexed: IAOP.
—BLDSC (1745.680000), IE, ingenta.
Published by: Australian Society for Operations Research Inc., QUT, Brisbane, QLD 4001, Australia. TEL 61-1-62688051, FAX 61-6-62688581. Ed., Adv. contact Ruhul Sarker. page AUD 200. Circ: 400.

658 GBR
A-Z OF BUSINESS INFORMATION SOURCES. Variant title: Croner's A-Z of Business Information Sources. Text in English. a. looseleaf. EUR 365.97 (effective 2001). **Document type:** *Trade.*
Related titles: CD-ROM ed.; Print ed.
Published by: Croner.C C H Group Ltd. (Subsidiary of: Wolters Kluwer N.V.), 145 London Rd, Kingston, Surrey KT2 6SR, United Kingdom. TEL 44-20-85473333, FAX 44-20-85472637, info@croner.co.uk, http://www.croner.co.uk.

658 GBR
A-Z OF EUROPEAN BUSINESS INFORMATION SOURCES. Variant title: Croner's A-Z of European Business Information Sources. Text in English. a. looseleaf. EUR 407.16 (effective 2001). **Document type:** *Trade.*
Related titles: CD-ROM ed.; Print ed.
Published by: Croner.C C H Group Ltd. (Subsidiary of: Wolters Kluwer N.V.), 145 London Rd, Kingston, Surrey KT2 6SR, United Kingdom. TEL 44-20-85473333, FAX 44-20-85472637, info@croner.co.uk, http://www.croner.co.uk.

A3 BAU; das oesterreichische Baumagazin. see *BUILDING AND CONSTRUCTION*

A3 ECO. see *ENVIRONMENTAL STUDIES*

A3 GAST; Oesterreichs Magazin fuer Gastronomie, Hotellerie und Touristik. see *HOTELS AND RESTAURANTS*

A3 UMWELT; das oesterreichische Oeko-Wirtschaftsmagazin. see *ENVIRONMENTAL STUDIES—Waste Management*

658 NLD ISSN 0922-2928
AANSPRAAK. Text in Dutch. 1988. m. EUR 148 (effective 2003).
—IE, Infotrieve.
Published by: Reed Business Information bv (Subsidiary of: Reed Business), Postbus 16400, Den Haag, 2500 BK, Netherlands. TEL 31-70-313-1500, FAX 31-70-313-1506, info@reedbusiness.nl, http://www.reedbusiness.nl.

658 CHL ISSN 0717-344X
HD70.C497
ABANTE; estudios en direccion de empresas. Text in Spanish. 1997. s-a. back issues avail.
Related titles: Online - full text ed.: (from EBSCO Publishing).
Published by: Pontificia Universidad Catolica de Chile, Escuela de Administracion, Casilla No. 76, Correo 17, Santiago, Chile. TEL 56-2-5531672, FAX 56-2-6864002, iarrieta@volcan.facea.puc.cl, http://www.faceapuc.cl/abante/.

658 USA ISSN 1528-2686
➤ **ACADEMY OF ENTREPRENEURSHIP JOURNAL.** Text in English. s-a. **Document type:** *Journal, Academic/Scholarly.*
Related titles: Online - full text ed.
Published by: (Academy of Entrepreneurship), Allied Academies, 145 Travis Rd., P. O. Box 2689, Cullowhee, NC 28723. http://www.alliedacademies.org/entrepreneurship/index.html. Ed. Jim & JoAnn Carland.

658 USA ISSN 1079-5545
➤ **ACADEMY OF MANAGEMENT EXECUTIVE**; the thinking manager's source. Text in English. 1987. q. USD 70 domestic to individuals; USD 90 foreign to individuals; USD 110 domestic to institutions; USD 135 foreign to institutions; USD 150 domestic to corporations; USD 165 foreign to corporations; USD 100 combined subscription domestic to individuals print & online eds.; USD 125 combined subscription foreign to individuals print & online eds.; USD 145 combined subscription domestic to institutions print & online eds.; USD 170 combined subscription foreign to institutions print & online eds.; USD 185 combined subscription domestic to corporations print & online eds.; USD 200 combined subscription foreign to corporations print & online eds. (effective 2004). adv. bk.rev. illus. back issues avail.; reprint service avail. from PQC. **Document type:** *Academic/Scholarly.* **Description:** Provides information in both theory and practice of management.
Formerly (until 1989): Academy of Management Executive (0896-3789)
Related titles: Online - full text ed.: (from EBSCO Publishing, Gale Group, Northern Light Technology, Inc., O C L C Online Computer Library Center, Inc., ProQuest Information & Learning).
Indexed: ABIn, ABS&EES, AgeL, BPI, CurCont, Emerald, PCI, QAb, SSCI, T&DA.
—BLDSC (3836.209900), IE. **CCC.**
Published by: Academy of Management, 235 Elm Rd, P O Box 3020, Briarcliff Manor, NY 10510-3020. http://www.aom.pace.edu/ame, http://www.aomonline.org. Ed. Dr. Robert C. Ford. adv.: page GBP 500, page USD 835. Circ: 13,700.

658 USA ISSN 0001-4273
➤ **ACADEMY OF MANAGEMENT JOURNAL.** Text in English. 1958. bi-m. USD 140 domestic individuals & academic libraries; USD 165 foreign individuals & academic libraries; USD 170 domestic to corporations; USD 180 foreign to corporations; USD 175 combined subscription domestic individuals & academic libraries for print & online eds.; USD 200 combined subscription foreign individuals & academic libraries for print & online eds.; USD 205 combined subscription domestic to corporations print & online eds.; USD 215 combined subscription foreign to corporations print & online eds. (effective 2004). adv. bk.rev. charts; tr.lit.; illus. index. reprint service avail. from PQC. **Document type:** *Journal, Academic/Scholarly.* **Description:** Articles and research notes of an empirical nature from original research.
Formerly (until 1962): The Journal of the Academy of Management (1535-3990)
Related titles: Microform ed.: (from PQC); Online - full text ed.: (from EBSCO Publishing, Gale Group, JSTOR (Web-based Journal Archive), O C L C Online Computer Library Center, Inc., ProQuest Information & Learning).
Indexed: ABIn, AHCMS, ASCA, AgeL, BAS, BPI, BPIA, BusI, CINAHL, CLOSS, CPM, CommAb, CurCont, Emerald, ErgAb, HECAB, IBSS, Inspec, M&MA, MEA&I, MEDLINE, ManagCont, ORMS, PersLit, PsySCAP, PsycInfo, PsycholAb, QAb, RASB, SCIMP, SSCI, T&DA, WorkRelAb, e-psyche.
—BLDSC (0570.587000), IE, Infotrieve, ingenta. **CCC.**
Published by: Academy of Management, 235 Elm Rd, P O Box 3020, Briarcliff Manor, NY 10510-3020. TEL 914-923-2607, FAX 914-923-2615, amj@cba.uiuc.edu, academy@pace.edu, http://www.aom.pace.edu/amjnew, http://www.aomonline.org. Ed. Amme Tsui. R&P Hope Tinsley. Adv. contact Terese Vivenzo. Circ: 11,500.

658 USA ISSN 1537-260X
HD30.4
➤ **ACADEMY OF MANAGEMENT LEARNING AND EDUCATION.** Text in English. 2002. 4/yr. USD 99 domestic individuals & academic libraries; USD 120 foreign individuals & academic libraries; USD 135 domestic to corporations; USD 150 foreign to corporations; USD 135 combined subscription domestic individuals & academic libraries for print & online eds.; USD 150 combined subscription foreign individuals & academic libraries for print & online eds.; USD 170 combined subscription domestic to corporations; USD 185 combined subscription foreign to corporations (effective 2004). **Document type:** *Journal, Academic/Scholarly.* **Description:** Presents theory, models, research, critique, dialogues and retrospectives that address the learning process, and enhance the practice of education in the management disciplines.
Related titles: Online - full text ed.: (from EBSCO Publishing).
Indexed: ABIn.
—BLDSC (0570.587100), IE, ingenta. **CCC.**
Published by: Academy of Management, 235 Elm Rd, P O Box 3020, Briarcliff Manor, NY 10510-3020. TEL 914-923-2607, FAX 914-923-2615, academy@pace.edu, http://www.aomonline.org.

658 658.3 USA ISSN 1557-5241
THE ACADEMY OF MANAGEMENT NEWS. Text in English. 1971. 3/yr. looseleaf. USD 115 membership (effective 2005). adv. bibl. back issues avail.; reprint service avail. from PQC. **Document type:** *Newsletter.* **Description:** Announcements, special features, and informed coverage of individual members and organizational elements of the Academy.
Formerly (until 1988): Academy of Management Newsletter (0161-5998)
Related titles: Online - full content ed.: ISSN 1557-6736.
Published by: Academy of Management, 235 Elm Rd, P O Box 3020, Briarcliff Manor, NY 10510-3020. TEL 914-923-2607, FAX 914-923-2615, newsletter@aomonline.org, academy@pace.edu, http://www.aom.pace.edu/newsletter, http://www.aomonline.org. Ed. Anthony M Townsend. Circ: 10,000 (controlled).

658 USA ISSN 1543-8643
HD29
ACADEMY OF MANAGEMENT. PROCEEDINGS AND MEMBERSHIP DIRECTORY. Text in English. 1938. a. USD 20 in North America; USD 25 elsewhere (effective 2004). adv. illus. index. back issues avail.; reprint service avail. from PQC. **Document type:** *Proceedings.* **Description:** Summary of research findings presented at the academy's annual meeting.
Former titles (until 1997): Academy of Management. Best Papers Proceedings (0896-7911); (until 1985): Academy of Management. Proceedings (0065-0668)
Media: CD-ROM. **Related titles:** Microform ed.: (from PQC).
Indexed: BPIA, BusI.
—CCC.
Published by: Academy of Management, 235 Elm Rd, P O Box 3020, Briarcliff Manor, NY 10510-3020. TEL 914-923-2607, FAX 914-923-2615, academy@pace.edu, http://www.aomonline.org. R&P Hope Tinsley. Adv. contact Terese Vivenzo. Circ: 4,000.

658 USA ISSN 0363-7425
HD28
➤ **ACADEMY OF MANAGEMENT REVIEW.** Text in English. 1976. q. USD 99 domestic individuals & academic libraries; USD 120 foreign individuals & academic libraries; USD 135 domestic to corporations; USD 150 foreign to corporations; USD 135 combined subscription domestic individuals & academic libraries for print & online eds.; USD 150 combined subscription foreign individuals & academic libraries for print & online eds.; USD 170 combined subscription domestic to corporations print & online eds.; USD 185 combined subscription foreign to corporations print & online eds. (effective 2004). adv. bk.rev. illus. Index. reprint service avail. from PQC. **Document type:** *Journal, Academic/Scholarly.* **Description:** Presents conceptual and theoretical manuscripts.
Related titles: Microform ed.: (from PQC); Online - full text ed.: (from EBSCO Publishing, Gale Group, JSTOR (Web-based Journal Archive), Northern Light Technology, Inc., O C L C Online Computer Library Center, Inc., ProQuest Information & Learning).
Indexed: ABIn, ADPA, AHCMS, ASEANManA, AgeL, BPI, BPIA, CPM, CurCont, Emerald, IBSS, Inspec, MEA&I, MEDLINE, ManagCont, PersLit, PsySCAP, PsycInfo, PsycholAb, QAb, RASB, SCIMP, SSCI, T&DA, e-psyche.
—BLDSC (0570.587600), IE, Infotrieve, ingenta. **CCC.**
Published by: Academy of Management, 235 Elm Rd, P O Box 3020, Briarcliff Manor, NY 10510-3020. TEL 914-923-2607, FAX 914-923-2615, academy@pace.edu, http://www.aom.pace.edu., http://www.aomonline.org. Ed. Richard J Klimoski. R&P Hope Tinsley. Adv. contact Terese Vivenzo. Circ: 11,500.

B

658 USA ISSN 1544-1458
HD30.28
➤ **ACADEMY OF STRATEGIC MANAGEMENT JOURNAL.** Text in English. s-a. **Document type:** *Journal, Academic/Scholarly.*
Related titles: Online - full text ed.
Published by: (Academy of Strategic Management), Allied Academies, 145 Travis Rd., P. O. Box 2689, Cullowhee, NC 28723. http://www.alliedacademies.org/strategic/index.html. Ed. William T Jackson.

658.02 CAN ISSN 1495-6802
ACCESS WEST. Text in English. 1997. q. **Document type:** *Newsletter.* **Description:** Features information about the department's programs and services in support of economic development and diversification in the West.
Related titles: Online - full text ed.: ISSN 1495-6543.
Published by: Western Economic Diversification Canada, 700-601 West Hastings St, Price Waterhouse Building, Vancouver, BC V6B 5G9, Canada. TEL 604-666-6256, FAX 604-666-2353, http://www.wd.gc.ca/mediacentre/accesswest/default_e.asp.

658 ESP ISSN 0044-5894
ACCION EMPRESARIAL; la revista del directivo. Text in Spanish. 1971. 4/yr. adv. bk.rev. bibl.; charts; illus.; stat.
—IE, Infotrieve.
Published by: Accion Social Empresarial Comision Nacional, Jose Maranon, 3, Madrid, 28010, Spain. TEL 593-27-58, FAX 5593-28-21. Ed. Alfonso Sanchez. Circ: 3,000.

ACCOUNTING, ACCOUNTABILITY & PERFORMANCE. see *BUSINESS AND ECONOMICS—Accounting*

ACCOUNTING OFFICE MANAGEMENT & ADMINISTRATION REPORT. see *BUSINESS AND ECONOMICS—Accounting*

658 USA ISSN 0147-1554
HC101 CODEN: ACBODW
ACROSS THE BOARD; reporting to management on business affairs. Text in English. 1939. 6/yr. USD 59 to non-members; USD 39 to members (effective 2005). adv. bk.rev. charts; illus. index. back issues avail.; reprints avail. **Document type:** *Magazine, Trade.* **Description:** Offers information and insights on matters of interest to managers in business and industry.
Formerly (until 1976): Conference Board Record (0010-5546); Supersedes: Conference Board Business-Management Record
Related titles: Online - full text ed.: (from bigchalk, EBSCO Publishing, H.W. Wilson, Northern Light Technology, Inc., O C L C Online Computer Library Center, Inc., ProQuest Information & Learning).
Indexed: ABIn, ABS&EES, ADPA, ASEANManA, ATI, AgeL, BAS, BLI, BPI, BPIA, BusI, CADCAM, CPM, DPD, Emerald, FutSurv, KES, M&MA, MEA&I, MEDLINE, ManagCont, PAIS, PROMT, PSI, PersLit, QAb, RASB, SSCI, T&DA, T&II.
—BLDSC (0578.887000), CASDDS, CISTI, IE, Infotrieve, ingenta. **CCC.**
Published by: Conference Board, Inc., 845 Third Ave, New York, NY 10022. TEL 212-339-0345, FAX 212-836-9740, atb@conference-board.com, http://www.conference-board.org. Ed. Albert Vogl. Pub. Matthew Budmen. Circ: 35,000.

658 ZAF ISSN 1684-1999
ACTA COMMERCII. Text in English. 2001. a.
Related titles: Online - full text ed.: (from International Network for the Availability of Scientific Publications, African Journals Online).
Published by: Rand Afrikaans University, Department of Business Management, PO Box 524, Auckland Park, 2006, South Africa. TEL 27-11-4893141, FAX 27-11-4892827, actacom@eb.rau.ac.za, http://www.inasp.info/ajol/journals/actac/about.html, http://general.rau.ac.za/.

658 FIN ISSN 1456-9426
HD28
ACTA POLYTECHNICA SCANDINAVICA. INDUSTRIAL MANAGEMENT AND BUSINESS ADMINISTRATION SERIES. Text in English. 2000. irreg. **Document type:** *Monographic series.*
Indexed: RefZh.
Published by: Finnish Academies of Technology, Mariankatu 8 B 11, Helsinki, 00170, Finland. TEL 358-9-278-2400, FAX 358-9-455-4626, facte@facte.com.

ACTION RESEARCH INTERNATIONAL. see *SCIENCES: COMPREHENSIVE WORKS*

658 ARG ISSN 0325-0814
ADMINISTRACION. Cover title: Revista de Ciencias Economicas. Temas de Administracion. Variant title: C G C E Administracion. Text in Spanish. 1913. q. adv. bk.rev.
Formerly (until 1972): Revista de Ciencias Economicas. Temas de Administracion (0325-0806); Supersedes in part (in 1970): Revista de Ciencias Economicas (0034-7779)
Published by: Colegio de Graduados en Ciencias Economicas, Viamonte, 1582, Capital Federal, Buenos Aires 1055, Argentina. Circ: 15,000.

658 CHL ISSN 0716-7628
HC191
ADMINISTRACION Y ECONOMIA UC. Variant title: Administracion y Economia Universidad Catolica. Text in Spanish. 1982. q. CLP 13 (effective 2002). adv.
Formerly (until 1990): Boletin Economico (0716-3894)
Related titles: Online - full text ed.
Published by: Pontificia Universidad Catolica de Chile, Facultad de Ciencias Economicas y Administrativas, Ave. Vicuna Mackenna 4860, Santiago, Chile. TEL 56-2-6864015, FAX 56-2-6864361, revista@volcan.facea.pcu.cl, http://www.faceapub.cl/, http://www.faceapuc.cl/. adv.: color page CLP 875,000.

658 USA ISSN 1549-974X
ADMINISTRATIVE PROFESSIONAL UPDATE. Abbreviated title: A A. Text in English. 1995. s-m. USD 195.50 (effective 2004). software rev. charts; tr.lit. **Document type:** *Newsletter.* **Description:** Provides information for the professional improvement of administrative assistants.
Formerly (until 2004): Administrative Assistant Adviser (1083-3846)
Published by: Progressive Business Publications, 370 Technology Dr, Malvern, PA 19355-1315. TEL 610-695-8600, 800-220-5000, FAX 610-647-8089, editor@pbp.com, http://www.pbp.com. Ed. Karen Dawson. R&P Curt Brown. Circ: 20,602 (paid).

658.4 CAN
➤ **ADMINISTRATIVE SCIENCES ASSOCIATION OF CANADA. ANNUAL CONFERENCE PROCEEDINGS.** Text in English. 1973. a. CND 350 domestic; USD 350 foreign. adv. illus. **Document type:** *Proceedings, Academic/Scholarly.*
Former titles: Canadian Association of Administrative Sciences. Annual Conference Proceedings (0318-5036); Association of Canadian Schools of Business. Annual Conference Proceedings (0066-9490)
—BLDSC (0696.521500).
Published by: Administrative Sciences Association of Canada, F.C. Manning School of Business, Acadia University, Wolfville, NS B0P 1X0, Canada. TEL 902-585-1285, http://www.asac.ca. Adv. contact Alain Gosselin. Circ: 900.

658 DEU ISSN 0720-6690
ADMINISTRATIVES MANAGEMENT. Text in German. 1976. irreg., latest vol.2, 1978. price varies. **Document type:** *Monographic series, Academic/Scholarly.*
Published by: Duncker und Humblot GmbH, Carl-Heinrich-Becker-Weg 9, Berlin, 12165, Germany. TEL 49-30-7900060, FAX 49-30-79000631, info@duncker-humblot.de, http://www.duncker-humblot.de.

ADULT DAY SERVICES LETTER. see *GERONTOLOGY AND GERIATRICS*

658 GBR
ADVANCED SERIES IN MANAGEMENT. Text in Dutch. 1983-1995; resumed 199?. irreg., latest 2003. price varies. **Document type:** *Monographic series, Academic/Scholarly.* **Description:** Aims to provide an integrated theoretical basis for studying various issues in management.
Indexed: Inspec, ZentMath.
—BLDSC.
Published by: Pergamon (Subsidiary of: Elsevier Science & Technology), The Boulevard, Langford Ln, East Park, Kidlington, Oxford OX5 1GB, United Kingdom. TEL 44-1865-843000, FAX 44-1865-843010, nlinfo-f@elsevier.nl, http://www.elsevier.com/wps/find/bookdescription.cws_home/BS_ASM/description#description, http://www.elsevier.nl. Ed. Ron Sanchez TEL 41-21-6180111. **Subscr. to:** Elsevier BV, PO Box 211, Amsterdam 1000 AE, Netherlands. TEL 31-20-485-3757, FAX 31-20-485-3432.

658 USA ISSN 0749-6826
HD30.28
ADVANCES IN APPLIED BUSINESS STRATEGY. Text in English. 1984. irreg., latest vol.9, 2005. price varies. back issues avail. **Document type:** *Monographic series, Academic/Scholarly.*
Related titles: Online - full text ed.: (from ScienceDirect).
—BLDSC (0698.934000). **CCC.**
Published by: J A I Press Inc. (Subsidiary of: Elsevier Science & Technology), 360 Park Ave S, New York, NY 10010-1710. TEL 212-989-5800, FAX 212-633-3990, usinfo-f@elsevier.com, http://www.elsevier.com/wps/find/bookdescription.cws_home/BS_AABS/description#description. Eds. A Heene, R Sanchez.

ADVANCES IN COMPETITIVENESS RESEARCH; ACR. see *BUSINESS AND ECONOMICS—International Commerce*

658 SGP
▼ ➤ **ADVANCES IN DOCTORAL RESEARCH IN MANAGEMENT.** Text in English. forthcoming 2006. irreg. USD 75, GBP 46 per vol. (effective 2006). 300 p./no.; **Document type:** *Monographic series, Academic/Scholarly.* **Description:** Covers methodological issues, techniques and approaches aimed at doctoral researchers in the management/business field.
Published by: World Scientific Publishing Co. Pte. Ltd., 5 Toh Tuck Link, Singapore, 596224, Singapore. TEL 65-466-5775, FAX 65-467-7667, series@wspc.com.sg, http://www.wspc.com/books/series/adrm_series.shtml, http://www.worldscientific.com. Ed. Luiz Moutinho. **Subscr. to:** Farrer Rd, PO Box 128, Singapore 912805, Singapore. TEL 65-382-5663, FAX 65-382-5919. **Dist. by:** World Scientific Publishing Ltd., 57 Shelton St, London WC2H 9HE, United Kingdom. TEL 44-20-78360888, FAX 44-20-78362020, sales@wspc.co.uk.; World Scientific Publishing Co., Inc., 1060 Main St, River Edge, NJ 07661. TEL 201-487-9655, 800-227-7562, FAX 201-487-9656, 888-977-2665, wspc@wspc.com.

658 USA ISSN 1074-7540
HB615
ADVANCES IN ENTREPRENEURSHIP, FIRM EMERGENCE AND GROWTH. Text in English. 1993. irreg., latest vol.8, 2005. price varies. back issues avail. **Document type:** *Monographic series, Academic/Scholarly.*
Related titles: Online - full text ed.: (from ScienceDirect).
—BLDSC (0705.465000). **CCC.**
Published by: J A I Press Inc. (Subsidiary of: Elsevier Science & Technology), 360 Park Ave S, New York, NY 10010-1710. TEL 212-989-5800, FAX 212-633-3990, usinfo-f@elsevier.com, http://www.elsevier.com/wps/find/bookdescription.cws_home/BS_AEFEG/description#description. Ed. J Edward Ketz.

658.15 332 USA ISSN 1046-5847
HG4001
ADVANCES IN FINANCIAL PLANNING AND FORECASTING. SUPPLEMENT. Text in English. 1989. irreg., latest vol.11, 2003. price varies. back issues avail. **Document type:** *Monographic series, Academic/Scholarly.*
—BLDSC (0706.580000). **CCC.**
Published by: J A I Press Inc. (Subsidiary of: Elsevier Science & Technology), 360 Park Ave S, New York, NY 10010-1710. TEL 212-989-5800, FAX 212-633-3990, usinfo-f@elsevier.com, http://www.elsevier.com/wps/find/bookdescription.cws_home/BS_AFPF/description#description. Ed. Cheng-Few Lee.

658 DEU ISSN 1611-3101
▼ **ADVANCES IN INFORMATION SYSTEMS AND MANAGEMENT SCIENCE.** Text in English, German. 2003. irreg., latest vol.4, 2003. price varies. **Document type:** *Monographic series, Academic/Scholarly.*
Published by: Logos Verlag Berlin, Comeniushof, Gubener Str 47, Berlin, 10243, Germany. TEL 49-30-42851090, FAX 49-30-42851092, redaktion@logos-verlag.de, http://www.logos-verlag.de.

658 USA ISSN 1572-0977
ADVANCES IN INTERDISCIPLINARY STUDIES OF WORK TEAMS. Text in English. 1994. a., latest vol.11, 2005. price varies. back issues avail. **Document type:** *Monographic series, Academic/Scholarly.*
Related titles: Online - full text ed.: (from ScienceDirect).
—BLDSC (0709.244000).
Published by: (University of North Texas, Department of Psychology, Center for the Study of Work Teams), J A I Press Inc. (Subsidiary of: Elsevier Science & Technology), 360 Park Ave S, New York, NY 10010-1710. TEL 212-989-5800, FAX 212-633-3990, usinfo-f@elsevier.com, http://www.elsevier.com/wps/find/bookdescription.cws_home/BS_AISWT/description#description. Ed. M Beyerlein.

ADVANCES IN INTERNATIONAL MANAGEMENT. see *BUSINESS AND ECONOMICS—International Commerce*

658 USA
ADVANCES IN ORGANIZATION DEVELOPMENT. Text in English. 1990. irreg., latest vol.3, 1995. USD 73.25. **Document type:** *Academic/Scholarly.*
Indexed: e-psyche.
Published by: Ablex Publishing Corporation (Subsidiary of: Greenwood Publishing Group Inc.), 88 Post Rd W, Westport, CT 06881. TEL 203-323-9606, FAX 203-357-8446. Ed. Fred Massarik.

658 NLD ISSN 1566-1075
ADVANCES IN ORGANIZATION STUDIES. Text in English. 1999. irreg.
—ingenta.
Published by: John Benjamins Publishing Co., PO Box 36224, Amsterdam, 1020 ME, Netherlands.

ADVANCES IN SERVICES MARKETING AND MANAGEMENT. see *BUSINESS AND ECONOMICS—Marketing And Purchasing*

658 USA ISSN 0742-3322
HD30.28
ADVANCES IN STRATEGIC MANAGEMENT. Text in English. 1983. irreg., latest vol.21, 2004. price varies. back issues avail. **Document type:** *Monographic series, Academic/Scholarly.* **Description:** Dedicated to communicating innovative, new research that advances theory and practice in Strategic Management.
Related titles: Online - full text ed.: (from ScienceDirect).
Indexed: SSCI.
—BLDSC (0711.584000), IE, ingenta. **CCC.**
Published by: J A I Press Inc. (Subsidiary of: Elsevier Science & Technology), 360 Park Ave S, New York, NY 10010-1710. TEL 212-989-5800, FAX 212-633-3990, usinfo-f@elsevier.com, http://www.elsevier.com/wps/find/bookdescription.cws_home/BS_ASTM/description#description. Ed. Joel A C Baum.

658 USA
ADVANCES IN THE MANAGEMENT OF ORGANIZATIONAL QUALITY. Text in English. 1996. irreg., latest vol.5, 2000. price varies. **Document type:** *Monographic series, Academic/Scholarly.* **Description:** Aims create an academic, theoretically driven dialogue on the management of quality efforts in organizations.
—BLDSC (0709.338500).
Published by: J A I Press Inc. (Subsidiary of: Elsevier Science & Technology), 360 Park Ave S, New York, NY 10010-1710. TEL 212-989-5800, FAX 212-633-3990, usinfo-f@elsevier.com, http://www.elsevier.nl/inca/tree/?key=B1AMOQ, http://www.elsevier.com. Eds. Donald B Fedor, Soumen Ghosh.

658 USA ISSN 1041-6749
HG4028.W65
ADVANCES IN WORKING CAPITAL MANAGEMENT. Text in English. 1988. irreg., latest vol.4, 2001. price varies. back issues avail. **Document type:** *Monographic series, Academic/Scholarly.*
—BLDSC (0712.165000).
Published by: J A I Press Inc. (Subsidiary of: Elsevier Science & Technology), 360 Park Ave S, New York, NY 10010-1710. TEL 212-989-5800, FAX 212-633-3990, usinfo-f@elsevier.com, http://www.elsevier.com/wps/find/bookdescription.cws_home/BS_AWCM/description#description. Ed. Yong H Kim.

ADVISOR (NEW YORK). see *BUSINESS AND ECONOMICS—Marketing And Purchasing*

658 GBR ISSN 0963-8296
AFTERSALES MANAGEMENT. Text in English. 1989. 10/yr. GBP 125. back issues avail. **Document type:** *Magazine, Trade.* **Description:** Practice management guide focused on profit-earning opportunities in the service, parts and bodyshop departments. Topics, ideas and new concepts to help improve performance and profits.
Formerly (until 1991): Sewells Training on Aftersales Management (0963-2549)
Published by: Emap Automotive Ltd., Sewells Information and Research, Wentworth House, Wentworth St, Peterborough, Northants PE1 1DS, United Kingdom. TEL 44-1733-468255, FAX 44-1733-468349, http://www.sewells.co.uk, http://www.emap.com. Eds. Chris Oakham, Jerry Connolly.

AGENCYINC. see *TRAVEL AND TOURISM*

658 ITA
AGENDA MONACI. Text in Italian. 1970. a. **Description:** Contains information on the first 1000 top ranking Italian companies.
Former titles: Guida Monaci. Agenda Nazionale (1122-8490); (until 1992): Guida Monaci. Agenda Edizione Nazionale (1123-0932); (until 1986): Guida Monaci. Agenda (1123-0924)
Published by: Guida Monaci SpA, Via Salaria 1319, Rome, 00138, Italy. TEL 39-06-8887777, FAX 39-06-8889996, guida.monaci@italybygm.it, http://www.italybygm.it.

AGGREGATES MANAGER. see *BUILDING AND CONSTRUCTION*

658 USA
AGILE ENTERPRISE. Text in English. 1996. irreg., latest 2002. price varies. adv. **Document type:** *Monographic series, Academic/Scholarly.* **Description:** Covers the new "agile" organizations which provide goods and information in an information-rich environment by coordinating intercompany processes. Includes articles on the following areas: enabling subsystems, organizational infrastructure, human resources, international aspects, legal, accounting and organizational issues, performance measures, and technology.
Formerly (until 1997): Agility and Virtual Organization (1083-1339)
—CCC.
Published by: (Agility Forum), John Wiley & Sons, Inc., 111 River St, Hoboken, NJ 07030-5774. Ed. Rick Dove. adv.: B&W page GBP 640, color page GBP 1,515; trim 210 x 279.

AIRLINE BUSINESS; the voice of airline managements. see *TRANSPORTATION—Air Transport*

AIRPORT SUPPORT. see *TRANSPORTATION—Air Transport*

658 SWE ISSN 0282-7336
AKTUELL SAEKERHET. Text in Swedish. 1982. bi-m. SEK 330 (effective 2000). adv. **Document type:** *Magazine, Trade.*
Incorporates (in 1985): Det Handlar om Saekerhet; Formerly (until vol.3, 1985): Aktuellt Foeretagsskydd
Published by: Saekerhetsfoerlaget, Midskogsgraend 5, Stockholm, 11543, Sweden. TEL 46-8-6614200, FAX 46-8-6600140. Ed. Kenneth Andren. Adv. contact Lennart Roennquist. B&W page SEK 20,900, color page SEK 25,900; trim 185 x 271. Circ: 25,000.

658 USA ISSN 1079-1191
THE ALLIANCE ANALYST. Abbreviated title: A A. Text in English. 1994. m. **Document type:** *Magazine, Corporate.* **Description:** Reports on issues of interest to senior executives and alliance managers.
Related titles: Online - full text ed.
Published by: Newcap Communications, Inc., 3133 Connecticut Ave NW, Apt. 1125, Washington, DC 20008-5113. helpdesk@allianceanalyst.com, http://www.allianceanalyst.com. Ed. James Bamford.

658 ESP ISSN 0002-6549
HD28
ALTA DIRECCION. Text in Spanish. 1965. bi-m. adv. bk.rev. charts; illus.; stat. index, cum.index. **Document type:** *Trade.* **Description:** Covers Deontologi of the company, financing and accounting, information systems, personnel management, stocks and capital, production, marketing, and economic activities.
Indexed: M&MA, PAIS, SCIMP.
—BLDSC (0802.500000), CINDOC, IE, Infotrieve. **CCC.**
Published by: Alta Direccion, S.A., C Balmes 191, 5o 4a, Barcelona, 08006, Spain. TEL 34-93-410-9619, FAX 34-93-410-9739, revista@altadireccion.es, http://www.altadireccion.es/. Ed. Rafael Badet Vilanova. Circ: 9,360.

658 ESP
ALTA DIRECCION. MONOGRAFIAS. Text in Spanish. irreg., latest vol.215, 2001. price varies. **Document type:** *Monographic series, Trade.*
Published by: Alta Direccion, S.A., C Balmes 191, 5o 4a, Barcelona, 08006, Spain. TEL 34-93-410-9619, FAX 34-93-410-9739, revista@altadireccion.es, http://www.altadireccion.es/.

658 340 USA ISSN 0191-863X
KF318.A1
ALTMAN WEIL PENSA REPORT TO LEGAL MANAGEMENT. Text in English. 1974. m. CND 245, USD 195 domestic; USD 220 foreign. bk.rev. bibl.; charts; illus.; stat. index. back issues avail. **Document type:** *Trade.* **Description:** Geared to the legal profession.
—CCC.
Published by: Altman Weil Pensa Publications, Inc., PO Box 625, Newtown, PA 19073. TEL 610-359-9900, FAX 610-359-0467, http://www.altmanweil.com. Ed. James Wilber. R&P Charles Huxsan. Circ: 1,000.

AMBULATORY OUTREACH. see *MEDICAL SCIENCES*

658 USA ISSN 0360-7100
HD30.23
AMERICAN INSTITUTE FOR DECISION SCIENCES. SOUTHEAST SECTION. PROCEEDINGS. Text in English. 1971. a. USD 10. abstr.; charts; pat. index. **Document type:** *Proceedings.*
Published by: American Institute for Decision Sciences, Southeast Section, Dept of Business Administration, Virginia Polytechnic Institute and State University, Blacksburg, VA 24061. TEL 203-961-6601. Ed. Bernard W Taylor III. Circ: 400.

658.8 796.7 USA ISSN 1549-9499
▼ **AMERICAN IRON RETAILER.** Text in English. 2004 (Aug./Sept.). bi-m. free (effective 2005). adv. **Document type:** *Magazine, Trade.*
Published by: T A M Communications Inc., 1010 Summer St, Stamford, CT 06905-5503. TEL 203-425-8777, FAX 203-425-8775. Eds. Marjorie Kleiman, Buzz Kanter. Adv. contact Steve Jaten.

THE AMERICAN JOURNAL OF EVALUATION. see *SOCIAL SCIENCES: COMPREHENSIVE WORKS*

AMERICAN JOURNAL OF MATHEMATICAL AND MANAGEMENT SCIENCES. see *MATHEMATICS*

AMERICAN JOURNAL OF MEDICAL QUALITY. see *MEDICAL SCIENCES*

658 USA ISSN 0065-9193
AMERICAN MANAGEMENT ASSOCIATION. SEMINAR PROGRAM. Text in English. 1963. irreg.
Published by: American Management Association, 1610 Broadway, New York, NY 10019. TEL 212-586-8100, http://www.amanet.org.

658 346.066 USA ISSN 0894-0622
AMERICAN SOCIETY OF CORPORATE SECRETARIES. LOS ANGELES CHAPTER. NEWSLETTER. Text in English. 1981. 3/yr. looseleaf. **Document type:** *Newsletter.* **Description:** Business and legal information for elected corporate secretaries in southwestern states.
Published by: American Society of Corporate Secretaries, Inc., Los Angeles Chapter, c/o American Society of Corporate Secretaries, 521 Fifth Ave, New York, NY 10175-0003. Ed. James K Baer. Circ: 300.

AMERICAN SOCIETY OF MECHANICAL ENGINEERS. MANAGEMENT DIVISION. NEWSLETTER. see *ENGINEERING—Engineering Mechanics And Materials*

AMERICAN VENTURE; for entrepreneurs and accredited investors. see *BUSINESS AND ECONOMICS—Investments*

ANNALS OF OPERATIONS RESEARCH. see *COMPUTERS*

ANNUAL CONFERENCE ON STATISTICS, COMPUTER SCIENCE AND OPERATIONS RESEARCH. PROCEEDINGS. see *COMPUTERS—Abstracting, Bibliographies, Statistics*

658 USA ISSN 1092-4876
HD28
➤ **ANNUAL EDITIONS: MANAGEMENT.** Text in English. 1991. a., latest 2003, 12th ed. USD 20.31 per vol. (effective 2004). illus. **Document type:** *Academic/Scholarly.*
Formerly (until 1992): Annual Editions: Readings in Management (0195-4784)
Published by: McGraw-Hill - Dushkin (Subsidiary of: McGraw-Hill Higher Education), 2460 Kerper Blvd, Dubuque, IA 52001. TEL 800-243-6532, customer.service@mcgraw-hill.com, http://www.dushkin.com/text-data/catalog/0072874414.mhtml. Ed. Fred H Maidment. Pub. Ian Nielsen. R&P Cheryl Greenleaf.

658 USA ISSN 1085-035X
HM134
(YEAR) ANNUAL. VOLUME 1: TRAINING; developing human resources. Text in English. 1972. a. USD 39.95 paperbound ed.; USD 89.95 looselead ed.. **Document type:** *Trade.* **Description:** Contains activities, instruments, and articles for use in human resource development.
Supersedes in part (in 1995): Annual. Developing Human Resources (1046-333X); Which was formerly (until 1984): Annual for Facilitators, Trainers, and Consultants (0732-037X); (until 1982): Annual Handbook for Group Facilitators (0094-601X)
—BLDSC (1073.611700), IE, ingenta.
Published by: Pfeiffer, 350 Sansome St, San Francisco, CA 94104-1304. Ed. J William Pfeiffer. Circ: 9,000.

B

658 USA ISSN 1085-0368
HM134
(YEAR) ANNUAL. VOLUME 2: CONSULTING. Text in English. 1972. a. looseleaf. USD 95 (effective 2005). **Document type:** *Trade.* **Description:** Contains activities, instruments, and articles for use in human resource development.
Supersedes in part (in 1995): Annual. Developing Human Resources (1046-333X); Which was formerly (until 1984): Annual for Faciltators, Trainers, and Consultants (0732-037X); (until 1982): Annual Handbook for Group Facilitators (0094-601X)
—BLDSC (1073.611700), IE, ingenta.
Published by: Pfeiffer, 350 Sansome St, San Francisco, CA 94104-1304. Ed. J William Pfeiffer.

APOTHEKEN-PRAXIS; Zeitschrift fuer Marketing - Management - Kommunikation. see *PHARMACY AND PHARMACOLOGY*

658 USA ISSN 0276-8976
HD30.23
➤ **APPLICATIONS OF MANAGEMENT SCIENCE.** Text in English. 1981. irreg., latest vol.11, 2004. price varies. back issues avail. **Document type:** *Monographic series, Academic/Scholarly.* **Description:** Presents state-of-the-art studies in the application of Management Science to the solution of significant managerial decision making problems.
Related titles: ♦ Supplement(s): Applications of Management Science. Supplement. ISSN 0884-1799.
Indexed: MathR.
—BLDSC (1571.150000), IE. **CCC.**
Published by: J A I Press Inc. (Subsidiary of: Elsevier Science & Technology), 360 Park Ave S, New York, NY 10010-1710. TEL 212-989-5800, FAX 212-633-3990, usinfo-f@elsevier.com, http://www.elsevier.com/wps/find/bookdescription.cws_home/BS_MANSC/description#description. Eds. G R Reeves, Kenneth D Lawrence.

658 USA ISSN 0884-1799
HD28
APPLICATIONS OF MANAGEMENT SCIENCE. SUPPLEMENT. Text in English. 1984. irreg., latest vol.1, 1984.
Related titles: ♦ Supplement to: Applications of Management Science. ISSN 0276-8976.
Published by: J A I Press Inc. (Subsidiary of: Elsevier Science & Technology), 360 Park Ave S, New York, NY 10010-1710. TEL 212-989-5800, FAX 212-633-3990, usinfo-f@elsevier.com, http://www.elsevier.com.

AQUACULTURE ECONOMICS & MANAGEMENT. see *FISH AND FISHERIES*

AQUATICS INTERNATIONAL; the source for facility products, services and management. see *SPORTS AND GAMES*

658.4 KWT ISSN 1029-855X
➤ **ARAB JOURNAL OF ADMINISTRATIVE SCIENCES.** Text in Arabic, English. 1993. 3/yr. KWD 3 domestic to individuals; USD 15 foreign to individuals; KWD 15 domestic Government; USD 60 foreign Government; KWD 0.75 newsstand/cover domestic (effective 2005). abstr.; bibl.; stat. back issues avail. **Document type:** *Magazine, Academic/Scholarly.* **Description:** Features management, accounting, finance, marketing, investment, management information system, organizational behavior, quality management, stock markets application of statistics in business, decision making in business, decision support, administration and other related fields.
Related titles: Fax ed.

Published by: Academic Publication Council, Kuwait University/Majliss an-Nushir al-Elmi, P O Box 13411, Keifan, 71955, Kuwait. TEL 965-4830173, FAX 965-4845372, ajoas@kuc01.kuniv.edu.kw, http://www.pubcouncil.kuniv.edu.kw/ajas. Ed. A A Al-Saffar. Circ: 2,000.

➤ **ASIA - PACIFIC BUSINESS SERIES.** see *BUSINESS AND ECONOMICS*

658.0071 NLD
ASIA PACIFIC EXECUTIVE EDUCATION DIRECTORY. Text in English. 1995. a. EUR 195 (effective 2005). adv. **Document type:** *Directory.* **Description:** Lists executive training programs at Asia Pacific business schools and management training centers.
Former titles: Asia Pacific Management Education Directory; Asian Management Education Directory (1383-6226)
Published by: E M D Centre, Naarderstraat 296, Huizen, 1272 NT, Netherlands. TEL 31-35-6951111, FAX 31-35-6951900, http://www.emdcentre.com/. Eds. Rino Schreuder, Yvonne Kuysters.

B

658 USA ISSN 0217-4561
HD28 CODEN: APJMFN
ASIA PACIFIC JOURNAL OF MANAGEMENT. Text mainly in English. 1983. q. EUR 318, USD 328, GBP 205 combined subscription to institutions print & online eds. (effective 2005). adv. bk.rev. reprint service avail. from PSC. **Document type:** *Journal, Academic/Scholarly.* **Description:** Contains articles on economic analysis, environment and development of the Asia-Pacific Region.
Related titles: Online - full text ed.: ISSN 1572-9958 (from EBSCO Publishing, Gale Group, IngentaConnect, Kluwer Online, O C L C Online Computer Library Center, Inc., ProQuest Information & Learning, Springer LINK, Swets Information Services).
Indexed: ABIn, APEL, BAS, BPI, BibLing, Emerald, Inspec, RASB, RefZh.
—BLDSC (1742.260700), IE, Infotrieve, ingenta. **CCC.**
Published by: (National University of Singapore, Faculty of Business Administration SGP), Springer-Verlag New York, Inc. (Subsidiary of: Springer Science+Business Media), 233 Spring St, New York, NY 10013. TEL 212-460-1500, FAX 212-460-1575, service@springer-ny.com, http://springerlink.metapress.com/openurl.asp?genre=journal&issn=0217-4561, http://www.springer-ny.com. Ed. Andrew Delios. Circ: 400. **Subscr. to:** Journal Fulfillment, PO Box 2485, Secaucus, NJ 07096-2485. TEL 201-348-4033, FAX 201-348-4505, journals@springer-ny.com.

ASIA PACIFIC JOURNAL OF OPERATIONAL RESEARCH. see *COMPUTERS*

658 USA
ASIA WEEKLY EXECUTIVE BRIEFING. Text in English. w. looseleaf. USD 795 (effective 2001). stat. 8 p./no.; back issues avail. **Document type:** *Bulletin, Consumer.* **Description:** Bulletin on political, economic and business events in India, Indonesia, Korea, Malaysia, The Philippines, Singapore and Thailand.
Formerly (until 2000): Southeast Asia Weekly Fax Bulletin
Media: Fax. **Related titles:** E-mail ed.
Published by: Orbis Publications, LLC, 1924 47th St NW, Washington, DC 20007-1901. TEL 202-298-7936, FAX 202-298-7938, sfoster@orbispub.com, http://www.orbispublications.com. R&P David Mosedale.

658 GBR ISSN 1472-4782
➤ **ASIAN BUSINESS & MANAGEMENT.** Text in English. 2002. 3/yr. USD 118 combined subscription in United States to individuals print & online; GBP 72 combined subscription elsewhere to individuals print & online; USD 535 combined subscription in United States to institutions print & online; GBP 324 combined subscription elsewhere to institutions print & online (effective 2005). bk.rev. abstr. **Document type:** *Journal, Academic/Scholarly.* **Description:** Seeks to encourage the awareness of social issues in the study of business and management in Asia.
Related titles: Online - full content ed.; Online - full text ed.: ISSN 1476-9328. GBP 243 in Europe to institutions; USD 365 elsewhere to institutions (effective 2004) (from EBSCO Publishing, Gale Group, IngentaConnect, O C L C Online Computer Library Center, Inc., ProQuest Information & Learning, Swets Information Services).
Indexed: ABIn, IBR, IBSS, IBZ, Inspec.
—BLDSC (1742.403100), IE. **CCC.**
Published by: Palgrave Macmillan Ltd. (Subsidiary of: Macmillan Publishers Ltd.), Houndmills, Basingstoke, Hants RG21 6XS, United Kingdom. TEL 44-1256-329242, FAX 44-1256-810526, abm@sheffield.ac.uk, http://www.palgrave-journals.com/abm, http://www.palgrave.com. Ed. Harukiyo Hasegawa. Pub. David Bull TEL 44-1256-329242. Adv. contact Robert Sloan TEL 44-20-88827199.

➤ **ASIAN INSTITUTE OF TECHNOLOGY. ABSTRACTS ON MANAGEMENT OF TECHNOLOGY AND INTERNATIONAL BUSINESS.** see *TECHNOLOGY: COMPREHENSIVE WORKS—Abstracting, Bibliographies, Statistics*

➤ **ASIAN INSTITUTE OF TECHNOLOGY. M O T I C MONOGRAPHS.** see *BUSINESS AND ECONOMICS—Abstracting, Bibliographies, Statistics*

658 IND ISSN 0972-8201
➤ **ASIAN JOURNAL OF MANAGEMENT CASES.** Text in English. s-a. INR 425 to individuals in India, Nepal & Bhutan; USD 18 SAARC to individuals; USD 61 in the Americas to individuals other Asian countries; INR 720 to institutions in India, Nepal & Bhutan; USD 212, GBP 121 to institutions; USD 221, GBP 126 combined subscription to institutions print & online eds. (effective 2006). **Document type:** *Journal, Academic/Scholarly.* **Description:** Focusing on real life management issues in the unique socio-economic environment of Asia. It covers all the major management areas including accounting and finance, business ethics, entrepreneurship, human resource management, marketing, organizational behavior and strategic management.
Related titles: Online - full text ed.: USD 210, GBP 120 to institutions (effective 2006) (from EBSCO Publishing, Sage Publications, Inc.).
Published by: Sage Publications India Pvt. Ltd. (Subsidiary of: Sage Publications, Inc.), M-32 Market, Greater Kailash-I, PO Box 4215, New Delhi, 110 048, India. TEL 91-11-6444958, FAX 91-11-6472426, http://www.indiasage.com/browse/journal.asp?Journalid=15&Subject_Name=&SubSubjectName=&mode=1, http://www.sagepub.com. Ed. Naim Sipra. **Subscr. in Europe, Middle East and Australasia to:** Sage Publications Ltd., 1 Oliver's Yard, 55 City Rd, London EC1 1SP, United Kingdom. TEL 44-20-73740645, FAX 44-20-73748741, subscription@sagepub.co.uk; **Subscr. in the Americas to:** Sage Publications, Inc., 2455 Teller Rd, Thousand Oaks, CA 91320. TEL 805-499-0721, FAX 805-499-0871, journals@sagepub.com.

658 PHL ISSN 0116-7790
➤ **THE ASIAN MANAGER.** Text in English. 1988. bi-m. PHP 650 domestic; USD 27 foreign; USD 5 newsstand/cover. adv. bk.rev. back issues avail. **Document type:** *Academic/Scholarly.* **Description:** Covers management trends and analysis, realistic management issues and the opinions of key Asian decision-makers.
Related titles: E-mail ed.; Online - full text ed.: (from LexisNexis).
Indexed: Emerald, IPP.
—BLDSC (1742.648000).
Published by: Asian Institute of Management, Joseph McMicking Campus, 123 Paseo de Roxas, Makati Mm, Philippines. TEL 63-2-892-4011, FAX 63-2-817-9240, tam@aim.edu.ph, http://www.aim.edu.ph. Ed. Patricia L Lontoc. Pub. Felipe Alfonso. R&P Millie Ferrer. Adv. contact Edythe Bautista. B&W page USD 1,659, color page USD 2,371; trim 210 x 276. Circ: 3,500 (paid); 18,500 (controlled).

658 USA ISSN 0731-2350
ASK!. Text in English. 1982. m. USD 95. bk.rev.
Published by: Accurate Information Service, 9711 MacArthur Blvd, Bethesda, MD 20817. TEL 301-365-0412. Ed. Louis V Lombardo.

ASSCOMPACT; Fachmagazin fuer Risiko- und Kapitalmanagement. see *INSURANCE*

658 USA ISSN 0098-9169
HV8290
ASSETS PROTECTION; for senior managers responsible for internal controls and safeguards for financial, physical and intellectual assets. Text in English. 1975. bi-m. USD 72 domestic; USD 84 in Canada & Mexico; USD 104 elsewhere (effective 2005). **Document type:** *Newsletter, Trade.* **Description:** Provides management with ideas and tools to create and maintain a practical, cost-effective compliance and protection programs for intellectual property assets.
Published by: Assets Protection Publishing, 5029 Sheboygan Ave #201, Madison, WI 53705. Ed., R&P Paul Shaw.

658 CAN ISSN 1498-6094
ASSOCIATION & MEETING DIRECTOR. Text in English. 2001. bi-m. CND 40 (effective 2005).
Address: 225-530 Century Street, Winnipeg, MB R3H 0Y4, Canada. TEL 888-573-1136, subscriptions@associationdirector.ca, http://www.associationdirector.ca. Ed. Vivian Shelley. Pub. Wayne Unruh. Circ: 14,000 (controlled).

658 AUS
ASSOCIATION C B E MANAGEMENT. Text in English. d. AUD 790 (effective 2001). adv. bk.rev.; Website rev. 1 p./no.; back issues avail. **Document type:** *Newspaper, Trade.* **Description:** Provides information for an audience of entrepreneurial managers in association and community business enterprises.
Media: E-mail.
Published by: Civic Chamber Australia, 19 Prospect St, Box Hill, VIC 3128, Australia. TEL 61-3-9899-3448, FAX 61-3-9899-3449, admin@civic-chamber.com.au, http://www.civic-chamber.com.au. adv.: page AUD 500; 180 x 250. Circ: 1,000.

658.00715 USA
ASSOCIATION EDUCATOR. Text in English. m. membership. adv. **Description:** For managers of educational programs of associations.
Former titles: Association Education Directory; Education Director
Published by: (Education Section), American Society of Association Executives, 1575 Eye St, N W, Washington, DC 20005-1168. TEL 202-626-2821, FAX 202-289-4049, http://www.asaenet.org. Circ: 1,600.

658.4 USA
ASSOCIATION EXECUTIVE. Text in English. 1985. bi-m. free membership (effective 2004). adv. **Document type:** *Magazine, Trade.*
Related titles: Online - full text ed.
Published by: (New York Society of Association Executives), Naylor Publications, Inc., 5950 NW 1st Pl, Gainesville, FL 32607-6018. TEL 800-369-6220, http://www.nysaenet.org/exec/index.cfm, http://www.naylor.com. Adv. contact Kathryn Hillgardner. B&W page USD 2,969.50; trim 8.375 x 10.875. Circ: 3,000.

658.45 USA
PN4073
ASSOCIATION FOR COMMUNICATION ADMINISTRATION. JOURNAL. Abbreviated title: J A C A. Text in English. 1972. 3/yr. USD 75, USD 60 membership (effective 2000). adv. bk.rev. reprint service avail. from PQC. **Document type:** *Academic/Scholarly.* **Description:** Incorporates information useful to academic administrators in all areas of the communication arts and sciences.
Former titles (until 1992): A C A Bulletin (0360-0939); Association of Departments and Administrators in Communication. Bulletin
Related titles: Microfilm ed.
Indexed: CIJE, ERA, ETA, HECAB, IJCS.
—BLDSC, IE.
Published by: Association for Communication Administration, 5105 F Backlick Rd, Annandale, VA 22003. TEL 703-750-0533, FAX 703-914-9471. Ed. Ronald Applbaum. R&P Ellie Bruner. Circ: 400.

658 011 USA
ASSOCIATION FOR CONVENTION OPERATIONS MANAGEMENT. CONVENTION PROCEEDINGS✶. Text in English. a. **Document type:** *Proceedings.*
Published by: Association for Convention Operations Management, 2965 Flowers Rd S, Ste 105, Atlanta, GA 30341-5520. TEL 404-351-3220, FAX 404-351-3348.

ASSOCIATION FOR INVESTMENT MANAGEMENT AND RESEARCH. MEMBERSHIP DIRECTORY. see *BUSINESS AND ECONOMICS—Investments*

658 USA
ASSOCIATION FOR QUALITY AND PARTICIPATION. ANNUAL CONFERENCE AND RESOURCE MART TRANSACTIONS. Text in English. 1979. a. USD 27.50. back issues avail. **Document type:** *Proceedings.* **Description:** Quality and productivity improvements through team problem solving.
Formerly: International Association of Quality Circles. Annual Conference and Resource Mart Transactions
Published by: American Society for Quality, 600 N Plankinton Ave, Milwaukee, WI 53203. TEL 513-381-1959, FAX 513-381-0070. Circ: 3,000.

658 USA ISSN 0004-5578
HF5001
ASSOCIATION MANAGEMENT. Text in English. 1949. m. USD 60; USD 5 per issue (effective 2005). adv. bk.rev. bibl.; illus. index, cum.index: 1970-1988. back issues avail.; reprints avail. **Document type:** *Magazine, Trade.* **Description:** Covers the management of an association.
Formerly: American Society of Association Executives. Journal
Related titles: Microform ed.: (from PQC); Online - full text ed.: (from EBSCO Publishing, Florida Center for Library Automation, Gale Group, H.W. Wilson, Northern Light Technology, Inc., O C L C Online Computer Library Center, Inc., ProQuest Information & Learning).
Indexed: ABIn, ATI, AgeL, BPI, BPIA, BldManAb, BusI, ConcrAb, LRI, MEDLINE, ManagCont, PAIS, PMA, PSI, T&II, WorkRelAb.
—BLDSC (1746.703000), IE, Infotrieve, ingenta.
Published by: American Society of Association Executives, 1575 I St, N W, Washington, DC 20005-1168. TEL 202-626-2723, FAX 202-371-8825, editorial@asaenet.org, http://www.asaenet.org/magazine. Eds. Keith C Skillman, Carol Schweitzer. Pub. Karl Ely. Adv. contacts Vernon Hemphill, Karl Ely. Circ: 24,000 (paid).

658 GBR ISSN 1368-4213
ASSOCIATION MANAGER. Text in English. 1997. bi-m. GBP 42 (effective 1999). adv. **Document type:** *Trade.* **Description:** Provides full coverage of all aspects of running and managing a modern and effective membership organization.
Published by: Plaza Publishing Ltd, 3 Rectory Grove, London, SW4 0DX, United Kingdom. TEL 44-171-819-1200, FAX 44-1719-191210. Ed. Daniel Phelan. Pub. Andrew Maiden. Adv. contact Alice Frackelton. B&W page GBP 1,195, color page GBP 1,395.

658 USA
ASSOCIATION NEWS (LOS ANGELES). Text in English. 1976. m. free to qualified personnel (effective 2004). adv. bk.rev. back issues avail. **Document type:** *Magazine, Trade.* **Description:** Contains information of interest to association executives and meeting planners.

Formerly: Western Association News (1062-5771)
Published by: Schneider Publishing Co., 11835 W Olympic Blvd, Ste 1265, Los Angeles, CA 90064. TEL 310-577-3700, FAX 310-577-3715, info@schneiderpublishing.com, http://www.associationnews.com/, http://www.schneiderpublishing.com/. Ed. Ann Shepphird. Pub., R&P Timothy Schneider. Adv. contact Sonia Simpson. B&W page USD 2,300, color page USD 3,285; 10 x 7. Circ: 10,000.

358.0029   GBR
ASSOCIATION OF M B AS ADDRESS BOOK. Text in English. 1969. a. GBP 80 per issue to non-members (effective 2001). adv. 500 p./no. 2 cols./p.; **Document type:** Directory.
Description: Lists all members of the association in alphabetical and geographical order, by business school and by business sector and company.
Formerly: Business Graduates Association Address Book (0308-0455)
Related titles: Diskette ed.
Indexed: Emerald.
Published by: (Association of M B As Ltd.), A P Information Services, Marlborough House, 298 Regents Park Rd, London, N3 2UU, United Kingdom. TEL 44-20-83499988, FAX 44-20-83499797, amba@ap-info.co.uk, info@apinfo.co.uk, http://www.ap-info.co.uk. Eds. Debbie Robel, Laura Storr. Adv. contact Caron Thomas TEL 44-1788-522279. page GBP 600; 150 x 210. Circ: 8,000.

ASSOCIATION OF TALENT AGENTS. NEWSLETTER. see THEATER

658   AUS   ISSN 1324-910X
ASSOCIATION TIMES. Text in English. 1994. m. looseleaf. AUD 77 (effective 2001). adv. bk.rev. 16 p./no. 6 cols./p.; back issues avail. **Document type:** Newspaper, Trade.
Description: Provides information for an audience of entrepreneurial managers across the twenty-two dominions, in the non-profit sector.
Former titles (until 1994): A M News (Box Hill) (1037-6445); (until 1991): Association Management (Box Hill) (1036-1871)
Published by: Civic Chamber Australia, 19 Prospect St, Box Hill, VIC 3128, Australia. TEL 61-3-9899-3448, FAX 61-3-9899-3449, admin@civic-chamber.com.au, http://civic.chamber.com.au, http://www.civic-chamber.com.au. Ed., Pub. Bernard Kelly. Adv. contact Warren Spence. B&W page AUD 3,553, color page USD 3,953; trim 383 x 259. Circ: 5,000 (paid and controlled).

AUDITOPICS. see BUSINESS AND ECONOMICS

658   AUT   ISSN 1813-6923
▼ **AUFSICHTSRAT AKTUELL.** Text in German. 2004. bi-m. EUR 86.24 (effective 2005). **Document type:** Journal, Trade.
Published by: Linde Verlag Wien GmbH, Scheydgasse 24, Vienna, W 1211, Austria. TEL 43-1-246300, FAX 43-1-2463023, office@lindeverlag.at, http://www.lindeverlag.at.

AUSTRALASIAN TRANSPORT NEWS. see TRANSPORTATION—Trucks And Trucking

AUSTRALIAN ADMINISTRATIVE LAW JOURNAL. see LAW—Corporate Law

658   AUS   ISSN 1324-3209
➤ **AUSTRALIAN AND NEW ZEALAND ACADEMY OF MANAGEMENT. JOURNAL.** Text in English. 1995. s-a. AUD 100 domestic; USD 133 foreign (effective 2005). bk.rev. abstr.; bibl.; illus.; stat. cum.index: 1995-2004. back issues avail.; reprints avail. **Document type:** Journal, Academic/Scholarly.
Description: Publishes academically rigorous papers and case studies that will advance knowledge on practical and theoretical aspects of management and the links between them.
Related titles: Online - full text ed.: (from O C L C Online Computer Library Center, Inc., ProQuest Information & Learning).
Indexed: ABIn.
—BLDSC (4706.400000).
Published by: Australian and New Zealand Academy of Management, ANZAM Secretariat, c/o School of Management, University of Technology, Sydney, Kuring-gai Campus, PO Box 222, Lindfield, NSW 2070, Australia. TEL 61-2-95145582, FAX 61-2-95145587, anzam@uts.edu.au, http://www.anzam.uts.edu.au/janzam/index.htm. Ed., Pub. Ken Parry. Circ: 200 (paid); 300 (controlled).

➤ **AUSTRALIAN DENTAL PRACTICE MAGAZINE.** see MEDICAL SCIENCES—Dentistry

658   AUS   ISSN 0313-7112
AUSTRALIAN GRADUATE SCHOOL OF MANAGEMENT. HANDBOOK. Text in English. 1976. a. AUD 4.
—ingenta.
Published by: University of New South Wales, Sydney, NSW 2052, Australia. TEL 61-2-385-2840, FAX 61-2-662-2163.

658   AUS   ISSN 0312-8962
➤ **AUSTRALIAN JOURNAL OF MANAGEMENT.** Text in English. 1976. s-a. AUD 40 domestic to individuals; USD 42 foreign to individuals; AUD 65 domestic to institutions; USD 68 foreign to institutions (effective 2004). bk.rev. back issues avail.
Document type: Journal, Academic/Scholarly. **Description:** Covers the management of firms, groups, industries, regulatory bodies, government and other institutions; encompasses both discipline & problem based research. Publishes management research in accounting, applied economics, finance, industrial relations, political science, psychology, statistics, and other disciplines, as well as research in areas such as marketing, corporate strategy, operations management, organization development, decision analysis and other problems.
Related titles: CD-ROM ed.; Microfiche ed.: (from PQC); Online - full text ed.: ISSN 1327-2020. 1996 (from EBSCO Publishing, Factiva, Florida Center for Library Automation, Gale Group, Northern Light Technology, Inc., O C L C Online Computer Library Center, Inc., ProQuest Information & Learning, R M I T Publishing).
Indexed: ABIn, AusPAIS, BPIA, Emerald, Inspec, JEL, ManagCont, PAIS, RefZh, WBA, WMB.
—BLDSC (1809.200000), IE, Infotrieve, ingenta.
Published by: Australian Graduate School of Management, Sydney, University Of New South Wales, NSW 2052, Australia. TEL 61-2-9931-9259, FAX 61-2-9662-7621, journal@agsm.unsw.edu.au, http://www.agsm.unsw.edu.au/~eajm/. Ed., R&P Robert E Marks TEL 61-2-9931-9271. Circ: 375 (paid).

658   AUS   ISSN 1325-8591
AUSTRALIAN PROJECT MANAGER. Text in English. 1974. q. AUD 25 (effective 2001). adv. bk.rev. back issues avail.
Document type: Magazine, Trade. **Description:** For project managers working in all types of organizations and industries.
Published by: (Australian Institute of Project Management), Banksia Media Group, L9, 139 Macquarie St, Sydney, NSW 2000, Australia. TEL 61-2-9252-7277, FAX 61-2-9252-7077, bmg@ihug.com.au. Ed. Kay Fay. R&P Leigh Cunningham. Circ: 4,000.

AUTOMOTIVE LOGISTICS. see TRANSPORTATION

AUTOTECHNOLOGY; international magazine for engineering, production and management. see TRANSPORTATION—Automobiles

658   ITA   ISSN 1127-5812
AZIENDA PUBBLICA; teoria e problemi di management. Text in Italian. 1988. bi-m. EUR 90 (effective 2005). **Document type:** Magazine, Trade.
Published by: Maggioli Editore, Via del Carpino 8/10, Santarcangelo di Romagna, RN 47822, Italy. TEL 39-0541-628111, FAX 39-0541-622020, editore@maggioli.it, http://www.maggioli.it.

658 338.642 352   ITA   ISSN 0394-2155
AZIENDITALIA; mensile per gli enti locali e le loro aziende. Text in Italian. 1986. m. EUR 104 (effective 2005). **Document type:** Magazine, Consumer.
Published by: IPSOA Editore (Subsidiary of: Wolters Kluwer Italia Srl), Strada 1, Palazzo F6, Milanofiori, Assago, MI 20090, Italy. TEL 39-02-82476888, FAX 39-02-82476436, http://www.ipsoa.it.

658   DEU   ISSN 0177-6932
B B E CHEF-TELEGRAMM; aktueller Beratungsbrief fuer die Unternehmensfuehrung im Einzelhandel. Text in German. 1966. s-m. EUR 16.80 per month (effective 2005). **Document type:** Magazine, Trade.
Formerly (until 1982): Chef-Telegramm (0171-841X)
Indexed: BiolDig.
Published by: (Betriebswirtschaftliche Beratungsstelle fuer den Einzelhandel), B B E Unternehmensberatung GmbH, Gothaer Allee 2, Cologne, 50969, Germany. TEL 49-221-93655130, FAX 49-221-93655112, info@bbe-verlag.de, http://www.bbe-verlag.de.

658   DEU   ISSN 0939-7620
B B E CHEF-TELEGRAMM. APOTHEKEN SPEZIAL. Text in German. 1988. fortn. EUR 16.80 per month (effective 2005). **Document type:** Journal, Trade.
Published by: (Betriebswirtschaftliche Beratungsstelle fuer den Einzelhandel), B B E Unternehmensberatung GmbH, Gothaer Allee 2, Cologne, 50969, Germany. TEL 49-221-93655130, FAX 49-221-93655112, info@bbe-verlag.de, http://www.bbe-verlag.de.

658   DEU   ISSN 0939-7639
B B E CHEF-TELEGRAMM. TEXTIL SPEZIAL. Text in German. 1982. fortn. EUR 16.80 per month (effective 2005). **Document type:** Journal, Trade.
Published by: (Betriebswirtschaftliche Beratungsstelle fuer den Einzelhandel), B B E Unternehmensberatung GmbH, Gothaer Allee 2, Cologne, 50969, Germany. TEL 49-221-93655130, FAX 49-221-93655112, info@bbe-verlag.de, http://www.bbe-verlag.de.

658   DEU
B B E DATA KOMPAKT. Text in German. w. EUR 23.50 per month (effective 2005). **Document type:** Newsletter, Trade.

Published by: B B E Unternehmensberatung GmbH, Gothaer Allee 2, Cologne, 50969, Germany. TEL 49-221-93655130, FAX 49-221-93655112, info@bbe-verlag.de, http://www.bbe-verlag.de.

658   DEU   ISSN 0939-7647
B B E STEUERPRAXIS. Text in German. 1977. fortn. EUR 16.50 per month (effective 2005). **Document type:** Journal, Trade.
Published by: (Betriebswirtschaftliche Beratungsstelle fuer den Einzelhandel), B B E Unternehmensberatung GmbH, Gothaer Allee 2, Cologne, 50969, Germany. TEL 49-221-93655130, FAX 49-221-93655112, info@bbe-verlag.de, http://www.bbe-verlag.de.

658   DEU
B D V T JOURNAL. Text in German. q. adv. **Document type:** Magazine, Trade.
Published by: Berufsverband der Verkaufsfoerderer und Trainer e.V., Elisenstr 12-14, Cologne, 50667, Germany. TEL 49-221-920760, FAX 49-221-9207610, info@bdvt.de, http://www.bdvt.de. adv.: B&W page EUR 900; trim 178 x 258. Circ: 3,500 (controlled).

658   DEU   ISSN 1610-563X
B F P - FUHRPARK UND MANAGEMENT. Text in German. 1977. 10/yr. EUR 30, EUR 51; EUR 4 newsstand/cover (effective 2004). adv. **Document type:** Magazine, Trade.
Former titles (until 2001): B F P - Betriebsfuhrpark (1616-1947); (until 1999): Betriebsfuhrpark (1437-6180)
Published by: Verlagsgesellschaft Gruetter GmbH & Co. KG, Postfach 910708, Hannover, 30427, Germany. TEL 49-511-4609300, FAX 49-511-4609320, info@gruetter.de, http://www.fuhrpark.de, http://www.gruetter.de. Ed. Hans-Joachim Mag. Adv. contact Susann Stenzel. B&W page EUR 4,980, color page EUR 6,780; trim 175 x 243. Circ: 49,812 (paid and controlled).

658   DEU   ISSN 0340-5370
B F U P - BETRIEBSWIRTSCHAFTLICHE FORSCHUNG UND PRAXIS. Abbreviated title: B F u P. Text in German. 1949. 6/yr. EUR 104; EUR 73.80 to students; EUR 20 newsstand/cover (effective 2004). bk.rev. charts. index. reprints avail. **Document type:** Journal, Trade.
Formerly (until 1973): Betriebswirtschaftliche Forschung und Praxis (0006-002X)
Related titles: Online - full text ed.: (from ProQuest Information & Learning).
Indexed: ASCA, DIP, ExcerpMed, IBR, IBZ, KES, SSCI.
—BLDSC (1946.895000), IDS, IE, Infotrieve, ingenta. **CCC.**
Published by: Verlag Neue Wirtschafts-Briefe GmbH & Co., Eschstr 22, Herne, 44629, Germany. TEL 49-2323-141900, FAX 49-2323-141123, info@nwb.de, http://www.nwb.de. Ed. Guenter Sieben. Circ: 1,150.

B O M A EXPERIENCE EXCHANGE REPORT; income - expense analysis for office buildings. see REAL ESTATE

B O M A.ORG. (Building Owners and Managers Association) see BUILDING AND CONSTRUCTION

BAKING MANAGEMENT. see FOOD AND FOOD INDUSTRIES—Bakers And Confectioners

658   GBR   ISSN 1746-5265
▼ ➤ **BALTIC JOURNAL OF MANAGEMENT.** Text in English. forthcoming 2006 (Jan.). 3/yr. EUR 303.41 in Europe; USD 359 in North America; AUD 479 in Australasia; GBP 216.41 in the UK & elsewhere (effective 2006). **Document type:** Journal, Academic/Scholarly. **Description:** Contributes to an understanding of different management cultures and provides readers with a fresh look at emerging management practices and research in the countries of the Baltic region and beyond.
Related titles: Online - full content ed.: forthcoming.
Published by: Emerald Group Publishing Limited, 60-62 Toller Ln, Bradford, W Yorks BD8 9BY, United Kingdom. TEL 44-1274-777700, FAX 44-1274-785200, infomation@emeraldinsight.com, http://www.emeraldinsight.com/bjm.htm. Ed. Dr. Asta Pundziene. Pub. Ms. Kate Snowden, R&P Ms. Anne-Marie Thorslund.

658   USA
BALTIMORE SMARTCEO. (Chief Executive Officer) Text in English. m. USD 29.95 (effective 2005). adv. **Document type:** Magazine, Trade. **Description:** Contains smart ideas to help educate, motivate and inspire decision-makers. Reaches decision-makers in Baltimore City and a five county area including Baltimore, Howard, Carroll, Anne Arundel and Harford counties.
Published by: SmartCEO, 2400 Boston St, Ste 330, Baltimore, MD 21224. TEL 410-342-9510, FAX 410-675-3782, http://baltimore.smartceo.com/. Ed. David Callahan. Pub. Craig Burns.

BANK UND MARKT; Zeitschrift fuer Management, Marketing, Technik, E-Commerce und Organisation. see BUSINESS AND ECONOMICS—Banking And Finance

658   CHN   ISSN 1002-3135
BEIJING GONGSHANG GUANLI/BEIJING INDUSTRIAL AND COMMERCIAL MANAGEMENT. Text in Chinese. 1987. bi-m.

B

Related titles: Online - full text ed.: (from East View Information Services).
Published by: Beijing Gongshang Xingzheng Guangli-ju, 18 Enjizhuang, Haidian-qu, Beijing, 100036, China. TEL 8311924. Ed. Chai Su'er.

658 GBR ISSN 1463-5771
HD62.15 CODEN: BQMTF9
➤ **BENCHMARKING**; an international journal. Text in English. 1994. 5/yr. EUR 4,501.16 in Europe; USD 4,529 in North America; AUD 5,909 in Australasia; GBP 3,152.66 in UK & elsewhere (effective 2006). reprint service avail. from PSC. **Document type:** *Journal, Academic/Scholarly.* **Description:** Provides a communication medium for all those working at a senior level in the quality technology and benchmarking fields.
Formerly (until 1998): Benchmarking for Quality Management and Technology (1351-3036)
Related titles: Online - full text ed.: (from EBSCO Publishing, Emerald Group Publishing Limited, Gale Group, IngentaConnect, O C L C Online Computer Library Center, Inc., ProQuest Information & Learning, Swets Information Services).
Indexed: ABIn, EmerIntel, Emerald, Inspec, M&MA.
—BLDSC (1891.290270), AskIEEE, IE, Infotrieve, ingenta. **CCC.**
Published by: Emerald Group Publishing Limited, 60-62 Toller Ln, Bradford, W Yorks BD8 9BY, United Kingdom. TEL 44-1274-777700, FAX 44-1274-785200, infomation@emeraldinsight.com, http://www.emeraldinsight.com/bij.htm. Ed. A Gunasekaran. **Subscr. addr. in N America:** Emerald Group Publishing Ltd., 44 Brattle St, 4th Fl, Cambridge, MA 02138. TEL 617-497-2175, 888-622-0075, FAX 617-354-6875.

➤ **BENEFITS & COMPENSATION INTERNATIONAL.** see *INSURANCE*

➤ **BENEFITS REPORT - ASIA.** see *BUSINESS AND ECONOMICS—Personnel Management*

➤ **BERLINGSKE NYHEDSMAGASIN.** see *BUSINESS AND ECONOMICS*

338 GBR ISSN 0889-3136
➤ **THE BEST OF LONG RANGE PLANNING.** Text in English. 1989. irreg., latest vol.13, 1993. price varies. back issues avail. **Document type:** *Monographic series, Academic/Scholarly.* **Description:** Brings together the best articles on a particular topic from the Long Range Planning journal, so that readers wishing to study a specific aspect of planning can find an authoritative and comprehensive view of the subject, conveniently published in one volume.
—CCC.
Published by: Elsevier Ltd., Books Division (Subsidiary of: Elsevier Science & Technology), Kidlington, PO Box 800, Oxford, OX2 1DX, United Kingdom. TEL 44-1865-843000, FAX 44-1865-843410, http://www.elsevier.com/wps/find/bookdescription.authors/BS_BLRP/description#description. **Subscr. to:** Elsevier BV, PO Box 211, Amsterdam 1000 AE, Netherlands. TEL 31-20-485-3757, FAX 31-20-485-3432, nlinfo-f@elsevier.nl, http://www.elsevier.nl.

➤ **BEST PRACTICE MEASUREMENT STRATEGIES.** see *COMMUNICATIONS*

658 ZAF ISSN 1019-567X
➤ **BESTUURSDINAMIKA/MANAGEMENT DYNAMICS.** Text in Afrikaans, English. 1992. q. ZAR 120 (effective 1999). **Document type:** *Academic/Scholarly.* **Description:** Publishes contributions of a scientific nature on the theory and practice of economic and management sciences.
Related titles: Online - full text ed.
Indexed: ISAP.
Published by: Suider-Afrika Instituut vir Bestuurswetenskaplikes/ Southern African Institute for Management Scientists, Dept of Business Management, Private Bag X1, Matieland, Stellenbosch 7602, South Africa. TEL 27-21-8082213, FAX 27-21-8082213, nst@maties.sun.ac.za, http://www.journals.co.za/ej/ejour_mandyn.html. Ed. N S Terblanche. Circ: 350.

658 NOR ISSN 0801-3322
➤ **BETA**; tidsskrift for bedriftsoekonomi. Text mainly in Norwegian; Text occasionally in Danish, Swedish. 1987. biennial. NOK 375 to individuals; NOK 650 to institutions; NOK 200 to students; NOK 175 per issue (effective 2005). bk.rev.; software rev. **Document type:** *Journal, Academic/Scholarly.* **Description:** Articles on business economics and management in the Scandinavian countries.
Related titles: Online - full text ed.
—Infotrieve. **CCC.**
Published by: Universitetsforlaget AS/Scandinavian University Press (Subsidiary of: Aschehoug & Co.), Sehesteds Gate 3, Postboks 508, Oslo, 0105, Norway. TEL 47-24-147500, FAX 47-24-147501, http://www.universitetsforlaget.no/tidsskrifter/article.jhtml?articleID=302. Ed. Odd Nordhaug.

➤ **BETRIEBS-BERATER**; Zeitschrift fuer Recht und Wirtschaft. see *LAW*

658 DEU ISSN 0344-5941
DER BETRIEBSLEITER. Text in German. 1958. 10/yr. EUR 81 domestic; EUR 95 foreign; EUR 7.50 newsstand/cover (effective 2004). adv. **Document type:** *Magazine, Trade.*
Formerly (until 1977): Betriebs-Management Service
Published by: Verlag fuer Technik und Wirtschaft GmbH & Co., Lise-Meitner-Str 2, Mainz, 55129, Germany. TEL 49-6131-992-0, FAX 49-6131-992100, info@vfmz.de, http://www.industrie-service.de. Ed. Michael Doeppert. Adv. contact Michael Spahn. B&W page EUR 4,100, color page EUR 5,330; trim 185 x 265. Circ: 17,000 (controlled). **Subscr. to:** Postfach 4029, Mainz 55030, Germany.

658.1 DEU ISSN 0523-0993
BETRIEBSPOLITISCHE SCHRIFTEN. Text in German. 1967. irreg., latest vol.25, 1982. price varies. **Document type:** *Monographic series, Academic/Scholarly.*
Published by: Duncker und Humblot GmbH, Carl-Heinrich-Becker-Weg 9, Berlin, 12165, Germany. TEL 49-30-7900060, FAX 49-30-79000631, info@duncker-humblot.de, http://www.duncker-humblot.de.

658 DEU ISSN 0342-7064
DIE BETRIEBSWIRTSCHAFT. Variant title: D B W. Text in German. 1908-1943; N.S. 1977. bi-m. adv. bk.rev. reprint service avail. from PQC. **Document type:** *Trade.* **Description:** Deals with the problems and solutions of private and public enterprises in all fields and areas of activity.
Related titles: Microform ed.: N.S. (from PQC).
Indexed: DIP, ExcerpMed, IBR, IBZ, SCIMP.
—BLDSC (1946.881950), IE, Infotrieve, ingenta. **CCC.**
Published by: Schaeffer - Poeschel Verlag, Postfach 103241, Stuttgart, 70028, Germany. TEL 49-711-2194102, FAX 49-711-2194119. Ed. Marita Rollnik Mollenhauer. Adv. contact Sabine Zobeley. Circ: 1,500.

658 332 DEU ISSN 0723-9629
BETRIEBSWIRTSCHAFTLICHE BLAETTER. Text in German. 1950. m. adv. bk.rev. index. reprints avail. **Document type:** *Magazine, Trade.*
Former titles (until 1981): Betriebswirtschaftliche Blaetter fuer die Praxis der Sparkassen und Landesbanken, Girozentralen (0172-0260); (Until 1975): Betriebswirtschaftliche Blaetter fuer die Praxis der Sparkassen und Girozentralen (0006-0011)
Indexed: DIP, IBR, IBZ.
—CCC.
Published by: (Deutscher Sparkassen- und Giroverband e.V.), Deutscher Sparkassenverlag GmbH, Am Wallgraben 115, Stuttgart, 70565, Germany. TEL 49-711-7820, FAX 49-711-7821709, webredaktion@dsv-gruppe.de, http://www.dsv-gruppe.de. Ed. Arnulf Sauter. adv.: B&W page EUR 2,800, color page EUR 4,270. Circ: 4,569 (paid).

658 DEU ISSN 0523-1027
BETRIEBSWIRTSCHAFTLICHE FORSCHUNGSERGEBNISSE. Text in German. 1959. irreg., latest vol.122, 2002. price varies. **Document type:** *Monographic series, Academic/Scholarly.*
Formerly (until 1962): Freie Universitaet Berlin. Institut fuer Industrieforschung. Veroeffentlichungen (0174-9307)
Published by: Duncker und Humblot GmbH, Carl-Heinrich-Becker-Weg 9, Berlin, 12165, Germany. TEL 49-30-7900060, FAX 49-30-79000631, info@duncker-humblot.de, http://www.duncker-humblot.de.

658 DEU ISSN 0523-1035
BETRIEBSWIRTSCHAFTLICHE SCHRIFTEN. Text in German. 1955. irreg., latest vol.155, 2003. price varies. **Document type:** *Monographic series, Academic/Scholarly.*
Published by: Duncker und Humblot GmbH, Carl-Heinrich-Becker-Weg 9, Berlin, 12165, Germany. TEL 49-30-7900060, FAX 49-30-79000631, info@duncker-humblot.de, http://www.duncker-humblot.de.

384.6 USA
BETTER BUSINESS BY TELEPHONE✶. Text in English. 1964. s-m. USD 5.95. adv. illus.; tr.lit.
Published by: Kirkley Press Inc., PO Box 20175, Baltimore, MD 21284-0175. Ed. Julie Fraunholz.

658 IND
BHAGAWAN MAHAVEER INTERNATIONAL MANAGEMENT REVIEW. Text in English. q.
Published by: Shri Attam Vallabh Jain Girls College, Institute of Management & Technology, Sudama Nagar, Hanumangarh Rd, Sriganganagar, 335 001, India. TEL 91-154-437371.

BIBLIOGRAPHY OF ECONOMIC AND SOCIAL DEVELOPMENT SRI LANKA. see *BUSINESS AND ECONOMICS—Abstracting, Bibliographies, Statistics*

BIKE BUSINESS; das Fachmagazin fuer professionelles Management im Motorrad- und Motorrad-Zubehoer-Handel. see *SPORTS AND GAMES—Bicycles And Motorcycles*

▼ **BIOEXECUTIVE INTERNATIONAL.** see *BIOLOGY—Biotechnology*

570 600 658 USA
▼ **BIOTECHNOLOGY MANAGEMENT PRACTICES.** Text in English. 2003. a. (in 2 vols.). USD 4,995 (effective 2004). **Document type:** *Trade.* **Description:** Annual study of management practices throughout all stages of a biotech's firm development.
Published by: Windhover Information, Inc., 10 Hoyt St, Norwalk, CT 06851. TEL 203-838-4401, ext 232, FAX 203-838-3214, custserv@windhover.com, http://www.windhover.com.

658 158 GBR
BIRKBECK COLLEGE. SCHOOL OF MANAGEMENT AND ORGANIZATIONAL PSYCHOLOGY. WORKING PAPER SERIES. Text in English. irreg. **Document type:** *Academic/Scholarly.*
Published by: Birkbeck College, Department of Management and Organizational Psychology (Subsidiary of: University of London), Malet St, Bloomsbury, London, WC1E 7HX, United Kingdom. TEL 44-20-7631-6751, FAX 44-20-7631-6750, c.caldwell@bbk.co.uk, http://www.bbk.ac.uk.

BIROTREND. see *BUSINESS AND ECONOMICS—Computer Applications*

BIZED. see *EDUCATION—Higher Education*

658 USA ISSN 1047-3718
BOARD AND ADMINISTRATOR: ASSOCIATION EDITION. Text in English. 1989. m. **Document type:** *Trade.*
Published by: Aspen Publishers, Inc. (Subsidiary of: Wolters Kluwer N.V.), 5301 Buckeystown Pike, Ste. 400, Frederick, MD 21704-8319. TEL 800-638-8437, customer.service@aspenpubl.com, http://www.aspenpub.com. **Dist. by:** Distribution Center, 7201 McKinney Circle, Frederick, MD 21701. TEL 301-698-7100, FAX 301-417-7550.

658 USA ISSN 1525-7878
BOARD & ADMINISTRATOR - FOR ADMINISTRATORS ONLY. Text in English. 1984. m. USD 185 (effective 2002). **Document type:** *Newsletter, Trade.* **Description:** Provides reports on the findings of administrators who share their strategies for improving their relationship with board members.
Formerly: Board & Administrator: Nonprofit Edition (0748-9471)
Related titles: Online - full text ed.: (from ProQuest Information & Learning).
Indexed: ABIn.
—CCC.
Published by: Aspen Publishers, Inc. (Subsidiary of: Wolters Kluwer N.V.), 5301 Buckeystown Pike, Ste. 400, Frederick, MD 21704-8319. TEL 800-638-8437, customer.service@aspenpubl.com, http://www.aspenpublishers.com, http://www.aspenpub.com. Ed. Jeff Stratton. **Dist. by:** Distribution Center, 7201 McKinney Circle, Frederick, MD 21701. TEL 301-698-7100, FAX 301-417-7550.

658 USA ISSN 1058-7640
BOARD AND ADMINISTRATOR: GOVERNMENT EDITION. Text in English. m. **Document type:** *Trade.*
Published by: Aspen Publishers, Inc. (Subsidiary of: Wolters Kluwer N.V.), 5301 Buckeystown Pike, Ste. 400, Frederick, MD 21704-8319. TEL 800-638-8437, customer.service@aspenpubl.com, http://www.aspenpub.com. **Dist. by:** Distribution Center, 7201 McKinney Circle, Frederick, MD 21701. TEL 301-698-7100, FAX 301-417-7550.

658 USA ISSN 0894-816X
BOARD AND ADMINISTRATOR: SCHOOL EDITION. Text in English. m. USD 243 (effective 2002). **Document type:** *Newsletter, Trade.* **Description:** Covers information to keeps superintendents in touch with the successful strategies other superintendents and school administrators use to build strong relationships with their boards.
—CCC.
Published by: (Center for Management Systems), Aspen Publishers, Inc. (Subsidiary of: Wolters Kluwer N.V.), 111Eighth Ave., 7th Fl, New York, NY 10011. TEL 212-771-0600, 800-638-8437, FAX 212-771-0885, customer.service@aspenpubl.com, http://www.aspenpub.com. Ed. Jeff Stratton. **Dist. by:** Distribution Center, 7201 McKinney Circle, Frederick, MD 21701. TEL 301-698-7100, FAX 301-417-7550.

658.4 USA ISSN 1061-4249
HD2741
BOARD LEADERSHIP; Policy Governance in Action. Text in English. 1992. bi-m. USD 435 domestic to institutions; USD 495 in Canada & Mexico to institutions; USD 546 elsewhere to institutions; USD 479 combined subscription domestic to institutions print and online eds.; USD 539 combined subscription in Canada & Mexico to institutions print and online eds.; USD 590 combined subscription elsewhere to institutions print and online eds. (effective 2006). 8 p./no.; back issues avail. **Document type:** *Journal, Academic/Scholarly.* **Description:** An approach to improving the way boards conduct business.
Related titles: Online - full text ed.: ISSN 1542-7862. USD 435 to institutions (effective 2006) (from EBSCO Publishing, O C L C Online Computer Library Center, Inc., Swets Information Services, Wiley InterScience).
—IE. **CCC.**

B

Published by: Jossey-Bass Inc., Publishers (Subsidiary of: John Wiley & Sons, Inc.), 989 Market St, San Francisco, CA 94103-1741. TEL 415-433-1740, 888-378-2537, FAX 800-605-2665, 415-433-0499, jbsubs@jbp.com, http://www.josseybass.com/cda/product/0,,BL,00.html. Ed. John Carver. Pub. Sue Lewis. Circ: 3,400 (paid).

658 360 USA ISSN 1058-5419
HD62.6
BOARD MEMBER; the periodical for members of the National Center for Nonprofit Boards. Text in English. 1992. 10/yr. USD 139 membership (effective 2005). bk.rev. illus.; tr.lit. back issues avail. **Document type:** *Newsletter.* **Description:** Covers board leadership issues and trends in the nonprofit sector, including case studies, interviews, current news.
—**CCC.**
Published by: National Center for Nonprofit Boards, 1828 L St, N W, Ste 900, Washington, DC 20036-5104. TEL 202-452-6262, 800-883-6262, FAX 202-452-6299, ncnb@ncnb.org, http://www.ncnb.org. Ed. Betsy J. Rosenblatt. R&P Lisa Polk. Circ: 13,000 (paid); 2,000 (controlled).

658 USA
BOARD OF DIRECTORS REPORT. Text in English. a. USD 640. charts. **Document type:** *Corporate.* **Description:** Provides data, reported by industry and company size, on board compensation and organization.
Published by: (Executive Compensation Service (ECS)), Wyatt Data Services, 218 Rte 17 N, Rochelle Park, NJ 07622-9832. TEL 201-843-1177, FAX 201-843-0101.

BOARDROOM. see *BUSINESS AND ECONOMICS*

BODYSHOP MANAGEMENT BRIEFINGS. see *TRANSPORTATION—Automobiles*

BOSS MAGAZINE; the construction industries' guide to greater wealth. see *BUILDING AND CONSTRUCTION*

658 794 USA
BOWLING CENTER MANAGEMENT. Text in English. m. free domestic to members; USD 50 domestic to non-members (effective 2005). adv. **Document type:** *Magazine, Trade.*
Published by: Luby Publishing, 122 S Michigan Ave, Ste 1506, Chicago, IL 60603-6107. TEL 312-341-1110, FAX 312-341-1180, email@lubypublishing.com, http://www.bcmmag.com/, http://www.lubypublishing.com. Pub. Michael Panozzo. Adv. contact Barbara Peltz.

658.0071 USA ISSN 1078-2257
HD20.15.U5
BRICKER'S INTERNATIONAL DIRECTORY. Text in English. 1969. a. USD 595 per issue (effective 2003). **Document type:** *Directory, Trade.* **Description:** Covers programs offered by university-based executive education programs worldwide specifically for middle-level and senior managers and executives.
Formed by the 1995 merger of: Bricker's International Directory, Volume 1: Long-Term University-Based Executive Programs (Year) (1054-7835); Bricker's International Directory, Volume 2: Short-Term University-Based Executive Programs (Year) (1054-7843); Which was formerly: Short-Term University-Based Executive Programs (Year) (1040-7618); Superseded in part (in 1989): Bricker's International Directory (0277-7312); Which was formerly (until 1980): Bricker's International Directory of University-Sponsored Executive Development Programs (0191-2682); (until 1977): Bricker's International Directory of University-Sponsored Executive Development Programs Including Marketing and Management Programs (0191-2992); (until 1976): Bricker's International Directory of University Executive Development Programs Including Marketing and Management Programs (0361-1108)
Published by: Thomson Peterson's (Subsidiary of: Thomson Corporation), Princeton Pike Corporate Center, 2000 Lenox Dr, 3rd Fl, Lawrenceville, NJ 08648. TEL 609-243-9111, FAX 609-243-9150, http://www.petersons.com. Ed. Barbara Lawrence.

658 GBR ISSN 1045-3172
HD28 CODEN: BJMAE4
➤ **BRITISH JOURNAL OF MANAGEMENT**; challenging management theory and practice. Text in English. 1990. 5/yr. EUR 152 combined subscription in Europe to individuals print & online eds.; USD 126 combined subscription in the Americas to individuals & Caribbean, print & online eds.; GBP 101 combined subscription elsewhere to individuals print & online eds.; USD 1,057 combined subscription in the Americas to institutions & Caribbean, print & online eds.; GBP 629 combined subscription elsewhere to institutions print & online eds. (effective 2006); subscr. includes International Journal of Management Reviews. back issues avail.; reprint service avail. from PSC. **Document type:** *Journal, Academic/Scholarly.* **Description:** Aims to provide an outlet for research and scholarship on managerial oriented themes and topics.
Related titles: Microform ed.: (from PQC); Online - full text ed.: ISSN 1467-8551. USD 1,005 in the Americas to institutions & Caribbean; GBP 598 elsewhere to institutions (effective 2006) (from Blackwell Synergy, EBSCO Publishing, Gale Group, IngentaConnect, O C L C Online Computer Library Center, Inc., Swets Information Services).
Indexed: ABIn, CPM, CurCont, ERA, Emerald, ErgAb, IAOP, IBSS, Inspec, M&MA, PsycInfo, PsycholAb, RASB, SCIMP, SSCI, SWA, TEA.
—BLDSC (2311.180000), IE, Infotrieve, ingenta. **CCC.**
Published by: (British Academy of Management), Blackwell Publishing Ltd., 9600 Garsington Rd, Oxford, OX4 2ZG, United Kingdom. TEL 44-1865-776868, FAX 44-1865-714591, customerservices@oxon.blackwellpublishing.com, http://www.blackwellpublishing.com/journals/BJOM. Ed. Gerard P Hodgkinson TEL 44-113-3434468. Circ: 1,072.

➤ **BUILDINGS**; the source for facilities decision-makers. see *BUILDING AND CONSTRUCTION*

658 341 FRA ISSN 1264-9120
BULLETIN EUROPEEN ET INTERNATIONAL. Text in French. 1995. bi-m. EUR 97 (effective 2005). **Document type:** *Bulletin, Trade.*
Published by: Editions Francis Lefebvre, 42 rue de Villiers, Levallois-Perret, 92300, France. TEL 33-1-41052222, http://www.efl.fr.

370 FRA
BULLETIN OFFICIEL DU TRAVAIL ET DE L'EMPLOI. Text in French. 1975. 23/yr. bk.rev.
Incorporates: Centre I N F F O. Bulletin de Liason (0758-0266)
Address: 26 rue Desaix, Paris, Cedex 15 75727, France. TEL 40-58-77-17.

658 340 FRA ISSN 0395-451X
BULLETIN RAPIDE DE DROIT DES AFFAIRES. Text in French. 1959. bi-m. EUR 135 combined subscription print & online eds. (effective 2005). pat.; stat. **Document type:** *Bulletin, Trade.*
Formerly: Documentation Rapide du Chef d'Entreprise (0012-4680)
Related titles: Online - full text ed.
Published by: Editions Francis Lefebvre, 42 rue de Villiers, Levallois-Perret, 92300, France. TEL 33-1-41052222, http://www.efl.fr.

658 GBR ISSN 1350-3197
BULLETPOINT. Text in English. 1993. 10/yr. GBP 345 (effective 2003). 16 p./no.; **Description:** Contains the latest thinking on subjects of practical interest to managers including teamwork, leadership, change, innovation, etc.
—BLDSC (2926.450000), IE, Infotrieve.
Published by: Bulletpoint Communications Ltd., Betchworth House, 57-65 Station Rd, Redhill, Surrey RH1 1DL, United Kingdom. TEL 44-1737-784300, FAX 44-1737-784301, http://www.bulletpointonline.com.

BUSINESS & MANAGEMENT EDUCATION FUNDING ALERT. see *EDUCATION*

358 USA
BUSINESS BREAKTHROUGHS. Variant title: Jay Abraham's Business Breakthroughs. Text in English. m. USD 99.95. **Description:** Provides management and marketing tips.
Published by: Phillips International, Inc., 7811 Montrose Rd, Potomac, MD 20854-3363. TEL 800-777-5005, FAX 301-340-2647. Ed. Jay Abraham.

658.45 USA ISSN 1080-5699
HF5717 CODEN: ABCACL
➤ **BUSINESS COMMUNICATION QUARTERLY.** Text in English. 1935. q. USD 314, GBP 203 to institutions; USD 326, GBP 211 combined subscription to institutions print & online eds. (effective 2006); includes Journal of Business Communication. adv. bk.rev. illus. index. reprint service avail. from PQC. **Document type:** *Journal, Academic/Scholarly.* **Description:** Practice-oriented publication covering teaching and organizational applications. Includes course outlines, descriptions of training programs, problems and solutions and more.
Former titles (until 1994): Association for Business Communication. Bulletin (8756-1972); (until 1985): A B C A Bulletin (American Business Communication Association) (0001-0383); A B W A Bulletin (American Business Writing Association)
Related titles: Microform ed.: (from PQC); Online - full text ed.: ISSN 1552-4191. USD 311, GBP 201 to institutions (effective 2006) (from EBSCO Publishing, Florida Center for Library Automation, Gale Group, Northern Light Technology, Inc., O C L C Online Computer Library Center, Inc., Sage Publications, Inc., Swets Information Services).
Indexed: ABIn, BPI, BPIA, BusEdI, BusI, CIJE, CommAb, HRA, Inspec, PAIS, SOPODA, T&II.
—BLDSC (2933.345000), IE, Infotrieve, ingenta.
Published by: (Association for Business Communication), Sage Publications, Inc., 2455 Teller Rd, Thousand Oaks, CA 91320. TEL 805-499-0721, 800-818-7243, FAX 805-499-0871, info@sagepub.com, http://www.sagepub.co.uk/journal.aspx?pid=105852, http://www.sagepub.com. Ed. Kathryn Riley. R&P, Adv. contact Pamela S Ouellette. page USD 200; 5.5 x 8.5. Circ: 2,475. **Subscr. overseas to:** Sage Publications Ltd., 1 Oliver's Yard, 55 City Rd, London EC1 1SP, United Kingdom. TEL 44-20-73740645, FAX 44-20-73748741, subscription@sagepub.co.uk.

658 USA ISSN 1064-0223
HF5387
BUSINESS ETHIC RESOURCE; a resource on ethics management for the CEO. Text in English. 1987. q. USD 36; USD 40 foreign (effective 1999). bk.rev. **Document type:** *Newsletter.* **Description:** Covers news of ethics related issues for the business community.
Published by: Business Ethics Foundation, 150 Buckminster Rd, Brookline, MA 02445-5806. TEL 617-232-1820, FAX 617-232-2775. Ed. William H P Smith. Pub. Verne E Henderson. Circ: 1,000.

658.3 658 USA
BUSINESS ETHICS NEWSLINE. Text in English. 1998. w. USD 650 (effective 1999). abstr.; charts; illus.; stat. back issues avail. **Document type:** *Newsletter.* **Description:** Abstract of week's news in ethics for businesses. Includes statistics, quotes, research reports and commentary.
Published by: Institute for Global Ethics, PO Box 563, Camden, ME 04843. TEL 207-236-6658, FAX 207-236-4014, ethics@globalethics.org, http://www.globalethics.org. Ed. Rushworth Kidder. Pub. Paula Blanchard.

B

658.00715 GBR ISSN 0951-1792
CODEN: BUEXE8
➤ **BUSINESS EXECUTIVE.** Text in English. 1987. s-a. GBP 20 (effective 2002). adv. bk.rev. index. back issues avail. **Document type:** *Academic/Scholarly.* **Description:** Covers innovations in business management and administration.
Incorporates (in 1993): Business Education International; Which was formerly: Institute of Commerce, London. Magazine (0046-9793)
Indexed: Inspec, M&MA, SOMA.
—BLDSC (2933.643000), AskIEEE, IE, ingenta.
Published by: (Association of Business Executives), Business Executive Ltd., William House, 14 Worple Rd, Wimbledon, London, SW19 4DD, United Kingdom. TEL 44-20-8879-1973, FAX 44-20-8946-7153, info@abeuk.com, http://www.abeuk.com. Ed. Sidney Callis. R&P, Adv. contact Sandra Whiting. B&W page GBP 350, color page GBP 450; trim 210 x 297. Circ: 22,000.

658 657 USA ISSN 1521-4818
HG4001 CODEN: COMGFZ
BUSINESS FINANCE. Text in English. 1995. m. free to qualified personnel (effective 2005). adv. **Document type:** *Magazine, Trade.* **Description:** Informs financial executives about the growing role of finance within organizations from changes in technology, business strategy and economic trends.
Formerly (until 1998): Controller Magazine (1083-1371)
Related titles: Online - full text ed.: (from EBSCO Publishing).
Indexed: ABIn.
—BLDSC, IE. **CCC.**
Published by: Penton Technology Media (Subsidiary of: Penton Media, Inc.), 221 E 29th St, Ste 242, Loveland, CO 80538. TEL 970-663-4700, 800-621-1544, FAX 970-663-3285, info@businessfinancemag.com, http://www.businessfinancemag.com. Ed. Laurie Brannen. Pub. David Blansfield.

658.8 USA
BUSINESS FUNDAMENTALS SERIES. Text in English. irreg. USD 24.95 per issue. back issues avail. **Document type:** *Monographic series.* **Description:** Each issue covers an important topic in management.
Published by: Harvard Business School Publishing, 60 Harvard Way, Boston, MA 02163. TEL 800-988-0866.

658 338 GBR
BUSINESS GAZETTE. Text in English. 1986. m. free. adv. bk.rev.; software rev.; video rev. 28 p./no. 6 cols./p.; back issues avail. **Document type:** *Newspaper, Trade.* **Description:** Covers financial, accounting, management, legal, TQM, technology, and training topics for owners and managers of small businesses in southern England.
Published by: Datateam Publishing Ltd, 15a London Rd, Maidstone, Kent ME16 8LY, United Kingdom. TEL 44-1622-687031, FAX 44-1622-757646, info@datateam.co.uk, http://www.datateam.co.uk/home/home.htm. Ed. William Campbell. Adv. contact Chris Lethbridge. Circ: 15,000 (controlled).

658 IND ISSN 0007-6783
BUSINESS HERALD; management magazine. Text in English. 1965. m. INR 32.50, USD 10. adv. bk.rev. abstr.; charts. index.
Related titles: Microform ed.: (from PQC).
Indexed: BibLing.
Published by: K.G.P. Nayar, Herald House, P O Box 133, Trivandrum, Kerala, India. Ed. T A A Latif. Circ: 3,000.

658 AUS ISSN 1447-364X
THE BUSINESS IMPROVER. Text in English. 2002. fortn. AUD 395 domestic; AUD 359.09 foreign (effective 2004). **Document type:** *Newsletter.* **Description:** Aimed at helping managers resolve the issues they need to address to win and keep customers and stay in business. Provides news and information on quality management, customer service and retention strategies, standards and other business improvement initiatives.
Related titles: Online - full content ed.

Published by: Crown Content, Level 1, 141 Capel St, Nth Melbourne, VIC 3051, Australia. TEL 6-13-93299800, FAX 6-13-93299698, max@crowncontent.com.au, scott@crowncontent.com.au, http://www.crowncontent.com.au/prod/newsletters/busimp.htm. Ed. Max Berry.

BUSINESS INFORMATION SEARCHER. see *LIBRARY AND INFORMATION SCIENCES*

658.785 USA ISSN 1547-2825
QA76.9.D3
BUSINESS INTELLIGENCE JOURNAL. Text in English. 1996. q. **Description:** Dedicated to helping organizations increase their understanding and use of business intelligence by educating decision makers and IS professionals on the proper deployment of data warehousing strategies and technologies.
Formerly (until Jul.2003): The Journal of Data Warehousing (1092-6208)
Related titles: Online - full text ed.: (from ProQuest Information & Learning).
Indexed: ABIn.
—BLDSC (2933.845000), IE, ingenta.
Published by: Data Warehousing Institute, 849-J Quince Orchard Blvd, Gaithersburg, MD 20879. TEL 301-947-3730, FAX 301-947-3733, info@dw-institute.com, http://www.dw-institute.com. Ed. Hugh J Watson.

BUSINESS INTELLIGENCE REPORT; strategies and trends for the successful business. see *BUSINESS AND ECONOMICS—Small Business*

658 500 400 GBR ISSN 0968-2015
BUSINESS MATTERS. Text in English. 1990. s-a. GBP 6 (effective 1999). illus. **Document type:** *Newsletter, Academic/Scholarly.*
Incorporates: Language Matters (0968-2023); Science Matters (0968-2031)
Indexed: Inspec, RICS.
Published by: Associated Examining Board, Associated Examining Board, Stag Hill House, Guildford, Surrey GU2 5XJ, United Kingdom. TEL 44-1483-506506, FAX 44-1483-300152. Ed., R&P George Turnbull TEL 44-1483-455228. Circ: 24,000.

BUSINESS MOTORING. see *TRANSPORTATION—Automobiles*

658 USA ISSN 1556-813X
▼ **BUSINESS PERFORMANCE MANAGEMENT.** Text in English. 2003 (Jun.). q. free to qualified personnel (effective 2003). **Document type:** *Magazine, Trade.*
Published by: Penton Media, Inc. (Subsidiary of: Pittway Company), 1300 E 9th St, Cleveland, OH 44114-1503. TEL 216-696-7000, FAX 216-696-0177, http://www.bpmmag.net/, http://www.penton.com. Ed., Pub. David Blansfield TEL 203-559-2849.

BUSINESS PROCESS MAGAZINE. see *COMPUTERS—Automation*

658 GBR ISSN 1463-7154
HD28
➤ **BUSINESS PROCESS MANAGEMENT JOURNAL**; developing re-engineering towards integrated process management. Text in English. 1995. 5/yr. EUR 4,033.54 in Europe; USD 4,199 in North America; AUD 5,079 in Australasia; GBP 2,826.41 in UK & elsewhere (effective 2006). reprint service avail. from PSC. **Document type:** *Journal, Academic/Scholarly.* **Description:** Examines how a variety of business processes intrinsic to organizational efficiency and effectiveness are integrated and managed for competitive success.
Formerly (until 1997): Business Process Re-Engineering and Management Journal (1355-2503)
Related titles: Online - full text ed.: (from EBSCO Publishing, Emerald Group Publishing Limited, Gale Group, IngentaConnect, O C L C Online Computer Library Center, Inc., ProQuest Information & Learning, Swets Information Services).
Indexed: ABIn, CPE, ERA, ETA, EmerIntel, Emerald, Inspec, MEA, RHEA, SEA, SENA, SOMA, TEA.
—BLDSC (2934.636500), IE, ingenta. **CCC.**
Published by: Emerald Group Publishing Limited, 60-62 Toller Ln, Bradford, W Yorks BD8 9BY, United Kingdom. TEL 44-1274-777700, FAX 44-1274-785200, infomation@emeraldinsight.com, http://www.emeraldinsight.com/bpmj.htm. Ed. Dr. Majed Al-Mashari. **Subscr. addr. in N America:** Emerald Group Publishing Ltd., 44 Brattle St, 4th Fl, Cambridge, MA 02138. TEL 617-497-2175, 888-622-0075, FAX 617-354-6875.

658 GBR ISSN 1472-7692
BUSINESS RATIO REPORT. MANAGEMENT CONSULTANCIES (YEAR). Text in English. 1987. a. GBP 275 (effective 2001). charts; stat. **Document type:** *Trade.*
Former titles (until 2000): Business Ratio. Management Consultancies (1468-3709); (until 1999): Business Ratio Plus. Management Consultancies (1357-6828); (until 1994): Business Ratio Report. Management Consultancies (1363-1934); (until 1992): Business Ratio Report. Management Consultants (0952-8539)

Published by: The Prospect Shop Ltd., Field House, 72 Oldfield Rd, Hampton, Middx TW12 2HQ, United Kingdom. TEL 44-20-8461-8730, 44-20-8481-8720, FAX 44-20-8783-1940, info@theprospectshop.co.uk.

650 USA
BUSINESS READER REVIEW. Text in English. 1998. m. free. back issues avail. **Document type:** *Newsletter.*
Media: Online - full text.
Address: PO Box 3627, Williamsburg, VA 23187. TEL 757-258-4746, FAX 757-258-3398, bizbooks@gte.net, http://home1.gte.net/bizbooks/.

658.8 CAN
BUSINESS RELATIONSHIPS QUARTERLY. Variant title: B R Q Newsletter. Text in English. q. free. **Document type:** *Newsletter.* **Description:** Offers tips and insights on helping one succeed at networking and relationship building in business.
Media: Online - full text.
Published by: Heritage Cards, 65 Victoria St, Dundas, ON L9H 2B9, Canada. TEL 888-355-6333, FAX 877-842-2222, brq-subscribe@heritagegreetingcards.com, http://www.heritagegreetingcards.com/newsletter.html.

BUSINESS SOLUTIONS. see *COMPUTERS—Electronic Data Processing*

BUSINESS STRATEGY AND THE ENVIRONMENT. see *ENVIRONMENTAL STUDIES*

658 GBR ISSN 0955-6419
HD28
BUSINESS STRATEGY REVIEW. Text in English. 1990. q. EUR 60 combined subscription in Europe to individuals print & online eds.; USD 67 combined subscription in the Americas to individuals & Caribbean (print & online eds.); GBP 40 combined subscription elsewhere to individuals print & online eds.; USD 203 combined subscription in the Americas to institutions & Caribbean (print & online eds.); GBP 178 combined subscription elsewhere to institutions print & online eds.; EUR 29 combined subscription in Europe to students print & online eds.; USD 32 combined subscription in the Americas to students & Caribbean (print & online eds.); GBP 19 combined subscription elsewhere to students print & online eds. (effective 2006). index. reprint service avail. from PSC. **Document type:** *Academic/Scholarly.* **Description:** Analyses and interprets contemporary research on strategic management and the wider business environment, publishing articles which combine disciplines and cross cultural boundaries.
Related titles: Online - full text ed.: ISSN 1467-8616. USD 193 in the Americas to institutions & Caribbean; GBP 169 elsewhere to institutions (effective 2006) (from Blackwell Synergy, EBSCO Publishing, Florida Center for Library Automation, Gale Group, IngentaConnect, O C L C Online Computer Library Center, Inc., Swets Information Services).
Indexed: ABIn, CPM, Emerald, Inspec, M&MA, SCIMP.
—BLDSC (2934.802000), IE, Infotrieve, ingenta. **CCC.**
Published by: (London Business School), Blackwell Publishing Ltd., 9600 Garsington Rd, Oxford, OX4 2ZG, United Kingdom. TEL 44-1865-776868, FAX 44-1865-714591, customerservices@oxon.blackwellpublishing.com, http://www.blackwellpublishing.com/journals/BSR. Ed. Stuart Crainer. Circ: 1,200.

BUSINESS WITHOUT BORDERS. see *LAW—Corporate Law*

BUSINESS WOMAN MAGAZINE. see *WOMEN'S INTERESTS*

658 AUS ISSN 1320-971X
BUSINESSDATE. Text in English. 1993. q. AUD 65.50 (effective 2003). back issues avail. **Document type:** *Academic/Scholarly.* **Description:** Presents various aspects of business for 12 grade students.
Related titles: Online - full text ed.: (from EBSCO Publishing).
Indexed: WBA, WMB.
Published by: Warringal Publications, 116 Argyle St, Fitzroy, VIC 3065, Australia. TEL 61-3-94160200, FAX 61-3-94160402. Ed. Bruce Watt. Pub. Colin Hobbs. Circ: 1,000.

658 USA ISSN 1529-0018
BUSINESSFINANCEMAG.COM. Text in English. d. adv. **Document type:** *Trade.*
Media: Online - full content.
Published by: Penton Technology Media (Subsidiary of: Penton Media, Inc.), 221 E 29th St, Ste 242, Loveland, CO 80538. TEL 970-663-4700, 800-621-1544, FAX 970-663-3285, info@businessfinancemag.com, http://www.businessfinancemag.com.

658 GBR ISSN 0965-9455
BUSINESSMATTERS. Text in English. 1992. bi-m. GBP 14.95. adv. bk.rev. **Document type:** *Trade.* **Description:** Promotes excellence among small business by providing advice on management and purchasing, sharing experiences, and providing news and entertainment.
Published by: (Guild of Master Craftsmen), G M C Publications Ltd., 166 High St, Lewes, E Sussex BN7 1XU, United Kingdom. TEL 44-1273-477374, FAX 44-1273-487692. Ed. Neil Bell. Pub. A E Phillips. Adv. contact Linda Grace. Circ: 30,000 (controlled).

BUTLER AVIATION'S ECHELON; the magazine for corporate executives. see *TRANSPORTATION—Air Transport*

C A S B O JOURNAL OF SCHOOL BUSINESS MANAGEMENT. see *EDUCATION*

C C A NEWS. see *BUSINESS AND ECONOMICS—Banking And Finance*

658.8 USA
C C C WORKING PAPER✶. Text in English. 1990. irreg. back issues avail. **Document type:** *Monographic series.*
Published by: Consortium on Competitiveness and Cooperation, Institute of Management, Innovation and Organization, F402 Haas School of Business, 1930, University of California at Berkeley, Berkeley, CA 94720-1930. TEL 510-642-4041, FAX 510-642-2826. Ed. Josef Chytry.

C E & TRADE. (Consumer Electronics) see *ELECTRONICS*

658 GBR
C E O. (Chief Executive Officer) Text in English. 2002 (Sept.). s-a. GBP 5.95 per issue to individuals; free to qualified personnel (effective 2005). adv. reprints avail. **Document type:** *Journal, Trade.* **Description:** Contains specialist articles, interviews and case studies from the world's most preeminent business personalities at the forefront of corporate development within government, business organisations and multi-national corporations.
Published by: S P G Media Ltd. (Subsidiary of: Sterling Publishing Group Plc.), Brunel House, 55-57 North Wharf Rd, London, W2 1LA, United Kingdom. TEL 44-20-79159600, FAX 44-20-77242089, info@spgmedia.com, info@sterlingpublications.com, http://ww.ceo-journal.com, http://www.spgmedia.com/. Ed. Mr. Dougal Thomson. Pub. Mr. William Crocker. R&P Mr. Derek Deschamps. Adv. contact Mr. Patrick Agyeman TEL 44-20-79159738. B&W page GBP 6,600, color page GBP 7,900.

658 FRA ISSN 0994-7205
C E R E G E. CENTRE DE RECHERCHE EN GESTION. (Centre Europeen de Recherche et d'Enseignement des Geosciences de l' Environnement) Text in French. 1980. irreg. Price varies. **Document type:** *Monographic series, Academic/Scholarly.*
Published by: Centre Europeen de Recherche et d'Enseignement des Geosciences de l' Environnement, Universite Aix-Marseille III, CNRS UMR 6635, Aix-en-Provence, 13545, France. TEL 31-4-42971500, FAX 31-4-42971505.

658 HKG
C F O ASIA. (Chief Financial Officer) Text in English. 10/yr. free to qualified personnel. adv. reprints avail. **Document type:** *Magazine, Trade.* **Description:** Covers the latest Asian trends in finance, information technology, human resources, risk management and other topics of interest to the chief financial officers.
Related titles: Online - full text ed.; ◆ Regional ed(s).: C F O. ISSN 8756-7113; ◆ C F O Europe. ISSN 1462-5601.
Published by: Economist Group, 15 Regent St, London, SW1Y 4LR, United Kingdom. TEL 44-20-7830-7000, FAX 44-20-7830-1178, http://www.cfoasia.com, http://www.economistgroup.com/. Ed. Carla Rapoport. Adv. contact Simon Cholmeley. B&W page USD 9,030, color page USD 12,040; 206 x 273. Circ: 19,052 (controlled).

658.8 GBR ISSN 1462-5601
C F O EUROPE. (Chief Financial Officer) Text in English. 1998. m. GBP 70 domestic; GBP 85 in Europe; free q (effective 2005). adv. charts; illus.; maps; stat. back issues avail.; reprints avail. **Document type:** *Magazine, Trade.* **Description:** Examines the broad implications of strategic decision-making in corporations while providing in-depth coverage of specialized financial issues.
Related titles: Online - full text ed.; ◆ Regional ed(s).: C F O. ISSN 8756-7113; ◆ C F O Asia.
—CCC.
Published by: Economist Group, 15 Regent St, London, SW1Y 4LR, United Kingdom. TEL 44-20-7830-7000, FAX 44-20-7830-1178, donnacolbourne@cfoeurope.com, http://www.cfoeurope.com. Ed. Janet Kersnar. Adv. contact Charlotte Hollingshead. Circ: 20,982 (controlled); 243 (paid).

330 DEU ISSN 1437-2878
C I M - CONFERENCE AND INCENTIVE MANAGEMENT. Text in German, English. 1986. bi-m. EUR 31 domestic; EUR 38 foreign; EUR 7 newsstand/cover (effective 2004). adv. **Document type:** *Magazine, Trade.* **Description:** Focuses on current topics, trends and technologies in the meeting and incentive business, as well as on well-targeted event marketing, both globally and locally.
Published by: C I M Verlag GmbH & Co. KG, Stephanstr 3, Darmstadt, 64295, Germany. TEL 49-6151-390701, FAX 49-6151-390778, info@cim-publications.de, http://www.cim-publications.de. adv.: B&W page EUR 3,910, color page EUR 5,140; trim 210 x 280. Circ: 17,155 (paid and controlled).

C I O ASIA. (Chief Information Officer) see *BUSINESS AND ECONOMICS—Computer Applications*

C I O AUSTRALIA. (Chief Information Officer) see *BUSINESS AND ECONOMICS—Computer Applications*

C I O GERMANY; IT-Strategie fuer Manager. (Chief Information Officer) see *BUSINESS AND ECONOMICS—Computer Applications*

C I O INDIA. see *BUSINESS AND ECONOMICS—Computer Applications*

C I O JAPAN. (Chief Information Officer) see *BUSINESS AND ECONOMICS—Computer Applications*

C I O KOREA. (Chief Information Officer) see *BUSINESS AND ECONOMICS—Computer Applications*

C I O NEW ZEALAND. (Chief Information Officer) see *BUSINESS AND ECONOMICS—Computer Applications*

C I O TAIWAN. (Chief Information Officer) see *BUSINESS AND ECONOMICS—Computer Applications*

C M A MANAGEMENT; for strategic business ideas. see *BUSINESS AND ECONOMICS—Accounting*

C O R S BULLETIN. see *COMPUTERS*

C P A CLIENT BULLETIN. see *BUSINESS AND ECONOMICS—Accounting*

C P A CONSULTANT. (Certified Public Accountant) see *BUSINESS AND ECONOMICS—Accounting*

C P A MANAGING PARTNER REPORT; management news for accounting executives. see *BUSINESS AND ECONOMICS—Accounting*

658 USA ISSN 1547-8904
HD49
C P M GLOBAL ASSURANCE. (Contingency Planning & Management) Text in English. 1996. m. USD 275 in US & Canada; USD 350 elsewhere; free (effective 2005). **Document type:** *Newsletter, Trade.* **Description:** Provides a central resource for technology, products, services, information, and management strategies that support business continuity to safeguard the physical, informational, and communication assets of a business; ensure the safety of employees and the public; and protect the financial well-being of the company.
Formerly (until Jan. 2004): Contingency Planning & Management (1086-0932)
Published by: Witter Publishing Co., Inc., 20 Commerce St., Flemington, NJ 08822-7700. info@witterpublishing.com, http://www.contingencyplanning.com/magazine/index.aspx, http://www.witterpublishing.com. Ed. Vanessa Van Gilson. Circ: 35,000 (paid and controlled).

658.812 USA
C R M MAGAZINE. (Customer Relationship Management) Text in English. m. free domestic to qualified personnel (effective 2005). **Document type:** *Magazine, Trade.* **Description:** Each issue incorporates vital information that will help you benefit from the experience of other companies, and ensure that your company becomes a CRM success story.
Published by: Information Today, Inc., 143 Old Marlton Pike, Medford, NJ 08055-8750. TEL 609-654-6266, FAX 609-654-4309, custserv@infotoday.com, http://www.destinationCRM.com, http://www.infotoday.com. Ed. Ginger Conlon. Pub. Bob Fernekees.

658 GBR
C R O M T E C WORKING PAPER SERIES. Text in English. 1989. irreg. price varies. **Document type:** *Monographic series, Academic/Scholarly.*
Published by: Centre for Research on Organisations, Management and Technical Change, University of Manchester, Institute of Science and Technology, School of Management, PO Box 88, Manchester, Lancs M60 1QD, United Kingdom. TEL 0161-200-3401, FAX 0161-200-3505, TELEX 666094.

658 AUS ISSN 1325-6114
C T C NEWSLETTER. (Competitive Tendering and Contracting Research) Text in English. 1992. s-a.
Published by: University of Sydney, Graduate School of Business., C37, Sydney, NSW 2006, Australia. TEL 61-2-351-0049, FAX 61-2-557-0740, ctcinfo@gsb.usyd.edu.au, http://www.usdy.edu.au/su/ctcr/newslett.html.

C T O MAGAZINE. (Chief Technology Officer) see *COMPUTERS—Computer Industry*

C X O; magazyn kadry zarzadzajacej. see *BUSINESS AND ECONOMICS—Computer Applications*

658 CAN ISSN 1484-9844
C Y A P FORUM. (Canada's Year of Asia Pacific) Text in English. 1997. irreg.
Published by: International Trade Canada, 125 Sussex Drive, Ottawa, ON K1A 0G2, Canada. TEL 613-944-4000, FAX 613-996-9709, http://www.itcan-cican.gc.ca/menu-en.asp.

658 BRA ISSN 1518-7322
CADERNOS DE POS-GRADUACAO EM ADMINISTRACAO DE EMPRESAS. Text in Portuguese; Abstracts in English. 2001. a. free (effective 2005). 100 p./no.; **Document type:** *Journal, Academic/Scholarly.*
Published by: Universidade Presbiteriana Mackenzie (Subsidiary of: Instituto Presbiteriano Mackenzie), Rua da Consolacao 896, Pr.2, Sao Paulo-SP, SP 01302-907, Brazil. FAX 55-11-32368302, 55-11-32142582, biblio.per@mackenzie.br, http://www.mackenzie.com.br. Ed. Mr. Reynaldo Cavalheiro Marcondes.

658 600 FRA ISSN 1261-0402
LES CAHIERS DU MANAGEMENT TECHNOLOGIQUE. Text in Multiple languages. 1991. q.
Indexed: RefZh.
Published by: Groupe E S C Grenoble, Europole, 12 Rue Pierre Semard, Grenoble, 38003, France. TEL 33-4-76706060, FAX 33-4-76706090, info@esc-grenoble.fr, http://www.esc-grenoble.com.

658 IND ISSN 0068-5356
CALCUTTA MANAGEMENT ASSOCIATION. ANNUAL REPORT. Text in English. 1959. a. membership.
Published by: Calcutta Management Association, 1 Shakespeare Sarani, Kolkata, West Bengal 700 071, India.

658 IND
CALCUTTA MANAGEMENT ASSOCIATION. NEWSLETTER. Text in English. 1959. m. membership. adv. bk.rev. **Document type:** *Newsletter.*
Published by: Calcutta Management Association, 1 Shakespeare Sarani, Kolkata, West Bengal 700 071, India. Ed. N K Sharan. Circ: 1,500.

658 USA
CALIFORNIA C E O. (Chief Executive Officer) Text in English. 2000. m. adv. **Document type:** *Magazine, Trade.* **Description:** Contains articles on well-known California business leaders as well as regular features on state-based industries, innovative management ideas and trends, and company success stories.
Published by: C E O Media Corp., 12201 Tukwila International Bl., Ste. 150, Tukwila, WA 98168-5121. TEL 206-441-8415, 888-700-4153, FAX 206-441-8325, http://www.californiaceo.com, http://www.fivash.com. Ed. Alastair Goldfisher. Pub. Scott Fivash. Adv. contact Sara Wilenski.

658 USA ISSN 0008-1256
➤ **CALIFORNIA MANAGEMENT REVIEW.** Text in English. 1958. q. USD 75 domestic to individuals; USD 115 foreign to individuals; USD 100 domestic to institutions; USD 140 foreign to institutions; USD 40 domestic to students; USD 60 foreign to students (effective 2004). adv. illus. index. back issues avail.; reprints avail. **Document type:** *Journal, Academic/Scholarly.* **Description:** Serves as a bridge of communication between those who study management and those who practice it.
Related titles: Microform ed.: (from PQC); Online - full text ed.: (from Chadwyck-Healey Inc., EBSCO Publishing, Northern Light Technology, Inc., O C L C Online Computer Library Center, Inc., ProQuest Information & Learning).
Indexed: AAR, ABCPolSci, ABIn, ABS&EES, ADPA, ASCA, ASEANManA, ATI, BAS, BLI, BPI, BPIA, BusI, CPM, CurCont, DIP, DPD, EAA, ESPM, Emerald, ExcerpMed, FamI, FutSurv, IBR, IBSS, IBZ, Inspec, JEL, KES, LogistBibl, M&MA, MEA&I, MEDLINE, ManagCont, ORMS, PAIS, PCI, PMA, PersLit, QC&AS, RASB, RefZh, RiskAb, SCIMP, SSCI, WBA.
—BLDSC (3015.060000), CISTI, IDS, IE, Infotrieve, ingenta, Linda Hall.
Published by: University of California at Berkeley, Haas School of Business, F 501 #1900, Berkeley, CA 94720-1900. TEL 510-642-7159, FAX 510-642-1318, cmr@haas.berkeley.edu, http://haas.berkeley.edu/news/cmr, http://www.hass.berkeley.edu. Circ: 6,500.

➤ **CALL CENTRE FOCUS.** see *COMMUNICATIONS—Telephone And Telegraph*

658 GBR
CAMBRIDGE STUDIES IN MANAGEMENT. Text in English. 1983. irreg., latest no.27, 2000. price varies. **Document type:** *Monographic series, Academic/Scholarly.*
—BLDSC (3015.994500), ingenta.
Published by: Cambridge University Press, The Edinburgh Bldg, Shaftesbury Rd, Cambridge, CB2 2RU, United Kingdom. TEL 44-1223-312393, FAX 44-1223-315052, information@cambridge.org, http://publishing.cambridge.org/series/csmn.

658 378 USA ISSN 1556-2999
▼ **CAMPUS FACILITY MAINTENANCE**; promoting a healthy and productive learning environment. Text in English. 2004. bi-m. adv. **Document type:** *Magazine, Trade.* **Description:** Provide facility directors/planners and operations managers at today's higher learning facilities with information designed to help them better run their operations and efficiently manage their staff.
Published by: Cygnus Business Media, Inc., 33 Inverness Center Pkwy, 2nd Fl, Birmingham, AL 35242. TEL 205-988-9708, 800-366-0676, FAX 205-987-3237, http://www.campusfacilitymaintenance.com/, http://www.cygnusb2b.com/. Ed. Richard DiPaolo TEL 618-845-2700 ext 217. Pub. Tracy Aston TEL 205-380-1431. Adv. contact Joe Ruzic TEL 205-380-1368. B&W page USD 6,400; trim 7.875 x 10.75. Circ: 20,005 (controlled).

658 CAN
CANADA SCHOOL OF PUBLIC SERVICE. ANNUAL REPORT. Text in English. 1990. a.
Former titles: Canadian Centre for Management Development. Annual Report (1187-2160); (until 1991): Canadian Centre for Management Development. Principal's Report (0848-4317)
—CISTI.
Published by: Canada School of Public Service, 373 Sussex Drive, Ottawa, ON K1N 6Z2, Canada. TEL 866-703-9598, FAX 819-953-7953.

658 CAN
CANADIAN BUSINESS MANAGEMENT MANUAL. Text in English. m. looseleaf. CND 560 (effective 2005). **Document type:** *Trade.* **Description:** Covers a wide range of topics for business managers including easy-to-read treatment of business and human resources issues, practical how-to examples, checklists and procedures.
Published by: C C H Canadian Ltd., 90 Sheppard Ave E, Ste 300, North York, ON M2N 6X1, Canada. TEL 416-224-2248, 800-268-4522, FAX 416-224-2243, cservice@cch.ca, http://www.cch.ca.

651.37 346.066 CAN
CANADIAN CORPORATE SECRETARY'S GUIDE. Text in English. 1978. bi-m. CND 680 (effective 2005). **Document type:** *Trade.* **Description:** Reference manual outlining the duties and responsibilities of corporate secretaries and administrators.
Supersedes: Canadian Corporate Secretary and Administrator
Related titles: CD-ROM ed.: CND 680 (effective 2005); Online - full text ed.: CND 680 (effective 2005).
Indexed: CBCABus.
Published by: (Institute of Chartered Secretaries and Administrators), C C H Canadian Ltd., 90 Sheppard Ave E, Ste 300, North York, ON M2N 6X1, Canada. TEL 416-224-2248, 800-268-4522, FAX 416-224-2243, cservice@cch.ca, http://www.cch.ca.

CANADIAN JOURNAL OF ADMINISTRATIVE SCIENCES/REVUE CANADIENNE DES SCIENCES DE L'ADMINISTRATION. see *BUSINESS AND ECONOMICS*

658 CAN ISSN 0045-5156
CANADIAN MANAGER. Text in English. 1942. q. CND 12, USD 18. adv. bk.rev. **Document type:** *Trade.* **Description:** Management techniques for middle to upper management.
Supersedes: Industrial Manager (0319-4027)
Related titles: Microfiche ed.: (from MML); Microform ed.: (from MML); Online - full text ed.: (from EBSCO Publishing, Florida Center for Library Automation, Gale Group, Micromedia ProQuest, Northern Light Technology, Inc., O C L C Online Computer Library Center, Inc., ProQuest Information & Learning).
Indexed: ABIn, BPIA, BusI, CBCABus, CBCARef, CBPI, CPerI, ManagCont, T&II.
—BLDSC (3037.820000), IE, ingenta. **CCC.**
Published by: (Canadian Institute of Management), Taylor Enterprises Ltd., 2175 Sheppard Ave E, Ste 310, Willowdale, ON M2J 1W8, Canada. TEL 416-493-0155, FAX 416-491-1670, office@cim.ca, http://www.cim.ca/NResources/CanadianManager.asp. Ed. Ruth Max. adv.: B&W page CND 1,600, color page CND 2,200; trim 10.88 x 8.13. Circ: 10,200.

CAREER DEVELOPMENT INTERNATIONAL. see *OCCUPATIONS AND CAREERS*

658 333.33 USA ISSN 0889-2288
CARLSONREPORT FOR SHOPPING CENTER MANAGEMENT. Text in English. 1982. m. USD 135 domestic; USD 145 foreign (effective 2000). adv. bk.rev.; software rev. abstr.; charts; illus.; maps; stat.; tr.lit. back issues avail. **Document type:** *Newsletter.* **Description:** Industry newsletter for shopping center management professionals at the mall and corporate level.
—**CCC.**
Published by: Raven Communications, Inc., PO Box 50038, Indianapolis, IN 46250. TEL 800-546-9889, ravencom@prodigy.net. Ed., Pub., R&P Major William R Wilburn. Circ: 1,500.

658 340 338 COL
CARTA DE GERENCIA. Text in Spanish. 1964. fortn. USD 64. bibl. **Document type:** *Academic/Scholarly.*
Published by: Legis S.A., Ave. Eldorado, 81-10, Apartado Aereo 98888, Bogota, CUND, Colombia. FAX 57-1-410-0628. Ed. Roberto Escobar. Circ: 10,000.

658 USA ISSN 0894-6043
CASE RESEARCH JOURNAL. Text in English. 1980. q. **Document type:** *Journal.* **Description:** Publishes teaching cases drawn from research in real organizations, covering all administration-related disciplines.

B

B

Published by: North American Case Research Association, c/o Bob Crowner, 3719 Meadow Lane, Saline, MI 48176. rpcnacra@worldnet.att.net, http://www.sba.muohio.edu/crj/. Ed. David W Rosenthal TEL 513-529-1203.

658 USA ISSN 1545-2816
HD45
CATALYST (FAIRFAX). Text in English. 2000. q. **Document type:** *Magazine, Trade.* **Description:** Explores how technology impacts business on a broad scale, addresses relevant market trends, explains technology in the context of profitability, interviews industry leaders, and highlights the new ways technology is changing how organizations interact with each other and their customers.
Published by: American Management Systems, Inc., 4050 Legato Rd, Fairfax, VA 22033. TEL 703-267-8000, FAX 703-267-5073, http://www.amsinc.com/Amscat/Catalyst.htm.

CATALYST DIRECTORY NEWSLETTER. see *NEW AGE PUBLICATIONS*

CATERING MANAGEMENT. see *FOOD AND FOOD INDUSTRIES*

CATERING SERVICE IDEA NEWSLETTER. see *FOOD AND FOOD INDUSTRIES*

658.5 USA ISSN 1072-5296
HD62.15
CENTER FOR QUALITY MANAGEMENT JOURNAL. Text in English. 1992. q.
Published by: Center for Quality Management, 150 Cambridge Park Dr, Cambridge, MA 02140. http://www.cqm.org/. Ed. David Walden.

CENTRAL EUROPEAN JOURNAL OF OPERATIONS RESEARCH. see *COMPUTERS*

CENTRE ON GOVERNANCE. see *PUBLIC ADMINISTRATION*

658 CAN
THE CEO REFRESHER. Text in English. m. adv. back issues avail. **Document type:** *Newsletter, Trade.* **Description:** Covers contemporary topics in creative leadership, competitive strategy, and performance improvement.
Media: Online - full text.
Published by: Refresher Publications, Inc., 17 Markland Drive, Etobicoke, ON M9C 1M8, Canada. vfr@refresher.com, http://www.refresher.com. Ed., Pub. Rick Sidorowicz.

658 USA
CERTIFIED LETTER. Text in English. 1979. q. free to members. bk.rev. back issues avail. **Document type:** *Newsletter.* **Description:** Newsletter about assessment, benchmaking and competency for general managers who have earned certification.
Formerly: I C P M Newsletter
Published by: Institute of Certified Professional Managers, James Madison University, Harrisonburg, VA 27807. TEL 703-568-3247, FAX 703-568-3587, adm-icpm@vas1.acs.jmu.edu. Circ: 5,300 (controlled).

CESTE I MOSTOVI/ROADS AND BRIDGES. see *ENGINEERING—Civil Engineering*

658 USA ISSN 0164-9914
CHAIN DRUG REVIEW; the reporter for the chain drug store industry. Text in English. 1978. fortn. (except m. in May, Dec. & Jul.). USD 125 manufacturers & sales representatives; USD 185 to libraries (effective 2005). adv. **Document type:** *Magazine, Trade.*
Related titles: Online - full text ed.: (from Gale Group, Northern Light Technology, Inc., O C L C Online Computer Library Center, Inc.).
Indexed: B&I.
—BLDSC (3128.734150).
Published by: Racher Press, Inc., 220 Fifth Ave, 18th Fl, New York, NY 10001. TEL 212-213-6000, 212-213-6000, FAX 212-213-6106, jwoldt@racherpress.com, http://www.chaindrugreview.com. Eds. David Pinto, Jeff Woldt. Pub. Susan Schinitsky. adv.: B&W page USD 10,189, color page USD 13,070. Circ: 46,000 (controlled).

658 MNG
CHANAR STANDART/QUALITY AND STANDARDS. Text in Mongol. 1982. bi-m.
Address: Ulan Bator, Mongolia. TEL 976-1-458032, FAX 976-1-453574. Ed. N Tsetsgee. Circ: 1,500.

THE CHANNEL. see *BUSINESS AND ECONOMICS—Computer Applications*

658 USA
CHAPTER RELATIONS. Text in English. bi-m. membership. adv. **Description:** Provides information on operating federations and associations composed of chapters (national and international); management techniques; activities calendar.
Published by: (Chapter Relations Section), American Society of Association Executives, 1575 Eye St, N W, Washington, DC 20005-1168. TEL 202-626-2775, FAX 202-842-1109, http://www.asaenet.org. Circ: 650.

CHARTER INDUSTRY; management magazine for the marine charter industry. see *SPORTS AND GAMES—Boats And Boating*

658 346 GBR ISSN 1363-5905
CHARTERED SECRETARY. Text in English. 1891. m. GBP 50 domestic to non-members; GBP 62 foreign to non-members (effective 2001). adv. bk.rev.; software rev.; Website rev. charts; illus. index. 52 p./no.; back issues avail. **Document type:** *Magazine, Trade.* **Description:** Contains practical articles on law, finance, health & safety, governance & compliance, and personnel-oriented problems and developments. For administrators and company secretaries.
Former titles (until 1996): Administrator (0263-3868); (until 1982): Professional Administration
Related titles: Online - full text ed.
Indexed: IMI, WBA.
—IE, Infotrieve.
Published by: Institute of Chartered Secretaries and Administration (I C S A), 16 Park Crescent, London, W1N 1AH, United Kingdom. TEL 44-20-7580-4741, FAX 44-20-7612-7034, 44-20-7323-1132, chartsec@isca.co.uk, chartsec@icsa.co.uk, http://www.icsa.org.uk/products/csmag1.html. Ed. Will Booth. Adv. contact Sean Murphy TEL 44-20-7250-4004. Circ: 28,000 (controlled).

658.4092 SWE ISSN 1401-0747
CHEF. Text in Swedish. 1995. 11/yr. SEK 495; SEK 45 newsstand/cover (effective 2000). adv. **Document type:** *Magazine, Trade.* **Description:** For leaders in all fields of endeavor.
Formed by the merger of (1926-1995): Arbetsledaren (0003-7842); (1965-1995): Personal (1104-7925); Which was formerly (until 1992): Personal, Manniskor och Arbete (0348-5242); (until 1978): Personaltjanst (0345-9284)
Published by: Affaerledarna A&L Foerlags HB, Riddargatan 23 A, Stockholm, 11457, Sweden. TEL 46-8-587-112-80, FAX 46-8-587-112-90, red@tidningenchef.com, http://www.tidningenchef.com. Pub. Henrik Frenkel. Adv. contact Andreas Forsberg. B&W page SEK 39,900, color page SEK 43,500; trim 215 x 276. Circ: 87,100.

651 DEU
CHEFBUERO; Das Magazin fuer Fuehrungskraefte. Text in German. 1988. 8/yr. EUR 31; EUR 5 newsstand/cover (effective 2004). adv. **Document type:** *Magazine, Trade.*
Published by: Chefbuero Verlag GmbH, Alt-Godshorn 75, Langenhagen, 30855, Germany. TEL 49-511-786790, FAX 49-511-7867914, chefbuero@chefbuero.de, http://www.chefbuero.de. Ed. Stefan Beuchel. Pub., Adv. contact Gerda Burkhardt. color page EUR 6,590, B&W page EUR 5,050; trim 184 x 268. Circ: 49,584 (paid and controlled).

CHICAGO ARTISTS' NEWS. see *ART*

658 AUS
CHIEF. Text in English. m. AUD 195 (effective 2004). **Document type:** *Magazine, Trade.* **Description:** Covers technology, trends in the industry, and profiles of leading Australian CEOs.
Published by: First Charlton Communications, Level 9, Tenix House, 100 Arthur St, North Sydney, NSW 2060, Australia. TEL 61-2-99556299, FAX 61-2-99571512, pctc@charlton.com.au, http://www.charlton.com.au/. Ed. Sarah Jones. Adv. contact Tony May TEL 61-2-99579809.

658 USA ISSN 0160-4724
HC10 CODEN: CHIEER
CHIEF EXECUTIVE MAGAZINE. Text in English. 1977. m. USD 95 domestic; USD 135 foreign; USD 10 newsstand/cover (effective 2005). adv. bk.rev. 72 p./no. 3 cols./p.; back issues avail.; reprints avail. **Document type:** *Magazine, Trade.* **Description:** Offers opinion written by and for CEOs in the US and elsewhere. Covers management, financial or business strategy, marketing, economic and public policy issues.
Related titles: Microform ed.: (from PQC); Online - full text ed.: (from Florida Center for Library Automation, Gale Group, O C L C Online Computer Library Center, Inc., ProQuest Information & Learning); Supplement(s): C E O Brief.
Indexed: ABIn, BPIA, PROMT.
—BLDSC (3172.824200), IE, ingenta.
Published by: Chief Executive Group, Inc., 110 Summit Ave., Montvale, NJ 07645. TEL 201-930-5959, FAX 201-930-5956, cevans@chiefevexcutive.net, http://www.chiefexecutive.net. Ed. William J Holstein. adv.: B&W page USD 17,395, color page USD 21,220. Circ: 42,033 (paid and free).

658 USA ISSN 1084-4147
CHIEF EXECUTIVE OFFICERS NEWSLETTER; for the entrepreneurial manager and the professionals who advise him. Text in English. 1979. m. looseleaf. USD 96 (effective 2005). bk.rev. **Document type:** *Newsletter.* **Description:** For the entrepreneurial manager and the professionals who advise him.
Formerly: Entrepreneurial Manager's Newsletter (0272-0396)
Related titles: Online - full text ed.
Published by: Chief Executive Officer's Club, Inc., 47 West St, Ste 5 A, New York, NY 10006-2949. TEL 212-978-8863, FAX 212-978-7622, info@ceoclubs.org, http://www.ceoclubs.org. Ed. Joseph R Mancuso. Circ: 3,000.

CHIEF EXECUTIVES COMPENSATION IN CANADA. see *BUSINESS AND ECONOMICS—Personnel Management*

658 170 IND ISSN 0971-9806
➤ **CHINMAYA MANAGEMENT REVIEW.** Text in English. 1997. s-a. INR 300 domestic; USD 20 foreign (effective 2001). bk.rev. back issues avail. **Document type:** *Academic/Scholarly.* **Description:** Maintains a broad focus and seeks to publish the best available scholarship on all aspects of ethics, values, spirituality and management.
Published by: Chinmaya Institute of Higher Learning, Chinmaya Institute of Management, 7 D'Costa Layout, 1st Cross, Cooketown, Bangalore, Karnataka 560 084, India. TEL 91-80-5476509, FAX 91-80-5476509, maganti@giasbg01.vsnl.net.in, http://www.chinmaya.org/html/chinmaya_management_review.html. Ed., R&P Mytrae Maganti. Circ: 500 (paid).

658.3 230 USA
CHRISTIAN MANAGEMENT REPORT. Text in English. 1979. 6/yr. USD 29.95 to non-members. adv. bk.rev. back issues avail. **Document type:** *Trade.* **Description:** Covers management areas of fund raising, computers, tax and legal, accounting and finance, communications, personnel and others for Christian ministries.
Published by: Christian Management Association, PO Box 4090, San Clemente, CA 92674. TEL 949-487-0900, FAX 949-487-0927, cma@cmaonline.org, ron@cmaonline.org, http://www.cmaonline.org. Ed. Ron Keener. Pub. John Pearson. Adv. contact Jim McDonald. Circ: 7,000.

658 200 USA ISSN 1521-3536
CHURCH BUSINESS. Text in English. 1996. m. USD 72 domestic; USD 78 in Canada; USD 147 elsewhere (effective 2005). adv. **Document type:** *Magazine, Trade.* **Description:** Dedicated to providing information that will be useful to running the business of a church.
Published by: Virgo Publishing, Inc., 3300 N. Central Ave., Ste 300, Phoenix, AZ 85012. TEL 480-990-1101, FAX 480-990-0819, cs@vpico.com, http://www.churchbusiness.com, http://www.vpico.com. adv.: B&W page USD 4,035, color page USD 1,200; trim 8.125 x 10.875.

CHURCH BUSINESS. PRODUCTS & TECHNOLOGY. see *RELIGIONS AND THEOLOGY*

658 USA
CHURCH EXECUTIVE; the first source of information for business administrators of America's largest churches. Text in English. 2001. m. free to qualified personnel; USD 39; USD 5 per issue (effective 2005). adv. **Document type:** *Magazine, Trade.*
Published by: Power Trade Media, LLC, 4742 N 24th St, Ste 340, Phoenix, AZ 85016-4884. TEL 602-265-7600, 800-541-2670, FAX 602-277-7588, subscriptions@churchexecutive.com, http://www.churchexecutive.com. Ed., Pub. Steve Kane. Adv. contact Rebecca Frockt. B&W page USD 2,100; trim 8.125 x 10.875. Circ: 18,500 (controlled).

658 ESP ISSN 0211-1535
CIRCULO DE EMPRESARIOS. BOLETIN. Text in Spanish. 1979. 3/yr.
—CINDOC.
Published by: Circulo de Empresarios, Serrano 1, 4o. Piso, Madrid, 28001, Spain. TEL 34-91-5781472, FAX 34-91-5774871.

658 ESP ISSN 1133-1771
CIRCULO DE EMPRESARIOS. PUBLICACIONES MONOGRAFICAS. Text in Spanish. 1987. a.
Formerly (until 1987): Circulo de Empresarios. Numero Monografico (0213-7445)
—CINDOC.
Published by: Circulo de Empresarios, Serrano 1, 4o. Piso, Madrid, 28001, Spain. TEL 34-91-5781472, FAX 34-91-5774871, asociacion@circulodeempresarios.org, http://www.circulodeempresarios.org/. Ed. Manuel Azpilicueta.

331 658.1 SWE ISSN 1400-0997
CIVILEKONOMEN. Text in Swedish. 1924. 8/yr. SEK 250 (effective 2001). adv. bk.rev. illus. index. **Document type:** *Magazine, Trade.*
Former titles (until vol.4, 1994): Civilekonomnytt (0280-915X); (until 1983): Ekonomen (0013-2977)
Related titles: Audio cassette/tape ed.
Published by: Civilekonomernas Riksfoerbund (CR), Fack 4720, Stockholm, 11692, Sweden. TEL 46-8-7832769, FAX 46-8-7832752, info@civilekonomerna.se, http://www.civilekonomerna.se. Ed. Unn Edberg. Adv. contact Ninni Westerlund. B&W page SEK 15,600, color page SEK 19,400; trim 196 x 260. Circ: 18,800.

658 USA ISSN 0009-8434
JK468.S4
CLASSIFICATION MANAGEMENT. Text in English. 1965. a. USD 30. **Document type:** *Newsletter.*
Published by: National Classification Management Society, 994 Old Eagle School Rd, Ste 1019, Wayne, PA 19087-1802. TEL 610-971-4856, FAX 610-971-4859, classmgmt@aol.com, http://www.classmgmt.com. Ed. Sharon K Tannahill. Circ: 1,800.

CLEAN AIR NEWS. see *ENVIRONMENTAL STUDIES—Pollution*

CLEANING BUSINESS; published monthly for the self-employed cleaning & maintenance professional. see *BUSINESS AND ECONOMICS—Small Business*

CLICK (TAMPA); your online medical management magazine. see *MEDICAL SCIENCES*

CLINICAL GOVERNANCE; an international journal. see *MEDICAL SCIENCES*

CLINICAL LEADERSHIP & MANAGEMENT REVIEW. see *MEDICAL SCIENCES—Experimental Medicine, Laboratory Technique*

CLINICIAN IN MANAGEMENT. see *MEDICAL SCIENCES*

367 658 AUS ISSN 0045-7205
CLUB MANAGEMENT IN AUSTRALIA✶ . Text in English. 1960. m. AUD 40. adv. charts; stat. **Document type:** *Trade.*
Former titles: Secretaries and Managers Journal of Australia; Club Managers Journal (0009-9597)
Published by: Club Managers' Association Australia, 67-73 St Hilliers Rd, Auburn, NSW 2144, Australia. TEL 61-2-9643-2300, FAX 61-2-9643-2400, http://www.cmaa.asn.au/. Adv. contact Judy Rayner. Circ: (controlled).

658 FRA
CODE DES SOCIETES. Text in French. irreg. looseleaf. **Document type:** *Trade.*
Published by: Joly Editions, 31 rue Falguiere, Paris, 75015, France. TEL 33-1-56541600, FAX 33-1-56541647. Ed. Daniel Lepeltier.

658 DEU ISSN 1437-7128
COGNITIVE STRATEGY CONCEPTS. Text in German. 1999. irreg., latest vol.2, 2000. price varies. **Document type:** *Monographic series, Academic/Scholarly.*
Published by: Logos Verlag Berlin, Comeniushof, Gubener Str 47, Berlin, 10243, Germany. TEL 49-30-42851090, FAX 49-30-42851092, redaktion@logos-verlag.de, http://www.logos-verlag.de.

658 ESP
COLECCION DIRECCION DE EMPRESAS Y ORGANIZACIONES. Text in Spanish. 1976. irreg. price varies. back issues avail. **Document type:** *Academic/Scholarly.*
Published by: (Universidad de Navarra, Instituto de Estudios Superiores de la Empresa), Ediciones Universidad de Navarra S.A., Pza. Los Sauces, 1-2, Baranain, (Navarra) 31010, Spain. TEL 34-948-856850, FAX 34-948-856854, eunsaedi@abc.ibernet.com, http://www.unav.es.

658 ESP
COLECCION LA EMPRESA Y SU ENTORNO. SERIE A C. Text in Spanish. 1967. irreg. price varies. **Document type:** *Monographic series.*
Formerly (until 1975): Universidad de Navarra. Instituto de Estudios Superiores de la Empresas. Coleccion I E S E. Serie A C (0078-8716)
Published by: (Universidad de Navarra, Instituto de Estudios Superiores de la Empresa), Ediciones Universidad de Navarra S.A., Pza. Los Sauces, 1-2, Baranain, (Navarra) 31010, Spain. TEL 34-948-256850, FAX 34-948-256854, eunsaedi@abc.ibernet.com, http://www.unav.es.

658 ESP ISSN 0212-0763
COLECCION LA EMPRESA Y SU ENTORNO. SERIE L. Text in Spanish. 1970. irreg. price varies. back issues avail. **Document type:** *Monographic series.*
Formerly (until 1975): Universidad de Navarra. Instituto de Estudios Superiores de la Empresa. Coleccion I E S E. Serie L (0078-8708)
Published by: (Universidad de Navarra, Instituto de Estudios Superiores de la Empresa.), Ediciones Universidad de Navarra S.A., Pza. Los Sauces, 1-2, Baranain, (Navarra) 31010, Spain. TEL 34-948-256850, FAX 34-948-256854, eunsaedi@abc.ibernet.com, http://www.unav.es.

658.4 USA ISSN 1085-911X
CODEN: CCEOE2
COLUMBUS C.E.O.✶ . Text in English. 1992. m. USD 20.05; USD 2.25 newsstand/cover. back issues avail.
Published by: Metropolitan C.E.O., PO Box 40907, Indianapolis, IN 46240-0907. TEL 317-257-8000, FAX 317-257-1482. Ed. Cindy Ludlow. Circ: 25,000 (controlled).

658 GBR
COMMERCIAL TRANSACTIONS CHECKLISTS. Text in English. 1997. base vol. plus updates 2/yr. looseleaf. GBP 339 (effective 2006). **Document type:** *Journal, Trade.*
Description: Provides an extensive range of checklists for use in various business transactions and activities.
Published by: Sweet & Maxwell Ltd., 100 Avenue Road, London, NW3 3PF, United Kingdom. TEL 44-20-74491111, FAX 44-20-74491144, customer.services@sweetandmaxwell.co.uk, http://www.sweetandmaxwell.co.uk. Ed. Neil Sinclair. **Subscr. to:** Cheriton House, North Way, Andover, Hants SP10 5BE, United Kingdom.

658.45 USA ISSN 0730-7799
CODEN: COBREC
COMMUNICATION BRIEFINGS. Text in English. 1981. m. USD 169 domestic; USD 299 foreign (effective 2005). bk.rev. index. back issues avail. **Document type:** *Newsletter, Consumer.*
Description: Contains articles, excerpts, news items, and departments on ideas and techniques to help improve writing, speaking, listening, organizing, problem-solving, and decision-making skills at the managerial and administrative levels.
—CASDDS, IE, Infotrieve. **CCC.**
Published by: Briefings Publishing Group (Subsidiary of: Douglas Publications, Inc.), 1101 King St, Ste 110, Alexandria, VA 22314. TEL 703-518-2343, 800-722-9221, FAX 703-684-2136, dhackett@briefings.com, customerservice@briefings.com, http://www.briefings.com. Eds. Deidre Hackett, Chris Vestal. Circ: 60,000 (paid and controlled).

658 USA ISSN 1539-008X
COMMUNICATION BULLETIN FOR MANAGERS AND SUPERVISORS. Text in English. 1998. s-m. USD 94.56 (effective 2002). bk.rev. **Document type:** *Newsletter.*
Description: Ideas and insights for better marketplace communication and personal success.
Formerly (until 2002): Communication Solutions (1523-4290)
Published by: Progressive Business Publications, 370 Technology Dr, Malvern, PA 19355-1315. TEL 610-695-8600, 800-220-5000, FAX 610-647-8089, editor@pbp.com, http://www.pbp.com. Ed. Ken Dooley. R&P Curt Brown.

658 FRA
COMMUNICATION MANAGEMENT CONSULTING NEWSLETTER. Text in English. w. **Document type:** *Newsletter.* **Description:** Presents a weekly analysis of American companies and their management.
Media: Online - full text.
Published by: European Press, France. infos@cmc.fr, http://www.cmc.fr/morning.htm.

658.45 USA
COMMUNICATION NEWS. Text in English. m. membership. adv.
Description: Features common public and employee relations problems faced by association executives who manage the communication of their association.
Published by: (Communication Section), American Society of Association Executives, 1575 Eye St, N W, Washington, DC 20005-1168. TEL 202-626-2739, FAX 202-408-9635, http://www.asaenet.org. Circ: 2,050.

COMMUNICATION NEWS. see *COMMUNICATIONS*

658.45 USA ISSN 0744-7612
CODEN: COMWEE
COMMUNICATION WORLD. Text in English. 1973. 7/yr. USD 150 to libraries; USD 270; free to members (effective 2005). adv. bk.rev. illus. back issues avail.; reprints avail. **Document type:** *Magazine, Trade.* **Description:** Publishes for members of IABC whose business is communication, public relations and related disciplines.
Former titles (until 1982): Journal of Communication Management (0745-1822); (until 1981): Journal of Organizational Communication (0162-5659); (until 1974): I A B C Journal (0092-7384)
Related titles: Online - full text ed.: (from bigchalk, EBSCO Publishing, Florida Center for Library Automation, Gale Group, Northern Light Technology, Inc., O C L C Online Computer Library Center, Inc., ProQuest Information & Learning, The Dialog Corporation).
Indexed: ABIn, BPIA, ManagCont, T&II.
—BLDSC (3363.469500), IE, ingenta. **CCC.**
Published by: International Association of Business Communicators, One Hallidie Plaza, Ste 600, San Francisco, CA 94102. TEL 415-544-4700, FAX 415-544-4747, ggordon@iabc.com, http://www.abc.com. Ed. Natasha Spring. adv.: B&W page USD 2,600, color page USD 3,395. Circ: 45,000 (paid and free).

621.388 USA
COMMUNICATIONS BUSINESS & FINANCE. Text in English. bi-w. USD 645 in North America; USD 825 elsewhere (effective 2005). **Document type:** *Newsletter.* **Description:** Deals exclusively with investment and finance activities in the converging telecom, cable television, wireless, and internet businesses, tracking the performance of telecom strategies, deals in the making, and investment trends and controversies.
Related titles: Online - full text ed.
Published by: Telecommunications Reports International, Inc. (Subsidiary of: Aspen Publishers, Inc.), 1333 H St., N.W., Ste. 100-E, Washington, DC 20005. http://www.tr.com. Eds. John Curran, Victoria Mason.

658 GBR ISSN 0264-4576
COMMUNICATIONS MANAGEMENT. Text in English. 1983. m. adv. **Document type:** *Trade.*
Formerly: C S and M (0264-455X)
Indexed: Inspec, M&MA.
Published by: E M A P Media (Subsidiary of: E M A P Business Communications), 33-39 Bowling Green Ln, London, EC1R 0DA, United Kingdom. TEL 44-171-837-1212, FAX 44-171-278-4008, TELEX 936566. Circ: 15,000.

658.45 GBR ISSN 0967-5841
COMMUNICATORS IN BUSINESS MAGAZINE. Text in English. 1992. 3/yr. GBP 50 (effective 2000). 32 p./no.; **Document type:** *Trade.* **Description:** Publishes features and news for policymakers in the communications industry.
Published by: British Association of Communicators in Business, 42 Borough High St, London, SE1 1XW, United Kingdom. TEL 44-207-378-7139, FAX 44-207-378-7140. Ed. Neil Jones. Circ: 3,000.

658.0071 USA ISSN 1043-0695
➤ **COMMUNIQUE (COLUMBUS, 1967).** Text in English. 1967. q. free to members. adv. charts; illus.; tr.lit. **Document type:** *Journal, Academic/Scholarly.*
Former titles: O E A Communique (0889-4817); Office Education Association. National Newsletter
Indexed: BusEdI, M&MA.
Published by: Business Professionals of America, 5454 Cleveland Ave, Columbus, OH 43231-4021. TEL 614-895-7277, FAX 614-895-1165, bpa@ix.netcom.com, http://www.bpa.orgbpa.html. Ed., R&P, Adv. contact Stephen Dziura. Circ: 45,000.

658 USA ISSN 1071-5967
COMMUNITY MANAGEMENT. Text in English. 1993. bi-m. looseleaf. USD 59 to non-members (effective 2002). adv. 10 p./no. 3 cols./p.; **Document type:** *Newsletter, Trade.*
Description: Presents strategies, trends and news for managers of condominiums and planned communities.
Published by: Community Associations Institute, 225 Reinekers Lane, Ste. 300, Alexandria, VA 22314. TEL 703-548-8600, FAX 703-836-6907, http://www.caionline.org. adv.: B&W page USD 3,675, color page USD 4,940; 7 x 10. Circ: 2,100 (paid). **Subscr. to:** The Crustacean Society, PO Box 1897, Lawrence, KS 66044-8897.

COMPANY CAR REPORT - EUROPE. see *BUSINESS AND ECONOMICS—Personnel Management*

658 340 AUS ISSN 0816-5521
COMPANY DIRECTOR. Text in English. 1983. m. AUD 295. adv. bk.rev.
Formed by the 1983 merger of: Director's Law Reporter (0311-0389); (1979-1983): Directors Early Warner; (1975-1983): Directors Economic Review
Published by: Australian Institute of Company Directors, Level 25, Australia Sq, 264-278 George St, Sydney, NSW 2000, Australia. TEL 61-2-82486600, FAX 61-2-82486633, aicd@companydirectors.com.au, http://www.companydirectors.com.au/0fra/f/ff5.html. Ed. Mark Phillips. Adv. contact Sarah Coles. Circ: 12,000.

658 HKG ISSN 1023-4128
COMPANY SECRETARY. Text in English. 1990. m. HKD 1,635.
Description: Contains commentary on developments in legal, accounting and company secretarial practices as they affect the Hong Kong and PRC business environment.
Published by: (Hong Kong Institute of Company Secretaries), Pearson Professional (HK) Ltd., Ste. 1808 Asian House, 1 Hennessy Rd, Wanchai, Hong Kong, Hong Kong. TEL 852-2863-2659, FAX 852-2520-6954, pphkg@hk.super.net.

658 GBR
COMPARATIVE MANAGEMENT. Text in English. q. GBP 45, USD 85. **Description:** Academic and management journal that focuses on the institutional, legal and cultural environment in which businesses operate. Has a heavy emphasis on Europe.
Published by: Debos Oxford Publications Ltd., 31 Warnborough Rd, Oxford, OX2 6JA, United Kingdom. Ed. Oscar Werdmuller.

COMPENSATION & BENEFITS UPDATE. see *BUSINESS AND ECONOMICS—Personnel Management*

COMPENSATION OF PLANT - FACILITIES MAINTENANCE - ENGINEERING MANAGERS & ENGINEERS. see *BUSINESS AND ECONOMICS—Labor And Industrial Relations*

650 CAN
COMPETIA ONLINE MAGAZINE. Text in English. irreg. USD 89 (effective 2000). bk.rev. back issues avail. **Description:** Includes articles and general resources on strategic planning.
Published by: Executive Resources, 1250 Rene Levesque W, Ste 2200, Montreal, PQ H3B 4W8, Canada. TEL 514-270-5222, FAX 514-270-5223, ian@compedia.com, http:/www.compedia.com.

658 USA ISSN 1521-5881
HD38.7
COMPETITIVE INTELLIGENCE MAGAZINE. Text in English. 1998. bi-m. free to members (effective 2004). **Document type:** *Magazine, Trade.* **Description:** Provides news and developments, with sharply focused articles on CI tools, techniques, and methods, along with first-person observations on becoming a more effective competitive intelligence professional.
Related titles: Online - full text ed.: (from Gale Group, IngentaConnect).
Indexed: ABIn.
—BLDSC (3363.993655), IE.

B

Published by: Society of Competitive Intelligence Professionals, 1700 Diagonal Rd, Ste 600, Alexandria, VA 22314. TEL 703-739-0696, FAX 703-739-2524, info@scip.org, http://www.scip.org. Ed., Pub. Stephen H Miller.

COMPETITIVENESS REVIEW; an international business journal. see *BUSINESS AND ECONOMICS—International Commerce*

658.32 USA ISSN 0274-8304
HD7106.U5
COMPLIANCE GUIDE FOR PLAN ADMINISTRATORS. Text in English. 1976. 3 base vols. plus m. updates. looseleaf. USD 1,059 base vol(s). print or online or CD-ROM ed. (effective 2004). **Description:** Provides step-by-step and sample guidance for complying with all pension law reporting and disclosure requirements.
Formerly: C C H Compliance Guide for Plan Administrators (0363-7476)
Related titles: CD-ROM ed.; Online - full text ed.
Indexed: ATI.
—**CCC.**
Published by: C C H Inc., 2700 Lake Cook Rd, Riverwoods, IL 60015. TEL 847-267-7000, 800-449-6439, cust_serv@cch.com, http://www.cch.com. Pub. Catherine Wolfe.

COMPUTATIONAL & MATHEMATICAL ORGANIZATION THEORY. see *MATHEMATICS—Computer Applications*

COMPUTATIONAL ECONOMICS. see *BUSINESS AND ECONOMICS—Computer Applications*

COMPUTER LAW & SECURITY REPORT. see *COMPUTERS—Computer Security*

COMPUTER MANAGER. see *COMPUTERS*

COMPUTERS & OPERATIONS RESEARCH. see *COMPUTERS*

651.3 USA ISSN 1551-8728
▼ **CONFLICT MANAGEMENT.** Text in English. 2004 (Fall). q. USD 90 to individuals; USD 190 to institutions (effective 2005).
Supersedes in part (in 2004): International Journal of Conflict Management (1044-4068)
Published by: Information Age Publishing, Inc., 411 W Putnam Ave, Ste 205, PO Box 4967, Greenwich, CT 06831. TEL 203-661-7602, FAX 203-661-7952, info@infoagepub.com, http://www.infoagepub.com.

658 FRA
CONSEIL NATIONAL DU PATRONAT FRANCAIS. ANNUAIRE. Text in French. a. index.
Published by: Conseil National du Patronat Francais, 31 av. Pierre 1er de Serbie, Paris, Cedex 16 75784, France.

658 GBR ISSN 1363-6804
CONSPECTUS. Text in English. 1992. m. free. **Document type:** *Trade.* **Description:** Publication for decision makers and management consultants who are interested in current developments in information technology.
Formerly (until 1996): Consultants' Conspectus (1351-0908)
Indexed: Inspec, MLA-IB.
—BLDSC (3420.099400), AskIEEE.
Published by: Prime Marketing Publications Ltd., Witton House, Lower Rd, Chorleywood, Rickmansworth, Herts WD3 5LB, United Kingdom. TEL 44-1923-285323, FAX 44-1923-285819, info@pmp.co.uk, conspectus@pmp.co.uk, http://www.pmp.co.uk. Ed. Tim Ring. Pub. Steve Markwell. Adv. contacts Ms. Megra Butterworth, Ms. Sharron Johns. Circ: 25,000.

CONSTRUCTION MANAGEMENT. see *BUILDING AND CONSTRUCTION*

658 GBR ISSN 1468-8441
CONSULTANTS ADVISORY. Text in English. 2000. 5/yr. free. **Document type:** *Trade.* **Description:** Aims to keep consultants integrators and analysts in the UK up-to-date with business and associated software and technology issues.
Indexed: Inspec.
Published by: Prime Marketing Publications Ltd., Witton House, Lower Rd, Chorleywood, Rickmansworth, Herts WD3 5LB, United Kingdom. TEL 44-1923-285323, FAX 44-1923-285819, info@pmp.co.uk, http://www.consultants-advisory.com. Ed. Tim Ring. Circ: 15,000 (controlled).

658.0029 USA ISSN 0196-1292
HD69.C6
CONSULTANTS & CONSULTING ORGANIZATIONS DIRECTORY; a reference guide to concerns and individuals engaged in consultation for business, industry and government. Text in English. a., latest vol.27, 2004. USD 940 (effective 2005); includes supplement. **Document type:** *Directory.* **Description:** Details on firms, individuals and organizations active in consulting fields.
Formerly: Consultants and Consulting Organizations (0589-4859)
Related titles: Online - full text ed.
—CISTI.
Published by: Gale Group (Subsidiary of: Thomson Corporation), 27500 Drake Rd, Farmington Hills, MI 48331-3535. TEL 248-699-8061, 800-877-4253, FAX 248-699-4253, galeord@gale.com, http://www.gale.com. Ed. Virgil Burton III.

658 USA ISSN 0045-8201
CONSULTANTS NEWS; independent commentary on management consulting since 1970. Text in English. 1970. m. USD 295 in US & Canada; USD 345 elsewhere (effective 2004). adv. bk.rev. index. back issues avail.; reprints avail. **Document type:** *Newsletter.* **Description:** Covers trends and developments in management consulting.
Related titles: Online - full text ed.: (from EBSCO Publishing, ProQuest Information & Learning).
Indexed: ATI.
Published by: Kennedy Professional Publishing, 60 East 42nd St, Ste 1263, New York, NY 10165. TEL 212-972-3793, FAX 212-972-1002, http://www.kennedyinfo.com/mc/cn.html. Eds. Delicia Yard, Jess Scheer. **Subscr. to:** Kennedy Information Inc., One Kennedy Place, Rte 12 S, Fitzwilliam, NH 03447. dyard@kennedyinfo.com, http://www.kennedyinfo.com.

658 USA ISSN 1534-0562
CONSULTING ALERT. Text in English. 2001. m. **Document type:** *Newsletter, Trade.*
Indexed: ATI.
Published by: Strafford Publications, Inc., 590 Dutch Valley Rd, N E, Postal Drawer 13729, Atlanta, GA 30324-0729. TEL 404-881-1141, FAX 404-881-0074, editors@straffordpub.com, http://www.straffordpub.com.

658 USA ISSN 1525-4321
HD69.C6
CONSULTING MAGAZINE. Text in English. 1999. bi-m.
Published by: Kennedy Information Inc., One Kennedy Place, Rte 12 S, Fitzwilliam, NH 03447. TEL 603-585-6544, 800-531-0007, FAX 603-585-9555, dyard@kennedyinfo.com, http://www.kennedyinfo.com.

658 USA ISSN 0273-4613
CONSULTING OPPORTUNITIES JOURNAL. Text in English. 1981. bi-m. USD 97 (effective 1999). adv. bk.rev. **Document type:** *Newsletter.*
Incorporates: Consultant's Digest
Published by: Consultants National Resource Center, PO Box 430, Clear Spring, MD 21722. TEL 301-791-9332. Ed. J Stephen Lanning. Pub., R&P Lew Williams. Circ: 3,000.

658.46 USA ISSN 1530-0153
HD69.C6
➤ **CONSULTING TO MANAGEMENT.** Text in English. 1982. q. (4 nos./vol.). USD 80; USD 120 combined subscription print & online; USD 24 per issue (effective 2004). adv. bk.rev. charts; illus. back issues avail.; reprint service avail. from PQC. **Document type:** *Journal, Academic/Scholarly.* **Description:** Covers all aspects of management consulting, including issues and trends, the consulting process, practice development and management, professional ethics, computer applications, and more.
Formerly (until 1999): Journal of Management Consulting (0168-7778)
Related titles: CD-ROM ed.; Microform ed.: (from PQC); Online - full text ed.: USD 100 (effective 2004) (from EBSCO Publishing, Northern Light Technology, Inc., O C L C Online Computer Library Center, Inc., ProQuest Information & Learning).
Indexed: ABIn, ADPA, ATI, BPI, BPIA, CPM, RASB.
—BLDSC (3424.010500), IE, Infotrieve, ingenta. **CCC.**
Published by: Journal of Management Consulting, Inc., 858 Longview Rd, Burlingame, CA 94010-6974. TEL 650-342-1954, FAX 650-344-5005, c2m@c2m.com, http://www.c2m.com/. Ed. Gerald A Simon. Adv. contact E Michael Shays. Circ: 8,500.

658 600 USA
CONSUMER GOODS TECHNOLOGY; improving business performance. Text in English. 1992. 10/yr. USD 190 domestic; USD 225 in Canada; USD 250 elsewhere (effective 2005). charts; illus.; stat. back issues avail.; reprints avail. **Document type:** *Magazine, Trade.*
Formerly: Consumer Goods Manufacturer (1070-9398)
Published by: Edgell Communications, Inc., 4 Middlebury Blvd, Randolph, NJ 07869-4214. edgell@edgellmail.com, http://www.consumergoods.com, http://www.edgellcommunications.com. Ed. Carol Fisher. Pub. Andrew Gaffney. Adv. contact Betty Schoonover. Circ: 25,000 (paid).

658.812 CAN ISSN 1498-2145
CONTACT MANAGEMENT. Text in English. 2001. q. CND 40 (effective 2005). **Document type:** *Magazine, Trade.* **Description:** Covers Canadian contact centre industry technology developments, management, profiles, association news and human resources.
Published by: August Communications, 225-530 Century St, Winnipeg, MB R3H 0Y4, Canada. TEL 204-957-0265, 888-573-1136, FAX 204-957-0217, 866-957-0217, info@august.ca, http://www.contactmanagement.ca, http://www.august.ca.

658 338.4 BEL
CONTACT TRANSPORT & LOGISTICS; le trait d'union industrie - prestataires de services - bindeteken tussen industrie en dienstverlenende sektor. Text in Dutch. bi-m. adv. illus. **Document type:** *Trade.*
Related titles: French ed.
Published by: Multi Media Management, Parc Artisanal 11-13, Blegny-Barchon, 4670, Belgium. TEL 32-4-3878787, FAX 32-4-3879087.

658.4013 MEX
CONTACTO; la revista de calidad total. Text in Spanish. m. MXP 280 (effective 1999). adv.
Related titles: Online - full text ed.
Address: INSURGENTES SUR 1032, Desp. 202. Piso 2o., Col Del Valle, Mexico City, DF 03100, Mexico. http://www.contacto.com.mx/. Circ: 18,000.

658 TWN
➤ **CONTEMPORARY MANAGEMENT RESEARCH.** Text in English. q. USD 150 to individuals; USD 200 to institutions (effective 2004). **Document type:** *Journal, Academic/Scholarly.* **Description:** Covers all fields of management, such as accounting, management information system, electronic commerce, information systems and technology, business administration, marketing, consumer behavior, Internet marketing, financial and banking, human resource, economics, international business, operations management, technology and innovation management, business ethics.
Published by: Academy of Taiwan Information Systems Research, PO Box 179-45, Taipei, 116, Taiwan. TEL 886-2-25009508, FAX 886-2-25175924, cmr@atisr.org, http://cmr.atisr.org/, http://www.atisr.org/. Ed. Wenchang Fang.

658.47 USA ISSN 1542-4340
HD49
▼ **CONTINUITY INSIGHTS**; strategies to assure integrity, availability and security. Text in English. 2003 (Jan./Feb.). bi-m. free in US & Canada to qualified personnel; USD 48 elsewhere (effective 2003). adv.
Published by: Communication Technologies, Inc., 301 S. Main St. Ste. 1 W., Doylestown, PA 18901. TEL 215-230-9556, FAX 215-230-9601, info@ctipublishing.com, http://www.continuityinsights.com. Ed. Christina Fuges. Pub. Robert S. Nakao. adv.: B&W page USD 5,195; trim 8 x 10.75.

658 USA ISSN 0190-3063
KF842
CONTRACT MANAGEMENT. Text in English. 1970 (vol.10). bi-m. free to members. adv. bibl.; charts; illus. **Document type:** *Magazine.* **Description:** Articles covering issues in contract management.
Former titles: N C M A Magazine; N C M A Newsletter (0027-6332)
Related titles: Online - full text ed.: (from Florida Center for Library Automation, Gale Group, O C L C Online Computer Library Center, Inc., ProQuest Information & Learning).
Indexed: ABIn, BPIA, BusI, ManagCont, T&II.
Published by: National Contract Management Association, 8260 Greensboro Dr, Ste 200, Ste. 200, Mc Lean, VA 22102-3886. TEL 571-382-0082, 800-344-8096, FAX 703-448-0939, couture@ncmahq.org, http://www.ncmahq.org/publications/cm. Ed. Terry Hoskins. adv.: B&W page USD 2,550.

658 690 USA ISSN 1533-5410
CONTRACTOR'S BUSINESS STRATEGIST. Text in English. m. USD 255 (effective 2004). **Document type:** *Newsletter, Trade.* **Description:** Strategies, legal tips, and how-to advice for successfully managing a construction company in the 1990s. Features model contract language, forms, guidelines, and more.
Formerly (until 2001): Construction Company Strategist (1089-733X)
Published by: Brownstone Publishers, Inc., 149 Fifth Ave, 16th Fl, New York, NY 10010-6801. TEL 212-473-8200, FAX 212-473-8786. Ed. Jane Czik.

658 GBR ISSN 0266-1713
➤ **CONTROL.** Text in English. 1964. 10/yr. GBP 60 (effective 2001). adv. bk.rev. 2 cols./p.; **Document type:** *Magazine, Academic/Scholarly.* **Description:** Contains technical articles related to operations management, materials management, inventory control, production and logistics.
Former titles (until 1995): B P I C S Control; (until 1983): B P I C S News
Indexed: Inspec.
—BLDSC (3461.776000).
Published by: Institute of Operations Management, Sir William Lyons Rd, University Of Warwick Science Park, Coventry, Warks CV4 7EZ, United Kingdom. TEL 44-2476-692266, FAX 44-2476-692305, iom@iomnet.org.uk, http://www.iomnet.org.uk. Ed. David Angove. R&P R G Turner. Adv. contact Theresa Pitt. B&W page GBP 1,000, color page GBP 1,250; 210 x 297. Circ: 5,000 (paid).

658 DEU ISSN 0343-267X
CONTROLLER MAGAZIN. Text in German. 1976. 6/yr. adv. bk.rev. charts; illus.; stat. index. back issues avail. **Document type:** *Trade.* **Description:** Publication of interest to controllers and managers. Covers new ideas and developments, new systems, new regulations, organization, planning and international news. Includes bibliographies and positions available.
Indexed: Inspec, RefZh.
—BLDSC (3463.111000).
Published by: (Controller Verein e.V., Muenchen), Management Service Verlag, Postfach 1168, Gauting, 82116, Germany. TEL 49-8153-8041, FAX 49-8153-8043, http://www.controllermagatin.de. Ed. Albrecht Deyle. Adv. contact Christa Kiessling. Circ: 6,500.

658 DEU
CONTROLLING & MANAGEMENT; Zeitschrift fuer Controlling & Management. Text in German. 1957. bi-m. EUR 114; EUR 75 to students; EUR 26 newsstand/cover (effective 2004). adv. bk.rev. reprint service avail. from SCH. **Document type:** *Magazine, Trade.*
Former titles: K R P (0931-9077); (until 1977): Kostenrechnungspraxis (0023-4265)
Indexed: RefZh, SCIMP.
—IE, Infotrieve. **CCC.**
Published by: Betriebswirtschaftlicher Verlag Dr. Th. Gabler GmbH (Subsidiary of: Springer Science+Business Media), Abraham-Lincoln-Str 46, Wiesbaden, 65189, Germany. TEL 49-611-78780, FAX 49-611-7878400, gabler.service@gwv-fachverlage.de, http://www.krp-online.de, http://www.gabler.de. Eds. Alexander Sasse, Joachim Sandt. Adv. contact Susanne Brettschneider. B&W page EUR 1,980, color page EUR 3,210. Circ: 4,800 (paid and controlled).

658 011 USA ISSN 1065-0938
CONVENE. Text in English. 1986. 10/yr. USD 50 domestic; USD 75 foreign (effective 2005). adv. **Document type:** *Trade.*
Published by: Professional Convention Management Association, 2301 S. Lake Shore Dr., # 1001, Chicago, IL 60616-1419. TEL 205-823-7262, FAX 205-822-3891, ckrause@pcma.org, http://www.pcma.org. Ed. Peter Shure. Pub. Roy B Evans Jr. R&P Carla Krause TEL 205-978-4917. Adv. contact John Oliver. Circ: 30,000.

658 USA* ISSN 0897-1447
CORNELL ENTERPRISE. Text in English. 19??. m. CND 21, USD 30. adv. bk.rev. charts; illus.
Former titles (until 1985): C G S M Enterprise (0741-6989); (until 1984): Cornell Executive (0734-192X); (until 1982): Executive (Ithaca) (0145-3963)
Related titles: Microfiche ed.: (from MML); Microform ed.
Indexed: ABIn, BPIA, BusI, CBPI, Inspec, ManagCont, PAIS, PROMT, T&II.
Published by: Johnson Graduate School of Management (Subsidiary of: Cornell University), Ithaca, NY 14853. http://www.johnson.cornell.edu/publications/enterprise/. Circ: 48,183.

658 USA ISSN 0746-8652
HD2745
CORPORATE BOARD. Text in English. 1980. bi-m. USD 520 to individuals; USD 2,900 to corporations (effective 2004). bk.rev. charts; stat. Index. 32 p./no.; back issues avail.; reprints avail. **Document type:** *Journal, Trade.*
Formerly (until 1983): Corporate Director (0196-2116)
Related titles: Online - full text ed.: (from EBSCO Publishing, Florida Center for Library Automation, Gale Group).
Indexed: BPIA, BusI, ManagCont, T&II.
—BLDSC (3472.060500), IE, ingenta. **CCC.**
Published by: Vanguard Publications, Inc., 4440 Hagadorn Rd, Okemos, MI 48864-2414. TEL 517-336-1700, FAX 517-336-1705, info@corporateboard.com, http://www.corporateboard.com. Ed. Ralph D Ward. Pub. Irving A Lesher III. R&P Judith Scheidt TEL 517-336-1600. Circ: 4,000 (paid).

658 USA
CORPORATE BOARD MEMBER; the magazine for directors of public companies. Text in English. q. USD 155 domestic (effective 2001). adv. back issues avail. **Document type:** *Magazine, Corporate.* **Description:** Written specifically for directors of public companies listed with Nasdaq and the New York and American Stock Exchanges.
Related titles: Online - full text ed.
Published by: Board Member Inc., 5110 Maryland Way, Ste 250, Brentwood, TN 37027. TEL 615-309-3200, FAX 615-371-0899, boardmember@boardmember.com, bankdirector@boardmember.com, http://www.boardmember.com/issues/current/.

658 USA
CORPORATE CITIZENSHIP REVIEW; the newsletter for the community relations professional. Text in English. bi-m. USD 225 in North America to non-members; USD 250 elsewhere to non-members (effective 2000). bk.rev. cum.index: 1989-1994; 1994-1996. back issues avail. **Document type:** *Newsletter.* **Description:** Covers trends and issues affecting corporations and their involvement in the community, corporate citizenship, and corporate social responsibility.
Formerly (until 2001): Corporate Community Relations Letter (1083-7930)
Published by: Boston College, Center for Corporate Community Relations, 55 Lee Rd, Chestnut Hill, MA 02467-3942. TEL 617-552-4545, FAX 617-552-8499, cccr@bc.edu, http://www.bc.edu/cccr. Ed. Sharron Kahn Luttrell. R&P Susan Thomas. Circ: 4,000.

CORPORATE COMMUNICATIONS; an international journal. see *COMMUNICATIONS*

CORPORATE COUNSEL. see *LAW—Corporate Law*

658 USA ISSN 0886-0475
KF1397
CORPORATE COUNSEL WEEKLY. Text in English. 1978. w. looseleaf. index. back issues avail. **Document type:** *Newsletter.* **Description:** Covers current developments in law that affect business, including the courts, federal regulatory agencies, the executive branch, states and professional associations.
Formerly (until 1981): B N A's Washington Memorandum (0162-5683)
Related titles: Online - full text ed.: ISSN 1522-5305 (from The Bureau of National Affairs, Inc.); ♦ Series of: Corporate Practice Series. ISSN 0162-5691.
—**CCC.**
Published by: The Bureau of National Affairs, Inc., 1231 25th St., NW, Washington, DC 20037. TEL 202-452-4200, FAX 202-822-8092, http://www.bna.com/products/corplaw/ccw.htm. Ed. Larry Lampert.

CORPORATE ENVIRONMENTAL STRATEGY; the journal of environmental leadership. see *ENVIRONMENTAL STUDIES*

658 GBR ISSN 1472-0701
➤ **CORPORATE GOVERNANCE**; the international journal of business in society. Text in English. 2001 (May). 5/yr. EUR 444.79 in Europe; USD 479 in North America; AUD 749 in Australasia; GBP 314.29 in UK & elsewhere (effective 2006). reprint service avail. from PSC. **Document type:** *Journal, Academic/Scholarly.* **Description:** Debates on board performance, corporate responsibility and CEO effectiveness through practical, real-world discussions and analysis of past, present and future concerns.
Related titles: Online - full text ed.: (from EBSCO Publishing, Emerald Group Publishing Limited, Gale Group, IngentaConnect, O C L C Online Computer Library Center, Inc., ProQuest Information & Learning, Swets Information Services).
Indexed: ABIn.
—BLDSC (3472.066060), IE, Infotrieve. **CCC.**
Published by: Emerald Group Publishing Limited, 60-62 Toller Ln, Bradford, W Yorks BD8 9BY, United Kingdom. TEL 44-1274-777700, FAX 44-1274-785200, slinacre@emeraldinsight.com, infomation@emeraldinsight.com, http://www.emeraldinsight.com/cg.htm. Eds. Andrew Kakabadse, Nada K Kakabadse. Pub. Simon Linacre.

658.4 346.066 USA
CORPORATE GOVERNANCE (SACRAMENTO). Text in English. 1995. d. free. adv. bk.rev. **Document type:** *Newsletter, Trade.* **Description:** Provides news, discussions and links to consultants, sites policies and organizations with a focus on corporate governance.
Media: Online - full text.
Published by: James McRichtie, Ed. & Pub., 2461 Second Ave, Sacramento, CA 95818. jm@corpgov.net, http://www.corpgov.net/.

THE CORPORATE GOVERNANCE ADVISOR. see *LAW—Corporate Law*

CORPORATE LEGAL TIMES; the management monthly for corporate legal executives. see *LAW—Corporate Law*

658 GBR ISSN 1363-3589
➤ **CORPORATE REPUTATION REVIEW**; an international journal. Text in English. 1996. q. GBP 85 in Europe to individuals; USD 135 in North America to individuals; GBP 100 elsewhere to individuals; GBP 200 in Europe to institutions; USD 320 in North America to institutions; GBP 215 elsewhere to institutions (effective 2004). adv. back issues avail.; reprint service avail. from PSC. **Document type:** *Academic/Scholarly.* **Description:** Provides an international forum for original research on corporate identity, corporate image, and corporate brand management.
Related titles: Online - full text ed.: ISSN 1479-1889 (from EBSCO Publishing, Gale Group, IngentaConnect, O C L C Online Computer Library Center, Inc., ProQuest Information & Learning, Swets Information Services).
Indexed: ABIn, PsycInfo, PsycholAb.
—BLDSC (3472.093040), IE, Infotrieve, ingenta. **CCC.**
Published by: (International Corporate Identity Group), Palgrave Macmillan Ltd. (Subsidiary of: Macmillan Publishers Ltd.), Houndmills, Basingstoke, Hants RG21 6XS, United Kingdom. TEL 44-1256-329242, FAX 44-1256-810526, journal-info@palgrave.com, http://www.palgrave-journals.com/. Eds. Cees B M van Riel, Charles Fombrun. Circ: 2,000 (paid).

333.72 GBR
CORPORATE RESPONSIBILITY MANAGEMENT. Text in English. 6/yr.
—BLDSC (3472.093050).
Published by: Melcrum Publishing, 1st Floor, Chelsea Reach, 79-89 Lots Rd, London, SW10 0RN, United Kingdom. TEL 44-20-7795-2205, FAX 44-20-7795-2156, info@melcrum.com, http://www.melcrum.com. Ed. Jason Sumner.

333.72 GBR ISSN 1535-3958
GE300
➤ **CORPORATE SOCIAL RESPONSIBILITY AND ENVIRONMENTAL MANAGEMENT.** Text in English. 1994. 5/yr. USD 925 to institutions; USD 1,018 combined subscription to institutions print & online eds. (effective 2006). adv. reprint service avail. from PSC. **Document type:** *Journal, Academic/Scholarly.* **Description:** Practical guidance on the development of tools, case studies and assessment methods for environmental impacts and concerns.
Former titles (until 2002): Eco-Management and Auditing (0968-9427); Corporate Social Responsibility and Environmental Management; Eco-Management and Auditing
Related titles: Online - full content ed.: ISSN 1535-3966. USD 925 to institutions (effective 2006); Online - full text ed.: (from EBSCO Publishing, ProQuest Information & Learning, Swets Information Services, Wiley InterScience).
Indexed: ABIn, ASFA, BIOBASE, EPB, ESPM, EnvAb, EnvEAb, Inspec, PollutAb, SWRA.
—BLDSC (3472.093215), IE, ingenta. **CCC.**
Published by: (E R P Environment), John Wiley & Sons Ltd. (Subsidiary of: John Wiley & Sons, Inc.), The Atrium, Southern Gate, Chichester, West Sussex PO19 8SQ, United Kingdom. TEL 44-1243-779777, FAX 44-1243-775878, customer@wiley.co.uk, http://www.wiley.com/WileyCDA/WileyTitle/productCd-CSR.html, http://www.wiley.co.uk. Ed. Dr. Richard Welford. adv.: B&W page GBP 650, color page GBP 1,550; trim 210 x 297. **Subscr. to:** John Wiley & Sons, Inc., 111 River St, Hoboken, NJ 07030-5774. TEL 201-748-6645, FAX 201-748-6088, subinfo@wiley.com.

658 GBR ISSN 1473-7825
▼ **CORPORATE VENTURING**; entrepreneurship, innovation and value creation. Text in English. 2003. q. GBP 495, USD 745 (effective 2003). 16 p./no. 2 cols./p.; back issues avail.; reprints avail. **Document type:** *Newsletter, Corporate.* **Description:** Focuses on successful strategies for sustainable growth.
Published by: Grist Ltd, 21 Noel St, 2nd Fl, London, W1F 8GP, United Kingdom. TEL 44-20-74341445, FAX 44-20-74841845, andrewrogers@gristonline.com, http://www.gristonline.com/. Ed. Mark Wellings TEL 44-20-74341447. R&P, Adv. contact Andrew Rogerson TEL 44-20-74341445.

658 USA ISSN 1058-2908
HG4057
CORPORATE YELLOW BOOK; who's who at the leading U.S. companies. Text in English. 1985. q. USD 400; USD 380 renewals (effective 2005). illus. Index. **Document type:** *Directory, Trade.* **Description:** Lists names, titles, addresses, and telephone numbers of corporate leaders. Provides internet addresses, business descriptions, approximate annual revenues, administrative stuff, board of directors, and their affiliations.
Former titles (until 1992): Corporate 1000 Yellow Book (1049-7943); (until 1990): Corporate 1000 (0882-3227)
Related titles: CD-ROM ed.; Online - full text ed.
—**CCC.**
Published by: Leadership Directories, Inc, 104 Fifth Ave, 2nd Fl, New York, NY 10011. TEL 212-627-4140, FAX 212-645-0931, info@leadershipdirectories.com, http://www.leadershipdirectories.com/cor.htm. Ed. Catherine Shih. Pub. David J Hurvits.

CORRECTIONAL INDUSTRIES ASSOCIATION NEWSLETTER. see *PUBLIC ADMINISTRATION*

658 338 USA ISSN 1096-4568
COST CONTROL STRATEGIES FOR MANUFACTURING EXECUTIVES. Text in English. 1997. m. USD 259 (effective 2000). index. back issues avail. **Document type:** *Newsletter.* **Description:** Discusses tested strategies to control costs for manufacturers.
Published by: Siefer Consultants, Inc., 525 Cayuga St, Storm Lake, IA 50588. TEL 712-732-7340, FAX 712-732-7906, siefer@ncn.net. Ed. Steve Herron.

COURAGEOUS CONTRARIAN. see *BUSINESS AND ECONOMICS—Investments*

LE COURRIER DES MAIRES ET DES ELUS LOCAUX. see *PUBLIC ADMINISTRATION—Municipal Government*

CREDIT & COLLECTION MANAGER'S LETTER. see *BUSINESS AND ECONOMICS—Banking And Finance*

CREDIT-CURIER. see *BUSINESS AND ECONOMICS—Economic Situation And Conditions*

CREDIT MANAGEMENT. see *BUSINESS AND ECONOMICS—Marketing And Purchasing*

CRITTENDEN GOLF DAILY. see *SPORTS AND GAMES—Ball Games*

▼ new title ➤ refereed ✶ unverified ♦ full entry avail.

658 GBR ISSN 0965-2841
CRONER'S COMPANY ADMINISTRATION. Key Title: Company Administration Briefing. Text in English. 1988. base vol. plus q. updates. looseleaf. GBP 432.78; GBP 314.16 updates.
Document type: *Trade.*
Published by: Croner.C C H Group Ltd. (Subsidiary of: Wolters Kluwer N.V.), 145 London Rd, Kingston, Surrey KT2 6SR, United Kingdom. TEL 44-20-85473333, FAX 44-20-85472637, info@croner.co.uk, http://www.croner.co.uk. Ed. Peter Durbin.

658 GBR ISSN 0969-7144
CRONER'S EXECUTIVE COMPANION. Text in English. 1978. base vol. plus bi-m. updates. looseleaf. EUR 325 (effective 2001). **Description:** Discusses a broad range of business questions ranging from finance, taxation, communications, and export to government and economic issues in the U.K.
Formerly: Management Information Manual
Related titles: CD-ROM ed.; Online - full text ed.
Published by: Croner.C C H Group Ltd. (Subsidiary of: Wolters Kluwer N.V.), 145 London Rd, Kingston, Surrey KT2 6SR, United Kingdom. TEL 44-20-85473333, FAX 44-20-85472637, info@croner.co.uk, http://www.croner.cch.co.uk, http://www.croner.co.uk. Ed. Lisbeth Louwner.

658 GBR
CRONER'S HEADS OF SCIENCE. Text in English. 1992. base vol. plus updates 3/yr. looseleaf. GBP 201.86 (effective 1999).
Document type: *Trade.*
Formerly: Heads of Science Briefing (0967-6813)
Related titles: Online - full text ed.
Published by: Croner.C C H Group Ltd. (Subsidiary of: Wolters Kluwer N.V.), 145 London Rd, Kingston, Surrey KT2 6SR, United Kingdom. TEL 44-20-85473333, FAX 44-20-85472637, info@croner.co.uk, http://www.croner.co.uk.

CRONER'S HEALTH & SAFETY MANAGER. see *OCCUPATIONAL HEALTH AND SAFETY*

658 GBR
CRONER'S OFFICE COMPANION. Text in English. 1994. base vol. plus q. updates. looseleaf. EUR 386.77 (effective 2001). adv. **Document type:** *Trade.*
Formerly: Office Companion Bulletin (1352-5573)
Related titles: CD-ROM ed.; Online - full text ed.
Published by: Croner.C C H Group Ltd. (Subsidiary of: Wolters Kluwer N.V.), 145 London Rd, Kingston, Surrey KT2 6SR, United Kingdom. TEL 44-20-85473333, FAX 44-20-85472637, info@croner.co.uk, http://www.croner.co.uk. Adv. contact Louise Saunders.

658 GBR ISSN 1352-7606
HD28
➤ **CROSS CULTURAL MANAGEMENT.** Text in English. 1994. q. EUR 597.04 in Europe; USD 599 in North America; AUD 739 in Australasia; GBP 401.29 in the UK & elsewhere (effective 2005). back issues avail.; reprint service avail. from PSC. **Document type:** *Journal, Academic/Scholarly.* **Description:** Publishes research papers, articles and monographs on all aspects of cross-cultural relationships at work.
Related titles: Online - full text ed.: (from EBSCO Publishing, Emerald Group Publishing Limited, Gale Group, IngentaConnect, O C L C Online Computer Library Center, Inc., ProQuest Information & Learning, Swets Information Services).
Indexed: ABIn, ERA, EmerIntel, PsycInfo, PsycholAb, SWA.
—BLDSC (3488.807000), IE, Infotrieve, ingenta. **CCC.**
Published by: Barmarick Publications, Enholmes Hall, Patrington, Hull, East Yorkshire HU12 0PR, United Kingdom. TEL 44-1964-630033, FAX 44-1964-631716, hr24@dial.pipex.com, http://www.emeraldinsight.com/ccm.htm. Ed. Samuel M Natale. R&P Barrie O Pettman. **Dist by:** Emerald Group Publishing Limited, 60-62 Toller Ln, Bradford, W Yorks BD8 9BY, United Kingdom. TEL 44-1274-777700, FAX 44-1274-785200, infomation@emeraldinsight.com, http://www.emeraldinsight.com/; **Dist in the US by:** Emerald Group Publishing Ltd., 44 Brattle St, 4th Fl, Cambridge, MA 02138. TEL 617-497-2175, 888-622-0075, FAX 617-354-6875, america@emeraldinsight.com.

658 COL ISSN 0120-3592
HD62.7
CUADERNOS DE ADMINISTRACION. SERIE ORGANIZACIONES. Text in Spanish. 1981. s-a. COP 12,000, USD 15 (effective 2004).
Indexed: IBSS.
Published by: Pontificia Universidad Javeriana, Facultad de Ciencias Economicas y Administrativas, Carrera 7 No 40-62 Piso 4o, Edificio Emilio Arango, Bogota, CUND, Colombia. TEL 57-1-3208320, FAX 57-1-2857289, cuadernos.administracion@javeriana.edu.co, http://www.javeriana.edu.co/cursad/cuadernos. Ed. Florentino Malaver Rodriguez.

CUADERNOS DE CIENCIAS ECONOMICAS Y EMPRESARIALES. see *BUSINESS AND ECONOMICS*

658.15 ESP ISSN 1138-5758
CUADERNOS DE ECONOMIA Y DIRECCION DE LA EMPRESA. Text in Spanish. 1998. q. EUR 55.48 domestic; EUR 75.73 in Europe (effective 2005). back issues avail.
Related titles: Online - full text ed.
—CINDOC.
Published by: Civitas, S.A., Barbara de Braganza, 10, Madrid, 28004, Spain. FAX 34-91-7252673, clientes@civitas.es, http://www.civitas.es/. Ed. Juan Jose Duran Herrera.

658 GBR
CUMBRIAN EXECUTIVE. Text in English. 1986. bi-m. GBP 15 (effective 1999). **Document type:** *Bulletin.*
Published by: Cumbrian Press, 3 Chatsworth Sq, Carlisle, Cumbria CA11 1HB, United Kingdom. TEL 44-1228-471444, FAX 44-1228-514747. Ed. Tony Thornton. Adv. contact Alan Taylor. Circ: 5,000.

658 USA ISSN 1529-2088
HD28
CURRENT TOPICS IN MANAGEMENT. Text in English. 1996. a., latest vol.9, 2005. USD 59.95 (effective 2005).
—CCC.
Published by: Transaction Publishers, 390 Campus Dr, Somerset, NJ 07830. TEL 888-999-6778, FAX 732-748-9801, trans@transactionpub.com, http://www.transactionpub.com. **Subscr. to:** Transaction Distribution Center, 390 Campus Dr., Somerset, NJ 08873. TEL 732-445-1245, orders@transactionpub.com.

CUSTOMER CONNECT. see *COMMUNICATIONS—Telephone And Telegraph*

658.812 GBR ISSN 1472-4367
CUSTOMER MANAGEMENT. Text in English. 1993. q. GBP 54 domestic; GBP 68 foreign (effective 2000).
Formerly (until 2000): Customer Service Management (1351-8321)
Indexed: M&MA.
—BLDSC (3506.120900), IE, ingenta.
Published by: CSM Group, 21 High St, Green St Green, Orpinton, Ken, BR6 6BG, United Kingdom. TEL 44-1689-862999, FAX 44-1689-862455. Ed. Phil Dourado.

658.812 USA ISSN 1529-8728
CUSTOMER RELATIONSHIP MANAGEMENT. Abbreviated title: C R M. Text in English. m. free to qualified personnel; USD 23.95 domestic; USD 38.95 in Canada & Mexico; USD 63.95 elsewhere (effective 2005). adv. **Document type:** *Magazine, Trade.* **Description:** Aims to help organizations leverage their customer knowledge to better identify, sell to and service their client's needs and improve profitability through higher levels of customer interaction.
Incorporates (in 2001): e C R M; Former titles (until 2000): Sales & Marketing Automation (1527-8662); (until 1999): Sales & Field Force Automation
Related titles: Online - full text ed.: (from EBSCO Publishing, Gale Group, O C L C Online Computer Library Center, Inc., ProQuest Information & Learning).
Indexed: ABIn, CompD, MicrocompInd.
—CCC.
Published by: C R M Media, LLC (Subsidiary of: Information Today, Inc.), 494 Eighth Ave, 8th Fl, New York, NY 10001-2509. TEL 212-251-0608, FAX 212-779-1152, crminfo@destinationcrm.com, http://www.destinationcrm.com/articles/magazine_index.asp. Ed. Ginger Conlon. Pub. Bob Fernekees. Adv. contact Joe Ferrick. B&W page USD 14,300, color page USD 18,990. Circ: 100,027.

658 659.1 USA ISSN 0145-8442
CUSTOMER SERVICE NEWSLETTER; the authority on managing the customer contact center. Text in English. 1973. m. USD 199 (effective 2005). 8 p./no.; back issues avail. **Document type:** *Newsletter, Corporate.* **Description:** Reports on practical techniques for improving customer service operations including: training, measurement, benchmarking, using new technology and more.
Related titles: Online - full text ed.
Indexed: LogistBibl.
Published by: Alexander Communications Group, Inc., 28 W 25th St, 8th Fl, New York, NY 10010. TEL 212-228-0246, FAX 212-228-0376, info@customerservicegroup.com, http://www.customerservicegroup.com. Eds. Masha Zagar, Susan Hash. Pub. Margaret Dewitt. R&P Mary Dalessandro.

658 USA ISSN 1525-1047
CUSTOMERS FIRST; a practical guide to profitable customer relations. Text in English. 1987. bi-w. (26/yr.). USD 245.70 5 copies (effective 2005). **Document type:** *Newsletter, Trade.* **Description:** Motivates and instructs employees on how to improve customer relations.
Formerly (until 1995): Customers
—CCC.
Published by: Dartnell Corp. (Subsidiary of: L R P Publications), 360 Hiatt Dr, Palm Beach Garden, FL 33418. TEL 561-622-6520, 800-621-5463, FAX 561-622-0757, custserve@lrp.com, http://www.shoplrp.com/product/p-28000.N.html, http://www.dartnellcorp.com/. Ed. Robert Stricklin.

658 USA ISSN 1527-6554
CUSTOMERS FIRST IN HOSPITALITY. Text in English. 1999. bi-w. (22/yr.). USD 207.90 (effective 2006). **Description:** Provides employees with the techniques, inspiration and guidance they need to raise their service awareness and improve their people skills to achieve total guest satisfaction. It is packed with practical advice, expert techniques, quick tips and problem-solving suggestions.
Published by: Dartnell Corp. (Subsidiary of: L R P Publications), 360 Hiatt Dr, Palm Beach Garden, FL 33418. TEL 561-622-6520, 800-621-5463, FAX 561-622-0757, custserve@lrp.com, http://www.shoplrp.com/product/p-28004.N.html, http://www.dartnellcorp.com/.

658 USA ISSN 1098-7266
HD2745
D & B REFERENCE BOOK OF CORPORATE MANAGEMENTS. (Dun & Bradstreet) Text in English. 1967. a.
Former titles (until 1997): Reference Book of Corporate Managements (0735-6498); (until 1981): Dun and Bradstreet Reference Book of Corporate Managements (0070-7627); Moody's Handbook of Corporate Managements (0545-0209)
Related titles: Online - full text ed.: (from Questel Orbit Inc.).
Published by: Dun's Marketing Services (Subsidiary of: Dun & Bradstreet, Inc.), 3 Sylvan Way, Parsippany, NJ 07054-3896. TEL 201-455-0900. Circ: 3,500.

658 GBR
➤ **D W P S.** (Doctoral Working Paper Series) Text in English. 1988; N.S. 1992 (Feb.). irreg. **Document type:** *Monographic series, Academic/Scholarly.*
Formerly (until 1992): Doctoral Working Papers Series (0952-2247)
Published by: Aston University, Aston Business School, Aston Triangle, Birmingham, W Mids B4 7ET, United Kingdom. TEL 44-121-3593611, FAX 44-121-3596350, dwps@aston.ac.uk, http://www.abs.aston.ac.uk/. Ed. P. Seltsikas. R&P P Seltsikas TEL 44-121-359-3611.

658 NLD ISSN 1380-6521
DAGELIJKS BELEID; tips & adviezen voor uw werk. Text in Dutch. 1982. m. EUR 62 (effective 2005). back issues avail. **Document type:** *Bulletin, Trade.* **Description:** Publication for managers in business and industry, covering managerial skills and management-employee relations.
—Infotrieve.
Published by: V N U Business Publications (Netherlands), Ceylonpoort 5-25, Haarlem, 2037 AA, Netherlands. TEL 31-23-5463463, FAX 31-23-5463931, http://www.dagelijksbeleid.nl. R&P Mieke Beumer. Circ: 4,800.

658.812 USA
DAILY CUSTOMER SERVICE NEWSLETTER. Text in English. d. (plus w. update). **Document type:** *Newsletter.* **Description:** Discusses how relationships with customers affect the bottom line.
Media: Online - full text.
Address: stacy@customeredge.com, http://www.customeredge.com/. Ed. Stacy Brice.

658 USA ISSN 0148-8155
DAILY REPORT FOR EXECUTIVES. Text in English. 1943. 5/w. looseleaf. USD 9,399 in United States (effective 2005 - 2006). m. index. 65 p./no.; back issues avail. **Description:** Covers legislative, regulatory, legal, tax, and economic developments which affect both national and international businesses.
Related titles: Online - full text ed.: ISSN 1523-567X (from The Bureau of National Affairs, Inc., Thomson West).
—CISTI. **CCC.**
Published by: The Bureau of National Affairs, Inc., 1231 25th St., NW, Washington, DC 20037. TEL 202-452-4200, 800-372-1033, 800-452-7773, FAX 202-822-8092, customercare@bna.com, bnaplus@bna.com, http://www.bna.com/products/corplaw/der.htm. Ed. Nancee L Simonson. Pub. Greg C McCaffery.

658 DNK ISSN 1397-3266
DANSK MANAGEMENT FORUM. Text in Danish. 1995. 3/yr. DKK 345 (effective 1999). **Document type:** *Trade.*
Address: Folke Bernadottes Alle 45, Copenhagen Oe, 2100, Denmark. TEL 45-33-48-88-88, FAX 45-33-48-88-89, forum@dmforum.dk, http://www.dmforum.dk. Ed. Ruth Znaider. Circ: 3,500.

658 USA ISSN 1525-0911
DARTNELL'S FIRST LINE SUPERVISOR. Text in English. 1967. bi-w. (26/yr.). USD 245.70 5 copies (effective 2005).
Document type: *Newsletter, Trade.* **Description:** Provides manufacturing, construction, and warehouse supervisors with instructional information to help them manage their work and workers better.
Published by: Dartnell Corp. (Subsidiary of: L R P Publications), 360 Hiatt Dr, Palm Beach Garden, FL 33418. TEL 561-622-6520, 800-621-5463, FAX 561-622-0757, custserve@lrp.com, http://www.shoplrp.com/product/p-18007.N.html, http://www.dartnellcorp.com/. Ed. Patrick Byrne.

658 USA ISSN 1525-089X
DARTNELL'S SUCCESSFUL SUPERVISOR; a bulletin of ideas and inspiration for those who manage people. Text in English. 1973. bi-w. (26/yr.). USD 245.70 for 5 copies (effective 2005).
Document type: *Newsletter, Trade.* **Description:** Provides supervisors with valuable information and innovative ideas on people management, decision making, problem solving, and time management.
Published by: Dartnell Corp. (Subsidiary of: L R P Publications), 360 Hiatt Dr, Palm Beach Garden, FL 33418. TEL 561-622-6520, 800-621-5463, FAX 561-622-0757, custserve@lrp.com, http://www.shoplrp.com/product/p-18006.N.html, http://www.dartnellcorp.com/. Ed. Kim Anderson.

658.785 USA
DATA WAREHOUSING CAREER NEWSLETTER. Text in English. 1996. w. back issues avail. **Document type:** *Newsletter, Trade.* **Description:** Contains a sampling of data warehousing job opportunities, as well as news and views from the field and articles on managing data warehousings.
Media: Online - full text.
Published by: Allen Davis & Associates, PO Box 2007, Amherst, MA 01004-2007. TEL 413-253-0600, FAX 413-253-3535, rmeyers@softwarejobs.com, http://softwarejobs.com/dataware.html/. Ed. Rachel Meyers.

DATABASES IN JAPAN. see *COMPUTERS—Data Base Management*

658 388 GBR ISSN 0963-2522
DEALER PRINCIPAL. Text in English. 1986. m. GBP 150 (effective 2002). back issues avail. **Document type:** *Magazine, Trade.* **Description:** Practice management guide focused on strategic issues within the Dealer Principal's domain, which directly affect bottom line management controls. Provides relevant subjects for in-dealership training, development and management discussion.
Published by: Emap Automotive Ltd., Sewells Information and Research, Wentworth House, Wentworth St, Peterborough, Northants PE1 1DS, United Kingdom. TEL 44-1733-468255, FAX 44-1733-468349, http://www.sewells.co.uk, http://www.emap.com. Ed. Jerry Connolly. Pub. Mr. Mike Gunnell.

DEALERSEDGE C F O REPORT. see *TRANSPORTATION—Automobiles*

658 IRL ISSN 1393-2993
➤ **DECISION**; Ireland's business review. Text in English. 1996. bi-m. EUR 95 (effective 2005). adv. bk.rev.; software rev. illus.; stat.; abstr.; charts. back issues avail. **Document type:** *Magazine, Trade.* **Description:** For people who think about business. Contains features, opinion and analysis piece designed for an audience of senior professionals.
Related titles: Online - full text ed.: (from O C L C Online Computer Library Center, Inc., ProQuest Information & Learning).
Indexed: ABIn, Emerald.
—BLDSC (3536.825000).
Published by: Dillon Publications Ltd., P.O. Box 7130, Dublin, 18, Ireland. TEL 353-1-2780841, FAX 353-1-2954368, info@decisionireland.com, http://www.decisionireland.com. Ed., Pub., R&P Frank Dillon. adv.: color page EUR 2,500; trim 190 x 234. Circ: 5,000 (controlled).

658.4 IND ISSN 0304-0941
HD28
DECISION. Text in English. 1974. q. INR 200, USD 30. adv. bk.rev. abstr. **Document type:** *Academic/Scholarly.*
Related titles: Online - full text ed.: (from EBSCO Publishing).
Indexed: IPsyAb.
Published by: Indian Institute of Management, Alipore P.O., P O Box 16757, Kolkata, West Bengal 700 027, India. TELEX 021-2501. Ed. Rahul Mukherjee. Circ: 300.

658 USA ISSN 1545-8490
HD30.23
▼ **DECISION ANALYSIS.** Text in English. 2004. q. USD 172 combined subscription domestic to non-members print & online eds.; USD 184 combined subscription foreign to non-members print & online eds.; USD 286 combined subscription domestic to institutions print & online eds.; USD 288 combined subscription foreign to institutions print & online eds. (effective 2005). **Document type:** *Journal, Academic/Scholarly.* **Description:** Focuses on the development and study of operational decision-making methods, drawing on all aspects of decision theory and decision analysis, with the ultimate objective of providing practical guidance for decision makers.
Related titles: Online - full text ed.: ISSN 1545-8504. USD 92 to non-members; USD 23 to members additional journal (effective 2004) (from EBSCO Publishing, Gale Group, Swets Information Services).
Indexed: ABIn.
—CCC.
Published by: I N F O R M S, 901 Elkridge Landing Rd., Ste. 400, Linthicum, MD 21090-2909. TEL 410-850-0300, FAX 410-684-2963, informs@informs.org, http://da.pubs.informs.org/, http://www.informs.org. Eds. Don N Kleinmuntz TEL 217-333-0694, Robert T Clemen TEL 919-660-8005. **Subscr. to:** PO Box 631704, Baltimore, MD 631704.

658 USA ISSN 0732-6823
HD30.23
DECISION LINE. Text in English. 1970. bi-m. (5/yr.). USD 6 to non-members (effective 1999). bibl. **Document type:** *Academic/Scholarly.*
Related titles: Online - full text ed.
—IE, Infotrieve.
Published by: Decision Sciences Institute, University Plaza, Atlanta, GA 30303. TEL 404-651-4073, http://www.decisionsciences.org. Ed. Barbara B Flynn. R&P Carol Latta TEL 404-651-4005. Circ: 5,000.

658 USA ISSN 0011-7315
HD30.23 CODEN: DESCDQ
➤ **DECISION SCIENCES.** Text in English. 1970. q. USD 291 combined subscription in the Americas to institutions & Caribbean (print & online eds.); GBP 217 combined subscription elsewhere to institutions print & online eds. (effective 2006); subscr. includes Decision Sciences Journal of Innovative Education. adv. illus.; abstr. back issues avail.; reprints avail. **Document type:** *Journal, Academic/Scholarly.*
Related titles: Microform ed.: (from PQC); Online - full text ed.: ISSN 1540-5915. USD 276 in the Americas to institutions & Caribbean; GBP 207 elsewhere to institutions (effective 2006) (from bigchalk, Blackwell Synergy, EBSCO Publishing, Gale Group, IngentaConnect, Northern Light Technology, Inc., O C L C Online Computer Library Center, Inc., ProQuest Information & Learning, Swets Information Services).
Indexed: AAR, ABIn, ASCA, ATI, BPI, BPIA, BusI, CIS, CMCI, CPM, CurCont, Emerald, ExcerpMed, IAOP, Inspec, JCQM, ManagCont, ORMS, QC&AS, SCIMP, SFA, SSCI, T&II, WildRev.
—BLDSC (3537.150000), AskIEEE, CISTI, IDS, IE, Infotrieve, ingenta. **CCC.**
Published by: (Decision Sciences Institute), Blackwell Publishing, Inc. (Subsidiary of: Blackwell Publishing Ltd.), Commerce Place, 350 Main St, Malden, MA 02148. TEL 781-388-8206, FAX 781-388-8232, subscrip@blackwellpub.com, http://www.blackwellpublishing.com/journals/DECI. Ed. Vicki Smith-Daniels. R&P Carol Latta TEL 404-651-4005. Circ: 4,000. **Subscr. to:** Blackwell Publishing Ltd., Journal Customer Services, 9600 Garsington Rd, PO Box 1354, Oxford OX4 2XG, United Kingdom. TEL 44-1865-778315, FAX 44-1865-471775.

658 USA
T57.95
DECISION SCIENCES INSTITUTE. PROCEEDINGS. Text in English. 1970. a. USD 25 (effective 1999). **Document type:** *Proceedings.*
Former titles (until 1990): Decision Sciences Institute. Annual Meeting Proceedings (0898-9567); (until 1986): American Institute for Decision Sciences. Meeting Proceedings (0360-375X)
Media: CD-ROM.
Indexed: BPIA, Englnd.
—BLDSC (6841.428200), CISTI.
Published by: Decision Sciences Institute, University Plaza, Atlanta, GA 30303. TEL 404-651-4073, http://www.decisionsciences.org. R&P Carol Latta TEL 404-651-4005. Circ: 2,500.

658 330 NLD ISSN 0167-9236
CODEN: DSSYDK
➤ **DECISION SUPPORT SYSTEMS.** Text in English. 1985. 8/yr. EUR 944 in Europe to institutions; JPY 125,200 in Japan to institutions; USD 1,056 to institutions except Europe and Japan (effective 2006). adv. abstr.; illus. Index. back issues avail.; reprints avail. **Document type:** *Academic/Scholarly.* **Description:** Covers the concept of using computers for supporting the decision process in managerial settings. Articles discuss operations research, management science, cognitive psychology and organizational behavior.
Related titles: Online - full text ed.: (from EBSCO Publishing, Gale Group, IngentaConnect, ScienceDirect, Swets Information Services).
Indexed: ABIn, AIA, AS&TI, ASCA, BrCerAb, C&ISA, CADCAM, CJA, CMCI, CPM, CerAb, CompAb, CompLI, CompR, CorrAb, CurCont, CybAb, E&CAJ, EMA, ESPM, Emerald, ErgAb, IAA, IAOP, Inspec, M&TEA, MBF, METADEX, PollutAb, PsycInfo, PsycholAb, RASB, RefZh, SSCI, SolStAb, WAA.
—BLDSC (3537.160000), AskIEEE, Ei, IDS, IE, Infotrieve, ingenta, Linda Hall. **CCC.**
Published by: Elsevier BV, North-Holland (Subsidiary of: Elsevier Science & Technology), Sara Burgerhartstraat 25, Amsterdam, 1055 KV, Netherlands. TEL 31-20-485-3911, FAX 31-20-485-2457, nlinfo-f@elsevier.nl, http://www.elsevier.com/locate/dss, http://www.elsevier.nl. Ed. A B Whinston. **Subscr. to:** Elsevier BV, PO Box 211, Amsterdam 1000 AE, Netherlands. TEL 31-20-485-3757, FAX 31-20-485-3432, http://www.elsevier.nl.

➤ **DELOVA SEDMITSA/BUSINESS WEEKLY.** see *BUSINESS AND ECONOMICS—Accounting*

658 GRC ISSN 0011-8087
DELTION DIIKISEOS EPICHIRISEON/BUSINESS ADMINISTRATION BULLETIN. Text in Greek. 1962. m. USD 100 in Europe; USD 200 in North America (effective 2000). adv. bk.rev. bibl.; charts; illus.; stat. index. **Document type:** *Bulletin.*
Published by: John Papamichalakis Ed. & Pub., 26 Rigillis St, Athens, 106 75, Greece. FAX 30-71-7240000, TELEX 219006 OLKI GR. Adv. contact Ecaterini Papamihalaki. Circ: 25,000.

DENTAL PRACTICE MANAGEMENT. see *MEDICAL SCIENCES—Dentistry*

658 616.5 USA ISSN 1547-6383
▼ **DERMATOLOGY BUSINESS MANAGEMENT**; the bridge between dermatology and business. Text in English. 2003 (Oct.). m. USD 200; USD 20 per issue (effective 2004). adv. **Document type:** *Magazine, Trade.*
Published by: Medical Business Publications, 4938 Brookview Dr., Dallas, TX 75220-3918. http://www.dbmmagazine.com. Ed. June Slowik. Pub. Mark P Hurley. adv.: B&W page USD 2,725; trim 8 x 10.75. Circ: 10,880.

658 USA ISSN 1057-2864
DESIGN FIRM MANAGEMENT & ADMINISTRATION REPORT. Abbreviated title: D F M A R. Text in English. 1991. m. looseleaf. USD 278.95 in US & Canada print & online eds.; USD 293 elsewhere print & online eds. (effective 2006). index. back issues avail. **Document type:** *Newsletter, Trade.* **Description:** Offers actionable strategies for improving design firm efficiency and profitability. Practical guidance on fees and billing rates; compensation and benefits for architects, engineers, and staff; purchasing automation and office equipment, etc.
Incorporates (1986-1991): Architect's Office Management and Administration Report (0890-9814); Formerly (until 1991): Engineering Office Management and Administration Report (0749-1557)
Related titles: Diskette ed.; E-mail ed.; Online - full content ed.: (from Northern Light Technology, Inc.); Online - full text ed.: (from LexisNexis, ProQuest Information & Learning).
Indexed: ABIn.
—CCC.
Published by: Institute of Management & Administration, Inc., 3 Park Ave, New York, NY 10016-5902. TEL 212-244-0360, FAX 212-564-0465, subserve@ioma.com, http://www.ioma.com/products/prod_detail.php?prodid=36. Ed. Stephen Kliment. Pub. Lee Rath. Circ: 2,000.

658 USA ISSN 1557-0614
T342
DESIGN MANAGEMENT REVIEW. Text in English. 1989. q. USD 110 domestic; USD 145 foreign (effective 2004). adv. bk.rev. **Document type:** *Journal, Trade.* **Description:** Devoted to exploring "how design" in products, communication, and environments.
Formerly (until 2004): Design Management Journal (1045-7194)
Related titles: Online - full text ed.: (from H.W. Wilson, O C L C Online Computer Library Center, Inc.).
Indexed: ABIn, BPI, DAAI.
—BLDSC (3559.978380), IE, Infotrieve, ingenta. **CCC.**
Published by: Design Management Institute, 29 Temple Place, 2nd Fl, Boston, MA 02111-1350. TEL 617-338-6380, FAX 617-338-6570, orders@dmi.org, http://www.dmi.org/dmi/html/publications/journal/journal_d.jsp. Ed. Thomas Walton. Pub. Anne McCuen-Bouchenoire. R&P Anne McCuen Bouchenoire. Adv. contact Emily Donahie.

658 DEU ISSN 0343-9496
DEUTSCHE VERWALTUNGSPRAXIS. Text in German. 1949. m. EUR 76.80; EUR 7.65 newsstand/cover (effective 2004). adv. bk.rev. abstr.; charts; illus.; stat. index. reprints avail. **Document type:** *Magazine, Trade.*
Published by: Maximilian-Verlag (Subsidiary of: Verlagsgruppe Koehler - Mittler), Striepenweg 31, Hamburg, 21147, Germany. TEL 49-40-79713322, FAX 49-40-79713324, c_grotzke@koehler-mittler.de, http://www.deutsche-verwaltungs-praxis.de, http://www.koehler-mittler.de. Adv. contact Rainer Metzner. B&W page EUR 1,483, color page EUR 2,251; trim 176 x 260. Circ: 7,850.

658 DEU
DIALOG & WANDEL. Text in German. q. **Document type:** *Magazine, Trade.* **Description:** Provides information and content on new ideas and trends in international management
Related titles: English ed.
Published by: (Plaut International Management Consulting), BurdaYukom Publishing GmbH (Subsidiary of: Hubert Burda Media Holding GmbH & Co. KG), Schleissheimer Str 141, Munich, 80797, Germany. TEL 49-89-306200, FAX 49-89-30620100, info@burdayukom.de, http://www.yukom.de. Circ: 15,000 (controlled).

658 JPN ISSN 0385-4272
DIAMOND HARVARD BUSINESS. Text in Japanese. 1976. bi-m. adv. **Description:** Covers commercial, chemical, fishing, electrical and machinery industries.
Related titles: ♦ Translation of: Harvard Business Review. ISSN 0017-8012.
Indexed: PAIS, RGAb.
Published by: Diamond Inc., 4-2 Kasumigaseki 1-chome, Chiyoda-ku, Tokyo, 100-0013, Japan. TEL 81-3-3504-6558, FAX 81-3-3591-3895. Ed. Yoshihiro Kamimuro. Pub. Mineo Iwamochi. Adv. contact Katsutoshi Hirose. B&W page JPY 400,000, color page JPY 470,000; trim 280 x 208. Circ: 12,500.

658 JPN
DIAMOND WEEKLY. Text in Japanese. 1913. w. adv.
Formerly: Bessatsu Daiyamondo (0385-3802)
Published by: Diamond Inc., 4-2 Kasumigaseki 1-chome, Chiyoda-ku, Tokyo, 100-0013, Japan. TEL 81-3-3504-6548. Ed. Yutaka Iwasa. Pub. Hiromichi Sone. Adv. contact Katsutoshi Hirose. B&W page USD 8,917, color page USD 11,562; trim 257 x 182. Circ: 100,287.

658 FRA
DICTIONNAIRE JOLY SOCIETES. Text in French. 12 base vols. plus q. updates. looseleaf. **Document type:** *Trade.*

Formed by the merger of: Dictionnaire Joly Societes Anonymes; Dictionnaire Joly Societes a Responsabilite Limitee
Related titles: CD-ROM ed.; Diskette ed.
Published by: Joly Editions, 31 rue Falguiere, Paris, 75015, France. TEL 33-1-56541600, FAX 33-1-56541647. Ed. Daniel Lepeltier.

658 FRA ISSN 0767-1555
DICTIONNAIRE PERMANENT: DIFFICULTES DES ENTREPRISES. Text in French. base vol. plus m. updates. looseleaf. EUR 242 base vol(s). (effective 2004). **Description:** Analyzes the performance of businesses at various levels from the most to least successful.
Related titles: CD-ROM ed.; Online - full text ed.
Published by: Editions Legislatives, 80 Avenue de la Marne, Montrouge, Cedex 92546, France. TEL 33-1-40923636, FAX 33-1-40923663, infocom@editions-legislatives.fr, http://www.editions-legislatives.fr. Pub. Michel Vaillant.

658 333.33 FRA ISSN 0758-7309
DICTIONNAIRE PERMANENT: GESTION IMMOBILIERE. Text in French. 1977. 2 base vols. plus m. updates. looseleaf. EUR 249 base vol(s). (effective 2004). **Description:** Discusses legal and fiscal problems linked with the management of urban real estate.
Published by: Editions Legislatives, 80 Avenue de la Marne, Montrouge, Cedex 92546, France. TEL 33-1-40923636, FAX 33-1-40923663, infocom@editions-legislatives.fr, http://www.editions-legislatives.fr. Ed. Roger Saint Alary. Pub. Michel Vaillant.

DIGITAL COAST DAILY. see *COMPUTERS—Internet*

338 384.33 USA
THE DIGITAL WOMAN ONLINE; women with their modems running. Text in English. q. free. adv. **Document type:** *Newsletter.* **Description:** Offers women in management and women who manage their own businesses timely tips and advice on how to put the Internet to their advantage.
Media: Online - full text.
Published by: Digital Woman Online, 713 Rogers Ct, Aledo, TX 76008-4448. rebecca@digital-women.com, http://www.digital-women.com/. Ed., R&P, Adv. contact Rebecca Game TEL 817-441-6619.

DIMENSIONS (RESTON). see *EDUCATION—Teaching Methods And Curriculum*

658 USA
DIMENSIONS IN TOTAL QUALITY SERIES✶. Text in English. 1994. irreg. USD 19.95. **Document type:** *Monographic series, Trade.* **Description:** Aims to provide business and engineering students with a full understanding of the serious issues behind the popularity of Total Quality Management.
Published by: Basil Blackwell Inc., 350 Main St, Malden, MA 02148. TEL 800-488-2665, FAX 617-547-0789. Ed. Michael J Stahl.

658 JOR ISSN 1026-373X
JQ1833.A1 CODEN: DUJOES
➤ **DIRASAT. ADMINISTRATIVE SCIENCES.** Text in Arabic, English. 1974. s-a. JOD 9 domestic to individuals; JOD 11 domestic to institutions; USD 30 foreign (effective 2005). index, cum.index. back issues avail. **Document type:** *Journal, Academic/Scholarly.* **Description:** Presents research papers and articles in administrative, economics, and accounting sciences.
Supersedes in part (in 1996): Dirasat. Series A: Humanities (0255-8033)
Indexed: IBSS, PsycInfo, PsycholAb, e-psyche.
—CASDDS, CISTI.
Published by: University of Jordan, Deanship of Academic Research, Dean of Academic Research, Amman, 11942, Jordan. TEL 962-6-5355000 ext 3200, FAX 962-6-5355599, dirasata@ju.edu.jo, http://www.ju.edu.jo/research/dar. Ed. Nabil Shawagfeh. Circ: 1,000 (controlled).

658 ESP ISSN 1132-175X
DIRECCION Y ORGANIZACION. Text in Spanish. 1992. q.
Related titles: Online - full text ed.
—CINDOC.
Published by: Universidad Politecnica de Madrid, CEPADE, Ave. de Brasil, 23, Madrid, 28020, Spain. TEL 34-91-5562485, FAX 34-91-5566011, infocepade@cepade.es, http://apolo.cepade.es/07revista/revista.stm.

DIRECT (NEW YORK, 1988); magazine of direct marketing management. see *BUSINESS AND ECONOMICS—Marketing And Purchasing*

658.3 BEL ISSN 0779-7672
LE DIRECTEUR. Text in French. 1977. s-m. index. back issues avail. **Document type:** *Newsletter.*
Supersedes (in 1993): Personeel - L'Employeur; Social Trends (French Edition) (0772-4802)
Related titles: Microfiche ed.; Dutch ed.
Published by: Biblo N.V., Brasschaatsteenweg 308, Kalmthout, 2920, Belgium. Ed. Jan Van Dyck.

DIRECTIONS. see *INSURANCE*

658 GBR ISSN 0012-3242
HC251
DIRECTOR. Text in English. 1947. m. GBP 42 domestic; GBP 57 in Europe; GBP 73 elsewhere (effective 2004). bk.rev. illus. Supplement avail.; reprint service avail. from PQC. **Document type:** *Magazine, Consumer.*
Related titles: Microform ed.: (from PQC); Online - full text ed.: (from EBSCO Publishing, Northern Light Technology, Inc., O C L C Online Computer Library Center, Inc., ProQuest Information & Learning).
Indexed: ABIn, ADPA, BPIA, BusI, CPM, Emerald, IMI, IndBusRep, Inspec, KES, M&MA, ManagCont, PAIS, PSI, RASB, WBA, WMB, WorkRelAb.
—BLDSC (3590.400000), IE, Infotrieve, ingenta. **CCC.**
Published by: (Institute of Directors), Director Publications Ltd., 116 Pall Mall, London, SW1Y 5EA, United Kingdom. TEL 44-20-78391233, FAX 44-20-79301949, director-ed@iod.com, enquiries@iod.com, http://www.iod.com, http://www.iod.com/. Ed. Tom Nash. Pub. Andrew Main Wilson. Adv. contact Edwards Hicks. Circ: 58,441.

658 IND ISSN 0012-3250
DIRECTOR; India's top management journal. Text in English. 1964. q. INR 100, USD 25 (effective 1999). adv. bk.rev.
Related titles: Online - full text ed.: (from Northern Light Technology, Inc.).
Published by: (Institute of Directors, India), India-International News Service, 12 India Exchange Place, Kolkata, West Bengal 700 001, India. Ed. H Kothari.

658 USA ISSN 0364-9156
HD2709
DIRECTORS & BOARDS; thought leadership in governance since 1976. Text in English. 1976. q. USD 325 domestic; USD 350 foreign (effective 2005). adv. bk.rev. illus. index. 92 p./no.; back issues avail.; reprints avail. **Document type:** *Journal, Trade.* **Description:** A forum for discussion and analysis of topics such as corporate governance, the role and responsibilities of the board, corporate strategy, CEO succession and human resource development, global business and management trends, and executive and director compensation.
Related titles: Microform ed.: (from PQC); Online - full text ed.: (from Florida Center for Library Automation, Gale Group, O C L C Online Computer Library Center, Inc.).
Indexed: ABIn, ADPA, ASEANManA, ATI, BLI, BPIA, BusI, CLI, Emerald, HospLI, LRI, M&MA, MEDLINE, ManagCont, PAIS, PROMT, T&II.
—BLDSC (3590.570000), IE, Infotrieve, ingenta.
Address: 1845 Walnut St, 9th Fl, Philadelphia, PA 19103-4709. TEL 215-567-3200, FAX 215-405-6078, info@directorsandboards.com, jkristie@directorsandboards.com, http://www.directorsandboards.com/. Ed. Barbara Wenger. Pub., R&P James Kristie. Adv. contact Scott Chase. Circ: 5,000.

658 USA
DIRECTOR'S MONTHLY. Text in English. 1977. m. USD 350. bk.rev. **Document type:** *Newsletter.* **Description:** Includes feature articles on current topics of concern to corporate directors; news updates and analysis; and legal, financial, and accounting briefs.
Published by: National Association of Corporate Directors, 1133 21st St NW, # 700, Washington, DC 20036-3390. TEL 202-775-0509, FAX 202-775-4857. Ed. Alexandra Reed Lajoux. Circ: 4,000.

DIRECTORS REWARDS. see *BUSINESS AND ECONOMICS—Labor And Industrial Relations*

658 USA ISSN 0193-4279
DIRECTORSHIP. Text in English. 1976. m. USD 495 domestic; USD 650 foreign (effective 2005). bk.rev. index. back issues avail. **Document type:** *Newsletter.*
Related titles: Online - full text ed.: (from EBSCO Publishing, Northern Light Technology, Inc., ProQuest Information & Learning).
Published by: Directorship Inc., 8 Sound Shore Dr, Ste 250, Greenwich, CT 06830-7242. TEL 203-861-7000, FAX 203-861-7007, editor@directorship.com, http://www.directorship.com/Newsletter.htm, http://directorship.com. Ed. B.E. Beebe. Pub. B E Beebe.

658 USA ISSN 1077-7199
DIRECTORY OF BUSINESS PERIODICAL SPECIAL ISSUES✶. Text in English. 1995. irreg.
Published by: Reference Press Inc., 6448 Hwy 290 E, Ste E 104, Austin, TX 78723.

658 IND ISSN 0070-5322
DIRECTORY OF COMPANY SECRETARIES. Text in English. 1969. irreg. INR 30, USD 9 (effective 2000). adv. **Document type:** *Directory.* **Description:** Lists names, addresses, education of company secretaries. Includes information about their professional organizations.
Published by: Kothari Publications, 12 India Exchange Pl., Kolkata, West Bengal 700 001, India. TEL 91-33-220-9563. Ed. H Kothari.

658 GBR ISSN 0070-5438
DIRECTORY OF DIRECTORS. Text in English. 1878. a. (in 2 vols.), latest vol.126, 2005. GBP 295 per vol. (effective 2005). adv. bibl. 2 cols./p.; **Document type:** *Directory, Corporate.* **Description:** Provides essential information on over 46,000 directors, who control the top 15,000 British companies.
Related titles: Online - full text ed.: (from Reed Information Services Ltd.).
—BLDSC (3593.400000).
Published by: Hemscott Plc., 2nd Fl, Finsbury Tower, 103-105 Bunhill Row, London, EC1Y 8TY, United Kingdom. TEL 44-20-7496-0055, FAX 44-20-7847-1716, Marketing@Hemscott.co.uk, http://www.dofd.com/, http://www.hemscott.com/. Ed. Richard Price. Circ: 2,400.

DIRECTORY OF DIRECTORS. see *BIOGRAPHY*

658.31 USA ISSN 1059-163X
HD38.25.U6
DIRECTORY OF EXECUTIVE RECRUITERS (CORPORATE ED.). Text in English. 1971. a. USD 179.95 per vol. (effective 2001). adv. **Document type:** *Directory.* **Description:** Lists over 5,000 executive recruiting firms in the United States, Canada and Mexico. Six indexes: functions, industries, geographic, recruiter specialties, key principals, and firms.
Published by: Kennedy Information Inc., One Kennedy Place, Rte 12 S, Fitzwilliam, NH 03447. TEL 212-972-3793, FAX 212-972-1002, subscribe@kennedyinfo.com, http://www.kennedyinfo.com/er/corpder.html. Adv. contact Carolyn D Edwards.

658.3 USA ISSN 0743-6890
HD69.C6
THE DIRECTORY OF MANAGEMENT CONSULTANTS. Text in English. 1976. biennial. USD 295 (effective 2001). adv. **Document type:** *Directory.* **Description:** Lists and indexes 1,800 management consulting firms by services, industries, geography, and key principals. For companies seeking to hire a management consultant and for competitive intelligence, etc.
Published by: Kennedy Information Inc., One Kennedy Place, Rte 12 S, Fitzwilliam, NH 03447. TEL 212-972-3793, FAX 212-972-1002, bookstore@kennedyinfo.com, http://www.kennedyinfo.com. Pub. David Beck. Adv. contact Carolyn D Edwards.

658.0029 GBR ISSN 0268-375X
DIRECTORY OF MANAGEMENT CONSULTANTS IN THE UK. Text in English. 1983. a. GBP 94.75. adv. **Document type:** *Directory.* **Description:** Lists more than 3,000 consultancy firms in the U.K. Includes statistical information on firms and articles addressing topical issues.
Related titles: Diskette ed.
—BLDSC (3594.485900).
Published by: Management Information Publishing, c/o Edward Peck, 32 Clerkenwell Green, London, EC1R 0DU, United Kingdom. adv.: B&W page GBP 700, color page GBP 1,100; trim 190 x 270. Circ: 2,200.

DIRECTORY OF TRAINING. see *COMPUTERS*

658 SCG ISSN 0419-3903
DIREKTOR; casopis za teoriju i praksu rukovodjenja i upravljanja. Text in Serbo-Croatian. 1969. m. YUN 1,300, USD 126.30. adv. bk.rev. charts; illus.
Published by: Privredni Pregled, Marsala Birjuzova 3-5, Belgrade, 11000. Ed. Slobodan Sindovic.

DIREKTOR INFORMACIONNOJ SLUZBY. see *BUSINESS AND ECONOMICS—Computer Applications*

658.5 BRA ISSN 0012-3366
DIRIGENTE INDUSTRIAL. Text in Portuguese. 1959. m. USD 70. adv. bk.rev. abstr.; bibl.; charts; illus.
Published by: Editora Visao Ltda., Rua Alvaro de Carvalho, 354, Centro, Sao Paulo, SP 01050-070, Brazil. TEL 256-5011, FAX 258-1919. Ed. Hamilton Lucas de Oliveira. Circ: 25,750.

658 ITA
DIRIGENTI INDUSTRIA. Text in Italian. 1946. m. adv. bk.rev. **Document type:** *Magazine, Trade.*
Published by: Associazione Lombarda Dirigenti Aziende Industriali, Via Pantano 9, Milan, 20122, Italy. TEL 39-02-58370, FAX 39-02-58304507, assolombarda@assolombarda.it, http://www.assolombarda.it. Ed. Bruno Losito.

658 USA ISSN 1020-8135
DISASTER RISK MANAGEMENT SERIES. Text in English. 1999. irreg., latest vol.2, 2000. **Document type:** *Monographic series.*
Indexed: GEOBASE.
Published by: World Bank Group, 1818 H St, NW, Washington, DC 20433. TEL 703-661-1580, FAX 703-661-1501, books@worldbank.org, http://www.worldbank.org/dmf/knowledge/publications.htm.

658 GBR ISSN 1461-6017
DISCUSSION PAPERS IN MANAGEMENT AND ORGANIZATION STUDIES. Text in English. 1992. irreg.
Formerly (until 1997): Discussion Papers in Management Studies (1363-8203)

—BLDSC (3597.948150).
Published by: University of Leicester, Faculty of Social Sciences, Leicester, Leics LE1 7RH, United Kingdom. TEL 44-116-252-5368, http://www.leicester.ac.uk/.

DISEASE MANAGEMENT NEWS. see *MEDICAL SCIENCES*

658   GBR   ISSN 0953-7147
DISTRIBUTION BUSINESS. Text in English. 1989. 10/yr. free to qualified personnel (effective 2003). adv. back issues avail.
Document type: *Magazine, Trade.* **Description:** Probes issues of current interest to retail business and industrial users of distribution services.
Published by: UK Transport Press Ltd., 8th Fl, Cygnet House, 12-14 Sydenham Rd, Croydon, CR9 2ET, United Kingdom. TEL 44-20-86807474, FAX 44-20-86499747, bernardsteel@uktpl.com, http://www.distributionb.com/frn/tpl/main/main.php, http://www.uktpl.com/. Ed. Peter Rowlands. Adv. contact Chris Propert Lewis. B&W page GBP 1,310, color page GBP 1,925; trim 210 x 297. Circ: 11,500 (controlled).

DISTRIBUTION CENTER MANAGEMENT; managing people, materials and costs in the warehouse and distribution center. see *BUSINESS AND ECONOMICS—Marketing And Purchasing*

DISTRIBUTION MANAGEMENT DIGEST. see *BUSINESS AND ECONOMICS—Marketing And Purchasing*

658 551   CHN   ISSN 1003-6369
DIZHI KEJI GUANLI/SCIENTIFIC AND TECHNOLOGICAL MANAGEMENT IN GEOLOGICAL EXPLORATION. Text in Chinese. 1986. bi-m. USD 1.50 per issue. **Document type:** *Academic/Scholarly.*
Related titles: Online - full text ed.: (from East View Information Services).
Indexed: CIN, ChemAb, ChemTitl.
Published by: Chengdu Ligong Daxue/Chengdu University of Technology, No.1 3rd East Road, Chengdu, Sichuan 610059, China. TEL 86-28-3334712, FAX 86-28-3341299. Ed. Xingjian Li, Circ: 2,000. **Co-sponsor:** Chinese Geological Society.

658   USA
DOLLARS & CENTS. Text in English. m. membership. adv. **Description:** For finance directors, chief executive officers, and personnel managers of associations. Legislative, financial, human resources, technology issues.
Published by: (Finance and Administration Section), American Society of Association Executives, 1575 Eye St, N W, Washington, DC 20005-1168. TEL 202-626-2781, FAX 202-842-1145, http://www.asaenet.org. Circ: 3,600.

658   USA   ISSN 1531-3085
HF5548.32
DOTCEO. Text in English. 2001. bi-m. free to qualified personnel. adv. **Document type:** *Magazine, Trade.* **Description:** Covers leadership issues, financing growth and resources issues, high-level technical briefings, and controversial opinion issues for the Internet CEO.
Published by: Chief Executive Group, Inc., 733 Third Ave, 24th Fl, New York, NY 10017. TEL 212-687-8288, FAX 212-687-8456, media@dotceo.com, http://www.dotceo.com. Ed. Christine Larson. Pub., Adv. contact Carol Evans. B&W page USD 9,840, color page USD 12,000; trim 8 x 10.5. Circ: 25,000 (controlled).

DRUG COST MANAGEMENT REPORT. see *PHARMACY AND PHARMACOLOGY*

380 658   AUS   ISSN 0818-5093
DUN'S GAZETTE. (In 5 state editions: N.S.W., Vic., S.A., W.A., Qld.) Text in English. 1887. w. looseleaf. AUD 425. adv. stat.
Formerly: Bradstreet Gazette
Related titles: Microfiche ed.
Published by: Dun & Bradstreet Information Services, 479 St. Kilda Rd, Melbourne, VIC 3004, Australia. TEL 61-3-98283333, FAX 61-3-98283300, http://www.dbapic.com.au. Circ: 10,000.

E B; Handbuch fuer Selbstaendige und Unternehmer. see *BUSINESS AND ECONOMICS*

658   GBR   ISSN 1474-1717
E-BUSINESS WORKFLOW. Text in English. 1993. 10/yr. GBP 250, USD 400 (effective 2002). software rev. 12 p./no. 3 cols./p.; back issues avail.; reprints avail. **Document type:** *Newsletter, Corporate.* **Description:** Includes news, workflow management system reviews, user case studies and supplier strategies.
Formerly (until Mar. 2001): Workflow World (1351-3273)
Related titles: E-mail ed.
Published by: SODAN, 20 Mead Rd, Uxbridge, Mddx UB8 1AU, United Kingdom. khales@sodan.co.uk, http://www.sodan.co.uk. Ed. Barry Knight. Pub., R&P Keith Hales.

330   USA
E C F O. Text in English. q.
Related titles: ♦ Supplement to: C F O. ISSN 8756-7113.

Published by: C F O Publishing Corporation (Subsidiary of: Economist Group), 253 Summer St, Boston, MA 02210. TEL 617-345-9700, FAX 617-951-4090, subscription@cfopub.com, juliahomer@cfopub.com, http://www.ecfonet.com. Ed. Julia Homer. **Subscr. to:** PO Box 1230, Skokie, IL 60076-9798.

658   USA   ISSN 1549-2842
HD4965.5.U6
THE E C S TOP MANAGEMENT HI-COMP REPORT. (Executive Compensation Service) Text in English. 1986. a. USD 490. **Document type:** *Trade.* **Description:** Presents data on the highest paid one-third of the sample.
Related titles: Diskette ed.
Published by: (Executive Compensation Service (ECS)), Wyatt Data Services, 218 Rte 17 N, Rochelle Park, NJ 07622-9832. TEL 201-843-1177, FAX 201-843-0101.

658   USA
E JOURNAL OF ORGANIZATIONAL LEARNING AND LEADERSHIP. Text in English. 2002. irreg. free (effective 2005). **Document type:** *Journal, Academic/Scholarly.*
Media: Online - full text.
Published by: weLEAD Inc., PO Box 202, Litchfield, OH 44253-0202. http://www.weleadinlearning.org/ejournal.htm, http://www.leadingtoday.org.

658   ESP
E S I C PRESS. Text in Spanish. m.
Published by: Escuela Superior de Gestion Comercial y Marketing, Ave. Valdenigrales, s-n, Pozuelo de Alarcon, Madrid, 28223, Spain. TEL 34-91-3527716, FAX 34-91-3528534, http://www.esic.es/.

658 332.6   USA
E S O P REPORT. (Employee Stock Ownership Plan) Text in English. 1979. m. bk.rev. **Document type:** *Newsletter, Trade.*
Incorporates: Profile
Published by: E S O P Association, 1726 M St, N W, Ste 501, Washington, DC 20036. TEL 202-293-2971, FAX 202-293-7568, http://www.esopassociation.org. Ed. Jim Leutkemeyer. R&P Jim Luetkemeyer. Circ: 3,300.

E-TAILER'S DIGEST. see *BUSINESS AND ECONOMICS— Marketing And Purchasing*

658   KEN   ISSN 0012-8341
EAST AFRICAN MANAGEMENT JOURNAL. Text in English. 1966. q. adv.
Published by: (East African Management Foundation), English Press Ltd., Accra Rd., PO Box 30127, Nairobi, Kenya. Ed. R A West. Circ: 5,000.

EAST EUROPEAN BUSINESS INFORMATION SEARCHER. see *LIBRARY AND INFORMATION SCIENCES*

658   LUX
ECHO DE L'INDUSTRIE. Text in French. 1920. m. LUF 800; LUF 1,000 foreign (effective 1999). adv. **Document type:** *Trade.*
Indexed: KES.
Published by: Federation des Industriels Luxembourgeois, 7 rue Gasperi, BP 1304, Luxembourg, L-1013, Luxembourg. TEL 352-4353661, FAX 352-432328, TELEX 60174, echo@fedil.lu. Ed. Nicolas Soisson. R&P, Adv. contact Georges Santer. Circ: 1,900.

ECONOMETRICS IN THE INFORMATION AGE; theory and practice of measurement. see *BUSINESS AND ECONOMICS—Banking And Finance*

658   ITA   ISSN 1120-5032
ECONOMIA & MANAGEMENT. Text in Italian. 1988. bi-m. EUR 129 domestic; EUR 155 foreign (effective 2005). **Document type:** *Magazine, Consumer.*
Related titles: Online - full text ed.
Indexed: SCIMP.
Published by: R C S Libri (Subsidiary of: R C S Mediagroup), Via Mecenate, 91, Milan, MI 20138, Italy. TEL 39-02-5095-2248, FAX 39-02-5095-2975, http://economiaemanagement.corriere.it. Ed. Luisa Finocchi. Pub. Gian Maria Fiameni. R&P Pia Barbieri. Adv. contact Alfio Patane. Circ: 10,000.

658   PRT   ISSN 0873-7444
ECONOMIA GLOBAL E GESTAO. Text in Portuguese. 1996. 3/yr. EUR 12 to individuals; EUR 17 to institutions; EUR 9 to students (effective 2002). **Document type:** *Journal, Academic/Scholarly.*
Published by: I N D E G - I S C T E, Av. Prof. Anibal de Bettencourt, Lisbon, 1600-189, Portugal. TEL 351-21-7826100, FAX 351-21-7938709, http://www.indeg.org.

ECONOMICS OF GOVERNANCE. see *BUSINESS AND ECONOMICS*

658   FRA
ECONOMIES ET SOCIETES. SERIE EGS. ECONOMIE ET GESTION DES SERVICES. Text in French. irreg.
Published by: Les Presses de l'I S M E A, BP 22, Paris, Cedex 13 75622, France. TEL 33-1-55489076, FAX 33-1-55489071, http://www.ismea.org. Ed. Gerard de Bernis.

658   USA
EDUCATIONFM. Text in English. irreg.
Indexed: CIJE.
Published by: Trade Press Publishing Corp., 2100 W Florist Ave, Milwaukee, WI 53209. TEL 414-228-7701, FAX 414-228-7701, 414-228-1134, http://www.tradepress.com.

658.45   ISR
EFFECTIVE COMMUNICATION. Text in English. 1998. bi-w. free. adv. **Document type:** *Newsletter.* **Description:** Discusses all aspects of business and personal communication, both written and oral.
Media: Online - full text. **Related titles:** E-mail ed.
Published by: Hodu Winning Documents, Aish Kodesh 11-6, Betar Illit, 99879, Israel. TEL 972-2-580-7297, FAX 972-8-926-1832, winn@internet-zahav.net, http://www.hodu.com/. Ed., Pub. Azriel Winnett.

658   USA   ISSN 1525-1039
EFFECTIVE TELEPHONE TECHNIQUES. Variant title: Dartnell's Effective Telephone Techniques. Text in English. 1991. bi-w. USD 245.70 5 copies (effective 2005). **Document type:** *Newsletter, Trade.* **Description:** Helps employees build profitable customer relations with every phone call.
—CCC.
Published by: Dartnell Corp. (Subsidiary of: L R P Publications), 360 Hiatt Dr, Palm Beach Garden, FL 33418. TEL 561-622-6520, 800-621-5463, FAX 561-622-0757, custserve@lrp.com, http://www.shoplrp.com/product/p-28001.N.html, http://www.dartnellcorp.com/. Ed. David Dee.

EINKAEUFER IM MARKT. see *BUSINESS AND ECONOMICS—Marketing And Purchasing*

658   DEU   ISSN 0722-4850
EINZELHANDELS BERATER. Text in German. 1958. m. **Document type:** *Journal, Trade.*
Indexed: KES.
Published by: (Betriebswirtschaftliche Beratungsstelle fuer den Einzelhandel), B B E Unternehmensberatung GmbH, Gothaer Allee 2, Cologne, 50969, Germany. TEL 49-221-93655130, FAX 49-221-93655112, info@bbe-verlag.de, http://www.bbe-verlag.de.

658   MEX
EJECUTIVOS DE FINANZAS. Text in Spanish. 1972. m. MXP 250 domestic; MXP 80 foreign (effective 2000). adv. bk.rev. **Document type:** *Trade.* **Description:** Covers finance and economics for top executives.
Published by: Instituto Mexicano de Ejecutivos de Finanzas A.C., PATRICIO SANZ 1516, Col Del Valle, Mexico City, DF 03100, Mexico. TEL 52-5-5598366, FAX 52-5-5754410, mexfin@ibm.net, http://www.imef.org.mx. Ed. Jose Antonio Castillo. Pub. Agustin Humarin Adame. Adv. contact Cristina Fernandez. B&W page USD 2,790, color page USD 3,420. Circ: 15,000.

658   POL   ISSN 0860-6846
HC337.P7
EKONOMIKA I ORGANIZACJA PRZEDSIEBIORSTWA. Text in Polish; Summaries in English. 1950. m. EUR 119 foreign (effective 2005). adv. bk.rev. **Document type:** *Journal, Corporate.* **Description:** Covers economy and financial management.
Formerly (until 1988): Ekonomika i Organizacja Pracy (0013-3043)
Published by: Instytut Organizacji i Zarzadzania w Przemysle, ul Zelazna 87, Warsaw, 00879, Poland. TEL 48-22-6546061, FAX 48-22-6204360, wydawnictwa@orgmasz.waw.pl, http://www.orgmasz.waw.pl. Ed. Wieslaw Grudzewski. Circ: 3,200. Dist. by: Ars Polona, Krakowskie Przedmiescie 7, Warsaw, Poland. TEL 48-22-9263914, FAX 48-22-9265334, arspolona@arspolona.com.pl, http://www.arspolona.com.pl.

658   UKR
EKONOMIKA I UPRAVLENIE. Text in Russian. 1996. bi-m. USD 245 in the Americas (effective 2000).
Indexed: RefZh.
Published by: Krymskoe Respublikanskoe Nauchno-Pedagogicheskoe Obshchestvo Intellekt, Ul. Zoi Zhil'tsovoi, 11, Simferopol', 333000, Ukraine. TEL 27-32-18.

658   NLD   ISSN 0921-5220
ELAN (DEVENTER); magazine voor directeuren en commissarissen. Text in Dutch. 1986. 10/yr. EUR 135; EUR 15 newsstand/cover (effective 2005). adv. bk.rev. illus. **Document type:** *Trade.* **Description:** Discusses corporate strategy, leadership, organization and other management issues.
Formed by the merger of (1981-1986): Management Monitor (0167-5664); Elan (Deurne) (0167-3939); Which was formerly: Management Totaal (0770-3716); Incorporates (1998-2001): OndernemersZaken (1388-8722); Which was formerly: Zakelijke Dienstverlening (1388-1485)
Indexed: ABIn, ADPA, ExcerpMed, KES, M&MA.
—IE.

Published by: (Nederlands Centrum van Directeuren en Commissarissen), Wolters Kluwer N.V., Postbus 23, Deventer, 7400 GA, Netherlands. TEL 31-570-673358, FAX 31-570-691555, elan@kluwer.nl, info@kluwer.nl, http://www.elanonline.nl. Ed. Jan Schoenmakers. Pub. Berend Jan Veldkamp. Adv. contact Eric-Jan Vis. B&W page EUR 2,500; 210 x 297. Circ: 10,744.

658 GBR ISSN 1477-7029
➤ **ELECTRONIC JOURNAL OF BUSINESS RESEARCH METHODS.** Variant title: E J B R M. Text in English. biennial. free (effective 2005). bk.rev. **Document type:** *Journal, Academic/Scholarly.* **Description:** Aims to publish articles and papers that contribute to the development of both the theory and practice of research methods employed across the whole field of business and management studies.
Media: Online - full content.
Indexed: InfoSAb.
Published by: Management Centre International Ltd., Curtis Farm, Kidmore End, Near Reading, RG4 9AY, United Kingdom. TEL 44-1189-724148, FAX 44-1189-724691, info@ejbrm.com, http://www.ejbrm.com/. Ed. Arthur Money.

➤ **ELECTRONIC JOURNAL OF THE ARGENTINE SOCIETY FOR INFORMATICS AND OPERATIONS RESEARCH.** see *COMPUTERS*

➤ **ELECTRONIC WORLD NEWS.** see *ELECTRONICS*

▼ ➤ **ELECTRONICS SUPPLY & MANUFACTURING.** see *ELECTRONICS*

658 ESP
ELITES; de los negocios. Text in Spanish. 1976. 6/yr. adv. bk.rev.
Address: P. de la Castellana 210, Madrid, 28046, Spain. TEL 3594779, FAX 3452782. Ed. Fernando Ruiz Ogarrio. Circ: 15,000.

EMANAGER. see *BUSINESS AND ECONOMICS—Computer Applications*

658.155 USA
EMENTOR. Text in English. 2002. m. **Description:** Provides information on credit and lending essentials and industry updates for risk management professionals.
Media: Online - full content.
Published by: Risk Management Association, One Liberty Place, Ste 2300, 1650 Market St, Philadelphia, PA 19103-7398.

658 USA
P95.54
➤ **EMERGENCE: COMPLEXITY AND ORGANIZATION.** Abbreviated title: E: C O. Text in English. 1999-2004; resumed 2004. q. USD 100 to individuals; USD 300 to institutions; USD 50 to students (effective 2005). adv. reprint service avail. from PSC. **Document type:** *Journal, Academic/Scholarly.* **Description:** Allows for practicing managers as well as academics to acquire, understand, and explore new mental models of thinking. Seeks to develop the concepts, applications, and research in management and leadership.
Formerly (until 2004): Emergence (Mahwah, Print Edition) (1521-3250)
—BLDSC (3733.167600), IE. **CCC.**
Published by: Institute for the Study of Coherence and Emergence, 395 Central St, Mansfield, MA 02048. TEL 508-406-3111, FAX 781-634-0357, e-co@isce.edu, http://www.http://www.emergence.org. adv.: page USD 275; trim 5 x 8.

658 004 USA
EMERSON'S DIRECTORY OF LEADING US TECHNOLOGY CONSULTING FIRMS. Text in English. 1999. bi-m. USD 195; USD 250 foreign. back issues avail. **Document type:** *Directory.* **Description:** Provides leading background information on US technology consultants, including key personnel, services provided, and industry expertise.
Related titles: Diskette ed.
Address: 12342 Northup Way, Bellevue, WA 98005. TEL 425-896-0655, FAX 425-869-0746, emerson@emersoncompany.com, http://www.emersoncompany.com. Ed. Christopher Ames. Pub., R&P James C Emerson.

EMPIRE FOOD SERVICE NEWS; your premier news advantage. see *FOOD AND FOOD INDUSTRIES—Grocery Trade*

EMPLOYEE ASSISTANCE PROGRAM MANAGEMENT LETTER. see *BUSINESS AND ECONOMICS—Labor And Industrial Relations*

EMPLOYEE BENEFIT NEWS. see *BUSINESS AND ECONOMICS—Labor And Industrial Relations*

EMPLOYEE BENEFITS DIRECTORY. see *HEALTH FACILITIES AND ADMINISTRATION*

658 USA
EMPLOYEE BENEFITS MANAGEMENT. Text in English. 1990. 6 base vols. plus s-m. updates. looseleaf. USD 999 base vol(s). print or online or CD-ROM ed. (effective 2004). **Description:** Offers practical guidance on the full spectrum of employee benefits including health plans, family leave, 401(k) plans, and more.
Related titles: CD-ROM ed.; Online - full text ed.
Indexed: ATI.
Published by: C C H Inc., 2700 Lake Cook Rd, Riverwoods, IL 60015. TEL 847-267-7000, 800-449-6439, cust_serv@cch.com, http://www.cch.com. Pub. Catherine Wolfe.

EMPLOYEE BENEFITS PLANNER. see *HEALTH FACILITIES AND ADMINISTRATION*

658 USA ISSN 1528-0764
EMPLOYEE MOTIVATION AND INCENTIVE STRATEGIES FOR MANAGERS AND FINANCE EXECUTIVES. Text in English. 1999. m. USD 259 (effective 2000). index. back issues avail. **Document type:** *Newsletter.* **Description:** Details proven employee motivation strategies.
Indexed: BLI.
Published by: Siefer Consultants, Inc., 525 Cayuga St, Storm Lake, IA 50588. TEL 712-732-7340, FAX 712-732-7906, siefer@ncn.net. Ed. Marty Gallagher. Pub. Dan Siefer. Circ: 500.

658 USA
EMPLOYEE MOTIVATION AND INCENTIVE STRATEGIES FOR MANUFACTURING EXECUTIVES. Text in English. 1998. m. USD 259 (effective 2000). index. back issues avail. **Document type:** *Newsletter.* **Description:** Profiles strategies manufacturers use to motivate employees.
Published by: Siefer Consultants, Inc., 525 Cayuga St, Storm Lake, IA 50588. TEL 712-732-7340, FAX 712-732-7906, siefer@ncn.net. Ed. Marty Gallagher. Circ: 1,600.

658 USA
EMPLOYEE RECRUITMENT AND RETENTION STRATEGIES FOR MANUFACTURING EXECUTIVES. Text in English. 1999. m. USD 259 (effective 2000). back issues avail. **Document type:** *Newsletter.*
Published by: Siefer Consultants, Inc., 525 Cayuga St, Storm Lake, IA 50588. TEL 712-732-7340, FAX 712-732-7906, siefer@ncn.net. Ed. Steve Herron. Circ: 500.

658 AUS ISSN 1326-5512
EMPLOYEE RELATIONS BRIEF✶ ; strategy, legal compliance and change management. Text in English. 199?. m. AUD 395. **Document type:** *Trade.*
Contact Corp. Auth.: Australian Human Resources Institute, Level 6, 601 Bourke St, Melbourne, VIC 3000, Australia. TEL 300-656746, FAX 61-3-99189201, jlsydney@mpx.com.au, http://www.ahri.com.au/.

658 790 658.8 USA ISSN 0744-3676
GV1
EMPLOYEE SERVICES MANAGEMENT; the journal of employee services, recreation, health and education. Text in English. 1958. 10/yr. USD 52 domestic; USD 67 foreign (effective 2005). adv. charts; illus.; tr.lit. Index. reprint service avail. from PQC. **Document type:** *Magazine, Trade.* **Description:** Employee services management's editorial program administration, wellness programs, management, athletic teams and leagues, travel and discount services, eldercare, and childcare.
Formerly (until 1982): Recreation Management (0034-1770)
Related titles: Microform ed.: (from PQC).
Indexed: SportS.
Published by: Employee Services Management Association, 568 Spring Rd., Ste. D, Elmhurst, IL 60126-3896. TEL 630-559-0020, FAX 630-559-0025, esmahq@esmassn.org, http://www.esmassn.org/magazineindex.htm. Ed. Cynthia M Helson. Circ: 5,000 (paid and free).

658 NZL ISSN 0046-1903
EMPLOYER. Text in English. 1971. 11/yr. membership or on exchange. adv. bk.rev. charts; illus.; stat. **Document type:** *Newsletter.* **Description:** Deals with all current issues affecting the employing community, with emphasis on public policy, particularly but not exclusively labor relations and economy as it affects business.
—**CCC.**
Published by: New Zealand Employers Federation, PO Box 1786, Wellington, New Zealand. TEL 64-4-4994111, FAX 64-4-4994112, nzef@nzef.org.nz, http://www.nzef.org.nz. Ed. John McCaskey. Adv. contact Jacqui McVie. Circ: 14,800.

EMPLOYER'S GUIDE TO THE HEALTH INSURANCE PORTABILITY & ACCOUNTABILITY ACT. see *INSURANCE*

▼ **EMPLOYMENT BENEFIT NEWS CANADA.** see *BUSINESS AND ECONOMICS—Labor And Industrial Relations*

EMPLOYMENT TERMS AND CONDITIONS. ASIA - PACIFIC. see *BUSINESS AND ECONOMICS—Personnel Management*

658 MEX ISSN 0187-7828
EMPRENDEDORES. Text in Spanish. 1987. bi-m. MXP 55 (effective 2000). **Description:** Designed for top-managers, CEOs and VIPs in small and medium organizations.
Published by: Universidad Nacional Autonoma de Mexico, Facultad de Contaduria y Administracion, Edificio de la Direccion, 2o. Piso, Cub. 21, Circuito Exterior, Ciudad Universitaria, Apartado Postal 70-287, Mexico City, DF 04510, Mexico. TEL 52-5-6228396, FAX 52-5-6161355, http://server.contad.unam.mx/. Ed. Adrian Mendez Salvatorio.

658 ESP
EMPRESAS Y EMPRESARIOS. Text in Spanish. 11/yr.
Related titles: ◆ Supplement to: AgentTravel.
Address: Conde de Romanones, 9, 3o izda., Madrid, 28012, Spain. TEL 1-369-28-60, FAX 1-369-35-86. Ed. Lilian Aguirre. Circ: 10,000.

650 USA ISSN 0071-0210
Z7164.C81
ENCYCLOPEDIA OF BUSINESS INFORMATION SOURCES. Text in English. irreg., latest vol.19, 2004. USD 415 (effective 2004). **Description:** On-line and other business information sources.
Formerly: Executives Guide to Information Sources
Published by: Gale Group (Subsidiary of: Thomson Corporation), 27500 Drake Rd, Farmington Hills, MI 48331-3535. TEL 248-699-8061, 800-877-4253, FAX 248-699-4253, galeord@gale.com, http://www.gale.com. Ed. James Woy.

658 USA
ENCYCLOPEDIC DICTIONARY OF ECONOMICS. Text in English. 1973. irreg., latest 1991, 4th ed. USD 27.18 per vol. (effective 2004). illus.
Formerly: Economics: Encyclopedia (0090-4422)
Published by: McGraw-Hill - Dushkin (Subsidiary of: McGraw-Hill Higher Education), 2460 Kerper Blvd, Dubuque, IA 52001. TEL 800-243-6532, customer.service@mcgraw-hill.com, http://www.dushkin.com/catalog/0879678844.mhtml. Ed. Don Cole. Pub. Jeffrey Hahn. R&P Cheryl Greenleaf.

658 ARG ISSN 1514-8602
ENFOQUES (BUENOS AIRES). Text in Spanish. 1999. m. ARS 600 (effective 2002).
Related titles: Online - full text ed.
Published by: La Ley Saeei, Tucuman 1471, Buenos Aires, 1050, Argentina. TEL 54-11-43784841, FAX 54-11-43720953, laley@teletel.com.ar, enfoques@la-ley.com.ar. Ed. Orlando Gualtieri. Circ: 1,000.

ENGINEERING MANAGEMENT. see *ENGINEERING*

ENJINIASU/ENGINEERS. see *ENGINEERING*

658 GBR ISSN 1350-3030
ENTERPRISE. Text in English. 1993. m.
Related titles: Online - full text ed.: (from EBSCO Publishing).
Published by: Martin Leach Publishing Ltd., 2-6 Northburgh St, 3rd Flr., London, EC1V 0AY, United Kingdom. TEL 44-207-6088016, FAX 44-870-1282550.

658 ZAF ISSN 1024-154X
ENTERPRISE 200; the business magazine for black entrepreneurs and decision makers. Text in English. 1994. a. ZAR 40. illus. **Document type:** *Trade.*
Published by: Mafube Publishing (Pty) Ltd., PO Box 2185, Houghton, Johannesburg 2041, South Africa. TEL 27-11-4833863, FAX 27-11-4833194. Ed., Pub., R&P Thami Mazwai. Adv. contact Cheryl Pheiffer. B&W page ZAR 10,450, color page ZAR 13,500; trim 210 x 297.

ENTERTAINMENT LAW & FINANCE. see *LAW*

ENTERTAINMENT MANAGEMENT. see *LEISURE AND RECREATION*

658 USA ISSN 1087-8955
HD30.4
➤ **ENTREPRENEURIAL EXECUTIVE.** Text in English. a. free (effective 2005). **Document type:** *Journal, Academic/Scholarly.*
Related titles: Online - full text ed.
Indexed: ABIn.
Published by: (Academy of Entrepreneurship), Allied Academies, 145 Travis Rd., P. O. Box 2689, Cullowhee, NC 28723. http://www.alliedacademies.org/entrepreneurship/ee.html. Ed. R Wilburn Clouse.

658 FRA ISSN 1243-4167
L'ENTREPRISE. Text in French. 1991. m. EUR 20.30 domestic; EUR 40.30 in the European Union; EUR 56.30 in US & Canada; EUR 49.30 in Africa; EUR 77.30 elsewhere (effective 2005). adv. bk.rev.
Formery (until 1992): L' Entreprise - A pour Affaires Economiques (1164-7027); Which was formed by the merger of (1985-1991): L' Entreprise (0769-6248); (1989-1991): A pour Affaires Economiques (0998-4887); Which was formerly (1983-1989): Tertiel (0765-0272)
—IE, Infotrieve.

Published by: Groupe Express-Expansion (Subsidiary of: Socpresse), 17 rue de l'Arrivee, Paris Cede, 75733, France. TEL 33-1-53911111, http://www.lentreprise.com, http://www.groupe-expansion.com.

658 BEL ISSN 0046-2160
HD83
L'ENTREPRISE ET L'HOMME. Text in French. 1923. 5/yr. USD 130 (effective 1998). adv. bk.rev. bibl.; charts; illus. **Document type:** *Corporate.*
Formerly (until 1971): Bulletin Social des Industriels (0773-4042)
Published by: Association Chretienne des Dirigeants et Cadres, Av Konrad Adenauer 8, Brussels, 1200, Belgium. TEL 32-2-771-47-31, FAX 32-2-772-46-33, adic@belgacom.net. Ed., R&P Krystyna Delahaye. Pub. Michel Dussenne. Adv. contact B Janssens Debisthoven. Circ: 6,500.

ENVIRONMENT & MANAGEMENT. see *ENVIRONMENTAL STUDIES*

658 USA ISSN 1069-0131
ENVIRONMENTAL COMPLIANCE ALERT. Abbreviated title: E C A. Text in English. 1993. s-m. USD 299. charts. **Document type:** *Newsletter.* **Description:** Provides current environmental regulations update.
Indexed: PAIS.
Published by: Progressive Business Publications, 370 Technology Dr, Malvern, PA 19355-1315. TEL 610-695-8600, 800-220-5000, FAX 610-647-8089, editor@pbp.com, http://www.pbp.com. Ed. Tom Gray. R&P Curt Brown. Circ: 12,254 (paid).

ENVIRONMENTAL EXCELLENCE. see *ENVIRONMENTAL STUDIES*

ENVIRONMENTAL MANAGER; the independent, weekly newsletter on industry and the environment. see *ENVIRONMENTAL STUDIES*

ENVIRONMENTAL QUALITY MANAGEMENT. see *ENVIRONMENTAL STUDIES*

658 USA
ENVIRONMENTAL SYSTEMS UPDATE. Text in English. m. USD 375 (effective 2005). **Document type:** *Journal, Trade.* **Description:** Tracks national and international developments with respect to the application and implementation of the ISO 14000 family of international standards.
Published by: Q S U Publishing Company, 3975 University Dr, Ste 230, Fairfax, VA 22030. TEL 703-359-8460, FAX 703-359-8462, news@qsuonline.com, http://www.qsuonline.com. Ed. Suzanne Leonard. Pub. Paul Scicchitano.

EQUIPMENT SOLUTIONS. see *FOOD AND FOOD INDUSTRIES*

ERHVERV OEST; erhverv/Koebenhavn-Sjaelland. see *BUSINESS AND ECONOMICS—Production Of Goods And Services*

658 DNK ISSN 1399-8080
ERHVERV/VEST. Variant title: Maanedsmagasinet Erhverv/Vest. Text in Danish. 1991. 11/yr. (11/yr.). DKK 280 (effective 2004). adv. reprints avail. **Document type:** *Magazine, Trade.*
Formerly (untill 1998): Erhverv/Jylland (0907-0699); Which was formed by the merger of (1990-1991): Erhverv/Syd- og Midtjylland (0906-4494); (1985-1991): Erhverv/ Nordjylland (0900-6028); Which was formed by the merger of (1985-1990): Erhverv/Syd- og Soenderjylland (0900-6036); (1985-1989): Erhverv/Midtjylland (0905-2607); Which was formerly (until 1989): Erhverv/Aarhus Amt (0900-6044); Incorporates (1983-?): Erhverv/Fyn (0900-5706); Which was formerly (until 1985): Erhverv paa Fyn (0906-7787); (1983): Erhvervs-Nyt (0900-5692)
Related titles: Online - full text ed.
Published by: Vestkystens Distriksblade A/S, Jernbanegade 18, Esbjerg, 6700, Denmark. TEL 45-75-155200, FAX 45-75-155804, info@mme-vest.dk, http://www.mme-vest.dk. Ed. Birthe Rasmussen. Adv. contact Freddy Larsen. page DKK 29,950. Circ: 51,684 (controlled).

658 ESP ISSN 0212-1867
ESIC MARKET. (Escuela Superior de Gestion Comercial y Marketing) Text in Spanish. 1970. 3/yr. back issues avail.
—CINDOC.
Published by: Escuela Superior de Gestion Comercial y Marketing, Ave. Valdenigrales, s-n, Pozuelo de Alarcon, Madrid, 28223, Spain. TEL 34-91-3527716, FAX 34-91-3528534, http://www.esic.es/. Ed. Jose Maria Curto de la Mano.

ESSENTIALS OF MANAGED HEALTH CARE. see *INSURANCE*

658 ESP ISSN 0425-3698
QE1 CODEN: TGSGAL
ESTUDIOS EMPRESARIALES. Text in Spanish. 1965. 3/yr. EUR 20 domestic; EUR 45 in Europe; USD 70 elsewhere (effective 2002). adv. bk.rev. bibl.; abstr.; charts; illus. **Document type:** *Academic/Scholarly.*
Indexed: JEL, PAIS.
—CINDOC, IE, Infotrieve.

Published by: Universidad de Deusto, Facultad de Ciencias Economicas y Empresariales, Apdo 1359, San Sebastian, Guipuzcoa 20080, Spain. TEL 34-943-273100, FAX 34-943-273932. Ed. Jose Luis Perez. Pub. Francisco Olarte. R&P Antxon Masse. Adv. contact Jose Sein. Circ: 2,000.

ETHIKOS; examining ethical and compliance issues in business. see *PHILOSOPHY*

ETHOS. see *SOCIOLOGY*

658.0029 GBR ISSN 1355-0292
THE EUROPEAN DIRECTORY OF MANAGEMENT CONSULTANTS. Text in English. 1990. biennial. GBP 140. adv. **Document type:** *Directory.* **Description:** Provides details on more than 3,250 consultancy firms in Western and Eastern Europe on national and international levels. Indexed by country.
Related titles: Diskette ed.
Published by: Management Information Publishing, c/o Edward Peck, 32 Clerkenwell Green, London, EC1R 0DU, United Kingdom. adv.: B&W page GBP 600, color page GBP 900; trim 210 x 297. Circ: 2,000.

658.00711 NLD ISSN 1570-0194
EUROPEAN EXECUTIVE EDUCATION DIRECTORY. Text in English. 1987. a. EUR 195 (effective 2005). adv. **Document type:** *Directory.* **Description:** Lists executive training programs at European business schools and management training centers.
Former titles (until 2001): European Management Education Directory (1383-6218); World Management Education Guide - Europe; European Management Education Guide
Published by: E M D Centre, Naarderstraat 296, Huizen, 1272 NT, Netherlands. TEL 31-35-6951111, FAX 31-35-6951900, http://www.emdcentre.com/. Eds. Rino Schreuder, Yvonne Kuysters.

658 BEL ISSN 0778-7936
EUROPEAN FORUM FOR MANAGEMENT DEVELOPMENT. Text in English. 1972. q.
—BLDSC (3664.132500), IE, ingenta.
Published by: European Foundation for Management Development, Rue Gachard 88, Brussels, 1050, Belgium. TEL 32-2-6290810, FAX 32-2-6290811, info@efmd.be, http://www.efmd.be.

EUROPEAN JOURNAL FOR SPORT MANAGEMENT. see *SPORTS AND GAMES*

EUROPEAN JOURNAL OF INFORMATION SYSTEMS. see *COMPUTERS—Information Science And Information Theory*

658.406 GBR ISSN 1460-1060
HD45
➤ **EUROPEAN JOURNAL OF INNOVATION MANAGEMENT.** Text in English. 1998. 4/yr. EUR 1,597.54 in Europe; USD 1,599 in North America; AUD 2,759 in Australasia; GBP 1,119.04 in UK & elsewhere (effective 2006). reprint service avail. from PSC. **Document type:** *Journal, Academic/Scholarly.* **Description:** Presents a European perspective on the latest developments in the management of innovation and the latest theoretical & practical developments in key areas of organizational success.
Related titles: Online - full text ed.: (from EBSCO Publishing, Emerald Group Publishing Limited, Gale Group, IngentaConnect, O C L C Online Computer Library Center, Inc., ProQuest Information & Learning, Swets Information Services).
Indexed: ABIn, EmerIntel, Inspec.
—BLDSC (3829.730430), IE, Infotrieve, ingenta. **CCC.**
Published by: Emerald Group Publishing Limited, 60-62 Toller Ln, Bradford, W Yorks BD8 9BY, United Kingdom. TEL 44-1274-777700, FAX 44-1274-785200, infomation@emeraldinsight.com, http://www.emeraldinsight.com/ejim.htm. Ed. Pervaiz Ahmed. **Subscr. addr. in N America:** Emerald Group Publishing Ltd., 44 Brattle St, 4th Fl, Cambridge, MA 02138. TEL 617-497-2175, 888-622-0075, FAX 617-354-6875.

658 USA ISSN 1555-4015
▼ ➤ **EUROPEAN JOURNAL OF MANAGEMENT.** Text in English. forthcoming 2006 (Jan.). s-a. USD 100 (effective 2006). **Document type:** *Journal, Academic/Scholarly.*
Published by: Academy of International Business and Economics, 983 Woodland Dr, Turlock, CA 95382-7281. TEL 209-656-7084, Review@aibe.org, http://www.AIBE.org, http://www.aibe.org.

003 NLD ISSN 0377-2217
T57.6 CODEN: EJORDT
➤ **EUROPEAN JOURNAL OF OPERATIONAL RESEARCH.** Text in Dutch. 1977. 24/yr. EUR 4,500 in Europe to institutions; JPY 597,500 in Japan to institutions; USD 5,034 to institutions except Europe and Japan (effective 2006). bk.rev. illus. reprints avail. **Document type:** *Journal, Academic/Scholarly.* **Description:** Publishes papers on the theory and practice of decision making.
Related titles: Microform ed.: (from PQC); Online - full text ed.: (from EBSCO Publishing, Gale Group, IngentaConnect, ScienceDirect, Swets Information Services).

Indexed: ABIn, AHCMS, ASCA, BPIA, BibInd, Biostat, BusI, C&ISA, CIS, CJA, CMCI, CPM, CivEngAb, CompAb, CompLI, CurCont, E&CAJ, EIA, ESPM, Emerald, EnerInd, EngInd, ExcerpMed, IAOP, ISMEC, Inspec, JCQM, ManagCont, MathR, MathSciNet, ORMS, QC&AS, RefZh, RiskAb, SCIMP, SFA, SSCI, ST&MA, SolStAb, T&II, ZentMath.
—BLDSC (3829.733200), AskIEEE, CISTI, Ei, IDS, IE, Infotrieve, ingenta, Linda Hall. **CCC.**
Published by: (Association of European Operational Research Societies), Elsevier BV, North-Holland (Subsidiary of: Elsevier Science & Technology), Sara Burgerhartstraat 25, Amsterdam, 1055 KV, Netherlands. TEL 31-20-485-3911, FAX 31-20-485-2457, nlinfo-f@elsevier.nl, http://www.elsevier.com/locate/ejor, http://www.elsevier.nl. Eds. Canon J. Teghem, R. Slowinski. **Subscr. to:** Elsevier BV, PO Box 211, Amsterdam 1000 AE, Netherlands. TEL 31-20-485-3757, FAX 31-20-485-3432.

658 GBR ISSN 0263-2373
HD28
➤ **EUROPEAN MANAGEMENT JOURNAL.** Text in English. 1983. 6/yr. EUR 135 in Europe to individuals; JPY 18,000 in Japan to individuals; USD 152 to individuals except Europe and Japan; EUR 685 in Europe to institutions; JPY 91,000 in Japan to institutions; USD 766 to institutions except Europe and Japan (effective 2006). adv. bk.rev. illus. Index. back issues avail.; reprint service avail. from PQC. **Document type:** *Journal, Academic/Scholarly.* **Description:** Publishes articles based on experience or research of immediate relevance to European business affairs, for both practicing managers and management academics.
Related titles: Microfilm ed.: (from PQC); Online - full text ed.: (from EBSCO Publishing, Gale Group, IngentaConnect, O C L C Online Computer Library Center, Inc., ScienceDirect, Swets Information Services).
Indexed: ABIn, BPI, CPM, Emerald, Inspec, M&MA, ORMS, PAIS, PCI, QC&AS, RefZh, SCIMP.
—BLDSC (3829.750430), IE, Infotrieve, ingenta. **CCC.**
Published by: Pergamon (Subsidiary of: Elsevier Science & Technology), The Boulevard, Langford Ln, East Park, Kidlington, Oxford OX5 1GB, United Kingdom. TEL 44-1865-843000, FAX 44-1865-843010, http://www.elsevier.com/locate/emj. Ed. Paul Stonham. Circ: 1,000. **Subscr. to:** Elsevier BV, PO Box 211, Amsterdam 1000 AE, Netherlands. TEL 31-20-485-3757, FAX 31-20-485-3432, nlinfo-f@elsevier.nl, http://www.elsevier.nl.

658 GBR ISSN 1740-4754
▼ **EUROPEAN MANAGEMENT REVIEW.** Text in English. 2004 (Spr). 3/yr. USD 140 combined subscription in United States to individuals; GBP 85 combined subscription elsewhere to individuals; USD 410 combined subscription in United States to institutions; GBP 249 combined subscription elsewhere to institutions (effective 2005); combined. subscr. includes print & online eds.. **Document type:** *Journal, Academic/Scholarly.* **Description:** Serves as a new forum for international management research.
Related titles: Online - full text ed.: ISSN 1740-4762. GBP 152 in Europe to institutions; USD 239 elsewhere to institutions (effective 2004) (from EBSCO Publishing, Gale Group, IngentaConnect, O C L C Online Computer Library Center, Inc., ProQuest Information & Learning, Swets Information Services).
Indexed: ABIn.
Published by: (European Academy of Management BEL), Palgrave Macmillan Ltd. (Subsidiary of: Macmillan Publishers Ltd.), Houndmills, Basingstoke, Hants RG21 6XS, United Kingdom. TEL 44-1256-329242, FAX 44-1256-810526, journal-info@palgrave.com, http://www.palgrave-journals.com/emr/index.html. Ed. Pierre Dussauge. **Subscr. to:** Subscriptions Dept, Houndmills, Basingstoke, Hants RG21 2XS, United Kingdom. TEL 44-1256-357893, FAX 44-1256-328339.

EUROPEAN SPORT MANAGEMENT QUARTERLY. see *SPORTS AND GAMES*

658.054678 GBR ISSN 1470-2126
EUROWIRED. Text in English. 2000. s-a. GBP 50 domestic; USD 95 elsewhere (effective 2003).
Related titles: Online - full text ed.: (from Gale Group).
—**CCC.**
Published by: Euromoney Institutional Investor Plc., Nestor House, Playhouse Yard, London, EC4V 5EX, United Kingdom. TEL 44-20-7779-8673, FAX 44-20-7779-8541, http://www.euromoney.com. Ed., Adv. contact Sean Nicklin TEL 44-20-77798114. **Subscr. to:** Eclipse, The In-house Fulfillment Bureau, PO Box 18083, London EC4V 5JS, United Kingdom. TEL 44-20-7779-8610, FAX 44-20-7779-8602, CustomerService@euromoneyplc.com.

658 PAK
EXECUTIVE. Text in English. 1975. a. free. adv. illus.
Published by: Institute of Business Administration, University of Karachi, University Campus, Karachi 32, Pakistan. Ed. Noman Afzal Tariq. Circ: 1,500.

▼ new title ➤ refereed ✶ unverified ♦ full entry avail.

658   USA   ISSN 1093-6114
EXECUTIVE ADVANTAGE. Variant title: Letitia Baldrige's Executive Advantage. Text in English. 1996. m. **Document type:** *Newsletter, Trade.* **Description:** Presents management and executives with the means to achive professional success.
Published by: Briefings Publishing Group (Subsidiary of: Douglas Publications, Inc.), 1101 King St, Ste 110, Alexandria, VA 22314. TEL 703-518-2343, 800-722-9221, FAX 703-684-2136, customerservice@briefings.com, http://www.briefings.com.

658 346.065   USA
▼ **EXECUTIVE COUNSEL;** legal insights inspiring business strategies. Text in English. 2004. bi-m. USD 99; USD 17.95 per issue (effective 2005). adv. **Document type:** *Magazine, Trade.*
Published by: Nienhouse Media, Inc., 640 Park Ave, Hinsdale, IL 60521. TEL 630-655-3202, FAX 630-655-3310, editor@executivecounsel.com, http://www.executivecounsel.com. Ed. Robert Nienhouse. adv.: color page USD 18,100; trim 8 x 10.5. Circ: 50,000.

658   USA
▼ **EXECUTIVE DECISION.** Text in English. 2004. bi-m. USD 19.95; USD 5.95 per issue (effective 2005). adv. **Document type:** *Magazine, Trade.*
Published by: United Publishing & Media, LLC, 779 North St, Greenwich, CT 06831-2706. TEL 203-622-8778, FAX 203-622-0391. Pub. Phillip G Wren TEL 203-622-8778 ext 10. Adv. contact Bill Ruha TEL 203-622-8778 ext 14. B&W page USD 6,915, color page USD 8,945; trim 8.25 x 10.875. Circ: 51,949 (paid).

658   PRT   ISSN 0874-0526
EXECUTIVE DIGEST. Text in Portuguese. 1995. m. EUR 56.16 (effective 2004). adv. **Document type:** *Magazine, Trade.*
Published by: Edimpresa Editora Lda., Rua Calvet de Magalhaes 242, Laveiras, Paco de Arcos, 2770-022, Portugal. TEL 351-21-4698000, FAX 351-21-4698501, edimpresa@edimpresa.pt, http://www.edimpresa.pt. adv.: page EUR 3,345; trim 205 x 275.

EXECUTIVE EMPLOYMENT LAW. see *LAW—Corporate Law*

658   GBR
EXECUTIVE GRAPEVINE. INTERIM MANAGEMENT IN EUROPE (YEAR); the definitive guide to interim management providers. Text in English. a. GBP 115 per issue (effective 2005). **Document type:** *Directory, Trade.*
Formerly: Executive Grapevine. The European Directory of Interim Management Providers (Year)
—BLDSC (4533.537600).
Published by: Executive Grapevine International Ltd., New Barnes Mill, Cottonmill Ln, St Albans, Herts AL1 2HA, United Kingdom. TEL 44-1727-844335, FAX 44-1727-844779, info@executive-grapevine.co.uk, http://www.executive-grapevine.co.uk/.

658 371.2   GBR   ISSN 1468-6821
EXECUTIVE GRAPEVINE. THE EUROPEAN DIRECTORY OF CAREER DEVELOPMENT CONSULTANTS. Text in English. 1988. a. GBP 60 (effective 2000). **Document type:** *Directory, Trade.* **Description:** Lists consultancies that provide services to both individual and corporate clients, including career counselling outplacement, psychological assessments, job search seminars, management development and training.
Former titles (until 1999): Executive Grapevine, Volume 3: European Directory of Career Development Consultants (1462-4222); (until 1997): Executive Grapevine, Volume 3: European Directory of Career Management and Outplacement Consultants (1367-6385); (until 1995): Executive Grapevine. Volume 3: Directory of Career Management and Outplacement Consultants
—BLDSC (3829.689496).
Published by: Executive Grapevine International Ltd., New Barnes Mill, Cottonmill Ln, St Albans, Herts AL1 2HA, United Kingdom. TEL 44-1727-844335, FAX 44-1727-844779, info@executive-grapevine.co.uk, http://www.executive-grapevine.co.uk. Ed. Helen Barrett.

658 371.2   GBR
EXECUTIVE GRAPEVINE. THE EUROPEAN DIRECTORY OF NON-EXECUTIVE DIRECTOR AND INTERIM MANAGEMENT PROVIDERS. Text in English. 1992. a. GBP 50 (effective 2000). **Document type:** *Directory.* **Description:** Profiles consultants active in carrying out assignments for temporary executive positions and non-executive directorship appointments.
Former titles (until 1998): Executive Grapevine, Volume 4: Directory of Non Executive Directors, Interim Management and Consultants; Executive Grapevine, Volume 4: Directory of Interim Management and Non Executive Directors
—BLDSC (3829.689553).
Published by: Executive Grapevine International Ltd., New Barnes Mill, Cottonmill Ln, St Albans, Herts AL1 2HA, United Kingdom. TEL 44-1727-844335, FAX 44-1727-844779, sales@executive-grapevine.co.uk, info@executive-grapevine.co.uk, http://www.executive-grapevine.co.uk. Ed. Helen Barrett.

658 371.42   GBR
EXECUTIVE GRAPEVINE, VOLUME 1: DIRECTORY OF EXECUTIVE RECRUITMENT CONSULTANTS - UK EDITION (YEAR); recruitment library. Text in English. 1979. a. GBP 130 (effective 2000). adv. **Document type:** *Directory.* **Description:** Provides up-to-date profiles and information on more than 750 executive recruitment consultancies based in the UK.
Published by: Executive Grapevine International Ltd., New Barnes Mill, Cottonmill Ln, St Albans, Herts AL1 2HA, United Kingdom. TEL 44-1727-844335, FAX 44-1727-844779, sales@executive-grapevine.co.uk, info@executive-grapevine.co.uk, http://www.executive-grapevine.co.uk. Ed. Helen Barrett.

658   GBR
EXECUTIVE GRAPEVINE, VOLUME 11: GRAPEVINE INDEX OF CHAIRMEN CHIEF EXECUTIVE & MANAGING DIRECTORS. Text in English. 1996. a. GBP 135 (effective 2000). **Description:** Focuses on both public and private companies. Serves as reference for individuals monitoring leading executives within corporate life. Indexed by company size, industry, and individuals' names.
Formerly: Executive Grapevine, Volume 11: Grapevine Index of Chief Executive & Managing Directors
—ingenta.
Published by: Executive Grapevine International Ltd., New Barnes Mill, Cottonmill Ln, St Albans, Herts AL1 2HA, United Kingdom. TEL 44-1727-844335, FAX 44-1727-844779, sales@executive-grapevine.co.uk, info@executive-grapevine.co.uk, http://www.executive-grapevine.co.uk.

658 371.2   GBR
EXECUTIVE GRAPEVINE, VOLUME 2: INTERNATIONAL DIRECTORY OF EXECUTIVE RECRUITMENT CONSULTANTS; Grapevine recruitment library. Text in English. 1993. a. GBP 120 (effective 2000). adv. **Document type:** *Directory.* **Description:** Lists and profiles executive recruiters in more than 65 non-UK nations. Lists functional specializations, remuneration levels, fees, and other data.
—BLDSC (4539.637500).
Published by: Executive Grapevine International Ltd., New Barnes Mill, Cottonmill Ln, St Albans, Herts AL1 2HA, United Kingdom. TEL 44-1727-844335, FAX 44-1727-844779, sales@executive-grapevine.co.uk, info@executive-grapevine.co.uk, http://www.executive-grapevine.co.uk. Ed. Helen Barrett. Adv. contact Jinny O'Gorman.

658 371.42   GBR
EXECUTIVE GRAPEVINE, VOLUME 5: GRAPEVINE INDEX OF WORLD'S LEADING EXECUTIVES. Text in English. 1993. a. GBP 200 (effective 2000). **Document type:** *Directory.* **Description:** Gives visibility to over 1000 of the world's leading corporations together with their senior executives and functional specialists.
Former titles: Executive Grapevine, Volume 5: Directory of Assessment and Development Consultants; Executive Grapevine, Volume 5: Directory of Executive and Management Development Consultants
Published by: Executive Grapevine International Ltd., New Barnes Mill, Cottonmill Ln, St Albans, Herts AL1 2HA, United Kingdom. TEL 44-1727-844335, FAX 44-1727-844779, sales@executive-grapevine.co.uk, info@executive-grapevine.co.uk, http://www.executive-grapevine.co.uk. Ed. Helen Barrett.

658.3 371.42   GBR
EXECUTIVE GRAPEVINE, VOLUME 6: THE GRAPEVINE INDEX OF SENIOR H R EXECUTIVES, U K EDITION; recruitment library. Text in English. 1995. a. GBP 135 (effective 2000). **Document type:** *Directory.* **Description:** Lists human resource directors and managers at the largest UK companies.
Former titles: Executive Grapevine, Volume 6: The Grapevine Index of H R Directors, U K Edition; Executive Grapevine, Volume 6: List of Human Resource Professionals
Published by: Executive Grapevine International Ltd., New Barnes Mill, Cottonmill Ln, St Albans, Herts AL1 2HA, United Kingdom. TEL 44-1727-844335, FAX 44-1727-844779, sales@executive-grapevine.co.uk, info@executive-grapevine.co.uk, http://www.executive-grapevine.co.uk. Ed. Helen Barrett.

658 371.2   GBR
EXECUTIVE GRAPEVINE, VOLUME 7: THE GRAPEVINE INDEX OF SENIOR I T EXECUTIVES; Grapevine recruitment library. Text in English. 1996. a. GBP 135 (effective 2000). **Document type:** *Directory.* **Description:** Aims to provide a focus and greater awareness of Information Technology positions and their function. Lists some of the UK's most influential IT directors and professional consultants.
Former titles: Executive Grapevine, Volume 7: The Directory of I T Professionals; Executive Grapevine, Volume 7: The Grapevine Index of I T Directors; Executive Grapevine, Volume 7: The Directory of I T Directors and Consultants
Published by: Executive Grapevine International Ltd., New Barnes Mill, Cottonmill Ln, St Albans, Herts AL1 2HA, United Kingdom. TEL 44-1727-844335, FAX 44-1727-844779, sales@executive-grapevine.co.uk, info@executive-grapevine.co.uk, http://www.executive-grapevine.co.uk. Ed. Helen Barrett.

EXECUTIVE GRAPEVINE, VOLUME 8: GRAPEVINE INDEX OF FINANCE EXECUTIVES. see *BUSINESS AND ECONOMICS—Banking And Finance*

EXECUTIVE GRAPEVINE, VOLUME 9: GRAPEVINE INDEX OF SALES & MARKETING DIRECTORS. see *BUSINESS AND ECONOMICS—Marketing And Purchasing*

▼ **EXECUTIVE INSIGHTS;** management strategies that drive results. see *HEALTH FACILITIES AND ADMINISTRATION*

658   USA
EXECUTIVE ISSUES. Text in English. irreg. **Description:** Forum for the discussion of topical business issues.
Published by: University of Pennsylvania, Wharton School, Wharton Executive Education Division, 255 S 38th St, Philadelphia, PA 19130. TEL 215-898-4560, FAX 215-386-4304, neveras@wharton.upenn.edu. Ed. Jeffrey J Barta.

658   USA
EXECUTIVE LEADERSHIP. Text in English. 1985. m. USD 96. 8 p./no.; **Document type:** *Newsletter.* **Description:** Provides fast-track managers with advice on developing their leadership abilities.
Former titles (until Aug. 2000): Executive Strategies (1042-0657); Career Letter for Managers
—CISTI. **CCC.**
Published by: National Institute of Business Management, PO Box 9266, Mclean, VA 22102-0266. TEL 703-905-8000. Ed. Lynn Miller. Pub. Philip W Clark. R&P Carolyn Frazier. Circ: 20,000.

658   USA
EXECUTIVE PERQUISITES REPORT. Text in English. a. USD 640. charts. **Document type:** *Trade.* **Description:** Provides information specific to company size and industry, on current US perquisite practices.
Published by: (Executive Compensation Service (ECS)), Wyatt Data Services, 218 Rte 17 N, Rochelle Park, NJ 07622-9832. TEL 201-843-1177, FAX 201-843-0101.

658   USA   ISSN 0271-0781
EXECUTIVE RECRUITER NEWS. Text in English. 1980. m. USD 229 in US & Canada; USD 269 elsewhere (effective 2004). adv. bk.rev. index. **Document type:** *Newsletter.* **Description:** Covers the recruiting industry, and contains news, analysis, practice advice, propriety data and opinion.
Published by: Kennedy Information Inc., One Phoenix Mill Ln., 5th Fl., Peterborough, NH 03458. TEL 603-924-1006, 800-531-0007, FAX 603-924-4460, ern-editor@kennedyinfo.com, http://www.kennedyinfo.com/er/ern.html. Ed. Joseph Daniel McCool. Adv. contact Carolyn D Edwards.

681.3   SWE   ISSN 1400-2523
EXECUTIVE REPORT; analysbrevet om hela it-industrin. Text in Swedish. 1990. 11/yr. SEK 3,490 (effective 2002). adv. **Document type:** *Magazine, Trade.*
Formerly (until 1993): C W Executive Report
Published by: I D G AB (Subsidiary of: I D G Communications Inc.), Sturegatan 11, Stockholm, 10678, Sweden. TEL 46-8-4536000, FAX 46-8-4536005, exr@idg.se, http://exr.idg.se, http://www.idg.se. Eds. David Lundblad TEL 46-8-4536271, Victor Falkteg TEL 46-8-4536262. Adv. contact Magnus Wallen.

658   USA
EXECUTIVE REPORT ON CUSTOMER RETENTION. Text in English. 1988. s-m. USD 239 (effective 2005). 8 p./no.; **Document type:** *Newsletter, Corporate.* **Description:** For senior managers concerned with corporate-level customer service policy. Covers how successful companies of all sizes are using innovative strategies to retain their best customers and attract new ones. Plus trends, statistics, timely news and information.
Formerly: Executive Report on Customer Satisfaction (1064-8623)
Published by: Alexander Communications Group, Inc., 28 W 25th St, 8th Fl, New York, NY 10010. TEL 212-228-0246, FAX 212-228-0376, info@customerservicegroup.com, info@alexcommgrp.com, http://www.customerservicegroup.com, http://www.alexcommgrp.com. Eds. Bob Weinstein, Susan Hash. Pub. Margaret Dewitt. R&P Mary Dalessandro.

658   USA   ISSN 1050-9003
EXECUTIVE SEARCH REVIEW. Text in English. 1989. 10/yr. USD 190 (effective 2002). adv. bk.rev. back issues avail.
Published by: Hunt - Scanlon Publishing Co., Inc., 20 Signal Rd, Stamford, CT 06902. TEL 203-629-3629, FAX 203-629-3701, http://www.hunt-scanlon.com/newsletters/search.htm. Eds. Christopher Hunt, Scott Scanlon. Circ: 10,000.

658   GBR   ISSN 0955-6230
EXECUTIVE SECRETARY. Text in English. 1989. q. GBP 75; GBP 85 in Europe; USD 150 in United States. bk.rev. **Document type:** *Trade.* **Description:** Provides a wide range of articles on important and often controversial topics within the executive secretary profession.

Published by: Salisbury House Publishing Ltd., 182 Hill Top Rd, Thornton, Bradford, BD13 3QL, United Kingdom. TEL 44-1274-832099, FAX 44-1274-831832, 100555.2456@compuserve.com. Ed. Jo Denby. Circ: 400.

658 GBR
EXECUTIVE STRATEGY. Text in English. q.
Address: 29 Tivoli Rd, Brighton, BN1 5BG, United Kingdom. TEL 0273-565505, FAX 0273-550072. Ed. Peter Bartram. Circ: 4,116.

658 USA ISSN 0733-5512
EXECUTIVE UPDATE. Text in English. 1983. m. membership. adv. back issues avail. **Document type:** *Magazine, Trade.* **Description:** Contains articles for association executives. Covers meetings, membership marketing, financial management, human resources.
Published by: Greater Washington Society of Association Executives, 1300 Pennsylvania Ave, N W, Washington, DC 20004. TEL 202-326-9502, FAX 202-326-0995, general@centeronline.org, http://www.gwsae.org/ExecutiveUpdate/.

658 GBR ISSN 1354-5558
EXECUTIVE WOMAN. Text in English. 1987. bi-m. GBP 15 domestic; GBP 35 foreign; GBP 2.50 newsstand/cover. adv. bk.rev. **Document type:** *Consumer.*
Published by: Saleworld Ltd., 2 Chantry Pl, Harrow, Mddx HA3 6NY, United Kingdom. TEL 44-181-420-1210, FAX 44-181-420-1691. Ed. Angela Giveon. Adv. contact Angie Greene. B&W page GBP 2,200, color page GBP 3,200. Circ: 70,000 (paid).

658 USA ISSN 1073-8355
HD58 CODEN: EXPMEG
EXPANSION MANAGEMENT; growth strategies for companies on the move. Text in English. 1986. m. free domestic (effective 2004). adv. back issues avail. **Document type:** *Magazine, Trade.* **Description:** Directed to executives responsible for site selection. Covers relocation topics, including real estate and industry trends, state profiles, family and employee issues.
Related titles: Online - full text ed.: (from EBSCO Publishing, Gale Group, ProQuest Information & Learning); ♦ Includes: Northeast Ohio Works.
—CCC.
Published by: Penton Media, Inc. (Subsidiary of: Pittway Company), 1350 Connecticut Ave NW, Washington, DC 20036. TEL 877-530-8801, 202-659-8500 ext 100, FAX 202-659-1554, information@penton.com, http://www.expansionmanagement.com, http://www.penton.com. Ed. Bill King. Pub. Gorton Wood. adv.: B&W page USD 5,855, color page USD 7,940. Circ: 45,000 (controlled).

658 USA ISSN 1046-3925
T396
EXPO (OVERLAND PARK); the magazine for exposition management. Text in English. 1989. 10/yr. USD 48 domestic; USD 59 in Canada & Mexico; USD 80 elsewhere (effective 2001); free to qualified personnel in N. America. adv. back issues avail. **Document type:** *Trade.* **Description:** For managers of trade shows and public expositions. Offers information on the administration and operation of trade shows, and current news on the industry.
Related titles: Online - full text ed.
Published by: (International Association for Exposition Management), Atwood Convention Publishing, 11600 College Blvd, Overland, Park, KS 66210. TEL 913-469-1185, FAX 913-469-0806, drorer@expoweb.com, http://www.expoweb.com. Ed. Cathy Chatfield Taylor. Pub. Donna Sanford. Adv. contact Kathy Hungerford. Circ: 7,500 (controlled).

658 332 NLD ISSN 1568-5802
F & A ACTUEEL. (Financieel en Administratief) Text in Dutch. 2001. m. EUR 230 (effective 2005). **Document type:** *Newsletter.*
Formed by the merger of (1999-2001): Financieel Management Actueel (1566-0044); (1992-2001): Fisc (0928-8457); (1991-2001): Fact (0926-4078); Which was formerly (until 1991): Feiten en Cijfers (0165-0238)
Published by: Wolters Kluwer N.V., Postbus 23, Deventer, 7400 GA, Netherlands. TEL 31-570-648904, FAX 31-570-637533, f&aactueel@kluwer.nl, info@kluwer.nl. Circ: 2,600.

F & W - FUEHREN UND WIRTSCHAFTEN IM KRANKENHAUS. see *HEALTH FACILITIES AND ADMINISTRATION*

658.5 628.5 DEU ISSN 1431-2271
HD28
F B - I E; Zeitschrift fuer Unternehmensentwicklung und Industrial Engineering. Text in German. 1975. bi-m. EUR 61.20 (effective 2003). adv. bk.rev. 48 p./no.; reprint service avail. from SCH. **Document type:** *Journal, Academic/Scholarly.* **Description:** Covers all aspects of industrial organization: market surveys, CA-systems, announcements of conferences and trade fairs.
Formerly (until 1995): Fortschrittliche Betriebsfuehrung und Industrial Engineering (0340-8302); Which was formed by the merger of (1959-1975): Fortschrittliche Betriebsfuehrung (0015-8216); (1966-1975): Industrial Engineering (0340-8272); Which was formerly (until 1971): Zeitschrift fuer Fuehrungskraefte im Arbeitsstudium und Industrial Engineering (0514-6410)
Indexed: ABIn, ADPA, CISA, DokArb, KES, RASB, SCIMP.
—IE. **CCC.**
Published by: R E F A - Verband fuer Arbeitsgestaltung Betriebsorganisation und Unternehmensentwicklung e.V., Wittichstr 2, Darmstadt, 64295, Germany. TEL 49-6151-8801181, FAX 49-6151-8801260, fbie@refa.de, http://www.refa.de. Ed. Manfred Stroh. Adv. contact Michael Brauckmann TEL 49-6157-991636. page EUR 1,265; trim 175 x 260. Circ: 4,000.

658 USA ISSN 1087-7827
HG4001 CODEN: FINMEE
➤ **F M.** (Financial Management) Text in English. 1972. q. USD 160 domestic; USD 175 renewals in Canada; USD 181 in Mexico; USD 201.50 elsewhere (effective 2004). adv. charts; illus. index. reprint service avail. from PQC,PSC. **Document type:** *Journal, Academic/Scholarly.* **Description:** Presents research papers and analysis on the economic aspects of operating a corporation, focusing on markets, stocks, financial leverage, pricing, trading, purchase-lease options, and cash flow, with news briefs on the latest developments in the field.
Formerly: Financial Management (0046-3892)
Related titles: Microform ed.: (from PQC); Online - full text ed.: (from EBSCO Publishing, Gale Group, H.W. Wilson, O C L C Online Computer Library Center, Inc., ProQuest Information & Learning).
Indexed: ABIn, ADPA, ASCA, ATI, BPI, BPIA, BusI, CPM, CurCont, ESPM, Emerald, IBSS, JEL, M&MA, MEA&I, ORMS, PAIS, PROMT, QC&AS, RiskAb, SCIMP, SSCI, T&II.
—BLDSC (3926.961000), CASDDS, IDS, IE, ingenta. **CCC.**
Published by: Financial Management Association International, University of South Florida, College of Business Administration, Ste 3331, Tampa, FL 33620-5500. TEL 813-974-2084, FAX 813-974-3318, fma@coba.usf.edu, http://www.fma.org. Ed. Lemma Senbet. Circ: 12,000.

658.4 USA
F M A BULLETIN✶. Text in English. 1948. 9/yr. USD 45. tr.lit.
Formerly: S F M A Bulletin (0049-2434)
Media: Duplicated (not offset).
Published by: Fulfillment Management Association, 60 E 42nd St, Ste 1146, New York, NY 10165. TEL 212-725-6140. Ed. Tracy Purcell. Circ: 600.

F M - DAS LOGISTIK-MAGAZIN. see *TRANSPORTATION*

F M I QUARTERLY. (Fails Management Institute) see *BUILDING AND CONSTRUCTION*

F M R A NEWS. see *AGRICULTURE—Agricultural Economics*

658 BRA ISSN 1517-8900
➤ **FACES.** Text in Portuguese. 2000. 2/yr. USD 20; USD 10 newsstand/cover (effective 2004). adv. **Document type:** *Journal, Academic/Scholarly.* **Description:** Deals with a broad spectrum of knowledge domains, perspectives and questions in management.
Published by: F U M E C - F A C E, Rua Cobre 200, Belo Horizonte, MG 30310-190, Brazil. TEL 55-31-32283060, FAX 55-31-32283060, faces@fumec.br, http://www.face.fumec.com.br/revista_faces/revista_face.shtm. Ed., R&P Cid Goncalves Filho. adv.: B&W page USD 100. Circ: 3,000 (paid and controlled).

➤ **FACILITIES.** see *BUILDING AND CONSTRUCTION*

658 USA ISSN 1523-6315
FACILITIES AND DESTINATIONS; the bible for convention, exposition and event management. Text in English. 1991. m. USD 36 domestic; USD 66 in Canada; USD 96 elsewhere. adv. **Document type:** *Journal, Trade.* **Description:** On convention, exposition, and event management from the facilities' viewpoints. Features include state and regional spotlights, special sections on entertainment, convention facility markets, and products and services.
Former titles (until 1999): Facilities (1084-3922); (until 1995): Agent and Manager (1065-5921)
—Linda Hall.
Published by: Bedrock Communications, Inc., 650 First Ave, 7th Fl, New York, NY 10016-3240. TEL 212-532-4150, FAX 212-213-6382, ber3@inch.com. Ed., R&P Michael Caffin. Adv. contact Mark Gold. B&W page USD 3,495, color page USD 4,470; trim 10.88 x 13.5. Circ: 30,000 (controlled).

658 USA ISSN 1524-0258
FACILITIES AND EVENT MANAGEMENT. Text in English. bi-m.
Published by: Bedrock Communications, Inc., 650 First Ave, 7th Fl, New York, NY 10016-3240. TEL 212-532-4150, FAX 212-213-6382.

FACILITIES MANAGER. see *EDUCATION—School Organization And Administration*

658.2 721 USA ISSN 1059-3667
TS177
FACILITY MANAGEMENT JOURNAL. Text in English. 1988. bi-m. free to members. adv. back issues avail. **Document type:** *Journal, Trade.* **Description:** Covers facility management and real estate issues, the environment, the bottom line, security, technology, innovation.
—CCC.
Published by: International Facility Management Association, 1 E Greenway Plaza, Ste 1100, Houston, TX 77046-0194. TEL 713-623-4362, FAX 713-623-6124, http://www.ifma.org/fmj/index.cfm?actionbig=16. Ed., Pub. Deborah Quinn Hensel. adv.: page USD 1,875. Circ: 15,500.

358 NLD ISSN 0924-8641
FACILITY MANAGEMENT MAGAZINE. Text in Dutch. 1988. 10/yr. adv. bk.rev. charts; illus.; stat.; tr.lit. **Document type:** *Trade.* **Description:** Features new product announcements, spatial organizing ideas, calendars of events and classes, as well as insights for upper management. Includes computer applications.
Formerly (until 1989): Gebouwmanagement (0169-2305)
Related titles: ♦ Supplement(s): Jaarbijlage Facility Management. ISSN 1386-8225.
—IE, Infotrieve.
Published by: (Nederlandse Facility Management Associatie), Arko Uitgeverij BV, Postbus 616, Nieuwegein, 3430 AP, Netherlands. TEL 31-30-605-1090, gerlings@arko.nl, http://www.arko.nl. Ed. F W van Waardhuizen. Pub. Marc Gerlings. Circ: 3,000.

658 USA ISSN 0888-0085
FACILITY MANAGER. Text in English. 1985. bi-m. USD 55 domestic to non-members; USD 110 foreign to non-members (effective 2005). adv. charts; illus. **Document type:** *Magazine, Trade.*
Formerly (until 1985): Auditorium News
Published by: International Association of Assembly Managers, 635 Fritz Dr, Coppell, TX 75019-4442. TEL 972-906-7441, FAX 972-906-7418, julie.herrick@iaam.org, http://www.iaam.org/Facility_manager/Pages/Facility_Issues.htm. Ed. R V Baugus. Circ: 3,600 (paid).

658.2 721 DEU ISSN 0947-0026
DER FACILITY MANAGER; Gebaeude und Anlagen besser planen, bauen, bewirtschaften. Text in German. 1994. 10/yr. EUR 74; EUR 9.60 newsstand/cover (effective 2004). adv. bk.rev.; software rev. bibl.; illus. back issues avail. **Document type:** *Magazine, Trade.* **Description:** Reports on all areas of facility management.
Published by: Forum Verlag Herkert GmbH, Mandichostr 18, Merching, 86504, Germany. TEL 49-8233-3810, FAX 49-8233-381212, service@forum-verlag.com, http://www.facility-manager.de, http://www.forum-verlag.com. Ed., R&P Martin Graeber. Adv. contact Helmut Junginger. B&W page EUR 3,700, color page EUR 5,200; trim 210 x 297. Circ: 9,906 (paid).

658 USA ISSN 1081-9517
FACILITY MANAGER'S ALERT. Abbreviated title: F M A. Text in English. 1995. s-m. USD 253. charts. **Document type:** *Newsletter.* **Description:** Keeps facility managers current on safety, environmental, and building code regulations.
Published by: Progressive Business Publications, 370 Technology Dr, Malvern, PA 19355-1315. TEL 610-695-8600, 800-220-5000, FAX 610-647-8089, editor@pbp.com, http://www.pbp.com. Ed. Bill Hatton. R&P Curt Brown. Circ: 10,250 (paid).

FAIRCHILD'S EXECUTIVE TECHNOLOGY. see *BUSINESS AND ECONOMICS—Computer Applications*

FARMING BUSINESS. see *AGRICULTURE—Dairying And Dairy Products*

658 332.6 USA ISSN 1085-9241
HF5001 CODEN: FACOFC
FAST COMPANY. Text in English. 1995. m. USD 12 domestic; USD 29 in Canada (effective 2005). adv. illus. back issues avail.; reprints avail. **Document type:** *Magazine, Consumer.* **Description:** Presents path-breaking businesses to find out what makes them tick, who they are, how they work, what they know, and what they can teach.
Related titles: ♦ Online - full content ed.: Fastcompany.com; Online - full text ed.: (from bigchalk, EBSCO Publishing, Florida Center for Library Automation, Gale Group, H.W. Wilson, LexisNexis, O C L C Online Computer Library Center, Inc., ProQuest Information & Learning).
Indexed: ABIn, BPI, MicrocompInd.
—BLDSC (3897.164000), IE, ingenta.
Published by: Fast Company, Inc. (Subsidiary of: Gruner + Jahr U.S.A. Publishing), 375 Lexington Ave, New York, NY 10017. TEL 212-499-2000, 800-542-6029, FAX 212-389-5497, subscriptions@fastcompany.com, http://www.fastcompany.com/. Ed. John Byrne. R&P Charles McEnrerey. Adv. contact Linda Sepp. B&W page USD 41,150, color page USD 61,470. Circ: 500,000. **Subscr. to:** PO Box 52760, Boulder, CO 80321-2760.

658 332.6 USA
FASTCOMPANY.COM. Text in English. w. adv. **Document type:** *Trade.*

B

Media: Online - full content. **Related titles:** Online - full text ed.: (from bigchalk, EBSCO Publishing, Florida Center for Library Automation, Gale Group, H.W. Wilson, LexisNexis, O C L C Online Computer Library Center, Inc., ProQuest Information & Learning); ♦ Print ed.: Fast Company. ISSN 1085-9241.
Published by: Fast Company, Inc. (Subsidiary of: Gruner + Jahr U.S.A. Publishing), 375 Lexington Ave., BSMT, New York, NY 10017-5644. TEL 617-973-0300, FAX 617-973-0373, content@fastcompany.com, subscriptions@fastcompany.com, http://www.fastcompany.com/homepage.

658 USA
FEDERAL CONTRACT MANAGEMENT: A MANUAL FOR THE CONTRACT PROFESSIONAL. Text in English. 1982. 3 base vols. plus irreg. updates. looseleaf. USD 706 base vol(s). (effective 2002). **Description:** Covers all major aspects of the federal government contracting (procurement) process, from basic concepts to sophisticated strategies. Written by experienced practitioners, it supplies abundant practical advice and tips for successful bidding for contracting work with governmental agencies and guidance relative to managing contract performance.
Published by: Matthew Bender & Co., Inc. (Subsidiary of: LexisNexis North America), 1275 Broadway, Albany, NY 12204. international@bender.com, http://bender.lexisnexis.com. Ed. Norman Steiger.

FEDERAL GRANTS MANAGEMENT HANDBOOK. see *BUSINESS AND ECONOMICS*

658 USA
JK404
FEDERAL MANAGER. Text in English. 1983. q. USD 24 (effective 1998). adv. **Document type:** *Trade.*
Formerly (until 1997): Federal Managers Quarterly (0893-8415)
Indexed: PersLit.
Published by: Federal Managers' Association, 1641 Prince St, Alexandria, VA 22314-2818. TEL 703-683-8700, FAX 703-683-8707, fma@ix.netcom.com, http://www.fpmi.com. Ed. Michael B Styles. R&P Frances Webb. Adv. contact Katherine Dibitetto. Circ: 25,000.

FEEDBACK FROM FUJITSU. see *COMPUTERS*

658 USA
FIERCE C I O. Text in English. d. free. adv. **Document type:** *Newsletter, Trade.* **Description:** Contains information on news, trends, insights and best practices in executive IT management.
Media: E-mail.
Published by: FierceMarkets, Inc., 1319 F St, NW, Ste 604, Washington, DC 20004. TEL 202-628-8778, info@fiercemarkets.com, http://www.fiercecio.com, http://www.fiercemarkets.com. Ed. Judy Mottl. Adv. contact Ryan Willumson.

658.812 USA
FIERCEENTERPRISE; the crm & enterprise it daily monitor. Text in English. d. free. adv. **Document type:** *Newsletter, Trade.* **Description:** Covers the latest enterprise software developments with a special emphasis on CRM (Customer Relationship Management).
Media: E-mail.
Published by: FierceMarkets, Inc., 1319 F St, NW, Ste 604, Washington, DC 20004. TEL 202-628-8778, info@fiercemarkets.com, http://www.fierceenterprise.com, http://www.fiercemarkets.com. Ed. Evan Koblentz. Adv. contact Ryan Willumson.

FINANCE & CONTROL. see *BUSINESS AND ECONOMICS—Banking And Finance*

658 FRA ISSN 1287-1141
FINANCE CONTROLE STRATEGIE. Variant title: Revue Finance Controle Strategie. Text in French. 1998. q. EUR 112 to individuals; EUR 180 to institutions (effective 2004).
Related titles: Online - full text ed.: (from ProQuest Information & Learning).
Indexed: ABIn, JEL.
Published by: Editions Economica, 49 rue Hericart, Paris, 75015, France. TEL 33-1-45781292, FAX 33-1-45750567, http://gerard.charreaux.free.fr/fcs/, http://www.economica.fr. Ed. Gerard Charreaux.

658 GBR ISSN 1366-9427
FINANCE MIDLANDS; the business magazine for the midlands. Text in English. 1993. bi-m. GBP 45 (effective 2000). adv. **Document type:** *Magazine, Consumer.* **Description:** Provides readers with a comprehensive source of information, opinion and insight on the business issues facing the midland region's most influential companies.
Published by: Hillgate Communications Ltd., Shand House, 14-20 Shand St, London, SE1 2ES, United Kingdom. TEL 44-207-645-3600, FAX 44-207-407-7771, http://www.hillgate.com. Ed. Arabella McIntyre-Brown. Pub. Sean Allison. Adv. contact Claire Rodgers. page GBP 2,450; trim 210 x 297.

658 GBR ISSN 1366-9419
FINANCE NORTH; the business magazine for the north. Text in English. 1993. bi-m. GBP 45 (effective 2000). adv. **Document type:** *Magazine, Trade.* **Description:** Focuses on corporate finance, professional services, investment, personnel management as well as the individuals who make news happen.
Published by: Hillgate Communications Ltd., Shand House, 14-20 Shand St, London, SE1 2ES, United Kingdom. TEL 44-207-645-3600, FAX 44-207-407-7771, http://www.hillgate.com. Ed. Arabella McIntyre-Brown. Pub. Sean Allison. Adv. contact Claire Rodgers. page GBP 2,450; trim 210 x 297.

658 USA
FINANCIAL ANALYSIS, PLANNING & REPORTING YEARBOOK. Text in English. a. USD 224.95 print & online eds. (effective 2003). **Description:** Covers the latest analytical techniques; performance measurement; and FASB, IRS, and SEC reporting requirements. Also describes approaches for assessing performance, measuring value, and analyzing new products, capital budgets, and financial statements.
Related titles: Online - full text ed.: USD 219 (effective 2003); ♦ Cumulative ed. of: I O M A's Report on Financial Analysis, Planning & Reporting. ISSN 1532-1673.
Published by: Institute of Management & Administration, Inc., 3 Park Ave, New York, NY 10016-5902. TEL 212-244-0360, FAX 212-564-0465, subserve@ioma.com, http://www.ioma.com. Ed. Andy Dzamba.

658 USA ISSN 0895-4186
HF5001 CODEN: FIEXAW
FINANCIAL EXECUTIVE; for today's global business leader. Text in English. 1932. 10/yr. USD 59 domestic; USD 75 foreign (effective 2005). adv. bk.rev. charts; illus. Index. 72 p./no. 3 cols./p.; back issues avail.; reprint service avail. from PQC. **Document type:** *Magazine, Trade.* **Description:** Examines professional and technical developments that affect financial executives' day-to-day responsibilities, as well as long-range issues that reflect financial executives' increasing involvement in the general management of their companies.
Former titles (until 1987): F E: The Magazine for Financial Executives (0883-7481); (until Jan. 1985): Financial Executive (0015-1998); Controller
Related titles: Microfilm ed.: (from PQC); Online - full text ed.: (from EBSCO Publishing, Florida Center for Library Automation, Gale Group, H.W. Wilson, Northern Light Technology, Inc., O C L C Online Computer Library Center, Inc., ProQuest Information & Learning, The Dialog Corporation).
Indexed: ABIn, ADPA, ASEANManA, ATI, AgeL, BPI, BPIA, CPM, Emerald, IMI, Inspec, KES, M&MA, ManagCont, ORMS, PAIS, PROMT, SCIMP, T&II.
—BLDSC (3926.954000), AskIEEE, IE, Infotrieve, ingenta. **CCC.**
Published by: Financial Executives International, 200 Campus Dr, Ste 200, Florham Park, NJ 07932-0674. TEL 973-765-1000, 800-336-0773, FAX 973-765-1018, eheffes@fei.org, http://www.fei.org/mag. Ed., Pub., R&P Jeffrey Marshall TEL 973-765-1024. Adv. contact Brenda Newkirk. B&W page USD 5,438, color page USD 7,142; trim 8.12 x 10.87. Circ: 17,000 (paid).

FINANCIAL INFORMATION SYSTEMS MANUAL. see *BUSINESS AND ECONOMICS—Accounting*

FINANCIAL MANAGEMENT STRATEGIES FOR MEDICAL OFFICES. see *HEALTH FACILITIES AND ADMINISTRATION*

658 330.9 USA
FINANCIAL MANAGEMENT SURVEY. Text in English. a. USD 300.
Published by: A C I L: The American Council of Independent Laboratories, 1629 K St, N W, Washington, DC 20006. TEL 202-887-5872, FAX 202-887-0021.

FINANCIAL MONITOR. see *BUSINESS AND ECONOMICS—Investments*

FINANCIAL PARTICIPATION - EUROPE. see *BUSINESS AND ECONOMICS—Personnel Management*

658 332 USA ISSN 0746-7915
HG1
FINANCIAL PLANNING. Text in English. 1972. m. USD 79 domestic; USD 89 foreign (effective 2005). adv. bk.rev. back issues avail.; reprints avail. **Document type:** *Magazine, Trade.*
Formerly (until 1983): The Financial Planner (0363-7441)
Related titles: Online - full text ed.: (from bigchalk, EBSCO Publishing, Gale Group, LexisNexis, O C L C Online Computer Library Center, Inc., ProQuest Information & Learning); Supplement(s): C P A Wealth Provider. 2001. free with subscr. to any financial planning publication by Source Media, Inc.
Indexed: ABIn, ATI, BLI, PAIS.
—**CCC.**
Published by: Source Media, Inc., One State St Plaza, 27th Fl, New York, NY 10004. TEL 212-803-6077, 800-221-1809, FAX 212-747-1154, custserv@sourcemedia.com, http://www.financial-planning.com, http://www.sourcemedia.com. Ed. Eric Garland. adv.: B&W page USD 10,110, color page USD 11,945. Circ: 100,000 (paid and controlled).

658 CAN ISSN 0071-5042
FINANCIAL POST DIRECTORY OF DIRECTORS. Text in English. 1931. a. CND 159.95. adv. **Document type:** *Directory.*
Formerly (until 1944): Directory of Canadian Directors (0317-3658)
Related titles: Online - full text ed.: (from F P Infomart Ltd.).
—BLDSC (3593.400000), CISTI. **CCC.**
Published by: Financial Post Datagroup, 300-1450 Don Mills Rd, Don Mills, ON M3B 3R5, Canada. TEL 416-350-6116, FAX 416-350-6501, fpdg@fpdata.finpost.com. Ed. Jean Graham. Circ: 3,000.

658 USA ISSN 1058-2878
HG65
FINANCIAL YELLOW BOOK; who's who at the leading U.S. financial institutions. Text in English. 1988. s-a. USD 295; USD 280 renewals (effective 2005). illus. Index. **Document type:** *Directory, Trade.* **Description:** Compiles contact information for more than 31,000 executives at public and private financial institutions and over 5,800 board members and their outside affiliations. Also lists major subsidiaries and divisions, business descriptions, information on assets, and administrative staff. Includes photographs, subject, organization, and name indexes.
Former titles (until 1992): Financial 1000 Yellow Book (1049-7935); (until 1990): Financial 1000 (0894-7627)
Related titles: CD-ROM ed.; Online - full text ed.
—**CCC.**
Published by: Leadership Directories, Inc, 104 Fifth Ave, 2nd Fl, New York, NY 10011. TEL 212-627-4140, FAX 212-645-0931, info@leadershipdirectories.com, http://www.leadershipdirectories.com/fin.htm. Ed. Don Doyle.

658 ITA ISSN 1593-2230
➤ **FINANZA MARKETING E PRODUZIONE;** rivista di economia d'impresa. (Special biennial English issue avail.) Text in Italian. 1983. q. EUR 22 per issue (effective 2005). bk.rev. **Document type:** *Academic/Scholarly.* **Description:** Publishes articles on management and economics of industrial, commercial and financial companies.
Published by: (Universita Commerciale Luigi Bocconi), E G E A SpA, Viale Isonzo 25, Milan, MI 20135, Italy. TEL 39-02-58365751, FAX 39-02-58365753, egea.edizioni@unibocconi.it, http://www.egeaonline.com. Ed. Giovanna Dossena. Adv. contact Luca Bubbi. Circ: 2,000 (controlled).

➤ **FITNESS MANAGEMENT.** see *PHYSICAL FITNESS AND HYGIENE*

➤ **FITNESS MANAGEMENT INTERNATIONAL.** see *PHYSICAL FITNESS AND HYGIENE*

658 USA
FIVE-YEAR INFORMATION RESOURCES MANAGEMENT PROGRAM. Text in English. a. **Document type:** *Government.* **Description:** Aims to improve management of information resources by strengthening and integrating the information resources management program planning and budgeting activities.
Related titles: Online - full text ed.
Published by: U.S. Department of Veterans Affairs, 810 Vermont Ave, N W 008C2, Washington, DC 20420. TEL 202-233-3557.

658 388 GBR ISSN 1358-8591
FLEET DEALER. Text in English. 1995. 10/yr. GBP 125 (effective 2002). back issues avail. **Document type:** *Magazine, Trade.* **Description:** Aimed specifically at fleet dealers who are supplying cars to fleets and business users. Designed to keep the fleet salesman up-to-date with issues and developments.
Published by: Emap Automotive Ltd., Sewells Information and Research, Wentworth House, Wentworth St, Peterborough, Northants PE1 1DS, United Kingdom. TEL 44-1733-468255, FAX 44-1733-468349, http://www.sewells.co.uk, http://www.emap.com.

FLEET MANAGEMENT. see *TRANSPORTATION—Automobiles*

658 GBR ISSN 1360-9505
FLEXIBLE WORKING. Text in English. 1996. 6/yr. GBP 210; GBP 221 foreign (effective 2000). bk.rev. **Document type:** *Trade.* **Description:** Presents articles and case studies in strategic planning, human resource management, facilities management, finance, and information technology.
Related titles: Online - full text ed.: (from Gale Group).
Indexed: Emerald.
Published by: Eclipse Group Ltd. (Subsidiary of: LexisNexis UK (Scottish Office)), 18-20 Highbury Place, London, N5 1QP, United Kingdom. TEL 44-20-7354-5858, FAX 44-20-7226-8618, publications@irseclipse.co.uk. Ed. Louis Wustemann. Pub. Andrew Brode.

FLORIDA COMMUNITY ASSOCIATION JOURNAL; journal for community association management. see *REAL ESTATE*

658 DEU
THE FOCUS. Text in English. s-a. **Document type:** *Magazine, Trade.* **Description:** Examines important developments in the field of management policy, corporate strategy and executive search.
Published by: Egon Zehnder International, Rheinallee 97, Duesseldorf, 40545, Germany. TEL 49-211-5502850, FAX 49-211-55028550, corporatecommunications@egonzehnder.com, http://www.ezifocus.com/focus/, http://www.egonzehnder.com. Ed. Ulrike Mertens.

658 GBR ISSN 1352-9501
FOCUS ON CHANGE MANAGEMENT. Text in English. 1994. 10/yr. GBP 295, USD 450 (effective 2000). adv. back issues avail. **Document type:** *Trade.*
—BLDSC (3964.203930). **CCC.**
Published by: Informa Law (Subsidiary of: Informa Publishing), Informa House, 30-32 Mortimer St, London, W1W 7RE, United Kingdom. TEL 44-207-5531000, FAX 44-207-5531593.

FOCUS ON IMAGING. see *PHOTOGRAPHY*

658 CAN ISSN 1494-684X
FOCUS ON STRATEGY. Text in English. 1996. q. free to members (effective 2002). **Description:** Contains executive briefings designed to serve those responsible for managing their organizations through times of change.
Published by: Strategic Leadership Forum, The Toronto Society for Strategic Management, 26 Rose Park Dr, Toronto, ON M4T 1R1, Canada. TEL 416-481-7228, FAX 416-489-3304, mstreet@inforamp.net, http://www.slf-canada.org.

FOOD PRODUCTION - MANAGEMENT; monthly publication of the canning, glass-packing, aseptic, and frozen food industry. see *FOOD AND FOOD INDUSTRIES*

FOOD SHOP. see *FOOD AND FOOD INDUSTRIES*

658 USA ISSN 0015-6914
CODEN: FORBA5
FORBES. Text in English. 1917. bi-w. USD 59.95 domestic; CND 89.95 in Canada; USD 137.95 elsewhere; USD 4.99 newsstand/cover (effective 2005). adv. charts; illus.; mkt. s-a. index. reprints avail. **Document type:** *Magazine, Consumer.* **Description:** Covers US and international business issues for executives, managers, and investors in US corporations.
Related titles: Microfiche ed.: (from PQC); Microform ed.: (from PQC); Online - full text ed.: Forbes.com (from EBSCO Publishing, Florida Center for Library Automation, Gale Group, O C L C Online Computer Library Center, Inc., ProQuest Information & Learning, The Dialog Corporation); ♦ Supplement(s): Forbes F Y I. ISSN 1066-9205.
Indexed: ABIPC, ABIn, AIA, ATI, Acal, AgeL, Agr, B&I, BLI, BPI, BPIA, BRI, BusI, CADCAM, CIN, ChemAb, ChemTitl, CompB, CompD, CurCont, DPD, EIA, Emerald, EnerInd, EnvAb, HlthInd, IPARL, InfoSAb, KES, LRI, MASUSE, MEA&I, MEDLINE, MagInd, ManagCont, MicrocompInd, ORMS, PRA, PROMT, PSI, QC&AS, RASB, RGAb, RGPR, RI-1, RI-2, RehabLit, RoboAb, SRI, SSCI, T&II, TOM, TelAb, Telegen, WBA, WMB.
—BLDSC (3985.525000), CASDDS, IDS, IE, Infotrieve, ingenta. **CCC.**
Published by: Forbes, Inc., 60 Fifth Ave, New York, NY 10011. TEL 212-620-2200, 800-888-9896, FAX 212-620-1873, subscriber@forbes.com, http://www.forbes.com, http://www.forbes.com/forbes. Ed. William Baldwin. Pub. Jeffrey M. Cunningham. Adv. contact William J. Flatley. B&W page USD 46,590, color page USD 70,820; trim 10.5 x 8. Circ: 819,884. **Subscr. to:** PO Box 10048, Des Moines, IA 50340-0048.

FORMATION EMPLOI. see *BUSINESS AND ECONOMICS—Personnel Management*

658 USA ISSN 0015-7805
FORMS OF BUSINESS AGREEMENTS. Text in English. q. looseleaf. USD 264. adv. bk.rev.
Published by: Resource Institution Of America Group, 90 Fifth Ave, New York, NY 10011-7629. TEL 800-562-0245, FAX 800-782-8242.

650 332.024 USA ISSN 0015-8259
HF5001 CODEN: FORTAP
FORTUNE. Text in English. 1930. bi-w. USD 19.99; USD 4.99 newsstand/cover (effective 2005). adv. bk.rev.; music rev.; software rev. mkt.; stat.; illus. Index. back issues avail.; reprints avail. **Document type:** *Magazine, Consumer.* **Description:** Publishes articles and commentary on business and financial issues and trends; covers most areas of investing and personal finances.
Related titles: CD-ROM ed.; Microform ed.: (from PQC); Online - full text ed.: Fortune.com (from EBSCO Publishing, Florida Center for Library Automation, Gale Group, H.W. Wilson, LexisNexis, O C L C Online Computer Library Center, Inc., ProQuest Information & Learning).
Indexed: ABIPC, ABIn, ABS&EES, AIA, AIAP, ATI, Acal, AgeL, Agr, BLI, BMT, BPI, BPIA, BRI, BusI, CADCAM, CBRI, CPM, CPerI, CompB, CompIU, CurCont, EIA, ELLIS, EnvAb, ExcerpMed, F&EA, HlthInd, ILD, IMI, IndBusRep, InfoSAb, Inpharma, Inspec, KES, LRI, M&MA, MASUSE, MEDLINE, MagInd, ManagCont, MicrocompInd, ORMS, PAIS, PCI, PCR2, PE&ON, PMR, PROMT, QC&AS, RAPRA, RASB, RGAb, RGPR, RI-1, RI-2, RPFIA, Reac, ResCtrInd, RoboAb, SRI, SSCI, T&II, TOM, TTI, TelAb, Telegen, WBA, WMB, WorkRelAb.
—CASDDS, CISTI, IDS, IE, Infotrieve, Linda Hall.
Published by: Time Inc., Business Information Group (Subsidiary of: Time Warner, Inc.), 1271 Ave of the Americas, New York, NY 10020. TEL 212-522-1212, 800-621-8000, FAX 212-522-0970, letters@fortune.com, http://www.fortune.com/fortune/. Ed. John Huey. Pub. Michael Federle. R&P Jo Mattern TEL 212-522-2582. adv.: B&W page USD 47,300, color page USD 71,700; trim 8 x 10.875. Circ: 818,791 (paid). **Subscr.to:** Fortune, PO Box 60001, Tampa, FL 33660-0001. **Dist. in UK by:** Comag, Tavistock Works, Tavistock Rd, W Drayton, Middx UB7 7QX, United Kingdom.

FORTUNE SMALL BUSINESS. see *BUSINESS AND ECONOMICS—Small Business*

658 NLD ISSN 1384-2102
FORUM (HAGUE); voor andernemend Nederland. Text in Dutch. 1968. s-w. free. adv. bk.rev. illus. index. **Document type:** *Magazine.*
Former titles (until 1995): Onderneming (0165-6643); Nederlandse Onderneming (0028-2294)
Related titles: Online - full text ed.: (from LexisNexis).
Indexed: CISA, KES.
—IE, Infotrieve, KNAW.
Published by: Confederation of Dutch Employers and Industry V N O - N C W, Bezuidenhoutseweg 12, PO Box 93002, The Hague, 2509 AA, Netherlands. TEL 31-70-3490166, FAX 31-70-3490181, forum@vno-ncw.nl, http://www.vno-ncw.nl/publicaties/forum, http://www.vno-ncw.nl. Ed. R G Smit. Circ: 30,000.

FRANCHISING ADVISER. see *LAW*

658.1 DEU ISSN 0532-6028
FRANKFURTER WIRTSCHAFTS- UND SOZIALWISSENSCHAFTLICHE STUDIEN. Text in German. 1957. irreg., latest vol.28, 1975. price varies. **Document type:** *Monographic series, Academic/Scholarly.*
Published by: (Johann Wolfgang Goethe Universitaet Frankfurt, Fachbereich Wirtschaftswissenschaft), Duncker und Humblot GmbH, Carl-Heinrich-Becker-Weg 9, Berlin, 12165, Germany. TEL 49-30-7900060, FAX 49-30-79000631, info@duncker-humblot.de, http://www.duncker-humblot.de.

361.73 USA ISSN 1547-2078
HV41.2
▼ **FUNDRAISING SUCCESS.** Text in English. 2003 (Nov./Dec.). bi-m. USD 10 per issue (effective 2003).
Published by: North American Publishing Co., 1500 Spring Garden St., Ste 1200, Philadelphia, PA 19130-4094. TEL 215-238-5300, FAX 215-238-5457, http://www.fundraisingsuccessmag.com, http://www.napco.com.

658 USA ISSN 1088-9590
FUNNY BUSINESS. Text in English. 1995. m. **Document type:** *Newsletter, Trade.* **Description:** Provides humor and insight for professional business communications.
—**CCC.**
Published by: Briefings Publishing Group (Subsidiary of: Douglas Publications, Inc.), 1101 King St, Ste 110, Alexandria, VA 22314. TEL 703-518-2343, 800-722-9221, FAX 703-684-2136, customerservice@briefings.com, http://www.briefings.com.

G-TWO COMPLIANCE REPORT. see *LAW*

658 USA ISSN 1544-9319
KF1371.A3
▼ **G P MANAGEMENT REPORT.** (General Partners) Text in English. 2003. 6/yr. USD 995 domestic; USD 1,070 foreign; USD 245 per issue (effective 2003).
Published by: Alternative Investor, 170 Linden St, 2nd Fl, Wellesley, MA 02482. TEL 781-304-1400, FAX 781-304-1440, info@AlternativeInvestor.Info, http://www.assetnews.com/products/news/GPmanagementReport.htm.

658 DEU ISSN 0940-8762
G V MANAGER; Fachmagazin der Fuehrungskraefte in Grossgastronomie und Gemeinschaftsverpflegung. (Gross Verbraucher) Text in German. 1950. 10/yr. EUR 75.70 domestic; EUR 95 foreign (effective 2005). adv. bk.rev. tr.lit. back issues avail. **Document type:** *Magazine, Trade.*
Related titles: Supplement(s): GVonline.
Published by: B & L MedienGesellschaft mbH & Co. KG, Anton-Ditt-Bogen 23, Munich, 80939, Germany. TEL 49-89-370600, FAX 49-89-37060111, muc@blmedien.de, http://www.gvmanager.de, http://www.blmedien.de. Ed. Annemarie Heinrichsdobler. Adv. contact Edda Evertz. B&W page EUR 4,201, color page EUR 5,858; trim 185 x 260. Circ: 15,800.

658 USA
HD28
GALLUP MANAGEMENT JOURNAL. Text in English. m. USD 95 (effective 2003). **Document type:** *Journal, Trade.*
Media: Online - full content. **Related titles:** Online - full text ed.: (from EBSCO Publishing); Print ed.: ISSN 1544-7278.
Published by: Gallup Organization, Editorial and Executive Offices, 1251 Ave of the Americas, Ste 2350, New York, NY 10020. TEL 888-274-5447, http://gmj.gallup.com/, http://www.gallup.com.

658 DEU
GAMES & BUSINESS; Fachzeitschrift fuer das moderne Muenzspiel. Text in German. 1952. m. adv. bk.rev. **Document type:** *Magazine, Trade.*
Formerly: Muenzautomat (0721-6823)
Published by: Universitaet-Druckerei und Verlag H. Schmidt GmbH, Robert-Koch-Str 8, Mainz, 55129, Germany. TEL 49-6131-506010, FAX 49-6131-506070. Ed. Stefan Dreizehnter. Pub. Manfred Schloesser. Adv. contact Alexandra Anstatt TEL 49-6131-9583651. Circ: 5,000.

GAS INDUSTRIES. see *PETROLEUM AND GAS*

658 FRA ISSN 0769-3508
HC271
GAZETTE DES COMMUNES, DES DEPARTEMENTS, DES REGIONS. Text in French. 1980. w. adv.
Formerly (until 1985): Gazette des Communes (0242-570X); Which was formed by the merger of (1934-1980): Gazette des Communes et du Personnel Communal (0242-5718); (1949-1980): L'Action Municipale (0001-7450)
Published by: Groupe Moniteur, 17 rue d'Uzes, Paris, 75002, France. TEL 33-1-40133030, FAX 33-1-40135106, TELEX 680 876F, gazette@gazettedescommunes.presse.fr, http://www.lagazettedescommunes.com/. Ed. Jean Dumonteil. Pub. Marc N Vigier. Circ: 27,092 (controlled).

658 690 NLD ISSN 0927-0140
GEBOUWBEHEER. Text in Dutch. 1990. 8/yr. EUR 132.50 (effective 2005). adv. illus. **Document type:** *Trade.* **Description:** Covers building management and maintenance, for public- and private sector managers.
—IE, Infotrieve.
Published by: Reed Business Information bv (Subsidiary of: Reed Business), Hanzestraat 1, Doetinchem, 7006 RH, Netherlands. TEL 31-314-349911, FAX 31-314-343839, info@reedbusiness.nl, http://www.productonline.reedbusiness.nl/product.asp?catalog%5Fname=RBI&category%5Fname=&product%5Fid=865%28Octopus%29, http://www.reedbusiness.nl. Ed. Gerrit Das TEL 31-314-349908. Adv. contact Cor van Nek. B&W page EUR 2,041, color page EUR 3,209; trim 285 x 215. Circ: 5,030.

GEDRAG & ORGANISATIE. see *HEALTH FACILITIES AND ADMINISTRATION*

658 JPN
GEKKAN GENDAI. Text in Japanese. 1967. m. **Description:** Covers general topics for businessmen.
Formerly: Monthly Gendai
Published by: Kodansha Ltd., 2-12-21 Otowa, Bunkyo-ku, Tokyo, 112-8001, Japan. TEL 81-3-3946-6201, FAX 81-3-3944-9915, http://www.kodansha.co.jp, http://www.toppan.co.jp/kodansha. Ed. Ryosuke Sasaki. Circ: 250,000.

658 305.4 GBR ISSN 0968-6673
HD6060.6 CODEN: GWORF8
➤ **GENDER, WORK AND ORGANIZATION.** Text in English. 1994. bi-m. EUR 44 combined subscription in Europe to individuals print & online eds.; USD 49 combined subscription in the Americas to individuals & Caribbean, print & online eds.; GBP 29 combined subscription elsewhere to individuals print & online eds.; USD 788 combined subscription in the Americas to institutions & Caribbean, print & online eds.; GBP 469, USD 380 combined subscription in developing nations to institutions print & online eds.; GBP 469 combined subscription elsewhere to institutions print & online eds.; EUR 27 combined subscription in Europe to students print & online eds.; USD 30 combined subscription in the Americas to students & Caribbean, print & online eds.; GBP 18 combined subscription elsewhere to students print & online eds. (effective 2006). adv. bk.rev. illus. reprint service avail. from PSC. **Document type:** *Journal, Academic/Scholarly.* **Description:** Dedicated to advancing theory, research, and applications of gender studies at work. Investigates various gender issues in the workplace.
Related titles: Online - full text ed.: ISSN 1468-0432. USD 749 in the Americas to institutions & Caribbean; GBP 222, USD 361 in developing nations to institutions; GBP 446 elsewhere to institutions (effective 2006) (from Blackwell Synergy, EBSCO Publishing, Gale Group, IngentaConnect, O C L C Online Computer Library Center, Inc., Swets Information Services).
Indexed: ABIn, CJA, CurCont, ERA, Emerald, ErgAb, FamI, FemPer, GEOBASE, HRA, IBSS, PsycInfo, PsycholAb, SOPODA, SSA, SSCI, SWA, SociolAb.
—BLDSC (4096.401680), IE, Infotrieve, ingenta. **CCC.**

Published by: Blackwell Publishing Ltd., 9600 Garsington Rd, Oxford, OX4 2ZG, United Kingdom. TEL 44-1865-776868, FAX 44-1865-714591, customerservices@oxon.blackwellpublishing.com, http://www.blackwellpublishing.com/journals/GWAO. Eds. David Knights, Deborah Kerfoot.

➤ **GEORGESON REPORT.** see *BUSINESS AND ECONOMICS—Investments*

➤ **GERER ET COMPRENDRE/TO MANAGE AND TO UNDERSTAND.** see *MINES AND MINING INDUSTRY*

658.338   BRA   ISSN 0104-530X
T55.4
GESTAO & PRODUCAO. Text in Portuguese. 1994. 3/yr. **Document type:** *Journal, Trade.*
Related titles: Online - full text ed.: free (effective 2005).
Published by: Universidade Federal de Sao Carlos, Departamento de Engenharia de Producao, Caixa Posta 676, Sao Paulo, 13565-905, Brazil. TEL 55-16-2608237, FAX 55-16-2608240.

658   FRA   ISSN 0766-9755
GESTION SOCIALE. Text in French. 1984. w. FRF 5,000 (effective 1997).
Published by: Groupe Liaisons S.A. (Subsidiary of: Wolters Kluwer BV), 1 Avenue Edouard Belin, Rueil Malmaison, Cedex 92856, France. TEL 33-1-41299696, FAX 33-1-41299880.

GIFT BASKET IDEA NEWSLETTER. see *GIFTWARE AND TOYS*

658   ITA
GIORNALE DEL DIRIGENTE. Text in Italian. 1974. m. (10/yr.). adv. bk.rev. **Document type:** *Magazine, Trade.*
Published by: Federazione Nazionale Dirigenti di Aziende Commerciali (FENDAC Servizi), Via Antonio Stoppani, 6, Milan, MI 20129, Italy. TEL 39-2-29516028, FAX 39-2-29516093, giornale@fendac.it. Ed. Guido Gay. Circ: 21,240.

GLOBAL BUSINESS & FINANCE REVIEW. see *BUSINESS AND ECONOMICS—International Commerce*

GLOBAL COMPETITIVENESS. see *BUSINESS AND ECONOMICS—International Development And Assistance*

GLOBAL MONEY MANAGEMENT. see *BUSINESS AND ECONOMICS—Investments*

GLOBAL REINSURANCE. see *INSURANCE*

658   DEU   ISSN 1616-976X
DER GMBH-GESCHAEFTSFUEHRER IN RECHT UND PRAXIS. Text in German. m. EUR 239 (effective 2004). adv. **Document type:** *Magazine, Trade.*
Published by: Verlag Praktisches Wissen GmbH (Subsidiary of: Wolters Kluwer Deutschland GmbH), Marlener Str 2, Offenburg, 77656, Germany. TEL 49-781-605300, FAX 49-781-59825, info@praktisches-wissen.de, http://www.praktisches-wissen.de. adv.: B&W page EUR 500, color page EUR 1,250. Circ: 2,056 (paid).

GODLY COUNSEL. see *RELIGIONS AND THEOLOGY*

GOLF CLUB MANAGEMENT & EQUIPMENT NEWS. see *SPORTS AND GAMES—Ball Games*

GOLF MANAGEMENT COMPANIES. see *SPORTS AND GAMES—Ball Games*

658   CHN   ISSN 1001-2516
HD70.C5
GONGYE QIYE GUANLI/INDUSTRIAL ENTERPRISE MANAGEMENT. Text in Chinese. 1978. m. CNY 168 (effective 2004). 176 p./no.; **Document type:** *Journal, Academic/Scholarly.*
Indexed: RASB.
Published by: Zhongguo Renmin Daxue, Shubao Zilio Zhongxin/Renmin University of China, Information Center for Social Server, Dongcheng-qu, 3, Zhangzizhong Lu, Beijing, 100007, China. 86-10-84043003, FAX 86-10-64015080, http://www.confucius.cn.net/bkdetail.asp?fzt=F31. **Dist. in US by:** China Publications Service, PO Box 49614, Chicago, IL 60649; **Dist. by:** China International Book Trading Corp, 35 Chegongzhuang Xilu, Haidian District, PO Box 399, Beijing 100044, China. TEL 86-10-68412045, FAX 86-10-68412023, cibtc@mail.cibtc.com.cn, http://www.cibtc.com.cn.

658   USA   ISSN 0145-6598
KF846.5
GOVERNMENT CONTRACTS SERVICE. Text in English. 1962. bi-m. looseleaf. USD 595; USD 495 renewals (effective 1999). index. back issues avail. **Description:** Information for managers interested in government contracts.
Published by: Procurement Associates, Inc., 733 N Dodsworth Ave, Covina, CA 91724. TEL 818-966-4576. Ed. Paul R McDonald Sr. Circ: 2,000.

658   USA
GOVERNMENT RELATIONS. Text in English. m. membership. **Description:** For government affairs managers of associations.
Published by: (Government Relations Section), American Society of Association Executives, 1575 Eye St, N W, Washington, DC 20005-1168. TEL 202-626-2703, FAX 202-371-1673, http://www.asaenet.org. Circ: 1,400.

658.155   USA
GOVERNMENTAL RISK MANAGEMENT MANUAL. Text in English. 1976. q. looseleaf. USD 200 (effective 2001). cum.index: 1976-1989. back issues avail. **Document type:** *Newsletter.*
Published by: Risk Management Publishing Co., 7311 E. Camino De Cima., Tucson, AZ 85750-2212. TEL 520-622-5174, FAX 520-884-8834. Ed. Nestor R Roos. R&P Marilyn Hall. Circ: 200 (paid).

GRAFISCH NEDERLAND; informatie voor en over grafisch management. see *PRINTING*

GRATIS. see *COMPUTERS—Internet*

658.340   GBR   ISSN 0960-7250
GREAT BRITAIN. DEPARTMENT OF TRADE AND INDUSTRY. ASSESSMENT PAPER. Text in English. 1987. irreg. —ingenta.
Published by: Great Britain. Department of Trade and Industry, 1 Victoria St, London, SW1H 0ET, United Kingdom. TEL 44-171-155000, dti.enquiries@dti.gsi.gov.uk, http://www.dti.gov.uk.

GREAT BRITAIN. HEALTH & SAFETY EXECUTIVE. TECHNOLOGY AND HEALTH SCIENCES DIVISION. SPECIALIST INSPECTOR REPORTS. see *PUBLIC HEALTH AND SAFETY*

GREEN PRODUCTIVITY. see *ENVIRONMENTAL STUDIES*

GREENER MANAGEMENT INTERNATIONAL; the journal of corporate environmental strategy and practice. see *ENVIRONMENTAL STUDIES*

658   NLD   ISSN 0926-2644
HD30.23   CODEN: GDNEEY
➤ **GROUP DECISION AND NEGOTIATION.** Text in English. 1992. bi-m. EUR 568, USD 578, GBP 355 combined subscription to institutions print & online eds. (effective 2005). adv. back issues avail.; reprint service avail. from PSC. **Document type:** *Journal, Academic/Scholarly.* **Description:** Publishes papers discussing all aspects of the process of group decision-making and negotiation, including descriptive, normative and design viewpoints.
Related titles: Microform ed.: (from PQC); Online - full text ed.: ISSN 1572-9907 (from EBSCO Publishing, Gale Group, IngentaConnect, Kluwer Online, O C L C Online Computer Library Center, Inc., ProQuest Information & Learning, Springer LINK, Swets Information Services).
Indexed: ABIn, ASCA, BibLing, CurCont, ESPM, IBSS, IPSA, IPsyAb, PSA, PsycInfo, PsycholAb, RiskAb, SOPODA, SSCI, e-psyche.
—BLDSC (4220.174200), IDS, IE, Infotrieve, ingenta. **CCC.**
Published by: (I N F O R M S USA), Springer-Verlag Dordrecht (Subsidiary of: Springer Science+Business Media), Van Godewijckstraat 30, Dordrecht, 3311 GX, Netherlands. TEL 31-78-6576050, FAX 31-78-6576474, http:// springerlink.metapress.com/openurl.asp?genre=journal&issn= 0926-2644, http://www.springeronline.com. Ed. Melvin F Shakun.

➤ **GROUP PRACTICE SOLUTIONS.** see *HEALTH FACILITIES AND ADMINISTRATION*

658   FRA   ISSN 1632-4366
GROUPE E S C GRENOBLE. PAPIERS DE RECHERCHE. Text in French. irreg. **Document type:** *Monographic series.*
Published by: Groupe E S C Grenoble, Europole, 12 Rue Pierre Semard, Grenoble, 38003, France. TEL 33-4-76706060, FAX 33-4-76706090, info@esc-grenoble.fr, http://www.esc-grenoble.com.

GROUPWARE MAGAZIN. see *COMMUNICATIONS—Computer Applications*

658   CHN   ISSN 1007-0591
GUANLI KEXUE/MANAGEMENT SCIENCE. Text in Chinese. 1996. m. CNY 66 (effective 2004). 64 p./no.; **Document type:** *Journal, Academic/Scholarly.* **Description:** Contains reprints of articles on management theories as well as related Chinese policies.
Published by: Zhongguo Renmin Daxue, Shubao Zilio Zhongxin/Renmin University of China, Information Center for Social Server, Dongcheng-qu, 3, Zhangzizhong Lu, Beijing, 100007, China. TEL 86-10-64039458, FAX 86-10-64015080, kyes@163.net, http://www.confucius.cn.net/bkdetail.asp?fzt= C3. **Dist. in US by:** China Publications Service, PO Box 49614, Chicago, IL 60649. TEL 312-288-3291, FAX 312-288-8570.

658   CHN   ISSN 1002-5502
HD70.C5
GUANLI SHIJIE∗ /JOURNAL OF MANAGEMENT WORLD. Text in Chinese. 1985. bi-m. USD 64.60. 224 p./no.; **Description:** Analyzes China's economic situations, policies and regulations as well as problems facing both managers and regulators.
Related titles: Online - full text ed.: (from East View Information Services).
Published by: (China, People's Republic. Zhonghua Renmin Gongheguo Guowuyuan/State Council of the People's Republic of China, Fazhan Yanjiu Zhongxin/Research Center for Economic Development), China Books & Periodicals Inc Ed. Li Kemu.

658   CHN   ISSN 1004-5414
GUANLI YU XIAOYI/MANAGEMENT AND BENEFIT. Text in Chinese. 1987. bi-m. CNY 1.50 per issue (effective 1993). adv. bk.rev. **Description:** Exchanges methods and experiences of management.
Published by: (Chinese Mechanical Engineering Society, Management Association), Zhongguo Tequ Jidian Zazhishe, No1, Shenhu Lu, Fuzhou, Fujian 350001, China. TEL 554120. Ed. Chen Peijing. Circ: 30,000. **Dist. overseas by:** Jiangsu Publications Import & Export Corp., 56 Gao Yun Ling, Nanjing, Jiangsu, China.

658.3   USA
GUERRILLA - TACTICS. Text in English. w. free. **Document type:** *Newsletter.* **Description:** Online magazine for small business, entrepreneurs, sales people and marketers of all kinds.
Media: Online - full text.
Published by: IPUB, 114 Linden St, Oakland, CA 94607. TEL 510-238-4512, FAX 510-286-8188, humans@ipub.com, http://www.gmarketing.com.

658   USA
GUIDE TO ARKANSAS FUNDING SOURCES. Text in English. 1981. biennial. USD 75. adv. **Document type:** *Bulletin.* **Description:** Financial and program information on all Arkansas-based private foundations, out-of-state foundations making grants in Arkansas, corporate donors to Arkansas charities.
Published by: Independent Community Consultants, Inc., PO Box 141, Hampton, AR 71744. TEL 501-798-4510, FAX 501-798-4513. Ed. Jerry Cronin. Adv. contact Monica Gilmore. Circ: 1,000.

THE GUIDE TO HOSPITAL PERFORMANCE. see *HEALTH FACILITIES AND ADMINISTRATION*

GUILDNOTES. see *ART*

H M : HOTEL MANAGEMENT. see *HOTELS AND RESTAURANTS*

658   DEU
HAMBURG NACHRICHTEN. Text in German. m.
Published by: Wirtschaftsvereinigung Handelsvertreter und Handelsmakler Hamburg - Schleswig Holstein, Raboisen 16, Hamburg, 20095, Germany. TEL 040-331025.

658   GBR   ISSN 1077-5730
HD30.28
HANDBOOK OF BUSINESS STRATEGY. Text in English. 1986. a. EUR 369 per issue in Europe; USD 439 per issue in North America; AUD 739 per issue in Australasia; GBP 259 per issue in the UK & elsewhere (effective 2006). reprint service avail. from PSC. **Document type:** *Journal, Trade.* **Description:** Provides busy executives with an immediate and ongoing resource to the most successful and enduring strategies in the marketplace today.
Formerly (until 1994): Handbook of Business Strategy. Yearbook (0894-4318)
—**CCC.**
Published by: Emerald Group Publishing Limited, 60-62 Toller Ln, Bradford, W Yorks BD8 9BY, United Kingdom. TEL 44-1274-777700, FAX 44-1274-785200, infomation@emeraldinsight.com, http:// www.emeraldinsight.com/hbs.htm. Ed. Ms. Patricia Coate.

HANDBOOK OF COST MANAGEMENT. see *BUSINESS AND ECONOMICS—Accounting*

HANDBOOKS IN OPERATIONS RESEARCH AND MANAGEMENT SCIENCE. see *COMPUTERS*

658   DEU   ISSN 0942-2609
HANDBUCH KULTURMANAGEMENT. Text in German. 1992. irreg. looseleaf. price varies. bk.rev.; software rev. bibl.; illus. **Document type:** *Directory, Trade.*
Published by: Dr. Josef Raabe Verlags GmbH, Rotebuehlstr 77, Stuttgart, 70178, Germany. TEL 49-711-629000, FAX 49-711-6290010, info@raabe.de, http://www.raabe.de. Ed. Peter Bendixen. Circ: 2,500 (controlled).

DER HANDEL; das Wirtschaftsmagazin fuer Handelsmanagement. see *BUSINESS AND ECONOMICS—Domestic Commerce*

658 331.1 NOR ISSN 0332-8066
HANDELSBESTYREREN. Text in Norwegian. 1920. m. (11/yr.). NOK 90. adv.
Published by: Handelsbestyrerforbundet, Arbeidersamfunnets Plass 1, Oslo, 0181, Norway. TEL 02-20-52-40, FAX 47-2-113194. Ed. Arne Randen. Circ: 1,450 (controlled).

658.01 DEU ISSN 0945-6570
HARVARD BUSINESS MANAGER. Text in German. 1979. m. EUR 120 domestic; EUR 141.60 foreign; EUR 14.50 newsstand/cover (effective 2003). adv. **Document type:** *Magazine, Trade.*
Formerly (until 1993): Harvard - Manager (0174-335X)
Indexed: DIP, IBR, IBZ.
—BLDSC (4265.794000), IE, ingenta.
Published by: Manager Magazin Verlagsgesellschaft mbH, Brandstwiete 19, Hamburg, 20457, Germany. TEL 49-40-3080050, FAX 49-40-30800549, mm_redaktion@manager-magazin.de, http://www.manager-magazin.de/harvard/. adv.: B&W page EUR 3,900; trim 178 x 252. Circ: 30,000 (paid and controlled).

HARVARD BUSINESS SCHOOL GUIDE TO CAREERS IN MANAGEMENT CONSULTING. see *OCCUPATIONS AND CAREERS*

HARVARD MANAGEMENT COMMUNICATION LETTER. see *JOURNALISM*

658 USA ISSN 1525-9595
HARVARD MANAGEMENT UPDATE. Text in English. 1996. m. USD 109 domestic; USD 129 in Canada & Mexico; USD 149 elsewhere (effective 2004). **Document type:** *Newsletter, Academic/Scholarly.* **Description:** Aims to help managers and their organizations be more effective. Includes a short list of "Web sites for managers," summaries of articles found in other business journals, and sources for further reading.
Formerly (until 199?): Management Update (Boston) (1088-8578)
Related titles: Online - full text ed.: (from EBSCO Publishing).
—BLDSC (4268.205000), IE, ingenta. **CCC.**
Published by: Harvard Business School Publishing, 60 Harvard Way, Boston, MA 02163. TEL 617-783-7500, 800-988-0866, FAX 617-783-7555, corpcustserv@hbsp.harvard.edu, MUOpinion@hbsp.harvard.edu, http://harvardbusinessonline.hbsp.harvard.edu/b01/en/newsletters/news-hmu_home.jhtml?_requestid=10416, http://www.hbsp.harvard.edu.

650 658.01 USA ISSN 0073-0785
HARVARD UNIVERSITY. GRADUATE SCHOOL OF BUSINESS ADMINISTRATION. PROGRAM FOR MANAGEMENT DEVELOPMENT. PUBLICATION. Text in English. 1960. a. price varies.
Published by: Harvard University, Graduate School of Business Administration, Soldiers Field Rd, Boston, MA 02163. TEL 617-495-6000.

HEALTH CARE MANAGEMENT HANDBOOK (YEAR). see *MEDICAL SCIENCES*

HEALTH CARE MANAGEMENT REVIEW. see *HEALTH FACILITIES AND ADMINISTRATION*

HEALTH CARE MANAGEMENT SCIENCE. see *HEALTH FACILITIES AND ADMINISTRATION*

658 USA ISSN 1060-0434
THE HEALTH CARE REGISTRATION; the newsletter for health care registration professionals. Text in English. 1991. m. USD 335 (effective 2004). **Document type:** *Newsletter, Trade.* **Description:** Covers simple, straightforward information, with tips on how to run the department more efficiently. Focuses on patient relations, with regular information on up-front collections, problems in admitting areas, employee management issues, and productivity.
Related titles: Online - full text ed.: (from EBSCO Publishing).
—**CCC.**
Published by: Aspen Publishers, Inc. (Subsidiary of: Wolters Kluwer N.V.), 5301 Buckeystown Pike, Ste. 400, Frederick, MD 21704-8319. TEL 800-638-8437, customer.service@aspenpubl.com, http://www.aspenpub.com. Ed. Laura J Merisalo. **Dist. by:** Distribution Center, 7201 McKinney Circle, Frederick, MD 21701. TEL 301-698-7100, FAX 301-417-7550.

HEALTH CLUB MANAGEMENT. see *LEISURE AND RECREATION*

HEALTHCARE LEADERSHIP REVIEW. see *HEALTH FACILITIES AND ADMINISTRATION*

HEALTHCARE RISK CONTROL SYSTEM; an information and consultation system. see *HEALTH FACILITIES AND ADMINISTRATION*

658 MEX
HECHO EN MEXICO. Text in English, Spanish. 1998. a. adv. **Document type:** *Yearbook.*
Related titles: Online - full text ed.
Published by: Grupo Internacional Editorial S A de C V, Rio Nazas 34, Col. Cuahutemoc, Mexico D F, 06500, Mexico. TEL 52-5-2099930, FAX 52-5-5660564, buzon@intermundo.com.mx, http://www.intermundo.com.mx/. Ed. Ana Luisa Ochoa. Adv. contact Fabrizio Tavano. color page MXP 30,000. Circ: 30,000.

658 GBR
HD28
HENLEY MANAGER UPDATE. Text in English. 1973. q. GBP 130, USD 280; GBP 32.50, USD 70 per issue (effective 2003); print subscr. includes online access. 45 p./no.; back issues avail.; reprints avail. **Document type:** *Journal, Academic/Scholarly.* **Description:** Aims to help the general manager keep abreast of the latest articles in specialist management journals.
Former titles: Manager Update (0957-4212); (until 1988): Journal of General Management. Supplement
Related titles: Online - full text ed.: GBP 75.20, USD 128 (effective 2003) (from EBSCO Publishing).
Indexed: ABIn.
—BLDSC (4295.650922), IE, ingenta. **CCC.**
Published by: (Henley Management College), Braybrooke Press Ltd., Remenham House, Remenham Hill, Henley-on-Thames, Oxon RG9 3EP, United Kingdom. TEL 44-1491412061, FAX 44-1491411428, braybrookepress@compuserve.com, http://www.braybrooke.co.uk/hm/index.htm. Ed. Keith MacMillan. Circ: 1,000.

HILDEBRANDT REPORT; a management and marketing newsletter for law firms. see *LAW*

658.2 JPN ISSN 0386-8230
HINSHITSU/JOURNAL OF THE JAPANESE SOCIETY FOR QUALITY CONTROL. Text in English. 1971. q. JPY 8,000 membership (effective 2005). **Document type:** *Journal, Academic/Scholarly.*
—BLDSC (7168.133000), IE, ingenta. **CCC.**
Published by: Nihon Hinshitsu Kanri Gakkai/Nihon Hinshitsu Kanri Gakkai, 1-2-1, Ko-enji Minami, Suginami-ku, Tokyo, 166-0003, Japan. TEL 81-3-53781506, FAX 81-3-53781507, office@jsqc.org, http://www.jsqc.org/.

658.3 JPN ISSN 0439-2795
HITACHI ZOSEN NEWS. Text in English. 1976 (vol.19). s-a. free. illus.
Indexed: BMT.
—BLDSC (4318.810000).
Published by: Hitachi Zosen Corporation, 1-1 Hitotsubashi 1-chome, Chiyoda-ku, Tokyo, 100-0003, Japan. FAX 03-3217-8545, TELEX 24490 SHIPYARD J. Ed. T Nishijima. Circ: 2,800.

380 658 JPN ISSN 0018-2796
HF53
➤ **HITOTSUBASHI JOURNAL OF COMMERCE AND MANAGEMENT.** Text in English. 1961. a. JPY 2,500 (effective 2001). charts; illus.; stat.; abstr.; bibl. cum.index. 65 p./no.; **Document type:** *Journal, Academic/Scholarly.*
Supersedes in part (1950-1960): Hitotsubashi Academy. Annals (0439-2841)
Indexed: BAS, ExcerpMed, IBSS, JEL, PAIS, PCI, RASB.
Published by: (Hitotsubashi Daigaku, Hitotsubashi Gakkai/Hitotsubashi University, Hitotsubashi Academy), Sanseido Publishing Company, Ltd., 2-22-14, Misakicho, Chiyoda-ku, Tokyo, 101-8371, Japan. FAX 81-3-3230-9569, info@sanseido-publ.co.jp, http://www.sanseido-publ.co.jp/. Ed. T Fujita. Circ: 700. **Dist. by:** Japan Publications Trading Co., Ltd., Book Export II Dept, PO Box 5030, Tokyo International, Tokyo 101-3191, Japan. TEL 81-3-32923753, FAX 81-3-32920410, infoserials@jptco.co.jp, http://www.jptco.co.jp.

658.00711 GBR
HOBSONS MANAGEMENT CASEBOOK. Text in English. a. GBP 9.99 per issue (effective 2002). **Description:** Recent graduates discuss their management careers.
Published by: (Careers Research and Advisory Centre), Hobsons PLC, Challenger House, 42 Adler St, London, E1 1EE, United Kingdom. TEL 44-1223-460366, FAX 44-1223-301506. **Dist. by:** Biblios Publishers' Distribution Services Ltd., Star Rd, Partridge Green, W Sussex RH13 8LD, United Kingdom. TEL 44-1403-710851, FAX 44-1403-711143.

658 USA ISSN 0738-7490
HOME BUSINESS IDEA POSSIBILITY NEWSLETTER. Text in English. 1991. a. looseleaf. USD 19.95 domestic; USD 21.95 in Canada; USD 28.95 foreign (effective 2003). 15 p./no.; **Document type:** *Newsletter.* **Description:** Offers ideas and suggestions on starting and operating a home-based business.
Published by: Sought After Publications, c/o Prosperity & Profits Unlimited, Box 416, Denver, CO 80201-0416. TEL 303-575-5676, mail@breadpudding.net. Ed., R&P A C Doyle.

658 HKG ISSN 0018-4594
HONG KONG MANAGER. Text in Chinese, English. 1965. q. HKD 200; HKD 300 foreign (effective 1999). adv. bk.rev. abstr.; charts; illus.; stat.; tr.lit. index. **Document type:** *Magazine, Trade.* **Description:** Covers the latest developments in management theories and skills.
Indexed: HongKongiana.
Published by: Hong Kong Management Association, 14-F Fairmont House, 8 Cotton Tree Dr, Central, Hong Kong, Hong Kong. TEL 852-2526-6516, FAX 852-2868-4387, TELEX 81903 HKMGR HX, http://www.hk.super.net/~hkma. Ed. Timothy Fong. Adv. contact S H So. B&W page HKD 6,800, color page HKD 9,500; trim 210 x 280. Circ: 13,000.

HOSPITAL MANAGEMENT INTERNATIONAL. see *HEALTH FACILITIES AND ADMINISTRATION*

HOSPITAL MATERIALS MANAGEMENT; the newsletter for materials management and group purchasing. see *HEALTH FACILITIES AND ADMINISTRATION*

330.1 USA
HG179
HOW TO AVOID FINANCIAL TANGLES. Text in English. 1938. irreg., latest 1997. USD 8 per issue.
Incorporates: How to Avoid Financial Tangles: Section B. Wills and Trusts, Taxes, and Help for the Widow; How to Avoid Financial Tangles: Section A. Elementary Property Problems and Financial Relationships
Indexed: RASB.
Published by: American Institute for Economic Research, PO Box 1000, Great Barrington, MA 01230. TEL 413-528-1216.

HUMAN CAPITAL. see *BUSINESS AND ECONOMICS—Personnel Management*

HUMAN RESOURCE MANAGEMENT. see *BUSINESS AND ECONOMICS—Personnel Management*

658 USA
HUMAN RESOURCES MANAGEMENT - IDEAS AND TRENDS. Text in English. 1981. bi-w. USD 265 (effective 2004). **Document type:** *Newsletter.* **Description:** Covers human resources developments in business and government.
Formerly: Human Resources Management - Ideas and Trends in Personnel (0745-0613)
Related titles: Series of: Human Resources Management Library.
—**CCC.**
Published by: C C H Inc., 2700 Lake Cook Rd, Riverwoods, IL 60015. TEL 847-267-7000, 800-449-6439, cust_serv@cch.com, http://www.cch.com. Pub. Catherine Wolfe.

658 NLD ISSN 0167-2533
CODEN: HSMADU
➤ **HUMAN SYSTEMS MANAGEMENT.** Abbreviated title: H S M. Text in English. 1980. q. EUR 397, USD 478 combined subscription print & online eds. (effective 2006). adv. bk.rev. illus. back issues avail.; reprints avail. **Document type:** *Journal, Academic/Scholarly.* **Description:** For managers and social scientists. Provides information on the science, technology and art of management. Articles cover productivity, performance and competence improvement.
Related titles: Online - full text ed.: (from EBSCO Publishing, Gale Group, IngentaConnect, O C L C Online Computer Library Center, Inc., ProQuest Information & Learning, Swets Information Services).
Indexed: ABIn, B&BAb, BPIA, BusI, CLOSS, CPM, CurCont, ERA, Emerald, EngInd, ErgAb, HRA, IBR, IBZ, IPSA, Inspec, M&MA, MEA, ManagCont, RASB, SCIMP, SOPODA, SSCI, TEA.
—BLDSC (4336.468000), AskIEEE, CISTI, Ei, IE, Infotrieve, ingenta. **CCC.**
Published by: I O S Press, Nieuwe Hemweg 6B, Amsterdam, 1013 BG, Netherlands. TEL 31-20-6883355, FAX 31-20-6203419, info@iospress.nl, order@iospress.nl, http://www.iospress.nl/html/01672533.php. Ed. M Zeleny TEL 212-636-6175. R&P Ms. Carry Koolbergen TEL 31-20-6382189. Adv. contact Ms. Jolijn van Eunen. Circ: 400. **Subscr. to:** I O S Press, Inc, 4502 Rachael Manor Dr., Fairfax, VA 22032-3631. iosbooks@iospress.com; Globe Publication Pvt. Ltd., C-62 Inderpuri, New Delhi 100 012, India. TEL 91-11-579-3211, 91-11-579-3212, FAX 91-11-579-8876, custserve@globepub.com, http://www.globepub.com; Kinokuniya Co. Ltd., Shinjuku 3-chome, Shinjuku-ku, Tokyo 160-0022, Japan. FAX 81-3-3439-1094, journal@kinokuniya.co.jp, http://www.kinokuniya.co.jp.

658 USA
I A A M NEWS. Text in English. bi-w. USD 90 to non-members (effective 2005). adv. **Document type:** *Newsletter, Trade.*
Published by: International Association of Assembly Managers, 635 Fritz Dr, Coppell, TX 75019-4442. TEL 972-906-7441, FAX 972-906-7418, http://www.iaam.org/IAAM_News/Pages/NLmenu.htm. Ed. R V Baugus. Adv. contact Rick Fritsche. Circ: 2,850.

658 IRL
I B E C - E S R I MONTHLY INDUSTRIAL SURVEY. Text in English. m. stat. **Document type:** *Bulletin.*
Formerly: Monthly Industrial Survey - Business Forecast
Published by: Irish Business and Employers Confederation, Confederation House, 84-86 Lower Baggot St., Dublin, 2, Ireland. TEL 353-1-6601011, FAX 353-1-6601717, http://www.iol.ie/ibec. Ed. David Croughan. **Co-sponsor:** Social Research Institute.

658 GBR
I.B.I.S. BEST SOLUTIONS. Text in English. 1997. q. **Document type:** *Trade.*
Published by: Institute of Business, Ideas on Solutions (I.B.I.S.), Osney House, 116 Curtain Rd, London, EC2A 3AH, United Kingdom. TEL 0171-8802700. Ed., Pub. Grahame White. Circ: 300,000.

658 USA ISSN 1058-5036
I C 2 MANAGEMENT AND MANAGEMENT SCIENCE SERIES. Text in English. 1991. irreg. price varies. **Document type:** *Monographic series, Academic/Scholarly.*
Published by: Greenwood Publishing Group Inc. (Subsidiary of: Harcourt International), 88 Post Rd W, PO Box 5007, Westport, CT 06881. TEL 203-226-3571, FAX 203-226-1502, webmaster@greenwood.com, http://www.greenwood.com.

330 DEU ISSN 1433-8025
I C E C E NEWS. Text in English. 199?. irreg. price varies. **Document type:** *Monographic series, Academic/Scholarly.*
Published by: (Innovation Centers in Central and Eastern Europe), Weidler Buchverlag Berlin, Luebecker Str 8, Berlin, 10559, Germany. TEL 49-30-3948668, FAX 49-30-3948698, weidler_verlag@yahoo.de, http://www.weidler-verlag.de.

658 DEU ISSN 0173-0665
I D - INFORMATIONSDIENST FUER DIE PERSONALABTEILUNG. Text in German. 1979. m. adv. bk.rev.
Address: In der Unteren Rombach 6L, Heidelberg, 69118, Germany. Ed. Wolfgang Reineke. Circ: 900.

I E E E ENGINEERING MANAGEMENT REVIEW. see *ENGINEERING*

I E E E INTERNATIONAL ENGINEERING MANAGEMENT CONFERENCE. PROCEEDINGS. see *ENGINEERING*

658 USA ISSN 0747-6221
I F M A NEWS. Text in English. 1982. m. USD 75 domestic to non-members; USD 100 foreign to non-members (effective 2000). adv. bk.rev. **Document type:** *Newsletter.* **Description:** Association news, industry codes, regulations and standards, research updates.
—CCC.
Published by: International Facility Management Association, 1 E Greenway Plaza, Ste 1100, Houston, TX 77046-0194. TEL 713-623-4362, FAX 713-623-6124. Ed., Pub., R&P Deborah Quinn Hensel. Adv. contact Jennifer Boecher. Circ: 15,500.

658 IND
I F M R PUBLICATIONS. Text in English. 1975 (no.12). irreg.
Published by: Institute for Financial Management and Research, Chennai, Tamil Nadu 600 034, India. **Dist. by:** Vora & Co., Publishers, Kalbadevi, 3 Round Bldg., Mumbai, Maharashtra 400 002, India.

658 MYS ISSN 1394-7680
I I U M JOURNAL OF ECONOMICS AND MANAGEMENT. (International Islamic University Malaysia) Text in English. 1996. s-a. MYR 75 domestic; USD 35 foreign (effective 2004). back issues avail. **Document type:** *Journal.*
Indexed: IndIslam, JEL.
Published by: (International Islamic University Malaysia, Kulliyyah of Economics and Management Sciences), I I U M Press, PO Box 70, Petaling Jaya, Salangor 46700, Malaysia. TEL 60-3-7547670, FAX 60-3-7546759, iiupress@iiu.edu.my, http://iiu.edu.my/publications/journals/journals.html.

370 FRA ISSN 0397-3301
I N F F O - FLASH. Text in French. 22/yr. bk.rev.
Published by: Centre I N F F O, Tour Europe, Paris La Defense, Cedex 92049, France. TEL 33-1-41252222, FAX 33-1-47737420, cinffo1@easynet.fr.

658 USA ISSN 1532-0545
HB1
➤ **I N F O R M S TRANSACTIONS ON EDUCATION.** (Institute for Operations Research and the Management Sciences) Text in English. 2000 (Sept.). 3/yr. free. **Document type:** *Journal, Academic/Scholarly.* **Description:** Its goal is to advance operations research and information management education at all levels worldwide.
Media: Online - full content.
Indexed: Inspec.
—CCC.
Published by: I N F O R M S, 901 Elkridge Landing Rd., Ste. 400, Linthicum, MD 21090-2909. TEL 410-850-0300, FAX 410-684-2963, informs@informs.org, http://ite.informs.org, http://www.informs.org. Ed. Erhan Erkut.

658 USA ISSN 1538-4934
I O M A'S REPORT ON CUSTOMER RELATIONSHIP MANAGEMENT. Text in English. 1997. m. USD 268.95 in US & Canada print & online eds.; USD 283 elsewhere print & online eds. (effective 2006). back issues avail. **Document type:** *Newsletter, Trade.* **Description:** Provides tips on how to boost the productivity, efficiency and visibility of the department.
Formerly (until 2002): I O M A's Report on Managing Customer Service (1093-6149)
Related titles: Online - full text ed.: (from EBSCO Publishing, Gale Group, LexisNexis, O C L C Online Computer Library Center, Inc., ProQuest Information & Learning).
—CCC.
Published by: Institute of Management & Administration, Inc., 3 Park Ave, New York, NY 10016-5902. TEL 212-244-0360, FAX 212-564-0465, subserve@ioma.com, http://www.ioma.com. Ed. Ann Podolske.

658 USA ISSN 1532-1673
I O M A'S REPORT ON FINANCIAL ANALYSIS, PLANNING & REPORTING. Variant title: Financial Analysis, Planning & Reporting. Text in English. 2000. m. USD 278.95 in US & Canada print & online eds.; USD 293 elsewhere print & online eds. (effective 2005). **Document type:** *Newsletter, Trade.* **Description:** Provides information on the latest techniques on financial analysis, performance measurement, and planning.
Related titles: Online - full text ed.: (from EBSCO Publishing, ProQuest Information & Learning); ♦ Cumulative ed(s).: Financial Analysis, Planning & Reporting Yearbook.
Indexed: ABIn.
—CCC.
Published by: Institute of Management & Administration, Inc., 3 Park Ave, New York, NY 10016-5902. TEL 212-244-0360, FAX 212-564-0465, subserve@ioma.com, http://www.ioma.com. Ed. Andy Dzamba.

614.8 658 USA ISSN 1524-1564
I O M A'S SAFETY DIRECTOR'S REPORT. Text in English. 1999. m. USD 268.95 in US & Canada print & online eds.; USD 283 elsewhere print & online eds. (effective 2005). **Document type:** *Newsletter, Trade.* **Description:** Provides information on workplace health and safety to safely run the department. Also gives the latest news on safety regulations and tips on cost-effective compliance.
Related titles: Online - full text ed.: (from EBSCO Publishing, Gale Group, O C L C Online Computer Library Center, Inc.); ♦ Cumulative ed(s).: Safety Director's Report Yearbook.
—CCC.
Published by: Institute of Management & Administration, Inc., 3 Park Ave, New York, NY 10016-5902. TEL 212-244-0360, FAX 212-564-0465, subserve@ioma.com, http://www.ioma.com/products/prod_detail.php?prodid=44. Ed. Garett Seivold.

658.5 CHE
HD45.A1 CODEN: IIOODN
I O NEW MANAGEMENT; Zeitschrift fuer Unternehmenswissenschaften und Fuehrungspraxis. Text in German; Summaries in German, French, English. 1932. m. CHF 158 domestic; EUR 118 in Europe; CHF 185 elsewhere; CHF 16 newsstand/cover (effective 2004). adv. bk.rev. illus.; stat. index. **Document type:** *Magazine, Trade.* **Description:** Features research in automation, manufacturing, production, technology, organization, personnel and marketing. Includes events, courses, new products, software news, and positions available.
Former titles (until 2003): New Management; (until 2001): I O Management (1422-3600); (until 1996): I O Management Zeitschrift (0019-9281); (until 1974): Industrielle Organisation (1016-8605)
Related titles: Microfilm ed.: (from PQC).
Indexed: ABIn, ADPA, CISA, DIP, ErgAb, ExcerpMed, IBR, IBZ, Inspec, KES, SCIMP.
—BLDSC (4563.774150), IE, ingenta, Linda Hall.
Published by: (Betriebswissenschaftliches Institut der Eidgenoessischen Technischen Hochschule Zuerich, Stiftung fuer Forschung und Beratung), HandelsZeitung Fachverlag AG, Seestr 344, Zuerich, 8027, Switzerland. TEL 41-1-2889414, FAX 41-1-2889301, io@handelszeitung.ch, verlag@handelszeitung.ch, http://www.newmanagement.ch, http://www.handelszeitung.ch. Pub. Ralph Buechi. Adv. contact Stefanie Dinges. B&W page CHF 4,150, color page CHF 6,700; trim 265 x 181. Circ: 15,000.

350 358 USA
I P M N NEWSLETTER. Text in English. q. free. back issues avail. **Document type:** *Newsletter, Trade.* **Description:** Informs members of the International Public Management Network of important news and forthcoming events.
Media: Online - full content.
Published by: International Public Management Network, c/o Atkinson Graduate School of Management, Willamette University, 900 State St, Salem, OR 97301. TEL 503-370-6440, FAX 503-370-3011, fthompso@willamette.edu, http://www.willamette.org/ipmn.

658 GBR ISSN 0958-5222
I P M S BULLETIN. Text in English. 1925. m. GBP 25 domestic; GBP 32.50 foreign (effective 2001). adv. bk.rev. illus. index. **Document type:** *Newspaper.* **Description:** Contains news and views for specialists and professionals.
Former titles: I P C S Bulletin (0265-0975); (until Jun. 1982): State Service (0039-0151)
Published by: Institution of Professionals Managers and Specialists, 75 York Rd, London, SE1 7AQ, United Kingdom. TEL 44-20-7902-6654, FAX 44-20-7928-5440, ipmshq@ipms.org.uk, http://www.ipms.org.uk. Ed., R&P Charles Harvey. Adv. contact T G Scott. Circ: 72,214 (controlled).

658 GBR ISSN 1360-8711
I R S PAY INTELLIGENCE. (Industrial Relations Services) Text in English. 1995. m. looseleaf. GBP 249 domestic; GBP 270 foreign; GBP 150 to Pay and Benefits Bulletin subscribers (effective 2003). 12 p./no.; **Document type:** *Trade.*
Related titles: Online - full text ed.: (from Gale Group, IngentaConnect).
—CCC.
Published by: I R S (Subsidiary of: LexisNexis UK (Scottish Office)), 18-20 Highbury Pl, London, N5 1QP, United Kingdom. TEL 44-20-7354-6742, 44-20-7354-5858, FAX 44-20-7226-8618, 44-20-7359-4000, publications@irseclipse.co.uk, http://www.irsonline.co.uk/pub_subjects/index_pub_pay.htm, http://www.irseclipse.co.uk.

I T - BUSINESS DAY. (Information Technology) see *BUSINESS AND ECONOMICS—Computer Applications*

I T - BUSINESS NEWS; Wochenzeitung fuer IT-Reseller und E-Solution-Provider. (Information Technology) see *BUSINESS AND ECONOMICS—Computer Applications*

I T - SOURCES. (Information Technology) see *BUSINESS AND ECONOMICS—Computer Applications*

658.45 GBR
I V C A UPDATE. Text in English. 1983. m. membership. adv. bk.rev. back issues avail. **Document type:** *Newsletter.* **Description:** Reviews the state of the visual and business communication industry.
Supersedes: I V C A Magazine (0952-7419); Which was formed by the 1987 merger of: B I S F A Magazine (0263-502X); I T V A (UK)
Published by: International Visual Communications Association, Bolsover House 5-6, Clipstone St, London, W1P 7EB, United Kingdom. TEL 0171-580-0962, FAX 0171-436-2606. Ed. Michael Smith. Circ: 1,500.

IBUSINESS. see *COMPUTERS—Information Science And Information Theory*

658 330 DEU ISSN 1617-5794
ICONOMY; Wirtschaftsmagazin fuer IT- und EBusiness-Strategien. Text in German. 1996. 4/yr. EUR 3.60 newsstand/cover (effective 2005). adv. illus.; stat. back issues avail. **Document type:** *Magazine, Trade.* **Description:** Contains information on the business impact of information and communication technology for the top management of medium and large sized companies.
Formerly (until 2001): IT.Services (1430-5208)
Published by: meetBIZ und Denkfabrik GmbH, Pastoratstr 6, Huerth, 50354, Germany. TEL 49-2233-61170, info@iconomy-online.de, http://www.iconomy-online.de. Ed., Pub. Wilfried Heinrich. Adv. contact Marc Warmbier. B&W page EUR 4,870, color page EUR 5,840; trim 210 x 297. Circ: 18,750 (paid and controlled).

658 LBN
AL-IDARI. Text in Arabic. 1976. m. LBP 75,000 domestic; USD 150 in US & Canada; USD 100 in Europe (effective 2003). adv. back issues avail. **Description:** Covers business management.
Published by: Dar As-Sayad S.A.L., C/o Said Freiha, Hazmieh, P O Box 1038, Beirut, Lebanon. TEL 961-5-456373, FAX 961-5-452700, contactpr@csi.com, alanwar@alanwar.com, http://www.alanwar.com. Ed. Hassan El Khoury. Adv. contact Said Freiha. color page USD 4,200; bleed 215 x 285. Circ: 25,350.

658 ZAF
IDEAS FOR A CHANGE. Text in English. 1997. s-a. ZAR 100 (effective 2000). illus. back issues avail. **Description:** Looks at techniques and approaches to understanding organizations and organization development.
Published by: Olive (OD and Training), 21 Sycamore Rd, Glenwood, Durban, KwaZulu-Natal 4001, South Africa. TEL 27-31-206-1534, FAX 27-31-205-2114, olive@oliveodt.co.za. Ed., R&P Warren Banks. Circ: 500 (paid).

658 DEU ISSN 0940-7693
DER IDEENBRIEF FUER DEN CHEF. Text in German. 1991. m. EUR 164.40 (effective 2004). index. back issues avail. **Document type:** *Newsletter, Trade.*
Published by: Verlag Norbert Mueller AG und Co. KG (Subsidiary of: S V Corporate Media GmbH), Emmy-Noether-Str 2, Munich, 80992, Germany. TEL 49-89-5485201, FAX 49-89-54852192, infoVNM@sv-corporate-media.de, http://www.vnm.de/svcm/index/includeVerzeichnis/nm[]briefe[]0940-7693/. Ed. Ralf Koschut. Circ: 2,500.

658 DEU ISSN 1439-4766
IDEENMANAGEMENT. Text in German. 1975. q. EUR 36.80; EUR 10.80 newsstand/cover (effective 2006). **Document type:** *Newspaper, Trade.*
Former titles (until 1999): Zeitschrift fuer Vorschlagswesen (0945-5892); (until 1994): Betriebliches Vorschlagswesen (0340-9279)
Indexed: DIP, IBR, IBZ.
—IE, Infotrieve. CCC.

Published by: (Deutsches Institut fuer Betriebswirtschaft), Erich Schmidt Verlag GmbH & Co. (Berlin), Genthiner Str 30G, Berlin, 10785, Germany. TEL 49-30-2500850, FAX 49-30-250085305, vertrieb@esvmedien.de, http://www.esv.info.

658 FRA
IMPACT MEDECIN; les dossiers de F M C du praticien. Text in French. 45/yr. **Document type:** *Newspaper.*
Address: 1 rue Paul Cezanne, Paris, Cedex 8 75375, France. Ed. Jean de Charon. Circ: 90,000.

658.2 DEU ISSN 0344-4546
IMPULS; Zeitung fuer Sicherheit im Betrieb. Text in German. 1968. m. membership.
Indexed: FLUIDEX, RILM.
Published by: Berufsgenossenschaft der Feinmechanik und Elektrotechnik, Postfach 510580, Cologne, 50941, Germany. **Co-sponsor:** Berufsgenossenschaft der Chemischen Industrie.

IN BUSINESS (MADISON); Dane county's business magazine. see *BUSINESS AND ECONOMICS—Domestic Commerce*

658 USA
▼ **IN THE BOARDROOM**; a global executive roundtable on innovation and new product development. Text in English. 2004. m. free to qualified personnel. **Description:** Offers a unique opportunity to learn about the latest product development strategies from leading executives in Europe, Asia and the U.S.
Media: Online - full content.
Published by: Penton Media, Inc. (Subsidiary of: Pittway Company), 1300 E 9th St, Cleveland, OH 44114-1503. TEL 216-696-7000, FAX 216-696-0177, http://www.intheboardroom.com/home/, http://www.penton.com.

658 674 USA ISSN 1094-8015
INDEPENDENT SAWMILL & WOODLOT MANAGEMENT. Text in English. 1997. bi-m. USD 19.95 in United States; USD 26.95 in Canada; USD 33.95 elsewhere (effective 2002). adv.
Published by: Sawmill Publishing, LLC, 3671 Enlow Rd., Ste B, Albany, OH 45710. sawmill@sawmillmag.com, http://sawmill.mag.com. Ed. Gregory Sharpless TEL 740-592-0552. Adv. contact Dairne Russell. **Subscr. to:** Independent Sawmill & Woodlot Management Subscription Services, P.O. Box 3000, Denville, NJ 07834-9242. TEL 800-875-2997.

658 IND ISSN 0019-5812
HD70.I4
INDIAN MANAGEMENT; business and management. Text and summaries in English. 1963. m. INR 112, USD 30. adv. bk.rev. charts; illus.; stat. index. back issues avail.; reprints avail.
Indexed: BAS, ManagAb.
Published by: All Indian Management Association, Management House, Lodi Rd., 14 Institutional Area, New Delhi, 110 003, India. TEL 617354, FAX 91-11-4626689, TELEX 031-74066 AIMA IN. Ed. Utpal K Banerjee. Pub. Vinod Shanbhag. Adv. contact Laila Ramanathan. B&W page INR 4,000, color page INR 8,000; trim 280 x 210. Circ: 10,000.

658 IND ISSN 0046-9025
INDIAN MANAGER. Text in English. 1970. q. INR 100, USD 28. adv. bk.rev. bibl.; charts.
Published by: Cochin University of Science and Technology, School of Management Studies, Cochin, Kerala 682 022, India. TEL 91-484-555310, FAX 91-484-532495. Eds. Jose T Payyappilly, K C Sankaranarayanan. Circ: 1,000.

INDIAN SOCIETY OF STATISTICS AND OPERATIONS RESEARCH. JOURNAL. see *COMPUTERS*

658.4 USA ISSN 1078-8476
HD38.25.I6
INDIANAPOLIS C.E.O.✶. Text in English. 1988. m. USD 19.95; USD 2.25 newsstand/cover. adv. back issues avail. **Document type:** *Trade.*
Related titles: Online - full text ed.: 1988.
Published by: Metropolitan C.E.O., PO Box 40907, Indianapolis, IN 46240-0907. TEL 317-257-8000, FAX 317-257-1482. Ed. Julie Sturgeon. Pub., Adv. contact Joe Cole. B&W page USD 3,830; trim 10.88 x 8.38. Circ: 30,000 (controlled).

INDUSTRIAL AND COMMERCIAL TRAINING. see *BUSINESS AND ECONOMICS—Personnel Management*

INDUSTRIAL ENGINEERING AND MANAGEMENT. see *ENGINEERING—Industrial Engineering*

658.5 USA ISSN 0019-8471
HD28 CODEN: IMNGDM
INDUSTRIAL MANAGEMENT. Text in English. 1952. bi-m. USD 59 domestic to non-members; USD 74 foreign to non-members (effective 2005); Free to Society members; USD 35 to IIE members. bk.rev. abstr.; charts; illus. Index. reprint service avail. from PQC. **Document type:** *Magazine, Trade.* **Description:** Offers management advice for professionals in various industries. Articles cover productivity improvement, management technologies, automation applications, and management techniques.
Related titles: Online - full text ed.: (from EBSCO Publishing, Florida Center for Library Automation, Gale Group, H.W. Wilson, Northern Light Technology, Inc., O C L C Online Computer Library Center, Inc., ProQuest Information & Learning).
Indexed: ABIn, BPI, BPIA, BusI, Emerald, EngInd, IMI, ISAP, Inspec, LRI, LogistBibl, ManagCont, ORMS, QC&AS, RASB, TTI, WorkRelAb.
—BLDSC (4457.700000), AskIEEE, Ei, IE, Infotrieve, ingenta, Linda Hall. **CCC.**
Published by: Institute of Industrial Engineers, Society for Engineering and Management Systems, 3577 Pkwy Ln Ste 200, Norcross, GA 30092. TEL 770-449-0460, 800-494-0460, FAX 770-441-3295, http://www.iienet.org/public/articles/index.cfm?Cat=640, http://www.iienet.org/public/articles/index.cfm?Cat=200. Circ: 3,000.

INDUSTRIAL SOCIETY. BRIEFING PLUS. see *BUSINESS AND ECONOMICS—Personnel Management*

658.3 JPN ISSN 0036-438X
INDUSTRIAL TRAINING/SANGYO KUNREN. Text in Japanese. 1955. m. JPY 9,600 to non-members; JPY 7,200 to members. adv. bk.rev. abstr.; stat.
Indexed: JTA.
Published by: Japan Industrial Training Association/Nihon Sangyo Kunren Kyokai, 6th Floor, Minamizuka Bldg, 2-17-3 Shibuya, Shibuya-ku, Tokyo, 150-0002, Japan. TEL 03-3409-3551, FAX 03-3409-7334. Ed. Fukuda Hiroshi. Circ: 5,000.

658 BEL ISSN 1780-4175
▼ **INDUSTRIE TECHNIQUE ET MANAGEMENT.** Text in French. 2004. 9/yr. EUR 50 (effective 2004). adv. **Document type:** *Magazine, Trade.*
Formed by the merger of (1999-2004): Industrie Magazine (1375-0712); (1995-2004): Technique et Management (1780-4159); Which was formerly (1972-1994): T M - Technique et Management (0774-4064)
Related titles: Dutch ed.: Industrie Technisch Management. ISSN 1780-4167. 2004.
Published by: Roularta Media Group, Research Park, Zellik, 1731, Belgium. TEL 32-2-4675611, FAX 32-2-4675757, communication@roularta.be, http://www.roularta.be. Circ: 37,000 (paid and controlled).

INDUSTRY REPORT ON PROFESSIONAL AND SCIENTIFIC PERSONNEL COMPENSATION. see *BUSINESS AND ECONOMICS—Personnel Management*

658 USA ISSN 1041-908X
HD4965.5.U6
INDUSTRY REPORT ON SUPERVISORY MANAGEMENT COMPENSATION. Text in English. a. USD 490. charts. **Document type:** *Trade.* **Description:** Supervisory pay data examined from an industry-by-industry perspective.
Related titles: ♦ Supplement(s): Supervisory Management Report - Geographic Edition.
Published by: (Executive Compensation Service (ECS)), Wyatt Data Services, 218 Rte 17 N, Rochelle Park, NJ 07622-9832. TEL 201-843-1177, FAX 201-843-0101.

INDUSTRY REPORT ON TECHNICIAN AND SKILLED TRADES PERSONNEL COMPENSATION. see *BUSINESS AND ECONOMICS—Personnel Management*

658 USA ISSN 0039-0895
TS300 CODEN: IWEEA4
INDUSTRYWEEK; the management resource. Text in English. 1882. 22/yr. USD 66 domestic; USD 82.50 in Canada & Mexico; USD 99 elsewhere; free to qualified personnel (effective 2005). adv. illus.; charts; mkt.; stat. s-a. index. reprint service avail. from PQC. **Document type:** *Magazine, Trade.* **Description:** Covers general management techniques for the purposes of improving industrial productivity, motivating employees and increasing profitability.
Incorporates (1985-1995): Electronics (0883-4989); Which was formerly (1984-1985): Electronics Week (0748-3252); (1930-1984): Electronics (0013-5070)
Related titles: Microform ed.: (from PQC); Online - full text ed.: (from bigchalk, EBSCO Publishing, Factiva, Florida Center for Library Automation, Gale Group, H.W. Wilson, LexisNexis, Northern Light Technology, Inc., O C L C Online Computer Library Center, Inc., ProQuest Information & Learning, The Dialog Corporation).
Indexed: ABIn, AIA, AS&TI, AgeL, B&I, BPI, BPIA, BusI, CADCAM, CompD, CompIU, CurCont, Emerald, EngInd, EnvAb, HlthInd, IMI, Inspec, LRI, MASUSE, MagInd, ManagCont, PROMT, PSI, PersLit, QAb, RASB, ResCtrInd, RoboAb, SRI, SoftBase, T&DA, T&II, TOM, TelAb, Telegen, WorkRelAb.
—BLDSC (4478.235000), AskIEEE, CISTI, Ei, IDS, IE, Infotrieve, ingenta, Linda Hall. **CCC.**
Published by: Penton Media, Inc. (Subsidiary of: Pittway Company), 1300 E 9th St, Cleveland, OH 44114-1503. TEL 216-696-7000, 800-659-5251, FAX 216-696-0177, information@penton.com, http://www.industryweek.com, http://www.penton.com. Eds. John R Russell, Patricia Panchak. adv.: B&W page USD 20,993, color page USD 27,558. Circ: 236,248 (controlled).

658 USA ISSN 0828-525X
INFO OUTLOOK (YEAR)✶; a guide to trends and sources for the information community. Text in English. 1985. irreg. free. back issues avail. **Document type:** *Newsletter.*
—**CCC.**
Published by: Information Plus Inc., PO Box 115, Buffalo, NY 14205-0115. TEL 716-852-2220, FAX 716-858-1653. Ed. D C Sawyer. Circ: 1,000.

658 GRC ISSN 1105-5502
INFORMATION. Text in Greek. 1986. m. adv. bk.rev. back issues avail. **Description:** Concerned with management marketing and economics on an international and national level in Greece.
Published by: Compupress S.A., 44 Syngrou Ave, Athens, 117 42, Greece. TEL 30-1-9238-672, FAX 30-1-921-6847. Ed. M Daskalakis. Pub. N O Manousos. Adv. contact V Giakamozis. Circ: 15,000.

658 GBR ISSN 1359-4214
INFORMATION AGE (BATH). Text in English. 1995. m. GBP 57.60; free domestic to qualified personnel (effective 2005). **Document type:** *Magazine, Trade.* **Description:** Focuses on the best ways to manage information.
Related titles: Online - full text ed.: (from Florida Center for Library Automation).
Indexed: Inspec.
—BLDSC (4481.724500). **CCC.**
Published by: Infoconomy Ltd, 17-18 Margaret St, London, W1W 8RP, United Kingdom. TEL 44-20-76129300, FAX 44-20-74369188, http://www.infoconomy.com/pages/information-age/index.adp. Ed. Dominic Tonner.

658 004 GBR
▼ **INFORMATION ECONOMICS JOURNAL.** Text in English. 2003 (Oct.). q. free to qualified personnel (effective 2003). **Document type:** *Journal, Trade.* **Description:** Covers economics of information and information technology with articles by authoritative contributors from around the world, providing insights and practical guidance on investment strategies and best practice.
Published by: Butler Group, Europa House, 184 Ferensway, Hull, HU1 3UT, United Kingdom. TEL 44-1482-586149, FAX 44-1482-323577, http://www.butlergroup.com/.

658 FRA ISSN 0153-9868
INFORMATION FISCALE ET SOCIALE✶. Text in French. 1964. m.
Published by: (Union des Fonctionnaires des Finances en Europe), Centre de Documentation et Informations, 191 av. Pierre Brossolette, B.P. 310, Montrouge, Cedex 92541, France. Ed. Jacques Michelot.

658 USA ISSN 1080-286X
T58.6 CODEN: INMAF8
INFORMATION MANAGEMENT (HERSHEY). Text in English. 1988. s-a. USD 50 to individuals; USD 70 to institutions (effective 2005). bk.rev. tr.lit. 24 p./no.; **Document type:** *Newsletter, Consumer.* **Description:** Offers a digest of information advancements in the information resources management field. Enumerates current and future issues and trends in the field of information technology.
Formerly: Information Management Bulletin (1046-9303)
Related titles: Online - full text ed.: (from ProQuest Information & Learning).
Indexed: ABIn, CompLI, InfoSAb, Inspec, LISA.
—BLDSC (4493.686300), AskIEEE, IE, ingenta. **CCC.**
Published by: (Information Resources Management Association), Idea Group Publishing (Subsidiary of: Idea Group Inc.), 701 E Chocolate Ave, Ste 200, Hershey, PA 17033-1240. jtravers@idea-group.com, http://www.idea-group.com/journals/details.asp?id=200. Ed. Rabbi Mehdi Khosrow-Pour. R&P Jan Travers. Circ: 800.

658 020 GBR ISSN 0968-5227
T58.64 CODEN: IMCSE4
➤ **INFORMATION MANAGEMENT & COMPUTER SECURITY.** Text in English. 1992. 5/yr. EUR 8,927.29 in Europe; USD 9,059 in North America; AUD 10,949 in Australasia; GBP 6,154.16 in UK & elsewhere (effective 2006). reprint service avail. from PSC. **Document type:** *Journal, Academic/Scholarly.*
Formed by merger of (1990-1992): International Journal of Information Resource Management (0956-4225); (1982-1992): Computer Control Quarterly (0813-7099)
Related titles: Online - full text ed.: (from EBSCO Publishing, Emerald Group Publishing Limited, Gale Group, IngentaConnect, O C L C Online Computer Library Center, Inc., ProQuest Information & Learning, Swets Information Services).
Indexed: ABIn, C&CSA, CompLI, ESPM, EmerIntel, Emerald, EngInd, InfoSAb, Inspec, LISA, MicrocompInd, RiskAb.
—BLDSC (4493.687056), AskIEEE, IE, Infotrieve, ingenta. **CCC.**
Published by: Emerald Group Publishing Limited, 60-62 Toller Ln, Bradford, W Yorks BD8 9BY, United Kingdom. TEL 44-1274-777700, FAX 44-1274-785200, infomation@emeraldinsight.com, http://www.emeraldinsight.com/imcs.htm. Eds. Mr. Kevin Fitzgerald, Ms. Margaret Hurley. Pub. Miss Rachel Murawa. R&P Mr. John Eggleton.

B

658 020 USA ISSN 1040-1628
CODEN: IRMAEZ
➤ **INFORMATION RESOURCES MANAGEMENT JOURNAL.**
Text in English. 1988. q. USD 95 to individuals; USD 315 to
institutions (effective 2005). adv. bk.rev. 48 p./no.; **Document
type:** *Journal, Academic/Scholarly.* **Description:** Provides the
latest research findings dealing with all aspects of information
resources management, managerial and organizational
applications, as well as implications of information technology
organizations.
Related titles: Online - full text ed.: ISSN 1533-7979 (from
EBSCO Publishing, O C L C Online Computer Library Center,
Inc., ProQuest Information & Learning).
Indexed: ABIn, BrCerAb, BusEdI, C&ISA, CerAb, CompLI,
CorrAb, E&CAJ, EMA, Emerald, IAA, InfoSAb, Inspec, LISA,
M&TEA, MBF, METADEX, MicrocompInd, SolStAb, WAA.
—BLDSC (4494.145000), AskIEEE, IE, Infotrieve, ingenta, Linda
Hall. **CCC.**
Published by: (Information Resource Management Association),
Idea Group Publishing (Subsidiary of: Idea Group Inc.), 701 E
Chocolate Ave, Ste 200, Hershey, PA 17033-1240. TEL
717-533-8845, 866-342-6657, FAX 717-533-7115,
irmj@idea-group.com, jtravers@idea-group.com,
http://www.idea-group.com/journals/details.asp?id=199. Ed.
Rabbi Mehdi Khosrow-Pour. Circ: 600 (controlled).

➤ **INFORMATION SCIENCE AND KNOWLEDGE
MANAGEMENT.** see *LIBRARY AND INFORMATION
SCIENCES*

651.8 USA ISSN 0743-8613
HD30.335
INFORMATION STRATEGY: THE EXECUTIVE'S JOURNAL. Text
in English. 1984. q. USD 195 (effective 2000 - 2001). adv.
bk.rev. index. 48 p./no. 2 cols./p.; back issues avail.; reprint
service avail. from SCH. **Document type:** *Journal, Trade.*
Description: Helps senior executives without DP backgrounds
make policy and strategy decisions about business and
information management, gain a competitive advantage
through the use of information systems, assess IS
departments, and manage IS applications.
Related titles: Online - full text ed.: (from EBSCO Publishing,
H.W. Wilson, O C L C Online Computer Library Center, Inc.).
Indexed: ABIn, BPI, CompLI, Emerald, Inspec, LISA, RASB.
—BLDSC (4496.352000), AskIEEE, CISTI, IE, Infotrieve,
ingenta. **CCC.**
Published by: Auerbach Publications (Subsidiary of: C R C
Press, LLC), 2000 Corporate Blvd., NW, Boca Raton, FL
33431. TEL 561-994-0555, FAX 561-374-3401,
auerbach@crcpress.com, http://www.auerbach-
publications.com/ejournals/issues/issue_archive.asp?section=
1077, http://www.auerbach-publications.com/home.asp. Ed. L
R DeJarnett. Pub., Adv. contact Richard O'Hanley TEL
212-845-4017. R&P Jamie Sigal TEL 561-994-0555. B&W
page USD 2,000; trim 10 x 7. Circ: 500.

658 USA ISSN 1094-1509
INFORMATION TECHNOLOGY ADVISER. Abbreviated title: I T A.
Text in English. 1997. s-m. USD 299. software rev. charts.
back issues avail. **Document type:** *Newsletter.* **Description:**
News and instructional materials on managing IT departments.
Related titles: Online - full text ed.
Published by: Progressive Business Publications, 370 Technology
Dr, Malvern, PA 19355-1315. TEL 610-695-8600,
800-220-5000, FAX 610-647-8089, editor@pbp.com,
http://www.pbp.com. Ed. Robin Nelson. R&P Curt Brown. Circ:
14,038 (paid).

658 ITA ISSN 1128-1928
INFORMAZIONI AZIENDALI E PROFESSIONALI. QUADERNI.
Text in Italian. 1976.
Published by: De Lillo Editore s.r.l., Via Mecenate 76/3, Milan,
20138, Italy. TEL 39-02-58013112, FAX 39-02-58012450,
http://www.delillo.it.

658 USA ISSN 1096-4126
THE INFORMED OUTLOOK. Text in English. 1996. m. USD 295
domestic to members; USD 342.40 in Canada to members;
USD 370 elsewhere to members; USD 325 domestic to
non-members; USD 374.50 in Canada to non-members; USD
400 elsewhere to non-members (effective 2000). **Document
type:** *Newsletter, Trade.* **Description:** Features regular
reports on developments and interpretations, conferences and
meetings, relevant new technologies and other
standards-related information.
Indexed: TTI.
Published by: (International Forum for Management Systems),
American Society for Quality Control, 600 N Plankinton Ave,
Milwaukee, WI 53203-2914. TEL 414-272-8575, FAX
414-272-1734, http://www.asq.org.

658.45 FRA ISSN 0985-8784
INFOS DE L'EXPRESSION D'ENTREPRISE. Text in French.
1987. w. **Description:** Covers important meetings, key
nominations, and current events in the world of corporate
communications.
Published by: Editions de l'Expression, 22 rue Plumet, Paris,
75015, France. TEL 47-34-02-70, FAX 47-34-00-46. Ed.
Patrice Legendre.

INFOTREND. see *BUSINESS AND ECONOMICS—Computer
Applications*

658 MEX
INGENIERIA DE COSTOS. Text in Spanish. 1970. 4/yr. MXP 25
per issue. adv.
Published by: (Sociedad Mexicana de Ingenieria de Costos,
A.C.), D'Pastrana Editores, S.A., Kepler 147-A, Mexico City 5,
DF, Mexico. Ed. Jorge L Castillo Tufino. Circ: 5,000
(controlled).

371.3 360 USA ISSN 1053-2587
HC79.T4
INNOVATING. Text in English. 1990. q. USD 40 (effective 2005).
bk.rev. back issues avail. **Document type:** *Journal,
Academic/Scholarly.* **Description:** Discusses innovative
assumptions, paradigms, and examples of leadership, for
individuals and organizations.
Related titles: Online - full text ed.: (from EBSCO Publishing).
Indexed: SWR&A.
Published by: The Rensselaerville Institute, 63 Huyck Rd,
Rensselaerville, NY 12147. TEL 518-797-3783, FAX
518-797-5270, info@rinstitute.org, http://www.rinstitute.org/.
Circ: 1,500.

338.92609505 AUS ISSN 1447-9338
➤ **INNOVATION: MANAGEMENT, POLICY & PRACTICE;** an
international journal for the publication of research in all fields
of innovation. Text in English. 1998. 4/yr. AUD 399 in
Australia, New Zealand, S. & S.E. Asia, S. America & Africa;
USD 399 elsewhere; AUD 499 combined subscription in
Australia, New Zealand, S. & S.E. Asia, S. America & Africa
for print & online eds.; USD 499 combined subscription
elsewhere print & online eds. (effective 2005). adv. **Document
type:** *Journal, Academic/Scholarly.* **Description:** Aims to
encourage, promote and advance innovation research
outcomes, research applications, policy development,
education and best practice.
Formerly (until 2002): R & D Enterprise: Asia Pacific (1440-1266)
Related titles: Online - full text ed.
Indexed: IBSS.
—BLDSC (4515.480850), IE.
Published by: eContent Management Pty Ltd., PO Box 1027,
Maleny, QLD 4552, Australia. TEL 61-7-54352900, FAX
61-7-54352911, info@e-contentmanagement.com,
http://www.innovation-enterprise.com, http://www.e-
contentmanagement.com. Ed. Mark Dodgson. Pub., R&P,
Adv. contact James Davidson. Circ: 500 (controlled).

658 NLD
INNOVATIONS IN FINANCIAL MARKETS AND INSTITUTIONS.
Text in English. irreg., latest vol.16, 2005. price varies.
Document type: *Monographic series.*
Published by: Springer-Verlag Dordrecht (Subsidiary of: Springer
Science+Business Media), Van Godewijckstraat 30, Dordrecht,
3311 GX, Netherlands. TEL 31-78-6576050, FAX
31-78-6576474, http://www.springeronline.com. Ed. Mark J
Flannery.

658 DEU ISSN 1437-787X
**INNOVATIVE BETRIEBSWIRTSCHAFTLICHE FORSCHUNG
UND PRAXIS.** Variant title: Schriftenreihe Innovative
Betriebswirtschaftliche Forschung und Praxis. Text in German.
1985. irreg., latest vol.163, 2005. price varies. **Document
type:** *Monographic series, Academic/Scholarly.*
Formerly (until 1998): Betriebswirtschaftliche
Forschungsergebnisse (1435-621X)
Published by: Verlag Dr. Kovac, Arnoldstr 49, Hamburg, 22763,
Germany. TEL 49-40-3988800, FAX 49-40-39888055,
info@verlagdrkovac.de, http://www.verlagdrkovac.de/3-1.htm.

658.8 USA
INNOVATIVE LEADER (ONLINE); monthly tool to increase
creativity and productivity. Text in English. 1992. m. free. adv.
bk.rev. illus. back issues avail. **Document type:** *Newsletter,
Trade.* **Description:** Provides a resource for managers to
stimulate creativity and productivity.
Former titles (until Mar. 2001): Innovative Leader (Print)
(1092-2156); (until Mar. 1997): R and D Innovator (1061-1894)
Media: Online - full content.
Published by: Winston J Brill Associates, 4134 Cherokee Dr,
Madison, WI 53711. TEL 608-231-6766, FAX 608-231-6794,
wbrill@winstonbrill.com, http://www.winstonbrill.com. Ed., Pub.,
R&P, Adv. contact Winston J Brill.

658 DEU ISSN 1439-7625
INNOVATIVES DIENSTLEISTUNGSMANAGEMENT. Text in
German. 2000. irreg., latest vol.15, 2004. price varies.
Document type: *Monographic series, Academic/Scholarly.*
Published by: Verlag Dr. Kovac, Arnoldstr 49, Hamburg, 22763,
Germany. TEL 49-40-3988800, FAX 49-40-39888055,
info@verlagdrkovac.de, http://www.verlagdrkovac.de/3-9.htm.

658 686.2 USA
INSIDE EDGE. Text in English. 1986. m. USD 50 domestic to
non-members; USD 72 foreign to non-members; USD 5
newsstand/cover (effective 2005). adv. bk.rev. back issues
avail. **Document type:** *Magazine, Trade.* **Description:** Covers
in-house printing, the copying and mailing management
industry, managerial and technical advances, and association
news.
Formerly: Perspectives (Liberty) (1073-0737)

Published by: International Publishing Management Association,
1205 W College St, Liberty, MO 64068-3733. TEL
816-781-1111, FAX 816-781-2790, ipmainfo@ipma.org,
http://www.ipma.org/inside_edge.html. Eds. Jeff Langford, Jeff
Langford. R&P, Adv. contact Jeff Langford. Circ: 2,300
(controlled).

INSIDE PUBLIC ACCOUNTING; the competitive advantage for
accounting firm leaders since 1987. see *BUSINESS AND
ECONOMICS—Accounting*

INSIDE RADIO; the latest news, trends and management
information. see *COMMUNICATIONS—Radio*

658 330.9 DEU
INSTITUT DER DEUTSCHEN WIRTSCHAFT. FORUM. Text in
German. 1951. w. EUR 43.01 (effective 2005). index. back
issues avail. **Document type:** *Journal, Trade.*
Formerly (until 1988): Institut der Deutschen Wirtschaft.
Vortragsreihe
Published by: (Institut der Deutschen Wirtschaft), Deutscher
Instituts Verlag GmbH, Gustav-Heinemann-Ufer 84-88,
Cologne, 50968, Germany. TEL 49-221-4981515, FAX
49-221-4981533, div@iwkoeln.de, http://www.iwkoeln.de. Circ:
1,300.

**INSTITUT PANAFRICAIN POUR LE DEVELOPPEMENT.
CENTRE DE FORMATION AU MANAGEMENT DES
PROJETS. BILAN DES ACTIVITES.** see *BUSINESS AND
ECONOMICS—International Development And Assistance*

**INSTITUT PANAFRICAIN POUR LE DEVELOPPEMENT.
CENTRE D'ETUDES ET DE RECHERCHES APPLIQUEES.
EVALUATION DU SEMINAIRE SUR LA METHODOLOGIE
DU MANAGEMENT DES PROJETS.** see *BUSINESS AND
ECONOMICS—International Development And Assistance*

658.007 IDN
**INSTITUTE FOR MANAGEMENT EDUCATION AND
DEVELOPMENT. REPORT.** Text in English. 1980. a. USD 20.
Published by: Institute for Management Education and
Development/Lembaga Pendidikan dan Pembinaan
Management, Jalan Mentang Raya 9, Jakarta, Indonesia. Circ:
10,000.

658 ZAF
**INSTITUTE OF ADMINISTRATION AND COMMERCE OF
SOUTH AFRICA. JOURNAL.** Text in Afrikaans, English. 1967.
4/yr. membership. adv. illus. back issues avail.
Formerly: Business and Administration (0007-6449)
Published by: Institute of Administration and Commerce,
Mowbray, PO Box 13450, Cape Town, 7705, South Africa.
TEL 27-21-4480876, FAX 27-21-4480872, info@iacsa.za,
http://www.iacsa.co.za. Circ: 7,200.

658 TZA
**INSTITUTE OF DEVELOPMENT MANAGEMENT. REPORT OF
THE ACTIVITIES OF THE INSTITUTE.** Text in English. 1973.
a. **Document type:** *Corporate.*
Published by: Institute of Development Management, PO Box 5,
Mzumbe-morogoro, Tanzania. Circ: 500.

658 DEU ISSN 0967-652X
Z699.5.E25
**INSTITUTE OF MANAGEMENT INTERNATIONAL DATABASES
PLUS.** Text in English. q. GBP 930 to individuals; GBP 699 to
members (effective 2001). **Document type:** *Trade.*
Description: Contains over 86,0000 abstracts of international
management materials arranged in five cross-searchable
databases including books, journal articles, management
working papers and audio-visual materials.
Former titles (until 1992): British Institute of Management
International Databases Plus; British Institute of Management
Databases on CD-ROM
Media: CD-ROM.
Published by: (Institute of Management ZWE), K.G. Saur Verlag
GmbH (Subsidiary of: Gale Group), Ortlerstr 8, Munchen,
81373, Germany. TEL 49-89-769020, FAX 49-89-76902150,
info@saur.de, http://www.saur.de.

**INSTITUTE OF PHARMACY MANAGEMENT INTERNATIONAL.
INSTITUTE NEWS.** see *PHARMACY AND PHARMACOLOGY*

658 IND ISSN 0971-1864
INSTITUTE OF PUBLIC ENTERPRISE. JOURNAL. Text in
English. 1978. q. INR 50, USD 20. adv. bk.rev. **Description:**
Devoted to professional and academic research in the
economics and management aspects of public enterprises.
Former titles (until 1990, vol.13, no.1): I P E Journal; I.P.E. News
Letter
Published by: Institute of Public Enterprise, Osmania University
Campus, Hyderabad, Andhra Pradesh 500 007, India. TEL
868937, TELEX 0425-7064 IPE IN. Ed. T L Sankar. Circ: 800.

658 ARG ISSN 0325-9072
**INSTITUTO PARA EL DESARROLLO DE EJECUTIVOS EN LA
ARGENTINA. REVISTA.** Key Title: Revista I D E A. Text in
Spanish. 1977. bi-m. USD 60 (effective 2001). adv. bk.rev.
back issues avail.
Formerly (until 1979): Instituto para el Desarrollo de Ejecutivos en
la Argentina. Noticias (0325-9064)

Indexed: IBSS.
Published by: Revista Idea, Moreno, 1850-3, Capital Federal, Buenos Aires 1094, Argentina. TEL 54-11-5861-4300, FAX 54-11-5861-4399, ifo@ideamail.com.ar, info@ideamail.com.ar, http:/www.ideared.org/, http://www.ideared.org/. Ed. Gerado Lopes-Alonso. Pub. Ruben D Puentedura. Adv. contact Beatriz Suescun. page USD 5,300. Circ: 1,000.

INTAND NEWSLETTER; the newsletter of the international network for transactional analysis, neuro-linguistic programming. see *PSYCHOLOGY*

658 USA
INTEGRATION MANAGEMENT; the newspaper for the global integrators. Text in English. irreg. adv. back issues avail. **Document type:** *Newspaper, Trade.* **Description:** Delivers news and analysis on the enterprise market and spotlights consulting strategies such as business process outsourcing, and risk rewards solutions.
Related titles: Online - full text ed.
Address: 10 G St, Ste 500, Washington, DC 20002-4228. TEL 703-848-2800, FAX 703-848-2353, jsweeney@technews.com, http://www.imnews.com. Ed. Jack Sweeney. Adv. contact Tony Carlson.

058 GBR ISSN 1741-1424
▼ **INTELLECT ASSET MANAGEMENT.** Variant title: I A M. Text in English. 2003. bi-m. GBP 335 (effective 2004). **Document type:** *Magazine, Trade.* **Description:** Designed to give its readers the inside track on how companies can ensure they extract the maximum value from the patents, trademarks, copyrights and trade secrets they own, as well as the know-how inside their employees' heads.
—BLDSC (4531.819150), IE.
Published by: Globe White Page Ltd., New Hibernia House, Winchester Walk, London, SE1 9AG, United Kingdom. TEL 44-20-72340606, FAX 44-20-72340808, info@globewhitepage.com, http://www.iam-magazine.com/. Ed. Joff Wild. Pub. Tony Harriss.

INTELLECTUAL PROPERTY STRATEGY YEARBOOK. see *PATENTS, TRADEMARKS AND COPYRIGHTS*

▼ **INTERDISCIPLINARY JOURNAL OF INFORMATION, KNOWLEDGE, AND MANAGEMENT.** see *LIBRARY AND INFORMATION SCIENCES*

003 USA ISSN 0092-2102
CODEN: INFAC
➤ **INTERFACES (LINTHICUM).** Text in English. 1971. bi-m. USD 172 combined subscription domestic to non-members print & online eds.; USD 204 combined subscription foreign to non-members print & online eds.; USD 286 combined subscription domestic to institutions print & online eds.; USD 296 combined subscription foreign to institutions print & online eds. (effective 2005). adv. bk.rev. illus.; charts; bibl. Index. back issues avail.; reprint service avail. from PQC. **Document type:** *Journal, Academic/Scholarly.*
Formerly: Institute of Management Sciences Bulletin (0020-2916)
Related titles: Microform ed.: (from PQC); Online - full content ed.: ISSN 1526-551X. USD 92 to non-members; USD 46 to members additional journal (effective 2004); Online - full text ed.: (from EBSCO Publishing, Gale Group, O C L C Online Computer Library Center, Inc., ProQuest Information & Learning, Swets Information Services).
Indexed: ABIn, AHCI, AS&TI, AgeL, BMT, BPI, BPIA, BusI, CIS, CMCI, CPM, CompAb, CompC, CompR, CurCont, DIP, DPD, Emerald, ErgAb, ExcerpMed, IAOP, IBR, IBSS, IBZ, IMI, Inspec, JCQM, LT&LA, ManagCont, ORMS, PMA, PsycholAb, QC&AS, RASB, SSCI, T&II, WorkRelAb.
—BLDSC (4533.461000), AskIEEE, IDS, IE, Infotrieve, ingenta, Linda Hall. **CCC.**
Published by: I N F O R M S, 901 Elkridge Landing Rd., Ste. 400, Linthicum, MD 21090-2909. TEL 410-850-0300, 800-446-3676, FAX 410-684-2963, informs@informs.org, http://interfaces.pubs.informs.org, http://www.informs.org. Ed. Terry P Harrison TEL 814-863-3357. R&P Candita Gerzevitz. Adv. contact Trish Allewalt. B&W page USD 700; trim 6.75 x 10. Circ: 4,000 (paid and controlled). **Subscr. to:** PO Box 631704, Baltimore, MD 631704.

330.9 FRA ISSN 1267-0669
INTERIEUR SYSTEMES; la construction seche en action. Text in French. bi-m. adv.
Indexed: RefZh.
Published by: Edial Editions, 126 rue du Temple, Paris, 75003, France. TEL 33-1-44788778, FAX 33-1-44788779, is.redaction@edial.fr, http://www.edial.fr. Ed. Jonas Tophoven. Pub. Nicole Bergmann. Adv. contact Thierry Meunier. Circ: 10,000.

THE INTERMOUNTAIN RETAILER. see *FOOD AND FOOD INDUSTRIES—Grocery Trade*

658 GBR ISSN 0965-5999
INTERNAL COMMUNICATION FOCUS. Text in English. 10/yr. GBP 380, USD 495 (effective 2000). back issues avail. **Document type:** *Trade.*
—CCC.

Published by: Informa Law (Subsidiary of: Informa Publishing), Informa House, 30-32 Mortimer St, London, W1W 7RE, United Kingdom. TEL 44-207-5531000, FAX 44-207-5531593. Ed. Vanessa Day. Pub. Frania Weaver.

INTERNATIONAL ABSTRACTS IN OPERATIONS RESEARCH. see *COMPUTERS—Abstracting, Bibliographies, Statistics*

INTERNATIONAL ARTS MANAGER. see *ART*

658.4012 GBR
INTERNATIONAL CENTRE FOR CORPORATE IDENTITY STUDIES. NEWSLETTER. Text in English. 1998. irreg. adv. **Document type:** *Newsletter.* **Description:** Offers information and resources to people interested in corporate identity and reputation.
Media: Online - full text.
Published by: University of Stratchclyde, International Centre for Corporate Identity Studies, Rm 512, Edward Salvesen Hall, Milne's Court, Lawnmarket, Edinburgh, EH1 2PF, United Kingdom. TEL 44-171-681-2448, shaun.powell@stratch.ac.uk, http://www.corporate-id.com/htm/magazine.htm. Ed., Adv. contact Shaun Powell.

658 GBR ISSN 1460-4124
INTERNATIONAL CONSULTANTS' GUIDE. Text in English. 1997. bi-m. free. **Document type:** *Trade.* **Description:** Intends to keep consultants, systems integrators, and analysts working in Europe and wider international markets up-to-date with business and associated software and technology issues.
Published by: Prime Marketing Publications Ltd., Witton House, Lower Rd, Chorleywood, Rickmansworth, Herts WD3 5LB, United Kingdom. TEL 44-1923-285323, FAX 44-1923-285819, info@pmp.co.uk, icg@pmp.co.uk, http://www.consultants-guide.com. Ed. Tim Ring. Pub. Steve Markwell. Adv. contacts Mark Mills, Ms. Zandra Christie. Circ: 20,000 (controlled).

INTERNATIONAL DIRECTORY OF BUSINESS AND MANAGEMENT SCHOLARS AND RESEARCH. see *OCCUPATIONS AND CAREERS*

INTERNATIONAL EMPLOYMENT RELATIONS REVIEW. see *BUSINESS AND ECONOMICS—Labor And Industrial Relations*

INTERNATIONAL FASHION GROUP. ANNUAL REPORT. see *CLOTHING TRADE—Fashions*

INTERNATIONAL FASHION GROUP. BULLETIN. see *CLOTHING TRADE—Fashions*

INTERNATIONAL FASHION GROUP. NEWSLETTER. see *CLOTHING TRADE—Fashions*

INTERNATIONAL HOSPITAL & AGED CARE JOURNAL. see *HEALTH FACILITIES AND ADMINISTRATION*

658 GBR ISSN 1741-9174
▼ ➤ **INTERNATIONAL JOURNAL OF AGILE SYSTEMS AND MANAGEMENT.** Text in English. 2005. 4/yr. USD 450; USD 545 combined subscription print & online eds. (effective 2005). **Document type:** *Journal, Academic/Scholarly.* **Description:** Aims to promote and coordinate knowledge developments in the emerging field of agile organization research, e-supply chain coordination and performance evaluation, knowledge transfer and the spread of good practice.
Related titles: Online - full text ed.: ISSN 1741-9182. USD 450 (effective 2005).
—BLDSC (4541.592500).
Published by: Inderscience Publishers, IEL Editorial Office, PO Box 735, Olney, Bucks MK46 5WB, United Kingdom. TEL 44-1234-240519, FAX 44-1234-240515, ijasm@inderscience.com, http://www.inderscience.com/ijasm. Ed. Dr. Yahaya Yusuf.

658.005 GBR ISSN 1468-5191
INTERNATIONAL JOURNAL OF APPLIED MANAGEMENT. Text in English. 1999. 3/yr. GBP 25 to individuals; GBP 75 to institutions (effective 2000). bk.rev.
Indexed: BrEdI.
—BLDSC (4542.088500), IE, ingenta.
Published by: (Dearne Valley Business School), Sheffield Hallam University Press, c/o Mrs. Monica Moseley, Pub., Sheffield Hallam University Press, Learning Centre, Sheffield, S Yorks S1 1WB, United Kingdom. TEL 44-114-2254702, FAX 44-114-2254478, m.mosely@shu.ac.uk. Ed. Robert H Haigh.

658 JPN ISSN 1618-7504
➤ **INTERNATIONAL JOURNAL OF ASIAN MANAGEMENT.** Text in English. 2001. a. EUR 95 combined subscription to institutions print & online eds. (effective 2005). 1000 p./no.; **Document type:** *Journal, Academic/Scholarly.* **Description:** Deals with the study of management in Asia and highlights specific problems of management relevant to the Asian region.
Related titles: Online - full text ed.: ISSN 1618-7512 (from EBSCO Publishing, ProQuest Information & Learning, Springer LINK, Swets Information Services).
—IE. **CCC.**

Published by: (International Federation of the East Asia Management Association), Springer-Verlag Tokyo (Subsidiary of: Springer Science+Business Media), 3-13 Hongo 3-chome, Bunkyo-ku, Tokyo, 113-0033, Japan. TEL 81-3-38120331, FAX 81-3-38187454, http://link.springer.de/link/service/journals/10276/, http://www.springer-tokyo.co.jp/. Ed. Tasuku Noguchi. Adv. contact Stephan Kroeck TEL 49-30-827875739. Circ: 1,000. **Subscr. in the Americas to:** Springer-Verlag New York, Inc., Journal Fulfillment, PO Box 2485, Secaucus, NJ 07096-2485. TEL 800-777-4643, 201-348-4033, FAX 201-348-4505, journals@springer-ny.com, http://www.springer-ny.com; **Subscr. to:** Springer GmbH Auslieferungsgesellschaft, Haberstr 7, Heidelberg 69126, Germany. TEL 49-6221-345-0, FAX 49-6221-345-4229, subscriptions@springer.de.

➤ **INTERNATIONAL JOURNAL OF BUSINESS.** see *BUSINESS AND ECONOMICS—International Commerce*

658 GBR
INTERNATIONAL JOURNAL OF BUSINESS CONTINUITY MANAGEMENT. Text in English. q. GBP 220, USD 350 (effective 2002). **Description:** Deals with the continuing challenges in business continuity and risk management.
Indexed: Inspec.
Published by: Survive, 107-111 Fleet St, London, EC4A 2AB, United Kingdom. TEL 44-020-7936-9026, FAX 44-020-7936-9126, http://www.survive.comg.

658 GBR ISSN 1740-0589
▼ ➤ **INTERNATIONAL JOURNAL OF BUSINESS ENVIRONMENT.** Text in English. 2005. q. USD 450 to institutions; USD 545 combined subscription to institutions print & online eds. (effective 2005). **Document type:** *Journal, Academic/Scholarly.* **Description:** Addresses managerial issues in the social, political, economic, competitive, and technological environments of business.
Related titles: Online - full text ed.: 2005. USD 430 (effective 2004).
Published by: Inderscience Publishers, IEL Editorial Office, PO Box 735, Olney, Bucks MK46 5WB, United Kingdom. TEL 44-1234-240519, FAX 44-1234-240515, ijbe@inderscience.com, editor@inderscience.com, http://www.inderscience.com/ijbe. **Subscr. to:** World Trade Centre Bldg, 29 route de Pre-Bois, Case Postale 896, Geneva 15 1215, Switzerland. FAX 41-22-7910885, subs@inderscience.com.

658 GBR ISSN 1746-0972
▼ ➤ **INTERNATIONAL JOURNAL OF BUSINESS INFORMATION SYSTEMS.** Text in English. 2005. q. USD 450, USD 545 to institutions (effective 2005). **Document type:** *Journal, Academic/Scholarly.* **Description:** Aims to promote the research and practice of new strategies, tools, techniques and technologies for the design, development and implementation of BIS.
Related titles: Online - full text ed.: ISSN 1746-0980.
Published by: Inderscience Publishers, IEL Editorial Office, PO Box 735, Olney, Bucks MK46 5WB, United Kingdom. TEL 44-1234-240519, FAX 44-1234-240515, ijbis@inderscience.com, info@inderscience.com, http://www.inderscience.com/ijbis. Ed. Angappa Gunasekaran.

658 GBR ISSN 1368-4892
HD28
➤ **INTERNATIONAL JOURNAL OF BUSINESS PERFORMANCE MANAGEMENT.** Abbreviated title: I J B P M. Text in English. 1998. q. USD 450 to institutions; USD 545 combined subscription to institutions print & online eds. (effective 2005). back issues avail.; reprints avail. **Document type:** *Journal, Academic/Scholarly.* **Description:** Aims to provide an interactive and global discussion forum for academics, professionals and practitioners working and interested in research and practice of performance measurement and management.
Related titles: Online - full text ed.: ISSN 1741-5039. USD 450 to institutions (effective 2005) (from EBSCO Publishing).
Indexed: ABIn, BrCerAb, C&ISA, CerAb, CorrAb, E&CAJ, EMA, IAA, Inspec, M&TEA, MBF, METADEX, WAA.
—BLDSC (4542.155860), IE, ingenta, Linda Hall. **CCC.**
Published by: Inderscience Publishers, IEL Editorial Office, PO Box 735, Olney, Bucks MK46 5WB, United Kingdom. TEL 44-1234-240519, FAX 44-1234-240515, ijbpm@inderscience.com, editor@inderscience.com, http://www.inderscience.com/ijbpm. Eds. Alan Stainer, Nelson Tang, Dr. Mohammed A Dorgham. R&P Jeanette Brooks. **Subscr. to:** World Trade Centre Bldg, 29 route de Pre-Bois, Case Postale 896, Geneva 15 1215, Switzerland. FAX 41-22-7910885, subs@inderscience.com.

B

658   GBR   ISSN 1741-8763
INTERNATIONAL JOURNAL OF BUSINESS PROCESS INTEGRATION AND MANAGEMENT. Text in English. q. USD 450 to institutions; USD 545 combined subscription to institutions print & online eds. (effective 2005). **Document type:** *Journal, Academic/Scholarly.* **Description:** Aims to establish an effective channel of communication between policy makers, government agencies, academic and research institutions and persons concerned with the complex role of business processes in e-business solutions, engineering design collaboration, logistics management, etc. It also aims to promote and coordinate developments in the field of business process integration and management.
Related titles: Online - full text ed.: ISSN 1741-8771. USD 450 to institutions (effective 2005).
Indexed: C&ISA, E&CAJ, IAA.
Published by: Inderscience Publishers, IEL Editorial Office, PO Box 735, Olney, Bucks MK46 5WB, United Kingdom. TEL 44-1234-240519, FAX 44-1234-240515, ijbpim@inderscience.com, info@inderscience.com, http://www.inderscience.com/ijbpim. Eds. Frank Leymann, Dr. Liang-Jie Zhang.

658 657   USA   ISSN 1554-5466
▼ ➤ **INTERNATIONAL JOURNAL OF BUSINESS RESEARCH.** Short title: I J B R(International Journal of Business Research). Text in English. 2004 (Oct.). s-a. USD 100 in US & Canada to individuals (effective 2005). **Document type:** *Journal, Academic/Scholarly.* **Description:** Contains original research papers in business, international business, economics and related topics.
Related titles: Online - full content ed.
Published by: Academy of International Business and Economics, PO Box 2536, Ceres, CA 95307. TEL 209-656-7084, review@aibe.org, AKhade@iabe.org, http://www.aibe.org. R&P Dr. Alan S Khade.

658 332   USA   ISSN 1553-9563
▼ ➤ **INTERNATIONAL JOURNAL OF BUSINESS STRATEGY.** Abbreviated title: I J B S(International Journal of Business Strategy). Text in English. 2004 (Oct.). s-a. USD 100 to individuals (effective 2005). **Document type:** *Journal, Academic/Scholarly.* **Description:** Contains original research papers in business policy including management, finance, marketing, OM, economics and related subjects.
Related titles: Online - full content ed.
Published by: International Academy of Business and Economics, 983 Woodland Dr, Turlock, CA 95382-7281, TEL 209-656-7084, AKhade@iabe.org, http://www.iabe.org, http://www.aibe.org. Ed. Dr. Bhavesh S Patel. R&P Dr. Alan S Khade TEL 209-656-7084.

▼ ➤ **INTERNATIONAL JOURNAL OF BUSINESS STUDIES.** see *BUSINESS AND ECONOMICS—International Commerce*

658.812   GBR   ISSN 1463-1415
INTERNATIONAL JOURNAL OF CALL CENTRE MANAGEMENT. Text in English. 1998. q. GBP 275 to individuals; GBP 138 academic; GBP 413 to libraries (effective 2001). adv. back issues avail. **Description:** Provides with the information required to develop and manage a Call Centre, advises at every stage from strategic conception to performance monitoring.
Related titles: Online - full text ed.: (from Gale Group).
—CCC.
Published by: Winthrop Publications Ltd., Brunel House, 55-57 North Wharf Rd, London, W2 1XR, United Kingdom. TEL 44-20-7915-9612, 44-20-7915-9634, 44-20-7915-9660, FAX 44-20-7915-9636, info@winpub.demon.co.uk, http://www.winthrop-publications.co.uk/CCMFrontpage.htm. adv.: page GBP 880.

658 332.6   USA   ISSN 1056-9219
HF1371   CODEN: ICMAFX
➤ **INTERNATIONAL JOURNAL OF COMMERCE AND MANAGEMENT.** Text in English. 1991. q. USD 60 domestic to individuals; USD 80 foreign to individuals; USD 120 domestic to institutions; USD 140 foreign to institutions (effective 2005). bk.rev. **Document type:** *Academic/Scholarly.* **Description:** Promotes the understanding of managers and organizations within and across nations. Directed toward academicians, policy makers and practitioners in business and non-profit organizations.
Related titles: Online - full text ed.: (from EBSCO Publishing, Factiva, Florida Center for Library Automation, Gale Group, O C L C Online Computer Library Center, Inc., ProQuest Information & Learning).
Indexed: ABIn, BRI, CBRI, CPM, ESPM, RiskAb, SOPODA.
—BLDSC (4542.172450), IE, ingenta.
Published by: Indiana University of Pennsylvania, International Academy of Business Disciplines, PO Box 1658, Indiana, PA 15705. TEL 754-357-5759, aaali@grove.iup.edu. Ed., R&P Abbas J Ali.

650.13   USA   ISSN 1044-4068
HD42   CODEN: IOCMEY
➤ **INTERNATIONAL JOURNAL OF CONFLICT MANAGEMENT.** Text in English. 1990. q. USD 38 in US & Canada to individual members; USD 53 elsewhere to individual members (effective 2004). adv. bk.rev. **Document type:** *Journal, Academic/Scholarly.* **Description:** Publishes original empirical and conceptual articles, case studies, simulations, and teaching notes on various aspects of conflict management.
Related titles: Online - full text ed.: (from EBSCO Publishing, Northern Light Technology, Inc., O C L C Online Computer Library Center, Inc., ProQuest Information & Learning).
Indexed: ABIn, ASCA, CurCont, ESPM, FamI, PSA, PerIslam, PsycInfo, PsycholAb, RiskAb, SOPODA, SSA, SSCI, SociolAb, e-psyche.
—BLDSC (4542.175700), IDS, IE, Infotrieve, ingenta. **CCC.**
Published by: International Association of Conflict Management, c/o Judi McLean Parks, IACM Executive Director, Olin School of Business, Washington University, Campus Box 1133, One Brookings Dr., St. Louis, MO 63130-4899. TEL 314-935-7603, FAX 314-935-6359, IACM@mail.olin.wustl.edu, http://www.iacm-conflict.org/ijcm/. Ed. Judi McLean Parks. adv.: B&W page USD 100. Circ: 999 (paid).

➤ **INTERNATIONAL JOURNAL OF CONTEMPORARY HOSPITALITY MANAGEMENT.** see *HOTELS AND RESTAURANTS*

658   GBR   ISSN 1461-4561
INTERNATIONAL JOURNAL OF CUSTOMER RELATIONSHIP MANAGEMENT. Text in English. 1998. q. GBP 295 to individuals; GBP 150 academic; GBP 450 to libraries (effective 2002). adv. **Description:** Gives you an insight into the experiences of companies wordwide who are setting the standarts for selling more products and services through better management of their external relationships. Helps to make strategic marketing decisions and guide a company to a customer-facing position.
Related titles: Online - full text ed.: (from Gale Group).
—BLDSC (4542.182200), IE, ingenta. **CCC.**
Published by: Winthrop Publications Ltd., Brunel House, 55-57 North Wharf Rd, London, W2 1XR, United Kingdom. TEL 44-20-7915-9612, 44-20-7915-9634, 44-20-7915-9660, info@winpub.demon.co.uk, http://www.winthrop-publications.co.uk/CRMfrontpage.htm. Ed. Stephen Calver. adv.: page GBP 450. Circ: 250.

658.4   GBR   ISSN 1741-3591
▼ **INTERNATIONAL JOURNAL OF DISCLOSURE AND GOVERNANCE.** Text in English. 2003 (Oct.). q. GBP 190 in Europe to institutions; USD 300 in North America to institutions; GBP 205 elsewhere to institutions (effective 2004). **Document type:** *Journal, Academic/Scholarly.* **Description:** Devoted exclusively to discussion and analysis of the most significant issues in corporate governance and the effective disclosure of information.
Related titles: Online - full text ed.: (from Gale Group, IngentaConnect, ProQuest Information & Learning).
Indexed: ABIn.
—BLDSC (4542.185700), IE.
Published by: Palgrave Macmillan Ltd. (Subsidiary of: Macmillan Publishers Ltd.), Houndmills, Basingstoke, Hants RG21 6XS, United Kingdom. TEL 44-1256-329242, FAX 44-1256-810526, journal-info@palgrave.com, http://www.palgrave-journals.com/. Eds. Barry Rider, Dr. Chizu Nakajima.

658.054   GBR   ISSN 1467-0305
INTERNATIONAL JOURNAL OF E-BUSINESS STRATEGY MANAGEMENT. Text in English. 1999. q. GBP 350 to individuals; GBP 175 academic; GBP 525 to libraries (effective 2001). adv. back issues avail. **Description:** Presents innovative and practical e-business solutions for companies operating in a business-to-business or business-to-consumer market. Provides a robust e-business strategy in the supply chain, customer-focused operations and internal activities.
Related titles: Online - full text ed.: (from Gale Group).
—BLDSC (4542.189700). **CCC.**
Published by: Winthrop Publications Ltd., Brunel House, 55-57 North Wharf Rd, London, W2 1XR, United Kingdom. TEL 44-20-7915-9612, 44-20-7915-9634, 44-20-7915-9660, FAX 44-20-7915-9636, info@winpub.demon.co.uk, http://www.winthrop-publications.co.uk/EBSMFrontpage.htm. Ed. Andrew Slade. adv.: page GBP 250.

658   GBR   ISSN 0951-354X
LB2805
THE INTERNATIONAL JOURNAL OF EDUCATIONAL MANAGEMENT. Text in English. bi-m. EUR 8,361.79 in Europe; USD 8,619 in North America; AUD 10,789 in Australasia; GBP 5,860.54 in UK & elsewhere (effective 2006). reprint service avail. from PSC. **Document type:** *Journal, Academic/Scholarly.* **Description:** Seeks to widen the horizons of education and management by focusing on a whole range of related issues. The Journal crosses the conventional boundaries which separate the two fields.
Related titles: Online - full text ed.: (from EBSCO Publishing, Emerald Group Publishing Limited, Gale Group, IngentaConnect, O C L C Online Computer Library Center, Inc., ProQuest Information & Learning, Swets Information Services).
Indexed: ABIn, BrEdI, CIJE, CPE, EAA, ERA, ETA, EmerIntel, Emerald, HRA, MEA, RHEA, SEA, SENA, SOMA, TEA.

—BLDSC (4542.199700), IE, Infotrieve, ingenta. **CCC.**
Published by: Emerald Group Publishing Limited, 60-62 Toller Ln, Bradford, W Yorks BD8 9BY, United Kingdom. TEL 44-1274-777700, FAX 44-1274-785200, infomation@emeraldinsight.com, http://www.emeraldinsight.com/ijem.htm. Ed. Brian Roberts.

658   GBR   ISSN 1741-1025
▼ ➤ **INTERNATIONAL JOURNAL OF ELECTRONIC MARKETING AND RETAILING.** Text in English. 2005. q. USD 450 to institutions; USD 545 to institutions print & online eds. (effective 2005). **Document type:** *Journal, Academic/Scholarly.* **Description:** Promotes the advancement, understanding, and practice of electronic marketing and retailing.
Related titles: Online - full text ed.: ISSN 1741-1033. USD 450 to institutions (effective 2005).
Published by: Inderscience Publishers, IEL Editorial Office, PO Box 735, Olney, Bucks MK46 5WB, United Kingdom. TEL 44-1234-240519, FAX 44-1234-240515, ijemr@inderscience.com, info@inderscience.com, http://www.inderscience.com/ijemr. Eds. Dinesh S Dave, Michael J Dotson. **Subscr. to:** World Trade Centre Bldg, 29 route de Pre-Bois, Case Postale 896, Geneva 15 1215, Switzerland. FAX 41-22-7910885, subs@inderscience.com.

658   GBR   ISSN 1471-4825
HV551.2   CODEN: IJEMB6
➤ **INTERNATIONAL JOURNAL OF EMERGENCY MANAGEMENT.** Abbreviated title: I J E M. Text in English. 2002. 4/yr. USD 450 to institutions; USD 545 combined subscription to institutions print & online eds. (effective 2005). bk.rev. back issues avail. **Document type:** *Journal, Academic/Scholarly.* **Description:** Provides a forum where researchers, planners, managers, response personnel and other interested parties can exchange knowledge and information on the use of innovative methods and technologies to improve the ability to avoid, mitigate, respond to, and recover from natural and technological disasters.
Related titles: Online - full content ed.: ISSN 1741-5071. USD 450 to institutions (effective 2005); Online - full text ed.: (from EBSCO Publishing).
Indexed: BrCerAb, C&ISA, CerAb, CivEngAb, CorrAb, E&CAJ, EMA, ESPM, ExcerpMed, H&SSA, I&DA, IAA, Inspec, M&TEA, MBF, METADEX, S&F, SolStAb, WAA, WAE&RSA.
—BLDSC (4542.232650), Linda Hall.
Published by: Inderscience Publishers, IEL Editorial Office, PO Box 735, Olney, Bucks MK46 5WB, United Kingdom. TEL 44-1234-240519, FAX 44-1234-240515, ijem@inderscience.com, editor@inderscience.com, http://www.inderscience.com/ijem. Ed. Jean-Luc Wybo. R&P Jeanette Brooks. Adv. contact Cheryl Busby. **Subscr. to:** World Trade Centre Bldg, 29 route de Pre-Bois, Case Postale 896, Geneva 15 1215, Switzerland. FAX 41-22-7910885.

330   GBR   ISSN 1745-3143
▼ ➤ **INTERNATIONAL JOURNAL OF ENTERPRISE SYSTEMS INTEGRATION AND INTEROPERABILITY.** Text in English. 2005. 4/yr. USD 450; USD 545 combined subscription print & online eds. (effective 2005). **Document type:** *Journal, Academic/Scholarly.* **Description:** To establish an effective channel of communication between manufacturers, scientists, academic and research institutions and persons concerned with the complex role of interoperating enterprises or parts of it. It also aims to promote and coordinate developments in the field of networked and synchronous enterprises.
Related titles: Online - full text ed.: ISSN 1745-3151. forthcoming. USD 450 (effective 2005).
Published by: Inderscience Publishers, IEL Editorial Office, PO Box 735, Olney, Bucks MK46 5WB, United Kingdom. TEL 44-1234-240519, FAX 44-1234-240515, ijesii@inderscience.com, info@inderscience.com, http://www.inderscience.com/ijesii. Ed. Michele Dassisti.

658 790.1   GBR   ISSN 1475-8954
▼ ➤ **INTERNATIONAL JOURNAL OF ENTERTAINMENT TECHNOLOGY AND MANAGEMENT.** Text in English. forthcoming 2006. q. USD 450 to institutions; USD 545 combined subscription to institutions print & online eds. (effective 2005). **Document type:** *Journal, Academic/Scholarly.*
Related titles: Online - full content ed.: ISSN 1741-8046. forthcoming 2006. USD 450 to institutions (effective 2005).
Published by: Inderscience Publishers, IEL Editorial Office, PO Box 735, Olney, Bucks MK46 5WB, United Kingdom. TEL 44-1234-240519, FAX 44-1234-240515, ijenttm@inderscience.com, editor@inderscience.com, http://www.inderscience.com/ijenttm. Ed. Dr. Mohammed A Dorgham. **Subscr. to:** World Trade Centre Bldg, 29 route de Pre-Bois, Case Postale 896, Geneva 15 1215, Switzerland. FAX 41-22-7910885, subs@inderscience.com.

658   USA   ISSN 1099-9264
HB615
➤ **INTERNATIONAL JOURNAL OF ENTREPRENEURSHIP.** Text in English. a. **Document type:** *Journal, Academic/Scholarly.*
Related titles: Online - full text ed.
Published by: (Academy of Entrepreneurship), Allied Academies, 145 Travis Rd., P. O. Box 2689, Cullowhee, NC 28723. http://www.alliedacademies.org/entrepreneurship/ije.html. Ed. Reagan McLaurin.

658 GBR ISSN 1368-275X
➤ **INTERNATIONAL JOURNAL OF ENTREPRENEURSHIP AND INNOVATION MANAGEMENT.** Abbreviated title: I J E I M. Text in English. 2000. 6/yr. USD 540 to institutions; USD 685 combined subscription to institutions print & online eds. (effective 2005). **Document type:** *Journal, Academic/Scholarly.* **Description:** Provides an interface between entrepreneurship and innovation, as well as business corporate strategy and government economic development.
Related titles: Online - full content ed.: ISSN 1741-5098. USD 540 to institutions (effective 2005); Online - full text ed.: (from EBSCO Publishing).
Indexed: ABIn, BrCerAb, C&ISA, CerAb, CorrAb, E&CAJ, EMA, IAA, Inspec, M&TEA, MBF, METADEX, SolStAb, WAA.
—BLDSC (4542.240550), IE, Linda Hall. **CCC.**
Published by: Inderscience Publishers, IEL Editorial Office, PO Box 735, Olney, Bucks MK46 5WB, United Kingdom. TEL 44-1234-240519, FAX 44-1234-240515, ijeim@inderscience.com, editor@inderscience.com, http://www.inderscience.com/ijeim. Ed. Dr. Mohammed A Dorgham. **Subscr. to:** World Trade Centre Bldg, 29 route de Pre-Bois, Case Postale 896, Geneva 15 1215, Switzerland. FAX 41-22-7910885, subs@inderscience.com.

658 GBR ISSN 1476-1297
▼ ➤ **INTERNATIONAL JOURNAL OF ENTREPRENEURSHIP AND SMALL BUSINESS.** Text in English. 2003. q. USD 450 to institutions; USD 545 combined subscription to institutions print & online eds. (effective 2005). **Document type:** *Journal, Academic/Scholarly.* **Description:** Provides an international forum in the fields of entrepreneurship and small business management.
Related titles: Online - full content ed.: ISSN 1741-8054. USD 450 to institutions (effective 2005); Online - full text ed.: (from EBSCO Publishing).
Indexed: C&ISA, E&CAJ, IAA, Inspec.
—BLDSC (4542.240560), IE.
Published by: Inderscience Publishers, IEL Editorial Office, PO Box 735, Olney, Bucks MK46 5WB, United Kingdom. TEL 44-1234-240519, FAX 44-1234-240515, ijesb@inderscience.com, editor@inderscience.com, http://www.inderscience.com/ijesb. Ed. Dr. Mohammed A Dorgham. **Subscr. to:** World Trade Centre Bldg, 29 route de Pre-Bois, Case Postale 896, Geneva 15 1215, Switzerland. FAX 41-22-7910885, subs@inderscience.com.

➤ **INTERNATIONAL JOURNAL OF ENVIRONMENTAL TECHNOLOGY AND MANAGEMENT.** see *ENVIRONMENTAL STUDIES*

658 GBR ISSN 1478-1476
▼ ➤ **INTERNATIONAL JOURNAL OF FORENSIC ENGINEERING AND MANAGEMENT.** Text in English. 2004. q. USD 450 to institutions; USD 545 combined subscription to institutions print & online eds. (effective 2005). **Document type:** *Journal, Academic/Scholarly.* **Description:** Provides information on failure in technical and societal systems.
Related titles: Online - full text ed.: ISSN 1479-3091. USD 450 to institutions (effective 2005).
Published by: Inderscience Publishers, IEL Editorial Office, PO Box 735, Olney, Bucks MK46 5WB, United Kingdom. TEL 44-1234-240519, FAX 44-1234-240515, ijfem@inderscience.com, info@inderscience.com, http://www.inderscience.com/ijfem. **Subscr. to:** World Trade Centre Bldg, 29 route de Pre-Bois, Case Postale 896, Geneva 15 1215, Switzerland. FAX 41-22-7910885, subs@inderscience.com.

➤ **INTERNATIONAL JOURNAL OF HOSPITALITY AND TOURISM ADMINISTRATION.** see *HOTELS AND RESTAURANTS*

➤ **INTERNATIONAL JOURNAL OF HOSPITALITY MANAGEMENT.** see *HOTELS AND RESTAURANTS*

658 NLD ISSN 0167-7187
HD28 CODEN: IJIODY
➤ **INTERNATIONAL JOURNAL OF INDUSTRIAL ORGANIZATION.** Text in English. 1983. 6/yr. EUR 1,159 in Europe to institutions; JPY 153,900 in Japan to institutions; USD 1,295 elsewhere to institutions (effective 2006). bk.rev. stat. index. back issues avail.; reprints avail. **Document type:** *Journal, Academic/Scholarly.* **Description:** Provides a full coverage of both theoretical and empirical work within the field of industrial organization, as well as covering traditional issues of market structure and performance.
Related titles: Microfiche ed.; Online - full text ed.: (from EBSCO Publishing, Gale Group, IngentaConnect, ScienceDirect, Swets Information Services).
Indexed: ABIn, ASCA, BAS, CPM, CREJ, CurCont, Emerald, Englnd, IBSS, Inspec, JEL, PCI, SCIMP, SPAA, SSCI.
—BLDSC (4542.304500), IDS, IE, Infotrieve, ingenta. **CCC.**
Published by: Elsevier BV, North-Holland (Subsidiary of: Elsevier Science & Technology), Sara Burgerhartstraat 25, Amsterdam, 1055 KV, Netherlands. TEL 31-20-485-3911, FAX 31-20-485-2457, ijlo@mgmt.purdue.edu, nlinfo-f@elsevier.nl, http://www.elsevier.com/locate/ijio, http://www.elsevier.nl. Eds. B. Caillaud, N. Gandal, P. Bajari. **Subscr. to:** Elsevier BV, PO Box 211, Amsterdam 1000 AE, Netherlands. TEL 31-20-485-3757, FAX 31-20-485-3432, http://www.elsevier.nl.

658 GBR ISSN 1744-2303
▼ ➤ **INTERNATIONAL JOURNAL OF INFORMATION AND OPERATIONS MANAGEMENT EDUCATION.** Text in English. 2005. q. USD 450, USD 545 to institutions (effective 2005). bk.rev. **Document type:** *Journal, Academic/Scholarly.* **Description:** Promotes research and practice of innovation and lifetime learning in information systems and operations management. Aims to help professionals working in the field of information systems and operations management, academic educators, industry consultants, and practitioners to contribute, to disseminate and to learn from each other's work.
Related titles: Online - full text ed.: ISSN 1744-2311.
Published by: Inderscience Publishers, IEL Editorial Office, PO Box 735, Olney, Bucks MK46 5WB, United Kingdom. ijiome@inderscience.com, http://www.inderscience.com/ijiome. Ed. Angappa Gunasekaran.

658 GBR ISSN 1479-3121
▼ ➤ **INTERNATIONAL JOURNAL OF INFORMATION SYSTEMS AND CHANGE MANAGEMENT.** Text in English. 2005. q. USD 450 to institutions; USD 545 combined subscription to institutions print & online eds. (effective 2005). **Document type:** *Journal, Academic/Scholarly.* **Description:** Promote the research and practice of information systems and change management. Aims to establish an effective channel of communication between academic educators, information systems workers, managers, industry consultants, and practitioners to contribute, disseminate and learn from each other's work.
Related titles: Online - full text ed.: ISSN 1479-313X. forthcoming 2005. USD 450 to institutions (effective 2005).
Published by: Inderscience Publishers, IEL Editorial Office, PO Box 735, Olney, Bucks MK46 5WB, United Kingdom. TEL 44-1234-240519, FAX 44-1234-240515, ijiscm@inderscience.com, info@inderscience.com, http://www.inderscience.com/ijiscm. Ed. David C Chou. **Subscr. to:** World Trade Centre Bldg, 29 route de Pre-Bois, Case Postale 896, Geneva 15 1215, Switzerland. FAX 41-22-7910885, subs@inderscience.com.

658 GBR ISSN 1471-8197
➤ **INTERNATIONAL JOURNAL OF INNOVATION AND LEARNING.** Text in English. 2001. q. USD 450; USD 545 combined subscription print & online eds. (effective 2005). **Document type:** *Journal, Academic/Scholarly.* **Description:** Aims to develop, promote and coordinate the development and practice of innovation and learning.
Formerly: International Journal of Innovation and Organizational Learning
Related titles: Online - full text ed.: ISSN 1741-8089. USD 450 to institutions (effective 2005) (from EBSCO Publishing).
Indexed: BrCerAb, C&ISA, CerAb, CorrAb, E&CAJ, EMA, IAA, Inspec, M&TEA, MBF, METADEX, WAA.
—BLDSC (4542.305700), IE, Linda Hall.
Published by: Inderscience Publishers, IEL Editorial Office, PO Box 735, Olney, Bucks MK46 5WB, United Kingdom. TEL 44-1234-240519, FAX 44-1234-240515, ijil@inderscience.com, editor@inderscience.com, http://www.inderscience.com/ijil. **Subscr. to:** World Trade Centre Bldg, 29 route de Pre-Bois, Case Postale 896, Geneva 15 1215, Switzerland. FAX 41-22-7910885, subs@inderscience.com.

658 GBR ISSN 1740-8822
▼ ➤ **INTERNATIONAL JOURNAL OF INNOVATION AND SUSTAINABLE DEVELOPMENT.** Text in English. 2005. 4/yr. USD 450; USD 545 combined subscription print & online eds. (effective 2005). bk.rev. **Document type:** *Journal, Academic/Scholarly.* **Description:** Provides a vehicle for dissemination and exchange of information between professionals, academics, researchers, policy-makers and educators and all others interested in innovative and challenging thinking about the complexities of sustainable development.
Related titles: Online - full text ed.: ISSN 1740-8830. USD 450 (effective 2005).
Published by: Inderscience Publishers, IEL Editorial Office, PO Box 735, Olney, Bucks MK46 5WB, United Kingdom. TEL 44-1234-240519, FAX 44-1234-240515, ijisd@inderscience.com, info@inderscience.com, http://www.inderscience.com/ijisd. Ed. Dr. Delyse V Springett.

▼ ➤ **INTERNATIONAL JOURNAL OF INNOVATION AND TECHNOLOGY MANAGEMENT.** see *ENGINEERING*

658 GBR ISSN 1363-9196
HD45
➤ **INTERNATIONAL JOURNAL OF INNOVATION MANAGEMENT.** Abbreviated title: I J I M. Text in English. 1997. q. SGD 276, USD 158, EUR 152 to individuals; SGD 689, USD 395, EUR 379 combined subscription to institutions print & online eds. (effective 2006). back issues avail. **Document type:** *Journal, Academic/Scholarly.* **Description:** Dedicated to the advancement of academic research and management practice in the field of innovation management.
Related titles: Online - full text ed.: (from EBSCO Publishing, O C L C Online Computer Library Center, Inc., Swets Information Services).
Indexed: IBSS.
—BLDSC (4542.305800), IE, Infotrieve, ingenta. **CCC.**
Published by: Imperial College Press (Subsidiary of: World Scientific Publishing Co. Pte. Ltd.), 57 Shelton St, London, WC2H 9HE, United Kingdom. TEL 44-20-7836-3954, FAX 44-20-7836-2002, edit@icpress.co.uk, http://www.worldscinet.com/ijim/ijim.shtml, http://www.icpress.co.uk/. Ed. Joe Tidd TEL 44-1273-686758. **Dist. in the US by:** World Scientific Publishing Co., Inc., 1060 Main St, River Edge, NJ 07661. TEL 201-487-9655, 800-227-7562, FAX 201-487-9656, 888-977-2665, wspc@wspc.com.

658 GBR ISSN 1476-1300
▼ ➤ **INTERNATIONAL JOURNAL OF INTERNET AND ENTERPRISE MANAGEMENT.** Short title: I J I E M. Text in English. 2003. q. USD 450 to institutions; USD 545 combined subscription to institutions print & online eds. (effective 2005). **Document type:** *Journal, Academic/Scholarly.* **Description:** Focuses on the emerging changes in enterprise management, its organisational structure, competitive strategies, and management methods, brought about by the internet and information technology applications, and their implications on the associated process, products, and services.
Related titles: Online - full content ed.: ISSN 1741-5330. USD 450 to institutions (effective 2005); Online - full text ed.: (from EBSCO Publishing).
Indexed: BrCerAb, C&ISA, CerAb, CorrAb, E&CAJ, EMA, ErgAb, IAA, Inspec, M&TEA, MBF, METADEX, WAA.
—BLDSC (4542.311100), IE, Linda Hall.
Published by: Inderscience Publishers, IEL Editorial Office, PO Box 735, Olney, Bucks MK46 5WB, United Kingdom. TEL 44-1234-240519, FAX 44-1234-240515, 44-1234-240515, ijiem@inderscience.com, editor@inderscience.com, http://www.inderscience.com/ijiem. Ed. Dr. Eldon Y Li TEL 805-756-2964. **Subscr. to:** World Trade Centre Bldg, 29 route de Pre-Bois, Case Postale 896, Geneva 15 1215, Switzerland. FAX 41-22-7910885, subs@inderscience.com.

B

658 GBR ISSN 1746-6962
▼ ➤ **INTERNATIONAL JOURNAL OF INVENTORY RESEARCH.** Text in English. forthcoming 2006. q. USD 450 to institutions; USD 545 combined subscription to institutions print & online (effective 2005). **Document type:** *Journal, Academic/Scholarly.*
Related titles: Online - full content ed.: ISSN 1746-6970. forthcoming 2006.
Published by: Inderscience Publishers, IEL Editorial Office, PO Box 735, Olney, Bucks MK46 5WB, United Kingdom. TEL 44-1234-240519, FAX 44-1234-240515, ijir@inderscience.com, info@inderscience.com, http://www.inderscience.com/ijir. Ed. Thomas L Urban.

658 GBR ISSN 1741-1009
▼ ➤ **INTERNATIONAL JOURNAL OF KNOWLEDGE AND LEARNING.** Text in English. 2005. 4/yr. USD 450; USD 545 combined subscription print & online eds. (effective 2005). **Document type:** *Journal, Academic/Scholarly.* **Description:** Aims to foster multidisciplinary discussion and research on knowledge-intensive approaches to learning management and learning processes at the individual, organizational and national levels.
Related titles: Online - full text ed.: ISSN 1741-1017. USD 450 (effective 2005).
—BLDSC (4542.311820).
Published by: Inderscience Publishers, IEL Editorial Office, PO Box 735, Olney, Bucks MK46 5WB, United Kingdom. TEL 44-1234-240519, FAX 44-1234-240515, ijkl@inderscience.com, info@inderscience.com, http://www.inderscience.com/ijkl. Ed. Miltiadis Lytras.

658.4038 003.54 USA ISSN 1548-0666
▼ **INTERNATIONAL JOURNAL OF KNOWLEDGE MANAGEMENT.** Text in English. 2005. q. USD 85 to individuals; USD 195 to institutions (effective 2005). **Document type:** *Journal, Academic/Scholarly.* **Description:** Covers all aspects of the knowledge management discipline, from organizational issues to technology support to knowledge representation. Provides a forum for global aspects of knowledge management and for differing cultural perspectives on the use of knowledge and knowledge management.
Related titles: Online - full text ed.: ISSN 1548-0658. 2005.
Indexed: C&ISA, E&CAJ, IAA.
Published by: (Information Resources Management Association), Idea Group Publishing (Subsidiary of: Idea Group Inc.), 701 E Chocolate Ave, Ste 200, Hershey, PA 17033-1240. TEL 717-533-8845, FAX 717-533-7115, cust@idea-group.com, http://www.idea-group.com/journals/details.asp?id=4288. Ed. Murray E Jennex.

658 GBR ISSN 1743-8268
▼ ➤ **INTERNATIONAL JOURNAL OF KNOWLEDGE MANAGEMENT STUDIES.** Text in English. 2005 (Nov.). 4/yr. USD 450; USD 545 combined subscription print & online eds. (effective 2005). **Document type:** *Journal, Academic/Scholarly.*
Related titles: Online - full text ed.: ISSN 1743-8276. USD 450 (effective 2005).
Published by: Inderscience Publishers, IEL Editorial Office, PO Box 735, Olney, Bucks MK46 5WB, United Kingdom. TEL 44-1234-240519, FAX 44-1234-240515, ijkms@inderscience.com, info@inderscience.com, http://www.inderscience.com/ijkms. Ed. P H J Hendriks.

658 GBR ISSN 1740-2875
▼ ➤ **INTERNATIONAL JOURNAL OF LEARNING AND CHANGE.** Text in English. 2004. q. USD 430; USD 520 combined subscription for print & online eds. (effective 2004). **Document type:** *Journal, Academic/Scholarly.*
Related titles: Online - full text ed.: ISSN 1740-2883. USD 430 (effective 2004).
Published by: Inderscience Publishers, IEL Editorial Office, PO Box 735, Olney, Bucks MK46 5WB, United Kingdom. TEL 44-1234-240519, FAX 44-1234-240515, ijlc@inderscience.com, info@inderscience.com, http://www.inderscience.com/ijlc. **Subscr. to:** World Trade Centre Bldg, 29 route de Pre-Bois, Case Postale 896, Geneva 15 1215, Switzerland. FAX 41-22-7910885, subs@inderscience.com.

658 GBR ISSN 0957-4093
➤ **THE INTERNATIONAL JOURNAL OF LOGISTICS MANAGEMENT.** Text in English. 1990. 2/yr. EUR 249.04 in Europe; USD 279 in North America; AUD 389 in Australasia; GBP 172.91 in the UK & elsewhere (effective 2006). adv. bk.rev. illus. back issues avail.; reprints avail. **Document type:** *Journal, Academic/Scholarly.* **Description:** Aims to provide executives and teachers with reports of current developments in the fields of logistics management and supply chain management. Facilitates the interchange of information about logistics management among business planners and researchers on a worldwide basis.
Related titles: Online - full text ed.: (from EBSCO Publishing, Northern Light Technology, Inc., O C L C Online Computer Library Center, Inc., ProQuest Information & Learning).
Indexed: ABIn, CLT&T, Emerald, HRIS, LogistBibl, TTI.
—BLDSC (4542.321800), IE, Infotrieve, ingenta. **CCC.**
Published by: (International Logistics Research Institute, Inc. USA), Emerald Group Publishing Limited, 60-62 Toller Ln, Bradford, W Yorks BD8 9BY, United Kingdom. TEL 44-1274-777700, FAX 44-1274-785200, infomation@emeraldinsight.com, http://www.emeraldinsight.com, http://www.emeraldinsight.com/. Eds. Douglas Lambert, Martin Christopher. R&P Mr. John Eggleton. Circ: 2,000 (paid).

658 GBR ISSN 1742-7967
▼ ➤ **INTERNATIONAL JOURNAL OF LOGISTICS SYSTEMS AND MANAGEMENT.** Text in English. 2004. q. USD 450 to institutions; USD 545 to institutions print & online eds. (effective 2005). **Document type:** *Journal, Academic/Scholarly.* **Description:** Acts as a vehicle to help professionals, academics and researchers, working in the field of logistics systems and management, to disseminate information and latest developments and to learn from each other's research.
Related titles: Online - full text ed.: ISSN 1742-7975. USD 450 to institutions (effective 2005) (from EBSCO Publishing).
Indexed: C&ISA, E&CAJ, IAA, Inspec.
—BLDSC (4542.321850).
Published by: Inderscience Publishers, IEL Editorial Office, PO Box 735, Olney, Bucks MK46 5WB, United Kingdom. TEL 44-1234-240519, FAX 44-1234-240515, ijlsm@inderscience.com, info@inderscience.com, http://www.inderscience.com/ijlsm. **Subscr. to:** World Trade Centre Bldg, 29 route de Pre-Bois, Case Postale 896, Geneva 15 1215, Switzerland. FAX 41-22-7910885, subs@inderscience.com.

658 657 GBR ISSN 0813-0183
➤ **INTERNATIONAL JOURNAL OF MANAGEMENT.** Text in English. 1984. q. GBP 90, USD 150 to individuals (effective 2004). **Document type:** *Journal, Academic/Scholarly.* **Description:** Includes Articles concerning the theory and practice of management.
Related titles: Online - full text ed.: (from EBSCO Publishing, O C L C Online Computer Library Center, Inc., ProQuest Information & Learning).
Indexed: ABIn, APEL, BusI, CPM, CurCont, Emerald, PMA, ST&MA, WorkRelAb.
—BLDSC (4542.325700), IE, Infotrieve, ingenta.
Address: PO Box 982, Poole, Dorset BH12 5YF, United Kingdom. intjnlmgmt@aol.com. Ed. Christopher Orpen. Circ: 1,000 (paid).

658 GBR ISSN 1462-4621
➤ **INTERNATIONAL JOURNAL OF MANAGEMENT AND DECISION MAKING.** Abbreviated title: I J A R G E. Text in English. 2000. q. USD 450 to institutions; USD 545 combined subscription to institutions print & online eds. (effective 2005). **Document type:** *Journal, Academic/Scholarly.* **Description:** Provides a new venue for high-quality papers focusing on the analytical and empirical study of management processes in private and public sector organizations.
Related titles: Online - full text ed.: ISSN 1741-5187. USD 450 (effective 2005) (from EBSCO Publishing).
Indexed: ABIn, BrCerAb, C&ISA, CerAb, CorrAb, E&CAJ, EMA, IAA, Inspec, M&TEA, MBF, METADEX, WAA.
—BLDSC (4542.325710), Linda Hall.
Published by: Inderscience Publishers, IEL Editorial Office, PO Box 735, Olney, Bucks MK46 5WB, United Kingdom. TEL 44-1234-240519, FAX 44-1234-240515, ijmdm@inderscience.com, editor@inderscience.com, http://www.inderscience.com/ijmdm. Ed. Dr. Mohammed A Dorgham. **Subscr. to:** World Trade Centre Bldg, 29 route de Pre-Bois, Case Postale 896, Geneva 15 1215, Switzerland. FAX 41-22-7910885, subs@inderscience.com.

658 GBR ISSN 1468-4330
➤ **INTERNATIONAL JOURNAL OF MANAGEMENT AND ENTERPRISE DEVELOPMENT.** Abbreviated title: I J M E D. Text in English. 2001. 4/yr. USD 450; USD 545 combined subscription print & online eds. (effective 2005). **Document type:** *Journal, Academic/Scholarly.* **Description:** Provides a forum for SME start-up developments and the associated management, product and organizational issues from concept to market.
Related titles: Online - full text ed.: ISSN 1741-8127. USD 450 to institutions (effective 2005) (from EBSCO Publishing).
Indexed: BrCerAb, C&ISA, CerAb, CorrAb, E&CAJ, EMA, IAA, Inspec, M&TEA, MBF, METADEX, WAA.
—BLDSC (4542.325715), IE, Linda Hall.
Published by: Inderscience Publishers, IEL Editorial Office, PO Box 735, Olney, Bucks MK46 5WB, United Kingdom. TEL 44-1234-240519, FAX 44-1234-240515, ijmed@inderscience.com, editor@inderscience.com, http://www.inderscience.com/ijmed. **Subscr. to:** World Trade Centre Bldg, 29 route de Pre-Bois, Case Postale 896, Geneva 15 1215, Switzerland. FAX 41-22-7910885, subs@inderscience.com.

658 IND ISSN 0970-7328
INTERNATIONAL JOURNAL OF MANAGEMENT AND SYSTEMS. Text in English. 1985. bi-m. USD 60 (effective 2000). **Document type:** *Academic/Scholarly.*
Formerly (until 1988): Indian Journal of Management and Systems (0970-0439)
Indexed: CIS, ST&MA.
Published by: (Technocrat Publications Centre), Hindustan Publishing Corporation (India), 4805-24, Bharat Ram Rd., 1st Fl., Flats 1 & 2, Darya Ganj, New Delhi, 110 002, India. TEL 91-11-325-4401, FAX 91-11-6193511, hpcpd@nda.vsnl.net.in, hpcpd@hpc.cc, http://www.hpc.cc, http://www.bizdelhi.com/publisher/hpc.

658 GBR ISSN 1478-1484
▼ **INTERNATIONAL JOURNAL OF MANAGEMENT CONCEPTS AND PHILOSOPHY.** Abbreviated title: I J M C P. Text in English. 2003. q. USD 450 to institutions; USD 545 combined subscription to institutions print & online eds. (effective 2005). **Document type:** *Journal, Trade.* **Description:** Addresses all aspects of management forms and function while encouraging cross-functional dialogue and approaches.
Related titles: Online - full text ed.: ISSN 1741-8135. USD 450 to institutions (effective 2005) (from EBSCO Publishing).
—BLDSC (4542.325751), IE.
Published by: Inderscience Publishers, IEL Editorial Office, PO Box 735, Olney, Bucks MK46 5WB, United Kingdom. TEL 44-1234-240519, FAX 44-1234-240515, ijmcp@inderscience.com, editor@inderscience.com, http://www.inderscience.com/ijmcp. Ed. Pervaiz K Ahmed. **Subscr. to:** World Trade Centre Bldg, 29 route de Pre-Bois, Case Postale 896, Geneva 15 1215, Switzerland. FAX 41-22-7910885, subs@inderscience.com.

658 GBR ISSN 1472-8117
THE INTERNATIONAL JOURNAL OF MANAGEMENT EDUCATION. Text in English. 2000. 3/yr. software rev. **Description:** Covers teaching and learning in business and management.
Indexed: BrEdI.
—BLDSC (4542.325760), IE.
Published by: Learning and Teaching Support Network Centre for Business, Management and Accountancy, Business Education Support Team, School of Management, University of East Anglia, Norwich, NR4 7TJ, United Kingdom. TEL 44-1603-593756, FAX 44-1603-593343, best@uea.ac.uk, http://www.business.ltsn.ac.uk.

658 AUS ISSN 1441-5410
INTERNATIONAL JOURNAL OF MANAGEMENT IN SMALL AND MEDIUM SIZED ENTERPRISES. Text in English. 2000. s-a.
Media: Online - full text.
Published by: University of Southern Queensland, Department of Human Resource Management and Employment Relations, Toowoomba, QLD 4350, Australia. hrm@usq.edu.au, http://www.usq.edu.au/faculty/business/dept_hrm/HRMJournal/IJMSMEHome.htm.

658 GBR ISSN 1477-9064
▼ ➤ **INTERNATIONAL JOURNAL OF MANAGEMENT PRACTICE.** Text in English. 2003. q. USD 450 to institutions; USD 545 combined subscription to institutions print & online eds. (effective 2005). **Document type:** *Journal, Academic/Scholarly.* **Description:** Publishes papers that are able to show how to turn theory into practice or describe leading managerial practices that enable business performance.
Related titles: Online - full text ed.: ISSN 1741-8143. USD 450 (effective 2005) (from EBSCO Publishing).
Indexed: BrCerAb, C&ISA, CerAb, CorrAb, E&CAJ, EMA, IAA, Inspec, M&TEA, MBF, METADEX, WAA.
—BLDSC (4542.325765), IE, Linda Hall.
Published by: Inderscience Publishers, IEL Editorial Office, PO Box 735, Olney, Bucks MK46 5WB, United Kingdom. TEL 44-1234-240519, FAX 44-1234-240515, ijmp@inderscience.com, editor@inderscience.com, http://www.inderscience.com/ijmp. Ed. Pervaiz K Ahmed. **Subscr. to:** World Trade Centre Bldg, 29 route de Pre-Bois, Case Postale 896, Geneva 15 1215, Switzerland. FAX 41-22-7910885, subs@inderscience.com.

658 GBR ISSN 1460-8545
HD28
INTERNATIONAL JOURNAL OF MANAGEMENT REVIEWS. Text in English. 1999. q. USD 865 combined subscription in the Americas to institutions print & online; GBP 535 combined subscription elsewhere to institutions print & online (effective 2004); Included with subscr. to British Journal of Management. reprint service avail. from PSC. **Document type:** *Journal, Academic/Scholarly.*
Related titles: Online - full text ed.: ISSN 1468-2370. USD 824 in the Americas to institutions; GBP 508 elsewhere to institutions (effective 2004) (from Blackwell Synergy, EBSCO Publishing, Gale Group, IngentaConnect, O C L C Online Computer Library Center, Inc., Swets Information Services).
Indexed: ABIn, CurCont, Emerald, SSCI.
—BLDSC (4542.325770), IE, Infotrieve, ingenta. **CCC.**
Published by: Blackwell Publishing Ltd., 9600 Garsington Rd, Oxford, OX4 2ZG, United Kingdom. TEL 44-1865-776868, FAX 44-1865-714591, customerservices@oxon.blackwellpublishing.com, http://www.blackwellpublishing.com/journal.asp?ref=1460-8545&site=1.

▼ **INTERNATIONAL JOURNAL OF MANAGERIAL FINANCE.** see *BUSINESS AND ECONOMICS—Banking And Finance*

658 374 GBR ISSN 1746-725X
▼ ➤ **INTERNATIONAL JOURNAL OF MOBILE LEARNING AND ORGANISATION.** Text in English. forthcoming 2006. q. USD 450 to institutions; USD 545 combined subscription to institutions (effective 2005). **Document type:** *Journal, Academic/Scholarly.*
Related titles: Online - full content ed.: ISSN 1746-7268. forthcoming 2006.
Published by: Inderscience Publishers, IEL Editorial Office, PO Box 735, Olney, Bucks MK46 5WB, United Kingdom. TEL 44-1234-240519, FAX 44-1234-240515, ijmlo@inderscience.com, info@inderscience.com, http://www.inderscience.com/ijmlo. Ed. Dr. Jason C H Chen.

658.575 GBR ISSN 1464-6684
INTERNATIONAL JOURNAL OF NEW PRODUCT DEVELOPMENT & INNOVATION MANAGEMENT✶. Text in English. 1998. q. adv. back issues avail. **Description:** Contains case studies and real-life examples guiding decision making and warning of potential problems, offers harness applied technology to create new market opportunities and develop an innovation culture in organizations.
Related titles: Online - full text ed.: (from Gale Group).
—**CCC.**
Published by: Winthrop Publications Ltd., Brunel House, 55-57 North Wharf Rd, London, W2 1XR, United Kingdom. TEL 44-20-7915-9612, 44-20-7915-9634, 44-20-7915-9660, FAX 44-20-7915-9636, info@winpub.demon.co.uk, http://www.winthrop-publications.co.uk/NPDFrontpage.htm. Ed. Margaret Bruce. adv.: page GBP 250.

658 GBR ISSN 0144-3577
TS155.A1 CODEN: IOPMDU
➤ **INTERNATIONAL JOURNAL OF OPERATIONS AND PRODUCTION MANAGEMENT.** Text in English. 1980. m. EUR 10,003.91 in Europe; USD 10,169 in North America; AUD 11,879 in Australasia; GBP 6,893.66 in UK & elsewhere (effective 2006). bk.rev. illus. cum.index. reprint service avail. from PSC. **Document type:** *Academic/Scholarly.* **Description:** Covers all aspects of operations management.
Related titles: CD-ROM ed.; Online - full text ed.: (from EBSCO Publishing, Emerald Group Publishing Limited, Florida Center for Library Automation, Gale Group, IngentaConnect, O C L C Online Computer Library Center, Inc., ProQuest Information & Learning, Swets Information Services).
Indexed: ABIn, ADPA, ASCA, BPIA, BrCerAb, BusI, C&ISA, CPM, CerAb, CivEngAb, CorrAb, CurCont, E&CAJ, EMA, EmerIntel, Emerald, EngInd, ErgAb, IAA, IAOP, Inspec, M&TEA, MBF, METADEX, SSCI, SolStAb, WAA.
—BLDSC (4542.425000), AskIEEE, Ei, IDS, IE, Infotrieve, ingenta, Linda Hall. **CCC.**
Published by: Emerald Group Publishing Limited, 60-62 Toller Ln, Bradford, W Yorks BD8 9BY, United Kingdom. TEL 44-1274-777700, FAX 44-1274-785200, rknowles@emeraldinsight.com, infomation@emeraldinsight.com, http://www.emeraldinsight.com/ijopm.htm. Eds. Dr. Andrew Taylor, Dr. Margaret Webster.

658.8 USA ISSN 1082-1910
TS155.A1
➤ **INTERNATIONAL JOURNAL OF OPERATIONS AND QUANTITATIVE MANAGEMENT.** Abbreviated title: I J O Q M. Text in English. 1995. 3/yr. USD 200 domestic; USD 215 foreign (effective 2003). adv. abstr. **Document type:** *Journal, Academic/Scholarly.* **Description:** Provides an international forum to discuss advancements in operations management, operations research, quantitative management, and management science.
Related titles: Online - full text ed.
Indexed: ESPM, IAOP, RiskAb.
—BLDSC (4542.427000), IE, ingenta.
Address: c/o Omprakash K. Gupta, Department of Management & Marketing, Prairie View A & M University, Prairie View, TX 77446-0638. TEL 936-857-2122, FAX 936-857-2243, Om_Gupta@pvamu.edu. Ed. Omprakash K. Gupta.

330 GBR ISSN 1742-5360
▼ ➤ **INTERNATIONAL JOURNAL OF OPPORTUNITY, GROWTH AND VALUE CREATION.** Text in English. 2005. 4/yr. USD 450; USD 545 combined subscription print & online eds. (effective 2005). **Document type:** *Journal, Academic/Scholarly.* **Description:** Provides an international forum in the field of management with the particular focus on the phenomena of opportunity, growth and value creation.
Related titles: Online - full text ed.: ISSN 1742-5379. USD 450 (effective 2005).
Published by: Inderscience Publishers, IEL Editorial Office, PO Box 735, Olney, Bucks MK46 5WB, United Kingdom. TEL 44-1234-240519, FAX 44-1234-240515, ijogvc@inderscience.com, info@inderscience.com, http://www.inderscience.com/ijogvc. Ed. Terrence E Brown.

658 GBR ISSN 1460-6739
➤ **INTERNATIONAL JOURNAL OF PROCESS MANAGEMENT AND BENCHMARKING.** Abbreviated title: I J P M B. Text in English. 2000. q. USD 450 to institutions; USD 545 combined subscription to institutions print & online eds. (effective 2005). **Document type:** *Journal, Academic/Scholarly.* **Description:** Provides a refereed reference in process management, TQM and benchmarking. Coverage is extended to private and public sectors, manufacturing and services industries.
Related titles: Online - full text ed.: ISSN 1741-816X. USD 450 to institutions (effective 2005).
Indexed: C&ISA, E&CAJ, IAA, Inspec.
—BLDSC (4542.484100).
Published by: Inderscience Publishers, IEL Editorial Office, PO Box 735, Olney, Bucks MK46 5WB, United Kingdom. TEL 44-1234-240519, FAX 44-1234-240515, ijpmb@inderscience.com, editor@inderscience.com, http://www.inderscience.com/ijpmb. Ed. Dr. Mohammed A Dorgham. **Subscr. to:** World Trade Centre Bldg, 29 route de Pre-Bois, Case Postale 896, Geneva 15 1215, Switzerland. FAX 41-22-7910885, subs@inderscience.com.

658 GBR ISSN 1477-9056
▼ ➤ **INTERNATIONAL JOURNAL OF PRODUCT DEVELOPMENT.** Text in English. 2003. 4/yr. USD 450 to institutions; USD 545 combined subscription to institutions print & online eds. (effective 2005). **Document type:** *Journal, Academic/Scholarly.* **Description:** Provides an authoritative source of information in the field of product development and innovation. It is devoted to the development, promotion and coordination of the science and practice of this field.
Related titles: Online - full text ed.: ISSN 1741-8178. USD 450 to institutions (effective 2005) (from EBSCO Publishing).
Indexed: BrCerAb, C&ISA, CerAb, CorrAb, E&CAJ, EMA, ErgAb, IAA, Inspec, M&TEA, MBF, METADEX, WAA.
—BLDSC (4542.484500), IE, Linda Hall.
Published by: Inderscience Publishers, IEL Editorial Office, PO Box 735, Olney, Bucks MK46 5WB, United Kingdom. TEL 44-1234-240519, FAX 44-1234-240515, ijpd@inderscience.com, editor@inderscience.com, http://www.inderscience.com/ijpd. Ed. Dr. Mohammed A Dorgham. **Subscr. to:** World Trade Centre Bldg, 29 route de Pre-Bois, Case Postale 896, Geneva 15 1215, Switzerland. FAX 41-22-7910885, subs@inderscience.com.

➤ **INTERNATIONAL JOURNAL OF PRODUCTION ECONOMICS.** see *ENGINEERING—Industrial Engineering*

658.54 GBR ISSN 1741-0401
HD56
➤ **INTERNATIONAL JOURNAL OF PRODUCTIVITY AND PERFORMANCE MANAGEMENT.** Text in English. 1952. 7/yr. (8/yr from 2004)). EUR 7,763.66 in Europe; USD 7,919 in North America; AUD 9,559 in Australasia; GBP 5,403.79 in UK & elsewhere (effective 2006). bk.rev. charts; illus.; abstr. index. reprint service avail. from PSC. **Document type:** *Journal, Academic/Scholarly.* **Description:** Provides new developments in work study techniques and practice designed to improve individual and organizational performance.
Former titles (until 2004): Work Study (0043-8022); Time and Motion Study
Related titles: CD-ROM ed.; Online - full text ed.: (from EBSCO Publishing, Emerald Group Publishing Limited, Gale Group, IngentaConnect, O C L C Online Computer Library Center, Inc., ProQuest Information & Learning, Swets Information Services).
Indexed: ABIn, ADPA, ASEANManA, CISA, ERA, ESPM, EmerIntel, Emerald, ErgAb, H&SSA, IMI, M&MA, ORMS, PsycInfo, PsycholAb, RASB, TEA, TTI, WorkRelAb.
—BLDSC (4542.486200), IE, Infotrieve, ingenta. **CCC.**
Published by: Emerald Group Publishing Limited, 60-62 Toller Ln, Bradford, W Yorks BD8 9BY, United Kingdom. TEL 44-1274-777700, FAX 44-1274-785200, infomation@emeraldinsight.com, http://www.emeraldinsight.com/ws.htm. Ed. John Heap.

658 338 GBR ISSN 1746-6474
▼ ➤ **INTERNATIONAL JOURNAL OF PRODUCTIVITY AND QUALITY MANAGEMENT.** Text in English. 2005. q. USD 450; USD 545 combined subscription (effective 2005). **Document type:** *Journal, Academic/Scholarly.*
Related titles: Online - full text ed.: ISSN 1746-6482.
Published by: Inderscience Publishers, IEL Editorial Office, PO Box 735, Olney, Bucks MK46 5WB, United Kingdom. TEL 44-1234-240519, FAX 44-1234-240515, ijpqm@inderscience.com, info@inderscience.com, http://www.inderscience.com/ijpqm. Ed. Angappa Gunasekaran.

➤ **INTERNATIONAL JOURNAL OF PROJECT MANAGEMENT.** see *BUSINESS AND ECONOMICS—Computer Applications*

658 GBR ISSN 1740-2891
▼ ➤ **INTERNATIONAL JOURNAL OF PROJECT ORGANISATION AND MANAGEMENT.** Variant title: International Journal of Project Planning and Management. Text in English. 2004. q. EUR 430, USD 450 print or online; EUR 520, USD 545 combined subscription print & online (effective 2005). **Document type:** *Journal, Academic/Scholarly.* **Description:** Fosters active dialogue about successful practice and theoretical research concerned with project management.
Related titles: Online - full text ed.: ISSN 1740-2905. USD 430 (effective 2004).
Published by: Inderscience Publishers, IEL Editorial Office, PO Box 735, Olney, Bucks MK46 5WB, United Kingdom. TEL 44-1234-240519, FAX 44-1234-240515, ijpom@inderscience.com, info@inderscience.com, http://www.inderscience.com/ijpom. **Subscr. to:** World Trade Centre Bldg, 29 route de Pre-Bois, Case Postale 896, Geneva 15 1215, Switzerland. FAX 41-22-7910885, subs@inderscience.com.

658 GBR ISSN 0951-3558
HD3840
➤ **THE INTERNATIONAL JOURNAL OF PUBLIC SECTOR MANAGEMENT.** Text in English. 7/yr. EUR 7,154.66 in Europe; USD 7,329 in North America; AUD 8,319 in Australasia; GBP 5,012.29 in UK & elsewhere (effective 2006). reprint service avail. from PSC. **Document type:** *Journal, Academic/Scholarly.* **Description:** Includes contributions from a wide diversity of interests within public sector management: the civil service, health and education services, local government and state organizations in developed and developing countries.
Related titles: Online - full text ed.: (from EBSCO Publishing, Emerald Group Publishing Limited, Gale Group, IngentaConnect, O C L C Online Computer Library Center, Inc., ProQuest Information & Learning, Swets Information Services).
Indexed: ABIn, ASSIA, EmerIntel, Emerald, GEOBASE, PAIS, RASB.
—BLDSC (4542.509200), IE, Infotrieve, ingenta. **CCC.**
Published by: Emerald Group Publishing Limited, 60-62 Toller Ln, Bradford, W Yorks BD8 9BY, United Kingdom. TEL 44-1274-777700, FAX 44-1274-785200, infomation@emeraldinsight.com, http://www.emeraldinsight.com/ijpsm.htm. Ed. Dr. Joyce Liddle.

658 GBR ISSN 0265-671X
TS156 CODEN: IJQMEZ
➤ **INTERNATIONAL JOURNAL OF QUALITY & RELIABILITY MANAGEMENT.** Text in English. 1985. 9/yr. EUR 9,394.91 in Europe; USD 9,509 in North America; AUD 10,799 in Australasia; GBP 6,469.54 in UK & elsewhere (effective 2006). bk.rev. reprint service avail. from PSC. **Document type:** *Journal, Academic/Scholarly.* **Description:** Aims to provide the essential information needed to achieve competitive standards in an easily assimilated form. Describes new techniques and systems - focusing particularly on their application.
Incorporates: International Journal of Quality Science (1359-8538)
Related titles: Online - full text ed.: (from EBSCO Publishing, Emerald Group Publishing Limited, Florida Center for Library Automation, Gale Group, IngentaConnect, O C L C Online Computer Library Center, Inc., ProQuest Information & Learning, Swets Information Services).
Indexed: ABIn, CPM, ERA, EmerIntel, Emerald, EngInd, ErgAb, Inspec, TEA.
—BLDSC (4542.510000), CISTI, Ei, IE, Infotrieve, ingenta. **CCC.**
Published by: Emerald Group Publishing Limited, 60-62 Toller Ln, Bradford, W Yorks BD8 9BY, United Kingdom. TEL 44-1274-777700, FAX 44-1274-785200, infomation@emeraldinsight.com, http://www.emeraldinsight.com/ijqrm.htm. Eds. Barrie Dale, Christian Madu.

658 GBR ISSN 1466-8297
CODEN: IJRABZ
➤ **INTERNATIONAL JOURNAL OF RISK ASSESSMENT AND MANAGEMENT.** Abbreviated title: I J R A M. Text in English. 2000. 4/yr. EUR 430, USD 450 to institutions print or online ed.; EUR 520, USD 545 combined subscription to institutions print & online eds. (effective 2005). **Document type:** *Journal, Academic/Scholarly.* **Description:** Provides a forum for discussion involving decision making and decision support systems for risk and disaster management on regional and global scales.
Related titles: Online - full text ed.: ISSN 1741-5241 (from EBSCO Publishing).
Indexed: ABIn, ASFA, BiolDig, BrCerAb, C&ISA, CerAb, CivEngAb, CorrAb, E&CAJ, EEA, EMA, EPB, ESPM, IAA, Inspec, M&GPA, M&TEA, MBF, METADEX, OceAb, RiskAb, SWRA, SolStAb, ToxAb, WAA, WRCInf.
—BLDSC (4542.538250), Linda Hall.
Published by: Inderscience Publishers, IEL Editorial Office, PO Box 735, Olney, Bucks MK46 5WB, United Kingdom. TEL 44-1234-240519, FAX 44-1234-240515, ijram@inderscience.com, http://www.inderscience.com/ijram. Ed. Dr. Mohammed A Dorgham. **Subscr. to:** World Trade Centre Bldg, 29 route de Pre-Bois, Case Postale 896, Geneva 15 1215, Switzerland. FAX 41-22-7910885, subs@inderscience.com.

▼ ➤ **INTERNATIONAL JOURNAL OF RURAL MANAGEMENT.** see *GEOGRAPHY*

658 338 GBR ISSN 0956-4233
HD9980.1
➤ **INTERNATIONAL JOURNAL OF SERVICE INDUSTRY MANAGEMENT.** Text in English. 1990. 5/yr. EUR 7,187.29 in Europe; USD 7,319 in North America; AUD 9,059 in Australasia; GBP 5,034.04 in UK & elsewhere (effective 2006). reprint service avail. from PSC. **Document type:** *Journal, Academic/Scholarly.* **Description:** Provides current information on research and developments worldwide in management within the service sector.
Related titles: Online - full text ed.: (from EBSCO Publishing, Emerald Group Publishing Limited, Gale Group, IngentaConnect, O C L C Online Computer Library Center, Inc., ProQuest Information & Learning, Swets Information Services).
Indexed: ABIn, ASCA, CPM, CurCont, EmerIntel, Emerald, H&TI, M&MA, RefZh, SSCI.
—BLDSC (4542.544680), IDS, IE, Infotrieve, ingenta. **CCC.**
Published by: Emerald Group Publishing Limited, 60-62 Toller Ln, Bradford, W Yorks BD8 9BY, United Kingdom. TEL 44-1274-777700, FAX 44-1274-785200, infomation@emeraldinsight.com, http://www.emeraldinsight.com/0956-4233.htm. Ed. Bo Edvardsson.

658 GBR ISSN 1744-2370
▼ ➤ **INTERNATIONAL JOURNAL OF SERVICES AND OPERATIONS MANAGEMENT.** Text in English. 2004. q. EUR 430, USD 450 to institutions print or online ed.; EUR 520, USD 545 to institutions print & online eds. (effective 2005). **Document type:** *Journal, Academic/Scholarly.*
Related titles: Online - full content ed.: ISSN 1744-2389.
Indexed: C&ISA, E&CAJ, IAA, Inspec.
—BLDSC (4542.544686).
Published by: Inderscience Publishers, IEL Editorial Office, PO Box 735, Olney, Bucks MK46 5WB, United Kingdom. TEL 44-1234-240519, FAX 44-1234-240515, ijsom@inderscience.com, info@inderscience.com, http://www.inderscience.com/ijsom. **Subscr. to:** World Trade Centre Bldg, 29 route de Pre-Bois, Case Postale 896, Geneva 15 1215, Switzerland. FAX 41-22-7910885, subs@inderscience.com.

658 GBR ISSN 1741-539X
▼ ➤ **INTERNATIONAL JOURNAL OF SERVICES OPERATIONS AND INFORMATICS.** Text in English. 2005. q. USD 450 to institutions; USD 545 to institutions print & online eds. (effective 2005). **Document type:** *Journal, Academic/Scholarly.*
Related titles: Online - full text ed.: ISSN 1741-5403. USD 450 to institutions (effective 2005).
Published by: Inderscience Publishers, IEL Editorial Office, PO Box 735, Olney, Bucks MK46 5WB, United Kingdom. TEL 44-1234-240519, FAX 44-1234-240515, ijsoi@inderscience.com, info@inderscience.com, http://www.inderscience.com/ijsoi. Ed. Robin G Qiu. **Subscr. to:** World Trade Centre Bldg, 29 route de Pre-Bois, Case Postale 896, Geneva 15 1215, Switzerland. FAX 41-22-7910885, subs@inderscience.com.

➤ **INTERNATIONAL JOURNAL OF SERVICES TECHNOLOGY AND MANAGEMENT.** see *BUSINESS AND ECONOMICS—Computer Applications*

▼ ➤ **INTERNATIONAL JOURNAL OF SIX SIGMA AND COMPETITIVE ADVANTAGE.** see *ENGINEERING—Industrial Engineering*

B

658 USA ISSN 1546-234X
GV713
INTERNATIONAL JOURNAL OF SPORT MANAGEMENT. Text in English. 2000. q. USD 62 domestic; USD 110 foreign (effective 2005). **Document type:** *Journal, Academic/Scholarly.* **Description:** Covers professional sport and recreation management and athletic administration.
Published by: American Press, 28 State St, Ste 1100, Boston, MA 02109. ampress@flash.net, http://americanboston.20megsfree.com/IJSM.html. Ed. William F Stier.

658 GBR ISSN 1475-8962
▼ ➤ **INTERNATIONAL JOURNAL OF SPORTS MANAGEMENT AND MARKETING.** Text in English. 2003. q. USD 450 to institutions print or online ed.; USD 545 combined subscription to institutions print & online eds. (effective 2005). **Document type:** *Journal, Academic/Scholarly.*
Related titles: Online - full content ed.: ISSN 1740-2808; Online - full text ed.: (from EBSCO Publishing).
Indexed: C&ISA, E&CAJ, IAA.
—BLDSC (4542.680700).
Published by: Inderscience Publishers, IEL Editorial Office, PO Box 735, Olney, Bucks MK46 5WB, United Kingdom. TEL 44-1234-240519, FAX 44-1234-240515, ijsmm@inderscience.com, editor@inderscience.com, http://www.inderscience.com/ijsmm. Ed. Dr. Mohammed A Dorgham. **Subscr. to:** World Trade Centre Bldg, 29 route de Pre-Bois, Case Postale 896, Geneva 15 1215, Switzerland. FAX 41-22-7910885, subs@inderscience.com.

B

658 GBR ISSN 1740-2859
▼ ➤ **INTERNATIONAL JOURNAL OF STRATEGIC CHANGE MANAGEMENT.** Text in English. 2005. q. USD 450 to institutions print or online ed.; USD 545 combined subscription to institutions print & online eds. (effective 2005). **Document type:** *Journal, Academic/Scholarly.* **Description:** Objectives are to establish an effective channel of communication between academic and research institutions, policy makers, government agencies and persons concerned with the complex issue of strategic change management.
Related titles: Online - full text ed.: ISSN 1740-2867.
Published by: Inderscience Publishers, IEL Editorial Office, PO Box 735, Olney, Bucks MK46 5WB, United Kingdom. TEL 44-1234-240519, FAX 44-1234-240515, ijscm@inderscience.com, info@inderscience.com, http://www.inderscience.com/ijscm. Ed. Dr. Patricia Ordonez de Pablos. **Subscr. to:** World Trade Centre Bldg, 29 route de Pre-Bois, Case Postale 896, Geneva 15 1215, Switzerland. FAX 41-22-7910885, subs@inderscience.com.

658 USA ISSN 1555-2411
▼ ➤ **INTERNATIONAL JOURNAL OF STRATEGIC MANAGEMENT.** Short title: I J S M(International Journal of Strategic Management). Text in English. 2004 (Dec.). s-a. USD 100 to individuals (effective 2005). **Document type:** *Journal, Academic/Scholarly.* **Description:** Contains original research papers in management, strategy, finance, marketing, OM, economics and related subjects.
Published by: International Academy of Business and Economics, 983 Woodland Dr, Turlock, CA 95382-7281. TEL 209-656-7084, AKhade@iabe.org, http://www.AIBE.org, http://www.iabe.org. Ed. Dr. Bhavesh S Patel.

658.421 338.04 GBR ISSN 1746-5370
▼ ➤ **INTERNATIONAL JOURNAL OF TECHNOENTREPRENEURSHIP.** Text in English. forthcoming 2006. q. USD 450 to institutions; USD 545 combined subscription to institutions (effective 2005). **Document type:** *Journal, Academic/Scholarly.* **Description:** Provides a platform of exchange for academics, researchers, managers and policy makers interested in the issues faced by entrepreneurs and intrapreneurs in fast-pacing technology intensive activities.
Related titles: Online - full content ed.: ISSN 1746-5389. forthcoming 2006.
Published by: Inderscience Publishers, IEL Editorial Office, PO Box 735, Olney, Bucks MK46 5WB, United Kingdom. TEL 44-1234-240519, FAX 44-1234-240515, ijte@inderscience.com, info@inderscience.com, http://www.inderscience.com/ijte. Ed. Francois Therin.

➤ **INTERNATIONAL JOURNAL OF TECHNOLOGY MANAGEMENT.** see *TECHNOLOGY: COMPREHENSIVE WORKS*

➤ **INTERNATIONAL JOURNAL OF TECHNOLOGY POLICY AND MANAGEMENT.** see *TECHNOLOGY: COMPREHENSIVE WORKS*

658 GBR ISSN 1742-7541
▼ ➤ **INTERNATIONAL JOURNAL OF TRADE AND GLOBAL MARKETS.** Text in English. forthcoming 2006. q. USD 450, USD 545 to institutions (effective 2005). **Document type:** *Journal, Academic/Scholarly.*
Related titles: Online - full text ed.: ISSN 1742-755X. forthcoming 2006.
Published by: Inderscience Publishers, IEL Editorial Office, PO Box 735, Olney, Bucks MK46 5WB, United Kingdom. TEL 44-1234-240519, FAX 44-1234-240515, ijgtm@inderscience.com, info@inderscience.com, http://www.inderscience.com/ijtgm.

➤ **INTERNATIONAL JOURNAL OF TRANSPORT MANAGEMENT.** see *TRANSPORTATION*

658 GBR ISSN 1741-5357
▼ ➤ **INTERNATIONAL JOURNAL OF VALUE CHAIN MANAGEMENT.** Text in English. 2005. 4/yr. USD 450 print or online ed.; USD 545 combined subscription print & online eds. (effective 2005). **Document type:** *Journal, Academic/Scholarly.* **Description:** Aims to establish an effective channel of communication between policy makers, corporate bodies, practitioners, academic, research institutions and government agencies, and to understand how enterprises harness new opportunities to create value, reinvent value chains and alter industry structures. It also aims to sketch possible research directions.
Related titles: Online - full text ed.: ISSN 1741-5365.
Published by: Inderscience Publishers, IEL Editorial Office, PO Box 735, Olney, Bucks MK46 5WB, United Kingdom. TEL 44-1234-240519, FAX 44-1234-240515, ijvcm@inderscience.com, info@inderscience.com, http://www.inderscience.com/ijvcm. Ed. B S Sahay.

➤ **INTERNATIONAL OIL NEWS.** see *PETROLEUM AND GAS*

➤ **INTERNATIONAL PENSION FUNDS AND THEIR ADVISORS.** see *BUSINESS AND ECONOMICS—Investments*

➤ **INTERNATIONAL PUBLIC MANAGEMENT JOURNAL.** see *PUBLIC ADMINISTRATION*

658 GBR ISSN 1067-9987
HF5549.A2
➤ **INTERNATIONAL REVIEW OF PROFESSIONAL ISSUES IN SELECTION AND ASSESSMENT.** Text in English. 1993. a., latest vol.2, 1996. price varies. **Document type:** *Monographic series, Academic/Scholarly.*
Published by: John Wiley & Sons Ltd. (Subsidiary of: John Wiley & Sons, Inc.), The Atrium, Southern Gate, Chichester, West Sussex PO19 8SQ, United Kingdom. TEL 44-1243-779777, FAX 44-1243-775878, customer@wiley.co.uk, http://www.wiley.co.uk.

➤ **INTERNATIONAL SERIES IN OPERATIONS RESEARCH AND MANAGEMENT SCIENCE.** see *BUSINESS AND ECONOMICS—Computer Applications*

650 USA ISSN 0020-8825
HD28
➤ **INTERNATIONAL STUDIES OF MANAGEMENT AND ORGANIZATION.** Text in English. 1971. q. USD 139 domestic to individuals; USD 197 foreign to individuals; USD 959 combined subscription domestic to institutions; USD 1,079 combined subscription foreign to institutions (effective 2006). adv. back issues avail.; reprint service avail. from PSC. **Document type:** *Journal, Academic/Scholarly.* **Description:** Publishes English translations of international articles on business administration.
Formerly (until 1971): International Journal of Management and Organization
Related titles: Online - full text ed.: 2002 (Mar.) (from EBSCO Publishing, Florida Center for Library Automation, Gale Group, H.W. Wilson, O C L C Online Computer Library Center, Inc., ProQuest Information & Learning, Swets Information Services).
Indexed: ABIn, APEL, BAS, BPI, BPIA, BusI, ESPM, Emerald, H&SSA, IBR, IBSS, IBZ, MEA&I, ManagCont, PAIS, RASB, RiskAb.
—BLDSC (4549.790000), IE, Infotrieve, ingenta, Linda Hall. **CCC.**
Published by: M.E. Sharpe, Inc., 80 Business Park Dr, Armonk, NY 10504. TEL 914-273-1800, 800-541-6563, FAX 914-273-2106, custserv@mesharpe.com, http://www.mesharpe.com/mall/results1.asp. Ed. J J Boddewyn. Adv. contact Barbara Ladd TEL 914-273-1800 ext 121. page USD 300; 8 x 5.

➤ **INTERNATIONAL TRANSACTIONS IN OPERATIONAL RESEARCH.** see *COMPUTERS*

658 USA
▼ **THE INTERNET JOURNAL OF MANAGEMENT SCIENCE.** Text in English. 2004. irreg. free to individuals; USD 500 to institutions (effective 2005). **Document type:** *Journal, Academic/Scholarly.*
Media: Online - full content.
Published by: Internet Scientific Publications, L.L.C., 23 Rippling Creek Dr, Sugar Land, TX 77479. TEL 832-443-1193, FAX 281-240-1533, wenker@ispub.com, http://www.ispub.com/ostia/index.php?xmlFilePath=journals/ijmas/front.xml.

658 USA
▼ ➤ **THE INTERNET JOURNAL OF ORGANIZATIONAL BEHAVIOR.** Text in English. 2004. irreg. free to individuals; USD 500 to individuals (effective 2004). **Document type:** *Journal, Academic/Scholarly.*
Media: Online - full content.
Published by: Internet Scientific Publications, L.L.C., 23 Rippling Creek Dr, Sugar Land, TX 77479. TEL 832-443-1193, FAX 281-240-1533, wenker@ispub.com, http://www.ispub.com/ostia/index.php?xmlFilePath=journals/ijob/front.xml.

658 USA
▼ ➤ **THE INTERNET JOURNAL OF STRATEGY.** Text in English. 2004. irreg. free to individuals; USD 500 to institutions (effective 2005). **Document type:** *Journal, Academic/Scholarly.*
Media: Online - full content.
Published by: Internet Scientific Publications, L.L.C., 23 Rippling Creek Dr, Sugar Land, TX 77479. TEL 832-443-1193, FAX 281-240-1533, wenker@ispub.com, http://www.ispub.com/ostia/index.php?xmlFilePath=journals/ijst/front.xml.

▼ ➤ **INTERVENTION RESEARCH**; international journal on culture, organization and management. see *SOCIAL SCIENCES: COMPREHENSIVE WORKS*

658 IRN
IQTISAD VA MUDIRIYAT/ECONOMIC AND MANAGEMENT QUARTERLY JOURNAL OF THE ISLAMIC AZAD UNIVERSITY. Text in English, Persian, Modern. 1991 (no.7). q. IRR 500 per issue. **Description:** Scholarly papers on topics in economics and management with an Islamic perspective.
Published by: Danishgah-i Azad-i Islami/Islamic Azad University of Iran, P O Box 19395-1775, Tehran, Iran.

IRYO KEIEI JOHO. see *HEALTH FACILITIES AND ADMINISTRATION*

658 RUS ISSN 1606-7789
ISKUSSTVO UPRAVLENIA. Text in Russian. 2000. 8/yr. RUR 440 domestic; RUR 55 per issue domestic (effective 2004). **Document type:** *Magazine, Trade.*
Published by: Izdatel'stvo Otkrytye Sistemy/Open Systems Publications, ul Rustaveli, dom 12A, komn 117, Moscow, 127254, Russian Federation. TEL 7-095-9563306, FAX 7-095-2539204, milov@osp.ru, info@osp.ru, http://www.osp.ru/imanagement. Ed. Grigorii Milov. Circ: 38,700.

338 USA ISSN 1096-9446
ISSUES AND ANSWERS IN SALES MANAGEMENT. Text in English. 1997. bi-w. USD 195 (effective 2005). **Document type:** *Newsletter, Trade.* **Description:** Contains techniques, comprehensive strategies and inside information on how to manage more effectively and stay informed about the rapidly changing world of sales management.
Published by: Clement Communications, Inc., 10 LaCrue Ave, PO Box 36, Concordville, PA 19331. TEL 610-459-4200, 888-358-5858, FAX 610-459-4582, editor@clement.com, http://www.clement.com.

658 CAN CODEN: BUQUAL
IVEY BUSINESS JOURNAL; improving the practice of management. Text in English. 1933. bi-m. CND 44.94 domestic; CND 48.30 Atlantic; USD 42 in United States; USD 60 overseas; CND 9.26 newsstand/cover (effective 2000). adv. bk.rev. illus. index. reprint service avail. from PQC. **Document type:** *Trade.* **Description:** For senior managers looking for ways to improve their management practices.
Former titles (until 2002): Ivey Business Journal (Print ed) (1481-8248); (until 1999): Ivey Business Quarterly (1480-6746); (until 1997): Business Quarterly (0007-6996); (until 1950): Quarterly Review of Commerce (0317-6797)
Media: Online - full content. **Related titles:** Microfiche ed.: (from MML); Microform ed.: (from MIM, MML, PQC); Online - full text ed.: (from Florida Center for Library Automation, Gale Group, H.W. Wilson, Micromedia ProQuest, O C L C Online Computer Library Center, Inc., ProQuest Information & Learning, The Dialog Corporation).
Indexed: ABIn, ADPA, ASEANManA, BPI, BPIA, BusI, CBCARef, CBPI, CPM, CPerI, CWPI, CurCont, Emerald, ICLPL, Inspec, M&MA, MEA&I, ManagCont, PAIS, PersLit, SCIMP, SSCI, T&DA, T&II.
—BLDSC (4589.042600), AskIEEE, CISTI, IE. **CCC.**
Published by: (University of Western Ontario, Richard Ivey School of Business), Ivey Management Services, 179 John St, Ste 501, Toronto, ON M5T 1X4, Canada. TEL 416-598-7775, FAX 416-598-0669, ibjonline@ivey.uwo.ca, ibj@ivey.uwo.ca, http://www.iveybusinessjournal.com, http://www.ivey.uwo.ca/publications/bq. Ed. Stephen Bernhut TEL 416-598-1741. Pub., Adv. contact Ed Pearce. Circ: 9,123 (paid); 6,500 (controlled).

658 USA ISSN 0730-9368
J. CROSS EXECUTIVE ALERT✶. Text in English. m. USD 60.
Published by: J. Cross Consulting Service, PO Box 846, San Diego, CA 92112. TEL 619-584-7727.

658 JPN ISSN 0287-5802
J M A JANARU/JAPAN MANAGEMENT ASSOCIATION. JOURNAL. Text in Japanese. 1942. m. adv.
Formed by the merger of (1951-1982): Manejimento (0287-5799); I E: Industrial Engineering (0445-0612)
Indexed: Inspec.
Published by: Nippon Noritsu Kyokai, 1-22 Shibakoen 3-chome, Minato-ku, Tokyo, 105-0011, Japan. Circ: 27,805.

658 NLD ISSN 1386-8225
JAARBIJLAGE FACILITY MANAGEMENT. Text in Dutch. 1995. a. free with Facility Management Magazine. illus. **Document type:** *Trade.* **Description:** Covers all aspects of managing facilities.

Formerly (until 1997): Facility Management (1383-6269)
Related titles: ♦ Supplement to: Facility Management Magazine. ISSN 0924-8641.
Published by: Arko Uitgeverij BV, Postbus 616, Nieuwegein, 3430 AP, Netherlands. TEL 31-30-605-1090, gerlings@arko.nl, http://www.arko.nl. Ed. F van Waardhuizen. Pub. Marc Gerlings. Circ: 3,000.

150 USA ISSN 0160-7146
JACOB MARSCHAK INTERDISCIPLINARY COLLOQUIUM ON MATHEMATICS IN THE BEHAVIORAL SCIENCES. Text in English. 1959. a. USD 5.50. **Document type:** *Monographic series.*
Published by: (U C L A Business Forecastng Project), University of California at Los Angeles, John E. Anderson Graduate School of Management, 110 Westwood Plaza, Ste B201, Los Angeles, CA 90095-1481. TEL 213-825-1581. Ed. Jeremy Anderson. Circ: 100. **Co-sponsor:** Western Managment Science Institute.

JAPAN (YEAR) MARKETING AND ADVERTISING YEARBOOK. see *ADVERTISING AND PUBLIC RELATIONS*

JIANZHU GUANLI XIANDAIHUA/CONSTRUCTION MANAGEMENT MODERNIZATION. see *BUILDING AND CONSTRUCTION*

658 CHN ISSN 1002-5766
HD70.C5
JINGJI GUANLI/ECONOMIC MANAGEMENT. Text in Chinese. 1979. m. CNY 18, USD 48.50. adv. bk.rev. **Description:** Covers theories, experiences and policies of Chinese and foreign economic management.
Indexed: RASB.
Published by: (Zhongguo Shehui Kexueyuan/Chinese Academy of Social Sciences, Gongye Jingji Yanjiusuo/Institute of Industrial Economics), Jingji Guanli Chubanshe/Economic Management Publishing House, 6 Tiao Xinjiekou, 8 Hongyuan Hutong, Beijing, 100035, China. TEL 86-10-2253956. Ed. Zhang Zuoyuan. Adv. contact Li Li. Circ: 110,000. **Dist. in US by:** China Books & Periodicals Inc, 360 Swift Ave., Ste. 48, S San Fran, CA 94080-6220. TEL 415-282-2994; **Dist. outside China by:** China International Book Trading Corp, 35 Chegongzhuang Xilu, Haidian District, PO Box 399, Beijing 100044, China. TEL 86-10-68412045, FAX 86-10-68412023, cibtc@mail.cibtc.com.cn, http://www.cibtc.com.cn.

658 CHN ISSN 1002-8668
JINGJI GUANLI WENZHAI/ECONOMIC MANAGEMENT DIGEST. Text in Chinese. 1987. s-m. CNY 120; USD 120 foreign. bk.rev. 32 p./no.; **Document type:** *Abstract/Index.* **Description:** Abstracts of articles and researches on economic policies, trends, investment environment, market conditions and economic management.
Published by: (Guojia Jingji Tizhi Gaige Weiyuanhui/State Commission for Restructuring Economic Systems), Jingji Guanli Wenzhai Bianjibu/State Commission for Restructuring the Economics, No 11 Rendinghu Beixiang, Huangshi Dajie, Beijing, 100011, China. TEL 86-10-6201-5945, FAX 86-10-6204-9117, cmie@public3.bta.net.cn. Ed. Haichun Chen. Pub., Adv. contact Jingrao Zhang. R&P Xinying Lin. **Dist. overseas by:** China International Book Trading Corp, 35 Chegongzhuang Xilu, Haidian District, PO Box 399, Beijing 100044, China.

658 330.1 CHN ISSN 1000-596X
HB9
JINGJI LILUN YU JINGJI GUANLI/ECONOMIC THEORY & BUSINESS MANAGEMENT. Text in Chinese. 1981. m. CNY 78 (effective 2004). **Document type:** *Journal, Academic/Scholarly.*
Indexed: RASB.
Published by: Zhongguo Renmin Daxue/Renmin University of China, Haidian-qu, 31, Zhongguancu Dajie, Beijing, 100080, China. etbm@263.net, http://jjllyjgl.periodicals.net.cn/default.html. **Dist. in US by:** China Books & Periodicals Inc, 360 Swift Ave., Ste. 48, S San Fran, CA 94080-6220. TEL 415-282-2994; **Dist. by:** China International Book Trading Corp, 35 Chegongzhuang Xilu, Haidian District, PO Box 399, Beijing 100044, China. TEL 86-10-68412045, FAX 86-10-68412023, cibtc@mail.cibtc.com.cn, http://www.cibtc.com.cn.

658 CHN ISSN 1003-3890
JINGJI YU GUANLI/ECONOMICS AND MANAGEMENT. Text in Chinese. 1986. bi-m. CNY 1.50 newsstand/cover. adv. bk.rev. **Document type:** *Academic/Scholarly.*
Formerly (until 1988): Hebei Jingji Guanli Ganbu Xueyuan Xuebao
Related titles: Online - full text ed.: (from East View Information Services).
Published by: Hebei Jingji Guanli Ganbu Xueyuan, Wu Qi Lu, Beijiao (North Suburb), Shijiazhuang, Hebei 050061, China. TEL 0311-639306. Ed. Liu Chunzhong. Circ: 5,000.

658 330 CHN ISSN 1000-7636
HC427.92
JINGJI YU GUANLI YANJIU/RESEARCH ON ECONOMICS AND MANAGEMENT. Text in Chinese. 1980. bi-m. USD 22.10. bk.rev. **Document type:** *Academic/Scholarly.*
Related titles: Online - full text ed.: (from East View Information Services).
Indexed: RASB.
Published by: Beijing Jingji Xueyuan/Beijing Institute of Economics, Hongmiao Chaoyangmen, Beijing, 100026, China. TEL 86-1-5061188. Ed. Ningwu Qu. **Dist. in US by:** China Books & Periodicals Inc, 360 Swift Ave., Ste. 48, S San Fran, CA 94080-6220. TEL 415-282-2994; **Dist. outside China by:** China International Book Trading Corp, 35 Chegongzhuang Xilu, Haidian District, PO Box 399, Beijing 100044, China.

658 CHN ISSN 1003-3475
JINGYING YU GUANLI. Text in Chinese. m.
Related titles: Online - full text ed.: (from East View Information Services).
Published by: Tianjin Qiye Guanli Xiehui, 16 Shuishang Gongyuan Lu, Nankai-qu, Tianjin 300191, China. TEL 348615. Ed. Song Fucheng.

658 CHN ISSN 1004-292X
JISHU JINGJI YU GUANLI YANJIU/TECHNOECONOMICS AND MANAGEMENT RESEARCH. Text in Chinese, English. 1980. bi-m. USD 4. adv.
Related titles: Online - full text ed.: (from East View Information Services).
Published by: Shanxi Sheng Jishu Jingji Yanjiu Zhongxin, 18 Wenyuanxiang, Rm. 233, Xinjian Nan Lu, Taiyuan, Shanxi 030001, China. TEL 86-351-2021450, FAX 86-351-4040802. Ed. Zhu Guanxin. Adv. contact Dai Ziwei. page USD 1,800. Circ: 280,000.

658 USA ISSN 1041-1488
JOB TRAINING AND PLACEMENT REPORT; the newsletter for professionals who support employment for people with disabities. Short title: J T P R. Text in English. 1978. m. USD 149 domestic; USD 162 foreign (effective 2003). adv. bk.rev. **Document type:** *Newsletter.* **Description:** For professionals and organizations who train and place people with disabilities into employment. Includes practical marketing tips, funding program opportunities and technologies available.
Formerly (until 1988): Information Management (0197-6524)
Related titles: Supplement(s): J T P R Plus.
Indexed: PROMT, RehabLit, e-psyche.
Published by: Impact Publications, Inc., E3430 Mountain View Lane, Box 322, Waupaca, WI 54981. TEL 715-258-2448, FAX 715-258-9048, info@impact-publications.com, http://www.impact-publications.com/JTPR/index.html. Ed. Karen Kolpien. Pub., R&P Scott Kolpien. Circ: 3,000.

658 IND
JODHPUR MANAGEMENT JOURNAL. Text in English. 1971. a. INR 15, USD 5. adv. bk.rev.
Published by: University of Jodhpur, Department of Management Studies, Jodhpur, Rajasthan 342 001, India. Ed. Raj K Agarwala. Circ: 1,000.

JOHN LINER LETTER. see *INSURANCE*

JOHN LINER REVIEW. see *INSURANCE*

JONESREPORT PLUS FOR SHOPPING CENTER MARKETING & MANAGEMENT. see *BUSINESS AND ECONOMICS—Marketing And Purchasing*

658 DEU ISSN 0949-6181
HC244.A1
➤ **JOURNAL FOR EAST EUROPEAN MANAGEMENT STUDIES.** Text in German, English. 1996. q. EUR 60 domestic; EUR 68 foreign (effective 2005). **Document type:** *Journal, Academic/Scholarly.* **Description:** Designed to promote a dialogue between East and West over issues emerging from management practice, theory and related research in the transforming societies of Central and Eastern Europe.
Related titles: Online - full text ed.: (from EBSCO Publishing, ProQuest Information & Learning).
Indexed: ABIn, DIP, IBR, IBSS, IBZ.
Published by: Rainer Hampp Verlag, Meringerzellerstr 10, Mering, 86415, Germany. TEL 49-8233-4783, FAX 49-8233-30755, Rainer_Hampp_Verlag@t-online.de, http://www.hampp-verlag.de/hampp_ZS02.htm. Ed. R Lang. **Dist. by:** Brockhaus Commission, Kreidlerstr 9, Kornwestheim 70806, Germany. TEL 49-7154-132739, FAX 49-7154-132713.

685 GBR ISSN 1746-966X
▼ ➤ **JOURNAL FOR GLOBAL BUSINESS ADVANCEMENT.** Text in English. 2005. q. USD 450 to institutions; USD 545 combined subscription to institutions (effective 2005). **Document type:** *Journal, Academic/Scholarly.* **Description:** Provides a vehicle to help professionals, academics, scholars, policy makers, entrepreneurs, consultants, and international civil servants working in the field of global business to disseminate information and to learn from each other(UNKNOWN CHARACTER)s work.
Related titles: Online - full content ed.: ISSN 1746-9678.
Published by: Inderscience Publishers, IEL Editorial Office, PO Box 735, Olney, Bucks MK46 5WB, United Kingdom. TEL 44-1234-240519, FAX 44-1234-240515, jgba@inderscience.com, info@inderscience.com, http://www.inderscience.com/jgba. Ed. Zafar U Ahmed.

658 DEU ISSN 0344-9327
➤ **JOURNAL FUER BETRIEBSWIRTSCHAFT.** Text in German. 1950. 4/yr. EUR 185.98 combined subscription to institutions print & online eds. (effective 2005). bk.rev. back issues avail.; reprint service avail. from SCH. **Document type:** *Journal, Academic/Scholarly.* **Description:** Covers the promotion of academic research in business administration and management.
Formerly (until 1974): Der Oesterreichische Betriebswirt (0472-5417)
Related titles: Online - full text ed.: ISSN 1614-631X (from Springer LINK).
Indexed: KES, RASB, RefZh, SCIMP.
—BLDSC (4951.520000), IE, Infotrieve, ingenta. **CCC.**
Published by: Springer-Verlag (Subsidiary of: Springer Science+Business Media), Tiergartenstr 17, Heidelberg, 69121, Germany. TEL 49-6221-3450, FAX 49-6221-345229, subscriptions@springer.de, http://www.springer.de. Adv. contact Stephan Kroeck TEL 49-30-827875739. Circ: 1,000.

▼ ➤ **JOURNAL OF ACCOUNTING AND ORGANISATIONAL CHANGE.** see *BUSINESS AND ECONOMICS—Accounting*

658 387.7 GBR ISSN 0969-6997
HE9781
➤ **JOURNAL OF AIR TRANSPORT MANAGEMENT.** Text in English. 1994. 6/yr. EUR 136 in Europe to individuals; JPY 17,900 in Japan to individuals; USD 152 to individuals except Europe and Japan; EUR 566 in Europe to institutions; JPY 75,100 in Japan to institutions; USD 634 to institutions except Europe and Japan (effective 2006). adv. bk.rev. illus. Index. back issues avail.; reprints avail. **Document type:** *Journal, Academic/Scholarly.* **Description:** Provides an international forum among practioners and academics for important issues affecting the air transport industry. Focuses on analyzing developments and trends while encouraging speculative and creative thought about new operational or managerial concepts or challenges.
Related titles: Microform ed.: (from PQC); Online - full text ed.: (from EBSCO Publishing, Gale Group, IngentaConnect, ScienceDirect, Swets Information Services).
Indexed: CLT&T, CurCont, ESPM, ErgAb, GEOBASE, H&SSA, H&TI, HRIS, RiskAb, SSCI.
—BLDSC (4926.550000), IE, Infotrieve, ingenta. **CCC.**
Published by: Pergamon (Subsidiary of: Elsevier Science & Technology), The Boulevard, Langford Ln, East Park, Kidlington, Oxford OX5 1GB, United Kingdom. TEL 44-1865-843000, FAX 44-1865-843010, http://www.elsevier.com/locate/jairtraman. Eds. K Button, S Morrison. **Subscr. to:** Elsevier BV, PO Box 211, Amsterdam 1000 AE, Netherlands. TEL 31-20-485-3757, FAX 31-20-485-3432, nlinfo-f@elsevier.nl, http://www.elsevier.nl.

339 USA ISSN 1077-1158
HD28
➤ **JOURNAL OF APPLIED MANAGEMENT AND ENTREPRENEURSHIP.** Text in English. 1994. q. free (effective 2005). bk.rev. back issues avail. **Document type:** *Journal, Academic/Scholarly.* **Description:** Dedicated to the study of general management and entrepreneurship.
Related titles: Online - full text ed.
Indexed: ABIn.
—BLDSC (4942.655000).
Published by: Nova Southeastern University, Wayne Huizenga Graduate School of Business and Entrepreneurship, 3301 College Ave, Ft Lauderdale, FL 33314. TEL 954-262-5000, 800-672-7223, harvey@huizenga.nova.edu, http://www.huizenga.nova.edu/jame. Ed. Jane Gibson. R&P Steve Harvey. Circ: 250 (paid); 750 (controlled).

658 GBR ISSN 0894-3257
BF448 CODEN: BDMAEU
➤ **JOURNAL OF BEHAVIORAL DECISION MAKING.** Text in English. 1988. 5/yr. USD 780 to institutions; USD 858 combined subscription to institutions print & online eds. (effective 2006). adv. back issues avail.; reprint service avail. from PSC. **Document type:** *Journal, Academic/Scholarly.* **Description:** Covers research in psychology, management science, sociology, political science and economics.
Related titles: Microform ed.: (from PQC); Online - full content ed.: ISSN 1099-0771. 1996. USD 780 to institutions (effective 2006); Online - full text ed.: (from EBSCO Publishing, ProQuest Information & Learning, Swets Information Services, Wiley InterScience).
Indexed: ABIn, CIS, CJA, CompAb, CurCont, ESPM, Emerald, ErgAb, HRA, Inspec, PsycInfo, PsycholAb, RiskAb, SOPODA, SSCI, ST&MA, e-psyche.
—BLDSC (4951.256600), AskIEEE, IDS, IE, Infotrieve, ingenta. **CCC.**
Published by: John Wiley & Sons Ltd. (Subsidiary of: John Wiley & Sons, Inc.), The Atrium, Southern Gate, Chichester, West Sussex PO19 8SQ, United Kingdom. TEL 44-1243-779777, FAX 44-1243-775878, customer@wiley.co.uk, http://www3.interscience.wiley.com/cgi-bin/jhome/4637, http://www.wiley.co.uk. Ed. George Wright. adv.: B&W page GBP 650, color page GBP 1,550; trim 200 x 260. Circ: 600. **Subscr. in N. America to:** John Wiley & Sons, Inc., 111 River St, Hoboken, NJ 07030-5774. TEL 201-748-6645, 800-225-5945, subinfo@wiley.com.

B

658 CAN ISSN 1701-9680
JOURNAL OF BUSINESS ADMINISTRATION AND POLICY ANALYSIS. Text in English. 1969. s-a. CND 24 (effective 1999). adv. bk.rev. bibl.; illus. reprint service avail. from PQC.
Formerly (until vols.23, 1995): Journal of Business Administration (0021-941X)
Related titles: Microform ed.: (from MML, PQC); Online - full text ed.: (from Gale Group).
Indexed: ABIn, BPIA, BusI, CBPI, CPM, CPerI, ManagCont.
—BLDSC (4954.660200), IE, ingenta. **CCC.**
Published by: University of British Columbia, Faculty of Commerce and Business Administration, Henry Angus Bldg, 2053 Main Mall, Vancouver, BC V6T 1Z2, Canada. TEL 604-822-9434, FAX 604-822-8489, peter.nemetz@commerce.ubc.ca. Ed. Peter N Nemetz. Circ: 400.

658 USA ISSN 1535-668X
HF5001
➤ **JOURNAL OF BUSINESS AND MANAGEMENT.** Text in English. 1993. q. USD 50 to individuals; USD 100 to institutions (effective 2003). **Document type:** *Journal, Academic/Scholarly.* **Description:** Aims to provide a forum for contributions in all areas of business and related public policy.
Related titles: Online - full text ed.: (from EBSCO Publishing, O C L C Online Computer Library Center, Inc., ProQuest Information & Learning).
Indexed: ABIn.
Published by: Colorado State University, College of Business, Management Department, 213 Rockwell Hall, Fort Collins, CO 80523. TEL 970-491-5221, FAX 970-491-3522, raymond.hogler@colostate.edu, charley.baer@colostate.edu, http://www.biz.colostate.edu/jbm.

➤ **JOURNAL OF BUSINESS AND TECHNICAL COMMUNICATION.** see *BUSINESS AND ECONOMICS*

▼ ➤ **JOURNAL OF BUSINESS CHEMISTRY.** see *CHEMISTRY*

658.45 USA ISSN 0021-9436
HF5718 CODEN: JBCOAO
➤ **JOURNAL OF BUSINESS COMMUNICATION.** Text in English. 1963. q. USD 314, GBP 203 to institutions; USD 326, GBP 211 combined subscription to institutions print & online eds. (effective 2006); Subscription incl. Business Communication Quarterly. adv. bk.rev. charts; illus. index. reprint service avail. from PQC. **Document type:** *Journal, Academic/Scholarly.* **Description:** Contains major papers dealing with important areas and aspects of business communication.
Former titles (until 1973): The A B C A Journal of Business Communication (0886-7216); (until 1969): The Journal of Business Communication (0885-2456)
Related titles: Microform ed.: (from PQC); Online - full content ed.: ISSN 1552-4582. USD 311, GBP 201 to institutions (effective 2006); includes Business Communication Quarterly (from Florida Center for Library Automation, Northern Light Technology, Inc.); Online - full text ed.: (from EBSCO Publishing, Gale Group, H.W. Wilson, O C L C Online Computer Library Center, Inc., Sage Publications, Inc., Swets Information Services).
Indexed: ABIn, AbAn, BPI, BPIA, BusEdI, BusI, CIJE, CommAb, HRA, Inspec, L&LBA, ManagCont, SOPODA.
—BLDSC (4954.665000), IE, Infotrieve, ingenta.
Published by: (Association for Business Communication), Sage Publications, Inc., 2455 Teller Rd, Thousand Oaks, CA 91320. TEL 805-499-0721, FAX 805-499-8096, JBC@list.flint.umich.edu, info@sagepub.com, http://www.sagepub.com/journal.aspx?pid=9888. Ed. Steven M Ralston. R&P, Adv. contact Pamela S Ouellette. page USD 275. Circ: 1,875.

658 USA ISSN 0735-3766
HD38.5
➤ **JOURNAL OF BUSINESS LOGISTICS.** Text in English. 1978. s-a. USD 74.95 to non-members (effective 2005). bk.rev. illus. reprints avail. **Document type:** *Journal, Academic/Scholarly.*
Related titles: Online - full text ed.: (from EBSCO Publishing, Northern Light Technology, Inc., O C L C Online Computer Library Center, Inc., ProQuest Information & Learning).
Indexed: ABIn, Emerald, HRIS, Inspec, LogistBibl.
—BLDSC (4954.703000), IE, Infotrieve, ingenta.
Published by: Council of Supply Chain Management Professionals, 2805 Butterfield Rd., Ste. 200, Oak Brook, IL 60523. TEL 630-574-0985, FAX 630-574-0989, CSCMPpublications@cscmp.org, http://www.cscmp.org/Website/Resources/JBL_Public.asp. Ed. Patricia Dougherty. Circ: 15,000.

658 330.01 USA ISSN 0148-2963
HF5001 CODEN: JBRED4
➤ **JOURNAL OF BUSINESS RESEARCH.** Text in English. 1973. 12/yr. EUR 175 in Europe to individuals; JPY 23,300 in Japan to individuals; USD 196 to individuals except Europe and Japan; EUR 1,591 in Europe to institutions; JPY 211,400 in Japan to institutions; USD 1,781 to institutions except Europe and Japan (effective 2006). adv. bk.rev. bibl.; illus. Index. reprint service avail. from PQC. **Document type:** *Journal, Academic/Scholarly.* **Description:** Applies theory developed from business research to actual business situations. Surveys theoretical and empirical advances in buyer behavior, finance, organizational theory and behavior, marketing, risk and insurance, and international business.
Formerly (until 1978): Southern Journal of Business (0038-4259)
Related titles: Microform ed.: (from PQC); Online - full text ed.: (from EBSCO Publishing, Gale Group, IngentaConnect, ScienceDirect, Swets Information Services).
Indexed: ABIn, ASCA, AgeL, BPI, BPIA, BusI, CPM, CommAb, CurCont, Emerald, FamI, IBSS, Inspec, JEL, MEA&I, ManagCont, ORMS, PAIS, PMA, PsycInfo, PsycholAb, QC&AS, RefZh, SSCI, T&II, WorkRelAb.
—BLDSC (4954.715000), IDS, IE, Infotrieve, ingenta. **CCC.**
Published by: Elsevier Inc. (Subsidiary of: Elsevier Science & Technology), 360 Park Ave. S, New York, NY 10010-1710. TEL 212-633-3730, 888-437-4636, FAX 212-633-3140, awoodside@freeman.tulane.edu, usinfo-f@elsevier.com, http://www.elsevier.com/locate/jbusres. Ed. Arch G Woodside. Adv. contact Michael Targowski. B&W page USD 820, color page USD 1,950. Circ: 1,750 (paid). **Subscr. outside the Americas to:** Elsevier BV, PO Box 211, Amsterdam 1000 AE, Netherlands. TEL 31-20-485-3757, FAX 31-20-485-3432.

658.4012 USA ISSN 0887-2058
HD28
➤ **JOURNAL OF BUSINESS STRATEGIES.** Text in English. 1984. s-a. USD 22.50 domestic; USD 32.50 foreign (effective 2004). 90 p./no. 1 cols./p.; back issues avail. **Document type:** *Journal, Academic/Scholarly.*
Related titles: Online - full text ed.: (from bigchalk, EBSCO Publishing, Florida Center for Library Automation, Gale Group, O C L C Online Computer Library Center, Inc., ProQuest Information & Learning).
Indexed: ABIn.
Published by: Gibson D. Lewis Center for Business and Economic Development, Sam Houston State University, Huntsville, TX 77341-2056. TEL 409-294-1518, FAX 409-294-3957, cbed@shsu.edu, http://coba.shsu.edu/jbs, http://coba.shsu.edu/cbr-home.htm. Ed., Pub., R&P, Adv. contact Jo Ann Duffy. Circ: 950.

658 GBR ISSN 0275-6668
HD28 CODEN: JBSTDK
JOURNAL OF BUSINESS STRATEGY. Text in English. 1980. bi-m. EUR 357.79 in Europe; USD 379 in North America; AUD 649 in Australasia; GBP 249.04 in the UK & elsewhere (effective 2006). illus. reprint service avail. from PQC,PSC. **Document type:** *Journal, Academic/Scholarly.* **Description:** Covers theory and practice of strategy, planning, implementation and competitive analysis.
Incorporates (1975-1995): Small Business Reports (0164-5382); Incorporates (1989-1994): Journal of European Business (1044-002X); Which incorporated (1990-1991): Journal of Pricing Management (1045-8425)
Related titles: Microform ed.: (from PQC); Online - full text ed.: (from EBSCO Publishing, Emerald Group Publishing Limited, Factiva, Florida Center for Library Automation, Gale Group, IngentaConnect, Northern Light Technology, Inc., O C L C Online Computer Library Center, Inc., ProQuest Information & Learning).
Indexed: ABIn, ABS&EES, ADPA, ASEANManA, Agr, BPI, BPIA, BusI, CPM, Emerald, Inspec, LRI, LogistBibl, M&MA, MEDLINE, ManagCont, PAIS, PROMT, QAb, RASB, SCIMP, SUSA, T&DA, T&II.
—BLDSC (4954.717000), CASDDS, IE, Infotrieve, ingenta. **CCC.**
Published by: Emerald Group Publishing Limited, 60-62 Toller Ln, Bradford, W Yorks BD8 9BY, United Kingdom. TEL 44-1274-777700, FAX 44-1274-785200, infomation@emeraldinsight.com, http://www.emeraldinsight.com/. Ed. Nanci Healy. R&P Mr. James Bender.

658.116 GBR ISSN 1469-7017
➤ **THE JOURNAL OF CHANGE MANAGEMENT.** Text in English. 2000. q. GBP 206, USD 340 combined subscription to institutions print & online eds. (effective 2006). bk.rev. reprint service avail. from PSC. **Document type:** *Journal, Academic/Scholarly.* **Description:** Offers a forum to explore all the strategic and tactical factors affecting and effecting change in organizations today.
Related titles: Online - full text ed.: ISSN 1479-1811. GBP 196, USD 323 to institutions (effective 2006) (from EBSCO Publishing, Gale Group, IngentaConnect, O C L C Online Computer Library Center, Inc., ProQuest Information & Learning, Swets Information Services); Special ed(s).
Indexed: ABIn, ErgAb, PsycInfo, PsycholAb.
—BLDSC (4955.250000), IE, ingenta. **CCC.**
Published by: Routledge (Subsidiary of: Taylor & Francis Group), 4 Park Sq, Milton Park, Abingdon, Oxon OX14 4RN, United Kingdom. TEL 44-1235-828600, FAX 44-1235-829000, info@routledge.co.uk, http://www.tandf.co.uk/journals/titles/14697017.asp, http://www.routledge.co.uk. Circ: 750 (paid). **Subscr. to:** Taylor & Francis Ltd, Journals Customer Service, Rankine Rd, Basingstoke, Hants RG24 8PR, United Kingdom. TEL 44-1256-813000, FAX 44-1256-330245, enquiry@tandf.co.uk.

658.45 GBR ISSN 1363-254X
HD30.3
➤ **JOURNAL OF COMMUNICATION MANAGEMENT.** Text in English. 1996. q. GBP 279 to institutions (effective 2006). adv. bk.rev.; software rev.; Website rev. 96 p./no. 2 cols./p.; back issues avail.; reprint service avail. from PSC. **Document type:** *Journal, Academic/Scholarly.* **Description:** Contains practitioner focused papers on the latest developments and thinking in the management of internal and external communications.
Related titles: Online - full content ed.: ISSN 1478-0852; Online - full text ed.: (from EBSCO Publishing, Gale Group, IngentaConnect, O C L C Online Computer Library Center, Inc., ProQuest Information & Learning, Swets Information Services).
Indexed: ABIn, CPM, CommAb, PsycInfo, PsycholAb.
—BLDSC (4961.634900), IE, Infotrieve, ingenta. **CCC.**
Published by: (Institute of Public Relations, International Association of Business Communicators USA), Emerald Group Publishing Limited, 60-62 Toller Ln, Bradford, W Yorks BD8 9BY, United Kingdom. TEL 44-1274-777700, FAX 44-1274-785200, subscriptions@emeraldinsight.com, infomation@emeraldinsight.com, http://www.emeraldinsight.com, http://www.emeraldinsight.com/. Eds. Anne Gregory, Emma Wood. R&P Mr. John Eggleton. Circ: 500 (paid); 1,200 (controlled).

658 CAN ISSN 1481-0468
➤ **JOURNAL OF COMPARATIVE INTERNATIONAL MANAGEMENT.** Text in English. 1998. s-a. USD 100 to institutional members; USD 50 to individuals (effective 2002). abstr. 110 p./no.; back issues avail. **Document type:** *Journal, Academic/Scholarly.* **Description:** Covers the field of comparative, international business and management for advancing understanding of organizations and management around the world through theoretical and empirical research.
Related titles: Online - full text ed.: (from Florida Center for Library Automation, Gale Group, O C L C Online Computer Library Center, Inc.).
Indexed: CPerI, IBSS.
Published by: Management Futures, 297 Kimble Dr, Fredericton,, NB E3B 6Y1 , Canada. TEL 506-454-1310, FAX 506-455-8421, http://www.managementfutures.com. Ed. Basu Sharma.

658 USA
▼ ➤ **JOURNAL OF COMPETITIVE INTELLIGENCE AND MANAGEMENT.** Text in English. 2003. q. **Document type:** *Journal, Academic/Scholarly.* **Description:** Publishes studies of those performing competitive intelligence activities and aims to identify how it has delivered benefits to those organizations and groups employing it.
Media: Online - full content.
Published by: Society of Competitive Intelligence Professionals, 1700 Diagonal Rd, Ste 600, Alexandria, VA 22314. TEL 703-739-0696, FAX 703-739-2524, info@scip.org, http://www.scip.org.

658 USA ISSN 1553-5347
➤ **JOURNAL OF CONTEMPORARY BUSINESS ISSUES.** Text in English. 1992. s-a. USD 20 domestic; USD 40 foreign (effective 2004 - 2005). back issues avail. **Document type:** *Journal, Academic/Scholarly.* **Description:** Publishes articles from a variety of disciplines, including accounting, business law and ethics, business education, economics, finance, management, marketing and supply chain management. Seeks papers with interest to a general business, especially material that would be interest to both academics and practitioners.
Published by: Western Illinois University, College of Business and Technology, Dept. of Marketing and Finance, 1 University Circle, Macomc, IL 61455. TEL 309-298-1592, FAX 309-298-2198, mfrjb@wiu.edu, RJ-Bauerly@wiu.edu. Ed., Pub., R&P Ronald J Bauerly. Circ: 10 (paid); 100 (controlled).

658 GBR ISSN 0966-0879
HD49
➤ **JOURNAL OF CONTINGENCIES AND CRISIS MANAGEMENT.** Text in English. 1993. q. EUR 80 combined subscription in Europe to individuals print & online eds.; USD 89 combined subscription in the Americas to individuals & Caribbean (print & online eds.); GBP 53 combined subscription elsewhere to individuals print & online eds.; USD 541 combined subscription in the Americas to institutions & Caribbean (print & online eds.); GBP 322 combined subscription elsewhere to institutions print & online eds. (effective 2006). reprint service avail. from PSC. **Document type:** *Journal, Academic/Scholarly.* **Description:** Discusses all aspects of contingency planning, scenario management, and crisis management for executives and researchers in corporate, agency, and government.
Related titles: Online - full text ed.: ISSN 1468-5973. USD 514 in the Americas to institutions & Caribbean; GBP 306 elsewhere to institutions (effective 2006) (from Blackwell Synergy, EBSCO Publishing, Gale Group, IngentaConnect, O C L C Online Computer Library Center, Inc., Swets Information Services).
Indexed: ABIn, ESPM, GEOBASE, H&SSA, IBSS, IPSA, PSA, PsycInfo, PsycholAb, RiskAb, SOPODA, SSA, SociolAb.
—BLDSC (4965.244000), IE, Infotrieve, ingenta. **CCC.**

Published by: Blackwell Publishing Ltd., 9600 Garsington Rd, Oxford, OX4 2ZG, United Kingdom. TEL 44-1865-776868, FAX 44-1865-714591, customerservices@oxon.blackwellpublishing.com, http://www.blackwellpublishing.com/journals/JCCM. Eds. Alexander Kouzmin TEL 61-2-9685-9705, Uriel Rosenthal TEL 31-71-527-3895.

658 382 GBR ISSN 1470-5001
HD60
➤ **THE JOURNAL OF CORPORATE CITIZENSHIP.** Short title: J C C. Text in English. 2001 (Jan). q. GBP 75, USD 125 to individuals; GBP 150, USD 250 to institutions (effective 2005). adv. bk.rev. charts; illus. 112 p./no.; back issues avail.; reprints avail. **Document type:** *Journal, Academic/Scholarly.* **Description:** Provides a global forum for researchers and practitioners to explore varying perspectives and to further define the role, scope and purpose of business in a globalised economy.
Related titles: Online - full text ed.: (from EBSCO Publishing, Gale Group, ProQuest Information & Learning).
Indexed: ABIn, IBSS.
—BLDSC (4965.336150). **CCC.**
Published by: Greenleaf Publishing, Aizlewood Business Centre, Aizlewoods Mill, Nursery St, Sheffield, S3 8GG, United Kingdom. TEL 44-144-2823475, FAX 44-144-2823476, info@greenleaf-publishing.com, http://www.greenleaf-publishing.com/jcc/jcchome.htm. Ed. Sandra Waddock. Pub., R&P, Adv. contact John Stuart. B&W page GBP 200; trim 131 x 208. Circ: 750 (paid).

➤ **JOURNAL OF CROSS-CULTURAL COMPETENCE & MANAGEMENT.** see *BUSINESS AND ECONOMICS—International Commerce*

658 GBR ISSN 1743-6540
▼ ➤ **JOURNAL OF DIGITAL ASSET MANAGEMENT.** Text in English. 2005. bi-m. GBP 265 in Europe; USD 480 in US & Canada; GBP 280 elsewhere (effective 2005). **Document type:** *Journal, Academic/Scholarly.* **Description:** Designed specifically for those involved in developing and deploying D A M systems and those concerned with managing digital assets.
Related titles: Online - full text ed.: (from Gale Group, IngentaConnect).
Published by: Palgrave Macmillan Ltd. (Subsidiary of: Macmillan Publishers Ltd.), Houndmills, Basingstoke, Hants RG21 6XS, United Kingdom. TEL 44-1256-329242, FAX 44-1256-810526, journal-info@palgrave.com, http://www.palgrave-journals.com/. Ed. Michael Moon.

➤ **JOURNAL OF ECONOMICS & MANAGEMENT STRATEGY.** see *BUSINESS AND ECONOMICS—Economic Systems And Theories, Economic History*

658.45 USA
JOURNAL OF EMPLOYEE COMMUNICATION MANAGEMENT. Abbreviated title: J E C M. Text in English. bi-m. USD 199. **Document type:** *Newsletter.* **Description:** Provides a strategic focus to the critical issues facing your communications department.
Published by: Lawrence Ragan Communications, Inc., 316 N Michigan Ave, Ste 300, Chicago, IL 60601. TEL 312-960-4106, 800-878-5331, FAX 312-960-4106, http://www.ragan.com.

658 338 NLD ISSN 0923-4748
TA190 CODEN: JETMEQ
➤ **JOURNAL OF ENGINEERING AND TECHNOLOGY MANAGEMENT.** Text in English. 1981. 4/yr. EUR 79 in Europe to individuals; JPY 10,500 in Japan to individuals; USD 87 to individuals except Europe and Japan; EUR 374 in Europe to institutions; JPY 49,400 in Japan to institutions; USD 417 to institutions except Europe and Japan (effective 2006). bk.rev. back issues avail.; reprints avail. **Document type:** *Journal, Academic/Scholarly.* **Description:** Links engineering and management disciplines to address issues involved in planning, development, and implementation of technological capabilities that shape and accomplish the strategic and operational objectives of an organization. Includes research and development, the managing of process technology and product technology.
Formerly (until 1989): Engineering Management International (0167-5419)
Related titles: Microform ed.: (from PQC); Online - full text ed.: (from EBSCO Publishing, Gale Group, IngentaConnect, ScienceDirect, Swets Information Services).
Indexed: ABIn, ASCA, ASFA, BPIA, BrCerAb, C&ISA, CerAb, CorrAb, CurCont, E&CAJ, EIA, EMA, ERA, ESPM, ETA, EngInd, EnvAb, H&SSA, IAA, Inspec, JOF, M&TEA, MBF, MEA, METADEX, ManagCont, RHEA, RefZh, SEA, SENA, SOMA, SSI, SolStAb, TEA, WAA.
—BLDSC (4978.550000), AskIEEE, CISTI, Ei, IDS, IE, Infotrieve, ingenta, Linda Hall. **CCC.**
Published by: Elsevier BV (Subsidiary of: Elsevier Science & Technology), Radarweg 29, Amsterdam, 1043 NX, Netherlands. TEL 31-20-4853911, FAX 31-20-4852457, nlinfo-f@elsevier.nl, http://www.elsevier.com/locate/jengtecman, http://www.elsevier.nl. Ed. Michael K Badawy TEL 703-538-8148.

658 IND ISSN 0971-3557
HB615 CODEN: JOENFP
➤ **JOURNAL OF ENTREPRENEURSHIP.** Text in English. 1992. s-a. GBP 122, USD 214 to institutions; GBP 127, USD 223 combined subscription to institutions print & online eds. (effective 2006). adv. bk.rev. abstr. index. back issues avail.; reprints avail. **Document type:** *Journal, Academic/Scholarly.* **Description:** Publishes original contributions, both conceptual and empirical. Useful to researchers, policymakers,and practicing entrepreneurs, as well as students and teachers of management and development processes.
Related titles: Online - full text ed.: GBP 121, USD 212 to institutions (effective 2006) (from EBSCO Publishing, Sage Publications, Inc.).
Indexed: ABIn, HRA.
—BLDSC (4979.354500). **CCC.**
Published by: (Entrepreneurship Development Institute of India), Sage Publications India Pvt. Ltd. (Subsidiary of: Sage Publications, Inc.), M-32 Market, Greater Kailash-I, PO Box 4215, New Delhi, 110 048, India. TEL 91-11-6444958, FAX 91-11-6472426, editors@indiasage.com, http://www.sagepub.co.uk/journal.aspx?pid=105639, http://www.indiasage.com/. Ed. Sasi Misra. Pub. Tejeshwar Singh. adv.: page USD 75. Circ: 500. **Subscr. to:** Sage Publications, Inc., 2455 Teller Rd, Thousand Oaks, CA 91320. TEL 805-499-0721, FAX 805-499-0871, journals@sagepub.com; Sage Publications Ltd., 1 Oliver's Yard, 55 City Rd, London EC1 1SP, United Kingdom. TEL 44-20-73740645, FAX 44-20-73748741, subscription@sagepub.co.uk.

658 370.7 USA ISSN 1098-8394
➤ **JOURNAL OF ENTREPRENEURSHIP EDUCATION.** Text in English. a. **Document type:** *Journal, Academic/Scholarly.*
Related titles: Online - full text ed.: ISSN 1528-2651.
Published by: (Academy of Entrepreneurship), Allied Academies, 145 Travis Rd., P. O. Box 2689, Cullowhee, NC 28723, http://www.alliedacademies.org/entrepreneurship/index-jee.html. Ed. Robin Anderson.

658 THA ISSN 0859-449X
HF3753.E85
JOURNAL OF EURO - ASIAN MANAGEMENT. Text in English. 1995. s-a. USD 40. **Document type:** *Academic/Scholarly.*
Published by: (Management of Technology Information Center), Asian Institute of Technology, School of Management, Klong Luang, PO Box 4, Pathum Thani, 12120, Thailand. TEL 66-2-516-0110, FAX 66-2-516-2126, TELEX 84276TH, marrof@ait.ac.th, http://www.ait.ac.th. Eds. Jyoti P Gupta, Patrick Gougeon. Circ: 500.

658.3 GBR ISSN 0309-0590
HF5549.5.T7 CODEN: JEITDP
➤ **JOURNAL OF EUROPEAN INDUSTRIAL TRAINING.** Text in English. 1977. 9/yr. EUR 13,146.79 in Europe to institutions; USD 12,779 in North America to institutions; AUD 12,259 in Australasia to institutions; GBP 8,764.16 to institutions in UK & elsewhere (effective 2006). charts; illus. index. reprint service avail. from PSC. **Document type:** *Journal, Academic/Scholarly.* **Description:** Covers latest research and practice in training and human resource development. Focuses on activity in or of relevance to Europe.
Formed by the merger of (1974-1977): Industrial Training International (0019-8811); (1966-1977): Journal of European Training (0261-3190)
Related titles: Online - full text ed.: (from EBSCO Publishing, Emerald Group Publishing Limited, Florida Center for Library Automation, Gale Group, IngentaConnect, O C L C Online Computer Library Center, Inc., ProQuest Information & Learning, Swets Information Services).
Indexed: ABIn, ADPA, ASEANManA, BPIA, BrEdI, BusI, CIJE, CPE, CPM, CurCont, ERA, ETA, EmerIntel, Emerald, ErgAb, HECAB, HRA, Inspec, M&MA, MEA, ManagCont, RHEA, SCIMP, SEA, SENA, SOMA, SPAA, SWA, T&DA, TEA.
—BLDSC (4979.605000), CISTI, IE, Infotrieve, ingenta. **CCC.**
Published by: Emerald Group Publishing Limited, 60-62 Toller Ln, Bradford, W Yorks BD8 9BY, United Kingdom. TEL 44-1274-777700, FAX 44-1274-785200, infomation@emeraldinsight.com, http://www.emeraldinsight.com/jeit.htm. Ed. Dr. Thomas Garavan. Pub. Ms. Paula Fernandez. R&P Mr. John Eggleton.

658 GBR ISSN 1472-5967
➤ **JOURNAL OF FACILITIES MANAGEMENT.** Text in English. 2002. q. GBP 219 to institutions (effective 2006). **Document type:** *Journal, Academic/Scholarly.* **Description:** Provides an international forum for the analysis and dissemination of best practice, new thinking and applied research in relation to the strategic, tactical and operational issues confronted by today's senior facilities manager.
Related titles: Online - full text ed.: ISSN 1741-0983 (from EBSCO Publishing, Gale Group, IngentaConnect, O C L C Online Computer Library Center, Inc., ProQuest Information & Learning, Swets Information Services).
Indexed: ABIn.
—BLDSC (4983.624000), IE, ingenta. **CCC.**
Published by: Emerald Group Publishing Limited, 60-62 Toller Ln, Bradford, W Yorks BD8 9BY, United Kingdom. TEL 44-1274-777700, FAX 44-1274-785200, subscriptions@emeraldinsight.com, infomation@emeraldinsight.com, http://www.emeraldinsight.com, http://www.emeraldinsight.com/. Ed. Michael Pitt. R&P Mr. John Eggleton.

658 651 658.3 ZAF
JOURNAL OF FACILITIES MANAGEMENT IN AFRICA. Abbreviated title: J F M Africa. Text in English. 2000 (Jun.). q. ZAR 130 domestic; USD 35 in Africa; USD 65 elsewhere (effective 2002). adv. **Description:** Covers the management and maintenance of outsourced non-core facilities and services.
Published by: Brooke Pattrick Publications, PO Box 422, Bedfordview, Transvaal 2008, South Africa. TEL 27-11-622-4666, FAX 27-11-616-7196, bestbook@brookepattrick.co.za, http://www.brookepattrick.com/facilities_management.html.

658 GBR ISSN 0277-6693
H61.4 CODEN: JOFODV
➤ **JOURNAL OF FORECASTING.** Text in English. 1981. 8/yr. USD 1,255 to institutions; USD 1,381 combined subscription to institutions print & online eds. (effective 2006). adv. illus. back issues avail.; reprint service avail. from PQC,PSC. **Document type:** *Journal, Academic/Scholarly.* **Description:** Provides a centralized focus on recent developments in the art and science of forecasting.
Related titles: Microform ed.: (from PQC); Online - full content ed.: ISSN 1099-131X. USD 1,255 to institutions (effective 2006); Online - full text ed.: (from EBSCO Publishing, O C L C Online Computer Library Center, Inc., ProQuest Information & Learning, Swets Information Services, Wiley InterScience).
Indexed: ABIn, ADPA, ASCA, BPIA, CIS, CLOSS, CPM, CREJ, CompAb, CurCont, ESPM, Emerald, EngInd, IAOP, IBSS, IndVet, JCQM, JEL, ORMS, PAIS, QC&AS, RASB, RefZh, RiskAb, SCIMP, SOPODA, SSCI, ST&MA, T&II, VetBull.
—BLDSC (4984.577000), CASDDS, IDS, IE, Infotrieve, ingenta. **CCC.**
Published by: John Wiley & Sons Ltd. (Subsidiary of: John Wiley & Sons, Inc.), The Atrium, Southern Gate, Chichester, West Sussex PO19 8SQ, United Kingdom. TEL 44-1243-779777, FAX 44-1243-775878, customer@wiley.co.uk, http://www3.interscience.wiley.com/cgi-bin/jhome/2966, http://www.wiley.co.uk. Ed. Derek Bunn. adv.: B&W page GBP 750, color page GBP 1,650; trim 200 x 260. **Subscr. in the Americas to:** John Wiley & Sons, Inc., 111 River St, Hoboken, NJ 07030-5774. TEL 201-748-6645, 800-225-5945, subinfo@wiley.com.

658 GBR ISSN 0306-3070
HD28 CODEN: JGMAAX
JOURNAL OF GENERAL MANAGEMENT. Text in English. 1973. q. GBP 173, USD 367.50 combined subscription print & online; GBP 41.25, USD 87.50 per issue (effective 2004). adv. bk.rev. illus. Index. reprints avail. **Document type:** *Journal, Academic/Scholarly.* **Description:** Aims to help top managers understand the main economic, social, political and technological issues that affect the success of their organization. Keeps the readers up-to-date with new developments in theory and practice of general management.
Formed by the merger of (1969-1973): Journal of Business Finance (0021-9452); (19??-1973): Journal of Business Policy (0021-9479)
Related titles: Online - full text ed.: GBP 88, USD 128 (effective 2004) (from EBSCO Publishing).
Indexed: ABIn, ADPA, APEL, ASEANManA, AgeL, BPIA, BusI, CPM, CurCont, Emerald, ExcerpMed, Inspec, KES, M&MA, ManagCont, PAIS, RASB, SCIMP, SSCI, WBA, WorkRelAb.
—BLDSC (4987.900000), IE, Infotrieve, ingenta. **CCC.**
Published by: Braybrooke Press Ltd., Remenham House, Remenham Hill, Henley-on-Thames, Oxon RG9 3EP, United Kingdom. TEL 44-1491412061, FAX 44-1491411428, braybrookepress@compuserve.com, http://www.braybrooke.co.uk/jogm/index.htm. Ed. Dr. Kevin Money. Circ: 1,000.

658 USA ISSN 1062-7375
T58.64 CODEN: JGLMEY
➤ **JOURNAL OF GLOBAL INFORMATION MANAGEMENT.** Text in English. 1993. q. USD 95 combined subscription to individuals print & online eds.; USD 315 combined subscription to institutions print & online eds. (effective 2005). 80 p./no.; **Document type:** *Journal, Academic/Scholarly.* **Description:** Publishes research and practical articles related to a broad range of topics in global information technology management, including managerial, technological, and behavioral aspects of international information systems.
Related titles: Online - full text ed.: ISSN 1533-7995. USD 68 to individuals; USD 212 to institutions (effective 2004) (from EBSCO Publishing, Florida Center for Library Automation, Gale Group, O C L C Online Computer Library Center, Inc., ProQuest Information & Learning).
Indexed: ABIn, BrCerAb, BusEdI, C&ISA, CerAb, CompD, CompLI, CorrAb, E&CAJ, EMA, ESPM, Emerald, IAA, InfoSAb, Inspec, LISA, M&TEA, MBF, METADEX, MicrocompInd, RiskAb, SolStAb, WAA.
—BLDSC (4996.270000), AskIEEE, IE, Infotrieve, ingenta, Linda Hall. **CCC.**
Published by: (Information Resources Management Association), Idea Group Publishing (Subsidiary of: Idea Group Inc.), 701 E Chocolate Ave, Ste 200, Hershey, PA 17033-1240. TEL 717-533-8845, FAX 717-533-8661, cust@idea-group.com, http://www.idea-group.com/journals/details.asp?id=99. Ed. Felix B Tan. Circ: 250 (paid).

➤ **JOURNAL OF HEALTHCARE INFORMATION MANAGEMENT.** see *HEALTH FACILITIES AND ADMINISTRATION*

B

658 GBR ISSN 1462-1797
JOURNAL OF HIGH-PERFORMANCE TEAMS. Text in English. 1995. q. GBP 195; GBP 235 foreign. adv. **Document type:** *Trade.* **Description:** Reports on the issues, trends and activities leading to superior team-based organizations and team-working performance.
Formerly (until vol.3, no.2, 1998): Teams (1359-8066)
Indexed: M&MA.
Published by: I F S International Ltd., Wolseley Rd, Wolseley Business Park, Kempston, Beds MK42 7PW, United Kingdom. TEL 44-1234-853605, FAX 44-1234-854499, rj@ifsinternational.demon.co.uk, IFSIntl@eWorld.com. Ed. Chris Ashton. Pub. David Crosby. R&P, Adv. contact Andrew Dec.

THE JOURNAL OF HIGH TECHNOLOGY MANAGEMENT RESEARCH. see *BUSINESS AND ECONOMICS—Computer Applications*

121 IND ISSN 0971-6858
HD38
➤ **JOURNAL OF HUMAN VALUES.** Text in English. 1995. s-a. GBP 120, USD 210 to institutions; GBP 125, USD 219 combined subscription to institutions print & online eds. (effective 2006). adv. back issues avail.; reprints avail. **Document type:** *Journal, Academic/Scholarly.* **Description:** Provides an international forum for ideas, principles, and processes concerning the application of human values to organizations and institutions, as well as the world at large.
Related titles: Microform ed.: (from PQC); Online - full text ed.: GBP 119, USD 208 to institutions (effective 2006) (from Sage Publications, Inc.).
Indexed: SOPODA, SSA, SociolAb.
—BLDSC (5003.441000), IE, ingenta.
Published by: (Indian Institute of Management, Management Centre for Human Values), Sage Publications India Pvt. Ltd. (Subsidiary of: Sage Publications, Inc.), M-32 Market, Greater Kailash-I, PO Box 4215, New Delhi, 110 048, India. TEL 91-11-6444958, FAX 91-11-6472426, editors@indiasage.com, http://www.sagepub.co.uk/journal.aspx?pid=105656, http://www.indiasage.com/. Eds. S K Chakraborty, Sanjoy Mukherjee. Pub. Tejeshwar Singh. Adv. contact Sunanda Ghosh. page USD 75. Circ: 600. **Subscr. to:** Sage Publications, Inc., 2455 Teller Rd, Thousand Oaks, CA 91320. TEL 805-499-0721, FAX 805-499-0871, journals@sagepub.com; Sage Publications Ltd., 1 Oliver's Yard, 55 City Rd, London EC1 1SP, United Kingdom. TEL 44-20-73740645, FAX 44-20-73748741, subscription@sagepub.co.uk.

658 USA ISSN 1547-5816
QA402.5
▼ **JOURNAL OF INDUSTRIAL AND MANAGEMENT OPTIMIZATION.** Text in English. 2005 (Feb.). q. USD 350 (effective 2005).
Related titles: Online - full text ed.: ISSN 1553-166X.
Published by: American Institute of Mathematical Sciences, PO Box 2604, Springfield, MO 65801-2604. TEL 417-836-5377, FAX 417-886-0559, http://aimsciences.org. Ed. Shouchuan Hu.

658 USA ISSN 1526-4726
HD30.2
JOURNAL OF INFORMATICS EDUCATION AND RESEARCH. Text in English. 1993. s-a. USD 45 domestic to individuals; USD 55 foreign to individuals; USD 75 domestic to institutions; USD 85 foreign to institutions (effective 2002). adv.
Formerly (until 1999): Journal of Education for M I S (1075-8909)
Published by: International Academy for Information Management, c/o Georgia Southern University, Dept. of Information Systems & Logistics, P. O. Box 8152, Statesboro, GA 30460. TEL 912-681-5205, FAX 912-681-0710, http://www.jier.org, http://www.iaim.org. Ed. Mary J. Granger.

658 USA ISSN 1081-0714
HD28
JOURNAL OF INNOVATIVE MANAGEMENT. Text in English. 1995. q. USD 99 in US & Canada; USD 119 elsewhere (effective 2004). **Document type:** *Journal, Trade.* **Description:** Contains stories from business leaders and managers from different industries and countries in the hopes of building better organizations, better economies, and a better world.
Related titles: Online - full text ed.: (from EBSCO Publishing).
—BLDSC (5006.990000).
Published by: G O A L - Q P C, 12B Manor Parkway, Salem, NH 03079-2841. TEL 603-890-8800, 800-643-4316, FAX 603-870-9122, service@goalqpc.com, http://www.goalqpc.com/journal.htm. Ed. Laurence Smith.

658 GBR ISSN 1469-1930
HD53
➤ **JOURNAL OF INTELLECTUAL CAPITAL.** Abbreviated title: J I C. Text in English. 2000. q. EUR 1,042.91 in Europe; USD 1,059 in North America; AUD 1,669 in Australasia; GBP 727.54 in UK & elsewhere (effective 2006). reprint service avail. from PSC. **Document type:** *Journal, Academic/Scholarly.* **Description:** Focuses on the study, measurement and report of intellectual capital. It reports on the developing and implementing innovative approaches to facilitate organizational transformation to superior performance.
Related titles: Online - full text ed.: (from EBSCO Publishing, Emerald Group Publishing Limited, Gale Group, IngentaConnect, O C L C Online Computer Library Center, Inc., ProQuest Information & Learning, Swets Information Services).
Indexed: ABIn.
—BLDSC (5007.538435), IE, Infotrieve, ingenta. **CCC.**
Published by: Emerald Group Publishing Limited, 60-62 Toller Ln, Bradford, W Yorks BD8 9BY, United Kingdom. TEL 44-1274-777700, FAX 44-1274-785200, infomation@emeraldinsight.com, http://www.emeraldinsight.com/jic.htm. Ed. Rory Chase. **Subscr. in N America to:** Emerald Group Publishing Ltd., 44 Brattle St, 4th Fl, Cambridge, MA 02138. TEL 617-497-2175, 888-622-0075, FAX 617-354-6875.

▼ ➤ **JOURNAL OF INTERNATIONAL BUSINESS AND ECONOMICS.** see *BUSINESS AND ECONOMICS—International Commerce*

▼ ➤ **JOURNAL OF INTERNATIONAL BUSINESS STRATEGY.** see *BUSINESS AND ECONOMICS—International Commerce*

➤ **JOURNAL OF INTERNATIONAL FINANCIAL MARKETS, INSTITUTIONS & MONEY.** see *BUSINESS AND ECONOMICS—Banking And Finance*

658 USA ISSN 1075-4253
HD62.4 CODEN: JIMAFI
➤ **JOURNAL OF INTERNATIONAL MANAGEMENT.** Text in English. 1995. 4/yr. EUR 74 in Europe to individuals; JPY 9,700 in Japan to individuals; USD 81 elsewhere to individuals; EUR 562 in Europe to institutions; JPY 74,500 in Japan to institutions; USD 628 elsewhere to institutions (effective 2006). adv. back issues avail. **Document type:** *Academic/Scholarly.* **Description:** Reports on the latest theoretical and empirical research into all major international management issues.
Related titles: Microform ed.: (from PQC); Online - full text ed.: (from EBSCO Publishing, Gale Group, IngentaConnect, ScienceDirect, Swets Information Services).
Indexed: IBSS, RefZh.
—BLDSC (5007.673200), IE, Infotrieve, ingenta. **CCC.**
Published by: Elsevier Inc. (Subsidiary of: Elsevier Science & Technology), 360 Park Ave. S, New York, NY 10010-1710. TEL 212-633-3730, 888-437-4636, usinfo-f@elsevier.com, http://www.elsevier.com/locate/intman. Ed. M Kotabe. adv.: B&W page GBP 640, color page GBP 1,515; trim 178 x 254. Circ: 850. **Subscr. outside the Americas to:** Elsevier BV, PO Box 211, Amsterdam 1000 AE, Netherlands. TEL 31-20-485-3757, FAX 31-20-485-3432.

658.4 USA ISSN 1543-5962
T58.64
➤ **JOURNAL OF INTERNATIONAL TECHNOLOGY AND INFORMATION MANAGEMENT.** Text in English. 1992. 3/yr. USD 65 domestic to non-members; USD 80 foreign to non-members (effective 2003). adv. bk.rev.; software rev. **Document type:** *Academic/Scholarly.* **Description:** Reports the findings of scholars and practitioners who are concerned with information management.
Formerly (until 2002): Journal of International Information Management (1063-519X)
Indexed: Inspec.
—BLDSC (5007.686820), AskIEEE, IE, ingenta.
Published by: International Information Management Association, Department of Information and Decision Sciences, California State University, San Bernardino, CA 92407. TEL 909-880-5786, FAX 909-880-5994, http://www.iima.org. Ed. C E Tarif Rohm Jr. R&P Walter T Stewart. Adv. contact Diana Catalano. Circ: 1,000 (paid).

658 GBR ISSN 1367-3270
HD53 CODEN: JKMAFW
➤ **JOURNAL OF KNOWLEDGE MANAGEMENT.** Text in English. 1997. q. (6/yr from 2004). EUR 2,065.16 in Europe; USD 2,129 in North America; AUD 2,659 in Australasia; GBP 1,445.29 in UK & elsewhere (effective 2006). reprint service avail. from PSC. **Document type:** *Journal, Academic/Scholarly.* **Description:** Dedicated to the exchange of research and practical information on all aspects of managing knowledge in organizations. Focuses on the identification of innovative knowledge management strategies and the application of theoretical concepts to real-world situations.
Related titles: Online - full text ed.: (from EBSCO Publishing, Emerald Group Publishing Limited, Gale Group, IngentaConnect, O C L C Online Computer Library Center, Inc., ProQuest Information & Learning, Swets Information Services).
Indexed: ABIn, CompLI, EmerIntel, Emerald, InfoSAb, Inspec, M&MA, MicrocompInd, PsycInfo, PsycholAb.
—BLDSC (5009.858000), IE, Infotrieve, ingenta. **CCC.**
Published by: Emerald Group Publishing Limited, 60-62 Toller Ln, Bradford, W Yorks BD8 9BY, United Kingdom. TEL 44-1274-777700, FAX 44-1274-785200, infomation@emeraldinsight.com, http://www.emeraldinsight.com/jkm.htm. Ed. Rory Chase.

➤ **JOURNAL OF KNOWLEDGE MANAGEMENT PRACTICE.** see *PHILOSOPHY*

658 USA ISSN 1548-0518
HD57.7
➤ **JOURNAL OF LEADERSHIP AND ORGANIZATIONAL STUDIES.** Text in English. 1993. q. USD 65; USD 48 to students (effective 2005). adv. bk.rev. index. back issues avail. **Document type:** *Journal, Academic/Scholarly.* **Description:** Provides materials, thoughts, sources and networking opportunities in leadership education in business and college settings.
Formerly (until Summer, 2002): Journal of Leadership Studies (1071-7919)
Related titles: Online - full text ed.: (from EBSCO Publishing, Gale Group, O C L C Online Computer Library Center, Inc., ProQuest Information & Learning).
Indexed: ABIn.
—BLDSC (5010.215000), IE, ingenta.
Published by: Baker College, Center for Graduate Studies, 1050 W Bristol Rd, Flint, MI 48507-9987. TEL 810-766-4390, FAX 810-766-4399, journal@baker.edu, http://www.baker.edu/departments/leadership/jls-main.htm. Ed. Richard Hodgetts. R&P, Adv. contact Dawn Prueter TEL 810-766-4024. Circ: 3,000 (paid).

➤ **JOURNAL OF LOSS PREVENTION IN THE PROCESS INDUSTRIES.** see *ENGINEERING—Chemical Engineering*

658 USA ISSN 0149-2063
HD28 CODEN: JOMADO
➤ **JOURNAL OF MANAGEMENT.** Text in English. 1975. bi-m. USD 441, GBP 285 to institutions; USD 459, GBP 297 combined subscription to institutions print & online eds. (effective 2006). adv. bk.rev. illus. index. back issues avail.; reprints avail. **Document type:** *Journal, Academic/Scholarly.* **Description:** Publishes original scholarly articles related to the study of management and organization from any area within the domain of management.
Related titles: Microfilm ed.: (from PQC); Online - full text ed.: ISSN 1557-1211. USD 437, GBP 282 to institutions (effective 2006) (from C S A, EBSCO Publishing, Florida Center for Library Automation, Gale Group, H.W. Wilson, HighWire Press, IngentaConnect, Northern Light Technology, Inc., O C L C Online Computer Library Center, Inc., Sage Publications, Inc., ScienceDirect, Swets Information Services).
Indexed: ABIn, ASCA, BPI, BPIA, BusI, CIJE, CPM, CurCont, Emerald, Inspec, M&MA, ManagCont, ORMS, PAIS, PMA, PsySCAP, PsycInfo, PsycholAb, QC&AS, RASB, SOPODA, SPAA, SSCI, WorkRelAb, e-psyche.
—BLDSC (5011.100000), IE, Infotrieve, ingenta. **CCC.**
Published by: (Southern Management Association GBR), Sage Publications, Inc., 2455 Teller Rd, Thousand Oaks, CA 91320. TEL 805-499-0721, FAX 805-499-0871, info@sagepub.com, http://www.sagepub.com/journal.aspx?pid=10604. Ed. David C Feldman. Circ: 2,000. **Subscr. oveseas to:** Sage Publications Ltd., 1 Oliver's Yard, 55 City Rd, London EC1 1SP, United Kingdom. TEL 44-20-73740645, FAX 44-20-73748741, subscription@sagepub.co.uk. **Co-sponsor:** Indiana University Graduate School of Business.

➤ **JOURNAL OF MANAGEMENT ACCOUNTING RESEARCH.** see *BUSINESS AND ECONOMICS—Accounting*

658 ARG
THE JOURNAL OF MANAGEMENT AND ECONOMICS. Text in English. 1997. q. back issues avail. **Document type:** *Academic/Scholarly.* **Description:** Publishes papers describing the results of original research in management and economics.
Media: Online - full text.
Published by: Universidad de Buenos Aires, Facultad de Ciencias Economicas, Ave. Cordoba No. 2122, Buenos Aires, 1120, Argentina. TEL 54-114-3744448, web@econ.uba.ar, http://www.econ.uba.ar/www/servicios/publicaciones/index.html.

658 USA ISSN 1385-3457
HD2741
➤ **JOURNAL OF MANAGEMENT & GOVERNANCE.** Text in English. 1997. q. EUR 382, USD 382, GBP 239 combined subscription to institutions print & online eds. (effective 2005). adv. reprint service avail. from PSC. **Document type:** *Journal, Academic/Scholarly.* **Description:** Focus on relationships among management, governance systems, and the institutional factors affecting organizational life. These relationships are proving increasingly critical in many areas of economic life, ranging from organizational change to more general issues of economic transformation.
Related titles: Online - full text ed.: ISSN 1572-963X (from EBSCO Publishing, Gale Group, IngentaConnect, Kluwer Online, O C L C Online Computer Library Center, Inc., ProQuest Information & Learning, Springer LINK, Swets Information Services).
Indexed: ABIn, BibLing, DIP, IBR, IBSS, IBZ, JEL, RefZh.
—BLDSC (5011.180000), IE, Infotrieve, ingenta. **CCC.**
Published by: Springer-Verlag New York, Inc. (Subsidiary of: Springer Science+Business Media), 233 Spring St, New York, NY 10013. TEL 212-460-1500, FAX 212-460-1575, service@springer-ny.com, http://springerlink.metapress.com/openurl.asp?genre=journal&issn=1385-3457, http://www.springer-ny.com. Ed. Anna Grandori. **Subscr. to:** Journal Fulfillment, PO Box 2485, Secaucus, NJ 07096-2485. TEL 201-348-4033, FAX 201-348-4505, journals@springer-ny.com.

658 GBR ISSN 0262-1711
HF5549.5.T7 CODEN: JMDEFD
THE JOURNAL OF MANAGEMENT DEVELOPMENT. Text in English. 1982. 9/yr. EUR 10,950.04 in Europe; USD 10,839 in North America; AUD 13,169 in Australasia; GBP 7,369.29 in UK & elsewhere (effective 2006). charts; illus. back issues avail.; reprint service avail. from PSC. **Document type:** *Journal, Academic/Scholarly.* **Description:** Covers evaluating assessment centers, experimental learning methods, new technology of management development, use of appraisal systems, value of a management training survey, team building, self-appraisal and self-development, management knowledge and more.
Related titles: Online - full text ed.: (from EBSCO Publishing, Emerald Group Publishing Limited, Florida Center for Library Automation, Gale Group, IngentaConnect, O C L C Online Computer Library Center, Inc., ProQuest Information & Learning, Swets Information Services).
Indexed: ABIn, ADPA, ASEANManA, BPIA, BrEdI, CIJE, CurCont, ERA, ETA, EmerIntel, Emerald, HRA, Inspec, M&MA, MEA, PsycInfo, PsycholAb, RASB, RHEA, SEA, SENA, SOMA, SWA, T&DA, T&II, TEA.
—BLDSC (5011.300000), IE, Infotrieve, ingenta. **CCC.**
Published by: Emerald Group Publishing Limited, 60-62 Toller Ln, Bradford, W Yorks BD8 9BY, United Kingdom. TEL 44-1274-777700, FAX 44-1274-785200, infomation@emeraldinsight.com, http://www.emeraldinsight.com/jmd.htm. Eds. Andrew Kakabadse, Nada K Kakabadse.

658.0071 USA ISSN 1052-5629
➤ **JOURNAL OF MANAGEMENT EDUCATION.** Text in English. 1975. bi-m. USD 419, GBP 271 to institutions; USD 436, GBP 282 combined subscription to institutions print & online eds. (effective 2006). adv. bk.rev. illus. back issues avail.; reprints avail. **Document type:** *Journal, Academic/Scholarly.* **Description:** Provides an international forum for the analysis and improvement of teaching and training business students and managers. Comprehensively covers such diverse areas as human resources, public administration, organizational behavior, management consultation, entrepreneurship and organizational communication.
Former titles (until 1977): Organizational Behavior Teaching Review; Exchange - The Organizational Behavior Teaching Journal (0162-1858); Teaching Organization Behavior; Teaching of Organization Behavior
Related titles: Online - full text ed.: ISSN 1552-6658. USD 415, GBP 268 to institutions (effective 2006) (from C S A, EBSCO Publishing, O C L C Online Computer Library Center, Inc., ProQuest Information & Learning, Sage Publications, Inc., Swets Information Services).
Indexed: ABIn, CPE, CurCont, ERA, ETA, Emerald, HRA, MEA, PMA, RHEA, SEA, SENA, SOMA, SOPODA, SPAA, TEA.
—BLDSC (5011.305000), IE, Infotrieve, ingenta. **CCC.**
Published by: (The Organizational Behavior Teaching Society), Sage Publications, Inc., 2455 Teller Rd, Thousand Oaks, CA 91320. TEL 805-499-0721, 800-818-7243, FAX 805-499-8096, 800-583-2665, info@sagepub.com, http://www.sagepub.com/journal.aspx?pid=181. Eds. Jane Schmidt-Wilk, Susan J Herman. Pub. Sara Miller McCune. R&P Tanya Udin TEL 805-499-0721 ext 7716. Adv. contact Kirsten Beaulieu TEL 805-499-0721 ext 7160. page USD 350. Circ: 950 (paid). **Subscr. overseas to:** Sage Publications Ltd., 1 Oliver's Yard, 55 City Rd, London EC1 1SP, United Kingdom. TEL 44-20-73740645, FAX 44-20-73748741, subscription@sagepub.co.uk.

658 GBR ISSN 1355-252X
HD30.5
➤ **JOURNAL OF MANAGEMENT HISTORY.** (Incorporated into Management Decision from 2001-2005 and relaunched as an independent title in 2006.) Text in English. 1995. 10/yr. GBP 249 worldwide (effective 2000). reprint service avail. from PSC. **Document type:** *Academic/Scholarly.* **Description:** Reflects on the historical development of management concepts and practices, with a view to how they inform the present and shape what we are and what we do.
Related titles: CD-ROM ed.; Online - full text ed.: (from EBSCO Publishing, Gale Group, IngentaConnect, O C L C Online Computer Library Center, Inc., Swets Information Services).
Indexed: EmerIntel, Emerald.
—BLDSC (5011.331000), Infotrieve. **CCC.**
Published by: Emerald Group Publishing Limited, 60-62 Toller Ln, Bradford, W Yorks BD8 9BY, United Kingdom. TEL 44-1274-777700, FAX 44-1274-785200, subscriptions@emeraldinsight.com, infomation@emeraldinsight.com, http://www.emeraldinsight.com/jmh.htm. Ed. David Lamond.

658 USA ISSN 1056-4926
HD28 CODEN: JMNIE6
➤ **JOURNAL OF MANAGEMENT INQUIRY.** Text in English. 1992. q. USD 458, GBP 296 to institutions; USD 477, GBP 308 combined subscription to institutions print & online eds. (effective 2006). adv. bk.rev. back issues avail.; reprints avail. **Document type:** *Journal, Academic/Scholarly.* **Description:** Provides a forum for nontraditional research and practice in the fields of management and organization. Provides reflections on experience from academics, consultants and executives. Promotes active, constructive exchanges between proponents of differing points of view.
Related titles: Online - full text ed.: ISSN 1552-6542. USD 454, GBP 293 to institutions (effective 2006) (from C S A, EBSCO Publishing, O C L C Online Computer Library Center, Inc., ProQuest Information & Learning, Sage Publications, Inc., Swets Information Services).
Indexed: ABIn, ASCA, CommAb, CurCont, Emerald, FamI, HRA, SFSA, SOPODA, SSCI, V&AA.
—BLDSC (5011.360000), IDS, IE, Infotrieve, ingenta. **CCC.**
Published by: (Western Academy of Management), Sage Publications, Inc., 2455 Teller Rd, Thousand Oaks, CA 91320. TEL 805-499-0721, 800-818-7243, FAX 805-499-8096, 805-499-0871, 800-583-2665, info@sagepub.com, http://www.sagepub.com/journal.aspx?pid=172. Eds. Kimberly B Boal, Paul M Hirsch, Susan Hanscom. Pub. Sara Miller McCune. R&P Tanya Udin TEL 805-499-0721 ext 7716. Adv. contact Kirsten Beaulieu TEL 805-499-0721 ext 7160. page USD 350. Circ: 650 (paid and free). **Subscr. overseas to:** Sage Publications Ltd., 1 Oliver's Yard, 55 City Rd, London EC1 1SP, United Kingdom. TEL 44-20-73740645, FAX 44-20-73748741, subscription@sagepub.co.uk.

658 AUS ISSN 1441-2543
JOURNAL OF MANAGEMENT PRACTICE. Text in English. 1999. s-a.
Media: Online - full text.
Published by: University of Southern Queensland, Department of Human Resource Management and Employment Relations, Toowoomba, QLD 4350, Australia. hrm@usq.edu.au, http://www.usq.edu.au/faculty/business/dept_hrm/HRMJournal/JMPHome.htm. Ed. Tesera Marchant.

658 IND ISSN 0972-5814
JOURNAL OF MANAGEMENT RESEARCH. Text in English. 2001. triennial. INR 900 domestic; USD 150 foreign (effective 2002). **Document type:** *Academic/Scholarly.*
Related titles: Online - full text ed.: (from EBSCO Publishing).
Published by: South Asia Publications, 29, Central Market, Ashok Vihar-I, New Delhi, 110 052, India. TEL 91-11-7241869, jmr@sapub.com. Ed. H D Gupta. Pub. Sanjay P Garg. Circ: 250 (paid).

351 USA ISSN 1042-7309
JA1
JOURNAL OF MANAGEMENT SCIENCE & POLICY ANALYSIS. Text in English. 1988. q.
Indexed: ABCPolSci, IPSA.
Published by: Marist College, Graduate Center for Public Policy and Administration, 3399 North Rd, Poughkeepsie, NY 12601.

658 GBR ISSN 1476-6086
▼ ➤ **JOURNAL OF MANAGEMENT, SPIRITUALITY & RELIGION;** an international refereed journal. Text in English. 2004. 3/yr. GBP 95, EUR 140, USD 170 (effective 2005). **Document type:** *Journal, Academic/Scholarly.*
—BLDSC (5011.450000).
Published by: Y. Altman, Pub., 262 Shakespeare Tower, Barbican, London, EC2Y 8DR, United Kingdom. jmsr04@go.com, http://www.jmsr.com. Eds. Jerry Biberman, Yochanan Altman.

658 IND ISSN 0972-3846
JOURNAL OF MANAGEMENT STUDIES. Text in English. 2000. a. INR 60 newsstand/cover domestic to individuals; GBP 15 newsstand/cover foreign to individuals; INR 100 newsstand/cover domestic to institutions; USD 20 newsstand/cover foreign to institutions (effective 2003).
Published by: Guru Nanak Dev University Press, Press & Publications Department, Amritsar, Punjab 143 005, India. TEL 91-183-258802, FAX 91-183-258819, dcse.gndu@yahoo.com.

658 GBR ISSN 0022-2380
HD28 CODEN: JMASB2
➤ **JOURNAL OF MANAGEMENT STUDIES.** Text in English. 1964. 8/yr., latest vol.39, no.8, 2002. USD 178 combined subscription in the Americas to individuals & Caribbean (print & online eds.); EUR 159 combined subscription in Europe to individuals print & online eds.; GBP 106 combined subscription elsewhere to individuals print & online eds.; GBP 781 combined subscription in Europe to institutions print & online eds.; USD 1,643 combined subscription in the Americas to institutions & Caribbean (print & online eds.); GBP 978 combined subscription elsewhere to institutions print & online eds.; USD 29 combined subscription in the Americas to students & Caribbean (print & online eds.); EUR 26 combined subscription in Europe to students print & online eds.; GBP 17 combined subscription elsewhere to students print & online eds. (effective 2006). adv. bk.rev. illus. Index. reprint service avail. from PQC,PSC. **Document type:** *Journal, Academic/Scholarly.* **Description:** Publishes articles on organization theory, strategic management, and human resource management.
Related titles: Online - full text ed.: ISSN 1467-6486. GBP 742 in Europe to institutions; USD 1,561 in the Americas to institutions; GBP 929 elsewhere to institutions (effective 2006) (from Blackwell Synergy, EBSCO Publishing, Gale Group, IngentaConnect, O C L C Online Computer Library Center, Inc., Swets Information Services).
Indexed: ABIn, ADPA, AHCMS, APEL, ASEANManA, BPI, BPIA, BusI, CPM, CurCont, DIP, EAA, Emerald, ErgAb, IAOP, IBR, IBSS, IBZ, ILD, IPSA, Inspec, KES, ManagCont, ORMS, PAA&I, PersLit, PsycInfo, PsycholAb, QC&AS, RASB, RefZh, SCIMP, SOMA, SOPODA, SSCI, WorkRelAb.
—BLDSC (5011.500000), IDS, IE, Infotrieve, ingenta. **CCC.**
Published by: Blackwell Publishing Ltd., 9600 Garsington Rd, Oxford, OX4 2ZG, United Kingdom. TEL 44-1865-776868, FAX 44-1865-714591, customerservices@oxon.blackwellpublishing.com, http://www.blackwellpublishing.com/journals/JMS. Eds. Mike Wright, Steven W Floyd, Timothy Clark. Circ: 1,600.

658 GHA ISSN 0022-2399
HD28
➤ **JOURNAL OF MANAGEMENT STUDIES.** Text in English. 1961. a. USD 5 domestic; USD 25 foreign (effective 2000). adv. bk.rev. illus. **Document type:** *Journal, Academic/Scholarly.*
Related titles: Microfiche ed.
Indexed: ASCA, CurCont, M&MA, PAIS, SPAA, SSCI, WBA.
Published by: University of Ghana, School of Administration, PO Box 78, Legon, Ghana. TEL 233-21-500592, FAX 233-21-500024, soa@ug.gn.apc.org. Ed., R&P Kwabena Adu Poku TEL 233-21-500381 ext 3358. adv.: page USD 250. Circ: 4,000.

658 USA ISSN 1045-3695
HD28 CODEN: JMAIE9
➤ **JOURNAL OF MANAGERIAL ISSUES.** Short title: J M I. Text in English. 1989. q., latest vol.14, 2002. USD 60 domestic to individuals; USD 125 foreign to individuals; USD 90 domestic to institutions (effective 2005). illus.; bibl. annual index. 135 p./no. 2 cols./p.; back issues avail.; reprints avail. **Document type:** *Journal, Academic/Scholarly.* **Description:** Serves as a bridge of communication between those who study management and those who practice it. Seeks to contribute to the practice of management and the theory of organizations.
Related titles: Microform ed.: (from PQC); Online - full text ed.: (from EBSCO Publishing, Florida Center for Library Automation, Gale Group, Northern Light Technology, Inc., O C L C Online Computer Library Center, Inc., ProQuest Information & Learning).
Indexed: ABIn, BusI, CIJE, CommAb, CurCont, ESPM, HRA, IPSA, InfoSAb, ORMS, PAA&I, PAIS, PRA, PsycInfo, PsycholAb, QC&AS, RiskAb, SOPODA, e-psyche.
—BLDSC (5011.525000), IE, ingenta. **CCC.**
Published by: Pittsburg State University, Department of Economics, Finance & Banking, 1701 South Broadway, Pittsburg, KS 66762-7533. TEL 620-235-4546, FAX 620-235-4572, chuck@pittstate.edu, http://www.pittstate.edu/econ/jmi.html. Ed., R&P Dr. Charles C Fischer TEL 620-235-4546. Circ: 1,000 (paid).

658 158 GBR ISSN 0268-3946
HF5548.7
➤ **JOURNAL OF MANAGERIAL PSYCHOLOGY.** Text in English. 1986. 8/yr. EUR 9,046.91 in Europe; USD 8,959 in North America; AUD 11,009 in Australasia; GBP 6,088.91 in UK & elsewhere (effective 2006). abstr. back issues avail.; reprint service avail. from PSC. **Document type:** *Journal, Academic/Scholarly.* **Description:** Offers practical guidance for personnel and training managers. Provides personnel managers with an essential digest of the latest legislation, research and publications affecting their profession.
Related titles: Online - full text ed.: (from EBSCO Publishing, Emerald Group Publishing Limited, Florida Center for Library Automation, Gale Group, IngentaConnect, O C L C Online Computer Library Center, Inc., ProQuest Information & Learning, Swets Information Services).
Indexed: ABIn, BrEdI, ERA, ESPM, EmerIntel, Emerald, ErgAb, H&SSA, HRA, M&MA, PsycInfo, PsycholAb, RiskAb, SOMA, T&DA, TEA, e-psyche.
—BLDSC (5011.530000), IE, Infotrieve, ingenta. **CCC.**
Published by: Emerald Group Publishing Limited, 60-62 Toller Ln, Bradford, W Yorks BD8 9BY, United Kingdom. TEL 44-1274-777700, FAX 44-1274-785200, infomation@emeraldinsight.com, http://www.emeraldinsight.com/jmp.htm. Ed. Yochanan Altman.

➤ **JOURNAL OF MANUFACTURING TECHNOLOGY MANAGEMENT.** see *ENGINEERING—Computer Applications*

658 GBR ISSN 1746-5664
▼ ➤ **JOURNAL OF MODELLING IN MANAGEMENT.** Text in English. forthcoming 2006 (May). 3/yr. EUR 303.41 in Europe; USD 359 in North America; AUD 479 in Australasia; GBP 216.41 in the UK & elsewhere (effective 2006). **Document type:** *Journal, Academic/Scholarly.*
Related titles: Online - full content ed.: forthcoming.
Published by: Emerald Group Publishing Limited, 60-62 Toller Ln, Bradford, W Yorks BD8 9BY, United Kingdom. TEL 44-1274-777700, FAX 44-1274-785200, infomation@emeraldinsight.com, http://www.emeraldinsight.com/. Ed. Dr. Luiz Moutinho. Pub. Ms. Kate Snowden. R&P Ms. Anne-Marie Thorslund.

658 USA
➤ **JOURNAL OF MODERN BUSINESS.** Text in English. 1998. q. free. back issues avail. **Document type:** *Academic/Scholarly.* **Description:** Covers management, marketing, and finance.
Media: Online - full text.
Published by: (College of Business Administration, University of Sarasota), D C Press, 5720 Third Ave W, Bradenton, FL 34209. drdwaldo@aol.com, http://www.dcpress.com/page2.html/. Ed. Douglas Waldo.

B

658 GBR ISSN 1057-9214
T57.95 CODEN: JMDAEY
JOURNAL OF MULTI-CRITERIA DECISION ANALYSIS. Text in English. 1992. bi-m. USD 630 to institutions; USD 693 combined subscription to institutions print & online eds. (effective 2006). adv. bk.rev.; software rev. back issues avail.; reprint service avail. from PSC. **Document type:** *Journal, Academic/Scholarly.* **Description:** Provides an international forum for the presentation and discussion of all aspects of research, application and evaluation of multicriteria decision analysis.
Related titles: Microform ed.: (from PQC); Online - full text ed.: ISSN 1099-1360. USD 630 to institutions (effective 2006) (from EBSCO Publishing, ProQuest Information & Learning, Swets Information Services, Wiley InterScience).
Indexed: ABIn, CIS, CurCont, ST&MA, ZentMath.
—BLDSC (5021.054000), IE, Infotrieve, ingenta. **CCC.**
Published by: John Wiley & Sons Ltd. (Subsidiary of: John Wiley & Sons, Inc.), The Atrium, Southern Gate, Chichester, West Sussex PO19 8SQ, United Kingdom. TEL 44-1243-779777, FAX 44-1243-775878, customer@wiley.co.uk, http://www3.interscience.wiley.com/cgi-bin/jhome/5725, http://www.wiley.co.uk. Ed. Valerie Belton. adv.: B&W page GBP 650, color page GBP 1,550; trim 200 x 260. Circ: 450. **Subscr. in the Americas to:** John Wiley & Sons, Inc., 111 River St, Hoboken, NJ 07030-5774. TEL 201-748-6645, 800-225-5945, subinfo@wiley.com.

B

658.15 NLD ISSN 1042-444X
HG4027.5
➤ **JOURNAL OF MULTINATIONAL FINANCIAL MANAGEMENT.** Text in Dutch. 1990. 5/yr. EUR 300 in Europe to institutions; JPY 39,900 in Japan to institutions; USD 335 elsewhere to institutions (effective 2006). abstr. back issues avail.; reprints avail. **Document type:** *Journal, Academic/Scholarly.* **Description:** Focuses on the management of multinational enterprises.
Related titles: Microform ed.: (from PQC); Online - full text ed.: (from EBSCO Publishing, Gale Group, IngentaConnect, ScienceDirect, Swets Information Services).
Indexed: CPM, IBSS, JEL.
—BLDSC (5021.065000), IE, Infotrieve, ingenta. **CCC.**
Published by: Elsevier BV, North-Holland (Subsidiary of: Elsevier Science & Technology), Sara Burgerhartstraat 25, Amsterdam, 1055 KV, Netherlands. TEL 31-20-485-3911, FAX 31-20-485-2457, nlinfo-f@elsevier.nl, http://www.elsevier.com/locate/mulfin, http://www.elsevier.nl. Eds. G. G. Booth, I Mathur. **Subscr. to:** Elsevier BV, PO Box 211, Amsterdam 1000 AE, Netherlands. TEL 31-20-485-3757, FAX 31-20-485-3432.

➤ **JOURNAL OF NURSING MANAGEMENT.** see *MEDICAL SCIENCES—Nurses And Nursing*

➤ **JOURNAL OF OPERATIONS MANAGEMENT.** see *ENGINEERING—Industrial Engineering*

658 GBR ISSN 0953-4814
➤ **THE JOURNAL OF ORGANIZATIONAL CHANGE MANAGEMENT.** Text in English. 1988. bi-m. EUR 8,949.04 in Europe; USD 9,219 in North America; AUD 11,329 in Australasia; GBP 6,262.91 in UK & elsewhere (effective 2006). reprint service avail. from PSC. **Document type:** *Journal, Academic/Scholarly.* **Description:** Focuses on organizational development, quality of work life, organizational behavior modification, and consultation.
Related titles: CD-ROM ed.; Online - full text ed.: (from EBSCO Publishing, Emerald Group Publishing Limited, Gale Group, IngentaConnect, O C L C Online Computer Library Center, Inc., ProQuest Information & Learning, Swets Information Services).
Indexed: ABIn, ASCA, CurCont, ESPM, EmerIntel, Emerald, ErgAb, HRA, M&MA, PollutAb, PsycInfo, PsycholAb, SSCI, e-psyche.
—BLDSC (5027.069000), IDS, IE, Infotrieve, ingenta. **CCC.**
Published by: Emerald Group Publishing Limited, 60-62 Toller Ln, Bradford, W Yorks BD8 9BY, United Kingdom. TEL 44-1274-777700, FAX 44-1274-785200, infomation@emeraldinsight.com, http://www.emeraldinsight.com/jocm.htm. Ed. Slawomir Magala.

658 384 USA ISSN 1544-0508
HD30.3
➤ **JOURNAL OF ORGANIZATIONAL CULTURE, COMMUNICATIONS AND CONFLICT.** Text in English. a. **Document type:** *Journal, Academic/Scholarly.*
Formerly: Academy of Managerial Communications Journal (1095-631X)
Related titles: Online - full text ed.
Published by: (Academy of Managerial Communications), Allied Academies, 145 Travis Rd., P. O. Box 2689, Cullowhee, NC 28723. TEL 828-293-9251, FAX 828-293-9407, info@alliedacademies.org, http://www.alliedacademies.org/communication/index.html.

658 USA ISSN 1531-1864
HD56
JOURNAL OF ORGANIZATIONAL EXCELLENCE. Text in English. 1981. q. USD 499 in North America; USD 523 elsewhere; USD 549 combined subscription in North America print & online eds.; USD 573 combined subscription elsewhere print & online eds. (effective 2006). adv. illus. reprint service avail. from PQC,PSC. **Document type:** *Journal, Trade.* **Description:** Focuses on productivity management, practical productivity programs, work innovation and design, human services, quality of work life, robotics, and systems improvement.
Incorporates (19??-2003): Competitive Intelligence Review (1058-0247); Which was formerly (until 1990): Competitive Intelligencer (1040-9645); Formerly (until 2000): National Productivity Review (0277-8556)
Related titles: Microform ed.: (from PQC); Online - full text ed.: ISSN 1531-6653. USD 499 (effective 2006) (from EBSCO Publishing, Gale Group, Northern Light Technology, Inc., O C L C Online Computer Library Center, Inc., ProQuest Information & Learning, Swets Information Services, Wiley InterScience).
Indexed: ABIn, ADPA, BPI, BPIA, BusI, Emerald, ManagCont, ORMS, PAIS, PersLit, QAb, QC&AS, RASB, T&DA, T&II.
—BLDSC (5027.095000), IE, Infotrieve, ingenta. **CCC.**
Published by: Jossey-Bass Inc., Publishers (Subsidiary of: John Wiley & Sons, Inc.), 989 Market St, San Francisco, CA 94103-1741. TEL 415-433-1740, FAX 415-433-0499, jbsubs@jbp.com, http://www3.interscience.wiley.com/cgi-bin/jhome/76507306, http://www.josseybass.com. Ed. Jane G Bensahel. adv.: B&W page USD 1,112, color page USD 1,365; trim 8.25 x 11. Circ: 500 (paid and controlled). **Subscr. outside of N. America to:** John Wiley & Sons Ltd., The Atrium, Southern Gate, Chichester, West Sussex PO19 8SQ, United Kingdom. TEL 44-1243-779777, FAX 44-1243-775878, cs-journals@wiley.co.uk.

JOURNAL OF PARK AND RECREATION ADMINISTRATION (ONLINE EDITION). see *SPORTS AND GAMES—Outdoor Life*

JOURNAL OF PHARMACEUTICAL MARKETING AND MANAGEMENT. see *PHARMACY AND PHARMACOLOGY*

658 GBR ISSN 1384-1289
HD72 CODEN: JPREF2
JOURNAL OF POLICY REFORM. Text in English. 1997. q. GBP 180, USD 298 combined subscription to institutions print & online eds. (effective 2006). reprint service avail. from PSC. **Document type:** *Journal, Academic/Scholarly.* **Description:** Focuses on a new, dynamic area of research which has emerged during the last decade: policy reform.
Related titles: Online - full text ed.: GBP 171, USD 283 (effective 2006) (from EBSCO Publishing, Gale Group, IngentaConnect, O C L C Online Computer Library Center, Inc., Swets Information Services).
Indexed: IBSS, IPSA, JEL.
—BLDSC (5040.844000), IE, Infotrieve, ingenta. **CCC.**
Published by: Routledge (Subsidiary of: Taylor & Francis Group), 4 Park Square, Milton Park, Abingdon, Oxon OX14 4RN, United Kingdom. TEL 44-1235-828600, FAX 44-1235-829000, http://www.tandf.co.uk/journals/titles/13841289.html, http://www.routledge.co.uk. Ed. Michael Connolly. **Subscr. to:** Taylor & Francis Ltd, Journals Customer Service, Rankine Rd, Basingstoke, Hants RG24 8PR, United Kingdom. TEL 44-1256-813000, FAX 44-1256-330245, enquiry@tandf.co.uk.

JOURNAL OF PRODUCT INNOVATION MANAGEMENT. see *BUSINESS AND ECONOMICS—Production Of Goods And Services*

658 338 USA ISSN 0895-562X
HD56
➤ **JOURNAL OF PRODUCTIVITY ANALYSIS.** Text in English. 1989. bi-m. EUR 598, USD 608, GBP 378 combined subscription to institutions print & online eds. (effective 2005). adv. illus. Index. reprint service avail. from PQC,PSC. **Document type:** *Journal, Academic/Scholarly.* **Description:** Publishes theoretical and applied research that addresses issues involving the measurement, explanation and improvement of productivity.
Related titles: Microform ed.; Online - full text ed.: ISSN 1573-0441 (from EBSCO Publishing, Gale Group, IngentaConnect, Kluwer Online, O C L C Online Computer Library Center, Inc., ProQuest Information & Learning, Springer LINK, Swets Information Services).
Indexed: ABIn, ASCA, BibLing, CurCont, Inspec, JEL, ORMS, QC&AS, RefZh, SSCI.
—BLDSC (5042.660000), IDS, IE, Infotrieve, ingenta. **CCC.**
Published by: Springer-Verlag New York, Inc. (Subsidiary of: Springer Science+Business Media), 233 Spring St, New York, NY 10013. TEL 212-460-1500, FAX 212-460-1575, service@springer-ny.com, http://springerlink.metapress.com/openurl.asp?genre=journal&issn=0895-562X, http://www.springer-ny.com. Ed. Robin C Sickles. **Subscr. to:** Journal Fulfillment, PO Box 2485, Secaucus, NJ 07096-2485. TEL 201-348-4033, FAX 201-348-4505, journals@springer-ny.com.

➤ **JOURNAL OF PROJECT & CONSTRUCTION MANAGEMENT.** see *ENGINEERING*

➤ **JOURNAL OF PROMOTION MANAGEMENT**; innovations in planning & applied research. see *ADVERTISING AND PUBLIC RELATIONS*

➤ **JOURNAL OF PUBLIC BUDGETING, ACCOUNTING & FINANCIAL MANAGEMENT.** see *PUBLIC ADMINISTRATION*

➤ **JOURNAL OF PUBLIC HEALTH MANAGEMENT AND PRACTICE.** see *PUBLIC HEALTH AND SAFETY*

➤ **JOURNAL OF QUALITY TECHNOLOGY**; a quarterly journal of methods, applications and related topics . see *ENGINEERING—Engineering Mechanics and Materials*

➤ **JOURNAL OF RELATIONSHIP MARKETING**; innovations & enhancements for customer service, relations & satisfaction. see *BUSINESS AND ECONOMICS*

658 USA ISSN 1539-1590
Q180.55.M3
THE JOURNAL OF RESEARCH ADMINISTRATION. Text in English. 1969. q. USD 165; USD 30 to students (effective 2005). adv. bk.rev. index. back issues avail.; reprints avail. **Document type:** *Journal, Academic/Scholarly.* **Description:** For researchers and administrators in universities, industry, nonprofit organizations and medical facilities.
Former titles (until 2000): S R A Journal (1062-8142); (until 1991): Society of Research Administrators. Journal (0038-0024)
Related titles: Microfilm ed.: (from PQC); Online - full text ed.: (from Florida Center for Library Automation, Gale Group, O C L C Online Computer Library Center, Inc., ProQuest Information & Learning).
Indexed: ABIn, ASCA, BPIA, BusI, CIJE, CurCont, Inspec, PAIS, RASB, SSCI.
—BLDSC (5051.860000), CISTI, IE, ingenta.
Published by: Society of Research Administrators, Inc., 1901 N Moore St., Ste. 1004, Arlington, VA 22209-1706. TEL 703-741-0140, FAX 703-741-0142, journal@srainternational.org, info@srainternational.org, http://www.srainternational.org/newweb/publications/journal/. Ed. Peggy Harrel. Circ: 3,600.

658 USA ISSN 1520-0361
HG179
JOURNAL OF RETIREMENT PLANNING. Text in English. 1998. bi-m. USD 225; USD 325 combined subscription print & online eds. (effective 2004). **Description:** Dedicated entirely to the complex and evolving issues surrounding retirement planning.
Related titles: Online - full text ed.: USD 245 (effective 2004).
Indexed: AgeL.
—**CCC.**
Published by: C C H Inc., 2700 Lake Cook Rd, Riverwoods, IL 60015. TEL 847-267-7000, 800-449-6439, cust_serv@cch.com, http://www.cch.com.

JOURNAL OF REVENUE AND PRICING MANAGEMENT. see *BUSINESS AND ECONOMICS—Accounting*

JOURNAL OF RISK AND UNCERTAINTY. see *BUSINESS AND ECONOMICS—Economic Systems And Theories, Economic History*

658 364 USA
THE JOURNAL OF SAFE MANAGEMENT OF DISRUPTIVE AND ASSAULTIVE BEHAVIOR. Text in English. 1980. q. **Document type:** *Trade.*
Published by: Crisis Prevention Institute, Inc., 3315-K N 124th St, Brookefield, WI 53005. FAX 262-783-5906, info@crisisprevention.com, http://www.crisisprevention.com. Ed. Diana B Kohn. Circ: 12,000.

JOURNAL OF SCHEDULING. see *COMPUTERS—Software*

658 IND ISSN 0972-4702
HD9980.1
➤ **JOURNAL OF SERVICES RESEARCH.** Text in English. 2001. s-a. INR 500 domestic; USD 75 in Asia; USD 150 elsewhere (effective 2002). bk.rev. abstr. back issues avail. **Document type:** *Journal, Academic/Scholarly.* **Description:** Publishes management related research focusing on service industries - hospitality, health management, financial services, infrastructure, education, information technology.
Related titles: CD-ROM ed.; Online - full text ed.: (from EBSCO Publishing).
Indexed: RRTA.
Published by: Institute for International Management & Technology, 336, Phase-IV, Udyog Vihar, Gurgaon, Haryana 122 001, India. TEL 91-124-6397783, FAX 91-124-6397784, iimt@imtobu.ac.in, http://www.iimtobu.ac.in. Ed. Dr. Vinnie Jauhari. Pub. Dr. Kamlesh Misra. Circ: 200 (paid); 800 (controlled).

➤ **JOURNAL OF SPORT MANAGEMENT.** see *SPORTS AND GAMES*

658 370 IRL
JOURNAL OF STRATEGIC MANAGEMENT EDUCATION. Text in English. 2002 (Summer). q. **Document type:** *Magazine, Academic/Scholarly.* **Description:** Contains case studies relating to strategic management, lectures and information on advances in strategic management/research topics.
Published by: Senate Hall Academic Publishing, PO Box 8261, Shankill, Co. Dublin, Ireland. TEL 353-1-2005066, FAX 353-1-2823701, info@senatehall.com, http://www.senatehall.com/jsme/index.html.

▼ **JOURNAL OF TECHNOLOGY MANAGEMENT IN CHINA.** see *TECHNOLOGY: COMPREHENSIVE WORKS*

JOURNAL OF WORKERS COMPENSATION. see *INSURANCE*

658 USA ISSN 1548-7717
HD30.2 CODEN: ACITCD
➤ **JOURNALS OF CASES ON INFORMATION TECHNOLOGY.** Text in English. 1999. q. USD 90 to individuals; USD 245 to institutions (effective 2005). 200 p./no. 1 cols./p.; **Document type:** *Journal, Academic/Scholarly.* **Description:** Aims to provide understanding and lessons learned in regard to all aspects of information technology utilization and management in organizations.
Former titles: Annals of Cases on Information Technology (1537-937X); (until 2002): Annals of Cases on Information Technology Applications and Management in Organizations (1098-8580)
Related titles: Online - full text ed.: ISSN 1548-7725 (from EBSCO Publishing, O C L C Online Computer Library Center, Inc., ProQuest Information & Learning).
Indexed: ABIn, BrCerAb, C&ISA, CerAb, CorrAb, E&CAJ, EMA, ESPM, IAA, InfoSAb, Inspec, M&TEA, MBF, METADEX, RiskAb, WAA.
—BLDSC (1040.147500), IE, ingenta, Linda Hall. **CCC.**
Published by: Idea Group Publishing (Subsidiary of: Idea Group Inc.), 701 E Chocolate Ave, Ste 200, Hershey, PA 17033-1240. TEL 717-533-8845, FAX 717-533-8661, cust@idea-group.com, http://www.idea-group.com. Ed. Rabbi Mehdi Khosrow-Pour. R&P Jan Travers. Circ: 300 (paid and controlled).

658 FRA ISSN 0755-0006
JURIS ASSOCIATIONS. Text in French. 1983. 20/yr. EUR 99; EUR 9.80 newsstand/cover (effective 2003). adv. index. back issues avail. **Document type:** *Trade.* **Description:** Presents case law related to the fiscal system,the administration and regulation of the non-profit sector for accountants, lawyers and administrators in France.
Media: CD-ROM.
Published by: Editions Juris-Service, 2 rue Andre-Lassagne, Lyon, 69001, France. TEL 33-04-72101001, FAX 33-04-78289383, info@juris-associations.com, http://www.editionsjuris.com. Ed. Xavier Delsol. Pub. Philippe Chagnon. Circ: 16,000.

658 MYS ISSN 0127-2713
JURNAL PENGURUSAN. Text in English, Malay. 1977. a. USD 15.
Indexed: APEL.
Published by: Penerbit Universiti Kebangsaan Malaysia, Ukm Bangi, Selangor 43600, Malaysia.

658 LKA
KALAMANAKARANAYA; management. Text in Singhalese. 1977. irreg.?. LKR 1.50.
Published by: University of Sri Lanka, Vidyodaya Campus, Management Studies Society, Gangodawila, Nugegoda, Sri Lanka.

658 NOR ISSN 0332-5423
KAPITAL. Text in Norwegian. 1971. fortn. (22/yr.). NOK 750. adv.
Published by: Periscopus A-S, Postboks 188, Lysaker, 1324, Norway. TEL 67-58 28 50, FAX 67-58-28-70. Ed. Trygve Hegnar. Circ: 45,000.

658 AUS ISSN 1444-7614
KEEPING GOOD COMPANIES. Text in English. 1948. m. AUD 90 domestic; AUD 118 foreign (effective 2004). adv. index. 64 p./no.; **Document type:** *Magazine, Corporate.* **Description:** Presents articles of interest to company secretaries on corporate governance, risk management, finance, economics, taxation, human resources and administration, principally in Australia and New Zealand.
Former titles (until 2000): Australian Company Secretary (1323-9406); (until 1995): Journal of Corporate Management (1038-2410); (until 1992): Corporate Management (1034-0408); (until 1989): Professional Administrator (0159-4672); (until 1980): Chartered Secretary (0009-1928)
Related titles: Online - full text ed.: (from Gale Group).
Indexed: AESIS, AusPAIS, IMI.
—**CCC.**
Published by: Chartered Secretaries Australia Ltd., GPO Box 1594, Sydney, NSW 2001, Australia. TEL 61-2-9223-5744, FAX 61-2-9232-7174, info@csaust.com, http://www.CSAust.com. Pub., R&P Catherine Britton. adv.: B&W page AUD 2,060, color page AUD 3,600; trim 210 x 297. Circ: 7,810.

658 330.1 JPN ISSN 0451-6222
HB9
KEIZAI RIRON/WAKAYAMA ECONOMIC REVIEW. Text in Japanese; Abstracts in English. 1950. 6/yr. JPY 500 (effective 2001). bk.rev. **Document type:** *Academic/Scholarly.*
Indexed: JPI, SSI.
Published by: Wakayama Daigaku, Keizai Gakkai/Wakayama University, Economic Society, 930 Sakaedani, Wakayama-shi, 640-510, Japan. TEL 81-73-547-7633, FAX 81-73-457-7630, keiken@emily.eco.wakayama-u.ac.jp. Circ: 1,600.

658 600 CHN ISSN 1009-1629
KEJI GUANLI/MANAGEMENT OF SCIENCE AND TECHNOLOGY. Text in Chinese. 1986. m. CNY 96 (effective 2004). 96 p./no.; **Document type:** *Journal, Academic/Scholarly.*
Formerly: Keji Guanli yu Chengjiu (1001-313X)
Published by: Zhongguo Renmin Daxue, Shubao Zilio Zhongxin/Renmin University of China, Information Center for Social Server, Dongcheng-qu, 3, Zhangzizhong Lu, Beijing, 100007, China. TEL 86-10-64039458, FAX 86-10-64015080, kyes@163.net, http://www.confucius.cn.net/bkdetail.asp?fzt=N1. **Dist. in US by:** China Publications Service, PO Box 49614, Chicago, IL 60649. TEL 312-288-3291, FAX 312-288-8570; **Dist. by:** China International Book Trading Corp, 35 Chegongzhuang Xilu, Haidian District, PO Box 399, Beijing 100044, China. TEL 86-10-68412045, FAX 86-10-68412023, cibtc@mail.cibtc.com.cn, http://www.cibtc.com.cn.

658 600 JPN ISSN 0914-7020
KENKYU GIJUTSU KEIKAKU/JOURNAL OF SCIENCE POLICY AND RESEARCH MANAGEMENT. Text in English, Japanese. 1986. 2/yr. JPY 8,000, USD 60 (effective 1998). bk.rev. abstr. **Document type:** *Journal, Trade.* **Description:** Contains special reports, articles, reviews, commentary, and news of the society.
—**CCC.**
Published by: Kenkyu Gijutsu Keikaku Gakkai/Japan Society for Science Policy and Research Management, c/o Institute for Policy Sciences, Toshiba EMI Nagatacho Bldg 5th Fl, 4-8 Nagata-cho 2-chome, Chiyoda-ku, Tokyo, 100-0014, Japan. TEL 81-3-5521-1741, FAX 81-3-5521-1901, hirasawa@nistep.go.jp. Ed. Ryo Hirasawa. Circ: 900.

KEY NOTE MARKET REPORT: DEBT MANAGEMENT (COMMERCIAL & CONSUMER). see *BUSINESS AND ECONOMICS—Banking And Finance*

KEY NOTE MARKET REPORT: DISCOUNT RETAILING. see *BUSINESS AND ECONOMICS—Marketing And Purchasing*

658 338 GBR
KEY NOTE MARKET REPORT: MANAGEMENT CONSULTANTS. Variant title: Management Consultants. Text in English. irreg., latest 2001, Apr. GBP 340 per issue (effective 2002). **Document type:** *Trade.* **Description:** Provides and overview of a specific UK market segment and includes executive summary, market definition, market size, industry background, competitor analysis, current issues, forecasts, company profiles, and more.
Formerly: Key Note Report: Management Consultants
Related titles: CD-ROM ed.; Online - full text ed.
Published by: Key Note Ltd., Field House, 72 Oldfield Rd, Hampton, Mddx TW12 2HQ, United Kingdom. TEL 44-20-8481-8750, FAX 44-20-8783-0049, info@keynote.co.uk, http://www.keynote.co.uk. Ed. Jenny Baxter.

KEYAN GUANLI/SCIENCE RESEARCH MANAGEMENT. see *SCIENCES: COMPREHENSIVE WORKS*

658 790 USA
KEYNOTES (OAK BROOK). Text in English. m. membership. **Document type:** *Newsletter.* **Description:** Information on effective implementation of employee recreation, sports and wellness education programs.
Published by: Employee Services Management Association, 568 Spring Rd., Ste. D, Elmhurst, IL 60126-3896. TEL 630-559-0020, FAX 630-559-0025, esmahq@esmassn.org, http://www.esmassn.org/. Ed. Karen G Beagley. Circ: 4,000.

658 KOR
KIYUP KYUNGYUNG/BUSINESS MANAGEMENT. Text in Korean. 1958. m. KRW 44,000 (effective 1991). adv. **Description:** Aims to impart concepts and techniques of enterprise management to help domestic industries develop competitive power in the world economy. Contains articles, comments, diary for top and middle managers, overseas economic information, field reports on productivity improvement, and case studies on industrial relations.
Published by: Korea Productivity Center, Jeokseon-dong Jongro-ku, 122-1 Sangsansung Blvd, Seoul, 110052, Korea, S. TEL 02-739-5868, FAX 02-736-0322, TELEX KPCENTR-K27672. Ed. Hiwhoa Moon. Circ: 30,000.

658 GBR ISSN 1092-4604
HD58.8 CODEN: KPMAFA
➤ **KNOWLEDGE AND PROCESS MANAGEMENT;** the journal of corporate transformation. Text in English. 1993. q. USD 735 to institutions; USD 809 combined subscription to institutions print & online eds. (effective 2006). adv. back issues avail.; reprint service avail. from PSC. **Document type:** *Journal, Academic/Scholarly.*
Formerly: Business Change and Re-engineering (0969-3866)
Related titles: Microform ed.: (from PQC); Online - full text ed.: ISSN 1099-1441. 1997. USD 735 to institutions (effective 2006) (from EBSCO Publishing, ProQuest Information & Learning, Swets Information Services, Wiley InterScience).
Indexed: ABIn, Emerald.
—BLDSC (5100.439500), IE, Infotrieve, ingenta. **CCC.**
Published by: John Wiley & Sons Ltd. (Subsidiary of: John Wiley & Sons, Inc.), The Atrium, Southern Gate, Chichester, West Sussex PO19 8SQ, United Kingdom. TEL 44-1243-779777, FAX 44-1243-775878, customer@wiley.co.uk, http://www.interscience.wiley.com/jpages/1092-4604/, http://www.wiley.co.uk. Ed. Anthony Wensley. adv.: B&W page GBP 650, color page GBP 1,550; trim 210 x 297. **Subscr. in N. America to:** John Wiley & Sons, Inc., 111 River St, Hoboken, NJ 07030-5774. TEL 201-748-6645, 800-225-5945, subinfo@wiley.com.

B

▼ ➤ **KNOWLEDGE MANAGEMENT RESEARCH & PRACTICE.** see *COMPUTERS*

658 GBR ISSN 1369-7633
KNOWLEDGE MANAGEMENT REVIEW. Variant title: K M Review. Text in English. 1998. bi-m. GBP 265; GBP 365 combined subscription print & online (effective 2004). **Document type:** *Journal, Trade.* **Description:** Provides key advice for senior managers in knowledge management, information management, strategic planning, total quality management, human resources, and internal communication, among others.
Related titles: Online - full text ed.: GBP 375 (effective 2004) (from EBSCO Publishing, ProQuest Information & Learning).
—BLDSC (5100.451500), IE, ingenta. **CCC.**
Published by: Melcrum Publishing, 1st Floor, Chelsea Reach, 79-89 Lots Rd, London, SW10 0RN, United Kingdom. TEL 44-171-229-9900, 877-226-2764, FAX 44-171-243-5554, 312-803-1871, http://www.melcrum.com. Ed. Victoria Mellor.

658 USA
KNOWLEDGE@WHARTON. Text in English. bi-w. free. **Document type:** *Journal, Academic/Scholarly.* **Description:** Offers the latest business insights, information and research from a variety of sources.
Media: Online - full text.
Published by: University of Pennsylvania, Wharton School, 430 Vance Hall, Philadelphia, PA 19104-6301. TEL 215-898-4560, FAX 215-386-4304, http://knowledge.wharton.upenn.edu, http://www.wharton.upenn.edu/. Ed. Mukul Pandya.

658 JPN ISSN 0085-2570
HF5001
KOBE UNIVERSITY. SCHOOL OF BUSINESS ADMINISTRATION. ANNALS. Text in English. 1957. irreg., latest 2000. per issue exchange basis. bibl.; charts. back issues avail. **Description:** Covers issues in business and economics in Japan.
Indexed: ATI, BAS.
Published by: Kobe Daigaku, School of Business Administration/Kobe University, Rokko-Dai-cho, Nada-ku, Kobe-shi, Hyogo-ken 657-0013, Japan. FAX 81-78-881-8100. Circ: (controlled).

KOBIETA I BIZNES/WOMEN & BUSINESS; akademicko-gospodarcze forum. see *BUSINESS AND ECONOMICS—Small Business*

658.5 JPN ISSN 0023-2777
KOJO KANRI/FACTORY MANAGEMENT. Text in Japanese. 1955. m. JPY 980. adv. bk.rev. abstr.; bibl.; charts; illus.; stat.; tr.lit. index. **Description:** Covers the business environment regarding management strategy, development of human ability, reorganization of production systems, measures taken by developed enterprises.
Indexed: JTA.
Published by: Industrial Daily News Ltd./Nikkan Kogyo Shinbunsha, 1-9-5 Otemachi Chivoda ku, Tokyo, 100-8066, Japan. Ed. Tomio Wada. Circ: 36,500.

KOMPASS PROFESSIONNEL. DISTRIBUTION, COMMERCE DE GROS. see *BUSINESS AND ECONOMICS—Trade And Industrial Directories*

650 KOR ISSN 0023-396X
KOREAN BUSINESS JOURNAL. Text in English, Korean. 1967. q. free or on exchange basis. adv. bk.rev. bibl.; charts; mkt. index.
Published by: Institute of Management Research, School of Management, Seoul National University, 56-1 Shinrim-Dong, Kwanak-Ku, Seoul, 151, Korea, S. Ed. Chung Nyun Kim. Circ: 2,000.

658.2 389 JPN ISSN 1347-0213
KUORITI MANEJIMENTO/QUALITY MANAGEMENT. Text in Japanese. 1950. m. JPY 18,100. adv. abstr.; charts; illus. index.
Formerly (until 2002): Hinshitsu Kanri (0018-1951)
Indexed: JTA.
—CISTI.
Published by: Union of Japanese Scientists and Engineers/Nihon Kagaku Gijutsu Renmei, 5-10-11 Sendagaya, Shibuya-ku, Tokyo, 151-0051, Japan. TEL 03-5379-1227, FAX 03-3225-1813. Ed. Kohei Suzue. Circ: 15,000.

KVALITETSMAGASINET. see *BUSINESS AND ECONOMICS*

KWALITEIT IN BEELD. see *HEALTH FACILITIES AND ADMINISTRATION*

658 KOR
KYUNG-YOUNG SHINMUN/MANAGEMENT NEWS. Text in Korean. 1955. bi-m. KRW 50,000, USD 62.50. adv. bk.rev.
Published by: (Korea University, Graduate School of Business Administration), Korea University Press, 1 Anam-dong, Sungbuk-ku, Seoul, 136-70, Korea, S. TEL 82-2-9261926, FAX 82-2-923-4661. Ed. Il Kweon Dong. Circ: 12,000.

B

L A M A MANAGER. see *LAW*

658 NGA ISSN 1118-3713
HD70.N6
L B S MANAGEMENT REVIEW. Text in English. 1996. s-a. USD 30 to individuals; USD 40 to institutions (effective 2004).
Related titles: Online - full text ed.: (from International Network for the Availability of Scientific Publications, African Journals Online).
Published by: Lagos Business School, 2 Ahmed Onibudo St, PO Box 73688, Lagos, Victoria Island, Nigeria. http://www.inasp.info/ajol/journals/lbsmr/about.html. Ed. Chantal Epie.

658 332 USA
L I M R A'S VISION; effective strategy for tomorrow's leaders. Text in English. 1996. bi-m. USD 59.97; USD 74.97 foreign (effective 1996). **Description:** Dedicated to leadership and business management issues affecting managers in the financial services industry.
Published by: L I M R A International, Inc., 300 Day Hill Rd, Windsor, CT 06095. TEL 800-235-4672.

658 USA
L R I GUIDES TO MANAGEMENT. MONOGRAPHS✱. Text in English. 1965. irreg., latest vol.7. price varies. **Document type:** *Monographic series.*
Formerly: Management Monographs (0076-3640)
Published by: Leadership Resources Inc., 491 Pass Run Dr, Luray, VA 22835-3532. Ed. Ronald E Kieloch.

LABORATORY INDUSTRY REPORT; the bi-monthly on lab management and marketing intelligence. see *SCIENCES: COMPREHENSIVE WORKS*

658 USA ISSN 1082-2186
CODEN: LAREFL
LAKEWOOD REPORT ON POSITIVE EMPLOYEE PRACTICES. Text in English. 1995. 12/yr. USD 128 domestic; USD 138 in Canada; USD 148 elsewhere. **Document type:** *Newsletter.* **Description:** Provides case studies from innovative companies and how-to information on the best business practices in business today.
Formed by the merger of (1990-1995): Total Quality (1053-1718); (1988-1995): Service Edge (1053-1734); Which incorporates: Front-Line Service (1053-1726)
Related titles: Microform ed.: (from PQC); Online - full text ed.: (from ProQuest Information & Learning).
Indexed: BLI.
—CCC.
Published by: Lakewood Publications, Inc., 50 S 9th St, Minneapolis, MN 55402. TEL 612-333-0471, FAX 612-333-6526. Ed. Brian McDermott.

LAMY DROIT DU DIRIGEANT D'ENTREPRISE. see *LAW—Corporate Law*

658 FRA ISSN 1635-9291
LAMY SOCIETES COMMERCIALES. FORMULAIRE. SOCIETE A RESPONSABILITE LIMITEE. Text in French. a. looseleaf. EUR 518.01 print & CD-ROM eds. (effective 2004).
Related titles: CD-ROM ed.; ♦ Supplement to: Lamy Societes Commerciales. ISSN 0983-6799.
Published by: Lamy S.A. (Subsidiary of: Wolters Kluwer France), 21/23 rue des Ardennes, Paris, 75935 Cedex 19, France. TEL 33-1-825080800, FAX 33-1-44721388, lamy@lamy.fr, http://www.lamy.fr. Ed. Jacques Demaison.

658 FRA ISSN 1635-9305
LAMY SOCIETES COMMERCIALES. FORMULAIRE. SOCIETE ANONIME A CONSEIL D'ADMINISTRATION. Text in French. base vol. plus s-a. updates. looseleaf. EUR 523.28 print & CD-ROM eds. (effective 2004).
Related titles: CD-ROM ed.; ♦ Supplement to: Lamy Societes Commerciales. ISSN 0983-6799.
Published by: Lamy S.A. (Subsidiary of: Wolters Kluwer France), 21/23 rue des Ardennes, Paris, 75935 Cedex 19, France. TEL 33-1-825080800, FAX 33-1-44721388, lamy@lamy.fr, http://www.lamy.fr. Ed. Jacques Demaison.

658 FRA ISSN 1635-9313
LAMY SOCIETES COMMERCIALES. FORMULAIRE. SOCIETE ANONIME A DIRECTOIRE ET CONSEIL DE SURVEILLANCE. Text in French. base vol. plus s-a. updates. looseleaf. EUR 523.28 print & CD-ROM eds. (effective 2004).
Related titles: CD-ROM ed.; ♦ Supplement to: Lamy Societes Commerciales. ISSN 0983-6799.
Indexed: SCI.
Published by: Lamy S.A. (Subsidiary of: Wolters Kluwer France), 21/23 rue des Ardennes, Paris, 75935 Cedex 19, France. TEL 33-1-825080800, FAX 33-1-44721388, lamy@lamy.fr, http://www.lamy.fr. Ed. Jacques Demaison.

658 FRA ISSN 1635-9321
LAMY SOCIETES COMMERCIALES. FORMULAIRE. SOCIETES AUTRES QUE SARL ET SA. REGROUPEMENT DES SOCIETES. Text in French. 2 base vols. plus s-a. updates. looseleaf. EUR 601.35 print & CD-ROM eds. (effective 2004).
Related titles: CD-ROM ed.; ♦ Supplement to: Lamy Societes Commerciales. ISSN 0983-6799.
Published by: Lamy S.A. (Subsidiary of: Wolters Kluwer France), 21/23 rue des Ardennes, Paris, 75935 Cedex 19, France. TEL 33-1-825080800, FAX 33-1-44721388, lamy@lamy.fr, http://www.lamy.fr.

LATIN AMERICAN BUSINESS REVIEW; published in cooperation and partnership with COPPEAD, EGADE, and USD. see *BUSINESS AND ECONOMICS—International Commerce*

658 CAN ISSN 0023-9038
LAVAL ADMINISTRATION. Text in English. 1969. q. free. adv. bk.rev. bibl.; charts; illus.; stat.
Supersedes: Economie et Commerce
Published by: Universite Laval, Faculte des Sciences de l'Administration, Cite Universitaire, Ste Foy, PQ G1K 7P4, Canada. Circ: 1,000.

648 340 USA ISSN 1071-7242
LAW OFFICE ADMINISTRATOR. Text in English. 1992. m. looseleaf. USD 167 (effective 2000). bk.rev. index. back issues avail. **Document type:** *Newsletter.* **Description:** Covers issues and regulations affecting the administration of law firms.
Published by: Ardmore Publishing Company, PO Box 11670, Atlanta, GA 30355. Ed. Bill Kimbro. Pub., R&P Susan Crawford. Circ: 2,500.

LAW PRACTICE; the business of practicing law. see *LAW*

658.4092 USA ISSN 1087-8149
HM141
LEADER TO LEADER. Text in English. 1996. q. USD 250 domestic; USD 290 in Canada & Mexico; USD 324 elsewhere; USD 275 combined subscription domestic print & online eds.; USD 315 combined subscription in Canada & Mexico print & online eds.; USD 349 combined subscription elsewhere print & online eds. (effective 2006). back issues avail. **Document type:** *Journal, Academic/Scholarly.* **Description:** Reports on management, leadership and strategy written by world-class executives, best-selling management authors, top consultants and respected social thinkers.
Related titles: Online - full text ed.: ISSN 1531-5355. USD 250 (effective 2006) (from EBSCO Publishing, O C L C Online Computer Library Center, Inc., ProQuest Information & Learning, Swets Information Services, Wiley InterScience).
Indexed: ABIn.
—IE.
Published by: (Peter F. Drucker Foundation for Nonprofit Management), Jossey-Bass Inc., Publishers (Subsidiary of: John Wiley & Sons, Inc.), 989 Market St, San Francisco, CA 94103-1741. TEL 415-433-1740, FAX 415-433-0499, jbsubs@jbp.com, http://www3.interscience.wiley.com/cgi-bin/jhome/73505673, http://www.josseybass.com. Ed. Frances Hesselbein. Pub. Sue Lewis. R&P Lorri Wimer TEL 415-433-1740. Circ: 8,900 (paid).

658 USA ISSN 1057-4816
LEADERSHIP (FAIRFIELD); with a human touch. Text in English. 1985. m. USD 1.35 per issue. **Description:** Contains wit, wisdom and common sense about the art of managing people.
Formerly (until 1991): Soundings (Fairfield) (0886-8123)
Published by: Economics Press, Inc., 1249, Caldwell, NJ 07007-1249. TEL 800-526-2554, FAX 201-227-9742. Ed. Arthur F Lenehan. Circ: 60,000.

658 USA ISSN 0195-9204
HF5001
LEADERSHIP (WASHINGTON, 1980). Text in English. 1980. a. adv. reprint service avail. from PQC.
Indexed: ChrPI, RI-1.
Published by: American Society of Association Executives, 1575 Eye St, N W, Washington, DC 20005-1168. TEL 202-626-2735, FAX 202-408-9635, http://www.asaenet.org. Ed. Ann Mahoney. Circ: 50,000.

LEADERSHIP AND MANAGEMENT IN ENGINEERING. see *ENGINEERING—Civil Engineering*

658 GBR ISSN 0143-7739
HD58.8
➤ **LEADERSHIP AND ORGANIZATION DEVELOPMENT JOURNAL.** Text in English. 1980. 8/yr. EUR 12,265.91 in Europe to institutions; USD 12,009 in North America to institutions; AUD 15,079 in Australasia to institutions; GBP 8,179.91 to institutions in UK & elsewhere (effective 2006). reprint service avail. from PSC. **Document type:** *Journal, Academic/Scholarly.* **Description:** Covers theory and practice in area of leadership and organization development. Adopts an interdisciplinary approach.
Related titles: Online - full text ed.: (from EBSCO Publishing, Emerald Group Publishing Limited, Florida Center for Library Automation, Gale Group, IngentaConnect, O C L C Online Computer Library Center, Inc., ProQuest Information & Learning, Swets Information Services).
Indexed: ABIn, ADPA, ASEANManA, BPIA, BrEdI, BusI, CPM, CurCont, ERA, ETA, EmerIntel, Emerald, ErgAb, HRA, M&MA, MEA, PsycholAb, SOMA, SWA, T&DA, T&II, TEA.
—BLDSC (5162.866000), IE, Infotrieve, ingenta. **CCC.**
Published by: Emerald Group Publishing Limited, 60-62 Toller Ln, Bradford, W Yorks BD8 9BY, United Kingdom. TEL 44-1274-777700, FAX 44-1274-785200, infomation@emeraldinsight.com, http://www.emeraldinsight.com/lodj.htm. Ed. Dr. Marie McHugh. Pub. Ms. Paula Fernandez. R&P Mr. John Eggleton.

658 USA ISSN 1080-1863
LEADERSHIP FOR THE FRONT LINES. Text in English. 1988. s-m. USD 149 to individuals; USD 7 newsstand/cover (effective 2002). index. **Document type:** *Newsletter.* **Description:** Focuses on how supervisors and team leaders can become more effective in their current positions by following detailed guidelines and specific steps to success.
Incorporates (in 1998): Human Side (1077-4335); Which was formerly (until 1992): Human Side of Supervision (0018-7135); Former titles (until 1994): Front Line Leadership (1077-5498); Front Line Supervisor's Bulletin (1067-8956)
Related titles: Online - full text ed.: (from EBSCO Publishing, Florida Center for Library Automation, Gale Group).
Published by: Bureau of Business Practice (Subsidiary of: Aspen Publishers, Inc.), 1185 Avenue of the Americas, 37th Fl, New York, NY 10036. TEL 860-442-4365, 800-243-0876, FAX 860-437-3555, rebecca_armitage@prenhall.com, http://www.bbpnews.com. Ed. Kathy Cipriani. Pub. Peter Garabedian. R&P Kathryn Mennone.

658.071 303.34 USA ISSN 1093-6092
HD57.7
LEADERSHIP IN ACTION. Text in English. 1980. bi-m. USD 345 domestic to institutions; USD 405 in Canada & Mexico to institutions; USD 456 elsewhere to institutions; USD 380 combined subscription domestic to institutions print & online eds.; USD 440 combined subscription in Canada & Mexico to institutions print & online eds.; USD 491 combined subscription elsewhere to institutions print & online eds. (effective 2006). 24 p./no.; back issues avail. **Document type:** *Newsletter, Academic/Scholarly.* **Description:** Covers management education, executive development, and leadership development.
Formerly: Issues and Observations (1065-464X)
Related titles: Online - full text ed.: ISSN 1532-1088. USD 345 (effective 2006) (from EBSCO Publishing, O C L C Online Computer Library Center, Inc., ProQuest Information & Learning, Swets Information Services, Wiley InterScience).
Indexed: ABIn, T&DA.
—IE. **CCC.**
Published by: (Center for Creative Leadership), Jossey-Bass Inc., Publishers (Subsidiary of: John Wiley & Sons, Inc.), 989 Market St, San Francisco, CA 94103-1741. TEL 415-433-1740, 888-378-2537, FAX 800-605-2665, 415-433-0499, jbsubs@jbp.com, http://www3.interscience.wiley.com/cgi-bin/jhome/73505682, http://www.josseybass.com. Ed. Martin J Wilcox. Pub. Sue Lewis. R&P Lorri Wimer TEL 415-433-1740. Circ: 3,500.

658 AUS
THE LEADERSHIP LETTER. Text in English. fortn. AUD 395 domestic; AUD 359.09 foreign (effective 2004). **Document type:** *Newsletter.* **Description:** Gives you advice, tips on strategic planning as well as provides you with leadership inspiration and motivation.
Related titles: Online - full content ed.
Published by: Crown Content, Level 1, 141 Capel St, Nth Melbourne, VIC 3051, Australia. TEL 6-13-93299800, FAX 6-13-93299698, leadership@crowncontent.com.au, scott@crowncontent.com.au, http://www.crowncontent.com.au/prod/newsletters/leadership.htm.

658 GBR ISSN 1048-9843
HD57.7 CODEN: LEQUEN
➤ **THE LEADERSHIP QUARTERLY.** Text in English. 1990. 6/yr. EUR 123 in Europe to individuals; JPY 16,200 in Japan to individuals; USD 136 to individuals except Europe and Japan; EUR 375 in Europe to institutions; JPY 49,700 in Japan to institutions; USD 419 to institutions except Europe and Japan; EUR 47 in Europe to students; JPY 6,100 in Japan to students; USD 53 to students except Europe and Japan (effective 2006). bk.rev. back issues avail. **Document type:** *Academic/Scholarly.* **Description:** Publishes timely leadership research and applications.
Related titles: Microform ed.: (from PQC); Online - full text ed.: (from EBSCO Publishing, Gale Group, IngentaConnect, ScienceDirect, Swets Information Services).
Indexed: ABIn, ASCA, CurCont, Emerald, PSA, PsycInfo, PsycholAb, SOPODA, SSA, SSCI, SociolAb, e-psyche.
—BLDSC (5162.866600), IE, Infotrieve, ingenta. **CCC.**
Published by: Pergamon (Subsidiary of: Elsevier Science & Technology), The Boulevard, Langford Ln, East Park, Kidlington, Oxford OX5 1GB, United Kingdom. TEL 44-1865-843000, FAX 44-1865-843010, http://www.elsevier.com/locate/leaqua. Ed. M D Mumford. **Subscr. to:** Elsevier BV, PO Box 211, Amsterdam 1000 AE, Netherlands. TEL 31-20-485-3757, FAX 31-20-485-3432, nlinfo-f@elsevier.nl, http://www.elsevier.nl.

658 USA
LEADERSHIP STRATEGIES. Text in English. m. USD 199 domestic; USD 299 foreign (effective 2005). **Document type:** *Newsletter, Trade.* **Description:** Provides articles and information on how to manage and lead effectively.
Published by: Briefings Publishing Group (Subsidiary of: Douglas Publications, Inc.), 1101 King St, Ste 110, Alexandria, VA 22314. TEL 703-518-2343, 800-722-9221, FAX 703-684-2136, customerservice@briefings.com, http://www.briefings.com.

658 338 USA ISSN 1525-5166
TS176
LEAN MANUFACTURING ADVISOR; strategies and tactics for implementing T P M and lean production. Text in English. 1979. m. USD 200 print or email ed. (effective 2005). bk.rev. abstr.; charts; illus.; stat. 12 p./no.; back issues avail. **Document type:** *Newsletter, Trade.* **Description:** Includes practical advice for implementing lean production and lean equipment management.
Formerly: Productivity (0275-8040)
Related titles: E-mail ed.
Indexed: PersLit, TTI.
Published by: Productivity Press, 444 Park Ave S., #503, New York, NY 10016. TEL 212-686-5900, FAX 212-686-5411, rbernstein@productivitypress.com, info@productivitypress.com, http://wwwproductivityinc.com, http://www.productivitypress.com. Ed. Ralph Bernstein. Pub. Maura May. R&P Cherise Windley. Circ: 300 (paid).

658 USA
LEARNINGFOUNT; a mailing list about business strategy. Text in English. 2000. 3/w. free. adv. back issues avail. **Document type:** *Newsletter.* **Description:** Features discussion of business strategy, problem solving and community building.
Formerly (until 1999): Learning Fountain Reviews
Media: Online - full text.
Published by: Learning Fountain Marketing, 3461 Marna Ave, Long Beach, CA 90808. TEL 562-598-9210, FAX 562-598-9210, paul@learningfountain.com, http://www.learningfountain.com/newsletr.htm. Ed., Pub. Paul Siegel. R&P, Adv. contact Paul Siegal. Circ: 1,500.

658 DNK ISSN 0905-8966
HD28
LEDELSE I DAG. Text in Danish. 1990. q. DKK 1,050; DKK 525 to students; DKK 300 (effective 2003). adv. bk.rev. **Document type:** *Trade.* **Description:** Directed to leaders and decision makers in business, industry and the public sector. Focuses on what is happening in management in Denmark, Scandinavia and internationally.
Related titles: Online - full text ed.
Published by: Ledernes Hovedorganisation/Danish Association of Managers and Executives, Vermlandsgade 63, Copenhagen S, 2300, Denmark. TEL 45-32-833283, FAX 45-32-833284, lh@lederne.dk, http://www.lederne.dk. Eds. Ulla Bechsgaard, Paul Hegedahl. Adv. contact Niels Hass. Circ: 2,000.

LEGAL ASSISTANT MANAGEMENT ASSOCIATION. DIRECTORY. see *LAW*

LEGAL BULLETIN. see *LAW*

LEGAL MANAGEMENT. see *LAW*

920 650 DEU ISSN 0935-4859
LEITENDE MAENNER UND FRAUEN DER WIRTSCHAFT. Text in German. 1952. a. EUR 296.55 (effective 1999). adv. **Document type:** *Trade.*
Formerly (until 1979): Leitende Maenner der Wirtschaft (0075-871X)
Published by: Hoppenstedt Bonnier Zeitschriften GmbH, Havelstr. 9, Darmstadt, 64295, Germany. TEL 49-6151-380-0, FAX 49-6151-380-360. Circ: 53,000.

LIBERIAN ECONOMIC AND MANAGEMENT REVIEW. see *BUSINESS AND ECONOMICS*

LIBRARY ADMINISTRATOR'S DIGEST. see *LIBRARY AND INFORMATION SCIENCES*

LOGISTIC. see *TRANSPORTATION*

658.5 BEL
LOGISTIC DIGEST. Text in Dutch, French. 1986. q. adv. illus. **Document type:** *Trade.*
Former titles: Professional Direct; Handleiding en Digest Industrial (0778-9173); (until 1992): Handling Digest (0775-2059)
Related titles: ◆ Supplement to: Logistic.
Published by: Technipress nv, Stationsstraat 30, Bus 1, Groot-Bijgaarden, 1702, Belgium. TEL 32-2-4818100, FAX 32-2-4818182.

658 ITA ISSN 1120-3587
LOGISTICA MANAGEMENT. Text in Italian. 1990. 10/yr. EUR 70 domestic; EUR 126 in Europe; EUR 135 elsewhere (effective 2002). adv. bk.rev. **Document type:** *Trade.* **Description:** Covers logistic topics: supply, materials handling, warehousing, distribution, packaging, transport.
Related titles: Online - full text ed.
Published by: Edizioni Ritman s.r.l., Piazza Quattro Novembre 4, Milan, 20124, Italy. TEL 39-02-6693690, FAX 39-02-66983635, logman@logisticamanagement.it, http://www.logisticamanagement.it. Ed. Massimo Merlino. Pub., R&P Alessandro Delfino. Adv. contact Fabrizio Marioli TEL 39-02-66719098. B&W page EUR 1,985, color page EUR 2,550; trim 245 x 170. Circ: 5,269 (controlled).

658.324 388.324 AUS
LOGISTICS AND MATERIALS HANDLING✶ ; the magazine for managers. Text in English. 1991. 6/yr. AUD 45; AUD 60 foreign (effective 1999). adv. **Document type:** *Trade.* **Description:** Covers materials handling, distribution and customer service for decision-making managers.
Published by: Publishing Services (Australia) Pty. Ltd., 244 St Pauls Terrace, Fortitude Valley, Brisbane, QLD 4000, Australia. TEL 61-7-3854-1286, FAX 61-7-3252-4829, lmh@pubserv.com.au, http://www.pubser.com.au/. Ed., R&P Andrew Stewart. Adv. contact Dave Rigby. B&W page AUD 1,645, color page AUD 2,695; trim 205 x 275. Circ: 8,213.

658 GBR ISSN 1353-5595
LOGISTICS MANAGER. Text in English. 1994. 8/yr. GBP 27.50 domestic; GBP 60 foreign. adv. bk.rev. abstr. back issues avail. **Document type:** *Trade.* **Description:** Provides comprehensive information on logistics applications in manufacturing and service industries and on materials storage and handling. Articles concentrate on improving productivity, systems analysis, cost reduction and management techniques.
Indexed: ADPA, Inspec.
—**CCC.**
Published by: Seven Kings Publications Ltd., 1a Sutton Court Rd, Sutton, Surrey SM1 1HW, United Kingdom. TEL 44-20-8661-1160, FAX 44-20-8661-1173. Ed., R&P Neil Asten. Adv. contact Richard Milbourn. Circ: 7,000.

LOGISTICS NEWS. see *TRANSPORTATION*

658 380.5 NLD ISSN 0922-8675
LOGISTIEKKRANT. Text in Dutch. 1988. 20/yr. EUR 179.50 (effective 2005). adv. illus. **Document type:** *Newspaper, Trade.* **Description:** Provides a management-oriented publication covering all aspects of logistics within a business operation, including internal transport and storage, packaging, computerization, and distribution.
Published by: Reed Business Information bv (Subsidiary of: Reed Business), Postbus 4, Doetinchem, 7000 BA, Netherlands. TEL 31-314-349911, 31-314-349309, info@reedbusiness.nl, http://www.reedbusiness.nl. Ed. H Stad. Pub. Martine L Lofvers. adv.: B&W page EUR 3,799, color page EUR 9,052; trim 307 x 465. Circ: 19,249.

658 CHE ISSN 1422-1896
LOGISTIK. Text in German, French. 1956. 10/yr. CHF 88 domestic; CHF 98 in Europe; CHF 101 elsewhere (effective 2001). adv. **Document type:** *Magazine, Trade.*
Former titles (until 1989): S G L Mitteilungen (1422-1918); (until 1985): S S R G Mitteilungen (1422-1926)
Published by: (Schweizerische Gesellschaft fuer Logistik), HandelsZeitung Fachverlag AG, Seestr 344, Zuerich, 8027, Switzerland. TEL 41-1-2889414, FAX 41-1-2889301, verlag@handelszeitung.ch, http://www.handelszeitung.ch. Ed. Kurt Bahnmueller. Adv. contact Jean-Claude Page TEL 41-1-2889410. Circ: 3,000 (paid).

658 DEU ISSN 0930-7834
LOGISTIK FUER UNTERNEHMEN; das Fachmagazin der internen und externen Logistik. Text in German. 1986. 9/yr. EUR 140.50 domestic; EUR 158 foreign (effective 2003). adv. bk.rev.; Website rev. abstr.; bibl. back issues avail.; reprints avail. **Document type:** *Magazine, Trade.* **Description:** Publishes articles on the whole spectrum of internal and external logistics up to and including e-logistics..
Related titles: Online - full text ed.: ISSN 1436-493X.
Indexed: Englnd, IBR, IBZ.
—Ei, IE, Infotrieve.
Published by: (Verein Deutscher Ingenieure e.V.), Springer V D I Verlag GmbH & Co. KG, Heinrichstr 24, Duesseldorf, 40239, Germany. TEL 49-211-61030, FAX 49-211-6103414, logistik@technikwissen.de, anzeigen@technikwissen.de, info@technikwissen.de, http://www.technikwissen.de/logistik/aktuell/news.asp. Ed. Eckard Muckelberg. Adv. contact Dagmar Schwarz TEL 49-211-6103370. B&W page EUR 4,308, color page EUR 5,388; trim 210 x 297. Circ: 20,000.

658.781 DNK ISSN 1602-2513
LOGISTIK HORISONT; nyhedsmagasinet om supply chain management. Text in Danish. 1970. m. DKK 698 (effective 2002). adv. bk.rev. illus.; charts.
Former titles (until 2001): Logistik Nyt (1600-1702); (until 1998): Virksomheds Nyt (0106-1666); (until 1975): Materialehaandtering og Transport Nyt (0025-5297); Materiale Haandtering
—**CCC.**
Published by: Horisont Gruppen A/S, Center Boulevard 5, Copenhagen S, 2300, Denmark. TEL 45-32-473230, FAX 45-32-473239. Ed. Jesper Baadsgaard. Circ: 13,000 (paid).

658 DNK ISSN 1602-186X
LOGISTIK HORISONT GUIDEN. Text in Danish. 2000. a. adv.
Formerly (until 2001): Logistik Guiden (1399-9168)
Related titles: Online - full content ed.
Published by: Horisont Gruppen A/S, Center Boulevard 5, Copenhagen S, 2300, Denmark. TEL 45-32-473230, FAX 45-32-473239, http://www.logistikguiden.dk. Ed. Jesper Baadsgaard. Circ: 13,000 (paid).

330 DEU ISSN 1611-4450
▼ **LOGISTIK-MANAGEMENT IN FORSCHUNG UND PRAXIS.** Text in German. 2003. irreg., latest vol.5, 2005. price varies. **Document type:** *Monographic series, Academic/Scholarly.*
Published by: Verlag Dr. Kovac, Arnoldstr 49, Hamburg, 22763, Germany. TEL 49-40-3988800, FAX 49-40-39888055, info@verlagdrkovac.de, http://www.verlagdrkovac.de.

338 GBR ISSN 0024-6301
HD1 CODEN: LRPJA4
➤ **LONG RANGE PLANNING.** Text in English. 1968. 6/yr. EUR 191 in Europe to individuals; JPY 25,400 in Japan to individuals; USD 213 to individuals except Europe and Japan; EUR 1,332 in Europe to institutions; JPY 177,000 in Japan to institutions; USD 1,491 to institutions except Europe and Japan (effective 2006). adv. bk.rev. charts; stat.; illus. Index. back issues avail.; reprints avail. **Document type:** *Journal, Academic/Scholarly.* **Description:** Provides authoritative information on developments and new thinking about problems and techniques of forward planning in business and government.
Related titles: Microfiche ed.: (from MIM); Microfilm ed.: (from PQC); Online - full text ed.: (from EBSCO Publishing, Gale Group, IngentaConnect, ScienceDirect, Swets Information Services).
Indexed: ABIn, ADPA, AIAP, APEL, ASCA, ASEANManA, AgeL, BPI, BPIA, BrRB, BusI, CLOSS, CPM, CurCont, EPB, Emerald, Englnd, EnvAb, ExcerpMed, F&EA, FutSurv, GEOBASE, Inspec, KES, M&MA, MEA&I, MEDLINE, ManagCont, ORMS, PAIS, PROMT, PsycInfo, PsycholAb, QAb, RASB, RefZh, SCIMP, SSCI, SUSA, T&II.
—BLDSC (5294.220000), CISTI, Ei, IDS, IE, Infotrieve, ingenta. **CCC.**
Published by: (Strategic Planning Society), Pergamon (Subsidiary of: Elsevier Science & Technology), The Boulevard, Langford Ln, East Park, Kidlington, Oxford OX5 1GB, United Kingdom. TEL 44-1865-843000, FAX 44-1865-843010, lrp@city.ac.uk, http://www.elsevier.com/locate/lrp. Ed. C. Baden-Fuller. Circ: 4,700. **Subscr. to:** Elsevier BV, PO Box 211, Amsterdam 1000 AE, Netherlands. TEL 31-20-485-3757, FAX 31-20-485-3432, nlinfo-f@elsevier.nl, http://www.elsevier.nl. **Co-sponsor:** European Strategic Planning Federation.

➤ **LOS ANGELES MASTERPLANNER.** see *SOCIAL SERVICES AND WELFARE*

➤ **LUND STUDIES IN ECONOMICS AND MANAGEMENT.** see *BUSINESS AND ECONOMICS—Economic Systems And Theories, Economic History*

658 USA
M A C NEWS. Text in English. 1986. q. looseleaf. back issues avail. **Description:** Covers shopping centers management and marketing.
Published by: (Mid-Atlantic Council of Shopping Center Managers), John Bachner Communications, Inc., 8811 Colesville Rd, Ste G106, Silver Spring, MD 20910. TEL 301-589-9121, FAX 301-589-2017. Ed. Diane B Perlman. Circ: 175.

330 DEU
M E R K U R - SCHRIFTEN ZUM INNOVATIVEN MARKETING-MANAGEMENT. Text in German. 2000. irreg., latest vol.10, 2005. price varies. **Document type:** *Monographic series, Academic/Scholarly.*
Published by: Verlag Dr. Kovac, Arnoldstr 49, Hamburg, 22763, Germany. TEL 49-40-3988800, FAX 49-40-39888055, info@verlagdrkovac.de, http://www.verlagdrkovac.de/3-6.htm.

▼ new title ➤ refereed ✶ unverified ◆ full entry avail.

658 NLD ISSN 0165-1722
HD28 CODEN: MMOODR
M & O; tijdschrift voor organisatiekunde en sociaal beleid. Text in Dutch; Summaries in English. 1947. bi-m. EUR 169 print & online eds. (effective 2005). adv. bk.rev. bibl.; charts; illus.; stat. index. **Document type:** *Trade.*
Formerly (until 1978): Mens en Onderneming (0025-9470)
Related titles: Online - full content ed.
Indexed: ABIn, AbHyg, CISA, ErgAb, PsycholAb, SOPODA, TDB. —IE, Infotrieve, KNAW.
Published by: Kluwer B.V. (Subsidiary of: Wolters Kluwer N.V.), Postbus 23, Deventer, 7400 GA, Netherlands. TEL 31-570-673449, FAX 31-570-691555, http://www.managementexecutive.nl, http://www.kluwer.nl. Circ: 4,400.

658 AUS ISSN 1445-0801
M H D SUPPLY CHAIN SOLUTIONS. Text in English. 1970. bi-m. AUD 72.60 domestic; AUD 88 Canada, Africa, USA, United Kingdom, Europe, Middle East; AUD 77 elsewhere (effective 2005). adv. bk.rev. **Document type:** *Magazine, Trade.* **Description:** Provides comprehensive coverage of automation in the materials handling, storage and distribution industry. Offers articles on the latest technology, systems in use and product developments in process.
Former titles (until 2000): Materials Handling & Distribution (0814-916X); (until Feb. 1984): Materials Handling and Storage (0047-6234)
Published by: (Australian Institute of Materials Management), Intermedia Group Pty. Ltd., Unit 7B, 87 Bay St., PO Box 55, Glebe, NSW 2037, Australia. TEL 61-2-96602113, FAX 61-2-96604419, info@intermedia.com.au, http://www.intermedia.com.au. Ed. Charles Pauka. Pub. Simon Grover. Adv. contact Simon Chan. B&W page AUD 1,280, color page AUD 2,300; trim 210 x 297. Circ: 7,000.

658 DEU ISSN 0938-8249
HD28 CODEN: MINRAY
➤ **M I R: MANAGEMENT INTERNATIONAL REVIEW**; journal of international business. Text in English. 1961. q. EUR 114 to individuals; EUR 228 to institutions; EUR 62 newsstand/cover (effective 2004). adv. bk.rev. illus.; stat. index. reprints avail. **Document type:** *Journal, Academic/Scholarly.*
Former titles (until 1990): Management International Review (0025-181X); (until 1966): Management International (0942-8771)
Related titles: Online - full text ed.: (from Florida Center for Library Automation, Gale Group, H.W. Wilson, Northern Light Technology, Inc., O C L C Online Computer Library Center, Inc., ProQuest Information & Learning).
Indexed: ABIn, ADPA, APEL, BAS, BPI, BPIA, BusI, CPM, CurCont, ESPM, Emerald, ExcerpMed, IBR, IBSS, IBZ, IndIslam, KES, M&MA, MEA&I, ManagCont, PAIS, RASB, RefZh, RiskAb, SCIMP, SSCI.
—BLDSC (5359.041000), IE, Infotrieve, ingenta. **CCC.**
Published by: Betriebswirtschaftlicher Verlag Dr. Th. Gabler GmbH (Subsidiary of: Springer Science+Business Media), Abraham-Lincoln-Str 46, Wiesbaden, 65189, Germany. TEL 49-611-78780, FAX 49-611-7878400, gabler.service@gwv-fachverlage.de, http://www.uni-hohenheim.de/~mir, http://www.gabler.de. Ed. Klaus Macharzina. adv.: B&W page EUR 950, color page EUR 1,850. Circ: 1,300 (paid and controlled).

658 AUS ISSN 1445-5382
M I S (AUSTRALIAN EDITION); managing information strategies. Text in English. 1992. 11/yr. AUD 84 domestic; AUD 118 foreign (effective 2002). **Document type:** *Magazine, Trade.*
Former titles (until 1999): M I S Australia (1327-9688); (until 1997): M I S (Sydney, 1995) (1442-2794); (until 1995): Managing Information Systems (1038-2534)
Related titles: ♦ Regional ed(s).: M I S (New Zealand Edition); M I S (UK Edition). GBP 49 domestic; GBP 85 in Europe (effective 2002); M I S (Asia Edition). SGD 63 (effective 2002).
Indexed: CompLI.
—IE.
Published by: Fairfax Business Media (Subsidiary of: John Fairfax Holdings Ltd.), 201 Sussex St, Sydney, NSW 2000, Australia. TEL 61-2-9282-2822, http://www.misweb.com/, http://www.fxj.com.au/.

658.5 USA ISSN 1532-9194
HD28 CODEN: SMRVAO
➤ **M I T SLOAN MANAGEMENT REVIEW.** Text in English. 1960. q. USD 89 domestic to individuals; USD 99 in Canada to individuals; USD 125 elsewhere to individuals (effective 2005). bk.rev. bibl.; charts; illus.; stat.; abstr. index. back issues avail.; reprint service avail. from PQC. **Document type:** *Journal, Academic/Scholarly.* **Description:** Articles on key issues that affect national and international senior management professionals, focusing on entrepreneurial technologies and business intelligence systems.
Former titles (until 2001): Sloan Management Review (0019-848X); (until 1970): Industrial Management Review (0884-8211)
Related titles: Microform ed.: (from PQC); Online - full text ed.: (from bigchalk, Chadwyck-Healey Inc., EBSCO Publishing, Florida Center for Library Automation, Gale Group, H.W. Wilson, Northern Light Technology, Inc., O C L C Online Computer Library Center, Inc., ProQuest Information & Learning).
Indexed: ABIn, AESIS, ASCA, ASEANManA, AgeL, BLI, BMT, BPI, BPIA, BusI, CADCAM, CMCI, CPM, CurCont, DPD, EAA, Emerald, EngInd, EnvAb, Inspec, JEL, KES, LogistBibl, M&MA, MEDLINE, ManagCont, ORMS, PAIS, PCI, PMA, PROMT, PersLit, QC&AS, RASB, SCIMP, SOPODA, SSCI, TelAb, WorkRelAb.
—BLDSC (5829.596680), AskIEEE, CISTI, IDS, IE, Infotrieve, ingenta. **CCC.**
Published by: (Sloan Management Review Association), Massachusetts Institute of Technology, 77 Massachusetts Ave, Room E60-100, Cambridge, MA 02139-4307. smr@mit.edu, http://web.mit.edu/smr. Ed. Jane Gebhart. Pub., Adv. contact Susan Petrie. R&P Patricia Fitzpatrick TEL 617-258-7485. Circ: 25,000. **Subscr. to:** EDS, Agents Department, CSC 6, PO Box 55254, Boulder, CO 80322-5254.

658 USA ISSN 1080-0794
M M R; reporter for supermarket, drug and discount chains. (Mass Market Retailers) Text in English. 1983. fortn. (except m. in May & Dec.). USD 185 domestic; USD 249 foreign; USD 125 domestic manufacturers (effective 2005). adv. **Document type:** *Magazine, Trade.* **Description:** Reports events and trends pertinent to the growth and development of the supermarket and the drug and discount chain industry.
Former titles (until 1994): Mass Market Retailers (0743-5258); (until 1984): ChainSigns (0739-3776)
Related titles: Online - full text ed.: (from Florida Center for Library Automation, Gale Group, O C L C Online Computer Library Center, Inc.).
Indexed: B&I.
Published by: Racher Press, Inc., 220 Fifth Ave, 18th Fl, New York, NY 10001. TEL 212-213-6000, FAX 212-213-6106, jwoldt@racherpress.com, http://www.massmarketretailers.com. Ed. David Pinto. adv.: B&W page USD 9,361, color page USD 10,649. Circ: 21,645 (controlled).

658 SWE
MAALARDALEN - BERGSLAGENS AFFAERER; med Gaevle-Dala. Text in Swedish. 1988. 6/yr. SEK 295 (effective 1996). adv.
Formerly: Begslagens Affaerer (0284-8732)
Published by: Affaersinfo, Fack 2041, Orebro, 70002, Sweden. TEL 46-19-170-760, FAX 46-19-125-642. Ed. Claes Goeran Hanberg. Adv. contact Ronny Stenbergh. Circ: 20,000.

M@BS. see *BUSINESS AND ECONOMICS—Abstracting, Bibliographies, Statistics*

658 EGY ISSN 1110-2284
AL MAGALLAT AL-MISRIYYAT LIL-DIRASAT AL-TIGARIYYAT/EGYPTIAN JOURNAL FOR COMMERCIAL STUDIES. Text in Arabic. 1977. s-a. EGP 15 domestic; USD 15 foreign (effective 2004). **Document type:** *Journal, Academic/Scholarly.*
Published by: Mansoura University, Faculty of Commerce, University Campus, Mansoura, Egypt. TEL 20-50-343974, FAX 20-50-354724, http://derp.sti.sci.eg/data/0033.htm, http://www.mans.edu.eg. Ed. Dr. Samir Abou-El-Futouh Saleh.

MAGALLAT AL-MUHASABT WA-AL-IDARAT WA-AL-TA'MIN LIL-BUHUTH AL-'ILMIYYAT/ACCOUNTING, MANAGEMENT AND INSURANCE REVIEW. see *BUSINESS AND ECONOMICS—Accounting*

658 EGY ISSN 1110-2306
MAGALLAT KULIYYAT AL-TIGARAT LIL-BUHUTH AL-'ILMIYAT/FACULTY OF COMMERCE FOR SCIENTIFIC RESEARCH. JOURNAL. Text in Arabic. 1965. s-a. EGP 5 staff members; EGP 10 to non-members (effective 2004). **Document type:** *Journal, Academic/Scholarly.*
Published by: Alexandria University, Faculty of Commerce, Alexandria University Campus, Alexandria, Egypt. TEL 20-3-4848717, FAX 20-3-4860913, http://derp.sti.sci.eg/data/0039.htm. Ed. Dr. Neamat-Allah Ebrahim.

658 NOR ISSN 1500-0788
MAGMA; tidsskrift for oekonomi og ledelse. Text in Norwegian. 1998. 6/yr. NOK 890; NOK 445 to students (effective 2003). adv.
Published by: Fagbokforlaget, Kanalveien 51, PO Box 6050, Postterminalen, Bergen, 5892, Norway. TEL 47-22-55388800, FAX 47-22-55388801, magna@fagbokforlaget.no, http://www.fagbokforlaget.no/magma. Ed. Magne Gaasemyr TEL 47-55-388829. Adv. contact Kjetil Hovda TEL 47-33-330468. Circ: 10,100.

658.2 FRA ISSN 1154-6433
MAINTENANCE AND ENTREPRISE. Text in French. 1991. 11/yr. FRF 550 domestic; FRF 650 foreign (effective 2000). bibl.; tr.lit. **Document type:** *Newspaper.*
Formed by the merger of (1970-1991): Maintenance (0025-0880); (1973-1991): Equipement Industriel, Achats et Entretien (0396-6666); Which was formerly (1952-1973): Achats et Entretien du Materiel Industriel (0001-4877)
Indexed: Inspec.
—CISTI, Infotrieve.
Published by: Golding, 4 bis rue de la Gare, Levallois-Perret, Cedex 92532, France. TEL 33-1-41404140, FAX 33-1-42709683, contact@golding.fr, http://www.golding.fr. Adv. contact Patrick Thuot. Circ: 7,500.

658 FRA
MAINTENANCE ET ENTREPRISES. Text in French. m.
Published by: Golding, 4 bis rue de la Gare, Levallois-Perret, Cedex 92532, France. TEL 33-1-41404140, FAX 33-1-42709683, contact@golding.fr, http://www.golding.fr.

658 USA ISSN 1080-188X
MAINTENANCE MANAGEMENT. Text in English. m. USD 159; USD 16 newsstand/cover (effective 2002). index. **Document type:** *Newsletter.* **Description:** Features interviews with experienced supervisors and other experts in the maintenance or supervisory field, sharing field-tested ways to upgrade maintenance machinery or procedures, and providing solutions to any of the myriad problems or tasks supervisors face daily.
Formerly: Maintenance Supervisor's Bulletin (0194-5912)
Related titles: Online - full text ed.: (from EBSCO Publishing, Florida Center for Library Automation, Gale Group).
Published by: Bureau of Business Practice (Subsidiary of: Aspen Publishers, Inc.), 1185 Avenue of the Americas, 37th Fl, New York, NY 10036. TEL 860-442-4365, 800-243-0876, FAX 860-437-3555, rebecca_armitage@prenhall.com, http://www.bbpnews.com. Ed. Peter Hawkins. Pub. Peter Garabedian. R&P Kathryn Mennone.

658 MYS ISSN 0025-1348
HD28
MALAYSIAN MANAGEMENT REVIEW. Text in English. 1966. 2/yr. MYR 28 to non-members. adv. bk.rev. charts; stat.
Indexed: BAS.
—BLDSC (5356.070000).
Published by: Malaysian Institute of Management/Institut Pengurusan Malaysia, 227 Jalan Ampang, Kuala Lumpur, 50450, Malaysia. TEL 03-264-5255, FAX 03-264-3171, actreg@manage.edu.my, http://www.jaring.my. Ed. Tarcisius Chin. Circ: 4,000. **Subscr. to:** PO Box 13015, Kuala Lumpur 50796, Malaysia.

658 USA ISSN 1552-3748
HD28
MANAGE (ONLINE). Text in English. 1948. q. free (effective 2005). adv. bk.rev. charts; illus. reprint service avail. from PQC. **Document type:** *Magazine, Trade.*
Formerly (until 2002): Manage (Print) (0025-1623)
Media: Online - full content. **Related titles:** Microform ed.: (from PQC); Online - full text ed.: (from Gale Group, O C L C Online Computer Library Center, Inc., ProQuest Information & Learning).
Indexed: ABIn, AgeL, BPIA, BusI, PersLit, WorkRelAb.
—BLDSC (5358.400000), IE.
Published by: National Management Association, 2210 Arbor Blvd, Dayton, OH 45439. TEL 937-294-0421, nma@nma1.org, http://nma1.org/breaktime/index.htm. Ed. Douglas E Shaw. Circ: 30,000 (paid and free).

MANAGED DENTAL CARE. see *MEDICAL SCIENCES—Dentistry*

658 330.9 FRA ISSN 1627-4792
MANAGEMENT. Text in French. 1995. m. EUR 25.99; EUR 3 newsstand/cover (effective 2002). adv. **Document type:** *Magazine, Trade.*
Formerly (until 1999): L' Essentiel du Management (1263-7807)
Related titles: Online - full text ed.
Published by: Prisma Presse, 6 rue Daru, Paris, 75379, France. TEL 33-1-56994700, FAX 33-1-56994740, management@prisma-presse.com, prisma@presse-info.fr, http://www.management.fr, http://www.prisma-presse.com. Ed. Eric Walther. Circ: 102,117 (paid). **Subscr. to:** Service Abonnements, B 140, Sainte Genevieve Cedex 60732, France. TEL 33-3-44625202.

658 FRA ISSN 1286-4692
➤ **M@N@GEMENT.** Text in Multiple languages. 1998. irreg. free (effective 2005). **Document type:** *Journal, Academic/Scholarly.* **Description:** Provides a forum to express and exchange ideas on management research, strategy, and organizational theory.
Media: Online - full content.
Published by: D M S P Research Center, Paris-Dauphine University, Paris, 75775 Cedex 16, France. management@dauphine.fr, http://www.dmsp.dauphine.fr/MANAGEMENT/. Eds. Bernard Forgues, Martin Evans.

658 POL ISSN 1429-9321
MANAGEMENT. Text in Polish. 1994. a.
Formerly (until 1997): Manufacturing Management (1233-748X)
Related titles: English Translation:.
Indexed: Inspec, RefZh.
Published by: Politechnika Zielonogorska, Wydzial Zarzadzania, Instytut Organizacji i Zarzadzania/Technical University of Zielona Gora, Institute of Organization and Management, Redakcja "Management", ul Podgorna 50, Zielona Gora, 65-246, Poland. TEL 48-68-3282540, 48-68-3282239, FAX 48-68-3253944, an.gr@wp.pl, http://www.ioz.uz.zgora.pl/management.html. Ed. Janina Stankiewicz.

B

658 SCG ISSN 0354-8635
MANAGEMENT. Text in English, Serbian. 1996. q. YUN 5,400 domestic; EUR 100 foreign (effective 2004). **Document type:** *Journal, Academic/Scholarly.* **Description:** Serves as an open discussion arena for new views, experiences and ideas concerning problems and management development tendencies in national and international perspective, with the aim of giving support to economic and social development.
Published by: Univerzitet u Beogradu, Fakultet Organizacionih Nauka/University of Belgrade, Faculty of Organizational Sciences, Jove Ilica 154, Belgrade, 11000. manage@fon.bg.ac.yu, http://management.fon.bg.ac.yu.

658 HRV ISSN 1331-0194
HD28
MANAGEMENT. Text in English. 1996. s-a. **Document type:** *Journal.*
Indexed: JEL, SSCI.
Published by: Sveučiliste u Splitu, Ekonomski Fakultet, Matice Hrvatske 31, Split, 21000, Croatia. TEL 385-21-430600, FAX 385-21-430701, nalf@efst.hr, http://www.efst.hr/management/. Ed. Marin Buble.

658 USA ISSN 0198-8557
JK671
MANAGEMENT (WASHINGTON); a magazine for government supervisors, managers, private contractors. Text in English. 1979. q. USD 5.50. adv. bk.rev.
Formerly: Civil Service Journal (0009-7985)
Indexed: BPIA, IUSGP, PersLit.
Published by: U.S. Office of Personnel Management, Office of Public Affairs, Washington, DC 20415. TEL 202-655-4000. Ed. David A Turner. Circ: 45,000. **Dist. by:** U.S. Government Printing Office, Superintendent of Documents, PO Box 371954, Pittsburgh, PA 15250-7954. TEL 202-512-1800, FAX 202-512-2250, orders@gpo.gov, http://www.access.gpo.gov.

MANAGEMENT ACCOUNTING QUARTERLY (ONLINE). see *BUSINESS AND ECONOMICS—Accounting*

362.1 GBR
MANAGEMENT AGENDA. Text in English. a. **Document type:** *Journal, Academic/Scholarly.*
—BLDSC (5359.074250).
Published by: Roffey Park Institute Ltd., Forest Rd, Horsham, RH12 4TD, United Kingdom. TEL 44-1293-851644, FAX 44-1293-851565.

658 IRN
MANAGEMENT AND DEVELOPMENT; scientific and specialized quarterly. Text in English, Persian, Modern. 1999. q. IRR 5,000 domestic; USD 60 foreign (effective 2001). **Document type:** *Academic/Scholarly.* **Description:** It helps to meet the scientific research and applied needs of the students, researchers and experts of management and specialists in water and power industry managers.It also help them to upgrade the level of their educational, scientific and technical knowledge.
Published by: Institute of Management Research and Education, No.42, Karyabi St., Vali-Asr Square, Tehran, Iran. TEL 98-21-8802462, FAX 98-21-8896780, m_sobhan2001@yahoo.com, imre@moe.or.ir, http://www.moe.gov.ir. Eds. Yoosof Mohammad Nezhad Ali Zaminy, Ali-Akbar Mohajeri.

658 GBR
MANAGEMENT AND INDUSTRIAL RELATIONS SERIES. Text in English. 1982. irreg. price varies. **Document type:** *Monographic series.*
Published by: Cambridge University Press, The Edinburgh Bldg, Shaftesbury Rd, Cambridge, CB2 2RU, United Kingdom. TEL 44-1223-312393, FAX 44-1223-315052, information@cambridge.org, http://www.cup.cam.ac.uk/. R&P Linda Nicol TEL 44-1223-325757.

658 GBR ISSN 1740-8776
▼ **MANAGEMENT & ORGANIZATION REVIEW.** Text in English. 2004. 3/yr. EUR 80 combined subscription in Europe to individuals print & online eds.; USD 89 combined subscription in the Americas to individuals & Caribbean, print & online eds.; GBP 53 combined subscription elsewhere to individuals print & online eds.; GBP 124, USD 201 combined subscription in developing nations to institutions print & online eds.; USD 418 combined subscription in the Americas to institutions & Caribbean, print & online eds.; GBP 249 combined subscription elsewhere to institutions print & online eds. (effective 2006). **Description:** Publishes innovative research contributing to management knowledge in three domains: fundamental research in management; international and comparative management; Chinese management.
Related titles: Online - full text ed.: ISSN 1740-8784. GBP 118, USD 198 in developing nations to institutions; USD 398 in the Americas to institutions; GBP 237 elsewhere to institutions (effective 2006) (from Blackwell Synergy, EBSCO Publishing, Gale Group, IngentaConnect, O C L C Online Computer Library Center, Inc., Swets Information Services).
—BLDSC (5359.008940), IE. **CCC.**
Published by: Blackwell Publishing Ltd., 9600 Garsington Rd, Oxford, OX4 2ZG, United Kingdom. TEL 44-1865-776868, FAX 44-1865-714591, customerservices@oxon.blackwellpublishing.com, http://www.blackwellpublishing.com/journals/MOR.

658 GBR ISSN 1744-9359
▼ **MANAGEMENT & ORGANIZATIONAL HISTORY.** Text in English. 2005. q. GBP 260, USD 454 to institutions; GBP 270, USD 473 combined subscription to institutions print & online eds. (effective 2006). **Document type:** *Journal, Academic/Scholarly.* **Description:** Publishes original, academic research concerning historical approaches to the study of management, organizations and organizing.
Related titles: Online - full text ed.: ISSN 1744-9367. GBP 257, USD 449 to institutions (effective 2006).
—**CCC.**
Published by: Sage Publications Ltd. (Subsidiary of: Sage Publications, Inc.), 1 Oliver's Yard, 55 City Rd, London, EC1 1SP, United Kingdom. TEL 44-20-73248500, FAX 44-20-73248600, info@sagepub.co.uk, http://www.sagepub.co.uk/journal.aspx?pid=107240. Eds. Charles Booth, Michael Rowlinson, Roy Stager Jacques. **Subscr. to:** Sage Publications, Inc., 2455 Teller Rd, Thousand Oaks, CA 91320. TEL 805-499-0721, FAX 805-499-0871, journals@sagepub.com.

658 345 USA
MANAGEMENT AND SUPERVISION OF LAW ENFORCEMENT PERSONNEL. Text in English. 1995. irreg. USD 34.95 (effective 2000). **Document type:** *Trade.* **Description:** A must for anyone studying for promotion in law enforcement. Topics include: principles of management and supervision associated with a police supervisor's role or managers role as a leader, planner, communicator, interviewer, performance evaluator, and human relations specialist.
Published by: Gould Publications, Inc. (Subsidiary of: LexisNexis), 1333 North US Hwy 17-92, Longwood, FL 32750-3724. TEL 407-695-9500, 800-717-7917, FAX 407-695-2906, info@gouldlaw.com, http://www.gouldlaw.com.

658 DEU ISSN 1433-9862
MANAGEMENT BERATER. Text in German. 1997. m. adv. **Document type:** *Magazine, Trade.*
Incorporates (1960-2000): Eco (1438-3136); Which was formerly (until 1999): Gablers Magazin (0932-3961); (until 1987): Betriebswirtschafts-Magazin (0005-9986)
Published by: Management Berater Verlagsgesellschaft mbH, Stuttgarter Str 18-24, Frankfurt Am Main, 60329, Germany. TEL 49-69-2600-0, FAX 49-69-2600249, http://www.management-berater.de.

658 USA
MANAGEMENT BULLETINS. Text in English. q. **Document type:** *Newsletter, Trade.*
Published by: Alexander Communications Group, Inc., 28 W 25th St, 8th Fl, New York, NY 10010. TEL 212-228-0246, FAX 212-228-0376, info@alexcommgrp.com, http://www.alexcommgrp.com.

658.16 GBR ISSN 1353-8950
MANAGEMENT BUY-OUTS. Text in English. 1988. q. GBP 350 (effective 1998). adv. **Document type:** *Academic/Scholarly.*
Formerly (until 1994): U K Management Buy-Outs (0961-0197)
Published by: (Centre for Management Buy-Out Research), University of Nottingham, School of Management and Finance, University Park, Nottingham, Notts NG7 2RD, United Kingdom. TEL 44-115-951-5494, FAX 44-115-951-5204, kenneth.robbie@nottingham.ac.uk, http://www.ccc.nottingham.ac.uk/~lizsmf/cmbor/html. Ed. Ren Robbie. Adv. contact Margaret Burdeed. Circ: 500.

658.45 USA ISSN 0893-3189
➤ **MANAGEMENT COMMUNICATION QUARTERLY**; an international journal. Text in English. 1987. q. USD 436, GBP 282 to institutions; USD 454, GBP 293 combined subscription to institutions print & online eds. (effective 2006). adv. bk.rev. illus. back issues avail.; reprints avail. **Document type:** *Journal, Academic/Scholarly.* **Description:** Brings together communication research from many fields, with a focus on managerial and organizational effectiveness.
Related titles: Online - full text ed.: ISSN 1552-6798. USD 432, GBP 279 to institutions (effective 2006) (from C S A, EBSCO Publishing, O C L C Online Computer Library Center, Inc., ProQuest Information & Learning, Sage Publications, Inc., Swets Information Services).
Indexed: ABIn, CIJE, CPM, CommAb, ESPM, HRA, PRA, RiskAb, SFSA, SOPODA, SPAA, V&AA.
—BLDSC (5359.013900), IE, Infotrieve, ingenta. **CCC.**
Published by: Sage Publications, Inc., 2455 Teller Rd, Thousand Oaks, CA 91320. TEL 805-499-0721, FAX 805-499-0871, ., info@sagepub.com, http://www.sagepub.com/journal.aspx?pid=78. Eds. Charles Conrad, Susan Hanscom. Pub. Sara Miller McCune. R&P Tanya Udin TEL 805-499-0721 ext 7716. Adv. contact Kirsten Beaulieu TEL 805-499-0721 ext 7160. page USD 350. Circ: 600 (paid). **Subscr. overseas to:** Sage Publications Ltd., 1 Oliver's Yard, 55 City Rd, London EC1 1SP, United Kingdom. TEL 44-20-73740645, FAX 44-20-73748741, subscription@sagepub.co.uk.

658 GBR ISSN 1351-0924
MANAGEMENT CONSULTANCY. Text in English. 1989. m. GBP 95 (effective 1999). adv. bk.rev. **Document type:** *Trade.* **Description:** Written for a wide consultancy readership, from large consultancies through to sole practitioners and niche players.
Related titles: Online - full text ed.: (from LexisNexis).
Indexed: Emerald, M&MA.
—BLDSC (5359.014630), IE, Infotrieve, ingenta. **CCC.**
Published by: V N U Business Publications Ltd., VNU House, 32-34 Broadwick St, London, W1A 2HG, United Kingdom. TEL 44-20-7316-9000, FAX 44-20-7316-9160, http://www.managementconsultancy.vnu.co.uk. Circ: 19,526.

658 USA ISSN 0956-3253
MANAGEMENT CONSULTANT INTERNATIONAL. Text in English. 1988. m. USD 1,100 domestic; GBP 670 in United Kingdom; EUR 945 elsewhere (effective 2005). **Document type:** *Newsletter.* **Description:** Gives worldwide news and trends in the management consultancy industry.
Related titles: Online - full text ed.: (from Gale Group, O C L C Online Computer Library Center, Inc.).
Indexed: B&I.
—Infotrieve.
Published by: Kennedy Information Inc., One Phoenix Mill Ln., 5th Fl., Peterborough, NH 03458. TEL 603-924-1006, 800-531-0007, FAX 603-924-4460, http://management_consultant_international.consultingcentral.com/vsf/international_consulting/. Adv. contact Brian Cuthbert.

658 GBR ISSN 1351-0894
MANAGEMENT CONSULTANTS NEWS. Text in English. 1989. 14/yr. GBP 48 domestic; GBP 120 elsewhere (effective 2000). adv. **Document type:** *Newsletter.* **Description:** Provides information for management consultancy professionals in Europe and the UK.
Published by: Prime Marketing Publications Ltd., Witton House, Lower Rd, Chorleywood, Rickmansworth, Herts WD3 5LB, United Kingdom. TEL 44-1923-285323, FAX 44-1923-285819, info@pmp.co.uk, mcn@pmp.co.uk, http://www.pmp.co.uk. Ed. Tim Ring. Pub., Adv. contact Steve Markwell. Circ: 11,000 (controlled).

MANAGEMENT CONSULTING; annotated bibliography of selected references. see *BUSINESS AND ECONOMICS—Abstracting, Bibliographies, Statistics*

658 IDN ISSN 0302-9859
HD70.I5
MANAGEMENT DAN USAHAWAN INDONESIA. Text in Indonesian. bi-m. IDR 5,500. **Document type:** *Journal, Academic/Scholarly.*
Published by: University of Indonesia, Institute of Management Studies, Jalan Salemba Raya 4, Box 404, Jakarta, 10430, Indonesia.

658 GBR ISSN 0025-1747
HD28 CODEN: MANDA4
➤ **MANAGEMENT DECISION.** (Incorporated from 2001-2005 the Journal of Management History which relaunched as an independent title in 2006.) Text in English. 1963. 10/yr. EUR 12,298.54 in Europe; USD 12,079 in North America; AUD 14,629 in Australasia; GBP 8,079.04 in UK & elsewhere (effective 2006). bk.rev. charts; illus. back issues avail.; reprint service avail. from PSC. **Document type:** *Journal, Academic/Scholarly.* **Description:** Presents important issues and topics in a style appropriate for a general managerial audience. Covers corporate planning, management training and development, personnel, industrial relations and more.
Incorporates: Management in Action (0030-0217); Which was formerly: Office Methods and Machines; Formerly (until 1967): Scientific Business
Related titles: Online - full text ed.: (from EBSCO Publishing, Emerald Group Publishing Limited, Florida Center for Library Automation, Gale Group, IngentaConnect, O C L C Online Computer Library Center, Inc., ProQuest Information & Learning, Swets Information Services).
Indexed: ABIn, ADPA, ASEANManA, BPI, BPIA, BrEdI, BusI, CPM, CurCont, EmerIntel, Emerald, IMI, Inspec, KES, M&MA, MResA, ManagCont, PAIS, RASB, SCIMP, WorkRelAb.
—BLDSC (5359.019000), AskIEEE, IE, Infotrieve, ingenta, Linda Hall. **CCC.**
Published by: Emerald Group Publishing Limited, 60-62 Toller Ln, Bradford, W Yorks BD8 9BY, United Kingdom. TEL 44-1274-777700, FAX 44-1274-785200, infomation@emeraldinsight.com, http://www.emeraldinsight.com/md.htm. Ed. John Peters. R&P Mr. James Bender.

658 CHE ISSN 0074-6703
MANAGEMENT DEVELOPMENT SERIES. Text in English. irreg. price varies. **Document type:** *Monographic series.*
Related titles: Microform ed.: (from ILO).
Published by: (International Labour Office), I L O Publications, PO Box 6, Geneva 22, 1211, Switzerland. TEL 41-22-799-6111, FAX 41-22-798-6358. **Dist. in US by:** I L O Publications Center, 9 Jay Gould Court, Ste. CT, PO Box 753, Waldorf, MD 20604. TEL 301-638-3152, FAX 301-843-0159, ilopubs@tasco1.com.

658 NLD ISSN 1571-862X
HF23
▼ **MANAGEMENT EXECUTIVE**; grensverleggend voor de ambitieuze manager. Text in Dutch. 2003. bi-m. EUR 152 (effective 2005). adv. **Document type:** *Trade.*

B

Formed by the merger of (1993-2003): Tijdschrift Management en Informatie (0929-1792); (1974-2003): Bedrijfskunde (0165-0971); Which was formerly (until 1974): Maandblad Bedrijfskunde; (2000-2003): Management Select (1567-7427); Which was formed by merger of (1990-1999): Management Selectuur (0923-8735); (1997-1999): P E M (1385-7673); Which was formerly (until 1996): P E M Select (0929-1660); (until 1993): P E M (0169-5061)
Related titles: Online - full content ed.
Indexed: KES, SCIMP.
—IE, Infotrieve, KNAW.
Published by: Wolters Kluwer N.V., Postbus 23, Deventer, 7400 GA, Netherlands. info@kluwer.nl, http://www.managementexecutive.nl/. Circ: 2,100.

658 DEU ISSN 1615-2107
MANAGEMENT - FORSCHUNG UND PRAXIS. Text in German. 2000. irreg., latest vol.6, 2004. price varies. **Document type:** *Monographic series, Academic/Scholarly.*
Published by: Verlag Dr. Kovac, Arnoldstr 49, Hamburg, 22763, Germany. TEL 49-40-3988800, FAX 49-40-39888055, info@verlagdrkovac.de, http://www.verlagdrkovac.de/3-12.htm.

B

658 USA
MANAGEMENT FORUM. Text in English. 1989. q. looseleaf. membership. bk.rev. back issues avail. **Document type:** *Newsletter.*
Published by: International Management Council, 430 S 20th St, 3, Omaha, NE 68102. TEL 402-345-1904, FAX 402-345-4480. Ed. Jodeen M Sterba. Circ: 6,000 (controlled).

658 IND ISSN 0025-1771
MANAGEMENT IDEAS. Text in English. 1963. m. USD 25. bk.rev. **Document type:** *Trade.* **Description:** Reports practical solutions to difficulties arising at work for business managers.
Published by: M.M.C. School of Management, 3rd Fl., New Marine Lines, 3-E 1 Court Chambers, Mumbai, Maharashtra 400 020, India. FAX 2000446. Ed. N H Atthreya. Circ: 1,000.

MANAGEMENT IN EDUCATION. see *EDUCATION—School Organization And Administration*

MANAGEMENT IN GOVERNMENT. see *PUBLIC ADMINISTRATION*

352.14 GBR ISSN 0263-4678
MANAGEMENT IN GOVERNMENT. Text in English. 1945. q. GBP 2.56. bk.rev. charts; illus. index. back issues avail.; reprint service avail. from PQC,SCH.
Incorporating (vol.37, 1982): Management Services in Government (0307-8558); O and M Bulletin (0048-6051)
Indexed: ABIn, BPIA, BusI, CISA, CurCont, Emerald, IMI, Inspec, ManagCont, PAIS, WTA.
Published by: Civil Service Department, Whitehall, London, SW1A 2AZ, United Kingdom. Circ: 7,300.

658.8 NGA ISSN 0025-178X
HD28
➤ **MANAGEMENT IN NIGERIA.** Text in English. 1965. q. NGN 1,000 domestic; USD 40 foreign (effective 2000). adv. bk.rev. charts; illus. back issues avail. **Document type:** *Journal, Academic/Scholarly.* **Description:** Examines ways in which to improve management effectiveness and efficiency. Informs readers of new management techniques in all management functions, including personnel, marketing, finance, production, and general administration.
Published by: Nigerian Institute of Management, 22 Idowu Taylor St, PO Box 2557, Victoria Island, Lagos, Nigeria. TEL 234-1-614116, 234-1-615105, 264-1-616203, FAX 264-1-614116, nim@rcl.nig.com. Ed. Dele Osundahunsi. R&P, Adv. contact Abdullateef M Ogbondeminu. Circ: 100,000.

658 USA ISSN 1067-9391
HD31
MANAGEMENT IN PRACTICE. Text in English. 1989. q. USD 220. **Document type:** *Journal, Academic/Scholarly.* **Description:** Publishes articles by academics and practitioners on current organization and management issues.
Former titles: Journal of Management Systems (1041-2808); (until 1991): Journal of Management in Practice (1042-1300)
—BLDSC (5011.512000). **CCC.**
Published by: (Association of Management), Maximilian Press, PO Box 64841, Virginia Beach, VA 23464-0841. TEL 757-482-0325, FAX 757-482-0325. Ed. Willem A Hamel. Circ: 2,000.

658 IND ISSN 0300-2667
HD28
MANAGEMENT INFORMATION SERVICE. Text in English. 1971 (vol.3). 10/yr. bk.rev. bibl.; stat.
Published by: University of Cochin, Foundation for Management Education, School of Management, Cochin, Kerala 682 022, India.

MANAGEMENT INFORMATION SYSTEMS. see *COMPUTERS—Information Science And Information Theory*

658 CAN ISSN 1206-1697
MANAGEMENT INTERNATIONAL. Text in English. 1996. s-a.
Related titles: Online - full text ed.: (from Micromedia ProQuest, ProQuest Information & Learning).
Indexed: ABIn.
Published by: Centre D'Etudes en Administration Internationale, Ecole Des Hautes Etudes Commerciales, 3000, Chemin de la Cote-Sainte-Catherine, Montreal, PQ H3T 2A7, Canada. TEL 514-340-6184, FAX 514-340-6177, andre.poirier@hec.ca.

658.4 UGA ISSN 0300-2144
HD70.U35
MANAGEMENT JOURNAL. Short title: Management. Text in English. 1968. a. UGX 2. adv. illus.
Formerly: M T A C Journal
Published by: Management Training and Advisory Centre, PO Box 4655, Kampala, Uganda. Circ: 2,500.

658 GBR ISSN 1350-5076
HD20.15.G7
MANAGEMENT LEARNING; journal for managerial and organizational learning. Text in English. 1994. q. GBP 422, USD 738 to institutions; GBP 439, USD 769 combined subscription to institutions print & online eds. (effective 2006). adv. bk.rev. **Document type:** *Journal, Academic/Scholarly.* **Description:** For managers concerned with issues of learning, change and development in organizations, including educators and practitioners in organizational behaviour, organizational change and development, organizational psychology, and human resources management.
Incorporates (in 1994): Management Education and Development (0047-5688)
Related titles: Online - full text ed.: ISSN 1461-7307. GBP 418, USD 730 to institutions (effective 2006) (from C S A, EBSCO Publishing, O C L C Online Computer Library Center, Inc., ProQuest Information & Learning, Sage Publications, Inc., Swets Information Services).
Indexed: ABIn, ASCA, BrEdI, CIJE, CPE, CPM, CommAb, CurCont, EAA, ERA, ETA, Emerald, HRA, IBSS, M&MA, MEA, PsycInfo, PsycholAb, RHEA, SCIMP, SEA, SENA, SOMA, SPAA, SSCI, T&DA, TEA, TMA, WorkRelAb, e-psyche.
—BLDSC (5359.042300), IDS, IE, Infotrieve, ingenta. **CCC.**
Published by: Sage Publications Ltd. (Subsidiary of: Sage Publications, Inc.), 1 Oliver's Yard, 55 City Rd, London, EC1 1SP, United Kingdom. TEL 44-20-73248500, FAX 44-20-73248600, info@sagepub.co.uk, http://www.sagepub.co.uk/journal.aspx?pid=105708. Eds. Bente Elkjaer, Russ Vince. Adv. contact Jenny Kirby. page GBP 220; trim 200 x 135. **Subscr. in the Americas to:** Sage Publications, Inc., 2455 Teller Rd, Thousand Oaks, CA 91320. TEL 805-499-0721, FAX 805-499-0871, journals@sagepub.com.

658 TWN ISSN 1011-7792
MANAGEMENT MAGAZINE. Text in Chinese. 1973. m. TWD 2,100 domestic; USD 148 in Asia; USD 161 elsewhere. adv. **Document type:** *Trade.*
Published by: Frank L. Hung, Ed. & Pub., 9th Fl, 118 Nanking E. Rd, Sec 5, Taipei, Taiwan. TEL 886-2-7150471, FAX 886-2-7135701. R&P Tony Hung. Adv. contact Kathy Kuo. Circ: 54,000.

658 CAN ISSN 1201-7817
MANAGEMENT MATTERS. Text in English. 1995. m. looseleaf. CND 229 (effective 2005). **Document type:** *Newsletter, Trade.* **Description:** Contains news stories, practical articles, and economic indicators, for HR managers and business people alike.
Related titles: Online - full text ed.: (from Micromedia ProQuest).
Published by: C C H Canadian Ltd., 90 Sheppard Ave E, Ste 300, North York, ON M2N 6X1, Canada. TEL 416-224-2248, FAX 416-224-2243, cservice@cch.ca, http://www.cch.ca.

658.5 SWE ISSN 1102-5581
MANAGEMENT OF TECHNOLOGY. Text in Swedish. 1982. q.
Formerly (until 1992): I M I T - Nytt (0280-6592)
Published by: Institute for Management of Innovation and Technology (IMIT), Fack 6501, Stockholm, 11383, Sweden.

MANAGEMENT OF VOLUNTARY ORGANISATIONS. see *SOCIAL SERVICES AND WELFARE*

658 USA ISSN 1050-2114
MANAGEMENT PORTFOLIO. Text in English. 1989. m. (except July-Aug. combined). membership only. tr.lit. back issues avail. **Document type:** *Trade.* **Description:** Covers news and instructive information for management of graphic arts businesses.
Indexed: ABIPC.
Published by: Printing Industries of America, Inc., 100 Daingerfield Rd, Alexandria, VA 22314. TEL 703-519-8100. Ed. Cliff Weiss. Circ: 10,000.

658 IND
MANAGEMENT PROFESSIONALS ASSOCIATION. EVENTS DIARY. Text in English. 1981. m. free.
Published by: Management Professionals Association, 25 Krishna St., T. Nagar, Chennai, Tamil Nadu 600 017, India. FAX 91-44-441514, TELEX 041 23189 MPA IN. Ed. J Sudershan. Circ: 30,000.

658 IND ISSN 0970-0447
MANAGEMENT PROFESSIONALS ASSOCIATION. JOURNAL. Text in English. 1981. m. free.
Published by: Management Professionals Association, 25 Krishna St., T. Nagar, Chennai, Tamil Nadu 600 017, India. FAX 91-44-441514. Ed. J Sudershan. Circ: 30,000.

658 USA ISSN 0025-1860
HD28 CODEN: MQMQAE
MANAGEMENT QUARTERLY; a guide to better management. Text in English. 1960. q. USD 25 to members; USD 150 to non-members (effective 2005). bk.rev. index, cum.index: 1960-1967. **Document type:** *Magazine, Trade.* **Description:** Designed to address the important management, board, industry and organizational issues affecting electric cooperatives.
Related titles: Microform ed.: (from PQC); Online - full text ed.: (from EBSCO Publishing, Florida Center for Library Automation, Gale Group, Northern Light Technology, Inc., O C L C Online Computer Library Center, Inc., ProQuest Information & Learning).
Indexed: ABIn, BPIA, BusI, IUSGP, ManagCont, WorkRelAb.
—BLDSC (5359.053000), IE, Infotrieve, ingenta.
Published by: (Management Services Department), National Rural Electric Cooperative Association, 4301 Wilson Blvd, Arlington, VA 22203-1860. TEL 703-907-5500, nreca@nreca.coop, http://www.nreca.org. Ed. June B Lane. Circ: 7,000.

658 USA ISSN 1536-5433
HD28
▼ **MANAGEMENT RESEARCH;** the journal of the Iberoamerican Academy of Management. Text in English. 2003. 3/yr. USD 69 domestic to individuals; USD 81 foreign to individuals; USD 279 domestic to institutions; USD 321 foreign to institutions (effective 2006). **Description:** Dedicated to advancing the understanding of management in private and public sector organizations through empirical investigation and theoretical analysis.
Formerly: Journal of Management Research
Related titles: Online - full text ed.: 2004 (Feb.) (from EBSCO Publishing, O C L C Online Computer Library Center, Inc., Swets Information Services).
Indexed: ABIn.
—**CCC.**
Published by: (Iberoamerican Academy of Management), M.E. Sharpe, Inc., 80 Business Park Dr, Armonk, NY 10504. TEL 914-273-1800, 800-541-6563, FAX 914-273-2106, mesinfo@usa.net, http://www.mesharpe.com/mall/results1.asp. Eds. Isabel Gutierrez, Luis Gomez-Mejia.

658 GBR ISSN 0140-9174
HD28
MANAGEMENT RESEARCH NEWS. Text in English. m. EUR 3,783.41 in Europe; USD 3,589 in North America; AUD 3,139 in Australasia; GBP 2,521.91 in the UK & elsewhere (effective 2005). bk.rev. bibl.; charts; stat.; abstr. back issues avail.; reprint service avail. from PSC. **Document type:** *Journal, Academic/Scholarly.* **Description:** Provides precise, informative and readable accounts of management research.
Related titles: Online - full text ed.: (from EBSCO Publishing, Emerald Group Publishing Limited, Gale Group, IngentaConnect, O C L C Online Computer Library Center, Inc., ProQuest Information & Learning, Swets Information Services).
Indexed: ABIn, CJA, EmerIntel.
—BLDSC (5359.058500), IE, Infotrieve, ingenta. **CCC.**
Published by: Barmarick Publications, Enholmes Hall, Patrington, Hull, East Yorkshire HU12 0PR, United Kingdom. FAX 44-1964-631716, hr24@dial.pipex.com, http://www.emeraldinsight.com/mrn.htm. Ed. Richard Dobbins. Pub. Barrie O Pettman. Circ: 400. **Dist. by:** Emerald Group Publishing Limited, 60-62 Toller Ln, Bradford, W Yorks BD8 9BY, United Kingdom. TEL 44-1274-777700, FAX 44-1274-785200; **Dist. in US:** Emerald Group Publishing Ltd., 44 Brattle St, 4th Fl, Cambridge, MA 02138. TEL 617-497-2175, 888-622-0075, FAX 617-354-6875, america@emeraldinsight.com.

658 USA ISSN 0025-1895
T58.A2
MANAGEMENT REVIEW. Text in English. 1923. m. USD 225 membership (effective 2005). bk.rev. charts; illus. index. reprints avail. **Document type:** *Magazine, Trade.* **Description:** Describes management trends, techniques and issues for middle and upper-level managers in the corporate and public sector.
Incorporates (1987-1990): A M A Council Reports (1041-7001); Management in Practice
Media: Online - full content (from Florida Center for Library Automation, Northern Light Technology, Inc.).
Indexed: ABIn, AgeL, Agr, BPI, BPIA, BRI, CBRI, CurCont, Emerald, IMI, LRI, M&MA, MEDLINE, ORMS, PAA&I, PAIS, PCI, PMA, PersLit, PsycholAb, QAb, QC&AS, RASB, T&DA, T&II, TTI, WorkRelAb.
—CISTI, IDS, IE, Linda Hall. **CCC.**
Published by: American Management Association, 1610 Broadway, New York, NY 10019. TEL 800-313-8650, amapubs@aol.com, http://www.amanet.org. Pub. Rosemary K. Carlough. Circ: 85,000.

658 USA ISSN 0025-1909
HD28 CODEN: MSCIAM
➤ **MANAGEMENT SCIENCE.** Text in English. 1954. m. USD 156 domestic to non-members; USD 211 foreign to non-members; USD 78 to members additional journal; USD 203 combined subscription domestic to non-members print & online eds.; USD 258 combined subscription foreign to non-members print & online eds.; USD 536 combined subscription domestic to institutions print or online eds.; USD 591 combined subscription foreign to institutions print or online eds.; USD 101 combined subscription foreign to members additional journal, print & online eds. (effective 2005). adv. bibl.; charts; illus.; stat. Index. back issues avail. **Document type:** *Journal, Academic/Scholarly.*
Incorporates: Management Technology: Monograph of the Institute of Management Science (0542-4917)
Related titles: Online - full content ed.: ISSN 1526-5501. USD 92 to non-members; USD 46 to members additional journal (effective 2004); Online - full text ed.: (from EBSCO Publishing, Gale Group, JSTOR (Web-based Journal Archive), O C L C Online Computer Library Center, Inc., ProQuest Information & Learning, Swets Information Services).
Indexed: ABIn, ASCA, ATI, AgeL, ArtHuCI, BMT, BPI, BPIA, BusI, C&ISA, CIS, CJA, CLOSS, CMCI, CPM, CompAb, CompC, CompR, CurCont, CybAb, E&CAJ, EAA, EIA, Emerald, EnerInd, EngInd, HRIS, IAA, IAOP, IBSS, IMI, Inspec, JCQM, KES, MEA&I, MResA, ManagCont, MathR, ORMS, PsycInfo, PsycholAb, RASB, RefZh, SCIMP, SOPODA, SSCI, SolStAb, ZentMath.
—BLDSC (5359.080000), AskIEEE, CISTI, Ei, IDS, IE, Infotrieve, ingenta, Linda Hall. **CCC.**
Published by: I N F O R M S, 901 Elkridge Landing Rd., Ste. 400, Linthicum, MD 21090-2909. TEL 410-850-0300, FAX 410-684-2963, informs@informs.org, http://mansci.pubs.informs.org, http://www.informs.org. Ed. Wallace J Hopp TEL 847-491-3669. R&P Candita Gerzevitz. Adv. contact Trish Allewalt. B&W page USD 1,000; trim 8.125 x 10.875. Circ: 5,000 (paid). **Subscr. to:** PO Box 631704, Baltimore, MD 631704.

658.5 GBR ISSN 0307-6768
CODEN: MASEDZ
MANAGEMENT SERVICES. Text in English. 1965. m. GBP 45; GBP 3.80 per issue (effective 2004). adv. bk.rev. charts; illus.; stat. reprint service avail. from PQC. **Document type:** *Journal, Trade.* **Description:** Contains news, views and features concerning the profession.
Formerly (until 1976): Work Study and Management Services (0043-8030)
Related titles: Microform ed.: (from PQC); Online - full text ed.: (from EBSCO Publishing, Northern Light Technology, Inc., O C L C Online Computer Library Center, Inc., ProQuest Information & Learning).
Indexed: ABIn, ADPA, ASEANManA, BMT, BrEdI, BrTechI, CISA, CPM, Emerald, EngInd, ILD, IMI, Inspec, M&MA, ORMS, PAA&I, RASB, SCIMP, TEA, WorkRelAb.
—BLDSC (5359.084000), AskIEEE, IE, Infotrieve, ingenta. **CCC.**
Published by: Institute of Management Services, Stowe House, Netherstowe, Lichfield, Staffs WS13 6TJ, United Kingdom. TEL 44-1543-266825, FAX 44-1543-266833, editor@msjournal.co.uk, admin@ims-stowe.fsnet.co.uk, http://www.ims-productivity.com/. Circ: 5,500.

658 GBR ISSN 0307-3041
THE MANAGEMENT SPECIALIST; the international aid to management specialists and education in Management. Text in English. 1971. 3/yr. GBP 7 per issue to non-members; free to members (effective 2003). adv.
Incorporates (1974-2000): Specialist International (0308-1559); Which was formerly (until 1976): Specialist (0307-305X)
—BLDSC (5359.093000).
Published by: The Institute of Management Specialists (Subsidiary of: The Academy of Multi-Skills), Academy House, Warwick Corner, 42 Warwick Rd, Kenilworth, Warks CV8 1HE, United Kingdom. TEL 44-1926-855498, FAX 44-1926-513100. Adv. contact Prof. H J Manners. B&W page GBP 400.

658 NLD ISSN 0166-1256
MANAGEMENT TEAM. Text in Dutch. 1979. 21/yr. EUR 66 to individuals; EUR 31.50 to students (effective 2005). adv. **Document type:** *Trade.*
Related titles: ♦ Supplement(s): View. ISSN 1382-7936.
—IE, Infotrieve, KNAW. **CCC.**
Published by: V N U Business Publications (Netherlands), Ceylonpoort 5-25, Haarlem, 2037 AA, Netherlands. TEL 31-23-5463463, FAX 31-23-5463931, http://www.mt.nl/, http://www.vnubp.nl. adv.: B&W page EUR 6,775, color page EUR 11,161. Circ: 230,000.

650 AUS ISSN 1440-5636
HD28
MANAGEMENT TODAY. Text in English. 1993. 10/yr. AUD 55 (effective 2004). adv. bk.rev. back issues avail. **Document type:** *Magazine, Trade.* **Description:** Keeps managers up to date with the latest in management thought, and equips them with an understanding of current issues that affect business life.
Formerly (until 1997): Management (1039-4729); Which incorporated (in 1994): A I M (Queensland); A I M (South Australia); A I M (Western Australia); Formed by the 1993 merger of: Management Review (0313-0835); Which had former titles (until 1975): Management Diary (0313-0843); A I M (Victoria); A I M (Tasmania); A I M (Australian Capital Territory); A I M (New South Wales) (0817-5713); (1970-1989) : A I M News (0813-6785)
Related titles: Online - full text ed.: (from R M I T Publishing).
Indexed: AESIS, Emerald.
—BLDSC (5359.150100), IE, Infotrieve, ingenta.
Published by: Australian Institute of Management, 181 Fitzroy St, St Kilda, VIC 3182, Australia. TEL 61-3-95348181, FAX 61-3-95345050, magazine@aim.com.au, enquiry@aim.com.au, http://www.aim.com.au/publications/managementtoday.html. adv.: B&W page AUD 2,000, color page AUD 3,000; 180 x 245. Circ: 33,201.

658 ZAF ISSN 1027-4324
MANAGEMENT TODAY. Text in English. 1985. m. ZAR 273.60 (effective 2004). adv. **Description:** Addresses key issues in the South African business environment.
Formerly (until 1997): Human Resource Management (1010-8092)
Related titles: Online - full content ed.
Published by: Havenga & Associates, Richard, PO Box 2239, Northcliff, 2114, South Africa. TEL 27-11-8886188, FAX 27-11-8882281, rha@icon.co.za, http://www.managementtoday.co.za/magazine.htm. Ed., Pub., Adv. contact Richard Havenga. B&W page ZAR 4,750; trim 210 x 297. Circ: 10,000.

658 MEX ISSN 0186-5609
MANAGEMENT TODAY; en espanol. Text in Spanish. 1973. every 45 days. USD 185 (effective 2004). adv. **Document type:** *Magazine, Trade.* **Description:** Presents recent investigations and new proposals in Management field, as well as Mexican firms real cases, evaluating and comparing their results and studying the tools and strategies applied.
Related titles: Online - full text ed.: (from Northern Light Technology, Inc.).
Indexed: ADPA, BrEdI, BrRB, HECAB, T&II.
Published by: Comunicacion Profesional Impresa, S.A., Baja California 275, Desp 601, Mexico City, DF 06170, Mexico. TEL 52-5-2869421, FAX 52-5-2869612, http://www.managementtoday.com.mx. Ed. Laura Serralde Diaz. R&P Rodolfo Serralde Solorzona. Adv. contact Jose Maria Serralde Diaz. color page MXP 3,360. Circ: 10,000 (paid).

658 GBR ISSN 0025-1925
HD70.G7 CODEN: MANTAI
MANAGEMENT TODAY. Text in English. 1966. m. GBP 45.60 domestic; GBP 70 in Europe; GBP 110 elsewhere (effective 2004). adv. bk.rev. bibl.; charts; illus.; stat. index. reprints avail. **Document type:** *Magazine, Trade.*
Supersedes: Manager
Related titles: Online - full text ed.: (from bigchalk, EBSCO Publishing, Florida Center for Library Automation, Gale Group, LexisNexis, Northern Light Technology, Inc., O C L C Online Computer Library Center, Inc., ProQuest Information & Learning).
Indexed: ABIn, ASEANManA, BMT, BPI, BPIA, BldManAb, BrCerAb, BrEdI, BusI, CPM, DAAI, Emerald, ExcerpMed, H&TI, IMI, IndBusRep, KES, LRI, M&MA, MEA&I, MagInd, ManagCont, RASB, RHEA, RICS, SCIMP, SOMA, T&II, WTA, WorkRelAb.
—BLDSC (5359.150000), IE, ingenta. **CCC.**
Published by: (Chartered Management Institute), Haymarket Business Publications Ltd., 174 Hammersmith Rd, London, W6 7JP, United Kingdom. TEL 44-20-8943-5000, FAX 44-20-82674268, hpg@haymarketgroup.com, http://www.clickmt.com, http://www.haymarketgroup.com. Adv. contact Peter Grant. Circ: 98,000. **Dist. by:** Seymour Distribution Ltd, 86 Newman St, London W1T 3EX, United Kingdom. TEL 44-20-73968000, FAX 44-20-73968002.

658 IND
MANAGEMENT TRAINING AND RESEARCH CENTRES IN INDIA. DIRECTORY. Text in English. 1982. irreg. INR 150, USD 20.
Published by: Information Research Academy, 37 Syed Amir Ali Ave, Flat #9, Kolkata, West Bengal 700 019, India. info@irakol.net, http://www.irakol.net. Ed. Partha Subir Guha.

MANAGEMENT UND KRANKENHAUS; Informationsdienst fuer alle Fuehrungskraefte im Krankenhaus. see *HEALTH FACILITIES AND ADMINISTRATION*

MANAGEMENTBLAD RIJKSDIENST. see *PUBLIC ADMINISTRATION*

658 DEU
MANAGEMENTFORSCHUNG. Text in German. 1991. a. price varies. **Document type:** *Monographic series, Academic/Scholarly.*
Published by: Betriebswirtschaftlicher Verlag Dr. Th. Gabler GmbH (Subsidiary of: Springer Science+Business Media), Abraham-Lincoln-Str 46, Wiesbaden, 65189, Germany. TEL 49-611-78780, FAX 49-611-7878400, gabler.service@gwv-fachverlage.de, http://www.gabler.de.

658 POL ISSN 1426-0204
MANAGER. Text in Polish. 1996. bi-m.
Published by: Grupa Wydawnicza INFOR Sp. z o.o., Ul Okopowa 58/72, Warsaw, 01042, Poland. TEL 48-22-5304208, 48-22-5304450, bok@infor.pl. Ed. Zdzislaw Krasnicki. Adv. contact Waldemar Krakowiak.

658 AUS
THE MANAGER; online insights to business thinking. Text in English. m. **Description:** Designed to introduce business and management students to the ideas that are shaping business thinking.
Media: Online - full text.
Published by: R M I T Business, 239 Bourke St, Melbourne, VIC 3000, Australia. TEL 61-3-9925-5555, FAX 61-3-9925-5624, duren@themanager.com.au, http://www.themanager.com.au/. Ed. David Uren.

658 SDN
MANAGER. Text in English. 1975. irreg. (1-2/yr.).
Published by: Management Development Centre, P O Box 2308, Khartoum, Sudan. Ed. Sowar El Dabab Ahmed.

658 GBR
HD28 CODEN: OMINEH
MANAGER; the British journal of administrative management. Text in English. 1964. bi-m. GBP 45 domestic to non-members; GBP 55 foreign to non-members (effective 2003). adv. bk.rev. index. reprint service avail. from SCH. **Document type:** *Journal, Trade.* **Description:** Aims to promote and develop, for the public benefit, the science of administrative management in all branches. Provides information to enable institute members to keep up to date with the latest techniques and developments in the field of administrative management.
Former titles: British Journal of Administrative Management (1353-5188); (until 1990): Office and Information Management International (1351-6019); Office Management International (0951-5062); (until 1987): British Journal of Administrative Management (0260-9096); (until 1981): Administrative Management (London) (0144-9079); Administrative Management Bulletin
Related titles: Online - full text ed.: (from EBSCO Publishing, O C L C Online Computer Library Center, Inc., ProQuest Information & Learning).
Indexed: ABIn, ADPA, ASEANManA, BPIA, BldManAb, EngInd, Inspec, LOIS.
—BLDSC (5359.199000), AskIEEE, Ei, IE, ingenta. **CCC.**
Published by: Institute of Administrative Management, 40 Chatsworth Parade, Petts Wood, Orpington, Kent BR5 1RW, United Kingdom. TEL 44-1689-875555, FAX 44-1689-870891, iadmin@cix.compulink.co.uk, http://www.InstAM.org. Adv. contact Raye Hallett. Circ: 15,000.

658 DEU ISSN 0341-4418
MANAGER MAGAZIN; Wirtschaft aus erster Hand. Text in German. 1971. m. EUR 64.80; EUR 6 newsstand/cover (effective 2003). adv. bk.rev. abstr.; bibl.; charts; illus.; stat. **Document type:** *Magazine, Trade.* **Description:** Covers all aspects of business and management trends and experiences.
Related titles: Microfiche ed.: (from PQC).
Indexed: ABIn, KES, M&MA, RASB, SCIMP.
—BLDSC (5359.230000), IE, Infotrieve, ingenta.
Published by: Manager Magazin Verlagsgesellschaft mbH, Brandstwiete 19, Hamburg, 20457, Germany. TEL 49-40-3080050, FAX 49-40-30800549, mm_redaktion@manager-magazin.de, http://www.manager-magazin.de. adv.: B&W page EUR 13,500, color page EUR 18,200; trim 175 x 252. Circ: 126,347 (paid). **Subscr. to:** Postfach 111053, Hamburg 20410, Germany. **Dist. by:** German Language Publications Inc., 153 S Dean St, Englewood, NJ 07631. TEL 800-457-4443, info@glpnews.com, http://www.glpnews.com.

658 GBR ISSN 0143-6570
HD30.22 CODEN: MDECDE
➤ **MANAGERIAL AND DECISION ECONOMICS**; the international journal of research and progress in management economics. Abbreviated title: M D E. Text in English. 1980. 8/yr. USD 1,485 to institutions; USD 1,634 combined subscription to institutions print & online eds. (effective 2006). adv. bk.rev. charts; illus.; stat. index. back issues avail.; reprints avail. **Document type:** *Journal, Academic/Scholarly.* **Description:** Deals with economic problems in the field of managerial and decision economics.
Related titles: Microform ed.: (from PQC); Online - full text ed.: ISSN 1099-1468. USD 1,485 to institutions (effective 2006) (from EBSCO Publishing, JSTOR (Web-based Journal Archive), ProQuest Information & Learning, Swets Information Services, Wiley InterScience).
Indexed: ABIn, CJA, CPM, CurCont, ESPM, Emerald, IABS, IBSS, JEL, ORMS, PAIS, PCI, QC&AS, RASB, RiskAb, ST&MA.
—BLDSC (5359.232000), IE, Infotrieve, ingenta. **CCC.**

B

Published by: John Wiley & Sons Ltd. (Subsidiary of: John Wiley & Sons, Inc.), The Atrium, Southern Gate, Chichester, West Sussex PO19 8SQ, United Kingdom. TEL 44-1243-779777, FAX 44-1243-775878, customer@wiley.co.uk, http://www3.interscience.wiley.com/cgi-bin/jhome/7976, http://www.wiley.co.uk. Ed. Paul Rubin. adv.: B&W page GBP 650, color page GBP 1,550; trim 200 x 260. Circ: 700. **Subscr. in the Americas to:** John Wiley & Sons, Inc., 111 River St, Hoboken, NJ 07030-5774. TEL 201-748-6645, 800-225-5945, subinfo@wiley.com.

658 GBR ISSN 0268-6902
➤ **MANAGERIAL AUDITING JOURNAL.** Text in English. 1986. 9/yr. EUR 8,785.91 in Europe; USD 9,069 in North America; AUD 10,339 in Australasia; GBP 6,154.16 in UK & elsewhere (effective 2006). back issues avail.; reprint service avail. from PSC. **Document type:** *Journal, Academic/Scholarly.* **Description:** Covers a broad range of issues including management implications of auditing, planning and implementing the auditing process, operations auditing, psychological aspects of the auditor's work, and the organizational structure of auditing.
Related titles: Online - full text ed.: (from EBSCO Publishing, Emerald Group Publishing Limited, Gale Group, IngentaConnect, O C L C Online Computer Library Center, Inc., ProQuest Information & Learning, Swets Information Services).
Indexed: ABIn, ATI, EmerIntel, Emerald, Inspec, SCIMP.
—BLDSC (5359.233000), IE, Infotrieve, ingenta. **CCC.**
Published by: Emerald Group Publishing Limited, 60-62 Toller Ln, Bradford, W Yorks BD8 9BY, United Kingdom. TEL 44-1274-777700, FAX 44-1274-785200, infomation@emeraldinsight.com, http://www.emeraldinsight.com/maj.htm.

658 GBR ISSN 0307-4358
HG4001
➤ **MANAGERIAL FINANCE.** Text in English. 1975. m. EUR 6,078.04 in Europe; USD 6,159 in North America; AUD 5,229 in Australasia; GBP 4,055.29 in the UK & elsewhere (effective 2005). index. back issues avail.; reprint service avail. from PSC. **Document type:** *Journal, Academic/Scholarly.* **Description:** Disseminates information about the practice of financial management, including financial objectives, security valuation, diversification, assessment of new projects, borrowing requirements, and dividends.
Related titles: Online - full text ed.: (from EBSCO Publishing, Emerald Group Publishing Limited, Gale Group, IngentaConnect, O C L C Online Computer Library Center, Inc., ProQuest Information & Learning, Swets Information Services).
Indexed: ABIn, ADPA, ATI, BPIA, BusI, CPM, CurCont, EmerIntel, Emerald, M&MA, ManagCont, PAIS, SCIMP, T&II.
—BLDSC (5359.240000), IE, Infotrieve, ingenta. **CCC.**
Published by: Barmarick Publications, Enholmes Hall, Patrington, Hull, East Yorkshire HU12 0PR, United Kingdom. TEL 44-1964-630033, FAX 44-1964-631716, hr24@dial.pipex.com, http://www.emeraldinsight.com/mf.htm. Ed. Richard Dobbins. Pub. Barrie O Pettman. Circ: 400. **Dist. by:** Emerald Group Publishing Limited, 60-62 Toller Ln, Bradford, W Yorks BD8 9BY, United Kingdom. TEL 44-1274-777700, FAX 44-1274-785200; **Dist. in US:** Emerald Group Publishing Ltd., 44 Brattle St, 4th Fl, Cambridge, MA 02138. TEL 617-497-2175, 888-622-0075, FAX 617-354-6875, america@emeraldinsight.com.

658 IND
MANAGER'S DIGEST. Text in English. 1971. s-a. USD 20 to individuals; USD 40 to institutions. bk.rev. **Document type:** *Academic/Scholarly.*
Published by: Management Development Centre, 1st Fl., 1 Shakespeare Sarani, Calcutta, West Bengal 700 071, India. TEL 91-33-282-1589, FAX 91-33-282-2755. Ed. M A Mabud. Circ: 500.

658 USA ISSN 1093-6157
MANAGER'S EDGE. Text in English. 1984. m. USD 177 domestic; USD 207 in Canada; USD 237 elsewhere (effective 2005). 8 p./no.; back issues avail. **Document type:** *Newsletter, Trade.* **Description:** Presents digest of techniques for leading, motivating and communicating with employees.
Related titles: Online - full text ed.
—CCC.
Published by: Briefings Publishing Group (Subsidiary of: Douglas Publications, Inc.), 1101 King St, Ste 110, Alexandria, VA 22314. TEL 703-518-2343, 800-722-9221, FAX 703-684-2136, bwalls@briefings.com, customerservice@briefings.com, http://www.briefings.com. Pub. Barbara Baker Clark. Circ: 21,000 (controlled and free).

658 USA ISSN 1099-7261
THE MANAGER'S INTELLIGENCE REPORT; an insider's fast track to better management. Text in English. 1994. m. USD 129. **Document type:** *Newsletter.* **Description:** For managers at all levels of organizations.
Published by: Lawrence Ragan Communications, Inc., 316 N Michigan Ave, Ste 300, Chicago, IL 60601. TEL 312-960-4100, 800-878-5331, FAX 312-335-9583, cservice@ragan.com, http://www.ragan.com. Ed. Steve Crescenzo.

658 346 USA ISSN 0889-4493
KF3455.A15
MANAGER'S LEGAL BULLETIN. Text in English. 1986. s-m. USD 66 (effective 2005). index. back issues avail. **Document type:** *Newsletter.* **Description:** Sets scenarios of potential legal problems in the workplace based on cases.
Published by: Alexander Hamilton Institute, Inc., 70 Hilltop Rd, Ramsey, NJ 07446-1119. TEL 201-825-3377, 800-879-2441, FAX 201-825-8696, mlb@ahipubs.com, http://www.ahipubs.com/cgi-bin/displayproducts.pl?ProductID=1MLB. Ed. Brian L P Zevnik.

658 USA ISSN 1541-7379
MANAGER'S SECURITY ALERT. Text in English. 2002 (Sept.). s-m. (only 1x in Dec.). USD 289 (effective 2002).
Published by: Institute of Business Publications, P. O. Box 1688, West Chester, PA 19380. TEL 610-408-8200, 800-817-3922, FAX 610-408-8199, iobp@comcast.net, http://www.iobp.com. Ed. Edward O'Loughlin.

658.00715 DEU ISSN 0938-6211
MANAGERSEMINARE; das Weiterbildungsmagazin. Text in German. 1990. 10/yr. EUR 70; EUR 8.50 newsstand/cover (effective 2003). adv. bk.rev.; software rev.; Website rev. charts; illus.; tr.lit. back issues avail. **Document type:** *Magazine, Consumer.* **Description:** Provides news and trends for human resource development.
Published by: managerSeminare Verlags GmbH, Endenicher Str 282, Bonn, 53121, Germany. TEL 49-228-97791-0, FAX 49-228-616164, info@managerseminare.de, http://www.managerseminare.de. Ed. Nicole Bussmann. Adv. contact Juergen Koch. Circ: 30,000 (controlled). **Dist. by:** Omnia Vertrieb GmbH, Waldstr 6, Weidenbach 56355, Germany. TEL 49-6775-1654, FAX 49-6775-1455.

658 USA
MANAGING 24/7. Text in English. m. USD 175 (effective 2005). **Document type:** *Newsletter, Trade.* **Description:** Provides information on best practices, the latest industry trends & practices, and advice on emerging shiftwork issues from the leading experts.
Formerly: 24/7 Shiftwork Solutions
Media: Online - full content.
Contact: Circadian Technologies, Inc., 24 Hartwell Ave, Lexington, MA 02421. TEL 781-676-6900, 800-284-5001, FAX 781-676-6999, info@circadian.com, http://www.circadian.com/publications/man247.html.

MANAGING AUTOMATION. see *COMPUTERS—Automation*

▼ **MANAGING IN TODAY'S GOVERNMENT.** see *PUBLIC ADMINISTRATION*

MANAGING INTELLECTUAL PROPERTY. see *PATENTS, TRADEMARKS AND COPYRIGHTS*

658 USA
MANAGING PARTNER; what's new and what's working in managing the small to mid-sized law firm. Text in English. m. USD 299 (effective 2001). **Document type:** *Newsletter, Trade.* **Description:** Provides a source of information for small and mid-sized law firms to improve client satisfaction and increase firm profits.
Published by: InfoCom Group, 5900 Hollis St, Ste L, Emeryville, CA 94608-2008. TEL 510-596-9300, 800-959-1059, FAX 510-596-9331, webmgr@infocomgroup.com, http://www.infocomgroup.com/partner.html.

MANAGING SCHOOL BUSINESS. see *EDUCATION—School Organization And Administration*

658 GBR ISSN 0960-4529
HF5415.5 CODEN: MSQUEU
➤ **MANAGING SERVICE QUALITY.** Text in English. 1990. bi-m. EUR 4,392.41 in Europe; USD 4,459 in North America; AUD 5,509 in Australasia; GBP 3,076.54 in UK & elsewhere (effective 2006). bk.rev. back issues avail.; reprint service avail. from PSC. **Document type:** *Journal, Academic/Scholarly.* **Description:** Provides managers in the service sector with the information needed to create the Total Quality organisation. Emphasis is placed on providing practitioners with the concepts, strategies, implementation methods, and continuous quality improvement techniques.
Related titles: Online - full text ed.: (from EBSCO Publishing, Emerald Group Publishing Limited, Gale Group, IngentaConnect, O C L C Online Computer Library Center, Inc., ProQuest Information & Learning, Swets Information Services).
Indexed: ABIn, BrEdI, EmerIntel, Emerald, M&MA.
—BLDSC (5359.305000), IE, Infotrieve, ingenta. **CCC.**
Published by: Emerald Group Publishing Limited, 60-62 Toller Ln, Bradford, W Yorks BD8 9BY, United Kingdom. TEL 44-1274-777700, FAX 44-1274-785200, infomation@emeraldinsight.com, http://www.emeraldinsight.com/msq.htm. Ed. Dr. Jay Kandampully.

▼ ➤ **MANAGING THE MARGIN**; strategies for generating new revenue and controlling costs. see *HEALTH FACILITIES AND ADMINISTRATION*

658 DNK ISSN 0905-4332
MANDAG MORGEN. Variant title: Ugebladet Mandag Morgen. Text in Danish. 1989. w. DKK 6,300 to individuals; DKK 2,205 to students (effective 2003). adv. **Description:** Strives through internal research to interpret global trends and developments.
Published by: Huset Mandag Morgen, Valkendorfsgade 13, PO Box 1127, Copenhagen K, 1009, Denmark. TEL 45-33-939323, FAX 45-33-141394, mm@mm.dk, salg@mm.dk, http://www.mm.dk. Eds. Peter Kjaergaard, Erik Rasmussen. adv.: color page DKK 25,000; 287 x 200.

658 NOR ISSN 1503-7096
▼ **MANDAG MORGEN NORGE.** Text in Norwegian. 2003. 44/yr. NOK 4,750; NOK 2,200 to students (effective 2003). adv. **Description:** Strives through internal research to interpret global trends and developments.
Published by: Mandag Morgen Norge AS, St. Olavs Gate 21B, Oslo, 0165, Norway. TEL 47-22-991818, FAX 47-22-991810, mail@mandagmorgen.no, http://www.mandagmorgen.no. Ed. Terje Osmundsen TEL 47-22-991819. Adv. contact Vibekea Brekke TEL 47-22-991832.

MANUFACTURERS' MART. see *BUSINESS AND ECONOMICS—Production Of Goods And Services*

658 GBR ISSN 0141-450X
MANUFACTURING. Text in English. 1978. a. GBP 7 per issue to non-members; free to members (effective 2003). adv. **Document type:** *Journal, Trade.*
—BLDSC (5365.965000).
Published by: The Institute of Manufacturing (Subsidiary of: The Academy of Multi-Skills), Academy House, Warwick Corner, 42 Warwick Rd, Kenilworth, Warwickshire CV8 1HE, United Kingdom. TEL 44-1926-855498, FAX 44-1926-513100. Pub. H J Manners. adv.: B&W page GBP 400.

MANUFACTURING AND LOGISTICS I T. see *COMPUTERS*

658 338 USA ISSN 1523-4614
HD28 CODEN: MSOMFV
➤ **MANUFACTURING AND SERVICE OPERATIONS MANAGEMENT.** Abbreviated title: M & S O M. Text in English. 1999. bi-m. USD 128 domestic to non-members; USD 144 foreign to non-members; USD 64 to members additonal journal; USD 168 combined subscription domestic to non-members print & online eds.; USD 184 combined subscription foreign to non-members print & online eds.; USD 84 combined subscription to members additional journal, print & online eds.; USD 272 combined subscription domestic to institutions print &/or online eds.; USD 288 combined subscription foreign to institutions print & online eds. (effective 2004); membership includes 1 free journal. adv. charts; illus.; bibl. back issues avail. **Document type:** *Journal, Academic/Scholarly.*
Related titles: Online - full content ed.: ISSN 1526-5498. USD 92 to non-members; USD 46 to members additional journal (effective 2004); Online - full text ed.: (from EBSCO Publishing, Gale Group, O C L C Online Computer Library Center, Inc., ProQuest Information & Learning, Swets Information Services).
Indexed: ABIn, EngInd, IAOP, Inspec.
—BLDSC (5313.535000). **CCC.**
Published by: I N F O R M S, 901 Elkridge Landing Rd., Ste. 400, Linthicum, MD 21090-2909. TEL 410-850-0300, 800-446-3676, FAX 410-684-2963, msomeditor@gsb.columbia.edu, informs@informs.org, http://www.msom.org/, http://www.informs.org. Ed. Garrett van Ryzin TEL 212-854-4280. R&P Candita Gerzevitz. Adv. contact Trish Allewalt. B&W page USD 400; trim 8.125 x 10.875. Circ: 1,000 (paid and controlled). **Subscr. to:** PO Box 631704, Baltimore, MD 631704.

658 GBR ISSN 0141-4518
MANUFACTURING MANAGEMENT (KENILWORTH). Text in English. 1978. a. GBP 7 per issue to non-members; free to members (effective 2003). adv. **Document type:** *Journal, Academic/Scholarly.*
—BLDSC (5367.232000).
Published by: The Institute of Manufacturing (Subsidiary of: The Academy of Multi-Skills), Academy House, Warwick Corner, 42 Warwick Rd, Kenilworth, Warwickshire CV8 1HE, United Kingdom. TEL 44-1926-855498, FAX 44-1926-513100. Pub. H J Manners. adv.: B&W page GBP 400.

338 BEL ISSN 1373-119X
LE MARCHE; hebdomadaire du dirigeant. Text in French. 1963. w. adv. bk.rev. charts; illus.; stat.; tr.lit.
Indexed: KES.
Published by: J.J. Gaudisart, Bd Lambermont 140, Brussels, 1030, Belgium. Circ: 15,300.

MARKET PROFILES FOR MEDICARE RISK CONTRACTING. see *HEALTH FACILITIES AND ADMINISTRATION*

658 ESP
MARKETING ACCION. Text in Spanish. q.
Published by: Escuela Superior de Gestion Comercial y Marketing, Ave. Valdenigrales, s-n, Pozuelo de Alarcon, Madrid, 28223, Spain. TEL 34-91-3527716, FAX 34-91-3528534, http://www.esic.es/.

658 IND
MARKETING & MANAGEMENT NEWS. Text in English. 1969. m. INR 150; USD 25 foreign (effective 1999). adv. bk.rev. illus. **Description:** Contains articles on agricultural and industrial services, and international marketing by professionals in the fields.
Former titles: Marketology Quarterly (0970-8219); (until 1982): Marketing Digest; Marketing and Management Monthly; Marketing and Management Digest; Management Digest
Published by: Institute of Marketing & Management, 62-F Sujan Singh Park, New Delhi, 110 003, India. TEL 91-11-4699224, FAX 91-11-4692874, TELEX 31-74043 IMM IN, immnd@nda.vsnl.net.in, http://www.immindia.com. Ed., R&P, Adv. contact Jagjit Singh. Circ: 30,000.

MARKETING MANAGEMENT. see *BUSINESS AND ECONOMICS—Marketing And Purchasing*

THE MARKETING MANAGER'S YEARBOOK. see *BUSINESS AND ECONOMICS—Marketing And Purchasing*

MARKETING SCIENCE; the marketing journal of INFORMS. see *BUSINESS AND ECONOMICS—Marketing And Purchasing*

658 DEU
MARKT-MANAGEMENT. Text in German. 1997. irreg., latest vol.3, 2002. EUR 32.50 per vol. (effective 2003). **Document type:** *Monographic series, Academic/Scholarly.*
Published by: Peter Lang GmbH Europaeischer Verlag der Wissenschaften, Eschborner Landstr 42-50, Frankfurt Am Main, 60489, Germany. TEL 49-69-7807050, FAX 49-69-78070543, zentrale.frankfurt@peterlang.com, http://www.peterlang.de. Eds. Axel Eggert, Wolfgang Mueller.

658 DEU ISSN 0343-043X
MASCHINEN ANLAGEN VERFAHREN. Abbreviated title: M A V. Text in German. 1958. 10/yr. EUR 6.30 newsstand/cover (effective 2005). adv. back issues avail. **Document type:** *Magazine, Trade.* **Description:** Discusses production engineering, automation and plant equipment.
Incorporates (1979-1993): Industrie-Ausruestungs-Magazin (0174-7215); Formerly (until 1972): Maschine plus Manager (0465-1219)
Indexed: ExcerpMed.
—CCC.
Published by: Konradin Verlag Robert Kohlhammer GmbH, Ernst Mey Str 8, Leinfelden-Echterdingen, 70771, Germany. TEL 49-711-75940, FAX 49-711-7594390, mav.redaktion@konradin.de, info@konradin.de, http://www.mav-online.de, http://www.konradin.de. Ed. Rudolf Beyer. Adv. contact Peter Hamberger. B&W page EUR 4,520, color page EUR 5,610; trim 190 x 270. Circ: 22,036 (paid and controlled).

MASSACHUSETTS PSYCHOLOGIST. see *PSYCHOLOGY*

658 DEU ISSN 0937-4183
MATERIALWIRTSCHAFT UND LOGISTIK IM UNTERNEHMEN; Materialwirtschaft fuer Manager. Text in German. 1979. m. **Document type:** *Trade.*
Formerly: Materialwirtschaft im Unternehmen (0179-499X)
—CCC.
Published by: Verlag Praxiswissen, Hauert 20, Dortmund, 44227, Germany. Ed. A Juenemann.

003 DEU ISSN 1432-2994
T57.6.A1 CODEN: ZMMRFZ
➤ **MATHEMATICAL METHODS OF OPERATIONS RESEARCH.** Text in English. 1957. bi-m. (in 2 vols., 3 nos./vol.). EUR 699 combined subscription to institutions print & online eds. (effective 2005). adv. bk.rev. charts. index. back issues avail.; reprints avail. **Document type:** *Journal, Academic/Scholarly.* **Description:** Consists of two main sections: theory section covers operations research and related optimization theory; applications section focuses on concrete problems of mathematical methods for the description and analysis of technical, social and economic systems.
Former titles: Z O R - Methods and Models of Operations Research; Z O R - Zeitschrift fuer Operations Research (0340-9422); Unternehmensforschung - Operations Research - Recherche Operationnelle (0042-0573)
Related titles: Online - full text ed.: ISSN 1432-5217 (from EBSCO Publishing, ProQuest Information & Learning, Springer LINK, Swets Information Services).
Indexed: ABIn, BrCerAb, C&ISA, CCMJ, CMCI, CerAb, CivEngAb, CompLI, CorrAb, CurCont, E&CAJ, EMA, EngInd, IAA, IAOP, Inspec, JCQM, JEL, M&TEA, MBF, METADEX, MathR, MathSciNet, ORMS, QC&AS, RASB, RefZh, ST&MA, SolStAb, WAA, ZentMath.
—BLDSC (5402.541000), AskIEEE, CISTI, Ei, IDS, IE, Infotrieve, ingenta, Linda Hall. **CCC.**
Published by: Physica-Verlag GmbH und Co. (Subsidiary of: Springer-Verlag), Postfach 105280, Heidelberg, 69042, Germany. TEL 49-6221-487492, FAX 49-6221-487177, physica@springer.de, http://link.springer.de/link/service/journals/00186/. Eds. Alexander Shapiro, Ulrich Rieder. Adv. contact Stephan Kroeck TEL 49-30-827875739. Circ: 1,900. **Subscr. in the Americas to:** Springer-Verlag New York, Inc., Journal Fulfillment, PO Box 2485, Secaucus, NJ 07096-2485. TEL 800-777-4643, 201-348-4033, FAX 201-348-4505, journals@springer-ny.com, http://www.springer-ny.com; **Subscr. to:** Springer GmbH Auslieferungsgesellschaft, Haberstr 7, Heidelberg 69126, Germany. TEL 49-6221-345-0, FAX 49-6221-345-4229, subscriptions@springer.de.

➤ **MATHEMATICS OF OPERATIONS RESEARCH.** see *COMPUTERS*

338.5 USA ISSN 0047-5394
HD28
THE MCKINSEY QUARTERLY. Text in English. 1964. q. free to qualified personnel. charts; illus. cum.index every 2 yrs. back issues avail.; reprints avail.
Related titles: Online - full text ed.: (from EBSCO Publishing, Florida Center for Library Automation, Gale Group, Northern Light Technology, Inc.).
Indexed: ABIn, ADPA, ASEANManA, ATI, BPI, CPM, Emerald, M&MA, T&II.
—BLDSC (5413.497000), IE, ingenta.
Published by: McKinsey & Co. Inc., 55 E 52nd St, New York, NY 10022. TEL 212-446-7000, http://www.mckinseyquarterly.com. Circ: 55,000.

658 DEU
MCKINSEY WISSEN. Text in German. q. EUR 60 domestic; EUR 66 in Europe; EUR 108 elsewhere (effective 2003). adv. **Document type:** *Magazine, Trade.*
Published by: Brand Eins Wissen GmbH & Co. KG (Subsidiary of: Brand Eins Verlag GmbH), Schauenburger Str 21, Hamburg, 20095, Germany. TEL 49-40-80805890, FAX 49-40-808058989, dialog@brandeins.de, http://www.brandeins-wissen.de/magazine/. Ed. Susanne Risch. Adv. contact Joachim Uetzmann. page EUR 5,000.

658 340.56 USA ISSN 1543-2114
KF1220.E83
MEALEY'S LITIGATION REPORT: EMPLOYER LIABILITY INSURANCE. Text in English. 2002 (Sept.). m. USD 735 (effective 2003). **Description:** Tracks insurance coverage litigation resulting from such employment issues as sexual harassment, age discrimination, workplace injury, wrongful termination, ADA, workplace violence, sexual preference discrimination, gender discrimination, pension and 401(k) fiduciary duty.
Published by: Mealey Publications & Conferences Group (Subsidiary of: LexisNexis North America), 217 W Church Rd., PO Box 62090, King of Prussia, PA 19406-0230. TEL 610-768-7800, 800-632-5397, FAX 610-768-0880, info@mealeys.com, http://www.mealeys.com. Eds. Beth Caputo, Scott M. Jacobs. Adv. contact Margaret D. Walker.

658 GBR ISSN 1368-3047
➤ **MEASURING BUSINESS EXCELLENCE.** Abbreviated title: M B E Quarterly. Text in English. 1997. q. EUR 662.29 in Europe; USD 639 in North America; AUD 1,059 in Australasia; GBP 466.54 in UK & elsewhere (effective 2006). reprint service avail. from PSC. **Document type:** *Journal, Academic/Scholarly.* **Description:** Contains cutting edge research papers and live case histories by leading management strategists providing international insights into non-financial ways to measure business improvements.
Incorporates (1997-2000): Quality Focus (1460-4248)
Related titles: Online - full text ed.: (from EBSCO Publishing, Emerald Group Publishing Limited, Gale Group, IngentaConnect, O C L C Online Computer Library Center, Inc., ProQuest Information & Learning, Swets Information Services).
Indexed: ABIn.
—BLDSC (5413.580925), IE, Infotrieve, ingenta. **CCC.**
Published by: Emerald Group Publishing Limited, 60-62 Toller Ln, Bradford, W Yorks BD8 9BY, United Kingdom. TEL 44-1274-777700, FAX 44-1274-785200, rknowles@emeraldinsight.com, infomation@emeraldinsight.com, http://www.emeraldinsight.com/mbe.htm. Ed. Mike Bourne. **Subscr. addr. in N America:** Emerald Group Publishing Ltd., 44 Brattle St, 4th Fl, Cambridge, MA 02138. TEL 617-497-2175, 888-622-0075, FAX 617-354-6875.

➤ **MEDFAX.** see *HEALTH FACILITIES AND ADMINISTRATION*

➤ **MEDIA MANAGEMENT REVIEW.** see *COMMUNICATIONS*

➤ **MEDICAL BUSINESS GULF COAST EDITION.** see *MEDICAL SCIENCES*

658 330.9 610 USA
MEDICAL BUSINESS REVIEW✶; medical business analysis for the doctor-executive. Text in English. 1981. m. looseleaf. USD 144. bk.rev. back issues avail.
Published by: Cast, Hursh & Associates, 4401 Taylor Rd, Fort Wayne, IN 46804-1913. TEL 219-436-3036. Ed. William Cast. Circ: 2,000.

658 USA ISSN 1052-4894
MEDICAL OFFICE MANAGER; the newsletter for physician office administrators. Text in English. 1987. m. looseleaf. USD 249 (effective 2005). bk.rev. index. back issues avail. **Document type:** *Newsletter.* **Description:** Covers issues and regulations affecting the management of medical practices.
Published by: Ardmore Publishing Company, PO Box 52843, Atlanta, GA 30355. TEL 404-367-1991, FAX 404-367-1995, susancrawford@ardmorepublishing.com. Ed., Pub., R&P Susan Crawford. Circ: 4,200 (paid and controlled).

MEDICAL OFFICE STAFF MANAGEMENT STRATEGIES. see *HEALTH FACILITIES AND ADMINISTRATION*

650 DNK
MEDLEMSSERVICE (COPENHAGEN). Text in Danish. 1987. 6/yr. free. bk.rev. illus. **Document type:** *Newsletter.*
Former titles: Nyhedsbrev; NetNyt (0902-4468); Netvaerk; Netvaerkstedet; D.M.C. Information (0107-8216)
Published by: Dansk Management Forum, Folke Bernadottes Alle 45, Copenhagen Oe, 2100, Denmark. TEL 45-33-48-88-88, FAX 45-33-48-88-99. Ed. Ruth Znaider. Circ: 3,500.

658 USA
MEETINGS & EXPOSITIONS. Text in English. m. membership. adv. **Description:** Features information for association meeting planning.
Formerly: Conventions and Expositions
Published by: (Meetings & Exhibitions Section), American Society of Association Executives, 1575 Eye St, N W, Washington, DC 20005-1168. TEL 202-626-2789, FAX 202-289-4049, http://www.asaenet.org. Circ: 3,500.

658 DEU ISSN 0941-8342
DER MEISTERBRIEF FUER DEN BETRIEBSLEITER; Arbeitstechnik, Betriebspraxis, Menschenfuehrung. Text in German. 1963. m. EUR 96 (effective 2004). index. back issues avail. **Document type:** *Newsletter, Trade.*
Formerly (until 1992): Meisterbrief (0171-3914)
Published by: Verlag Norbert Mueller AG und Co. KG (Subsidiary of: S V Corporate Media GmbH), Emmy-Noether-Str 2, Munich, 80992, Germany. TEL 49-89-5485201, FAX 49-89-54852192, infoVNM@sv-corporate-media.de, http://www.vnm.de/svcm/index/includeVerzeichnis/nm[]briefe[]0941-8342/. Ed. Stefan Uhlig. Circ: 1,600.

658 CHN ISSN 1002-8315
MEITAN QIYE GUANLI/COAL INDUSTRY MANAGEMENT. Text in Chinese. 1985. m.
Related titles: Online - full text ed.: (from East View Information Services).
Published by: Beijing Meitan Guanli Ganbu Xueyuan, 2 Dingfu Zhuang, Chaoyang-qu, Beijing, 199924, China. TEL 571031. Ed. Zhou Peiyu.

658 USA
MEMBERSHIP DEVELOPMENTS. Text in English. m. membership. adv. **Description:** Provides membership recruitment and retention techniques, job listings, and a calendar of events for membership professionals of associations.
Formerly: Membership Marketer
Published by: (Membership Section), American Society of Association Executives, 1575 Eye St, N W, Washington, DC 20005-1168. TEL 202-626-2829, FAX 202-408-9635, http://www.asaenet.org. Circ: 2,650.

658 GBR ISSN 0963-6404
THE MENTOR MANAGEMENT DIGEST. Text in English. 1991. 10/yr. GBP 80 for 6 nos.. bk.rev. **Document type:** *Bulletin.* **Description:** Provides information on the realities and practice of management, human resources, training and staff development.
Published by: Mentor Management Digest, 33 Kingsley Pl, Newcastle upon Tyne, Northd NE6 5AN, United Kingdom. TEL 0191-265-0838, FAX 0191-224-2868. Ed. Chris Ashton. Circ: 1,000.

658 332 USA
MERGERS & ACQUISITIONS CONSULTANT✶; the management report and information resource. Text in English. 1968. m. USD 297; USD 333 foreign. adv. bk.rev. charts; illus.; stat. **Description:** Covers all aspects of mergers, acquisitions, divestitures, leveraged buyouts, corporate restructurings, and joint ventures world-wide. Profiles acquirers, sellers, intermediaries and professional M and A service forms.
Published by: Princeton Research Institute, Management Centers, PO Box 2702, Scottsdale, AZ 85252-2702. TEL 609-396-0305.

METALL I LIT'E UKRAINY. see *METALLURGY*

THE MICROENTERPRISE JOURNAL. see *BUSINESS AND ECONOMICS—Small Business*

▼ **MID-ATLANTIC EXECUTIVE LEGAL ADVISOR.** see *LAW—Corporate Law*

658 USA
MIDDLE MANAGEMENT AND CLERICAL COMPENSATION REPORT - MEXICO. Text in English. a. USD 860. charts. **Document type:** *Trade.* **Description:** Comprehensive information on what companies in Mexico are paying their middle management and clerical personnel.

Published by: (Executive Compensation Service (ECS)), Wyatt Data Services, 218 Rte 17 N, Rochelle Park, NJ 07622-9832. TEL 201-843-1177, FAX 201-843-0101.

658 USA
MIDDLE MANAGEMENT COMPENSATION - REGRESSION ANALYSIS REPORT. Text in English. a. USD 690. charts. **Document type:** *Trade.* **Description:** Presents salary and total compensation equations for each position which are presented separately for ten industry categories.
Related titles: ◆ Supplement to: Regional Report on Middle Management Compensation.
Published by: (Executive Compensation Service (ECS)), Wyatt Data Services, 218 Rte 17 N, Rochelle Park, NJ 07622-9832. TEL 201-843-1177, FAX 201-843-0101.

658 USA
MIDDLE MANAGEMENT HI - COMP REPORT. Text in English. a. USD 490. **Document type:** *Trade.* **Description:** Presents data on the highest paid one-third of the sample.
Published by: (Executive Compensation Service (ECS)), Wyatt Data Services, 218 Rte 17 N, Rochelle Park, NJ 07622-9832. TEL 201-843-1177, FAX 201-843-0101.

658 USA ISSN 0270-9023
HD4965.5.U6
MIDDLE MANAGEMENT REPORT. Text in English. a. (in 2 vols.). USD 690. **Document type:** *Trade.* **Description:** Allows you to compare your rates and policies with other companies in your industry and of your size.
Published by: (Executive Compensation Service (ECS)), Wyatt Data Services, 218 Rte 17 N, Rochelle Park, NJ 07622-9832. TEL 201-843-1177, FAX 201-843-0101.

658 USA ISSN 1528-5251
TS176
MIDRANGE E R P. (Enterprise Resource Planning) Text in English. 1997. m. USD 60 domestic; USD 96 in Canada; USD 195 elsewhere; USD 7 newsstand/cover domestic; USD 9 newsstand/cover in Canada; USD 20 newsstand/cover elsewhere (effective 2000). **Document type:** *Trade.* **Description:** Provides information on manufacturing software principles, practices and applications that enhance competitiveness, profitability, productivity and quality.
Related titles: Online - full content ed.
Published by: Penton Media, Inc. (Subsidiary of: Pittway Company), 1300 E 9th St, Cleveland, OH 44114-1503. http://www.penton.com.

658 381 FRA ISSN 0076-8812
MILLESIME. Text in French. 1953. a. adv. bk.rev.
Published by: Association des Anciens Eleves de l'Ecole Superieur de Commerce de Paris, 79 av. de la Republique, Paris, 75011, France. Circ: 8,000.

658 USA
MINDPLAY; creativity & innovation in today's business environment. Text in English. 1989. q. USD 135 to members (effective 2000). adv. **Document type:** *Newsletter.* **Description:** Presents ideas and information related to building 21st century thinking skills. For business managers, trainers, team leaders, new-product developers, and consultants.
Published by: Innovation Network, 451 E 58th Ave, 4625, Box 468, Denver, CO 80216. TEL 303-308-1088, FAX 303-295-6108, staff@thinksmart.com. Ed. Ruth Ann Hattori. Pub. Joyce Wycoff. Adv. contact Glenda Chipps.

MINI-STORAGE MESSENGER. see *BUSINESS AND ECONOMICS—Domestic Commerce*

MODERN BAKING. see *FOOD AND FOOD INDUSTRIES—Bakers And Confectioners*

MODERN CAR CARE. see *TRANSPORTATION—Automobiles*

658 GBR ISSN 0951-6522
HD28 CODEN: MODMEF
MODERN MANAGEMENT. Text in English. 1949. bi-m. GBP 30; GBP 39 foreign (effective 1999). adv. bk.rev.; film rev. charts; illus. reprints avail. **Document type:** *Newsletter.*
Former titles: Supervisory Management (Lichfield) (0950-9895); Supervisor (0039-5862)
Indexed: ADPA, ASEANManA, BusI, Emerald, PROMT, SWA.
—BLDSC (5889.048000), IE, Infotrieve. **CCC.**
Published by: Institute for Supervision and Management, Stowe House, Netherstowe, Lichfield, Staffs WS13 6TJ, United Kingdom. TEL 44-1543-251346, FAX 44-1543-415804, info@ismstowe-info.demon.co.uk. Ed. R G Hewitt. R&P R.G. Hewitt. Circ: 25,000.

658 CZE ISSN 1210-4094
MODERNI OBCHOD. Text in Czech, Slovak. 1992. 11/yr. CZK 693 (effective 2003). adv. **Document type:** *Magazine, Trade.* **Description:** Provides information on management in the wholesale and retail trade in the Czech Republic and Slovak Republic.
Published by: Ceske a Slovenske Odborne Nakladatelstvi (Subsidiary of: Deutscher Fachverlag GmbH), Drtinova 10, Prague 5, 150 00, Czech Republic. TEL 420-2-27018400, FAX 420-2-27018401, mobchod@con-praha.cz, prodej@con-praha.cz, http://www.con-praha.cz/en/mo. Ed. Eva Klanova. Adv. contact Jan Krajc. B&W page CZK 88,700, color page CZK 103,000; trim 210 x 297. Circ: 14,000.

658 CZE ISSN 0026-8720
HD28
MODERNI RIZENI. Text in Czech. 1965. m. CZK 1,020; CZK 85 newsstand/cover (effective 2003). adv. bk.rev. abstr.; charts; illus. cum.index: 1966-1970. **Document type:** *Magazine, Trade.*
Indexed: RASB.
Published by: Economia a.s., Dobrovskeho 25, Prague 7 7, 170 55, Czech Republic. TEL 420-2-33071111, FAX 420-2-33072003, moderni.rizeni@economia.cz, economia@economia.cz, http://www.economia.cz. Ed. Eva Motejzikova. adv.: page CZK 39,000; trim 143 x 216. Circ: 8,200.

658.568 AUS ISSN 1444-1861
MOMENTUM. Text in English. 1984. bi-m. AUD 60 domestic; AUD 100 foreign (effective 2002). adv. bk.rev.; software rev.; video rev. tr.lit. back issues avail. **Document type:** *Magazine, Trade.* **Description:** Discusses quality issues and practices.
Former titles (until 2000): The Quality Magazine (1039-558X); (until 1992): Quality Australia (0813-0272)
—BLDSC (7168.152480), IE.
Published by: (Australian Quality Council, Quality Society of Australasia), Brandmedia, 180 Bourke Road, Alexandria, NSW 2015, Australia. TEL 61-2-93530070, FAX 61-2-99014677, magazine@qsanet.com. Ed. Maureen Jordan. Pub. Mallory Holland TEL 61-2-9353-0071. adv.: B&W page AUD 1,925, color page AUD 2,585; trim 210 x 275. Circ: 10,580.

MOTIVATIONAL MANAGER. see *COMMUNICATIONS*

MOTOR FLEET SUPERVISION; principles and practices. see *BUSINESS AND ECONOMICS—Personnel Management*

MOUSE. see *COMPUTERS*

658 AUS ISSN 1444-2558
➤ **MT. ELIZA BUSINESS REVIEW.** Text in English. 1980. s-a. AUD 25 (effective 2003). adv. bk.rev. **Document type:** *Journal, Academic/Scholarly.* **Description:** For top management in the Asia-Pacific region. Presents thoughtful articles on innovations in global leadership and management thinking.
Former titles (until 1999): Monash Mt. Eliza Business Review (1329-1610); (until 1997): Practising Manager (0159-1193)
Related titles: Online - full text ed.: (from ProQuest Information & Learning).
Indexed: ABIn, AusPAIS, Emerald.
—BLDSC (5980.874542), IE, ingenta.
Published by: Mt. Eliza Business School, PO Box 7262, St Kilda Rd Post Office, Melbourne, VIC 3004, Australia. TEL 61-3-86966666, FAX 61-3-86966677, publications@mteliza.com.au, http://www.mteliza.com.au/. adv.: B&W page AUD 2,700, color page AUD 3,200; trim 210 x 275. Circ: 6,000.

➤ **MULTIFAMILY EXECUTIVE.** see *HOUSING AND URBAN PLANNING*

658 332.6 USA
MULTINATIONAL MANAGERS AND DEVELOPING COUNTRIES. Text in English. 1987. irreg., latest vol.5, 1996. price varies. **Document type:** *Monographic series.* **Description:** Discussions of the social, economic, and ethical issues faced by managers of multinational corporations in the context of today's global community.
Published by: University of Notre Dame Press, 310 Flanner Hall, Notre Dame, IN 46556. TEL 219-631-6346, FAX 219-631-8148, undpress1@nd.edu, undpress.1@nd.edu, http://www.undpress.nd.edu. R&P Ann Bromley. **Dist. overseas by:** Eurospan University Press Group, Order Dept, 3 Henrietta St, London WC2E 8LU, United Kingdom. TEL 44-20-7240-0856, FAX 44-20-7379-0609, http://www.eurospan.co.uk.

MUNDO EJECUTIVO. see *BUSINESS AND ECONOMICS*

MUSIC MANAGEMENT & INTERNATIONAL PROMOTION; the magazine behind the business news. see *MUSIC*

658 USA
MWORLD. Text in English. 2002. q. USD 225 to members; USD 25 newsstand/cover (effective 2002).
Published by: American Management Association (A M A), 1601 Broadway, New York, NY 10019. TEL 212-586-8100, 800-262-9699, FAX 212-903-8168, customerservice@amanet.org, http://www.amanet.org. Ed. Florence M Stone.

658.00715 USA
N A I E C NEWSLETTER. Text in English. 1964. bi-m. USD 25. adv. bk.rev. cum.index. back issues avail. **Document type:** *Newsletter.* **Description:** Provides information on industry involvement in education, including summaries of studies and research projects, news of events, conferences, legislation and resources.
Published by: National Association for Industry - Education Cooperation, 235 Hendricks Blvd, Buffalo, NY 14226-3304. TEL 716-837-7047, FAX 716-834-7047, naiec@pcom.net, http://www2.pcom.net/naiec. Ed. Vito Pace. Adv. contact Donald M Clark. Circ: 728.

N A P A M A NEWS. see *THEATER*

658 USA ISSN 1098-9714
HD9697.U4
N A R D A INDEPENDENT RETAILER. Text in English. 1943. m. USD 78 domestic; USD 100 foreign; USD 6.50 newsstand/cover (effective 2005). adv. charts; illus. index. 32 p./no. 3 cols./p.; back issues avail.; reprints avail. **Document type:** *Magazine, Trade.* **Description:** Serves independent retailers selling and servicing major appliances, consumer electronics products, furniture, computers, sewing machines and other hard goods. Emphasizes ideas to help the reader become better and more profitable businessmen.
Formerly (until 199?): N A R D A News (0047-8717)
Published by: North American Retail Dealers Association, 10 E 22nd St, Ste 310, Lombard, IL 60148-6191. TEL 630-953-8950, FAX 630-953-8957, nardahdq@narda.com, http://www.narda.com. Ed. Jennifer M Ichalek. Circ: 2,500 (paid).

658 USA
N A W REPORT. Text in English. 1972. 6/yr. membership. bk.rev. **Document type:** *Newsletter.* **Description:** Covers business issues affecting wholesaling.
Former titles: Channels; N A W Newsletter
Published by: National Association of Wholesaler - Distributors, 1725 K St, N W, Washington, DC 20006. TEL 202-872-0885. Circ: 10,000.

658 USA
N C U R A NEWSLETTER. (National Council of University Research Administrators) Text in English. bi-m.
Published by: National Council of University Research Administrators, 1 Dupont Cir, N W, Ste 220, Washington, DC 20036. TEL 202-466-3894, FAX 202-223-5573, http://www.ncura.edu.

658 NLD ISSN 1380-7374
N I V E MANAGEMENT MAGAZINE. Text in Dutch. 1976. 6/yr. EUR 56.72 to non-members (effective 2005). adv. illus. **Document type:** *Journal, Trade.*
Former titles (until 1994): N M2 (N I V E Management Magazine) (0926-4221); (until 1992): N2 (N I V E Nieuws) (0926-423X); (until 1991): N I V E Nieuws (0926-4000)
Published by: N I V E - Nederlandse Vereniging voor Management, Postbus 266, Voorburg, 2270 AG, Netherlands. TEL 31-70-3001500, FAX 31-70-3001599, info@nive.org. Circ: 10,000.

658 331.88 CZE
N O S. (Noviny Odboroveho Svazu Statnich Organu a Organizaci) Variant title: Odvorovy Svaz Statnich Organu a Organizaci. Noviny. Text in Czech. 1965 (vol.10). s-m. USD 16.70. **Document type:** *Trade.*
Formerly (until 1990): Sluzba Lidu (0037-7082)
Published by: (Odvorovy Svaz Statnich Organu a Organizaci), Kveta Dedovska, Ed. & Pub., Konevova 134, Prague 3, 130 00, Czech Republic. **Subscr. to:** Artia, Ve Smeckach 30, Prague 1 111 27, Czech Republic.

658 PRI ISSN 1554-6357
▼ **N P E R C I INFORMA;** informacion de vanguardia para las organizaciones sin fines de lucro en Puerto Rico. (Non-Profit Evaluation & Resource Center Inc.) Text in Spanish. 2004. q. **Document type:** *Newsletter, Trade.*
Media: Online - full content.
Published by: Non-Profit Evaluation & Resource Center, Inc., 53 Esmerelda Ave P M B 010, Guaynabo, 00969-4429, Puerto Rico. TEL 787-464-4644, FAX 787-780-1851, nperci@nperci.org, http://www.charityadvantage.com/npercipr/Newsletters.asp, http://www.nperci.org.

658 621.3 USA ISSN 1541-7611
NANOTECH BUSINESS UPDATE. Text in English. 2002. bi-w. USD 395 to individuals; USD 999 university library; USD 1,500 to corporations (effective 2002). **Document type:** *Magazine, Trade.* **Description:** Designed to inform, educate, and discuss nanotechnology with reliable straight talk, news and insight without any hype or exaggeration.
Media: Online - full content.
Published by: San Francisco Consulting Group, 480 5th St., 1st Fl., San Francisco, CA 94107. TEL 415-495-7305, FAX 415-276-2359, http://www.sfcgcorp.com/whatnbu.htm. Ed. Marc Rothchild. R&P David Ewing. Adv. contact Tracy Brien. Circ: 2,876 (paid and controlled).

658 JPN ISSN 0912-6147
NANZAN KEIEI KENKYU/NANZAN MANAGEMENT REVIEW. Text in Japanese. 1952. 3/yr. free. **Document type:** *Academic/Scholarly.*
Supersedes in part (in 1986): Akademia. Keizai Keieigaku-hen (0389-844X); Which superseded in part (in 1975): Akademia (0515-8680)
—BLDSC (6015.343910).
Published by: Nanzan University, 18 Yamazato-cho, Showa-ku, Nagoya-shi, Aichi-ken 466-8673, Japan. TEL 81-52-832-3111, FAX 81-52-832-6157.

NASHA SPRAVA. see *BUSINESS AND ECONOMICS—Investments*

658 615 USA ISSN 1079-1116
NATIONAL ASSOCIATION OF CHAIN DRUG STORES. EXECUTIVE NEWSLETTER. Variant title: N A C D S Executive Newsletter. Text in English. bi-w. free. **Document type:** *Newsletter, Trade.* **Description:** Contains government and pharmacy activities on issues of concern to top level chain drug store executives. Includes member news, as well as activities of the Association.
Published by: National Association of Chain Drug Stores, 413 N Lee St, Box 1417 D49, Alexandria, VA 22313-1417. TEL 703-549-3001, FAX 703-836-4869, jcovert@nacds.org, http://www.nacds.org. Ed. John Covert. Circ: 43,000 (controlled).

658.00711 338 USA ISSN 1553-1600
HF1101
NATIONAL BUSINESS EDUCATION ASSOCIATION YEARBOOK. Text in English. 1963. a. USD 40 to non-members; USD 20 to members (effective 2005). bibl. back issues avail.; reprint service avail. from PQC. **Document type:** *Yearbook, Trade.* **Description:** In-depth coverage of a single topic relating to business education.
Formerly (until 1997): National Business Education Yearbook (1049-0256); Supersedes in part (in 1987): Business Education Forum (0007-6678); Which incorporated in part (1963-1982): National Business Education Yearbook (0547-4728)
Related titles: Microform ed.: (from PQC).
Indexed: ABIn, BusEdI, EduInd.
—BLDSC (6021.259000), ingenta.
Published by: National Business Education Association, 1914 Association Dr, Reston, VA 20191-1596. TEL 703-860-8300, FAX 703-620-4483, nbea@nbea.org, http://www.nbea.org. Circ: 15,000.

658 USA ISSN 1045-1668
K14 CODEN: NCMJB9
➤ **NATIONAL CONTRACT MANAGEMENT JOURNAL.** Text in English. 1966. s-a. USD 35. bk.rev. bibl.; charts; illus. **Document type:** *Academic/Scholarly.* **Description:** Publishes research and in-depth studies of issues in contract management.
Former titles: National Contract Management Quarterly Journal (0163-2124); National Contract Management Journal (0027-9064)
Related titles: Online - full text ed.: (from Northern Light Technology, Inc., O C L C Online Computer Library Center, Inc., ProQuest Information & Learning).
Indexed: ABIn, AUNI, BPIA, BusI, Inspec, RASB, T&II.
Published by: National Contract Management Association, 8260 Greensboro Dr, Ste 200, Ste. 200, Mc Lean, VA 22102-3886.

➤ **NATIONAL CREDITOR-DEBTOR REVIEW.** see *BUSINESS AND ECONOMICS—Banking And Finance*

658.4 MYS
NATIONAL PRODUCTIVITY CORPORATION, MALAYSIA. ANNUAL REPORT/PERBADANAN PRODUKTIVITI NEGARA. LAPURAN TAHUNAN. Text in English, Malay. 1962. a. free.
Formerly: National Productivity Centre, Malaysia. Annual Report (0126-8392)
Published by: National Productivity Centre/Pusat Daya Pengeluaran Negara, Sultan St., PO Box 64, Petaling Jaya, 46904, Malaysia. TEL 03-7557266, FAX 03-7578068, TELEX MA-36312. Circ: 2,000.

658.8 SGP
➤ **NATIONAL UNIVERSITY OF SINGAPORE. FACULTY OF BUSINESS ADMINISTRATION. RESEARCH PAPER SERIES.** Text in English. 1994. irreg. on exchange basis. back issues avail. **Document type:** *Monographic series, Academic/Scholarly.* **Description:** Publishes research in all areas of business administration.
Formerly (until 1996): National University of Singapore. Faculty of Business Administration. Working Papers
Published by: National University of Singapore, Faculty of Business Administration, 17 Law Link, Singapore, 117591, Singapore. TEL 65-874-3079, 65-874-3098, fbasimhl@nus.edu.sg, http://www.fba.nus.edu.sg/fba.

658 USA ISSN 1546-9522
HD30.3
▼ **NEGOTIATION.** Text in English. 2003. m. USD 99 domestic; USD 119 in Canada & Mexico; USD 139 elsewhere (effective 2004).
Published by: Harvard Business School Publishing, 60 Harvard Way, Boston, MA 02163. TEL 617-783-7500, FAX 617-783-7555, corpcustserv@hbsp.harvard.edu, http://www.hbsp.harvard.edu. Ed. Katie Shonk.

658 DEU
DER NEUE GMBH-BERATER VON A-Z. Text in German. base vol. plus updates 13/yr. EUR 129 (effective 2004). **Document type:** *Directory, Trade.*
Published by: Verlag Praktisches Wissen GmbH (Subsidiary of: Wolters Kluwer Deutschland GmbH), Marlener Str 2, Offenburg, 77656, Germany. TEL 49-781-605300, FAX 49-781-59825, info@praktisches-wissen.de, http://www.praktisches-wissen.de.

DIE NEUE VERWALTUNG. see *PUBLIC ADMINISTRATION*

NEW DIRECTIONS FOR EVALUATION. see *SOCIAL SCIENCES: COMPREHENSIVE WORKS*

NEW ENGLAND ACCOUNTING RESEARCH STUDIES (NO.). see *BUSINESS AND ECONOMICS—Accounting*

▼ **NEW ENGLAND FOOD SERVICE.** see *FOOD AND FOOD INDUSTRIES—Grocery Trade*

NEW JERSEY STATE BAR ASSOCIATION. CREDITOR AND DEBTOR RELATIONS SECTION. NEWSLETTER. see *BUSINESS AND ECONOMICS—Banking And Finance*

NEW MANAGEMENT. see *COMMUNICATIONS—Postal Affairs*

658 361.7 USA
HD2769.2.U6
THE NEW NONPROFIT ALMANAC AND DESK REFERENCE; the essential facts and figures for managers, researchers, and volunteers. Text in English. 1984. irreg. USD 40 per vol. (effective 2004).
Former titles (until 2002): Nonprofit Almanac (1060-7889); (until 1993): Dimensions of the Independent Sector (0887-9893)
Published by: Jossey-Bass Inc., Publishers (Subsidiary of: John Wiley & Sons, Inc.), 433 California St, San Francisco, CA 94104. http://www.josseybass.com.

NEW YORK MASTERPLANNER. see *SOCIAL SERVICES AND WELFARE*

658 NZL ISSN 1174-5339
NEW ZEALAND MANAGEMENT; the leaders' magazine. Text in English. 1955. m. NZD 67.96 (effective 2005). adv. bk.rev. illus. reprint service avail. from PQC. **Document type:** *Journal, Trade.* **Description:** Trade publication for business and professional executives in New Zealand.
Formerly (until 1998): Management (0025-1658); Incorporates: E.Office; Which was formerly: New Zealand Office Products News
Related titles: Microfilm ed.: (from PQC); Online - full text ed.: (from EBSCO Publishing, Gale Group, O C L C Online Computer Library Center, Inc., ProQuest Information & Learning).
Indexed: ABIn, INZP, Inpharma, PE&ON, Reac, WBA, WMB, WorkRelAb.
—BLDSC (5358.800000), IE, ingenta. **CCC.**
Published by: Profile Publishing Ltd., Wellesley St, PO Box 5544, Auckland, New Zealand. TEL 64-9-6308940, FAX 64-9-6301046, info@profile.co.nz, http://www.management.co.nz/, http://www.profile.co.nz/. Ed. Ruth Le Pla. Pub. Reg Birchfield. Adv. contact Diana Graham. Circ: 9,578.

NEWS TO YOU?. see *HANDICAPPED—Visually Impaired*

NEWSINC.; The business of the newspaper business. see *PUBLISHING AND BOOK TRADE*

658 070 USA
PN4734
NEWSPAPER FINANCIAL EXECUTIVES QUARTERLY. Text in English. 1949. q. USD 100. adv. bk.rev. index, cum.index. reprint service avail. from PQC. **Description:** Contains original articles contributed by members and others about accounting, information processing, profit planning, cost control, systems and procedures, and related problems in the newspaper field.
Former titles (until 1994): Newspaper Financial Executives Journal (0889-4590); Newspaper Controller (0028-9558)
Related titles: Online - full text ed.: (from ProQuest Information & Learning).
Indexed: ABIn, ATI.
Published by: International Newspaper Financial Executives, 21525 Ridgetop Circle, Ste 200, Sterling, VA 20166-6510. TEL 703-648-1160, FAX 703-476-5961. Ed. Jeanie E Ingram. Circ: 1,200.

658 NLD ISSN 0929-7774
NIEUWSBRIEF ABSENT!. Cover title: Absent!. Text in Dutch. 1994. bi-m. **Document type:** *Newsletter.*
Published by: Samsom H.D. Tjeenk Willink B.V. (Subsidiary of: Wolters Kluwer N.V.), Postbus 316, Alphen aan den Rijn, 2400 AH, Netherlands. TEL 31-1720-66822, FAX 31-1720-66639.

658 NGA ISSN 0331-0612
NIGERIAN JOURNAL OF BUSINESS MANAGEMENT. Text in English. 1977. bi-m. USD 115.20. adv. illus.
Published by: Fred Atoki Publishing Co. Ltd., Plot 25 Kekere-Ekun St., Orile-Iganmu, PO Box 7313, Lagos, Nigeria. Ed. F O A Atoki. Circ: 20,600.

658 NGA ISSN 0189-2568
NIGERIAN MANAGEMENT REVIEW. Text in English. 1985. q. (in 1 vol.). USD 38.03 to individuals; USD 40 to institutions. adv. bk.rev. **Document type:** *Trade.*
Published by: Centere for Management Development, Management Village, PMB 21578, Ikeja, Lagos, Nigeria. TEL 234-64-901120-2. Ed. Udo Udo Aka. Circ: 25,000.

658 JPN
NIHON KEIEI KOGAKUKAI ROMBUNSHI/JAPAN INDUSTRIAL MANAGEMENT ASSOCIATION. COMMUNICATIONS. Text in Japanese. bi-m. **Document type:** *Journal, Trade.*
Published by: Nihon Keiei Kogakukai/Japan Industrial Management Association, Gakkai Center C21, 5-16-9 Honkomagome, Bunkyo-ku, Tokyo, 113-8622, Japan. TEL 81-3-5814-5801, FAX 81-3-5814-5820, http://edpex104.bcasj.or.jp/jima/.

658 JPN ISSN 0386-4812
NIHON KEIKEI KOGAKKAISHI/JAPAN INDUSTRIAL MANAGEMENT ASSOCIATION. JOURNAL. Text in Japanese; Summaries in English. 1950. bi-m.
Formerly (until 1974): J I M A News (0386-4804)
Indexed: JCT.
—**CCC.**
Published by: Nihon Keikei Kogakkai, Nihon Gakkai Jimu Senta, 16-9 Honkomagome 5-chome, Bunkyo-ku, Tokyo, 113-0021, Japan.

658 ISR ISSN 0333-5658
HD28
NIHUL; Israel managers magazine. Text in Hebrew. 1978. bi-m. ILS 432 (effective 2000).
Indexed: IHP.
Published by: Israel Management Center, P O Box 33033, Tel Aviv, Israel. TEL 972-3-6957205, FAX 972-3-6953104. Ed. Avraham Tal.

658 JPN ISSN 0913-3429
NIKKEI DESIGN. Text in Japanese. 1987. m. JPY 18,860 (effective 1999). adv. **Document type:** *Trade.* **Description:** Covers a whole spectrum of interests in Japan's diverse design community.
Published by: Nikkei Business Publications Inc. (Subsidiary of: Nihon Keizai Shimbun, Inc.), 2-7-6 Hirakawa-cho, Chiyoda-ku, Tokyo, 102-8622, Japan. TEL 81-3-5210-8311, FAX 81-3-5210-8530, info@nikkeibpnyc.com, info@nikkeibp-america.com, http://www.nikkeibp.com. Ed. Takehiko Katsuo. Pub. Ginjiro Takahashi. Adv. contact Kazuhiro Hatto. B&W page JPY 306,000, color page JPY 522,000; trim 210 x 280. Circ: 16,608. **Dist. in America by:** Nikkei Business Publications America Inc., 575 Fifth Ave, 20th Fl, New York, NY 10017.

658.8 BEL ISSN 1373-8488
➤ **NON MARCHAND.** Text in French. s-a. EUR 55 (effective 2005). bk.rev. abstr. back issues avail. **Document type:** *Monographic series, Academic/Scholarly.* **Description:** Covers issues in managing nonprofit organizations.
Indexed: DIP, IBR, IBZ.
Published by: De Boeck Universite, Fond Jean-Paques 4, Louvain-la-Neuve, 1348, Belgium. TEL 32-10-482511, FAX 32-10-482519, info@universite.deboeck.com, http://universite.deboeck.com/revues/nonmarchand. Ed. Michel Coippel. Circ: 500 (paid). **Subscr. to:** Acces S.P.R.L.. TEL 32-10-4852570, acces+cde@deboeck.be.

658 ITA ISSN 1122-9322
NON PROFIT; diritto e management degli enti non commerciali. Text in Italian. 1994. q. EUR 122 (effective 2005). **Document type:** *Magazine, Trade.* **Description:** Addresses issues facing management of non-profit enterprises.
Published by: Maggioli Editore, Via del Carpino 8/10, Santarcangelo di Romagna, RN 47822, Italy. TEL 39-0541-628111, FAX 39-0541-622020, editore@maggioli.it, http://www.maggioli.it. Ed. Paolo Sciume.

658 USA ISSN 1531-5428
NONPROFIT BUSINESS ADVISOR. Text in English. 1990. m. USD 189 (effective 2006). **Document type:** *Newsletter, Trade.* **Description:** Covers fresh guidance on such hot button topics as taxation, donations, compensation, commercial ventures, retirement plans and technology. For the chief executive, top financial officer or savvy fundraiser, Nonprofit business advisor offers intelligence-not fluff.
Formerly (until 1999): Nonprofit Business Alert (1527-9189)
—**CCC.**
Published by: L R P Publications, 747 Dresher Rd, PO Box 980, Horsham, PA 19044. TEL 215-784-0860, 800-341-7874, FAX 215-784-9639, custserve@lrp.com, http://www.shoplrp.com/product/p-9500.html, http://www.lrp.com.

B

658 USA ISSN 1074-6331
NONPROFIT FINANCIAL ADVISOR. Text in English. 1994. m. USD 169 domestic; USD 203 foreign (effective 2000).
Document type: *Newsletter, Trade.*
Published by: Aspen Publishers, Inc. (Subsidiary of: Wolters Kluwer N.V.), 5301 Buckeystown Pike, Ste. 400, Frederick, MD 21704-8319. TEL 800-638-8437, customer.service@aspenpubl.com, http://www.aspenpub.com. Ed. Mark A Yahoudy. **Dist. by:** Distribution Center, 7201 McKinney Circle, Frederick, MD 21701. TEL 301-698-7100, FAX 301-417-7550.

658.048 USA ISSN 1048-6682
HD62.6 CODEN: NMLEES
➤ **NONPROFIT MANAGEMENT AND LEADERSHIP.** Text in English. 1990. q. USD 195 domestic; USD 235 in Canada & Mexico; USD 269 elsewhere; USD 215 combined subscription domestic; USD 255 combined subscription in Canada & Mexico; USD 289 combined subscription elsewhere (effective 2006). bk.rev. illus. Index. back issues avail.; reprint service avail. from PSC. **Document type:** *Journal, Academic/Scholarly.* **Description:** Offers authoritative insights of top executives and researchers on the common concerns of all nonprofit managers.
Related titles: Online - full text ed.: ISSN 1542-7854. USD 195 (effective 2006) (from EBSCO Publishing, O C L C Online Computer Library Center, Inc., Swets Information Services, Wiley InterScience).
Indexed: ABIn, ASG, BPI, CIJE, EAA, HRA, IBSS, JEL, MEDLINE, RI-1, RI-2, SOPODA, SPAA, SSA, SociolAb, V&AA.
—BLDSC (6117.340150), IE, ingenta. **CCC.**
Published by: Jossey-Bass Inc., Publishers (Subsidiary of: John Wiley & Sons, Inc.), 989 Market St, San Francisco, CA 94103-1741. TEL 415-433-1740, 888-378-2537, FAX 800-605-2665, 415-433-0499, jbsubs@jbp.com, http://www.josseybass.com/WileyCDA/WileyTitle/productCd-NML.html. Ed. Roger A Lohman. R&P Lorri Wimer TEL 415-433-1740. Circ: 1,050. **Co-sponsor:** Editorial sponsoring bodies: Mandel Center for Nonprofit Organizations of Case Western Reserve University; London School of Economics Centre for Voluntary Organisation.

658 USA ISSN 1084-8371
HD62.6
THE NONPROFIT QUARTERLY. Key Title: The New England Nonprofit Quarterly. Text in English. 1994. q. USD 49; USD 14.95 newsstand/cover (effective 2005). adv. **Document type:** *Magazine, Trade.* **Description:** Reviews current ideas and trends concerning nonprofit/voluntary organizations and activities.
Published by: Third Sector New England, Lincoln Plaza, Suite 700, 89 South St, Boston, MA 02111. TEL 617-523-6565, 800-281-7770, FAX 617-523-2070, http://www.nonprofitquarterly.org/. adv.: B&W page USD 2,450, color page USD 2,700; trim 8 x 10.625.

658 USA ISSN 0896-5048
NONPROFIT TIMES; the leading publication for nonprofit news and management. Text in English. 1987. m. USD 65 domestic; USD 89 in Canada; USD 129 elsewhere (effective 2005). adv. bk.rev. bibl.; charts; illus.; stat.; tr.lit. index. back issues avail. **Document type:** *Trade.* **Description:** News and "how to" information on funding, management for any nonprofit organization.
Related titles: Microfiche ed.; Online - full text ed.: (from Gale Group).
Published by: Davis Information Group, 240 Cedar Knolls Rd, Ste 318, Cedar Knolls, NJ 07927-1621. TEL 201-734-1700, FAX 201-734-1777, nptimes@haven.ios.com, http://www.nptimes.com/. Ed. Kevin Landers. R&P Paul Clolery. Circ: 34,000.

658 NOR ISSN 1500-4066
NORGES HANDELSHOEYSKOLE. INSTITUTT FOR FORETAKSOEKONOMI. DISCUSSION PAPER. Text in English. 1990. irreg. **Document type:** *Monographic series.*
Formerly (until 1997): Norges Handelshoeyskole. Institutt for Foretaksoekonomi. Working Paper (0803-2777); Incorporates (1994-1997): Norges Handelshoeyskole. Institutt for Matematikk og Statistikk. Discussion Paper (0805-1127)
Indexed: ASFA, ESPM.
Published by: Norges Handelshoeyskole, Institutt for Foretaksoekonomi/Norwegian School of Economics and Business Administration, Institute of Finance and Management Science, Helleveien 30, Bergen, 5045, Norway. TEL 47-5595-9293, FAX 47-5595-9650, for.postmottak@nhh.no, http://www.nhh.no/for/res-pub.htm.

658 ITA
IL NUOVO MANAGEMENT. Text in Italian. 1999. 3/yr. EUR 39 domestic; EUR 69 foreign (effective 2003).
Published by: (Universita degli Studi di Bergamo, Dipartimento di Economia Aziendale), Franco Angeli Edizioni, Viale Monza 106, Milan, 20127, Italy. TEL 39-02-2837141, FAX 39-02-26144793, redazioni@francoangeli.it, http://www.francoangeli.it.

O B G MANAGEMENT. (Obstetrics and Gynecology) see *MEDICAL SCIENCES—Obstetrics And Gynecology*

658 ZAF ISSN 1025-1073
O D DEBATE; reflecting on organisations and development. Text in English. 1994. q. ZAR 110 domestic; ZAR 140 other African countries; ZAR 210 elsewhere (effective 2000). adv. bk.rev.
Description: Focuses on development approaches and techniques. Aimed at development practicioners, or those involved with change.
Indexed: ISAP.
Published by: Olive (OD and Training), 21 Sycamore Rd, Glenwood, Durban, KwaZulu-Natal 4001, South Africa. TEL 27-31-206-1534, FAX 27-31-252114, olive@oliveodt.co.za, http://www.epages.net/olive. Eds. Andra Hellberg Phillips, Davine Thaw. Adv. contact Evangeline Govender. Circ: 1,500.

658 USA ISSN 1086-2609
HD58.8
O D PRACTITIONER. (Organization Development) Text in English. 1968. q. USD 160 domestic membership; USD 175 in Canada & Mexico membership; USD 180 elsewhere membership (effective 2004). **Document type:** *Journal, Trade.*
Related titles: Online - full text ed.
—BLDSC (6235.158500), IE, ingenta. **CCC.**
Published by: Organization Development Network, Inc, 71 Valley St, Ste 301, South Orange, NJ 07079-2825. TEL 973-763-7337, FAX 973-763-7488, odnetwork@odnetwork.org, http://www.odnetwork.org. Ed. Marilyn Blair.

O D T U GELISME DERGISI/M E T U STUDIES IN DEVELOPMENT. (Orta Dogu Teknik Universitesi) see *BUSINESS AND ECONOMICS—Economic Systems And Theories, Economic History*

658 GBR ISSN 0953-5543
➤ **O R INSIGHT.** Text in English. 1987. q. free to members; GBP 60 (effective 2003). adv. bk.rev. back issues avail. **Document type:** *Academic/Scholarly.* **Description:** To inform managers and management scientists about the scope and potential of operational research interventions.
Related titles: Online - full content ed.: free to members; Available only to members of the Operational Research Society.
Indexed: CPM, CompAb, IAOP.
—BLDSC (6277.373000), IE, ingenta.
Published by: Operational Research Society, Seymour House, Tudor Court, 12 Edward St, Birmingham, Warks B1 2RX, United Kingdom. TEL 44-121-233-9300, FAX 44-121-233-0321, faulkner@orsoc.org.uk, http://www.orsoc.org.uk. Eds. Brian Lehaney, Steve Clarke. R&P, Adv. contact Christine Faulkner. Circ: 3,000 (controlled).

➤ **O R - M S TODAY.** see *SCIENCES: COMPREHENSIVE WORKS*

➤ **O R SPECTRUM;** quantitative approaches in management. (Operations Research) see *COMPUTERS*

658.333714 DEU ISSN 1435-6228
OEKO-MANAGEMENT; Studien zur oekologischen Betriebsfuehrung. Text in German. 1994. irreg., latest vol.9, 2004. price varies. **Document type:** *Monographic series, Academic/Scholarly.*
Published by: Verlag Dr. Kovac, Arnoldstr 49, Hamburg, 22763, Germany. TEL 49-40-3988800, FAX 49-40-39888055, info@verlagdrkovac.de, http://www.verlagdrkovac.de/3-2.htm.

005.74 DNK ISSN 0900-8322
OEKONOMISTYRING OG INFORMATIK. Text in Danish. 1986. 7/yr. DKK 1,800 domestic (effective 2003). back issues avail. **Document type:** *Journal, Academic/Scholarly.* **Description:** Contains theoretical and practical information for professionals in the fields of management accounting, management information systems and leadership.
Published by: Jurist- og Oekonomforbundets Forlag, Lyngbyvej 17, PO Box 2702, Copenhagen OE, 2100, Denmark. TEL 45-39-315500, FAX 45-39-135555, oekinfo@djoef.dk, fl@djoef.dk, http://www.djoef.dk/forlag/oekinfo. Ed. Preben Melander. Circ: 1,000.

OF COUNSEL; the monthly legal practice report. see *LAW*

OFFICE PERSONNEL REPORT. see *BUSINESS AND ECONOMICS—Personnel Management*

651 USA ISSN 1096-5807
HF5547.A2 CODEN: SCTYA7
OFFICEPRO. Text in English. 1942. 8/yr. USD 25 domestic; USD 59 foreign (effective 2005). adv. bk.rev.; software rev.; Website rev. illus.; stat.; charts. index. back issues avail.; reprint service avail. from PQC. **Document type:** *Magazine, Trade.* **Description:** Offers information and other tips for office professionals concerning office technology, productivity improvement, management and training, and career advancement.
Formerly (until 1997): Secretary (0037-0622)
Related titles: Online - full text ed.: (from EBSCO Publishing).
Indexed: BusEdI, CIJE, PersLit.
—CASDDS, IE. **CCC.**
Published by: Stratton Publishing and Marketing Inc., 5285 Shawnee Rd, Ste 510, Alexandria, VA 22312-2334. TEL 703-914-9200, FAX 703-914-6777, officepro@iaap-hq.org, pubpros@strattonpub.com, http://www.iaap-hq.org/officepro/toc.htm, http://www.strattonpub.com. Ed. Angela Hickman Brady. Pub. Deborah J Stratton. Adv. contacts Alison Bashion TEL 800-335-7500, Deborah S Sollosi. B&W page USD 3,420, color page USD 4,590; trim 8.25 x 10.88. Circ: 36,000 (paid).

658 USA ISSN 1522-516X
HD9561
OIL & GAS EXECUTIVE. Text in English. 1998. q., latest vol.3, no.2, 2000.
Indexed: PetrolAb.
—PADDS. **CCC.**
Published by: Society of Petroleum Engineers, Inc., PO Box 833836, Richardson, TX 75083-3836. TEL 972-952-9393, FAX 972-952-9435, spedal@spe.org.

658 GBR ISSN 0305-0483
HD28 CODEN: OMEGA6
➤ **OMEGA.** Text in English. 1973. 6/yr. EUR 1,037 in Europe to institutions; JPY 137,700 in Japan to institutions; USD 1,161 elsewhere to institutions (effective 2006). adv. bk.rev. abstr.; bibl.; illus. Index. reprints avail. **Document type:** *Academic/Scholarly.* **Description:** Reports on the latest developments in management, including research results and applications, as well as assessments of specific management techniques.
Related titles: Microfilm ed.: (from PQC); Online - full text ed.: (from EBSCO Publishing, Florida Center for Library Automation, Gale Group, IngentaConnect, ScienceDirect, Swets Information Services).
Indexed: ABIn, ADPA, ApMecR, BPIA, BibInd, BusI, CIJE, CJA, CMCI, CPM, CurCont, DPD, Emerald, EngInd, ExcerpMed, FamI, HECAB, IAOP, IMFL, Inspec, MEA&I, ManagCont, ORMS, QC&AS, RASB, RefZh, SCIMP, SSCI, T&II.
—BLDSC (6256.426000), AskIEEE, IDS, IE, Infotrieve, ingenta, Linda Hall. **CCC.**
Published by: Pergamon (Subsidiary of: Elsevier Science & Technology), The Boulevard, Langford Ln, East Park, Kidlington, Oxford OX5 1GB, United Kingdom. TEL 44-1865-843000, FAX 44-1865-843010, OMEGA@umich.edu, http://www.elsevier.com/locate/omega. Ed. B Lev. Circ: 1,400. **Subscr. to:** Elsevier BV, PO Box 211, Amsterdam 1000 AE, Netherlands. TEL 31-20-485-3757, FAX 31-20-485-3432, nlinfo-f@elsevier.nl, http://www.elsevier.nl.

658 USA
ON THE LEARNING EDGE; business and personal coaching services. Text in English. 1998. m. free. back issues avail. **Document type:** *Newsletter.* **Description:** Contains practical tools to help stretch your learning edge to achieve increased levels of success, satisfaction and energy. Topics include management and organization skills.
Related titles: Online - full text ed.
Published by: On The Learning Edge, PO Box 177, San Anselmo, CA 94979-0177. TEL 415-457-4277, ontheedge@theedgecoach.com, http://www.theedgecoach.com. Ed. Sheila Adams Sapper.

658 352.84 USA ISSN 1087-6391
ON THE MARK. Text in English. 1995. q. back issues avail. **Document type:** *Newsletter.* **Description:** Provides news and insight into conformity assessment issues to help companies manage global certification problems.
Published by: Underwriters Laboratories Inc., Corporate Communications, 333 Pfingsten Rd., Northbrook, IL 60062-2096. TEL 847-272-8800, FAX 847-272-8129, nissenm@ul.com, http://www.ul.com. Ed. Michael Nissen. Circ: 80,000 (controlled).

ONLINE BUSINESS ANALYST. see *COMPUTERS—Internet*

OPERATING RESULTS OF INDEPENDENT SUPERMARKETS. see *BUSINESS AND ECONOMICS—Small Business*

OPERATIONAL RESEARCH SOCIETY. JOURNAL. see *COMPUTERS*

OPERATIONAL RISK. see *INSURANCE*

OPERATIONS RESEARCH. see *COMPUTERS*

OPERATIONS RESEARCH/COMPUTER SCIENCE INTERFACE SERIES. see *COMPUTERS*

OPERATIONS RESEARCH PROCEEDINGS. see *COMPUTERS*

658.4 JPN ISSN 0453-4514
T57.6.A1 CODEN: JORJA5
➤ **OPERATIONS RESEARCH SOCIETY OF JAPAN. JOURNAL/NIHON OPERESHONZU RISACHI GAKKAI RONBUNSHI.** Text in English. 1957. q. free to members. index. back issues avail. **Document type:** *Academic/Scholarly.* **Description:** Publishes original operations research and management science work and quality reviews of interest to OR practitioners.
Related titles: Online - full text ed.: (from EBSCO Publishing, Gale Group, IngentaConnect, Swets Information Services).

Indexed: ASCA, CCMJ, CIS, CMCI, IAOP, Inspec, JCQM, JTA, MathR, MathSciNet, RefZh, SCI, SSCI, ST&MA, ZentMath. —BLDSC (4836.010000), AskIEEE, CISTI, IDS, IE, Infotrieve, ingenta, Linda Hall. **CCC.**

Published by: Nihon Opereshonzu Risachi Gakkai/Operations Research Society of Japan, Gakkai-Center Bldg., 2-4-16 Yayoi, Bunkyo-ku, Tokyo, 113-0032, Japan. TEL 81-3-38153351, FAX 81-3-38153352, jimukyoku@orsj.or.jp, http://www.orsj.or.jp/. Ed. Naoki Katoh. Circ: 3,000.

➤ **OPERATIONS UPDATE (NEW YORK).** see *BUSINESS AND ECONOMICS*

003 JPN ISSN 0030-3674
T57.6.A1

OPERESHONZU RISACHI/OPERATIONS RESEARCH. Variant title: Operations Research Society of Japan. Communications. Text in Japanese. 1956. m. JPY 970 newsstand/cover (effective 2005). bk.rev. abstr. Index. **Document type:** *Journal, Academic/Scholarly.*

Formerly: Keiei Kagaku - Management Science (0451-5978)

Indexed: CMCI, IAOP, RefZh.
—CISTI. **CCC.**

Published by: (Nihon Opereshonzu Risachi Gakkai/Operations Research Society of Japan), J U S E Press, Ltd., 5-4-2, Sendagaya, Shibuya-ku, Tokyo, 151-0051, Japan. TEL 81-3-53791240, FAX 81-3-33563419, http://www.juse-p.co.jp/. Circ: 4,200.

OPHTHALMOLOGY MANAGEMENT. see *MEDICAL SCIENCES—Ophthalmology And Optometry*

658 IND ISSN 0030-3887
HD20.5 CODEN: OPSEAN

OPSEARCH; journal of the Operational Research Society of India. Text in English. 1964. bi-m. USD 90 to institutions (effective 2006). adv. bk.rev. charts; illus. index. **Document type:** *Journal, Academic/Scholarly.*

Indexed: Biostat, CCMJ, CIS, CurCont, IAOP, Inspec, JCQM, MathR, MathSciNet, ORMS, QC&AS, ST&MA, ZentMath.
—BLDSC (6272.700000), AskIEEE, IE, Infotrieve, ingenta. **CCC.**

Published by: (Operational Research Society of India, Care Institute for Systems Studies and Analyses), Scientific Publishers, 5-A New Pali Rd., Near Hotel Taj Hari Mahal, PO Box 91, Jodhpur, Rajasthan 342 003, India. TEL 91-291-2433323, FAX 91-291-2512580, info@scientificpub.com, http://www.scientificpub.com/bookdetails.php?booktransid=343&bookid=339. Ed. N K Jaiswal. Circ: 2,000.

OPTIMUM ONLINE; the journal of public sector management. see *PUBLIC ADMINISTRATION*

658 DEU ISSN 0048-2129

➤ **ORDO**; Jahrbuch fuer die Ordnung von Wirtschaft und Gesellschaft. Text in German, English. 1948. a. EUR 78 (effective 2005). adv. 700 p./no.; **Document type:** *Yearbook, Academic/Scholarly.*

Indexed: DIP, IBR, IBSS, IBZ, IPSA, RASB.
—CCC.

Published by: Lucius und Lucius Verlagsgesellschaft mbH, Gerokstr 51, Stuttgart, 70184, Germany. TEL 49-711-242060, FAX 49-711-242088, lucius@luciusverlag.com, http://www.luciusverlag.com. Ed. H Schueller. Pub. Wulf von Lucius. adv.: page EUR 450; 120 x 195. Circ: 650 (controlled).

658 GBR ISSN 1350-6269

ORGANISATIONS & PEOPLE. Text in English. 1994. q. GBP 81 membership to individuals; GBP 56 membership to students, retired persons or unemployed (effective 2001). **Document type:** *Trade.*

Related titles: Online - full text ed.

Indexed: Emerald, HRA, M&MA.
—BLDSC (6289.370000), IE, ingenta. **CCC.**

Published by: Association for Management Education and Development, 62 Paul St, London, EC2A 4NA, United Kingdom. TEL 44-207-613-4121, FAX 44-207-613-4737, amed.office@management.org.uk, http://www.amed.management.org.uk/default.shtm.

658 CHE ISSN 0473-2839

DER ORGANISATOR✱. Text in German. 10/yr. **Document type:** *Trade.*

Published by: Verlag Organisator AG, Loewenstr 16, Zurich, 8021, Switzerland. TEL 01-4011212, FAX 01-4010815. Ed. Franz Schnyder. Circ: 15,000.

658 SCG ISSN 0351-3432

ORGANIZACIJA SAMOUPRAVLJANJA OUR✱; casopis za pitanja stimulativne raspodele i obracuna po ekonomskim jedinicama. Text in Serbo-Croatian. 1962. m. YUN 500.

Former titles: Radna Jedinica (0013-3221); Ekonomska Jedinica

Published by: Zavod za Ekonomske Ekspertize, c/o Economical Society of Serbia, Nusiceva 6-111, P.O. Box 490, Belgrade. Ed. Dr. Bogdan Orlovic. Circ: 2,000.

658 330 POL ISSN 0137-5466

ORGANIZACJA I KIEROWANIE/ORGANIZATION AND MANAGEMENT. Text in Polish; Summaries in English. 1975. q. EUR 49 domestic (effective 2005). adv. **Document type:** *Journal, Academic/Scholarly.* **Description:** Covers cybernetics, computer science, sociology of organization, economics of organization and related fields.

Indexed: AgrLib, RASB.

Published by: (Polska Akademia Nauk, Komitet Nauk Organizacj i Zarzadzania), Instytut Organizacji i Zarzadzania w Przemysle, ul Zelazna 87, Warsaw, 00879, Poland. TEL 48-22-6546061, FAX 48-22-6204360, wydawnictwa@orgmasz.waw.pl, http://www.orgmasz.waw.pl/w/org_pol/wydaw/kwart/k_head.htm. Ed. Zbigniew Dworzecki. **Dist. by:** Ars Polona, Krakowskie Przedmiescie 7, Warsaw, Poland. TEL 48-22-9263914, FAX 48-22-9265334, arspolona@arspolona.com.pl, http://www.arspolona.com.pl.

658 GBR ISSN 1350-5084
HM131 CODEN: OGANF4

➤ **ORGANIZATION**; the interdisciplinary journal of organization, theory and society. Text in English. 1994. bi-m. GBP 580, USD 1,015 to institutions; GBP 604, USD 1,057 combined subscription to institutions print & online eds. (effective 2006). adv. bk.rev. **Document type:** *Journal, Academic/Scholarly.* **Description:** Seeks to construct analytical narratives and ethical discourses appropriate to the radically changing structural, theoretical, and ideological realities organizations now face. Along with analyses of specific processes, it pays particular attention to the links between intellectual developments, changes in organizational forms and practices, and broader social, cultural, and institutional transformations.

Related titles: Online - full content ed.; Online - full text ed.: ISSN 1461-7323. GBP 574, USD 1,005 to institutions (effective 2006) (from C S A, EBSCO Publishing, O C L C Online Computer Library Center, Inc., ProQuest Information & Learning, Sage Publications, Inc., Swets Information Services).

Indexed: ABIn, ASCA, CPE, CPM, CommAb, CurCont, Emerald, FamI, HRA, IBSS, IPSA, PAA&I, PSA, RASB, SOPODA, SSA, SSCI, SWA, SociolAb, UAA.
—BLDSC (6290.630000), IDS, IE, Infotrieve, ingenta. **CCC.**

Published by: Sage Publications Ltd. (Subsidiary of: Sage Publications, Inc.), 1 Oliver's Yard, 55 City Rd, London, EC1 1SP, United Kingdom. TEL 44-20-73248500, FAX 44-20-73248600, info@sagepub.co.uk, http://www.sagepub.co.uk/journal.aspx?pid=105723. Eds. Linda Smircich, Marta Calas, Mike Reed. Adv. contact Jenny Kirby. page GBP 195; trim 192 x 116. Circ: 1,100. **Subscr. in the Americas to:** Sage Publications, Inc., 2455 Teller Rd, Thousand Oaks, CA 91320. TEL 805-499-0721, FAX 805-499-0871, journals@sagepub.com.

➤ **ORGANIZATION & ENVIRONMENT.** see *OCCUPATIONAL HEALTH AND SAFETY*

658 USA ISSN 0889-6402
HD58.8

ORGANIZATION DEVELOPMENT JOURNAL; guiding the future of people working together. Text in English. 1983. q., latest vol.20. USD 80; free to members (effective 2004). adv. bk.rev. 100 p./no.; back issues avail.; reprint service avail. from PQC. **Document type:** *Journal, Trade.* **Description:** Offers practical information for those interested in organization development and management development.

Related titles: Microform ed.: (from PQC); Online - full text ed.: (from EBSCO Publishing, Northern Light Technology, Inc., O C L C Online Computer Library Center, Inc., ProQuest Information & Learning).

Indexed: ABIn, BibInd, Emerald, PsycInfo, PsycholAb, QAb, T&DA, e-psyche.
—BLDSC (6290.716000), IE, ingenta.

Published by: Organization Development Institute, 11234 Walnut Ridge Rd, Chesterland, OH 44026. TEL 440-729-7419, don@odinstitute.org, http://www.odinstitute.org. Ed. Dr. Steven Cady. Pub., R&P, Adv. contact Dr. Donald W Cole TEL 440-729-7419. page USD 125. Circ: 800 (paid).

658 USA ISSN 1541-6518
HD30.4

▼ ➤ **ORGANIZATION MANAGEMENT JOURNAL.** Text in English. 2004. 3/yr. free (effective 2004). **Document type:** *Journal, Academic/Scholarly.*

Media: Online - full content.

Published by: Western New England College, School of Business, 1215 Wilbraham Rd., Springfield, MA 01119. TEL 413-782-1702, http://www.wnec.edu/omj. Ed. Jeanie M. Forray.

658 USA ISSN 1047-7039
HD28 CODEN: ORSCEZ

➤ **ORGANIZATION SCIENCE.** Text in English. 1990. q. USD 138 domestic to non-members; USD 162 foreign to non-members; USD 69 to members additonal journal; USD 180 combined subscription domestic to non-members print & online eds.; USD 204 combined subscription foreign to non-members print & online eds.; USD 90 combined subscription to members additonal journal, print & online eds.; USD 272 combined subscription domestic to institutions print &/or online eds.; USD 296 combined subscription foreign to institutions print & online eds. (effective 2004); membership includes 1 free journal. adv. illus.; bibl.; charts. back issues avail. **Document type:** *Journal, Academic/Scholarly.* **Description:** Interdisciplinary forum for research on organizations from diverse fields such as management, sociology, economics, political science, and psychology.

Related titles: Online - full content ed.: ISSN 1526-5455. USD 92 to non-members; USD 46 to members additional journal; USD 272 to institutions (effective 2004); Online - full text ed.: (from EBSCO Publishing, Gale Group, JSTOR (Web-based Journal Archive), ProQuest Information & Learning, Swets Information Services).

Indexed: ABIn, ASCA, CMCI, CurCont, Emerald, IBSS, ORMS, PsycInfo, PsycholAb, QC&AS, SOPODA, SSCI, e-psyche.
—BLDSC (6290.728000), IDS, IE, Infotrieve, ingenta. **CCC.**

Published by: I N F O R M S, 901 Elkridge Landing Rd., Ste. 400, Linthicum, MD 21090-2909. TEL 410-850-0300, 800-446-3676, FAX 410-684-2963, os-mg-editor@gsm.uci.edu, informs@informs.org, http://web.gsm.uci.edu/orgsci/, http://www.informs.org. Ed. Claudia Bird Schoonhoven TEL 949-824-7474. R&P Candita Gerzevitz. Adv. contact Trish Allewalt. B&W page USD 400; trim 8.125 x 10.875. Circ: 1,900.

658 USA ISSN 1551-7470

➤ **ORGANIZATIONAL ANALYSIS.** Text in English. 1993. q. USD 90 to individuals; USD 190 to institutions (effective 2005). adv. bk.rev. illus. Index. reprints avail. **Document type:** *Magazine, Academic/Scholarly.* **Description:** Publishes articles that includes relevant subject matter in the areas of human resources management, organizational behavior, organizational theory, and strategic management.

Formerly (until 2004): The International Journal of Organizational Analysis (1055-3185)

Related titles: Online - full text ed.: (from EBSCO Publishing, Northern Light Technology, Inc., O C L C Online Computer Library Center, Inc., ProQuest Information & Learning).

Indexed: ABIn, CPM, ESPM, IBSS, IPsyAb, PerIslam, PsycInfo, PsycholAb, RiskAb, SOPODA, SSA, SociolAb, e-psyche.
—BLDSC (4542.435200), IE, ingenta. **CCC.**

Published by: (Center for Advanced Studies in Management), Information Age Publishing, Inc., 411 W Putnam Ave, Ste 205, PO Box 4967, Greenwich, CT 06831. TEL 203-661-7602, FAX 203-661-7952, order@infoagepub.com, http://www.infoagepub.com/www/products/product4/oa.htm. Ed. Daniel J Svyantek. adv.: B&W page USD 100.

658 USA ISSN 0749-5978
BF636.A1 CODEN: OBDPFO

➤ **ORGANIZATIONAL BEHAVIOR AND HUMAN DECISION PROCESSES.** Text in English. 1966. 6/yr. EUR 904 in Europe to individuals; JPY 94,400 in Japan to individuals; USD 726 elsewhere to individuals; EUR 1,980 in Europe to institutions; JPY 206,700 in Japan to institutions; USD 1,586 elsewhere to institutions; EUR 427 in Europe to students; JPY 44,700 in Japan to students; USD 340 elsewhere to students (effective 2006). adv. bibl.; charts; stat.; illus. Index. back issues avail.; reprints avail. **Document type:** *Journal, Academic/Scholarly.* **Description:** Features articles that describe original empirical research and theoretical developments in all areas of human decision processes and organizational psychology.

Formerly (until 1985): Organizational Behavior and Human Performance (0030-5073)

Related titles: Online - full text ed.: ISSN 1095-9920. USD 1,632 (effective 2002) (from EBSCO Publishing, Gale Group, IngentaConnect, O C L C Online Computer Library Center, Inc., ScienceDirect, Swets Information Services).

Indexed: ABIn, ASCA, AgeL, BPI, BPIA, BusI, CINAHL, CIS, CJA, CPM, CommAb, CurCont, DIP, ErgAb, FamI, HRA, IBR, IBSS, IBZ, ILD, LRI, MEA&I, MEDLINE, PsySCAP, PsycInfo, PsycholAb, RASB, RI-1, RI-2, SCIMP, SOPODA, SSCI, T&II, e-psyche.
—BLDSC (6290.749000), IDS, IE, Infotrieve, ingenta. **CCC.**

Published by: Academic Press (Subsidiary of: Elsevier Science & Technology), 525 B St, Ste 1900, San Diego, CA 92101-4495. TEL 619-231-6616, 800-894-3434, FAX 619-699-6422, apsubs@acad.com, http://www.elsevier.com/locate/obhdp, http://www.academicpress.com. Ed. D A Harrison.

658 GBR ISSN 0090-2616
HD28 CODEN: ORDYA
ORGANIZATIONAL DYNAMICS. Text in English. 1972. 4/yr. EUR 76 in Europe to individuals; JPY 10,100 in Japan to individuals; USD 83 to individuals except Europe and Japan; EUR 165 in Europe to institutions; JPY 21,800 in Japan to institutions; USD 189 in Mexico to institutions; USD 189 in United States to institutions; USD 189 in Canada to institutions; USD 189 to institutions except Europe and Japan (effective 2006). bk.rev. illus.; abstr. index. back issues avail.; reprints avail. **Document type:** *Trade.* **Description:** Features articles and interviews with leading managers and behavioral scientists on the application of the behavioral sciences in organizations.
Related titles: Microform ed.: (from PQC); Online - full text ed.: (from EBSCO Publishing, Florida Center for Library Automation, Gale Group, H.W. Wilson, IngentaConnect, Northern Light Technology, Inc., O C L C Online Computer Library Center, Inc., ScienceDirect, Swets Information Services).
Indexed: ABIn, ADPA, ASCA, ASEANManA, AgeL, BPI, BPIA, BusI, CPM, CurCont, EmerIntel, Emerald, Inspec, MEDLINE, ManagCont, PMA, PersLit, PsySCAP, PsycInfo, PsycholAb, QAb, RASB, SCIMP, SSCI, T&DA, T&II, WorkRelAb, e-psyche.
—BLDSC (6290.770000), IDS, IE, Infotrieve, ingenta. **CCC.**
Published by: (American Management Association USA), Pergamon (Subsidiary of: Elsevier Science & Technology), The Boulevard, Langford Ln, East Park, Kidlington, Oxford OX5 1GB, United Kingdom. TEL 44-1865-843000, FAX 44-1865-843010, http://www.elsevier.com/locate/orgdyn. Ed. Fred Luthans. Circ: 4,000. **Subscr. to:** Elsevier BV, PO Box 211, Amsterdam 1000 AE, Netherlands. TEL 31-20-485-3757, FAX 31-20-485-3432, nlinfo-f@elsevier.nl, http://www.elsevier.nl.

658 USA ISSN 1094-4281
HD28
ORGANIZATIONAL RESEARCH METHODS. Text in English. 1998. q. USD 623, GBP 402 to institutions; USD 648, GBP 419 combined subscription to institutions print & online eds. (effective 2006). back issues avail. **Document type:** *Journal, Academic/Scholarly.* **Description:** Addresses questions about existing quantitative and qualitative methods and research designs currently used by organizational researchers.
Related titles: Online - full text ed.: ISSN 1552-7425. USD 616, GBP 398 to institutions (effective 2006) (from C S A, EBSCO Publishing, O C L C Online Computer Library Center, Inc., ProQuest Information & Learning, Sage Publications, Inc., Swets Information Services).
Indexed: ABIn, BrCerAb, C&ISA, CerAb, CorrAb, CurCont, DIP, E&CAJ, EMA, ERA, ESPM, HRA, IAA, IBR, IBZ, M&TEA, MBF, METADEX, PsycInfo, PsycholAb, RiskAb, SSA, SSCI, SociolAb, WAA.
—BLDSC (6290.787500), IE, Infotrieve, ingenta, Linda Hall. **CCC.**
Published by: (Research Methods Division), Sage Publications, Inc., 2455 Teller Rd, Thousand Oaks, CA 91320. TEL 805-499-0721, 800-818-7243, FAX 805-499-0871, 800-583-2665, info@sagepub.com, http://www.sagepub.com/journal.aspx?pid=146. Ed. Herman Aguinis. R&P Tanya Udin TEL 805-499-0721 ext 7716. Adv. contact DeAnna Vega Hammersley. **Subscr. overseas to:** Sage Publications Ltd., 1 Oliver's Yard, 55 City Rd, London EC1 1SP, United Kingdom. TEL 44-20-73740645, FAX 44-20-73748741, subscription@sagepub.co.uk. **Co-sponsor:** Academy of Management, Research Methods Division.

ORGANIZATIONS AND CHANGE. see *BUSINESS AND ECONOMICS—Personnel Management*

658 RUS
ORGANIZATSIYA UPRAVLENIYA. Text in Russian. 1971. irreg.
Published by: Izdatel'stvo Ekonomika, Berezhkovskaya nab 6, Moscow, 121864, Russian Federation.

658 USA ISSN 1556-8997
THE ORGANIZED EXECUTIVE. Text in English. 1996. m. USD 97 (effective 2005). **Document type:** *Newsletter, Trade.* **Description:** Presents executives and management with effective ideas on how to accomplish tasks more efficiently.
Formerly: Stephanie Winston's The Organized Executive (1092-2024)
—IE.
Published by: Briefings Publishing Group (Subsidiary of: Douglas Publications, Inc.), 1101 King St, Ste 110, Alexandria, VA 22314. TEL 703-518-2343, 800-722-9221, FAX 703-684-2136, customerservice@briefings.com, http://www.briefings.com. Ed. Alice Baumgarner.

658 ITA ISSN 0474-635X
ORGANIZZARSI. Text in Italian. 1962. q. adv.
Published by: ORGA Srl, Via Vitruvio 3, Milan, 20124, Italy. TEL 39-02-29512102, FAX 39-02-2047052, orga@orga.it, http://www.orga.it. Ed. Pierluigi Malinverni.

ORION. see *COMPUTERS*

658 USA
OTO'S SCOPE✶. Text in English. 1983. 3/yr. membership. **Document type:** *Newsletter.*
Published by: Association of Otolaryngology Administrators, P O Box 503269, Saint Louis, MO 63150-0001. TEL 319-356-2371. Ed. Richard M Harding. Circ: 600.

OUTSOURCING CENTER; the journal for strategic outsourcing. see *COMPUTERS*

658 GBR
OXFORD INSTITUTE OF RETAIL MANAGEMENT. RESEARCH PAPERS. RETAIL DEVELOPMENT, PLANNING AND POLICY. Text in English. 198?. irreg., latest vol.31, 1994. GBP 25. **Document type:** *Monographic series.*
Published by: Oxford Institute of Retail Management, Templeton College, Kennington, Oxford, OX1 5NY, United Kingdom. TEL 44-1865-735422, FAX 44-1865-736374.

P B L BUSINESS LEADER. see *OCCUPATIONS AND CAREERS*

658 CAN ISSN 1487-475X
P E M: INDUSTRIAL SOURCEBOOK. Text in English. 1978. a. CND 12 domestic; USD 20 in United States (effective 2005). adv. **Document type:** *Directory, Trade.* **Description:** Provides a resource of thousands of industrial products and services and Canadian supplier contacts.
Former titles (until 1997): Industrial Sourcebook (1205-4917); (until 1996): P E M: Sourcebook (1187-1547); Industrial Products and Services
Related titles: Online - full text ed.; ◆ Supplement to: P E M: Plant Engineering and Maintenance. ISSN 0710-362X.
Indexed: ABIn.
Published by: C L B Media, Inc. (Subsidiary of: Canada Law Book Inc.), 240 Edward St, Aurora, ON L4G 3S9, Canada. TEL 905-727-0077, FAX 905-727-0017, ar@industrialsourcebook.com, http://www.industrialsourcebook.com, http://www.clbmedia.ca. adv.: page CND 3,950; trim 10.88 x 8. Circ: 18,519 (controlled).

658 628.5 CAN ISSN 0710-362X
P E M: PLANT ENGINEERING AND MAINTENANCE. Text in English. 1978. bi-m. CND 40 domestic; USD 60 in United States; USD 75 elsewhere (effective 2005). adv. **Document type:** *Magazine, Trade.* **Description:** Committed to helping Canada's industrial managers meet the challenges of running and operating a competitive industrial facility.
Former titles (until 1981): Maintenance Engineering Management (0227-664X); (until 1980): Maintenance Management (0707-1965)
Related titles: Microfiche ed.: (from MML); Online - full text ed.; ◆ Supplement(s): P E M: Industrial Sourcebook. ISSN 1487-475X.
Indexed: ABIn.
—BLDSC (6516.095000), CISTI. **CCC.**
Published by: C L B Media, Inc. (Subsidiary of: Canada Law Book Inc.), 240 Edward St, Aurora, ON L4G 3S9, Canada. TEL 905-727-0077, FAX 905-727-0017, http://www.pem-mag.com, http://www.clbmedia.ca. Circ: 18,100.

P M A DIRECTORY. see *BUSINESS AND ECONOMICS—Trade And Industrial Directories*

658 CHE
P M E MAGAZINE. Text in German. 10/yr. CHF 105 domestic; CHF 130 in Europe; CHF 139 elsewhere (effective 2001). adv. **Document type:** *Magazine, Trade.*
Published by: HandelsZeitung Fachverlag AG, Seestr 344, Zuerich, 8027, Switzerland. TEL 41-1-2889414, FAX 41-1-2889301, infopme@pme.ch, verlag@handelszeitung.ch, http://www.handelszeitung.ch. Ed. Francois Schaller. Pub. Ralph Buechi. Circ: 20,000.

658 USA
P M E-ZINE. Text in English. 1983. s-m. USD 24. adv. bk.rev. charts; illus.; tr.lit. **Document type:** *Newsletter, Trade.* **Description:** Covers use of applied behavioral analysis concepts to business, education, family and government, with emphasis on business.
Formerly: Performance Management Magazine (Print Edition) (0734-029X)
Media: Online - full content.
Published by: Aubrey Daniels International, 3353 Peachtree Rd NE, Ste 920, Atlanta, GA 30326. TEL 678-904-6140, FAX 678-904-6141, http://www.pmezine.com/article_type.asp?TID=1, http://www.aubreydaniels.com. Ed. Gail Snyder. Circ: 3,000.

658 USA ISSN 1040-8754
HD69.P75
P M NETWORK. (Project Management) Text in English. 1987. m., latest vol.17, 2003. free to members. adv. bk.rev. charts. Index. 64 p./no. 3 cols./p.; back issues avail. **Document type:** *Magazine, Trade.* **Description:** Professional magazine covering industry applications and practical issues in managing projects. Its mission is to keep the project management decision-maker abreast of the latest news of techniques and best practices.
Related titles: Online - full text ed.: (from EBSCO Publishing, H.W. Wilson, O C L C Online Computer Library Center, Inc., ProQuest Information & Learning).
Indexed: BPI.
—BLDSC (6451.077450), IE, Infotrieve, ingenta. **CCC.**
Published by: Project Management Institute, 4 Campus Blvd, Newtown Square, PA 19073. TEL 610-356-4600, FAX 610-356-4647, pmihq@pmi.org, http://www.pmi.org/info/PIR_PMNetworkOnline.asp. Ed. Dan Goldfischer. Pub. Gary Boyler. R&P Laurie Miller. Adv. contacts Libby Barwis TEL 215-540-9447, Richard Barwis. B&W page USD 2,655, color page USD 4,890; trim 10.88 x 8.13. Circ: 103,000 (paid).

P O S - MANAGER. see *FOOD AND FOOD INDUSTRIES—Grocery Trade*

THE PAINT DEALER; dedicated to the retail paint market. see *PAINTS AND PROTECTIVE COATINGS*

658 PAK ISSN 0969-8027
CODEN: PMAREY
PAKISTAN MANAGEMENT REVIEW. Text in English. 1960. q. PKR 180, USD 55. adv. bk.rev. charts; illus.; stat. index, cum.index: 1960-1969, 1970-1979.
Indexed: BAS, INIS AtomInd.
—BLDSC (6343.035000).
Published by: Pakistan Institute of Management, Shahrah-Iran, Clifton, Karachi 6, Pakistan. TEL 537123. Ed. Zarrar R Zubair. Circ: 1,600.

658 ITA
PANORAMI; riflessioni, discussioni e proposte sul diritto e l'amministrazione. Text in Italian. 1990. s-a. EUR 20.66 domestic; EUR 36.15 foreign (effective 2003).
Published by: Rubbettino Editore, Viale Rosario Rubbettino 10, Soveria Mannelli, CZ 88049, Italy. TEL 39-0968-662034, FAX 39-0968-662055, segreteria@rubbettino.it, http://www.rubbettino.it. Ed. Alessandro Corbino.

658 ESP ISSN 1132-2640
PAPELES DE TRABAJO. Text in Spanish. 1985. s-a.
Related titles: ◆ Supplement to: Cuadernos de Ciencias Economicas y Empresariales. ISSN 0211-4356.
Published by: Universidad de Malaga, Facultad de Ciencias Economicas y Empresariales, Campus de El Ejido, Malaga, 29071, Spain. TEL 34-95-2131148, FAX 34-95-2132031, cumalaga@uma.es, http://www.uma.es/.

PARCEL SHIPPING & DISTRIBUTION; small shipment logistics management. see *TRANSPORTATION*

PARFUEMERIE JOURNAL. see *BEAUTY CULTURE—Perfumes And Cosmetics*

PARKS & REC BUSINESS. see *SPORTS AND GAMES—Outdoor Life*

PARKS AND RECREATION; journal of park and recreation management. see *LEISURE AND RECREATION*

658 332 GBR
PARTNERS IN BUSINESS. Text in English. 1994. irreg., latest vol.2, 1995. **Document type:** *Trade.* **Description:** Contains articles on how to help a business grow with sections on finances, management, customer service, and human resource issues.
Published by: Bank of Scotland, Business Banking, c/o UK Banking, Uberior House,, 61 Grassmarket, Bank Of Scotland, Edinburgh, EH1 2JF, United Kingdom. TEL 44-131-243-5944, FAX 44-131-243-5738. Ed. Chris Baur. **Co-sponsor:** Insider Group.

659 COL ISSN 1657-6276
PENSAMIENTO & GESTION. Text in Spanish. 1997. s-a. COP 12,000 (effective 2002).
Published by: Universidad del Norte, Ediciones Uninorte, Km 5 Via a Puerto Colombia, Barranquilla, Colombia. TEL 57-5-3509218, FAX 57-5-3509489, ediciones@uninorte.edu.co, http://www.uninorte.edu.co. Circ: 2,500.

PEOPLE DYNAMICS. see *BUSINESS AND ECONOMICS—Personnel Management*

658 300 HUN ISSN 1416-3837
H1
➤ **PERIODICA POLYTECHNICA. SOCIAL AND MANAGEMENT SCIENCES.** Text in English, German. 1993. s-a. USD 18 (effective 2002). bk.rev.; Website rev. **Document type:** *Journal, Academic/Scholarly.*
Formerly (until 1996): Periodica Polytechnica. Humanities and Social Sciences (1216-0555)
Indexed: EngInd, RefZh.
Published by: Budapesti Muszaki es Gazdasagtudomanyi Egyetem/Budapest University of Technology and Economics, Periodica Polytechnica, Budapest, 1521, Hungary. TEL 36-1-4631469, FAX 36-1-4632270, perpol@goliat.eik.bme.hu, http://www.pp.bme.hu. Ed. T Koltai. Circ: 400. **Subscr. to:** Acquisition Department Central Library, Budapest 1521, Hungary.

658 RUS ISSN 1682-6000
PERSONAL MIKS. Text in Russian. 2001. bi-m. RUR 1,650 domestic (effective 2004). **Document type:** *Magazine, Trade.*

B

Published by: Rimus, pr Dobroliubova, 11 liter, St Petersburg, 197198, Russian Federation. TEL 7-812-2304683, info@personal-mix.ru, http://www.personal-mix.ru. Ed. Vera Minina.

650 NOR ISSN 1503-3449
PERSONAL OG LEDELSE. Text in Norwegian. 1991. 8/yr. NOK 850 (effective 2005). adv. **Document type:** *Magazine, Trade.*
Former titles (until 2002): Personal (0808-2693); (until 1997): Bedre Oekonomi og Personal (0803-642X); Which was formed by the merger of (1987-1991): Bedre Lonnsomhet (0802-6076); Which was formerly (until 1989): Finansmagasinet (0801-5651); (1985-1991): Bedre paa Jobben (0802-9253); Which was formerly (until 1989): Jeg og Jobben (0801-7425); (until 1986): Jeg (0800-8094)
Published by: Vanebo Fagpresse AS, PO Box 130, Kirkenaer, 2260, Norway. TEL 47-62-941000, FAX 47-62-941010, firmapost@vanebo.no, http://www.personalogledelse.no/, http://www.vanebo.no. Eds. Ole Alvik, Ove Hansrud TEL 47-62-829100. Adv. contact Kjetil Hovda. B&W page NOK 14,500, color page NOK 19,000; 190 x 265.

658 USA ISSN 0893-2549
CODEN: PRPSEB
PERSONAL REPORT FOR THE PROFESSIONAL SECRETARY. Text in English. 1974. m. USD 39. **Document type:** *Newsletter.* **Description:** Professional secretary's guide to accelerated career advancement.
Formerly: Research Institute Personal Report for the Professional Secretary (0276-6035)
—CASDDS. **CCC.**
Published by: National Institute of Business Management, PO Box 9225, Mclean, VA 22102-0225. TEL 703-905-8000. Ed. Barry Lenson. Pub. Michelle S Cox. R&P Carolyn Frazier. Circ: 20,000.

267 USA ISSN 0745-3027
BV1000
PERSPECTIVES (BLOOMINGTON). Text in English. 1919. 8/yr. USD 20 (effective 1999 & 2000). adv. bk.rev. back issues avail. **Document type:** *Trade.*
Incorporated (in 1985): Journal of Physical Education and Program (0735-0139); Which was formerly (until 1981): Journal of Physical Education (0022-3662); (until 1975): Forum
Indexed: SportS.
Published by: Association of Professional Directors of Y M C A's, 8200, Humboldt, MN 55431. TEL 612-885-0273, FAX 612-885-0227. Ed. Steve Kendall. Pub. James G Stooke. Adv. contact Paul Carr. page USD 1,046; trim 11.25 x 8.63. Circ: 5,500.

PETERSON'S JOB OPPORTUNITIES FOR BUSINESS MAJORS. see *OCCUPATIONS AND CAREERS*

PHARMACEUTICAL OUTSOURCING DECISONS. see *PHARMACY AND PHARMACOLOGY*

PHARMAVOICE. see *PHARMACY AND PHARMACOLOGY*

330 USA ISSN 1530-342X
PHYSICIAN COMPENSATION REPORT. Text in English. 2001. m. USD 379 (effective 2001). **Description:** Includes data, benchmarks, and the specifics of hundresds of actual physician pay plans, plus news and strategies that can help medical groups enhance revenues.
Related titles: Online - full text ed.
Published by: Atlantic Information Services, Inc., 1100 17th St, NW, Ste 300, Washington, DC 20036. Pub. Richard Biehl.
Co-publisher: Medical Group Management Association.

THE PHYSICIAN'S ADVISORY. see *HEALTH FACILITIES AND ADMINISTRATION*

PHYSICIAN'S MANAGEMENT MANUALS. see *MEDICAL SCIENCES*

PHYSICIAN'S PRACTICE DIGEST; business journal for physicians. see *MEDICAL SCIENCES*

658.2 620 CAN
PLANT; canada's industry publication. Text in English. 1941. 18/yr. USD 128.75 foreign (effective 2004); includes all supplements. adv. bk.rev. illus.; tr.lit. reprint service avail. from PQC. **Document type:** *Newspaper, Trade.* **Description:** Provides news and technical information of interest to Canada's manufacturing and processing industries, from raw material resourcing through to finished products.
Former titles: Plant - Canada's Industrial Newsletter (0845-4213); (until 1988): Plant Management and Engineering (0315-9183); Plant Administration and Engineering (0032-0773)
Related titles: Online - full text ed.: (from Micromedia ProQuest, ProQuest Information & Learning); ♦ Supplement(s): Plant Sites & Locations. ISSN 0841-2375; Plant Controls & Instrumentation; Plant Automation; Plant Brochure Guide; Plant Action Pac.
Indexed: BPIA, CBCARef, CBPI.
—CISTI. **CCC.**
Published by: Rogers Media Publishing Ltd, One Mount Pleasant Rd, 11th Fl, Toronto, ON M4Y 2Y5, Canada. TEL 416-764-2000, FAX 416-764-3941, http://www.plant.ca, http://www.rogers.com. Ed. Joe Terrett. Pub. Dan Bordun. Circ: 34,000.

658 690 GBR ISSN 1352-8637
PLANT MANAGERS JOURNAL. Text in English. 1973. m. GBP 50 domestic; GBP 69, USD 104 elsewhere (effective 2000). adv. **Document type:** *Trade.* **Description:** Journal for buyers of construction equipment focusing on plant hire, building and civil engineering, quarries, utilities, the military, and industry in the UK.
Related titles: Online - full text ed.: (from EBSCO Publishing, Gale Group).
—CCC.
Published by: Reed Business Information Ltd. (Subsidiary of: Reed Business), Quadrant House, The Quadrant, Brighton Rd, Sutton, Surrey SM2 5AS, United Kingdom. TEL 44-208-652-3500, FAX 44-208-652-8977, rbi.subscriptions@qss-uk.com, http://www.reedbusiness.co.uk/. Ed. David Nunn TEL 44-20-8652-4643. Pub. Trevor Parker. Adv. contact Steve Beard TEL 44-20-8652-4652. Circ: 10,084. **Subscr. to:** Quadrant Subscription Services, PO Box 302, Haywards Heath, W Sussex RH16 3YY, United Kingdom. TEL 44-1444-445566, FAX 44-1444-445447.

658 POL ISSN 0860-2506
POLITECHNIKA WARSZAWSKA. ORGANIZACJA I ZARZADZANIE PRZEMYSLEM. PRACE NAUKOWE. Text in Polish. 1983. irreg., latest no.13, 1999. price varies. **Document type:** *Academic/Scholarly.*
—Linda Hall.
Published by: Oficyna Wydawnicza Politechniki Warszawskiej/Publishing House of the Warsaw University of Technology, ul Polna 50, Warsaw, 00644, Poland. bgpw@bg.pw.edu.pl, http://www.wpw.pw.edu.pl.

POLITICAL RISK YEARBOOK (SET). see *BUSINESS AND ECONOMICS—Banking And Finance*

POLITICAL RISK YEARBOOK. VOLUME 1: NORTH & CENTRAL AMERICA. see *BUSINESS AND ECONOMICS—Banking And Finance*

POLITICAL RISK YEARBOOK. VOLUME 2: MIDDLE EAST & NORTH AFRICA. see *BUSINESS AND ECONOMICS—Banking And Finance*

POLITICAL RISK YEARBOOK. VOLUME 3: SOUTH AMERICA. see *BUSINESS AND ECONOMICS—Banking And Finance*

POLITICAL RISK YEARBOOK. VOLUME 4: SUB-SAHARAN AFRICA. see *BUSINESS AND ECONOMICS—Banking And Finance*

POLITICAL RISK YEARBOOK. VOLUME 5: EAST ASIA & THE PACIFIC. see *BUSINESS AND ECONOMICS—Banking And Finance*

POLITICAL RISK YEARBOOK. VOLUME 6: WEST EUROPE. see *BUSINESS AND ECONOMICS—Banking And Finance*

POLITICAL RISK YEARBOOK. VOLUME 7: EAST EUROPE. see *BUSINESS AND ECONOMICS—Banking And Finance*

POLITICAL RISK YEARBOOK. VOLUME 8: CENTRAL AND SOUTH AFRICA. see *BUSINESS AND ECONOMICS—Banking And Finance*

658 USA ISSN 1099-7237
HM263
POSITIVE LEADERSHIP. Text in English. m. USD 99. **Document type:** *Newsletter.* **Description:** Designed to improve performance through value-centered management.
Published by: Lawrence Ragan Communications, Inc., 316 N Michigan Ave, Ste 300, Chicago, IL 60601. TEL 312-960-4106, 800-878-5331, FAX 312-960-4106, http://www.ragan.com.

POWER, FINANCE & RISK. see *BUSINESS AND ECONOMICS—Banking And Finance*

658 IND
PRAGYA FEATURES. Text in English.
Published by: Shri Attam Vallabh Jain Girls College, Institute of Management & Technology, Sudama Nagar, Hanumangarh Rd, Sriganganagar, 335 001, India. TEL 91-154-437371.

PRAJNAN (PUNE); journal of social and management sciences. see *BUSINESS AND ECONOMICS—Banking And Finance*

PRATT'S BANK ASSET/LIABILITY MANAGEMENT. see *BUSINESS AND ECONOMICS—Banking And Finance*

658 IND
PRAXIS; Business Line's journal on management. Text in English. **Document type:** *Journal, Trade.* **Description:** Covers topics on management.
Published by: Kasturi & Sons Ltd., Kasturi Bldgs., 859-860 Anna Salai, Chennai, Tamil Nadu 600 002, India. TEL 9144-28589060, FAX 9144-28545703, bleditor@thehindu.co.in, thehindu@vsnl.com, http://www.hindubusinessline.com/praxis/index.htm, http://www.thehindu.com.

658 DEU ISSN 0937-6828
PRAXIS-HANDBUCH UNTERNEHMENSFUEHRUNG. Text in German. 1990. bi-m. looseleaf. **Document type:** *Trade.*
Published by: W R S Verlag GmbH & Co. KG (Subsidiary of: Rudolf Haufe Verlag GmbH & Co. KG), Fraunhoferstr 5, Planegg, 82152, Germany. TEL 49-89-895170, FAX 49-89-89517250, info@wrs.de, http://www.wrs.de.

▼ **PRAXISFUEHRUNG PROFESSIONELL.** see *MEDICAL SCIENCES—Physical Medicine And Rehabilitation*

PRESENCES IN BUSINESS. see *BUSINESS AND ECONOMICS—Economic Situation And Conditions*

658 JPN ISSN 0032-7751
PRESIDENT; business in-sight magazine. Text in Japanese. 1963. m. JPY 10,800. adv. bk.rev. charts; illus. index. **Document type:** *Trade.* **Description:** General business interest magazine whose core readers are corporate owners and executive managers. Highlights successful people and their strategies and important business trends.
Published by: President Inc. (Subsidiary of: Time Inc.), Bridgestone Hirakawa-cho Bldg 1st Fl, 2-13-12 Hirakawa-cho, Chiyoda-ku, Tokyo, 102-0093, Japan. TEL 81-3-3237-3711, FAX 81-3-3237-3745, TELEX J24914 PREMAG. Eds. Hirofumi Kabashima, Norihisa Yamamoto. Adv. contact Takashi Kikuchi. B&W page JPY 1,260,000, color page JPY 1,900,000; trim 275 x 210. Circ: 273,323.

368.5 USA ISSN 1044-4998
PRINCIPAL'S REPORT. Text in English. 1989. m. looseleaf. USD 278.95 combined subscription in US & Canada print & online eds.; USD 293 combined subscription elsewhere print & online eds. (effective 2006). index. back issues avail. **Document type:** *Newsletter, Trade.* **Description:** Looks to show owners and partners in design firms how to improve partner distributions and their leadership of the firm. Includes advice on how to increase margins, compensation and benefits for both principals and staff, retirement plan alternatives, partnership agreements, "rainmaking," tax strategies, increasing staff productivity, etc.
Related titles: Diskette ed.; E-mail ed.; Online - full content ed.: (from Northern Light Technology, Inc.); Online - full text ed.: (from LexisNexis, ProQuest Information & Learning).
Indexed: ABIn.
—CCC.
Published by: Institute of Management & Administration, Inc., 3 Park Ave, New York, NY 10016-5902. TEL 212-244-0360, FAX 212-564-0465, subserve@ioma.com, http://www.ioma.com/products/prod_detail.php?prodid=37. Ed. Stephen Kliment. Pub. Lee Rath. R&P Sofie Kourkoutakis.

658.321 USA ISSN 1072-5318
KF6436
PRINCIPLES OF PAYROLL ADMINISTRATION; the complete learning and reference guide. Text in English. 1988. a. looseleaf. USD 150 (effective 1998). **Document type:** *Trade.* **Description:** Outlines laws and procedures that apply to payroll administration. Also covers items relating to benefits.
Published by: W G & L Financial Reporting & Management Research (Subsidiary of: R I A), 395 Hudson St, New York, NY 10014. TEL 212-367-6300, FAX 212-367-6718, http://www.InsideHR.com. Ed. Debera J Salam. **Subscr. to:** The Park Square Bldg., 31 St James Ave, Boston, MA 02116-4112. TEL 800-950-1207.

PRINTING MANAGER. see *PRINTING*

650 USA ISSN 1053-8577
PRISM (BOSTON). Text in English. 1988. s-a. **Document type:** *Journal, Trade.*
—IE.
Published by: Arthur D. Little, Inc., 68 Fargo St, Boston, MA 02210. TEL 617-443-0309, FAX 617-443-0166, marketng@adlittle.com, http://www.adl.com/insights/prism/.

658 USA ISSN 0895-3228
PRIVATE PRACTICE NEWS✶. Text in English. 1987. m. looseleaf. USD 69. bk.rev. index. back issues avail.
Published by: Private Practice Institute, PO Box 1485, Shawnee, OK 74802-1485. Ed. Katherine O'Halloran. Circ: 700.

PRIVATE PRACTICE SUCCESS. see *HEALTH FACILITIES AND ADMINISTRATION*

658 SCG ISSN 0350-9435
PRIVREDA I RUKOVODJENJE. Text in Serbo-Croatian. 1967. m. YUN 1,200, USD 130. adv. bk.rev. charts; illus.; stat. index.
Formerly: Menadzer u Privredi (0025-9225)
Published by: Tanjug Economic Service/Tanjug Redakcija Ekonomskih Informacija, Novinska agencija Tanjug, Oblicev Venac 2, B P 439, Belgrade, 11000. Ed. Dragoslav Pavlovic. Circ: 1,700.

658 ITA ISSN 0032-9363
PROBLEMI DI GESTIONE; selezione da riviste straniere. Text in Italian. 1968. 6/yr. bk.rev. charts. index. **Document type:** *Monographic series.*
Formerly: Studi di Economia della Produzione Industriale
Indexed: PAIS.
Published by: Centro di Formazione e Studi (Formez), Comprensorio Olivetti, Via Campi Flegrei, 34, Arco Felice, NA 80072, Italy. TEL 39-81-5250111, FAX 39-81-8041348. Ed. Roberto Stampacchia. R&P Elio Flora. Circ: 1,000 (controlled).

658 UKR ISSN 1727-7051
▼ ➤ **PROBLEMS & PERSPECTIVES IN MANAGEMENT.** Text in English. 2003. q. USD 300 foreign (effective 2005). adv. back issues avail. **Document type:** *Journal, Academic/Scholarly.* **Description:** Covers both theoretical and practical issues in finance and investment management and business administration. Aimed at researchers, scholars, lecturers, college students and practitioners alike.
Related titles: CD-ROM ed.; Online - full content ed.: ISSN 1810-5467; Online - full text ed.: (from EBSCO Publishing); ♦ Ukrainian ed.: Problemy i Perspektyvy Upravlinnya v Ekonomitsi.
Indexed: IBSS.
Published by: Dilovi Perspektyvy, Karbysheva lane 138, office 4, Sumy, 40018, Ukraine. TEL 380-542-345455, FAX 380-542-345455, head@businessperspectives.sumy.ua, http://www.businessperspectives.org. Ed. Serhiy Kozmenko. Adv. contact Natalia Ivakhnenko. B&W page USD 200. Circ: 1,000.

B

658 UKR
▼ **PROBLEMY I PERSPEKTYVY UPRAVLINNYA V EKONOMITSI.** Text in Ukrainian. 2003. q. UAK 240 domestic; USD 300 foreign (effective 2005). **Document type:** *Journal, Academic/Scholarly.* **Description:** Designed for researchers, scholars, lecturers, students in institutions of higher education, and practitioners alike, it aims at improvement of existing methods and development of new methods in the management of macro- and microeconomic processes, and the further dissemination of research results.
Related titles: ♦ English ed.: Problems & Perspectives in Management. ISSN 1727-7051.
Published by: Dilovi Perspektyvy, Karbysheva lane 138, office 4, Sumy, 40018, Ukraine. TEL 380-542-345455, FAX 380-542-345455, head@businessperspectives.sumy.ua, http://www.businessperspectives.org. Ed. Serhiy Kozmenko.

658 RUS ISSN 0257-9928
PROBLEMY TEORII I PRAKTIKI. Text in Russian; Summaries in English. 1983. s-m. RUR 108,000. adv. **Document type:** *Monographic series.* **Description:** Presents theoretical and practical aspects of management.
Related titles: Supplement(s): Programmnye Produkty i Sistemy. ISSN 0236-235X. 1988.
Indexed: WAE&RSA.
Published by: (Mezhdunarodnyi Naucho-issledovatel'skii Institut Problem Upravleniya), Editorial Board Problemy Teorii i Praktiki, Ul Medvedeva 13, str 1, Moscow, 103006, Russian Federation. TEL 7-095-9730660, FAX 7-095-9730543. Ed. V Silin. Circ: 5,000.

658 338 USA ISSN 1059-1478
TS155.A1 CODEN: POMAEN
➤ **PRODUCTION AND OPERATIONS MANAGEMENT.** Text in English. 1992. q. USD 80 domestic membership (effective 2004). adv. illus. reprints avail. **Document type:** *Journal, Academic/Scholarly.*
Related titles: Online - full text ed.: (from EBSCO Publishing, O C L C Online Computer Library Center, Inc., ProQuest Information & Learning).
Indexed: ABIn, CMCI, CurCont, Inspec.
—BLDSC (6853.076600), AskIEEE, IE, Infotrieve, ingenta.
Published by: Production and Operations Management Society, College of Engineering, Florida International University, EAS 2460, 10555 W Flagle St, Miami, FL 33174. TEL 305-348-1413, FAX 305-348-6890, poms@fiu.edu, http://www.poms.org. Ed. Kalyan Singhal. Pub., R&P, Adv. contact Sushil K Gupta. Circ: 1,200 (paid).

658 ZAF
PRODUCTIVITY; for excellence in management. Text in English. 1990 (vol.16)-2000 (vol.26); resumed 2001 (Jun.). bi-m. ZAR 12.50 newsstand/cover (effective 2001). adv. **Document type:** *Magazine, Corporate.*
Formerly (until 1999): Productivity S A (1018-7227)
Indexed: ISAP.
Published by: Mafube Publishing, PO Box 2185, Houghton, 2041, South Africa.

658 TTO
PRODUCTIVITY NEWS. Text in English. 1974. q. free. bibl. **Description:** Focuses on management and productivity issues related to Trinidad and Tobago.
Former titles: M D C News; (until 1976): Trinidad and Tobago Management Development Centre. Quarterly Newsletter
Published by: Management Development Centre, Library, Salvatori Bldg, PO Box 1301, Port-of-Spain, Trinidad, Trinidad & Tobago. TEL 809-623-1961, FAX 809-623-2111. Ed. Heather Baldwin-MacDowell. Circ: 1,000.

PROFESSIONAL ADVISOR. see *ADVERTISING AND PUBLIC RELATIONS*

PROFESSIONAL AND SCIENTIFIC PERSONNEL REPORT - GEOGRAPHIC EDITION. see *BUSINESS AND ECONOMICS—Personnel Management*

658 GBR ISSN 1470-7799
PROFESSIONAL BUSINESS & TECHNICAL MANAGEMENT. Text in English. 1983. 3/yr. GBP 7 per issue to non-members; free to members (effective 2003). adv.
Formed by the merger of (1987-2001): Professional Management (0951-1814); (1986-2001): B.T.M. Bulletin (Business and Technical Management) (0268-5868)
Indexed: Inspec.
—BLDSC (6857.340000), IE, ingenta.
Address: Academy House, Warwick Corner, 42 Warwick Rd, Kenilworth, Warks CV8 1HE, United Kingdom. TEL 44-1926-855498, FAX 44-1926-513100. Adv. contact H J Manners. B&W page GBP 400.

PROFESSIONAL MANAGEMENT REVIEW. see *BUSINESS AND ECONOMICS—Marketing And Purchasing*

658 GBR ISSN 0969-6695
THE PROFESSIONAL MANAGER. Text in English. 1972. bi-m. GBP 18 domestic to non-members; GBP 21 in Europe to non-members; GBP 24 elsewhere to non-members (effective 2002). adv. bk.rev. abstr. index, cum.index. back issues avail.; reprints avail. **Document type:** *Journal, Trade.* **Description:** Provides timely information on every aspect of management, covering major news trends, techniques, views and issues. Features practical articles designed to help managers with their continuing professional development.
Formed by the Nov. 1992 merger of: Industrial Management (0962-4732); Management News; Which was previously: Management Review and Digest (0307-3580); Management Abstracts (0025-1666)
Indexed: BMT, BldManAb, ERA, Emerald, Inspec, M&MA, RASB, SOMA, WTA.
—BLDSC (6859.555000), IE, Infotrieve, ingenta.
Published by: Chartered Management Institute, 2 Savoy Ct, 3rd Fl, Strand, London, WC2R 0EZ, United Kingdom. TEL 44-20-7497-0580, FAX 44-20-7497-0463, join@managers.org.uk, http://www.managers.org.uk. Ed., R&P Sue Mann TEL 44-20-7421-2717. Adv. contact Nathalie Ferguson TEL 44-20-7421-2705. B&W page GBP 2,600, color page GBP 2,950; trim 205 x 280. Circ: 84,000 (controlled).
Subscr. to: Publications Subscription, Registrars Dept., Chartered Management Institute, Cottingham Rd, Corby, Northants NN17 1TT, United Kingdom. TEL 44-1536-204222, FAX 44-1536-201651.

658.4 GBR
PROFESSIONAL OFFICER. Text in English. 1986. m. GBP 5 to non-members. adv. bk.rev. back issues avail. **Document type:** *Newspaper.*
Published by: Federated Union of Managerial and Professional Officers, Terminus House, Terminus St, Harlow, CM20 1TZ, United Kingdom. TEL 44-1274-434444, FAX 44-1279-451176. Ed., R&P David Candler. Adv. contact Jenny Pearce. Circ: 12,500 (controlled).

658 720 620 USA
PROFESSIONAL SERVICES MANAGEMENT JOURNAL. Text in English. 1973. m. USD 247 domestic; USD 287 foreign; USD 350 combined subscription domestic print & online eds.; USD 390 combined subscription foreign print & online eds. (effective 2002). index. back issues avail. **Document type:** *Newsletter.* **Description:** Strategies for design firms worldwide.
Former titles (until Aug. 2002): P S M J - Best Practices (1542-3069); (until 2002): P S M J - Principal Strategies; (until 1998): Professional Services Management Journal (P S M J) (0732-2119)
Related titles: Online - full text ed.
—BLDSC (6864.220310).
Published by: P S M J Resources, Inc., 10 Midland Ave, Newton, MA 02458. TEL 617-965-0055, 800-537-7765, FAX 617-965-5152, psmj@tiac.com, http://www.psmj.com. Ed. Susan Yoder. Pub. Frank A Stasiowski. R&P Christa Matukaitis.

658 DEU
PROFIT IM HANDEL. Text in German. fortn. EUR 9 per month (effective 2005). **Document type:** *Newsletter, Trade.*
Published by: B B E Unternehmensberatung GmbH, Gothaer Allee 2, Cologne, 50969, Germany. TEL 49-221-93655130, FAX 49-221-93655112, info@bbe-verlag.de, http://www.bbe-verlag.de.

658 747 USA ISSN 8750-6106
PROGRESSIVE RENTALS✱; the magazine of the home entertainment, appliance, and furniture rental industry. Text in English. 1981. bi-m. USD 30. adv. bk.rev. index. back issues avail. **Document type:** *Trade.* **Description:** Trade magazine for the "rental-purchase" industry.
Formerly: A P R Oach (0736-1874)
Published by: Association of Progressive Rental Organizations, 9015 Mountain Ridge Dr, 220, Austin, TX 78759-7252. TEL 512-794-0095, FAX 512-794-0097, http://www.apro-rto.com. Ed., R&P Julie Sherrier. Adv. contact Cindy Ganther. Circ: 2,862 (paid).

658.404 346 USA ISSN 1071-4324
PROJECT FINANCE MONTHLY. Text in English. 1990. m. USD 245. adv. **Document type:** *Newsletter, Trade.*
Published by: Information Forecast, Inc., 6800 Owensmouth Ave., Ste. 300, Canoga Park, CA 91303-3159. TEL 818-888-4444, FAX 818-888-4440, information@forecast.com, http://www.informationforecast.com. Ed., R&P, Adv. contact Wyanne Chase. Pub. William Meyer. page USD 500. Circ: 1,000 (controlled).

658 USA ISSN 8756-9728
HD69.P75
➤ **PROJECT MANAGEMENT JOURNAL.** Short title: P M J. Text in English. 1970. q. free to members (effective 2004). adv. bk.rev. abstr. index. 64 p./no. 2 cols./p.; back issues avail.; reprints avail. **Document type:** *Journal, Academic/Scholarly.* **Description:** Peer-reviewed professional journal devoted to theory and practice in the field of project management.
Formerly (until 1984): Project Management Quarterly (0147-5363)
Related titles: Online - full text ed.: (from EBSCO Publishing, H.W. Wilson, O C L C Online Computer Library Center, Inc., ProQuest Information & Learning).
Indexed: ABIn, BPI, ESPM, Emerald, PAA&I, RiskAb.
—BLDSC (6924.847810), IE, ingenta. **CCC.**
Published by: Project Management Institute, 4 Campus Blvd, Newtown Square, PA 19073. TEL 610-356-4600, FAX 610-356-4647, pmihq@pmi.org, http://www.pmi.org/info/PIR_PMJournal.asp. Ed. Parviz F Rad. Pub. Linda Cherry TEL 610-355-1623. Adv. contacts Libby Barwis, Richard Barwis. B&W page USD 2,655, color page USD 4,890. Circ: 85,000 (paid).

658 GBR ISSN 1366-6851
PROJECT MANAGER TODAY. Text in English. 1989. 11/yr. GBP 32.50 domestic; GBP 45 in the European Union; GBP 55 elsewhere (effective 2002). software rev. **Description:** Provides case studies, articles, and software reviews for project managers.
Formerly (until 1996): Project Management Today (0957-1353)
Indexed: Emerald, Inspec.
—BLDSC (6924.847843), IE, Infotrieve, ingenta. **CCC.**
Published by: Larchdrift Projects Ltd., 12 Moor Place Farm, Plough Lane, Bramshill, Hook, Hants RG27 0RF, United Kingdom. TEL 44-118-932-6663, FAX 44-118-932-6665, http://www.pmtoday.co.uk. Ed. Ken Lane.

658 DEU ISSN 0942-1017
PROJEKTMANAGEMENT. Text in German. 1990. 4/yr. EUR 15 newsstand/cover (effective 2005). adv. **Document type:** *Trade.*
Published by: (Deutsche Gesellschaft fuer Projektmanagement e.V.), T Ue V Verlag GmbH, Am Grauen Stein 1, Cologne, 51105, Germany. TEL 49-221-8063535, FAX 49-221-8063510, verlag@tuev-rheinland.de, http://www.tuev-rheinland.de. Adv. contact Gudrun Karafiol. B&W page EUR 854, color page EUR 1,439; trim 183 x 250. Circ: 4,800 (controlled).

PROPERTY MANAGEMENT ASSOCIATION. BULLETIN. see *REAL ESTATE*

PROPOZYTSIYA. see *AGRICULTURE*

658 POL ISSN 0137-7221
PRZEGLAD ORGANIZACJI✱. Text in Polish. 1926. m. **Description:** Covers management and organization issues.
Formerly (until 1962): Towarzystwo Naukowe Organizacji i Kierownictwa. Biuletyn
Indexed: AgrLib, RASB.
Published by: Towarzystwo Naukowe Organizacji i Kierownictwa, Ul Koszykowa 6, Bl. C, Warsaw, 00564, Poland. Ed. Marek Dziduszko. Circ: 6,000.

658 SVN ISSN 0351-3564
HD4420.8
PUBLIC ENTERPRISE. Text in English. q.
Indexed: PAIS.
—BLDSC (6963.385000), ingenta.
Published by: International Center for Public Enterprises in Developing Countries, Dunajska 104, P.O. Box 2592, Ljubljana, 1001, Slovenia.

PUBLIC FINANCE AND MANAGEMENT. see *BUSINESS AND ECONOMICS—Public Finance, Taxation*

PUBLIC MANAGEMENT BULLETIN. see *PUBLIC ADMINISTRATION*

658 351 GBR ISSN 1471-9037
JA8
➤ **PUBLIC MANAGEMENT REVIEW**; an international journal of research and theory. Text in English. 1999. q. GBP 317, USD 497 combined subscription to institutions print & online eds. (effective 2006). adv. bk.rev. back issues avail.; reprint service avail. from PSC. **Document type:** *Journal, Academic/Scholarly.* **Description:** Covers the strategic and operational management of public services, and studies the implementation and development of public management in cross-national and regional research papers.
Formerly (until 2001): Public Management (1461-667X)
Related titles: Online - full text ed.: ISSN 1471-9045. GBP 301, USD 472 to institutions (effective 2006) (from EBSCO Publishing, Gale Group, IngentaConnect, Northern Light Technology, Inc., O C L C Online Computer Library Center, Inc., Swets Information Services).
Indexed: ESPM, IBSS, PAIS, PSA, RiskAb.
—BLDSC (6967.717700), IE, Infotrieve, ingenta. **CCC.**
Published by: Routledge (Subsidiary of: Taylor & Francis Group), 4 Park Sq, Milton Park, Abingdon, Oxon OX14 4RN, United Kingdom. TEL 44-1235-828600, FAX 44-1235-829000, info@routledge.co.uk, http://www.tandf.co.uk/journals/titles/14719037.asp, http://www.routledge.co.uk. Ed. Stephen P Osborne. R&P Sally Sweet. **Subscr. to:** Taylor & Francis Ltd, Journals Customer Service, Rankine Rd, Basingstoke, Hants RG24 8PR, United Kingdom. TEL 44-1256-813000, FAX 44-1256-330245, enquiry@tandf.co.uk.

658 USA ISSN 1566-7170
CODEN: PORACC
PUBLIC ORGANIZATION REVIEW; a global journal. Text in English. 2001. q. EUR 324, USD 324, GBP 218 combined subscription to institutions print & online eds. (effective 2005). bk.rev. reprint service avail. from PSC. **Document type:** *Journal, Academic/Scholarly.* **Description:** Seeks to advance knowledge of public organizations around the world and focusing on 'public' broadly defined, to include governmental, non-profit, and non-governmental organizations, and their impacts on human life and society, as well as their influence in shaping human civilization.
Related titles: Online - full text ed.: ISSN 1573-7098 (from EBSCO Publishing, Gale Group, IngentaConnect, Kluwer Online, O C L C Online Computer Library Center, Inc., ProQuest Information & Learning, Springer LINK, Swets Information Services).
Indexed: ABIn, BibLing, IPSA, RefZh.
—BLDSC (6967.852000), IE, Infotrieve, ingenta. **CCC.**
Published by: Springer-Verlag New York, Inc. (Subsidiary of: Springer Science+Business Media), 233 Spring St, New York, NY 10013. TEL 212-460-1500, FAX 212-460-1575, service@springer-ny.com, http://springerlink.metapress.com/openurl.asp?genre=journal&issn=1566-7170, http://www.springer-ny.com. Ed. Ali Farazmand. **Subscr. to:** Journal Fulfillment, PO Box 2485, Secaucus, NJ 07096-2485. TEL 201-348-4033, FAX 201-348-4505, journals@springer-ny.com.

PUBLIC PERFORMANCE AND MANAGEMENT REVIEW. see *PUBLIC ADMINISTRATION*

658.155 USA ISSN 0891-7183
PUBLIC RISK. Text in English. 1986. 10/yr. USD 125. adv. bk.rev. index. back issues avail. **Document type:** *Trade.* **Description:** Provides news and features on public sector risk management topics. Covers association business, pooling issues and legislation.
Published by: Public Risk Management Association, 500 Montgomery St., # 750, Alexandria, VA 22314-1565. TEL 703-528-7701, FAX 703-528-7966. Ed. Lisa Gidley. Circ: 2,200.

PUBLISHER & EXECUTIVE EDITOR. see *JOURNALISM*

658.048 USA
PULSE! (WASHINGTON). Text in English. 1986. irreg. (12-24/yr.). free. bk.rev. **Document type:** *Newsletter, Trade.* **Description:** For nonprofit management and governance support organizations and professionals as well as those interested in nonprofit management issues.
Formerly (until 1997): N M A Bulletin Board
Media: Online - full text. **Related titles:** E-mail ed.
Published by: Alliance for Nonprofit Management, 1899 L St, N W, 6th Fl, Washington, DC 20036. TEL 202-955-8406, FAX 202-822-8419, alliance@allianceonline.org, http://www.allianceonline.org. Ed. Roni Posner. R&P Laura Pruteanu. Circ: 2,500.

PURCHASING MANAGEMENT BULLETIN. see *BUSINESS AND ECONOMICS—Marketing And Purchasing*

658 MMR
PYINNYA LAWKA JOURNAL. Text in Burmese. q.
Published by: Sarpay Beikman Management Board, 529 Merchant St., Botahtaung PO, Yangon, Myanmar. Circ: 18,000.

658 JPN ISSN 0914-5001
Q C CIRCLE. (Quality Control) Text in Japanese. 1962. m. JPY 10,000. charts.
Formerly (until 1988): Quality Control for the Foreman (0914-3831)
Indexed: JTA.
Published by: Union of Japanese Scientists and Engineers/Nihon Kagaku Gijutsu Renmei, 5-10-11 Sendagaya, Shibuya-ku, Tokyo, 151-0051, Japan. TEL 03-5379-1227, FAX 03-3225-1813. Ed. Kohei Suzue. Circ: 182,000.

330 DEU
Q M - QUANTITATIVE METHODEN IN FORSCHUNG UND PRAXIS. Text in German. 2002. irreg., latest vol.7, 2004. price varies. **Document type:** *Monographic series, Academic/Scholarly.*
Published by: Verlag Dr. Kovac, Arnoldstr 49, Hamburg, 22763, Germany. TEL 49-40-3988800, FAX 49-40-39888055, info@verlagdrkovac.de, http://www.verlagdrkovac.de.

658 338 NZL ISSN 0111-4158
Q-NEWZ. Text in English. 1979. m. NZD 137 to members (effective 2001). adv. bk.rev. charts; illus.; stat.; tr.lit. **Document type:** *Newsletter, Corporate.*
Published by: New Zealand Organisation for Quality Inc., P.O. Box 622, Palmerston North, New Zealand. TEL 64-6-3505825, FAX 64-6-3505820, quality@nzoq.org.nz, http://www.nzoq.org.nz. Ed., R&P Joyce Wenmoth. Adv. contact Helen Baines. B&W page NZD 450. Circ: 1,400 (paid).

658 338.642 CHN ISSN 1003-2320
QIYE GUANLI/ENTERPRISE MANAGEMENT. Text in Chinese. 1980. m. USD 34.10 (effective 1995).
Related titles: Online - full text ed.: (from East View Information Services).
Published by: Qiye Guanli Zazhishe, 17 Zizhuyuan Nanlu, Beijing, 100044, China. TEL 86-10-8414646. Ed. Zhu Tao. Circ: 200,000. **Dist. in US by:** China Books & Periodicals Inc, 360 Swift Ave., Ste. 48, S San Fran, CA 94080-6220. TEL 415-282-2994.

QUADERNI DI ECONOMIA DEL LAVORO. see *BUSINESS AND ECONOMICS—Labor And Industrial Relations*

658 DEU ISSN 1617-7754
QUALITAETSMANAGEMENT. Text in German. 2001. irreg., latest vol.8, 2004. price varies. **Document type:** *Monographic series, Academic/Scholarly.*
Published by: Verlag Dr. Kovac, Arnoldstr 49, Hamburg, 22763, Germany. TEL 49-40-3988800, FAX 49-40-39888055, info@verlagdrkovac.de, http://www.verlagdrkovac.de/3-16.htm.

▼ **QUALITATIVE RESEARCH IN ACCOUNTING AND MANAGEMENT.** see *BUSINESS AND ECONOMICS—Accounting*

658 GBR ISSN 1746-5648
▼ ➤ **QUALITATIVE RESEARCH IN ORGANIZATIONS AND MANAGEMENT**; an international journal. Text in English. forthcoming 2006 (May). 3/yr. EUR 303.41 in Europe; USD 359 in North America; AUD 479 in Australasia; GBP 216.41 in the UK & elsewhere (effective 2006). **Document type:** *Journal, Academic/Scholarly.* **Description:** Seeks to provide a forum for qualitative researchers through which they can share their work with others and discuss issues of research practice of particular pertinence to qualitative approaches.
Related titles: Online - full content ed.: forthcoming.
Published by: Emerald Group Publishing Limited, 60-62 Toller Ln, Bradford, W Yorks BD8 9BY, United Kingdom. TEL 44-1274-777700, FAX 44-1274-785200, qrom@emeraldinsight.com, infomation@emeraldinsight.com, http://www.emeraldinsight.com/qrom.htm. Eds. Dr. Catherine Cassell, Dr. Gillian Symon. Pub. Ms. Kate Snowden. R&P Ms. Anne-Marie Thorslund.

➤ **QUALITY ASSURANCE IN EDUCATION.** see *EDUCATION*

658 BEL ISSN 0923-3962
QUALITY LINK. Text in English. 1988. bi-m. free. back issues avail. **Document type:** *Newsletter.* **Description:** Covers past and future activities of the foundation.
Published by: European Foundation for Quality Management, Av des Pleiades 15, Brussels, 1200, Belgium. TEL 32-2-7753511, FAX 32-2-7753535. Ed. Marion Loveday. Circ: 13,000.

658 USA ISSN 0360-9936
TS156.A1 CODEN: QULTDP
QUALITY MAGAZINE; improving your manufacturing process. Text in English. 1962. m. USD 74 domestic; USD 85 foreign; USD 10 newsstand/cover domestic; USD 15 newsstand/cover foreign; free to qualified personnel (effective 2005). adv. charts; illus.; stat.; tr.lit. index. reprint service avail. from PQC. **Document type:** *Journal, Academic/Scholarly.* **Description:** Targets manufacturing professionals responsible for testing, inspecting, measuring, evaluating and documenting manufacturing processes and finished products.
Former titles: Quality Management and Engineering; Quality Assurance
Related titles: Microform ed.: 1962 (from PQC); Online - full text ed.: (from EBSCO Publishing, Florida Center for Library Automation, Gale Group, H.W. Wilson, Northern Light Technology, Inc., O C L C Online Computer Library Center, Inc., ProQuest Information & Learning); Supplement(s): N D T and Materials Test.
Indexed: ABIn, AIA, AS&TI, BPIA, BrCerAb, C&ISA, CADCAM, CerAb, CorrAb, E&CAJ, EMA, IAA, Inspec, M&TEA, MBF, METADEX, ORMS, QAb, QC&AS, RASB, RoboAb, SolStAb, WAA.
—BLDSC (7168.127000), CISTI, Ei, IE, Infotrieve, ingenta, Linda Hall. **CCC.**
Published by: B N P Media, 2401 W Big Beaver, Ste 700, Troy, MI 48084. williams@bnpmedia.com, http://www.qualitymag.com, http://www.bnpmedia.com/. Eds. Rebecca Hennessy, Thomas A Williams. Circ: 64,000 (paid).

658 USA ISSN 1080-0883
QUALITY MANAGEMENT. Text in English. s-m. USD 167 (effective 1999). index. **Document type:** *Newsletter, Trade.* **Description:** Covers a vast range of quality topics pertaining to quality in manufacturing, including TQM, benchmarking, customer relationships, manufacturing and supplier quality, cycle time reduction, controlling quality costs, and innovative quality techniques and technologies.
Former titles: Quality Assurance Bulletin (1040-0664); (until 1988): Quality Control Supervisor's Bulletin (0199-6223)
Published by: Bureau of Business Practice (Subsidiary of: Aspen Publishers, Inc.), 1185 Avenue of the Americas, 37th Fl, New York, NY 10036. TEL 860-442-4365, 800-243-0876, FAX 860-437-3555, http://www.bbpnews.com. Ed. Peter Hawkins. Pub. Peter Garabedian. R&P Kathryn Mennone.

658 USA ISSN 1097-8704
QUALITY MANAGEMENT ALERT. Abbreviated title: Q M A. Text in English. 1998. s-m. USD 299. charts; illus. **Document type:** *Newsletter.* **Description:** Keeps quality managers current by providing them with ISO quality standards updates.
Published by: Progressive Business Publications, 370 Technology Dr, Malvern, PA 19355-1315. TEL 610-695-8600, 800-220-5000, FAX 610-647-8089, editor@pbp.com, http://www.pbp.com. Ed. Jim McCanney. R&P Curt Brown. Circ: 2,500 (paid).

658 USA ISSN 1068-6967
HD62.15
QUALITY MANAGEMENT JOURNAL. Text in English. 1993. q. USD 50 domestic to members; USD 80 in Canada to members; USD 74 foreign to members; USD 75 domestic to non-members; USD 90 in Canada to non-members; USD 90 foreign to non-members; USD 130 domestic to institutions; USD 160 in Canada to institutions; USD 150 foreign to institutions. adv. illus. reprints avail. **Document type:** *Journal, Academic/Scholarly.*
Related titles: Online - full text ed.: (from O C L C Online Computer Library Center, Inc., ProQuest Information & Learning).
Indexed: ABIn, Emerald, Inspec.
—BLDSC (7168.152630), IE, Infotrieve, ingenta. **CCC.**
Published by: American Society for Quality Control, 600 N Plankinton Ave, Milwaukee, WI 53203-2914. TEL 414-272-8575, FAX 414-272-1734, http://www.asq.org/pub/qmj/. Ed. Barbara Flynn. Circ: 14,000.

658 USA ISSN 0033-524X
TS156.A1 CODEN: QUPRB3
QUALITY PROGRESS. Text in English. 1944. m. USD 80 domestic to non-members; USD 110 foreign to non-members; USD 50 domestic to members; USD 90 foreign to members (effective 2005). adv. bk.rev. bibl.; charts; illus. index. reprint service avail. from PQC. **Document type:** *Journal, Trade.* **Description:** Contains articles of a semi-technical nature discussing techniques and philosophies pertaining to quality control/quality assurance in manufacturing and service industries.
Supersedes in part (in 1968): Industrial Quality Control (0884-822X)
Related titles: Microform ed.: (from PQC); Online - full text ed.: (from H.W. Wilson, O C L C Online Computer Library Center, Inc., ProQuest Information & Learning).
Indexed: ABIn, AS&TI, ASCA, B&BAb, BPIA, C&ISA, CIS, CurCont, E&CAJ, Emerald, EngInd, ExcerpMed, GALA, ISMEC, Inspec, ORMS, QAb, QC&AS, RASB, SSCI, SolStAb, TTI.
—BLDSC (7168.153000), CISTI, Ei, IDS, IE, Infotrieve, ingenta, Linda Hall. **CCC.**
Published by: American Society for Quality Control, 600 N Plankinton Ave, Milwaukee, WI 53203-2914. TEL 414-272-8575, FAX 414-272-1734, ddonaldson@asq.com, cs@asq.org, http://qualityprogress.asq.org, http://www.asq.org. Ed. Debbie Donaldson. Pub. William Tony. R&P Paul Omera. Adv. contacts Christian Dreyer, Kathy Arnold, Phil Edmunds. Circ: 133,000 (paid and controlled).

658 USA ISSN 1058-0417
QUALITY QUIPS NEWSLETTER. Text in English. 1991. q. USD 30 (effective 2000). adv. bk.rev. back issues avail. **Document type:** *Newsletter.* **Description:** Provides information, instruction, examples of quality performance, and improvement to the business world.
Published by: Q P Publishing, PO Box 237, Finleyville, PA 15332-0237. TEL 724-348-8949, swoggerdl@usaor.net. Ed., Pub., Adv. contact Nancy Sue Swoger. Circ: 5,000.

B

658 USA ISSN 1060-1821
QUALITY SYSTEMS UPDATE. Text in English. 1991. m. USD 375 (effective 2005). **Document type:** *Journal, Trade.* **Description:** Contains information on all the latest ISO 9000 and QS-9000 breaking news.
Published by: Q S U Publishing Company, 3975 University Dr, Ste 230, Fairfax, VA 22030. TEL 703-359-8460, FAX 703-359-8462, news@qsuonline.com, http://www.qsuonline.com. Ed. Suzanne Leonard. Pub. Paul Scicchitano.

658 CHN ISSN 1002-7106
QUANLI KEXUE WENZHAI/DIGEST OF MANGEMENT SCIENCE. Text in Chinese. m. CNY 7.80 domestic (effective 2000). **Document type:** *Academic/Scholarly.*
Related titles: Online - full content ed.: (from WanFang Data Corp.); Online - full text ed.: (from East View Information Services).
Published by: Zhongguo Kexue Jishu Xinsi Yanjiusuo, 15 Beijing Fu-xing Lu, Beijing, 10038, China. TEL 86-1-68515544 ext 2960, FAX 86-1-68537104, zhougz@istic.ac.cn.

658 GBR ISSN 0033-6807
T175.5 CODEN: RDMAAW
➤ **R & D MANAGEMENT.** Text in English. 1970. 5/yr. EUR 132 combined subscription in Europe to individuals print & online eds.; USD 148 combined subscription in the Americas to individuals & Caribbean, print & online eds.; GBP 88 combined subscription elsewhere to individuals print & online eds.; GBP 615 combined subscription in Europe to institutions print & online eds.; USD 1,255 combined subscription in the Americas to institutions & Caribbean, print & online eds.; GBP 747 combined subscription elsewhere to institutions print & online eds. (effective 2006). adv. bk.rev. illus. reprints avail. **Document type:** *Journal, Academic/Scholarly.* **Description:** Aims to improve the efficiency of research and development management by providing a forum for applying theoretical aspects to the practical needs of industry and government.
Related titles: Online - full text ed.: ISSN 1467-9310. GBP 584 in Europe to institutions; USD 1,193 in the Americas to institutions & Caribbean; GBP 710 elsewhere to institutions (effective 2006) (from Blackwell Synergy, EBSCO Publishing, Gale Group, IngentaConnect, O C L C Online Computer Library Center, Inc., Swets Information Services).
Indexed: ABIn, ADPA, ASCA, BMT, BPI, BPIA, BrCerAb, BrRB, BusI, CLOSS, CPM, CurCont, ERA, Emerald, EngInd, HECAB, IAOP, IBR, IBZ, Inspec, M&MA, ORMS, PAIS, PCI, QC&AS, RASB, RefZh, SCIMP, SSCI, T&II, TEA, WTA.
—BLDSC (7218.400000), AskIEEE, CINDOC, CISTI, Ei, IDS, IE, Infotrieve, ingenta, Linda Hall. **CCC.**
Published by: Blackwell Publishing Ltd., 9600 Garsington Rd, Oxford, OX4 2ZG, United Kingdom. TEL 44-1865-776868, FAX 44-1865-714591, customerservices@oxon.blackwellpublishing.com, http://www.blackwellpublishing.com/journals/RADM. Eds. Alan W Pearson TEL 44-1612-756338, Jeff Butler. Circ: 1,150.

➤ **R E M: THE REAL ESTATE MAGAZINE.** see *REAL ESTATE*

658 DEU ISSN 1619-7372
HD28 CODEN: RTNLBD
R K W - MAGAZIN. Text in German. 1983. q. adv. bk.rev. illus.; pat. index. reprints avail. **Document type:** *Magazine, Trade.*
Former titles (until 2002): W & P - Wirtschaft und Produktivitaet (1438-7670); (until 1999): Wirtschaft & Produktivitaet (0724-3057); Which was formed by the merger of (19??-1983): R K W Kurznachrichten (0481-5106); (1950-1983): Rationalisierung (0034-0057)
Indexed: ABIn, ExcerpMed, PAIS.
—CCC.
Published by: R K W - Rationalisierungs- und Innovationszentrum der Deutschen Wirtschaft e.V., Duesseldorfer Str 40, Eschborn, 65760, Germany. TEL 49-6196-4952810, FAX 49-6196-4954801, rkw@rkw.de, http://www.rkw.de. Circ: 13,000.

658 DEU
RADAR FUER TRENDS. Text in German. 1983. s-m. USD 336. back issues avail. **Document type:** *Newsletter.*
Published by: (Institut fuer Trend-Forschung), Muditax GmbH, Postfach 1230, Worpswede, 27723, Germany. TEL 04792-2656, FAX 04792-2686. Ed. Gerd Gerken. Circ: 1,500.

RADIO ONLY MAGAZINE; the monthly management tool. see *COMMUNICATIONS—Radio*

658.45 USA ISSN 0197-6060
RAGAN REPORT; a weekly survey of ideas and methods for communication executives. Text in English. 1970. w. USD 287 (effective 2004). bk.rev. **Document type:** *Newsletter, Trade.*
Published by: Lawrence Ragan Communications, Inc., 316 N Michigan Ave, Ste 300, Chicago, IL 60601. TEL 312-960-4140, 800-878-5331, FAX 312-960-4106, cservice@ragan.com, http://www.ragan.com. Ed. David Murray. Circ: 3,000.

RANGE MANAGEMENT NEWSLETTER. see *AGRICULTURE*

RASSEGNA ITALIANA DI VALUTAZIONE. see *SOCIAL SCIENCES: COMPREHENSIVE WORKS*

REALITES INDUSTRIELLES. see *MINES AND MINING INDUSTRY*

REASON IN PRACTICE; the journal of philosophy of management. see *PHILOSOPHY*

658 GBR ISSN 0956-5698
HF5735 CODEN: RMJOFP
➤ **RECORDS MANAGEMENT JOURNAL.** Text in English. 3/yr. EUR 357.79 in Europe; USD 309 in North America; AUD 609 in Australasia; GBP 249.04 in UK & elsewhere (effective 2006). bk.rev. **Document type:** *Journal, Academic/Scholarly.* **Description:** Reports research and best practice in records, information and archives management. Publishes research results, case studies and critical comment of value to records professionals, educators and students.
Related titles: Online - full text ed.: (from EBSCO Publishing, Emerald Group Publishing Limited, Gale Group, IngentaConnect, O C L C Online Computer Library Center, Inc., ProQuest Information & Learning, Swets Information Services).
Indexed: ABIn, CompLI, InfoSAb, Inspec, LISA.
—BLDSC (7325.792500), AskIEEE, IE, Infotrieve, ingenta.
Published by: Emerald Group Publishing Limited, 60-62 Toller Ln, Bradford, W Yorks BD8 9BY, United Kingdom. TEL 44-1274-777700, FAX 44-1274-785200, editorial@emeraldinsight.com, infomation@emeraldinsight.com, http://www.emeraldinsight.com/rmj.htm. Eds. Mrs. Catherine Hare, Dr. Julie McLeod. R&P Mr. James Bender. **Dist. in N America:** Emerald Group Publishing Ltd., 44 Brattle St, 4th Fl, Cambridge, MA 02138. TEL 617-497-2175, 888-622-0075, FAX 617-354-6875.

➤ **RECYCLAGE RECUPERATION.** see *ENVIRONMENTAL STUDIES—Waste Management*

➤ **REFERATIVNYI ZHURNAL. EKONOMICHESKIE ASPEKTY ORGANIZATSII I TEKHNIKI SISTEM UPRAVLENIYA.** see *BUSINESS AND ECONOMICS—Abstracting, Bibliographies, Statistics*

➤ **REFERATIVNYI ZHURNAL. ORGANIZATSIYA UPRAVLENIYA.** see *BUSINESS AND ECONOMICS—Abstracting, Bibliographies, Statistics*

658 USA ISSN 1524-1734
HD58.82
➤ **REFLECTIONS**; the SoL journal on knowledge, learning and change. Text in English. 1999. 4/yr. USD 55 combined subscription in US & Canada to individuals print & online eds.; USD 75 combined subscription elsewhere to individuals print & online eds.; USD 175 combined subscription in US & Canada to non-profit organizations print & online eds.; USD 195 combined subscription elsewhere to non-profit organizations print & online eds.; USD 275 combined subscription in US & Canada to corporations print & online eds.; USD 295 combined subscription elsewhere to corporations print & online eds.; USD 15 newsstand/cover (effective 2003). back issues avail. **Document type:** *Journal, Academic/Scholarly.* **Description:** Provides a unique forum where three key constituencies - researchers, consultants, and managerial practitioners - can learn together how knowledge and skills are generated, disseminated and utilized.
Related titles: ◆ Online - full text ed.: Reflections Online. ISSN 1536-0148.
—BLDSC (7332.330920), IE, Infotrieve, ingenta. **CCC.**
Published by: Society for Organizational Learning, 25 1st St., Ste. 414, Cambridge, MA 02141-1826. jane@solonline.org, info@solonline.org, http://mitpress.mit.edu/reflections, http://www.solonline.org.

658 USA ISSN 1536-0148
REFLECTIONS ONLINE. Text in English. 4/yr. USD 44 to individuals; USD 220 to institutions; USD 140 to non-profit organizations (effective 2003). **Document type:** *Academic/Scholarly.*
Media: Online - full text (from EBSCO Publishing, Gale Group, IngentaConnect, O C L C Online Computer Library Center, Inc., Swets Information Services). **Related titles:** ◆ Print ed.: Reflections. ISSN 1524-1734.
Published by: Society for Organizational Learning, 25 1st St., Ste. 414, Cambridge, MA 02141-1826. jane@solonline.org, info@solonline.org, http://mitpress.mit.edu/reflections, http://www.solonline.org.

658 USA
REGIONAL REPORT ON MIDDLE MANAGEMENT COMPENSATION. Text in English. a. USD 690. charts. **Document type:** *Trade.* **Description:** Analyzes the geographic influences affecting middle management pay.
Related titles: ◆ Supplement(s): Middle Management Compensation - Regression Analysis Report.
Published by: (Executive Compensation Service (ECS)), Wyatt Data Services, 218 Rte 17 N, Rochelle Park, NJ 07622-9832. TEL 201-843-1177, FAX 201-843-0101.

REGISTRY NEWS. see *SPORTS AND GAMES—Horses And Horsemanship*

RELIGIOUS CONFERENCE MANAGER. see *RELIGIONS AND THEOLOGY*

REMUNERATION REPORT - AUSTRIA. see *BUSINESS AND ECONOMICS—Personnel Management*

REMUNERATION REPORT - BELGIUM. see *BUSINESS AND ECONOMICS—Personnel Management*

REMUNERATION REPORT - DENMARK. see *BUSINESS AND ECONOMICS—Personnel Management*

REMUNERATION REPORT - FINLAND. see *BUSINESS AND ECONOMICS—Personnel Management*

REMUNERATION REPORT - FRANCE. see *BUSINESS AND ECONOMICS—Personnel Management*

REMUNERATION REPORT - GERMANY. see *BUSINESS AND ECONOMICS—Personnel Management*

REMUNERATION REPORT - GREECE. see *BUSINESS AND ECONOMICS—Personnel Management*

REMUNERATION REPORT - IRELAND. see *BUSINESS AND ECONOMICS—Personnel Management*

REMUNERATION REPORT - ITALY. see *BUSINESS AND ECONOMICS—Personnel Management*

REMUNERATION REPORT - LUXEMBOURG. see *BUSINESS AND ECONOMICS—Personnel Management*

REMUNERATION REPORT - NETHERLANDS. see *BUSINESS AND ECONOMICS—Personnel Management*

REMUNERATION REPORT - NORWAY. see *BUSINESS AND ECONOMICS—Personnel Management*

REMUNERATION REPORT - PORTUGAL. see *BUSINESS AND ECONOMICS—Personnel Management*

REMUNERATION REPORT - SPAIN. see *BUSINESS AND ECONOMICS—Personnel Management*

REMUNERATION REPORT - SWEDEN. see *BUSINESS AND ECONOMICS—Personnel Management*

REMUNERATION REPORT - SWITZERLAND. see *BUSINESS AND ECONOMICS—Personnel Management*

REMUNERATION REPORT - TURKEY. see *BUSINESS AND ECONOMICS—Personnel Management*

REMUNERATION REPORT - UNITED KINGDOM. see *BUSINESS AND ECONOMICS—Personnel Management*

658 NLD ISSN 0926-3314
RENDEMENT; tijdschrift voor winstverbetering. Text in Dutch. 1991. 10/yr. EUR 149; EUR 17 newsstand/cover (effective 2005). adv. **Document type:** *Trade.* **Description:** For senior managers, directors, financial executives and others with corporate financial responsibilities.
—IE, Infotrieve.
Published by: Rendement Uitgeverij BV, Postbus 27020, Rotterdam, 3003 LA, Netherlands. TEL 31-10-2433933, FAX 31-10-2439028, redactie@rendement.nl, http://www.rendement.nl/. Ed. Jacqueline Groebbe. Pub. Luc Muijser. Adv. contact Johan de Vassy. Circ: 10,500.

628 614 DNK ISSN 0906-270X
RENT I DANMARK. Text in Danish. 1974. 8/yr. DKK 236. adv. bk.rev.
Formerly: Renhold Vedligehold (0900-856X)
Published by: Forlaget Thorsgaard ApS, Holmensvej 5, PO Box 5, Frederikssund, 3600, Denmark. TEL 42-31-21-05, FAX 47-38-36-33, post@thorsgaard.dk. Ed. Kim Thorsgaard. Pub. Forlaget Thorsgaard. Adv. contact Erik Hvalsoe. B&W page DKK 13,450, color page DKK 16,450; trim 297 x 210. Circ: 6,350 (controlled).

658 338.642 USA ISSN 0272-7323
REP TALK✶. Text in English. 1978. m. USD 117. **Description:** Features business management for the independent representative.
Published by: Berman Publications, 11718 Barrington Ct, Ste 341, Los Angeles, CA 90049-2930. TEL 408-246-4582. Ed. Norma Zonay. Circ: 300.

658 USA ISSN 1066-8063
HD4965.5.C3
REPORT ON CANADIAN EXECUTIVE AND MIDDLE MANAGEMENT REMUNERATION. Text in English. a. USD 930. **Document type:** *Trade.*
Formerly: Report on Canadian Executive Remuneration (1050-0766)
Published by: (Executive Compensation Service (ECS)), Wyatt Data Services, 218 Rte 17 N, Rochelle Park, NJ 07622-9832. TEL 201-843-1177, FAX 201-843-0101.

REPORT ON EXECUTIVE REMUNERATION. see *BUSINESS AND ECONOMICS—Personnel Management*

REPORT ON HUMAN RESOURCES COMPENSATION. see *BUSINESS AND ECONOMICS—Personnel Management*

REPORT ON OFFICE PERSONNEL REMUNERATION. see *BUSINESS AND ECONOMICS—Personnel Management*

658 301 GBR ISSN 1529-2096
RESEARCH IN ETHICAL ISSUES IN ORGANIZATIONS. Text in English. 1999. a., latest 2003. price varies. **Document type:** *Monographic series, Academic/Scholarly.* **Description:** Explores the central and unique role of organizational ethics in creating and sustaining a flourishing, pluralistic, free enterprise economy.
Related titles: Online - full text ed.: (from ScienceDirect).
—BLDSC (7739.905000).
Published by: J A I Press Ltd. (Subsidiary of: Elsevier Science & Technology), The Boulevard, Langford Ln, Kidlington, Oxford, OX5 1GB, United Kingdom. TEL 44-1865-843000, FAX 44-1865-843010, http://www.sciencedirect.com/science/bookseries/15292096. Ed. M L Pava.

658 USA ISSN 1064-4857
HD62.4
RESEARCH IN GLOBAL STRATEGIC MANAGEMENT. Text in English. 1990. a., latest vol.10, 2004. price varies. back issues avail. **Document type:** *Monographic series, Academic/Scholarly.*
Related titles: Online - full text ed.: (from ScienceDirect).
—BLDSC (7741.143000). **CCC.**
Published by: J A I Press Inc. (Subsidiary of: Elsevier Science & Technology), 360 Park Ave S, New York, NY 10010-1710. TEL 212-989-5800, FAX 212-633-3990, usinfo-f@elsevier.com, http://www.elsevier.com/wps/find/bookdescription.cws_home/BS_RGSM/description#description. Ed. A Rugman.

658.406 USA ISSN 0897-3016
RESEARCH IN ORGANIZATIONAL CHANGE AND DEVELOPMENT. Text in English. 1987. a., latest vol.15, 2005. price varies. back issues avail. **Document type:** *Monographic series, Academic/Scholarly.* **Description:** Addresses managing emotional issues raised during change, measuring the impact of change, improving the methods used to conduct research on organizational change, and increasing intervention effectiveness.
Related titles: Online - full text ed.: (from ScienceDirect).
—BLDSC (7750.605000), IE. **CCC.**
Published by: J A I Press Inc. (Subsidiary of: Elsevier Science & Technology), 360 Park Ave S, New York, NY 10010-1710. TEL 212-989-5800, FAX 212-633-3990, usinfo-f@elsevier.com, http://www.elsevier.com/wps/find/bookdescription.cws_home/704753/description#description. Eds. R W Woodman, W A Pasmore.

658 USA ISSN 1082-0396
RESEARCH IN STRATEGIC MANAGEMENT AND INFORMATION TECHNOLOGY. Text in English. 1994. a., latest vol.2, 1999. price varies. **Document type:** *Monographic series, Academic/Scholarly.*
—**CCC.**
Published by: J A I Press Inc. (Subsidiary of: Elsevier Science & Technology), 360 Park Ave S, New York, NY 10010-1710. TEL 212-989-5800, FAX 212-633-3990, usinfo-f@elsevier.com, http://www.elsevier.com/wps/find/bookdescription.cws_home/BS_RSMIT/description#description. Eds. J C Henderson, N Venkatraman.

658 USA ISSN 0279-8050
HC101
RESEARCH INSTITUTE REPORT. Text in English. w. **Document type:** *Trade.*
—**CCC.**
Published by: R I A (Subsidiary of: Thomson Corporation), 395 Hudson St, New York, NY 10014. TEL 212-367-6300, RIA.CustomerServices@Thomson.com, http://ria.thomson.com/.

658 USA ISSN 1068-4867
RESEARCH MANAGEMENT REVIEW. Text in English. 1987. s-a. free (effective 2005). **Document type:** *Journal, Academic/Scholarly.*
Media: Online - full content.
Indexed: CIJE.
Published by: National Council of University Research Administrators, 1 Dupont Cir, N W, Ste 220, Washington, DC 20036. TEL 202-466-3894, FAX 202-223-5573, http://www.ncura.edu/rmr. Ed. William Sharp.

658 USA ISSN 1040-9556
HD42
RESEARCH ON NEGOTIATION IN ORGANIZATIONS. Text in English. 1986. irreg., latest vol.7, 1999. price varies. back issues avail. **Document type:** *Monographic series, Academic/Scholarly.*
—BLDSC (7743.708000), IE. **CCC.**
Published by: J A I Press Inc. (Subsidiary of: Elsevier Science & Technology), 360 Park Ave S, New York, NY 10010-1710. TEL 212-989-5800, FAX 212-633-3990, usinfo-f@elsevier.com, http://www.elsevier.com/wps/find/bookdescription.cws_home/BS_RNO/description#description. Ed. R J Lewicki.

658 GBR
➤ **RESEARCH PAPERS IN MANAGEMENT STUDIES.** Text in English. 1987. irreg., latest vol.21, 2002. price varies. abstr.; bibl.; charts; illus. back issues avail. **Document type:** *Monographic series, Academic/Scholarly.*
Related titles: Online - full text ed.
—ingenta.
Published by: University of Cambridge, Judge Institute of Management Studies, Trumpington St, Cambridge, Cambs CB2 1AG, United Kingdom. TEL 44-1223-339700, FAX 44-1223-339701, research-support@jims.cam.ac.uk, http://www.jims.cam.ac.uk. Ed. G Meeks.

➤ **RESEARCH POLICY.** see *SCIENCES: COMPREHENSIVE WORKS*

658 USA ISSN 0895-6308
T175.5 CODEN: RTMAEC
➤ **RESEARCH TECHNOLOGY MANAGEMENT;** international journal of research management. Text in English. 1958. bi-m. USD 95 in North America to individuals; USD 190 in North America to institutions (effective 2005). bk.rev. charts; illus. index. 64 p./no.; back issues avail.; reprints avail. **Document type:** *Journal, Academic/Scholarly.* **Description:** Covers the management and administration of industrial research, technological innovation, development, science and engineering.
Formerly: Research Management (0034-5334)
Related titles: Microfilm ed.: (from PQC); Online - full text ed.: (from bigchalk, EBSCO Publishing, Florida Center for Library Automation, Gale Group, H.W. Wilson, IngentaConnect, O C L C Online Computer Library Center, Inc., ProQuest Information & Learning).
Indexed: ABIPC, ABIn, ABS&EES, ADPA, ASCA, ASEANManA, ASFA, BPI, BPIA, BusI, CADCAM, CMCI, CPM, CurCont, EIA, ESPM, Emerald, EngInd, EnvAb, H&SSA, HECAB, IUSGP, KES, M&MA, ORMS, PAIS, PROMT, RASB, RiskAb, SCIMP, SSCI, TelAb, WRCInf, WorkRelAb.
—BLDSC (7773.714500), CASDDS, CISTI, Ei, IDS, IE, Infotrieve, ingenta, Linda Hall. **CCC.**
Published by: Industrial Research Institute, 2200 Clarendon Blvd, Arlington, VA 22201. TEL 703-647-2580, FAX 703-647-2581, http://www.iriinc.org/webiri/rtm.cfm. Ed. Michael F Wolff. Pub. C F Larson. R&P Lodita Vallarta. Circ: 3,000 (paid). **Subscr. to:** Sheridan Press.

658 IND
RESEARCHES IN MANAGEMENT IN ASIA SERIES. Text in English. 1997. irreg. price varies. **Document type:** *Monographic series, Academic/Scholarly.*
Indexed: S&F.
Published by: Hindustan Publishing Corporation (India), 4805-24, Bharat Ram Rd., 1st Fl., Flats 1 & 2, Darya Ganj, New Delhi, 110 002, India. TEL 91-11-325-4401, FAX 91-11-6193511, hpcpd@nda.vsnl.net.in, hpcpd@hpc.cc, http://www.bizdelhi.com/publisher/hpc, http://www.hpc.cc.

RESISTANT PEST MANAGEMENT. see *AGRICULTURE*

RESOURCE MANAGEMENT. see *MILITARY*

658 FRA ISSN 1282-7959
RESUMES. Text in French. 1997. m. EUR 256.70 domestic; EUR 271.70 foreign (effective 2005).
Published by: Groupe Express-Expansion (Subsidiary of: Socpresse), 17 rue de l'Arrivee, Paris Cede, 75733, France. TEL 33-1-53911111, http://www.lexpansion.com, http://www.groupe-expansion.com.

RETAIL BANKER INTERNATIONAL. see *BUSINESS AND ECONOMICS—Banking And Finance*

658 USA
RETAIL OPPORTUNITY LETTER. Text in English. 1975. m. USD 77. back issues avail.
Former titles: Productive Management; Executive Management
Published by: Management Facts Co., Inc., 6223 E Lake Dr, Haslett, MI 48840-8737. TEL 517-339-8025. Ed. John Moon.

658.8 USA ISSN 0360-506X
RETAILING TODAY✶. Text in English. 1966. m. USD 70; USD 82 foreign (effective 1999). **Document type:** *Newsletter.* **Description:** For CEO's in retailing. Commentary on current trends, with emphasis on ethical business practices.
Published by: Robert Kahn and Associates, 3684 Happy Valley Rd, Lafayette, CA 94549-3040. TEL 510-254-4434, FAX 510-284-5612, Bobkahn@earthlink.net. Ed., Pub. Robert Kahn. Circ: 1,200.

▼ **REVIEW OF BUSINESS RESEARCH.** see *BUSINESS AND ECONOMICS—International Commerce*

REVIEW OF INDUSTRIAL ORGANIZATION. see *BUSINESS AND ECONOMICS—Economic Systems And Theories, Economic History*

REVIEW OF THE ELECTRONIC AND INDUSTRIAL DISTRIBUTION INDUSTRIES. see *ELECTRONICS*

REVIEW OF URBAN & REGIONAL DEVELOPMENT STUDIES. see *BUSINESS AND ECONOMICS—International Development And Assistance*

658.8 ARG ISSN 1514-9358
REVISTA CIENTIFICA DE UCES. (Revista Cientifica de Universidad de Ciencias Empresariales y Sociales) Text in Spanish. 1997. q. back issues avail.
Related titles: Online - full text ed.
Published by: Universidad de Ciencias Empresariales y Sociales, Departamento de Investigacion, Paraguay, 1401 9o. Piso, Buenos Aires, 1061, Argentina. TEL 54-114-8130228, informes@uces.edu.ar, http://www.uces.edu.ar/publicaciones3.htm.

658 BRA ISSN 0080-2107
JA5
➤ **REVISTA DE ADMINISTRACAO.** Abbreviated title: R A U S P. Variant title: Universidade de Sao Paulo. Revista de Administracao. Text and summaries in Portuguese, English, Spanish. 1977. q. BRL 50 domestic; USD 60 foreign (effective 2002). adv. bk.rev.; Website rev. bibl.; illus.; abstr. cum. index. back issues avail. **Document type:** *Journal, Academic/Scholarly.* **Description:** Publishes original articles and research papers in the field of business administration and related topics.
Related titles: CD-ROM ed.
Indexed: PAIS.
Published by: Universidade de Sao Paulo, Instituto de Administracao, Pinheiros, Caixa Postal 11498, Sao Paulo, SP 05422-970, Brazil. TEL 55-11-818-5922, FAX 55-11-8145500, TELEX 11-838299, rausp@edu.usp.br, http://www.rausp.usp.br, http://www.usp.br/fea/adm/rausp. Ed. Decio Zylbersztajn. Pub. Roberto Fava Scare. R&P Sonia Maria Eira-Velha. Adv. contact Alexandre Bourroul. page USD 2,000; trim 210 x 280. Circ: 3,000 (paid); 500 (free).

658 BRA ISSN 0034-7590
HD28
REVISTA DE ADMINISTRACAO DE EMPRESAS/BUSINESS ADMINISTRATION JOURNAL. Text in Portuguese. 1961. q. USD 100 foreign (effective 2001). adv. bk.rev. bibl. Index. **Document type:** *Academic/Scholarly.* **Description:** Provides original articles by both Brazilian and foreign authors, including notes, commentaries and information on topics of interest to the administrator. Covers practical administrative aspects as well as research linked to administration.
Indexed: HAPI, JEL, PAIS, RASB.
Published by: (Fundacao Getulio Vargas), Escola de Administracao de Empresas de Sao Paulo, Centro de Pesquisas e Publicacoes, Av. 9 de Julho, 2029, Sao Paulo, 01313-902, Brazil. TEL 55-11-2817779, FAX 55-11-281-7871, rae@fgvsp.br, http://www.fgvsp.br/rae. Ed. Thomaz Wood Jr. Adv. contact Else Flejlau. Circ: 17,000.

658 651 BRA ISSN 1518-6776
HD28
➤ **REVISTA DE ADMINISTRACAO MACKENZIE.** Text in Portuguese; Abstracts in English. 2000. s-a. free (effective 2005). **Document type:** *Journal, Academic/Scholarly.*
Indexed: IBSS.
Published by: Universidade Presbiteriana Mackenzie (Subsidiary of: Instituto Presbiteriano Mackenzie), Rua da Consolacao 896, Pr.2, Sao Paulo-SP, SP 01302-907, Brazil. FAX 55-11-32368302, 55-11-32142582, mazilber@mackenzie.com.br, biblio.per@mackenzie.br, http://www.mackenzie.com.br. Ed., R&P Moises Ari Zilber.

➤ **REVISTA DE GESTION PUBLICA Y PRIVADA.** see *PUBLIC ADMINISTRATION*

658 351 COL
REVISTA GESTION. Variant title: Gestion. Text in Spanish. s-a. **Document type:** *Journal, Academic/Scholarly.* **Description:** Examines issues in management in the private sector and public administration.
Published by: Universidad del Norte, Division de Ciencias Juridicas, Apdo Aereo 1569, Barranquilla, Colombia. http://www.uninorte.edu.co/publicacion/ediciones/public.htm.

658 BRA ISSN 0104-088X
TS156.A1
REVISTA INDICADORES DA QUALIDADE E PRODUTIVIDADE. Text in Portuguese. 1993. s-a.
Published by: Instituto de Pesquisa Economica Aplicada, Av Presidente Antonio Carlos, 51 Andar 13, Centro, Rio De Janeiro, RJ 20020-010, Brazil. TEL 021-2121117, FAX 021-2205533, editrj@ipea.gov.br, http://www.ipea.gov.br.

658 PRT
REVISTA PORTUGUESA E BRASILEIRA DE GESTAO. Text in Portuguese. 1985. q. EUR 20 to individuals; EUR 30 to institutions; EUR 15 to students (effective 2002). **Document type:** *Journal, Academic/Scholarly.*
Formerly (until 2002): Revista Portuguesa de Gestao
Related titles: Online - full text ed.
Published by: I N D E G - I S C T E, Av. Prof. Anibal de Bettencourt, Lisbon, 1600-189, Portugal. TEL 351-21-7826100, FAX 351-21-7938709, http://www.indeg.org/rpbg/index.html. Ed. Jorge Nascimento Rodrigues.

B

▼ new title ➤ refereed ✶ unverified ♦ full entry avail.

658 COL ISSN 0120-341X
HD28
REVISTA UNIVERSIDAD E A F I T. Text in Spanish. 1965. q. COP 40,000 domestic to individuals; USD 30 foreign to individuals; COP 20,000 domestic to students (effective 2000). adv. bk.rev. bibl.; charts; illus.; stat. index, cum.index. **Document type:** *Academic/Scholarly.*
Former titles: Revista E A F I T - Temas Administrativos (0120-033X); Temas Administrativos (0040-2877)
Indexed: IBR, IBSS, INIS AtomInd.
Published by: (Escuela de Administracion y Finanzas y Tecnologias), Editorial E A F I T, Apartado Aereo 3300, Medellin, ANT, Colombia. TEL 57-4-2660500, FAX 57-4-2664284, anrestre@sigma.eafit.edu.co, http://www.eafit.edu.co/revista/index.html. Ed. Felix Londono. Circ: 2,000.

658 VEN ISSN 1315-9984
HC236
➤ **REVISTA VENEZOLANA DE GERENCIA.** Text in Spanish. 1996. s-a. **Document type:** *Academic/Scholarly.* **Description:** Covers all aspects of management.
Indexed: GEOBASE, PSA, SociolAb.
Published by: Universidad del Zulia, Vicerrectorado Academico, Division de Estudio para Graduados, Facultad de Ciencias Economicas y Sociales, Primer piso, cubiculo 11, Apartado Postal 15401, Maracaibo, Estado Zulia, Venezuela. TEL 58-61-528397, FAX 58-61-528397, revista_venezolana_gerencia@luz.ve, http://www.luz.ve/vice_academico/rvg.html. Ed. Haydee Ochoa Henriquez.

➤ **LA REVUE ADMINISTRATIVE.** see *PUBLIC ADMINISTRATION*

658 346 FRA ISSN 1156-2935
REVUE DE JURISPRUDENCE DE DROIT DES AFFAIRES. Text in French. 1991. m. EUR 243 combined subscription print & CD ROM eds. (effective 2005). **Document type:** *Magazine, Trade.*
Related titles: CD-ROM ed.
Published by: Editions Francis Lefebvre, 42 rue de Villiers, Levallois-Perret, 92300, France. TEL 33-1-41052222, http://www.efl.fr.

658 FRA ISSN 1160-7742
LA REVUE DES SCIENCES DE GESTION; direction et gestion des entreprises. Text in French. 1965. bi-m. EUR 175 domestic; EUR 197 in Europe; EUR 245 elsewhere (effective 2003). adv. bk.rev. abstr.; bibl.; charts; stat. 100 p./no. 2 cols./p.; reprint service avail. from SCH. **Document type:** *Magazine, Corporate.* **Description:** Offers observations on putting management and business methods into practice. Geared towards managers, executives and directors in the public and private sectors.
Former titles (until 1999): Direction et Gestion (1291-2905); (until 1997): Direction et Gestion des Entreprises (0012-320X)
Related titles: Online - full text ed.: (from ProQuest Information & Learning).
Indexed: ABIn, PAIS, PdeR, RASB, SCIMP.
—BLDSC (3590.295000), IE, ingenta.
Published by: Direction et Gestion S.A.R.L., BP 49, Epinay Sur Orge, 91360, France. TEL 33-1-69099339, FAX 33-1-69093897, lrdsdg@infonie.fr. Ed. Philippe Naszalyi. R&P, Adv. contact Yves Soulabail. B&W page EUR 760, color page EUR 1,500; trim 270 x 210. Circ: 3,500.

658 FRA ISSN 1167-7848
REVUE FIDUCIAIRE - CONSEIL. Key Title: RF Conseil. Text in French. 1990. m. index. back issues avail. **Description:** Covers all the elements of managing a business.
Formerly (until 1992): Fidu-Conseil (1150-1790)
Published by: Groupe Revue Fiduciaire, 100 rue La Fayette, Paris, Cedex 10 75485, France. TEL 33-1-41835252, FAX 33-1-41835253, http://www.grouperf.com. Ed. Laurence Faidherbes.

658 FRA ISSN 1240-4640
REVUE FIDUCIAIRE - PAYE. Key Title: RF Paye. Text in French. m. index. back issues avail. **Description:** Covers the latest news and laws on wages.
Published by: Groupe Revue Fiduciaire, 100 rue La Fayette, Paris, Cedex 10 75485, France. TEL 33-1-41835252, FAX 33-1-41835253, http://www.grouperf.com. Ed. Nicolas Raymond.

658 FRA ISSN 0338-4551
REVUE FRANCAISE DE GESTION. Text in French. 1975. 6/yr. EUR 135 in the European Union; EUR 170 elsewhere (effective 2003). adv. bk.rev. **Description:** Bibliographic guide offering critical analyses of recent publications that give managerial advice as it applies to all industries.
Incorporates (1945-1975): Hommes et Techniques (0018-4381); (1975-1976): Direction (0338-4543); (1986-1987): Formation et Gestion (0765-7587); Which was formerly: Enseignement et Gestion (0765-7579); Supersedes in part (in 1975): Management France (0542-4801); Which was previously (until 1969): C N O F: Comite National de l'Organisation Francaise (0998-5476); (1927-1934): Comite National de l'Organisation Francaise. Bulletin (0998-5484)
Related titles: Online - full text ed.: (from ProQuest Information & Learning).
Indexed: ABIn, CPM, JEL, KES, M&MA, PAIS, RASB, SCIMP.
—BLDSC (7904.160000), IE, Infotrieve, ingenta. **CCC.**
Published by: (Fondation Nationale pour l'Enseignement de la Gestion des Entreprises), Lavoisier, 11 rue Lavoisier, Paris, 75008, France. TEL 33-1-42653995, FAX 33-1-42650246, info@lavoisier.fr, http://www.lavoisier.fr. Ed. Jean-Claude Tarondeau. **Subscr. to:** Lavoisier - Dept Abonnements, 14 rue de Provigny, Cachan 94236, France. TEL 33-1-47406700, FAX 33-1-47406702, abo@lavoisier.fr.

658 FRA ISSN 0242-9780
REVUE FRANCAISE DE GESTION INDUSTRIELLE. Text in French. 1982. q. adv. **Description:** Designed for all those involved in the decision-making of company strategy, service organizations and data processing consultants, as well as teachers. Provides articles on management philosophy, methodology and strategy, including practical case studies and specific problems of special interest.
Indexed: SCIMP.
—BLDSC (7904.165000), IE, ingenta. **CCC.**
Published by: (Association Francaise de Gestion Industrielle), Dunod, 5 rue Laromiguiere, Paris, 75005, France. TEL 33-1-40463500, FAX 33-1-40464995, infos@dunod.com, http://www.dunod.com. Ed. C Montagnon. Circ: 1,300.

658 CAN ISSN 1192-9480
REVUE INTERNATIONALE EN GESTION ET MANAGEMENT DE PROJETS. Text in French. 1993. s-a. **Description:** Contains research from academics and professionals in the field of Project Management. Also includes sharing reflections and experiences in the field.
Published by: Universite du Quebec a Rimouski, 300 allee des Ursulines, Rimouski, PQ G5L 3A1, Canada. rigmp100@hotmail.com.

REWARD MANAGEMENT REWARDS. see *BUSINESS AND ECONOMICS—Labor And Industrial Relations*

658 ITA ISSN 0391-6960
RIFORMA AMMINISTRATIVA. Text in Italian. 1961. m. bk.rev. reprints avail. **Document type:** *Magazine, Trade.*
Published by: Federazione Nazionale Dirigenti Stato, Via Ezio, 12, Rome, RM 00192, Italy. TEL 06-32-11-535. Ed. Dr. Arcangelo D'Ambrosio. Circ: 10,000.

658 690.1 USA
RINKSIDER; independent voice of the industry!. Text in English. 1956. bi-m. USD 20 (effective 1995). adv. 56 p./no. 4 cols./p.; **Document type:** *Newspaper, Trade.* **Description:** Provides rink operators with promotional ideas and legislative, insurance, operational and supplier news.
Published by: Target Publishing Co., Inc. (Columbus), 2470 E Main St, Columbus, OH 43209. TEL 614-235-1022, FAX 614-235-3584. Ed. Susie Young. Pub., Adv. contact Linda Katz. Circ: 3,000 (controlled).

658 USA ISSN 1053-556X
HG9395
RISK & BENEFITS JOURNAL (MARINA DEL REY). Text in English. 1991. bi-m.
Published by: Allied Health Care Publications, 6701 Center Dr W, Ste 450, Los Angeles, CA 90045. TEL 310-642-4400.

658 USA ISSN 1556-1569
▼ **RISK MITIGATION EXECUTIVE.** Text in English. 2005 (May). m. USD 795 (effective 2005). **Document type:** *Newsletter, Trade.* **Description:** Covers such risk mitigation topics as security analysis and planning, risk and crisis management, business continuity planning and due diligence, security litigation and law, employee hiring and HR best practices.
Published by: Cygnus Business Media, Inc., 1233 Janesville Ave, Fort Atkinson, WI 53538-0803. TEL 920-563-1698, 800-547-7377, FAX 920-568-2244.

658.155 GBR
RISK TRANSFER; the global publication for risk professionals. Text and summaries in English. 1995. 10/yr. GBP 195 (effective 2004). adv. **Document type:** *Bulletin, Academic/Scholarly.*
Formerly: Risk Management Bulletin (1363-9498)
Related titles: Online - full content ed.: GBP 145 (effective 2004).
Published by: Ark Group Ltd, 86-88 Upper Richmond Rd, London, SW15 2UR, United Kingdom. TEL 44-20-87852700, FAX 44-20-87859373, info@ark-group.com, http://www.risktransfermagazine.com/, http://www.ark-group.com. Ed. Roger Crombie. Pub. Andreas Silbermann. Adv. contact John Eddington. B&W page GBP 1,450, color page GBP 1,650. Circ: 1,000 (paid); 1,500 (controlled).

362 DEU ISSN 1612-8931
▼ **RISKNEWS**; Das Fachmagazin fuer Risikomanagement. Text in German. 2004. bi-m. EUR 94; EUR 104 combined subscription print & online eds. (effective 2005). adv. **Document type:** *Magazine, Trade.* **Description:** Examines all aspects of risk management, including topics such as methods and instruments for the identification, analysis, evaluation, reduction, financing and control of risks, best practice in various areas of industry and business, experience reports, software solutions, and procedure models.
Related titles: Online - full text ed.: ISSN 1616-0045 (from EBSCO Publishing, Swets Information Services, Wiley InterScience).
—**CCC.**
Published by: Wiley - V C H Verlag GmbH & Co. KGaA (Subsidiary of: John Wiley & Sons, Inc.), Boschstr 12, Weinheim, 69469, Germany. erben@risknews.de, http://www.risktech.de. Ed. Roland Franz Erben. Adv. contact Angela Schimpf. B&W page EUR 1,950; trim 180 x 260. Circ: 3,500 (paid and controlled).

658.155 USA ISSN 0896-2308
RISKWATCH. Text in English. 1985. m. USD 125. **Document type:** *Newsletter.* **Description:** A current events watchdog for public sector risk managers.
Published by: Public Risk Management Association, 500 Montgomery St., # 750, Alexandria, VA 22314-1565. TEL 703-528-7701, FAX 703-528-7966. Ed. Rona Kobell. Circ: 2,500.

658 FRA ISSN 1760-2009
▼ **RISQUES & MANAGEMENT INTERNATIONAL.** Text in French. 2003. s-a. EUR 34 (effective 2004). **Document type:** *Journal, Academic/Scholarly.*
Published by: L' Harmattan, 5 rue de l'Ecole Polytechnique, Paris, 75005, France. TEL 33-1-43257651, FAX 33-1-43258203, http://www.editions-harmattan.fr.

657 DEU ISSN 1437-7802
ROSTOCKER BEITRAEGE ZU CONTROLLING UND RECHNUNGSWESEN. Text in German. 1998. irreg., latest vol.9, 2004. price varies. **Document type:** *Monographic series, Academic/Scholarly.*
Published by: Verlag Dr. Kovac, Arnoldstr 49, Hamburg, 22763, Germany. TEL 49-40-3988800, FAX 49-40-39888055, info@verlagdrkovac.de, http://www.verlagdrkovac.de/3-5.htm.

658 GBR
ROUTLEDGE ADVANCES IN MANAGEMENT AND BUSINESS STUDIES. Text in English. 1997. irreg., latest 2002, Oct. price varies. back issues avail. **Document type:** *Monographic series, Academic/Scholarly.* **Description:** Features leading-edge studies addressing all the major issues in business and management today.
—BLDSC (8026.470000), ingenta.
Published by: Routledge (Subsidiary of: Taylor & Francis Group), 4 Park Square, Milton Park, Abingdon, Oxon OX14 4RN, United Kingdom. TEL 44-1235-828600, FAX 44-1235-829000, info@routledge.co.uk, http://www.reference.routledge.com/research/business/amb.html, http://www.tandf.co.uk.

S A DIRECTORY OF BLACK MANAGERS. see *BUSINESS AND ECONOMICS—Trade And Industrial Directories*

658 ZAF ISSN 1026-6550
THE S A I M A S. Text in English. q. ZAR 140 domestic to non-members; ZAR 250 foreign to non-members (effective 2003). adv. bk.rev. 16 p./no.; back issues avail. **Document type:** *Journal, Corporate.* **Description:** Concerned with the enhancement, practice, and development of management services methodologies and techniques.
Formerly: South African Institute of Organization and Methods. Newsletter
Published by: South African Institute of Management Services/Suidelike Afrika Instituut vir Bestuursdienste, PO Box 693, Pretoria, 0001, South Africa. TEL 27-12-318-5797, FAX 27-12-318-5797, saimas@global.co.za, http://www.global.co.za/~assoc. Ed., Adv. contact Hercules A du Plessis. page ZAR 600. Circ: 1,200.

658 USA ISSN 0749-7075
➤ **S A M ADVANCED MANAGEMENT JOURNAL.** Variant title: Advanced Management Journal. Text in English. 1935. q. USD 54 domestic; USD 69 foreign (effective 2004). adv. bk.rev. charts; illus.; stat.; tr.lit. index. back issues avail.; reprints avail. **Document type:** *Journal, Trade.* **Description:** Features articles by business professionals on business in real world settings.
Former titles (1975-1984): Advanced Management Journal (0362-1863); (1969-1974): S A M Advanced Management Journal (0036-0805)
Related titles: Microform ed.: (from PQC); Online - full text ed.: ISSN 0567-977X (from EBSCO Publishing, Gale Group, H.W. Wilson, O C L C Online Computer Library Center, Inc., ProQuest Information & Learning).
Indexed: ABIn, ADPA, ATI, AgeL, BPI, BPIA, BusI, CPM, DPD, Emerald, M&MA, MEA&I, ManagCont, PMA, PROMT, RASB, SCIMP.
—BLDSC (8071.870000), IDS, IE, Infotrieve, ingenta. **CCC.**
Published by: Society for Advancement of Management, Texas A&M University Corpus Christi, College of Business, 6300 Ocean Dr, FC 111, Corpus Christi, TX 78412. TEL 361-825-6045, FAX 361-825-2725, moustafa@falcon.tamucc.edu, http://www.cob.tamucc.edu/sam/, http://www.enterprise.tamucc.edu/sam. Ed. Moustafa H Abdelsamad. Circ: 5,000.

658 USA
S A M INTERNATIONAL MANAGEMENT CONFERENCE. PROCEEDINGS. Text in English. 1990. a. USD 35; USD 45 foreign. charts; stat. back issues avail. **Document type:** *Proceedings.* **Description:** Disseminates research in critical issues facing business leaders, such as competing in the global marketplace, working in the information age, and managing a diverse staff.

Published by: Society for Advancement of Management, Texas A&M University Corpus Christi, College of Business, 6300 Ocean Dr, FC 111, Corpus Christi, TX 78412. TEL 361-825-6045, FAX 361-825-2725, moustafa@falcon.tamucc.edu, http://www.enterprise.tamucc.edu/sam/. Ed. Moustafa H Abdelsamad.

658.1 USA ISSN 0163-6707
S A V E PROCEEDINGS. Text in English. 1967. a.
—Linda Hall.
Published by: Society of American Value Engineers Inc., 136 S Keowee St, Dayton, OH 45402. TEL 937-224-7283, FAX 937-222-5794, info@value-eng.org, http://www.value-eng.org/catalog_conference.php.

658 USA ISSN 1546-9824
▼ **S C M EXPERT.** (Supply Chain Management) Text in English. 2003 (Sept.). 10/yr. USD 595 (effective 2005). **Document type:** *Newsletter, Trade.*
Related titles: Online - full content ed.
Published by: Wellesley Information Services (Subsidiary of: United Communications Group), 990 Washington St, Dedham, MA 02026-6714. TEL 781-329-0419, FAX 781-320-9466, customer@scmexpertonline.com, customer@eview.com, http://www.SCMexpertOnline.com, http://www.wispubs.com. Eds. Michael Nadeau, Bonnie Penzias.

658.8 IND
S D I NEWS SERVICE. Text in English. 1998. fortn. INR 500, USD 100. **Document type:** *Trade.* **Description:** Covers various topics in business and management.
Published by: National Institute of Small Industry Extension Training, Yousufguda, Hyderabad, Andhra Pradesh 500 045, India. TEL 91-40-238544, FAX 91-40-238547. Ed. Mary H Powell.

S M E - I T GUIDE; information technology for a successful business. (Small and Medium-Sized Enterprise - Information Technology) see *BUSINESS AND ECONOMICS—Computer Applications*

658 USA
S R A NEWSLETTER✶ . Text in English. bi-m. USD 50. adv. back issues avail. **Document type:** *Newsletter.* **Description:** Covers SRA news and issues affecting members.
Published by: Society of Research Administrators, Inc., 1901 N Moore St., Ste. 1004, Arlington, VA 22209-1706. TEL 202-857-1141, FAX 202-223-4579. Ed. Bruce Steinert. Adv. contact Amy McNamara. Circ: 2,800.

S S O R YOKOSHU/PROCEEDINGS OF S S O R. see *COMPUTERS—Abstracting, Bibliographies, Statistics*

S T E P RAPPORT/S T E P REPORT. (Studies in Technology, Innovation and Economic Policy) see *SOCIOLOGY*

658 USA ISSN 1542-0116
SAFETY 21 FOR SUPERVISORS. Text in English. 2002 (Nov.). 24/yr. USD 99.60 (effective 2003).
Published by: Business 21 Publishing, 477 Baltimore Pike, Springfield, PA 19064. TEL 484-479-2700, FAX 610-543-2292. Ed. Louis Greenstein. Pub. Stephen Meyer.

SAFETY DIRECTOR'S REPORT YEARBOOK. see *PUBLIC HEALTH AND SAFETY*

SAFETY MANAGEMENT. see *OCCUPATIONAL HEALTH AND SAFETY*

SALARY SURVEY (WASHINGTON). see *BUSINESS AND ECONOMICS—Economic Situation And Conditions*

658 GBR ISSN 1356-1952
SALES MANAGEMENT. Text in English. m. GBP 125 (effective 2002). back issues avail. **Document type:** *Trade.*
Description: Practice management guide identifying techniques and controls essential to profitable new and used car sales. Explores new profit opportunities and explains the tactics behind successful sales and F&I operations—providing clear and concise solutions which can be implemented with confidence.
Former titles (until 1994): Sales Manager (0963-2530); (until 1991): Sales Management
Published by: Emap Automotive Ltd., Sewells Information and Research, Wentworth House, Wentworth St, Peterborough, Northants PE1 1DS, United Kingdom. TEL 44-1733-468255, FAX 44-1733-468349, http://www.sewells.co.uk, http://www.emap.com. Ed. Jerry Connolly. Pub. Mr. Mike Gunnell.

658.8 NLD ISSN 1381-0553
SALES MANAGEMENT. Text in Dutch. 1987. 10/yr. EUR 135; EUR 49 to students; EUR 15 newsstand/cover (effective 2005). adv. **Document type:** *Trade.*
Formerly (until 1994): Verkopen (Deurne) (0774-9082)
—IE.
Published by: Wolters Kluwer N.V., Postbus 23, Deventer, 7400 GA, Netherlands. info@kluwer.nl, http://www.sales-online.nl. Ed. Bernhard Rittger. Adv. contact Eric-Jan Vis. B&W page EUR 1,850; trim 190 x 268. Circ: 4,696.

658 RUS
SAMARSKII GOSUDARSTVENNYI UNIVERSITET. VESTNIK. GUMANITARNAYA SERIYA. EKONOMIKA I MENEDZHMENT. Text in Russian. 1998. a., latest 2003. **Document type:** *Journal, Academic/Scholarly.*
Published by: (Samarskii Gosudarstvennyi Universitet), Izdatel'stvo Samarskii Universitet/Publishing House of Samara State University, ul Akademika Pavlova 1, k 209, Samara, 443011, Russian Federation. vestnikNS@ssu.samara.ru, http://www.ssu.samara.ru/~vestnik/content/econ.html. Ed. G P Yarovoi.

658 FIN ISSN 0786-2113
SAMPOVISIO. Text in Finnish. bi-m. **Document type:** *Trade.*
Formerly: Riskienhallinta (0782-0496)
Published by: Helsinki Media Company Oy, PL 2, Helsinki, 00040, Finland. TEL 358-9-1201, FAX 358-9-120-5988. Ed. Tuomo Paasi. Circ: 60,000.

SAMSOM SUBSIDIE-INFO. see *BUSINESS AND ECONOMICS—Production Of Goods And Services*

SAN DIEGO MASTERPLANNER. see *SOCIAL SERVICES AND WELFARE*

SATELLITE NEWS. see *COMMUNICATIONS—Television And Cable*

658 GBR ISSN 0956-5221
HD28
➤ **SCANDINAVIAN JOURNAL OF MANAGEMENT.** Text in English. 1984. 4/yr. EUR 683 in Europe to institutions; JPY 90,800 in Japan to institutions; USD 764 elsewhere to institutions (effective 2006). reprints avail. **Document type:** *Academic/Scholarly.* **Description:** Dedicated to the advancement of understanding of management in private and public organizations through empirical investigation and theoretical analysis.
Formerly (until 1989): Scandinavian Journal of Management Studies (0281-7527)
Related titles: Microfilm ed.: (from PQC); Online - full text ed.: (from EBSCO Publishing, Gale Group, IngentaConnect, ScienceDirect, Swets Information Services).
Indexed: Emerald, PsycInfo, PsycholAb, e-psyche.
—BLDSC (8087.517240), IE, Infotrieve, ingenta. **CCC.**
Published by: Pergamon (Subsidiary of: Elsevier Science & Technology), The Boulevard, Langford Ln, East Park, Kidlington, Oxford OX5 1GB, United Kingdom. TEL 44-1865-843000, FAX 44-1865-843010, http://www.elsevier.com/locate/scajman. Ed. Janne Tienari. **Subscr. to:** Elsevier BV, PO Box 211, Amsterdam 1000 AE, Netherlands. TEL 31-20-485-3757, FAX 31-20-485-3432, nlinfo-f@elsevier.nl, http://www.elsevier.nl.

658 AUS ISSN 0819-6990
SCANFILE. Text in English. 1979. m. AUD 220 (effective 2004). abstr. back issues avail. **Document type:** *Bulletin, Abstract/Index.* **Description:** Covers current and emerging issues in research management and science and technology policy, including policy, management, social and economic issues of R and D and corporate intelligence.
Media: Online - full content. **Related titles:** CD-ROM ed.
Published by: C S I R O, Corporate Library and Information Service, PO Box 225, Dickson, ACT 2602, Australia. TEL 61-2-6276-6217, FAX 61-2-6276-6217, ashq@libary.csiro.au, http://www.csiro.au/. Ed., Pub. Carol Murray. Circ: 150.

658 DEU ISSN 1612-1767
▼ **SCHRIFTEN ZU ORGANISATION UND INFORMATION.** Text in German. 2003. irreg., latest vol.6, 2005. price varies. **Document type:** *Monographic series, Academic/Scholarly.*
Published by: Rainer Hampp Verlag, Meringerzellerstr 10, Mering, 86415, Germany. TEL 49-8233-4783, FAX 49-8233-30755, Rainer_Hampp_Verlag@t-online.de, http://www.hampp-verlag.de.

657 DEU ISSN 1435-6236
SCHRIFTEN ZUM BETRIEBLICHEN RECHNUNGSWESEN UND CONTROLLING. Text in German. 1991. irreg., latest vol.26, 2005. price varies. **Document type:** *Monographic series, Academic/Scholarly.*
Published by: Verlag Dr. Kovac, Arnoldstr 49, Hamburg, 22763, Germany. TEL 49-40-3988800, FAX 49-40-39888055, info@verlagdrkovac.de, http://www.verlagdrkovac.de/3-3.htm.

658 DEU ISSN 1612-2690
▼ **SCHRIFTEN ZUM INTERNATIONALEN MANAGEMENT.** Text in German. 2003. irreg., latest vol.12, 2005. price varies. **Document type:** *Monographic series, Academic/Scholarly.*
Published by: Rainer Hampp Verlag, Meringerzellerstr 10, Mering, 86415, Germany. TEL 49-8233-4783, FAX 49-8233-30755, Rainer_Hampp_Verlag@t-online.de, http://www.hampp-verlag.de.

658 DEU
SCHRIFTEN ZUR GESCHICHTE DER BETRIEBSWIRTSCHAFTLEHRE. Text in German. irreg., latest vol.17, 1999. price varies. **Document type:** *Monographic series, Academic/Scholarly.*
Address: Nussbauer Berg 36, Bergisch Gladbach, 51467, Germany. info@bwl-geschichte.de, http://www.bwl-geschichte.de.

658 DEU
SCHRIFTEN ZUR NACHHALTIGEN UNTERNEHMENSENTWICKLUNG. Text in German. irreg., latest vol.4, 2004. price varies. **Document type:** *Monographic series, Academic/Scholarly.*
Published by: Rainer Hampp Verlag, Meringerzellerstr 10, Mering, 86415, Germany. TEL 49-8233-4783, FAX 49-8233-30755, Rainer_Hampp_Verlag@t-online.de, http://www.hampp-verlag.de.

SCOTTISH BUSINESS INSIDER. see *BUSINESS AND ECONOMICS—Banking And Finance*

658.45 USA ISSN 1069-210X
SE HABLA ESPANOL✶ . Text in English. 1993. 24/yr. USD 119 (effective 1999). **Document type:** *Newsletter.*
Published by: Hispanic Business Inc., 425 Pine Ave, Santa Barbara, CA 93117-3700. TEL 805-682-5843, FAX 805-563-1239, info@hbinc.com. Ed. Vaughn Hagerty. Pub. Jesus Chavarria.

SECURITY JOURNAL. see *CRIMINOLOGY AND LAW ENFORCEMENT—Security*

658 658.3 USA ISSN 0145-9406
HD38 CODEN: SECME6
SECURITY MANAGEMENT. Text in English. 1957. m. USD 48 in North America to non-members; USD 115 elsewhere to non-members; USD 38 to members; USD 4 per issue domestic; USD 5 per issue in Canada (effective 2005). adv. bk.rev. charts; illus.; stat. cum.index. back issues avail.; reprint service avail. from PQC. **Document type:** *Magazine, Trade.*
Formerly: Industrial Security (0019-8773)
Related titles: Microform ed.: (from PQC); Online - full text ed.: Security Management Online (from EBSCO Publishing, Florida Center for Library Automation, Gale Group, Northern Light Technology, Inc., O C L C Online Computer Library Center, Inc., ProQuest Information & Learning).
Indexed: ABIn, AC&P, BPI, BPIA, BusI, CJA, CJPI, ESPM, Inspec, LRI, ManagCont, PSI, RiskAb, T&II.
—BLDSC (8217.210000), AskIEEE, IE, Infotrieve, ingenta. **CCC.**
Published by: American Society for Industrial Security, 1625 Prince St, Alexandria, VA 22314-2818. TEL 703-519-6200, FAX 703-519-6299, sharowitz@asisonline.org, asis@asisonline.org, http://www.securitymanagement.com, http://www.asisonline.org. Ed. Sherry Harowitz. Pub. Denny White. R&P Nello Caramat TEL 703-518-1451. Adv. contact Sandra Wade. B&W page USD 4,300, color page USD 5,850. Circ: 35,000 (paid and free).

658.5 MEX
SEGURINOTAS. Text in Spanish. 1955. m. USD 4.
Published by: Instituto Tecnologico y de Estudios Superiores de Monterrey, Departamento de Seguridad Industrial, Sucursal de Correos "J", Monterrey, Mexico. Ed. Marco Antonio Ledesma. Circ: 2,400.

658 GBR ISSN 0963-2638
➤ **SELECTION AND DEVELOPMENT REVIEW.** Text in English. 1984. bi-m. GBP 37, USD 50; free to qualified personnel (effective 2003). adv. bk.rev. back issues avail. **Document type:** *Academic/Scholarly.* **Description:** Focuses on selection and development issues for professional people whose job it is to assess other people.
Formerly: Guidance and Assessment Review (0265-1610)
Indexed: e-psyche.
—BLDSC (8235.144870), IE, ingenta.
Published by: The British Psychological Society, St Andrews House, 48 Princess Rd E, Leicester, LE1 7DR, United Kingdom. TEL 44-116-2549568, FAX 44-116-2470787, mail@bps.org.uk, http://www.bps.org.uk. Eds. John Boddy, Tuvia Melamed. R&P, Adv. contact Geoff Ellis TEL 44-116-2529523.

➤ **SELF-STORAGE ALMANAC.** see *BUSINESS AND ECONOMICS—Domestic Commerce*

➤ **SELF-STORAGE NOW.** see *BUSINESS AND ECONOMICS—Domestic Commerce*

658.85 USA ISSN 1069-1952
HF5438
SELLING. Text in English. 1993. m.
Related titles: Online - full text ed.: (from EBSCO Publishing, Factiva, Gale Group).
Indexed: ABIn.
—CCC.
Published by: Capital Cities - A B C, Inc., 825 Seventh Ave, New York, NY 10019. TEL 212-887-8560, FAX 212-887-8493.

SELLING POWER; advisory for sales and marketing executives. see *BUSINESS AND ECONOMICS—Marketing And Purchasing*

658 USA ISSN 0739-6236
SERVICE DEALER'S NEWSLETTER; business and personal insights for service dealers and managers. Text in English. 1984. m., latest vol.18. USD 97 (effective 2001). bk.rev.
Description: How-to tips on improving sales and profits for owners and managers of service-repair businesses.

Published by: Whitaker Newsletters Inc., 241, Burtonsville, MD 20866-0241. TEL 908-889-6336, FAX 908-889-6339. Ed. Carly Lombardi. Circ: 6,000.

SERVICE LINE LEADER. see *HEALTH FACILITIES AND ADMINISTRATION*

648 658 NLD ISSN 0928-3021
SERVICE MANAGEMENT (ALPHEN AAN DEN RIJN); vakblad voor facilitaire dienstverlening. Text in Dutch. 1974. 11/yr. adv. illus. **Document type:** *Trade.*
Former titles (until 1992): Bedrijfshuishouding (0165-1323); (until 1978): Schoonmaak en Hygiene (0928-3471)
Published by: Samsom Bedrijfsinformatie BV (Subsidiary of: Wolters Kluwer N.V.), Postbus 4, Alphen aan den Rijn, 2400 MA, Netherlands. TEL 31-172-466533, FAX 31-172-422886. Circ: 14,838 (paid).

658 CHN ISSN 1000-2154
HB9
SHANGYE JINGJI YU GUANLI/ECONOMICS AND BUSINESS ADMINISTRATION. Text in Chinese. 1981. m. CNY 6.50, USD 0.80 (effective 2000). adv. bk.rev. **Document type:** *Academic/Scholarly.* **Description:** Studies the theories and practices of Chinese economic reform. Guides the development of commercial enterprises in China. Aimed at academic staff, students and business administrators.
Related titles: Online - full text ed.: (from East View Information Services).
Indexed: ABIn.
Published by: Hangzhou Shangxueyuan/Hangzhou University of Commerce, 29 Jiaogong Rd, Hangzhou, Zhejiang 310035, China. TEL 86-571-8081002, FAX 86-571-8053079. Eds. Xiangping Zhong, Zuguang Hu. Adv. contact Huaizheng Li. Circ: 5,000 (paid). **Dist. in US by:** China Books & Periodicals Inc, 360 Swift Ave., Ste. 48, S San Fran, CA 94080-6220. TEL 415-282-2994.

658 CHN ISSN 1005-4367
SHANGYE QIYE GUANLI/MANAGEMENT OF COMMERCIAL ENTERPRISE. Text in Chinese. m. 112 p./no.; **Description:** Cover the management of commercial enterprises.
Published by: Zhongguo Renmin Daxue, Shubao Zilio Zhongxin/Renmin University of China, Information Center for Social Server, Dongcheng-qu, 3, Zhangzizhong Lu, Beijing, 100007, China. TEL 86-10-64039458, FAX 86-10-64015080, kyes@163.net, http://www.confucius.cn.net/. **Dist. in US by:** China Publications Service, PO Box 49614, Chicago, IL 60649. TEL 312-288-3291, FAX 312-288-8570; **Dist. by:** China International Book Trading Corp, 35 Chegongzhuang Xilu, Haidian District, PO Box 399, Beijing 100044, China. TEL 86-10-68412045, FAX 86-10-68412023, cibtc@mail.cibtc.com.cn, http://www.cibtc.com.cn.

658 333.33 USA ISSN 1089-7364
SHOPPING CENTER MANAGEMENT INSIDER. Text in English. 1995. m. USD 287 (effective 2004). **Document type:** *Newsletter.* **Description:** Tested management techniques, legal insights, and "how-to" guidelines for running a shopping center or mall. Includes model notices to tenants, letters, agreements and rules.
Published by: Brownstone Publishers, Inc., 149 Fifth Ave, 16th Fl, New York, NY 10010-6801. TEL 212-473-8200, FAX 212-473-8786, rbarton@brownstone.com, http://www.brownstone.com. Ed. Robin Barton. Pub. John M Striker. R&P Mike Koplin. Circ: 2,000 (paid).

SHUIYUN GUANLI/WATER TRANSPORTATION MANAGEMENT. see *TRANSPORTATION—Ships And Shipping*

658 JPN
SHUKAN GENDAI. Text in Japanese. 1954. w. JPY 8,650; JPY 350 newsstand/cover (effective 2005). **Document type:** *Magazine, Consumer.* **Description:** Covers general topics for businessmen.
Published by: Kodansha Ltd., 2-12-21 Otowa, Bunkyo-ku, Tokyo, 112-8001, Japan. TEL 81-3-39451111, wgendai@kodansha.co.jp, http://books.bitway.ne.jp/kodansha/wgendai/scoopengine/, http://www.kodansha.co.jp. Circ: 950,000 (paid).

658 DEU ISSN 0344-8746
SICHERHEITS-BERATER; Informationsdienst zu Problemen der Sicherheit in Betrieb, Unternehmen und Verwaltung. Text in German. 1974. s-m. **Document type:** *Bulletin.*
—IE, Infotrieve. **CCC.**
Published by: Verlagsgruppe Handelsblatt GmbH, Kasernenstr. 67, Duesseldorf, 40213, Germany. TEL 49-211-887-0, FAX 49-211-133522. Ed. Rainer A H von zur Muehlen. Circ: 1,900.

658 NLD ISSN 0166-6967
SIGMA; tijdschrift voor excellent ondernemen. Text in Dutch. 1955. 6/yr. EUR 190 (effective 2005). adv. **Document type:** *Trade.* **Description:** Professional journal for quality professionals.
Indexed: RefZh.
—IE, Infotrieve.
Published by: Kluwer Business Media, Postbus 23, Deventer, 7400 GA, Netherlands. TEL 31-570-648955, FAX 31-570-614795, http://www.sigma-online.nl. Eds. Wilma Berenschot TEL 31-570-648891, Mariet Ebbinge TEL 31-570-648308. Circ: 2,725.

SIGNCRAFT; the guide to profitable and creative sign production. see *ADVERTISING AND PUBLIC RELATIONS*

658 USA
HD2745
SIGNIFICANT DATA FOR DIRECTORS. Text in English. 1977. a. USD 95 (effective 1999). back issues avail. **Document type:** *Trade.*
Formerly (until 1999): Significant Issues Facing Directors (0193-4201)
Published by: Directorship Inc., 8 Sound Shore Dr, Ste 250, Greenwich, CT 06830-7242. TEL 203-861-7000, FAX 203-861-7007. Ed. B E Beebe.

SILICON ALLEY DAILY. see *COMPUTERS—Internet*

SILICON IRAN. see *COMPUTERS—Internet*

658 SGP ISSN 0129-5977
HD28
➤ **SINGAPORE MANAGEMENT REVIEW.** Text in English. 1979. s-a. adv. back issues avail. **Document type:** *Journal, Academic/Scholarly.* **Description:** Covers the latest business issues in Singapore and the Asian region. Numerous researchers and academics contribute articles that focus on both local and regional business perspectives and issues. The aim of the journal is to make the latest developments and advances in the theory and practice of management accessible to all managers and senior executives. It also helps to foster the exchange of ideas and perspectives between academics and practitioners.
Related titles: Online - full text ed.: (from EBSCO Publishing, Gale Group, Northern Light Technology, Inc., ProQuest Information & Learning).
Indexed: ABIn, ASEANManA, BAS, EI, Emerald.
—BLDSC (8285.476000).
Published by: Singapore Institute of Management, Management House, 41 Namly Ave, Singapore, 267616, Singapore. TEL 1800-468-8866, FAX 65-469-1559, http://www1.sim.edu.sg/sim/pub/gen/sim_pub_gen_content.cfm?mnuid=163, http://www.sim.edu.sg. Ed. Hing-Man Leung. adv.: color page SGD 1,200. **Co-sponsor:** National University of Singapore, Faculty of Business Administration.

➤ **SIR FREDERIC HOOPER AWARD ESSAY.** see *BUSINESS AND ECONOMICS*

➤ **SIX SIGMA FORUM.** see *BUSINESS AND ECONOMICS—Production Of Goods And Services*

➤ **SMALL BUSINESS NEWS - DAYTON.** see *BUSINESS AND ECONOMICS—Small Business*

➤ **SMALL BUSINESS NEWS. PHILADELPHIA/SOUTH JERSEY.** see *BUSINESS AND ECONOMICS—Small Business*

➤ **SMALL BUSINESS NEWS - WASHINGTON D C.** see *BUSINESS AND ECONOMICS—Small Business*

658 USA ISSN 1544-7464
SMART SUPERVISION. Text in English. 2002. bi-w. USD 149.50 (effective 2005). **Document type:** *Newsletter, Trade.* **Description:** Provides information and training tips for supervisors on all aspects of their job from time management and presentations to interviewing and training to safety and employment law.
Published by: Clement Communications, Inc., 10 LaCrue Ave, PO Box 36, Concordville, PA 19331. TEL 610-459-4200, 888-358-5858, FAX 610-459-4582, editor@clement.com, http://www.clement.com.

SMETKOVODSTVENO FINANSISKA REVIJA; spisanie za smetkovodstveno-finansiska i organizaciona problematika na rabotnite organizacii. see *BUSINESS AND ECONOMICS—Accounting*

SOBSTVENOST I PRAVO. see *BUSINESS AND ECONOMICS—Small Business*

SOCIAL MARKETING QUARTERLY. see *BUSINESS AND ECONOMICS—Marketing And Purchasing*

658 BEL ISSN 1373-8593
SOCIAL PROFIT JAARBOEK/SOCIAL PROFIT YEARBOOK. Text in Dutch. 1998. a., latest 2004. EUR 28 per issue (effective 2005). bk.rev. **Document type:** *Consumer.* **Description:** Management cases and theory for not-for-profit organizations.
Related titles: Online - full content ed.
Published by: Standaard Uitgeverij, Belgielei 147a, Antwerp, 2018, Belgium. TEL 32-3-285-7200, FAX 32-3-230-1225. Ed. Dirk Vermeulen. R&P Eric Willems. Adv. contact Katie Thys. Circ: 1,500.

SOCIETY OF MANAGEMENT ACCOUNTANTS OF CANADA. ANNUAL REPORT. see *BUSINESS AND ECONOMICS—Accounting*

SOCIETY OF PHOTOGRAPHER AND ARTIST REPRESENTATIVES. NEWSLETTER. see *PHOTOGRAPHY*

SOCIO-ECONOMIC PAPERS. see *RELIGIONS AND THEOLOGY*

658 JPN ISSN 0286-9713
SOSHIKI KAGAKU/ORGANIZATIONAL SCIENCE. Text in Japanese. 1967. q. **Document type:** *Journal, Academic/Scholarly.*
—BLDSC (6290.840000), IE.
Published by: Soshiki Gakkai/Academic Association for Organizational Science, Togin bldg. 6F 603, 1-4-2 Marunouchi, Chiyoda-ku, Tokyo, 100-0005, Japan. TEL 81-3-52202896, FAX 81-3-52202968, organizationalhome@hotmail.com, http://wwwsoc.nii.ac.jp/aos/OSmagazine/index.html, http://wwwsoc.nii.ac.jp/aos/index.html.

658 USA ISSN 0747-2196
SOUNDVIEW EXECUTIVE BOOK SUMMARIES. Text in English. 1979. m. USD 139 domestic; USD 169 foreign (effective 2004). adv. bk.rev. illus. Index. reprints avail. **Document type:** *Newsletter.* **Description:** Concise, 8-page distillations of new business books.
Formerly (until 198?): Soundview Summaries (0195-1718)
Published by: Concentrated Knowledge, Inc., 10 LaCrue Ave, Concordville, PA 19331. TEL 888-358-1000, FAX 800-453-5062, sales@summary.ccm, http://www.summary.com/. Ed. Roger Griffith. Pub. Cynthia Folino. Adv. contact Robert Carter. Circ: 43,000 (paid).

658 ZAF ISSN 0378-9098
CODEN: SAJMDC
➤ **SOUTH AFRICAN JOURNAL OF BUSINESS MANAGEMENT/SUID-AFRIKAANSE TYDSKRIF VIR BEDRYFSLEIDING.** Text and summaries in English. 1970. q. adv. bk.rev. charts; illus.; stat. **Document type:** *Journal, Abstract/Index.* **Description:** Publishes articles of real significance for business practice.
Formerly (until 1979): Bedryfsleiding - Business Management (0045-1614)
Related titles: Online - full text ed.: (from EBSCO Publishing).
Indexed: ABIn, ADPA, BiolAb, CurCont, ISAP.
Published by: (Association for Professional Managers in South Africa), South African Bureau for Scientific Publications, PO Box 11663, Pretoria, Hatfield 0028, South Africa. TEL 27-12-322-6404, FAX 27-12-320-7803, bspman@icon.co.zaac.za, http://www.journals.co.za/ej/ejour_busman.html, http://www.safest.org.za/bsp. Ed., Adv. contact Linda Human. Circ: 900.

658 ZAF ISSN 1015-8812
➤ **SOUTH AFRICAN JOURNAL OF ECONOMIC AND MANAGEMENT SCIENCES.** Text in English. 1988. s-a. bibl. 220 p./no.; reprints avail. **Document type:** *Journal, Academic/Scholarly.* **Description:** Contains articles and research on the creation, dissemination and application of knowledge in economic and related sciences.
Formerly (until 2000): Suid-Afrikaanse Tydskrift vis Ekonomiese a Bergfswetemskapf
Related titles: Online - full text ed.
Indexed: JEL.
—BLDSC (8338.856000), IE, ingenta.
Published by: University of Pretoria, Faculty of Economic and Management Sciences/Universiteit van Pretoria, Pretoria, 0002, South Africa. TEL 27-12-420-3453, FAX 27-12-362-5207, slaing@hakuna.up.ac.za, http://www.journals.co.za/ej/ejour_ecoman.html, http://www.up.ac.za/academic/economic. Ed. M L Truv. Circ: 110 (paid); 120 (controlled).

658 GBR ISSN 1560-683X
➤ **SOUTH AFRICAN JOURNAL OF INFORMATION MANAGEMENT.** Text in English. 1999. 4/yr. free (effective 2005). **Description:** Publishes articles in the areas of research and development as they relate to Information Management theory, technologies, applications and services.
Media: Online - full content.
Indexed: InfoSAb.
Published by: Interworld Publications, 12 The Fairway, New Barnet, EN5 1HN, United Kingdom. TEL 44-20-84495938, FAX 44-20-84470599, interword@icon.co.za, http://general.rau.ac.za/infosci/raujournal/default.asp?to=scope.

658 IND ISSN 0971-5428
HD70.S62
➤ **SOUTH ASIAN JOURNAL OF MANAGEMENT.** Text in English. 1994. q. INR 450, USD 60 (effective 2003). **Document type:** *Academic/Scholarly.*
Related titles: Online - full text ed.: (from ProQuest Information & Learning).
Indexed: ABIn, PAA&I.
Published by: Association of Management Development Institutions in South Asia, No.1228, Road No.60, Jubilee Hills, Hyderabad, 500 033, India. TEL 91-40-3546090, FAX 91-40-3544801, http://www.amdisa.org. Ed. Matthew J Manimala TEL 91-080—26582450.

658 USA
SOUTHWEST ACADEMY OF MANAGEMENT. ANNUAL MEETING PROCEEDINGS. Text in English. a.
—BLDSC (1087.904000).

Published by: Southwest Academy of Management, The University of Texas at San Antonio, College of Business, Office of the Dean, 6900 North Loop 1604 West, San Antonio, TX 78249-0631. ddamonte@coastal.edu, http://www.shsu.edu/~mgt_swam. Ed. Darla Domke-Damonte TEL 843-349-2129.

658 USA
SOUTHWEST ACADEMY OF MANAGEMENT NEWSLETTER. Text in English. q.
Published by: Southwest Academy of Management, The University of Texas at San Antonio, College of Business, Office of the Dean, 6900 North Loop 1604 West, San Antonio, TX 78249-0631. dduchon@utsa.edu, http://www.shsu.edu/~mgt_swam. Ed. Dennis Duchon TEL 210-458-5373.

658 DEU ISSN 1439-4057
SOZIALMARKT AKTUELL. Text in German. 1995. m. **Document type:** *Magazine, Trade.*
Formerly (until 2000): Gemeinnuetzigkeit und Management (0949-2992)
Published by: Verlag R.S. Schulz GmbH (Subsidiary of: Wolters Kluwer Deutschland GmbH), Enzianstr. 4a, Starnberg, 82319, Germany. TEL 49-89-360070, FAX 49-89-36007310, info@wolters-kluwer.de, http://www.rss.de.

658 DEU ISSN 0936-9198
SOZIALVERSICHERUNGS-BERATER; Unternehmer-Handbuch fuer zeit- und kostensparenden Umgang mit den Sozialversicherungsvorschriften. Text in German. 1989. 8/yr. looseleaf. **Document type:** *Bulletin.* **Description:** How-to information for social security.
Related titles: Online - full text ed.
Published by: V N R Verlag fuer die Deutsche Wirtschaft AG, Theodor-Heuss-Str 2-4, Bonn, 53095, Germany. TEL 49-228-9550120, FAX 49-228-359710, gsc@vnr.de, http://www.personalverlag.de/produkte/svb/svb.html, http://www.vnr.de. Eds. H Max, H G Kalinowski.

SPORT BESTUUR & MANAGEMENT; vakblad voor sportbestuurders, sportkader en sportoverheden. see *SPORTS AND GAMES*

658 AUS ISSN 1441-3523
GV713
SPORT MANAGEMENT REVIEW. Text in English. 1998. s-a. AUD 50 in Australia & New Zealand to individuals; AUD 60 elsewhere to individuals; AUD 100 in Australia & New Zealand to institutions; AUD 110 elsewhere to institutions (effective 2002). **Description:** Covers management, marketing, and governance of sport at all levels and in all its manifestations as entertainment, recreation, or occupation.
Related titles: Online - full text ed.: (from EBSCO Publishing).
Indexed: RRTA, WAE&RSA.
—BLDSC (8419.628500).
Published by: Sport Management Association of Australia & New Zealand, Bowater School of Management & Marketing, Deakin University, 221 Burwood Hwy, Burwood, VIC 3125 , Australia. http://www.gu.edu.au/school/lst/services/smaanz/. Ed. David Shilbury.

658 790.1 DEU
SPORTMANAGEMENT. Text in German. 1966. a. EUR 24.50 (effective 2002). adv. **Document type:** *Magazine, Trade.*
Published by: Philippka-Verlag, Postfach 150105, Muenster, 48061, Germany. TEL 49-251-230050, FAX 49-251-2300599, info@philippka.de, http://www.philippka.de. Ed. Konrad Honig. Adv. contact Peter Moellers TEL 49-251-2300528. B&W page EUR 705, color page EUR 1,380.

SPRINGER SERIES IN OPERATIONS RESEARCH. see *COMPUTERS*

SPROUTS; working papers on information environments, systems and organizations. see *COMPUTERS—Information Science And Information Theory*

STABLE MANAGEMENT. see *SPORTS AND GAMES—Horses And Horsemanship*

STAFFING MANAGEMENT. see *BUSINESS AND ECONOMICS—Personnel Management*

338 669 GBR
STAINLESS STEEL MARKET INFORMATION. Text in English. m.
Published by: Alloy Metals & Steel Publications, Frampton Fen, PO Box 106, Boston, Lincs PE20 1SE, United Kingdom. TEL 44-1205-365050, FAX 44-1205-365080, amspublications@cwcom.net, http://www.stainlesssteelfocus.com/.

THE STANDARD (BOSTON); New England's insurance weekly. see *INSURANCE*

658 338 USA ISSN 0361-3623
HG4057
STANDARD & POOR'S REGISTER OF CORPORATIONS, DIRECTORS AND EXECUTIVES. Text in English. 1928. base vol. plus a. updates. USD 675. **Document type:** *Directory, Trade.* **Description:** Lists some 55,000 companies, giving such information as addresses and telephone numbers, key officers and directors, numbers of employees, S.I.C. codes, their principal products, and annual sales.
Formerly (until 1973): Poor's Register of Corporations, Directors and Executives (0079-3825)
Related titles: CD-ROM ed.: (from The Dialog Corporation); Diskette ed.; Magnetic Tape ed.; Online - full text ed.; Supplement(s):.
Published by: Standard & Poor's (Subsidiary of: McGraw-Hill Companies, Inc.), 55 Water St, New York, NY 10041. TEL 212-208-8280, FAX 212-412-0305. Ed. Lily Deangelis. Pub. Tom Lupo. R&P Peggy Smith.

658 USA
STANDARDS WATCH; a briefing on standards for business information management professionals. Text in English. 1997. q. USD 25 domestic to members by fax; USD 100 foreign to members by fax; USD 75 domestic to non-members by fax; USD 120 foreign to non-members by fax. **Document type:** *Newsletter.* **Description:** Covers major developments in standardization within information and document management technologies that could affect business information management professionals in the future.
Published by: A I I M International, 1100 Wayne Ave, Ste 1100, Silver Spring, MD 20910. TEL 301-587-8202, FAX 301-587-2711, aiim@aiim.org. Ed. Marilyn Wright.

658 NOR ISSN 0803-0103
JN7461
STAT OG STYRING; tidsskrift for bedre styring og ressurutnyttelse i offentlige sektor. Text in Norwegian. 1956. 5/yr. NOK 298 to individuals; NOK 598 to institutions (effective 2003). adv. **Document type:** *Academic/Scholarly.* **Description:** Focuses on government and leadership issues.
Formerly (until 1990): Administrasjonsnytt (0400-518X)
Published by: (Directorate of Organization and Management), Fagbokforlaget, Kanalveien 51, PO Box 6050, Postterminalen, Bergen, 5892, Norway. TEL 47-22-55388800, FAX 47-22-55388801, http://www.fagbokforlaget.no/statogstyring. Ed. Hans Christian Erlandsen TEL 47-22-017103. Adv. contact Thorhild Nyborg TEL 47-64-952627. Circ: 3,700.

658 336.2 DEU ISSN 0945-5558
STEUER-BRIEF FUER DEN GMBH-GESCHAEFTSFUEHRER. Text in German. m. EUR 5.80 per issue (effective 2005). **Document type:** *Journal, Trade.*
Published by: Deubner Verlag GmbH & Co. KG, Oststr 11, Cologne, 50996, Germany. TEL 49-221-9370180, FAX 49-221-93701890, kundenservice@deubner-verlag.de, http://www.vrp.de.

STORES. see *CRIMINOLOGY AND LAW ENFORCEMENT—Security*

658 GBR ISSN 1086-1718
HD58.8 CODEN: STCHFT
➤ **STRATEGIC CHANGE.** Text in English. 1992. 8/yr. USD 695 to institutions; USD 765 combined subscription to institutions print & online eds. (effective 2006). adv. bk.rev. illus. back issues avail.; reprints avail. **Document type:** *Journal, Academic/Scholarly.* **Description:** Provides information on the planning and implementation of organizational change to meet the demands of changing business, economic and social environments.
Formerly (until 1996): Journal of Strategic Change (1057-9265)
Related titles: Microform ed.: (from PQC); Online - full text ed.: ISSN 1099-1697. 1997. USD 695 to institutions (effective 2006) (from EBSCO Publishing, ProQuest Information & Learning, Swets Information Services, Wiley InterScience).
Indexed: ABIn, CPM, Emerald, Inspec, SOMA.
—BLDSC (8474.031423), IE, Infotrieve, ingenta. **CCC.**
Published by: John Wiley & Sons Ltd. (Subsidiary of: John Wiley & Sons, Inc.), The Atrium, Southern Gate, Chichester, West Sussex PO19 8SQ, United Kingdom. TEL 44-1243-779777, FAX 44-1243-775878, customer@wiley.co.uk, http://www3.interscience.wiley.com/cgi-bin/jhome/6184, http://www.wiley.co.uk. Ed. Graham Beaver. adv.: B&W page GBP 650, color page GBP 1,550; trim 210 x 297. Circ: 450. **Subscr. in N. America to:** John Wiley & Sons, Inc., 111 River St, Hoboken, NJ 07030-5774. TEL 201-748-6645, 800-225-5945, subinfo@wiley.com

658.45 GBR ISSN 1363-9064
STRATEGIC COMMUNICATION MANAGEMENT; a new information architecture. Text in English. bi-m. GBP 225; GBP 325 combined subscription print & online (effective 2004). **Document type:** *Magazine, Trade.* **Description:** Features case studies, special reports, reviews and practical tips for professional communicators.
Related titles: Online - full content ed.: GBP 275 (effective 2004); Online - full text ed.: (from EBSCO Publishing).
—BLDSC (8474.031426), IE, ingenta. **CCC.**
Published by: Melcrum Publishing, 1st Floor, Chelsea Reach, 79-89 Lots Rd, London, SW10 0RN, United Kingdom. TEL 877-226-2764, 44-20-7795-2205, FAX 312-803-1871, 44-20-7795-2156, http://www.melcrum.com. Ed. Victoria Mellor. R&P Robin Crumb.

658 GBR ISSN 0143-2095
HD30.28 CODEN: SMAJD8
➤ **STRATEGIC MANAGEMENT JOURNAL.** Text in English. 1979. 13/yr. USD 1,650 to institutions; USD 1,815 combined subscription to institutions print & online eds. (effective 2006). adv. illus.; abstr. Index. back issues avail.; reprint service avail. from PQC,ISI,PSC. **Document type:** *Journal, Academic/Scholarly.* **Description:** Concerned with all aspects of strategic management and improving both theory and practice.
Related titles: Microform ed.: (from PQC); Online - full text ed.: ISSN 1097-0266. 1997. USD 1,650 to institutions (effective 2006) (from EBSCO Publishing, JSTOR (Web-based Journal Archive), O C L C Online Computer Library Center, Inc., ProQuest Information & Learning, Swets Information Services, Wiley InterScience).
Indexed: ABIn, ADPA, ASCA, ASEANManA, ArtHuCI, BAS, BPI, BPIA, BusI, CJA, CPM, CurCont, ESPM, Emerald, Englnd, IBSS, Inspec, M&MA, ManagCont, ORMS, PROMT, QC&AS, RASB, RiskAb, SCIMP, SSCI.
—BLDSC (8474.031460), CISTI, Ei, IDS, IE, Infotrieve, ingenta. **CCC.**
Published by: John Wiley & Sons Ltd. (Subsidiary of: John Wiley & Sons, Inc.), The Atrium, Southern Gate, Chichester, West Sussex PO19 8SQ, United Kingdom. TEL 44-1243-779777, FAX 44-1243-775878, customer@wiley.co.uk, http://www.interscience.wiley.com/jpages/0143-2095, http://www.wiley.co.uk. Ed. Dan Schendel. Pub. Diane Taylor. R&P Diane Southern TEL 44-1243-770347. adv.: B&W page GBP 650, color page GBP 1,550; trim 200 x 260. Circ: 4,000. **Subscr. in the Americas to:** John Wiley & Sons, Inc., 111 River St, Hoboken, NJ 07030-5774. TEL 201-748-6645, 800-225-5945, subinfo@wiley.com

658 GBR ISSN 1476-1270
HD30.28
▼ **STRATEGIC ORGANIZATION.** Text in English. 2003 (Feb.). q. GBP 346, USD 605 to institutions; GBP 360, USD 630 combined subscription to institutions print & online eds. (effective 2006). **Document type:** *Journal, Academic/Scholarly.* **Description:** Publishes high-quality, disciplined-grounded conceptual and empirical research of interest to researchers, teachers, students, and practitioners of strategic management and organization.
Related titles: Online - full text ed.: ISSN 1741-315X. GBP 342, USD 599 to institutions (effective 2006) (from C S A, EBSCO Publishing, O C L C Online Computer Library Center, Inc., Sage Publications, Inc., Swets Information Services).
Indexed: IBSS, Inspec.
—BLDSC (8474.031502), IE. **CCC.**
Published by: Sage Publications Ltd. (Subsidiary of: Sage Publications, Inc.), 1 Oliver's Yard, 55 City Rd, London, EC1 1SP, United Kingdom. TEL 44-20-73248500, FAX 44-20-73248600, info@sagepub.co.uk, http://www.sagepub.co.uk/journal.aspx?pid=105788. Eds. Joel A C Baum, P Devereaux Jennings, Royston Greenwood. **Subscr. in the Americas to:** Sage Publications, Inc., 2455 Teller Rd, Thousand Oaks, CA 91320. TEL 805-499-0721, FAX 805-499-0871, journals@sagepub.com.

658 DEU
STRATEGIE. Text in German. q. **Document type:** *Magazine, Trade.* **Description:** Provides information and content on new management and technology ideas and trends.
Published by: (Deutsche Gesellschaft fuer Mittelstandsberatung GmbH), BurdaYukom Publishing GmbH (Subsidiary of: Hubert Burda Media Holding GmbH & Co. KG), Schleissheimer Str 141, Munich, 80797, Germany. TEL 49-89-306200, FAX 49-89-30620100, info@burdayukom.de, http://www.yukom.de. Circ: 15,000 (controlled).

331 DEU ISSN 0934-4179
STRATEGIE- UND INFORMATIONSMANAGEMENT. Text in German. 1989. irreg., latest vol.16, 2005. price varies. **Document type:** *Monographic series, Academic/Scholarly.*
Published by: Rainer Hampp Verlag, Meringerzellerstr 10, Mering, 86415, Germany. TEL 49-8233-4783, FAX 49-8233-30755, Rainer_Hampp_Verlag@t-online.de, http://www.hampp-verlag.de.

658 DEU ISSN 1617-7762
STRATEGISCHES MANAGEMENT. Text in German. 2001. irreg., latest vol.24, 2005. price varies. **Document type:** *Monographic series, Academic/Scholarly.*
Published by: Verlag Dr. Kovac, Arnoldstr 49, Hamburg, 22763, Germany. TEL 49-40-3988800, FAX 49-40-39888055, info@verlagdrkovac.de, http://www.verlagdrkovac.de/3-15.htm.

B

658 GBR ISSN 1087-8572
HD28 CODEN: STLEFV
➤ **STRATEGY & LEADERSHIP.** Text in English. 1972. bi-m. EUR 1,097.29 in Europe; USD 639 in North America; AUD 1,829 in Australasia; GBP 771.04 in UK & elsewhere (effective 2006). bk.rev. charts; illus. back issues avail.; reprint service avail. from PSC. **Document type:** *Journal, Academic/Scholarly.*
Description: Essential tool for the implementation of power strategies, highlighting the importance of long range planning and strong leadership, it features significant, unique articles and case studies that tackle a variety of issues.
Incorporates (1996-2001): The Antidote (1363-8483); Formerly (until 1996): Planning Review (0094-064X); Which superseded (in 1985): Managerial Planning (0025-1941); Which was formerly: Budgeting
Related titles: Online - full text ed.: (from EBSCO Publishing, Emerald Group Publishing Limited, Florida Center for Library Automation, Gale Group, IngentaConnect, Northern Light Technology, Inc., O C L C Online Computer Library Center, Inc., ProQuest Information & Learning, Swets Information Services).
Indexed: ABIn, ADPA, ASEANManA, ATI, BPI, BusI, CPM, Emerald, Inspec, M&MA, ManagCont, PAIS, PROMT, RASB, RefZh, SCIMP.
—BLDSC (8474.037950), CASDDS, IE, Infotrieve, ingenta. **CCC.**
Published by: Emerald Group Publishing Limited, 60-62 Toller Ln, Bradford, W Yorks BD8 9BY, United Kingdom. TEL 44-1274-777700, FAX 44-1274-785200, infomation@emeraldinsight.com, http://www.emeraldinsight.com/sl.htm. Ed. Mr. Robert Randall. R&P Mr. James Bender. **Subscr. addr. N America:** Emerald Group Publishing Ltd., 44 Brattle St, 4th Fl, Cambridge, MA 02138. TEL 617-497-2175, 888-622-0075, FAX 617-354-6875.

658 GBR
STRATEGY AND RISK MANAGEMENT S + R M. Text in English. 2002. m. **Document type:** *Newsletter.*
Incorporates (1987-2001): Environmental Impact (0966-8985)
—BLDSC (8474.037980), ingenta.
Published by: Prisconsult, 1 Port Hill, Nuffield, Henley-on-Thames, Oxon RG9 5RL, United Kingdom. TEL 44-1491-641337, pamela.shimell@prisconsult.com, http://www.prisconsult.com/.

658 ITA ISSN 0391-8769
STUDI ORGANIZZATIVI. Text in Italian. 1969. q. EUR 48 domestic; EUR 73 foreign (effective 2003).
Published by: Franco Angeli Edizioni, Viale Monza 106, Milan, 20127, Italy. TEL 39-02-2837141, FAX 39-02-26144793, redazioni@francoangeli.it, http://www.francoangeli.it. Ed. Piero Bontadini.

658 NLD ISSN 0081-8194
➤ **STUDIES IN MATHEMATICAL AND MANAGERIAL ECONOMICS.** Text in Dutch. 1964. irreg., latest vol.38, 1995. price varies. back issues avail. **Document type:** *Monographic series, Academic/Scholarly.* **Description:** Presents original research in theoretical and empirical microeconomics.
Indexed: IAOP, MathR, RASB, ZentMath.
—BLDSC (8491.047000).
Published by: Elsevier BV, North-Holland (Subsidiary of: Elsevier Science & Technology), Sara Burgerhartstraat 25, Amsterdam, 1055 KV, Netherlands. TEL 31-20-485-3911, FAX 31-20-485-2457, nlinfo-f@elsevier.nl, http://www.elsevier.nl. Eds. H Gleiser, S Martin. **Subscr. to:** Elsevier BV, PO Box 211, Amsterdam 1000 AE, Netherlands. TEL 31-20-485-3757, FAX 31-20-485-3432, http://www.elsevier.nl.

658.311 338.09 NLD
➤ **STUDIES IN PRODUCTIVITY ANALYSIS.** Text in English. 1981. irreg., latest vol.9, 1987. price varies. **Document type:** *Monographic series, Academic/Scholarly.*
Published by: Springer-Verlag Dordrecht (Subsidiary of: Springer Science+Business Media), Van Godewijckstraat 30, Dordrecht, 3311 GX, Netherlands. TEL 31-78-6576050, FAX 31-78-6576474, http://www.springeronline.com.

658 USA
SUCCESS ORIENTATION; the management newsletter for executives, for supervisors, for salesmen, and for personal development. Text in English. 1969. q. USD 29.95 (effective 1999). bk.rev. **Document type:** *Newsletter.*
Published by: (Jordan International Enterprises), Success Publications, Inc., PO Box 487, Roswell, GA 30077. TEL 770-992-6060, 800-672-8677. Ed. Dupree Jordan Jr. R&P Margaret Jordan. Circ: 2,800.

658 USA ISSN 1533-7170
SUCCESSFUL COST CONTROL STRATEGIES FOR C E OS, MANAGERS, & ADMINISTRATORS. Text in English. 1991. m. USD 279 (effective 2001). index. back issues avail. **Document type:** *Newsletter.* **Description:** Details proven cost-control strategies.
Former titles (until 2001): Employee Cost Control Strategies for C E Os, Managers, & Administrators (1531-0698); (until 2000): Cost Control Strategies for Managers, Controllers & Finance Executives (1096-2441); Incorporates: Cost Control Strategies for Financial Institutions; Formerly (until 1997): Cost Controller (1063-2735)
Indexed: BLI.
Published by: Siefer Consultants, Inc., 525 Cayuga St, Storm Lake, IA 50588. TEL 712-732-7340, FAX 712-732-7906, siefer@ncn.net. Ed. Dana Siefer. Circ: 3,200.

SUCCESSFUL OFFICER CALL STRATEGIES. see *BUSINESS AND ECONOMICS—Banking And Finance*

658 GBR
SUCCESSFUL SUPERVISOR✶. Text in English. 1990. 24/yr. GBP 120. bk.rev. **Document type:** *Newsletter.*
Published by: Fulcrum Publishing Ltd., 254 Goswell Rd, London, EC1V 7EB, United Kingdom. TEL 44-1483-35753, FAX 44-1483-37086. Ed. Jenny Hayes.

SUPERVISION; the magazine of industrial relations and operating management. see *BUSINESS AND ECONOMICS—Labor And Industrial Relations*

SUPERVISION; Mensch - Arbeit - Organisation. see *BUSINESS AND ECONOMICS—Labor And Industrial Relations*

658 USA ISSN 1521-8066
SUPERVISORS LEGAL UPDATE. Abbreviated title: S L U. Text in English. 1998. s-m. USD 94.56. **Document type:** *Newsletter.* **Description:** Information to help managers understand and comply with federal and state employment laws.
Published by: Progressive Business Publications, 370 Technology Dr, Malvern, PA 19355-1315. TEL 610-695-8600, 800-220-5000, FAX 610-647-8089, editor@pbp.com, http://www.pbp.com. Ed. Dave Clemens. R&P Curt Brown. Circ: 1,000 (paid).

658 USA ISSN 1077-9337
SUPERVISOR'S MEMORY JOGGER. Text in English. 1956. m. USD 16.20 (effective 1999). **Document type:** *Trade.*
Published by: Bureau of Business Practice (Subsidiary of: Aspen Publishers, Inc.), 1185 Avenue of the Americas, 37th Fl, New York, NY 10036. TEL 860-442-4365, 800-243-0876, FAX 860-437-3555, rebecca_armitage@prenhall.com, http://www.bbpnews.com. Ed. Brendan Johnston. Pub. Peter Garabedian. R&P Kathryn Mennone.

658 USA
SUPERVISORY MANAGEMENT REPORT - GEOGRAPHIC EDITION. Text in English. a. USD 490. charts. reprints avail. **Document type:** *Trade.* **Description:** Features a wide variety of data cuts ranging from broad regional scans to city-by-city analyses.
Related titles: ♦ Supplement to: Industry Report on Supervisory Management Compensation. ISSN 1041-908X.
Published by: (Executive Compensation Service (ECS)), Wyatt Data Services, 218 Rte 17 N, Rochelle Park, NJ 07622-9832. TEL 201-843-1177, FAX 201-843-0101.

658 USA ISSN 1529-8167
SUPPLY CHAIN E-BUSINESS. Text in English. m.
Indexed: CompLI.
Published by: Keller International Publishing Corp., 150 Great Neck Rd, Great Neck, NY 11021. TEL 516-829-9210, FAX 516-824-5414, info@supplychainbrain.com, http://www.supplychainbrain.com, http://www.kellerpubs.com.

658 GBR ISSN 1359-8546
HF5415.7
➤ **SUPPLY CHAIN MANAGEMENT**; an international journal. Text in English. 1996. 5/yr. EUR 1,782.41 in Europe; USD 1,849 in North America; AUD 2,309 in Australasia; GBP 1,249.54 in UK & elsewhere (effective 2006). back issues avail.; reprints avail. **Document type:** *Journal, Academic/Scholarly.* **Description:** Focuses on risk management and the logistics of multiple sourcing that brings additional costs for multi-product enterprises.
Related titles: Online - full text ed.: (from EBSCO Publishing, Emerald Group Publishing Limited, Gale Group, IngentaConnect, O C L C Online Computer Library Center, Inc., ProQuest Information & Learning, Swets Information Services).
Indexed: ABIn, CurCont, EmerIntel, Inspec, LogistBibl, SSCI.
—BLDSC (8547.630600), IE, Infotrieve, ingenta. **CCC.**
Published by: Emerald Group Publishing Limited, 60-62 Toller Ln, Bradford, W Yorks BD8 9BY, United Kingdom. TEL 44-1274-777700, FAX 44-1274-785200, infomation@emeraldinsight.com, http://www.emeraldinsight.com/scm.htm. Ed. Andrew Fearne.

658 USA ISSN 1521-9747
HF5415.7
SUPPLY CHAIN MANAGEMENT REVIEW. Text in English. 1997. bi-m. (in 1 vol.). USD 209 in US & Canada; USD 241 foreign; USD 59.95 newsstand/cover (effective 2004). adv. **Document type:** *Magazine, Trade.* **Description:** Aimed at high-level corporate and supply chain executives. Provides in-depth information on managing the supply chain, which encompasses all of the activities involved in moving goods from the raw materials stage to the end user.
Related titles: Online - full text ed.: (from EBSCO Publishing, Florida Center for Library Automation, Gale Group, O C L C Online Computer Library Center, Inc., ProQuest Information & Learning).
Indexed: ABIn, CLT&T, HRIS, LogistBibl.
—BLDSC (8547.630620), IE, ingenta. **CCC.**
Published by: Reed Business Information (Subsidiary of: Reed Business), 275 Washington St, Newton, MA 02458. TEL 617-558-4241, FAX 617-558-4480, http://www.manufacturing.net/scm/, http://www.reedbusiness.com. Ed. Frank Quinn TEL 617-558-4359. Pub. Susan M Fitzgerald TEL 617-558-4519. Circ: 12,000. **Subscr. to:** Reed Business Information, PO Box 15565, North Hollywood, CA 91615-5565. TEL 888-343-5567, http://www.pubservice.com/CH.htm.

658 360 IND ISSN 0586-0008
HD28
SURVEY; a quarterly journal. Text in English. 1973 (vol.13). q. USD 10. adv. bk.rev. **Document type:** *Academic/Scholarly.* **Description:** Covers the study of management and welfare in India and abroad including labor economics, human relations, personnel management, sociology, psychology, economics, and public systems management.
Published by: Indian Institute of Social Welfare and Business Management, College Square West, Kolkata, West Bengal 700 073, India. Ed. A C Ray. Circ: 800.

SURVEY REPORT ON VARIABLE PAY PROGRAMS. see *BUSINESS AND ECONOMICS—Personnel Management*

658.2 ITA ISSN 0391-7045
SVILUPPO E ORGANIZZAZIONE. Text in Italian. 1970. bi-m. adv. bk.rev. charts. reprint service avail. from PQC.
Related titles: Microform ed.: (from PQC).
Published by: Edizioni Scientifiche Tecniche Europee s.r.l., Via Giorgio Vasari, 15, Milan, MI 20135, Italy. TEL 39-02-55018039, FAX 39-02-5455644, edizioni.este@iol.it. Ed. Raoul C D Nacamulli. R&P Gianni Ceriani. Adv. contact Emma Samarati. Circ: 6,200 (paid); 1,800 (controlled).

658 300 GBR ISSN 0883-7066
QA402 CODEN: SDREEG
➤ **SYSTEM DYNAMICS REVIEW.** Text in English. 1975. q. USD 650 to institutions; USD 715 combined subscription to institutions print & online eds. (effective 2006). adv. bk.rev. back issues avail.; reprint service avail. from PSC. **Document type:** *Journal, Academic/Scholarly.* **Description:** Provides information and advances in the application of the perspective and methods of system dynamics to societal, technical, managerial, and environmental problems.
Supersedes: Dynamica (0306-7564)
Related titles: Microform ed.: (from PQC); Online - full text ed.: ISSN 1099-1727. 1996. USD 650 to institutions (effective 2006) (from EBSCO Publishing, ProQuest Information & Learning, Swets Information Services, Wiley InterScience).
Indexed: ABIn, ASCA, CurCont, EngInd, GEOBASE, IAOP, Inspec, PsycInfo, PsycholAb, RASB, SSCI, e-psyche.
—BLDSC (8589.151000), AskIEEE, CISTI, Ei, IDS, IE, Infotrieve, ingenta. **CCC.**
Published by: (System Dynamics Society), John Wiley & Sons Ltd. (Subsidiary of: John Wiley & Sons, Inc.), The Atrium, Southern Gate, Chichester, West Sussex PO19 8SQ, United Kingdom. TEL 44-1243-779777, FAX 44-1243-775878, customer@wiley.co.uk, http://www3.interscience.wiley.com/cgi-bin/jhome/11215, http://www.wiley.co.uk. Ed. Brian Dangerfield. adv.: B&W page GBP 650, color page GBP 1,550; trim 200 x 260. Circ: 900. **Subscr. in the Americas to:** John Wiley & Sons, Inc., 111 River St, Hoboken, NJ 07030-5774. TEL 201-748-6645, 800-225-5945, subinfo@wiley.com.

658 USA ISSN 1094-429X
Q295 CODEN: SPARFL
➤ **SYSTEMIC PRACTICE AND ACTION RESEARCH.** Short title: S P A R. Text in English. 1988. bi-m. EUR 708, USD 728, GBP 448 combined subscription to institutions print & online eds. (effective 2005). adv. bk.rev. reprint service avail. from PSC. **Document type:** *Journal, Academic/Scholarly.*
Description: Provides an interdisciplinary approach to the study of systems. Attempts to find ways to utilize and apply the concepts of system science.
Formerly (until 1998): Systems Practice (0894-9859)
Related titles: Microfilm ed.: (from PQC); Online - full text ed.: ISSN 1573-9295 (from EBSCO Publishing, Gale Group, IngentaConnect, Kluwer Online, O C L C Online Computer Library Center, Inc., ProQuest Information & Learning, Springer LINK, Swets Information Services).
Indexed: ABIn, ASCA, BibLing, CMCI, CompLI, CurCont, EngInd, FamI, IMFL, Inspec, ORMS, QC&AS, RASB, SSCI.
—BLDSC (8589.267300), CISTI, Ei, IDS, IE, Infotrieve, ingenta. **CCC.**
Published by: (University of Lincoln, Business School GBR), Plenum US (Subsidiary of: Springer Science+Business Media), 233 Spring St, New York, NY 10013. TEL 212-460-1500, FAX 212-460-1575, service@springer-ny.com, http://springerlink.metapress.com/openurl.asp?genre=journal&issn=1094-429X, http://www.springeronline.com. Ed. Robert L Flood.

➤ **SYSTEMS DEVELOPMENT MANAGEMENT.** see *COMPUTERS—Computer Systems*

➤ **SYSTEMS RESEARCH AND BEHAVIORAL SCIENCE.** see *COMPUTERS—Computer Systems*

658 003 USA
➤ **THE SYSTEMS THINKER (EMAIL EDITION).** (files in PDF format) Text in English. 1990. 10/yr. USD 109 to individuals; USD 189 to libraries (effective 2003). bk.rev. back issues avail. **Document type:** *Newsletter, Academic/Scholarly.*
Description: Presents a systems perspective on current issues and challenges facing managers in the business world.
Formerly: The Systems Thinker (Print Edition) (1050-2726)
Media: E-mail. **Related titles:** CD-ROM ed.: price varies.
—BLDSC (8589.472000), IE, ingenta.
Published by: Pegasus Communications, Inc., 1 Moody St, Waltham, MA 02154-5339. TEL 802-862-0095, 800-272-0945, FAX 802-864-7626, info@pegasuscom.com, http://www.thesystemsthinker.com/, http://www.pegasuscom.com. Circ: 5,000 (paid).

658 GBR ISSN 0954-478X
HD62.15 CODEN: TQMMEF
➤ **THE T Q M MAGAZINE.** (Total Quality Management) Text in English. bi-m. EUR 5,371.16 in Europe; USD 5,479 in North America; AUD 6,069 in Australasia; GBP 3,761.66 in UK & elsewhere (effective 2006). bk.rev. reprint service avail. from PSC. **Document type:** *Journal, Academic/Scholarly.*
Description: Aims to improve quality by bringing ideas, case studies, reviews and techniques to working managers and the scholars and research sectors.
Incorporates: Training for Quality (0968-4875); (1993-1998): Strategic Insights into Quality (0968-0829); Asia Pacific Journal of Marketing Logistics; Which was formerly (until 1993): Asia Pacific International Journal of Marketing (0954-7517); (until 1996): Asia Pacific Journal of Quality Management (0954-3570)
Related titles: Online - full text ed.: (from EBSCO Publishing, Emerald Group Publishing Limited, Gale Group, IngentaConnect, O C L C Online Computer Library Center, Inc., ProQuest Information & Learning, Swets Information Services).
Indexed: ABIn, BrEdI, CPM, CurCont, ERA, EmerIntel, Emerald, EngInd, ErgAb, M&MA, MEA, QAb, TEA.
—BLDSC (8873.783000), Ei, IE, Infotrieve, ingenta, Linda Hall. **CCC.**
Published by: Emerald Group Publishing Limited, 60-62 Toller Ln, Bradford, W Yorks BD8 9BY, United Kingdom. TEL 44-1274-777700, FAX 44-1274-785200, tqm@emeraldinsight.com, infomation@emeraldinsight.com, http://www.emeraldinsight.com/tqm.htm. Ed. Dr. Alex Douglas.

➤ **TABAK PLUS GEMAK**; vakblad voor de tabaksdetailhandel. see *TOBACCO*

658 USA ISSN 1080-0387
CODEN: PRASF5
THE TAKE - CHARGE ASSISTANT. Text in English. 1995. m. USD 75; USD 95 in Canada & Mexico; USD 110 elsewhere (effective 2000). **Document type:** *Newsletter.* **Description:** Helps office professionals manage stress; develop a strong verbal professional image; build verbal, written, and mathematics skills; hone their management and interpersonal skills; and balance their professional and personal lives.
Related titles: Online - full text ed.: (from Gale Group, O C L C Online Computer Library Center, Inc.).
—**CCC.**
Published by: American Management Association, 1610 Broadway, New York, NY 10019. TEL 212-586-8100, 800-313-8650, FAX 212-903-8083, amapubs@aol.com, http://www.amanet.org.

TAX & BUSINESS ADVISER. see *BUSINESS AND ECONOMICS—Accounting*

658.153 USA ISSN 0747-8607
KF6289.8.E9
TAX MANAGEMENT COMPENSATION PLANNING JOURNAL. Text in English. 1973. m. USD 426 (effective 1999). s-a. index, cum.index. back issues avail. **Document type:** *Trade.*
Description: Reviews major employee benefit plans in use as well as developments in retirement, profit sharing, welfare plans, stock options, and other employee compensation arrangements.
Former titles (until 1983): Compensation Planning Journal (0148-690X); (until 1977): Executive Compensation Journal (0094-789X); (until 1974): Tax Management Ecexutive Compensation Journal (0093-6995)
Related titles: Microform ed.: (from PQC); Online - full text ed.: ISSN 1544-0788 (from Northern Light Technology, Inc., ProQuest Information & Learning, The Bureau of National Affairs, Inc., Thomson West); ♦ Series: Tax Management Compensation Planning.
Indexed: ATI, BPIA, BusI, CLI, FamI, LII, LRI.
—**CCC.**
Published by: Tax Management Inc. (Subsidiary of: The Bureau of National Affairs, Inc.), 1231 25th St, N W, Washington, DC 20037. TEL 202-452-4200, 800-372-1033, http://www.bna.com. Ed. Glenn B Davis.

658 USA ISSN 1069-6539
CODEN: TMBRFG
TEAM MANAGEMENT BRIEFINGS. Text in English. 1993. m. USD 178 domestic; USD 198 in Canada; USD 258 elsewhere (effective 2005). **Document type:** *Newsletter, Trade.*
Description: Contains tips and ideas for managing teams of employees.
—CISTI, IE.
Published by: Briefings Publishing Group (Subsidiary of: Douglas Publications, Inc.), 1101 King St, Ste 110, Alexandria, VA 22314. TEL 703-518-2343, 800-722-9221, FAX 703-684-2136, customerservice@briefings.com, http://www.briefings.com. Ed. Joe McGavin. Pub. Michelle Cox.

658 GBR ISSN 1352-7592
HD66
➤ **TEAM PERFORMANCE MANAGEMENT**; an international journal. Text in English. 1995. q. EUR 1,445.29 in Europe to institutions; USD 1,469 in North America to institutions; AUD 1,989 in Australasia to institutions; GBP 1,010.29 to institutions in UK & elsewhere (effective 2006). back issues avail.; reprint service avail. from PSC. **Document type:** *Journal, Academic/Scholarly.* **Description:** Covers applied research related to all aspects of work teams and collaborative work arrangements.
Incorporates: Journal of High Performance Teams
Related titles: CD-ROM ed.; Online - full text ed.: (from EBSCO Publishing, Emerald Group Publishing Limited, Gale Group, IngentaConnect, O C L C Online Computer Library Center, Inc., ProQuest Information & Learning, Swets Information Services).
Indexed: ABIn, EmerIntel, Emerald, ErgAb.
—BLDSC (8614.560200), IE, Infotrieve, ingenta. **CCC.**
Published by: Emerald Group Publishing Limited, 60-62 Toller Ln, Bradford, W Yorks BD8 9BY, United Kingdom. TEL 44-1274-777700, FAX 44-1274-785200, infomation@emeraldinsight.com, http://www.emeraldinsight.com/tpm.htm. Ed. Dr. Linda S Wing. Pub. Ms. Paula Fernandez. R&P Mr. John Eggleton.

658 USA
TECHCOMP REVIEW. Text in English. 1988. q. USD 10. back issues avail. **Description:** Examines the interface between technology and competition within the context of various industries.
Published by: Central Michigan University, School of Business Administration, Smith Hall, Mt Pleasant, MI 48859. TEL 517-774-3450. Ed. S Benjamin Prasad. Circ: 500.

TECHNICIAN AND SKILLED TRADES PERSONNEL REPORT - GEOGRAPHIC EDITION. see *BUSINESS AND ECONOMICS—Personnel Management*

658 600 DEU ISSN 0344-9696
TECHNOLOGIE-NACHRICHTEN - MANAGEMENT-INFORMATIONEN. Text in German. 1968. s-m.
—IE, Infotrieve. **CCC.**
Published by: T N V GmbH, An den Eichen, Hennef, 53773, Germany. TEL 02248-1881, FAX 02248-1796. Ed. Nicola Gasterstaedt. Circ: 500.

TECHNOLOGIE UND MANAGEMENT. see *TECHNOLOGY: COMPREHENSIVE WORKS*

TECHNOLOGY ANALYSIS & STRATEGIC MANAGEMENT. see *TECHNOLOGY: COMPREHENSIVE WORKS*

658 382 600 USA ISSN 1072-0782
➤ **TECHNOLOGY TRANSFER SOCIETY. INTERNATIONAL SYMPOSIUM AND EXHIBIT. ANNUAL MEETING PROCEEDINGS.** Text in English. 1990. a. USD 75 (effective 1998). bk.rev. cum.index. back issues avail. **Document type:** *Proceedings, Academic/Scholarly.* **Description:** Contains full text papers presented at the symposium on methods, models and case studies of technology transfer.
Indexed: Agr.
Published by: Technology Transfer Society, 230 E. Ohio St., Flr. 4, Chicago, IL 60611-3268. TEL 312-644-0828, FAX 312-644-8557, 102234.166@compuserve.com.

➤ **TELEMARKETER.** see *BUSINESS AND ECONOMICS—Marketing And Purchasing*

658 SWE ISSN 1102-3597
TEMA ARKIV. Variant title: Svensk Arkivtidskrift. Text in Swedish. 1991. q. SEK 200 (effective 1998). adv. bk.rev.
Formed by the merger of (1983-1991): Arkivforum (0281-2371); (1951-1991): Arkivinformation (0571-0731)
Published by: Foereningsarkivet, Noerrmalmsgatan 4, Sundsvall, 85185, Sweden. TEL 46-8-24-17-60, FAX 46-60-19-21-36, ove.norberg@sundsvall.se. Ed. Owe Norberg. Adv. contact Harriet Kvist. Circ: 10,000.

658 SWE ISSN 1650-4224
TEMPO (STOCKHOLM). Text in Swedish. 1971. 5/yr.
Former titles (until 2001): Nu (1403-5693); (until 1998): Smaafoeretag & Utveckling (1102-4283); (until 1991): S I N D - Info (1101-8208)
Published by: N U T E K. Verket foer Naeringslivsutveckling/ Swedish Business Development Agency, Liljeholmsvaegen 32, Stockholm, 11786, Sweden. TEL 46-8-6819100, FAX 46-8-196826, nutek@nutek.se, http://www.nutek.se. Ed. Sven-Oskar Ruhmen. Circ: 22,000.

TEORIE VEDY/THEORY OF SCIENCE. see *SCIENCES: COMPREHENSIVE WORKS*

▼ **TEXAS APARTMENTS.** see *REAL ESTATE*

658 GBR
THAMESMAN PUBLICATIONS. OCCASIONAL PAPERS. Text in English. 1978. irreg. bk.rev. **Document type:** *Monographic series.*
Published by: Oxford Brookes University, School of Business, Oxford Brookes University, Wheatley, Oxford, OX33 1HX, United Kingdom. FAX 0865-485830. Ed. B Axford.

658 SWE ISSN 1403-9427
TIDNINGEN G; Sveriges affaers och industritidning. Text in Swedish. 1988. 4/yr. SEK 185 (effective 2004). adv. **Document type:** *Journal, Trade.*
Former titles (until 1997): G (1104-8107); (until 1992): Tidningen G (1988) (1101-4687)
Published by: Active Media AB, Arabygatan 82, Vaexjoe, 35246, Sweden. TEL 46-470-711865, FAX 46-470-13042, red@tidningeng.com, http://www.tidningeng.com. Ed. Tina Jukas. Pub. Soeren Moellmark. Adv. contact Johnny Lindman. Circ: 8,000.

658 NLD ISSN 1388-2635
TIJDSCHRIFT ADMINISTRATIE. Text in Dutch. 1992. 10/yr. EUR 122.50; EUR 12.75 per issue (effective 2003). **Document type:** *Journal, Trade.*
Formerly (until 1998): Nieuwsbrief Administratie (0927-6076)
—Infotrieve.
Published by: Kluwer B.V. (Subsidiary of: Wolters Kluwer N.V.), Postbus 23, Deventer, 7400 GA, Netherlands. TEL 31-570-673449, FAX 31-570-691555, http://www.kluwer.nl.

658 NLD ISSN 0928-8627
HD28
TIJDSCHRIFT VOOR BEDRIJFSADMINISTRATIE. Text in Dutch. 1894. 10/yr. adv. bk.rev. charts; illus. **Description:** Publishes studies on all aspects of business administration, industrial organization, management economics, and relevant issues in law, computerization, accounting and statistics.
Former titles (until 1993): Maandblad voor Bedrijfsadministratie en Bedrijfsorganisatie; Maandblad voor Bedrijfsadministratie en Organisatie (0024-8630)
Indexed: ExcerpMed, KES.
—IE, Infotrieve.
Published by: Reed Business Information bv (Subsidiary of: Reed Business), Postbus 16400, Den Haag, 2500 BK, Netherlands. TEL 31-70-3624800, FAX 31-70-3605606. Circ: 9,000.

658 NLD ISSN 0169-5304
TIJDSCHRIFT VOOR INKOOP & LOGISTIEK. Cover title: I & L. Text in Dutch. 1985. 10/yr. EUR 137.27 domestic; EUR 142.57 foreign (effective 2005). adv. **Document type:** *Trade.*
Description: Covers news and issues of importance to purchasing managers and logistics managers, with particular emphasis on the integral business approach.
—IE, Infotrieve.
Published by: (Nederlandse Vereniging voor Inkoopmanagement), Sdu Uitgevers bv, Postbus 34, The Hague, 2516 BC, Netherlands. sdu@sdu.nl, http://www.ienl.nl, http://www.sdu.nl/. Ed. Paul van Haaster. adv.: B&W page EUR 2,300; trim 180 x 267. Circ: 7,970. **Subscr. to:** Postbus 20014, The Hague 2500 EA, Netherlands. TEL 31-70-3789880, FAX 31-70-3789783. **Co-sponsor:** Vereniging voor Logistiek Management.

TINBERGEN MAGAZINE. see *BUSINESS AND ECONOMICS—Economic Systems And Theories, Economic History*

658 SGP
TODAY'S MANAGER. Text in English. 1995. bi-m. **Document type:** *Trade.* **Description:** Cover stories encapsulate a variety of leading-edge business and management topics including Information Technology, Human Resource, Communications, Marketing, and Public Relations. Business trends, developments, issues, and changes affecting management professionals are discussed and illustrated.
Published by: Singapore Institute of Management, Management House, 41 Namly Ave, Singapore, 267616, Singapore. TEL 65-874-3067, FAX 65-462-5751, http://www1.sim.edu.sg/sim/pub/gen/sim_pub_gen_content.cfm?mnuid=164. Ed. Roland Tan Chee Teik. Circ: 18,500.

658 USA ISSN 1089-5949
CODEN: TPAEEQ
TOM PETERS FAST FORWARD. Text in English. 1986. m. USD 150; USD 200 foreign. bk.rev. **Document type:** *Newsletter.*
Description: Presents management case studies and commentary on organizational change and innovation.
Formerly: Tom Peters on Achieving Excellence (0887-5332)
—CASDDS. **CCC.**
Published by: T P G Communications, 555 Hamilton Ave, Palo Alto, CA 94301. TEL 415-326-4496, 800-827-3095, FAX 415-326-7065, oaex@aol.com. Ed. Liz Mitchell. Pub. Tom Peters. **Subscr. to:** PO Box 652, Mt Morris, IL 61054-0652.

658 USA
TOMORROW'S BUSINESS✶. Text in English. 1996. m. **Document type:** *Newsletter.* **Description:** Examines future business trends for middle- to upper-middle management.
Address: 493 Santa Barbara Dr, Los Altos, CA 94022-3810. TEL 703-759-7947, FAX 703-759-7655, sarahengel@aol.com. Ed. Sarah Engel.

658 USA
TOP EXECUTIVE COMPENSATION. Text in English. 1960. a. USD 195 to non-members; USD 55 to members (effective 2003). illus.; stat. **Document type:** *Monographic series.* **Description:** Analyzes compensation of the five highest-paid executives in approximately 900 companies representing seven major types of business.
Related titles: Microfiche ed.: (from CIS).
Indexed: SRI.
Published by: Conference Board, Inc., 845 Third Ave, New York, NY 10022. TEL 212-759-0900, FAX 212-980-7014, http://www.conference-board.org.

658 AUT
TOP GEWINN. Text in German. 1990. m. adv. **Document type:** *Consumer.* **Description:** Contains information about stock markets, careers, management news, and real estate.
Published by: Wailand und Waldstein GmbH, Stiftgasse 31, Vienna, W 1070, Austria. TEL 43-1-52124-0, FAX 43-1-5212440, gewinn@gewinn.vienna.at, http:// www.gewinn.co.at. Eds., Pubs. Georg Wailand, Georg Waldstein. Adv. contact Raimund Jacoba. Circ: 42,000.

658 LUX
TOP MANAGEMENT & FINANCE LUXEMBOURG. Text in French, English. 1998. a. EUR 220 per issue (effective 2004). **Document type:** *Directory, Trade.* **Description:** Contains complete biographies of members of the board for over 1,200 companies in Luxembourg.
Published by: Top Edilux sarl, 156 route d'Arlon, Luxembourg, 8010, Luxembourg. TEL 32-2-6462740, FAX 32-2-6462017. Ed., Pub., R&P Alain Renier. Circ: 2,000 (paid).

658 920 BEL ISSN 0779-5920
TOP MANAGEMENT BELGIUM. Text in Dutch, English, French. 1984. a. bk.rev. **Document type:** *Directory, Trade.*
Related titles: CD-ROM ed.
Published by: Who's Who International S A, Av des Casernes 41A, Brussels, 1040, Belgium. TEL 32-2-6462740, FAX 32-2-6462017, info@topmanagement.be, http:// www.topmanagement.net. Ed., Pub., R&P Alain Renier. Adv. contact Thierry Roberti Lintermans. Circ: 5,000.

658 USA
TOP MANAGEMENT COMPENSATION - REGRESSION ANALYSIS REPORT. Text in English. a. USD 690. charts. **Document type:** *Trade.* **Description:** Calculates salary and total compensation levels for companies in different industries.
Published by: (Executive Compensation Service (ECS)), Wyatt Data Services, 218 Rte 17 N, Rochelle Park, NJ 07622-9832. TEL 201-843-1177, FAX 201-843-0101.

658 FRA
TOP MANAGEMENT FRANCE. Text in French. 1984. a. EUR 435 (effective 2005). bk.rev. **Document type:** *Directory, Trade.* **Description:** Contains complete biographies of members of the board for over 14,500 companies in France.
Published by: Alan Renier & Ass, 17 bis passage Jean Nicot, Paris, 75007, France. TEL 33-1-45558571, FAX 33-1-47530826, http://www.topmanagement.net. Ed., Pub. Alain Renier. Adv. contact Thierry de Longvilliers. Circ: 10,000 (paid).

658 USA
TOP MANAGEMENT REMUNERATION REPORT - EUROPE. Text in English. a. USD 940. charts. **Document type:** *Trade.* **Description:** Provides a comprehensive guide to total compensation practices for executives in 17 Western European countries and Turkey.
Published by: (Executive Compensation Service (ECS)), Wyatt Data Services, 218 Rte 17 N, Rochelle Park, NJ 07622-9832. TEL 201-843-1177, FAX 201-843-0101.

658 USA
TOP MANAGEMENT REPORT. Text in English. a. (in 2 vols.). USD 690. **Document type:** *Trade.* **Description:** Features analyses of executive pay reported by company size for over 50 industry categories.
Published by: (Executive Compensation Service (ECS)), Wyatt Data Services, 218 Rte 17 N, Rochelle Park, NJ 07622-9832. TEL 201-843-1177, FAX 201-843-0101.

658 AUT
TOP SERVICE. Text in German. bi-m.
Address: Nikolsdorfergasse 7-11, Vienna, W 1051, Austria. TEL 01-555585, FAX 01-555585215, TELEX 0111669. Ed. Michael Stenzel. Circ: 105,200.

658 GBR ISSN 1478-3363
CODEN: TQMAED
➤ **TOTAL QUALITY MANAGEMENT & BUSINESS EXCELLENCE.** Text in English. 1990. 10/yr. GBP 840, USD 1,443 combined subscription to institutions print & online eds. (effective 2006). adv. bk.rev. index. back issues avail.; reprint service avail. from PSC. **Document type:** *Journal, Academic/Scholarly.*
Formerly (until 2003): Total Quality Management (0954-4127)
Related titles: Online - full text ed.: ISSN 1478-3371. GBP 798, USD 1,371 to institutions (effective 2006) (from EBSCO Publishing, Gale Group, IngentaConnect, Northern Light Technology, Inc., O C L C Online Computer Library Center, Inc., ProQuest Information & Learning, Swets Information Services).
Indexed: ABIn, ASCA, ATI, CIS, CJA, CPM, CurCont, ERA, Emerald, IBSS, Inspec, RHEA, SSCI, ST&MA, TTI, WBA, WMB.
—BLDSC (8870.274950), IDS, IE, ingenta. **CCC.**
Published by: Routledge (Subsidiary of: Taylor & Francis Group), 4 Park Sq, Milton Park, Abingdon, Oxon OX14 4RN, United Kingdom. TEL 44-1235-828600, FAX 44-1235-829000, journals@routledge.com, http://www.tandf.co.uk/journals/titles/ 14783363.asp, http://www.routledge.co.uk. Ed. Gopal K Kanji. **Subscr. to:** Taylor & Francis Ltd, Journals Customer Service, Rankine Rd, Basingstoke, Hants RG24 8PR, United Kingdom. TEL 44-1256-813000, FAX 44-1256-330245, enquiry@tandf.co.uk.

338.4791 GBR ISSN 1479-053X
▼ ➤ **TOURISM AND HOSPITALITY PLANNING & DEVELOPMENT.** Text in English. 2004. 3/yr. GBP 173, USD 286 combined subscription to institutions print & online eds. (effective 2006). bk.rev. **Document type:** *Journal, Academic/Scholarly.* **Description:** Focuses on bringing together researchers and practitioners, individuals and organisations interested in both the theoretical and the practical aspects of planning and development.
Related titles: Online - full text ed.: ISSN 1479-0548. GBP 164, USD 272 to institutions (effective 2006) (from EBSCO Publishing, Gale Group, IngentaConnect, O C L C Online Computer Library Center, Inc., Swets Information Services).
—BLDSC (8870.920610).
Published by: Routledge (Subsidiary of: Taylor & Francis Group), 4 Park Sq, Milton Park, Abingdon, Oxon OX14 4RN, United Kingdom. TEL 44-1235-828600, FAX 44-1235-829000, journals@routledge.com, http://www.tandf.co.uk/journals/titles/ 1479053X.asp, http://www.routledge.co.uk. Eds. Bob Brotherton, Les Lumsdon. **Subscr. to:** Taylor & Francis Ltd, Journals Customer Service, Rankine Rd, Basingstoke, Hants RG24 8PR, United Kingdom. TEL 44-1256-813000, FAX 44-1256-330245, enquiry@tandf.co.uk.

➤ **TOURISM MANAGEMENT.** see *TRAVEL AND TOURISM*

➤ **TOURIST ATTRACTIONS AND PARKS.** see *LEISURE AND RECREATION*

658 USA ISSN 0893-2662
T391
TRADESHOW AND EXHIBIT MANAGER. Text in English. 1986. bi-m. USD 80 domestic; USD 110 foreign (effective 2005). adv. bk.rev. charts; illus.; tr.lit. index. back issues avail. **Document type:** *Magazine, Trade.*
Related titles: ♦ Supplement to: Tradeshow Directory.
Published by: Goldstein and Associates, 1150 Yale St, Ste 12, Santa Monica, CA 90403-4738. TEL 310-828-1309. Ed. Les Plesko. Pub. Steve Goldstein. Circ: 18,000 (paid).

658.071 USA ISSN 0095-5892
CODEN: TRNGB6
TRAINING; the magazine covering the human side of business. Text in English. 1964. m. USD 78 domestic; USD 88 in Canada; USD 154 elsewhere (effective 2005). adv. bk.rev. charts; illus.; stat.; tr.lit. Index. back issues avail.; reprint service avail. from PQC. **Document type:** *Magazine, Trade.* **Description:** Covers all aspects of training, management and organizational development, motivation and performance improvement.
Formerly: Training in Business and Industry (0041-0896)
Related titles: Microform ed.: (from PQC); Online - full text ed.: (from bigchalk, EBSCO Publishing, Florida Center for Library Automation, Gale Group, H.W. Wilson, O C L C Online Computer Library Center, Inc., ProQuest Information & Learning).
Indexed: ABIn, AgeL, Agr, BPI, BPIA, BibAg, BusI, CIJE, Emerald, MEDLINE, ManagCont, PersLit, QAb, SFSA, WorkRelAb.
—BLDSC (8883.480000), CASDDS, CISTI, IE, Infotrieve, ingenta. **CCC.**
Published by: V N U Business Publications (Subsidiary of: V N U Business Media), 50 S Ninth St, Minneapolis, MN 55402. TEL 612-333-0471, FAX 612-333-6526, edit@trainingmag.com, bmcomm@vnuinc.com, http://www.trainingmag.com, http://www.vnubusinessmedia.com/. Ed. Tammy Gordon. Pub. Stacy Marmolejo TEL 612-340-4779. adv.: B&W page USD 7,800, color page USD 9,940; trim 8 x 10.875. Circ: 50,000 (paid). **Subscr. to:** PO Box 2104, Skokie, IL 60076-7804.

658 DEU ISSN 0939-2688
TRAINING AKTUELL; Spezial-Informationsdienst fuer die gesamte Weiterbildungsbranche. Text in German. 1990. m. EUR 154 (effective 2003); includes ManagerSeminare. adv. bk.rev.; software rev. charts; illus.; tr.lit. back issues avail. **Document type:** *Newsletter, Trade.* **Description:** Reports on all aspects of human resources functions: politics, training, associations, learning technologies, media and literature, computer-based training, and job markets.
Published by: managerSeminare Verlags GmbH, Endenicher Str 282, Bonn, 53121, Germany. TEL 49-228-97791-0, FAX 49-228-616164, info@managerseminare.de, http://www.managerseminare.de. Ed. Nicole Bussmann. Adv. contact Juergen Koch. Circ: 2,500 (controlled).

TRAINING AND DEVELOPMENT IN AUSTRALIA. see *BUSINESS AND ECONOMICS—Labor And Industrial Relations*

658 GBR ISSN 0951-3507
TRAINING AND MANAGEMENT DEVELOPMENT METHODS. Text in English. 1987. 5/yr. EUR 8,329 in Europe; USD 9,139 in North America; AUD 9,489 in Australasia; GBP 5,739 in UK & elsewhere (effective 2006). **Document type:** *Journal, Academic/Scholarly.* **Description:** Concentrates on presenting usable, up-to-date learning methods. Includes practical examples of exercises and case studies.
Related titles: Online - full text ed.: (from O C L C Online Computer Library Center, Inc., ProQuest Information & Learning).
Indexed: ABIn, ErgAb, M&MA, T&DA.
—BLDSC (8883.501180), IE, Infotrieve. **CCC.**
Published by: Emerald Group Publishing Limited, 60-62 Toller Ln, Bradford, W Yorks BD8 9BY, United Kingdom. TEL 44-1274-777700, FAX 44-1274-785200, infomation@emeraldinsight.com, http:// www.emeraldinsight.com/tmdm.htm. Ed. David Pollitt.

658.071 GBR ISSN 1352-1187
TRAINING MANAGEMENT. Text in English. 198?. fortn. **Document type:** *Magazine, Trade.*
—**CCC.**
Published by: Inside Communications Ltd., One Canada Square, Canary Wharf, London, E14 5AP, United Kingdom. TEL 44-20-77728300, FAX 44-20-77728599, ic@insidecom.co.uk, Katie.richardson@mrn.co.uk, http://www.insidecom.co.uk.

658.0029 GBR ISSN 1470-7268
THE TRAINING MANAGER'S YEARBOOK. Abbreviated title: TMY. Text in English. 2000. a. GBP 80 (effective 2001). adv. stat. 800 p./no. 2 cols./p.; **Document type:** *Directory, Trade.* **Description:** Lists training contacts in over 5,500 major UK companies, also over 3000 suppliers and advisers, including venues, products and services.
Formerly (until 1999): The Management Training Directory (0267-8802)
Related titles: Diskette ed.
Published by: A P Information Services, Marlborough House, 298 Regents Park Rd, London, N3 2UU, United Kingdom. TEL 44-20-83499988, FAX 44-20-83499797, tmy@ap-info.co.uk, info@apinfo.co.uk, http://www.trainingmanagers.co.uk, http://www.ap-info.co.uk. Ed. Helen Irwin. Pub. Alan Philipp. Adv. contact James Johnston. B&W page GBP 600, color page GBP 900; trim 210 x 297. Circ: 4,500.

TRANSPORT MANAGEMENT. see *TRANSPORTATION*

TRANSPORTATION EXECUTIVE UPDATE. see *TRANSPORTATION—Trucks And Trucking*

658.5 FRA ISSN 0041-185X
HD28
TRAVAIL ET METHODES; revue des techniques nouvelles au service de l'entreprise. Text in French. 1947. m. adv. bk.rev. charts; illus. cum.index. **Document type:** *Magazine, Corporate.*
Indexed: CISA, ExcerpMed, KES, RASB.
Published by: Editions Entreprises et Techniques, 5 bis, rue Fontaine au Roi, Paris, 75011, France. TEL 48-05-25-70. Ed. G Fuchs. Circ: 10,000.

TRAVEL INDUSTRY DIGEST. see *TRAVEL AND TOURISM*

TREASURY & RISK MANAGEMENT. see *BUSINESS AND ECONOMICS—Investments*

658 336 AUS
TRENDS, TIPS AND TAX. Text in English. 1992. s-a. looseleaf. AUD 1,300. **Document type:** *Trade.* **Description:** Comprehensive practical guide to current employment and reward issues in Australia, including taxation review.
Published by: Cullen Egan Dell, Level 8, 50 Bridge St, Sydney, NSW 2000, Australia. TEL 61-2-9375-6800, FAX 61-2-9233-6800. Ed. Marilyn Earl. Circ: 140.

TYOTEHOSEURAN METSATIEDOTE. see *AGRICULTURE*

658 PHL ISSN 0042-0158
U E BUSINESS REVIEW; a magazine for business leaders. Text in English. 1958. 3/yr. abstr.; charts; stat. index.
Published by: (College of Business Administration), University of the East, Sampaloc, Manila, Philippines.

U K KOMPASS REGIONAL SALES GUIDE. see *BUSINESS AND ECONOMICS—Trade And Industrial Directories*

658.47 SWE ISSN 0280-8072
U & D. (Underhaall & Driftsaekerhet) Text in Swedish. 1981. 11/yr. SEK 1,144 domestic; SEK 1,352 elsewhere (effective 2003). adv. **Document type:** *Magazine, Trade.*

Published by: Mentor Online AB, Tryffelslingan 10, PO Box 72001, Lidingoe, 18172, Sweden. TEL 46-8-6704100, FAX 46-8-6616455, http://www.maintenancenet.se/uochd/. Ed., Pub. Anders Aastroem TEL 46-42-4901941. Adv. contact Mikael Joensson TEL 46-42-4901945. B&W page SEK 21,900, color page SEK 30,600; 203 x 302. Circ: 3,700.

658 USA ISSN 0740-2678
HD2425
U S ASSOCIATION EXECUTIVE. Text in English. 1982. w. USD 95. adv. **Document type:** *Newspaper.* **Description:** Publishes news about the association management profession and association suppliers.
Published by: Custom News, Inc., 4341 Montgomery Ave, Bethesda, MD 20814-4401. TEL 301-951-1881, FAX 301-656-2845. Ed. Diane Kirsh. Circ: 18,500.

U.S. DEPARTMENT OF AGRICULTURE. RURAL BUSINESS - COOPERATIVE SERVICE. SERVICE REPORT. see *AGRICULTURE*

658 USA
UNIT LOAD MANAGEMENT. Text in English. bi-m. USD 48 domestic; USD 60 in Canada; USD 100 elsewhere; free domestic to qualified personnel (effective 2002). adv. **Document type:** *Magazine, Trade.* **Description:** Dedicated to users of supply chain packaging systems. Each issue is full of information and ideas that directly benefits decision makers involved in unit load management, such as senior executives, packaging engineers, logistics professionals, managers of distribution centers and purchasing agents.
Published by: Industrial Reporting, Inc., 10244 Timber Ridge Dr, Ashland, VA 23005. TEL 804-550-0326, 800-805-0263 (Subscribe), FAX 804-550-2181, http://www.unitload.com/.

UNIVERSAL DIRECTORY - CONFERENCES - EXHIBITIONS - FUNCTIONS. see *MEETINGS AND CONGRESSES*

658 ECU
UNIVERSIDAD CENTRAL DEL ECUADOR. INSTITUTO DE ESTUDIOS ADMINISTRATIVOS. BOLETIN. Text in Spanish. bi-m. **Document type:** *Bulletin.*
Published by: Universidad Central del Ecuador, Instituto de Estudios Administrativos, Casilla 3474, Ave. AMERICA, 1396, Quito, Pichincha, Ecuador.

658 650 URY
UNIVERSIDAD DE LA REPUBLICA. INSTITUTO DE ADMINISTRACION. BOLETIN. Text in Spanish. 1976. irreg., latest vol.4, 1979. **Document type:** *Bulletin.*
Published by: Universidad de la Republica, Instituto de Administracion, Av. Dieciocho De Julio, 1953 Piso 4, Montevideo, 11206, Uruguay.

658 URY ISSN 0077-1287
UNIVERSIDAD DE LA REPUBLICA. INSTITUTO DE ADMINISTRACION. CUADERNO. Text in Spanish. 1956. irreg., latest vol.80, 1979. price varies.
Published by: Universidad de la Republica, Instituto de Administracion, Av. Dieciocho De Julio, 1953 Piso 4, Montevideo, 11206, Uruguay.

658 DEU ISSN 0935-381X
UNIVERSITAET MANNHEIM. INDUSTRIESEMINAR. ABHANDLUNGEN. Text in German. 1956. irreg., latest vol.56, 2001. price varies. **Document type:** *Monographic series, Academic/Scholarly.*
Formerly (until 1981): Universitaet Koeln. Industrieseminar. Abhandlungen (0531-0350)
Published by: (Universitaet Mannheim, Industrieseminar), Duncker und Humblot GmbH, Carl-Heinrich-Becker-Weg 9, Berlin, 12165, Germany. TEL 49-30-7900060, FAX 49-30-79000631, info@duncker-humblot.de, http://www.duncker-humblot.de.

658 CHE
UNIVERSITAET ZUERICH. INSTITUT FUER BETRIEBSWIRTSCHAFTLICHE FORSCHUNG. SCHRIFTENREIHE. Text in German. 1971. irreg., latest vol.93, 2003. price varies. **Document type:** *Monographic series, Academic/Scholarly.*
Published by: (Universitaet Zuerich, Institut fuer Betriebswirtschaftliche Forschung), Paul Haupt AG, Falkenplatz 14, Bern, 3001, Switzerland. TEL 41-31-3012425, FAX 41-31-3014669, verlag@haupt.ch, http://www.haupt.ch.

658 MEX
UNIVERSITARIO EJECUTIVO. Text in Spanish. m. MXP 150; MXP 550 Including Hecho en Mexico (effective 2001). adv. back issues avail. **Document type:** *Trade.*
Related titles: Online - full text ed.
Published by: Grupo Internacional Editorial S A de C V, Rio Nazas 34, Col. Cuahutemoc, Mexico D F, 06500, Mexico. TEL 52-5-2099930, FAX 52-5-5660564, buzon@intermundo.com.mx, http://www.intermundo.com.mx/. Ed. Ana Luisa Ochoa. Adv. contact Fabrizio Tavano. color page MXP 45,000. Circ: 15,000.

UNIVERSITATEA POLITEHNICA DIN TIMISOARA. BULETINUL STIINTIFIC. SERIA MANAGEMENT INGINERIE, ECONOMICA, INGINERIA, TRANSPORTURILOR. see *ENGINEERING*

003 BEL ISSN 0008-9737
T57.6 CODEN: CCROAT
UNIVERSITE LIBRE DE BRUXELLES. CENTRE D'ETUDES DE RECHERCHE OPERATIONNELLE. CAHIERS/OPERATIONS RESEARCH, STATISTICS AND APPLIED MATHEMATICS. Text in English, French. 1958. q. USD 20. adv. bk.rev. charts. cum.index.
Indexed: CIS, CompR, IAOP, Inspec, ZentMath.
—CISTI, Ei.
Published by: Universite Libre de Bruxelles, Centre d'Etudes de Recherche Operationnelle, c/o Institut de Statistique, Bd du Triomphe, CP 210, Brussels, 1050, Belgium. FAX 32-2-650-51-13.

658 GBR
UNIVERSITY OF BRADFORD. SCHOOL OF MANAGEMENT. WORKING PAPER SERIES. Text in English. irreg. **Document type:** *Monographic series, Academic/Scholarly.*
Formerly: University of Bradford. Management Centre. Working Paper Series
—BLDSC (9350.936300).
Published by: University of Bradford, School of Management, Emm Ln, Bradford, BD9 4JL, United Kingdom. TEL 44-1274-384387, FAX 44-1274-546866, k.a.cousens@bradford.ac.uk, management@bradford.ac.uk, http://www.brad.ac.uk/acad/management/.

UNIVERSITY OF NEW ENGLAND. DEPARTMENT OF ACCOUNTING & FINANCIAL MANAGEMENT. WORKING PAPERS. see *BUSINESS AND ECONOMICS—Accounting*

658 GBR ISSN 1356-3548
UNIVERSITY OF SOUTHAMPTON. DEPARTMENT OF MANAGEMENT. DISCUSSION PAPERS. Text in English. a. free. **Document type:** *Academic/Scholarly.*
—BLDSC (3597.887530).
Published by: University of Southampton, Department of Management, Southampton, Hants SO17 1BJ, United Kingdom. TEL 44-1703-593076, FAX 44-1703-593844, bvt@socsci.soton.ac.uk. Circ: 150.

330.099305 NZL ISSN 1174-7366
UNLIMITED; inspiring business. Text in English. 1998. 11/yr. NZD 89 domestic; NZD 95 in Australasia; NZD 110 elsewhere; NZD 8.95 newsstand/cover (effective 2004). adv. **Document type:** *Magazine, Trade.* **Description:** Aims to identify and analyze advancing trends in the way businesses develop and operate.
Related titles: Online - full text ed.: UnlimitedNet.
—**CCC.**
Published by: I D G Communications Ltd., Wellesley St., PO Box 6813, Auckland, 1036, New Zealand. TEL 64-9-377-9902, FAX 64-9-377-4604, idg@idg.co.nz, http://unlimited.co.nz, http://www.idg.net.nz. adv.: B&W page NZD 2,540, color page NZD 3,380; trim 235 x 315. Circ: 7,232 (paid and controlled).

658 DEU ISSN 1435-5418
UNTERNEHMENSBERATER. Text in German. 1997. q. EUR 46.01; EUR 12.78 newsstand/cover (effective 2002). adv. **Document type:** *Magazine, Trade.*
Published by: Dr. Curt Haefner Verlag GmbH, Bachstr 14-16, Heidelberg, 69121, Germany. TEL 49-6221-6446-0, FAX 49-6221-644640, info@haefner-verlag.de, http://www.haefner-verlag.de/fachzeitschr/unternber/index.php. adv.: B&W page EUR 1,534, color page EUR 2,556. Circ: 12,000 (paid and controlled).

658 DEU ISSN 0173-3664
UNTERNEHMER MAGAZIN. Text in German. 1953. m. EUR 7.50 newsstand/cover (effective 2002). adv. bk.rev. charts; illus.; stat. index. back issues avail. **Document type:** *Magazine, Consumer.* **Description:** Covers news and practical information for those owning a business. Features automation, finance, economics, and international trade.
Former titles (until 1980): Junge Wirtschaft (0022-6416); (until 1971): Die Aussprache (0004-8240)
Published by: (Arbeitsgemeinschaft Selbstaendiger Unternehmer e.V.), Unternehmerwirtschaft Verlags-GmbH, Postfach 201328, Bonn, 53143, Germany. TEL 49-228-954590, FAX 49-228-9545980, unternehmer-magazin@t-online.de. Ed., Adv. contact Reinhard Nenzel. B&W page EUR 4,350, color page EUR 5,100; trim 178 x 252. Circ: 17,500. **Co-sponsor:** Bundesverband Junger Unternehmer.

658 CHE ISSN 0042-059X
DIE UNTERNEHMUNG; swiss journal of business research and practice. Text in German. 1947. 6/yr. CHF 115 domestic; EUR 84 in Europe; CHF 132 elsewhere; CHF 68 domestic to students; EUR 51 in Europe to students; CHF 82 elsewhere to students; CHF 22 newsstand/cover (effective 2005). adv. bk.rev. charts; illus. index. reprints avail. **Document type:** *Journal, Trade.*
Indexed: DIP, IAOP, IBR, IBZ, KES, PAIS, SCIMP, SSCI.
—IE, Infotrieve. **CCC.**
Published by: Versus Verlag AG, Merkurstr 45, Zuerich, 8032, Switzerland. TEL 41-44-2510892, FAX 41-44-2626738, manfred.bruhn@unibas.ch, info@versus.ch, http://www.unternehmung.ch, http://www.versus.ch. Ed. Manfred Bruhn. adv.: B&W page CHF 750; trim 138 x 195. Circ: 1,700 (paid and controlled).

658 TZA ISSN 0856-1435
UONGOZI: JOURNAL OF MANAGEMENT DEVELOPMENT. Text in English. 1976. 3/yr. TZS 2,000 domestic; USD 23 in Africa; USD 30 elsewhere. adv. bk.rev. **Document type:** *Academic/Scholarly.*
Formerly: Tanzania Management Journal
Related titles: Diskette ed.
Published by: Institute of Development Management, PO Box 5, Mzumbe-morogoro, Tanzania. TEL 255-56-4380-4. Ed. P C Ndunguru. Adv. contact S K Fimnbo. page USD 30. Circ: 3,000.

UTILITY WEEK. see *ENERGY*

658 SWE ISSN 1651-355X
V I N N O V A ANALYS. Text in Swedish. 2001. irreg. price varies. back issues avail. **Document type:** *Monographic series, Academic/Scholarly.*
Formerly (until 2002): V I N N O V A Innovation i Fokus (1650-3147)
Related titles: Online - full content ed.
Published by: V I N N O V A/Swedish Agency for Innovation Systems, Maester Samuelsgatan 36, Stockholm, 10158, Sweden. TEL 46-8-4733000, FAX 46-8-4733005, vinnova@vinnova.se, http://www.vinnova.se.

658 SWE ISSN 1651-3541
V I N N O V A FORUM. Variant title: Innovationspolitik i Fokus. Text in Swedish. 2001. irreg., latest 2004. price varies. back issues avail. **Document type:** *Monographic series, Academic/Scholarly.*
Formerly (until 2002): V I N N O V A Debatt (1650-3139); Which incorporated (1999-2001): Transportpolitik i Fokus (1404-1367)
Related titles: Online - full content ed.
Published by: V I N N O V A/Swedish Agency for Innovation Systems, Maester Samuelsgatan 36, Stockholm, 10158, Sweden. TEL 46-8-4733000, FAX 46-8-4733005, vinnova@vinnova.se, http://www.vinnova.se.

658 SWE ISSN 1651-3568
V I N N O V A POLICY. Text in Swedish. 2002. bi-m. free (effective 2005). back issues avail. **Document type:** *Magazine, Consumer.*
Related titles: Online - full text ed.
Published by: V I N N O V A/Swedish Agency for Innovation Systems, Maester Samuelsgatan 36, Stockholm, 10158, Sweden. TEL 46-8-4733000, FAX 46-8-4733005, vinnovanytt@vinnova.se, vinnova@vinnova.se, http://www.vinnova.se. Eds. Krystyna Nilsson TEL 46-8-4733077, Per Eriksson TEL 46-8-4733001.

658 SWE ISSN 1650-3104
V I N N O V A RAPPORT. Text in Swedish. 2001. irreg. price varies. back issues avail. **Document type:** *Monographic series, Academic/Scholarly.*
Incorporates (2001-2001): V I N N O V A Meddelande (1650-3112)
Related titles: Online - full content ed.
—BLDSC (9236.888000).
Published by: V I N N O V A/Swedish Agency for Innovation Systems, Maester Samuelsgatan 36, Stockholm, 10158, Sweden. TEL 46-8-4733000, FAX 46-8-4733005, vinnova@vinnova.se, http://www.vinnova.se.

658 IND ISSN 0083-5102
VAIKUNTH MEHTA NATIONAL INSTITUTE OF COOPERATIVE MANAGEMENT. PUBLICATIONS. Text in English. irreg.
Published by: Vaikunth Mehta National Institute of Cooperative Management, University Rd., Pune, Maharashtra 411 007, India.

658 USA ISSN 1543-2815
▼ **VALUE-ADDED SELLING 21.** Text in English. 2003. 24/yr. USD 99.60 (effective 2004).
Published by: Business 21 Publishing, 477 Baltimore Pike, Springfield, PA 19064. TEL 484-479-2700, FAX 610-543-2292, http://www.b21pubs.com. Ed., Pub. Stephen Meyer.

658 USA ISSN 0275-4371
VALUE ENGINEERING AND MANAGEMENT DIGEST - DEFENSE CONTRACT GUIDE. Text in English. 1960. m. USD 180 (effective 2000). bk.rev. **Document type:** *Newsletter.* **Description:** Provides the only English-language commercial publication devoted primarily to value-engineering and analysis. Covers management news and related disciplines.
Former titles: Cost Reduction Digest; Value Engineering Digest - Defense Contract Guide (0010-9622)
Published by: Tufty Communications Co., 2107 National Press Bldg, Washington, DC 20045. TEL 202-347-8998, htufty@capaccess.org, http://www.valuedigest.com. Ed. Harold G Tufty. Circ: 5,000.

658.1 657 USA ISSN 1554-6098
HF5681.V3
THE VALUE EXAMINER; a professional development journal for the consulting disciplines. Text in English. 1991. bi-m. USD 185 domestic; USD 225 foreign (effective 2005). **Document type:** *Journal, Trade.*
Formerly (until May/Jun. 2004): The Valuation Examiner (1094-3137)
Related titles: Online - full text ed.: ISSN 1554-6101.

Published by: National Association of Certified Valuation Analysts, 1111 Brickyard Rd Ste 200, Salt Lake City, UT 84106-5401. TEL 801-486-0600, FAX 801-486-7500, nacva1@nacva.com, http://www.nacva.com. Ed. Jeanne Shaw.

658.2 USA ISSN 1547-4135
GV415
VENUES TODAY. Text in English. 2002 (Jul.). m. USD 200 (effective 2003). adv. **Document type:** *Magazine, Trade.*
Related titles: Online - full text ed.: ISSN 1547-4143.
Address: 18350 Mt. Langley Ste. 200, Fountain Valley, CA 92708. TEL 714-378-5400, FAX 714-378-0040, info@venuestoday.com, http://www.venuestoday.com. Ed., Pub. Linda Deckard.

658 CHE
VERBANDS MANAGEMENT. Text in English, French, German. 1976. q. CHF 90. adv. **Document type:** *Bulletin.*
Published by: Forschungsinstitut fuer Verbands- und Genossenschafts-Management, Universitaet Freiburg, Postfach 284, Fribourg, 1701, Switzerland. TEL 41-26-3008400, FAX 41-26-3009755. Ed. Guido Kaufmann. R&P, Adv. contact Michel Mueller. Circ: 900.

B

DER VEREIN. see *CLUBS*

658 366 DEU ISSN 0943-285X
VEREIN UND MANAGEMENT. Text in German. 1992. bi-m. EUR 25; EUR 5 newsstand/cover (effective 2002). adv. bk.rev.; software rev.; Website rev. 56 p./no. 3 cols./p.; back issues avail. **Document type:** *Magazine, Trade.*
Published by: Non Profit Verlag, Zollernstr 4, Konstanz, 78462, Germany. TEL 49-7531-282141, FAX 49-7531-282179, verlag@nonprofit.de, http://www.nonprofit.de. Eds. Hans-Willy Brockes, Wolfgang Happes. Adv. contact Christel Willig TEL 49-9087-90055. B&W page EUR 525, color page EUR 1,065; trim 185 x 265. Circ: 5,000 (paid).

658 DEU ISSN 0178-5893
VERKAUFSLEITER SERVICE; Beratungsbrief zur Aussendienstfuehrung. Text in Dutch, English, Finnish, French, German, Italian, Spanish, Swedish. 1972. bi-w. EUR 324 (effective 2004). bk.rev. tr.lit. index. back issues avail. **Document type:** *Newsletter, Trade.*
Published by: Verlag Norbert Mueller AG und Co. KG (Subsidiary of: S V Corporate Media GmbH), Emmy-Noether-Str 2, Munich, 80992, Germany. TEL 49-89-5485201, FAX 49-89-54852192, infoVNM@sv-corporate-media.de, http://www.verkaufspower.de/svcm/index/includeVerzeichnis/nm[]briefe[]0178-5893/, http://www.vnm.de. Ed. Andrea Krukow. Circ: 2,900.

624 658 LTU ISSN 1648-0627
HF37.L78
VERSLAS/BUSINESS: THEORY & PRACTICE; teorija i praktika. Abbreviated title: Verslas teor. prakt. Text in Lithuanian, English, German, Russian. 2000. q. back issues avail. **Document type:** *Journal, Academic/Scholarly.*
Indexed: BrCerAb, C&ISA, CerAb, CorrAb, E&CAJ, EMA, IAA, M&TEA, MBF, METADEX, WAA.
—Linda Hall.
Published by: (Vilniaus Gedimino Technikos Universitetas/Vilnius Gediminas Technical University), Lidykla Technika, Sauletekio al. 11, Vilnius, 2040, Lithuania. Ed. R Ginevicius.

658 DEU
DER VERTRAULICHE UNTERNEHMERBRIEF. Text in German. 8/yr. **Document type:** *Magazine, Trade.*
Published by: (Genossenschaftsverband Bayern e.V.), BurdaYukom Publishing GmbH (Subsidiary of: Hubert Burda Media Holding GmbH & Co. KG), Schleissheimer Str 141, Munich, 80797, Germany. TEL 49-89-306200, FAX 49-89-30620100, info@burdayukom.de, http://www.yukom.de. Circ: 70,000 (controlled).

658 DEU ISSN 0409-1728
VERTRIEBSWIRTSCHAFTLICHE ABHANDLUNGEN. Text in German. 1958. irreg., latest vol.33, 1991. price varies. **Document type:** *Monographic series, Academic/Scholarly.*
Published by: Duncker und Humblot GmbH, Carl-Heinrich-Becker-Weg 9, Berlin, 12165, Germany. TEL 49-30-7900060, FAX 49-30-79000631, info@duncker-humblot.de, http://www.duncker-humblot.de.

658 NZL ISSN 1173-4523
VICTORIA UNIVERSITY OF WELLINGTON. G S B G M WORKING PAPER SERIES. (Graduate School of Business and Government Management) Text in English. 1990. irreg., latest no.10, 1994. **Document type:** *Academic/Scholarly.*
Formerly (until 2000): Victoria University of Wellington. Graduate School of Business and Government Management. Working Paper Series (0114-7420)
—BLDSC (4223.694000).
Published by: Victoria University of Wellington, Graduate School of Business & Government Management, P.O. Box 600, Wellington, New Zealand. TEL 64-4-495-5085, FAX 64-4-496-5435, monica.cartner@vuw.ac.nz.

658 NLD ISSN 1382-7936
VIEW. Text in Dutch. 1995. q. adv. **Document type:** *Trade.*
Related titles: ♦ Supplement to: Management Team. ISSN 0166-1256.
Indexed: ABM, MRD.
Published by: Benelux Periodieken B.V., Postbus 397, Veenendaal, 3900 AJ, Netherlands. TEL 31-8385-21422, FAX 31-8385-23136.

658 USA ISSN 1061-6187
VIEWPOINT (NEW YORK, 1972). Text in English. 1972. q. **Document type:** *Journal.*
Published by: Marsh & McLennan Companies, 1166 Avenue of the Americas, New York, NY 10036-2774. TEL 212-345-5000, http://www.mmc.com/views2/index.php.

658 IND ISSN 0256-0909
HD28
➤ **VIKALPA**; journal for decision makers. Text and summaries in English. 1976. q. INR 600 domestic to individuals; USD 40 foreign to individuals; INR 1,000 domestic to institutions; INR 800 domestic Academic institutions; USD 50 foreign to institutions; INR 400 domestic to students (effective 2005). adv. bk.rev. abstr. back issues avail. **Document type:** *Academic/Scholarly.* **Description:** Covers management-related topics. Largest audience consists of libraries, management institutes, companies, students and academies.
Related titles: Online - full text ed.: (from EBSCO Publishing).
Indexed: BAS, IAOP, IPsyAb, PAA&I, PsycInfo, PsycholAb, e-psyche.
—BLDSC (9236.373000), IE, Infotrieve, ingenta.
Published by: Indian Institute of Management Ahmedabad, Publications Department, Vastrapur, Ahmedabad, Gujarat 380 015, India. TEL 91-79-6324801, FAX 91-79-6427896, vikalpa@iimahd.ernet.in, http://www.iimahd.ernet.in/vikalpa. Ed. I M Pandey. adv.: B&W page INR 22,000, color page INR 35,000, B&W page USD 1,250, color page USD 1,750; trim 180 x 220. Circ: 3,500.

658 IND
HD28
➤ **VISION**; the journal of business perspective. Text in English. 1987. s-a. INR 400, USD 25 (effective 2000). bk.rev. **Document type:** *Academic/Scholarly.* **Description:** Provides a forum for research and practical results of interest and relevance to business managers. Includes behavioral science, development banking, quantitative techniques, modern trends and developments in management.
Formerly (until Jan. 1997): M D I Management Journal (0970-6623)
Indexed: BAS, PAA&I.
Published by: Management Development Institute, Mehrauli Rd., P O Box 60, Gurgaon, Haryana 122001, India. TEL 91-124-340173, FAX 91-124-341189, mandev.mdi@axcess.net.in. Ed. Anup Singh. Circ: 500.

➤ **VISIONS (NEW YORK).** see *BUSINESS AND ECONOMICS—Production Of Goods And Services*

➤ **VLAAMS TIJDSCHRIFT VOOR SPORTBEHEER.** see *SPORTS AND GAMES*

➤ **WAGE - HOUR ALERT.** see *BUSINESS AND ECONOMICS—Labor And Industrial Relations*

658 339 USA ISSN 1048-4981
HD38.25.U6
WASHINGTON C E O; connecting the ceo community. (Chief Executive Officer) Text in English. 1989. m. USD 34.95 (effective 2005). adv. **Document type:** *Magazine, Trade.* **Description:** For top corporate executives. Provides state-wide business news on the personalities, events, trends and ideas which shape the character, dynamics and direction of the state's economy.
Related titles: Online - full text ed.
Published by: C E O Media Corp., 12201 Tukwila International Bl., Ste. 150, Tukwila, WA 98168-5121. TEL 206-441-8415, FAX 206-441-8325, feedback@waceo.com, http://www.washingtonceo.com, http://www.fivash.com. Eds. Jeff Bond, Scott Fivash. Pub. Scott Fivash. adv.: B&W page USD 4,595, color page USD 5,475; trim 8.38 x 10.88. Circ: 24,000.

658 USA
WASHINGTON SMARTCEO. (Chief Executive Officer) Text in English. m. USD 29.95 (effective 2005). adv. **Document type:** *Magazine, Trade.* **Description:** Contains smart ideas to help educate, motivate and inspire decision-makers. Reaches decision-makers in the District of Columbia, Northern Virginia, and the Maryland counties of Montgomery and Prince Georges.
Published by: SmartCEO, 2400 Boston St, Ste 330, Baltimore, MD 21224. TEL 410-342-9510, FAX 410-675-3782, http://washington.smartceo.com/. Ed. Timothy Burn. Pub. Craig Burns.

WASHINGTON STATE BAR ASSOCIATION. CREDITOR - DEBTOR LAW SECTION NEWSLETTER. see *BUSINESS AND ECONOMICS—Banking And Finance*

WATERLINE. see *TRANSPORTATION—Ships And Shipping*

658 AUT ISSN 1430-7928
WER LEITET - DIE FUEHRUNGSKRAEFTE DER OESTERREICHISCHEN WIRTSCHAFT. Text in German. 1986. a. **Document type:** *Directory.*
Media: CD-ROM.
Published by: Hoppenstedt und Co. Wirtschaftsverlag GmbH, Fichtnergasse 2-4, Vienna, W 1130, Austria. TEL 43-1-8763700, FAX 43-1-876370050. Circ: 50,000.

658.562 USA ISSN 0083-8217
WEST COAST RELIABILITY SYMPOSIUM. Text in English. 1964 (5th). irreg., latest 1991.
Published by: (Los Angeles Section), American Society for Quality Control, 600 N Plankinton Ave, Milwaukee, WI 53203-2914. TEL 213-331-6204.

WESTERN TECHNOLOGY & MANAGEMENT. see *TECHNOLOGY: COMPREHENSIVE WORKS*

658.8 USA
WHARTON LEADERSHIP DIGEST. Text in English. 1996. m. free. back issues avail. **Document type:** *Newsletter.* **Description:** Forwards information updates of interest to persons engaged in and writing about leadership issues, particularly the management of change.
Media: E-mail.
Published by: University of Pennsylvania, Wharton Center for Leadership and Change Management, 2000 Steinberg Hall Dietrich Hall, Philadelphia, PA 19104-6370. TEL 215-898-7684, FAX 215-573-2122, lead@wharton.upenn.edu, http://leadership.wharton.upenn.edu/leaders/digest/current.shtml. Ed. Michael Useem.

658 USA
WHAT IT COSTS TO RUN AN AGENCY. Text in English. 1955. a. USD 39.75 (effective 2001).
Published by: Rough Notes Co., Inc., PO Box 1990, Carmel, IN 46032-4990. TEL 317-582-1600, 800-428-4384, FAX 317-816-1003, rnc@roughnotes.com, http://www.roughnotes.com.

WHAT'S NEW IN BENEFITS & COMPENSATION. see *BUSINESS AND ECONOMICS—Personnel Management*

WHAT'S WORKING IN CREDIT & COLLECTION. see *LAW—Corporate Law*

658.9 USA
WHAT'S WORKING IN SALES MANAGEMENT. Abbreviated title: W S M. Text in English. s-m. USD 264; USD 330 foreign. bk.rev. charts. **Document type:** *Newsletter.* **Description:** Information that helps sales managers provide the leadership necessary to increase sales performance and improve their company's bottom line.
Formerly (until 1992): Effective Sales Management (1069-1103)
Published by: Progressive Business Publications, 370 Technology Dr, Malvern, PA 19355-1315. TEL 610-695-8600, 800-220-5000, FAX 610-647-8089, editor@pbp.com, http://www.pbp.com. Ed. Leah Rapposelli. R&P Curt Brown. Circ: 13,080 (paid).

658 USA
WHAT'S WORKING IN W M S; strategies and tactics for getting the most value from your warehouse management system. (Warehouse Management Systems) Text in English. 1998. m. USD 297 domestic; USD 327 foreign (effective 2005). software rev. charts; illus. index. 12 p./no.; back issues avail.; reprints avail. **Document type:** *Newsletter, Trade.* **Description:** This regularly updated service shows managers how to use warehouse management systems to get control of their warehouses.
Formerly (until 1999): Warehouse Management & Control Systems (1079-0101)
Related titles: Online - full text ed.
Published by: Alexander Communications Group, Inc., 28 W 25th St, 8th Fl, New York, NY 10010. TEL 212-228-0246, FAX 212-228-0376, info@alexcommgrp.com, http://www.distributiongroup.com/wms.php, http://www.alexcommgrp.com. Ed. Troy Reynolds. Pub. Margaret Dewitt. R&P Mary Dalessandro.

658.00711 USA
WHICH M B A?; a critical guide to the world's best programmes. (Master's in Business Administration) Text in English. 1989. a. USD 49.99 (effective 2003). **Document type:** *Directory.* **Description:** Outlines the master's-level programs in business administration offered by universities worldwide.
—BLDSC (9310.897000).
Published by: Economist Intelligence Unit, 111 W 57th St, New York, NY 10019. TEL 212-554-0600, 800-938-4685, FAX 212-586-1181, http://www.eiu.com. Ed. George Bickerstaffe.

658 338 GBR ISSN 0140-6582
HG4132.Z5 CODEN: WOWCEK
WHO OWNS WHOM. CONTINENTAL EUROPE. Text in English. 1961. a. (in 3 vols.). GBP 575 (effective 2000). index. **Document type:** *Directory.*
Formerly (until 1977): Who Owns Whom. Continental Edition (0083-9302)
Related titles: Online - full text ed.
—BLDSC (9311.922000), CISTI. **CCC.**

Published by: Dun & Bradstreet Ltd., 50-100 Holmers Farm Way, High Wycombe, Bucks HP12 4UL, United Kingdom. TEL 44-1494-423689, FAX 44-1494-422332.

658.31 920 USA ISSN 0092-4598
HF5549.5.T7
WHO'S WHO IN TRAINING AND DEVELOPMENT. Text in English. 1970. a. USD 40 to members; USD 50 to libraries (effective 2003). adv. illus. **Document type:** *Directory.*
Formerly: American Society for Training and Development. Membership Directory (0569-776X)
Published by: American Society for Training & Development, 1640 King St, Box 1443, Alexandria, VA 22313. TEL 703-683-8100, FAX 703-683-9591, http://www.astd.org. Circ: 28,000.

658 JPN ISSN 0286-7877
WILL. Text in Japanese. 1962. m. JPY 8,450. adv. bk.rev.
Former titles (until 1982): Chuokoron Keieimondai - Chuokoron Management Affairs (0385-7379); (until 1972): Bessatsu Chuokoron. Keieimondai (0409-2465)
Published by: Chuokoron-Sha Inc., 2-8-7 Kyobashi, Chuo-ku, Tokyo, 104-0031, Japan. TEL 03-3563-1866, FAX 03-3561-5920.

WIRTSCHAFT UND GESELLSCHAFT IM BERUF. see *EDUCATION—Teaching Methods And Curriculum*

658 USA
WOMEN DIRECTORS OF THE TOP 1000 CORPORATIONS. Text in English. 1986. a. USD 50 to individuals; USD 100 to institutions. index. back issues avail. **Document type:** *Directory.*
Published by: National Women's Economic Alliance Foundation, 1440 New York Ave N W, Ste 300, Washington, DC 20005. TEL 202-393-5257. Ed. Elise Garfinkel.

658 CAN ISSN 1185-4863
WOMEN IN MANAGEMENT. Text in English. 1990. q.
—CISTI.
Published by: University of Western Ontario, 1151 Richmond St., Suite 2, London, ON N6A 5B8, Canada. TEL 519-661-2111, http://www.uwo.ca.

658 GBR ISSN 0964-9425
HD6054.3
➤ **WOMEN IN MANAGEMENT REVIEW.** Text in English. 1985. 8/yr. EUR 9,405.79 in Europe to institutions; USD 9,409 in North America to institutions; AUD 12,549 in Australasia to institutions; GBP 6,480.41 elsewhere to institutions (effective 2006). bk.rev. reprint service avail. from PSC. **Document type:** *Journal, Academic/Scholarly.* **Description:** Current research and practice in the field of gender and management.
Former titles (until 1992): Women in Management Review & Abstracts (0955-8357); (until 1989): Women in Management Review (0267-4602)
Related titles: CD-ROM ed.; Online - full text ed.: (from EBSCO Publishing, Emerald Group Publishing Limited, Gale Group, IngentaConnect, O C L C Online Computer Library Center, Inc., ProQuest Information & Learning, Swets Information Services).
Indexed: ABIn, CJA, CPM, ERA, ETA, EmerIntel, Emerald, FemPer, HRA, MEA, RHEA, SEA, SENA, SOMA, SWA, T&DA, TEA.
—BLDSC (9343.299000), IE, Infotrieve, ingenta. **CCC.**
Published by: Emerald Group Publishing Limited, 60-62 Toller Ln, Bradford, W Yorks BD8 9BY, United Kingdom. TEL 44-1274-777700, FAX 44-1274-785200, infomation@emeraldinsight.com, http://www.emeraldinsight.com/wimr.htm. Ed. Dr. Sandra Fielden. Pub. Ms. Paula Fernandez. R&P Mr. John Eggleton.

➤ **WORKERS' COMPENSATION OUTLOOK.** see *INSURANCE*

658.45 USA ISSN 1099-7245
THE WORKING COMMUNICATOR. Text in English. 1981. m. USD 107. bk.rev. **Document type:** *Newsletter.* **Description:** Provides advice on writing, speaking and editing better for those involved in organizational communications.
Former titles (until 1991): Bottom Line Communicator; Business Writer
Published by: Lawrence Ragan Communications, Inc., 316 N Michigan Ave, Ste 300, Chicago, IL 60601. TEL 312-960-4140, 800-878-5331, FAX 312-960-4106, cservice@ragan.com, http://www.ragan.com. Ed. John Cowan. Circ: 7,000.

658 USA ISSN 1049-4855
WORKING SMART. Text in English. 1972. m. USD 66 (effective 2004). **Document type:** *Newsletter, Trade.* **Description:** Covers a broad range of management topics, including team building, enhancing supervisory skills, getting more done with less, dealing with difficult people, streamlining paperwork, improving customer service, hiring and firing, and more.
Formerly (until 1990): Personal Report for the Executive (0048-3443)
Indexed: PersLit.
—**CCC.**

Published by: National Institute of Business Management, 1750 Old Meadow Rd. Ste. 302, McLean, VA 22102-4315. TEL 703-905-8000, 800-543-2052, customer@nibm.net, http://www.nibm.net/newsletter.asp?pub=PRE, http://www.nibm.net/home.asp.

WORKPLACE. see *INTERIOR DESIGN AND DECORATION*

658.5 GBR ISSN 0374-4795
TS155.A1
WORKS MANAGEMENT. Text in English. 1947. m. GBP 78 domestic; GBP 115 foreign (effective 2005). adv. bk.rev. back issues avail. **Document type:** *Magazine, Trade.* **Description:** Covers all types of factory technology and services, with particular emphasis on productivity and people.
Formerly: Istitution of Works Managers. Journal
Related titles: Online - full text ed.: (from EBSCO Publishing, Northern Light Technology, Inc., O C L C Online Computer Library Center, Inc., ProQuest Information & Learning).
Indexed: ABIn, ADPA, ASEANManA, CISA, Emerald, Inspec, M&MA, RASB.
—BLDSC (9352.200000), IE, ingenta. **CCC.**
Published by: Findlay Publications Ltd., Franks Hall, Franks Ln, Horton Kirby, Kent DA4 9LL, United Kingdom. TEL 44-1322-860000, FAX 44-1322-862644, enquiries@findlay.co.uk, http://www.worksmanagement.co.uk/, http://www.findlay.co.uk/. Ed. Adam Lawrence. Pub. Chris Wyles. Adv. contact Rob Fisher. Circ: 25,035.

658 HKG ISSN 1022-7784
WORLD EXECUTIVE'S DIGEST - CHINA EDITION/JINGLIREN WENZHAI. Text in Chinese. m. USD 35. **Document type:** *Trade.*
Related titles: CD-ROM ed.; Online - full text ed.
Published by: Asian Sources Media Group, GPO Box 12367, Hong Kong, Hong Kong. TEL 852-2555-4777, FAX 852-2834-5201, asmgroup@singnet.com.sg, http://www.asiansources.wed.com. Ed. Jeff Zhou. Pub. Barrie C Goodridge. adv.: B&W page USD 4,210, color page USD 5,610; trim 273 x 206. Circ: 46,350.

658 686.2 USA
WORLD LEADERS IN PRINT. Text in English, German, Spanish, Japanese. 2001. a. free (effective 2004). adv. **Document type:** *Magazine, Trade.* **Description:** Provides management perspective and vision for top executives of the world's largest graphic communications companies.
Published by: Reed Business Information (Subsidiary of: Reed Business), 2000 Clearwater Dr, Oak Brook, IL 60525. TEL 847-390-2997, FAX 847-390-2530, http://www.worldleadersinprint.com, http://www.reedbusiness.com. Ed. Mathew Miller. Pub. Terry McCoy Jr. TEL 646-746-7312. adv.: color page USD 14,822; trim 254 x 271. Circ: 25,000 (controlled).

658 GBR ISSN 1746-0573
▼ ➤ **WORLD REVIEW OF ENTREPRENEURSHIP, MANAGEMENT AND SUSTAINABLE DEVELOPMENT.** Text in English. 2005. q. USD 450, USD 545 to institutions (effective 2005). bk.rev. **Document type:** *Journal, Academic/Scholarly.* **Description:** Publishes original papers, review papers, conceptual papers, business and management case studies, conference reports, management reports, notes, commentaries, and news. Special Issues devoted to important topics in Business, Management and Entrepreneurship will occasionally be published.
Related titles: Online - full text ed.: ISSN 1746-0581.
Published by: Inderscience Publishers, IEL Editorial Office, PO Box 735, Olney, Bucks MK46 5WB, United Kingdom. TEL 44-1234-240519, FAX 44-1234-240515, wremsd@inderscience.com, info@inderscience.com, http://www.inderscience.com/wremsd. Ed. Dr. Allam Ahmed.

➤ **WORLD SCIENTIFIC ASIAN ECONOMIC PROFILES.** see *BUSINESS AND ECONOMICS—Banking And Finance*

➤ **WORLDPROFIT ONLINE MAGAZINE.** see *BUSINESS AND ECONOMICS—Small Business*

658 CHN ISSN 1002-5499
HD70.C5
XIANDAI QIYE DAOKAN/MODERN ENTERPRISE HERALD. Text in Chinese. 1987. m. CNY 117.60 (effective 2004). **Document type:** *Trade.*
Related titles: Online - full text ed.: (from WanFang Data Corp.).
Address: A-2, Fuxingmen Wei Dajie, 601, Zhonghua Dasha, Beijing, 100045, China. TEL 86-10-62184856, jyglz@163.net, http://xdqydk.periodicals.net.cn/default.html. **Dist. by:** China International Book Trading Corp, 35 Chegongzhuang Xilu, Haidian District, PO Box 399, Beijing 100044, China. TEL 86-10-68412045, FAX 86-10-68412023, cibtc@mail.cibtc.com.cn, http://www.cibtc.com.cn.

YELLOW SHEET (BALLWIN); the practical newsletter on agency management. see *ADVERTISING AND PUBLIC RELATIONS*

658 FIN ISSN 0358-4208
YRITYSTALOUS/LEADER'S MAGAZIN. Text in Finnish. 1969. 6/yr. EUR 245 (effective 2004). adv. bk.rev. charts; illus. index. **Document type:** *Journal, Trade.*
Former titles (until 1981): Tehokas Yritys (0356-5327); (until 1974): Yritystalous (0044-1309); Which was formed by the merger of (1954-1969): Liiketalous (0457-8848); (1943-1969): Tehostaja (0374-4590)
Indexed: Inspec.
Published by: Rastor Publications, Wavulinintie 3, Helsinki, 00210, Finland. TEL 358-9-41360300, FAX 358-9-41360200, rastor@rastor.fi, http://www.rastor.fi/julkaisut/yritystalous/. Ed. Liisa Kokko. adv.: B&W page EUR 1,080; 177 x 240. Circ: 2,500.

YUGOSLAV JOURNAL OF OPERATIONS RESEARCH; an international journal dealing with theoretical and computational aspects of operations research, systems science, and management science. see *COMPUTERS*

658 DEU ISSN 0044-2372
HD28
Z F B. (Zeitschrift fuer Betriebswirtschaft) Text in German. 1931. m. EUR 198; EUR 111 to students (effective 2004); EUR 23 newsstand/cover (effective 2003). adv. bk.rev. illus. reprint service avail. from SCH. **Document type:** *Magazine, Trade.*
Indexed: DIP, ExcerpMed, IBR, IBZ, JEL, KES, PAIS, RASB, RefZh, SCIMP, SSCI.
—BLDSC (9453.890000), IE, Infotrieve, ingenta. **CCC.**
Published by: Betriebswirtschaftlicher Verlag Dr. Th. Gabler GmbH (Subsidiary of: Springer Science+Business Media), Abraham-Lincoln-Str 46, Wiesbaden, 65189, Germany. TEL 49-611-78780, FAX 49-611-7878400, gabler.service@gwv-fachverlage.de, http://www.zfb-online.de, http://www.gabler.de. Ed. Ralf Wettlaufer. Adv. contact Thomas Werner. B&W page EUR 1,350, color page EUR 2,250. Circ: 2,300 (paid and controlled).

658 DEU ISSN 0341-2687
Z F B F. (Zeitschrift fuer Betriebswirtschaftliche Forschung) Text in German. 1906. m. EUR 153; EUR 76.50 to students; EUR 14 newsstand/cover (effective 2005). adv. bk.rev. charts; stat. index, cum.index. reprint service avail. from SCH. **Document type:** *Journal, Academic/Scholarly.*
Former titles (until 1974): Schmalenbachs Zeitschrift fuer Betriebswirtschaftliche Forschung (0036-6196); (until 1963): Zeitschrift fuer Handelswissenschaftliche Forschung (1619-6147)
Related titles: Online - full text ed.: (from EBSCO Publishing).
Indexed: DIP, ELLIS, ExcerpMed, IBR, IBZ, KES, SCIMP.
—IE, Infotrieve. **CCC.**
Published by: (Schmalenbach-Gesellschaft), Verlagsgruppe Handelsblatt GmbH, Kasernenstr 67, Duesseldorf, 40213, Germany. TEL 49-211-8870, FAX 49-211-371792, zfbf@bwl.uni-muenchen.de, leser-service@vhb.de, http://www.vhb.de/zfbf/home.html. Ed. Wolfgang Ballwieser. Adv. contact Regina Hamdorf. B&W page EUR 1,280, color page EUR 2,330. Circ: 3,000 (paid and controlled).

658 DEU ISSN 0722-7485
HF5001
Z F O - ZEITSCHRIFT FUER FUEHRUNG UND ORGANISATION. Text in German. 1930. bi-m. adv. bk.rev. illus.; tr.lit. back issues avail.; reprint service avail. from SCH. **Document type:** *Trade.*
Former titles (until 1982): Z O - Zeitschrift fuer Organisation (0722-7477); (until 1970): Z fuer O - Zeitschrift fuer Organisation (0722-7604); (until 1951): Zeitschrift fuer Organisation (0044-3212)
Indexed: ABIn, DIP, ExcerpMed, IBR, IBZ, Inspec, RASB, RefZh.
—BLDSC (9462.205000), IE, Infotrieve, ingenta.
Published by: Schaeffer - Poeschel Verlag, Postfach 103241, Stuttgart, 70028, Germany. TEL 49-711-2194102, FAX 49-711-2194119. Circ: 4,200.

658 POL ISSN 1230-3747
ZARZADZANIE NA SWIECIE. Text in Polish. 1985. m.
Published by: (Redakcja Zagraniczna), Polska Agencja Prasowa (P.A.P.)/Polish Press Agency, Al Jerozolimskie 7, Warsaw, 00950, Poland. Ed. Marek Fijalkowski.

658 CHN ISSN 1006-7582
HD30.28
ZHANLUE YU GUANLI/STRATEGY AND MANAGEMENT. Text in Chinese. 1993. bi-m. **Document type:** *Journal, Academic/Scholarly.*
Related titles: Online - full text ed.: (from East View Information Services).
—BLDSC (8474.037970).
Published by: Zhongguo Zhanlue yu Guanli Yanjiuhui/China Society for Strategy and Management Research, 33, Zhongguancun Nanlu, Guojia Tushuguan, Shuguan Xingzhenluo 5-ceng, Beijing, 100081, China. TEL 86-10-68482774, FAX 86-10-68416354, nova@public.bta.net.cn, cssm@cssm.org.cn, http://xueshu.newyouth.beida-online.com/zlygl/index.php3, http://www.cssm.org.cn/.

658 CHN ISSN 1011-5358
HC427.92.A1
ZHONGGUO JINGJI NIANJIAN/ALMANAC OF CHINA'S ECONOMY. Text in Chinese. 1981. a. CNY 70. adv. **Document type:** *Academic/Scholarly.* **Description:** Covers Chinese economic policies, development in economic construction, and economic statistics.
Indexed: RASB.

Published by: (Chinese Academy of Social Sciences, Institute of Industrial Economics), Jingji Guanli Chubanshe/Economic Management Publishing House, 6 Tiao Xinjiekou, 8 Hongyuan Hutong, Beijing, 100035, China. TEL 86-10-2253956, FAX 86-10-8312679. Ed. Wang Haibo. Adv. contact Li Li. Circ: 15,000. **Dist. in US by:** China Books & Periodicals Inc, 360 Swift Ave., Ste. 48, S San Fran, CA 94080-6220. TEL 415-282-2994; **Dist. outside China by:** China International Book Trading Corp, 35 Chegongzhuang Xilu, Haidian District, PO Box 399, Beijing 100044, China. TEL 86-10-68412045, FAX 86-10-68412023, cibtc@mail.cibtc.com.cn, http://www.cibtc.com.cn.

658 USA ISSN 1068-1310
THE ZWEIG LETTER. Text in English. 1992. w. USD 325 (effective 2005). **Document type:** *Newsletter, Trade.* **Description:** Contains advice, frank opinions, industry news, and real-life management practices for architecture, engineering, and environmental consulting firms.
Published by: Zweig White Information Services, One IBM Plaza, 330 N Wabash, Chicago, IL 60611. TEL 312-628-5870, FAX 312-628-5878, info@mercormedia.com, http://www.zweigwhite.com/trends/thezweigletter/index.asp, http://www.mercormedia.com/.

▼ **4 O R**; quarterly journal of the Belgian, French and Italian operations research societies. (Operations Research) see *COMPUTERS*

658 USA
▼ **6 L**; the premiere journal for Six Sigma and Lean professionals. Text in English. 2004. m. USD 375 (effective 2005). **Document type:** *Journal, Trade.* **Description:** Provides a guide to the latest available resources on Six Sigma and Lean manufacturing.
Published by: Q S U Publishing Company, 3975 University Dr, Ste 230, Fairfax, VA 22030. TEL 703-359-8460, FAX 703-359-8462, news@qsuonline.com, http://www.qsuonline.com. Ed. Suzanne Leonard. Pub. Paul Scicchitano.

BUSINESS AND ECONOMICS—Marketing And Purchasing

see also ADVERTISING AND PUBLIC RELATIONS

A A D A NEWS. see *ANTIQUES*

A & E PUBLISHING WORLDWIDE E-MAGAZINE. see *COMPUTERS—Internet*

A B A BANK MARKETING. see *BUSINESS AND ECONOMICS—Banking And Finance*

A B C'S OF NET MARKETING E-ZINE. see *COMPUTERS—Internet*

658 USA
A F & P A STATISTICAL ROUNDUP. Text in English. 1984. m. USD 157 to non-members; USD 57 to members. back issues avail. **Description:** Covers topics of interest to forest products companies, focusing on industry statistics.
Former titles: N F P A Statistical Roundup; National Forest Products Association. Economics Monthly
Indexed: SRI.
Published by: American Forest & Paper Association, 1111 19th St, N W, Washington, DC 20036. TEL 202-463-2700, FAX 202-463-2785. Ed. Alberto Goetzl. Circ: 100.

658 USA ISSN 1059-7425
A I M∗. (Age of Information Marketing) Text in English. 1979. q. back issues avail.
Formerly (until 1989): Marketing Trends (0882-4754)
Related titles: French ed.: 1979; German ed.: 1979; Italian ed.: 1979; Portuguese ed.: 1979; Spanish ed.: 1979.
Published by: Nielsen Marketing Research (Subsidiary of: Dun & Bradstreet Corporation), 150 N Martingale Rd, Schaumburg, IL 60173-2408. Circ: 30,000.

A L A WORLDWIDE DIRECTORY AND FACT BOOK. see *MILITARY*

658.8 USA ISSN 0888-1839
HF5410
A M A EDUCATORS' PROCEEDINGS. Text in English. a. USD 50 to non-members; USD 40 to members (effective 2000). adv. **Document type:** *Proceedings.*
Related titles: Seasonal ed(s).: A M A Educators' Proceedings (Summer Edition).
—BLDSC (0806.279500). **CCC.**
Published by: American Marketing Association, 311 S Wacker Dr, Ste 5800, Chicago, IL 60606. TEL 312-542-9000, 800-262-1150, FAX 312-542-9001, info@ama.org, http://www.ama.org. Eds. Gregory T Gundlach, Patrick E Murphy. R&P Rochelle Amos TEL 312-542-9022. Adv. contact Richard Ballschmiede.

658.8 USA
HF5411
A M A WINTER EDUCATORS' CONFERENCE. PROCEEDINGS. Text in English. 1944. a. USD 50 to non-members; USD 40 to members (effective 2000). adv. index. **Document type:** *Proceedings.*
Formerly: A M A Annual Marketing Educators' Conference. Proceedings (1054-0806); Supersedes: American Marketing Association. Proceedings (0065-9231); Incorporates: A M A Combined Proceedings Series; A M A Papers of the Conferences; A M A Abstracts of Papers of the Conferences (0065-9215)
Indexed: BPIA, BusI.
—BLDSC (0806.324000). **CCC.**
Published by: American Marketing Association, 311 S Wacker Dr, Ste 5800, Chicago, IL 60606. TEL 312-542-9000, 800-262-1150, FAX 312-542-9001, info@ama.org, http://www.ama.org. Ed. Francesca Van Gorp. R&P Rochelle Amos TEL 312-542-9022. Adv. contact Richard Ballschmiede.

A M I'S WEST EUROPEAN PLASTICS INDUSTRY REPORT. see *PLASTICS*

658.8 USA
A M R NEWSLETTER∗. Text in English. m. **Document type:** *Newsletter.* **Description:** Includes case studies and industry developments.
Published by: Association Marketing Roundtable, 3770 Parkview Way, Naples, FL 33940-2737. TEL 202-244-7256.

336 USA
A M SHOW DAYS. Text in English. bi-m. **Document type:** *Magazine, Trade.*
Published by: Cygnus Business Media, Inc., 1233 Janesville Ave, Fort Atkinson, WI 53538-0803. TEL 800-547-7377, FAX 920-563-1702, http://www.amonline.com/showdays/index.html, http://www.cygnusb2b.com. Pub. Gloria Cosby. **Subscr. to:** PO Box 470, Fort Atkinson, WI 53538.

658 USA
A P R. (Accessory & Performance Retailer) Text in English. 2002 (Sep.). bi-m. adv. **Document type:** *Magazine, Trade.* **Description:** Focuses on over-the-counter specialty automotive products.
Published by: National Business Media, Inc., PO Box 1416, Broomfield, CO 80038. TEL 303-469-5730, 303-469-0424, 800-669-0424, aprpublisher@nbm.com.

A S A E ASSOCIATE MEMBER UPDATE. see *BUSINESS AND ECONOMICS—Management*

658 011 DEU ISSN 0934-9790
A U M A HANDBOOK INTERNATIONAL. Text in German. s-a. free. **Document type:** *Directory.* **Description:** Trade fairs and exhibitions outside of Germany which are of importance to the German economy.
Formerly: A U M A Kalender Ausland (0721-2720)
Published by: Ausstellungs- und Messe-Ausschuss der Deutschen Wirtschaft e.V./Association of the German Trade Fair Industry, Lindenstr 8, Cologne, 50674, Germany. TEL 49-221-20907-0, FAX 49-221-2090712, info@auma.de, http://auma.de. Ed. Kornelia Gelhausen. Circ: 8,000.

658 011 DEU ISSN 0939-7078
A U M A HANDBOOK REGIONAL. Text in German. 1973. a. free. back issues avail. **Document type:** *Directory.* **Description:** Lists dates, groups of offers, visitor, exhibitor and space figures, including information on visitor structures of the regional exhibitions in Germany.
Formed by the merger of: A U M A Zahlenspiegel Regional (0724-0457); A U M A Kalender Regional (0721-2747)
Published by: Ausstellungs- und Messe-Ausschuss der Deutschen Wirtschaft e.V./Association of the German Trade Fair Industry, Lindenstr 8, Cologne, 50674, Germany. TEL 49-221-20907-0, FAX 49-221-2090712, info@auma.de, http://auma.de. Eds. Harald Koetter, Manuela Goerzen. Circ: 8,000.

658 DEU
HF5474.G3
A U M A HANDBOOK TRADE FAIR CENTER GERMANY. Text in English, German. s-a. free. **Document type:** *Directory.* **Description:** Lists dates, groups of offers, visitor, exhibitor and space figures, including information on visitor structures of the international trade fairs in Germany.
Formerly: A U M A Handbook Germany - Trade Fair Country (0933-6206); Which was formed by the merger of: A U M A Kalender Messeplatz Deutschland (0930-8768); A U M A Zahlenspiegel Messeplatz Deutschland (0724-0554); Deutsche Messen und Ausstellungen - Ein Zahlenspiegel (0084-9766)
Published by: Ausstellungs- und Messe-Ausschuss der Deutschen Wirtschaft e.V./Association of the German Trade Fair Industry, Lindenstr 8, Cologne, 50674, Germany. TEL 49-221-20907-0, FAX 49-221-2090712, info@auma.de, http://auma.de. Eds. Harald Koetter, Mathias Wuestefeld. Circ: 12,000.

A U M A INFOBLAETTER; Daten und Fakten ueber Messen und Ausstellungen im In- und Ausland. see *ADVERTISING AND PUBLIC RELATIONS*

A U M A - MITTEILUNGEN. see *ADVERTISING AND PUBLIC RELATIONS*

A U M A TRADE FAIR SELECTIONS. see *MEETINGS AND CONGRESSES*

A V INVEST. (Audio Video) see *COMMUNICATIONS*

658.82 AUT
A3 BOOM!; Magazin fuer Media, Marketing, Werbung, Medien. Text in German. 10/yr. adv. **Document type:** *Magazine, Trade.*
Published by: A3 Wirtschaftsverlag GmbH, Hagenauertalstr 40, Giesshuebl, N 2372, Austria. TEL 43-2236-42528, FAX 43-2236-26311, a3@a3verlag.com, http://www.a3verlag.com. Ed. Herwig Stindl. Adv. contact Hannes Walter. B&W page EUR 4,400; trim 185 x 250. Circ: 13,300 (paid and controlled).

658.8 DEU ISSN 0001-3374
ABSATZWIRTSCHAFT; Zeitschrift fuer Marketing. Text in German. 1958. m. EUR 111 domestic; EUR 118 foreign; EUR 9 newsstand/cover (effective 2004). adv. bk.rev. abstr.; charts; illus.; stat. index. reprint service avail. from PQC. **Document type:** *Magazine, Trade.*
Related titles: Online - full text ed.
Indexed: ABIn, ADPA, DIP, ExcerpMed, IBR, IBZ, KES, M&MA, PAIS, SCIMP.
—BLDSC (0551.450000), IE, Infotrieve. **CCC.**
Published by: Verlagsgruppe Handelsblatt GmbH, Kasernenstr 67, Duesseldorf, 40213, Germany. TEL 49-211-887-0, FAX 49-211-133522, m.trumm@vhb.de, leser-service@vhb.de, http://www.absatzwirtschaft.de, http://www.vhb.de. Ed. F Paelike. adv.: page EUR 5,720. Circ: 29,794 (paid and controlled). **Subscr. to:** Postfach 102753, Duesseldorf 40018, Germany.

658.8 USA ISSN 0092-0703
HF5415
➤ **ACADEMY OF MARKETING SCIENCE. JOURNAL.** Text in English. 1973. q. USD 423, GBP 273 to institutions; USD 440, GBP 284 combined subscription to institutions print & online eds. (effective 2006). adv. bk.rev.; software rev. bibl.; charts; illus. back issues avail.; reprint service avail. from PQC,PSC. **Document type:** *Journal, Academic/Scholarly.* **Description:** Furthers the science of marketing as an economic, ethical, and social force worldwide by conducting research and disseminating the results.
Related titles: Microform ed.; Online - full text ed.: ISSN 1552-7824. USD 418, GBP 270 to institutions (effective 2006) (from C S A, EBSCO Publishing, O C L C Online Computer Library Center, Inc., ProQuest Information & Learning, Sage Publications, Inc., Swets Information Services, The Dialog Corporation).
Indexed: ABIn, ATI, BPIA, BusI, CommAb, CurCont, Emerald, HRA, JCQM, M&MA, ManagCont, PAIS, PSI, PsycInfo, PsycholAb, SOPODA, SSCI, e-psyche.
—BLDSC (4674.967000), IDS, IE, Infotrieve, ingenta. **CCC.**
Published by: (Academy of Marketing Science), Sage Publications, Inc., 2455 Teller Rd, Thousand Oaks, CA 91320. TEL 805-499-0721, FAX 805-499-0871, info@sagepub.com, http://www.sagepub.com/journal.aspx?pid=20. Ed. George M Zinkhan. R&P Tanya Udin TEL 805-499-0721 ext 7716. Adv. contact DeAnna Vega Hammersley. Circ: 3,000. **Subscr. overseas to:** Sage Publications Ltd., 1 Oliver's Yard, 55 City Rd, London EC1 1SP, United Kingdom. TEL 44-20-73740645, FAX 44-20-73748741, subscription@sagepub.co.uk.

658.834 USA ISSN 1526-1794
➤ **ACADEMY OF MARKETING SCIENCE REVIEW.** Text in English. 1997. irreg. free (effective 2005). **Document type:** *Journal, Academic/Scholarly.* **Description:** Publishes conceptual and measure development papers in marketing and consumer behavior.
Formerly (until 1998): Journal of Consumer and Market Research (1097-4202)
Media: Online - full text (from ProQuest Information & Learning).
Indexed: ABIn.
—**CCC.**
Published by: Academy of Marketing Science, School of Business Administration, University of Miami, PO Box 248012, Coral Gables, FL 33124-6536. TEL 305-284-6673, FAX 305-284-3762, amsreview@ams-web.org, http://www.amsreview.org/. Ed., R&P Joseph A Cote TEL 360-546-9753. Circ: 1,400.

658.8 USA ISSN 1528-2678
➤ **ACADEMY OF MARKETING STUDIES JOURNAL.** Text in English. s-a. **Document type:** *Journal, Academic/Scholarly.*
Related titles: Online - full text ed.
Published by: (Academy of Marketing Studies), Allied Academies, 145 Travis Rd., P. O. Box 2689, Cullowhee, NC 28723. http://www.alliedacademies.org/marketing/index.html. Ed. Newell Wright.

➤ **ACCUSUBMIT!**; mercenary Internet marketing. see *COMPUTERS—Internet*

658.8 MEX
ADCEBRA; revista Mexicana de mercadotecnia, publicidad y comunicacion. Text in Spanish. 1992. m. MXP 399, USD 150; MXP 40 newsstand/cover (effective 2002). adv. bk.rev. charts; stat.; illus. back issues avail. **Document type:** *Magazine, Trade.* **Description:** Covers consumer-product marketing and promotion in Mexico. Includes product news, strategies, and personality profiles.
Published by: Editorial la Cebra, REVOLUCION 528-700, San Pedro de los Pinos, Mexico City, DF 03800, Mexico. TEL 52-5-273-7717, FAX 52-5-273-7866, info@adcebra.com, http://www.adcebra.com. Ed. Andrzej R Rattinger. Pub. Andrzej A Rattinger. Adv. contact Luz Maria Lopez. page USD 3,300. Circ: 10,000 (paid).

658.8 NLD ISSN 1384-2897
ADFO DIRECT. Text in Dutch. 1984. 10/yr. EUR 115; EUR 49 to students; EUR 12 newsstand/cover (effective 2005). adv. **Document type:** *Journal, Trade.* **Description:** Covers in depth all aspects of direct marketing and sales promotion.
Former titles (until 1996): Adfodirect Magazine (0926-7689); (until 1991): D M Magazine (Direct Marketing) (0923-8670); (until 1989): Direct Effect (0169-0183)
Related titles: ♦ Supplement(s): AdfoXtract. ISSN 1569-5344.
Indexed: BusI.
—IE.
Published by: Adformatie Groep (Subsidiary of: Wolters Kluwer N.V.), Postbus 75462, Amsterdam, 1070 AL, Netherlands. TEL 31-20-5733644, FAX 31-20-6793581, http://www.adformatie.nl/adfodirect/. Ed. Arjo van der Gaag. Pub. Berend Jan Veldkamp. Circ: 10,000.

659 NLD ISSN 0926-7670
ADFOMEDIANIEUWS. Text in Dutch. 1991. s-m. adv. **Document type:** *Newsletter.*
Published by: Samsom Bedrijfsinformatie BV (Subsidiary of: Wolters Kluwer N.V.), Postbus 4, Alphen aan den Rijn, 2400 MA, Netherlands. TEL 31-172-466775, FAX 31-172-440681.

ADFORMATIE BUREAUBIJLAGE. see *ADVERTISING AND PUBLIC RELATIONS*

658.8 NLD ISSN 1569-5344
ADFOXTRACT. Text in Dutch. 2001. 10/yr. EUR 105; EUR 12 newsstand/cover (effective 2005). abstr.; charts; illus. back issues avail. **Document type:** *Newsletter, Trade.* **Description:** Pays attention to recent direct marketing and special promotion actions and abstracts the Dutch and international professional literature.
Formed by the merger of (1993-2001): Adfo Corporate Sponsoring Actueel (1388-4972); Which was formerly (until 1998): Sponsoring Actueel (1380-6793); (1995-2001): AdfoFlash (1389-8884); Which was formerly (until 1999): Adfo Direct Digest (1384-2870); (until 1996): Digest D M & S P (1382-9858)
Related titles: Online - full content ed.; ♦ Supplement to: Adfo Direct. ISSN 1384-2897.
Published by: Adformatie Groep (Subsidiary of: Wolters Kluwer N.V.), Postbus 75462, Amsterdam, 1070 AL, Netherlands. TEL 31-20-5733644, FAX 31-20-6793581, http://www.adformatie.nl/adfoxtract/.

ADLINE; the marketing magazine for the regions. see *ADVERTISING AND PUBLIC RELATIONS*

ADMAP. see *ADVERTISING AND PUBLIC RELATIONS*

ADMEDIA. see *ADVERTISING AND PUBLIC RELATIONS*

ADVANCE CONSULTANCY NEWS. see *COMPUTERS—Internet*

658.8 USA ISSN 1069-0964
HF5410
ADVANCES IN BUSINESS MARKETING AND PURCHASING. Text in English. 1986. irreg., latest vol.13, 2005. price varies. back issues avail. **Document type:** *Monographic series, Academic/Scholarly.* **Description:** Offers a collection of papers written by senior marketing scholars based on their presentations upon receiving the Society for Marketing Advances Distinguished Marketing Scholar Award.
Formerly (until 1992): Advances in Business Marketing (0894-5969)
Related titles: Online - full text ed.: (from ScienceDirect).
—BLDSC (0700.760000). **CCC.**
Published by: J A I Press Inc. (Subsidiary of: Elsevier Science & Technology), 360 Park Ave S, New York, NY 10010-1710. TEL 212-989-5800, FAX 212-633-3990, usinfo-f@elsevier.com, http://www.elsevier.com/wps/find/bookdescription.cws_home/BS_ABMP/description#description. Ed. A G Woodside.

658 USA ISSN 0098-9258
HF5415.3
➤ **ADVANCES IN CONSUMER RESEARCH.** Text in English. 1973. a., latest vol.30, 2003. USD 99 per vol. (effective 2005). back issues avail.; reprints avail. **Document type:** *Proceedings, Academic/Scholarly.* **Description:** Publishes proceedings of the annual conference of the Association for Consumer Research. Contains papers on all aspects of consumer behavior, including the mental and emotional processes and physical actions that people engage in when selecting, purchasing, using, and discarding products and services so as to satisfy needs and desires.
Related titles: Online - full text ed.: (from EBSCO Publishing).
Indexed: ABIn, BPIA, ChPerI, CurCont, ManagCont, RILM, SSCI.
—BLDSC (0704.136000), IE, Infotrieve, ingenta.
Published by: Association for Consumer Research, c/o Rajiv Vaidyanathan, UMD Labovitz School of Business & Economics, 11 E Superior St., Ste. 210, Duluth, MN 55802. TEL 218-726-7853, FAX 218-726-6338, acr@acrweb.org, http://www.vancouver.wsu.edu/acr/home.htm, http://www.acrwebsite.org. Circ: 1,500 (paid). **Subscr. to:** c/o James Muncy, College of Business Administration, Valdosta State University, Valdosta, GA 31698. TEL 229-244-4270, FAX 229-244-7881.

658 USA ISSN 1474-7979
ADVANCES IN INTERNATIONAL MARKETING. Text in English. 1986. a., latest vol.15, 2005. price varies. back issues avail. **Document type:** *Monographic series, Academic/Scholarly.*
Related titles: Online - full text ed.: (from ScienceDirect).
Indexed: ABIn.
—BLDSC (0709.253400). **CCC.**
Published by: (Michigan State University, The Eli Broad Graduate School of Management), J A I Press Inc. (Subsidiary of: Elsevier Science & Technology), 360 Park Ave S, New York, NY 10010-1710. TEL 212-989-5800, FAX 212-633-3990, usinfo-f@elsevier.com, http://www.elsevier.com/wps/find/bookdescription.cws_home/BS_AIM/description#description. Ed. S Cavusgil.

658 657 USA ISSN 1067-5671
HD9980.1
ADVANCES IN SERVICES MARKETING AND MANAGEMENT. Text in English. 1992. a., latest vol.7, 1998. price varies. back issues avail. **Document type:** *Monographic series, Academic/Scholarly.* **Description:** Focuses on new, fresh ideas in services marketing and management. Encourages scholars new to the area of services to pursue innovative and interdisciplinary services-related research.
Related titles: Online - full text ed.
Indexed: SSCI.
—BLDSC (0711.384000). **CCC.**
Published by: J A I Press Inc. (Subsidiary of: Elsevier Science & Technology), 360 Park Ave S, New York, NY 10010-1710. TEL 212-989-5800, FAX 212-633-3990, usinfo-f@elsevier.com, http://www.elsevier.com/wps/find/bookdescription.cws_home/BS_ASMM/description#description. Eds. D E Bowen, S W Brown, T E Swartz.

658.8 USA
ADVANTAGES. Text in English. m. **Document type:** *Magazine, Trade.* **Description:** Filled with sales-friendly product showcases, dependable ideas, proven sales tips, and helpful case histories.
Published by: Advertising Specialty Institute, 4800 Street Rd, Trevose, PA 19053. TEL 215-953-4000, FAX 215-953-3034, info@asicentral.com, http://www.asicentral.com/asp/open/ProductsAndServices/dist/magazines/advantages/index.asp.

ADVERTISING AGE; the international newspaper of marketing. see *ADVERTISING AND PUBLIC RELATIONS*

ADVERTISING AGE CHINA. see *ADVERTISING AND PUBLIC RELATIONS*

ADVERTISING, MARKETING, AND PUBLIC RELATIONS RESOURCES; an internet miniguide. see *BUSINESS AND ECONOMICS—Abstracting, Bibliographies, Statistics*

ADVERTISING SUCCESS. see *COMPUTERS—Internet*

ADVERTLINK; a newspaper on advertising and marketing. see *ADVERTISING AND PUBLIC RELATIONS*

658 330.9 USA
ADVISOR (NEW YORK). Text in English. q. **Description:** Contains business news and feature articles relevant to the direct marketing industry. Covers recent acquisitions, strategies, and other topics.
Published by: Vos, Gruppo, & Capell, Inc., 60 E 42nd St, Ste 3810, New York, NY 10165. TEL 212-697-5753.

AFTERSALES MANAGEMENT. see *BUSINESS AND ECONOMICS—Management*

658.8 USA ISSN 0749-2332
HF5419
AGENCY SALES; the marketing magazine for manufacturers' agencies and their principals. Text in English. 1949. m. USD 54 domestic; USD 60.50 in Canada; USD 66.50 elsewhere (effective 2005). adv. bk.rev. charts; bibl.; tr.lit. **Document type:** *Magazine, Trade.* **Description:** Articles, news updates and announcements on marketing issues that affect manufacturers' agents and their principals.
Incorporates: Manufacturers' Agents National Association. Rep Letter; Former titles: Agency Sales Magazine (0162-3656); Agency Sales - With Agent and Representative (0044-6718)
Related titles: Online - full text ed.: (from Florida Center for Library Automation, Gale Group, Northern Light Technology, Inc., O C L C Online Computer Library Center, Inc., ProQuest Information & Learning).
Indexed: ABIn, BPIA, LRI, T&II.
—BLDSC (0736.228990), IE, ingenta.
Published by: Manufacturers' Agents National Association, 1 Spectrum Pointe, Ste 150, Lake Forest, Orange, CA 92630-2283. TEL 949-859-4040, 877-626-2776, FAX 949-855-2973, mana@manaonline.org, http://www.manaonline.org. Ed. Jack Foster. Adv. contact Jane Holm. B&W page USD 2,074, color page USD 3,171; 7.375 x 9.75. Circ: 9,000 (paid).

AGRAFOOD BIOTECH. see *BIOLOGY—Biotechnology*

▼ **AIRCRAFT OWNER**; the monthly buyers guide for aviation products and services. see *TRANSPORTATION—Air Transport*

658 USA ISSN 0191-9113
ALABAMA & GULF COAST RETAILING NEWS. Text in English. 1970. m. free. adv. **Document type:** *Newspaper.*
Published by: Retailing Newspapers Inc., PO Box 81489, Conyers, GA 30013-9420. TEL 770-786-1375, FAX 770-787-1213, insider@insidernewspapers.com, http://www.insidernewspapers.com.

658.7 USA ISSN 0002-4325
ALABAMA PURCHASOR. Text in English. 1945. m. USD 24.
Published by: Purchasing Management Association of Alabama, c/o Sid Donaldson, Ed, Box 11506, Birmingham, AL 35202. TEL 205-879-3515. Circ: 9,310.

658 USA
ALERT (ROCKY HILL). Text in English. m. USD 35 to non-members (effective 1998). adv. **Document type:** *Newsletter.*
Related titles: Microform ed.: (from PQC).
Published by: Marketing Research Association, Inc., 1344 Silas Deane Hwy, Ste 306, Box 230, Rocky Hill, CT 06067-0230. TEL 860-257-4008, FAX 860-257-3990. Ed. Lisa Asadourian. Adv. contact Christy Becker. Circ: 2,500.

657 PER
ALERTA PUBLICITARIA. Text in Spanish. s-a.
Media: Online - full text.
Published by: Pontificia Universidad Catolica del Peru, Facultad de Ciencias y Artes de la Comunicacion, Ave. Universitaria Cdra, 18, San Miguel, Lima, 32, Peru. TEL 51-1-4602870, FAX 51-1-2613175, epublici@macareo.pucp.edu.pe, comunic@pucp.edu.pe, http://www.pucp.edu.pe/fac/comunic/alerta_publicitaria/.

ALFORJA; revista de distribucion y produccion. see *FOOD AND FOOD INDUSTRIES*

658 ESP ISSN 1575-3646
ALIMARKET. COMERCIALES. Text in Spanish. 1995. a. price varies. adv. **Document type:** *Directory, Trade.*
Related titles: Online - full text ed.
Published by: Publicaciones Alimarket S.A., Albasanz 14 3o, Madrid, 28037, Spain. TEL 34-91-3274340, FAX 34-91-3274522, informa@alimarket.es, http://www.alimarket.es. R&P Carlos Guerrero.

658 ESP ISSN 1134-8135
ALIMARKET. DISTRIBUCION. Text in Spanish. 1993. a. price varies. adv. **Document type:** *Directory, Trade.*
Related titles: Online - full text ed.
Published by: Publicaciones Alimarket S.A., Albasanz 14 3o, Madrid, 28037, Spain. TEL 34-91-3274340, FAX 34-91-3274522, informa@alimarket.es, http://www.alimarket.es. Ed. Carlos Guerrero.

658 338.642 GBR ISSN 1366-2295
ALL ABOUT MAKING MONEY; your guide to financial success. Text in English. 1997. m. GBP 2.45 newsstand/cover. adv. software rev. charts; illus. 100 p./no.; **Document type:** *Consumer.* **Description:** Reports on various ways to make money through business enterprises and investments.
Published by: Partridge Publications, Avenue Lodge 60, 59-60 East St, Brighton, E Sussex BN1 1HN, United Kingdom. TEL 44-1273-719900, MM_editorial@partridgelimited.demon.co.uk, http://www.makingmoney.co.uk. Ed. Ted Rowe. Pub. Matthew Tudor. **Dist. by:** Comag Specialist Division, Tavistock Works, Tavistock Rd, W Drayton, Mddx UB7 7QX, United Kingdom. TEL 44-1895-433800, FAX 44-1895-433801.

ALL ABOUT NET PROFITS. see *BUSINESS AND ECONOMICS*

658.84 USA ISSN 1089-2435
HC110.C6
ALL ABOUT WOMEN CONSUMERS. Text in English. a. USD 269 (effective 2001). adv. **Document type:** *Directory, Trade.* **Description:** Examines women's behavior and attitudes in the fields of online, health, retail, finance, family and other markets.
Published by: E P M Communications, 160 Mercer St, 3rd Fl, New York, NY 10012-3212. TEL 212-941-0099, FAX 212-941-1622, info@epmcom.com, http://www.epmcom.com.

B

658 DEU
ALLENSBACHER MARKT-ANALYSE - WERBETRAEGER-ANALYSE. Text in English, German. 1959. a. stat. index. back issues avail. **Document type:** *Bulletin.* **Description:** Contains market and media research; information on markets and media for advertising agencies and publishers.
Formerly: Allensbacher Werbetraeger-Analyse
Related titles: CD-ROM ed.; Magnetic Tape ed.
Published by: Institut fuer Demoskopie Allensbach, Radolfzellerstr 8, Allensbach, 78476, Germany. TEL 49-7533-8050, FAX 49-7533-3048, info@ifd-allensbach.de. R&P Johannes Schneller. Circ: 1,300.

658.8 URY
ALTA GERENCIA. Text in Spanish. 1982. m. USD 45; USD 90 foreign. adv. back issues avail. **Document type:** *Academic/Scholarly.*
Former titles: Marketing Directo; Marketing S
Published by: C I E C C Universidad Abierta, Dr. Mario Cassinoni, 1157, Montevideo, 11215, Uruguay. TEL 598-2-412174, FAX 598-2-487221. Ed., R&P Edgardo Martinez Zimarioff. Adv. contact Laura Paz. Circ: 9,000 (paid).

658 910.09 CAN ISSN 0843-462X
AM-CAN REPORT; marketing & trade journal. Text in English. 1989. q. CND 10, USD 10 (effective 1991). adv. bk.rev. **Document type:** *Trade.*
Published by: (Am-Can International Club), Small Business World Magazine, 2433 Southvale Crescent, Ottawa, ON K1B 4T8, Canada. TEL 613-733-4260. Ed. Mohamed Talib. Circ: 5,000.

658.0029 USA ISSN 0065-8103
HF5421
AMERICAN DROP-SHIPPERS DIRECTORY. Text in English. 1964. biennial. USD 15. adv. bk.rev. **Document type:** *Directory.* **Description:** Lists more than 500 wholesale sources of supply, of which 200 will make drop-shipments.
Published by: World Wide Trade Service, PO Box 53232, Bellevue, WA 98005. Ed. Randall Lucas. Circ: 8,500 (controlled).

669 USA ISSN 0002-9998
HD9506.U6
AMERICAN METAL MARKET - DAILY; the world metal information network. Text in English. 1882. d. (Mon.-Fri.). USD 775 in North America; USD 1,050 in Central America; USD 1,050 in South America; USD 1,050 in Europe; USD 1,195 elsewhere (effective 2005). adv. bk.rev. charts; illus.; mkt.; stat. back issues avail. **Document type:** *Newspaper, Trade.* **Description:** Covers all aspects of metals business, including production, trade, activity on commodities markets, supply and demand; covers nonferrous, ferrous, precious metals, scrap and competing materials.
Incorporates (1972-1982): Metalworking News (0026-1025)
Related titles: E-mail ed.; Microfiche ed.; Microfilm ed.: (from FCM); Online - full content ed.; Online - full text ed.: American Metal Market Online (from EBSCO Publishing, Factiva, Florida Center for Library Automation, Gale Group, Northern Light Technology, Inc., O C L C Online Computer Library Center, Inc., The Dialog Corporation); Alternate Frequency ed(s).: w.
Indexed: BrCerAb, BusI, C&ISA, CADCAM, CIN, CerAb, ChemAb, ChemTitl, CivEngAb, CorrAb, E&CAJ, EMA, IAA, LRI, M&TEA, MBF, METADEX, RoboAb, SolStAb, T&II, WAA.
—CASDDS, Linda Hall. **CCC.**
Published by: American Metal Market LLC (Subsidiary of: Metal Bulletin plc), 1250 Broadway, New York, NY 10001. TEL 212-213-6202, 800-947-9553, FAX 212-213-6273, http://www.amm.com. Pub. Martin Abbott. adv.: B&W page USD 3,640, color page USD 4,540. Circ: 9,600 (paid). Wire service: DJNS, KR, AP, RN.

669 USA
AMERICAN METAL MARKET - WEEKLY. Text in English. 52/yr. USD 435 in North America (effective 2003).
Published by: American Metal Market LLC (Subsidiary of: Metal Bulletin plc), 1250 Broadway, New York, NY 10001. TEL 800-947-9553, FAX 212-213-1804, 212-213-6273, http://www.amm.com.

658.85 USA ISSN 0003-0902
HF5438 CODEN: AMSLB6
AMERICAN SALESMAN; the national magazine for sales professionals. Text in English. 1955. m. USD 60.55 domestic (effective 2005). **Document type:** *Magazine, Trade.* **Description:** Articles provide practical ways for salespeople to solve daily problems, improve techniques, stimulate creative ideas, develop personality, and gain confidence.
Related titles: Microfilm ed.; Online - full text ed.: (from EBSCO Publishing, Florida Center for Library Automation, Gale Group, Northern Light Technology, Inc., O C L C Online Computer Library Center, Inc., ProQuest Information & Learning).
Indexed: ABIn, BPIA, BusI, ManagCont, T&II.
—BLDSC (0856.200000), IE, ingenta. **CCC.**
Published by: National Research Bureau, 320 Valley St, Burlington, IA 52601-5513. TEL 319-752-5415, FAX 319-752-3421, national@willinet.net. Ed. Teresa Levinson. Pub. Michael Darnall. Circ: 1,500 (paid).

658.8 USA
AMERICAN TELEMARKETING ASSOCIATION. JOURNAL★. Abbreviated title: J A T A. Text in English. 10/yr. adv. **Document type:** *Newsletter.* **Description:** Provides legislative information, coverage of the association's activities, and educational information on topics relating to telemarketing as an industry.
Published by: American Telemarketing Association, 1620 I St NW Ste 615, Washington, DC 20006-4005. TEL 213-463-2330, FAX 213-462-3372. Ed. Roberta Black. Adv. contact Carole Morgan. Circ: 1,200.

ANALYSIS OF BANK MARKETING EXPENDITURES. see *BUSINESS AND ECONOMICS—Banking And Finance*

658.7 SWE
ANBUDSJOURNALEN; Sveriges marknadsdatabas foer offentlig upphandling. Text in Swedish. 1994. 41/yr. SEK 1,900; SEK 75 newsstand/cover. adv. **Document type:** *Newspaper, Trade.*
Published by: AnbudsJournalen i Sverige AB, Box 406, Falun, 79128, Sweden. TEL 46-23-652-00, FAX 46-23-652-05, info@ajour.se, http://www.ajour.se. Ed. Stefan Elg. Adv. contact Anna Astroem. B&W page SEK 8,000; trim 250 x 365. Circ: 3,100 (paid and controlled).

380.1 IND ISSN 0376-5512
HD4295.A5
ANDHRA PRADESH STATE TRADING CORPORATION LIMITED. ANNUAL REPORT. Key Title: Annual Report - Andhra Pradesh State Trading Corporation Limited. Text in English. a.
Published by: Andhra Pradesh State Trading Corporation Limited, 5-10-174 Fatchmaiden Rd., Hyderabad, Andhra Pradesh 500 004, India.

ANLAEG BRUTTO. see *BUILDING AND CONSTRUCTION*

ANLAEG NETTO. see *BUILDING AND CONSTRUCTION*

658.8 FRA ISSN 0066-300X
ANNUAIRE DU MARKETING. Text in French. 1964. a. adv. bk.rev.
Published by: Association Nationale pour le Developpement des Techniques de Marketing, 221 rue La Fayette, Paris, 75010, France. Circ: 1,500.

658 USA ISSN 1052-6838
HF5415.2
ANNUAL ADVANCED RESEARCH TECHNIQUES FORUM. Text in English. 1991. a. USD 35 to non-members; USD 25 to members (effective 2000). adv. **Document type:** *Proceedings.*
—**CCC.**
Published by: American Marketing Association, 311 S Wacker Dr, Ste 5800, Chicago, IL 60606. TEL 312-542-9000, 800-262-1150, FAX 312-542-9001, info@ama.org, http://www.ama.org. Ed. Francesca Van Gorp. R&P Rochelle Amos TEL 312-542-9022. Adv. contact Richard Ballschmiede.

658.8 USA ISSN 0730-2606
HF5415
➤ **ANNUAL EDITIONS: MARKETING.** Text in English. 1973. a., latest 2003, 26th ed. USD 20.31 per vol. (effective 2004). illus. **Document type:** *Academic/Scholarly.*
Former titles: Readings in Marketing; Annual Editions: Readings in Marketing
Published by: McGraw-Hill - Dushkin (Subsidiary of: McGraw-Hill Higher Education), 2460 Kerper Blvd, Dubuque, IA 52001. TEL 800-243-6532, customer.service@mcgraw-hill.com, http://www.dushkin.com/text-data/catalog/0072861304.mhtml. Ed. John E Richardson. Pub. Ian Nielsen. R&P Cheryl Greenleaf.

➤ **ANSURNEWS SITE PROMOTION NEWSLETTER.** see *COMPUTERS—Internet*

➤ **ANUNCIOS**; semanario de la publicidad. see *ADVERTISING AND PUBLIC RELATIONS*

➤ **ANZEIGEN BEOBACHTER MOEBEL.** see *INTERIOR DESIGN AND DECORATION—Furniture And House Furnishings*

➤ **APPAREL SALES - MARKETING COMPENSATION SURVEY.** see *CLOTHING TRADE*

658 714 USA ISSN 1041-388X
TH6485
AQUA: THE BUSINESS MAGAZINE FOR THE SPA AND POOL INDUSTRY★. Text in English. 1976. m. USD 48; USD 90 foreign (effective 1999). **Description:** Contains market information, business management advice for retailers and builders of swimming pools and spas.
Incorporates (1972-1988): Flotation Sleep Industry (0164-5749); Former titles: Spa and Sauna (0886-9472); Spa and Sauna Trade Journal (0164-4858)
Indexed: EPB.
Published by: A B Publications, 4130 Lien Rd, Madison, WI 53704-3602. TEL 608-249-0186, FAX 608-249-1153. Ed. Alan Sanderfoot. Circ: 5,000.

658 BRA
O ARAUTO DO VENDEDOR. Text in Portuguese. 1953. q. free. illus.
Published by: Sindicato Empregados Vendedores e Viajantes do Comercio no Estado do Sao Paulo, Rua Santo Amaro No. 255 (Bela Vista), Sao Paulo, SP CEP 01315, Brazil. TEL 55-11-37-4531, FAX 55-11-36-2160. Ed. Lilly D Portella. Circ: 10,000.

ARGUS (DUTCH EDITION); vakblad voor de detailhandel in gedekte tafel, lifestyle, geschenkartikelen and huishoudelektro. see *GIFTWARE AND TOYS*

ARGUS (FRENCH EDITION); revue professionelle pour les detaillants en art de table, electro-menager, articles cadeaux et lifestyle. see *GIFTWARE AND TOYS*

ARGUS FUNDAMENTALS. see *PETROLEUM AND GAS*

ARGUS GLOBAL MARKETS. see *PETROLEUM AND GAS*

658 USA
ARROWTRADE MAGAZINE; a magazine for retailers, distributors & manufacturers of bowhunting equipment. Text in English. 1996. bi-m. adv. tr.lit. 128 p./no. 3 cols./p.; back issues avail. **Document type:** *Magazine, Trade.*
Published by: Arrow Trade Publishing Corporation, 2295 E Newman Rd, Lake City, MI 49651. TEL 888-796-2083, 888-796-2084, FAX 231-328-3006, atrade@freeway.net. Ed., Pub., R&P Tim Dehn. Adv. contact Matt Granger. B&W page USD 1,444, color page USD 2,203; trim 7.25 x 10. Circ: 10,000.

THE ART OF SELF PROMOTION; nuts and bolts for manageable marketing. see *BUSINESS AND ECONOMICS—Small Business*

658 GBR ISSN 1355-5855
➤ **ASIA PACIFIC JOURNAL OF MARKETING AND LOGISTICS.** Text in English. 1989. q. EUR 2,065.16 in Europe; USD 1,949 in North America; AUD 969 in Australasia; GBP 1,380.04 in the UK & elsewhere (effective 2005). reprint service avail. from PSC. **Document type:** *Journal, Academic/Scholarly.*
Formerly (until 1993): Asia Pacific International Journal of Marketing (0954-7517)
Related titles: Online - full text ed.: (from EBSCO Publishing, Emerald Group Publishing Limited, Gale Group, IngentaConnect, O C L C Online Computer Library Center, Inc., Swets Information Services).
Indexed: ABIn.
—BLDSC (1742.260720), IE, ingenta. **CCC.**
Published by: Barmarick Publications, Enholmes Hall, Patrington, Hull, East Yorkshire HU12 0PR, United Kingdom. TEL 44-1964-630033, 44-1964-630033, FAX 44-1964-631716, hr24@dial.pipex.com. Ed. Oliver H M Yan. **Dist. by:** Emerald Group Publishing Limited, 60-62 Toller Ln, Bradford, W Yorks BD8 9BY, United Kingdom. TEL 44-1274-777700, FAX 44-1274-785200.

658.8 HKG ISSN 1561-7343
ASIAN BRAND NEWS; the essential read for marketing professionals. Text in English. 1999. m. adv. **Document type:** *Magazine, Trade.* **Description:** Contains a mix of marketing news, intelligence and insights on regional marketing campaigns, brand repositionings, and the movers and shakers behind the campaigns.
Published by: Media & Marketing Ltd., 28/F, Dorset House, 979 Kings Rd, Quarry Bay, Hong Kong. TEL 852-2577-2628, FAX 852-2576-9171, askme@media.com.hk, http://www.media.com.hk. Ed. Sharon Desker Shaw. Pub. Ken McKenzie. Adv. contact Steve Bruce. B&W page HKD 7,668, color page HKD 10,958; trim 181 x 265. Circ: 800 (paid and controlled).

658.8 SGP ISSN 0218-6101
➤ **ASIAN JOURNAL OF MARKETING.** Abbreviated title: A J M. Text in English. 1992. a. bk.rev. **Document type:** *Journal, Academic/Scholarly.* **Description:** Discusses marketing matters of interest to academicians and practitioners alike in Singapore and throughout the world.
Incorporates (1976-199?): Singapore Marketing Review (0217-5320)
—**CCC.**
Published by: National University of Singapore, Faculty of Business Administration, 17 Law Link, Singapore, 117591, Singapore. TEL 65-874-3079, 65-874-3098, http://www.fba.nus.edu.sg/qm/journals/AJM.html, http://www.fba.nus.edu.sg/fba. **Co-sponsor:** Marketing Institute of Singapore.

➤ **ASSOCIATE PROGRAMS NEWSLETTER**; successful affiliate marketing. see *COMPUTERS—Internet*

658 USA
AUCTION BULLETIN. Text in English. 1965. fortn. looseleaf. USD 460. **Document type:** *Trade.*
Related titles: Video ed.
Published by: John B. Tamke, Ed. & Pub., PO Box 5, Laconia, NH 03246. TEL 603-366-2553, FAX 603-366-5734. Circ: 622.

658   USA
AUCTION PRICE GUIDE. Text in English. s-a. USD 39.95. **Description:** Lists actual prices paid at auction for merchandise.
Published by: Cowles Publishing Co., 999 W Riverside Ave, Box 2160, Spokane, WA 99201-1010. TEL 509-459-5000, FAX 509-459-5258.

658.84   USA   ISSN 0004-7465
THE AUCTIONEER. Text in English. 1950. m. membership. adv. illus. **Document type:** *Trade.* **Description:** Provides members of NAA with information on association activities, industry issues and general auction news.
Published by: National Auctioneers Association, 8880 Ballentine, Overland, Park, KS 66214-1985. TEL 913-541-8084, FAX 913-894-5281, naahq@aol.com. Ed., R&P Ed Hiscock. Circ: 5,900.

AUDIOVIDEO INTERNATIONAL. see *ELECTRONICS*

658.8005   AUS   ISSN 1441-3582
AUSTRALASIAN MARKETING JOURNAL. Abbreviated title: A M J. Text in English. 1993. s-a. **Document type:** *Academic/Scholarly.*
Formerly (until 1997): Asia-Australia Marketing Journal (1320-1646)
Related titles: Online - full text ed.: (from ProQuest Information & Learning).
Indexed: ABIn, Emerald.
—BLDSC (1795.740000), IE, ingenta.
Published by: (Australia - New Zealand Marketing Academy), University of New South Wales, School of Marketing, Sydney, NSW 2052, Australia. TEL 61-2-93853187, FAX 61-2-93137767, Enquiries.amj@unsw.edu.au, ceinfo@unsw.edu.au, http://www2.fce.unsw.edu.au.
Co-sponsor: Australian Marketing Institute.

AUSTRALIA. BUREAU OF STATISTICS. INFORMATION PAPER: INTRODUCTION OF CONCURRENT SEASONAL ADJUSTMENT INTO THE RETAIL TRADE SERIES. see *BUSINESS AND ECONOMICS—Abstracting, Bibliographies, Statistics*

AUSTRALIA. BUREAU OF STATISTICS. INFORMATION PAPER: SEASONAL INFLUENCES ON RETAIL TRADE. see *BUSINESS AND ECONOMICS—Abstracting, Bibliographies, Statistics*

AUSTRALIA. BUREAU OF STATISTICS. MARKET RESEARCH SERVICES, AUSTRALIA. see *BUSINESS AND ECONOMICS—Abstracting, Bibliographies, Statistics*

AUSTRALIA. BUREAU OF STATISTICS. NEW SOUTH WALES OFFICE. RETAILING IN NEW SOUTH WALES. see *BUSINESS AND ECONOMICS—Abstracting, Bibliographies, Statistics*

AUSTRALIA. BUREAU OF STATISTICS. RETAIL INDUSTRY, AUSTRALIA. see *BUSINESS AND ECONOMICS— Abstracting, Bibliographies, Statistics*

AUSTRALIA. BUREAU OF STATISTICS. RETAIL INDUSTRY, AUSTRALIA: COMMODITY SALES. see *BUSINESS AND ECONOMICS—Abstracting, Bibliographies, Statistics*

AUSTRALIA. BUREAU OF STATISTICS. RETAIL INDUSTRY, STATE AND TERRITORY SUMMARY. see *BUSINESS AND ECONOMICS—Abstracting, Bibliographies, Statistics*

AUSTRALIA. BUREAU OF STATISTICS. RETAIL TRADE, AUSTRALIA: COMMODITY DETAILS. see *BUSINESS AND ECONOMICS—Abstracting, Bibliographies, Statistics*

AUSTRALIA. BUREAU OF STATISTICS. RETAIL TRADE SPECIAL DATA SERVICE: CUSTOMISED REPORTS - DATA REPORT. see *BUSINESS AND ECONOMICS—Abstracting, Bibliographies, Statistics*

AUSTRALIA. BUREAU OF STATISTICS. RETAIL TRADE SPECIAL DATA SERVICES: PERFORMANCE REPORTS - DATA REPORT. see *BUSINESS AND ECONOMICS— Abstracting, Bibliographies, Statistics*

AUSTRALIA. BUREAU OF STATISTICS. RETAIL TRADE SPECIAL DATA SERVICES: SELF COMPARISON REPORTS - DATA REPORT. see *BUSINESS AND ECONOMICS— Abstracting, Bibliographies, Statistics*

AUSTRALIA. BUREAU OF STATISTICS. RETAILING IN AUSTRALIA. see *BUSINESS AND ECONOMICS— Abstracting, Bibliographies, Statistics*

AUSTRALIA. BUREAU OF STATISTICS. WHOLESALE INDUSTRY, AUSTRALIA. see *BUSINESS AND ECONOMICS—Abstracting, Bibliographies, Statistics*

AUSTRALIAN DENTAL PRACTICE MAGAZINE. see *MEDICAL SCIENCES—Dentistry*

THE AUSTRALIAN DIRECT MARKETING DIRECTORY. see *BUSINESS AND ECONOMICS—Trade And Industrial Directories*

AUSTRALIAN FARM JOURNAL. see *AGRICULTURE*

658   AUS
AUSTRALIAN SERVICE MANAGER JOURNAL. Text in English. 1994. bi-m. AUD 59; AUD 79 foreign (effective 1999). adv. back issues avail. **Document type:** *Trade.*
Address: PO Box 271, Lutwyche, QLD 4030, Australia. TEL 61-7-3356-6155, FAX 61-7-3356-6130, aaen@smartchat.net.au. Ed. A J McMahon. Adv. contact Tony McMahon. Circ: 3,200 (paid).

658   AUS   ISSN 0817-3192
HD2930.A1
AUSTRALIA'S TOP 500 COMPANIES. Text in English. 1986. a. AUD 265. adv.
Published by: Dun & Bradstreet Marketing Pty. Ltd., 19 Havilah St, Chatswood, NSW 2067, Australia. TEL 61-2-9352700, FAX 61-2-9352777, http://www.dbmarketing.com.au. Pub., R&P Sue Francis. Circ: 2,000.

658 388.3   USA   ISSN 1075-9409
AUTO RENTAL NEWS. Text in English. 1988. bi-m. (plus Factbook in April). USD 25 domestic; USD 30 in Canada; USD 75 elsewhere (effective 2005). illus.; mkt. **Document type:** *Magazine, Trade.* **Description:** For the car rental industry.
Published by: Bobit Business Media, 3520 Challenger St, Torrance, CA 90503. TEL 310-533-2400, FAX 310-533-2500, http://www.autorentalnews.com/, http://www.bobit.com. Ed. Cathy Stephens. Pub. Sherb Brown. Circ: 17,000 (controlled).

AUTO REVISTA. see *TRANSPORTATION—Automobiles*

658.8   GBR
AUTO VENDING. Text in English. 1991. m. GBP 55; GBP 65 in Europe. adv. **Document type:** *Trade.*
Formerly: Automatic Vending
Published by: Rephoto Publishing Ltd., Plough Rd, Smallfield, Horley, Surrey RH6 9EZ, United Kingdom. TEL 44-1342-844444, FAX 44-1342-844488, rephotopublishingltd@btinternet.com, http://www.auto-vending.co.uk. Ed. Amanda Roberts. Pub. Phil Reynolds. Adv. contact Hugh Jenkins. Circ: 7,000.

658.87   DEU   ISSN 0005-1039
AUTOMATEN-MARKT; Spiegel der Branche. Text in German. 1949. m. EUR 80, EUR 97 (effective 2004). adv. bk.rev. illus.; pat. **Document type:** *Magazine, Trade.* **Description:** Covers coin machines and the amusement business.
Indexed: RASB, RefZh.
Published by: Sigert Verlag GmbH, Ekbertstr 14, Braunschweig, 38122, Germany. TEL 49-531-8092914, FAX 49-531-8092937, info@automatenmarkt.de, http://www.automatenmarkt.de. Ed. Olaf Weinstein. Adv. contact Rudolf Watzlawek. B&W page EUR 1,655, color page EUR 2,570. Circ: 5,000 (paid and controlled).

658.8   USA   ISSN 1061-1797
TJ1560
AUTOMATIC MERCHANDISER. Text in English. 1958. m. (11/yr, plus a. product issue). USD 66 (effective 2005). adv. bk.rev. illus.; stat.; charts. index. back issues avail.; reprints avail. **Document type:** *Magazine, Trade.* **Description:** For vending machine operators, office coffee service operators and mobile caterers; features comprehensive reference of products, equipment, accessories and services.
Formerly (until 1992): American Automatic Merchandiser (0002-7545)
Related titles: Microform ed.; Online - full text ed.: (from Gale Group, Northern Light Technology, Inc., ProQuest Information & Learning).
—CCC.
Published by: Cygnus Business Media, Inc., 1233 Janesville Ave, Fort Atkinson, WI 53538-0803. TEL 920-563-1698, 800-547-7377, FAX 920-563-1699, gloria.cosby@amoline.com, http://www.cygnusb2b.com. Ed. Elliot Maras. Pub. Gloria Cosby. adv.: B&W page USD 3,085, color page USD 4,735. Circ: 15,300 (controlled).

AUTOMOTIVE WEEK; the Greensheet. see *TRANSPORTATION—Automobiles*

AVIATORS HOT LINE. see *AERONAUTICS AND SPACE FLIGHT*

B A G - HANDELSMAGAZIN. see *BUSINESS AND ECONOMICS—Domestic Commerce*

B & T WEEKLY. (Broadcasting and Television) see *ADVERTISING AND PUBLIC RELATIONS*

B B I'S MONITOR OF TECHNOLOGY ASSESSMENT AND REIMBURSEMENT; cost, outcome and payment data critical to medical product markets. see *HEALTH FACILITIES AND ADMINISTRATION—Computer Applications*

B B S I. (Beauty & Barber Supply Institute) see *BEAUTY CULTURE*

658.8   GBR
B P M A NEWS. Text in English. 1972. 6/yr. free. adv. bk.rev.
Formerly: British Premium Merchandise Association News
Published by: (British Promotional Merchandise Association), Headline Promotions, Wellington House, 6 Ashford Rd, Maidstone, Kent ME14 5BH, United Kingdom. Ed. Leonard Baskett. Circ: 15,400.

658   GBR   ISSN 1468-599X
B R A D DIRECT. Text in English. 1989. s-a. GBP 200. **Document type:** *Trade.*
Former titles (until 1998): B R A D Direct Marketing (1368-6593); (until 1996): B R A D Direct Marketing Lists, Rates and Data (0954-7746)
—BLDSC (2265.906600).
Published by: (British Rate and Data), E M A P - Finance & Freight Ltd., 151 Roseberry Ave, London, EC1R 40X, United Kingdom. TEL 44-171-505-3510, FAX 44-171-505-3535.

658   DEU   ISSN 0171-838X
B T E MARKETING-BERATER; Magazin fuer den Textileinzelhandel. Text in German. 1967. m. EUR 35.10; EUR 3.25 newsstand/cover (effective 2004). adv. bk.rev. charts; illus.; tr.lit. **Document type:** *Journal, Trade.*
Formerly (until 1975): B T E - Werbedienst (0005-3376)
Published by: (Bundesverband des Deutschen Textileinzelhandels e.V.), Institut des Deutschen Textileinzelhandels GmbH, An Lyskirchen 14, Cologne, 50676, Germany. TEL 49-221-92150955, FAX 49-221-92150910, marketingberater@bte.de, info@bte.de, http://www.bte.de/fachpublikationen/marketingberater.htm. Ed. Kirsten Reinhardt. Adv. contact Manuela Carlier. B&W page EUR 2,220, color page EUR 3,552. Circ: 12,995 (paid and controlled).

B T H A BUYERS GUIDE. see *GIFTWARE AND TOYS*

658.8   USA   ISSN 1530-2369
HF5801   CODEN: BUMAED
B TO B; the magazine for marketing and e-commerce strategists. Variant title: Advertising Age's B to B. Text in English. 1935. 26/yr. USD 59 domestic; USD 69 in Canada; USD 89 elsewhere (effective 2005). adv. bk.rev. charts; illus.; tr.lit. index. back issues avail.; reprint service avail. from PQC. **Document type:** *Magazine, Trade.*
Former titles (until 1999): Advertising Age's Business Marketing (1087-948X); (until 1993): Business Marketing (0745-5933); (until 1983): Industrial Marketing (0019-8498)
Related titles: Microform ed.: (from MIM, PQC); Online - full text ed.: (from EBSCO Publishing, Florida Center for Library Automation, Gale Group, H.W. Wilson, O C L C Online Computer Library Center, Inc., ProQuest Information & Learning); Supplement(s): B to B Media Business. ISSN 1549-4926.
Indexed: ABIn, ADPA, ASEANManA, ATI, B&I, BLI, BPI, BPIA, BusI, CompIU, Emerald, Inspec, KES, LRI, LogistBibl, M&MA, MEA&I, ManagCont, MicrocompInd, PAIS, RASB, SoftBase, T&II.
—BLDSC (1854.154000), AskIEEE, CASDDS, IDS, IE. **CCC.**
Published by: Crain Communications, Inc., 360 N Michigan Ave, Chicago, IL 60601-3806. TEL 312-649-5200, ebooker@crain.com, http://www.btobonline.com/, http://www.crain.com. Eds. Ellis Booker, Steve Yahn. Pub. Robert Felsenthol. Adv. contact David Bernstein. Circ: 47,853 (controlled).

658.8   USA
B2B MARKETINGONE. Text in English. m. **Document type:** *Newsletter, Trade.*
Media: Online - full content.
Published by: Penton Media, Inc. (Subsidiary of: Pittway Company), 1300 E 9th St, Cleveland, OH 44114-1503. TEL 216-696-7000, 216-696-7000, 800-659-5251, information@penton.com, http://www.B2BmarketingTrends.com, http://www.pentonmedia.com.

658.8   USA
▼ **B2B MARKETINGTRENDS.** Text in English. 2005. q. **Document type:** *Magazine, Trade.* **Description:** Includes information and tools designed to help marketers stay current with b2b marketing trends and carry "how-to" articles, white papers, case studies and marketing solutions.
Published by: Penton Media, Inc. (Subsidiary of: Pittway Company), 1300 E 9th St, Cleveland, OH 44114-1503. TEL 216-696-7000, 800-659-5251, FAX 216-696-0177, information@penton.com, http://www.B2BmarketingTrends.com, http://www.pentonmedia.com. Circ: 5,000 (controlled).

658   TWN
BACKBONE TECHNOLOGIES. Text in Chinese. m. **Description:** Contains information on telecommunica-tions infrastructure, construction products and services in the Taiwan domestic market.
Published by: Arco Publications Inc., 4F, No. 5, Sec. 1, Pa-Te Rd, Taipei, Taiwan. Circ: 18,000.

BAKERY PRODUCTION AND MARKETING NEWSLETTER. see *FOOD AND FOOD INDUSTRIES—Bakers And Confectioners*

B

658.8   PRT
BAREME - IMPRENSA; base regular de meios. Text in Portuguese. q. **Description:** Provides information on press audiences for analysis and advertising planning.
Formerly: Bareme - Base Regular de Meios
Related titles: Magnetic Tape ed.; Online - full text ed.
Published by: Marktest, Rua de S. Jose 183-2, Lisbon, 1169-116, Portugal. TEL 351-213-470866, FAX 351-213-460894, BImprensa@markestest.pt, dcomerc@marktest.pt, http://www.marktest.pt/produtos_servicos/Bareme_Imprensa/default.asp.

658.8   PRT
BAREME - RADIO; base regular de meios. Text in Portuguese. q. **Description:** Radio audience studies used for analysis and advertising planning.
Formerly: Indice de Audience Semanal
Related titles: Magnetic Tape ed.; Online - full text ed.
Published by: Marktest, Rua de S. Jose 183-2, Lisbon, 1169-116, Portugal. TEL 351-213-470866, FAX 351-213-460894, BRadio@marktest.pt, dcomerc@marktest.pt, http://www.marktest.pt/produtos_servicos/Bareme_Radio/default.asp.

658.8   GBR   ISSN 1353-7520
BARGAIN BUYER. Text in English. 1994. w. GBP 0.45 newsstand/cover. **Document type:** *Consumer.*
Published by: Bristol Evening Post, Temple Way, Bristol, Bristol Evening Post Ltd, Bristol, BS99 7HD, United Kingdom. TEL 44-117-9343000, FAX 44-117-9343571, mail@epost.co.uk, subscriptions@bepp.co.uk.

658   USA   ISSN 0882-6218
BARNARD'S RETAIL MARKETING REPORT. Text in English. 1984. bi-m. USD 179 domestic; USD 199 foreign; USD 45 newsstand/cover (effective 2005). adv. bk.rev. back issues avail. **Document type:** *Newsletter.* **Description:** Covers and forecasts retailing trends with emphasis on marketing.
Published by: Barnard Enterprises, Inc., 304 Hillside Ave., Apt. E2, Nutley, NJ 07110-1172. retailfriends@earthlink.net, http://www.retailtrends.com. Ed. Kurt Barnard. Adv. contact Wendy Barnard. Circ: 10,000 (controlled and free).

BEDROOM MAGAZINE. see *INTERIOR DESIGN AND DECORATION—Furniture And House Furnishings*

BEER HANDBOOK. see *BEVERAGES*

658.8   USA
▼ **BENEFITS SELLING.** Text in English. 2003. m. free to qualified personnel (effective 2005). **Document type:** *Magazine, Trade.* **Description:** Designed specifically for brokers, advisors and agents focused on the sale of group and voluntary products.
Published by: Wiesner Publishing, LLC, 7009 S Potomac St, Ste 200, Centennial, CO 80112. TEL 303-397-7600, FAX 303-397-7619, http://www.benefitssellingmag.com, http://www.wiesnerpublishing.com.

658.7   DEU   ISSN 0341-4507
BESCHAFFUNG AKTUELL. Text in German. 1954. 13/yr. EUR 111.15 domestic; EUR 117.65 foreign; EUR 7.70 newsstand/cover (effective 2004). adv. bk.rev. Supplement avail.; back issues avail. **Document type:** *Magazine, Trade.* **Description:** For materials management, industrial purchasing and logistics. Covers marketing, the economy, materials, quality control, and recycling. Includes reports and lists of events, positions available, and a list of suppliers and advertisers.
Formerly: Industrielle Einkauf (0019-9265)
—IE. CCC.
Published by: (Bundesverband Materialwirtschaft und Einkauf e.V.), Konradin Verlag Robert Kohlhammer GmbH, Ernst Mey Str 8, Leinfelden-Echterdingen, 70771, Germany. TEL 49-711-75940, FAX 49-711-7594399, ba.redaktion@konradin.de, info@konradin.de, http://www.beschaffung-aktuell.de/O/123/Y/6477/default.aspx, http://www.konradin.de. Ed. Heinz Kruse. Adv. contact Dietmar Gutekunst. B&W page EUR 4,680, color page EUR 5,970; trim 190 x 270. Circ: 20,032.

658.7   DEU
BESCHAFFUNG SPECIAL. Text in German. 1985. m. EUR 1 newsstand/cover (effective 2004). adv. **Document type:** *Magazine, Trade.*
Published by: ProPress Verlag GmbH, Am Buschhof 8, Bonn, 53227, Germany. TEL 49-228-970970, FAX 49-228-444296, redaktion-bs@t-online.de. adv.: B&W page EUR 7,611, color page EUR 10,545. Circ: 101,400 (paid and controlled).

658   DEU
BESCHAFFUNGS-MARKT. Text in German. a. adv. **Document type:** *Journal, Trade.*
Published by: Konradin Verlag Robert Kohlhammer GmbH, Ernst Mey Str 8, Leinfelden-Echterdingen, 70771, Germany. TEL 49-711-75940, FAX 49-711-7594399, info@konradin.de, http://www.konradin.de. Ed. Heinz Kruse. Adv. contact Dietmar Gutekunst. B&W page EUR 4,680, color page EUR 5,970; trim 190 x 270. Circ: 20,000 (controlled)

658   CHE
BESCHAFFUNGSMANAGEMENT. Text in French, German. 10/yr. CHF 60 (effective 2000). adv. **Document type:** *Magazine, Trade.*
Formerly: Einkaeufer Revue de l'Acheteur
Published by: Schweizerischer Verband fuer Materialwirtschaft und Einkauf/Association Suisse pou l'Approvisionnement et l'Achat, Postfach, Zuerich, 8027, Switzerland. TEL 41-1-2016606, FAX 41-1-2026175. Ed. J Luzius Ruppert. Circ: 4,000.

BESKRIVELSESTEKSTER. see *BUILDING AND CONSTRUCTION*

658.7   PHL
BEST BALIK BUYS∗. Text in English. 1991. s-a. adv. **Document type:** *Catalog.* **Description:** Product and price listing catalogue informs readers of the many advantages of shopping at Duty Free Philippines outlets.
Related titles: Special ed(s).: Balikbayan Program's Duty Free Catalogue.
Published by: (Duty Free Philippines), Eastgate Publishing Corporation, Rm.704 Prestige Tower Condominium, Emerald Ave., Ortigas Center, Pasig Mm, 1605, Philippines. TEL 63-2-6312921, FAX 63-2-631-2992, http://www.eastgateph.com/. Ed. Cecile G Mauricio. Adv. contact Gina C Sancaez. Circ: 75,000.

658.8   AUT
▼ **BEST OF DIRECT MARKETING.** Text in German. 2003. a. EUR 10.95 (effective 2005). **Document type:** *Directory, Trade.*
Published by: Manstein Zeitschriften Verlagsgesellschaft mbH, Brunner Feldstr 45, Perchtoldsdorf, N 2380, Austria. TEL 43-1-866480, FAX http://www.manstein.at, 43-1-86648100, office@manstein.at.

BESTSELLER. see *ADVERTISING AND PUBLIC RELATIONS*

BETRIEBSLEITER-KATALOG. see *ENGINEERING—Industrial Engineering*

BICYCLE RETAILER AND INDUSTRY NEWS. see *SPORTS AND GAMES—Bicycles And Motorcycles*

BIKE EUROPE. see *SPORTS AND GAMES—Bicycles And Motorcycles*

658   USA   ISSN 1064-4180
► **BIOMEDICAL MARKET NEWSLETTER.** Text in English. 1991. m. USD 695; USD 790 foreign; USD 995 by email. charts; illus.; stat.; tr.lit. **Document type:** *Newsletter.* **Description:** Covers business, financial, regulations and marketing on medical equipment, devices, clinical tests, supplies and instruments worldwide.
Related titles: Online - full text ed.: (from Gale Group, Northern Light Technology, Inc., O C L C Online Computer Library Center, Inc.).
Indexed: B&I.
Published by: Biomedical Market Newsletter, Inc., 3237 Idaho Pl, Costa Mesa, CA 92626-2207. TEL 714-434-9500, 800-875-8181, FAX 714-434-9755. Pub., R&P David G Anast.

► **BIZ - E.** see *COMPUTERS—Internet*

► **BIZNEWS.** see *COMPUTERS—Internet*

► **BIZREPORT NEWSLETTER.** see *COMPUTERS—Internet*

658.8   DEU   ISSN 1611-8308
BLACHREPORT; Fachinformationen fuer Event-Marketing, Incentives, Promotions und Sponsoring. Text in German. 1998. bi-w. EUR 183.50 domestic; EUR 237.70 foreign (effective 2005). adv. bk.rev. back issues avail. **Document type:** *Newsletter, Trade.*
Related titles: CD-ROM ed.; Online - full text ed.
Published by: Aktiv Media GmbH, Hopfenfeld 5, Uetze, 31311, Germany. TEL 49-5173-98270, FAX 49-5173-982739, info@blachreport.de, info@aktivmedia-online.de, http://www.blachreport.de, http://www.aktivmedia-online.de. Ed., Pub. Peter Blach. Adv. contact Ulf-Gundo Sanders TEL 49-7144-843200. B&W page EUR 900, color page EUR 1,450; trim 185 x 240. Circ: 1,000 (paid).

BOOK MARKETING UPDATE. see *PUBLISHING AND BOOK TRADE*

BOOK PUBLISHING RESOURCE GUIDE. see *PUBLISHING AND BOOK TRADE*

658.8   USA
BOOMER MARKET ADVISOR. Text in English. 2002. m. **Document type:** *Magazine, Trade.* **Description:** Dedicated to serving the leading financial planners that specialize in selling variable products.
Formerly: (until 2004): Variable Product Specialist (1542-6106)
Published by: Wiesner Publishing, LLC, 7009 S Potomac St, Ste 200, Centennial, CO 80112. TEL 303-397-7600, FAX 303-397-7619, http://www.boomermarketadvisor.com, http://www.wiesnerpublishing.com.

658.8   USA
HF5415.A2
BRADFORD'S INTERNATIONAL DIRECTORY OF MARKETING RESEARCH AGENCIES. Text in English. 1944. a. USD 90 (effective 2000). adv. 272 p./no.; **Document type:** *Directory.* **Description:** Contains over 1,800 listings, which include company name, address, phone and fax numbers, e-mail addresses and website URLs, as well as a short statement on the expertise provided and facilities available.
Formerly: Bradford's Directory of Marketing Research Agencies and Management Consultants in the United States and the World (0068-063X)
—CCC.
Published by: Business Research Services, Inc., 4701 Sangamore Rd., Ste. S155, Bethesda, MD 20816-2532. TEL 202-364-6947, 800-845-8420, FAX 202-686-3228, brspubs@sba8a.com. Ed., Pub. Thomas D Johnson. Circ: 1,000 (paid).

BRAIN/BUREIN. see *ADVERTISING AND PUBLIC RELATIONS*

BRIDAL BUYER. see *MATRIMONY*

658.8   PRT
BRIEFING; publicidade - media - marketing. Text in Portuguese. w. adv. **Document type:** *Magazine, Trade.*
Related titles: Online - full text ed.
Published by: Edicoes Expansao Economica Lda., Rue Mario Castelhano, 40-1, Queluz de Baixo, Barcarena, 2749-502, Portugal. TEL 351-21-496-95-40, FAX 351-21-436-95-39, webmaster@expansao.iol.pt, http://www.briefing.iol.pt, http://www.expansao.iol.pt. Ed. Benedita Trindade. Adv. contact Hugo Santinho.

658.8   GBR
BRITISH COMMERCIAL AGENTS REVIEW. Text in English. 1967. m. GBP 48, USD 80 (effective 2001). adv. 12 p./no.; **Document type:** *Journal, Trade.* **Description:** Promotion and enhancement of the services of manufacturers' agents in the United Kingdom.
Formerly: British Agents Review (0007-022X)
Published by: British Agents Register (B.A.R.) Ltd., 24 Mount Parade, Harrogate, W Yorks HG1 1BP, United Kingdom. FAX 44-1423-561204, info@agentsregister.com, http://www.agentsregister.com. Ed., R&P, Adv. contact Andrew Turner TEL 44-1423-560608. B&W page GBP 560, color page GBP 980; trim 10.5 x 7. Circ: 4,500 (paid).

BUILDING INTELLIGENCE. see *BUILDING AND CONSTRUCTION*

658   USA
BUSINESS 2 BUSINESS∗; for business and marketing communicators. Text in English. q. USD 215 to corporations includes national BMA membership; USD 140 to qualified personnel includes national BMA membership (effective 2000). **Description:** Provides members with commentary, advice, and association news.
Formerly: New Jersey B M A News
Published by: Business Marketing Association, New Jersey Chapter, c/o Nancy A. Rago, Membership Chair, Brigham & Rago Marketing Communications, 18 Bank St, Ste 200, Morristown, NJ 07060. TEL 973-425-0011, FAX 973-425-0044, nancy@brigham-rago.com, http://www.bma-nj.org/member.htm.

658.8   USA
BUSINESS ADVANTAGE NEWSLETTER. Text in English. irreg. free. **Document type:** *Newsletter.* **Description:** Focuses on marketing and promoting business on the Internet.
Media: Online - full text.
Address: CookieJim@aol.com. Pub. Jim Smoot.

BUSINESS CREDIT. see *BUSINESS AND ECONOMICS—Banking And Finance*

658 388.3   USA
BUSINESS DRIVER. Text in English. a. USD 7.50 per vol.; free to qualified personnel (effective 2005). illus. **Document type:** *Magazine, Trade.* **Description:** Car value issues and driver safety for business car drivers.
Related titles: Online - full text ed.
Published by: Bobit Business Media, 3520 Challenger St, Torrance, CA 90503. TEL 310-533-2400, FAX 310-533-2500, mike.antich@bobit.com, http://fleet-central.com/index.cfm, http://www.bobit.com. Ed. Mike Antich. Pub. Sherb Brown. Circ: 400,000 (controlled). **Subscr. to:** PO Box 1068, Skokie, IL 60076.

658 388.3   USA
BUSINESS FLEET; managing 10-50 company vehicles. Text in English. 2000. q. adv. **Document type:** *Trade.* **Description:** Provides information on more economical and efficient ways of operating small fleets, and to inform the audience of the latest vehicles, products, and services available to small companies.
Related titles: Online - full content ed.
Published by: Bobit Business Media, 3520 Challenger St, Torrance, CA 90503. TEL 310-533-2592, FAX 310-533-2503, selliott@bobit.com, http://www.fleet-central.com/bf/home.cfm, http://fleet-central.com. Ed. Steve Elliott. Circ: 100,000 (paid). **Subscr. to:** PO Box 1068, Skokie, IL 60076.

658   USA
BUSINESS INFORMATION MARKETS (YEAR): THE STRATEGIC OUTLOOK. Text in English. 1975. a. USD 2,390 (effective 2006). **Document type:** *Directory, Trade.* **Description:** Provides information on the $30 billion market, as well as profiles and forecasts for ten major industry segments: general business periodicals, trade magazines and newspapers, looseleafs, newsletters, print and online databases, business books, research services, report publishing, information on demand, face-to-face services, and audiovisual services. **Formerly:** Business and Professional Online Information Markets **Related titles:** Online - full text ed.: USD 2,295 (effective 2005). **Published by:** SIMBA Information (Subsidiary of: R.R. Bowker LLC), 60 Long Ridge Rd., Ste 300, Stamford, CT 06902. TEL 203-325-8193, 800-307-2529, FAX 203-325-8915, info@simbanet.com, http://www.simbanet.com/publications/report_bim.htm.

BUSINESS INTELLIGENCE REPORT; strategies and trends for the successful business. see *BUSINESS AND ECONOMICS—Small Business*

BUSINESS MONITOR: RETAILING. see *BUSINESS AND ECONOMICS—Abstracting, Bibliographies, Statistics*

BUSINESS MONITOR: WHOLESALING. see *BUSINESS AND ECONOMICS—Abstracting, Bibliographies, Statistics*

THE BUSINESS OF E-MAIL. see *COMPUTERS—Internet*

BUSINESS OPPORTUNITIES. see *BUSINESS AND ECONOMICS—International Commerce*

BUSINESS RATIO. ADVERTISING AGENCIES. see *ADVERTISING AND PUBLIC RELATIONS*

BUSINESS RATIO. ANTIQUES AND FINE ART DEALERS AND AUCTIONEERS. see *ANTIQUES*

BUSINESS RATIO. BAKERIES. see *FOOD AND FOOD INDUSTRIES—Bakers And Confectioners*

BUSINESS RATIO. BREWERS. see *BEVERAGES*

BUSINESS RATIO. BUILDERS MERCHANTS. see *BUILDING AND CONSTRUCTION*

658.8   GBR   ISSN 1469-6363
BUSINESS RATIO. CASH AND CARRY. Text in English. 1980. a. GBP 275 (effective 2001). charts; stat. **Document type:** *Trade.* **Former titles** (until 1999): Business Ratio Plus: Cash & Carry (1357-8847); (until 1994): Business Ratio Report. Cash and Carry (0261-7560) **Published by:** The Prospect Shop Ltd., Field House, 72 Oldfield Rd, Hampton, Middx TW12 2HQ, United Kingdom. TEL 44-20-8461-8730, 44-20-8481-8720, FAX 44-20-8783-1940, info@theprospectshop.co.uk.

BUSINESS RATIO. CERAMIC MANUFACTURERS. see *CERAMICS, GLASS AND POTTERY*

BUSINESS RATIO. CHEMICAL DISTRIBUTORS. see *CHEMISTRY*

BUSINESS RATIO. CLOTHING MANUFACTURERS. see *CLOTHING TRADE*

BUSINESS RATIO. CLOTHING RETAILERS. see *CLOTHING TRADE*

BUSINESS RATIO. COMMERCIAL HORTICULTURE & GARDEN CENTRES. see *GARDENING AND HORTICULTURE*

BUSINESS RATIO. CONFECTIONERY MANUFACTURERS. see *FOOD AND FOOD INDUSTRIES—Bakers And Confectioners*

BUSINESS RATIO. DOMESTIC FURNITURE MANUFACTURERS. see *INTERIOR DESIGN AND DECORATION—Furniture And House Furnishings*

BUSINESS RATIO. DYERS & FINISHERS. see *CLEANING AND DYEING*

BUSINESS RATIO. ELECTRICAL INSTALLATION EQUIPMENT MANUFACTURERS. see *ENGINEERING—Electrical Engineering*

BUSINESS RATIO. ELECTRICAL WHOLESALERS. see *ELECTRONICS*

BUSINESS RATIO. ELECTRONIC COMPONENT DISTRIBUTORS. see *ELECTRONICS*

BUSINESS RATIO. ELECTRONIC COMPONENT MANUFACTURERS. see *ELECTRONICS*

BUSINESS RATIO. ENGINEERING DISTRIBUTORS. see *ENGINEERING*

BUSINESS RATIO. FROZEN FOOD DISTRIBUTORS. see *FOOD AND FOOD INDUSTRIES*

BUSINESS RATIO. FROZEN FOOD PRODUCERS. see *FOOD AND FOOD INDUSTRIES*

BUSINESS RATIO. GROCERY WHOLESALERS. see *FOOD AND FOOD INDUSTRIES—Grocery Trade*

BUSINESS RATIO. HYDRAULIC AND PNEUMATIC EQUIPMENT MANUFACTURERS. see *ENGINEERING—Hydraulic Engineering*

BUSINESS RATIO. INDUSTRIAL FASTENER DISTRIBUTORS. see *BUSINESS AND ECONOMICS—Production Of Goods And Services*

BUSINESS RATIO. INDUSTRIAL FASTENER MANUFACTURERS. see *BUSINESS AND ECONOMICS—Production Of Goods And Services*

658.8   GBR   ISSN 1470-3394
BUSINESS RATIO. MAIL ORDER & CATALOGUE HOUSES. Text in English. 1981. a. GBP 275 (effective 2001). charts; stat. **Document type:** *Directory.* **Former titles** (until 2000): Business Ratio Plus: Mail Order & Catalogue Houses (1354-3407); (until 1994): Business Ratio Report: Mail Order and Catalogue Houses (0267-856X); Which superseded in part (1985-1993): Business Ratio Report. Direct Marketing (0261-3859) **Published by:** The Prospect Shop Ltd., Field House, 72 Oldfield Rd, Hampton, Middx TW12 2HQ, United Kingdom. TEL 44-20-8461-8730, 44-20-8481-8720, FAX 44-20-8783-1940, info@theprospectshop.co.uk.

658.8   GBR   ISSN 1467-9116
BUSINESS RATIO. MARKET RESEARCH AGENCIES. Text in English. 1987. a. GBP 275 (effective 2001). charts; stat. **Document type:** *Trade.* **Former titles** (until 1999): Business Ratio Plus: Market Research Agencies (1356-7373); (until 1994): Business Ratio Report. Market Research (0952-5173) **Published by:** The Prospect Shop Ltd., Field House, 72 Oldfield Rd, Hampton, Middx TW12 2HQ, United Kingdom. TEL 44-20-8461-8730, 44-20-8481-8720, FAX 44-20-8783-1940, info@theprospectshop.co.uk.

BUSINESS RATIO. METAL STOCKHOLDERS. see *METALLURGY*

BUSINESS RATIO. MINING & QUARRYING. see *MINES AND MINING INDUSTRY*

BUSINESS RATIO. NEWSPAPER PUBLISHERS. see *JOURNALISM*

BUSINESS RATIO. PAPER AND BOARD MANUFACTURERS. see *PAPER AND PULP*

BUSINESS RATIO. PAPER MERCHANTS. see *PAPER AND PULP*

BUSINESS RATIO. PERIODICAL PUBLISHERS. see *PUBLISHING AND BOOK TRADE*

BUSINESS RATIO. PHARMACEUTICAL MANUFACTURERS & DEVELOPERS. see *PHARMACY AND PHARMACOLOGY*

BUSINESS RATIO. PLASTICS PACKAGING MANUFACTURERS. see *PACKAGING*

BUSINESS RATIO PLUS: AIR CONDITIONING INDUSTRY. see *HEATING, PLUMBING AND REFRIGERATION*

BUSINESS RATIO PLUS: BOOKSELLERS. see *PUBLISHING AND BOOK TRADE*

BUSINESS RATIO PLUS: COMPUTER EQUIPMENT DISTRIBUTORS. see *COMPUTERS—Computer Industry*

BUSINESS RATIO PLUS: COMPUTER SERVICES; an industry sector analysis. see *COMPUTERS—Computer Industry*

BUSINESS RATIO PLUS: COMPUTER SOFTWARE HOUSES. see *COMPUTERS—Software*

BUSINESS RATIO PLUS: COTTON & MAN - MADE FIBRE PROCESSORS. see *TEXTILE INDUSTRIES AND FABRICS*

BUSINESS RATIO PLUS: FOOD PROCESSORS. see *FOOD AND FOOD INDUSTRIES*

BUSINESS RATIO PLUS: LEATHER MANUFACTURERS & PROCESSORS. see *LEATHER AND FUR INDUSTRIES*

BUSINESS RATIO PLUS: MACHINE TOOL MANUFACTURERS. see *MACHINERY*

BUSINESS RATIO PLUS: READY MIXED CONCRETE & AGGREGATES INDUSTRY. see *BUILDING AND CONSTRUCTION*

BUSINESS RATIO: POULTRY PROCESSORS. see *AGRICULTURE—Poultry And Livestock*

BUSINESS RATIO. PRINTERS. INTERMEDIATE. see *PRINTING*

BUSINESS RATIO. PRINTERS. MAJOR. see *PRINTING*

BUSINESS RATIO REPORT: ASSOCIATION FOOTBALL LEAGUE CLUBS; an industry sector analysis. see *SPORTS AND GAMES—Ball Games*

BUSINESS RATIO REPORT: CARPET INDUSTRY; an industry sector analysis. see *INTERIOR DESIGN AND DECORATION—Furniture And House Furnishings*

BUSINESS RATIO REPORT. COMPOUND ANIMAL FEEDSTUFFS. see *AGRICULTURE—Feed, Flour And Grain*

BUSINESS RATIO REPORT: CONTRACT & OFFICE FURNITURE INDUSTRY; an industry sector analysis. see *INTERIOR DESIGN AND DECORATION—Furniture And House Furnishings*

BUSINESS RATIO REPORT: COURIERS AND DESPATCH SERVICES; an industry sector analysis. see *TRANSPORTATION—Trucks And Trucking*

658.8   GBR   ISSN 1473-107X
BUSINESS RATIO REPORT. DEPARTMENT & VARIETY STORES. Text in English. 1980. a. GBP 275 (effective 2001). charts; stat. **Document type:** *Trade.* **Former titles** (until 2001): Business Ratio. Department & Variety Stores (1469-7343); (until 2000): Business Ratio Plus: Department and Variety Stores (1366-8757); (until 1997): Business Ratio Plus. Department Stores (1358-3735); (until 1994): Business Ratio Report. Department Stores (0261-779X) **Published by:** The Prospect Shop Ltd., Field House, 72 Oldfield Rd, Hampton, Middx TW12 2HQ, United Kingdom. TEL 44-20-8461-8730, 44-20-8481-8720, FAX 44-20-8783-1940, info@theprospectshop.co.uk.

658.8   GBR   ISSN 0267-8578
BUSINESS RATIO REPORT: DIRECT MARKETING SERVICES; an industry sector analysis. Text in English. 1981. a. GBP 275 (effective 2001). charts; stat. **Document type:** *Trade.* **Supersedes in part** (1985-1993): Business Ratio Report. Direct Marketing (0261-3859) **Published by:** The Prospect Shop Ltd., Field House, 72 Oldfield Rd, Hampton, Middx TW12 2HQ, United Kingdom. TEL 44-20-8461-8730, 44-20-8481-8720, FAX 44-20-8783-1940, info@theprospectshop.co.uk.

BUSINESS RATIO REPORT. ELECTRICAL CONTRACTORS (YEAR). see *ENGINEERING—Electrical Engineering*

BUSINESS RATIO REPORT: EXHIBITION AND CONFERENCE ORGANISERS; an industry sector analysis. see *MEETINGS AND CONGRESSES*

BUSINESS RATIO REPORT: FOOTWEAR DISTRIBUTORS; an industry sector analysis. see *SHOES AND BOOTS*

BUSINESS RATIO REPORT: FOOTWEAR MANUFACTURERS; an industry sector analysis. see *SHOES AND BOOTS*

BUSINESS RATIO REPORT. FREIGHT FORWARDERS. see *TRANSPORTATION*

BUSINESS RATIO REPORT. HAND & SMALL TOOL MANUFACTURERS. see *ENGINEERING*

BUSINESS RATIO REPORT. HEATING AND VENTILATING EQUIPMENT MANUFACTURERS (YEAR). see *HEATING, PLUMBING AND REFRIGERATION*

BUSINESS RATIO REPORT. HOUSEBUILDERS. INTERMEDIATE (YEAR). see *BUILDING AND CONSTRUCTION*

BUSINESS RATIO REPORT. HOUSEBUILDERS. MAJOR (YEAR). see *BUILDING AND CONSTRUCTION*

BUSINESS RATIO REPORT. INDUSTRIAL CHEMICAL MANUFACTURERS. see *CHEMISTRY*

BUSINESS RATIO REPORT. INSURANCE BROKERS AND INTERMEDIARIES. see *INSURANCE*

BUSINESS RATIO REPORT. IRON FOUNDERS (YEAR). see *METALLURGY*

BUSINESS RATIO REPORT. MANAGEMENT CONSULTANCIES (YEAR). see *BUSINESS AND ECONOMICS—Management*

BUSINESS RATIO REPORT: METAL FINISHERS; an industry sector analysis. see *METALLURGY*

BUSINESS RATIO REPORT. NON-FERROUS FOUNDERS (YEAR). see *METALLURGY*

BUSINESS RATIO REPORT. PAINT & PRINTING INK MANUFACTURERS (YEAR). see *PAINTS AND PROTECTIVE COATINGS*

BUSINESS RATIO REPORT: PAINTING AND DECORATING CONTRACTORS AND MERCHANTS; an industry sector analysis. see *INTERIOR DESIGN AND DECORATION*

BUSINESS RATIO REPORT: PAPER & BOARD PACKAGING; an industry sector analysis. see *PACKAGING*

BUSINESS RATIO REPORT. PRINTED CIRCUIT MANUFACTURERS (YEAR). see *ELECTRONICS*

BUSINESS RATIO REPORT. TEXTILE RENTAL, LAUNDERERS & DRY CLEANERS (YEAR). see *CLEANING AND DYEING*

BUSINESS RATIO REPORT: THE DEFENCE INDUSTRY; an industry sector analysis. see *MILITARY*

BUSINESS RATIO REPORT: THE DOMESTIC ELECTRICAL APPLIANCE INDUSTRY; an industry sector analysis. see *ELECTRONICS*

BUSINESS RATIO REPORT. THE FOOD INGREDIENTS INDUSTRY (YEAR). see *FOOD AND FOOD INDUSTRIES*

BUSINESS RATIO REPORT. THE GREETING CARD INDUSTRY. see *GIFTWARE AND TOYS*

BUSINESS RATIO REPORT: THE MEDICAL EQUIPMENT INDUSTRY; an industry sector analysis. see *MEDICAL SCIENCES*

BUSINESS RATIO. RETAIL AND WHOLESALE CHEMISTS. see *PHARMACY AND PHARMACOLOGY*

BUSINESS RATIO. THE AGRICULTURAL EQUIPMENT INDUSTRY. see *MACHINERY*

BUSINESS RATIO. THE BETTING AND GAMING INDUSTRY. see *SPORTS AND GAMES*

BUSINESS RATIO. THE FIRE PROTECTION EQUIPMENT INDUSTRY. see *FIRE PREVENTION*

BUSINESS RATIO. THE FORGING INDUSTRY. see *METALLURGY*

BUSINESS RATIO. THE KITCHEN AND BATHROOM FURNITURE AND FITTINGS INDUSTRY. see *INTERIOR DESIGN AND DECORATION*

BUSINESS RATIO. THE OPTICAL INDUSTRY. see *PHYSICS—Optics*

BUSINESS RATIO. THE PHOTOGRAPHIC INDUSTRY. see *PHOTOGRAPHY*

BUSINESS RATIO. THE REFRIGERATION EQUIPMENT INDUSTRY. see *HEATING, PLUMBING AND REFRIGERATION*

BUSINESS RATIO. VEHICLE DEALERS. see *TRANSPORTATION—Automobiles*

658.8   USA
BUSINESS THEME E-ZINE. Text in English. m. **Document type:** *Newsletter.* **Description:** Provides tips for sales professionals, small business owners and marketing.
Media: E-mail.
Address: internetsearch@hotmail.com. Ed. Kim Busch.

658   AUS   ISSN 1031-1343
THE BUSINESS WHO'S WHO AUSTRALIAN PRODUCTS AND TRADENAMES GUIDE. Text in English. 1967. a. AUD 350. adv. back issues avail. **Document type:** *Directory.* **Description:** Lists products and services divided into industry sectors, trade names and agencies, company address details.
Former titles: Business Who's Who Australian Buying Reference (0311-5070); Riddell's Australian Purchasing Yearbook (0085-5715)
Related titles: CD-ROM ed.
Published by: Dun & Bradstreet Marketing Pty. Ltd., 19 Havilah St, Chatswood, NSW 2067, Australia. TEL 61-2-9352700, FAX 61-2-9352777, http://www.dbmarketing.com.au. Ed. Thyle Carroll. Pub., R&P, Adv. contact Sue Francis. Circ: 2,000.

658   GBR
BUSINESSES & ASSETS. Text in English. 1983. m. GBP 85. adv. bk.rev. back issues avail. **Document type:** *Trade.*
Published by: Businesses & Assets Ltd., Business MarketPl, East Common, Gerrards Cross, Bucks SL9 7AG, United Kingdom. TEL 01753-891000, FAX 01753-880342. Ed. Lesley Carroll. Adv. contact Robert Spencer. B&W page GBP 850, color page GBP 1,000; 180 x 257. Circ: 15,000.

658.8
BUSY MARKETING TIPS. Text in English. 3/w. software rev. **Document type:** *Newsletter.* **Description:** Includes website marketing tips, answers and software reviews for beginners.
Media: E-mail.
Published by: Busy Marketing, 2482 Wooding Ct, San Jose, CA 95128. TEL 408-298-1927, tips@busymarketing.com, http://www.busymarketing.com. Ed., Pub., R&P Dawn Gray TEL 408-910-9816. Circ: 1,000 (free).

658   FRA
BUYING AND SELLING IN EUROPE; europages newsletter. Text in French. q. **Document type:** *Directory.*
Published by: Euredit S.A., 47 rue Louis Blanc, Paris La Defense, Cedex 92984, France. TEL 33-1-41164900, FAX 33-1-41164950, comments@europages.com, http://www.europages.com. Ed. Edouard Prisse.

658   USA   ISSN 1082-0035
BUYING STRATEGY FORECAST; the bi-weekly source of short-term buying forecasts and strategies. Variant title: Purchasing Magazine's Buying Strategy Forecast. Text in English. 1985 (vol.10). s-m. USD 275 Print or online ed. (effective 2005). **Document type:** *Newsletter, Trade.* **Description:** News and graphic analysis of trends in and projections of commodities and products investments and pricing.
Formerly: Buying Strategy Forecast for Purchasing Managers (0733-0103)
Related titles: Online - full text ed.
—CCC.
Published by: Reed Business Information (Subsidiary of: Reed Business), 275 Washington St, Newton, MA 02458. TEL 617-964-3030, http://www.manufacturing.net/pur/index.asp?layout=siteInfoWebzine&view=Detail&doc_id=30802, http://www.reedbusiness.com. Ed. Tom Stundza.

658 659.1   USA   ISSN 1063-3383
BUZZ (ROCHESTER); perspectives on marketing technology. Text in English. 1992. m. free to qualified personnel. **Document type:** *Newsletter.* **Description:** Focuses on marketing communications trends and techniques.
Published by: Buck & Pulleyn, Inc., 1160 Pittsford Victor Rd #A, Pittsford, NY 14534-3899. TEL 585-248-2300, FAX 585-248-5315, http://www.pulleyn.com. Ed. Cathy Rubino. R&P Cecelia Stone.

658.8 380.14   GBR
C B I DISTRIBUTIVE TRADES SURVEY. Text in English. m. GBP 425 to non-members; GBP 255 to members (effective 1999). adv. **Description:** Covers latest trends in retail, wholesale and the motor trades, with qualitative information on sales, stocks, imports, suppliers, investment, and the general business situation.
Formerly: Distributive Trades Survey (0266-1802)
Published by: Confederation of British Industry, Centre Point, 103 New Oxford St, London, WC1A 1DU, United Kingdom. TEL 44-171-395-8164, FAX 44-171-240-1578. Ed. Sudhair Junankar, R&P Wendy Hayes TEL 44-171-395-8036. Adv. contact Frances Hughes.

C C N MATTHEWS C C E DIRECTORY. see *ADVERTISING AND PUBLIC RELATIONS*

658 384   USA
C C NEWS (EMAIL); the business newspaper for call centers and customer care professionals. (Call Center) Text in English. m. free (effective 2005). adv. **Document type:** *Newspaper, Trade.* **Description:** Covers news and trends of the customer care and call center industry.
Formerly: C C News (Print)
Media: E-mail. **Related titles:** Online - full text ed.
Published by: United Publications, Inc., 106 Lafayette St, PO Box 995, Yarmouth, ME 04096. TEL 207-846-0600, FAX 207-846-0657, info@ccnews.com, http://www.ccnews.com, http://www.unitedpublications.com/. Ed. Bernie Monegain. adv.: B&W page USD 7,550, color page USD 8,925.

658.8   ITA
C E D E M NOTIZIE* . Text in Italian. fortn.
Published by: Centro di Documentazione Economica e di Marketing, Via Giacinto Bruzzesi, 27, Milan, MI 20146, Italy.

658.8 659.1   CAN
C M A COMMUNICATOR. Text in English. q. CND 30 to non-members. adv. **Document type:** *Newsletter.*
Former titles: Communicator (Don Mills); Direct Marketing Communicator (0834-0722); (until 1986): Canadian Direct Marketing Communicator (0831-7852); (until 1985): C D M A Update (0831-7844); (until 1985): Direct Marketing Communicator (0821-7602); (until 1983): Communicator (0821-7599)

Published by: Canadian Marketing Association, One Concorde Gate, Ste. 607, Don Mills, ON M3C 3N6, Canada. TEL 416-391-2362, FAX 416-441-4062. Ed., R&P Elizbeth Lewis. Adv. contact Katherine Brasch. Circ: 2,500.

658.8 630   GHA   ISSN 0007-8611
C M B NEWSLETTER. Text in English. 1956. q. free. **Document type:** *Newsletter.*
Published by: Ghana Cocoa Marketing Board, PO Box 933, Accra, Ghana. Ed. Nana M B Sarpong II. Circ: 3,000.

C P A CLIENT BULLETIN. see *BUSINESS AND ECONOMICS—Accounting*

658 657   USA   ISSN 0279-1021
C P A MARKETING REPORT. Text in English. 1981. m. looseleaf. USD 374 (effective 2004). back issues avail. **Document type:** *Newsletter.* **Description:** Helps public accounting firms design, implement and evaluate effective programs to attract new clients, enhance the firm's image, improve client relations and build sound practices.
Incorporates (1978-1987): C P A Proposal Alert
Related titles: Online - full text ed.: (from EBSCO Publishing).
Indexed: ATI.
—CCC.
Published by: Strafford Publications, Inc., 590 Dutch Valley Rd, N E, Postal Drawer 13729, Atlanta, GA 30324-0729. TEL 404-881-1141, 800-926-7926, FAX 404-881-0074, 404-881-0041, editors@straffordpub.com, custserv@straffordpub.com, http://www.aspenpub.com. Ed. Jon McKenna. Pub. Richard M Ossoff. R&P Marianne Mueller.

THE C S R ADVISOR. (Customer Service Representative) see *INSURANCE*

658.8   AUS
C T G GAZETTE* . Text in English. 1964. q. AUD 0.24 per issue.
Published by: (Commercial Travellers' Guild), Paragon Publications, 9 Minyon St, Brunswick Heads, NSW 2483, Australia. **Co-sponsor:** New South Wales Sales Representatives.

CABLE THEFT NEWSLETTER. see *COMMUNICATIONS— Television And Cable*

658   FRA   ISSN 0249-5570
CAHIERS DE RECHERCHE EN GESTION DES ENTREPRISES. Text in French. 1977. 2/yr. back issues avail. **Document type:** *Academic/Scholarly.*
Published by: Universite de Rennes I, Laboratoire Economie et Gestion des Entreprises, 7 place Hoche, Rennes, 35000, France. TEL 99-25-35-06, FAX 99-38-80-84. Ed. Alain Galesne.

CALIFORNIA. DEPARTMENT OF CONSUMER AFFAIRS. ANNUAL REPORT. see *CONSUMER EDUCATION AND PROTECTION*

658   DEU
CALL CENTER & C R M MARKTFUEHRER. Text in German. 1998. 2/yr. EUR 9.50 newsstand/cover (effective 2004). adv. **Document type:** *Magazine, Trade.*
Published by: telepublic Verlag GmbH & Co. Medien KG, Podbielskistr. 325, Hannover, 30659, Germany. TEL 49-511-3348400, FAX 49-511-3348499, info@teletalk.de. adv.: B&W page EUR 2,800, color page EUR 3,340; trim 210 x 297. Circ: 8,260 (paid and controlled).

658   USA   ISSN 1064-5543
CALL CENTER MAGAZINE. Text in English. 1988. m. free in US & Canada to qualified personnel (effective 2005). **Document type:** *Trade.* **Description:** For call center management; helps them choose and buy, implement and manage technology — hardware, software and services used in telephone call centers.
Formerly (until 1992): Inbound - Outbound Magazine (1042-6116)
Related titles: Online - full text ed.: (from EBSCO Publishing, Florida Center for Library Automation, Gale Group, H.W. Wilson, LexisNexis, O C L C Online Computer Library Center, Inc., ProQuest Information & Learning).
Indexed: ABIn, BPI, CurCont, SoftBase.
—IDS. CCC.
Published by: C M P Media LLC (Subsidiary of: United News & Media), 600 Community Dr, Manhasset, NY 11030. Callcenter@halldata.com, http://www.callcentermagazine.com/. Ed. Keith Dawson. Pub. Ruthann Fisher TEL 215-396-4037. Circ: 60,758.

658   DEU   ISSN 1433-0199
CALL CENTER PROFI; das Magazin fuer Call Center, e-Marketing und CRS. Text in German. 1998. 10/yr. EUR 57; EUR 48 to students; EUR 9.50 newsstand/cover (effective 2004). adv. **Document type:** *Magazine, Trade.*
Related titles: Online - full text ed.

Published by: Betriebswirtschaftlicher Verlag Dr. Th. Gabler GmbH (Subsidiary of: Springer Science+Business Media), Abraham-Lincoln-Str 46, Wiesbaden, 65189, Germany. TEL 49-611-78780, FAX 49-611-7878400, callcenterprofi@bertelsmann.de, gabler.service@gwv-fachverlage.de, http://www.callcenterprofi.de, http://www.gabler.de. Ed. Simone Fojut. Adv. contact Annette Oberlaender-Renner. B&W page EUR 3,520, color page EUR 4,990. Circ: 10,484 (paid and controlled).

658 SWE
CALLCENTER. Text in Swedish. 6/yr. SEK 295 (effective 2001). adv. **Document type:** *Magazine, Trade.*
Published by: Tidningen Callcenter i Sverige AB, Soedra Jaernvaegsgatan 58, Box 33, Ljusdal, 82721, Sweden. TEL 46-651-16810, FAX 46-651-16831, info@callcentermedia.com, http://www.callcentermedia.com. Ed. Tomas Burvall. Pub., Adv. contact Sune Frost. B&W page SEK 17,500, color page SEK 22,500; trim 210 x 280.

658.8 USA ISSN 1050-4621
CAMPUS MARKETPLACE. Text in English. 1994. w. USD 350 to non-members; free to members (effective 2005). 4 p./no.; **Document type:** *Newsletter, Consumer.* **Description:** Publishes news and tips for NACS members.
Related titles: Supplement(s): Campus Marketplace Bulletin.
Published by: National Association of College Stores, 500 E Lorain St, Oberlin, OH 44074-1298. TEL 440-775-7777, 800-626-8518, FAX 440-775-4769, info@nacs.org, thecollegestore@nacs.org, http://www.nacs.org. Circ: 10,137 (controlled).

CANADIAN ASSOCIATION OF EXPOSITION MANAGERS. COMMUNIQUE. see *MEETINGS AND CONGRESSES*

CANADIAN COMMERCIAL LAW GUIDE. see *LAW—Corporate Law*

658.7 CAN ISSN 0822-7799
CANADIAN DIRECTORY OF SHOPPING CENTRES. Text in English. 1975. a. **Document type:** *Directory, Trade.* **Description:** Contains information on over 2,200 Canadian shopping centers with 30,000 sq. ft. of gross leasable area and non-traditional retail areas such as subway stations, hospitals, hotels, universities, colleges and airports.
Published by: Rogers Media Publishing Ltd, One Mount Pleasant Rd, 11th Fl, Toronto, ON M4Y 2Y5, Canada. TEL 416-764-2000, FAX 416-764-3941, http://www.retailinfonet.com/cdsc.html, http://www.rogers.com.

CANADIAN ENVIRONMENTAL DIRECTORY; complete guide to the business of environmental management. see *ENVIRONMENTAL STUDIES*

658 CAN ISSN 0829-4836
HF5415.2
➤ **CANADIAN JOURNAL OF MARKETING RESEARCH.** Text in English; Summaries in French. 1980. a. CND 25 per issue to non-members; free to members (effective 2005). adv. bk.rev. back issues avail. **Document type:** *Academic/Scholarly.*
Indexed: MResA.
—BLDSC (3031.950000), IE, ingenta. **CCC.**
Published by: Professional Marketing Research Society, 2175 Sheppard Ave E, Ste 310, Toronto, ON M2J 1W8, Canada. TEL 416-493-4080. Ed., R&P, Adv. contact Chuck Chakrapani. Circ: 2,000.

➤ **CANADIAN PHARMACEUTICAL MARKETING.** see *PHARMACY AND PHARMACOLOGY*

658 CAN ISSN 0226-9864
CANADIAN RETAILER (TORONTO). Text in English. 1974. 6/yr. CND 36.75 domestic; CND 52.50 in United States (effective 2005). adv. **Document type:** *Magazine, Trade.* **Description:** Designed for retail decision-makers looking for the latest industry research, advice and analysis.
Published by: Retail Council of Canada, 1255 Bay St, Ste 800, Toronto, ON M5R 2A9, Canada. TEL 416-922-6678, 888-373-8245, FAX 416-922-8011, 877-790-4271, trogers@retailcouncil.org, http://www.retailcouncil.org/cdnretailer. Circ: 10,000.

CANADIAN TRANSPORTATION & LOGISTICS. see *TRANSPORTATION*

CARD TALK. see *ADVERTISING AND PUBLIC RELATIONS*

658 388.3 USA
CARLINK NEWS. Text in English. 1999. m. **Document type:** *Trade.*
Published by: Northwest Automotive Publishing Co., PO Box 46937, Seattle, WA 98146-0937. TEL 206-935-3336, FAX 206-937-9732, nwautopub@galaxy-7.net. Ed. J B Smith. Circ: 15,000 (paid).

CARTOON OPPORTUNITIES. see *ART*

658 USA ISSN 1526-5927
CASES IN CORPORATE ACQUISITIONS, BUYOUTS, MERGERS & TAKEOVERS. Text in English. 1999. irreg., latest 1999. USD 395 per issue (effective 2005). 1507 p./no.; **Document type:** *Trade.* **Description:** Analyzes 300 notable mergers and acquisitions in the United States and abroad.
Published by: Gale Group (Subsidiary of: Thomson Corporation), 27500 Drake Rd, Farmington Hills, MI 48331-3535. TEL 248-699-4253, 800-877-4253, FAX 800-414-5043, galeord@gale.com, http://www.gale.com/servlet/ItemDetailServlet?region=9&imprint=000&titleCode=CCABMT&type=4&id=113688, http://www.galegroup.com.

658 ZAF
CASH 'N' CARRY NEWS. Text in English. 1993. m. adv. illus. **Document type:** *Trade.*
Published by: Complete Publishing (Pty.) Ltd., PO Box 87745, Houghton, Johannesburg 2041, South Africa. TEL 27-11-7892112, FAX 27-11-789-5347.

CASINO INTERNATIONAL. see *SPORTS AND GAMES*

CAST POLYMER CONNECTION. see *PLASTICS*

658.8 USA ISSN 1524-2307
CATALOG SUCCESS. Text in English. 1999. m. free to qualified personnel. **Document type:** *Magazine, Trade.* **Description:** provides information, case studies and advice from leading experts on catalog creative, production/printing, e-commerce, fulfillment, merchandising, database marketing, lists and media, and customer relationship management.
Related titles: Online - full text ed.: (from H.W. Wilson, O C L C Online Computer Library Center, Inc.).
Indexed: BPI.
Published by: North American Publishing Co., 1500 Spring Garden St., Ste 1200, Philadelphia, PA 19130-4094. TEL 215-238-5300, FAX 215-238-5457, http://www.catalogsuccess.com/, http://www.napco.com. Ed. Donna Loyle.

380.1 384.33 GBR ISSN 1362-2315
CATALOGUE & MAIL ORDER BUSINESS. Text in English. 1995 (no.30). m. GBP 75 domestic; GBP 85 overseas (effective 2000). adv. software rev. stat.; tr.lit. back issues avail. **Document type:** *Newspaper, Trade.* **Description:** Focused journal for catalog, home shopping and e-commerce based business.
Related titles: E-mail ed.; Online - full content ed.
Published by: Catalogue Development Centre Ltd., 151 High St, Ilfracombe, Devon EX34 9EZ, United Kingdom. TEL 44-1271-866112, FAX 44-1271-866040, info@catalog-biz.com, edit@catalog-biz.com, http://www.catalog-biz.com. Ed. Jane Revell Higgins. Pub. Jane Revell-Higgins. R&P Phil Randles TEL 44-1372-386687. Adv. contact Lee Barham. B&W page GBP 1,095, color page GBP 2,495. Circ: 8,500 (paid and controlled).

CELLULAR INTEGRATION. see *COMMUNICATIONS—Telephone And Telegraph*

658.8 USA ISSN 1087-0601
HF5428
CHAIN STORE AGE; the news magazine for retail executives. Text in English. 1925. m. USD 105 domestic; USD 125 in Canada; USD 165 foreign; USD 10 per issue (effective 2005). adv. illus. 160 p./no.; back issues avail.; reprints avail. **Document type:** *Magazine, Trade.* **Description:** Provides managers of chain retail stores with practical advice and news on trends.
Former titles (until 1995): Chain Store Age Executive with Shopping Center Age (0193-1199); (until 1975): Chain Store Age Executives Edition Including Shopping Center Age (0885-1425)
Related titles: Microfiche ed.: (from CIS); Online - full text ed.: (from EBSCO Publishing, Gale Group, H.W. Wilson, O C L C Online Computer Library Center, Inc., ProQuest Information & Learning).
Indexed: ABIn, B&I, BPI, BusI, CompC, Inspec, LogistBibl, PROMT, RPFIA, SRI, T&II.
—BLDSC (3128.740100), AskIEEE, IE, ingenta. **CCC.**
Published by: Lebhar-Friedman, Inc., 425 Park Ave, New York, NY 10022. TEL 212-756-5252, 212-756-5000, FAX 212-756-5215, mforseter@lf.com, info@lf.com, http://www.chainstoreage.com, http://www.lf.com. Ed. Murray Forseter. Pubs. Dan Bagan TEL 212-756-5256, Murray Forseter. Adv. contact Dan Bagan TEL 212-756-5256. B&W page USD 8,215, color page USD 10,515; 7 x 10. Circ: 35,000 (paid and controlled).

CHANNELMARKER LETTER. see *COMPUTERS—Computer Industry*

THE CHARLESTON REPORT; business insights into the library market. see *LIBRARY AND INFORMATION SCIENCES*

658 IRL ISSN 0790-438X
CHECKOUT. Text in English. 1966. m. EUR 111.23 (effective 2005). adv. **Document type:** *Trade.*
Indexed: KES.
Published by: Checkout Publications Ltd., Adelaide Hall, 3 Adelaide St., Dun Laoghaire, Co. Dublin, Ireland. TEL 353-1-2300322, FAX 353-1-2300629, info@checkout.ie, http://www.checkout.ie. Ed. Terence Cosgrave. Adv. contact Pat Murray. Circ: 6,500 (controlled).

CHEMICAL INDUSTRIES NEWSLETTER. see *CHEMISTRY*

CHEMICAL YELLOW PAGES DIRECTORY. see *CHEMISTRY*

CHICAGO ARTISTS' NEWS. see *ART*

658.7 USA ISSN 0009-367X
CHICAGO PURCHASOR. Text in English. 1923. q. USD 15. adv. **Document type:** *Trade.*
Published by: Purchasing Management Association of Chicago, 2250 E Devon Ave, Ste 236, Des Plaines, IL 60018-4509. Ed., R&P, Adv. contact Jackie Stinson TEL 847-298-1940. B&W page USD 775, color page USD 1,425. Circ: 3,600 (controlled).

658 USA
▼ **CHIEF MARKETING OFFICERS MAGAZINE.** Variant title: C M O Magazine. Text in English. 2004. m. USD 65 in US & Canada; USD 95 elsewhere (effective 2004). **Document type:** *Magazine, Trade.* **Description:** Covers everything from building brand to using technology to manage customer relationships, from defending marketing budget to measuring the return on marketing investments.
Published by: C X O Media Inc. (Subsidiary of: I D G Communications Inc.), 492 Old Connecticut Path, PO Box 9208, Framingham, MA 01701-9208. TEL 508-872-0080, FAX 508-879-7784, http://www.cmomagazine.com/, http://www.cxo.com/. Ed. Lew McCreary.

B

CHILE MARKETING AND FINANCIAL STATISTICS. see *BUSINESS AND ECONOMICS—Abstracting, Bibliographies, Statistics*

CHIMES (SUDBURY). see *AGRICULTURE—Dairying And Dairy Products*

540 660 658 CHN
CHINA CHEMICAL MARKET NEWSLETTER. Text in English. bi-m. **Document type:** *Newsletter, Trade.* **Description:** Updates you of the latest trends of Chinese chemical industry, markets and producers.
Related titles: Online - full text ed.
Published by: A M I D Co., 1st Fl, Rm 101, 4 Jifa Bldg, Heiniucheng Rd, Hexi District, Tianjin, 300381, China. TEL 86-22-23950735, 425-844-8585, FAX 425-844-8515, amid@chinaindustrynet.com, http://www.chinaindustrynet.com/research/newsletter.htm.

658 338.476 667.6 CHN
CHINESE MARKETS FOR AUTOMOTIVE COATINGS. Text in English. irreg., latest 2001. EUR 3,745 per issue print or online (effective 2003). **Document type:** *Trade.* **Description:** Examines China's economic trends, investment environment, industry development, supply and demand, industry capacity, industry structure, marketing channels and major industry participants.
Related titles: Online - full text ed.
Published by: A M I D Co., 1st Fl, Rm 101, 4 Jifa Bldg, Heiniucheng Rd, Hexi District, Tianjin, 300381, China. TEL 86-22-23950735, 425-844-8585, FAX 425-844-8515, amid@chinaindustrynet.com, http://www.researchandmarkets.com/reports/29773/, http://www.chinaindustrynet.com/. **Dist. by:** Research and Markets Ltd., Guinness Centre, Taylors Lane, Dublin 8, Ireland. TEL 353-1-4957318, FAX 353-86-8797580, orders@researchandmarkets.com, http://www.researchandmarkets.com.

658 338.476 CHN
CHINESE MARKETS FOR AUTOMOTIVE COMPONENTS. Text in English. irreg., latest 2001. EUR 3,745 per issue print or online (effective 2003). 302 p./no.; **Document type:** *Trade.* **Description:** Examines China's economic trends, investment environment, industry development, supply and demand, industry capacity, industry structure, marketing channels and major industry participants.
Related titles: Online - full text ed.
Published by: A M I D Co., 1st Fl, Rm 101, 4 Jifa Bldg, Heiniucheng Rd, Hexi District, Tianjin, 300381, China. TEL 86-22-23950735, 425-844-8585, FAX 425-844-8515, amid@chinaindustrynet.com, http://www.researchandmarkets.com/reports/29771/, http://www.chinaindustrynet.com/. **Dist. by:** Research and Markets Ltd., Guinness Centre, Taylors Lane, Dublin 8, Ireland. TEL 353-1-4957318, FAX 353-86-8797580, orders@researchandmarkets.com, http://www.researchandmarkets.com.

658 621.381 338.476 CHN
CHINESE MARKETS FOR AUTOMOTIVE ELECTRONICS. Text in English. irreg., latest 2001. EUR 3,745 per issue print or online (effective 2003). 234 p./no.; **Document type:** *Trade.* **Description:** Examines China's economic trends, investment environment, industry development, supply and demand, industry capacity, industry structure, marketing channels and major industry participants.

Related titles: Online - full text ed.
Published by: A M I D Co., 1st Fl, Rm 101, 4 Jifa Bldg, Heiniucheng Rd, Hexi District, Tianjin, 300381, China. TEL 86-22-23950735, 425-844-8585, FAX 425-844-8515, amid@chinaindustrynet.com, http://www.researchandmarkets.com/reports/29772/, http://www.chinaindustrynet.com/. **Dist. by:** Research and Markets Ltd., Guinness Centre, Taylors Lane, Dublin 8, Ireland. TEL 353-1-4957318, FAX 353-86-8797580, orders@researchandmarkets.com, http://www.researchandmarkets.com.

658 690 CHN
CHINESE MARKETS FOR BUILDING MATERIALS. Text in English. irreg., latest 2001. EUR 3,745 per issue print or online (effective 2003). 185 p./no.; **Document type:** *Trade.*
Description: Examines China's economic trends, investment environment, industry development, supply and demand, industry capacity, industry structure, marketing channels and major industry participants.
Related titles: Online - full text ed.
Published by: A M I D Co., 1st Fl, Rm 101, 4 Jifa Bldg, Heiniucheng Rd, Hexi District, Tianjin, 300381, China. TEL 86-22-23950735, 425-844-8585, FAX 425-844-8515, amid@chinaindustrynet.com, http://www.researchandmarkets.com/reports/29777/, http://www.chinaindustrynet.com/. **Dist. by:** Research and Markets Ltd., Guinness Centre, Taylors Lane, Dublin 8, Ireland. TEL 353-1-4957318, FAX 353-86-8797580, orders@researchandmarkets.com, http://www.researchandmarkets.com.

658 540 660 CHN
CHINESE MARKETS FOR DIMETHYLFORMAMIDE. Text in English. irreg., latest 2001. EUR 3,745 per issue print or online (effective 2003). 148 p./no.; **Document type:** *Trade.*
Description: Examines China's economic trends, investment environment, industry development, supply and demand, industry capacity, industry structure, marketing channels and major industry participants.
Related titles: Online - full text ed.
Published by: A M I D Co., 1st Fl, Rm 101, 4 Jifa Bldg, Heiniucheng Rd, Hexi District, Tianjin, 300381, China. TEL 86-22-23950735, 425-844-8585, FAX 425-844-8515, amid@chinaindustrynet.com, http://www.researchandmarkets.com/reports/29781/, http://www.chinaindustrynet.com/. **Dist. by:** Research and Markets Ltd., Guinness Centre, Taylors Lane, Dublin 8, Ireland. TEL 353-1-4957318, FAX 353-86-8797580, orders@researchandmarkets.com, http://www.researchandmarkets.com.

658 572.57 547.77 CHN
CHINESE MARKETS FOR FATTY ACIDS. Text in English. irreg., latest 2001. EUR 3,745 per issue print or online (effective 2003). 168 p./no.; **Document type:** *Trade.* **Description:** Examines China's economic trends, investment environment, industry development, supply and demand, industry capacity, industry structure, marketing channels and major industry participants.
Related titles: Online - full text ed.
Published by: A M I D Co., 1st Fl, Rm 101, 4 Jifa Bldg, Heiniucheng Rd, Hexi District, Tianjin, 300381, China. TEL 86-22-23950735, 425-844-8585, FAX 425-844-8515, amid@chinaindustrynet.com, http://www.researchandmarkets.com/reports/29766/, http://www.chinaindustrynet.com/. **Dist. by:** Research and Markets Ltd., Guinness Centre, Taylors Lane, Dublin 8, Ireland. TEL 353-1-4957318, FAX 353-86-8797580, orders@researchandmarkets.com, http://www.researchandmarkets.com.

658 668.14 663.1 547 CHN
CHINESE MARKETS FOR FATTY ALCOHOL. Text in English. irreg., latest 2001. EUR 3,745 per issue print or online (effective 2003). 170 p./no.; **Document type:** *Trade.*
Description: Examines China's economic trends, investment environment, industry development, supply and demand, industry capacity, industry structure, marketing channels and major industry participants.
Related titles: Online - full text ed.
Published by: A M I D Co., 1st Fl, Rm 101, 4 Jifa Bldg, Heiniucheng Rd, Hexi District, Tianjin, 300381, China. TEL 86-22-23950735, 425-844-8585, FAX 425-844-8515, amid@chinaindustrynet.com, http://www.researchandmarkets.com/reports/29770/, http://www.chinaindustrynet.com/. **Dist. by:** Research and Markets Ltd., Guinness Centre, Taylors Lane, Dublin 8, Ireland. TEL 353-1-4957318, FAX 353-86-8797580, orders@researchandmarkets.com, http://www.researchandmarkets.com.

658 664 CHN
CHINESE MARKETS FOR FLAVORS & FRAGRANCES. Text in English. irreg., latest 2001. EUR 3,745 per issue print or online (effective 2003). 201 p./no.; **Document type:** *Trade.*
Description: Examines China's economic trends, investment environment, industry development, supply and demand, industry capacity, industry structure, marketing channels and major industry participants.
Related titles: Online - full text ed.
Published by: A M I D Co., 1st Fl, Rm 101, 4 Jifa Bldg, Heiniucheng Rd, Hexi District, Tianjin, 300381, China. TEL 86-22-23950735, 425-844-8585, FAX 425-844-8515, amid@chinaindustrynet.com, http://www.researchandmarkets.com/reports/29783/, http://www.chinaindustrynet.com/. **Dist. by:** Research and Markets Ltd., Guinness Centre, Taylors Lane, Dublin 8, Ireland. TEL 353-1-4957318, FAX 353-86-8797580, orders@researchandmarkets.com, http://www.researchandmarkets.com.

658 540 CHN
CHINESE MARKETS FOR METHANOL. Text in English. irreg., latest 2001. EUR 3,745 per issue (effective 2003). 161 p./no.; **Document type:** *Trade.* **Description:** Examines China's economic trends, investment environment, industry development, supply and demand, industry capacity, industry structure, marketing channels and major industry participants.
Related titles: Online - full text ed.
Published by: A M I D Co., 1st Fl, Rm 101, 4 Jifa Bldg, Heiniucheng Rd, Hexi District, Tianjin, 300381, China. TEL 86-22-23950735, 425-844-8585, FAX 425-844-8515, amid@chinaindustrynet.com, http://www.researchandmarkets.com/reports/29769/, http://www.chinaindustrynet.com/. **Dist. by:** Research and Markets Ltd., Guinness Centre, Taylors Lane, Dublin 8, Ireland. TEL 353-1-4957318, FAX 353-86-8797580, orders@researchandmarkets.com, http://www.researchandmarkets.com.

658 688.8 CHN
CHINESE MARKETS FOR PACKAGING MATERIALS. Text in English. irreg., latest 2001. EUR 3,745 per issue print or online (effective 2003). 215 p./no.; **Document type:** *Trade.*
Description: Examines China's economic trends, investment environment, industry development, supply and demand, industry capacity, industry structure, marketing channels and major industry participants.
Related titles: Online - full text ed.
Published by: A M I D Co., 1st Fl, Rm 101, 4 Jifa Bldg, Heiniucheng Rd, Hexi District, Tianjin, 300381, China. TEL 86-22-23950735, 425-844-8585, FAX 425-844-8515, amid@chinaindustrynet.com, http://www.researchandmarkets.com/reports/29778/, http://www.chinaindustrynet.com/. **Dist. by:** Research and Markets Ltd., Guinness Centre, Taylors Lane, Dublin 8, Ireland. TEL 353-1-4957318, FAX 353-86-8797580, orders@researchandmarkets.com, http://www.researchandmarkets.com.

661.804 658 CHN
CHINESE MARKETS FOR PETROCHEMICALS. Text in English. irreg., latest 2001. USD 3,745 per issue print or online (effective 2003). 266 p./no.; **Document type:** *Trade.*
Description: Examines China's economic trends, investment environment, industry development, supply and demand, industry capacity, industry structure, marketing channels and major industry participants.
Related titles: Online - full text ed.
Published by: A M I D Co., 1st Fl, Rm 101, 4 Jifa Bldg, Heiniucheng Rd, Hexi District, Tianjin, 300381, China. TEL 86-22-23950735, 425-844-8585, FAX 425-844-8515, amid@chinaindustrynet.com, http://www.researchandmarkets.com/reports/29775/, http://www.chinaindustrynet.com/. **Dist. by:** Research and Markets Ltd., Guinness Centre, Taylors Lane, Dublin 8, Ireland. TEL 353-1-4957318, FAX 353-86-8797580, orders@researchandmarkets.com, http://www.researchandmarkets.com.

338.476 658 665.5 CHN
CHINESE MARKETS FOR PETROLEUM ADDITIVES. Text in English. irreg., latest 2001. EUR 3,745 per issue print or online (effective 2003). 178 p./no.; **Document type:** *Trade.*
Description: Examines China's economic trends, investment environment, industry development, supply and demand, industry capacity, industry structure, marketing channels and major industry participants.
Related titles: Online - full text ed.
Published by: A M I D Co., 1st Fl, Rm 101, 4 Jifa Bldg, Heiniucheng Rd, Hexi District, Tianjin, 300381, China. TEL 86-22-23950735, 425-844-8585, FAX 425-844-8515, amid@chinaindustrynet.com, http://www.researchandmarkets.com/reports/29776, http://www.chinaindustrynet.com/. **Dist. by:** Research and Markets Ltd., Guinness Centre, Taylors Lane, Dublin 8, Ireland. TEL 353-1-4957318, FAX 353-86-8797580, orders@researchandmarkets.com, http://www.researchandmarkets.com.

668.4 658 CHN
CHINESE MARKETS FOR PLASTIC ADDITIVES. Text in English. irreg., latest 2001. EUR 3,745 per issue print or online (effective 2003). 230 p./no.; **Document type:** *Trade.*
Description: Examines China's economic trends, investment environment, industry development, supply and demand, industry capacity, industry structure, marketing channels and major industry participants.
Related titles: Online - full text ed.
Published by: A M I D Co., 1st Fl, Rm 101, 4 Jifa Bldg, Heiniucheng Rd, Hexi District, Tianjin, 300381, China. TEL 86-22-23950735, 425-844-8585, FAX 425-844-8515, amid@chinaindustrynet.com, http://www.researchandmarkets.com/reports/29779/, http://www.chinaindustrynet.com/. **Dist. by:** Research and Markets Ltd., Guinness Centre, Taylors Lane, Dublin 8, Ireland. TEL 353-1-4957318, FAX 353-86-8797580, orders@researchandmarkets.com, http://www.researchandmarkets.com.

658 668.4 668.661 CHN
CHINESE MARKETS FOR PLASTIC COMPOUNDING. Text in English. irreg., latest 2001. EUR 3,745 per issue print or online (effective 2003). 219 p./no.; **Document type:** *Trade.*
Description: Examines China's economic trends, investment environment, industry development, supply and demand, industry capacity, industry structure, marketing channels and major industry participants.
Related titles: Online - full text ed.
Published by: A M I D Co., 1st Fl, Rm 101, 4 Jifa Bldg, Heiniucheng Rd, Hexi District, Tianjin, 300381, China. TEL 86-22-23950735, 425-844-8585, FAX 425-844-8515, amid@chinaindustrynet.com, http://www.researchandmarkets.com/reports/29768/, http://www.chinaindustrynet.com/. **Dist. by:** Research and Markets Ltd., Guinness Centre, Taylors Lane, Dublin 8, Ireland. TEL 353-1-4957318, FAX 353-86-8797580, orders@researchandmarkets.com, http://www.researchandmarkets.com.

667.5 686.2 658 CHN
CHINESE MARKETS FOR PRINTING INKS. Text in English. irreg., latest 2001. EUR 3,745 per issue print or online (effective 2003). 186 p./no.; **Document type:** *Trade.*
Description: Examines China's economic trends, investment environment, industry development, supply and demand, industry capacity, industry structure, marketing channels and major industry participants.
Related titles: Online - full text ed.
Published by: A M I D Co., 1st Fl, Rm 101, 4 Jifa Bldg, Heiniucheng Rd, Hexi District, Tianjin, 300381, China. TEL 86-22-23950735, 425-844-8585, FAX 425-844-8515, amid@chinaindustrynet.com, http://www.researchandmarkets.com/reports/29782/, http://www.chinaindustrynet.com/. **Dist. by:** Research and Markets Ltd., Guinness Centre, Taylors Lane, Dublin 8, Ireland. TEL 353-1-4957318, FAX 353-86-8797580, orders@researchandmarkets.com, http://www.researchandmarkets.com.

668.494 658 CHN
CHINESE MARKETS FOR REINFORCED PLASTICS. Text in English. irreg., latest 2001. EUR 3,745 per issue print or online (effective 2003). 167 p./no.; **Document type:** *Trade.*
Description: Examines China's economic trends, investment environment, industry development, supply and demand, industry capacity, industry structure, marketing channels and major industry participants.
Related titles: Online - full text ed.
Published by: A M I D Co., 1st Fl, Rm 101, 4 Jifa Bldg, Heiniucheng Rd, Hexi District, Tianjin, 300381, China. TEL 86-22-23950735, 425-844-8585, FAX 425-844-8515, amid@chinaindustrynet.com, http://www.researchandmarkets.com/reports/29767/, http://www.chinaindustrynet.com/. **Dist. by:** Research and Markets Ltd., Guinness Centre, Taylors Lane, Dublin 8, Ireland. TEL 353-1-4957318, FAX 353-86-8797580, orders@researchandmarkets.com, http://www.researchandmarkets.com.

658 USA
CLOSEOUT NEWS. Text in English. 1987. m. USD 50 domestic; USD 84 foreign (effective 2005). adv. **Document type:** *Newspaper.* **Description:** Covers surplus and closeout merchandise of all types.
Contact: Target Media Partners Inc., 5900 Wilshire Blvd, Ste 650, Los Angeles, CA 90036. TEL 323-930-3123, FAX 323-525-2531, info@thecloseoutnews.com, http://www.thecloseoutnews.com. adv.: color page USD 1,600; 8.75 x 12.75. Circ: 80,000 (controlled and free).

658 531.64 USA ISSN 1098-0105
COALDAT MARKETING REPORT. Text in English. 1986. m. USD 595 (effective 1999). **Document type:** *Newsletter.*
Description: Monitors all utility coal purchases and determines market reach, size and share for coal based on quality, transportation and price.
Formed by the 199? merger of: COALDAT Marketing Report. Productivity Report, State/County Format (1042-945X); Which was formerly: COALDAT Productivity Report. State/County Format (0893-9748); and: COALDAT Marketing Report. Productivity Report, Controlling Company Format (1042-9468); Which was formerly: COALDAT Productivity Report. Controlling Company Format (0893-973X); and: COALDAT Marketing Report. Utility Format (0895-2361); Which was formerly: COALDAT Utility Format (1041-0996); and: COALDAT Marketing Report. Supplier Format (1043-0474);

Which was formerly: COALDAT Supplier Format (1041-097X); Which was formerly: COALDAT Marketing Report. Supplier Format (0895-237X); and: COALDAT Marketing Report. Producing District Format (1043-1845); Which was formerly: COALDAT Producing District Format (1041-0988); Which was formerly: COALDAT Marketing Report. Producing District Format (0895-2353)
Related titles: Online - full text ed.
Published by: Financial Times Energy (Subsidiary of: Platts), 1200 G St NW, Ste. 1100, Washington, DC 20005-3814. TEL 703-528-1244, 800-424-2908, FAX 703-528-7821, http://www.ftenergy.usa.com.

658 GBR ISSN 1357-7441
COIN SLOT INTERNATIONAL. Variant title: Coin Slot. Coinslot International. Text in English. 1958. w. GBP 40 in United Kingdom; USD 90 rest of Europe; USD 160 in the Americas & the Middle East; USD 180 in the Far East (effective 2000). **Document type:** *Newspaper, Trade.* **Description:** Features articles on the UK coin operated amusement business, suppliers, manufacturers and personalities.
Published by: World's Fair Ltd., Albert Mill, Albert St, PO Box 57, Oldham, Lancs OL8 3WF, United Kingdom. TEL 44-161-683-8000, FAX 44-161-683-8001, coinslot@worldsfair.co.uk, http://www.coinslot.co.uk, http://www.worldsfair.co.uk. Ed. Mike Beevers.

378 658.8 USA
THE COLLEGE STORE. Text in English. 1928. bi-m. USD 64 to non-members; USD 54 to members (effective 2005). adv. charts; illus.; mkt.; stat. index, cum.index. 100 p./no. 3 cols./p.; back issues avail.; reprint service avail. from PQC. **Document type:** *Magazine, Trade.*
Formerly: College Store Journal (0010-115X)
Related titles: Online - full text ed.: (from PQC).
Indexed: CIJE.
Published by: National Association of College Stores, 500 E Lorain St, Oberlin, OH 44074-1298. TEL 440-775-7777, 800-626-8518, FAX 440-775-4769, thecollegestore@nacs.org, http://www.nacs.org. Ed., R&P Keith Galestock TEL 440-775-7777 ext 2330. Pub. Cynthia D'Angelo. Adv. contact Michelle van Wormer. B&W page USD 1,660, color page USD 3,145. Circ: 10,000 (controlled).

658.0711 USA ISSN 0010-1141
COLLEGE STORE EXECUTIVE. Text in English. 1970. 10/yr. USD 35 domestic; USD 40 foreign (effective 2005). adv. bk.rev. charts; illus.; stat. **Document type:** *Magazine, Trade.*
Published by: Executive Business Media, Inc., 825 Old Country Rd, PO Box 1500, Westbury, NY 11590. TEL 516-334-3030, FAX 516-334-8958. Ed. Ken Baglino. Pub. Murry Greenwald. R&P Fred Schaen. Circ: 10,600 (controlled).

658.8 USA ISSN 1065-0296
COLLEGIATE TRENDS. Text in English. 1985. q. USD 95; USD 150 foreign (effective 1997). charts. back issues avail. **Document type:** *Newsletter.* **Description:** Covers media marketing aimed at the college market.
Published by: Strategic Marketing Communications, Inc., 550 N Maple Ave, Ridgewood, NJ 07450. TEL 201-612-8100, FAX 201-612-1444, http://www.sancinc.com. Ed. Robert Doran. Pub. Eric Weil. Circ: 3,000 (paid).

658.7 338 USA ISSN 0095-3423
COMMERCE BUSINESS DAILY; synopsis of United States government proposed procurement, sales, and contract awards. Text in English. 1950. d. (Mon.-Fri.). USD 316 (effective 2001). **Document type:** *Government.* **Description:** For businesses interested in selling to the U.S. Government. Contains a listing of products and services the Government needs, with information on how and when to bid.
Related titles: Online - full text ed.: (from LexisNexis, Northern Light Technology, Inc., The Dialog Corporation).
Published by: (U.S. and Foreign Commercial Service), U.S. International Trade Administration (Subsidiary of: U.S. Department of Commerce), 14th St., N.W, Between Constitution Ave. & E St., Washington, DC 20230. cbd-support@gpo.gov, http://cbdnet.access.gpo.gov/. Circ: 30,000. **Subscr. to:** U.S. Government Printing Office, Superintendent of Documents, PO Box 371954, Pittsburgh, PA 15250-7954. TEL 202-512-1800, FAX 202-512-2250, orders@gpo.gov, http://www.access.gpo.gov.

657.04 ZAF
THE COMMERCIAL AND FINANCIAL ACCOUNTANT. Text in Afrikaans. 1982. bi-m. ZAR 137.50 (effective 2000). adv. **Document type:** *Newsletter, Trade.*
Formerly: F A C T - Technical Bulletin
Related titles: Online - full text ed.
Published by: Instituut van Kommersiele en Finansiele Rekenmeesters van Suider-Afrika/Institute of Commercial and Financial Accountants of South Africa, 66 Oxford Rd, Block 3, Rivera Office Park, Riviera, South Africa. TEL 27-11-486-0283, FAX 27-11-486-0632, tlee@cfasa.co.za. Ed., R&P, Adv. contact Tania Lee TEL 27-11-486-0212. color page ZAR 4,588.20. Circ: 7,100. **Subscr. to:** PO Box 1791, Houghton, Johannesburg 2041, South Africa.

COMMODITIES - U S A. see *BUSINESS AND ECONOMICS—International Commerce*

COMMUNITY PHARMACY. see *PHARMACY AND PHARMACOLOGY*

658.8 659.1 USA ISSN 0888-482X
KF2028.A15
COMPENDIUM OF GOVERNMENT ISSUES AFFECTING DIRECT MARKETING. Text in English. a. USD 29.95. **Document type:** *Trade.*
Published by: Direct Marketing Association (Washington), 1111 19th St N W, Ste 1100, Washington, DC 20036-3603. TEL 202-955-5030, FAX 202-955-0085. **Dist. by:** PMDS Book Distribution Center, PO Box 39, Annapolis, MD 20701-0391. TEL 301-604-0187, FAX 301-206-9789.

658 USA ISSN 0886-1994
THE COMPETITIVE ADVANTAGE; the newsletter for sales and marketing professionals. Text in English. 1985. m. USD 99 (effective 2005). bk.rev. reprint service avail. from WSH. **Document type:** *Newsletter, Trade.* **Description:** Provides sales, marketing and management tools to make careers and companies more prosperous.
—CCC.
Published by: Briefings Publishing Group (Subsidiary of: Douglas Publications, Inc.), 1101 King St, Ste 110, Alexandria, VA 22314. TEL 703-518-2343, 800-722-9221, FAX 703-684-2136, customerservice@briefings.com, http://www.briefings.com. Ed. Katie May. Pub. Michelle Cox.

COMPOSANTS INSTRUMENTATION ELECTRONIQUES. see *ELECTRONICS*

COMPOSITES INDUSTRY MONTHLY. see *ENGINEERING—Engineering Mechanics And Materials*

658.7 ITA
COMPRARE OGGI; rivista di management degli approvvigionamenti. Text in Italian. 1987. 6/yr. USD 155 foreign (effective 2004).
Published by: (Associazione Italiana di Management degli Approvvigionamenti (ADACI)), Societa Editoriale Farmaceutica, Via Ausonio 12, Milan, MI 20123, Italy. TEL 39-02-89404545, FAX 39-02-89401168, info@sef.it, http://www.sef.it. Ed. Giancarlo Lubner. Circ: 3,000.

658.7 ESP ISSN 0212-8268
COMPRAS Y EXISTENCIAS. Text in Spanish. 1980. 6/yr. adv. bk.rev. **Document type:** *Trade.*
Published by: Compras y Existencias S.L., Maria de Molina, 44, 6o Dcha., Madrid, 28006, Spain. TEL 34-1-5618263, FAX 34-1-5644091. Ed. Simon Pallares. Pub. Sonsoles Monis. Adv. contact Mariano Fernandez. Circ: 3,000 (paid).

658.7 CAN ISSN 0841-9485
HC120.C6
CONFERENCE BOARD OF CANADA. INDEX OF CONSUMER ATTITUDES. Text in English. q. membership. charts; stat.
Former titles (until 1988): Conference Board of Canada. Consumer Attitudes and Buying Intentions (0827-5831); (until 1985): Conference Board of Canada. Survey of Consumer Buying Intentions (0381-7377)
Indexed: CSI.
Published by: (Contemporary Research Centre Ltd.), Conference Board of Canada, 255 Smyth Rd, Ste 100, Ottawa, ON K1H 8M7, Canada. TEL 613-526-3280, FAX 613-526-4857.

658.8 USA ISSN 0573-665X
HC107.C8
CONNECTICUT MARKET DATA. Text in English. 1957. biennial. USD 25 (effective 2001). back issues avail. **Document type:** *Government.* **Description:** Presents demographics, economic statistics, business support programs, transportation, labor force, markets, education, housing and income information.
Related titles: Diskette ed.; Microfiche ed.: (from CIS).
Indexed: SRI.
Published by: Department of Economic and Community Development, 505 Hudson St, 3rd Fl, Hartford, CT 06106-7107. TEL 860-270-8165, FAX 860-270-8188, decd@po.state.ct.us, http://www.state.ct.us.

658 FRA ISSN 0767-0672
CONQUERIR✶ . Text in French. 10/yr. **Description:** For marketing and business directors.
Published by: Editions Conquetes, 9 Ave. Fremiet, Paris, 75016, France. TEL 43-06-04-62, TELEX 201 746. Ed. Alain Gazo. Circ: 20,000.

658 GBR
CONSUMER✶ . Text in English. 6/yr.
Address: Akela House, Low Rd, Tasburgh, Norwich, Norfolk NR15 1AR, United Kingdom. Ed. Madeleine Munday. Circ: 8,500.

658.8 GBR
CONSUMER ASIA (YEAR). Text in English. a., latest 2001. GBP 675 domestic; EUR 1,090 in Europe; USD 1,090 elsewhere (effective 2003). **Document type:** *Trade.* **Description:** Analyzes the various consumer markets throughout Asian countries, including, China, Hong Kong, India, Indonesia, Japan, Malaysia, Philippines, Singapore, South Korea, Taiwan, Thailand, and Vietnam.
Published by: Euromonitor, 60-61 Britton St, London, EC1 5UX, United Kingdom. TEL 44-20-7251-8024, FAX 44-20-7608-3149, info@euromonitor.com, http://www.euromonitor.com. **Affiliates:** Euromonitor International (Asia) Pte Ltd.; Euromonitor International.

658.8 GBR
CONSUMER CHINA (YEAR). Text in English. 1996. a. GBP 675 domestic; EUR 1,090 in Europe; USD 1,090 elsewhere (effective 2003). charts; stat. **Document type:** *Trade.* **Description:** Evaluates the various consumer markets in China and Hong Kong.
Published by: Euromonitor, 60-61 Britton St, London, EC1 5UX, United Kingdom. TEL 44-20-7251-8024, FAX 44-20-7608-3149, info@euromonitor.com, http://www.euromonitor.com. **Affiliates:** Euromonitor International; Euromonitor International (Asia) Pte Ltd.

658.7 USA ISSN 1046-1876
CONSUMER CONFIDENCE SURVEY. Text in English. 1968. m. USD 150 to non-members; USD 95 to members (effective 2003). charts; stat. **Document type:** *Newsletter.* **Description:** Buyer appraisal of business conditions and employment.
Formerly (until 1987): Consumer Attitudes and Buying Plans (0547-7204)
Related titles: Online - full text ed.: (from Factiva, Gale Group).
Indexed: PROMT, SRI.
—CISTI.
Published by: Conference Board, Inc., 845 Third Ave, New York, NY 10022. TEL 212-759-0900, FAX 212-980-7014, http://www.conference-board.org. Circ: 1,000.

658.8 GBR ISSN 0967-3601
CONSUMER EASTERN EUROPE (YEAR). Text in English. 1992. a. GBP 775 domestic; EUR 1,290 in Europe; USD 1,290 elsewhere (effective 2003). charts; stat. **Document type:** *Trade.* **Description:** Analyzes economic and political trends that present business opportunities in countries in Eastern Europe, including, Bulgaria, Czech Republic, Hungary, Poland, Romania, Russia, Slovakia, and the Ukraine.
Published by: Euromonitor, 60-61 Britton St, London, EC1 5UX, United Kingdom. TEL 44-20-7251-8024, FAX 44-20-7608-3149, info@euromonitor.com, http://www.euromonitor.com.

658.8 GBR ISSN 0308-4353
HD7022
CONSUMER EUROPE (YEAR). Text in English. 1977. a. GBP 795 domestic; EUR 1,290 in Europe; USD 1,290 elsewhere (effective Apr. 2002). charts; stat. **Document type:** *Trade.* **Description:** Provides a statistical guide to 330 consumer markets, with volume and value sales data broken down across countries in Europe, including, Austria, Belgium, Denmark, Finland, France, Germany, Greece, Ireland, Italy, Netherlands, Norway, Portugal, Spain, Sweden, Switzerland, and the UK. Presents statistical tables of production, sales, distribution, and consumption.
Published by: Euromonitor, 60-61 Britton St, London, EC1 5UX, United Kingdom. TEL 44-20-7251-8024, FAX 44-20-7608-3149, info@euromonitor.com, http://www.euromonitor.com.

658.8 GBR ISSN 1464-102X
HF5415.12.E8
CONSUMER GOODS EUROPE; a monthly bulletin providing detailed analysis of the European market for consumer goods. Text in English. 1963. m. GBP 695, USD 1,200 (effective 2000). charts; mkt.; stat.; tr.lit. cum.index: 1995-1999. back issues avail.; reprints avail. **Document type:** *Newsletter, Corporate.* **Description:** Monitors consumer goods markets, marketing and distribution in Western Europe.
Formerly (until 1998): Marketing in Europe (0025-3723)
Related titles: CD-ROM ed.; Diskette ed.; E-mail ed.; Microfilm ed.: (from WMP); Online - full text ed.
Indexed: CPM, IndBusRep, KES, RASB.
—BLDSC (3424.310200), IE, Infotrieve, ingenta. **CCC.**
Published by: Retail Intelligence, 48 Bedford Sq, London, WC1B 3DP, United Kingdom. TEL 44-20-7696-9006, FAX 44-20-7696-9004, sales@cior.com, lmweiss@lf.com, http://www.cior.com. Ed., R&P Shane Collins. **Subscr. in US to:** Lebhar-Friedman, Inc., 425 Park Ave, New York, NY 10022. TEL 212-756-5159, 212-756-5038, FAX 212-756-5038.

658.8 GBR ISSN 1464-1852
CONSUMER GOODS U K. Text in English. m. GBP 545, USD 925 (effective 2000). **Document type:** *Trade.* **Description:** Contains consumer spending forecasts, product sector overviews, consumer product surveys, topical news review, and company profiles.
Formerly: Marketing Retail Business
Indexed: CPM.
Published by: Corporate Intelligence on Retailing, 48 Bedford Sq, London, WC1 B3DP, United Kingdom. TEL 44-20-7814-3814, FAX 44-20-7696-9004, sales@cior.com, http://www.cior.com. Ed. Nick Wall. R&P Teri Hawksworth TEL 44-20-7814-3814.

B

▼ new title ➤ refereed ✶ unverified ♦ full entry avail.

658.8 GBR
CONSUMER INTERNATIONAL. Text in English. 1994. a. GBP 795 domestic; EUR 1,190 in Europe; USD 1,190 elsewhere (effective Jun. 2002). charts; stat. **Document type:** *Trade.*
Description: Provides statistical coverage of the non-European consumer markets, and include, Argentina, Australia, Brazil, Canada, Chile, China, Columbia, Hong Kong, India, Indonesia, Japan, Malaysia, Mexico, New Zealand, Philippines, Singapore, South Africa, South Korea, Taiwan, Turkey, Thailand, USA, Venezuela, and Vietnam.
Published by: Euromonitor, 60-61 Britton St, London, EC1 5UX, United Kingdom. TEL 44-20-7251-8024, FAX 44-20-7608-3149, info@euromonitor.com, http://www.euromonitor.com.

658.8 GBR
CONSUMER LATIN AMERICA (YEAR). Text in English. 1993. biennial. GBP 675 domestic; EUR 1,090 in Europe; USD 1,090 elsewhere (effective 2003). charts; stat. **Document type:** *Directory.* **Description:** Provides essential information for companies looking to sell products or services in Latin America, and includes, Argentina, Brazil, Chile, Colombia, Mexico, and Venezuela.
Published by: Euromonitor, 60-61 Britton St, London, EC1 5UX, United Kingdom. TEL 44-20-7251-8024, FAX 44-20-7608-3149, info@euromonitor.com, http://www.euromonitor.com.

B

658.8 GBR
CONSUMER MIDDLE EAST (YEAR). Text in English. 1997. a. GBP 675 domestic; EUR 1,090 in Europe; USD 1,090 elsewhere (effective 2003). **Description:** Details the latest consumer trends in the Middle Eastern countries, including, Algeria, Egypt, Jordan, Kuwait, Israel, Morocco, Saudi Arabia, Tunisia, Turkey, and United Arab Emirates.
Published by: Euromonitor, 60-61 Britton St, London, EC1 5UX, United Kingdom. TEL 44-20-7251-8024, FAX 44-20-7608-3149, info@euromonitor.com, http://www.euromonitor.com.

658 CAN ISSN 1206-9744
CONSUMER QUARTERLY. Variant title: Bulletin Trimestriel sur la Consommation. Text in English, French. 1996. q.
Related titles: Online - full text ed.: ISSN 1494-0264.
Published by: Industry Canada, Office of Consumer Affairs, C D Howe Bldg, 235 Queen St, Ottawa, ON K1A 0H5, Canada. TEL 613-952-3466, FAX 613-952-6927, http://strategis.ic.gc.ca/epic/internet/inoca-bc.nsf/en/ca00039e.html. Ed. Cathy Enright.

658.8 GBR ISSN 0952-9543
HC101
CONSUMER U S A (YEAR). Text in English. irreg. GBP 675 domestic; EUR 1,090 in Europe; USD 1,090 elsewhere (effective 2003). **Document type:** *Directory, Trade.*
Description: Provides key statistics and background information on U.S. businesses. Includes a comprehensive statistical database on market size for 350 market sectors, profiles of consumer goods manufacturers, a directory of U.S. retailers, and a guide to official and nonofficial business information sources.
Published by: Euromonitor, 60-61 Britton St, London, EC1 5UX, United Kingdom. TEL 44-20-7251-8024, FAX 44-20-7608-3149, info@euromonitor.com, http://www.euromonitor.com.

658 CAN ISSN 1193-7513
CONTACT (TORONTO). Text in English. 1940. 6/yr. CND 105 to members (effective 2000). adv. bk.rev. charts; illus.; stat.; tr.lit. back issues avail. **Document type:** *Directory, Trade.*
Description: Discusses upcoming events and news. Includes educational information for members.
Former titles (until 1991): Contact - Commercial Travellers' Association of Canada (0834-3845); (until 1985): Canadian Salesman (0576-6044); (until 1960): C T A Bulletin (0319-6798)
Related titles: French ed.: Contact - Association Canadienne des Professionnels de la Vente. ISSN 1193-7521.
Published by: Canadian Professional Sales Association/ Association Canadienne des Professionnels de la Vente, 145 Wellington St W, Ste 610, Toronto, ON M5J 1H8, Canada. TEL 416-408-2685, FAX 416-408-2684, maryk@cpsa.com, http://www.cpsa.com. Ed. Mary Klonizakis. Pub. Sharon Armstrong. Adv. contact Nadine Hoffman. Circ: 32,000 (controlled).

CONTEMPORARY TEA TIME. see *FOOD AND FOOD INDUSTRIES*

658.8 DEU
CONTEXT. Text in German. fortn. adv. **Document type:** *Journal, Trade.*
Published by: Verlag Helga Marcotty, Josefstr 66, Nettetal, 41334, Germany. adv.: B&W page EUR 805. Circ: 1,090 (controlled).

CONTRACTORS HOT LINE. see *BUILDING AND CONSTRUCTION*

658 ZAF
CONVENIENCE STORE RETAILING. Text in English. 1988. m. ZAR 60. adv. **Document type:** *Trade.*
Formerly: Independent Retailer
Published by: Complete Publishing (Pty.) Ltd., PO Box 87745, Houghton, Johannesburg 2041, South Africa. TEL 27-11-7892112, FAX 27-11-789-5347. Circ: 15,000.

658.8 USA
COOL NEWS OF THE DAY. Text in English. 1998. d. **Document type:** *Newsletter, Trade.* **Description:** Features marketing insights from current news headlines and trends.
Media: Online - full content. **Related titles:** E-mail ed.; Print ed.
Published by: David X. Manners Company, Inc., 107 Post Rd E, Westport, CT 06880. TEL 203-227-7060, FAX 203-227-7067, coolnewseditor@reveries.com, http://www.reveries.com/coolnews/index.html, http://www.dxmanners.com.

380.1 DNK ISSN 0109-3401
COPENHAGEN BUSINESS SCHOOL. MARKETING INSTITUTE. WORKING PAPER. Text in Danish, English. 1983. irreg., latest 1996, Oct. 7. price varies. charts. cum.index. back issues avail. **Document type:** *Monographic series, Academic/Scholarly.*
Related titles: Online - full text ed.
Published by: Copenhagen Business School, Department of Marketing/Handelshoejskolen. Institut for Afsaetningsoekonomi, Solbjerg Plads 3C, Frederiksberg C, 2000, Denmark. TEL 45-38-152100, FAX 45-38-152101, reception.marketing@cbs.dk, http://uk.cbs.dk/content/view/pub/6659, http://www.cbs.dk. Ed. Hans S Solgaard. Circ: 200.

COPENHAGEN SCHOOL OF BUSINESS. FORUM FOR ADVERTISING RESEARCH. RESEARCH PAPER. see *BUSINESS AND ECONOMICS*

658 USA
COPY CHICAGO. Text in English. m. membership. **Document type:** *Newsletter.* **Description:** Contains announcements of association events.
Published by: Business Marketing Association (Wilmette), 1920 N. Clark St., Apt. 10A, Chicago, IL 60614-5455. TEL 708-256-3883. Ed. Kirsten Reilly.

658.7 USA
COPYRIGHT INFORMATION PURCHASING & USAGE; best practices of American corporations. Text in English. irreg. USD 295 domestic; EUR 316 foreign (effective 2003). **Description:** Examines how American companies buy and use books, directories, online databases, and other media. Also provides advice on developing digital resources, monitoring information usage, internal pricing, and other issues.
Related titles: Online - full text ed.: USD 295 domestic; EUR 316 foreign (effective 2003).
Published by: Primary Research Group, 850 Seventh Avenue, Suite 1200, New York, NY 10019. TEL 212-245-2327, FAX 212-245-1430, primarydat@mindspring.com, http://www.primaryresearch.com. **Dist. by:** Research and Markets Ltd., Guinness Centre, Taylors Lane, Dublin 8, Ireland. TEL 353-1-4957318, FAX 353-86-8797580, orders@researchandmarkets.com, http://www.researchandmarkets.com.

THE CORPORATE LOGO; the monthly sales magazine for promotional product distributors. see *ADVERTISING AND PUBLIC RELATIONS*

658 USA
CORPORATE TRAINING MARKET (YEAR): FORECASTS & ANALYSIS. Text in English. 1997. a. USD 2,075 (effective 2006). **Document type:** *Directory, Trade.* **Description:** Analyzes the multi-billion dollar market for corporate training and professional development, covering every medium.
Former titles: IT & Soft Skills Corporate Training; Corporate Training Markets (Year); Lifelong Learning Market Report: Analysis and Forecast (Year)
Related titles: Online - full text ed.: USD 1,995 (effective 2005).
Published by: SIMBA Information (Subsidiary of: R.R. Bowker LLC), 60 Long Ridge Rd., Ste 300, Stamford, CT 06902. TEL 203-325-8193, 800-307-2529, FAX 203-325-8915, info@simbanet.com, http://www.simbanet.com/publications/report_ctm.htm.

658 668.5 648 JPN
COSMETICS & TOILETRIES & HOUSEHOLD PRODUCTS MARKETING NEWS IN JAPAN. Text in English. 1979. m. USD 795 (effective 2003). **Document type:** *Trade.*
Description: Covers new product introductions to the Japanese market and also provides a great deal of marketing news and data. Includes such topics as bath products, cosmetics, deodorants & foot care, depilatories, hair products, household products, men's toiletries, OTC pharmaceuticals, perfume, sanpro & paper, skin care, toilet soap, toothpaste, oral hygiene and pet products.
Related titles: Online - full text ed.
Published by: Pacific Research Consulting, 4-18-2, Shikahama, Adachi-ku, Tokyo, 123-0864, Japan. TEL 212-532-8815, 81-3-38999953, FAX 81-3-38999968, prc@abelia.ocn.ne.jp, prcnyrep@hotmail.com, http://www.prcjapan.com/cosmeandhouse.html.

658.8 USA ISSN 0898-6614
COUNCIL OF LOGISTICS MANAGEMENT ANNUAL CONFERENCE PROCEEDINGS. Text in English. 1975 (vol.13). a. USD 40 per issue (effective 2004). bk.rev. charts. **Document type:** *Proceedings.*
Former titles: N C P D M Annual Conference Proceedings; National Council of Physical Distribution Management. Annual Conference Proceedings.; National Council of Physical Distribution Management. Annual Meeting Proceedings
Indexed: HRIS, LogistBibl.
Published by: Council of Supply Chain Management Professionals, 2805 Butterfeld Rd., Ste. 200, Oak Brook, IL 60523. TEL 630-574-0985, FAX 630-574-0989, CSCMPpublications@cscmp.org, http://www.cscmp.org/. Ed. Jessica D'Amico. Circ: 15,000.

COUNSEL. see *ADVERTISING AND PUBLIC RELATIONS*

CREATIV VERPACKEN; Marken, Design, Erfolge. see *PACKAGING*

658.8 MEX
CREATIVA; publicidad, comunicacion y medios. Text in Spanish. m. free. back issues avail. **Description:** Includes news, short articles and reviews on advertising, marketing and mass media.
Related titles: Online - full text ed.
Published by: B & M Disenadores de Medios S.A. de C.V., RIO VOLGA 13 Piso 2, Col Cuauhtemoc, Mexico City, DF 06500, Mexico. TEL 52-5-207-0528, FAX 52-5-525-5963, revista@creativa.com.mx, http://www.creativa.com.mx/.

658 659 USA
CREATIVE MARKETING; incentives in retail promotion. Text in English. 1979. bi-m. bk.rev. stat. back issues avail. **Document type:** *Newsletter.* **Description:** Covers incentive retail promotion, including trading stamps, continuities, tape plans, games and sweepstakes, traffic builders and direct premiums.
Incorporates (1978-1996): A R M S Register
Published by: Association of Retail Marketing Services, 10 Drs James Parker Blvd., Ste. 103, Red Bank, NJ 07701-1500. TEL 732-842-5070, FAX 732-219-1938, info@goarms.com, http://www.goarms.com. Ed., R&P Karen Kircher. Circ: 4,200.

A CREATIVE NEWSLETTER. see *COMPUTERS—Internet*

658.8 659.1 GBR ISSN 0262-1037
CREATIVE REVIEW. Text in English. 1980. m. GBP 49.95 domestic; GBP 68 in Europe; GBP 83 in North America; GBP 95 rest of world (effective 2000). adv. abstr. back issues avail. **Document type:** *Trade.* **Description:** Aimed at creative professionals, largely in the advertising and design industries, around the world.
Related titles: CD-ROM ed.; Microform ed.: (from PQC); Online - full text ed.: (from EBSCO Publishing, Gale Group, H.W. Wilson, LexisNexis, O C L C Online Computer Library Center, Inc., ProQuest Information & Learning).
Indexed: ABIn, ABM, ArtInd, DAAI.
—BLDSC (3487.245000), IE.
Published by: Centaur Publishing, St Giles House, 50 Poland St, London, W1V 4AX, United Kingdom. TEL 44—20-7970-4000, FAX 44-207-970-4099, http://www.mad.co.uk/cr/index.asp. Ed. Patrick Burgoyne. Pub. Jess MacDermot. **Dist. by:** Comag Specialist Division, Tavistock Works, Tavistock Rd, W Drayton, Mddx UB7 7QX, United Kingdom. TEL 44-1895-433800, FAX 44-1895-433801.

658 USA
CREATIVE SELLING. Text in English. m. USD 109 domestic; USD 127 foreign (effective 2001). **Document type:** *Newsletter, Trade.* **Description:** Publishes advice on sales and marketing.
Published by: Bentley-Hall, Inc., 120 Walton St, Ste 201, Syracuse, NY 13202. TEL 315-422-4488, 800-724-9700, FAX 800-724-3881, sales@creativeselling.com, sales@bentley-hall.com, http://www.creativeselling.com, http://www.bentley-hall.com. Ed. Michelle Brunton. Pub. Bob Popyk.

332.7 658 GBR ISSN 0265-2099
CODEN: CEMNEJ
CREDIT MANAGEMENT. Text in English. 1950. m. GBP 55 domestic; GBP 65 foreign (effective 2005). adv. bk.rev. charts; illus.; stat. **Document type:** *Journal, Academic/Scholarly.*
Description: Offers full coverage of consumer, trade, and export news and editorials.
Related titles: Online - full text ed.: (from EBSCO Publishing, Northern Light Technology, Inc., O C L C Online Computer Library Center, Inc., ProQuest Information & Learning).
Indexed: ABIn, Emerald, Inspec, RefZh.
—BLDSC (3487.283000), AskIEEE, IE, ingenta. **CCC.**
Published by: Institute of Credit Management, The Water Mill, Station Rd, South Luffenham, Leics LE15 8NB, United Kingdom. TEL 44-1780722900, FAX 44-1780721333, editorial@icm.org.uk, info@icm.org.uk, http://www.icmjournal.org.uk/, http://www.icm.org.uk. Ed., R&P, Adv. contact Rob Beddington TEL 44-1780-722900. B&W page GBP 955; 177 x 263. Circ: 10,000.

CRONER'S BUYING AND SELLING LAW. see *LAW*

CROSS AND TALK; for communications between you and the world. see *COMMUNICATIONS*

676.282 658 USA ISSN 1544-0745
HD9999.G493
CUSTOM GIFT RETAILER. Text in English. 2002. bi-m. free in US & Canada; USD 51 in Mexico; USD 67 elsewhere (effective 2003). adv. **Document type:** *Magazine, Trade.*
Published by: National Business Media, Inc., PO Box 1416, Broomfield, CO 80038. TEL 303-469-0424, 800-669-0424, FAX 303-469-5730, http://www.nbm.com.

658 USA ISSN 1352-0415
CUSTOMER LOYALTY TODAY. Text in English.
Related titles: Online - full text ed.: (from Gale Group, O C L C Online Computer Library Center, Inc.).
Published by: Center for Information Based Competition, 2349 Donamere Circle, Centerville, OH 45459. TEL 937-439-1104, FAX 937-439-1078, informationmasters@att.net, http://www.informationmasters.com.

658 USA
CUSTOMER PROFIT REPORT✶. Text in English. bi-w. USD 199. **Description:** Includes strategies for improving customer satisfaction, customer retention, profitability, and quality. For managers, directors, VP's of marketing, customer service and distribution.
Formerly: Customer Assurance Report
Published by: Marketing Publications Inc., 4120 Military Rd NW, Washington, DC 20015-2930. TEL 301-585-0730, FAX 301-585-3084. Ed. Warren Blanding.

658 GBR
THE CUSTOMER REPORT. Text in English. 2001. bi-m. adv. **Document type:** *Trade.* **Description:** Analyzes current developments in customer management.
Related titles: Online - full content ed.
Published by: Centaur Publishing, St Giles House, 50 Poland St, London, W1V 4AX, United Kingdom. TEL 44-20-7970-4000, markt@centaur.co.uk, http://www.mad.co.uk/clt/, http://www.centaur.co.uk.

658 USA ISSN 1092-8014
THE CUSTOMER SERVICE ADVANTAGE. Text in English. 1997. s-m. USD 253. charts. **Document type:** *Newsletter.* **Description:** Information on how to provide exceptional service that delights customers. Includes instructional materials.
Published by: Progressive Business Publications, 370 Technology Dr, Malvern, PA 19355-1315. TEL 610-695-8600, 800-220-5000, FAX 610-647-8089, editor@pbp.com, http://www.pbp.com. Ed. Julie Power. R&P Curt Brown.

658 004 NLD ISSN 1381-3641
CUSTOMERBASE. Text in Dutch. 1994. bi-m. EUR 75 (effective 2003).
—Infotrieve.
Published by: F & G Publishing, Posbus 1245, Heerhugowaard, 1700 BE, Netherlands. TEL 31-72-5762888, FAX 31-72-5762889, info@fngpubli.com, http://www.customerbase.nl/, http://www.fngpubli.com. Ed. Teun Putter.

D & A. see *MEDICAL SCIENCES—Orthopedics And Traumatology*

658 GBR ISSN 1472-3166
D & B EUROPA. (Dun & Bradstreet) Text in English. 1989. a. GBP 520 (effective 2000). **Document type:** *Directory.*
Formerly (until 1992): Duns Europa (0957-5812)
Published by: Dun & Bradstreet Ltd., 50-100 Holmers Farm Way, High Wycombe, Bucks HP12 4UL, United Kingdom. TEL 44-1494-423689, FAX 44-1494-422332.

658.8 USA ISSN 1543-3587
HF5487
▼ **D C VELOCITY**; logistics solutions for distribution center management. (Distribution Center) Text in English. 2003 (Jan.). m. USD 59 in US & Canada; USD 129 elsewhere (effective 2003). adv.
Published by: Agile Business Media LLC, 1300 S. Grove Ave., Barrington, IL 60010. TEL 847-713-0000, FAX 847-304-8603, http://www.dcvelocity.com. Eds. Peter Bradley, Mitch MacDonald. Pub. Jim Indelicato.

658.8 USA
THE D M A INSIDER. Text in English. 4/yr. **Document type:** *Magazine, Trade.*
Published by: (Direct Marketing Association), Pohly & Partners Inc., 27 Melcher St., 2nd Fl., Boston, MA 02210. TEL 617-451-1700, FAX 617-338-7767, http://www.pohlypartners.com. Circ: 30,000 (controlled).

658.8 659.1 USA ISSN 1049-6092
HF5415.126
D M A STATISTICAL FACT BOOK. Text in English. a. USD 395 (effective 2005). charts; stat. reprint service avail. from PQC. **Description:** Covers many aspects of direct marketing including: media and market growth and usage trends, consumer and business attitudes and buying habits, expectations and outlooks, production and operating cost figures and environmental issues concerns.
Formerly: Fact Book on Direct Marketing
Indexed: SRI.
Published by: (Library & Resource Center), Direct Marketing Association, 1120 Ave of the Americas, New York, NY 10036-6700. TEL 212-768-7277, FAX 212-768-4546.

658.8 GBR
D M BUSINESS; the direct marketing - direct mail business magazine. Text in English. 1997. bi-m. GBP 26 (effective 1999). adv. **Document type:** *Trade.* **Description:** Provides direct marketing and direct mail service information for end users.
Published by: Anthony Harvey Associates, 43 Maiden Ln, London, WC2E 7LJ, United Kingdom. TEL 44-171-240-9363, FAX 44-171-379-4103, aha@dircon.co.uk. Ed. Frank Wainwright. Adv. contact Noel Harvey. color page GBP 1,600. Circ: 13,000 (controlled).

658 025.04 DEU
D M M V SPECIAL. (Deutscher Multimedia Verband) Text in German. irreg. adv. **Document type:** *Journal, Trade.*
Published by: Europa Fachpresse Verlag GmbH (Subsidiary of: Sueddeutsche Verlag), Emily-Noether-Str 2-E, Munich, 80992, Germany. TEL 49-89-54852-0, FAX 49-89-54852333. Adv. contact Sabine Vockrodt.

668.8 USA ISSN 0194-3588
D M NEWS. (Direct Marketing) Text in English. 1979. w. USD 49 (effective 2005). adv. software rev.; Website rev. stat.; tr.lit. 60 p./no.; back issues avail.; reprints avail. **Document type:** *Newspaper, Trade.*
Incorporates (in 2002): iMarketing News (1528-2465)
Related titles: Online - full text ed.: (from O C L C Online Computer Library Center, Inc.); ♦ Supplement(s): D M News International.
Published by: Courtenay Communications Corp., 100 Avenue of the Americas, 6th Fl, New York, NY 10013-1689. TEL 212-925-7300, FAX 212-925-8797, editor@dmnews.com, http://www.dmnews.com. Ed., R&P Tad Clarke. Pub. Adrian Courtenay. Adv. contact Charlton Cham. Circ: 40,000 (controlled).

D M NEWS INTERNATIONAL. see *BUSINESS AND ECONOMICS—International Commerce*

658.879 USA ISSN 1530-6259
D S N RETAILING TODAY. (Discount Store News) Text in English. 1962. fortn. (23/yr.). free to qualified personnel. adv. illus.; tr.lit.; abstr. back issues avail.; reprint service avail. from PQC. **Document type:** *Newspaper, Trade.* **Description:** Covers merchandising and operational methods; includes reports on developments.
Formerly: Discount Store News (0012-3587)
Related titles: Microfiche ed.: (from CIS); Microform ed.: (from PQC); Online - full text ed.: (from EBSCO Publishing, Factiva, Florida Center for Library Automation, Gale Group, Northern Light Technology, Inc., O C L C Online Computer Library Center, Inc., ProQuest Information & Learning, The Dialog Corporation); ♦ Supplement(s): Apparel Merchandising. ISSN 0746-889X.
Indexed: ABIn, B&I, BusI, PAIS, SRI, T&II.
—BLDSC (3630.457200). **CCC.**
Published by: Lebhar-Friedman, Inc., 425 Park Ave, New York, NY 10022. TEL 212-756-5000, 800-766-6999, FAX 212-756-5395, info_dsn@lf.com, info@lf.com, http://www.dsnretailingtoday.com/, http://www.lf.com. Ed. Tim Craig. Pub. Paula Lashinsky. adv.: B&W page USD 12,225, color page USD 15,120. Circ: 32,805.

D T C PERSPECTIVES. (Direct-to-Customer) see *PHARMACY AND PHARMACOLOGY*

DAGENS HANDEL. see *BUSINESS AND ECONOMICS—Domestic Commerce*

658.8 SWE ISSN 1403-8498
DAGENS MEDIA; affaerstidningen om marknadsfoering och medieval. Text in Swedish. 1998. 22/yr. SEK 1,595 (effective 2004). adv. **Document type:** *Magazine, Trade.*
Related titles: Online - full text ed.
Published by: Dagens Media Sverige AB, Vaestmanngatan 15, Stockholm, 11124, Sweden. TEL 46-8-54522200, FAX 46-8-5452215, info@dagensmedia.se, http://www.dagensmedia.se. Ed., Pub. Rolf Van Den Brink TEL 46-8-54522203. Adv. contact Mathias Kallio TEL 46-8-54522212. B&W page SEK 21,500, color page SEK 28,300; trim 230 x 345.

DAGLIGVARU AFFAERER. see *FOOD AND FOOD INDUSTRIES—Grocery Trade*

658 RUS
DAIDZHEST MARKETING. Text in Russian. 1999. s-a.
Related titles: ♦ Supplement to: Prakticheskii Marketing.
Published by: B C I Marketing, ul Malaya Cherkizovskaya, dom 66, Moscow, 107392, Russian Federation. bcimarketing@mtu-net.ru, http://www.bci-marketing.aha.ru. Eds. Suren Grigoryan, Tatiana Chudina. Circ: 100.

DAILY SUGAR REPORT. see *FOOD AND FOOD INDUSTRIES—Bakers And Confectioners*

DANSK FAGPRESSEKATALOG. see *ADVERTISING AND PUBLIC RELATIONS*

DANSK PRESSE. see *JOURNALISM*

DANSKE MALERMESTRE. see *PAINTS AND PROTECTIVE COATINGS*

658 USA ISSN 1525-0962
DARTNELL'S SALESMANSHIP. Text in English. 1972. bi-w. USD 76.70. reprint service avail. from PQC. **Document type:** *Newsletter.* **Description:** Enhances personal and corporate salespeople-training programs with instructive performance tips.
—**CCC.**
Published by: Dartnell Corp. (Subsidiary of: L R P Publications), 360 Hiatt Dr, Palm Beach Garden, FL 33418. TEL 800-621-5463, FAX 561-622-2423, custserve@lrp.com, http://www.dartnellcorp.com/. Ed. Terry Breen.

005.74 USA ISSN 1523-3367
DATABASE MARKETER. Text in English. 1992. m. USD 329. **Document type:** *Newsletter.* **Description:** Includes comparisons, vital statistics, and real case studies on topics such as pricing, technology, and ethics.
Former titles: Cowles - SIMBA Report on Database Marketing; (until 199?): Cowles Report on Database Marketing (1072-401X)
—**CCC.**
Published by: SIMBA Information (Subsidiary of: R.R. Bowker LLC), 60 Long Ridge Rd., Ste 300, Stamford, CT 06902. TEL 203-325-8193, 800-307-2529, 888-269-5372, FAX 203-325-8915, info@simbanet.com, http://www.simbanet.com.

658 683.83 USA
DEALERSCOPE MERCHANDISING FIRST OF THE MONTH. Text in English. 1990. m. free to qualified personnel. adv. **Document type:** *Trade.* **Description:** Retail news about consumer electronics and major appliances for large chains and department store management.
Published by: North American Publishing Co., 1500 Spring Garden St., Ste 1200, Philadelphia, PA 19130-4094. TEL 215-238-5300, FAX 215-238-5457. Ed. Richard Sherwin. Circ: 30,000.

658 USA
DECA DIMENSIONS. Text in English. 1947. bi-m. **Document type:** *Trade.*
Address: 1908 Association Dr, Reston, VA 20191. TEL 703-860-5000, FAX 703-860-4013, carol_lund@deca.org, http://www.deca.org. Ed. Carol Lund. Circ: 160,000 (paid).

656.8 FRA ISSN 1253-0476
DECISIONS MARKETING. Abbreviated title: D C. Text in French. 199?. q.
Related titles: Online - full text ed.: (from ProQuest Information & Learning).
Indexed: ABIn.
Published by: E S S E C Business School, Avenue Bernard Hirsch BP 105, Cergy-Pontoise, Cedex 95021, France. TEL 33-1-34433136, FAX 33-1-34433111, billet@essec.fr, http://www.essec.com.

658.8 BEL ISSN 0779-7389
DECISIONS MARKETING. Text in French. 1993. 3/yr.
Published by: C E C O E D U C, Avenue des Naiades 11, Bruxelles, B-1170, Belgium. a_philippart@ hotmail.com.

DECO FLEUR. see *GIFTWARE AND TOYS*

DEFENSE CONTRACTS INTERNATIONAL. see *MILITARY*

DELANEY REPORT. see *ADVERTISING AND PUBLIC RELATIONS*

380.1 381.1 DNK ISSN 0109-1751
DETAILBLADET. Text in Danish. 1983. 23/yr. DKK 300 per issue (effective 2004). adv. illus. **Document type:** *Newsletter, Trade.*
Published by: Erhvervs-Bladet A-S, Vesterbrogade 12, Copenhagen V, 1780, Denmark. TEL 45-33-267200, FAX 45-33-267282, hd@detailbladet.dk, http://www.erhvervsbladet.dk/detailbladet/detailbladet.asp. Ed. Henrik Denman. Circ: 37,000.

381 NLD ISSN 0168-0021
DETAILHANDEL MAGAZINE. Short title: D H Magazine. Text in Dutch. 1971. w. illus. **Document type:** *Journal, Trade.*
Formerly (until 1982): Detailhandelsbulletin (0167-031X)
—IE, Infotrieve.
Published by: Hoofdbedrijfschap Detailhandel, Postbus 90703, The Hague, 2509 LS, Netherlands. TEL 31-70-338-5600, FAX 31-70-338-5711, info@hbd.nl, http://www.hbd.nl/tovhbd.htm.

658 USA ISSN 0149-7421
HF5415.1
DEVELOPMENTS IN MARKETING SCIENCE. Text in English. 1977. a. USD 50 per issue (effective 2005). adv. back issues avail. **Document type:** *Proceedings.*
—BLDSC (3579.084600), IE, ingenta. **CCC.**
Published by: Academy of Marketing Science, School of Business Administration, University of Miami, PO Box 248012, Coral Gables, FL 33124-6536. TEL 305-284-6673, FAX 305-284-3762, amsrev@vancouver.wsu.edu, amsreview@ams-web.org, http://www.amsreview.org. Eds. Elizabeth Wilson, Joseph F Hair Jr. Circ: 500.

658 USA
DICKINSON'S D T C MARKETER. (Direct-To-Consumer) Text in English. bi-w. USD 655 domestic; USD 715 elsewhere (effective 2005). **Document type:** *Newsletter, Trade.*
Formerly: Dickinson's F D A Marketer
Published by: Ferdic Inc., PO Box 28, Camp Hill, PA 17011. TEL 717-731-1426, FAX 717-731-1427, info@fdaweb.com, http://www.fdaweb.com. Ed., Pub. James G Dickinson TEL 520-684-3112.

658.8 CAN ISSN 1495-5636
DIGITAL MARKETING (TORONTO, 2000). Text in English. 1933. bi-m. adv. **Document type:** *Magazine, Trade.* **Description:** Covers all aspects of emerging technology and marketing.
Supersedes in part (in 2000): Marketing Magazine (1196-4650); Which was formerly (until 1993): Marketing (0025-3642); Incorporates (in 1994): Digital Marketing (Toronto, 1994) (1202-631X); (1973-1982): Canadian Premiums & Incentives (0319-6267)
Related titles: Online - full text ed.: (from H.W. Wilson, Micromedia ProQuest, O C L C Online Computer Library Center, Inc., ProQuest Information & Learning).
Indexed: ABIn.
—BLDSC (3588.397015), CISTI.
Published by: Rogers Media Publishing Ltd, One Mount Pleasant Rd, 11th Fl, Toronto, ON M4Y 2Y5, Canada. TEL 416-764-2000, FAX 416-764-3941, http://www.rogers.com.

DIMENSIONS (RESTON). see *EDUCATION—Teaching Methods And Curriculum*

658 FRA ISSN 1147-7776
DIRECT. Text in French. 1990. 9/yr.
Related titles: Online - full text ed.: (from Northern Light Technology, Inc.).
Published by: Marketing Mix S.A., 15 bis rue Ernest Renan, BP 62, Issy-les-Moulineaux, Cedex 92133, France. TEL 40-93-01-02, FAX 40-93-03-40. Ed. Bruno Le Prat. Circ: 5,500.

658.8 USA ISSN 1046-4174
HF5415.126
DIRECT (NEW YORK, 1988); magazine of direct marketing management. Text in English. 1988. 16/yr. USD 85 domestic; USD 96 in Canada; USD 218 elsewhere (effective 2005). adv. bk.rev. illus.; stat.; tr.lit. back issues avail.; reprint service avail. from PQC. **Document type:** *Magazine, Trade.* **Description:** Reports on the latest developments in direct marketing.
Related titles: Online - full text ed.: (from EBSCO Publishing, Gale Group, H.W. Wilson, O C L C Online Computer Library Center, Inc.).
Indexed: B&I, BPI.
—**CCC.**
Published by: Primedia Business Magazines & Media, Inc. (Subsidiary of: Primedia, Inc.), 249 W 17th St, New York, NY 10011. TEL 212-462-3600, FAX 212-206-3622, inquiries@primediabusiness.com, http://www.directmag.com, http://www.primediabusiness.com. Ed. Ray Schultz. adv.: B&W page USD 8,370, color page USD 11,560. Circ: 600 (paid); 37,500 (controlled). **Subscr. to:** 2104 Harvell Circle, Bellevue, NE 68005. TEL 402-505-7173, 866-505-7173, FAX 402-293-0741.

DIRECT DISTRIBUTION. see *PUBLISHING AND BOOK TRADE*

658 BEL
DIRECT EFFECT. Text in Flemish. m. **Description:** Explores direct marketing.
Published by: C E D Samsom (Subsidiary of: Wolters Samsom Belgie n.v.), Kouterveld 14, Diegem, 1831, Belgium. TEL 32-2-7231111.

658.8 659.1 USA ISSN 0743-7625
DIRECT LINE. Text in English. m.
Published by: Direct Marketing Association, 1120 Ave of the Americas, New York, NY 10036-6700. TEL 212-768-7277, FAX 212-768-4547.

658.8 USA
HF5861 CODEN: DIMADI
DIRECT MARKETING (ONLINE EDITION); using direct response advertising to enhance marketing database. Text in English. 1938. m. adv. illus. Index. reprint service avail. from PQC. **Document type:** *Magazine, Trade.* **Description:** Regular departments, columns and special features provide timely insight on the people, organizations, trends and developments, strategies and tactics.
Former titles (until 2004): Direct Marketing (Print Edition) (0012-3188); (until 1968): Reporter of Direct Mail Advertising
Media: Online - full text (from Gale Group, O C L C Online Computer Library Center, Inc., ProQuest Information & Learning). **Related titles:** Microform ed.: (from PQC).
Indexed: ABIn, ASEANManA, B&I, BLI, BPI, BPIA, Emerald, Inspec.
—BLDSC (3590.240000), AskIEEE, CASDDS, IE, ingenta. **CCC.**
Published by: Hoke Communications, 224 Seventh St, Garden City, NY 11530. TEL 516-746-6700, 800-229-6700, FAX 516-294-8141, 71410.2423@compuserve.com, http://netplaza.com/cgi-bin/document/plaza/business/1025/storepg2.html. Ed., R&P Joseph Gatti. Pub., Adv. contact Henry Hoke. Circ: 11,000.

658.8 659.1 USA
DIRECT MARKETING ASSOCIATION. ANNUAL REPORT. Text in English. a. **Document type:** *Corporate.*
Published by: Direct Marketing Association, 1120 Ave of the Americas, New York, NY 10036-6700. TEL 212-768-7277, FAX 212-768-4547.

658 JPN
DIRECT MARKETING IN JAPAN. Text in English. irreg. USD 200 per issue. **Document type:** *Directory.* **Description:** Covers 80 specialist and non-specialist direct marketers.
Published by: Dodwell Marketing Consultants, Kowa no 35 Bldg, 14-14 Akasaka 1-chome, Minato-ku, Tokyo, 107-0052, Japan. TEL 03-3589-0207, FAX 03-5570-7132. Circ: 1,000.

658.8 GBR ISSN 0969-6881
DIRECT MARKETING INTERNATIONAL. Text in English. 1990. m. **Document type:** *Trade.*
Formed by the 1989 merger of: Direct Marketing World; World List News; (1987-1989): Database Marketing (0953-8828); (1988-1989): Tele direct (0958-0891)
Related titles: Online - full content ed.
—**CCC.**
Published by: Charterhouse Communications Group Ltd., Arnold House, 36-41 Holywell Ln, London, EC2A 3ET, United Kingdom. TEL 44-20-7827-5454, info@themoneypages.com, http://www.charterhouse-communications.co.uk.

658 USA ISSN 0192-3137
HF5415.1
DIRECT MARKETING MARKET PLACE; the networking source of the direct marketing industry. Short title: D M M P. Text in English. 1980. a. USD 345 per issue (effective 2005). adv. stat.; tr.lit. index. back issues avail. **Document type:** *Directory.* **Description:** Lists over 31,000 key executives, leading direct marketing companies, major firms, suppliers, and creative sources in the US. Provides information on key decision makers, advertising budget, direct marketing expenditures, sales, and billing.
Published by: National Register Publishing (Subsidiary of: Marquis Who's Who), 562 Central Ave, New Providence, NJ 07974. TEL 800-473-7020, FAX 908-673-1189, NRPsales@marquiswhoswho.com, http://www.dirmktgplace.com, http://www.nationalregisterpub.com. Circ: 3,000.

658.8 CAN ISSN 1187-7111
DIRECT MARKETING NEWS. Text in English. 1988. 12/yr. USD 60. adv. bk.rev. **Description:** Provides articles on telemarketing, direct marketing, database marketing, loyalty and relationship management, data warehousing and call centres in direct marketing.
Formerly (until 1992): Canadian Direct Marketing News (0844-3238)
Indexed: CBCARef.
Published by: Lloydmedia Inc., 1200 Markham Rd, Ste 301, Scarborough, ON M1H 3C3, Canada. TEL 416-439-4083, FAX 416-439-4086. Ed. Ron Glen. Adv. contact Tom Kjaersgaard. B&W page CND 3,195, color page CND 4,495; trim 15 x 9.5. Circ: 7,500 (controlled).

658 USA ISSN 1085-1321
DIRECT RESPONSE. Text in English. 1971. m. USD 79 domestic; USD 88 foreign (effective 2000). adv. bk.rev. **Document type:** *Newsletter.* **Description:** Contains original articles and a digest of the latest in direct marketing. Test results, new trends, case studies are outlined.
Related titles: Online - full text ed.: (from Florida Center for Library Automation).
Published by: Creative Direct Marketing Group, 2360 Plaza Del Amo, Ste 105, Torrance, CA 90501-2800. TEL 310-212-5727, FAX 310-212-5773. Ed. Bill Tannebring. Pub. Craig A Huey. R&P Craig Huey.

DIRECT RESPONSE SPECIALIST. see *ADVERTISING AND PUBLIC RELATIONS*

658.8 USA
DIRECT SELLING ASSOCIATION. WORLD FEDERATION NEWS. Text in English. 6/yr. membership only. illus. **Document type:** *Bulletin, Trade.*
Formerly: Direct Selling Association. International Bulletin
Published by: (Direct Selling Association), World Federation of Direct Selling Associations, 1275 Pennsylvania Ave N W, Ste 800, Washington, DC 20004. TEL 202-347-8866, FAX 202-463-4569, info@wfdsa.org, http://www.wfdsa.org. Ed., R&P Anna Fernau.

DIRECTION (ALLENDALE). see *ADVERTISING AND PUBLIC RELATIONS*

658.8 659.1 USA ISSN 0883-9727
DIRECTIONS (NEW YORK). Text in English. bi-m. reprint service avail. from PQC.
Formerly (until 1985): Direct Marketing Journal (0747-8100)
Published by: Direct Marketing Association, 1120 Ave of the Americas, New York, NY 10036-6700. TEL 212-768-7277, FAX 212-768-4547.

378 USA ISSN 0084-988X
DIRECTORY OF COLLEGE STORES. Text in English. 1956. irreg. USD 75 (effective 2000). **Document type:** *Directory.*
Published by: B. Klein Publications, PO Box 6578, Delray Beach, FL 33482. TEL 407-496-3316, FAX 407-496-5546. Ed. Bernard Klein.

DIRECTORY OF DEPARTMENT STORES; includes: resident buyers, mail order firms. see *BUSINESS AND ECONOMICS—Trade And Industrial Directories*

DIRECTORY OF DISCOUNT AND GENERAL MERCHANDISE STORES (YEAR). see *BUSINESS AND ECONOMICS—Trade And Industrial Directories*

DIRECTORY OF MAIL ORDER CATALOGS. see *BUSINESS AND ECONOMICS—Trade And Industrial Directories*

DIRECTORY OF MAJOR MALLS. see *REAL ESTATE*

DIRECTORY OF PREMIUM, INCENTIVE & TRAVEL BUYERS. see *BUSINESS AND ECONOMICS—Investments*

330 DEU ISSN 0946-0446
DIREKT MARKETING. Text in German. 1965. m. EUR 89; EUR 57.22 to students; EUR 7.50 newsstand/cover (effective 2005). adv. **Document type:** *Magazine, Trade.*
Incorporates (1998-2004): Database Marketing; Formerly (until 1970): Direktwerbung und Verkaufsfoerderung (0012-3315)
Related titles: Supplement(s): Direkt Marketing Trend. ISSN 1616-4105. 2000.
Published by: I M Marketing-Forum GmbH, Englerstr 26, Ettlingen, 76275, Germany. TEL 49-7243-54000, FAX 49-7243-540054, info@im-marketing-forum.de, http://www.im-marketing-forum.de. Ed. Andrea Braendli. adv.: B&W page EUR 2,225, color page EUR 2,800. Circ: 13,430 (paid and controlled).

658.8 DEU
DIREKT MEHR. Text in German. 4/yr. **Document type:** *Newsletter, Trade.*
Published by: (Deutsche Post AG), Medienfabrik Guetersloh GmbH, Carl-Bertelsmann-Str 33, Guetersloh, 33311, Germany. TEL 49-5241-2348010, FAX 49-5241-2348022, kontakt@medienfabrik-gt.de, http://www.medienfabrik-gt.de. Circ: 150,000 (controlled).

658.8 DEU
DIREKTMARKETING PRAXIS. Text in German. 1996. m. EUR 47; EUR 31.17 to students; EUR 4.90 newsstand/cover (effective 2005). adv. **Document type:** *Magazine, Trade.*
Formerly: Praxisletter Mailings (1434-6958)
Published by: I M Marketing-Forum GmbH, Englerstr 26, Ettlingen, 76275, Germany. TEL 49-7243-54000, FAX 49-7243-540054, info@im-marketing-forum.de, http://www.im-marketing-forum.de. adv.: B&W page EUR 3,650, color page EUR 4,200. Circ: 30,000 (controlled).

658.8 DEU ISSN 0946-2430
DISPLAY; das Magazin fuer Verkaufsfoerderung und Marketing. Text in German. 1993. bi-m. EUR 45 domestic; EUR 50 in Europe; EUR 117 elsewhere; EUR 5 newsstand/cover (effective 2005). adv. charts; illus.; stat. **Document type:** *Magazine, Trade.*
Published by: Display Verlags GmbH, Wellingsbuettler Weg 148, Hamburg, 22391, Germany. TEL 49-40-5360054, FAX 49-40-5360111, info@display.de, http://www.display.de. Ed. Juergen Bethge. Adv. contact Thorsten Brandmann. B&W page EUR 3,420, color page EUR 4,360; trim 187 x 255. Circ: 18,429 (paid).

658.8 DEU
DISPLAY INTERNATIONAL; the international magazine for p.o.p. marketing. Text in English, German, Italian, Russian. 1995. q. EUR 35 domestic; EUR 40 in Europe; EUR 90 elsewhere; EUR 7 newsstand/cover (effective 2005). adv. charts; illus.; stat. **Document type:** *Magazine, Trade.*
Published by: Display Verlags GmbH, Wellingsbuettler Weg 148, Hamburg, 22391, Germany. TEL 49-40-5360054, FAX 49-40-5360111, info@display.de, http://www.display.de. Ed. Juergen Bethge. Adv. contact Thorsten Brandmann. B&W page EUR 1,730, color page EUR 2,500; trim 187 x 255. Circ: 18,909 (paid).

658.8 ESP
DISTRIBUCION ACTUALIDAD. Text in Spanish. 1975. m. (11/yr.). adv. bk.rev. **Document type:** *Trade.*
Indexed: B&I.

Published by: Ediciones y Estudios S.A., Enrique Larreta, 5-1o, Madrid, 28036, Spain. TEL 1-733-91-14, FAX 1-315-74-19. Ed. Alicia Davara. Pub. Miguel de Haro. Adv. contact Choni Velasco.

658.7   USA   ISSN 0894-7651
DISTRIBUTION CENTER MANAGEMENT; managing people, materials and costs in the warehouse and distribution center. Text in English. 1966. m. USD 199 (effective 2005). charts; illus.; stat. 8 p./no.; **Document type:** *Newsletter, Trade.* **Description:** Provides practical strategies and industry news to help distribution center and warehouse professionals improve distribution center efficiency.
Former titles (until 1979): Warehouse and Physical Distribution Productivity; (until 1973): Distribution-Warehouse Cost Digest (0012-3927)
Indexed: LogistBibl.
Published by: Alexander Communications Group, Inc., 28 W 25th St, 8th Fl, New York, NY 10010. TEL 212-228-0246, FAX 212-228-0376, info@distributiongroup.com, http://www.distributiongroup.com. Ed. Troy Reynolds.

658.8   BEL   ISSN 0012-3935
DISTRIBUTION D'AUJOURD'HUI; le mensuel des fabricants et commercants dynamiques. Text in French. 1960. 10/yr. adv. **Document type:** *Trade.* **Description:** Examines the economic aspects, commercial techniques and marketing involved in distribution. Includes new product announcements.
Formerly (until 1968): Revue Belge de la Distribution (0773-1183)
Related titles: Flemish ed.: Distributie Vandaag. ISSN 0773-1175.
Indexed: KES.
Published by: Comite Belge de la Distribution/Belgisch Comite voor de Distributie, Rue Marianne 34, Bruxelles, 1180, Belgium. TEL 32-2-345-9923, FAX 32-2-346-0204, http://www.cbd-bcd.be. Ed. Wim Van Meerbeeck. adv.: B&W page EUR 1,910, color page EUR 2,550; trim 185 x 265.

658   USA
DISTRIBUTION MANAGEMENT DIGEST. Text in English. 1987. q. adv. **Document type:** *Newsletter.*
Published by: Business Marketing & Publishing Inc., PO Box 7457, Wilton, CT 06897. TEL 203-834-9959. Adv. contact George B Young. B&W page USD 965.

338.025   USA   ISSN 1079-2414
HD2346.U5
DIVERSITY SUPPLIERS & BUSINESS MAGAZINE. Text in English. 1994. a. USD 3.50 newsstand/cover. bk.rev. illus. back issues avail. **Document type:** *Trade.* **Description:** Seeks to introduce small-business people to corporate America.
Related titles: Online - full text ed.: (from EBSCO Publishing, Florida Center for Library Automation, Gale Group, SoftLine Information).
Indexed: ENW.
Published by: Hispanic Times Enterprises, 3007 W Florida Ave, Ste 201, Hemet, CA 92545. TEL 213-484-6450, FAX 213-483-7037, foxiekoji@aol.com. Ed. Jane Rifkin. Pub. Humberto Salazar Lopez. adv.: page USD 3,500; trim 10.88 x 8.25. Circ: 15,000 (controlled).

658   NLD
DOCUMENTATIE REVUE. Text in Dutch. s-a. free to qualified personnel. adv. **Document type:** *Trade.* **Description:** Aimed at the purchasing department, management and executives of production and trade enterprises.
Published by: Reed Business Information bv (Subsidiary of: Reed Business), Hanzestraat 1, Doetinchem, 7006 RH, Netherlands. TEL 31-314-349911, FAX 31-314-343839, info@reedbusiness.nl, http://www.reedbusiness.nl. Ed. J F F van Bruggen. Adv. contact Cor van Nek. Circ: 15,000 (controlled).

DOOR & WINDOW RETAILING. see *BUILDING AND CONSTRUCTION*

658   FRA   ISSN 0769-5918
DOSSIERS DU MARKETING DIRECT. Text in French. 1984. 11/yr. **Description:** Educational review dedicated to direct marketing.
Published by: Centre Francais pour la Promotion du Marketing Direct, 4 rue de Commaille, Paris, 75007, France. TEL 42-22-90-33, FAX 42-22-23-89. Ed. M C Ferreira. Circ: 2,000.

658   USA
DROP SHIPPING MARKETING METHODS; a handbook of methods and policies. Text in English. 1992. a. USD 18 (effective 2005). **Document type:** *Directory, Trade.* **Description:** Covers many facets of drop shipping and direct marketing. Twenty four articles covering all aspects of drop shipping as a means of shifting storage & order fulfillment backward to the Mfgr. or major distributor.
Published by: Drop Shipping News (Subsidiary of: Consolidated Marketing Services, Inc.), PO Box 7838, New York, NY 10150. TEL 212-688-8797, http://www.drop-shipping-news.com. Ed., Pub. Nicholas T Scheel.

658   USA
DROP SHIPPING NEWS. Text in English. 1977. **Document type:** *Newsletter, Trade.* **Description:** Covers all facets of drop shipping as a marketing function by shifting the risk of inventory possession backward through channels of distribution.
Address: PO Box 7838, New York, NY 10150. TEL 212-688-8797, nscheel@drop-shipping-news.com, http://www.drop-shipping-news.com. Ed., Pub. Nicholas T Scheel.

DROP SHIPPING SOURCE DIRECTORY OF MAJOR CONSUMER PRODUCT LINES. see *BUSINESS AND ECONOMICS—Trade And Industrial Directories*

▼ **DRUG DELIVERY & COMMERCE.** see *PHARMACY AND PHARMACOLOGY*

381.45   USA   ISSN 0191-7587
DRUG STORE NEWS. Text in English. 1960. 17/yr. free to qualified personnel (effective 2005). adv. illus.; tr.lit. reprint service avail. from PQC. **Document type:** *Magazine, Trade.*
Supersedes: Chain Store Age Drug Magazine
Related titles: Microfiche ed.: (from CIS); Microform ed.: (from PQC); Online - full text ed.: (from EBSCO Publishing, Factiva, Florida Center for Library Automation, Gale Group, Northern Light Technology, Inc., O C L C Online Computer Library Center, Inc., ProQuest Information & Learning).
Indexed: ABIn, B&I, IPA, SRI, T&II.
—CCC.
Published by: Lebhar-Friedman, Inc., 425 Park Ave, New York, NY 10022. TEL 212-756-5000, FAX 212-756-5395, info@lf.com, http://www.drugstorenews.com, http://www.lf.com. Ed. Tony Lisanti TEL 212-756-5105. Pub. John Kenlon TEL 212-756-5238. adv.: B&W page USD 13,440, color page USD 17,120; bleed 11 x 14.25. Circ: 45,000.

658.8   USA
E-BIZ. Text in English. d. back issues avail. **Document type:** *Newsletter, Trade.* **Description:** Reports on news and trends regarding electronic commerce and interactive marketing.
Media: Online - full text.
Published by: Digitrends, 225 S Sepulveda Blvd, Ste 360, Manhattan Beach, CA 90266. TEL 310-374-1898, 888-881-5861, FAX 310-374-4233, khaney@digitrends.net, shays@digitrends.net, http://www.digitrends.net/ebiz/index.html. Ed. Scott Hays. Adv. contact Mike Pubentz TEL 949-349-9454 ext 22.

658.7   GBR
E C TENDERS. (European Communities) Text in English. w. GBP 120 (effective 1999). **Document type:** *Trade.* **Description:** Official source for information on public procurement opportunities from the European Union, the European economic area and beyond.
Media: CD-ROM.
Published by: Business Information Publications Ltd., Park House, 300 Glasgow Rd, Shawfield, Glasgow, G73 1SQ, United Kingdom. TEL 44-141-3328247, FAX 44-141-3312652, bip@bipcontracts.com, bip@bipsolutions.com, http://www.bipcontracts.com.

E-COM. see *COMPUTERS—Internet*

E-COMMERCE MAGAZIN; Geschaeftserfolg im Internet. see *BUSINESS AND ECONOMICS—Computer Applications*

658   USA   ISSN 1098-9854
E-COMMERCE PRACTITIONER. Text in English. 1998. m. **Document type:** *Journal, Trade.*
Related titles: Online - full text ed.: (from O C L C Online Computer Library Center, Inc.).
Published by: Auerbach Publications (Subsidiary of: C R C Press, LLC), 2000 Corporate Blvd., NW, Boca Raton, FL 33431. TEL 212-286-1010, FAX 212-297-9176, orders@crcpress.com, http://www.auerbach-publications.com/home.asp.

658 025.04   USA
E-COMMERCE TIMES. Text in English. 1999. d. Free. **Description:** Provides independent, up-to-date information about electronic commerce, with everything from success stories and daily news, to feature articles, product guides, newsmaker profiles, and an e-commerce events calendar and message board.
Media: Online - full content.
Address: 15821 Ventura Blvd Ste 635, Encino, CA 91436. TEL 818-461-9700, editorial@ecommercetimes.com, http://www.ecommercetimes.com/.

658   BEL
E M O T A - A E V P C POSITION PAPERS. Text mainly in English; Text occasionally in French. 1995. irreg. free. back issues avail. **Document type:** *Bulletin, Trade.* **Description:** Comments on issues of importance to professionals in Europe's mail order business industry.
Media: Online - full content.

Published by: European Mail Order and Distance Selling Trade Association/Association Europeenne de Vente par Correspondance et a Distance, BDC, Heizel Esplanade, Box 47, Brussels, 1020, Belgium. TEL 32-2-477-1799, FAX 32-2-478-9165, info@emota-aevpc.org, http://www.emota-aevpc.org/mailorder/opn.htm.

658.8 608   USA   ISSN 1539-7386
HF5826.5
E P M ENTERTAINMENT MARKETING SOURCEBOOK. Text in English. 1992. a. USD 295 (effective 2001). **Document type:** *Directory, Trade.* **Description:** Provides information on entertainment firms, sponsors, and service providers to the promotion and marketing industries.
Related titles: CD-ROM ed.
Published by: E P M Communications, 160 Mercer St, 3rd Fl, New York, NY 10012-3212. TEL 212-941-0099, FAX 212-941-1622, info@epmcom.com, http://www.epmcom.com. Ed. Michael Bush. Pub., R&P Barbara Perrin.

658.8 620   GBR   ISSN 0144-476X
E R A TECHNOLOGY NEWS. (Electrical Research Association) Text in English. 1979. s-a. free. **Document type:** *Newspaper.* **Description:** Covers component and system design and devleopment, company assessment and technological consultancy.
Indexed: Inspec.
Published by: E R A Technology Ltd., Cleeve Rd, Leatherhead, Surrey KT22 7SA, United Kingdom. TEL 44-1372-367007, FAX 44-1372-367009, info@era.co.uk. Circ: 900 (controlled).

E R M; the monthly magazine for electrical retailers. (Electrical Retailing Magazine) see *ENGINEERING—Electrical Engineering*

658   NLD   ISSN 0928-1525
E R M. (Elektro Retail Magazine) Text in Dutch. 1928. m. (11/yr.). EUR 83.50 (effective 2005). bk.rev. bibl.; charts; illus.; mkt.; pat.; stat.; tr.lit. index. **Document type:** *Trade.*
Former titles (until 1992): E R M Journaal (0921-5131); (until 1988): E R M (0165-5205); Elektrotechnisch Vakblad E R M; (until 1976): Electro Radio Mercuur (0013-4619); (until 1945): Electro Radio Techniek (0926-6100)
Indexed: KES.
—IE.
Published by: Pressure Media Uitgevers, Postbus 47, Dronten, 8250 AA, Netherlands. TEL 31-321-339465, FAX 31-321-339754, erm@pressuremedia.nl, info@pressuremedia.nl, http://www.ermonline.nl, http://www.pressuremedia.nl. Circ: 4,500.

E R T DIRECTORY (YEAR). (Electrical & Radio Trading) see *ELECTRONICS*

E R T WEEKLY; the only weekly serving the electrical retailing industry. (Electrical and Radio Trading) see *COMMUNICATIONS—Radio*

E S I C PRESS. see *BUSINESS AND ECONOMICS—Management*

658.8   NLD
HF5415.2
E S O M A R DIRECTORY (YEAR). Text in English. 1965. a. (in 3 vols.). **Document type:** *Directory, Trade.*
Former titles: E S O M A R Handbook; E S O M A R Directory (0923-8212); (until 1988): Handbook of Marketing Research (0071-3074)
Related titles: CD-ROM ed.: EUR 350 (effective 2003).
Published by: E S O M A R - The World Association of Research Professionals, Vondelstraat 172, Amsterdam, 1054 GV, Netherlands. TEL 31-20-664-2141, FAX 31-20-664-2922, email@esomar.org, http://www.esomar.org.

658.8   NLD
E S O M A R MARKETING RESEARCH CONGRESS. Text in English. a. **Document type:** *Proceedings, Trade.*
Formerly: E S O M A R Congress. Proceedings (0071-3082)
Related titles: CD-ROM ed.: EUR 215 to members; EUR 270 to non-members (effective 2003).
Indexed: MResA.
Published by: E S O M A R - The World Association of Research Professionals, Vondelstraat 172, Amsterdam, 1054 GV, Netherlands. TEL 31-20-664-2141, FAX 31-20-664-2922, email@esomar.org, http://www.esomar.org.

658.8   NLD
HF5415.2
➤ **E S O M A R - THE WORLD ASSOCIATION OF RESEARCH PROFESSIONALS**; marketing intelligence and decision making. (European Society for Opinion and Marketing Research) Text in English. m. membership. adv. bk.rev.; software rev. charts; stat. back issues avail. **Document type:** *Magazine, Academic/Scholarly.*
Former titles: European Society for Opinion and Marketing Research. Research World; European Society for Opinion and Marketing Research. Newsbrief; Which incorporated (19??-1999): Marketing and Research Today (0923-5957); Which was formerly (until 1989): European Research (0304-4297); (until 1973): European Marketing Research Review (0014-3014)
Related titles: Online - full text ed.

▼ *new title*   ➤ *refereed*   ✳ *unverified*   ◆ *full entry avail.*

Indexed: ABIn, ADPA, BPIA, CPM, Emerald, KES, M&MA, MResA, PAIS, PROMT, RASB, SCIMP.
—IE. **CCC.**
Address: Vondelstraat 172, Amsterdam, 1054 GV, Netherlands. TEL 31-20-664-2141, FAX 31-20-664-2922, email@esomar.org, http://www.esomar.org. Ed. Kathy Joe. Adv. contact Debby Koot. Circ: 4,000.

658.8 380.1 USA
THE E-TACTICS LETTER. Text in English. 1991. m. USD 149 (effective 2002). 4 p./no. 3 cols./p.; back issues avail. **Document type:** *Newsletter, Trade.* **Description:** Covers how businesses use new technologies to market and distribute data.
Formerly (until 2002): Sarah Stambler's Marketing with Technology News (1070-809X)
Media: E-mail. **Related titles:** Fax ed.: USD 249 (effective 2002); Online - full text ed.: (from Factiva, Gale Group).
Published by: E-Tactics, Inc., 370 Central Park W, Ste 210, New York, NY 10025. TEL 212-222-1713, FAX 212-678-6357, sarah@e-tactics.com, http://www.e-tactics.com. Ed., R&P Sarah Stambler. Circ: 2,500 (paid).

658.87 USA ISSN 1522-6891
E-TAILER'S DIGEST. Text in English. 1998. 3/w. free. back issues avail. **Description:** Includes articles and news pertaining to retail business.
Media: Online - full text.
Published by: Webbers Communications, PO Box 3214, North Conway, NH 03860. TEL 603-447-1024, etd@gapent.com, http://www.gapent.com/etailer/. Ed. George Matyjewicz.

658.8 AUT
E & W P.O.S.; das Insider-Magazin fuer Verkaufsprofis. (Elektro und Wirtschaft) Text in German. 2000. bi-m. adv. **Document type:** *Magazine, Trade.*
Published by: Elektro und Wirtschaft Verlagsgesellschaft mbH, Wilhelminenstrasse 91-IIC, Vienna, W 1160, Austria. TEL 43-1-48531490, FAX 43-1-486903230, redaktion@elektro.at, http://www.elektro.at. Adv. contact Sylvia Populorum. page EUR 2,600; trim 180 x 255. Circ: 8,000 (paid and controlled).

ECHO DES M.I.N.; mensuel de la filiere fruits et legumes. *see AGRICULTURE*

070.5 USA ISSN 0362-1200
EDITOR & PUBLISHER MARKET GUIDE. Text in English. 1924. a. USD 172.50 per issue (effective 2004). adv. reprint service avail. from PQC. **Document type:** *Directory, Trade.* **Description:** Marketing reference with both quantitative and qualitative data for all US counties and daily newspaper cities in the US and Canada.
Formerly (until 1924): Space Buyers' Guide Number
Related titles: CD-ROM ed.: USD 495; Microfiche ed.: (from CIS, PQC); Online - full text ed.
Indexed: SRI.
—**CCC.**
Published by: Editor & Publisher Co., Inc. (Subsidiary of: V N U Business Publications), 770 Broadway, New York, NY 10003-9595. TEL 646-654-5883, FAX 646-654-5518, edpub@editor&publisher.com, http://www.editorandpublisher.com. Circ: 2,645.

685 658 DEU ISSN 0930-8458
EINKAEUFER IM MARKT. Text in German. 1969. fortn. EUR 204 (effective 2003). index. **Document type:** *Newsletter, Trade.*
Related titles: E-mail ed.
—**CCC.**
Published by: Vereinigte Wirtschaftsdienste GmbH, Niederurseler Allee 8-10, Eschborn, 65760, Germany. TEL 49-6196-4050, FAX 49-6196-405303, feedback@vwd.de, http://www.vwd-einkaeufer.de, http://www.vwd.de.

658 CHE ISSN 1421-864X
EINKAUF - MATERIALWIRTSCHAFT - LOGISTIK. Text in German. 1960. 10/yr. CHF 71; CHF 85 foreign (effective 2000). adv. bk.rev. **Document type:** *Magazine, Trade.*
Formerly (until 1995): Einkaeufer - Materialwirtschaft - Logistik (1421-8577)
Address: Postfach 1222, Sarnen, 6060, Switzerland. TEL 41-41-6600766, FAX 41-41-6600717, consult.keller@bluewin.ch. Ed. Benno Keller. Adv. contact Sylvia Biener. Circ: 6,500.

658 RUS
EKSKLUZIVNYI MARKETING. Text in Russian. 1998. bi-m. **Document type:** *Magazine, Trade.*
Related titles: ◆ Supplement to: Prakticheskii Marketing.
Published by: B C I Marketing, ul Malaya Cherkizovskaya, dom 66, Moscow, 107392, Russian Federation. bcimarketing@mtu-net.ru, http://www.bci-marketing.aha.ru. Ed. Tatiana Chudina. Circ: 100.

658.8 RUS
EKSPRESS-INFORMATSIYA. MARKETING NEFTI I NEFTEPRODUKTOV. Text in Russian. m. USD 159 in United States.
Address: Ul Bolotnaya 12, Moscow, 113035, Russian Federation. TEL 7-095-2311204, FAX 7-095-2332434. **US dist. addr.:** East View Information Services, 3020 Harbor Ln. N., Minneapolis, MN 55447. TEL 612-550-0961.

658.8 621.3 USA ISSN 0149-5771
ELECTRICAL MARKETING. Text in English. 1975. s-m. USD 525 to individuals; USD 325 to members (effective 2005); Members of either "National Electrical Manufacturers Representatives Association" (NEMRA) or "National Association of Electrical Distributors" (NAED). charts; pat. back issues avail. **Document type:** *Newsletter, Trade.* **Description:** Electrical industry news and information.
Related titles: Online - full content ed.: USD 1,000 group subscr. (effective 2005) (from PQC).
—**CCC.**
Published by: Primedia Business Magazines & Media, Inc. (Subsidiary of: Primedia, Inc.), 9800 Metcalf Ave, Overland Park, KS 66212-2216. TEL 913-341-1300, FAX 913-967-1898, inquiries@primediabusiness.com, http://www.electricalmarketing.com/, http://www.primediabusiness.com. Ed. Dale Funk. **Subscr. to:** PO Box 12993, Overland Park, KS 66282-2993. TEL 800-441-0294, FAX 913-967-1331.

ELECTRICAL PRODUCT NEWS. *see ENGINEERING—Electrical Engineering*

658 USA
ELECTRICAL SALES BUILDERS. Text in English. 1987. q. USD 29.50 (effective 1999). **Document type:** *Newsletter.*
Published by: Business Marketing & Publishing Inc., PO Box 7457, Wilton, CT 06897. TEL 203-834-9959. Ed. George B Young. adv.: B&W page USD 965.

658 683.83 USA ISSN 0013-4430
TK1
ELECTRICAL WHOLESALING. Text in English. 1920. m. USD 20 domestic; USD 22 in Canada; USD 40 elsewhere; free to qualified personnel (effective 2005). adv. illus.; tr.lit. reprint service avail. from PQC. **Document type:** *Magazine, Trade.* **Description:** Independent voice of the industry for owners, managers and sales people in electrical distributorships.
Related titles: Microform ed.: (from PQC); Online - full text ed.: (from bigchalk, EBSCO Publishing, Florida Center for Library Automation, Gale Group, H.W. Wilson, O C L C Online Computer Library Center, Inc., ProQuest Information & Learning).
Indexed: ABIn, BPI, SRI.
—**CCC.**
Published by: Primedia Business Magazines & Media, Inc. (Subsidiary of: Primedia, Inc.), 9800 Metcalf Ave, Overland Park, KS 66212-2216. TEL 913-341-1300, FAX 913-967-7276, bmacarthur@primediabusiness.com, inquiries@primediabusiness.com, http://industryclick.com/magazine.asp?siteid=13&magazineid=32, http://www.primediabusiness.com. Ed. Jim Lucy TEL 913-967-1743. Pub. Robert MacArthur TEL 312-840-8422. adv.: B&W page USD 4,975, color page USD 7,005. Circ: 24,234 (paid and controlled). **Subscr. to:** PO Box 12993, Overland Park, KS 66282-2993. TEL 800-441-0294, FAX 913-967-1331.

ELECTRONIC COMMERCE ADVISOR. *see BUSINESS AND ECONOMICS—Banking And Finance—Computer Applications*

380.10285 GBR ISSN 1019-6781
➤ **ELECTRONIC MARKETS/ELEKTRONISCHE MAERKTE.** Variant title: International Journal of Electronic Commerce and Business Media. Text in English, German. 1991. q. GBP 360, USD 592 combined subscription to institutions print & online eds. (effective 2006). reprint service avail. from PSC. **Document type:** *Journal, Academic/Scholarly.* **Description:** Forum for advancing the understanding and practice of electronic markets and commerce.
Related titles: Online - full text ed.: ISSN 1422-8890. GBP 342, USD 562 to institutions (effective 2006) (from EBSCO Publishing, Gale Group, IngentaConnect, O C L C Online Computer Library Center, Inc., Swets Information Services).
Indexed: ABIn, CompLI, IBSS, Inspec.
—BLDSC (3702.595250), IE, Infotrieve, ingenta. **CCC.**
Published by: (University of St. Gallen, Media Communications Management Institute CHE), Routledge (Subsidiary of: Taylor & Francis Group), 4 Park Square, Milton Park, Abingdon, Oxon OX14 4RN, United Kingdom. TEL 44-1235-828600, FAX 44-1235-829000, http://www.tandf.co.uk/journals/routledge/10196781.asp, http://www.routledge.com. Ed. Beat Schmid. Circ: 4,000. **Subscr. to:** Taylor & Francis Ltd, Journals Customer Service, Rankine Rd, Basingstoke, Hants RG24 8PR, United Kingdom. TEL 44-1256-813000, FAX 44-1256-330245, enquiry@tandf.co.uk.

651.8 USA
ELECTRONIC RETAILING. Text in English. 1994. m. USD 44.95; USD 5 newsstand/cover. **Document type:** *Magazine, Trade.* **Description:** Focuses on the new sales opportunities afforded by emerging electronic media such as commercial online services, the Internet, WWW, interactive kiosks, CD-ROM and more.
Related titles: Online - full text ed.
Published by: G P G Publishing, Inc. (Subsidiary of: R.J. Gordon & Co.), 9200 Sunset Blvd, Ste 710, Los Angeles, CA 90069. TEL 818-782-7328, FAX 818-782-7450, webmaster@elrond.worldshop.com, http://www.eretail.com. Ed. Kathy St Louis. Pub. Deborah Carver. adv.: B&W page USD 2,450. Circ: 21,500.

658 DEU ISSN 1615-0260
MARKET; Webmagazin fuer Online-Marketing und E-Commerce. Text in German. 1997. fortn. EUR 98 (effective 2005). adv. software rev. charts; stat. back issues avail. **Document type:** *Magazine, Trade.*
Former titles (until 2000): W & V New Media Report (1438-0455); (until 1997): New Media Report (1433-6553)
Published by: Europa Fachpresse Verlag GmbH (Subsidiary of: Sueddeutsche Verlag), Emily-Noether-Str 2-E, Munich, 80992, Germany. TEL 49-89-5485200, FAX 49-89-54852108, webmaster@efv.de, http://www.emar.de. R&P Markus Baeuchle TEL 49-89-54852165. Adv. contact Sabine Vockrodt. Circ: 2,600 (paid); 2,400 (controlled).

EMBROIDERY / MONOGRAM BUSINESS. *see NEEDLEWORK*

658.8 POL
EMERGING EUROPE RETAIL UPDATE. Text in English. bi-w. EUR 700 foreign (effective 2005). **Document type:** *Newsletter, Trade.* **Description:** Contains overview of the news from the retail industry in the Czech Republic, Hungary, Poland, Russia and Slovakia, supplied and verified by market analysts from the respective countries.
Media: E-mail.
Published by: Polish Market Review Ltd., ul Supniewskiego 9, Krakow, 31527, Poland. TEL 48-12-4280360, FAX 48-12-4134012, pmr@pmrpublications.com, http://www.pmrpublications.com.

658 CAN
EMERGING MARKETS ANALYST. Text in English. m. USD 895. **Description:** Provides a forecast and analysis of emerging capital markets.
Formed by the merger of: Emerging Markets Analyst. Annual Backgrounders; Emerging Markets Analyst. Country Quarterlies; Emerging Markets Analyst. Monthly Bulletin
Address: 1002 Sherbrooke St W, 16th Fl, Montreal, PQ H3A 3L6, Canada. TEL 514-499-9706, FAX 514-499-9709. **Subscr. to:** PO Box 238, Chazy, NY 12921.

658 GBR
EMERGING MARKETS HANDBOOK. Text in English. s-a. GBP 160; GBP 175 foreign. **Document type:** *Trade.* **Description:** Covers over 800 leading companies in emerging markets.
Published by: Financial Times Information Ltd., Extel, Fitzroy House, 13-17 Epworth St, London, EC2A 4DL, United Kingdom. TEL 44-20-7825-8000, FAX 44-20-7608-2032, eic@ft.com, http://www.info.ft.com.

THE EMERGING MARKETS MONITOR; the weekly brief for global investors. *see BUSINESS AND ECONOMICS—Investments*

608 658.8 USA ISSN 1048-5112
ENTERTAINMENT MARKETING LETTER. Text in English. 1988. 24/yr. USD 449 domestic; USD 509 foreign (effective 2005). s-a. index. back issues avail. **Document type:** *Newsletter, Trade.* **Description:** Covers promotion, marketing, contests sponsorship, in-theater advertising, and product placement, for entertainment companies and sponsors.
Related titles: Online - full text ed.: (from Factiva, Gale Group, Northern Light Technology, Inc., O C L C Online Computer Library Center, Inc.).
Indexed: B&I.
Published by: E P M Communications, 160 Mercer St, 3rd Fl, New York, NY 10012-3212. TEL 212-941-0099, FAX 212-941-1622, info@epmcom.com, http://www.epmcom.com/html/entertainment/eml/. Ed. Michael Bush. Pub., R&P Barbara Perrin.

ENVIRONMENT BUSINESS MAGAZINE. *see ENVIRONMENTAL STUDIES*

ENVIRONMENT NEWS. *see ENVIRONMENTAL STUDIES*

EQUINE OZ. *see ADVERTISING AND PUBLIC RELATIONS*

658 DEU ISSN 1435-7720
DER ERFOLGREICHE VERKAUFSPROFI. Text in German. 1998. irreg. looseleaf. **Document type:** *Trade.*
Published by: W R S Verlag GmbH & Co. KG (Subsidiary of: Rudolf Haufe Verlag GmbH & Co. KG), Fraunhoferstr 5, Planegg, 82152, Germany. info@wrs.de, http://www.wrs.de.

658 DNK ISSN 0014-0155
ERHVERVS-BLADET. Text in Danish. 1964. d. DKK 900 (effective 2004). adv. **Document type:** *Newspaper, Trade.*
Incorporates (1931-1982): Frit Erhverv (0108-8769); Which was formerly (until 1972): Dansk Grossist-Tidende (0011-6300)
Related titles: Online - full text ed.
Published by: Erhvervs-Bladet A-S, Vesterbrogade 12, Copenhagen V, 1780, Denmark. TEL 45-33-267200, FAX 45-33-267282, red@erhvervsbladet.dk, http://www.erhvervsbladet.dk/. Eds. Klaus Dalgas, Carsten Steno. Adv. contact Peter Lenthe TEL 45-33-267242. Circ: 106,000.

658.8 ESP ISSN 0213-4950
ESMA INFORM. Variant title: Escuela Superior de Marketing y Administracion Inform. Text in Spanish. 1960. q. **Document type:** *Bulletin.*
Former titles (until 1985): Boletin de Marketing y Administracion de Empresas (0210-3508); (until 1976): Promoventas (0212-6362); (until 1970): Ventas (0505-2084)

Published by: Escuela Superior de Marketing y Administracion Inform, Consejo de Ciento 42, Barcelona, 08014, Spain. TEL 3-426-99-88, FAX 3-426-76-21, esma@nexus.es, http://www.esma.edu.es. Ed. Cesar Duch.

ESSEX COUNTY COUNCIL. PLANNING. SUBJECT MONITORING REPORTS. RETAILING. see *PUBLIC ADMINISTRATION—Municipal Government*

658.8 ESP ISSN 0212-9469
ESTUDIOS SOBRE CONSUMO. Text in Spanish. 1984. 3/yr. EUR 30.05 (effective 2005).
—CINDOC.
Published by: Instituto Nacional del Consumo, Principe de Vergara, 54, Madrid, 28006, Spain. TEL 34-91-4311836, FAX 34-91-4311892, inc@consumo-inc.es, http://www.consumo-inc.es/publicac/interior/periodic/frame/centro.htm. Ed. Ismael Diaz Yubero.

658 FRA ISSN 0984-774X
ETAT DE L'OPINION. Text in French. 1984. a. **Document type:** *Magazine, Consumer.*
Formerly (until 1987): Opinion Publique (0980-2991)
Published by: (S O F R E S), Editions du Seuil, 27 Rue Jacob, Paris, 75006, France. TEL 33-1-40465050, FAX 33-1-40464300, contact@seuil.com, http://www.seuil.com. Eds. Jerome Jaffre, Olivier Duhamel.

ETAT-KALKULATOR. see *ADVERTISING AND PUBLIC RELATIONS*

ETHNIC MEDIA & MARKETS. see *ADVERTISING AND PUBLIC RELATIONS*

658 DEU ISSN 1614-6530
EURO. Text in German. 1960. m. EUR 42.60; EUR 4 newsstand/cover (effective 2003). adv. back issues avail. **Document type:** *Magazine, Trade.* **Description:** Offers advice on how to manage financial affairs and supplies decision makers and investors with key information on stock market trends and corporate strategy.
Former titles (until 2004): D M Euro (1614-6506); (until 2001): D M (0416-5551)
—IE, Infotrieve. **CCC.**
Published by: Verlagsgruppe Handelsblatt GmbH, Kasernenstr 67, Duesseldorf, 40213, Germany. TEL 49-211-887-0, FAX 49-211-328721, dm@vhb.de, leser-service@vhb.de, http://www.dmeuro.com, http://www.vhb.de. adv.: B&W page EUR 12,561, color page EUR 16,958; trim 8.25 x 11.0625. Circ: 202,681 (paid). **Subscr. to:** Postfach 3752, Nuernberg 90018, Germany.

658 BEL
EURO UPDATE. Text in English. bi-m. charts; illus.; stat. back issues avail. **Document type:** *Newsletter, Trade.* **Description:** Discusses issues of interest to professionals involved in European mail-order sales and marketing.
Media: Online - full content.
Published by: European Mail Order and Distance Selling Trade Association/Association Europeenne de Vente par Correspondance et a Distance, BDC, Heizel Esplanade, Box 47, Brussels, 1020, Belgium. TEL 32-2-477-1799, FAX 32-2-478-9165, info@emota-aevpc.org, http://www.emota-aevpc.org/members/nletters/euro_update.htm.

EUROMARKETING VIA EMAIL. see *ADVERTISING AND PUBLIC RELATIONS*

THE EUROPEAN CLOTHING RETAIL HANDBOOK. see *CLOTHING TRADE*

658.5 GBR
THE EUROPEAN D I Y RETAILING HANDBOOK. (Do-it-Yourself) Text in English. a. GBP 95, USD 195. **Document type:** *Trade.* **Description:** Meets the needs of those requiring accessible market information as well as a general overview of the DIY and related trades across Europe.
Published by: Corporate Intelligence on Retailing, 48 Bedford Sq, London, WC1 B3DP, United Kingdom. TEL 44-20-7696-9006, FAX 44-20-76969006, sales@cior.com, http://www.cior.com. **Subscr. in US to:** Lebhar-Friedman, Inc., 425 Park Ave, New York, NY 10022. TEL 212-756-5159, FAX 212-756-5038.

658.5 GBR
THE EUROPEAN FORECOURT RETAILING HANDBOOK. Text in English. a. **Description:** Provides reviews of the forecourt sector accross Europe.
Published by: Corporate Intelligence on Retailing, 48 Bedford Sq, London, WC1 B3DP, United Kingdom. TEL 44-20-7696-9006, FAX 44-20-7696-9004, sales@cior.com, http://www.cior.com. **Subscr. in US to:** Lebhar-Friedman, Inc., 425 Park Ave, New York, NY 10022. TEL 212-756-5159, FAX 212-756-5038.

658.8 GBR ISSN 0309-0566
HF5410
➤ **EUROPEAN JOURNAL OF MARKETING.** Abstracts in English, French, German. 1967. m. EUR 10,417.16 in Europe; USD 10,569 in North America; AUD 12,929 in Australasia; GBP 7,176.41 in UK & elsewhere (effective 2006). bk.rev. abstr.; bibl.; charts; stat. index. reprint service avail. from PSC. **Document type:** *Journal, Academic/Scholarly.* **Description:** Presents the practical applications of new ideas and developments in marketing research. Covers marketing planning, customer policy and service, marketing of services, history of advertising, and product development.
Incorporates: Journal of Advertising History (0143-0793); Formerly: British Journal of Marketing (0007-1099)
Related titles: Online - full text ed.: (from EBSCO Publishing, Emerald Group Publishing Limited, Florida Center for Library Automation, Gale Group, IngentaConnect, O C L C Online Computer Library Center, Inc., ProQuest Information & Learning, Swets Information Services).
Indexed: ABIn, ADPA, ASEANManA, BPIA, BusI, CPM, CurCont, EmerIntel, Emerald, M&MA, MResA, ManagCont, PsycInfo, PsycholAb, SCIMP, SSCI, T&II, WBA, WMB.
—BLDSC (3829.731000), CISTI, IE, Infotrieve, ingenta. **CCC.**
Published by: Emerald Group Publishing Limited, 60-62 Toller Ln, Bradford, W Yorks BD8 9BY, United Kingdom. TEL 44-1274-777700, FAX 44-1274-785200, help@emeraldinsight.com, infomation@emeraldinsight.com, http://www.emeraldinsight.com/ejm.htm. Eds. Dr. Audrey Gilmore, David Carson. **Subscr. in N America:** Emerald Group Publishing Ltd., 44 Brattle St, 4th Fl, Cambridge, MA 02138. TEL 617-497-2175, 888-622-0075, FAX 617-354-6875.

➤ **EUROPEAN LENSES & TECHNOLOGY.** see *MEDICAL SCIENCES—Ophthalmology And Optometry*

➤ **EUROPEAN MARKETING DATA AND STATISTICS (YEAR).** see *BUSINESS AND ECONOMICS—Abstracting, Bibliographies, Statistics*

➤ **EUROPEAN MARKETING FORECASTS.** see *BUSINESS AND ECONOMICS—Abstracting, Bibliographies, Statistics*

658 GBR ISSN 0966-7717
EUROPEAN MARKETING POCKET BOOK (YEAR). Text in English. a. GBP 32 per issue (effective 2000). **Document type:** *Trade.* **Description:** Source of international marketing, media and advertising data covering 37 countries.
—**CCC.**
Published by: N T C Publications Ltd. (Subsidiary of: World Advertising Research Center Ltd.), Farm Rd, Henley-on-Thames, Oxon RG9 1EJ, United Kingdom. TEL 44-1491-411000, FAX 44-1491-571188, ntc@ntc.co.uk.

658 USA ISSN 0960-0191
HF5429.6.E85
EUROPEAN RETAIL. Text in English. 1990. 24/yr. GBP 975 (effective 2005). **Document type:** *Trade.* **Description:** Contains news and analysis, features and surveys, country profiles and details, and implications of EC legislation.
Related titles: Microform ed.: (from PQC).
Indexed: ABIn.
—**CCC.**
Published by: Economist Intelligence Unit, 111 W 57th St, New York, NY 10019. TEL 212-554-0600, FAX 212-586-1181, newyork@eiu.com, http://www.eiu.com.

658.5 GBR
THE EUROPEAN RETAIL HANDBOOK. Text in English. a. GBP 95 (effective 2000). **Document type:** *Trade.* **Description:** Contains information about the retail trade across 27 European countries.
Published by: Corporate Intelligence on Retailing, 48 Bedford Sq, London, WC1 B3DP, United Kingdom. TEL 44-20-7696-9006, FAX 44-20-7696-9004, sales@cior.com, http://www.cior.com. **Subscr. in US to:** Lebhar-Friedman, Inc., 425 Park Ave, New York, NY 10022. TEL 212-756-5159, FAX 212-756-5038.

658.8 NLD
EUROPEAN SOCIETY FOR OPINION AND MARKETING RESEARCH. MONOGRAPH SERIES. Text in Dutch. 1995. irreg., latest vol.8, 1999. CHF 75 to members; CHF 90 to non-members. **Document type:** *Monographic series, Trade.*
Published by: E S O M A R - The World Association of Research Professionals, Vondelstraat 172, Amsterdam, 1054 GV, Netherlands. TEL 31-20-664-2141, FAX 31-20-664-2922, email@esomar.org, http://www.esomar.org.

EUROPE'S AUTOMOTIVE COMPONENTS BUSINESS. see *TRANSPORTATION—Automobiles*

658 306.4 GBR ISSN 0966-0259
EUROSLOT. Text in English. 1990. m. GBP 55 domestic; EUR 130 in Europe; USD 165 in the Americas & the Middle East; USD 195 in the Far East (effective 2004). adv. **Document type:** *Magazine, Trade.* **Description:** Focuses on the coin-op amusement and gaming industry and out-of-home electronic gaming market.
—**CCC.**
Published by: Datateam Publishing Ltd, 15a London Rd, Maidstone, Kent ME16 8LY, United Kingdom. TEL 44-1622-687031, FAX 44-1622-757646, euroslot@datateam.co.uk, info@datateam.co.uk, http://www.datateam.co.uk/business_publications/euro_slot.htm, http://www.datateam.co.uk/home/home.htm. adv.: B&W page GBP 1,750, B&W page EUR 2,888, B&W page USD 2,538, color page GBP 1,900, color page EUR 3,135, color page USD 2,755; trim 202 x 278.

EVALUATING YOUR FIRM'S INJURY & ILLNESS RECORD. WHOLESALE & RETAIL TRADE INDUSTRIES. see *OCCUPATIONAL HEALTH AND SAFETY*

658.8 SWE
EVENT & EXPOMARKETING; facktidningen foer maessor, events och utstaellingar. Text in Swedish. 1984. 6/yr. SEK 450 domestic; SEK 500 foreign (effective 2001). adv. **Document type:** *Magazine, Trade.* **Description:** Covers trade fairs, exhibitions, and other similar forms of marketing in Scandinavia.
Former titles: ExpoMarketing (1103-436X); (until 1992): Maessor och Kongresser (0282-793X)
Published by: Kellerman & Oeqvist AB, Fack 515, Nykoping, 61110, Sweden. TEL 46-155-219815, FAX 46-155-219859, red@expomarketing.se, http://www.expomarketing.se. Ed., Pub., R&P Roland Oeqvist. Adv. contact Anne Eriksson. B&W page SEK 14,000, color page SEK 18,000; trim 185 x 275. Circ: 7,000.

658.8 USA
EVENT MARKETER. Text in English. 2002. 7/yr. free to qualified personnel. **Document type:** *Magazine, Trade.* **Description:** Provides marketers with access to the trends, best practices, and resources they need to produce better, more strategic and powerful event marketing programs.
Published by: Red 7 Media, LLC, 33 South Main St, Norwalk, CT 06854. TEL 203-854-6730, FAX 203-854-6735, http://www.eventmarketer.com, http://www.m10report.com. Ed. Dan Hanover. Pub. Kerry Smith. Adv. contact Chip Berry.

658 011 GBR
EVENT ORGANISER. Text in English. 1991. bi-m. GBP 35; GBP 50 foreign. adv. tr.lit. back issues avail. **Document type:** *Trade.* **Description:** Publishes news and articles on the events industry for suppliers and organizers.
Published by: (Event Services Association), Trade Publications Ltd., Trade Publications Ltd, 8 Home Farm, Ardington, Wantage, Oxon OX12 8PN, United Kingdom. TEL 44-1235-821820, FAX 44-1235-862200. Ed. Simon Ambrose. adv.: B&W page GBP 975; 210 x 296. Circ: 7,000. **Dist. by:** Alpha Mail, Remmers House, 14 Victoria Way, Burgess Hill, W Sussex RH15 9NF, United Kingdom. TEL 44-1444-071555, FAX 44-1444-071355.

EVENT SOLUTIONS. see *MEETINGS AND CONGRESSES*

EXCERPTA MEDICA. SECTION 36: HEALTH POLICY, ECONOMICS AND MANAGEMENT. see *HEALTH FACILITIES AND ADMINISTRATION—Abstracting, Bibliographies, Statistics*

658 GBR
EXECUTIVE GRAPEVINE, VOLUME 9: GRAPEVINE INDEX OF SALES & MARKETING DIRECTORS. Text in English. 1996. a. GBP 90 (effective 1999). **Description:** For marketing professionals, and those who need to monitor movements, and identify individuals within sales & marketing in the UK.
Published by: Executive Grapevine International Ltd., New Barnes Mill, Cottonmill Ln, St Albans, Herts AL1 2HA, United Kingdom. TEL 44-1727-844335, FAX 44-1727-844779, executive.grapevine@dial.pipex.com, info@executive-grapevine.co.uk, http://www.d-net.com/executive.grapevine, http://www.executive-grapevine.co.uk.

EXECUTIVE OUTLOOK. see *FOOD AND FOOD INDUSTRIES—Grocery Trade*

658 USA ISSN 0887-6878
EXHIBIT BUILDER. Text in English. 1983. bi-m. (7/yr.). USD 40 (effective 2004). adv. bk.rev. **Document type:** *Trade.* **Description:** Devoted to design and construction techniques. Provides successful case histories, new products and covers the services and products marketplace.
Published by: Exhibit Builder, Inc., PO Box 4144, Woodland, CA 91365. TEL 818-225-0100, FAX 818-225-0138, http://www.exhibitbuilder.net. Ed. Judy Pomerantz. Pub., R&P, Adv. contact Jill Brookman. Circ: 15,000.

EXHIBIT BUILDER SOURCE BOOK DIRECTORY (YEAR). see *BUSINESS AND ECONOMICS—Trade And Industrial Directories*

658.8 USA
EXHIBIT MARKETING MAGAZINE. Text in English. 1989. q. adv. **Document type:** *Trade.* **Description:** Offers advice to business trade show exhibitors to help them sell and exhibit.
Published by: Eaton Hall Publishing, 256 Columbia Tpke, Florham Park, NJ 07932. TEL 201-514-5900, FAX 201-514-5977. Ed., Pub. Scott Goldman. R&P Karen Mellion. Adv. contact Gary Puro. Circ: 31,000.

B

658 338.642 USA ISSN 0739-6821
T391 CODEN: EXHIDV
EXHIBITOR MAGAZINE; the magazine for trade show and event marketing management. Text in English. 1981. m. USD 78 domestic; USD 108 in Canada; USD 125 in Mexico; USD 165 elsewhere; USD 9.50 newsstand/cover; USD 14 newsstand/cover in Canada (effective 2002). adv. back issues avail. **Document type:** Magazine, Trade. **Description:** Aims at people who plan, implement or oversee trade show exhibiting programs. Highlights the strategic, logistical, and tactical aspects of trade show marketing and exhibit program management.
Incorporates (in 1995): Buyers Guide: an Illustrated Guide to Trade Show Displays and Accessories
—CASDDS.
Published by: Exhibitor Publications, Inc., 206 S Broadway, Ste 745, Rochester, MN 55904-6565. TEL 507-289-6556, FAX 507-289-5253, http://www.exhibitornet.com. Ed. Lee Knight. Pub. Randy Acker. R&P Randy Ackler. Adv. contact John Pavek. B&W page USD 2,930, color page USD 3,300; trim 10.38 x 8.5. Circ: 15,000. **Subscr. to:** PO Box 368, Rochester, MN 55903-0368.

F E D M A - MEMBERSHIP NEWS. see ADVERTISING AND PUBLIC RELATIONS

F M A TODAY. see PETROLEUM AND GAS

658 ZAF
F M C G RETAILER. Text in English. 1978. m. ZAR 60. adv. illus. **Document type:** Trade.
Published by: Complete Publishing (Pty.) Ltd., PO Box 87745, Houghton, Johannesburg 2041, South Africa. TEL 27-11-7892112, FAX 27-11-789-5347. Circ: 7,000.

658 664 USA
F P P SERIES IN FOOD PRODUCTS MARKETING. (Food Products Press) Text in English. irreg. price varies. **Document type:** Monographic series. **Description:** Aims to develop a better understanding of food marketing by focusing attention on specific food industries and sectors and on specific food marketing activities.
Published by: Haworth Press, Inc., Food Products Press, 10 Alice St, Binghamton, NY 13904-1580. TEL 607-722-5857, FAX 607-722-1424, getinfo@haworthpress.com, http://www.haworthpress.com. Ed. John L Stanton.

658.7 GBR ISSN 0014-6579
FACTORY EQUIPMENT NEWS. Text in English. 1949. m. GBP 52; GBP 71 in Europe; USD 197 in US & Canada; GBP 102 elsewhere (effective 1999). **Document type:** Trade.
Published by: Wilmington Publishing Ltd. (Subsidiary of: Wilmington Group Plc), Maidstone Rd, Footscray, Sidcup, Kent DA14 5HZ, United Kingdom. TEL 44-1322-277788, FAX 44-1322-276474, wbp@wilmington.co.uk. Ed. Judith Ruthven. Circ: 50,058.

FAIRCHILD'S EXECUTIVE TECHNOLOGY. see BUSINESS AND ECONOMICS—Computer Applications

658 615 USA
FAMILY ALMANAC. Text in English. 1915. a. free at participating pharmacies (effective 2003). illus. **Document type:** Consumer.
Former titles: N A R D Almanac and Health Guide; N A R D Almanac
Published by: Creative Publishing, 1608 South Dakota Ave, Sioux Falls, SD 57105. TEL 605-336-9434, 800-423-7158, FAX 605-338-3501, kal1303567@aol.com. Ed. Ken Alvine. Circ: 125,000 (controlled).

FARMERS HOT LINE. see AGRICULTURE

FEDERAL ADVERTISING AND MARKETING LAW GUIDE. see LAW

658 910.09 CAN ISSN 0836-6926
FETES ET FESTIVALS. Text in English. 1982. q. CND 23.54 (effective 2000). adv. bibl.; illus.; stat. back issues avail.
Formerly: Tam Ti Delam (0705-3428)
Indexed: CMPI.
Published by: Societe des Fetes et Festivals du Quebec, 4545 Av Pierre de Coubertin, P O Box 1000, succ M, Montreal, PQ H1V 3R2, Canada. TEL 514-252-3037, FAX 514-254-1617. Ed. Pierre Paul Leduc. Circ: 5,500.

FIBEROPTICS MARKETING INTELLIGENCE (ONLINE EDITION). see PHYSICS—Optics

658.8 330 USA ISSN 1527-4470
FIELD FORCE AUTOMATION. Text in English. 1999. m. free domestic to qualified personnel; USD 15 in Canada; USD 15 in Mexico; USD 40 elsewhere (effective 2003). **Document type:** Magazine, Academic/Scholarly. **Description:** Targeted to today's executives and managers charged with assimilating mobile technology into the business processes of the enterprise.
Related titles: Online - full text ed.

Published by: Freedom Technology Media Group, 156 W 56th St, 3rd Fl, New York, NY 10019. TEL 212-333-7600, 800-537-4638, spencere@curtco.com, http://www.destinationffa.com, http://www.curtco.com. Ed. Teresa Von Fuchs. Adv. contact Ed Meskill TEL 212-314-7640. Circ: 50,000.

658 ITA ISSN 1121-3906
FIERE NEL MONDO. Text in Italian. 1981. a. adv.
Published by: Centro Italiano Pubblicita s.r.l., Via C. Pisacane 26, Milan, MI 20129, Italy. TEL 39-2-29419135, FAX 39-2-29419056. Ed. Bonisolli Lanfranco.

FINANCIAL MARKETING (LONDON). see BUSINESS AND ECONOMICS—Investments

658.8 CAN ISSN 1481-4900
HC111
FINANCIAL POST MARKETS CANADIAN DEMOGRAPHICS. Text in English. 1925. a. CND 145; CND 695 includes CD-ROM. adv. **Description:** Contains extensive demographic data for more than 700 Canadian markets. Includes information on population, language, households, income, education, retail sales, lifestyles and more.
Former titles (until 1999): Canadian Markets (0832-2503); (until 1985): Financial Post Canadian Markets (0227-6038); (until 1981): Financial Post Survey of Markets (0707-154X); (until 1978): Financial Post Survey of Markets and Business Year Book (0707-1558); (until 1976): Survey of Markets and Business Yearbook (0071-5077)
Related titles: CD-ROM ed.
—CISTI.
Published by: Financial Post Datagroup, 300-1450 Don Mills Rd, Don Mills, ON M3B 3R5, Canada. TEL 416-350-6516, FAX 416-350-6501, fpdg@fpdata.finpost.com. Ed. Jean Graham. Circ: 3,000.

658 GBR ISSN 1393-9580
FINANCIAL SERVICES DISTRIBUTION. Text in English. 1995. m. GBP 997, EUR 1,597, USD 1,697 (effective 2005). **Document type:** Trade. **Description:** Covers branches, ATMs, agents, advisers, telephone, internet, co-branding and affinity partners, supermarkets and post offices in the distribution of financial services.
Former titles (until 2000): Distribution Management Briefing (1393-7413); (until 1998): Direct Delivery International (1393-2551)
Related titles: Online - full text ed.: (from Gale Group, ProQuest Information & Learning).
Indexed: BLI.
Published by: Lafferty Publications Ltd., The Colonnades, 82 Bishops Bridge Rd, London, W2 6BB, United Kingdom. TEL 44-20-75635700, FAX 44-20-75635701, cuserv@lafferty.com, http://www.lafferty.com/newsletter_publication.php?id=3. Ed. Patrick Frazer.

658.8 GBR
FINANCIAL TIMES. MANAGEMENT REPORTS. Text in English. irreg. price varies. **Document type:** Monographic series, Trade. **Description:** Each volume researches a particular U.K. or international market.
Published by: Financial Times Business Information, Management Reports (Subsidiary of: Financial Times Group), 102-108 Clerkenwell Rd, London, EC1M 5SA, United Kingdom. TEL 44-171-814-9770, FAX 44-171-411-4415. **Orders to:** F T B I, 126 Jermyn St, London, Mddx SW1Y 4UJ, United Kingdom. TEL 44-1209-612493, FAX 44-1209-612811.

FIZZZ; fuer die Szenengastronomie. see BEVERAGES

658 388.5 USA
FLEET ASSOCIATION DIRECTORY. Text in English. 1991. a. USD 20 (effective 2000). adv. **Document type:** Directory, Trade. **Description:** Directory for car fleet associations.
Published by: Bobit Business Media, 3520 Challenger St, Torrance, CA 90503. TEL 310-533-2400, FAX 310-533-2500. adv.: B&W page USD 1,700; trim 10.88 x 8.

658 388.5 USA
FLEET FINANCIALS. Text in English. 1987. 3/yr. USD 28 domestic; USD 34 in Canada; USD 75 elsewhere; USD 10 per issue (effective 2005). charts; mkt. **Document type:** Magazine, Trade. **Description:** For top executives at companies having car fleets.
Published by: Bobit Business Media, 3520 Challenger St, Torrance, CA 90503. TEL 310-533-2400, FAX 310-533-2500, mikeantich@bobit.com, http://fleet-central.com. Ed. Mike Antich. Pub. Sherb Brown. Circ: 16,000 (controlled).

FLORAL MANAGEMENT; business news for the floral industry. see GARDENING AND HORTICULTURE—Florist Trade

FLORIDA COUNTY MIGRATION FLOWS 1981-1996. see BUSINESS AND ECONOMICS—Economic Situation And Conditions

658 USA
FOCUS (RESEARCH TRIANGLE PARK). Text in English. q. free to qualified personnel (effective 2003). adv. **Document type:** Magazine, Trade.
Published by: Motor & Equipment Manufacturers Association, 10 Laboratory Dr, PO Box 13966, Research Triangle Park, NC 27709-3966. TEL 919-549-4800, FAX 919-549-4824, info@mema.org, http://www.mema.org/public/publications/focus.php. adv.: B&W page USD 2,075; trim 8.5 x 10.

658.8 USA ISSN 0884-7185
FOOD BROKER QUARTERLY. Text in English. 1985. q. USD 40. adv. back issues avail. **Document type:** Trade. **Description:** For management executives of food broker, retail and foodservice sales organizations and packaged goods manufacturers.
Published by: National Food Brokers Association, 1010 Wisconsin Ave NW, # 9, Washington, DC 20007-3603. TEL 202-789-2844, FAX 202-842-0839. Ed., R&P Julie Legg. Circ: 2,800.

FOOD DISTRIBUTION RESEARCH SOCIETY. NEWSLETTER. see FOOD AND FOOD INDUSTRIES

FOOD MARKETING & TECHNOLOGY. see FOOD AND FOOD INDUSTRIES

FOOD, NONFOOD UND GETRAENKE. see FOOD AND FOOD INDUSTRIES

FOOD TRADE NEWS. see FOOD AND FOOD INDUSTRIES

FOOTWEAR TODAY. see SHOES AND BOOTS

FOREIGN TRADE FAIRS NEW PRODUCTS NEWSLETTER. see BUSINESS AND ECONOMICS—International Commerce

658.8029 GBR ISSN 1352-2485
FORMER SOVIET UNION MARKETING, MEDIA & ADVERTISING DIRECTORY. Text in English. 1993. a. **Document type:** Directory.
Published by: Hughes Publishing Ltd., 43 Lower Belgrave St, London, SW1W 0LS, United Kingdom.

658.8 USA
FORTUNE NOW NEWSLETTER. Text in English. 10/yr. USD 97 (effective 2005). **Document type:** Newsletter.
Address: PO Box 890084, Houston, TX 77289. TEL 281-280-9800, FAX 413-556-5465, bigalnews@fortunenow.com, http://www.fortunenow.com.

658.8 USA ISSN 1555-0753
▼ **FOUNDATIONS AND TRENDS IN MARKETING.** Text in English. forthcoming 2006. q.
Related titles: Online - full text ed.: ISSN 1555-0761. forthcoming 2006.
Published by: Now Publishers Inc., PO Box 1024, Hanover, MA 02339. TEL 781-871-0245, FAX 781-871-6172, http://www.nowpublishers.com. Pub., R&P Mike Casey.

FRAMES QUARTERLY. see MEDICAL SCIENCES—Ophthalmology And Optometry

658.8 GBR ISSN 1363-7274
FRANCHISE INTERNATIONAL. Text in English. 1985. 10/yr. GBP 25 domestic; GBP 50 in Europe; GBP 95 elsewhere (effective 1999); GBP 3.95 newsstand/cover. adv. bk.rev. index. back issues avail. **Document type:** Magazine, Trade. **Description:** Promotes ideas, hints, advice, and information on all aspects of promoting franchise business opportunities.
Related titles: Online - full text ed.
Published by: Franchise Development Services Ltd., Franchise House, Franchise Development Services Ltd, 56 Surrey St, Norwich, NR1 3FD, United Kingdom. TEL 44-1603-620301, FAX 44-1603-630174, fds@norwich.com, http://www.franchise-group.com. Ed. Dennis Chaplin. Pub. Roy Seaman. Adv. contact Paul Cairnie. color page GBP 3,000, color page USD 4,500; trim 210 x 297. Circ: 100,000. **Subscr. to:** Rouen House, Rouen House, Rouen Rd, Norwich NR1 1RB, United Kingdom. **Dist. by:** Comag, Tavistock Works, Tavistock Rd, W Drayton, Middx UB7 7QX, United Kingdom. FAX 44-1895-433801.

658.8 GBR
THE FRANCHISE MAGAZINE. Text in English. bi-m. GBP 25; GBP 2.50 newsstand/cover (effective 1999). **Document type:** Trade. **Description:** Provides assistance to those seeking business franchising opportunities compatible with their resources and abilities.
Published by: Franchise Development Services Ltd., Franchise House, Franchise Development Services Ltd, 56 Surrey St, Norwich, NR1 3FD, United Kingdom. TEL 44-1603-620301, FAX 44-1603-630174. **Dist. by:** Diamond Magazine Distribution, Rye Wharf, Harbour Rd, Rye, E Sussex TN31 7TE, United Kingdom. TEL 44-1797-225229, FAX 44-1797-225657.

658 USA
FRANCHISE NEWS. Text in English. 1985. m. USD 23 (effective 2003). adv. bk.rev. abstr.; bibl.; charts; illus.; maps; stat.; tr.mk. Index. reprints avail. **Document type:** *Newsletter, Trade.* **Description:** Contains business reports, tips, law updates, and other information in the field of franchising.
Media: Duplicated (not offset). **Related titles:** Duplicated (not offset) ed.
Published by: GlobalXchange Corp, 3820 Premier Ave, Memphis, TN 38118. TEL 901-368-3333, FAX 901-368-1144, franmark@msn.com. Ed. William Richey. R&P, Adv. contact Christina Pauline. Circ: 10,000.

FRANCHISE TIMES (ROSEVILLE). see *BUSINESS AND ECONOMICS—Production Of Goods And Services*

FRANCHISING ADVISER. see *LAW*

341 USA ISSN 1524-4814
FRANCHISING WORLD. Text in English. 1960. 8/yr., latest vol.33, 2001. USD 50 (effective 2005). adv. bibl.; stat. 90 p./no. 3 cols./p.; **Document type:** *Magazine, Trade.* **Description:** For franchisers and people interested in the industry; reports on news and trends in franchising.
Former titles: Franchising Opportunities; (until 1989): Franchising World (1041-7311); International Franchise Association. Quarterly Legal Bulletin; International Franchise Association. Legal Bulletin (0020-6792)
Related titles: Microform ed.: (from PQC); Online - full text ed.: (from bigchalk, EBSCO Publishing, Florida Center for Library Automation, Gale Group, H.W. Wilson, Northern Light Technology, Inc., O C L C Online Computer Library Center, Inc., ProQuest Information & Learning).
Indexed: ABIn, BPI.
—BLDSC (4032.782600), IE, ingenta.
Published by: International Franchise Association, 1350 New York Ave, N W, Ste 900, Washington, DC 20005. TEL 202-628-8000, FAX 202-628-0812, TELEX 323175, ifa@franchise.org, http://www.franchise.org. Ed., R&P Terry Hill TEL 202-628-8000. Pub. Don DeBolt. Adv. contact Guy Mitchell TEL 202-628-8000. Circ: 12,000.

FRASER'S CANADIAN TRADE DIRECTORY. see *BUSINESS AND ECONOMICS—Trade And Industrial Directories*

658 PRY ISSN 1607-2871
FREENEWS MARKETINERAS. Text in Spanish. 2000. w.
Media: Online - full text.
Published by: MDA Creative Marketing, G.R. de Francia, 910, Asuncion, Paraguay. TEL 595-21-583258, FAX 595-21-440239, http://www.marketineros.com/ultimaFN.htm. Ed. Migue Angel Alzaa.

FRESH PRODUCE WORKSHOP. see *FOOD AND FOOD INDUSTRIES*

FRESHLINE. see *FOOD AND FOOD INDUSTRIES*

658.8 639.2 CAN ISSN 0703-6639
FRESHWATER FISH MARKETING CORPORATION. ANNUAL REPORT. Text in English, French. 1970. a.
Related titles: Online - full content ed.: ISSN 1701-428X.
Published by: Freshwater Fish Marketing Corporation, 1199 Plessis Rd, Winnipeg, MB R2C 3L4, Canada. TEL 204-983-6600, FAX 204-983-6497, sales@freshwaterfish.com, http://www.freshwaterfish.com.

FRESNO DAILY LEGAL REPORT. see *CRIMINOLOGY AND LAW ENFORCEMENT*

658.5 659.1 USA ISSN 0046-5097
FRIDAY REPORT. Text in English. 1961. w. looseleaf. USD 165; USD 215 foreign (effective 1996). stat. back issues avail. **Document type:** *Newsletter.* **Description:** Covers the direct response advertising community; new campaigns, postal news, pertinent legislation, executive moves, new direct marketing lists, calendar of events.
—CCC.
Published by: Hoke Communications, 224 Seventh St, Garden City, NY 11530. TEL 516-746-6700, FAX 516-229-8141. Ed. Henry Hoke. Circ: 900.

658 ISL ISSN 1017-3544
FRJALS VERSLUN. Text in Icelandic. 1939. 10/yr. ISK 7,100 (effective 2002). adv. **Document type:** *Magazine, Trade.* **Description:** Focuses on trade, business and politics.
Published by: Heimur hf., Borgartuni 23, Reykjavik, 105, Iceland. TEL 354-512-7575, FAX 354-561-8646, http://www.heimur.is. adv.: B&W page ISK 46,900, color page ISK 94,900. Circ: 8,500.

658 GBR
FRONTIER BRANDS; trade magazine for buyers of tax and duty-free goods. Text in English. 1993. 3/yr. **Document type:** *Trade.*
Formerly: International Marketing (0969-2495)
Indexed: B&I.
Published by: Wilmington Publishing, 6-8 Underwood St, London, N1 7JQ, United Kingdom. TEL 44-20-7549-2548, FAX 44-20-7549-2550. Ed. Wendy Richmond. Pub. Colin Bailey Wood. Circ: 5,000 (controlled).

FUTURE OF TECHNOLOGY ADVERTISING & MARKETING REPORT (YEAR). see *ADVERTISING AND PUBLIC RELATIONS*

658.8 USA
THE FUTURE PROFIT NEWSLETTER. Text in English. m. free. **Document type:** *Newsletter.* **Description:** Includes marketing tips, and articles from entrepreneurs making their living online.
Media: Online - full text.
Published by: Future Profit Newsletter Webmaster@Future-Profit.com, FreeNewsletter@Future-Profit.com, http://www.Future-Profit.com. Ed. Jason Skinner.

658 GBR
GALLOWAY GAZETTE AND STRANRAER NEWS. Text in English. 1870. w. GBP 21.30. adv. film rev. back issues avail.
Published by: Galloway Gazette Ltd., 71 Victoria St, Newton Stewart, DG8 6NL, United Kingdom. Ed. Alex Shand. Circ: 9,580.

658 POL ISSN 1232-1893
GAZETA NA TARGI. Text in Polish. 1991. irreg.
Related titles: ♦ Supplement to: Gazeta Wyborcza. ISSN 0860-908X.
Published by: Agora S.A., ul Czerska 8/10, Warsaw, 00732, Poland. TEL 48-22-6994301, FAX 48-22-6994603, http://www.gazeta.pl.

658 POL ISSN 1425-8234
GAZETA STOLECZNA SUPERMARKET. Variant title: Gazeta Stoleczna. Czesc B, Supermarket. Text in Polish. 1994. d.
Related titles: ♦ Supplement to: Gazeta Wyborcza. ISSN 0860-908X.
Published by: Agora S.A., ul Czerska 8/10, Warsaw, 00732, Poland. TEL 48-22-6994301, FAX 48-22-6994603, http://www.gazeta.pl.

658 POL ISSN 0137-9550
GAZETA TARGOWA. Text in Polish. 1971. m. adv. **Document type:** *Newspaper, Consumer.*
Published by: Polish Institute of Fairs, Ul K Libelta 26, Poznan, 61707, Poland. TEL 48-61-524897, FAX 48-61-526108. Ed. Kazimierz Marcinkowski. Pub. Alojzy A Kuca. Adv. contact Krystyna Just. Circ: 20,000.

340 USA ISSN 1078-2060
KF915.Z9
GILBERT LAW SUMMARIES. SALES & LEASE OF GOODS. Text in English. irreg., latest vol.12, 1992. USD 19.95 (effective 2000). **Document type:** *Trade.* **Description:** Reviews the legal aspects of the sale or lease of all types of goods.
Supersedes (in 199?): Gilbert Law Summaries. Sales
Published by: Gilbert Law Summaries (Subsidiary of: B A R / B R I Group), 111 W Jackson, 7th Fl, Chicago, IL 60604. TEL 312-853-3662, 800-787-8717, FAX 312-853-3622, http://www.gilbertlaw.com. Ed. Douglas J Whaley.

GLOBAL. see *ADVERTISING AND PUBLIC RELATIONS*

GLOBAL MARKET SHARE PLANNER. see *BUSINESS AND ECONOMICS—Trade And Industrial Directories*

658.87 SWE ISSN 0046-6050
GOETEBORGS - KOEPMANNEN. Text in Swedish. 1941. m. SEK 10, USD 2.
Published by: Goeteborgs Koepmannafoerbund, Fack 53 200, Goeteborg, 400 15, Sweden. Ed. Sten Olof Palm. Circ: 3,000.

GOLF MARKETING & OPERATIONS. see *SPORTS AND GAMES—Ball Games*

658 CAN ISSN 0840-870X
JL186
GOVERNMENT BUSINESS OPPORTUNITIES. Text in English, French. 3/w. CND 525; CND 628.50 foreign. **Document type:** *Government.*
Formed by the 1989 merger of: Bulletin des Marches Publics (0713-133X); Bulletin of Business Opportunities (0713-1321)
Published by: Canada Communication Group, 45 Sacre-Coeur Blvd, Hull, PQ K1A 0S7, Canada. TEL 819-956-7864, FAX 819-956-5134. adv.: B&W page CND 600. Circ: 3,235.

GOVERNMENT PRODUCT NEWS. see *PUBLIC ADMINISTRATION*

658 CAN ISSN 0046-6220
GOVERNMENT PURCHASING GUIDE. Text in English. 1969. m. CND 35, USD 50. adv. back issues avail. **Document type:** *Directory, Government.* **Description:** For those who initiate, specify, review or purchase for all levels of government.
Published by: Moorshead Magazines Ltd., 505 Consumers Rd, Ste 500, Toronto, ON M2J 4V8, Canada. TEL 416-491-3699, FAX 416-491-3996. Ed. Tammie Hall. Adv. contact Peter Irvine. B&W page USD 3,555, color page USD 4,350. Circ: 17,233 (controlled).

GRAIN & FEED MARKETING. see *AGRICULTURE—Feed, Flour And Grain*

GRAPHIC FACTS (YEAR). see *ENGINEERING—Chemical Engineering*

GREEN WORLD. see *GARDENING AND HORTICULTURE*

658 USA ISSN 8756-534X
HF5415.2
GREENBOOK; international directory of marketing research companies and services. Text in English. 1963. a. USD 125. **Document type:** *Directory.* **Description:** Lists more than 2,200 marketing research companies and allied services from 90 countries.
Related titles: Online - full text ed.
Published by: American Marketing Association, New York Chapter, 60 E 42nd St, Ste 1765, New York, NY 10165-0006. TEL 212-687-3280, FAX 212-557-9242, http://www.greenbook.org. Circ: 6,000.

▼ **GREENSCAPE HOT LINE.** see *GARDENING AND HORTICULTURE*

GROENLAND. see *BUILDING AND CONSTRUCTION*

GUERRILLA - TACTICS. see *BUSINESS AND ECONOMICS—Management*

658 ESP
GUIA DEL MARKETING. Text in Spanish. 1970. a. adv. **Document type:** *Directory.* **Description:** Guide for marketing and advertising professionals where one can find information on Spanish research institutes, advertising agencies, marketing schools, tele-sales, consultants, data banks and marketing models.
Published by: Ediciones y Estudios S.A., Enrique Larreta, 5-1o, Madrid, 28036, Spain. TEL 91-315-98-45, FAX 91-315-56-28. Ed. Miguel de Haro. Circ: 8,000 (paid).

GUIA VENEZOLANA DE PUBLICIDAD Y MERCADEO. see *ADVERTISING AND PUBLIC RELATIONS*

GUIDA MARKETING. see *BUSINESS AND ECONOMICS—Trade And Industrial Directories*

GUIDE DU PAPIER ARTS GRAPHIQUES. see *PAPER AND PULP*

658.8029 GRC ISSN 1105-4964
GUIDE OF CONSUMER GOODS IN GREECE/ODEGOS PROIONTON EUREIAS KATANALOSEOS. Text in Greek. 1976. biennial. USD 200. adv. **Document type:** *Directory, Trade.* **Description:** Provides marketing data on the production, imports, consumption, and advertising of important consumer brands and lists the suppliers of these products.
Published by: Report - D. Michaelidis, 8 Polytechniou St, Athens, 104 33, Greece. TEL 30-1-5243-778, FAX 30-1-8222-040. Ed. Christine Shilioti. Pub. Vasso Michaelidis. R&P Demetre Michaelidis. Adv. contact Demetre Kontis. color page GRD 650,000; 230 x 300. Circ: 10,000 (paid).

GUIDELINES. see *COMMUNICATIONS—Telephone And Telegraph*

658.8 GBR ISSN 1350-4746
HF5415.12.P35
GULF MARKETING REVIEW. Text in English. 1993. q. adv. **Document type:** *Trade.* **Description:** For people interested in doing business in the Middle East.
Published by: Emap Business International Ltd. (Subsidiary of: Emap Business Communications Ltd.), c/o EMAP Communications, Scriptor Court, 155 Farringdon Rd, London, EC1R 3AD, United Kingdom. TEL 44-20-78416600, tracey.bigmore@emap.com, http://www.emap.com. Ed. Karen Thomas. Pub. Edmund O'Sullivan. Adv. contact Richard Mair.

H N MAGAZINE. see *GENERAL INTEREST PERIODICALS—Great Britain*

658 USA ISSN 0746-9985
H S M A I MARKETING REVIEW. Text in English. 1982. q. USD 65 (effective 2004). adv. **Document type:** *Journal, Trade.* **Description:** Contains articles by industry professionals about cutting edge issues facing practitioners of sales and marketing.
Formerly (until 198?): H S M A Marketing Review (0744-9011)
Indexed: H&TI.
Published by: Hospitality Sales and Marketing Association International, 8201 Greensboro Dr., Ste. 300, Mc Lean, VA 22102-3814. TEL 202-789-0089, FAX 202-789-1725, http://www.hsmai.org/Resources/review.cfm. Ed., R&P Ilsa Whittemore. Pub. Robert Gilbert. Adv. contact Marjorie Lane. B&W page USD 1,000, color page USD 1,800; trim 8.5 x 11. Circ: 10,000 (paid and controlled).

658 DEU
HAMBURGER SCHRIFTEN ZUR MARKETINGFORSCHUNG. Text in German. irreg., latest vol.33, 2005. price varies. **Document type:** *Monographic series, Academic/Scholarly.*
Published by: Rainer Hampp Verlag, Meringerzellerstr 10, Mering, 86415, Germany. TEL 49-8233-4783, FAX 49-8233-30755, Rainer_Hampp_Verlag@t-online.de, http://www.hampp-verlag.de.

B

HANDBOOK OF MAGAZINE PRODUCTION. see *PUBLISHING AND BOOK TRADE*

658 JPN
HANDBOOK OF MARKETING. Text in Japanese. a. **Document type:** *Trade.* **Description:** Provides detailed explanations of changes in the distribution industry during the year.
Published by: Nihon Keizai Shimbun Inc., 1-9-5 Ote-Machi, Chiyoda-ku, Tokyo, 100-0004, Japan. TEL 81-3-32700251, FAX 81-3-52552661.

658 CHE
HANDEL HEUTE; die Zeitschrift des schweizer Detailhandels. Text in German. 1978. 6/yr. CHF 38.50. adv. bk.rev. tr.lit. **Document type:** *Trade.* **Description:** Trends and news of the international retail business.
Published by: Handel Heute Verlags AG, Industriestr 5, Boesingen, 3178, Switzerland. TEL 41-31-7409730, FAX 41-31-7409739, handel-heute@21st-century.net. Eds. Martin Schnoeller, Urs Bretscher. Pub. Urs Bodmer. Adv. contact Walter Egli. page CHF 5,980; trim 275 x 210. Circ: 34,500.

658 POL ISSN 1425-8242
HANDLOWA. Text in Polish. 1991. w. **Document type:** *Newspaper, Consumer.*
Related titles: ♦ Supplement to: Gazeta Wyborcza. ISSN 0860-908X.
Published by: Agora S.A., ul Czerska 8/10, Warsaw, 00732, Poland. TEL 48-22-6994301, FAX 48-22-6994603, http://www.gazeta.pl.

HARDWARE MERCHANDISING; the information source for home improvement retailers. see *BUILDING AND CONSTRUCTION—Hardware*

HARDWARE RETAILER. see *BUILDING AND CONSTRUCTION—Hardware*

362 USA ISSN 1556-9349
HEALTHCARE MARKET STRATEGIST. Text in English; Summaries in English. 2000. m. USD 287 combined subscription plrnt, online & email eds. (effective 2006). bk.rev.; Website rev. abstr.; bibl.; charts; illus.; stat. Index. back issues avail.; reprints avail. **Document type:** *Newsletter, Trade.* **Description:** To help healthcare CEOs, strategic planners, business development staff, and marketers better understand their markets, define their organization's mission, develop their market strategies, and implement their strategies through the use of tools such as marketing and advertising.
Formerly: C O R Healthcare Market Strategist (1529-1863); Which was formed by the 2000 merger of: Healthcare Market Strategist; Healthcare Marketing Abstracts (0891-5016)
Related titles: E-mail ed.; Online - full text ed.
—BLDSC (3470.255500). **CCC.**
Published by: C O R Health, Llc. (Subsidiary of: H C Pro, Inc.), PO Box 40959, Santa Barbara, CA 93140. TEL 805-564-2177, FAX 805-564-2146, info@corhealth.com, http://www.corhealth.com. Ed. Bridget Meaney. Pub. Dean H Anderson TEL 805-564-2177.

HEALTHCARE MARKETER'S EXECUTIVE BRIEFING. see *MEDICAL SCIENCES*

HEARTH & HOME; hearth, barbecue and patio. see *INTERIOR DESIGN AND DECORATION—Furniture And House Furnishings*

658 USA ISSN 1083-1428
HELLER REPORT: INTERNET STRATEGIES FOR EDUCATION MARKETS. Text in English. m. USD 397 domestic; USD 537 foreign (effective 2001). adv. **Document type:** *Newspaper.* **Description:** News and analysis of business opportunities in online content, hardware, software and services.
Related titles: Online - full text ed.: (from Florida Center for Library Automation, Gale Group).
Indexed: CompD.
Published by: Nelson B. Heller & Associates, 1625 Broadway., Ste. 250, Denver, CO 80202-4765. TEL 847-441-2920, FAX 847-926-0202, mary@HellerReports.com, http://www.HellerReports.com. Ed. Mark Axelson. Pub., R&P Nelson B Heller TEL 847-674-6282. Adv. contact Robert James. Circ: 1,000.

HERSTELLER UND LIEFERANTEN KATALOG. see *ENGINEERING—Industrial Engineering*

658.8 USA
HI-TECH BUYERS GUIDE. Text in English. 1946. a. USD 39.95. adv. **Document type:** *Directory.*
Former titles: E I A Guide (0070-7821); Western Industrial Purchasing Guide and Electronic - Sources
Published by: Directories of Industry, Inc., 431 1/2 Begonia Ave., Corona Dl Mar, CA 92625-2841. TEL 714-792-1090, FAX 714-792-1095. Circ: 32,000.

658 USA
HIGH TECH SELLING. Text in English. 1982. s-m. USD 208 (effective 1999). index. **Document type:** *Newsletter.* **Description:** Offers skill and career-building ideas for sales professionals, particularly in the industrial, wholesale, pharmaceutical, high-tech and financial services fields.
Formerly: Professional Selling (1077-436X)
Published by: Bureau of Business Practice (Subsidiary of: Aspen Publishers, Inc.), 1185 Avenue of the Americas, 37th Fl, New York, NY 10036. TEL 860-442-4365, 800-243-0876, FAX 860-437-3555, rebecca_armitage@prenhall.com, http://www.bbpnews.com. Ed. Deborah Cottrill. Pub. Peter Garabedian. R&P Kathryn Mennone.

HILDEBRANDT REPORT; a management and marketing newsletter for law firms. see *LAW*

658 659 USA
HISPANIC MARKET WEEKLY. Text in English. 1993. w. adv.
Related titles: Online - full text ed.
Published by: Solmark, Inc., 2625 Ponce de Leon Blvd, Ste 285, Coral Gables, FL 33134. TEL 305-448-5838, FAX 305-448-6573, http://www.hmweekly.com, http://www.hmwonline.com/. Ed., Pub. Arturo Villar. Adv. contact Leila Winick TEL 310-200-6513.

658.80711 GBR
HOBSONS MARKETING, RETAILING AND SALES CASEBOOK. Text in English. a. GBP 9.99 per issue (effective 2002). **Description:** Recent graduates discuss their careers in marketing, retailing, and sales.
Published by: (Careers Research and Advisory Centre), Hobsons PLC, Challenger House, 42 Adler St, London, E1 1EE, United Kingdom. TEL 44-1223-460366, FAX 44-1223-301506. **Dist. by:** Biblios Publishers' Distribution Services Ltd., Star Rd, Partridge Green, W Sussex RH13 8LD, United Kingdom. TEL 44-1403-710851, FAX 44-1403-711143.

658.8 GBR ISSN 1364-5382
HOLLIS BUSINESS ENTERTAINMENT (YEAR). Text in English. 1995. a., latest 2003, 9th Ed. GBP 125 per vol. for 9th Ed. (2003); GBP 117 per vol. for 8th Ed. (2002) (effective 2002). adv. **Document type:** *Directory.* **Description:** Provides a guide to corporate hospitality: venues, events, and specialist suppliers. Includes spectator activities in sports, arts and entertainment, and shows and exhibitions.
Published by: Hollis Publishing Ltd., Harlequin House, 7 High St, Teddington, Middx TW11 8EL, United Kingdom. TEL 44-20-8977-7711, FAX 44-20-8977-1133, orders@hollis-pr.co.uk, http://www.hollis-pr.com/publications/entertain.htm, http://www.hollis-pr.co.uk/. Ed. Julie Rylance. Pub. Gary Zabel. Adv. contact Jane Ireland. B&W page GBP 1,000, color page GBP 1,500; 126 x 174. Circ: 1,000.

HOME FURNISHINGS EXECUTIVE. see *INTERIOR DESIGN AND DECORATION—Furniture And House Furnishings*

HOME SCHOOL MARKET GUIDE; how to sell curriculum, books, educational toys and games, software programs, DVDs and other educational products to the home school market. see *EDUCATION—Teaching Methods And Curriculum*

HOMECARE MONDAY. see *MEDICAL SCIENCES—Nurses And Nursing*

658 USA
HONG KONG DIRECTORY TO 10,000 EXPORTERS & IMPORTERS. Text in English. 1986. biennial. USD 155. **Document type:** *Directory.*
Formerly (until 1987): Hong Kong Bargain Guide to Factory Outlets
Related titles: Diskette ed.
Published by: Howard Spriggle Publishers, PO Box 550, Ocean View, DE 19970-9801. Ed. Ken Wood. Circ: 500.

HONG KONG SPECIAL ADMINISTRATIVE REGION OF CHINA. CENSUS AND STATISTICS DEPARTMENT. AVERAGE WHOLESALE PRICES OF SELECTED BUILDING MATERIALS. see *BUILDING AND CONSTRUCTION—Abstracting, Bibliographies, Statistics*

HORIZONT SPORT BUSINESS. see *SPORTS AND GAMES*

658.8 USA ISSN 1052-8733
HOSPITAL REVENUE REPORT. Text in English. 1983. 25/yr. USD 379. **Description:** Describes the necessary steps to designing and implementing specific marketing campaigns. Covers projections on costs and the response of patients and businesses.
Incorporates (in 1990): Health Care Marketer (0896-1204); Which incorporated (1985 - Sep. 1987): Urgent Care Business Report (0883-8712); Health Care Marketer was formerly (until 1986): Health Care Marketer and Target Market (0884-6596); Which incorporated: Cost Containment (0198-9872)
Indexed: MEDLINE.
—**CCC.**
Published by: United Communications Group, 11300 Rockville Pike Ste 1100, Rockville, MD 20852-3030. TEL 301-961-8777, FAX 301-816-8945. Ed. Lori Launi.

668.5 USA ISSN 0090-8878
HD9999.S7 CODEN: HPPIAB
HOUSEHOLD & PERSONAL PRODUCTS INDUSTRY; the magazine for the detergent, soap, cosmetic and toiletries, wax, polish and aerosol industries. Short title: H A P P I. Text in English. 1964. m. USD 55; free to qualified personnel (effective 2005). adv. bk.rev. charts; illus.; pat.; stat.; tr.lit.; tr.mk. index. **Document type:** *Magazine, Trade.*
Formerly: Detergents and Specialties (0011-958X)
Related titles: Online - full text ed.: (from Gale Group, O C L C Online Computer Library Center, Inc.).
Indexed: B&I, CBNB, CIN, ChemAb, ChemTitl, CurPA, ExcerpMed, PROMT.
—BLDSC (4334.880000), CASDDS, IE, Infotrieve, ingenta. **CCC.**
Published by: Rodman Publications, Inc., 70 Hilltop Rd, 3rd Fl, Ramsey, NJ 07446. TEL 201-825-2552, FAX 201-825-0553, tomb@rodpub.com, http://www.happi.com. Ed. Tom Branna. Pub. Art Larger. Adv. contact Beth Russo. B&W page USD 3,455, color page USD 4,820. Circ: 18,000 (controlled).

HOUSEWARES CANADA. see *INTERIOR DESIGN AND DECORATION—Furniture And House Furnishings*

658.8 USA
THE HUB MAGAZINE. Text in English. 2000. q. adv. **Document type:** *Magazine, Trade.* **Description:** Features roundtable discussions of marketing ideas and trends.
Related titles: Online - full content ed.
Published by: David X. Manners Company, Inc., 107 Post Rd E, Westport, CT 06880. TEL 203-227-7060, FAX 203-227-7067, info@hubmagazine.com, http://www.hubmagazine.com, http://www.dxmanners.com. Ed., Pub. Tim Manners.

658.8 HUN ISSN 0237-1553
HC267.A2
HUNGARIAN BUSINESS HERALD. Text in English, German. 1969. q. USD 17.50.
Formerly (until 1985): Marketing in Hungary (0025-3731)
Indexed: KES, PAIS, PROMT, RASB.
Published by: Magyar Kereskedelmi Kamara, Kossuth Lajos ter 608, Budapest, 1055, Hungary. Ed. Gerd Biro. Circ: 4,000.
Co-sponsor: Orszagos Piackutato Intezet.

HUSBYGNING BRUTTO. see *BUILDING AND CONSTRUCTION*

HUSBYGNING NETTO. see *BUILDING AND CONSTRUCTION*

658 SWE ISSN 1652-5590
I C A NYHETER. Text in Swedish. 1968. 44/yr. SEK 1,485 (effective 2004). adv. 5 cols./p.; **Document type:** *Magazine, Consumer.*
Formerly (until 2000): I C A - Nyheter och Debatt (0347-3899)
Related titles: Online - full text ed.: ISSN 1402-4659.
Published by: Forma Publishing Group, Port-Anders Gata T3, PO Box 6630, Vaesteraas, 11384, Sweden. TEL 46-21-194000, FAX 46-21-194186, icanyheter@formapg.se, http://www.ica-nyheter.net, http://www.formapg.se. Ed., Pub. Aake Bergholm. Adv. contact Hakan Broberg. page SEK 59.50; 195 x 270. Circ: 23,300.

I C A S T BUYER'S GUIDE. (International Convention of Allied Sportfishing Trades) see *FISH AND FISHERIES*

658 USA
I E G SPONSORSHIP REPORT; the international newsletter of event sponsorship and lifestyle marketing. Text in English. 1982. bi-w. USD 415 domestic; USD 440 in Canada & Mexico; USD 495 elsewhere. adv. index. back issues avail. **Document type:** *Newsletter.* **Description:** Presents case studies and quantitative analysis along with breaking news, positions available and agency action.
Formerly: Special Events Report
Published by: International Events Group, Inc., 640 N LaSalle, Ste 600, Chicago, IL 60610. TEL 312-944-1727, FAX 312-944-1897, ieg@sponsorship.com, http://www.sponsorship.com. Ed. Lesa Ukman. R&P Jon Ukman. Adv. contact Meg Pound. Circ: 14,000.

658 394.2 USA
GT3930
I E G SPONSORSHIP SOURCEBOOK. Text in English. 1984. a. USD 199 domestic; USD 214 in Canada & Mexico; USD 226 elsewhere. adv. **Document type:** *Directory.* **Description:** Sourcebook on international events like the America's Cup and Los Angeles Marathon to regional crowd pleasers such as the Texas State Fair and Miami's Calle Ocho. Covers attendance, budget, sponsors and contacts of approximately 3,000 events, and lists suppliers and organizations that fuel the business.
Former titles (until 1994): I E G Directory of Sponsorship Marketing (1058-613X); (until 1990): Official (Year) Directory of Festivals, Sports and Special Events (0894-0649); (until 1987): Official International Directory of Special Events and Festivals (0743-4170)
Related titles: Diskette ed.
Published by: International Events Group, Inc., 640 N LaSalle, Ste 600, Chicago, IL 60610. TEL 312-944-1727, FAX 312-944-1897, ieg@sponsorship.com, http://www.sponsorship.com. Ed. Lesa Ukman. Pub. Jon Ukman. Adv. contact Meg Pound. Circ: 7,000.

658.7 USA ISSN 0019-8285
TJ1
I E N: INDUSTRIAL EQUIPMENT NEWS; what's new in equipment, parts, materials, software - all products useful to the US industrial marketplace. Text in English. 1933. m. USD 35 domestic; USD 50 in Canada & Mexico; USD 115 elsewhere; USD 3.50 newsstand/cover (effective 2005). adv. illus.; tr.lit. reprint service avail. from PQC. **Document type:** *Magazine, Trade.* **Description:** Provides new product information to the industry.
Related titles: ♦ Supplement(s): Industrial Literature Review.
Indexed: BrCerAb, C&ISA, CerAb, CivEngAb, CorrAb, E&CAJ, EMA, IAA, M&TEA, MBF, METADEX, SolStAb, WAA.
—Linda Hall.
Published by: Thomas Publishing Company, Five Penn Plaza, New York, NY 10001. TEL 212-629-1546, FAX 212-629-1542, subscriptioninfo@ienonline.com, info@thomasimg.com, http://www.ienonline.com, http://www.thomaspublishing.com. Pub. Ciro Buttacavoli. adv.: page USD 16,530. Circ: 208,174 (controlled).

I G P C NEWSLETTER. (International Guild of Professional Consultants) see *BUSINESS AND ECONOMICS—Small Business*

658 CHE
I H A NEWS. Text in German. q. **Document type:** *Trade.*
Published by: I H A Institut fuer Marktanalysen, Obermattweg 9, Hergiswil Nw, 6052, Switzerland. TEL 041-959111, FAX 041-959123. Ed. P Hofer. Circ: 10,000.

658 ROM ISSN 1221-6992
I M A S BULLETIN. Text in Romanian. 1991. m.?. USD 196.
Published by: Institutul de Marketing si Sondaje/Institute for Marketing and Public Opinion Polls, PO Box 56-52, Bucharest, 77750, Romania.

658 IRL ISSN 0791-6809
I M J. (Irish Marketing Journal) Text in English. 1974. m. EUR 150 (effective 2005). adv. bk.rev. illus.; tr.lit. back issues avail. **Document type:** *Directory, Trade.* **Description:** Features comprehensive news and features on advertising, direct marketing, media, sales promotion, public relations, design, and graphics.
Former titles (until 1989): Irish Marketing and Advertising Journal (0791-1092); (until 1987): I M J. Irish Marketing & Advertising Journal (0790-7516); (until 1980): I M J. Irish Marketing Journal (0332-4559)
Related titles: Online - full text ed.
Published by: Irish Marketing Journal, 45 Upper Mount St, Dublin, 2, Ireland. TEL 353-1-6611660, FAX 353-1-6611630, editor@irishmarketingjournal.ie, info@irishmarketingjournal.ie, http://www.adworld.ie. Ed. Seamus Bagnall. Pub. John McGee. Adv. contact Derek Doyle. Circ: 25,000.

658 330 USA
I N T I X NEWSLETTER. Text in English. 1981. 8/yr. free. adv. **Document type:** *Newsletter.* **Description:** Covers customer service, marketing, survey results, use of credit cards, and software for the ticketing industry worldwide.
Formerly: B O M I Newsletter (1071-6254)
Published by: The International Ticketing Association, 250 W 57th St, Ste 722, New York, NY 10107. TEL 212-581-0600, FAX 212-581-0885, info@intix.org, http://www.intix.org. Ed. Laura-Ilene Harding. Pub., R&P, Adv. contact Patricia G Spira TEL 212-381-0600. Circ: 1,400 (controlled).

658.8 659.1 ESP ISSN 0214-7459
I.P. MARK. (Informacion de Publicidad y Marketing) Text in Spanish. 1962. 20/yr. EUR 150 domestic; EUR 275 foreign (effective 2005). bk.rev. **Description:** Contains advertising news, reports on advertising communications, public relations, services, launching of new products and campaigns.
Formerly (until 1973): I.P. Informacion de la Publicidad (0214-7483)
Indexed: RILM.
—CINDOC.
Published by: Ediciones y Estudios S.A., Enrique Larreta, 5-1o, Madrid, 28036, Spain. TEL 34-1-7339114, FAX 34-1-3157419, http://www.ipmark.com/portal/index.php. Ed. Manuel G Carbajo. Pub. Miguel de Haro. Circ: 5,500.

I Q DIRECTORY; interactive resources. see *BUSINESS AND ECONOMICS—Trade And Industrial Directories*

I T COST MANAGEMENT SOURCEBOOK. (Information Technology) see *COMPUTERS—Electronic Data Processing*

658 GBR
I T MARKETING SOURCE BOOK. Text in English. 1994. irreg. GBP 75 (effective 1996). adv. **Document type:** *Directory.* **Description:** Guide to marketing in computer industry providing specialist help for sales and marketing professionals.
Published by: V N U Business Publications Ltd., VNU House, 32-34 Broadwick St, London, W1A 2HG, United Kingdom. TEL 44-20-7316-9000, FAX 44-20-7316-9620. Ed. Peter Chare. Pub. Melanie Williams.

I-TIPS NEWSLETTER. see *COMPUTERS—Internet*

658 CHE
IDEE A'JOUR. Text in German. 10/yr. **Document type:** *Bulletin.*
Published by: Vereinigung fuer Werbekommunikation, Froebelstr 33, Zuerich, 8032, Switzerland. Ed. Fridolin Kretz. Circ: 3,000.

338.642 658 USA ISSN 1077-3045
I'M TOO BUSY TO READ MARKETING REPORT SERVICE✶. Text in English. 1992. m. USD 149; USD 169 foreign (effective 1996). bk.rev. back issues avail. **Document type:** *Newsletter.* **Description:** Covers advertising, sales, public relations, and customer relations.
Formerly (until 1994): Win - Win Marketing Newsletter for Small Business (1063-5904)
Published by: Win - Win Marketing, 16501 Franklin Rd, Fort Bragg, CA 95437-8714. TEL 408-247-0122, FAX 408-249-5754, towin@aol.com. Ed. Frankie Kangas.

658.8 USA ISSN 0536-5856
IMPRINT; the promotional idea magazine. Text in English. 1967. q. USD 20 domestic; USD 50 foreign (effective 2004). adv. **Document type:** *Magazine, Trade.* **Description:** Delivers promotional ideas and solutions right to end-buyers.
Published by: Advertising Specialty Institute, 4800 Street Rd, Trevose, PA 19053. TEL 215-953-4000, FAX 215-953-3034, info@asicentral.com, http://www.asicentral.com/asp/open/ProductsAndServices/dist/magazines/imprint/index.asp. adv.: color page USD 4,225; trim 8.375 x 10.5.

658 GBR ISSN 1366-5448
IN-STORE MARKETING. Text in English. 1997. m. GBP 39.50 domestic; GBP 58 in Europe; GBP 88 in United States; GBP 88 elsewhere (effective 2001). adv. **Document type:** *Magazine, Trade.* **Description:** Covers news and trends about the point-of-purchase marketing industry.
Related titles: Online - full content ed.; Online - full text ed.: (from EBSCO Publishing, Gale Group, H.W. Wilson, LexisNexis, O C L C Online Computer Library Center, Inc., ProQuest Information & Learning).
Indexed: ABIn, BPI.
Published by: Centaur Publishing, St Giles House, 50 Poland St, London, W1V 4AX, United Kingdom. TEL 44-20-7970-4000, matthewv@centaur.co.uk, http://www.mad.co.uk/ism/, http://www.centaur.co.uk. adv.: color page GBP 2,750.

658.85 USA ISSN 1042-5195
CODEN: INCNEU
INCENTIVE; managing & marketing through motivation. Text in English. 1905. m. USD 59 domestic; USD 75 in Canada; USD 195 elsewhere (effective 2005). adv. reprints avail. **Document type:** *Magazine, Trade.* **Description:** Serves executives responsible for incentive programs geared to motivate employees, customers and dealers.
Formerly (until 1988): Incentive Marketing (0019-3364); Which incorporated: Incentive Travel
Related titles: Online - full text ed.: (from EBSCO Publishing, Florida Center for Library Automation, Gale Group, O C L C Online Computer Library Center, Inc., ProQuest Information & Learning).
Indexed: ABIn, BLI, BusI, H&TI, SRI.
—BLDSC (4374.890000), IE, ingenta. **CCC.**
Published by: V N U Business Publications (Subsidiary of: V N U Business Media), 770 Broadway, New York, NY 10003-9595. TEL 646-654-7604, FAX 646-654-5351, acohen@incentivemag.com, bmcomm@vnuinc.com, http://www.incentivemag.com, http://www.vnubusinessmedia.com/. Ed. Andy Cohen TEL 646-654-7636. Adv. contact Tim Reid TEL 646-654-4460. B&W page USD 6,330, color page USD 7,240. Circ: 40,050 (controlled). **Subscr. to:** PO Box 1255, Skokie, IL 60076.

658 DEU ISSN 1439-8575
INCENTIVE CONGRESS JOURNAL; magazine for motivation and sales promotion. Text in German. 1986. 4/yr. EUR 25 domestic; EUR 45 foreign (effective 2005). adv. bk.rev. back issues avail. **Document type:** *Magazine, Trade.* **Description:** Professional magazine for incentives, meetings, conventions, exhibitions, and business travel.
Formerly (until 1997): Incentive Journal (0933-7849)
Published by: E C - GmbH, Keltenring 22, Egamting, 85658, Germany. TEL 49-8095-87260, FAX 49-8095-872629, ec@icj-mm.de, http://www.incentive-journal.de. Ed., Pub. Gerald W Huft. Adv. contact Ivo Baumann. B&W page EUR 3,690, color page EUR 4,590; trim 190 x 265. Circ: 12,000 (paid and controlled).

658.8 NLD
INCREASE YOUR SALES VOLUME; for businessmen and opportunity seekers. Text in English. 1980. bi-m. USD 15. adv. bk.rev.
Published by: International Business & Information Services, Beukelsdijk 9a, Rotterdam, 3021 AA, Netherlands. Ed. Roy K Benschop.

INDEPENDENT WOMEN'S SPECIALTY STORES & BOUTIQUES. see *CLOTHING TRADE*

658.8 IND ISSN 0019-5316
INDIAN JOURNAL OF MARKETING; journal of marketing, advertisement and sales management. Text in English. 1968. m. INR 60, USD 25. adv. bk.rev. charts; stat.
Published by: Associated Management Consultants (P) Ltd., Y-21 Hauz Khas, New Delhi, 110 016, India. Ed. J Gilani. Circ: 2,500.

658.8 ITA ISSN 1591-6243
INDUSTRIA & DISTRIBUZIONE; rivista di economia e gestione dei rapporti di canale. Text in Italian. 1999. q. EUR 96 domestic; EUR 120 foreign (effective 2003). **Document type:** *Journal, Academic/Scholarly.*
Formed by the merger of (1979-1999): Commercio (1591-5743); (1991-1999): Trade Marketing (1591-6235)
Published by: Franco Angeli Edizioni, Viale Monza 106, Milan, 20127, Italy. TEL 39-02-2837141, FAX 39-02-26144793, redazioni@francoangeli.it, http://www.francoangeli.it.

658.5 USA ISSN 0019-8153
TJ1 CODEN: INDDAZ
INDUSTRIAL DISTRIBUTION; for industrial distributors and their sales personnel. Text in English. 1911. m. USD 109.90 domestic; USD 131.90 in Canada; USD 126.90 in Mexico; USD 254.90 elsewhere; USD 10 per issue domestic; USD 15 per issue foreign; free to qualified personnel (effective 2004). adv. bk.rev. charts; illus.; mkt.; stat.; tr.lit. index. reprint service avail. from PQC. **Document type:** *Magazine, Trade.* **Description:** For general line, specialist and combination industrial distributor firms. Provides how-to information and industry news, with an emphasis on increasing sales and profits.
Formerly: Industrial Distribution Marketplace
Related titles: Microfiche ed.: (from CIS); Microform ed.; Online - full text ed.: (from EBSCO Publishing, Factiva, Florida Center for Library Automation, Gale Group, H.W. Wilson, LexisNexis, Northern Light Technology, Inc., O C L C Online Computer Library Center, Inc., ProQuest Information & Learning, The Dialog Corporation).
Indexed: ABIn, BPI, BPIA, BusI, EngInd, LogistBibl, ManagCont, SRI, T&II.
—BLDSC (4450.200000), Ei, IE, ingenta, Linda Hall. **CCC.**
Published by: Reed Business Information (Subsidiary of: Reed Business), 275 Washington St, Newton, MA 02458. TEL 617-558-4787, FAX 617-630-3922, http://www.inddist.com, http://www.reedbusiness.com. Ed. John Keough TEL 617-558-4432. Pub. Craig Riley TEL 617-558-4780. adv.: B&W page USD 8,080, color page USD 10,055; trim 10.5 x 7.88. Circ: 40,000 (paid and controlled). **Subscr. to:** Reed Business Information, PO Box 9020, Maple Shade, NJ 08052-9020. TEL 303-470-4466, FAX 303-470-4691.

658.7 GBR ISSN 0019-8277
INDUSTRIAL EQUIPMENT NEWS. Text in English. 1951. m. GBP 65 (effective 2003). bk.rev.; film rev. illus.; mkt.; stat. back issues avail.; reprint service avail. from PQC. **Document type:** *Trade.* **Description:** Provides an industrial product and corporate product and services purchaser guide.
Related titles: Microform ed.: (from PQC).
Indexed: AEA, BMT, CoppAb, CurPA, FLUIDEX, T&II.
Published by: Nexus Media Ltd. (Subsidiary of: Highbury House Communications PLC), Nexus House, Azalea Dr, Swanley, Kent BR8 8HU, United Kingdom. TEL 44-1322-660070, FAX 44-1322-616311, info@nexusmedia.com, http://www.hhc.co.uk/ien. Ed. James Stagg TEL 44-1322-660070 ext 2145. Adv. contact Daniel Coyne. Circ: 36,000.

INDUSTRIAL MACHINE TRADER. see *MACHINERY*

658.83 USA ISSN 0019-8501
HF5415.12.E8 CODEN: IMMADX
➤ **INDUSTRIAL MARKETING MANAGEMENT.** Text in English. 1971. 8/yr. EUR 121 in Europe to individuals; JPY 16,100 in Japan to individuals; USD 137 to individuals except Europe and Japan; EUR 808 in Europe to institutions; JPY 107,200 in Japan to institutions; USD 904 to institutions except Europe and Japan (effective 2006). adv. illus. back issues avail.; reprints avail. **Document type:** *Journal, Academic/Scholarly.* **Description:** Provides in-depth case studies geared to the needs of managers, executives and professionals.
Related titles: Microform ed.: (from PQC); Online - full text ed.: (from EBSCO Publishing, Gale Group, IngentaConnect, ScienceDirect, Swets Information Services).
Indexed: ABIn, ADPA, ASCA, BPI, BPIA, BusI, CPM, CurCont, Emerald, FamI, IBSS, IMI, Inspec, KES, M&MA, ManagAb, ManagCont, PAIS, RASB, RefZh, SCIMP, SSCI.
—BLDSC (4457.750000), IDS, IE, Infotrieve, ingenta. **CCC.**
Published by: Elsevier Inc. (Subsidiary of: Elsevier Science & Technology), 360 Park Ave. S, New York, NY 10010-1710. TEL 212-989-5800, 888-437-4636, FAX 212-633-3990, a.gaskin@elsevier.com, usinfo-f@elsevier.com, http://www.elsevier.com/locate/indmarman. Ed. Peter J. LaPlaca. adv.: B&W page USD 1,060, color page USD 2,995. Circ: 1,060 (paid and free).

658.8 USA
THE INDUSTRIAL MARKETING PRACTITIONER. Text in English. 1996. m. looseleaf. USD 199; USD 240 foreign (effective 1998). back issues avail. **Document type:** *Newsletter.* **Description:** Marketing know-how for industrial markets.
Related titles: Online - full text ed.

B

Published by: Amber Publishing, 1551 S Valley Forge Rd, Ste 246, Lansdale, PA 19446. TEL 215-362-7200, FAX 215-362-6249, publisher@practitioner.com, http://www.practitioner.com. Ed. Dane Claussen. adv.: B&W page USD 200; trim 10 x 8. Circ: 1,000 (paid).

658.7 USA ISSN 0019-8641
INDUSTRIAL PURCHASING AGENT. Text in English. 1956. bi-m. USD 25 (effective 2005). adv. bk.rev.; film rev.; software rev.; Website rev. charts; illus.; stat.; tr.lit. back issues avail.; reprint service avail. from PQC. **Document type:** *Magazine, Trade.* **Description:** Reports new product releases with or without photos for largest US industrial concerns.
Published by: Publications for Industry, 21 Russell Woods Rd., Great Neck, NY 11021-4644. TEL 516-487-0990, FAX 516-487-0809, ipa@publicationsforindustry.com, info@publicationsforindustry.com, http://www.publicationsforindustry.com/ipa/ipa_index.html. Ed. Pearl Shaine Panes. Pub. Jack S Panes. Adv. contact B Grillo. B&W page USD 2,087; trim 10.3 x 14.2. Circ: 25,000 (controlled).

B

INDUSTRY WORLD. see *BEVERAGES*

INFO PRESSE COMMUNICATIONS; le seul magazine d'affaires francophones des communications au Canada. see *ADVERTISING AND PUBLIC RELATIONS*

658 USA ISSN 1058-0344
INFOMERCIAL MARKETING REPORT. Text in English. 1991. m. USD 395; USD 435 in Canada; USD 445 elsewhere. adv. bk.rev. back issues avail. **Document type:** *Newsletter.* **Description:** Deals with all the behind-the-scenes-activities of the infomercial industry with quarterly media figures and an annual list of the top ten grossing infomercials.
Published by: Steven Dworman Enterprises, 12254 Montana Ave, Suite A, Los Angeles, CA 90049. TEL 310-979-6090, FAX 310-472-6004, clarkkent@aol.com. Ed., Pub. Steve Dworman. Adv. contact Clare Jacoby. Circ: 3,000.

INFORMATION SYSTEMS SPENDING; an analysis of trends and strategies. see *COMPUTERS—Electronic Data Processing*

658 DEU ISSN 0940-7707
INFORMATIONEN FUER DEN VERKAUFS INNENDIENST. Text in Dutch, French, German. 1975. m. EUR 165.60 (effective 2004). back issues avail. **Document type:** *Journal, Trade.*
Published by: Verlag Norbert Mueller AG und Co. KG (Subsidiary of: S V Corporate Media GmbH), Emmy-Noether-Str 2, Munich, 80992, Germany. TEL 49-89-5485201, FAX 49-89-54852192, infoVNM@sv-corporate-media.de, http://www.vnm.de/svcm/index/includeVerzeichnis/nm[]briefe[]0940-7707/. Ed. Hilger Veenema. Circ: 2,500.

INFORMATIONSDIENST GROSS- UND AUSSENHANDEL. see *BUSINESS AND ECONOMICS—International Commerce*

INNOVATIVE LEADER (ONLINE); monthly tool to increase creativity and productivity. see *BUSINESS AND ECONOMICS—Management*

INNOVATIVE NEW PACKAGING IN JAPAN. see *PACKAGING*

INSIDE. see *INTERIOR DESIGN AND DECORATION*

659 USA ISSN 1099-9639
INSIDE DIRECT MAIL. Text in English. 1984. m. **Document type:** *Newsletter, Consumer.*
Formerly (until 1998): Who's Mailing What! (8755-2671)
Published by: North American Publishing Co., 1500 Spring Garden St., Ste 1200, Philadelphia, PA 19130-4094. TEL 215-238-5300, hmummert@napco.com, http://www.insidedirectmail.com. Ed. Hallie Mummert. Circ: 1,000 (paid).

658.8 USA ISSN 1084-2624
INSIDE RESEARCH. Text in English. 1990. m. **Document type:** *Newsletter, Trade.* **Description:** Provides information and insight on the global marketing research industry.
Address: PO Box 296, Barrington, IL 60011. TEL 847-526-0707, LnGold@att.net. Ed. Larry Gold.

INSIDE SPORTING GOODS. see *SPORTS AND GAMES*

658.7 USA ISSN 1538-733X
HD39.5
INSIDE SUPPLY MANAGEMENT; resouces to create your future. Text in English. m. free membership (effective 2005). adv. **Document type:** *Magazine, Trade.* **Description:** Publishes articles relating to purchasing and materials management.
Former titles (until 2002): Purchasing Today (1086-5853); (until 1995): N A P M Insights (1047-7470); (until 1990): Insight (Tempe)
Published by: Institute for Supply Management, 2055 E Centennial Circle, PO Box 22160, Tempe, AZ 85285-2160. TEL 602-752-6276, FAX 602-752-7890, http://www.ism.ws/Pubs/ISMMag/index.cfm. Ed. Roberta Duffy TEL 480-752-6276 ext 3085. adv.: B&W page USD 5,207; trim 8.125 x 10.875. Circ: 44,770 (paid and controlled).

658.7 GBR
INTERCON. Text in English. d. GBP 696. **Document type:** *Trade.* **Description:** Daily listing of international public sector contract opportunities and notices.
Related titles: CD-ROM ed.: GBP 560; Online - full text ed.
Published by: Business Information Publications Ltd., Park House, 300 Glasgow Rd, Shawfield, Glasgow, G73 1SQ, United Kingdom. TEL 44-141-3328247, FAX 44-141-3312792, bip@bipcontracts.com, bip@bipsolutions.com, http://www.bipcontracts.com.

658 USA ISSN 1096-1747
HG4501
INTERMARKET REVIEW✶. Key Title: Martin J. Pring's Intermarket Review. Text in English. 1984. m. USD 265 domestic; USD 300 in Canada; USD 420 elsewhere (effective 1999). **Description:** Summarizes activity of the world's principal financial markets with special emphasis on the U.S. bond and stock markets; up-to-date information on currencies, international debt, equity markets, commodity indexes and precious metals. Includes an asset allocation section, a PTG stock of the month feature and over 40 charts.
Formerly: Pring Market Review (0892-189X)
Related titles: E-mail ed.; Fax ed.
Published by: International Institute for Economic Research, Inc., 1539 S Orange Ave, Sarasota, FL 34239-2035. TEL 804-694-0415, FAX 804-694-0028, info@pring.com, http://www.pring.com. Ed. Martin J Pring.

382 658 USA ISSN 0020-7004
INTERNATIONAL INTERTRADE INDEX; new foreign products - marketing techniques. Text in English. 1950. m. looseleaf. USD 45 (effective 2001). mkt.; tr.lit. back issues avail. **Document type:** *Newsletter.* **Description:** Provides descriptions of new imported products available from foreign manufacturers for import into the US.
Formerly: International Import Index
Related titles: ◆ Supplement(s): Foreign Trade Fairs New Products Newsletter. ISSN 0883-4687.
Address: PO Box 636, Federal Sq, Newark, NJ 07101. TEL 973-686-2382, FAX 973-622-1740. Ed. John E Felber.

INTERNATIONAL JOURNAL OF ADVERTISING; the quarterly review of marketing communications. see *ADVERTISING AND PUBLIC RELATIONS*

658.8005 GBR ISSN 1472-8249
INTERNATIONAL JOURNAL OF APPLIED MARKETING. Text in English. 2002. 3/yr. GBP 25, USD 50 to individuals; GBP 75, USD 150 to institutions (effective 2003). **Document type:** *Journal, Academic/Scholarly.*
—BLDSC (4542.088700), IE.
Published by: Sheffield Hallam University Press, c/o Mrs. Monica Moseley, Pub., Sheffield Hallam University Press, Learning Centre, Sheffield, S Yorks S1 1WB, United Kingdom. TEL 44-114-2254702, FAX 44-114-2254478, m.mosely@shu.ac.uk, http://www.shu.ac.uk/shupress/. Ed. Robert H Haigh.

THE INTERNATIONAL JOURNAL OF BANK MARKETING. see *BUSINESS AND ECONOMICS—Banking And Finance*

INTERNATIONAL JOURNAL OF BUSINESS. see *BUSINESS AND ECONOMICS—International Commerce*

658.8 GBR ISSN 1744-6635
▼ ➤ **INTERNATIONAL JOURNAL OF BUSINESS FORECASTING AND MARKET INTELLIGENCE.** Text in English. 2005. q. USD 450 to institutions; USD 545 to institutions print & online eds. (effective 2005). **Document type:** *Journal, Academic/Scholarly.* **Description:** Aims to further the development of the field of business forecasting and marketing intelligence as well as related disciplines.
Related titles: Online - full text ed.: ISSN 1744-6643. USD 450 to institutions (effective 2005).
Published by: Inderscience Publishers, IEL Editorial Office, PO Box 735, Olney, Bucks MK46 5WB, United Kingdom. TEL 44-1234-240519, FAX 44-1234-240515, ijbfmi@inderscience.com, info@inderscience.com, editor@inderscience.com, http://www.inderscience.com/ijbfmi. **Subscr. to:** World Trade Centre Bldg, 29 route de Pre-Bois, Case Postale 896, Geneva 15 1215, Switzerland. FAX 41-22-7910885, subs@inderscience.com.

▼ ➤ **INTERNATIONAL JOURNAL OF BUSINESS RESEARCH.** see *BUSINESS AND ECONOMICS—Management*

▼ ➤ **INTERNATIONAL JOURNAL OF BUSINESS STRATEGY.** see *BUSINESS AND ECONOMICS—Management*

▼ ➤ **INTERNATIONAL JOURNAL OF BUSINESS STUDIES.** see *BUSINESS AND ECONOMICS—International Commerce*

▼ ➤ **INTERNATIONAL JOURNAL OF ELECTRONIC MARKETING AND RETAILING.** see *BUSINESS AND ECONOMICS—Management*

658.7 GBR ISSN 1477-5360
▼ **INTERNATIONAL JOURNAL OF INTEGRATED SUPPLY MANAGEMENT.** Abbreviated title: I J I S M. Text in English. 2003. q. USD 450 to institutions; USD 545 combined subscription to institutions print & online eds. (effective 2005). **Document type:** *Journal, Academic/Scholarly.* **Description:** Provides information on a wide variety of supply management issues including purchasing and other incoming supply issues, internal materials management, information systems and quality issues, and outbound supply, logistics, and customer service issues.
Related titles: Online - full text ed.: ISSN 1741-8097. USD 450 to institutions (effective 2005) (from EBSCO Publishing).
Indexed: BrCerAb, C&ISA, CerAb, CorrAb, E&CAJ, EMA, IAA, Inspec, M&TEA, MBF, METADEX, WAA.
—BLDSC (4542.310250), IE, Linda Hall.
Published by: Inderscience Publishers, IEL Editorial Office, PO Box 735, Olney, Bucks MK46 5WB, United Kingdom. TEL 44-1234-240519, FAX 44-1234-240515, ijism@inderscience.com, editor@inderscience.com, http://www.inderscience.com/ijism. Ed. Dr. Mohammed A Dorgham. **Subscr. to:** World Trade Centre Bldg, 29 route de Pre-Bois, Case Postale 896, Geneva 15 1215, Switzerland. FAX 41-22-7910885, subs@inderscience.com.

▼ **INTERNATIONAL JOURNAL OF INTERNET MARKETING AND ADVERTISING.** see *COMPUTERS—Internet*

658.8 659 GBR ISSN 1470-7853
HF5415.2 CODEN: JMRSBJ
➤ **INTERNATIONAL JOURNAL OF MARKET RESEARCH.** Text in English. 1959. q. GBP 210, EUR 370, USD 350 to institutions (effective 2005). adv. bk.rev. bibl.; charts; illus. index. back issues avail.; reprint service avail. from PQC,SCH. **Document type:** *Journal, Academic/Scholarly.* **Description:** Contains papers and shorter notes covering important technical advances, practical applications, appraisals of specific problem areas and issues of current concern, together with correspondence and reviews covering the broad field of marketing and social research.
Former titles (until 1999): Market Research Society. Journal (0025-3618); (until 1968): Commentary
Related titles: Microfilm ed.: (from PQC); Online - full text ed.: (from EBSCO Publishing, Gale Group, O C L C Online Computer Library Center, Inc., ProQuest Information & Learning).
Indexed: ABIn, ADPA, BPIA, BusI, CJA, CPM, CommAb, CurCont, Emerald, HRIS, M&MA, ManagCont, PAIS, PsySCAP, PsycInfo, PsycholAb, RILM, SCIMP, SSCI, e-psyche.
—BLDSC (4542.329600), IDS, IE, ingenta. **CCC.**
Published by: (Market Research Society), N T C Publications Ltd. (Subsidiary of: World Advertising Research Center Ltd.), Farm Rd, Henley-on-Thames, Oxon RG9 1EJ, United Kingdom. TEL 44-1491-411000, FAX 44-1491-571188, katherine-goldsmith@ntc.co.uk, http://www.ijmr.com/, http://www.warc.com. Ed. Peter Mouncey. R&P, Adv. contact Katherine Goldsmith. Circ: 3,500.

658 361.73 GBR ISSN 1465-4520
➤ **INTERNATIONAL JOURNAL OF NONPROFIT AND VOLUNTARY SECTOR MARKETING.** Text in English. 1996. q. USD 440 to institutions; USD 484 combined subscription to institutions print & online eds. (effective 2006). adv. abstr. 96 p./no. 2 cols./p.; back issues avail.; reprint service avail. from PSC. **Document type:** *Journal, Academic/Scholarly.* **Description:** Forum for papers and case studies on marketing in the not-for-profit sector.
Formerly (until 1999): Journal of Nonprofit and Voluntary Sector Market (1360-8576)
Related titles: Online - full text ed.: ISSN 1479-103X. USD 440 to institutions (effective 2006) (from EBSCO Publishing, Gale Group, IngentaConnect, O C L C Online Computer Library Center, Inc., ProQuest Information & Learning, Swets Information Services, Wiley InterScience).
Indexed: ABIn, CPM.
—BLDSC (4542.398000), IE, Infotrieve, ingenta. **CCC.**
Published by: John Wiley & Sons Ltd. (Subsidiary of: John Wiley & Sons, Inc.), The Atrium, Southern Gate, Chichester, West Sussex PO19 8SQ, United Kingdom. TEL 44-1243-779777, FAX 44-1243-775878, cs-journals@wiley.co.uk, http://www.interscience.wiley.com/journal/nvsm, http://www.wiley.co.uk. Pub. Claire Plimmer. Circ: 200 (paid).

658 GBR ISSN 1743-5110
▼ ➤ **INTERNATIONAL JOURNAL OF PRODUCT LIFECYCLE MANAGEMENT.** Text in English. 2004. q. USD 450 to institutions; USD 545 to institutions print & online eds. (effective 2005). **Document type:** *Journal, Academic/Scholarly.* **Description:** Devoted to the development, promotion and coordination of the science and practice of the PLM field.
Related titles: Online - full text ed.: ISSN 1743-5129. USD 450 to institutions (effective 2005).
Published by: Inderscience Publishers, IEL Editorial Office, PO Box 735, Olney, Bucks MK46 5WB, United Kingdom. TEL 44-1234-240519, FAX 44-1234-240515, ijplm@inderscience.com, info@inderscience.com, http://www.inderscience.com/ijplm. **Subscr. to:** World Trade Centre Bldg, 29 route de Pre-Bois, Case Postale 896, Geneva 15 1215, Switzerland. FAX 41-22-7910885, subs@inderscience.com.

658 NLD ISSN 0167-8116
HF5415.2 CODEN: IJRME6
➤ **INTERNATIONAL JOURNAL OF RESEARCH IN MARKETING.** Text in English. 1984. 4/yr. EUR 81 in Europe to individuals; JPY 10,700 in Japan to individuals; USD 89 to individuals except Europe and Japan; EUR 597 in Europe to institutions; JPY 79,300 in Japan to institutions; USD 668 to institutions except Europe and Japan (effective 2006). adv. bk.rev. bibl.; charts; illus. Index. back issues avail.; reprints avail. **Document type:** *Journal, Academic/Scholarly.*
Description: Communicates developments in marketing theory and thought, and results of empirical research.
Related titles: Microform ed.: (from PQC); Online - full text ed.: (from EBSCO Publishing, Gale Group, IngentaConnect, ScienceDirect, Swets Information Services).
Indexed: ABIn, CPM, CurCont, Emerald, Faml, MResA, RASB, RefZh, SCIMP, SSCI.
—BLDSC (4542.535000), CISTI, IDS, IE, Infotrieve, ingenta. **CCC.**
Published by: (European Marketing Academy), Elsevier BV, North-Holland (Subsidiary of: Elsevier Science & Technology), Sara Burgerhartstraat 25, Amsterdam, 1055 KV, Netherlands. TEL 31-20-485-3911, FAX 31-20-485-2457, nlinfo-f@elsevier.nl, http://www.elsevier.com/locate/ijresmar, http://www.elsevier.nl. Ed. H Gatignon. Circ: 800.

658 GBR ISSN 0959-0552
HF5429 CODEN: IRDMEQ
INTERNATIONAL JOURNAL OF RETAIL AND DISTRIBUTION MANAGEMENT. Text in English. 1986. m. EUR 9,862.54 in Europe; USD 9,989 in North America; AUD 12,149 in Australasia; GBP 6,806.66 in UK & elsewhere (effective 2006). cum.index. reprint service avail. from PSC. **Document type:** *Journal, Academic/Scholarly.* **Description:** Focuses on issues of strategic significance in retailing and distribution worldwide and provides a forum for researchers and practitioners in the field. All academic articles are reviewed anonymously.
Formerly: International Journal of Retailing (0268-3903)
Related titles: CD-ROM ed.; Online - full text ed.: (from EBSCO Publishing, Emerald Group Publishing Limited, Florida Center for Library Automation, Gale Group, IngentaConnect, O C L C Online Computer Library Center, Inc., ProQuest Information & Learning, Swets Information Services).
Indexed: ABIn, CJA, CPM, EmerIntel, Emerald, Inspec, M&MA.
—BLDSC (4542.537800), AskIEEE, IE, Infotrieve, ingenta. **CCC.**
Published by: Emerald Group Publishing Limited, 60-62 Toller Ln, Bradford, W Yorks BD8 9BY, United Kingdom. TEL 44-1274-777700, FAX 44-1274-785200, help@emeraldinsight.com, infomation@emeraldinsight.com, http://www.emeraldinsight.com/ijrdm.htm. Ed. John Fernie TEL 44-131-4513880. **Subscr. addr. in N America:** Emerald Group Publishing Ltd., 44 Brattle St, 4th Fl, Cambridge, MA 02138. TEL 617-497-2175, 888-622-0075, FAX 617-354-6875.

INTERNATIONAL JOURNAL OF SPORTS MARKETING & SPONSORSHIP. see *SPORTS AND GAMES*

▼ **INTERNATIONAL JOURNAL OF STRATEGIC MANAGEMENT.** see *BUSINESS AND ECONOMICS—Management*

658 GBR ISSN 1741-878X
▼ ➤ **INTERNATIONAL JOURNAL OF TECHNOLOGY MARKETING.** Text in English. 2005. 4/yr. USD 450 print or online ed.; USD 545 combined subscription print & online eds. (effective 2005). **Document type:** *Journal, Academic/Scholarly.* **Description:** Promotes discussion on the advancement of marketing practice and theory, with emphasis on technology and technology intensive products.
Related titles: Online - full text ed.: ISSN 1741-8798.
Published by: Inderscience Publishers, IEL Editorial Office, PO Box 735, Olney, Bucks MK46 5WB, United Kingdom. TEL 44-1234-240519, FAX 44-1234-240515, ijtmkt@inderscience.com, info@inderscience.com, http://www.inderscience.com/ijmkt.

➤ **INTERNATIONAL MARKETING DATA AND STATISTICS (YEAR).** see *BUSINESS AND ECONOMICS—Abstracting, Bibliographies, Statistics*

➤ **INTERNATIONAL MARKETING FORECASTS.** see *BUSINESS AND ECONOMICS—Abstracting, Bibliographies, Statistics*

658 GBR ISSN 0265-1335
HF1416
➤ **INTERNATIONAL MARKETING REVIEW.** Text in English. 1983. bi-m. EUR 9,177.41 in Europe; USD 9,249 in North America; AUD 11,229 in Australasia; GBP 6,328.16 in UK & elsewhere (effective 2006). adv. bk.rev. abstr.; charts; illus. cum.index. back issues avail.; reprint service avail. from PSC. **Document type:** *Journal, Academic/Scholarly.* **Description:** Aims to push back the boundaries of thinking and practice in the field of international marketing and is not a home for general marketing papers.
Incorporates: Industrial Marketing and Purchasing (0268-3911)
Related titles: CD-ROM ed.; Online - full text ed.: (from EBSCO Publishing, Emerald Group Publishing Limited, Gale Group, IngentaConnect, O C L C Online Computer Library Center, Inc., ProQuest Information & Learning, Swets Information Services).
Indexed: ABIn, CPM, CurCont, EmerIntel, Emerald, M&MA, PsycInfo, PsycholAb, RASB, SCIMP, SSCI.
—BLDSC (4543.976250), IE, Infotrieve, ingenta. **CCC.**
Published by: Emerald Group Publishing Limited, 60-62 Toller Ln, Bradford, W Yorks BD8 9BY, United Kingdom. TEL 44-1274-777700, FAX 44-1274-785200, help@emeraldinsight.com, infomation@emeraldinsight.com, http://www.emeraldinsight.com/imr.htm. Ed. Jeryl Whitelock TEL 44-161-245-5987. Circ: 900. **Subscr. addr. in N America:** Emerald Group Publishing Ltd., 44 Brattle St, 4th Fl, Cambridge, MA 02138. TEL 617-497-2175, 888-622-0075, FAX 617-354-6875.

➤ **INTERNATIONAL NEW PRODUCT REPORT.** see *FOOD AND FOOD INDUSTRIES—Grocery Trade*

663 USA ISSN 1086-1238
INTERNATIONAL PRODUCT ALERT. Text in English. 1983. s-m. USD 795 (effective 2005). Index. back issues avail. **Document type:** *Newsletter, Trade.* **Description:** Reports new product launches throughout twenty countries overseas. Includes coverage of foods, beverages, health and beauty aids, household and pet products.
Related titles: Online - full text ed.: (from CompuServe Inc., Data-Star, Factiva, Gale Group, O C L C Online Computer Library Center, Inc.).
Indexed: B&I.
—CCC.
Published by: Marketing Intelligence Service Ltd., 6473D Route 64, Naples, NY 14512-9726. TEL 585-374-6326, FAX 585-374-5217, mi@productscan.com, http://www.productscan.com/index.cfm?nid=6. Ed. Sherie Heins.

658 GBR ISSN 0959-3969
HF5428
➤ **THE INTERNATIONAL REVIEW OF RETAIL, DISTRIBUTION AND CONSUMER RESEARCH.** Text in English. 1990. 5/yr. GBP 502, USD 832 combined subscription to institutions print & online eds. (effective 2006). bk.rev. illus. Index. back issues avail.; reprint service avail. from PSC. **Document type:** *Journal, Academic/Scholarly.* **Description:** Provides an international forum for theoretical research and reflection on practice for both retailing scholars and retailing professionals.
Related titles: Online - full text ed.: ISSN 1466-4402. GBP 477, USD 790 to institutions (effective 2006) (from EBSCO Publishing, Gale Group, IngentaConnect, O C L C Online Computer Library Center, Inc., Swets Information Services).
Indexed: ABIn, CPM, DIP, IBR, IBSS, IBZ, PsycInfo, PsycholAb.
—BLDSC (4547.630000), IE, Infotrieve, ingenta. **CCC.**
Published by: Routledge (Subsidiary of: Taylor & Francis Group), 4 Park Sq, Milton Park, Abingdon, Oxon OX14 4RN, United Kingdom. TEL 44-1235-828600, FAX 44-1235-829000, info@routledge.co.uk, http://www.tandf.co.uk/journals/titles/09593969.asp, http://www.routledge.co.uk. Eds. John Dawson, Leigh Sparks. Circ: 550. **Subscr. in US & Canada to:** Taylor & Francis Inc., Customer Services Dept, 325 Chestnut St, 8th Fl, Philadelphia, PA 19106; **Subscr. to:** Taylor & Francis Ltd, Journals Customer Service, Rankine Rd, Basingstoke, Hants RG24 8PR, United Kingdom. TEL 44-1256-813000, FAX 44-1256-330245, enquiry@tandf.co.uk.

330 DEU ISSN 1615-0619
INTERNATIONAL SALES VOICE; Business-Englisch fuer Ihren beruflichen Erfolg. Text in English, German. 1996. m. EUR 141.60 (effective 2004). **Document type:** *Newsletter, Trade.*
Formerly (until 1999): International Sales Force (1432-6221)
Published by: Verlag Norbert Mueller AG und Co. KG (Subsidiary of: S V Corporate Media GmbH), Emmy-Noether-Str 2, Munich, 80992, Germany. TEL 49-89-5485201, FAX 49-89-54852192, infoVNM@sv-corporate-media.de, http://www.vnm.de/svcm/index/includeVerzeichnis/nm[]briefe[]1615-0619/.

658 NLD ISSN 0923-6716
➤ **INTERNATIONAL SERIES IN QUANTITATIVE MARKETING.** Text in English. 1989. irreg., latest vol.17, 2004. price varies. **Document type:** *Monographic series, Academic/Scholarly.*
Published by: Springer-Verlag Dordrecht (Subsidiary of: Springer Science+Business Media), Van Godewijckstraat 30, Dordrecht, 3311 GX, Netherlands. TEL 31-78-6576050, FAX 31-78-6576474, http://www.springeronline.com. Ed. Jehoshua Eliashberg.

➤ **INTERNATIONAL TRADESHOW DIRECTORY.** see *BUSINESS AND ECONOMICS—Trade And Industrial Directories*

658.0029 USA
INTERNATIONAL VENDING BUYER'S GUIDE AND DIRECTORY. Text in English. 1946. a. USD 35 (effective 1998). adv. **Document type:** *Directory.*
Incorporates: Vending Buyer's Guide
Published by: Vending Times, Inc., 1375 Broadway, 6th Fl, New York, NY 10018-7001. TEL 212-302-4700, FAX 212-221-3311. Ed. Timothy Sanford. R&P Victor Lavay. Adv. contact Steve Zarolnick. Circ: 16,500.

658 DEU ISSN 0170-3625
INTERNATIONALE BEITRAEGE ZUR MARKT-, MEINUNGS- UND ZUKUNFTSFORSCHUNG. Text in German. 1968. irreg. price varies. adv. bk.rev. **Document type:** *Monographic series, Academic/Scholarly.*
Formerly (until 1972): Internationale Beitraege zur Markt- und Meinungsforschung (0539-1431)
Published by: Wickert Institute GmbH & Co. KG, Hohnsen 32, Hildesheim, 31134, Germany. TEL 49-5121-7790070, FAX 49-5121-7790076, mail@wickert-institute.de, http://www.wickert-institute.de. Circ: 2,700.

658 USA
▼ ➤ **THE INTERNET JOURNAL OF MARKETING.** Text in English. 2004. irreg. free to individuals; USD 500 to institutions (effective 2005). **Document type:** *Journal, Academic/Scholarly.*
Media: Online - full content.
Published by: Internet Scientific Publications, L.L.C., 23 Rippling Creek Dr, Sugar Land, TX 77479. TEL 832-443-1193, FAX 281-240-1533, wenker@ispub.com, http://www.ispub.com/ostia/index.php?xmlFilePath=journals/ijma/front.xml.

➤ **INTERNET MARKETING REPORT.** see *COMPUTERS—Internet*

➤ **INTERNET MARKETING UPDATE.** see *COMPUTERS—Internet*

➤ **INTERNET YELLOW PAGES (YEAR): BUSINESS MODELS AND MARKET OPPORTUNITIES.** see *BUSINESS AND ECONOMICS—Computer Applications*

➤ **INTERSERVICE.** see *MILITARY*

658.8 ESP ISSN 1131-6144
INVESTIGACION Y MARKETING. Text in Spanish. 3/yr.
—CINDOC.
Address: Urgell 152, Apdo. 37104, Barcelona, 08036, Spain. TEL 3-453-98-10, FAX 3-451-00-15. Ed. Gloria Batista. Circ: 1,000.

658.8 332.6 PAK ISSN 0021-0064
INVESTMENT & MARKETING. Text in English. 1965. m. PKR 250, USD 100. adv. bk.rev. charts; illus.; mkt.; stat.
Published by: Business Promoters, 10-B Pak Chambers, West Wharf Rd., P O Box 7578, Karachi, Pakistan. TEL 92-21-201272, FAX 92-21-551959, TELEX SADIQ-PK-21404. Ed. S B Hassan. Circ: 15,000.

IPROSPERITY WEB BUSINESS E-ZINE. see *COMPUTERS—Internet*

658 IRL ISSN 0790-7362
➤ **IRISH MARKETING REVIEW.** Text in English. 1986. 2/yr. bk.rev. **Document type:** *Academic/Scholarly.* **Description:** Examines research and practice in marketing from a generalist and international perspective.
Related titles: Microform ed.: (from PQC); Online - full text ed.: (from Northern Light Technology, Inc., O C L C Online Computer Library Center, Inc., ProQuest Information & Learning).
Indexed: ABIn, CPM.
—BLDSC (4572.908000), IE, ingenta.
Published by: (Dublin Institute of Technology, College of Marketing and Design), Marketing Institute, Marketing House, South County Business Park, Leopardstown, Dublin, 18, Ireland. TEL 353-1-2952355, FAX 353-1-2952453, http://www.mii.ie. Circ: 3,500.

➤ **ISOURCE BUSINESS.** see *COMPUTERS—Internet*

➤ **ISOURCE BUSINESS ONLINE.** see *COMPUTERS—Internet*

658.8 GBR
IT MARKETING NEWS. Text in English. 1997. d. adv.
Media: Online - full text.
Published by: Joslin Shaw Ltd, Windsor Centre, Windsor St, London, Islington N1 8QG, United Kingdom. TEL 44-20-226-9177, geo@joshaw.co.uk, http://www.itmarketingnews.co.uk. Ed. George Shaw. adv.: online banner USD 500.

ITALIAN FOOD AND BEVERAGE TECHNOLOGY. see *FOOD AND FOOD INDUSTRIES*

658 JPN
J E T R O MARKETING SERIES. Text in Japanese. irreg.
Published by: Japan External Trade Organization, 2-5 Toranomom 2-chome, Minato-ku, Tokyo, 105-8466, Japan. TEL 81-3-3587-5521, FAX 81-3-3582-0504.

658 GBR
J N C Z MARKETING NEWSLETTER. Text in English. irreg. (approx. m.). **Document type:** *Newsletter.* **Description:** Focuses on home business success in the UK, including features on network marketing companies.
Related titles: E-mail ed.
Published by: J N C Z Marketing, 119 Cholmley Gardens, London, NW6 1AA, United Kingdom. TEL 44-171-4316271, FAX 44-171-4311099, lloyd@night.co.uk, http://www.information-web.com/news/jncz-id.htm. Ed. Lloyd Daley.

B

▼ new title ➤ refereed ✶ unverified ◆ full entry avail.

658.8 NLD ISSN 1387-9014
JAARBOEK DIRECT MARKETING. Text in Dutch. 1997. a. free with subscr to Adfo Direct. charts; illus.; mkt. **Document type:** *Journal, Trade.* **Description:** Offers insight into the most important developments during the year and the directions direct marketing and sales promotion will take.
Published by: Adformatie Groep (Subsidiary of: Wolters Kluwer N.V.), Postbus 4, Alphen aan den Rijn, MA, Netherlands. TEL 44-172-466844, abonnementen@adfo.nl, http://www.adformatie.nl/adfoshop/directjaarboek.html.

658.8 SWE ISSN 1651-7326
▼ **JAERN, BYGG, FAERG/BUILDING MATERIAL AND HARDWARE TRADE JOURNAL.** Text in Swedish. 2003. m. SEK 400 domestic; SEK 550 foreign (effective 2005). adv. bk.rev. charts; illus.; tr.lit.; tr.mk. **Document type:** *Magazine, Trade.* **Description:** Contains news and reports on the various building materials and hardware trades and their businesses.
Formed by the merger of (1993-2003): Jaernaffaerer med Bygg-och Faergaktuellt (1104-8123); (1993-2003): Bygg och Jaernhandeln (1103-3754); Which was formed by the merger of (1914-1993): Jaernhandlaren (0021-552X); (1976-1993): Bygg- och Traevaruhandeln (0347-5220); Which was formerly (1973-1976): Trae- och Byggvaruhandlaren (0346-3419); (1939-1973): Traevaruhandlaren (0041-1884)
Published by: Foerlags AB Verkstadstidningen, Raasundevaegen 166, PO Box 2082, Solna, 16902, Sweden. TEL 46-8-51493400, FAX 46-8-51493409, http://www.jarnbyggfarg.se, http://www.vtf.se. Ed. Lars Cyrus TEL 46-8-51493420. Adv. contact Thomas af Kleen TEL 46-851493422. B&W page SEK 12,500, color page SEK 21,500; 190 x 269. Circ: 7,500. **Co-sponsors:** Sveriges Jaernhandlarefoerbund; Sveriges Bygg & Traevaruhandelsfoerbund.

B

659.8 DEU ISSN 0021-3985
HC79.C6
JAHRBUCH DER ABSATZ- UND VERBRAUCHSFORSCHUNG. Text in German. 1955. q. EUR 54; EUR 43.20 to students; EUR 15 newsstand/cover (effective 2006). adv. bk.rev. reprint service avail. from SCH. **Document type:** *Yearbook, Academic/Scholarly.*
Indexed: DIP, IBR, IBZ, KES, PAIS.
—CCC.
Published by: (Gesellschaft fuer Konsum-, Markt- und Absatzforschung), Duncker und Humblot GmbH, Carl-Heinrich-Becker-Weg 9, Berlin, 12165, Germany. TEL 49-30-7900060, FAX 49-30-79000631, info@duncker-humblot.de, http://www.duncker-humblot.de. Ed. F Wimmer. adv.: page EUR 550; trim 115 x 185. Circ: 1,200 (paid and controlled).

JAPAN (YEAR) MARKETING AND ADVERTISING YEARBOOK. see *ADVERTISING AND PUBLIC RELATIONS*

JAPAN AIR CONDITIONING, HEATING & REFRIGERATION NEWS. see *HEATING, PLUMBING AND REFRIGERATION*

JAPAN FOOD SERVICE JOURNAL. see *HOTELS AND RESTAURANTS*

658.8 JPN
JAPAN MARKETING DATA. Text in English. a. USD 63.
Published by: Intercontinental Marketing Corp., I.P.O. Box 5056, Tokyo, 100-3191, Japan. TEL 81-3-3661-7458, tc9w-ball@asahi-net.or.jp.

JAPAN. STATISTICS BUREAU. MANAGEMENT AND COORDINATION AGENCY. MONTHLY REPORT OF RETAIL PRICES SURVEY/NIHON TOKEI KYOKAI. KOURI BUKKA TOKEI CHOSA HOKOKU. see *BUSINESS AND ECONOMICS—Abstracting, Bibliographies, Statistics*

JAPAN TOY AND GAME JOURNAL. see *SPORTS AND GAMES*

658 659.1 USA
HF5429.7
JONESREPORT PLUS FOR SHOPPING CENTER MARKETING & MANAGEMENT. Text in English. 1978 (Sept.). m. USD 145 domestic; USD 170 foreign (effective 2005). bk.rev. back issues avail. **Document type:** *Newsletter.* **Description:** Supplies international news about marketing and management for shopping center managers and marketing directors. Includes articles on management, marketing, leasing, operations, insurance, advertising, retailing and public relations,.
Formerly: Jonesreport (0889-485X)
—CCC.
Published by: Raven Communications, Inc., PO Box 50038, Indianapolis, IN 46250. TEL 317-576-9889, FAX 317-576-0441, ravencom@comcast.net, ravencom@prodigy.net. Ed., Pub., R&P Major William R Wilburn. Circ: 1,500.

658 GBR
JOURNAL OF ASIA PACIFIC MARKETING. Text in English. 2002. q. **Document type:** *Journal, Academic/Scholarly.*
Published by: Barmarick Publications, Enholmes Hall, Patrington, Hull, East Yorkshire HU12 0PR, United Kingdom. TEL 44-1964-630033, FAX 44-1964-631716, http://www.barmarick.co.uk/.

658 GBR ISSN 1350-231X
➤ **THE JOURNAL OF BRAND MANAGEMENT.** Text in English. 1993. bi-m. GBP 345 in Europe to institutions; USD 550 in US & Canada to institutions; GBP 360 elsewhere to institutions (effective 2005). adv. abstr. 92 p./no. 2 cols./p.; back issues avail.; reprint service avail. from PSC. **Document type:** *Journal, Academic/Scholarly.* **Description:** For those concerned with the launch, development, management and evaluation of brands.
Related titles: Online - full text ed.: ISSN 1479-1803 (from EBSCO Publishing, Gale Group, IngentaConnect, O C L C Online Computer Library Center, Inc., ProQuest Information & Learning, Swets Information Services).
Indexed: ABIn, CommAb, Emerald, RefZh.
—BLDSC (4954.295000), IE, Infotrieve, ingenta. **CCC.**
Published by: Palgrave Macmillan Ltd. (Subsidiary of: Macmillan Publishers Ltd.), Houndmills, Basingstoke, Hants RG21 6XS, United Kingdom. TEL 44-1256-329242, FAX 44-1256-810526, enquiries@hspublications.co.uk, journal-info@palgrave.com, http://www.henrystewart.com/journals/bm/, http://www.palgrave-journals.com/. Circ: 2,000 (paid).

➤ **JOURNAL OF BUSINESS (SPOKANE).** see *BUSINESS AND ECONOMICS—Banking And Finance*

658.8 GBR ISSN 0885-8624
➤ **THE JOURNAL OF BUSINESS AND INDUSTRIAL MARKETING.** Text in English. 1985. 7/yr. EUR 7,611.41 in Europe; USD 2,579 in North America; AUD 9,479 in Australasia; GBP 5,327.66 in UK & elsewhere (effective 2006). adv. bk.rev. illus. index. reprint service avail. from PSC. **Document type:** *Journal, Academic/Scholarly.* **Description:** Informs academics and professionals on new ideas relating to business-to-business marketing. For example, how one company or organization markets its goods/services/ideas to another company or organization.
Related titles: Online - full text ed.: (from EBSCO Publishing, Emerald Group Publishing Limited, Florida Center for Library Automation, Gale Group, IngentaConnect, O C L C Online Computer Library Center, Inc., ProQuest Information & Learning, Swets Information Services).
Indexed: ABIn, BPI, CurCont, DSA, EmerIntel, Emerald, FS&TA.
—BLDSC (4954.661060), IDS, IE, Infotrieve, ingenta. **CCC.**
Published by: Emerald Group Publishing Limited, 60-62 Toller Ln, Bradford, W Yorks BD8 9BY, United Kingdom. TEL 44-1274-777700, FAX 44-1274-785200, help@emeraldinsight.com, infomation@emeraldinsight.com, http://www.emeraldinsight.com/jbim.htm. Ed. Wesley J Johnston. Circ: 3,000. **Subscr. addr. in N America:** Emerald Group Publishing Ltd., 44 Brattle St, 4th Fl, Cambridge, MA 02138. TEL 617-497-2175, 888-622-0075, FAX 617-354-6875.

658 USA ISSN 1051-712X
HF5415.1263
➤ **JOURNAL OF BUSINESS-TO-BUSINESS MARKETING;** innovations in basic and applied research for industrial marketing. Abbreviated title: J B B M. Text in English. 1993. q. USD 340 combined subscription domestic to institutions print & online eds.; USD 459 combined subscription in Canada to institutions print & online eds.; USD 493 combined subscription elsewhere to institutions print & online eds. (effective 2006). adv. bk.rev. 120 p./no. 1 cols./p.; back issues avail.; reprint service avail. from HAW. **Document type:** *Journal, Academic/Scholarly.* **Description:** Features diverse approaches to business marketing theory development and problem solving.
Related titles: Online - full text ed.: ISSN 1547-0628 (from EBSCO Publishing, O C L C Online Computer Library Center, Inc., PQC, Swets Information Services).
Indexed: ABIn, CPM, CommAb, DIP, HRA, IBR, IBZ, M&MA, ORMS, RefZh.
—BLDSC (4954.664000), Haworth, IE. **CCC.**
Published by: Haworth Press, Inc., 10 Alice St, Binghamton, NY 13904-1580. TEL 607-722-5857, 800-429-6784, FAX 607-722-1424, 800-895-0582, getinfo@haworthpress.com, http://www.haworthpress.com/web/JBBM. Ed. J David Lichtental. Pub. William Cohen. R&P Ruth Ann Heath TEL 607-722-5857 ext 316. Adv. contact Rebecca Miller-Baum TEL 607-722-5857 ext 337. B&W page USD 315, color page USD 550; trim 4.375 x 7.125. Circ: 252 (paid).

658.8 AUS ISSN 1442-4827
JOURNAL OF CHINA MARKETING. Text in English. 2000. **Description:** Publishes research articles pertaining to all areas of marketing in China.
Media: Online - full text.
Published by: Griffith University, School of Marketing, Nathan Campus, Nathan, QLD 4111, Australia. TEL 61-7-3875-7232, FAX 61-7-3875-7126, t.tam@mailbox.gu.edu.au, http://www.china-marketing-centre.com/.

JOURNAL OF CONSUMER BEHAVIOUR; an international research review. see *CONSUMER EDUCATION AND PROTECTION*

658.8 GBR ISSN 0736-3761
HF5410
➤ **THE JOURNAL OF CONSUMER MARKETING.** Text in English. 1983. 7/yr. EUR 7,611.41 in Europe; USD 2,719 in North America; AUD 9,809 in Australasia; GBP 5,327.66 in UK & elsewhere (effective 2006). adv. bk.rev. abstr.; illus. index. back issues avail.; reprint service avail. from PSC. **Document type:** *Journal, Academic/Scholarly.* **Description:** Edited for marketers and marketing academics who wish to develop further insight into how people behave as consumers worldwide.
Related titles: CD-ROM ed.; Microform ed.: (from PQC); Online - full text ed.: (from EBSCO Publishing, Emerald Group Publishing Limited, Florida Center for Library Automation, Gale Group, IngentaConnect, O C L C Online Computer Library Center, Inc., ProQuest Information & Learning, Swets Information Services).
Indexed: ABIn, BLI, BPI, CPM, CommAb, CurCont, CurPA, EmerIntel, Emerald, H&TI, PsycInfo, PsycholAb, SCIMP, e-psyche.
—BLDSC (4965.211600), IDS, IE, Infotrieve, ingenta. **CCC.**
Published by: Emerald Group Publishing Limited, 60-62 Toller Ln, Bradford, W Yorks BD8 9BY, United Kingdom. TEL 44-1274-777700, FAX 44-1274-785200, help@emeraldinsight.com, infomation@emeraldinsight.com, http://www.emeraldinsight.com/jcm.htm. Ed. Richard C Leventhal TEL 866-858-7490. Circ: 4,000. **Subscr. addr. in N America:** Emerald Group Publishing Ltd., 44 Brattle St, 4th Fl, Cambridge, MA 02138. TEL 617-497-2175, 888-622-0075, FAX 617-354-6875.

658.8 USA ISSN 0093-5301
HF5415.3 CODEN: JCSRBL
➤ **JOURNAL OF CONSUMER RESEARCH.** Text in English. 1974. q. USD 145 combined subscription to individuals print & online eds.; USD 195 combined subscription to institutions print & online eds.; USD 24 per issue to individuals; USD 48 per issue to institutions (effective 2006). adv. bk.rev. abstr.; illus. index. 148 p./no.; back issues avail.; reprint service avail. from PQC,PSC. **Document type:** *Journal, Academic/Scholarly.* **Description:** Focuses on scholarly research aimed at describing and explaining consumer behavior, in the broadest sense of that term.
Related titles: CD-ROM ed.; Microform ed.: (from PQC); Online - full text ed.: ISSN 1537-5277 (from bigchalk, EBSCO Publishing, Florida Center for Library Automation, Gale Group, JSTOR (Web-based Journal Archive), ProQuest Information & Learning, The Dialog Corporation).
Indexed: ABIn, ASCA, AgeL, Agr, ArtHuCI, BPI, BPIA, BibAg, BusI, CIS, CommAb, CurCont, CurPA, ErgAb, FS&TA, FamI, H&TI, HRIS, IAOP, JCQM, JEL, L&LBA, MResA, ManagCont, PsySCAP, PsycInfo, PsycholAb, RASB, RILM, SCIMP, SFSA, SOPODA, SPAA, SSCI, SWA, T&II, e-psyche.
—BLDSC (4965.215000), CISTI, IDS, IE, Infotrieve, ingenta. **CCC.**
Published by: (Association for Consumer Research), University of Chicago Press, Journals Division, Journals Division, PO Box 37005, Chicago, IL 60637. TEL 773-753-3347, FAX 773-753-0811, 877-705-1879, JCR@bus.wisc.edu, subscriptions@press.uchicago.edu, http://www.journals.uchicago.edu/JCR. Ed. John Deighton. adv.: page USD 615; trim 8.5 x 11. Circ: 2,800 (paid).

658 USA ISSN 0899-8620
HF5415.32
➤ **JOURNAL OF CONSUMER SATISFACTION, DISSATISFACTION AND COMPLAINING BEHAVIOR.** Variant title: C S & D & C B. Text in English. 1988. a. USD 15 domestic; USD 18 foreign (effective 2004). back issues avail. **Document type:** *Journal, Academic/Scholarly.*
Related titles: Online - full text ed.: (from O C L C Online Computer Library Center, Inc., ProQuest Information & Learning).
Indexed: ABIn, H&TI, ISAP, e-psyche.
—BLDSC (4965.216000), IE, Infotrieve, ingenta. **CCC.**
Published by: Consumer Satisfaction, Dissatisfaction and Complaining Behavior, Inc., CS/D&CB, c/o H. Keith Hunt, Ed., 632 TNRB, Brigham Young University, Provo, UT 84602. TEL 801-378-2080, FAX 801-226-7650, hkhunt@byu.edu, http://www.csdcb.org. Ed. H Keith Hunt.

➤ **JOURNAL OF CONTEMPORARY BUSINESS ISSUES.** see *BUSINESS AND ECONOMICS—Management*

658 GBR ISSN 1475-3928
HF5415.5
➤ **JOURNAL OF CUSTOMER BEHAVIOR.** Text in English. 2002. 3/yr. GBP 60 to individuals; GBP 150 to institutions; GBP 250 combined subscription to institutions print & online eds. (effective 2005). **Document type:** *Journal, Academic/Scholarly.* **Description:** Designed to bridge the perceived gap between consumer behavior and organizational buyer behavior.
Related titles: Online - full text ed.: ISSN 1477-6421. GBP 58.75 to individuals; GBP 250 to institutions (effective 2005) (from EBSCO Publishing, Gale Group, IngentaConnect, Swets Information Services).
—BLDSC (4965.955200). **CCC.**
Published by: Westburn Publishers Ltd., 23 Millig St, Helensburgh, Argyll, G84 9LD, United Kingdom. TEL 44-1436-678699, FAX 44-1436-670328, journals@westburn.co.uk, http://www.westburn.co.uk/jcb/. Ed. Michael J Baker. R&P Dr. Anne Foy.

➤ **THE JOURNAL OF DATABASE MARKETING & CUSTOMER STRATEGY MANAGEMENT.** see *BUSINESS AND ECONOMICS—Computer Applications*

▼ ➤ **JOURNAL OF DIGITAL ASSET MANAGEMENT.** see *BUSINESS AND ECONOMICS—Management*

658.8 GBR ISSN 1746-0166
JOURNAL OF DIRECT, DATA AND DIGITAL MARKETING PRACTICE. Text in English. 1999. q. GBP 90 in Europe to individuals teaching, researching or otherwise working full time at an educational establishment; USD 135 in North America to individuals teaching, researching or otherwise working full time at an educational establishment; GBP 105 elsewhere to individuals teaching, researching or otherwise working full time at an educational establishment; GBP 120 in Europe to institutions; USD 180 in North America to institutions; GBP 135 elsewhere to institutions (effective 2004). bk.rev.; software rev.; Website rev. 104 p./no. 1 cols./p.; back issues avail.; reprints avail. **Document type:** *Journal, Trade.* **Description:** Publishes in-depth, peer-reviewed, practitioner-oriented articles written by leading international practitioners, expert consultants and respected academics.
Formerly (until 2005): Interactive Marketing (1463-5178)
Related titles: Online - full text ed.: ISSN 1746-0174 (from EBSCO Publishing, Gale Group, IngentaConnect, O C L C Online Computer Library Center, Inc., ProQuest Information & Learning).
Indexed: ABIn.
—BLDSC (4531.872260), IE, ingenta. **CCC.**
Published by: (Institute of Direct Marketing), Palgrave Macmillan Ltd. (Subsidiary of: Macmillan Publishers Ltd.), Houndmills, Basingstoke, Hants RG21 6XS, United Kingdom. TEL 44-1256-329242, FAX 44-1256-810526, journal-info@palgrave.com, http://www.palgrave-journals.com/. Eds. Derek Holder, Robin Fairlie. Circ: 6,000 (paid and free).

658.8 150 NLD ISSN 0167-4870
HB74.P8
➤ **JOURNAL OF ECONOMIC PSYCHOLOGY.** Text in English. 1981. 6/yr. EUR 174 in Europe to individuals; JPY 23,100 in Japan to individuals; USD 196 elsewhere to individuals; EUR 509 in Europe to institutions; JPY 67,600 in Japan to institutions; USD 569 elsewhere to institutions (effective 2006). adv. index. back issues avail.; reprints avail. **Document type:** *Academic/Scholarly.* **Description:** Presents research on behavioral aspects of economic phenomena and processes, especially socio-psychological.
Related titles: Microform ed.: (from PQC); Online - full text ed.: (from EBSCO Publishing, Gale Group, IngentaConnect, ScienceDirect, Swets Information Services).
Indexed: ABIn, ASCA, BPIA, CJA, CREJ, CurCont, Emerald, FS&TA, FamI, HRIS, HortAb, IBSS, IPsyAb, JEL, ManagCont, PSI, PsycInfo, PsycholAb, RASB, SSCI, T&II, WAE&RSA, e-psyche.
—BLDSC (4973.054100), IDS, IE, Infotrieve, ingenta. **CCC.**
Published by: (Society "European Research in Economic Psychology"), Elsevier BV, North-Holland (Subsidiary of: Elsevier Science & Technology), Sara Burgerhartstraat 25, Amsterdam, 1055 KV, Netherlands. TEL 31-20-485-3911, FAX 31-20-485-2457, nlinfo-f@elsevier.nl, http://www.elsevier.com/locate/joep, http://www.elsevier.nl. Ed. S. Kemp. **Subscr. to:** Elsevier BV, PO Box 211, Amsterdam 1000 AE, Netherlands. TEL 31-20-485-3757, FAX 31-20-485-3432, http://www.elsevier.nl.

658 AUS ISSN 1326-4443
➤ **JOURNAL OF EMPIRICAL GENERALISATIONS IN MARKETING SCIENCE.** Text in English. 1996. irreg. free (effective 2005). back issues avail. **Document type:** *Academic/Scholarly.*
Media: Online - full text.
Published by: University of South Australia North Terrace, Marketing Science Centre, PO Box 2471, Adelaide, SA 5001, Australia. TEL 61-8-83020715, FAX 61-8-83020123, Byron.Sharp@marketingsciencecentre.com, http://www.empgens.com. Ed. Byron M Sharp.

658 382 USA ISSN 1049-6483
HF1416.6.E86 CODEN: JEMAEN
➤ **JOURNAL OF EUROMARKETING.** Abbreviated title: J E M. Text in English. 1991. q. USD 480 combined subscription domestic to institutions print & online eds.; USD 648 combined subscription in Canada to institutions print & online eds.; USD 696 combined subscription elsewhere to institutions print & online eds. (effective academic year 2005 - 2006). adv. bk.rev. 120 p./no. 1 cols./p.; back issues avail.; reprint service avail. from HAW. **Document type:** *Journal, Academic/Scholarly.* **Description:** Provides a forum that fosters a conceptual understanding of the European markets and marketing systems as well as analytical insights; highlights the past, present, and future of European marketing.
Related titles: Microfiche ed.: (from PQC); Microform ed.; Online - full text ed.: ISSN 1528-6967 (from EBSCO Publishing, O C L C Online Computer Library Center, Inc., ProQuest Information & Learning, Swets Information Services).
Indexed: ABIn, CPM, CommAb, DIP, DSA, Emerald, GEOBASE, HortAb, IBR, IBZ, M&MA, NutrAb, PHN&I, RRTA, SOPODA, SUSA, WAE&RSA.
—BLDSC (4979.602750), Haworth, IE, Infotrieve, ingenta. **CCC.**
Published by: International Business Press (Subsidiary of: Haworth Press, Inc.), 10 Alice St, Binghamton, NY 13904. TEL 607-722-5857, 800-429-6784, FAX 607-771-0012, 800-895-0582, getinfo@haworthpress.com, http://www.haworthpress.com/web/JEM. Ed. Erdener Kaynak TEL 717-566-3054. Pub. William Cohen. R&P Ruth Ann Heath TEL 607-722-5857 ext 316. Adv. contact Rebecca Miller-Baum TEL 607-722-5857 ext 337. B&W page USD 315, color page USD 550; trim 4.375 x 7.125. Circ: 153 (paid).

658 746.92 GBR ISSN 1361-2026
HD9940.A1
JOURNAL OF FASHION MARKETING AND MANAGEMENT. Text in English. 1996. q. EUR 716.66 in Europe; USD 669 in North America; AUD 1,349 in Australasia; GBP 499.16 in UK & elsewhere (effective 2006). adv. back issues avail.; reprint service avail. from PSC. **Document type:** *Journal, Academic/Scholarly.* **Description:** Provides a forum for research in the marketing and management of clothing, as opposed to textiles.
Related titles: Online - full text ed.: (from EBSCO Publishing, Emerald Group Publishing Limited, Gale Group, IngentaConnect, O C L C Online Computer Library Center, Inc., ProQuest Information & Learning, Swets Information Services).
Indexed: ABIn, CPM, TTI, WTA.
—BLDSC (4983.860000), IE, Infotrieve, ingenta. **CCC.**
Published by: Emerald Group Publishing Limited, 60-62 Toller Ln, Bradford, W Yorks BD8 9BY, United Kingdom. TEL 44-1274-777700, FAX 44-1274-785200, editorial@emeraldinsight.com, infomation@emeraldinsight.com, http://www.emeraldinsight.com/jfmm.htm. Ed. Mr. Richard Jones. R&P Mr. James Bender. Circ: 600 (paid). **Subscr. addr. in N America:** Emerald Group Publishing Ltd., 44 Brattle St, 4th Fl, Cambridge, MA 02138. TEL 617-497-2175, 888-622-0075, FAX 617-354-6875.

658 332.1 GBR ISSN 1363-0539
➤ **JOURNAL OF FINANCIAL SERVICES MARKETING.** Text in English. 1996. q. GBP 340 in Europe; USD 535 in North America; GBP 355 elsewhere (effective 2005). adv. bk.rev. abstr.; bibl.; charts. 96 p./no. 2 cols./p.; back issues avail.; reprint service avail. from PSC. **Document type:** *Journal, Academic/Scholarly.* **Description:** Keeps readers in touch with how the world's leading financial service providers are designing and marketing their products.
Related titles: Online - full text ed.: ISSN 1479-1846 (from EBSCO Publishing, Gale Group, IngentaConnect, O C L C Online Computer Library Center, Inc., ProQuest Information & Learning, Swets Information Services); Special ed(s).
Indexed: ABIn.
—BLDSC (4984.265500), IE, ingenta. **CCC.**
Published by: Palgrave Macmillan Ltd. (Subsidiary of: Macmillan Publishers Ltd.), Houndmills, Basingstoke, Hants RG21 6XS, United Kingdom. TEL 44-1256-329242, FAX 44-1256-810526, journal-info@palgrave.com, http://www.palgrave-journals.com/. Circ: 600 (paid).

➤ **JOURNAL OF FOOD DISTRIBUTION RESEARCH.** see *FOOD AND FOOD INDUSTRIES*

➤ **JOURNAL OF FOOD PRODUCTS MARKETING;** innovations in food advertising, food promotion, food publicity, food sales promotion. see *FOOD AND FOOD INDUSTRIES*

➤ **JOURNAL OF FOODSERVICE BUSINESS RESEARCH.** see *HOTELS AND RESTAURANTS*

657 USA ISSN 0891-1762
HF1009.5 CODEN: JGMAE3
➤ **JOURNAL OF GLOBAL MARKETING.** Abbreviated title: J G M. Text in English. 1987. q. USD 500 combined subscription domestic to institutions print & online eds.; USD 675 combined subscription in Canada to institutions print & online eds.; USD 725 combined subscription elsewhere to institutions print & online eds. (effective academic year 2005 - 2006). adv. bk.rev. illus. 120 p./no. 1 cols./p.; back issues avail.; reprint service avail. from HAW. **Document type:** *Journal, Academic/Scholarly.* **Description:** Addresses marketing challenges, opportunities, and problems encountered by firms, industries, and governments on a global scale.
Related titles: Microfiche ed.: (from PQC); Microform ed.; Online - full text ed.: ISSN 1528-6975 (from EBSCO Publishing, O C L C Online Computer Library Center, Inc., Swets Information Services).
Indexed: ABIn, BPI, BusEdI, CPM, CommAb, CurCont, ESPM, Emerald, HRA, IBR, IBZ, IPSA, M&MA, PAIS, PsycInfo, PsycholAb, RefZh, RiskAb.
—BLDSC (4996.300000), Haworth, IDS, IE, Infotrieve, ingenta. **CCC.**
Published by: International Business Press (Subsidiary of: Haworth Press, Inc.), 10 Alice St, Binghamton, NY 13904. TEL 607-722-5857, 800-429-6784, FAX 607-771-0012, 800-895-0582, getinfo@haworthpress.com, http://www.haworthpress.com/web/JGM/. Ed. Erdener Kaynak TEL 717-566-3054. Pub. William Cohen. R&P Ruth Ann Heath TEL 607-722-5857 ext 316. Adv. contact Rebecca Miller-Baum TEL 607-722-5857 ext 337. B&W page USD 315, color page USD 550; trim 4.375 x 7.125. Circ: 425 (paid).

➤ **THE JOURNAL OF HIGH TECHNOLOGY MANAGEMENT RESEARCH.** see *BUSINESS AND ECONOMICS—Computer Applications*

658.8 USA ISSN 1539-0942
RA965.5 CODEN: JHMPAH
➤ **JOURNAL OF HOSPITAL MARKETING & PUBLIC RELATIONS.** Abbreviated title: J H M P R. Text in English. 1987. s-a. USD 400 combined subscription domestic to institutions print & online eds.; USD 540 combined subscription in Canada to institutions print & online eds.; USD 580 combined subscription elsewhere to institutions print & online eds. (effective academic year 2005 - 2006). adv. bk.rev. 120 p./no.; back issues avail.; reprint service avail. from HAW. **Document type:** *Journal, Academic/Scholarly.* **Description:** Presents new and effective ways of marketing hospital services. Shares current marketing applications and methodologies by professional hospital marketing consultants and educators.
Formerly (until 2002): Journal of Hospital Marketing (0883-7570)
Related titles: Microfiche ed.: (from PQC); Microform ed.; Online - full text ed.: ISSN 1539-0934. 2002. free to institutions (effective 2003); free with print subs. (from EBSCO Publishing, O C L C Online Computer Library Center, Inc., Swets Information Services).
Indexed: CINAHL, CurCont, DIP, ExcerpMed, HospLI, IBR, IBZ, MCR, MEDLINE, RefZh.
—BLDSC (5003.295000), GNLM, Haworth. **CCC.**
Published by: Best Business Books (Subsidiary of: Haworth Press, Inc.), 10 Alice St, Binghamton, NY 13904. TEL 607-722-5857, 800-429-6784, FAX 607-771-0012, 800-896-0582, getinfo@haworthpress.com, http://www.haworthpress.com/web/JHMPR. Ed. Tony Carter. Pub. William Cohen. R&P Ruth Ann Heath TEL 607-722-5857 ext 316. Adv. contact Rebecca Miller-Baum TEL 607-722-5857 ext 337. B&W page USD 315, color page USD 550; trim 4.375 x 7.125. Circ: 207 (paid).

➤ **JOURNAL OF HOSPITALITY & LEISURE MARKETING;** the international forum for research, theory & practice. see *HOTELS AND RESTAURANTS*

658.8 USA ISSN 1094-9968
HF5415.126
➤ **JOURNAL OF INTERACTIVE MARKETING.** Text in English. 1987. q. USD 845 domestic; USD 885 in Canada & Mexico; USD 919 elsewhere; USD 930 combined subscription domestic print & online eds.; USD 970 combined subscription in Canada & Mexico print & online eds.; USD 1,004 combined subscription elsewhere print & online eds. (effective 2006). adv. bk.rev.; software rev. back issues avail.; reprint service avail. from PSC. **Document type:** *Journal, Academic/Scholarly.* **Description:** Offers an exchange of ideas in the field of direct marketing and the emerging field of interactive marketing. Designed to provide a bridge between direct-marketing practitioners and the academic research community.
Formerly: Journal of Direct Marketing (0892-0591); Which incorporated (1986-1987): Journal of Direct Marketing Research (0888-9295)
Related titles: Microform ed.: (from PQC); Online - full text ed.: ISSN 1520-6653. 1998. USD 845 (effective 2006) (from EBSCO Publishing, ProQuest Information & Learning, Swets Information Services, The Dialog Corporation, Wiley InterScience).
Indexed: ABIn, BPI, CommAb, CurCont, Emerald.
—BLDSC (5007.539600), IDS, IE, Infotrieve, ingenta. **CCC.**
Published by: (Direct Marketing Educational Foundation, Inc.), Jossey-Bass Inc., Publishers (Subsidiary of: John Wiley & Sons, Inc.), 989 Market St, San Francisco, CA 94103-1741. TEL 415-433-1740, FAX 415-433-0499, jbsubs@jbp.com, http://www3.interscience.wiley.com/cgi-bin/jhome/38979, http://www.josseybass.com. Eds. Russell S Winer, Venkatesh Shankar. adv.: B&W page GBP 640, color page GBP 1,515; trim 216 x 279. Circ: 1,000. **Subscr. outside the Americas to:** John Wiley & Sons Ltd., The Atrium, Southern Gate, Chichester, West Sussex PO19 8SQ, United Kingdom. TEL 44-1243-843335, 0800-243407, FAX 44-1243-843232.

658 640.73 USA ISSN 0896-1530
HF5415.2 CODEN: JIMREY
➤ **JOURNAL OF INTERNATIONAL CONSUMER MARKETING.** Text in English. 1988. q. USD 480 combined subscription domestic to institutions print & online eds.; USD 648 combined subscription in Canada to institutions print & online eds.; USD 696 combined subscription elsewhere to institutions print & online eds. (effective academic year 2005 - 2006). adv. bk.rev. back issues avail.; reprint service avail. from HAW. **Document type:** *Journal, Academic/Scholarly.* **Description:** Publishes articles written by practitioners and public policymakers as well as academicians from a variety of countries. Offers managerial insights to practicing international business persons as well as to policymakers in governments and international agencies and organizations to enable them to formulate need-oriented action programs and policies.
Formerly: International Journal of Cross-Cultural Consumer Behavior
Related titles: Microfiche ed.: (from PQC); Microform ed.; Online - full text ed.: ISSN 1528-7068. free to institutions (effective 2003); free with print subs. (from EBSCO Publishing, O C L C Online Computer Library Center, Inc., ProQuest Information & Learning, Swets Information Services).

B

Indexed: ABIn, BusEdI, CPM, DIP, ESPM, FS&TA, IBR, IBZ, M&MA, PsycInfo, PsycholAb, RiskAb, SOPODA, TTI.
—BLDSC (5007.633000), Haworth, IE, Infotrieve, ingenta. **CCC.**
Published by: International Business Press (Subsidiary of: Haworth Press, Inc.), 10 Alice St, Binghamton, NY 13904. TEL 607-722-5857, 800-429-6784, FAX 607-771-0012, 800-895-0582, getinfo@haworthpress.com, http://www.haworthpress.com/web/JICM. Ed. Erdener Kaynak TEL 717-566-3054. Pub. William Cohen. R&P Ruth Ann Heath TEL 607-722-5857 ext 316. Adv. contact Rebecca Miller-Baum TEL 607-722-5857 ext 337. B&W page USD 315, color page USD 550; trim 4.375 x 7.125. Circ: 266 (paid).

658.8 USA ISSN 1069-031X
HF1416
➤ **JOURNAL OF INTERNATIONAL MARKETING.** Text in English. 1992. q. USD 95 domestic to individuals; USD 120 foreign to individuals; USD 180 domestic to institutions; USD 205 foreign to institutions; USD 53 to members (effective 2005). adv. bk.rev. abstr.; bibl.; charts; illus.; stat. reprint service avail. from PQC,PSC. **Document type:** *Journal, Academic/Scholarly.* **Description:** Dedicated to advancing international marketing practice, research and theory.
Related titles: Microform ed.: (from PQC); Online - full text ed.: ISSN 1547-7215 (from bigchalk, EBSCO Publishing, H.W. Wilson, Northern Light Technology, Inc., O C L C Online Computer Library Center, Inc., ProQuest Information & Learning).
Indexed: ABIn, BPI, CurCont, Emerald, SSCI, WBA, WMB.
—BLDSC (5007.673400), IDS, IE, ingenta. **CCC.**
Published by: American Marketing Association, 311 S Wacker Dr, Ste 5800, Chicago, IL 60606. TEL 312-542-9000, 800-262-1150, FAX 312-542-9001, info@ama.org, http://www.marketingpower.com/live/content1055.php, http://www.ama.org/pubs/jim/index.html. Ed. S Tamer Cavusgil. Pub. Jack Hollfelder. R&P Rochelle Amos TEL 312-542-9022. Adv. contact Sally Schmidt. page USD 335. Circ: 850. **Subscr. to:** Allen Press Inc., PO Box 1897, Lawrence, KS 66044.

658.8 382 AUS ISSN 1324-5864
➤ **JOURNAL OF INTERNATIONAL MARKETING AND EXPORTING.** Text in English. 1996. s-a. AUD 66 domestic; AUD 77 foreign (effective 2003). adv. back issues avail. **Document type:** *Journal, Academic/Scholarly.* **Description:** Provides a forum for academics and practitioners to disseminate scholarly information in the areas of exporting, marketing, and management.
Published by: University of Southern Queensland, Research Centre for International Marketing, Exporting and Trade, Department of Marketing, Faculty of Business (Toowoomba), GPO Box K789, Perth, W.A. 6001, Australia. gogunmok@ecel.uwa.edu.au, http://www.imm.ecel.uwa.edu.au/reschdx/cime/journal_new.html. Ed. Gabriel Ogunmokun. Adv. contact Derry Simpson. Circ: 300.

658.8 GBR ISSN 1356-0565
HF5438
➤ **JOURNAL OF INTERNATIONAL SELLING & SALES MANAGEMENT.** Text in English. 1995. 3/yr., latest vol.8, 2002. GBP 50 (effective 2003). bk.rev. abstr. back issues avail. **Document type:** *Journal, Academic/Scholarly.* **Description:** Covers selling, marketing, marketing research and international business.
Indexed: Emerald.
—BLDSC (5007.686430), IE, ingenta.
Published by: (Institute of Industrial Selling), European Marketing Association/Association Europeenne pour le Marketing, 18 St Peters Steps, Brixham, Devon TQ5 9TE, United Kingdom. Ed. David W Newill. Adv. contact David Newill. **Co-sponsors:** Industrial Marketing Association, Sales Section; Federacion Internacional de Marketing.

➤ **JOURNAL OF INTERNET PURCHASING.** see *COMPUTERS—Internet*

658 USA ISSN 0276-1467
HF5410
➤ **JOURNAL OF MACROMARKETING.** Text in English. 1981. s-a. USD 282, GBP 182 to institutions; USD 293, GBP 190 combined subscription to institutions print & online eds. (effective 2006). bk.rev. illus. back issues avail.; reprints avail. **Document type:** *Journal, Academic/Scholarly.* **Description:** Focuses on important social issues and how they are impacted by marketing and on how society influences the conduct of macromarketing. Covers wide range of social science and business disciplines including management, economics, sociology, and history. Articles may involve explanatory theory, empirical studies or methodological treatment of tests.
Related titles: Online - full text ed.: ISSN 1552-6534. USD 279, GBP 180 to institutions (effective 2006) (from C S A, EBSCO Publishing, Northern Light Technology, Inc., O C L C Online Computer Library Center, Inc., Sage Publications, Inc., Swets Information Services).
Indexed: ABIn, BPIA, CPM, CommAb, HRA, PRA, RefZh.
—BLDSC (5010.745000), IE, Infotrieve, ingenta. **CCC.**
Published by: Sage Publications, Inc., 2455 Teller Rd, Thousand Oaks, CA 91320. TEL 805-499-0721, FAX 805-499-0871, info@sagepub.com, http://www.sagepub.com/journal.aspx?pid=204. Ed. Clifford J Shultz II. **Subscr. to:** Sage Publications Ltd., 1 Oliver's Yard, 55 City Rd, London EC1 1SP, United Kingdom. TEL 44-20-73740645, FAX 44-20-73748741, subscription@sagepub.co.uk.

➤ **JOURNAL OF MANAGERIAL ISSUES.** see *BUSINESS AND ECONOMICS—Management*

658 USA ISSN 0022-2429
HF5415.A2 CODEN: JMKTAK
➤ **JOURNAL OF MARKETING.** Text in English. 1934. q. USD 95 domestic to individuals; USD 120 foreign to individuals; USD 235 domestic to institutions; USD 265 foreign to institutions; USD 53 to members (effective 2005). adv. bk.rev. abstr.; bibl.; charts; illus.; stat. index. back issues avail.; reprint service avail. from PQC,PSC. **Document type:** *Journal, Academic/Scholarly.* **Description:** Designed to bridge the gap between marketing theory and application.
Related titles: Microform ed.: (from PQC); Online - full text ed.: ISSN 1547-7185 (from Chadwyck-Healey Inc., EBSCO Publishing, Gale Group, H.W. Wilson, JSTOR (Web-based Journal Archive), Northern Light Technology, Inc., O C L C Online Computer Library Center, Inc., ProQuest Information & Learning).
Indexed: ABIn, ADPA, ASCA, ASEANManA, ATI, AcaI, BAS, BLI, BPI, BPIA, BRI, BusI, CBRI, CIS, CPM, CommAb, CompAb, CurCont, CurPA, DIP, Emerald, H&TI, IBR, IBZ, IMI, JCQM, JEL, KES, LogistBibl, M&MA, MResA, ManagCont, PAIS, PCI, PROMT, PsySCAP, PsycInfo, PsycholAb, RASB, RILM, RPFIA, RefZh, SCIMP, SSCI, T&II, e-psyche.
—BLDSC (5012.100000), CASDDS, CISTI, IDS, IE, Infotrieve, ingenta. **CCC.**
Published by: American Marketing Association, 311 S Wacker Dr, Ste 5800, Chicago, IL 60606. TEL 312-542-9000, 800-262-1150, FAX 312-542-9001, info@ama.org, http://www.marketingpower.com, http://www.ama.org. Ed. Ruth N Bolton. Pub. Jack Hollfelder. R&P Rochelle Amos TEL 312-542-9022. Adv. contact Sally Schmidt. page USD 335. Circ: 10,000 (paid).

658 USA ISSN 1046-669X
HF5415.129 CODEN: JMKCE7
➤ **JOURNAL OF MARKETING CHANNELS**; distribution systems, strategy, and management. Abbreviated title: J M C. Text in English. 1991. q. USD 350 combined subscription domestic to institutions print & online eds.; USD 472.50 combined subscription in Canada to institutions print & online eds.; USD 507.50 combined subscription elsewhere to institutions print & online eds. (effective academic year 2005 - 2006). adv. bk.rev. 120 p./no. 1 cols./p.; back issues avail.; reprint service avail. from HAW. **Document type:** *Journal, Academic/Scholarly.* **Description:** Focuses on distribution systems, strategy and management.
Related titles: Microfiche ed.: (from PQC); Microform ed.; Online - full text ed.: ISSN 1540-7039. free to institutions (effective 2003); free with print subs. (from EBSCO Publishing, O C L C Online Computer Library Center, Inc., Swets Information Services).
Indexed: ABIn, CPM, FS&TA, HRA, IBR, IBZ, Inspec, M&MA, RRTA, RefZh, SOPODA, WAE&RSA.
—BLDSC (5012.113000), AskIEEE, Haworth, IE, Infotrieve, ingenta. **CCC.**
Published by: Best Business Books (Subsidiary of: Haworth Press, Inc.), 10 Alice St, Binghamton, NY 13904. TEL 607-722-5857, 800-429-6784, FAX 607-771-0012, 800-896-0582, getinfo@haworthpress.com, http://www.haworthpress.com/web/JMC. Ed. Lou E Belton. Pub. William Cohen. R&P Ruth Ann Heath TEL 607-722-5857 ext 316. Adv. contact Rebecca Miller-Baum TEL 607-722-5857 ext 337. B&W page USD 315, color page USD 550; trim 4.375 x 7.125. Circ: 271 (paid).

658.82 GBR ISSN 1352-7266
HF5415.123
➤ **JOURNAL OF MARKETING COMMUNICATIONS.** Text in English. 1995. q. GBP 506, USD 831 combined subscription to institutions print & online eds. (effective 2006). bibl. back issues avail.; reprint service avail. from PSC. **Document type:** *Journal, Academic/Scholarly.* **Description:** Devoted to publishing research papers and information articles on all aspects of marketing communications and promotion management.
Related titles: Online - full text ed.: ISSN 1466-4445. GBP 481, USD 789 (effective 2006) (from EBSCO Publishing, Gale Group, IngentaConnect, O C L C Online Computer Library Center, Inc., Swets Information Services).
Indexed: CPM, CurCont, DIP, Emerald, IBR, IBZ, PsycInfo, PsycholAb.
—BLDSC (5012.114000), IDS, IE, Infotrieve, ingenta. **CCC.**
Published by: Routledge (Subsidiary of: Taylor & Francis Group), 4 Park Sq, Milton Park, Abingdon, Oxon OX14 4RN, United Kingdom. TEL 44-1235-828600, FAX 44-1235-829000, info@routledge.co.uk, http://www.tandf.co.uk/journals/titles/13527266.asp, http://www.routledge.co.uk. Ed. Philip J Kitchen. R&P Sally Sweet. **Subscr. to:** Taylor & Francis Ltd, Journals Customer Service, Rankine Rd, Basingstoke, Hants RG24 8PR, United Kingdom. TEL 44-1256-813000, FAX 44-1256-330245.

658.8071 USA ISSN 0273-4753
HF5415
➤ **JOURNAL OF MARKETING EDUCATION.** Text in English. 1979. 3/yr. USD 379, GBP 245 to institutions; USD 394, GBP 255 combined subscription to institutions print & online eds. (effective 2006). adv. illus. Index. reprints avail. **Document type:** *Journal, Academic/Scholarly.* **Description:** Provides outstanding value to business educators. Each new issue provides many developmental insights, as well as action-oriented suggestions that are particularly helpful on a day-to-day basis. Forum for the exchange of ideas, information and experiences related to the process of marketing.
Related titles: Online - full text ed.: ISSN 1552-6550. USD 375, GBP 242 to institutions (effective 2006) (from C S A, EBSCO Publishing, O C L C Online Computer Library Center, Inc., ProQuest Information & Learning, Sage Publications, Inc., Swets Information Services).
Indexed: ABIn, BusEdI.
—BLDSC (5012.115000), IE, Infotrieve, ingenta. **CCC.**
Published by: Sage Publications, Inc., 2455 Teller Rd, Thousand Oaks, CA 91320. TEL 805-499-0721, 800-818-7243, FAX 805-499-8096, 800-583-2665, info@sagepub.com, http://www.sagepub.com/journal.aspx?pid=117. Ed. Douglas J Lincoln. Adv. contact Kirsten Beaulieu TEL 805-499-0721 ext 7160. B&W page USD 350. Circ: 400. **Subscr. to:** Sage Publications Ltd., 1 Oliver's Yard, 55 City Rd, London EC1 1SP, United Kingdom. TEL 44-20-73740645, FAX 44-20-73748741, subscription@sagepub.co.uk. **Co-sponsor:** Marketing Educators' Association.

➤ **JOURNAL OF MARKETING FOR HIGHER EDUCATION.** see *EDUCATION—Higher Education*

658 GBR ISSN 0267-257X
➤ **JOURNAL OF MARKETING MANAGEMENT.** Text in English. 1985. 5/yr. free to members (effective 2004). adv. bk.rev.; software rev. a.index. 1200 p./no. 1 cols./p.; reprints avail. **Document type:** *Journal, Academic/Scholarly.* **Description:** Concerned with all aspects of the management of marketing and is intended to provide a forum for the exchange of the latest research ideas and best practice in the field of marketing as a whole.
Related titles: Online - full text ed.: ISSN 1472-1376. GBP 75 to individuals; GBP 475 to institutions (effective 2002) (from EBSCO Publishing, Gale Group, IngentaConnect, Swets Information Services).
Indexed: ABIn, CPM, Emerald.
—BLDSC (5012.125000), IE, Infotrieve, ingenta. **CCC.**
Published by: Westburn Publishers Ltd., 23 Millig St, Helensburgh, Argyll, G84 9LD, United Kingdom. TEL 44-1436-678699, FAX 44-1436-670328, jmm@westburn.co.uk, journals@westburn.co.uk, http://www.journalofmarketingmanagement.com/jmm/, http://www.westburn.co.uk/. Ed. Susan Hart. R&P Dr. Anne Foy. Circ: 1,800.

658.83 USA ISSN 0022-2437
HF5415.2 CODEN: JMKRAE
➤ **JOURNAL OF MARKETING RESEARCH.** Text in English. 1964. q. USD 95 domestic to non-members; USD 120 foreign to non-members; USD 235 domestic to institutions; USD 265 foreign to institutions; USD 53 to members (effective 2005). adv. bk.rev. charts; illus. index, cum.index every 5 yrs. back issues avail.; reprint service avail. from PQC,PSC. **Document type:** *Journal, Academic/Scholarly.* **Description:** Covers methodology and problems of research in marketing, discusses current trends and experiments in social psychology and other behavioral sciences as they affect marketing.
Related titles: Microform ed.: (from PQC); Online - full text ed.: ISSN 1547-7193 (from Chadwyck-Healey Inc., EBSCO Publishing, Gale Group, H.W. Wilson, JSTOR (Web-based Journal Archive), O C L C Online Computer Library Center, Inc., ProQuest Information & Learning).
Indexed: ABIn, ASCA, ATI, AgeL, BPI, BPIA, BusI, CIS, CPM, CommAb, CurCont, CurPA, DIP, ESPM, Emerald, FS&TA, FamI, IBR, IBZ, JCQM, JEL, KES, M&MA, MResA, ManagCont, ORMS, PAIS, PCI, PsySCAP, PsycInfo, PsycholAb, QC&AS, RASB, RefZh, RiskAb, SCIMP, SSCI, ST&MA, T&II, e-psyche.
—BLDSC (5012.150000), CISTI, IDS, IE, Infotrieve, ingenta. **CCC.**
Published by: American Marketing Association, 311 S Wacker Dr, Ste 5800, Chicago, IL 60606. TEL 312-542-9000, 800-262-1150, FAX 312-542-9001, info@ama.org, http://www.marketingpower.com/live/content1054C363.php. Eds. Dick R Wittink, Wagner A. Kamakura. Pub. Jack Hollfelder. R&P Rochelle Amos TEL 312-542-9022. Adv. contacts Sally Schmitz, Richard Ballschmiede. B&W page USD 900. Circ: 9,000.

658.8 USA ISSN 1069-6679
HF5410
➤ **JOURNAL OF MARKETING THEORY AND PRACTICE.** Short title: J M T P. Text in English. 1992. q. USD 80 domestic to individuals; USD 96 foreign to individuals; USD 195 domestic to institutions; USD 227 foreign to institutions (effective 2006). adv. abstr.; bibl.; charts; stat. 80 p./no. 2 cols./p.; back issues avail. **Document type:** *Journal, Academic/Scholarly.* **Description:** Looks to bridge the gap im marketing between practicioners and academicians.

Related titles: Fax ed.; Microform ed.; Online - full text ed.: (from EBSCO Publishing, O C L C Online Computer Library Center, Inc., ProQuest Information & Learning).
Indexed: ABIn.
—BLDSC (5012.155000), IE, ingenta.
Published by: M.E. Sharpe, Inc., 80 Business Park Dr, Armonk, NY 10504. TEL 914-273-1800, 800-541-6563, FAX 914-273-2106, info@mesharpe.com, http://www.mesharpe.com. adv.: B&W page USD 500. Circ: 1,000 (paid).

658.8 610 615 NGA ISSN 0331-0124
JOURNAL OF MEDICAL AND PHARMACEUTICAL MARKETING. Text in English. 1972. bi-m. USD 115.20. adv. illus.
Related titles: Online - full text ed.
Indexed: IPA.
Published by: Fred Atoki Publishing Co. Ltd., Plot 25 Kekere-Ekun St., Orile-Iganmu, PO Box 7313, Lagos, Nigeria. Circ: 16,000.

JOURNAL OF MEDICAL MARKETING; device, diagnostic and pharmaceutical marketing. see *PHARMACY AND PHARMACOLOGY*

JOURNAL OF MODERN BUSINESS. see *BUSINESS AND ECONOMICS—Management*

658.8 USA ISSN 1049-5142
CODEN: JNPMEZ
➤ **JOURNAL OF NONPROFIT & PUBLIC SECTOR MARKETING.** Abbreviated title: J N P S M. Text in English. 1986. s-a. USD 400 combined subscription domestic to institutions print & online eds.; USD 540 combined subscription in Canada to institutions print & online eds.; USD 580 combined subscription elsewhere to institutions print & online eds. (effective 2006). adv. bk.rev. 120 p./no. 1 cols./p.; back issues avail.; reprint service avail. from HAW. **Document type:** *Journal, Academic/Scholarly.* **Description:** Provides a forum for the development of marketing thought and for the dissemination of marketing knowledge in the nonprofit and public sector of the economy.
Former titles (until 1991): Journal of Marketing for Mental Health; Psychotherapy Marketing and Practice Development Reports (0883-7589)
Related titles: Microfiche ed.: (from PQC); Microform ed.; Online - full text ed.: ISSN 1540-6997. free to institutions (effective 2003); free with print subs. (from EBSCO Publishing, Swets Information Services).
Indexed: ABIn, DIP, HRA, IBR, IBZ, M&MA, MEDLINE, PAIS, PSA, PsycInfo, PsycholAb, SWR&A.
—BLDSC (5022.842300), GNLM, Haworth, IE, ingenta. **CCC.**
Published by: Haworth Press, Inc., 10 Alice St, Binghamton, NY 13904-1580. TEL 607-722-5857, 800-429-6784, FAX 607-722-1424, getinfo@haworthpress.com, http://www.haworthpress.com/web/JNPSM. Ed. Walter W Wymer Jr. Pub. William Cohen. R&P Ruth Ann Heath TEL 607-722-5857 ext 316. Adv. contact Rebecca Miller-Baum TEL 607-722-5857 ext 337. B&W page USD 315, color page USD 550; trim 4.375 x 7.125. Circ: 153 (paid).

658 USA ISSN 0885-3134
HF5438
➤ **JOURNAL OF PERSONAL SELLING AND SALES MANAGEMENT.** Text in English. 1980. q. USD 65 domestic to individuals; USD 81 foreign to individuals; USD 219 combined subscription domestic to institutions print & online eds.; USD 251 combined subscription foreign to institutions print & online eds. (effective 2006). bk.rev. bibl.; charts. cum.index: 1980-1994. back issues avail.; reprints avail. **Document type:** *Journal, Academic/Scholarly.* **Description:** Covers most aspects of personal selling and sales management. Purpose is to bridge gap between academic and business communities involved in selling and sales management. Audience consists of academics, researchers, trainers, sales executives, and students.
Related titles: Microfilm ed.: (from PQC); Online - full text ed.: ISSN 1557-7813. 2002 (Dec.) (from EBSCO Publishing, Gale Group, O C L C Online Computer Library Center, Inc., ProQuest Information & Learning, Swets Information Services).
Indexed: ABIn, ESPM, PsycInfo, RiskAb.
—BLDSC (5030.870000), IE, ingenta.
Published by: (Phi Sigma Epsilon), M.E. Sharpe, Inc., 80 Business Park Dr, Armonk, NY 10504. TEL 914-273-1800, 800-541-6563, FAX 914-273-2106, custserv@mesharpe.com, http://www.mesharpe.com/mall/results1.asp. Ed. Greg W Marshall. Circ: 500 (paid).

➤ **JOURNAL OF PHARMACEUTICAL MARKETING AND MANAGEMENT.** see *PHARMACY AND PHARMACOLOGY*

➤ **JOURNAL OF POLITICAL MARKETING**; political campaigns in the new millennium. see *POLITICAL SCIENCE*

658 GBR ISSN 1061-0421
HF5415.153
THE JOURNAL OF PRODUCT AND BRAND MANAGEMENT. Text in English. 1992. 7/yr. EUR 7,611.41 in Europe; USD 2,719 in North America; AUD 9,809 in Australasia; GBP 5,327.66 in UK & elsewhere (effective 2006). reprint service avail. from PSC. **Document type:** *Journal, Academic/Scholarly.* **Description:** Offers a direct route to worldwide research at the cutting edge of product and brand management and pricing. Offering expert analysis and practical recommendations to aid decision making and stimulate further research activity, it provides an invaluable source of knowledge for academics and corporate practitioners.
Incorporates: Pricing Strategy and Practice (0968-4905)
Related titles: Online - full content ed.; Online - full text ed.: (from EBSCO Publishing, Emerald Group Publishing Limited, Gale Group, IngentaConnect, O C L C Online Computer Library Center, Inc., ProQuest Information & Learning, Swets Information Services).
Indexed: ABIn, Emerald, Inspec.
—BLDSC (5042.648000), IE, Infotrieve, ingenta. **CCC.**
Published by: Emerald Group Publishing Limited, 60-62 Toller Ln, Bradford, W Yorks BD8 9BY, United Kingdom. TEL 44-1274-777700, FAX 44-1274-785200, infomation@emeraldinsight.com, http://www.emeraldinsight.com/jpbm.htm. Eds. Michelle A Morganosky TEL 217-333-3217, Richard C Leventhal TEL 866-858-7490. **Subscr. addr. in N America:** Emerald Group Publishing Ltd., 44 Brattle St, 4th Fl, Cambridge, MA 02138. TEL 617-497-2175, 888-622-0075, FAX 617-354-6875.

658.8 USA ISSN 0748-6766
HF5410
➤ **JOURNAL OF PUBLIC POLICY & MARKETING.** Text in English. 1982. s-a. USD 75 domestic to individuals; USD 100 foreign to individuals; USD 115 domestic to institutions; USD 135 foreign to institutions; USD 53 to members (effective 2005). adv. abstr. back issues avail.; reprint service avail. from PSC. **Document type:** *Journal, Academic/Scholarly.* **Description:** Covers the public policy, legal, and regulatory activities related to the marketing arena.
Formerly (until 1982): Journal of Marketing and Public Policy (0743-9156)
Related titles: Online - full text ed.: ISSN 1547-7207 (from EBSCO Publishing, H.W. Wilson, Northern Light Technology, Inc., O C L C Online Computer Library Center, Inc., ProQuest Information & Learning).
Indexed: ABIn, ASCA, BPI, CommAb, CurCont, LRI, PAIS, PRA, PsycInfo, PsycholAb, SSCI, V&AA.
—BLDSC (5043.645000), IDS, IE, ingenta. **CCC.**
Published by: American Marketing Association, 311 S Wacker Dr, Ste 5800, Chicago, IL 60606. TEL 312-542-9000, 800-262-1150, FAX 312-542-9001, info@ama.org, http://www.marketingpower.com, http://www.ama.org. Eds. J Craig Andrews, Joel B. Cohen. Pub. Jack Hollfelder. R&P Rochelle Amos TEL 312-542-9022. Adv. contacts Richard Ballschmiede, Sally Schmitz. Circ: 700 (paid). **Subscr. to:** Allen Press Inc., PO Box 1897, Lawrence, KS 66044. TEL 785-843-1235, FAX 785-843-1235, 785-843-1274, http://www.allenpress.com/.

658 GBR ISSN 1478-4092
HD39.5 CODEN: EJPMFL
➤ **JOURNAL OF PURCHASING & SUPPLY MANAGEMENT.** Text in English. 1994. 6/yr. EUR 100 in Europe to individuals; JPY 13,500 in Japan to individuals; USD 125 elsewhere to individuals; EUR 402 in Europe to institutions; JPY 53,400 in Japan to institutions; USD 450 elsewhere to institutions (effective 2006). bk.rev. back issues avail. **Document type:** *Academic/Scholarly.* **Description:** Covers every aspect of the purchasing of goods and services in all contexts.
Formerly: European Journal of Purchasing and Supply Management (0969-7012)
Related titles: Microform ed.: (from PQC); Online - full text ed.: (from EBSCO Publishing, Gale Group, IngentaConnect, ScienceDirect, Swets Information Services).
Indexed: Inspec.
—BLDSC (5043.673000), IE, ingenta. **CCC.**
Published by: Pergamon (Subsidiary of: Elsevier Science & Technology), The Boulevard, Langford Ln, East Park, Kidlington, Oxford OX5 1GB, United Kingdom. TEL 44-1865-843000, FAX 44-1865-843010, http://www.elsevier.com/locate/pursup. Ed. Finn Wynstra. **Subscr. to:** Elsevier BV, PO Box 211, Amsterdam 1000 AE, Netherlands. TEL 31-20-485-3757, FAX 31-20-485-3432, nlinfo-f@elsevier.nl, http://www.elsevier.nl.

658.87 GBR ISSN 0022-4359
HF5001
➤ **JOURNAL OF RETAILING.** Text in English. 1925. 4/yr. EUR 128 in Europe to individuals; JPY 16,800 in Japan to individuals; USD 141 to individuals except Europe and Japan; EUR 346 in Europe to institutions; JPY 46,000 in Japan to institutions; USD 387 to institutions except Europe and Japan (effective 2006). adv. bk.rev. bibl.; charts; illus. cum.index every 2 and 10 yrs. back issues avail.; reprint service avail. from PQC,ISI. **Document type:** *Academic/Scholarly.* **Description:** Devoted to advancing the state of knowledge and its application with respect to all aspects of retailing, its management, evolution, and current theory.
Related titles: Microform ed.: (from PQC); Online - full text ed.: (from EBSCO Publishing, Florida Center for Library Automation, Gale Group, H.W. Wilson, IngentaConnect, Northern Light Technology, Inc., O C L C Online Computer Library Center, Inc., ScienceDirect, Swets Information Services, The Dialog Corporation).
Indexed: ABIn, ADPA, ASCA, ASEANManA, ATI, AgeL, BPI, BPIA, BusI, CPM, CurCont, ESPM, Emerald, IBR, IBZ, KES, M&MA, ManagCont, ORMS, PAIS, PsycInfo, PsycholAb, RDA, RPFIA, RefZh, RiskAb, SSCI, T&II, WAE&RSA, e-psyche.
—BLDSC (5052.040000), IE, Infotrieve, ingenta. **CCC.**
Published by: (New York University, Leonard N. Stern School of Business USA), Pergamon (Subsidiary of: Elsevier Science & Technology), The Boulevard, Langford Ln, East Park, Kidlington, Oxford OX5 1GB, United Kingdom. TEL 44-1865-843000, FAX 44-1865-843010, http://www.elsevier.com/locate/jretai. Eds. Dhruv Grewal, Michael Levy. Circ: 3,200. **Subscr. to:** Elsevier BV, PO Box 211, Amsterdam 1000 AE, Netherlands. TEL 31-20-485-3757, FAX 31-20-485-3432, nlinfo-f@elsevier.nl, http://www.elsevier.nl.

658.8 GBR ISSN 0969-6989
HF5428
➤ **JOURNAL OF RETAILING AND CONSUMER SERVICES.** Text in English. 1994. 6/yr. EUR 215 in Europe to individuals; JPY 28,600 in Japan to individuals; USD 241 to individuals except Europe and Japan; EUR 657 in Europe to institutions; JPY 87,100 in Japan to institutions; USD 735 to institutions except Europe and Japan (effective 2006). back issues avail. **Document type:** *Academic/Scholarly.* **Description:** Provides a forum for research and debate in the rapidly developing and converging fields of retailing and services studies.
Related titles: Microform ed.: (from PQC); Online - full text ed.: (from EBSCO Publishing, Gale Group, IngentaConnect, ScienceDirect, Swets Information Services).
Indexed: GEOBASE, RefZh, WTA.
—BLDSC (5052.041000), IE, Infotrieve, ingenta. **CCC.**
Published by: Pergamon (Subsidiary of: Elsevier Science & Technology), The Boulevard, Langford Ln, East Park, Kidlington, Oxford OX5 1GB, United Kingdom. TEL 44-1865-843000, FAX 44-1865-843010, http://www.elsevier.com/locate/jretconser. Ed. Harry Timmermans. **Subscr.to:** Elsevier BV, PO Box 211, Amsterdam 1000 AE, Netherlands. TEL 31-20-485-3757, FAX 31-20-485-3432, nlinfo-f@elsevier.nl, http://www.elsevier.nl.

658 USA ISSN 1094-6705
HF5415.5
➤ **JOURNAL OF SERVICE RESEARCH.** Text in English. 1998. q. USD 605, GBP 391 to institutions; USD 630, GBP 407 combined subscription to institutions print & online eds. (effective 2006). adv. **Document type:** *Journal, Academic/Scholarly.* **Description:** Provides an outlet for the most advanced research in service marketing, service operations, service human resources and organizational design, service information systems, and customer satisfaction and service quality.
Related titles: Online - full content ed.: (from C S A, EBSCO Publishing); Online - full text ed.: ISSN 1552-7379. USD 599, GBP 387 to institutions (effective 2006) (from O C L C Online Computer Library Center, Inc., ProQuest Information & Learning, Sage Publications, Inc., Swets Information Services).
Indexed: ABIn, H&TI, HRA, PsycInfo, PsycholAb, RefZh.
—BLDSC (5064.010700), IE. **CCC.**
Published by: (Vanderbilt University, Center for Service Marketing), Sage Publications, Inc., 2455 Teller Rd, Thousand Oaks, CA 91320. TEL 805-499-0721, 800-818-7243, FAX 805-499-8096, 800-583-2665, info@sagepub.com, http://www.sagepub.com/journal.aspx?pid=3. Ed. A Parasuraman. R&P Tanya Udin TEL 805-499-0721 ext 7716. Adv. contact Kirsten Beaulieu TEL 805-499-0721 ext 7160. B&W page USD 350, color page USD 1,150. **Subscr. In US, Europe, Middle East, & Africa to:** Sage Publications Ltd., 1 Oliver's Yard, 55 City Rd, London EC1 1SP, United Kingdom. TEL 44-20-73740645, FAX 44-20-73748741, subscription@sagepub.co.uk.

658.8 GBR ISSN 0887-6045
HD9980.1
THE JOURNAL OF SERVICES MARKETING. Text in English. 1986. 7/yr. EUR 7,611.41 in Europe; USD 2,719 in North America; AUD 9,809 in Australasia; GBP 5,327.66 in UK & elsewhere (effective 2006). adv. bk.rev. illus. index. back issues avail.; reprint service avail. from PSC. **Document type:** *Journal, Academic/Scholarly.* **Description:** This fully peer reviewed journal is written for both practitioners and academics. It publishes research articles, case studies, creative concepts and applications and other thought provoking items in the field of services marketing.
Related titles: Online - full text ed.: (from EBSCO Publishing, Emerald Group Publishing Limited, Gale Group, IngentaConnect, O C L C Online Computer Library Center, Inc., ProQuest Information & Learning, Swets Information Services).
Indexed: ABIn, EmerIntel, Emerald.
—BLDSC (5064.011000), IE, Infotrieve, ingenta. **CCC.**

Published by: Emerald Group Publishing Limited, 60-62 Toller Ln, Bradford, W Yorks BD8 9BY, United Kingdom. TEL 44-1274-777700, FAX 44-1274-785200, help@emeraldinsight.com, infomation@emeraldinsight.com, http://www.emeraldinsight.com/jsm.htm. Ed. Charles Martin. Circ: 1,000. **Subscr. in N America:** Emerald Group Publishing Ltd., 44 Brattle St, 4th Fl, Cambridge, MA 02138. TEL 617-497-2175, 888-622-0075, FAX 617-354-6875.

▼ **JOURNAL OF STRATEGIC E-COMMERCE.** see *BUSINESS AND ECONOMICS—Computer Applications*

658 GBR ISSN 0965-254X
HF5415.13
➤ **JOURNAL OF STRATEGIC MARKETING.** Text in English. 1993. q. GBP 502, USD 830 combined subscription to institutions print & online eds. (effective 2006). bibl. reprint service avail. from PSC. **Document type:** *Journal, Academic/Scholarly.* **Description:** Publishes articles and research dedicated to exploring the relationship between marketing and strategic management.
Related titles: Online - full text ed.: ISSN 1466-4488. GBP 477, USD 789 to institutions (effective 2006) (from EBSCO Publishing, Gale Group, IngentaConnect, O C L C Online Computer Library Center, Inc., Swets Information Services).
Indexed: ABIn, CPM, Emerald, IBR, IBZ.
—BLDSC (5066.872950), IE, Infotrieve, ingenta. **CCC.**
Published by: Routledge (Subsidiary of: Taylor & Francis Group), 4 Park Sq, Milton Park, Abingdon, Oxon OX14 4RN, United Kingdom. TEL 44-1235-828600, FAX 44-1235-829000, info@routledge.co.uk, http://www.tandf.co.uk/journals/titles/0965254X.asp, http://www.routledge.co.uk. Ed. Nigel F Piercy. R&P Sally Sweet. **Subscr. to:** Taylor & Francis Ltd, Journals Customer Service, Rankine Rd, Basingstoke, Hants RG24 8PR, United Kingdom. TEL 44-1256-813000, FAX 44-1256-330245, enquiry@tandf.co.uk.

658.7 USA ISSN 1523-2409
HF5437.A2 CODEN: JOPUAS
➤ **JOURNAL OF SUPPLY CHAIN MANAGEMENT**; a global review of purchasing and supply. Text in English; Summaries in French, German, Spanish. 1965. q. USD 93 combined subscription in the Americas to individuals print & online eds.; EUR 87, GBP 58 combined subscription in Europe to individuals print & online eds.; USD 191 combined subscription in the Americas to institutions print & online eds.; GBP 118 combined subscription elsewhere to institutions print & online eds. (effective 2006). adv. bk.rev. charts; illus. Index. back issues avail.; reprint service avail. from PSC,SCH. **Document type:** *Journal, Academic/Scholarly.* **Description:** Publishes articles dealing with concepts from business, supply chain management, economics, operations management, logistics, information systems, the behavioral sciences, and other disciplines which contribute to the advancement of knowledge in the various areas of purchasing, materials and supply management, supply chain management, and related fields.
Former titles (until 1999): International Journal of Purchasing & Materials Management (1055-6001); (until 1991): Journal of Purchasing and Materials Management (0094-8594); Journal of Purchasing (0022-4030)
Related titles: Microform ed.: (from PQC); Online - full text ed.: ISSN 1745-493X. USD 181 in the Americas to institutions; GBP 112 elsewhere to institutions (effective 2006) (from Blackwell Synergy, EBSCO Publishing, Florida Center for Library Automation, Gale Group, H.W. Wilson, O C L C Online Computer Library Center, Inc., ProQuest Information & Learning, The Dialog Corporation).
Indexed: ABIn, ASEANManA, BPI, BPIA, BusI, CPM, DPD, Emerald, IMI, LogistBibl, M&MA, ManagCont, T&II.
—BLDSC (5067.260000), IE, Infotrieve, ingenta. **CCC.**
Published by: (Institute for Supply Management), Blackwell Publishing, Inc. (Subsidiary of: Blackwell Publishing Ltd.), Commerce Place, 350 Main St, Malden, MA 02148. TEL 781-388-8206, FAX 781-388-8232, subscrip@blackwellpub.com, http://www.blackwellpublishing.com/journal.asp?ref=1523-2409. Ed. Alvin Williams. Circ: 3,000.

➤ **JOURNAL OF TRAVEL & TOURISM MARKETING.** see *TRAVEL AND TOURISM*

➤ **JOURNAL OF VACATION MARKETING**; an international journal for the tourism and hospitality industries. see *TRAVEL AND TOURISM*

▼ ➤ **JOURNAL OF WEBSITE PROMOTION**; innovations in internet business research, theory, and practice. see *COMPUTERS—Internet*

659 NOR ISSN 0022-8214
KAMPANJE!; tidsskrift for markedsfoering. Text in Norwegian. 1964. fortn. (20/yr.). NOK 845; NOK 445 to students; NOK 75 per issue (effective 2002). adv. **Description:** Articles on a variety of marketing subjects and media, information and communication in general.
Incorporates (in 1986): Markedsfoering (0025-3502)
—**CCC.**
Published by: Hjemmet-Mortensen AS, PO Box 5001, Majorstua, Oslo, 0301, Norway. TEL 47-22-58-50-00, FAX 47-22-58-05-66, kampanje@hm-media.no, http://www.kampanje.com. Ed. Lasse Gimnes TEL 47-22-58-59-51. Adv. contact Bente Dahlen TEL 47-22-58-55-22. color page NOK 28,500; 185 x 238. Circ: 9,047.

KART MARKETING INTERNATIONAL; the monthly trade magazine for the karting industry. see *SPORTS AND GAMES*

658 NLD ISSN 1571-4276
KARWEI MANAGEMENT. Text in Dutch. 1968. bi-m. EUR 65.49 domestic; EUR 80.49 in Europe (effective 2005). adv. charts; illus.; mkt.; stat. back issues avail. **Document type:** *Trade.* **Description:** For retailers of do-it-yourself products, hardware, tools, paint, wallpaper, and glass.
Former titles (until 2002): Karwei (0165-4357); (until 1969): Keukenkompas
Published by: Quorum Uitgevers, PO Box 123, Zutphen aan den Rijn, 7200 AC, Netherlands. TEL 31-575-515515, FAX 31-575-512199, redactie@qumedia.nl, info@qumedia.nl, http://www.karwei.net, http://www.qumedia.nl. Ed. Hugo Schrameyer. Pub., R&P Arnold Jansen. Adv. contact Monique Sueters. page EUR 1,495; trim 190 x 277. Circ: 5,150.

659 FIN ISSN 0783-5167
KEHITTYVAE KAUPPA. Text in Finnish. 1968. fortn. adv. bk.rev. tr.lit. index. **Document type:** *Magazine.*
Former titles (until 1986): Kauppias (0355-3078); (until 1974): K-Kauppias (0358-8440); (until 1973): Kaupias (0022-9512)
Published by: K-Kauppiasliitto ry, Koydenpunojankatu 2 a D, Helsinki, 00180, Finland. TEL 358-9-15668510, FAX 358-9-15668525, etunimi.sukunimi@k-kauppiasliitto.fi, http://www.k-kauppiasliitto.fi/. Ed. Arto Jaakkola. Circ: 21,368 (controlled).

KEY (BATTLEGROUND). see *ADVERTISING AND PUBLIC RELATIONS*

KEY NOTE MARKET ASSESSMENT. AUDIO VISUAL RETAILING. see *ELECTRONICS*

KEY NOTE MARKET ASSESSMENT. BABY FOODS. see *FOOD AND FOOD INDUSTRIES*

658 664 GBR
KEY NOTE MARKET ASSESSMENT. COOKING AND EATING. Text in English. 2001. irreg., latest 2001, Dec. GBP 730 per issue (effective 2002). **Description:** Provides an overview on cooking and eating in the UK, including industry structure, market size and trends, developments, prospects, and major company profiles.
Published by: Key Note Ltd., Field House, 72 Oldfield Rd, Hampton, Mddx TW12 2HQ, United Kingdom. TEL 44-20-8481-8750, FAX 44-20-8783-0049, info@keynote.co.uk, http://www.keynote.co.uk. Ed. Simon Taylor.

KEY NOTE MARKET ASSESSMENT. FISH INDUSTRY. see *FISH AND FISHERIES*

KEY NOTE MARKET ASSESSMENT. FORECOURT RETAILING. see *PETROLEUM AND GAS*

KEY NOTE MARKET ASSESSMENT. HEALTHY EATING. see *FOOD AND FOOD INDUSTRIES*

KEY NOTE MARKET ASSESSMENT. HOLIDAY PURCHASING PATTERNS. see *TRAVEL AND TOURISM*

KEY NOTE MARKET ASSESSMENT. HOME ENTERTAINMENT. see *LEISURE AND RECREATION*

KEY NOTE MARKET ASSESSMENT. HOT BEVERAGES. see *BEVERAGES*

KEY NOTE MARKET ASSESSMENT. IN-CAR ENTERTAINMENT. see *SOUND RECORDING AND REPRODUCTION*

KEY NOTE MARKET ASSESSMENT. INTERNET ADVERTISING. see *ADVERTISING AND PUBLIC RELATIONS*

KEY NOTE MARKET ASSESSMENT. INTERNET SERVICE PROVIDERS. see *COMPUTERS—Internet*

KEY NOTE MARKET ASSESSMENT. LIFESTYLE & SPECIALIST MAGAZINES. see *JOURNALISM*

658 GBR
KEY NOTE MARKET ASSESSMENT. MARKET FORECASTS. Text in English. 2001. a., latest 2002, Mar. GBP 730 per issue (effective 2002). **Description:** Offers insight into forthcoming changes in UK industry, looking at sales forecasts and developing trends for key growth markets.
Published by: Key Note Ltd., Field House, 72 Oldfield Rd, Hampton, Mddx TW12 2HQ, United Kingdom. TEL 44-20-8481-8750, FAX 44-20-8783-0049, info@keynote.co.uk, http://www.keynote.co.uk. Ed. Simon Taylor.

KEY NOTE MARKET ASSESSMENT. MARKETING TO CHILDREN 4-11. see *CHILDREN AND YOUTH—About*

658 GBR
KEY NOTE MARKET ASSESSMENT. MEN'S & WOMEN'S BUYING HABITS. Text in English. 2002. irreg., latest 2002, Jan. GBP 730 per issue (effective 2002). **Description:** Provides an in-depth strategic analysis across a broad range of industries and contains an examination on the scope, dynamics and shape of key UK markets in the consumer, financial, lifestyle and business to business sectors.
Published by: Key Note Ltd., Field House, 72 Oldfield Rd, Hampton, Mddx TW12 2HQ, United Kingdom. TEL 44-20-8481-8750, FAX 44-20-8783-0049, info@keynote.co.uk, http://www.keynote.co.uk. Ed. Simon Taylor.

KEY NOTE MARKET ASSESSMENT. MOTOR FINANCE. see *TRANSPORTATION—Automobiles*

KEY NOTE MARKET ASSESSMENT. NON-FOOD SALES IN SUPERMARKETS. see *FOOD AND FOOD INDUSTRIES—Grocery Trade*

658 GBR
KEY NOTE MARKET ASSESSMENT. RETAIL DEVELOPMENT. Text in English. 2001. irreg., latest 2001, May. GBP 730 per issue (effective 2002). **Description:** Provides an in-depth strategic analysis across a broad range of industries and contains an examination on the scope, dynamics and shape of key UK markets in the consumer, financial, lifestyle and business to business sectors.
Published by: Key Note Ltd., Field House, 72 Oldfield Rd, Hampton, Mddx TW12 2HQ, United Kingdom. TEL 44-20-8481-8750, FAX 44-20-8783-0049, info@keynote.co.uk, http://www.keynote.co.uk. Ed. Simon Taylor.

658.878 GBR
KEY NOTE MARKET ASSESSMENT. SUPERMARKET OWN LABELS. Variant title: Supermarket Own Labels Market Assessment. Text in English. 2000 (Jan). irreg., latest 2000. GBP 730 per issue (effective 2002). **Description:** Provides an in-depth strategic analysis across a broad range of industries and contains an examination on the scope, dynamics and shape of key UK markets in the consumer, financial, lifestyle and business to business sectors.
Published by: Key Note Ltd., Field House, 72 Oldfield Rd, Hampton, Mddx TW12 2HQ, United Kingdom. TEL 44-20-8481-8750, FAX 44-20-8783-0049, info@keynote.co.uk, http://www.keynote.co.uk.

KEY NOTE MARKET ASSESSMENT. SWEET & SALTY SNACKS. see *FOOD AND FOOD INDUSTRIES*

KEY NOTE MARKET ASSESSMENT. TEENAGE MAGAZINES. see *JOURNALISM*

658 GBR
KEY NOTE MARKET ASSESSMENT. THE GREY CONSUMER MARKET. Variant title: Grey Market in the U K. Text in English. 1994. irreg., latest 2000, Aug. GBP 730 per issue (effective 2002). **Document type:** *Trade.* **Description:** Provides an in-depth strategic analysis across a broad range of industries and contains an examination on the scope, dynamics and shape of key UK markets in the consumer, financial, lifestyle and business to business sectors.
Formerly (until 2000): Key Note Market Review: Grey Market in the U K (1356-6180)
Related titles: CD-ROM ed.; Online - full text ed.
Published by: Key Note Ltd., Field House, 72 Oldfield Rd, Hampton, Mddx TW12 2HQ, United Kingdom. TEL 44-20-8481-8750, FAX 44-20-8783-0049, info@keynote.co.uk, http://www.keynote.co.uk. Ed. Kim Thomasson.

KEY NOTE MARKET ASSESSMENT. TRENDS IN FOOD SHOPPING. see *FOOD AND FOOD INDUSTRIES—Grocery Trade*

KEY NOTE MARKET ASSESSMENT. TWEENAGERS. see *CHILDREN AND YOUTH—About*

KEY NOTE MARKET ASSESSMENT. VEGETARIAN FOODS. see *FOOD AND FOOD INDUSTRIES*

KEY NOTE MARKET ASSESSMENT. VITAMINS & SUPPLEMENTS. see *PHARMACY AND PHARMACOLOGY*

KEY NOTE MARKET REPORT: BICYCLES. see *SPORTS AND GAMES—Bicycles And Motorcycles*

KEY NOTE MARKET REPORT: BIOTECHNOLOGY. see *BIOLOGY—Biotechnology*

KEY NOTE MARKET REPORT: BUS & COACH OPERATORS. see *TRANSPORTATION*

658 338   GBR
KEY NOTE MARKET REPORT: CASH & CARRY OUTLETS.
Variant title: Cash & Carry Outlets Market Report. Text in English. irreg., latest 2001, June. GBP 340 per issue (effective 2002). **Document type:** *Trade.* **Description:** Provides an overview of a specific UK market segment and includes executive summary, market definition, market size, industry background, competitor analysis, current issues, forecasts, company profiles, and more.
Formerly (until 1995): Key Note Report: Cash and Carry Outlets (0954-4283)
Related titles: CD-ROM ed.; Online - full text ed.
Published by: Key Note Ltd., Field House, 72 Oldfield Rd, Hampton, Mddx TW12 2HQ, United Kingdom. TEL 44-20-8481-8750, FAX 44-20-8783-0049, info@keynote.co.uk, http://www.keynote.co.uk. Ed. Jacob Howard.

KEY NOTE MARKET REPORT: CLOTHING RETAILING. see *CLOTHING TRADE*

658 338   GBR
KEY NOTE MARKET REPORT: CONVENIENCE RETAILING.
Variant title: Convenience Retailing Market Report. Text in English. 199?. irreg., latest 2001, Jan. GBP 340 per issue (effective 2002). **Document type:** *Trade.* **Description:** Provides an overview of the UK convenience retailing market, including industry structure, market size and trends, developments, prospects, and major company profiles.
Formerly (until 1995): Key Note Report: Convenience Retailing (1352-6537)
Related titles: CD-ROM ed.; Online - full text ed.
Published by: Key Note Ltd., Field House, 72 Oldfield Rd, Hampton, Mddx TW12 2HQ, United Kingdom. TEL 44-20-8481-8750, FAX 44-20-8783-0049, info@keynote.co.uk, http://www.keynote.co.uk. Ed. Emma Wiggin.

KEY NOTE MARKET REPORT: CORPORATE GIFTWARE. see *GIFTWARE AND TOYS*

395.3   GBR   ISSN 1462-4540
KEY NOTE MARKET REPORT: CORPORATE HOSPITALITY.
Variant title: Corporate Hospitality Market Report. Text in English. 1998. irreg., latest 2002, Mar. GBP 340 per issue (effective 2002). **Description:** Provides and overview of a specific UK market segment and includes executive summary, market definition, market size, industry background, competitor analysis, current issues, forecasts, company profiles, and more.
Published by: Key Note Ltd., Field House, 72 Oldfield Rd, Hampton, Mddx TW12 2HQ, United Kingdom. TEL 44-20-8481-8750, FAX 44-20-8783-0049, info@keynote.co.uk, http://www.keynote.co.uk. Ed. Jenny Baxter.

KEY NOTE MARKET REPORT: DIGITAL T V. see *COMMUNICATIONS—Television And Cable*

658   GBR   ISSN 1460-0927
KEY NOTE MARKET REPORT: DIRECT MARKETING. Variant title: Direct Marketing Market Report. Text in English. 1987. irreg., latest 2001, Sept. GBP 340 per issue (effective 2002). **Document type:** *Trade.* **Description:** Provides an overview of the UK direct marketing sector, including industry structure, market size and trends, developments, prospects, and major company profiles.
Formerly: Key Note Report: Direct Marketing (0950-3765)
Related titles: CD-ROM ed.; Online - full text ed. —CCC.
Published by: Key Note Ltd., Field House, 72 Oldfield Rd, Hampton, Mddx TW12 2HQ, United Kingdom. TEL 44-20-8481-8750, FAX 44-20-8783-0049, info@keynote.co.uk, http://www.keynote.co.uk. Ed. Emily Pattullo.

658   GBR   ISSN 1469-5219
KEY NOTE MARKET REPORT: DISCOUNT RETAILING. Text in English. 1999. a., latest 2001, Nov. GBP 340 per issue (effective 2002). **Description:** Provides an overview of a specific UK market segment and includes executive summary, market definition, market size, industry background, competitor analysis, current issues, forecasts, company profiles, and more.
Published by: Key Note Ltd., Field House, 72 Oldfield Rd, Hampton, Mddx TW12 2HQ, United Kingdom. TEL 44-20-8481-8750, FAX 44-20-8783-0049, info@keynote.co.uk, http://www.keynote.co.uk. Ed. Lyndsey Barker.

KEY NOTE MARKET REPORT: DISTILLERS (WHISKY). see *BEVERAGES*

KEY NOTE MARKET REPORT: DRY BATTERIES. see *ENGINEERING—Electrical Engineering*

KEY NOTE MARKET REPORT: ELECTRICAL WHOLESALE. see *ENGINEERING—Electrical Engineering*

KEY NOTE MARKET REPORT: ELECTRICITY INDUSTRY. see *ENERGY—Electrical Energy*

KEY NOTE MARKET REPORT: ELECTRONIC COMPONENT DISTRIBUTION. see *ELECTRONICS*

KEY NOTE MARKET REPORT: ELECTRONIC GAMES. see *COMPUTERS—Computer Games*

KEY NOTE MARKET REPORT: EQUIPMENT FOR THE DISABLED. see *HANDICAPPED*

KEY NOTE MARKET REPORT: EQUIPMENT LEASING. see *BUSINESS AND ECONOMICS—Small Business*

KEY NOTE MARKET REPORT: FIBRES. see *TEXTILE INDUSTRIES AND FABRICS*

KEY NOTE MARKET REPORT: FIRE PROTECTION EQUIPMENT. see *FIRE PREVENTION*

KEY NOTE MARKET REPORT: FISH & FISH PRODUCTS. see *FISH AND FISHERIES*

KEY NOTE MARKET REPORT: FITTED KITCHENS. see *INTERIOR DESIGN AND DECORATION—Furniture And House Furnishings*

KEY NOTE MARKET REPORT: FOOD FLAVOURINGS & INGREDIENTS. see *FOOD AND FOOD INDUSTRIES*

KEY NOTE MARKET REPORT: FOOD SEASONINGS. see *FOOD AND FOOD INDUSTRIES*

KEY NOTE MARKET REPORT: FRUIT & VEGETABLES. see *FOOD AND FOOD INDUSTRIES—Grocery Trade*

KEY NOTE MARKET REPORT: FRUIT JUICES & HEALTH DRINKS. see *BEVERAGES*

KEY NOTE MARKET REPORT: GARDEN EQUIPMENT. see *GARDENING AND HORTICULTURE*

KEY NOTE MARKET REPORT: GIFTWARE. see *GIFTWARE AND TOYS*

KEY NOTE MARKET REPORT: GLASSWARE. see *CERAMICS, GLASS AND POTTERY*

KEY NOTE MARKET REPORT: HAND LUGGAGE & LEATHER GOODS. see *LEATHER AND FUR INDUSTRIES*

KEY NOTE MARKET REPORT: HEALTH CLUBS AND LEISURE CENTRES. see *PHYSICAL FITNESS AND HYGIENE*

KEY NOTE MARKET REPORT: HOME FURNISHINGS. see *INTERIOR DESIGN AND DECORATION—Furniture And House Furnishings*

KEY NOTE MARKET REPORT: HOME LEISURE. see *LEISURE AND RECREATION*

381.1 658   GBR
KEY NOTE MARKET REPORT: HOME SHOPPING. Variant title: Home Shopping. Text in English. 1993. irreg., latest 2001, May. GBP 340 per issue (effective 2002). **Document type:** *Trade.* **Description:** Provides and overview of a specific UK market segment and includes executive summary, market definition, market size, industry background, competitor analysis, current issues, forecasts, company profiles, and more.
Formerly: Key Note Report: Home Shopping (1354-2702)
Related titles: CD-ROM ed.; Online - full text ed.
Published by: Key Note Ltd., Field House, 72 Oldfield Rd, Hampton, Mddx TW12 2HQ, United Kingdom. TEL 44-20-8481-8750, FAX 44-20-8783-0049, info@keynote.co.uk, http://www.keynote.co.uk. Ed. Phillippa Smith.

KEY NOTE MARKET REPORT: HORTICULTURAL RETAILING. see *GARDENING AND HORTICULTURE*

KEY NOTE MARKET REPORT: HOUSEBUILDING. see *BUILDING AND CONSTRUCTION*

KEY NOTE MARKET REPORT: HOUSEHOLD APPLIANCES (BROWN GOODS). see *ELECTRONICS*

KEY NOTE MARKET REPORT: HOUSEHOLD APPLIANCES (WHITE GOODS). see *INTERIOR DESIGN AND DECORATION—Furniture And House Furnishings*

KEY NOTE MARKET REPORT: HOUSEHOLD FURNITURE. see *INTERIOR DESIGN AND DECORATION—Furniture And House Furnishings*

KEY NOTE MARKET REPORT: HOUSEHOLD SOAPS & DETERGENTS. see *CLEANING AND DYEING*

KEY NOTE MARKET REPORT: INDUSTRIAL FASTENERS. see *ENGINEERING—Engineering Mechanics And Materials*

KEY NOTE MARKET REPORT: INDUSTRIAL PUMPS. see *ENGINEERING—Hydraulic Engineering*

KEY NOTE MARKET REPORT: INSURANCE COMPANIES. see *INSURANCE*

KEY NOTE MARKET REPORT: INTERNET USAGE IN BUSINESS. see *COMPUTERS—Internet*

KEY NOTE MARKET REPORT: JEWELLERY & WATCHES. see *JEWELRY, CLOCKS AND WATCHES*

KEY NOTE MARKET REPORT: LABORATORY EQUIPMENT. see *MEDICAL SCIENCES*

KEY NOTE MARKET REPORT: LIGHTING EQUIPMENT. see *INTERIOR DESIGN AND DECORATION—Furniture And House Furnishings*

KEY NOTE MARKET REPORT: LINGERIE. see *CLOTHING TRADE*

658   GBR
KEY NOTE MARKET REPORT: MAIL ORDER. Variant title: Mail Order. Text in English. irreg., latest vol.8, 1991. GBP 265 (effective 1999). **Document type:** *Trade.*
Published by: Key Note Ltd., Field House, 72 Oldfield Rd, Hampton, Mddx TW12 2HQ, United Kingdom. TEL 44-20-8481-8750, FAX 44-20-8783-0049, info@keynote.co.uk, http://www.keynote.co.uk.

658   GBR
KEY NOTE MARKET REPORT: MARKET RESEARCH AGENCIES. Text in English. 1999. irreg., latest 1999. GBP 340 per issue (effective 2002). **Description:** Provides and overview of a specific UK market segment and includes executive summary, market definition, market size, industry background, competitor analysis, current issues, forecasts, company profiles, and more.
Published by: Key Note Ltd., Field House, 72 Oldfield Rd, Hampton, Mddx TW12 2HQ, United Kingdom. TEL 44-20-8481-8750, FAX 44-20-8783-0049, info@keynote.co.uk, http://www.keynote.co.uk. Ed. Jane Griffiths.

KEY NOTE MARKET REPORT: MEAT & MEAT PRODUCTS. see *FOOD AND FOOD INDUSTRIES*

KEY NOTE MARKET REPORT: MEDICAL EQUIPMENT. see *MEDICAL SCIENCES*

KEY NOTE MARKET REPORT: MEN'S MAGAZINES. see *PUBLISHING AND BOOK TRADE*

KEY NOTE MARKET REPORT: METALWORKING MACHINE TOOLS. see *ENGINEERING—Industrial Engineering*

KEY NOTE MARKET REPORT: MILK & DAIRY PRODUCTS. see *AGRICULTURE—Dairying And Dairy Products*

KEY NOTE MARKET REPORT: MOBILE PHONES. see *COMMUNICATIONS—Telephone And Telegraph*

KEY NOTE MARKET REPORT: MORTGAGE FINANCE. see *BUSINESS AND ECONOMICS—Banking And Finance*

KEY NOTE MARKET REPORT: MULTIMEDIA IN U K. see *COMMUNICATIONS*

658   GBR
KEY NOTE MARKET REPORT: OWN BRANDS. Variant title: Own Brands. Text in English. irreg., latest 2001, Mar. GBP 340 per issue (effective 2002). **Document type:** *Trade.* **Description:** Provides an overview of a specific UK market segment and includes executive summary, market definition, market size, industry background, competitor analysis, current issues, forecasts, company profiles, and more.
Formerly: Key Note Report: Own Brands
Related titles: CD-ROM ed.; Online - full text ed.
Published by: Key Note Ltd., Field House, 72 Oldfield Rd, Hampton, Mddx TW12 2HQ, United Kingdom. TEL 44-20-8481-8750, FAX 44-20-8783-0049, info@keynote.co.uk, http://www.keynote.co.uk. Ed. Jenny Baxter.

KEY NOTE MARKET REPORT: PERISHABLE FAST-MOVING CONSUMER GOODS. see *FOOD AND FOOD INDUSTRIES*

KEY NOTE MARKET REPORT: PLASTICS PROCESSING. see *PLASTICS*

KEY NOTE MARKET REPORT: POWER TOOLS. see *MACHINERY*

KEY NOTE MARKET REPORT: PROTECTIVE CLOTHING & EQUIPMENT. see *CLOTHING TRADE*

658   GBR
KEY NOTE MARKET REPORT: SHOPFITTING. Variant title: Shop Fitting. Text in English. irreg., latest 2002, Jan. GBP 3,340 per issue (effective 2002). **Document type:** *Trade.* **Description:** Provides an overview of a specific UK market segment and includes executive summary, market definition, market size, industry background, competitor analysis, current issues, forecasts, company profiles, and more.

Formerly: Key Note Report: Shopfitting
Related titles: CD-ROM ed.; Online - full text ed.
Published by: Key Note Ltd., Field House, 72 Oldfield Rd,
Hampton, Mddx TW12 2HQ, United Kingdom. TEL
44-20-8481-8750, FAX 44-20-8783-0049, info@keynote.co.uk,
http://www.keynote.co.uk. Ed. Jenny Baxter.

KEY NOTE MARKET REPORT: SPORTS SPONSORHIP. see
SPORTS AND GAMES

KEY NOTE MARKET REPORT: T V & VIDEO RENTAL. see
ELECTRONICS

KEY NOTE MARKET REPORT: THE GAS INDUSTRY. see
PETROLEUM AND GAS

KEY NOTE MARKET REPORT: THE OIL AND GAS INDUSTRY.
see *PETROLEUM AND GAS*

KEY NOTE MARKET REPORT: THE TAKE HOME TRADE. see
BEVERAGES

KEY NOTE MARKET REPORT: THE UNDER-16S MARKET. see
CHILDREN AND YOUTH—About

KEY NOTE MARKET REPORT: THE UNDER-5S MARKET. see
CHILDREN AND YOUTH—About

KEY NOTE MARKET REPORT: TOYS & GAMES. see
GIFTWARE AND TOYS

KEY NOTE MARKET REPORT: TYRE INDUSTRY. see *RUBBER*

KEY NOTE MARKET REPORT: WALLCOVERINGS. see
INTERIOR DESIGN AND DECORATION

KEY NOTE MARKET REPORT: WINDOWS & DOORS. see
*INTERIOR DESIGN AND DECORATION—Furniture And
House Furnishings*

KEY NOTE MARKET REPORT: YOUTH MARKET IN THE U.K.
see *CHILDREN AND YOUTH—About*

658   GBR   ISSN 1360-032X
KEY NOTE MARKET REVIEW: RETAILING IN THE U K. Variant
title: Retailing in the U K. Text in English. 1991. irreg. (7th
Edition), latest 1998, Sep. GBP 565 per issue (effective 1999).
Document type: *Trade.* **Description:** Designed to keep you
up to date with the developments and opportunities across
entire industry sectors. They provide a comprehensive
analysis of the industry by drawing together key related
market segments under one cover.
Related titles: CD-ROM ed.; Online - full text ed.
Published by: Key Note Ltd., Field House, 72 Oldfield Rd,
Hampton, Mddx TW12 2HQ, United Kingdom. TEL
44-20-8481-8750, FAX 44-20-8783-0049, info@keynote.co.uk,
http://www.keynote.co.uk. Ed. Simon Howitt.

**KEY NOTE MARKET REVIEW: U K D I Y & HOME
IMPROVEMENTS.** (United Kingdom Do It Yourself) see
INTERIOR DESIGN AND DECORATION

KEY NOTE MARKET REVIEW: U K DRINKS MARKET. see
BEVERAGES

KEY NOTE MARKET REVIEW: U K FOOD MARKET. see *FOOD
AND FOOD INDUSTRIES*

KEY NOTE MARKET REVIEW: U K INSURANCE MARKET. see
INSURANCE

KEY NOTE MARKET REVIEW: U.K. OFFICE EQUIPMENT. see
*BUSINESS AND ECONOMICS—Office Equipment And
Services*

658.8   GBR
KEY NOTE MARKET REVIEW: U K PET MARKET. Text in
English. 1994. irreg. GBP 465 (effective 1999). **Document
type:** *Trade.*
Related titles: CD-ROM ed.; Online - full text ed.
Published by: Key Note Ltd., Field House, 72 Oldfield Rd,
Hampton, Mddx TW12 2HQ, United Kingdom. TEL
44-20-8481-8750, FAX 44-20-8783-0049, info@keynote.co.uk,
http://www.keynote.co.uk. Ed. Eleanor Hughes.

**KEY NOTE MARKET REVIEW: U K PHARMACEUTICAL
INDUSTRY.** see *PHARMACY AND PHARMACOLOGY*

658   GBR
KEY NOTE MARKET REVIEW: WHOLESALING IN THE U K.
Variant title: Wholesaling in the U K Market Review. Text in
English. 1994. irreg. latest 1994, Apr. GBP 565 per issue
(effective 2002). **Document type:** *Trade.* **Description:**
Designed to keep you up to date with the developments and
opportunities across entire industry sectors. They provide a
comprehensive analysis of the industry by drawing together
key related market segments under one cover.
Related titles: CD-ROM ed.; Online - full text ed.

Published by: Key Note Ltd., Field House, 72 Oldfield Rd,
Hampton, Mddx TW12 2HQ, United Kingdom. TEL
44-20-8481-8750, FAX 44-20-8783-0049, info@keynote.co.uk,
http://www.keynote.co.uk.

**KEY NOTE PLUS MARKET REPORT. COSMETICS &
FRAGRANCES.** see *BEAUTY CULTURE—Perfumes And
Cosmetics*

**KEY NOTE PLUS MARKET REPORT. DARK SPIRITS &
LIQUEURS.** see *BEVERAGES*

**KEY NOTE PLUS MARKET REPORT. FAST FOOD & HOME
DELIVERY OUTLETS.** see *FOOD AND FOOD INDUSTRIES*

KEY NOTE PLUS MARKET REPORT. FOOTWEAR. see *SHOES
AND BOOTS*

KEY NOTE PLUS MARKET REPORT. FROZEN FOODS. see
FOOD AND FOOD INDUSTRIES

KEY NOTE PLUS MARKET REPORT. GREETINGS CARDS. see
GIFTWARE AND TOYS

KEY NOTE PLUS MARKET REPORT. HEALTH FOODS. see
FOOD AND FOOD INDUSTRIES

**KEY NOTE PLUS MARKET REPORT. PREMIUM LAGERS,
BEERS & CIDERS.** see *BEVERAGES*

KEY NOTE PLUS MARKET REPORT. SAUCES & SPREADS.
see *FOOD AND FOOD INDUSTRIES*

KEY NOTE PLUS MARKET REPORT. SOFT DRINKS. see
BEVERAGES

KEY NOTE PLUS MARKET REPORT. TOILETRIES. see
BEAUTY CULTURE

KEY NOTE PLUS MARKET REPORT. WINE. see *BEVERAGES*

658   GBR   ISSN 1464-8121
KIDS MARKETING REPORT. Text in English. 1998. m. GBP 335
(effective 2001). adv. **Document type:** *Newsletter, Trade.*
Description: Publishes news and trends about selling and
marketing to children.
Related titles: Online - full content ed.; Online - full text ed.:
(from Gale Group, O C L C Online Computer Library Center,
Inc.).
Published by: Centaur Publishing, St Giles House, 50 Poland St,
London, W1V 4AX, United Kingdom. TEL 44-20-7970-4000,
joannap@centaur.co.uk, http://www.mad.co.uk/kmr/,
http://www.centaur.co.uk.

658   CAN   ISSN 1205-7746
KIDSCREEN. Text in English. 1996. m. CND 79; USD 59 in
United States; USD 99 elsewhere. adv. **Document type:**
Trade. **Description:** Covers the business of children's
entertainment production and programming and the marketing
of child-oriented licensed products and services.
Related titles: Online - full text ed.: (from bigchalk, LexisNexis,
Micromedia ProQuest); Supplement(s): Kidscreen Retail.
Published by: Brunico Communications Inc., 366 Adelaide St W,
Ste 500, Toronto, ON M5V 1R9, Canada. TEL 416-408-2300,
FAX 416-408-0870, circ@brunico.com, http://
www.brunico.com. Ed. Mary Maddever. Pub. Ken Faier. adv.:
B&W page CND 3,470, color page CND 4,385; trim 11 x 8.5.

658   CHE
KIOSKINHABER. Text in German. m.
Address: Postfach 330, Winterthur, 8401, Switzerland. TEL
052-821315. Ed. Peter Sutter. Circ: 800.

380.14   NOR
KJOEPMANNEN. Text in Norwegian. m. (11/yr.). adv.
Published by: Bergens Kjoepmannsforening, Taarnplass 3,
Bergen, 5000, Norway. Circ: 1,000.

KOEPMANNEN VAEST. see *BUSINESS AND
ECONOMICS—Domestic Commerce*

658.8   SWE   ISSN 1100-4924
KONFERENS VAERLDEN; en facktidskrift foer konferenser,
motivation & incentive och affaersresor. Text in Swedish.
1989. 8/yr. SEK 420; SEK 54 newsstand/cover (effective
1997). adv. bk.rev. **Document type:** *Trade.*
Published by: Foerlagshuset Stocom AB, Fack 1106,
Sundbyberg, 17222, Sweden. TEL 46—8-98-02-60, FAX
46-8-98-16-80, konferensvarlden@stocom.se,
bjorn.stromberg@stocom.se, roger.kellerman@stocom.se,
http://www.stocom.se. Ed. Roger Kellerman. Pub. Bjorn A
Stromberg. Adv. contact Eva Svenander.

330   DEU   ISSN 1615-1550
DER KUNDEN-MANAGER; Beratung fuer ein optimales
Kundenmanagement. Text in German. 1994. m. EUR 153.60
(effective 2004). **Document type:** *Newsletter, Trade.*
Formerly (until 2000): Kundenbindung (0946-1094)

Published by: Verlag Norbert Mueller AG und Co. KG (Subsidiary
of: S V Corporate Media GmbH), Emmy-Noether-Str 2,
Munich, 80992, Germany. TEL 49-89-5485201, FAX
49-89-54852192, infoVNM@sv-corporate-media.de,
http://www.vnm.de/svcm/index/includeVerzeichnis/
nm[]briefe[]1615-1550/.

L M S; new developments in laboratory equipment. (Laboratory
Marketing Spectrum) see *MEDICAL SCIENCES—
Experimental Medicine, Laboratory Technique*

L O M A LINE. see *PETROLEUM AND GAS*

658.87   FRA   ISSN 0024-2632
L S A. (Libre Service Actualites) Text in French. 1958. w. EUR
170.10 domestic; EUR 230.49 foreign (effective 2002). adv.
bk.rev. abstr.; bibl.; charts; illus.; stat.; tr.lit.; tr.mk. index.
Related titles: Online - full text ed.: (from O C L C Online
Computer Library Center, Inc.).
Indexed: B&I; KES, PROMT.
—BLDSC (5300.385000), IE, ingenta.
Published by: Groupe Industrie Services Info, 12-14 Rue
Mederic, Paris, Cedex 17 75815, France. TEL 33-1-56794300,
FAX 33-1-56794301, http://www.lsa.fr. Circ: 37,000.

LABTALK. see *MEDICAL SCIENCES—Ophthalmology And
Optometry*

658   DEU   ISSN 0171-015X
LAGERTECHNIK. Text in German. 1967. a. **Document type:**
Magazine, Trade.
Published by: Henrich Publikationen GmbH, Schwanheimer Str
110, Frankfurt Am Main, 60528, Germany. TEL
49-69-96777234, FAX 49-69-96777111, http://www.henrich.de.
Ed. Martin Spiekermann. Circ: 15,000.

658.8   CAN   ISSN 0705-212X
LAWN & GARDEN TRADE. Text in English. 4/yr. CND 15, USD
33 (effective 1999). adv. bk.rev. **Document type:** *Trade.*
Description: Marketing news, trends, new products covering
Canada's lawn, garden and outdoor power equipment
industries.
Address: 2585 Skymark Ave, Ste 306, Mississauga, ON L4W
4L5, Canada. TEL 905-624-8218, FAX 905-624-6764. Ed.
Peter Tasler. Adv. contact Norm Rosen. Circ: 14,000
(controlled).

LEADS. see *BUSINESS AND ECONOMICS—Economic Situation
And Conditions*

LEBENSMITTEL ZEITUNG SPEZIAL; das Marketing-
Themenmagazin. see *FOOD AND FOOD INDUSTRIES*

LEGAL ASPECTS OF SELLING AND BUYING. see *LAW—Civil
Law*

LENSES. see *MEDICAL SCIENCES—Ophthalmology And
Optometry*

LESSONS OF YELLOW PAGES COMPETITION. see *BUSINESS
AND ECONOMICS—Trade And Industrial Directories*

658   FRA   ISSN 0759-0024
LETTRE DE LA COMMUNICATION. Text in French. 47/yr.
Address: 5 rue Papillon, Paris, 75009, France. TEL 42-46-58-10,
FAX 40-22-07-18. Ed. Nathalie Leclerc. Circ: 1,200.

LEWIS LETTER ON CABLE MARKETING. see
COMMUNICATIONS—Television And Cable

658   USA   ISSN 1521-611X
K12
LICENSE!; the idea marketplace for the licensing industry. Text in
English. 1998. m. USD 59.95 domestic; USD 79 in Canada &
Mexico; USD 199 elsewhere (effective 2005). adv. back issues
avail. **Document type:** *Magazine, Trade.* **Description:**
Discusses news and tips on all forms of licensing in marketing
and merchandising.
Related titles: Online - full text ed.: (from EBSCO Publishing,
Gale Group).
—CCC.
Published by: Advanstar Communications, Inc., One Park Ave,
2nd Fl, New York, NY 10016. TEL 212-951-6600, FAX
212-951-6793, info@advanstar.com, http://
www.licensemag.com, http://www.advanstar.com. Eds. James
Mammarella TEL 212-951-6707, Laura Liebeck. Pub., Adv.
contact Steven Ekstract TEL 212-951-6684. R&P James
Mammarella TEL 212-951-6707. B&W page USD 6,390, color
page 8,140; trim 8.125 x 10.875. Circ: 20,075.

658   GBR
LICENSE! EUROPE. Text in English. GBP 48 in Europe; GBP 64
elsewhere; GBP 12 newsstand/cover in Europe; GBP 16
newsstand/cover elsewhere (effective 2004). **Description:**
Discusses news and tips on all forms of licensing in marketing
and merchandising.
Published by: Advanstar Communications, Unit C, First Fl., Lamb
House, Church St., Chiswick, London, W4 2PD, United
Kingdom. TEL 44-208-9870900, FAX 44-208-9870901,
info@advanstar.com, http://www.advanstar.com.

THE LICENSING BOOK. see *PATENTS, TRADEMARKS AND COPYRIGHTS*

THE LICENSING LETTER. see *PATENTS, TRADEMARKS AND COPYRIGHTS*

658 388.3   USA   ISSN 1556-3103
LIGHT TRUCK AND SUV ACCESSORY BUSINESS & PRODUCT NEWS. (Sports Utility Vehicle) Text in English. 1996. bi-m. free to qualified personnel; USD 48 (effective 2005). adv. **Document type:** *Magazine, Trade.*
Former titles (until 2005): Sport Truck & S U V Accessory Business (1529-5079); (until 2000): Sport Truck Accessory Digest (1522-3973)
—CCC.
Published by: Cygnus Business Media, Inc., 1233 Janesville Ave, Fort Atkinson, WI 53538-0803. TEL 920-563-1698, FAX 920-568-2244, rvtd@aol.com. Ed. Pat Walker. Pub. John Spaulding. Adv. contact Maryellen Ley. color page USD 5,840, B&W page USD 4,715. Circ: 15,000 (paid).

LIGHTING. see *INTERIOR DESIGN AND DECORATION— Furniture And House Furnishings*

LIMOUSINE & CHAUFFEURED TRANSPORTATION. see *TRANSPORTATION—Automobiles*

658   USA
THE LITTLE NEWSLETTER. Text in English.
Media: E-mail.
Published by: Little Newsletter Ed. Wilma Thibodeaux.

658 659.2   BEL   ISSN 1373-3397
LOBBYING IN THE EUROPEAN UNION. Text and summaries in English, French, German. 1998. biennial. EUR 73 per issue (effective 2004). **Document type:** *Directory.*
—CCC.
Published by: Euroconfidentiel s.a., Rue de Rixensart 18, Genval, 1332, Belgium. TEL 32-2-6520284, FAX 32-2-6530180, nigel.hunt @infoboard.be.

658.8   USA
▼ **LOCAL MEDIA JOURNAL.** Text in English. 2004. 24/yr. USD 995 (effective 2005). **Document type:** *Journal, Trade.* **Description:** Provides information and analysis of the opportunities available in directional advertising as it relates to local business.
Media: Online - full content.
Published by: The Kelsey Group, Inc., 600 Executive Dr, Princeton, NJ 08540-1528. TEL 609-921-7200, FAX 609-921-2112, svasil@kelseygroup.com, tkg@kelseygroup.com, http://www.kelseygroup.com/ lmj_info.htm.

658   USA
LOGISTICS COMMENT. Text in English. 1968. q. free to members (effective 2003). bk.rev. **Document type:** *Bulletin.* **Description:** Provides information about the Council of interest to members.
Indexed by: CLT&T.
Published by: Council of Supply Chain Management Professionals, 2805 Butterfield Rd., Ste. 200, Oak Brook, IL 60523. TEL 630-574-0985, FAX 630-574-0989, clmadmin@clm1.org, CSCMPpublications@cscmp.org, http://www.cscmp.org/. Ed. Madeleine Holodnicki. Circ: 15,000.

LOGISTICS MANAGEMENT. see *TRANSPORTATION*

LOGISTIIKKA/LOGISTICS. see *TRANSPORTATION*

658.8   USA   ISSN 0099-099X
THE LOS ANGELES MARKET. Text in English. 1973. irreg.
Published by: Conference Board, Inc., 845 Third Ave, New York, NY 10022. TEL 212-339-0345, FAX 212-980-7014, atb@conference-board.org, http://www.conference-board.org.

658.8   GBR   ISSN 1354-5868
LOYALTY MAGAZINE; the magazine about profiting from relationships. Text in English. 1992. bi-m. GBP 98, USD 145, EUR 159 (effective 2005). adv. **Document type:** *Magazine, Trade.* **Description:** Offers advice for persons concerned with customer relationships, retention and loyalty.
Related titles: Online - full content ed.
—CCC.
Published by: C & M Publications Ltd., 3 A Market Pl, Uppingham, Leics LE15 9QH, United Kingdom. TEL 44-1572-820088, FAX 44-1572-820099, publisher@cm-media.net, http://www.loyaltymagazine.com, http://www.cm-media.net/. Ed., R&P Annich McIntosh. Adv. contact Marie Sinclair. B&W page GBP 1,000, color page GBP 1,500. Circ: 5,000 (paid); 7,000 (controlled).

658   USA   ISSN 1542-5266
LUXURY BUSINESS. Text in English. 2002 (Nov.). bi-m. USD 195 (effective 2002).
Published by: Unity Marketing, 188 Cocalico Creek Rd., Stevens, PA 17578. TEL 717-336-1600, FAX 717-336-1601, http://www.unitymarketingonline.com. Ed., Pub. Pam Danziger.

---

658 739.27   USA
LUXURY INTERNATIONAL. Text in English. q. USD 25 domestic; USD 42.50 foreign; USD 10 per issue domestic (effective 2004). **Description:** Provides the latest design trends, expert market analysis and insight for jewelers in the U.S., South America, México, Europe, the Middle East, Asia, and Australia.
Published by: J C K, International Publishing Group (Subsidiary of: Reed Business Information), Valley Forge Park Place, 1018 W 9th Ave, King of Prussia, PA 19406. TEL 610-205-1000, FAX 610-205-1139, http:// www.reedbusiness.com/index.asp?layout= theListProfile&theListID=788&groupid=39&industryid=39. Ed. Carrie Soucy TEL 646-746-7126. Pub. Frank Dallahan TEL 610-205-1101. Circ: 4,000. **Subscr. to:** Reed Business Information, 360 Park Ave South, New York, NY 10010.

M A C NEWS. see *BUSINESS AND ECONOMICS—Management*

M & A E-NEWS. see *COMPUTERS—Internet*

M & S MAGAZINE. see *GENERAL INTEREST PERIODICALS—Great Britain*

658   DEU
M D - MARKETING DIGEST; Fachbereichszeitschrift der Fachhochschule fuer Wirtschaft, Pforzheim. Text in German. 1983. s-a. adv. bk.rev. back issues avail. **Document type:** *Academic/Scholarly.*
Published by: Verein der Foerder und Absolventen (FAV), Fachhochschule fuer Wirtschaft, Tiefenbronner Str 65, Pforzheim, 75175, Germany. TEL 07231-603-0. Ed. Philip Staehler. Circ: 1,700.

658.8   USA   ISSN 0092-4857
HC106.6
M E I MARKETING ECONOMICS GUIDE∗ . Text in English. 1973. a. USD 30. illus.; stat.
Related titles: Diskette ed.: 1973; Magnetic Tape ed.: 1973.
Published by: Marketing Economics Institute, Ltd., 186 26 Avon Rd, Jamaica, NY 11432-5823. Ed. Alfred Hong.

658.8   ESP   ISSN 1130-8761
M K MARKETING Y VENTAS PARA DIRECTIVOS. Text in Spanish. 1987. 11/yr. EUR 199 combined subscription Print & online eds. (effective 2005). adv. **Document type:** *Trade.*
Related titles: Online - full text ed.
Published by: Grupo Especial Directivos (Subsidiary of: Wolters Kluwer BV), Orense 16, Madrid, 28020, Spain. TEL 34-902-250520, FAX 34-902-250502, clientes@edirectivos.com, http://www.marketingmk.com, http://www.e-directivos.com. Ed. Begona de Miguel. Adv. contact Juan Manuel Castro. Circ: 9,637 (controlled).

658.8   USA
M L M INSIDER. (Multi-Level Marketing) Text in English. 1991. bi-m. **Document type:** *Newsletter, Trade.* **Description:** Provides network marketers with accurate, objective, unbiased, and current information on all aspects of the network marketing industry.
Related titles: Online - full text ed.
Published by: Network Resources, Inc., 3741 N E 163rd St, Ste 123, N Miami, FL 33160. TEL 305-947-5600, FAX 305-947-8655, coreya@mlminsider.com, http:// www.mlminsider.com. Ed. Rod Cook. Pub. Corey Augenstein.

658.8   USA
M L M WOMAN NEWSLETTER. (Multi-Level Marketing) Text in English. m. free. **Document type:** *Newsletter, Trade.* **Description:** Dedicated to issues of interest to women in network marketing.
Media: Online - full text.
Published by: Regent Press, 2073 N Oxnard Blvd, 251, Oxnard, CA 93030. regent@west.net, http://www.mlmwoman.com. Ed., Pub. Linda Locke.

M L S. (Marketing Library Services) see *LIBRARY AND INFORMATION SCIENCES*

M O D CONTRACTS BULLETIN. see *MILITARY*

M O D DEFENCE CONTRACTS BULLETIN. see *MILITARY*

M P A: SALES EDGE. see *ADVERTISING AND PUBLIC RELATIONS*

M P R EXCHANGE. see *HEALTH FACILITIES AND ADMINISTRATION*

M R A A NEWSLETTER. see *SPORTS AND GAMES—Boats And Boating*

658   USA
M R A BLUE BOOK RESEARCH SERVICES DIRECTORY. Text in English. 1973. a. USD 120 to non-members; USD 80 to members. adv. **Document type:** *Directory.* **Description:** Outlines research and data-collection company capabilities and facilities.
Formerly: M R A Research Service Directory

Published by: Marketing Research Association, Inc., 1344 Silas Deane Hwy, Ste 306, Box 230, Rocky Hill, CT 06067-0230. TEL 860-257-4008, FAX 860-257-3990. Ed., R&P, Adv. contact Maureen Peruta. Circ: 1,400.

MADE FOR EXPORT & ELECTRONIC COMMERCE. see *BUSINESS AND ECONOMICS—International Commerce*

MAGA SCENE. see *PUBLISHING AND BOOK TRADE*

THE MAGAZINE; everything you need to know to make it in the magazine business. see *PUBLISHING AND BOOK TRADE*

658.8 659.1   USA
MAGNET MARKETING & SALES. Text in English. 1976. q. free. back issues avail. **Document type:** *Newsletter, Trade.* **Description:** Features results-oriented articles and information on advertising, marketing, public relations, design, creative sales and fundraising for businesses.
Former titles: Magnet Marketing; (until 1991): Good Impressions
Published by: Graham Communications, 40 Oval Rd, Ste 2, Quincy, MA 02170-3813. http://www.grahamcomm.com/. Ed., Pub. John R Graham. Circ: 3,500 (controlled).

MAIL MARKETING. see *ADVERTISING AND PUBLIC RELATIONS*

MAIL ORDER BUSINESS DIRECTORY. see *BUSINESS AND ECONOMICS—Trade And Industrial Directories*

658   CAN
MAIL ORDER EUROPE BUSINESS DIRECTORY ON CD-ROM. Text in English. a. CND 495 domestic; USD 495 in United States (effective 2000). **Document type:** *Directory, Trade.* **Description:** Lists some 3,250 European mail order companies in 25 countries. Surveys national markets and more than 400 home-shopping Web sites.
Media: CD-ROM.
Published by: (European Mail Order and Distance Selling Trade Association/Association Europeenne de Vente par Correspondance et a Distance BEL), International Press Publications Inc, 90 Nolan Ct, Ste 21, Markham, ON L3R 4L9, Canada. TEL 905-946-9588, 800-679-2514, FAX 905-946-9590, ipp@interlog.com, http://interlog.com/~ipp/ international.html, http://www.interlog.com/~ipp. **Co-sponsor:** National Mail Order Association.

658   CAN
MAIL ORDER U S A BUSINESS DIRECTORY ON CD-ROM. Text in English. a. CND 495 per vol. (effective 2000). **Document type:** *Directory, Trade.* **Description:** Lists the top 2,000 US mail order firms and profiles 11 market segments. Includes more than 1,000 home-shopping Web sites.
Media: CD-ROM.
Published by: (National Mail Order Association USA), International Press Publications Inc, 90 Nolan Ct, Ste 21, Markham, ON L3R 4L9, Canada. TEL 905-946-9588, 800-679-2514, FAX 905-946-9590, ipp@interlog.com, http://interlog.com/~ipp/international.html, http:// www.interlog.com/~ipp.

658.8   USA   ISSN 0464-591X
MAINLY MARKETING∗ ; the Schoonmaker report to technical managements. Text in English. 1962. m. USD 200. bk.rev. charts; stat. cum.index. back issues avail. **Description:** Attempts to help readers market better to and for high technology companies.
Published by: Schoonmaker Associates, 2405 Antigua Cir Apt E4, Coconut Creek, FL 33066-1013. TEL 516-473-8741. Ed. W K Schoonmaker. Circ: 1,000.

MAJOR MARKET SHARE COMPANIES: ASIA PACIFIC. see *BUSINESS AND ECONOMICS—Trade And Industrial Directories*

MAJOR MARKET SHARE COMPANIES: EUROPE & SOUTH AFRICA. see *BUSINESS AND ECONOMICS—Trade And Industrial Directories*

MAJOR MARKET SHARE COMPANIES: THE AMERICAS. see *BUSINESS AND ECONOMICS—Trade And Industrial Directories*

MAJOR PERFORMANCE RANKINGS. see *BUSINESS AND ECONOMICS—Trade And Industrial Directories*

MAKE-UP ARTIST MAGAZINE. see *BEAUTY CULTURE*

362   USA   ISSN 1079-9494
MANAGED CARE MARKETING. Text in English. 1995. q. **Document type:** *Journal, Trade.*
Related titles: Online - full text ed.: (from Gale Group, O C L C Online Computer Library Center, Inc.); ♦ Supplement to: Med Ad News. ISSN 1067-733X.
—CCC.
Published by: Engel Publishing Partners, 828 A Newtown-Yardley Rd, Newtown, PA 18940. TEL 215-867-0044, FAX 215-867-0053, info@engelpub.com, http://www.engelpub.com.

MANAGEMENT AND MARKETING ABSTRACTS. see *BUSINESS AND ECONOMICS—Abstracting, Bibliographies, Statistics*

MANAGEMENT IN NIGERIA. see *BUSINESS AND ECONOMICS—Management*

658 IRL
MANDATE NEWS. Text in English. 1904. 4/yr. free to members (effective 2001). **Document type:** *Trade.*
Former titles: Distributive Worker (0790-8776); (until 1921): Drapers' Assistant (0790-8768)
Related titles: Online - full content ed.
Published by: Mandate Trade Union, O'Lehane House, 9 Cavendish Row, Dublin, 1, Ireland. TEL 353-1-8746321, FAX 353-1-8729581, mandate@mandate.ie, http://www.mandate.ie/news.htm. Ed. Owen Nulty. Circ: 7,500.

MANIPULACION DE MATERIALES EN LA INDUSTRIA. see *BUILDING AND CONSTRUCTION*

MANUAL OF CREDIT AND COMMERCIAL LAWS. see *BUSINESS AND ECONOMICS—Banking And Finance*

658 FRA ISSN 0183-3308
MARCHAND FORAIN. Text in French. m.
Address: 2 Place de l'Amirande, BP 52, Avignon, Cedex 1 84005, France. TEL 90-82-54-03, TELEX 432 770. Ed. Michel Pierre. Circ: 24,000.

MARKEDSFOERING. see *ADVERTISING AND PUBLIC RELATIONS*

658 DEU ISSN 0342-1236
MARKENARTIKEL. Text in German. 1934. m. EUR 11.50 newsstand/cover (effective 2003). adv. **Document type:** *Magazine, Trade.*
—IE.
Published by: E. Albrecht Verlags KG, Freihamer Str 2, Graefelfing, 82166, Germany. TEL 49-89-858530, FAX 49-89-85853199, av@albrecht.de. adv.: B&W page EUR 1,308, color page EUR 2,352. Circ: 3,590 (paid and controlled).

658.8 ESP
MARKERAMA. Text in Spanish. 6/yr.
Address: Consell de Cent, 366, pra., Barcelona, 08009, Spain. TEL 3-302-25-27, FAX 3-412-33-26. Ed. Cesar Dutch. Circ: 3,500.

380.14 GBR
MARKET INTELLIGENCE (LONDON, 1972). Text in English. 1972. m. GBP 3,995 (effective 1999). Index. back issues avail. **Document type:** *Trade.*
Formerly: Mintel (0305-3504)
Related titles: CD-ROM ed.; Online - full text ed.
Indexed: FS&TA, SCIMP.
Published by: Mintel International Group Ltd., 18-19 Long Ln., London, EC1A 9PL, United Kingdom. TEL 44-20-76064533, FAX 44-20-76065932, info@mintel.com, http://www.mintel.com. Ed. James McCoy. Circ: 600.

▼ **MARKET INTELLIGENCE MONTHLY.** see *PUBLISHING AND BOOK TRADE*

052 ZAF
MARKET PLACE. Text in English. 1978. fortn. ZAR 204 (effective 2000). adv. bk.rev. **Document type:** *Trade.*
Published by: Caxton Printing & Publishing Co., PO Box 1610, Parklands, Johannesburg 2121, South Africa. TEL 27-11-889-0600, FAX 27-11-889-0758. R&P Heather Holt. Adv. contact Carla Feirao. Circ: 3,500.

658.83 GBR ISSN 0308-3446
MARKET RESEARCH EUROPE. Text in English. 1968. m. GBP 825 domestic; EUR 1,310 in Europe; USD 1,310 elsewhere (effective 2003). charts; illus.; mkt.; stat. index. **Document type:** *Journal, Trade.* **Description:** Each issue contains 5 or 6 market reports with business analysis of European consumer markets.
Former titles: Euromonitor Review (0014-2441); Which incorporates: Market Research in Benelux (0047-598X); Market Research in Germany (0047-5998); Market Research in Italy (0047-6005)
Media: Duplicated (not offset). **Related titles:** Online - full text ed.
Indexed: BPIA, CPM, FS&TA, IPackAb, KES, PROMT, RASB, SCIMP.
—IE, Infotrieve.
Published by: Euromonitor, 60-61 Britton St, London, EC1 5UX, United Kingdom. TEL 44-20-7251-8024, FAX 44-20-7608-3149, info@euromonitor.com, http://www.euromonitor.com. **Subscr. to:** Euromonitor International. **Dist. by:** Euromonitor International, 122 S. Michigan Ave., Ste. 810, Chicago, IL 60603-6131. TEL 800-577-3876.

658.83 GBR ISSN 0308-3047
HC260.C6
MARKET RESEARCH G B. Variant title: Market Research Great Britain. Text in English. 1960. m. GBP 825 domestic; EUR 1,190 in Europe; USD 1,190 elsewhere (effective 2003). mkt.; stat. **Document type:** *Journal, Trade.* **Description:** Each issue contains 5 or 6 markets reports with business analysis of consumer markets in the UK.
Formerly: Market Research (0025-3588)
Related titles: Online - full text ed.
Indexed: CPM, FS&TA, IPackAb, KES, SCIMP.
—BLDSC (5381.585000), IE, Infotrieve.
Published by: Euromonitor, 60-61 Britton St, London, EC1 5UX, United Kingdom. TEL 44-20-7251-8024, FAX 44-20-7608-3149, info@euromonitor.com, http://www.euromonitor.com. **Dist. by:** Euromonitor International, 122 S. Michigan Ave., Ste. 810, Chicago, IL 60603-6131. TEL 312-922-1115, FAX 312-522-1157.

MARKET RESEARCH MONITOR. see *BUSINESS AND ECONOMICS—Economic Situation And Conditions*

658.8 GBR ISSN 0963-7257
MARKET RESEARCH REPORTER. Text in English. 1992. 20/yr. GBP 395, USD 789 (effective 1999). **Document type:** *Newsletter.* **Description:** Keeps market research professionals up to date on the findings of new market reports, covering both consumer and industrial markets.
Published by: MarketScape, 5th Fl, 29-30 Warwick St, London, W1R 5RD, United Kingdom. TEL 44-1717-273443, FAX 44-1727-834012, em72@dial.pipex.com. Ed., Pub. Anne P Smith. R&P A P Smith.

658.8 GBR
MARKET RESEARCH SOCIETY. ANNUAL CONFERENCE PROCEEDINGS. Text in English. a.
—BLDSC (1082.287000).
Published by: Market Research Society, 15 Northburgh St, London, EC1V 0JR, United Kingdom. TEL 44-20-74904911, FAX 44-20-74900608, info@marketresearch.org.uk, http://www.marketresearch.org.uk.

658.8 GBR
MARKET RESEARCH SOCIETY. MEMBERS' REGISTER. Text in English. 1998. a. **Document type:** *Directory, Corporate.*
Formerly: Market Research Society. Members' Handbook (1461-3336); Supersedes in part (1969-1998): Market Research Society. Yearbook (0076-4523)
Media: CD-ROM. **Related titles:** Print ed.
—**CCC.**
Published by: Market Research Society, 15 Northburgh St, London, EC1V 0JR, United Kingdom. TEL 44-20-74904911, FAX 44-20-74900608, info@mrs.org.uk, http://www.mrs.org.uk. Adv. contact Debra Lestrade TEL 44-20-7566-1843. Circ: 8,000.

MARKET RESEARCH SOURCEBOOK. see *BUSINESS AND ECONOMICS—Trade And Industrial Directories*

MARKET SHARE TRACKER. see *BUSINESS AND ECONOMICS—Trade And Industrial Directories*

658 332.6 IND
MARKET SURVEY CUM DETAILED TECHNO ECONOMIC FEASIBILITY REPORTS. Text in English. irreg. INR 3,150, USD 150 per issue (effective 1999). **Document type:** *Proceedings.* **Description:** Describes in detail projects readily available, including market survey, manufacturing techniques, raw materials, plant and machinery, personnel requirements, land and building, and financial aspects.
Published by: Small Industry Research Institute, 4-43 Roop Nagar, P O Box 2106, New Delhi, 110 007, India. TEL 91-11-2910805, FAX 91-11-2923955.

658.7 GBR ISSN 1361-9055
MARKET TRADER & SHOPKEEPER; the retailer's weekly. Variant title: Market Trader. Text in English. 1925. w. GBP 35 in United Kingdom; USD 55 rest of Europe; USD 150 in the Americas & Middle East; USD 160 in the Far East (effective 2000). adv. **Document type:** *Newspaper, Trade.* **Description:** Publishes articles on the UK local retail markets & shopkeeping business sector, suppliers, manufacturers and personalities.
Published by: World's Fair Ltd., Albert Mill, Albert St, PO Box 57, Oldham, Lancs OL8 3WF, United Kingdom. TEL 44-161-683-8000, FAX 44-161-683-8001, mt@worldsfair.co.uk, http://www.worldsfair.co.uk. Ed. Michael Mellor.

658.8 GBR
THE MARKETER. Text in English. 1988. 10/yr. GBP 59 in United Kingdom; GBP 67 in Europe; GBP 75 elsewhere (effective 2001). adv. bk.rev. back issues avail. **Document type:** *Magazine, Trade.* **Description:** Covers marketing trends and techniques.
Formerly (until 2004): Marketing Business (0954-1543)
Indexed: Emerald, Inspec.
—BLDSC (5381.626400), IE, ingenta. **CCC.**
Published by: Chartered Institute of Marketing, Moor Hall, Cookham, Maidenhead, Berks SL6 9QH, United Kingdom. TEL 44-1628-427500, FAX 44-1628-427329, corporatecommunications@cim.co.uk, cim@communications-team.co.uk, http://www.cim.co.uk. Pub. Mark Flanders. R&P Dawn Southgate. Adv. contact Rob Brown TEL 44-20-7923-5400. Circ: 42,700 (controlled).

338.47665 USA
THE MARKETER (TOPEKA). Text in English. bi-m. free to members. **Document type:** *Magazine, Trade.*
Formerly: Kansas Oil Marketer
Published by: Petroleum Marketers and Convenience Store Association of Kansas, 201 N W Hwy 24, Ste 320, Topeka, KS 66608. TEL 785-233-9655, FAX 785-354-4374, andy@pmcaofks.org, http://www.pmcaofks.org. Ed. Andy Anderson. Circ: 800 (paid).

MARKETING ST. KILDA. see *BUSINESS AND ECONOMICS—Computer Applications*

658 DEU ISSN 0344-1369
MARKETING; Zeitschrift fuer Forschung und Praxis. Text in German. 1979. q. EUR 144 domestic; EUR 153.90 foreign; EUR 102 to students; EUR 40.50 newsstand/cover (effective 2005). adv. back issues avail.; reprint service avail. from SCH. **Document type:** *Journal, Trade.*
Related titles: Online - full text ed.: (from Northern Light Technology, Inc.).
Indexed: ABIn, ADPA, DIP, IBR, IBZ, RASB, SCIMP.
—BLDSC (5381.630100), IE, Infotrieve.
Published by: Verlag C.H. Beck oHG, Wilhelmstr 9, Munich, 80801, Germany. TEL 49-89-38189338, FAX 49-89-38189398, abo.service@beck.de, http://www.beck.de. adv.: page EUR 1,200; trim 186 x 260. Circ: 1,200.

658.8 RUS
MARKETING. Text in Russian. bi-m. USD 154 in United States (effective 2004). **Document type:** *Magazine, Trade.*
Indexed: RefZh.
Published by: Tsentr Marketingovykh Issledovanii i Menedzhmenta, Ryazanskii pr-t 99, ofis 522, Moscow, 109542, Russian Federation. Ed. A P Chelenkov. **US dist. addr.:** East View Information Services, 3020 Harbor Ln. N., Minneapolis, MN 55447. TEL 800-477-1005, FAX 800-800-3839, eastview@eastview.com, http://www.eastview.com.

658.8 GBR ISSN 0025-3650
CODEN: MARKBC
MARKETING. Text in English. 1980. w. GBP 74 in the European Union & Ireland; GBP 230 elsewhere (effective 2005). adv. bk.rev. abstr.; illus. reprints avail. **Document type:** *Magazine, Trade.*
Related titles: Microform ed.: (from PQC); Online - full text ed.: (from bigchalk, EBSCO Publishing, Gale Group, LexisNexis, Northern Light Technology, Inc., O C L C Online Computer Library Center, Inc., ProQuest Information & Learning).
Indexed: ABIn, ADPA, ASEANManA, BPIA, BusI, CBPI, CPerI, Emerald, IndBusRep, Inspec, LRI, M&MA, ManagCont, PSI.
—BLDSC (5381.630000), AskIEEE, IE, Infotrieve. **CCC.**
Published by: Haymarket Magazines Ltd. (Subsidiary of: Haymarket Publishing Ltd.), 174 Hammersmith Rd, London, W6 7JP, United Kingdom. TEL 44-20-82675000, FAX 44-20-82674268, hpg@haymarketgroup.com, http://www.haymarketgroup.com/. Ed. Craig Smith TEL 44-20-82674341. Pub. Mike Hewitt. Circ: 40,291.

658.8 SCG ISSN 0354-3471
MARKETING (BEOGRAD). Text in English, Serbian. 1969. q. USD 45 to individuals; USD 65 to institutions; USD 90 to libraries; effective 1998. adv. bk.rev. bibl. reprints avail. **Document type:** *Academic/Scholarly.* **Description:** Presents the theory and practice of marketing in Serbia and all over the world.
Formerly (until 1992): Marketing (Zagreb) (0581-1023)
Published by: Institut Ekonomskih Nauka, 12 Zmaj Jovina St, Belgrade, 11000. TEL 381-11-2622357, FAX 381-11-181471, ien@ien.bg.ac.yu, http://www.ien.bg.ac.yu. Ed. Mile Jovic. R&P, Adv. contact Jovan Zubovic. Circ: 2,000.

MARKETING ACCION. see *BUSINESS AND ECONOMICS—Management*

658.8 USA ISSN 0896-4742
MARKETING ADVENTS. Text in English. 1954. m. USD 135 to members (effective 2000). adv. **Document type:** *Newsletter.* **Description:** Provides information on developments pertinent to the direct marketing industry, plus news and information about the Association.
Indexed: ManagCont, T&II.
Published by: Direct Marketing Association (Washington), 801 Roeder Rd., # 575, Silver Spring, MD 20910-4467. TEL 703-821-3629, FAX 703-821-3694, http://www.dmaw.org. Ed. Nancy Scott. R&P S Marshall. Adv. contact L Hegler. Circ: 1,850.

658 659.1 GBR
MARKETING & CREATIVE HANDBOOK. Text in English. 1985. a. GBP 35 per issue (effective 1998). adv. **Document type:** *Directory.* **Description:** Provides information on the UK's marketing services, creative and advertising companies.

Address: Ste. 5, 74 Oak Rd, Horfield, Bristol, Glos BS7 8RZ, United Kingdom. TEL 44-117-9446144, http://www.mch.co.uk. Ed. Nikki Bealing. Adv. contact Clive Hicklin. page GBP 1,025. Circ: 65,000.

MARKETING & MANAGEMENT NEWS. see *BUSINESS AND ECONOMICS—Management*

658.8 ITA
MARKETING & MANAGERS. Text in Italian. 1988. 11/yr.
Published by: Multispe s.r.l., Piazza Della Conciliazione, 2, Milan, MI 20123, Italy. TEL 39-2-48007589, FAX 39-2-4984494. Ed. Giancarlo Spezia.

658.8 CZE ISSN 1212-9496
MARKETING & MEDIA. Text in Czech. 2000. w. CZK 2,450; CZK 50 newsstand/cover (effective 2003). adv. **Document type:** *Magazine, Trade.*
Related titles: Online - full text ed.
Published by: Economia a.s., Dobrovskeho 25, Prague 7 7, 170 55, Czech Republic. TEL 420-2-33071111, FAX 420-2-33072003, mm@economia.cz, economia@economia.cz, http://www.MaM.cz, http://www.economia.cz. Ed. Daniel Koppl. Adv. contact Lukas Polak. page CZK 58,000; trim 226 x 326.

658 GBR
MARKETING AND RETAILING WORKING PAPER SERIES. Text in English. irreg. **Document type:** *Monographic series.*
—BLDSC (5381.636520).
Published by: University of Ulster, Faculty of Business and Management, Coleraine, Co Londonderry BT52 1SA, United Kingdom. TEL 44-1265-324168, FAX 44-1265-324910, b.quinn@ulst.ac.uk. Ed. Barry Quinn.

MARKETING BONANZA NEWSLETTER. see *COMPUTERS—Internet*

MARKETING BOOK. see *ADVERTISING AND PUBLIC RELATIONS*

658 NZL
➤ **MARKETING BULLETIN (ONLINE EDITION).** Text in English. 1990. irreg. free. back issues avail. **Document type:** *Bulletin, Academic/Scholarly.* **Description:** Provides a forum for disseminating ideas and information relating to the theory and practice of marketing and marketing research.
Formerly: Marketing Bulletin (Print Edition) (0113-6895)
Media: Online - full text.
Indexed: ABIn, WBA.
Published by: Massey University, Department of Marketing, c/o Mike Brennan, Ed., Private Bag 11222, Palmerston North, New Zealand. TEL 64-6-3569099, FAX 64-6-3502260, M.Brennan@massey.ac.nz, http://marketing-bulletin.massey.ac.nz/index.asp. Ed. Mike Brennan.

658.8 USA ISSN 0886-6368
MARKETING BULLETING. Text in English. 1959. irreg.
Published by: U.S. Department of Agriculture, Agricultural Marketing Service, 1400 Independence Ave, S W, Washington, DC 20250. TEL 202-720-8317, FAX 202-690-0031.

MARKETING C D BUSINESS. see *BUSINESS AND ECONOMICS—Trade And Industrial Directories*

658 659 USA
MARKETING CONSENSUS GUIDE. Text in English. 1995. a. USD 800 (effective 1999). bk.rev.; music rev.; software rev. tr.lit. **Document type:** *Trade.* **Description:** Comprehensive guide to marketing and advertising practices worldwide for leading multinational marketers and advertising agencies.
Related titles: E-mail ed.; Fax ed.; Online - full text ed.
Published by: Marketing Strategist Communications, Ltd., 7 Coppel Dr, Tenafly, NJ 07670-2903. TEL 201-567-4447, FAX 201-568-8538, frohlinger@worldnet.att.net. Ed., Pub. Joseph Frohlinger.

658 BRA
MARKETING E NEGOCIOS. Text in Portuguese. m. BRL 70,000 per issue.
Published by: Grupo Editorial Letter, Rua Otaviano Hudson, 26, Copacabana, Rio De Janeiro, RJ 22030-030, Brazil. FAX 021-275-2346. Circ: 40,000.

MARKETING E PUBLICIDADE. see *ADVERTISING AND PUBLIC RELATIONS*

658.8 USA ISSN 0098-1397
HC102
MARKETING ECONOMICS KEY PLANTS✶; guide to industrial purchasing power. Text in English. 1960. biennial. USD 120. stat.
Formerly: Market Statistics Key Plant Directory (0076-4531)
Related titles: Magnetic Tape ed.: 1960.
Published by: Marketing Economics Institute, Ltd., 186 26 Avon Rd, Jamaica, NY 11432-5823. Ed. Alfred Hong.

MARKETING EDUCATION REVIEW. see *EDUCATION—Higher Education*

658.8 USA ISSN 1085-2115
MARKETING EDUCATORS' JOURNAL. Text in English. 1985. s-a.
Formerly: Marketing & Distributive Educators' Digest
Published by: Marketing Education Association, Box 27473, Tempe, AZ 85285-7473. TEL 602-750-6735, mea@nationalmea.org, http://www.nationalmea.org/.

658.8 USA
A MARKETING ENERGIZER FOR CONSULTANTS. Text in English. 1997. m. free. bk.rev. back issues avail. **Document type:** *Newsletter.* **Description:** Offers tips, news and strategies on how to gain more qualified prospects and increase revenues.
Media: Online - full text.
Published by: Hanson Marketing Group, Inc., 8011 Nauajo St., Philadelphia, PA 19118. TEL 215-836-5866, FAX 215-836-4465, hanson@voicenet.com, http://www.hansonmarketing.com/freezine.html. R&P Shirley Hanson.

MARKETING FOR LAWYERS NEWSLETTER. see *LAW*

658 USA
MARKETING FORUM. Text in English. q. membership. adv. **Description:** Provides information on strategic marketing, marketing resources, successful marketing strategies; marketing case studies; 'how-to' articles; calendar of events.
Published by: (Marketing Section), American Society of Association Executives, 1575 Eye St, N W, Washington, DC 20005-1168. TEL 202-626-2723, FAX 202-371-8825, http://www.asaenet.org. Circ: 650.

658.8 GBR ISSN 0965-5328
HF5415.12.G7
THE MARKETING HANDBOOK. Text in English. 1982. a., latest vol.13, 2002-2003. GBP 70 per vol. (effective 2002). adv. **Description:** Provides coverage in the UK within the following categories: marketing consultants, market research, design, direct marketing, sales promotion, creative services, print and related services, exhibition and conference services.
Formerly (until 1990): U.K. Marketing Handbook
—BLDSC (5381.645700).
Published by: Hollis Publishing Ltd., Harlequin House, 7 High St, Teddington, Middx TW11 8EL, United Kingdom. TEL 44-20-8977-7711, FAX 44-20-8977-1133, orders@hollis-pr.co.uk, http://www.hollis-pr.com/publications/marketing.htm, http://www.hollis-pr.co.uk/. Ed. Gillie Mayer. adv.: B&W page GBP 1,525, color page GBP 2,025; 130 x 270. Circ: 5,000.

658.8 613.7 USA ISSN 1094-1304
RA410.A1
MARKETING HEALTH SERVICES. Text in English. 1981. q. USD 53 to members; USD 75 to individuals; USD 94 foreign to individuals; USD 90 domestic to institutions; USD 110 foreign to institutions (effective 2005). adv. bk.rev. abstr.; bibl.; charts; illus.; stat. index. back issues avail.; reprint service avail. from PQC,PSC. **Document type:** *Magazine, Academic/Scholarly.* **Description:** Geared to meet the needs of health care marketers with articles from professionals on provocative and relevant topics.
Formerly (until 1996): Journal of Health Care Marketing (0737-3252)
Related titles: Microfiche ed.: (from MIM, PQC); Online - full text ed.: (from Northern Light Technology, Inc.); (from EBSCO Publishing, Factiva, Gale Group, H.W. Wilson, LexisNexis, O C L C Online Computer Library Center, Inc., ProQuest Information & Learning).
Indexed: ABIn, BPI, CINAHL, CurCont, ExcerpMed, INI, MEDLINE, PAIS.
—BLDSC (5381.645800), GNLM, IDS, IE, Infotrieve, ingenta, KNAW. **CCC.**
Published by: American Marketing Association, 311 S Wacker Dr, Ste 5800, Chicago, IL 60606. TEL 312-542-9000, 312-542-9000, 800-262-1150, FAX 312-542-9001, 312-542-9001, info@ama.org, http://www.ama.org. Ed. Kent Seltman. Pub. Jack Hollfelder. Adv. contact Richard Ballschmiede. B&W page USD 740, color page USD 1,690. Circ: 4,000.

658 381 RUS ISSN 1606-1454
MARKETING I PRAKTIKA PREDPRINIMATEL'STVA. Text in Russian. 1999. w. free (effective 2004).
Media: Online - full text.
Published by: Al'yans Midiya, Bolotnaya ul 12, str 3, Moscow, 115035, Russian Federation. TEL 7-095-2345380, FAX 7-095-2345363, allmedia@allmedia.ru, http://www.businesspress.ru, http://allmedia.ru.

658.8 POL ISSN 1231-7853
MARKETING I RYNEK. Text in Polish. 1994. m. PLZ 32 per issue (effective 2003). bk.rev. 40 p./no.; **Document type:** *Journal.*
Indexed: AgrLib.
Published by: Polskie Wydawnictwo Ekonomiczne, ul Canaletta 4, Warsaw, 00099, Poland. TEL 48-22-8278001, FAX 48-22-8275567, mir@pwe.com.pl, pwe@pwe.com.pl, marketing@pwe.com.pl, http://www.marketingirynek.pl, http://www.pwe.com.pl. Ed. Ireneusz Rutkowski. Adv. contact Monika Kolodziejczyk TEL 48-22-8278001 ext 320.

658.8 GBR
MARKETING IN ACTION SERIES. Text in English. irreg., latest vol.5. GBP 12.95. adv. **Document type:** *Monographic series.*
Published by: Kogan Page Ltd., 120 Pentonville Rd, London, N1 9JN, United Kingdom. FAX 44-20-7837-6348. Ed. Norman Hart. Adv. contact Linda Batham.

658.8 NGA ISSN 0331-8400
MARKETING IN NIGERIA; for business, economics, commerce, industry. Text in English. 1972. m. NGN 10. adv. bk.rev. charts; illus.; stat.; tr.lit. **Document type:** *Trade.*
Published by: Alpha Publications, 18 A Modele St., PMB 1163, Surulere, Lagos State, Nigeria. Ed. Charles Dodoo. Circ: 30,000.

658 GBR ISSN 0263-4503
HF5410
MARKETING INTELLIGENCE & PLANNING. Text in English. 7/yr. EUR 12,265.91 in Europe; USD 12,179 in North America; AUD 14,259 in Australasia; GBP 8,296.54 in UK & elsewhere (effective 2006). reprint service avail. from PSC. **Document type:** *Journal, Academic/Scholarly.* **Description:** Aims to help the marketing researcher and practitioner increase marketing effectiveness. Covers strategic planning, advertising effectiveness research, understanding buyer behavior, technological forecasting, the effective use of concept testing and more.
Incorporates (1955-1989): Selling (0037-1599); Journal of Sales Management (0266-3007); (1995-200?): Journal of Marketing Practice: Applied Marketing Science (1355-2538)
Related titles: CD-ROM ed.; Online - full text ed.: (from EBSCO Publishing, Emerald Group Publishing Limited, Florida Center for Library Automation, Gale Group, IngentaConnect, O C L C Online Computer Library Center, Inc., ProQuest Information & Learning, Swets Information Services).
Indexed: ABIn, CPM, EmerIntel, Emerald, M&MA, PsycInfo, PsycholAb.
—BLDSC (5381.646700), CISTI, IE, Infotrieve, ingenta. **CCC.**
Published by: Emerald Group Publishing Limited, 60-62 Toller Ln, Bradford, W Yorks BD8 9BY, United Kingdom. TEL 44-1274-777700, FAX 44-1274-785200, help@emeraldinsight.com, infomation@emeraldinsight.com, http://www.emeraldinsight.com/mip.htm. Ed. Keith Crosier. **Subscr. in N America:** Emerald Group Publishing Ltd., 44 Brattle St, 4th Fl, Cambridge, MA 02138. TEL 617-497-2175, 888-622-0075, FAX 617-354-6875.

B

658.8 DEU ISSN 0025-3774
MARKETING JOURNAL. Text in German. 1968. bi-m. adv. bk.rev. abstr.; bibl.; illus.; stat. index. **Document type:** *Trade.*
Indexed: KES.
—IE, Infotrieve.
Published by: Marketing Journal Gesellschaft fuer angewandtes Marketing mbH, Koopstr 20-22, Hamburg, 20144, Germany. TEL 49-40-4103148, FAX 49-40-4101276, marketingjournal@t-online.de. Ed. Wolfgang K A Disch. Circ: 5,000.

MARKETING LAW REPORTING SERVICE. see *LAW*

658.8 USA ISSN 0923-0645
HF5415.2 CODEN: MLETEK
➤ **MARKETING LETTERS**; a journal of research in marketing. Text in English. 1990. q. EUR 448, USD 458, GBP 285 combined subscription to institutions print & online eds. (effective 2005). adv. illus. reprint service avail. from PQC,PSC. **Document type:** *Journal, Academic/Scholarly.* **Description:** Publishes empirical findings, methodological papers, and theoretical and conceptual insights across areas of research in marketing.
Related titles: Microform ed.: (from PQC); Online - full text ed.: ISSN 1573-059X (from EBSCO Publishing, Gale Group, IngentaConnect, Kluwer Online, O C L C Online Computer Library Center, Inc., ProQuest Information & Learning, Springer LINK, Swets Information Services).
Indexed: ABIn, BibLing, CurCont, IBSS, RefZh, SSCI.
—BLDSC (5381.648050), IE, Infotrieve, ingenta. **CCC.**
Published by: Springer-Verlag New York, Inc. (Subsidiary of: Springer Science+Business Media), 233 Spring St, New York, NY 10013. TEL 212-460-1500, FAX 212-460-1575, service@springer-ny.com, http://springerlink.metapress.com/openurl.asp?genre=journal&issn=0923-0645, http://www.springer-ny.com. Eds. Barton A Weitz, Charles B Weinberg. **Subscr. to:** Journal Fulfillment, PO Box 2485, Secaucus, NJ 07096-2485. TEL 201-348-4033, FAX 201-348-4505, journals@springer-ny.com.

658.8 659.1 CAN ISSN 1196-4650
HF5410
MARKETING MAGAZINE; Canada's weekly newspaper for marketing, advertising and sales executives. Text in English. 1933. w. CND 89 domestic; CND 120 foreign (effective 2005). adv. bk.rev. illus.; tr.lit. index, cum.index. **Document type:** *Newspaper, Trade.* **Description:** Serves the information needs of sales, advertising, and marketing executives in business, industry, and advertising agencies. Prepares a series of special reports on major media plus advertising and sales forecasts.
Incorporates (in 1994): Digital Marketing (Toronto, 1994) (1202-631X); Formerly (until 1993): Marketing (0025-3642); Which incorporates (1973-1982): Canadian Premiums & Incentives (0319-6267)

Related titles: Microform ed.: (from MML, PQC); Online - full text ed.: Marketing Online (from EBSCO Publishing, H.W. Wilson, Micromedia ProQuest, O C L C Online Computer Library Center, Inc., ProQuest Information & Learning).
Indexed: ABIn, BPI, CBCABus, CBCARef, CBPI, CPerl, PAIS, T&II.
—BLDSC (5381.648410), CISTI. **CCC.**
Published by: Rogers Media Publishing Ltd, One Mount Pleasant Rd, 11th Fl, Toronto, ON M4Y 2Y5, Canada. TEL 416-764-1593, FAX 416-764-1419, http://www.marketingmag.ca, http://www.rogers.com. Pub. Richard Elliott TEL 416-764-1570. Circ: 12,000.

658.8 NZL ISSN 0111-9044
MARKETING MAGAZINE. Text in English. 1981. m. NZD 95 domestic; NZD 145.50 in Australia; NZD 199.50 elsewhere (effective 2000). adv. bk.rev. back issues avail. **Document type:** *Trade.* **Description:** Marketing strategy in practice for marketing-oriented executives.
Incorporates (1990-1992): Direct Marketing (1170-3520)
Related titles: Online - full text ed.: (from EBSCO Publishing, Gale Group, ProQuest Information & Learning).
Indexed: ABIX, ABIn, INZP, Inpharma, PE&ON, Reac, WBA, WMB.
—BLDSC (5381.648400).
Published by: Profile Publishing Ltd., Wellesley St, PO Box 5544, Auckland, New Zealand. TEL 64-9-630-8940, FAX 64-9-630-1046, info@profile.co.nz, http://www.profile.co.nz/. Ed. Ruth Le Pla. Adv. contact Vernene Medcalf. Circ: 4,046.

658 USA ISSN 1061-3846
HF5415.13
MARKETING MANAGEMENT. Text in English. 1992. q. USD 53 to members; USD 70 to individuals; USD 105 to institutions (effective 2005). adv. reprint service avail. from PSC. **Document type:** *Magazine, Trade.* **Description:** For senior marketing management in the production and service markets; focuses on analysis, real marketplace applications, as well as insider and senior-level insights and opinions on the issues and trends facing today's business professionals.
Related titles: Microform ed.: (from PQC); Online - full text ed.: Marketing Management Online (from EBSCO Publishing, H.W. Wilson, Northern Light Technology, Inc., O C L C Online Computer Library Center, Inc., ProQuest Information & Learning).
Indexed: ABIn, BPI, CRIA, CRICC, CurCont, Emerald, LogistBibl.
—BLDSC (5381.648420), IDS, IE, Infotrieve, ingenta. **CCC.**
Published by: American Marketing Association, 311 S Wacker Dr, Ste 5800, Chicago, IL 60606. TEL 312-542-9000, 800-262-1150, FAX 312-542-9001, info@ama.org, http://www.marketingpower.com, http://www.ama.org. Ed. Carolyn Pollard Neal. Pub. Jack Hollfelder. adv.: B&W page USD 1,200. Circ: 5,000.

658 USA
MARKETING MANAGEMENT JOURNAL. Text in English. s-a. USD 35 membership; USD 35 to non-members; USD 35 to libraries (effective 2003).
Formerly: Journal of Marketing Management (1071-1988)
Published by: Marketing Management Association, c/o Paul C. Thistlethwaite, Exec. Sec., Dept. of Marketing and Finance, Western Illinois Univ., Macomb, IL 61455. TEL 309-298-1401, FAX 309-298-2198, mfpct@wiu.edu, http://www.mmaglobal.org. Ed. Charles E Pettijohn TEL 417-836-4188.

658 GBR ISSN 0964-5454
THE MARKETING MANAGER'S YEARBOOK. Abbreviated title: MMY. Text in English. 1991. a. GBP 125 (effective 2001). adv. **Document type:** *Directory, Trade.* **Description:** Lists sales/marketing directors and managers in over 10000 major UK companies and organizations, plus 4000 advisers and suppliers to the marketing sector.
—BLDSC (5381.648450).
Published by: A P Information Services, Marlborough House, 298 Regents Park Rd, London, N3 2UU, United Kingdom. TEL 44-20-83499988, FAX 44-20-83499797, mmy@ap-info.co.uk, info@apinfo.co.uk, http://www.ap-info.co.uk. Ed. Helen Irwin. Pub. Alan Philipp. Adv. contact James Johnston. B&W page CND 1,550, color page CND 1,900. Circ: 4,450.

658.8 USA
THE MARKETING MINUTE. Text in English. w. free. back issues avail. **Document type:** *Trade.* **Description:** Includes informative marketng vignettes.
Media: Online - full text.
Published by: Marcia Yudkin Marketing TEL 781-934-5406, 888-562-7469, marcia@yudkin.com, http://www.jobshow.com/MM_email.html. Ed. Marcia Yudkin.

658 ZAF ISSN 0256-0348
MARKETING MIX. Text in English. 1982. m. ZAR 96. adv. bk.rev. illus.
Indexed: ISAP.
Published by: Systems Publishers (Pty) Ltd., PO Box 41345, Craighall, Gauteng 2024, South Africa. TEL 27-11-789-1808, FAX 27-11-789-4725, TELEX 4-24952. Ed. Gisele Wertheim Aymes. Circ: 7,530.

658.8 NLD ISSN 0025-3782
MARKETING MIX DIGEST. Text in Dutch. 1965. 11/yr. adv. bk.rev. abstr.; illus.; stat. index. **Document type:** *Trade.*
Published by: Wolters Kluwer N.V., Leeuwenburg 101, Deventer, 7411 TH, Netherlands. TEL 31-5700-48999, FAX 31-5700-11504. **Subscr. to:** Intermedia bv, Postbus 4, Alphen aan den Rijn 2400 MA, Netherlands. TEL 31-172-466321, FAX 31-172-435527.

MARKETING MUSING ON ART; sell fine art for a change. see *ART*

658.8 USA ISSN 0025-3790
HF5415 CODEN: MKNWAT
MARKETING NEWS; reporting on marketing and its association. Text in English. 1967. bi-w. USD 100 to non-members; USD 130 to institutions (effective 2000). adv. bk.rev. charts; illus.; tr.lit. reprints avail. **Document type:** *Newspaper, Trade.* **Description:** Covers the most recent innovations in marketing as it is practiced in today's leading companies.
Related titles: Microform ed.: (from MIM, PQC); Online - full text ed.: (from EBSCO Publishing, Gale Group, H.W. Wilson, LexisNexis, Northern Light Technology, Inc., O C L C Online Computer Library Center, Inc., ProQuest Information & Learning).
Indexed: ABIn, B&I, BPI, BPIA, BusI, Inspec, ManagCont, PROMT, T&II.
—BLDSC (5381.648500), AskIEEE, CASDDS, CISTI. **CCC.**
Published by: American Marketing Association, 311 S Wacker Dr, Ste 5800, Chicago, IL 60606. TEL 312-542-9000, 800-262-1150, FAX 312-542-9001, info@ama.org, http://www.ama.org/pubs/mn/pub2.html. Pub. Jack Hollfelder. R&P Rochelle Amos TEL 312-542-9022. Adv. contact Daniel C Bello. Circ: 38,000.

658 PHL
MARKETING PROFILES OF STRATEGIC INDUSTRIES. Text in English. 1991. a.
Published by: Board of Investments, Ortigas Bldg, Ortigas Ave, PO Box 676, Rizal, Philippines. TEL 63-2-8953666, FAX 63-2-8953521.

THE MARKETING PULSE; the exclusive insight provider to the entertainment, marketing, advertising and media industries. see *ADVERTISING AND PUBLIC RELATIONS*

MARKETING RECREATION CLASSES. see *EDUCATION—Guides To Schools And Colleges*

380.1 658.8 USA ISSN 1064-3893
CODEN: MRRPED
THE MARKETING REPORT. Abbreviated title: T M R. Text in English. 1992. s-m. USD 264 domestic; USD 330 foreign (effective 2005). **Document type:** *Newsletter.* **Description:** Business-to-business marketing news and success stories.
Published by: Progressive Business Publications, 370 Technology Dr, Malvern, PA 19355-1315. TEL 610-695-8600, 800-220-5000, FAX 610-647-8089, editor@pbp.com, http://www.pbp.com. Ed. Michael Boyette. R&P Curt Brown. Circ: 17,201 (paid).

658.8 USA ISSN 1040-8460
HF5415.2
➤ **MARKETING RESEARCH**; a magazine of management and applications. Text in English. 1989. bi-m. USD 53 domestic to members; USD 75 domestic to non-members; USD 94 foreign to non-members; USD 90 domestic to institutions; USD 146 foreign to institutions (effective 2005). adv. bk.rev. illus. Index. back issues avail.; reprint service avail. from PSC. **Document type:** *Magazine, Academic/Scholarly.* **Description:** Promotes a new and broader AMA definition of marketing research that stresses developing and evaluating hypotheses and theories rather than merely analyzing data. For managers and practitioners of marketing research.
Related titles: Online - full text ed.: (from EBSCO Publishing, Gale Group, H.W. Wilson, LexisNexis, O C L C Online Computer Library Center, Inc., ProQuest Information & Learning).
Indexed: ABIn, BLI, BPI, CurCont, Emerald, MResA.
—BLDSC (5381.649700), IDS, IE, Infotrieve, ingenta. **CCC.**
Published by: American Marketing Association, 311 S Wacker Dr, Ste 5800, Chicago, IL 60606. TEL 312-542-9000, 800-262-1150, 800-262-1150, FAX 312-542-9001, info@ama.org, http://www.marketingpower.com/, http://www.ama.org/pubs/mr/index.html. Ed. Chuck Chakrapani. Pub. Jack Hollfelder. Adv. contact Richard Ballschmiede. B&W page USD 910, color page USD 1,860. Circ: 3,500 (paid).

➤ **MARKETING RESULTS**; vakblad voor verkopers van drogisterijartikelen. see *PHARMACY AND PHARMACOLOGY*

658 USA
MARKETING REVIEW. Text in English. 1947. m. USD 40. adv. index. **Description:** News magazine with articles on marketing and marketing research related practices and theories.
Indexed: Hospl.
Published by: American Marketing Association, New York Chapter, 60 E 42nd St, Ste 1765, New York, NY 10165-0006. TEL 212-687-3280, FAX 212-447-0994. Ed. Hal Marcus. Circ: 5,000.

658 GBR ISSN 1469-347X
HF5415.2
➤ **THE MARKETING REVIEW.** Text in English. 2000. q. GBP 60 to individuals; GBP 180 to institutions; GBP 325 combined subscription to institutions print & online (effective 2005). back issues avail. **Document type:** *Journal, Academic/Scholarly.* **Description:** Aims to provide clear, well written and authoritative discussions and reviews of current issues, with regular features on theory, hot topics, research methods, data analysis and skills and professional development.
Related titles: Online - full text ed.: ISSN 1472-1384. GBP 15 to individuals (effective 2002) (from EBSCO Publishing, Gale Group, IngentaConnect, Swets Information Services).
—BLDSC (5381.661000), IE. **CCC.**
Published by: Westburn Publishers Ltd., 23 Millig St, Helensburgh, Argyll, G84 9LD, United Kingdom. TEL 44-1436-678699, FAX 44-1436-670328, tmr@westburn.co.uk, journals@westburn.co.uk, http://www.themarketingreview.com/, http://www.westburn.co.uk/. Ed. Dr. Jim A Blythe. Pub., R&P Dr. Anne Foy.

658 USA ISSN 0732-2399
HF5410
➤ **MARKETING SCIENCE**; the marketing journal of INFORMS. Text in English. 1982. q. USD 128 domestic to non-members; USD 144 foreign to non-members; USD 168 combined subscription domestic to non-members print & online eds.; USD 184 combined subscription foreign to non-members print & online eds.; USD 84 combined subscription to members print & online eds.; USD 272 combined subscription domestic to institutions print & online eds.; USD 288 combined subscription foreign to institutions print & online eds. (effective 2004). adv. charts; bibl.; illus. Index. back issues avail. **Document type:** *Journal, Academic/Scholarly.*
Related titles: Online - full content ed.: ISSN 1526-548X. USD 92 to non-members; USD 272 to institutions (effective 2004); Online - full text ed.: (from EBSCO Publishing, Gale Group, JSTOR (Web-based Journal Archive), O C L C Online Computer Library Center, Inc., ProQuest Information & Learning, Swets Information Services).
Indexed: ABIn, ASCA, BPI, CMCI, CPM, CurCont, Emerald, IAOP, IBSS, JCQM, JEL, ORMS, PsycInfo, PsycholAb, QC&AS, SOPODA, SSCI.
—BLDSC (5381.665000), IDS, IE, Infotrieve, ingenta. **CCC.**
Published by: I N F O R M S, 901 Elkridge Landing Rd., Ste. 400, Linthicum, MD 21090-2909. TEL 410-850-0300, 800-446-3676, FAX 410-684-2963, iol_publications@mail.informs.org, informs@informs.org, http://bear.cba.ufl.edu/centers/MKS/index.asp, http://www.informs.org. Ed. Steven M. Shugan. R&P Candita Gerzevitz. Adv. contact Trish Allewalt. B&W page USD 400; trim 8.125 x 10.875. Circ: 1,800. **Subscr. to:** PO Box 631704, Baltimore, MD 631704.

658.8 USA ISSN 0733-5768
MARKETING SCIENCE INSTITUTE. NEWSLETTER. Variant title: M S I Newsletter. Text in English. 1969. s-a. free. illus. **Document type:** *Newsletter.* **Description:** Covers events, research findings, conferences, and membership of the Institute, a research center whose purpose is to advance marketing practice and knowledge.
Published by: Marketing Science Institute, 1000 Massachusetts Ave, Cambridge, MA 02138-5396. TEL 617-491-2060, FAX 617-491-2065, pubs@msi.org, msi@msi.org, http://www.msi.org. Ed. Susan Keane. Circ: 8,000.

658.8 USA
MARKETING SCIENCE INSTITUTE. PUBLICATIONS. Text in English. 1961. a. free. **Document type:** *Catalog.*
Published by: Marketing Science Institute, 1000 Massachusetts Ave, Cambridge, MA 02138-5396. TEL 617-491-2060, FAX 617-491-2065, pubs@msi.org, msi@msi.org. Circ: 8,000.

658.8 USA
MARKETING SCIENCE INSTITUTE. RESEARCH PRIORITIES. Text in English. biennial. free. **Document type:** *Academic/Scholarly.* **Description:** Establishes research priorities for projects funded by the Institute, a non-profit research center whose purpose is to advance marketing practice and knowledge.
Formerly: Marketing Science Institute. Research Briefs
Published by: Marketing Science Institute, 1000 Massachusetts Ave, Cambridge, MA 02138-5396. TEL 617-491-2060, FAX 617-491-2065, pubs@msi.org, msi@msi.org. Circ: 5,000.

658.8306073 USA ISSN 0542-7398
HF5415.2
MARKETING SCIENCE INSTITUTE. REVIEW. Text in English. 1969. s-a. free membership (effective 2005). **Document type:** *Newsletter.* **Description:** Includes interviews, highlights from recent conferences, awards, competitions, and other news.
Published by: Marketing Science Institute, 1000 Massachusetts Ave, Cambridge, MA 02138-5396. TEL 617-491-2060, FAX 617-491-2065, msi@msi.org, http://www.msi.org/msi/publications.cfm#MSI_Review. Ed. Susan Keane.

658 GBR ISSN 0967-0556
MARKETING SERIES. Text in English. 1991. irreg. price varies. **Document type:** *Monographic series.* **Description:** Covers marketing issues in developing countries, from initial analysis and methodology via policy formulation and monitoring to implementation.

Related titles: CD-ROM ed.; Online - full text ed.
Indexed: WAE&RSA.
—BLDSC (5381.688000).
Published by: Natural Resources Institute, Central Ave, Chatham Maritime, Kent, ME4 4TB, United Kingdom. TEL 44-1634-880088, FAX 44-1634-880066, publications@nri.org, http://www.nri.org.

658 NZL
MARKETING SERVICES DIRECTORY. Text in English. a. NZD 39.95 domestic; NZD 89.95 foreign (effective 2000). **Document type:** *Trade.* **Description:** Lists professional & industry associations, advertising agencies, direct marketing agencies, designers, market researchers, printers, typesetters, lithographers, packaging companies, video & film producers, sales promotion consultants, and exhibition organisers.
Published by: Profile Publishing Ltd., Wellesley St, PO Box 5544, Auckland, New Zealand. TEL 64-9-6301040, FAX 64-9-630-1046, info@profile.co.nz, http://www.profile.co.nz/. Adv. contact Vernene Medcalf.

MARKETING SMARTER WITH SEARCH ENGINES. see *COMPUTERS—Internet*

658 GBR ISSN 0961-7752
MARKETING SUCCESS. Text in English. 1990. q. GBP 20 in United Kingdom; GBP 25 foreign (effective 2001). **Document type:** *Newsletter.*
Published by: Chartered Institute of Marketing, Moor Hall, Cookham, Maidenhead, Berks SL6 9QH, United Kingdom. TEL 44-1628-427500, FAX 44-1628-427499, corporatecommunications@cim.co.uk, http://www.cim.co.uk. Adv. contact Sue Ward. Circ: 35,000.

658.8 720 620 USA
MARKETING TACTICS. Variant title: A E M J. Text in English. m. USD 194 (effective 1998). index. back issues avail. **Document type:** *Newsletter.* **Description:** Marketing for architects and engineers.
Formerly (until 1998): A - E Marketing Journal (0732-7943)
Published by: P S M J Resources, Inc., 10 Midland Ave, Newton, MA 02458. TEL 617-965-0055, FAX 617-965-5152, psmj@tiac.com. Ed. Winslow Pettingall. Pub. Frank Stasiowski.

MARKETING THE LAW FIRM. see *LAW*

658.8 GBR ISSN 1470-5931
HF5410
➤ **MARKETING THEORY**; an international review. Text in English. 2001 (Sept.). q. GBP 301, USD 526 to institutions; GBP 313, USD 548 combined subscription to institutions print & online eds. (effective 2006). adv. **Document type:** *Journal, Academic/Scholarly.* **Description:** Publishes theory and research at the forefront of current and emergent developments in marketing. Issues covered include modern and post-modern representations of marketing, radical assessments of contemporary marketing theory and practice, the ethics of marketing, ethnicity and cultural identity, competing histories of marketing thought and critical accounts of marketing in society.
Related titles: Online - full text ed.: ISSN 1741-301X. GBP 298, USD 521 to institutions (effective 2006) (from C S A, EBSCO Publishing, O C L C Online Computer Library Center, Inc., Sage Publications, Inc., Swets Information Services).
Indexed: ABIn, CommAb, PsycInfo, PsycholAb, RefZh.
—BLDSC (5381.691800), IE. **CCC.**
Published by: Sage Publications Ltd. (Subsidiary of: Sage Publications, Inc.), 1 Oliver's Yard, 55 City Rd, London, EC1 1SP, United Kingdom. TEL 44-20-73248500, FAX 44-20-73248600, info@sagepub.co.uk, http://www.sagepub.co.uk/journal.aspx?pid=105709. Eds. Barbara Stern, Pauline Maclaran. **Subscr. in the Americas to:** Sage Publications, Inc., 2455 Teller Rd, Thousand Oaks, CA 91320. TEL 805-499-0721, FAX 805-499-0871, journals@sagepub.com.

658 USA
MARKETING TIDBITS. Text in English. m. free. **Document type:** *Newsletter.* **Description:** Covers different marketing issues that challenge small businesses, marketing executives, and do-it-yourself entrepreneurs.
Media: Online - full text.
Address: newsletter@seegertmktg.com, http://www.seegertmktg.com/newsletter.html. Ed. Liz Seegert.

658 USA
MARKETING TO THE EMERGING MAJORITIES. Text in English. 1988. m. USD 325 domestic; USD 355 foreign (effective 2005). 8 p./no.; **Document type:** *Newsletter, Trade.* **Description:** Presents facts, comprehensive overviews, projections and predictions, micromarketing information and shirtsleeve tidbits on how to best reach blacks, Hispanics, and Asian Americans.
Formerly: Minority Markets Alert (1041-7524)
Related titles: Online - full text ed.: (from Gale Group, Northern Light Technology, Inc., O C L C Online Computer Library Center, Inc.).
Indexed: B&I, CWI.
Published by: E P M Communications, 160 Mercer St, 3rd Fl, New York, NY 10012-3212. info@epmcom.com, http://www.epmcom.com. Ed. Michael Bush. Pub., R&P Barbara Perrin.

658.84 USA ISSN 1525-2329
MARKETING TO WOMEN; addressing women and women's sensibilities. Text in English. 1987. m. USD 337 domestic; USD 367 foreign (effective 2001). charts; stat. back issues avail. **Document type:** *Newsletter, Trade.* **Description:** Covers psychographics, demographics and the purchasing behavior of women. Provides marketing tips and techniques that are effective with women consumers.
Former titles (until 1999): About Women & Marketing (1089-2958); (until 1996): About Marketing to Women (1089-2427); (until 1995): Marketing to Women (1047-1677); (until 1989): Women Scope: Surveys of Women (1040-5240); (until 1989): Marketing to Women (0894-5861)
Related titles: Microform ed.; Online - full text ed.: (from Factiva, Florida Center for Library Automation, Gale Group, Northern Light Technology, Inc., O C L C Online Computer Library Center, Inc., ProQuest Information & Learning, SoftLine Information).
Indexed: ABIn, B&I, CWI, GendWatch.
Published by: E P M Communications, 160 Mercer St, 3rd Fl, New York, NY 10012-3212. TEL 212-941-0099, FAX 212-941-1622, info@epmcom.com, http://www.epmcom.com. Ed. Lisa Gallay. Pub. Barbara Perrin.

MARKETING TREASURES. see *LIBRARY AND INFORMATION SCIENCES*

658.8 HRV ISSN 1330-2612
MARKETING U PRAKSI. Text in Croatian. 1993. bi-m. **Document type:** *Magazine, Trade.*
Published by: Trend d.o.o., Trg Petra Svacica 12-II, Zagreb, 10000, Croatia. TEL 385-1-4856895, FAX 385-1-4554536.

658 AUS
MARKETING UPDATE NEWSLETTER. Text in English. 1996. s-a. **Document type:** *Newsletter.* **Description:** Covers marketing and business information.
Media: Online - full text.
Published by: Exton Enterprises, PO Box 394, Mount Ommaney, QLD 4074, Australia. exton@gil.com.au, http://www.gil.com.au/comm/emerald. Ed. Rahan Exton.

658 POL ISSN 1425-8315
MARKETING W PRAKTYCE. Text in Polish. 1996. m. PLZ 90 (effective 2001).
Published by: Grupa Wydawnicza INFOR Sp. z o.o., Ul Okopowa 58/72, Warsaw, 01042, Poland. TEL 48-22-5304208, 48-22-5304450, bok@infor.pl. Ed. Zdzislaw Krasnicki. Adv. contact Waldemar Krakowiak.

658.8 GBR ISSN 0141-9285
MARKETING WEEK. Text in English. 1978. w. GBP 80; GBP 103 in Europe; GBP 165 elsewhere; GBP 2.20 newsstand/cover (effective 1999). adv. **Document type:** *Trade.* **Description:** Specifically geared towards marketing management.
Related titles: Microform ed.: (from PQC); Online - full text ed.: (from bigchalk, EBSCO Publishing, Gale Group, H.W. Wilson, LexisNexis, O C L C Online Computer Library Center, Inc., ProQuest Information & Learning).
Indexed: ABIn, ABM, BPI, Emerald, M&MA.
—BLDSC (5381.694000), IE, ingenta. **CCC.**
Published by: Centaur Publishing, St Giles House, 50 Poland St, London, W1V 4AX, United Kingdom. TEL 44—20-7970-4000, FAX 44-20-7970-4009, mw.editorial@chiron.co.uk, http://www.marketing-week.co.uk. Ed. Stuart Smith. Pub. Annie Swift. Adv. contact Debbie Rimmer. Circ: 39,254 (paid). **Dist. by:** Comag, Tavistock Works, Tavistock Rd, W Drayton, Middx UB7 7QX, United Kingdom. TEL 44-1895-444055, FAX 44-1895-433602.

659 USA ISSN 1521-1274
HC79.H53
MARKETING WITH HONORS; directory of awards competitions. Text in English. 1996. a. USD 595 (effective 2001). **Document type:** *Directory, Trade.* **Description:** Lists more than 500 product and service awards, sponsored by trade shows, professional associations, and national and local government organizations.
Published by: Marcus & Company, 241 Perkins St., Apt. B302, Jamaica Plain, MA 02130-4040. TEL 617-232-1370, FAX 617-232-0535, lmarcus@marketingwithhonors.com, http://www.marketingwithhonors.com. Ed. Lynne S Marcus.

658 CAN ISSN 0714-7422
MARKETNEWS. Text in English. 1975. m. CND 48.15, USD 95 (effective 1998). adv.
Formerly (until 1982): Audio Marketnews (0382-6120)
Published by: Bomar Publishing, 364 Supertest Rd, Ste 200, North York, ON M3J 2M2, Canada. TEL 416-667-9945, FAX 416-667-0609. Ed. Robert Franner. Pub. Robert Grierson. R&P Bob Grierson. Adv. contact Mary Thomson. Circ: 11,200.

MARKETONS I T DATABANK. see *COMPUTERS—Information Science And Information Theory*

658 ZAF
MARKETPLACE; an insight into advertising, marketing, research, sales. Text in English. 1976. 22/yr. ZAR 121 (effective 1996). adv. bk.rev. **Document type:** *Trade.* **Description:** Covers all aspects of the South African advertising industry in print and broadcast media, with news of successful campaigns and analysis of trends in South Africa and the World.
Published by: C T P Ltd., PO Box 1610, Parklands, Johannesburg 2121, South Africa. TEL 27-11-889-0600, FAX 27-11-889-0680. Ed., R&P Lynne Kloot. Adv. contact B Ferreira. Circ: 3,000.

658 USA
MARKETPULSE✶. Text in English. 1985. irreg. (approx. 4/yr.). free to qualified personnel.
Published by: (Dependable Lists, Inc.), SpeciaLists Ltd., 1200 Harbor Blvd., 9th Fl., Weehawken, NJ 07087-6728. Ed. Ray Lewis.

658.8 GBR ISSN 0076-4647
MARKETS YEAR BOOK. Text in English. 1955. a. GBP 12.99 (effective 2000). **Document type:** *Trade.* **Description:** Listing of different markets in England, Wales and Scotland providing market days, owners and superintendents, number of stalls, plus directory of suppliers.
Published by: World's Fair Ltd., Albert Mill, Albert St, PO Box 57, Oldham, Lancs OL8 3WF, United Kingdom. TEL 44-161-683-8000, FAX 44-161-683-8001, wfair@worldsfair.co.uk, http://www.worldsfair.co.uk. Circ: 10,000.

658.8 AUT ISSN 0025-3863
DER MARKT; Zeitschrift fuer Absatzwirtschaft und Marketing. Text in German. 1962. q. EUR 38 domestic; EUR 42 foreign; EUR 24 to students; EUR 12 newsstand/cover (effective 2005). bk.rev. charts. index. **Document type:** *Magazine, Trade.*
Indexed: DIP, IBR, IBZ, SCIMP.
Published by: Oesterreichische Gesellschaft fuer Absatzwirtschaft, Augasse 2-6, Vienna, W 1090, Austria. TEL 43-1-313364400, FAX 43-1-31336732, http://www.wu-wien.ac.at/project/dermarkt/local.html. Circ: 1,250.

658 635 DEU ISSN 0930-8741
MARKT IN GRUEN; Marketing-Magazin. Text in German. 1985. 10/yr. EUR 77 domestic; EUR 92 foreign; EUR 10 newsstand/cover (effective 2004). adv. **Document type:** *Magazine, Trade.*
Published by: Verlag Siegfried Rohn GmbH & Co. KG, Stolberger Str 84, Cologne, 50933, Germany. TEL 49-221-54974, FAX 49-221-5497278, rohn@rudolf-mueller.de, http://www.rohn.de. Ed. Ulrike Neugebauer. Adv. contact Jenny Jones Steinkamp. B&W page EUR 2,820, color page EUR 4,950; trim 185 x 270. Circ: 6,846.

658.8 DEU
MARKT INTERN. Text in German. 1981. fortn. back issues avail.
Published by: Markt Intern Verlag GmbH, Grafenberger Allee 30, Duesseldorf, 40237, Germany. TEL 0211-6698-0. Ed. Erhard Liemen.

658.8 DEU
MARKT UND KONSUM. Text in German. irreg., latest vol.13, 2002. EUR 42.50 per vol. (effective 2003). **Document type:** *Monographic series, Academic/Scholarly.*
Published by: Peter Lang GmbH Europaeischer Verlag der Wissenschaften, Eschborner Landstr 42-50, Frankfurt Am Main, 60489, Germany. TEL 49-69-7807050, FAX 49-69-78070543, zentrale.frankfurt@peterlang.com, http://www.peterlang.de.

658.8 DEU ISSN 0933-7105
HF5415.2
MARKTFORSCHUNG UND MANAGEMENT; Zeitschrift fuer Marktorientierte Unternehmenspolitik. Variant title: M & M. Text in German. 1957. bi-m. adv. bk.rev. bibl. **Document type:** *Trade.*
Former titles: Marktforschung (0170-723X); Marktforscher (0465-0166); Incorporated: G F M-Mitteilungen zur Markt- und Absatzforschung (0016-3511)
Indexed: KES, PAIS.
—**CCC.**
Published by: Schaeffer - Poeschel Verlag, Postfach 103241, Stuttgart, 70028, Germany. TEL 49-711-2194102, FAX 49-711-2194119. Eds. Dr. Fred Becker, Dr. Ulli Arnold. Circ: 1,500.

658 DEU
MARKTFUEHRER MOBILE SOLUTIONS. Text in German. 2000. 2/yr. EUR 3.50 newsstand/cover (effective 2003). adv. **Document type:** *Magazine, Trade.*
Published by: telepublic Verlag GmbH & Co. Medien KG, Podbielskistr. 325, Hannover, 30659, Germany. TEL 49-511-3348400, FAX 49-511-3348499, info@teletalk.de. adv.: B&W page EUR 3,540, color page EUR 4,080. Circ: 43,125 (paid and controlled).

MASTER GUIDE. see *PHOTOGRAPHY*

▼ new title ➤ refereed ✶ unverified ♦ full entry avail.

658.85 USA ISSN 0199-3887
MASTER SALESMANSHIP. Text in English. 197?. bi-w. USD 156 (effective 2005). **Document type:** *Newsletter, Trade.*
Description: Contains advice and tips on how to sell as well as articles on other issues related to salesmanship.
Published by: Clement Communications, Inc., 10 LaCrue Ave, PO Box 36, Concordville, PA 19331. TEL 610-459-4200, 888-358-5858, FAX 610-459-4582, editor@clement.com, http://www.clement.com.

658.7 GBR ISSN 0142-114X
MATERIALS HANDLING BUYERS GUIDE. Text in English. 1963. a. GBP 44 domestic; GBP 49 foreign (effective 1999). adv. index. **Document type:** *Directory.* **Description:** A directory of unit load handling and storage equipment available on the UK market, with tabular presentation of which companies supply what products, and a fully updated list of suppliers' names and addresses.
Formerly: Manual of Materials Handling and Ancilliary Equipment (0076-4167)
Published by: Turret R A I plc, Armstrong House, 38 Market Sq, Uxbridge, Middx UB8 1TG, United Kingdom. TEL 44-1895-454545, FAX 44-1895-454647.

658.7 IND ISSN 0543-0313
MATERIALS MANAGEMENT JOURNAL OF INDIA. Text in English. 1960. m. INR 32. adv. bk.rev.
Incorporates: Eastern Purchasing Journal
Published by: P.G. Menon Ed. & Pub., D-409 Defence Colony, New Delhi, 110 003, India. Circ: 2,000.

MATERIALWIRTSCHAFT UND LOGISTIK IM UNTERNEHMEN; Materialwirtschaft fuer Manager. see *BUSINESS AND ECONOMICS—Management*

MCGUIRE'S HOME BUSINESS NEWSLETTER. see *COMPUTERS—Internet*

338 USA ISSN 1079-1604
CODEN: MMRTEO
MEAT MARKETING & TECHNOLOGY. Text in English. m. adv. **Document type:** *Magazine, Trade.* **Description:** Provides information for the U.S. and Canadian meat processing industry.
Indexed: Agr.
Published by: Marketing and Technology Group, Inc., 1415 N Dayton St, Chicago, IL 60622. TEL 312-266-3311, FAX 312-266-3363, http://www.meatingplace.com. adv.: B&W page USD 3,955, color page USD 5,405; trim 8 x 10.75.

658.8 615.19 USA ISSN 1067-733X
MED AD NEWS. Text in English. 1982. m. USD 190 (effective 2005). adv. charts; illus.; stat. back issues avail. **Document type:** *Newsletter, Trade.* **Description:** Covers news about products on the market, business news, promotions, advertising agency news, FDA, drug approvals in the U.S. and the world.
Formerly: Medical Advertising News (0745-0907)
Related titles: Online - full text ed.: (from EBSCO Publishing, Gale Group, Northern Light Technology, Inc., O C L C Online Computer Library Center, Inc., ProQuest Information & Learning); ♦ Supplement(s): Managed Care Marketing. ISSN 1079-9494.
Indexed: ABIn, B&I, Inpharma, PE&ON, Reac.
—BLDSC (5424.621800), IE. **CCC.**
Published by: Engel Publishing Partners, 828 A Newtown-Yardley Rd, Newtown, PA 18940. TEL 215-867-0044, FAX 215-867-0053, http://www.pharmabusiness.com/magazines/medad/, http://www.engelpub.com. Ed. Styli Engel. Pub., Adv. contact Lisa Banket. R&P Miriam Rodriguez. B&W page USD 6,180, color page USD 7,680; trim 10.875 x 14.5. Circ: 3,970 (paid); 12,722 (controlled).

MEDIA & MARKETING EUROPE. see *ADVERTISING AND PUBLIC RELATIONS*

302.230688 GBR ISSN 1473-4613
MEDIA BUSINESS. Text in English. 1999. w. **Document type:** *Magazine, Trade.*
Formerly (until 2001): Campaign Media Business (1467-758X)
Related titles: Online - full text ed.: (from Gale Group).
Published by: Haymarket Business Publications Ltd., 174 Hammersmith Rd, London, W6 7JP, United Kingdom. TEL 44-20-8943-5000, FAX 44-20-82674268, http://www.haymarketgroup.com.

MEDIA DIRECTORY. see *ADVERTISING AND PUBLIC RELATIONS*

658 USA
MEDIA INC. Text in English. 1987. q. **Document type:** *Trade.*
Published by: Pacific Northwest Media, Marketing and Creative Services News, Box 24365, Seattle, WA 98124-0365. TEL 206-382-9220, FAX 206-382-9437, media@media-inc.com, http://www.media-inc.com. Ed. Betsy Model. Pub. James Baker. Circ: 10,000 (paid).

658.8 ITA
MEDIA KEY; mensile professionale di comunicazione, media e marketing. Text in Italian. 1982. m. (10/yr.). includes TV Key and Global. adv. **Document type:** *Trade.* **Description:** Covers marketing, media research and planning, and advertising.
Formerly: Media Key Synthesis
Related titles: ♦ Supplement(s): Global.
Published by: Media Key s.r.l., Via Lippi Filippino, 33 C, Milan, MI 20131, Italy. TEL 39-2-70638348, FAX 39-2-2363662. Ed. Roberto Albano. Adv. contact Silvana Carazzina. Circ: 10,500.

MEDIA MAP OF EASTERN EUROPE. see *COMMUNICATIONS—Television And Cable*

070.5 GBR
MEDIA MAP OF WESTERN EUROPE. Text in English. 1990. a. GBP 195 (effective 1999). **Description:** Examines in detail the western European media market. Covers consumer media in 17 countries and contains details of national media regulations together with profiles of the major players. Includes a media directory. Covers television and cable as well as print media.
Supersedes in part (in 1997): Media Map (1355-0055)
Published by: (Communications and Information Technology Research Ltd.), C I T Publications Ltd., 3 Colleton Crescent, Exeter, Devon EX2 4DG, United Kingdom. TEL 44-1392-315-555, FAX 44-1392-315-556, citpubs@eurobell.co.uk, http://www.telecoms-data.com. Ed. Tania Harvey.

MEDIA MAP YEARBOOK. see *COMMUNICATIONS—Television And Cable*

658 BEL
MEDIA MARKT. Text in Flemish. 11/yr. Supplement avail.
Description: Depicts marketing and advertisement.
Published by: C E D Samsom (Subsidiary of: Wolters Samsom Belgie n.v.), Kouterveld 14, Diegem, 1831, Belgium. TEL 32-2-7231111.

658 DEU ISSN 1433-9366
MEDIA UND MARKETING; das Magazin fuer Entscheider in Marketing und Medien. Text in German. 1997. m. EUR 55 domestic; EUR 70 foreign; EUR 5.45 newsstand/cover (effective 2005). adv. **Document type:** *Magazine, Trade.* **Description:** Covers all aspects of marketing and advertising, including the effects of media and technology on global markets.
Published by: Europa Fachpresse Verlag GmbH (Subsidiary of: Sueddeutsche Verlag), Emily-Noether-Str 2-E, Munich, 80992, Germany. TEL 49-89-5485200, FAX 49-89-54852108, mediaundmarketing@efv.de, webmaster@efv.de, http://www.mediaundmarketing.de, http://www.wuv.de. Ed. Christian Faltin. Adv. contact Edith Lockenvitz. B&W page EUR 4,160, color page EUR 5,490. Circ: 7,127 (paid).

658.8 HUN ISSN 1416-7336
MEDIAFIGYELO. Text in Hungarian. 1996. fortn. adv. **Document type:** *Magazine, Trade.* **Description:** Covers all aspects of marketing and the media in Hungary.
Published by: Sanoma Budapest Kiadoi Rt. (Subsidiary of: Sanoma Magazines Finland Corporation), Bokor Utca 15-19, Budapest, 1037, Hungary. TEL 36-1-4371100, FAX 36-1-2502303, mediafigyelo@sanomabp.hu, info@sanomabp.hu, http://www.mediafigyelo.hu, http://www.sanoma.hu. Adv. contact Piroska Bosanszki. page HUF 300,000; trim 205 x 285. Circ: 1,500 (paid).

MEDICAL MARKETING & MEDIA. see *PHARMACY AND PHARMACOLOGY*

659.1 USA ISSN 1054-3066
MEDICAL NEWS REPORT. Text in English. 1991. m. USD 175 (effective 2005). **Document type:** *Newsletter, Trade.*
Description: Aimed at health care public relations professionals; reports on crisis communications, medical topics making news, media relations, and public relations management.
Published by: Standish Publishing Co., PO Box 335, Ardmore, PA 19003. TEL 610-519-9220, FAX 610-519-9221, medicalnewsreport@.com. Ed. Kim Standish. Circ: 400 (paid and controlled).

MEDIEN DIALOG; Gespraech - Diskussion - Meinung - Information. see *COMMUNICATIONS—Television And Cable*

MEDISTAT. see *INSTRUMENTS*

MEMBERSHIP DEVELOPMENTS. see *BUSINESS AND ECONOMICS—Management*

658.8 ESP ISSN 1137-7615
MERCADOCONTINUO. Text in Spanish. 1992. m.
—CINDOC.
Published by: Ediciones 9, C. Mendez Nunez, 59, Villagarcia de Arosa, Pontevedra 36600, Spain. TEL 34-986-502468.

338.0029 USA
MERCHANDISE MART RESOURCE GUIDE. Text in English. 1952. a. USD 5. adv.
Former titles: Merchandise Mart Buyers Guide; (until 1979): Merchandise Mart Directory (0539-3876)
Published by: Merchandise Mart Properties, Inc., 470 Merchandise Mart, Chicago, IL 60654. TEL 312-527-4141. Circ: 60,000.

658 USA
MERCHANTS NEWS. Text in English. m. USD 39.95 domestic; USD 99 foreign (effective 2001). adv. **Document type:** *Magazine, Trade.* **Description:** Publishes information to match retailers with new wholesale merchandise.
Related titles: Online - full text ed.
Address: 432 W. Boynton Beach Blvd., Boynton Beach, FL 33435-4027. TEL 800-453-3532, http://www.merchantsnews.com/.

MERLE'S MISSION. see *COMPUTERS—Internet*

METALS SOURCING GUIDE. see *METALLURGY*

MICHIGAN MANUFACTURERS DIRECTORY. see *BUSINESS AND ECONOMICS—Trade And Industrial Directories*

658.8 ITA ISSN 1121-4228
MICRO & MACRO MARKETING. Text in Italian. 1992-1995; resumed 199?. 3/yr. EUR 45 domestic to individuals; EUR 84 foreign to individuals; EUR 75 domestic to institutions print & online eds.; EUR 129 foreign to institutions print & online eds. (effective 2004). **Document type:** *Academic/Scholarly.*
Related titles: Online - full text ed.
Published by: Societa Editrice Il Mulino, Strada Maggiore 37, Bologna, 40125, Italy. TEL 39-051-256011, FAX 39-051-256034, riviste@mulino.it, http://www.mulino.it. Circ: 2,000.

MID-WEEK PETROLEUM ARGUS. see *PETROLEUM AND GAS*

658 659 FRA ISSN 0295-3943
MIDI MEDIA. Text in French. 11/yr. **Description:** Covers TV, radio, press, publicity and marketing in the South of France.
Published by: Media Sud Communication, 5 rue Alsace Lorraine, BP 27, Toulouse, Cedex 6 31012, France. TEL 61-55-54-94, FAX 61-25-03-09. Ed. Jean Paul Bobin. Circ: 10,000.

658 USA
MIDWEST RETAILER. Text in English. 1971. m. free to qualified personnel (effective 2004). adv. **Document type:** *Magazine, Trade.* **Description:** Provides news of products, marketing changes, personnel and trends in the flooring industry.
Address: 8528 Columbus Ave, Bloomington, MN 55420. TEL 952-854-7610, FAX 952-854-6460. Ed., R&P Joan Thomasberg. Adv. contact John Thomasberg. B&W page USD 1,456. Circ: 6,200 (free).

MILCH-MARKETING. see *AGRICULTURE—Dairying And Dairy Products*

MILITARY REALTOR. see *MILITARY*

MILJOE. see *BUILDING AND CONSTRUCTION*

MILK MARKET ADMINISTRATOR'S BULLETIN. see *AGRICULTURE—Dairying And Dairy Products*

790.13 USA ISSN 0191-6904
CODEN: LHYGD7
MODEL RETAILER. Text in English. 1971. m. USD 85; free to qualified personnel (effective 2005). adv. bk.rev. **Document type:** *Magazine, Trade.*
Related titles: Online - full text ed.
Published by: Kalmbach Publishing Co., 21027 Crossroads Circle, PO Box 1612, Waukesha, WI 53187-1612. TEL 262-796-8776, FAX 262-796-0126, adsales@modelretailer.com, customerservice@kalmbach.com, http://www.modelretailer.com, http://www.kalmbach.com. Ed. Hal Miller. Pub. Kevin Keefe. Adv. contact Richard Albers. B&W page USD 2,303, color page USD 3,224. Circ: 4,317 (controlled).

658.8 USA ISSN 0544-6538
MODERN DISTRIBUTION MANAGEMENT. Text in English. 1967. bi-w. USD 245 domestic; USD 265 foreign (effective 2001). 8 p./no.; back issues avail. **Document type:** *Newsletter, Trade.* **Description:** Publishes information about industrial maintenance, repair & operations (MRO) products and their distribution channels.
Published by: Modern Distribution Management, Inc., P O Box 13507, Minneapolis, MN 55414. TEL 612-623-1074, FAX 612-623-1087, tom@mdm.com, http://www.mdm.com. Ed. Thomas P. Gale.

MOM'S OLD-FASHIONED INTERNET GAZETTE. see *COMPUTERS—Internet*

658 659.1 CAN ISSN 0700-3528
MONDAY REPORT ON RETAILERS. Text in English. 1973. w. CND 330. index. **Document type:** *Newsletter, Trade.*
Related titles: Online - full text ed.: (from Micromedia ProQuest, ProQuest Information & Learning).
Published by: Rogers Media Publishing Ltd, One Mount Pleasant Rd, 11th Fl, Toronto, ON M4Y 2Y5, Canada. TEL 416-764-2000, FAX 416-764-3941, http://www.retailinfonet.com, http://www.rogers.com.

MOTORCYCLE WORLD. see *SPORTS AND GAMES—Bicycles And Motorcycles*

658 USA
MR. CHEAP'S ATLANTA; shopping, bargains, factory outlets, off-price stores, cheap eats, cheapplaces to stay and much more. Text in English. irreg. USD 9.95 (effective 2005).
Published by: Adams Media Corporation (Subsidiary of: F & W Publications, Inc.), 57 Littlefield St, Avon, MA 02322. TEL 508-427-7100, 800-872-5627, FAX 508-427-6790, jobbanklist@adamsmedia.com, http://www.adamsmedia.com.

658 USA
MR. CHEAP'S CHICAGO; shopping, bargains, factory outlets, off-price stores, cheap eats, cheapplaces to stay and much more. Text in English. 1994. irreg., latest 2000, 2nd ed. USD 9.95 domestic; USD 14.95 in Canada (effective 2005). **Document type:** *Trade.* **Description:** Covers places where anyone can save money on shopping, restaurants, lodging and entertainment.
Related titles: Diskette ed.; E-mail ed.; Fax ed.; Online - full text ed.
Published by: Adams Media Corporation (Subsidiary of: F & W Publications, Inc.), 57 Littlefield St, Avon, MA 02322. TEL 508-427-7100, 800-872-5627, FAX 508-427-6790, jobbanklist@adamsmedia.com, http://www.adamsmedia.com. Eds. Jennifer Wood, Michelle Lang. Pub. Bob Adams. R&P, Adv. contact Nancy True TEL 781-607-5260.

658 USA ISSN 1529-1170
MR. CHEAP'S NEW YORK; shopping, bargains, factory outlets, off-price stores, cheapeats, cheapplaces to stay and much more. Text in English. 1993. irreg., latest 2000, 2nd ed. USD 9.95 domestic; USD 14.95 in Canada (effective 2005). **Document type:** *Trade.* **Description:** Covers places where anyone can save money on shopping, restaurants, lodging and entertainment.
Related titles: Diskette ed.; E-mail ed.; Fax ed.; Online - full text ed.
Published by: Adams Media Corporation (Subsidiary of: F & W Publications, Inc.), 57 Littlefield St, Avon, MA 02322. TEL 508-427-7100, 800-872-5627, FAX 508-427-6790, jobbanklist@adamsmedia.com, http://www.adamsmedia.com. Eds. Jennifer Wood, Michelle Kelly. Pub. Bob Adams. R&P, Adv. contact Nancy True TEL 781-607-5260.

658 USA
MR. CHEAP'S WASHINGTON D.C.; shopping, bargains, factory outlets, off-price stores, cheap eats, cheapplaces to stay and much more. Text in English. irreg. USD 9.95 (effective 2005).
Published by: Adams Media Corporation (Subsidiary of: F & W Publications, Inc.), 57 Littlefield St, Avon, MA 02322. TEL 508-427-7100, 800-872-5627, FAX 508-427-6790, jobbanklist@adamsmedia.com, http://www.adamsmedia.com.

069 USA ISSN 1040-6999
MUSEUM STORE. Text in English. 1973. q. USD 34; USD 59 foreign (effective 1999). adv. **Document type:** *Trade.* **Description:** Provides information for museum store buyers and managers.
Formerly: M U S T
Published by: Museum Store Association, Inc., 4100 E Mississippi Ave, 800, Denver, CO 80245-3055. TEL 303-504-9223, FAX 303-504-9585, http://www.msaweb.org. Ed. Dawn Sawrel. Adv. contact Johnny Chavez. Circ: 3,400.

MUSIC AND SOUND RETAILER; the newsmagazine for musical instrument and sound product merchandisers. see *MUSIC*

MUSIC INC. see *MUSIC*

MY LITTLE SALESMAN TRUCK AND TRAILER CATALOG. see *TRANSPORTATION—Trucks And Trucking*

658.8 IND
N A F E D MARKETING REVIEW. Text in English. 1971. m. INR 18. adv. bk.rev.
Published by: National Agricultural Cooperative Marketing Federation of India Ltd., 1 Siddharth Enclave, (Nafed House), Ashram Chowk, New Delhi, 110 014, India. TEL 6845106, FAX 31-75347, TELEX 31-75358-NFD-IN. Eds. K Janakiram, V Mewawalla. Circ: 1,500.

N A U M D NEWS. see *CLOTHING TRADE*

N A U M D OFFICE REPORTS. see *CLOTHING TRADE*

658.87 DNK ISSN 1395-1831
N B. Text in Danish. 1995. m. DKK 550; DKK 50 newsstand/cover (effective 2002). adv. illus. reprints avail. **Document type:** *Trade.*
Formed by the merger of (1923-1995): Kiosk og Service (0903-9287); Which was formerly (until 1987): Kioskejer-Bladet (0023-172X); (1983-1995): Vin & Tobak (0908-1798)
Published by: Naerbutikkernes Landsforening, Mellemdammen 8, Ribe, 6760, Denmark. TEL 45-75-42-45-77, FAX 45-75-42-42-79. Ed. Hans Jorgen Staun. Adv. contact Hans Joergen Staun. B&W page DKK 9,750, color page DKK 15,150; trim 185 x 265. Circ: 8,000.

N B W A HANDBOOK. see *BEVERAGES*

N B W A LEGISLATIVE AND REGULATORY ISSUES ALERT. see *BEVERAGES*

658.8 USA
N M O A - MAIL ORDER DIGEST; direct marketing for the entrepreneurial company. Text in English. 1972. m. looseleaf. USD 99 to non-members (effective 2001); membership. bk.rev.; software rev. stat. back issues avail. **Document type:** *Newsletter, Trade.* **Description:** Reports on effective sales techniques for mail order marketers, new products, government activities, and general data.
Related titles: Online - full content ed.; Supplement(s): Washington Newsletter.
Published by: National Mail Order Association, 2807 Polk St NE, Minneapolis, MN 55418-2954. TEL 612-788-1673, FAX 612-788-1147, editor@nmoa.org, info@nmoa.org, http://www.nmoa.org. Circ: 2,000.

658.8 796 USA ISSN 1045-2087
GV743
N S G A RETAIL FOCUS. Text in English. 1947. bi-m. free to members; USD 50 (effective 2005). bk.rev. charts; illus.; stat. **Document type:** *Magazine, Trade.* **Description:** Covers retail and industry news for corporate executive members of the Association.
Former titles: N S G A Sports Retailer (0884-6278); Sports Retailer (0279-6678); Selling Sporting Goods (0037-1610)
Indexed: SportS.
Published by: National Sporting Goods Association, 1601 Feehanville Dr, Ste 300, Mt. Prospect, IL 60056-6305. TEL 800-815-5422, http://www.nsga.org. Ed., Pub. Larry N Weindruch. Circ: 2,000 (paid).

N S S R A COST OF DOING BUSINESS SURVEY. see *SPORTS AND GAMES—Abstracting, Bibliographies, Statistics*

688 USA
N S S R A NEWSLETTER. Text in English. 1988. q. membership. back issues avail. **Document type:** *Newsletter, Trade.* **Description:** Provides information to ski and snowboard shops on industry issues of shop guidelines, litigation, exposure, and marketing.
Formerly: N S R A Newsletter
Published by: National Ski & Snowboard Retailers Association, 1601 Feehanville Dr, Ste 300, Mt. Prospect, IL 60056-6035. TEL 847-391-9825, FAX 847-391-9827, nsgatdoyle@aol.com, info@nssra.com, http://www.nssra.com. Ed., Pub., R&P Thomas B Doyle. Circ: 500 (controlled).

658 USA
N Y AUCTION ADVERTISER. Text in English. m.
Published by: Brooklyn Journal Publications, Inc., 129 Montague St, Brooklyn, NY 11201. TEL 718-624-6033, FAX 718-875-5302.

NARUZHNAYA REKLAMA ROSSII. see *ADVERTISING AND PUBLIC RELATIONS*

NATIONAL AGRI-MARKETING ASSOCIATION NEWS. see *AGRICULTURE*

NATIONAL ASSOCIATION OF BEVERAGE RETAILERS. NEWS AND VIEWS. see *BEVERAGES*

658 USA ISSN 0739-327X
NATIONAL AUCTION BULLETIN; the where, what and when of auctions. Text in English. 1983. bi-m. USD 49; USD 49 foreign (effective 1999). adv. 8 p./no. 2 cols./p.; back issues avail. **Document type:** *Bulletin, Consumer.* **Description:** Lists auctions for confiscated, liquidated, bankrupt, antique and collectible surplus.
Published by: National Auction Bulletin Inc., 2501 N W 17th Lane, Ste 1, Pompano Beach, FL 33064-1515. TEL 954-917-4107, 800-327-2049, FAX 954-917-4108, nabinc@bellsouth.net, http://www.nabinc.com. Pub., R&P I. Goldman. Adv. contact I Goldman. B&W page USD 425. Circ: 1,650 (paid); 150 (controlled).

NATIONAL AUCTIONS & SALES. see *BUSINESS AND ECONOMICS—Domestic Commerce*

NATIONAL BEER WHOLESALERS ASSOCIATION. BEER PERSPECTIVES NEWSLETTER. see *BEVERAGES*

NATIONAL BEER WHOLESALERS ASSOCIATION. DISTRIBUTOR PRODUCTIVITY REPORT. see *BEVERAGES*

NATIONAL DIRECTORY OF MAILING LISTS. see *BUSINESS AND ECONOMICS—Trade And Industrial Directories*

NATIONAL GARDENING. see *GARDENING AND HORTICULTURE*

NATIONAL GARDENING SURVEY (YEAR); an exclusive market research report for the lawn and garden industry. see *GARDENING AND HORTICULTURE*

658.8 USA
TX795.A1
NATIONAL ICE CREAM AND YOGURT RETAILERS ASSOCIATION. YEARBOOK. Text in English. 1941. a. USD 25 (effective 2000). adv. illus. **Document type:** *Directory.*
Formerly: National Ice Cream Retailers Association. Yearbook (8756-1719)
Published by: National Ice Cream and Yogurt Retailers Association, Inc., 1841 Hicks Rd, Ste C, Rolling Meadows, IL 60008-1251. TEL 614-486-1444, FAX 614-486-4711. Ed. Don Buckley. R&P D L Buckley. Adv. contact Julie Buckley. Circ: 1,100 (paid).

NATIONAL SPORTING GOODS ASSOCIATION BUYING GUIDE. see *SPORTS AND GAMES*

NATIONWIDE DIRECTORY OF GIFT, HOUSEWARES & HOME TEXTILE BUYERS. see *GIFTWARE AND TOYS*

NATIONWIDE DIRECTORY OF MEN'S AND BOYS' WEAR BUYERS. see *CLOTHING TRADE*

NATIONWIDE DIRECTORY OF SPORTING GOODS BUYERS. see *SPORTS AND GAMES*

NATIONWIDE DIRECTORY OF WOMEN'S AND CHILDREN'S WEAR BUYERS. see *CLOTHING TRADE*

NATIONWIDE MAJOR MASS MARKET MERCHANDISERS. see *CLOTHING TRADE*

613.2 USA ISSN 0164-338X
CODEN: NFMEEI
NATURAL FOODS MERCHANDISER; new ideas, trends, products for the natural and organic foods industry. Text in English. 1979. 12/yr. USD 175 domestic; USD 190 in Canada; USD 205 elsewhere; free (effective 2005). adv. bk.rev. charts; illus.; mkt.; pat.; stat.; tr.lit. back issues avail. **Document type:** *Magazine, Trade.* **Description:** Provides information to companies involved in the development, marketing, sales and distribution of natural and organic products and dietary supplements.
Related titles: Online - full text ed.: (from EBSCO Publishing, Gale Group, O C L C Online Computer Library Center, Inc., ProQuest Information & Learning).
Indexed: B&I.
—CCC.
Published by: New Hope Natural Media (Subsidiary of: Penton Media, Inc.), 1401 Pearl St, Boulder, CO 80302. TEL 303-998-9000, 888-721-4321, FAX 303-998-9020, customerservice@newhope.com, http://www.newhope.com/nfm-online/nfm_backs/apr_03/index.cfm. Ed. Lisa Everitt. adv.: B&W page USD 5,150, color page USD 8,060; trim 10.75 x 14.75. Circ: 500 (paid); 15,000 (controlled).

NATURAL PRODUCTS INDUSTRY INSIDER. see *NUTRITION AND DIETETICS*

NEA DIMOSSIOTIS. see *ADVERTISING AND PUBLIC RELATIONS*

658.8 MEX
NEO; la vanguardia en mercadotecnia y negocios. Text in Spanish. m. MXP 350 domestic; USD 95 in US & Canada; USD 125 elsewhere (effective 2001). adv.
Related titles: Online - full text ed.: ISSN 1605-5721. 1999.
Published by: Bouleau Comunicaciones, S.A. de C.V., Homero 527 PH, Col. Polanco, Mexico, D.F., 11560, Mexico. TEL 52-5-2542525, FAX 52-5-2804415, http://www.revistaneo.com/. Ed. Jean Pierre Bouleau-Durroty. Adv. contact Carlos Casanueva. Circ: 7,228.

658.8 DNK
THE NET MARKET NEWS. Text in Danish. irreg. free. **Document type:** *Newsletter.* **Description:** Developed to help increase online marketing success.
Media: Online - full text.
Published by: Veritus Communications, Benediktevej 40, Viborg, 8800, Denmark. bizinc@netlane.com, netmarketnews@writeme.com, http://come.to/netmarketnews. Ed. Mcdonald Uche.

NET MARKETING INFO. see *COMPUTERS—Internet*

658.8 USA
NETWORK MARKETING TODAY. Text in English. 1997. 3/yr. **Document type:** *Newsletter, Trade.* **Description:** Contains positive sales, training and recruitment information.
Published by: Network Resources, Inc., 3741 N E 163rd St, Ste 123, N, Miami, FL 33160. TEL 305-947-5600, FAX 305-947-8655, coreya@mlminsider.com, http://www.mlminsider.com. Ed. Corey Augenstein.

658.8 USA ISSN 1539-3151
NETWORKING TIMES; moving the heart of business. Text in English. 2002 (Apr.). bi-m. USD 77.77 domestic; USD 87.77 in Canada; USD 7.97 newsstand/cover domestic; USD 10.97 newsstand/cover in Canada (effective 2004). adv. **Document type:** *Magazine, Trade.* **Description:** Contains articles and features on network marketing and communication.
Related titles: Online - full text ed.: USD 27.77 (effective 2002).

Published by: Gabriel Media Group, Inc., PO Box 55743, Sherman Oaks, CA 91413-0743. FAX 818-981-3759, customercare@networkingtimes.net, http://www.networkingtimes.net. Ed. John Milton Fogg. Pub. Bob Proctor.

658.7 USA
NEW ENGLAND PURCHASER. Text in English. 1921. q. membership. bk.rev. **Document type:** *Newsletter.* **Description:** Includes information about association news, seminars, and events.
Formerly: New England Purchaser - Connecticut Purchaser; Which was formed by the merger of: New England Purchaser (0028-4858); Connecticut Purchaser (0010-6208)
Published by: Purchasing Management Association of Boston, Inc., 200 Baker Ave, Ste 306, Concord, MA 01742-2112. TEL 508-371-2522, FAX 978-369-9130. Ed. Christiane Loup. Circ: 1,600.

NEW FOOD PRODUCTS IN JAPAN. see *FOOD AND FOOD INDUSTRIES—Grocery Trade*

658.8 790.1 GBR ISSN 0968-9400
NEW LEISURE MARKETS. Text in English. 10/yr. GBP 595 (effective 1999). **Document type:** *Trade.* **Description:** Each report analyzes a sector of the UK leisure market.
Published by: MarketScape, 5th Fl, 29-30 Warwick St, London, W1R 5RD, United Kingdom. TEL 44-1717-273443, FAX 44-1727-834012, em72@dial.pipex.com. Ed., Pub. Anne P Smith. R&P A P Smith.

658 GBR
NEW PRODUCT DEVELOPMENT NEWS. Text in English. 1983. m. GBP 450, USD 695; USD 745 foreign. **Document type:** *Consumer.*
Published by: Mintel International Group Ltd., 18-19 Long Ln., London, EC1A 9PL, United Kingdom. TEL 44-20-76064533, FAX 44-20-76065932. Ed. David Jago. Circ: 120.

NEW PRODUCT REVIEW. see *NUTRITION AND DIETETICS*

658.8 USA ISSN 0099-1007
HC108.N7
THE NEW YORK MARKET. Text in English. 1973. irreg.
Published by: Conference Board, Inc., 845 Third Ave, New York, NY 10022. TEL 212-339-0345, FAX 212-980-7014, atb@conference-board.com, http://www.conference-board.org.

658 NZL ISSN 1174-1023
NEW ZEALAND RETAIL; New Zealand's leading retail magazine. Variant title: Retail. Text in English. m. NZD 68 domestic; NZD 97 foreign (effective 1999); NZD 6.95 newsstand/cover. adv. charts; illus.; maps; stat.; tr.lit. back issues avail. **Document type:** *Trade.* **Description:** Covers all aspects of retailing, wholesaling and distribution.
Former titles (until 1997): Merchant (0113-468X); (until 1987): Retail News
Indexed: INZP.
—CCC.
Published by: (Retail and Wholesale Merchants Association of New Zealand Inc.), Retailer Publishing Co., P.O. Box 12086, Wellington, New Zealand. TEL 64-4-472-3733, FAX 64-4-472-1071, nzretailAibm.net, nzretail@ibm.net. Ed., R&P Martin Craig. Adv. contact Andre Dromgool. B&W page NZD 1,535, color page NZD 2,135. Circ: 3,800 (paid); 2,100 (controlled).

658 338 USA
NEWS & VIEWS (PORTLAND). Text in English. m. membership only. adv. bk.rev. **Document type:** *Newsletter.* **Description:** Discusses forms and systems management and current BFMA communications.
Published by: Business Forms Management Association, Inc., 319 S W Washington St, Ste 710, Portland, OR 97204-2604. TEL 503-227-3393, FAX 503-274-7667, Paul@bfma.org, http://www.bfma.org/~bfma/. Ed., R&P, Adv. contact Paul Telles. Circ: 2,000.

658.8 USA
NEWS AT THE PRESS. Text in English. 1998. bi-m. free. **Document type:** *Newsletter.* **Description:** Provides consumers with tips and facts on products for the entire family.
Media: Online - full text.
Published by: Watermelon Press, Inc., 64989 Hunnell Rd, Bend, OR 97701-8925. TEL 541-385-1399, FAX 541-685-1360, news@watermelonpress.com, http://www.watermelonpress.com.

658 CAN
NEWS CANADA. Text in English. 1981. m. free. adv.
Related titles: ◆ English ed.: Actualite Canada.
Published by: News Canada Inc., 366 Adelaide St, N W, Ste 606, Toronto, ON M5V 1R9, Canada. TEL 416-599-9900, FAX 416-599-9700. Ed. Linda Kroboth. Pub. Ruth Douglas. R&P Angela Skura. Adv. contact Yvonne Larkin. Circ: 1,546.

658.8 USA
NEWS SCAN. Text in English. m. **Document type:** *Newsletter, Trade.*

Published by: General Merchandise Distributors Council, 1275 Lake Plaza Dr, Colorado Springs, CO 80906-3583. TEL 719-576-4260, FAX 719-576-2661, info@gmdc.org, http://www.gmdc.org.

658.8 070.172 USA ISSN 0896-8284
HF6107
NEWSPAPER MARKETING. Text in English. bi-m. USD 60 to individuals (effective 2004). adv. bk.rev. **Document type:** *Magazine, Trade.* **Description:** Provides NAA Federation members with the latest news on industry issues, hot ideas and revenue-generating tips.
Formerly: I N A M E News (0745-5089)
Published by: Newspaper Association of America, 1921 Gallows Rd, Ste 600, Vienna, VA 22182-3900. TEL 703-902-1600, FAX 703-476-6015, http://www.naa.org/artpage.cfm?AID=6475&SID=34. Adv. contact Marc Benson. B&W page USD 1,500, color page USD 2,050. Circ: 11,399 (paid and controlled).

658 USA
NICHE (BALTIMORE); the magazine for progressive retailers. Text in English. 1988. q. **Document type:** *Trade.*
Published by: Rosen Group, 3000 Chestnut Ave, Baltimore, MD 21211-2743. TEL 410-889-3093, FAX 410-243-7089, hoped@rosengrp.com. Ed. Hope Daniels. Circ: 20,000.

658.8 USA
NIELSEN ALLIANCE✶. Text in English. 1942. 3/yr. free. stat.
Supersedes (in 1992): Nielsen Researcher (0885-6206)
Indexed: ABIn, PAIS, PROMT.
Published by: Nielsen Marketing Research (Subsidiary of: Dun & Bradstreet Corporation), 150 N Martingale Rd, Schaumburg, IL 60173-2408. TEL 708-498-6300. Ed. Paul J J Payack. Circ: 20,000.

658 BEL
NIEUWSBRIEF DIREKT MARKETING EN VERKOOP. Text in Flemish. w. Supplement avail. **Document type:** *Newsletter.*
Published by: C E D Samsom (Subsidiary of: Wolters Samsom Belgie n.v.), Kouterveld 14, Diegem, 1831, Belgium. TEL 32-2-7231111.

NIKKEI IMAGE CLIMATE FORECAST. see *ADVERTISING AND PUBLIC RELATIONS*

658 JPN
NIKKEI QUARTERLY NEWSLETTER ON COMMODITIES. Text in Japanese. q. **Document type:** *Newsletter.* **Description:** Contains price, demand, and sales trends of 500 categories from basic materials to consumer commodities.
Published by: Nihon Keizai Shimbun Inc., Nikkei Research Institute of Industry and Markets, 1-9-5 Ote-Machi, Chiyoda-ku, Tokyo, 1000004, Japan. TEL 81-3-5294-2574, FAX 81-3-5294-2593.

658 JPN
NIKKEI WEEKLY NEWSLETTER ON COMMODITIES. Text in Japanese. w. **Document type:** *Newsletter.* **Description:** Contains pricing and demand forecasts for various commodities.
Published by: Nihon Keizai Shimbun Inc., Nikkei Research Institute of Industry and Markets, 1-9-5 Ote-Machi, Chiyoda-ku, Tokyo, 1000004, Japan. TEL 81-3-5294-2574, FAX 81-3-5294-2593, TELEX J22308 NIKKEI.

331.88 NOR ISSN 0333-4570
NORSKE HANDELSREISENDE. Text in Norwegian. 1907. m. (10/yr.).
Published by: Norges Handelsreisendesforbund, Pilestredet 17, Oslo, 0164, Norway. Circ: 4,200.

NORTH AMERICAN MEAT PROCESSORS ASSOCIATION. NEWSFAX. see *FOOD AND FOOD INDUSTRIES*

NOVAYA POLIGRAFIYA. see *ADVERTISING AND PUBLIC RELATIONS*

658 RUS ISSN 1606-1519
NOVOSTI SISTEMY M M TS. (Mezhregional'nyi Marketingovyi Tsentr) Text in Russian. 1999. w. free (effective 2004). **Document type:** *Consumer.*
Media: Online - full text.
Published by: Al'yans Midiya, Bolotnaya ul 12, str 3, Moscow, 115035, Russian Federation. TEL 7-095-2345380, FAX 7-095-2345363, allmedia@allmedia.ru, http://www.businesspress.ru, http://allmedia.ru.

O T C BUSINESS NEWS. see *PHARMACY AND PHARMACOLOGY*

658.8029 USA
OFF-PRICE RETAIL DIRECTORY✶. Text in English. a. USD 142.95; to members (non-members and foreign $179); contact diskette $59 (effective 1999). adv. Supplement avail. **Document type:** *Directory.* **Description:** Contains details on off-price retail chains in the U.S., with 600 listings altogether.
Published by: (Off-Price Specialists, Inc.), Value Retail News, 29399 US HWY 19 N, Ste 370, Clearwater, FL 33761-2138. TEL 727-536-4047. Ed. Linda Humphers. Pub., R&P Ellis Rowland. Adv. contact Karen Knobeloch.

▼ **OFF-ROAD RETAILER.** see *TRANSPORTATION—Automobiles*

OFFICIAL SCHOOL BUS RESALE GUIDE. see *TRANSPORTATION*

658.87 USA ISSN 0030-1841
OKLAHOMA RETAILER. Text in English. 1961. m. USD 12 (effective 2000). adv. bk.rev. illus. reprint service avail. from PQC. **Document type:** *Trade.* **Description:** Covers appliances, electronics, plumbing, heating and air conditioning, furniture and home furnishings, home building and remodeling business in Oklahoma.
Related titles: Microfilm ed.: (from PQC).
Published by: Oklahoma Retailer Publishing Co., Inc., 4405 NW 4th St., Ste. 135, Oklahoma City, OK 73107-6541. TEL 405-528-0903. Ed., Pub., R&P, Adv. contact Fred Singleton. Circ: 4,900 (controlled).

658.85 ZAF ISSN 0030-2368
ON THE ROAD (CAPE TOWN). Text in English. 1914. m. ZAR 24. adv. bk.rev. **Document type:** *Newspaper, Trade.*
Published by: Southern Africa Commercial Travellers Association/Suidelike-Afrikaanse Handelsreisigersvereniging, Box 828, Cape Town, South Africa. TEL 27-21-216777, FAX 27-21-4197435. Ed., R&P, Adv. contact Morrie Silber. Circ: 2,500.

658.8 USA ISSN 1540-5249
ONE TO ONE (STAMFORD). Cover title: 1 to 1. Text in English. bi-m. Free to qualified subscribers.. **Document type:** *Magazine, Trade.* **Description:** Covers issues about one-to-one marketing which emphasizes focusing more on customers' needs.
Indexed: B&I.
Published by: Peppers and Rogers Group, 470 West Ave, Stamford, CT 06902. TEL 203-642-5121, 800-626-8121, thomas.schmalzl@1to1.com, http://www.1to1.com/. Ed. Lynn Dougherty TEL 203-642-5237.

658.575 USA
THE ONLINE INVENTOR. Text in English. 1998. m. free. back issues avail. **Document type:** *Newsletter.* **Description:** E-zine about getting a new product into the market, from inventing and prototyping through market research, patenting, finding a licensee, manufacturing and promoting it.
Media: Online - full text.
Published by: Market Launchers, Inc., 2614 S. 24th St., Quincy, IL 62305-2751. TEL 217-224-7735, 800-337-5758, FAX 217-224-7736, Niemann7@marketlaunchers.com, http://www.marketlaunchers.com. Ed., Pub., R&P, Adv. contact Paul Niemann TEL 217-224-7735. Circ: 700 (controlled).

ONLINE LOGISTICS BIBLIOGRAPHY. see *BUSINESS AND ECONOMICS—Abstracting, Bibliographies, Statistics*

658.7 USA ISSN 0030-4786
OREGON PURCHASOR✶. Text in English. 1928. m. USD 12; free. adv. bk.rev.
Published by: Purchasing Management Association of Oregon, c/o Decorators West, Box 25191, Portland, OR 97225-0191. TEL 503-245-2296. Eds. Annette Ross, Rick Drury. Circ: 2,200 (controlled).

364.4 USA
OUNCE OF PREVENTION✶; survey of security & loss prevention in the retail industry. Text in English. a. USD 65 to non-members; USD 35 to members; USD 13 to institutions.
Indexed: SRI.
Published by: Retail Industry Leaders Association, 1700 N Moore St, Ste 2250, Arlington, VA 22209-1903. TEL 202-861-0774, FAX 202-785-4588.

OUTDOOR POWER EQUIPMENT OFFICIAL GUIDE. see *AGRICULTURE—Agricultural Equipment*

658.8029 USA
OUTLET PROJECT DIRECTORY✶. Text in English. a. USD 142.95. adv. Supplement avail. **Document type:** *Directory.* **Description:** Provides details on existing and planned outlet centers worldwide, plus megamalls and value centers, with 496 listings altogether.
Published by: (Off-Price Specialists, Inc.), Value Retail News, 29399 US HWY 19 N, Ste 370, Clearwater, FL 33761-2138. TEL 727-536-4047, FAX 727-536-4384. Ed. Linda Humphers. Pub., R&P Ellis Rowland. Adv. contact Karen Knobeloch.

658.8029 USA
OUTLET RETAIL DIRECTORY✶. Text in English. a. USD 142.95. adv. Supplement avail. **Document type:** *Directory.* **Description:** Contains details on manufacturers' outlet retail chains in the U.S.
Published by: (Off-Price Specialists, Inc.), Value Retail News, 29399 US HWY 19 N, Ste 370, Clearwater, FL 33761-2138. TEL 727-536-4047, FAX 727-536-4384. Ed. Linda Humphers. Pub., R&P Ellis Rowland. Adv. contact Karen Knobeloc.

658.8 USA
P M C OF N Y NEWSLETTER. Text in English. 1950. m. USD 195 to members (effective 2000). **Document type:** *Newsletter.* **Description:** Information regarding incentives.

Published by: Premium Marketing Club of New York, Inc., 244 Broad St, Red Bank, NJ 07701. TEL 732-842-5070, FAX 732-219-1938, pmc@pmc-ny.com, http://www.pmc-ny.com. Ed. Karen Kircher. Circ: 300 (paid).

658 388.3 USA
P M L; the market letter for Porsche automobiles. Text in English. 1981. m. **Document type:** *Trade.*
Published by: P M L Consulting, PO Box 567, Socorro, NM 87801-0567. pmletter@aol.com, http://www.pmletter.com. Ed., Pub. Pat Van Buskirk. Circ: 1,500 (paid).

658.7 USA
P M NEWS★. Text in English. 1926. m. membership only. adv. illus. **Document type:** *Newsletter.*
Former titles (until 1991): Mid-Atlantic Purchasing (0031-7322); Philadelphia Purchasor
Published by: Purchasing Management Association of Philadelphia, 852 N Marion Way, Chandler, AZ 85225-9031. Ed. Ginger Ale Baker. Circ: 3,000.

658 DEU ISSN 1619-2753
P M - TRENDLETTER FUER PROFIS IM MARKETING. Text in German. 1984. 22/yr. EUR 393.60 (effective 2004). index. back issues avail. **Document type:** *Newsletter, Trade.*
Formerly (until 2002): Beratungsbrief fuer Produktmanager und Marketingleiter (1430-9939)
Published by: Medienmenschen GmbH, Neubiberger Str 15, Munich, 81737, Germany. TEL 49-89-68890448, FAX 49-89-681575, info@medienmenschen.de, http://www.medienmenschen.de/marketing_produktinfo.htm. Circ: 600.

P-O-P TIMES. (Point-of-Purchase) see *BUSINESS AND ECONOMICS—Economic Situation And Conditions*

P S R S. (Publishing Sales Representative's Source) see *PUBLISHING AND BOOK TRADE*

PABLISITI. see *ADVERTISING AND PUBLIC RELATIONS*

658 DEU ISSN 0342-3743
PACK REPORT. Text in German. 1968. m. EUR 99 domestic; EUR 105 in the European Union; EUR 110.30 elsewhere; EUR 11 newsstand/cover (effective 2003). adv. **Document type:** *Magazine, Trade.*
Incorporates (1960-1994): Verpackung (0042-4269); (1990-1994): European Packaging (1430-0974)
Indexed: FS&TA, IPackAb, KES, P&BA, PST.
—IE, Infotrieve. **CCC.**
Published by: Deutscher Fachverlag GmbH, Mainzer Landstr 251, Frankfurt Am Main, 60326, Germany. TEL 49-69-759501, FAX 49-69-75952999, heidrun.dangl@dfv.de, info@dfv.de, http://www.dfv.de. Ed. Annette von der Heide. Adv. contact Gudrun Bitterlich. B&W page EUR 2,608, color page EUR 3,748; trim 185 x 270. Circ: 10,529 (paid and controlled).

PACKAGING: A WORLD SURVEY. see *PACKAGING*

PAPERCAST. see *PAPER AND PULP*

791.06 658 GBR ISSN 1462-4796
PARK WORLD. Text in English. 1990. m. GBP 55 domestic; EUR 130 in Europe; USD 165 in the Americas & the Middle East; USD 195 in the Far East (effective 2004). adv. **Document type:** *Magazine, Trade.* **Description:** Focuses on the theme and amusement park and family entertainment center industry and is read by operators, developers and decision makers.
Supersedes in part (in 1998): Euroslot (0966-0259)
Indexed: RASB.
—**CCC.**
Published by: Datateam Publishing Ltd, 15a London Rd, Maidstone, Kent ME16 8LY, United Kingdom. TEL 44-1622-687031, FAX 44-1622-757646, parkworld@datateam.co.uk, info@datateam.co.uk, http://www.datateam.co.uk/business_publications/park_world.htm, http://www.datateam.co.uk/home/home.htm. adv.: B&W page GBP 1,100, B&W page EUR 1,825, B&W page USD 1,850, color page GBP 1,300, color page EUR 2,160, color page USD 2,200; trim 229 x 306. Circ: 6,500.

PARTY & PAPER RETAILER. see *LEISURE AND RECREATION*

PEERLESS EXPRESS ZINE. see *COMPUTERS—Internet*

PENNSYLVANIA MARKETING BULLETIN. see *FORESTS AND FORESTRY—Lumber And Wood*

658 691 USA ISSN 0898-0047
PEOPLE & PROFITS; Bill Lee's tips, tactics and how-to's for the building supply, hardware and home center industry. Text in English. 1988. m. USD 147. charts; illus.; stat.; tr.lit. index. back issues avail.
Published by: Lee Resources, Inc., PO Box 16711, Greenville, SC 29606. TEL 803-288-0461, FAX 803-234-6961. Ed. Beth White. Circ: 1,100 (paid).

658 CHE
PERSOENLICH. Text in German. 23/yr.
Published by: Persoenlich Verlags AG, Hauptplatz 5, Rapperswil SG, 8640, Switzerland. TEL 055-261717, FAX 055-271593. Ed. Erich Liebi. Circ: 1,600.

PET BUSINESS. see *PETS*

658 659.1 DEU ISSN 0721-5665
PHARMA-MARKETING JOURNAL. Text in German. 1976. bi-m. adv. bk.rev. 36 p./no.; **Document type:** *Journal, Trade.*
—GNLM, IE, Infotrieve.
Published by: I F A M Institut, Kaiser-Wilhelm-Ring 43, Duesseldorf, 40545, Germany. TEL 49-211-55986-0, FAX 49-211-575043, info@ifam-online.de. Ed. Malte W Wilkes. Adv. contact Uwe Rothstein. Circ: 1,100.

615.1 658.8 POL
PHARMA POLAND NEWS. Text in English. bi-w. EUR 400 foreign (effective 2005). **Document type:** *Newsletter, Trade.* **Description:** Contains pharmaceutical sector news as well as curent trends, statistics and analyses of the Polish pharmaceutical market.
Media: E-mail.
Published by: Polish Market Review Ltd., ul Supniewskiego 9, Krakow, 31527, Poland. TEL 48-12-4280360, FAX 48-12-4134012, pmr@pmrpublications.com, http://www.pmrpublications.com.

PHARMACEUTICAL MARKETERS DIRECTORY. see *PHARMACY AND PHARMACOLOGY*

PHARMACY RETAILER. see *PHARMACY AND PHARMACOLOGY*

658.8029 USA ISSN 1072-2572
HF5035
PHELON'S DISCOUNT - JOBBING TRADE. Text in English. 1890. a., latest vol.14, 2001. USD 175 (effective 2001). 300 p./no.; **Document type:** *Directory.* **Description:** Lists the executives and buyers in the discount, mass merchandising, and wholesaling industries.
Published by: Phelon Sheldon & Marsar, Inc., 1364 Georgetowne Circle, Sarasota, FL 34232-2048. TEL 941-342-7990, 800-234-8804, FAX 941-342-7994, PSMpublishing@aol.com. Ed., Pub., R&P, Adv. contact Joseph R Marsar Jr. Circ: 2,000 (paid).

658.8 USA ISSN 0098-9312
THE PHILADELPHIA MARKET. Text in English. irreg.
Published by: Conference Board, Inc., 845 Third Ave, New York, NY 10022. TEL 212-339-0345, FAX 212-980-7014, atb@conference-board.com, http://www.conference-board.org.

658.84 USA
PHONE SALES PRESENTATIONS FOR SERVICE-TYPE BUSINESSES, ETC. - A NEWSLETTER. Text in English. 1991. irreg. looseleaf. USD 15.95 per issue (effective 2001). **Document type:** *Directory.* **Description:** Provides scripts for telemarketing presentations for various types of businesses.
Published by: Prosperity & Profits Unlimited Distribution Services, PO Box 416, Denver, CO 80201-0416. TEL 303-575-5676, FAX 970-292-2136, mail@curriculumresourceonline.com, http://www.telemarketingscripts.20m.com/. Ed. A Doyle.

658.8 FIN ISSN 0032-0242
PIRKKA. Text in Finnish. 1933. 10/yr. EUR 37 (effective 2005). adv. illus. **Document type:** *Magazine, Trade.*
Published by: K-Kauppiasliitto ry, Koydenpunojankatu 2 a D, Helsinki, 00180, Finland. TEL 358-9-15668510, FAX 358-9-15668525, etunimi.sukunimi@pirkka.fi, http://www.pirkka.fi. Ed. Riita Korhonen. adv.: B&W page EUR 7,820, color page EUR 9,810; trim 216 x 265. Circ: 1,201,126 (controlled).

PIZZA MARKETING QUARTERLY. see *HOTELS AND RESTAURANTS*

PIZZA MARKETING QUARTERLY AUSTRALIA & NEW ZEALAND. see *HOTELS AND RESTAURANTS*

▼ **PLACE BRANDING.** see *ADVERTISING AND PUBLIC RELATIONS*

658 DEU ISSN 0724-9632
PLANUNG & ANALYSE; die Fachzeitschrift fuer Marktforschung und Marketing. Text in German. 1973. 7/yr. EUR 131.50 domestic; EUR 138.57 in the European Union; EUR 131.50 elsewhere; EUR 22.50 newsstand/cover (effective 2003). adv. bk.rev. back issues avail. **Document type:** *Magazine, Trade.*
Formerly (until 1983): Interview und Analyse (0343-9690)
—IE, Infotrieve.
Published by: Deutscher Fachverlag GmbH, Mainzer Landstr 251, Frankfurt Am Main, 60326, Germany. TEL 49-69-759501, FAX 49-69-75952999, info@planung-analyse.de, info@dfv.de, http://www.planung-analyse.de, http://www.dfv.de. Ed. Karin Duerr. adv.: B&W page EUR 2,040, color page EUR 2,910; trim 175 x 272. Circ: 1,950 (paid and controlled).

PLASTICS BRIEF: THERMOPLASTICS MARKETING NEWSLETTER. see *PLASTICS*

658.8029 USA ISSN 1532-5954
HF5429.3
PLUNKETT'S RETAIL INDUSTRY ALMANAC. Text in English. 1997. a. USD 249.99 (effective 2005); includes CD-ROM. **Document type:** *Directory, Trade.* **Description:** Presents the trends and a thorough analysis of careers, suppliers, finances, and future growth within the retail industry.
Related titles: CD-ROM ed.
Published by: Plunkett Research, Ltd, PO Drawer 541737, Houston, TX 77254-1737. TEL 713-932-0000, FAX 713-932-7080, info@plunkettresearch.com, http://www.plunkettresearch.com. Ed., Pub. Jack W Plunkett.

658.8 FRA ISSN 0150-1844
POINTS DE VENTE. Text in French. 1962. w. FRF 588; FRF 840 foreign. adv. bk.rev.
Incorporates: Rayons Jardin (0249-1605)
Related titles: Online - full text ed.
Indexed: KES.
Published by: Groupe Liaisons S.A. (Subsidiary of: Wolters Kluwer BV), 1 Avenue Edouard Belin, Rueil Malmaison, Cedex 92856, France. TEL 33-1-41299899, FAX 33-1-41299908.

POLISH MARKET REVIEW. see *BUSINESS AND ECONOMICS—Investments*

POLITICHESKII MARKETING. see *POLITICAL SCIENCE*

658 GBR
POOL. Text in English. q. Free. adv. **Document type:** *Magazine, Trade.* **Description:** Comments on business, marketing and communications strategies.
Media: Online - full content.
Published by: Through the Loop Consulting Ltd, 155 Lichfield Court, Sheen Rd, Richmond, Surrey TW9 1AZ, United Kingdom. TEL 44-20-83346300, FAX 44-20-89401447, info@throughtheloop.com, http://www.poolonline.com, http://www.throughtheloop.com/.

797.2 790.1 CAN ISSN 0711-2998
POOL & SPA MARKETING. Text in English. 1976. 7/yr. CND 25, USD 25 (effective 2005). adv. bk.rev. charts; tr.lit.; stat. **Document type:** *Trade.* **Description:** Provides product, marketing and business information to manufacturers, dealers and service personnel in the swimming pool, spa and sauna industry in Canada and the Eastern United States.
Formerly: Canadian Pool and Spa Marketing (0227-3330)
—**CCC.**
Published by: Hubbard Marketing & Publishing Ltd., 270 Esna Park Dr, Unit 12, Markham, ON L3R 1H3, Canada. TEL 905-513-0090, 800-268-5503, FAX 905-513-1377, http://www.poolspamarketing.com/. Ed. David Barnsley. Pub. Richard Hubbard. R&P R Hubbard. Adv. contact Anita Bradley. B&W page USD 1,135, color page USD 1,885; trim 10.88 x 8.13. Circ: 8,000.

POTATO COUNTRY. see *AGRICULTURE—Crop Production And Soil*

658.8 USA ISSN 1522-9564
HF5410
POTENTIALS; ideas and products that motivate. Text in English. 1968. m. USD 59 domestic; USD 75 in Canada; USD 117 elsewhere; free to qualified personnel (effective 2005). adv. illus. reprints avail. **Document type:** *Magazine, Trade.* **Description:** Designed to stimulate ideas by serving as a source for the latest new products, techniques and strategies required to meet today's marketplace challenges and future marketing goals.
Formerly (until 1998): Potentials in Marketing (0032-5619); Which incorporated (1976-1989): Marketing Communications (0164-4343)
Related titles: Online - full text ed.: (from EBSCO Publishing, Florida Center for Library Automation, Gale Group, O C L C Online Computer Library Center, Inc., ProQuest Information & Learning).
Indexed: ABIn, AgeL, BPI.
—IE. **CCC.**
Published by: V N U Business Publications (Subsidiary of: V N U Business Media), 770 Broadway, New York, NY 10003-9595. TEL 646-654-7604, info@potentialsmag.com, bmcomm@vnuinc.com, http://www.potentialsmag.com/, http://www.vnubusinessmedia.com/. Ed. Melinda Ligos TEL 646-654-7353. adv.: B&W page USD 9,756, color page USD 12,771. Circ: 50,450 (controlled). **Subscr. to:** PO Box 2085, Skokie, IL 60076-7985. TEL 847-763-9050, FAX 847-763-9037.

POWER AND GAS MARKETING. see *PETROLEUM AND GAS*

PRACTICE BUILDERS. see *ADVERTISING AND PUBLIC RELATIONS*

658 RUS
PRAKTICHESKII MARKETING. Text in Russian. 1997. m. **Document type:** *Magazine, Trade.*
Related titles: ♦ Supplement(s): Ekskluzivnyi Marketing; ♦ Politicheskii Marketing; ♦ Daidzhest Marketing; ♦ Reklamodatel'.

Published by: B C I Marketing, ul Malaya Cherkizovskaya, dom 66, Moscow, 107392, Russian Federation. bcimarketing@mtu-net.ru, http://www.bci-marketing.aha.ru. Ed. Suren Grigoryan. Circ: 900.

658.8   GBR   ISSN 0955-0836
PRECISION MARKETING. Text in English. 1988. w. GBP 95.90 in Europe; GBP 141 in US & Canada; GBP 176 elsewhere (effective 2005). adv. **Document type:** *Magazine, Trade.* **Description:** Provides in-depth information on direct marketing, loyalty campaigns, sales promotion, sponsorship and all the other techniques which leading edge marketers are using to win new customers and sell more to their existing customers.
Related titles: Online - full text ed.: (from EBSCO Publishing, Gale Group, H.W. Wilson, Northern Light Technology, Inc., O C L C Online Computer Library Center, Inc., ProQuest Information & Learning); Supplement(s): Agency Showcase. ISSN 0957-4913. 1989.
Indexed: ABIn, BPI, Emerald.
—BLDSC (6603.996800). **CCC.**
Published by: Centaur Communications Ltd., 50 Poland St, London, W1V 7AX, United Kingdom. TEL 44-20-79704000, pmcirc@centaur.co.uk, customer.service@centaur.co.uk, http://www.mad.co.uk/publications/pm/, http://www.centaur.co.uk/. Ed. Charlie McKelvey TEL 44-20-79704000. Pub. Declan Gough. Adv. contact Ian Sinclair.

PRESENTATIONS; technology and techniques for effective communication. see *ADVERTISING AND PUBLIC RELATIONS*

PRICING ADVISOR. see *CONSUMER EDUCATION AND PROTECTION*

PRINTTHOUGHTS; occasional comments on matters of interest in the print world. see *PRINTING*

PRODUCER PRICE INDEXES. see *BUSINESS AND ECONOMICS—Abstracting, Bibliographies, Statistics*

PRODUCT ALERT. see *FOOD AND FOOD INDUSTRIES*

659.1 615   USA   ISSN 1078-6937
HF5415.15
PRODUCT MANAGEMENT TODAY. Text in English. 1990. m. USD 80.60 (effective 2004). adv. **Document type:** *Magazine, Trade.* **Description:** Covers marketing, product management, managed care marketing and career development issues affecting the product management team, service healthcare manufacturers and service sector companies.
—CCC.
Published by: Product Management Today, Inc., 28 Jones Ave, Flourtown, PA 19031. TEL 215-233-9384, FAX 215-233-9320. Ed. Peter Ciszewski. Pub. Thomas Lyons Drake. Circ: 9,600 (controlled).

PROFESSIONAL ADVISOR. see *ADVERTISING AND PUBLIC RELATIONS*

PROFESSIONAL CANDY BUYER. see *FOOD AND FOOD INDUSTRIES*

▼ **PROFESSIONAL DOOR DEALER.** see *BUILDING AND CONSTRUCTION*

658   ZAF
PROFESSIONAL MANAGEMENT REVIEW. Cover title: P M R. Text in English. 1990. m. ZAR 190; ZAR 20 newsstand/cover (effective 1999). adv. bk.rev.; software rev.; tel.rev. abstr.; charts; illus.; stat. index. back issues avail. **Document type:** *Trade.* **Description:** Presents expertise and intelligence on business and management issues affecting South Africa and the region.
Formerly: Professional Marketing Review (1016-0051)
Related titles: Online - full text ed.
Indexed: ISAP.
Published by: P M R cc, PO Box 1200, Parklands, Johannesburg 2121, South Africa. TEL 27-11-880-4720, FAX 27-11-880-4724, pmr@iafrica.com, http://www.fast.co.za/pmr/. Ed. Ray Wood. Adv. contact R Curtin. color page ZAR 10,600; trim 210 x 273.

658   GBR   ISSN 0969-1847
PROFESSIONAL MARKETING. Text in English. 1993. m. GBP 225 (effective 2002). bk.rev. back issues avail. **Document type:** *Trade.*
Published by: Professional Marketing International, 29 Throgmorton St, London, EC2N 2AT, United Kingdom. TEL 44-20-7786-9786, FAX 44-20-7786-9799, pm@pmint.co.uk, http://www.pmint.co.uk. Ed., Adv. contact Nadia Cristina.

658.8   AUS   ISSN 1327-1903
PROFESSIONAL MARKETING. Text in English. 1992. bi-m. AUD 154 (effective 2000); included with B&T Weekly. adv. **Document type:** *Trade.* **Description:** Coverage includes regular analysis of marketing strategies, latest international trends, the top brands, and the people who drive them.
Formerly: Australian Professional Marketing (1038-9598)

Published by: (Australian Marketing Institute), Reed Business Information Pty Ltd (Subsidiary of: Reed Business Information International), Locked Bag 2999, Chatswood, NSW 2067, Australia. customerservice@reedbusiness.com.au, http://www.bandt.com.au. Ed. Tony Burrett. Pub. Barrie Parsons. Adv. contact Jacqui Brown. Circ: 11,530 (paid).

658.72   USA   ISSN 1070-0455
PROFESSIONAL PURCHASING. Text in English. 1972. m. USD 99 to non-members (effective 2000); 115 USD to non-members (Effective 2001). adv. bk.rev. index. back issues avail.; reprints avail. **Document type:** *Newsletter.* **Description:** Provides information on price, job openings in purchasing, and answers to purchasing problems. Information on purchasing methods.
Published by: American Purchasing Society, Inc., 430 W Downer Pl, P O Box 256, Aurora, IL 60506-5035. TEL 630-859-0250, FAX 630-859-0270, propurch@aol.com, http://www.american-purchasing.com. Ed., Pub. & R&P Harry E Hough. Adv. contact Richard Hough. Circ: 3,000 (paid); 7,500 (controlled).

658.7   CAN
PROGRESSIVE PURCHASING. Text in English, French. 1982. q. USD 130 to non-members; free to members (effective 1999). adv. bk.rev. **Document type:** *Newsletter.*
Formerly: P M A C News; Supersedes: Action (0319-5023)
Published by: Purchasing Management Association of Canada, 2 Carlton St, Ste 1414, Toronto, ON M5B 1J3, Canada. TEL 416-977-7111, FAX 416-977-8886, info@pmac.ca, http://www.pmac.ca. Ed., Pub. & R&P Alexandra Marshall. Adv. contact Janice Lauzon. Circ: 10,000.

381.1   ZAF   ISSN 1607-9892
HF5429.6.S6
PROGRESSIVE RETAILING. Text in English. 1995. m. ZAR 336 domestic; ZAR 422 foreign (effective 2003).
Published by: Primedia Publishing, 366 Pretoria Ave, Ferndale, Randburg, Transvaal 2194, South Africa. TEL 27-11-787-5725, FAX 27-11-787-5776, http://www.primemags.co.za.

659.2   USA
PROMODISPATCH. Text in English. bi-w. free. **Document type:** *Newsletter.* **Description:** Devoted to interactive and high-tech public relations and marketing.
Media: Online - full text.
Address: promodispatch@taprootcom.com, http://www.taprootcom.com/prodispatch.html. Ed. Melissa Meehan.

658.8   USA   ISSN 1539-3216
PROMOTIONAL MARKETING; the source of product information for distributors. Text in English.
Published by: North American Publishing Co., 1500 Spring Garden St., Ste 1200, Philadelphia, PA 19130-4094. TEL 215-238-5300, FAX 215-238-5457, http://www.promotionalmktg.com, http://www.napco.com. Ed. Bill Drennan.

PROMOTIONAL PRODUCTS BUSINESS. see *ADVERTISING AND PUBLIC RELATIONS*

658.85   GBR   ISSN 0266-7991
HF5415
PROMOTIONS AND INCENTIVES. Text in English. 1961. 10/yr. GBP 47 in United Kingdom; GBP 58 in Europe; GBP 95 elsewhere (effective 2001). adv. bk.rev. charts; illus.; stat.; tr.lit. back issues avail.; reprint service avail. from PQC. **Document type:** *Journal, Trade.*
Former titles: Incentive Marketing and Sales Promotion (0305-2230); Incentive Marketing (0019-3356)
Related titles: Microfilm ed.: (from PQC); Online - full content ed.: (from Florida Center for Library Automation); Online - full text ed.: (from Gale Group, O C L C Online Computer Library Center, Inc., ProQuest Information & Learning).
Indexed: ABIn, AIAP, Emerald.
—BLDSC (6925.500000), IE, ingenta. **CCC.**
Published by: Haymarket Business Publications Ltd., 174 Hammersmith Rd, London, W6 7JP, United Kingdom. TEL 44-20-8943-5000, FAX 44-20-82674268, admin.promoinc@haynet.com, http://www.haymarketgroup.com, http://www.factiva.com. Ed. Bhavna Mistry. Adv. contact Paul Mann TEL 44-20-8267-4361. Circ: 7,000. **Subscr. to:** c/o Promotions and Incentives, Units 12 & 13, Cranleigh Gardens Industrial Estate, Southall, Midds UB1 2DB, United Kingdom.

PROMOWEAR; for the business of promotional products. see *CLOTHING TRADE*

658.8   USA
PROOF. Text in English. m. membership. adv. **Document type:** *Newsletter.*
Published by: Direct Marketing Club of New York, 224 Seventh St, Garden City, NY 11530-9619. Ed., R&P Debra Ray. Adv. contact S Boysen.

PROSPER; your complete guide to making money. see *BUSINESS AND ECONOMICS—Small Business*

PROSPERITY BUILDER NEWSLETTER. see *COMPUTERS—Internet*

PSYCHOLOGY & MARKETING. see *PSYCHOLOGY*

PUBBLICITA ITALIA. see *ADVERTISING AND PUBLIC RELATIONS*

658   USA   ISSN 1053-9751
HM261
PUBLIC PULSE. Text in English. 1986. m. USD 297; USD 347 foreign. **Document type:** *Newsletter.* **Description:** Tracks what people are thinking, doing and buying, through proprietary survey data.
Related titles: Online - full text ed.
Indexed: CCR.
Published by: Roper Starch Worldwide, 205 E 42nd St, New York, NY 10017. TEL 212-599-0700, FAX 212-867-7008. Ed. John Berry.

658.7   GBR   ISSN 1460-7190
PUBLIC SECTOR PROPERTY. Text in English. 1996. m. (plus w. updates). GBP 240; GBP 266 in Europe; GBP 302 elsewhere. **Document type:** *Trade.* **Description:** Dedicated to providing the building trade with details of new contract opportunities for companies of all sizes throughout the UK.
Formerly (until 1997): Public Sector Property Contracts and Tenders (1366-5596)
Related titles: CD-ROM ed.; Diskette ed.; Online - full text ed.
Published by: Business Information Publications Ltd., Park House, 300 Glasgow Rd, Shawfield, Glasgow, G73 1SQ, United Kingdom. TEL 44-141-3328247, FAX 44-141-3312652, bip@bipcontracts.com, bip@bipsolutions.com, http://www.bipcontracts.com.

PUBLICIDAD Y MERCADEO. see *ADVERTISING AND PUBLIC RELATIONS*

070.5   USA
PUBLISHING POYNTERS; book and information marketing news and ideas from Dan Poynter. Text in English. 1986. bi-w. USD 9.95 for 2 yrs. (effective 2005). bk.rev.; software rev.; Website rev. stat.; tr.lit. back issues avail. **Document type:** *Newsletter, Trade.* **Description:** Book and information marketing news and ideas from Dan Poynter.
Related titles: E-mail ed.; Online - full text ed.
Published by: Para Publishing, PO Box 8206-236, Santa Barbara, CA 93118-8206. TEL 805-968-7277, FAX 805-968-1379, danpoynter@parapublishing.com, http://www.parapublishing.com. Ed., Pub., Adv. contact Dan Poynter. R&P Monique Tihanyi. Circ: 17,000 (controlled); 500 (paid).

658.7   IND   ISSN 0014-6544
PURCHASING. Text in English. 1964. m. INR 25. adv. bk.rev. illus.
Formerly: Factory
Related titles: Online - full text ed.: (from Northern Light Technology, Inc.).
Indexed: T&II.
Published by: India Publications Co., Denabank House, 2nd Fl., 31 Hamam St., Mumbai, Maharashtra 400 001, India. Ed. Eric Martin.

658.7   USA   ISSN 0033-4448
HF5001
PURCHASING (NEWTON); the magazine of total supply chain management. Text in English. 1936. 19/yr. (plus guide and directory) (in 2 vols.). USD 109.90 domestic; USD 152.90 in Canada; USD 142.90 in Mexico; USD 279.90 elsewhere; USD 10 per issue domestic; free to qualified personnel (effective 2005). adv. bk.rev. charts; illus.; mkt.; tr.lit. index. back issues avail.; reprints avail. **Document type:** *Magazine, Trade.* **Description:** Provides price and market news and forecasts on industrial products, components and materials, office products, business systems, transportation. Reports latest purchasing tactics, strategies and techniques.
Related titles: Microform ed.; Online - full text ed.: (from EBSCO Publishing, Factiva, Florida Center for Library Automation, Gale Group, H.W. Wilson, O C L C Online Computer Library Center, Inc., ProQuest Information & Learning); ◆ Supplement(s): Chemical Yellow Pages Directory; ◆ Metals Sourcing Guide.
Indexed: ABIn, BPI, BPIA, BrCerAb, BusI, C&ISA, CerAb, CorrAb, E&CAJ, EMA, EngInd, IAA, Inspec, KES, LRI, M&TEA, MBF, METADEX, SolStAb, T&II, WAA.
—BLDSC (7160.500000), AskIEEE, IE, ingenta, Linda Hall. **CCC.**
Published by: Reed Business Information (Subsidiary of: Reed Business), 275 Washington St, Newton, MA 02458. TEL 617-558-4291, FAX 617-558-4327, kdoyle@reedbusiness.com, http://www.purchasing.com, http://www.reedbusiness.com. Ed. Doug Smock TEL 617-558-4224. Pub. Kathy Doyle TEL 617-558-4491. adv.: B&W page USD 12,915, color page USD 15,230; trim 10.5 x 7.88. Circ: 97,097 (paid and controlled). **Subscr. to:** Reed Business Information, PO Box 9020, Maple Shade, NJ 08052-9020. TEL 303-470-4466, FAX 303-470-4691, http://www.pubservice.com/CH.htm.

658.7   CAN   ISSN 1497-1569
HF5437
PURCHASING B2B. Text in English. 1959. 10/yr. CND 94 domestic; CND 156 foreign (effective 2001). adv. illus. **Document type:** *Magazine, Trade.* **Description:** Covers technology developments, management issues, sector-by-sector trends, and legal issues, offering up-to-date news coverage, expert commentary and profiles of Canadian supply-chain professionals.
Formerly (until 2000): Modern Purchasing (0026-833X)
Related titles: Microfiche ed.: (from MML); Microform ed.: (from MML, PQC); Online - full text ed.: (from Micromedia ProQuest, ProQuest Information & Learning).
Indexed: CBCABus, CBCARef, CBPI.
Published by: Rogers Media Publishing Ltd, One Mount Pleasant Rd, 11th Fl, Toronto, ON M4Y 2Y5, Canada. TEL 416-764-2000, FAX 416-764-3941, http://www.purchasingb2b.ca. adv.: page CND 4,410; 7 x 10. Circ: 20,425.

658   USA   ISSN 1080-3203
CODEN: PMBUFF
PURCHASING MANAGEMENT BULLETIN. Text in English. 1968. m. USD 169 to individuals; USD 17 newsstand/cover (effective 2002). index. **Document type:** *Newsletter.* **Description:** Profiles noteworthy purchasing techniques in action at identified companies, including vendor selection and rating systems, vendor certification and partnering, sole sourcing, negotiations, value and cost analysis, and buyer training and development.
Formerly: Purchasing Executive's Bulletin (1077-4351)
Related titles: Online - full text ed.: (from Florida Center for Library Automation, Gale Group).
Published by: Bureau of Business Practice (Subsidiary of: Aspen Publishers, Inc.), 1185 Avenue of the Americas, 37th Fl, New York, NY 10036. TEL 860-442-4365, 800-243-0876, FAX 860-437-3555, rebecca_armitage@prenhall.com, http://www.bbpnews.com. Ed. Wayne Mullen. Pub. Peter Garabedian. R&P Kathryn Mennone.

658   GBR   ISSN 1352-2752
HF5415.2
➤ **QUALITATIVE MARKET RESEARCH;** an international journal. Text in English. 1994. q. EUR 1,206.04 in Europe; USD 1,499 in North America; AUD 2,009 in Australasia; GBP 847.16 in UK & elsewhere (effective 2006). reprint service avail. from PSC. **Document type:** *Journal, Academic/Scholarly.* **Description:** Furthers the frontiers of knowledge and understanding of qualitative market research and its applications, exploring many contemporary issues and new developments in marketing.
Related titles: Online - full text ed.: (from EBSCO Publishing, Emerald Group Publishing Limited, Gale Group, IngentaConnect, O C L C Online Computer Library Center, Inc., ProQuest Information & Learning, Swets Information Services).
Indexed: ABIn, EmerIntel, Emerald, PsycInfo, PsycholAb.
—BLDSC (7168.124320), IE, Infotrieve, ingenta. **CCC.**
Published by: Emerald Group Publishing Limited, 60-62 Toller Ln, Bradford, W Yorks BD8 9BY, United Kingdom. TEL 44-1274-777700, FAX 44-1274-785200, help@emeraldinsight.com, infomation@emeraldinsight.com, http://www.emeraldinsight.com/qmr.htm. Ed. Len Tiu Wright.
Subscr. addr. in N America: Emerald Group Publishing Ltd., 44 Brattle St, 4th Fl, Cambridge, MA 02138. TEL 617-497-2175, 888-622-0075, FAX 617-354-6875.

▼ ➤ **QUANTITATIVE MARKETING AND ECONOMICS.** see *BUSINESS AND ECONOMICS*

658 600   GBR   ISSN 0952-7532
QUIDDITY; polemical review of new developments in publishing. Text in English. 1987. m. **Description:** For publishers and others concerned with electronic information, media and communication.
—IE.
Address: 3 Abbey Orchard St, London, SW1P 2JJ, United Kingdom. TEL 01-222-1339. Ed. Graham Lea.

658.8   USA   ISSN 0893-7451
CODEN: QMREEN
QUIRK'S MARKETING RESEARCH REVIEW. Text in English. 1986. 11/yr. USD 70 domestic; USD 100 in Canada & Mexico; USD 119 elsewhere (effective 2004). adv. bk.rev. **Document type:** *Magazine, Trade.* **Description:** Focuses on research techniques for the marketing industry. Includes case histories and industry product and personnel news.
Published by: Quirk Enterprises, 8030 Cedar Ave S, Ste 229, Minneapolis, MN 55425. TEL 952-854-5101, FAX 952-854-8191, info@quirks.com, http://www.quirks.com/, http://www.quirks.com/. Ed., R&P Joseph Rydholm. Pub. Tom Quirk. Adv. contact Evan Tweed. Circ: 15,500 (controlled).

658   USA
R A C DIGEST✶ . Text in English. bi-m. USD 65 to members. **Document type:** *Bulletin.*
Published by: (Retail Advertising Conference), Retail Advertising and Marketing Association International, 333 N Michigan Ave, Ste 3000, Chicago, IL 60601-4105. TEL 312-245-9011, FAX 312-245-9015.

R & I MENU. (Restaurants & Institutions) see *HOTELS AND RESTAURANTS*

658.8   DEU
R B CONGRESS MARKETING. Text in German. 1967. m. looseleaf. USD 110. **Document type:** *Newsletter.*
Related titles: ♦ Supplement to: R B Reisebuero-Marketing & Hotel-Marketing.
Published by: R B Redaktions Buero, Schraemelstr 126, Munich, 81247, Germany. TEL 49-89-88888888, FAX 49-89-8110655. Ed. Hans Nechleba. Circ: 1,190 (paid).

658.7   USA   ISSN 0887-3003
HD9940.U4
R T W REVIEW. Variant title: Retailing in Today's World Review. Text in English. 1985. bi-m. USD 179 domestic; USD 199 in Canada; USD 249 elsewhere (effective 2000). adv. bk.rev. back issues avail. **Document type:** *Newsletter, Trade.* **Description:** Trade publication for the retail industry featuring alternative retail formats for the new millennium, comprehensive retail coverage, merchandising strategies and emerging industry trends.
Published by: Creative Concepts Group, 1970 Norhardt Dr., Unit D, Brookfield, WI 53045-5086. TEL 414-425-5503, FAX 414-425-2501, rtwrev@aol.com. Ed., R&P Lauren Daniel-Falk. Adv. contact Kelly Smith. Circ: 5,000. **Subscr. to:** P O Box 27688, Milwaukee, WI 53227.

910 658.8   USA   ISSN 0361-9923
G1019
RAND MCNALLY COMMERCIAL ATLAS AND MARKETING GUIDE. Text in English. 1876-1982; resumed. a., latest 134th ed. USD 395 (effective 2004). charts; stat. index.
Published by: Rand McNally & Co., 8255 N Central Park Ave, Skokie, IL 60076-2970. TEL 800-333-0136 ext 6171, http://www.randmcnally.com. Ed. David Zapenski.

658   FRA   ISSN 0767-3701
RECHERCHE ET APPLICATIONS EN MARKETING. Text in French. 1986. q. EUR 72 domestic; EUR 80 foreign (effective 2005). **Document type:** *Journal, Academic/Scholarly.* **Description:** Aims to validate research and to show the applications of marketing to the professional world.
Related titles: Online - full text ed.: (from ProQuest Information & Learning).
Indexed: ABIn, CPM, M&MA, SCIMP.
—BLDSC (7306.740000), IE, ingenta. **CCC.**
Published by: (Association Francaise du Marketing), Presses Universitaires de Grenoble, 1041 Rue des Residences, Grenoble, 38040, France. TEL 33-4-76825651, FAX 33-4-76827835, pug@oug.fr, http://www.pug.fr.

RECRUITMENT, RETENTION & RESTRUCTURING REPORT; strategies for recruiters, managers, R&R committees, & human resource directors. see *MEDICAL SCIENCES—Nurses And Nursing*

REGIONAL ECONOMIES AND MARKETS; a quarterly analysis from the Conference Board. see *BUSINESS AND ECONOMICS—Economic Situation And Conditions*

REGIONAL OFFICIAL GUIDES: TRACTORS AND FARM EQUIPMENT. see *AGRICULTURE—Agricultural Equipment*

658   GBR   ISSN 1364-4424
REGIONAL SALES LEADS - CENTRAL MANCHESTER. Text in English. 1995. a. GBP 249.
Related titles: Diskette ed.
Published by: The Prospect Shop Ltd., Field House, 72 Oldfield Rd, Hampton, Middx TW12 2HQ, United Kingdom. TEL 44-20-8461-8730, 44-20-8481-8720, FAX 44-20-8783-1940, info@theprospectshop.co.uk.

658.8 659.1   RUS
REKLAMODATEL'. Text in Russian. m. **Document type:** *Magazine, Trade.*
Related titles: ♦ Supplement to: Prakticheskii Marketing.
Published by: B C I Marketing, ul Malaya Cherkizovskaya, dom 66, Moscow, 107392, Russian Federation. bcimarketing@mtu-net.ru, http://www.inforeklama.ru/rd, http://www.bci-marketing.aha.ru.

RENOVERING OG DRIFT - NETTO. see *BUILDING AND CONSTRUCTION*

338   USA   ISSN 0034-4524
RENTAL EQUIPMENT REGISTER; serving the rental profession. Short title: R E R. Text in English. 1957. m. USD 79 domestic; USD 85 in Canada; USD 190 elsewhere (effective 2005). adv. illus.; tr.lit. **Document type:** *Magazine, Trade.* **Description:** Edited for owners and managers of equipment rental and sales centers that are engaged in the rental of tools, contractor equipment, homeowner equipment, towing devices and outdoor power equipment.
Related titles: Online - full text ed.: (from bigchalk, EBSCO Publishing, Florida Center for Library Automation, Gale Group, H.W. Wilson, O C L C Online Computer Library Center, Inc.).
Indexed: BPI.
—CCC.

Published by: Primedia Business Magazines & Media, Inc. (Subsidiary of: Primedia, Inc.), 9800 Metcalf Ave, Overland Park, KS 66212-2216. TEL 913-341-1300, FAX 913-967-7276, aaron_smith@intertec.com, inquiries@primediabusiness.com, http://rermag.com, http://www.primediabusiness.com. Ed. Michael Roth. Pub., Adv. contact Bob MacArthur. R&P Greg Vargas TEL 800-543-4116. B&W page USD 1,810, color page USD 2,505; trim 8.25 x 10.88. Circ: 17,500 (controlled). **Subscr. to:** PO Box 12993, Overland Park, KS 66282-2993, TEL 800-441-0294, FAX 913-967-1331.

658.8 338   USA   ISSN 1042-9085
HD9999.L438
RENTAL MANAGEMENT. Text in English. 1970. m. USD 24 domestic; free to qualified personnel (effective 2005). adv. tr.lit. reprints avail. **Document type:** *Magazine, Trade.* **Description:** Articles cover news of equipment rental industry; analyze operating philosophies of innovators; describe business strategies; interpret the effects of business, legislative and regulatory trends; asset management, technology, marketing, merchandising and product news.
Formerly: Rental Age (0098-8529)
Related titles: Online - full text ed.
Published by: American Rental Association, 1900 19th St, Moline, IL 61265. TEL 309-764-2475, 800-334-2177, FAX 309-764-1533, brian.alm@ararental.org, http://www.rentalmanagementmag.com, http://ararental.org. Ed., R&P Brian Alm. Pub. Ken Hughes. adv.: B&W page USD 2,548, color page USD 3,643. Circ: 19,400 (paid and controlled).

REP TALK. see *BUSINESS AND ECONOMICS—Management*

658.8 659.1   GBR   ISSN 0969-6709
RESEARCH. Text in English. 1966. m. GBP 130 domestic; GBP 145, EUR 210, USD 228 foreign (effective 2005). adv. 86 p./no.; **Document type:** *Magazine, Trade.*
Formerly: M R S Newsletter (0961-5172)
—CCC.
Published by: Market Research Society, 15 Northburgh St, London, EC1V 0JR, United Kingdom. TEL 44-20-74904911, FAX 44-20-74900608, info@mrs.org.uk, http://www.research-live.com/, http://www.mrs.org.uk. Ed. Marc Brenner. Pub. Peter Greenwood. R&P Nicola Potts. Adv. contact Debra Lestrade TEL 44-20-7566-1843. Circ: 7,300.

658.8   USA   ISSN 0739-358X
RESEARCH ALERT (NEW YORK). Text in English. 1981. fortn. USD 389 domestic; USD 449 foreign (effective 2005). Index. 12 p./no.; back issues avail.; reprints avail. **Document type:** *Newsletter, Trade.* **Description:** Reports on consumer marketing studies.
Incorporates (1989-199?): Affluent Markets Alert (1041-7508)
Related titles: Online - full text ed.: (from Factiva, Gale Group, O C L C Online Computer Library Center, Inc.).
Indexed: B&I.
Published by: E P M Communications, 160 Mercer St, 3rd Fl, New York, NY 10012-3212. TEL 212-941-0099, FAX 212-941-1622, info@epmcom.com, http://www.epmcom.com. Ed., Pub., R&P Barbara Perrin.

658.8   USA   ISSN 1542-9172
HF5415.33.U6
RESEARCH ALERT YEARBOOK. Text in English. a. USD 295 (effective 2001). **Document type:** *Yearbook, Trade.* **Description:** Data and findings gleaned from more than 1,000 reports, studies, polls and focus groups that help to evaluate current and future plans, spot emerging trends, keep tabs on competitors, and identify new opportunities.
Published by: E P M Communications, 160 Mercer St, 3rd Fl, New York, NY 10012-3212. TEL 212-941-0099, FAX 212-941-1622, info@epmcom.com, http://www.epmcom.com.

658.8   USA   ISSN 1087-9641
RESEARCH BUSINESS REPORT. Text in English. 1995. m. (11/yr.). USD 480 (effective 2001). bk.rev. charts; illus.; stat. 8 p./no.; back issues avail. **Document type:** *Newsletter.* **Description:** Focuses on technological, methodological, economic, and business changes in marketing research.
Published by: R F L Communications, Inc., PO Box 4514, Skokie, IL 60076-4514. TEL 847-673-6284, FAX 847-673-6286, info@rflonline.com, http://www.rflonline.com. Ed., Pub. Robert Lederer.

658   GBR   ISSN 1462-026X
THE RESEARCH BUYER'S GUIDE (YEAR). Text in English. a., latest 2001. GBP 40 per issue (effective 2000); free to members. 1088 p./no.; **Document type:** *Directory, Trade.* **Description:** Provides research buyers information on companies and consultants throughout UK and Ireland. It includes markets, services and locations, names and overviews.
Formerly (until 1998): Orgs Book (1365-0491); Which superseded in part (in 1997): Market Research Society Yearbook (0076-4523)
Related titles: Online - full content ed.; Print ed.
—BLDSC (7734.495000). **CCC.**

Published by: Market Research Society, 15 Northburgh St, London, EC1V 0JR, United Kingdom. TEL 44-20-74904911, FAX 44-20-74900608, rbg@mrs.org.uk, info@mrs.org.uk, http://www.rbg.org.uk, http://www.mrs.org.uk. Pub. Damian Cerase. Adv. contact Debra Lestrade TEL 44-20-7566-1843. Circ: 9,000 (controlled).

658.8 USA ISSN 1094-8570
RESEARCH CONFERENCE REPORT. Text in English. 1997. m. (11/yr.). USD 480 (effective 2001). charts; illus.; stat. back issues avail. **Document type:** *Newsletter.* **Description:** Summarizes presentations made about market research issues at conferences, seminars, and symposiums held around the world.
Published by: R F L Communications, Inc., PO Box 4514, Skokie, IL 60076-4514. TEL 847-673-6284, FAX 847-673-6286, info@rflonline.com, http://www.rflonline.com. Ed., Pub., R&P Robert Lederer.

658.8 USA ISSN 1521-7590
RESEARCH DEPARTMENT REPORT. Text in English. 1998. 9/yr. USD 350. charts; illus.; stat. back issues avail. **Document type:** *Newsletter.* **Description:** Profiles successful market research departments at major companies around the world.
Published by: R F L Communications, Inc., PO Box 4514, Skokie, IL 60076-4514. TEL 847-673-6284, FAX 847-673-6286, info@rflonline.com. Ed., Pub. Robert Lederer.

658 USA ISSN 0885-2111
HF5415.3
➤ **RESEARCH IN CONSUMER BEHAVIOR**; a research annual. Text in English. 1985. a., latest vol.9, 2000. price varies. **Document type:** *Monographic series, Academic/Scholarly.* **Description:** Presents state of the art research papers and theoretical essays on consumption behavior.
—BLDSC (7737.005000), ingenta. **CCC.**
Published by: J A I Press Inc. (Subsidiary of: Elsevier Science & Technology), 360 Park Ave S, New York, NY 10010-1710. TEL 212-989-5800, FAX 212-633-3990, usinfo-f@elsevier.com, http://www.elsevier.com/wps/find/bookdescription.cws_home/BS_RCB/description#description. Eds. C J Schultz, Russell W Belk.

658.8 USA ISSN 0191-3026
HF5415.2
RESEARCH IN MARKETING; an annual compilation of research. Text in English. 1979. a., latest vol.15, 1999. price varies. **Document type:** *Monographic series, Academic/Scholarly.*
Related titles: Online - full text ed.; Supplement(s): Choice Models for Buyers Behavior.
Indexed: BPIA, PsycholAb, T&II.
—BLDSC (7741.916000). **CCC.**
Published by: J A I Press Inc. (Subsidiary of: Elsevier Science & Technology), 360 Park Ave S, New York, NY 10010-1710. TEL 212-989-5800, FAX 212-633-3990, usinfo-f@elsevier.com, http://www.elsevier.com/wps/find/bookdescription.cws_home/BS_RM/description#description. Ed. J N Seth.

RESPONSE MAGAZINE; multi-channel direct advertising. see *ADVERTISING AND PUBLIC RELATIONS*

658 BEL ISSN 1378-725X
RETAIL (FRENCH EDITION). Text in French. 2002. 11/yr. EUR 61 domestic (effective 2004). **Document type:** *Magazine, Consumer.*
Related titles: Dutch ed.: Retail (Dutch Edition). ISSN 1378-7268.
Published by: Professional Media Group, Torhoutsesteenweg 226 bus 2/6, Zedelgem, B-8210, Belgium. TEL 32-50-240404, FAX 32-50-240445, info@pmgroup.be, http://www.pmgroup.be.

658.87 GBR
RETAIL & CONSUMER PRODUCTS RETAIL TRADE REVIEW. Text in English. 1958. m. GBP 225, USD 375 (effective 1999). index. **Document type:** *Trade.* **Description:** Contains statistical analysis and forecasts for individual UK retail trade sectors. Reviews the 15 largest UK retail sectors and profiles the top 50 UK retail groups, providing information on financial results, recent acquisitions, number of stores, analysis of trading strategies and future plans.
Formerly (until 1994): Retail Business. Retail Trade Reviews (0951-9742); Which superseded in part (in 1987): Retail Business (0034-6012)
Related titles: Microform ed.: (from WMP).
Indexed: ABIn, CPM, IndBusRep, KES, SCIMP.
Published by: Corporate Intelligence on Retailing, 48 Bedford Sq, London, WC1 B3DP, United Kingdom. TEL 44-20-7696-9006, FAX 44-20-7696-9004, sales@cior.com, http://www.cior.com. **Subscr. in US to:** Lebhar-Friedman, Inc., 425 Park Ave, New York, NY 10022. TEL 212-756-5159, FAX 212-756-5038.

658 381 GBR ISSN 1465-9409
RETAIL DETAILS. Text in English. 1999. bi-w. GBP 295 (effective 1999). back issues avail. **Document type:** *Magazine.* **Description:** Features retail news, analysis, figures and statistics together with quantitative research.
Published by: Corporate Intelligence Group, 48 Bedford Sq, London, WC1B 3DP, United Kingdom. TEL 44-171-814-3724, FAX 44-171-696-9004.

658.0029 GBR
RETAIL DIRECTORY OF EUROPE (YEAR). Text in English. 1953. a., latest 2002. GBP 170 (effective 2001). adv. 1000 p./no. 3 cols./p.; **Document type:** *Directory, Trade.* **Description:** Contains information on thousands of Europe's leading retailers across 29 countries and lists named buyers and decision-makers with full contact details.
Former titles: Directory of European Retailers & International Buying Agents; Stores of the World Directory (0081-5829)
Related titles: Diskette ed.; E-mail ed.; Online - full content ed.
Published by: Hemming Information Services Ltd. (Subsidiary of: Hemming Group Ltd.), 32 Vauxhall Bridge Rd, London, SW1V 288, United Kingdom. TEL 44-20-79736402, FAX 44-20-72335057, h-info@hemming-group.co.uk, http://www.retaildirectory.co.uk, https://www.h-info.co.uk/. Ed. Louise Baker. Pub. Yvonne Phillips. Adv. contact Lydia Lee TEL 44-20-7973-4647. Circ: 3,500 (paid).

381.029 GBR
RETAIL DIRECTORY OF THE UK (YEAR). Text in English. 1939. a., latest 2002. GBP 170 (effective 2001). adv. 1300 p./no. 3 cols./p.; **Document type:** *Directory, Trade.* **Description:** Directory of U.K. retailers with full company details including type of trade, number of branches, executives, and buyers.
Incorporates: London Shop Surveys (0140-3206); Former titles: Stores, Shops, Hypermarkets Retail Directory (0305-4012); Stores and Shops Retail Directory (0081-5810)
Related titles: Diskette ed.; E-mail ed.; Online - full content ed.
—BLDSC (7785.502710).
Published by: Hemming Information Services Ltd. (Subsidiary of: Hemming Group Ltd.), 32 Vauxhall Bridge Rd, London, SW1V 288, United Kingdom. TEL 44-20-79736402, FAX 44-20-72335057, h-info@hemming-group.co.uk, http://www.retaildirectory.co.uk, https://www.h-info.co.uk/. Ed. James de Bunsen. Pub. Yvonne Phillips. Adv. contact Lydia Lee TEL 44-20-7973-4647. Circ: 4,000 (paid).

RETAIL INFO SYSTEMS NEWS DIRECTORY. see *BUSINESS AND ECONOMICS—Computer Applications*

658 384 USA
RETAIL IN$IGHTS. Text in English. m. USD 348 (effective 2003). **Document type:** *Newsletter, Trade.* **Description:** Provides a complete, concise resource designed to keep your sales people out selling instead of in the office researching.
Published by: Executive Decision Systems, Inc., 6421 W Weaver Drive, Littleton, CO 80123. TEL 800-837-3662, http://www.retailinsights.com.

658.8 GBR ISSN 0265-2536
RETAIL INTELLIGENCE. Key Title: Mintel Retail Intelligence Quarterly. Text in English. 1980. bi-m. GBP 3,995 (effective 1999). back issues avail. **Document type:** *Trade.* **Description:** Provides commercial insight into the retail trade using exclusive research.
Related titles: CD-ROM ed.; Online - full text ed.
Published by: Mintel International Group Ltd., 18-19 Long Ln., London, EC1A 9PL, United Kingdom. TEL 44-20-76064533, FAX 44-20-76065932. Ed. Neil Mason. Circ: 150.

658.879 USA ISSN 1530-8154
HF5001 CODEN: DISMAD
RETAIL MERCHANDISER. Text in English. 1961. m. USD 99 domestic; USD 109 in Canada; USD 171 elsewhere (effective 2005). adv. illus. back issues avail.; reprint service avail. from PQC. **Document type:** *Magazine, Trade.* **Description:** Covers all phases of the mass merchandising retail industry.
Formerly (until May 2000): Discount Merchandiser (0012-3579)
Related titles: Microform ed.: (from PQC); Online - full text ed.: (from EBSCO Publishing, Florida Center for Library Automation, Gale Group, H.W. Wilson, Northern Light Technology, Inc., O C L C Online Computer Library Center, Inc., ProQuest Information & Learning).
Indexed: ABIn, BPI, BPIA, PAIS, PROMT, SRI.
—BLDSC (7785.503850), IE, ingenta. **CCC.**
Published by: V N U Business Publications (Subsidiary of: V N U Business Media), 770 Broadway, New York, NY 10003-9595. debby@retail-merchandiser.com, bmcomm@vnuinc.com, http://www.retail-merchandiser.com/, http://www.vnubusinessmedia.com/. Ed. Deborah Garbato. Pub. Chris Loretto. Circ: 34,188 (controlled). **Subscr. to:** PO Box 2016, Skokie, IL 60076.

RETAIL NEWS. see *PHARMACY AND PHARMACOLOGY*

658 IRL
RETAIL NEWS. Text in English. 10/yr. EUR 85 (effective 2005). adv. **Document type:** *Trade.* **Description:** Informs the independent retailer of new product lines.
Former titles: Grocery Review (0017-4440); Irish Grocery and Allied Trades Review; R G D A T A Review
Published by: (Retail Grocery Dairy and Allied Trades Association), Tara Publishing Co. Ltd., Poolbeg House, 1-2 Poolbeg St, Dublin, 2, Ireland. TEL 353-1-2413000, FAX 353-1-2413020, info@tarapublishingco.com, http://www.retailnews.ie. Ed. John Walshe TEL 353-1-2413093. Adv. contact Kathleen Belton TEL 353-1-2413095. B&W page EUR 2,000, color page EUR 2,895; trim 210 x 297. Circ: 3,368.

658 IRL
RETAIL NEWS DIRECTORY. Text in English. a. EUR 60 (effective 2005). adv. **Document type:** *Directory.*
Published by: Tara Publishing Co. Ltd., Poolbeg House, 1-2 Poolbeg St, Dublin, 2, Ireland. TEL 353-1-2413000, FAX 353-1-2413020, retailnews@tarapublishingco.com, info@tarapublishingco.com. Ed. Fergus Farrell. Adv. contact Kathleen Belton TEL 353-1-2413095. B&W page EUR 1,905, color page EUR 2,695; trim 210 x 297.

658.87 GBR
RETAIL NEWS FAX. Text in English. d. GBP 395 (effective 2000). **Document type:** *Trade.*
Related titles: Online - full text ed.
Published by: Corporate Intelligence on Retailing, 48 Bedford Sq, London, WC1 B3DP, United Kingdom. TEL 44-20-7696-9006, FAX 44-20-7696-9004, sales@cior.com, http://www.cior.com. **Subscr. in US to:** Lebhar-Friedman, Inc., 425 Park Ave, New York, NY 10022. TEL 212-756-5159, FAX 212-756-5038.

658 GBR ISSN 0966-3711
RETAIL POCKET BOOK. Text in English. a. GBP 32 per issue (effective 2000). **Document type:** *Trade.* **Description:** Provides facts and figures on UK and European retail markets and retailers.
Published by: N T C Publications Ltd. (Subsidiary of: World Advertising Research Center Ltd.), Farm Rd, Henley-on-Thames, Oxon RG9 1EJ, United Kingdom. TEL 44-1491-411000, FAX 44-1491-571188, info@ntc.co.uk.

658.5 GBR ISSN 1461-1139
THE RETAIL RANKINGS. Text in English. 1989. a. GBP 395 (effective 2000). **Description:** Reference database of the UK retail trade: 800 companies and their 1,600 retail operations. Covers all UK retailers with sales above GBP3,000,000. They are ranked first by their total retail sales and then separated out and expanded by operation within 39 retail sectors.
—BLDSC (7785.504245).
Published by: Corporate Intelligence on Retailing, 48 Bedford Sq, London, WC1 B3DP, United Kingdom. TEL 44-20-7696-9006, FAX 44-20-7696-9004, sales@cior.com, http://www.cior.com. **Subscr. in US to:** Lebhar-Friedman, Inc., 425 Park Ave, New York, NY 10022. TEL 212-756-5159, FAX 212-756-5038.

658.8 GBR ISSN 0144-6835
RETAIL REVIEW. Text in English. 1973. 10/yr. GBP 93 (effective 1997). bk.rev. back issues avail. **Document type:** *Newsletter.* **Description:** Covers a wide range of retail news.
Published by: Co-operative Wholesale Society Ltd., Library & Information Unit, New Century House, Co-Operative Wholesale Society Ltd, Manchester, M60 4ES, United Kingdom. TEL 0161-827-6686, FAX 0161-834-4507. Ed. R D Hilton. Circ: 2,000.

RETAIL SALES. see *BUSINESS AND ECONOMICS—Abstracting, Bibliographies, Statistics*

658 GBR
RETAIL SOLUTIONS MAGAZINE. Text in English. q. **Document type:** *Trade.*
Published by: Emap Maclaren Ltd. (Subsidiary of: Emap Business Communications Ltd.), c/o EMAP Communications, Scriptor Court, 155 Farringdon Rd, London, EC1R 3AD, United Kingdom. TEL 44-20-78416600, tracey.bigmore@emap.com, http://www.emap.com.

330 DEU ISSN 1615-5521
RETAIL TECHNOLOGY JOURNAL; information, communication and security technologies within the trade. Text in German. 1999. q. EUR 32.73 (effective 2001). adv. bk.rev. tr.lit. back issues avail. **Document type:** *Magazine, Trade.* **Description:** Reports on current developments in retail technology and investment trends.
Published by: E H I - EuroHandelsinstitut e.V., Spichernstr 55, Cologne, 50672, Germany. TEL 49-221-57993-0, FAX 49-221-5799345, redaktion@ehi.org, http://www.ehi.org. Ed., R&P Winfried Lambertz TEL 49-221-5799340. Pub. Dr. Bernd Hallier. Adv. contact Claudia Husseck TEL 49-221-5799364. B&W page EUR 2,569.75, color page EUR 3,885.82. Circ: 12,000 (paid and controlled).

658.83 GBR ISSN 0966-7067
RETAIL TRADE INTERNATIONAL (YEAR). Text in English. 1998. a., latest 2002. GBP 5,000 domestic complete set; EUR 8,000 in Europe complete set; USD 8,000 elsewhere complete set; GBP 450 per issue domestic per individual counrty report; EUR 700 per issue in Europe per individual counrty report; USD 700 per issue elsewhere per individual counrty report (effective 2003). stat. **Document type:** *Directory, Trade.* **Description:** Contains statistical analysis examining trends in retailing and the distribution of consumer goods throughout the world.
Formerly: Retail Trade Europe
Related titles: Online - full text ed.: Retail Trade International on the Internet. GBP 7,000 domestic; EUR 10,000 in Europe; USD 10,000 elsewhere (effective 2003); Series: Retail Trade International - United Kingdom; Retail Trade International - India; Retail Trade International - Argentina; Retail Trade International - Australia; Retail Trade International - Austria; Retail Trade International - Belgium; Retail Trade International - Brazil; Retail Trade International - Bulgaria; Retail Trade International - Canada; Retail Trade International - Chile;

Retail Trade International - China; Retail Trade International - Colombia; Retail Trade International - Czech Republic; Retail Trade International - Denmark; Retail Trade International - Egypt; Retail Trade International - Finland; Retail Trade International - France; Retail Trade International - Greece; Retail Trade International - Hong Kong; Retail Trade International - Hungary; Retail Trade International - Indonesia; Retail Trade International - Ireland; Retail Trade International - Israel; Retail Trade International - Japan; Retail Trade International - Malaysia; Retail Trade International - Mexico; Retail Trade International - Morocco; Retail Trade International - Netherlands; Retail Trade International - New Zealand; Retail Trade International - Norway; Retail Trade International - Philippines; Retail Trade International - Poland; Retail Trade International - Portugal; Retail Trade International - Romania; Retail Trade International - Russia; Retail Trade International - Saudi Arabia; Retail Trade International - Singapore; Retail Trade International - Slovakia; Retail Trade International - South Africa; Retail Trade International - South Korea; Retail Trade International - Spain; Retail Trade International - Sweden; Retail Trade International - Switzerland; Retail Trade International - Taiwan; Retail Trade International - Thailand; Retail Trade International - Turkey; Retail Trade International - Ukraine; Retail Trade International - United States; Retail Trade International - Venezuela; Retail Trade International - Vietnam.
Published by: Euromonitor, 60-61 Britton St, London, EC1 5UX, United Kingdom. TEL 44-20-7251-8024, FAX 44-20-7608-3149, info@euromonitor.com, http://www.euromonitor.com.

658 333.33 USA ISSN 1544-4236
HF5430
RETAIL TRAFFIC. Text in English. 1972. m. free domestic to qualified personnel; USD 115 domestic; USD 127 in Canada; USD 139 elsewhere (effective 2005). charts; illus.; tr.lit. reprint service avail. from PQC. **Document type:** *Magazine, Trade.* **Description:** Serves the fields of building, development, construction, design, financing, leasing, management and promotion of shopping centers, chain stores, and other related product and service industries.
Formerly (until May 2003): Shopping Center World (0049-0393); Incorporates (1975-1991): Shopping Center World Product and Service Directory
Related titles: Microform ed.: (from PQC); Online - full text ed.: (from bigchalk, EBSCO Publishing, Gale Group, H.W. Wilson, Northern Light Technology, Inc., O C L C Online Computer Library Center, Inc., ProQuest Information & Learning); ♦ Supplement(s): Outlet Retailer.
Indexed: ABIn, B&I, BPI, SRI.
—CCC.
Published by: Primedia Business Magazines & Media, Inc. (Subsidiary of: Primedia, Inc.), 249 W 17th St, New York, NY 10011. TEL 212-462-3600, FAX 212-206-3622, bkarlin@primediabusiness.com, inquiries@primediabusiness.com, http://retailtrafficmag.com/, http://www.primediabusiness.com. Ed. Beth Karlin. Pub. Warren Bimblick. Circ: 36,553 (controlled).

658.8 POL
RETAIL UPDATE POLAND. Text in English. w. EUR 370 foreign (effective 2005). **Document type:** *Newsletter, Trade.* **Description:** Provides analyses of current trends in the Polish retail trade and the behaviour and preferences of Polish consumers.
Media: E-mail.
Published by: Polish Market Review Ltd., ul Supniewskiego 9, Krakow, 31527, Poland. TEL 48-12-4280360, FAX 48-12-4134012, pmr@pmrpublications.com, http://www.pmrpublications.com.

658 GBR ISSN 1360-8215
RETAIL WEEK. Text in English. 1988. w. GBP 105; GBP 135 in Europe; GBP 180 elsewhere. adv. **Document type:** *Newspaper, Trade.*
Related titles: Online - full text ed.: (from LexisNexis).
Indexed: B&I.
Published by: Emap Maclaren Ltd. (Subsidiary of: Emap Business Communications Ltd.), c/o EMAP Communications, Scriptor Court, 155 Farringdon Rd, London, EC1R 3AD, United Kingdom. TEL 44-20-78416600, john@maclaren.emap.co.uk, tracey.bigmore@emap.com, http://www.emap.com. Ed. John Porter. Adv. contact Ian Springs. Circ: 12,722.

658 MLT
RETAILER. Text in English, Maltese. m. USD 6 to non-members. adv. bk.rev. **Document type:** *Bulletin, Trade.*
Published by: Association of General Retailers and Traders, Republic St., Valletta, Malta. TEL 356-234170, FAX 356-246925, grtu@waldonet.net.mt, http://www.grtu.org.mt. Ed. Vincent Farrugia. R&P Joseph Bonnici TEL 356-232881.

658.8 AUS
RETAILER. Text in English. 1891. m. AUD 60 (effective 2000). adv. bk.rev. **Document type:** *Trade.* **Description:** Covers QRTSA initiatives, legislative changes, members' activities, new products and retailing developments.
Formerly: Retailer of Queensland (0034-6144); Incorporates: Queensland Shopkeeper (0033-622X)
Published by: (Queensland Retail Traders and Shopkeepers Association), The Magazine Publishing Company Pty Ltd, 34 Station St, Nundah, QLD 4012, Australia. TEL 61-7-38660000, FAX 61-7-38660066, tmpc@powerup.com.au, retailer@tmpc.com.au, http://www.asumall.com.au.magazine/retailer.htm. Ed. Emily Holme. Adv. contact Alan Kirk. B&W page AUD 1,691, color page AUD 2,683; trim 210 x 275. Circ: 5,500.

658.87 USA ISSN 0192-9151
RETAILER AND MARKETING NEWS. Text in English. 1964. m. USD 12 (effective 2000). adv. bk.rev. illus. **Document type:** *Magazine, Trade.* **Description:** Regional business trade journal serving the appliance, consumer electronic and furniture industry in the northern half of Texas.
Formerly: North Texas Retailer (0029-2907)
Published by: R A M Nvest, Inc., 3111 Cole Ave, Dallas, TX 75204. TEL 214-871-2930, FAX 214-871-2931. Ed., Pub. Michael J Anderson. Circ: 8,000 (controlled).

RETAILING TODAY. see *BUSINESS AND ECONOMICS—Management*

658 USA
▼ **REVENUE**; the internet affiliate marketing standard. Text in English. 2004. q. USD 25 (effective 2004). **Document type:** *Magazine, Trade.*
Published by: Montgomery Research, Inc., 300 Montgomery St, Ste 1135, San Francisco, CA 94104. TEL 415-397-2400, info@mriresearch.com, http://www.revenuetoday.com/, http://www.mriresearch.com/index.asp. Ed. Tom Murphy. Pub. Nick Smith. Adv. contact Chris Smith. Circ: 125,000 (paid and controlled).

658.8 USA
REVERIES. Text in English. 1996. **Document type:** *Magazine, Trade.* **Description:** Publishes interviews and profiles of marketing professionals.
Media: Online - full content.
Published by: David X. Manners Company, Inc., 107 Post Rd E, Westport, CT 06880. TEL 203-227-7060, FAX 203-227-7067, editor@reveries.com, http://www.reveries.com/, http://www.dxmanners.com. Ed., Pub. Tim Manners.

658.8 USA ISSN 1548-6435
HF5415.2
▼ ➤ **REVIEW OF MARKETING RESEARCH.** Text in English. 2004. a. USD 95 per issue (effective 2004). **Document type:** *Academic/Scholarly.*
Published by: M.E. Sharpe, Inc., 80 Business Park Dr, Armonk, NY 10504. TEL 914-273-1800, 800-541-6563, FAX 914-273-2106, custserv@mesharpe.com, http://www.mesharpe.com.

658 USA ISSN 1546-5616
HF5410
▼ ➤ **REVIEW OF MARKETING SCIENCE.** Text in English. 2003 (Aug.). m. USD 35 to individuals; USD 225 to institutions (effective 2006). **Document type:** *Academic/Scholarly.*
Media: Online - full content (from O C L C Online Computer Library Center, Inc.).
Published by: (University of Texas at Dallas, School of Management), Berkeley Electronic Press, 2809 Telegraph Ave., Ste 202, Berkeley, CA 94705. TEL 510-665-1200, FAX 510-665-1201, info@bepress.com, http://www.bepress.com/romsjournal. Ed. Ram C Rao.

658 ESP
REVISTA ESPANOLA DE INVESTIGACION DE MARKETING. Text in Spanish. s-a.
Published by: Escuela Superior de Gestion Comercial y Marketing, Ave. Valdenigrales, s-n, Pozuelo de Alarcon, Madrid, 28223, Spain. TEL 34-91-3527716, FAX 34-91-3528534, http://www.esic.es/.

REVISTA PUBLICIDAD Y MERCADEO. see *ADVERTISING AND PUBLIC RELATIONS*

658 ARG
REVISTA TIENDA. Text in Spanish. 1964. m.
Address: Carlos Pellegrini, 1175 A Piso 7, Capital Federal, Buenos Aires 1009, Argentina. TEL 54-114-3938526. Ed. Hernan Bianchi. Circ: 9,000.

REVOLUTION; the magazine for news-media marketing. see *BUSINESS AND ECONOMICS—Computer Applications*

658.8 FRA ISSN 0035-3051
REVUE FRANCAISE DU MARKETING. Text in French. 1964. 5/yr. adv. bk.rev. abstr.; bibl.; charts; illus.; mkt.
Related titles: Online - full text ed.: (from ProQuest Information & Learning).
Indexed: ABIn, ADPA, CPM, M&MA, PAIS, RASB, SCIMP, SSCI.
—BLDSC (7904.190000), CISTI, IE, Infotrieve, ingenta.
Published by: Association Nationale pour le Developpement des Techniques de Marketing, 221 rue La Fayette, Paris, 75010, France. TEL 33-1-40389710, FAX 33-1-40380508. Ed. Dominique Servant Chamonet. Adv. contact Pierre Cagnat. Circ: 3,000.

658 ISR
RIV'ON HESHEV. Text in Hebrew. q.
Published by: Cheshev Ltd., P O Box 40021, Tel Aviv, 61400, Israel. TEL (03)216291.

RUSSIA AND CHINA TRAVEL NEWS; weekly news - travel - trade - tranportation - marketing - media. see *TRAVEL AND TOURISM*

S A C I SLANTS. see *CHEMISTRY*

658.8 USA ISSN 1532-9550
S A M MAGAZINE. (Sales Advertising Marketing) Text in English. 2000. bi-m. free to qualified personnel. adv. back issues avail. **Document type:** *Magazine, Trade.* **Description:** Provides comprehensive and concise coverage of all forms of marketing: print, mail, trade shows, the Web, in-store, or live.
Related titles: Online - full text ed.: (from O C L C Online Computer Library Center, Inc., ProQuest Information & Learning).
Indexed: ABIn.
Address: 117 W Micheltorena St, Ste C, Santa Barbara, CA 93101. TEL 805-965-5858, FAX 805-963-1143, editorial@sammag.com, http://www.sammag.com. Ed. Leslie Dinaberg. Pub. John Katnic. Adv. contact Dan Alpern. B&W page USD 7,500, color page USD 9,350; bleed 7.625 x 10.375.

658.8 DEU ISSN 1437-3106
S A Z SPORT. Text in German. 1974. fortn. EUR 90 domestic; EUR 105 in Europe; EUR 160 elsewhere (effective 2005). adv. **Document type:** *Magazine, Trade.* **Description:** Business journal for the sporting goods industry.
Former titles (until 1994): S A Z (1437-3092); (until 1994): S A Z - Sport Artikel Zeitung (0933-9469)
Published by: S A Z Verlag GmbH, Rumfordstr 42, Munich, 80469, Germany. TEL 49-89-2121100, FAX 49-89-21211039, anzsport@saz.de, http://www.saz.de/sazsport/. Ed. Florian Bergener. Pub. Horst Frankl. Adv. contact Ulrich Onnasch. color page EUR 4,490; trim 230 x 315. Circ: 8,500.

658 DEU
S B ARTIKEL; German self-service trade magazine. (Selbstbedienung) Text in German. 1968. m.
Published by: Verlag fuer Handel und Marketing GmbH, Ruhrstr 2, Hagen, 58097, Germany. TEL 02331-21044, FAX 02331-15213. Ed. Meno Schramm. Circ: 21,000.

658.8 USA
S D M DEALER - INSTALLER MARKETPLACE. (Security Distributing and Marketing) Text in English. 13/yr. free domestic to qualified personnel; USD 185 foreign (effective 2002). adv. **Document type:** *Trade.* **Description:** Product tabloid that reaches dealers, installers and distributors of electronic security products and services in the United States.
Related titles: Online - full text ed.
Published by: B N P Media, 755 W Big Beaver Rd, Ste 1000, Troy, MI 48084-4903. TEL 248-362-3700, FAX 248-362-0317, http://www.sdmmag.com, http://www.bnpmedia.com/. Ed. Bill Zalud TEL 630-694-4029. adv.: B&W page USD 4,270, color page USD 4,700; 8 x 10.75. Circ: 28,000 (paid). **Subscr. to:** PO Box 3212, Northbrook, IL 60065. TEL 847-291-5224, FAX 847-291-4816.

658.8 USA
S D M MUNDO MERCANTIL. (Security Distributing and Marketing) Text in Spanish. bi-m. USD 70; USD 128 in Canada; USD 120 in Mexico. adv. charts; illus.; tr.lit. **Document type:** *Trade.* **Description:** Product tabloid for end-users, dealers and distributors of security products and equipment in Mexico, Central America and South America.
Published by: B N P Media, 755 W Big Beaver Rd, Ste 1000, Troy, MI 48084-4903. TEL 248-362-3700, FAX 248-362-0317, swhitehurst@cahners.com, http://www.sdmmag.com/sdmmundo.htm, http://www.bnpmedia.com/. adv.: B&W page USD 1,700, color page USD 2,330. Circ: 10,000 (controlled). **Subscr. to:** PO Box 3212, Northbrook, IL 60065. TEL 847-291-5224, FAX 847-291-4816.

S G B; the national newsmagazine of the sporting goods industry. see *SPORTS AND GAMES*

658 790.1 USA
S G M A COMPREHENSIVE QUARTERLY SALES TRENDS REPORT. Text in English. q. **Document type:** *Trade.*
Published by: Sporting Goods Manufacturers Association, 6650 W. Indiantown Rd., Ste. 220, Jupiter, FL 33458-4629. TEL 561-842-4100. Ed. Sebastian Dicasoli.

658 USA
S M N NEWSLETTER. (Sales Marketing Network) Text in English. 1996 (Oct.). m. (plus irreg. updates). free (effective 2004). **Document type:** *Trade.* **Description:** Enables users to access articles on a wide array of topics, including direct marketing, event marketing, promotions and incentives, incentive travel, planning and hosting meetings (along with information on destinations worldwide), doing business on the Internet, sales management and training, and motivation.
Media: Online - full text.

▼ new title ➤ refereed ✶ unverified ♦ full entry avail.

Published by: Selling Communications, Inc., One Bridge St, Ste 77, Irvington, NY 10533. TEL 914-591-7600, FAX 914-591-7699, selling@sellingcommunications.com, http://www.sellingcommunications.com. Ed., Pub. Bruce Bolger. R&P Jay Levin. Adv. contact Jim Kilmetis TEL 914-591-7600 ext 229.

658.8 USA
S P WEEKLY; voice of the industry. (Service Provider Weekly) Text in English. 2001. w. back issues avail.
Media: Online - full text.
Published by: GM Media Corp, 5201 Blue Lagoon Dr 8th Fl, Miami, FL 33126. TEL 305-228-4566, FAX 305-675-2881, info@gmmediacorp.com, http://www.spweekly.com/, http://www.gmmediacorp.com. Ed. Matthew Thomas.

S R D S LIFESTYLE MARKET ANALYST. see *BUSINESS AND ECONOMICS—Abstracting, Bibliographies, Statistics*

S R D S THE BULLET; the latest in list activity. (Standard Rate and Data Service) see *ADVERTISING AND PUBLIC RELATIONS—Abstracting, Bibliographies, Statistics*

658 USA ISSN 1541-1834
S R O. (Staging, Rental, Operations) Text in English. 2002. bi-m. USD 70 domestic; USD 90 foreign (effective 2004).
Description: Provides practical information to staging professionals, rental agencies, as well as the meeting/event planners they serve, who are producing high-quality, technology-rich staged events for entertainment and business.
Related titles: Online - full text ed.: (from EBSCO Publishing, Gale Group, H.W. Wilson, O C L C Online Computer Library Center, Inc., ProQuest Information & Learning).
Indexed: BPI.
—CCC.
Published by: Primedia Business Magazines & Media, Inc. (Subsidiary of: Primedia, Inc.), 9800 Metcalf Ave, Overland Park, KS 66212-2216. TEL 913-341-1300, FAX 913-967-1898, inquiries@primediabusiness.com, http://www.sromagazine.biz, http://www.primediabusiness.com. Pub. Jeff Victor. **Subscr. to:** 2104 Harvell Circle, Bellevue, NE 68005.

381.2060489 DNK ISSN 0900-1891
SAELGEREN. Text in Danish. 1901. 11/yr. DKK 420 membership (effective 2003). adv. bk.rev. back issues avail. **Document type:** *Trade.* **Description:** Written for professional sales people.
Former titles (until 1972): Handelsrejsendebladet (0900-2251); (until 1935): Organet for Danske Handelsrejsende
Related titles: Online - full text ed.
Published by: Danske Saelgere, Noerre Farimagsgade 49, Copenhagen K, 1364, Denmark. TEL 45-33-740200, FAX 45-33-740290, info@danske-saelgere.dk, http://www.danske-saelgere.dk. Ed. Peter Hjort. R&P Frits Vanwyk TEL 45-3374-0603. Adv. contact Frits Van Wyk. page DKK 21,000; trim 186 x 266. Circ: 21,000 (paid).

SAFEWAY MAGAZINE. see *WOMEN'S INTERESTS*

658.8 JPN
SALES. Text in Japanese. 1956. m. JPY 8,160.
Published by: Diamond Inc., 4-2 Kasumigaseki 1-chome, Chiyoda-ku, Tokyo, 100-0013, Japan. Ed. Takeshi Sato.

SALES AND IDEA BOOK. see *ADVERTISING AND PUBLIC RELATIONS*

658.8 USA
SALES & MARKETING DIGEST (BELVIDERE). Text in English. m.
Published by: Marsili Publishing Inc., 2464 Circle Dr, Belvidere, IL 61008-9758. TEL 815-547-4311. Ed. Ray Marsili.

650 USA
SALES & MARKETING DIGEST (NEW YORK). (Includes special bonus report) Text in English. m. USD 19.
Related titles: Special ed(s).
Published by: Sales & Marketing Digest, 160 Fifth Ave, Ste 812A, New York, NY 10010.

658.8 USA ISSN 0163-7517
HF5438
SALES & MARKETING MANAGEMENT. Text in English. 1918. m. USD 48 domestic; USD 67 in Canada; USD 146 elsewhere (effective 2005). adv. bk.rev. illus.; tr.lit. reprint service avail. from PQC. **Document type:** *Magazine, Trade.* **Description:** Supplies information to executives responsible for sales and marketing within their own organizations.
Formerly (until 1975): Sales Management (0885-9019)
Related titles: Microfiche ed.: (from CIS); Microform ed.: (from PQC); Online - full text ed.: (from bigchalk, EBSCO Publishing, Factiva, Florida Center for Library Automation, Gale Group, H.W. Wilson, O C L C Online Computer Library Center, Inc., ProQuest Information & Learning).
Indexed: ABIn, ASEANManA, BLI, BPI, BPIA, ChPerl, CurCont, Emerald, Inspec, KES, LRI, M&MA, MagInd, PAIS, SRI.
—BLDSC (8070.670000), AskIEEE, IDS, IE, Infotrieve, ingenta. CCC.

Published by: V N U Business Publications (Subsidiary of: V N U Business Media), 770 Broadway, 7th Fl, New York, NY 10003. edit@salesandmarketing.com, bmcomm@vnuinc.com, http://www.salesandmarketing.com/, http://www.vnubusinessmedia.com/. Ed. Jennifer Gilbert. Pub. Jackie Augustine. adv.: B&W page USD 12,040, color page USD 15,585. Circ: 60,000. **Subscr. to:** PO Box 10667, Riverton, NJ 08076-0667. TEL 856-786-9085, 800-821-6897, FAX 856-786-4415.

SALES AND MARKETING PERSONNEL REPORT. see *BUSINESS AND ECONOMICS—Personnel Management*

658 USA
SALES & MARKETING REPORT; practical ideas for successful selling. Text in English. m. USD 119. **Document type:** *Newsletter.* **Description:** Provides information on how to develop strategic sales coaching, build a high-performance sales team, boost morale and productivity, and manage your time more effectively.
Published by: Lawrence Ragan Communications, Inc., 316 N Michigan Ave, Ste 300, Chicago, IL 60601. TEL 312-960-4106, 800-878-5331, FAX 312-960-4106, cservice@ragan.com, http://www.ragan.com. Ed. Steve Crescenzo. Pub. Mark Ragan.

658 USA ISSN 1066-5463
HF5415.13
SALES AND MARKETING STRATEGIES & NEWS; comprehensive news source for successful sales & marketing strategies. Text in English. 1991. 7/yr. USD 39.95 domestic; USD 54 in Canada & Mexico; USD 150 elsewhere; USD 6.95 per issue (effective 2005). adv. bk.rev. **Document type:** *Magazine, Trade.*
Related titles: Supplement(s): Sales and Marketing Strategies & News. Directory. USD 52.95 per issue domestic; USD 67.95 per issue foreign (effective 2004).
—CCC.
Published by: Douglas Publications, Inc., 2807 N Parham Rd, Ste 200, Richmond, VA 23294. TEL 804-762-9600, FAX 804-217-8999, info@douglaspublications.com, http://www.salesandmarketingnews.com, http://www.douglaspublications.com. Circ: 62,000 (controlled).

658.8 USA
SALES & SERVICE EXCELLENCE. Text in English. m. USD 99 (effective 2005). **Document type:** *Magazine.*
Related titles: Online - full text ed.
Published by: Executive Excellence Publishing, 1366 East 1120 South, Provo, UT 84606. TEL 800-304-9782, FAX 801-377-5960, info@eep.com, http://www.eep.com/Merchant//newsite/smeindex.htm.

658.81 USA
SALES AND SERVICE FOR AN UNFAIR ADVANTAGE. Text in English. 1998. bi-m. free. back issues avail. **Document type:** *Newsletter.* **Description:** Includes vital information for salespeople, sales managers, and business owners who must sell.
Media: Online - full text.
Published by: Professional Strategies Inc., 139 George Sandys., Williamsburg, VA 23185-8938. TEL 757-259-1684, FAX 757-259-1141, pweber@prostrategies.com, http://www.prostrategies.com. Ed. Pat Weber. Pub., R&P Patricia Weber.

658.81 GBR ISSN 1361-9691
SALES ARENA; improving sales and marketing success through technology, business images and people. Text in English. 1994. m. GBP 60. adv. software rev. tr.lit. back issues avail. **Document type:** *Trade.* **Description:** Looks at the use of technology and technological services relevant to sales directors and their staff. Focuses on how technology can improve sales and marketing results. Includes coverage of computer automation and computer software.
Published by: Carys Publishing Ltd., Carys House, Chalk Rd, Ifold, Loxwood, Billingshurst, W Sussex RH14 0UD, United Kingdom. TEL 44-1403-752879. Ed. Rhys Parry. Adv. contact Carolyn Parry. color page GBP 625. Circ: 10,000 (controlled).

658 USA ISSN 8756-8780
SALES AUTOMATION SUCCESS. Text in English. 1985. 10/yr. looseleaf. USD 97 (effective 2005). bk.rev. tr.lit. Index. **Document type:** *Newsletter, Trade.* **Description:** Discusses how to use computer technology in direct sales to close more orders.
Related titles: Online - full text ed.
Published by: Denali Group, Inc., 2815 N W Pine Cone Dr, Ste 100, Issaquah, WA 98027-8698. TEL 425-392-3514, FAX 425-391-7982, richbohn@sellmorenow.com, http://www.sellmorenow.com. Ed., R&P Jean Schodde. Pub. Richard N Bohn. Circ: 5,000 (paid).

658 DEU ISSN 1616-7902
SALES BUSINESS; das Entscheidermagazin. Text in German. 1991. 10/yr. EUR 78.60; EUR 60 to students; EUR 7.30 newsstand/cover (effective 2005). adv. **Document type:** *Magazine, Trade.*
Formerly (until 2001): Sales Profi (0940-6786)
Related titles: Online - full text ed.

Published by: Betriebswirtschaftlicher Verlag Dr. Th. Gabler GmbH (Subsidiary of: Springer Science+Business Media), Abraham-Lincoln-Str 46, Wiesbaden, 65189, Germany. TEL 49-611-78780, FAX 49-611-7878400, salesbusiness@bertelsmann.de, gabler.service@gwv-fachverlage.de, http://www.salesbusiness.de, http://www.gabler.de. Ed. Volker Hassman. Adv. contact Stefan Kaffenberger. B&W page EUR 4,355, color page EUR 5,810. Circ: 16,485 (paid and controlled).

658.81 USA
SALES LEAD REPORT; for business-to-business marketing and sales professionals. Text in English. 1990. irreg. free. **Document type:** *Newsletter, Corporate.* **Description:** Covers articles of interest to business-to-business sales and marketing professionals and management.
Related titles: E-mail ed.; Fax ed.; Online - full content ed.
Published by: Mac McIntosh Inc., 601 Pendar Rd, North Kingston, RI 02852-6620. TEL 401-294-7730, FAX 401-679-0176, mcintosh@salesleadexperts.com, http://www.imninc.com/macmcintosh. Ed., Pub., R&P Mr. M H McIntosh. Circ: 12,000 (controlled).

SALES MANAGEMENT. see *BUSINESS AND ECONOMICS—Management*

SALES MANAGEMENT. see *BUSINESS AND ECONOMICS—Management*

658.8 JPN
SALES MANAGER. Text in Japanese. 1966. m. JPY 8,160. **Document type:** *Trade.*
Published by: Diamond Inc., 4-2 Kasumigaseki 1-chome, Chiyoda-ku, Tokyo, 100-0013, Japan. Ed. Takeshi Sato.

SALES MARKETING REWARDS. see *BUSINESS AND ECONOMICS—Labor And Industrial Relations*

658.8 USA ISSN 1077-9329
SALES MEMORY JOGGER. Text in English. 1956. m. USD 22.80 (effective 1999). **Document type:** *Trade.* **Description:** Includes monthly calender and information organizer to help sales people in the field keep appointments and track expenses.
Published by: Bureau of Business Practice (Subsidiary of: Aspen Publishers, Inc.), 1185 Avenue of the Americas, 37th Fl, New York, NY 10036. TEL 860-442-4365, 800-243-0876, FAX 860-437-3555, rebecca_armitage@prenhall.com, http://www.bbpnews.com. Ed. Brendan Johnston. Pub. Peter Garabedian. R&P Kathryn Mennone.

658.8 GBR ISSN 0957-6193
SALES PROMOTION. Text in English. 1989. m. adv. **Document type:** *Magazine, Trade.* **Description:** Provides vital industry information and news on promotional marketing and incentive strategies.
Published by: Archant Specialist Ltd. (Subsidiary of: Archant), The Mill, Bearwalden Business Park, Royston Rd, Wendens Ambo, Essex CB11 4GB, United Kingdom. TEL 44-1799-544200, salespromotion.sales@archant.co.uk, farine.clarke@archant.co.uk, http://www.salespromo.co.uk, http://www.archant.co.uk/. adv.: color page GBP 1,690; trim 210 x 297. **Dist. by:** Seymour Distribution Ltd, 86 Newman St, London W1T 3EX, United Kingdom. TEL 44-20-73968000, FAX 44-20-73968002.

658.8 CAN ISSN 1206-6435
SALES PROMOTION. Text in English. 1994. bi-m. CND 40 domestic; USD 60 in United States; USD 75 elsewhere (effective 2005). adv. **Document type:** *Magazine, Trade.* **Description:** Examines the leading areas of promotional expenditure, and their role in the marketing mix.
Formerly (until 1997): Sales Promotion Sourcing Guide (1483-4006)
Published by: C L B Media, Inc. (Subsidiary of: Canada Law Book Inc.), 240 Edward St, Aurora, ON L4G 3S9, Canada. TEL 905-727-0077, FAX 905-727-0017, http://www.clbmedia.ca. Circ: 14,000 (controlled).

658 910.03 USA
SALES WAYS. Text in English. 1984. bi-m. looseleaf. free to qualified personnel. **Document type:** *Newsletter.* **Description:** Contains articles of interest to the black salesperson.
Formerly: National Alliance Report
Published by: (National Alliance of Black Salesmen & Women), Time Crest Publishing, PO Box 2814, Manhattanville Sta, New York, NY 10027. TEL 212-409-4925. Ed. Franklyn Bryant. Circ: 2,000.

658 USA
SALESDOCTORS MAGAZINE; seeking cures for the common close. Text in English. 1995. w. free. adv. bk.rev. **Document type:** *Trade.* **Description:** Information for sales professionals, sales managers, trainers, marketing and customer service professionals and business owners.
Formerly (until Sept. 1996): SalesDoctors (1086-9476)
Media: Online - full text.
Published by: SeaBird Associates, Inc., 3011 NE 7th Dr., Boca Raton, FL 33431-6904. TEL 561-997-9345, FAX 561-997-9375, salesdoctors@worldnet.att.net, http://www.salesdoctors.com. Ed., R&P Donna Siegel. Pub., Adv. contact Art Siegel. Circ: 120,000 (controlled).

658 NOR ISSN 1503-6987
SALG & MARKEDSFOERING. Text in Norwegian. 2000. 10/yr. NOK 560 domestic (effective 2005). adv. **Document type:** *Magazine, Trade.*
Formerly (until 2003): Salg og Suksess (1502-3842)
Published by: Vanebo Fagpresse AS, PO Box 130, Kirkenaer, 2260, Norway. TEL 47-62-941000, FAX 47-62-941010, firmapost@vanebo.no, http://www.vanebo.no. Ed. Ove Hansrud TEL 47-62-829100. Adv. contacts Lars Erik Bratli TEL 47-62-946705, Lena Oerbog. page NOK 12,000; 190 x 265.

658 USA
SAM; what matters most in sales, advertising & marketing today. (Sales, Advertising and Marketing) Text in English. 2000. bi-m. free. adv. Website rev.; bk.rev. reprints avail. **Document type:** *Magazine, Trade.* **Description:** Provides comprehensive, concise, no-nonsense coverage of the things that matter most wherever marketing occurs: in print, through the mail, trade shows, in person, or on the Web.
Related titles: Online - full text ed.
Published by: SAM Magazine, 117 W Micheltorena St, Ste C, Santa Barbara, CA 93101. TEL 805-965-5858, FAX 805-963-1143, info@sammag.com, http://www.sammag.com. Ed. Leslie Dinaberg. Pub. John Katnic. Adv. contact Dan Alpern. Circ: 50,000 (controlled).

658 USA ISSN 0036-4436
HD9999.S383
SANITARY MAINTENANCE; the journal of the sanitary supply industry. Text in English. 1943. m. USD 60; free to qualified personnel (effective 2005). adv. illus.; tr.lit. index. reprint service avail. from PQC. **Document type:** *Magazine, Trade.* **Description:** Serves the needs of distribution executives in the sanitary supply industry by covering market trends, product news, application methods, and management.
Related titles: Microfilm ed.: (from PQC); Online - full text ed.: (from Northern Light Technology, Inc., ProQuest Information & Learning).
—Linda Hall.
Published by: Trade Press Publishing Corp., 2100 W Florist Ave, Milwaukee, WI 53209. TEL 414-228-7701, FAX 414-228-1134, http://www.cleanlink.com/sm/toc.asp?id=sm0504, http://www.tradepress.com. Eds. Seiche Sanders, Dick Yake. Pub., Adv. contact R Geissler. R&P Tim Rowe TEL 414-228-7701 ext 515. color page USD 4,495. Circ: 16,000 (paid).

658 CHE
ST. GALLISCH - APPENZELLISCHE GEWERBE ZEITUNG. Text in German. m.
Address: Oberer Graben 12, St. Gallen 1, 9000, Switzerland. TEL 071-229191. Ed. A Muehlematter. Circ: 8,500.

SATELLITE NEWS. see *COMMUNICATIONS—Television And Cable*

640.73 ITA ISSN 1592-0518
LE SCELTE DEL CONSUMATORE; mensile di informazione e orientamento del consumatore. Text in Italian. 1965. m. free to members; EUR 21 (effective 2004). bk.rev. **Document type:** *Magazine, Consumer.*
Former titles (until 1992): U N C Notizie (1592-050X); (until 1976): Le Scelte del Consumatore (1592-0496); (until 1967): Il Consumatore (1592-0488)
Published by: Unione Nazionale Consumatori, Via Caio Duilio 13, Rome, RM 00192, Italy. TEL 39-06-3269531, FAX 39-06-3234616, info@consumatori.it, http://www.consumatori.it. Ed. Vincenzo Dona. Circ: 140,000.

SCHOOL MARKETING NEWSLETTER. see *EDUCATION—School Organization And Administration*

658.8 DEU ISSN 0343-5970
SCHRIFTEN ZUM MARKETING. Text in German. 1975. irreg., latest vol.44, 1997. **Document type:** *Monographic series, Academic/Scholarly.*
Published by: Duncker und Humblot GmbH, Carl-Heinrich-Becker-Weg 9, Berlin, 12165, Germany. TEL 49-30-7900060, FAX 49-30-79000631, info@duncker-humblot.de, http://www.duncker-humblot.de.

658 CHE
SCHWEIZERISCHE DETAILLISTEN ZEITUNG. Text in German. m.
Address: Huebstr 34, Postfach 97, Effretikon, 8307, Switzerland. TEL 052-325051. Ed. Hermann Keller. Circ: 5,200.

658.8 CHE ISSN 0302-2048
SCHWEIZERISCHE GESELLSCHAFT FUER MARKTFORSCHUNG. GESCHAEFTSBERICHT. Text in German. irreg., latest vol.37, 1977. stat.
Published by: Schweizerische Gesellschaft fuer Marktforschung, Bleicherweg 21, Zuerich, 8022, Switzerland.

658 CHE
SCHWEIZERISCHE GEWERBE ZEITUNG. Text in German. w.
Address: Schwarztorstr 26, Bern, 3001, Switzerland. TEL 031-257785, FAX 031-262366. Ed. Ernst Tschanz. Circ: 21,932.

658.7 GBR
SCOTTISH TRADES AND SHOPS HOLIDAYS. Text in English. a. GBP 1.75. **Document type:** *Consumer.*
Published by: William Culross & Son Ltd., Queen St, Coupar Angus, Perthshire, United Kingdom.

SCRIPT (DUTCH EDITION); vakblad voor de kantoorvakhandel. see *BUSINESS AND ECONOMICS—Office Equipment And Services*

SCRIPT (FRENCH EDITION); revue professionelle de la papeterie et de la bureautique. see *BUSINESS AND ECONOMICS—Office Equipment And Services*

658 USA ISSN 1079-8307
SEASON'S GREETINGS. Text in English. 1995. q. USD 36. adv. bk.rev. back issues avail. **Document type:** *Trade.*
Published by: Byrne - McCoy Worldwide, Inc., 150 Fifth Ave, New York, NY 10011. TEL 212-691-1100, FAX 212-691-6185, byrnemccoy@aol.com. Ed. Christopher Byrne. Pub. Robert McCoy. Adv. contact Bruce Karaban. page USD 36; trim 10.88 x 8.13. Circ: 22,500. **Subscr. to:** PO Box 1284 JAF, New York, NY 10116-1284.

658.8 USA ISSN 0049-0016
HD9999.S453
SECURITY DISTRIBUTING & MARKETING. Variant title: S D M Magazine. Text in English. 1971. 13/yr. USD 82 domestic; USD 135 in Canada; USD 125 in Mexico; USD 185 elsewhere; USD 10 per issue domestic; USD 15 per issue foreign; free to members (effective 2005). adv. bk.rev. charts; illus. index. reprint service avail. from PQC. **Document type:** *Magazine, Trade.* **Description:** For the security professional concerned with sales, installation, service and distribution of security, technology and management.
Formerly: S D M Security Distribution & Marketing
Related titles: Microfiche ed.: (from CIS); Microform ed.: (from PQC); Online - full text ed.: (from EBSCO Publishing, Florida Center for Library Automation, Gale Group, O C L C Online Computer Library Center, Inc., ProQuest Information & Learning).
Indexed: ABIn, CJPI, SRI.
—BLDSC (8217.180000). **CCC.**
Published by: B N P Media, 755 W Big Beaver Rd, Ste 1000, Troy, MI 48084-4903. TEL 248-362-3700, FAX 248-362-0317, http://www.sdmmag.com, http://www.bnpmedia.com/. Eds. Laura Stepanek, Bill Zalud TEL 630-694-4029. adv.: B&W page USD 4,270, color page USD 5,490. Circ: 28,012.
Co-sponsor: National Fire and Burglar Alarm Association.

SECURITY RETAILER. see *CRIMINOLOGY AND LAW ENFORCEMENT—Security*

658 620.11 JPN
SEISANZAI/INDUSTRIAL MARKETING. Text in Japanese. 1964. m. JPY 12,000; JPY 14,000 foreign (effective 2000). adv. **Document type:** *Trade.*
Published by: News Digest Publishing Co. Ltd., 5-3 Uchiyama 3-chome, Chikusa-ku, Nagoya, 4640075, Japan. TEL 81-52-732-2455, FAX 81-52-732-2459, news-co@tcp-ip.or.jp, http://MediaZone.tcp-net.ad.jp/news-co. Ed. Tokuei Hattori. Pub. Hachiro Higuchi. R&P K Chaya. Adv. contact H Higuchi. Circ: 30,000.

658.8 GRC ISSN 1105-4972
SELF SERBIS/SELF SERVICE REVIEW. Text in Greek. 1972. m. USD 75. adv. bk.rev. index. back issues avail. **Document type:** *Trade.* **Description:** Contains news and articles on retail and wholesale business and on the marketing of consumer goods.
Published by: Vasso Michaelidis Editions, 5 Polytechniou St, Athens, 104 33, Greece. TEL 30-1-522-2413, FAX 30-1-522-2040. Ed. Xenix Magliori. Pub., Adv. contact Vasso Michaelidis. R&P Demetre Michaelidis. Circ: 9,000 (paid).

658 USA ISSN 1093-2216
HF5438
SELLING POWER; advisory for sales and marketing executives. Text in English. 1981. 9/yr. USD 33 domestic to individuals; USD 56 in Canada to individuals; USD 76 elsewhere to individuals; USD 5 newsstand/cover (effective 2005); price varies for institutions. adv. bk.rev. charts; illus. back issues avail. **Document type:** *Magazine, Trade.*
Formerly (until 1996): Personal Selling Power (0738-8594)
Related titles: Online - full text ed.
Published by: Personal Selling Power, Inc., PO Box 5467, Fredericksburg, VA 22403-0467. TEL 540-752-7000, FAX 540-752-7001, generalinfo@sellingpower.com, http://www.sellingpower.com. Ed. Laura B Gschwandtner. Pub. Gerhard Gschwandtner. R&P Jeff Macharyas. Adv. contact John D Nuzzi. Circ: 193,533.

658 USA ISSN 1050-382X
HC110.C6
SELLING TO SENIORS; the monthly report on the mature market. Text in English. 1987. m. USD 294 (effective 2005). index. 18 p./no. 2 cols./p.; **Document type:** *Newsletter.* **Description:** Practical advice on effective ways to reach the "over 50" market.
Related titles: Online - full text ed.
Indexed: BLI.
—**CCC.**
Published by: (Community Development Services, Inc.), C D Publications, Inc., 8204 Fenton St, Silver Spring, MD 20910-2889. TEL 301-588-6380, FAX 301-588-6385, sts@cdpublications.com, info@cdpublications.com, http://www.cdpublications.com. Ed. Jean Van Ryzin. R&P Mike Gerecht.

SELL'S PRODUCTS & SERVICES DIRECTORY. see *BUSINESS AND ECONOMICS—Trade And Industrial Directories*

658.8 USA
SENIOR MARKET ADVISOR. Text in English. 2000. m. free to qualified personnel (effective 2005). **Document type:** *Magazine, Trade.* **Description:** Designed to fulfill the information needs of financial service providers involved in the over-50 market.
Published by: Wiesner Publishing, LLC, 7009 S Potomac St, Ste 200, Centennial, CO 80112. TEL 303-397-7600, FAX 303-397-7619, http://www.seniormarketadvisor.com, http://www.wiesnerpublishing.com.

658 USA ISSN 1538-9022
SERVICE REVENUE. Text in English. 2002. bi-m. USD 119 (effective 2004). **Document type:** *Magazine, Trade.* **Description:** Reports on the challenges and successes of marketing and selling services.
Media: Online - full content. **Related titles:** Print ed.: USD 189.
Published by: Center for Services Marketing, Inc., 3000 Hess Ave, Bldg II, Golden, CO 80401. TEL 720-746-1900, FAX 720-746-1902, info@csmhub.com, http://www.csmhub.com.

658.8 USA ISSN 1533-2969
➤ **SERVICES MARKETING QUARTERLY.** Abbreviated title: S M Q. Text in English. 1985. q. (in 2 vols.). USD 475 combined subscription domestic to institutions print & online eds.; USD 641.25 combined subscription in Canada to institutions print & online eds.; USD 688.75 combined subscription elsewhere to institutions print & online eds. (effective academic year 2005 - 2006). adv. bk.rev. 120 p./no. 1 cols./p.; back issues avail.; reprint service avail. from HAW. **Document type:** *Journal, Academic/Scholarly.* **Description:** Covers current techniques and trends in the service marketing industry.
Formerly (until 2000): Journal of Professional Services Marketing (0748-4623)
Related titles: Microfiche ed.: (from PQC); Microform ed.; Online - full text ed.: ISSN 1533-2977. free to institutions (effective 2003); free with print subs. (from EBSCO Publishing, O C L C Online Computer Library Center, Inc., ProQuest Information & Learning, Swets Information Services).
Indexed: ABIn, AHCMS, DIP, H&TI, IBR, IBZ, IPARL, MEDLINE, PAIS, PsycholAb, RRTA, RefZh.
—BLDSC (8252.806000), Haworth, IE, Infotrieve, ingenta. **CCC.**
Published by: Best Business Books (Subsidiary of: Haworth Press, Inc.), 10 Alice St, Binghamton, NY 13904. TEL 607-722-5857, 800-429-6784, FAX 607-771-0012, 800-896-0582, getinfo@haworthpress.com, http://www.haworthpress.com/web/SMQ. Eds. David Loudon TEL 318-342-1186, Robert Stevens TEL 318-342-1201. Pub. William Cohen. R&P Ruth Ann Heath TEL 607-722-5857 ext 316. Adv. contact Rebecca Miller-Baum TEL 607-722-5857 ext 337. B&W page USD 315, color page USD 550; trim 4.375 x 7.125. Circ: 293 (paid).

➤ **SHANGYE JINGJI/COMMERICAL ECONOMY.** see *BUSINESS AND ECONOMICS—Domestic Commerce*

658.8029 USA
SHELDON'S MAJOR STORES & CHAINS. Text in English. 1885. a., latest vol.116, 2001. USD 200 per issue (effective 2004). adv. 450 p./no.; back issues avail. **Document type:** *Directory.* **Description:** Lists executives and buyers in the major retailing stores and chains industry throughout North America.
Published by: Phelon Sheldon & Marsar, Inc., 1364 Georgetowne Circle, Sarasota, FL 34232-2048. TEL 941-342-7990, 800-234-8804, FAX 941-342-7994, PSMpublishing@aol.com. Ed., Pub., R&P, Adv. contact Joseph R Marsar Jr. page USD 500; 7 x 9. Circ: 5,000.

658 CHN
SHICHANG BAO/MARKET NEWS. Text in Chinese. 6/w. CNY 92.76. adv. **Document type:** *Newspaper, Consumer.*
Related titles: ♦ Alternate Frequency ed(s).: Shichang Zhoubao. w.
Published by: Renmin Ribao Chubanshe, 2 Jintai Xilu, Chaoyangmenwai, Beijing, 100733, China. **Dist. in the US by:** China Books & Periodicals Inc, 360 Swift Ave., Ste. 48, S San Fran, CA 94080-6220. TEL 415-282-2994, FAX 415-282-0994; **Dist. by:** China International Book Trading Corp, 35 Chegongzhuang Xilu, Haidian District, PO Box 399, Beijing 100044, China. TEL 86-10-68412045, FAX 86-10-68412023, cibtc@mail.cibtc.com.cn, http://www.cibtc.com.cn.

658.8 CHN ISSN 1009-1351
SHICHANG YINGXIAO/MARKETING. Text in English. 1998. m. CNY 66 (effective 2004). **Document type:** *Journal, Academic/Scholarly.*
Formerly (until 1999): Shichang Yingxiaoxue
Related titles: Alternate Frequency ed(s).: a. USD 38.20 (effective 2001).

B

Published by: Zhongguo Renmin Daxue, Shubao Zilio Zhongxin/Renmin University of China, Information Center for Social Server, Dongcheng-qu, 3, Zhangzizhong Lu, Beijing, 100007, China. TEL 86-10-64039458, FAX 86-10-64015080, kyes@163.net, http://www.confucius.cn.net/bkdetail.asp?fzt= F512. **Dist. in the US by:** China Publications Service, PO Box 49614, Chicago, IL 60649. TEL 312-288-3291, FAX 312-288-8570; **Dist. outside of China by:** China International Book Trading Corp, 35 Chegongzhuang Xilu, Haidian District, PO Box 399, Beijing 100044, China. TEL 86-10-68412045, FAX 86-10-68412023, cibtc@mail.cibtc.com.cn, http://www.cibtc.com.cn/.

658   CHN
SHICHANG YINGXIAO WENZHAI KA/MARKETING ABSTRACTS ON CARDS. Text in Chinese. q. CNY 30 (effective 2004). **Document type:** Abstract/Index.
Media: Cards.
Published by: Zhongguo Renmin Daxue, Shubao Zilio Zhongxin/Renmin University of China, Information Center for Social Server, Dongcheng-qu, 3, Zhangzizhong Lu, Beijing, 100007, China. TEL 86-10-64039458, FAX 86-10-64015080, kyes@163.net, http://www.confucius.cn.net/bkdetail.asp?fzt= WF512. **Dist. in the US by:** China Publications Service, PO Box 49614, Chicago, IL 60649. TEL 312-288-3291, FAX 312-288-8570; **Dist. outside of China by:** China International Book Trading Corp, 35 Chegongzhuang Xilu, Haidian District, PO Box 399, Beijing 100044, China. TEL 86-10-68412045, FAX 86-10-68412023, cibtc@mail.cibtc.com.cn, http://www.cibtc.com.cn/.

SHOOTING SPORTS RETAILER. see *SPORTS AND GAMES*

658   USA
SHOP-AT-HOME DIRECTORY. Text in English. 1987. every 6 wks. adv. **Document type:** Directory, Consumer.
Related titles: Online - full content ed.
Published by: Belcaro Group, Inc., 7100 E. Belleview Ave., Ste. 305, Greenwood Village, CO 80111-1636. TEL 303-843-0302, FAX 303-843-0377, sales@shopathome.com, http://www.shopathome.com. Ed. Linda Muhiz. Adv. contact Marc Braunstein. Circ: 5,000,000 (paid).

658 664   USA   ISSN 1077-5099
SHOPPER REPORT. Text in English. 1979. m. USD 195 (effective 2000). **Document type:** Trade. **Description:** Includes satisfaction polls drawn from a national panel of 5,000 shoppers. Most poll statements are taken directly from the consumer's own reports of their experiences.
Related titles: Online - full text ed.: (from Data-Star, The Dialog Corporation).
Published by: Consumer Network, Inc,, PO Box 42753, Philadelphia, PA 19101-2753. TEL 215-235-2400, FAX 215-235-6967, http://www.monadoyle.com. Ed. Mona Doyle. R&P Chas Ebner. Circ: 450.

SHOPPING CENTER DIGEST; the locations newsletter. see *REAL ESTATE*

658   GBR   ISSN 0964-1793
SHOPPING CENTRE. Text in English. 1991. m. GBP 50 domestic; GBP 65 in Europe; GBP 120 elsewhere (effective 2005). adv. **Document type:** Magazine, Trade.
Published by: William Reed Publishing Ltd., Broadfield Park, Brighton Rd, Pease Pottage, Crawley, W Sussex RH11 9RT, United Kingdom. TEL 44-7714-451955, patrick.morgan@william-reed.co.uk, subs@william-reed.co.uk, http://www.william-reed.co.uk/magazines/s_shop_centre.html. Ed. Pat Morgan. Pub. John Lewis. Adv. contact Graham Harvey. Circ: 13,216.

SHORTRUNS; for publishers of books, journals, magazines and newsletters. see *PUBLISHING AND BOOK TRADE*

SKI INDUSTRY LETTER. see *SPORTS AND GAMES—Outdoor Life*

658   USA   ISSN 1538-702X
HD9969.B433
SLEEP SAVVY; the magazine for sleep products professionals. Text in English. 2002 (Mar./Apr.). bi-m. USD 30 domestic; USD 40 foreign; USD 8 newsstand/cover (effective 2002). adv.
Published by: (Better Sleep Council), International Sleep Products Association, 501 Whythe St, Alexandria, VA 22314-1917. TEL 703-683-8371, FAX 703-683-4503, info@sleepproducts.org, http://www.sleepproducts.org. Ed. Nancy Butler. Adv. contact Kerri Bellias.

SMEDJAN (ONLINE EDITION). see *BUSINESS AND ECONOMICS—Economic Systems And Theories, Economic History*

SMOKESHOP. see *TOBACCO*

658.8   USA   ISSN 1524-5004
HF5414
➤ **SOCIAL MARKETING QUARTERLY.** Text in English. 1994. q. USD 173, GBP 105 combined subscription to institutions print & online eds. (effective 2006). back issues avail. **Document type:** Journal, Academic/Scholarly. **Description:** Covers theoretical, research and practical issues confronting social marketers. Publishes original work and fosters a cooperative exploration of ideas and practices in order to build bridges among various disciplines so that innovative change strategies and alliances are created.
Related titles: Online - full text ed.: ISSN 1539-4093. USD 164, GBP 100 to institutions (effective 2006) (from EBSCO Publishing, Gale Group, IngentaConnect, Swets Information Services).
Indexed: PAIS.
—BLDSC (8318.124600), IE. **CCC.**
Published by: Taylor & Francis Inc. (Subsidiary of: Taylor & Francis Group), 325 Chestnut St, Ste 800, Philadelphia, PA 19016. TEL 215-625-8900, 800-354-1420, FAX 215-625-8914, info@taylorandfrancis.com, http://www.tandf.co.uk/journals/titles/15245004.asp, http://www.taylorandfrancis.com. Ed. Dr. Carol A. Bryant. Circ: 400 (paid and controlled). **Subsc. in Europe:** Taylor & Francis Ltd, Journals Customer Service, Rankine Rd, Basingstoke, Hants RG24 8PR, United Kingdom. TEL 44-1256-813000, FAX 44-1256-330245.

➤ **SOUTH AFRICA. STATISTICS SOUTH AFRICA. STATISTICAL RELEASE. RETAIL TRADE SALES.** see *BUSINESS AND ECONOMICS—Abstracting, Bibliographies, Statistics*

➤ **SOUTH AFRICA. STATISTICS SOUTH AFRICA. STATISTICAL RELEASE. RETAIL TRADE SALES (FINAL).** see *BUSINESS AND ECONOMICS—Abstracting, Bibliographies, Statistics*

➤ **SOUTH AFRICA. STATISTICS SOUTH AFRICA. STATISTICAL RELEASE. RETAIL TRADE SALES - PRELIMINARY.** see *BUSINESS AND ECONOMICS— Abstracting, Bibliographies, Statistics*

➤ **SOUTH AFRICA. STATISTICS SOUTH AFRICA. STATISTICAL RELEASE. TOTAL VALUE OF WHOLESALE TRADE SALES - EXPECTED SALES.** see *BUSINESS AND ECONOMICS—Abstracting, Bibliographies, Statistics*

➤ **SOUTH AFRICA. STATISTICS SOUTH AFRICA. STATISTICAL RELEASE. WHOLESALE TRADE SALES.** see *BUSINESS AND ECONOMICS—Abstracting, Bibliographies, Statistics*

658.7   USA   ISSN 0049-1624
SOUTHERN PURCHASER. Text in English. 1970. q. free to members. adv. illus. **Document type:** Magazine, Trade. **Description:** Covers buyer-seller relationships, purchasing and allied subjects, management, economic conditions, markets and trends, products, methods, association and personal news, news from suppliers and educational programs.
Published by: N A P M - Carolinas-Virginia., Inc., 2300 West Meadowview Rd, Ste 117, Greensboro, NC 27409-2932. TEL 336-292-9228, FAX 336-292-8415, bhempstead@aol.com, http://www.napm-cv.org. Ed., Pub. Betty A Hempstead. adv.: B&W page USD 585, color page USD 1,095; trim 10 x 7. Circ: 3,000 (controlled).

SPECIAL EVENTS MAGAZINE. see *HOTELS AND RESTAURANTS*

658   HKG
SPECIAL ISSUES FOR CHINESE EXPORT COMMODITIES FAIR/ZHONGGUO CHUKOU SHANGPIN JIAOYIHUI TEKAN. Text in Chinese, English. s-a. HKD 60, USD 33.
Published by: Economic Information & Agency, 342 Hennessy Rd 10th Fl, 10 th Fl, Wanchai, Hong Kong. TEL 5-738217, FAX 852-5-8388304.

659   USA
SPECIALISTS' MARKETPLUS NEWSLETTER∗. Text in English. 1970. 6/yr. USD 36; USD 49 foreign. adv. bk.rev. **Document type:** Newsletter. **Description:** Latest techniques for analyzing, evaluating and improving mailing lists, including the profitable marketing of those lists.
Former titles: Dependable's List Marketing Newsletter (0399-7189); Dependable's List Letter
Media: Duplicated (not offset).
Published by: SpeciaLists Ltd., 1200 Harbor Blvd., 9th Fl., Weehawken, NJ 07087-6728. TEL 212-677-6760. Ed. Ray Lewis. Circ: 9,500.

658   ITA
SPONSORNEWS. Text in Italian. 12/yr.
Published by: Edizioni Imago International Srl, Corso Indipendenza 6, Milan, 20129, Italy. TEL 39-02-70009474, FAX 39-02-70009480, edizionimago@tin.it.

SPORT MARKETING QUARTERLY; for professionals in the business of marketing sport. see *SPORTS AND GAMES*

SPORT SHOP NEWS; national magazine for sporting goods buyers and retailers. see *SPORTS AND GAMES*

SPORT UND MODE. see *SPORTS AND GAMES*

SPORTING GOODS INTELLIGENCE; news and analysis of the international market. see *SPORTS AND GAMES*

SPORTS LICENSING INTERNATIONAL. see *SPORTS AND GAMES*

SPORTS MARKET PLACE. see *SPORTS AND GAMES*

SPORTS MARKETING. see *SPORTS AND GAMES*

SPORTS MARKETING LETTER. see *SPORTS AND GAMES*

658.8   DEU   ISSN 1269-3626
SPORTS RETAIL EUROPE; the only European trade magazine for sporting goods retailers. Abbreviated title: S R E. Text in English. 1996. s-a. **Document type:** Trade.
Published by: S A Z Verlag GmbH, Rumfordstr 42, Munich, 80469, Germany. TEL 49-89-212110-0, FAX 49-89-21211029.

SPOWI - SPORTARTIKEL WIRTSCHAFT. see *SPORTS AND GAMES*

658 340   USA
STATE CAPITOL WATCH∗. Text in English. 1987. 26/yr. back issues avail. **Document type:** Newsletter.
Published by: Retail Industry Leaders Association, 1700 N Moore St, Ste 2250, Arlington, VA 22209-1903. TEL 202-861-0774, FAX 202-785-4588. Ed. Jennifer Keehan. Circ: 275.

THE STATE OF THE MARKET. see *BUSINESS AND ECONOMICS—Economic Situation And Conditions*

STATS - MONTHLY STATISTICAL AND MARKETING DIGEST. see *STATISTICS*

STORE WINDOWS. see *ADVERTISING AND PUBLIC RELATIONS*

658   USA   ISSN 0749-5153
STRATEGIC HEALTH CARE MARKETING. Text in English. 1984. m. USD 279 (effective 2004). bk.rev. index. back issues avail. **Document type:** Newsletter, Trade. **Description:** Covers strategies and techniques in a wide range of service settings - from hospitals to physicians' offices.
—**CCC.**
Published by: Health Communications, Inc., 11 Heritage Lane, Box 594, Rye, NY 10580. TEL 914-967-6741, FAX 914-967-3054, healthcomm@aol.com, http://www.strategichealthcare.com. Ed., Pub. Michele von Dambrowski.

658.9   USA
STRATEGIC SALES MANAGEMENT. Text in English. 1960. s-m. USD 187.80 (effective 1999). index. **Document type:** Newsletter. **Description:** Provides interview-based articles with sales managers about effective ways to hire, train, motivate, and manage a sales force and get results.
Formerly (until 1997): Sales Manager's Bulletin (0036-3421)
Published by: Bureau of Business Practice (Subsidiary of: Aspen Publishers, Inc.), 1185 Avenue of the Americas, 37th Fl, New York, NY 10036. TEL 860-442-4365, 800-243-0876, FAX 860-437-3555, rebecca_armitage@prenhall.com, http://www.bbpnews.com. Ed. Karen Barretta. Pub. Peter Garabedian. R&P Kathryn Mennone.

658   FRA
STRATEGIES NEWSLETTER; le premier quotidien electronique de la communication. Text in French. 44/yr. **Document type:** Newsletter, Trade. **Description:** Reports on issues in communication, the media, and marketing.
Formerly: Groupe Strategies. Newsletter
Media: Online - full content.
Published by: Groupe Strategies SA (Subsidiary of: Reed Business Information France), 2 rue Maurice Hartmann, BP62, Issy-les-Moulinaux, Cedex 92133, France. TEL 33-1-46294629, FAX 33-1-40930314, infos@groupe-strategies.fr, http://www.groupe-strategies.fr. Circ: 300. **Subscr. to:** 99 rue d'Amsterdam, Paris 75008 , France.

658   CAN   ISSN 1187-4309
STRATEGY; Canadian marketing report. Text in English. 1989. 25/yr. CND 69.50 domestic; USD 93.50 in United States; USD 186 elsewhere (effective 2005). adv. **Document type:** Magazine, Trade. **Description:** Covers the marketing and advertising industries in Canada.
Formerly (until 1991): Playback Strategy (0848-4457)
Related titles: Microfilm ed.: (from MML); Microform ed.: (from MML); Online - full text ed.: (from EBSCO Publishing, LexisNexis, Micromedia ProQuest).
Indexed: CBCARef, CBPI, CPerl.
—**CCC.**

Published by: Brunico Communications Inc., 366 Adelaide St W, Ste 500, Toronto, ON M5V 1R9, Canada. TEL 416-408-2300, FAX 416-408-0870, circ@brunico.com, http://www.strategymag.com, http://www.brunico.com. Ed. Patrick Allossery. adv.: B&W page CND 3,570, color page CND 4,465. Circ: 18,000.

658.8 DEU ISSN 0579-5923
STRUKTUR UND WACHSTUM. REIHE ABSATZWIRTSCHAFT. Text in German. 1970. irreg., latest vol.14, 1994. price varies. **Document type:** *Monographic series, Academic/Scholarly.*
Published by: Duncker und Humblot GmbH, Carl-Heinrich-Becker-Weg 9, Berlin, 12165, Germany. TEL 49-30-7900060, FAX 49-30-79000631, duh-werbung@duncker-humblot.de, http://www.duncker-humblot.de.

658 USA ISSN 1014-1472
STUDIES IN THE PROCESSING, MARKETING AND DISTRIBUTION OF COMMODITIES. Text in English. 1984. irreg. USD 15 (effective 1997).
Related titles: French ed.: Etudes sur la Transformation, la Commercialisation et la Distribution des Produits de Base. ISSN 1014-1480; Spanish ed.: Estudios sobre la Elaboracion, la Comercializacion y la Distribucion de los Productos Basicos. ISSN 1014-1529; Russian ed.: Pererabotka i Marketing Medi : Oblasti dla Mezhdunarodnogo Sotrudnicestva. ISSN 1014-4854; Chinese ed.: Tong de Jiagong he Xiaoshou : ke Jinxing Guoji Hezuo de Lingyu. ISSN 1014-4862; Arabic ed.: Dirasat fi Taghiz al-Sila' al-Asasiyyat wa-Taswiqi-ha wa-Tawzi'i-ha. ISSN 1014-4870.
Published by: (United Nations, Conference on Trade and Development (UNCTAD)), United Nations Publications, Rm DC2-853, United Nations Bldg, 2 United Nations Plaza, New York, NY 10017. TEL 212-963-8302, 800-253-9646, FAX 212-963-3489, publications@un.org,http://www.un.org/Pubs.

658.8 GBR
SUB-CONTRACT NEWS. Text in English. m. free. **Document type:** *Newsletter.* **Description:** Reports on marketing ideas, industry events, and contracts awarded in the world of manufacturing.
Media: Online - full text.
Published by: Sub-Contract UK Ltd., The Square, Basing View, Basingstoke, Hamps RG21 4EB, United Kingdom. TEL 44-01256-394500, FAX 44-01256-394600, sales@subcontract.co.uk, http://www.subcontract.co.uk/News/Default.asp.

SUBSCRIPTIONS STRATEGY; the direct marketing newsletter for publishers. see *PUBLISHING AND BOOK TRADE*

658.8 USA ISSN 0148-4052
HF5438 CODEN: SUMTEJ
SUCCESSFUL MEETINGS; the authority on meetings and incentive travel management. Text in English. 1952. m. USD 79 domestic; USD 95 in Canada; USD 195 elsewhere; free (effective 2005). adv. bk.rev. illus. back issues avail.; reprints avail. **Document type:** *Magazine, Trade.* **Description:** Designed for meeting planners, company presidents, vice-presidents, marketing executives, promotion managers, association executives, convention and show managers, training directors, exhibit managers, incentive travel managers.
Former titles: S M - Successful Meetings (0095-4241); S M - Sales Meetings (0048-8917)
Related titles: Microform ed.: (from PQC); Online - full text ed.: (from EBSCO Publishing, Florida Center for Library Automation, Gale Group, Northern Light Technology, Inc., O C L C Online Computer Library Center, Inc., ProQuest Information & Learning).
Indexed: ABIn, ADPA, BPIA, BusI, H&TI, HospI, PAIS, PROMT, PSI, ResCtrInd, T&II.
—BLDSC (8504.200000), CASDDS, IE, ingenta. **CCC.**
Published by: V N U Business Publications (Subsidiary of: V N U Business Media), 770 Broadway, New York, NY 10003-9595. TEL 646-654-7604, bmcomm@vnuinc.com, http://www.successmtgs.com, http://www.vnubusinessmedia.com/. adv.: color page USD 22,050; trim 8 x 10.75. Circ: 72,050. **Subscr. to:** PO Box 1258, Skokie, IL 60076-8258.

658.8 ZAF
SUCCESSFUL SALESMANSHIP✶. Text in English. m. ZAR 184; ZAR 269.40 foreign (effective 2000). adv. **Document type:** *Trade.*
Published by: (Successful Salesmanship (Pty.) Ltd.), T M L Business Publishing (Subsidiary of: Times Media Ltd.), PO Box 182, Pinegowrie, Gauteng 2123, South Africa. TEL 27-11-789-2144, FAX 27-11-789-3196. Ed. Lynette Dicey. Adv. contact Gerald Dreyer.

658 USA
SUCCESSFUL SCHMOOZING. Text in English. w. **Description:** For business owners, freelancers, salespersons and consultants who are interested in cultivating more referrals, getting free sales leads, and more.
Media: Online - full text.
Address: monique@connectionbank.com, http://www.connectionbank.com/commctr.html. Ed. Monique Harris.

SUCCESSFUL TRADE SHOW STRATEGIES; profitable tips and ideas for the trade show exhibitor. see *BUSINESS AND ECONOMICS—Domestic Commerce*

658.8 USA ISSN 1050-1789
HF5428
SULLIVAN'S RETAIL PERFORMANCE MONITOR. Text in English. 1972. s-w. USD 395 domestic; USD 435 in Canada & Mexico; USD 450 elsewhere (effective 2000). bk.rev. tr.lit. index. **Document type:** *Newsletter, Trade.* **Description:** Covers retail business and economics, sales and earnings, openings and closings, stock performance and more.
Former titles (until 1990): Upscale Discounting (1041-3219); (until 1987): C S M Merchandiser (0898-7254); (until 1986): Catalog Showroom Merchandiser (0194-3022)
Indexed: T&II.
Published by: C S M Communications Co., Inc., 7519 Hurstbourne Green Dr., Charlotte, NC 28277-2507. TEL 516-265-3900, FAX 516-265-3281. Ed. John Walsh. Pub. Ralph H Sullivan.

SUNSHINE ARTIST; America's premier show & festival guide for artists and craftspeople. see *ART*

SUNWEAR VISION. see *MEDICAL SCIENCES—Ophthalmology And Optometry*

658.878 SWE ISSN 0039-5781
SUPERMARKET. Text in Swedish. 1960. 8/yr. SEK 1,795 (effective 2005). adv. **Document type:** *Magazine, Trade.* **Description:** Provides information concerning trade trends and developments for food and grocery retailing decision-makers.
Formerly (until 1969): Sjaelvbetjaening (0583-4600); Incorporates (1992-2002): Dagens Konsument (1102-6154); (1982-1986): Butik Special (0280-6193)
Published by: Forma Publishing Group, Port-Anders Gata T3, PO Box 6630, Vaesteraas, 11384, Sweden. TEL 46-21-194000, FAX 46-21-194186, http://www.formapg.se/tidning.asp?iPageId=127. Ed., Pub. David Jansson. Adv. contact Haakan Broberg. Circ: 7,700.

658 BRA
SUPERMERCADO MODERNO. Text in Portuguese. 1969. m. BRL 70 domestic; USD 28.29 foreign (effective 2001). adv. **Document type:** *Trade.*
Published by: Informa Publicacoes Especializadas Ltda., Rua Brigadeiro Tobias, 356 Andar 9 O, Centro, Sao Paulo, SP 01032-000, Brazil. TEL 55-11-3327-4400, FAX 55-11-229-9373, edi_sm@lund.com.br, http://www.sm.com.br. Ed. Valdir Orsetti. Pub. Sheila Suly-Hissa. Adv. contact Sergio Luis Alvim Veiga de Oliveira. page BRL 9,000. Circ: 23,000.

658 USA ISSN 1046-3771
SUPPLIER SELECTION & MANAGEMENT REPORT. Abbreviated title: S S M R. Text in English. 1989. m. looseleaf. USD 298.95 in US & Canada print & online eds.; USD 313 elsewhere print & online eds. (effective 2005). Index. back issues avail. **Document type:** *Newsletter, Trade.* **Description:** Shows purchasing and materials managers how to choose suppliers, achieve inventory accuracy, maintain JIT methods, develop procurement strategies that help achieve corporate business objectives.
Related titles: Diskette ed.; E-mail ed.; Online - full content ed.: (from Northern Light Technology, Inc.); Online - full text ed.: (from EBSCO Publishing, Florida Center for Library Automation, Gale Group, LexisNexis, O C L C Online Computer Library Center, Inc., ProQuest Information & Learning).
Indexed: ABIn.
—CCC.
Published by: Institute of Management & Administration, Inc., 3 Park Ave, New York, NY 10016-5902. TEL 212-244-0360, FAX 212-564-0465, subserve@ioma.com, http://www.ioma.com/products/prod_detail.php?prodid=32. Ed. Joe Mazel.

658 USA ISSN 1557-5128
▼ **SUPPLY CHAIN SOLUTIONS.** Text in English. 2005 (July). 6/yr. USD 45 to non-members; USD 30 to members (effective 2005). **Document type:** *Newsletter, Trade.*
Published by: Healthcare Financial Management Association, 2 Westbrook Corporate Center, Ste 700, Westchester, IL 60154-5700. TEL 708-531-9600, 800-252-4362, FAX 708-531-0032, http://www.hfma.org/.

658.7 GBR ISSN 1362-2021
HD39.5 CODEN: SUMAFV
SUPPLY MANAGEMENT. Text in English. 1996. fortn. GBP 80 domestic; GBP 110 foreign (effective 2005). adv. bk.rev.; software rev. mkt.; tr.lit. index. back issues avail. **Document type:** *Magazine, Trade.* **Description:** Targets purchasing and supply chain professionals.
Formed by the merger of (1950-1996): Procurement Weekly (0306-1922); Which was formerly (until 1973): Purchasing Bulletin (0033-4456); (19??-1996): Purchasing and Supply Management (0265-2072); Which was formerly (until 1977): Purchasing and Supply (0309-7242); (until 1976): Procurement (0305-9073); (until 1973): Purchasing Journal (0033-4472)
Related titles: Online - full text ed.: (from O C L C Online Computer Library Center, Inc., ProQuest Information & Learning).
Indexed: ABIn, Emerald, Inspec, M&MA, RDA.
—BLDSC (8547.638140), AskIEEE, IE, ingenta. **CCC.**

Published by: (Chartered Institute of Purchasing and Supply), Redactive Publishing Ltd., 1 Benjamin St, London, EC1M 5EA, United Kingdom. TEL 44-20-73242746, FAX 44-20-73242791, editorial@supplymanagement.co.uk, http://www.supplymanagement.co.uk/. Ed. Geraint John. adv.: B&W page GBP 1,800, color page GBP 2,500; trim 210 x 297. Circ: 25,977.

658.7 USA
THE SURVEY OF ACADEMIC AND SPECIAL LIBRARIES. Text in English. irreg. USD 73 domestic; EUR 78 foreign (effective 2003). **Description:** Covers the purchasing policies and technology practices of academic and special libraries in North America.
Related titles: Online - full text ed.: USD 73 domestic; EUR 75 foreign (effective 2003).
Published by: Primary Research Group, 850 Seventh Avenue, Suite 1200, New York, NY 10019. TEL 212-245-2327, FAX 212-245-1430, primarydat@mindspring.com, http://www.primaryresearch.com. **Dist. by:** Research and Markets Ltd., Guinness Centre, Taylors Lane, Dublin 8, Ireland. TEL 353-1-4957318, FAX 353-86-8797580, orders@researchandmarkets.com, http://www.researchandmarkets.com.

658 378 USA
THE SURVEY OF COLLEGE MARKETING PROGRAMS. Text in English. irreg. USD 245 domestic; EUR 262 foreign (effective 2003). **Description:** Reports on college marketing practices, including internet marketing, radio and television advertising, use of surveys by colleges, trends in visits to guidance counselors, and other facets of college enrollment marketing.
Related titles: Online - full text ed.: USD 245 domestic; EUR 270 foreign (effective 2003).
Published by: Primary Research Group, 850 Seventh Avenue, Suite 1200, New York, NY 10019. TEL 212-245-2327, FAX 212-245-1430, primarydat@mindspring.com, http://www.primaryresearch.com. **Dist. by:** Research and Markets Ltd., Guinness Centre, Taylors Lane, Dublin 8, Ireland. TEL 353-1-4957318, FAX 353-86-8797580, orders@researchandmarkets.com, http://www.researchandmarkets.com.

658.8 HRV ISSN 1330-0180
SUVREMENA TRGOVINA. Text in Croatian. 1976. bi-m. **Document type:** *Magazine, Trade.*
Formerly (until 1992): Supermarket (0350-4824)
Published by: Ideje, Frankopanska 18, Zagreb, 10000, Croatia. TEL 385-1-4849066, FAX 385-1-4849066, suvremena.trgovina@zg.tel.hr. Ed. Tihomir Sertic.

SWITZERLAND. CENTER FOR TRADE FAIRS. see *BUSINESS AND ECONOMICS—International Commerce*

▼ **T B I BUYERS' BRIEFING.** (Television Business International) see *COMMUNICATIONS—Television And Cable*

T M A NEWSLINE. (Telecommunications Managers Association) see *COMMUNICATIONS*

658 389 GBR ISSN 1475-1364
T S TODAY; the trading standards review. (Trading Standards) Text in English. 1894. m. GBP 5 newsstand/cover (effective 2001). adv. bk.rev. illus. index. **Document type:** *Trade.*
Former titles (until July 2001): Trading Standards Review (0953-8704); (until 1988): Fairtrader (Southend-on-Sea) (0951-4473); (until 1987): Institute of Trading Standards Administration Monthly Review (0302-3249); (until 1972): Institute of Weights and Measures Administration Monthly Review (0020-319X)
—BLDSC (9067.426000), CISTI.
Published by: Institute of Trading Standards Administration, 3/5 Hadleigh Business Centre, 351 London Rd, Hadleigh, Essex SS7 2BT, United Kingdom. TEL 44-1702-559922, FAX 44-1702-559902, pressoffice@tsi.org.uk. Eds. Matt Adams, Tony Northcott. Adv. contact Amanda Wilkins TEL 44-1870-872-9009. Circ: 2,300.

TAIWAN ELECTRONICS INDUSTRY. see *ELECTRONICS*

658.8 659.1 USA ISSN 0889-5333
HF5410
TARGET MARKETING; the leading magazine for integrated database marketing. Text in English. 1978. m. USD 65; USD 85 in Canada; USD 110 elsewhere (effective 1999); free to qualified personnel. adv. bibl.; charts; stat.; tr.lit. back issues avail. **Document type:** *Magazine, Trade.* **Description:** Covers all aspects of selling and marketing through the mail and other direct-response media. For writers, designers, catalogers, printers, list managers and those in allied industries for the latest news in regulations, direct-marketing techniques, equipment, and marketing strategy.
Former titles (until 1986): Zip Target Marketing (0739-6953); (until 1983): Zip (0160-4090)
Related titles: Online - full text ed.: (from bigchalk, Florida Center for Library Automation, Gale Group, H.W. Wilson, Northern Light Technology, Inc., O C L C Online Computer Library Center, Inc., ProQuest Information & Learning).
Indexed: ABIn, BPI, BPIA, GALA, ManagCont.
—BLDSC (8606.253500), IE, ingenta. **CCC.**

Published by: North American Publishing Co., 1500 Spring Garden St., Ste 1200, Philadelphia, PA 19130-4094. TEL 215-238-5300, FAX 215-238-5457, phatch@napco.com, http://www.targetonline.com, http://www.napco.com. Eds. Denny Hatch, Hallie Mummert. Pub., Adv. contact Peggy Hatch. R&P Kristen Monte. Circ: 36,796.

658.8 790.1 USA ISSN 1097-119X
TEAM MARKETING REPORT. Text in English. 1988. m. USD 195 domestic; USD 205 foreign (effective 2005). adv. **Document type:** *Newsletter, Trade.* **Description:** Reports on innovative and successful trends in sports marketing and sports sponsorships.
Published by: Team Marketing Report Inc., 1653 North Wells., Ste 2F, Ste. 2100, Chicago, IL 60614. TEL 312-280-2311, FAX 312-280-2322, editor@teammarketing.com, http://www.teammarketing.com. R&P, Adv. contact Andrew J Arkin. Circ: 5,000 (paid).

TECHNOLOGY ADVERTISING & BRANDING REPORT. see *ADVERTISING AND PUBLIC RELATIONS*

TELCO BUSINESS REPORT; executive briefings on the Bell operating companies - regional holding companies and independent telcos. see *COMMUNICATIONS—Telephone And Telegraph*

B

658 338.642 USA ISSN 8750-9067
HF5415.1265
TELEMARKETER. Text in English. 1980. s-m. USD 285. adv. bk.rev. cum.index: 1980-1988. back issues avail. **Description:** Aspects of the telemarketing industry: sales, lead generation, fund raising.
Formerly: A I S 800 Report
Published by: Actel Marketing, 163 Third Ave, Ste 303, New York, NY 10003. TEL 212-674-2545. Ed. Aldyn McKean. Circ: 2,000.

658.84 USA ISSN 0736-167X
TELEMARKETING UPDATE. (Special editions avail.: Secretarial Script Presentations, Catering Service Script Presentations, Copier Service Business Script Presentations, Small Business Telemarketing Script Presentations) Text in English. 1985. a. looseleaf. USD 200 (effective 2005). 4 p./no. 2 cols./p.; **Document type:** *Newsletter.* **Description:** Provides ideas on telemarketing, scripts and how to.
Related titles: Supplement(s): Telecommagazine Service Guide.
—CCC.
Published by: Prosperity and Profits Unlimited, PO Box 416, Denver, CO 80201-0416. TEL 303-575-5676, FAX 303-575-1187, starsuccess@excite.com, http://www.newsreleasemedia.com, http://www.telemarketingscripts.20m.com/. Ed., R&P A Doyle TEL 303-575-5676. Circ: 5,000 (paid and controlled).

658.8 USA ISSN 0882-1461
CODEN: TSERE4
TELEPHONE SELLING REPORT. Text in English. 1984. bi-m. USD 69 (effective 2001). bk.rev. back issues avail. **Document type:** *Newsletter.* **Description:** Training newsletter with how-to ideas and tips on phone selling and prospecting.
Published by: Business By Phone, Inc., 13254 Stevens St, Omaha, NE 68137-1728. TEL 402-895-9399, FAX 402-896-3353, http://www.businessbyphone.com. Ed. Art Sobczak.

658 DEU ISSN 0944-0690
TELETALK. Text in German. 1993. m. EUR 53, EUR 76, EUR 90 (effective 2003). adv. **Document type:** *Magazine, Trade.*
Related titles: Online - full text ed.
Published by: telepublic Verlag GmbH & Co. Medien KG, Podbielskistr. 325, Hannover, 30659, Germany. TEL 49-511-3348400, FAX 49-511-3348499, info@teletalk.de, http://www.teletalk.de. Ed. Arne Graevemeyer. Adv. contact Irmgard Ditgens TEL 49-511-3348410. B&W page EUR 2,900, color page EUR 3,515; trim 210 x 297. Circ: 21,606 (paid and controlled).

658 DEU ISSN 1618-1808
TELETRAFFIC MARKTFUEHRER. Text in German. 1997. 2/yr. **Document type:** *Magazine, Trade.*
Formerly (until 2001): TeleTraffic (1434-7059)
Published by: telepublic Verlag GmbH & Co. Medien KG, Podbielskistr. 325, Hannover, 30659, Germany. TEL 49-511-3348400, FAX 49-511-3348499, info@teletalk.de.

THETA MARKET RESEARCH REPORTS. see *MEDICAL SCIENCES*

658 CHE ISSN 0254-9697
THEXIS. Text in German. 1984. 6/yr. CHF 60.
Published by: Forschungsinstitut fuer Absatz und Handel, Bodanstr 8, St. Gallen, 9000, Switzerland. TEL 071-302820, FAX 071-232274. Ed. Peter Ritter. Circ: 8,500.

658.0029 USA ISSN 0362-7721
T12
THOMAS REGISTER OF AMERICAN MANUFACTURERS. Variant title: Thomas Register. Text in English. 1908. irreg. (in 16 vols.). USD 29.95 (effective 2005). index. **Document type:** *Catalog.* **Description:** Lists nearly every industrial product or service offered in North America.
Related titles: CD-ROM ed.: (from The Dialog Corporation); Online - full text ed.
—CISTI.
Published by: Thomas Publishing Company, Five Penn Plaza, New York, NY 10001. TEL 212-629-1546, 800-733-1127, FAX 212-629-1542, info@thomasimg.com, http://www.thomaspublishing.com/pagetr.html.

TIDINGS (CAMDEN). see *BUSINESS AND ECONOMICS—Domestic Commerce*

TIE LINES. see *CLOTHING TRADE*

658.8 NLD ISSN 0165-1439
TIJDSCHRIFT VOOR MARKETING. Text in Dutch. 1967. 11/yr. EUR 135; EUR 49 to students; EUR 15 newsstand/cover (effective 2005). adv. bk.rev. bibl.; charts; illus. **Document type:** *Trade.*
Formerly: N I A (0027-6618); Incorporates (1999-2002): Connect (1389-9902)
Indexed: KES.
—IE, Infotrieve, KNAW.
Published by: (Nederlands Instituut voor Marketing (NIMA)), Wolters Kluwer N.V., Postbus 23, Deventer, 7400 GA, Netherlands. TEL 31-570-673358, FAX 31-570-611504, 31-570-691555, info@kluwer.nl, http://www.marketingonline.nl/. Ed. Theo van Vugt. Pub. Judith Kuiperi. Adv. contact Eric-Jan Vis. B&W page EUR 2,300; trim 190 x 268. Circ: 10,191.

TODAY FAX. see *ADVERTISING AND PUBLIC RELATIONS*

688 635.9 USA ISSN 1082-0434
TODAY'S HOSPITAL GIFT SHOP BUSINESS. Text in English. 1978. bi-m. USD 50 domestic; USD 70 in Canada & Mexico; USD 85 elsewhere (effective 2005). adv. 16 p./no. 2 cols./p.; back issues avail.; reprints avail. **Document type:** *Newsletter, Trade.* **Description:** For persons involved with hospital gift shops.
Published by: Nason & Associates, PO Box 8204, Asheville, NC 28814. TEL 828-298-1322, FAX 828-298-1312. Ed., Pub., R&P Marilyn Nason TEL 828-298-1314. Adv. contact Michelle Ramsey. page USD 500; 8 x 10. Circ: 8,500 (paid and controlled).

658 BRA
TOP 5. Text in Portuguese. 1996. a. adv.
Published by: Informa Publicacoes Especializadas Ltda., Rua Brigadeiro Tobias, 356 Andar 9 O, Centro, Sao Paulo, SP 01032-000, Brazil. TEL 55-11-3327-4400, FAX 55-11-229-9373, edi_sm@lund.com.br, http://www.sm.com.br. adv.: page BRL 10,000. Circ: 23,200 (free).

658 GBR
TOP MARKETS. Text in English. irreg., latest 2002, Mar. GBP 730 per issue (effective 2002). **Description:** Gives you insight into forthcoming changes in UK industry, looking at sales forecasts and developing trends for key growth markets.
Published by: Key Note Ltd., Field House, 72 Oldfield Rd, Hampton, Mddx TW12 2HQ, United Kingdom. TEL 44-20-8481-8750, FAX 44-20-8783-0049, info@keynote.co.uk, http://www.keynote.co.uk. Ed. Simon Taylor.

TOP SOCIETY. see *BUILDING AND CONSTRUCTION*

TOPICAL ISSUES IN PROCUREMENT SERIES. see *PUBLIC ADMINISTRATION*

TOPICATOR; classified guide to articles in the advertising/communications/marketing periodical press. see *ADVERTISING AND PUBLIC RELATIONS—Abstracting, Bibliographies, Statistics*

658.83 USA
TOPLINE. Text in English. 1978. q. looseleaf. free. charts; illus.; stat. back issues avail. **Document type:** *Newsletter, Trade.* **Description:** Contains market research information gleaned from McCollum Spielman studies of TV and print advertising.
Published by: McCollum-Spielman Worldwide, Inc., 1111 Marcus Ave., Ste. MZ200, New Hyde Park, NY 11042-1034. TEL 516-482-0310, FAX 516-482-3228. Ed. Paula Kay Pierce. Circ: 5,000 (controlled).

THE TORONTO BUSINESS AND MARKET GUIDE. see *BUSINESS AND ECONOMICS*

381.45002 USA ISSN 1070-3179
THE TOWERS CLUB U S A INFO MARKETING REPORT; money-making news for independent business persons and information merchants. Text in English. 1974. 10/yr. looseleaf. USD 69.95 (effective 1999). adv. bk.rev. back issues avail. **Document type:** *Newsletter, Trade.* **Description:** Aimes at people interested in direct marketing and self-publishing. Contains insider news, tips, and sources especially for home-based entrepreneurs. Also includes mail order mini-clinics, success stories of self-publishers and marketers, and letters to the editor.
Former titles: Jerry Buchannan's Info Marketing Report (1066-5250); (until 1993): Towers Club U S A Newsletter (0193-4953)
Published by: Towers Club, U.S.A., Inc., PO Box 65404, Vancouver, WA 98665-0014. TEL 206-574-3084, FAX 206-576-8969. Ed., Pub., R&P, Adv. contact Jerry Buchanan. Circ: 185 (paid).

TOWNSEND PROFILE. see *PLASTICS*

TOYS; das Magazin der Branche. see *GIFTWARE AND TOYS*

658.7 GBR
TRACKER. Text in English. d. GBP 980 (effective 1999). **Document type:** *Trade.* **Description:** Provides daily automated information on contract announcements and opportunities.
Media: Online - full text.
Published by: Business Information Publications Ltd., Park House, 300 Glasgow Rd, Shawfield, Glasgow, G73 1SQ, United Kingdom. TEL 44-141-3328247, FAX 44-141-3312652, bip@bipcontracts.com, bip@bipsolutions.com, http://www.bipcontracts.com.

658.8 ITA
TRADE BIANCO. Text in Italian. m. (11/yr.). EUR 25 (effective 2005). **Document type:** *Magazine, Trade.*
Published by: Editoriale Duesse SpA, Via Donatello 5b, Milan, 20131, Italy. TEL 39-02-277961, FAX 39-02-27796300, e-duesse@e-duesse.it, http://www.e-duesse.it.

658 ITA
TRADE CONSUMER ELECTRONICS. Text in Italian. m. (10/yr.). EUR 25 (effective 2005). **Document type:** *Magazine, Trade.*
Published by: Editoriale Duesse SpA, Via Donatello 5b, Milan, 20131, Italy. TEL 39-02-277961, FAX 39-02-27796300, e-duesse@e-duesse.it, http://www.e-duesse.it.

TRADE SHOWS & EXHIBITS SCHEDULE. see *BUSINESS AND ECONOMICS—Trade And Industrial Directories*

658.8 GBR ISSN 0955-0828
THE TRADER; the UK's No. 1 stock buying magazine. Text in English. 1969. m. GBP 24 domestic; GBP 52 in Europe; GBP 85 elsewhere; GBP 2 newsstand/cover (effective 2000). adv. tr.lit.
Formerly (until 1969): Small Trader and Wholesaler (0037-7252)
Published by: United Advertising Publications plc., Link House, 25 West St, Poole, Dorset BH15 1LL, United Kingdom. TEL 44-1202-445302, FAX 44-1202-445309, trader@unitedadvertising.co.uk. Pub., Adv. contact Angela Boyer. B&W page GBP 437, color page GBP 899; trim 180 x 276. Circ: 25,000 (paid). **Subscr. to:** Trader Subscriptions, Garrard House 2-6, Homesdale Rd, Bromley BR2 9WL, United Kingdom. TEL 44-181-289-7951. **Dist. by:** Seymour Distribution Ltd, 86 Newman St, London W1T 3EX, United Kingdom. TEL 44-20-73968000, FAX 44-20-73968002.

TRADESHOW. see *ADVERTISING AND PUBLIC RELATIONS*

TRADESHOW WEEK; since 1971, the only weekly source of news & statistics on the tradeshow industry. see *ADVERTISING AND PUBLIC RELATIONS*

658 USA ISSN 0000-1023
T394
TRADESHOW WEEK DATA BOOK (YEAR); the annual statistical directory of US and Canadian tradeshows and public shows. Text in English. 1985. a. USD 439 (effective 2004). adv. 2000 p./no.; **Document type:** *Directory.* **Description:** Details trade and public shows in the US and Canada; lists marketing, statistical and historical data on expositions.
—CCC.
Published by: Reed Business Information (Subsidiary of: Reed Business), 5700 Wilshire Blvd, Ste 120, Los Angeles, CA 90036. TEL 323-965-2093, FAX 323-965-5334, http://www.tradeshowweek.com, http://www.reedbusiness.com.

TRADESHOW WEEK'S BUYER'S GUIDE. see *ADVERTISING AND PUBLIC RELATIONS*

TRADESHOW WEEK'S MAJOR EXHIBIT HALL DIRECTORY. see *ADVERTISING AND PUBLIC RELATIONS*

658.7 USA
TRAILS ADVOCATE. Text in English. 1984. bi-m. USD 15 (effective 2000). adv. bk.rev. maps; stat.; tr.lit. cum.index. back issues avail. **Document type:** *Newsletter.* **Description:** Discusses land acquisition, trail development and promotion.
Published by: Iowa Trails Council, Inc., PO Box 131, Center Point, IA 52213-0131. TEL 319-849-1844, FAX 319-849-2866, tomneenan1@aol.com. Ed., Adv. contact Tom F Neenan. Circ: 1,400.

658 GBR ISSN 1357-3489
TRAVEL RETAILER INTERNATIONAL. Text in English. 1991. m. GBP 150 combined subscription domestic print & online eds.; EUR 225 combined subscription in Europe print & online eds.; USD 260 combined subscription elsewhere print & online eds. (effective 2005). **Document type:** *Trade.*
Related titles: Online - full text ed.: (from EBSCO Publishing, Florida Center for Library Automation, Gale Group, O C L C Online Computer Library Center, Inc., ProQuest Information & Learning).

Indexed: ABIn, B&I.
—CCC.
Published by: Euromoney Institutional Investor Plc., Nestor House, Playhouse Yard, London, EC4V 5EX, United Kingdom. TEL 44-20-7779-8673, FAX 44-20-7779-8541, information@euromoneyplc.com, http://www.travelretailworld.com, http://www.euromoney.com. Ed. Liz Miller. Circ: 5,000 (controlled). **Subscr. to:** Quadrant Subscription Services, PO Box 18083, London EC4V 5JS, United Kingdom. TEL 44-20-7779-8610, FAX 44-20-7779-8602.

TRAVELWRITER MARKETLETTER. see *JOURNALISM*

658.8 NLD ISSN 0165-537X
TREND; vakblad voor de eigentijdse ondernemer in glas, porselein, aardewerk, luxe- en huishoudelijke artiklen, kunstnijverheids- en geschenkartikelen. Text in Dutch. 1974. 11/yr. adv. **Document type:** *Trade.*
Published by: Blauw Media Uitgeverij B.V., Postbus 1043, Maarssen, 3600 BA, Netherlands. TEL 31-346-574040, FAX 31-346-576056, trend@blauwmedia.demon.nl, bmu@blauwmedia.demon.nl, http://www.blauwmedia.demon.nl. Circ: 4,500.

658.8 NLD ISSN 0165-4438
TREND-BOUTIQUE; vakblad voor de eigentijdse ondernemer in lederwaren, bijoux en modeaccessoires. Text in Dutch. 1980. 6/yr. EUR 37.25 (effective 2005). adv. **Document type:** *Journal, Trade.*
Published by: Blauw Media Uitgeverij B.V., Postbus 1043, Maarssen, 3600 BA, Netherlands. TEL 31-346-574040, FAX 31-346-576056, trendboutique@blauwmedia.demon.nl, bmu@blauwmedia.demon.nl, http://www.blauwmedia.demon.nl. Circ: 2,400.

658 FRA ISSN 0397-5258
TRIBUNE DE LA VENTE✱. Text in French. m. (11/yr.).
Formerly (until 1976): Depositaire de France (0011-8966)
Address: 7 rue du 4 Septembre, Paris, 75002, France.

658 USA
TROUBLED COMPANY PROSPECTOR. Text in English. w. USD 780 for 6 mos. (effective 2002). **Document type:** *Journal, Trade.* **Description:** Profiles firms in transition.
Media: E-mail.
Published by: Beard Group, Inc, PO Box 9867, Washington, DC 20016. TEL 240-629-3300, FAX 240-629-3360, info@beard.com, http://www.beard.com. Ed. Chris McHugh. Pub., R&P Christopher Beard.

TRUCK SALES & LEASING. see *TRANSPORTATION—Trucks And Trucking*

658 SCG ISSN 0564-3619
HG37.Y8
TRZISTE, NOVAC, KAPITAL/MONEY MARKET CAPITAL. Text mainly in Serbo-Croatian; Text occasionally in English. 1966. q. CSD 7,000 (effective 2005). tr.lit. **Document type:** *Journal, Trade.*
Related titles: CD-ROM ed.
Indexed: RASB, RefZh.
Published by: Privredna Komora Srbije, Centar za Naucnoistrazivacki Rad i Ekonomske Analize/Serbian Chamber for Industry, Scientific Research Centre for Economic Analyses, Knez Mihailova 10/I, Beograd, 11000. TEL 381-11-180074, jelenav@pks.co.yu, http://www.pks.co.yu. Pub. Radovan Kovacevic.

THE U K CALL CENTRE MARKET PERFORMANCE REPORT. see *COMMUNICATIONS—Telephone And Telegraph*

658.87 GBR ISSN 1465-9212
U K RETAIL REPORT. Text in English. 1988. m. GBP 595, USD 1,000 (effective 2000). charts; mkt.; stat.; tr.lit. cum.index: 1995-1999. back issues avail. **Document type:** *Newsletter, Corporate.* **Description:** Provides market studies, profiles of leading companies, and analysis of specific sectors of the retail market.
Formerly (until 1996): Retail Trade Review
Related titles: E-mail ed.; Online - full text ed.: (from Gale Group).
Indexed: ABIn.
Published by: Retail Intelligence, 48 Bedford Sq, London, WC1B 3DP, United Kingdom. TEL 44-20-7696-9006, FAX 44-20-7696-9004, sales@cior.com, http://www.cior.com. Ed. Ben Perkins. R&P Teri Hawksworth TEL 44-20-7814-3814. **Subscr. in US to:** Lebhar-Friedman, Inc., 425 Park Ave, New York, NY 10022. TEL 212-756-5159, FAX 212-756-5038.

U S D A BROILER MARKET NEWS REPORT. see *AGRICULTURE—Poultry And Livestock*

U S D A EGG MARKET NEWS REPORT. see *AGRICULTURE—Poultry And Livestock*

658 304.6 USA
U S MARKET FORECASTS. Text in English. 1996. a. **Document type:** *Directory.* **Description:** Provides in-depth profiles of every US city or town with 2,500 residents or more. Includes Market Guide information.
Media: CD-ROM.
Published by: Editor & Publisher Co., Inc. (Subsidiary of: V N U Business Publications), 770 Broadway., New York, NY 10003-9596. TEL 212-675-4380, FAX 212-929-1259, edpub@mediainfo.com, edpub@editor&publisher.com, http://www.mediainfo.com, http://www.editorandpublisher.com. Ed. Thomas C Dahlin. Pubs. D Colin Phillps, D. Colin Phillips. R&P D. Colin Phillips.

U S TRANSACTIONS MONTHLY. see *BUSINESS AND ECONOMICS—Banking And Finance*

U S TRANSACTIONS PRIME CUSTOMER QUARTERLY. see *BUSINESS AND ECONOMICS—Banking And Finance*

U S TRANSACTIONS SMALL BUSINESS QUARTERLY. see *BUSINESS AND ECONOMICS—Banking And Finance*

658 387 USA ISSN 1072-6098
UNDERWATER MAGAZINE✱. Text in English. 1989. bi-m. USD 50; free to qualified personnel (effective 2004). adv. bk.rev. illus.; tr.lit. back issues avail. **Document type:** *Magazine, Trade.* **Description:** Covers commercial diving for construction, engineering, the oil and gas industry, and scientific research.
—Linda Hall.
Published by: (Association of diving Contractors International, Inc., Association of Diving Contractors), Doyle Publishing Co., Inc., 607 Mason St., # 2, Tomball, TX 77375-4451. editor@doylepublishing.com, http://diveweb.com/uw. Ed. Daron Jones. Pubs. Howie Doyle TEL 281-440-0278, William H. Doyle. R&P Howie Doyle TEL 281-440-0278. Adv. contacts Jo Anne Hudson, Marlene Breedlove. Circ: 15,000 (controlled).

658.8 HUN ISSN 1416-3586
UNGARISCHE WIRTSCHAFT. Text in Hungarian. 1971. q.
Former titles (until 1995): Ungarische Wirtschaftshefte (0237-1545); (until 1985): Marketing in Ungarn (0134-0980)
Indexed: PAIS.
Published by: Magyar Kereskedelmi Kamara, Kossuth Lajos ter 608, Budapest, 1055, Hungary. TEL 36-1-1531225, FAX 36-1-1531285.

658.8 ZAF
UNIVERSITY OF STELLENBOSCH. BUREAU FOR ECONOMIC RESEARCH. RETAIL SURVEY. Text in English; Summaries in Afrikaans. 1986. q. ZAR 830 (effective 2003). **Description:** Discusses the latest market research on the behavior of South African consumers, including repercussions for wholesale and retail trade.
Formerly (until vol.9, 1994): University of Stellenbosch. Bureau for Economic Research. Trade and Commerce (0258-9311); Supersedes (in 1986): Consumer Survey Report (0379-6086)
Related titles: Online - full text ed.
Published by: Universiteit Stellenbosch, Bureau for Economic Research/Stellenbosch University, University, Private Bag 5050, Stellenbosch, 7599, South Africa. TEL 27-21-8872810, FAX 27-21-8899225, hhman@maties.sun.ac.za, http://www.journals.co.za/ej/ejour_retailmotor.html, http://www.sun.ac.za/. Ed. L Ellis. Circ: 600.

658 GBR
UNIVERSITY OF STRATHCLYDE. DEPARTMENT OF MARKETING. WORKING PAPER SERIES. Text in English. irreg. **Document type:** *Monographic series.*
—BLDSC (9350.214670).
Published by: University of Strathclyde, Department of Marketing, Stenhouse Bldg, 173 Cathedral St, Glasgow, G4 0RQ, United Kingdom. TEL 0141-552-4400, FAX 0141-552-2802. Ed. Susan Shaw.

UNIVERSO VISUAL. see *MEDICAL SCIENCES—Ophthalmology And Optometry*

658 USA
UP-TO-DATE PRICE MAGAZINE; published for distributors (wholesalers) of candy, tobacco, grocery, health & beauty aids, and sundry products. Text in English. 1957. m. USD 35.
Address: 21 W Delilah Rd, Pleasantville, NJ 08232. TEL 800-331-7061, FAX 609-646-2692. Circ: 1,100.

658.8 USA ISSN 1062-5062
UPLINE. Text in English. 1990. m. USD 79 domestic; USD 89 in Canada; USD 99 foreign (effective 2001). bk.rev.; software rev. 48 p./no.; back issues avail. **Document type:** *Journal, Trade.* **Description:** Covers issues of interest to network marketing professionals.
Formerly (until 1992): M L M Success (1054-3988)
Related titles: Online - full text ed.
Published by: M L M Publishing, Inc., 221 N. Figueroa St., Los Angeles, CA 90012-2639. TEL 818-947-4444, 877-898-8882, FAX 804-979-1602, 818-947-4440, editors@upline.com, customerservice@upline.com, http://www.upline.com/journal/. Ed. Uma Outka. Pub. N Ridgely Goldsborough. Circ: 8,000 (paid).

643.3 USA
V D T A NEWS. Text in English. m. free. adv.
Published by: Vacuum Dealers Trade Association, 2724 Second Ave, Des Moines, IA 50313-4933. TEL 515-282-9101. Ed., Adv. contact Judy Patterson. Circ: 19,000.

643.3 USA
V D T A PHONE DIRECTORY AND PRODUCT GUIDE. Text in English. a. **Document type:** *Directory.*
Published by: Vacuum Dealers Trade Association, 2724 Second Ave, Des Moines, IA 50313-4933. TEL 515-282-9101.

692.5 DNK
V & S GENERALBESKRIVELSE. Text in Danish. 1995. irreg. DKK 590 (effective 2000).
Related titles: ◆ Supplement(s): V & S Generalbeskrivelse. Supplement.
Published by: V & S Byggedata, 551 Frederikssundvej 194, Broenshoej, 2700, Denmark. TEL 45-38-60-77-11, FAX 45-38-60-77-55, bygdat@vs-byggedata.dk, bygdat@vs.byggedata.dk. Ed. Carl Friis Skovsen.

692.5 DNK
V & S GENERALBESKRIVELSE. SUPPLEMENT. Text in Danish. 1995. irreg. DKK 200 (effective 2000).
Related titles: ◆ Supplement to: V & S Generalbeskrivelse.
Published by: V & S Byggedata, 551 Frederikssundvej 194, Broenshoej, 2700, Denmark. TEL 45-38-60-77-11, FAX 45-38-60-77-55, bygdat@vs-byggedata.dk, bygdat@vs.byggedata.dk. Ed. Carl Friis Skovsen.

692.3 DNK
V & S REGLER FOR OPMAALING AF BYGGERI. Text in Danish. 1994. irreg. DKK 200 (effective 1999). **Document type:** *Trade.*
Published by: V & S Byggedata, 551 Frederikssundvej 194, Broenshoej, 2700, Denmark. TEL 45-38-60-77-11, FAX 45-38-60-77-55, bygdat@vs-byggedata.dk, bygdat@vs.byggedata.dk. Ed. Carl Friis Skovsen.

658 USA
VALUE RETAIL NEWS; the journal of outlet & off-price retailing & development. Text in English. 1983. m. USD 144, USD 175 to non-members; USD 99 to members (effective 2005). adv. bk.rev. **Document type:** *Magazine, Trade.* **Description:** Covers real-estate leasing and related news of outlet and off-price retailers and developers.
Formerly: Off-Price News
Published by: International Council of Shopping Centers, 665 Fifth Ave, New York, NY 10022. TEL 212-421-8181, lhumphers@icsc.org, http://www.valueretailnews.com. Ed. Linda Humphers. Adv. contact Karen Knobeloch. B&W page USD 3,135, color page USD 4,240.

659.1 USA ISSN 1540-6016
HF5438.8.K48
VELOCITY. Text in English. 1990. 4/yr. USD 120 (effective 2000). adv. bk.rev. **Document type:** *Trade.* **Description:** Covers strategies for successful customer management, including case studies of customer-supplier partnerships and benchmark data from Fortune 1000 companies.
Former titles (until 1999): N A M A Journal; N A M A News
Published by: Strategic Account Management Association, 150 N Wacker Dr, Ste 2222, Chicago, IL 60606-1607. TEL 312-251-3131, FAX 312-251-3132. Ed. Maria Susano. Pub. Lisa Napolitano. R&P, Adv. contact Katherine Gotsick. Circ: 2,000 (controlled).

658.8 GBR ISSN 0954-6235
VENDING INTERNATIONAL. Text in English. 1967. m. GBP 50. adv. **Document type:** *Magazine, Trade.* **Description:** Focuses on the automated refreshment industry and its related products, services & developments.
Formerly: International Vending Times
Indexed: PROMT.
Published by: Datateam Publishing Ltd, 15a London Rd, Maidstone, Kent ME16 8LY, United Kingdom. TEL 44-1622-687031, FAX 44-1622-757646, vending@datateam.co.uk, info@datateam.co.uk, http://www.datateam.co.uk/business_publications/vending_international.htm, http://www.datateam.co.uk/home/home.htm. Ed. Geoff Manners. Pub. Nick Carpenter. Adv. contact Odell Gardner. B&W page GBP 1,100, color page GBP 1,650; trim 195 x 280.

658 ITA
VENDING MAGAZINE; of automatic merchandising. Text in Italian; Summaries in English, Italian. 1976. 10/yr. EUR 75 domestic; EUR 95 in Europe; EUR 121 elsewhere (effective 2005). adv. back issues avail. **Document type:** *Magazine, Trade.*
Related titles: Online - full content ed.
Published by: Vending Press s.r.l., Corso Mocalieri 21-A, Turin, TO 10131, Italy. TEL 39-11-6602900, FAX 39-11-6600120, http://www.vendingpress.it/. Ed. Gian Franco Fassio. Adv. contact Silvana Ferrero. B&W page EUR 847, color page EUR 1,418; 21 x 29.7. Circ: 6,000.

658.87 USA ISSN 0042-3327
VENDING TIMES; vending - feeding - coffee service - music & games. Text in English. 1961. m. USD 35 (effective 2005). adv. illus. reprints avail. **Document type:** *Magazine, Trade.*
Incorporates (in 1974): Vend (0042-3297); V-T Music and Games
Related titles: Microform ed.: (from PQC); Online - full text ed.
Indexed: BusI, PROMT, SRI, T&II.

Published by: Vending Times, Inc., 1375 Broadway, 6th Fl, New York, NY 10018-7001. TEL 212-302-4700, FAX 212-221-3311, vendtime@idt.net, http://www.vendingtimes.com. Ed. T.R. Sanford. Pub. Alicia Lavay-Kertes. Adv. contact Steve Zarolnick. Circ: 17,500 (paid).

670.29 USA
VENDOR PRODUCT COMPARISON (DESIGN ENGINEERING). Text in English. 1984. m. USD 835. adv. **Description:** Provides product and subject access to manufacturers of comparative products necessary for design engineering.
Formerly: Design Engineering Services Index
Published by: I H S Energy (Subsidiary of: I H S Energy Group), 15 Inverness Way East, Englewood, CO 80112. FAX 303-799-4085, http://ihsenergy.com. Ed. Liz Maynard Prigge. Circ: 2,600.

658 MEX
VENTAS Y MERCADOTECNIA✶. Text in Spanish. m. adv.
Published by: Editorial Grupo Infocorp S.A. de C.V., Manuel M Ponce 304, Col. Guadalupe Inn, Mexico, D.F., 01020, Mexico. Ed. Milo Escobedo Fournier. Circ: 10,969.

VENTE EQUIPEMENTS MENAGERS. see *ELECTRONICS*

658.87 DEU ISSN 0049-5999
DER VERSANDHAUSBERATER✶. Text in German. 1961. w. bk.rev. **Document type:** *Newsletter.* **Description:** Weekly newsletter for catalog and mail order industries in German speaking countries.
Media: Duplicated (not offset).
Published by: Versandhausberater, Esternaystr 32, Waldbronn, 76337, Germany. Ed. Klaus Prochazka. Circ: 400.

658.8 USA
VERTICAL SYSTEMS RESELLER; the news source for channel management. Text in English. 1992. m. USD 190 domestic; USD 225 in Canada; USD 250 elsewhere (effective 2005). adv. software rev. illus.; tr.lit.; charts; stat. **Document type:** *Magazine, Trade.* **Description:** Target markets: retail, hospitality, warehousing/distribution, manufacturing, healthcare and the public sector (government, education, utilities).
Formerly (until Jan. 2004): Retail Systems Reseller (1071-2224)
Related titles: Online - full text ed.
Indexed: CompLI, MicrocompInd.
—**CCC.**
Published by: Edgell Communications, Inc., 4 Middlebury Blvd, Randolph, NJ 07869-4214. edgell@edgellmail.com, http://verticalsystemsreseller.com, http://www.edgellcommunications.com. Ed. Ralph Bernstein. Pub. Michael Kachmar. adv.: B&W page USD 3,100, color page USD 3,800; trim 10.88 x 8.13. Circ: 30,000.

VERZEICHNIS DER VERSANDHANDELS. see *BUSINESS AND ECONOMICS—Trade And Industrial Directories*

VIEW MAGAZINE/REVISTA VIEW. see *MEDICAL SCIENCES—Ophthalmology And Optometry*

VISION MONDAY. see *MEDICAL SCIENCES—Ophthalmology And Optometry*

VITRINA. RESTORANNYI BIZNES. see *HOTELS AND RESTAURANTS*

658.8 ITA ISSN 0042-7837
VOCE DELLA FIERA; bisettimanale di economia e problemi di mercato. Text in Italian. 1964. s-w. adv. bk.rev. illus.; stat.
Published by: Organizzazione "X" di Armando Rositani, Corso Cavour, 113, Bari, BA 70121, Italy. TEL 39-80-5214363, FAX 39-80-5214363. Ed. Armando Rositani. Adv. contact Mariuccia Verrone. Circ: 10,000.

658.87 USA
THE VOICE OF THE NEBRASKA GROCERY INDUSTRY. Text in English. 1906. bi-m. USD 75 to non-members (effective 2001). adv. 32 p./no.; **Document type:** *Magazine, Trade.* **Description:** Covers company development, market trends, merchandising ideas, promotion plans, government regulations.
Formerly: Nebraska Retailer (0028-1948)
Published by: Nebraska Grocery Industry Association, 5533 S. 27th St., Ste. 104, Lincoln, NE 68512-1664. TEL 402-423-5533, FAX 402-423-8686. Ed., Pub., Adv. contact Kathy Siefken. Circ: 500 (paid and free).

658.8 USA
▼ **WALL STREET JOURNAL ONLINE (MEDIA & MARKETING EDITION).** Text in English. 2003. d. USD 79; USD 59 with subscr. to Wall Street Journal Online; USD 39 with subscr. to Wall Street Journal (effective 2003). **Description:** Provides the latest news and information on the media and marketing industries as well as regular content from the Wall Street Journal Online.
Media: Online - full content. **Related titles:** Special ed. of: Wall Street Journal Online. USD 79 (effective 2004) (from bigchalk, Factiva, O C L C Online Computer Library Center, Inc., ProQuest Information & Learning).
Published by: Dow Jones Company, 200 Burnett Rd, Chicopee, MA 01020. http://online.wsj.com/public/media?mod=0%5F0006, http://www.wsj.com.

WEARABLES BUSINESS. see *CLOTHING TRADE*

384.33 658.8 USA ISSN 1094-8112
WEB MARKETING TODAY. Text in English. 1995. m. free. adv. back issues avail. **Document type:** *Newsletter, Trade.* **Description:** Provides information on how to use websites for promotion and marketing.
Media: Online - full content (from Florida Center for Library Automation). **Related titles:** E-mail ed.; Online - full text ed.: (from Gale Group).
Published by: Wilson Internet Services, P O Box 308, Rocklin, CA 95677-0308. TEL 916-652-4659, rfwilson@wilsonweb.com, http://www.wilsonweb.com/wmt/. Ed., Pub. Ralph F. Wilson.

658 USA ISSN 1091-1405
WEB MARKETING UPDATE. Text in English. 1996. m. USD 347 (effective 2004). back issues avail. **Document type:** *Newsletter.* **Description:** Includes news briefs, trend roundups, new application developments, and Web success updates.
—**CCC.**
Published by: Computer Economics, Inc., 2082 Business Center Dr., Ste 240, Irvine, CA 92612. TEL 949-831-8700, FAX 949-442-7688, info@compecon.com, http://www.computereconomics.com. Ed. Anne Zalatan. Pub. Bruno Bassi.

658.8 USA
THE WEBBIZ TELEGRAM. Text in English. w. free. **Document type:** *Newsletter.* **Description:** Features articles from entrepreneurs, news, and business-related classifieds.
Media: Online - full text.
Published by: WebBiz Telegram success@topher.net, http://www.tex-net.net. Ed. Harold Mounce.

WEEKLY PETROLEUM ARGUS. see *PETROLEUM AND GAS*

WEIN UND MARKT; Das Wirtschaftsmagazin fuer Handel und Erzeuger. see *BEVERAGES*

WESTERN - ENGLISH INDUSTRY REPORT. see *CLOTHING TRADE*

WESTERN LUMBER (YEAR) BUYERS MANUAL. see *FORESTS AND FORESTRY—Lumber And Wood*

658 GBR ISSN 0265-296X
WHAT TO BUY FOR BUSINESS. Text in English. m. back issues avail. **Document type:** *Trade.* **Description:** Reports on faxes, photocopiers, mobile phones, computer software, and a whole range of other business equipment and services.
Formerly: Better Buys for Business
Related titles: Online - full text ed.
Indexed: BrCerAb, Inspec, RAPRA.
—BLDSC (9309.625000), AskIEEE, IE, Infotrieve. **CCC.**
Published by: Highbury Business Communications (Subsidiary of: Highbury House Communications PLC), Ann Boleyn House, 9-13 Ewell Rd, Cheam, Surrey SM3 8BZ, United Kingdom. TEL 44-20-87226000, http://www.hhc.co.uk/whattobuyforbusiness. Ed. Sarah White TEL 44-20-87226023.

WHAT'S NEW FOR FAMILY FUN CENTERS. see *BUSINESS AND ECONOMICS—Trade And Industrial Directories*

658.8 GBR
WHAT'S NEW IN MARKETING (ONLINE). Text in English. 1986. m. free. adv. **Document type:** *Trade.* **Description:** Offers regular advice on everything from e-marketing to effective exhibiting.
Formerly: What's New in Marketing (Print) (0269-2058)
Media: Online - full content.
Indexed: ABIn.
—**CCC.**
Published by: Chartered Institute of Marketing, Moor Hall, Cookham, Maidenhead, Berks SL6 9QH, United Kingdom. TEL 44-1628-427500, FAX 44-1628-427499, wnim@cim.co.uk, http://www.wnim.com, http://www.cim.co.uk.

658 USA ISSN 1088-2359
WHAT'S WORKING FOR AMERICAN COMPANIES IN INTERNATIONAL SALES & MARKETING. Text in English. 1996. s-m. USD 391. charts; stat.; tr.lit. **Document type:** *Newsletter.* **Description:** Helps international sales and marketing executives identify local partners, expand distributor networks, overcome language and cultural barriers, and deal with local laws and regulations.
Published by: Progressive Business Publications, 370 Technology Dr, Malvern, PA 19355-1315. TEL 610-695-8600, 800-220-5000, FAX 610-647-8089, editor@pbp.com, http://www.pbp.com. Ed. Lyn McCafferty. R&P Curt Brown. Circ: 2,379 (paid).

381.45002 USA
WHAT'S WORKING IN DIRECT MARKETING AND FULFILLMENT. Text in English. 1982. bi-w. USD 182. cum.index: 1982-86. back issues avail. **Description:** Reports on innovative and unusual ways marketers are boosting response, cutting costs, and speeding fulfillment.
Published by: United Communications Group, 11300 Rockville Pike Ste 1100, Rockville, MD 20852-3030. TEL 301-816-8950, FAX 301-816-8945. Ed. Barbara Weckstein Kaplowitz.

WHAT'S WORKING IN SALES MANAGEMENT. see *BUSINESS AND ECONOMICS—Management*

WHAT'S WORKING ONLINE. see *COMPUTERS—Internet*

658.0029 GBR ISSN 1367-806X
HD9652.3
WHERE TO BUY CHEMICALS, PLANT AND SERVICES. Text in English. 1930. a. (June). GBP 113 domestic; GBP 122, USD 222 foreign (effective Jun. 2005). reprint service avail. from PQC. **Document type:** *Directory, Trade.* **Description:** Lists U.K. chemical traders and distributors. Includes sections for general and fine chemicals; plant, materials and apparatus; and services to the chemical industry.
Formerly (until 1990): Where to Buy: Chemicals and Chemical Plant (0308-0021)
Related titles: ◆ Supplement to: Specialty Chemicals.
—BLDSC (9310.775500).
Published by: D M G Business Media Ltd. (Subsidiary of: D M G World Media Ltd.), Queensway House, 2 Queensway, Redhill, Surrey RH1 1QS, United Kingdom. TEL 44-1737-768611, FAX 44-1737-855477, info@uk.dmgworldmedia.com, http://www.dmgworldmedia.com/BusinessMediaPublications.html.

WHITE PAGES & DIRECTORY LISTINGS (YEAR). see *BUSINESS AND ECONOMICS—Trade And Industrial Directories*

658.8 GBR
HG4538
WHO OWNS WHOM. NORTH & SOUTH AMERICA. Text in English. 1969. a. GBP 375 (effective 2000). index. **Document type:** *Directory.*
Former titles: Who Owns Whom. North America (0308-8502); (until 1976): Who Owns Whom. North American Edition (0083-9310)
Related titles: Online - full text ed.
—BLDSC (9311.935000), CISTI. **CCC.**
Published by: Dun & Bradstreet Ltd., 50-100 Holmers Farm Way, High Wycombe, Bucks HP12 4UL, United Kingdom. TEL 44-1494-423689, FAX 44-1494-422332.

658 USA ISSN 1049-0116
HF5465.5
WHOLESALE-BY-MAIL CATALOG. Text in English. 1979. a.
Published by: St. Martin's Press (Subsidiary of: Holtzbrink Publishers), 175 Fifth Ave, New York, NY 10010. TEL 212-674-5151.

658 USA
WHOLESALE SOURCE MAGAZINE; for distributors and retailers of general merchandise. Text in English. m. USD 20 domestic; USD 35 in Canada & Mexico; USD 75 foreign (effective 2001). adv. **Document type:** *Magazine, Trade.* **Description:** Reports on industry news and issues of interest to distributors and retailers of general merchandise.
Published by: Show Communications, 423 Lenni Rd, Lenni, PA 19052. TEL 800-297-4036, FAX 610- 361-0117, showcomm@aol.com, http://wsmag.com/indexmain.htm. Ed. John Valania. Pub. Jack McAndrew. adv.: B&W page USD 800, color page USD 1,850.

WHO'S WHO IN DIRECT MARKETING. see *BUSINESS AND ECONOMICS—Trade And Industrial Directories*

658.8 NLD ISSN 1387-2907
WIE WERKT WAAR BIJ ADVERTEERDERS (GEDRUKTE VERSIE). Text in Dutch. 1996. s-a. EUR 130 includes diskette (effective 2005). adv. **Document type:** *Directory, Trade.* **Description:** Lists the names and adresses of contact persons at the 500 most important advertisers.
Related titles: Supplement(s): Wie Werkt Waar bij Adverteerders (Diskette). ISSN 1567-9241.
Published by: Adformatie Groep (Subsidiary of: Wolters Kluwer N.V.), Postbus 75462, Amsterdam, 1070 AL, Netherlands. TEL 31-20-5733644, FAX 31-20-6793581, http://www.adformatie.nl.

658.8 NLD ISSN 1387-2915
WIE WERKT WAAR IN DE MEDIA (GEDRUKTE VERSIE). Text in Dutch. 1995. s-a. EUR 119 incl. diskette (effective 2005). adv. **Document type:** *Directory, Trade.* **Description:** Lists the names and adresses of publishers, managing editors, editors, advertising, and acquisitions personnel of the most important media outlets.
Related titles: Supplement(s): Wie Werkt Waar in de Media (Diskette). ISSN 1567-9268.
Published by: Adformatie Groep (Subsidiary of: Wolters Kluwer N.V.), Postbus 75462, Amsterdam, 1070 AL, Netherlands. TEL 31-20-5733644, FAX 31-20-6793581, http://www.adformatie.nl.

WINDOW & DOOR. see *BUILDING AND CONSTRUCTION*

658.7   GBR
WINNING EDGE; the magazine for professional sales & marketing personnel. Text in English. 1976. m. free to members (effective 2005). adv. bk.rev. illus. **Document type:** *Magazine, Trade.* **Description:** Covers sales techniques, evaluation of markets for products and services, methods for attracting customers, sales team development, conference venues, business travel, and news in sales and marketing, video reviews, sales training, international trade news, and appointments.
Former titles (until 2005): Sales & Marketing Professional (1470-3009); (until 2000): Sales and Marketing Management (0264-3200); (until 1981): Sales Management (0140-5179); Which incorporates: Sales Engineering (0306-5618); (until 1976): Professional Salesmanship
Related titles: Online - full text ed.: (from The Dialog Corporation).
Indexed: ADPA, ATI, BusI, CPM, Emerald, MagInd, RASB, T&II.—BLDSC (9319.418125), IE.
Published by: (Institute of Sales and Marketing Management), The Institute of Sales & Marketing Management, Harrier Court, Woodside Rd, Romeland Hill, Lower Woodside, LU1 4DQ, United Kingdom. TEL 44-1582-840001, FAX 44-1582-849142, sales@ismm.co.uk, http://www.ismm.co.uk/magazine.php. Ed., R&P Stuart Morgan. Adv. contact Mike Wright TEL 44-1536-747333. page GBP 2,050; trim 210 x 297. Circ: 15,000.

WIRTSCHAFT UND WETTBEWERB; Zeitschrift fuer Kartellrecht, Wettbewerbsrecht und Marktorganisation. see *BUSINESS AND ECONOMICS—Production Of Goods And Services*

WOLFF'S GUIDE TO THE LONDON METAL EXCHANGE. see *METALLURGY*

WOOD PRODUCTS: INTERNATIONAL TRADE AND FOREIGN MARKETS. see *AGRICULTURE—Agricultural Economics*

WORLD CONSUMER INCOME AND EXPENDITURE PATTERNS. see *BUSINESS AND ECONOMICS—Trade And Industrial Directories*

WORLD CONSUMER MARKETS; on the internet. see *BUSINESS AND ECONOMICS—Trade And Industrial Directories*

WORLD COSMETICS AND TOILETRIES MARKETING DIRECTORY; the definitive information source for the world cosmetics and toiletries industry. see *BEAUTY CULTURE—Perfumes And Cosmetics*

658.8029   GBR
HF5415.124
WORLD DIRECTORY OF MARKETING INFORMATION SOURCES. Text in English. 1990. biennial, latest 2003, Mar. GBP 395, USD 650, EUR 650 per issue (effective 2003). **Document type:** *Directory.* **Description:** Provides a guide to business research organizations throughout the world.
Formerly (until 1995): European Directory of Marketing Information Sources (0950-656X)
Published by: Euromonitor, 60-61 Britton St, London, EC1 5UX, United Kingdom. TEL 44-20-7251-8024, FAX 44-20-7608-3149, info@euromonitor.com, http://www.euromonitor.com. Dist. by: Current Pacific Ltd., PO Box 36-536, Northcote, Auckland, New Zealand. TEL 64-9-480-1388, FAX 64-9-480-1387, info@cplnz.com, http://www.cplnz.com.

WORLD DRINKS DATABOOK. see *BEVERAGES*

WORLD DRINKS MARKETING DIRECTORY; the ultimate guide to the global drinks industry. see *BEVERAGES*

380   IND
WORLD FAIRS GUIDE; devoted to industrial expansion, trade fairs, export, tourism and travel trade. Text in English. 1959. m. INR 140, USD 25. adv. bk.rev. tr.lit.
Formerly: Trade Digest (0041-042X)
Media: Duplicated (not offset).
Published by: (International Trade Fair Association), Trade Digest Publications, S-185 Greater Kailash-2, New Delhi, 110 048, India. TEL 6414185. Ed. C L Khanna. Circ: 7,500.

WORLD FOOD MARKETING DIRECTORY. see *FOOD AND FOOD INDUSTRIES*

658.87   USA   ISSN 0049-8106
WORLD GIFT REVIEW MONTHLY NEWSLETTER∗ . Text in English. 1965. m. looseleaf. USD 14. adv. bk.rev. **Document type:** *Newsletter.*
Published by: World Gift Review Co., 59 Hille Pl, Ridgefield, NJ 07660-2025. Ed. John W Slawenski. Circ: 9,600.

WORLD LEADING GLOBAL BRAND OWNERS. see *BUSINESS AND ECONOMICS—Trade And Industrial Directories*

658.8 663.1   GBR
THE WORLD MARKET FOR ALCOHOLIC DRINKS. Text in English. a. GBP 5,050 per vol. domestic; EUR 7,900 per vol. in Europe; USD 7,900 per vol. elsewhere (effective Jun. 2002). **Document type:** *Trade.*
Related titles: Series of: Strategy 2000 Series.

Published by: Euromonitor, 60-61 Britton St, London, EC1 5UX, United Kingdom. TEL 44-20-7251-8024, FAX 44-20-7608-3149, info@euromonitor.com, http://www.euromonitor.com.

658.8 676   GBR
THE WORLD MARKET FOR AWAY FROM HOME DISPOSABLE PAPER PRODUCTS. Text in English. a., latest 2001, Aug. GBP 4,660 per vol. domestic; EUR 7,000 per vol. in Europe; USD 7,000 per vol. elsewhere (effective 2003). **Document type:** *Trade.*
Related titles: Series of: Strategy 2000 Series.
Published by: Euromonitor, 60-61 Britton St, London, EC1 5UX, United Kingdom. TEL 44-20-7251-8024, FAX 44-20-7608-3149, info@euromonitor.com, http://www.euromonitor.com.

THE WORLD MARKET FOR BAKERY PRODUCTS. see *FOOD AND FOOD INDUSTRIES—Bakers And Confectioners*

THE WORLD MARKET FOR BEER. see *BEVERAGES*

THE WORLD MARKET FOR CONFECTIONERY. see *FOOD AND FOOD INDUSTRIES—Bakers And Confectioners*

658.8 664   GBR
THE WORLD MARKET FOR CONSUMER FOODSERVICE. Text in English. a., latest 2003, Jan. GBP 5,050 per vol. domestic; EUR 7,900 per vol. in Europe; USD 7,900 per vol. elsewhere (effective 2003). **Document type:** *Trade.*
Related titles: Series of: Strategy 2000 Series.
Published by: Euromonitor, 60-61 Britton St, London, EC1 5UX, United Kingdom. TEL 44-20-7251-8024, FAX 44-20-7608-3149, info@euromonitor.com, http://www.euromonitor.com.

658.8 642   GBR
THE WORLD MARKET FOR CONTRACT FOODSERVICE. Text in English. a., latest 2002, May. GBP 5,050 per vol. domestic; EUR 7,900 per vol. in Europe; USD 7,900 per vol. elsewhere (effective May. 2002). **Document type:** *Trade.*
Related titles: Series of: Strategy 2000 Series.
Published by: Euromonitor, 60-61 Britton St, London, EC1 5UX, United Kingdom. TEL 44-20-7251-8024, FAX 44-20-7608-3149, info@euromonitor.com, http://www.euromonitor.com.

668.55 658.8   GBR
THE WORLD MARKET FOR COSMETICS AND TOILETRIES. Text in English. irreg., latest 2002. GBP 5,750 domestic; EUR 9,000 in Europe; USD 9,000 elsewhere (effective Jul. 2002). **Document type:** *Trade.* **Description:** Provides strategic analysis at the global level for the cosmetics and toiletries market.
Related titles: Series of: Strategy 2000 Series.
Published by: Euromonitor, 60-61 Britton St, London, EC1 5UX, United Kingdom. TEL 44-20-7251-8024, FAX 44-20-7608-3149, info@euromonitor.com, http://www.euromonitor.com.

THE WORLD MARKET FOR DAIRY PRODUCTS. see *AGRICULTURE—Dairying And Dairy Products*

658.8 664.6 613.26   GBR
THE WORLD MARKET FOR DIETETIC FOOD. Text in English. a., latest 2002, Nov. GBP 5,050 per vol. domestic; EUR 7,900 per vol. in Europe; USD 7,900 per vol. elsewhere (effective Nov. 2002). **Document type:** *Trade.*
Related titles: Series of: Strategy 2000 Series.
Published by: Euromonitor, 60-61 Britton St, London, EC1 5UX, United Kingdom. TEL 44-20-7251-8024, FAX 44-20-7608-3149, info@euromonito.commed, info@euromonitor.com.

658.8 646.7 668.5   GBR
THE WORLD MARKET FOR ETHNIC COSMETICS & TOILETRIES. Text in English. a., latest 2002, Feb. GBP 4,660 per vol. domestic; EUR 7,000 per vol. in Europe; USD 7,000 per vol. elsewhere (effective Feb. 2002).
Related titles: Series of: Strategy 2000 Series.
Published by: Euromonitor, 60-61 Britton St, London, EC1 5UX, United Kingdom. TEL 44-20-7251-8024, FAX 44-20-7608-3149, info@euromonitor.com, http://www.euromonitor.com.

THE WORLD MARKET FOR HOUSEHOLD CARE. see *CLEANING AND DYEING*

THE WORLD MARKET FOR ICE CREAM. see *FOOD AND FOOD INDUSTRIES*

THE WORLD MARKET FOR O T C HEALTHCARE. (Over the Counter) see *PHARMACY AND PHARMACOLOGY*

664.6 658.8   GBR
THE WORLD MARKET FOR PET FOOD AND PET CARE PRODUCTS. Text in English. a., latest 2002, Apr. GBP 5,050 per vol. domestic; EUR 7,900 per vol. in Europe; USD 7,900 per vol. elsewhere (effective Apr. 2002). **Document type:** *Trade.* **Description:** Provides a comprehensive and strategic review of pet food markets from a global perspective.

Formerly: The World Market for Pet Food
Related titles: Series of: Strategy 2000 Series.
Published by: Euromonitor, 60-61 Britton St, London, EC1 5UX, United Kingdom. TEL 44-20-7251-8024, FAX 44-20-7608-3149, info@euromonitor.com, http://www.euromonitor.com.

THE WORLD MARKET FOR SAVOURY SNACKS. see *FOOD AND FOOD INDUSTRIES*

THE WORLD MARKET FOR SOFT DRINKS. see *BEVERAGES*

THE WORLD MARKET FOR SPIRITS. see *BEVERAGES*

THE WORLD MARKET FOR TOBACCO. see *TOBACCO*

THE WORLD MARKET FOR TRAVEL AND TOURISM. see *TRAVEL AND TOURISM*

643 658.8   GBR
THE WORLD MARKET FOR WHITE GOODS. Text in English. irreg., latest 2001. GBP 5,050 domestic; EUR 7,900 in Europe; USD 7,900 elsewhere (effective 2003). **Document type:** *Trade.*
Published by: Euromonitor, 60-61 Britton St, London, EC1 5UX, United Kingdom. TEL 44-20-7251-8024, FAX 44-20-7608-3149, info@euromonitor.com, http://www.euromonitor.com.

THE WORLD MARKET FOR WINE. see *BEVERAGES*

WORLD MARKETING DATA AND STATISTICS. see *BUSINESS AND ECONOMICS—Trade And Industrial Directories*

WORLD MARKETING FORECASTS; on the internet. see *BUSINESS AND ECONOMICS—Trade And Industrial Directories*

658.83   GBR
WORLD RETAIL DATA AND STATISTICS (YEAR). Text in English. 1999. irreg., latest 2003. GBP 395 domestic; EUR 650 in Europe; USD 650 elsewhere (effective 2003). **Document type:** *Directory, Trade.* **Description:** Combines an extensive range of retailing statistics across 50 countries worldwide with up-to-date information on socio-economic trends and consumer expenditure patterns.
Published by: Euromonitor, 60-61 Britton St, London, EC1 5UX, United Kingdom. TEL 44-20-7251-8024, FAX 44-20-7608-3149, info@euromonitor.com, http://www.euromonitor.com.

WORLD RETAIL DIRECTORY AND SOURCEBOOK. see *BUSINESS AND ECONOMICS—Trade And Industrial Directories*

WORLDPROFIT ONLINE MAGAZINE. see *BUSINESS AND ECONOMICS—Small Business*

658.8   GBR   ISSN 0043-9304
WORLD'S FAIR. Text in English. 1904. w. GBP 35 in United Kingdom; GBP 50 rest of Europe; GBP 100 elsewhere; GBP 0.76 newsstand/cover (effective 2000). adv. bk.rev. charts; illus.; mkt.; pat.; tr.mk. **Document type:** *Newspaper, Trade.* **Description:** News and features of interest to those involved in amusement parks, traveling fair and circus industries, steam preservation, and the world of magic.
Incorporates: Coin Slot (0010-0420); Market Trader
Indexed: RASB.
Published by: World's Fair Ltd., Albert Mill, Albert St, PO Box 57, Oldham, Lancs OL8 3WF, United Kingdom. TEL 44-161-683-8000, FAX 44-161-683-8001, wfair@worldsfair.co.uk, http://www.worldsfair.co.uk. Ed. Michael Mellor. Circ: 30,000.

380.14   GBR   ISSN 0309-4960
WORLDWIDE MARKETING OPPORTUNITIES DIGEST. Text in English. 1978. bi-m. USD 150. adv. **Document type:** *Trade.*
Published by: International Commercial Network Ltd., Yorks, 24 Mount Parade, Harrogate, Yorks HG1 1BP, United Kingdom. FAX 0423-561204, TELEX 94014165 AGTS G. Ed. M A Lewis. Circ: 2,000.

658   TWN   ISSN 1813-4483
▼ ➤ **XINGXIAO PINGLUN/MARKETING REVIEW.** Text in Chinese, English. 2004. q. TWD 1,200, USD 50 (effective 2004 & 2005). abstr.; bibl.; charts; illus. back issues avail. **Document type:** *Journal, Academic/Scholarly.* **Description:** Covers marketing research for scholars.
Published by: Academy of Taiwan Information Systems Research, PO Box 179-45, Taipei, 116, Taiwan. TEL 886-2-25009508, FAX 886-2-25175924, chang@atisr.org, http://marketingreview.atisr.org/, http://www.atisr.org/.

658   USA   ISSN 1041-7516
YOUTH MARKETS ALERT. Text in English. 1989. fortn. USD 447 domestic; USD 507 foreign (effective 2005). 8 p./no.; back issues avail. **Document type:** *Newsletter, Trade.* **Description:** Covers all the latest research and marketing tactics on youth markets.

Related titles: Online - full text ed.: (from Factiva, Gale Group, Northern Light Technology, Inc., O C L C Online Computer Library Center, Inc.).
Indexed: B&I.
Published by: E P M Communications, 160 Mercer St, 3rd Fl, New York, NY 10012-3212. info@epmcom.com, http://www.epmcom.com. Ed. Michael Bush. Pub., R&P Barbara Perrin.

658.8 USA ISSN 1549-9588
THE ZWEIG A-E MARKETING LETTER. Text in English. 2/m. USD 275 (effective 2005). **Document type:** *Newsletter, Trade.* **Description:** Provides information on marketing practices, techniques, and campaigns that are effective for A/E firms.
Formerly (until 2004): Revolutionary Marketing (1526-4483)
Published by: Zweig White Information Services, One IBM Plaza, 330 N Wabash, Chicago, IL 60611. TEL 312-628-5870, FAX 312-628-5878, info@mercormedia.com, http://www.zweigwhite.com/trends/marketing/index.asp, http://www.mercormedia.com/.

20/20. see *MEDICAL SCIENCES—Ophthalmology And Optometry*

20/20 ASIA. see *MEDICAL SCIENCES—Ophthalmology And Optometry*

20/20 EUROPE. see *MEDICAL SCIENCES—Ophthalmology And Optometry*

B

BUSINESS AND ECONOMICS—Office Equipment And Services

651 FRA ISSN 0758-8763
ANNUAIRE BUREAUTIQUE INFORMATIQUE. Text in French. 1972. a.
Formerly: Annuaire de la Mecanographie, Materiel de Bureau, Informatique
Published by: Editions Louis Johanet, 38 bd Henri Sellier, Suresnes, 92156, France.

ANNUAL BOOK OF A S T M STANDARDS. VOLUME 15.08. SENSORY EVALUATION; LIVESTOCK, MEAT, AND POULTRY EVALUATION SYSTEMS, VACUUM CLEANERS; SECURITY SYSTEMS AND EQUIPMENT; DETENTION AND CORRECTIONAL FACILITIES; FOOD SERVICE EQUIPMENT. see *ENGINEERING—Engineering Mechanics And Materials*

ARCHIV FUER STENOGRAFIE, TEXTVERARBEITUNG, BUEROTECHNIK. see *EDUCATION—Teaching Methods And Curriculum*

651 333.33 USA
ARIZONA BUSINESS MAGAZINE. Text in English. 1985. q. USD 30 (effective 2005). adv. **Document type:** *Magazine, Consumer.* **Description:** Focus on virtually every facet of the business community — from development and construction to the environment, building management and architecture.
Former titles: Arizona Business and Development; Office Guide to Phoenix
Address: 3101 N. Central Ave., Ste. 1030, Phoenix, AZ 85012-2654. TEL 602-277-6045, FAX 602-650-0827, editors@azbusmag.com, http://www.azbusinessmagazine.com. Ed. Greg Sexton. Pub. Michael Atkinson. Circ: 26,000 (paid).

004 330 USA
AUTOMOTIVE MANAGEMENT INFORMATION SYSTEMS COUNCIL NEWSLETTER. Text in English. 1979. s-a. free to members. **Document type:** *Newsletter.*
Formerly: Automotive Manufacturers E D T Council Newsletter
Published by: Automotive Management Information Systems Council, PO Box 13966, Durham, NC 27709-3966. TEL 201-569-8500. Circ: 150 (controlled).

651.2 DEU ISSN 1617-9757
B I T - BUSINESS INFORMATION TECHNOLOGY. Text in German. 1964. bi-m. EUR 69 domestic; EUR 76.80 foreign; EUR 12 newsstand/cover (effective 2004). adv. **Document type:** *Magazine, Trade.*
Former titles (until 2001): B I T - Buerowelt im Trend (1438-227X); (until 1996): B I T - Bueroorganisation, Informationstechnik, Telekommunikation (0941-9055); (until 1989): B I T - Buero- und Informationstechnik (0006-3843); (until 1970): B I T - Berichte, Informationen, Tatsachen (0408-1099)
Indexed: ABIn, RefZh.
—CCC.
Published by: B I T Verlag Weinbrenner GmbH & Co. KG, Fasanenweg 18, Leinfelden-Echterdingen, 70771, Germany. TEL 49-711-75910, FAX 49-711-7591336, info@bitverlag.de, http://www.bitverlag.de/bitverlag/bit/index.asp?br=e&sc=8&z=BIT. Pub. Karl Heinz Weinbrenner. Adv. contact Christa Winkler. B&W page EUR 3,640, color page EUR 5,200. Circ: 11,750 (paid and controlled).

651 USA ISSN 1078-5809
B P I A. BUSINESS PRODUCTS INDUSTRY REPORT. Text in English. 1970. bi-w. USD 40 to non-members; USD 10 to members (effective 2005). stat. **Document type:** *Newsletter, Trade.*
Formerly (until 1994): N O P A Industry Report (0746-5467)
Published by: National Office Products Association, 301 N Fairfax St, Alexandria, VA 22314. TEL 703-549-9040, FAX 703-683-7552, info@iopfad.org, http://www.iopfda.org, http://www.iofda.org. Ed. Sandra Selva. Circ: 9,000.

651.2 USA
B T A HOTLINE ONLINE. Text in English. 1968. s-m. (except. Feb. m.). free (effective 2005). adv. back issues avail. **Document type:** *Magazine, Trade.* **Description:** Features industry news, association news and information on new products.
Former titles (until 2000): B T A Hotline (Print); Business Equipment Hotline; Hotline (Kansas City)
Media: Online - full content.
Published by: Business Technology Association, 12411 Wornall Rd, Kansas City, MO 64145-1166. TEL 816-941-3100, 800-366-6950, FAX 816-941-2829, brent@bta.org, http://www.bta.org. Ed. Brent Hoskins. Pub. Mike Wukitsch. Adv. contact Julie Birch.

653 DEU ISSN 0005-7010
BAYERISCHE BLAETTER FUER STENOGRAPHIE. Text in German. 1849. bi-m. adv. bk.rev. charts; illus.; stat. index, cum.index. **Document type:** *Bulletin, Trade.* **Description:** Contains essays and other infomration on the pedagogy, systematics, and development of shorthand typewriting and computing.
Published by: Stenographen-Zentralverein Gabelsberger e.V., Uhlandstr 16, Ottobrunn, 85521, Germany. TEL 49-89-23392535, info@stenografenzentralverein.de, http://www.stenografenzentralverein.de. Ed. Hans-Andreas Kroiss. Pub., R&P Hannes Steiner. Circ: 800.

BETRIEBSWIRTSCHAFTLICHE BLAETTER. see *BUSINESS AND ECONOMICS—Management*

651.2 USA ISSN 1084-2055
HF5548
BETTER BUYS FOR BUSINESS. Text in English. 1986. 10/yr. USD 134 domestic; USD 141 in Canada; USD 235 elsewhere. **Document type:** *Consumer.* **Description:** Consumer guide to document imaging equipment.
Formerly (until Jan. 1996): What to Buy for Business (0886-6163); Which incorporated (in 1983): Better Buys for Business
Indexed: Consl, Inspec.
Published by: What to Buy for Business, Inc., 370 Technology Dr, Malvern, PA 19355. TEL 805-963-3539, FAX 805-963-3740, orders@betterbuys.com, http://www/betterbuys.com. Ed. Jon Bees. Pub. John Derrick. R&P Michelle Gaitan.

651.37 ZAF ISSN 0378-9144
BOARDROOM. Text in English. 1954. m. ZAR 18. adv. bk.rev.
Formerly (until 1976): Chartered Secretary
Indexed: ISAP.
Published by: Southern African Institute of Chartered Secretaries and Administrators, PO Box 1917, Johannesburg, Transvaal 2000, South Africa. TEL 27-11-296116. Ed. Graham Hulley. Circ: 9,444.

651 DEU ISSN 0938-1511
BOSS; Fachzeitschrift fuer den PBS- und BBO-Handel. Text in German. 1978. 12/yr. EUR 84 domestic; EUR 93.60 foreign; EUR 6.50 newsstand/cover (effective 2004). adv. illus. **Document type:** *Magazine, Trade.*
Published by: B I T Verlag Weinbrenner GmbH & Co. KG, Fasanenweg 18, Leinfelden-Echterdingen, 70771, Germany. TEL 49-711-75910, FAX 49-711-7591336, info@bitverlag.de, http://www.bitverlag.de. adv.: B&W page EUR 2,600, color page EUR 3,860. Circ: 6,587 (paid and controlled).

651.37 GBR
BRISTOL SECRETARY MAGAZINE. Text in English. 1988. m. GBP 12 (effective 1999). adv. back issues avail. **Document type:** *Trade.*
Published by: Media West Ltd., 30 Drakes Way, Portishead, Bristol, BS20 6XA, United Kingdom. TEL 44-1275-845846. Ed. H B Childs. Adv. contact Rob McCabe. B&W page GBP 500, color page GBP 750; trim 186 x 272. Circ: 5,800 (paid).

651 DEU
BUERO UND SERVICE REPORT. Variant title: B & S Report. Text in German. 2002. 10/yr. EUR 95 (effective 2004). adv. **Document type:** *Magazine, Trade.*
Published by: Verlag Frank Nehring GmbH, Uhlandstr 17, Berlin, 13156, Germany. TEL 49-30-4790710, FAX 49-30-47907120, info@officeabc.de, http://www.bueroserviceabc.de/branchenreport.htm, http://www.officeabc.de. Ed. Bernd Fahland. Pub. Frank Nehring. Adv. contact Kerstin Schier. page EUR 1,800; trim 178 x 252. Circ: 4,970 (paid and controlled).

651.2 DEU
DER BUEROMASCHINEN- UND BUEROBEDARFSHANDEL. Text in English, German. 1999. q. EUR 40 (effective 2001). adv. bk.rev.; software rev. bibl.; charts; illus.; mkt.; pat.; stat.; tr.lit. **Document type:** *Magazine, Trade.* **Description:** Covers all trade involving office machinery and equipment.
Published by: Zeitungs- und Zeitschriftenverlag Heinrichs, Brueggekamp 1, Barsinghausen, 30890, Germany. TEL 49-5105-2289. Ed., Pub. Gerhard Heinrichs. adv.: B&W page EUR 4,000, color page EUR 6,000; trim 192 x 295.

651 DEU ISSN 1434-2782
BUEROSPEZIAL; das Fachmagazin fuer Ergonomie im Office. Text in German. 1997. bi-m. EUR 45; EUR 8 newsstand/cover (effective 2004). adv. **Document type:** *Magazine, Trade.*
Published by: Verlag Frank Nehring GmbH, Uhlandstr 17, Berlin, 13156, Germany. TEL 49-30-4790710, FAX 49-30-47907120, info@officeabc.de, http://www.buerospezial.de, http://www.officeabc.de. Ed. Robert Nehring. Pub. Frank Nehring. Adv. contact Kerstin Schier. color page EUR 3,900; trim 178 x 252. Circ: 9,800 (paid and controlled).

651.2 USA ISSN 1099-9221
THE BUSINESS CONSUMER'S ADVISOR. Text in English. m. USD 195 (effective 2005). back issues avail. **Document type:** *Newsletter, Consumer.* **Description:** Offers advice on purchasing and using office equipment, supplies and office services.
Formerly (until 1998): Update: The Executive's Purchasing Advisor (0897-0939)
Published by: Buyers Laboratory, Inc., 20 Railroad Ave, Hackensack, NJ 07601-3309. info@buyerslab.com, http://www.buyerslab.com. Ed. Lynn Nannariello. Pub. Burt Meerow. R&P Jane Lyons. Circ: 2,200.

651 USA
BUSINESS CONSUMER'S NETWORK. Text in English. 1962. m. looseleaf. USD 795 (effective 2000 - 2001). illus. **Document type:** *Newsletter.* **Description:** The Business Consumer's Network combines two newsletters (Digital Imaging Review, The Business Consumer's Advisor, and FAXreporter), test findings for each product category, and printer specifications.
Former titles: Buyers Laboratory Report on Office Products (Full-O); Buyers Laboratory Test Reports. Series 1: Test Reports of Office Products
Published by: Buyers Laboratory, Inc., 20 Railroad Ave, Hackensack, NJ 07601-3309. TEL 201-488-0404, FAX 201-488-0461, info@buyerslab.com, http://www.buyerslab.com. Ed. Daria Hoffman. Pub. Burt Meerow. R&P Jane Lyons. Adv. contact John Ahrens. Circ: 2,300.

651.2 GBR ISSN 0007-6708
BUSINESS EQUIPMENT DIGEST. Text in English. 1961. m. GBP 78 in United Kingdom; GBP 99 in Europe; GBP 143.50 elsewhere (effective 2000). adv. bk.rev. mkt.; tr.lit. **Document type:** *Trade.*
Indexed: B&I, BldManAb, BrCerAb, CISA, CSNB, Emerald, Inspec, LHB, M&MA, WSCA.
—BLDSC (2933.620000), AskIEEE, IE, ingenta. **CCC.**
Published by: I M L Group Plc., Blair House, 184 High St, Tonbridge, Kent TN9 1BQ, United Kingdom. TEL 01732-359990, FAX 01732-770049, imlgroup@dial.pipex.com. Ed. Eric Fordham. Pub. Peter Middup. R&P Valerie Billingsby. Adv. contact Tim Boden. Circ: 30,300.

651.2 NLD ISSN 1567-1917
BUSINESS IN OFFICE. Text in Dutch. 1992. bi-m. adv. bk.rev.; software rev. illus. back issues avail. **Document type:** *Trade.* **Description:** Covers office facility management and design.
Former titles (until 2000): Quintessence van Office & Management (1389-7845); (until 1999): Quintessence van Office en Facility Management (1388-073X); (until 1997): Quintessence van Office en Management (1388-0713); (until 1996): Office en Management (1384-0150); (until 1995): Office en Quality (0929-502X)
Published by: Brinkman Publishers Groep B.V, Postbus 155, Nijmegen, 6500 AD, Netherlands. TEL 31-24-372-2911, FAX 31-24-377-9441, redactiebrinkman@compuserve.com. Ed. P R van der Heijden. Pub. Heltjo Brinkman.

651.2 USA ISSN 1081-0374
HF5548
BUSINESS PRODUCTS UPDATE. Text in English. 1929. bi-m. USD 40 to non-members; USD 10 to members. adv. **Document type:** *Trade.*
Former titles (until 1994): N O P A Office Market Update (1060-3522); (until 1990): Special Report to the Office Products Industry; Business Products (0007-6988)
Published by: National Office Products Association, 301 N Fairfax St, Alexandria, VA 22314. TEL 703-549-9040, FAX 703-683-7552. Ed. Sandra Selva. adv.: B&W page USD 1,395, color page USD 2,205; trim 11 x 8.25. Circ: 9,000.

651 GBR ISSN 1467-8950
BUSINESS RATIO. STATIONERY DISTRIBUTORS. Text in English. 1985. irreg., latest vol.11, 1995. GBP 275 (effective 2001).
Former titles (until 1999): Business Ratio Plus: Stationery Distributors (1356-0778); (until 1993): Business Ratio Report: Stationery Distributors (0268-2427)
Published by: The Prospect Shop Ltd., Field House, 72 Oldfield Rd, Hampton, Middx TW12 2HQ, United Kingdom. TEL 44-20-8461-8730, 44-20-8481-8720, FAX 44-20-8783-1940, info@theprospectshop.co.uk.

651 GBR ISSN 1467-8969
BUSINESS RATIO. STATIONERY MANUFACTURERS. Text in English. 1972. irreg. GBP 275 (effective 2001). **Document type:** *Trade.*
Former titles (until 1999): Business Ratio Plus: Stationery Manufacturers (1356-0182); (until 1993): Business Ratio Report: Stationery Manufacturers (0261-9571)
Published by: The Prospect Shop Ltd., Field House, 72 Oldfield Rd, Hampton, Middx TW12 2HQ, United Kingdom. TEL 44-20-8461-8730, 44-20-8481-8720, FAX 44-20-8783-1940, info@theprospectshop.co.uk.

651.2 USA ISSN 1521-7027
BUSINESS SOLUTIONS. Text in English. 1986. m. free in US & Canada to qualified personnel (effective 2005). adv. back issues avail. **Document type:** *Magazine, Trade.*
Former titles (until 199?): Business Systems Magazine (1079-7467); (until 1994): Business Systems Dealer (1066-7997); (until 1992): Business Machine Dealer (1055-7822); (until 1990): Business Electronics Dealer (0893-6013); Business Electronics (0889-4035)
Indexed: MicrocompInd, TelAb.
Published by: Corry Publishing Inc., 5539 Peach St, Erie, PA 16506. TEL 814-868-9935, FAX 814-864-2037, editor@corrypub.com, CarlyR@corrypub.com, http://www.businesssolutionsmag.com/, http://www.corrypub.com. Pub. John Clifton. Adv. contact Carrie Brocious. B&W page USD 7,850, color page USD 9,550; trim 10.88 x 8.25. Circ: 45,000 (controlled and free).

651 688 ITA
C L. (CartoLibraio) Text in Italian. 1965. 8/yr. EUR 30 domestic; EUR 45 foreign (effective 2005). adv. bk.rev. **Description:** Covers the market of selling Italian school supplies, gift articles, stamps, stationery, office supplies and more both on the national and international scale.
Indexed: CERDIC.
Published by: Editoriale Delfino, via Calabria, 15, Milano, 20090, Italy. TEL 39-02-2692-6030, FAX 39-02-2187-1402, http://www.editorialedelfino.it/ita/cartoleria.php. Circ: 15,500.

651.2 CAN ISSN 0045-5210
C O M D A KEY. Key Title: COMDA Key. Text in English. 1945. bi-m. membership.
Published by: Canadian Office Machine Dealers Association, 3464 Kingston Rd, Ste 204, Scarborough, ON M1M 1R5, Canada. TEL 416-261-1607, FAX 416-261-1679. Ed. Frank Stephen. adv.: B&W page USD 430; trim 11 x 8.5. Circ: 1,837 (controlled).

CANADIAN FACILITY MANAGEMENT & DESIGN. see *INTERIOR DESIGN AND DECORATION*

676.282 ITA
CARTOLERIA. Text in Italian. 9/yr.
Published by: Linea Commerciale, Via Della Stradella, 14, Monza, MI 20052, Italy. TEL 39-39-737312. Ed. B Nicola Giordano. Pub. Mario Paleari. Adv. contact Elisabetta Caslini. Circ: 10,700.

▼ **CHRISTIAN SCHOOL PRODUCTS.** see *EDUCATION*

CLERICAL SALARY REVIEW. see *BUSINESS AND ECONOMICS—Abstracting, Bibliographies, Statistics*

651.3 BEL ISSN 0779-5513
COMPTABILITE ET FISCALITE PRATIQUES. Text in French. 1923. 10/yr. adv. bk.rev. **Document type:** *Consumer.*
Formerly (until 1992): La Vie au Bureau (0779-5505)
Published by: Editions Kluwer (Subsidiary of: Wolters Kluwer Belgique), Avenue Louise 326, Brussels, 1050, Belgium. TEL 32-800-16868, FAX 32-2-3003003, customer@editionskluwer.be, http://www.editionskluwer.be/ek/home.asp. Circ: 8,000.

COMPUTERS & OFFICE EQUIPMENT: LATIN AMERICAN INDUSTRIAL REPORT. see *COMPUTERS*

651 DEU ISSN 0947-1510
CONTROLLING INSTRUMENTE. Text in German. 1994. bi-m. looseleaf. **Document type:** *Trade.*
Published by: W R S Verlag GmbH & Co. KG (Subsidiary of: Rudolf Haufe Verlag GmbH & Co. KG), Fraunhoferstr 5, Planegg, 82152, Germany. info@wrs.de, http://www.wrs.de.

621.38 USA ISSN 1543-5660
HD9802.3.A1
COPIER (YEAR). Variant title: Orion Copier Blue Book. Text in English. 1991. a. USD 39 (effective 1999). **Document type:** *Directory.*
Formerly (until 1994): Office Equipment (1056-859X)
Related titles: CD-ROM ed.; Diskette ed.
Published by: Orion Research Corp., 14555 N Scottsdale Rd, Ste 330, Scottsdale, AZ 85254-3457. TEL 800-844-0759, FAX 800-375-1315, orion@bluebook.com, http://www.netzone.com/orion.

651.2 ITA
COPIER - DUPLICATOR GUIDE (YEAR). Text in Italian. 1990. a. **Document type:** *Catalog.*
Published by: Editoriale Directa S.r.l., Viale Sondrio 7, Milan, MI 20124, Italy. Ed., R&P, Adv. contact Andrea Ganassini.

651.2 GBR
CORPORATE OFFICE. Text in English. m. GBP 35 domestic; GBP 56.95 foreign (effective Oct. 2001). **Document type:** *Trade.*
Former titles: Office Buyer; (until 1991): Office Supplies Buyer
Published by: Peebles Media Group, Bergius House, Clifton St, Glasgow, G3 7LA, United Kingdom. TEL 44-141-567-6000, FAX 44-141-353-2336, corporateoffice@peeblesmedia.com, info@peeblesmedia.com, http://www.peeblesmedia.com/co/index.htm. Ed. Kathryn Hanks. Adv. contact Liz Rowntree. Circ: 7,300.

651.37 USA
CORPORATE SECRETARY'S GUIDE. Text in English. 1950. base vol. plus m. updates. looseleaf. USD 785 base vol(s). print or online ed. (effective 2004). **Description:** Covers information on corporate developments and helps to file standard SEC documents. Provides a comprehensive resource for this multi-faceted function, giving all the current information on ever-changing regulations and requirements and get the job done better and faster.
Formerly (until 1988): Stock Transfer Guide
Related titles: CD-ROM ed.; Online - full text ed.
Published by: C C H Inc., 2700 Lake Cook Rd, Riverwoods, IL 60015. TEL 847-267-7000, 800-449-6439, cust_serv@cch.com, http://www.cch.com. Pub. Stacey Caywood.

653 ITA ISSN 0010-9290
CORRIERE STENOGRAFICO. Text in Italian. 1912. q. adv. bk.rev.
Published by: Unione Stenografica Italiana, Sala Stampa, Via Vittorio Alfieri, 10, Turin, TO 10121, Italy. Ed. Piero Molino. Circ: 5,000.

653 DEU ISSN 0011-5169
D S T Z - DEUTSCHE STENOGRAFENZEITUNG. Text in German. 1892. m. index. **Document type:** *Trade.*
—CCC.
Published by: (Deutscher Stenografenbund e. V.), Heckner Druck- und Verlagsgesellschaft mbH & Co. KG, Postfach 1559, Wolfenbuettel, 38285, Germany. FAX 05331-800858. Ed. Helga Protz.

651.3 SWE ISSN 0349-3725
DAGENS SEKRETERARE; tidningen foer sekreterare, kontorister och administratoerer. Text in Swedish. 1980. 9/yr. SEK 480 (effective 2002). adv. bk.rev. 40 p./no. 3 cols./p.; **Document type:** *Magazine, Trade.* **Description:** For professional secretaries in Scandinavia.
Published by: Today Press AB, Fack 1413, Uppsala, 75144, Sweden. TEL 46-18-150-200, FAX 46-18-150-210, redaktion@ds.todaypress.se, http://www.ds.nu. Ed. Birgitta Baecklund. Adv. contact Inger Kwarnmark. B&W page SEK 18,000, color page SEK 21,500; trim 185 x 270. Circ: 5,400.

DANSKE MOEBLER. see *INTERIOR DESIGN AND DECORATION—Furniture And House Furnishings*

651.2 USA
DIGITAL INFORMATION NETWORK. Text in English. 1978. m. looseleaf. USD 725 (effective 2005). **Document type:** *Newsletter, Trade.* **Description:** Provides news and analysis of digital office products, new products, new technologies, market trends and options for copiers and multifunctional products.
Formerly: Copier Review (0899-6164)
Published by: Buyers Laboratory, Inc., 20 Railroad Ave, Hackensack, NJ 07601-3309. TEL 201-488-0404, FAX 201-488-0461, info@buyerslab.com, http://www.buyerslab.com. Ed. Daria Hoffman. R&P Jane Lyons. Circ: 3,000 (paid and controlled).

651 USA ISSN 1079-736X
DISASTER RECOVERY JOURNAL; the journal dedicated to business continuity. Text in English. 1987. q. free (effective 2005). adv. 112 p./no.; **Document type:** *Journal, Trade.* **Description:** Covers all aspects of business contingency planning and disaster recovery.
Related titles: Online - full text ed.
Published by: Systems Support, Inc., PO Box 510110, St. Louis, MO 63151. TEL 314-894-0276, FAX 314-894-7474, drj@drj.com, http://www.drj.com. Eds. Janette Ballman, Jon Seals, Richard Arnold. Pub. Richard Arnold. Adv. contact Bob Arnold. color page USD 4,187. Circ: 63,000 (controlled).

DISCRIMINATION CASE LAW DIGEST. see *BUSINESS AND ECONOMICS—Labor And Industrial Relations*

651 658.503 FRA
DOCUTIQUE; le management du document d'entreprise. Text in French. 1998. q. FRF 120; FRF 160 in Europe; FRF 200 elsewhere. **Document type:** *Trade.* **Description:** Covers the management of documents in businesses.
Related titles: CD-ROM ed.; E-mail ed.; Fax ed.; Online - full text ed.
Published by: Golding, 4 bis rue de la Gare, Levallois-Perret, Cedex 92532, France. TEL 33-1-41404140, FAX 33-1-42709683, contact@golding.fr, http://www.golding.fr. Adv. contact Patrick Thuot.

651 VEN
E P O: CATALOGO DE EQUIPOS PARA OFICINA. (Equipos para Oficina) Text in Spanish. 1976. a. adv.
Published by: M.G. Ediciones Especializadas, S.A., Av. Maturin, No. 15, Urb. Los Cedros, El Bosque, Caracas, 1050, Venezuela. Ed. Montserrat Giol.

651.2 USA ISSN 1062-9645
E T CETERA. Text in English. 1987. q. USD 20 in North America; USD 25 elsewhere (effective 1999). adv. bk.rev. back issues avail. **Document type:** *Newsletter.* **Description:** Covers the history of typewriters, calculators and other office machines.
Indexed: IBZ.
Published by: Early Typewriter Collectors Association, 2591 Military Ave, Los Angeles, CA 90064-1933. TEL 310-477-5229, dcrehr@earthlink.net, http://home.earthlink.net/~dcrehr/etc.html. Ed., Pub., R&P, Adv. contact Darryl Rehr. Circ: 250.

ENTREPRENEUR'S HOME OFFICE. see *BUSINESS AND ECONOMICS—Small Business*

EQUAL OPPORTUNITIES REVIEW. see *BUSINESS AND ECONOMICS—Labor And Industrial Relations*

EQUIP-MART. see *MACHINERY*

651 DEU ISSN 0343-6691
ERFOLG. Text in German. 1951. 6/yr. adv. **Document type:** *Consumer.*
Published by: Hans Holzmann Verlag GmbH, Gewerbestr 2, Bad Woerishofen, 86825, Germany. FAX 08247-354170, info@holzmannverlag.de. Ed. Erwin Stroebele. Circ: 15,400.

ERHVERV/VEST. see *BUSINESS AND ECONOMICS—Management*

651.3 USA ISSN 1527-4047
CODEN: CRSLEW
ESSENTIAL ASSISTANT. Text in English. 1960. s-m. USD 155 (effective 2002). index. **Document type:** *Newsletter, Trade.* **Description:** Includes interviews with experts in the business world that will help educate office professionals about the latest trends and innovations, as well as offer practical information they can apply on the job.
Former titles (until 1999): Creative Secretary's Letter (1079-1795); (until 1994): Prentice Hall Creative Secretary's Letter (1059-633X); Professional Secretary - Administrative Support Letter; (until 1990): P.S. for Professional Secretaries (0273-9682); (until 1978): P.S. for Private Secretaries (0030-8285)
Related titles: Online - full text ed.: (from Gale Group).
Indexed: HistAb.
Published by: Wicks Business Information LLC, 1375 Kings Hwy., Ste. 450, Fairfield, CT 06824-5398.

ETAGE; Chef-Informationen. see *BUSINESS AND ECONOMICS*

651.2 USA ISSN 0894-5748
EXEC-U-TARY. Text in English. 1975. m. USD 25 domestic; USD 30 in Canada; USD 35 elsewhere (effective 2000). adv. bk.rev. stat. back issues avail. **Document type:** *Newsletter.*
Published by: National Association of Executive Secretaries and Administrative Assistants, 900 S Washington St, Ste G 13, Falls Church, VA 22046. TEL 703-237-8616. Ed., Adv. contact Ruth Ludeman. Circ: 7,000 (paid).

651.2 AUS ISSN 1320-3975
F M FACILITY MANAGEMENT. Text in English. 1993. bi-m. AUD 40 domestic; AUD 120 foreign (effective 2004). adv. **Document type:** *Magazine, Trade.* **Description:** Examines the planning, design and management of buildings and their associating building systems, equipment and furniture, to enable and enhance an organization's ability to meet its fundamental business objectives.
Published by: Niche Media Pty Ltd (Subsidiary of: Waivcom Worldwide Ltd.), 165 Fitzroy St, St Kilda, VIC 3182, Australia. TEL 61-3-95255566, 800-804-160, FAX 61-3-95255628, subscription@niche.com.au, http://www.niche.com.au. Ed. Max Winter. Adv. contact Grace Banas. color page AUD 3,000; trim 210 x 297. Circ: 5,000 (controlled).

651 GBR
F M FOCUS. (Facilities Management) Variant title: F M Focus Newsletter. Text in English. q. GBP 60; GBP 70 foreign. **Document type:** *Newsletter.*
Published by: I R S (Subsidiary of: LexisNexis UK (Scottish Office)), 18-20 Highbury Pl, London, N5 1QP, United Kingdom. TEL 44-20-7354-6742, FAX 44-20-7226-8618, publications@irseclipse.co.uk, http://www.irseclipse.co.uk.

658.2 BEL ISSN 1370-7582
FACILITIES. Text in French. 1996. 7/yr. EUR 25 (effective 2004). adv. **Document type:** *Magazine, Trade.* **Description:** Contains information on the management of internal services such cleaning, catering, security, environment and telecommunications.
Published by: Roularta Media Group, Research Park, Zellik, 1731, Belgium. TEL 32-2-4675611, FAX 32-2-4675757, communication@roularta.be, http://www.roularta.be. Circ: 9,000 (paid and controlled).

658.2 GBR ISSN 1471-0315
THE FACILITIES BUSINESS. Text in English. 2000. bi-w. GBP 72; GBP 6 newsstand/cover (effective 2001). 45 p./no. 3 cols./p.; **Document type:** *Magazine, Trade.* **Description:** Provides news, updates and advice on all aspects of facilities management.
Indexed: Inspec.
—CCC.
Published by: Builder Group plc., Exchange Tower, 2 Harbour Exchange Sq, London, E14 9GE, United Kingdom. TEL 44-20-7560-4000, FAX 44-20-7560-4404, http://www.facilitiesbusiness.co.uk. Ed. Kate Lowe. Adv. contact Richard Myles TEL 44-20-7560-4229. Circ: 15,000.

658.2 GBR ISSN 1351-668X
FACILITIES MANAGEMENT. Text in English. 1994. m. GBP 305 domestic; GBP 326 foreign (effective 2003); includes Management Guide. adv. 28 p./no.; Supplement avail. **Document type:** *Journal, Trade.* **Description:** Covers topics in strategic planning, property and building management, energy management, fire and security, health and safety, and the workplace.
Related titles: Online - full content ed.; Online - full text ed.: (from Gale Group).
Indexed: IBuildSA.
—BLDSC (3863.455600), IE, Infotrieve.
Published by: I R S (Subsidiary of: LexisNexis UK (Scottish Office)), 18-20 Highbury Pl, London, N5 1QP, United Kingdom. TEL 44-20-7354-6742, 44-20-7354-5858, FAX 44-20-7226-8618, 44-20-7359-4000, publications@irseclipse.co.uk, http://www.irsonline.co.uk/pub_subjects/index_pub_facilities.htm, http://www.irseclipse.co.uk. Ed. Kate Lowe.

651.2 USA
FAX MAGAZINE*. Text in English. 1987. q. adv.
Published by: Technical Data Publishing Corporation, 195A State Rte 33, Hartfield, VA 23071. TEL 201-770-2633. Ed. William M Rowe. Circ: 25,000.

651.3 USA ISSN 0016-1616
FROM NINE TO FIVE; tips and information for success in the office. Text in English. 1960. bi-w. (26/yr.). looseleaf. USD 245.70 for 5 copies (effective 2005). bk.rev. illus.; tr.lit. index: 1960-62. reprint service avail. from PQC. **Document type:** *Newsletter, Trade.* **Description:** Provides office support staff tips on how to develop skills to overcome problems, how to work with other members of their team, and how to increase the company's success by increasing their own.
Related titles: Microform ed.: (from PQC).
—CCC.
Published by: Dartnell Corp. (Subsidiary of: L R P Publications), 360 Hiatt Dr, Palm Beach Garden, FL 33418. TEL 561-622-6520, 800-621-5463, FAX 561-622-0757, custserve@lrp.com, http://www.shoplrp.com/product/p-18008.N.html, http://www.dartnellcorp.com/. Ed. Kim Andersen. Circ: 31,000.

653 IND
G K ROUND-UP. Text in English. 1977. m. INR 27. adv. bk.rev.
Published by: Delhi Shorthand School, 2-58 Ramesh Nagar, New Delhi, 110 015, India. Ed. Dharma Vira. Circ: 5,200.

651 688 ITA
GIORNALE IN CARTOLERIA. Text in Italian. 1988. bi-m. EUR 20 (effective 2005). adv.
Published by: Raddicchi Editore S.R.L., Via San Giovanni B. De La Salle, 4, Milan, MI 20132, Italy. TEL 39-02-26300330, FAX 39-02-2566849. Ed. Rossella Radicchi. Circ: 13,786.

652 GBR ISSN 0269-9486
GREETINGS. Text in English. 1970. bi-m. GBP 30; GBP 40 foreign. adv. **Document type:** *Trade.*
Published by: (Greeting Card & Calendar Association), Lema Publishing Co., Unit 1, Queen Mary's Ave, Watford, Herts WD1 7JR, United Kingdom. TEL 44-1293-250909, FAX 44-1293-250995, TELEX 8952440. Ed. Nicholas Eyriey. Pub. Malcolm Naish. Adv. contact Toni Sheppard. Circ: 20,000.

HABITAT UFFICIO. see *INTERIOR DESIGN AND DECORATION*

651.2 DEU ISSN 0938-6556
HECKNERS HEFTE FUER TEXTVERARBEITUNG. Text in German. bi-m. **Document type:** *Trade.*
Formerly: Musterdiktate fuer Kurzschrift, Maschinenschreiben und Phonotypie
Published by: Heckner Druck- und Verlagsgesellschaft mbH & Co. KG, Postfach 1559, Wolfenbuettel, 38285, Germany. FAX 05331-800858.

HOME BUSINESS MAGAZINE; the home-based entrepreneur's magazine. see *BUSINESS AND ECONOMICS—Small Business*

651 USA
HOW TO MANAGE YOUR LAW OFFICE. Text in English. 1973. base vol. plus a. updates. looseleaf. USD 230 base vol(s). (effective 2002). **Description:** Provides readers with cutting edge information about effective techniques in law office administration. It includes discussions on topics ranging from the intricacies of personnel management to law office ergonomics to how law offices can utilize the Internet. Written by the well-respected consulting firm, Altman Weil, Inc., How to Manage Your Law Office offers the reader a wealth of practical tips and recommendations from how to build a law practice to how to manage case control and paper volume. Additionally, in each release, key statistics regarding compensation, billing rates, and overhead expenses, among others, are updated with data from Altman Weil's surveys and reports.
Published by: Matthew Bender & Co., Inc. (Subsidiary of: LexisNexis North America), 1275 Broadway, Albany, NY 12204. international@bender.com, http://bender.lexisnexis.com. Eds. Mary Ann Altman, Robert Weil.

I E E E SYMPOSIUM ON MASS STORAGE SYSTEMS. DIGEST OF PAPERS. see *COMPUTERS*

651 USA
IMAGE SOURCE MAGAZINE. Text in English. m. free domestic to qualified personnel (effective 2005). adv. **Document type:** *Magazine, Trade.*
Published by: Imaging Network, 4061 S W 47th Ave, Fort Lauderdale, FL 33314. TEL 954-453-0700, 800-989-6077, FAX 954-581-0815, info@imagingnetwork.com, http://www.imagingnetwork.com. adv.: color page USD 2,000. Circ: 45,000 (controlled).

651 USA ISSN 1524-1041
INDUSTRY FOCUS. Text in English. 1981. a. USD 48 domestic; USD 64 in Canada & Mexico; USD 84 elsewhere (effective 2000). adv. bk.rev. back issues avail. **Document type:** *Newsletter.* **Description:** Deals with every facet of business support service operations: pricing, successful new sales techniques for adding clients, dealing with clients and employees, work scheduling, forms and contracts, financial management, equipment/software, and technology. Also includes industry survey results regarding rates and other pertinent issues.
Formerly: National Association of Secretarial Services. Newsletter
Published by: Association of Business Support Services International, Inc., 5852 Oak Meadow Dr., Yorba Linda, CA 92886-5930. TEL 714-282-9398, 800-237-1462, FAX 714-282-8630, abssi4you@aol.com, http://www.abssi.org. Ed., R&P, Adv. contact Lynette M Smith. B&W page USD 1,200; trim 7.5 x 10. Circ: 1,000 (paid).

651.2 FRA ISSN 1264-6253
INFO BURO MAG. Text in French. 1995. 7/yr. USD 45.71 (effective 2001). adv. **Document type:** *Magazine, Trade.* **Description:** Includes communications by and for purchasers in the grocery trade.
Related titles: Online - full content ed.
Published by: Helios International, 35 av. de l'Opera, Paris, 75002, France. TEL 33-4-90893300, FAX 33-4-90882849, info@infoburomag.com, http://www.infoburomag.com. Ed. Annick Lagadec. Pub. Christophe Durrieu. Adv. contact Didier Libs. B&W page USD 3,860, color page USD 5,160. Circ: 35,000 (paid).

004 AUS ISSN 0816-200X
INFORMAA QUARTERLY. Text in English. 1985. q. AUD 38 domestic to non-members; AUD 50 foreign to non-members; free to members (effective 2005). bk.rev. tr.lit. Index. back issues avail. **Document type:** *Magazine, Trade.* **Description:** Contains articles and information provided by various sources throughout Australia on the issues effecting the industry.
Related titles: Microfiche ed.
—BLDSC (4478.890500), IE, ingenta.
Published by: Records Management Association of Australia, GPO Box 1059, Brisbane, QLD 4001, Australia. TEL 61-7-32102171, FAX 61-7-32101313, admin@rmaa.com.au, http://www.rmaa.com.au. Circ: 2,500.

651 CHE
INFORMATIK UND BUERO TREND. Text in German. q. adv. **Document type:** *Trade.*
Published by: Eulach Verlag AG, Wartstr 6, Winterthur, 8401, Switzerland. TEL 052-2124021, FAX 052-2133207. Ed. Rene Donze. Pub. Willy Grueninger. Adv. contact Beda Schoenenberger. Circ: 20,000.

651.2 USA ISSN 1385-951X
CODEN: ITMNAG
➤ **INFORMATION TECHNOLOGY & MANAGEMENT.** Text in English. 2000. q. EUR 384, USD 384, GBP 240 combined subscription to institutions print & online eds. (effective 2005). adv. reprint service avail. from PSC. **Document type:** *Journal, Academic/Scholarly.* **Description:** Covers information technology and information systems, along with the interaction between these two fields. Pays particular attention to the impact of changing information technology on information systems and the organizations being supported by these systems.
Related titles: Online - full text ed.: ISSN 1573-7667 (from EBSCO Publishing, Gale Group, IngentaConnect, Kluwer Online, O C L C Online Computer Library Center, Inc., ProQuest Information & Learning, Springer LINK, Swets Information Services).
Indexed: ABIn, BibLing, BrCerAb, BrEdI, C&ISA, CerAb, CompLI, CorrAb, E&CAJ, EMA, IAA, Inspec, M&TEA, MBF, METADEX, SolStAb, WAA.
—BLDSC (4496.368720), IE, Infotrieve, ingenta, Linda Hall. CCC.
Published by: Springer-Verlag New York, Inc. (Subsidiary of: Springer Science+Business Media), 233 Spring St, New York, NY 10013. TEL 212-460-1500, FAX 212-460-1575, service@springer-ny.com, http://springerlink.metapress.com/openurl.asp?genre=journal&issn=1385-951X, http://www.springer-ny.com. Eds. H Pirkul, Varghese S Jacob. **Subscr. to:** Journal Fulfillment, PO Box 2485, Secaucus, NJ 07096-2485. TEL 201-348-4033, FAX 201-348-4505, journals@springer-ny.com.

➤ **INFORMATION TECHNOLOGY, LEARNING, AND PERFORMANCE JOURNAL.** see *COMPUTERS*

621.382 AUS ISSN 1322-3526
INFORMATION TECHNOLOGY MANAGEMENT; non-technical report on IT and its applications. Text in English. 1989. a., latest 2001. USD 425 domestic; USD 455 in North America & Europe (effective 2001). 240 p./no.; **Document type:** *Trade.* **Description:** Telecommunication and broadcasting technologies and applications, including pay TV, optical fiber, EDI, Videotex, ISDN and more.
Published by: Paul Budde Communication Pty. Ltd., 2643 George Downes Dr, Bucketty, NSW 2250, Australia. TEL 61-2-4998-8144, FAX 61-2-4998-8247, sally@budde.com.au, http://www.budde.com.au. Ed. Paul Budde. Circ: 150.

651 GRC
INNOVATIVE BUSINESS TECHNOLOGIES. Text in Greek. 1986. m. **Document type:** *Trade.* **Description:** Covers office automation technologies in the Greek and international markets.
Published by: Business Press S.A., 44 Syngrou Ave, Athens, 117 42, Greece. TEL 30-1-9238-672, FAX 30-1-9216-847. Ed. Antonis Kassanos. Circ: 10,000.

INTERNATIONAL DIRECTORY OF OFFICE EQUIPMENT, STATIONERY AND SUPPLIES IMPORTERS. see *BUSINESS AND ECONOMICS—Trade And Industrial Directories*

658.2 GBR ISSN 1365-702X
TS155
➤ **INTERNATIONAL JOURNAL OF FACILITIES MANAGEMENT.** Text in English. 1997. q. GBP 125; GBP 210 foreign. adv. bk.rev. bibl. **Document type:** *Academic/Scholarly.*
Related titles: Online - full text ed.
—BLDSC (4542.244870), IE.
Published by: Thomson Professional (Subsidiary of: International Thomson Publishing Group), 2-6 Boundary Row, London, SE1 8HN, United Kingdom. TEL 44-171-865-0066, FAX 44-171-522-9621, GeneralInfo@Thomson.com. Ed. Keith Alexander. Adv. contact Gemma Heiser. **Dist. by:** Mercury UMD Ltd., Mills Rd, Quarry Wood, Aylesford, Kent ME26 7W2, United Kingdom. TEL 44-1622-792111, FAX 44-1622-792444.

651 ITA
INTERNATIONAL STATIONERY; events in the world of stationery. Text in Italian. 1988. q.
Published by: Raddicchi Editore S.R.L., Via San Giovanni B. De La Salle, 4, Milan, MI 20132, Italy. TEL 02-263-00-330, FAX 02-25-66-849. Circ: 7,500.

651.2 FRA
INTERNATIONAL STATIONERY GUIDE; the global office, school and soho database for the international buyer. Key Title: I S G. Text in English, French, German, Italian, Spanish. 1993. a. USD 130 CD-ROM included (effective 2001). adv. **Document type:** *Directory, Trade.* **Description:** Lists manufacturers, suppliers, exporters and importers of stationery products at the international level.
Related titles: CD-ROM ed.
Published by: Helios International, 35 av. de l'Opera, Paris, 75002, France. TEL 33-4-90893300, FAX 33-4-90882849, info@is-guide.com, http://www.is-guide.com. Adv. contact Sandrine Descamps. B&W page USD 1,730, color page USD 2,520; trim 297 x 210. Circ: 24,000.

650 USA ISSN 1541-1141
INVENTORY MANAGEMENT REPORT. Text in English. 1986. m. looseleaf. USD 268.95 in US & Canada print & online eds.; USD 283 elsewhere print & online eds. (effective 2005). index. back issues avail. **Document type:** *Newsletter, Trade.* **Description:** Looks to demonstrate how to reduce inventory and costs, better manage materials hadling, and improve cash flow and profitability. Includes benchmark information on fill rates, customer service, cycle counting, reducing lead time, improving warehouse and distribution management, and more. Also provides cost-cutting tactics, evaluations of automation equipment, as well as salary data for managers and staff.
Formerly (until 2002): Inventory Reduction Report (1049-9849)

Related titles: Diskette ed.; E-mail ed.; Online - full content ed.: (from Northern Light Technology, Inc.); Online - full text ed.: (from EBSCO Publishing, Gale Group, LexisNexis, O C L C Online Computer Library Center, Inc.).
Indexed: LogistBibl.
—CCC.
Published by: Institute of Management & Administration, Inc., 3 Park Ave, New York, NY 10016-5902. TEL 212-244-0360, FAX 212-564-0465, subserve@ioma.com, http://www.ioma.com. Ed. Joe Mazel. Pub. Perry Patterson. R&P Sofie Kourkoutakis.

651 USA ISSN 1531-3905
ITBEAT MAGAZINE✱. Text in English. 2000. m. adv. **Document type:** *Magazine, Trade.* **Description:** Focuses on bringing real world solutions to business problems by explaining the latest developments and technological innovations in the industry.
Published by: MindBuilder Group, Inc., 1 S. Wacker Dr, Chicago, IL 60606-4616. TEL 847-753-8000, 877-753-8889, info@itbeat.com, http://www.itbeat.com. Ed. Karen Rosenthal. Circ: 250,000 (controlled).

JOURNAL OF FACILITIES MANAGEMENT IN AFRICA. see *BUSINESS AND ECONOMICS—Management*

651.2 DEU ISSN 0178-594X
K M I BUEROWIRTSCHAFT - LEHRE UND PRAXIS; Fachzeitschrift fuer Kurzschrift, Maschinenschreiben und Informationsverarbeitung. Text in German. 1986. q. adv. bk.rev. **Document type:** *Trade.*
Published by: Winklers Verlag, Postfach 111552, Darmstadt, 64230, Germany. TEL 49-6151-8768-0, FAX 49-6151-876860. Circ: 3,600.

K O M MAGASINET; magasinet for kommunikation og sprog. see *LABOR UNIONS*

651 NLD ISSN 0929-7871
KANTOOR BUSINESS MAGAZINE; vaktijdschrift voor de handel in kantoor- en schrijfartikelen, papeterie en wenskaarten. Short title: K B M. Text in Dutch. 1993. m. EUR 77 domestic; EUR 86 foreign (effective 2005). adv. illus.; stat. index. **Document type:** *Trade.* **Description:** Discusses the office supply and stationery industry.
Which was formed by the 1993 merger of: Best of Seven (0929-788X); K B M - Kantoormarkt (0169-7285); Which was formerly (until 1984): K B M (0169-3204); Which was formed by the 1980 merger of: Band (0005-4909); K B (0165-4403); Which was formerly: Kantoorboekhandel (0039-0364)
Published by: Magenta Communicatie Projecten, Postbus 134, Groesbeek, 6560 AC, Netherlands. TEL 31-24-3454150, FAX 31-24-3976071, kbm@kantoornet.nl, http://www.kantoornet.nl. Ed. Emiel te Walvaart TEL 31-24-3454154. Pub. Joost Heessels. Adv. contacts Annet Poelen, Paqui Tamayo. B&W page EUR 1,365, color page EUR 2,345; trim 285 x 268. Circ: 4,250.

651 NLD ISSN 0022-8893
KANTOOR EN EFFICIENCY; het hele kantoor in een tijdschrift. Text in Dutch. 1962. m. EUR 88 domestic; EUR 97 foreign (effective 2005). adv. bk.rev. charts; illus.; stat. index. **Document type:** *Magazine, Consumer.* **Description:** Covers office organization and practice featuring the latest news and research in automation, software, programming, information processing, office machines, office furnishings and more. Includes list of events and exhibitions.
Incorporates (1993-2000): Telewerken (0929-9459); (1992-1995): K en E Interieur (0927-9571)
Indexed: KES.
—IE.
Published by: Magenta Communicatie Projecten, Postbus 134, Groesbeek, 6560 AC, Netherlands. TEL 31-24-3454150, FAX 31-24-3976071, k-e@kantoornet.nl, http://www.kantoornet.nl. Ed. Monique Berkelmans TEL 31-24-3454156. Pub. Joost Heessels. Adv. contacts Annet Poelen, Paqui Tamayo. B&W page EUR 2,040, color page EUR 3,495; trim 185 x 268. Circ: 8,000.

651 NLD ISSN 0022-8907
KANTOOR - SCHOOL - HUIS✱; voorlichtingsblad voor gebruikers van kantoorartikelen. Text in Dutch. 1951. bi-m.
Address: Waldecklaan 41, Hilversum, Netherlands. Ed. B W De Veer. Circ: 10,000.

KEY NOTE MARKET ASSESSMENT. SMALL OFFICE HOME OFFICE (SOHO) - PRODUCT. see *BUSINESS AND ECONOMICS—Small Business*

651 GBR
KEY NOTE MARKET REPORT: OFFICE FURNITURE. Variant title: Office Furniture. Text in English. irreg., latest 2002, Jan. GBP 340 per issue (effective 2002). **Document type:** *Trade.* **Description:** Provides an overview of a specific UK market segment and includes executive summary, market definition, market size, industry background, competitor analysis, current issues, forecasts, company profiles, and more.
Formerly: Key Note Report: Office Furniture (0954-5085)
Related titles: CD-ROM ed.; Online - full text ed.
—CCC.
Published by: Key Note Ltd., Field House, 72 Oldfield Rd, Hampton, Mddx TW12 2HQ, United Kingdom. TEL 44-20-8481-8750, FAX 44-20-8783-0049, info@keynote.co.uk, http://www.keynote.co.uk. Ed. Dominic Fenn.

651 GBR ISSN 1367-4137
KEY NOTE MARKET REPORT: PHOTOCOPIERS & FAX MACHINES. Text in English. 1992. irreg., latest 2000, Oct. GBP 340 per issue (effective 2002). **Document type:** *Trade.* **Description:** Provides an overview of a specific UK market segment and includes executive summary, market definition, market size, industry background, competitor analysis, current issues, forecasts, company profiles, and more.
Formerly (until 1997): Key Note Report: Photocopiers and Fax Machines (1352-6995)
Related titles: CD-ROM ed.; Online - full text ed.
Published by: Key Note Ltd., Field House, 72 Oldfield Rd, Hampton, Mddx TW12 2HQ, United Kingdom. TEL 44-20-8481-8750, FAX 44-20-8783-0049, info@keynote.co.uk, http://www.keynote.co.uk. Ed. Jacob Howard.

651 GBR ISSN 1363-0865
KEY NOTE MARKET REPORT: STATIONERY (PERSONAL & OFFICE). Variant title: Stationery (Personal & Office). Text in English. 1996. a., latest 2002, Mar. GBP 340 per issue (effective 2002). **Document type:** *Trade.* **Description:** Provides an overview of a specific UK market segment and includes executive summary, market definition, market size, industry background, competitor analysis, current issues, forecasts, company profiles, and more.
Formerly: Key Note Report: Stationery (Personal and Office) (1354-2354)
Related titles: CD-ROM ed.; Online - full text ed.
Published by: Key Note Ltd., Field House, 72 Oldfield Rd, Hampton, Mddx TW12 2HQ, United Kingdom. TEL 44-20-8481-8750, FAX 44-20-8783-0049, info@keynote.co.uk, http://www.keynote.co.uk. Ed. Lyndsey Barker.

651 658 GBR ISSN 1357-1354
KEY NOTE MARKET REVIEW: U.K. OFFICE EQUIPMENT. Text in English. 1989. irreg. (4th Edition), latest 1998, Apr. GBP 565 per issue (effective 2002). **Document type:** *Trade.* **Description:** Designed to keep you up to date with the developments and opportunities across entire industry sectors. They provide a comprehensive analysis of the industry by drawing together key related market segments under one cover.
Formerly (until 1994): Market Review. U.K. Office Equipment (0960-4235)
Related titles: CD-ROM ed.; Online - full text ed.
Published by: Key Note Ltd., Field House, 72 Oldfield Rd, Hampton, Mddx TW12 2HQ, United Kingdom. TEL 44-20-8481-8750, FAX 44-20-8783-0049, info@keynote.co.uk, http://www.keynote.co.uk. Ed. Simon Howitt.

KOMPUTERY I BIURO. see *COMPUTERS*

381.456762 DNK ISSN 1603-8630
KONTOR/PAPIR; fagblad for den danske kontorartikelbranche. Text in Danish. 1949. 10/yr. free to qualified personnel. adv. bk.rev. illus. index. 3 cols./p.; back issues avail. **Document type:** *Magazine, Trade.* **Description:** Internal newsletter for the paper trade.
Formerly (until 2004): Papirhandleren (0031-143X)
Published by: (Detail-Papirhandlerforeningen i Danmark), Pressto Kommunikation, Ulvedalen 2, PO Box 120, Soenderborg, 6400, Denmark. TEL 45-74-431444, post@pressto.dk, http://www.pressto.dk. Ed., R&P Bjarke Larsen TEL 45-74-431444. Adv. contact Jette Petersen. B&W page DKK 5,995, color page DKK 7,995; trim 257 x 186. Circ: 3,300.

651.8 651.3 SWE ISSN 0023-3722
KONTORSVAERLDEN✱. Text in Swedish. 1911. q. SEK 26.
Published by: Sveriges Kontoristfoerening, Fack 1341, Stockholm, 11183, Sweden. Ed. Birger Ernblad. Circ: 2,000.

651 DEU
KULT AM PULT; das Journal fuer erlesene Schreibtischkultur. Text in German. 4/yr. EUR 18 domestic; EUR 22.40 foreign (effective 2004). **Document type:** *Journal, Trade.*
Published by: B I T Verlag Weinbrenner GmbH & Co. KG, Fasanenweg 18, Leinfelden-Echterdingen, 70771, Germany. TEL 49-711-75910, FAX 49-711-7591368, info@bitverlag.de, http://www.bitverlag.de.

651.3 331.8 DNK ISSN 0903-7497
LAEGESEKRETAER NYT. Text in Danish. 1968. 11/yr. adv.
Published by: Dansk Laegesekretaerforening - H K, H C Andersens Boulevard 50, Copenhagen V, 1780, Denmark. TEL 45-33-30-43-43, FAX 45-33-30-44-49, www.dl-hk.dk. Ed. Niels Stoktoft Overgaard. adv.: color page DKK 6,600; 175 x 245. Circ: 9,600.

651.3 SWE ISSN 0345-746X
LAEKARSEKRETERAREN. Text in Swedish. 1964. 10/yr. SEK 300 (effective 2000). **Document type:** *Trade.*
Published by: Sveriges Laekarsekreterarfoerbund (LSF), Sandsjoen 48, Lockryd, Svenljunga, 51291, Sweden. TEL 46-33-280566, FAX 46-33-280505, http://www.lakarsekreterarforbundet.a.se. Ed. Ewalena Sternfeldt.

651 340 USA
LAW PRACTICE NEWS. Text in English. irreg. (2-4/yr.). membership. back issues avail. **Document type:** *Academic/Scholarly.* **Description:** Covers the management of law offices.
Formerly: Office Management News
Published by: (Law Practice Section), State Bar of Wisconsin, 5302 Eastpark Blvd, Madison, WI 53718. FAX 608-257-5502, service@wisbar.org. Circ: 1,025.

651.2 USA
M.I.M EUROPE. (Marking Industry Magazine) Text in English. 6/yr. free to qualified personnel (effective 2004). **Document type:** *Magazine, Trade.*
Published by: Marking Devices Publishing, 136 W Vallette St, Ste 6, Elmhurst, IL 60126-4377. TEL 630-832-5200, 888-627-5464, FAX 630-832-5206, info@makingdevices.com, http://www.markingdevices.com. Circ: 2,100.

651 NLD ISSN 1382-3590
MANAGEMENT SUPPORT MAGAZINE. Text in Dutch. 1983. m. adv. illus. **Document type:** *Trade.*
Incorporates (in 2002): Management Assistant (1375-7806); Former titles (until 1995): Secretaresse Magazine (0169-0582); (until 1985): Secretaresse Nieuwsbrief (0926-8847)
—IE, Infotrieve.
Published by: Samsom Bedrijfsinformatie BV (Subsidiary of: Wolters Kluwer N.V.), Postbus 4, Alphen aan den Rijn, 2400 MA, Netherlands. TEL 31-172-469954, FAX 31-172-422804. Circ: 11,000.

B

651.2 USA ISSN 0164-4939
MARKING INDUSTRY MAGAZINE. Text in English. 1907. m. USD 54 (effective 2004); includes a. buyer's guide Marking Products & Equipment. adv. bk.rev. illus.; tr.lit. **Document type:** *Magazine, Trade.* **Description:** Designed for those firms engaged in the manufacturing, distribution and-or sales of marking products: rubber stamps and dies, steel stamps and dies; engraved plates and signs - plastic or metal.
Formerly: Marking Industry (0025-3839)
Published by: Marking Devices Publishing, 136 W Vallette St, Ste 6, Elmhurst, IL 60126-4377. TEL 630-832-5200, FAX 630-832-5206, info@makingdevices.com, http://www.markingdevices.com. Ed. Kathy Strickland. Pub., Adv. contact David Hachmeister. Circ: 1,500 (paid).

651.2 USA
MARKING PRODUCTS & EQUIPMENT BUYERS' GUIDE. Text in English. 1908. a. USD 30 per issue (effective 2004). adv. **Document type:** *Directory, Trade.*
Published by: Marking Devices Publishing, 136 W Vallette St, Ste 6, Elmhurst, IL 60126-4377. TEL 630-832-5200, FAX 630-832-5206, info@makingdevices.com, http://www.markingdevices.com. Ed. Kathy Strickland. Pub., Adv. contact David Hachmeister. B&W page USD 830, color page USD 1,500; trim 10.88 x 8.38.

651.2 USA
MARKING TIME. Text in English. q. USD 25 domestic; USD 50 foreign (effective 2004). **Document type:** *Magazine, Trade.* **Description:** Contains new product information provided by various companies that do business with time and attendance retailers and vendors. Includes original articles that offer practical examples of the use of various time and attendance products.
Published by: Marking Devices Publishing, 136 W Vallette St, Ste 6, Elmhurst, IL 60126-4377. TEL 630-832-5200, 888-627-5464, FAX 630-832-5206, info@makingdevices.com, http://www.markingdevices.com.

651.2 DEU ISSN 0933-8241
MENSCH UND BUERO; ambience, architecture, communication, furnishing. Text in German. 1987. bi-m. EUR 61.50 domestic; EUR 79.20 foreign (effective 2005). adv. bk.rev. **Document type:** *Magazine, Trade.*
Published by: Konradin Verlag Robert Kohlhammer GmbH, Ernst Mey Str 8, Leinfelden-Echterdingen, 70771, Germany. TEL 49-711-75940, FAX 49-711-7594399, info@menschundbuero.de, info@konradin.de, http://www.menschundbuero.de, http://www.konradin.de. Ed. Wilhelm Kluemper. Adv. contact Matthias Knecht. B&W page EUR 7,040; trim 205 x 266. Circ: 40,000.

651.2 333.33 USA
METRO CHICAGO OFFICE GUIDE. Text in English. q. adv.
Published by: Law Bulletin Publishing Co., 415 N State St, Chicago, IL 60610-4674. TEL 312-922-9278. Circ: 10,000.

651 330 GBR ISSN 0143-1374
MIND YOUR OWN BUSINESS. Text in English. 1978. 10/yr. GBP 54 (effective 1999). adv. bk.rev. back issues avail. **Document type:** *Trade.*
Indexed: Inspec, M&MA.
—BLDSC (5775.574000), AskIEEE.
Published by: Market Place Publishing Ltd., Scorpio House, 106 Church Rd, London, SE19 2UB, United Kingdom. TEL 44-181-771-3614, FAX 44-181-771-4592, 101737.2100@compuserve.com. Ed. Martin Read. Pub. Laurence Allen. Adv. contact Mark Povey. Circ: 32,134.

651.2 USA ISSN 0196-3287
HD9800.U5
N O P A MEMBERSHIP DIRECTORY AND BUYER'S GUIDE (YEAR). Text in English. 1906. a. USD 80 to non-members.
Published by: National Office Products Association, 301 N Fairfax St, Alexandria, VA 22314. TEL 703-549-9040, FAX 703-683-7552. Ed. Sandra Selva.

653 DEU ISSN 0028-3371
NEUE STENOGRAPHISCHE PRAXIS. Text in German. 1953. q. adv. bk.rev. abstr.; illus.; stat.
Published by: Verband der Parlaments- und Verhandlungsstenographen, Postfach 120409, Bonn, 53046, Germany. Ed. Dr. Karl Gutzler. Circ: 600.

380.1029 NGA ISSN 0331-0973
HF5286.5.A3
NIGERIAN YELLOW PAGES. Text in English. 1971. a. **Document type:** *Directory.*
Former titles (until 1979): Nigerian Office and Residential Directory; Nigerian Office and Quarters Directory (0085-4190)
Published by: I C I C (Directory Publishers) Ltd., PMB 3204, Surulere, Lagaos State, Nigeria. Ed. Olu Adeyemi.

NOVA SCOTIA BUSINESS JOURNAL. see *BUSINESS AND ECONOMICS—Small Business*

338 GBR
O P D REFERENCE BOOK & BUYERS GUIDE. (Office Products Dealer) Text in English. 1954. a. GBP 50 (effective 2003). adv. **Document type:** *Trade.* **Description:** Contains up to date information on the entire office products market, providing comprehensive and current facts, figures and contacts in the fast moving office products market.
Formerly: Stationery Trade Reference Book and Buyers Guide (0081-461X)
Published by: Nexus Media Ltd. (Subsidiary of: Highbury House Communications PLC), Nexus House, Azalea Dr, Swanley, Kent BR8 8HU, United Kingdom. TEL 44-1322-660070, FAX 44-1322-616311, info@nexusmedia.com, http://www.hhc.co.uk/. Ed. Alison Bowie TEL 44-1322-660070 ext 2316. Adv. contact Andre Daffon TEL 44-1322-660070 ext 2118.

629.8 USA
OBSERVER (APTOS); office systems trends. Text in English. 1980. 6/yr. USD 95. **Description:** Contains information on office systems technology and educational computer use. Articles cover office automation, communications, information processing, microcomputers, hardware, software, industry news and technological developments.
Formerly: Word Processing News
Published by: Automated Office Resources, 812 Via Tornasol, Aptos, CA 95003-5624. Ed. Paula Cecil. Circ: 2,500.

OF COUNSEL; the monthly legal practice report. see *LAW*

651 DEU
OFFICE; Magazin fuer das moderne Buero. Text in German. 5/yr. EUR 19; EUR 3.80 newsstand/cover (effective 2003). adv. **Document type:** *Magazine, Trade.*
Published by: Trend Medien Verlag GmbH, Herdweg 20, Stuttgart, 70174, Germany. TEL 49-711-18790-0, FAX 49-711-1879045, office@office-verlag.de, http://www.office-verlag.de. Ed., Pub., R&P Klaus Vetterle. Adv. contact Ulrike Ehlers. B&W page EUR 4,750, color page EUR 6,650; trim 184 x 278. Circ: 32,350.

330 DEU
OFFICE AND PAPER; das Branchenmagazin fuer Buerobedarf und Papeterie. Text in German. 1947. m. EUR 74; EUR 9.70 newsstand/cover (effective 2002). adv. **Document type:** *Magazine, Trade.*
Published by: Goeller Verlag GmbH, Aschmattstr 8, Baden-Baden, 76532, Germany. TEL 49-7221-502200, FAX 49-7221-502222, verlag@goeller-verlag.de, http://www.officeandpaper.com/index2.html. Pub. Ulrich Goeller. Adv. contact Branka Di Stefano. B&W page EUR 2,380, color page EUR 3,790. Circ: 8,639 (paid and controlled).

651.2 GBR ISSN 1479-4632
OFFICE AND STATIONERY NEWS. Variant title: O & S N. Text in English. 1983. m. GBP 82.50 domestic; GBP 95 foreign (effective Oct. 2001). bk.rev. **Document type:** *Magazine, Trade.*
Former titles (until Jan., 2003): Stationery Trade News (0951-7820); Which incorporates: Office Dealer
—CCC.
Published by: Datateam Publishing Ltd, 15a London Rd, Maidstone, Kent ME16 8LY, United Kingdom. TEL 44-1622-687031, FAX 44-1622-757646, info@datateam.co.uk, http://www.datateam.co.uk/business_publications/office_and_stationery_news.htm, http://www.datateam.co.uk/home/home.htm. Circ: 6,400.

658 ITA ISSN 1120-0138
OFFICE AUTOMATION. Text in Italian. 1981. 11/yr. EUR 68 domestic; EUR 140 foreign (effective 2005). adv. **Document type:** *Magazine, Consumer.* **Description:** Specializes in data processing, networking, telecommunications and systems for the office. For sector professionals.
Indexed: B&I.
Published by: Soiel International, Via Martiri Oscuri 3, Milan, MI 20127, Italy. TEL 39-02-26148855, FAX 39-02-26149333, info@soiel.it, http://www.soiel.it. Ed., Pub. Grazia Gargiulo. Circ: 14,800.

651.2 HKG
OFFICE CATALOGUE (HONG KONG). Text in Chinese, English; Summaries in English. 1996. a. HKD 199 domestic; USD 35 foreign; HKD 199 newsstand/cover. back issues avail. **Document type:** *Catalog, Trade.*
Formerly: Office Supplies Catalogue
Published by: Communication Management Ltd., 1811 Hong Kong Plaza, 188 Connaught Rd W, Hong Kong, Hong Kong. FAX 852-2858-2671, cmail@cmlink.com. Ed. M P Gopalan. Pub. Lina Ross. Circ: 22,000.

670.29 USA ISSN 1050-7612
OFFICE DEALER; updating the office products industry. Text in English. 1987. 6/yr. USD 36 (effective 2000). adv. bk.rev.
Formerly: Office Systems Dealer (Year) (0896-0852)
Published by: Quality Publishing Inc., PO Box 1028, Mt Airy, NC 27030. TEL 336-783-0000, FAX 336-783-0045, http://www.os-od.com. Ed. Lisa Bouchey. Pub. Richard Kunkel. R&P, Adv. contact Debbie Hooker. Circ: 17,000. **Subscr. to:** Office Systems, PO Box 3219, Lowell, MA 01853.

651 DEU ISSN 0937-4639
OFFICE DESIGN. Text in German. 1985. bi-m. **Document type:** *Bulletin.*
Published by: Verlagsgruppe Handelsblatt GmbH, Kasernenstr 67, Duesseldorf, 40213, Germany. TEL 49-211-887-0, FAX 49-211-133522.

651.2 GBR ISSN 0030-0187
OFFICE EQUIPMENT NEWS∗. Text in English. 1956. m. (10/yr.). adv. bk.rev. charts; illus.; tr.lit. **Document type:** *Trade.*
Indexed: BMT, BrCerAb, Inspec, RASB.
—IE. **CCC.**
Published by: Wilmington Publishing Ltd. (Subsidiary of: Wilmington Group Plc), Maidstone Rd, Footscray, Sidcup, Kent DA14 5HZ, United Kingdom. TEL 44-1322-277788, FAX 44-1322-276474, wbp@wilmington.co.uk. Ed. Andy Drew. Circ: 55,236 (controlled).

651.2 747 ITA ISSN 1120-012X
OFFICE LAYOUT. Text in Italian. 1985. 6/yr. EUR 52 domestic; EUR 150 foreign (effective 2005). adv. **Document type:** *Magazine, Trade.* **Description:** Covers office organization, schemes and furnishings. Presents the best in production, design, furnishings, lighting, security and automation.
Published by: Soiel International, Via Martiri Oscuri 3, Milan, MI 20127, Italy. TEL 39-02-26148855, FAX 39-02-26149333, info@soiel.it, http://www.soiel.it. Ed., Pub. Grazia Gargiulo. Adv. contact Andrea Bobbiesk. Circ: 16,000.

651.2 USA ISSN 0197-4602
HF5548
OFFICE PRODUCTS ANALYST; a monthly report devoted to the analysis of office products. Abbreviated title: O P A. Text in English. 1976. m. USD 195; USD 225 foreign (effective 1999). charts; stat. back issues avail. **Document type:** *Newsletter.* **Description:** Provides comparisons of copying, duplicating, facsimile, word processing and microcomputer equipment. Tracks pricing, supplies, service and technology trends.
Indexed: CompB.
Published by: Industry Analysts, Inc., 50 Chestnut St, Rochester, NY 14604. TEL 716-232-5320, FAX 716-458-3950, theopa001@aol.com, http://www.industranalysysts.com. Ed. Kathy Dwyer. Pub., R&P Louis E Slawelsky. Circ: 1,000.

651.2 GBR
OFFICE PRODUCTS DEALER. Text in English. 1881. m. (10/yr.). GBP 78; GBP 110 foreign. adv. **Document type:** *Trade.* **Description:** Covers business machines, EOS and furniture to software systems, e-commerce and traditional stationery.
Formerly: Stationery Trade Review (0039-0372)
Indexed: B&I.
Published by: Nexus Media Ltd. (Subsidiary of: Highbury House Communications PLC), Nexus House, Azalea Dr, Swanley, Kent BR8 8HU, United Kingdom. TEL 44-1322-660070, FAX 44-1322-616311, info@nexusmedia.com, http://www.officeproductsdealer.co.uk/, http://www.hhc.co.uk/. Ed. Alison Bowie TEL 44-1322-660070 ext 2316. Adv. contact Daniel Emerson. B&W page GBP 1,100, color page GBP 1,700; trim 297 x 420. Circ: 5,194.

651 004 GBR ISSN 1360-8460
OFFICE PRODUCTS INTERNATIONAL. Cover title: O P I. Text in English. 1991. m. GBP 195 in United Kingdom; USD 295 foreign (effective 2001). adv. tr.lit. back issues avail. **Document type:** *Magazine, Trade.* **Description:** Provides information for the office products industry worldwide, focusing on news, finance consideration of the industry, interaction with the IT industry and changes within each distribution channel.
Related titles: Online - full text ed.: (from Florida Center for Library Automation, Gale Group, O C L C Online Computer Library Center, Inc., ProQuest Information & Learning).
Indexed: ABIn.
—CCC.
Published by: Mondiale Corporation Ltd., Condor House, 5-14 St Paul's Churchyard, London, EC4M 8BE, United Kingdom. TEL 44-20-7236-0389, FAX 44-20-7236-0393, opi@opi.net, http://www.opi.net. Ed. Colin Carter. Pub. Michelle Pester. R&P Steve Hilleard TEL 44-20-7634-9445. adv.: color page USD 5,000; trim 277 x 200.

651 USA ISSN 0739-3156
HD8039.M39 CODEN: OFPRDE
OFFICE PROFESSIONAL. Text in English. 1981. m. USD 87 (effective 2004). back issues avail.; reprints avail. **Document type:** *Newsletter, Trade.*
Related titles: Online - full text ed.
—CCC.
Published by: Professional Training Associates, Inc. (Subsidiary of: McMurry Publishing), 2055 W Army Trail Rd, Ste 1, Addison, IL 80101-1493. TEL 800-424-2112, FAX 630-628-0550, top@protrain.com, http://www.protrain.com/cart/top.html. Ed. Diane Moore. Pub. Natalie Young. Circ: 9,000 (paid).

651 USA ISSN 1073-4252
OFFICE RELOCATION MAGAZINE∗. Text in English. 1992. bi-m. USD 39. adv. **Document type:** *Trade.*
Published by: O R M Group, Attn: J Barthelmess, 354 W Lancaster Ave, Haverford, PA 19041. TEL 610-649-6565, FAX 610-642-8020. Pub. Larry Dillon. Adv. contact Jay Barthelmes. B&W page USD 5,992, color page USD 7,792; trim 10.88 x 8.25. Circ: 38,000 (controlled).

OFFICE SECRETARY. see *BUSINESS AND ECONOMICS—Personnel Management*

651 USA ISSN 1529-1804
HF5548 CODEN: OFSYEH
OFFICE SOLUTIONS; the magazine for office professionals. Text in English. 1984. 6/yr. USD 36; free to qualified personnel (effective 2005). adv. bk.rev. illus. 56 p./no.; reprints avail. **Document type:** *Magazine, Trade.* **Description:** Covers all aspects of office automation with an emphasis on the concerns of the small mid-size company. Features include articles on telecommunications, imaging, filing, computers, computer supplies, software, office equipment, office supplies, mail center technology and furniture.
Formerly (until 2000): Office Systems (Year) (8750-3441); Incorporates: Managing Office Technology (1070-4051); Which was formerly (until June 1993): Modern Office Technology (0746-3839); (1956-1983): Modern Office Procedures (0026-8208)
Related titles: Microform ed.: (from PQC); Online - full text ed.: (from EBSCO Publishing, Florida Center for Library Automation, Gale Group, H.W. Wilson, O C L C Online Computer Library Center, Inc., ProQuest Information & Learning).
Indexed: ABIn, BPI, CompD, ConsI, Inspec, MagInd, MicrocompInd, RASB, SoftBase.
—BLDSC (6237.681000), IE, ingenta. **CCC.**
Published by: OfficeVision, Inc., 252 N Main St, Ste 200, Mt Airy, NC 27030. TEL 336-783-0000, FAX 336-783-0045, osod@os-od.com, http://www.os-od.com. Ed. Simon DeGroot. Pub. Richard Kunkel. Adv. contact Bessie Comer. B&W page USD 8,390, color page USD 9,980. Circ: 81,250 (paid and controlled).

651 GBR ISSN 0269-2430
OFFICE TRADE NEWS. Text in English. 1982. 10/yr. GBP 49 domestic; GBP 62 in Europe; USD 146 in US & Canada; GBP 92 elsewhere (effective 1999). **Document type:** *Trade.*
Published by: Wilmington Publishing Ltd. (Subsidiary of: Wilmington Group Plc), Maidstone Rd, Footscray, Sidcup, Kent DA14 5HZ, United Kingdom. TEL 44-1322-277788, FAX 44-1322-276474, wbp@wilmington.co.uk. Ed. Glynn Pritchard. Circ: 9,012.

651.2 USA ISSN 0164-5951
CODEN: OWNEEH
OFFICE WORLD NEWS. Abbreviated title: O W N. Text in English. 1972. bi-m. USD 50; free to qualified personnel (effective 2005). adv. bk.rev. charts; illus.; tr.lit. **Document type:** *Magazine, Trade.* **Description:** Covers the full range of business systems and supplies for the dealers, wholesalers, manufacturers and sales representatives of office, furniture and technology products.
Formerly: Office Products News
Related titles: Online - full text ed.: (from Northern Light Technology, Inc., ProQuest Information & Learning).
Indexed: ABIn, Inspec, PROMT.
—AskIEEE. **CCC.**
Published by: Imaging Network, 4061 S W 47th Ave, Fort Lauderdale, FL 33314. TEL 954-453-0700, 800-989-6077, FAX 954-581-0815, ownews@att.net, http://www.imagingnetwork.com/. Ed. Kevin Self. adv.: color page USD 5,995. Circ: 19,000 (paid and free).

651 ESP ISSN 0030-0624
OFICINA MODERNA; revista de papeleria, material, maquinas y muebles para oficina. Text in Spanish. 1961. bi-m. bk.rev. bibl.; illus. **Document type:** *Trade.* **Description:** Covers the world of stationery, includes sales, advertising and manufacturing of the industry.
Published by: (Asociacion Nacional de Empresarios de Papeleria y Objetos de Escritorio), Reclamo Tecnico S.A., De Casanova, 212, Barcelona, 08036, Spain. TEL 34-3-3212149, FAX 34-3-3223812. Ed. Jorge Foix Cusco. Adv. contact Enrique Estrada. Circ: 6,000.

651.2 ESP ISSN 0030-0640
OFICINAS; mobiliario, instalacion, iluminacion, ergonomia, diseno oficinas. Text in Spanish. 1968. 6/yr. EUR 100 domestic; EUR 106.25 in Europe; EUR 162.11 rest of world (effective 2006). adv. **Document type:** *Consumer.* **Description:** Informs on all aspects of buildings, from architecture to ergonomics, including interior design and furnishings.
Published by: Cetisa Editores S.A., Enrique Granados, 7, Barcelona, 08019, Spain. TEL 34-93-2431040, FAX 34-93-3492350, info@cetisa.com, http://www.cetisa.com/ofi/index.html. Ed. Santiago Pena. R&P Lluis Lleida. Adv. contact Xavier Cuatracasas. page EUR 3,365; 250 x 297. Circ: 6,500.

ORGANIZATIONAL SYSTEMS RESEARCH ASSOCIATION. CONFERENCE PROCEEDINGS. see *COMPUTERS*

652 DEU ISSN 0935-9958
P B S AKTUELL. (Papierwaren, Buerobedarf, Schreibwaren) Text in German. 1976. 10/yr. EUR 30; EUR 3 newsstand/cover (effective 2005). adv. index. **Document type:** *Magazine, Trade.*
Published by: B I T Verlag Weinbrenner GmbH & Co. KG, Fasanenweg 18, Leinfelden-Echterdingen, 70771, Germany. TEL 49-711-75910, FAX 49-711-7591368, info@bitverlag.de, http://www.pbsaktuell.de, http://www.bitverlag.de. Ed. Christine Schott. Adv. contact Christa Winkler. B&W page EUR 4,810, color page EUR 6,730; trim 210 x 297. Circ: 17,774 (paid and controlled).

651.2 DEU ISSN 0344-726X
P B S REPORT. Text in German. 1967. m. EUR 68; EUR 8 newsstand/cover (effective 2005). adv. bk.rev. **Document type:** *Magazine, Trade.*
Published by: Umschau Zeitschriftenverlag Breidenstein GmbH, Brueningstr 580, Frankfurt Am Main, 65929, Germany. TEL 49-69-2600601, FAX 49-69-2600659, kontakt@pbs-report.de, info@uzv.de, http://www.pbsreport.de, http://www.uzv.de. Ed. Werner Stark. Adv. contact Torsten Wessel. B&W page EUR 2,600, color page EUR 3,890; trim 170 x 270. Circ: 7,845 (paid).

676.282 ESP ISSN 0212-8489
PAPELERIA. Text in Spanish. 1979. q. **Document type:** *Directory, Consumer.* **Description:** Covers office and school supplies, paper industry, and fine arts.
Published by: Ser-Graf, Vilamari, 81, Barcelona, 08015, Spain. TEL 34-3-2260424, FAX 34-3-2263298. Pub. Antonio Palazon Serrano. Adv. contact Javier Palazon Barriuso. Circ: 5,000.

651.2 FRA ISSN 0031-1324
LE PAPETIER DE FRANCE; professional magazine for stationers, retailers, suppliers and stores. Text in French. 1947. m. (11/yr.). USD 110. adv. bk.rev.; rec.rev. charts; illus.; pat.; tr.mk. index. **Document type:** *Magazine, Trade.*
—CCC.
Published by: Helios International, 35 av. de l'Opera, Paris, 75002, France. TEL 33-1-42604010, FAX 33-4-90882849, info@papetierdefrance.com, http://www.papetierdefrance.com. Ed. Jean-Francois Aubry. Circ: 12,500.

651.2 SWE ISSN 1104-2400
PAPPER & KONTOR. Text in Swedish. 1918. 6/yr. SEK 360 (effective 2001). adv. bk.rev. charts; illus.; mkt.; pat.; tr.lit. index. **Document type:** *Magazine, Trade.*
Former titles: Papper och Kontor Data (1101-8887); (until 1989): Papper och Kontor (0349-7925); (until 1981): Bok och Papper; (until 1980): Pappershandlaren (0031-1456)
Published by: Kontors- och Pappershandelns Riksfoerbund, Birkagatan 16C, Stockholm, 11386, Sweden. pok@svb.se. Ed., Pub. Uno Palmstroem. Adv. contact Eva Lindell-Nilsson. B&W page SEK 8,600, color page SEK 13,400; trim 210 x 297. Circ: 2,600.

651.2 FIN ISSN 1459-6636
PORTAALI. Text in Finnish. 1975. m. EUR 74 (effective 2005). adv. bk.rev. illus. index. 48 p./no. 4 cols./p.; **Document type:** *Magazine, Trade.*
Formerly (until 2003): Uudistuva Konttori (0355-9912); Incorporates (1973-2003): Toimisto (0781-4593); Which was formerly (until 1984): Konttoriuutiset (0355-7928)
Related titles: Microfiche ed.
Published by: Nantucket Oy, Taipaleentie A 6, Humppila, 31640, Finland. TEL 358-3-4378590, FAX 358-3-4378591, toimitus@portaalilehti.fi, http://www.portaalilehti.fi/. Ed. Risto Anttila. Adv. contact Leena Royna-Anttila. B&W page EUR 1,730, color page EUR 1,980; 210 x 297. Circ: 13,500.

PRAVO I PRIVREDA. see *LAW*

651 GBR ISSN 0965-4739
CODEN: PFMAES
PREMISES AND FACILITIES MANAGEMENT. Text in English. 1986. m. GBP 78 domestic; GBP 99 in Europe; GBP 143.50 elsewhere (effective 2000). adv. bk.rev. **Document type:** *Trade.*
Indexed: IBuildSA, Inspec, RICS.
—BLDSC (6607.644630), AskIEEE, IE, ingenta.
Published by: I M L Group Plc., Blair House, 184 High St, Tonbridge, Kent TN9 1BQ, United Kingdom. TEL 01732-359990, FAX 01732-770049, imlgroup@dial.pipex.com. Ed. Jane Fenwick. Pub. Peter Middup. R&P Valerie Billingsby. Adv. contact Ian Webb. Circ: 11,300.

PRESTIGE CORPORATE INTERIORS. see *INTERIOR DESIGN AND DECORATION*

651.2 ITA
PRIMA COPIA; the printing and imaging magazine. Text in Italian. 1986. m. EUR 49.95 domestic; EUR 74.95 in the European Union; EUR 99.95 elsewhere (effective 2002). **Document type:** *Magazine, Trade.*
Formerly (until 2001): Copia (1123-6795)
Indexed: B&AI.
Published by: Editoriale Directa S.r.l., Viale Sondrio 7, Milan, MI 20124, Italy. TEL 39-02-67479048, FAX 39-02-67479253, info@primacopia.it, http://www.primacopia.it, http://www.e-directa.com. Ed., R&P, Adv. contact Andrea Ganassini. Circ: 17,000.

PRINT IT MAGAZINE; regular updates on PC and Mac driven printers. see *COMPUTERS—Personal Computers*

651.2 DEU
PRODUKTUEBERSICHT: KOPIERER - VOLLFARB - GROSSFORMATKOPIERER. Text in German. 1986. s-a. EUR 48; EUR 36 per issue (effective 2005). adv. reprints avail. **Document type:** *Magazine, Trade.*
Formerly: Lexikon Buerotechnik
Published by: Comkotext GmbH, Buedericher Str 14, Willich, 47877, Germany. TEL 49-2154-883955, FAX 49-2154-884990, comkotext@t-online.de, http://www.comkotext.de. Ed. Wolfgang Broetzmann. Circ: 5,000.

651.2 DEU
PRODUKTUEBERSICHT: SEITEN - LASERDRUCKER. Text in German. s-a. EUR 48; EUR 36 per issue (effective 2005). **Document type:** *Directory, Trade.*
Published by: Comkotext GmbH, Buedericher Str 14, Willich, 47877, Germany. TEL 49-2154-883955, FAX 49-2154-884990, comkotext@t-online.de, http://www.comkotext.de. Ed. Wolfgang Broetzmann.

651.2 DEU
PRODUKTUEBERSICHT: TELEFAX - MOBILFAX. Text in German. s-a. EUR 48; EUR 36 per issue (effective 2005). **Document type:** *Directory, Trade.*
Published by: Comkotext GmbH, Buedericher Str 14, Willich, 47877, Germany. TEL 49-2154-883955, FAX 49-2154-884990, comkotext@t-online.de, http://www.comkotext.de. Ed. Wolfgang Broetzmann.

651 VEN
PROOFICINAS. Text in Spanish. 1978. a. adv.
Published by: Publicaciones Araguaney, Edificio Lec piso 3, Calle 8, La Urbina, Caracas, DF 1073, Venezuela.

651 352 GBR ISSN 1466-2167
PUBLIC SERVICE WORKPLACE. Text in English. 1999. m. bk.rev. tr.lit. back issues avail. **Document type:** *Trade.*
Published by: Market Place Publishing Ltd., Scorpio House, 106 Church Rd, London, SE19 2UB, United Kingdom. TEL 44-181-771-3614, FAX 44-181-771-4592. Ed. Joanna Knight. Pub. Laurence Allen. adv.: B&W page GBP 1,270, color page GBP 1,905; trim 210 x 297. Circ: 10,688 (controlled).

651 GBR
QUALITY TODAY BUYERS GUIDE. Text in English. a. GBP 30 per issue (effective 2003). **Document type:** *Trade.*
Published by: Nexus Media Ltd. (Subsidiary of: Highbury House Communications PLC), Nexus House, Azalea Dr, Swanley, Kent BR8 8HU, United Kingdom. TEL 44-1322-660070, FAX 44-1322-616311, info@nexusmedia.com, http://www.hhc.co.uk/qtbuyersguide. Ed. Brendan Coyne. Circ: 10,000.

651.2 USA ISSN 1053-7503
HD9696.C6
RECHARGER; serving the office products recycling industry. Text in English. m. USD 45 in US & Canada; USD 105 elsewhere (effective 2003). adv. **Document type:** *Magazine, Trade.* **Description:** Contains information and articles on all aspects of the office products and equipment recycling industry.
Related titles: Online - full text ed.
Published by: Recharger Magazine (Subsidiary of: 101 Communications, Llc.), 2800 W. Sahara Ave., Ste. 5C, Las Vegas, NV 89102-4381. info@recharger.com, http://www.rechargermag.com. adv.: B&W page USD 800, color page USD 1,145; trim 8 x 10.75.

651 USA ISSN 1096-9624
Z699.5.A7
RECORDS & INFORMATION MANAGEMENT REPORT; issues in information technology. Text in English. 1984. 10/yr. USD 182 domestic; USD 222 foreign (effective 2006). 16 p./no. 3 cols./p.; back issues avail. **Document type:** *Magazine, Trade.*
Formerly: Records and Retrieval Report (8756-0089)
Related titles: Online - full text ed.: 2004 (Feb.) (from EBSCO Publishing, O C L C Online Computer Library Center, Inc., Swets Information Services).
—BLDSC (7325.342000), IE, ingenta. **CCC.**
Published by: M.E. Sharpe, Inc., 80 Business Park Dr, Armonk, NY 10504. TEL 914-273-1800, 800-541-6563, FAX 914-273-2106, custserv@mesharpe.com, http://www.mesharpe.com/mall/results1.asp. Ed. Richard J Cox.

651 658.7 USA
▼ **RELIGIOUS PRODUCT NEWS.** Text in English. 2003. m. free to qualified personnel (effective 2005). adv. **Document type:** *Magazine, Trade.* **Description:** Provides the latest information and resources about products, furnishings, building supplies, technology, media and more for today's growing churches.
Published by: Valor Media Concepts, Inc., PO Box 36577, Birmingham, AL 35236. TEL 205-620-2888, 888-548-2567, FAX 205-620-4040, info@rpnmag.com, http://www.rpnmag.com/. Pub. Loren Stiffler TEL 205-620-2888 ext 225. adv.: color page USD 3,700; trim 8 x 10.625.

648.5 NOR ISSN 1501-987X
RENHOLD. Text in Norwegian. 2000. 6/yr. NOK 370 (effective 2005). adv. illus. **Document type:** *Magazine, Trade.*
Formed by the merger of (1978-2000): Renholdsnytt (0802-2100); (1992-2000): Rengjoering og Vedlikehold (0804-1563)
Published by: Vanebo Fagpresse AS, PO Box 130, Kirkenaer, 2260, Norway. TEL 47-62-941000, FAX 47-62-941010, firmapost@vanebo.no, http://www.vanebo.no. Eds. Paal Soensteli, Hans Degerdal TEL 47-62-941013. Adv. contact Roy Utgaard TEL 47-62-946995. B&W page NOK 10,300, color page NOK 13,950; 190 x 265. Circ: 4,233.

B

REVISTA DE ADMINISTRACAO MACKENZIE. see *BUSINESS AND ECONOMICS—Management*

651.2 USA
S E R O M D A SCENE✶. Text in English. bi-m.
Published by: South Eastern Regional Office Machine Dealers Association, 12411 Wornall Rd, Kansas City, MO 64145-1119. TEL 615-690-8996, FAX 615-690-3328. Ed. Betsy Morrow. Circ: 1,000.

S I G GROUP BULLETIN. (Special Interest Group) see *COMPUTERS—Computer Systems*

676.282 658.8 BEL ISSN 0778-9106
SCRIPT (DUTCH EDITION); vakblad voor de kantoorvakhandel. Text in Dutch. 1932. 8/yr. (plus 20 e-mails). EUR 50 (effective 2005). adv. bk.rev. illus.; tr.lit. Supplement avail. **Document type:** *Journal, Trade.* **Description:** Reports on new products and sales and marketing techniques for retailers and distributors of office and stationery supplies.
Formerly: Script, De Papierhandel (0774-9848); Which superseded in part (in 1986): Papetier (0774-9910)
Related titles: ◆ French ed.: Script (French Edition).
Published by: Professional Media Group, Torhoutsesteenweg 226 bus 2/6, Zedelgem, B-8210, Belgium. TEL 32-50-240404, FAX 32-50-240445, info@pmgroup.be, http://www.retail-script.be/?lang=n, http://www.pmgroup.be. adv.: color page EUR 2,025; trim 297 x 210. Circ: 6,467 (controlled).

658.5 BEL
SCRIPT (FRENCH EDITION); revue professionelle de la papeterie et de la bureautique. Text in French. 1977. 8/yr. (plus 20 e-mails). EUR 50 (effective 2005). adv. bk.rev. illus.; tr.lit. Supplement avail. **Document type:** *Journal, Trade.* **Description:** Reports on new products and sales and marketing techniques and distributors of office and stationery supplies.
Formerly: Script, Le Papetier (0774-9856); Which superseded in part (in 1986): Papetier (0774-9910)
Related titles: ◆ Dutch ed.: Script (Dutch Edition). ISSN 0778-9106.
Published by: Professional Media Group, Torhoutsesteenweg 226 bus 2/6, Zedelgem, B-8210, Belgium. TEL 32-50-240404, FAX 32-50-240445, info@pmgroup.be, http://www.retail-script.be/?lang=f, http://www.pmgroup.be. adv.: color page EUR 2,025; trim 297 x 210. Circ: 8,600 (controlled).

SECRETARY: F Y I. see *RELIGIONS AND THEOLOGY—Protestant*

651 USA ISSN 0164-3320
HD9999.S45 CODEN: SEDEEL
SECURITY DEALER. Text in English. 1972. m. free to qualified personnel; USD 65 (effective 2005). adv. illus. **Document type:** *Magazine, Trade.* **Description:** Publishes articles on security equipment applications and installations.
Related titles: Online - full text ed.: (from Gale Group, ProQuest Information & Learning).
—CCC.
Published by: Cygnus Business Media, Inc., 3 Huntington Quadrangle, Ste 301N, Melville, NY 11747-3601. TEL 631-845-2700, FAX 631-845-7109, http://www.securityinfowatch.com, http://www.cygnusb2b.com. Ed. Susan A Brady. Circ: 26,000 (controlled).

651 POL ISSN 1425-5782
SEKRETARIAT. Text in Polish. 1996. m. PLZ 60 (effective 2001).
Published by: Grupa Wydawnicza INFOR Sp. z o.o., Ul Okopowa 58/72, Warsaw, 01042, Poland. TEL 48-22-5304208, 48-22-5304450, bok@infor.pl. Ed. Janusz Walewski. Adv. contact Waldemar Krakowiak.

651 CHE
SIGNAL STENOGRAPHIQUE. Text in French. 6/yr.
Address: Libellule 12, Lausanne, 1010, Switzerland. TEL 021-331453. Ed. Gabrielle Fasnacht. Circ: 1,200.

651.2 ITA
SISTEMI UOMINI MACCHINE ORGANIZZAZIONE. Short title: S U M O. Text in Italian. 1958. 5/yr.
Published by: Gruppo Editoriale J C E, Via Patecchio 2, Milan, MI 20141, Italy. TEL 39-02-57316011, FAX 39-02-57316291, info@jce.it, http://www.jce.it. Ed. Pasquale Satalino. Circ: 30,000.

653 SVK ISSN 0231-6978
SLOVENSKY STENOGRAF. Text in Slovak. 1945. 10/yr. USD 29 (effective 2000).
Published by: P A R E N T E S, Sutazna 18, Bratislava, 82108, Slovakia. TEL 42-1-7-559606266. Ed. Marta Hajna. Circ: 15,000.

SOCIETY OF DESIGN ADMINISTRATION. NATIONAL PUBLICATION. see *ARCHITECTURE*

651 USA
SOUTH FLORIDA OFFICE GUIDE✶. Text in English. 1982. q. USD 30. adv. reprints avail.
Formerly: Office Guide to Miami (0743-5983)
Published by: South Florida Office Guides, Inc., 2450 Hollywood Blvd, 701, Hollywood, FL 33020-6619. TEL 305-570-7800, FAX 305-570-8380. Ed. Jann Sabin. Circ: 14,000.

653 IND
SPEEDTYPE. Text in English. 1978. q. INR 12. adv. bk.rev.
Published by: Delhi Shorthand School, 2-58 Ramesh Nagar, New Delhi, 110 015, India. Ed. Dharma Vira. Circ: 2,600.

653 IND
SPEEDWRITER. Text in English. 1975. m. INR 55. adv. bk.rev.
Description: Model test papers for various shorthand examinations.
Published by: Delhi Shorthand School, 2-58 Ramesh Nagar, New Delhi, 110 015, India. Ed. Dharma Vira. Circ: 5,000.

651.2 TWN
STATIONERY & OFFICE BUYERS' GUIDE. Text in English. 1983. a. USD 35 per issue (effective 2005). adv. **Document type:** *Directory, Trade.* **Description:** Covers stationery and office products produced in Taiwan for export.
Former titles: Stationery and Office Products Buyer's Guide; Taiwan Stationery and Office Products Buyer's Guide (1024-9001)
Published by: Interface Global Taiwan Co., Ltd., PO Box 173-12, Taipei, 116, Taiwan. TEL 886-2-29180500, FAX 886-2-89119381, service@asiatrademart.com, http://www.asiatrademart.com. Ed. Daniel Foong. Pub. Herbert Chen. R&P Donald Shapiro. Adv. contact Melody Lin TEL 886-2-2351-3180. **Subscr. in U.S. to:** Trade Winds Inc., PO Box 820519, Dallas, TX 75382. TEL 877-861-1188, FAX 972-699-1189, twinds8888@aol.com.

651.2 ZAF
STATIONERY & OFFICE PRODUCTS S A. Text in English. 1916. 9/yr. ZAR 135; ZAR 500 foreign (effective 1999). bk.rev. illus.; tr.lit. **Document type:** *Trade.*
Former titles: Office Products S A; Stationery; South African Stationery Trades Journal (0038-2701)
Published by: (National Office Products and Stationery Association of Southern Africa), R.D. Whales Associates, PO Box 73005, Fairland, Johannesburg 2030, South Africa. TEL 27-11-6786317, FAX 27-11-4767035. Ed. Robin Whales. Circ: 6,000.

651.2 TWN
STATIONERY AND OFFICE SUPPLIES. Text in English. s-a. USD 30.
Published by: Taiwan Trade Pages Corp., P.O. Box 72-50, Taipei, Taiwan. TEL 02-3050759, FAX 886-2-3071000.

652 GBR ISSN 1475-8644
STATIONERY & OFFICE UPDATE. Text in English. 1990. m. GBP 28 domestic; GBP 50 in Europe; GBP 70 elsewhere (effective 2004). adv. **Document type:** *Magazine, Trade.* **Description:** Contains news product information, literature, company profiles, overviews of market sectors,and industry trends.
Formerly (until 1998): Stationery Update (1367-5990)
—CCC.
Published by: Datateam Publishing Ltd, 15a London Rd, Maidstone, Kent ME16 8LY, United Kingdom. TEL 44-1622-687031, FAX 44-1622-757646, stationery@datateam.co.uk, info@datateam.co.uk, http://www.datateam.co.uk/business_publications/stationary_office_update.htm, http://www.datateam.co.uk/home/home.htm. Ed. Roger Hooper. Pub. Nick Carpenter. R&P Bob Foreman. Adv. contact Sidney French. B&W page GBP 720, color page GBP 1,075; trim 280 x 420. Circ: 6,000 (controlled).

651.2 AUS ISSN 1033-758X
STATIONERY NEWS. Text in English. 1989. m. AUD 58 domestic; AUD 75 in New Zealand; AUD 85 in Asia; AUD 115 elsewhere (effective 2005). adv. **Document type:** *Magazine, Trade.* **Description:** Provides advertisers access to the buyers in each important link of the Australian stationery and office product reseller chain, including: office product dealers; stationery and office supply wholesalers; stationery retailers, superstores and mail order houses; newsagents throughout Australia; retail chain and department store buyers; manufacturers, importers and agents.
Published by: Yaffa Publishing Group Pty Ltd., 17-21 Bellevue St, Surry Hills, NSW 2010, Australia. TEL 61-2-92812333, FAX 61-2-92812750, yaffa@yaffa.com.au, http://www.yaffa.com.au. Ed. Amy Hurrell. Pub. Michael Merrick. Adv. contact Max Yaffa. B&W page AUD 2,090, color page AUD 2,860; trim 210 x 297. Circ: 6,000.

653 ITA ISSN 0039-2960
STUDI GRAFICI. Text in Italian. 1925. bi-m. adv. bk.rev. bibl.; illus.; stat. index.
Published by: Accademia Italiana di Stenografia, c/o Giuseppe Aliprandi, Ed., Via Dei Soncin, 17, Padua, PD 35122, Italy.
Co-sponsor: Primo Centro Italiano di Studi Dattilografici.

621.382 DEU ISSN 0946-6703
TEL-COM - BRIEF; Telekommunikation, Datenverarbeitung und Organisation. Text in German. 1987. m. EUR 179.80 (effective 2005). bk.rev. index. **Document type:** *Bulletin, Trade.*
Former titles: Tel-Com D V und Orga-Brief; Former titles: Telcom-Brief (0939-1649); D V und O R G A Brief (0932-2698)
Published by: Deutscher Wirtschaftsdienst (Subsidiary of: Wolters Kluwer Deutschland GmbH), Schoenhauser Str 64, Cologne, 50968, Germany. TEL 49-221-93763-0, FAX 49-221-9376399. Circ: 500.

651 747 USA ISSN 1059-0307
NA4170
TODAY'S FACILITY MANAGER; the magazine of facilities - interior planning team. Text in English. 1982. m. USD 30 (effective 2005). adv. bk.rev. illus. back issues avail. **Document type:** *Magazine, Trade.*
Former titles (until 1990): Business Interiors (1044-3584); (until 1988): Corporate Design (0894-3575); (until 1987): Corporate Design and Realty (8750-8206); (until 1984): Corporate Design (0744-2750)
Indexed: ABIn, AIAP.
Published by: Group C Communications, 44 Apple St, Ste 3, Tinton Falls, NJ 07724. TEL 732-842-7433, FAX 732-758-6634, schwartz@groupc.com, connie@groupc.com, http://www.todaysfacilitymanager.com, http://www.groupc.com. Ed. Heidi Schwartz. Pub., Adv. contact Susan Coene. B&W page USD 6,755. Circ: 50,000 (controlled).

652 GBR ISSN 0266-3295
TROPHY & ENGRAVING NEWS. Abbreviated title: T E N. Text in English. 1984. m. GBP 32 in British Isles; GBP 40 in Europe; GBP 52.50 elsewhere (effective 2000). **Description:** Provides a forum for the trophy engraving, industrial, and incentive marking trades.
Incorporates: Trophy and Incentive Marketing
Published by: Hill Media Ltd., 119 High St, Berkhamsted, Herts HP4 2DJ, United Kingdom. TEL 44-1442-878787, FAX 44-1442-870888. Ed. Fleur Dolphin. Pub., R&P, Adv. contact Colin Gallimore.

U.S. SITES AND DEVELOPMENT. see *REAL ESTATE*

U.S. SITES AND DEVELOPMENT ANNUAL DIRECTORY. see *REAL ESTATE*

U.S. SITES AND DEVELOPMENT RELOCATION JOURNAL. see *REAL ESTATE*

UFFICIOSTILE. see *INTERIOR DESIGN AND DECORATION*

052 GBR
UNLIMITED; the office management magazine. Text in English. 1998. q. GBP 20 (effective 2005). adv. 96 p./no.; back issues avail. **Document type:** *Magazine, Consumer.* **Description:** Provides features and information on the inner workings of the business and corporate workplace and lifestyle.
Published by: Tomorrows Business Ltd., Claridge House, 29 Barnes High St, London, SW13 9LW, United Kingdom. TEL 44-20-82821682, FAX 44-20-82821683, info@officemanagement.uk.com, http://www.officemanagement.uk.com/unlimited_html/. Ed. Debi Arnold. adv.: page GBP 5,225; 220 x 307.

676.282 USA
W S A DIGEST✶. (Wholesale Stationers' Association) Text in English. bi-m.
Formerly: Wholesaler Digest
Published by: Office Products Wholesalers Association, 5024 R Campbell Blvd, Baltimore, MD 21236-5974. TEL 708-297-6882. Ed. Carole Rosebaugh.

651 GBR ISSN 0269-2996
WAREHOUSE COMPUTING. Text in English. 6/yr.
Address: Turret House, 171 High St, Rickmansworth, Herts WD3 1SN, United Kingdom. TEL 0923-777000, TELEX 888095-UKPUBS-G. Ed. Nick Allen. Circ: 18,300.

651 USA ISSN 1062-7650
HD9803.U6
THE WORKSTATION REPORT; (year) buyer's guide to office furniture. Text in English. 1986. a. USD 49.95. back issues avail. **Description:** Provides an overview of contract products, product services, and news digest for previous year.
Published by: Design Network International Ltd., P O Box 638, Highland, IL 60035-0638. TEL 708-831-0300, FAX 708-926-8230. Ed. Elizabeth Work.

651.2 CHN
ZHONGGUO WENFANG SIBAO/CHINESE FOUR TREASURES OF THE STUDY. Text in Chinese. q. **Description:** Features traditional Chinese office stationery: writing brush, ink stick, ink slab and paper.
Published by: Zhongguo Wenfang Sibao Xiehui/Chinese Association of Four Treasures of the Study, 99 Liulichang, Xuanwu-qu, Beijing, 100050, China. TEL 3017839. Ed. Huang He.

653 IND
40 MINUTES; an I Q monthly. Text in English. 1981. m. INR 27. adv. bk.rev.
Published by: Delhi Shorthand School, 2-58 Ramesh Nagar, New Delhi, 110 015, India. Ed. Dharma Vira. Circ: 3,500.

BUSINESS AND ECONOMICS—Personnel Management

658.3 345 USA
A C J S EMPLOYMENT BULLETIN. Text in English. 1993. m. (Oct.- Apr.). USD 45; USD 15 per issue (effective 2001); free with ACJS membership. **Document type:** *Bulletin.* **Description:** Lists job vacancies in criminal justice field.
Published by: Academy of Criminal Justice Sciences, 7339 Hanover Pkwy., Ste. A, Greenbelt, MD 20770-3640. info@acjs.org, http://www.acjs.org. Circ: 3,400.

658.3 USA ISSN 1539-5138
HD5723
A M A SURVEY ON STAFFING AND STRUCTURE. Text in English. 1996. a. **Document type:** *Trade.*
Formerly (until 1998): A M A Survey on Job Creation, Job Elimination, and Downsizing (1539-512X)
Published by: American Management Association International, 1601 Broadway, New York, NY 10019. TEL 800-714-6395, FAX 212-903-8168, 518-891-3653, customerservice@amanet.org, http://www.amanet.org.

658.3 CAN
A S A C E-BULLETIN. Text in English. 2000. s-a. **Document type:** *Bulletin, Academic/Scholarly.*
Media: Online - full content.
Published by: Administrative Sciences Association of Canada, F.C. Manning School of Business, Acadia University, Wolfville, NS B0P 1X0, Canada. TEL 902-585-1285, jean.mills@acadiau.ca, http://www.asac.ca.

658.0029 USA
A S T D BUYERS GUIDE AND CONSULTANTS DIRECTORY. Text in English. a. USD 45 to non-members (effective 2003). adv. **Document type:** *Directory.*
Former titles: Training Resources; A S T D Consultant Directory (0098-5619)
Related titles: Online - full text ed.
Published by: American Society for Training & Development, 1640 King St, Box 1443, Alexandria, VA 22313. TEL 703-683-8100, FAX 703-683-9591, http://www.astd.org. Ed., Adv. contact Jan Throckmorton.

ABHIGYAN; the journal of foundation for organization research and education. see *SOCIAL SCIENCES: COMPREHENSIVE WORKS*

THE ACADEMY OF MANAGEMENT NEWS. see *BUSINESS AND ECONOMICS—Management*

ACCOUNTANT'S GUIDE TO EMPLOYEE BENEFIT PLANS. see *BUSINESS AND ECONOMICS—Accounting*

ACTUARIAL UPDATE. see *INSURANCE*

658.3 CAN ISSN 1191-7881
ADMINISTRATIVE ASSISTANT'S UPDATE. Text in English. 1986. m. CND 149 domestic; USD 125.21 foreign (effective 2005). **Document type:** *Newsletter, Trade.* **Description:** professional insights, tips and information designed to help administrative assistants and secretaries in their daily tasks.
Formerly (until 1992): Secretary's Update (0833-2878)
Related titles: Online - full text ed.: (from Micromedia ProQuest, Northern Light Technology, Inc., ProQuest Information & Learning).
Published by: Carswell (Subsidiary of: Thomson Corporation), One Corporate Plaza, 2075 Kennedy Rd, Toronto, ON M1T 3V4, Canada. TEL 416-609-8000, 800-387-5164, FAX 416-298-5094, carswell.customerrelations@thomson.com, http://www.carswell.com/description.asp?docid=2962. Ed. Joyce Grant.

658.3 GBR ISSN 0960-6580
ADULT AND YOUTH TRAINING. Text in English. 1988. 12/yr. free. **Document type:** *Government.*
Formed by the 1990 merger of: Employment Training News (0955-4130); Youth Training News (0952-9853)
Published by: Training Agency, Employment Department, Information Services Branch, Rm E810, Moorfoot, Sheffield, S Yorks S1 4PQ, United Kingdom. TEL 01742-704289, FAX 01742-730982. Ed. Howard Woollin. Circ: 35,000.

658.3 371.42 USA ISSN 1523-4223
HF5549.A2
➤ **ADVANCES IN DEVELOPING HUMAN RESOURCES.** Text in English. 2001. q. USD 84, GBP 51 to individuals; USD 362, GBP 234 to institutions; USD 377, GBP 244 combined subscription to institutions print & online eds. (effective 2006). adv. back issues avail. **Document type:** *Journal, Academic/Scholarly.* **Description:** Focuses on issues that help you work more effectively in human resources development. Spans the realms of performance learning and integrity within an organizational context.
Related titles: Online - full text ed.: ISSN 1552-3055. USD 359, GBP 232 to institutions (effective 2006) (from C S A, EBSCO Publishing, O C L C Online Computer Library Center, Inc., ProQuest Information & Learning, Sage Publications, Inc., Swets Information Services).
Indexed: ABIn, HRA, PsycInfo, PsycholAb.
—BLDSC (0704.243120), IE, ingenta. **CCC.**
Published by: Sage Publications, Inc., 2455 Teller Rd, Thousand Oaks, CA 91320. TEL 805-499-0721, FAX 805-499-0871, info@sagepub.com, http://www.sagepub.com/journal.aspx?pid=267. Ed. Wendy E A Ruona. Adv. contact Kirsten Beaulieu TEL 805-499-0721 ext 7160. B&W page USD 325, color page USD 745. **Subscr. outside the US to:** Sage Publications Ltd., 1 Oliver's Yard, 55 City Rd, London EC1 1SP, United Kingdom. TEL 44-20-73740645, FAX 44-20-73748741, subscription@sagepub.co.uk. **Co-sponsor:** Academy of Human Resource Development.

➤ **AFFIRMATIVE ACTION REGISTER**; for effective equal opportuniy recruitment. see *OCCUPATIONS AND CAREERS*

658.3 USA ISSN 1547-349X
AFFIRMATIVE ACTION SOLUTIONS. Text in English. 2000 (Aug.). m. USD 395 (effective 2003).
Published by: Business & Legal Reports, Inc., PO Box 6001, Old Saybrook, CT 06475-6001. TEL 860-510-0100, 800-727-5257, FAX 860-510-7225, service@blr.com, http://www.blr.com. Ed. Sandra K. Romano. Pub. Robert L Brady.

658.3 USA
AGENCY ISSUES. Text in English. bi-m. adv. back issues avail. **Document type:** *Newsletter, Government.* **Description:** Short articles on trends in public personnel for agency members of IPMA.
Media: E-mail.
Published by: International Personnel Management Association, 1617 Duke St, Alexandria, VA 22314. TEL 703-549-7100, FAX 703-684-0948, publications@ipma-hr.org, http://www.ipma-hr.org. Ed. Karen D Smith. Adv. contact Logan Hunter-Thompson TEL 703-549-7100. online banner USD 200. Circ: 3,000.

AMERICANS WITH DISABILITIES CASES. see *LAW*

658.3 USA ISSN 1092-6577
HF5549.A2
➤ **ANNUAL EDITIONS: HUMAN RESOURCES.** Text in English. 1989. a., latest 2003, 14th ed. USD 20.31 per vol. (effective 2004). illus. **Document type:** *Academic/Scholarly.* **Description:** Explores the current environment of human resources management; meeting human resource requirements; creating a productive work environment; developing effective human resources; implementing compensation and security; fostering employee/management relationships; and international human resource management.
Published by: McGraw-Hill - Dushkin (Subsidiary of: McGraw-Hill Higher Education), 2460 Kerper Blvd, Dubuque, IA 52001. TEL 800-243-6532, customer.service@mcgraw-hill.com, http://www.dushkin.com/text-data/catalog/0072874430.mhtml. Ed. Fred H Maidment. Pub. Ian Nielsen. R&P Cheryl Greenleaf.

658.3 CAN
ANNUAL SURVEY OF HOURLY PAID EMPLOYEES IN ONTARIO. Text in English. a. CND 395 (effective 1998 & 1999).
Published by: Central Ontario Industrial Relations Institute, 111 Richmond St W, Ste 1002, Toronto, ON M5H 2G4, Canada. TEL 416-368-2364, FAX 416-368-7217.

658.3 CAN
ANNUAL SURVEY OF SALARIED EMPLOYEES IN ONTARIO. Text in English. a. CND 395 (effective 1998).
Published by: Central Ontario Industrial Relations Institute, 111 Richmond St W, Ste 1002, Toronto, ON M5H 2G4, Canada. TEL 416-368-2364, FAX 416-368-7217.

(YEAR) ANNUAL. VOLUME 1: TRAINING; developing human resources. see *BUSINESS AND ECONOMICS—Management*

(YEAR) ANNUAL. VOLUME 2: CONSULTING. see *BUSINESS AND ECONOMICS—Management*

APPLIED H.R.M. RESEARCH. (Human Resources Management) see *PSYCHOLOGY*

ARBEJDSMARKEDSPOLITISK AGENDA. see *BUSINESS AND ECONOMICS—Labor And Industrial Relations*

658.3 ITA ISSN 1126-5760
ARGOMENTI DI DIRITTO DEL LAVORO. Text in Italian. 1995. irreg. EUR 30.99 (effective 2003). **Document type:** *Academic/Scholarly.*
Published by: C E D A M, Via Giuseppe Jappelli 5-6, Padua, PD 35121, Italy. TEL 39-049-8239111, FAX 39-049-8752900, info@cedam.com, http://www.cedam.com.

658.3 GBR ISSN 1038-4111
HF5549.A2
➤ **ASIA PACIFIC JOURNAL OF HUMAN RESOURCES.** Short title: Asia Pacific J H R. Text in English. 1962. 3/yr. GBP 234, USD 409 to institutions; GBP 243, USD 426 combined subscription to institutions print & online eds. (effective 2006). adv. bk.rev. **Document type:** *Journal, Academic/Scholarly.* **Description:** Presents leading thinking and commentary on a range of human resouces topics.
Former titles: Asia Pacific Human Resource Management (1032-3627); (until 1989): Human Resource Management Australia (0156-904X); Personnel Management (0048-346X)
Related titles: Online - full text ed.: ISSN 1744-7941. GBP 231, USD 404 to institutions (effective 2006) (from C S A, EBSCO Publishing, O C L C Online Computer Library Center, Inc., Sage Publications, Inc., Swets Information Services).
Indexed: ABIn, ADPA, AESIS, ASEANManA, AusPAIS, BusI, CISA, CPM, Emerald, FamI, HECAB, HRA, M&MA, PsycInfo, PsycholAb, SCIMP.
—BLDSC (1742.260690), IE, ingenta. **CCC.**
Published by: (Australian Human Resources Institute AUS), Sage Publications Ltd. (Subsidiary of: Sage Publications, Inc.), 1 Oliver's Yard, 55 City Rd, London, EC1 1SP, United Kingdom. TEL 44-20-73248500, FAX 44-20-73248600, info@sagepub.co.uk, http://www.sagepub.co.uk/journal.aspx?pid=105476. Ed. Robin Kramar. adv.: page GBP 200. Circ: 14,000. **Subscr. in the Americas to:** Sage Publications, Inc., 2455 Teller Rd, Thousand Oaks, CA 91320. TEL 805-499-0721, FAX 805-499-0871, journals@sagepub.com.

658.3 AUS ISSN 1325-6858
AUSTRALIAN BENEFITS REVIEW. Text in English. 1992. a. looseleaf. AUD 450. charts; stat. **Document type:** *Trade.* **Description:** Provides information on a range of benefits policies, remuneration and package designs.
Published by: Cullen Egan Dell, Level 8, 50 Bridge St, Sydney, NSW 2000, Australia. TEL 61-2-9375-9800, FAX 61-2-9233-6800. Ed. Marilyn Earl. Circ: 560.

658.3 AUS ISSN 1328-2506
AUSTRALIAN CALL CENTRE AND CUSTOMER SERVICE REMUNERATION REVIEW. Text in English. 1994. a. AUD 1,500 (effective 1999). **Document type:** *Trade.* **Description:** Focuses on positions relevant to organizations having a strong customer service focus.
Published by: Cullen Egan Dell, Level 8, 50 Bridge St, Sydney, NSW 2000, Australia. TEL 61-2-9375-9800, FAX 61-2-9233-6800. Ed. Jackie Taggart. Circ: 31.

658.3 USA ISSN 0005-3228
B N A POLICY AND PRACTICE SERIES. Text in English. 1945. w. looseleaf. bibl.; charts. cum.index. back issues avail. **Document type:** *Newsletter.* **Description:** Notification and reference service covering five major areas of employer-employee relations. Covered are personnel management, labor relations, fair employment practices, compensation, and wages and hours.
Former titles (until 1968): Labor Policy and Practice; (until 1950): Manual Labor Supervision
Related titles: Online - full text ed.; ♦ Series: B N A's SafetyNet. ISSN 1091-2894; ♦ Air Pollution Control (Washington). ISSN 0196-7150; ♦ Bulletin to Management. ISSN 0525-2156; ♦ B N A Policy and Practice Series. Fair Employment Practices. ISSN 0149-2683; ♦ Water Pollution Control. ISSN 0194-0147; ♦ Fair Employment Practices Summary of Latest Developments. ISSN 1545-4460; ♦ Labor Relations (Washington, DC). ISSN 0149-2713; ♦ Personnel Management. ISSN 0149-2675; ♦ B N A Policy and Practice Series. Wages and Hours. ISSN 0149-2691.
—**CCC.**
Published by: The Bureau of National Affairs, Inc., 1231 25th St., NW, Washington, DC 20037. TEL 202-452-4200, 800-372-1033, FAX 202-785-7167, customercare@bna.com, http://www.bna.com. Ed. Bill L Manville. Pub. Greg C McCaffery.

B N A POLICY AND PRACTICE SERIES. COMPENSATION. see *BUSINESS AND ECONOMICS—Labor And Industrial Relations*

B N A'S AMERICANS WITH DISABILITIES ACT MANUAL. NEWSLETTER. see *LAW—Legal Aid*

658.3 USA ISSN 1072-1967
KF3464.A15
B N A'S EMPLOYMENT DISCRIMINATION REPORT. Text in English. 1993. w. back issues avail. **Description:** Covers decisional, legislative and regulatory developments of equal employment opportunity, including all facets of employment discrimination: race, national origin, religion, age, sex and disability.
Related titles: Online - full text ed.: ISSN 1521-5288 (from The Bureau of National Affairs, Inc.).
—**CCC.**
Published by: The Bureau of National Affairs, Inc., 1231 25th St., NW, Washington, DC 20037. TEL 202-452-4200, FAX 202-822-8092, http://www.bna.com/products/lit/edr.htm.

B W C FOCUS; Ohio workers' Compensation safety and risk magazine. see *BUSINESS AND ECONOMICS—Labor And Industrial Relations*

BANQUES RESSOURCES HUMAINES. see *BUSINESS AND ECONOMICS—Banking And Finance*

658.3 AUS ISSN 1321-6287
BENCHMARKING H R. Text in English. 1993. fortn. AUD 450 domestic; AUD 409.09 foreign (effective 2004). **Document type:** *Newsletter.* **Description:** Covers emerging workforce issues; contains answers for human resources professionals who need to keep up-to-date with the latest trends and developments in employment law and employee relations.
Related titles: Online - full content ed.
Published by: Crown Content, Level 1, 141 Capel St, Nth Melbourne, VIC 3051, Australia. TEL 6-13-93299800, FAX 6-13-93299698, max@crowncontent.com.au, scott@crowncontent.com.au, http://www.crowncontent.com.au/prod/newsletters/benchmarking.htm. Ed. Max Berry.

BENEFITS & COMPENSATION INTERNATIONAL. see *INSURANCE*

658.3 CAN ISSN 1191-0763
BENEFITS AND PENSIONS MONITOR. Text in English. 1991. 6/yr. CND 115.56 domestic; CND 172 foreign (effective 2005). adv. **Document type:** *Trade.* **Description:** For those who invest pension funds, administer pension plans and-or manage employee benefit programs in Canada.
Indexed: CBCARef.
—**CCC.**
Published by: Powershift Communications Inc., 245 Fairview Mall Dr, Ste 501, North York, ON M2J 4T1, Canada. TEL 416-494-1066, FAX 416-494-2536, http://www.bpmmagazine.com/. Circ: 17,022.

658.3 USA ISSN 1063-9217
BENEFITS COMMUNICATOR. Text in English. 1992. bi-m. USD 98 (effective 1998). **Document type:** *Newsletter.* **Description:** Reports on trends and issues in benefits communication and administration.
Published by: H R Communication Services, PO Box 671, Richmond, VA 23218. TEL 804-751-5003. Ed., R&P Ann Black.

658.3 657 USA
BENEFITS COORDINATOR. Text in English. 1989. 7 base vols. plus bi-w. updates. looseleaf. USD 885.
Indexed: ATI.
Published by: W G & L Financial Reporting & Management Research (Subsidiary of: R I A), 395 Hudson St, New York, NY 10014. TEL 212-367-6300, FAX 212-367-6718, http://www.InsideHR.com. **Subscr. to:** The Park Square Bldg., 31 St James Ave, Boston, MA 02116-4112. TEL 800-950-1207.

658.3 USA ISSN 1553-8419
▼ **BENEFITS COST CONTROL ADVISOR.** Text in English. 2005 (Mar.). m. USD 197 (effective 2005).
Published by: M. Lee Smith Publishers LLC, PO Box 5094, Brentwood, TN 37024. TEL 615-373-7517, 800-274-6774, FAX 615-373-5183, custserv@mleesmith.com, http://www.mleesmith.com. Ed. Kathy Carlson.

658.3 USA
BENEFITS GUIDE. Text in English. and m. newsletter), base vol. plus bi-m. updates. looseleaf. USD 340 (effective 1998). **Document type:** *Trade.* **Description:** Provides current information that deals with managed care (for AIDS and other catastrophic diseases), flexible benefits, cafeteria plans, family leave, COBRA, health care, continuation coverage and retiree health benefits. Includes federal and state laws.
Formerly: Managing Employee Benefits (1057-3364)
—**CCC.**
Published by: W G & L Financial Reporting & Management Research (Subsidiary of: R I A), 395 Hudson St, New York, NY 10014. TEL 212-367-6300, FAX 212-367-6718, http://www.InsideHR.com. Ed. Martin Censor. **Subscr. to:** The Park Square Bldg., 31 St James Ave, Boston, MA 02116-4112. TEL 800-950-1207.

BENEFITS LAW JOURNAL. see *LAW—Legal Aid*

B

658.3 USA ISSN 1520-3220
BENEFITS LEGAL ALERT. Text in English. 1998. m. USD 120 (effective 1999). back issues avail. **Document type:** *Newsletter.*
Published by: Alexander Hamilton Institute, Inc., 70 Hilltop Rd, Ramsey, NJ 07446-1119. TEL 201-825-3377, 800-879-2441, FAX 201-825-8696, bla@ahipubs.com, http://www.ahipubs.com. Ed. Brian L P Zevnik.

658.3 USA ISSN 0199-3100
HD4928.N62
BENEFITS NEWS ANALYSIS. Text in English. 1979. 6/yr. USD 89. adv. **Description:** Provides analysis of corporate employee benefit practices. Includes review of benefit program changes at a number of major corporations.
Published by: Benefits News Analysis, Inc., PO Box 4033, New Haven, CT 06525. TEL 203-393-2272. Ed. Faisal A Saleh. Circ: 10,000.

331 USA ISSN 8756-1263
HD4928.N62
BENEFITS QUARTERLY. Text in English. 1985. q. USD 100, CND 140 (effective 2004). adv. bk.rev. illus.; charts. Index. back issues avail.; reprints avail. **Document type:** *Journal, Trade.* **Description:** In-depth articles on benefit-related topics, plus notes and comments; updates on current literature and legal-legislative-regulatory developments.
Related titles: Online - full text ed.: (from EBSCO Publishing, Northern Light Technology, Inc., O C L C Online Computer Library Center, Inc., ProQuest Information & Learning).
Indexed: ABIn, AgeL, INI, MEDLINE, PAIS.
—BLDSC (1891.485000), IE, Infotrieve, ingenta. **CCC.**
Published by: International Society of Certified Employee Benefit Specialists, Inc., 18700 W. Bluemound Rd., PO Box 209, Brookfield, WI 53008-0209. TEL 414-786-8771, FAX 414-786-8650, bq@vanderhei.com, iscebs@ifebp.org, http://www.iscebs.org/bqinfo/default.asp. Ed. Jack L Vanderhei. R&P, Adv. contact Sandra L Becker. Circ: 17,000.

658 USA
BENEFITS REPORT - ASIA. Text in English. a. USD 1,150. charts. **Description:** Provides employee benefits information for 11 Asian countries.
Published by: (Executive Compensation Service (ECS)), Wyatt Data Services, 218 Rte 17 N, Rochelle Park, NJ 07622-9832. TEL 201-843-1177, FAX 201-843-0101.

658 USA
BENEFITS REPORT - EUROPE. Text in English. a. USD 940. **Description:** Comprehensive guide to pensions and related employee benefits, both occupational and statutory; covers 17 Western European countries and Turkey.
Published by: (Executive Compensation Service (ECS)), Wyatt Data Services, 218 Rte 17 N, Rochelle Park, NJ 07622-9832. TEL 201-843-1177, FAX 201-843-0101.

658.3 340 USA
BENEFITS REVIEW BOARD SERVICE LONGSHORE REPORTER. Text in English. 1974. 3 base vols. plus m. updates. looseleaf. USD 966 base vol(s). (effective 2003). **Description:** Features full text of Benefits Review Board decisions, the Longshore and Harbor Workers' Compensation Act, and other relevant longshore material. It includes complete headnote texts of all longshore BRB opinions and decisions, selected ALJ decisions, and all court opinions on appeal from the BRB with fully keyed digest to all these sources.
Published by: Matthew Bender & Co., Inc. (Subsidiary of: LexisNexis North America), 1275 Broadway, Albany, NY 12204. international@bender.com, http://bender.lexisnexis.com.

BENEFITS SURVEY. see *BUSINESS AND ECONOMICS—Abstracting, Bibliographies, Statistics*

658.31243 USA
LC1072.I58
BEST 109 INTERNSHIPS. Text in English. 1994. a. USD 21 per issue (effective 2004).
Former titles (until 2000): America's Top Internships; (until 1998): Princeton Review Student Advantage Guide to America's Top Internships (1520-8990); (until 1997): Th Princeton Review Student Access Guide to America's Top 100 Internships (1073-5801)
Published by: Random House Inc. (Subsidiary of: W. Bertelsmann Verlag GmbH & Co. KG), 1745 Broadway, New York, NY 10019. TEL 212-782-9000, http://www.randomhouse.com.

658.3 USA
BIOWORLD EXECUTIVE COMPENSATION REPORT. Text in English. a. USD 499 (effective 2005). **Document type:** *Magazine, Trade.*
Published by: Thomson American Health Consultants, Inc. (Subsidiary of: Thomson Corporation, Healthcare Information Group), 3525 Piedmont Rd, N E, Bldg 6, Ste 400, Atlanta, GA 30305. TEL 404-262-5511, FAX 800-284-3291, customerservice@ahcpub.com, http://www.bioworld.com/servlet/com.accumedia.web.Dispatcher?next=execCompensation, http://www.ahcpub.com.

658.3 GBR
BLUEPRINT (NOTTINGHAM). Text in English. 1970. 10/yr. free to current employees. back issues avail. **Description:** Informs employees of Boots The Chemests in the UK and overseas.
Formerly (until 1995): Boots Company News
Published by: Boots The Chemests, 1 Thane Rd W., Nottingham, NG2 3AA, United Kingdom. TEL 44-115-959-2365, FAX 44-115-959-5684. Ed., R&P David Shelton. Circ: 32,000 (controlled).

BOARD OF DIRECTORS REPORT. see *BUSINESS AND ECONOMICS—Management*

658.3 AUS ISSN 1327-6123
BOARD REMUNERATION AND PRACTICE REPORT. Text in English. 1994. a. AUD 700 (effective 1999). **Document type:** *Trade.* **Description:** Focuses on issues relating to the remuneration and performance of directors.
Published by: Cullen Egan Dell, Level 8, 50 Bridge St, Sydney, NSW 2000, Australia. TEL 61-2-9375-9800, FAX 61-2-9233-6800. Ed. James Cooper. Circ: 75.

BRANCH OPERATIONS MANAGEMENT SERVICE. see *BUSINESS AND ECONOMICS—Banking And Finance*

THE BRITISH JOURNAL OF OCCUPATIONAL TRAINING. see *EDUCATION*

658.3 USA
BUILDING BLOCKS IN TOTAL COMPENSATION. Text in English. 1991. irreg. (5-10/yr.). USD 24.95 per issue to non-members (effective 2000); USD 19.95 per issue to members. **Document type:** *Monographic series.* **Description:** Provides instructional approaches to various aspects of compensation and benefits administration.
Published by: American Compensation Association, 14040 N Northsight Blvd, Scottsdale, AZ 85260. TEL 480-922-2020. Ed. Denise Constantine. R&P Betty Laurie TEL 480-922-2008.

658.3 USA ISSN 0525-2156
HF5549.2.U5
BULLETIN TO MANAGEMENT. Text in English. 1947. w. looseleaf. USD 317 (effective 2005 - 2006). charts; stat. 8 p./no.; back issues avail. **Document type:** *Newsletter.* **Description:** Summaries of current developments, discussions of real-life job situations, statistical charts and graphs, and ready-to-use policy studies.
Related titles: Online - full text ed.: (from The Bureau of National Affairs, Inc.); ♦ Series of: B N A Policy and Practice Series. ISSN 0005-3228.
Indexed: PersLit.
—**CCC.**
Published by: The Bureau of National Affairs, Inc., 1231 25th St., NW, Washington, DC 20037. TEL 202-452-4200, 800-372-1033, 800-452-7773, FAX 202-822-8092, customercare@bna.com, bnaplus@bna.com, http://www.bna.com/products/hr/btmn.htm. Ed. Bill L Manville. Pub. Greg C McCaffery.

BUSINESS ETHICS NEWSLINE. see *BUSINESS AND ECONOMICS—Management*

BUSINESS FINANCE. see *BUSINESS AND ECONOMICS—Management*

658.3 GBR ISSN 1472-9245
BUSINESS RATIO REPORT. PLANT HIRE (YEAR). Text in English. 1973. a. GBP 275 (effective 2001). charts; stat. **Document type:** *Trade.*
Former titles (until 2000): Business Ratio. Plant Hire (1468-8948); (until 1999): Business Ratio Plus: Plant Hire (1358-1902); (until 1994): Business Ratio Report. Plant Hire (0261-9377)
Published by: The Prospect Shop Ltd., Field House, 72 Oldfield Rd, Hampton, Middx TW12 2HQ, United Kingdom. TEL 44-20-8461-8730, 44-20-8481-8720, FAX 44-20-8783-1940, info@theprospectshop.co.uk.

658.3 657 USA ISSN 0745-0877
C P A PERSONNEL REPORT. Text in English. 1982. m. looseleaf. USD 345 (effective 2004). back issues avail. **Document type:** *Newsletter.* **Description:** Helps firms excel in recruiting staff, competing with other firms to attract the best talent, making informed hiring and firing decisions and staying abreast of evaluation, compensation and benefits strategies, and management and motivational techniques.
Related titles: Online - full text ed.: (from EBSCO Publishing).
Indexed: ATI.
—**CCC.**
Published by: Aspen Publishers, Inc. (Subsidiary of: Wolters Kluwer N.V.), 111Eighth Ave., 7th Fl, New York, NY 10011. TEL 212-771-0600, FAX 212-771-0885, customer.service@aspenpubl.com, http://www.aspenpublishers.com.

658.3 CHN ISSN 1609-4964
CAIZHI. Text in Chinese. m. CNY 358 (effective 2004). **Document type:** *Magazine, Trade.*
Published by: Shanghai Caizhi Wenhua Chuanbo Youxian Gongsi/Fortune & Wisdom Culture Communication (ShangHai) Co.Ltd, Room 3003, Kerry Everbright City Tower 2, 218 TianMu Xi Road, ShangHai, 200070, China. TEL 86-21-63538132, FAX 86-21-63539323, caizhi@aphr.org, http://www.aphr.org/caizhi/. **Subscr. to:** 218, Tianmu Xilu, Jialibuyecheng, 2-Ceng, 3003-Shi, Shanghai 200070, China. TEL 86-21-63538132 ext 12.

658.3 USA
CALIFORNIA PAYROLL REPORT. Text in English. s-m. USD 228 (effective 2002). **Document type:** *Newsletter.* **Description:** Covers new federal and California laws and regulations, and the latest payroll-related court cases.
Formerly: California Payroll Letter
Published by: Aspen Publishers, Inc. (Subsidiary of: Wolters Kluwer N.V.), 111Eighth Ave., 7th Fl, New York, NY 10011. TEL 212-771-0600, FAX 212-771-0885, customer.service@aspenpubl.com, http://www.aspenpublishers.com. Ed. Susan Driscoll.

CANADIAN ASSOCIATION OF SPECIAL LIBRARIES AND INFORMATION SERVICES. NATIONAL SALARY SURVEY. see *LIBRARY AND INFORMATION SCIENCES—Abstracting, Bibliographies, Statistics*

CANADIAN CASES ON EMPLOYMENT LAW (3RD SERIES). see *LAW*

658.3 CAN ISSN 1209-6539
CANADIAN DIRECTORY OF SEARCH FIRMS. Text in English. 1997. a. CND 59.95 (effective 2003). **Document type:** *Directory, Consumer.* **Description:** Provides comprehensive information on every major headhunter or job search firm in Canada.
Published by: Mediacorp Canada Inc., 21 New St, Toronto, ON M5R 1P7, Canada. TEL 416-964-6069, FAX 416-964-3202, info@mediacorp2.com, http://www.mediacorp2.com.

658.3 CAN ISSN 0838-228X
CANADIAN H R REPORTER; the national journal of human resource management. Text in English. 1987. bi-w. CND 149 (effective 2005). adv. bk.rev. back issues avail. **Document type:** *Journal, Trade.* **Description:** For the human resources market including practitioners and related professionals. Covers news, developments, trends and products across Canada.
Related titles: Microform ed.: (from PQC); Online - full text ed.: (from Micromedia ProQuest, O C L C Online Computer Library Center, Inc., ProQuest Information & Learning).
Indexed: ABIn, CBCARef.
—CCC.
Published by: Carswell (Subsidiary of: Thomson Corporation), One Corporate Plaza, 2075 Kennedy Rd, Toronto, ON M1T 3V4, Canada. TEL 416-609-8000, 800-387-5164, FAX 416-298-5094, carswell.customerrelations@thomson.com, http://www.hrreporter.com, http://www.carswell.com. Circ: 8,100.

CANADIAN LEGAL & LEGISLATIVE BENEFITS REPORTER. see *LAW*

658.3 ESP ISSN 1130-8117
CAPITAL HUMANO. Text in Spanish. 1988. 11/yr. EUR 210 combined subscription Print & online eds. (effective 2005). adv.
Related titles: Online - full text ed.
Indexed: RILM.
—CINDOC.
Published by: Grupo Especial Directivos (Subsidiary of: Wolters Kluwer BV), Orense 16, Madrid, 28020, Spain. TEL 34-902-250520, FAX 34-902-250502, clientes@edirectivos.com, http://www.capitalhumano.es, http://www.e-directivos.com. Ed. Jose Antonio Carazo. Adv. contact Jorge Martinez. Circ: 10,000.

658.3 USA
CAREER - OUTPLACEMENT; newsletter for human resource professionals, executives and managers. Text in English. 1988. q. USD 24 (effective 1997). **Document type:** *Newsletter.* **Description:** Each issue includes one feature article on topical subject, one case study, one book review, and chart of recent unemployment rates by state.
Published by: Career Management Consultants, Inc., 2040 Linlestown Rd, Ste 205, Harrisburg, PA 17110. TEL 717-233-2272, FAX 717-233-2129, jackate@darrington.net. Ed. Kate Duttro. Pub. Louis Persico.

658.3 331.1 USA
CASS RECRUITMENT MEDIA. Text in English. bi-m. **Document type:** *Trade.*
Address: 9071 Mill Creek Rd, Ste 419, Levittown, PA 19054. TEL 215-269-8190, FAX 215-733-3990, paula.lipp@casscom.com, http://www.casscom.com. Ed. Paula Lipp.

CATALYST DIRECTORY NEWSLETTER. see *NEW AGE PUBLICATIONS*

CENTRE I N F F O. FICHES PRATIQUES. see *EDUCATION—Adult Education*

658.300715 FRA ISSN 0242-259X
CENTRE I N F F O. GUIDES TECHNIQUES. Text in French. 1979. irreg.
Published by: Centre I N F F O, Tour Europe, Paris La Defense, Cedex 92049, France. TEL 33-1-41252222, FAX 33-1-47737420, cinffo1@easynet.fr.

CHEERS; Kuaile Gongzouren Zazhi. see *BUSINESS AND ECONOMICS—Labor And Industrial Relations*

658 USA
CHIEF EXECUTIVE OFFICERS' TOTAL COMPENSATION REPORT - MEXICO. Text in English. a. USD 775. charts. **Description:** Comprehensive source of information for the compensation practices and the prevalence and amount of fringe benefits for CEOs in Mexico.
Published by: (Executive Compensation Service (ECS)), Wyatt Data Services, 218 Rte 17 N, Rochelle Park, NJ 07622-9832. TEL 201-843-1177, FAX 201-843-0101.

658 USA ISSN 1185-524X
CHIEF EXECUTIVES COMPENSATION IN CANADA. Text in English. 1975. a. **Document type:** *Trade.*
Former titles (until 1990): Remuneration of Chief Executives in Canada (0707-3879); (until 1977): Remuneration of Chief Executive Officers in Canada (0701-1059)
Published by: (Executive Compensation Service (ECS)), Wyatt Data Services, 218 Rte 17 N, Rochelle Park, NJ 07622-9832. TEL 201-843-1177, FAX 201-843-0101.

CHILE. INSTITUTO NACIONAL DE ESTADISTICAS. INDICE DE REMUNERACIONES. see *BUSINESS AND ECONOMICS—Abstracting, Bibliographies, Statistics*

658.3 HKG
CHINA STAFF. Text in English. 10/yr. HKD 3,500 domestic; GBP 296 in United Kingdom; USD 480 elsewhere (effective 2003). **Document type:** *Trade.* **Description:** Provides a definitive guide to the law and practice of human resources in China such as dealing with the regulators, work force management in China, updates of legal issues, and compensation & benefits.
Formerly: China Staff - Hong Kong Staff
Related titles: Online - full text ed.
Indexed: HongKongiana.
Published by: C C H Hong Kong Ltd., Rm 1608, 16/F Harcourt House, 39 Gloucester Rd, Wanchai, Hong Kong. TEL 852-2526-7614, FAX 852-2521-7874, support@cch.com.hk, http://www.asialaw.com/cs/, http://www.cch.com.hk/.

658.3 USA
▼ **CHOICE**; the magazine for professional coaching. Text in English. 2003. q. USD 43.55 (effective 2005). adv. back issues avail. **Document type:** *Magazine, Trade.* **Description:** Forwards the global conversation about professional coaching, by providing, diverse perspectives, thought-provoking commentary, insightful discussion, and access to services, tools, resources and practical information.
Published by: Choice Global Media, 8581 Santa Monica Blvd, #113, Los Angeles, CA 90069. TEL 310-274-5542, FAX 310-671-3752, publisher@choice-online.com, http://www.choice-online.com/. Ed. Maureen A Ford TEL 416-423-5552. Pub. Bradford C Stauffer TEL 310-274-5542. Adv. contact Garry T Schleifer TEL 416-925-6643. B&W page USD 1,575, color page USD 2,075; trim 7.625 x 10.375. Circ: 2,000.

659.142 CAN ISSN 0708-4471
CIRCUIT FERME; journal des employes de Radio-Canada. Text in English. 1965. s-m. free. **Description:** Internal news for CBC radio and TV employees.
Published by: Canadian Broadcasting Corporation, 1400 E Rene Levesque, Montreal, PQ H3C 3A8, Canada. TEL 514-597-4343, FAX 514-597-6000. Ed. Boris Volkoff. Circ: 7,000.

658.3 ITA ISSN 1594-6754
CLASS. Text in Italian. 1986. m. adv. bk.rev. **Document type:** *Magazine, Consumer.*
Published by: Class Editori, Via Marco Burigozzo 5, Milan, MI 20122, Italy. TEL 39-02-582191, http://www.classeditori.com. Ed. Paolo Panerai. Circ: 90,000 (controlled).

658 USA
COMPANY CAR REPORT - EUROPE. Text in English. a. USD 940. charts. **Description:** Provides information on how multinational companies set up and administer their company car policies in 17 Western European countries and Turkey.
Published by: (Executive Compensation Service (ECS)), Wyatt Data Services, 218 Rte 17 N, Rochelle Park, NJ 07622-9832. TEL 201-843-1177, FAX 201-843-0101.

352.14 USA ISSN 0732-5282
JS361
COMPENSATION (WASHINGTON, 1982); an annual report on local government executive salaries and fringe benefits. Text in English. 1982. a. USD 180 (effective 2000).
Indexed: ATI.
Published by: International City/County Management Association, 777 N Capitol St, N E Ste 500, Washington, DC 20002-4201. TEL 202-962-3564, 800-745-8780, FAX 202-962-3500. Ed., R&P Sebia Clark. Circ: 900.

658.3 331.21 USA ISSN 1094-5660
HF5549.5.C67
COMPENSATION & BENEFITS LIBRARY ON C D. Text in English. 1993 (Oct.). m. USD 1,494 to individuals (effective 2005 - 2006).
Media: CD-ROM. **Related titles:** Online - full text ed.: (from The Bureau of National Affairs, Inc.).
—CCC.
Published by: The Bureau of National Affairs, Inc., 1231 25th St., NW, Washington, DC 20037. TEL 202-452-4200, 800-372-1033, FAX 202-785-7167, customercare@bna.com, http://www.bna.com. **Subscr. to:** 9435 Key West Ave, Rockville, MD 20850.

COMPENSATION & BENEFITS SOFTWARE CENSUS. see *BUSINESS AND ECONOMICS—Computer Applications*

658 USA
COMPENSATION AND BENEFITS SURVEY FOR EXECUTIVE LEVELS - MEXICO. Text in English. a. USD 1,030. **Document type:** *Trade.* **Description:** Contains compensation information on more than 60 executive positions in Mexico.
Published by: (Executive Compensation Service (ECS)), Wyatt Data Services, 218 Rte 17 N, Rochelle Park, NJ 07622-9832. TEL 201-843-1177, FAX 201-843-0101.

331.21 USA
KF1424.A15
COMPENSATION & BENEFITS UPDATE. Text in English. 1974. m. USD 149. back issues avail.; reprint service avail. from PQC. **Document type:** *Newsletter.* **Description:** Provides information on the latest ideas and developments in the field of employee benefits. Offers advice and up-to-date coverage on IRS actions, employment law, benefits planning, social security developments, and related topics.
Former titles (until 1997): Benefits and Compensation Update (1074-6293); (until 1994): Employee Benefits Report (0884-478X); (until 1984): Executive Compensation and Employee Benefits Report (0273-9046); (until 1980): Executive Compensation Report (0162-7503); Incorporates: Employee Benefit and ERISA Case Law Service
Related titles: Microform ed.: (from PQC).
Indexed: LII.
—CCC.
Published by: W G & L Financial Reporting & Management Research (Subsidiary of: R I A), 395 Hudson St, New York, NY 10014. TEL 212-367-6300, FAX 212-367-6718, http://www.InsideHR.com. Ed. Dennis Tosh. **Subscr. to:** The Park Square Bldg., 31 St James Ave, Boston, MA 02116-4112. TEL 800-950-1207.

658.3 USA
COMPENSATION GUIDE. Text in English. base vol. plus q. updates. USD 290. **Document type:** *Trade.* **Description:** Aims to provide new plan ideas to make it easier to attract and keep quality employees while keeping costs down. Includes alternative awards, job analysis and evaluation, salary surveys, base pay programs, performance management, etc.
Published by: W G & L Financial Reporting & Management Research (Subsidiary of: R I A), 395 Hudson St, New York, NY 10014. TEL 212-367-6300, FAX 212-367-6718, http://www.InsideHR.com. Ed. Martin Censor. **Subscr. to:** The Park Square Bldg., 31 St James Ave, Boston, MA 02116-4112. TEL 800-950-1207.

658 USA
COMPENSATION REPORT - HONG KONG. Text in English. a. USD 900. charts. **Document type:** *Trade.*
Published by: (Executive Compensation Service (ECS)), Wyatt Data Services, 218 Rte 17 N, Rochelle Park, NJ 07622-9832. TEL 201-843-1177, FAX 201-843-0101.

658 USA
COMPENSATION REPORT - TAIWAN. Text in English. a. USD 900. **Document type:** *Trade.*
Published by: (Executive Compensation Service (ECS)), Wyatt Data Services, 218 Rte 17 N, Rochelle Park, NJ 07622-9832. TEL 201-843-1177, FAX 201-843-0101.

658 USA
COMPENSATION REPORT - THE PHILIPPINES. Text in English. a. USD 900. charts. **Document type:** *Trade.*
Published by: (Executive Compensation Service (ECS)), Wyatt Data Services, 218 Rte 17 N, Rochelle Park, NJ 07622-9832. TEL 201-843-1177, FAX 201-843-0101.

658.3 GBR ISSN 1469-3348
COMPETENCY & EMOTIONAL INTELLIGENCE BENCHMARKING. Text in English. 1999. a. Included with subscr. to Competency & Emotional Intelligence Quarterly. **Document type:** *Trade.*
Formerly (until 2000): Competency - The Annual Benchmarking Survey (1464-7850)
Related titles: Online - full text ed.: Competency & Emotional Intelligence Benchmarking Online. ISSN 1469-3356. 1999 (from Gale Group, IngentaConnect); ♦ Supplement to: Competency & Emotional Intelligency Quarterly. ISSN 1469-333X.
—BLDSC (3363.992245).
Published by: I R S (Subsidiary of: LexisNexis UK (Scottish Office)), 18-20 Highbury Pl, London, N5 1QP, United Kingdom. TEL 44-20-7354-6742, 44-20-7354-5858, FAX 44-20-7226-8618, 44-20-7359-4000, publications@irseclipse.co.uk, http://www.irseclipse.co.uk.

658.3 GBR ISSN 1469-3313
COMPETENCY & EMOTIONAL INTELLIGENCE MONTHLY (ONLINE). Text in English. 1998. m. Included with subscr. to Competency & Emotional Intelligence Quarterly. **Document type:** *Trade.*
Formerly (until 1999): Competency - The Monthly Bulletin (Print) (1464-0783)
Media: Online - full text (from Gale Group). **Related titles:** ♦ Supplement to: Competency & Emotional Intelligency Quarterly. ISSN 1469-333X.
Published by: I R S (Subsidiary of: LexisNexis UK (Scottish Office)), 18-20 Highbury Pl, London, N5 1QP, United Kingdom. TEL 44-20-7354-6742, 44-20-7354-5858, FAX 44-20-7226-8618, 44-20-7359-4000, publications@irseclipse.co.uk, http://www.irseclipse.co.uk.

658.3 GBR ISSN 1469-333X
COMPETENCY & EMOTIONAL INTELLIGENCY QUARTERLY. Text in English. 1993. q. GBP 259 domestic; GBP 275 foreign (effective 2003); Subscription includes Competency & Emotional Intelligence Benchmarking, Competency & Emotional Intelligence Monthly (Online), Competency & Emotional Intelligence Quarterly, Competency & Emotional Intelligence Literature, and Competency - The Cumulative Index. bk.rev.; software rev. abstr.; tr.lit. index. back issues avail. **Document type:** *Journal, Academic/Scholarly.* **Description:** Business focused, concentrating on how real organizations are implementing competency.
Formerly (until 1999): Competency (Quarterly) (1351-5802)
Related titles: Online - full text ed.: Competency & Emotional Intelligency Quarterly Online. ISSN 1469-3321. 1997 (from EBSCO Publishing, Gale Group, IngentaConnect); ♦ Supplement(s): Competency & Emotional Intelligence Monthly (Online). ISSN 1469-3313; ♦ Competency & Emotional Intelligence Benchmarking. ISSN 1469-3348.
Indexed: BrEdI, M&MA.
—BLDSC (3363.992244), IE, ingenta. **CCC.**
Published by: I R S (Subsidiary of: LexisNexis UK (Scottish Office)), 18-20 Highbury Pl, London, N5 1QP, United Kingdom. TEL 44-20-7354-6742, 44-20-7354-5858, FAX 44-20-7226-8618, 44-20-7359-4000, publications@irseclipse.co.uk, http://www.irseclipse.co.uk/pub_subjects/index_pub_human.htm. Ed. Neil Rankin. Pub. Andrew Brode.

658.3 NLD ISSN 1384-6639
➤ **CONCEPTS AND TRANSFORMATION**; international journal of action research and organizational renewal. Text in English. 1996. 3/yr., latest vol.6, 2001. EUR 165 combined subscription print & online eds. (effective 2004). bk.rev. 300 p./no.; back issues avail. **Document type:** *Journal, Academic/Scholarly.* **Description:** Includes information on the relationship between theory and practice in the conduct of social science.
Related titles: Online - full text ed.: ISSN 1569-9692 (from EBSCO Publishing, Gale Group, IngentaConnect, Swets Information Services).
Indexed: DIP, IBR, IBZ, L&LBA, PSA, SSA, SociolAb.
—BLDSC (3399.412600).
Published by: John Benjamins Publishing Co., PO Box 36224, Amsterdam, 1020 ME, Netherlands. TEL 31-20-630-4747, FAX 31-20-673-9773, subscription@benjamins.nl, http://www.benjamins.com.

658.3 AUS ISSN 1325-6769
CONSTRUCTION AND ENGINEERING REMUNERATION REVIEW. Text in English. 1990. a. AUD 1,975 (effective 1999). **Document type:** *Trade.* **Description:** Includes remuneration data for over 70 positions in the Australian construction and engineering industry.
Published by: Cullen Egan Dell, Level 8, 50 Bridge St, Sydney, NSW 2000, Australia. TEL 61-2-9375-9800, FAX 61-2-9233-6800. Ed. Paul Adams. Circ: 41.

658.3 AUS ISSN 1325-6785
CONSUMER GOODS INDUSTRY REVIEW. Text in English. 1992. a. AUD 1,000 (effective 1999). **Document type:** *Trade.* **Description:** Surveys over 50 representative positions within the consumer goods industry.
Published by: Cullen Egan Dell, Level 8, 50 Bridge St, Sydney, NSW 2000, Australia. TEL 61-2-9375-9800, FAX 61-2-9233-6800. Ed. Paul Adams. Circ: 18.

658.3 USA ISSN 1548-8942
HF5549.5.T4
▼ **CONTINGENT WORKFORCE STRATEGIES.** Text in English. 2004 (Mar). 8/yr. USD 96; free to qualified personnel (effective 2004). adv. **Document type:** *Magazine, Trade.* **Description:** Provides information for businesses and managers who use temporary/contract workers as part of their overall workforce/staffing strategy.
Published by: Staffing Industry Analysts, Inc., 881 Fremont Ave, Los Altos, CA 94024. TEL 650-948-9303, 800-950-9496, FAX 650-948-9345, http://www.staffingindustry.com/publications/cws.html. Pub. Ron Mester. adv.: B&W page USD 14,000; trim 8.375 x 10.875. Circ: 8,000.

▼ *new title* ➤ *refereed* ✱ *unverified* ♦ *full entry avail.*

658.3 AUS ISSN 1325-6963
CORPORATE BENCHMARK MONITOR. Text in English. 1992. a. AUD 425 (effective 1999). **Document type:** *Trade.*
Description: Provides managers and professionals in Australian organizations with accurate, concise, and relevant data on a range of organizational and cost issues.
Published by: Cullen Egan Dell, Level 8, 50 Bridge St, Sydney, NSW 2000, Australia. TEL 61-2-9375-9800, FAX 61-2-9233-6800. Ed. Chris Lupton. Circ: 210.

CRONER AT C C H EMPLOYMENT CASE DIGEST. see *BUSINESS AND ECONOMICS—Labor And Industrial Relations*

658.3 GBR
CRONER'S A-Z FOR H R PROFESSIONALS. (Human Resources) Text in English. 1992. base vol. plus updates 3/yr. GBP 387.98 (effective 1999). bk.rev. **Document type:** *Trade.*
Former titles: Croner's Human Resources; Human Resources Briefing (0965-299X)
Related titles: Online - full text ed.
Published by: Croner.C C H Group Ltd. (Subsidiary of: Wolters Kluwer N.V.), 145 London Rd, Kingston, Surrey KT2 6SR, United Kingdom. TEL 44-20-85473333, FAX 44-20-85472637, info@croner.co.uk, http://www.croner.co.uk.

CRONER'S EMPLOYMENT LAW. see *LAW*

331.125 GBR ISSN 0070-1580
CRONER'S REFERENCE BOOK FOR EMPLOYERS. Text in English. 1947. base vol. plus m. updates. looseleaf. GBP 503 (effective 2000). **Description:** Provides comprehensive information on legal requirements and other information needed by UK employers.
Related titles: CD-ROM ed.; Diskette ed.; Online - full text ed.; ♦ Series: Employer's Guide to Maternity Online; Employment Relations Act Online; ♦ Employer's Briefing. ISSN 0963-5343; ♦ Key Rates and Data; ♦ Guide to Managing Fair Dismissal; ♦ Supplement(s): Employer's Briefing. ISSN 0963-5343.
—BLDSC (3487.826000).
Published by: Croner.C C H Group Ltd. (Subsidiary of: Wolters Kluwer N.V.), 145 London Rd, Kingston, Surrey KT2 6SR, United Kingdom. TEL 44-20-85473333, FAX 44-20-85472637, info@croner.co.uk, http://www.croner.co.uk, http://www.croner.cch.co.uk.

331.125 GBR ISSN 1367-8728
CRONER'S REFERENCE BOOK FOR EMPLOYERS - MAGAZINE. Text in English. 1997. 10/yr. **Document type:** *Trade.* **Description:** Alerts human-resource professionals and executives to legal and other developments affecting them and their companies.
—BLDSC (3487.827000).
Published by: Croner.C C H Group Ltd. (Subsidiary of: Wolters Kluwer N.V.), 145 London Rd, Kingston, Surrey KT2 6SR, United Kingdom. TEL 44-20-85473333, FAX 44-20-85472637, info@croner.co.uk, http://www.croner.co.uk. Pub. Catriona Banting.

CROSS & COCKADE INTERNATIONAL. see *MILITARY*

658 USA ISSN 1070-3160
CULTURAL DIVERSITY AT WORK. Text in English. 1998. bi-m. USD 99 (effective 2004). **Document type:** *Newsletter, Trade.*
Description: Contains articles on the best practices and innovative approaches on all topics concerning diversity in the workplace.
Formerly (until 1991): Training and Culture Newsletter (1043-1322)
Published by: The GilDeane Group, Inc., 13751 Lake City Way NE, Ste 210, Seattle, WA 98125-8612. TEL 206-362-0336, info@diversitycentral.com, http://www.diversityhotwire.com/learning/cultural_diversity_at_work/about.html.

658.3 USA ISSN 0145-8450
THE CUSTOMER COMMUNICATOR; toals, tips and tactics for the frontline customer service professional. Text in English. 1976. m. USD 200 for 10 copies (effective 2004). 4 p./no.; back issues avail.; reprints avail. **Document type:** *Newsletter, Corporate.* **Description:** The training and motivation source for front-line customer service representatives.
Related titles: Online - full text ed.
Published by: Alexander Communications Group, Inc., 28 W 25th St, 8th Fl, New York, NY 10010. TEL 212-228-0246, FAX 212-228-0376, info@customerservicegroup.com, info@alexcommgrp.com, http://www.customerservicegroup.com, http://www.alexcommgrp.com. Eds. Bill Keenan, Susan Hash. Pub. Margaret Dewitt. R&P Mary Dalessandro.

658.3 USA ISSN 1525-0903
DARTNELL'S GETTING ALONG; your personal guide to building productive work relationships. Text in English. 1990. bi-w. USD 76.70. **Document type:** *Newsletter, Trade.* **Description:** Helps employees work with subordinates, superiors and co-workers as individuals to get things done effectively.
—CCC.
Published by: Dartnell Corp. (Subsidiary of: L R P Publications), 360 Hiatt Dr, Palm Beach Garden, FL 33418. TEL 561-622-6520, 800-621-5463, FAX 561-622-0757, custserve@lrp.com, http://www.dartnellcorp.com/. Ed. Kim Anderson.

658.3 USA ISSN 1525-0873
DARTNELL'S TEAMWORK. Text in English. 1987. bi-w. (26/yr.). USD 245.70 5 copies (effective 2005). **Document type:** *Newsletter.* **Description:** Offers insight, wisdom and new concepts that will have an immediate, positive impact on the relations between employees.
—CCC.
Published by: Dartnell Corp. (Subsidiary of: L R P Publications), 360 Hiatt Dr, Palm Beach Garden, FL 33418. TEL 561-622-6520, 800-621-5463, FAX 561-622-0757, custserve@lrp.com, http://www.shoplrp.com/product/p-18000.N.html, http://www.dartnellcorp.com/.

658.3 USA
DEMOGRAPHIC PROFILE OF THE FEDERAL WORKFORCE. Text in English. a. **Document type:** *Government.*
Related titles: Online - full content ed.
Published by: U.S. Office of Personnel Management, 1900 E. St. N.W., Washington, DC 20415. TEL 202-606-1800, fedstats@opm.gov, General@opm.gov, http://www.opm.gov/feddata/demograp/demograp.asp. **Subscr. to:** U.S. Department of Commerce, National Technical Information Service, 5285 Port Royal Rd, Springfield, VA 22161. TEL 703-605-6060, 800-363-2068, FAX 703-605-6880, subscriptions@ntis.gov.

658.3 GBR ISSN 1477-7282
DEVELOPMENT AND LEARNING IN ORGANIZATIONS; an international journal. Text in English. 1989. bi-m. EUR 2,652.41 in Europe; GBP 2,829 in North America; AUD 3,709 in Australasia; GBP 1,858.54 in UK & elsewhere (effective 2006). bk.rev. reprint service avail. from PSC. **Document type:** *Journal, Academic/Scholarly.* **Description:** Features expert appraisal and reviews of the latest thinking in organizational learning, training and development. Also includes suggested reading, current issues and web reviews. Written specifically for busy managers, consultants and researchers.
Former titles (until 2003): Training Strategies for Tomorrow (1369-7234); (until 1998): Training Tomorrow (0957-0004); Which incorporated (1978-1996): Training Digest Europe (1350-9489); (1994-1996): Training Network (1351-1157)
Related titles: Online - full text ed.: (from EBSCO Publishing, Emerald Group Publishing Limited, Gale Group, IngentaConnect, O C L C Online Computer Library Center, Inc., ProQuest Information & Learning, Swets Information Services).
Indexed: ABIn, ErgAb.
—BLDSC (3578.787000), IE, ingenta. **CCC.**
Published by: Emerald Group Publishing Limited, 60-62 Toller Ln, Bradford, W Yorks BD8 9BY, United Kingdom. TEL 44-1274-777700, FAX 44-1274-785200, infomation@emeraldinsight.com, http://www.emeraldinsight.com/dlo.htm. Ed. Ian Cunningham.

658.3 NLD ISSN 1384-6671
DIALOGUES ON WORK AND INNOVATION. Text in English. 1996. irreg., latest vol.3, 1996. price varies. back issues avail. **Document type:** *Monographic series.* **Description:** Presents empirically based studies, as well as theoretical reflections on the practice of organizational renewal.
—BLDSC (3579.775970).
Published by: John Benjamins Publishing Co., PO Box 36224, Amsterdam, 1020 ME, Netherlands. TEL 31-20-676-2325, FAX 31-20-6792956, http://www.benjamins.nl. Ed. Hans van Beinum.

658.3 346 USA
DISABILITIES IN THE WORKPLACE. Text in English. base vol. plus q. updates. looseleaf. USD 385. **Document type:** *Trade.*
Description: Provides information on the American Disabilities Act and related federal and state laws. Gives analysis and practical guidance to plan long-term compliance strategies.
Published by: W G & L Financial Reporting & Management Research (Subsidiary of: R I A), 395 Hudson St, New York, NY 10014. TEL 212-367-6300, FAX 212-367-6718, http://www.InsideHR.com. Ed. Diane Roberts. **Subscr. to:** The Park Square Bldg., 31 St James Ave, Boston, MA 02116-4112. TEL 800-950-1207.

658.3 USA ISSN 1545-2808
HF5549.5.M5
➤ **DIVERSITY FACTOR (ONLINE).** Text in English. 1992. q. USD 36 to individuals; USD 425 to institutions (effective 2003). bk.rev. illus. **Document type:** *Newsletter, Academic/Scholarly.* **Description:** Provides theoretical and practical information on the changing work force for corporations and public and private institutions.
Formerly (until 2003): Diversity Factor (Print) (1067-7194)
Media: Online - full content. **Related titles:** Online - full text ed.: (from Gale Group, IngentaConnect, O C L C Online Computer Library Center, Inc., ProQuest Information & Learning).
Indexed: ABIn, SRRA.
—IDS. **CCC.**
Published by: Diversity Factor, 8194 Batesville Rd., Afton, VA 22920-1723. TEL 201-833-0011, FAX 201-833-4184, http://diversityfactor.rutgers.edu. Ed. Wendy A. Conklin. Pub. Elsie Y Cross. R&P Susan Levitt. Circ: 1,500.

➤ **DIVERSITYINC.** see *LAW—Corporate Law*

658.314 USA
DOCUMENTING EMPLOYEE DISCIPLINE. Text in English. 1994 (2nd ed.). latest 2002, 4th ed., base vol. plus irreg. updates. USD 46 (effective 2003).
Published by: Michie Company (Subsidiary of: LexisNexis North America), 701 E Water St, Charlottesville, VA 22902-5389. TEL 434-972-7600, 800-446-3410, FAX 434-972-7677, http://www.michie.com. Eds. Lee T Paterson, Mike Deblieux.

364 USA ISSN 1055-6281
CODEN: GMLEEJ
DRUG DETECTION REPORT; the newsletter on drug testing in the workplace. Text in English. 1991. bi-w. looseleaf. USD 337 in US & Mexico; USD 355 elsewhere; USD 387 combined subscription print & email eds. (effective 2005). **Document type:** *Newsletter.* **Description:** Provides information to help protect companies and employees with coverage of key issues surrounding drug and alcohol testing in the workplace.
Related titles: E-mail ed.: ISSN 1545-7834. USD 277 (effective 2005); Online - full text ed.: (from Factiva, Florida Center for Library Automation, Gale Group, Northern Light Technology, Inc.).
—CCC.
Published by: Business Publishers, Inc., 8737 Colesville Rd., Flr. 10, Silver Spring, MD 20910-3976. TEL 800-274-6737, custserv@bpinews.com, http://www.bpinews.com/hs/pages/ddr.cfm. Ed. Dave Speights. Pub. L A Eiserer.

658.3 USA ISSN 0887-137X
E B R I ISSUE BRIEF. Text in English. 1982. m. USD 199 (effective 2005). cum.index. back issues avail. **Document type:** *Monographic series.* **Description:** Provides evaluations of evolving employee benefit issues and trends, including critical analyses of employee benefit program policies and proposals.
Related titles: E-mail ed.: USD 49; Microform ed.: (from PQC); Online - full text ed.: (from ProQuest Information & Learning).
Indexed: AgeL, MEDLINE.
—CCC.
Published by: Employee Benefit Research Institute, 2121 K St, N W, Ste 600, Washington, DC 20037-1896. TEL 202-659-0670, FAX 202-775-6312, info@ebri.org, http://www.ebri.org. Ed., R&P Stephen Blakely TEL 202-775-6341. Circ: 3,500.

THE E C S TOP MANAGEMENT HI-COMP REPORT. (Executive Compensation Service) see *BUSINESS AND ECONOMICS—Management*

E M A REPORTER. see *BUSINESS AND ECONOMICS—Labor And Industrial Relations*

E R I S A AND BENEFITS LAW JOURNAL. (Employee Retirement Income Security Act) see *LAW*

658.3 FRA
ECOLE ET PROFESSIONS. Text in French. 1982. 6/yr. adv. bk.rev. **Description:** For personnel officers and training institutes.
Former titles (until 1997): Relations Ecoles - Professions (1143-354X); (until 1986): Cahiers des Relations Ecoles Professions (0299-9625)
Published by: Informations Developpement Entreprises, 24 rue de Lisbonne, Paris, 75008, France. TEL 33-1-53890289, FAX 33-1-53890290. Ed. Thierry Silvester. Circ: 5,000.

658.3 DEU ISSN 0945-1773
EDITION Q U E M. (Qualifikations Entwicklungs Management) Text in German. 1993. irreg., latest vol.14, 2002. EUR 29.90 per vol. (effective 2003). **Document type:** *Monographic series, Academic/Scholarly.*
Published by: (Arbeitsgemeinschaft Betriebliche Weiterbildungsforschung, Qualifikations - Entwicklungs - Management), Waxmann Verlag GmbH, Steinfurter Str 555, Muenster, 48159, Germany. TEL 49-251-26504-0, FAX 49-251-2650426, info@waxmann.com, http://www.waxmann.com.

ELECTRONIC RECRUITING NEWS. see *COMPUTERS—Internet*

658.3 USA
EMPLOYEE ASSISTANCE. Text in English. 1990. m. USD 299 (effective 2004). **Document type:** *Newsletter.*
Formerly: Employee Assistance Professional Report (1061-7728)
Published by: Stevens Publishing Corporation, 5151 Beltline Rd, 10th Fl, Dallas, TX 75240. FAX 972-687-6769, custserv@stevenspublishing.com, http://www.stevenspublishing.com/. Ed. Darla Bean. Circ: 300 (paid).

658.3 158 USA ISSN 1097-6221
EMPLOYEE ASSISTANCE REPORT; supporting EAP and HR professionals. Text in English. m. USD 189 domestic; USD 199 foreign (effective 2003). **Document type:** *Newsletter.*
Description: Offers employee-assistance and human-resources professionals tips on how to best serve company employees. Covers relevant issues and developments in the field.
Indexed: e-psyche.
Published by: Impact Publications, Inc., E3430 Mountain View Lane, Box 322, Waupaca, WI 54981. TEL 715-258-2448, FAX 715-258-9048, info@impact-publications.com, http://www.impact-publications.com/EAR/index.html. Ed. Karen Kolpien. Pub., R&P Scott Kolpien.

658.3 USA ISSN 1545-3839
HD4928.N6
▼ **EMPLOYEE BENEFIT ADVISER.** Text in English. 2003 (Mar.). bi-m. USD 19.95 (effective 2005). adv. **Document type:** *Newsletter, Trade.* **Description:** Provides coverage of the ever-changing business of employee benefits selling and the most effective ways to market products and services.
Related titles: Online - full text ed.: (from Gale Group).
—CCC.
Published by: Thomson Financial Media, One State St Plaza, 27th Fl, New York, NY 10004-1549. TEL 212-803-8200, FAX 212-292-5216, 800-235-5552, http://www.employeebenefitadviser.com, http://www.thomsonmedia.com. Ed. David Albertson. Pub. Jim Callan. adv.: B&W page USD 6,683; trim 8 x 10.75. Circ: 20,040.

658.3 USA ISSN 0013-6808
HD7106.U5 CODEN: EBPVAL
EMPLOYEE BENEFIT PLAN REVIEW. Text in English. 1946. m. USD 210 (effective 2004). stat.; illus. index. back issues avail.; reprint service avail. from PQC. **Document type:** *Magazine, Trade.*
Incorporates (in 2002): Compensation & Benefits Report
Related titles: Microform ed.: (from PQC); Online - full text ed.: (from EBSCO Publishing, Northern Light Technology, Inc., O C L C Online Computer Library Center, Inc., ProQuest Information & Learning).
Indexed: ABIn, AgeL, BPI, BPIA, BusI, CINAHL, HlthInd, LII, LRI, MEDLINE, ManagCont, PersLit, T&II, WBSS.
—BLDSC (3737.032500), IE, Infotrieve, ingenta. **CCC.**
Published by: Aspen Publishers, Inc. (Subsidiary of: Wolters Kluwer N.V.), 111Eighth Ave., 7th Fl, New York, NY 10011. TEL 212-771-0600, FAX 212-771-0885, editor@spencernet.com, http://www.spencernet.com. Ed. Steve Huth. Circ: 2,100 (paid).

331.255 GBR ISSN 1366-8722
EMPLOYEE BENEFITS. Text in English. 1997. m. GBP 45 domestic; GBP 60 in Europe; GBP 89.50 elsewhere (effective 2001). adv. **Document type:** *Magazine, Trade.* **Description:** Publishes news and research on the latest developments affecting employee benefits.
Related titles: Online - full content ed.; Online - full text ed.: (from EBSCO Publishing, Gale Group, H.W. Wilson, O C L C Online Computer Library Center, Inc., ProQuest Information & Learning).
Indexed: ABIn, BPI.
Published by: Centaur Publishing, St Giles House, 50 Poland St, London, W1V 4AX, United Kingdom. TEL 44-20-7970-4000, employee-benefits@centaur.co.uk, http://www.employeebenefits.co.uk/, http://www.centaur.co.uk. adv.: color page GBP 2,386.

657 USA ISSN 0273-768X
EMPLOYEE BENEFITS COMPLIANCE COORDINATOR. Text in English. 4 base vols. plus m. updates. looseleaf. USD 905 (effective 2005). **Document type:** *Trade.* **Description:** Provides guidance to alltypes of employee benefit plans and how to comply with the various requirements imposed by the Internal Revenue Service, the Department of Labor, and the Social Security Administration.
—CCC.
Published by: W G & L Financial Reporting & Management Research (Subsidiary of: R I A), 395 Hudson St, New York, NY 10014. TEL 212-367-6300, FAX 212-367-6300, http://www.InsideHR.com. **Subscr. to:** The Park Square Bldg., 31 St James Ave, Boston, MA 02116-4112. TEL 800-950-1207.

658.3 USA
EMPLOYEE BENEFITS HANDBOOK. Text in English. 2 base vols. plus s-a. updates. looseleaf. USD 195. **Document type:** *Trade.* **Description:** Provides explanations of employee benefits statutes and regulations, illustrating the steps to take to keep a plan in compliance.
Published by: W G & L Financial Reporting & Management Research (Subsidiary of: R I A), 395 Hudson St, New York, NY 10014. TEL 212-367-6300, FAX 212-367-6718, http://www.InsideHR.com. Ed. Martin Censor. **Subscr. to:** The Park Square Bldg., 31 St James Ave, Boston, MA 02116-4112. TEL 800-950-1207.

EMPLOYEE BENEFITS IN MERGERS AND ACQUISITIONS. see *LAW—Corporate Law*

EMPLOYEE BENEFITS ISSUES: THE MULTIEMPLOYER PERSPECTIVE; proceedings of the annual employee benefits conference with papers from other multi-employer conferences. see *BUSINESS AND ECONOMICS—Labor And Industrial Relations*

658.3 GBR ISSN 1351-055X
EMPLOYEE DEVELOPMENT BULLETIN; practice and policy in training and development; recruitment, selection and retention. Text in English. 1990. m. GBP 169 domestic; GBP 180 foreign (effective 2003). index. 16 p./no.; back issues avail. **Document type:** *Journal, Trade.* **Description:** Provides practical coverage of issues relating to employers' skill needs: recruitment and selection, assessment, training, and development.
Formerly (until 1995): Recruitment and Development Report (0959-146X)
Related titles: Online - full text ed.
Indexed: LRI.
Published by: I R S (Subsidiary of: LexisNexis UK (Scottish Office)), 18-20 Highbury Pl, London, N5 1QP, United Kingdom. TEL 44-20-7354-6742, 44-20-7354-5858, FAX 44-20-7226-8618, 44-20-7359-4000, publications@irseclipse.co.uk, http://www.irsonline.co.uk/pub_subjects/index_pub_human.htm, http://www.irseclipse.co.uk. Ed. Neil Rankin. Pub. Andrew Brode.

658.3 USA
EMPLOYEE INVOLVEMENT ASSOCIATION. STATISTICAL REPORT. Text in English. 1943. a. USD 150 domestic; USD 210 in Canada (effective 2001).
Formerly: National Association of Suggestion Systems. Statistical Report (0077-3441)
Published by: Employee Involvement Association, 525 SW 5th Street, Ste. A, Des Moines, IA 50309-4501. TEL 515-282-8192, FAX 515-282-9117, eia@assoc-mgmt.com, http://www.eia.net. Circ: 1,000.

EMPLOYEE MOTIVATION & INCENTIVE STRATEGIES FOR FINANCIAL INSTITUTIONS. see *BUSINESS AND ECONOMICS—Banking And Finance*

658.3 362.128 USA ISSN 0889-5422
KF3457.3.A15
EMPLOYEE TESTING & THE LAW; reporting legal, technical, and business developments in employee testing. Text in English. 1986. m. looseleaf. USD 295. bk.rev. index. back issues avail. **Description:** Covers legal and business issues involved in polygraphs, paper and pencil, drug and AIDS testing.
Related titles: Microform ed.: (from PQC).
Indexed: CJPI, e-psyche.
Published by: Vanguard Information Publications, PO Box 667, Chapel Hill, NC 27514. TEL 919-967-2420, FAX 919-967-6294. Ed. Ted Shults. Circ: 2,000.

658.3 GBR
EMPLOYEES RELOCATION REPORT. Text in English. q. GBP 100 to non-members; GBP 60 to members. adv. **Description:** Serves as journal for the Council. Covers domestic and international relocation issues of concern to human resources and relocation specialists. Includes feature articles, news items and reports from the Council conferences.
Published by: (Employee Relocation Council), Confederation of British Industry, Centre Point, 103 New Oxford St, London, WC1A 1DU, United Kingdom. TEL 44-171-395-8160, FAX 44-171-240-1578. Ed. Thomas Hadley. R&P Wendy Hayes TEL 44-171-395-8036. Adv. contact Frances Hughes.

EMPLOYER'S BRIEFING. see *LAW—Corporate Law*

658.3 344.01 USA
EMPLOYER'S COMPLIANCE REVIEW (FEDERAL). Text in English. irreg., latest vol.2, 1993. USD 54.
Published by: LexisNexis (Subsidiary of: LexisNexis North America), PO Box 7587, Charlottesville, VA 22906-7587. TEL 804-972-7600, 800-562-1197, FAX 804-972-7666, llp.customer.support@lexis-nexis.com, http://www.lexislawpublishing.com. Ed. Lee T Paterson.

658.3 GBR ISSN 1364-9493
EMPLOYERS LAW. Text in English. m. GBP 95 domestic; GBP 149, USD 224 elsewhere (effective 2000). adv. **Document type:** *Trade.* **Description:** Designed to meet the growing needs of personnel professionals by providing a regular insight into the law at work. Features advice on model policies and highlights some of the year's most important cases.
Related titles: Online - full text ed.: (from EBSCO Publishing).
—CCC.
Published by: Reed Business Information Ltd. (Subsidiary of: Reed Business), Quadrant House, The Quadrant, Brighton Rd, Sutton, Surrey SM2 5AS, United Kingdom. TEL 44-20-8652-3946, FAX 44-208-652-8977, rbi.subscriptions@qss-uk.com, http://www.reedbusiness.co.uk/. Adv. contact Sally Collett. **Subscr. to:** Quadrant Subscription Services, PO Box 302, Haywards Heath, W Sussex RH16 3YY, United Kingdom. TEL 44-1444-445566, FAX 44-1444-445447.

658.3 GBR ISSN 0966-1662
EMPLOYMENT CASE DIGEST. Text in English. 1992. m. **Document type:** *Trade.*
Related titles: ♦ Supplement to: Personnel in Practice.
—BLDSC (3487.806500).
Published by: Croner.C C H Group Ltd. (Subsidiary of: Wolters Kluwer N.V.), 145 London Rd, Kingston, Surrey KT2 6SR, United Kingdom. TEL 44-20-85473333, FAX 44-20-85472637, info@croner.co.uk, http://www.croner.co.uk.

344.01 658.3 USA
EMPLOYMENT DISCRIMINATION (NEW YORK). Text in English. 1973. 10 base vols. plus irreg. updates. looseleaf. USD 1,416 base vol(s). (effective 2003). **Description:** Discusses substantive and procedural law governing employment discrimination based on sex, age, race, religion, national origin and more.
Related titles: CD-ROM ed.
Published by: Matthew Bender & Co., Inc. (Subsidiary of: LexisNexis North America), 1275 Broadway, Albany, NY 12204. international@bender.com, http://bender.lexisnexis.com. Ed. Lex Larson.

EMPLOYMENT DISCRIMINATION VERDICTS AND SETTLEMENTS. see *BUSINESS AND ECONOMICS—Labor And Industrial Relations*

EMPLOYMENT IN THE MAINSTREAM. see *POLITICAL SCIENCE—Civil Rights*

344.01 USA
EMPLOYMENT LAW MANUAL. Text in English. a. USD 162. **Document type:** *Trade.* **Description:** Contains advice and information to help avoid and defend against legal battles in wrongful discharge, sexual harassment, alleged discrimination, family leave and affirmative action.
Published by: W G & L Financial Reporting & Management Research (Subsidiary of: R I A), 395 Hudson St, New York, NY 10014. TEL 212-367-6300, FAX 212-367-6718, http://www.InsideHR.com. Ed. Diane Roberts. **Subscr. to:** The Park Square Bldg., 31 St James Ave, Boston, MA 02116-4112. TEL 800-950-1207.

658.3 332.2 USA
KF3512
EMPLOYMENT LAW SERIES. QUALIFIED RETIREMENT PLANS. Text in English. 1987. 2 base vols. plus a. updates. USD 188.50 base vol(s). print & diskette eds. (effective 2004). **Document type:** *Trade.* **Description:** Provides step-by-step guidance through all legal requirements and compliance filings. Model plans on disk allow you to easily draft qualified retirement plans that are accurate and complete.
Formerly: Qualified Retirement and Other Employee Benefit Plans (1047-224X)
Indexed: ATI.
Published by: Thomson West (Subsidiary of: Thomson Corporation, The), 610 Opperman Dr, Eagan, MN 55123-1396. TEL 651-687-8000, 800-328-9352, FAX 651-687-7302, http://www.westgroup.com/store/product.asp?product%5Fid=17350347&catalog%5Fname=wgstore, http://west.thomson.com. Ed. Michael J Canan.

EMPLOYMENT LAW UPDATE (EVANSVILLE). see *LAW*

658.3 GBR
EMPLOYMENT NEWSLETTER. Text in English. q. **Document type:** *Newsletter.*
Published by: Lovell White Durrant, 65 Holburn Viaduct, London, EC1A 2DY, United Kingdom. TEL 44-20-7236-0066, FAX 44-20-7248-4212, publications@lovellwhitedurrant.com, http://www.lovellwhitedurrant.com.

THE EMPLOYMENT REPORT. see *BUSINESS AND ECONOMICS—Labor And Industrial Relations*

EMPLOYMENT STANDARDS HANDBOOK AND DIGEST. see *LAW*

658 USA
EMPLOYMENT TERMS AND CONDITIONS. ASIA - PACIFIC. Text in English. a. **Document type:** *Trade.* **Description:** Provides information on terms and conditions of employment for 11 Asian nations.
Formerly: Employment Terms and Conditions Report Report - Asia
Published by: (Executive Compensation Service (ECS)), Watson Wyatt Data Services, 1717 H St NW, Flr. 8, Washington, DC 20006-3907. TEL 301-581-4600, FAX 301-581-4688, survey_service@watsonwyatt.com, http://www.watsonwyatt.com.

658 USA
EMPLOYMENT TERMS AND CONDITIONS - EUROPE. Text in English. a. USD 940. **Document type:** *Trade.* **Description:** Guide to employment law and practice across Western Europe.
Published by: (Executive Compensation Service (ECS)), Wyatt Data Services, 218 Rte 17 N, Rochelle Park, NJ 07622-9832. TEL 201-843-1177, FAX 201-843-0101.

659.3 USA
EMPLOYMENT TESTING MANUAL. Text in English. a. looseleaf. USD 185. **Document type:** *Trade.* **Description:** Provides guidance on the use of all types of tests for applicants or employees. Covers government laws and regulations, benefits of tests, choosing and evaluating testing programs, and record-keeping.
Published by: W G & L Financial Reporting & Management Research (Subsidiary of: R I A), 395 Hudson St, New York, NY 10014. TEL 212-367-6300, FAX 212-367-6718, http://www.InsideHR.com. Ed. Rodney Eubanks. **Subscr. to:** The Park Square Bldg., 31 St James Ave, Boston, MA 02116-4112. TEL 800-950-1207.

B

▼ *new title* ➤ *refereed* ✶ *unverified* ♦ *full entry avail.*

658.3 USA
ENCYCLOPEDIA OF PERFORMANCE APPRAISAL. Text in English. irreg. USD 149.95 (effective 1999). **Document type:** *Trade.* **Description:** Explains all types of performance-appraisal systems and how to select the right method and forms for the situation. Contains over 90 ready-to-use forms needed for legal documentation, employee development and compensation administration.
Published by: Business & Legal Reports, Inc., PO Box 6001, Old Saybrook, CT 06475-6001. TEL 203-245-7448, FAX 203-245-0483, service@blr.com. Pub. Robert L Brady.

ENROLLED ACTUARIES REPORT. see *INSURANCE*

658.3 USA ISSN 1094-3757
ENROLLMENT MANAGEMENT REPORT. Text in English. 1997. m. USD 198 (effective 2006). **Document type:** *Newsletter, Trade.* **Description:** Provides news and practical guidance on administering all aspects of enrollment management, including records and registration, recruitment, admissions, financial aid, retention, and more.
Related titles: Online - full text ed.: (from LexisNexis).
—CCC.
Published by: L R P Publications, 747 Dresher Rd, PO Box 980, Horsham, PA 19044. TEL 215-784-0860, 800-341-7874, FAX 215-784-9639, custserve@lrp.com, http://www.shoplrp.com/product/p-31039.html, http://www.lrp.com.

B

658.3 FRA ISSN 0765-5762
LC1060
ENTREPRISES FORMATION. Text in French. 1950. 8/yr. adv. bk.rev. bibl.; charts; illus.; stat. **Document type:** *Trade.*
Formed by the 1985 merger of: Objectif Formation (0294-8230); Which superseded (1951-1972): Notre Formation (0029-4551); And: Entreprise et Formation Permenante (0223-5145); Which superseded (in 1980): Revue du Formation Permenante - Revue de l'Entreprise (0223-436X); Which was formed by the merger of (1973-1979): Revue de la Formation Permenante (0181-186X); And: Revue de l'Entreprise (0153-7156); Which superseded (in 1979): Ingenieurs et Techniciens - Production et Gestion (0399-7782); Which was formed by the merger of (1924-1976): Ingenieurs et Techniciens (0020-1227); And: Production et Gestion (0398-2475); Which superseded (1944-1973): Etude du Travail (0014-1925)
Indexed: Inspec, PAIS, RefZh.
—BLDSC, CISTI. **CCC.**
Published by: Association Nationale pour la Formation Professionnelle des Adultes, 13 pl du General de Gaulle, Montreuil, Cedex 93108, France. TEL 33-1-48705400, FAX 33-1-48707470. Ed. Didier Guibert. Circ: 6,000.

658.3 USA
ESSENTIAL FACTS: EMPLOYMENT. Text in English. a. looseleaf. USD 150. **Document type:** *Trade.* **Description:** Provides information for the Human Resources professional in the areas of: recruitment, selection, contracts, wages, employment benefits, discrimination, sexual harassment and privacy.
Published by: W G & L Financial Reporting & Management Research (Subsidiary of: R I A), 395 Hudson St, New York, NY 10014. TEL 212-367-6300, FAX 212-367-6718, http://www.InsideHR.com. Ed. Diane Roberts. **Subscr. to:** The Park Square Bldg., 31 St James Ave, Boston, MA 02116-4112. TEL 800-950-1207.

658.3 BOL
ESTUDIOS DE RECURSOS HUMANOS. Text in Spanish. 1978. irreg., latest vol.10, 1985. **Document type:** *Monographic series, Academic/Scholarly.*
Published by: Centro de Investigaciones Sociales, Casilla 6931 - C.C., La Paz, Bolivia. TEL 591-2-352931. Ed. Antonio Cisneros.

658.3 DEU ISSN 0071-2493
EUROPEAN ASSOCIATION FOR PERSONNEL MANAGEMENT. CONGRESS REPORTS. Text in French. 1963. irreg. (Madrid), latest 1977. **Document type:** *Proceedings.*
Published by: European Association for Personnel Management/Europaische Vereinigung fuer Personalfuerung, Deutsche Gesellschaft fuer Personalfuerung, Niederkasseler Lohweg 16, Dusseldorf, 40547, Germany. TEL 49-21-15978150, FAX 49-21-15978179, ellerbrake@dgfp.de, http://www.eapm.org.

EXECUTIVE COMPENSATION SURVEY REPORT. see *BUSINESS AND ECONOMICS—Labor And Industrial Relations*

EXECUTIVE GRAPEVINE, VOLUME 6: THE GRAPEVINE INDEX OF SENIOR H R EXECUTIVES, U K EDITION; recruitment library. see *BUSINESS AND ECONOMICS—Management*

658.3 AUS
EXECUTIVE INCENTIVE PLANS IN AUSTRALIA. Text in English. 1998. a. **Document type:** *Trade.* **Description:** Contains analyses of current practices in executive reward policies.
Published by: Cullen Egan Dell, Level 8, 50 Bridge St, Sydney, NSW 2000, Australia. TEL 61-2-9378-9800, FAX 61-2-9233-6800. Ed. James Cooper.

EXECUTIVE PERQUISITES REPORT. see *BUSINESS AND ECONOMICS—Management*

THE EXECUTIVE REPORT ON MANAGED CARE. see *INSURANCE*

EXECUTIVE REPORT ON PHYSICIAN ORGANIZATIONS. see *INSURANCE*

F & W - FUEHREN UND WIRTSCHAFTEN IM KRANKENHAUS. see *HEALTH FACILITIES AND ADMINISTRATION*

FAIR EMPLOYMENT COMPLIANCE; a confidential letter to management. see *BUSINESS AND ECONOMICS—Labor And Industrial Relations*

357.63 USA ISSN 0163-7665
JK671
FEDERAL PERSONNEL GUIDE; employment, pay, benefits, postal service, civil service. Text in English. 1979. a. USD 14.95 newsstand/cover worldwide (effective 2004 - 2005). adv. **Document type:** *Directory.* **Description:** Summarizes and explains, in plain English, the most important rules and regulations that affect their pay, benefits, careers and retirement. Also includes directories of Federal agencies, organizations, associations and more. The Federal Personnel Guide is in effect an "employee handbook" for civilian employees of the U.S. Federal Government and Postal Service.
Related titles: CD-ROM ed.: Federal Personnel Guide on CD-ROM; Online - full text ed.: Federal Personnel Guide on LAN. ISSN 1540-0018 (from Northern Light Technology, Inc.).
Indexed: PersLit.
—IE. **CCC.**
Published by: Key Communications Group Inc., 5617 Warwick Pl., Chevy Chase, MD 20815-5503. info@fedguide.com, keycom@bellatlantic.net, http://www.fedguide.com. Ed. Ms. Sandra M Harris. Pub., R&P, Adv. contact Mr. Frank S Joseph TEL 301-656-0451. B&W page USD 3,095; trim 7.25 x 9.5. Circ: 60,000. **Dist. by:** Quality Books Inc.; **Dist. to book trade by:** Biblio Distribution, Inc., 4501 Forbes Blvd, Ste 200, Lanham, MD 20706. TEL 800-462-6420, FAX 800-338-4550, custserv@nbnbooks.com, http://www.bibliodistribution.com/.

658.3 USA
FEDERAL QUALITY NEWS. Text in English. bi-m. USD 13; USD 16.25 foreign. back issues avail. **Document type:** *Government.*
Published by: U.S. Office of Personnel Management, 1900 E. St. N.W., Washington, DC 20415. TEL 202-606-2424. **Subscr. to:** U.S. Government Printing Office, Superintendent of Documents.

658.3 336 USA
FINANCIAL INSTITUTIONS RETIREMENT FUND. ANNUAL REPORT. Text in English. a. **Document type:** *Corporate.*
Published by: Financial Institutions Retirement Fund, Pentegna Group, 108 Corporate Park Dr, White Plains, NY 10604. TEL 914-694-1300. Ed. Gail E Janensch.

658 USA
FINANCIAL PARTICIPATION - EUROPE. Text in English. a. USD 545. charts. **Document type:** *Trade.* **Description:** Provides survey data for 17 Western European countries regarding company practices on incentive programs that link awards to company performance.
Published by: (Executive Compensation Service (ECS)), Wyatt Data Services, 218 Rte 17 N, Rochelle Park, NJ 07622-9832. TEL 201-843-1177, FAX 201-843-0101.

658.3 USA ISSN 0164-6397
HV8138
FIRE AND POLICE PERSONNEL REPORTER. Text in English. 1975. m. USD 335 to institutions (effective 2003); includes Monthly Law Summaries, Law Enforcement Liability Reporter and Jail and Prisoner Law Bulletin. bk.rev. index. **Document type:** *Newsletter.* **Description:** Contains articles on litigation arising out of employee disciplinary action or labor laws. Articles cover more than 200 topics, such as age, race, sex, national origin and disability discrimination; collective bargaining rights, etc.
Formerly: Fire Department Personnel Reporter
Media: Online - full content.
Published by: Aele Law Enforcement Legal Center, 841 W Touhy Ave, Park Ridge, IL 60068-3351. TEL 847-685-0700, FAX 847-685-9700, fp@aele.org, aele@aol.com, http://www.aele.org. Circ: 950 (paid).

FIRST DRAFT. see *PUBLISHING AND BOOK TRADE*

331.125 CAN ISSN 0831-4535
KE3254.A13
FOCUS ON CANADIAN EMPLOYMENT AND EQUALITY RIGHTS. Text in English. 1986. m. looseleaf. CND 409 (effective 2005). **Document type:** *Trade.* **Description:** Reports on developments in the field including legislation and government programs and initiatives. Includes case notes and advice.
Related titles: Online - full text ed.: (from Micromedia ProQuest).
Indexed: CBCABus.
Published by: C C H Canadian Ltd., 90 Sheppard Ave E, Ste 300, North York, ON M2N 6X1, Canada. TEL 416-224-2248, 800-268-4522, FAX 416-224-2243, cservice@cch.ca, http://www.cch.ca.

FORDYCE LETTER; commentary and information provided exclusively for those involved in the personnel, search, employment, recruiting and outplacement professions. see *LAW—Corporate Law*

FORMANDSBLADET. see *BUILDING AND CONSTRUCTION*

658 370.113 FRA ISSN 0759-6340
HD5715.5.F8
FORMATION EMPLOI. Text in French. 1983. q. EUR 53 domestic; EUR 56 in the European Union; EUR 57.50 DOM-TOM; EUR 60 elsewhere (effective 2003).
Indexed: IBSS, JEL, RASB, SociolAb.
Published by: (Centre d'Etudes et de Recherches sur les Qualifications), Documentation Francaise, 29-31 quai Voltaire, Paris, Cedex 7 75344, France. FAX 33-1-40157230.

FRONTLINE SUPERVISION; employment law advice for people who manage people. see *LAW—Corporate Law*

658.3 USA ISSN 1061-7469
HD6983
GEOGRAPHIC REFERENCE REPORT (YEAR); annual report of costs, wages, salaries, and human resource statistics US and Canada. Text in English. 1987. a. USD 489 (effective 2005). **Document type:** *Academic/Scholarly.*
Former titles (until 1993): Geographic Reference (1057-8498); (until 1990): Geographic Entry Level Salary Survey and Relocation Reference
Published by: E R I Economic Research Institute, 8575 164th Ave NE, Ste. 100, Redmond, WA 98052-3679. TEL 800-627-3697, FAX 800-753-4415, info@erieri.com, http://www.erieri.com. R&P Briana Bennitt.

GEWERBEARCHIV; Zeitschrift fuer Gewerbe- und Wirtschaftsverwaltungsrecht. see *LAW—Corporate Law*

658.3 NLD ISSN 0921-1896
GIDS VOOR PERSONEELSMANAGEMENT. Text in Dutch. 1958. 11/yr. EUR 159 (effective 2005). adv. **Document type:** *Trade.*
Formerly (until 1987): Gids voor Personeelsbeleid, Arbeidsvraagstukken, Sociale Verzekering (0165-0289)
—IE, Infotrieve, KNAW.
Published by: Wolters Kluwer N.V., Postbus 23, Deventer, 7400 GA, Netherlands. FAX 31-570-691555, gids@kluwer.nl, info@kluwer.nl. Ed. Ton Hesp. Circ: 8,607.

658.3 USA ISSN 1542-5665
GLOBAL H R REPORT. Text in English. 2002 (Oct.). w. USD 295 in United States (effective 2005 - 2006). **Description:** Contains detailed information on managing expatriate and local national employees, from setting up compensation packages to improving retention after repatriation; suggestions on how to best manage the international HR function itself; and tips on keeping worldwide workforces safe and secure.
Media: Online - full content. **Related titles:** Online - full text ed.: (from The Bureau of National Affairs, Inc.).
—CCC.
Published by: The Bureau of National Affairs, Inc., 1231 25th St., NW, Washington, DC 20037. TEL 202-452-4200, 800-372-1033, http://www.bna.com/products/hr/ghrn.htm.

THE GUIDE TO BACKGROUND INVESTIGATIONS; a comprehensive source directory for employee screening and background investigations. see *CRIMINOLOGY AND LAW ENFORCEMENT—Security*

659.3 USA
GUIDE TO EMPLOYEE DISCIPLINE AND TERMINATION. Text in English. base vol. plus s-a. updates. looseleaf. USD 195. **Document type:** *Trade.* **Description:** Provides explanations and analysis of proper procedures to follow before, during, and after an employee termination.
Published by: W G & L Financial Reporting & Management Research (Subsidiary of: R I A), 395 Hudson St, New York, NY 10014. TEL 212-367-6300, FAX 212-367-6718, http://www.InsideHR.com. Ed. Linda Mark. **Subscr. to:** The Park Square Bldg., 31 St James Ave, Boston, MA 02116-4112. TEL 800-950-1207.

658.3 USA
GUIDE TO EMPLOYEE HANDBOOKS. Text in English. a. looseleaf. USD 180 (effective 1998). **Document type:** *Trade.* **Description:** Points out how to best update existing employee handbooks, covering key legal issues.
Indexed: ATI.
Published by: W G & L Financial Reporting & Management Research (Subsidiary of: R I A), 395 Hudson St, New York, NY 10014. TEL 212-367-6300, FAX 212-367-6718, http://www.InsideHR.com. Ed. Robert J Nobile. **Subscr. to:** The Park Square Bldg., 31 St James Ave, Boston, MA 02116-4112. TEL 800-950-1207.

658.3 USA
GUIDE TO EMPLOYEE LEAVE. Text in English. base vol. plus s-a. updates. looseleaf. USD 195. **Document type:** *Trade.* **Description:** Provides current information covering all types of employee leave policies, procedures and laws. Explains how to coordinate leave policies, how to administer leave, and how to treat benefits while employees are on leave.

Published by: W G & L Financial Reporting & Management Research (Subsidiary of: R I A), 395 Hudson St, New York, NY 10014. TEL 212-367-6300, FAX 212-367-6718, http://www.InsideHR.com. Ed. Martin Censor. **Subscr. to:** The Park Square Bldg., 31 St James Ave, Boston, MA 02116-4112.

658.3 USA
GUIDE TO EMPLOYEE RECRUITMENT & HIRING. Text in English. base vol. plus s-a. updates. looseleaf. USD 195. **Document type:** *Trade.* **Description:** Provides current information about recruiting, interviewing, selecting and hiring employees. Includes information about compliance with federal and state laws and regulations.
Published by: W G & L Financial Reporting & Management Research (Subsidiary of: R I A), 395 Hudson St, New York, NY 10014. TEL 212-367-6300, FAX 212-367-6718, http://www.InsideHR.com. Ed. Rodney Eubanks. **Subscr. to:** The Park Square Bldg., 31 St James Ave, Boston, MA 02116-4112. TEL 800-950-1207.

331.133 USA
GUIDE TO EQUAL EMPLOYMENT PRACTICES. Text in English. 2 base vols. plus s-a. updates. looseleaf. USD 269. **Document type:** *Trade.* **Description:** Serves as a practical guide to handling fair employment issues and employment discrimination issues in the workplace. Includes coverage of federal and state laws, discrimination as it affects employment practices, and dealings with discrimination lawsuits and administrative proceedings.
Published by: W G & L Financial Reporting & Management Research (Subsidiary of: R I A), 395 Hudson St, New York, NY 10014. TEL 212-367-6300, FAX 212-367-6718, http://www.InsideHR.com. Ed. Linda Mark. **Subscr. to:** The Park Square Bldg., 31 St James Ave, Boston, MA 02116-4112.

658.3 USA
GUIDE TO H R POLICIES AND PROCEDURES MANUALS. (Human Resources) Text in English. a. looseleaf. USD 195. **Document type:** *Trade.* **Description:** Provides guidance and sample policies and procedures for creating an effective manual.
Published by: W G & L Financial Reporting & Management Research (Subsidiary of: R I A), 395 Hudson St, New York, NY 10014. TEL 212-367-6300, FAX 212-367-6718, http://www.InsideHR.com. Ed. Diane Roberts. **Subscr. to:** The Park Square Bldg., 31 St James Ave, Boston, MA 02116-4112. TEL 800-950-1207.

658.3 HKG ISSN 1012-7887
H K STAFF; Hong Kong's human resources journal. Text in Chinese. 1988. 10/yr. HKD 1,450, USD 200. **Document type:** *Trade.* **Description:** Covers employee benefits, contracts, employment law, migration, provident funds, salaries, tax, trade unions, training, and work permits.
Related titles: Online - full text ed.: (from Gale Group).
Indexed: HongKongiana.
Published by: Asia Law & Practice Ltd. (Subsidiary of: Euromoney Institutional Investor Plc.), 5/F Printing House, 6 Duddell St, Central Hong Kong, Hong Kong. TEL 852-544-9918, FAX 852-544-0040. **Dist. in US by:** American Educational Systems, PO Box 246, New York, NY 10024-0246. TEL 800-431-1579.

658.3 340 USA
H R ADVISOR: LEGAL & PRACTICAL GUIDANCE. (Human Resources) Text in English. bi-m. USD 175. **Document type:** *Trade.* **Description:** Gives analysis and practical guidance for handling HR and employment issues. Includes information on how to prevent lawsuits.
Published by: W G & L Financial Reporting & Management Research (Subsidiary of: R I A), 395 Hudson St, New York, NY 10014. TEL 212-367-6300, FAX 212-367-6718, http://www.InsideHR.com. Ed. Rodney Eubanks. **Subscr. to:** The Park Square Bldg., 31 St James Ave, Boston, MA 02116-4112. TEL 800-950-1207.

H R BANKER. see *BUSINESS AND ECONOMICS—Banking And Finance*

658.3 332.1 USA ISSN 1553-8192
H R BANKER (AUSTIN); for hr professionals in financial institutions. (Human Resources) Text in English. 2000 (Jan). m. USD 395 (effective 2005). **Document type:** *Newsletter.*
Published by: AlexInformation, 807 Las Cimas Pkwy Ste 300, Austin, TX 78746. TEL 512-652-4400, FAX 512-652-4499, inforeply@alexinformation.com, http://www.alexinformation.com. Ed. Allie Buzzell.

658.3 AUS
H R D ALERT. (Human Resource Development) Text in English. 1999. m. 4 p./no.; **Document type:** *Newsletter, Consumer.*
Media: E-mail.
Published by: Desert Wave Publishing, PO Box 2361, Alice Spring, N.T. 0871, Australia. TEL 61-8-8953-4409, http://www.dwave.com.au/. Ed., R&P Robin Henry. Circ: 894 (controlled).

658.3 USA ISSN 1540-2711
HF5549.2.U5
H R DEPARTMENT BENCHMARKS AND ANALYSIS. (Human Resources) Text in English. 2002. a. USD 1,195 per issue (effective 2005). **Document type:** *Trade.*
Related titles: Online - full text ed.: (from The Bureau of National Affairs, Inc.).
—CCC.
Published by: The Bureau of National Affairs, Inc., 1231 25th St., NW, Washington, DC 20037. TEL 800-372-1033, customercare@bna.com, http://www.bna.com.

658.3 USA ISSN 1546-9832
▼ **H R EXPERT.** Text in English. 2003. 10/yr. USD 595 (effective 2005). back issues avail. **Document type:** *Newsletter, Trade.*
Related titles: Online - full content ed.
Published by: Wellesley Information Services (Subsidiary of: United Communications Group), 990 Washington St, Dedham, MA 02026-6714. TEL 781-329-0419, FAX 781-320-9466, customer.service@hrexpertonline.com, customer@eview.com, http://www.HRExpertOnline.com, http://www.wispubs.com. Eds. Michael Nadeau, Bonnie Penzias.

658.3 USA
H R FLORIDA REVIEW MAGAZINE. (Human Resources) Text in English. 2000. s-a. adv. **Document type:** *Magazine, Trade.* **Description:** Contains information such as an executive focus, feature articles, trends of human resources and future outlooks for the industry.
Published by: (H R Florida State Council), Naylor Publications, Inc., 5950 NW 1st Pl, Gainesville, FL 32607-6018. TEL 800-369-6220, editor@hrflorida.org, http://www.hrflorida.org/displaycommon.cfm?an=6, http://www.naylor.com. Ed. Tim Smith. Pub. Steve Stramm. Adv. contact Ray Goodwin. B&W page USD 1,529.50; trim 8.375 x 10.875. Circ: 3,003 (paid).

658.3 USA ISSN 1554-0936
▼ **H R HERO'S HIRING & FIRING**; proven strategies for managing your toughest tasks. (Human Resources) Text in English. 2005 (Mar.). m. USD 197 (effective 2005). **Document type:** *Newsletter.* **Description:** Presents proven practices and guidance on this most crucial part of HR management.
Published by: M. Lee Smith Publishers LLC, PO Box 5094, Brentwood, TN 37024. TEL 615-373-7517, 800-274-6774, FAX 615-373-5183, custserv@mleesmith.com, http://www.hrhero.com/hire-fire, http://www.mleesmith.com.

658.3 USA ISSN 1548-4211
▼ **H R INSIGHT.** (Human Resources) Text in English. 2004 (May). m. USD 197 (effective 2005). **Document type:** *Newsletter.*
Published by: M. Lee Smith Publishers LLC, PO Box 5094, Brentwood, TN 37024. TEL 615-373-7517, 800-274-6774, FAX 615-373-5183, custserv@mleesmith.com, http://www.hrhero.com/insight.shtml, http://www.mleesmith.com.

THE H R INTERNET AND TECHNOLOGY LETTER. see *BUSINESS AND ECONOMICS—Computer Applications*

658.3 NLD ISSN 0923-1420
H R M SELECT; het beste uit de internationale vakpers. (Human Resource Management) Text in Dutch. 1989. 4/yr. **Document type:** *Trade.*
—IE, Infotrieve.
Published by: Wolters Kluwer N.V., Leeuwenburg 101, Deventer, 7411 TH, Netherlands. TEL 31-5700-48999, FAX 31-5700-11504. **Subscr. to:** Intermedia bv, Postbus 4, Alphen aan den Rijn 2400 MA, Netherlands. TEL 31-172-466321, FAX 31-172-435527.

658.3 346 USA ISSN 1047-3149
HF5549.A2 CODEN: HMAGFG
H R MAGAZINE; the business of people. (Human Resources) Text in English. 1950. m. USD 70 domestic to non-members; USD 90 in Canada to non-members; USD 125 elsewhere to non-members (effective 2005). adv. bk.rev.; software rev. charts; illus. index. back issues avail.; reprint service avail. from PQC. **Document type:** *Magazine, Trade.* **Description:** Expounds on issues related to human resources: emphasizes knowledge of the human resource management profession and contributes to its progress.
Former titles: Personnel Administrator (0031-5729); (until 1954): Personnel News
Related titles: Online - full text ed.: (from EBSCO Publishing, Florida Center for Library Automation, Gale Group, H.W. Wilson, O C L C Online Computer Library Center, Inc., ProQuest Information & Learning).
Indexed: ABIn, ADPA, ASEANManA, AgeL, BPI, BPIA, BRI, BusI, CBRI, CIJE, EAA, Emerald, LRI, M&MA, MEDLINE, ManagCont, PAIS, PMA, PROMT, PersLit, PsycholAb, QAb, RASB, T&DA, T&II.
—BLDSC (4335.267450), IE, Infotrieve, ingenta. **CCC.**
Published by: Society for Human Resource Management, 1800 Duke St, Alexandria, VA 22314-3499. TEL 703-548-3440, FAX 703-548-6490, shrm@shrm.org, http://www.shrm.org/hrmagazine. Ed. Patrick Mirza. Pub. Gary Rubin. R&P Nicole Gauin TEL 703-535-6138. Adv. contact Reema Hamoui. Circ: 195,000.

658.3 USA ISSN 1047-3157
H R NEWS. (Human Resources) Text in English. 1990. m. **Document type:** *Bulletin, Trade.*
Formerly (until 1989): Resource (Berea) (0746-7850)
Indexed: AgeL.
—CCC.
Published by: Society for Human Resource Management, 1800 Duke St, Alexandria, VA 22314-3499. TEL 800-283-7476, shrm@shrm.org, http://www.shrm.org.

658.3 USA ISSN 1098-4763
HF5549.A2
H R - O D. (Human Resources - Organizational Dynamics) Text in English. 1998. m.
Published by: American Management Association International, 1601 Broadway, New York, NY 10019. TEL 212-586-8100, FAX 212-903-8168.

658.3 331 USA ISSN 1541-3551
HF5549.2.U5
H R O TODAY. Variant title: Human Resources Outsourcing Today. Text in English. 2002. m. USD 150 domestic; USD 170 in Canada; USD 185 elsewhere (effective 2005). **Document type:** *Magazine, Trade.*
Published by: Outsourcing Today, LLC, 103 Eisenhower Pkwy, 2nd fl, Roseland, NJ 07068. TEL 973-439-0060, FAX 973-439-0061, info@outsourcingtoday.com, http://www.hrotoday.com. Ed. Margo Alderton. Pub. Jay Whitehead TEL 973-439-0060 ext 202.

658.3 USA ISSN 1098-9293
H R ON CAMPUS. (Human Resources) Text in English. 1998. m. USD 180 (effective 2005). **Description:** Provides literature information to solve institutions human resource challenges.
Related titles: Online - full text ed.
—CCC.
Published by: L R P Publications, 747 Dresher Rd, PO Box 980, Horsham, PA 19044. TEL 215-784-0860, 800-341-7874, FAX 215-784-9639, custserve@lrp.com, http://www.shoplrp.com/product/p-31040.html, http://www.lrp.com. Ed. David Shadovitz.

H R - P C (ONLINE); computer technology for human resource management. see *BUSINESS AND ECONOMICS—Computer Applications*

658.3 USA
H R P S BEST PRACTICES SERIES. Text in English. 1994. irreg. USD 32 to non-members; USD 25 to members. **Description:** Provides a review and assessment of concepts, approaches, methods, and applications in subject areas of interest and value to HR executives and planners.
Published by: Human Resource Planning Society, 317 Madison Ave, Ste 1509, New York, NY 10017. TEL 212-490-6387, FAX 212-682-6851, info@hrps.org, http://www.hrps.org.

658.3 USA
H R P S CORPORATE SPONSOR FORUM PROCEEDINGS. Text in English. a. USD 32 to non-members; USD 25 to members. **Document type:** *Proceedings.*
Published by: Human Resource Planning Society, 317 Madison Ave, Ste 1509, New York, NY 10017. TEL 212-490-6387, FAX 212-682-6851, info@hrps.org, http://www.hrps.org.

658.3 USA
H R P S RESEARCH SYMPOSIUM PROCEEDINGS. Text in English. biennial. USD 64 to non-members; USD 50 to members. **Document type:** *Proceedings.*
Published by: Human Resource Planning Society, 317 Madison Ave, Ste 1509, New York, NY 10017. TEL 212-490-6387, FAX 212-682-6851, info@hrps.org, http://www.hrps.org.

658.3 USA
H R POLICIES & PRACTICES UPDATE. (Human Resources) Text in English. bi-w. USD 155 (effective 1998). **Document type:** *Newsletter.* **Description:** Addresses current employment law problems confronting human resources managers. Provides "how-to" information on complying with regulations, preparing employee handbooks, and interviewing job applicants in order to avoid costly errors.
Formerly: Personnel Practice Ideas
Related titles: Microform ed.: (from PQC).
Published by: W G & L Financial Reporting & Management Research (Subsidiary of: R I A), 395 Hudson St, New York, NY 10014. TEL 212-367-6300, FAX 212-367-6718, http://www.InsideHR.com. **Subscr. to:** The Park Square Bldg., 31 St James Ave, Boston, MA 02116-4112. TEL 800-950-1207.

658.3 USA ISSN 1098-3392
HF5549.A2
H R PRACTITIONERS GUIDE. Text in English. m. **Document type:** *Trade.*
Media: CD-ROM.
—CCC.
Published by: The Bureau of National Affairs, Inc., 1231 25th St., NW, Washington, DC 20037. TEL 800-372-1033. **Subscr. to:** 9435 Key West Ave, Rockville, MD 20850.

658.3 CAN
H R PROFESSIONAL; the magazine for Canadian human resources professionals. (Human Resources) Text in English. 1985. 6/yr. CND 55 domestic; USD 70 in United States; USD 80 in Europe (effective 2005). adv. bk.rev. **Document type:** *Magazine, Trade.* **Description:** Provides timely information and analysis on human resources issues, trends and practices, including recruitment, retention, benefits, compensation, training and development, occupational health and safety, HR technology, employment law, and more.

Former titles (until 2003): Human Resources Professional (0847-9453); (until 1989): H R Professional (0833-8892)
Indexed: CBCARef, CBPI.
—CCC.
Published by: (Human Resources Professionals Association of Ontario), Naylor Communications Ltd., 920 Yonge St, Ste 600, Toronto, ON M4W 3C7, Canada. TEL 800-665-2456, FAX 800-709-5551, http://www.hrprofessional.org, http://www.naylor.com. Ed. Shawn D Phelps. Pub. David Long. adv.: B&W page CND 1,939, color page CND 2,938; trim 8.37 x 10.8. Circ: 13,000.

658.3 346.066 USA
H R SERIES: COMPENSATION & BENEFITS. (Human Resources) Text in English. 1990. and newsletter), 3 base vols. plus m. updates. looseleaf. USD 560. **Description:** Covers pay plan design, job evaluation, all types of benefits, executive compensation, and complex legal requirements.
Formerly: Compensation Strategy and Management (1057-4859)
Related titles: Series of: H R Series.
—CCC.
Published by: W G & L Financial Reporting & Management Research (Subsidiary of: R I A), 395 Hudson St, New York, NY 10014. TEL 212-367-6300, FAX 212-367-6718, http://www.InsideHR.com. Ed. Amy Middleton. **Subscr. to:** The Park Square Bldg., 31 St James Ave, Boston, MA 02116-4112. TEL 800-950-1207.

658.3 346 USA
H R SERIES: FAIR EMPLOYMENT PRACTICES. (Human Resouces) Text in English. and newsletters), 3 base vols. plus m. updates. looseleaf. USD 560. **Document type:** *Trade.* **Description:** Contains equal employment opportunity and affirmative action information with analysis, resources directories, fact sheets, sample forms, model policies, and other tools.
Related titles: Series of: H R Series.
Published by: W G & L Financial Reporting & Management Research (Subsidiary of: R I A), 395 Hudson St, New York, NY 10014. TEL 212-367-6300, FAX 212-367-6718, http://www.InsideHR.com. Ed. Joe Lustig. **Subscr. to:** The Park Square Bldg., The Park Square Bldg, 31 St. James Ave, Boston, MA 02116-4101. TEL 800-950-1207.

658.3 USA
H R SERIES: POLICIES AND PRACTICES. Text in English. base vol. plus m. updates. looseleaf. USD 560 (effective 1998). **Document type:** *Newsletter.* **Description:** Provides clear understanding of legal issues and contains key government required forms.
Formerly: Human Resources Policies and Practices
Related titles: Series of: H R Series.
Published by: W G & L Financial Reporting & Management Research (Subsidiary of: R I A), 395 Hudson St, New York, NY 10014. TEL 212-367-6300, FAX 212-367-6718, http://www.InsideHR.com. Ed. Lee Lunsford. **Subscr. to:** The Park Square Bldg., 31 St James Ave, Boston, MA 02116-4112. TEL 800-950-1207.

658.3 DEU ISSN 1439-3174
H R SERVICES; die Welt der Personaldienstleistungen. (Human Resources) Text in German. 2000. 6/yr. EUR 40; EUR 8 newsstand/cover (effective 2004). adv. **Document type:** *Magazine, Trade.*
Published by: Datakontext Fachverlag GmbH, Augustinusstr 9 d, Frechen, 50226, Germany. TEL 49-2234-966100, FAX 49-2234-966109, info@datakontext.com, http://www.datakontext-press.de/HR/hr_hauptframe.htm. Adv. contact Gabriele Beuder. B&W page EUR 2,300, color page EUR 4,025; trim 178 x 246. Circ: 13,400 (paid and controlled).

658.3 USA ISSN 1545-360X
▼ **THE H R SPECIALIST.** (Human Resources) Text in English. 2003 (Jul.). m. USD 97 (effective 2003).
—CCC.
Published by: National Institute of Business Management, 1750 Old Meadow Rd. Ste. 302, McLean, VA 22102-4315. TEL 703-905-8000, 800-543-2052, customer@nibm.net, http://www.hrspecialist.net, http://www.nibm.net/home.asp. Ed. Joe McGavin. Pub. Steve Sturm.

658.3 USA ISSN 1543-9046
H R STRATEGIC ADVISOR. (Human Resources) Text in English. 2002 (Nov.). m. USD 197 in US & Canada; USD 227 elsewhere (effective 2003).
Published by: Belden Communications, LLC, P. O. Box 7029, Wilton, CT 06897-7029. TEL 203-563-9797, 866-563-9797, FAX 203-563-9898, info@beldencom.com. Ed., Pub. Lawrence A. deQuintal.

658.3 CAN
H R STRATEGIES & TACTICS✶. (Human Resources) Text in English. 1976. 10/yr. free. bk.rev. bibl. back issues avail. **Document type:** *Newsletter.* **Description:** Investigates business issues through strategic human resource management.
Former titles (until 1998): H R Planning Newsletter (0733-0332); (until 1981): Manpower Planning (0364-7358)
Media: Online - full text.
—CCC.
Address: 2603-10 Yonge St, Toronto, ON M5E 1R4, Canada. TEL 416-363-0480, FAX 416-363-7848, info@hrstrategy.com, http://www.hrstrategy.com. Ed., Pub., R&P James W Peters TEL 414-347-7733. Circ: 8,000 (paid).

658.3 AUS ISSN 1325-6831
HI - TECH TELECOMMUNICATIONS AND INFORMATION TECHNOLOGY. Text in English. 1992. a. AUD 1,500 (effective 1999). **Document type:** *Trade.* **Description:** Includes remuneration and benefits data for the hi-tech industry.
Published by: Cullen Egan Dell, Level 8, 50 Bridge St, Sydney, NSW 2000, Australia. TEL 61-2-9375-9800, FAX 61-2-9233-6800. Ed. Paulina Wladdimiro. Circ: 37.

658.3 USA ISSN 1526-2987
HIRING THE BEST. Text in English. 1998. m. USD 487 one time charge (effective 2005). **Document type:** *Newsletter, Trade.* **Description:** Helps executives recruit, screen and retain the best employees.
Published by: Briefings Publishing Group (Subsidiary of: Douglas Publications, Inc.), 1101 King St, Ste 110, Alexandria, VA 22314. TEL 703-518-2343, 800-722-9221, FAX 703-684-2136, customerservice@briefings.com, http://www.briefings.com.

HOME HEALTH EXECUTIVE COMPENSATION REPORT. see *HEALTH FACILITIES AND ADMINISTRATION*

HOSPITAL AND HEALTH CARE REPORT. see *HEALTH FACILITIES AND ADMINISTRATION*

658.3 USA ISSN 1059-6038
HF5549.A2
HRFOCUS; the hands-on tool for human resources professionals. Text in English. 1919. m. USD 271.95 combined subscription in US & Canada print & online eds.; USD 283 combined subscription elsewhere print & online eds. (effective 2006). adv. bk.rev. charts; illus. index. back issues avail.; reprints avail. **Document type:** *Newsletter, Trade.* **Description:** Keeps human resources managers abreast of progressive personnel practices and current developments in the field.
Formerly (until 1991): Personnel (0031-5702)
Related titles: Microform ed.: (from PQC); Online - full text ed.: (from EBSCO Publishing, Factiva, Florida Center for Library Automation, Gale Group, H.W. Wilson, O C L C Online Computer Library Center, Inc., ProQuest Information & Learning); ♦ Cumulative ed(s).: HRfocus Yearbook.
Indexed: ABIn, ASEANManA, ATI, AcaI, BPI, BPIA, CPM, CurCont, EAA, Emerald, ExcerpMed, HospLI, KES, M&MA, MEDLINE, ManagCont, ORMS, PCI, PMA, PersLit, PsycholAb, RASB, SSCI, T&II, WorkRelAb.
—BLDSC (4335.266800), CISTI, IDS, IE, Infotrieve, ingenta. **CCC.**
Published by: Institute of Management & Administration, Inc., 3 Park Ave, New York, NY 10016-5902. TEL 212-244-0360, FAX 212-564-0465, subserve@ioma.com, http://www.ioma.com. Ed. Sue Sandler. Circ: 8,000 (controlled).

658.3 USA
HRFOCUS YEARBOOK. Text in English. a. USD 224.95 print & online eds. (effective 2003). **Description:** Covers retention and perfomance management, compensation, benefits, training, legal issues, technology, management, and special reports on strategic planning, hiring, international human resources, and performance management.
Related titles: Online - full text ed.: USD 219 (effective 2003); ♦ Cumulative ed. of: HRfocus. ISSN 1059-6038.
Published by: Institute of Management & Administration, Inc., 3 Park Ave, New York, NY 10016-5902. TEL 212-244-0360, FAX 212-564-0465, subserve@ioma.com, http://www.ioma.com. Ed. Sue Sandler.

658.3 USA ISSN 1043-8998
HE5549.A2
HUMAN CAPITAL. Text in English. 1989. q. free. **Document type:** *Newsletter, Consumer.* **Description:** For human resource directors and senior executives of Fortune 1,000 firms. Focuses on senior management methods for investing in and creating a productive, innovative workforce.
Published by: Douglas Publications, Inc., 2807 N Parham Rd, Ste 200, Richmond, VA 23294. TEL 804-762-9600, FAX 804-217-8999, info@douglaspublications.com, http://www.humancapitalmag.com, http://www.douglaspublications.com. Circ: 65,000.

658.3 USA ISSN 1550-0365
HUMAN CAPITAL (RICHMOND); exceeding corporate goals through superior human capital management. Text in English. 1999. 7/yr., latest vol.4, no.1. USD 49 domestic; USD 54 in Canada & Mexico; USD 150 elsewhere; USD 6.95 newsstand/cover (effective 2005). adv. **Document type:** *Magazine, Trade.*
Formerly: Human Capital Strategies & News (1533-9327)
Related titles: Supplement(s): Human Capital Magazine. Buying Guide. USD 25 (effective 2004).
—CCC.
Published by: Douglas Publications, Inc., 2807 N Parham Rd, Ste 200, Richmond, VA 23294. TEL 804-762-9600, FAX 804-217-8999, info@humancapitalmag.com, info@douglaspublications.com, http://www.humancapitalmag.com/, http://www.douglaspublications.com.

658.3 USA
HUMAN RESOURCE DEPARTMENT MANAGEMENT REPORT YEARBOOK. Text in English. a. USD 224.95 print & online eds. (effective 2003). **Description:** Provides practical tips and strategies to enhance human resource department performance.
Related titles: Online - full text ed.: USD 219 (effective 2003); ♦ Cumulative ed. of: I O M A's Human Resources Department Management Report. ISSN 1092-5910.
Published by: Institute of Management & Administration, Inc., 3 Park Ave, New York, NY 10016-5902. TEL 212-244-0360, FAX 212-564-0465, subserve@ioma.com, http://www.ioma.com. Ed. Susan Patterson.

658.3 GBR ISSN 1367-8868
HF5549.5.M3
HUMAN RESOURCE DEVELOPMENT INTERNATIONAL; enhancing performance, learning, and integrity. Short title: H R D I. Text in English. 1998. q. GBP 316, USD 525 combined subscription to institutions print & online eds. (effective 2006). bk.rev. back issues avail.; reprint service avail. from PSC. **Document type:** *Journal, Academic/Scholarly.* **Description:** Brings HRD theory into the workplace and studies the development of organizations, their strategy and policy, and the processes of life-long learning and collectivity among organizations throughout the world.
Related titles: Online - full text ed.: ISSN 1469-8374. GBP 300, USD 499 to institutions (effective 2006) (from EBSCO Publishing, Gale Group, IngentaConnect, O C L C Online Computer Library Center, Inc., Swets Information Services).
Indexed: BrEdI, ErgAb, HRA, IBSS.
—BLDSC (4336.432750), IE, Infotrieve, ingenta. **CCC.**
Published by: Routledge (Subsidiary of: Taylor & Francis Group), 4 Park Square, Milton Park, Abingdon, Oxon OX14 4RN, United Kingdom. TEL 44-1235-828600, FAX 44-1235-829000, info@routledge.co.uk, http://www.tandf.co.uk/journals/titles/13678868.asp. Eds. K Peter Kuchinke, Rob Poell, Jean Woodall. R&P Sally Sweet. **Subscr. to:** Taylor & Francis Ltd, Journals Customer Service, Rankine Rd, Basingstoke, Hants RG24 8PR, United Kingdom. TEL 44-1256-813000, FAX 44-1256-330245, enquiry@tandf.co.uk. **Co-sponsors:** Academy of Human Resource Development; University Forum for Human Resource Development; Euresform.

658.3 USA ISSN 1044-8004
HF5549.15 CODEN: HRDQER
➤ **HUMAN RESOURCE DEVELOPMENT QUARTERLY.** Text in English. 1990. q. USD 256 domestic to institutions; USD 296 in Canada & Mexico to institutions; USD 330 elsewhere to institutions; USD 282 combined subscription domestic to institutions print & online eds.; USD 322 combined subscription in Canada & Mexico to institutions print & online eds.; USD 356 combined subscription elsewhere to institutions print & online eds. (effective 2006). bk.rev. Index. back issues avail.; reprint service avail. from PSC. **Document type:** *Journal, Academic/Scholarly.* **Description:** Draws together the work of scholars and practitioners in a range of related areas, including training, management, industrial psychology, organizational behavior and adult education. Presents a comprehensive resource for information on the latest advances in human resource development theory and research.
Related titles: Microfiche ed.: (from PQC); Online - full text ed.: ISSN 1532-1096. USD 256 (effective 2006) (from EBSCO Publishing, Northern Light Technology, Inc., O C L C Online Computer Library Center, Inc., ProQuest Information & Learning, Swets Information Services, Wiley InterScience).
Indexed: ABIn, BPI, BusEdI, CIJE, Emerald, JEL, PsycInfo, PsycholAb, QAb, SOPODA, T&DA, e-psyche.
—BLDSC (4336.432800), IE, Infotrieve, ingenta. **CCC.**
Published by: (American Society for Training & Development), Jossey-Bass Inc., Publishers (Subsidiary of: John Wiley & Sons, Inc.), 989 Market St, San Francisco, CA 94103-1741. TEL 415-433-1740, 888-378-2537, FAX 415-433-0499, jbsubs@jbp.com, http://www.josseybass.com/WileyCDA/WileyTitle/productCd-HRDQ.html. Ed. Darlene F Russ-Eft. Circ: 12,000 (paid). **Co-sponsor:** Academy of Human Resource Development.

351.73 371.43 USA ISSN 1534-4843
HF5549.15
HUMAN RESOURCE DEVELOPMENT REVIEW. Text in English. 2002. q. USD 334, GBP 215 to institutions; USD 347, GBP 224 combined subscription to institutions print & online eds. (effective 2006). **Document type:** *Journal, Academic/Scholarly.* **Description:** Publishes articles that make theoretical contributions in papers devoted to theory development, foundations of HRD, theory building methods, and integrative reviews of the literature.
Related titles: Online - full text ed.: ISSN 1552-6712. USD 330, GBP 213 to institutions (effective 2006) (from C S A, EBSCO Publishing, O C L C Online Computer Library Center, Inc., ProQuest Information & Learning, Sage Publications, Inc., Swets Information Services).
Indexed: ABIn, HRA.
—BLDSC (4336.432810), IE. **CCC.**

Published by: Sage Publications, Inc., 2455 Teller Rd, Thousand Oaks, CA 91320. TEL 805-499-0721, 800-818-7243, FAX 805-499-0871, 800-583-2665, info@sagepub.com, http://www.sagepub.com/journal.aspx?pid=282. Ed. Richard Torraco. **Subscr. to:** Sage Publications Ltd., 1 Oliver's Yard, 55 City Rd, London EC1 1SP, United Kingdom. TEL 44-20-73740645, FAX 44-20-73748741, subscription@sagepub.co.uk.

658.3 BHR
▼ **HUMAN RESOURCE MAGAZINE.** Text in English. 2003 (Oct.-Dec.). q. **Document type:** *Magazine, Trade.*
Published by: Bahrain Society for Training and Development, PO Box 11435, Manama, Bahrain. TEL 973-825518, FAX 973-825517, bstd@batelco.com.bh, http://www.bstd.com.bh/.

658.3 USA ISSN 0090-4848
HF5549.A2 CODEN: HRMAFP
➤ **HUMAN RESOURCE MANAGEMENT.** Text in English. 1961. q. USD 665 domestic; USD 705 in Canada & Mexico; USD 739 elsewhere; USD 732 combined subscription domestic print & online eds.; USD 772 combined subscription in Canada & Mexico print & online eds.; USD 806 combined subscription elsewhere print & online eds. (effective 2006). adv. bk.rev. illus. Index. back issues avail.; reprint service avail. from PQC,PSC. **Document type:** *Journal, Academic/Scholarly.* **Description:** Discusses new theories, techniques, case studies, models and research trends of significance to practicing managers.
Formerly (until 1971): Management of Personnel Quarterly (0025-1852)
Related titles: Microform ed.: (from PQC); Online - full text ed.: ISSN 1099-050X. USD 665 (effective 2006) (from EBSCO Publishing, ProQuest Information & Learning, Swets Information Services, Wiley InterScience).
Indexed: ABIn, ADPA, ASCA, ASEANManA, AgeL, BPI, BPIA, BusI, CINAHL, CPM, CurCont, EAA, ESPM, Emerald, FamI, H&SSA, HRA, ISAP, MEDLINE, ManagCont, PAIS, PSI, PersLit, PsycInfo, PsycholAb, RASB, RefZh, SCIMP, SSCI, T&DA, T&II.
—BLDSC (4336.433000), CISTI, IDS, IE, Infotrieve, ingenta. **CCC.**
Published by: John Wiley & Sons, Inc., 111 River St, Hoboken, NJ 07030-5774. TEL 201-748-6000, FAX 201-748-5915, uscs-wis@wiley.com, http://www.wiley.com/WileyCDA/WileyTitle/productCd-HRM.html. Ed. Mark Huselid. adv.: B&W page GBP 640, color page GBP 1,515; trim 210 x 279. **Subscr. to:** John Wiley & Sons Ltd., The Atrium, Southern Gate, Chichester, West Sussex PO19 8SQ, United Kingdom. TEL 44-1243-779777, FAX 44-1243-775878, cs-journals@wiley.co.uk.

658.3 GBR ISSN 0967-0734
HF5549.A2
HUMAN RESOURCE MANAGEMENT INTERNATIONAL DIGEST; incorporating Management Development Review. Text in English. 1993. bi-m. EUR 7,948.54 in Europe; USD 8,059 in North America; AUD 10,569 in Australasia; GBP 5,566.91 in UK & elsewhere (effective 2006). reprint service avail. from PSC. **Document type:** *Journal, Academic/Scholarly.* **Description:** Covers all aspects of human resource management in all types of organization, with the emphasis on international experience for the widest possible scope.
Incorporates (1987-1998): Management Development Review; Which incorporated (1993-1996): Financial Services Training Journal (0967-4969); Formerly (until 1993): Target Management Development Review (0962-2519)
Related titles: Online - full text ed.: 2002 (from EBSCO Publishing, Emerald Group Publishing Limited, Gale Group, IngentaConnect, O C L C Online Computer Library Center, Inc., ProQuest Information & Learning, Swets Information Services).
Indexed: ABIn, EmerIntel, M&MA, TEA.
—BLDSC (4336.434045), IE, Infotrieve, ingenta. **CCC.**
Published by: Emerald Group Publishing Limited, 60-62 Toller Ln, Bradford, W Yorks BD8 9BY, United Kingdom. TEL 44-1274-777700, FAX 44-1274-785200, infomation@emeraldinsight.com, http://www.emeraldinsight.com/hrmid.htm. Ed. David Pollitt. **Subscr. addr. in N America:** Emerald Group Publishing Ltd., 44 Brattle St, 4th Fl, Cambridge, MA 02138.

658.3 GBR ISSN 0954-5395
➤ **HUMAN RESOURCE MANAGEMENT JOURNAL.** Text in English. 198?. q. GBP 120 domestic to individuals & charities; GBP 135 foreign to individuals & charities; GBP 185 domestic to institutions; GBP 200 foreign to institutions; GBP 165 domestic educational institutions; GBP 180 foreign educational institutions (effective 2005); includes online access. bk.rev. 96 p./no.; **Document type:** *Journal, Academic/Scholarly.* **Description:** Covers topics in human resources management for practitioners and academics.
Related titles: Online - full text ed.: (from bigchalk, EBSCO Publishing, Gale Group, IngentaConnect, Northern Light Technology, Inc., O C L C Online Computer Library Center, Inc., ProQuest Information & Learning).
Indexed: ABIn, Emerald, Inspec, M&MA.
—BLDSC (4336.434050), IE, Infotrieve, ingenta. **CCC.**

Published by: I R S (Subsidiary of: LexisNexis UK (Scottish Office)), 18-20 Highbury Pl, London, N5 1QP, United Kingdom. TEL 44-20-7354-6742, 44-20-7354-5858, FAX 44-20-7226-8618, 44-20-7359-4000, publications@irseclipse.co.uk, http://www.irseclipse.co.uk/pub_subjects/index_pub_human.htm. Ed. John Purcell. **Co-publishers:** Personnel Publications Ltd.; Permanent Press.

658.3 USA
HUMAN RESOURCE MANAGEMENT NEWS; the weekly newsletter for the human resource management field. Text in English. 1951. s-m. USD 295; USD 345 foreign (effective 1999). charts; stat. index. back issues avail. **Document type:** *Newsletter.* **Description:** Contains HR news, trends and technology since 1951. Now includes "What's Ahead in HR" as a regular feature.
Formerly: Industrial Relations News (0019-8714)
Related titles: Online - full text ed.
Published by: Kennedy Information Inc., One Kennedy Place, Rte 12 S, Fitzwilliam, NH 03447. TEL 212-972-3793, 800-531-0007, FAX 212-972-1002, hrmn-editor@kennedyinfo.com, http://www.kennedyinfo.com. Ed. Stephanie Overman. Pub. David Beck.

658.3 GBR ISSN 1053-4822
HF5549.2.U5 CODEN: HRMRE7
➤ **HUMAN RESOURCE MANAGEMENT REVIEW.** Text in English. 1991. 4/yr. EUR 123 in Europe to individuals; JPY 16,200 in Japan to individuals; USD 136 to individuals except Europe and Japan; EUR 375 in Europe to institutions; JPY 49,700 in Japan to institutions; USD 419 to institutions except Europe and Japan (effective 2006). back issues avail. **Document type:** *Journal, Academic/Scholarly.* **Description:** Publishes conceptual and theoretical articles pertaining to human resource management and allied fields.
Related titles: Microform ed.: (from PQC); Online - full text ed.: (from EBSCO Publishing, Gale Group, IngentaConnect, ScienceDirect, Swets Information Services).
Indexed: ABIn, ASCA, AgeL, CurCont, Inspec, PsycInfo, PsycholAb, SOPODA, SSCI, e-psyche.
—BLDSC (4336.434100), IE, Infotrieve, ingenta. **CCC.**
Published by: Pergamon (Subsidiary of: Elsevier Science & Technology), The Boulevard, Langford Ln, East Park, Kidlington, Oxford OX5 1GB, United Kingdom. TEL 44-1865-843000, FAX 44-1865-843010, http://www.elsevier.com/locate/hrmr. Ed. Rodger W. Griffeth. **Subscr. to:** Elsevier BV, PO Box 211, Amsterdam 1000 AE, Netherlands. TEL 31-20-485-3757, FAX 31-20-485-3432, nlinfo-f@elsevier.nl, http://www.elsevier.nl.

658.3 GBR ISSN 0957-6142
HUMAN RESOURCE MANAGER. Text in English. 1989. 2/yr. free. bk.rev. **Document type:** *Trade.* **Description:** Covers topical issues concerning payroll, personnel and pensions administration in the U.K., as well as related issues.
Formed by the merger of (1981-1988): Payroll Manager (0262-981X); Personnel Matters
Address: Thorpe Park, Peterborough Rd, Peterborough, Cambs PE7 3BY, United Kingdom. TEL 44-1733-555777, FAX 44-1733-312347. Ed. Diana Probert. R&P Liz Phillips. Circ: 6,000 (controlled).

658.3 USA ISSN 0199-8986
HF5549.5.M3 CODEN: EJUPEK
HUMAN RESOURCE PLANNING. Text in English. 1978. q. USD 150 to non-members; USD 37.50 per issue to non-members; free to members (effective 2005). adv. bk.rev. illus. Index. back issues avail.; reprints avail. **Document type:** *Magazine, Trade.* **Description:** Contains current theory, research and practice in strategic human resource management. Focuses on the HR practices that contribute to the achievement of organizational effectiveness.
Related titles: Microfilm ed.; Online - full text ed.: (from EBSCO Publishing, Florida Center for Library Automation, Gale Group, H.W. Wilson, Northern Light Technology, Inc., O C L C Online Computer Library Center, Inc., ProQuest Information & Learning).
Indexed: ABIn, BPI, BPIA, CPM, Emerald, PersLit, T&II.
—BLDSC (4336.434500), IE, Infotrieve, ingenta.
Published by: Human Resource Planning Society, 317 Madison Ave, Ste 1509, New York, NY 10017. TEL 212-490-6387, FAX 212-682-6851, info@hrps.org, http://www.hrps.org/publications/planning.shtml. Ed., Adv. contact Beverly Bachtle Pinzon. Circ: 3,500 (paid).

658.3 USA ISSN 1540-8027
HUMAN RESOURCES 21. Text in English. 2002 (Aug.). 23/yr. USD 399 (effective 2002).
Published by: Business 21 Publishing, 477 Baltimore Pike, Springfield, PA 19064. TEL 484-479-2700, FAX 610-543-2292. Ed. Louis Greenstein. Pub. Stephen Meyer.

HUMAN RESOURCES ABSTRACTS; an international information service. see *BUSINESS AND ECONOMICS—Abstracting, Bibliographies, Statistics*

331.12 CAN ISSN 1492-6032
HUMAN RESOURCES ADVISOR NEWSLETTER (ATLANTIC EDITION). Text in English. 1999. base vol. plus bi-m. updates. looseleaf. CND 363.80 combined subscription for print ed. base vol. plus updates (effective 2002). 500 p./no.; **Document type:** *Trade.*
Related titles: CD-ROM ed.: 2002; ◆ Regional ed(s).: Human Resources Advisor Newsletter (Ontario Edition). ISSN 1203-1151; ◆ Human Resources Advisor Newsletter (Western Edition). ISSN 1206-8977.
Published by: First Reference, Inc., 50 Viceroy Rd, Unit 1, Concord, ON L4K 3A7, Canada. TEL 905-761-7305, 800-750-8175, FAX 905-761-7306, info@firstreference.com, http://www.firstreference.com/frhome.htm.

331.12 CAN ISSN 1203-1151
HUMAN RESOURCES ADVISOR NEWSLETTER (ONTARIO EDITION). Text in English. 1995. base vol. plus bi-m. updates. looseleaf. CND 363.80 combined subscription for print ed. base vol. & updates; CND 461.55 combined subscription for CD-ROM & print eds. base vol. & updates (effective 2002). Index. 500 p./no.; **Document type:** *Trade.*
Related titles: CD-ROM ed.: CND 391 per issue (effective 2002); Online - full text ed.: (from Micromedia ProQuest); ◆ Regional ed(s).: Human Resources Advisor Newsletter (Western Edition). ISSN 1206-8977; ◆ Human Resources Advisor Newsletter (Atlantic Edition). ISSN 1492-6032.
Published by: First Reference, Inc., 50 Viceroy Rd, Unit 1, Concord, ON L4K 3A7, Canada. TEL 905-761-7305, 800-750-8175, FAX 905-761-7306, info@firstreference.com, http://www.firstreference.com/frhome.htm.

331.12 CAN ISSN 1206-8977
HUMAN RESOURCES ADVISOR NEWSLETTER (WESTERN EDITION). Text in English. 1997. base vol. plus bi-m. updates. looseleaf. CND 363.80 combined subscription for print ed. base vol. plus 6 months subscr. of updates. **Document type:** *Trade.*
Related titles: Online - full text ed.: (from Micromedia ProQuest); ◆ Regional ed(s).: Human Resources Advisor Newsletter (Ontario Edition). ISSN 1203-1151; ◆ Human Resources Advisor Newsletter (Atlantic Edition). ISSN 1492-6032.
Published by: First Reference, Inc., 50 Viceroy Rd, Unit 1, Concord, ON L4K 3A7, Canada. TEL 905-761-7305, 800-750-8175, FAX 905-761-7306, info@firstreference.com, http://www.firstreference.com/frhome.htm.

658.3 USA
HUMAN RESOURCES GUIDE. Text in English. base vol. plus m. updates. looseleaf. USD 400. **Document type:** *Trade.* **Description:** Provides answers and practical guidance on employment issues from hiring, termination, and union-management relations to compensation, benefits, work rules and discipline, and safety and health. Includes information on state laws.
Published by: W G & L Financial Reporting & Management Research (Subsidiary of: R I A), 395 Hudson St, New York, NY 10014. TEL 212-367-6300, FAX 212-367-6718, http://www.InsideHR.com. Ed. Rodney Eubanks. **Subscr. to:** The Park Square Bldg., The Park Square Bldg, 31 St. James Ave, Boston, MA 02116-4101. TEL 800-950-1207.

658.3 USA
▼ **HUMAN RESOURCES INNOVATOR.** Abbreviated title: H R Innovator. Text in English. 2003. 6/yr. free (effective 2003). **Document type:** *Magazine, Trade.*
Published by: Innovator Media, LLC, 112 Titus Mill Rd, Pennington, NJ 08534. TEL 609-818-9301, FAX 609-818-9218, http://www.hrinnovator.com/s. Ed. Matt Damsker. Pub. Bill Corsini.

658.3 USA ISSN 1094-3072
HUMAN RESOURCES LIBRARY. Text in English. 1993. m. USD 21.52 (effective 2005). **Document type:** *Trade.* **Description:** Provides regularly updated information on policies, laws, and regulations, as well as expert analyses and guidance.
Media: CD-ROM. **Related titles:** Online - full content ed.: ISSN 1528-0225. USD 17.95 (effective 2005); Online - full text ed.: (from The Bureau of National Affairs, Inc.).
—**CCC.**
Published by: B N A Inc. (Subsidiary of: The Bureau of National Affairs, Inc.), 1231 25th St, NW, Washington, DC 20037. TEL 202-452-4343, FAX 202-452-4997, customercare@bna.com, http://www.bna.com/products/hr/hrlw.htm.

658.3 USA
HUMAN RESOURCES LIBRARY (LAWYERS' EDITION). Text in English. m. **Document type:** *Trade.* **Description:** Provides regularly updated information on policies, laws, regulations, and cases, as well as expert analyses and guidance, for human resources professionals, employment attorneys, corporate legal departments, and anyone who writes or reviews employment policies.
Media: CD-ROM. **Related titles:** Online - full content ed.
Published by: B N A Inc. (Subsidiary of: The Bureau of National Affairs, Inc.), 1231 25th St, NW, Washington, DC 20037. TEL 202-452-4343, FAX 202-452-4997, customercare@bna.com, http://www.bna.com/products/hr/hlaw.htm.

331.21 USA ISSN 0745-063X
HUMAN RESOURCES MANAGEMENT - COMPENSATION. Text in English. 1981. 2 base vols. plus m. updates. looseleaf. USD 529 base vol(s). print or online or CD-ROM ed. (effective 2004). **Description:** Provides access to a wide range of compensation problems faced by personnel professionals. Includes the full text of federal wage laws and key regulations.
Related titles: CD-ROM ed.; Online - full text ed.; Series of: Human Resources Management Library.
Published by: C C H Inc., 2700 Lake Cook Rd, Riverwoods, IL 60015. TEL 847-267-7000, 800-449-6439, cust_serv@cch.com, http://www.cch.com. Pub. Catherine Wolfe.

658.3 USA ISSN 0745-2179
HUMAN RESOURCES MANAGEMENT - EMPLOYMENT RELATIONS. Text in English. 1981. 2 base vols. plus m. updates. looseleaf. USD 529 base vol(s). print or online or CD-ROM ed. (effective 2004). **Description:** Covers reliable explanations on employers' right to discharge employees plus other issues affecting both union/management relations as well as a nonunion workplace.
Related titles: CD-ROM ed.; Online - full text ed.; Series of: Human Resources Management Library.
Published by: C C H Inc., 2700 Lake Cook Rd, Riverwoods, IL 60015. TEL 847-267-7000, 800-449-6439, cust_serv@cch.com, http://www.cch.com. Pub. Catherine Wolfe.

HUMAN RESOURCES MANAGEMENT - O S H A COMPLIANCE. see *OCCUPATIONAL HEALTH AND SAFETY*

658.3 USA ISSN 0745-0621
HUMAN RESOURCES MANAGEMENT - PERSONNEL PRACTICES & COMMUNICATIONS. Text in English. 2 base vols. plus m. updates. looseleaf. USD 529 base vol(s). print or online or CD-ROM ed. (effective 2004). **Description:** Practical "how to" help for developing, implementing and communicating workable HR policies to HR professionals. Includes sample HR policies, checklists, step-by-step procedures.
Related titles: CD-ROM ed.; Online - full text ed.; Series of: Human Resources Management Library.
Published by: C C H Inc., 2700 Lake Cook Rd, Riverwoods, IL 60015. TEL 847-267-7000, 800-449-6439, cust_serv@cch.com, http://www.cch.com. Pub. Catherine Wolfe.

658.3 CAN
HUMAN RESOURCES POLICYPRO (ONTARIO EDITION). Text in English. base vol. plus bi-m. updates. looseleaf. CND 396.75 combined subscription for print ed. base vol. plus updates & CD-ROM ed. (effective 2002). **Document type:** *Trade.*
Published by: First Reference, Inc., 50 Viceroy Rd, Unit 1, Concord, ON L4K 3A7, Canada. TEL 905-761-7305, 800-750-8175, FAX 905-761-7306, info@firstreference.com, http://www.firstreference.com/frhome.htm.

658.3 AUS
HUMAN RESOURCES REPORT. Text in English. fortn. AUD 425 (effective 1999). **Document type:** *Newsletter.* **Description:** Analyzes trends in employment and human resources management.
Published by: Newsletter Information Services, PO Box 2095, Manly, NSW 2095, Australia. TEL 61-2-9977-7500, FAX 61-2-9977-3310, customer.support@newsinfo.com.au, http://www.newsinfo.com.au. Ed. Peter Schwab.

658.3 USA ISSN 0073-3873
HUMAN RESOURCES RESEARCH ORGANIZATION. PROFESSIONAL PAPERS★ . Text in English. 1966. irreg. free.
Related titles: Microform ed.: 1966 (from NTI).
Indexed: PsycholAb.
Published by: Human Resources Research Organization, 66 Canal Center Plaza, Ste 400, Alexandria, VA 22314. TEL 703-549-3611.

HUMANISME ET ENTREPRISE; revue informant des problemes humains, sociaux et economiques dans l'entreprise. see *BUSINESS AND ECONOMICS—Labor And Industrial Relations*

658.3 331 USA ISSN 1073-4627
HF5549.2.U5
HUNT - SCANLON'S SELECT GUIDE TO HUMAN RESOURCE EXECUTIVES. Text in English. 1992. a. USD 269 (effective 2002). **Document type:** *Directory.*
Formerly (until 1994): Hunt - Scanlon's Directory of Human Resource Executives (1067-4462)
Published by: Hunt - Scanlon Publishing Co., Inc., 20 Signal Rd, Stamford, CT 06902. TEL 203-629-3629, FAX 203-629-3701, http://www.hunt-scanlon.com/shop.

658.3 USA ISSN 1089-991X
HF5549.A2
➤ **I H R I M - LINK.** Text in English. 1996. bi-m. subscr. incld. with memebership. **Document type:** *Journal, Academic/Scholarly.*
Formed by the 1996 merger of: Association of Human Resource Systems Professionals. Review (1075-2986); Canadian Association of Human Resource Systems Professionals Resource
Published by: International Association for Human Resource Information Management, PO Box 1086, Burlington, MA 01803. TEL 512-453-6363, 800-946-6363, FAX 781-998-8011, moreinfo@ihrim.org, http://www.ihrim.org/pubonline/link/index.asp. R&P Kevin Miles. Circ: 6,000 (paid).

658.3 USA
HD4926
I O M A'S COMPLETE GUIDE TO BEST PRACTICES IN PERFORMANCE MANAGEMENT. Text in English. 1996. q. USD 274.95 combined subscription in US & Canada print & online eds.; USD 293 combined subscription elsewhere print & online eds. (effective 2006). back issues avail. **Document type:** *Newsletter, Trade.* **Description:** Helps HR and compensation executives improve their company's productivity through the use of variable pay and bonus programs for all types of employees.
Formerly: I O M A's Pay for Performance Report (1086-9581)
Related titles: Online - full text ed.: (from EBSCO Publishing, Florida Center for Library Automation, Gale Group, LexisNexis, O C L C Online Computer Library Center, Inc., ProQuest Information & Learning); ◆ Cumulative ed(s).: Pay for Performance Report Yearbook.
Indexed: ABIn.
—CCC.
Published by: Institute of Management & Administration, Inc., 3 Park Ave, New York, NY 10016-5902. TEL 212-244-0360, FAX 212-564-0465, subserve@ioma.com, http://www.ioma.com. Ed. Ann Podolske. R&P Sofie Kourkoutakis.

658.3 USA ISSN 1092-5910
I O M A'S HUMAN RESOURCES DEPARTMENT MANAGEMENT REPORT. Variant title: Human Resource Department Management Report. Text in English. 1997. m. USD 268.95 in US & Canada print & online eds.; USD 283 elsewhere print & online eds. (effective 2005). software rev. back issues avail. **Document type:** *Newsletter, Trade.* **Description:** Shows HR department heads how to boost staff motivation and productivity, improve departmental automation and cut costs while improving service. Provides salary data, budget advice, new automation evaluations, and career planning advice, etc.
Related titles: Diskette ed.; E-mail ed.; Online - full content ed.: (from Florida Center for Library Automation); Online - full text ed.: (from EBSCO Publishing, Gale Group, LexisNexis, O C L C Online Computer Library Center, Inc.); ◆ Cumulative ed(s).: Human Resource Department Management Report Yearbook.
—CCC.
Published by: Institute of Management & Administration, Inc., 3 Park Ave, New York, NY 10016-5902. TEL 212-244-0360, FAX 212-564-0465, subserve@ioma.com, http://www.ioma.com. Ed. Susan Patterson. R&P Sofie Kourkoutakis.

658.3 USA ISSN 1068-4239
I O M A'S REPORT ON COMPENSATION & BENEFITS FOR LAW OFFICES. Variant title: Compensation & Benefits for Law Offices. Text in English. 1990. m. looseleaf. USD 278.95 in US & Canada; USD 293 elsewhere (effective 2006). index. back issues avail. **Document type:** *Newsletter, Trade.* **Description:** Looks to keep compensation to lawyers and support staff competitive. Shows how to contain benefits, training and recruiting costs. Covers health and life insurance, 401K plans and other deferred compensation programs, HMOs and PPOs, COBRA, flexible spending accounts, etc.
Former titles (until 1993): I O M A's Report on Controlling Benefits Costs for Law, Design, C P A and Other Professional Services Firms (1062-7936); (until 1992): Professional Service Firms Report on Controlling Benefits and Deferred Compensation (1053-5349)
Related titles: Diskette ed.; E-mail ed.; Online - full content ed.; Online - full text ed.: (from EBSCO Publishing, LexisNexis, ProQuest Information & Learning).
Indexed: ABIn.
—CCC.
Published by: Institute of Management & Administration, Inc., 3 Park Ave, New York, NY 10016-5902. TEL 212-244-0360, FAX 212-564-0465, subserve@ioma.com, http://www.ioma.com. Ed. Lisa Isom-Rodriguez. Pub. Lee Rath. R&P Sofie Kourkoutakis.

658.3 USA ISSN 1059-2741
I O M A'S REPORT ON MANAGING 401K PLANS. Text in English. 1992. m. looseleaf. USD 291.95 combined subscription in US & Canada print & online eds.; USD 303 combined subscription elsewhere print & online eds. (effective 2006). back issues avail. **Document type:** *Newsletter, Trade.* **Description:** Covers how-to techniques for getting the maximum benefit from 401(k) plans while keeping costs to a minimum. Shows how to adminster plans with less effort and how to reduce fiduciary liability. Includes surveys, trends, new products and service legislation.
Related titles: Diskette ed.; E-mail ed.; Online - full text ed.: (from EBSCO Publishing, Florida Center for Library Automation, Gale Group, O C L C Online Computer Library Center, Inc., ProQuest Information & Learning); ◆ Cumulative ed(s).: Managing 401k Plans Yearbook.
Indexed: ABIn, BLI.
—CCC.
Published by: Institute of Management & Administration, Inc., 3 Park Ave, New York, NY 10016-5902. TEL 212-244-0360, FAX 212-564-0465, subserve@ioma.com, http://www.ioma.com. Ed. Rebecca Morrow. Pub. Perry Patterson. R&P Sofie Kourkoutakis.

658.3 USA ISSN 1098-5662
I O M A'S REPORT ON MANAGING BENEFITS PLANS. Text in English. 1991. m. looseleaf. USD 271.95 in US & Canada print & online eds.; USD 283 elsewhere print & online eds. (effective 2006). index. back issues avail. **Document type:** *Newsletter, Trade.* **Description:** Examines cost reduction strategies for HR, benefits managers in corporate environments.
Formerly: I O M A's Report on Reducing Benefits Costs (1056-7984)
Related titles: Diskette ed.; E-mail ed.; Online - full content ed.; Online - full text ed.: (from EBSCO Publishing, Florida Center for Library Automation, Gale Group, LexisNexis, O C L C Online Computer Library Center, Inc., ProQuest Information & Learning); ◆ Cumulative ed(s).: Managing Benefits Plans Yearbook.
Indexed: ABIn.
—CCC.
Published by: Institute of Management & Administration, Inc., 3 Park Ave, New York, NY 10016-5902. TEL 212-244-0360, FAX 212-564-0465, subserve@ioma.com, http://www.ioma.com/products/prod_detail.php?prodid=5. Ed. Rebecca Morrow. Pub. Perry Patterson.

658.3 USA ISSN 1526-7164
HF5549
I O M A'S REPORT ON MANAGING TRAINING & DEVELOPMENT. Text in English. 1999. m. USD 248.95 in US & Canada print & online eds.; USD 263 elsewhere print & online eds. (effective 2005). **Document type:** *Newsletter, Trade.* **Description:** Covers the latest news and developments on learning and performance development for training managers, including cost-control, budgeting, training options, and ways to reduce course failure and increase new hire retention rates.
Related titles: Online - full text ed.: (from EBSCO Publishing, Gale Group, O C L C Online Computer Library Center, Inc.); ◆ Cumulative ed(s).: Managing Training & Development Yearbook.
—CCC.
Published by: Institute of Management & Administration, Inc., 3 Park Ave, New York, NY 10016-5902. TEL 212-244-0360, FAX 212-564-0465, subserve@ioma.com, http://www.ioma.com/products/prod_detail.php?prodid=6. Ed. Susan Patterson.

331.21 USA ISSN 1067-4551
I O M A'S REPORT ON SALARY SURVEYS. Text in English. 1993. m. looseleaf. USD 281.95 in US & Canada print & online eds.; USD 293 elsewhere print & online eds. (effective 2006). index. back issues avail. **Document type:** *Newsletter, Trade.* **Description:** Survey data and guidance on setting and managing compensation.
Related titles: Diskette ed.; E-mail ed.; Online - full content ed.; Online - full text ed.: (from EBSCO Publishing, Gale Group, LexisNexis, O C L C Online Computer Library Center, Inc., ProQuest Information & Learning); ◆ Cumulative ed(s).: Report on Salary Surveys Yearbook.
Indexed: ABIn.
—CCC.
Published by: Institute of Management & Administration, Inc., 3 Park Ave, New York, NY 10016-5902. TEL 212-244-0360, FAX 212-564-0465, subserve@ioma.com, http://www.ioma.com/products/prod_detail.php?prodid=9. Ed. Laime Vaitkus. Pub. Perry Patterson.

658.3 USA
I P M A NEWS. Text in English. 1935. m. adv. illus. **Document type:** *Newsletter.* **Description:** News articles on national developments in the public personnel field.
Formerly: International Personnel Management Association. Personnel News (0031-5788)
Published by: International Personnel Management Association, 1617 Duke St, Alexandria, VA 22314. TEL 703-549-7100, FAX 703-684-0948, publications@ipma-hr.org, http://www.ipma-hr.org. Ed., Adv. contact Karen Smith. Circ: 6,000.

658.3 GBR ISSN 1362-4997
I R S MANAGEMENT REVIEW; using human resources to achieve strategic objectives. (Industrial Relations Services) Text in English. 1996. q. GBP 325 domestic; GBP 335 foreign; GBP 145 newsstand/cover (effective 2001). **Document type:** *Trade.* **Description:** Provides information on the effects of, and reasons behind, many current management practices, containing research and named case studies.
Related titles: Online - full content ed.; Online - full text ed.: (from EBSCO Publishing).
—BLDSC (4581.699000).
Published by: Eclipse Group Ltd. (Subsidiary of: LexisNexis UK (Scottish Office)), 18-20 Highbury Place, London, N5 1QP, United Kingdom. TEL 44-20-7354-5858, publications@irseclipse.co.uk, http://www.irseclipse.co.uk. Ed. Paul Suff.

658.3 USA
I T A A COMPENSATION AND NON-CASH BENEFITS SURVEYS. Text in English. a. price varies.

Published by: Information Technology Association of America, 1401 Wilson Blvd., Ste. 1100, Arlington, VA 22209-2318. TEL 703-522-5055, FAX 703-525-2279. **Subscr. to:** c/o William M. Mercer, The National Survey Group, 1417 Lake Cook Rd, Deerfield, IL 60015. TEL 800-333-3070.

658.3   GBR   ISSN 0954-7940
I T TRAINING. (Information Technology) Text in English. 1989. 6/yr. GBP 37 domestic; GBP 46 in Europe; GBP 66 elsewhere (effective 2001). adv. tr.lit. **Document type:** *Magazine, Trade.* **Description:** Discusses challenges and problems trainers in the computer profession are likely to encounter.
Related titles: Online - full text ed.: (from EBSCO Publishing, ProQuest Information & Learning).
Indexed: BrEdI.
—BLDSC (4587.680000).
Published by: Haymarket Business Publications Ltd., 174 Hammersmith Rd, London, W6 7JP, United Kingdom. TEL 44-20-8267-4419, FAX 44-20-8267-4927, ittraining.sales@haynet.com, http://www.train-net.co.uk. Ed. Donna Murphy. Adv. contact Ben Guynan. Circ: 10,000.

IDEAS AND SOLUTIONS; magazine for businesses, products and services. see *BUSINESS AND ECONOMICS—Production Of Goods And Services*

IMPACT (AURORA); labour law & management practices. see *BUSINESS AND ECONOMICS—Labor And Industrial Relations*

IN DEPTH (NEW YORK); report to management. see *BUSINESS AND ECONOMICS—Labor And Industrial Relations*

658.3   CHE
INDEX. Text in German. m. adv. **Document type:** *Trade.*
Published by: Mapag Marketing Pool AG, Redingstr 20, Postfach, Basel, 4028, Switzerland. TEL 061-3128888, FAX 061-3128884. Ed. Heinz Werner. Adv. contact Ruth Nebiker. B&W page CHF 3,400, color page CHF 4,900; trim 250 x 184. Circ: 10,500.

658.3   IND   ISSN 0970-3330
➤ **INDIAN JOURNAL OF TRAINING & DEVELOPMENT.** Text in English. 1971. q. INR 150, USD 30. adv. bk.rev. **Document type:** *Academic/Scholarly.* **Description:** Leading professional journal devoted to the cause of human resources.
Former titles (until 1977): Training and Development (0970-3322); (until 1976): I S T D Review (0377-029X)
Indexed: CRIA, CRICC, IPsyAb, M&MA, PAA&I.
Published by: Indian Society for Training & Development, B-41, Institutional Area, Behind Qutab Hotel, New Delhi, 110 016, India. TEL 91-11-6867710, FAX 91-11-6867607, islal@ren.02.nic.in. Ed. Krishan C Sethi. Pub., Adv. contact Amrit Lal. Circ: 3,500 (paid).

658.5   GBR   ISSN 0019-7858
HF5549.5.T7   CODEN: ILCTAU
INDUSTRIAL AND COMMERCIAL TRAINING. Text in English. 1969. 7/yr. EUR 10,232.29 in Europe; USD 10,329 in North America; AUD 12,209 in Australasia; GBP 6,882.79 elsewhere (effective 2006). bk.rev. charts; illus. back issues avail.; reprint service avail. from PQC,PSC. **Document type:** *Journal, Academic/Scholarly.* **Description:** Focuses on the practical application of training and development theories and techniques. An information resource for training practitioners.
Related titles: CD-ROM ed.; Microform ed.: (from PQC); Online - full text ed.: (from EBSCO Publishing, Emerald Group Publishing Limited, Gale Group, IngentaConnect, O C L C Online Computer Library Center, Inc., ProQuest Information & Learning, Swets Information Services).
Indexed: ABIn, ADPA, BPIA, BrEdI, BusI, CISA, CPE, ERA, ETA, EmerIntel, Emerald, ErgAb, HECAB, HRA, Inspec, M&MA, MEA, RHEA, SEA, SENA, SOMA, T&DA, TEA, WorkRelAb.
—BLDSC (4444.970000), AskIEEE, IE, Infotrieve, ingenta. **CCC.**
Published by: Emerald Group Publishing Limited, 60-62 Toller Ln, Bradford, W Yorks BD8 9BY, United Kingdom. TEL 44-1274-777700, FAX 44-1274-785200, infomation@emeraldinsight.com, http:// www.emeraldinsight.com/ict.htm. Ed. Mr. Bryan Smith. Pub. Ms. Paula Fernandez. R&P Mr. John Eggleton.

INDUSTRIAL RELATIONS AND MANAGEMENT LETTER. see *BUSINESS AND ECONOMICS—Labor And Industrial Relations*

658   GBR
INDUSTRIAL SOCIETY. BRIEFING PLUS. Text in English. m. **Description:** Bulletin on management and training matters.
Published by: Industrial Society, Robert Hyde House, 48 Bryanston Sq, London, W1HY 7LN, United Kingdom. TEL 44-171-479-2127. Ed. Jill Moreau.

658   USA
INDUSTRY REPORT ON PROFESSIONAL AND SCIENTIFIC PERSONNEL COMPENSATION. Text in English. a. USD 690. charts. **Document type:** *Trade.* **Description:** Industry-by-industry examination of current professional employee compensation rates and policies.
Related titles: ◆ Supplement to: Professional and Scientific Personnel Report - Geographic Edition.

Published by: (Executive Compensation Service (ECS)), Wyatt Data Services, 218 Rte 17 N, Rochelle Park, NJ 07622-9832. TEL 201-843-1177, FAX 201-843-0101.

INDUSTRY REPORT ON SUPERVISORY MANAGEMENT COMPENSATION. see *BUSINESS AND ECONOMICS— Management*

658   USA   ISSN 1063-0058
TA158
INDUSTRY REPORT ON TECHNICIAN AND SKILLED TRADES PERSONNEL COMPENSATION. Text in English. 1992. a. USD 490. charts. **Document type:** *Trade.* **Description:** Technician and skilled trades personnel pay data reviewed from an industry-by-industry point of view.
Related titles: ◆ Supplement(s): Technician and Skilled Trades Personnel Report - Geographic Edition.
Published by: (Executive Compensation Service (ECS)), Wyatt Data Services, 218 Rte 17 N, Rochelle Park, NJ 07622-9832. TEL 201-843-1177, FAX 201-843-0101.

658.3   USA
INFO-NEWS NEWSLETTER. Text in English. m. free. **Document type:** *Newsletter.* **Description:** Includes business success tips, free offers, and business building resources to help you profit online and off.
Media: Online - full text.
Published by: Total Success Solutions, Inc. Ed. Brian Rooney.

658.3   AUS   ISSN 1325-6866
INFORMATION TECHNOLOGY JOB FAMILY REMUNERATION REVIEW. Text in English. 1988. a. AUD 1,350 (effective 1999). **Document type:** *Trade.* **Description:** Provides data on positions in the information technology job family.
Published by: Cullen Egan Dell, Level 8, 50 Bridge St, Sydney, NSW 2000, Australia. TEL 61-2-9375-9800, FAX 61-2-9233-6800. Ed. Paulina Wladdimiro. Circ: 36.

658.3 336   ITA
INFORMATORE PIROLA. Text in Italian. 1964. w. (48/yr.). EUR 227 (effective 2005). bk.rev. **Document type:** *Magazine, Trade.*
Published by: Editrice Il Sole 24 Ore SpA, Via Paolo Lomazzo 52, Milan, 20154, Italy. TEL 39-02-30221, FAX 39-02-312055, info@ilsole24ore.com, http://www.ilsole24ore.com. Circ: 14,500.

658.3   USA
INSIDE OUT (BALTIMORE). Text in English. 2001. w. Free to qualified subscribers. **Document type:** *Newsletter, Trade.* **Description:** Covers workforce issues that affect a company's corporate culture.
Media: E-mail.
Published by: People Notion, PMB 149, 798 Kenilworth Drive, Baltimore, MD 21204. TEL 410-821-3090, 888-799-4369, FAX 410-821-3091, info@peoplenotion.com, http:// www.peoplenotion.com.

658.3   CAN   ISSN 1492-6040
INSIDE POLICIES NEWSLETTER. Text in English. 2000. q. looseleaf. **Document type:** *Newsletter, Trade.*
Published by: First Reference, Inc., 50 Viceroy Rd, Unit 1, Concord, ON L4K 3A7, Canada. TEL 905-761-7305, 800-750-8175, FAX 905-761-7306, info@firstreference.com, http://www.firstreference.com/frhome.htm.

658.3   GBR
INSIGHT (LONDON, 1984); journal of technical and vocational education initiative. Text in English. 1984. 4/yr. free.
Published by: Employment Department, Information Branch, Rm E801, Moorfoot, Sheffield, S Yorks S1 4PQ, United Kingdom. Circ: 55,000.

658.3   AUS   ISSN 1325-6882
INSURANCE INDUSTRY REMUNERATION REVIEW. Text in English. 1985. a. AUD 1,500 (effective 1999). **Document type:** *Trade.* **Description:** Includes remuneration and benefits data for insurance staff with analysis of remuneration and human resources policies and practices.
Published by: Cullen Egan Dell, Level 8, 50 Bridge St, Sydney, NSW 2000, Australia. TEL 61-2-9375-9800, FAX 61-2-9233-6800. Ed. Paulina Wladdmiro. Circ: 25.

INTAND NEWSLETTER; the newsletter of the international network for transactional analysis, neuro-linguistic programming. see *PSYCHOLOGY*

658.3   RUS
INTERFAX. BUSINESS OFFERS/INTERFAX. DELOVYE PREDLOZHENIYA. Text in Russian. m. **Document type:** *Trade.*
Published by: Interfax Ltd., 1-ya Tverskaya-Yamskaya 2, Moscow, 127006, Russian Federation. TEL 7-095-2509840, FAX 7-095-2509727. **US dist. addr.:** East View Information Services, 3020 Harbor Ln. N., Minneapolis, MN 55447. TEL 612-550-0961.

658.3   USA
INTERNATIONAL ASSOCIATION FOR HUMAN RESOURCE INFORMATION MANAGEMENT E-JOURNAL. Text in English. bi-m. **Document type:** *Journal, Trade.* **Description:** Includes reviews of timely articles and books that are of specific interest to current and emerging thought leaders and senior executives in the HR and IT field. In addition, the IHRIM e-Journal also includes interviews with business leaders and strategists with expertise in global industry trends and international business, as well as excerpts from recent surveys and white papers.
Media: Online - full content.
Published by: International Association for Human Resource Information Management, PO Box 1086, Burlington, MA 01803. TEL 512-453-6363, 800-946-6363, FAX 781-998-8011, moreinfo@ihrim.org, http://www.ihrim.org/resources/eJournal/ ejindex.asp.

658.3   USA   ISSN 1098-5565
INTERNATIONAL ASSOCIATION FOR HUMAN RESOURCE INFORMATION MANAGEMENT JOURNAL. Abbreviated title: I H R I M Journal. Text in English. 1997. q. USD 120 to non-members (effective 2004). **Document type:** *Magazine, Trade.* **Description:** Provides information to current and emerging thought leaders and senior management and dedicated to increasing individual and organizational effectiveness in the workplace through visionary and evolving uses of technology.
Published by: International Association for Human Resource Information Management, PO Box 1086, Burlington, MA 01803. TEL 512-453-6363, 800-946-6363, FAX 781-998-8011, moreinfo@ihrim.org, http://www.ihrim.org/pubonline/journal/ index.asp.

658.3 332.6   USA   ISSN 1081-4876
HD4906
INTERNATIONAL H R JOURNAL. (Human Resources) Text in English. 1992. bi-m. **Document type:** *Trade.* **Description:** Analyzes issues in international company human resources management, covering major new laws and regulations that affect international compensation and benefits.
Formerly (until 1995): Journal of International Compensation and Benefits (1068-2309)
—CCC.
Published by: W G & L Financial Reporting & Management Research (Subsidiary of: R I A), 395 Hudson St, New York, NY 10014. TEL 212-367-6300, FAX 212-367-6718, http://www.InsideHR.com. Ed. Charles J Boylan. **Subscr. to:** The Park Square Bldg., 31 St James Ave, Boston, MA 02116-4112. TEL 800-950-1207.

658.3 340.9   USA
INTERNATIONAL HUMAN RESOURCES GUIDE. Text in English. base vol. plus s-a. updates. looseleaf. USD 259. **Document type:** *Trade.* **Description:** Aims to serve as a reference to help H R professionals succeed in the international arena.
Published by: W G & L Financial Reporting & Management Research (Subsidiary of: R I A), 395 Hudson St, New York, NY 10014. TEL 212-367-6300, FAX 212-367-6718, http://www.InsideHR.com. Eds. Elizabeth Shaw, Linda Mark. **Subscr. to:** The Park Square Bldg., 31 St James Ave, Boston, MA 02116-4112. TEL 800-950-1207.

658.3 621.39   GBR   ISSN 1742-7207
▼ **INTERNATIONAL JOURNAL OF COGNITIVE PERFOMANCE SUPPORT.** Text in English. 2005. q. USD 450 to institutions; USD 545 to institutions print & online eds. (effective 2005). **Document type:** *Journal, Academic/Scholarly.* **Description:** Provides a forum and arena for professionals, academics, researchers and software system designers working in the fields of human-machine interaction, engineering, information management, learning and human resource management.
Related titles: Online - full text ed.: ISSN 1742-7215. USD 450 to institutions (effective 2005).
Published by: Inderscience Publishers, IEL Editorial Office, PO Box 735, Olney, Bucks MK46 5WB, United Kingdom. TEL 44-1234-240519, FAX 44-1234-240515, ijcps@inderscience.com, info@inderscience.com, http://www.inderscience.com/ijcps. Ed. Dr. Mohammed A Dorgham. **Subscr. to:** World Trade Centre Bldg, 29 route de Pre-Bois, Case Postale 896, Geneva 15 1215, Switzerland. FAX 41-22-7910885, subs@inderscience.com.

658.3   GBR   ISSN 1470-5958
HD28
➤ **INTERNATIONAL JOURNAL OF CROSS CULTURAL MANAGEMENT.** Text in English. 2001 (Apr.). 3/yr. GBP 230, USD 402 to institutions; GBP 239, USD 419 combined subscription to institutions print & online eds. (effective 2006). **Document type:** *Journal, Academic/Scholarly.* **Description:** Provides new outlet for studies of diversity management alongside organizational culture and international management issues. The journal will be of particular relevance to scholars working in the fields of organizational behaviour, HRM, organizational psychology, international and comparative management and international industrial relations.
Related titles: Online - full text ed.: ISSN 1741-2838. GBP 228, USD 398 to institutions (effective 2006) (from C S A, EBSCO Publishing, O C L C Online Computer Library Center, Inc., ProQuest Information & Learning, Sage Publications, Inc., Swets Information Services).
Indexed: ABIn, CommAb, DIP, HRA, IBR, IBSS, IBZ, IndIslam, PsycInfo, PsycholAb, e-psyche.

▼ *new title*   ➤ *refereed*   ✱ *unverified*   ◆ *full entry avail.*

—BLDSC (4542.179500), IE. **CCC.**
Published by: Sage Publications Ltd. (Subsidiary of: Sage Publications, Inc.), 1 Oliver's Yard, 55 City Rd, London, EC1 1SP, United Kingdom. TEL 44-20-73248500, FAX 44-20-73248600, info@sagepub.co.uk, http://www.sagepub.co.uk/journal.aspx?pid=105590. Eds. Terence Jackson, Zeynep Aycan. **Subscr. in the Americas to:** Sage Publications, Inc., 2455 Teller Rd, Thousand Oaks, CA 91320. TEL 805-499-0721, FAX 805-499-0871, journals@sagepub.com.

658.3 GBR ISSN 0958-5192
HF5549.A2 CODEN: IHMGEH
➤ **INTERNATIONAL JOURNAL OF HUMAN RESOURCE MANAGEMENT.** Text in English. 1990. m. GBP 814, USD 1,310 combined subscription to institutions print & online eds. (effective 2006). back issues avail.; reprint service avail. from PSC. **Document type:** *Journal, Academic/Scholarly.*
Description: Provides a forum for human resource management scholars and professionals.
Related titles: Online - full text ed.: ISSN 1466-4399. GBP 773, USD 1,245 to institutions (effective 2006) (from EBSCO Publishing, Gale Group, IngentaConnect, O C L C Online Computer Library Center, Inc., Swets Information Services).
Indexed: ABIn, BrEdI, CurCont, DIP, Emerald, ErgAb, HRA, IBR, IBSS, IBZ, M&MA, PsycInfo, PsycholAb, SOPODA, SPAA, SSCI.
—BLDSC (4542.288500), IE, Infotrieve, ingenta. **CCC.**
Published by: Routledge (Subsidiary of: Taylor & Francis Group), 4 Park Square, Milton Park, Abingdon, Oxon OX14 4RN, United Kingdom. TEL 44-1235-828600, FAX 44-1235-829000, http://www.tandf.co.uk/journals/titles/09585192.asp, http://www.routledge.co.uk. Ed. Michael Poole. R&P Sally Sweet. **Subscr. to:** Taylor & Francis Ltd, Journals Customer Service, Rankine Rd, Basingstoke, Hants RG24 8PR, United Kingdom. TEL 44-1256-813000, FAX 44-1256-330245, enquiry@tandf.co.uk.

658.3 GBR ISSN 1465-6612
HD4904.7 CODEN: IJHRAZ
➤ **INTERNATIONAL JOURNAL OF HUMAN RESOURCES DEVELOPMENT AND MANAGEMENT.** Abbreviated title: I J H R D M. Text in English. 2001. 4/yr. USD 450; USD 545 combined subscription print & online eds. (effective 2005). **Document type:** *Journal, Academic/Scholarly.* **Description:** Provides a forum for discussion and information on all aspects of human resources development and manangement in manufacturing and services enterprises in a changing and dynamic global environmental.
Related titles: Online - full content ed.: ISSN 1741-5160. USD 450 (effective 2005); Online - full text ed.: (from EBSCO Publishing).
Indexed: ABIn, BrCerAb, C&ISA, CerAb, CorrAb, E&CAJ, EMA, ErgAb, IAA, Inspec, M&TEA, MBF, METADEX, WAA.
—BLDSC (4542.288520), IE, ingenta, Linda Hall.
Published by: Inderscience Publishers, IEL Editorial Office, PO Box 735, Olney, Bucks MK46 5WB, United Kingdom. TEL 44-1234-240519, FAX 44-1234-240515, ijhrdm@inderscience.com, editor@inderscience.com, http://www.inderscience.com/ijhrdm. Ed. Dr. Mohammed A Dorgham. **Subscr. to:** World Trade Centre Bldg, 29 route de Pre-Bois, Case Postale 896, Geneva 15 1215, Switzerland. FAX 41-22-7910885, subs@inderscience.com.

658.3 GBR ISSN 1479-4853
▼ ➤ **INTERNATIONAL JOURNAL OF LEARNING AND INTELLECTUAL CAPITAL.** Text in English. 2004. q. USD 450 to institutions; USD 545 combined subscription to institutions print & online eds. (effective 2005). **Document type:** *Journal, Academic/Scholarly.* **Description:** Provides a selection of new perspectives that collectively articulate a knowledge-based view of strategy management.
Related titles: Online - full text ed.: ISSN 1479-4861. USD 430 (effective 2004) (from EBSCO Publishing).
Indexed: BrCerAb, C&ISA, CerAb, CorrAb, E&CAJ, EMA, IAA, Inspec, M&TEA, MBF, METADEX, WAA.
—BLDSC (4542.314600), IE, Linda Hall.
Published by: Inderscience Publishers, IEL Editorial Office, PO Box 735, Olney, Bucks MK46 5WB, United Kingdom. TEL 44-1234-240519, FAX 44-1234-240515, ijlic@inderscience.com, info@inderscience.com, http://www.inderscience.com/ijlic. Ed. Dr. Patricia Ordonez de Pablos. **Subscr. to:** World Trade Centre Bldg, 29 route de Pre-Bois, Case Postale 896, Geneva 15 1215, Switzerland. FAX 41-22-7910885, subs@inderscience.com.

658.3 GBR ISSN 0965-075X
HF5549.5.S38
➤ **INTERNATIONAL JOURNAL OF SELECTION AND ASSESSMENT.** Text in English. 1993. q. EUR 89 combined subscription in Europe to individuals print & online eds.; USD 99 combined subscription in the Americas to individuals & Caribbean, print & online eds.; GBP 59 combined subscription elsewhere to individuals print & online eds.; USD 627 combined subscription in the Americas to institutions & Caribbean, print & online eds.; GBP 373 combined subscription elsewhere to institutions print & online eds.; EUR 69 combined subscription in Europe to students print & online eds.; USD 77 combined subscription in the Americas to students & Caribbean, print & online eds.; GBP 46 combined subscription elsewhere to students print & online eds. (effective 2006). reprint service avail. from PSC. **Document type:** *Journal, Academic/Scholarly.*
Related titles: Microform ed.: (from PQC); Online - full text ed.: ISSN 1468-2389. 1997. USD 597 in the Americas to institutions & Caribbean; GBP 355 elsewhere to institutions (effective 2006) (from Blackwell Synergy, EBSCO Publishing, Gale Group, IngentaConnect, O C L C Online Computer Library Center, Inc., Swets Information Services).
Indexed: ABIn, ASCA, CurCont, DIP, Emerald, ErgAb, HRA, IBR, IBZ, PsycInfo, PsycholAb, SSCI.
—BLDSC (4542.544640), IDS, IE, Infotrieve, ingenta. **CCC.**
Published by: Blackwell Publishing Ltd., 9600 Garsington Rd, Oxford, OX4 2ZG, United Kingdom. TEL 44-1865-776868, FAX 44-1865-714591, customerservices@oxon.blackwellpublishing.com, http://www.blackwellpublishing.com/journals/IJSA. Eds. Deniz S Ones TEL 612-625-4551, Jesus F Salgado TEL 34-981-563100 ext 13803.

658.3 GBR ISSN 1360-3736
HF5549.5.T7
➤ **INTERNATIONAL JOURNAL OF TRAINING & DEVELOPMENT.** Text in English. 1996. q. EUR 102 combined subscription in Europe to individuals print & online eds.; USD 114 combined subscription in the Americas to individuals & Caribbean (print & online eds.); GBP 68 combined subscription elsewhere to individuals print & online eds.; USD 576 combined subscription in the Americas to institutions & Caribbean (print & online eds.); GBP 342 combined subscription elsewhere to institutions print & online eds.; EUR 54 combined subscription in Europe to students print & online eds.; USD 60 combined subscription in the Americas to students & Cariibean (print & online eds.); GBP 38 combined subscription elsewhere to students print & online eds. (effective 2006). reprint service avail. from PSC. **Document type:** *Journal, Academic/Scholarly.* **Description:** Aims to be an international forum for the reporting of high-quality research, analysis and debate for the benefit of the academic and corporate communities, as well as those engaged in public policy formulation and implementation.
Related titles: Online - full text ed.: ISSN 1468-2419. 1997. USD 511 in the Americas to institutions & Caribbean; GBP 304 elsewhere to institutions (effective 2005) (from Blackwell Synergy, EBSCO Publishing, Gale Group, IngentaConnect, O C L C Online Computer Library Center, Inc., Swets Information Services).
Indexed: ABIn, CIJE, Emerald, ErgAb, M&MA, PsycInfo, PsycholAb.
—BLDSC (4542.695870), IE, Infotrieve, ingenta. **CCC.**
Published by: Blackwell Publishing Ltd., 9600 Garsington Rd, Oxford, OX4 2ZG, United Kingdom. TEL 44-1865-776868, FAX 44-1865-714591, customerservices@oxon.blackwellpublishing.com, http://www.blackwellpublishing.com/journals/IJTD. Eds. William J Rothwell TEL 814-863-2596, Dr. Paul Lewis TEL 44-113-2334511.

658.3 GBR ISSN 1740-8938
➤ **INTERNATIONAL JOURNAL OF WORK ORGANISATION AND EMOTION.** Text in English. q. USD 450 to institutions; USD 545 to institutions print & online eds. (effective 2005). **Document type:** *Journal, Academic/Scholarly.* **Description:** Aims to act as a focal point for the dissemination of theoretical and empirical developments in the area of emotion work and emotional labor.
Related titles: Online - full text ed.: ISSN 1740-8946. USD 450 to institutions (effective 2005).
—BLDSC (4542.701850).
Published by: Inderscience Publishers, IEL Editorial Office, PO Box 735, Olney, Bucks MK46 5WB, United Kingdom. TEL 44-1234-240519, FAX 44-1234-240515, ijwoe@inderscience.com, info@inderscience.com, http://www.inderscience.com/ijwoe. **Subscr. to:** World Trade Centre Bldg, 29 route de Pre-Bois, Case Postale 896, Geneva 15 1215, Switzerland. FAX 41-22-7910885, subs@inderscience.com.

➤ **INTERNATIONAL PRESS CUTTING SERVICE: LABOUR WELFARE - INDUSTRIAL LEGISLATION AND PERSONNEL MANAGEMENT.** see *BUSINESS AND ECONOMICS—Labor And Industrial Relations*

658.3 USA ISSN 0749-2685
HD69.C6
INTERNATIONAL REGISTRY OF ORGANIZATION DEVELOPMENT PROFESSIONALS AND ORGANIZATION DEVELOPMENT HANDBOOK. Text in English. 1973. a., latest vol.28, 2003. USD 30 (effective 2003). 400 p./no.; back issues avail. **Document type:** *Directory.* **Description:** Lists member's credentials, criteria for becoming a registered O.D., descriptions of all O.D. and O.B. academic programs, O.D. networks and the O.D. international code of ethics, a statement on the knowledge and skill necessary to be competent in the field, and a variety of additional information.
Published by: Organization Development Institute, 11234 Walnut Ridge Rd, Chesterland, OH 44026. TEL 440-729-7419, don@odinstitute.org, http://www.odinstitute.org. Ed., R&P, Adv. contact Dr. Donald W Cole TEL 440-729-7419. Circ: 500.

658.3 USA ISSN 0731-4531
INTERNATIONAL SOCIETY OF CERTIFIED EMPLOYEE BENEFIT SPECIALISTS. NEWSBRIEFS. Text in English. 1982. bi-m. membership. bk.rev. abstr. **Document type:** *Newsletter.* **Description:** Contains news of society activities, articles on benefit-related topics, updates on current developments and literature in the field.
Published by: International Society of Certified Employee Benefit Specialists, Inc., 18700 W. Bluemound Rd., PO Box 209, Brookfield, WI 53008-0209. TEL 414-786-8771, FAX 414-786-8650, iscebs@ifebp.org. Ed. Mary Brennan. Circ: 3,800.

INTERNSHIPS. see *OCCUPATIONS AND CAREERS*

658.3 GBR
INTERVIEWER. Text in English. w. GBP 1.50 newsstand/cover. adv. **Document type:** *Trade.* **Description:** Provides current ideas, information and trends in personnel recruitment and management.
Published by: Inside Communications Ltd., One Canada Square, Canary Wharf, London, E14 5AP, United Kingdom. FAX 44-1732-464939, ic@insidecom.co.uk, http://www.insidecom.co.uk. Ed. Rosalind Renshaw. Circ: 30,000.

658.3 GBR ISSN 1472-0361
JOB WATCH. Text in English. 2000. w. adv. **Document type:** *Newspaper, Consumer.*
Published by: Archant Regional Ltd. (Subsidiary of: Archant), Newspaper House, 2 Whalebone Lane S, Dagenham, Essex RM8 1HB, United Kingdom. TEL 44-20-84912000, nigel.websper@archant.co.uk, http://www.archant.co.uk/.

658.3 FRA
JOURNAL AUX SYNDIQUES. Text in French. 10/yr.
Formerly (until 1984): Voix des Employes et Cadres (0766-2793)
Published by: Federation Nationale des Personnels des Organismes Sociales, 263 rue de Paris, Montreuil, Cedex 93515, France. Circ: 50,000.

658.3 FRA ISSN 1268-4368
JOURNAL DE L'ACTION SOCIALE. Text in French. 1995. 10/yr.
Published by: Action Municipale SARL, 17 rue d' Uzes, Paris, Cedex 2 75108, France. TEL 33-1-40133030, FAX 33-1-40135106. Ed. Jean Dumonteil. Pub. Marc N Vigier.

658.3 USA ISSN 1040-9602
HD66
JOURNAL FOR QUALITY AND PARTICIPATION. Text in English. 1978. 6/yr. USD 45 domestic to individual members; USD 65 in Canada to individual members; USD 70 elsewhere to individual members; USD 75 domestic to individuals; USD 85 foreign to individuals; USD 95 to institutions (effective 2005). adv. bk.rev. back issues avail. **Document type:** *Newsletter, Trade.* **Description:** Covers quality management, employee involvement, quality teams and continuous improvement.
Formerly: Quality Circles Journal
Related titles: Online - full content ed.; Online - full text ed.: (from EBSCO Publishing, O C L C Online Computer Library Center, Inc., ProQuest Information & Learning).
Indexed: ABIn, Emerald, QAb, RefZh, T&DA.
—BLDSC (5043.684000), IE, Infotrieve, ingenta. **CCC.**
Published by: American Society for Quality, 600 N Plankinton Ave, Milwaukee, WI 53203. TEL 414-272-8575, 800-248-1946, FAX 414-272-1734, aqp@aqp.org, http://www.asq.org/pub/jqp, http://www.aqp.org. Ed. Ned Hamson. Circ: 11,000.

658.3 USA ISSN 0893-780X
KF3509.A15
JOURNAL OF COMPENSATION & BENEFITS. Text in English. 1937. bi-m. illus. reprints avail. **Document type:** *Trade.* **Description:** Provides analysis of plan design, administration and record keeping, accounting, tax planning, fiduciary responsibilities, employment law affecting benefits, life and health insurance and legislation. Shows how to avoid legal or compliance problems.
Related titles: Online - full text ed.: (from EBSCO Publishing).
Indexed: ABIn, ATI, AgeL, BPI.
—BLDSC (4963.385000), IE, ingenta. **CCC.**
Published by: W G & L Financial Reporting & Management Research (Subsidiary of: R I A), 395 Hudson St, New York, NY 10014. TEL 212-367-6300, FAX 212-367-6718, http://www.InsideHR.com. Ed. Diane Roberts. **Subscr. to:** The Park Square Bldg., 31 St James Ave, Boston, MA 02116-4112. TEL 800-950-1207.

JOURNAL OF DEFERRED COMPENSATION; nonqualified plans and executive compensation. see *BUSINESS AND ECONOMICS—Labor And Industrial Relations*

JOURNAL OF EDUCATION AND WORK. see *EDUCATION—Teaching Methods And Curriculum*

658.3 USA ISSN 1555-5240
HF5549.5.A4
➤ **JOURNAL OF EMPLOYEE ASSISTANCE & WORKPLACE BEHAVIORAL HEALTH.** Abbreviated title: E A Q. Text in English. q. USD 565 combined subscription domestic to institutions print & online eds.; USD 762.75 combined subscription in Canada to institutions print & online eds.; USD 819.25 combined subscription elsewhere to institutions print & online eds. (effective academic year 2005 - 2006). adv. bk.rev. illus. 120 p./no. 1 cols./p.; back issues avail.; reprint service avail. from HAW. **Document type:** *Journal, Academic/Scholarly.* **Description:** Covers development of scholarly and research literature regarding work-based alcoholism programs and the employee assistance movement.
Former titles (until 2005): Employee Assistance Quarterly (0749-0003); (until 1984): Labor Management Alcoholism Journal (0361-1205)
Related titles: Microfiche ed.: (from PQC); Microform ed.; Online - full text ed.: ISSN 1555-5259 (from EBSCO Publishing, O C L C Online Computer Library Center, Inc., Swets Information Services).
Indexed: BibInd, DIP, ExcerpMed, FamI, HRA, IBR, IBZ, IMFL, PAIS, PRA, PsycInfo, PsycholAb, RefZh, SOPODA, SSA, SUSA, SWR&A, SociolAb, V&AA, e-psyche.
—BLDSC (3737.032400), Haworth, IE, ingenta. **CCC.**
Published by: Haworth Press, Inc., 10 Alice St, Binghamton, NY 13904-1580. TEL 607-722-5857, 800-429-6784, FAX 607-722-1424, 800-895-0582, getinfo@haworthpress.com, http://www.haworthpress.com/web/EAQ. Ed. R Paul Maiden. Pub. William Cohen. R&P Ruth Ann Heath TEL 607-722-5857 ext 316. adv.: B&W page USD 315, color page USD 550; trim 4.375 x 7.125. Circ: 381 (paid).

➤ **JOURNAL OF FACILITIES MANAGEMENT IN AFRICA.** see *BUSINESS AND ECONOMICS—Management*

658.3 USA ISSN 0022-166X
HD5701 CODEN: JHREA9
➤ **JOURNAL OF HUMAN RESOURCES**; education, manpower and welfare economics. Text in English. 1966. q. USD 64 combined subscription to individuals print & online eds.; USD 190 combined subscription to institutions print & online eds. (effective 2006). adv. bk.rev. abstr.; bibl.; charts; stat.; illus. Index. back issues avail.; reprint service avail. from PQC,PSC. **Document type:** *Journal, Academic/Scholarly.* **Description:** Publishes academic papers using the best available empirical methods, principally in the field of economics.
Related titles: Microform ed.: (from MIM, PQC); Online - full text ed.: ISSN 1548-8004. USD 181 (effective 2006) (from EBSCO Publishing, Florida Center for Library Automation, Gale Group, H.W. Wilson, IngentaConnect, JSTOR (Web-based Journal Archive), O C L C Online Computer Library Center, Inc., ProQuest Information & Learning).
Indexed: ABIn, AHCMS, AMHA, ASCA, ASG, AgeL, BPIA, BusI, CIJE, CINAHL, CJA, CurCont, DIP, EAA, ERA, ESPM, ETA, Emerald, EngInd, FamI, GEOBASE, H&SSA, HRA, IBR, IBSS, IBZ, IndMed, Inspec, JEL, MCR, MEA, MEA&I, MEDLINE, ManagCont, PAIS, PCI, PMA, PRA, PSA, PersLit, RASB, RDA, RHEA, RiskAb, SEA, SENA, SFSA, SOMA, SPAA, SRRA, SSA, SSCI, SSI, SWA, SWR&A, SociolAb, TEA, V&AA, WAE&RSA.
—BLDSC (5003.430000), GNLM, IDS, IE, Infotrieve, ingenta. **CCC.**
Published by: (University Of Wisconsin At Madison, Industrial Relations Research Institute), University of Wisconsin Press, Journal Division, 1930 Monroe St, 3rd Fl, Madison, WI 53711-2059. TEL 608-263-0668, FAX 608-263-1173, jhr@ssc.wisc.edu, journals@uwpress.wisc.edu, http://www.wisc.edu/wisconsinpress/journals/journals/jhr.html. Ed. Jonathon S Skinner. adv.: page USD 390; trim 6.125 x 9.25. Circ: 2,000 (paid). **Co-sponsor:** Institute for Research on Poverty.

➤ **JOURNAL OF MULTICULTURAL COUNSELING AND DEVELOPMENT.** see *PSYCHOLOGY*

➤ **JOURNAL OF ORGANIZATIONAL BEHAVIOR MANAGEMENT.** see *PSYCHOLOGY*

658.3 GBR ISSN 1474-7472
HD7088
JOURNAL OF PENSION ECONOMICS AND FINANCE. Text in English. 2002. 3/yr. GBP 100 to institutions; USD 150 in North America to institutions; GBP 106 combined subscription to institutions print & online eds.; USD 161 combined subscription in North America to institutions print & online eds. (effective 2006). abstr. reprint service avail. from PSC. **Document type:** *Journal, Academic/Scholarly.* **Description:** Focuses on the economics and finance of pensions and retirement income.
Related titles: Online - full text ed.: ISSN 1475-3022. GBP 97 to institutions; USD 150 in North America to institutions (effective 2006) (from EBSCO Publishing, O C L C Online Computer Library Center, Inc., Swets Information Services).
—BLDSC (5030.512000), IE, Infotrieve. **CCC.**
Published by: Cambridge University Press, The Edinburgh Bldg, Shaftesbury Rd, Cambridge, CB2 2RU, United Kingdom. TEL 44-1223-312393, FAX 44-1223-315052, journals@cambridge.org, http://www.cup.cam.ac.uk/. Eds. J Michael Orzsag, Moshe Milevsky, Steven Haberman. **Subscr. to:** Cambridge University Press, 100 Brook Hill Dr, West Nyack, NY 10994. TEL 845-353-7500, FAX 845-353-4141, journals_subscriptions@cup.org

JOURNAL OF PERSONNEL EVALUATION IN EDUCATION. see *EDUCATION*

658.30715 USA ISSN 0276-928X
LC5251
JOURNAL OF STAFF DEVELOPMENT. Text in English. 1980. 4/yr. USD 49 domestic; USD 59 in Canada; USD 84 elsewhere (effective 2005). adv. bk.rev. back issues avail.
Related titles: Microfilm ed.; Online - full text ed.: (from H.W. Wilson, O C L C Online Computer Library Center, Inc., ProQuest Information & Learning).
Indexed: ABIn, CIJE, EduInd.
—BLDSC (5066.500000), IE, Infotrieve, ingenta. **CCC.**
Published by: National Staff Development Council, 5995 Fairfield Rd, Ste 4, tel, Oxford, OH 45056. TEL 513-523-6029, FAX 513-523-0638, nsdcoffice@aol.com, http://www.nsdc.org/library/publications/jsd/index.cfm. Ed. Paul Burden. Circ: 6,000.

658.3 GBR ISSN 1366-5626
HF5549.5.T7
➤ **JOURNAL OF WORKPLACE LEARNING: EMPLOYEE COUNSELLING TODAY.** Text in English. 1997. 8/yr. EUR 8,883.79 in Europe; USD 9,119 in North America; AUD 11,339 in Australasia; GBP 6,219.41 in UK & elsewhere (effective 2006). reprint service avail. from PSC. **Document type:** *Journal, Academic/Scholarly.* **Description:** Encompasses formal, informal and incidental learning in the workplace for individuals, groups and teams, as well as work-based learning, and off-the-job learning for the workplace. Also relevant are such topics as assessment of workplace learning, knowledge management and growth of the learning individual within the workplace.
Formed by the merger of: Journal of Workplace Learning; (1989-1997): Employee Counselling Today (0955-8217)
Related titles: Online - full text ed.: (from EBSCO Publishing, Emerald Group Publishing Limited, Gale Group, IngentaConnect, O C L C Online Computer Library Center, Inc., ProQuest Information & Learning, Swets Information Services).
Indexed: ABIn, CIJE, CPE, ERA, ETA, EmerIntel, Emerald, ErgAb, HRA, MEA, PsycInfo, PsycholAb, RHEA, SEA, SENA, SOMA, SWA, TEA, e-psyche.
—BLDSC (5072.638000), IE, Infotrieve, ingenta. **CCC.**
Published by: Emerald Group Publishing Limited, 60-62 Toller Ln, Bradford, W Yorks BD8 9BY, United Kingdom. TEL 44-1274-777700, FAX 44-1274-785200, infomation@emeraldinsight.com, http://www.emeraldinsight.com/jwl.htm. Ed. Dr. Darryl Dymock. **Subscr. addr. N America:** Emerald Group Publishing Ltd., 44 Brattle St, 4th Fl, Cambridge, MA 02138. TEL 617-497-2175, 888-622-0075, FAX 617-354-6875.

658.3 RUS
KADRY. NOVYE ZAKONY I KOMMENTARII. Text in Russian. bi-m. USD 95 in United States.
Address: Ul Rozhdestvenka 8, str 2, Moscow, 103031, Russian Federation. TEL 7-095-2685647, FAX 7-095-9639626. Ed. L P Larina. **US dist. addr.:** East View Information Services, 3020 Harbor Ln. N., Minneapolis, MN 55447. TEL 612-550-0961.

331.128 338 GBR ISSN 1365-814X
KEY NOTE MARKET REPORT: EMPLOYMENT AGENCIES. Variant title: Employment Agencies Market Report. Text in English. 198?. irreg., latest 1999, Aug. GBP 340 per issue (effective 2002). **Document type:** *Trade.* **Description:** Provides an overview of the UK employment agencies market, including industry structure, market size and trends, developments, prospects, and major company profiles.
Formerly (until 1995): Key Note Report: Employment Agencies (0268-9294)
Related titles: CD-ROM ed.; Online - full text ed.
Published by: Key Note Ltd., Field House, 72 Oldfield Rd, Hampton, Mddx TW12 2HQ, United Kingdom. TEL 44-20-8481-8750, FAX 44-20-8783-0049, info@keynote.co.uk, http://www.keynote.co.uk. Ed. Simon Howitt.

658.3 GBR
KEY NOTE MARKET REPORT: RECRUITMENT AGENCIES (PERMANENT). Text in English. 2000. irreg., latest 2001, Nov. GBP 340 per issue (effective 2002). **Description:** Provides an overview of a specific UK market segment and includes executive summary, market definition, market size, industry background, competitor analysis, current issues, forecasts, company profiles, and more.
Published by: Key Note Ltd., Field House, 72 Oldfield Rd, Hampton, Mddx TW12 2HQ, United Kingdom. TEL 44-20-8481-8750, FAX 44-20-8783-0049, info@keynote.co.uk, http://www.keynote.co.uk. Ed. Lyndsey Barker.

658.3 GBR
KEY NOTE MARKET REPORT: RECRUITMENT AGENCIES (TEMPORARY AND CONTRACT). Text in English. 2001. irreg., latest 2001, Dec. GBP 340 per issue (effective 2002). **Description:** Provides an overview of a specific UK market segment and includes executive summary, market definition, market size, industry background, competitor analysis, current issues, forecasts, company profiles, and more.
Published by: Key Note Ltd., Field House, 72 Oldfield Rd, Hampton, Mddx TW12 2HQ, United Kingdom. TEL 44-20-8481-8750, FAX 44-20-8783-0049, info@keynote.co.uk, http://www.keynote.co.uk. Ed. Lyndsey Barker.

658.3 GBR
KEY NOTE MARKET REPORT: RECRUITMENT AGENCIES (TEMPORARY). Text in English. 2000. irreg., latest 2000, Dec. GBP 340 per issue (effective 2002). **Description:** Provides an overview of a specific UK market segment and includes executive summary, market definition, market size, industry background, competitor analysis, current issues, forecasts, company profiles, and more.
Published by: Key Note Ltd., Field House, 72 Oldfield Rd, Hampton, Mddx TW12 2HQ, United Kingdom. TEL 44-20-8481-8750, FAX 44-20-8783-0049, info@keynote.co.uk, http://www.keynote.co.uk. Ed. Jacob Howard.

B

658.3 DEU ISSN 1432-3257
KOMPETENZENTWICKLUNG. Text in German. 1996. a. EUR 24 per vol. (effective 2003). **Document type:** *Monographic series, Academic/Scholarly.*
Published by: (Arbeitsgemeinschaft Betriebliche Weiterbildungsforschung, Qualifikations - Entwicklungs - Management), Waxmann Verlag GmbH, Steinfurter Str 555, Muenster, 48159, Germany. TEL 49-251-26504-0, FAX 49-251-2650426, info@waxmann.com, http://www.waxmann.com.

658.3 FRA ISSN 1635-7728
LAMY ADMINISTRATION DU PERSONNEL. Text in French. 2002. a. EUR 344.99 print & CD-ROM eds. (effective 2004). **Description:** Presents fiscal problems faced by corporate personnel.
Formerly: Interessement du Personnel a l'Entreprise
Related titles: CD-ROM ed.; Online - full text ed.: EUR 102 (effective 2003).
Published by: Lamy S.A. (Subsidiary of: Wolters Kluwer France), 21/23 rue des Ardennes, Paris, 75935 Cedex 19, France. TEL 33-1-825080800, FAX 33-1-44721388, lamy@lamy.fr, http://www.lamy.fr.

LAW OFFICE ADMINISTRATOR. see *BUSINESS AND ECONOMICS—Management*

LAW OFFICE MANAGEMENT & ADMINISTRATION REPORT. see *LAW*

LAW OFFICE MANAGEMENT & ADMINISTRATION YEARBOOK. see *LAW*

LAWYER HIRING & TRAINING REPORT. see *LAW*

658.3 USA
HF5549.A2
LEADERSHIP EXCELLENCE; the newsletter of personal development, managerial effectiveness, and organizational productivity. Text in English. 1983. m. USD 129 domestic; USD 149 foreign (effective 2005). bk.rev. **Document type:** *Newsletter.* **Description:** Deals with news regarding personal development, managerial effectiveness, and organizational productivity.
Formerly (until 2005): Executive Excellence (8756-2308)
Related titles: Online - full text ed.: (from EBSCO Publishing, Northern Light Technology, Inc., O C L C Online Computer Library Center, Inc.).
Indexed: ABIn.
—BLDSC (3836.214100), IE, Infotrieve, ingenta. **CCC.**
Published by: Executive Excellence Publishing, 1366 East 1120 South, Provo, UT 84606. TEL 800-304-9782, FAX 801-377-5960, info@eep.com, http://www.eep.com. Ed. Kenneth M Shelton. R&P Adam Anderson. Circ: 25,500.

658.3 GBR ISSN 0969-6474
HD58.82
➤ **THE LEARNING ORGANIZATION**; an international journal. Text in English. 1994. 5/yr. EUR 3,185.29 in Europe; USD 3,209 in North America; AUD 3,829 in Australasia; GBP 2,228.29 in UK & elsewhere (effective 2006). reprint service avail. from PSC. **Document type:** *Journal, Academic/Scholarly.* **Description:** Brings ideas, debates issues, techniques, case examples and opinion to those exploring the Learning Organization concept in the context of their own organization.
Related titles: CD-ROM ed.; Online - full text ed.: (from EBSCO Publishing, Emerald Group Publishing Limited, Gale Group, IngentaConnect, O C L C Online Computer Library Center, Inc., ProQuest Information & Learning, Swets Information Services).
Indexed: ABIn, BrEdI, CIJE, CPE, ERA, ETA, EmerIntel, Emerald, ErgAb, HRA, M&MA, MEA, RHEA, SEA, SENA, SOMA, TEA, e-psyche.
—BLDSC (5179.328300), IE, Infotrieve, ingenta. **CCC.**

Published by: Emerald Group Publishing Limited, 60-62 Toller Ln, Bradford, W Yorks BD8 9BY, United Kingdom. TEL 44-1274-777700, FAX 44-1274-785200, infomation@emeraldinsight.com, http://www.emeraldinsight.com/tlo.htm. Ed. Dr. Steven Cavaleri. **Subscr. addr. in N America:** Emerald Group Publishing Ltd., 44 Brattle St, 4th Fl, Cambridge, MA 02138. TEL 617-497-2175, 888-622-0075, FAX 617-354-6875.

658.3 USA ISSN 1557-2102
▼ **LEGAL ALERT FOR SUPERVISORS.** Text in English. 2005 (June). s-m. USD 99 (effective 2006). **Document type:** *Newsletter, Trade.*
Published by: Institute of Business Publications, P. O. Box 1688, West Chester, PA 19380. TEL 610-408-8200, 800-817-3922, FAX 610-408-8199, iobp@comcast.net, http://www.iobp.com. Ed. Jim McCanney.

658.3 340 USA ISSN 1545-2468
▼ **LEGAL FOR SUPERVISORS 21.** Text in English. 2003. s-m. USD 99.60 (effective 2004).
Published by: Business 21 Publishing, 477 Baltimore Pike, Springfield, PA 19064. TEL 484-479-2700, FAX 610-543-2292.

658.3 346 USA
LEGAL GUIDE TO HUMAN RESOURCES. Text in English. base vol. plus s-a. updates. looseleaf. USD 175. **Document type:** *Trade.* **Description:** Examines HR-related transactions, from recruiting and hiring to termination, compensation, and benefits practices. Gives practical advice to keep in legal compliance.
Published by: W G & L Financial Reporting & Management Research (Subsidiary of: R I A), 395 Hudson St, New York, NY 10014. TEL 212-367-6300, FAX 212-367-6718, http://www.InsideHR.com. Ed. Rodney Eubanks. **Subscr. to:** The Park Square Bldg., 31 St James Ave, Boston, MA 02116-4112. TEL 800-950-1207.

658.3 DEU ISSN 0024-0737
DER LEITENDE ANGESTELLTE; Zeitschrift fuer Fuehrungskraefte in der Wirtschaft. Text in German. 1950. 10/yr. adv. bk.rev.
Published by: MSK-Verlag GmbH, Schlehenstr 45, Hamm, 59063, Germany. Ed. Jost J Kroeger. Circ: 43,500.

LIBRARY PERSONNEL NEWS. see *LIBRARY AND INFORMATION SCIENCES*

▼ **LIBRARY WORKLIFE.** see *LIBRARY AND INFORMATION SCIENCES*

658.311 USA ISSN 0076-0889
LOOKING INTO LEADERSHIP SERIES* . Text in English. 1961. irreg. price varies. **Document type:** *Monographic series.*
Published by: Leadership Resources Inc., 491 Pass Run Dr, Luray, VA 22835-3532. TEL 703-876-8944.

658.3 IND
MANAGEMENT DIGEST. Text in English. 1973. bi-m. INR 250, USD 100. **Document type:** *Abstract/Index.*
Formerly: S E N D O C Bulletin. Part 3: Management and Behavioral Sciences (0970-8731)
Published by: National Institute of Small Industry Extension Training, Small Enterprises National Documentation Centre, Yousufguda, Hyderabad, Andhra Pradesh 500 045, India. TEL 91-40-238544, FAX 91-40-238547. Ed. C Kondiah.

MANAGEMENT IN NIGERIA. see *BUSINESS AND ECONOMICS—Management*

658.3 USA
MANAGING 401K PLANS YEARBOOK. Text in English. a. USD 224.95 print & online eds. (effective 2003). **Description:** Covers legislative and regulatory actions, 401(k) management, plan design and administration, fees, investment options and manager rankings, and communication strategies.
Related titles: Online - full text ed.: USD 219 (effective 2003); ♦ Cumulative ed. of: I O M A's Report on Managing 401k Plans. ISSN 1059-2741.
Published by: Institute of Management & Administration, Inc., 3 Park Ave, New York, NY 10016-5902. TEL 212-244-0360, FAX 212-564-0465, subserve@ioma.com, http://www.ioma.com. Ed. Rebecca Morrow.

658.3 USA
MANAGING BENEFITS PLANS YEARBOOK. Text in English. a. USD 224.95 print & online eds. (effective 2003). **Description:** Covers the various methods used to enhance benefits, control costs, automate enrollment and administration, negotiate effectively with managed-care providers, and work better with outsourced service providers.
Related titles: Online - full text ed.: USD 219 (effective 2003); ♦ Cumulative ed. of: I O M A's Report on Managing Benefits Plans. ISSN 1098-5662.
Published by: Institute of Management & Administration, Inc., 3 Park Ave, New York, NY 10016-5902. TEL 212-244-0360, FAX 212-564-0465, subserve@ioma.com, http://www.ioma.com. Ed. Susan Patterson.

658.3 GBR ISSN 1355-1515
MANAGING BEST PRACTICE. Text in English. 1994. 12/yr. GBP 435 (effective 1998). adv. bk.rev. **Document type:** *Catalog.* **Description:** Aims to provide best-practice advice, examples, options, and differing experience from a range of organizations, which together supply practical pointers to achieving excellence in managing personnel.
—BLDSC (5359.284500), IE, ingenta. **CCC.**
Published by: Industrial Society, Robert Hyde House, 48 Bryanston Sq, London, W1HY 7LN, United Kingdom. TEL 44-171-479-2127. R&P Gill Hyatt. Adv. contact Debbie Marshal. **Subscr. to:** Sales Unit, Quadrant Ct, 49 Calthorpe Rd, Edgbaston, Birmingham B15 1TH, United Kingdom. TEL 44-121-4102020.

658 USA ISSN 1521-5326
MANAGING EMPLOYEES UNDER F M L A AND A D A. (Federal Family & Medical Leave Act and Americans with Disabilities Act) Text in English. 1998. bi-w. USD 149.50 (effective 2005). **Document type:** *Newsletter, Trade.* **Description:** Helps managers and supervisors stay abreast of new FMLA and ADA regulations and developments.
Published by: Clement Communications, Inc., 10 LaCrue Ave, PO Box 36, Concordville, PA 19331. TEL 610-459-4200, 888-358-5858, FAX 610-459-4582, editor@clement.com, http://www.clement.com.

658.3 USA ISSN 1525-8181
MANAGING PEOPLE AT WORK. Text in English. 1984. m. USD 117 (effective 2005). back issues avail.; reprints avail. **Document type:** *Newsletter, Trade.*
Former titles (until 1999): Making the Most of People at Work (1521-7159); (until 1998): Practical Supervision (0742-7859)
Related titles: Online - full text ed.
—**CCC.**
Published by: McMurry Publishing, 1010 E Missouri Ave, Phoenix, AZ 85014-2601. TEL 602-395-5850, 888-626-8779, FAX 602-395-5853, mpaw@mcmurry.com, info@mcmurry.com, http://www.managingpeopleatwork.com/newsletters/mpaw/, http://www.mcmurry.com. Ed. Mike Clark Madison. R&P Dennis E. Murphy. Circ: 12,000 (paid).

MANAGING SCHOOL BUSINESS. see *EDUCATION—School Organization And Administration*

658.3 344.73 USA ISSN 1526-0739
MANAGING TODAY'S FEDERAL EMPLOYEES. Text in English. 1989. m. USD 155 (effective 2006). s.a. index. back issues avail. **Document type:** *Newsletter, Government.* **Description:** Keeps supervisors up-to-date on their personnel management responsibilities. Includes case decisions and policy changes that affect the federal sector.
Former titles: Guideposts for Effective Leadership - Tackling Federal Workplace Issues; Personnel Management Guideposts for Federal Supervisors (1082-9156)
Related titles: Online - full text ed.
—**CCC.**
Published by: L R P Publications, 747 Dresher Rd, PO Box 980, Horsham, PA 19044. TEL 215-784-0860, 800-341-7874, FAX 215-784-9639, custserve@lrp.com, http://www.shoplrp.com/product/p-40351A.html, http://www.lrp.com. Ed. Drew Long.

658.3 USA
MANAGING TRAINING & DEVELOPMENT YEARBOOK. Text in English. a. USD 224.95 print & online eds. (effective 2003). **Description:** Provides strategies, techniques, and ideas for improving training results and using the most effective performance measurement methods.
Related titles: Online - full text ed.: USD 219 (effective 2003); ♦ Cumulative ed. of: I O M A's Report on Managing Training & Development. ISSN 1526-7164.
Published by: Institute of Management & Administration, Inc., 3 Park Ave, New York, NY 10016-5902. TEL 212-244-0360, FAX 212-564-0465, subserve@ioma.com, http://www.ioma.com. Ed. Susan Patterson.

MANNESMANN MAGAZIN. see *BUSINESS AND ECONOMICS—Domestic Commerce*

658.3 ISR ISSN 0792-0970
➤ **MASHABEI ENOSH/HUMAN RESOURCES**; human resources magazine. Text in Hebrew. 1988. m. ILS 702, USD 150 (effective 2003). bk.rev.; Website rev. 64 p./no.; back issues avail.; reprints avail. **Document type:** *Magazine, Academic/Scholarly.*
Indexed: IHP.
Published by: Eush Ltd., P O Box 3202, Herzliyya, 46104, Israel. TEL 972-9-950-0882, FAX 972-9-958-2785, http://www.hrisrael.co.il. Eds., Pubs. Chanoch Sadan, Nava Eldar. R&P, Adv. contact Nava Eldar. Circ: 2,500 (paid).

➤ **MASSACHUSETTS PRACTICE SERIES. EMPLOYMENT LAW.** see *LAW—Corporate Law*

➤ **MIDDLE MANAGEMENT AND CLERICAL COMPENSATION REPORT - MEXICO.** see *BUSINESS AND ECONOMICS—Management*

➤ **MIDDLE MANAGEMENT COMPENSATION - REGRESSION ANALYSIS REPORT.** see *BUSINESS AND ECONOMICS—Management*

➤ **MIDDLE MANAGEMENT HI - COMP REPORT.** see *BUSINESS AND ECONOMICS—Management*

➤ **MIDDLE MANAGEMENT REPORT.** see *BUSINESS AND ECONOMICS—Management*

➤ **MINDPLAY**; creativity & innovation in today's business environment. see *BUSINESS AND ECONOMICS—Management*

➤ **MOBILITY (WASHINGTON).** see *REAL ESTATE*

658.3 BOL
MONOGRAFIAS DE RECURSOS HUMANOS. Text in Spanish. 1978. irreg., latest vol.4, 1985. price varies. **Document type:** *Monographic series, Academic/Scholarly.*
Published by: Centro de Investigaciones Sociales, Casilla 6931 - C.C., La Paz, Bolivia. TEL 591-2-352931. Ed. Antonio Cisneros.

658.3 388.324 USA
MOTOR FLEET SUPERVISION; principles and practices. Text in English. 1983. irreg. USD 20 per issue. **Document type:** *Academic/Scholarly.*
Published by: National Committee for Motor Fleet Supervisor Training, A 364 Engineering Bldg, Michigan State University, Lansing, MI 48824-1226. TEL 517-353-1790. Ed. Jack Burkert.

658.3 DEU
MUSTERARBEITSVERTRAEGE UND ZEUGNISSE FUER DIE BETRIEBLICHE PRAXIS. Text in German. 1992. q. looseleaf. **Document type:** *Trade.*
Published by: W E K A Media GmbH & Co. KG, Roemerstr 16, Kissing, 86438, Germany. service@weka.de, http://www.weka.de. Ed. Wolf Hunold. Circ: 1,100 (paid).

658.300711 USA ISSN 0271-1672
N A S P A FORUM. Text in English. bi-m. bk.rev. back issues avail. **Document type:** *Newsletter, Academic/Scholarly.*
Published by: National Association of Student Personnel Administrators, 1875 Connecticut Ave, N W, Ste 418, Washington, DC 20009-5728. TEL 202-265-7500, FAX 202-797-1157, office@naspa.org, http://www.naspa.org. Ed. Gwen Dungy. R&P, Adv. contact Carla Dicks TEL 202-265-7500 ext 3009. Circ: 8,000.

658.3 USA ISSN 1060-4979
N L S HANDBOOK. (National Longitudinal Surveys) Text in English. 1987. a. **Document type:** *Directory, Government.*
Published by: U.S. Department of Labor, Bureau of Labor Statistics, Postal Square Bldg., 2 Massachusetts Ave, NE, Washington, DC 20212-0001 . TEL 202-691-5200, FAX 202-691-6325, http://www.bls.gov.

NATIONAL PUBLIC EMPLOYMENT REPORTER. see *BUSINESS AND ECONOMICS—Labor And Industrial Relations*

658.3 USA ISSN 1073-2047
NATIONAL RELOCATION & REAL ESTATE. Text in English. 1980. m. **Document type:** *Trade.*
Published by: R I S Publishing Inc., 50 Water St, Norwalk, CT 06854. TEL 203-855-1234, FAX 203-852-7208, frank@rismedia.com, http://www.rismedia.com. Ed. Frank Sziros. Circ: 33,000.

THE NAVIGATOR (RALEIGH). see *SCIENCES: COMPREHENSIVE WORKS*

658.3 346 DEU
NEUE ARBEITSRECHT VON A-Z FUER DEN GESCHAEFTSFUEHRER. Text in German. 1992. q. looseleaf. **Document type:** *Trade.*
Published by: W E K A Media GmbH & Co. KG, Roemerstr 16, Kissing, 86438, Germany. TEL 08233-23410, http://www.weka.de. Eds. A Mueller, W Schoen. Circ: 4,000 (paid).

658.3 DEU ISSN 0941-5610
DIE NEUE PERSONAL-PRAXIS VON A-Z. Text in German. 1992. base vol. plus updates 13/yr. EUR 99.70 (effective 2004). **Document type:** *Directory, Trade.*
Published by: Verlag Praktisches Wissen GmbH (Subsidiary of: Wolters Kluwer Deutschland GmbH), Marlener Str 2, Offenburg, 77656, Germany. TEL 49-781-605300, FAX 49-781-59825, info@praktisches-wissen.de, http://www.praktisches-wissen.de.

NEW HAMPSHIRE WORKERS' COMPENSATION MANUAL. see *LAW—Corporate Law*

658.3 NZL ISSN 1175-5407
➤ **NEW ZEALAND JOURNAL OF HUMAN RESOURCES MANAGEMENT.** Text in English. 2001. irreg. free. bk.rev. **Document type:** *Journal, Academic/Scholarly.* **Description:** Collates, reviews and publishes original material on the development and practice of human resource management in New Zealand and the South Pacific region.
Media: Online - full content.

Published by: Human Resources Institute of New Zealand, PO Box 11-450, Wellington, New Zealand. TEL 64-4-4992966, FAX 64-4-4992966, hrinz@hrinz.org.nz, http://www.hrinz.org.nz/info/academic_journal/. Ed. Paul Toulson. R&P, Adv. contact Peter Marshall.

➤ **NOTIZIARIO DEL LAVORO E PREVIDENZA.** see *LAW—Corporate Law*

➤ **OF COUNSEL**; the monthly legal practice report. see *LAW*

658 USA
OFFICE PERSONNEL REPORT. Text in English. a. USD 490. charts. **Document type:** *Trade.* **Description:** Complete information concerning office personnel salary.
Published by: (Executive Compensation Service (ECS)), Wyatt Data Services, 218 Rte 17 N, Rochelle Park, NJ 07622-9832. TEL 201-843-1177, FAX 201-843-0101.

658.3 651 GBR ISSN 0951-6824
OFFICE SECRETARY. Variant title: O S Magazine. Text in English. 1986. bi-m. GBP 27 domestic; GBP 32 foreign (effective Oct. 2002). **Document type:** *Trade.*
—CCC.
Published by: Peebles Media Group, Bergius House, Clifton St, Glasgow, G3 7LA, United Kingdom. TEL 44-141-567-6000, FAX 44-141-353-2336, os@peeblesmedia.com, info@peeblesmedia.com, http://www.peeblesmedia.com/os/index.htm. Ed. Emma Smith. Adv. contact Paul Ormond. Circ: 46,000.

658.3 USA ISSN 0078-4001
OHIO. DIVISION OF STATE PERSONNEL. ANNUAL REPORT. Text in English. 1960. a. free.
Published by: Division of State Personnel, Department of Administrative Services, 30 E Broad St, Columbus, OH 43215. TEL 614-466-6341.

658.3 USA
OKLAHOMA. PUBLIC EMPLOYEES RETIREMENT SYSTEM. ANNUAL REPORT. Text in English. a.
Published by: Public Employees Retirement System, 580 Jim Thorpe Bldg, Box 53007, Oklahoma City, OK 73152. TEL 405-521-2381.

658.3 DEU
OPEL POST. Text in German. 10/yr. back issues avail. **Document type:** *Newsletter, Trade.*
Published by: Adam Opel AG, Friedrich-Lutzmann-Ring, Ruesselsheim, 65423, Germany. TEL 49-6142-770, FAX 49-6142-778800, kunden.info.center@de.opel.com, http://www.opel.de. Ed. Norbert Giesen. Circ: 80,000.

658.3 NLD ISSN 0922-0895
OPLEIDING & ONTWIKKELING; tijdschrift over human resource development. Text in Dutch. 1988. 10/yr. **Document type:** *Trade.* **Description:** Discussion of practical and theoretical issues in personnel management and development.
—IE, Infotrieve.
Published by: Reed Business Information bv (Subsidiary of: Reed Business), Postbus 16400, Den Haag, 2500 BK, Netherlands. TEL 31-70-3624800, FAX 31-70-3605606.

658.3 150 DEU ISSN 1618-808X
ORGANISATIONSBERATUNG, SUPERVISION, COACHING. Text in German. 1994. q. EUR 48; EUR 36.01 to students; EUR 13.50 newsstand/cover (effective 2004). **Document type:** *Journal, Academic/Scholarly.*
Formerly: Organisationsberatung, Supervision, Clinical Management (0946-9834)
Indexed: DIP, IBR, IBSS, IBZ, e-psyche.
Published by: V S - Verlag fuer Sozialwissenschaften (Subsidiary of: Springer Science+Business Media), Abraham-Lincoln-Str 46, Wiesbaden, 65189, Germany. TEL 49-611-78780, FAX 49-611-7878400, info@vs-verlag.de, http://www.vs-verlag.de.

658 SVN ISSN 1318-5454
CODEN: ORKAEN
➤ **ORGANIZACIJA**; journal of management, informatics and human resources. Text in Slovenian, English; Summaries in English. 1972. m. SIT 16,600 domestic; USD 80 foreign (effective 2003). adv. bk.rev. bibl.; charts; abstr. 60 p./no. 2 cols./p.; back issues avail. **Document type:** *Journal, Academic/Scholarly.*
Former titles (until Jan. 1995): Organizacija in Kadri (0350-1531); Moderna Organizacija (0047-777X); Organizacija Kadrovska Politika (0030-5022)
Indexed: ErgAb, Inspec, PSA, SociolAb.
—BLDSC (6289.980000), AskIEEE.
Published by: Moderna Organizacija, Fakulteta za Organizacijske Vede, Univerza v Mariboru, Kidriceva 55a, Kranj, 4000, Slovenia. TEL 386-4-2374226, FAX 386-4-2374299, omik@fov.uni-mb.si, http://www.fov.uni-mb.si/mzalozba/revija.htm. Ed. Joze Zupancic. Adv. contact Nada Arh. Circ: 3,200 (paid).

➤ **ORGANIZATION DEVELOPMENT JOURNAL**; guiding the future of people working together. see *BUSINESS AND ECONOMICS—Management*

658.3 USA
ORGANIZATIONS AND CHANGE. Text in English. m. USD 110 (effective 2003). **Document type:** *Newsletter.* **Description:** Lists meetings, jobs, and consulting opportunities in the field of organization development.
Published by: Organization Development Institute, 11234 Walnut Ridge Rd, Chesterland, OH 44026. TEL 440-729-7419, don@odinstitute.org, http://www.odinstitute.org. Ed., R&P, Adv. contact Dr. Donald W Cole TEL 440-729-7419.

ORGANIZE YOUR LUCK!. see *OCCUPATIONS AND CAREERS*

658.3 BEL ISSN 0030-543X
ORIENTATIONS; la revue du droit social et de la gestion du personnel. Text in English. 1971. m. bk.rev. bibl. index. Supplement avail.
Related titles: Dutch ed.: Orientatie. ISSN 0773-350X. 1970.
Indexed: HongKongiana.
Published by: C E D Samsom (Subsidiary of: Wolters Samsom Belgie n.v.), Kouterveld 14, Diegem, 1831, Belgium. TEL 32-2-7231111.

658.3 GBR ISSN 0966-7660
OVERSEAS JOBS EXPRESS. Text in English. 1991. 26/yr. GBP 52; GBP 63 in Europe; GBP 73 elsewhere. adv. bk.rev. **Document type:** *Newspaper.* **Description:** Lists international employment opportunities and vacancies. Provides information to persons interested in living and/or working abroad.
Address: Premier House, Shoreham Airport, Shoreham-by-Sea, Sussex BN43 5FF, United Kingdom. TEL 44-1273-440220, FAX 44-1273-440229, editor@overseasjobs.com, http://www.overseasjobs.com. Ed., R&P David Creffield. Adv. contact Mike Dorrinston. Circ: 20,000 (paid).

658.3 NLD ISSN 0165-3334
P W; vakblad voor personeelsmanagement. (Personeelswerk) Key Title: PW (Amsterdam). Text in Dutch. 1977. fortn. (20 times a year). EUR 139; EUR 59 to students; EUR 6.75 newsstand/cover to students (effective 2005); includes 3 special guides. adv. bk.rev. stat.; illus. index. 72 p./no.; back issues avail. **Document type:** *Trade.* **Description:** Covers personnel management issues.
Incorporates (1985-1993): P W Nieuws en Actualiteit (0929-3280); Incorporates (1983-1985): Training en Opleiding (0929-3272)
—IE, Infotrieve. **CCC.**
Published by: V N U Business Publications (Netherlands), Ceylonpoort 5-25, Haarlem, 2037 AA, Netherlands. TEL 31-23-5463463, FAX 31-23-5463931, redactie@pwnet.nl, http://www.pwnet.nl. Ed. Toine Al TEL 31-23-5463418. Adv. contact Christian van Essen TEL 31-23-5463386. B&W page EUR 3,024; trim 190 x 260. Circ: 12,444.

PARTNERS IN BUSINESS. see *BUSINESS AND ECONOMICS—Management*

331 GBR ISSN 0143-8328
PAY AND BENEFITS BULLETIN. Short title: P A B B. Text in English. 1979. fortn. GBP 195; GBP 220 foreign (effective 1999). reprint service avail. from PQC. **Document type:** *Trade.* **Description:** Analyzes pay awards, surveys topical pay issues, summarizes pay-review settlements, and provides key negotiating statistics.
Related titles: Online - full text ed.
Indexed: LRI.
Published by: I R S (Subsidiary of: LexisNexis UK (Scottish Office)), 18-20 Highbury Pl, London, N5 1QP, United Kingdom. TEL 44-20-7354-5858, FAX 44-207-226-8618. Ed. Paul Thompson.

658.3 CAN ISSN 1181-8093
PAY EQUITY COMMISSION OF ONTARIO. ANNUAL REPORT. Text in English. 1990. a.
Published by: Pay Equity Commission of Ontario, 400 University Ave, 11th Fl, Toronto, ON M7A 1T7, Canada. TEL 800-387-8813, FAX 416-314-8741.

658.3 USA
PAY FOR PERFORMANCE REPORT YEARBOOK. Text in English. a. USD 224.95 print & online eds. (effective 2003). **Description:** Presents case studies, surveys, opinion pieces, highlights from top human resources and compensation conferences, resources, contact information, and more.
Related titles: Online - full text ed.: USD 219 (effective 2003); ♦ Cumulative ed. of: I O M A's Complete Guide to Best Practices in Performance Management.
Published by: Institute of Management & Administration, Inc., 3 Park Ave, New York, NY 10016-5902. TEL 212-244-0360, FAX 212-564-0465, subserve@ioma.com, http://www.ioma.com. Ed. Ann Podolske.

PAY MAGAZINE. see *OCCUPATIONS AND CAREERS*

658.3 DEU ISSN 1615-2670
PAYROLL; Infodienst fuer die Lohn- & Gehaltsabrechnung. Text in German. 2000. bi-m. EUR 66; EUR 11.50 newsstand/cover (effective 2005). adv. **Document type:** *Journal, Trade.* **Description:** Contains information and advice on managing employee payrolls and investments.
Published by: Hermann Luchterhand Verlag GmbH (Subsidiary of: Wolters Kluwer Deutschland GmbH), Heddesdorfer Str 31, Neuwied, 56564, Germany. TEL 49-2631-8012222, FAX 49-2631-8012223, info@luchterhand.de, http://www.payroll-info.de, http://www.luchterhand.de. Ed. Claudia Ossola-Haring.

658.3 USA ISSN 1085-7508
PAYROLL LEGAL ALERT. Text in English. 1995. m. USD 119 (effective 1999). back issues avail. **Document type:** *Newsletter.*
Published by: Alexander Hamilton Institute, Inc., 70 Hilltop Rd, Ramsey, NJ 07446-1119. TEL 201-825-3377, 800-879-2441, FAX 201-825-8696, payla@ahipubs.com, http://www.ahipubs.com. Ed. Alice Gilman.

658.3 GBR ISSN 0950-8147
PAYROLL MANAGER'S REVIEW. Text in English. 1986. m. GBP 74 in United Kingdom; GBP 94 overseas (effective 2000). **Document type:** *Trade.*
Published by: Butterworths Tolley (Subsidiary of: LexisNexis UK (Scottish Office)), 2 Addiscombe Rd, Croydon, Surrey CR9 5AF, United Kingdom. TEL 44-20-8686-9141, FAX 44-20-8686-3155, http://www.tolley.co.uk. Eds. Ciarom Molloy, Mike Nicholas. Circ: 4,000.

B

658.3 657 USA
PENSION COORDINATOR. Text in English. 1987. 13 base vols. plus w. updates. looseleaf. USD 820. **Description:** Provides analysis of pension law, planning articles, official source materials and compliance tools.
Indexed: ATI.
Published by: R I A (Subsidiary of: Thomson Corporation), 395 Hudson St, New York, NY 10014. TEL 212-367- 6300, 212-367-6300.

368.37 GBR ISSN 1478-5315
➤ **PENSIONS**; an international journal. Text in English. 1995. q. GBP 235 in Europe to institutions & Libraries; USD 360 in US & Canada to institutions & Libraries; GBP 250 elsewhere to institutions & Libraries (effective 2005). adv. bk.rev.; Website rev. 96 p./no. 2 cols./p.; back issues avail. **Document type:** *Journal, Academic/Scholarly.* **Description:** Keeps readers abreast of the latest thinking and best practice in the design, administration, management, actuarial issues, documentation and investment strategies for pension plans.
Former titles (until vol.8, no.1, 2002): Journal of Pensions Management (1462-222X); (until vol.3, no.4, 1998): Journal of Pensions Management and Marketing (1369-7455); Journal of Pensions Management (1359-1207)
Related titles: Online - full text ed.: (from EBSCO Publishing, O C L C Online Computer Library Center, Inc., ProQuest Information & Learning).
Indexed: ABIn.
—BLDSC (6422.720060), IE, ingenta. **CCC.**
Published by: Palgrave Macmillan Ltd. (Subsidiary of: Macmillan Publishers Ltd.), Houndmills, Basingstoke, Hants RG21 6XS, United Kingdom. TEL 44-1256-329242, FAX 44-1256-810526, journal-info@palgrave.com, http://www.palgrave-journals.com/. Circ: 500 (paid).

658.3 GBR ISSN 0269-7505
PENSIONS MANAGEMENT. Text in English. 1985. m. GBP 69; GBP 5.95 newsstand/cover (effective 1999). adv. bk.rev. **Document type:** *Trade.* **Description:** Directed to pension professionals in the U.K. Covers all aspects of benefit planning and investment from personal and company pension schemes.
Related titles: Microform ed.: (from PQC); Online - full text ed.: (from Gale Group).
Indexed: ABIn, BLI.
—BLDSC (6422.720170), IE, ingenta.
Published by: Financial Times Business Information, Magazines (Subsidiary of: Financial Times Group), Tabernacle Court, 16-28 Tabernacle St, London, EC2A 4DD, United Kingdom. TEL 44-20-7405-6969, FAX 44-20-7405-5276. Circ: 12,087.
Dist. by: Seymour Distribution Ltd, 86 Newman St, London W1T 3EX, United Kingdom. FAX 44-207-396-8002, enquiries@seymour.co.uk.

658.3 GBR ISSN 1366-8765
PENSIONS WEEK. Text in English. w. GBP 162 (effective 2005). adv. **Document type:** *Magazine, Trade.* **Description:** Keeps pensions professionals up to date with pensions and the changes taking place in the industry.
Related titles: Online - full text ed.: (from Gale Group, O C L C Online Computer Library Center, Inc.).
Indexed: B&I.
Published by: Financial Times Business Information, Magazines (Subsidiary of: Financial Times Group), Tabernacle Court, 16-28 Tabernacle St, London, EC2A 4DD, United Kingdom. TEL 44-20-73828000, FAX 44-20-73828099, matthew.craig@ft.com, http://www.ftbusiness.com/product_pensionweek2.htm. Ed. Matthew Craig. Pub. Angus Cushley. Adv. contact Tim Baker. B&W page GBP 2,425, color page GBP 3,890; trim 210 x 297. Circ: 8,299 (paid).

▼ *new title* ➤ *refereed* ✶ *unverified* ♦ *full entry avail.*

658.3 ZAF ISSN 1019-6196
PEOPLE DYNAMICS. Text in English. 1973. m. (11/yr). ZAR 252 domestic; ZAR 367 in Southern Africa; ZAR 437 elsewhere (effective 2000). adv. bk.rev. illus. **Document type:** *Trade.*
Description: Discusses issues relating to all aspects of human resources administration and planning, with particular focus on the impact of changes in South Africa.
Former titles (until Feb 1992): I P M Journal - I P B Joernaal (1011-4149); (until 1985): I P M Manpower Journal (1011-4270); (until 1982): People and Profits (0301-6005)
Indexed: ISAP.
—BLDSC (6422.876530), IE, ingenta.
Published by: Institute of People Management, PO Box 31390, Braamfontein, Johannesburg 2017, South Africa. TEL 27-11-482-4970, FAX 27-11-482-5542, alan.hosking@pixie.co.za. Ed. Alan Hosking. R&P Linda Brims. Adv. contact Barbara Spence. B&W page ZAR 4,660, color page ZAR 5,893; trim 297 x 210. Circ: 9,302.

PERSONAL; Zeitschrift fuer Human Resource Management. see *BUSINESS AND ECONOMICS—Labor And Industrial Relations*

658.3 DEU ISSN 0937-3012
DAS PERSONAL. Text in German. 1990. bi-m. looseleaf. **Document type:** *Trade.*
Published by: W R S Verlag GmbH & Co. KG (Subsidiary of: Rudolf Haufe Verlag GmbH & Co. KG), Fraunhoferstr 5, Planegg, 82152, Germany. info@wrs.de, http://www.wrs.de.

658.3 DEU ISSN 1610-0506
PERSONAL MANAGER; H R International. Text in German. 2002. q. EUR 58; EUR 17 newsstand/cover (effective 2004). adv. **Document type:** *Magazine, Trade.*
Published by: Datakontext Fachverlag GmbH, Augustinusstr 9 d, Frechen, 50226, Germany. TEL 49-2234-966100, FAX 49-2234-966109, info@datakontext.com, http://www.datakontext-press.de/personal_manager/hrman_hauptframe.html. adv.: B&W page EUR 1,800, color page EUR 3,150. Circ: 10,000 (paid and controlled).

658.3 SWE ISSN 1402-5744
PERSONAL & LEDARSKAP, P & L. Text in Swedish. 1970. 11/yr. SEK 600 (effective 2001). adv. bk.rev. abstr. cum.index. **Document type:** *Magazine, Trade.*
Former titles: P och L. Personalarbete och Ledarskap (1104-6600); (until 1993): Utbildningstidningen (0049-5735)
Published by: Epok Media AB, Fack 22022, Orebro, 70202, Sweden. TEL 46-19-24-70-70, FAX 46-19-24-70-75, personal@epok.se, http://www.personal-ledarskap.com. Ed., Pub. Kent Seifors. adv.: B&W page SEK 19,500, color page SEK 24,000; trim 185 x 265. Circ: 15,300.

658.3 DEU ISSN 1610-0492
PERSONAL PLUS. Text in German. q. EUR 198 (effective 2004). **Document type:** *Trade.*
Media: CD-ROM.
Published by: Verlag Praktisches Wissen GmbH (Subsidiary of: Wolters Kluwer Deutschland GmbH), Marlener Str 2, Offenburg, 77656, Germany. TEL 49-781-605300, FAX 49-781-59825, info@praktisches-wissen.de, http://www.praktisches-wissen.de.

658.3 DEU ISSN 1611-3152
PERSONAL PRAXIS AKTUELL; Rechtsreport fuer Personalentscheidungen im Betrieb. Abbreviated title: P R P. Text in German. m. EUR 69; EUR 5.75 newsstand/cover (effective 2004). adv. **Document type:** *Journal, Trade.*
Published by: Hermann Luchterhand Verlag GmbH (Subsidiary of: Wolters Kluwer Deutschland GmbH), Heddesdorfer Str 31, Neuwied, 56564, Germany. TEL 49-2631-8012222, FAX 49-2631-8012223, info@luchterhand.de, http://www.luchterhand.de. Ed. Sabrina Kullmann. Adv. contact Christian Roller.

658.3 DEU ISSN 0723-3868
PERSONALFUEHRUNG. Text in German. 1967. m. EUR 116; EUR 9.80 newsstand/cover (effective 2005). adv. bk.rev. reprints avail. **Document type:** *Journal, Trade.*
—IE, Infotrieve.
Published by: Deutsche Gesellschaft fuer Personalfuehrung e.V., Niederkasseler Lohweg 16, Duesseldorf, 40547, Germany. TEL 49-211-59780, FAX 49-211-5978149, personalfuehrung@dgfp.de, graf@dgfp.de, http://www1.dgfp.com. Ed. Thomas Hartge. Adv. contact Josi Kemmann. Circ: 6,000.

331 DEU ISSN 1612-4855
▼ **DER PERSONALLEITER.** Text in German. 2003. 10/yr. EUR 98; EUR 9.80 newsstand/cover (effective 2005). **Document type:** *Journal, Trade.*
Published by: Hermann Luchterhand Verlag GmbH (Subsidiary of: Wolters Kluwer Deutschland GmbH), Heddesdorfer Str 31, Neuwied, 56564, Germany. TEL 49-2631-8012222, FAX 49-2631-8012223, info@luchterhand.de, http://www.luchterhand.de.

658.3 DEU
PERSONALMAGAZIN; Management, Recht, Lohn & Gehalt. Text in German. 1999. m. EUR 97 (effective 2004). adv. **Document type:** *Magazine, Trade.*
Published by: Rudolf Haufe Verlag GmbH & Co. KG, Hindenburgstr 64, Freiburg Im Breisgau, 79102, Germany. TEL 49-761-36830, FAX 49-761-3683195, personalmagazin@haufe.de, online@haufe.de, http://www.personal-magazin.de, http://www.haufe.de. Ed. Reiner Straub. Adv. contact Thomas Herrmann. B&W page EUR 6,500, color page EUR 7,900. Circ: 49,067 (paid and controlled).

658.3 DEU ISSN 0175-9299
KK5932.A13
DER PERSONALRAT. Text in German. 1984. m. EUR 79.80; EUR 8 newsstand/cover (effective 2005). adv. **Document type:** *Journal, Trade.*
Indexed: DIP, IBR, IBZ.
Published by: Bund-Verlag GmbH, Heddernheimer Landstr 144, Frankfurt Am Main, 60439, Germany. TEL 49-69-79501020, FAX 49-69-79501010, kontakt@bund-verlag.de, http://www.bund-verlag.de. adv.: page EUR 1,990; trim 180 x 260.

658.3 DEU ISSN 0476-3475
DIE PERSONALVERTRETUNG; Fachzeitschrift des gesamten Personalwesens fuer Personalvertretungen und Dienststellen. Text in German. 1958. m. EUR 93.60; EUR 9.40 newsstand/cover (effective 2006). adv. **Document type:** *Newspaper, Trade.*
Indexed: DIP, IBR, IBZ.
—CCC.
Published by: Erich Schmidt Verlag GmbH & Co. (Berlin), Genthiner Str 30G, Berlin, 10785, Germany. TEL 49-30-2500850, FAX 49-30-250085305, redaktionpv@esvmedien.de, vertrieb@esvmedien.de, http://www.esv.info. Ed. Frank Bieler. Adv. contact Helmut Lanzinger TEL 49-89-8299600. page EUR 1,590; trim 130 x 208.

PERSONALVERTRETUNGSRECHT DES BUNDES UND DER LAENDER. see *BUSINESS AND ECONOMICS—Labor And Industrial Relations*

658.3 DEU ISSN 0341-4698
PERSONALWIRTSCHAFT; Zeitschrift fuer erfolgreiches Personalmanagement. Text in German. 1974. m. EUR 149.80; EUR 52.50 to students; EUR 13.20 newsstand/cover (effective 2005). adv. index. back issues avail.; reprints avail. **Document type:** *Journal, Trade.*
Formerly (until 1975): Praxis der Personalarbeit (0341-4701)
Indexed: DIP, IBR, IBZ.
—IE, Infotrieve. **CCC.**
Published by: Hermann Luchterhand Verlag GmbH (Subsidiary of: Wolters Kluwer Deutschland GmbH), Heddesdorfer Str 31, Neuwied, 56564, Germany. TEL 49-2631-8012222, FAX 49-2631-8012223, personalwirtschaft@luchterhand.de, info@luchterhand.de, http://www.personalwirtschaft.de, http://www.luchterhand.de. Ed. Reiner Straub. Adv. contact Christian Roller. B&W page EUR 1,615, color page EUR 2,935. Circ: 5,000.

658.3 DEU ISSN 1439-5258
PERSONALWIRTSCHAFT (HAMBURG). Text in German. 1999. irreg., latest vol.6, 2005. price varies. **Document type:** *Monographic series, Academic/Scholarly.*
Published by: Verlag Dr. Kovac, Arnoldstr 49, Hamburg, 22763, Germany. TEL 49-40-3988800, FAX 49-40-39888055, info@verlagdrkovac.de, http://www.verlagdrkovac.de/3-10.htm.

658.3 DEU ISSN 0940-8002
PERSONALWIRTSCHAFTLICHE SCHRIFTEN. Text in German. 1992. irreg., latest vol.23, 2005. price varies. **Document type:** *Monographic series, Academic/Scholarly.*
Published by: Rainer Hampp Verlag, Meringerzellerstr 10, Mering, 86415, Germany. TEL 49-8233-4783, FAX 49-8233-30755, Rainer_Hampp_Verlag@t-online.de, http://www.hampp-verlag.de.

658.3 NLD ISSN 0031-5656
PERSONEELBELEID. Text in Dutch. 1965. m. (11/yr.). EUR 139 domestic; EUR 167 foreign (effective 2005). adv. bk.rev. charts; illus. **Document type:** *Journal, Trade.*
Related titles: Diskette ed.
Indexed: KES.
—IE, Infotrieve, KNAW.
Published by: (Nederlandse Vereniging voor Personeelbeleid), Sdu Uitgevers bv, Postbus 20025, The Hague, 2500 EA, Netherlands. TEL 31-70-3789321, FAX 31-70-3789766, personeelbeleid@sdu.nl, sdu@sdu.nl, http://www.sdu.nl/. Ed. Henk Vlaming. Circ: 8,300. **Subscr. to:** Postbus 20014, The Hague 2500 EA, Netherlands. TEL 31-70-3789880, FAX 31-70-3789783.

658.3 POL ISSN 1641-0793
PERSONEL I ZARZADZANIE. Text in Polish. s-m. PLZ 150 (effective 2001).
Published by: Grupa Wydawnicza INFOR Sp. z o.o., Ul Okopowa 58/72, Warsaw, 01042, Poland. TEL 48-22-5304208, 48-22-5304450, bok@infor.pl. Ed. Wojciech Gladykowski. Adv. contact Waldemar Krakowiak.

658.3 FRA ISSN 0223-5692
PERSONNEL. Variant title: La Revue Personnel. Text in French. 195?. m. reprints avail. **Document type:** *Magazine, Trade.*
Former titles (until 1968): Direction de Personnel (1247-9578); (until 1963): A N D C P. Revue Bimestrielle (1247-9586)
Indexed: AgeL, RASB.
—BLDSC (6428.033000).
Published by: A N D C P/National Association of Directors and Personnel Officers, 91 Rue Miromesnil, Paris, 75008, France. TEL 33-1-56881828, FAX 33-1-56881829, andcp@andcp.fr, http://www.andcp.fr. Ed. Jacques Laurioz. Circ: 7,000.

658.3 GBR ISSN 1351-0614
PERSONNEL ASSISTANT'S HANDBOOK BULLETIN. Text in English. 1993. base vol. plus m. updates. looseleaf. GBP 184.36. **Document type:** *Trade.*
Published by: Croner.C C H Group Ltd. (Subsidiary of: Wolters Kluwer N.V.), 145 London Rd, Kingston, Surrey KT2 6SR, United Kingdom. TEL 44-20-85473333, FAX 44-20-85472637, info@croner.co.uk, http://www.croner.co.uk.

658.3 GBR
PERSONNEL IN PRACTICE. Variant title: Croner's Personnel in Practice. Text in English. base vol. plus q. updates. looseleaf. GBP 411 (effective 1999). **Document type:** *Trade.*
Related titles: Supplement(s): Croner at C C H Employment Case Digest; ♦ Employment Case Digest. ISSN 0966-1662.
Indexed: M&MA.
Published by: Croner.C C H Group Ltd. (Subsidiary of: Wolters Kluwer N.V.), 145 London Rd, Kingston, Surrey KT2 6SR, United Kingdom. TEL 44-20-85473333, FAX 44-20-85472637, info@croner.co.uk, http://www.croner.co.uk.

658.3 USA ISSN 1084-6913
THE PERSONNEL LEGAL ALERT. Text in English. 1989. s-m. USD 139 (effective 2005). back issues avail. **Document type:** *Newsletter.* **Description:** Provides personnel managers with up-to-date information on important court decisions, government regulations, and trends in employment law.
Formerly (until 19??): Personnel Alert (1044-2189)
Published by: Alexander Hamilton Institute, Inc., 70 Hilltop Rd, Ramsey, NJ 07446-1119. TEL 201-825-3377, 800-879-2441, FAX 201-825-8696, pla@ahipubs.com, http://www.ahipubs.com. Ed. Brian L P Zevnik.

658.3 USA ISSN 0149-2675
KF3315
PERSONNEL MANAGEMENT. Text in English. 1969. w. looseleaf. USD 938 (effective 2001). back issues avail.; reprints avail. **Document type:** *Newsletter.* **Description:** Practical guide to handling non-legal employee relations problems, in areas such as hiring, termination, workplace safety, grievances, training, and productivity.
Related titles: Online - full text ed.; ♦ Series of: B N A Policy and Practice Series. ISSN 0005-3228.
Indexed: AgeL, BAS, M&MA.
—CCC.
Published by: The Bureau of National Affairs, Inc., 1231 25th St., NW, Washington, DC 20037. TEL 202-452-4200, 800-372-1033, 800-452-7773, FAX 202-822-8092, customercare@bna.com, bnaplus@bna.com, http://www.bna.com/. Ed. Bill L Manville. Pub. Greg C McCaffery.

658.3 331.21 USA
PERSONNEL MANAGER'S ENCYCLOPEDIA OF PREWRITTEN PERSONNEL POLICIES. Text in English. base vol. plus bi-m. updates. looseleaf. USD 199.95 (effective 1999). **Description:** Contains over 350 policies on more than 100 subjects such as attendance and time-off, workplace violence, compensation, employee benefits, and discipline.
Published by: Business & Legal Reports, Inc., PO Box 6001, Old Saybrook, CT 06475-6001. TEL 203-245-7448, FAX 203-245-0483, service@blr.com. Pub. Robert L Brady.

658.3 GBR ISSN 0265-704X
THE PERSONNEL MANAGER'S YEARBOOK. Abbreviated title: PMY. Text in English. 1984. a., latest vol.17. GBP 109.95 (effective 2001). adv. stat. Index of major companies by region and by business activity. SIC code. 1400 p./no.; **Document type:** *Directory, Trade.* **Description:** Lists key personnel, recruitment and training executives in the U.K.'s 9,000 largest companies and organizations. Also lists 5,000 providers of services to the industry.
Related titles: Diskette ed.
—BLDSC (6428.089100).
Published by: A P Information Services, Marlborough House, 298 Regents Park Rd, London, N3 2UU, United Kingdom. TEL 44-20-83499988, FAX 44-20-83499797, pmy@ap-info.co.uk, info@apinfo.co.uk, http://www.ap-info.co.uk. Ed. Laura Storr. Pub. Alan Philipp. Adv. contact James Johnston. B&W page GBP 915, color page GBP 1,500; trim 210 x 297. Circ: 6,000.

658.3 USA
PERSONNEL POLICIES AND BENEFITS FOR THE APPAREL INDUSTRY. Text in English. irreg. USD 60 to non-members; USD 25 to members. **Document type:** *Trade.*
Supersedes in part: Apparel Plant Wages and Personnel Policies (0084-6678)
Published by: American Apparel Manufacturers Association, 1601 N. Kent St., Ste. 1200, Arlington, VA 22209-2105. TEL 703-524-1864, FAX 703-522-6741.

658.3 GBR
PERSONNEL POLICIES IN EUROPE. Text in English. q. GBP 600. **Document type:** *Directory.* **Description:** Covers relevant personnel practices in European countries.
Published by: P-E Inbucon Ltd., Brooks House, 34 Paradise Rd, Richmond-upon-Thames, Surrey TW9 1SE, United Kingdom. TEL 44-181-334-5727, FAX 44-181-334-5739, meis@easynet.co.uk. R&P Rosemary Hook.

PERSONNEL PSYCHOLOGY. see *PSYCHOLOGY*

658.3 GBR ISSN 0048-3486
HF5549.A2
➤ **PERSONNEL REVIEW.** Text in English. 1971. bi-m. EUR 11,385.04 in Europe; USD 11,569 in North America; AUD 13,879 in Australasia; GBP 7,580.66 in UK & elsewhere (effective 2006). bk.rev. bibl.; charts; illus.; abstr. cum.index. back issues avail.; reprint service avail. from PSC. **Document type:** *Journal, Academic/Scholarly.* **Description:** Seeks to present the latest research and developments in all disciplines of relevance to the personnel specialist. Covers organizational behavior and design, personnel and occupational psychology, education, training and development, staff planning and more.
Related titles: CD-ROM ed.; Online - full text ed.: (from EBSCO Publishing, Emerald Group Publishing Limited, Florida Center for Library Automation, Gale Group, IngentaConnect, O C L C Online Computer Library Center, Inc., ProQuest Information & Learning, Swets Information Services).
Indexed: ABIn, ADPA, ASCA, ASEANManA, BPIA, BrEdI, BusI, CPM, CurCont, EAA, EmerIntel, Emerald, HECAB, HRA, Inspec, M&MA, ManagCont, PRA, PsycInfo, PsycholAb, SCIMP, SOMA, SSCI, SWA, T&DA, TEA, V&AA, WorkRelAb.
—BLDSC (6428.098000), IDS, IE, Infotrieve, ingenta. **CCC.**
Published by: (Institute of Personnel Management), Emerald Group Publishing Limited, 60-62 Toller Ln, Bradford, W Yorks BD8 9BY, United Kingdom. TEL 44-1274-777700, FAX 44-1274-785200, infomation@emeraldinsight.com, http://www.emeraldinsight.com/pr.htm. Ed. Tom Redman.

➤ **PERSONNEL REWARDS.** see *BUSINESS AND ECONOMICS—Labor And Industrial Relations*

658.3 330 USA ISSN 1536-3376
HF5549.5.D37
PERSONNEL SOFTWARE CENSUS. VOL. 1: DEPARTMENTAL SOFTWARE. Text in English. 1989. a. USD 79.95; USD 119.95 for print and electronic version (effective 2000). adv. **Document type:** *Directory.* **Description:** Lists HR software with 1,300 125-word listings and complete vendor contact information. Covers micro, midrange, mainframe and Internet-based systems for employment, skills, payroll, training, performance, attendance and timekeeping, health and safety.
Supersedes in part: Personnel Software Census (1065-4615)
Related titles: CD-ROM ed.: ISSN 1536-3341; E-mail ed.
Published by: Advanced Personnel Systems, 1247, Roseville, CA 95678-8247. TEL 916-781-2900, FAX 916-781-2901, frantz@hrcensus.com, http://www.hrcensus.com. Ed. Richard B Frantzreb. Circ: 1,000 (paid).

658.3 330 USA
HF5549.5.D37
PERSONNEL SOFTWARE CENSUS. VOL. 2: HUMAN RESOURCE INFORMATION SYSTEMS. Text in English. 1989. a. USD 79.95; USD 119.95 with online ed. (effective 2000). adv. **Description:** Lists 120 HR information systems with 750 word listings and complete vendor contact information. Covers micro, midrange, mainframe, client/server and Internet-based systems. Also includes brief listings of systems marketed outside the US & Canada as well as systems for special industries (education,government, healthcare, etc.) Special feature: directory of 50 HR systems consulting firms.
Supersedes in part: Personnel Software Census (1065-4615)
Media: Diskette. **Related titles:** CD-ROM ed.: ISSN 1536-335X; E-mail ed.; Print ed.: ISSN 1536-3384.
Published by: Advanced Personnel Systems, 1247, Roseville, CA 95678-8247. TEL 916-781-2900, FAX 916-781-2901, frantz@hrcensus.com, http://www.hrcensus.com. Ed. Richard B Frantzreb. Circ: 1,000 (paid).

658.3 GBR ISSN 0959-5848
PERSONNEL TODAY. Text in English. 1987. w. GBP 86 (effective 2005). adv. bk.rev. **Document type:** *Magazine, Trade.* **Description:** Written for directors, managers, officers and assistants in personnel, training, recruitment, industrial relations and human resources.
Related titles: Online - full text ed.: (from EBSCO Publishing, Gale Group, H.W. Wilson, O C L C Online Computer Library Center, Inc.).
Indexed: BPI, Emerald.
—BLDSC (6428.102100), IE, ingenta. **CCC.**
Published by: Reed Business Information Ltd. (Subsidiary of: Reed Business), Quadrant House, The Quadrant, Brighton Rd, Sutton, Surrey SM2 5AS, United Kingdom. TEL 44-20-86523500, FAX 44-20-86528932, personnel.today@rbi.co.uk, rbi.subscriptions@qss-uk.com, http://www.personneltoday.com/, http://www.reedbusiness.co.uk/. Ed. David Nunn TEL 44-20-8652-4643. Pub. Susan Downey. R&P Toby Wolpe. Adv. contact Trevor Parker. Circ: 51,396. **Subscr. to:** Quadrant Subscription Services, PO Box 302, Haywards Heath, W Sussex RH16 3YY, United Kingdom. TEL 44-1444-445566, FAX 44-1444-445447.

658.3 IND ISSN 0970-8405
PERSONNEL TODAY. Text in English. 1949. q. USD 50 (effective 2000). adv. bk.rev. illus. **Document type:** *Academic/Scholarly.*
Formerly (until 1980): Industrial Relations (0019-8684)
Published by: National Institute of Personnel Management, 45 Jhowtalla Rd., Kolkata, West Bengal 700 019, India. TEL 91-33-2475650, FAX 91-33-2408179, nipma@cal2.vsnl.net.in. Ed. B D Pande. Circ: 6,000.

658.3 AUS ISSN 1325-6920
PHARMACEUTICAL INDUSTRY REMUNERATION REVIEW. Text in English. 1986. biennial. AUD 1,550 (effective 1999). **Document type:** *Trade.*
Published by: Cullen Egan Dell, Level 8, 50 Bridge St, Sydney, NSW 2000, Australia. TEL 61-2-9375-9800, FAX 61-2-9233-6800. Ed. James Cooper. Circ: 65.

POLICIES, PRACTICES, AND EMPLOYEE BENEFITS SURVEY. see *BUSINESS AND ECONOMICS—Labor And Industrial Relations*

658.3 GBR
PRACTICAL TRAINING. Text in English. 1982. m. (except Aug.). GBP 18.77. adv. bk.rev. **Document type:** *Trade.* **Description:** Provides professional trainers with lively, in-depth, and accessible articles covering core training topics across all industry sectors, along with news and reviews.
Formerly (until 1995): Training and Development
Indexed: CPE, ETA, TEA.
Published by: (Institute of Training and Development), Kay Davis Publishing, 166 Pullman Ct, Streatham Hill, London, SW2 4S2, United Kingdom. TEL 0171-671-2060. Ed. Eva Tyler. Pub., Adv. contact Kay Davis. Circ: 23,000.

PRAVO I PRIVREDA. see *LAW*

658.3 DEU
PRAXIS UND RECHT. Text in German. q. free. **Document type:** *Magazine, Trade.*
Published by: Deutsche Angestellten Krankenkasse, Nagelsweg 27-35, Hamburg, 20097, Germany. service@dak.de, http://www.dak.de.

658.3 DEU ISSN 1611-6089
▼ **PRAXISORIENTIERTE PERSONAL- UND ORGANISATIONSFORSCHUNG.** Text in German. 2003. irreg., latest vol.8, 2005. price varies. **Document type:** *Monographic series, Academic/Scholarly.*
Published by: Rainer Hampp Verlag, Meringerzellerstr 10, Mering, 86415, Germany. TEL 49-8233-4783, FAX 49-8233-30755, Rainer_Hampp_Verlag@t-online.de, http://www.hampp-verlag.de.

658.3 388 USA
PREVIEW (TROY). Text in English. m. software rev.; video rev. charts; illus.; stat. **Description:** Training and education publication for Chevrolet dealers and dealership managers.
Published by: Chevrolet Motor Division, PO Box 500, Troy, MI 48007-0500. Ed. Duane Rose. Adv. contact Heidi Dilloway.

658 USA
PROFESSIONAL AND SCIENTIFIC PERSONNEL REPORT - GEOGRAPHIC EDITION. Text in English. a. USD 690. charts. **Document type:** *Trade.* **Description:** Provides geographic analyses of salaries and total cash compensation for a full spectrum of professional positions.
Related titles: ♦ Supplement(s): Industry Report on Professional and Scientific Personnel Compensation.
Published by: (Executive Compensation Service (ECS)), Wyatt Data Services, 218 Rte 17 N, Rochelle Park, NJ 07622-9832. TEL 201-843-1177, FAX 201-843-0101.

658.3 USA ISSN 0091-0260
HF5549.A2 CODEN: PPMNCX
➤ **PUBLIC PERSONNEL MANAGEMENT.** Text in English. 1972. q. USD 110 domestic; USD 135 foreign (effective 2005). adv. bk.rev. abstr.; bibl.; illus.; stat.; charts. index. reprint service avail. from PQC. **Document type:** *Journal, Academic/Scholarly.* **Description:** Articles on labor relations, assessment issues, comparative personnel policies, governmental reform and other areas of concern to personnel managers in the public sector.
Formerly (until 1973): Personnel Administration and Public Personnel Review (0885-6591); Which was formed by the merger of (1940-1972): Public Personnel Review (0033-3638); (1938-1972): Personnel Administration (0031-5710)
Related titles: Microform ed.: (from MIM, PQC); Online - full text ed.: USD 75 (effective 2004) (from bigchalk, EBSCO Publishing, Florida Center for Library Automation, Gale Group, H.W. Wilson, Northern Light Technology, Inc., O C L C Online Computer Library Center, Inc., ProQuest Information & Learning).
Indexed: ABCPolSci, ABIn, ADPA, ASCA, ATI, AgeL, BPI, BPIA, BRI, BusI, CBRI, CIJE, CINAHL, CJA, CurCont, DPD, EAA, Emerald, FamI, MEA&I, PAIS, PMA, PersLit, PsySCAP, PsycInfo, PsycholAb, QAb, SPAA, SSCI, T&DA, T&II, WorkRelAb, YAE&RB, e-psyche.
—BLDSC (6967.890000), CISTI, IDS, IE, Infotrieve, ingenta. **CCC.**
Published by: International Personnel Management Association, 1617 Duke St, Alexandria, VA 22314. TEL 703-549-7100, FAX 703-684-0948, publications@ipma-hr.org, http://www.ipma-hr.org. Ed. Caroline Wilson. adv.: page USD 600; 6 x 9. Circ: 7,000 (paid).

658.3 USA
QUALIFIED PLAN ADMINISTRATOR'S MANUAL. Text in English. and newsletters), base vol. plus q. updates. looseleaf. USD 270. **Document type:** *Trade.* **Description:** Provides practical guidance on administering qualified retirement plans and staying in compliance with regulations.
Published by: W G & L Financial Reporting & Management Research (Subsidiary of: R I A), 395 Hudson St, New York, NY 10014. TEL 212-367-6300, FAX 212-367-6718, http://www.InsideHR.com. Ed. Martin Censor. **Subscr. to:** The Park Square Bldg., 31 St James Ave, Boston, MA 02116-4112. TEL 800-950-1207.

658.3 USA ISSN 1072-9135
THE QUALITY YEARBOOK. Text in English. 1994. a.
Published by: McGraw-Hill Companies, Inc., 1221 Ave of the Americas, New York, NY 10020. TEL 212-512-4736, FAX 212-512-6904.

658.3 CAN ISSN 1703-5465
QUARTERLY LABOUR MARKET AND INCOME REVIEW/REVUE TRIMESTRIELLE SUR LE MARCHE DU TRAVAIL ET LE REVENU. Text in English, French. 2001. q.
Published by: Human Resources Development Canada, Applied Research Branch, 165 Hotel de Ville St, Phase II, 7th Fl, Hull, PQ K1A OJ2, Canada. FAX 819-953-8868, http://www.hrsdc.gc.ca, http://dsp-psd.communication.gc.ca/Collection/RH62-2-3-1E.pdf.

331 650 AUS ISSN 0314-2558
QUARTERLY SALARY REVIEW. Text in English. 1968. q. AUD 2,300. **Document type:** *Trade.* **Description:** Covers positions at all levels of corporate, administrative and technical functions. Provides global view of salary movements in Australia.
Published by: Cullen Egan Dell, Level 8, 50 Bridge St, Sydney, NSW 2000, Australia. TEL 61-2-9375-9800, FAX 61-2-9375-6800. Ed. Matt Darian. Circ: 650.

658.3 DEU
R K W KONTAKT. Text in German. 1955. bi-m. free to members. bk.rev. **Document type:** *Newsletter, Trade.*
Published by: Rationalisierungs- und Innovationszentrum der Deutschen Wirtschaft e.V., Landesgruppe Bayern, Gustav-Heinemann-Ring 212, Munich, 81739, Germany. TEL 49-89-670040-0, FAX 49-89-67004040, info@rkw-bayern.de, http://www.rkw-bayern.de. Ed. Rudolf Donnert. Circ: 2,500.

RECRUIT!. see *INSURANCE*

331.1 658.3 USA
RECRUITER. Text in English. q. back issues avail. **Document type:** *Newsletter, Trade.* **Description:** Contains tips on day-to-day agency management for field managers on such topics as recruiting, retention, cost control, and motivation.
Related titles: Online - full content ed.; Esperanto ed.; Chinese ed.
Published by: L I M R A International, Inc., 300 Day Hill Rd, Windsor, CT 06095. TEL 860-688-3358, FAX 860-298-9555, http://www.limra.com/.

658.0029 USA
RECRUITING AND SEARCH REPORT; executive search - headhunter directories. Text in English. 1980. w. looseleaf. USD 15. bk.rev. bibl.; charts; stat. back issues avail. **Description:** Executive search firm directories by their industry and functional area of expertise.
Related titles: Diskette ed.
Published by: Recruiting & Search Report, PO Box 9433, Panama City, FL 32417. TEL 850-235-3733, FAX 850-233-9695. Ed., Pub. Kenneth J Cole. Circ: 7,000.

RECRUITING TRENDS; the monthly newsletter for the recruiting executive. see *BUSINESS AND ECONOMICS—Labor And Industrial Relations*

REFERATIVNYI ZHURNAL. KADRY, EKONOMIKA OBRAZOVANIYA. see *BUSINESS AND ECONOMICS—Abstracting, Bibliographies, Statistics*

REGIONAL REPORT ON MIDDLE MANAGEMENT COMPENSATION. see *BUSINESS AND ECONOMICS—Management*

658.3   AUS
REINSURANCE INDUSTRY REMUNERATION REVIEW. Text in English. 1992. a. AUD 950 (effective 1999). **Document type:** *Trade.* **Description:** Provides data on the remuneration and benefits practices of reinsurance companies.
Published by: Cullen Egan Dell, Level 8, 50 Bridge St, Sydney, NSW 2000, Australia. TEL 61-2-9375-9800, FAX 61-2-9233-6800. Ed. Paul Adams. Circ: 11.

RELATIONS INDUSTRIELLES/INDUSTRIAL RELATIONS. see *BUSINESS AND ECONOMICS—Labor And Industrial Relations*

658.3 333.33   USA   ISSN 0275-7613
THE RELOCATION REPORT. Text in English. 1977. s-m. looseleaf. USD 227 (effective 1999). bk.rev. back issues avail. **Document type:** *Newsletter, Trade.* **Description:** Provides relocation industry news for real estate brokers, appraisers and corporate relocation specialists.
—CCC.
Published by: Federal News Service, PO Box 8548, Silver Spring, MD 20907-8548. TEL 301-608-9322, FAX 410-740-5039, dezu@erols.com. Ed. Dona Dezube. Pub., R&P Margaret Waitt.

658.3   GBR
REMUNERATION IN EUROPE. Text in English. a. GBP 475 (effective 1998). **Document type:** *Directory.* **Description:** Salary and benefits information for directors down to middle managers.
Published by: P-E Inbucon Ltd., Brooks House, 34 Paradise Rd, Richmond-upon-Thames, Surrey TW9 1SE, United Kingdom. TEL 44-181-334-5727, FAX 44-181-334-5739, meis@easynet.co.uk. R&P Rosemary Hook.

658   USA
REMUNERATION REPORT - AUSTRIA. Text in English. a. USD 825. **Document type:** *Trade.*
Published by: (Executive Compensation Service (ECS)), Wyatt Data Services, 218 Rte 17 N, Rochelle Park, NJ 07622-9832. TEL 201-843-1177, FAX 201-843-0101.

658   USA
REMUNERATION REPORT - BELGIUM. Text in English. a. USD 825. **Document type:** *Trade.*
Published by: (Executive Compensation Service (ECS)), Wyatt Data Services, 218 Rte 17 N, Rochelle Park, NJ 07622-9832. TEL 201-843-1177, FAX 201-843-0101.

658   USA
REMUNERATION REPORT - DENMARK. Text in English. a. USD 825. **Document type:** *Trade.*
Published by: (Executive Compensation Service (ECS)), Wyatt Data Services, 218 Rte 17 N, Rochelle Park, NJ 07622-9832. TEL 201-843-1177, FAX 201-843-0101.

658   USA
REMUNERATION REPORT - FINLAND. Text in English. a. USD 825. **Document type:** *Trade.*
Published by: (Executive Compensation Service (ECS)), Wyatt Data Services, 218 Rte 17 N, Rochelle Park, NJ 07622-9832. TEL 201-843-1177, FAX 201-843-0101.

658   USA
REMUNERATION REPORT - FRANCE. Text in English. a. USD 825. **Document type:** *Trade.*
Published by: (Executive Compensation Service (ECS)), Wyatt Data Services, 218 Rte 17 N, Rochelle Park, NJ 07622-9832. TEL 201-843-1177, FAX 201-843-0101.

658   USA
REMUNERATION REPORT - GERMANY. Text in English. a. USD 825. **Document type:** *Trade.*
Published by: (Executive Compensation Service (ECS)), Wyatt Data Services, 218 Rte 17 N, Rochelle Park, NJ 07622-9832. TEL 201-843-1177, FAX 201-843-0101.

658   USA
REMUNERATION REPORT - GREECE. Text in English. a. USD 825. **Document type:** *Trade.*
Published by: (Executive Compensation Service (ECS)), Wyatt Data Services, 218 Rte 17 N, Rochelle Park, NJ 07622-9832. TEL 201-843-1177, FAX 201-843-0101.

658   USA
REMUNERATION REPORT - IRELAND. Text in English. a. USD 825. **Document type:** *Trade.*
Published by: (Executive Compensation Service (ECS)), Wyatt Data Services, 218 Rte 17 N, Rochelle Park, NJ 07622-9832. TEL 201-843-1177, FAX 201-843-0101.

658   USA
REMUNERATION REPORT - ITALY. Text in English. a. USD 825. **Document type:** *Trade.*
Published by: (Executive Compensation Service (ECS)), Wyatt Data Services, 218 Rte 17 N, Rochelle Park, NJ 07622-9832. TEL 201-843-1177, FAX 201-843-0101.

658   USA
REMUNERATION REPORT - LUXEMBOURG. Text in English. a. USD 825. **Document type:** *Trade.*
Published by: (Executive Compensation Service (ECS)), Wyatt Data Services, 218 Rte 17 N, Rochelle Park, NJ 07622-9832. TEL 201-843-1177, FAX 201-843-0101.

658   USA
REMUNERATION REPORT - NETHERLANDS. Text in English. a. USD 825. **Document type:** *Trade.*
Published by: (Executive Compensation Service (ECS)), Wyatt Data Services, 218 Rte 17 N, Rochelle Park, NJ 07622-9832. TEL 609-843-1177, FAX 201-843-0101.

658   USA
REMUNERATION REPORT - NORWAY. Text in English. a. USD 825. **Document type:** *Trade.*
Published by: (Executive Compensation Service (ECS)), Wyatt Data Services, 218 Rte 17 N, Rochelle Park, NJ 07622-9832. TEL 201-843-1177, FAX 201-843-0101.

658   USA
REMUNERATION REPORT - PORTUGAL. Text in English. a. USD 825. **Document type:** *Trade.*
Published by: (Executive Compensation Service (ECS)), Wyatt Data Services, 218 Rte 17 N, Rochelle Park, NJ 07622-9832. TEL 201-843-1177, FAX 201-843-0101.

658   USA
REMUNERATION REPORT - SPAIN. Text in English. a. USD 825. **Document type:** *Trade.*
Published by: (Executive Compensation Service (ECS)), Wyatt Data Services, 218 Rte 17 N, Rochelle Park, NJ 07622-9832. TEL 201-843-1177, FAX 201-843-0101.

658   USA
REMUNERATION REPORT - SWEDEN. Text in English. a. USD 825. **Document type:** *Trade.*
Published by: (Executive Compensation Service (ECS)), Wyatt Data Services, 218 Rte 17 N, Rochelle Park, NJ 07622-9832. TEL 201-843-1177, FAX 201-843-0101.

658   USA
REMUNERATION REPORT - SWITZERLAND. Text in English. a. USD 825. **Document type:** *Trade.*
Published by: (Executive Compensation Service (ECS)), Wyatt Data Services, 218 Rte 17 N, Rochelle Park, NJ 07622-9832. TEL 201-843-1177, FAX 201-843-0101.

658   USA
REMUNERATION REPORT - TURKEY. Text in English. a. USD 825. **Document type:** *Trade.*
Published by: (Executive Compensation Service (ECS)), Wyatt Data Services, 218 Rte 17 N, Rochelle Park, NJ 07622-9832. TEL 201-843-1177, FAX 201-843-0101.

658   USA
REMUNERATION REPORT - UNITED KINGDOM. Text in English. a. USD 825. **Document type:** *Trade.*
Published by: (Executive Compensation Service (ECS)), Wyatt Data Services, 218 Rte 17 N, Rochelle Park, NJ 07622-9832. TEL 201-843-1177, FAX 201-843-0101.

658.3   CHN   ISSN 1000-7628
RENCAI KAIFA/TALENT EXPLOITATION. Text in Chinese. 1986. m. CNY 60 (effective 2004). adv. bk.rev. **Document type:** *Academic/Scholarly.* **Description:** Promotes reform on personnel management system.
Related titles: Online - full text ed.: (from East View Information Services).
Published by: Shanghai Rencai Yanjiuhui/Shanghai Society of Talents Research, 278-288, Fuxing Xilu, Dingxianghuayuang 4-hao-Luo 3-Luo, Shanghai, 200031, China. TEL 86-21-3274690. Ed. Zuo Chao. Circ: 50,000. **Dist. outside of China by:** China International Book Trading Corp, 35 Chegongzhuang Xilu, Haidian District, PO Box 399, Beijing 100044, China. TEL 86-10-68412045, FAX 86-10-68412023, cibtc@mail.cibtc.com.cn, http://www.cibtc.com.cn/.

658.3   CHN
RENLI ZIYUAN BAO. Text in Chinese. every 3 wks. **Document type:** *Newspaper, Trade.*
Related titles: Online - full content ed.
Published by: Sichuan Ribao Baoye Jituan, Renmin Zhonglu, Section 1, no.1, Chengdu, 610013, China. TEL 86-28-86261724, FAX 86-28-86262701, scjob@scol.com.cn, http://scjob.scol.com.cn/.

658.3   CHN   ISSN 1009-7678
RENLI ZIYUAN KAIFA GUANLI/HUMAN RESOURCES DEVELOPMENT AND MANAGEMENT. Text in Chinese. m. CNY 70.80 (effective 2004). **Document type:** *Journal, Academic/Scholarly.*

Published by: Zhongguo Renmin Daxue, Shubao Zilio Zhongxin/Renmin University of China, Information Center for Social Server, Dongcheng-qu, 3, Zhangzizhong Lu, Beijing, 100007, China. TEL 86-10-64039458, FAX 86-10-64015080, kyes@163.net, http://www.confucius.cn.net/bkdetail.asp?fzt= F102. **Dist. by:** China International Book Trading Corp, 35 Chegongzhuang Xilu, Haidian District, PO Box 399, Beijing 100044, China. TEL 86-10-68412045, FAX 86-10-68412023, cibtc@mail.cibtc.com.cn, http://www.cibtc.com.cn; China Publications Service, PO Box 49614, Chicago, IL 60649. TEL 312-288-3191, FAX 312-288-8570.

RENTAL MANAGEMENT. see *BUSINESS AND ECONOMICS—Marketing And Purchasing*

REPORT ON CANADIAN EXECUTIVE AND MIDDLE MANAGEMENT REMUNERATION. see *BUSINESS AND ECONOMICS—Management*

658   USA   ISSN 1060-0205
REPORT ON EXECUTIVE REMUNERATION. Text in English. 1988. a. **Document type:** *Trade.*
Published by: (Executive Compensation Service (ECS)), Wyatt Data Services, 218 Rte 17 N, Rochelle Park, NJ 07622-9832. TEL 201-843-1177, FAX 201-843-0101.

658   USA   ISSN 1063-1968
HF5549.2.U5
REPORT ON HUMAN RESOURCES COMPENSATION. Text in English. a. USD 340. charts. **Document type:** *Trade.* **Description:** Provides a complete perspective on compensation in the human resources field.
Published by: (Executive Compensation Service (ECS)), Wyatt Data Services, 218 Rte 17 N, Rochelle Park, NJ 07622-9832. TEL 201-843-1177, FAX 201-843-0101.

658   USA   ISSN 1057-9494
REPORT ON OFFICE PERSONNEL REMUNERATION∗. Text in English. 1981. a. USD 600. **Document type:** *Trade.* **Description:** Geographically focused pay information reported for 71 office personnel positions.
Former titles (until 1990): Report on Canadian Office Personnel Remuneration (1044-6028); (until 1987): Office Personnel Remuneration, Canada (0835-6718); (until 1985): Report on Office Personnel Remuneration, Canada (0829-5441); Office Personnel Canada (0229-1649)
Published by: (Executive Compensation Service (ECS)), Wyatt Data Services, 218 Rte 17 N, Rochelle Park, NJ 07622-9832. TEL 201-585-9808, FAX 201-585-0127.

331.21   USA
REPORT ON SALARY SURVEYS YEARBOOK. Text in English. a. USD 224.95 print & online eds. (effective 2003). **Description:** Reports on salary surveys in the areas of accounting and finance human resources, customer service, marketing, logistics, purchasing, and mail center and office services.
Related titles: Online - full text ed.: USD 219 (effective 2003); ♦ Cumulative ed. of: I O M A's Report on Salary Surveys. ISSN 1067-4551.
Published by: Institute of Management & Administration, Inc., 3 Park Ave, New York, NY 10016-5902. TEL 212-244-0360, FAX 212-564-0465, subserve@ioma.com, http://www.ioma.com. Ed. Laime Vaitkus.

658.3   SGP   ISSN 0218-5180
HF5549.A2
➤ **RESEARCH AND PRACTICE IN HUMAN RESOURCE MANAGEMENT.** Text in English. 1993. a. (Jul.). SGD 18.54 newsstand/cover domestic; USD 35 newsstand/cover foreign. **Document type:** *Journal, Academic/Scholarly.* **Description:** Synthesizes theory and practice in human resources management to seek out new solutions to problems relating to the human side of business enterprise.
—BLDSC (7715.697000).
Published by: Singapore Human Resources Institute, 60A Collyer Quay, 5th Level, Change Alley Aerial Plaza Tower, Singapore, 049322, Singapore. TEL 65-438-0012, FAX 65-438-0029, shri@singnet.com.sg, http://www.fba.nus.edu.sg/rphrm, http://www.shri.org.sg. **Co-sponsor:** National University of Singapore, Faculty of Business Administration.

658.3   USA   ISSN 0742-7301
HF5549.A2
RESEARCH IN PERSONNEL AND HUMAN RESOURCES MANAGEMENT. Text in English. 1983. a., latest vol.24, 2005. price varies. back issues avail. **Document type:** *Monographic series, Academic/Scholarly.* **Description:** Designed to promote theory and research on important substantive and methodological topics in the field of human resources management.
Related titles: Online - full text ed.: (from ScienceDirect).
—BLDSC (7755.071000), IE, ingenta. **CCC.**
Published by: J A I Press Inc. (Subsidiary of: Elsevier Science & Technology), 360 Park Ave S, New York, NY 10010-1710. TEL 212-989-5800, FAX 212-633-3990, usinfo-f@elsevier.com, http://www.elsevier.com/wps/find/bookdescription.cws_home/ BS_RPHR/description#description. Eds. Gerald Ferris, J Martocchio.

336 346.066 USA
RETIREMENT AND BENEFIT PLANNING; strategy and design for businesses and tax-exempt organizations. Text in English. 1991. base vol. plus a. updates. looseleaf. USD 105.
Description: Comprehensive review of laws and planning principles covering retirement plans from a legal perspective. Covers the emerging areas of retirement planning, and the benefits and responsibilities for employers and employees.
Published by: LexisNexis (Subsidiary of: LexisNexis North America), PO Box 7587, Charlottesville, VA 22906-7587. TEL 804-972-7600, 800-562-1197, FAX 804-972-7666, llp.customer.support@lexis-nexis.com, http://www.lexislawpublishing.com. Ed. Randolph M Goodman.

658.3 FRA ISSN 1163-913X
REVUE DE GESTION DES RESSOURCES HUMAINES. Text in French. 1991. q. **Document type:** *Trade.* **Description:** Seeks to develop, verify, and advance knowledge in human resources management.
Related titles: Online - full text ed.: (from ProQuest Information & Learning).
Indexed: ABIn.
Published by: (Association de la Gestion des Ressources Humaines), Editions E S K A, 12 avenue du 4 septembre, Paris, 75002, France. TEL 33-1-4286-5593, FAX 33-1-4260-4535, eska@eska.fr, http://www.eska.fr.

658.3 FRA
REVUE RESSOURCES HUMAINES. Text in French. 4/yr.
Published by: Societe Formac, 45 rue de Turbigo, Paris, 75003, France. Ed. Brigitte Bouillon. Circ: 7,500.

658 910.9 USA ISSN 0731-9150
RUNZHEIMER REPORTS ON RELOCATION. Text in English. 1982. m. looseleaf. USD 354. back issues avail. **Document type:** *Newsletter.*
—CCC.
Published by: Runzheimer International, Runzheimer Park, Rochester, WI 53167. TEL 262-971-2200, http://www.runzheimer.com. Ed. Nat Workman.

658 910.09 USA
RUNZHEIMER REPORTS ON TRAVEL MANAGEMENT (ONLINE EDITION). Text in English. 1981. m. looseleaf. free to qualified personnel. back issues avail. **Document type:** *Newsletter, Trade.* **Description:** Offers travel administrators a reliable source of information each month on industry practices and benchmarking data.
Formerly: Runzheimer Reports on Travel Management (Print Edition) (0730-8663)
—CCC.
Published by: Runzheimer International, Runzheimer Park, Rochester, WI 53167. TEL 262-971-2200, 800-558-1702, FAX 262-971-2254, webmaster@runzheimer.com, http://www.runzheimer.com/tmc/scripts/rrtm.asp.

S B B ZEITUNG; Informationen fuer die Mitarbeiterinnen und Mitarbeiter der Schweizerischen Bundesbahnen. see *TRANSPORTATION—Railroads*

658.3 USA ISSN 1063-1917
S E R AMERICA. (Service, Employment, Redevelopment) Text in English. 1972. q. USD 25 to individuals; USD 100 to institutions. adv. bibl.; stat. **Description:** Discusses the development and utilization of human resources with special emphasis on the needs of Hispanics in the areas of education, training, employment, business and economic opportunities.
Former titles (until 1986): S E R Network News; S E R News; Adelante S E R
Published by: S E R - Jobs for Progress, Inc., 1925 W. John Carpenter Fwy., Ste. 5D, Irving, TX 75063-3209. TEL 214-541-0616, FAX 214-650-1860. Ed. Juan J Constantino. Adv. contact Sherri Seidel. Circ: 15,000.

658.3 USA
S E R NETWORK DIRECTORY. (Service, Employment, Redevelopment) Text in English. a. **Document type:** *Directory.* **Description:** Resource information guide in the areas of education, training, employment, business and economic opportunities for the development and utilization of America's human resources, with emphasis on the needs of Hispanics.
Published by: S E R - Jobs for Progress, Inc., 1925 W. John Carpenter Fwy., Ste. 5D, Irving, TX 75063-3209. TEL 214-541-0616, FAX 214-650-1860. Ed. Obie Gonzalez.
Co-sponsors: League of United Latin American Citizens (LULAC); American G.I. Forum.

658.3 USA ISSN 1096-1585
HD5873
S I REVIEW; tools and techniques for staffing industry professionals. Cover title: Si Review. Text in English. 1996. 10/yr. included in the subscr. to Staffing Industry Report. adv. software rev. illus.; tr.lit. back issues avail. **Document type:** *Trade.*
Published by: Staffing Industry Analysts, Inc., 881 Fremont Ave, Los Altos, CA 94024. TEL 650-948-9303, FAX 650-948-9345, http://www.staffingindustry.com/. Eds. Doris Hisey, Peter Yessne. Pub. Peter Yessne. R&P Joanne Jaime TEL 650-948-9303 ext. 216. Adv. contact Grant Landes. page USD 1,950; trim 11 x 8.5. Circ: 21,000.

SALARY INCREASE SURVEY REPORT. see *OCCUPATIONS AND CAREERS*

658 USA
SALES AND MARKETING PERSONNEL REPORT. Text in English. a. USD 490. charts. **Document type:** *Trade.* **Description:** Evaluates how the pay packages of the sales and marketing staff compare to the marketplace.
Published by: (Executive Compensation Service (ECS)), Wyatt Data Services, 218 Rte 17 N, Rochelle Park, NJ 07622-9832. TEL 201-843-1177, FAX 201-843-0101.

658.3 BEL ISSN 0774-7217
SAMSOM SOCIAAL OVERLEG. Text in Flemish. 1986. m.
Related titles: French ed.: Samsom Concertation Sociale. ISSN 0774-7209.
Published by: C E D Samsom (Subsidiary of: Wolters Samsom Belgie n.v.), Kouterveld 14, Diegem, 1831, Belgium. TEL 32-2-7231111.

658.3 340 DEU ISSN 0943-5980
SCHNELLBRIEF FUER PERSONALWIRTSCHAFT UND ARBEITSRECHT; aktuelle Gesetzgebung, neue Rechtsprechung und alle wichtigen Trends fuer die Personalarbeit. Text in German. 1993. s-m. EUR 134 domestic; EUR 158.70 foreign; EUR 6.30 newsstand/cover (effective 2005). **Document type:** *Journal, Trade.*
Published by: Verlag C.H. Beck oHG, Wilhelmstr 9, Munich, 80801, Germany. TEL 49-89-38189338, FAX 49-89-38189398, abo.service@beck.de, http://www.beck.de.

658.3 GBR
SELECTION. Text in English. 1969. 10/yr. free to members. adv. **Document type:** *Trade.* **Description:** Includes issues surrounding recruiting and training and qualifications for recruiters.
Published by: (Institute of Employment Consultants), Builder Group Plc., 3rd Fl, Steward House, 16a Commercial Way, Woking, Surrey GU21 1ET, United Kingdom. TEL 44-1483-766442, FAX 44-1483-714979, iec@iec.org.uk, http://www.iec.org.uk. Ed. Susan B Smith Feci. Adv. contact Richard Myles. Circ: 7,000.

SHESHUNOFF TRAINING SERIES. see *BUSINESS AND ECONOMICS—Banking And Finance*

658.3 USA
SMART WORKPLACE PRACTICES. Text in English. 1981. m. USD 149 membership (effective 2000 - 2001). bk.rev. back issues avail. **Document type:** *Newsletter.* **Description:** Focuses on how managers and supervisors can deal safely, effectively and profitably with their employees.
Formerly: Employer Advocate
Published by: Independent Small Business Employers of America, 1431 4th St SW, Box 305, Mason City, IA 50401-2736. TEL 641-424-3187, 800-728-3187, FAX 641-424-1673, employer@employerhelp.org, http://www.employerhelp.org. Ed., Pub. Jim Collison. Circ: 1,200 (paid).

SOUNDVIEW EXECUTIVE BOOK SUMMARIES. see *BUSINESS AND ECONOMICS—Management*

658.3 GBR
SPEAKING UP BY SECTOR✶. Text in English. irreg., latest vol.3, 1995. GBP 20. adv. **Document type:** *Monographic series.*
—BLDSC.
Published by: Public Concern at Work, Suite 302, 16 Baldwins Gardens, London, EC1N 7RJ, United Kingdom. TEL 44-171-404-6609, FAX 44-171-404-6576, whistle@pcaw.demon.co.uk. Ed., R&P, Adv. contact Guy Dehn.

658.3 USA
SPENCER'S BENEFITS REPORTS. Text in English. 1996. w. **Description:** Serves as a complete reference and news guide to pension, 401(K) and health care plans.
Related titles: CD-ROM ed.: USD 1,250 (effective 2000).
Published by: Charles D. Spencer & Associates, Inc., 250 S Wacker Dr, Ste 600, Chicago, IL 60606-5834. TEL 312-993-7900, FAX 312-993-7910, editor@spencernet.com, http://www.spencernet.com. Ed. Steve Huth.

658.3 USA ISSN 0740-0217
SPENCER'S RESEARCH REPORTS ON EMPLOYEE BENEFITS. Text in English. 1953. w. looseleaf. USD 725 (effective 2000). bk.rev.
Formerly: E B P R Research Reports
Published by: Charles D. Spencer & Associates, Inc., 250 S Wacker Dr, Ste 600, Chicago, IL 60606-5834. TEL 312-993-7900. Ed. Seymour Larock.

658 USA ISSN 0897-8484
STAFF LEADER. Text in English. 1987. m. USD 263 (effective 2002). **Document type:** *Newsletter, Trade.* **Description:** Guides nonprofit administrators through the toughest of personnel problems.
Formerly (until 1989): Staff (0895-7568)
Related titles: Online - full text ed.: (from EBSCO Publishing).
—CCC.
Published by: Aspen Publishers, Inc. (Subsidiary of: Wolters Kluwer N.V.), 5301 Buckeystown Pike, Ste. 400, Frederick, MD 21704-8319. TEL 800-638-8437, customer.service@aspenpubl.com, http://www.aspenpub.com. Ed. John Gillis. **Dist. by:** Distribution Center, 7201 McKinney Circle, Frederick, MD 21701. TEL 301-698-7100, FAX 301-417-7550.

658.3 USA ISSN 1051-3051
HD5873
STAFFING INDUSTRY REPORT. Text in English. 1990. s-m. USD 385 in North America includes annual Staffing Industry Resource Guide and 2 m. supplements; USD 490 elsewhere includes annual Staffing Industry Resource Guide and 2 m. supplements (effective 2000). adv. index. Supplement avail.; back issues avail. **Document type:** *Trade.* **Description:** Reports company news, industry trends, and financial data regarding the temporary help, PEO, and employment services industry. Covers a variety of temporary-help staffing issues.
Published by: Staffing Industry Analysts, Inc., 881 Fremont Ave, Los Altos, CA 94024. TEL 650-948-9303, FAX 650-948-9345. Eds. Peter Yessne, Tim Murphy. Pub. Peter Yessne. R&P Joanne Jaime TEL 650-948-9303 ext. 216. Adv. contact Grant Landes. Circ: 3,000 (paid).

658.8029 USA ISSN 1553-8168
HD5873
STAFFING INDUSTRY SUPPLIER DIRECTORY. Text in English. 1993. a. USD 129 per issue (effective 2005). adv. **Document type:** *Directory.* **Description:** Serves as a resource and supplier directory for staffing industry professionals involved in temporary help, employment search, etc.
Former titles (until 2004): Staffing Industry Supplier Directory & Buyers Guide (1542-8567); (until 2001): Staffing Industry Resource Guide (1072-3749)
Published by: Staffing Industry Analysts, Inc., 881 Fremont Ave, Los Altos, CA 94024. TEL 650-948-9303, 800-950-9496, FAX 650-948-9345, http://www.staffingindustry.com/. Ed., Pub. Peter Yessne. R&P Joanne Jaime TEL 650-948-9303 ext. 216. Adv. contact Grant Landes. Circ: 5,000.

658.3 USA ISSN 1555-2586
HF5549.A2
STAFFING MANAGEMENT. Text in English. 1986. q. USD 35 domestic; USD 85 foreign (effective 2005). back issues avail. **Document type:** *Magazine, Trade.* **Description:** Covers the latest techniques and trends in recruiting and retaining employees.
Former titles (until 2005): Employment Management Today (1528-5766); (until 1996): E M A Journal (1070-8863)
—CCC.
Published by: (Employment Management Association), Society for Human Resource Management, 1800 Duke St, Alexandria, VA 22314-3499. TEL 703-548-3440, FAX 703-836-0367, shrm@shrm.org, http://www.shrm.org/ema/emt/. R&P Rebecca Hastings. Adv. contact Reema Hamoui. Circ: 6,000.

STERN'S CYBERSPACE SOURCEFINDER; HR and business management Internet directory. see *BUSINESS AND ECONOMICS—Abstracting, Bibliographies, Statistics*

658.3 USA
STERN'S MANAGEMENT REVIEW. Text in English. 1992. q. USD 36 (effective 2001). bk.rev. **Document type:** *Newsletter.* **Description:** Reviews important professional literature in human resources management and expounds on noteworthy issues.
Formerly: Stern's H R New and Forthcoming
Published by: (Stern & Associates), Michael Daniels, Publishers, PO Box 3233, Culver City, CA 90231-3233. TEL 310-838-4437, 800-773-0029, FAX 310-838-2344, stern@hrconsultant.com, http://www.hrconsultant.com. Eds. Gerry Stern, Yvette Borcia. Pub. Michael Daniels. Circ: 2,000 (paid).

STERN'S SOURCEFINDER; the master directory to human resources and business management information and resources. see *BUSINESS AND ECONOMICS—Abstracting, Bibliographies, Statistics*

658.3 336.2 DEU ISSN 0944-5765
STEUER-BRIEF FUER DAS PERSONALBUERO. Text in German. 1993. m. EUR 5.80 per issue (effective 2005). **Document type:** *Journal, Trade.*
Published by: Deubner Verlag GmbH & Co. KG, Oststr 11, Cologne, 50996, Germany. TEL 49-221-9370180, FAX 49-221-93701890, kundenservice@deubner-verlag.de, http://www.vrp.de.

658.3 GBR ISSN 1475-4398
STRATEGIC H R REVIEW. (Human Resource) Text in English. bi-m. GBP 225, USD 355; GBP 325, USD 495 combined subscription print & online (effective 2005). 40 p./no.; **Document type:** *Journal, Trade.* **Description:** Provides case studies, practitioners' insights, research, and many practical ideas.
Related titles: Online - full content ed.: GBP 275, USD 440 (effective 2005); Online - full text ed.: (from EBSCO Publishing, O C L C Online Computer Library Center, Inc., ProQuest Information & Learning).
—CISTI. CCC.

B

Published by: Melcrum Publishing, 1st Floor, Chelsea Reach, 79-89 Lots Rd, London, SW10 0RN, United Kingdom. TEL 44-20-7795-2205, FAX 44-20-7795-2156, info@melcrum.com, http://www.melcrum.com/cgi-bin/melcrum/eu_content.pl?docurl=pub%20shrr%20home.

658 USA
SUCCESSFUL BENEFITS COMMUNICATOR. Text in English. 1992. m. USD 179. **Document type:** *Newsletter.*
Published by: I O M A, 29 W 35th St, 5th Fl, New York, NY 10001-2299. TEL 212-244-0360.

658.313 USA
SUPERVISOR'S GUIDE TO EMPLOYEE PERFORMANCE REVIEWS. Text in English. 1992. irreg., latest 2002, 4th ed. USD 36 per vol. (effective 2005). **Description:** A manual for effective employee performance reviews that explains the necessity of a review policy and provides methods for writing and presenting reviews.
Published by: Michie Company (Subsidiary of: LexisNexis North America), 701 E Water St, Charlottesville, VA 22902-5389. TEL 434-972-7600, 800-446-3410, FAX 434-972-7677, http://www.michie.com. Eds. Lee T Paterson, Mike Deblieux.

658 USA ISSN 1069-4978
SUPERVISOR'S GUIDE TO EMPLOYMENT PRACTICES. Text in English. 1993. bi-w. USD 149.50 (effective 2005). **Document type:** *Newsletter, Trade.* **Description:** Created to help managers and supervisors prevent employee relations problems and lawsuits.
Published by: Clement Communications, Inc., 10 LaCrue Ave, PO Box 36, Concordville, PA 19331. TEL 610-459-4200, 888-358-5858, FAX 610-459-4582, editor@clement.com, http://www.clement.com.

SUPERVISORS LEGAL UPDATE. see *BUSINESS AND ECONOMICS—Management*

SUPERVISORY MANAGEMENT REPORT - GEOGRAPHIC EDITION. see *BUSINESS AND ECONOMICS—Management*

SURVEY OF SALARIES. see *BUSINESS AND ECONOMICS—Abstracting, Bibliographies, Statistics*

658 USA ISSN 1554-091X
HD4965.5.U6
SURVEY REPORT ON EXPATRIATE COMPENSATION, POLICIES AND PRACTICES. Text in English. a. USD 1,090 per issue (effective 2005). charts. **Document type:** *Trade.*
Former titles: The E C S Report on Expatriate and Inpatriate Compensation Policies and Practices (1096-5661); (until 1997): The E C S Report on Expatriate Compensation Policies and Practices (1089-7577); Report on Expatriate Compensation Policies and Practices (1069-434X); Expatriate Compensation Policies and Practices (1069-4420); (until 1985): Report on Expatriate Compensation Policies and Practices (0885-2197)
Published by: (Executive Compensation Service (ECS)), Wyatt Data Services, 218 Rte 17 N, Rochelle Park, NJ 07622-9832. TEL 201-843-1177, FAX 201-843-0101.

658 USA
SURVEY REPORT ON VARIABLE PAY PROGRAMS. Text in English. a. USD 640. charts. **Document type:** *Trade.* **Description:** Features annual survey data from over 400 variable-pay plans; provides information on the prevalence, eligibility, target and actual award levels of the country's most frequently used forms of alternative rewards.
Published by: (Executive Compensation Service (ECS)), Wyatt Data Services, 218 Rte 17 N, Rochelle Park, NJ 07622-9832. TEL 201-843-1177, FAX 201-843-0101.

331.259 USA ISSN 1535-7740
HF5549.5.T7 CODEN: TDABCX
➤ **T+ D.** Variant title: T & D. Text in English. 1945. m. USD 99 domestic; USD 125 in Canada & Mexico; USD 165 elsewhere (effective 2005). adv. bk.rev. charts; illus.; tr.lit. index. back issues avail.; reprint service avail. from PQC. **Document type:** *Magazine, Trade.*
Former titles (until 2001): Training and Development (1055-9760); (until 1991): Training and Development Journal (0041-0861); (until 1966): Training Directors Journal
Related titles: Microfilm ed.: (from PQC); Online - full text ed.: (from bigchalk, EBSCO Publishing, Florida Center for Library Automation, Gale Group, H.W. Wilson, O C L C Online Computer Library Center, Inc., ProQuest Information & Learning).
Indexed: ABIn, ADPA, ASCA, AgeL, BLI, BPI, BusI, CIJE, CPE, CWI, CurCont, ERA, Emerald, HRA, Inspec, KES, MEDLINE, ManagCont, ORMS, PMA, PersLit, PsySCAP, PsycholAb, QAb, RASB, SSCI, T&DA, T&II, WorkRelAb.
—BLDSC (8595.853000), AskIEEE, CISTI, IDS, IE. **CCC.**
Published by: American Society for Training & Development, 1640 King St, Box 1443, Alexandria, VA 22313. TEL 703-683-8100, FAX 703-683-9591, http://www.astd.org/astd/publications/td_magazine. Ed. Patricia A Galagan. R&P V Small. Adv. contact Mark Stout. Circ: 50,000.

658 USA
TA158
TECHNICIAN AND SKILLED TRADES PERSONNEL REPORT - GEOGRAPHIC EDITION. Text in English. a. USD 490. charts. **Document type:** *Trade.* **Description:** Provides data on salaries and total cash compensation for a full spectrum of technician and skilled trades personnel, analyzed from a geographic perspective.
Related titles: ◆ Supplement to: Industry Report on Technician and Skilled Trades Personnel Compensation. ISSN 1063-0058.
Published by: (Executive Compensation Service (ECS)), Wyatt Data Services, 218 Rte 17 N, Rochelle Park, NJ 07622-9832. TEL 201-843-1177, FAX 201-843-0101.

658.3 DEU
TEMPRA 365. Text in German. 1999. bi-m. EUR 33; EUR 5.50 newsstand/cover (effective 2004). adv. **Document type:** *Magazine, Trade.*
Published by: (Bundesverband Sekretariat und Bueromanagement e.V.), Verlag Frank Nehring GmbH, Uhlandstr 17, Berlin, 13156, Germany. TEL 49-30-4790710, FAX 49-30-47907120, info@officeabc.de, http://www.officeabc.de/bsb/index.htm. Ed. Bernd Fahland. Pub. Frank Nehring. Adv. contact Kerstin Schier. page EUR 3,500; trim 178 x 252. Circ: 6,600 (paid and controlled).

658.3 346.066 USA ISSN 0749-8233
TERMINATION OF EMPLOYMENT; employer and employee rights. Text in English. report bulletins and), base vol. plus m. updates. looseleaf. USD 550 (effective 1998). **Document type:** *Trade.* **Description:** Emphasizes preventive measures and provides explanations of key federal laws and court cases that restrict an employer's rights to hire and fire at will.
—**CCC.**
Published by: W G & L Financial Reporting & Management Research (Subsidiary of: R I A), 395 Hudson St, New York, NY 10014. TEL 212-367-6300, FAX 212-367-6718, http://www.InsideHR.com. Ed. Kenneth McCulloch. **Orders to:** The Park Square Bldg., 31 St James Ave, Boston, MA 02116-4112. TEL 800-950-1207.

658.3 338 AUS
TIME MANAGEMENT. Text in English. 1986. m. AUD 195; AUD 220 foreign (effective 1999). **Document type:** *Newsletter.*
Formerly: Timewatch (0818-1918)
Address: Unit 1, 11-13 Lakewood Dr, Braseside, VIC 3195, Australia. TEL 61-3-9580-9994, FAX 61-3-9580-9229. Ed. Lowell Tarling. Pub. Brad Tonini.

TIMING ANALYSIS PROJECTION. see *STATISTICS*

658.3 340 GBR
TOLLEY'S EMPLOYMENT LAW-LINE NEWSLETTER; news update for employment professionals. Text in English. 1993. m. GBP 135 in United Kingdom; GBP 104 overseas (effective 2000). adv. **Document type:** *Bulletin, Trade.*
Former titles (until 2001): Tolley's Employment Law-Line (1467-3347); (until 1998): Tolley's Employment Law and Practice (1467-5544); (until 1996): Tolley's Journal of Employment Law and Practice (0969-6385)
—BLDSC (8863.685820).
Published by: Butterworths Tolley (Subsidiary of: LexisNexis UK (Scottish Office)), 2 Addiscombe Rd, Croydon, Surrey CR9 5AF, United Kingdom. TEL 44-20-8686-9141, FAX 44-20-8686-3155, http://www.tolley.co.uk. Ed. Helen Bradford. Adv. contact Graham Joy.

658.3 GBR ISSN 1365-5590
TOLLEY'S PAYROLL HANDBOOK. Text in English. 1987. a. **Document type:** *Trade.* **Description:** Comprehensive and practical guide to payroll department procedures.
Published by: Butterworths Tolley (Subsidiary of: LexisNexis UK (Scottish Office)), 2 Addiscombe Rd, Croydon, Surrey CR9 5AF, United Kingdom. TEL 44-20-8686-9141, FAX 44-20-8686-3155, http://www.tolley.co.uk. Ed. Mike Nicholas.

TOP EXECUTIVE COMPENSATION. see *BUSINESS AND ECONOMICS—Management*

TOP MANAGEMENT COMPENSATION - REGRESSION ANALYSIS REPORT. see *BUSINESS AND ECONOMICS—Management*

TOP MANAGEMENT REMUNERATION REPORT - EUROPE. see *BUSINESS AND ECONOMICS—Management*

331 AUS ISSN 1325-6947
TOP MANAGEMENT REMUNERATION REVIEW. Text in English. 1975. a. AUD 1,800; avail. to Australian organizations only. **Document type:** *Trade.* **Description:** Contains detailed remuneration review of senior management positions in Australia for contributors.
Published by: Cullen Egan Dell, Level 8, 50 Bridge St, Sydney, NSW 2000, Australia. TEL 61-2-9375-9800, FAX 61-2-9233-6800. Ed. James Cooper. Circ: 85.

TOPICS (CAMBRIDGE). see *BUSINESS AND ECONOMICS—Labor And Industrial Relations*

658.3 USA
TOTAL COMPENSATION HANDBOOK. Text in English. a. USD 276.45; USD 396.45 foreign. **Document type:** *Trade.*
Published by: W G & L Financial Reporting & Management Research (Subsidiary of: R I A), 395 Hudson St, New York, NY 10014. TEL 212-367-6300, FAX 212-367-6718. **Subscr. to:** The Park Square Bldg., 31 St James Ave, Boston, MA 02116-4112. TEL 800-950-1207.

658.3 USA
HD4973
TOTAL SALARY INCREASE BUDGET SURVEY. Variant title: Report on the Total Salary Increase Budget Survey. Text in English. a. USD 95 to non-members; USD 75 to members (effective 1999). **Document type:** *Trade.* **Description:** Results of ACA annual survey of salary budgets, including trend information.
Formerly: Salary Budget Survey (1041-6633)
Indexed: SRI.
Published by: American Compensation Association, 14040 N Northsight Blvd, Scottsdale, AZ 85260. TEL 480-922-2020. R&P Betty Laurie TEL 480-922-2008.

TRAINING; the magazine covering the human side of business. see *BUSINESS AND ECONOMICS—Management*

658.3 ESP ISSN 1137-2230
TRAINING & DEVELOPMENT DIGEST. Text in Spanish. 1996. 6/yr., latest vol.29, 2001. adv. bk.rev.; software rev. bibl.; charts; illus. back issues avail. **Document type:** *Magazine, Trade.* **Description:** Deals with human resources and training.
Published by: Griker & Asociados, Ferraz, 15, Madrid, 28008, Spain. TEL 91-547-07-98, FAX 91-547-02-28, ricardo@griker.es, info@grikes.es. Pub. Ricardo Esteban. Adv. contact Francisca Martinez. Circ: 8,000.

TRAINING AND DEVELOPMENT IN AUSTRALIA. see *BUSINESS AND ECONOMICS—Labor And Industrial Relations*

TRAINING AND DEVELOPMENT YEARBOOK. see *BUSINESS AND ECONOMICS—Abstracting, Bibliographies, Statistics*

658 GBR ISSN 1465-6523
TRAINING JOURNAL. Text in English. 1965. 12/yr. GBP 98 in United Kingdom; GBP 115 in Europe; EUR 178.81, USD 158.77 elsewhere (effective 2001). adv. bk.rev. charts; illus. **Document type:** *Journal, Trade.* **Description:** Contains news, topical articles, independent reviews and news product releases.
Formerly (until 1999): Training Officer (0041-090X)
Related titles: Online - full text ed.: (from EBSCO Publishing, ProQuest Information & Learning).
Indexed: ABIn, ADPA, ASEANManA, BldManAb, BrEdI, CPE, Emerald, HECAB, Inspec, LT&LA, M&MA, SWA, T&DA.
—BLDSC (8883.504380), AskIEEE, IE, ingenta.
Published by: Fenman Limited, Clive House, The Business Park, Ely, Cambs CB7 4EH, United Kingdom. TEL 44-1353-654877, 44-1353-665577, 44-1353-654818, FAX 44-1353-663644, service@fenman.co.uk, ads@mi-pro.co.uk, sue@fenman.co.uk, http://www.trainingjournal.co.uk/. Ed. Debbie Carter TEL 44-1353-654815. Pub. Martin Delahoussaye.

371.42 GBR ISSN 1475-3294
TRAINING MAGAZINE; the independent voice of training & development managers. Text in English. 1994. 10/yr. GBP 39 domestic; GBP 78, USD 117 elsewhere (effective 2001). **Description:** Provides training professionals with news, data, comment and advice. It also organises conferences and campaigns on issues of concern to its readers.
Formerly (until 2001): Training (1364-7504)
Related titles: Online - full text ed.: (from EBSCO Publishing, Gale Group, H.W. Wilson, O C L C Online Computer Library Center, Inc.).
Indexed: BPI.
—BLDSC (8883.504640), IE. **CCC.**
Published by: Reed Business Information Ltd. (Subsidiary of: Reed Business), Quadrant House, The Quadrant, Brighton Rd, Sutton, Surrey SM2 5AS, United Kingdom. FAX 44-20-86528932, http://www.reedbusiness.com/products/training.asp. Ed. Stephanie Sparrow. **Subscr. to:** Quadrant Subscription Services, PO Box 302, Haywards Heath, W Sussex RH16 3YY, United Kingdom. TEL 44-1444-475603, FAX 44-1444-445447.

TRAINING MANAGEMENT. see *BUSINESS AND ECONOMICS—Management*

658.3 GBR
TRAINING NEWS. Text in English. bi-m. **Document type:** *Trade.*
Address: PO Box 1, Atherstone, Warks CV9 1BE, United Kingdom. TEL 01827-718081, FAX 01926-413900. Ed. Paul Carter.

658.3 GBR ISSN 1365-1935
TRAINING TECHNOLOGY AND HUMAN RESOURCES. Text in English. 1988. bi-m. GBP 36; GBP 44 foreign. adv. bk.rev. **Document type:** *Trade.*
Formerly (until 1992): Training Technology (0952-0503)
Indexed: BrEdI, Inspec.
—BLDSC (8883.574800), AskIEEE, IE, ingenta.

B

Published by: M R Publishing Ltd., International Centre, Spindle Way, Crawley, W Sussex RH10 1TG, United Kingdom. TEL 44-1293-537003, FAX 44-1293-531105. Ed., Pub., R&P Michael Randle. Adv. contact Pat Randle. Circ: 5,700; 300 (paid).

658.3 GBR ISSN 1353-5730
TRANSTERRA HUMAN RESOURCES REVIEW. Text in English. 1993. bi-m. GBP 110, USD 215 (effective 2000). adv. **Document type:** *Trade.*
Published by: Transterra Ltd., 2 Copperfields Orchard, Kemsing, Sevenoaks, Kent TN15 6QH, United Kingdom. TEL 44-1702-761687, FAX 44-1702-761687, transterra@exl.co.uk, http://www.transterra.co.uk. Ed. R Keoph. R&P S Klenke. Adv. contact S. Klenke.

658.3 USA
TRAVEL MANAGER'S EXECUTIVE BRIEFING. Text in English. 1979. 24/yr. USD 437 (effective 2000). index. back issues avail. **Document type:** *Newsletter.* **Description:** For travel managers of major corporations. Provides current information on developments in the field of travel and expense cost control.
Formerly: Travel Expense Management (0272-569X)
—CCC.
Published by: American Business Publishing, 1913 Atlantic Ave., Ste. F4, Manasquan, NJ 08736. TEL 732-292-1100, FAX 732-292-1111, info@themcic.com, http://www.themcic.com. Ed. Jennifer L DeFalco. Pub. Robert K Jenkins. R&P Jillian Philipp. Circ: 425.

658.3 DEU ISSN 1612-8419
▼ **TRIERER BEITRAEGE ZUM DIVERSITY MANAGEMENT.** Text in German. 2003. irreg., latest vol.2, 2005. price varies. **Document type:** *Monographic series, Academic/Scholarly.*
Published by: Rainer Hampp Verlag, Meringerzellerstr 10, Mering, 86415, Germany. TEL 49-8233-4783, FAX 49-8233-30755, Rainer_Hampp_Verlag@t-online.de, http://www.hampp-verlag.de.

658.3 GBR
U K SURVEY OF SALARIES AND BENEFITS. Text in English. a. GBP 400 (effective 1998). **Document type:** *Directory.* **Description:** Salary and benefits information for chairmen down to junior managers.
Published by: P-E Inbucon Ltd., Brooks House, 34 Paradise Rd, Richmond-upon-Thames, Surrey TW9 1SE, United Kingdom. TEL 44-181-334-5727, FAX 44-181-334-5739, meis@easynet.co.uk. R&P Rosemary Hook.

658.3 382 USA
U.S. CHAMBER OF COMMERCE. (YEAR) EMPLOYEE BENEFITS STUDY. Text in English. 1947. s-a. USD 95 to non-members; USD 50 to members (effective 2003). charts; stat. 50 p./no.; back issues avail. **Document type:** *Trade.* **Description:** Serves as a reference guide for employees, employers, and benefits specialists.
Formerly: U.S. Chamber of Commerce. Employee Benefits (0194-3499)
Published by: (Statistics Research Center), U.S. Chamber of Commerce, Business Information and Development Dept., 1615 H St N W, Washington, DC 20062-2000. http://www.uschamber.com. Ed. Chamain O'Mahony. R&P Gregory Melia TEL 202-463-5381.

658.3 USA
U.S. OFFICE OF PERSONNEL MANAGEMENT. NOTICE AND POSTING SYSTEM. Text in English. irreg. USD 122 (effective 2001). **Document type:** *Government.* **Description:** Contains notices of OPM regulatory changes, operating information, and variations.
Published by: U.S. Office of Personnel Management, 1900 E. St. N.W., Washington, DC 20415. http://www.opm.gov/. **Subscr. to:** U.S. Government Printing Office, Superintendent of Documents, PO Box 371954, Pittsburgh, PA 15250-7954. TEL 202-512-1800, FAX 202-512-2250, orders@gpo.gov, http://www.access.gpo.gov.

658.3 USA
U.S. OFFICE OF PERSONNEL MANAGEMENT OPERATING MANUALS. QUALIFICATION STANDARDS FOR GENERAL SCHEDULE POSITIONS. Text in English. base vol. plus irreg. updates. looseleaf. USD 107 for basic manual & updates (effective 2001). **Document type:** *Government.* **Description:** Furnishes current qualification standards for various grade-level occupations in the Office of Personnel Management, under the Classification Act of 1949.
Published by: U.S. Office of Personnel Management, 1900 E. St. N.W., Washington, DC 20415. **Subscr. to:** U.S. Government Printing Office, Superintendent of Documents, PO Box 371954, Pittsburgh, PA 15250-7954. TEL 202-512-1800, FAX 202-512-2250, orders@gpo.gov, http://www.access.gpo.gov.

658.3 USA
U.S. OFFICE OF PERSONNEL MANAGEMENT OPERATING MANUALS. THE FEDERAL WAGE SYSTEM. Text in English. base vol. plus irreg. updates. looseleaf. USD 40 for basic manual & updates (effective 2001). **Document type:** *Government.*
Published by: U.S. Office of Personnel Management, 1900 E. St. N.W., Washington, DC 20415. **Subscr. to:** U.S. Government Printing Office, Superintendent of Documents, PO Box 371954, Pittsburgh, PA 15250-7954. TEL 202-512-1800, FAX 202-512-2250, orders@gpo.gov, http://www.access.gpo.gov.

658.3 USA
U.S. OFFICE OF PERSONNEL MANAGEMENT OPERATING MANUALS. THE FEDERAL WAGE SYSTEM NONAPPROPRIATED FUND. Text in English. base vol. plus irreg. updates. looseleaf. USD 25 for basic manual & updates (effective 2001). **Document type:** *Government.*
Published by: U.S. Office of Personnel Management, 1900 E. St. N.W., Washington, DC 20415. **Subscr. to:** U.S. Government Printing Office, Superintendent of Documents, PO Box 371954, Pittsburgh, PA 15250-7954. TEL 202-512-1800, FAX 202-512-2250, orders@gpo.gov, http://www.access.gpo.gov.

658.3 USA
U.S. OFFICE OF PERSONNEL MANAGEMENT OPERATING MANUALS. THE GUIDE TO PROCESSING PERSONNEL ACTIONS. Text in English. base vol. plus irreg. updates. looseleaf. USD 190 for basic manual & updates (effective 2001). **Document type:** *Government.*
Published by: U.S. Office of Personnel Management, 1900 E. St. N.W., Washington, DC 20415. **Subscr. to:** U.S. Government Printing Office, Superintendent of Documents, PO Box 371954, Pittsburgh, PA 15250-7954. TEL 202-512-1800, FAX 202-512-2250, orders@gpo.gov, http://www.access.gpo.gov.

658.3 USA
U.S. OFFICE OF PERSONNEL MANAGEMENT. PERFORMANCE AND ACCOUNTABILITY REPORT FOR FISCAL YEAR. Text in English. 2002. a. **Document type:** *Government.*
Formed by the merger of: Program Performance Report; (1997-2001): Accountability Report for Fiscal Year
Related titles: Online - full content ed.
Published by: U.S. Office of Personnel Management, Division for Management & Chief Financial Officer, Center for Financial Services&Deputy Chief Financial Office, Theodore Roosevelt Bldg, 1900 E St. NW, Washington, DC 20415. TEL 202-606-2171, cgbrown@opm.gov, General@opm.gov, http://www.opm.gov/.

658.3 IND
UTPADAKTA. Text in Hindi. m. INR 25, USD 13. **Description:** Carries informative articles and features for supervisors and workers who want to achieve higher productivity.
Published by: National Productivity Council, Business Management Section, Utpadakta Bhawan Lodi Rd., New Delhi, 110 003, India. TEL 4690331.

VAN ZYL, RUDD INDUSTRIAL RELATIONS AND HUMAN RESOURCES DIARY. see *BUSINESS AND ECONOMICS—Labor And Industrial Relations*

658.3 USA ISSN 0888-6628
WHAT TO DO ABOUT PERSONNEL PROBLEMS IN (STATE). Text in English. 1985. s-m. looseleaf. USD 395 (effective 2005). adv. back issues avail. **Document type:** *Newsletter.* **Description:** Contains state-specific and federal information on human resource management, a 400 page answer book on all important policy and regulation topics and an annual wage and salary survey.
Incorporates: Personnel Manager's Policy and Practice Update; What to do about Your Personnel Problems Today
—CCC.
Published by: Business & Legal Reports, Inc., PO Box 6001, Old Saybrook, CT 06475-6001. TEL 203-318-0000, 800-727-5257, FAX 203-245-2559. Ed. Kelly Leisten. Pub. Robert L Brady. R&P Kathy Long. Adv. contact Cathy Zajack. Circ: 21,100 (paid).

658.3 USA
WHAT'S AHEAD IN HUMAN RESOURCES. Text in English. 1973. s-m. USD 145 (effective 1999). bk.rev. **Document type:** *Newsletter.*
Formerly: What's Ahead in Personnel (0899-3076)
Indexed: PersLit.
Published by: Kennedy Information Inc., One Kennedy Place, Rte 12 S, Fitzwilliam, NH 03447. TEL 603-585-3101, 800-531-0007, FAX 603-585-9555. Ed. John Hickey.

331.21 USA ISSN 1076-0466
WHAT'S NEW IN BENEFITS & COMPENSATION. Abbreviated title: W N B & C. Text in English. 1994. s-m. USD 299. charts; stat. **Document type:** *Newsletter.* **Description:** Benefits administration news and updates for managers.
Published by: Progressive Business Publications, 370 Technology Dr, Malvern, PA 19355-1315. TEL 610-695-8600, 800-220-5000, FAX 610-647-8089, editor@pbp.com, http://www.pbp.com. Ed. Richard P Kern. R&P Curt Brown. Circ: 13,064 (paid).

658.3 USA ISSN 1088-3223
WHAT'S WORKING IN HUMAN RESOURCES. Abbreviated title: W H R. Text in English. 1996. s-m. USD 299. back issues avail. **Document type:** *Newsletter.* **Description:** Provides information on how to improve the performance of your human resources. Covers employment law.
Related titles: Online - full text ed.
Published by: Progressive Business Publications, 370 Technology Dr, Malvern, PA 19355-1315. TEL 610-695-8600, 800-220-5000, FAX 610-647-8089, editor@pbp.com, http://www.pbp.com. Ed. Tom Gorman. R&P Curt Brown. Circ: 22,395 (paid).

331 USA ISSN 1075-8550
CODEN: WILRE2
THE WILLIAMS REPORT. Text in English. 1982. m. USD 157. bk.rev. back issues avail. **Document type:** *Newsletter.* **Description:** Reviews employee communications ideas, plans, and strategies.
Former titles: Communications Ideas, Plans and Strategies Report; Communication Illustrated; Employee Communication (0736-7635)
Published by: Joe Williams Communications, Inc., PO Box 924, Bartlesville, OK 74005. TEL 918-336-2267. Ed., Pub. Joe Williams.

WOMEN'S BUSINESS JOURNAL. see *WOMEN'S INTERESTS*

WORK AND STRESS. see *PSYCHOLOGY*

658.3 USA ISSN 1546-9859
WORK - LIFE TODAY; the newsletter for work/life professionals. Text in English. 1997. m. USD 355 (effective 2003). **Document type:** *Newsletter.* **Description:** Helps human resource professionals develop successful and cost-effective family-friendly benefit programs.
Published by: Balance Media LLC, 7300 Baylor Ave. Ste. G, College Park, MD 20740. TEL 301-345-9122, FAX 301-345-9139, http://www.worklifetoday.com. Ed. Sharon O'Malley.

WORKERS COMPENSATION; exposures, coverage, claims. see *INSURANCE*

658.3 346 USA
WORKER'S COMPENSATION GUIDE. Text in English. base vol. plus s-a. updates. looseleaf. USD 180. **Document type:** *Trade.* **Description:** Serves as a resource of ideas and techniques for reducing worker's compensation costs. Includes federal regulations and state compensation laws.
Published by: W G & L Financial Reporting & Management Research (Subsidiary of: R I A), 395 Hudson St, New York, NY 10014. TEL 212-367-6300, FAX 212-367-6718, http://www.InsideHR.com. Ed. Steve Levinson. **Subscr. to:** The Park Square Bldg., 31 St James Ave, Boston, MA 02116-4112. TEL 800-950-1207.

658.3 USA
WORKFORCE DIVERSITY FOR ENGINEERING AND I T PROFESSIONALS. Text in English. 1994. q. USD 15 (effective 1999). **Document type:** *Trade.*
Formerly: W D (Workforce Diversity)
Published by: Equal Opportunity Publications, Inc., 445 Broad Hollow Rd, Ste 425, Melville, NY 11747. TEL 631-421-9421, FAX 631-421-0359, info@eop.com, http://www.eop.com.

658.3 USA ISSN 1547-5565
HF5549.A2 CODEN: PEJOAA
WORKFORCE MANAGEMENT. Text in English. 1922. m. USD 59 domestic; USD 99 in Canada; USD 169 elsewhere (effective 2005). adv. illus. index. back issues avail.; reprint service avail. from PQC. **Document type:** *Magazine, Trade.* **Description:** Aims to provide tools to help readers solve HR issues. Provides information about the impact of current events on HR. Includes a section on "Trends & Resources" with trends, strategies for solving problems, and resources necessary for action.
Former titles (until 2003): Workforce (Costa Mesa) (1092-8332); (until 1997): Personnel Journal (0031-5745); (until 1927): Journal of Personnel Research (0886-750X)
Related titles: Online - full text ed.: (from bigchalk, EBSCO Publishing, Florida Center for Library Automation, Gale Group, H.W. Wilson, O C L C Online Computer Library Center, Inc., ProQuest Information & Learning); Supplement(s): Workforce Tools; Workforce.
Indexed: ABIn, ADPA, ASCA, ASEANManA, ASG, AcaI, AgeL, Agr, BLI, BPI, BPIA, BRI, BusI, CBRI, CIJE, CISA, CPM, CurCont, DPD, EAA, ERA, Emerald, ExcerpMed, FamI, IMI, KES, LOIS, M&MA, MEDLINE, ManagCont, ORMS, PAIS, PCI, PMA, PROMT, PSI, PersLit, PsySCAP, PsycholAb, QAb, RASB, RPFIA, SCIMP, SSCI, T&DA, TEA, WorkRelAb.
—BLDSC (9348.527777), CASDDS, CISTI, IDS, IE, Infotrieve, ingenta. **CCC.**
Published by: Crain Communications, Inc., 1155 Gratiot Ave, Detroit, MI 48207-2997. TEL 313-444-6000, FAX 313-446-1687, tostiv@workforcemag.com, http://www.workforceonline.com, http://www.crain.com. Ed. Carroll Lachnit. Pubs. Margaret Magnus, Todd Johnson. adv.: B&W page USD 6,175, color page USD 8,210. Circ: 30,000 (paid).

658.3 USA
▼ **WORKFORCE PERFORMANCE SOLUTIONS.** Text in English. 2005 (Apr.). bi-m. USD 95 (effective 2005). adv. **Document type:** *Magazine, Trade.* **Description:** Designed for decision-makers with enterprise-level responsibilities, including enterprise development, human resources, workforce development and related executives to help establish performance management systems that successfully align individual and team performance with corporate strategy.
Published by: MediaTec Publishing, Inc., 444 N Michigan Ave, Chicago, IL 60611. TEL 312-828-2800, FAX 312-828-1105, http://www.wpsmag.com. Eds. Tim Sosbe, Norman B Kamikow. Pub. Jim Yeakel. adv.: B&W page USD 6,906, color page USD 7,595; trim 8 x 10.125. Circ: 25,000 (controlled).

658.3 USA ISSN 1525-0857
WORKING TOGETHER; a bulletin of inspiration and ideas for achievement-minded people. Text in English. bi-w. (26/yr.). USD 254 5 copies (effective 2005). **Document type:** *Newsletter, Trade.* **Description:** Helps employees appreciate the benefits of cooperation and involvement—for themselves and for their companies.
—CCC.
Published by: Dartnell Corp. (Subsidiary of: L R P Publications), 360 Hiatt Dr, Palm Beach Garden, FL 33418. TEL 561-622-6520, 800-621-5463, FAX 561-622-0757, custserve@lrp.com, http://www.shoplrp.com/product/p-18004.N.html, http://www.dartnellcorp.com/. Ed. Dionne Ellis. Circ: 25,000.

658.3 DEU ISSN 1438-471X
WORKING@OFFICE; das Magazin fuer die Frau im Buero. Text in German. 1999. m. EUR 81; EUR 63 to students; EUR 7 newsstand/cover (effective 2005). adv. **Document type:** *Magazine, Trade.*
Formed by the merger of (1955-1999): Sekretariat (0171-4937); Which was formerly (until 1979): Gabriele (0016-3708); (1951-1999): Assistenz (0722-3587); Which was formerly (until 1982): Sekretaerin (0170-5377)
Related titles: Online - full text ed.
—IE. CCC.
Published by: Betriebswirtschaftlicher Verlag Dr. Th. Gabler GmbH (Subsidiary of: Springer Science+Business Media), Abraham-Lincoln-Str 46, Wiesbaden, 65189, Germany. TEL 49-611-78780, FAX 49-611-7878400, workingoffice@bertelsmann.de, gabler.service@gwv-fachverlage.de, http://www.workingoffice.de, http://www.gabler.de. Ed. Maria Akhavan-Hezavei. Adv. contact Elisabeth Massfeller. B&W page EUR 4,260, color page EUR 5,745. Circ: 30,484 (paid and controlled).

WORKLIFE (KINGSTON). see *BUSINESS AND ECONOMICS—Labor And Industrial Relations*

658.3 CAN ISSN 1487-9107
WORKPLACE TODAY. Text in English. 1991. m. CND 96 domestic (effective 2001); Free to qualified subscribers. back issues avail. **Document type:** *Magazine, Trade.* **Description:** Reports on legal information, case studies, and labor trends of interest to managers and supervisors.
Former titles (until 1998): H R Today (1204-4334); (until 1995): Recruiting & Supervision Today (1187-9378)
Related titles: Online - full text ed.
—CISTI.
Published by: Institute of Professional Management, Ste 2210-1081, Ambleside Dr, Ottawa, ON K2B 8C8, Canada. TEL 613-721-5957, FAX 613-721-5850, info@workplace.ca, http://www.workplace.ca/magazine/index.html. Ed., Pub. Brian W. Pascal. Adv. contact Nathaly Pinchuk.

658.3 CHE
WORKS. Text in English. 1919. 12/yr. membership. **Document type:** *Newspaper.*
Formerly (until 1997): Schweizer Arbeitnehmer
Indexed: AIAP.
Address: Badenerstr 41, Zuerich, 8004, Switzerland. TEL 41-1-2410757, FAX 41-1-2411409. Ed Andreas Hubli. Circ: 13,300.

WORKSITE WELLNESS WORKS. see *PUBLIC HEALTH AND SAFETY*

331.21 USA ISSN 1529-9457
HF5549.5.C67
WORLDATWORK JOURNAL. Text in English. 1992. q. USD 95 (effective 2005). adv. **Document type:** *Trade.* **Description:** Contains strategic articles on compensation and benefits.
Formerly (until 2000): A C A Journal (1068-0918)
Related titles: Microform ed.: (from PQC); Online - full text ed.: (from ProQuest Information & Learning).
Indexed: ATI.
—BLDSC (9360.457000), IE, ingenta.
Published by: American Compensation Association, 14040 N Northsight Blvd, Scottsdale, AZ 85260. TEL 480-951-9191, FAX 480-483-8352, worldatworkjournal@worldatwork.org, http://www.worldatwork.org/. Ed. Denise Constantine. Pub. Don Griffith. R&P Betty Laurie TEL 480-922-2008. Adv. contact Becky Tignor.

658.3 GBR
WORLDWIDE SURVEY OF INTERNATIONAL ASSIGNMENT POLICIES AND PRACTICES. EUROPEAN EDITION. Text in English. 1981. a.
Former titles: Survey of Policies and Practices for European Expatriates; Survey of Policies and Practices for U K Expatriates
Published by: Organization Resources Counselors Inc., Buckingham Ct, 78 Buckingham Gate, London, SW1E 6PE, United Kingdom. TEL 44-171-222-9321, FAX 44-171-799-2018.

WRONGFUL DISMISSAL. see *LAW*

WYNAGRODZENIA. see *LAW*

658.3 USA ISSN 0731-1109
KF889.A1
YOU AND THE LAW; quick and easy advice for managing employment law changes. Text in English. 1970. m. looseleaf. USD 125. bibl. **Document type:** *Newsletter.*
Formerly (until 1978): Your Business and the Law (0093-3503)
—CCC.
Published by: National Institute of Business Management, PO Box 9206, Mclean, VA 22102-0206. TEL 703-905-8000. Ed. Michael Levin Epstein. Pub. Michelle S Cox. R&P Carolyn Frazier. Circ: 15,000.

YOUR FINANCIAL FUTURE; Standard & Poor's guide to retirement planning. see *BUSINESS AND ECONOMICS—Investments*

658.3 DEU ISSN 0179-6437
ZEITSCHRIFT FUER PERSONALFORSCHUNG. Text in German. 1987. q. EUR 60 domestic; EUR 68 foreign (effective 2005). reprint service avail. from SCH. **Document type:** *Journal, Academic/Scholarly.* **Description:** Concerned with state-of-the-art research in the area of strategic and operative human resource management (HRM) in organizations.
Related titles: Microfilm ed.; Online - full text ed.: (from ProQuest Information & Learning).
Indexed: ABIn, DIP, IBR, IBSS, IBZ.
Published by: Rainer Hampp Verlag, Meringerzellerstr 10, Mering, 86415, Germany. TEL 49-8233-4783, FAX 49-8233-30755, Rainer_Hampp_Verlag@t-online.de, http://www.hampp-verlag.de/hampp_ZS04.htm. **Dist. by:** Brockhaus Commission, Kreidlerstr 9, Kornwestheim 70806, Germany. TEL 49-7154-132739, FAX 49-7154-132713.

658.3 CHN ISSN 1004-4124
ZHONGGUO RENLI ZIYUAN KAIFA/HUMAN RESOURCE DEVELOPMENT OF CHINA. Text in Chinese. 1991. m. **Document type:** *Journal, Academic/Scholarly.*
Related titles: Online - full text ed.: (from East View Information Services, WanFang Data Corp.).
Address: Xicheng-qu, 38, Baiwanzhuangzi-qu, Beijing, 100037, China. TEL 86-10-88363163, FAX 86-10-88364504, hrdchina@263.net, http://zgrlzykf.periodicals.net.cn/.

658.3 CHN
ZHONGGUO RENSHI BAO/CHINESE PERSONNEL GAZETTE. Text in Chinese. 1995. 2/w. CNY 54 (effective 2004). **Document type:** *Newspaper, Trade.*
Published by: Zhonghua Renmin Gongheguo Renshibu, Dongcheng-qu, 7, Hepingli Zhongjie, Beijing, 100013, China. http://www.rensb.com/. **Dist. by:** China International Book Trading Corp, 35 Chegongzhuang Xilu, Haidian District, PO Box 399, Beijing 100044, China. TEL 86-10-68412045, FAX 86-10-68412023, cibtc@mail.cibtc.com.cn, http://www.cibtc.com.cn.

ZIMBABWE JOURNAL OF EDUCATIONAL RESEARCH. see *EDUCATION*

BUSINESS AND ECONOMICS—Production Of Goods And Services

A B C BELGE POUR LE COMMERCE ET L'INDUSTRIE. see *BUSINESS AND ECONOMICS—Trade And Industrial Directories*

A B C LUXEMBOURGEOIS POUR LE COMMERCE ET L'INDUSTRIE. see *BUSINESS AND ECONOMICS—Trade And Industrial Directories*

388 USA
A C M A NEWSLETTER. Text in English. q. membership. adv. **Document type:** *Newsletter.*
Published by: American Cutlery Manufacturers Association, 112 J Elden St, Herndon, VA 20170-4809. TEL 703-709-8253, FAX 703-709-1036, acma@erols.com. Ed. David W Barrack. R&P Sarah Jane Gatley. Adv. contact Sarah-Jane Gatley.

338 658 USA
A I M - R NEWS. Text in English. m. **Description:** Covers management and industry news.
Published by: Association of Industry Manufacturers Representatives, 222 Merchandise Mart Plaza, Ste 1360, Chicago, IL 60654. TEL 312-464-0090. Ed. Betchie Bistrom. Circ: 250.

338 PRT ISSN 0870-287X
HC391
A I P INFORMACAO. Text in Portuguese. 1975. 12/yr. USD 40 (effective 2000). adv. bk.rev. **Document type:** *Bulletin.*
—BLDSC (0773.452000).
Published by: Associacao Industrial Portuguesa, Praca das Industrias, Lisbon Codex, 1399, Portugal. TEL 351-21-3600100, FAX 351-21-3639047, TELEX 15650 AIPFIL P. Ed. Rui Ferreira Leite. Adv. contact Benvindo Teixeira. Circ: 4,000.

A P I C S - THE PERFORMANCE ADVANTAGE. see *BUSINESS AND ECONOMICS—Management*

338.9 JPN ISSN 0066-846X
HC415.I52
A P O ANNUAL REPORT. Text in English. 1962. a. free.
Related titles: Microfiche ed.: (from CIS)
Indexed: IIS.
Published by: Asian Productivity Organization, 1-2-10Hirakawa-cho, Chiyoda-ku, Tokyo, 102-0093, Japan. FAX 81-3-5226-3950, apo@gol.com, http://www.apo-tokyo.com. Circ: 3,200.

338 JPN ISSN 0044-9229
HC411
A P O NEWS. Text in Japanese. 1961. m. free. bk.rev. **Document type:** *Bulletin.*
Formerly (until 1971): Asian Productivity Monthly Bulletin (0571-2971)
Published by: Asian Productivity Organization, 1-2-10Hirakawa-cho, Chiyoda-ku, Tokyo, 102-0093, Japan. FAX 81-3-5226-3950, apo@gol.com, http://www.apo-tokyo.com. Circ: 6,000.

338 JPN ISSN 0919-0589
HC415.I52
A P O PRODUCTIVITY JOURNAL. Text in English. 1993. 2/yr. USD 10 to Asia & Oceania; USD 23 elsewhere (effective 2000).
—BLDSC (1568.862000).
Published by: Asian Productivity Organization, 1-2-10Hirakawa-cho, Chiyoda-ku, Tokyo, 102-0093, Japan. FAX 81-3-5226-3950, apo@gol.com, http://www.apo-tokyo.com. Circ: 1,000.

338 380 DEU ISSN 0938-7927
ACQUISA; die Zeitschrift fuer erfolgreiches Absatzmanagement. Text in German. 1952. m. EUR 89 domestic; EUR 99 foreign; EUR 7.50 newsstand/cover (effective 2004). adv. **Document type:** *Magazine, Trade.*
Formerly: Industrie- und Handelsvertreter (0019-9214)
Related titles: Online - full text ed.
Published by: Max Schimmel Verlag GmbH & Co. KG (Subsidiary of: Rudolf Haufe Verlag GmbH & Co. KG), Im Kreuz 9, Wuerzburg, 97076, Germany. TEL 49-931-2791420, FAX 49-931-2791444, info@acquisa.de, info@schimmelverlag.de, http://www.acquisa.de, http://www.schimmelverlag.de. Ed. Martin Hausmann. Pub. Martina Schimmel-Schloo. Adv. contact Christian Schwert. B&W page EUR 5,140, color page EUR 6,100. Circ: 25,331 (paid and controlled).

338 CAN ISSN 1481-8345
ADVANCED MANUFACTURING. Text in English. 1999. bi-m. CND 40 domestic; USD 60 in United States; USD 75 elsewhere (effective 2005). adv. **Document type:** *Magazine, Trade.* **Description:** Publishes new ideas, on theory and technology, for senior management of manufacturing companies.
Related titles: Online - full content ed.
—Linda Hall.
Published by: C L B Media, Inc. (Subsidiary of: Canada Law Book Inc.), 240 Edward St, Aurora, ON L4G 3S9, Canada. TEL 905-727-0077, FAX 905-727-0017, http:// www.advancedmanufacturing.com. adv.: B&W page USD 4,510, color page USD 6,830.

338 SWE ISSN 1651-9264
AFFAERSTIDNINGEN NAERINGSLIV. Text in Swedish. 1984. 7/yr. SEK 395 (effective 2003). adv.
Formerly (until 2003): Svenskt Naeringsliv (0281-6989)
Published by: Infoteam AS, Goeteborgsvaegen 27-29, PO Box 2079, Saevedalen, 43302, Sweden. TEL 46-31-3409800, FAX 46-31-3409801, info@naringsliv.se, http://www.naringsliv.se. Ed. Peter Friden. Adv. contact Christer Andersson. Circ: 30,000.

668 USA ISSN 1055-3509
AGGLOMERATIONS. Text in English. 1990. bi-m. **Document type:** *Newsletter, Trade.* **Description:** Keeps detergent industry professionals abreast of developments worldwide.
Published by: Colin A. Houston & Associates, Inc., 20 Milltown Rd, Ste 206, Brewster, NY 10509. TEL 845-279-7891, FAX 845-279-7751, http://www.colin-houston.com/ AGGLOMERATIONS/agglomerations.htm.

B

338.7   DEU   ISSN 0002-3752
KK2451.3
DIE AKTIENGESELLSCHAFT; Zeitschrift fuer das gesamte Aktienwesen. Abbreviated title: A. G. Text in German. 2/m. EUR 349; EUR 17.45 newsstand/cover (effective 2005). adv. bk.rev. index, cum.index: 1956-1965. reprints avail. **Document type:** *Journal, Trade.*
Indexed: ELLIS, IBR, IBZ.
—IE, Infotrieve. **CCC.**
Published by: (Schutzgemeinschaft der Kleinaktionaere e.V.), Verlag Dr. Otto Schmidt KG, Gustav-Heinemann-Ufer 58, Cologne, 50968, Germany. TEL 49-221-93738460, FAX 49-221-93738943, dieaktiengesellschaft@otto-schmidt.de, info@otto-schmidt.de, http://www.die-aktiengesellschaft.de, http://www.otto-schmidt.de. Ed. Birgitta Peters. Adv. contact Renate Becker. B&W page EUR 2,300. color page EUR 4,025. Circ: 2,400 (paid and controlled).

338   DEU
DER AKTIONAERSREPORT. Text in German. m. EUR 50 (effective 2005). **Document type:** *Bulletin, Trade.*
Formerly (until 1995): Aktionaersbrief
Published by: Schutzgemeinschaft der Kleinaktionaere e.V., Karlsplatz 3, Munich, 80335, Germany. TEL 49-89-59998733, FAX 49-89-54887858, info@sdk.org, http://www.sdk.org.

ALFORJA; revista de distribucion y produccion. see *FOOD AND FOOD INDUSTRIES*

338   PAK
ALL PAKISTAN TEXTILE MILLS ASSOCIATION. CHAIRMAN'S REVIEW∗. Text in English. a. free.
Formerly: All Pakistan Textile Mills Association. Annual Report
Published by: All Pakistan Textile Mills Association, Moulvi Tamizuddin Khan Rd., Lalazat 44 A, P O Box 5446, Karachi, 74000, Pakistan.

ALUMINIUM INTERNATIONAL TODAY; the journal of aluminium production and processing. see *METALLURGY*

338   USA   ISSN 0002-8908
AMERICAN INDUSTRY. Text in English. 1946. bi-m. USD 25 (effective 2005). adv. bk.rev.; software rev.; Website rev. charts; illus.; tr.lit. back issues avail.; reprint service avail. from PQC. **Document type:** *Newspaper, Trade.* **Description:** New product releases with or without photos for largest US industrial concerns.
Related titles: Microfiche ed.: Microfilm ed.: (from PQC).
Published by: Publications for Industry, 21 Russell Woods Rd., Great Neck, NY 11021-4644. TEL 516-487-0990, FAX 516-487-0809, ai@publicationsforindustry.com, http://www.publicationsforindustry.com. Ed., Pub. Jack S Panes. Adv. contact B Grillo. B&W page USD 2,087; trim 14.25 x 10.38. Circ: 28,000 (controlled).

621.75   USA   ISSN 1041-7958
TJ1   CODEN: AMMAAA
AMERICAN MACHINIST; strategies & innovations for competitive manufacturing. Text in English. 1877. m. USD 85 domestic; USD 95 in Canada; USD 120 elsewhere; free to qualified personnel (effective 2005). adv. bk.rev. charts; illus.; tr.lit. Index. back issues avail.; reprints avail. **Document type:** *Magazine, Trade.* **Description:** Covers all aspects of manufacturing industry. Topics of articles include machine vision, computer-integrated manufacturing, robotics, lasers, computerized numerical control, and manufacturing systems.
Former titles (until 1988): American Machinist and Automated Manufacturing (0886-0335); (until 1986): American Machinist (0002-9858); (until 1968): American Machinist - Metalworking Manufacturing (0096-5154); (until 1960): American Machinist (0360-5892)
Related titles: Microform ed.: (from PMC, PQC); Online - full text ed.: (from bigchalk, EBSCO Publishing, Florida Center for Library Automation, Gale Group, H.W. Wilson, Northern Light Technology, Inc., O C L C Online Computer Library Center, Inc., ProQuest Information & Learning).
Indexed: ABIn, AIA, AS&TI, BrCerAb, C&ISA, CADCAM, CISA, Cadscan, CerAb, ChemAb, CivEngAb, CorrAb, E&CAJ, EMA, EngInd, FLUIDEX, IAA, IPackAb, ISR, Inspec, LRI, LeadAb, M&TEA, MBF, METADEX, RASB, RefZh, RoboAb, SRI, SolStAb, WAA, Zincscan.
—BLDSC (0841.000000), CASDDS, CISTI, Ei, IDS, IE, Infotrieve, ingenta, Linda Hall. **CCC.**
Published by: Penton Media, Inc. (Subsidiary of: Pittway Company), 1300 E 9th St, Cleveland, OH 44114-1503. TEL 216-931-9240, FAX 216-931-9524, ameditor@penton.com, http://www.americanmachinist.com/, http://www.penton.com. Ed. Thomas J Grasson TEL 216-931-9240. Pub. Robert Rosenbaum. adv.: B&W page USD 7,265, color page USD 9,275; trim 7.625 x 10.5. Circ: 82,000 (paid and controlled).
Subscr. to: PO Box 95759, Cleveland, OH 44101.

AMERICAN VENTURE; for entrepreneurs and accredited investors. see *BUSINESS AND ECONOMICS—Investments*

ANDHRA PRADESH PRODUCTIVITY COUNCIL. TARGET. see *AGRICULTURE*

338   BEL   ISSN 0003-505X
LES ANNONCES DE L'INDUSTRIE. Text in French. 1946. w. EUR 93.77 (effective 2003). adv. tr.lit. **Document type:** *Trade.*

Published by: Editions Kluwer (Subsidiary of: Wolters Kluwer Belgique), Avenue Louise 326, Brussels, 1050, Belgium. TEL 32-800-16868, FAX 32-2-3003003, customer@editionskluwer.be, http://www.editionskluwer.be/ek/home.asp. Ed. Michel Verstrepen. Circ: 5,021 (controlled).

ANNUAL EDITIONS: DEVELOPING WORLD. see *GEOGRAPHY*

338.925   USA
ANNUAL REPORT ON PRIVATIZATION. Text in English. biennial. USD 85 to individuals; USD 90 to institutions (effective 1999). adv. **Document type:** *Directory, Corporate.* **Description:** Covers contracting, infrastructure and public sector innovations in privatization and alternative service delivery.
Published by: ResourceWomen, 3415 S Sepulveda Blvd, Ste 400, Los Angeles, CA 90034-6060. TEL 310-391-2245, FAX 310-391-4395, adriantm@aol.com. Ed. Eileen Paul. Adv. contact Mike Griffin. Circ: 25,000.

ANNUAL REPORT ON THE NIGERIAN OIL INDUSTRY. see *PETROLEUM AND GAS*

338 347.7   USA   ISSN 1526-520X
ANTITRUST & TRADE REGULATION DAILY. Text in English. d. USD 2,296 (effective 2005 - 2006). back issues avail. **Document type:** *Newsletter, Trade.* **Description:** Covers federal, state, and international legal issues about competition and deceptive trade practices.
Media: Online - full text (from The Bureau of National Affairs, Inc.).
—**CCC.**
Published by: The Bureau of National Affairs, Inc., 1231 25th St., NW, Washington, DC 20037. TEL 800-372-1033, 800-452-7773, FAX 800-253-0332, customercare@bna.com, http://www.bna.com/products/corplaw/atrd.htm. **Subscr. to:** 9435 Key West Ave, Rockville, MD 20850.

338   DEU   ISSN 1611-6607
HC10
➤ **APPLIED ECONOMICS QUARTERLY.** Text in English, German; Summaries in English. 1954. q. EUR 68 to individuals; EUR 98 to institutions; EUR 68 to students; EUR 24 newsstand/cover (effective 2006). adv. bk.rev. charts; stat. index. reprints avail. **Document type:** *Journal, Academic/Scholarly.* **Description:** Publishes empirical, policy-oriented papers in all fields of economics.
Formerly (until 2003): Konjunkturpolitik (0023-3498)
Indexed: DIP, IBR, IBSS, IBZ, JEL, KES, PAIS, RASB.
—BLDSC (1571.974000), IE, Infotrieve, ingenta. **CCC.**
Published by: Duncker und Humblot GmbH, Carl-Heinrich-Becker-Weg 9, Berlin, 12165, Germany. TEL 49-30-7900060, FAX 49-30-79000631, info@duncker-humblot.de, http://www.duncker-humblot.de. Ed. Rainer Winkelmann. adv.: page EUR 450; trim 115 x 185. Circ: 500 (paid and controlled).

➤ **APPROPRIATE TECHNOLOGY**; practical approaches to development. see *AGRICULTURE—Agricultural Economics*

338   BHR
ARAB INDUSTRY REVIEW. Text in English. 1984. a. USD 35.
Published by: Falcon Publishing, PO Box 5028, Manama, Bahrain. Ed. S Gangulyey. Circ: 10,000.

330   DEU   ISSN 1439-5134
ARBEITSPAPIERE - DISTRIBUTION & HANDEL. Variant title: Westfaelische Wilhelms-Universitaet Muenster. Lehrstuhl fuer Betriebswirtschaftslehre, insb. Distribution und Handel. Arbeitspapiere. Text in German. 1992. irreg., latest vol.16, 2001. **Document type:** *Monographic series, Academic/Scholarly.*
Published by: Westfaelische Wilhelms-Universitaet Muenster, Lehrstuhl fuer Betriebswirtschaftslehre, insb. Distribution und Handel, Am Stadtgraben 13-15, Muenster, 48143, Germany. TEL 49-251-8322808, FAX 49-251-8322032, 02diah@wiwi.uni-muenster.de, http://www.marketing-centrum.de/ifhm/.

ARGENTINA. INSTITUTO NACIONAL DE ESTADISTICA Y CENSOS. ENCUESTA INDUSTRIAL ANUAL (YEAR). see *BUSINESS AND ECONOMICS—Abstracting, Bibliographies, Statistics*

ARGENTINA. INSTITUTO NACIONAL DE ESTADISTICA Y CENSOS. ESTADISTICA DE PRODUCTOS INDUSTRIALES. see *BUSINESS AND ECONOMICS—Abstracting, Bibliographies, Statistics*

ARGENTINA. INSTITUTO NACIONAL DE ESTADISTICA Y CENSOS. SERIE NOMENCLADORES Y CORRESPONDENCIAS. see *BUSINESS AND ECONOMICS—Abstracting, Bibliographies, Statistics*

338   IND   ISSN 0004-3567
HC431
➤ **ARTHA-VIKAS**; a journal of economic development. Text in English. 1965. s-a. INR 75, USD 30 to individuals; INR 150, USD 40 to institutions (effective 2000). adv. bk.rev. back issues avail. **Document type:** *Academic/Scholarly.* **Description:** Publishes research articles and reviews on economic development, particularly rural economic development.
Indexed: AEA, ForAb, HortAb, I&DA, JEL, RDA, S&F, TOSA, WAE&RSA.
Published by: Sardar Patel University, Department of Economics, Artha-Vikas, Vallabh Vidyanagar, Gujarat 388 120, India. TEL 91-2692-46545, FAX 91-2692-46475, TELEX 017225 VUIA, root@patelernet.in, root@patel.ernet.in. Ed., R&P, Adv. contact A S Patel. Pub. Harish Desai. B&W page INR 2,500. Circ: 150.

338 332.6   HKG   ISSN 1015-504X
ASIAN MANUFACTURERS JOURNAL. Text in Chinese. 1988. bi-m. HKD 210; USD 75 in Asia; USD 102 elsewhere. adv. **Document type:** *Trade.* **Description:** Introduces made-in-Asia consumer goods including gifts, toys, electronics, fashion, and fashion accessories, and household items to buyers in Europe and North America.
Related titles: Online - full text ed.
Address: GPO Box 6217, Hong Kong, Hong Kong. TEL 852-2558-8131, FAX 852-2897-5087, TELEX HX82169, enquiry@amj.com, http://www.amj.com. Ed. Terence Hung. Adv. contact Joseph Cheng. Circ: 32,000.

338   COL   ISSN 0120-9515
ASOCIACION NACIONAL DE INDUSTRIALES. REVISTA BIMESTRAL. Text in Spanish. 1966. bi-m. COP 10,800. adv. bk.rev. bibl.; charts; stat.
Formerly: Asociacion Nacional de Industriales. Revista Trimestral (0004-4865)
Indexed: PAIS.
—BLDSC (7840.870000).
Published by: Asociacion Nacional de Industriales, Centro Coltejer, P. 8, Apartado Aereo 997, Medellin, ANT, Colombia. FAX 251-8830, TELEX 66631. Ed. Fabio Echeverri Correa. Circ: 2,000.

338   USA
ASSOCIATION OF HOME APPLIANCE MANUFACTURERS. TRENDS AND FORECASTS. Text in English. **Document type:** *Newsletter.* **Description:** Reports on shipment trends of major appliances. Includes ten-year summary and two-year forecast.
Related titles: Online - full text ed.
Published by: Association of Home Appliance Manufacturers, 1111 19th St, N W, Ste 402, Washington, DC 20036. TEL 202-872-5955, FAX 202-872-9354, http://www.aham.org.

338   ITA   ISSN 0004-5918
ASSOCIAZIONE DEGLI INDUSTRIALI DI AREZZO. NOTIZIARIO∗. Text in Italian. 1945. m. free. stat. index, cum.index.
Indexed: BrCerAb, F&EA.
Published by: Associazione degli Industriali di Arezzo, C.P. 214, Via Roma, 2, Arezzo, AR 52100, Italy. Ed. Dr. Guido Goti. Circ: 500.

338.9   CAN   ISSN 1483-9067
ATLANTIC CANADA OPPORTUNITIES AGENCY. PERFORMANCE REPORT. Text in English, French. 1996. a.
Related titles: Online - full text ed.: ISSN 1490-5132.
Published by: (Atlantic Canada Opportunities Agency), Treasury Board of Canada Secretariat, Corporate Communications, West Tower, Rm P-135, 300 Laurier Ave W, Ottawa, ON K1A 0R5, Canada. TEL 613-995-2855, FAX 613-996-0518, services-publications@tbs-sct.gc.ca, http://www.acoa.ca/e/library/parliament.shtml, http://www.tbs-sct.gc.ca.

338   FRA
ATLAS DES USINES DE FRANCE. Text in French. a.
Published by: Groupe Industrie Services Info, 12-14 Rue Mederic, Paris, Cedex 17 75815, France. http://www.industrie-technologie.com. Circ: 70,000.

AUFBEREITUNGS-TECHNIK - MINERAL PROCESSING. see *MINES AND MINING INDUSTRY*

AUSTRALIA. BUREAU OF STATISTICS. AUSTRALIAN AND NEW ZEALAND STANDARD PRODUCT CLASSIFICATION - WEBSITE VERSION. see *BUSINESS AND ECONOMICS—Abstracting, Bibliographies, Statistics*

AUSTRALIA. BUREAU OF STATISTICS. CONSTANT PRICE ESTIMATES OF MANUFACTURING PRODUCTION, AUSTRALIA. see *BUSINESS AND ECONOMICS—Abstracting, Bibliographies, Statistics*

AUSTRALIA. BUREAU OF STATISTICS. INFORMATION PAPER: AVAILABILITY OF STATISTICS RELATED TO MANUFACTURING. see *BUSINESS AND ECONOMICS—Abstracting, Bibliographies, Statistics*

B

AUSTRALIA. BUREAU OF STATISTICS. INNOVATION IN MANUFACTURING, AUSTRALIA. see *BUSINESS AND ECONOMICS—Abstracting, Bibliographies, Statistics*

AUSTRALIA. BUREAU OF STATISTICS. MANUFACTURING, AUSTRALIA. see *BUSINESS AND ECONOMICS—Abstracting, Bibliographies, Statistics*

AUSTRALIA. BUREAU OF STATISTICS. MANUFACTURING PRODUCTION, AUSTRALIA. see *BUSINESS AND ECONOMICS—Abstracting, Bibliographies, Statistics*

AUSTRALIA. BUREAU OF STATISTICS. NEW SOUTH WALES OFFICE. MANUFACTURING INDUSTRY, NEW SOUTH WALES AND AUSTRALIAN CAPITAL TERRITORY. see *BUSINESS AND ECONOMICS—Abstracting, Bibliographies, Statistics*

AUSTRALIA. BUREAU OF STATISTICS. SOUTH AUSTRALIAN OFFICE. MANUFACTURING INDUSTRY, SOUTH AUSTRALIA. see *BUSINESS AND ECONOMICS—Abstracting, Bibliographies, Statistics*

AUSTRALIA. BUREAU OF STATISTICS. SOUTH AUSTRALIAN OFFICE. SALES OF GOODS AND SERVICES BY BUSINESSES INVOLVED IN WATER RELATED ACTIVITY IN SOUTH AUSTRALIA. see *BUSINESS AND ECONOMICS—Abstracting, Bibliographies, Statistics*

AUSTRALIA. BUREAU OF STATISTICS. VICTORIAN OFFICE. MANUFACTURING INDUSTRY, VICTORIA. see *BUSINESS AND ECONOMICS—Abstracting, Bibliographies, Statistics*

338 AUS ISSN 1328-259X
AUSTRALIAN BUSINESS NEWS. Text in English. 1931. bi-m. free to members. adv. bk.rev. charts; illus.; stat.; tr.lit. back issues avail. **Document type:** *Newspaper, Trade.*
Formerly: Manufacturer's Bulletin (Sydney, 1991) (1037-7271); (until 1991): A C M Bulletin (N.S.W. Edition) (1035-3941); (until 1990): Manufacturers' Bulletin (Sydney, 1931) (0816-9098)
Related titles: Online - full text ed.
Published by: Australian Business Ltd., 140 Arthur St, North Sydney, NSW 2060, Australia. TEL 61-2-9927-7461, FAX 61-2-9927-7461, ron.krueger@australianbusiness.com.au, krueger@asol.net, http://www.australianbusiness.com.au/abmagazine, http://asol.net. Ed., Pub. Ron Krueger. adv.: B&W page AUD 1,850, color page AUD 2,850; trim 250 x 297. Circ: 6,500.

AUSZUEGE AUS DEN EUROPAEISCHEN PATENTANMELDUNGEN. TEIL 3A. UEBRIGE VERARBEITUNGSINDUSTRIE UND ARBEITSVERFAHREN, FAHRZEUGBAU, ERNAEHRUNG, LANDWIRTSCHAFT. see *PATENTS, TRADEMARKS AND COPYRIGHTS*

AUTOMOTIVE COMPONENTS ANALYST; monthly analysis of developments in the global components industry. see *TRANSPORTATION—Automobiles*

AUTOMOTIVE SUPPLY. see *TRANSPORTATION—Automobiles*

AVANCE DE INFORMACION ECONOMICA. INDICADORES DE LA ACTIVIDAD INDUSTRIAL. see *BUSINESS AND ECONOMICS—Abstracting, Bibliographies, Statistics*

AVANCE DE INFORMACION ECONOMICA. INDICADORES DEL SECTOR MANUFACTURERO; 145 clases de actividad. see *BUSINESS AND ECONOMICS—Abstracting, Bibliographies, Statistics*

B A M A ANNUAL REPORT. see *CHEMISTRY*

338 BGR
BALKAN INDUSTRIAL REVIEW. Text in English. bi-m. **Description:** Covers industrial products & services of the Balkan region - Bulgaria, Romania, Yugoslavia, Macedonia, Greece and Turkey.
Published by: TLL Media Ltd., Dimitar Nestorov Blvd., Bl. 119, Entr. 3, Apt. 63, Sofia, 1612, Bulgaria. TEL 359-2-9516364, 359-2-9526486, FAX 359-2-9886981, office@tllmedia.bg, editors@tllmedia.bg, http://www.tllmedia.bg/review/index.en.chtm, http://www.tllmedia.bg/contact.en.chtm. Circ: 12,000.

330.9 MAR ISSN 0851-1934
HG3382.A8
BANQUE NATIONALE POUR LE DEVELOPPEMENT ECONOMIQUE. RAPPORT ANNUEL. Text in Arabic, English, French. 1960. a. free. illus.; stat. **Document type:** *Corporate.*
Published by: Banque Nationale pour le Developpement Economique, Place des Alaouites, 12, B P 407, Rabat, 10000, Morocco. TEL 212-7-70-60-40, FAX 212-7-70-37-06, TELEX BDMAROC 319 42 M. Circ: 4,000.

338 USA
BAXTER; a world economic and investment service. Text in English. 1924. m. USD 175 (effective 2000). charts; stat. back issues avail. **Document type:** *Newsletter.*
Published by: Baxter Brothers, Inc, 1030 E Putnam Ave, Box 2200, Greenwich, CT 06836. TEL 203-637-4559, FAX 203-637-9652, bill@baxterinvestment.com, http://www.baxterinvestment.com. Ed. William J Baxter Jr. **Subscr. to:** Rte 25, Cutchogue, NY 11935.

BAYER ALKALIZER. see *BIOLOGY*

338 DEU
BEIERSDORF JOURNAL. Text in German. 1960. q. bk.rev. **Document type:** *Corporate.*
Formerly: Hauskurier
Published by: Beiersdorf AG, Unnastr 48, Hamburg, 20253, Germany. FAX 49-40-4909143, http://www.beiersdorf.com. Ed., R&P Dr. Matthias Schatz. Circ: (controlled).

338 DEU ISSN 0343-0413
HD72
BEITRAEGE ZUR WIRTSCHAFTS- UND SOZIALPOLITIK. Text in German. 1963. 8/yr. EUR 77; EUR 10.50 newsstand/cover (effective 2002). **Document type:** *Journal, Academic/Scholarly.*
Former titles (until 1975): Institut der Deutschen Wirtschaft (0342-3808); (until 1973): Deutsches Industrieinstitut Beitraege (0012-1282)
Indexed: RefZh.
Published by: Deutscher Instituts Verlag GmbH, Gustav-Heinemann-Ufer 84-88, Cologne, 50968, Germany. TEL 49-221-4981452, FAX 49-221-4981445, div@iwkoeln.de, http://www.iwkoeln.de/verlag/reihen/rb.htm. Circ: 1,200.

338.9 BEL
BENELUX ECONOMIC UNION. CONSEIL CENTRAL DE L'ECONOMIE. RAPPORT DU SECRETAIRE SUR L'ACTIVITE DU CONSEIL. Text in French. 1950. a. free.
Formerly: Benelux Economic Union. Conseil Consultatif Economique et Social. Rapport du Secretaire Concernant les Activites du Conseil (0522-8948)
Published by: (Conseil Central de l'Economie), Benelux Economic Union, Rue de la Regence 39, Brussels, 1000, Belgium. TEL 32-2-519-3811, FAX 32-2-513-4206, http://www.benelux.be/fr/home_frame.htm.

BESTUUR EN BELEID V Z W. see *BUSINESS AND ECONOMICS*

338 DEU ISSN 0341-4477
BETRIEB UND MEISTER. Text in German. 1968. m. EUR 31.20 domestic; EUR 34.20 foreign; EUR 2.70 newsstand/cover (effective 2004). adv. bk.rev. back issues avail. **Document type:** *Journal, Trade.* **Description:** Focuses on production aspects of goods and services for masterworkmen and technicians in industry.
—IE, Infotrieve. **CCC.**
Published by: Konradin Verlag Robert Kohlhammer GmbH, Ernst Mey Str 8, Leinfelden-Echterdingen, 70771, Germany. TEL 49-711-75940, FAX 49-711-7594399, info@konradin.de, http://www.betriebmeister.de, http://www.konradin.de. Ed. Rudolf Beyer. Adv. contact Walter Schwager. B&W page EUR 3,900, color page EUR 4,990; trim 190 x 270. Circ: 16,315 (paid and controlled).

BIOQUALITY. see *PHARMACY AND PHARMACOLOGY*

BIOTECHNOLOGY INTERNATIONAL YEARBOOK (YEAR). see *BIOLOGY—Biotechnology*

338 DEU ISSN 0172-018X
BLAETTER FUER VORGESETZTE. Text in German. 1957. m. looseleaf. abstr. **Document type:** *Newsletter, Trade.*
Published by: (Bundesarbeitgeberverband Chemie), Dr. Curt Haefner Verlag GmbH, Bachstr 14-16, Heidelberg, 69121, Germany. TEL 49-6221-64460, FAX 49-6221-644640, info@haefner-verlag.de, http://www.haefner-verlag.de. Ed. Hans Guenter Glass. Circ: 23,400.

338.0972 MEX ISSN 0187-7321
BOLETIN INDUSTRIAL. Text in Spanish. 1983. m. free. adv. **Document type:** *Magazine, Trade.*
Published by: Editorial Nova S.A. de C.V., Goldsmith 37-401, Polanco Reforma, Mexico City, DF 11550, Mexico. TEL 52-55-5286080, FAX 52-55-5283194, informes@boletinindustrial.com, bolind@viernes.iwm.com.mx, http://www.boletinindustrial.com. Ed., Adv. contact Humberto Valades. Circ: 37,000 (controlled).

BOTSWANA MANUFACTURING DIRECTORY. see *BUSINESS AND ECONOMICS—Trade And Industrial Directories*

338.981 BRA
BRAZIL DEVELOPMENT SERIES/SERIES DESENVOLVIMENTO BRASILEIRO. Text in English, Portuguese. 1971. a. USD 20. illus.
Published by: (Brazilian Institute of Economic Studies), TELEPRESS Servicos de Imprensa Ltda., Rua Albuquerque Lins, 1315, S Cecilia, Sao Paulo, SP 01230-001, Brazil. Ed. Olavo G Otero. Circ: 10,000.

338 DEU
BUDERUS POST. Text in German. 1950. q. bk.rev. back issues avail. **Document type:** *Corporate.*
Published by: Buderus Aktiengesellschaft, Sophienstr 30-32, Wetzlar, 35573, Germany. TEL 49-6441-418-0, FAX 49-6441-418901. Ed. Hans Spiegelhalter. Circ: 13,500.

338 GBR ISSN 0955-3754
CODEN: BMINEA
BULK MATERIALS INTERNATIONAL. Text in English. 1988. 10/yr.
Indexed: RefZh.
Address: 77a High Rd, London, NW10 2SU, United Kingdom. TEL 081-451-6578, FAX 081-459-0712. Ed. Richard Miller. Circ: 10,000.

338 GRC
BUSINESS FILE SPECIAL SURVEY SERIES. Text in English. 1991. q. EUR 35 domestic; EUR 35 in Cyprus; EUR 20 domestic to students; EUR 20 in Cyprus to students; EUR 58 foreign (effective 2005). adv. bk.rev. charts; illus.; tr.mk. back issues avail. **Document type:** *Journal, Trade.* **Description:** Covers a particular Greek industrial sector.
Formerly: Industrial Review Special Survey Series (1106-8825)
Related titles: CD-ROM ed.; ♦ Supplement to: Oikonomike Biomehanike Epitheorese. ISSN 1109-1584.
Published by: Kerkyra Monoprosopi Ltd Publications, 6 - 8 Vlahava St, Athens, 105 51, Greece. TEL 30-1-331-4714, FAX 30-1-325-2283, http://www.oikonomiki.gr. Ed. Dimitris Karamanos. Pub. Alexandra K Vovolini Laskaridis. Adv. contact Anastasia Rammou.

BUSINESS MONITOR: SERVICE TRADES. see *BUSINESS AND ECONOMICS—Abstracting, Bibliographies, Statistics*

BUSINESS RATIO. DOMESTIC FURNITURE MANUFACTURERS. see *INTERIOR DESIGN AND DECORATION—Furniture And House Furnishings*

BUSINESS RATIO. FROZEN FOOD PRODUCERS. see *FOOD AND FOOD INDUSTRIES*

BUSINESS RATIO. HYDRAULIC AND PNEUMATIC EQUIPMENT MANUFACTURERS. see *ENGINEERING—Hydraulic Engineering*

338 658.8 GBR ISSN 1469-8862
BUSINESS RATIO. INDUSTRIAL FASTENER DISTRIBUTORS. Text in English. 1979. a. GBP 275 (effective 2001). charts; stat. **Document type:** *Trade.*
Former titles (until 2000): Business Ratio Plus: Industrial Fastener Distributors (1358-8060); (until 1995): Business Ratio Report: Industrial Fastener Distributors (0261-846X)
Published by: The Prospect Shop Ltd., Field House, 72 Oldfield Rd, Hampton, Middx TW12 2HQ, United Kingdom. TEL 44-20-8461-8730, 44-20-8481-8720, FAX 44-20-8783-1940, info@theprospectshop.co.uk.

338 658.8 GBR ISSN 1469-8919
BUSINESS RATIO. INDUSTRIAL FASTENER MANUFACTURERS. Text in English. 1978. a. GBP 275 (effective 2001). charts; stat. **Document type:** *Trade.*
Former titles (until 2000): Business Ratio Plus: Industrial Fastener Manufacturers (1359-6020); (until 1995): Business Ratio Report: Industrial Fastener Manufacturers (0261-8478)
Published by: The Prospect Shop Ltd., Field House, 72 Oldfield Rd, Hampton, Middx TW12 2HQ, United Kingdom. TEL 44-20-8461-8730, 44-20-8481-8720, FAX 44-20-8783-1940, info@theprospectshop.co.uk.

BUSINESS RATIO. JOINERY MANUFACTURERS. see *BUILDING AND CONSTRUCTION—Carpentry And Woodwork*

BUSINESS RATIO REPORT. HEATING AND VENTILATING EQUIPMENT MANUFACTURERS (YEAR). see *HEATING, PLUMBING AND REFRIGERATION*

BUSINESS RATIO REPORT. INDUSTRIAL CHEMICAL MANUFACTURERS. see *CHEMISTRY*

BUSINESS RATIO. THE HOTEL INDUSTRY. see *HOTELS AND RESTAURANTS*

338 678.2 GBR ISSN 1470-6873
BUSINESS RATIO. THE RUBBER AND TYRE INDUSTRY. Text in English. a. GBP 275 (effective 2001). **Description:** Analyses and compares the financial performance of companies within a given UK industry sector. Includes company and industry performance summaries, trends, and forecasts.
Former titles (until 2000): Business Ratio Plus: The Rubber & Tyre Industry (1357-6836); (until 1994): Business Ratio Report: Rubber Manufacturers and Processors
Published by: The Prospect Shop Ltd., Field House, 72 Oldfield Rd, Hampton, Middx TW12 2HQ, United Kingdom. TEL 44-20-8461-8730, 44-20-8481-8720, FAX 44-20-8783-1940, info@theprospectshop.co.uk.

650 PHL ISSN 0116-3930
BUSINESS WORLD. Text in English. 1987. d. looseleaf. PHP 2,080. adv. bk.rev. charts; illus.; mkt.; stat. index. back issues avail. **Document type:** *Newspaper.* **Description:** Business and financial daily newspaper covering world economy, stock markets, commodities futures market, and corporate world.

B

Formerly: Business Day (0007-6635); Which incorporates: A S E A N's Largest Corporations; Philippines' Largest Exporters
Related titles: Online - full text ed.: (from Gale Group, LexisNexis, ProQuest Information & Learning).
Indexed: ABIn, B&I.
Published by: BusinessWorld Publishing Corp., No. 95 Balete Drive Extension, New Manila, Quezon City, 1112, Philippines. TEL 632-7270091, FAX 632-7276014, marketng@bworld.com.ph. Ed., Pub. Raul L Locsin. Adv. contact Danilo Ocampo. page PHP 92,340; 58 x 69. Circ: 52,000.

C B I - PANNEL KERR FORSTER - S M E TRENDS REPORT. see *BUSINESS AND ECONOMICS—Small Business*

338   USA
C. BREWER TODAY✳ . Text in English. 1957. q. free. **Document type:** *Newsletter.*
Formerly (until 1976): Brewer Monthly Letter
Media: Duplicated (not offset).
Published by: C. Brewer & Co. Ltd., PO Box 1826, Papaikou, HI 96781-1826. TEL 808-536-4461. Ed. Mr. Kim L Peterson. R&P Kim Peterson TEL 808-969-8057. Circ: 2,000 (controlled).

338   AUS   ISSN 0085-1280
HC601
C E D A GROWTH SERIES. Text in English. 1961. irreg. price varies.
Related titles: Online - full text ed.: (from R M I T Publishing).
Indexed: AnBrAb, AusPAIS, BiolAb, PoultAb, VetBull.
Published by: Committee for Economic Development of Australia, 123 Lonsdale St, Melbourne, VIC 3000, Australia. FAX 61-3-9663-7271.

330   USA   ISSN 0889-7395
C R A REVIEW. Text in English. 1974. q. free. charts; illus.; stat. back issues avail. **Document type:** *Newsletter.* **Description:** Highlights work CRA has done as economics management consultant in a wide range of industries.
Formerly (until 1986): C R A Research Review
Published by: Charles River Associates Incorporated, John Hancock Tower, 200 Clarendon St, Boston, MA 02116. TEL 617-425-3000, FAX 617-425-3132. Ed. Charles Tucker. Circ: 15,000.

338   BRA
CADASTRO INDUSTRIAL DO PARA. Text in Portuguese. irreg.
Published by: Federacao das Industrias, Av. Nazare, 759, Belem, Para, Brazil.

CALIBRE (ENGLISH EDITION). see *METROLOGY AND STANDARDIZATION*

CAMARA DE INDUSTRIALES DE CARACAS. NOTI. see *BUSINESS AND ECONOMICS*

338   MEX
CAMARA NACIONAL DE LA INDUSTRIA DE TRANSFORMACION. BOLETIN INFORMATIVO. Text in Spanish. m. free.
Published by: Camara Nacional de la Industria de Transformacion, Apdo. Postal 60-468, Av. San Antonio 256, Mexico City, DF 03849, Mexico. TEL 5-563-3500. Ed. Iris Arzate Rios. Circ: (controlled).

338.7   CMR
CAMEROON DEVELOPMENT CORPORATION. ANNUAL REPORT AND ACCOUNTS/RAPPORT ANNUEL ET COMPTE - RENDU FINANCIER. Key Title: Annual Report and Accounts - Cameroon Development Corporation. Text in English, French. 1947. a. free. illus. **Document type:** *Corporate.* **Description:** Purpose is to acquire lands for the planting of tropical crops and process semi-finished and finished products for local and overseas markets.
Published by: Cameroon Development Corporation, Fako Division, South West Province, Bota - Limbe, Cameroon. TEL 332251, FAX 332654, TELEX 5242 KN. Circ: 5,000.

338.9   CAN   ISSN 1484-1193
T23.A1
CANADA. INDUSTRY CANADA. REPORT ON FEDERAL SCIENCE AND TECHNOLOGY. Variant title: Minding Our Future. Text in English, French. 1997. a.
—CISTI.
Published by: Industry Canada/Industrie Canada, Distribution Services, Communications & Marketing Branch, Rm 268D, West Tower, C.D. Howe Bldg, 235 Queen St, Ottawa, ON K1A 0H5, Canada. TEL 613-947-7466, FAX 613-954-6436, publications@ic.gc.ca, http://www.ic.gc.ca.

338.971   CAN   ISSN 1706-0516
CANADA. PARLIAMENT. HOUSE OF COMMONS. STANDING COMMITTEE ON INDUSTRY, SCIENCE AND TECHNOLOGY. MINUTES OF PROCEEDINGS. Text in English. 1986. irreg.
Former titles (until 2001): Canada. Parliament. House of Commons. Standing Committee on Industry. Minutes of Proceedings (1200-7382); (until 1995): Canada. Parliament. House of Commons. Standing Committee on Industry. Minutes of Proceedings and Evidence (1200-054X); (until 1994): Canada. Parliament. House of Commons. Standing Committee on Industry, Science and Technology, Regional and Northern

Development. Minutes of Proceedings and Evidence (0848-2977); Which superseded in part (in 1989): Canada. Parliament. House of Commons. Standing Committee on Aboriginal Affairs and Northern Development. Minutes of Proceedings and Evidence (0833-367X); (in 1989): Canada. Parliament. House of Commons. Standing Committee on Research, Science and Technology. Minutes of Proceedings and Evidence (0837-4848); (in 1989): Canada. Parliament. House of Commons. Standing Committee on Regional Industrial Expansion. Minutes of Proceedings and Evidence (0838-889X)
Related titles: Online - full text ed.: ISSN 1498-766X. 1995.
Published by: House of Commons, Standing Committee on Industry, Science and Technology, Information Service, Ottawa, ON K1A 0A9, Canada. TEL 613-992-4793, info@parl.gc.ca.

338.9   CAN   ISSN 1483-9369
CANADA. WESTERN ECONOMIC DIVERSIFICATION CANADA. PERFORMANCE REPORT. Text in English, French. 1997. a.
Related titles: Online - full text ed.: ISSN 1490-5035.
Published by: (Western Economic Diversification Canada), Treasury Board of Canada Secretariat, Corporate Communications, West Tower, Rm P-135, 300 Laurier Ave W, Ottawa, ON K1A 0R5, Canada. TEL 613-995-2855, FAX 613-996-0518, services-publications@tbs-sct.gc.ca, http://www.wd.gc.ca/rpts/plans/default_e.asp, http://www.tbs-sct.gc.ca.

CANADIAN ENGINEERING & INDUSTRIAL YEAR BOOK. see *ENGINEERING*

338   CAN   ISSN 0713-1348
CANADIAN FISHERIES. LANDINGS/PECHES CANADIENNES. DEBARQUEMENTS. Text in English. 1976. a.
Formerly (until 1981): Canadian Fisheries. Primary Sector Activities (0225-7246)
Indexed: ESPM.
Published by: (Department of Fisheries and Oceans, Statistical Services), Department of Fisheries and Oceans, Communications Directorate, 200 Kent St, 13th Fl, Sta 13228, Ottawa, ON K1A 0E6, Canada. TEL 613-993-0999, FAX 613-990-1866, info@dfo-mpo.gc.ca, http://www.ncr.dfo.ca.

338   CAN   ISSN 0835-9946
CANADIAN FISHERIES. PRODUCTS AND INVENTORIES/ PECHES CANADIENNES. PRODUITS ET STOCKS. Text in English, French. 1979. m. **Document type:** *Government.*
Formerly (until 1987): Canadian Fisheries. Products and Stocks (0225-722X)
Indexed: ASFA.
Published by: (Department of Fisheries and Oceans, Statistical Services), Department of Fisheries and Oceans, Communications Directorate, 200 Kent St, 13th Fl, Sta 13228, Ottawa, ON K1A 0E6, Canada. TEL 613-993-0999, FAX 613-990-1866, info@dfo-mpo.gc.ca, http://www.ncr.dfo.ca.

338.2 622   CAN   ISSN 0826-6166
CANADIAN INSTITUTE OF MINING AND METALLURGY. SPECIAL VOLUME. Text in English. irreg., latest vol.55. price varies.
Former titles (until 1982): C I M. Special Volume (0713-7672); (until 1977): Canadian Institute of Mining and Metallurgy. Special Volume (0576-5447)
—CISTI. CCC.
Published by: Canadian Institute of Mining, Metallurgy and Petroleum, 3400 de Maisonneuve Blvd W, Ste 1210, Montreal, PQ H3Z 3B8, Canada. TEL 514-939-2710, FAX 514-939-2714, cim@cim.org, http://www.cim.org/publications/specialVols.cfm.

338.6041   GBR   ISSN 1465-1629
CAPEX SCOREBOARD. Text in English. 1998. q.
—BLDSC (3050.653850).
Published by: Company Reporting Ltd., 11 John's Place, Edinburgh, Scotland EH6 7EL, United Kingdom. TEL 44-131-5618000, FAX 44-131-5618001, capex@comrep.co.uk, info@comrep.co.uk, http://www.companyreporting.com.

CASH ALMANACH. see *FOOD AND FOOD INDUSTRIES*

338.47665   USA   ISSN 1529-2509
CASPIAN INVESTOR. Text in English. 199?. 10/yr. USD 1,849 domestic; USD 1,949 foreign (effective 2005). **Document type:** *Journal, Trade.* **Description:** Contains news and analysis of issues and events affecting the energy market in the Caspian region.
Published by: WorldTrade Executive, Inc., 2250 Main St, Ste 100, PO Box 761, Concord, MA 01742. TEL 978-287-0301, FAX 978-287-0302, info@wtexec.com, http://www.wtexec.com/casp.html. Ed. Inna Gaiduk. Pub. Gary A Brown. Adv. contact John Martel.

CENSO DOS SERVICOS. see *BUSINESS AND ECONOMICS—Abstracting, Bibliographies, Statistics*

CENSO INDUSTRIAL. see *BUSINESS AND ECONOMICS— Abstracting, Bibliographies, Statistics*

338   USA   ISSN 0090-7111
HC107.M2
CENSUS OF MAINE MANUFACTURES. Text in English. 1948. a. free. charts; stat. **Document type:** *Government.* **Description:** Covers Maine manufacturing establishments ranging from the single proprietorships to the largest corporations.
Related titles: ◆ Series of: U.S. Bureau of Labor Statistics. Bulletin. ISSN 0082-9021.
Published by: (Maine. Technical Services Division), Department of Labor, Bureau of Labor Standards, 45 State House Station, Augusta, ME 04333-0045. TEL 207-624-6440, FAX 207-624-6449, webmaster_bls@state.me.us. Ed., R&P Barbara Chenoweth. Circ: 437.

338.47   PRI   ISSN 0552-5276
CENSUS OF MANUFACTURING INDUSTRIES OF PUERTO RICO. Text in English, Spanish. a. free. stat. **Document type:** *Government.*
Published by: Department of Labor, Bureau of Labor Statistics, 505 Munoz Rivera Ave., Hato Rey, 00918, Puerto Rico. TEL 787-754-5351. Ed. Antonio Padilla Torres. Circ: 1,000.

330   NLD   ISSN 0926-8235
CENTRAL ECONOMIC PLAN. Text in English. 1961. a.
Related titles: ◆ Dutch ed.: Netherlands. Centraal Planbureau. Centraal Economisch Plan. ISSN 0166-9478.
Published by: Sdu Uitgevers bv, Christoffel Plantijnstraat 2, The Hague, 2515 TZ, Netherlands.

338   ESP   ISSN 0214-6320
CENTRO DE INVESTIGACION Y CONTROL DE LA CALIDAD. Text in Spanish. 3/yr. free.
Indexed: IECT.
Published by: Instituto Nacional del Consumo, Principe de Vergara, 54, Madrid, 28006, Spain.

338 660   CHE   ISSN 1020-0746
HD9656.A1
CHEMICAL INDUSTRY IN (YEAR) - ANNUAL REVIEW. Text in English. 1971. a. USD 100 (effective 2001). charts; stat. **Document type:** *Yearbook, Trade.*
Formerly (until 1992): Annual Review of the Chemical Industry (0255-4291)
Related titles: Microfiche ed.: (from CIS).
Indexed: IIS.
—BLDSC (3148.270000), Linda Hall. CCC.
Published by: United Nations, Economic Commission for Europe (ECE), Palais des Nations, Geneva 10, 1211, Switzerland. TEL 41-22-9173254, FAX 41-22-9170178, info.ece@unece.org, http://www.unece.org.

CHEMICAL INDUSTRY SOURCEBOOK AND STRATEGIC OVERVIEW. see *CHEMISTRY*

338   IND
CHEMICAL PRODUCTS FINDER. Text in English. 1982. m. INR 1,200, USD 38. adv. bk.rev. abstr.; charts; illus. **Description:** Covers new products and news briefs.
Published by: IPFonline Ltd., 33 D'Silva Rd, Mylapore, Chennai, 600 004, India. TEL 91-44-4661588, FAX 91-44-4661617. Ed. A G Bhat. adv.: B&W page INR 8,500, color page INR 12,500; trim 205 x 280.

CHILE. INSTITUTO NACIONAL DE ESTADISTICAS. INDICE DE PRODUCCION Y VENTA FISICA DE INDUSTRIAS MANUFACTURERAS. see *BUSINESS AND ECONOMICS—Abstracting, Bibliographies, Statistics*

CHILE. INSTITUTO NACIONAL DE ESTADISTICAS. INDUSTRIAS MANUFACTURERAS. see *BUSINESS AND ECONOMICS—Abstracting, Bibliographies, Statistics*

338   TWN
CHINA DEVELOPMENT CORPORATION. ANNUAL REPORT. Text in Chinese. 1959. a. illus.; stat.
Published by: China Development Corporation, No 125 Nanking E. Rd, Sec 5, Taipei, Taiwan.

338   USA   ISSN 1047-1308
TS1033
CIRCLE Y OF YOAKUM. Text in English. a.
Published by: Circle Y, Inc., 201 W Morris St, PO Box 797, Yoakum, TX 77995.

338   USA
CITY PRODUCTS AND SERVICES GUIDE. Text in English. 1983. a. adv. **Document type:** *Government.* **Description:** Contains listings of businesses offering goods and services to Minnesota cities.
Published by: League of Minnesota Cities, 145 University Ave W, St Paul, MN 55103-2044. TEL 612-281-1200, FAX 612-281-1299, http://www.lmnc.org. Adv. contact Gayle Brodt.

CLEANER PRODUCTION. see *OCCUPATIONAL HEALTH AND SAFETY*

B

338 USA ISSN 1073-9602
CLEANER TIMES. Text in English. 1989. m. USD 36 domestic; USD 59 foreign (effective 2000). adv. bk.rev. illus.; tr.lit. index. back issues avail. **Document type:** *Trade.* **Description:** Emphasizes information, application, and productivity for persons engaged in the manufacturing, distribution, or use of high pressure water systems and accessories.
Published by: Advantage Publishing, 1000 Nix Rd., Little Rock, AR 72211-3235. bstark@adpub.com, http://www.adpub.com. Ed. Beth Stark. Pub., R&P Charlene Yarbrough TEL 501-280-9111. Adv. contact Chuck Prieur. page USD 1,350; trim 10.875 x 8.5. Circ: 10,000.

COLOMBIA. DEPARTAMENTO ADMINISTRATIVO NACIONAL DE ESTADISTICA. ANUARIO DE INDUSTRIA MANUFACTURERA. see *BUSINESS AND ECONOMICS—Abstracting, Bibliographies, Statistics*

338 ESP ISSN 0213-0637
COMERCIO INDUSTRIA. Text in Spanish. 1970. m. adv. bk.rev. bibl.; charts; illus. index. **Document type:** *Trade.*
Formerly (until 1980): Comercio e Industria. Suplemento Quincenal (0210-2595); Incorporated (in 1982): Comercio e Industria (0210-2579); Which was formed by the merger of (1930-1970): Comercio (0010-2261); (1923-1970): Industria (0019-7432); Incorporated (1962-1969): Industria. Suplemento Quincenal (0210-2587)
Indexed: ChemAb.
—CINDOC.
Published by: Camara Oficial de Comercio e Industria de Madrid, Huertas, 13, Madrid, 28012, Spain. TEL 34-91-538-3513, FAX 34-91-538-3677, cpd2@camaramadrid.es, http://www.camaramadrid.es. Ed. Jose Diez Clavero. Circ: 158,773.

COMMERCE BUSINESS DAILY; synopsis of United States government proposed procurement, sales, and contract awards. see *BUSINESS AND ECONOMICS—Marketing And Purchasing*

650 IND ISSN 0010-4027
KNS956.A15
COMPANY NEWS AND NOTES. Text in English. 1962. m. INR 42. adv. bk.rev. bibl.; charts; stat. index. **Document type:** *Newsletter, Trade.*
Indexed: PAA&I, RASB.
Published by: Department of Company Affairs, Shastri Bhawan, Dr. Rajendraprasad Rd., New Delhi, India. Circ: 12,000. **Dist. by:** Controller of Publications, Civil Lines, New Delhi 110 006, India.

338 USA
COMPASS MAGAZINE✶. Text in English. 1965. 4/yr. USD 2. adv. bk.rev. charts; illus.
Former titles: Compass Quarterly; (until 1979): Compass (Asbury Park) (0010-4191)
Published by: (Monmouth-Ocean Development Council), McLoughlin & Co. Publications, PO Box 7236, Shrewsbury, NJ 07702-7236. TEL 908-741-0547, FAX 908-842-5568. Ed. Carolann M Perry. Circ: 7,000.

COMPUTERS IN FURNITURE AND CABINET MANUFACTURING. INTERNATIONAL SYMPOSIUM PROCEEDINGS. see *COMPUTERS—Automation*

338 CAN ISSN 1206-0917
CONFERENCE BOARD OF CANADA. PERFORMANCE AND POTENTIAL. Text in English. 1996. a.
—CISTI.
Published by: Conference Board of Canada, 255 Smyth Rd, Ste 100, Ottawa, ON K1H 8M7, Canada. TEL 613-526-3280, 866-711-2262, FAX 613-526-4857, corpcomm@conferenceboard.ca, http://www.conferenceboard.ca/pubs1.htm.

CONGRESO MEXICANO DE CONTROL DE CALIDAD. ANNUAL PROCEEDINGS. see *METROLOGY AND STANDARDIZATION*

338 CAN
CONJONCTURE ECONOMIQUE DES REGIONS DU QUEBEC EN (YEAR). Text in English. 1960. a. free. **Document type:** *Government.* **Description:** Report on the economic situation of the Quebec economy.
Former titles: Quebec (Province). Ministere de l'Industrie, du Commerce et de la Technologie. Direction de l'Analyse et de la Conjoncture Industrielle; Quebec (Province). Ministere de l'Industrie, du Commerce et de la Technologie. Direction de l'Analyse et de la Prevision Economique; Quebec (Province). Ministere de l'Industrie et du Commerce. Direction de l'Analyse et de la Prevision Economiques
Published by: Ministere de l'Industrie, du Commerce et de la Technologie (Quebec), 710 place D Youville, Quebec, PQ G1R 4Y4, Canada. TEL 418-691-5967, FAX 418-646-6435. R&P Rose Marie Auger TEL 418-691-5950. Circ: 1,500.

330.9 GBR ISSN 1351-0959
CONSENSUS FORECASTS - U S A. Text in English. m. USD 424 (effective 2003). 12 p./no.; back issues avail. **Document type:** *Journal, Academic/Scholarly.* **Description:** Surveys U.S. economic and financial forecasters for predictions regarding future growth, inflation, merchandise trade and interest rates. Each issue features reference data and analysis of the economic and political situation in the U.S. along with surveys of international economic forecasts.
Published by: Consensus Economics Inc., 53 Upper Brook St, London, W1K 2LT, United Kingdom. TEL 44-20-7491-3211, FAX 44-20-7409-2331, editors@consensuseconomics.com, http://www.consensuseconomics.com. Ed. Claire V M Hubbard. Pub. Philip M Hubbard.

338.021 GBR
CONSUMER GOODS INTELLIGENCE. Text in English. irreg. stat. **Document type:** *Trade.*
Formerly: Consumer Goods Europe
Published by: Mintel International Group Ltd., 18-19 Long Ln., London, EC1A 9PL, United Kingdom. TEL 44-20-76064533, FAX 44-20-76065932, info@mintel.com, http://reports.mintel.com/sinatra/mintel/new/, http://www.mintel.com.

CONTACT TRANSPORT & LOGISTICS; le trait d'union industrie - prestataires de services - bindeteken tussen industrie en dienstverlenende sektor. see *BUSINESS AND ECONOMICS—Management*

338 CRI
CORPORACION COSTARRICENSE DE FINANCIAMIENTO INDUSTRIAL. MEMORIA ANUAL. Text in Spanish. a.
Published by: Corporacion Costarricense de Financiamiento Industrial, Apdo. 10067, San Jose, Costa Rica.

338 VEN
CORPORACION DE LOS ANDES. REVISTA. Text in Spanish. 1966. q. free. charts; illus.; stat.
Formerly: Corpoandes (0010-8944)
Published by: Corporacion de los Andes, Edificio Sede, La Isla, Merida, Venezuela.

COST CONTROL STRATEGIES FOR MANUFACTURING EXECUTIVES. see *BUSINESS AND ECONOMICS—Management*

330.95957 USA ISSN 1520-1325
COUNTRY REVIEW. SINGAPORE. Text in English. a. USD 39.95 (effective 2004). **Description:** Covers demographic, political, economic, social, corporate, cultural, and environmental information.
Related titles: Online - full text ed.: USD 39.95 single country; USD 99 standard - 192 countries (effective 2004).
Published by: Commercial Data International, CountryWatch, Two Riverway, Ste 1770, Houston, TX 77056. TEL 713-355-6500, FAX 713-355-2008, 800-879-3885, editor@countrywatch.com, http://www.countrywatch.com/.

338 USA
THE CRITICAL PATH; provocative musings for the irreverent product developer. Text in English. m. free.
Media: Online - full text.
Published by: Management Roundtable, Inc., 92 Crescent St, Waltham, MA 02453-4315. TEL 781-891-8080, FAX 781-398-1889, http://www.pdbpr.com. Pub. Gregg Tong.

338 IND
CURRENT DYNAMICS. Text in English. 1971. m. INR 24, USD 14. adv. charts.
Published by: Space Age Publishers, 237 Netaji Subhas Rd., Kolkata, West Bengal 700 047, India. Ed. J Chakravarty.

338 USA ISSN 0498-8477
CURRENT INDUSTRIAL REPORTS. (Consists of 70 series.) Text in English. m. (and q. online, a. consolidated report in printed format and online). charts; stat. back issues avail.; reprint service avail. from CIS. **Document type:** *Government.*
Related titles: Microfiche ed.: (from CIS); Online - full text ed.
Indexed: ABIPC, AmStI, CurPA, RASB, WSCA.
Published by: U.S. Bureau of the Census (Subsidiary of: U.S. Department of Commerce), Customer Services, Washington, DC 20233. TEL 301-457-4100, FAX 301-457-4714, http://www.census.gov/.

338 USA ISSN 0364-1880
HD9724
CURRENT INDUSTRIAL REPORTS: MANUFACTURERS' SHIPMENTS, INVENTORIES, AND ORDERS AND UNITED STATES DEPARTMENT OF COMMERCE NEWS: ADVANCE REPORT ON DURABLE GOODS MANUFACTURERS' SHIPMENTS AND ORDERS. Text in English. m. (plus a. summary). USD 70 (effective 2001). charts; stat. back issues avail. **Document type:** *Government.* **Description:** Compiles data on the total production, value, shipment, and consumption of various products manufactured by U.S. industries.
Related titles: Online - full text ed.
Indexed: ABIPC, AmStI, CurPA, WSCA.
Published by: U.S. Bureau of the Census (Subsidiary of: U.S. Department of Commerce), Customer Services, Washington, DC 20233. TEL 301-457-4100, FAX 301-457-4714, http://www.census.gov/. **Subscr. to:** U.S. Government Printing Office, Superintendent of Documents, PO Box 371954, Pittsburgh, PA 15250-7954. TEL 202-512-1800, FAX 202-512-2250, orders@gpo.gov, http://www.access.gpo.gov.

338 USA
CURRENT INDUSTRIAL REPORTS: MANUFACTURING TECHNOLOGY - FACTORS AFFECTING ADOPTION (YEAR). Text in English. irreg. price varies. **Document type:** *Government.*
Related titles: Online - full text ed.
Published by: U.S. Bureau of the Census (Subsidiary of: U.S. Department of Commerce), Customer Services, Washington, DC 20233. TEL 301-457-4100, FAX 301-457-4714, http://www.census.gov/. **Subscr. to:** U.S. Government Printing Office, Superintendent of Documents. TEL 202-783-3238.

CYPRUS. DEPARTMENT OF STATISTICS AND RESEARCH. MONTHLY ECONOMIC INDICATORS. see *BUSINESS AND ECONOMICS—Economic Situation And Conditions*

CYPRUS TIME OUT; tourist and business guide. see *TRAVEL AND TOURISM*

338.094 DNK ISSN 1604-0708
D I BUSINESS. (Dansk Industri) Variant title: Dansk Industri Business. Text in Danish. 1900. 40/yr. DKK 600 to non-members (effective 2004). adv. bk.rev. charts; illus. 12 p./no.; **Document type:** *Newsletter, Trade.* **Description:** Focuses on Danish industry and economy as well as worldwide markets as they relate to Danish commerce.
Former titles (until 2004): Industrien (Ugebrevet) (0907-7332); (until 1992): Industriens Ugebrev (0906-9267); (until 1991): Dansk Industri (0045-9623); (until 1972): Tidsskrift for Industri (0040-7070)
Related titles: Online - full text ed.
Published by: Dansk Industri (DI)/Confederation of Danish Industries, H. C. Andersens Boulevard 18, Copenhagen V, 1787, Denmark. TEL 45-33-773377, FAX 45-33-773300, redaktion@di.dk, di@di.dk, http://www.di.dk. Circ: 16,174 (controlled).

D I S P. (Dokumente und Informationen zur Schweizerischen Orts-, Regional- und Landesplanung) see *HOUSING AND URBAN PLANNING*

338 330.9 USA ISSN 1051-5933
HC101
D R I - MCGRAW-HILL U S MARKETS REVIEW: INDUSTRY FOCUS. Key Title: U S Markets Review: Industry Focus. Text in English. s-a. back issues avail. **Document type:** *Trade.*
Former titles: U S Industry Review; Interindustry Review
Published by: D R I - McGraw-Hill, 24 Hartwell Ave, Lexington, MA 02173. TEL 617-863-5100, FAX 617-860-6332. Ed. Vivien Singer.

338 330.9 USA ISSN 1069-6482
HC107.A13
D R I - MCGRAW-HILL U S MARKETS REVIEW: METRO FOCUS. Key Title: U S Markets Review: South. Metro Focus. Text in English. 1992. q. **Document type:** *Trade.*
Published by: D R I - McGraw-Hill, 24 Hartwell Ave, Lexington, MA 02173. TEL 617-863-5100, FAX 617-860-6332. Ed. Sara Johnson.

338 330.9 USA ISSN 1069-6431
HC107.A14
D R I - MCGRAW-HILL U S MARKETS REVIEW: MIDWEST. STATE FOCUS. Key Title: U S Markets Review: Midwest. State Focus. Text in English. q. **Document type:** *Trade.*
Formerly (until 1992): D R I - McGraw-Hill U S Markets Review: Midwestern Focus (1051-4422)
Published by: D R I - McGraw-Hill, 24 Hartwell Ave, Lexington, MA 02173. TEL 617-863-5100, FAX 617-860-6332. Ed. Sara Johnson.

338 330.9 USA ISSN 1069-6466
HC107.A115
D R I - MCGRAW-HILL U S MARKETS REVIEW: NORTHEAST. METRO FOCUS. Key Title: U S Markets Review: Northeast. Metro Focus. Text in English. 1992. q. **Document type:** *Trade.*
Published by: D R I - McGraw-Hill, 24 Hartwell Ave, Lexington, MA 02173. TEL 617-863-5100, FAX 617-860-6332. Ed. Sara Johnson.

338 330.9 USA ISSN 1069-6423
HC107.A115
D R I - MCGRAW-HILL U S MARKETS REVIEW: NORTHEAST. STATE FOCUS. Key Title: U S Markets Review: Northeast. State Focus. Text in English. q. **Document type:** *Trade.*
Formerly (until 1992): D R I - McGraw-Hill U S Markets Review: Northeastern Focus (1051-4430)
Published by: D R I - McGraw-Hill, 24 Hartwell Ave, Lexington, MA 02173. TEL 617-863-5100, FAX 617-860-6332. Ed. Sara Johnson.

338 330.9 USA ISSN 1056-6058
HC101
D R I - MCGRAW-HILL U S MARKETS REVIEW: REGIONAL FORECAST SUMMARY. Key Title: U S Markets Review: Regional Forecast Summary. Text in English. q. **Document type:** *Trade.*
Published by: D R I - McGraw-Hill, 24 Hartwell Ave, Lexington, MA 02173. TEL 617-860-5100, FAX 617-860-6332. Ed. Sara Johnson.

338 330.9 USA ISSN 1056-6066
HC101
D R I - MCGRAW-HILL U S MARKETS REVIEW: REGIONAL PREVIEW. Key Title: U S Markets Review: Regional Preview. Text in English. q. **Document type:** *Trade.*
Published by: D R I - McGraw-Hill, 24 Hartwell Ave, Lexington, MA 02173. TEL 617-863-5100, FAX 617-860-6332. Ed. Sara Johnson.

338 330.9 USA ISSN 1069-6458
HC107.A13
D R I - MCGRAW-HILL U S MARKETS REVIEW: SOUTH. STATE FOCUS. Key Title: U S Markets Review: South. State Focus. Text in English. q. **Document type:** *Trade.*
Formerly (until 1992): D R I - McGraw-Hill U S Markets Review: Southern Focus (1051-4449)
Published by: D R I - McGraw-Hill, 24 Hartwell Ave, Lexington, MA 02173. TEL 617-860-6332, FAX 617-860-6332. Ed. Sara Johnson.

338 330.9 USA ISSN 1069-6474
HC107.A17
D R I - MCGRAW-HILL U S MARKETS REVIEW: WEST. METRO FOCUS. Key Title: U S Markets Review: West. Metro Focus. Text in English. 1992. q. **Document type:** *Trade.*
Published by: D R I - McGraw-Hill, 24 Hartwell Ave, Lexington, MA 02173. TEL 617-863-5100, FAX 617-860-6332. Ed. Sara Johnson.

338 330.9 USA ISSN 1069-644X
HC107.A17
D R I - MCGRAW-HILL U S MARKETS REVIEW: WEST. STATE FOCUS. Key Title: U S Markets Review: West. State Focus. Text in English. q. **Document type:** *Trade.*
Formerly (until 1992): D R I - McGraw-Hill U S Markets Review: Western Focus (1051-4457)
Published by: D R I - McGraw-Hill, 24 Hartwell Ave, Lexington, MA 02173. TEL 617-863-5100, FAX 617-860-6332. Ed. Sara Johnson.

D V D RESOURCES DIRECTORY. (Digital Video Disc) see *COMMUNICATIONS—Video*

650 DNK ISSN 1602-7191
DANSK EXPORT. Text in Danish. 2002. q. adv. stat. **Document type:** *Trade.*
Formed by the merger of (1970-2002): Eksport Kontakt (1398-1161); (1910-2002): Dansk Arbejde (0906-396X); Which was formerly (until 1980): Debat (Greve Strand) (0906-3951); (until 1976): Dansk Arbejde (0011-6181)
Published by: Dansk Eksportforening for Gruppesamarbejde/ Danish Export Group Association, Tvaergade 15 A, PO Box 827, Silkeborg, 8600, Denmark. TEL 45-86-813888, FAX 45-86-813114, export@dega.dk, http://www.dega.dk.

DEFENCE AND PEACE ECONOMICS. see *MILITARY*

DELAWARE VALLEY REGIONAL PLANNING COMMISSION. ANNUAL REPORT. see *TRANSPORTATION*

338 JPN
DENKYU KOGYOKAIHO/JAPAN ELECTRIC LAMP MANUFACTURES ASSOCIATION. BULLETIN. Text in Japanese. 1952. m.
Published by: Nihon Denkyu Kogyokai/Japan Electric Lamp Manufactures Association, 7-1 Yuraku-cho 1-chome, Chiyoda-ku, Tokyo, 100-0006, Japan.

338 ARG ISSN 0046-001X
HD85.S7 CODEN: LBMEBX
➤ **DESARROLLO ECONOMICO;** revista de ciencias sociales. Text in Spanish. 1961. q. ARS 60 domestic; USD 74 in the Americas; USD 76 in Europe; USD 80 elsewhere. bk.rev. bibl.; charts. cum.index: 1958-1990. back issues avail. **Document type:** *Academic/Scholarly.*
Indexed: ASCA, AmH&L, DIP, GEOBASE, HAPI, HistAb, IBR, IBSS, IBZ, ILD, IPSA, JEL, PAIS, PCI, PSA, RASB, RRTA, SOPODA, SSA, SSCI, SociolAb, WAE&RSA.
—BLDSC (3555.727000), IDS, IE, Infotrieve, ingenta.
Published by: Instituto de Desarrollo Economico y Social, Araoz, 2836, Capital Federal, Buenos Aires 1425, Argentina. TEL 54-114-8044949, FAX 54-114-8045856. Ed. Juan Carlos Torre. Circ: 2,000.

385 COL ISSN 0418-7547
DESARROLLO INDOAMERICANO. Text in Spanish. 1966. m. COP 2,000, USD 120.
Indexed: HAPI, IBR, PAIS, RASB.
Address: Carrera 54, 58-132, Apartado Aereo 50122, Barranquilla, ATL, Colombia. Ed. Jose Consuegra.

338.9 JOR
DEVELOPMENT✶ /TANMIYAH. Text in Arabic. 1973. m.
Published by: Ministry of Information, P O Box 1794, Amman, Jordan. Ed. George Bandak.

338 PHL
DEVELOPMENT ACADEMY OF THE PHILIPPINES. PRESIDENT'S REPORT TO THE BOARD OF TRUSTEES✶. Text in English. 1974. a. illus.
Formerly: Development Academy of the Philippines. Annual Report
Published by: (Office of Special Services), Development Academy of the Philippines, President's Office, PO Box No. 12788, Ortigas Center, Pasig City, Philippines. TEL 63-631-0921, FAX 63-631-2123, academy@dap.edu.ph, http://www.dap.edu.ph/. Circ: (controlled).

DEVELOPMENTS IN STEELMAKING CAPACITY OF NON-O E C D COUNTRIES/CAPACITES DE PRODUCTION D'ACIER DANS LES PAYS NON O C D E. see *METALLURGY*

338 IDN ISSN 0125-9970
DINAMIKA. Text in Javanese. 1972. q. IDR 250 per issue. adv. charts; stat.
Published by: Wast Java Chamber of Commerce and Industry/Kamar Dagang dan Industri Jawa Barat, Sunijaraja 3, Bandung, West Java, Indonesia. Ed. Ajan Sujana. Circ: 2,500.

643.6029 USA
DIRECTORY OF APPLIANCES, EQUIPMENT, CONSTRUCTION MATERIALS, AND COMPONENTS EVALUATED IN ACCORDANCE WITH INTERNATIONAL PUBLICATIONS. Text in English. a. **Document type:** *Directory.*
Published by: Underwriters Laboratories Inc., Publications, 33 Pfingsten Rd, Northbrook, IL 60062-2096. TEL 847-272-8800, FAX 847-272-0472.

DIRECTORY OF MANUFACTURERS AND DISTRIBUTORS; hobby greenhouses, solariums, sunrooms, window greenhouses and cold frames. see *GARDENING AND HORTICULTURE*

338 SGP
DIRECTORY OF S P S B PRODUCTS & COMPANIES & ACCREDITED LABORATORIES. Text in English. 1976. a. **Document type:** *Directory.* **Description:** Lists certified companies and products under the various certification schemes operated by P S B. Circulates to is and used by purchasers in both public and private sectors as a guide to products and services.
Former titles: Directory of S I S I R Certified Products and Companies and Accredited Laboratories; Directory of Certified Products and Companies and Accredited Laboratories in Singapore (0218-3021); Directory of Certified Products in Singapore (0217-8311)
Related titles: CD-ROM ed.; Online - full text ed.
Published by: (Singapore Productivity and Standards Board), Times Trade Directories Pointe Ltd., 1 New Industrial Rd, Times Centre, Singapore, 536196, Singapore. TEL 65-284-8844, FAX 65-285-0161, ttd@corp.tpl.com.sq. Circ: 6,000.

338 JPN
DIRECTORY OF THE NATIONAL PRODUCTIVITY ORGANIZATIONS IN A P O MEMBER COUNTRIES. Text in English. 1962. irreg., latest 1996. **Document type:** *Directory.*
Former titles: Profiles of the National Productivity Organizations in A P O Member Countries; Asian Productivity Organization. Review of Activities of National Productivity Organizations (0571-3005)
Published by: Asian Productivity Organization, 1-2-10Hirakawa-cho, Chiyoda-ku, Tokyo, 102-0093, Japan. FAX 81-3-5226-3950, apo@gol.com, http://www.apo-tokyo.com. Ed. Philip Mathews. Circ: 1,500.

338 AGO
DIVULGACAO. Text in Portuguese. 1969. a. charts; illus.
Published by: Camara Municipal du Lobito, Caixa Postal Tres, Lobito, Angola.

DOMINICAN REPUBLIC. SECRETARIA DE ESTADO DE INDUSTRIA Y COMERCIO. REVISTA. see *BUSINESS AND ECONOMICS—Domestic Commerce*

338 PAK
E I P INDUSTRIAL RESEARCH SERVICE. Text in English. 1977. w. looseleaf. PKR 5,000, USD 400 (effective 1999). adv. charts; stat. **Document type:** *Trade.*
Published by: Economic and Industrial Publications, Al-Masiha, 47, Abdullah Haroon Rd., P O Box 7843, Karachi, 74400, Pakistan. TEL 92-21-7728434. Ed., Pub., R&P Iqbal Haidari TEL 92-21-7728963. Adv. contact A M Khan. Circ: 1,000.

338 USA ISSN 0012-8147
T1
EARLY AMERICAN INDUSTRIES ASSOCIATION. CHRONICLE. Text in English. 1933. q. USD 30 (effective 2002). bk.rev. illus. index. reprint service avail. from PQC. **Document type:** *Journal, Academic/Scholarly.*
Related titles: Online - full text ed.: (from bigchalk, ProQuest Information & Learning).
Indexed: ABIn, AIAP, HistAb.
—Linda Hall.
Published by: Early American Industries Association, 167 Bakerville Rd, South Dartmouth, MA 02748. TEL 508-993-4198. Ed. Patty MacLeish. R&P Elton Hall. Circ: 3,300.

L'EAU, L'INDUSTRIE, LES NUISANCES. see *WATER RESOURCES*

338.9 ESP ISSN 0422-2784
ECONOMIA INDUSTRIAL. Text in Spanish. 1964. s-m. USD 95. adv. charts; illus.; stat.; tr.lit. cum.index.
Related titles: ♦ Supplement to: Spain. Ministerio de Industria. Informe sobre Infra-Utilizacion de la Capacidad Productiva.
Indexed: INIS AtomInd, JEL, KES, PAIS, RefZh, SCIMP.
—CINDOC.
Published by: Ministerio de Industria Comercio y Turismo, Doctor Fleming, 7 2o, Madrid, 28036, Spain. TEL 250-0202. Ed. Arcadio Lopez. Circ: 5,000.

338 ITA ISSN 0390-6140
HC301
ECONOMIA PUBBLICA. Text in Italian. 1971. bi-m. (8/yr.). EUR 72 domestic; EUR 98 foreign (effective 2003). adv. bk.rev. abstr.; bibl.; charts; stat. index.
Formerly: Bollettino dell'Economia Pubblica (0390-6159)
Indexed: DIP, ELLIS, IBR, IBZ, PAIS.
—Infotrieve.
Published by: (Centro Italiano di Ricerche e Informazione Sull'Economia delle Imprese Pubbliche e di Pubblico Interesse), Franco Angeli Edizioni, Viale Monza 106, Milan, 20127, Italy. TEL 39-02-2837141, FAX 39-02-26144793, redazioni@francoangeli.it, http://www.francoangeli.it. Ed. Alberto Mortara. Circ: 6,000.

338 USA ISSN 1539-2503
ECONOMIC DEVELOPMENT NOW. Text in English. 2001. 22/yr.
Published by: International Economic Development Council, 734 15th Street, NW, Ste. 900, Washington, DC 20005. TEL 202-223-7800, FAX 202-223-4745, http://www.iedconline.org. Ed. Constance Parten.

338 USA ISSN 0742-3713
ECONOMIC DEVELOPMENT REVIEW. Text in English. 1983. 4/yr. USD 60 to individuals; USD 75 foreign to individuals; USD 48 to institutions; USD 63 foreign to institutions. adv. bk.rev. reprint service avail. from PQC. **Document type:** *Academic/Scholarly.*
Former titles (1965-1981): American Industrial Development Council Journal; Supersedes: American Economic Development Council. Newsletter; American Industrial Development Council Newsletter; American Industrial Development Council. Professional Notes
Related titles: Microform ed.: (from PQC); Online - full text ed.: (from EBSCO Publishing, Northern Light Technology, Inc., O C L C Online Computer Library Center, Inc., ProQuest Information & Learning).
Indexed: ABIn, Agr, BPIA, JEL, ManagCont, PAIS, T&II.
—BLDSC (3652.740000), IE, Infotrieve, ingenta.
Published by: American Economic Development Council, 734 15th St NW., Ste 900, Washington, DC 20005-1013. TEL 202-223-7800, FAX 202-223-4745, aedc@aedc.com, http://www.iedconline.org. Ed. Katie Burns. Pub. Jenny Murphy. R&P, Adv. contact Marion Morgan. page USD 950; trim 11 x 8.5. Circ: 5,000.

338 USA ISSN 0739-8956
HC107.T3
ECONOMIC GROWTH IN TENNESSEE, ANNUAL REPORT. Text in English. a. (plus q. updates). free. stat. **Document type:** *Government.*
Formerly (until 1981): Industrial Growth in Tennessee, Annual Report (0099-1872)
Published by: Department of Economic and Community Development, Rachel Jackson Bldg, 8th Fl, Nashville, TN 37243-0405. TEL 615-741-1995. Ed. Ray Dickerson.

338 ECU
ECUADOR. MINISTERIO DE INDUSTRIAS, COMERCIO E INTEGRACION. BOLETIN DE INFORMACION DE LAS EMPRESAS ACOGIDAS A LA LEY DE FOMENTO INDUSTRIAL. Text in Spanish. 1974. a.
Published by: Ministerio de Industrias Comercio e Integracion, Quito, Pichincha, Ecuador.

338 AUT
EINKAUFSFUEHRER FUER WISSENSCHAFT UND FORSCHUNG. Text in German. bi-m.
Address: Sommerhaidenweg 124, Vienna, W 1190, Austria. TEL 01-443295, FAX 01-442825. Circ: 9,000.

338 RUS ISSN 0869-4672
EKONOMIST. Text in Russian. 1923. m. USD 94. bk.rev. stat. index. **Document type:** *Government.*
Formerly (until 1992): Planovoe Khozyaistvo (0370-0356)
Related titles: Microfiche ed.: (from EVP).
Indexed: CDSP, ChemAb, IBSS, MaizeAb, PotatoAb, RASB, RRTA, RefZh, TriticAb, WAE&RSA.
—CISTI, East View.

B

Address: Smolenskii bulv 4, Moscow, 119898, Russian Federation. TEL 7-095-2461637. Ed. P A Ignatovakii. Circ: 23,380. **US dist. addr.:** East View Information Services, 3020 Harbor Ln. N., Minneapolis, MN 55447. TEL 763-550-0961, FAX 763-559-2931, eastview@eastview.com, http://www.eastview.com.

338 IND ISSN 0970-7441
ELECTRONIC PRODUCTS FINDER. Text in English. 1985. m. INR 800, USD 28. adv. bk.rev. abstr.; charts; illus.
Description: Covers new products and news briefs.
Published by: IPFonline Ltd., 33 D'Silva Rd, Mylapore, Chennai, 600 004, India. TEL 91-44-4661698, FAX 91-44-4661617. Ed. Milton D'Silva. adv.: B&W page INR 6,000, color page INR 10,600; trim 205 x 280. Circ: 8,000.

ELECTRONICS SPECIFIER. see *ENGINEERING—Electrical Engineering*

338 ARG
ENERGIA INDUSTRIAL. Text in Spanish. 6/yr.
Published by: Editorial Golova s.r.l., Avda. De Mayo, 863, Capital Federal, Buenos Aires 1084, Argentina. Circ: 4,000.

ENQUETE SUR LES ENTREPRISES INDUSTRIELLES ET COMMERCIALES DU TOGO. see *BUSINESS AND ECONOMICS—Domestic Commerce*

338 FRA ISSN 0751-588X
ENTREPRISES RHONE - ALPES. Text in French. 1942. 10/yr. EUR 435 (effective 2004); Includes Bref Rhone-Alpes. adv. illus.; mkt.; tr.lit. index. **Document type:** *Magazine, Consumer.*
Supersedes: Metallurgie (0026-0878)
Indexed: Cadscan, ChemAb, LeadAb, Zincscan.
Published by: Societe des Medias Economiques, Immeuble Les Lauriers, 513 Rue du Saint-Souci, Limonest, 69579, France. TEL 33-4-37497790, FAX 33-4-78645169, bref@smebref.com, http://www.brefonline.com. Circ: 3,012.

EQUIPMENT MANUFACTURERS INSTITUTE. FIRST OF THE WEEK NEWSLETTER. see *AGRICULTURE—Agricultural Equipment*

EQUIPMENT MANUFACTURERS INSTITUTE. RETAIL SALES REPORTS. see *AGRICULTURE—Agricultural Equipment*

EQUIPMENT MANUFACTURERS INSTITUTE. STATE OF THE INDUSTRY. see *AGRICULTURE—Agricultural Equipment*

338 621.9 ESP ISSN 1130-9571
EQUIPOS PRODUCTOS INDUSTRIALES. Text in Spanish. 1991. 9/yr. free to qualified personnel (effective 2003). adv. **Document type:** *Trade.* **Description:** Covers new products for industry.
Published by: Reed Business Information SA (Subsidiary of: Reed Business Information International), Zancoeta 9, Bilbao, 48013, Spain. TEL 34-944-285600, FAX 34-944-425116, rbi@rbi.es, http://www.rbi.es. Ed. Lluis Lahoz. Adv. contact Eduardo Lazaro. Circ: 27,000.

338 658 DNK ISSN 1600-7093
ERHVERV OEST; erhverv/Koebenhavn-Sjaelland. Text in Danish. 1989. 11/yr. DKK 275 (effective 2005). adv. **Document type:** *Magazine, Trade.*
Formerly (until 1999): Erhverv/Koebenhavn, Sjaelland (0905-0329); Which was formed by the merger of (1985-1989): Erhverv/Koebenhavn (0900-6079); (1985-1989): Erhverv/Sjaelland, Lolland-Falster, Moen og Bornholm (0902-6622); Which was formerly (until 1987): Erhverv/Sjaelland (0900-6052)
Related titles: Online - full text ed.
Published by: Dansk Erhvervskommunikation, Alhambravej 20, Frederiksberg C, 1826, Denmark. TEL 45-33-211636, FAX 45-33-213051, pr@mag-erhverv.dk, http://www.mag-erhverv.dk/. Ed. Esben Bilenberg. adv.: B&W page DKK 18,950, color page DKK 21,950; 185 x 263. Circ: 45,621 (controlled).

ERHVERV/VEST. see *BUSINESS AND ECONOMICS—Management*

338 ITA ISSN 0014-0554
ESPANSIONE. Text in Italian. 1969. m. (11/yr.). EUR 35 (effective 2005). adv. **Document type:** *Magazine, Consumer.*
Indexed: PAIS.
Published by: Arnoldo Mondadori Editore SpA, Via Mondadori 1, Segrate, 20090, Italy. TEL 39-02-66814363, FAX 39-030-3198412, http://www.mondadori.com. Ed. Redento Mori. Circ: 42,000.

338.9 ETH ISSN 0378-0813
HC591.A3
ETHIOPIAN JOURNAL OF DEVELOPMENT RESEARCH. Text in English. 1974. s-a. USD 7 per issue. bk.rev. charts; stat.
Indexed: PLESA.
Published by: Addis Ababa University, Institute of Development Research, PO Box 1176, Addis Ababa, Ethiopia. TELEX 21205. Ed. T Mulat. Circ: 1,000.

EUROPEAN ASSOCIATION OF FISHERIES ECONOMISTS. BULLETIN. see *FISH AND FISHERIES*

EUROPEAN INTELLIGENCE; a review of the European business economy: fortnightly report on company initiatives E E C (mergers, affiliations etc.) plus community news and articles. see *BUSINESS AND ECONOMICS—Economic Situation And Conditions*

338 GBR
EUROPEAN QUALITY TODAY. Text in English. 3/yr. free. adv. **Document type:** *Magazine, Trade.*
Published by: Nexus Media Ltd. (Subsidiary of: Highbury House Communications PLC), Nexus House, Azalea Dr, Swanley, Kent BR8 8HU, United Kingdom. TEL 44-1322-660070, FAX 44-1322-616311, info@nexusmedia.com, http://www.hhc.co.uk/europeanqt. adv.: B&W page GBP 1,545, color page GBP 1,815; trim 210 x 297. Circ: 10,000.

338 GBR ISSN 1352-9633
EUROPEAN RETAIL DIGEST; providing global insights for the retail industry. Text in English. q. GBP 350 to institutions includes single user online access (effective 2001). stat. 70 p./no. 2 cols./p.; back issues avail.; reprints avail. **Document type:** *Trade.* **Description:** Provides a guide to trends and developments in retailing within Europe.
Related titles: Online - full text ed.: (from EBSCO Publishing, Gale Group).
Indexed: CPM.
—BLDSC (3829.924900), IE, ingenta. **CCC.**
Published by: Oxford Institute of Retail Management, Templeton College, Kennington, Oxford, OX1 5NY, United Kingdom. TEL 44-1865-735422, FAX 44-1865-736374, publications@templeton.oxford.ac.uk, http://www.templeton.oxford.ac.uk. Ed. Christine Cuthbertson. R&P Melanie Goddard TEL 44-1865-422730.

338.47004 USA
EUROPEAN SERVICES INDUSTRY. Text in English. 1994. bi-m. USD 65. **Document type:** *Trade.*
Published by: Association for Services Management International, 1342 Colonial Blvd., Ste. 25, Ft. Myers, FL 33907. TEL 813-275-7887, FAX 813-275-0794. Ed. Leonard Mafrica. adv.: B&W page USD 3,150. Circ: 8,500.

EUROPEAN SIGN MAGAZINE. see *ADVERTISING AND PUBLIC RELATIONS*

338 PRT ISSN 0872-1866
EXAME. Text in Portuguese. 1989. m. EUR 65.52 (effective 2004). adv. **Document type:** *Magazine, Trade.*
Published by: Edimpresa Editora Lda., Rua Calvet de Magalhaes 242, Laveiras, Paco de Arcos, 2770-022, Portugal. TEL 351-21-4698000, FAX 351-21-4698501, exame@acj.pt, edimpresa@edimpresa.pt, http://www.edimpresa.pt. adv.: page EUR 4,265; trim 205 x 275. Circ: 24,223.

338 FRA ISSN 0014-4703
HC271
L'EXPANSION. Text in French. 1967. m. EUR 18.55 domestic; EUR 36.55 in the European Union; EUR 51.55 in US & Canada; EUR 44.55 in Africa; EUR 70.55 elsewhere (effective 2005). adv. reprint service avail. from PQC.
Related titles: Microform ed.: (from PQC); Online - full text ed.
Indexed: ELLIS, IndVet, KES, M&MA, PAIS, RASB, SCIMP, WAE&RSA.
—BLDSC (3836.430000), IE, Infotrieve, ingenta. **CCC.**
Published by: Groupe Express-Expansion (Subsidiary of: Socpresse), 17 rue de l'Arrivee, Paris Cede, 75733, France. TEL 33-1-53911111, http://www.lexpansion.com, http://www.groupe-expansion.com. Circ: 149,000.

338 MEX ISSN 0185-2728
HF3231
EXPANSION. Text in Spanish. 1969. fortn. USD 98 in US & Canada; USD 106 in Latin America; USD 116 in Europe. adv. illus. **Document type:** *Consumer.* **Description:** Covers business news of Mexico.
Related titles: Online - full text ed.: ISSN 1563-7433. 1999.
Published by: Grupo Editorial Expansion (Subsidiary of: Capital Cities - A B C, Inc.), SALAMANCA 35, Col Roma, Mexico City, DF 06700, Mexico. servicioaclientes@expansion.com.mx, http://www.expansion.com.mx/expansion/, http://www.gee.com.mx. Ed. Diego Arrazola. R&P David Estrello. Adv. contact Manuel Mier Y Concha. Circ: 23,516.

F D C CONTROL NEWSLETTER. (Food, Drug, and Cosmetics) see *FOOD AND FOOD INDUSTRIES*

338 640.73 BEL ISSN 0771-2987
F E B BULLETIN. Text in French. 1895. m. USD 89. adv. bk.rev. charts; illus. index. **Document type:** *Bulletin.*
Former titles (until 1983): Federation des Entreprises de Belgique. Bulletin (0773-185X); (until 1972): Federation des Industries Belges. Bulletin (0014-9349); (until 1940): Comite Central Industriel de Belgique. Bulletin (0773-1841); (until 1912): Comite Central du Travail Industriel. Bulletin (0773-1833)
Related titles: Dutch ed.: V B O Bulletin. ISSN 1378-3483. 1946.
Published by: Federation des Entreprises de Belgique/Verbond van Belgische Ondernemingen, Ravenstein 4, Brussels, 1000, Belgium. Circ: 6,500.

F E W A TIPS. see *AGRICULTURE—Agricultural Equipment*

338 NGA
F I I R O TECHNICAL INFORMATION BULLETIN FOR INDUSTRY. Text in English. 1972. q. NGN 10; free to research organizations. charts; illus. **Document type:** *Bulletin, Government.*
Published by: Federal Institute of Industrial Research Oshodi, PMB 21023, Ikeja, Lagos, Nigeria. TELEX 26006. Circ: 1,000.

F T BIOTECHNOLOGY & PHARMACEUTICAL COMPANIES DATABASE CD-ROM (YEARS). (Financial Times) see *BIOLOGY—Biotechnology*

338.4 USA
F T C NEWSNOTES. (Federal Trade Commission) Text in English. 1951. w. free. back issues avail.; reprint service avail. from CIS. **Document type:** *Government.* **Description:** Summarizes rulemaking procedures, speeches, and other noteworthy occurrences.
Related titles: Microfiche ed.: (from CIS); Online - full content ed.
Indexed: AmStI, PROMT, RASB.
Published by: U.S. Federal Trade Commission, Office of Public Affairs, Sixth St and Pennsylvania Ave, N W, Washington, DC 20580. TEL 202-382-4357, http://www.ftc.gov/opa/newsnotes/. Ed. Victoria Streitfeld. **Subscr. to:** U.S. Government Printing Office, Superintendent of Documents, PO Box 371954, Pittsburgh, PA 15250-7954. TEL 202-512-1800, FAX 202-512-2250, orders@gpo.gov, http://www.access.gpo.gov.

338 USA
FEDERAL SUPPLY CODE FOR MANUFACTURERS, UNITED STATES AND CANADA★. (In 2 parts: Cataloging Handbook H 4-1, Name to Code; Cataloging Handbook H 4-2, Code to Name) Text in English. bi-m. USD 24.
Media: Microfiche.
Published by: U.S. Defense Logistics Agency, 8725 John J Kingman Rd, Ste 2533, Fort Belvoir, VA 22060-6221. TEL 202-274-6000. **Dist. by:** U.S. Government Printing Office, Superintendent of Documents, PO Box 371954, Pittsburgh, PA 15250-7954. TEL 202-512-1800, FAX 202-512-2250, orders@gpo.gov, http://www.access.gpo.gov.

338 640.73 BEL ISSN 0773-1884
FEDERATION DES ENTREPRISES DE BELGIQUE. RAPPORT ANNUEL. Text in French. a. **Document type:** *Corporate.*
Formerly: Federation des Industries Belges. Rapport Annuel (0071-4178)
Related titles: Dutch ed.: Verbon van Belgische Ondernemingen. Jaarlijks Verslag. ISSN 0773-1892.
Published by: Federation des Entreprises de Belgique/Verbond van Belgische Ondernemingen, Ravenstein 4, Brussels, 1000, Belgium.

338 EGY
FEDERATION OF EGYPTIAN INDUSTRIES. MONTHLY BULLETIN. Text in English. m. **Document type:** *Bulletin.*
Published by: Federation of Egyptian Industries/Ittihad al-Sinaat al-Misriyah, 26A Sharia Sherif Pasha, P O Box 251, Cairo, Egypt.

338 639.2 ITA
FILIERA PESCA E ACQUACOLTURA. Text in Italian. irreg. free.
Description: This report covers the statistics of fishing production, marketing, import-export and sales in Italy plus in depth articles on specific topics related to fishing.
Published by: Istituto di Servizi per il Mercato Agricolo Alimentare, via Cornelio Celso, 6, Rome, 00161, Italy. TEL 039-06-85561-251, FAX 039-06-85561-286, urp@ismea.it, http://www.ismea.it/.

FINANCIAL SURVEY. THE FISH INDUSTRY; company data for success. see *BUSINESS AND ECONOMICS—Trade And Industrial Directories*

FINITE ELEMENTS IN ANALYSIS AND DESIGN. see *ENGINEERING—Computer Applications*

338 DEU ISSN 0938-8044
FIRMEN DER NEUEN BUNDESLAENDER. Text in German. 1990. a. EUR 263.32. **Document type:** *Directory.*
Incorporates: Offizielles Verzeichnis der Treuhandanstalt
Related titles: CD-ROM ed.; Online - full text ed.: (from Data-Star, The Dialog Corporation).
Published by: Hoppenstedt Bonnier Zeitschriften GmbH, Havelstr. 9, Darmstadt, 64295, Germany. TEL 49-6151-380-0, FAX 49-6151-380-360. Circ: 22,000.

338.3072 NOR ISSN 1500-6891
FISKERIFORSKNING INFO. Text in English. 1998. s-m.
Related titles: ◆ Norwegian ed.: Fiskeriforskning Informerer. ISSN 1500-130X.
Published by: Fiskeriforskning - Norsk Institutt for Fiskeri- og Havbruksforskning/Norwegian Institute of Fisheries and Aquaculture Research, Muninbakken 9-13, Breivika, Tromsoe, 9291, Norway. TEL 47-77-62-90-00, FAX 47-77-62-91-00.

338.3072 NOR ISSN 1500-130X
FISKERIFORSKNING INFORMERER. Text in Norwegian. 1998. m. **Description:** Details research at the institute.
Related titles: ◆ English ed.: Fiskeriforskning Info. ISSN 1500-6891.

Published by: Fiskeriforskning - Norsk Institutt for Fiskeri- og Havbruksforskning/Norwegian Institute of Fisheries and Aquaculture Research, Muninbakken 9-13, Breivika, Tromsoe, 9291, Norway. TEL 47-77-62-90-00, FAX 47-77-62-91-00.

THE FLAGSTAFF INSTITUTE. JOURNAL. see *BUSINESS AND ECONOMICS—International Commerce*

338 SWE ISSN 0348-7830
FOERETAG OCH SAMHAELLE. Text in Swedish. 1975. q. SEK 120 (effective 1990).
Published by: S N S - Studieforbundet Naeringsliv och Samhaelle, Skoldungagatan 2, Stockholm, 11427, Sweden.

650 ESP ISSN 0015-6035
FOMENTO DE LA PRODUCCION; revista de la industria, el comercio y las finanzas. Text in Spanish. 1946. s-m. illus.; stat.
Address: De Casanova, 57, Barcelona, 08011, Spain. TEL 3-253-06-97, FAX 3-323-38-85. Ed. Ramon Carlos Baratech.

330 FRA ISSN 0071-6847
FONDS DE DEVELOPPEMENT ECONOMIQUE ET SOCIAL. CONSEIL DE DIRECTION. RAPPORT. Text in French. a.
Published by: (France. Ministere de l'Economie et des Finances), Imprimerie Nationale, BP 514, Douai, Cedex 59505, France. TEL 27-93-70-90, FAX 27-93-70-96.

FOOD AND DRUG LETTER. see *PHARMACY AND PHARMACOLOGY*

338.8 JPN
FOREIGN-AFFILIATED ENTERPRISES IN JAPAN★. Text in English. 1967. a. JPY 13,000. illus.; stat.
Published by: Ministry of International Trade and Industry/Tsusho Sangyo-sho Daijin Kanbo Chosa Tokei-bu, 1-3-1 Kasumigaseki, Chiyoda-ku, Tokyo, 100-0013, Japan. TEL 03-501-1511.

330 FIN ISSN 0533-070X
FORUM FOER EKONOMI OCH TEKNIK. Text in Swedish. 1968. m. EUR 75 (effective 2003). adv. bk.rev. charts; illus.; tr.lit. index. **Document type:** *Journal.* **Description:** Swedish languaged journal covering business, management and technology in Finland.
Formed by the merger of: Mercator (0025-9837); Tekniskt Forum (0040-2362)
Related titles: Online - full text ed.
Indexed: RASB.
—Linda Hall.
Published by: Foerlags Ab Forum foer Ekonomi och Teknik, Georgsgatan 27 A, Helsinki, 00100, Finland. TEL 358-9-54955500, FAX 358-9-54955577, http://www.forum-fet.fi. Ed. Patrik Lindfors TEL 358-9-54955533. Adv. contact Sam Bjorklund TEL 358-9-54955522. Circ: 12,000.

338 669 USA
▼ **FORWARD.** Text in English. 2004. bi-m. adv. **Document type:** *Magazine, Trade.*
Published by: Imagination Publishing, 2222 N. Elston Ave., 2nd Fl., Chicago, IL 60614. TEL 773-252-3200, FAX 773-252-3290, http://www.imaginepub.com. Adv. contact Ruth Keefer. B&W page USD 4,950, color page USD 5,270; trim 8.5 x 10.75.

338.9 USA ISSN 1555-0737
▼ **FOUNDATIONS AND TRENDS IN ECONOMIC GROWTH.** Text in English. forthcoming 2006. q.
Related titles: Online - full text ed.: ISSN 1555-0745. forthcoming 2006.
Published by: Now Publishers Inc., PO Box 1024, Hanover, MA 02339. TEL 781-871-0245, FAX 781-871-6172, http://www.nowpublishers.com. Pub., R&P Mike Casey.

338 FRA
FRANCE. DIRECTION GENERALE DE LA CONCURRENCE ET DE LA CONSOMMATION. BULLETIN OFFICIEL - SERVICE DES PRIX. Text in French. 1941. irreg. **Document type:** *Bulletin, Government.*
Formerly: France. Direction Generale de la Concurrence et des Prix. Bulletin Officiel des Services des Prix (0071-870X)
Related titles: Microfiche ed.
Published by: (France. Direction General de la Concurrence et de la Consommation), Direction des Journaux Officiels, 26 rue Desaix, Paris, 75727 Cedex 15 , France. TEL 33-1-40587500, info@journal-officiel.gouv.fr, http://www.journal-officiel.gouv.fr.

658 338 USA ISSN 1530-3748
HF5429.23
FRANCHISE TIMES (ROSEVILLE). Text in English. 1968. 10/yr. looseleaf. USD 35 domestic; USD 80 in Canada; USD 115 elsewhere (effective 2005). bk.rev. Index. back issues avail.; reprints avail. **Document type:** *Magazine, Trade.* **Description:** Business publication that profiles successful franchise busiensses and updates owners and operators on the latest in finance, technology, and real estate issues.
Formerly: Continental Franchise Review (0045-8376)
Published by: Franchise Times, 2808 Anthony Lane S, Mpls, MN 55418. TEL 612-767-3200, FAX 612-767-3230, info@franchisetimes.com, http:franchisetimes.com. Ed. Kristine McKenzie. Pub. Mary Jo Larson. Circ: 15,000 (controlled).

FRONTLINE SOLUTIONS. see *COMPUTERS—Automation*

338 USA ISSN 1047-6555
G M P TRENDS. (Good Manufacturing Practice) Text in English. 1977. 2/m. USD 370 in US & Canada; USD 410 elsewhere (effective 2004). **Document type:** *Newsletter, Trade.* **Description:** Contains observations and reports made by FDA investigators during inspections of manufacturing plants producing pharmaceutical preparations and medical device products.
Related titles: Online - full text ed.: USD 550 in US & Canada; USD 590 elsewhere (effective 2004).
—CCC.
Published by: G M P Trends, Inc., PO Box 8001, Boulder, CO 80306. TEL 303-443-8716, FAX 303-443-3317, gmp@gmptrends.com, https://www.gmptrends.com.

GARDEN CENTRE UPDATE. see *GARDENING AND HORTICULTURE*

338 USA
▼ **GEAR SOLUTIONS**; your resource for machines, services and tooling for the gear industry. Text in English. 2003. m. free to qualified personnel (effective 2005). adv. **Document type:** *Magazine, Trade.* **Description:** Keeps readers updated on the latest industry news.
Related titles: Online - full text ed.
Published by: Media Solutions, Inc., 226D Yeager Parkway, Pelham, AL 35124. TEL 800-366-3185, FAX 205-380-1580, info@gearsolutionsonline.com, http://www.gearsolutionsonline.com. Pub. David Cooper. Adv. contact Chad Morrison. B&W page USD 2,300; trim 8.375 x 10.875. Circ: 10,250 (paid and controlled).

330 DEU ISSN 0072-159X
GERMANY. SACHVERSTAENDIGENRAT ZUR BEGUTACHTUNG DER GESAMTWIRTSCHAFTLICHEN ENTWICKLUNG. JAHRESGUTACHTEN. Text in German. 1964. a. reprint service avail. from SCH. **Document type:** *Government.*
Published by: Statistisches Bundesamt, Gustav-Stresemann-Ring 11, Wiesbaden, 65180, Germany. TEL 49-611-75-1, FAX 49-611-724000, http://www.statistik-bund.de. Circ: 3,300.

GESTAO & PRODUCAO. see *BUSINESS AND ECONOMICS—Management*

338 BEL ISSN 0773-0543
HD28
GESTION 2000; management & prospective. Text in English, French. 1985. 6/yr. EUR 177.63 in Europe; EUR 185.07 elsewhere (effective 2002). adv. bk.rev. bibl. index. **Document type:** *Journal, Academic/Scholarly.* **Description:** Covers all aspects of management, including strategy, marketing, finance, human resources and production, from an international perspective.
Formed by the merger of (1941-1985): Annales des Sciences Economiques Appliquees (0003-4207); Which was formerly (1937-1940): Annales des Sciences Commerciales et Economiques (0770-2566); (1981-1985): Demain (0772-103X); Which was formerly (until 1980): Etudes et Expansion (0770-2809); (until 1976): Societe d'Etudes et d'Expansion. Revue (0037-9263); (until 1961): Societe d'Etudes et d'Expansion. Revue Bimestrielle (0378-0937); (until 1958): Societe Belge d'Etudes et d'Expansion. Bulletin Bimestriel (0772-3857); (1907-1920): L' Association des Licencies Sortis de l'Universite de Liege. Bulletin (0770-2027)
Indexed: IBSS, KES, M&MA, PAIS, SCIMP.
—BLDSC (4163.790000), IE, Infotrieve, ingenta.
Published by: Recherches et Publications en Management a.s.b.l., Verte Voie 20, Louvain-la-Neuve, 1348, Belgium. TEL 32-10-453435, FAX 32-10-454060, gestion2000@skynet.be, http://gestion-2000.com. Ed. Etienne Cracco. R&P Brigitte Evrard. Adv. contact Ctistina Soster. Circ: 1,500.

338 GHA
GHANA MANUFACTURER. Text in English. 1974. q. free. adv. **Document type:** *Trade.*
Published by: Association of Ghana Industries, PO Box 8624, Accra - North, Ghana. TEL 233-21-777283, FAX 233-21-773143. Ed. Eddie Imbeah Amoakuh. Circ: 1,200.

681 CUB ISSN 1605-9069
GIGA ONLINE. Text in Spanish. 1999. bi-m.
Media: Online - full text.
Published by: Copextel, S.A., Ave. 3ra. y 78 Edif. Habana, Miramar Trade Center, Havana, Cuba. TEL 53-78-2047819, giga@ciolumbus.cu, http://www.giga.islagrande.cu/online/home.asp. Ed. Norma Marquez.

338 GBR ISSN 1474-0893
GLOBAL S M T & PACKAGING. (Surface Mount Technology) Text in English. 2001. m.
Indexed: Inspec.
—CCC.
Published by: Trafalgar Publications Limited, 65 High St, Glastinbury, Somerset BA6 9DS, United Kingdom. TEL 44-1458-833207, FAX 44-1458-832143, http://www.trafalgarpublications.net.

338 USA
GOODS AND SERVICES BULLETIN. Text in English. 1984. w. USD 45. **Document type:** *Bulletin.*
Published by: State Bookstore, Commonwealth of Massachusetts, State House, Rm 116, Boston, MA 02133. Circ: 1,950.

353 POL ISSN 1231-2037
TS149
GOSPODARKA MATERIALOWA I LOGISTYKA. Text in Polish. 1949. m. EUR 196 foreign (effective 2005). bk.rev. charts; illus.; stat. index. 28 p./no.; **Document type:** *Magazine, Trade.*
Formerly (until 1994): Gospodarka Materialowa (0017-2405)
Indexed: RASB, RefZh.
Published by: Polskie Wydawnictwo Ekonomiczne, ul Canaletta 4, Warsaw, 00099, Poland. TEL 48-22-8264182, gmil@pwe.com.pl, pwe@pwe.com.pl, http://www.gmil.pl, http://www.pwe.com.pl. Ed. Teresa Dudzik. Adv. contact Monika Kolodziejczyk TEL 48-22-8278001 ext 320. **Dist. by:** Ars Polona, Krakowskie Przedmiescie 7, Warsaw, Poland. TEL 48-22-9263914, FAX 48-22-9265334, arspolona@arspolona.com.pl, http://www.arspolona.com.pl.

338 USA ISSN 1064-6795
HD3858
GOVERNMENT CONTRACTS AND SUBCONTRACTS LEADS DIRECTORY. Text in English. 1964. a. USD 89.50 (effective 2004). **Document type:** *Directory, Trade.*
Formerly (until 1992): Government Contracts Directory (0072-5137)
Published by: Government Data Publications, Inc., 2300 M St, N W, Washington, DC 20037. TEL 800-275-4688, FAX 718-998-5960, gdp@govdata.com, http://www.govdata.com. Ed. Siegfried Lobel.

338 USA ISSN 0887-4085
HD3858
GOVERNMENT PRIMECONTRACTS MONTHLY. Text in English. 1976. m. USD 96 (effective 2005). 2 cols./p.; **Document type:** *Magazine, Trade.*
Published by: Government Data Publications, Inc., 2300 M St, N W, Washington, DC 20037. TEL 800-275-4688, FAX 718-998-5960, gdp@govdata.com, http://www.govdata.com. Ed. Siegfried Lobel.

GREAT BRITAIN. DEPARTMENT OF TRADE AND INDUSTRY. ENERGY PAPER. see *BUSINESS AND ECONOMICS—Domestic Commerce*

GREAT BRITAIN. SEA FISH INDUSTRY AUTHORITY. FISHERIES ECONOMICS NEWSLETTER. see *FISH AND FISHERIES*

GREECE. NATIONAL STATISTICAL SERVICE. PRODUCTION OF MANUFACTURED ITEMS. see *BUSINESS AND ECONOMICS—Abstracting, Bibliographies, Statistics*

338 DEU
GROSSUNTERNEHMEN IN OESTERREICH. Text in German. 1979. a. **Document type:** *Directory.*
Formerly: Oesterreich 2000
Published by: Hoppenstedt Bonnier Zeitschriften GmbH, Havelstr. 9, Darmstadt, 64295, Germany. TEL 49-6151-380-0, FAX 49-6151-380-360. Circ: 11,000.

338 DEU ISSN 1215-7481
GROSSUNTERNEHMEN IN UNGARN. Text in English, German. 1992. a. EUR 838.52. **Document type:** *Directory.*
Media: CD-ROM. **Related titles:** Hungarian ed.: Magyarorszag Nagy Vallalatai es Vallalkozasai. ISSN 1215-6906.
Published by: Hoppenstedt Bonnier Zeitschriften GmbH, Havelstr. 9, Darmstadt, 64295, Germany. TEL 49-6151-380-0, FAX 49-6151-380-360. Circ: 16,000.

338 USA ISSN 0017-4815
HT390 CODEN: GRCHDH
➤ **GROWTH AND CHANGE**; a journal of urban and regional policy. Text in English. 1970. q. USD 71 combined subscription in the Americas to individuals & Caribbean (print & online eds.); EUR 96 combined subscription in Europe to individuals print & online eds.; GBP 64 combined subscription elsewhere to individuals print & online eds.; USD 221 combined subscription in the Americas to institutions & Caribbean (print & online eds.); GBP 181 combined subscription elsewhere to institutions print & online eds. (effective 2006). adv. bk.rev. illus. index. reprints avail. **Document type:** *Journal, Academic/Scholarly.* **Description:** Interdisciplinary journal focusing on regional economic development and related policy issues.
Related titles: Microform ed.: (from PQC); Online - full text ed.: ISSN 1468-2257. USD 210 in the Americas to institutions & Caribbean; GBP 172 elsewhere to institutions (effective 2006) (from Blackwell Synergy, EBSCO Publishing, Florida Center for Library Automation, Gale Group, IngentaConnect, O C L C Online Computer Library Center, Inc., Swets Information Services).
Indexed: ABCPolSci, ABIn, ASCA, ASFA, AgeL, Agr, ArtHuCI, BAS, BPIA, BibInd, BusI, CurCont, EIA, ESPM, EnerInd, FamI, GEOBASE, HRA, IBSS, IPSA, JEL, KES, MEA&I, PAIS, PRA, PSA, PollutAb, PopulInd, RASB, RRTA, RefZh, S&F, SPAA, SSCI, SUSA, SWRA, SociolAb, T&II, UAA, V&AA, WAE&RSA, WorkRelAb, e-psyche.

—BLDSC (4223.020000), IDS, IE, Infotrieve, ingenta. **CCC.**
Published by: (Alabama. Center for Business and Economic Research, University of Kentucky), Blackwell Publishing, Inc. (Subsidiary of: Blackwell Publishing Ltd.), Commerce Place, 350 Main St, Malden, MA 02148. TEL 781-388-8206, FAX 781-388-8232, subscrip@blackwellpub.com, http://www.blackwellpublishing.com/journals/GROW. Ed. Thomas R Leinbach TEL 859-257-1276.

338   ESP   ISSN 1130-5185
GRUPO I N I (RESUMEN DE ACTIVIDADES). Text in Spanish. 1940. a. free. illus.
Formerly (until 1980): Spain. Instituto Nacional de Industria. Resumen de Actividades - Memoria (1130-5177)
Published by: Instituto Nacional de Industria, Plaza Marques de Salamanca 8, Madrid, 28006, Spain.

330.9   SEN
GUIDE DE L'INVESTISSEUR INDUSTRIEL AU SENEGAL. Text in French. irreg. XOF 3,000. illus.
Published by: Societe Nationale d'Etude et de Promotion Industrielle, 14 rue Maunoury, BP 100, Dakar, Senegal.

338   IND
GUJARAT INDUSTRIAL DEVELOPMENT CORPORATION. ANNUAL REPORT. Text in English. a. illus.; stat.
Published by: Gujarat Industrial Development Corporation, Ashram Rd., Ahmedabad, Gujarat 380 009, India.

338.7409489   DNK   ISSN 0905-5878
HD28
GULDNUMMERET. DANMARKS 500 STOERSTE VIRKSOMHEDER. Text in Danish. 1975. a. DKK 10. adv.
Document type: Directory.
Formerly (until 1989): Danmarks 200 Stoerste Virksomheder (0106-9977)
Published by: A-S Boersen Magasiner, Moentergade 19, Copenhagen K, 1140, Denmark. Ed. Kristian Lund. Adv. contact Willy Joergensen.

338 628.5   BHR   ISSN 0965-2809
HD9576.A67
GULF INDUSTRY MANUFACTURING & TRADING. Text in English. bi-m. USD 68 (effective 2001). adv. charts; illus.; stat.; tr.lit. 96 p./no. 3 cols./p.; **Document type:** Trade.
Description: For individuals with an involvement or interest in the industrial development of the Gulf region, including industrialists, factory managers, major distributors of industrial products, and government officials.
Formerly: Gulf Industry and Saudi Arabia Review; Incorporates: Shipping and Transport News International. Yearbook and Directory (1352-2051); Shipping and Transport News International (0958-8485); Which was formerly: Shipping and Transport News; Incorporates: Middle East Shipping and Transport (0958-8477); Gulf Shipping and Transport
Published by: Al Hilal Publishing & Marketing Group, Exhibition Ave, PO Box 224, Manama, Bahrain. TEL 973-293131, FAX 973-293400, hilalmg@traderarabic.net, hilalcirc@tradearabia.net, http://www.gulfindustryonline.com. Ed. Salvador Almeida. Pub. A M Abdul Rahman. adv.: B&W page USD 2,015, color page USD 2,890; trim 210 x 282. Circ: 11,483.

683.4   USA   ISSN 1050-6616
TS535
GUNMAKER; the journal on custom gunmaking. Text in English. 1983. q. USD 75 domestic; USD 100 foreign (effective 2003). adv. bk.rev. cum.index: 1983-1998. back issues avail.
Document type: Journal, Trade. **Description:** Contains technical and general interest articles on custom gunmaking.
Published by: American Custom Gunmakers Guild, Inc., 22 Vista View, Cody, WY 82414-9606. acgg@acgg.org. Ed. Stephen Nelson. Adv. contact Jan Billeb. page USD 400; trim 10 x 8. Circ: 350 (paid).

338   DEU   ISSN 0073-0068
HANDBUCH DER GROSSUNTERNEHMEN. Text in German. 1953. a. (2 vols.). EUR 409.03 (effective 1999). adv.
Document type: Directory.
Related titles: Online - full text ed.: (from Data-Star, G B I, The Dialog Corporation).
Published by: Hoppenstedt Bonnier Zeitschriften GmbH, Havelstr. 9, Darmstadt, 64295, Germany. TEL 49-6151-380-0, FAX 49-6151-380-360. Circ: 23,500.

HARRIS CONNECTICUT MANUFACTURERS DIRECTORY. see BUSINESS AND ECONOMICS—Trade And Industrial Directories

HARRIS DELAWARE MANUFACTURERS DIRECTORY. see BUSINESS AND ECONOMICS—Trade And Industrial Directories

HARRIS GEORGIA MANUFACTURERS DIRECTORY. see BUSINESS AND ECONOMICS—Trade And Industrial Directories

HARRIS MASSACHUSETTS MANUFACTURERS DIRECTORY. see BUSINESS AND ECONOMICS—Trade And Industrial Directories

HARRIS NATIONAL MANUFACTURERS DIRECTORY (YEAR). see BUSINESS AND ECONOMICS—Trade And Industrial Directories

HARRIS NATIONAL MANUFACTURERS DIRECTORY. MIDWEST EDITION (YEAR). see BUSINESS AND ECONOMICS—Trade And Industrial Directories

HARRIS NATIONAL MANUFACTURERS DIRECTORY. NORTHEAST EDITION (YEAR). see BUSINESS AND ECONOMICS—Trade And Industrial Directories

HARRIS NATIONAL MANUFACTURERS DIRECTORY. SOUTHEAST EDITION (YEAR). see BUSINESS AND ECONOMICS—Trade And Industrial Directories

HARRIS NEW ENGLAND MANUFACTURERS DIRECTORY. see BUSINESS AND ECONOMICS—Trade And Industrial Directories

HARRIS RHODE ISLAND MANUFACTURERS DIRECTORY. see BUSINESS AND ECONOMICS—Trade And Industrial Directories

HARRIS SOUTH CAROLINA MANUFACTURERS DIRECTORY. see BUSINESS AND ECONOMICS—Trade And Industrial Directories

HARRIS TEXAS MANUFACTURERS DIRECTORY. see BUSINESS AND ECONOMICS—Trade And Industrial Directories

HARRIS U S MANUFACTURERS DIRECTORY. WEST EDITION. see BUSINESS AND ECONOMICS—Trade And Industrial Directories

338.9   USA
HAWAII. DEPARTMENT OF BUSINESS, ECONOMIC DEVELOPMENT & TOURISM. ANNUAL REPORT. Text in English. 1962. a., latest 1999. free. **Document type:** Government.
Former titles: Hawaii. Department of Business and Economic Development. Annual Report (1041-0635); (until 1987): Hawaii. Department of Planning and Economic Development. Annual Report (0073-1072)
Media: Online - full text.
Published by: Department of Business, Economic Development & Tourism, Communications & Publications, P O Box 2359, Honolulu, HI 96804. TEL 808-586-2404, FAX 808-586-2427, http://www.hawaii.gov/dbedt/. Circ: 1,500.

338.9   USA
HAWAII'S ECONOMY NEWSLETTER. Text in English. q. free. **Document type:** Newsletter. **Description:** Provides periodic analysis of Hawaii's economy conducted by state economic research division.
Published by: Department of Business, Economic Development & Tourism, Communications & Publications, P O Box 2359, Honolulu, HI 96804. TEL 808-586-2404, FAX 808-587-2790, virion@dbedt.hawaii.gov, http://www.hawaii.gov/dbedt/.

338   USA
HEALTH OF THE REP NEWSLETTER. Text in English. m. **Document type:** Newsletter. **Description:** Covers the world of manufacturing.
Published by: (United Association Manufacturers' Representatives), Keith Kittrell & Associates, Inc., P O Box 986, Dana Point, CA 92639. TEL 714-240-4966. Ed. Karen K Mazzola.

HEBEI GONGYE KEJI/HEBEI JOURNAL OF INDUSTRIAL SCIENCE AND TECHNOLOGY. see TECHNOLOGY: COMPREHENSIVE WORKS

338   JPN   ISSN 0915-194X
HIROSHIMA KENRITSU SEIBU KOGYO GIJUTSU SENTA KENKYU HOKOKU. Text in Japanese. 1958. a.
Former titles (until 1987): Hiroshima Kenritsu Seibu Kogyo Gijutsu Senta Hokoku (0910-4429); (until 1983): Kure Kogyo Shikenjo Hokoku (0385-8669)
Indexed by: BrCerAb, C&ISA, CerAb, CorrAb, E&CAJ, EMA, IAA, M&TEA, MBF, METADEX, WAA.
—BLDSC (2814.570000), IE.
Published by: Western Hiroshima Prefecture, Industrial Research Institute/Hiroshima Kenritsu Seibu Kogyo Gijutsu Senta Hokoku, 2-chome-10-1 Aga-Minami, Hiroshima, Kure 737-0004, Japan.

338.00711   GBR   ISSN 1351-8097
HOBSONS I T CASEBOOK. (Information Technology) Text in English. a. GBP 9.99 per issue (effective 2002). **Description:** Recent graduates discuss their careers in the industry.
Published by: (Careers Research and Advisory Centre), Hobsons PLC, Challenger House, 42 Adler St, London, E1 1EE, United Kingdom. TEL 44-1223-460366, FAX 44-1223-301506. **Dist. by:** Biblios Publishers' Distribution Services Ltd., Star Rd, Partridge Green, W Sussex RH13 8LD, United Kingdom. TEL 44-1403-710851, FAX 44-1403-711143.

338   JPN
HOKKOHKEN NEWS. Text in Japanese. bi-m. free. **Document type:** Newsletter.
Formerly: Hokkaishi News
Published by: Hokkaido National Industrial Research Institute, 2-17 Tsukisamu-Higashi, Toyohira-ku, Sapporo-shi, Hokkaido 062-0000, Japan. FAX 81-11-857-8901.

338   HKG
HONG KONG PRODUCTIVITY COUNCIL ANNUAL REPORT. Text in Chinese, English. 1968. a.
Formerly: Hong Kong Productivity Council and Centre Annual Report
Published by: Hong Kong Productivity Council, HKPC Bldg, 78 Tat Chee Ave, Kowloon, Hong Kong. TEL 852-2788-5678, FAX 852-2788-5900. Ed. Betty Lee. Circ: 5,000.

338   HKG
HONG KONG PRODUCTIVITY NEWS. Text in Chinese, English. 1967. m. adv.
Published by: Hong Kong Productivity Council, HKPC Bldg, 78 Tat Chee Ave, Kowloon, Hong Kong. TEL 852-2788-5678, FAX 852-2788-5052. Ed. Wendy Tsang. adv.: B&W page HKD 5,600, color page HKD 8,300; 266 x 370. Circ: 7,000.

330   HKG
HONG KONG SPECIAL ADMINISTRATIVE REGION OF CHINA. CENSUS AND STATISTICS DEPARTMENT. QUARTERLY INDEX OF INDUSTRIAL PRODUCTION. Text in Chinese, English. 1984. q. HKD 40; HKD 10 newsstand/cover (effective 2002). stat. back issues avail. **Document type:** Government.
Description: Shows the up-to-date trends of the output of the manufacturing industries.
Published by: Census and Statistics Department/Zhengfu Tongjichu, Industrial Production Statistics Section, 16/F Chuang's Hung Hom Plaza, 83 Wuhu St, Hung Hom, Kowloon, Hong Kong. http://www.info.gov.hk/censtatd/eng/public/pub_list/IPS/qsip_index.html, http://www.statisticalbookstore.gov.hk. **Subscr. to:** Information Services Department, Publications Sales Section, 4/F, Murray Bldg, Garden Rd, Hong Kong, Hong Kong. TEL 852-2842-8844, FAX 852-2598-7482, puborder@isd.gcn.gov.hk, http://www.info.gov.hk/isd/book_e.htm. **Dist. by:** Government Publications Centre, Low Block, Ground Fl, Queensway Government Offices, 66 Queensway, Hong Kong, Hong Kong. TEL 852-2537-1910, FAX 852-2523-7195.

HONG KONG SPECIAL ADMINISTRATIVE REGION OF CHINA. CENSUS AND STATISTICS DEPARTMENT. REPORT ON ANNUAL SURVEY OF INDUSTRIAL PRODUCTION. see BUSINESS AND ECONOMICS—Abstracting, Bibliographies, Statistics

HUNGARIAN EXPORT & PRODUCTION DATABASE ON CD-ROM. see BUSINESS AND ECONOMICS—International Commerce

HUNGARY. KOZPONTI STATISZTIKAI HIVATAL. IPARSTATISZTIKAI EVKONYV. see BUSINESS AND ECONOMICS—Abstracting, Bibliographies, Statistics

HUTCHINS' U K BUILDING COSTS HANDBOOK (YEAR). see BUILDING AND CONSTRUCTION

338   IRL
I B E C - E S R I BUSINESS FORECAST. Text in English. 1974. m. **Document type:** Bulletin.
Formerly: C I I - E S R I Business Forecast
Published by: Irish Business and Employers Confederation, Confederation House, 84-86 Lower Baggot St., Dublin, 2, Ireland. TEL 353-1-6601011, FAX 353-1-6601717, http://www.iol.ie/ibec. Ed. David Croughan. Circ: (controlled).

338   IRL
I B E C NEWS. Text in English. 1965. m. looseleaf. **Document type:** Newsletter.
Formerly (until 1992): C I I Newsletter
Published by: Irish Business and Employers Confederation, Confederation House, 84-86 Lower Baggot St., Dublin, 2, Ireland. TEL 353-1-6601011, FAX 353-1-6601717, http://www.iol.ie/ibec. Ed. Karin MacArthur. Circ: 6,000 (controlled).

338   USA   ISSN 1533-435X
I D I I SOFTWARE NEWSLETTER. Text in English. 2000. 2/m. free. adv. **Document type:** Newsletter, Trade. **Description:** Aims to educate and inform professionals in software for warehousing, logistics, and supply chain.
Media: Online - full content.
Published by: Industrial Data & Information Inc., Rte 1, Box 580, Webbers Falls, OK 74470. TEL 918-464-2222, FAX 918-464-2221, editor@idii.com, info@idii.com, http://www.idii.com/esn/index.htm#current. Ed., Pub. Phil Obal.

THE I E A JOURNAL OF ERGONOMICS. see ENGINEERING

I E E E - C P M T ELECTRONICS MANUFACTURING TECHNOLOGY (I E M T). (Components, Packaging, and Manufacturing Technology Society) see ELECTRONICS

338 DEU ISSN 0170-5660
I F O STUDIEN ZUR INDUSTRIEWIRTSCHAFT. Text in German. 1967. irreg., latest vol.58, 1998. price varies. **Document type:** *Monographic series.*
Published by: I F O Institut fuer Wirtschaftsforschung, Poschingerstr 5, Munich, 81679, Germany. TEL 49-89-9224-0, FAX 49-89-985369, ifo@ifo.de, http://www.ifo.de. Circ: 500.

I I R R REPORT. see *BUSINESS AND ECONOMICS—International Development And Assistance*

338.0029 USA
I S O 9000 REGISTERED FIRMS DIRECTORY. (International Organization for Standardization) Text in English. s-a. (2 vols./yr.). **Document type:** *Directory.* **Description:** Lists firms complying with ISO 9000 standards.
Published by: Underwriters Laboratories Inc., Publications, 33 Pfingsten Rd, Northbrook, IL 60062-2096. TEL 847-272-8800, FAX 847-272-0472.

338 658.3 USA
IDEAS AND SOLUTIONS; magazine for businesses, products and services. Text in English. 1986. m. adv. bk.rev. **Document type:** *Journal, Trade.*
Published by: Gibbs Publishing Company, PO Box 97, Sylva, NC 28779-0097. Ed. James Calvin Gibbs. Circ: 2,500.

338 USA
THE ILLINOIS MANUFACTURER. Text in English. 1991. bi-m. USD 30. adv. back issues avail.; reprints avail. **Document type:** *Magazine, Trade.* **Description:** Featuring articles on manufacturing related issues.
Related titles: Online - full content ed.
Published by: The Illinois Manufacturers Association, 1301 W 22nd St., Ste. 610, Oak Brook, IL 60523. TEL 630-368-5300, FAX 630-218-7467, ima@ima-net.org, http://www.ima-net.org/. Ed., R&P, Adv. contact Laurie Kaczmar TEL 630-368-5300 ext. 3122. page USD 1,340; trim 11 x 8.5. Circ: 7,000.

INDEPENDENT SAWMILL & WOODLOT MANAGEMENT. see *BUSINESS AND ECONOMICS—Management*

338 IND ISSN 0970-6119
INDIAN CEMENT REVIEW. Text in English. 1986. m. USD 100. **Document type:** *Trade.*
Indexed: CRIA, CRICC.
Published by: Wadhera Publications, General Assurance Bldg., 232 Dr D.N. Rd., Mumbai, Maharashtra 400 001, India. TEL 91-22-2046918. Ed. Roshanlal Wadhera. Circ: 3,500.

338 USA
INDIANA MANUFACTURER. Text in English. m.
Published by: Industrial Marketing, Inc., PO Box 4310, Lexington, KY 40544-4310. TEL 800-264-3303.

338 URY ISSN 0376-9941
HC231
INDICE INDUSTRIAL - ANUARIO DE LA INDUSTRIA URUGUAYA. Text in Spanish. 1957. a.
Address: Sarandi, 456, Montevideo, 11007, Uruguay. TEL 2-951963. Ed. W M Trias. Circ: 6,000.

INDICES DA PRODUCAO INDUSTRIAL. see *MINES AND MINING INDUSTRY*

338 621.9 ESP ISSN 0213-6295
INDUEQUIPO. Text in Spanish. 1986. 6/yr. **Description:** Covers industrial equipment.
Address: Pza. Republica del Ecuador 6, Madrid, 28016, Spain. TEL 2509943, FAX 1-4582606. Ed. Sergio R Sanchez. Circ: 7,000.

338 GTM ISSN 0019-7408
INDUSTRIA. Text in Spanish. 1957. m. USD 1 per issue. adv. bibl.; charts; illus.; mkt.; stat.; tr.lit. index, cum.index. **Document type:** *Newspaper.*
Formerly: Revista Industria
Published by: Camara de Industria de Guatemala, Ruta 6, 9-21, Guatemala City Zona, Guatemala. TEL 502-2-340849, FAX 502-2-341090. Ed. Luis Anibal Blanco. Adv. contact Ana Graciela Lopez de Ruiz. Circ: 3,000.

338 PRT
INDUSTRIA. Text in Portuguese. 12/yr.
Published by: Confederacao Industria Portuguesa, Av. 5 de Outubro, 35 - 1o, Lisbon, 1000, Portugal. TEL 54-70-20.

338 ITA ISSN 0019-7416
L'INDUSTRIA; rivista di economia politica industriale. Text in Italian. 1887. q. EUR 64 domestic to individuals; EUR 97 foreign to individuals; EUR 111 combined subscription domestic to institutions print & online eds.; EUR 148 combined subscription foreign to institutions print & online eds. (effective 2005). adv. charts. index. back issues avail. **Document type:** *Academic/Scholarly.*
Incorporates (1975-1979): Rivista di Economia e Politica Industriale (0390-041X)
Related titles: Online - full text ed.
Indexed: ELLIS, IBSS, JEL, PAIS, RefZh. —IE.
Published by: Societa Editrice Il Mulino, Strada Maggiore 37, Bologna, 40125, Italy. TEL 39-051-256011, FAX 39-051-256034, lindustria@economia.unife.it, riviste@mulino.it, http://www.mulino.it/edizioni/riviste/scheda_rivista.php?issn=0019-7416. Ed. Patrizio Bianchi. Circ: 1,600.

338 BOL
INDUSTRIA BOLIVIANA. Text in Spanish. 1973 (vol.23). s-m.
Published by: Camara Nacional de Industrias, Casilla 611, La Paz, Bolivia.

338 BRA ISSN 0019-7602
HC186
INDUSTRIA E DESENVOLVIMENTO∗. Text in Portuguese. 1968. m. adv. bk.rev. abstr.; bibl.; charts; illus.; stat.
Published by: Federacao e Centro das Industrias do Estado de Sao Paulo, c/o C N I, Av. Nilo Pecanha 50, Andar 34, Rio de Janiero, RJ 20044, Brazil. Ed. Ney Lima Figueiredo. Circ: 27,000.

338 ESP
INDUSTRIA ESPANOLA. Text in Spanish. 4/yr.
Published by: Ministerio de Industria, Paseo Castellana, 210, Madrid, 28046, Spain. TEL 34-91-4570803, FAX 34-91-4572938. Ed. Fernando Escribano.

338 ESP ISSN 0210-1815
INDUSTRIA INTERNACIONAL. Text in Spanish. 1965. m.
Published by: Publicaciones Internacionales S.A., Paseo Castellana, 210, Madrid, 28046, Spain. TEL 34-91-4570806, FAX 34-91-4572938. Ed. F Escribano. Circ: 6,000 (controlled).

338 ITA ISSN 0019-7661
INDUSTRIA LOMBARDA. Text in Italian. 1947. w. **Document type:** *Newsletter.*
Published by: Associazione Industriale Lombarda, Via Pantano 9, Milan, MI 20122, Italy. TEL 39-02-58370, FAX 39-02-58304507, assolombarda@assolombarda.it, http://www.assolombarda.it. Ed. Giuliano Faliva. Circ: 16,000.

338 PAN
INDUSTRIA MANUFACTURERA. Text in Spanish. 1997. a. PAB 1.50 (effective 2000). **Description:** Offers information via company surveys for the most relevant aspect of manufacturing activity. Geared towards organization's management and productive structure.
Published by: Direccion de Estadistica y Censo, Contraloria General, Apdo. 5213, Panama City, 5, Panama. TEL 507-210-4800, FAX 507-210-4801, cgrdec@contraloria.gob.pa.

338 PER
INDUSTRIA PERUANA. Text in Spanish. 1896. m. USD 100. adv.
Published by: Sociedad de Industrias, Los Laureles, 365, San Isidro, Lima 27, Peru. Ed. Rolando Celi Burneo. Circ: 6,000.

LKA ISSN 0019-8064
INDUSTRIAL CEYLON. Text in English. 1960-1980; resumed. 32/yr. adv. charts; stat.; tr.lit.
Indexed: SLSI.
Published by: Ceylon National Chamber of Industries, Flat No. 20, 1st. Fl., Galle Face Court, Columbo, Sri Lanka. Ed. P Sangarapillai. Circ: 800.

338 IND ISSN 0019-8099
INDUSTRIAL COURIER. Text in English. 1969. q. INR 2.50. adv. bk.rev. charts; illus.; stat.
Published by: N. K. Lahiri Ed. & Pub., 45-9 Choudhurypara Lane, Howrah, 711 104, India. Circ: 3,000.

338 PAK
INDUSTRIAL DEVELOPMENT. Text in English. 1972. bi-m. PKR 20. adv. bk.rev.
Related titles: Microfiche ed.: (from PQC).
Indexed: T&II.
Published by: Press Corporation of Pakistan, P O Box 3138, Karachi, 75400, Pakistan. TEL 21-455-3703, FAX 21-7736198. Ed. Saeed Hafeez. Circ: 5,000.

338 IND ISSN 0019-8188
INDUSTRIAL ECONOMIST. Text in English. 1968. fortn. INR 200; USD 50 foreign (effective 2003). adv. bk.rev. charts; illus.; stat. **Document type:** *Newspaper.* **Description:** Contains analysis of corporate performance, stock markets, policy critique, global glimpses, information technology and politicao-economic policy issues.
Address: S-15 Industrial Estate, Guindy, Chennai, Tamil Nadu 600 032, India. TEL 91-44-234-2248, FAX 91-44-234-5676, inderom@eth.net, indecom@eth.net. Ed., Pub., R&P S Viswanathan. Adv. contact S Kalyan Ramanathan. B&W page INR 25,000, color page INR 40,000; trim 280 x 205. Circ: 10,000.

338 EGY ISSN 0019-820X
INDUSTRIAL EGYPT. Text in Arabic, English. 1924. q. adv.
Indexed: KES.
Published by: Federation of Egyptian Industries/Ittihad al-Sinaat al-Misriyah, 26A Sharia Sherif Pasha, P O Box 251, Cairo, Egypt. TEL 02-3928317, FAX 02-3928075, TELEX 92624. Ed. Darwish M Darwish. Circ: 900.

338 IND ISSN 0019-8269
INDUSTRIAL ENTERPRISE∗. Text in English. 1968. m. INR 15. adv. bk.rev. charts; illus.; tr.lit.
Published by: Cactus Publications, 55-1-2 Sastitola Rd., Kolkata, West Bengal 700 011, India. Ed. B N Nobis.

338 IND
INDUSTRIAL EXPANSION. Text in English. 1969. q. INR 10. adv. charts; tr.lit.
Address: K.S. South Extension Part 1, New Delhi, India. Ed. Usha Datta.

338 IND ISSN 0377-0036
T1
INDUSTRIAL HERALD. Text in English. 1965 (vol.20). m. INR 150 (effective 2000). adv. bk.rev. illus. 80 p./no.; **Document type:** *Journal, Trade.*
Formerly: Indsearch
Published by: (Industrial & Scientific Research Association), Gopali & Co., 407-408 Mount Rd., Chennai, Tamil Nadu 600 035, India. TEL 91-44-4330979, FAX 91-44-4332413, motorindia@usa.net, http://www.motorindia.org. Pub. R Kalidasan. Adv. contact R. Kalidasan. color page INR 16,000, B&W page INR 8,000; 23 x 18. Circ: 25,000.

338 IND ISSN 0019-8412
INDUSTRIAL INDIA. Text in English. 1950. m. INR 750 in India; USD 150 subscr - mailed in United States (effective 2005). adv. bk.rev. illus.
Incorporating: Index Port
Indexed: PROMT.
Published by: (All-India Manufacturers' Organization), Chary Publications Pvt Ltd, 311 Raikar Chambers, Govandi East, Mumbai, Maharashtra 400088, India. TEL 91-22-25556428, 91-22-55974256, FAX 91-22-25556433, charypublications@hathway.com, http://www.charypublications.com. Ed., Pub., R&P Mr. Mahadevan Iyer. Adv. contact Mrs. Pravita Iyer TEL 91-22-55974257.

338 CAN ISSN 0836-737X
INDUSTRIAL PROCESS PRODUCTS AND TECHNOLOGY. Text in English. 1987. 6/yr. CND 35 domestic; CND 47 in United States; CND 50 elsewhere (effective 2000). adv. **Document type:** *Trade.* **Description:** For the chemical process industries and other primary and secondary manufacturing industries utilizing chemicals or chemical engineering processes.
Published by: Swan Erickson Publishing Inc., 1011 Upper Middle Rd E Ste 1235, Oakville, ON L6H 5Z9, Canada. TEL 905-475-4231, FAX 905-475-3512, http://www.ippt.ca. Ed. Glen Scholey. Pub. Bob Erickson. Adv. contact Michael Swan. B&W page CND 3,575; trim 16.5 x 11.25. Circ: 23,598.

338 PRI ISSN 0019-8633
INDUSTRIAL PUERTO RICO. Text in English. 1965. bi-m. adv. bk.rev. charts; illus.; stat.
Published by: Antilles Publishing, 721 Hernandez St., Miramar Towers, Apt. 12B, Santurce, 00908, Puerto Rico. Ed. Mary Kay Murphy Aivaziar. Circ: 7,500 (controlled).

338 IND
INDUSTRIAL SITUATION IN INDIA. Text in English. 1972. q. USD 5.
Indexed: BAS.
Published by: Manjari Chaudhuri, 188-78. Prince Anwar Shah Rd., Calcutta, West Bengal 700 045, India.

338 CMR
INDUSTRIE CAMEROUNAISE. Text in French. a.
Published by: Syndicat des Industries du Cameroun, BP 673, Douala, Cameroon.

338 DEU ISSN 0174-6146
INDUSTRIE-SERVICE. Text in German. 1960. 10/yr. EUR 81 domestic; EUR 95 foreign; EUR 7.50 newsstand/cover (effective 2004). adv. illus. **Document type:** *Magazine, Trade.*
Published by: Verlag fuer Technik und Wirtschaft GmbH & Co., Lise-Meitner-Str 2, Mainz, 55129, Germany. TEL 49-6131-992-0, FAX 49-6131-992100, info@vfmz.de, http://www.industrie-service.de. Ed. Michaela Heider Peschel. Adv. contact Michael Spahn. B&W page EUR 6,150, color page EUR 7,530; trim 185 x 265. Circ: 55,000.

338 FRA ISSN 1167-7287
INDUSTRIES. Text in French. 1994. m. free. adv. bk.rev. charts; illus.; stat. back issues avail. **Document type:** *Directory, Government.* **Description:** Provides business leaders and industrial players with useful information, such as sector news, government initiatives, reports on general business topics, export news, legal changes and industry meetings.
Formerly: Lettre 101 (0294-0620); Which was formed by the merger of: Recherche et Technologie (0752-5575); Industrie et Energie Francaises (0249-9819)
Related titles: Online - full text ed.
Indexed: INIS AtomInd.
Published by: Ministere de l'Economie, des Finances, et de l'Industrie, 139 rue de Bercy, Paris, Cedex 12 75572, France. TEL 33-1-53188815, http://www.finances.gouv.fr, http://lekiosque.finances.gouv.fr. Ed. Jerome Chevaillier. Pub. Michel le Clainche. Circ: 50,200.

338 JPN ISSN 0446-1266
INDUSTRIES OF JAPAN. Text in English. 1958. a. JPY 800. stat.

B

Published by: (Mainichi Daily News), Mainichi Shinbunsha/Mainichi Newspapers, 1-1-1 Hitotsubashi, Chiyoda-ku, Tokyo, 100-8051, Japan. TEL 81-3-3212-0321, FAX 81-3-3211-0895.

INDUSTRY AND HIGHER EDUCATION. see *EDUCATION—Higher Education*

338 GBR ISSN 0264-4932
INDUSTRY NORTHWEST. Text in English. 1973. m. GBP 25. adv.
Published by: Industry Northwest Publications Ltd., 3 Parsonage, Manchester, Lancs M3 2WB, United Kingdom. TEL 061-832-2143, FAX 061-832-5589. Ed. Deborah Humphreys. Circ: 14,200.

INFOPESCA. NOTICIAS COMERCIALES. see *AGRICULTURE*

338 ITA ISSN 0020-0786
INFORMAZIONE INDUSTRIALE (TURIN). Text in Italian. 1920. s-m. bk.rev. illus.
Published by: Unione Industriale di Torino, Via Manfredo Fanti, 17, Turin, TO 10128, Italy. Ed. Giancarlo Forconi. Circ: 5,000.

B

620 DNK ISSN 0446-2491
INGENIOERENS INDKOEBSBOG. Text in Danish. 1960. a. (in 2 vols.). adv. **Document type:** *Catalog, Trade.*
Incorporates (1974-2002): Elektronik Indkoebsbogen (0108-8149)
Related titles: CD-ROM ed.: ISSN 1395-4938. 1995; Online - full text ed.
Published by: T D C Forlag A/S, Roedovrevej 241, Roedovre, 2610, Denmark. TEL 45-80-361350, FAX 45-70-113636, fagbogdanmark@tdc.dk, http://li.dk/, http://www.tdc.dk. Circ: 15,000.

338.064 CAN ISSN 1488-433X
INNOVATION ANALYSIS BULLETIN. Text in English. 1999. 3/yr. free (effective 2005). **Description:** Covers current issues in science and technology, advanced technologies, innovation in industry, and electronic media.
Media: Online - full content.
Published by: (Statistics Canada, Science, Innovation and Electronic Information Division), Statistics Canada, Publications Sales and Services, Ottawa, ON K1A 0T6, Canada. TEL 613-951-8116, infostats@statcan.ca, http://www.statcan.ca/english/freepub/88-003-XIE/free.htm.

338 USA
INNOVATION GROUP MEMBERSHIP NEWSLETTER (ONLINE EDITION). Text in English. 1991. m. free to members (effective 2005). **Document type:** *Newsletter, Consumer.* **Description:** Discusses products of interest to local and county governments.
Formerly (until 2005): Innovation Group Membership Newsletter (Print Edition); Incorporates (1988-1998): Innovative Products Letters (1058-8523)
Media: Online - full text.
Published by: Innovation Groups, Inc., 6604 Harney Rd., Ste. L, Tampa, FL 33610. http://www.ig.org. Circ: 14,000.

338 AUS ISSN 0310-5660
INSIDE RETAILING. Text in English. 1971. w. AUD 417. charts; stat. index. back issues avail. **Document type:** *Newsletter, Trade.* **Description:** Covers retailing in general.
Indexed: ABIX.
Published by: Ian Huntley Pty. Ltd., 233 Military Rd, Cremorne, NSW 2090, Australia. TEL 61-2-9953-5788, FAX 61-2-9953-2280. Ed. Murray White. **Dist. by:** Current Pacific Ltd., PO Box 36-536, Northcote, Auckland, New Zealand. TEL 64-9-480-1388, FAX 64-9-480-1387, info@cplnz.com, http://www.cplnz.com.

INSTITUTE OF PUBLIC ENTERPRISE. JOURNAL. see *BUSINESS AND ECONOMICS—Management*

338 330.9 PER ISSN 1022-0437
INSTITUTO DE ESTUDIOS PERUANOS. DOCUMENTOS DE TRABAJO. SERIE TALLERES. Key Title: Serie Talleres I E P. Variant title: Documentos de Trabajo. Serie Talleres I E P. Text in Spanish. 1985. irreg. price varies. back issues avail. **Document type:** *Monographic series, Academic/Scholarly.* **Description:** Publishes new research into the factories of Peru.
Related titles: ♦ Series of: Instituto de Estudios Peruanos. Documentos de Trabajo. ISSN 1022-0356.
Published by: (Instituto de Estudios Peruanos), I E P Ediciones (Subsidiary of: Instituto de Estudios Peruanos), Horacio Urteaga 694, Jesus Maria, Lima, 11, Peru. TEL 51-14-3326194, FAX 51-14-3326173, libreria@iep.org.pe, http://iep.perucultural.org.pe.

INTEGRATED DESIGN AND PROCESS TECHNOLOGY. see *ENGINEERING*

352 FRA ISSN 0240-9925
INTER REGIONS; les cahiers de l'expansion regionale. Text in French. 1979. 11/yr. adv. **Document type:** *Bulletin.*
Formed by the merger of: Inter Regions; (1961-1979): Cahiers de l'Expansion Regionale (0014-4711)
Indexed: PAIS.
Published by: Conseil National des Economies Regionales (C N E R), 219 bd. Saint-Germain, Paris, 75007, France. TEL 33-1-42223529, FAX 33-1-45499149. Ed. Anne France Braquehais. Adv. contact Elisabeth Cornu.

INTERACTIVE GLOBAL NEWS. see *BUSINESS AND ECONOMICS—International Commerce*

INTERNATIONAL CONFERENCE ON ION IMPLANTATION TECHNOLOGY. PROCEEDINGS. see *COMPUTERS—Circuits*

INTERNATIONAL INTERCONNECT TECHNOLOGY CONFERENCE. PROCEEDINGS. see *COMPUTERS—Circuits*

INTERNATIONAL JOURNAL FOR MANUFACTURING SCIENCE AND PRODUCTION. see *ENGINEERING—Industrial Engineering*

INTERNATIONAL JOURNAL OF INDUSTRIAL ERGONOMICS. see *ENGINEERING*

338 GBR ISSN 1742-4208
▼ ➤ **INTERNATIONAL JOURNAL OF MASS CUSTOMISATION.** Text in English. 2005. 4/yr. USD 450 (effective 2005). **Document type:** *Journal, Academic/Scholarly.* **Description:** Covers fundamental issues of mass customization, including variety, modularity, commonality, adaptability, flexibility, reusability, customizability, and economies of scale and scope.
Related titles: Online - full text ed.: ISSN 1742-4216. USD 450 (effective 2005).
Published by: Inderscience Publishers, IEL Editorial Office, PO Box 735, Olney, Bucks MK46 5WB, United Kingdom. TEL 44-1234-240519, FAX 44-1234-240515, ijmassc@inderscience.com, info@inderscience.com, http://www.inderscience.com/ijmassc. Ed. George Huang.

➤ **INTERNATIONAL JOURNAL OF PRODUCTION ECONOMICS.** see *ENGINEERING—Industrial Engineering*

338 620 GBR ISSN 0020-7543
TS155.A1 CODEN: IJPRB8
➤ **INTERNATIONAL JOURNAL OF PRODUCTION RESEARCH.** Text and summaries in English, French, German. 1961. s-m. GBP 3,228, USD 5,326 combined subscription to institutions print & online eds. (effective 2006). adv. bk.rev. bibl.; charts; illus. index. reprint service avail. from PSC. **Document type:** *Journal, Academic/Scholarly.* **Description:** Publishes papers on the technology and fundamental behavior of production resources, with the complex and cross-disciplinary problems of analysis and control that arise in combining these resources within the design of production systems.
Related titles: Microform ed.: (from MIM, PQC); Online - full text ed.: ISSN 1366-588X. 1997. GBP 3,067, USD 5,060 to institutions (effective 2006) (from EBSCO Publishing, Gale Group, IngentaConnect, O C L C Online Computer Library Center, Inc., Swets Information Services).
Indexed: ABIn, ASCA, B&BAb, BrCerAb, C&ISA, CADCAM, CMCI, CPM, Cadscan, CerAb, CivEngAb, CorrAb, CurCont, CybAb, E&CAJ, EMA, Emerald, EngInd, ErgAb, IAA, IAOP, ISMEC, ISR, Inspec, JCQM, LeadAb, M&TEA, MBF, MEA&I, METADEX, ORMS, PROMT, PsycholAb, RASB, SCI, SSCI, SolStAb, WAA, ZentMath, Zincscan.
—BLDSC (4542.486000), AskIEEE, CISTI, Ei, IDS, IE, Infotrieve, ingenta, Linda Hall. **CCC.**
Published by: Taylor & Francis Ltd (Subsidiary of: Taylor & Francis Group), 4 Park Sq, Milton Park, Abingdon, OX14 4RN, United Kingdom. TEL 44-1235-828600, FAX 44-1235-829000, info@tandf.co.uk, http://www.tandf.co.uk/journals/titles/00207543.asp. Ed. J E Middle. **Subscr. in N. America to:** Taylor & Francis Inc., Customer Services Dept, 325 Chestnut St, 8th Fl, Philadelphia, PA 19106. TEL 215-625-8900, 800-354-1420, FAX 215-625-8914, customerservice@taylorandfrancis.com; **Subscr. to:** Journals Customer Service, Rankine Rd, Basingstoke, Hants RG24 8PR, United Kingdom. TEL 44-1256-813000, FAX 44-1256-330245, enquiry@tandf.co.uk. **Co-sponsors:** Institution of Production Engineers; American Institute of Industrial Engineers; Society of Manufacturing Engineers.

▼ ➤ **INTERNATIONAL JOURNAL OF PRODUCTIVITY AND QUALITY MANAGEMENT.** see *BUSINESS AND ECONOMICS—Management*

➤ **INTERNATIONAL JOURNAL OF SERVICE INDUSTRY MANAGEMENT.** see *BUSINESS AND ECONOMICS—Management*

338 NLD ISSN 0924-6363
➤ **INTERNATIONAL STUDIES IN THE SERVICE ECONOMY.** Text in English. 1990. irreg., latest vol.5, 1995. price varies. back issues avail. **Document type:** *Monographic series, Academic/Scholarly.*
—BLDSC (4549.818000), ingenta.
Published by: Springer-Verlag Dordrecht (Subsidiary of: Springer Science+Business Media), Van Godewijckstraat 30, Dordrecht, 3311 GX, Netherlands. TEL 31-78-6576050, FAX 31-78-6576474, http://www.springeronline.com. Eds. Geza Feketekuty, Orio Giarini.

338 HUN ISSN 0021-0749
IPARGAZDASAG✶. Text in Hungarian; Contents page in German, Russian. 1947. m. USD 36. charts; illus.; stat.
Formerly (until 1959): Tobbtermeles (0369-0075)
Published by: Szervezesi es Vezetesi Tudomanyos Tarsasag, Fo utca 68, Budapest, 1027, Hungary. TEL 2021456. Ed. Dr. Istvan Harsanyi. **Subscr. to:** Kultura, PO Box 149, Budapest 1389, Hungary.

338 IRN ISSN 0578-6959
IRAN. MINISTRY OF ECONOMY. REPORT ON COMMENCEMENT AND OPERATION PERMITS FOR INDUSTRIAL ESTABLISHMENTS✶. Text in English. q. free. stat.
Published by: Ministry of Finance and Economic Affairs, Teheran, Iran.

338 JPN ISSN 0075-3289
JAPAN CENSUS OF MANUFACTURES: REPORT BY COMMODITIES✶. Text in Japanese. 1909. a. JPY 4,600.
Published by: (Japan. Research and Statistics Division), Ministry of International Trade and Industry/Tsusho Sangyo-sho Daijin Kanbo Chosa Tokei-bu, 1-3-1 Kasumigaseki, Chiyoda-ku, Tokyo, 100-0013, Japan. TEL 03-501-1511. Circ: 800.

600 330 JPN ISSN 0910-8300
HC461
JAPAN ECONOMIC ALMANAC; an annual in-depth report on the state of the Japanese economy. Text in English. 1962. a. JPY 9,800, USD 59.50. adv. **Document type:** *Trade.*
Formerly (until 1985): Industrial Review of Japan (0537-5452)
Related titles: Online - full text ed.
Indexed: RASB.
—CISTI.
Published by: Nihon Keizai Shimbun Inc., 1-9-5 Ote-Machi, Chiyoda-ku, Tokyo, 100-0004, Japan. TEL 81-3-32700251, FAX 81-3-52552661. Ed. Norimichi Okai. Adv. contact Kazuo Onodera. Circ: 5,000.

JAPANESE FINANCE AND INDUSTRY: QUARTERLY SURVEY. see *BUSINESS AND ECONOMICS—Banking And Finance*

338 TZA ISSN 0856-0110
HG3729.T352
JENGA; N D C's industrial magazine. Text in English. 1968. s-a. TZS 10 per issue. charts; illus. **Document type:** *Trade.*
Published by: National Development Corporation, PO Box 2669, Dar Es Salaam, Tanzania. TEL 255-51-26271, TELEX 41068. Circ: 6,000.

338 CHN ISSN 1002-5626
JIAYONG DIANQI/HOUSEHOLD APPLIANCE. Text in Chinese. 1980. m. CNY 8.64. adv. index. 40 p./no.; **Document type:** *Consumer.* **Description:** Covers popular science, especially the practical knowledge and information to serve household appliance customers, amateurs, and maintenance personnels.
Related titles: Online - full text ed.: (from East View Information Services).
Published by: Ministry of Light Industry, Beijing Household Electric Appliances Research Institute, 6 Yuetan Beixiaojie, Beijing, 100037, China. TEL 86-11-8311220, FAX 86-11-8312464. Ed. Zhang You Liang. Circ: 400,000.

JIXIE SHEJI YU ZHIZAO/MACHINERY DESIGN & MANUFACTURE. see *MACHINERY*

338 USA ISSN 0746-8881
JOB SHOP TECHNOLOGY. (In 3 regional eds.: Western, Eastern, Mid-Western) Text in English. 1984. q. free to qualified personnel. adv. **Document type:** *Trade.* **Description:** Dedicated to help product manufacturers understand parts and services provided by job shops.
Published by: Edwards Publishing, 16 Waterbury Rd, Box 7193, Prospect, CT 06712-1237. TEL 203-758-4474, 800-317-0474, FAX 203-758-4475, http://www.jobshoptechnology.com. Ed. John P Wright. Pub. Dave Edwards. R&P John Wright. Adv. contact Rob Eichner. Circ: 100,000 (controlled).

338 SGP ISSN 0219-6867
TS176
➤ **JOURNAL OF ADVANCED MANUFACTURING SYSTEMS.** Abbreviated title: J A M S. Text in English. 2002. s-a. SGD 121, EUR 65, USD 71 to individuals; SGD 175, EUR 94, USD 103 combined subscription to institutions print & online eds. (effective 2006). back issues avail. **Document type:** *Journal, Academic/Scholarly.* **Description:** Publishes original papers pertaining to state-of-the-art research and development, product development, process planning, resource planning, applications, and tools in the areas related to advanced manufacturing.
Related titles: Online - full content ed.; Online - full text ed.: (from EBSCO Publishing, O C L C Online Computer Library Center, Inc., Swets Information Services).
Indexed: BrCerAb, C&ISA, CerAb, CorrAb, E&CAJ, EMA, IAA, M&TEA, MBF, METADEX, SolStAb, WAA.
—BLDSC (4918.945770), IE, ingenta, Linda Hall. **CCC.**

Published by: World Scientific Publishing Co. Pte. Ltd., 5 Toh Tuck Link, Singapore, 596224, Singapore. wspc@wspc.com.sg, http://www.worldscinet.com/journals/jams/jams.shtml, http://www.worldscientific.com. **Subscr. to:** Farrer Rd, PO Box 128, Singapore 912805, Singapore. TEL 65-382-5663, FAX 65-382-5919, sales@wspc.com.sg. **Dist. by:** World Scientific Publishing Co., Inc., 1060 Main St, River Edge, NJ 07661. TEL 201-487-9655, 800-227-7562, FAX 201-487-9656, 888-977-2665.; World Scientific Publishing Ltd., 57 Shelton St, London WC2H 9HE, United Kingdom. TEL 44-20-78360888, FAX 44-20-78362020, sales@wspc.co.uk.

➤ **JOURNAL OF CLEANER PRODUCTION.** see *ENGINEERING—Industrial Engineering*

➤ **JOURNAL OF COMMERCE, INDUSTRY & TRANSPORTATION.** see *BUSINESS AND ECONOMICS—Domestic Commerce*

➤ **JOURNAL OF ENGINEERING AND TECHNOLOGY MANAGEMENT.** see *BUSINESS AND ECONOMICS—Management*

➤ **JOURNAL OF INDUSTRY, COMPETITION AND TRADE**; from theory to policy. see *BUSINESS AND ECONOMICS*

338 GBR ISSN 1526-6125
➤ **JOURNAL OF MANUFACTURING PROCESSES.** Text in English. 1999. 2/yr. EUR 363 in Europe to institutions; JPY 48,200 in Japan to institutions; USD 406 to institutions except Europe and Japan (effective 2006). **Document type:** *Journal, Academic/Scholarly.* **Description:** Contains research papers on manufacturing processes.
Related titles: Microform ed.; Online - full text ed.: (from O C L C Online Computer Library Center, Inc., ProQuest Information & Learning).
Indexed: Inspec.
—BLDSC (5011.640000), CISTI, Linda Hall. **CCC.**
Published by: (Society of Manufacturing Engineers USA), Elsevier Ltd. (Subsidiary of: Elsevier Science & Technology), The Boulevard, Langford Ln, Kidlington, Oxford, OX5 1GB, United Kingdom. TEL 44-1865-843000, FAX 44-1865-843010, nlinfo-f@elsevier.nl, http://www.elsevier.com/locate/manpro. Ed. J T Black. **Subscr. in the US & Canada to:** Society of Manufacturing Engineers, Customer Service, PO Box 6020, Dearborn, MI 48121. TEL 800-733-4763, FAX 313-240-8252.

338.948 SWE ISSN 1650-5891
DL55
JOURNAL OF NORDREGIO. Text in English. 1990. q. free (effective 2004). **Document type:** *Journal, Academic/Scholarly.* **Description:** Focuses on regional development, business and environment in the Nordic countries.
Former titles (until 2001): North (0809-0432); (until 1997): Nord Revy (0802-8818); Which incorporated: Nordic Impacts: Digest of Current Regional Developments
Related titles: Online - full text ed.
Published by: Nordregio. Nordic Centre for Spatial Studies, PO Box 1658, Stockholm, 11186, Sweden. TEL 47-8-4635400, FAX 47-8-4635401, nordregio@nordregio.se, http://www.nordregio.se. Ed. Jon P. Knudsen TEL 47-8-37275690.

338 658 USA ISSN 0737-6782
HF5415.153 CODEN: JPIMDD
➤ **JOURNAL OF PRODUCT INNOVATION MANAGEMENT.** Text in English. 1984. bi-m. USD 661 combined subscription in the Americas to institutions & Caribbean (print & online eds.); GBP 475 combined subscription elsewhere to institutions print & online eds. (effective 2006). adv. bk.rev. illus. Index. back issues avail.; reprint service avail. from PSC. **Document type:** *Journal, Academic/Scholarly.* **Description:** Dedicated to the advancement of management practice in all of the functions involved in the total process of product innovation.
Related titles: Online - full text ed.: ISSN 1540-5885. USD 630 in the Americas to institutions & Caribbean; GBP 452 elsewhere to institutions (effective 2006) (from Blackwell Synergy, EBSCO Publishing, Gale Group, IngentaConnect, O C L C Online Computer Library Center, Inc., ScienceDirect, Swets Information Services).
Indexed: ABIn, ASCA, BPIA, BrCerAb, C&ISA, CPM, CerAb, CivEngAb, CommAb, CorrAb, CurCont, E&CAJ, EMA, ESPM, Emerald, Englnd, IAA, ISR, Inspec, M&MA, M&TEA, MBF, METADEX, ManagCont, ORMS, QC&AS, RASB, RefZh, RiskAb, SCI, SSCI, SolStAb, WAA.
—BLDSC (5042.650000), AskIEEE, CISTI, Ei, IDS, IE, Infotrieve, ingenta, Linda Hall.
Published by: (Product Development & Management Association), Blackwell Publishing, Inc. (Subsidiary of: Blackwell Publishing Ltd.), Commerce Place, 350 Main St, Malden, MA 02148. TEL 781-388-8206, FAX 781-388-8232, subscrip@blackwellpub.com, http://www.blackwellpublishing.com/journals/JPIM. Ed. Anthony Di Benedetto. Adv. contact Martine Cariou-Keen. B&W page USD 820, color page USD 1,950. Circ: 2,500.

➤ **JOURNAL OF PRODUCTIVITY ANALYSIS.** see *BUSINESS AND ECONOMICS—Management*

338 EGY ISSN 1110-2543
JOURNAL OF PRODUCTIVITY AND DEVELOPMENT/ MAGALLAT AL-ANTAAGIYYAT WA AL-TANMIYYAT. Text in English. 1993. s-a. **Document type:** *Journal, Academic/Scholarly.*
Published by: Zagazig University, Institute of Efficient Productivity, Zagazig, Egypt. TEL 20-55-363635 ext.19043, http://derp.sti.sci.eg/data/0269.htm. Ed. Dr. Abdel-Rahman Esmaeil El-Salehi.

338 GBR ISSN 0967-3237
➤ **JOURNAL OF TARGETING, MEASUREMENT AND ANALYSIS FOR MARKETING.** Text in English. 1992. q. GBP 245 in Europe to institutions; USD 370 in North America to institutions; GBP 260 rest of world to institutions (effective 2004). adv. bk.rev.; software rev. abstr.; bibl.; charts; stat. 96 p./no. 2 cols./p.; back issues avail.; reprint service avail. from PSC. **Document type:** *Journal, Academic/Scholarly.* **Description:** Publishes rigorous papers on practical matters that allow marketers to measure and target their prospective and existing customers more effectively and efficiently.
Related titles: Online - full content ed.: ISSN 1479-1862. 2000; Online - full text ed.: (from EBSCO Publishing, Gale Group, IngentaConnect, O C L C Online Computer Library Center, Inc., ProQuest Information & Learning, Swets Information Services).
Indexed: ABIn, Emerald.
—BLDSC (5068.185000), IE, Infotrieve, ingenta. **CCC.**
Published by: Palgrave Macmillan Ltd. (Subsidiary of: Macmillan Publishers Ltd.), Houndmills, Basingstoke, Hants RG21 6XS, United Kingdom. TEL 44-1256-329242, FAX 44-1256-810526, journal-info@palgrave.com, http://www.palgrave-journals.com/. Ed. Jonathan Reynolds. Circ: 1,000 (paid).

338 340 DEU ISSN 0931-6000
➤ **DAS JURISTISCHE BUERO.** Text in German. 1956. m. EUR 178.50; EUR 15.90 newsstand/cover (effective 2005). adv. **Document type:** *Journal, Academic/Scholarly.*
Published by: Hermann Luchterhand Verlag GmbH (Subsidiary of: Wolters Kluwer Deutschland GmbH), Heddesdorfer Str 31, Neuwied, 56564, Germany. TEL 49-2631-8012222, FAX 49-2631-8012223, info@luchterhand.de, http://www.luchterhand.de. Adv. contact Margret Sock-Freiberg. B&W page EUR 970, color page EUR 2,035. Circ: 2,900 (paid and controlled).

650 AUT ISSN 0022-9253
KASTNER & OEHLER FIRMEN ZEITUNG. Text in German. 1951. q. free. bk.rev. charts; illus.
Published by: Kastner und Oehler, Sackstrasse 7-13, Graz, St 8012, Austria. Ed. Martin Kastner. Circ: 3,500.

KELLY'S INDUSTRIAL PAGES. see *BUSINESS AND ECONOMICS—Trade And Industrial Directories*

THE KENTUCKY MANUFACTURER. see *BUSINESS AND ECONOMICS*

670.29 KEN
KENYA ASSOCIATION OF MANUFACTURERS. MEMBERS LIST AND INTERNATIONAL STANDARD INDUSTRIAL CLASSIFICATION. Text in English. 1959. biennial. USD 50. adv. **Document type:** *Directory, Trade.* **Description:** Contains contact information and export markets for members and information about the association as well as an overview of the Kenyan manufacturing sector, agencies that assist manufacturing and export enterprises in Kenya, trends of Kenyan exports from 1963, the top ten sources of Kenyan imports and the top ten export markets for Kenyan goods.
Formerly: Kenya Association of Manufacturers. Industrial Index and Members List
Published by: Kenya Association of Manufacturers, PO Box 30225, Nairobi, Kenya. kam@users.africaonline.co.ke. Circ: 500.

KENYA. CENTRAL BUREAU OF STATISTICS. DEVELOPMENT ESTIMATES. see *BUSINESS AND ECONOMICS—Abstracting, Bibliographies, Statistics*

KENYA. CENTRAL BUREAU OF STATISTICS. ESTIMATES OF RECURRENT EXPENDITURES. see *BUSINESS AND ECONOMICS—Abstracting, Bibliographies, Statistics*

KENYA. CENTRAL BUREAU OF STATISTICS. ESTIMATES OF REVENUE EXPENDITURES. see *BUSINESS AND ECONOMICS—Abstracting, Bibliographies, Statistics*

KENYA. CENTRAL BUREAU OF STATISTICS. SURVEYS OF INDUSTRIAL PRODUCTION. see *BUSINESS AND ECONOMICS—Abstracting, Bibliographies, Statistics*

338 IND ISSN 0047-3359
KERALA INDUSTRY; journal of industry & trade. Text in English. 1956. m. INR 50. adv. bk.rev. abstr.; bibl.; charts; illus.; stat.; tr.lit. reprint service avail. from PQC. **Document type:** *Trade.*
Related titles: Microform ed.: (from PQC).
Published by: Department of Industries and Commerce, P O Box 108, Trivandrum, Kerala 695 001, India. nicker1!jaitha@ren.nic.in, dictvm@sanchar.net.in, http://www.keralaindustry.org. Ed. R Rengaraja Iyengar. Circ: 1,500.

338 GBR
THE KEY NOTE GUIDE TO TELEWORKING. Text in English. irreg. GBP 265 (effective 1999). **Document type:** *Trade.*
Published by: Key Note Ltd., Field House, 72 Oldfield Rd, Hampton, Mddx TW12 2HQ, United Kingdom. TEL 44-20-8481-8750, FAX 44-20-8783-0049, info@keynote.co.uk, http://www.keynote.co.uk.

338 GBR
KEY NOTE MARKET ASSESSMENT. BATHROOMS & SHOWERS. Variant title: Bathrooms & Showers Market Assessment. Text in English. 1995. irreg., latest 2000, May. GBP 730 per issue (effective 2002). **Document type:** *Journal, Trade.* **Description:** Provides an overview of a specific UK market segment and includes executive summary, market definition, market size, industry background, competitor analysis, current issues, forecasts, company profiles, and more.
Former titles: M A P S Strategic Market Report. Bathrooms and Showers (1368-3705); (until 1996): M A P S Strategic Market Report. Bathrooms (1358-9024)
Published by: Key Note Ltd., Field House, 72 Oldfield Rd, Hampton, Mddx TW12 2HQ, United Kingdom. TEL 44-20-8481-8750, FAX 44-20-8783-0049, info@keynote.co.uk, http://www.keynote.co.uk.

338 GBR
KEY NOTE MARKET ASSESSMENT. BEDS, BEDROOMS & UPHOLSTERED FURNITURE. Variant title: Beds, Bedrooms & Upholstered Furniture Market Assessment. Text in English. 2000. irreg., latest 2000, Aug. GBP 730 per issue (effective 2002). mkt.; stat. **Document type:** *Trade.* **Description:** Provides an in-depth strategic analysis across a broad range of industries and contains an examination on the scope, dynamics and shape of key UK markets in the consumer, financial, lifestyle and business to business sectors.
Published by: Key Note Ltd., Field House, 72 Oldfield Rd, Hampton, Mddx TW12 2HQ, United Kingdom. TEL 44-20-8481-8750, FAX 44-20-8783-0049, info@keynote.co.uk, http://www.keynote.co.uk.

KEY NOTE MARKET ASSESSMENT. BOOK RETAILING ON THE INTERNET. see *PUBLISHING AND BOOK TRADE*

KEY NOTE MARKET ASSESSMENT. BOTTLED WATER. see *BEVERAGES*

KEY NOTE MARKET ASSESSMENT. BRIDALWEAR. see *CLOTHING TRADE*

KEY NOTE MARKET ASSESSMENT. BUSINESS TRAVEL. see *TRAVEL AND TOURISM*

KEY NOTE MARKET ASSESSMENT. CALL CENTRES. see *COMMUNICATIONS—Telephone And Telegraph*

KEY NOTE MARKET ASSESSMENT. CHARITY FUNDING. see *SOCIAL SERVICES AND WELFARE*

KEY NOTE MARKET ASSESSMENT. CHILDCARE. see *CHILDREN AND YOUTH—About*

KEY NOTE MARKET ASSESSMENT. COFFEE AND SANDWICH SHOPS. see *HOTELS AND RESTAURANTS*

KEY NOTE MARKET ASSESSMENT. COMMERCIAL DYNAMICS IN FINANCIAL SERVICES. see *BUSINESS AND ECONOMICS—Banking And Finance*

KEY NOTE MARKET ASSESSMENT. CONTRACEPTIVES. see *BIRTH CONTROL*

KEY NOTE MARKET ASSESSMENT. CUSTOMER MAGAZINES & CONTRACT PUBLISHING. see *PUBLISHING AND BOOK TRADE*

330 338 GBR
KEY NOTE MARKET ASSESSMENT. CUSTOMER RELATIONSHIP MANAGEMENT. Text in English. 2002. irreg., latest 2002, Jan. GBP 730 per issue (effective 2002). **Description:** Provides an in-depth strategic analysis across a broad range of industries and contains an examination on the scope, dynamics and shape of key UK markets in the consumer, financial, lifestyle and business to business sectors.
Published by: Key Note Ltd., Field House, 72 Oldfield Rd, Hampton, Mddx TW12 2HQ, United Kingdom. TEL 44-20-8481-8750, FAX 44-20-8783-0049, info@keynote.co.uk, http://www.keynote.co.uk. Ed. Simon Taylor.

KEY NOTE MARKET ASSESSMENT. DIET & FAT-FREE FOODS. see *FOOD AND FOOD INDUSTRIES*

KEY NOTE MARKET ASSESSMENT. DIRECT INSURANCE. see *INSURANCE*

KEY NOTE MARKET ASSESSMENT. DIRECT MORTGAGES. see *BUSINESS AND ECONOMICS—Banking And Finance*

B

KEY NOTE MARKET ASSESSMENT. DOMESTIC TELECOMMUNICATIONS. see *COMMUNICATIONS— Telephone And Telegraph*

KEY NOTE MARKET ASSESSMENT. ELECTRONIC BANKING. see *BUSINESS AND ECONOMICS—Banking And Finance*

KEY NOTE MARKET ASSESSMENT. FINANCIAL SERVICES MARKETING TO A BS. see *BUSINESS AND ECONOMICS—Banking And Finance*

KEY NOTE MARKET ASSESSMENT. FINANCIAL SERVICES MARKETING TO C1C2DE. see *BUSINESS AND ECONOMICS—Banking And Finance*

KEY NOTE MARKET ASSESSMENT. FUNCTIONAL FOODS. see *FOOD AND FOOD INDUSTRIES*

KEY NOTE MARKET ASSESSMENT. GENERAL INSURANCE. see *INSURANCE*

KEY NOTE MARKET ASSESSMENT. GLOBAL TIMBER. see *FORESTS AND FORESTRY—Lumber And Wood*

KEY NOTE MARKET ASSESSMENT. INDEPENDENT FINANCIAL ADVISORS. see *BUSINESS AND ECONOMICS—Banking And Finance*

KEY NOTE MARKET ASSESSMENT. NEW MEDIA MARKETING. see *COMMUNICATIONS*

KEY NOTE MARKET ASSESSMENT. SUPERMARKET SERVICES. see *FOOD AND FOOD INDUSTRIES—Grocery Trade*

621.822   GBR
KEY NOTE MARKET REPORT: BEARINGS. Text in English. 2001. irreg., latest 2001, July. GBP 340 per issue (effective 2002). mkt.; stat. **Document type:** *Trade.* **Description:** Provides an overview of a specific UK market segment and includes executive summary, market definition, market size, industry background, competitor analysis, current issues, forecasts, company profiles, and more. **Published by:** Key Note Ltd., Field House, 72 Oldfield Rd, Hampton, Mddx TW12 2HQ, United Kingdom. TEL 44-20-8481-8750, FAX 44-20-8783-0049, info@keynote.co.uk, http://www.keynote.co.uk. Ed. Dominic Fenn.

373 306.4   GBR   ISSN 1360-4414
KEY NOTE MARKET REPORT: BETTING & GAMING. Variant title: Betting & Gaming. Betting & Gaming Market Report. Text in English. 1987. irreg., latest 2001, Oct. GBP 340 per issue (effective 2002). **Document type:** *Trade.* **Description:** Provides an overview of a specific UK market segment and includes executive summary, market definition, market size, industry background, competitor analysis, current issues, forecasts, company profiles, and more. **Formerly** (until 1995): Key Note Report: Betting and Gaming **Related titles:** CD-ROM ed.; Online - full text ed. **Published by:** Key Note Ltd., Field House, 72 Oldfield Rd, Hampton, Mddx TW12 2HQ, United Kingdom. TEL 44-20-8481-8750, FAX 44-20-8783-0049, info@keynote.co.uk, http://www.keynote.co.uk. Ed. Dominic Fenn.

KEY NOTE MARKET REPORT: BOOK PUBLISHING. see *PUBLISHING AND BOOK TRADE*

KEY NOTE MARKET REPORT: BOOKSELLING. see *PUBLISHING AND BOOK TRADE*

KEY NOTE MARKET REPORT: BREAKFAST CEREALS. see *FOOD AND FOOD INDUSTRIES*

KEY NOTE MARKET REPORT: BREWERIES & THE BEER MARKET. see *BEVERAGES*

KEY NOTE MARKET REPORT: BRICKS & TILES. see *BUILDING AND CONSTRUCTION*

KEY NOTE MARKET REPORT: BUILDING CONTRACTING. see *BUILDING AND CONSTRUCTION*

KEY NOTE MARKET REPORT: BUILDING MATERIALS. see *BUILDING AND CONSTRUCTION*

KEY NOTE MARKET REPORT: BUILDING SOCIETIES. see *BUILDING AND CONSTRUCTION*

KEY NOTE MARKET REPORT: BUSINESS PRESS. see *JOURNALISM*

338 780.384   GBR   ISSN 1460-7492
KEY NOTE MARKET REPORT: C DS & TAPES. Variant title: C Ds & Tapes Market Report. Text in English. 1997. irreg. (2nd Ed.), latest 1999, Feb. GBP 340 per issue (effective 2002). **Document type:** *Trade.* **Description:** Provides an overview of a specific UK market segment and includes executive summary, market definition, market size, industry background, competitor analysis, current issues, forecasts, company profiles, and more.

Published by: Key Note Ltd., Field House, 72 Oldfield Rd, Hampton, Mddx TW12 2HQ, United Kingdom. TEL 44-20-8481-8750, FAX 44-20-8783-0049, info@keynote.co.uk, http://www.keynote.co.uk. Ed. Dominic Fenn.

338   GBR
KEY NOTE MARKET REPORT: C T NS. (Confectioners, Tobacconists & Newsagents) Variant title: C T Ns Market Report. Confectioners, Tobacconists & Newsagents Market Report. Text in English. irreg., latest 2000, May. GBP 340 per issue (effective 2002). **Document type:** *Trade.* **Description:** Provides an overview of a specific UK market segment and includes executive summary, market definition, market size, industry background, competitor analysis, current issues, forecasts, company profiles, and more. **Formerly:** Key Note Report: C T Ns (0957-7319) **Related titles:** CD-ROM ed.; Online - full text ed. **Published by:** Key Note Ltd., Field House, 72 Oldfield Rd, Hampton, Mddx TW12 2HQ, United Kingdom. TEL 44-20-8481-8750, FAX 44-20-8783-0049, info@keynote.co.uk, http://www.keynote.co.uk. Ed. Jenny Baxter.

KEY NOTE MARKET REPORT: CABLE & SATELLITE T V. see *COMMUNICATIONS—Television And Cable*

KEY NOTE MARKET REPORT: CABLING & WIRING. see *COMMUNICATIONS—Television And Cable*

KEY NOTE MARKET REPORT: CAMERAS & CAMCORDERS. see *PHOTOGRAPHY*

KEY NOTE MARKET REPORT: CAR DEALERS. see *TRANSPORTATION—Automobiles*

KEY NOTE MARKET REPORT: CARPETS & FLOORCOVERINGS. see *INTERIOR DESIGN AND DECORATION—Furniture And House Furnishings*

KEY NOTE MARKET REPORT: CASH & CARRY OUTLETS. see *BUSINESS AND ECONOMICS—Marketing And Purchasing*

KEY NOTE MARKET REPORT: CATERING EQUIPMENT. see *HOTELS AND RESTAURANTS*

KEY NOTE MARKET REPORT: CHARITIES. see *SOCIAL SERVICES AND WELFARE*

KEY NOTE MARKET REPORT: CHEMICAL INDUSTRY. see *ENGINEERING—Chemical Engineering*

KEY NOTE MARKET REPORT: CHILDRENSWEAR. see *CLOTHING TRADE*

KEY NOTE MARKET REPORT: CHINA & EARTHENWARE. see *CERAMICS, GLASS AND POTTERY*

KEY NOTE MARKET REPORT: CIDER. see *BEVERAGES*

338 791.43 792   GBR   ISSN 1472-2011
KEY NOTE MARKET REPORT: CINEMAS & THEATRES. Variant title: Cinemas & Theatres Market Report. Text in English. irreg., latest 2001, Dec. GBP 340 per issue (effective 2002). **Document type:** *Trade.* **Description:** Provides an overview of the UK cinema and theater markets, including industry structure, market size and trends, developments, prospects, and major company profiles. **Formerly** (until 2000): Key Note Report: Cinemas & Theatres (0954-514X) **Published by:** Key Note Ltd., Field House, 72 Oldfield Rd, Hampton, Mddx TW12 2HQ, United Kingdom. TEL 44-20-8481-8750, FAX 44-20-8783-0049, info@keynote.co.uk, http://www.keynote.co.uk. Ed. Emily Pattullo.

KEY NOTE MARKET REPORT: CIVIL ENGINEERING. see *ENGINEERING—Civil Engineering*

KEY NOTE MARKET REPORT: CLOSED CIRCUIT T V. see *COMMUNICATIONS—Television And Cable*

KEY NOTE MARKET REPORT: CLOTHING MANUFACTURING. see *CLOTHING TRADE*

KEY NOTE MARKET REPORT: CLOTHING RETAILING. see *CLOTHING TRADE*

KEY NOTE MARKET REPORT: COMMERCIAL RADIO. see *COMMUNICATIONS—Radio*

KEY NOTE MARKET REPORT: COMMERCIAL T V. see *COMMUNICATIONS—Television And Cable*

KEY NOTE MARKET REPORT: COMMERCIAL VEHICLES. see *TRANSPORTATION—Automobiles*

KEY NOTE MARKET REPORT: COMPUTER HARDWARE. see *COMPUTERS—Hardware*

KEY NOTE MARKET REPORT: COMPUTER SERVICES. see *COMPUTERS—Computer Industry*

KEY NOTE MARKET REPORT: COMPUTER SOFTWARE. see *COMPUTERS—Software*

KEY NOTE MARKET REPORT: CONSUMER INTERNET USAGE. see *COMPUTERS—Internet*

KEY NOTE MARKET REPORT: CONSUMER MAGAZINES. see *PUBLISHING AND BOOK TRADE*

KEY NOTE MARKET REPORT: CONTRACT CATERING. see *HOTELS AND RESTAURANTS*

KEY NOTE MARKET REPORT: CONTRACT CLEANING. see *CLEANING AND DYEING*

KEY NOTE MARKET REPORT: CONVENIENCE RETAILING. see *BUSINESS AND ECONOMICS—Marketing And Purchasing*

KEY NOTE MARKET REPORT: COURIER & EXPRESS SERVICES. see *COMMUNICATIONS—Postal Affairs*

KEY NOTE MARKET REPORT: CREDIT & OTHER FINANCE CARDS. see *BUSINESS AND ECONOMICS—Banking And Finance*

338   GBR
KEY NOTE MARKET REPORT: CUTLERY. Variant title: Cutlery. Text in English. irreg., latest vol.8, 1991. GBP 265 (effective 1999). **Document type:** *Trade.* **Published by:** Key Note Ltd., Field House, 72 Oldfield Rd, Hampton, Mddx TW12 2HQ, United Kingdom. TEL 44-20-8481-8750, FAX 44-20-8783-0049, info@keynote.co.uk, http://www.keynote.co.uk.

KEY NOTE MARKET REPORT: DEFENCE EQUIPMENT. see *MILITARY*

KEY NOTE MARKET REPORT: DISPOSABLE PAPER PRODUCTS. see *PAPER AND PULP*

KEY NOTE MARKET REPORT: DOMESTIC HEATING. see *HEATING, PLUMBING AND REFRIGERATION*

KEY NOTE MARKET REPORT: DRY CLEANING & LAUNDRY SERVICES. see *CLEANING AND DYEING*

KEY NOTE MARKET REPORT: ELECTRICAL CONTRACTING. see *ENGINEERING—Electrical Engineering*

KEY NOTE MARKET REPORT: ELECTRONIC COMPONENT MANUFACTURING. see *ELECTRONICS*

KEY NOTE MARKET REPORT: EMPLOYMENT AGENCIES. see *BUSINESS AND ECONOMICS—Personnel Management*

KEY NOTE MARKET REPORT: FINANCE HOUSES. see *BUSINESS AND ECONOMICS—Banking And Finance*

KEY NOTE MARKET REPORT: FOOTBALL CLUBS & FINANCE. see *SPORTS AND GAMES—Ball Games*

KEY NOTE MARKET REPORT: FRANCHISING. see *BUSINESS AND ECONOMICS—Small Business*

KEY NOTE MARKET REPORT: FREIGHT FORWARDING. see *TRANSPORTATION*

KEY NOTE MARKET REPORT: HEATING, VENTILATING & AIR CONDITIONING. see *HEATING, PLUMBING AND REFRIGERATION*

KEY NOTE MARKET REPORT: HEAVY INDUSTRIAL CLEANING. see *CLEANING AND DYEING*

KEY NOTE MARKET REPORT: MANAGEMENT CONSULTANTS. see *BUSINESS AND ECONOMICS— Management*

KEY NOTE MARKET REPORT: OPHTHALMIC GOODS & SERVICES. see *MEDICAL SCIENCES—Ophthalmology And Optometry*

338   GBR   ISSN 1473-4087
KEY NOTE MARKET REPORT: SLIMMING MARKET. Text in English. irreg., latest 2000, Nov. GBP 340 per issue (effective 2002). **Document type:** *Monographic series.* **Description:** Provides an overview of a specific UK market segment and includes executive summary, market definition, market size, industry background, competitor analysis, current issues, forecasts, company profiles, and more. **Former titles** (until 2000): Key Note Report: Slimming Market (1352-7185); (until 1989): Key Note Report: Slimming Products (0265-7953) **Related titles:** CD-ROM ed.; Online - full text ed. **Published by:** Key Note Ltd., Field House, 72 Oldfield Rd, Hampton, Mddx TW12 2HQ, United Kingdom. TEL 44-20-8481-8750, FAX 44-20-8783-0049, info@keynote.co.uk, http://www.keynote.co.uk.

338.0029 GBR
KEY NOTE MARKET REVIEW: BUSINESS INFORMATION IN THE U K. Variant title: Business Information in the U K. Text in English. irreg., latest 1998, Aug. GBP 565 per issue (effective 2002). **Document type:** *Trade.* **Description:** Provides an overview of the UK business information sector, including industry structure, market size and trends, developments, prospects, and major company profiles.
Published by: Key Note Ltd., Field House, 72 Oldfield Rd, Hampton, Mddx TW12 2HQ, United Kingdom. TEL 44-20-8481-8750, FAX 44-20-8783-0049, info@keynote.co.uk, http://www.keynote.co.uk. Ed. Phillippa Smith.

338 GBR
KEY NOTE MARKET REVIEW: CONTRACTED-OUT SERVICES. Text in English. 2001. irreg., latest 2001, Nov. GBP 565 per issue (effective 2002). **Description:** Provides an overview of the UK contracted-out services market, including industry structure, market size and trends, developments, prospects, and major company profiles.
Published by: Key Note Ltd., Field House, 72 Oldfield Rd, Hampton, Mddx TW12 2HQ, United Kingdom. TEL 44-20-8481-8750, FAX 44-20-8783-0049, info@keynote.co.uk, http://www.keynote.co.uk. Ed. Dominic Fenn.

KEY NOTE MARKET REVIEW: CORPORATE SERVICES IN THE U K. see *BUSINESS AND ECONOMICS—Trade And Industrial Directories*

338 GBR
KEY NOTE MARKET REVIEW: PROCESS PLANT INDUSTRY. Text in English. 199?. irreg., latest 2000, Dec. GBP 565 per issue (effective 2002). **Document type:** *Trade.* **Description:** Designed to keep you up to date with the developments and opportunities across entire industry sectors. They provide a comprehensive analysis of the industry by drawing together key related market segments under one cover.
Former titles (until 2000): Key Note Market Report: Process Plant (1462-4192); (until 1998): Key Note Report: Process Plant (1352-7118)
Related titles: CD-ROM ed.; Online - full text ed.
Published by: Key Note Ltd., Field House, 72 Oldfield Rd, Hampton, Mddx TW12 2HQ, United Kingdom. TEL 44-20-8481-8750, FAX 44-20-8783-0049, info@keynote.co.uk, http://www.keynote.co.uk. Ed. Emma Wiggin.

KEY NOTE MARKET REVIEW: THE ENERGY INDUSTRY. see *ENERGY*

KEY NOTE MARKET REVIEW: U K CATERING MARKET. see *HOTELS AND RESTAURANTS*

KEY NOTE MARKET REVIEW: U K CLOTHING & FOOTWEAR. see *CLOTHING TRADE*

KEY NOTE MARKET REVIEW: U K COMPUTER MARKET. see *COMPUTERS—Computer Industry*

KEY NOTE MARKET REVIEW: U K CONSTRUCTION INDUSTRY. see *BUILDING AND CONSTRUCTION*

KEY NOTE MARKET REVIEW: U K DEFENCE INDUSTRY. see *MILITARY*

338 GBR
KEY NOTE MARKET REVIEW: U K DISTRIBUTION. Text in English. irreg., latest 2001, Mar. GBP 565 per issue (effective 2002). **Document type:** *Trade.*
Related titles: CD-ROM ed.; Online - full text ed.
Published by: Key Note Ltd., Field House, 72 Oldfield Rd, Hampton, Mddx TW12 2HQ, United Kingdom. TEL 44-20-8481-8750, FAX 44-20-8783-0049, info@keynote.co.uk, http://www.keynote.co.uk. Ed. Dominic Fenn.

KEY NOTE MARKET REVIEW: U K HEALTHCARE. see *MEDICAL SCIENCES*

KEY NOTE PLUS MARKET REPORT. BISCUITS & CAKES. see *FOOD AND FOOD INDUSTRIES—Bakers And Confectioners*

KEY NOTE PLUS MARKET REPORT. CANNED FOODS. see *FOOD AND FOOD INDUSTRIES*

KEY NOTE PLUS MARKET REPORT. CHILLED FOODS. see *FOOD AND FOOD INDUSTRIES*

KEY NOTE PLUS MARKET REPORT. CIGARETTES & TOBACCO. see *TOBACCO*

KEY NOTE PLUS MARKET REPORT. CONFECTIONARY. see *FOOD AND FOOD INDUSTRIES—Bakers And Confectioners*

KEY NOTE PLUS MARKET REPORT. ETHNIC FOODS. see *FOOD AND FOOD INDUSTRIES*

KEY NOTE PLUS MARKET REPORT. HOTELS. see *HOTELS AND RESTAURANTS*

KEY NOTE PLUS MARKET REPORT. WHITE SPIRITS AND SPECIALITY DRINKS. see *BEVERAGES*

KHADI GRAMODYOG; journal of rural economy. see *AGRICULTURE—Agricultural Economics*

338 NOR
KOEFFBLADET - I N. Text in Norwegian. m. (10/yr.). NOK 120. adv.
Published by: (Kjoepmennenes Oekonomiske Fellesforetagende A-L), K Oe F F-Gruppen A-S, Jappe Ippesvei 3, Kristiansund N, 6500, Norway. FAX 073-70950. Ed. Per Gunnar Aakvik. Circ: 11,117.

338.12 SWE ISSN 1650-9951
KONJUNKTURBAROMETERN. MAANAD. Variant title: Konjunkturbarometern.Kvartal. Text in Swedish. 2002. m. SEK 1,743; SEK 182 per issue (effective 2005). charts; stat. back issues avail. **Document type:** *Magazine, Consumer.* **Description:** Consists of a survey of 1900 business enterprizes in Sweden.
Formed by the merger of (1994-2002): Konjunkturbarometer. Tjaenstenaeringar (1402-8786); (1996-2002): Maanardsbarometer (1403-7122); (1994-2002): Konjunkturbarometern. Tillverkningsindustri och Byggindustri (1402-8778); Which was formerly (1954-1994): Konjunkturbarometern (0345-6390)
Related titles: Online - full text ed.
Published by: Konjunkturinstitutet/National Institute of Economic Research, Kungsgatan 12-14, PO Box 3116, Stockholm, 10362, Sweden. TEL 46-8-4535900, FAX 46-8-4535980, ki@konj.se, http://www.konj.se. Ed. Roger Knudsen TEL 46-8-4535906.

KONJUNKTUREN. see *BUSINESS AND ECONOMICS—Economic Situation And Conditions*

338 SWE ISSN 1650-996X
KONJUNKTURINSTITUTET. SPECIALSTUDIER. Text in Swedish; Text occasionally in English. 1990. irreg., latest vol.7, 2005. free (effective 2005). back issues avail. **Document type:** *Monographic series, Academic/Scholarly.*
Former titles (until 2002): Konjunkturinstitutet. K I Dokument (1403-8331); (until 1996): Konjunkturinstitutet. Arbetspapper (1101-802X)
Published by: Konjunkturinstitutet/National Institute of Economic Research, Kungsgatan 12-14, PO Box 3116, Stockholm, 10362, Sweden. TEL 46-8-4535900, FAX 46-8-4535980, ki@konj.se, http://www.konj.se.

338 SWE ISSN 0023-3463
HC371
KONJUNKTURLAEGET. Text in Swedish. 1937. q. SEK 937; SEK 932 per issue (effective 2005). charts; stat. **Document type:** *Journal, Academic/Scholarly.* **Description:** Forecasts and analysis of Swedish and international economy.
Formerly (until 1960): Meddelanden fraan Konjunkturinstitutet. Serie A
Related titles: Online - full text ed.; ◆ English ed.: The Swedish Economy. ISSN 0039-7296.
Published by: Konjunkturinstitutet/National Institute of Economic Research, Kungsgatan 12-14, PO Box 3116, Stockholm, 10362, Sweden. TEL 46-8-4535900, FAX 46-8-4535980, ki@konj.se, http://www.konj.se. Ed. Mats Dillon TEL 46-8-4535966.

658.83 SCG ISSN 0023-3471
KONJUNKTURNI BAROMETAR✶. Text in Serbo-Croatian. 1962. m. YUN 600. stat.
Published by: Zavod za Trzisna Istrazivanja, Belgrade Stock Exchange, Omladinskih Brigada 1, P.O. Box 214, Belgrade, 11070. Ed. Julije Drasinover. Circ: (controlled).

KOREA (REPUBLIC). NATIONAL STATISTICAL OFFICE. ANNUAL REPORT ON MONTHLY INDUSTRIAL PRODUCTION STATISTICS. see *BUSINESS AND ECONOMICS—Abstracting, Bibliographies, Statistics*

KOTHARI'S INDUSTRIAL DIRECTORY OF INDIA. see *BUSINESS AND ECONOMICS—Trade And Industrial Directories*

338 JPN
KYUSHU KOGYO GIJUTSU SHIKENJO NENPO/GOVERNMENT INDUSTRIAL RESEARCH INSTITUTE, KYUSHU. ANNUAL REPORT. Text in Japanese. a. abstr.
Published by: Kyushu Kogyo Gijutsu Shikenjo/Government Industrial Research Institute, Kyushu, 807-1 Shuku-Machi-Kyushu, Tosu-shi, Saga-ken 841-0000, Japan.

338 DEU ISSN 1611-8243
L G A IMPULSE. Text in German. 1874. q. bk.rev. index. **Document type:** *Magazine, Consumer.* **Description:** Contains testing reports and new technology information in all areas of building and construction, fire prevention, engineering, and environmental studies.
Former titles (until 2002): L G A Rundschau (0023-6268); (until 1969): B L G A Rundschau (0408-1102)
Published by: Landesgewerbeanstalt Bayern, Tillystr 2, Nuernberg, 90431, Germany. TEL 49-911-65550, FAX 49-911-6554235, lga@lga.de, http://www.lga.de. Eds. Rainer Weiskirchen, Susanne Morgenroth. Circ: 3,000.

338 JPN ISSN 0287-2404
L T C B RESEARCH; review of Japanese industry. Text in English. 1970. q. free. charts; stat.
Formerly: Chogin Research (0009-4951)
Indexed: KES, PAIS, RASB.
Published by: Long Term Credit Bank of Japan Ltd., Economics Division, 2-4 Ote-Machi 1-chome, Chiyoda-ku, Tokyo, 100-0004, Japan. Ed. Sawako Hagtwara.

LANDSCAPE MANAGEMENT; commercial magazine for lawn, landscape and grounds managers. see *GARDENING AND HORTICULTURE*

LARGE AND MEDIUM SCALE MANUFACTURING AND ELECTRICITY INDUSTRY SURVEY. see *BUSINESS AND ECONOMICS—Abstracting, Bibliographies, Statistics*

368.5 USA ISSN 0733-513X
KF1296.A15
LEADER'S PRODUCT LIABILITY LAW AND STRATEGY. Text in English. 1982. m. looseleaf. USD 299 (effective 2004). index. back issues avail. **Document type:** *Newsletter.* **Description:** Publishes tips and strategies for product liability practitioners, with reports on trends, court decisions, administrative rulings, legislative proposals, and news of settlements.
Formerly (until 1988): Leader's Product Liability Newsletter
Related titles: Online - full text ed.
—CCC.
Published by: A L M, 345 Park Ave., S, New York, NY 10010. TEL 212-313-9000, 800-888-8300, FAX 212-481-8255, dwenger@amlaw.com, apress@amlaw.com, http://www.alm.com. Ed. Stephanie McEvily. Pub. S Wise.

LEAN MANUFACTURING ADVISOR; strategies and tactics for implementing T P M and lean production. see *BUSINESS AND ECONOMICS—Management*

LEBENSMITTEL MARKT. see *FOOD AND FOOD INDUSTRIES*

LEHKA PROMYSLOVIST'; naukovo-vyrobnychyi zhurnal. see *TEXTILE INDUSTRIES AND FABRICS*

330 FRA ISSN 0399-8606
LA LETTRE DE L'EXPANSION. Text in French. 1970. w. EUR 807.50 domestic; EUR 862.50 in the European Union; EUR 872.50 elsewhere (effective 2005). charts.
Published by: Groupe Express-Expansion (Subsidiary of: Socpresse), 17 rue de l'Arrivee, Paris Cede, 75733, France. TEL 33-1-53911111, http://www.lexpansion.com, http://www.groupe-expansion.com.

338 380.5 LBR
LIBERIA. MINISTRY OF COMMERCE, INDUSTRY AND TRANSPORTATION. ANNUAL REPORT✶. Text in English. a.
Published by: Ministry of Commerce Industry and Transportation, PO Box 9041, Monrovia, Liberia.

338 LBR
LIBERIA. MINISTRY OF PLANNING AND ECONOMIC AFFAIRS. ANNUAL REPORT TO THE PEOPLE'S REDEMPTION COUNCIL✶. Text in English. 1965. a. USD 5.
Formerly: Liberia. Ministry of Planning and Economic Affairs. Annual Report to the Session of the Legislature of the Republic of Liberia (0459-2182); Which supersedes: Liberia. Department of Planning and Economic Affairs. Annual Report
Published by: Ministry of Planning and Economic Affairs, PO Box 9016, Monrovia, Liberia.

LIFE SCIENCE TODAY. see *PHARMACY AND PHARMACOLOGY*

LIGHTING EQUIPMENT NEWS. see *INTERIOR DESIGN AND DECORATION—Furniture And House Furnishings*

338 IND ISSN 0076-0269
LOCATIONS OF INDUSTRIES IN GUJARAT STATE. Text in English. 1956. irreg. INR 7.30.
Published by: Bureau of Economics and Statistics, Sector No. 18, Gandhinagar, Gujarat, India.

338 NOR ISSN 1502-198X
LOENNSOMHETSUNDERSOEKELSER FOR VANLIG GODT DREVNE OG VEL UTSTYRTE FISKEFARTOEY I STOERRELSEN 8 METER STOERSTE LENGDE OG OVER, SOM BRUKES TIL FISKE AARET RUNDT. Variant title: Lonnsomhetsundersokelser for Vanlig Godt Drevne og vel Utstyrte Fartoy Itorrelsen 8 Meter Storste Lengde og Over, som Brukes til Fiske Aret Rundt. Text in Norwegian. 1970. a.
Former titles (until 1998): Loennsomhetsundersoekelser for Vanlig Godt Drevne og vel Utstyrte Fartoeyer paa 13 M 1.1 og over Som Brukes til Fiske Aaret Rundt (0801-504X); (until 1981): Loennsomhetsundersoekelser for Vanlig Godt Drevne og Vel Utstyrte Fartoeyer over 40 Fot, som Brukes til Fiske Aaret Rundt (0801-5031)
Indexed: ASFA, ESPM.
Published by: Budsjettnemnda for Fiskenaeringen, Fiskerideriktoratet, Postboks 185, Sentrum, Bergen, 5804, Norway. TEL 55-23-80-00, FAX 55-23-80-90, http://www.fiskeridir.no.

629 CZE ISSN 1211-0957
LOGISTIKA. Text in Czech. 1995. m. CZK 825; CZK 75 newsstand/cover (effective 2003). adv. **Document type:** *Magazine, Trade.*
Published by: Economia a.s., Dobrovskeho 25, Prague 7 7, 170 55, Czech Republic. TEL 420-2-33071111, FAX 420-2-33072003, logistika@economia.cz, economia@economia.cz, http://www.economia.cz. adv.: page CZK 48,000; trim 185 x 254.

LOOKOUT - FOODS. see *FOOD AND FOOD INDUSTRIES*

LUBRICANTS WORLD. see *PETROLEUM AND GAS*

LYS; miljoe-design-teknik. see *ENGINEERING—Electrical Engineering*

338 IND ISSN 0541-5357
HC431
M B I'S INDIAN INDUSTRIES ANNUAL. Text in English. 1963. a. INR 20.
Published by: Chary Publications Pvt Ltd, 311 Raikar Chambers, Govandi East, Mumbai, Maharashtra 400088, India.

338 USA
M E M A MARKET ANALYSIS; a bimonthly report on the vehicle parts industry. Text in English. 1976. bi-m. USD 250 (effective 1997). bk.rev. **Document type:** *Trade.*
Published by: Motor & Equipment Manufacturers Association, 10 Laboratory Dr, PO Box 13966, Research Triangle Park, NC 27709-3966. TEL 919-549-4800, FAX 919-549-4824, info@mema.org, http://www.Afmkt.com/ME.MA, http://www.mema.org/. Ed. F Hampshire. Circ: 750.

338 NLD ISSN 0024-8843
MAATSCHAPPIJBELANGEN. Text in Dutch. 1832. m. adv. bk.rev. bibl.; charts; illus.; stat.; tr.lit. index. back issues avail.
Indexed: ELLIS, ExcerpMed.
—IE, Infotrieve, KNAW.
Published by: Nederlandsche Maatschappij voor Nijverheid en Handel/Netherlands Society for Industry and Trade, PO Box 205, Haarlem, 2000 AE, Netherlands. TEL 31-23-5360624, FAX 31-23-5360122, info@nmnh.nl, http://www.nmnh.nl. Ed. E A Nieuwenhuijzen Kruseman. Circ: 10,500. **Dist. by:** Wyt Uitgeefgroep B.V., Postbus 6438, Rotterdam 3002 AK, Netherlands.

338 USA
▼ **MADE IN U.S.A.** Text in English. 2005. bi-m. USD 36 combined subscription print & online eds. (effective 2005). adv. **Document type:** *Magazine, Consumer.* **Description:** Covers American companies, workers and products.
Address: 255 NE 2nd Ave., Ste. 313, Delray Beach, FL 33444. TEL 561-279-8155, FAX 561-279-9588, http://www.madeinusamag.com/. Eds. Adam Reiser, Julie Reiser. Pub. Julie Reiser. adv.: B&W page USD 15,188, color page USD 18,750.

338 ESP ISSN 0210-0762
MAESTRIA INDUSTRIAL. Text in Spanish. 1963. m. adv. bk.rev. bibl.; charts.
Published by: Federacion de Asociaciones de Maestros Industriales de Espana/Federation of Industrial Managers' Associations of Spain, Lillo, 1-2o Acia 3, Madrid, 28041, Spain. TEL 34-91-2179659. Ed. Fidel Astudillo Jimenez. Circ: 5,000.

MAGAZINE RECYCLING BENELUX. see *ENVIRONMENTAL STUDIES—Waste Management*

338.0029 USA ISSN 1045-6317
HD9727.M2
MAINE MANUFACTURING DIRECTORY. Text in English. 1965. a. USD 65 (effective 2000). adv. **Document type:** *Directory.* **Description:** Lists manufacturers in Maine, organized alphabetically, geographically and by product.
Former titles (until 1985): Maine Marketing Directory (0145-9007); (until 1975): Directory of Maine Manufacturers
Published by: Tower Publishing Co., 588 Saco Rd, Standish, ME 04084-6239. TEL 207-642-5400, 800-969-8693, FAX 207-642-5463.

MALAYSIA. DEPARTMENT OF STATISTICS. ANNUAL STATISTICS OF MANUFACTURING INDUSTRIES, MALAYSIA - PART A/MALAYSIA. JABATAN PERANGKAAN. PERANGKAAN TAHUNAN INDUSTRI PEMBUSATAN, MALAYSIA - BAHAGIAN A. see *BUSINESS AND ECONOMICS—Abstracting, Bibliographies, Statistics*

MALAYSIA. DEPARTMENT OF STATISTICS. ANNUAL STATISTICS OF MANUFACTURING INDUSTRIES, MALAYSIA - PART B/MALAYSIA. JABATAN PERANGKAAN. PERANGKAAN TAHUNAN INDUSTRI PEMBUATAN, MALAYSIA - BAHAGIAN B. see *BUSINESS AND ECONOMICS—Abstracting, Bibliographies, Statistics*

MALAYSIA. DEPARTMENT OF STATISTICS. ANNUAL SURVEY OF MANUFACTURING INDUSTRIES, MALAYSIA/ MALAYSIA. JABATAN PERGANGKAAN. PENYIASATAN TAHUNAN INDUSTRI PEMBUATAN, MALAYSIA. see *BUSINESS AND ECONOMICS—Abstracting, Bibliographies, Statistics*

MALAYSIA. DEPARTMENT OF STATISTICS. INDEX OF INDUSTRIAL PRODUCTION, MALAYSIA/MALAYSIA. JABATAN PERANGKAAN. INDEKS PENGELUARAN PERIDUSTRIAN, MALAYSIA. see *BUSINESS AND ECONOMICS—Abstracting, Bibliographies, Statistics*

MALAYSIA. DEPARTMENT OF STATISTICS. INDUSTRIAL SURVEYS, MALAYSIA/MALAYSIA. JABATAN PERANGKAAN. PENYIASATAN - PENYIASATAN PERINDUSTRIAN, MALAYSIA. see *BUSINESS AND ECONOMICS—Abstracting, Bibliographies, Statistics*

MALAYSIA. DEPARTMENT OF STATISTICS. MONTHLY MANUFACTURING STATISTICS, MALAYSIA. see *BUSINESS AND ECONOMICS—Abstracting, Bibliographies, Statistics*

MALAYSIA. DEPARTMENT OF STATISTICS. MONTHLY RUBBER STATISTICS, MALAYSIA/MALAYSIA. JABATAN PERANGKAAN. PERANGKAAN GETAH BULANAN, MALAYSIA. see *RUBBER—Abstracting, Bibliographies, Statistics*

MANAGEMENT BRIEFING. see *METROLOGY AND STANDARDIZATION*

338 USA
▼ **MANAGING OFFSHORE**; strategy and tactics for global sourcing. Text in English. 2004. m. USD 495 (effective 2004). **Document type:** *Trade.* **Description:** Examines the sourcing of services across the entire spectrum of application development, application maintenance, infrastructure, business process outsourcing, and call/contact centers.
Media: Online - full content.
Published by: C M P Media LLC (Subsidiary of: United News & Media), 600 Community Dr, Manhasset, NY 11030. TEL 516-562-5000, FAX 516-733-8584, rweston@cmp.com, feedback@cmp.com, http://www.managingoffshore.com, http://www.cmp.com. Ed. Rusty Weston.

338 MEX ISSN 1405-1559
MANUFACTURA. Text in Spanish. 1994. m.?. USD 55 in US & Canada; USD 60 in Latin America; USD 64 elsewhere. **Document type:** *Consumer.* **Description:** Provides product news, industry news and in-depth features on plant operations, design and development, processing, and automation - instrumentation.
Related titles: Online - full text ed.: ISSN 1605-4776. 1997.
Published by: Grupo Editorial Expansion (Subsidiary of: Capital Cities - A B C, Inc.), SALAMANCA 35, Col Roma, Mexico City, DF 06700, Mexico. servicioaclientes@expansion.com.mx, http://www.manufacturaweb.com.

338 USA ISSN 1537-3606
THE MANUFACTURER; promoting best practices in manufacturing. Text in English. 2001 (Oct.). m. USD 59 (effective 2005). adv.
Published by: Conquest Business Media, Inc., 900 Cummings Ctr., Ste. 309-U, Beverly, MA 01915. TEL 978-299-1200, FAX 978-299-1201, http://www.themanufacturerus.com. Ed. Jill Rose.

338 USA
MANUFACTURER OF MICHIGAN. Text in English. m.
Related titles: Online - full text ed.
Published by: Industrial Marketing, Inc., PO Box 4310, Lexington, KY 40544-4310. TEL 800-264-3303.

338 USA ISSN 0191-7234
MANUFACTURERS' MART. Text in English. 1978. m. USD 12 to industries located out of New England; free to industries in New England (effective 2005). adv. bk.rev. 32 p./no. 4 cols./p.; back issues avail.; reprints avail. **Document type:** *Directory, Trade.* **Description:** Seeks to show plant managers how to more effectively run their plants.
Related titles: Online - full text ed.
Published by: Manufacturers Mart Publications, 16 High St, Westerly, RI 02891-1850. TEL 401-348-0797, FAX 401-348-0799, info@manufacturersmart.com, http://www.manufacturersmart.com/. Ed. Linda Smith. Adv. contact Jeane Caseley. Circ: 30,000 (controlled).

338 AUS ISSN 0025-2530
MANUFACTURERS' MONTHLY. Text in English. 1961. m. AUD 26.51 (effective 2001). adv. bk.rev. illus.; stat. **Document type:** *Trade.*
Related titles: Online - full text ed.: (from EBSCO Publishing, Gale Group, LexisNexis).
Indexed: ABIX.
Published by: Reed Business Information Pty Ltd (Subsidiary of: Reed Business Information International), Locked Bag 2999, Chatswood, NSW 2067, Australia. http://www.reedbusiness.com.au. Circ: 15,068.

338 USA ISSN 1529-7659
HD9721
MANUFACTURING & DISTRIBUTION U S A. Text in English. 2000. biennial, latest 2002. USD 395 (effective 2004).
Formed by the merger of (1989-2000): Manufacturing U S A (1044-7024); (1995-2000): Wholesale and Retail Trade U S A (1084-8622)
Published by: Gale Group (Subsidiary of: Thomson Corporation), 27500 Drake Rd, Farmington Hills, MI 48331-3535. TEL 800-877-4253, FAX 248-699-8035, gale.galeord@thomson.com, http://www.galegroup.com.

MANUFACTURING AND SERVICE OPERATIONS MANAGEMENT. see *BUSINESS AND ECONOMICS—Management*

338 USA
MANUFACTURING AND TECHNOLOGY NEWS. Text in English. 1994. bi-m. USD 395 domestic; USD 445 foreign (effective 2000). adv. bk.rev. abstr.; bibl.; illus. index. back issues avail. **Document type:** *Newsletter, Trade.* **Description:** Covers advanced manufacturing, trends, manufacturing research and development, and government policies affecting manufacturing.
Formerly: Manufacturing News (1078-2397)
Related titles: Online - full text ed.: (from Factiva, Florida Center for Library Automation, Gale Group).
—IDS. **CCC.**
Published by: Publishers & Producers, PO Box 36, Annandale, VA 22003. TEL 703-750-2664, FAX 703-750-0064, editor@manufacturingnews.com, mfgnews@erols.com, http://www.manufacturingnews.com. Ed., Pub. Richard McCormack. R&P, Adv. contact Anne Anderson.

338 USA ISSN 1554-3404
TS155.A1 CODEN: MASYES
MANUFACTURING BUSINESS TECHNOLOGY. Abbreviated title: M B T. Text in English. 1983. m. USD 85 domestic; USD 102 in Canada & Mexico; USD 305 elsewhere; USD 8 newsstand/cover domestic; USD 10 newsstand/cover foreign; free to qualified personnel (effective 2005). adv. bk.rev. illus. back issues avail.; reprints avail. **Document type:** *Magazine, Trade.* **Description:** Dedicated to information technologies with a primary focus on enterprise management and supply-chain software, computer hardware and data collection technologies.
Former titles (until 2005): M S I (1533-7758); (until 2001): Manufacturing Systems (0748-948X); (until 198?): Manufacturing Operations (0743-023X)
Related titles: Online - full text ed.: (from EBSCO Publishing, Gale Group, H.W. Wilson, LexisNexis, O C L C Online Computer Library Center, Inc., ProQuest Information & Learning).
Indexed: ABIn, AIA, AS&TI, B&I, BrCerAb, C&ISA, CADCAM, CerAb, CompLI, CorrAb, E&CAJ, EMA, ESPM, EngInd, H&SSA, IAA, M&TEA, MBF, METADEX, ORMS, QC&AS, SoftBase, SolStAb, TTI, WAA.
—BLDSC (5980.868420), CISTI, IE, ingenta, Linda Hall. **CCC.**
Published by: Reed Business Information (Subsidiary of: Reed Business), 2000 Clearwater Dr, Oak Brook, IL 60525. TEL 630-288-8101, FAX 630-288-8764, kparker@reedbusiness.com, http://www.manufacturingsystems.com, http://www.reedbusiness.com. Ed. Kevin Parker TEL 630-320-7046. Pub. Steven Rourke TEL 630-288-8755. adv.: B&W page USD 11,890, color page USD 12,780; trim 10.5 x 7.88. Circ: 97,179 (controlled). **Subscr. to:** Reed Business Information, PO Box 9020, Maple Shade, NJ 08052-9020. TEL 303-470-4466, FAX 303-470-4691.

338 USA
MANUFACTURING ENGINEERING AND MATERIALS PROCESSING SERIES. Text in English. 1977. irreg., latest vol.55, 1999. price varies. adv. **Document type:** *Monographic series.*
Indexed: CIN, ChemAb, ChemTitl, Inspec.
—BLDSC (5367.110000), ingenta.
Published by: Marcel Dekker Inc. (Subsidiary of: Taylor & Francis Group), 270 Madison Ave, New York, NY 10016-0602. TEL 212-696-9000, FAX 212-685-4540, journals@dekker.com, http://www.dekker.com. Pub. Russell Dekker. R&P Julia Mulligan. Adv. contact Eridania Perez.

MANUFACTURING I T. see *COMPUTERS—Computer Systems*

338 IRL
MANUFACTURING IRELAND. Text in English. m. adv. **Document type:** *Magazine, Trade.*
Published by: Advance Publications Ltd., Acorn House, 38 St. Peters Rd., Phibsboro, Dublin, 7, Ireland. TEL 353-1-8686640, FAX 353-1-8686651, apladmin@eircom.net. adv.: B&W page EUR 1,872, color page EUR 2,533; 185 x 268.5. Circ: 6,524 (controlled).

338 NLD ISSN 1572-4417
➤ **MANUFACTURING RESEARCH AND TECHNOLOGY.** Text in Dutch. 1985. irreg., latest vol.23, 1995. price varies. back issues avail. **Document type:** *Monographic series, Academic/Scholarly.* **Description:** Reviews developments in manufacturing research and technology.

Published by: Elsevier BV (Subsidiary of: Elsevier Science & Technology), Radarweg 29, Amsterdam, 1043 NX, Netherlands. TEL 31-20-4853911, FAX 31-20-4852457, nlinfo-f@elsevier.nl, http://www.elsevier.nl.

670 USA ISSN 1096-6668
MANUFACTURING SCIENCE AND ENGINEERING. Text in English. 1993. a. USD 330 in US & Canada to non-members; USD 370 elsewhere to non-members; USD 50 in US & Canada to members; USD 90 elsewhere to members (effective 2004). **Document type:** *Journal, Academic/Scholarly.* **Description:** Covers computer-integrated manufacturing; design for manufacturing; expert systems in manufacturing; grinding and abrasive machining; inspection and quality control; machine tool control; manufacturing automation; metal forming and forging; material removal by machining; nontraditional manufacturing processes; process simulation; production systems optimization; rail transportation; robotics and flexible tooling; sensors; textile production; welding.
Related titles: Online - full content ed.: USD 43 (effective 2004).
—BLDSC (1745.203930). **CCC.**
Published by: American Society of Mechanical Engineers, Three Park Ave, New York, NY 10016-5990. TEL 212-591-7782, FAX 212-591-7841, infocentral@asme.org, http://scitation.aip.org/ASMEJournals/Manufacturing/, http://www.asme.org. Ed. Kornel F Ehmann TEL 847-491-3263.

338 USA
MANUFACTURING SURVEY. Text in English. m. USD 30 (effective 2000). **Description:** Nationwide survey of 1,000 manufacturing firms regarding their production, new orders, unfilled orders, exports and finished goods inventories for the upcoming three months.
Related titles: Online - full text ed.: free.
Published by: Dun & Bradstreet, Economic Analysis Department (Subsidiary of: Dun & Bradstreet Corporation), c/o Judy Webb, 3 Sylvan Way, Parsippany, NJ 07054. FAX 973-254-4063, http://www.dnb.com. R&P Judy Webb.

338 IND
MARCH OF KARNATAKA. Text in English. m. INR 3. adv. charts; illus.; stat.
Formerly (Nov. 1973): March of Mysore
Published by: Department of Information and Tourism, 5 Infantry Rd., Bangalore, Karnataka, India.

MARINE RESOURCE ECONOMICS. see *EARTH SCIENCES—Oceanography*

338 PAK ISSN 0464-9974
MARKET BULLETIN. Text in English, Gujarati. 1952. 2/w. PKR 400, USD 75. adv. bk.rev. **Document type:** *Bulletin.*
Address: Kazgi Bazar, P O Box 4553, Karachi, 74000, Pakistan. TEL 2416735. Ed. A D Karim. Circ: 2,000.

338 DEU ISSN 1615-4932
MASCHINENMARKT WISSEN. Text in German. 1970. m. **Document type:** *Magazine, Trade.*
Former titles (until 2000): Industrie Meister (0940-8436); (until 1991): Meister - Zeitung (0341-759X)
—IE. **CCC.**
Published by: Vogel Verlag und Druck GmbH & Co. KG, Max-Planck-Str 7-9, Wuerzburg, 97064, Germany. TEL 49-931-4182550, FAX 49-931-4182022, http://www.vogel-medien.de. Ed. Dietmar Kuhn. Adv. contact Helmut Sieber. Circ: 9,979 (controlled). **Dist. in US bu:** Vogel Europublishing Inc., 632 Sunflower Ct., San Ramos, CA 94583. TEL 510-648-1170.

338 DEU ISSN 1436-8331
MATERIAL MANAGEMENT. Text in German. 1994. bi-m. EUR 28 domestic; EUR 46 foreign; EUR 7 newsstand/cover (effective 2004). adv. **Document type:** *Magazine, Trade.*
Published by: Verlagsgesellschaft Gruetter GmbH & Co. KG, Postfach 910708, Hannover, 30427, Germany. TEL 49-511-4609300, FAX 49-511-4609320, info@gruetter.de, http://www.material-management.de, http://www.gruetter.de. Ed. Walter Dorsch. Adv. contact Erika Knauer. B&W page EUR 3,440, color page EUR 4,670; trim 184 x 260. Circ: 20,172 (paid and controlled).

(YEAR) MEDIA MANUFACTURING MARKETPLACE. see *COMMUNICATIONS*

MEDICAL PRODUCT MANUFACTURING NEWS. see *INSTRUMENTS*

338 AUT
MEGATECH; das oesterreichische Technikmagazin. Text in German. 1989. 12/yr. EUR 24 domestic; EUR 54 foreign (effective 2005). adv. back issues avail. **Document type:** *Magazine, Trade.*
Related titles: Online - full text ed.
Published by: Oesterreichischer Wirtschaftsverlag GmbH (Subsidiary of: Sueddeutscher Verlag GmbH), Wiedner Hauptstr 120-124, Vienna, W 1051, Austria. TEL 43-1-546640, FAX 43-1-54664406, megatech@wirtschaftsverlag.at, office@wirtschaftsverlag.at, http://www.megatech.at, http://www.wirtschaftsverlag.at. Ed. Christof Lampert. Adv. contact Brigitte Goeschl. color page EUR 6,900; trim 185 x 255. Circ: 13,100.

338 BRA ISSN 0104-3234
MELHORES E MAIORES. Text in Portuguese. 1973. a. USD 3.59. adv. charts; illus.; stat. **Document type:** *Consumer.* **Description:** Annual balance of the 500 major businesses in Brazil.
Related titles: ♦ Supplement to: Exame. ISSN 0102-2881.
Published by: Editora Abril, S.A., Av. Otaviano Alves de Lima 4,400, Sao Paulo, SP, Brazil. TEL 011-877-1322, FAX 011-877-1437. Ed. Jose Roberto Guzzo. Circ: 11,700.

338.925 POL
MERGERS&ACQUISITIONS NEWS. Text in English. bi-w. EUR 602 foreign (effective 2005). **Document type:** *Newsletter, Trade.*
Published by: Polish Market Review Ltd., ul Supniewskiego 9, Krakow, 31527, Poland. TEL 48-12-4280360, FAX 48-12-4134012, pmr@pmrpublications.com, http://www.pmrpublications.com.

METAL COMPONENT DESIGN. see *METALLURGY*

338 DEU
METTLER-TOLEDO MAGAZIN; Waegen und Analysieren in Labor und Produktion. Text in German. q. **Document type:** *Bulletin.*
Published by: Mettler-Toledo GmbH, Ockerweg 3, Giessen, 35396, Germany. TEL 49-641-507111, FAX 49-641-507128, http://www.mt.com/central. Eds. Daniela Damminger, Michael Schreiber.

338 658 HUN ISSN 0580-4485
TS156.A1
MINOSEG ES MEGBIZHATOSAG. Text in Hungarian; Summaries in English, French, German, Russian; Some issues in English, German, Russian, Spanish. 1966. bi-m. USD 38.50. adv. bk.rev. abstr.
Indexed: Inspec.
—CISTI.
Published by: Prodinform Muszaki Tanacsado Vallalat/Prodinform Technical Consulting Company, Munkacsy Mihaly utca 16, PO Box 453, Budapest, 1372, Hungary. TEL 323-770, TELEX 22-7750 PROD-H. Ed. Gabriel Gyozo. Circ: 4,000. **Subscr. to:** Kultura Foreign Trade Company, PO Box 149, Budapest 1389, Hungary.

338 USA ISSN 0540-4193
MISSOURI'S NEW AND EXPANDING INDUSTRY. Text in English. 1952. a. free. bk.rev. **Document type:** *Government.* **Description:** Data and graphs on annual measures of manufacturing growth and development in the state, based on qualified activities announced by companies.
Formerly: Missouri New and Expanding Manufacturers
Published by: Department of Economic Development, PO Box 118, Jefferson City, MO 65102. TEL 573-751-9072, FAX 573-751-7385, gbeahan@mail.state.mo.us. Ed. Gary W Beahan. Circ: 400 (controlled).

338 DEU ISSN 0930-3618
MITTELSTAENDISCHE UNTERNEHMEN. Text in German. 1986. a. EUR 296.55 for 3 vols.. **Document type:** *Trade.*
Related titles: CD-ROM ed.; Online - full text ed.: (from Data-Star, G B I, The Dialog Corporation).
Published by: Hoppenstedt Bonnier Zeitschriften GmbH, Havelstr. 9, Darmstadt, 64295, Germany. TEL 49-6151-380-0, FAX 49-6151-380-360. Circ: 55,000.

338 USA
MODERN CORPORATION CHECKLISTS (SUPPLEMENT). Text in English. a. looseleaf. USD 151.45; USD 241.95 foreign (effective 1998). **Document type:** *Trade.* **Description:** Covers all aspects of company practices with checklists from firms and law departments.
Published by: W G & L Financial Reporting & Management Research (Subsidiary of: R I A), 395 Hudson St, New York, NY 10014. TEL 212-367-6300, FAX 212-367-6718. **Subscr. to:** The Park Square Bldg., 31 St James Ave, Boston, MA 02116-4112. TEL 800-950-1207.

MOFET. see *MACHINERY*

338 CAN ISSN 0840-8238
MONTHLY SURVEY OF MANUFACTURING. Text in English. m.
Former titles (until 1988): Inventories, Shipments and Orders in Manufacturing Industries (0701-7367); (until 1952): Inventories and Shipments by Manufacturing Industries (0701-7375); Inventories and Shipments by Manufacturing Industries, Excluding Newfoundland (0827-0570); (until 1950): Inventories and Shipments by Manufacturing Industries (0827-0562); Monthly Report on Inventories and Shipments by Manufacturing Industries in Canada, Excluding Newfoundland (0827-0554); (until 1949): Monthly Report on Inventories and Shipments by Manufacturing Industries (0827-0546)
Published by: Statistics Canada, Industry Division, Rm 1500, Main Building, Holland Ave, Ottawa, ON K1A 0T6, Canada.

MOROCCO. DIRECTION DE LA STATISTIQUE. INDICE DES PRIX A LA PRODUCTION INDUSTRIELLE, ENERGETIQUE ET MINIERE. see *BUSINESS AND ECONOMICS—Abstracting, Bibliographies, Statistics*

MOROCCO. DIRECTION DE LA STATISTIQUE. INDICE DES PRIX DE GROS. see *BUSINESS AND ECONOMICS—Abstracting, Bibliographies, Statistics*

MOROCCO. DIRECTION DE LA STATISTIQUE. INDICE DU COUT DE LA VIE. see *BUSINESS AND ECONOMICS—Abstracting, Bibliographies, Statistics*

388 ESP
MOVICARGA. Text in Spanish. 1973. 12/yr. adv. **Document type:** *Trade.* **Description:** Includes information on cranes, aerial working platforms, forklift trucks, and reach stackers.
Address: Venezuela 2, 10 D, Pol. Vallaeguado, Apdo. 115, Coslada, (Madrid) 28820, Spain. TEL 34-1-673-58-12, FAX 34-1-673-59-11, gilusan@tsai.es, http://www.movicarga.com/ayuda.asp. Ed. Macarena Garcia. Pub. Luis Garcia Sanchez. Adv. contact Carlos Vivas. Circ: 6,000.

MOZAMBIQUE. INSTITUTO NACIONAL DE ESTATISTICA. ESTATISTICAS INDUSTRIAIS. see *BUSINESS AND ECONOMICS—Abstracting, Bibliographies, Statistics*

330 DEU ISSN 1615-4843
MUENSTERANER SCHRIFTEN ZUR DISTRIBUTIONS- UND HANDELFORSCHUNG. Text in German. 1998. irreg., latest vol.8, 2001. **Document type:** *Monographic series, Academic/Scholarly.*
Published by: Westfaelische Wilhelms-Universitaet Muenster, Lehrstuhl fuer Betriebswirtschaftslehre, insb. Distribution und Handel, Am Stadtgraben 13-15, Muenster, 48143, Germany. TEL 49-251-8322808, FAX 49-251-8322032, 02diah@wiwi.uni-muenster.de, http://www.marketing-centrum.de/ifhm/.

338 ESP
MUNDO INDUSTRIAL. Text in Spanish. 1967. 9/yr. EUR 24 domestic; EUR 84 foreign (effective 2005). adv. Website rev. index. **Document type:** *Newspaper, Newspaper-distributed.*
Published by: Ediciones Roda, S.L., Corcega 204 bajos, Tda. 2, Barcelona, 08036, Spain. TEL 34-93-419-2881, FAX 34-93-419-2463, correo@edicionesroda.es, http://www.edicionesroda.es/principal-mi.htm. Ed. Antonio Castro. Adv. contact Carlos Castro. Circ: 10,000.

338 USA
N A P S A RESULTS∗. Text in English. bi-m. USD 50. adv. **Document type:** *Newsletter.* **Description:** Provides news of the appliance parts aftermarket and other items of interest to association members.
Published by: National Appliance Parts Suppliers Association, PO Box 87907, Vancouver, WA 98687-7907. TEL 360-834-3805, FAX 312-922-2734. Circ: 500.

N A U M D NEWS. see *CLOTHING TRADE*

N A U M D OFFICE REPORTS. see *CLOTHING TRADE*

N A U M D POSTAL UPDATE. see *CLOTHING TRADE*

338 NGA
N N D C NEWSLETTER. Text in English. 1978. q. illus. **Document type:** *Newsletter.*
Published by: New Nigeria Development Company Ltd., PMB 2120, Kaduna, Nigeria.

338 NOR ISSN 0804-4597
HC361
NAERINGSLIVETS UKEAVIS. Text in Norwegian. 1919. fortn. NOK 150. adv. illus.; tr.lit. index.
Formerly (until 1993): Apropos (0802-247X); Which superseded in part (in 1988): Norges Industri (0029-1706)
Indexed: RASB.
Published by: Naeringslivets Forlag, Postboks 5145, Majorstua, Oslo, 0302, Norway. Circ: 4,200.

NAPETCOR. see *PETROLEUM AND GAS*

338 DNK
NATIONAL AGENCY OF INDUSTRY AND TRADE. ANNUAL REPORTS (YEAR)/AARSBERETNINGER. Text in Danish. 1982. a. free.
Former titles: Investering i Produktion (0108-2329); Denmark. Egnsudviklingsraadet. Beretning
Published by: National Agency of Industry and Trade, Soendergade 25, PO Box 983, Silkeborg, 8600, Denmark. TEL 86-825655, FAX 45-86-801629, TELEX 63346. Circ: 5,000.

NATIONAL HOUSEWARES MANUFACTURERS ASSOCIATION. STATE OF THE INDUSTRY REPORT. see *BUSINESS AND ECONOMICS—Abstracting, Bibliographies, Statistics*

338 IND
NATIONAL PRODUCTS NEWS. Text in English. 1989. m. INR 150; INR 15 newsstand/cover. adv. **Document type:** *Trade.*
Published by: Seven Hills Publications Pvt. Ltd., Nahar & Seth Industrial Estate, A-Wing Gala No. 3061 3rd Fl., Pannalal Silk Mills Compound, L.B.S. Marg, Bhandup (W), Mumbai, Maharashtra 400 078, India. TEL 5645479. Ed. A S Mani. Adv. contact P V Murali. B&W page INR 8,000, color page INR 18,000; trim 200 x 280. Circ: 12,700.

B

NEDERLANDS A B C DIENSTVERLENERS. see *BUSINESS AND ECONOMICS—Trade And Industrial Directories*

NEDERLANDS A B C VOOR HANDEL EN INDUSTRIE. see *BUSINESS AND ECONOMICS—Trade And Industrial Directories*

338.9   NPL   ISSN 0077-6548
NEPAL INDUSTRIAL DEVELOPMENT CORPORATION. ANNUAL REPORT. Text in English. 1959. a. free. **Document type:** *Corporate.*
Published by: Nepal Industrial Development Corporation, N.I.D.C. Bldg., Durbar Marg, P O Box 10, Kathmandu, Nepal. TEL 977-1-228322, FAX 977-1-227428.

338.9   NPL   ISSN 0077-6556
HC497.N5
NEPAL INDUSTRIAL DEVELOPMENT CORPORATION. INDUSTRIAL DIGEST. Text in English. 1966. a. NPR 30, USD 5.
Published by: Nepal Industrial Development Corporation, N.I.D.C. Bldg., Durbar Marg, P O Box 10, Kathmandu, Nepal. Ed. Ramesh Nath Dhungel.

330   NLD   ISSN 0166-9478
NETHERLANDS. CENTRAAL PLANBUREAU. CENTRAAL ECONOMISCH PLAN. Key Title: Centraal Economisch Plan. Text in Dutch. 1946. a. **Document type:** *Government.*
Related titles: ◆ English ed.: Central Economic Plan. ISSN 0926-8235.
—IE, Infotrieve, KNAW.
Published by: (Netherlands. Centraal Planbureau), Sdu Uitgevers bv, Christoffel Plantijnstraat 2, The Hague, 2515 TZ, Netherlands. FAX 31-70-347-5778.

338.9   CAN
T177.C2
NEW BRUNSWICK. RESEARCH AND PRODUCTIVITY COUNCIL. ANNUAL REPORT∗ . Text in English. 1962. a. free. **Document type:** *Government.*
Formerly: New Brunswick. Research and Productivity Council. Report (0077-8117)
—CISTI.
Published by: Research and Productivity Council, 921 College Hill Rd, Fredericton, NB E3B 6Z9, Canada. TEL 506-452-8994, FAX 506-452-1395. Ed. Peter Lewell. Circ: 500.

338   USA   ISSN 0028-4378
NEW BUSINESS INCORPORATIONS. Text in English. 1947. m. USD 25 (effective 2000). **Description:** Provides the number of new incorporations in each of the 50 states, with commentary and comparisons to previous periods.
Related titles: Microfiche ed.: (from CIS).
Indexed: SRI.
Published by: Dun & Bradstreet, Economic Analysis Department (Subsidiary of: Dun & Bradstreet Corporation), c/o Judy Webb, 3 Sylvan Way, Parsippany, NJ 07054. FAX 973-254-4063, http://www.dnb.com. R&P Judy Webb.

338   AUS
NEW ENGINEER JOURNAL. Text in English. 1999. q., latest vol.6. AUD 45 to non-members (effective 2003). illus. **Document type:** *Trade.* **Description:** Offers technical and business advice for professionals in manufacturing who need to know about changes in technology, management, and the competition. Coordinates the marketing, financial, and production aspects of all types of manufacturing.
Formerly: Manufacturing World
Published by: (Manufacturing Society of Australia (ManSA)), Research Publications Pty., 27 A Boronia Rd, Vermont, VIC 3133, Australia. TEL 61-3-98748982, FAX 61-3-98730100. Pub. Ted Colville. Circ: 2,000 (paid).

380.1029   USA
NEW HAMPSHIRE MANUFACTURING DIRECTORY. Text in English. a. USD 65 (effective 2000). **Document type:** *Directory.* **Description:** Lists manufacturers in New Hampshire alphabetically, geographically and by product.
Formerly: New Hampshire Marketing Directory (0276-2110)
Published by: Tower Publishing Co., 588 Saco Rd, Standish, ME 04084-6239. TEL 207-642-5400, 800-969-8693, FAX 207-642-5463.

338   GBR
NEW INDUSTRIAL PRODUCTS; the journal for new product launches. Text in English. 1992. bi-m. Free to qualified subscribers. adv. **Document type:** *Journal, Trade.* **Description:** Publishes information about new products and services in industry and commerce.
Related titles: Online - full content ed.
Published by: Harcourt Business Publications, Harcourt House, 11 Whitehead Grove, Balsall Common, West Midlands CV7 7US, United Kingdom. TEL 44-1676-530011, FAX 44-1676-530022, harcourtbp@msn.com, http://www.newindustrialproducts.co.uk.

338   USA   ISSN 0028-5560
HC107.N5
NEW JERSEY BUSINESS. Text in English. 1954. m. USD 21 domestic; USD 22 foreign; USD 2.50 newsstand/cover (effective 2005). adv. charts; illus. reprints avail. **Document type:** *Magazine, Consumer.*
Related titles: Online - full text ed.: (from bigchalk, Northern Light Technology, Inc., O C L C Online Computer Library Center, Inc., ProQuest Information & Learning).
Indexed: ABIn, BusDate, ORMS, PAIS.
Published by: New Jersey Business Magazine, 310 Passaic Ave, Fairfield, NJ 07004. TEL 973-882-5004, FAX 973-882-4648, a.birritteri@njbmagazine.com, http://www.njbmagazine.com/. Ed. Anthony Birritteri. Pub. Phillip A Battista. Adv. contact Al Leone. Circ: 28,000 (paid).

338   GBR   ISSN 0954-3538
NEW MATERIALS INTERNATIONAL∗ . Text in English. 1986. m. USD 250. pat.; tr.lit. index. back issues avail. **Document type:** *Newsletter.* **Description:** Contains news of new materials for the manufacturing industry; also covers materials processing.
—BLDSC (6084.474570).
Published by: C M P Information Ltd. (Subsidiary of: United Business Media), Miller Freeman House, 30 Calderwood St, London, SE18 6QH, United Kingdom. TEL 44-20-8855-7777, FAX 44-20-8854-8058. Ed. John Mortimer.

338   NGA   ISSN 0189-1316
NEW NIGERIA DEVELOPMENT COMPANY LIMITED. ANNUAL REPORT AND ACCOUNTS. Text in English. 1969. a. free. **Document type:** *Corporate.*
Supersedes (in 1978): Northern Nigeria Development Corporation. Report
Published by: New Nigeria Development Company Ltd., PMB 2120, Kaduna, Nigeria.

338   GBR
NEW PRODUCT NEWSLETTER. Text in English. m.
Published by: New Product Newsletter Co. Ltd., 1a Chesterfield St, London, W1X 7HF, United Kingdom.

NEW YORK MANUFACTURERS DIRECTORY. see *BUSINESS AND ECONOMICS—Trade And Industrial Directories*

333.79 658   NZL   ISSN 1171-5375
NEW ZEALAND MANUFACTURER. Text in English. 1949. 11/yr. NZD 65 domestic; NZD 95 in Australasia; NZD 140 elsewhere (effective 1999). adv. bk.rev. charts; illus.; mkt.; tr.lit. **Document type:** *Trade.*
Former titles (until 1992): Manufacturer (0113-9320); (until Apr. 1988): New Zealand Manufacturer (0113-0498); Which was formerly (until 1985): Manufacturer (0110-6279); (until 1975): New Zealand Manufacturer (0028-8411)
Related titles: Online - full text ed.: (from Northern Light Technology, Inc., O C L C Online Computer Library Center, Inc., ProQuest Information & Learning).
Indexed: ABIn, INZP.
—CCC.
Published by: New Zealand Manufacturers Federation, 3 Church St, PO Box 11-543, Wellington 1, New Zealand. TEL 64-4-473-3000, FAX 64-4-473-3004, j_mcburney@manufacturers.org.nz, http://manufacturers.org.nz. Ed. Julie McBurney. R&P Gilbert Peterson. Adv. contact David Neilson. Circ: 4,000 (controlled).

664.94   NZL   ISSN 1173-0161
NEW ZEALAND SEAFOOD INDUSTRY ECONOMIC REVIEW. Text in English. 1993. irreg. free (effective 2005).
Formerly: New Zealand Fishing Industry Economic Review (1171-4212)
Indexed: ESPM.
Published by: New Zealand Seafood Industry Council, Seafood Industry House, 74 Cambridge Terrace, Private Bag 24-901, Wellington, New Zealand. TEL 64-4-3854005, FAX 64-4-3852727, info@seafood.co.nz, http://www.seafood.co.nz. Ed. Ms. Sarah Crysell.

338 310   NZL
NEW ZEALAND. STATISTICS NEW ZEALAND. ECONOMIC SURVEY OF MANUFACTURING. Text in English. q. stat. **Document type:** *Government.* **Description:** Provides quick economic indicators of how the manufacturing sector is faring in the general economic conditions present at the time.
Published by: Statistics New Zealand/Te Tari Tatau, PO Box 2922, Wellington, New Zealand. TEL 64-4-495-4600, FAX 64-4-473-2626, info@stats.govt.nz, http://www.stats.govt.nz.

338 310   NZL
NEW ZEALAND. STATISTICS NEW ZEALAND. PRODUCTION STATISTICS. Text in English. q. stat. **Document type:** *Government.*
Published by: Statistics New Zealand/Te Tari Tatau, PO Box 2922, Wellington, New Zealand. TEL 64-4-495-4600, FAX 64-4-473-2626, info@stats.govt.nz, http://www.stats.govt.nz.

NEWS & VIEWS (PORTLAND). see *BUSINESS AND ECONOMICS—Marketing And Purchasing*

338   JPN
NIKKEI SANGYO SHIMBUN/NIKKEI INDUSTRIAL DAILY. Text in Japanese. 1973. d. (except Sun.). adv. **Document type:** *Newspaper.* **Description:** Provides in-depth coverage of developments in industry, including new products and technologies.
Indexed: B&I.
Published by: Nihon Keizai Shimbun Inc., 1-9-5 Ote-Machi, Chiyoda-ku, Tokyo, 100-0004, Japan. TEL 81-3-32700251, FAX 81-3-52552661. Ed. Shinichi Kamata. Adv. contact Hideaki Nakajima. B&W page JPY 2,460,000; trim 533 x 385. Circ: 231,048.

338   JPN   ISSN 0388-709X
NIKKO FORAMU/NIKKO PRODUCER - GOODS FORUM. Text in Japanese. 1980. m. JPY 400 per issue.
Published by: Nihon Kogyo Shinbunsha, 7-2 Ote-Machi 1-chome, Chiyoda-ku, Tokyo, 100-0004, Japan.

338   FRA   ISSN 0078-0960
NOMENCLATURE DES ENTREPRISES NATIONALES A CARACTERE INDUSTRIEL OU COMMERCIAL ET DES SOCIETES D'ECONOMIE MIXTE D'INTERET NATIONAL. Text in French. irreg. price varies.
Published by: (France. Ministere de l'Economie et des Finances), Imprimerie Nationale, BP 514, Douai, Cedex 59505, France. TEL 27-93-70-90, FAX 27-93-70-96.

338   DEU
NORDDEUTSCHES HANDWERK. Text in German. 1895. s-m. adv. bk.rev. **Document type:** *Bulletin, Trade.*
Formerly: Nordwestdeutsches Handwerk (0029-1617)
—CCC.
Published by: Schluetersche GmbH und Co. KG, Hans-Boeckler-Allee 7, Hannover, 30173, Germany. TEL 49-511-85500, FAX 49-511-85502405, anzeigen@schluetersche.de, http://www.schluetersche.de. Ed. Irmke Froemling. Circ: 85,400 (paid); 89,000 (controlled).

338.3   NOR
NORGES HANDELSHOEYSKOLE. SENTER FOR FISKERIOEKONOMI INSTITUTT. DISCUSSION PAPER SERIES. Text in Multiple languages. 1982. a. **Document type:** *Monographic series, Academic/Scholarly.*
Formerly: Norges Handelshoeyskole. Fiskerioekonomisk Institutt. Discussion Paper Series (0803-4435)
Indexed: ASFA, ESPM.
Published by: Norges Handelshoeyskole, Senter for Fiskerioekonomi/Norwegian School of Economics and Business Administration, Center for Fisheries Economics, Helleveien 30, Bergen, 5045, Norway. TEL 47-55-95-90-00.

338.3   NOR   ISSN 0804-1105
NORGES HANDELSHOEYSKOLE. SENTER FOR FISKERIOEKONOMI. SAERTRYKKSERIE. Text in Multiple languages. 1983. irreg. **Document type:** *Monographic series.*
Formerly (until 1992): Norges Handelshoeyskole. Fiskerioekonomisk Institutt. Saertrykkserie (0801-9002)
Indexed: ASFA, ESPM.
Published by: Norges Handelshoeyskole, Senter for Fiskerioekonomi/Norwegian School of Economics and Business Administration, Center for Fisheries Economics, Helleveien 30, Bergen, 5045, Norway. TEL 47-55-95-90-00, http://www.nhh.no.

NORTH CAROLINA MANUFACTURERS DIRECTORY. see *BUSINESS AND ECONOMICS—Trade And Industrial Directories*

338   DOM   ISSN 0254-2153
NOTAS DE DESARROLLO. Text in Spanish. 1967. q. free. illus.
Indexed: MRD.
Published by: Fundacion Dominicana de Desarrollo, Apdo. 857, Z.P.I, Santo Domingo, Dominican Republic. Circ: 2,000.

NOYCE PUBLISHING. RELIGION AND DEVELOPMENT SERIES. see *RELIGIONS AND THEOLOGY*

O I T NEWS; news from the U.S. Department of Energy's Office of Industrial Technologies. (Office of Industrial Technologies) see *ENERGY*

338   NOR   ISSN 0332-5555
HC361
OEKONOMISK RAPPORT. Text in Norwegian. 1962. 22/yr. NOK 745. adv. bk.rev. charts; illus.; stat. index.
Formerly (until 1975): Bedriftsoekonomisk Informasjon (0045-1606)
Published by: A-S Hjemmet, Kristian Iv S Gate 13, Oslo, 0164, Norway. Ed. Kjell Thompson. Circ: 30,000.

OFFICIAL IOWA MANUFACTURERS DIRECTORY. see *BUSINESS AND ECONOMICS—Trade And Industrial Directories*

338   USA
OHIO MANUFACTURER. Text in English. m.
Related titles: Online - full text ed.
Published by: Industrial Marketing, Inc., PO Box 4310, Lexington, KY 40544-4310. TEL 800-264-3303.

338 GRC ISSN 1109-1584
OIKONOMIKE BIOMEHANIKE EPITHEORESE; monthly business magazine. Text in Greek. 1934. m. EUR 42 domestic to individuals; EUR 42 in Cyprus to individuals; EUR 105 elsewhere to individuals (effective 2005). adv. bk.rev. charts; illus.; stat.; tr.lit.; tr.mk. index. Supplement avail. **Document type:** *Magazine, Trade.* **Description:** Covers Greek financial and political current events, industrial and technological advances.
Former titles: Viomichaniki Economiki Epitheorissis; (until 1998): Viomichaniki Epitheorissis (0042-6415)
Related titles: ♦ Supplement(s): Business File Special Survey Series.
Published by: Kerkyra Monoprosopi Ltd Publications, 6 - 8 Vlahava St, Athens, 105 51, Greece. TEL 30-1-331-4714, FAX 30-1-325-2283, http://www.oikonomiki.gr/OBEMagazine.asp?MagID=1&Lang=GR. Circ: 25,000 (paid).

338 NLD ISSN 1383-3391
ONDERNEMEN!; magazine voor de ondernemd Nederland. Text in Dutch. 1995. 10/yr. EUR 59 (effective 2005). adv. bk.rev. stat. **Document type:** *Trade.*
Formed by the merger of (1979-1995): Ondernemers-Visie (0165-1897); (1979-1995): Ondernemer (Rijswijk) (0927-3611); Which was formerly (1975-1979): Zelfstandig Ondernemerschap (1383-4142); Which was formed by the merger of (1968-1975): Ondernemer (1383-4150); (1947-1975): Modern Ondernemerschap (0026-8216)
Published by: (Vereniging M K B Nederland), Scope Publishing B.V., Postbus 23, Ouderkerk aan de Amstel, 1190 AA, Netherlands. TEL 31-20-3113799, FAX 31-20-6964874, ondernemen@mkb.nl, info@scopepublishing.nl, http://www.mkb.nl/Ondernemen!, http://www.scopepublishing.nl/. Ed. Andre Vermeulen. Pub. Walter Vesters. Adv. contact Edgar van Bueren TEL 31-20-3113793. Circ: 145,000.

338 FRA ISSN 0755-6225
OPTION QUALITE; reglementation, technologie, controle des produits. Text in French. 1983. m. EUR 245.04 print & CD-ROM eds. (effective 2004). 20 p./no.; **Description:** Provides information on how to track and improve the quality of products for professionals in the food industry.
Related titles: CD-ROM ed.
Published by: Lamy S.A. (Subsidiary of: Wolters Kluwer France), 21/23 rue des Ardennes, Paris, 75935 Cedex 19, France. TEL 33-1-825080800, FAX 33-1-44721388, lamy@lamy.fr, http://www.lamy.fr.

338 NGA
OYO STATE. MINISTRY OF ECONOMIC PLANNING AND COMMUNITY DEVELOPMENT. ANNUAL REPORT✶. Text in English. a. **Document type:** *Government.*
Formerly: Western State. Ministry of Economic Planning and Community Development. Annual Report
Published by: Government Printer, Ibadan, Oyo, Nigeria.

338 330 CAN
LES P M E AU QUEBEC. ETAT DE LA SITUATION. (Petite et Moyenne Entreprise) Text in English. a. free. **Document type:** *Government.* **Description:** Reports on the situation of the small and medium businesses in Quebec in the previous year.
Formerly: Quebec (Province). Ministere de Direction de l'analyse de la conjoncure industrielle.
Published by: Ministere de Direction de l'analyze de la conjuncture industrielle, 710 place D Youville, 9e etage, Quebec, PQ G1R 4Y4, Canada. TEL 418-691-5993, FAX 418-643-0221, http://www.micst.gouv.qc.ca. Circ: 1,000.

PADDLESPORTS PRO. see *SPORTS AND GAMES—Boats And Boating*

338.9 PAK ISSN 0078-8201
PAKISTAN INDUSTRIAL DEVELOPMENT CORPORATION. REPORT. Text in English. 1952. a.
Published by: Pakistan Industrial Development Corporation, PIDC House, Dr. Ziauddin Ahmad Rd., Karachi 4, Pakistan.

338 PAK ISSN 0078-8392
PAKISTAN. OFFICE OF THE ECONOMIC ADVISER. GOVERNMENT SPONSORED CORPORATIONS AND OTHER INSTITUTIONS. Text in English. 1965. a. free.
Published by: Office of the Economic Adviser, Islamabad, Pakistan. Circ: (controlled).

338.9 PAK ISSN 0078-8414
PAKISTAN. PLANNING AND DEVELOPMENT DIVISION. DEVELOPMENT PROGRAMME. Text in English. 1971. a. USD 20.
Published by: Planning and Development Division, Block "P", Islamabad, Pakistan.

PARAGUAY INDUSTRIAL Y COMERCIAL. see *BUSINESS AND ECONOMICS—Domestic Commerce*

PATENT DIGEST. see *PATENTS, TRADEMARKS AND COPYRIGHTS*

338 USA
PEOPLE AND PRODUCTS. Text in English. m. **Document type:** *Newsletter, Trade.*
Published by: General Merchandise Distributors Council, 1275 Lake Plaza Dr, Colorado Springs, CO 80906-3583. TEL 719-576-4260, FAX 719-576-2661, info@gmdc.org, http://www.gmdc.org.

338.9 BRA ISSN 0100-0551
HC186
➤ **PESQUISA E PLANEJAMENTO ECONOMICO.** Text in Portuguese. 1971. 3/yr. BRL 20; BRL 30 foreign. adv. bk.rev. **Document type:** *Journal, Academic/Scholarly.* **Description:** Presents research and studies in economic and social planning.
Formerly: Pesquisa e Planejamento (0304-2308)
Indexed: HAPI, IBR, IBSS, JEL, PAIS.
Published by: Instituto de Pesquisa Economica Aplicada, Av Presidente Antonio Carlos, 51 Andar 13, Centro, Rio De Janeiro, RJ 20020-010, Brazil. TEL 55-21-38048117, FAX 55-21-22205533, ppe@ipea.gov.br, http://www.ipea.gov.br. Ed. Octavio Augusto Fontes Tourinho. Adv. contact Angelica Ferreira de Barros. Circ: 1,000.

➤ **PESQUISA INDUSTRIAL.** see *BUSINESS AND ECONOMICS—Abstracting, Bibliographies, Statistics*

➤ **PHARMACEUTICALS (YEAR): INTERNATIONAL YEARBOOK.** see *PHARMACY AND PHARMACOLOGY*

➤ **PHARMAFILE INTERNATIONAL.** see *PHARMACY AND PHARMACOLOGY*

338 PHL ISSN 0116-6891
HD9736.P5
PHILIPPINES. NATIONAL STATISTICS OFFICE. INDUSTRY TRENDS. Text in English. m. 32 p./no.; **Document type:** *Government.* **Description:** Discusses the results of the Survey of Key Enterprises in Manufacturing, a special study conducted by NSO to provide flash indicators on the performance of growth-oriented industries.
Published by: National Statistics Office, Ramon Magsaysay Blvd, PO Box 779, Manila, Philippines. FAX 63-2-610794.

338.060284 AUS
PLANT & EQUIPMENT. Text in English. 1992. m. (11/yr.). AUD 42; AUD 4.60 newsstand/cover (effective 2003). adv. **Document type:** *Trade.* **Description:** Presents news for the manufacturing industries, warehousing and business in general. Helps in making decisions about buying and selling factory equipment.
Published by: A C P Trader International Group (Subsidiary of: A C P Publishing Pty. Ltd.), 54-58 Park St, Sydney, NSW 1028, Australia. TEL 61-2-92828000, FAX 61-2-92674361, http://www.factoryhub.com.au/mag-peaus.asp, http://www.tradergroup.com.au/. Adv. contact Rick Smith. B&W page AUD 800, color page AUD 1,740; trim 180 x 255. Circ: 9,490. **Subscr. to:** Magshop, Reply Paid 4967, Sydney, NSW 2001, Australia. TEL 61-2-92828000, magshop@acp.com.au, http://magshop.com.au.

338 ZAF
PLANT EQUIPMENT HIRE & RATES. Text in English. 1976. m. (11/yr.). ZAR 200 domestic; ZAR 250 in Africa; USD 160 elsewhere (effective 2000). adv. **Document type:** *Trade.* **Description:** Features company news, information on manufactured parts, articles on people in the profession, plant news, and listings of manufacturers and hire equipment and services available.
Former titles: Plant Equipment Hire and Rate Review; Plant
Published by: Brooke Pattrick Publications, PO Box 422, Bedfordview, Transvaal 2008, South Africa. TEL 27-11-622-4666, FAX 27-11-616-7196, bestbook@brookepattrick.co.za, Bpattric@global.co.za. Ed. Edith Webster. Pub. John Pattrick. Adv. contact Dave Herald. B&W page ZAR 3,500, color page ZAR 5,000; trim 180 x 250. Circ: 2,656 (controlled).

338 USA ISSN 1083-5636
CODEN: BBMTF6
PLANT PROSPECTOR. Text in English. 1995. w. USD 780 for 6 mos. (effective 2002). **Document type:** *Journal, Trade.* **Description:** Identifies regional & local businesses in transition through layoffs & work force reductions.
Media: E-mail.
Published by: Beard Group, Inc, PO Box 9867, Washington, DC 20016. TEL 240-629-3300, FAX 240-629-3360, info@beard.com, http://www.beard.com. Pub., R&P Christopher Beard.

338.9 DEU ISSN 0079-2284
PLANUNGSSTUDIEN. Text in German. 1969. irreg., latest vol.21, 1984. price varies. **Document type:** *Monographic series, Academic/Scholarly.*
Published by: Nomos Verlagsgesellschaft mbH und Co. KG, Waldseestr 3-5, Baden-Baden, 76530, Germany. TEL 49-7221-2104-0, FAX 49-7221-210427, nomos@nomos.de, http://www.nomos.de. Ed. Joseph H Kaiser.

PLASTICS INSIGHTS. see *PLASTICS*

PLASTICS: LATIN AMERICAN INDUSTRIAL REPORT. see *PLASTICS*

338 POL ISSN 0239-9415
T55.4
POLITECHNIKA POZNANSKA. ZESZYTY NAUKOWE. ORGANIZACJA I ZARZADZANIE. Text in Polish; Summaries in English. 1969. irreg., latest vol.35, 2002. price varies. 100 p./no.; **Document type:** *Monographic series, Academic/Scholarly.* **Description:** Covers ergonomics, quality engineering, production engineering and management, marketing and infomatics, economics, business law.
Formerly: Politechnika Poznanska. Zeszyty Naukowe. Ekonomika i Organizacja Przemyslu (0137-690X)
Published by: (Politechnika Poznanska), Wydawnictwo Politechniki Poznanskiej, Pl M Sklodowskiej Curie 2, Poznan, 60965, Poland. TEL 48-61-6653516, FAX 48-61-6653583, office_ed@put.poznan.pl, http://www.ed.put.poznan.pl. Ed. Leszek Pacholski. Circ: 80.

338 680 AUS
POOL & SPA REVIEW. Text in English. 1973. q. AUD 45; AUD 85 foreign. adv. tr.lit. **Document type:** *Trade.*
Former titles: Pool and Spa Industry Review; (until Mar. 1983): Caspa (0311-0001)
Published by: Wallacia (Sales) Pty. Ltd., 4 Coppabella Rd, Dural, NSW 2158, Australia. TEL 61-2-651-2044, FAX 61-9-651-2825. Ed. Ben Smith. Circ: 2,900.

338 621.9 USA
POWER PRODUCTS BUSINESS. Text in English. 1975. m. looseleaf. USD 365. stat. **Document type:** *Newsletter.* **Description:** News and market information regarding engine manufacturers, components and engine-powered equipment.
Former titles: Engine Power Perspective (1056-4063); Diesel Power Perspective (0743-0787)
Published by: Power Systems Research, 1301 Corporate Center Dr., Ste. 113, St. Paul, MN 55121. TEL 612-454-0144, FAX 612-454-0760. Ed. Gordon Gilbert. Pub. Geroge Zirnhelt. R&P George Zirnhelt. Circ: 150 (paid).

338 CIV
PRINCIPALES INDUSTRIES INSTALLEES EN COTE D'IVOIRE. Text in French. 1968. a. free.
Formerly: Principales Industries Ivoiriennes
Published by: Chambre de Commerce et d'Industrie de Cote d'Ivoire, BP 1399, Abidjan, Ivory Coast. TEL 225-20-331600, FAX 225-20323942, info@cci-ci.org, http://www.cci-ci.org.

338.1 CUB ISSN 1681-9993
PRISMA. Text in Spanish. 1999. bi-m.
Media: Online - full text.
Published by: Prensa Latina Agencia Informativa Latinoamericana, Calle 23 No. 201,, Vedado, La Habana, Cuba. TEL 53-78-4127902, http://www.prensalatina.com/. Ed. Edilberto Mendez Amador.

338 PHL ISSN 0115-4419
PRIVATE DEVELOPMENT CORPORATION OF THE PHILIPPINES. INDUSTRY DIGEST. Text in English. 1977. bi-m. USD 55.
Indexed: IPP.
Published by: Private Development Corporation of the Philippines/Pribadong Korporasyon sa Pagpapaunlad ng Pilipinas, P.O. Box 757, Makati, Manila, 3117, Philippines. TEL 02-8100231, FAX 02-8195376.

338 USA ISSN 0190-9851
PRIVATE LABEL; the publication for store brand leaders. Text in English. 1979. 7/yr. USD 85 domestic; USD 105 in Canada; USD 175 elsewhere (effective 2004). adv. bk.rev. **Document type:** *Magazine, Trade.*
Incorporates (in 1990): Private Label Executive Edition
Related titles: Online - full text ed.
Indexed: B&I, RPFIA.
Published by: E.W. Williams Publications Co., 2125 Center Ave, Ste 305, Fort Lee, NJ 07024-5898. TEL 201-592-7007, FAX 201-592-7171, http://www.privatelabelmag.com. Ed. Peter Berlinski. Pub. Andrew H Williams. R&P Tony Faber. Adv. contact Charles Loomer. Circ: 28,000.

338 658.8 USA ISSN 0886-5582
PRIVATE LABEL INTERNATIONAL; the magazine for store labels (own brands) and generics. Text in English; Summaries in French, German. 1986. s-a. USD 20; USD 45 foreign (effective 1999). adv. **Document type:** *Trade.*
Published by: E.W. Williams Publications Co., 2125 Center Ave, Ste 305, Fort Lee, NJ 07024-5898. TEL 201-592-7007, FAX 201-592-7171. Ed. Peter Berlinski. Pub. Andrew H Williams. R&P Tony Faber. Adv. contact Charles Loomer.

330 BIH ISSN 0350-9788
PRIVREDNE NOVINE✶. Text in Serbo-Croatian. 1972. w. BAD 1,000.
Published by: Oslobodjenje, Dzemala Bijedica 185, Sarajevo, 71000, Bosnia Herzegovina. Ed. Ljubomir Solomunovic.

338 USA
PRODUCT DEVELOPMENT BEST PRACTICES REPORT. Text in English. m. USD 247; USD 30 per issue (effective 2004). **Document type:** *Newsletter.* **Description:** Provides case studies, and perspectives on strategies for manufacturing excellence.
Formerly: Design for Manufacture Alert (1049-8400)
Related titles: Online - full text ed.

B

Published by: Management Roundtable, Inc., 92 Crescent St, Waltham, MA 02453-4315. Ed. David Vermette. Pub., R&P Alexander J Cooper TEL 781-891-8080 ext 212.

338 365.34 005.8   GBR   ISSN 1740-7540
▼ **PRODUCT ID**; the journal of automatic prodict id technolgy. Text in English. 2003. q. GBP 599, EUR 899, USD 955 (effective 2004). **Document type:** *Journal.* **Description:** Covers how the new ID technologies will work, analysis of products, possible applications, cost models and case studies.
Published by: Pira International, Randalls Rd, Leatherhead, Surrey KT22 7RU, United Kingdom. TEL 44-1372-802080, FAX 44-1372-802079, publications@pira.co.uk, http://www.piranet.com/pira/bookseo.htm/253.

346.066   USA   ISSN 1535-1629
PRODUCT LIABILITY DAILY. Text in English. d. back issues avail. **Document type:** *Newsletter, Trade.* **Description:** Reports on product liability law, regulation, and litigation issues.
Media: Online - full text (from The Bureau of National Affairs, Inc.).
—CCC.
Published by: The Bureau of National Affairs, Inc., 1231 25th St., NW, Washington, DC 20037. TEL 800-372-1033, 800-452-7773, FAX 800-253-0332, customercare@bna.com, http://www.bna.com/products/lit/pldm.htm. Subscr. to: 9435 Key West Ave, Rockville, MD 20850.

PRODUCT SAFETY LETTER. see *PUBLIC HEALTH AND SAFETY*

PRODUCTION AND OPERATIONS MANAGEMENT. see *BUSINESS AND ECONOMICS—Management*

PRODUCTION PLANNING & CONTROL. see *ENGINEERING—Computer Applications*

338   PER   ISSN 0032-9908
PRODUCTIVIDAD. Text in Spanish. 1961. a. free. adv. abstr.; charts; illus. **Document type:** *Government.*
Published by: Ministerio de Trabajo y Promocion Social, Centro Nacional de Productividad (CENIP), Ave. Paseo De La Republica, 3101 Piso 9, Apdo Postal 5442, San Isidro, Lima 100, Peru. TEL 51-14-417033. Ed. Alfonso Luna Victoria Sanchez. Circ: 2,500.

658.5   IND   ISSN 0032-9924
PRODUCTIVITY. Text in English. 1959. q. INR 300, USD 80. adv. bk.rev. illus.; stat. index, cum.index: vols.1-17 (1959-1976). **Document type:** *Academic/Scholarly.* **Description:** Provides research based techno-managerial expertise for invigorating the economy.
Indexed: CRIA, CRICC, ILD, PAA&I, TTI.
Published by: (National Productivity Council), New Age International Pvt. Ltd., Journals Division, 4835-24 Ansari Rd., Darya Ganj, New Delhi, 110 002, India. TEL 91-11-326-1487, FAX 91-11-326-7437. Ed. D P Upadhyay. Circ: 3,000.

338   IND   ISSN 0970-5597
PRODUCTIVITY NEWS. Text in English. 1963. m. INR 50, USD 24. adv. bk.rev. illus. **Document type:** *Trade.* **Description:** Provides a wide coverage of significant developments in all sectors of national economy.
Published by: National Productivity Council, Business Management Section, Utpadakta Bhawan Lodi Rd., New Delhi, 110 003, India. Ed. Harkirat Singh. Circ: 2,500.

338   USA
PRODUCTS & SERVICES∗**.** Text in English. a. USD 49 to members; USD 65 to non-members. adv. **Document type:** *Directory.* **Description:** Contains contacts in a directory of product and service companies.
Published by: Value Retail News, 29399 US HWY 19 N, Ste 370, Clearwater, FL 33761-2138. TEL 727-536-4047, FAX 727-536-4047. Ed. Linda Humphers. Pub., R&P Ellis Rowland. Adv. contact Karen Knobeloch.

338.0029   USA
PRODUCTS CERTIFIED FOR CANADA DIRECTORY. Text in English. s-a. (2 vols./yr.). USD 30 (effective 1999). **Document type:** *Directory.* **Description:** Identifies companies that have demonstrated an ability to produce appliances, equipment, construction materials and components evaluated by UL in accordance with Canadian standards and other recognized documents for the product categories covered.
Published by: Underwriters Laboratories Inc., Publications, 33 Pfingsten Rd, Northbrook, IL 60062-2096. TEL 847-272-8800, FAX 847-272-0472.

PRODUCTS LIABILITY (COLORADO SPRINGS). see *LAW*

PRODUCTS LIABILITY: DESIGN AND MANUFACTURING DEFECTS. see *LAW*

338   URY
PRODUCTS OF URUGUAY. Text in Spanish. 1899. m. free. adv. **Document type:** *Directory.*
Former titles: Camara de Industrias del Uruguay. Guia de Socios y de Productos; Union Industrial Uruguaya. Guia de Socios y de Productos (0041-6908)

Published by: Camara de Industrias del Uruguay, Av. Lib. Brig. Gral. Lavalleja 1672, Montevideo, Uruguay. TEL 9023402.

338   DEU   ISSN 0344-6166
PRODUKTION; Die Wirtschaftszeitung fuer die deutsche Industrie. Text in German. 1962. w. EUR 69; EUR 2.80 newsstand/cover (effective 2005). adv. charts; illus. **Document type:** *Newspaper, Trade.* **Description:** Reports on new developments in production, improvements in company organization, economic trends in companies, markets and industry branches.
Former titles (until 1978): Produktion. Ausgabe fuer Betriebsleiter (0344-6069); (until 1975): Produktion (0032-9967)
Indexed: RefZh.
Published by: Verlag Moderne Industrie AG & Co. KG, Justus-von-Liebig-Str 1, Landsberg, 86899, Germany. TEL 49-8191-1250, FAX 49-8191-125211, pro@mi-verlag.de, info@mi-verlag.de, http://www.produktion.de/pr/, http://www.mi-verlag.de. Ed. Eduard Altmann. Adv. contact Michael Klotz. B&W page EUR 9,980; trim 190 x 270. Circ: 47,185 (paid and controlled).

338   USA
PROFILE (SKOKIE); a newsmagazine for the people of Brunswick. Text in English. 1964. q. free. back issues avail. **Description:** News of the activities of Brunswick Corporation and its people.
Published by: Brunswick Corporation, One N Field Ct, Lake Forest, IL 60045-4811. TEL 847-735-4457, FAX 847-735-4765. Ed., R&P Eugene Fisher. Circ: 30,000 (controlled).

338   ITA   ISSN 0391-8351
PROGRAMMAZIONE IN SARDEGNA. Text in Italian. 1966. 6/yr. free. bk.rev. stat.
Published by: Centro Regionale di Programmazione, Via Goffredo Mameli, 88, Cagliari, CA 09123, Italy. TEL 070-6064659, FAX 070-6064684. Circ: 5,500.

338   RUS   ISSN 0033-1163
T4   CODEN: PAKBAG
PROMYSHLENNOST' ARMENII. Text in Russian. 1958. m. charts. index.
Indexed: ChemAb, RASB.
—CASDDS.
Published by: Izdatel'stvo Kniga, Ul Gor'kogo 50, Moscow, 125047, Russian Federation.

338   RUS   ISSN 0033-1171
HD28
PROMYSHLENNOST' BELORUSSII. Text in Russian. 1958. m. charts. index.
Indexed: ChemAb, RASB.
Published by: Izdatel'stvo Kniga, Ul Gor'kogo 50, Moscow, 125047, Russian Federation.

338.9   VEN
PROSPECCION SIGLO 21. VENEZUELA ANO 2000∗**.** Text in Spanish. 1969. q. bibl.; stat.
Published by: Universidad Catolica Andres Bello, Centro de Estudios del Futuro de Venezuela, Apdo 29068, Caracas, DF 1023-A, Venezuela.

338   GBR
▼ **PROTOTYPE.** Text in English. 2003. q. free to qualified personnel. **Document type:** *Magazine, Trade.* **Description:** Covers prototyping, technology, and direct manufacturing market.
Related titles: Online - full content ed.
Published by: Electronic Design Automation Ltd., 63-66 Hatton Garden, London, EC1N 8SR, United Kingdom. TEL 44-20-76811000, FAX 44-20-72425124, eda@edaltd.co.uk, http://www.edaltd.co.uk/magdownloads/. Ed. Al Dean.

333.7   USA   ISSN 0079-7634
➤ **PUBLIC POLICY ISSUES IN RESOURCE MANAGEMENT.** Text in English. 1965. irreg., latest 1986. price varies. **Document type:** *Monographic series, Academic/Scholarly.*
Published by: (University of Washington, Graduate School of Public Affairs), University of Washington Press, PO Box 50096, Seattle, WA 98145-5096. TEL 206-543-4050.

338   USA
THE PUBLIC PURCHASER. Text in English. 1998. bi-m. **Document type:** *Trade.*
Published by: C Q Press, Inc. (Subsidiary of: Congressional Quarterly, Inc.), 1255 22nd St., N.W., Ste. 400, Washington, DC 20037. TEL 202-729-1800, 800-432-2250, FAX 800-380-3810, customerservice@cq.com, http://www.cqpress.com/gethome.asp. Ed. Penelope Lemor. Circ: 25,000.

PUMP INDUSTRY ANALYST. see *MACHINERY*

338.7   IND
PUNJAB STATE INDUSTRIAL DEVELOPMENT CORPORATION. ANNUAL REPORT∗**.** Text in English. a. illus.; stat.
Published by: Punjab State Industrial Development Corporation, United Commercial Bank Bldg., 3rd Fl., Sector 17-B, Chandigarh, Haryana, India.

Q-NEWZ. see *BUSINESS AND ECONOMICS—Management*

338   ITA   ISSN 0391-6146
QUALE IMPRESA. Text in Italian. 1974. m. **Document type:** *Trade.*
Published by: Servizio Italiano Pubblicazioni Internazionali, Viale Pasteur 6, Rome, 00144, Italy. TEL 39-06-5903601, FAX 39-06-5903339. Ed. Paulo Annunziato. Circ: 10,000.

QUALITAET UND ZUVERLAESSIGKEIT; Zeitschrift fuer industrielles Qualitaetsmanagement. see *METROLOGY AND STANDARDIZATION*

QUALITY ASSURANCE INSTITUTE. JOURNAL. see *METROLOGY AND STANDARDIZATION*

QUALITY TODAY. see *METROLOGY AND STANDARDIZATION*

QUARTERLY BUSINESS FAILURES. see *BUSINESS AND ECONOMICS—Economic Situation And Conditions*

338.5   JPN   ISSN 0913-1841
HC462.9
QUARTERLY FORECAST OF JAPANESE ECONOMY. Text in Japanese; Summaries in English. 1967. 3/yr. JPY 18,000 (effective 2000). stat. **Description:** Provides an unbiased short-term forecast of Japanese business and economy.
Former titles: Quarterly Forecast of Japan's Economy by the S A Method (0910-075X); Eighteen Month Forecast of Japan's Economy (0013-2594)
Indexed: PROMT.
Published by: (Economic Analysis Division), Japan Center for Economic Research, Nikkei Kayabacho Bldg, 6-1 Nihonbashikayaba-cho 2-chome, Chuo-ku, Tokyo, 103-0025, Japan. TEL 81-3-3639-2801, FAX 81-3-3639-2839. Circ: (controlled).

338   AUS   ISSN 0728-067X
QUEENSLAND. DEPARTMENT OF PRIMARY INDUSTRIES. CONFERENCE AND WORKSHOP SERIES. Text in English. 1981. irreg.
Indexed: ESPM.
Published by: Queensland, Department of Primary Industries, 80 Ann St., GPO Box 46, Brisbane, QLD 4001, Australia. TEL 61-7-34046999, FAX 61-7-34046900, callweb@dpi.qld.gov.au, http://www.dpi.qld.gov.au.

658   USA
R N AND W P L ENCYCLOPEDIA. (Registered Number & Wool Products Label) Text in English. a. USD 275 (effective 2000). **Document type:** *Directory, Trade.* **Description:** Lists RN and WPL identification numbers issued by the Federal Trade Commission.
Formerly: R N and W P L Encyclopedia and Yearbook
Media: Magnetic Tape. **Related titles:** Diskette ed.
Published by: Douglas Publications, Inc., Salesman's Guide, 2807 N Parham Rd, Ste 210, Richmond, VA 23294. TEL 804-762-4455, FAX 804-935-0271, http://www.douglaspublications.com. Ed. Chasity Roberts.

R S A JOURNAL. see *ART*

338   DEU   ISSN 1614-0923
▼ ▼ **R T EJOURNAL;** forum fuer rapid technolgie. (Rapid Technology) Text in English, German. 2004. irreg. free (effective 2005). **Document type:** *Journal, Academic/Scholarly.* **Description:** Publishes articles in the field of generative or additive manufacturing, also known as rapid technology.
Media: Online - full content.
Published by: Di P P - N R W, Postfach 270451, Cologne, 50510, Germany. TEL 49-221-40075124, FAX 49-221-40075190, dipp@hbz-nrw.de, http://www.rtejournal.de, http://www.dipp.nrw.de. Ed. Andreas Gebhardt.

338.7   IND
RAJASTHAN STATE WAREHOUSING CORPORATION. ANNUAL REPORT AND ACCOUNTS. Text in English. a. stat.
Published by: Rajasthan State Warehousing Corporation, Govind Bhavan, Subhash Marg, C-Scheme, Jaipur, Rajasthan 1, India.

REFERATIVNYI ZHURNAL. LEGKAYA PROMYSHLENNOST'. TEKHNOLOGIYA I OBORUDOVANIYE. see *BUSINESS AND ECONOMICS—Abstracting, Bibliographies, Statistics*

338.9   RUS   ISSN 0131-8330
REGIONAL'NAYA NAUKA O RAZMESHCHENII PROIZVODITEL'NYKH SIL∗**;** sbornik referativnykh rabot. Text in Russian. irreg. illus.
Published by: Rossiiskaya Akademiya Nauk, Sibirskoe Otdelenie, Institut Ekonomiki, Pr-t Akad Lavrent'eva 17, k 338, Novosibirsk, 630090, Russian Federation.

REHABILITATION INDUSTRIES CORPORATION. ANNUAL REPORT. see *MEDICAL SCIENCES—Physical Medicine And Rehabilitation*

338 USA ISSN 1067-0904
RENTAL PRODUCT NEWS. Text in English. 1978. bi-m. (plus a. product issue). USD 55 (effective 2005). adv. illus. **Document type:** *Magazine, Trade.* **Description:** Provides a complete source of product news and information for businesses involved in construction, industrial equipment, lawn maintenance gear and do-it-yourself tools.
Former titles: Rental (0898-7106); Rental Product News (0163-3112)
Related titles: Online - full text ed.: (from Gale Group, ProQuest Information & Learning).
—CCC.
Published by: Cygnus Business Media, Inc., 1233 Janesville Ave, Fort Atkinson, WI 53538-0803. TEL 920-563-1698, 800-547-7377, FAX 920-563-1699, http:// www.cygnusbusinessmedia.com. Pub., Adv. contact David Davel. Circ: 20,500 (controlled).

784 USA ISSN 0360-7348
ML1
REPLAY; a monthly publication for the coin-operated amusement machine industry. Key Title: RePlay Magazine. Text in English. 1975. m. USD 65 domestic; USD 90 in Canada & Mexico (effective Jun. 2001); USD 240 elsewhere (effective 2001). adv. illus. back issues avail. **Document type:** *Magazine, Trade.*
Published by: Replay Publishing, Inc., PO Box 7004, Tarzana, CA 91357. TEL 818-776-2280, FAX 818-776-2888, editor@replaymag.com, http://www.replaymag.com. Ed. Steve White. Pub. Ed Adlum. Adv. contact Barry Zweben. Circ: 4,116.

REPORT OF THE (YEAR) BUSINESS TRADE AND SERVICES SURVEY. see *BUSINESS AND ECONOMICS—Abstracting, Bibliographies, Statistics*

REPORT OF THE (YEAR) INDUSTRIAL CENSUS. see *BUSINESS AND ECONOMICS—Abstracting, Bibliographies, Statistics*

REPORT ON SMALL SCALE MANUFACTURING INDUSTRIES SURVEY. see *BUSINESS AND ECONOMICS—Abstracting, Bibliographies, Statistics*

REPRESENTATIVE. see *AGRICULTURE—Agricultural Equipment*

338.767 IND ISSN 0304-811X
HD9745.I44
REPUBLIC FORGE COMPANY. ANNUAL REPORT. Key Title: Annual Report - Republic Forge Company. Text in English. 1971 (14th ed.). a. stat.
Published by: Republic Forge Company, Maula Ali, Hyderabad, Andhra Pradesh 40, India.

RESEARCH DISCLOSURE. see *PATENTS, TRADEMARKS AND COPYRIGHTS*

338.5 LUX ISSN 0378-4479
HC241.2
RESULTS OF THE BUSINESS SURVEY CARRIED OUT AMONG MANAGEMENTS IN THE COMMUNITY. Text in Dutch, English, French, German, Italian. 1962. m. USD 130.
Formerly: Results of the Business Survey Carried Out Among Heads of Enterprises in the Community (0034-5857)
Indexed: ECI, IIS, RASB.
Published by: (European Commission BEL), European Commission, Office for Official Publications of the European Union, 2 Rue Mercier, Luxembourg, L-2985, Luxembourg.
Dist. in the U.S. by: Bernan Associates, Bernan, 4611-F Assembly Dr., Lanham, MD 20706-4391. TEL 301-459-0056, 800-274-4447.

338 COL ISSN 0034-8686
HC10
REVISTA DE PLANEACION Y DESARROLLO. Variant title: Planeacion y Desarrollo. Text in Spanish. 1969. irreg. COP 10,000 (effective 2005).
Indexed: AbHyg, AmH&L, HAPI, HistAb, IBR, IBSS, ILD, PAIS, RASB, RDA, TriticAb, WAE&RSA.
Published by: Departamento Nacional de Planeacion, Biblioteca, Calle 26 No. 13-19 2o piso, Bogota, DE, Colombia. TEL 57-1-5960300, morrego@@dnp.gov.co, http://www.dnp.gov.co/. Circ: 2,000.

REVUE D'ECONOMIE INDUSTRIELLE. see *BUSINESS AND ECONOMICS—Economic Situation And Conditions*

338 FRA ISSN 1282-5247
LA REVUE DES ENTREPRISES. Text in French. 1956 (no.142). m. adv. bk.rev. illus.; stat. index.
Former titles (until 1997): C N P F la Revue des Entreprises (0766-5520); (until 1981): C N P F Patronat (0399-8975); (until 1972): Patronat (0990-5618); (until 1969): Patronat Francais (0031-3165)
Indexed: CISA, PAIS, RASB.
Published by: Conseil National du Patronat Francais, 31 av. Pierre 1er de Serbie, Paris, Cedex 16 75784, France. TEL 40-69-44-44, FAX 47-23-47-32. Ed. Michel Frois. Circ: 20,000.

RIVISTA DELLE SOCIETA. see *LAW—Constitutional Law*

RIVISTA DI DIRITTO INDUSTRIALE. see *PATENTS, TRADEMARKS AND COPYRIGHTS*

ROLLADEN & SONNENSCHUTZ; Fachzeitschrift fuer das Rolladen- und Jalousiebauer-Handwerk. see *ARTS AND HANDICRAFTS*

RUMANIA. COMISIA NATIONALA PENTRU STATISTICA. BULETIN STATISTIC INDUSTRIE/RUMANIA. NATIONAL COMMISSION FOR STATISTICS. STATISTICAL BULLETIN - INDUSTRY. see *BUSINESS AND ECONOMICS—Abstracting, Bibliographies, Statistics*

338.47665 USA ISSN 1072-155X
RUSSIAN PETROLEUM INVESTOR. Text in English. 1992. m. USD 2,673 domestic; USD 2,773 foreign (effective 2005). **Document type:** *Journal, Trade.* **Description:** Covers key political and business events affecting the oil and gas industry in Central Asia, Russia, the Caspian, and the Baltics.
Related titles: Online - full content ed.
Published by: WorldTrade Executive, Inc., 2250 Main St, Ste 100, PO Box 761, Concord, MA 01742. TEL 978-287-0301, FAX 978-287-0302, smahapatra@wtexec.com, info@wtexec.com, http://www.wtexecutive.com/cms/content.jsp?id=com.tms.cms.section.Section_1018, http://www.wtexec.com. Ed. Inna Gaiduk. Pub. Gary A Brown. Adv. contact Jay Stanley.

SAMSOM BESLOTEN VENNOOTSCHAPPEN MET BEPERKTE AANSPRAKELIJKHEID. see *BUSINESS AND ECONOMICS*

338 BEL ISSN 0778-6158
SAMSOM SUBSIDIE-INFO. Text in Flemish. 1990. s-m. **Description:** Highlights sources of financing and support measures.
Published by: C E D Samsom (Subsidiary of: Wolters Samsom Belgie n.v.), Kouterveld 14, Diegem, 1831, Belgium. TEL 32-2-7231111.

339.3 DEU ISSN 0179-3608
SCHRIFTEN ZU DISTRIBUTION UND HANDEL. Text in German. 1986. irreg., latest vol.35, 2001. **Document type:** *Monographic series, Academic/Scholarly.*
Published by: (Westfaelische Wilhelms-Universitaet Muenster, Lehrstuhl fuer Betriebswirtschaftslehre, insb. Distribution und Handel), Peter Lang GmbH Europaeischer Verlag der Wissenschaften, Eschborner Landstr 42-50, Frankfurt Am Main, 60489, Germany. TEL 49-69-7807050, FAX 49-69-78070543, zentrale.frankfurt@peterlang.com, http://www.peterlang.de.

338 DEU ISSN 1860-1758
▼ **SCHRIFTEN ZUR OEKOTROPHOLOGIE.** Text in German. 2005. irreg. price varies. **Document type:** *Monographic series, Academic/Scholarly.*
Published by: Verlag Dr. Kovac, Arnoldstr 49, Hamburg, 22763, Germany. TEL 49-40-3988800, FAX 49-40-39888055, info@verlagdrkovac.de, http://www.verlagdrkovac.de/17-4.htm.

338 CHE
SCHWEIZER INDUSTRIE UND VERKEHRS REVUE. Text in German. q.
Published by: Verlag Hugo Zwerger, Stationsstr 9, Postfach, Aadorf, 8355, Switzerland. TEL 052-473738. Ed. H Zwerger. Circ: 4,000.

338 COD ISSN 0377-5135
T175 CODEN: STICD8
SCIENCES, TECHNIQUES, INFORMATIONS C R I A C. Text in French. irreg. illus.
Formerly: Centre de Recherche Industrielles en Afrique Centrale. Bulletin d'Information
Published by: Centre de Recherches Industrielles en Afrique Centrale, BP 54, Lubumbashi, Congo, Dem. Republic.

338 DEU ISSN 0936-6962
SCOPE; Industrie-Magazin fuer Fuehrungskraefte. Text in German. 1961. m. free. **Document type:** *Trade.*
Incorporates: Cogito (0178-8728); Formerly (until 1986): Scope-Journal (0048-9735)
Related titles: Online - full text ed.: (from LexisNexis).
—GNLM.
Published by: Hoppenstedt Bonnier Zeitschriften GmbH, Havelstr. 9, Darmstadt, 64295, Germany. TEL 49-6151-380311, FAX 49-6151-380341, info@hopp.de, hbz@hopp.de, http://www.scope-online.de, http://www.hoppenstedt-zeitschriften.de. Ed. Dieter Capelle. Circ: 80,000 (controlled).

SECOM ANNUAL REPORT (YEAR). see *CRIMINOLOGY AND LAW ENFORCEMENT—Security*

SENEGAL. MINISTERE DE L'ECONOMIE, DES FINANCES ET DU PLAN. INDICE DE LA PRODUCTION INDUSTRIELLE. see *BUSINESS AND ECONOMICS—Abstracting, Bibliographies, Statistics*

SENEGAL. MINISTERE DE L'ECONOMIE, DES FINANCES ET DU PLAN. INDICE DES PRIX A LA CONSOMMATION. see *BUSINESS AND ECONOMICS—Abstracting, Bibliographies, Statistics*

338 USA ISSN 1058-1626
HD9981.1
SERVICE INDUSTRIES U S A; industry analyses, statistics and leading organizations. Text in English. 1992. biennial, latest 1998, 4th ed. USD 240 (effective 2003).
Published by: Gale Group (Subsidiary of: Thomson Corporation), 27500 Drake Rd, Farmington Hills, MI 48331-3535. TEL 248-699-8061, 800-877-4253, FAX 248-699-4253, galeord@gale.com, http://www.gale.com. Ed. Arsen J Darnay.

338 FRA
SERVICES-MARCHE COMMUN EUROPEEN. Text in French. 1965. q. adv. bk.rev. Supplement avail.
Related titles: Magnetic Tape ed.
Published by: Services G.E.C.E., 23 rue de l'Esperance, Paris, 75013, France. Circ: 40,000.

658 JPN
SEVEN - ELEVEN JAPAN. (YEAR) ANNUAL REPORT. Text in English. 1974. a. charts; illus.; mkt.; stat. **Document type:** *Corporate.*
Published by: Seven - Eleven Japan Co. Ltd. (Subsidiary of: Ito-Yokado Co., Ltd.), 1-4 Shibakoen 4-chome, Minato-ku, Tokyo, 105-0011, Japan. TEL 03-3459-3711, FAX 03-3438-3724.

338 CHN ISSN 1004-7816
SHANGHAI ZHILIANG✻ /SHANGHAI QUALITY. Text in Chinese. 1983. m. **Document type:** *Journal, Academic/Scholarly.*
Published by: Shanghai Zhiliang Zhishe, 74, Taian Lu, 304-nong, Shanghai, 200052, China. sg@sag.org.cn, http://shzl.periodicals.net.cn/default.html. **Co-sponsors:** Shanghai Zhiliang Kexue Yanjiuyuan; Shanghai Zhiliang Guanli Xiehui/Shanghai Quality Administration Society.

338 USA
SHAVINGS FROM THE CHRONICLE OF THE EARLY AMERICAN INDUSTRIES ASSOCIATION. Text in English. 1971. 6/yr. USD 30 (effective 2002); includes Chronicle. bk.rev. reprint service avail. from PQC. **Document type:** *Newsletter, Academic/Scholarly.*
Published by: Early American Industries Association, 167 Bakerville Rd, South Dartmouth, MA 02748. Ed. Terry L Hansen. Circ: 3,300.

SIGNALS. see *BUSINESS AND ECONOMICS—Small Business*

338.9 SGP ISSN 0080-9683
HC445.8
SINGAPORE. ECONOMIC DEVELOPMENT BOARD. ANNUAL REPORT. Text in English. 1962. a. price varies.
Published by: Economic Development Board, 250 N. Bridge Rd, 24-00 Raffles City Tower, Singapore, 0617, Singapore. TEL 336-2288. Circ: 10,000.

338 SGP
TA368
SINGAPORE STANDARDS CATALOGUE. Text in English. 1977. biennial. **Document type:** *Catalog.*
Published by: Singapore Productivity and Standards Board, One Science Park Dr., Singapore Science Park, Singapore, 118221, Singapore. TEL 65-7729786, FAX 65-7761280. Circ: 1,500.

SISTEMAS DE CALIDAD. see *METROLOGY AND STANDARDIZATION*

333 USA ISSN 1080-7799
SITE SELECTION. Text in English. 1956. bi-m. USD 85 per issue domestic; USD 125 per issue foreign (effective 2005). adv. illus. cum.index: 1956-1994. reprint service avail. from PQC,ISI. **Document type:** *Magazine, Trade.* **Description:** Focuses on business expansion planning with original research and analysis, interviews, case studies and industry reports. Features major reference guides to new plant construction, area economic development agencies, Utilities. Covers infrastructure and political-business climates.
Former titles (until 1994): Site Selection and Industrial Development (1041-3073); (until 1984): Site Selection Handbook (0192-0901); (until 1977): Industrial Development's Site Selection Handbook (0149-4600); (until 1976): Site Selection Handbook (0080-9810); (until 1970): Industrial Development's Site Selection Handbook; Incorporated (in 1984): Industrial Development (0097-3033); Which was formerly (until 1967): Industrial Development and Manufacturers Record (0019-8137); Which was formed by the 1958 merger of: Manufacturers Record; (1954-1958): Industrial Development (0148-7582)
Related titles: Microform ed.: (from PQC); Online - full text ed.: (from H.W. Wilson, O C L C Online Computer Library Center, Inc.).
Indexed: ABIn, BPI, BPIA, BusI, LRI, ManagCont, PAIS, PROMT, T&II.
—BLDSC (8286.424950), IE, ingenta. **CCC.**
Published by: Conway Data, Inc., 6625 The Corners Pkwy, Ste 200, Norcross, GA 30092. TEL 770-446-6996, FAX 770-263-8825, mark.arend@conway.com, http://www.sitenet.com. Ed. Mark Arend. Pub. H. McKinley Conway. adv.: B&W page USD 7,220, color page USD 9,560; trim 8.125 x 10.875. Circ: 45,000.

338 USA ISSN 1539-4069
SIX SIGMA FORUM. Text in English. 2001. q. USD 75 domestic to individuals; USD 85 foreign to individuals; USD 120 domestic to institutions; USD 150 foreign to institutions (effective 2005). adv. **Document type:** *Magazine, Trade.*
Description: Covers topics about applying Six Sigma methodology to achieve defect-free business processes.
Related titles: Online - full text ed.: (from O C L C Online Computer Library Center, Inc., ProQuest Information & Learning).
Indexed: ABIn.
Published by: American Society for Quality, PO Box 3005, Milwaukee, WI 53201-3005. TEL 800-248-1946, FAX 414-272-1734, cs@asq.org, http://www.sixsigmaforum.com, http://www.asq.org.

338 NOR ISSN 0333-3868
SKATTEBETALEREN. Text in Norwegian. 1952. 7/yr. NOK 145 (effective 1998). adv. bk.rev. **Document type:** *Consumer.*
Formerly: Skatt og Budsjett
Published by: Skattebetalerforeningen, Postboks 213, Sentrum, Oslo, 0103, Norway. TEL 47-22-42-07-27, FAX 47-22-33-71-80. Ed. Erik Stenbeck. adv.: B&W page NOK 12,700, color page NOK 17,200. Circ: 24,090.

658 USA ISSN 1547-0369
SMART CUSTOMER SERVICE. Text in English. 1996. bi-w. USD 195 (effective 2005). **Document type:** *Newsletter, Trade.*
Description: Provides a practical guide based on the experiences and recommendations of customer service and management experts.
Formerly (until 199?): The Supervisor's Guide to Improved Customer Service and Retention (1089-7100)
Published by: Clement Communications, Inc., 10 LaCrue Ave, PO Box 36, Concordville, PA 19331. TEL 610-459-4200, 888-358-5858, FAX 610-459-4582, editor@clement.com, http://www.clement.com.

338 SEN
SOCIETE NATIONALE D'ETUDE ET DE PROMOTION INDUSTRIELLE. BULLETIN D'INFORMATION INDUSTRIELLE. Text in French. bi-m. XOF 3,000.
Published by: Societe Nationale d'Etude et de Promotion Industrielle, 14 rue Maunoury, BP 100, Dakar, Senegal.

338.0029 USA ISSN 1055-906X
SORKINS DIRECTORY OF BUSINESS & GOVERNMENT (CHICAGO EDITION). Text in English. 1983. a. (print edition; q. , electronic editions). USD 1,550 for Chicago ed.; USD 945 for St. Louis ed.; USD 945 for Kansas City ed.. **Document type:** *Directory.* **Description:** Features profiles of major companies in the region, and their executives. Includes government and non-profit organizations.
Related titles: CD-ROM ed.; Online - full text ed.; Regional ed(s).: Sorkins Directory of Business & Government (St. Louis Edition). ISSN 0748-0458; Sorkins Directory of Business & Government (Kansas City Edition). ISSN 0894-1033.
Published by: Sorkins Directories, Inc., 1001, Craig, MO 63146. TEL 314-872-2101, 800-758-3228, FAX 314-872-2102, http://www.sorkins.com. Ed. Murray Sorkin. Pubs. Murray Sorkin, Pam Sorkin.

SOUTH AFRICA. STATISTICS SOUTH AFRICA. CENSUS OF MANUFACTURING - MATERIALS PURCHASED AND MANUFACTURES SOLD. see *BUSINESS AND ECONOMICS—Abstracting, Bibliographies, Statistics*

SOUTH AFRICA. STATISTICS SOUTH AFRICA. CENSUS OF MANUFACTURING - PRINCIPAL STATISTICS ON A REGIONAL BASIS PART-I. see *BUSINESS AND ECONOMICS—Abstracting, Bibliographies, Statistics*

SOUTH AFRICA. STATISTICS SOUTH AFRICA. CENSUS OF MANUFACTURING - STATISTICS ACCORDING TO MAJOR GROUPS AND SUBGROUPS. see *BUSINESS AND ECONOMICS—Abstracting, Bibliographies, Statistics*

SOUTH AFRICA. STATISTICS SOUTH AFRICA. STATISTICAL RELEASE. CENSUS OF MANUFACTURING. see *BUSINESS AND ECONOMICS—Abstracting, Bibliographies, Statistics*

SOUTH AFRICA. STATISTICS SOUTH AFRICA. STATISTICAL RELEASE. MANUFACTURING - CAPITAL EXPENDITURE ON NEW ASSETS. see *BUSINESS AND ECONOMICS—Abstracting, Bibliographies, Statistics*

SOUTH AFRICA. STATISTICS SOUTH AFRICA. STATISTICAL RELEASE. MANUFACTURING - PRODUCTION AND SALES. see *BUSINESS AND ECONOMICS—Abstracting, Bibliographies, Statistics*

SOUTH AFRICA. STATISTICS SOUTH AFRICA. STATISTICAL RELEASE. MANUFACTURING STATISTICS: BASIC METAL AND FABRICATED METAL PRODUCTS, MACHINERY AND EQUIPMENT, MOTOR VEHICLES AND PARTS AND MISCELLANEOUS PRODUCTS. see *BUSINESS AND ECONOMICS—Abstracting, Bibliographies, Statistics*

SOUTH AFRICA. STATISTICS SOUTH AFRICA. STATISTICAL RELEASE. MANUFACTURING STATISTICS: CHEMICAL, RUBBER, PLASTIC, GLASS AND NON-METALLIC MINERAL PRODUCTS. see *BUSINESS AND ECONOMICS—Abstracting, Bibliographies, Statistics*

SOUTH AFRICA. STATISTICS SOUTH AFRICA. STATISTICAL RELEASE. MANUFACTURING STATISTICS: PRODUCTS MANUFACTURED: FOODS, BEVERAGES AND TOBACCO PRODUCTS. see *BUSINESS AND ECONOMICS—Abstracting, Bibliographies, Statistics*

SOUTH AFRICA. STATISTICS SOUTH AFRICA. STATISTICAL RELEASE. MANUFACTURING STATISTICS: PRODUCTS MANUFACTURED: TEXTILES, CLOTHING, LEATHER AND LEATHER PRODUCTS, WOOD AND WOOD PRODUCTS, PAPER AND PAPER PRODUCTS AND PRINTING. see *BUSINESS AND ECONOMICS—Abstracting, Bibliographies, Statistics*

SOUTH AFRICA. STATISTICS SOUTH AFRICA. STATISTICAL RELEASE. UTILIZATION OF PRODUCTION CAPACITY. see *BUSINESS AND ECONOMICS—Abstracting, Bibliographies, Statistics*

SOUTHERN FARM EQUIPMENT MANUFACTURERS. NEWSLETTER. see *AGRICULTURE—Agricultural Equipment*

338 ESP
SPAIN. MINISTERIO DE INDUSTRIA. RESULTADOS DE LA ENCUESTA DE COYUNTURA INDUSTRIAL: SECTOR INDUSTRIAL. Text in Spanish. 1963. irreg. included with the review Economia Industrial. bk.rev.
Published by: Ministerio de Industria, Paseo Castellana, 160, Madrid, 28046, Spain. Circ: 10,000.

338 FIN ISSN 1457-0637
SPARRAAJA. Text in Finnish. 1966. 8/yr. EUR 100 (effective 2005). adv. **Document type:** *Magazine, Trade.*
Former titles (until 2000): Myyntineuvoja (0355-3256); (until 1973): A & O -Myyntineuroja
Published by: Suomen Spar oy, Tiilenpolttajankatu 5, PO Box 140, Vantaa, 01720, Finland. TEL 358-20-5321, FAX 358-20-5326023, info@spar.fi, http://www.spar.fi. adv.: page EUR 2,790. Circ: 3,500.

SPORTING GOODS AGENTS ASSOCIATION. MEMBERSHIP ROSTER. see *SPORTS AND GAMES*

SPORTS GOODS BUYER'S GUIDE. see *SPORTS AND GAMES*

STANDARD & POOR'S REGISTER OF CORPORATIONS, DIRECTORS AND EXECUTIVES. see *BUSINESS AND ECONOMICS—Management*

STANDARDS IN DEFENCE NEWS. see *METROLOGY AND STANDARDIZATION*

338 794.8 USA ISSN 0739-1048
STAR TECH JOURNAL. Text in English. 1979. m. USD 81. adv. **Document type:** *Trade.* **Description:** Provides information on the technology of the coin-op entertainment industry.
Published by: Star Tech Journal, Inc., PO Box 35, Medford, NJ 08055. TEL 609-654-5544, FAX 609-654-1441, info@startechjournal.com, http://www.startechjournal.com. Ed., Pub. James Calore. Circ: 4,500.

338 600 USA
START. Text in English. m. USD 39.95 domestic; USD 49.95 in Canada; USD 69.95 elsewhere (effective 2001). adv. **Document type:** *Magazine, Trade.* **Description:** Defines concepts, explains technologies, and translates technical solutions into business benefits for manufacturing executives around the world.
Related titles: Online - full text ed.
Published by: Specialty Publishing Co., 135 E Saint Charles Rd, Carol Stream, IL 60188. TEL 630-933-0844, FAX 630-933-0845, info@startmag.com, http://www.startmag.com. Ed. John Buell. Pub. Peggy Smedley. Adv. contact Robert Parzy.

354 AUS
STATE DEVELOPMENT 2000 (PLUS). Text in English. 1973. bi-m. back issues avail. **Document type:** *Government.*
Description: Highlights Queensland's innovative manufacturers with stories of their achievements.
Former titles (until 1998): Better Business for Queensland; (until May, 1996): Queensland. Department of Tourism, Small Business and Industry. Industry; Which incorporated (in Dec. 1992): Queensland. Department of Business, Industry and Regional Development. Client Update; Formerly (until Nov. 1990): Queensland. Department of Manufacturing and Commerce. Industry; (until Dec. 1989): Queensland. Department of Industry Development. Industry
Published by: Department of State Development, Level 22, 111 George St, Brisbane, QLD 4000, Australia. TEL 61-7-3234-1653, FAX 61-7-3234-1520, bron.mcclain@sd.qld.gov.au. Circ: 10,000.

338 GRC ISSN 0072-7458
HC295
STATE OF GREEK INDUSTRY IN (YEAR). Text in English. 1940-1977; resumed 1984. a. free.
Published by: Federation of Greek Industries, 5 Xenophontos St, Athens, 105 57, Greece. Circ: 4,000.

STATIONERY & OFFICE BUYERS' GUIDE. see *BUSINESS AND ECONOMICS—Office Equipment And Services*

338 FRA ISSN 1249-2965
STRATEGIQUE LOGISTIQUE. Text in French. 1997. m. (10/yr.). EUR 68.60 domestic; EUR 91.47 foreign (effective 2002).
Indexed: RefZh.
Published by: Societe d'Edition pour la Promotion de la Logistique, 31 Cours des Juillottes, Maisons-Alfort, 94700, France. TEL 33-1-41790888, FAX 33-1-48939851, http://www.logisticsstrategy.com.

338 DEU ISSN 1613-9100
▼ **STUDIEN ZUM KONSUMENTENVERHALTEN.** Text in German. 2004. irreg., latest vol.2, 2005. price varies. **Document type:** *Monographic series, Academic/Scholarly.*
Published by: Verlag Dr. Kovac, Arnoldstr 49, Hamburg, 22763, Germany. TEL 49-40-3988800, FAX 49-40-39888055, info@verlagdrkovac.de, http://www.verlagdrkovac.de/3-19.htm.

STUDIES IN INDUSTRIAL ORGANIZATION. see *BUSINESS AND ECONOMICS—Economic Systems And Theories, Economic History*

SUB-CONTRACT NEWS. see *BUSINESS AND ECONOMICS—Marketing And Purchasing*

338 ESP
SUMINISTROS INDUSTRIALES. Text in Spanish. 6/yr.
Description: Covers professional hardware and associated industries.
Address: Via Augusta, 59, 8o Of. 812, Barcelona, 08006, Spain. TEL 3-2378865, FAX 3-4158688. Ed. Salvador Beltran Nunez. Circ: 5,000.

SUPPLY CHAIN PHARMAFILE. see *PHARMACY AND PHARMACOLOGY*

338 USA ISSN 1520-9288
SUPPLY CHAIN REPORT. Text in English. 1998. w. free (effective 2004). **Document type:** *Newsletter.*
Published by: Penton Media, Inc. (Subsidiary of: Pittway Company), 1300 E 9th St, Cleveland, OH 44114-1503. TEL 216-696-7000, FAX 216-696-0177, http://www.penton.com.

SUPPLY, DISTRIBUTION, MANUFACTURING & SERVICE; supply and service companies & equipment manufacturers. see *PETROLEUM AND GAS*

338 ISR ISSN 0081-9743
SURVEYS AND DEVELOPMENT PLANS OF INDUSTRY IN ISRAEL/HATA'ASIYAH BE-YISRAEL. Text in English. 1964. a. free. **Document type:** *Government.*
Formerly: Survey of Industry in Israel
Related titles: Hebrew ed.
Published by: Ministry of Industry and Trade, Jerusalem, Israel. Ed. H Ross. Circ: 1,000.

SVERIGES STOERSTA FOERETAG/LARGEST COMPANIES IN SWEDEN; med nyckeltal foer naeringslivet under (aar); with financial data for Sweden's 10,000 largest companies. see *BUSINESS AND ECONOMICS—Trade And Industrial Directories*

338 SWE ISSN 1100-7818
SWEDEN. KONJUNKTURINSTITUTET. WORKING PAPERS. Text in English. 1984. irreg. free (effective 2005). back issues avail. **Document type:** *Monographic series, Academic/Scholarly.*
Description: Contains research results from the National Institute of Economic Research, Sweden.
Formerly (until 1989): Konjunkturinstitutet.. Meddelandeserie (0282-5392)
Published by: Konjunkturinstitutet/National Institute of Economic Research, Kungsgatan 12-14, PO Box 3116, Stockholm, 10362, Sweden. TEL 46-8-4535900, FAX 46-8-4535980, ki@konj.se, http://swopec.hhs.se/nierwp, http://www.konj.se.

338 SWE ISSN 0039-7296
HC371
THE SWEDISH ECONOMY. Text in English. 1961. q. SEK 937; SEK 937 per issue (effective 2005). charts; stat. index. **Document type:** *Journal, Academic/Scholarly.*
Related titles: Online - full text ed.: (from Gale Group); ♦ Swedish ed.: Konjunkturlaeget. ISSN 0023-3463.
Indexed: KES, PAIS, PROMT, RASB.
Published by: Konjunkturinstitutet/National Institute of Economic Research, Kungsgatan 12-14, PO Box 3116, Stockholm, 10362, Sweden. TEL 46-8-4535900, FAX 46-8-4535980, ki@konj.se, http://www.konj.se. Ed. Mats Dillon TEL 46-8-4535966.

338 658.0029 USA
SYSTEM SAFETY SOCIETY. DIRECTORY OF CONSULTANTS✶. Text in English. a. USD 50; to non-members; members $10. **Document type:** *Directory.* **Description:** Lists consultants in system and product safety.
Published by: System Safety Society, Inc., PO Box 70, Unionville, VA 22567-0070. http://www.system-safety.org/. Circ: 1,100.

T V NEWS (NEW YORK). see *COMMUNICATIONS—Television And Cable*

338 TWN ISSN 0039-9108
TAIWAN INDUSTRIAL PANORAMA. Text in Chinese. 1962. m. free. stat.
Indexed: KES.
Published by: Ministry of Economic Affairs, Industrial Development & Investment Center, 7 Roosevelt Rd, Sec 1, 10th Fl, Taipei, Taiwan. TEL 02-3947213, FAX 02-3926835, TELEX 10634-INVEST. Ed. Ming Ching Su. Circ: 5,000.

TAIWAN TOYS & CHILDREN'S ARTICLES BUYERS' GUIDE. see *GIFTWARE AND TOYS*

338.5 JPN
HC462.9
TANKAN REPORT - SHORT-TERM ECONOMIC SURVEY OF ENTERPRISES IN JAPAN. Text in Japanese. 1970. q. JPY 1,220 per issue (effective 1998). stat. 190 p./no.; **Description:** Provides detailed results of the short-term economic surveys conducted in March, June, September, and December, by the Bank of Japan. Aims to be useful for analyzing economic trends.
Former titles: Tankan - Short-Term Economic Survey of Enterprises in Japan (0916-670X); (until 1990): Kigyo Tanki Keizai Kansoku Chosa - Short-Term Economic Survey of Enterprises in Japan (0387-0642); Which incorporates: Shuyo Kigyo Tanki Keizai Kansoku Chosa - Short-Term Economic Survey of Principal Enterprises in Japan (0387-0634); Supersedes (in 1974): Shuyo Kigyo, Chusho Kigyo Tanki Keizai Kansoku (0387-0626); Which was formed by the 1970 merger of: Shuyo Kigyo Tanki Keizai Kansoku (0549-3188); Which was formerly (until 1966): Chusho Kigyo no Gyokyo Yosoku (0387-060X)
Media: Microform.
Published by: (Research and Statistics Department), Bank of Japan/Nippon Ginko, c/o Public Relations Department, 2-1-1 Hongoku-cho-Nihonbashi, Chuo-ku, Tokyo, 1030000, Japan. TEL 81-3-3279-1111, FAX 81-3-3510-1374, http://www.boj.or.jp/en.index.htm. **Dist. by:** Tokiwa Sohgoh Service Co. Ltd., Publication and Research Department, Kyodo Bldg, 2-4 Hongokucho, Nihonbashi 3-chome, Chuo-ku, Tokyo 103-0027, Japan. TEL 81-3-3270-5713, FAX 81-3-3270-5710; **Overseas dist. by:** Japan Publications Trading Co., Ltd., Book Export II Dept, PO Box 5030, Tokyo International, Tokyo 101-3191, Japan. TEL 81-3-32923753, FAX 81-3-32920410, infoserials@jptco.co.jp, http://www.jptco.co.jp.

338 TZA
TANZANIA. PLANNING COMMISSION. MACRO PLANNING DEPARTMENT. HALI YA UCHUMI WA TAIFA - ANNUAL ECONOMIC SURVEY. Text in English. 1973. a. USD 3. stat. **Document type:** *Government.*
Former titles: Tanzania. Ministry of Planning and Economic Affairs. Hali Ya Uchumi Wa Taifa - Annual Economic Survey; Tanzania. Ministry of Economic Affairs and Development Planning. Hali Ya Uchumi Wa Taifa - Annual Economic Survey
Published by: Planning Commission, Macro Planning Department, PO Box 9242, Dar Es Salaam, Tanzania. TEL 255-51-29418, TELEX 41651 DEPLAN TZ. Circ: 1,000. **Subscr. to:** Government Publications Agency, PO Box 1801, Dar Es Salaam, Tanzania.

338 USA ISSN 1051-1636
TS155.A1
TARGET (WHEELING); innovation at work. Text in English. 1985. 4/yr. free to libraries. bk.rev. cum.index: 1983-1994. back issues avail. **Document type:** *Trade.*
Published by: Association for Manufacturing Excellence, 380 W Palatine Rd, Wheeling, IL 60090-5863. TEL 847-520-3282, FAX 847-520-0163, info@ame.org, http://www.ame.org/main.php. Ed. Robert W Hall. R&P Joann Weitzenfled. Adv. contact Dennis Frantsve. Circ: 6,500.

TECH TALK. see *METROLOGY AND STANDARDIZATION*

338 JPN ISSN 0911-5544
T1
➤ **TECHNO JAPAN;** a monthly survey of Japanese technology and industry. Text in English. 1968. m. JPY 24,000; JPY 28,000 in Asia; JPY 32,000 in Central America; JPY 32,000 in Europe; JPY 34,000 elsewhere (effective 1999). adv. s-a. index. back issues avail. **Document type:** *Academic/Scholarly.*
Formerly (until 1985): Technocrat (0040-1609)
Indexed: AJEE, JCT, JTA, RASB.
—BLDSC (8755.460800), CISTI, IE, ingenta.
Published by: Fuji Technology Press Ltd., 4F Toranomon Sangyo Bldg, 2-29, Toranomon 1-chome, Minato-ku, Tokyo, 105-0001, Japan. TEL 81-3-35080051, FAX 81-3-35920648, tae00762@niftyserve.or.jp. Ed., Pub. Keiji Hayashi. Circ: 18,756.

➤ **TECHNOLOGY, RISK AND SOCIETY;** an international series in risk analysis. see *BUSINESS AND ECONOMICS—Economic Systems And Theories, Economic History*

➤ **TECNOINDUSTRIA.** see *TECHNOLOGY: COMPREHENSIVE WORKS*

338.3 UKR ISSN 0233-9897
TEKHNICHESKII PROGRESS I EFFEKTIVNOST' PROIZVODSTVA. Text in Russian. irreg. USD 10. illus.
Formerly (until 1981): Ekonomika Promyslovosti
Related titles: ♦ Series: Informatsionno-Izmeritel'naya Tekhnika; ♦ Magnitnoimpul'snaya Obrabotka Metallov; ♦ Elektroenergetika i Avtomatizatsiya Energoustanovok. ISSN 0453-7998; Kharkivskyi Politekhnichnyi Instytut. Vestnik.
Published by: Kharkivs'kyi Politekhnichnyi Instytut, Ul Frunze 21, Kharkov, 310002, Ukraine.

384.6 GBR ISSN 1359-5466
TELECOM MARKETS. Text in English. 1984. fortn. GBP 995, EUR 1,493, USD 1,890; GBP 2,985, EUR 4,478, USD 5,671 combined subscription print & online eds. (effective 2004). **Document type:** *Newsletter, Trade.* **Description:** Provides information and analysis on telecommunications markets: convergence between deregulation and free markets, telephony and computing, voice, image and data, state monopoly, and private capital.
Formerly (until 1992): FinTech 1 Telecom Markets (0267-1484)
Related titles: Microform ed.: (from PQC); Online - full text ed.: (from Data-Star, Gale Group, Northern Light Technology, Inc., O C L C Online Computer Library Center, Inc., ProQuest Information & Learning).
Indexed: B&I.
—BLDSC (8779.462800), IE, Infotrieve, ingenta. **CCC.**
Published by: Baskerville (Subsidiary of: T & F Informa plc), Sheepen Place, Colchester, Essex C03 3LP, United Kingdom. TEL 44-20-70175537, FAX 44-20-70174783, telecoms.enquiries@informa.com, http://www.baskerville.telecoms.com/. Ed. Anthony Cox.

338 BRA ISSN 0495-0879
TENDENCIA. Text in Portuguese. 1973. m. USD 26. illus. **Document type:** *Consumer.*
Published by: Bloch Editores S.A., Edificio Manchete, Rua do Russel, 766-804, Gloria, Rio De Janeiro, RJ 22210010, Brazil. TEL 021-5554000, FAX 021-2059998. Ed. Antonio Cunha. Circ: 50,000.

338 AUS ISSN 0812-2288
TENDERS AUSTRALIA. Text in English. 1905. w. AUD 165 for 1 category of Tenders; AUD 285 for 3 fax or 6 email categories of Tenders; AUD 385 for 6 fax or unlimited email categories of Tenders (effective 2000). adv. **Document type:** *Trade.* **Description:** Lists tenders invited and accepted in Australia. Covers relevant indutry news stories and has industry specific spotlights.
Formerly: Tenders (0040-3113)
Media: E-mail. **Related titles:** Fax ed.
Published by: Reed Business Information Pty Ltd (Subsidiary of: Reed Business Information International), Locked Bag 2999, Chatswood, NSW 2067, Australia. tenders-readerservices@reedbusiness.com.au, customerservice@reedbusiness.com.au, http://www.infolink.com.au/tenders/default.asp, http://www.reedbusiness.com.au. Ed. Katrina Mathieson. Pub. Paul Spotswood. Adv. contact Jonathan Sismey. Circ: 1,500.

THAI JOURNAL OF DEVELOPMENT ADMINISTRATION. see *PUBLIC ADMINISTRATION*

THEORETICAL ISSUES IN ERGONOMICS SCIENCE. see *ENGINEERING*

TIE LINES. see *CLOTHING TRADE*

338 NLD ISSN 1570-9361
TIJDSCHRIFT VOOR OPENBARE FINANCIEN. Text in Dutch. 1968. 6/yr. EUR 102 (effective 2005). adv. charts; stat. **Document type:** *Academic/Scholarly.*
Formerly (until 2003): Openbare Uitgaven (0030-3488)
Indexed: KES.
—IE, Infotrieve, KNAW.
Published by: Sdu Uitgevers bv, Postbus 20025, The Hague, 2500 EA, Netherlands. TEL 31-70-3789911, FAX 31-70-3854321, sdu@sdu.nl, http://www.sdu.nl/. Eds. A P Ros, C A de Kam. Circ: 1,000. **Subscr. to:** Postbus 20014, The Hague 2500 EA, Netherlands. TEL 31-70-3789880, FAX 31-70-3789783.

TIME MANAGEMENT. see *BUSINESS AND ECONOMICS—Personnel Management*

338.0029 USA
TOOLING AND MANUFACTURING ASSOCIATION. PURCHASING GUIDE. Text in English. biennial. USD 125. adv. **Document type:** *Directory.*
Formerly: Tool and Die Institute Purchasing Guide
Published by: Tooling and Manufacturing Association, 1177 S Dee Rd, Park Ridge, IL 60068. TEL 708-825-1120. Ed. Jeffrey Hayes. Circ: 18,000.

338 ZAF ISSN 0563-8895
TOP COMPANIES. Text in English. 1967. a. illus. **Description:** Provides detailed financial and production information on South Africa's top 300 industrial companies, with additional information on other sectors of the economy, including mining, life insurance, health care, banking and the financial markets.
Related titles: ♦ Supplement to: Financial Mail. ISSN 0015-2013.
Published by: Times Media Limited, PO Box 1746, Saxonwold, Johannesburg 2133, South Africa. TEL 27-11-280-3000, FAX 27-11-280-3773. Circ: 35,000.

338 PAK ISSN 0041-0411
HF41 CODEN: SDEFDL
TRADE CHRONICLE; Pakistan's leading magazine of commerce, industry and public affairs. Text in English. 1953. m. USD 90 (effective 1999). adv. bk.rev. illus.; mkt.; pat.; tr.lit.; tr.mk. **Document type:** *Trade.*
Published by: Chronicle Publications, Iftikhar Chambers Altaf Hussain Rd., P O Box 5257, Karachi, 74000, Pakistan. FAX 92-21-2635007, arsidiqi@khi.fascom.com. Ed., R&P Abdul Rauf Siddiqi TEL 92-21-2631587. Pub., Adv. contact Abdul Rab Siddiqi. Circ: 1,100 (paid); 5,500 (controlled).

TRADEWINDS. see *SPORTS AND GAMES—Outdoor Life*

338 340 GBR
TRANSFER OF UNDERTAKINGS. Text in English. 1998. base vol. plus updates 3/yr. looseleaf. GBP 425 base vol(s).; GBP 285, EUR 429 updates in Europe; GBP 300, USD 545 updates elsewhere (effective 2006). **Document type:** *Trade.*
Published by: Sweet & Maxwell Ltd., 100 Avenue Road, London, NW3 3PF, United Kingdom. TEL 44-20-74491111, FAX 44-20-74491144, customer.services@sweetandmaxwell.co.uk, http://www.sweetandmaxwell.co.uk. **Subscr. to:** Cheriton House, North Way, Andover, Hants SP10 5BE, United Kingdom.

338 MEX ISSN 0041-1124
TRANSFORMACION. Text in Spanish. 1957. m. MXP 35. adv. bk.rev. charts; illus.; stat.
Indexed: PAIS.
Published by: Camara Nacional de la Industria de Transformacion, Apdo. Postal 60-468, Av. San Antonio 256, Mexico City, DF 03849, Mexico. TEL 5-563-3500. Ed. Iris Arzate Rios. Circ: 25,000.

338.9 TUR ISSN 0082-6944
TURKEY. DEVLET PLANAMA TESKILATI. YILI PROGRAMI UCUNCU BES YIL/TURKEY. STATE PLANNING ORGANIZATION. ANNUAL PROGRAM OF THE FIVE YEAR DEVELOPMENT PLAN. Text in Turkish. 1963. a.
Published by: State Planning Organization/Devlet Planlama Teskilati, Ankara, Turkey. Circ: 5,000.

338 GBR
U K S M A COUNCIL'S REPORT AND FINANCIAL STATEMENTS. Text in English. a. **Document type:** *Corporate.*
Formerly (until 1996): S R A M A Council's Report and Financial Statements
Published by: U K Spring Manufacturers' Association, Henry St, Sheffield, S Yorks S3 7EQ, United Kingdom. TEL 44-114-2760542, FAX 44-114-2760554, uksma@uksma.org.uk.

U.S. BUREAU OF THE CENSUS. (YEAR) ECONOMIC CENSUS. MANUFACTURING. see *BUSINESS AND ECONOMICS—Abstracting, Bibliographies, Statistics*

338 USA ISSN 0565-4408
HC110.P6
U.S. ECONOMIC DEVELOPMENT ADMINISTRATION. ANNUAL REPORT. Variant title: Jobs for America. Text in English. 1968. a.
Formerly (until 1969): U.S. Economic Development Administration. Progress Report (0885-0380)
Published by: U.S. Department of Commerce, Economic Development Administration, 14th St & Constitution Ave, NW, Washington, DC 20230. http://www.eda.gov/AboutEDA/Annualreport.xml.

338 USA
U S SURVEY OF BUSINESS EXPECTATIONS. Text in English. 1947. q. USD 40 (effective 2000). **Description:** Nationwide survey of 3,000 business executives regarding their expectations for sales, profits, prices, inventories, employment, new orders and exports in the upcoming quarter.
Formerly: Business Expectations (0007-7178)
Indexed: SRI.
Published by: Dun & Bradstreet, Economic Analysis Department (Subsidiary of: Dun & Bradstreet Corporation), c/o Judy Webb, 3 Sylvan Way, Parsippany, NJ 07054. FAX 973-254-4063, http://www.dnb.com. R&P Judy Webb. **Subscr. to:** PO Box 1861, New York, NY 10017-1861.

354 UGA
UGANDA ESTIMATES OF DEVELOPMENT EXPENDITURES. Text in English. a., latest 1977. UGX 20; price varies.
Published by: Government Printer, PO Box 33, Entebbe, Uganda. **Subscr. to:** Chief Government Statistician, Ministry of Planning and Economic Development, PO Box 7086, Kampala, Uganda.

B

▼ new title ➤ refereed ✶ unverified ♦ full entry avail.

UNIFICAZIONE & CERTIFICAZIONE. see *BUSINESS AND ECONOMICS—Economic Systems And Theories, Economic History*

338 ARG ISSN 0457-1673
UNIVERSIDAD NACIONAL DE LA PLATA. INSTITUTO DE LA PRODUCCION. SERIE CONTRIBUCIONES*. Text in Spanish. 1960. irreg. charts; stat.
Published by: Universidad Nacional de la Plata, Instituto de la Produccion, Calle 47, Y 117, La Plata, Buenos Aires 1900, Argentina. Ed. Servando R M Dozo.

UNIVERSITY OF YORK. CENTRE FOR DEFENCE ECONOMICS. RESEARCH MONOGRAPH SERIES. see *MILITARY*

338 MYS ISSN 0126-8937
USAHALUAN. Text in English. 1972. 4/yr. free. adv. charts; illus.
Formerly: M I D F Reports
Published by: Malaysian Industrial Development Finance Berhad, Bangunan MIDF, Jalan Tun Razak, Kuala Lumpur, Malaysia. TEL 60-3-2613908, FAX 60-3-2613908, TELEX MIDFKL MA 30534. Circ: 3,000.

B

338 BEL ISSN 1374-5271
USINE ENTERPRISE. Text in French. 1924. 10/yr. adv. bk.rev. **Document type:** *Trade.*
Formerly (until 1999): L' Usine Industrial Digest (1374-5263)
Related titles: Dutch ed.: Het Bedrijf Industrial Digest. ISSN 1374-528X.
Published by: Benefalux S.A., Avenue Montjoie, 226, Bruxelles, 1080, Belgium. TEL 32-2-345-0191, FAX 32-2-347-2038. Ed. R Blanpain. Circ: 17,000.

338 FIN ISSN 0356-8091
VALTIONYHTIOT. Text in Finnish. 1969. a.
Published by: Valtionyhtioiden Neuvottelukunta, Aleksanterinkatu 10, Helsinki, 00170, Finland. Ed. Wd Ritva Hainari. Circ: 8,000.

338 USA
HC107.V53
VERMONT ECONOMIC DEVELOPMENT AUTHORITY. ANNUAL REPORT. Text in English. 1975. a. free (effective 2005). **Document type:** *Government.*
Formerly: Vermont Industrial Development Authority. Annual Report (0363-2067)
Published by: Vermont Economic Development Authority (V E D A), 58 E State St., Ste 5, Montpelier, VT 05602-3043. info@veda.org, http://www.veda.org/. Circ: 400 (controlled).

670.29 USA
VERMONT MANUFACTURING & WHOLESALE - DISTRIBUTOR DIRECTORY. Text in English. a. USD 65 (effective 2000). adv. **Document type:** *Directory.* **Description:** Lists more than 1,000 manufacturing and wholesale firms in Vermont in three sections: alphabetical, geographical and product.
Former titles: Vermont Manufacturing Directory; Vermont Business Phone Book and Manufacturers Directory; Vermont Marketing Directory
Published by: Tower Publishing Co., 588 Saco Rd, Standish, ME 04084-6239. TEL 207-642-5400, 800-969-8693, FAX 207-642-5463. Ed. Mary Ann Hildreth. Pub. Michael L Lyons.

338 NPL
VIKAS: NEPAL JOURNAL OF DEVELOPMENT. Text in English. 1975. s-a.
Published by: National Planning Commission, Secretariat, Kathmandu, Nepal.

338 658 USA
VISIONS (NEW YORK). Text in English. q. free to members. adv.
—BLDSC (9240.952700).
Published by: (Product Development and Management Association), Elsevier Inc. (Subsidiary of: Elsevier Science & Technology), 360 Park Ave. S, New York, NY 10010-1710. TEL 212-633-3730, 888-437-4636, usinfo-f@elsevier.com, http://www.pdma.org/visions/, http://www.elsevier.com. Ed. John H Liebe. adv.: B&W page USD 1,281.

LA VOLONTE DES P M E. (Petites et Moyennes Entreprises) see *BUSINESS AND ECONOMICS—Domestic Commerce*

338 NLD ISSN 0165-3954
VRAAG & AANBOD. Text in Dutch. 1898. w. (Fri.). EUR 179 domestic; EUR 186.80 in Europe; EUR 194.60 elsewhere (effective 2005). adv. **Document type:** *Trade.* **Description:** Covers news, market developments, technology, economics, management and entrepreneurial information for small and medium-sized industrial companies, commercial, construction and professional service firms.
Incorporates (1983-2001): De Metaalkrant (1389-0662); Which was formerly (until 1999): Handel en Techniek (1384-3893)
Related titles: Regional ed(s).: Vraag en Aanbod. Regio Noord; Vraag en Aanbod. Regio Oost; Vraag en Aanbod. Regio West. ISSN 0168-0315; Vraag en Aanbod. Regio Zuid; ♦ Supplement(s): Wie Levert Produkten en Diensten. ISSN 0928-7949; ♦ Wie Levert Merken. ISSN 0928-7930; ♦ Wie Levert Regio.
Published by: Uitgeverij Nassau, Postbus 23, Deventer, 7400 GA, Netherlands. TEL 31-570-665500, FAX 31-570-665599, info@wknassau.nl. Ed. Rolf Elling. Pub. Rob van Berkel. Adv. contact Henk Meijerink. Circ: 21,038.

338 BEL ISSN 0773-4778
VRAAG EN AANBOD. Text in Dutch. 1954. w. EUR 122.95 (effective 2005). adv. bk.rev. **Document type:** *Trade.*
Published by: Kluwer Uitgevers (Subsidiary of: Wolters Kluwer Belgique), Ragheno Business Park, Motstraat 30, Mechelen, B-2800, Belgium. TEL 32-15-800-94571, info@kluwer.be, http://www.vraageenaanbod.be, http://www.kluwer.be. Circ: 15,000.

VYAVASAYA KERALAM. see *BUSINESS AND ECONOMICS—Domestic Commerce*

W E P Z A NEWSLETTER. (World Economic Processing Zones Association) see *BUSINESS AND ECONOMICS—International Commerce*

WARD'S AUTOWORLD. see *TRANSPORTATION—Automobiles*

WASHINGTON DRUG LETTER (WASHINGTON, 1979). see *PHARMACY AND PHARMACOLOGY*

WATCH IT MADE IN THE U. S. A.; a visitor's guide to the companies that make your favorite products. see *TRAVEL AND TOURISM*

WHO OWNS WHOM. CONTINENTAL EUROPE. see *BUSINESS AND ECONOMICS—Management*

338 GBR
WINNERS PRODUCT CARDS. Text in English. 11/yr. looseleaf. free to qualified personnel. adv. **Document type:** *Trade.*
Media: Cards.
Published by: Nexus Media Ltd. (Subsidiary of: Highbury House Communications PLC), Nexus House, Azalea Dr, Swanley, Kent BR8 8HU, United Kingdom. TEL 44-1322-660070, FAX 44-1322-616311, info@nexusmedia.com, http://www.hhc.co.uk/winners. adv.: B&W page GBP 1,100, color page GBP 1,300; 105 x 148.

338 628.5 USA
WIRELINE (ALEXANDRIA). Text in English. q. USD 150 to non-members. back issues avail. **Document type:** *Newsletter.*
Published by: American Wire Producers Association, 801 N. Fairfax St., Ste. 211, Alexandria, VA 22314-1776. TEL 703-549-6003, FAX 703-684-6048. Ed., R&P David Woodbury. Pub. Kimberly Korbel.

658 340 338 DEU ISSN 0043-6151
K27
WIRTSCHAFT UND WETTBEWERB; Zeitschrift fuer Kartellrecht, Wettbewerbsrecht und Marktorganisation. Text in German. 1952. m. adv. bk.rev. abstr.; bibl. index. reprint service avail. from PQC. **Document type:** *Bulletin.*
Indexed: ELLIS, FLP, IBR, IBZ, KES, PAIS.
—IE, Infotrieve. **CCC.**
Published by: Verlagsgruppe Handelsblatt GmbH, Kasernenstr 67, Duesseldorf, 40213, Germany. TEL 49-211-887-0, FAX 49-211-133522.

WISCONSIN MANUFACTURERS DIRECTORY. see *BUSINESS AND ECONOMICS—Trade And Industrial Directories*

THE WORLD MARKET FOR HOT DRINKS. see *BEVERAGES*

THE WORLD MARKET FOR O T C HEALTHCARE. (Over the Counter) see *PHARMACY AND PHARMACOLOGY*

WORLD STEEL STATISTICS MONTHLY. see *METALLURGY—Abstracting, Bibliographies, Statistics*

338.4 GBR ISSN 0954-0180
HD9696.A3
YEARBOOK OF WORLD ELECTRONICS DATA VOL. 1: WEST EUROPE. Text in English. 1973. a. GBP 850; GBP 1,150 w/ CD ROM; USD 1,360; USD 1,840 w/ CD ROM (effective 2003). adv. illus.; stat. back issues avail. **Description:** Production and markets statistics for electronics products in Western European countries.
Formerly: Mackintosh Yearbook of West European Electronics Data (0306-5774)
Related titles: Diskette ed.: USD 803.
—BLDSC (9417.653250). **CCC.**
Published by: Reed Electronics Research, Unit 4 Harvard House, Grove Technology Park, Wantage, Oxon OX12 9FF, United Kingdom. TEL 44-1235-227310, FAX 44-1235-868811, info@rer.co.uk, http://www.rer.co.uk/. Circ: 450.

338.4 GBR ISSN 0954-0172
HD9696.A1
YEARBOOK OF WORLD ELECTRONICS DATA VOL. 2: AMERICA, JAPAN, & ASIA - PACIFIC. Text in English. 1983. a., latest 2003, 20th ed. GBP 1,195; GBP 1,495 w/ CD ROM; USD 1,912; USD 2,392 w/ CD ROM (effective 2003). adv. charts; illus.; stat. **Description:** Production and markets statistics for electronics products worldwide.
Formerly: Mackintosh Yearbook of International Electronics Data (0264-0724)
Related titles: Diskette ed.: USD 1,204.
—**CCC.**
Published by: Reed Electronics Research, Unit 4 Harvard House, Grove Technology Park, Wantage, Oxon OX12 9FF, United Kingdom. TEL 44-1235-227310, FAX 44-1235-868811, info@rer.co.uk, http://www.rer.co.uk/.

338 382 GBR
YEARBOOK OF WORLD ELECTRONICS DATA VOL. 3: EMERGING COUNTRIES. Text in English. 1990. biennial, latest 2002, 7th ed. GBP 745 base vol(s).; GBP 1,045 base vol(s). w/ CD ROM; USD 1,192 base vol(s).; USD 1,672 base vol(s). w/ CD ROM (effective 2003). **Description:** This volume of the set includes several emerging markets including China, Mexico and Turkey.
Published by: Reed Electronics Research, Unit 4 Harvard House, Grove Technology Park, Wantage, Oxon OX12 9FF, United Kingdom. TEL 44-1235-227310, FAX 44-1235-868811, info@rer.co.uk, http://www.rer.co.uk/.

338.4 GBR
YEARBOOK OF WORLD ELECTRONICS DATA VOL. 4: EAST EUROPE. Text in English. a., latest 2003, 7th ed. GBP 745; GBP 1,045 combined subscription w/ CD ROM; USD 1,192; USD 1,672 combined subscription w/ CD ROM (effective 2003). **Description:** Production and market statistics for electronics products in Eastern Europe and the world.
Formerly: Yearbook of World Electronics Data Vol. 4: East Europe & World Summary
Published by: Reed Electronics Research, Unit 4 Harvard House, Grove Technology Park, Wantage, Oxon OX12 9FF, United Kingdom. TEL 44-1235-227310, FAX 44-1235-868811, info@rer.co.uk, http://www.rer.co.uk/.

338.9689 ZMB
ZAMBIA. MINISTRY OF PLANNING AND FINANCE. ANNUAL REPORT. Text in English. 1971. a. **Document type:** *Government.*
Formed by the merger of: Zambia. Ministry of Development and National Guidance. Annual Report; Zambia. Ministry of Finance. Annual Report (0084-4896)
Published by: Ministry of Planning and Finance, PO Box RW 62, Lusaka, Zambia. **Subscr. to:** Government Printer, PO Box 136, Lusaka, Zambia.

330 DEU ISSN 0342-2852
HC281
ZEITSCHRIFT FUER UNTERNEHMENSGESCHICHTE. Text in German. 1956. 2/yr. EUR 34.90 domestic; EUR 40.60 foreign; EUR 24.50 to students; EUR 19.90 newsstand/cover (effective 2005). adv. bk.rev. back issues avail.; reprints avail. **Document type:** *Journal, Academic/Scholarly.*
Formerly: Tradition
Indexed: AmH&L, DIP, HistAb, IBR, IBSS, IBZ, JEL, RASB, SCIMP.
—IE, Infotrieve. **CCC.**
Published by: (Gesellschaft fuer Unternehmensgeschichte), Verlag C.H. Beck oHG, Wilhelmstr 9, Munich, 80801, Germany. TEL 49-89-38189338, FAX 49-89-38189398, abo.service@beck.de, http://www.beck.de. Adv. contact Susanne Szoradi. page EUR 1,700; trim 122 x 195. Circ: 800.

338 CHN
ZHILIANG GUANLI/QUALITY CONTROL. Text in Chinese. m.
Published by: Zhiliang Guanli Zazhishe, No 12 Zhongjing Jidao, Xidan, Beijing, 100032, China. TEL 667131. Ed. Liu Yuanzhang.

338 690 RUS ISSN 0044-4464
ZHILISHCHNOE I KOMMUNAL'NOE KHOZYAISTVO. Text in Russian. 1951. m. USD 106 foreign (effective 2004). bk.rev. bibl.; charts; illus.; stat.; tr.lit. index.
Indexed: ChemAb, RASB, RefZh.
—East View.
Address: Lubyanskii pr-d 25, Moscow, 101000, Russian Federation. TEL 7-095-9782737, FAX 7-095-9247834. Ed. Margarita Nazarenko. Circ: 12,700. **Dist. by:** M K - Periodica, ul Gilyarovskogo 39, Moscow 129110, Russian Federation. TEL 7-095-2845008, FAX 7-095-2813798, info@periodicals.ru, http://www.mkniga.ru.

338 CHN
ZHONGGUO TECHAN BAO/CHINA SPECIAL NATIVE PRODUCTS. Text in Chinese. 3/w. CNY 99 (effective 2004). **Document type:** *Newspaper, Trade.*
Address: 228, Beiyuan Lu Datunyi, Yayuncun, Zhaoyang-qu, Beijing, 100101, China. TEL 86-10-64933845, FAX 86-10-64925784, chinaspcom@hotmail.com, http://www.chinasp.com.cn/. **Dist. by:** China International Book Trading Corp, 35 Chegongzhuang Xilu, Haidian District, PO Box 399, Beijing 100044, China. TEL 86-10-68412045, FAX 86-10-68412023, cibtc@mail.cibtc.com.cn, http://www.cibtc.com.cn.

729.39 645.3 NLD ISSN 1381-8813
ZONVAK. Text in Dutch. 1984. bi-m. EUR 79.80 domestic; EUR 94.80 in Europe (effective 2005). adv. charts; illus. back issues avail. **Document type:** *Journal, Trade.* **Description:** Offers information on news and developments in the products and techniques for home decorating.

Published by: Quorum Uitgevers, PO Box 123, Zutphen aan den Rijn, 7200 AC, Netherlands. TEL 31-575-515515, FAX 31-575-512199, redactie@qumedia.nl, info@qumedia.nl, http://www.zonvak.nl, http://www.qumedia.nl. Ed. Derk-Jan Rouwenhorst TEL 31-575-51551530. Pub. Arnold Jansen. Adv. contact Annemarie van Berkel TEL 31-575-51551523. B&W page EUR 1,393; trim 210 x 297. Circ: 1,341.

BUSINESS AND ECONOMICS—Public Finance, Taxation

336.2 DEU ISSN 1617-2272
DER A O STEUER-BERATER. Text in German. 2001. m. EUR 119; EUR 11.90 newsstand/cover (effective 2005). adv. **Document type:** *Journal, Trade.*
Related titles: Online - full text ed.
Published by: Verlag Dr. Otto Schmidt KG, Gustav-Heinemann-Ufer 58, Cologne, 50968, Germany. TEL 49-221-93738460, FAX 49-221-93738943, info@otto-schmidt.de, http://www.aostb.de, http://www.otto-schmidt.de. adv.: B&W page EUR 555, color page EUR 971. Circ: 1,893 (paid and controlled).

336.2 USA
▼ **A T A JOURNAL OF LEGAL TAX RESEARCH.** Text in English. 2003. irreg. USD 125 (effective 2005). **Document type:** *Journal, Academic/Scholarly.* **Description:** Publishes creative and innovative studies employing legal research methodologies that logically and clearly identify, describe and illuminate important current tax issues including the history, development and congressional intent of specific provisions, propose improvements in tax systems and unique solutions to problems, and critically analyze proposed or recent tax rule changes from both technical and policy perspectives.
Media: Online - full content.
Published by: American Taxation Association (Subsidiary of: American Accounting Association), c/o W. Eugene Seago, Pamplin College of Business, Virginia Poly Inst & State University, Blackburg, VA 24061-0101. TEL 540-231-6564, FAX 540-231-2511, http://www.atasection.org/legal.html. Ed. W. Eugene Seago.

336 USA ISSN 0163-1241
KF6369.8.C5
ABINGDON CLERGY INCOME TAX GUIDE. Text in English. 1972. a. USD 12.95. **Description:** Offers clergy of all denominations information on filling out federal income tax forms.
Formerly (until 1978): Clergy's Federal Income Tax Guide (0090-9866)
Published by: Abingdon Press, 201 Eighth Ave S, Box 801, Nashville, TN 37202-0801. TEL 800-251-3320, FAX 615-749-6417.

336 BEL ISSN 0773-2163
ACCOUNTANCY THEMA'S; veertiendaagse nieuwsbrief voor bedrijfsrevisoren, accountants, en administratieve en financiele managers. Text in French. 1983. s-m. bk.rev. index. Supplement avail. **Description:** Contains articles on up-to-date accountancy, practical accountancy and financial analysis.
Published by: C E D Samsom (Subsidiary of: Wolters Samsom Belgie n.v.), Kouterveld 14, Diegem, 1831, Belgium. TEL 32-2-7231111. Circ: 1,500.

ACCOUNTING, ACCOUNTABILITY & PERFORMANCE. see *BUSINESS AND ECONOMICS—Accounting*

ACCOUNTING AND TAX INDEX. see *BUSINESS AND ECONOMICS—Abstracting, Bibliographies, Statistics*

336 333.33 340 USA
ADVANCED TAX PLANNING FOR REAL PROPERTY TRANSACTIONS. Text in English. a. USD 40 (effective 1999).
Published by: Continuing Education of the Bar - California, University of California, 300 Frank H Ogawa Plaza, Ste 410, Oakland, CA 94612-2001. TEL 510-642-6211, FAX 510-642-3788. **Co-sponsor:** State Bar of California.

336.2 USA ISSN 1058-7497
HJ2240
ADVANCES IN TAXATION. Text in English. 1987. a., latest vol.16, 2004. price varies. back issues avail. **Document type:** *Monographic series, Academic/Scholarly.*
Related titles: Online - full text ed.: (from ScienceDirect).
Indexed: ATI.
—BLDSC (0711.595750), IE, ingenta. **CCC.**
Published by: J A I Press Inc. (Subsidiary of: Elsevier Science & Technology), 360 Park Ave S, New York, NY 10010-1710. TEL 212-989-5800, FAX 212-633-3990, usinfo-f@elsevier.com, http://www.elsevier.com/wps/find/bookseriesdescription.cws_home/BS_AT/description. Ed. T M Porcano.

ADVISOR'S EDGE; canada's magazine for the financial professional. see *BUSINESS AND ECONOMICS—Investments*

▼ **ADVISOR'S EDGE REPORT.** see *BUSINESS AND ECONOMICS—Investments*

336.2 NLD
AFRICAN TAX SYSTEMS. Text in English. 1971. 6 base vols. plus q. updates. looseleaf. USD 1,060 base vol(s).; USD 600 updates (effective 2002). **Document type:** *Trade.* **Description:** Provides essential information to help overcome obstacles to international trade, including in-depth description of tax systems and investment regulations.
Published by: (International Bureau of Fiscal Documentation), I B F D Publications BV, H J E Wenckebachweg 210, PO Box 20237, Amsterdam, 1000 HE, Netherlands. TEL 31-20-554-0100, FAX 31-20-620-8626, info@ibfd.nl, http://www.ibfd.nl. Ed. Elizabeth de Brauw-Itay. **Co-sponsor:** United Nations, Economic Commission for Africa/Commission Economique pour l'Afrique.

331 AUS ISSN 1322-1833
H96
➤ **AGENDA**; a journal of policy analysis and reform. Text in English. 1994. q. AUD 55 in Australia & New Zealand; AUD 75 elsewhere; AUD 15 newsstand/cover (effective 2004). adv. bk.rev. charts; stat. index. 96 p./no.; back issues avail. **Document type:** *Journal, Academic/Scholarly.* **Description:** Provides analysis of public policy in all areas. Written in layman's terms for non-specialists.
Related titles: Online - full text ed.
Indexed: AESIS, AusPAIS, IPSA, JEL.
Published by: (Centre for Applied Economics), Australian National University, School of Economics, PO Box 3265, Canberra, ACT 2601, Australia. TEL 61-2-6125-0385, FAX 61-2-6125-5124, http://ecocomm.anu.edu.au/economics/agenda/. Eds. Franco Papandrea TEL 61-2-6201-5083, Graeme Wells. Adv. contact Graeme Wells. page AUD 400; 8 x 5. Circ: 550.

336 FRA
AGRICULTURAL POLICIES IN O E C D COUNTRIES: MONITORING AND EVALUATION. Text in French. a. price varies. charts; stat.
Former titles (until 1996): O E C D Agricultural Policies, Markets and Trade. Monitoring and Outlook (1017-8562); O E C D Agricultural Policy Reports
Related titles: Online - full text ed.; French ed.: Politiques Agricoles des Pays de l'O C D E.
Indexed: IIS, WAE&RSA.
Published by: Organization for Economic Cooperation and Development, 2 Rue Andre Pascal, Paris, 75775 Cedex 16, France. TEL 33-1-45248200, FAX 33-1-45248500, http://www.oecd.org. **U.S. orders to:** O E C D Turpin North America, PO Box 194, Downingtown, PA 19335-0194. TEL 610-524-5361, 800-456-6323, FAX 610-524-5417, bookscustomer@turpinna.com.

AGRICULTURAL TAXATION STUDIES. see *AGRICULTURE—Agricultural Economics*

336.2 USA ISSN 1044-4130
K1
AKRON TAX JOURNAL. Text in English. 1983. a. USD 13 (effective 2003). **Document type:** *Journal, Academic/Scholarly.*
Related titles: Online - full text ed.: (from H.W. Wilson, LexisNexis, O C L C Online Computer Library Center, Inc.).
Indexed: CLI, ILP, LRI.
Published by: University of Akron, School of Law, 150 University Ave, Akron, OH 44325. TEL 330-972-7335, FAX 330-258-2343, taxjournal@uakron.edu, http://www2.uakron.edu/lawrev/tax_journal.htm, http://www.uakron.edu.

336.2 AUT ISSN 1563-3675
AKTUELLE STEUER NEWS; der 14-taegige Infobrief zu Steuern, Rechnungswesen & Recht. Abbreviated title: AStN. Text in German. 2000. fortn. EUR 90; EUR 8 newsstand/cover (effective 2005). **Document type:** *Bulletin, Trade.* **Description:** Focuses on all aspects of taxes and taxation laws.
Published by: Manzsche Verlags- und Universitaetsbuchhandlung GmbH, Johannesgasse 23, Vienna, W 1010, Austria. TEL 43-1-531610, FAX 43-1-53161181, verlag@manz.at, http://www.manz.at.

336.2 DEU ISSN 0948-1850
AKTUELLES STEUERRECHT. Text in German. 1995. q. EUR 130 (effective 2004). **Document type:** *Magazine, Trade.*
Published by: (Steuerberaterverband Niedersachsen), Richard Boorberg Verlag GmbH und Co. KG, Scharrstr 2, Stuttgart, 70563, Germany. TEL 49-711-73850, FAX 49-711-7385100, mail@boorberg.de, http://www.boorberg.de.

ALABAMA. DEPARTMENT OF REVENUE. ANNUAL REPORT. see *PUBLIC ADMINISTRATION—Municipal Government*

ALABAMA. DEPARTMENT OF REVENUE. COUNTY LINES NEWSLETTER. see *PUBLIC ADMINISTRATION—Municipal Government*

ALABAMA. DEPARTMENT OF REVENUE. GENERAL SUMMARY OF STATE TAXES. see *PUBLIC ADMINISTRATION—Municipal Government*

ALABAMA. DEPARTMENT OF REVENUE. REVENUE REVIEW NEWSLETTER. see *PUBLIC ADMINISTRATION—Municipal Government*

336 USA
ALASKA. DEPARTMENT OF REVENUE. REVENUE SOURCES. Text in English. 197?. q. **Document type:** *Government.*
Formerly: Alaska. Department of Administration. Revenue Sources
Published by: Department of Revenue, Research Section, Pouch SA, Juneau, AK 99801. TEL 907-465-3682. Ed. Vincent D Wright.

ALASKA. DEPARTMENT OF REVENUE. STATE INVESTMENT PORTFOLIO. see *BUSINESS AND ECONOMICS—Investments*

336.2 CAN
ALBERTA, N.W.T. & YUKON TAX REPORTS. Text in English. m. CND 582 (effective 2005). **Document type:** *Trade.* **Description:** Provides in-depth information and source material with respect to various taxes imposed in Alberta, the Yukon, the Northwest Territories, and Nunavut.
Related titles: CD-ROM ed.: CND 531 (effective 2005); Online - full text ed.: CND 515 (effective 2005).
Published by: C C H Canadian Ltd., 90 Sheppard Ave E, Ste 300, North York, ON M2N 6X1, Canada. TEL 416-224-2248, 800-268-4522, FAX 416-224-2243, cservice@cch.ca, http://www.cch.ca.

ALGEMEEN FISKAAL TIJDSCHRIFT; informatie voor de belastingkundige en de administratieve en financiele managers. see *BUSINESS AND ECONOMICS—Accounting*

336 DZA
ALGERIA. DIRECTION DES DOUANES. BULLETIN COMPARATIF TRIMESTRIEL. Text in French. q.
Published by: Direction des Douanes, 19, rue du Docteur Saadane, Algiers, Algeria.

336 USA
ALL STATES TAX GUIDE. Text in English. 2 base vols. plus m. updates. looseleaf. USD 1,060 (effective 2005). **Description:** Provides concise state-by-state summaries of all taxes, with citations to official materials. It offers tables, charts and checklists containing key rules, tax rates and important tax return deadline information, as well as valuable lists of official state contacts, which include addresses and phone numbers.
Related titles: CD-ROM ed.: USD 670 (effective 2005); Online - full content ed.: USD 705 (effective 2005).
Published by: R I A (Subsidiary of: Thomson Corporation), 395 Hudson St, New York, NY 10014. TEL 212-367-6300, RIA.CustomerServices@Thomson.com, http://ria.thomson.com/estore/detail.aspx?id=PASTW&site=recommendations.

336.2 USA ISSN 0148-9976
KF6750
ALL STATES TAX HANDBOOK (YEAR). Text in English. a. USD 30. **Description:** Provides comparisons of different tax rates and structures for all fifty states and the District of Columbia.
Indexed: ATI.
Published by: R I A (Subsidiary of: Thomson Corporation), 395 Hudson St, New York, NY 10014. TEL 212- 367-6300.

336 GBR ISSN 0268-1269
ALLIED DUNBAR TAX HANDBOOK. Text in English. 1984. a. GBP 19.99. **Document type:** *Bulletin.* **Description:** Advice and information on the workings of income tax, capital gains tax, corporate tax, inheritance tax and value added tax in the United Kingdom.
Formerly (until 1985): Allied Dunbar Tax Guide (0268-0254)
Published by: Longman Group Ltd., Law Tax and Finance Division, 21-27 Lambs Conduit St, London, WC1N 3NJ, United Kingdom. TEL 071-242-2548, FAX 071-831-8119.

336.2 USA ISSN 1043-6960
KF6369
ALTERNATIVE MINIMUM TAX. Text in English. 1994. base vol. plus s-a. updates. looseleaf. USD 220 (effective 1999). **Document type:** *Trade.* **Description:** Analyzes the complexities of the alternative minimum tax and how it applies in both corporate and individual situations.
Indexed: ATI.
Published by: W G & L Financial Reporting & Management Research (Subsidiary of: R I A), 90 Fifth Ave, New York, NY 10011. TEL 212-645-4800, FAX 212-337-4280, http://www.riag.com. Ed. Daniel J Lathorpe. **Subscr. to:** 117 E Stevens Ave,, Valhalla, NY 10595.

336.76 ARG ISSN 0325-2582
AMBITO FINANCIERO. Text in Spanish. 1976. d. ARS 400, USD 200 (effective 2003). adv.
Related titles: Microfilm ed.; Online - full text ed.: Ambitoweb.
Indexed: B&I.
Published by: Editorial Amfin S.A., Avda. Paseo Colon, 1196, Capital Federal, Buenos Aires 1063, Argentina. TEL 54-114-3491500, FAX 54-114-3491505, http://www.ambito.com. Ed. Julio A Ramos. adv.: B&W page ARS 18,270. Circ: 133,300.

AMERICA REPORT. see *BUSINESS AND ECONOMICS—Economic Situation And Conditions*

B

▼ new title ➤ refereed ✶ unverified ♦ full entry avail.

AMERICAN BAR ASSOCIATION. SECTION OF TAXATION. NEWSLETTER. see *LAW*

AMERICAN HORSE COUNCIL TAX BULLETIN. see *SPORTS AND GAMES—Horses And Horsemanship*

336.2 USA ISSN 0883-3451
KF6272
AMERICAN INSTITUTE OF CERTIFIED PUBLIC ACCOUNTANTS. TAX DIVISION NEWSLETTER. Text in English. 1985. q.
Related titles: Online - full text ed.: (from LexisNexis, ProQuest Information & Learning).
Indexed: ATI.
Published by: American Institute of Certified Public Accountants, Harborside Financial Ctr., 201 Plaza Three, 3rd Fl, Jersey City, NJ 07311-9801. TEL 888-777-7077, FAX 800-302-5766, journal@aicpa.org, http://www.aicpa.org.

336 USA ISSN 0739-7569
K1
AMERICAN JOURNAL OF TAX POLICY. Text in English. 1981. s-a. USD 22. back issues avail.; reprint service avail. from WSH. **Document type:** *Academic/Scholarly.*
Related titles: Microfiche ed.: (from WSH); Microform ed.: (from WSH); Online - full text ed.: (from H.W. Wilson, LexisNexis, Thomson West).
Indexed: ILP, LRI.
Published by: American College of Tax Counsel, PO Box 870382, Tuscaloosa, AL 35487-0382. TEL 205-348-7372, FAX 205-348-3917. Ed., R&P James D Bryce. Circ: 1,300.

336 ASM
AMERICAN SAMOA GOVERNMENT. COMPREHENSIVE ANNUAL FINANCIAL REPORT. Text in English. a. **Document type:** *Government.*
Indexed: SPPI.
Published by: American Samoa Government, Treasury Department, Pago Pago, 96799, American Samoa.

336 USA ISSN 0198-9073
HF5681.T3
AMERICAN TAXATION ASSOCIATION. JOURNAL. Text in English. 1979. s-a. USD 30 (effective 2005). adv. bk.rev.; software rev. abstr.; illus. reprint service avail. from PSC.
Description: Provides articles on tax topics.
Related titles: Online - full text ed.: (from EBSCO Publishing, Factiva, Florida Center for Library Automation, Gale Group, O C L C Online Computer Library Center, Inc., ProQuest Information & Learning).
Indexed: ABIn, ATI.
—IE. **CCC.**
Published by: (American Taxation Association), American Accounting Association, 5717 Bessie Dr, Sarasota, FL 34233-2399. TEL 941-921-7747, FAX 941-923-4093, http://www.uni.edu/ata/jata/html, http://aaahq.org. Ed. Terrence J Shevlin. R&P Mary Cole.

336 IND
ANDHRA PRADESH STATE FINANCIAL CORPORATION. REPORT AND ACCOUNTS. Text in English. 1956. a. stat.
Formerly: Andhra Pradesh State Financial Corporation. Report
Published by: Andhra Pradesh State Financial Corporation, 5-9 194 Chirag Ali Lane, Hyderabad, Andhra Pradesh 500 001, India. TELEX 0425-6428-ASFC-IN.

336.2 FRA
▼ **L'ANNEE FISCALE.** Text in French. 2003. a. EUR 75 domestic (effective 2005). **Document type:** *Journal, Trade.*
Published by: Presses Universitaires de France, 6 Avenue Reille, Paris, 75685 Cedex 14, France. TEL 33-1-58103100, FAX 33-1-58103182, revues@puf.com, http://www.puf.com.

ANNUAL EDITIONS: DEVELOPING WORLD. see *GEOGRAPHY*

343.052 AUS
ANSWER BOOK, INCOME TAX LAW PRINCIPLES, INCOME TAX LAW APPLICATIONS. Text in English. 1985. a., latest 2003. AUD 35 (effective 2003). **Document type:** *Academic/Scholarly.*
Former titles: Question Book, Income Tax Law for Accountants, Income Tax Law for Tax Agents. Answers to Questions (Year) (1440-0286); (until 1998): Question Budget, Income Tax Law for Accountants, Income Tax Law for Tax Agents. Answers to Questions (Year) (1325-2143); (until 1996): Question Budget, Taxation Law and Practice. Answers to Questions (Year) (1034-5167)
Published by: Alan Kirby, Ed. & Pub., PO Box 632, Hurstville, NSW 2232, Australia. TEL 61-2-95794959.

336.2 DEU
ARBEITGEBER-TIP; Informationsdienst fuer die erfolgreiche Personalarbeit. Text in German. m. **Document type:** *Newsletter, Trade.* **Description:** Provides employers with up-to-date news and information on taxation and social security issues.
Published by: V S R W Verlag Dr. Hagen Pruehs GmbH, Rolandstr 48, Bonn, 53179, Germany. TEL 49-228-95124-0, FAX 49-228-9512490, vsrw@vsrw.de, http://www.vsrw.de/Informationsdienste/Arbeitgeber_Tip/Arbeitgeber-Tip.shtml.

ARGUS (DALAROE); aarsbok foer Tullmuseum och Tullhistoriska Foereningen. see *MUSEUMS AND ART GALLERIES*

336.2 HKG ISSN 1027-5592
ASIA - PACIFIC JOURNAL OF TAXATION. Text in Hebrew. 1997. q. HKD 300 domestic; HKD 470 foreign (effective 2004).
Description: Addresses issues in the field of taxation of relevance to Hong Kong, China and the Asian Pacific region.
Published by: (Hong Kong Polytechnic University SGP), Taxation Institute of Hong Kong, 21/F Kam Sang Building, 255-257 Des Voeux Road Central, Hong Kong, Hong Kong. TEL 852-2810-0438, FAX 852-2523-1263, http://www.af.polyu.edu.hk/about_journal_apjt.html.

336 NLD ISSN 1385-3082
K4456.2
ASIA - PACIFIC TAX BULLETIN. Cover title: A P T B. Text in English. 1983; N.S. 1995. bi-m. EUR 285 (effective 2005). back issues avail. **Document type:** *Bulletin.* **Description:** Provides news and analysis of taxation and investment issues in Asia and the Pacific region, including significant reports and documents.
Supersedes (in 1995): A P T I R C Bulletin (0218-3536); Formerly (until 1991): Asian-Pacific Tax and Investment Research Centre Bulletin (0217-6661)
Related titles: Online - full text ed.: (from Swets Information Services).
Indexed: FLP.
—IE, Infotrieve.
Published by: (International Bureau of Fiscal Documentation), I B F D Publications BV, H J E Wenckebachweg 210, PO Box 20237, Amsterdam, 1000 HE, Netherlands. TEL 31-20-5540100, FAX 31-20-6228658, info@ibfd.nl, http://www.ibfd.nl. **Subscr. to:** I B F D Publications USA, Inc, PO Box 805, Valatie, NY 12184-0805. TEL 800-908-6330.

AURA WEALTH NEWSLETTER; economic survival in perilous times. see *BUSINESS AND ECONOMICS—Economic Situation And Conditions*

AUSTRALIA AND THE I M F (YEAR). (International Monetary Fund) see *BUSINESS AND ECONOMICS—International Development And Assistance*

AUSTRALIA AND THE WORLD BANK. see *BUSINESS AND ECONOMICS—International Development And Assistance*

AUSTRALIA. BUREAU OF STATISTICS. INFORMATION PAPER: A.B.S. STATISTICS AND THE NEW TAX SYSTEM. see *BUSINESS AND ECONOMICS—Abstracting, Bibliographies, Statistics*

AUSTRALIA. BUREAU OF STATISTICS. INFORMATION PAPER: EXPANDED USE OF BUSINESS INCOME TAX DATA IN A.B.S. ECONOMIC STATISTICS - EXPERIMENTAL ESTIMATES FOR SELECTED INDUSTRIES. see *BUSINESS AND ECONOMICS—Abstracting, Bibliographies, Statistics*

AUSTRALIA. BUREAU OF STATISTICS. INFORMATION PAPER: THE USE OF INDIVIDUAL TAXPAYER DATA FOR A.B.S. REGIONAL STATISTICS - WAGE AND SALARY INDICATORS FOR SMALL AREAS. see *BUSINESS AND ECONOMICS—Abstracting, Bibliographies, Statistics*

AUSTRALIA. BUREAU OF STATISTICS. STANDARDS FOR CASH INCOME STATISTICS. see *STATISTICS*

AUSTRALIA. BUREAU OF STATISTICS. TAXATION REVENUE, AUSTRALIA. see *BUSINESS AND ECONOMICS—Abstracting, Bibliographies, Statistics*

336.2 AUS
AUSTRALIA. DEPARTMENT OF INDUSTRY, SCIENCE AND TOURISM. ANNUAL REPORT. Text in English. 1954. a. free. **Document type:** *Corporate.*
Former titles (until Mar. 1996): Australia. Department of Industry, Science and Technology. Annual Report; (until July 1994): Australia. Department of Industry, Technology and Regional Development. Annual Report; (until 1992): Australia. Department of Industry, Technology and Commerce. Annual Report (0728-6856); (until 1981): Australia. Department of Police and Customs. Review of Activities; Australia. Department of Industry and Commerce. Annual Report (0067-1347)
Published by: Department of Industry, Science and Resources, PO Box 9839, Canberra City, ACT 2601, Australia. TEL 61-6-2136000, FAX 61-6-2137000. Circ: 8,000.

AUSTRALIA. DEPARTMENT OF THE TREASURY. ANNUAL REPORT. see *BUSINESS AND ECONOMICS—Economic Situation And Conditions*

AUSTRALIA. DEPARTMENT OF THE TREASURY. BUDGET. see *BUSINESS AND ECONOMICS—Economic Situation And Conditions*

336.3 330.9 AUS ISSN 1031-4121
AUSTRALIA. DEPARTMENT OF THE TREASURY. TAX EXPENDITURES STATEMENT. Key Title: Tax Expenditures Statement. Short title: T E S. Text in English. 1986. a. charts; stat. back issues avail. **Document type:** *Government.*
Description: Provides details on the financial benefits that individuals and businesses in Australia derive from taxation concessions of various kinds.
Related titles: Online - full text ed.
Published by: (Australia. Department of the Treasury), AusInfo, GPO Box 1920, Canberra Mc, ACT 2610, Australia. TEL 61-2-6295-4512, FAX 61-2-6295-4455, http://www.ausinfo.gov.au, http://www.treasury.gov.au. **Orders to:** AusInfo Mail Order Sales, GPO Box 84, Canberra, ACT 2601, Australia. FAX 61-2-6295-4888.

AUSTRALIAN SOCIAL POLICY (CANBERRA). see *SOCIAL SERVICES AND WELFARE*

336 AUS
AUSTRALIAN STAMP DUTIES BULLETIN. Text in English. 1979. 4 base vols. plus bi-m. updates. looseleaf. AUD 1,593.90 (effective 2005). **Document type:** *Bulletin, Academic/Scholarly.*
Published by: LexisNexis Butterworths (Subsidiary of: LexisNexis Asia Pacific), Tower 2, 475-495 Victoria Ave, Chatswood, NSW 2067, Australia. TEL 61-2-94222189, FAX 61-2-94222406, http://www.lexisnexis.com.au/aus/products/catalog/current_htm/ASDL.asp?productid=ASDL&jurisdiction=1&category=0&medium=book/2/3/4/6/7/8/9/11/1/&author, http://www.lexisnexis.com.au/aus/default.asp.

336 AUS
AUSTRALIAN STAMP DUTIES LAW. Text in English. 4 base vols. plus bi-m. updates. looseleaf. AUD 1,155 (effective 2000). adv.
Formerly: Australian Revenue and Stamp Duties
Published by: LexisNexis Butterworths (Subsidiary of: LexisNexis Asia Pacific), Tower 2, 475-495 Victoria Ave, Chatswood, NSW 2067, Australia. TEL 61-2-94222189, FAX 61-2-94222406, http://www.lexisnexis.com.au/aus/default.asp. Ed. Carolyn Mathews. R&P Deanne Castellino. Adv. contact Mary Greenfield. **Dist. in N. America by:** Wm. W. Gaunt & Sons Inc., Gaunt Bldg, 3011 Gulf Dr, Holmes Beach, FL 34217-2199.

336 340 AUS ISSN 0812-695X
➤ **AUSTRALIAN TAX FORUM;** a journal of taxation policy, law and reform. Text in English. 1984. q. AUD 176, AUD 220 (effective 2002). adv. index. back issues avail.; reprint service avail. from WSH. **Document type:** *Academic/Scholarly.*
Description: Publishes papers on tax analysis and policy, tax law and tax reform in Australia.
Related titles: Microfiche ed.: (from PQC); Online - full text ed.: (from Northern Light Technology, Inc., ProQuest Information & Learning, R M I T Publishing).
Indexed: ATI, CLI, ILP, JEL, LRI, PAIS.
Published by: Taxation Institute of Australia, 9th Fl., 64 Castlereagh St, Sydney, NSW 2000, Australia. TEL 61-2-92323422, FAX 61-2-92216953, publications@taxinstitute.com.au, http://www.taxinstitute.com.au/cda/journals/1,1314,11,00.html. Ed. Richard Vann. R&P Alex Moham. Circ: 500 (paid).

336 AUS ISSN 1325-7935
KU2790
AUSTRALIAN TAX HANDBOOK. Text in English. 1938. a. (in 3 vols.). AUD 120 for print, online or CD ed. (effective 2003). **Document type:** *Monographic series, Trade.* **Description:** Covers all aspects of Australian income tax law and related taxes and provides clear overviews, introductions and worked examples.
Former titles (until 1995): Butterworths Australian Tax Handbook (1033-0313); (until 1988): Australian Income Tax Guide
Related titles: CD-ROM ed.; Online - full content ed.
Published by: Australian Tax Practice (Subsidiary of: Thomson Legal & Regulatory Ltd.), PO Box 3502, Rozelle, NSW 2039, Australia. ATPOnlineService@thomson.com.au, http://onlineecom01.thomson.com.au/thomson/Catalog.asp?EES_CMD=SI&EES_ID=101260, http://www.atp-online.com.au/

336 AUS ISSN 1325-7927
AUSTRALIAN TAX LEGISLATION. Text in English. 1979. a. AUD 230 (effective 2003). **Document type:** *Monographic series, Trade.* **Description:** Covers all tax and related legislation, including three indexes, conversion tables, legislation interpreter and detailed history notes.
Former titles (until 1996): Butterworths Australian Tax Legislation (1033-1506); (until 1988): Butterworths Income Tax Assessment Act and Related Legislation (1033-1492); (until 1985): Butterworths Income Tax Assessment Act, Regulations, Taxation Administration Act (1033-1484); (until 1984): Butterworths Income Tax Assessment Act and Related Legislation (0811-4676); (until 1982): Butterworths Income Tax Legislation Handbook (0811-4668)
Published by: Australian Tax Practice (Subsidiary of: Thomson Legal & Regulatory Ltd.), PO Box 3502, Rozelle, NSW 2039, Australia. ATPOnlineService@thomson.com.au, http://www.atp-online.com.au/.

336.2 AUS ISSN 1321-5779
AUSTRALIAN TAX PLANNING LAW JOURNAL. Text in English. 1994. q. AUD 99. bk.rev. back issues avail. **Document type:** *Journal, Academic/Scholarly.* **Description:** Provides analysis of the law as it relates to tax planning for scholars, professionals, consumers and businesses.
Published by: Australian Law Publishers Pty. Ltd., 254 Hawken Dr, St Lucia, QLD 4067, Australia. TEL 61-7-38709111, FAX 61-7-38702222, la510737@student.uq.edu.au. Ed. Russell Mathews. Circ: 200.

336.2 340 AUS ISSN 0311-094X
K1
AUSTRALIAN TAX REVIEW. Text in English. 1971. q. AUD 380 (effective 2004). charts; stat. reprint service avail. from WSH. **Document type:** *Journal, Academic/Scholarly.* **Description:** Provides discussion of tax issues and problems from recent cases or legislation.
Related titles: Online - full text ed.: (from O C L C Online Computer Library Center, Inc., ProQuest Information & Learning, R M I T Publishing).
Indexed: ABIn, ATI, AusPAIS, CANZLLI, CLI, ILP, LRI, LegCont, PAIS.
—BLDSC (1822.500000), IE, ingenta.
Published by: Lawbook Co. (Subsidiary of: Thomson Legal & Regulatory Ltd.), PO Box 3502, Rozelle, NSW 2039, Australia. LRA.Service@thomson.com, http://onlineecom01.thomson.com.au/thomson/Catalog.asp?EES_CMD=SI&EES_ID=101833, http://www.lawbookco.com.au. Ed. Peter Hill.

336.2 AUS ISSN 1321-7488
AUSTRALIAN TAXATION LAW JOURNAL. Text in English. 1994. q. AUD 99. bk.rev. **Document type:** *Journal, Academic/Scholarly.* **Description:** Provides analysis of the law as it relates to taxation for scholars, professionals and consumers.
Published by: Australian Law Publishers Pty. Ltd., 254 Hawken Dr, St Lucia, QLD 4067, Australia. TEL 61-7-38709111, FAX 61-7-38702222, Ed. Russell Mathews.

336 352 ITA ISSN 1590-1785
AZIENDITALIA FINANZA E TRIBUTI. Text in Italian. 1998. fortn. EUR 136 (effective 2005). **Document type:** *Magazine, Consumer.*
Published by: IPSOA Editore (Subsidiary of: Wolters Kluwer Italia Srl), Strada 1, Palazzo F6, Milanofiori, Assago, MI 20090, Italy. TEL 39-02-82476888, FAX 39-02-82476436, http://www.ipsoa.it.

B B E STEUERPRAXIS. see *BUSINESS AND ECONOMICS—Management*

336 DEU ISSN 1437-9864
B D Z MAGAZIN. Text in German. 1999. m. adv. **Document type:** *Magazine, Trade.*
Published by: Bund der Deutschen Zollbeamten, Friedrichstr 169-170, Berlin, 10117, Germany. TEL 49-30-40816600, FAX 49-30-40816633, post@bdz.dbb.de, http://www.bdz.dbb.de. adv.: B&W page EUR 2,150, color page EUR 2,930. Circ: 32,000 (controlled).

336 NLD ISSN 0166-8528
B & G. Variant title: Bank en Gemeenten. Text in Dutch. 1974. 10/yr. adv. bk.rev. **Document type:** *Journal, Trade.* **Description:** Publishes in-depth articles concerning financial and organizational matters affecting local and regional authorities.
Formerly: Gemeentefinancien (0016-6057)
—IE, Infotrieve.
Published by: Bank Nederlandse Gemeenten N. V., Koninginnegracht 2, The Hague, 2514 AA, Netherlands. TEL 31-70-3750820, FAX 31-70-3454743, http://www.bng.nl. Ed. J G Klaassens. R&P J.G. Klaassens. Circ: 10,000 (paid and controlled). **Co-sponsor:** Vereniging van Nederlandse Gemeenten.

336.2 DEU ISSN 1431-3928
B F H - P R; Entscheidungen des Bundesfinanzhofes fuer die Praxis der Steuerberatung von A bis Z. (Bundesfinanzhof - Praxis) Text in German. 1996. m. EUR 198 (effective 2004). adv. **Document type:** *Magazine, Trade.*
Published by: Verlag fuer Deutsche Steuerberater AG (Subsidiary of: Wolters Kluwer Deutschland GmbH), Marlener Str 2, Offenburg, 77656, Germany. TEL 49-781-9900646, FAX 49-781-9900644, info@steuern-online.de, http://www.steuern-online.de. adv.: B&W page EUR 920, color page EUR 1,687. Circ: 1,790 (paid).

B N A'S BANKING REPORT (PRINT EDITION); legal and regulatory developments in the financial services industry. see *LAW*

336.2714 NLD ISSN 0922-9566
B T W BRIEF. (Belasting Toegevoegde Waarde) Text in Dutch. 1989. 10/yr. back issues avail. **Document type:** *Trade.* **Description:** Covers practical issues, recent jurisprudence and developments relating to value added taxation in the Netherlands.
Published by: Uitgeverij Fed bv (Subsidiary of: Wolters Kluwer N.V.), Postbus 23, Deventer, 7400 GA, Netherlands. TEL 31-570-633155, FAX 31-570-633834. Eds. J L M J Vervloed, S T M Beelen.

336.2 BEL ISSN 1383-7613
B T W BULLETIN. (Belasting Toegevoegde Waarde) Text in Dutch. 1992. fortn. EUR 186.41 (effective 2003). 4 p./no.; **Document type:** *Newsletter.*
Formerly (until 1995): Europees Belasting Toegevoegde Waarde-Nieuws (0927-9296)
—Infotrieve.
Published by: (Price Waterhouse Coopers GBR), Kluwer Uitgevers (Subsidiary of: Wolters Kluwer Belgique), Ragheno Business Park, Motstraat 30, Mechelen, B-2800, Belgium. TEL 32-15-800-94571, info@kluwer.be, http://www.kluwer.be.

336 BHR
BAHRAIN. MONETARY AGENCY. ANNUAL REPORT. Text in English. a. charts; stat. **Document type:** *Government.*
Published by: Monetary Agency, PO Box 27, Manama, Bahrain. TEL 535535, FAX 533342.

BALANCE OF PAYMENTS OF TRINIDAD AND TOBAGO. see *BUSINESS AND ECONOMICS—Abstracting, Bibliographies, Statistics*

336 382 ESP ISSN 1136-5331
BALANZA DE PAGOS DE ESPANA. Text in Spanish. 1971. a. USD 4.50.
Published by: (Spain. Ministerio de Economia y Hacienda), Banco de Espana, Alcala 50, Madrid, 28014, Spain. TEL 34-91-3385180, FAX 34-91-3385320, http://www.bde.es. Circ: 1,500.

336 PAN
BANCO NACIONAL DE PANAMA. INFORMACION ECONOMICA Y FINANCIERA DE LA REPUBLICA DE PANAMA. Text in Spanish. 1978. a. free. charts; stat.
Published by: (Banco Nacional de Panama), Gerencia de Planificacion Economica y Financiera (Subsidiary of: Banco Nacional de Panama), Apdo 5220, Panama City, 5, Panama. FAX 507-69-5645. Circ: 1,000.

BANGLADESH BANK. STATISTICS DEPARTMENT. ANNUAL BALANCE OF PAYMENTS. see *BUSINESS AND ECONOMICS—Abstracting, Bibliographies, Statistics*

BANGLADESH BANK. STATISTICS DEPARTMENT. BALANCE OF PAYMENTS. see *BUSINESS AND ECONOMICS—Abstracting, Bibliographies, Statistics*

THE BANK INCOME TAX RETURN MANUAL. see *BUSINESS AND ECONOMICS—Banking And Finance*

336.3 CAN ISSN 1490-7291
HJ8513
BANK OF CANADA. SUMMARY OF GOVERNMENT OF CANADA DIRECT SECURITIES AND LOANS. Variant title: Resume des Titres et Emprunts Emis par le Gouvernement du Canada. Text in English, French. 1982. a. free (effective 2004).
Formerly (until 1988): Bank of Canada. Summary of Government of Canada Direct and Guaranteed Securities and Loans (0831-9383)
Related titles: Online - full text ed.: ISSN 1702-6431.
Published by: Bank of Canada, Publications Distribution, Communications Services, 234 Wellington St, Ottawa, ON K1A 0G9, Canada. TEL 613-782-8248, FAX 613-782-8874, publications@bank-banque-canada.ca, http://www.bankofcanada.ca/en/guide_idx.htm.

382 336 JPN
BANK OF JAPAN. BALANCE OF PAYMENTS MONTHLY. Text in English, Japanese. 1965. m. JPY 900 per issue. **Description:** Contains systematic records of Japan's cross-border economic transactions.
Formerly: Bank of Japan. Japan's Balance of Payments. Summary Report (0549-317X)
Published by: (International Department), Bank of Japan/Nippon Ginko, c/o Public Relations Department, 2-1-1 Hongoku-cho-Nihonbashi, Chuo-ku, Tokyo, 1030000, Japan. TEL 81-3-3271-1111, FAX 81-3-3510-1374, http://www.boj.or.jp/en.index.htm. **Dist. by:** Tokiwa Sohgoh Service Co. Ltd., Publication and Research Department, Kyodo Bldg, 2-4 Hongokucho, Nihonbashi 3-chome, Chuo-ku, Tokyo 103-0027, Japan. TEL 81-3-3270-5713, FAX 81-3-3270-5710; **Overseas dist. by:** Japan Publications Trading Co., Ltd., Book Export II Dept, PO Box 5030, Tokyo International, Tokyo 101-3191, Japan. TEL 81-3-32923753, FAX 81-3-32920410, infoserials@jptco.co.jp, http://www.jptco.co.jp.

336 382 LBY ISSN 0075-921X
BANK OF LIBYA. BALANCE OF PAYMENTS✶. Text in Arabic, English. 1954. a. free.
Published by: Bank of Libya, P O Box 1103, Tripoli, Libya.

BANKRUPTCY PRACTICE SERIES. CHAPTER 11: REORGANIZATIONS. see *LAW—Corporate Law*

336 BRB
BARBADOS. MINISTRY OF FINANCE AND ECONOMIC AFFAIRS. FINANCIAL STATEMENT AND BUDGETARY PROPOSALS. Text in English. 1974. bi-m. USD 6 (effective 1995). **Document type:** *Government.*
Formerly (until 1988): Barbados. Ministry of Finance and Planning. Financial Statement and Budgetary Proposals
Published by: Ministry of Finance and Economic Affairs, Government Printery, Bay St., St Michael, Barbados. Circ: 500.

336 ESP
BASQUE REGION. OGASUN ETA FINANTZA SAILA. (YEAR) RAKO AURREKONTUAK/BASQUE REGION. DEPARTAMENTO DE HACIENDA Y FINANZAS. PRESUPUESTOS (YEAR). Text in Spanish. a.
Published by: (Basque Region. Ogasun eta Finantza Saila/Departamento de Hacienda y Finanzas, Basque Region. Aurrekontu Zuzendaritza/Direccion de Presupuestos), Eusko Jaurlaritzaren Argitalpen-Zerbitzu Nagusia/Servicio Central de Publicaciones del Gobierno Vasco, Donostia-San Sebastian, 1, Vitoria-gasteiz, Alava 01010, Spain. Circ: 500.

B

336.2 DEU ISSN 0171-9513
DER BAYERISCHE STEUERZAHLER✶. Text in German. 1966. m. adv. charts; illus.
Formerly (until 1973): Bayern Nachrichten (0005-7223)
Published by: Bund der Steuerzahler Landesverband Bayern e.V., Nymphenburger Strasse 118, Munich, 80636, Germany. TEL 49-89-126008-0, FAX 49-89-12600827, info@steuerzahler-bayern.de, http://www.steuerzahler-bayern.de. Circ: 40,000.

336 DEU
BECK'SCHE STEUER CD; Gesetzgebung - Verwaltung - Rechtsprechung. Text in German. base vol. plus q. updates. EUR 125 base vol(s). per vol.; EUR 55 updates per issue (effective 2005). **Document type:** *Trade.*
Media: CD-ROM.
Published by: Verlag C.H. Beck oHG, Wilhelmstr 9, Munich, 80801, Germany. TEL 49-89-38189338, FAX 49-89-38189398, abo.service@beck.de, http://www.beck.de.

BEKNOPT OVERZICHT VAN DE SOCIALE ZEKERHEID IN BELGIE/SURVEY OF SOCIAL SECURITY IN BELGIUM. see *PUBLIC ADMINISTRATION*

336.2 NLD ISSN 0167-4293
BELASTINGBLAD. Text in Dutch. 1982. bi-w. adv. back issues avail. **Document type:** *Trade.*
—IE, Infotrieve.
Published by: Kluwer B.V. (Subsidiary of: Wolters Kluwer N.V.), Postbus 23, Deventer, 7400 GA, Netherlands. TEL 31-570-673449, FAX 31-570-691555, juridisch@kluwer.nl, http://www.kluwer.nl.

336.2 NLD
BELASTINGMAGAZINE. Text in Dutch. 10/yr. EUR 165 (effective 2003). **Description:** Aimed at the financial advisor.
Published by: Elsevier Financiele Informatie (Subsidiary of: Reed Business Information bv), Postbus 1872, Amsterdam, 1000 BW, Netherlands. TEL 0800-022-1313, FAX 31-20-515-9740, http://www.elsevierfiscaal.nl. Eds. D de Ruiter, M Keijzer.

DE BELGISCH TIJDSCHRIFT VOOR SOCIALE ZEKERHEID/BELGIAN SOCIAL SECURITY JOURNAL. see *PUBLIC ADMINISTRATION*

BELGIUM. FEDERAAL MINISTERIE VAN SOCIALE ZAKEN, VOLKSGEZONDHEID EN LEEFMILIEU. ALGEMEEN VERSLAG OVER DE SOCIALE ZEKERHEID. see *PUBLIC ADMINISTRATION*

BELGIUM. FEDERAAL MINISTERIE VAN SOCIALE ZAKEN, VOLKSGEZONDHEID EN LEEFMILIEU. HANIDGIDS/GUIDE OF THE DISABLED PERSON. see *HANDICAPPED*

336.2 BEL ISSN 0005-853X
BELGIUM. MINISTERE DES FINANCES. ADMINISTRATION DES CONTRIBUTIONS. BULLETIN DES CONTRIBUTIONS. Text in French. 1925. m. EUR 61.94 (effective 2004). charts; stat. **Document type:** *Government.*
Formerly (until 1960): Belgium. Ministere des Finances. Bulletin des Contributions Directes (0772-7194); Which superseded in part (in 1931): Belgium. Ministere des Finances. Bulletin des Contributions Directes et du Cadastre (0772-7186)
Related titles: Dutch ed.: Belgium. Ministerie van Financien. Hoofdbestuur der Directe Belastingen. Bulletin der Belastingen. ISSN 0772-7208.
Published by: Ministere des Finances, Administration Centrale des Contributions Directes/Ministerie van Financien, Hoofdbestuur der Directe Belastingen, Rijksadministratief Centrum, Financietoren, Kruidtuinlaan 50, Bus 32, Brussels, 1010, Belgium. TEL 32-2-2103816, FAX 32-2-2104118. Ed. Ph Cousin. Circ: 1,856.

BELGIUM. MINISTERE FEDERAL DES AFFAIRES SOCIALES, DE LA SANTE PUBLIQUE ET DE L'ENVIRONNEMENT. RAPPORT GENERAL SUR LA SECURITE SOCIALE. see *INSURANCE*

▼ new title ➤ refereed ✶ unverified ♦ full entry avail.

336 BEL ISSN 0779-8601
BELGIUM. MINISTERIE VAN FINANCIEN. DOCUMENTATIEBLAD/BELGIUM. MINISTERE DES FINANCES. BULLETIN DE DOCUMENTATION. Text in Dutch, English, French. 1941. bi-m. EUR 61.97 domestic; EUR 78.33 in the European Union; EUR 85.77 elsewhere; EUR 12.39 per issue (effective 2005). **Document type:** *Bulletin.* **Description:** Covers issues and topics relating to Belgian public finance and economic policy.
Related titles: Supplement(s): Ministerie van Financien. Studie- en Documentatiedienst. Fiscaal Memento. ISSN 0779-8504. 1989; Ministere des Finances. Service d'Etudes et de Documentation. Memento Fiscal. ISSN 0779-8512.
Published by: Ministerie van Financien, Studie- en Documentatiedienst/Ministere des Finances, Services d'Etudes et de Documentation, RAC Financietoren, Kruidtuinlaan 50, Bus 30, Brussels, 1010, Belgium. TEL 32-2-2103902, FAX 32-2-2103946, http://www.docufin.be/websedsdd/intersalgnl/thema/publicaties/documenta/documenta.htm#bestelvoorwaarden, http://www.docufin.be/websedsdd/index.htm. Circ: 1,150.

BERKELEY JOURNAL OF INTERNATIONAL LAW. see *LAW—International Law*

336.2 NLD ISSN 0165-0130
KKM3564.3
BESLISSINGEN IN BELASTINGZAKEN. Key Title: B N B. Beslissingen in Belastingzaken. Nederlandse Belastingrechtspraak. Text in Dutch. 1953. bi-w.
—IE, Infotrieve.
Published by: Kluwer B.V. (Subsidiary of: Wolters Kluwer N.V.), Postbus 23, Deventer, 7400 GA, Netherlands. TEL 31-570-673449, FAX 31-570-691555, juridisch@kluwer.nl, http://www.kluwer.nl. Circ: 3,000.

336 DEU ISSN 0174-5395
BETRIEBSPRUEFUNG; besser vorbereiten-erfolgreicher verhandeln-weniger nachzahlen. Text in German. 1984. q. looseleaf. **Document type:** *Trade.*
Published by: Rudolf Haufe Verlag GmbH & Co. KG, Hindenburgstr 64, Freiburg Im Breisgau, 79102, Germany. TEL 49-761-3683-0, online@haufe.de.

336.2 DEU ISSN 1619-0688
BETRIEBSWIRTSCHAFTLICHE MANDANTENBETREUUNG. Text in German. 2002. m. EUR 198 (effective 2004). **Document type:** *Journal, Trade.*
Published by: Vogel Verlag und Druck GmbH & Co. KG, Max-Planck-Str 7-9, Wuerzburg, 97064, Germany. TEL 49-931-4180, FAX 49-931-4182100, marliese_bernhardt@vogel-medien.de, http://www.iww.de/steuerberater/bwmandbetreuung/infoindex.php, http://www.vogel-medien.de.

336.2 DEU ISSN 1616-1297
BETRIEBSWIRTSCHAFTLICHE STEUERLEHRE IN FORSCHUNG UND PRAXIS. Text in German. 2000. irreg., latest vol.18, 2005. price varies. **Document type:** *Monographic series, Academic/Scholarly.*
Published by: Verlag Dr. Kovac, Arnoldstr 49, Hamburg, 22763, Germany. TEL 49-40-3988800, FAX 49-40-39888055, info@verlagdrkovac.de, http://www.verlagdrkovac.de/3-13.htm.

BILANZIERUNG PLUS. see *BUSINESS AND ECONOMICS—Accounting*

336.2 DEU ISSN 1612-524X
BILANZIERUNGS-RICHTLINIEN SPECIAL; Das Special-Wissen fuer alle Bilanzierungsfaelle. Text in German. 2002. base vol. plus updates 5/yr. EUR 198 base vol(s).; EUR 49 updates per issue (effective 2004). **Document type:** *Trade.*
Published by: Verlag fuer Deutsche Steuerberater AG (Subsidiary of: Wolters Kluwer Deutschland GmbH), Marlener Str 2, Offenburg, 77656, Germany. TEL 49-781-9900646, FAX 49-781-9900644, info@steuern-online.de, http://www.steuern-online.de.

336 USA
BOND TELLER. Text in English. 1971. 2/yr. free. charts. **Document type:** *Newsletter, Government.* **Description:** Provides information for employees of financial institutions.
Related titles: Online - full content ed.
Published by: U.S. Department of the Treasury, Bureau of Public Debt, 999 E St Ste 501, Washington, DC 20239-0001. TEL 304-480-6112, FAX 304-480-7959, OAdmin@bpd.treas.gov, http://www.publicdebt.treas.gov/sav/savbtell.htm. Circ: 205,000.

336 BWA ISSN 0068-0451
HJ80N
BOTSWANA. ANNUAL STATEMENTS OF ACCOUNTS. Text in English. a. BWP 11. **Document type:** *Government.*
Published by: Central Statistics Office, c/o Government Statistician, Private Bag 0024, Gaborone, Botswana. TEL 267-31-352200, FAX 267-31-352201, csobots@gov.bw, http://www.gov.bw/cso/index.html. **Subscr. to:** Government Printer, Private Bag 0081, Gaborone, Botswana. TEL 267-353202, FAX 267-312001, http://www.gov.bw.

336.2 BWA
BOTSWANA. DEPARTMENT OF INCOME TAX. ANNUAL REPORT. Text in English. 1972. a. free. **Document type:** *Government.*
Published by: Department of Taxes, Private Bag 0013, Gaborone, Botswana. TEL 267-352444, FAX 267-374642. Ed. Denis V Moishegare.

336.2 CAN ISSN 0045-3056
BRITISH COLUMBIA TAX REPORTER. Text in English. m. CND 582 (effective 2005). index. **Document type:** *Trade.* **Description:** Provides in-depth information and source material with respect to various B.C. taxes, including corporation capital tax, income tax (personal and corporate), social service tax (sales tax), hotel room tax, etc.
Related titles: CD-ROM ed.: CND 531 (effective 2005); Online - full text ed.: CND 515 (effective 2005).
Published by: C C H Canadian Ltd., 90 Sheppard Ave E, Ste 300, North York, ON M2N 6X1, Canada. TEL 416-224-2248, 800-268-4522, FAX 416-224-2243, cservice@cch.ca, http://www.cch.ca.

336.2 GBR ISSN 0007-1870
K2
BRITISH TAX REVIEW. Text in English. 1956. bi-m. GBP 355, EUR 534 in Europe; GBP 375, USD 681 elsewhere; GBP 178, EUR 267 in Europe to students; GBP 188, USD 341 elsewhere to students (effective 2006). adv. bk.rev. reprints avail. **Document type:** *Bulletin, Trade.* **Description:** Offers comments on topical matters such as draft legislation and consultative documents, case notes, and case law.
Related titles: Online - full text ed.
Indexed: ATI, CLI, CREJ, CurCont, FamI, ILP, LJI, LRI, LegCont, PAIS, PCI, RRTA, SSCI, WAE&RSA, WBA.
—BLDSC (2345.350000), IE, Infotrieve, ingenta. **CCC.**
Published by: Sweet & Maxwell Ltd., 100 Avenue Road, London, NW3 3PF, United Kingdom. TEL 44-20-74491111, FAX 44-20-74491144, customer.services@sweetandmaxwell.co.uk, http://www.sweetandmaxwell.co.uk. Eds. David Oliver, Judith Freedman. Adv. contact Jackie Wood. **Subscr. outside the UK to:** Cheriton House, North Way, Andover, Hants SP10 5BE, United Kingdom. TEL 44-1264-342706, sminfo@itps.co.uk.

BUCHEN, BILANZIEREN UND STEUERN SPAREN VON A-Z. see *BUSINESS AND ECONOMICS—Accounting*

336 CYP
HJ68
BUDGET. Text in English. a. **Document type:** *Government.*
Incorporates (in 2000): Cyprus. Development Estimates (0084-9510)
Published by: Government Printing Office, Director, Nicosia, Cyprus. TEL 357-2-302202, FAX 357-2-303175.

336 PAK
BUDGET OF THE GOVERNMENT OF PAKISTAN. DEMANDS FOR GRANTS AND APPROPRIATIONS. Text in English. a. free to qualified personnel.
Supersedes: Pakistan. Ministry of Finance. Budget of the Central Government (0078-8317)
Published by: Finance Division, Islamabad, Pakistan.

BUILDING SOCIETY TAXATION MANUAL. see *LAW—Estate Planning*

336 FRA ISSN 0242-5912
HJ47
BULLETIN FISCAL. Text in French. 1977 (vol.43). m. EUR 96 (effective 2005). adv. **Document type:** *Bulletin, Trade.*
Former titles: Bulletin de Documentation Pratique des Taxes sur le Chiffre d'Affaires (0007-4276); Bulletin de Documentation Pratiques des Impots Directs et des Taxes sur le Chiffre d'Affaires (0007-4268)
Published by: Editions Francis Lefebvre, 42 rue de Villiers, Levallois-Perret, 92300, France. TEL 33-1-41052222, http://www.efl.fr.

336.2 NLD ISSN 0007-4624
K4430.A15
BULLETIN FOR INTERNATIONAL FISCAL DOCUMENTATION. Text in English. 1946. m. looseleaf. USD 400 (effective 2005). adv. bk.rev. bibl. index. back issues avail.; reprints avail. **Document type:** *Bulletin, Trade.* **Description:** Provides detailed analysis of developments in tax policy and law.
Related titles: Online - full text ed.: (from Swets Information Services).
Indexed: ATI, CREJ, CurCont, ELLIS, FLP, IBSS, IBZ, IPARL, JEL, KES, MEA&I, PAIS, RASB, SSCI.
—BLDSC (2865.050000), IE, Infotrieve, ingenta.
Published by: (International Bureau of Fiscal Documentation), I B F D Publications BV, H J E Wenckebachweg 210, PO Box 20237, Amsterdam, 1000 HE, Netherlands. TEL 31-20-5540100, FAX 31-20-6228658, info@ibfd.nl, http://www.ibfd.nl. Ed. David Hughes. **Subscr. to:** I B F D Publications USA, Inc, PO Box 805, Valatie, NY 12184-0805. TEL 800-908-6330. **Co-sponsor:** International Fiscal Association.

336 FRA ISSN 0427-2129
BULLETIN OFFICIEL DES DOUANES. Text in French. 1954. d. **Document type:** *Bulletin.*
Published by: (France. Direction Generale des Douanes et Droits Indirects), Imprimerie Nationale, BP 514, Douai, Cedex 59505, France. TEL 27-93-70-70, FAX 27-93-70-96.

336 FRA ISSN 0982-801X
BULLETIN OFFICIEL DES IMPOTS. (In 14 series) Text in French. d.
Published by: Imprimerie Nationale, BP 514, Douai, Cedex 59505, France. TEL 27-93-70-70, FAX 27-93-70-96.

336 DEU ISSN 0175-5366
BUNDESSTEUERBLATT. AUSGABE A. Text in German. 1951. s-m. EUR 43.20 (effective 2004). **Document type:** *Journal, Trade.*
—IE, Infotrieve.
Published by: Stollfuss Verlag GmbH & Co. KG, Dechenstr 7, Bonn, 53115, Germany. TEL 49-228-7240, FAX 49-228-72491181, info@stollfuss.de, http://www.stollfuss.de/programm/products/0400010.htm.

336 USA ISSN 1524-3583
K2
BUSINESS ENTITIES. Text in English. 1999. bi-m. USD 215 (effective 2004). **Document type:** *Journal, Trade.*
Formed by the merger of (1984-1999): Journal of Partnership Taxation (0749-4513); (1989-1999): Journal of S Corporation Taxation (1045-1471); (1994-1999): Journal of Limited Liability Companies (1076-0865)
Related titles: Online - full text ed.: (from ProQuest Information & Learning).
Indexed: ABIn, ATI, ILP.
—BLDSC (2933.597000), IE, ingenta. **CCC.**
Published by: W G & L Financial Reporting & Management Research (Subsidiary of: R I A), 395 Hudson St, New York, NY 10014. TEL 617-423-2020, FAX 617-423-2026. Ed. Jerald D August.

336.2 USA
BUSINESS ORGANIZATIONS WITH TAX PLANNING. Text in English. 1963. 16 base vols. plus q. updates. looseleaf. USD 2,888 (effective 2003). Supplement avail. **Description:** Provides in-depth analysis of corporation law and all relevant aspects of federal corporate taxation.
Related titles: CD-ROM ed.
Published by: Matthew Bender & Co., Inc. (Subsidiary of: LexisNexis North America), 1275 Broadway, Albany, NY 12204. international@bender.com, http://bender.lexisnexis.com. Ed. Zolman Cavitch.

336.207 GBR ISSN 1351-0819
BUSINESS TAX PLANNING. Text in English. 1993. m. GBP 120.
Indexed: ELJI, LJI.
Published by: Longman Group Ltd., Law Tax and Finance Division, 21-27 Lambs Conduit St, London, WC1N 3NJ, United Kingdom. TEL 071-242-2548, FAX 071-831-8119.

336.2 GBR ISSN 0525-3063
BUTTERWORTHS BUDGET TAX TABLES. Text in English. 1966. a. GBP 7.45, USD 10 (effective 2000). charts. **Document type:** *Trade.* **Description:** Contains details and explanations of the budget proposals, set out under distinctive headings.
Published by: Butterworths Tolley (Subsidiary of: LexisNexis UK (Scottish Office)), Halsbury House, 35 Chancery Ln, London, Mddx WC2A 1EL, United Kingdom. TEL 44-20-74002500, FAX 44-20-74002583, TELEX DX Chancery Lane 1023, order.line@butterworths.co.uk, http://www.butterworths.co.uk. Ed. Derek Bond. Circ: 13,000.

336.2 GBR ISSN 0141-1500
BUTTERWORTHS ORANGE TAX HANDBOOK. Text in English. 1976. a., latest 2000-2001. GBP 46.95 (effective 2000). adv. **Document type:** *Trade.* **Description:** Contains up-to-date text of all legislation and other material relating to inheritance tax, national insurance contributions, stamp duty and value added tax, insurance premium tax, landfill tax and petroleum revenue tax.
Published by: Butterworths Tolley (Subsidiary of: LexisNexis UK (Scottish Office)), Halsbury House, 35 Chancery Ln, London, Mddx WC2A 1EL, United Kingdom. TEL 44-20-74002500, FAX 44-20-7400-2842, order.line@butterworths.co.uk, http://www.butterworths.co.uk/. Ed. Moiz Sadikali.

BUTTERWORTHS REGIONAL LEVIES REPORT. see *LAW*

336 ZAF
BUTTERWORTHS TAX ALERT. Text in English. m. looseleaf. ZAR 222.30. **Document type:** *Abstract/Index.* **Description:** Update service containing details of all changes to the tax law, as well as summaries and commentary covering all tax cases, legislation, fiscal rulings, and other relevant tax developments.
Published by: LexisNexis Butterworths South Africa (Subsidiary of: LexisNexis Europe and Africa), PO Box 792, Durban, KwaZulu-Natal 4000, South Africa. TEL 27-31-2683111, FAX 27-31-2683110.

336 NZL
BUTTERWORTHS TAXATION LIBRARY. Text in English. 3 base vols. plus updates 8/yr. looseleaf. NZD 99. **Description:** Contains consolidated statutes, regulations and case references.

Published by: Butterworths of New Zealand Ltd. (Subsidiary of: LexisNexis Asia Pacific), P.O. Box 472, 203-207 Victoria St, Wellington, New Zealand. TEL 64-4-3851479, FAX 64-4-385-1598. Ed. Stephen Gibbs.

336 ZAF
BUTTERWORTHS V A T GRAM; early information about changes to V A T. (Value Added Tax) Text in English. q. looseleaf.
Supersedes (in 1995): Juta's V A T News
Published by: LexisNexis Butterworths South Africa (Subsidiary of: LexisNexis Europe and Africa), PO Box 792, Durban, KwaZulu-Natal 4000, South Africa. TEL 27-31-294247, FAX 27-31-283255. Eds. Anne Bennett, Des Kruger.

336.2 GBR ISSN 0141-3856
BUTTERWORTHS YELLOW TAX HANDBOOK. Text in English. 1962. a. GBP 49.95 (effective 2000). adv. **Description:** Provides the text of the legislation relating to income tax, capital gains tax and corporation tax in the amended and updated form needed for accurate assessments.
Formerly: Butterworths Tax Handbook (0068-452X)
Published by: Butterworths Tolley (Subsidiary of: LexisNexis UK (Scottish Office)), Halsbury House, 35 Chancery Ln, London, Mddx WC2A 1EL, United Kingdom. TEL 44-20-74002500, FAX 44-20-7400-2842, order.line@butterworths.co.uk, http://www.butterworths.co.uk/. Ed. Moiz Sadikali.

336.2 USA
KF6285.B45
C C H FEDERAL TAX WEEKLY NEWSLETTER. (Commerce Clearing House) Text in English. 1951. w. looseleaf. USD 345 (effective 2005). index. **Document type:** *Newsletter.* **Description:** U.S. Federal tax analysis.
Former titles: Bender's Federal Tax Week; U S Tax Week (0041-8129)
Related titles: CD-ROM ed.; Online - full text ed.
—CCC.
Published by: C C H Inc., 2700 Lake Cook Rd, Riverwoods, IL 60015. TEL 847-267-7000, 800-449-6439, FAX 800-224-8299, cust_serv@cch.com, http://www.cch.com. Pub. Kevin Robert.

336 338.91 NLD
C C S O WORKING PAPERS. (Centrum voor Conjunctuur en Structuuronderzoek) Text in English, Dutch. irreg. **Document type:** *Academic/Scholarly.*
Formerly: C C S O Quarterly Journal
Related titles: Online - full text ed.
Published by: Rijksuniversiteit Groningen, Faculteit der Economische Wetenschappen/University of Groningen, Faculty of Economics, P.O. Box 800, Groningen, 9700 AV, Netherlands. http://www.eco.rug.nl/ccso/.

C G T CAPITAL LOSSES. (Capital Gains Tax) see *BUSINESS AND ECONOMICS—Investments*

343.73 USA ISSN 1066-1867
C P A CLIENT TAX LETTER. (Certified Public Accountant) Text in English. q. USD 111. **Document type:** *Newsletter.*
Related titles: Online - full text ed.
Indexed: ATI.
Published by: American Institute of Certified Public Accountants, Harborside Financial Ctr., 201 Plaza Three, 3rd Fl, Jersey City, NJ 07311-9801. TEL 888-777-7077, FAX 800-302-5766, journal@aicpa.org, http://www.aicpa.org.

336 690 USA ISSN 1047-5796
C P A CONSTRUCTION NICHE BUILDER. Text in English. 1989. m. USD 257 to individuals; USD 26 newsstand/cover (effective 2002). **Document type:** *Newsletter.* **Description:** Devoted to strategies and techniques for CPAs serving the construction industry.
Related titles: Online - full text ed.: (from Florida Center for Library Automation, Gale Group).
Indexed: ATI.
Published by: Aspen Publishers, Inc. (Subsidiary of: Wolters Kluwer N.V.), 5301 Buckeystown Pike, Ste. 400, Frederick, MD 21704-8319. customer.service@aspenpubl.com, http://www.aspenpublishers.com. Eds. Kristen E Clark, Kristen E. Clark. Pub. Sid Bernstein.

C P A G'S HOUSING BENEFIT AND COUNCIL TAX BENEFIT LEGISLATION (YEAR). see *SOCIAL SERVICES AND WELFARE*

C P A G'S INCOME - RELATED BENEFITS: THE LEGISLATION. see *SOCIAL SERVICES AND WELFARE*

336 USA
C S E A ANNUAL REPORT. Text in English. a. membership. adv. back issues avail. **Document type:** *Corporate.* **Description:** Informs members and other interested parties of society activities, progress and financial standing.
Published by: California Society of Enrolled Agents, 3200 Ramos Circle, Sacramento, CA 95827. TEL 916-366-6646, FAX 916-366-6674. Circ: 4,000 (controlled).

CAHIERS DE DROIT FISCAL INTERNATIONAL. see *LAW—International Law*

336 CHN ISSN 1005-4375
HJ1404
CAIZHENG YU SHUIWU/PUBLIC FINANCE AND TAXATION. Text in Chinese. m. CNY 180 (effective 2004). 96 p./no.; **Document type:** *Journal, Academic/Scholarly.* **Description:** Covers the systems, policies and regulations of Chinese taxation, and government budget and expenditure.
Formerly (until 1993): Caizheng, Jinrong (1001-3393)
Indexed: RASB.
Published by: Zhongguo Renmin Daxue, Shubao Zilio Zhongxin/Renmin University of China, Information Center for Social Server, Dongcheng-qu, 3, Zhangzizhong Lu, Beijing, 100007, China. TEL 86-10-84043003, FAX 86-10-64015080, kyes@163.net, http://www.confucius.cn.net/bkdetail.asp?fzt=F61. **Dist. in US by:** China Publications Service, PO Box 49614, Chicago, IL 60649. TEL 312-371-1761, FAX 312-288-8570.

336.2 USA ISSN 1093-1724
CAL - TAX DIGEST. Text in English. 1960. m. USD 96 to non-members; USD 50 to libraries; free to members (effective 2005). bk.rev. charts; stat. 24 p./no. 3 cols./p.; back issues avail. **Document type:** *Magazine, Trade.* **Description:** Features in-depth monthly analysis and commentary on important public finance topics.
Formerly (until 1997): Cal - Tax News (0008-0543)
Indexed: CalPI.
♦ **Published by:** California Taxpayers Association, 1215 K St, Ste 1250, Sacramento, CA 95814-3953. TEL 916-441-0490, FAX 916-441-1619, reroach@caltax.org, http://www.caltax.org/digest.htm. Ed., R&P Ronald W Roach. Circ: 4,000 (paid and controlled).

336 USA
CALIFORNIA AND NEW YORK TAX ANALYSIS (ONLINE EDITION). Text in English. 1983. 5 base vols. plus m. updates. looseleaf. USD 1,175 (effective 2004). **Description:** Provide practical, transaction-oriented examples and tax planning strategies on how to minimize tax liabilities in the two states levying the most taxes—California and New York.
Former titles: California Tax Analysis (Print Edition); California Taxation
Media: Online - full text. **Related titles:** CD-ROM ed.: USD 641 (effective 2004).
Published by: C C H Inc., 2700 Lake Cook Rd, Riverwoods, IL 60015. TEL 847-267-7000, 800-449-6439, FAX 800-224-8299, cust_serv@cch.com, http://www.cch.com. Eds. Philip Plant, Robert A Peterson. Pub. Kevin Robert.

336.24 345 USA
CALIFORNIA CLOSELY HELD CORPORATIONS: TAX PLANNING AND PRACTICE GUIDE. Text in English. 1987. 3 base vols. plus irreg. updates. looseleaf. USD 570 (effective 1999). **Description:** Examines all appropriate federal and California securities laws and corporate law. Provides complete tax planning guidance and how-to advice on structuring corporate transactions with shareholders.
Related titles: CD-ROM ed.
Published by: Matthew Bender & Co., Inc. (Subsidiary of: LexisNexis North America), 1275 Broadway, Albany, NY 12204. international@bender.com, http://bender.lexisnexis.com. Ed. Robert Wood.

CALIFORNIA COMMUNITY PROPERTY WITH TAX ANALYSIS. see *LAW—Family And Matrimonial Law*

336 USA
THE CALIFORNIA ENROLLED AGENT. Text in English. 1977. m. (10/yr.). USD 50 (effective 2000). adv. back issues avail. **Description:** Professional tax preparation topics, technical articles and organization news.
Published by: California Society of Enrolled Agents, 3200 Ramos Circle, Sacramento, CA 95827. TEL 916-366-6646, FAX 916-366-6674, evp@aol.com, http://www.csea.org. Ed., R&P Catherine A Apker. Adv. contact Lorelei Grenon. Circ: 4,400.

336.2 USA
CALIFORNIA FAMILY TAX PLANNING. Text in English. 1963. 2 base vols. plus irreg. updates. looseleaf. USD 523 base vol(s). (effective 2003). **Description:** Provides plans, methods, procedures and sample forms for optimum family tax savings under California and federal income, estate and gift tax law.
Published by: Matthew Bender & Co., Inc. (Subsidiary of: LexisNexis North America), 1275 Broadway, Albany, NY 12204. international@bender.com, http://bender.lexisnexis.com. Eds. Ralph S Rice, Terence R Rice.

336 USA ISSN 0068-5801
CALIFORNIA. STATE BOARD OF EQUALIZATION. ANNUAL REPORT. Text in English. 1879. a. free. **Document type:** *Government.* **Description:** Includes information on tax revenue, programs, operations, court decisions, regulations and legislation for California property taxes, sales and use taxes, excise taxes, fuel taxes, and environmental fees.
Indexed: SRI.
Published by: State Board of Equalization, PO Box 942879, Sacramento, CA 94279-0001. TEL 916-322-8825, FAX 916-324-1258, http://www.boe.ca.gov. Ed. Katherine Evatt. Circ: 4,000.

336.2 USA
CALIFORNIA TAX HANDBOOK (YEAR). Text in English. a. USD 25. **Description:** Explains all of California's state taxes, with tips, suggestions and cautions.
Published by: R I A (Subsidiary of: Thomson Corporation), 395 Hudson St, New York, NY 10014. TEL 212- 367-6300.

336.2 USA
CALTAXLETTER. Text in English. 1995. w. USD 350 to non-members; USD 250 to members (effective 2000). back issues avail. **Document type:** *Bulletin.* **Description:** Offers weekly news and analysis on issues affecting California taxpayers.
Published by: California Taxpayers Association, 1215 K St, Ste 1250, Sacramento, CA 95814-3953. TEL 916-441-0490, FAX 916-441-1619, reraoch@caltax.org, http://www.caltax.org. Ed., R&P Ronald W Roach.

336 CAN ISSN 1200-3557
CANADA. DEPARTMENT OF FINANCE. ANNUAL FINANCIAL REPORT OF THE GOVERNMENT OF CANADA. Text in English. 1994. a.
Published by: Canada. Department of Finance, Distribution Centre, West Tower, Rm P-135, 300 Laurier Ave W, Ottawa, ON K1A 0G5, Canada. TEL 613-995-2855, FAX 613-996-0518, http://www.fin.gc.ca/.

336.36 CAN ISSN 1484-4591
HJ13
CANADA. DEPARTMENT OF FINANCE. DEBT MANAGEMENT REPORT. Text in English. 1991. a.
Formerly (until 1997): Canada. Department of Finance. Debt Operations Report (1204-1076)
Related titles: Online - full text ed.: ISSN 1487-0177.
—CISTI.
Published by: Canada. Department of Finance, Distribution Centre, West Tower, Rm P-135, 300 Laurier Ave W, Ottawa, ON K1A 0G5, Canada. TEL 613-995-2855, FAX 613-996-0518, services-distribution@fin.gc.ca, http://www.fin.gc.ca/purl/dmr-e.html.

336 CAN ISSN 1706-3035
CANADA. DEPARTMENT OF FINANCE. ECONOMIC AND FISCAL UPDATE. Text in English. 1995. a.
Former titles (until 2002): Canada. Department of Finance. Economic Update (1700-019X); (until 2001): Canada. Department of Finance. Economic Statement and Budget Update (1495-9860); (until 2000): Canada. Department of Finance. Economic and Fiscal Update (1209-210X)
—CISTI.
Published by: Canada. Department of Finance, Distribution Centre, West Tower, Rm P-135, 300 Laurier Ave W, Ottawa, ON K1A 0G5, Canada. TEL 613-995-2855, FAX 613-996-0518, services-distribution@fin.gc.ca, http://www.fin.gc.ca/access/budinfoe.html.

336.2 CAN ISSN 1495-6489
CANADA. DEPARTMENT OF FINANCE. TAX EXPENDITURES AND EVALUATIONS. Text in English. 1994. a. CND 16 (effective 2004). **Description:** Provides estimates and projections of all federal tax expenditures.
Supersedes in part (in 2000): Canada. Department of Finance. Government of Canada Tax Expenditures (1200-8591)
Related titles: Online - full text ed.: ISSN 1495-737X.
—CISTI.
Published by: Canada. Department of Finance, Distribution Centre, West Tower, Rm P-135, 300 Laurier Ave W, Ottawa, ON K1A 0G5, Canada. TEL 613-995-2855, FAX 613-996-0518, services-distribution@fin.gc.ca, http://www.fin.gc.ca/.

336 CAN ISSN 0708-9031
CANADA. DEPARTMENT OF NATIONAL REVENUE. EXCISE NEWS. Text in English, French. 1971. q. free.
Formerly: Federal Sales Tax News
Published by: Department of National Revenue, Customs and Excise Branch, 320 Queen St, Tower A 9th Fl, Ottawa, ON K1A 0L5, Canada. TEL 613-994-7990. Circ: 80,000.

336.02 CAN
CANADA. DEPARTMENT OF NATIONAL REVENUE. REPORT: CUSTOMS, EXCISE AND TAXATION. Text in English, French. a.
Published by: Department of National Revenue, Customs and Excise Branch, 320 Queen St, Tower A 9th Fl, Ottawa, ON K1A 0L5, Canada. TEL 613-995-6447.

336.24 CAN ISSN 0008-2694
CANADA INCOME TAX GUIDE. Text in English. 1952. m. CND 584 (effective 2005). index. **Document type:** *Trade.* **Description:** Provides a concise and basic explanation of the federal income tax law with illustrative examples.
Related titles: CD-ROM ed.: CND 531 (effective 2005); Online - full text ed.: CND 515 (effective 2005).
Published by: C C H Canadian Ltd., 90 Sheppard Ave E, Ste 300, North York, ON M2N 6X1, Canada. TEL 416-224-2248, 800-268-4522, FAX 416-224-2243, cservice@cch.ca, http://www.cch.ca.

336 CAN
CANADA INCOME TAX GUIDE WITH CANADIAN INCOME TAX ACT, REGULATIONS & RULINGS. Text in English. m. looseleaf. CND 1,045 (effective 2005). **Document type:** *Trade.* **Description:** Explanation of the federal income tax law with illustrative examples. Consolidated texts of the income tax act and regulations with historical notes, references to related sections, summaries of amendments.
Related titles: CD-ROM ed.: CND 954 (effective 2005); Online - full text ed.: CND 926 (effective 2005).
Published by: C C H Canadian Ltd., 90 Sheppard Ave E, Ste 300, North York, ON M2N 6X1, Canada. TEL 416-224-2248, 800-268-4522, FAX 416-224-2243, cservice@cch.ca, http://www.cch.ca.

CANADA. STATISTICS CANADA. STATISTIQUES SUR LE SECTEUR PUBLIC. see *BUSINESS AND ECONOMICS—Abstracting, Bibliographies, Statistics*

336.2 CAN ISSN 0008-2740
KE5665.8
CANADA TAX CASES. Text in English. 1948. 24/yr. looseleaf. CND 899 domestic; USD 761.86 foreign (effective 2005). index. **Description:** Reports all judgments concerning federal taxation handed down by the Supreme Court of Canada, the Federal Court, the Tax Court, and the upper courts of the provinces. Includes comprehensive headnotes, editorial notes regarding significant decisions, topical and statutory indexes and tables of appeals.
Published by: Carswell (Subsidiary of: Thomson Corporation), One Corporate Plaza, 2075 Kennedy Rd, Toronto, ON M1T 3V4, Canada. TEL 416-609-8000, 800-387-5164, FAX 416-298-5094, carswell.customerrelations@thomson.com, http://www.carswell.com. Ed. Richard Pound.

336.2 CAN ISSN 0008-2759
CANADA TAX SERVICE; a loose-leaf tax information service. Text in English. 1948. 15/yr. looseleaf. CND 2,280 domestic; USD 1,932.21 foreign (effective 2005). charts. index. **Description:** Provides section-by-section treatment of the Income Tax Act. All relevant information follows each statutory provision and includes full historical notes, detailed commentary and analysis, precedent-setting cases, numerical examples where appropriate, interpretation bulletins, information circulars, and income tax regulations.
Published by: Carswell (Subsidiary of: Thomson Corporation), One Corporate Plaza, 2075 Kennedy Rd, Toronto, ON M1T 3V4, Canada. TEL 416-609-8000, 800-387-5164, FAX 416-298-5094, carswell.customerrelations@thomson.com, http://www.carswell.com. Ed. David N Finkelstein.

CANADA'S TAX TREATIES. see *LAW*

336.2 CAN ISSN 0317-6495
CANADIAN CURRENT TAX. Text in English. 1974. m. CND 275 (effective 2001). **Document type:** *Newsletter.* **Description:** Discusses developments in all aspects of tax law for lawyers and accountants.
Indexed: ICLPL.
Published by: LexisNexis Butterworths Canada Inc. (Subsidiary of: LexisNexis North America), 123 Commerce Valley Dr E, Ste 700, Markham, ON L3T 7W8, Canada. TEL 905-479-2665, FAX 905-479-2826, http://www.lexisnexis.ca/canadiancurrenttax.htm. Ed. Vern Krishna.

336 CAN
CANADIAN G S T & COMMODITY TAX CASES. Text in English. bi-w. looseleaf. CND 550 (effective 2005). **Document type:** *Trade.* **Description:** Contains full-text decisions pertaining to the GST, FST, Provincial Sales Tax, gasoline tax and tobacco tax.
Published by: C C H Canadian Ltd., 90 Sheppard Ave E, Ste 300, North York, ON M2N 6X1, Canada. TEL 416-224-2248, 800-268-4522, FAX 416-224-2243, cservice@cch.ca, http://www.cch.ca.

336.2714 CAN ISSN 1181-7097
CANADIAN G S T MONITOR. (Goods and Services Tax) Text in English. 1994. m. looseleaf. CND 217 (effective 2005). **Document type:** *Newsletter, Trade.*
Related titles: Online - full text ed.: (from Micromedia ProQuest).
Published by: C C H Canadian Ltd., 90 Sheppard Ave E, Ste 300, North York, ON M2N 6X1, Canada. TEL 416-224-2248, 800-268-4522, FAX 416-224-2243, 800-461-4131, cservice@cch.ca, http://www.cch.ca.

336 CAN
CANADIAN GOODS AND SERVICES TAX REPORTER. Text in English. m. looseleaf. CND 729 (effective 2005). **Document type:** *Trade.* **Description:** Provides up-to-date developments concerning the goods and services tax as they occur. Includes detailed commentary on and analysis of the tax.
Related titles: CD-ROM ed.: CND 885 (effective 2005); Online - full text ed.: CND 859 (effective 2005).
Published by: C C H Canadian Ltd., 90 Sheppard Ave E, Ste 300, North York, ON M2N 6X1, Canada. TEL 416-224-2248, 800-268-4522, FAX 416-224-2243, cservice@cch.ca, http://www.cch.ca.

340 336.2 CAN ISSN 0317-9060
CANADIAN INCOME TAX ACT WITH REGULATIONS. Key Title: Canadian Income Tax Act with Income Tax Regulations. Text in English. 194?. irreg., latest 2005, 79th ed. CND 84.95 per issue (effective 2005). **Document type:** *Trade.* **Description:** Consolidated texts of the Income Tax Act and Regulations with historical notes, references to related sections, summaries of amendments, interpretation bulletins and advance rulings.
Formerly (until 1966): Canadian Income Tax Act (0317-9079)
Published by: C C H Canadian Ltd., 90 Sheppard Ave E, Ste 300, North York, ON M2N 6X1, Canada. TEL 416-224-2248, 800-268-4522, FAX 416-224-2243, cservice@cch.ca, http://www.cch.ca.

336.2 CAN ISSN 0316-1331
KE5759
CANADIAN MASTER TAX GUIDE. Text in English. 1945. a., latest 2005, 60th ed. CND 69.95 per issue (effective 2005). **Document type:** *Trade.* **Description:** Explains Canadian federal income taxation.
Related titles: CD-ROM ed.: CND 139 per issue (effective 2005).
Indexed: ATI.
—CISTI.
Published by: C C H Canadian Ltd., 90 Sheppard Ave E, Ste 300, North York, ON M2N 6X1, Canada. TEL 416-224-2248, 800-268-4522, FAX 416-224-2243, cservice@cch.ca, http://www.cch.ca.

CANADIAN MONEYSAVER; your personal finance guide. see *BUSINESS AND ECONOMICS—Investments*

CANADIAN PETROLEUM TAX JOURNAL. see *PETROLEUM AND GAS*

336 333.33 CAN
CANADIAN REAL ESTATE INCOME TAX GUIDE. Text in English. q. looseleaf. CND 474 (effective 2005). **Document type:** *Trade.* **Description:** Covers tax implications associated with the acquisition, ownership and disposition of Canadian real estate.
Related titles: CD-ROM ed.: CND 428 (effective 2005); Online - full text ed.: CND 424 (effective 2005).
Indexed: CBCABus.
Published by: C C H Canadian Ltd., 90 Sheppard Ave E, Ste 300, North York, ON M2N 6X1, Canada. TEL 416-224-2248, 800-268-4522, FAX 416-224-2243, cservice@cch.ca, http://www.cch.ca.

336.2 CAN ISSN 0316-3571
HJ2449
CANADIAN TAX FOUNDATION. TAX CONFERENCE. REPORT OF PROCEEDINGS. Text in English. 1947. a. **Document type:** *Proceedings.* **Description:** Technical papers reflecting the notable public finance and tax developments of the year.
Related titles: CD-ROM ed.; Online - full text ed.
Indexed: ATI, CLI, ILP, LRI.
—CISTI.
Published by: Canadian Tax Foundation/L'Association Canadienne d'Etudes Fiscales, 595 Bay St, Ste 1200, Toronto, ON M5G 2N5, Canada. TEL 416-599-0283, FAX 416-599-9283, http://www.ctf.ca. R&P Laurel Amalia.

336 CAN ISSN 1192-2672
HJ13
CANADIAN TAX HIGHLIGHTS. Text in English. 1993. m. CND 160 (effective 1999). **Document type:** *Newsletter.* **Description:** Fast-breaking tax information, including matters of particular importance to small and medium-sized businesses.
Related titles: Online - full text ed.
Indexed: ABIn, ATI.
Published by: Canadian Tax Foundation/L'Association Canadienne d'Etudes Fiscales, 595 Bay St, Ste 1200, Toronto, ON M5G 2N5, Canada. TEL 416-599-0283, FAX 416-599-9283, http://www.ctf.ca. Ed. Vivien Morgan. R&P Laurel Amalia. Circ: 9,000.

336.2 CAN ISSN 0008-5111
CANADIAN TAX JOURNAL. Text in English. 1953. q. free to members; CND 300 to non-members (effective 2005). bk.rev. bibl.; charts. index. **Document type:** *Academic/Scholarly.* **Description:** Disseminates the results of research in and informed comment on taxation and public finance, with particular reference to Canada.
Related titles: CD-ROM ed.; Online - full text ed.: (from Micromedia ProQuest, O C L C Online Computer Library Center, Inc., ProQuest Information & Learning).
Indexed: ABIn, ATI, BPIA, CBCARef, CBPI, CLI, CPerI, FamI, ICLPL, ILP, JEL, LII, LRI, PAIS.
—BLDSC (3044.930000), IE, Infotrieve, ingenta.
Published by: Canadian Tax Foundation/L'Association Canadienne d'Etudes Fiscales, 595 Bay St, Ste 1200, Toronto, ON M5G 2N5, Canada. TEL 416-599-0283, 877-733-0283, FAX 416-599-9283, http://www.ctf.ca/publications/journal.asp. Eds. Alan MacNaughton, Scott Wilkie. R&P Laurel Amalia. Circ: 9,000.

336 340 CAN
CANADIAN TAX OBJECTIONS AND APPEAL PROCEDURES. Text in English. 1991. q. looseleaf. CND 603 (effective 2005). **Document type:** *Trade.* **Description:** Deals with objections and appeals relating to federal income tax, the Goods and Services Tax and other federal taxes.
Indexed: CBCABus.
Published by: C C H Canadian Ltd., 90 Sheppard Ave E, Ste 300, North York, ON M2N 6X1, Canada. TEL 416-224-2248, 800-268-4522, FAX 416-224-2243, cservice@cch.ca, http://www.cch.ca.

336.2 CAN ISSN 0008-512X
CANADIAN TAX PAPERS. Text in English. irreg., latest vol.103, 1999. price varies. **Document type:** *Monographic series.*
Indexed: ATI, CPerI.
—CISTI.
Published by: Canadian Tax Foundation/L'Association Canadienne d'Etudes Fiscales, 595 Bay St, Ste 1200, Toronto, ON M5G 2N5, Canada. TEL 416-599-0283, FAX 416-599-9283, http://www.ctf.ca. Ed. Laurel Amalia.

336.2 CAN ISSN 0008-5138
CANADIAN TAX REPORTER. Text in English. 1939. w. looseleaf. CND 2,354 (effective 2005). index. **Document type:** *Trade.* **Description:** Reports on federal corporate and personal income tax laws, regulations and rulings with comprehensive digests of all court decisions relating to federal income tax with a list of appeals filed.
Related titles: CD-ROM ed.: CND 1,476 (effective 2005); Online - full text ed.: CND 2,148 (effective 2005).
Published by: C C H Canadian Ltd., 90 Sheppard Ave E, Ste 300, North York, ON M2N 6X1, Canada. TEL 416-224-2248, 800-268-4522, FAX 416-224-2243, cservice@cch.ca, http://www.cch.ca.

336.2 CAN ISSN 0225-0608
THE CANADIAN TAXPAYER. Text in English. 1979. 24/yr. CND 359 per issue domestic; USD 304.24 per issue foreign (effective 2005). **Document type:** *Newsletter.*
Published by: Carswell (Subsidiary of: Thomson Corporation), One Corporate Plaza, 2075 Kennedy Rd, Toronto, ON M1T 3V4, Canada. TEL 416-609-8000, 800-387-5164, FAX 416-298-5094, carswell.customerrelations@thomson.com, http://www.carswell.com. Ed. Arthur B C Drache.

336.2 332.6 USA ISSN 0008-5855
CAPITAL CHANGES REPORTS. Text in English. 1928. 7 base vols. plus w. updates. looseleaf. price quoted by a CCH sales representative. cum.index. **Description:** Provides the facts and figures to compute a security holder's gain or loss from capital changes.
Related titles: CD-ROM ed.: USD 1,625 (effective 2000); Online - full text ed.: USD 1,785 (effective 2000).
—CCC.
Published by: C C H Inc., 2700 Lake Cook Rd, Riverwoods, IL 60015. TEL 847-267-7000, 800-449-6439, cust_serv@cch.com, http://www.cch.com. Pub. Stacey Caywood.

336.2 343.05 GBR
CAPITAL TAXES AND ESTATE PLANNING IN EUROPE. Text in English. 1991. s-a. looseleaf. GBP 159. cum.index. back issues avail. **Document type:** *Trade.* **Description:** Aimed at practitioners who specialize in private client work covering trusts, probate and taxation. Provides a guide to capital taxes and estate planning in EU member states and other important jurisdictions within Europe which have favorable tax regimes.
Published by: F T Law & Tax (Subsidiary of: Financial Times Professional Ltd.), 21-27, Lambs Conduit St, London, WC1N 3NJ, United Kingdom. TEL 44-20-7420-7500, FAX 44-20-7420-7510. Ed. Timothy Lyons. Pub. Karin Stevens. Circ: 330. **Subscr. to:** Pearson Professional Ltd., Journals Subscription Department, Fourth Ave., PO Box 77, Harlow, Essex CM19 5AA, United Kingdom. TEL 44-1279-623924, FAX 44-1279-639609.

336 CYM
CAYMAN ISLANDS MONETARY AUTHORITY. ANNUAL REPORT. Text in English. 1972. a. free. adv. illus. **Document type:** *Corporate.*
Former titles: Cayman Islands Monetary Authority. Report; (until 1997): Cayman Islands. Currency Board. Report (0303-8718)
Published by: Cayman Islands Monetary Authority, Elizabethan Square, PO Box 10052 APO, Grand Cayman, Cayman Isl. TEL 345-949-7089, FAX 345-945-1145, TELEX CP 4260 CIGOVT, admin@cimoney.com.ky. Adv. contact Cindy Bush. Circ: 250.

CD-ROM DER AUSLANDSZOELLE. see *BUSINESS AND ECONOMICS—International Commerce*

336 BLZ ISSN 1025-1618
CENTRAL BANK OF BELIZE. ANNUAL REPORT AND ACCOUNTS. Text in English. a. BZD 20 (effective 2001). **Document type:** *Corporate.*
Formerly (until 1982): Monetary Authority of Belize. Annual Report and Accounts
Published by: Central Bank of Belize, Library, PO Box 852, Belize City, Belize. TEL 501-2-36194, FAX 501-2-36226, cenbank@btl.net.

CENTRAL BANK OF BELIZE. ANNUAL STATISTICAL DIGEST. see *BUSINESS AND ECONOMICS—Abstracting, Bibliographies, Statistics*

336   BLZ
CENTRAL BANK OF BELIZE. QUARTERLY ECONOMIC REVIEW. Text in English. 1977. 3/yr. free.
Former titles (until 1982): Central Bank of Belize. Quarterly Review (1025-1634); Belize. Monetary Authority. Quarterly Review
Published by: Central Bank of Belize, Library, PO Box 852, Belize City, Belize. TEL 501-2-77216, FAX 501-2-76383, TELEX 225 MONETARY BZ, cenbank@btl.net.

336.73 USA ISSN 0272-6017
HJ275
CHANGING PUBLIC ATTITUDES ON GOVERNMENTS AND TAXES; a commission survey. Text in English. a. USD 10. **Document type:** *Government.*
Published by: U.S. Advisory Commission on Intergovernmental Relations, 800 K St, N W, Ste 450 South Bldg, Washington, DC 20575. TEL 202-653-5640.

343.04   USA
CHARITABLE CONTRIBUTIONS AND FEDERAL TAXES. Text in English. 1993. base vol. plus irreg. updates. USD 105.
Published by: LexisNexis (Subsidiary of: LexisNexis North America), PO Box 7587, Charlottesville, VA 22906-7587. TEL 804-972-7600, 800-562-1197, FAX 804-974-7666, llp.customer.support@lexis-nexis.com, http:// www.lexislawpublishing.com. Ed. Allan J Samansky.

336   USA ISSN 1535-9379
KF6388.A15
CHARITABLE GIFT PLANNING NEWS. Text in English. 1983. 10/yr. looseleaf. USD 168 (effective 2000). bk.rev. index: 1983-1997. back issues avail. **Document type:** *Newsletter.* **Description:** Covers current legislative, court cases, and tax laws affecting charities.
Published by: Terry Simmons, Jerry McCoy, Eds. & Pubs., PO Box 551606, Dallas, TX 75355-1606. TEL 214-328-4244, FAX 214-349-2209, carolcgpn@aol.com, http://www.imnopstuff.com. Eds. Jerry Mc Coy, Terry Simmons. Adv. contact Carol Stone. Circ: 600 (paid).

336   USA ISSN 0278-0593
CHARITABLE GIVING AND SOLICITATION. Text in English. 1981. base vol. plus updates 13/yr. looseleaf. USD 640 (effective 2005). **Description:** Focuses on laws governing charitable giving and solicitation, with numerous tips and proven fund-raising ideas.
—CCC.
Published by: W G & L Financial Reporting & Management Research (Subsidiary of: R I A), 90 Fifth Ave, New York, NY 10011. TEL 212-645-4280, FAX 212-337-4280, http://www.riag.com. Ed. Ruth Culhane.

CHARTERED INSTITUTE OF PUBLIC FINANCE AND ACCOUNTANCY. ADMINISTRATION OF JUSTICE. ESTIMATES & ACTUALS. see *CRIMINOLOGY AND LAW ENFORCEMENT—Abstracting, Bibliographies, Statistics*

CHARTERED INSTITUTE OF PUBLIC FINANCE AND ACCOUNTANCY. ARCHIVES STATISTICS. ESTIMATES. see *BUSINESS AND ECONOMICS—Abstracting, Bibliographies, Statistics*

CHARTERED INSTITUTE OF PUBLIC FINANCE AND ACCOUNTANCY. CAPITAL EXPENDITURE AND DEBT FINANCING STATISTICS. ACTUALS. see *BUSINESS AND ECONOMICS—Abstracting, Bibliographies, Statistics*

CHARTERED INSTITUTE OF PUBLIC FINANCE AND ACCOUNTANCY. CEMETERIES STATISTICS. ACTUALS. see *PUBLIC HEALTH AND SAFETY—Abstracting, Bibliographies, Statistics*

CHARTERED INSTITUTE OF PUBLIC FINANCE AND ACCOUNTANCY. CHARGES FOR LEISURE SERVICES. ACTUALS. see *SPORTS AND GAMES—Abstracting, Bibliographies, Statistics*

CHARTERED INSTITUTE OF PUBLIC FINANCE AND ACCOUNTANCY. COUNCIL TAX STATISTICS. ESTIMATES. see *BUSINESS AND ECONOMICS—Abstracting, Bibliographies, Statistics*

CHARTERED INSTITUTE OF PUBLIC FINANCE AND ACCOUNTANCY. CREMATORIA STATISTICS. ACTUALS. see *PUBLIC HEALTH AND SAFETY—Abstracting, Bibliographies, Statistics*

CHARTERED INSTITUTE OF PUBLIC FINANCE AND ACCOUNTANCY. EDUCATION STATISTICS. ACTUALS. see *EDUCATION—Abstracting, Bibliographies, Statistics*

CHARTERED INSTITUTE OF PUBLIC FINANCE AND ACCOUNTANCY. EDUCATION STATISTICS. ESTIMATES. see *EDUCATION—Abstracting, Bibliographies, Statistics*

CHARTERED INSTITUTE OF PUBLIC FINANCE AND ACCOUNTANCY. ENVIRONMENTAL HEALTH STATISTICS. ACTUALS. see *PUBLIC HEALTH AND SAFETY—Abstracting, Bibliographies, Statistics*

CHARTERED INSTITUTE OF PUBLIC FINANCE AND ACCOUNTANCY. FINANCE AND GENERAL STATISTICS. ESTIMATES. see *BUSINESS AND ECONOMICS— Abstracting, Bibliographies, Statistics*

CHARTERED INSTITUTE OF PUBLIC FINANCE AND ACCOUNTANCY. FIRE STATISTICS. ACTUALS & ESTIMATES. see *FIRE PREVENTION—Abstracting, Bibliographies, Statistics*

CHARTERED INSTITUTE OF PUBLIC FINANCE AND ACCOUNTANCY. HIGHWAYS AND TRANSPORTATION. ACTUALS & ESTIMATES. see *TRANSPORTATION— Abstracting, Bibliographies, Statistics*

CHARTERED INSTITUTE OF PUBLIC FINANCE AND ACCOUNTANCY. HIGHWAYS AND TRANSPORTATION STATISTICS. ESTIMATES & ACTUALS. see *TRANSPORTATION—Abstracting, Bibliographies, Statistics*

CHARTERED INSTITUTE OF PUBLIC FINANCE AND ACCOUNTANCY. HOMELESSNESS STATISTICS. ACTUALS. see *HOUSING AND URBAN PLANNING—Abstracting, Bibliographies, Statistics*

CHARTERED INSTITUTE OF PUBLIC FINANCE AND ACCOUNTANCY. HOUSING RENTS STATISTICS. ACTUALS. see *HOUSING AND URBAN PLANNING— Abstracting, Bibliographies, Statistics*

CHARTERED INSTITUTE OF PUBLIC FINANCE AND ACCOUNTANCY. HOUSING REVENUE ACCOUNT STATISTICS. ESTIMATES & ACTUALS. see *HOUSING AND URBAN PLANNING—Abstracting, Bibliographies, Statistics*

CHARTERED INSTITUTE OF PUBLIC FINANCE AND ACCOUNTANCY. LEISURE AND RECREATION STATISTICS. ESTIMATES. see *SPORTS AND GAMES—Abstracting, Bibliographies, Statistics*

CHARTERED INSTITUTE OF PUBLIC FINANCE AND ACCOUNTANCY. LEISURE CHARGES STATISTICS. ACTUALS. see *SPORTS AND GAMES—Abstracting, Bibliographies, Statistics*

CHARTERED INSTITUTE OF PUBLIC FINANCE AND ACCOUNTANCY. LOCAL GOVERNMENT COMPARATIVE STATISTICS. ESTIMATES. see *PUBLIC ADMINISTRATION— Abstracting, Bibliographies, Statistics*

CHARTERED INSTITUTE OF PUBLIC FINANCE AND ACCOUNTANCY. MEMBERS' YEARBOOK (YEAR). see *BUSINESS AND ECONOMICS—Accounting*

CHARTERED INSTITUTE OF PUBLIC FINANCE AND ACCOUNTANCY. PERSONAL SOCIAL SERVICES STATISTICS. ACTUALS. see *SOCIAL SERVICES AND WELFARE—Abstracting, Bibliographies, Statistics*

CHARTERED INSTITUTE OF PUBLIC FINANCE AND ACCOUNTANCY. PERSONAL SOCIAL SERVICES STATISTICS. ESTIMATES. see *SOCIAL SERVICES AND WELFARE—Abstracting, Bibliographies, Statistics*

CHARTERED INSTITUTE OF PUBLIC FINANCE AND ACCOUNTANCY. PLANNING AND DEVELOPMENT STATISTICS. ESTIMATES & ACTUALS. see *HOUSING AND URBAN PLANNING—Abstracting, Bibliographies, Statistics*

CHARTERED INSTITUTE OF PUBLIC FINANCE AND ACCOUNTANCY. POLICE STATISTICS. ACTUALS. see *CRIMINOLOGY AND LAW ENFORCEMENT—Abstracting, Bibliographies, Statistics*

CHARTERED INSTITUTE OF PUBLIC FINANCE AND ACCOUNTANCY. POLICE STATISTICS. ESTIMATES. see *CRIMINOLOGY AND LAW ENFORCEMENT—Abstracting, Bibliographies, Statistics*

CHARTERED INSTITUTE OF PUBLIC FINANCE AND ACCOUNTANCY. PROBATION. ESTIMATES & ACTUALS. see *SOCIAL SERVICES AND WELFARE—Abstracting, Bibliographies, Statistics*

CHARTERED INSTITUTE OF PUBLIC FINANCE AND ACCOUNTANCY. PUBLIC LIBRARIES STATISTICS. ACTUALS. see *LIBRARY AND INFORMATION SCIENCES—Abstracting, Bibliographies, Statistics*

CHARTERED INSTITUTE OF PUBLIC FINANCE AND ACCOUNTANCY. PUBLIC LIBRARIES STATISTICS. ESTIMATES. see *LIBRARY AND INFORMATION SCIENCES—Abstracting, Bibliographies, Statistics*

CHARTERED INSTITUTE OF PUBLIC FINANCE AND ACCOUNTANCY. RATING REVIEW (SCOTLAND) STATISTICS. ACTUALS. see *BUSINESS AND ECONOMICS—Abstracting, Bibliographies, Statistics*

CHARTERED INSTITUTE OF PUBLIC FINANCE AND ACCOUNTANCY. RATING REVIEW (SCOTLAND) STATISTICS. ESTIMATES. see *BUSINESS AND ECONOMICS—Abstracting, Bibliographies, Statistics*

CHARTERED INSTITUTE OF PUBLIC FINANCE AND ACCOUNTANCY. REVENUE COLLECTION STATISTICS. ACTUALS. see *BUSINESS AND ECONOMICS—Abstracting, Bibliographies, Statistics*

CHARTERED INSTITUTE OF PUBLIC FINANCE AND ACCOUNTANCY. TRADING STANDARDS STATISTICS. ACTUALS & ESTIMATES. see *BUSINESS AND ECONOMICS—Abstracting, Bibliographies, Statistics*

CHARTERED INSTITUTE OF PUBLIC FINANCE AND ACCOUNTANCY. WASTE COLLECTION & DISPOSAL STATISTICS. ACTUALS. see *ENVIRONMENTAL STUDIES—Abstracting, Bibliographies, Statistics*

336   GBR
CHECK YOUR TAX AND MONEY FACTS∗ . Text in English. a. **Document type:** *Consumer.* **Description:** Addresses public finance, taxation and general economic topics.
Formerly: Check Your Tax
Published by: W. Foulsham & Co. Ltd., Chippenham, Bennetts Close, Slough, Bucks SL1 5AP, United Kingdom.

336 343.05   USA
CHIEF COUNSEL ADVICE SERVICE. Text in English. w. USD 1,299 (effective 1999). back issues avail. **Description:** Contains U.S. Internal Revenue Service letter rulings and technical advice, weekly memoranda, and copyrighted summaries and indexes.
Formed by the merger of: Tax Analysts Letter Ruling Service; I R S Technical Advice Memorandums and I R S Letter Rulings (1066-6303); Incorporates (in 1995): Letter Ruling Review (1047-1596); Which was formerly (in 1988): Letter Ruling Alert (0898-4409)
Related titles: CD-ROM ed.
—CCC.
Published by: Tax Analysts, 6830 N Fairfax Dr, Arlington, VA 22213. TEL 703-553-4400, 800-955-3444, FAX 703-533-4444.

336   CHL
CHILE. DIRECCION DE PRESUPUESTOS. CALCULO DE ENTRADAS DE LA NACION. Text in Spanish. a. charts.
Published by: Direccion de Presupuestos, Piso 12 Of. 24-25, Teatinos, 120, Santiago, Chile. FAX 56-2-6713-814.

336   CHL
CHILE. DIRECCION DE PRESUPUESTOS. EXPOSICION SOBRE EL ESTADO DE LA HACIENDA PUBLICA. Text in Spanish. 1914. a. charts; stat.
Published by: Direccion de Presupuestos, Piso 12 Of. 24-25, Teatinos, 120, Santiago, Chile. FAX 56-2-6713-814.

336   CHL
CHILE. DIRECCION DE PRESUPUESTOS. INSTRUCCIONES PARA LA EJECUCION DE LA LEY DE PRESUPUESTOS. Text in Spanish. a. charts.
Published by: Direccion de Presupuestos, Piso 12 Of. 24-25, Teatinos, 120, Santiago, Chile. FAX 56-2-6713-814.

336   CHL
CHILE. DIRECCION DE PRESUPUESTOS. LEY DE PRESUPUESTOS PARA EL SECTOR PUBLICO. Text in Spanish. 1884. a. charts.
Published by: Direccion de Presupuestos, Piso 12 Of. 24-25, Teatinos, 120, Santiago, Chile. FAX 56-2-6713-814.

336   CHL
CHILE. SERVICIO DE IMPUESTOS INTERNOS. BOLETIN OFICIAL. (Includes annuals: Indice de Materias del Boletin, Textos Legales Actualizados) Text in Spanish. 1954. m. CLP 83,000, USD 219 to individuals; CLP 98,000, USD 258 to institutions. index. **Document type:** *Bulletin, Government.* **Description:** Covers administration and jurisprudence on taxes.
Formerly: Chile. Servicio de Impuestos Internos. Boletin (0716-145X)
Published by: Servicio de Impuestos Internos, Oficina de Comunicaciones, Teatinos, 120 Piso 1, Santiago, Chile. TEL 56-2-6921330, FAX 56-2-6921353. Ed. Bernardo Lara Berrios. Pub. Gonzalo Vergara Gomez. Circ: 4,000.

336.2   HKG
CHINA TAX REVIEW. Text in English. 1994. 10/yr. HKD 2,750 domestic; USD 385 foreign (effective 2001). **Document type:** *Newsletter.* **Description:** Provides up-to-date information on developments related to individual and corporate taxation in China.

B

Published by: Asia Law & Practice Ltd. (Subsidiary of: Euromoney Institutional Investor Plc.), 5/F Printing House, 6 Duddell St, Central Hong Kong, Hong Kong. TEL 852-2523-3399, FAX 852-2521-6110, info@euromoneyhk.com, http://www.asialaw.com/.

336   PRT   ISSN 0870-340X
CIENCIA E TECNICA FISCAL. Text in Portuguese. 1961. bi-m. adv. bk.rev. charts. **Document type:** *Government.*
Formerly (until 1964): Direccao Geral das Contribucoes e Impostos. Serie A, Ciencia e Tecnica Fiscal (0870-6999)
Indexed: PAIS.
Published by: Ministerio das Financas, Direccao Geral da Administracao Publica, Av. 24 de Julho 80-80J, Lisbon, 1249-084, Portugal. TEL 351-21-3915300, FAX 351-21-3900148, geral@dgap.gov.pt, http://www.dgap.gov.pt/0abert/dgapmf_site.htm. Circ: 3,400.

CLIENT TAX NEWSLETTER. see *BUSINESS AND ECONOMICS—Accounting*

CLIENT'S MONTHLY ALERT; monthly roundup of significant business & tax developments. see *BUSINESS AND ECONOMICS—Accounting*

336   FRA   ISSN 0294-1546
CODE GENERAL DES IMPOTS. Text in French. 1975. a.
Description: Allows access to regulatory and legislative texts concerning French fiscal law.
Published by: (France. Direction Generale des Impots), Imprimerie Nationale, BP 514, Douai, Cedex 59505, France. TEL 27-93-70-90, FAX 27-93-70-96.

336.2 340   CAN   ISSN 1701-0950
COLLECTION FISCALE. Text in French. 1998. m. CND 1,025 (effective 2005). **Description:** Publishes the full texts of statutes and detailed commentary of federal and provincial income taxes.
Formerly (until 2001): Collection Fiscale du Quebec (1489-5277)
Related titles: CD-ROM ed.: ISSN 1486-0074. CND 1,695 (effective 2005).
Published by: C C H Canadian Ltd., 90 Sheppard Ave E, Ste 300, North York, ON M2N 6X1, Canada. TEL 416-224-2248, 800-268-4522, FAX 416-224-2243, 800-461-4131, cservice@cch.ca, http://www.cch.ca.

336   USA
COLLEGE OF WILLIAM AND MARY. MARSHALL-WYTHE SCHOOL OF LAW. TAX CONFERENCE. Text in English. 1955. a. USD 2,115 for complete set. **Document type:** *Academic/Scholarly.* **Description:** Examines topics in taxation and tax law.
Indexed: CLI, LRI.
Published by: College of William and Mary, Marshall-Wythe School of Law, PO Box 8795, Williamsburg, VA 23187-8795 . TEL 757-221-9833. **Dist. in US & Canada by:** Wm. W. Gaunt & Sons Inc., Gaunt Bldg, 3011 Gulf Dr, Holmes Beach, FL 34217-2199. TEL 941-778-5252, 800-942-8683.

COLLIER ON BANKRUPTCY TAXATION. see *LAW—Corporate Law*

336   COL
COLOMBIA. MINISTERIO DE HACIENDA Y CREDITO PUBLICO. PROYECTO DE PRESUPUESTO GENERAL DE LA NACION. Text in Spanish. a. charts. **Document type:** *Government.*
Formerly: Colombia. Direction General del Presupuesto. Proyecto de Presupuesto (0588-3598)
Published by: Ministerio de Hacienda y Credito Publico, Direccion General del Presupuesto, Carrera 7a, 6-45 Pisos 1o 7o 8o, Bogota, CUND, Colombia. FAX 57-1-286-5345.

336.2   LUX   ISSN 0377-0192
HJ2599.5
COMMISSION OF THE EUROPEAN COMMUNITIES. DIRECTORATE OF TAXATION. INVENTORY OF TAXES. Text in English. a. USD 110.
Published by: European Commission, Office for Official Publications of the European Union, 2 Rue Mercier, Luxembourg, L-2985, Luxembourg.

354.67   CMR
COMPTES NATIONAUX DU CAMEROUN. Text in French. a. XAF 4,000. **Document type:** *Government.*
Published by: Direction de la Statistique et de la Comptabilite Nationale/Department of Statistics and National Accounts, BP 660, Yaounde, Cameroon.

332   USA
COMPTROLLER'S HANDBOOK. Text in English. base vol. plus irreg. updates. USD 150; USD 25 per issue (effective 2005). **Document type:** *Trade.* **Description:** Presents policies and procedures for the examination of the commercial activities of national banks.
Related titles: Supplement(s): Comptroller's Handbook for Asset Management. USD 50 newsstand/cover (effective 2000); Comptroller's Handbook for Compliance. USD 60 newsstand/cover (effective 2000).

Published by: U.S. Office of the Comptroller of the Currency, Administrator of National Banks, 250 E St, S W, Washington, DC 20219. TEL 202-874-5000, FAX 202-874-5263, http://www.occ.treas.gov/handbook/chndbk.htm.

354   COD
CONSEILLER COMPTABLE. Variant title: Revue Zairoise de la Comptabilite. Text in French. 1974. q. XAF 10, USD 13. adv. bk.rev. illus.
Published by: Conseil Permanent de la Comptabilite, Departement des Finances et du Budget, 17, av. du Port, Building S.N.C.Z, BP 308, Kinshasa, Congo, Dem. Republic. Ed. Kinzonzi Mvutukidi Ngindu K. Circ: 1,000.

350   USA   ISSN 0148-009X
KF6499.C58
THE CONSOLIDATED TAX RETURN (SUPPLEMENT). Text in English. base vol. plus s-a. updates. looseleaf. USD 245 (effective 1999). **Document type:** *Trade.*
Published by: W G & L Financial Reporting & Management Research (Subsidiary of: R I A), 90 Fifth Ave, New York, NY 10011. TEL 212-645-4800, FAX 212-337-4280, http://www.riag.com.

CONSTRUCTION CONTROLLER'S MANUAL. see *BUSINESS AND ECONOMICS—Accounting*

336.2   DEU   ISSN 1438-8723
CONSULTANT; Steuern - Wirtschaft - Finanzen. Text in German. 1999. 10/yr. EUR 79 domestic; EUR 89 foreign; EUR 7.90 newsstand/cover (effective 2004). adv. **Document type:** *Magazine, Trade.*
Published by: Max Schimmel Verlag GmbH & Co. KG (Subsidiary of: Rudolf Haufe Verlag GmbH & Co. KG), Im Kreuz 9, Wuerzburg, 97076, Germany. TEL 49-931-2791420, FAX 49-931-2791444, info@schimmelverlag.de, http://www.consultant-magazin.de, http://www.schimmelverlag.de. adv: B&W page EUR 5,900, color page EUR 6,500. Circ: 20,659 (paid and controlled).

336   ESP   ISSN 0069-9292
CONTABILIDAD NACIONAL DE ESPANA. Text in Spanish. a.
Published by: Instituto Nacional de Estadistica; P. de la Castellana, 183, Madrid, 28071, Spain.

336   USA   ISSN 1528-5294
CORPORATE BUSINESS TAXATION MONTHLY. Text in English. m. USD 295 (effective 2005). **Document type:** *Journal, Trade.*
Description: Discusses the tax issues involved with running a corporate business today.
Related titles: Online - full text ed.: (from EBSCO Publishing, Gale Group, ProQuest Information & Learning).
Indexed: ATI, CLI, LRI.
—CCC.
Published by: C C H Tax and Accounting (Subsidiary of: Wolters Kluwer N.V.), 2700 Lake Cook Rd, Riverwoods, IL 60015. TEL 800-449-8114, FAX 773-866-3895, http://tax.cchgroup.com/Store/Products/Product+Detail.htm?cs_id=CCE%2DCCH%2D2626%28CCE%29&cs_catalog=TADS.

CORPORATE COUNSEL'S GUIDE TO LEGAL AUDITS & INVESTIGATIONS. see *LAW—Corporate Law*

336.2   CAN   ISSN 0070-0282
KE5884
CORPORATE MANAGEMENT TAX CONFERENCE. Text in English. 1959. a. price varies. **Document type:** *Proceedings.*
Description: Technical papers with analysis of a tax topic of interest to the corporate sector.
Related titles: CD-ROM ed.; Online - full text ed.
Indexed: ATI, CLI, ILP, LRI.
—CISTI.
Published by: Canadian Tax Foundation/L'Association Canadienne d'Etudes Fiscales, 595 Bay St, Ste 1200, Toronto, ON M5G 2N5, Canada. TEL 416-599-0283, FAX 416-599-9283, http://www.ctf.ca. R&P Laurel Amalia.

338 336.2   USA   ISSN 1534-715X
K10
CORPORATE TAXATION. Text in English. 1973. bi-m. USD 290 (effective 2005). adv. bk.rev. illus. reprints avail. **Document type:** *Journal, Trade.* **Description:** Provides analysis and guidance for practitioners who must stay on top of all the latest developments and their planning implications. Covers corporate reorganizations, compensation and fringe benefits, tax accounting, international developments, closely held corporations, and consolidated tax returns.
Formerly (until Jan. 2001): Journal of Corporate Taxation (0094-0593)
Related titles: Microform ed.: (from MIM, PQC); Online - full text ed.: (from ProQuest Information & Learning).
Indexed: ABIn, ASCA, ATI, BLI, BPI, BPIA, BusI, CLI, CurCont, FamI, ILP, LRI, ManagCont, PAIS, SSCI, T&II.
—BLDSC (3472.093285), IDS, IE, ingenta. CCC.
Published by: W G & L Financial Reporting & Management Research (Subsidiary of: R I A), 395 Hudson St, New York, NY 10014. TEL 212-645-4800, FAX 212-337-4280, http://www.riahome.com, http://www.wgl.com/tax/jct.html. Ed. Gersham Goldstein.

336   GBR   ISSN 1461-2569
CORPORATE TAXATION REVIEW. Text in English. 1998. q. GBP 140 (effective 1998). **Description:** Contains technical analysis of current corporate taxation issues.
Published by: Key Haven Publications plc., 7 Crescent Stables, 139 Upper Richmond Rd, London, SW15 2TN, United Kingdom. TEL 44-20-8780-2522, FAX 44-20-8780-1693. Ed. Julian Ghosh.

362.1   USA   ISSN 1046-1302
CORPORATION AND PARTNERSHIP TAX RETURN GUIDE. Text in English. a.
Published by: R I A (Subsidiary of: Thomson Corporation), 395 Hudson St, New York, NY 10014. TEL 212-367-6300, RIA.CustomerServices@Thomson.com, http://ria.thomson.com/

336   CRI
COSTA RICA. DIRECCION GENERAL DE LA TRIBUTACION DIRECTA. ESTADISTICA DEMOGRAFIA FISCAL DEL IMPUESTO SOBRE LA RENTA. PERIODOS. Text in Spanish. 1974 (no.71). irreg. free.
Published by: Direccion General de Tributacion Directa, San Jose, Costa Rica. Circ: 250.

336   CRI   ISSN 0070-0576
COSTA RICA. MINISTERIO DE HACIENDA OFICINA DEL PRESUPUESTO. INFORME∗. Text in Spanish. a.
Published by: Ministerio de Hacienda, Oficina del Presupuesto, San Jose, Costa Rica.

COUNCIL TAX HANDBOOK. see *SOCIAL SERVICES AND WELFARE*

COUNTRY COMMERCE. AMERICAS. see *BUSINESS AND ECONOMICS—International Commerce*

COUNTRY COMMERCE. ARGENTINA. see *BUSINESS AND ECONOMICS—International Commerce*

COUNTRY COMMERCE. ASIA. see *BUSINESS AND ECONOMICS—International Commerce*

COUNTRY COMMERCE. AUSTRALIA. see *BUSINESS AND ECONOMICS—International Commerce*

COUNTRY COMMERCE. AUSTRIA. see *BUSINESS AND ECONOMICS—International Commerce*

COUNTRY COMMERCE. BELGIUM. see *BUSINESS AND ECONOMICS—International Commerce*

COUNTRY COMMERCE. BRAZIL. see *BUSINESS AND ECONOMICS—International Commerce*

COUNTRY COMMERCE. CANADA. see *BUSINESS AND ECONOMICS—International Commerce*

COUNTRY COMMERCE. CENTRAL AMERICA; including El Salvador, Guatemala, Honduras and Costa Rica. see *BUSINESS AND ECONOMICS—International Commerce*

COUNTRY COMMERCE. CHILE. see *BUSINESS AND ECONOMICS—International Commerce*

COUNTRY COMMERCE. CHINA. see *BUSINESS AND ECONOMICS—International Commerce*

COUNTRY COMMERCE. COLOMBIA. see *BUSINESS AND ECONOMICS—International Commerce*

COUNTRY COMMERCE. CZECH REPUBLIC. see *BUSINESS AND ECONOMICS—International Commerce*

COUNTRY COMMERCE. DENMARK. see *BUSINESS AND ECONOMICS—International Commerce*

COUNTRY COMMERCE. ECUADOR. see *BUSINESS AND ECONOMICS—International Commerce*

COUNTRY COMMERCE. EGYPT. see *BUSINESS AND ECONOMICS—International Commerce*

COUNTRY COMMERCE. EUROPEAN UNION. see *BUSINESS AND ECONOMICS—International Commerce*

COUNTRY COMMERCE. FINLAND. see *BUSINESS AND ECONOMICS—International Commerce*

COUNTRY COMMERCE. FRANCE. see *BUSINESS AND ECONOMICS—International Commerce*

COUNTRY COMMERCE. GERMANY. see *BUSINESS AND ECONOMICS—International Commerce*

COUNTRY COMMERCE. GREECE. see *BUSINESS AND ECONOMICS—International Commerce*

B

COUNTRY COMMERCE. HONG KONG. see *BUSINESS AND ECONOMICS—International Commerce*

COUNTRY COMMERCE. HUNGARY. see *BUSINESS AND ECONOMICS—International Commerce*

COUNTRY COMMERCE. INDIA. see *BUSINESS AND ECONOMICS—International Commerce*

COUNTRY COMMERCE. INDONESIA. see *BUSINESS AND ECONOMICS—International Commerce*

COUNTRY COMMERCE. IRELAND. see *BUSINESS AND ECONOMICS—International Commerce*

COUNTRY COMMERCE. ISRAEL. see *BUSINESS AND ECONOMICS—International Commerce*

COUNTRY COMMERCE. ITALY. see *BUSINESS AND ECONOMICS—International Commerce*

COUNTRY COMMERCE. JAPAN. see *BUSINESS AND ECONOMICS—International Commerce*

COUNTRY COMMERCE. KENYA. see *BUSINESS AND ECONOMICS—International Commerce*

COUNTRY COMMERCE. LUXEMBOURG. see *BUSINESS AND ECONOMICS—International Commerce*

COUNTRY COMMERCE. MALAYSIA. see *BUSINESS AND ECONOMICS—International Commerce*

COUNTRY COMMERCE. MEXICO. see *BUSINESS AND ECONOMICS—International Commerce*

COUNTRY COMMERCE. MIDDLE EAST - AFRICA. see *BUSINESS AND ECONOMICS—International Commerce*

COUNTRY COMMERCE. NETHERLANDS. see *BUSINESS AND ECONOMICS—International Commerce*

COUNTRY COMMERCE. NEW ZEALAND. see *BUSINESS AND ECONOMICS—International Commerce*

COUNTRY COMMERCE. NIGERIA. see *BUSINESS AND ECONOMICS—International Commerce*

COUNTRY COMMERCE. NORWAY. see *BUSINESS AND ECONOMICS—International Commerce*

COUNTRY COMMERCE. PAKISTAN. see *BUSINESS AND ECONOMICS—International Commerce*

COUNTRY COMMERCE. PANAMA. see *BUSINESS AND ECONOMICS—International Commerce*

COUNTRY COMMERCE. PERU. see *BUSINESS AND ECONOMICS—International Commerce*

COUNTRY COMMERCE. PHILIPPINES. see *BUSINESS AND ECONOMICS—International Commerce*

COUNTRY COMMERCE. POLAND. see *BUSINESS AND ECONOMICS—International Commerce*

COUNTRY COMMERCE. PORTUGAL. see *BUSINESS AND ECONOMICS—International Commerce*

COUNTRY COMMERCE. PUERTO RICO. see *BUSINESS AND ECONOMICS—International Commerce*

COUNTRY COMMERCE. RUSSIA. see *BUSINESS AND ECONOMICS—International Commerce*

COUNTRY COMMERCE. SAUDI ARABIA. see *BUSINESS AND ECONOMICS—International Commerce*

COUNTRY COMMERCE. SINGAPORE. see *BUSINESS AND ECONOMICS—International Commerce*

COUNTRY COMMERCE. SOUTH AFRICA. see *BUSINESS AND ECONOMICS—International Commerce*

COUNTRY COMMERCE. SOUTH KOREA. see *BUSINESS AND ECONOMICS—International Commerce*

COUNTRY COMMERCE. SPAIN. see *BUSINESS AND ECONOMICS—International Commerce*

COUNTRY COMMERCE. SWEDEN. see *BUSINESS AND ECONOMICS—International Commerce*

COUNTRY COMMERCE. SWITZERLAND. see *BUSINESS AND ECONOMICS—International Commerce*

COUNTRY COMMERCE. TAIWAN. see *BUSINESS AND ECONOMICS—International Commerce*

COUNTRY COMMERCE. THAILAND. see *BUSINESS AND ECONOMICS—International Commerce*

COUNTRY COMMERCE. TURKEY. see *BUSINESS AND ECONOMICS—International Commerce*

COUNTRY COMMERCE. UNITED KINGDOM. see *BUSINESS AND ECONOMICS—International Commerce*

COUNTRY COMMERCE. UNITED STATES OF AMERICA. see *BUSINESS AND ECONOMICS—International Commerce*

COUNTRY COMMERCE. URUGUAY. see *BUSINESS AND ECONOMICS—International Commerce*

COUNTRY COMMERCE. VENEZUELA. see *BUSINESS AND ECONOMICS—International Commerce*

COUNTRY COMMERCE. VIETNAM. see *BUSINESS AND ECONOMICS—International Commerce*

CRED-ALERT. see *BUSINESS AND ECONOMICS—Banking And Finance*

CRIMINAL TAX FRAUD. see *LAW—Criminal Law*

336   HRV   ISSN 1331-1743
HC404.A1
➤ CROATIA. INSTITUTE OF PUBLIC FINANCE. OCCASIONAL PAPER SERIES. Text in English. 1997. q. free. 30 p./no.; back issues avail. Document type: *Academic/Scholarly.*
Related titles: Online - full text ed.
Published by: Institut za Javne Financije/Institute of Public Finance, Katanciceva 5. Zagreb, 10000, Croatia. TEL 385-1-4819363, FAX 385-1-4819365, skreb@ijf.hr, http://www.ijf.hr/ocpapers/index.htm. Ed. Marina Kesner Skreb.

336   GBR
CRONER'S GUIDE TO CORPORATION TAX. Variant title: Guide to Corporation Tax. Text in English. 1978. base vol. plus q. updates. looseleaf. GBP 389.88; GBP 285.48 updates (effective 1999). Document type: *Trade.* Description: Covers computation and administration of corporation tax.
Published by: Croner.C C H Group Ltd. (Subsidiary of: Wolters Kluwer N.V.), 145 London Rd, Kingston, Surrey KT2 6SR, United Kingdom. TEL 44-20-85473333, FAX 44-20-85472637, info@croner.co.uk, http://www.croner.co.uk. Ed. Peter Durbin.

336.2   GBR
CRONER'S REFERENCE BOOK FOR V A T. Text in English. 1973. base vol. plus m. updates. looseleaf. GBP 392.96 (effective 1999). Description: Provides in-depth coverage of the Value Added Tax.
Formerly: Croner's Reference Book for Value Added Tax
Published by: Croner.C C H Group Ltd. (Subsidiary of: Wolters Kluwer N.V.), 145 London Rd, Kingston, Surrey KT2 6SR, United Kingdom. TEL 44-20-85473333, FAX 44-20-85472637, info@croner.co.uk, http://www.croner.co.uk. Ed. Peter Durbin.

336.2   GBR
CRONER'S REFERENCE SERVICE FOR THE SELF-EMPLOYED AND SMALLER BUSINESS. Text in English. 1976. base vol. plus m. updates. looseleaf. GBP 235.67 (effective 1999). Document type: *Trade.* Description: Includes comprehensive coverage of current information about VAT, taxation, health and safety issues, national Insurance, employment, consumer and company law.
Former titles: Croner's Reference Book for the Self-Employed and Smaller Business; Croner's Reference Book for the Self-Employed (0141-707X)
Published by: Croner.C C H Group Ltd. (Subsidiary of: Wolters Kluwer N.V.), 145 London Rd, Kingston, Surrey KT2 6SR, United Kingdom. TEL 44-20-85473333, FAX 44-20-85472637, info@croner.co.uk, http://www.croner.co.uk. Ed. Waynne Meek.

336.2   GBR
CRONER'S TAX SERIES. Text in English. 1978. a. GBP 18.70. Document type: *Trade.*
Incorporates: Capital Gains Tax Handbook (Year); Formerly: Corporation Tax Handbook (Year)
Published by: Croner.C C H Group Ltd. (Subsidiary of: Wolters Kluwer N.V.), 145 London Rd, Kingston, Surrey KT2 6SR, United Kingdom. TEL 44-20-85473333, FAX 44-20-85472637, info@croner.co.uk, http://www.croner.co.uk.

336.2   ESP   ISSN 0210-2919
CRONICA TRIBUTARIA. Text in Spanish. 1972. q. back issues avail.
—CINDOC.
Published by: Instituto de Estudios Fiscales, Avda Cardenal Herrera Oria, 378, Madrid, 28035, Spain. TEL 34-91-3398800, FAX 34-91-3398964, http://www.ief.es/. Subscr. to: Ministerio de Economia y Hacienda, Centro de Publicaciones, Pz Campillo del Mundo Nuevo, 3, Madrid 28005, Spain. TEL 91-527-1437.

336   NGA
CROSS RIVER STATE. MINISTRY OF ECONOMIC DEVELOPMENT AND RECONSTRUCTION. STATE DEVELOPMENT PLAN✳. Text in English. 197?. irreg. illus.; stat. Document type: *Government.*

Formerly: South-Eastern State. Ministry of Economic Development and Reconstruction. State Development Plan
Published by: Ministry of Economic Development and Reconstruction, Calabar, South-Eastern State, Nigeria. Dist. by: Cross River State Government Printer, Calabar, South-Eastern, Nigeria.

336   ESP   ISSN 1133-9470
CUADERNOS DE ACTUALIDAD. Text in Spanish. 1990. m.
Related titles: ◆ Supplement to: Hacienda Publica Espanola. ISSN 0210-1173.
—CINDOC.
Published by: Instituto de Estudios Fiscales, Avda Cardenal Herrera Oria, 378, Madrid, 28035, Spain. TEL 34-91-3398800, FAX 34-91-3398964, http://www.ief.es/.

336   USA
CUMULATIVE LIST OF ORGANIZATIONS. Text in English. a. USD 135 (effective 2001). Supplement avail. Document type: *Government.* Description: Lists the names of tax-exempt organizations.
Published by: U.S. Internal Revenue Service, 1111 Constitution Ave, N W, Washington, DC 20224. Subscr. to: U.S. Government Printing Office, Superintendent of Documents, 732 N Capitol St, NW, Washington, DC 20401. TEL 202-512-1800, 866-512-1800, FAX 202-512-2168, gpoaccess@gpo.gov, http://www.access.gpo.gov.

336.73   USA   ISSN 0082-9439
HJ9011
CURRENT GOVERNMENTS REPORTS: CITY GOVERNMENT FINANCES. Text in English. 1965. a. price varies. back issues avail. Document type: *Government.*
Media: Online - full text. Related titles: Microfiche ed.
Published by: U.S. Bureau of the Census (Subsidiary of: U.S. Department of Commerce), c/o Donna Hirsch, Governments Division, 4700 Silver Hill Rd., Washington, DC 20233. TEL 800-242-2184, http://www.census.gov.

336   USA   ISSN 0098-678X
HJ9011
CURRENT GOVERNMENTS REPORTS: COUNTY GOVERNMENT FINANCES. Text in English. a. price varies. Document type: *Government.*
Media: Online - full text. Related titles: Microfiche ed.
Published by: U.S. Bureau of the Census (Subsidiary of: U.S. Department of Commerce), c/o Donna Hirsch, Governments Division, 4700 Silver Hill Rd., Washington, DC 20233. TEL 800-242-2184, http://www.census.gov/mp/www/pub/gov/ msgov12h.html.

336   USA   ISSN 0095-3741
HJ257.2
CURRENT GOVERNMENTS REPORTS: GOVERNMENT FINANCES. Key Title: Governmental Finances (Washington). Text in English. a. price varies. stat. back issues avail. Document type: *Government.*
Media: Online - full text (from CompuServe Inc., The Dialog Corporation). Related titles: Microfiche ed.
Published by: U.S. Bureau of the Census (Subsidiary of: U.S. Department of Commerce), c/o Donna Hirsch, Governments Division, 4700 Silver Hill Rd., Washington, DC 20233. TEL 800-242-2184, http://www.census.gov.

336.2   USA
CURRENT GOVERNMENTS REPORTS: STATE AND LOCAL GOVERNMENT SPECIAL STUDIES. Text in English. irreg. Document type: *Government.*
Related titles: Microfiche ed.
Published by: U.S. Bureau of the Census (Subsidiary of: U.S. Department of Commerce), c/o Donna Hirsch, Governments Division, 4700 Silver Hill Rd., Washington, DC 20233. TEL 800-242-2184, http://www.census.gov.

336   USA   ISSN 0270-0808
HJ2385
CURRENT GOVERNMENTS REPORTS: STATE GOVERNMENT TAX COLLECTIONS. Text in English. 1965. a. price varies. Document type: *Government.*
Formerly (until 1977): State Tax Collections (0095-4152)
Media: Online - full text.
Published by: U.S. Bureau of the Census (Subsidiary of: U.S. Department of Commerce), Customer Services, Washington, DC 20233. TEL 301-457-4100, FAX 301-457-4714, http://www.census.gov/.

336   USA
CURRENT LEGAL FORMS WITH TAX ANALYSIS. Text in English. 1948. 34 base vols. plus q. updates. looseleaf. USD 1,980 base vol(s). (effective 2002). Description: Highly annotated forms, agreements, and legal documentation with tax introductions, practice backgrounds and annotations to case law and tax code.
Related titles: CD-ROM ed.
Published by: Matthew Bender & Co., Inc. (Subsidiary of: LexisNexis North America), 1275 Broadway, Albany, NY 12204. international@bender.com, http://bender.lexisnexis.com. Eds. Jacob Rabkin, Mark Johnson.

B

▼ *new title*   ➤ *refereed*   ✳ *unverified*   ◆ *full entry avail.*

336.2 IND ISSN 0971-0043
CURRENT TAX REPORTER. Text in English. 1972. w. INR 2,520 (effective 2000). adv. bk.rev. bibl. **Document type:** *Newspaper.* **Description:** Contains Supreme Court and High Court decisions.
Formerly: Current Tax Reporter (Supreme Court)
Address: 34 Heavy Industrial Area, Jodhpur, Rajasthan 342 003, India. TEL 91-291-745452, FAX 91-291-745470, http://www.ctr-india.com. Ed. Raman Bissa. Pub., R&P, Adv. contact K Kumar. Circ: 10,000.

336 USA ISSN 0162-6442
KF6687.A2
CUSTOMS BULLETIN AND DECISIONS; regulations, rulings, decisions, and notices concerning customs and related matters and decisions of Court of Customs and Patent Appeals and Customs Court. Text in English. 1967. w. USD 220 (effective 2001). back issues avail.; reprint service avail. from PQC. **Document type:** *Bulletin, Government.* **Description:** Contains regulations, rulings, decisions, and notices concerning U.S. Customs and related matters of the U.S. Customs Service.
Former titles (until 197?): Customs Bulletin (0011-4146); Weekly Treasury Decisions
Related titles: Microform ed.: (from PQC); Online - full text ed.: ISSN 1555-0575.
—CISTI.
Published by: U.S. Customs Service, National Support Staff, Rm B338, 1301 Constitution Ave, N W, Washington, DC 20229. **Subscr. to:** U.S. Government Printing Office, Superintendent of Documents, PO Box 371954, Pittsburgh, PA 15250-7954. TEL 202-512-1800, FAX 202-512-2250, orders@gpo.gov, http://www.access.gpo.gov.

CUSTOMS IMPORTS AND EXPORTS JOURNAL. see *BUSINESS AND ECONOMICS—International Commerce*

336 USA ISSN 1063-7443
CUSTOMS RECORD. Text in English. 1988. w. USD 625 domestic; USD 750 out of North America (effective 2001). **Document type:** *Newsletter.* **Description:** Reports on all activity at the US Customs Service; changes in special tariff programs; federal court cases and decisions; and Congressional legislation and reports.
Published by: International Business Reports, 582, Walterville, OR 97489-0582. TEL 541-746-4008, FAX 541-746-3948. Eds. Edward P Kemp, Emilio G Collado.

336 JPN
CUSTOMS TARIFF SCHEDULES. Text in Japanese, English. a. JPY 23,301. **Document type:** *Government.*
Published by: Japan Tariff Association, c/o Jibiki Daini Bldg, 4-7-8 Koji-Machi, Chiyoda-ku, Tokyo, 102-0083, Japan.

336 CYP ISSN 0070-2323
HJ68
CYPRUS. BUDGET: ESTIMATES OF REVENUE AND EXPENDITURE. Text in English, Greek. a., latest 2001. CYP 6, USD 30 (effective 2000). **Document type:** *Government.*
Published by: Government Printing Office, Director, Nicosia, Cyprus. TEL 357-2-302202, FAX 357-2-303175.

CYPRUS. MINISTRY OF LABOUR AND SOCIAL INSURANCE. ANNUAL REPORT. see *BUSINESS AND ECONOMICS—Labor And Industrial Relations*

336 CYP
HG3729.C85
CYPRUS. PUBLIC LOANS FUND. ACCOUNTS AND STATISTICS FOR THE YEAR. Text in English. 1954. a. CYP 1.50. stat. **Document type:** *Government.*
Formerly: Cyprus. Loan Commissioners. Accounts and Statistics for the Year (0574-8305)
Published by: Loan Commissioners, Loan Commissioner's Office, Nicosia, Cyprus. TEL 357-2-401197, FAX 357-2-675580. Circ: 350.

336 DEU
D A T E V MAGAZIN. Text in German. 1994. bi-m. adv. **Document type:** *Magazine, Trade.*
Published by: D A T E V eG, Paumgartnerstr 6-14, Nuernberg, 90429, Germany. TEL 49-911-2760, FAX 49-911-2763196, info@datev.de, http://www.datev.de. adv.: B&W page EUR 3,290, color page EUR 5,750. Circ: 42,000 (controlled).

355.4 USA ISSN 1058-076X
UC267 CODEN: DCAEEV
D C A A CONTRACT AUDIT MANUAL✶. Text in English. s-a. USD 54 domestic; USD 67.50 foreign (effective 2000). **Document type:** *Government.* **Description:** Establishes auditing policies and procedures for Department of Defense D.C.A.A. personnel.
Related titles: Online - full text ed.: ISSN 1554-9801.
Indexed: ATI.
Published by: U.S. Defense Contract Audit Agency, c/o Superintendent of Documents, U.S. Government Printing Office, Box 371954, Pittsburgh, PA 15250-7954. TEL 202-512-1800, FAX 202-512-2250, http://www.dcaa.mil/cam.htm.

D S T G MAGAZIN. see *PUBLIC ADMINISTRATION*

336 USA ISSN 0092-6884
KF6289.A1
DAILY TAX REPORT; from today's daily report for executives. Text in English. 1954. d. looseleaf. USD 3,215 in United States (effective 2005 - 2006). bi-w. & bi-m. indexes. 25 p./no.; back issues avail. **Description:** Tax notification service designed to give tax professionals rapid notification and comprehensive coverage of national legislative, regulatory, judicial, and policy developments.
Media: E-mail. **Related titles:** Online - full text ed.: ISSN 1522-8800 (from The Bureau of National Affairs, Inc., Thomson West).
—CCC.
Published by: The Bureau of National Affairs, Inc., 1231 25th St., NW, Washington, DC 20037. TEL 202-452-4200, 800-372-1033, 800-452-7773, FAX 202-822-8092, customercare@bna.com, bnaplus@bna.com, http://www.bna.com/products/corplaw/dtr.htm. Ed. Nancee L Simonson. Pub. Greg C McCaffery.

336 USA
DAILY TAXFAX. Text in English. d. USD 2,249. **Document type:** *Trade.* **Description:** Summarizes the day's tax news developments, including court decisions and congressional announcements, classified by Internal Revenue Code section, state, and country.
Related titles: Fax ed.; ◆ Supplement to: Highlights & Documents. ISSN 0889-3055.
Published by: Tax Analysts, 6830 N Fairfax Dr, Arlington, VA 22213. TEL 703-553-4400, 800-955-3444, FAX 703-533-4444.

336 EGY
DALIL AL-DARA'IB/TAX GUIDE. Text in Arabic. 1989. irreg. USD 30 in North America.
Published by: Mu'assasat al-Ahram, Al-Ahram Building, Al-Galaa St., Cairo, Egypt. TEL 20-2-5747411, FAX 20-2-5792899.

336 346 DNK ISSN 1398-4810
DANSKE SKATTELOVE; love, domme, afgoerelser. Text in Danish. 1989. a. DKK 675 (effective 2004). **Description:** Current Danish tax laws with comments.
Formerly (until 1998): Danske Skattelove med Henvisninger (0905-2135); Which was formed by the merger of (1987-1989): Skattelove (0902-5537); (1984-1989): Kommenterede Skattelove (0109-4963)
Published by: Magnus Informatik AS (Subsidiary of: Wolters Kluwer N.V.), Palaegade 4, PO Box 9026, Copenhagen K, 1022, Denmark. TEL 45-70-203314, FAX 45-33-960161, magnus@magnus.dk, http://www.magnus.dk.

336 BGR
DANUCHNO OBLAGANE. Text in Bulgarian. a. USD 24 foreign (effective 2002).
Related titles: CD-ROM ed.
Published by: Izdatelski Kompleks Trud i Pravo/Labour and Law Publishing House, Pl. Makedonia 1, Fl. 7, Sofia, 1040, Bulgaria. TEL 359-2-9875110, FAX 359-2-9870612, office@trudipravo.bg, http://www.trudipravo.bg. **Dist. by:** Sofia Books, ul Silivria 16, Sofia 1404, Bulgaria. TEL 359-2-9586257, info@sofiabooks-bg.com, http://www.sofiabooks-bg.com.

336.2 NLD
DATABASE OF CORPORATE TAXATION AND CROSS-BORDER PAYMENTS IN O E C D COUNTRIES. Text in English. 3/yr. USD 565; USD 345 renewals. **Description:** Contains developments in corporate taxation in developed countries. Includes information on taxation of resident and non-resident companies and holding companies, as well as taxation of foreign-source income.
Media: Diskette.
Published by: (International Bureau of Fiscal Documentation), I B F D Publications BV, H J E Wenckebachweg 210, PO Box 20237, Amsterdam, 1000 HE, Netherlands. TEL 31-20-626-7726, FAX 31-20-620-8626.

336.2 NLD
DATABASE OF TAXATION OF PRIVATE INCOME IN O E C D COUNTRIES. Text in English. 3/yr. USD 565 (effective 2000). **Document type:** *Trade.* **Description:** Contains information on the taxation of resident and non-resident individuals, with particular reference to dividends and interest. Features a transitional comparison of taxes borne on dividends and a list of tax-exempt government bonds.
Media: Diskette.
Published by: (International Bureau of Fiscal Documentation), I B F D Publications BV, H J E Wenckebachweg 210, PO Box 20237, Amsterdam, 1000 HE, Netherlands. TEL 31-20-554-0100, FAX 31-20-620-8626, http://www.ibfd.nl.

336.2 NLD
DATABASE ON CORPORATE WITHHOLDING TAXES IN THE O E C D. Text in English. 3/yr. **Description:** Keeps track of the latest withholding tax rates on patent royalties, interest and dividends in the most important OECD countries and the implications for corporate income taxation purposes.
Published by: I B F D Publications BV, H J E Wenckebachweg 210, PO Box 20237, Amsterdam, 1000 HE, Netherlands. TEL 31-20-554-0100, FAX 31-20-620-8626, info@ibfd.nl, http://www.ibfd.nl.

336 GBR
DE VOIL: VALUE ADDED TAX. Text in English. 5 base vols. plus m. updates. looseleaf. GBP 525, USD 475. **Document type:** *Trade.* **Description:** Contains the text of the relevant Acts of Parliament, statistics instruments, EC directives & regulational, relevant & excise press releases plus customer excise notices.
Related titles: CD-ROM ed.
Published by: Butterworths Tolley (Subsidiary of: LexisNexis UK (Scottish Office)), Halsbury House, 35 Chancery Ln, London, Mddx WC2A 1EL, United Kingdom. TEL 44-20-74002500, FAX 44-20-7400-2842, order.line@butterworths.co.uk, http://www.butterworths.co.uk/.

336 GBR ISSN 1363-9560
DE VOIL'S INDIRECT TAX INTELLIGENCE. Text in English. 1991. m. GBP 62.95. **Document type:** *Trade.* **Description:** Provides practical advice on achieving the optimum tax position. Incorporates all changes introduced by UK and EU legislation and case law.
Formerly (until 1996): V A T Planning (0964-5985)
Indexed: ELJI, LJI.
Published by: Butterworths Tolley (Subsidiary of: LexisNexis UK (Scottish Office)), Halsbury House, 35 Chancery Ln, London, Mddx WC2A 1EL, United Kingdom. TEL 44-20-74002500, FAX 44-20-7400-2842. Ed. Alan Buckett.

336 AUS ISSN 1442-1046
DEDUCTIONS. Text in English. 1995. q. **Document type:** *Government.*
Media: Online - full text.
Published by: Department of Communications Information Technology and the Arts, 38 Sydney Ave, Forrest, ACT 2603, Australia. TEL 61-2-6277-7480, FAX 61-2-6273-4154, artbeat@dca.gov.au, http://www.dca.gov.au/.

336 USA ISSN 0084-9685
DELAWARE. STATE TREASURER. ANNUAL REPORT✶. Text in English. a. free. **Document type:** *Government.*
Published by: Division of Accounting, Thomas Collins Building, 540 S. Dupont Hwy, Ste 3, Dover, DE 19901. TEL 302-739-4231. Ed. Betty Surgay. Circ: (controlled).

336 DNK ISSN 0909-1424
HJ56
DENMARK. FINANSMINISTERIET. BUDGETREDEGOERELSE. Text in Danish. 1979. a. **Document type:** *Government.*
Former titles (until 1994): Denmark. Finansministeriet. Udgiftsanalyser (0905-7544); (until 1990): Denmark. Finansministeriet. Redegoerelse om den Offentlige Sektor (0904-3098); (until 1988): Denmark. Finansministeriet. Budgetdepartmentet. Budgetredegoerelse (0106-3006)
Published by: Finansministeriet/Ministry of Finance, Christiansborg Slotsplads, Copenhagen K, 1218, Denmark. TEL 45-33-923333, fm@fm.dk, http://www.fm.dk/1024/visPublikationesForside.asp?artikelID=6400. Circ: 3,000. **Dist. by:** Schultz Information A-S.

336 USA
DEPRECIATION & CAPITAL PLANNING. Text in English. 1991. base vol. plus s-a. updates. looseleaf. USD 215 (effective 1999). **Document type:** *Trade.* **Description:** Complete planning reference to all changes in depreciation and investment credits.
Published by: W G & L Financial Reporting & Management Research (Subsidiary of: R I A), 90 Fifth Ave, New York, NY 10011. TEL 212-645-4800, FAX 212-337-4280.

336.2 340 USA
DEPRECIATION HANDBOOK. Text in English. 1990. base vol. plus a. updates. looseleaf. USD 256 base vol(s). (effective 2005). **Description:** covers depreciation and cost recovery, the accelerated cost recovery system, leased property, depletion, the rehabilitation tax credit, pollution control facilities, energy credits and investment tax credit transitional rules.
Related titles: CD-ROM ed.
Published by: Matthew Bender & Co., Inc. (Subsidiary of: LexisNexis North America), 1275 Broadway, Albany, NY 12204. TEL 518-487-3575, 800-252-9257, FAX 518-462-3788, international@bender.com, http://bender.lexisnexis.com. Eds. Bruce Benesh, M Kevin Bryant.

DERIVATIVES & FINANCIAL INSTRUMENTS. see *BUSINESS AND ECONOMICS—Investments*

336.2 USA ISSN 1546-6272
DERIVATIVES FINANCIAL PRODUCTS REPORT. Text in English. 1999. q. USD 320 in US & Canada (effective 2004). adv. **Document type:** *Magazine, Trade.*
Formerly (until 2003): Derivatives Report (1536-397X)
—CCC.
Published by: R I A (Subsidiary of: Thomson Corporation), 395 Hudson St, New York, NY 10014. TEL 212-367-6300, 800-950-1216, http://www.riahome.com. Ed. Mark H Leeds. Adv. contact Terry Storholm.

336.2 DEU ISSN 1431-3936
DEUTSCHE BILANZIERUNGS-RICHTLINIEN. Text in German. 1997. 3 base vols. plus updates 9/yr. EUR 129 base vol(s). (effective 2004). **Document type:** *Trade.*

B

Published by: Verlag fuer Deutsche Steuerberater AG (Subsidiary of: Wolters Kluwer Deutschland GmbH), Marlener Str 2, Offenburg, 77656, Germany. TEL 49-781-9900646, FAX 49-781-9900644, info@steuern-online.de, http://www.steuern-online.de.

336.2 DEU ISSN 1431-0678
DEUTSCHE ERBRECHTSZEITSCHRIFT. Text in German. 1996. q. EUR 4.90 newsstand/cover (effective 2004). adv. **Document type:** *Magazine, Trade.*
Published by: (Deutsche Gesellschaft fuer Erbrechtskunde e.V.), S V Corporate Media GmbH (Subsidiary of: Sueddeutscher Verlag GmbH), Emmy-Noether-Str 2, Munich, 80992, Germany. TEL 49-89-5485201, FAX 49-89-54852192, info@sv-medien-service.de, http://www.sv-medien-service.de/svcm/. adv.: B&W page EUR 2,150, color page EUR 3,710. Circ: 10,000 (controlled).

336.2 DEU ISSN 0724-5637
HJ2670
DEUTSCHE STEUER-ZEITUNG. Text in German. 1913. s-m. EUR 237.80; EUR 12.30 newsstand/cover (effective 2005). adv. charts; illus. index. **Document type:** *Newspaper, Trade.*
Formerly: Deutsche Steuer-Zeitung: Ausgabe A (0012-0774)
Indexed: IBR, IBZ.
—CCC.
Published by: (Germany. Bundesministerium der Finanzen), Stollfuss Verlag GmbH & Co. KG, Dechenstr 7, Bonn, 53115, Germany. TEL 49-228-7240, FAX 49-228-72491181, info@stollfuss.de, http://www.stollfuss.de/programm/products/0400120.htm. Ed. E Stoecker. adv.: B&W page EUR 1,435, color page EUR 2,255. Circ: 2,700 (paid and controlled).

336.2 DEU
DEUTSCHE STEUERBERATER-RICHTLINIEN; Problemloesungen fuer die Steuerberatungspraxis nach Sachverhalten von A-Z. Text in German. 4 base vols. plus updates 14/yr. EUR 129 base vol(s). (effective 2004). **Document type:** *Directory, Trade.*
Published by: Verlag fuer Deutsche Steuerberater AG (Subsidiary of: Wolters Kluwer Deutschland GmbH), Marlener Str 2, Offenburg, 77656, Germany. TEL 49-781-9900646, FAX 49-781-9900644, info@steuern-online.de, http://www.steuern-online.de.

332.6 DEU
DEUTSCHE UMWANDLUNGS-RICHTLINIEN. Text in German. base vol. plus updates 2/yr. EUR 149 base vol(s). (effective 2004). **Document type:** *Trade.*
Published by: Verlag fuer Deutsche Steuerberater AG (Subsidiary of: Wolters Kluwer Deutschland GmbH), Marlener Str 2, Offenburg, 77656, Germany. TEL 49-781-9900646, FAX 49-781-9900644, info@steuern-online.de, http://www.steuern-online.de.

343.04 DEU ISSN 1431-956X
KK7104.3
DEUTSCHES STEUERRECHT - ENTSCHEIDUNGSDIENST. Abbreviated title: DStR - E. Text in German. 1997. 2/m. **Document type:** *Journal, Trade.*
Related titles: ♦ Supplement to: DStR - Deutsches Steuerrecht. ISSN 0949-7676.
Published by: Verlag C.H. Beck oHG, Wilhelmstr 9, Munich, 80801, Germany. TEL 49-89-38189338, FAX 49-89-38189398, abo.service@beck.de, http://www.beck.de.

336.1 DEU ISSN 1431-4096
DEUTSCHLAND SPEZIAL OST; Steuer- und Wirtschaftsrecht der neuen Bundeslaender. Text in German. 1990. w. EUR 199.20; EUR 8 newsstand/cover (effective 2002). **Document type:** *Journal, Trade.*
Formerly (until 1994): DDR Spezial (0939-5733)
Published by: Verlag Neue Wirtschafts-Briefe GmbH & Co., Eschstr 22, Herne, 44629, Germany. TEL 49-2323-141900, FAX 49-2323-141123, info@nwb.de, http://www.nwb.de. Ed. Thomas Toeben. Circ: 2,500 (paid).

336 FRA ISSN 1638-2242
DICTIONNAIRE PERMANENT: GESTION FISCALE. Text in French. 1957. 3 base vols. plus bi-m. updates. looseleaf. EUR 330 base vol(s). (effective 2004). bibl. index, cum.index. **Description:** Covers fiscal laws for individuals and businesses.
Formerly (until 2001): Dictionnaire Permanent: Fiscal (0012-2491)
Related titles: CD-ROM ed.; Online - full text ed.
Published by: Editions Legislatives, 80 Avenue de la Marne, Montrouge, Cedex 92546, France. TEL 33-1-40923636, FAX 33-1-40923663, infocom@editions-legislatives.fr, http://www.editions-legislatives.fr. Ed. Emmanuelle Kaufman. Pub. Michel Vaillant. Circ: 9,000.

336.2 ITA ISSN 1122-4436
HD671
DIPARTIMENTO DEL TERRITORIO. RIVISTA. Key Title: Rivista del Dipartimento del Territorio. Text in Italian; Summaries in English, French, German, Italian. 1934. 3/yr. adv. bk.rev. bibl.; charts; illus.; tr.lit. index.
Formerly (until 1993): Rivista del Catasto e dei Servizi Tecnici Erariali (0035-5860)
—CISTI.
Published by: Ministero delle Finanze, Dipartimento del Territorio, Largo Giacomo Leopardi, 5, Rome, RM 00185, Italy. TEL 34-6-48168432. Ed. Enrico Vitelli.

336.2 IND
DIRECT TAXES BULLETIN. Text in English, Hindi. 1961. q. INR 114, USD 41.04. **Document type:** *Bulletin, Government.*
Published by: Government of India, Department of Publications, Civil Lines, New Delhi, 110 054, India. TEL 11-2517409.

355.6 USA ISSN 1058-0158
UC267
DIRECTORY OF D C A A OFFICES✶. Text in English. s-a. USD 20 domestic; USD 25 foreign (effective 2000). **Document type:** *Directory, Government.* **Description:** Lists personnel at the Defense Contract Audit Agency headquarters and regional offices, as well as those working at the Defense Contract Audit Institute.
Related titles: Online - full text ed.: ISSN 1554-9461.
Published by: U.S. Defense Contract Audit Agency, c/o Superintendent of Documents, U.S. Government Printing Office, Box 371954, Pittsburgh, PA 15250-7954. TEL 202-512-1800, FAX 202-512-2250.

336 USA
DIVORCE TAX PLANNING STRATEGIES. Text in English. 1990. base vol. plus a. updates. looseleaf. USD 200. Supplement avail. **Document type:** *Trade.* **Description:** Includes relevant provisions from the Tax Reform Acts of 1984 and 1986, former and current Code provisions and Congressional Committee Reports, as well as Temporary Regulations interpreting recent legislative changes.
Formerly (until 1989): Tax Strategies for Separations and Divorce
Published by: Shepard's (Subsidiary of: LexisNexis North America), 555 Middle Creek Pkwy, Colorado Springs, CO 80921. TEL 800-743-7393, customer_service@shepards.com, http://www.shepards.com, http://www.lexisnexis.com/shepards/. Ed. William J Brown.

336 346.01 USA ISSN 0730-6555
CODEN: RESSBM
DIVORCE TAXATION. Text in English. 1981. Report Bulletins and), base vol. plus m. updates. looseleaf. USD 645 (effective 2005). **Description:** Explains tax consequences of spousal and child support payments, property rights and interests, and special marital assets. Highlights provisions of new legislation.
Published by: W G & L Financial Reporting & Management Research (Subsidiary of: R I A), 90 Fifth Ave, New York, NY 10011. TEL 212-645-4800, FAX 212-337-4280, 212-367-6718. Ed. Marjorie A O'Connell.

DOCUMENTARY CREDIT WORLD. see *BUSINESS AND ECONOMICS*

336.2 CAN ISSN 0046-0567
KE5665.8
DOMINION TAX CASES. Text in English. s-m. looseleaf. CND 987 (effective 2005). index. **Document type:** *Trade.* **Description:** Digests full texts of federal income tax judgments from the Tax, Federal and Supreme Courts of Canada and selected provincial courts.
Related titles: CD-ROM ed.: CND 954 (effective 2005); Online - full text ed.: CND 926 (effective 2005).
Indexed: CBCABus.
Published by: C C H Canadian Ltd., 90 Sheppard Ave E, Ste 300, North York, ON M2N 6X1, Canada. TEL 416-224-2248, 800-268-4522, FAX 416-224-2243, cservice@cch.ca, http://www.cch.ca.

336.2 CAN
DOMINION TAX CASES NEWSLETTER. Text in English. m. looseleaf. CND 217 (effective 2005). **Document type:** *Newsletter, Trade.* **Description:** Provides summaries of recent tax cases.
Published by: C C H Canadian Ltd., 90 Sheppard Ave E, Ste 300, North York, ON M2N 6X1, Canada. TEL 416-224-2248, 800-268-4522, FAX 416-224-2243, 800-461-4131, cservice@cch.ca, http://www.cch.ca.

336.2 338.642 POL ISSN 1231-3084
DORADCA PODATNIKA. Text in Polish. 1993. w. PLZ 1,290 (effective 2003). adv. back issues avail. **Description:** Deals with income taxes (individual and corporate), value added tax, revenue fees and charges.
Formerly (until 1994): Jak Prowadzic Ksiegi Podatkowe (1231-3076)
Related titles: CD-ROM ed.; Online - full content ed.
Published by: Grupa Wydawnicza INFOR Sp. z o.o., Ul Okopowa 58/72, Warsaw, 01042, Poland. TEL 48-22-7613030, FAX 48-22-7613031, bok@infor.pl, http://www.doradcapodatnika.infor.pl, http://www.infor.pl. Ed. Grazyna Gonciarska. Adv. contact Waldemar Krakowiak.

382 NLD ISSN 1569-352X
DOUANERECHTSPRAAK. Text in Dutch. 1953. bi-m. looseleaf. index.
Former titles (until 2001): U T C (0167-4064); (until 1979): Uitspraken van de Tariefcommissie (0041-5588)
Related titles: ♦ Supplement to: In- en Uitvoer Nieuws. ISSN 0019-3178.
—IE.
Published by: (Netherlands. Tariefcommissie), Kluwer B.V. (Subsidiary of: Wolters Kluwer N.V.), Postbus 23, Deventer, 7400 GA, Netherlands. TEL 31-570-673449, FAX 31-570-691555, juridisch@kluwer.nl, http://www.kluwer.nl. Circ: 1,300.

336 GBR
DOUBLE TAXATION CONVENTIONS. Text in English. 2001. base vol. plus updates 2/yr. looseleaf. GBP 345 base vol(s).; GBP 199, EUR 299 updates in Europe; GBP 210, USD 356 updates elsewhere (effective 2005). **Document type:** *Journal, Trade.*
Published by: Sweet & Maxwell Ltd., 100 Avenue Road, London, NW3 3PF, United Kingdom. TEL 44-20-74491111, FAX 44-20-74491144, customer.services@sweetandmaxwell.co.uk, http://www.sweetandmaxwell.co.uk. **Subscr. to:** Cheriton House, North Way, Andover, Hants SP10 5BE, United Kingdom.

343.04 DEU ISSN 0949-7676
DSTR - DEUTSCHES STEUERRECHT; Wochenschrift fuer Steuerrecht, Gesellschaftsrecht und Betriebswirtschaft. Text in German. 1962. w. EUR 234 domestic; EUR 347.60 foreign; EUR 5 newsstand/cover (effective 2005). adv. bk.rev. index, cum.index covering 10 yrs. back issues avail. **Document type:** *Journal, Trade.*
Formerly (until 1990): Deutsches Steuerrecht (0012-1347)
Related titles: Audio CD ed.: DStR Audio-CD. ISSN 1617-089X. EUR 216 domestic; EUR 281.10 foreign; EUR 20.50 newsstand/cover (effective 2005); Audio cassette/tape ed.: DStR - Cassetten. ISSN 0949-4774. EUR 190 domestic; EUR 255.10 foreign; EUR 19 newsstand/cover (effective 2004); CD-ROM ed.: DStR-CD. ISSN 1431-2921. EUR 298 base vol(s). per vol.; EUR 79 updates per issue (effective 2005); ♦ Supplement(s): Deutsches Steuerrecht - Entscheidungsdienst. ISSN 1431-956X.
Indexed: DIP, IBR, IBZ.
—IE. **CCC.**
Published by: (Bundessteuerberaterkammer), Verlag C.H. Beck oHG, Wilhelmstr 9, Munich, 80801, Germany. TEL 49-89-38189338, FAX 49-89-38189398, abo.service@beck.de, http://www.dstr.de, http://www.beck.de. adv.: B&W page EUR 3,100, color page EUR 5,425; trim 186 x 260. Circ: 25,135 (controlled).

DUTCH BUSINESS LAW. see *LAW—Corporate Law*

336 340 AUS
DUTIES LEGISLATION. Text in English. 1979. 3-4 updates/yr.), 2 base vols. plus q. updates. looseleaf. AUD 605 (effective 2004). **Document type:** *Trade.* **Description:** Concentrates on the N.S.W. Stamp Duties Act 1920 and regulations, the A.C.T. Taxation (Administration) Act 1969 and other relevant stamp duties legislation.
Supersedes (in 1998): Stamp Duties N.S.W. and A.C.T. (0727-7970)
Published by: Lawbook Co. (Subsidiary of: Thomson Legal & Regulatory Ltd.), PO Box 3502, Rozelle, NSW 2039, Australia. LRA.Service@thomson.com, http://onlineecom01.thomson.com.au/thomson/Catalog.asp?EES_CMD=SI&EES_ID=100409, http://www.lawbookco.com.au/. Eds. D Graham Hill, W D M Cannon.

332.6 AUS
DUTIES LEGISLATION QUEENSLAND. Text in English. 1981. 4-5 updates/yr.), base vol. plus q. updates. looseleaf. AUD 600 (effective 2004). **Document type:** *Trade.* **Description:** Covers Duties Act 2001 and the Taxation Administration Act 2001 and Regulations as well as the forms, practice directions and revenue rulings of the Office of State Revenue.
Former titles (until 2002): Stamp Duties (Queensland); Law of Stamp Duties in Queensland (0725-6892)
Published by: Lawbook Co. (Subsidiary of: Thomson Legal & Regulatory Ltd.), PO Box 3502, Rozelle, NSW 2039, Australia. LRA.Service@thomson.com, http://onlineecom01.thomson.com.au/thomson/Catalog.asp?EES_CMD=SI&EES_ID=101942, http://www.lawbookco.com.au/. Ed. Dr. Jeff G Mann.

336 GBR
DYMONDS CAPITAL TAXES. Text in English. 1985. 3 base vols. plus updates 3/yr. looseleaf. GBP 575 base vol(s).; GBP 399, EUR 600 updates in Europe; GBP 415, USD 754 updates elsewhere (effective 2006). **Document type:** *Journal, Trade.*
Published by: Sweet & Maxwell Ltd., 100 Avenue Road, London, NW3 3PF, United Kingdom. TEL 44-20-74491111, FAX 44-20-74491144, customer.services@sweetandmaxwell.co.uk, http://www.sweetandmaxwell.co.uk. **Subscr. to:** Cheriton House, North Way, Andover, Hants SP10 5BE, United Kingdom.

336 USA
KF6272
E A JOURNAL. (Enrolled Agents) Text in English. 1983. bi-m. USD 48 (effective 1998). adv. 50 p./no. 3 cols./p.; **Document type:** *Trade.* **Description:** Provides timely and informative articles on the technical aspects of taxation, IRS policies and procedures, and tax practice.
Formerly: E A (8750-7072)

Published by: National Association of Enrolled Agents, 1120 Connecticut Ave NW, Ste. 460, Washington, DC 20036-3953. TEL 301-212-9608, FAX 301-990-1611, szuber@naeahq.org, mmitchell@naeahq.org, scranford@naeahq.org, http://www.naea.org. Ed. William Matesevac. R&P Sharon Cranford. Adv. contact Margaret M Mitchell. Circ: 9,500.

336 USA ISSN 0891-592X
E ALERT. Text in English. 1985. s-m. USD 16 to members. **Document type:** *Newsletter, Trade.*
Published by: National Association of Enrolled Agents, 1120 Connecticut Ave NW, Ste. 460, Washington, DC 20036-3953. TEL 301-212-9608, FAX 301-990-1611, cweiss@naea.org, szuber@naeahq.org. Ed. William Matesevac. Circ: 9,000.

336 NLD
E C CORPORATE TAX LAW. (European Commission) Text in English. 4 base vols. plus s-a. updates. looseleaf. USD 930 base vol(s).; USD 420 updates (effective 2002). **Document type:** *Trade.* **Description:** Provides detailed coverage and assessment of EC corporate tax directives and their impact on multinational companies doing business in Europe.
Published by: (International Bureau of Fiscal Documentation), I B F D Publications BV, H J E Wenckebachweg 210, PO Box 20237, Amsterdam, 1000 HE, Netherlands. TEL 31-20-554-0100, FAX 31-20-620-8626, info@ibfd.nl, http://www.ibfd.nl. Ed. Otmat Thommes.

336 BEL ISSN 1011-4637
E C S C FINANCIAL REPORT. (European Coal and Steel Community) Text in English. 1956. a. **Document type:** *Newsletter.*
Related titles: Microfiche ed.: (from CIS); Dutch ed.; French ed.; German ed.; Italian ed.
Indexed: IIS.
—BLDSC (3659.633700).
Published by: European Commission, Rue de la Loi - Wetstraat 200, Brussels, 1049, Belgium. Circ: (controlled). **Dist. in the U.S. by:** European Community Information Service, 2100 M St, NW Ste 707, Washington, DC 20037.

336 GBR ISSN 1350-1089
K5
E C TAX JOURNAL. Text in English. 1995. 3/yr. GBP 99 (effective 1998). **Document type:** *Bulletin.* **Description:** Provides a forum to discuss E.C. tax issues related to both particular member states and to the E.C. as a whole.
—BLDSC (3647.257755), IE, ingenta.
Published by: Key Haven Publications plc., 7 Crescent Stables, 139 Upper Richmond Rd, London, SW15 2TN, United Kingdom. TEL 44-20-8780-2522, FAX 44-20-8780-1693. Ed. Timothy Lyons.

336 341 NLD ISSN 0928-2750
E C TAX REVIEW. (European Communities) Text in Dutch. 1992. q. price varies. back issues avail. **Document type:** *Monographic series, Academic/Scholarly.* **Description:** Covers current developments in taxation in the EC, including current cases before the European Court of Justice and relevant national EC tax cases.
Related titles: Online - full text ed.: (from EBSCO Publishing, Kluwer Online, O C L C Online Computer Library Center, Inc., Swets Information Services); ♦ Supplement to: Intertax. ISSN 0165-2826.
Indexed: DIP, ELJI, IBR, IBZ.
—BLDSC (3647.257770), IE, Infotrieve, ingenta. **CCC.**
Published by: Kluwer Law International (Subsidiary of: Aspen Publishers, Inc.), Laan van Meerdervoort 70, PO Box 85889, The Hague, 2508 CN, Netherlands. TEL 31-70-3081500, FAX 31-70-3081515, sales@kluwerlaw.com, http://www.kluwerlaw.com. Ed. Frans Vanistendael.

336.2 USA
HJ5709.5.U6
E-COMMERCE TAX ALERT. Text in English. m. USD 410; USD 615 combined subscription print & online eds. (effective 2004). **Document type:** *Newsletter.* **Description:** Focuses on the complex world of e-commerce taxation. Every aspect of cybertaxation is covered: compliance and sourcing issues, e-cash implications, the latest in the heated internet tax debate, and more.
Related titles: Online - full text ed.: USD 515 includes archive issues (effective 2004).
Published by: C C H Inc., 2700 Lake Cook Rd, Riverwoods, IL 60015. TEL 847-267-7000, 800-449-6439, cust_serv@cch.com, http://www.cch.com.

336.2 USA ISSN 1530-1001
E-COMMERCE TAX REPORT. Text in English. 2000. d. **Document type:** *Newsletter, Trade.* **Description:** Keeps you at the forefront of e-commerce tax developments with timely news and authoritative, comprehensive analysis.
Related titles: ♦ Online - full text ed.: E-Commerce Tax Report (Online Edition). ISSN 1530-101X.
Published by: B N A Inc. (Subsidiary of: The Bureau of National Affairs, Inc.), 1231 25th St, NW, Washington, DC 20037. TEL 202-452-4343, FAX 202-452-4997, customercare@bna.com, http://www.bna.com/products/tax/etax.htm.

336.2 USA ISSN 1530-101X
E-COMMERCE TAX REPORT (ONLINE EDITION). Variant title: Ecommerce Tax Report. Text in English. 2000. d. back issues avail. **Document type:** *Newsletter, Trade.* **Description:** Keeps you at the forefront of e-commerce tax developments with timely news and authoritative, comprehensive analysis.
Media: Online - full text (from The Bureau of National Affairs, Inc.). **Related titles:** ♦ Print ed.: E-Commerce Tax Report. ISSN 1530-1001.
—CCC.
Published by: B N A Inc. (Subsidiary of: The Bureau of National Affairs, Inc.), 1231 25th St, NW, Washington, DC 20037. TEL 202-452-4343, FAX 202-452-4997, customercare@bna.com, http://www.bna.com/products/tax/etax.htm.

E I U INVESTING, LICENSING AND TRADING. (Economist Intelligence Unit) see *BUSINESS AND ECONOMICS—International Commerce*

E Z - VOPROS - OTVET. (Ekonomika i Zhizn') see *BUSINESS AND ECONOMICS—Accounting*

THE ECONOMIC AND BUDGET OUTLOOK; an update. see *BUSINESS AND ECONOMICS—Economic Situation And Conditions*

ECONOMIC EDGE. see *BUSINESS AND ECONOMICS—Economic Situation And Conditions*

336 ECU
ECUADOR. CORPORACION FINANCIERA NACIONAL. MEMORIA. Text in Spanish. a. free. charts; illus.; stat. **Document type:** *Government.* **Description:** Reviews the activities of the association. Includes statistics on the financial status of the CFN.
Formerly (until 1977): Ecuador. Comision de Valores. Corporacion Financiera Nacional. Memoria (0589-7688)
Published by: Corporacion Financiera Nacional, Juan Leon Mera 130 y Av Patria, Quito, Ecuador. TEL 593-2-564900, FAX 593-2-223823, http://www.cfn.fin.ec/.

336 ECU
ECUADOR. DIRECCION GENERAL DE RECAUDACIONES. BOLETIN✶. Text in Spanish. irreg. charts; stat. **Document type:** *Bulletin, Government.*
Published by: Direccion General de Recaudaciones, Quito, Pichincha, Ecuador.

336 RUS ISSN 0869-7302
EKSPRESS - ZAKON. Text in Russian. 1992. 52/yr. USD 712 foreign. adv. index. back issues avail. **Document type:** *Bulletin.* **Description:** Collection of legal and normative acts.
—East View.
Published by: Izdatel'stvo Infra-M, Dmitrovskoe shosse 107, Moscow, 127247, Russian Federation. TEL 7-095-4855779, FAX 7-095-4855318, relcom-contract@infram.msk.ru. Ed. Vladimir M Prudnikov. R&P Regina Bouglo. Adv. contact Galina Tabachnikova. Circ: 3,000 (controlled).

336.2 346.052 368.382 USA ISSN 1550-0470
▼ **ELDER CLIENT PLANNER.** Text in English. 2004 (Jun). m. USD 249 (effective 2005). **Document type:** *Newsletter, Trade.* **Description:** Contains information for CPAs and tax professionals who work with older clients and retirement plans.
Related titles: Online - full text ed.: ISSN 1550-4581.
Published by: Spidell Publishing, Inc., 1158 N Gilbert St, Anaheim, CA 92801-1401. TEL 714-776-7850, FAX 714-776-9906, http://www.elderclientplanner.com/, http://www.spidell.com. Ed. Nathan Orme.

336.2 NLD
ELSEVIER B T W ALMANAK (YEAR). (Belasting Toegevoegde Waarde) Text in Dutch. a., latest 2003. EUR 49.95 base vol(s). (effective 2003). charts. **Document type:** *Trade.* **Description:** Provides an comprehensive, up-to-date reference for the Dutch value-added (excise) tax.
Related titles: CD-ROM ed.: EUR 50.38 base vol(s). (effective 2003).
Published by: Elsevier Financiele Informatie (Subsidiary of: Reed Business Information bv), Postbus 1872, Amsterdam, 1000 BW, Netherlands. TEL 0800-022-1313, FAX 31-20-515-9740, http://www.elsevierfiscaal.nl.

336.2 NLD
ELSEVIER BELASTING ALMANAK (YEAR). Text in Dutch. a. EUR 19.95 per vol. (effective 2003). charts; stat. **Document type:** *Journal, Trade.* **Description:** Offers a comprehensive reference to taxation in the Netherlands.
Related titles: CD-ROM ed.
Published by: Elsevier Financiele Informatie (Subsidiary of: Reed Business Information bv), Postbus 1872, Amsterdam, 1000 BW, Netherlands. TEL 0800-022-1313, FAX 31-20-515-9740, efihelp@ebi.nl, http://www.elsevierfiscaal.nl.

336.2 NLD
ELSEVIER BELASTING CD-ROM (YEAR). Text in Dutch. 1985. a. EUR 40.76 base vol(s). (effective 2003). charts; stat. **Document type:** *Trade.* **Description:** Covers all aspects of Dutch tax policy and tax law.
Media: CD-ROM.
Published by: Elsevier Financiele Informatie (Subsidiary of: Reed Business Information bv), Postbus 1872, Amsterdam, 1000 BW, Netherlands. TEL 0800-022-1313, FAX 31-20-515-9740, efihelp@ebi.nl, http://www.elsevierfiscaal.nl.

336.2 NLD
ELSEVIER LOON DISKETTE 2000. Text in Dutch. a. charts. **Document type:** *Trade.* **Description:** Helps financial professionals make income and income tax calculations, using data reflecting the year's updates in the tax code.
Media: Diskette. **Related titles:** ♦ Supplement to: Elsevier Loonheffing Almanak (Year). ISSN 1388-4387.
Published by: Elsevier Financiele Informatie (Subsidiary of: Reed Business Information bv), Postbus 1872, Amsterdam, 1000 BW, Netherlands. TEL 0800-022-1313, FAX 31-20-515-9740, efihelp@ebi.nl, http://www.elsevierfiscaal.nl/products/products_fiscaal.asp.

336.2 NLD ISSN 1388-4387
ELSEVIER LOONHEFFING ALMANAK (YEAR). Text in Dutch. 1984. a., latest 2003. EUR 49.95 base vol(s). 2000 ed (effective 2003). charts. 400 p./no.; **Document type:** *Trade.* **Description:** Acts as a comprehensive, up-to-date reference on income taxes in the Netherlands.
Former titles (until 1997): Elseviers Almanak voor de Loonheffing (1387-5930); (until 1991): Elseviers Almanak voor de Loonbelasting (0923-4969)
Related titles: CD-ROM ed.: EUR 50.38 base vol(s). per vol. (effective 2003); ♦ Supplement(s): Elsevier Loon Diskette 2000.
Published by: Elsevier Financiele Informatie (Subsidiary of: Reed Business Information bv), Postbus 1872, Amsterdam, 1000 BW, Netherlands. TEL 0800-022-1313, FAX 31-20-515-9740, efihelp@ebi.nl, http://www.elsevierfiscaal.nl/products/products_fiscaal.asp.

ELSEVIER SOCIALE VERZEKERINGEN ALMANAK. see *INSURANCE*

336.2 NLD ISSN 1386-8179
ELSEVIER V P B ALMANAK. Variant title: Elsevier Vennootschapsbelasting Almanak. Text in Dutch. 1970. a., latest 2002. EUR 45.75 (effective 2003). charts. 290 p./no.; **Document type:** *Trade.* **Description:** Provides a comprehensive, up-to-date reference source for corporate income tax law and strategy in the Netherlands.
Former titles (until 1997): Elseviers Almanak voor de Vennootschapsbelasting (0925-1960); (until 1982): Elseviers Vennootschapsbelasting (0925-9112)
Related titles: CD-ROM ed.: EUR 44.12 (effective 2003); ♦ Diskette ed.: Elsevier V P B Diskette (Year).
Published by: Elsevier Financiele Informatie (Subsidiary of: Reed Business Information bv), Postbus 1872, Amsterdam, 1000 BW, Netherlands. TEL 0800-022-1313, FAX 31-20-515-9740, efihelp@ebi.nl, http://www.elsevierfiscaal.nl/Default.asp?pagetype=products&ProdID=86&doc=/ElsCart/DetailPage.asp.

336.2 NLD
ELSEVIER V P B DISKETTE (YEAR). (Venootschapsbelasting) Text in English. a., latest 2002. EUR 209.35 (effective 2003). charts; stat. **Document type:** *Trade.* **Description:** Enables financial professionals to estimate and calculate corporate income taxes, providing them with the year's updates in taxation.
Media: Diskette. **Related titles:** CD-ROM ed.: EUR 44.12 (effective 2003); ♦ Print ed.: Elsevier V P B Almanak. ISSN 1386-8179.
Published by: Elsevier Financiele Informatie (Subsidiary of: Reed Business Information bv), Postbus 1872, Amsterdam, 1000 BW, Netherlands. TEL 0800-022-1313, FAX 31-20-515-9740, efihelp@ebi.nl, http://www.elsevierfiscaal.nl/Default.asp?pagetype=products&ProdID=88&doc=/ElsCart/DetailPage.asp.

336 USA
EMPLOYMENT TAX FORMS. Text in English. 1991. 3 base vols. plus irreg. updates. looseleaf. USD 389 base vol(s). (effective 2004). **Description:** Includes periodic reports, reproducible federal and state employment tax forms and information returns filed by employers; selected federal Revenue Procedures and Social Security Administration Technical Publication and Information Bulletin (TIB-4); and due date calendar.
Published by: C C H Inc., 2700 Lake Cook Rd, Riverwoods, IL 60015. TEL 847-267-7000, 800-449-6439, cust_serv@cch.com, http://www.cch.com. Pub. Catherine Wolfe.

336.2 GBR ISSN 0958-6245
ENCYCLOPEDIA OF RATING & LOCAL TAXATION. Text in English. 1988. 2 base vols. plus updates 2/yr. looseleaf. GBP 559 base vol(s).; GBP 389, EUR 585 updates in Europe; GBP 400, USD 727 updates elsewhere (effective 2006). **Document type:** *Trade.*
Published by: Sweet & Maxwell Ltd., 100 Avenue Road, London, NW3 3PF, United Kingdom. TEL 44-20-74491111, FAX 44-20-74491144, customer.services@sweetandmaxwell.co.uk, http://www.sweetandmaxwell.co.uk. **Subscr. to:** Cheriton House, North Way, Andover, Hants SP10 5BE, United Kingdom.

ENVIRONMENT AND PLANNING C: GOVERNMENT & POLICY. see *PUBLIC ADMINISTRATION*

336.2 657 GBR ISSN 1361-0104
ENVIRONMENTAL TAXATION AND ACCOUNTING. Text in English. 1996. q. GBP 95; GBP 105 foreign. **Document type:** *Newsletter.*
Published by: Cameron May Ltd., 69 Bondway, London, SW8 1SQ, United Kingdom. TEL 44-20-7582-7567, FAX 44-20-7793-8353, 100615.1547@compuserve.com. Ed., R&P Amanda Pritchett TEL 44-171-608-3828.

ERNST & YOUNG FINANCIAL PLANNING REPORTER. see *BUSINESS AND ECONOMICS—Investments*

336 DEU ISSN 1437-9112
DER ERTRAG-STEUER-BERATER. Text in German. 1999. m. EUR 136; EUR 13.60 newsstand/cover (effective 2005). adv. **Document type:** *Magazine, Trade.*
Published by: Verlag Dr. Otto Schmidt KG, Gustav-Heinemann-Ufer 58, Cologne, 50968, Germany. TEL 49-221-93738460, FAX 49-221-93738943, info@otto-schmidt.de, http://www.estb.de, http://www.otto-schmidt.de. Ed. Annette Stuhldreier. Adv. contact Renate Becker. B&W page EUR 825, color page EUR 1,444. Circ: 3,436 (paid and controlled).

336 ESP ISSN 1135-7509
ESTUDIOS DEL MINISTERIO FISCAL. Text in Spanish. 1995. s-a. back issues avail.
Published by: Ministerio de Justicia, Centro de Publicaciones, San Bernardo 62, Planta Baja, Madrid, 28071, Spain. TEL 34-91-3902187, FAX 34-91-3902192, http://www.mju.es/publicaciones/.

ESTUDIOS ECONOMICOS. see *BUSINESS AND ECONOMICS—Economic Systems And Theories, Economic History*

332 FRA
ETUDES JURIF. Text in French. s-a. (plus 2 updates). looseleaf. price varies per no.
Published by: (Societe Jurif), Cahiers Fiscaux Europeens, 51 av. Reine Victoria, Nice, 06000, France. TEL 93-81-03-26, FAX 93-53-66-28.

336 DEU
EURO STEUER TELEX; Spezialdienst mit Kennziffen Service. Text in German. 1987. s-m. adv. bk.rev. index. back issues avail. **Document type:** *Journal, Trade.*
Formerly: Steuer Telex International (0930-7656)
Published by: Deubner Verlag GmbH & Co. KG, Oststr 11, Cologne, 50996, Germany. TEL 49-221-9370180, FAX 49-221-93701890, kundenservice@deubner-verlag.de, http://www.vrp.de. Ed. Peter Deubner.

327.17 LUX ISSN 1015-8642
EUROPEAN COMMUNITIES. COST. Text in English. 1988. irreg. —BLDSC (3477.229000).
Published by: European Commission, Office for Official Publications of the European Union, 2 Rue Mercier, Luxembourg, L-2985, Luxembourg. TEL 352-49-92-81, FAX 352-48-85-73, http://europa.eu.int.

EUROPEAN JOURNAL OF SOCIAL SECURITY. see *INSURANCE*

336 NLD ISSN 0925-9759
KJC7101.3
EUROPEAN TAX HANDBOOK (YEAR). Text in English. 1990. a. EUR 180 (effective 2005). **Document type:** *Trade.* **Description:** Provides extensive up-to-date summaries of the taxation of corporations and individuals in 35 countries in Western, Central and Eastern Europe, including a chapter on the EC.
—BLDSC (3830.247850).
Published by: (International Bureau of Fiscal Documentation), I B F D Publications BV, H J E Wenckebachweg 210, PO Box 20237, Amsterdam, 1000 HE, Netherlands. TEL 31-20-5540100, FAX 31-20-6228658, 31-20-6228658, info@ibfd.nl, http://www.ibfd.nl. **Subscr. to:** I B F D Publications USA, Inc, PO Box 805, Valatie, NY 12184-0805. TEL 800-908-6330.

336.2 NLD ISSN 0014-3138
KJC7101.3
EUROPEAN TAXATION. Text in English. 1961. m. USD 690 (effective 2002). adv. index. back issues avail.; reprints avail. **Document type:** *Academic/Scholarly.* **Description:** Offers comprehensive analysis of current issues in European tax law, including topical articles, case law, discussions of rulings and decisions.
Related titles: CD-ROM ed.; Online - full text ed.: (from Swets Information Services).
Indexed: ABIn, ATI, CREJ, ELJI, ELLIS, FLP, KES, PAIS, SCIMP. —BLDSC (3830.250000), IE, Infotrieve, ingenta.
Published by: (International Bureau of Fiscal Documentation), I B F D Publications BV, H J E Wenckebachweg 210, PO Box 20237, Amsterdam, 1000 HE, Netherlands. TEL 31-20-554-0100, FAX 31-20-620-8626, info@ibfd.nl, http://www.ibfd.nl. Ed. M R Nettinga Arnheim. **Subscr. to:** I B F D Publications USA, Inc, PO Box 805, Valatie, NY 12184-0805. TEL 518-758-2245, FAX 518-758-2246.
Co-sponsor: Confederation Fiscale Europeenne.

336.2 NLD
EUROPEAN TAXATION DATA BASE ON CD-ROM. Text in English. 4/yr. USD 3,380 (effective 2002). **Document type:** *Trade.* **Description:** Provides a comprehensive description of tax systems of European countries, with original texts (and translations) of laws, and EC draft directives.
Media: CD-ROM.
Published by: (International Bureau of Fiscal Documentation), I B F D Publications BV, H J E Wenckebachweg 210, PO Box 20237, Amsterdam, 1000 HE, Netherlands. TEL 31-20-554-0100, FAX 31-20-620-8626, info@ibfd.nl, http://www.ibfd.nl.

336 BEL
EUROPEAN UPDATE. Text in English. 1991. bi-m. free. adv. **Document type:** *Newsletter.* **Description:** Covers political, legal and business related developments in the EC and Eastern Europe.
Former titles (until June 1992): Touche Ross European Commentary (0254-9166); Fideurope European Commentary
Related titles: CD-ROM ed.: Justis European Commentaries. ISSN 1366-4433. GBP 250 (from Context Ltd.).
Published by: Deloitte Touche Tohmatsu Europe Services, Rue Royale 326, Brussels, 1210, Belgium. TEL 32-2-2195696, FAX 32-2-2231995, 106372.3145@compuserve.com. Ed., Pub., R&P, Adv. contact Graham Branton. Circ: 16,000.

EXCISE AND CUSTOMS REPORTER. see *BUSINESS AND ECONOMICS—International Commerce*

EXCISE TAX QUARTERLY. see *TRANSPORTATION—Trucks And Trucking*

336 USA ISSN 0273-7612
EXECUTIVE COMPENSATION & TAXATION COORDINATOR. Text in English. 1978. 3 base vols. plus m. updates. looseleaf. USD 865 (effective 2005); includes m. Executive Compensation Alert. **Document type:** *Trade.* **Description:** Provides an analysis of tax laws affecting executive compensation, and official source materials.
—CCC.
Published by: R I A (Subsidiary of: Thomson Corporation), 395 Hudson St, New York, NY 10014. TEL 212-367-6300, RIA.CustomerServices@Thomson.com, http://ria.thomson.com/estore/detail.aspx?ID=ECTC&SITE=/pension/products.

336.2 USA
EXEMPT ORGANIZATION MASTER LIST ON CD-ROM. Text in English. q. (a. versions avail.). USD 199 for q.; USD 149 for a.. **Description:** Includes over 1 million official IRS descriptions of organizations that qualify for exempt status. Provides information such as deductibility of contributions, addresses, accounting periods, and principal activities.
Media: CD-ROM.
Published by: Tax Analysts, 6830 N Fairfax Dr, Arlington, VA 22213. TEL 703-553-4400, 800-955-3444, FAX 703-533-4444.

336 USA ISSN 0899-3831
KF6449.A15
THE EXEMPT ORGANIZATION TAX REVIEW. Text in English. 1988. m. USD 649 (effective 1999). back issues avail. **Document type:** *Trade.* **Description:** Provides news and commentary on tax developments affecting nonprofit organizations and includes full-text documents of important court cases and rulings.
Related titles: Online - full text ed.: (from LexisNexis).
—CCC.
Published by: Tax Analysts, 6830 N Fairfax Dr, Arlington, VA 22213. TEL 703-553-4400, 800-955-3444, FAX 703-533-4444. Ed. Carolyn Wright. Pub. Thomas F Field.

332.6 USA
EXEMPT ORGANIZATIONS REPORTS LIBRARY. Text in English. 1971. 3 base vols. plus m. updates. USD 1,055 base vol(s). (effective 2004).
Former titles: Exempt Organizations Reports (0279-2427); (until 1981): Private Foundations Reports (0273-5873)
Related titles: CD-ROM ed.: USD 1,222 (effective 2004); Online - full text ed.
Indexed: ATI.
—CCC.
Published by: C C H Inc., 2700 Lake Cook Rd, Riverwoods, IL 60015. TEL 847-267-7000, 800-449-6439, FAX 800-224-8299, cust_serv@cch.com, http://www.cch.com. Pub. Kevin Robert.

EXEMPTIONS FROM CAPITAL GAINS TAX. see *BUSINESS AND ECONOMICS—Investments*

336 GBR ISSN 1362-0053
EXTEL CAPITAL GAINS TAX SERVICE. Text in English. 1966. base vol. plus m. updates. GBP 425 per vol.; GBP 485 per vol. with updates. **Description:** Details the CGT position on all UK securities quoted on the London and Republic of Ireland Stock Exchanges and authorised unit trusts existing on and after the base date of 31 March 1982.
Formerly (until 1995): Capital Gains Tax Service
Published by: Financial Times Information Ltd., Fitzroy House, 13-17 Epworth St, London, EC2A 4DL, United Kingdom. TEL 44-20-7825-8000, FAX 44-20-7608-2032, justine.dye@ft.com, http://www.ft.com.

EXTEL DIVIDEND & INTEREST RECORD. see *BUSINESS AND ECONOMICS—Banking And Finance*

336 DEU ISSN 0174-3163
F L F. (Finanzierung, Leasing, Factoring) Text in German. 1954. bi-m. adv. bk.rev. back issues avail. **Document type:** *Magazine, Trade.* **Description:** Financing, leasing, factoring.
Formerly (until 1980): Teilzahlungswirtschaft (0492-5661)
Indexed: IBR, IBZ.
Published by: Verlag fuer Absatzwirtschaft GmbH, Ulrich-von-Hassell-Str 64, Bonn, 53123, Germany. TEL 49-228-9191323, FAX 49-228-9191321, info@flf.de. Circ: 2,000.

343.48904 DNK ISSN 0907-7723
F S RS AFGIFTSLOVE; med noter. (Foreningen af Statsautoriserede Revisorer) Text in Danish. 1993. a. price varies. **Document type:** *Trade.*
Published by: (Foreningen af Statsautoriserede Revisorer/Institute of State Authorized Public Accountants in Denmark), Forlaget Thomson S/A, Nytorv 5, Copenhagen K, 1450, Denmark. TEL 45-33-740700, FAX 45-33-121636, thomson@thomson.dk, http://www/thomson.dk. Ed. Jens Drejer.

343.48904 DNK ISSN 0908-4185
F S RS SKATTE- OG AFGIFTSLOVE. SUPPLEMENT. (Foreningen af Statsautoriserede Revisorer) Variant title: Supplement til FSRs Afgiftslove med Noter. Text in Danish. 1991. a.
Formerly (until 1993): F S Rs Skattelove med Noter. Supplement (0906-494X)
Related titles: ♦ Supplement to: F S Rs Skattelove med Noter. ISSN 0905-4367.
Published by: (Foreningen af Statsautoriserede Revisorer/Institute of State Authorized Public Accountants in Denmark), Forlaget Thomson S/A, Nytorv 5, Copenhagen K, 1450, Denmark. TEL 45-33-740700, FAX 45-33-121636, thomson@thomson.dk, http://www/thomson.dk.

343.48904 DNK ISSN 0905-4367
F S RS SKATTELOVE MED NOTER. (Foreningen af Statsautoriserede Revisorer) Text in Danish. 1958. a. DKK 846.25 (effective 1999); price varies. **Document type:** *Trade.*
Formerly (until 1990): Skattelove (0108-6022)
Related titles: ♦ Supplement(s): F S Rs Skatte- og Afgiftslove. Supplement. ISSN 0908-4185.
Published by: (Foreningen af Statsautoriserede Revisorer/Institute of State Authorized Public Accountants in Denmark), Forlaget Thomson S/A, Nytorv 5, Copenhagen K, 1450, Denmark. TEL 45-33-740700, FAX 45-33-121636, thomson@thomson.dk, http://www/thomson.dk.

336 USA ISSN 0071-3678
HJ257
FACTS AND FIGURES ON GOVERNMENT FINANCE. Text in English. 1941. a., latest 36th edition. USD 55, USD 75 per issue (effective 2005). stat. **Document type:** *Academic/Scholarly.* **Description:** Provides statistical documentation of current and historical tax and spending activity at all levels of government.
Related titles: Microfiche ed.: (from CIS).
Indexed: ATI, SRI.
Published by: Tax Foundation, 2001 L St NW, Ste. 1050, Washington, DC 20036-4971. tf@taxfoundation.org, http://www.taxfoundation.org/tfbooks.html. Ed. David Hoffman. R&Ps Alicia Hansen, Bill Ahern.

FARM AND RANCH TAX LETTER. see *AGRICULTURE—Agricultural Economics*

FARM INCOME TAX MANUAL. see *AGRICULTURE—Agricultural Economics*

336 GBR ISSN 0268-9863
KD5494.F37
FARM TAX BRIEF; practical guidance on effective tax planning and the law relating to agricultural land. Text in English. 1986. 10/yr. GBP 204; GBP 229, USD 458 foreign (effective 2000). back issues avail. **Document type:** *Newsletter.* **Description:** Provides expert analysis and comment, practical articles and planning points, comprehensive news coverage and guidance on tax planning and the law relating to agricultural land.
Indexed: ELJI, LJI, RICS.
Published by: (Country Landowners Association), Monitor Press Ltd. (Subsidiary of: T & F Informa plc), Suffolk House, Church Field Rd, Sudbury, Suffolk CO10 2YA, United Kingdom. TEL 44-1787-378607, FAX 44-1787-881147, http://www.monitorpress.co.uk. Ed. Richard Williams. Pub. Zoe Turner. R&P Liz Dittner.

FARM TAX SAVER. see *AGRICULTURE—Agricultural Economics*

FARMERS' TAX GUIDE. see *AGRICULTURE*

336.2 NLD
FED FISCALE BROCHURES. Text in Dutch. 1964. irreg., latest 1996. price varies. back issues avail. **Document type:** *Monographic series.*
Published by: Uitgeverij Fed bv (Subsidiary of: Wolters Kluwer N.V.), Postbus 23, Deventer, 7400 GA, Netherlands. TEL 31-570-633155, FAX 31-570-633834.

▼ new title ➤ refereed ✶ unverified ♦ full entry avail.

336.2 NLD
FED FISCALE STUDIESERIE. Text in Dutch. irreg., latest vol.30, 1996. price varies. back issues avail. **Document type:** *Monographic series.*
Published by: Uitgeverij Fed bv (Subsidiary of: Wolters Kluwer N.V.), Postbus 23, Deventer, 7400 GA, Netherlands. TEL 31-570-633155, FAX 31-570-633834.

FEDERAL ESTATE AND GIFT TAX REPORTS. see *LAW—Estate Planning*

353 145 USA
FEDERAL ESTATE AND GIFT TAXATION (SUPPLEMENT). Text in English. base vol. plus s-a. updates. looseleaf. USD 390 (effective 1999). **Document type:** *Trade.*
Formerly: Stephens, Maxfield and Lind's Federal Estate and Gift Taxation (Supplement)
Published by: W G & L Financial Reporting & Management Research (Subsidiary of: R I A), 90 Fifth Ave, New York, NY 10011. TEL 212-645-4800, FAX 212-337-4280.

336 USA ISSN 0414-0141
FEDERAL EXCISE TAX REPORTS. Variant title: Federal Excise Tax Reporter. Text in English. 1913. base vol. plus m. updates. looseleaf. USD 509 base vol(s). (effective 2004). **Description:** Offers complete, timely coverage of federal excise taxes, with monthly reports to keep you apprised of the latest developments and tax law changes.
Related titles: CD-ROM ed.: USD 454 (effective 2004); Online - full text ed.
Published by: C C H Inc., 2700 Lake Cook Rd, Riverwoods, IL 60015. TEL 847-267-7000, 800-449-6439, FAX 800-224-8299, cust_serv@cch.com, http://www.cch.com. Ed. D Newquist. Pub. Kevin Robert.

FEDERAL GRANT DEADLINE CALENDAR. A SUPPLEMENT TO THE GUIDE TO FEDERAL FUNDING FOR EDUCATION. see *EDUCATION—School Organization And Administration*

336.2 343.05 USA
FEDERAL INCOME, GIFT, AND ESTATE TAXATION. Text in English. 1942. 9 base vols. plus irreg. updates. looseleaf. USD 1,070 base vol(s). (effective 2002). Supplement avail. **Description:** This comprehensive treatise on federal taxation combines the highest level of tax scholarship with a practical approach.
Indexed: ATI.
Published by: Matthew Bender & Co., Inc. (Subsidiary of: LexisNexis North America), 1275 Broadway, Albany, NY 12204. international@bender.com, http://bender.lexisnexis.com. Ed. Jacob Rabkin.

353 USA ISSN 1066-1972
KF6369
FEDERAL INCOME TAX LAW. Text in English. base vol. plus a. updates. looseleaf. USD 104.95 domestic; USD 162.45 foreign (effective 1999). **Document type:** *Trade.*
Former titles: Federal Income Tax Law (Supplement); Stanley and Kilcullen's Federal Income Tax Law (Supplement)
Published by: W G & L Financial Reporting & Management Research (Subsidiary of: R I A), 90 Fifth Ave, New York, NY 10011. TEL 212-645-4800, FAX 212-337-4280.

336 CAN
FEDERAL INCOME TAX LITIGATION IN CANADA. Text in English. 1998. s-a. looseleaf. CND 200 (effective 2001). **Document type:** *Trade.* **Description:** Serves as a guide for non-specialist lawyers and accountants representing clients in disputes with Revenue Canada.
Published by: LexisNexis Butterworths Canada Inc. (Subsidiary of: LexisNexis North America), 123 Commerce Valley Dr E, Ste 700, Markham, ON L3T 7W8, Canada. TEL 905-479-2665, FAX 905-479-2826, http://www.lexisnexis.ca/federalincometaxlitigationincanada.htm. Ed. J S Johnson.

336 USA ISSN 1043-7371
KF6356.99
FEDERAL INCOME TAX REGULATIONS (NEW YORK). Text in English. 1988. s-a. USD 52.
Published by: R I A (Subsidiary of: Thomson Corporation), 395 Hudson St, New York, NY 10014. TEL 212-367-6300, RIA.CustomerServices@Thomson.com, http://ria.thomson.com/.

353 332 USA
FEDERAL INCOME TAXATION OF BANKS AND FINANCIAL INSTITUTIONS (SUPPLEMENT). Text in English. base vol. plus q. updates. USD 575 (effective 1998). **Document type:** *Trade.*
Published by: W G & L Financial Reporting & Management Research (Subsidiary of: R I A), 90 Fifth Ave, New York, NY 10011. TEL 212-645-4800, FAX 212-337-4280.

336.2 USA
FEDERAL INCOME TAXATION OF INVENTORIES. Text in English. 1979. 3 base vols. plus s-a. updates. looseleaf. USD 760 base vol(s). (effective 2002). **Description:** This definitive work analyzes every aspect of inventory taxation, including valuation of goods, UNICAP rules, LIFO inventories, what must be included in inventory for tax purposes, and more.
Related titles: CD-ROM ed.: USD 781 (effective 2002).
Published by: Matthew Bender & Co., Inc. (Subsidiary of: LexisNexis North America), 1275 Broadway, Albany, NY 12204. international@bender.com, http://bender.lexisnexis.com. Ed. Leslie Schneider.

368.32 USA
FEDERAL INCOME TAXATION OF LIFE INSURANCE COMPANIES. Text in English. 1988. irreg. (in 2 vols.). looseleaf. USD 674 (effective 2002). **Description:** provides comprehensive analysis of the special tax provisions that apply to life insurance companies.
Related titles: CD-ROM ed.
Published by: Matthew Bender & Co., Inc. (Subsidiary of: LexisNexis North America), 1275 Broadway, Albany, NY 12204. international@bender.com, http://bender.lexisnexis.com.

FEDERAL INCOME TAXATION OF REAL ESTATE. see *REAL ESTATE*

FEDERAL SOCIAL SECURITY LAWS. see *INSURANCE*

336 USA ISSN 0162-1092
FEDERAL TAX ARTICLES. Text in English. 1962. base vol. plus m. updates. USD 676 base vol(s). (effective 2004). **Description:** Summaries of law review and professional journal articles covering federal tax issues.
—CCC.
Published by: C C H Inc., 2700 Lake Cook Rd, Riverwoods, IL 60015. TEL 847-267-7000, 800-449-6439, FAX 800-224-8299, cust_serv@cch.com, http://www.cch.com. Pub. Kevin Robert.

336 346.066 USA
FEDERAL TAX COLLECTIONS, LIENS AND LEVIES. Text in English. 1988. base vol. plus s-a. updates. USD 285 base vol(s). (effective 2005). **Document type:** *Trade.*
Related titles: Online - full text ed.: USD 425 (effective 2005).
Indexed: ATI.
Published by: R I A (Subsidiary of: Thomson Corporation), 395 Hudson St, New York, NY 10014. RIAhome@riag.com, http://www.riahome.com/estore/detail.asp?ID=FCL. Ed. Willam Elliott.

336.2 USA ISSN 0738-8632
FEDERAL TAX COORDINATOR 2D. Text in English. 1970. 35 base vols. plus w. updates. looseleaf. USD 2,610 (effective 2005). **Document type:** *Trade.* **Description:** Provides analysis of federal tax law, including commentary and practical guidance, and official source materials.
Former titles: Federal Tax Coordinator; Tax Coordinator (0039-999X)
Related titles: CD-ROM ed.; Online - full text ed.; ◆ Supplement(s): R I A Tax Guide Developments; ◆ Federal Tax Coordinator 2d. Weekly Alert. ISSN 0163-996X.
Indexed: ATI.
—CCC.
Published by: R I A (Subsidiary of: Thomson Corporation), 395 Hudson St, New York, NY 10014. TEL 212-367-6300, RIA.CustomerServices@Thomson.com, http://ria.thomson.com/EStore/detail.aspx?ID=WEB1.

343 USA ISSN 1090-4875
KF6289
(YEAR) FEDERAL TAX COURSE. Text in English. 1957. a. USD 180 (effective 2002). **Document type:** *Trade.* **Description:** Offers the knowledge and know-how to deal effectively with all current developments and changes in the federal tax structure.
Published by: Aspen Law & Business (Subsidiary of: Wolters Kluwer N.V.), 1185 Ave of the Americas, 37th Fl, New York, NY 10036. TEL 212-597-0210, 800-638-8437, FAX 212-597-0336, customer.service@aspenpubl.com, http://www.aspenpub.com. **Dist. by:** Aspen Publishers, Inc., Distribution Center, 7201 McKinney Circle, Frederick, MD 21701. TEL 301-698-7100, FAX 301-417-7550.

336.2 USA ISSN 1520-5800
FEDERAL TAX COURSE LETTER. Text in English. 1995. m. USD 186 (effective 2004). **Document type:** *Newsletter.* **Description:** Provides reports on the changes in tax laws and what to do about them before they take effect.
Published by: Aspen Publishers, Inc. (Subsidiary of: Wolters Kluwer N.V.), 111Eighth Ave., 7th Fl, New York, NY 10011. TEL 212-771-0600, FAX 212-771-0885, customer.service@aspenpubl.com, http://www.aspenpub.com. Ed. Susan Flax Posner.

336 USA ISSN 0274-6298
KF6286
FEDERAL TAX FORMS. Text in English. 1973. 3 base vols. plus irreg. updates. USD 479 base vol(s). (effective 2004). **Description:** Compilation of income, estate, gift, excise and employment tax forms, supplementary schedules and official Internal Revenue Service instructions.
Published by: C C H Inc., 2700 Lake Cook Rd, Riverwoods, IL 60015. TEL 847-267-7000, 800-449-6439, FAX 800-224-8299, cust_serv@cch.com, http://www.cch.com. Pub. Kevin Robert.

336 USA
FEDERAL TAX GUIDE. Text in English. 1958. 9 base vols. plus bi-m. updates. looseleaf. USD 1,044 base vol(s). (effective 2004). **Description:** Concise source that explains federal income, estate and gift, payroll and selected excise taxes, and points out tax savings and tax planning opportunities.
Formerly: Federal Tax Guide Reports (0162-1661)
Related titles: CD-ROM ed.: USD 953 (effective 2004).
Indexed: ATI.
—CCC.
Published by: C C H Inc., 2700 Lake Cook Rd, Riverwoods, IL 60015. TEL 847-267-7000, 800-449-6439, FAX 800-224-8299, cust_serv@cch.com, http://www.cch.com. Pub. Kevin Robert.

336.2 USA
FEDERAL TAX GUIDEBOOK. Text in English. 1972. 2 base vols. plus s-a. updates. looseleaf. USD 261 base vol(s). (effective 2003). Supplement avail. **Description:** A concise, practice-oriented guidebook on federal taxation for the practitioner.
Published by: Matthew Bender & Co., Inc. (Subsidiary of: LexisNexis North America), 1275 Broadway, Albany, NY 12204. international@bender.com, http://bookstore.lexis.com/bookstore/catalog?action=product&prod_id=10467&cat_id=J&pcat_id=65&pub_id=1, http://bender.lexisnexis.com. Ed. Alan Prigal.

350 347 USA
FEDERAL TAX LITIGATION (SUPPLEMENT). Text in English. base vol. plus a. updates. USD 235 (effective 1999). **Document type:** *Trade.*
Former titles: Federal Tax Litigation; Tax Court Practice (Supplement)
Published by: W G & L Financial Reporting & Management Research (Subsidiary of: R I A), 90 Fifth Ave, New York, NY 10011. TEL 212-645-4800, FAX 212-337-4280.

336.2 USA ISSN 0888-0522
KF6365
FEDERAL TAX MANUAL. Text in English. 1960. m. looseleaf. USD 374 1-4 (effective 2004).
Former titles: Federal Tax Compliance Reports; (until 1986): Federal Tax Compliance Manual (0748-1462); Federal Tax Return Manual (0071-4143)
Published by: C C H Inc., 2700 Lake Cook Rd, Riverwoods, IL 60015. TEL 847-267-7000, 800-449-6439, FAX 800-224-8299, cust_serv@cch.com, http://www.cch.com. Pub. Kevin Robert.

FEDERAL TAX VALUATION DIGEST. see *LAW—Estate Planning*

336 USA
KF6272.I44
FEDERAL TAXATION. Text in English. 1954. q. looseleaf. USD 68; USD 38 to non-profit organizations (effective 2006). **Document type:** *Newsletter, Trade.*
Published by: (Section of Federal Taxation), Illinois State Bar Association, Illinois Bar Center, 424 S Second St, Springfield, IL 62701. TEL 217-525-1760, 800-252-8908, sanderson@isba.org, http://www.isba.org. Ed. Michael L English. Circ: 1,200.

336 USA
FEDERAL TAXATION OF BANKRUPTCY WORKOUTS. Text in English. base vol. plus a. updates. looseleaf. USD 195 (effective 1998). Supplement avail. **Document type:** *Trade.* **Description:** Provides comprehensive coverage of bankruptcy and tax issues.
Indexed: ATI.
Published by: W G & L Financial Reporting & Management Research (Subsidiary of: R I A), 90 Fifth Ave, New York, NY 10011. TEL 212-645-4800, FAX 212-337-4280. Ed. Chris Trower.

FEDERAL TAXATION OF OIL AND GAS TRANSACTIONS. see *PETROLEUM AND GAS*

FEDERAL TAXES AFFECTING REAL ESTATE. see *REAL ESTATE*

336 343.73 USA ISSN 1083-5652
KF6272
FEDERAL TAXES WEEKLY ALERT. Text in English. 1995. w. USD 255 (effective 2005). **Document type:** *Newsletter, Trade.* **Description:** Features fast-breaking developments in Congress, the courts, the Treasury, the IRS, and other federal agencies.
Formed by the merger of (197?-1995): Federal Tax Coordinator 2d. Weekly Alert (0163-996X); (19??-1995): Tax Guide: Weekly Alert (0195-6531)
Related titles: Online - full content ed.: USD 305 (effective 2005).
—CCC.
Published by: R I A (Subsidiary of: Thomson Corporation), 395 Hudson St, New York, NY 10014. TEL 212-367-6300, RIA.CustomerServices@Thomson.com, http://ria.thomson.com/EStore/detail.aspx?ID=WWA.

336 FRA ISSN 0150-5467
FEUILLET RAPIDE FISCAL SOCIAL. Text in French. 1978 (vol.33). bi-w. EUR 204 combined subscription print & online eds. (effective 2005). **Document type:** *Magazine, Trade.*
Related titles: Online - full text ed.

Published by: Editions Francis Lefebvre, 42 rue de Villiers, Levallois-Perret, 92300, France. TEL 33-1-41052222, http://www.efl.fr.

336.2 SWE ISSN 1402-5965
FICKDATA. Text in Swedish. 1981-2000; resumed 2003. a.
Document type: *Government.*
Formerly (until 1996): Skattefoervaltningen. Riksskatteverket. Fickdata (0284-5024)
Published by: Skatteverket/Swedish National Tax Board (Subsidiary of: Skattefoervaltningen), Solna Strandvaeg 6, Solna, 17194, Sweden. TEL 46-771-778778, huvudkontoret@skatteverket.se, http://www.skatteverket.se/broschyrer/611/index.html. **Dist. by:** Fritzes Kundtjaenst, c/o Norstedts Juridik AB, Stockholm 10647, Sweden. TEL 46-8-6909190, FAX 46-8-6909191, order.fritzes@nj.se, http://www.fritzes.se, http://www.fritzes.se.

336 336.73 USA
FIDUCIARY TAX GUIDE. Text in English. 1990. base vol. plus m. updates. looseleaf. USD 551 base vol(s). (effective 2004).
Description: Offers expert analysis of fiduciary tax issues that can help estate and trust administrators avoid turning personal responsibility into personal liability.
Published by: C C H Inc., 2700 Lake Cook Rd, Riverwoods, IL 60015. TEL 847-267-7000, 800-449-6439, FAX 800-224-8299, cust_serv@cch.com, http://www.cch.com. Pub. Kevin Robert.

336.2 USA ISSN 0736-0975
FIDUCIARY TAX RETURN GUIDE. Text in English. 1977. a.
Published by: R I A (Subsidiary of: Thomson Corporation), 395 Hudson St, New York, NY 10014. TEL 212-367-6300, http://ria.thomson.com/.

FIJI. BUREAU OF STATISTICS. ECONOMIC AND FUNCTIONAL CLASSIFICATION OF GOVERNMENT ACCOUNTS. see *BUSINESS AND ECONOMICS—Abstracting, Bibliographies, Statistics*

336 GBR ISSN 0267-4424
FINANCIAL ACCOUNTABILITY & MANAGEMENT. Text in English. 1985. q. GBP 75, EUR 113 combined subscription in Europe to individuals print & online eds.; USD 148 combined subscription in the Americas to individuals & Caribbean (print & online eds.); GBP 88 combined subscription elsewhere to individuals print & online eds.; GBP 311 combined subscription in Europe to institutions print & online eds.; USD 660 combined subscription in the Americas to institutions & Caribbean (print & online eds.); GBP 393 combined subscription elsewhere to institutions print & online eds. (effective 2006). adv. reprint service avail. from PSC,PQC.
Document type: *Journal, Trade.*
Related titles: Microform ed.; Online - full text ed.: ISSN 1468-0408. GBP 295 in Europe to institutions; USD 627 in the Americas to institutions & Caribbean; GBP 373 elsewhere to institutions (effective 2006) (from Blackwell Synergy, EBSCO Publishing, Gale Group, IngentaConnect, O C L C Online Computer Library Center, Inc., Swets Information Services).
Indexed: ABIn, ATI, BPI, CPM, ESPM, Emerald, PAIS, PSI, RefZh, RiskAb, SCIMP.
—BLDSC (3926.932000), IE, Infotrieve, ingenta. **CCC.**
Published by: Blackwell Publishing Ltd., 9600 Garsington Rd, Oxford, OX4 2ZG, United Kingdom. TEL 44-1865-776868, FAX 44-1865-714591, customerservices@oxon.blackwellpublishing.com, http://www.blackwellpublishing.com/journals/FAM. Ed. Irvine Lapsley.

FINANCIAL AND MONETARY POLICY STUDIES. see *BUSINESS AND ECONOMICS—Banking And Finance*

FINANCIAL FOCUS; wealth producer and protector. see *BUSINESS AND ECONOMICS—Investments*

FINANCIAL INSTITUTIONS RETIREMENT FUND. ANNUAL REPORT. see *BUSINESS AND ECONOMICS—Personnel Management*

336 332 USA
FINANCIAL SERVICES DOCUMENT WATCH - PUBLIC FINANCE EDITION. (Consists of 4 eds.: Banking; Insurance; Public Finance; Thrift) Text in English. irreg. **Document type:** *Newsletter.* **Description:** Real-time delivery of key documents in the public finance sector.
Supersedes in part: Insurance Document Watch
Published by: American Banker Newsletters, Thomson Financial Services Company, One State St Plaza, 26th Fl, New York, NY 10004. TEL 800-407-8241, FAX 212-747-1098, glicke@tfn.com. Pub. David Schutt.

336.2 GBR ISSN 0141-0741
FINANCIAL TIMES WORLD TAX REPORT. Variant title: World Tax Report. Text in English. 1972. m. GBP 405; GBP 435 foreign. bk.rev. stat. index. back issues avail. **Document type:** *Newsletter.* **Description:** Provides a survey of world developments in taxation divided by country. Contains news and commentary about international tax issues, including tax reform, proposals, double-taxation treaties, compliance, tax havens, and government budgets worldwide.
Formerly (until 1977): Financial Times Tax Newsletter (0306-3089)
Related titles: Microfiche ed.; Online - full text ed.: (from ProQuest Information & Learning, The Dialog Corporation).
Indexed: ATI.
Published by: Financial Times Professional Publishing (Subsidiary of: Financial Times Group), Maple House, 149 Tottenham Court Rd, London, W1P 9LL, United Kingdom. TEL 44-20-7896-2222, FAX 44-20-7896-2276. Ed. Jonathan Schwarz. Pub. John McLachlan.

657 336.2 RUS ISSN 1727-8023
FINANSOVAYA GAZETA. EKSPO. Text in Russian. 1998. m.
Document type: *Newspaper, Trade.*
Published by: Redaktsiya Mezhdunarodnogo Ezhenedel'nika Finansovaya Gazeta, A-ya 598, Glavpochtamt, Moscow, 101000, Russian Federation. fingazeta@fingazeta.ru, http://www.fingazeta.ru/stranic/buklet/ex.htm.

FINANSOVYE I BUKHGALTERSKIE KONSUL'TATSII. see *BUSINESS AND ECONOMICS—Banking And Finance*

336 SWE ISSN 1650-0504
FINANSPLAN OCH SAMMANDRAG. Cover title: Sweden. Finansdepartementet Presenterar Regeringens Budgetfoerslag: Finansplan, Sammandrag. Text in Swedish. 1963. a. **Document type:** *Government.*
Former titles (until 1999): Sweden. Finansdepartementet. Regeringens Budgetfoerslag (0347-7169); (until 1971): Sweden. Finansdepartementet. Sammandrag av Statsverkspropositionen (0586-1446)
Published by: Finansdepartementet/Ministry of Finance, Drottninggatan 21, Stockholm, 10333, Sweden. TEL 46-8-4051000, FAX 46-8-217386, info@finance.ministry.se, http://www.regeringen.se/sb/d/1468. **Subscr. to:** Fritzes Offentliga Publikationer, c/o Norstedts Juridik AB, Stockholm 10647, Sweden. TEL 46-8-6909190, FAX 46-8-6909191, fritzes@nj.se, http://www.fritzes.se.

336 DNK ISSN 0106-2905
HJ56
FINANSREDEGOERELSE. Text in Danish. 1966. a. **Document type:** *Government.*
Former titles (until 1978): Budgetredegoerelse (0105-9890); (until 1973): Budgetoverslag (0418-6478); Incorporates (1979-1982): Budgetoversigt. Statens og Kommunernes Budgetter (0106-2409)
Related titles: Online - full text ed.
Published by: Finansministeriet/Ministry of Finance, Christiansborg Slotsplads, Copenhagen K, 1218, Denmark. TEL 45-33-923333, fm@fm.dk, http://www.fm.dk/1024/visPublikationesForside.asp?artikelID=6668. **Dist. by:** Schultz Information A-S.

336.2 DEU ISSN 1438-3292
KK7163.A13
FINANZ-RUNDSCHAU ERTRAGSTEUERRECHT. Text in German. 19??. s-m. EUR 249; EUR 12.45 newsstand/cover (effective 2005). adv. bk.rev. bibl. index. reprints avail.
Document type: *Journal, Trade.*
Formed by the merger of (1946-19??): Finanz-Rundschau fuer Einkommensteuer. Ausgabe A (0940-452X); Which was formerly (until 1991): Finanz-Rundschau fuer Einkommensteuer und Koerperschaftsteuer. Ausgabe A (0176-7771); (until 1984): Finanz-Rundschau. Ausgabe A (0340-9007); (1946-19??): Finanz-Rundschau fuer Einkommensteuer. Ausgabe B (0940-4538); Which was formerly (until 1991): Finanz-Rundschau fuer Einkommensteuer und Koerperschaftsteuer. Ausgabe B (0176-778X); (until 1984): Finanz-Rundschau. Ausgabe B (0340-9015); Both of which superseded in part (in 1953): Finanz-Rundschau (0015-2196)
Indexed: IBZ.
—IE. **CCC.**
Published by: Verlag Dr. Otto Schmidt KG, Gustav-Heinemann-Ufer 58, Cologne, 50968, Germany. TEL 49-221-93738460, FAX 49-221-93738943, info@otto-schmidt.de, http://www.finanzrundschau.de, http://www.otto-schmidt.de. Ed. Wolfgang Lingemann. adv.: B&W page EUR 1,125, color page EUR 1,969. Circ: 3,070 (paid and controlled).

352.14 ITA ISSN 0394-8307
LA FINANZA LOCALE; rivista mensile di contabilita e tributi degli enti locali e delle regioni. Text in Italian. 1981. m. (11/yr.). EUR 100 to individuals; EUR 168 to institutions (effective 2005). **Document type:** *Magazine, Trade.* **Description:** Dedicated to the research and discussion of themes regarding finance of companies and public bodies at the municipal, regional and provincial levels.
Related titles: ♦ Supplement(s): Dipartimento Funzione Pubblica On Line.
Published by: Maggioli Editore, Via del Carpino 8/10, Santarcangelo di Romagna, RN 47822, Italy. TEL 39-0541-628111, FAX 39-0541-622020, editore@maggioli.it, http://www.maggioli.it. Eds. Franceso Tesauro, Mario Trimeloni.

332 DEU ISSN 0015-2218
HJ105
FINANZARCHIV. Text in German. 1884. q. EUR 149 to individuals; EUR 2,740 to institutions (effective 2005). adv. bk.rev. index. reprints avail. **Document type:** *Journal, Academic/Scholarly.* **Description:** Covers all aspects of public finance.
Related titles: Online - full text ed.: (from Gale Group, IngentaConnect).
Indexed: ELLIS, IBR, IBSS, IBZ, JEL, KES, PAIS, PCI, RASB.
—IE, Infotrieve. **CCC.**
Published by: Mohr Siebeck, Wilhelmstr 18, Tuebingen, 72074, Germany. TEL 49-7071-9230, FAX 49-7071-51104, info@mohr.de, http://www.mohr.de/fa.html. Eds. Bernd Genser, Harry Huizinga, Wolfgang Richter. R&P Jill Sopper. Adv. contact Tilman Gaebler.

FINANZAS PUBLICAS ESTATALES Y MUNICIPALES DE MEXICO. see *BUSINESS AND ECONOMICS—Abstracting, Bibliographies, Statistics*

336 ITA ISSN 0015-2242
IL FINANZIERE. Text in Italian. 1886. m. free to members. adv. bk.rev. bibl.; illus.; stat. index. **Document type:** *Magazine, Trade.*
Published by: Comando Generale della Guardia di Finanza, Ufficio Stampa, Viale XX1 Aprile 55, Rome, RM 00162, Italy. TEL 39-06-44221, http://www.gdf.it. Ed. Luciano Carta. Circ: 70,000.

336.2 340 AUT ISSN 0015-2277
FINANZRECHTLICHE ERKENNTNISSE DES VERWALTUNGSGERICHTSHOFES; Beilage zur Oesterreichischen Steuer-Zeitung. Text in German. 1948. s-m. ATS 3,060 (effective 2001). 24 p./no.; **Document type:** *Bulletin, Trade.*
Published by: LexisNexis Verlag ARD Orac GmbH & Co. KG (Subsidiary of: LexisNexis Europe and Africa), Marxergasse 25, Vienna, W 1030, Austria. TEL 43-1-53452-0, FAX 43-1-53452141, verlag@orac.at, http://www.lexisnexis.at/. Circ: 5,200.

336 FIN ISSN 0533-1099
HC340.2.A1
FINLAND. KANSANTALOUSOSASTO. KANSANTALOUDEN KEHITYSARVIO. SUMMARY: NATIONAL BUDGET FOR FINLAND. Text in Finnish; Summaries in English. 1966. a.
Published by: (Finland. Valtiovarainministerio, Kansantalousosasto/Ministry of Finance. Economics Department), Valtion Painatuskeskus/Government Printing Centre, Annankatu 44, Helsinki, 00100, Finland.

343.05 336.2 BEL ISSN 0775-0781
FISCAAL JAARBOEK. Text in Dutch. 1986. a. EUR 136.65 (effective 2003). **Document type:** *Trade.* **Description:** Reviews developments in taxation and revenue law during the preceding year.
Published by: Kluwer Uitgevers (Subsidiary of: Wolters Kluwer Belgique), Ragheno Business Park, Motstraat 30, Mechelen, B-2800, Belgium. TEL 32-15-800-94571, info@kluwer.be, http://www.kluwer.be.

336.2 340 NLD ISSN 0927-5746
FISCAAL ONDERNEMINGSRECHT. Variant title: Tijdschrift Fiscaal Ondernemingsrecht. Text in Dutch. 1992. bi-m. adv.
Document type: *Academic/Scholarly.*
—IE, Infotrieve.
Published by: Kluwer B.V. (Subsidiary of: Wolters Kluwer N.V.), Postbus 23, Deventer, 7400 GA, Netherlands. TEL 31-570-673449, FAX 31-570-691555, juridisch@kluwer.nl, http://www.kluwer.nl. Circ: 800 (paid).

343.05 BEL
FISCAAL PRAKTIJKBOEK DIRECTE BELASTINGEN. Text in Dutch. a. EUR 126.81 (effective 2003). back issues avail.
Document type: *Trade.*
Published by: Kluwer Uitgevers (Subsidiary of: Wolters Kluwer Belgique), Ragheno Business Park, Motstraat 30, Mechelen, B-2800, Belgium. TEL 32-15-800-94571, info@kluwer.be, http://www.kluwer.be. Ed. Willy Maeckelbergh.

336.2 NLD ISSN 0165-0335
FISCAAL WEEKBLAD FED. Text in Dutch. 1940. w. looseleaf. back issues avail. **Document type:** *Trade.*
Formerly (until 1985): Losbladig Fiscaal Weekblad Fed (1382-4902)
Published by: Uitgeverij Fed bv (Subsidiary of: Wolters Kluwer N.V.), Postbus 23, Deventer, 7400 GA, Netherlands. TEL 31-570-633155, FAX 31-570-633834.

336 CAN ISSN 0839-8224
THE FISCAL MONITOR. Text in English. 1986. m.
Published by: Canada. Department of Finance, Distribution Centre, West Tower, Rm P-135, 300 Laurier Ave W, Ottawa, ON K1A 0G5, Canada. TEL 613-995-2855, FAX 613-996-0518, services-distribution@fin.gc.ca, http://www.fin.gc.ca/serialse/2004/fiscmon-e.html.

336 USA ISSN 0143-5671
HG11
➤ **FISCAL STUDIES.** Text in English. 1979. q. USD 367 combined subscription in the Americas to institutions & Caribbean (print & online eds.); GBP 219 combined subscription elsewhere to institutions print & online eds. (effective 2005). adv. abstr. back issues avail.; reprint service avail. from PSC. **Document type:** *Journal, Academic/Scholarly.* **Description:** Covers articles concerned with the whole range of ways in which government action affects individuals and the private sector of the economy.

▼ *new title* ➤ *refereed* ✶ *unverified* ♦ *full entry avail.*

Related titles: Microfilm ed.: (from PQC); Online - full text ed.: ISSN 1475-5890. 1999. USD 317 in the Americas to institutions & Caribbean (effective 2005); GBP 204 elsewhere to institutions (effective 2006) (from Blackwell Synergy, EBSCO Publishing, Gale Group, IngentaConnect, Northern Light Technology, Inc., O C L C Online Computer Library Center, Inc., ProQuest Information & Learning, Swets Information Services).
Indexed: ABIn, ATI, CPM, CREJ, CurCont, IBSS, JEL, RRTA, SSCI, WAE&RSA, WBA.
—BLDSC (3934.479000), IE, Infotrieve, ingenta. **CCC.**
Published by: (Institute for Fiscal Studies GBR), Blackwell Publishing, Inc. (Subsidiary of: Blackwell Publishing Ltd.), Commerce Place, 350 Main St, Malden, MA 02148. TEL 781-388-8206, FAX 781-388-8232, http://www.blackwellpublishing.com/fisc. R&P, Adv. contact Emma Hyman TEL 44-20-7291-4850. Circ: 1,350 (paid).

343.05 336.2 BEL ISSN 0772-733X
FISCALE JURISPRUDENTIE/JURISPRUDENCE FISCALE. Text in Dutch, French. 1982. 10/yr. EUR 356.17 (effective 2003). back issues avail. **Document type:** *Trade.* **Description:** Covers Belgian, European and international taxation law, local and regional tax issues, and relevant judicial decisions.
Published by: Kluwer Uitgevers (Subsidiary of: Wolters Kluwer Belgique), Ragheno Business Park, Motstraat 30, Mechelen, B-2800, Belgium. TEL 32-15-800-94571, info@kluwer.be, http://www.kluwer.be.

343.05 336.2 BEL ISSN 0774-658X
DE FISCALE KOERIER. Text in Dutch. 1986. fortn. EUR 289.50 (effective 2003). **Document type:** *Newsletter.* **Description:** Covers the latest developments in taxation law.
Related titles: French ed.: Courrier Fiscal. ISSN 0774-9775.
Published by: Kluwer Uitgevers (Subsidiary of: Wolters Kluwer Belgique), Ragheno Business Park, Motstraat 30, Mechelen, B-2800, Belgium. TEL 32-15-800-94571, info@kluwer.be, http://www.kluwer.be. Ed. Stefan Sablon.

336 NLD ISSN 1382-3507
FISCALE PRAKTIJKVRAGEN. Text in Dutch. 1946. 10/yr. adv. **Document type:** *Trade.* **Description:** Contains questions and answers for the tax law practice.
Formerly (until 1995): Fiscale en Administratieve Praktijkvragen (0165-2966)
Indexed: KES.
Published by: Kluwer B.V. (Subsidiary of: Wolters Kluwer N.V.), Postbus 23, Deventer, 7400 GA, Netherlands. TEL 31-570-673449, FAX 31-570-691555, juridisch@kluwer.nl, http://www.kluwer.nl. Ed. E P J Wasch.

332 FRA ISSN 0242-5599
K21
FISCALITE EUROPEENNE. (Editions avail. for 9 regions: Allemagne, Belgique, Espagne, France, Grande-Bretagne, Italie, Luxembourg, Monaco, Pays-Bas) Text in French. 1968. q. looseleaf. price varies.
Indexed: PAIS.
—IE, Infotrieve.
Published by: Cahiers Fiscaux Europeens, 51 av. Reine Victoria, Nice, 06000, France. TEL 93-81-03-26, FAX 93-53-66-28, TELEX 461682 FONTANE. Ed. Pierre Fontaneau.

336 FRA
FISCALITE EUROPEENNE: DROIT INTERNATIONAL DES AFFAIRES. Text in French. 1970. q. looseleaf.
Formerly: Fiscalite Europeenne Revue
Indexed: ELLIS.
Published by: Cahiers Fiscaux Europeens, 51 av. Reine Victoria, Nice, 06000, France. TEL 93-81-03-26, FAX 93-53-66-28, TELEX 461682. Ed. Pierre Fontaneau.

336 ITA ISSN 1124-9307
IL FISCO. Variant title: Rivista il Fisco. Text in Italian. 1977. w. EUR 374 combined subscription (effective 2006). bk.rev. abstr.; bibl. index. **Document type:** *Magazine, Trade.* **Description:** Offers laws, rules and regulations involved with the Ministry of Finance.
Related titles: Online - full text ed.
Published by: E T I - Wolters Kluwer Italia Professionale SpA (Subsidiary of: Wolters Kluwer Italia Srl), Viale Maresciallo Pilsudski 124, Rome, 00197, Italy. TEL 39-06-3217774, FAX 39-06-3217808, http://www.ilfisco.it. Circ: 49,615.

343.05 BEL ISSN 0774-3289
FISCOLEX B T W. Text in Dutch. 1985. a. EUR 189.67 (effective 2003). **Document type:** *Trade.*
Related titles: French ed.: Fiscolex C I R.
Published by: Kluwer Uitgevers (Subsidiary of: Wolters Kluwer Belgique), Ragheno Business Park, Motstraat 30, Mechelen, B-2800, Belgium. TEL 32-15-800-94571, info@kluwer.be, http://www.kluwer.be. Ed. Stefan Sablon.

343.05 BEL ISSN 1378-6814
FISCOLEX REGIONALE BELASTINGEN/FISCOLEX IMPOTS REGIONIAUX ET PROVINCIAUX. Text in Dutch, French. 1993. a. EUR 162 (effective 2003). back issues avail. **Document type:** *Trade.*
Formerly (until 2001): Fiscolex Regionale en Provinciale Belastingen (1370-1045)

Published by: Kluwer Uitgevers (Subsidiary of: Wolters Kluwer Belgique), Ragheno Business Park, Motstraat 30, Mechelen, B-2800, Belgium. TEL 32-15-800-94571, info@kluwer.be, http://www.kluwer.be. Ed. Paul Van Orshoven.

336 BEL ISSN 0772-4845
LE FISCOLOGUE. Text in French. 1980. 45/yr. EUR 321 (effective 2005). index. back issues avail. **Document type:** *Newsletter.*
Related titles: Microfiche ed.; Dutch ed.: Fiskoloog. ISSN 0772-4837.
Published by: Biblo N.V., Brasschaatsteenweg 308, Kalmthout, 2920, Belgium. TEL 32-3-620-0280, FAX 32-3-620-0363, http://www.fiscologue.be/fiscoloog/default.asp. Ed. Jan Van Dyck.

336 BEL ISSN 0772-1463
LE FISCOLOGUE INTERNATIONAL. Text in French. 1983. m. EUR 246.80 domestic (effective 2005). index. back issues avail. **Document type:** *Newsletter.*
Related titles: Microfiche ed.; Dutch ed.: Fiskoloog Internationaal. ISSN 0771-7520; English ed.: Fiskoloog (English edition). ISSN 0772-1447.
Published by: Biblo N.V., Brasschaatsteenweg 308, Kalmthout, 2920, Belgium. TEL 32-3-620-0280, FAX 32-3-620-0363, fiscologue@biblo.be, http://www.fiscologue.be/fiscoloogint/content.asp. Ed. Jan Van Dyck.

363.3 CAN ISSN 0700-1576
FISHERIES IMPROVEMENT LOANS ACT. ANNUAL REPORT. Variant title: Loi sur les Prets Aidant aux Operations de Peche. Rapport Annuel. Text in English, French. 1968. a.
Related titles: Online - full text ed.: ISSN 1700-7496.
Indexed: ESPM.
Published by: Department of Fisheries and Oceans, Communications Directorate, 200 Kent St, 13th Fl, Sta 13228, Ottawa, ON K1A 0E6, Canada. TEL 613-993-0999, FAX 613-990-1866, info@dfo-mpo.gc.ca, http://www.ncr.dfo.ca.

336 USA
FLORIDA BAR. TAX SECTION BULLETIN. Text in English. irreg. (2-4/yr.). membership. **Document type:** *Newsletter.*
Published by: The Florida Bar, 651 E Jefferson St, Tallahassee, FL 32399-2300. TEL 850-561-5630. Circ: 1,900.

THE FLORIDA TAX REVIEW. see *LAW*

336.2 USA
FOREIGN TAX AND TRADE BRIEFS. Text in English. 1951. 2 base vols. plus m. updates. looseleaf. USD 503 base vol(s). (effective 2002). **Description:** Handle critical international business ventures with the one information service that gives the latest foreign tax, trade policy, and currency rates on a regular monthly basis. It includes the latest tax and trade information for over 110 foreign countries.
Published by: Matthew Bender & Co., Inc. (Subsidiary of: LexisNexis North America), 1275 Broadway, Albany, NY 12204. international@bender.com, http://bender.lexisnexis.com. Ed. Walter Diamond.

FOREIGN TAX LAW BI-WEEKLY BULLETIN. see *LAW*

336 DEU ISSN 0933-8497
FORMELN FUER DIE STEUER- UND WIRTSCHAFTSPRAXIS. Text in German. 1973. irreg. looseleaf. price varies. **Document type:** *Monographic series, Trade.*
Published by: Erich Schmidt Verlag GmbH & Co. (Berlin), Genthiner Str 30G, Berlin, 10785, Germany. TEL 49-30-250085-0, FAX 49-30-25008521, vertrieb@esvmedien.de, http://www.erich-schmidt-verlag.de.

336 DEU ISSN 0933-8276
FORMULARBUCH DER STEUER- UND WIRTSCHAFTSPRAXIS. Text in German. 1961. irreg. price varies. **Document type:** *Monographic series, Trade.*
Published by: Erich Schmidt Verlag GmbH & Co. (Berlin), Genthiner Str 30G, Berlin, 10785, Germany. TEL 49-30-250085-0, FAX 49-30-25008511, esv@esvmedien.de, http://www.erich-schmidt-verlag.de.

657.6 DEU ISSN 0720-6909
FORSCHUNGSERGEBNISSE AUS DEM REVISIONSWESEN UND DER BETRIEBSWIRTSCHAFTLICHEN STEUERLEHRE. Text in German. 1974. irreg., latest vol.18, 2003. price varies. **Document type:** *Monographic series, Academic/Scholarly.*
Published by: Duncker und Humblot GmbH, Carl-Heinrich-Becker-Weg 9, Berlin, 12165, Germany. TEL 49-30-7900060, FAX 49-30-79000631, info@duncker-humblot.de, http://www.duncker-humblot.de.

336.2 FRA ISSN 0997-4768
FRANCE. CONSEIL DES IMPOTS. RAPPORT AU PRESIDENT DE LA REPUBLIQUE. Text in French. 1972. irreg. price varies. **Document type:** *Proceedings, Government.*
Related titles: Microfiche ed.
Published by: (France. Conseil des Impots), Direction des Journaux Officiels, 26 rue Desaix, Paris, 75727 Cedex 15, France. TEL 33-1-40587500, info@journal-officiel.gouv.fr, http://www.journal-officiel.gouv.fr. **Co-sponsor:** Ministere de l'Environnement et du Cadre de Vie.

336 382.1 FRA
FRANCE. DIRECTION DE LA BALANCE DES PAIEMENTS. LA BALANCE DES PAIEMENTS ET LA POSITION EXTERIEURE DE LA FRANCE. Text in French. 1982. a. EUR 22 (effective 2002). charts; stat. **Document type:** *Government.* **Description:** Presents a statistical and macroeconomic panorama of the economic, financial and monetary climates beyond France.
Former titles: France. Ministere de l'Economie, des Finances et du Budget. Balance des Paiements et la Position Exterieure de la France; France. Ministere de l'Economie, des Finances et du Budget. Balance des Paiements de la France (0292-6733); France. Ministere de l'Economie et des Finances. Balance des Paiements entre la France et l'Exterieur (0071-8890)
Published by: Banque de France, Service Relations avec le Public, 48 rue Croix-des-Petits-Champs, Paris, 75049, France. TEL 33-1-42923908, FAX 33-1-42923940, http://www.banque-france.fr.

336.1 FRA
FRANCE. DIRECTION GENERALE DES IMPOTS. BULLETIN OFFICIEL D'ANNONCES DES DOMAINES. Text in French. 1947. s-m. adv. bk.rev. illus.
Published by: (France. Service des Domaines), Direction Generale des Impots, 17 rue Scribe, Paris, Cedex 9 75436, France. TEL 94-94-78-78. Ed. J Gaillard. Circ: 38,000.

336 340 FRA ISSN 0767-1237
FRANCE. DIRECTION GENERALE DES IMPOTS. PRECIS DE FISCALITE. Text in French. 1980. a.
Formerly (until 1980): France. Direction Generale des Impots. Precis de Fiscalite Cadastre Domaine Publicite Fonciere (0767-1229)
Published by: (France. Direction Generale des Impots), Imprimerie Nationale, BP 514, Douai, Cedex 59505, France. TEL 27-93-70-90, FAX 27-93-70-96.

336 FRA ISSN 0071-8742
FRANCE. INSPECTION GENERALE DES FINANCES. ANNUAIRE. Text in French. 1952. a.
Published by: (France. Inspection Generale des Finances), Imprimerie Nationale, BP 514, Douai, Cedex 59505, France. TEL 27-93-70-90, FAX 27-93-70-96.

336.2 340 GBR
FRENCH TAX AND BUSINESS LAW GUIDE. Text in English. 1983. base vol. plus updates 6/yr. looseleaf. GBP 825 base vol(s).; GBP 735, EUR 1,106 updates in Europe; GBP 765, USD 1,390 updates elsewhere (effective 2006). **Document type:** *Journal, Trade.*
Published by: Sweet & Maxwell Ltd., 100 Avenue Road, London, NW3 3PF, United Kingdom. TEL 44-20-74491111, FAX 44-20-74491144, customer.services@sweetandmaxwell.co.uk, http://www.sweetandmaxwell.co.uk. **Subscr. to:** Cheriton House, North Way, Andover, Hants SP10 5BE, United Kingdom.

336 USA
FRINGE BENEFITS TAX GUIDE. Text in English. 1985. base vol. plus m. updates. USD 629 base vol(s). print or online or CD-ROM ed. (effective 2004). **Description:** Examines the treatment of more than 50 "perks" from both the employer and employee viewpoints. Coverage of government regulations and recent trends provides the basis for evaluating salary supplements for compensation and benefits planning. Discussions focus on the federal tax treatment of each fringe benefit.
Related titles: CD-ROM ed.; Online - full text ed.
Indexed: ATI.
Published by: C C H Inc., 2700 Lake Cook Rd, Riverwoods, IL 60015. TEL 847-267-7000, 800-449-6439, cust_serv@cch.com, http://www.cch.com. Pub. Stacey Caywood.

336 DEU ISSN 0944-291X
FUER SIE PRIVAT. Text in German. 1985. m. **Document type:** *Newsletter, Consumer.*
Published by: V S R W Verlag Dr. Hagen Pruehs GmbH, Rolandstr 48, Bonn, 53179, Germany. TEL 49-228-951240, FAX 49-228-9512490, vsrw@vsrw.de, http://www.vsrw.de. Ed., R&P Hagen Pruehs. Adv. contact Christiane Hellwig. Circ: 9,500 (controlled).

336 USA
G A A F R REVIEW. (Governmental Accounting, Auditing and Financial Reporting) Text in English. m. USD 75 to non-members; USD 40 to members. **Document type:** *Newsletter.*
Published by: Government Finance Officers Association, 203 N LaSalle St, Ste 2700, Chicago, IL 60601-1210. Subscriptions@gfoa.org, http://www.gfoa.org.

336 CAN ISSN 0847-3528
G S T & COMMODITY TAX. (Goods and Services Tax) Text in English. 1987. 10/yr. CND 249 domestic (effective 2005). **Document type:** *Newsletter.* **Description:** Covers the latest developments in the GST, federal and provincial sales and commodity taxes, and customs and excise duties.
Formerly (until 1989): De Boo Commodity Tax Reports (0835-6726)

Published by: Carswell (Subsidiary of: Thomson Corporation), One Corporate Plaza, 2075 Kennedy Rd, Toronto, ON M1T 3V4, Canada. TEL 416-609-8000, 800-387-5164, FAX 416-298-5094, carswell.customerrelations@thomson.com, http://www.carswell.com. Ed. Barry Hull.

336   CAN
G S T GUIDE FOR BUSINESS. Text in English. 1991. 6/yr. looseleaf. CND 269 domestic; USD 227.96 foreign (effective 2005). charts; stat. index. back issues avail. **Description:** Provides up-to-date information on the statutes, Canada Customs and Revenue Agency requirements affecting compliance and rebates.
Published by: Carswell (Subsidiary of: Thomson Corporation), One Corporate Plaza, 2075 Kennedy Rd, Toronto, ON M1T 3V4, Canada. TEL 416-609-8000, 800-387-5164, FAX 416-298-5094, carswell.customerrelations@thomson.com, http://www.carswell.com. Ed. Bart Singh. Circ: 3,000.

354.67   GAB
GABON. DIRECTION GENERALE DES FINANCES ET DU BUDGET. PROJET DU BUDGET GENERAL. Text in French. irreg. stat.
Published by: Direction Generale des Finances et du Budget, Ministere de l'Economie et des Finances, Libreville, Gabon.

336.2 340   GBR
GAMMIE & DE SOUZA: LAND TAXATION. Text in English. 1986. 2 base vols. plus updates 3/yr. looseleaf. GBP 799 base vol(s).; GBP 645, EUR 970 updates in Europe; GBP 660, USD 1,199 updates elsewhere (effective 2006). **Document type:** Journal, Trade.
Published by: Sweet & Maxwell Ltd., 100 Avenue Road, London, NW3 3PF, United Kingdom. TEL 44-20-74491111, FAX 44-20-74491144, customer.services@sweetandmaxwell.co.uk, http://www.sweetandmaxwell.co.uk. **Subscr. to:** Cheriton House, North Way, Andover, Hants SP10 5BE, United Kingdom.

336   DEU   ISSN 1432-4741
GEBUEHREN DER STEUERBERATENDEN BERUFE. Text in German. 1998. irreg. price varies. **Document type:** Monographic series, Trade.
Published by: Erich Schmidt Verlag GmbH & Co. (Berlin), Genthiner Str 30G, Berlin, 10785, Germany. TEL 49-30-250085-0, FAX 49-30-25008511, esv@esvmedien.de, http://www.erich-schmidt-verlag.de.

336   DEU   ISSN 0947-658X
GERMAN TAX NEWS. Text in German. bi-m. EUR 66 (effective 2004). **Document type:** Newsletter, Trade.
Published by: Hermann Luchterhand Verlag GmbH (Subsidiary of: Wolters Kluwer Deutschland GmbH), Heddesdorfer Str 31, Neuwied, 56564, Germany. TEL 49-2631-8012222, FAX 49-2631-8012223, info@luchterhand.de, http://www.luchterhand.de. Ed. Mathias Kessler.

336.2   DEU   ISSN 0947-501X
GESTALTENDE STEUERBERATUNG. Text in German. m. EUR 240 (effective 2004). **Document type:** Journal, Trade.
Published by: (Institut fuer Wirtschaftspublizistik), Vogel Verlag und Druck GmbH & Co. KG, Max-Planck-Str 7-9, Wuerzburg, 97064, Germany. TEL 49-931-4180, FAX 49-931-4182100, marliese_bernhardt@vogel-medien.de, http://www.iww.de/steuerberater/gestaltendesb/infoindex.php, http://www.vogel-medien.de. **Subscr. to:** DataM-Services GmbH, Fichtestr 9, Wuerzburg 97074, Germany. TEL 49-931-417001, FAX 49-931-4170499, swestenberger@datam-services.de, http://www.datam-services.de.

336   FRA   ISSN 1244-4383
GESTION ET FINANCES DES COLLECTIVITES LOCALES. Text in French. 1995. a. looseleaf. EUR 540.16 print & CD-ROM eds. (effective 2004).
Related titles: CD-ROM ed.: ISSN 1284-1218; Online - full text ed.
Published by: Lamy S.A. (Subsidiary of: Wolters Kluwer France), 21/23 rue des Ardennes, Paris, 75935 Cedex 19, France. TEL 33-1-825080800, FAX 33-1-44721388, lamy@lamy.fr, http://www.lamy.fr.

354.667   GHA
GHANA. SUPREME MILITARY COUNCIL. BUDGET PROPOSALS. Text in English. a. GHC 1. stat. **Document type:** Government.
Published by: Supreme Military Council, Ministry of Finance, Accra, Ghana.

GILBERT LAW SUMMARIES. ESTATE AND GIFT TAX. see LAW—Estate Planning

340   USA
GILBERT LAW SUMMARIES. INCOME TAX 1 (INDIVIDUAL). Text in English. irreg., latest vol.18, 199?. USD 21.95 (effective 2000). **Document type:** Trade. **Description:** Reviews the principles of the individual income tax.
Published by: Gilbert Law Summaries (Subsidiary of: B A R / B R I Group), 111 W Jackson, 7th Fl, Chicago, IL 60604. TEL 312-853-3662, 800-787-8717, FAX 312-853-3622, http://www.gilbertlaw.com. Ed. Michael R Asimow.

GILBERT LAW SUMMARIES. INCOME TAX 2 (CORPORATE). see LAW—Corporate Law

336.2   ITA   ISSN 0391-1853
GIURISPRUDENZA DELLE IMPOSTE. Text in Italian. 1928. bi-m. EUR 82.63 in the European Union; EUR 123.95 elsewhere (effective 2002). adv. **Description:** Contains the most important decisions of Italian and European courts concerning taxes, and includes current essays and studies of tax issues.
Published by: Casa Editrice Dott. A. Giuffre (Subsidiary of: LexisNexis Europe and Africa), Via Busto Arsizio, 40, Milan, MI 20151, Italy. TEL 39-02-28089200, FAX 39-02-38009582, giuffre@giuffre.it, http://www.giuffre.it. Ed. Claudio Berliri. Circ: 5,800.

GLASS'S GUIDE TO COMPANY CAR TAX. see TRANSPORTATION—Automobiles

336   USA
GLOBAL ASSET PROTECTION. Text in English. 1993. m. USD 50 (effective 2000). **Document type:** Newsletter, Trade. **Description:** Presents a variety of global methods of assest protection.
Former titles (until 2000): Jacobs Report on Asset Protection Strategies (1521-5695); (until 1993): Jacobs Report on Investment and Retirement Tax Planning
Related titles: Online - full text ed.: (from Northern Light Technology, Inc.).
Published by: Offshore Press Inc., 4500 W. 72nd Terrace, Prairie Village, KS 66208. TEL 913-362-9667, FAX 913-362-9667, vkj@rpifs.com, http://www.rpifs.com. Ed., Pub., R&P Vernon K Jacobs

GLOBAL BANKING & FINANCIAL POLICY REVIEW (YEARS). see BUSINESS AND ECONOMICS—Banking And Finance

336   DEU   ISSN 0939-5547
DIE GMBH. Text in German. 1991. bi-m. looseleaf. **Document type:** Trade.
Published by: W R S Verlag GmbH & Co. KG (Subsidiary of: Rudolf Haufe Verlag GmbH & Co. KG), Fraunhoferstr 5, Planegg, 82152, Germany. info@wrs.de, http://www.wrs.de.

347.72   DEU   ISSN 0932-2345
GMBH-STEUERPRAXIS. Text in German. 1978. m. **Document type:** Magazine, Trade. **Description:** Contains the latest news and information on corporate and business taxation procedures and policies.
Published by: V S R W Verlag Dr. Hagen Pruehs GmbH, Rolandstr 48, Bonn, 53179, Germany. TEL 49-228-95124-0, FAX 49-228-9512490, vsrw@vsrw.de, http://www.gmbh-steuerpraxis.de, http://www.vsrw.de.

347.72   DEU
GMBH-STEUERPRAXIS-RATGEBER. Text in German. a. **Document type:** Bulletin, Trade.
Published by: V S R W Verlag Dr. Hagen Pruehs GmbH, Rolandstr 48, Bonn, 53179, Germany. TEL 49-228-95124-0, FAX 49-228-9512490, vsrw@vsrw.de, http://www.vsrw.de/GmbH_Ratgeber/gmbhratgeber.shtml.

336.2   DEU   ISSN 1435-3369
GMBH-TIP. Text in German. 1998. fortn. **Document type:** Newsletter, Trade. **Description:** Contains up-to-date information for corporations on financial and taxation issues and trends.
Published by: V S R W Verlag Dr. Hagen Pruehs GmbH, Rolandstr 48, Bonn, 53179, Germany. TEL 49-228-95124-0, FAX 49-228-9512490, vsrw@vsrw.de, http://www.vsrw.de/Informationsdienste/GmbH_Tip/GmbH-Tip.shtml.

336   USA   ISSN 0731-583X
KF1432.1
GOING PUBLIC HANDBOOK; going public, the integrated disclosure system and exempt financing. Text in English. 1982. latest 2003 ed., 2 base vols. plus a. updates. USD 304 per vol. (effective 2004). **Document type:** Trade. **Description:** Provides practitioners with the basics of public financing and with numerous hard-to-find and crucial sample documents and forms.
Indexed: ATI.
Published by: Thomson West (Subsidiary of: Thomson Corporation, The), 610 Opperman Dr, Eagan, MN 55123-1396. TEL 651-687-8000, 800-328-4880, FAX 651-687-7302, customer.service@westgroup.com, http://west.thomson.com/product/14974166/product.asp. Ed. Harold S Bloomenthal.

352.1   USA   ISSN 0883-7856
HJ9103
GOVERNMENT FINANCE REVIEW. Text in English. 1985. bi-m. USD 30 (effective 2005). adv. bk.rev. illus. index. back issues avail.; reprint service avail. from PQC. **Document type:** Magazine, Government. **Description:** Covers the spectrum of public finance issues.
Formed by the merger of (197?-1985): Government Financial Management Resources in Review (0272-6823); (1926-1985): Governmental Finance (0091-4835); Which was formerly (until 1971): Municipal Finance (0027-3473)

Related titles: Microform ed.: (from PQC); Online - full text ed.: (from Florida Center for Library Automation, Gale Group, H.W. Wilson, Northern Light Technology, Inc., O C L C Online Computer Library Center, Inc., ProQuest Information & Learning).
Indexed: ABCPolSci, ABIn, ATI, BLI, BPI, BPIA, LRI, ManagCont, PAIS, PROMT, SPAA, T&II.
—BLDSC (4204.102500), IE, Infotrieve, ingenta.
Published by: Government Finance Officers Association, 203 N LaSalle St, Ste 2700, Chicago, IL 60601-1210. TEL 312-977-9700, FAX 312-977-4806, GFR@gfoa.org, Subscriptions@gfoa.org, http://www.gfoa.org/services/gfr. adv.: B&W page USD 1,385. Circ: 16,000 (paid).

336   USA   ISSN 0886-2915
HJ9773
GOVERNMENTAL ACCOUNTING STANDARDS BOARD. TECHNICAL BULLETIN. Abbreviated title: G A S B Technical Bulletin. Text in English. 1984. irreg. USD 8 per issue (effective 2004).
Published by: Governmental Accounting Standards Board, 401 Merritt 7, P O Box 5116, Norwalk, CT 06856-5116. TEL 203-847-0700, FAX 203-849-9714, http://www.gasb.org/.

339.20941   GBR
GREAT BRITAIN. BOARD OF INLAND REVENUE. SURVEY OF PERSONAL INCOMES. Key Title: Survey of Personal Incomes. Text in English. 1972. irreg. GBP 4.95. stat. **Document type:** Government.
Published by: H.M.S.O., Publications Centre, PO Box 276, London, SW8 5DT, United Kingdom. **Subscr. to:** H.M.S.O., Atlantic House, Holborn Viaduct, London EC1P 1BN, United Kingdom.

GREAT BRITAIN. DEPARTMENT OF THE ENVIRONMENT, TRANSPORT AND THE REGIONS. HOUSING CONSULTATION PAPERS. see HOUSING AND URBAN PLANNING

352.448   GBR
GREAT BRITAIN. H M CUSTOMS & EXCISE. MANAGEMENT PLAN. Text in English. biennial. **Document type:** Government.
Published by: H M Customs and Excise, Business Unit, New Kings Beam House, 11th Fl, 22 Upper Ground, London, SE1 9PJ, United Kingdom. TEL 44-171-865-5570, FAX 44-171-865-5626.

336   GBR
GREAT BRITAIN. H M TREASURY. GOVERNMENT PROCUREMENT: PROGRESS REPORT TO THE PRIME MINISTER (YEAR). Text in English. a. **Document type:** Government.
Formerly (until 1993): Great Britain. H M Treasury. Government Purchasing: Progress Report to the Prime Minister (Year)
Published by: (Great Britain. H M Treasury), Stationery Office, 51 Nine Elms Ln, London, SW8 5DA, United Kingdom. TEL 44-20-7873-0011, FAX 44-20-7873-8247. **Subscr. to:** PO Box 276, London SW8 5DT, United Kingdom. TEL 44-20-7873-8466, FAX 44-20-7873-8222.

336   GBR
GREAT BRITAIN. TREASURY. SUPPLY ESTIMATES. Text in English. 1850. a. price varies. stat. index. **Document type:** Government.
—BLDSC (8547.630700).
Published by: Stationery Office, 51 Nine Elms Ln, London, SW8 5DA, United Kingdom. TEL 44-20-7873-0011, FAX 44-20-7873-8247, book.orders@theso.co.uk, http://www.national-publishing.co.uk. Circ: 500.

GREECE. NATIONAL STATISTICAL SERVICE. PROVISIONAL NATIONAL ACCOUNTS OF GREECE. see BUSINESS AND ECONOMICS—Abstracting, Bibliographies, Statistics

GREECE. NATIONAL STATISTICAL SERVICE. QUARTERLY NATIONAL ACCOUNTS OF GREECE. see BUSINESS AND ECONOMICS—Abstracting, Bibliographies, Statistics

336.2   GUM   ISSN 0072-7873
GUAM. DEPARTMENT OF REVENUE AND TAXATION. REPORT. Text in English. 1969. a. USD 2.
Published by: Department of Revenue and Taxation, Office of the Director, Bldg 13-1 Mariner Ave, Tiyan, Barrigada, 96913, Guam. TEL 671-475-5000, FAX 671-472-2643, revtax@ns.gov.gu, http://mail.admin.gov.gu/revtax/diroff.html. Circ: 100.

336   CHN
GUANGXI SHENJI/GUANGXI AUDIT. Text in Chinese. bi-m.
Published by: Guangxi Shenji Ju, Xinghu Lu, Nanning, Guangxi 530022, China. TEL 42327. Ed. Cui Chusheng.

336   CHN
GUANGXI SHUIWU/GUANGXI TAXATION. Text in Chinese. bi-m.
Published by: Guangxi Shuiwu Ju/Guangxi Bureau of Taxation, 82 Taoyuan Lu, Nanning, Guangxi 530021, China. TEL 28920. Ed. Li Qiaoyu.

B

336 CAN ISSN 0432-9368
LE GUIDE DU CONTRIBUABLE CANADIEN. Text in English. 1954. a. CND 58.95.
Published by: C C H - F M Ltd., 90 Sheppard Ave E, Ste 300, North York, ON M2N 6X1, Canada. TEL 416-224-2248, 800-268-4522, FAX 416-224-2243, http://camelot.ca.cch.com. Ed. Pierrette Gregoire.

336 FRA ISSN 1290-0222
GUIDE PERMANENT: PAIE. Text in French. 1996. base vol. plus m. updates. looseleaf. EUR 117 base vol(s). (effective 2004).
Published by: Editions Legislatives, 80 Avenue de la Marne, Montrouge, Cedex 92546, France. TEL 33-1-40923636, FAX 33-1-40923663, infocom@editions-legislatives.fr, http://www.editions-legislatives.fr. Pub. Michel Vaillant.

336.2 USA
GUIDE TO AUDITING HEALTH CARE BILLING PRACTICES. Text in English. 1999. base vol. plus updates 12/yr. looseleaf. USD 321 (effective 2001). **Description:** Includes step-by-step guidance on recognizing problems, auditing components of the billing process, auditing IS billing systems, special billing problems and more.
Published by: Atlantic Information Services, Inc., 1100 17th St, NW, Ste 300, Washington, DC 20036. Ed. Frances Fernald. Pub. Richard Biehl.

B

GUIDE TO FEDERAL FUNDING FOR EDUCATION. see *EDUCATION—School Organization And Administration*

336.2 USA
GUIDE TO FEDERAL TAX ISSUES FOR COLLEGES AND UNIVERSITIES. Text in English. 2000. base vol. plus updates 4/yr. looseleaf. USD 483 to non-members; USD 383 to members; USD 609 combined subscription to non-members print & CD-ROM eds.; USD 509 combined subscription to members print & CD-ROM eds. (effective 2003). **Document type:** *Newsletter.* **Description:** Assists colleges and universities with complex tax challenges.
Related titles: CD-ROM ed.: USD 483 to non-members; USD 383 to members (effective 2003).
Published by: (National Association of College and University Business Officers), Atlantic Information Services, Inc., 1100 17th St, NW, Ste 300, Washington, DC 20036. TEL 202-775-9008, FAX 202-331-9542. Ed. Frances Fernald. Pub. Richard Biehl.

336.2 JPN ISSN 0072-8551
KNX3541.2
GUIDE TO JAPANESE TAXES. Text in English. 1965. a. JPY 7,000; JPY 8,500 foreign (effective 1998). **Description:** Provides extensive and up-to-date information on Japanese taxes based on laws, regulations and circulars.
Related titles: Japanese ed.
Indexed: ATI.
Published by: Zaikei Shoho Sha. Co. Ltd., 1-2-14 Higashi-Shinbashi, Minato-ku, Tokyo, 105-0021, Japan. FAX 81-3-3572-5189. Ed., R&P Yasuyuki Nagatomi TEL 81-3-3572-0624. Circ: 5,000.

336 USA
GUIDE TO PENSION AND PROFIT SHARING PLANS: TAXATION, SELECTION AND DESIGN. Text in English. 1984. base vol. plus a. updates. looseleaf. USD 115. Supplement avail. **Document type:** *Trade.* **Description:** Assists in the selection, design and analysis of the tax consequences of pension, profit sharing and other deferred compensation plans based on specific financial objectives.
Related titles: Series of: Tax and Estate Planning Series.
Published by: Shepard's (Subsidiary of: LexisNexis North America), 555 Middle Creek Pkwy, Colorado Springs, CO 80921. TEL 800-743-7393, customer_service@shepards.com, http://www.shepards.com, http://www.lexisnexis.com/shepards/. Ed. David S Dunkle.

336.2 USA
GUIDE TO SALES AND USE TAXES (YEAR). Text in English. a. USD 60. **Description:** Provides state-by-state coverage of sales and use taxes in every state and the District of Columbia.
Related titles: ◆ Supplement to: State and Local Taxes: Sales and Use Taxes.
Published by: R I A (Subsidiary of: Thomson Corporation), 395 Hudson St, New York, NY 10014. TEL 212- 367-6300. Ed. George Wohar Jr.

336 NLD
GUIDE TO THE EUROPEAN V A T DIRECTIVES; commentary on the Value Added Tax of the European Community. Text in English, Multiple languages. 1993. 6 base vols. plus updates 3/yr. looseleaf. USD 1,100 base vol(s).; USD 605 updates (effective 2002). **Document type:** *Trade.* **Description:** Provides comprehensive information on VAT legislation within the EU, including historical background and general introduction, and title-by-title commentary on the VAT Directives. Text of the Directives is presented in the nine working languages of the EU.
Published by: (International Bureau of Fiscal Documentation), I B F D Publications BV, H J E Wenckebachweg 210, PO Box 20237, Amsterdam, 1000 HE, Netherlands. TEL 31-20-554-0100, FAX 31-20-620-8626, info@ibfd.nl, http://www.ibfd.nl. Eds. B J M Terra, Julie Kajus.

336.2 NLD
GUIDES TO EUROPEAN TAXATION: TAXATION & INVESTMENT IN CENTRAL AND EAST EUROPEAN COUNTRIES. Text in English. 1983. 3 base vols. plus updates 3/yr. looseleaf. USD 1,060 base vol(s).; USD 565 updates (effective 2002). **Document type:** *Trade.* **Description:** Details the taxation systems for companies and individuals in Hungary, Poland, the Czech Republic, Slovakia, Bulgaria, Romania, Croatia and Russia, and includes profiles of taxation systems in Albania, Belarus, Estonia, and other states of the region.
Formerly: Guides to European Taxation: Taxation in European Socialist Countries
Published by: (International Bureau of Fiscal Documentation), I B F D Publications BV, H J E Wenckebachweg 210, PO Box 20237, Amsterdam, 1000 HE, Netherlands. TEL 31-20-554-0100, FAX 31-20-620-8626, info@ibfd.nl, http://www.ibfd.nl. Ed. G M M Michielse.

336.2 NLD
GUIDES TO EUROPEAN TAXATION: TAXATION OF COMPANIES IN EUROPE. Text in English. 5 base vols. plus bi-m. updates. looseleaf. USD 1,810 base vol(s).; USD 1,080 updates (effective 2002). **Document type:** *Trade.* **Description:** Systematically examines all forms of taxation at each stage of a company's life.
Published by: (International Bureau of Fiscal Documentation), I B F D Publications BV, H J E Wenckebachweg 210, PO Box 20237, Amsterdam, 1000 HE, Netherlands. TEL 31-20-554-0100, FAX 31-20-620-8626, info@ibfd.nl, http://www.ibfd.nl. Ed. L J Kesti.

336.2 NLD
GUIDES TO EUROPEAN TAXATION: TAXATION OF INDIVIDUALS IN EUROPE. Text in English. 1991. 2 base vols. plus updates 3/yr. looseleaf. USD 1,000 base vol(s).; USD 440 updates (effective 2002). **Document type:** *Trade.* **Description:** Analyzes and compares the taxation of resident and non-resident individuals in the 12 EC countries, Austria, Finland, Norway, Sweden, Switzerland, and Turkey.
Published by: (International Bureau of Fiscal Documentation), I B F D Publications BV, H J E Wenckebachweg 210, PO Box 20237, Amsterdam, 1000 HE, Netherlands. TEL 31-20-554-0100, FAX 31-20-620-8626, info@ibfd.nl, http://www.ibfd.nl. Ed. Catherine S Bobbett.

336.2 NLD
GUIDES TO EUROPEAN TAXATION: TAXATION OF PATENT ROYALTIES, DIVIDENDS, INTEREST IN EUROPE. Text in English. 1963. base vol. plus updates 3/yr. looseleaf. USD 565 base vol(s).; USD 340 updates (effective 2002). bibl. **Description:** Provides a country by country description of all withholding taxes (with base and rates) on corporate cross-border payments in Europe.
Published by: (International Bureau of Fiscal Documentation), I B F D Publications BV, H J E Wenckebachweg 210, PO Box 20237, Amsterdam, 1000 HE, Netherlands. TEL 31-20-554-0100, FAX 31-20-620-8626, info@ibfd.nl, http://www.ibfd.nl. Ed. P M Smit.

336.2 NLD
GUIDES TO EUROPEAN TAXATION: TAXATION OF PRIVATE INVESTMENT INCOME. Text in English. base vol. plus updates 3/yr. looseleaf. USD 565 base vol(s).; USD 345 updates (effective 2002). **Document type:** *Trade.* **Description:** Provides country-by-country outlines of the taxation of investment and investment income for resident and non-resident individuals in the 12 EC countries, Austria, Finland, Norway, Sweden, Switzerland, and the USA.
Published by: (International Bureau of Fiscal Documentation), I B F D Publications BV, H J E Wenckebachweg 210, PO Box 20237, Amsterdam, 1000 HE, Netherlands. TEL 31-20-554-0100, FAX 31-20-620-8626, info@ibfd.nl, http://www.ibfd.nl. Ed. Bernard P Dik.

336.2 NLD
GUIDES TO EUROPEAN TAXATION: VALUE ADDED TAXATION IN EUROPE. Text in English. 4 base vols. plus q. updates. looseleaf. USD 1,035 base vol(s).; USD 515 updates (effective 2002). bibl. **Document type:** *Trade.* **Description:** Analyzes VAT structures and their effect on international trade.
Published by: (International Bureau of Fiscal Documentation), I B F D Publications BV, H J E Wenckebachweg 210, PO Box 20237, Amsterdam, 1000 HE, Netherlands. TEL 31-20-554-0100, FAX 31-20-620-8626, info@ibfd.nl, http://www.ibfd.nl. Ed. Julie Kajus.

336 IND ISSN 0533-649X
GUJARAT STATE FINANCIAL CORPORATION. ANNUAL REPORT. Text in English. a. illus.; stat.
Published by: Gujarat State Financial Corporation, Jaladarshan Bldg., Ashram Rd., Navrangpura, PO Box 4030, Ahmedabad, Gujarat 380 009, India.

GUYANA. AUDITOR GENERAL. REPORT ON THE PUBLIC ACCOUNTS. see *BUSINESS AND ECONOMICS—Abstracting, Bibliographies, Statistics*

336 GBR
H M CUSTOMS AND EXCISE OFFICIAL V A T GUIDES. Text in English. irreg. looseleaf. GBP 147. **Document type:** *Bulletin.* **Description:** Reproduction of official VAT leaflets with index, table of cases and table of statutes.
Published by: Longman Group UK Ltd., Law Tax and Finance Division, 21-27 Lambs Conduit St, London, WC1N 3NJ, United Kingdom. TEL 44-20-7242-2548, FAX 44-207-831-8119.

336.2 ISR ISSN 0334-3065
K22
HA-RIVA'ON HA-YISRE'ELI L'MISSIM/ISRAELI TAX REVIEW. Text in Hebrew. 1965. q. ILS 180, USD 46 (effective 2000). adv. bk.rev. abstr.; bibl.; charts; stat. index. **Document type:** *Government.*
Formerly: Riv'on l'Inyanei Misim - Quarterly Tax Journal (0035-7138)
Indexed: IHP.
Published by: State Revenue Administration, Custom Sq., 32 Agron St., Jerusalem, Israel. TEL 972-2-6703201, FAX 972-2-6258602, misim@mof.gov.il. Ed. Mira Dror. Circ: 1,800.

336 ESP ISSN 0210-1173
HJ1244
HACIENDA PUBLICA ESPANOLA. Text in Spanish. 1964. 9/yr. bk.rev. bibl. index.
Supersedes (in 1979): Economia Financiera Espanola (0210-1181)
Related titles: Online - full text ed.; ◆ Supplement(s): Cuadernos de Actualidad. ISSN 1133-9470.
Indexed: IBSS, JEL, PAIS, PCI.
—CINDOC.
Published by: Instituto de Estudios Fiscales, Avda Cardenal Herrera Oria, 378, Madrid, 28035, Spain. FAX 34-91-3398964, 34-91-3398964, http://www.ief.es/. **Subscr. to:** Ministerio de Economia y Hacienda, Centro de Publicaciones, Pz Campillo del Mundo Nuevo, 3, Madrid 28005, Spain. TEL 91-527-1437.

343.05 BEL ISSN 1376-6066
HANDBOEK PERSONENBELASTING. Text in Dutch. 1992. a. EUR 442.49 (effective 2003). **Document type:** *Trade.*
Formerly (until 1999): Jaarboek Personenbelasting (0779-6609)
Published by: Kluwer Uitgevers (Subsidiary of: Wolters Kluwer Belgique), Ragheno Business Park, Motstraat 30, Mechelen, B-2800, Belgium. TEL 32-15-800-94571, info@kluwer.be, http://www.kluwer.be. Ed. Ludo Dillen.

343.05 336.2 BEL ISSN 0779-1186
HANDBOEK VOOR FISCAAL RECHT. Text in Dutch. 1955. a. **Document type:** *Trade.* **Description:** Provide general reference information relating to taxation in Belgium.
Related titles: French ed.: Manuel de Droit Fiscal. ISSN 0779-1178.
Published by: Kluwer Uitgevers (Subsidiary of: Wolters Kluwer Belgique), Ragheno Business Park, Motstraat 30, Mechelen, B-2800, Belgium. TEL 32-15-800-94571, info@kluwer.be, http://www.kluwer.be.

336 USA ISSN 0163-4615
HG61
HANDBOOK OF BUSINESS FINANCE AND CAPITAL SOURCES. Text in English. 1979. a. USD 125.
Published by: Interfinance Corporation, 1815 Major Dr N., Minneapolis, MN 55422-4152. TEL 612-588-6067. Ed. Dileep Rao.

336.2 NLD
HANDBOOK ON THE 1989 DOUBLE TAXATION CONVENTION BETWEEN THE FEDERAL REPUBLIC OF GERMANY AND THE UNITED STATES OF AMERICA. Text in English, German. 1966. 3 base vols. plus a. updates. looseleaf. USD 630 base vol(s).; USD 130 updates (effective 2002). **Document type:** *Trade.* **Description:** Discusses the effects of the Double Taxation Convention between the Federal Republic of Germany and the United States of America of 1989.
Formerly (until 1989): Handbook on the U.S. - German Tax Convention
Published by: (International Bureau of Fiscal Documentation), I B F D Publications BV, H J E Wenckebachweg 210, PO Box 20237, Amsterdam, 1000 HE, Netherlands. TEL 31-20-554-0100, FAX 31-20-620-8626, info@ibfd.nl, http://www.ibfd.nl. Ed. J C Amico.

336 DEU ISSN 0171-2365
HANDBUCH DER STEUERVERANLAGUNGEN: EINKOMMENSTEUER, KOERPERSCHAFTSTEUER, GEWERBESTEUER, UMSATZSTEUER. Text in German. 1964. a. EUR 82 (effective 2003). **Document type:** *Bulletin, Trade.*
Related titles: CD-ROM ed.: Veranlagungs-CD.
Published by: (Deutsches Wissenschaftliches Steuerinstitut der Steuerberater und Steuerbevollmaechtigten e.V.), Verlag C.H. Beck oHG, Wilhelmstr 9, Munich, 80801, Germany. TEL 49-89-38189338, FAX 49-89-38189398, bestellung@beck.de, http://www.beck.de.

336 USA
HANDY - WHITMAN INDEX OF PUBLIC UTILITY CONSTRUCTION COSTS. (Issued separately by subject area: Electric, Gas, Water) Text in English. 1924. s-a. price varies. stat. index. **Document type:** *Bulletin.* **Description:** Compiles construction cost indices for various categories of plant capital for the electric, gas, and water utility industries.
Published by: Whitman, Requardt & Associates, LLP, 801 S. Caroline St., Baltimore, MD 21231-3311. TEL 410-235-3450, FAX 410-243-5716. Circ: 600.

350.827 USA ISSN 1066-0925
KF6654.599
HARMONIZED TARIFF SCHEDULE OF THE UNITED STATES. Text in English. 1963. latest 2001, base vol. plus irreg. updates. looseleaf. USD 67 (effective 2001). **Document type:** *Government.* **Description:** Shows the American nomenclature for imported articles and their rates of duty. Includes the text of N.A.F.T.A. For importers and customs brokers.
Formerly (until 1987): Tariff Schedules of the United States Annotated (0082-173X)
Related titles: CD-ROM ed.: USD 63 (effective 2001); Online - full text ed.: ISSN 1555-0230; ◆ Series of: U S I T C Publication. ISSN 0196-9153.
—CISTI.
Published by: U.S. International Trade Commission, Office of Tariff Affairs and Trade Agreements, 500 E St, SW, Washington, DC 20436. http://www.usitc.gov/. **Subscr. to:** U.S. Government Printing Office, Superintendent of Documents, PO Box 371954, Pittsburgh, PA 15250-7954. TEL 202-512-1800, FAX 202-512-2250, orders@gpo.gov, http://www.access.gpo.gov.

336 GBR
HARRISON'S INLAND REVENUE INDEX TO TAX CASES. Text in English. irreg. looseleaf. GBP 233. **Document type:** *Bulletin.* **Description:** Synopsis of all Inland Revenue reports of tax cases back to 1875, indexed alphabetically and by subject.
Published by: (Solicitor's Office of the Inland Revenue), Longman Group UK Ltd., Law Tax and Finance Division, 21-27 Lambs Conduit St, London, WC1N 3NJ, United Kingdom. TEL 44-20-7242-2548, FAX 44-207-831-8119.

HEALTH CARE FINANCING REVIEW. see *MEDICAL SCIENCES*

HEALTH CARE FINANCING REVIEW. STATISTICAL SUPPLEMENT. see *PUBLIC HEALTH AND SAFETY*

336 USA
HIGHLIGHTS & DOCUMENTS ON MICROFICHE. Text in English. a. USD 499 (effective 1999). **Document type:** *Trade.*
Media: Microfiche. **Related titles:** ◆ Cumulative ed. of: Highlights & Documents. ISSN 0889-3055.
Published by: Tax Analysts, 6830 N Fairfax Dr, Arlington, VA 22213. TEL 703-553-4400, 800-955-3444, FAX 703-533-4444.

336 790.13 USA
HOBBY - BUSINESS WORLD. Text in English. 1976. w. USD 520 domestic (effective 2001). bk.rev. back issues avail. **Document type:** *Trade.*
Published by: Cricket Communications, Inc., PO Box 527, Ardmore, PA 19003. TEL 215-789-2480, FAX 215-747-6684, TELEX 6505179983. Ed. Mark E Battensby.

▼ **HOMELAND SECURITY FUNDING WEEK.** see *PUBLIC ADMINISTRATION*

HONG KONG SPECIAL ADMINISTRATIVE REGION OF CHINA. CENSUS AND STATISTICS DEPARTMENT. GROSS DOMESTIC PRODUCT (ANNUAL EDITION). see *BUSINESS AND ECONOMICS—Abstracting, Bibliographies, Statistics*

336.2 DEU ISSN 1433-0261
DER HONORAR-BRIEF FUER STEUERBERATER. Text in German. 1998. m. EUR 179.60 (effective 2004). **Document type:** *Magazine, Trade.*
Published by: Verlag fuer Deutsche Steuerberater AG (Subsidiary of: Wolters Kluwer Deutschland GmbH), Marlener Str 2, Offenburg, 77656, Germany. TEL 49-781-9900646, FAX 49-781-9900644, info@steuern-online.de, http://www.steuern-online.de.

HORSE OWNERS AND BREEDERS TAX HANDBOOK. see *SPORTS AND GAMES—Horses And Horsemanship*

336.2 USA
HOW TO SAVE TIME AND TAXES PREPARING FIDUCIARY INCOME TAX RETURNS. Text in English. 1969. base vol. plus s-a. updates. looseleaf. USD 246 base vol(s). (effective 2002). **Description:** Comprehensive coverage of the federal income taxation of trusts and estates, with an item-by-item, line-by-line preparation guide to Federal Form 1041. Provides the background necessary for effective tax planning.
Related titles: CD-ROM ed.
Published by: Matthew Bender & Co., Inc. (Subsidiary of: LexisNexis North America), 1275 Broadway, Albany, NY 12204. international@bender.com, http://bender.lexisnexis.com. Eds. Joseph O'Connell, Stowell Rounds.

336 CHN
HUBEI CAISHUI. Text in Chinese. m.
Published by: Hubei Sheng Shuiwu Ju, Hongshan Lu, Wuchang-qu, Wuhan, Hubei 430071, China. TEL 813317. Ed. Chen Tai'an.

I C A O'S POLICIES ON TAXATION IN THE FIELD OF INTERNATIONAL AIR TRANSPORT. see *AERONAUTICS AND SPACE FLIGHT*

I D W FACHNACHRICHTEN. see *BUSINESS AND ECONOMICS—Accounting*

336 GBR
I F A C INTERNATIONAL PUBLIC SECTOR GUIDELINE (NO.). Text in English. 1990. irreg., latest vol.3, 1992. back issues avail.
Indexed: ATI.
Published by: Institute of Public Finance and Accountancy, 3 Robert St, London, WC2N 6BH, United Kingdom. TEL 44-171-543-5600, FAX 44-171-543-5700.

336 NLD ISSN 1016-7560
I F A CONGRESS SEMINAR SERIES. Text in Dutch. 1977. a. price varies. back issues avail. **Document type:** *Proceedings, Academic/Scholarly.*
—BLDSC (4363.260000).
Published by: (International Fiscal Association), Kluwer Law International (Subsidiary of: Aspen Publishers, Inc.), Laan van Meerdervoort 70, PO Box 85889, The Hague, 2508 CN, Netherlands. TEL 31-70-3081500, FAX 31-70-3081515, sales@kluwerlaw.com, http://www.kluwerlaw.com.

336.2 DEU
I N F - DIE INFORMATION FUER STEUERBERATER UND WIRTSCHAFTSPRUEFER. Text in German. 1970. fortn. EUR 169 (effective 2005). **Document type:** *Journal, Trade.*
Formerly: Die Information ueber Steuer und Wirtschaft (0174-1942); Which was formed by the merger of (1952-1970): Die Information ueber Steuer und Wirtschaft. Ausgabe L (0174-1918); Which was formerly (until 1960): Die Information ueber Steuer und Wirtschaft fuer Land- und Forstwirtschaft, Garten- und Weinbau (0174-190X); (194?-1970): Die Information ueber Steuer und Wirtschaft. Ausgabe A (0174-1934); Which was formerly (until 1960): Die Information ueber Steuer und Wirtschaft fuer Industrie, Handel, Handwerk und Gewerbe (0174-1926); Which incorporated (1949-1960): Der Steuerpraktiker (0174-1896); (1962-1966): Steuern und Finanzen (0039-1301)
Published by: Rudolf Haufe Verlag GmbH & Co. KG, Hindenburgstr 64, Freiburg Im Breisgau, 79102, Germany. TEL 49-761-36830, FAX 49-761-3683195, online@haufe.de, http://www.haufe.de.

336.2 USA
I R S FEDERAL TAX PRODUCTS CD-ROM. Text in English. a. USD 21 (effective 2001). **Document type:** *Government.* **Description:** Contains current year tax forms, instructions and publications, prior-year tax forms and instructions, prior-year taxpayer information publications, popular tax forms which may be filled-in electronically, Internal Revenue Service Bulletins.
Media: CD-ROM. **Related titles:** ◆ Print ed.: U.S. Internal Revenue Service. Bulletin. ISSN 0020-5761.
Published by: U.S. Internal Revenue Service, 1111 Constitution Ave, N W, Washington, DC 20224. **Subscr. to:** U.S. Department of Commerce, National Technical Information Service, 5285 Port Royal Rd, Springfield, VA 22161. TEL 703-605-6060, 800-363-2068, FAX 703-605-6880, subscriptions@ntis.gov.

336 USA ISSN 0148-1940
KF6282.A2
I R S LETTER RULINGS REPORTER. (Internal Revenue Service) Text in English. base vol. plus w. updates. USD 1,575 base vol(s). (effective 2004). **Description:** Features the full text of IRS responses to inquiries concerning application of the tax rules to specific situations along with the text of revenue procedures relating to the IRS Letter Rulings.
Related titles: CD-ROM ed.: USD 1,365 (effective 2004); Online - full text ed.
—CCC.
Published by: C C H Inc., 2700 Lake Cook Rd, Riverwoods, IL 60015. TEL 847-267-7000, 800-449-6439, FAX 800-224-8299, cust_serv@cch.com, http://www.cch.com. Pub. Kevin Robert.

336 USA ISSN 1084-0141
KF6301
I R S PUBLICATIONS. (Internal Revenue Service) Text in English. 1977. 3 base vols. plus irreg. updates. looseleaf. USD 409 base vol(s). (effective 2004). **Description:** Includes approximately 150 current IRS publications intended for public use by taxpayers and their advisors.
Related titles: CD-ROM ed.: USD 253 (effective 2000); Online - full text ed.
Indexed: ATI.
Published by: C C H Inc., 2700 Lake Cook Rd, Riverwoods, IL 60015. TEL 847-267-7000, 800-449-6439, FAX 800-224-8299, cust_serv@cch.com, http://www.cch.com. Pub. Kevin Robert.

ILLINOIS PROPERTY TAX STATISTICS. see *BUSINESS AND ECONOMICS—Abstracting, Bibliographies, Statistics*

336 ROM ISSN 1223-5180
IMPOZITE SI TAXE. Text in Romanian. m. adv.
Indexed: RASB.
Published by: Tribuna Economica SA, Bd. Gh. Magheru 28-30, Bucharest, 70159, Romania. TEL 40-1-6595158, FAX 40-1-3102934, tribunae@tribunaeconomica.ro. **Dist. by:** Rodipet S.A., Piata Presei Libere 1, sector 1, PO Box 33-57, Bucharest 3, Romania. TEL 40-21-2224126, 40-21-2226407, rodipet@rodipet.ro.

332 ESP ISSN 0213-0548
IMPUESTOS; revista de doctrina, legislacion y jurisprudencia. Text in Spanish. 1984. bi-w. back issues avail.
Related titles: ◆ Supplement(s): Legislacion Fiscal. ISSN 1135-9145.
—CINDOC.
Published by: La Ley, Calle Collado Mediano, No. 9, Las Rozas (Madrid), 28230, Spain. TEL 34-902-420010, FAX 34-902-420012, clientes@laley.net, http://www.laley.net/. Ed. Julio Banacloche.

336 ARG ISSN 0325-3635
IMPUESTOS; revista critica mensual de jurisprudencia y legislacion. Text in Spanish. 1942. m. USD 600. Supplement avail. **Description:** Critical review of tax jurisprudence and legislation.
Published by: Ediciones la Ley S.A., Tucuman, 1471, Capital Federal, Buenos Aires 1050, Argentina. TEL 54-114-495481, FAX 54-114-4760953. Ed. Marcelo Lascano.

336 CAN
INCOME TAX AND FAMILY LAW HANDBOOK. Text in English. a. looseleaf. CND 225 (effective 2001). **Document type:** *Trade.* **Description:** Explains the Federal Income Tax Act and provincial tax statutes relevant to family law issues in Canada.
Published by: LexisNexis Butterworths Canada Inc. (Subsidiary of: LexisNexis North America), 123 Commerce Valley Dr E, Ste 700, Markham, ON L3T 7W8, Canada. TEL 905-479-2665, FAX 905-479-2826, http://www.lexisnexis.ca/incometaxandfamilylawhandbook.htm. Ed. Mary Lou Benotto.

336 ZAF
INCOME TAX IN SOUTH AFRICA. Text in English. 3 base vols. plus a. updates. looseleaf. ZAR 615. Supplement avail. **Description:** Provides comprehensive coverage of the legal principles of income tax, and practical advice on tax planning and tax solutions.
Formerly: Income Tax Service
Published by: LexisNexis Butterworths South Africa (Subsidiary of: LexisNexis Europe and Africa), PO Box 792, Durban, KwaZulu-Natal 4000, South Africa. TEL 27-31-2683111, FAX 27-31-2683110.

336 USA
INCOME TAX REGULATIONS. Text in English. 1913. m. USD 125 1-4 sets (effective 2004). **Description:** The standard reference for all serious tax professionals and students. Full text reproduction of the official text of the federal income tax regulations, including unemployment insurance regulations.
Formerly (until 1983): Federal Income Tax Regulations
Published by: C C H Inc., 2700 Lake Cook Rd, Riverwoods, IL 60015. TEL 847-267-7000, 800-449-6439, FAX 800-224-8299, cust_serv@cch.com, http://www.cch.com. **Subscr. to:** 4025 W. Peterson Ave., Chicago, IL 60646-6085. TEL 773-866-6000, 800-835-5224, FAX 773-866-3895.

336.24 IND ISSN 0019-3453
INCOME TAX REPORTS; a journal of the law of income tax, wealth tax, gift tax and estate duty. Text in English. 1933. w. INR 940.
Published by: Company Law Institute of India Pvt. Ltd., 88, Thayagaraya Rd., Chennai, Tamil Nadu 600 017, India. Circ: 16,500.

336 USA
INCOME TAXATION: ACCOUNTING METHODS AND PERIODS. Text in English. 1983. base vol. plus a. updates. looseleaf. USD 235. Supplement avail. **Document type:** *Trade.* **Description:** Provides guidance and planning ideas on adopting an accounting method or period, working within the I.R.S. rules applicable to requesting a change in an accounting method or period, and installment sales, for both dealers and non-dealers.
Related titles: Series of: Taxation Series.
Published by: Shepard's (Subsidiary of: LexisNexis North America), 555 Middle Creek Pkwy, Colorado Springs, CO 80921. TEL 800-743-7393, customer_service@shepards.com, http://www.shepards.com, http://www.lexisnexis.com/shepards/. Ed. George G Baumfeind.

343.7305 USA ISSN 1095-8711
KF6584
INCOME TAXATION FIDUCIARIES AND BENEFICIARIES. Text in English. 1995. a. (in 2 vols.), latest 2003. USD 289 (effective 2003). **Document type:** *Trade.* **Description:** Clarifies complex issues with step-by-step procedures that ensure the most advantageous outcomes for fiduciary and beneficiary clients.

B

▼ new title ➤ refereed ✶ unverified ◆ full entry avail.

Published by: Panel Publishers, Inc. (Subsidiary of: Aspen Publishers, Inc.), 1185 Ave of the Americas, 37th Fl, New York, NY 10036. TEL 212-597-0200, 800-638-8437, FAX 212-597-0331, customer.service@aspenpubl.com, http://www.aspenpublishers.com. **Dist. by:** Aspen Publishers, Inc., Distribution Center, 7201 McKinney Circle, Frederick, MD 21701. TEL 301-698-7100, FAX 301-417-7550.

336 340 USA ISSN 1057-4824
KF6482
INCOME TAXATION OF NATURAL RESOURCES. Text in English. bi-m. USD 550. **Description:** Provides comprehensive explanations of tax regulations governing intangible costs and their impact on exploration, development, and exploitation of oil, gas, solid minerals, and timber resources.
Published by: R I A (Subsidiary of: Thomson Corporation), 395 Hudson St, New York, NY 10014. TEL 212- 367-6300. Ed. C W Russell.

336.2 IND ISSN 0073-6120
INDIA. CENTRAL BOARD OF REVENUE. CENTRAL EXCISE MANUAL✶ . Text in English. a. INR 6.25, USD 2.85.
Published by: Central Board of Revenue, Ministry of Finance, New Delhi, India.

336 IND
INDIA. FINANCE DEPARTMENT. BUDGET OF THE CENTRAL GOVERNMENT. Text in English. a. charts; stat.
Supersedes: India. Ministry of Finance. Budget (0536-9290)
Published by: Finance Department, New Delhi, India.

336.2 GBR
INDONESIA & PHILIPPINES TAX REVIEW✶ . Text in English. 10/yr. HKD 2,800 in Hong Kong; USD 380 elsewhere. **Document type:** *Newsletter.* **Description:** Provides advice on complicated tax issues and developments for companies operating in Indonesia and the Philippines.
Published by: Euromoney Institutional Investor Plc., Nestor House, Playhouse Yard, London, EC4V 5EX, United Kingdom. TEL 44-20-7779-8888, information@euromoneyplc.com, http://www.euromoneyplc.com/.

INFORMACION DINAMICA DE CONSULTA. see *LAW—Corporate Law*

336 USA
INFORMATION RETURNS GUIDE. Text in English. 1987. base vol. plus m. updates. looseleaf. USD 362 base vol(s). (effective 2003). **Description:** Gathers together all the requirements for reporting transactions affecting the tax liabilities of payees.
Published by: C C H Inc., 2700 Lake Cook Rd, Riverwoods, IL 60015. TEL 847-267-7000, 800-449-6439, FAX 800-224-8299, cust_serv@cch.com, http://www.cch.com. Pub. Kevin Robert.

INFORMATORE PIROLA. see *BUSINESS AND ECONOMICS—Personnel Management*

INFORMAZIONI AZIENDALI E PROFESSIONALI. QUADERNI. see *BUSINESS AND ECONOMICS—Management*

336 340 ZAF
INFOTAX. Text in English. 1997. q. ZAR 1,000, USD 230. **Description:** Aims to provide complete information on South African taxation.
Media: CD-ROM. **Related titles:** Diskette ed.; ◆ Includes: S A Tax Review. ISSN 1019-8474.
Published by: InfoMedia Technologies (Pty) Ltd., PO Box 44597, Claremont, Cape Town 7735, South Africa. TEL 27-21-689 5075, FAX 27-21-689-5025, infomedia@iafrica.com, http://www.pix.za/taxfax/taxfax.html. Ed. Marius van Blerck.

336 USA
INHERITANCE, ESTATE AND GIFT TAX REPORTS - FEDERAL AND ALL STATES. Text in English. m. USD 1,778 (effective 2004).
Formed by the 2003 merger of: Inheritance, Estate and Gift Tax Reports - Federal; Inheritance, Estate and Gift Tax Reports - All States
Published by: C C H Inc., 2700 Lake Cook Rd, Riverwoods, IL 60015. TEL 847-267-7000, 800-449-6439, FAX 800-224-8299, cust_serv@cch.com, http://www.cch.com.

336 SWE ISSN 1651-095X
INKOMSTSKATTELAGEN. Text in Swedish. 2001. a. SEK 1,450 (effective 2002).
Published by: Norstedts Juridik AB (Subsidiary of: Wolters Kluwer N.V.), Stockholm, 10647, Sweden. TEL 46-8-6909190, FAX 46-8-6909191.

336 GBR
INLAND REVENUE OFFICIAL TAX GUIDES. Text in English. irreg. **Description:** Reproduces all current Inland Revenue leaflets; indexed, with tables of cases and statutes.
Published by: Longman Group UK Ltd., Law Tax and Finance Division, 21-27 Lambs Conduit St, London, WC1N 3NJ, United Kingdom. TEL 44-20-7242-2548, FAX 44-207-831-8119.

336 GBR
INLAND REVENUE PRACTICES AND CONCESSIONS. Text in English. 1981. 4 base vols. plus updates 2/yr. looseleaf. GBP 495 base vol(s).; GBP 475, EUR 715 updates in Europe; GBP 485, USD 881 updates elsewhere (effective 2006). **Document type:** *Journal, Trade.*
Published by: Sweet & Maxwell Ltd., 100 Avenue Road, London, NW3 3PF, United Kingdom. TEL 44-20-74491111, FAX 44-20-74491144, customer.services@sweetandmaxwell.co.uk, http://www.sweetandmaxwell.co.uk. **Subscr. to:** Cheriton House, North Way, Andover, Hants SP10 5BE, United Kingdom.

336 GBR ISSN 1350-410X
INLAND REVENUE PRACTICES AND CONCESSIONS YEARBOOK. Text in English. 1992. irreg. looseleaf. GBP 160. **Document type:** *Bulletin.* **Description:** Commentary on the Inland Revenue's interpretation of tax legislation.
Published by: Longman Group UK Ltd., Law Tax and Finance Division, 21-27 Lambs Conduit St, London, WC1N 3NJ, United Kingdom. TEL 44-20-7242-2548, FAX 44-207-831-8119.

336.1 DEU
INSTITUT "FINANZEN UND STEUERN." I F ST SCHRIFTEN. Text in German. 1954. irreg., latest vol.367, 1998. price varies. index, cum.index. back issues avail. **Document type:** *Monographic series.*
Formerly: Institut "Finanzen und Steuern." Gruene Briefe (0067-9941)
Published by: Institut "Finanzen und Steuern" e.V., Postfach 7269, Bonn, 53105, Germany. TEL 49-228-982210, FAX 49-228-9822150.

336.1 DEU ISSN 0067-995X
INSTITUT "FINANZEN UND STEUERN." SCHRIFTENREIHE. Text in German. 1950. irreg., latest vol.126, 1989. price varies. index, cum.index. back issues avail. **Document type:** *Monographic series.*
Published by: Institut "Finanzen und Steuern" e.V., Postfach 7269, Bonn, 53105, Germany. TEL 49-228-982210, FAX 49-228-9822150.

336 332 AUT
INSTITUT FUER FINANZWISSENSCHAFT UND STEUERRECHT. GELBE BRIEFE. Text in German. 1960. 6/yr. membership. abstr. **Document type:** *Bulletin.*
Published by: Institut fuer Finanzwissenschaft und Steuerrecht, Seilerstaette 24, Vienna, W 1010, Austria. TEL 01-5129910. Ed. Anton Matzinger. Circ: 730.

336 332 AUT
INSTITUT FUER FINANZWISSENSCHAFT UND STEUERRECHT. MITTEILUNGSBLATT. Text in German. 1960. 4/yr. membership. **Document type:** *Newsletter.*
Published by: Institut fuer Finanzwissenschaft und Steuerrecht, Seilerstaette 24, Vienna, W 1010, Austria. TEL 01-5129910. Ed. Anton Matzinger.

336.2 GBR ISSN 0961-3153
INSTITUTE FOR FISCAL STUDIES. COMMENTARY. Text in English. 198?. irreg.
—BLDSC (4363.338600), IE.
Published by: Institute for Fiscal Studies, 7 Ridgmount St, 3d Fl, London, WC1E 7AE, United Kingdom. TEL 44-20-72914800, FAX 44-20-73234780, mailbox@ifs.org.uk, http://www.ifs.org.uk.

336.2 GBR ISSN 1369-4685
INSTITUTE FOR FISCAL STUDIES. WORKING PAPERS. Variant title: Institute for Fiscal Studies. Working Paper Series. Text in English. 1979. irreg.
—BLDSC (4363.343505).
Published by: Institute for Fiscal Studies, 7 Ridgmount St, 3d Fl, London, WC1E 7AE, United Kingdom. TEL 44-20-72914800, FAX 44-20-73234780, mailbox@ifs.org.uk, http://www.ifs.org.uk.

336 GBR ISSN 0260-6496
INSTITUTE OF CHARTERED ACCOUNTANTS IN ENGLAND AND WALES. TAX DIGEST. Text in English. 1980. irreg. GBP 210; GBP 241.50 foreign (effective 2000). **Document type:** *Trade.*
—BLDSC (8611.590000), IE, ingenta.
Published by: (Institute of Chartered Accountants in England and Wales), A B G Professional Information (Subsidiary of: Croner.C C H Group Ltd.), 145 London Rd, Kingston upon Thames, KT2 6SR, United Kingdom. TEL 44-20-85473333, FAX 44-20-85472637, lovellv@croner.cch.co.uk, http://www.abgweb.com/. Circ: 1,500.

368 USA ISSN 0890-9164
KF6495.I5
THE INSURANCE TAX REVIEW. Text in English. 1986. m. USD 649 (effective 1999). back issues avail. **Document type:** *Trade.* **Description:** Covers federal and state taxation of insurance companies, products and policyholders with full text documents and commentary.
Related titles: Online - full text ed.: (from LexisNexis).
—CCC.
Published by: Tax Analysts, 6830 N Fairfax Dr, Arlington, VA 22213. TEL 703-553-4400, 800-955-3444, FAX 703-533-4444.

343.04 AUS ISSN 1328-4762
INTAX. Text in English. 11/yr. AUD 300 (effective 2003). **Document type:** *Magazine, Trade.* **Description:** Covers news and tax related issues.
Related titles: Online - full content ed.: AUD 300 for practices with up to 20 practitioners (effective 2003).
Published by: Australian Tax Practice (Subsidiary of: Thomson Legal & Regulatory Ltd.), PO Box 3502, Rozelle, NSW 2039, Australia. ATPOnlineService@thomson.com.au, http://onlineecom01.thomson.com.au/thomson/Catalog.asp?EES_CMD=SI&EES_ID=100207, http://www.atp-online.com.au/

336 ARG
INTER-AMERICAN CENTER OF TAX ADMINISTRATORS. INFORMATIVO - NEWSLETTER✶ . Text in English, Spanish. 1968. bi-m. USD 12. bk.rev. illus. back issues avail.
Published by: Inter-American Center of Tax Administrators/Centro Interamericano de Administradores Tributarios, San Jose 83, 2do piso, Buenos Aires, Argentina. Circ: 2,500.

336 USA ISSN 0885-0437
KF6275.99
INTERNAL REVENUE ACTS. Text in English. 1954. a., latest 2003. USD 72 per vol. (effective 2004). back issues avail. **Document type:** *Trade.*
Related titles: Microfiche ed.: (from WSH).
Published by: Thomson West (Subsidiary of: Thomson Corporation, The), 610 Opperman Dr, Eagan, MN 55123-1396. TEL 651-687-8000, 800-328-9352, FAX 651-687-7302, http://west.thomson.com/product/15511682/product.asp.

336 USA ISSN 0163-7177
KF6276.526.A19
INTERNAL REVENUE CODE. Cover title: Complete Internal Revenue Code. Text in English. a. USD 92.75 (effective 2005). **Document type:** *Trade.* **Description:** Contains more than 40 years of legislative history, back to 1954, including coverage of the latest Code changes prior to publication. This comprehensive, portable paperback provides the entire Code in one convenient, easy-to-use volume.
Indexed: ATI.
—CCC.
Published by: R I A (Subsidiary of: Thomson Corporation), 395 Hudson St, New York, NY 10014. TEL 212-367-6300, RIA.CustomerServices@Thomson.com, http://ria.thomson.com/tax_accounting/internal_revenue_code.asp.

336 USA ISSN 0364-0620
KF6282.A2
INTERNAL REVENUE CUMULATIVE BULLETIN. Text in English. 1922. a. USD 47. reprint service avail. from WSH. **Document type:** *Government.*
Formerly (until 1969): Internal Revenue Bulletin. Cumulative Bulletin (0145-6040)
Related titles: Microfiche ed.: (from WSH).
Published by: U.S. Internal Revenue Service, 1111 Constitution Ave, N W, Washington, DC 20224. TEL 800-829-1040, http://www.irs.gov. **Dist. by:** Bernan Press, 4611-F Assembly Dr, Lanham, MD 20706-4391. http://www.bernan.com.

336 USA
INTERNAL REVENUE MANUAL - ABRIDGED AND ANNOTATED. Variant title: Internal Revenue Manual. Text in English. 3 base vols. plus q. updates. looseleaf. USD 449.50 (effective 2004). 4000 p./no.; **Document type:** *Trade.* **Description:** Provides an abridgement, supplemented with annotations, of the IRS's massive official Internal Revenue Manual.
Published by: Thomson West (Subsidiary of: Thomson Corporation, The), 610 Opperman Dr, Eagan, MN 55123-1396. TEL 651-687-8000, 800-328-4880, FAX 651-687-7302, customer.service@westgroup.com, http://west.thomson.com/product/13514919/product.asp. Ed. Bryan Gates.

336 USA
INTERNAL REVENUE MANUAL - AUDIT AND ADMINISTRATION. Text in English. 1977. 6 base vols. plus irreg. updates. USD 1,394 base vol(s). (effective 2004). **Document type:** *Government.* **Description:** This two-part product includes Administration & Audit. Administration: Six volumes covering MSSPs administration, collection, employee plans and exempt organizations, appeals, criminal investigation and inspection divisions, including the division on penalty administration. Updated on a weekly basis or as needed, depending on the availability of material from the IRS. Audit: Four volumes containing MSSPs and procedural information pertaining generally to examination principles and to audits on specific tax issues such as the oil and gas industry. Published as often as the IRS updates the material.
Related titles: CD-ROM ed.: USD 1,202 (effective 2004); Online - full text ed.
Published by: C C H Inc., 2700 Lake Cook Rd, Riverwoods, IL 60015. TEL 847-267-7000, 800-449-6439, FAX 800-224-8299, cust_serv@cch.com, http://www.cch.com. Pub. Kevin Robert.

336 CHE ISSN 0074-1744
INTERNATIONAL ASSOCIATION OF STATE LOTTERIES. (REPORTS OF CONGRESS). (Reports published in host country) Text in English. 1974. biennial. CHF 8, USD 300. adv. bk.rev. **Document type:** *Proceedings.*
Published by: International Association of State Lotteries, Hirschengraben 62, PO Box 644, Zuerich, 8021, Switzerland. Circ: 1,000.

336 NLD ISSN 0074-2104
INTERNATIONAL BUREAU OF FISCAL DOCUMENTATION. ANNUAL REPORT. Text in English. 1953. a. free. **Document type:** *Corporate.* **Description:** Discusses IBFD's activities over the past year and its plans for the future.
Indexed: RASB.
—BLDSC (1309.900000).
Published by: (International Bureau of Fiscal Documentation), I B F D Publications BV, H J E Wenckebachweg 210, PO Box 20237, Amsterdam, 1000 HE, Netherlands. TEL 31-20-554-0100, FAX 31-20-620-8626, http://www.ibfd.nl. Ed. H M A L Hamaekers.

336.2 BEL ISSN 1378-4048
INTERNATIONAL CUSTOMS JOURNAL/BULLETIN INTERNATIONAL DES DOUANES. Text in English, French, German, Italian, Spanish. 1891. irreg. price varies.
Published by: International Customs Tariffs Bureau/Bureau International des Tarifs Douaniers, Rue de l'Association 38, Brussels, 1000, Belgium. Circ: 4,500. **Subscr. in the US to:** U.S. Department of Commerce, National Technical Information Service, 5285 Port Royal Rd, Springfield, VA 22161. TEL 703-605-6060, 800-363-2068, FAX 703-605-6880, subscriptions@ntis.gov.

INTERNATIONAL ENERGY: LAW AND TAXATION REVIEW. see *ENERGY*

336.2 USA
INTERNATIONAL FINANCE: TAX & REGULATION ADVISOR. Text in English. s-m. USD 945 domestic; USD 975 foreign (effective 2005). adv. **Document type:** *Newsletter, Trade.* **Description:** Contains solid, trusted, timely advice on corporate finance regulatory issues ranging from international accounting regulations, governmental hurdles for regional tax planning and financing strategies, to regulatory issues such antitrust, securities regulation or financial governance matters.
Published by: WorldTrade Executive, Inc., 2250 Main St, Ste 100, PO Box 761, Concord, MA 01742. TEL 978-287-0301, FAX 978-287-0302, smahapatra@wtexec.com, info@wtexec.com, http://www.wtexecutive.com/cms/content.jsp?id=com.tms.cms.section.Section_1024_sub_options, http://www.wtexec.com. Pub. Gary A Brown. Adv. contact Jay Stanley.

336.2 NLD
THE INTERNATIONAL GUIDE TO ADVANCE RULINGS. Text in English. 1997. 3 base vols. plus a. updates. looseleaf. USD 625 base vol(s).; USD 275 updates (effective 2002). **Document type:** *Trade.* **Description:** Presents information concerning advance private rulings.
Published by: (International Bureau of Fiscal Documentation), I B F D Publications BV, H J E Wenckebachweg 210, PO Box 20237, Amsterdam, 1000 HE, Netherlands. TEL 31-20-554-0100, FAX 31-20-620-8626, info@ibfd.nl, http://www.ibfd.nl.

336 NLD
INTERNATIONAL GUIDE TO MERGERS AND ACQUISITIONS. Text in English. 1992. 3 base vols. plus s-a. updates. looseleaf. USD 940 base vol(s).; USD 450 updates (effective 2002). **Document type:** *Trade.* **Description:** Provides practical advice for tax specialists involved in domestic and transnational mergers, acquisitions and reorganizations, covering relevant tax regulations, legislation, and company law.
Published by: (International Bureau of Fiscal Documentation), I B F D Publications BV, H J E Wenckebachweg 210, PO Box 20237, Amsterdam, 1000 HE, Netherlands. TEL 31-20-554-0100, FAX 31-20-620-8626, info@ibfd.nl, http://www.ibfd.nl. Ed. Claudia Daiber.

336 NLD
THE INTERNATIONAL GUIDE TO PARTNERSHIPS. Text in English. 1996. base vol. plus a. updates. looseleaf. USD 590 base vol(s).; USD 160 updates (effective 2002). **Document type:** *Trade.* **Description:** Provides complete coverage of the company and tax law applying to partnerships, including international aspects.
Published by: (International Bureau of Fiscal Documentation), I B F D Publications BV, H J E Wenckebachweg 210, PO Box 20237, Amsterdam, 1000 HE, Netherlands. TEL 31-20-554-0100, FAX 31-20-620-8626, info@ibfd.nl, http://www.ibfd.nl. Ed. Kees van Raad.

336.2 332.6 GBR
THE INTERNATIONAL GUIDE TO TAXATION OF LIFE ASSURANCE AND MUTUAL FUNDS. Text in English. base vol. plus irreg. updates. looseleaf. GBP 525 for base volume; GBP 233 for update; USD 1,030 for base volume; USD 466 for update (effective 2000). **Document type:** *Trade.* **Description:** Answers questions on taxation that buyers and sellers of financial services products raise.
Published by: Monitor Press Ltd. (Subsidiary of: T & F Informa plc), Suffolk House, Church Field Rd, Sudbury, Suffolk CO10 2YA, United Kingdom. TEL 44-1787-378607, FAX 44-1787-881147. Ed. Tony Wickenden. **Subscr. in the US to:** IBC (USA), 290 Eliot St, Box 91004, Ashland, MA 01721-9104. TEL 508-881-2800, FAX 508-881-0982.

336 NLD
THE INTERNATIONAL GUIDE TO THE TAXATION OF HOLDING COMPANIES. Text in English. 2001. base vol. plus a. updates. USD 540 base vol(s). (effective 2002).
Published by: I B F D Publications BV, H J E Wenckebachweg 210, PO Box 20237, Amsterdam, 1000 HE, Netherlands. TEL 31-20-554-0100, FAX 31-20-620-8626, info@ibfd.nl, http://www.ibfd.nl.

336.2 332.63 346.04 NLD
THE INTERNATIONAL GUIDE TO THE TAXATION OF REAL ESTATE. Text in English. 1999. 2 base vols. plus a. updates. looseleaf. USD 700 base vol(s).; USD 275 updates (effective 2002). **Document type:** *Trade.* **Description:** Examines how real estate investments are dealt with internationally, looking at three possibilities: by individuals, directly or indirectly through resident companies, or through non-resident companies.
Published by: (International Bureau of Fiscal Documentation), I B F D Publications BV, H J E Wenckebachweg 210, PO Box 20237, Amsterdam, 1000 HE, Netherlands. TEL 31-20-554-0100, FAX 31-20-620-8626, info@ibfd.nl, http://www.ibfd.nl. **Subscr. to:** I B F D Publications USA, Inc, PO Box 805, Valatie, NY 12184-0805.

336 NLD
THE INTERNATIONAL GUIDE TO THE TAXATION OF SPORTSMEN AND SPORTSWOMEN. Text in English. 2001. base vol. plus s-a. updates. USD 540 base vol(s). (effective 2002).
Published by: I B F D Publications BV, H J E Wenckebachweg 210, PO Box 20237, Amsterdam, 1000 HE, Netherlands. TEL 31-20-554-0100, FAX 31-20-620-8626, info@ibfd.nl, http://www.ibfd.nl.

336 NLD
THE INTERNATIONAL GUIDE TO THE TAXATION OF TRANSFERS OF TECHNOLOGY. Text in English. 2001. base vol. plus a. updates. USD 450 base vol(s). (effective 2002).
Published by: I B F D Publications BV, H J E Wenckebachweg 210, PO Box 20237, Amsterdam, 1000 HE, Netherlands. TEL 31-20-554-0100, FAX 31-20-620-8626, info@ibfd.nl, http://www.ibfd.nl.

336.2 NLD
THE INTERNATIONAL GUIDE TO THE TAXATION OF TRUSTS. Text in English. 1999. base vol. plus a. updates. looseleaf. USD 565 base vol(s).; USD 60 updates (effective 2002). **Document type:** *Trade.* **Description:** Explains the principles governing the taxation of trusts in countries surveyed, stating clearly where the difficulties and points of uncertainty are.
Published by: (International Bureau of Fiscal Documentation), I B F D Publications BV, H J E Wenckebachweg 210, PO Box 20237, Amsterdam, 1000 HE, Netherlands. TEL 31-20-554-0100, FAX 31-20-620-8626, info@ibfd.nl, http://www.ibfd.nl.

INTERNATIONAL INCOME TAX & ESTATE PLANNING. see *LAW—Estate Planning*

336 341 USA
INTERNATIONAL INCOME TAX RULES OF THE UNITED STATES. Text in English. 1989. latest 2000, 2 base vols. plus irreg. updates. looseleaf. USD 270 (effective 2003). Supplement avail. **Description:** Describes international tax rules of the United States, concentrating on the tax rules that resolve potential conflicts between the US claims for tax revenue from transnational income and the claims of other national tax jurisdictions.
Published by: Michie Company (Subsidiary of: LexisNexis North America), 701 E Water St, Charlottesville, VA 22902-5389. TEL 434-972-7600, 800-446-3410, FAX 434-972-7677, http://www.michie.com. Ed. Michael J McIntyre.

336 USA
INTERNATIONAL PERSONAL TAX PLANNING ENCYCLOPEDIA. Variant title: Lawrence International Personal Tax Planning Encyclopaedia. Text in English. 1990. 2 base vols. plus a. updates. looseleaf. USD 175. Supplement avail.
Published by: LexisNexis (Subsidiary of: LexisNexis North America), PO Box 7587, Charlottesville, VA 22906-7587. TEL 800-562-1197, FAX 804-972-7666, llp.customer.support@lexis-nexis.com, http://www.lexislawpublishing.com. Ed. Robert C Lawrence III.

336 IND
INTERNATIONAL PRESS CUTTING SERVICE: CENTRAL EXCISE NOTIFICATIONS AND NEWS. Text in English. w. INR 725, USD 85 (effective 1999). **Document type:** *Newsletter.* **Description:** Contains news about excise notifications in India.
Published by: International Press Cutting Service, PO Box 121, Allahabad, Uttar Pradesh 211 001, India. TEL 91-532-622392.

336.2 332 IND ISSN 0047-1097
INTERNATIONAL PRESS CUTTING SERVICE: TAXATION - FINANCE - COMPANY LAW. Text in English. 1967. w. INR 735, USD 85 (effective 1999). bk.rev. index. **Document type:** *Newsletter.* **Description:** Covers laws concerning tax, finance and Company Laws in India.
Media: Duplicated (not offset).
Published by: International Press Cutting Service, PO Box 121, Allahabad, Uttar Pradesh 211 001, India. TEL 91-532-622392. Ed. Nandi Khanna. Circ: 1,200.

INTERNATIONAL STUDIES ON SOCIAL SECURITY. see *INSURANCE*

336.2 USA ISSN 0074-896X
INTERNATIONAL TAX AGREEMENTS. Text in English, French, Spanish. 1948. 3/w. **Description:** Provides information on the status of international taxation agreements on: income and fortune; movable capital; commercial, industrial and agricultural enterprises; and maritime and air transport enterprises.
Published by: United Nations, Dag Hammarskjold Library, United Nations, New York, NY 10017.

336 USA ISSN 0927-5940
HJ2240 CODEN: ITPFEB
➤ **INTERNATIONAL TAX AND PUBLIC FINANCE.** Text in English. 1993. bi-m. EUR 648, USD 668, GBP 428 combined subscription to institutions print & online eds. (effective 2005). back issues avail.; reprint service avail. from PSC. **Document type:** *Journal, Academic/Scholarly.* **Description:** Publishes theoretical and empirical studies of tax policies, including expenditure and financial policies.
Related titles: Online - full text ed.: ISSN 1573-6970 (from EBSCO Publishing, Gale Group, IngentaConnect, Kluwer Online, O C L C Online Computer Library Center, Inc., ProQuest Information & Learning, Springer LINK, Swets Information Services).
Indexed: ABIn, AgeL, BibLing, CurCont, ESPM, IBR, IBSS, IBZ, JEL, RefZh, RiskAb, SSCI.
—BLDSC (4550.392500), IDS, IE, Infotrieve, ingenta. **CCC.**
Published by: Springer-Verlag New York, Inc. (Subsidiary of: Springer Science+Business Media), 233 Spring St, New York, NY 10013. TEL 212-460-1500, FAX 212-460-1575, service@springer-ny.com, http://springerlink.metapress.com/openurl.asp?genre=journal&issn=0927-5940, http://www.springer-ny.com. Eds. John D Wilson, Michael Devereux. **Subscr. to:** Journal Fulfillment, PO Box 2485, Secaucus, NJ 07096-2485. TEL 201-348-4033, FAX 201-348-4505, journals@springer-ny.com.

336.2 USA
INTERNATIONAL TAX HAVENS. Text in English. 1990. a. USD 60.
Published by: LexisNexis (Subsidiary of: LexisNexis North America), PO Box 7587, Charlottesville, VA 22906-7587. TEL 804-972-7600, 800-562-1197, FAX 804-972-7666, llp.customer.support@lexis-nexis.com, http://www.lexislawpublishing.com. Ed. Anthony S Ginsberg.

336.2 USA ISSN 0097-7314
HJ2240
INTERNATIONAL TAX JOURNAL. Text in English. 1974. q. USD 297 (effective 2004). adv. bk.rev. charts; illus. back issues avail.; reprint service avail. from WSH. **Document type:** *Journal, Trade.* **Description:** Articles, columns and tax notes pertaining to the international tax market.
Related titles: Microfiche ed.: (from WSH); Microform ed.: (from PQC, WSH); Online - full text ed.: (from EBSCO Publishing, Gale Group, ProQuest Information & Learning).
Indexed: ABIn, ATI, BPI, BPIA, BusI, CLI, IBR, ILP, LRI, LegCont, PAIS, T&II.
—BLDSC (4550.398000), IE, Infotrieve, ingenta. **CCC.**
Published by: Panel Publishers, Inc. (Subsidiary of: Aspen Publishers, Inc.), 1185 Ave of the Americas, 37th Fl, New York, NY 10036. TEL 212-597-0200, 800-638-8437, FAX 212-597-0331, customer.service@aspenpubl.com, http://www.aspenpublishers.com. Ed. Tom Whitehill. **Dist. by:** Aspen Publishers, Inc., Distribution Center, 7201 McKinney Circle, Frederick, MD 21701. TEL 301-698-7100, FAX 301-695-7931.

336.2 USA ISSN 1535-7783
INTERNATIONAL TAX MONITOR. Text in English. d. USD 1,054 domestic (effective 2005 - 2006). back issues avail. **Document type:** *Newsletter, Trade.* **Description:** Provides international news and analysis, focusing on tax and accounting developments affecting transnational enterprises.
Media: Online - full text (from The Bureau of National Affairs, Inc.).
—CCC.

Published by: The Bureau of National Affairs, Inc., 1231 25th St., NW, Washington, DC 20037. TEL 800-372-1033, 800-452-7773, FAX 800-253-0332, customercare@bna.com, http://www.bna.com/products/tax/itdm.htm. **Subscr. to:** 9435 Key West Ave, Rockville, MD 20850.

336.2   GBR   ISSN 0300-1628
K9
INTERNATIONAL TAX REPORT; maximizing tax opportunities worldwide. Text in English. 1972. m. GBP 525; GBP 550, USD 1,100 foreign (effective 2000). bk.rev. bibl.; charts; stat. index. back issues avail. **Document type:** *Newsletter.* **Description:** Reports changes in international tax legislation and gives practical advice on tax planning strategies. Contains a conference calendar and a summary of world tax developments.
Incorporates: International Tax Digest (0955-498X)
Related titles: Online - full text ed.: (from Data-Star, ProQuest Information & Learning).
Indexed: ATI, RASB.
—CCC.
Published by: Monitor Press Ltd. (Subsidiary of: T & F Informa plc), Suffolk House, Church Field Rd, Sudbury, Suffolk CO10 2YA, United Kingdom. TEL 44-1787-378607, FAX 44-1787-881147, http://www.monitorpress.co.uk. Ed. Richard P Casna. Pub. Mary Ann Bonomo. Circ: 850.

INTERNATIONAL TAX REVIEW. see *BUSINESS AND ECONOMICS—International Commerce*

336   GBR
INTERNATIONAL TAX SYSTEMS AND PLANNING TECHNIQUES. Text in English. base vol. plus updates 2/yr. looseleaf. GBP 425 base vol(s).; GBP 415, EUR 617 updates in Europe; GBP 425, USD 776 updates elsewhere (effective 2005). **Document type:** *Bulletin.* **Description:** Advice on tax management and planning for multi-national businesses.
Published by: Gee Publishing Ltd. (Subsidiary of: Sweet & Maxwell Ltd.), 100 Avenue Road, Swiss Cottage, London, NW3 3PG, United Kingdom. TEL 44-20-73937400, FAX 44-20-73937915, customerliaison@gee.co.uk, http://www.gee.co.uk

336   USA
INTERNATIONAL TAXATION: CORPORATE AND INDIVIDUAL. Text in English. 1980. base vol. plus a. updates. USD 195. Supplement avail. **Document type:** *Trade.* **Description:** Examines the international tax consequences of transactions carried out by and occurring between corporations and their shareholders.
Formerly (until 1994): International Taxation
Related titles: Series of: International Publications Series.
Published by: Shepard's (Subsidiary of: LexisNexis North America), 555 Middle Creek Pkwy, Colorado Springs, CO 80921. TEL 800-743-7393, customer_service@shepards.com, http://www.shepards.com, http://www.lexisnexis.com/shepards/. Eds. Philip F Postlewaite, Tamara L Frantzen.

336.2   GBR
INTERNATIONAL TAXATION OF LOW TAX TRANSACTIONS. Text in English. 1996. s-a. looseleaf. USD 450. back issues avail.
Published by: B N A International Inc. (Subsidiary of: The Bureau of National Affairs, Inc.), 29th Fl, Millbank Tower, 21-24 Millbank, London, SW1P 4QP, United Kingdom. TEL 44-20-75594800, FAX 44-20-75594848, TELEX 262570 BNALDN G. Ed. S Joel Kolko.

341.57 665.5   USA   ISSN 1550-0845
INTERNATIONAL TAXATION SERIES. Text in English. 1972. base vol. plus m. updates. looseleaf. USD 4,900 base vol(s).; USD 2,400 updates (effective 2005). **Description:** Presents an overview of the taxation of oil and gas, with a summary and analysis for every country.
Published by: Barrows Co., Inc., 116 E 66th St, New York, NY 10021. TEL 212-772-1199, FAX 212-288-7242, barrows@bellatlantic.net, http://www.barrowscompany.com. Eds. G H Barrows, Marta Guerra.

INTERNATIONAL TRANSFER PRICING JOURNAL. see *BUSINESS AND ECONOMICS—Banking And Finance*

336.2   NLD   ISSN 0925-0832
K4573.A15
INTERNATIONAL V A T MONITOR. (Value Added Taxation) Text in English. 1990. bi-m. EUR 525 (effective 2005). back issues avail. **Document type:** *Trade.* **Description:** Covers current issues in VAT, including outlines of VAT policy and legislation within particular countries, case reviews, and relevant EC developments.
Related titles: Microfiche ed.; Online - full text ed.: (from Swets Information Services).
—IE.
Published by: (International Bureau of Fiscal Documentation), I B F D Publications BV, H J E Wenckebachweg 210, PO Box 20237, Amsterdam, 1000 HE, Netherlands. TEL 31-20-5540100, FAX 31-20-6228658, info@ibfd.nl, http://www.ibfd.nl. **Customer service in N. America:** I B F D Publications USA, Inc, PO Box 805, Valatie, NY 12184-0805. TEL 800-908-6330.

336.2   USA
INTERNATIONAL WITHHOLDING TAX TREATY GUIDE. Text in English. 1974. base vol. plus irreg. updates. looseleaf. USD 262 base vol(s). (effective 2002). **Description:** Provides the withholding tax rates for more than 1,800 treaties, worldwide, paid on: Interest on foreign loans, dividends, royalties, firm royalties, rentals, bank deposits, technical fees, shipping and aircraft income.
Published by: Matthew Bender & Co., Inc. (Subsidiary of: LexisNexis North America), 1275 Broadway, Albany, NY 12204. international@bender.com, http://bender.lexisnexis.com. Ed. Water Diamond.

336.2   DEU   ISSN 0020-9368
INTERNATIONALE WIRTSCHAFTS-BRIEFE; Zeitschrift fuer internationales Steuer- und Wirtschaftsrecht. Abbreviated title: I W B. Text in German. 1954. fortn. looseleaf. EUR 288; EUR 14 newsstand/cover (effective 2002). stat. index, cum.index. **Document type:** *Journal, Trade.*
—IE, Infotrieve. **CCC.**
Published by: (Deutsche Vereinigung fuer Internationales Steuerrecht), Verlag Neue Wirtschafts-Briefe GmbH & Co., Eschstr 22, Herne, 44629, Germany. TEL 49-2323-141900, FAX 49-2323-141123, info@nwb.de, http://www.nwb.de. Eds. Heinz-Klaus Kroppen, Helmut Becker. Circ: 3,500.

336   DEU   ISSN 0942-6744
K9
INTERNATIONALES STEUERRECHT; Zeitschrift fuer europaeische und internationale Steuer- und Wirtschaftsberatung. Abbreviated title: I St R. Text in German. 1992. 24/yr. EUR 380 domestic; EUR 419.20 foreign; EUR 302 to students; EUR 17.80 newsstand/cover (effective 2005). adv. reprint service avail. from SCH. **Document type:** *Journal, Trade.*
Indexed: IBR, IBZ.
Published by: (Bundessteuerberaterkammer), Verlag C.H. Beck oHG, Wilhelmstr 9, Munich, 80801, Germany. TEL 49-89-38189338, FAX 49-89-38189398, abo.service@beck.de, http://www.beck.de. adv.: B&W page EUR 1,550, color page EUR 2,712.50; trim 186 x 260. Circ: 2,700.

336.2013   USA   ISSN 1092-2180
KF6750.A15
INTERSTATE TAX INSIGHTS. Text in English. 1981. m. looseleaf. USD 195 (effective 2000). bk.rev. index. 16 p./no. 2 cols./p.; back issues avail. **Document type:** *Newsletter.*
Formerly (until Dec. 1996): Interstate Tax Report (0731-5651)
Published by: Interstate Tax Corporation, 83 East Ave., Ste. 110, Norwalk, CT 06851-4902. TEL 203-854-0704, FAX 203-853-9510. Ed. Caryl Nackenson Sheiber. Adv. contact Kay Tsahirides TEL 203-854-0704. Circ: 1,050.

INTERTAX; international tax review. see *BUSINESS AND ECONOMICS—International Commerce*

336.2   CAN   ISSN 0821-5340
INTRODUCTION TO FEDERAL INCOME TAXATION IN CANADA (YEAR). Text in English. 1981. a., latest 24th ed. USD 104.95 per issue (effective 2005). **Description:** Comprehensive text designed for students of taxation and appropriate for others in accounting, business, economics, and law interested in developing a general understanding of federal tax law. Contents are arranged in the same sequence as the organization of the Income Tax Act.
Published by: C C H Canadian Ltd., 90 Sheppard Ave E, Ste 300, North York, ON M2N 6X1, Canada. TEL 416-224-2248, 800-268-4522, FAX 416-224-2243, 800-461-4131, cservice@cch.ca, http://www.cch.ca. Ed. James Barnett.

INVESTING, LICENSING AND TRADING. GLOBAL EDITION. see *BUSINESS AND ECONOMICS—International Commerce*

INVESTING, LICENSING AND TRADING. SLOVAKIA. see *BUSINESS AND ECONOMICS—International Commerce*

336.2   NLD
INVESTMENT FUNDS. Text in English. 1996. 2 base vols. plus a. updates. looseleaf. USD 810 base vol(s).; USD 330 updates (effective 2002). **Document type:** *Directory, Trade.* **Description:** Provides an international guide to the taxation and regulation of mutual investment funds and their investors.
Published by: (International Bureau of Fiscal Documentation), I B F D Publications BV, H J E Wenckebachweg 210, PO Box 20237, Amsterdam, 1000 HE, Netherlands. TEL 31-20-554-0100, FAX 31-20-620-8626, info@ibfd.nl, http://www.ibfd.nl. Ed. Dali Bouzoraa.

IRELAND. CENTRAL STATISTICS OFFICE. BALANCE OF INTERNATIONAL PAYMENTS. see *BUSINESS AND ECONOMICS—Abstracting, Bibliographies, Statistics*

IRELAND. CENTRAL STATISTICS OFFICE. NATIONAL INCOME AND EXPENDITURE. see *BUSINESS AND ECONOMICS—Abstracting, Bibliographies, Statistics*

IRELAND. CENTRAL STATISTICS OFFICE. SUPPLY AND USE AND INPUT-OUTPUT TABLES. see *BUSINESS AND ECONOMICS—Abstracting, Bibliographies, Statistics*

336   IRL   ISSN 0075-0670
IRELAND. DEPARTMENT OF FINANCE. FINANCIAL STATEMENT OF THE MINISTER FOR FINANCE. Text in English. a.
Published by: Department of Finance, Dublin, Ireland.

336.2   IRL
IRISH TAX REVIEW. Text in English. bi-m. adv. **Document type:** *Magazine, Trade.* **Description:** Contains information on all aspects of taxation in Ireland.
Published by: Institute of Taxation in Ireland, 19 Sandymount Ave., Dublin, 4, Ireland. TEL 353-1-6688222, FAX 353-1-6688387, http://www.taxireland.ie. Adv. contact Martin Lambe. B&W page EUR 900, color page EUR 1,300. Circ: 5,200 (controlled).

IRREVOCABLE TRUSTS. see *LAW*

ISRAEL. CENTRAL BUREAU OF STATISTICS. LOCAL AUTHORITIES IN ISRAEL: FINANCIAL DATA. see *BUSINESS AND ECONOMICS—Abstracting, Bibliographies, Statistics*

336   ISR
ISRAEL. DEPARTMENT OF CUSTOMS AND V A T. YALKUT. (Value Added Tax) Text in Hebrew; Abstracts occasionally in English, Multiple languages. 1955. irreg. ILS 30, USD 20. **Document type:** *Government.*
Formerly: Israel. Department of Customs and Excise. Yalkut (0578-8250)
Published by: Department of Customs and V A T, Publication & Instruction Section, 32 Agron St, P O Box 320, Jerusalem, 91002, Israel. Circ: 1,500.

336   ISR
ISRAEL. KNESSET. VA'ADAT HA-KESAFIM. MISPARIM AL VA'ADAT HA-KESAFIM/ISRAEL. KNESSET. FINANCE COMMITTEE. DATA ON ACTIVITIES. Text in Hebrew. 1972. a.
Media: Duplicated (not offset).
Published by: (Israel. Finance Committee), Knesset, Jerusalem, Israel. Ed. Ivor Kershner. Circ: (controlled).

336   USA
IT'S YOUR MONEY (JEFFERSON CITY). Text in English. 1981. w.
Published by: Department of the Treasury, State Capitol, Jefferson City, MO 65101. TEL 314-751-2411. Ed. John Robinson. Circ: 700.

336   CIV
IVORY COAST. MINISTERE DE L'ECONOMIE, DES FINANCES ET DU PLAN. COMPTES DE LA NATION. Text in French. 1966. a. XOF 20,000.
Formerly: Ivory Coast. Ministere du Plan. Comptes de la Nation (1013-5863)
Published by: Ministere de l'Economie des Finances et du Plan, BP V125, Abidjan, Ivory Coast. TEL 225-21-48-92.

336.2   USA   ISSN 1056-3121
J.K. LASSER'S MONTHLY TAX LETTER *. Text in English. m. USD 24. **Document type:** *Newsletter.*
Former titles (until 1991): J.K. Lasser's Monthly Tax Service (0895-3147); (until 1987): Monthly Tax Service (0736-1505)
Published by: (J.K. Lasser Tax Institute), Prentice Hall, 405 Murray Hill Pkwy., E Rutherford, NJ 07073-2136.

336.24   USA   ISSN 0084-4314
J.K. LASSER'S YOUR INCOME TAX. Text in English. 1937. a. USD 14.95.
Published by: (J.K. Lasser Institute), Macmillan General Reference, 300 Park Ave., S, New York, NY 10010-5313. TEL 212-654-8500. Ed. Bernard Greisman.

336.2   USA   ISSN 0075-2061
KF6369
J.K. LASSER'S YOUR INCOME TAX, PROFESSIONAL EDITION. Text in English. 1962. a. USD 50.
Published by: (J.K. Lasser Institute), Macmillan General Reference, 300 Park Ave., S, New York, NY 10010-5313. TEL 212-654-8500.

336   DEU
JAHRBUCH DER FACHANWAELTE FUER STEUERRECHT. Text in German. a. back issues avail. **Document type:** *Yearbook, Trade.*
Published by: Verlag Neue Wirtschafts-Briefe GmbH & Co., Eschstr 22, Herne, 44629, Germany. TEL 49-2323-141900, FAX 49-2323-141123, info@nwb.de, http://www.nwb.de. Circ: 1,300 (paid).

336   USA
JAPANESE INTERNATIONAL TAXATION. Text in English. 1983. base vol. plus a. updates. looseleaf. USD 275 per vol. (effective 2005).
Published by: Juris Publishing, Inc., 71 New St, Huntington, NY 11743-3301. TEL 631-351-5430, 800-887-4064, FAX 631-351-5712, info@jurispub.com, http://www.jurispub.com/books.asp?id=102.

336.2 USA
JOINT FEDERAL/STATE TAX PRACTITIONER NEWSLETTER. Text in English. a. **Document type:** *Government.*
Published by: Department of Treasury, Division of Taxation, Technical Services, Taxpayer Services Branch, PO Box 281, Trenton, NJ 08646-0281. http://www.state.nj.us/treasury/taxation/.

JOURNAL DE DROIT FISCAL. see *LAW*

JOURNAL D'ECONOMIE MEDICALE. see *MEDICAL SCIENCES*

JOURNAL OF ACCOUNTING AND PUBLIC POLICY. see *BUSINESS AND ECONOMICS—Accounting*

JOURNAL OF CONSTRUCTION ACCOUNTING AND TAXATION. see *BUSINESS AND ECONOMICS—Accounting*

JOURNAL OF FINANCIAL PLANNING. see *BUSINESS AND ECONOMICS—Investments*

JOURNAL OF INTERNATIONAL ACCOUNTING, AUDITING AND TAXATION. see *BUSINESS AND ECONOMICS—Accounting*

336 USA ISSN 1049-6378
K4464.A13
JOURNAL OF INTERNATIONAL TAXATION. Text in English. 1990. base vol. plus m. updates. USD 350 (effective 2004). adv. charts. reprints avail. **Document type:** *Journal, Trade.* **Description:** Offers broad-based, in-depth coverage of U.S. taxation issues as they relate to international transactions. Also covers foreign taxation matters.
Related titles: Microform ed.: (from PQC); Online - full text ed.: (from ProQuest Information & Learning).
Indexed: ABIn, ABS&EES.
—BLDSC (5007.686800), IE, ingenta. **CCC.**
Published by: W G & L Financial Reporting & Management Research (Subsidiary of: R I A), 90 Fifth Ave, New York, NY 10011. TEL 212-645-4800, FAX 212-337-4280, http://www.wgl.com/tax/joit.html. Ed. Robert Gallagher. Adv. contact Margaret Lord York. Circ: 2,500.

336 USA ISSN 1533-3124
KF6750.A15
JOURNAL OF MULTISTATE TAXATION & INCENTIVES. Text in English. 1991. 10/yr. USD 255 (effective 1999). reprint service avail. from WSH. **Document type:** *Trade.* **Description:** Covers developments on planning in-state and local taxation nationwide; of interest to those involved in multistate operations and individuals with assets or investments in more than one state.
Formerly (until 1999): Journal of Multistate Taxation (1054-8394)
Related titles: Microform ed.: (from PQC); Online - full text ed.
Indexed: ATI.
—CCC.
Published by: W G & L Financial Reporting & Management Research (Subsidiary of: R I A), 90 Fifth Ave, New York, NY 10011. TEL 212-645-4800, FAX 212-337-4280. Pub. Joe Trapani. Circ: 2,200.

331.252 USA ISSN 0148-2181
K16
JOURNAL OF PENSION PLANNING AND COMPLIANCE. Text in English. 1974. q. USD 265 (effective 2004). back issues avail.; reprint service avail. from WSH. **Document type:** *Journal, Trade.* **Description:** Technical articles on major issues confronting the pension community.
Formerly: Pension and Profit-Sharing Tax Journal
Related titles: Microfiche ed.: (from WSH); Microform ed.: (from PQC, WSH); Online - full text ed.: (from EBSCO Publishing, Florida Center for Library Automation, Gale Group, ProQuest Information & Learning).
Indexed: ABIn, ATI, BPIA, BusI, CLI, FamI, ILP, LII, LRI, LegCont, ManagCont, PAIS, T&II.
—BLDSC (5030.520000), IE, ingenta. **CCC.**
Published by: Panel Publishers, Inc. (Subsidiary of: Aspen Publishers, Inc.), 1185 Ave of the Americas, 37th Fl, New York, NY 10036. TEL 212-597-0200, 800-638-8437, FAX 212-597-0331, customer.service@aspenpubl.com, http://www.aspenpublishers.com. Ed. Bruce J McNeil. **Dist. by:** Aspen Publishers, Inc., Distribution Center, 7201 McKinney Circle, Frederick, MD 21701. TEL 301-698-7100, FAX 301-695-7931.

JOURNAL OF PRACTICAL ESTATE PLANNING. see *LAW—Estate Planning*

336 333.33 GBR ISSN 1357-1419
JOURNAL OF PROPERTY TAX ASSESSMENT & ADMINISTRATION. Text in English. 1994. 3/yr. **Document type:** *Academic/Scholarly.*
—BLDSC (5042.781200), IE, ingenta.
Published by: University of Ulster, School of the Built Environment, Coleraine, Londonderry BT52 1SA, United Kingdom. Eds. Alastair Adair, William McCluskey.

336 USA ISSN 1538-2338
K10
JOURNAL OF PROPERTY VALUATION AND TAXATION. Text in English. 1989. q. USD 225 to individuals; USD 70 newsstand/cover (effective 2002). back issues avail. **Document type:** *Journal, Trade.* **Description:** Commentary on issues and legislation affecting property tax, property valuation and property appraisal.
Former titles (until 2001): Journal of Property Tax Management (1521-5962); Journal of Property Taxation (1041-4797)
Related titles: Online - full text ed.: (from EBSCO Publishing, Florida Center for Library Automation, Gale Group).
Indexed: ATI, CLI, LRI.
Published by: Panel Publishers, Inc. (Subsidiary of: Aspen Publishers, Inc.), 1185 Ave of the Americas, 37th Fl, New York, NY 10036. TEL 212-597-0200, 800-638-8437, FAX 212-597-0331, customer.service@aspenpubl.com, http://www.aspenpublishers.com. Eds. James T Collins, Sheree L Nelson.

336 USA ISSN 0744-6713
K10
JOURNAL OF STATE TAXATION. Text in English. q. USD 260 (effective 2004). back issues avail.; reprint service avail. from WSH. **Document type:** *Journal, Trade.* **Description:** Articles on state and local tax planning and compliance for tax management professionals.
Related titles: Microfiche ed.: (from WSH); Microform ed.: (from PQC, WSH); Online - full text ed.: (from EBSCO Publishing, Florida Center for Library Automation, Gale Group, ProQuest Information & Learning).
Indexed: ABIn, ATI, BPI, BPIA, CLI, ILP, LRI, LegCont, PAIS.
—CCC.
Published by: Panel Publishers, Inc. (Subsidiary of: Aspen Publishers, Inc.), 1185 Ave of the Americas, 37th Fl, New York, NY 10036. TEL 212-597-0200, 800-638-8437, FAX 212-597-0331, customer.service@aspenpubl.com, http://www.aspenpublishers.com. Ed. James T Collins. **Dist. by:** Aspen Publishers, Inc., Distribution Center, 7201 McKinney Circle, Frederick, MD 21701. TEL 301-698-7100, FAX 301-695-7931.

336.2 USA ISSN 1541-9169
KF299.T3
JOURNAL OF TAX PRACTICE MANAGEMENT. Text in English. 2002 (Sept.). bi-m. USD 225 (effective 2005). **Document type:** *Journal, Trade.* **Description:** Provides tax practitioners with up-to-date commentary and analysis on the issues that confront practitioners in a variety of areas, including human resources, client relationships, marketing and sales, technology, organizational development, compensation, strategic planning, and more.
Related titles: Online - full text ed.: (from EBSCO Publishing).
Indexed: ABIn.
Published by: C C H Inc., 2700 Lake Cook Rd, Riverwoods, IL 60015. TEL 847-267-7000, 800-449-6439, cust_serv@cch.com, http://www.cch.com. Ed. Jeffrey S Pawlow.

336.2 USA ISSN 0022-4863
CODEN: JOTAAM
JOURNAL OF TAXATION; a national journal of current developments, analysis, and commentary for tax professionals. Text in English. 1954. m. USD 270 in US & Canada (effective 2004). adv. bk.rev. charts; illus.; tr.lit. index. 64 p./no. 3 cols./p.; reprint service avail. from WSH,PQC. **Document type:** *Magazine, Trade.* **Description:** Contains articles on key tax developments. Provides analysis of significant court decisions and revenue rulings.
Related titles: Microform ed.: (from PQC); Online - full text ed.: (from ProQuest Information & Learning, Thomson West).
Indexed: ABIn, ASCA, ATI, AgeL, BLI, BPI, BPIA, BusI, CLI, CurCont, FamI, ILP, JEL, LOIS, LRI, LegCont, ManagCont, PAIS, SSCI, T&II.
—BLDSC (5068.200000), IDS, IE, Infotrieve, ingenta. **CCC.**
Published by: R I A (Subsidiary of: Thomson Corporation), 395 Hudson St, New York, NY 10014. TEL 212-367-6300, FAX 212-337-4186, RIAhome@riag.com, http://www.riahome.com. Ed. Joseph I Graf. Pub. Linda Scheffel. Adv. contact Terry Storholm. Circ: 14,000.

JOURNAL OF TAXATION AND REGULATION OF FINANCIAL INSTITUTION. see *BUSINESS AND ECONOMICS—Banking And Finance*

336 346.066 USA ISSN 1541-0803
K10
JOURNAL OF TAXATION OF CORPORATE TRANSACTIONS. Text in English. 2002. q. USD 225 (effective 2004). 48 p./no.; **Document type:** *Journal, Corporate.* **Description:** Covers critical developments in the corporate tax arena from the perspective of the transactional practitioner. It focuses on the relevance of these developments to practical strategies and planning opportunities.
Related titles: Online - full text ed.: USD 245 (effective 2004).
—CCC.
Published by: C C H Inc., 2700 Lake Cook Rd, Riverwoods, IL 60015. TEL 847-267-7000, 800-449-6439, FAX 800-224-8299, cust_serv@cch.com, http://www.cch.com. Ed. Kenneth L Harris. **Subscr. to:** 4025 W. Peterson Ave., Chicago, IL 60646-6085. TEL 773-866-6000, 800-835-5224, FAX 773-866-3895.

336 USA ISSN 1069-1294
KF6410.A15
JOURNAL OF TAXATION OF EMPLOYEE BENEFITS. Text in English. 1993. bi-m. reprint service avail. from WSH. **Document type:** *Trade.*
Related titles: Microform ed.: (from PQC).
—CCC.
Published by: W G & L Financial Reporting & Management Research (Subsidiary of: R I A), 90 Fifth Ave, New York, NY 10011. TEL 212-645-4800, FAX 212-337-4280, http://www.riatax.com/journals/jourhom.html. Ed. Deborah Walker. **Subscr. to:** 117 E Stevens Ave,, Valhalla, NY 10595.

336 USA ISSN 1043-0539
KF6449.A15
JOURNAL OF TAXATION OF EXEMPT ORGANIZATIONS. Text in English. 1989. bi-m. reprint service avail. from WSH. **Document type:** *Trade.* **Description:** Gives advice, strategies, and analysis of the current tax situation for tax-exempt organizations.
Related titles: Online - full text ed.
Indexed: ATI.
—CCC.
Published by: W G & L Financial Reporting & Management Research (Subsidiary of: R I A), 90 Fifth Ave, New York, NY 10011. TEL 212-645-4800, FAX 212-337-4280, http://www.riatax.com/journals/jourhom.html. Ed. Joseph E Lundy.

336.2 USA ISSN 1529-9287
JOURNAL OF TAXATION OF FINANCIAL PRODUCTS. Text in English. 2000. q. USD 225 (effective 2004). **Document type:** *Journal.* **Description:** Focuses exclusively on the analysis of the tax ramifications of financial products. It offers discussions on cutting-edge strategies and industry specific insights into regulatory developments, state and local tax, and international tax issues.
Related titles: Online - full text ed.: USD 245 (effective 2004).
—CCC.
Published by: C C H Inc., 2700 Lake Cook Rd, Riverwoods, IL 60015. TEL 847-267-7000, 800-449-6439, cust_serv@cch.com, http://www.cch.com.

336 USA ISSN 0747-9115
K10
JOURNAL OF TAXATION OF INVESTMENTS. Text in English. 1983. q. USD 203 domestic; USD 233 foreign (effective 2005). reprint service avail. from WSH. **Document type:** *Journal, Trade.* **Description:** Provides indispensable planning guidance on individual, institutional and corporate strategies for limiting the tax impact on investment portfolios.
Related titles: Online - full text ed.
Indexed: ABIn, ATI, CLI, FamI, ILP, LRI.
—BLDSC (5068.210000), IE, ingenta. **CCC.**
Published by: Civic Research Insitute, 4490 US Route 27, PO Box 585, Kingston, NJ 08528. TEL 609-683-4450, FAX 609-683-7291, order@civicresearchinstitute.com, http://www.civicresearchinstitute.com/tax1.html. Ed. Kevin M Keyes.

JUSTICE TECHNOLOGY MONITOR. see *CRIMINOLOGY AND LAW ENFORCEMENT*

343.24 ZAF
JUTA'S INCOME TAX. Text in English. 3 base vols. plus irreg. updates. looseleaf. ZAR 1,750 (effective 2001). **Document type:** *Academic/Scholarly.*
Published by: Juta & Company Ltd., Law and Professional Publishing Division, PO Box 14373, Kenwyn, 7790, South Africa. TEL 27-21-7975101, FAX 27-21-7970121, cserv@juta.co.za, http://www.juta.co.za.

KANO (STATE). PUBLIC FINANCE STATISTICS OF KANO STATE & LOCAL GOVERNMENT COUNCILS. see *BUSINESS AND ECONOMICS—Abstracting, Bibliographies, Statistics*

336 JPN ISSN 0286-1933
Q183.J32 CODEN: KCBSDI
KANZEI CHUO BUNSEKIJOHO* /CENTRAL CUSTOMS LABORATORY. REPORTS. Text in Japanese; Summaries in English, Japanese. 1965. a.
Indexed: CIN, ChemAb, ChemTitl, FS&TA, MSB.
—CASDDS.
Published by: Okurasho, Kanzei Chuo Bunsekijo/Ministry of Finance, Central Customs Laboratory, 6-3-5 Kasiwanoha, Kashiwa, Chiba 277-0882, Japan. ccl@mof.go.jp, http://www.customs.go.jp/ccl/.

336 IND
KARNATAKA. FINANCE DEPARTMENT. ANNUAL REPORT. Text in English. a.
Supersedes: Mysore. Finance Department. Annual Report
Published by: Finance Department, Bangalore, Karnataka, India.

KEEP UP TO DATE ON ACCOUNTS PAYABLE. see *BUSINESS AND ECONOMICS—Accounting*

▼ new title ➤ refereed * unverified ♦ full entry avail.

B

336.3 USA ISSN 0095-1498
HJ9243.4
KENTUCKY LOCAL DEBT REPORT; a detailed statement of the bonded indebtedness of all Kentucky units of local government. Text in English. 1971. a. **Document type:** *Government.* **Description:** Contains comprehensive data for all local government bonded indebtedness (county, city, school, special district) presented for each unit of local government by purpose.
Published by: Office of the Controller, State Local Debt Office, 702 Capital Ave, Rm 069, Capitol Annex, Frankfort, KY 40601. TEL 502-564-3710. Ed. Nancy Rodgers.

336 KEN ISSN 0075-5931
KENYA. PUBLIC ACCOUNTS COMMITTEE. ANNUAL REPORT. Text in English. a. **Document type:** *Government.*
Published by: (Kenya. Public Accounts Committee), Government Printing and Stationery Department, PO Box 30128, Nairobi, Kenya.

343.73 347.3 USA ISSN 0023-1762
HJ9
KIPLINGER TAX LETTER. Text in English. 1925. fortn. USD 59 (effective 2004). charts; stat. **Document type:** *Newsletter, Consumer.* **Description:** News focusing on tax issues and problems associated with personal or business financial management.
Related titles: Online - full text ed.: (from bigchalk, Florida Center for Library Automation, Gale Group, H.W. Wilson, LexisNexis, O C L C Online Computer Library Center, Inc., ProQuest Information & Learning).
Indexed: BPI.
—CCC.
Published by: Kiplinger Washington Editors, Inc., 1729 H St, N W, Washington, DC 20006. TEL 888-419-0424, FAX 202-778-8976, http://www.kiplinger.com/newsletter/tax.html. Ed., Pub. Knight A Kiplinger.

336.2 NLD ISSN 0923-5051
KLUWER BELASTINGGIDS. Text in Dutch. 1971. a. adv.
Document type: *Trade.*
Published by: Kluwer B.V. (Subsidiary of: Wolters Kluwer N.V.), Postbus 23, Deventer, 7400 GA, Netherlands. TEL 31-570-673449, FAX 31-570-691555, juridisch@kluwer.nl, http://www.kluwer.nl. Circ: 80,000 (paid).

336.2 NLD ISSN 0923-8468
KLUWER LOONBELASTINGGIDS. Variant title: Loonbelastinggids. Text in Dutch. 1982. a. EUR 39.75 (effective 2003). adv.
Published by: Kluwer B.V. (Subsidiary of: Wolters Kluwer N.V.), Postbus 23, Deventer, 7400 GA, Netherlands. TEL 31-570-673449, FAX 31-570-691555, juridisch@kluwer.nl, http://www.kluwer.nl. Circ: 2,500 (paid).

336.249 NLD
KLUWER SOVAC SERIES ON SOCIAL SECURITY. Variant title: Sovac Series on Social Security. Text in Dutch. irreg., latest 1996, Nov. EUR 164 (effective 2004). **Document type:** *Monographic series, Academic/Scholarly.*
—BLDSC (5099.737000).
Published by: Kluwer Law International (Subsidiary of: Aspen Publishers, Inc.), Laan van Meerdervoort 70, PO Box 85889, The Hague, 2508 CN, Netherlands. TEL 31-70-3081500, FAX 31-70-3081515, sales@kluwerlaw.com, http://www.kluwerlaw.com.

336.2 DEU ISSN 0450-7126
KOMMUNALE STEUER - ZEITSCHRIFT; Zeitschrift fuer das gesamte Gemeindeabgabenwesen. Text in German. 1952. m. **Document type:** *Journal, Trade.*
—IE, Infotrieve.
Published by: Verlag Reckinger & Co, Postfach 1754, Siegburg, 53707, Germany. TEL 49-2241-65096, FAX 49-2241-56975.

336.2 657 RUS ISSN 0869-7272
KONSUL'TANT/CONSULTANT; informatsionno-spravochnyi zhurnal dlia bukhgalterov i rukovoditelii predpriyatii. Text in Russian. 1993. bi-w. USD 295 in United States.
Indexed: RASB.
—East View.
Published by: Mezhdunarodnyi Tsentr Finansovo-Ekonomicheskogo Razvitiya, Ul Komdiva Orlova 2-37, korp 3, Moscow, 127106, Russian Federation. TEL 7-095-2825123, FAX 7-095-2866116. Ed. O I Parkani. **US dist. addr.:** East View Information Services, 3020 Harbor Ln. N., Minneapolis, MN 55447. TEL 612-550-0961.

336.2 657 RUS
KONSUL'TANT BUKHGALTERA. Text in Russian. m. USD 199.95 in United States.
Indexed: RASB.
Published by: Izdatel'stvo Delo i Servis, A-ya 530, Moscow, 121096, Russian Federation. TEL 7-095-1626504, FAX 7-095-1617091. Ed. Yu I Ivanov. **US dist. addr.:** East View Information Services, 3020 Harbor Ln. N., Minneapolis, MN 55447. TEL 612-550-0961.

336.2 657 RUS
KONSUL'TANT DIREKTORA. Text in Russian. 24/yr. USD 319.95 in United States.

Published by: Izdatel'skii Dom Infra M, Dmitrovskoe shosse 8-a, Moscow, 127214, Russian Federation. TEL 7-095-4855779, FAX 7-095-4855318. Ed. V M Prudnikov. **US dist. addr.:** East View Information Services, 3020 Harbor Ln. N., Minneapolis, MN 55447. TEL 612-550-0961.

▼ **DER KONZERN IN RECHT UND WIRTSCHAFT;** Zeitschrift fuer Gesellschaftrecht, Steuerrecht, Bilanzrecht und Rechnungslegung der verbundenen Unternehmen. see *LAW—Corporate Law*

L V AKTUELL. see *LAW*

336 FRA
LAMY FISCALITE DES OPERATIONS INTERNATIONALES. Text in French. irreg. EUR 746.94 print & CD-ROM eds. (effective 2004).
Related titles: Online - full text ed.: EUR 217 (effective 2003).
Published by: Lamy S.A. (Subsidiary of: Wolters Kluwer France), 21/23 rue des Ardennes, Paris, 75935 Cedex 19, France. TEL 33-1-825080800, FAX 33-1-44721388, lamy@lamy.fr, http://www.lamy.fr.

LAND AND LIBERTY; quarterly journal for land value taxation and free trade. see *REAL ESTATE*

336.2 NLD
LATIN AMERICAN TAXATION DATA BASE ON CD-ROM. Text in Dutch. 4/yr. looseleaf. USD 760 (effective 2002). **Document type:** *Trade.* **Description:** Covers international taxation issues pertaining to Latin America.
Media: CD-ROM.
Published by: (International Bureau of Fiscal Documentation), I B F D Publications BV, H J E Wenckebachweg 210, PO Box 20237, Amsterdam, 1000 HE, Netherlands. TEL 31-20-554-0100, FAX 31-20-620-8626, info@ibfd.nl, http://www.ibfd.nl.

336.2 USA
LEGALINES: INCOME TAX KEYED TO THE FREELAND CASEBOOK. Text in English. irreg., latest vol.9. USD 18.95 per vol. **Document type:** *Trade.*
Published by: Gilbert Law Summaries (Subsidiary of: B A R / B R I Group), 111 W Jackson, 7th Fl, Chicago, IL 60604. TEL 312-853-3662, 800-787-8717, FAX 312-853-3622, http://www.gilbertlaw.com.

336.2 USA
LEGALINES: INCOME TAX KEYED TO THE KLEIN CASEBOOK. Text in English. irreg., latest vol.11. USD 18.95 per vol. **Document type:** *Trade.*
Published by: Gilbert Law Summaries (Subsidiary of: B A R / B R I Group), 111 W Jackson, 7th Fl, Chicago, IL 60604. TEL 312-853-3662, 800-787-8717, FAX 312-853-3622, http://www.gilbertlaw.com.

LEGALINES: PARTNERSHIP & CORPORATE TAX KEYED TO THE SURREY CASEBOOK. see *LAW—Corporate Law*

332 ESP ISSN 1135-9145
LEGISLACION FISCAL. Text in Spanish. 1996. bi-w.
Related titles: ◆ Supplement to: Impuestos. ISSN 0213-0548.
Published by: La Ley, Calle Collado Mediano, No. 9, Las Rozas (Madrid), 28230, Spain. TEL 34-902-420010, FAX 34-902-420012, clientes@laley.net, http://www.laley.net/. Ed. Julio Banacloche.

336 343.05 USA
HJ3698.A295T38
LEGISLATIVE TAX BILL SERVICE. Text in English. 1966. w. (during legislature session). USD 1,000 (effective 1999). s-a. index. **Description:** Covers tax legislation introduced during the legislative session.
Published by: Tax Foundation of Hawaii, 126 Queen St, Ste 304, Honolulu, HI 96813-4415. Ed. Lowell L Kalapa. Circ: 415.

336 LSO ISSN 0075-8817
LESOTHO. TREASURY. REPORT ON THE FINANCES AND ACCOUNTS. Text in English. a. ZAR 4. **Document type:** *Government.*
Published by: Treasury, PO Box 401, Maseru, Lesotho.

LEXIKON DES STEUER- UND WIRTSCHAFTSRECHTS. see *LAW*

336 LBR ISSN 0304-727X
HJ89.L5
LIBERIA. MINISTRY OF FINANCE. ANNUAL REPORT✱ . Text in English. 1972. a. charts; stat.
Published by: Ministry of Finance, Broad St., Monrovia, Liberia.

336.666 LBR
LIBERIA. MINISTRY OF PLANNING AND ECONOMIC AFFAIRS. GOVERNMENT ACCOUNTS✱ . Text in English. a., latest 1980. USD 3. stat.
Published by: Ministry of Planning and Economic Affairs, PO Box 9016, Monrovia, Liberia.

---

336 USA
LIFE AND TAXES. Text in English. 1968. a. free. bk.rev.
Document type: *Newsletter.* **Description:** Covers recent regional gatherings, future events and activities. Includes anti-tax articles.
Formerly: New England War Tax Resistance Newsletter
Published by: New England War Tax Resistance, PO Box 397174, Cambridge, MA 02139. TEL 617-859-0662. Circ: 800.

336 USA ISSN 0892-516X
LIMITED PARTNERSHIP INVESTMENT REVIEW. Text in English. 1980. m. USD 197. adv. bk.rev. charts; stat. index. back issues avail. **Description:** Offers detailed analyses of risks, tax consequences, general partners' track records.
Formerly (until June 1987): Tax Shelter Investment Review
Related titles: Online - full text ed.
Published by: Limited Partnership Investment Review, Inc., 55 Morris Ave, Springfield, NJ 07081. TEL 201-467-8700, FAX 201-467-0368. Ed. David W Kennedy.

336 USA
LIQUOR CONTROL LAW REPORTS; federal and all states. Text in English. 9 base vols. plus bi-w. updates. USD 4,143 base vol(s). (effective 2004). **Description:** Covers the taxation and regulation of alcoholic beverages since the repeal of Prohibition in 1933. Covers the latest information about the taxation on alcoholic beverages in all 50 states, the District of Columbia, and Puerto Rico.
Published by: C C H Inc., 2700 Lake Cook Rd, Riverwoods, IL 60015. TEL 847-267-7000, 800-449-6439, FAX 800-224-8299, cust_serv@cch.com, http://www.cch.com. Pub. Kevin Robert.

LIST OF PARTIES EXCLUDED FROM FEDERAL PROCUREMENT AND NONPROCUREMENT PROGRAMS. see *PUBLIC ADMINISTRATION*

336 USA
LITIGATION OF FEDERAL TAX CONTROVERSIES. Text in English. 1986. base vol. plus a. updates. looseleaf. USD 125. Supplement avail. **Document type:** *Trade.* **Description:** Covers Tax Court practice, tax-refund litigation and general civil tax litigation, with emphasis on prelitigation strategy.
Related titles: Series of: Tax and Estate Planning Series.
Published by: Shepard's (Subsidiary of: LexisNexis North America), 555 Middle Creek Pkwy, Colorado Springs, CO 80921. TEL 800-743-7393, customer_service@shepards.com, http://www.shepards.com, http://www.lexisnexis.com/shepards/. Eds. F Gerald Burnett, Gerald Kafka.

336 USA ISSN 0085-2821
HJ9011.M3
LOCAL GOVERNMENT FINANCES IN MARYLAND. Text in English. 1948. a., latest vol.999, 2001. free. stat. **Document type:** *Government.* **Description:** Gives a financial report on the counties, incorporated municipalities, and special districts of Maryland.
Media: Duplicated (not offset). **Related titles:** Microfiche ed.: (from PQC).
Indexed: SRI.
Published by: Department of Legislative Services Library, 90 State Circle, Annapolis, MD 21401. TEL 410-946-5400, FAX 410-946-5405. Circ: (controlled).

336 GBR ISSN 1356-9805
LOCAL MANAGEMENT AND FINANCE. Text in English. fortn. GBP 95 domestic; GBP 110 foreign (effective 2002). adv. **Description:** Current awareness bulletin covering local government finance and management.
Formerly: Find - Financial Digest (0269-2503)
Published by: London Research Centre, Research Library, 81 Black Prince Rd, London, SE1 7SZ, United Kingdom. TEL 020-7983-4672, FAX 020-7983-4674, sue.williams@london.gov.uk. Adv. contact Sue Williams.

336.1 360 USA ISSN 0741-3173
HJ275.2
LOCAL - STATE FUNDING REPORT. Text in English. 1972. w. (50/yr.). USD 279. **Document type:** *Newsletter.* **Description:** Summarizes information on funding from federal and private sector sources. Covers developments in Congress, the White House and federal agencies.
Formerly (until 1983): Local Government Funding Report (0273-4451)
—CCC.
Published by: Government Information Services (Subsidiary of: Thompson Publishing Group), 1725 K St, N W, 7th Fl, Washington, DC 20006. TEL 800-876-0226, FAX 202-739-9657. Eds. Don Hoffman, Lisa Hayes.

351.72 DEU ISSN 0931-5802
LOHNSTEUER-MITTEILUNGEN. Text in German. 198?. m. EUR 37 (effective 2004). **Document type:** *Magazine, Trade.*
Published by: Datakontext Fachverlag GmbH, Augustinusstr 9 d, Frechen, 50226, Germany. TEL 49-2234-966100, FAX 49-2234-966109, info@datakontext.com, http://www.datakontext-press.de/lstmitteilungen/lstmit_hauptframe.htm.

336.2 CAN ISSN 0710-1759
LOI DE L'IMPOT SUR LE REVENU DU CANADA ET REGLEMENT. Text in English. a., latest 2004, 33rd ed. CND 85 per issue (effective 2005). index. **Document type:** *Trade.*

Former titles: Loi de l'Impot sur le Revenu du Canada; Loi de l'Impot sur le Revenu Canadien (0076-048X)
Published by: C C H Canadian Ltd., 90 Sheppard Ave E, Ste 300, North York, ON M2N 6X1, Canada. TEL 416-224-2248, 800-268-4522, FAX 416-224-2243, cservice@cch.ca, http://www.cch.ca. Ed. Pierrette Gregoire.

336 GBR ISSN 0951-7618
LONGMAN TAX DIGEST. Text in English. 1987. m. GBP 50, USD 95. **Description:** Digests all developments in taxation.
—CCC.
Published by: Longman Group UK Ltd., Law Tax and Finance Division, 21-27 Lambs Conduit St, London, WC1N 3NJ, United Kingdom. TEL 44-20-7242-2548, FAX 44-207-831-8119. Ed. Mike Truman.

336.2 NLD
LOONBRIEF. Text in Dutch. 10/yr. index. back issues avail. **Document type:** *Trade.*
Published by: Uitgeverij Fed bv (Subsidiary of: Wolters Kluwer N.V.), Postbus 23, Deventer, 7400 GA, Netherlands. TEL 31-570-633155, FAX 31-570-633834. Eds. G J M Jacobs, W Seijbel.

336.17 CAN ISSN 0709-5724
LOTO - QUEBEC. RAPPORT ANNUEL. Text in French. 1970. a. illus. **Document type:** *Corporate.*
Related titles: English ed.: Loto - Quebec. Annual Report. ISSN 0709-5740.
Published by: Societe des Loteries du Quebec, Public Affairs, 500 Sherbrooke St W, Montreal, PQ H3A 3G6, Canada. TEL 514-282-8000, FAX 514-873-8999, TELEX 05560178. Circ: 15,000.

LOTTERY & CASINO NEWS. see *SPORTS AND GAMES*

LOTTERY, PARIMUTUEL & CASINO REGULATION - STATE CAPITALS. see *LAW*

336 DNK ISSN 0106-8466
KJR7
LOVTIDENDE B FOR KONGERIGET DANMARK. Text in Danish. 1896. s-a. DKK 200 (effective 2000). index. **Document type:** *Government.* **Description:** Official organ for promulgating the State Budget in accordance with Danish law.
Published by: Justisministeriet, Sekretariatet for Retsinformation, Axeltorv 6, 5 sal, Copenhagen V, 1609, Denmark. TEL 45-33-32-52-22, FAX 45-33-91-28-01, retsinfo@retsinfo.dk, http://www.retsinfo.dk. Ed. Nina Koch. Circ: 448.

336 USA
LOW-INCOME HOUSING TAX CREDIT HANDBOOK. Text in English. a. USD 275 per issue (effective 2003). **Document type:** *Trade.* **Description:** Offers guidance through laws, regulations, and judicial decisions concerning the low-income housing tax credit.
Published by: Thomson West (Subsidiary of: Thomson Corporation, The), 610 Opperman Dr, Eagan, MN 55123-1396. TEL 651-687-8000, 800-328-4880, FAX 651-687-7302, http://www.westgroup.com/store/product.asp?product%5Fid=13974235&catalog%5Fname=wgstore, http://west.thomson.com. Eds. Jon E Krabbenschmidt, Michael J Novogradac.

336 LUX ISSN 0076-1559
LUXEMBOURG. MINISTERE DES FINANCES. BUDGET DE L'ETAT. Text in French. a. free. **Document type:** *Government.*
Published by: Ministere des Finances, 3 rue de la Congregation, Luxembourg, L-1352, Luxembourg. Circ: (controlled). **Subscr. to:** Service Central des Imprimes, Dept. Diffusion, B.P. 1302, Luxembourg L-1013, Luxembourg.

336 LUX
LUXEMBOURG. MINISTERE DES FINANCES. PROJET DE LOI CONCERNANT LE BUDGET DES RECETTES ET DES DEPENSES DE L'ETAT. Text in French. a. free. **Document type:** *Government.*
Published by: Ministere des Finances, 3 rue de la Congregation, Luxembourg, L-1352, Luxembourg. **Subscr. to:** Service Central des Imprimes, Dept. Diffusion, B.P. 1302, Luxembourg L-1013, Luxembourg.

343 USA ISSN 1085-3693
KF6499.M4
THE M & A TAX REPORT. (Mergers & Acquisitions) Text in English. 1992. m. USD 416 (effective 2004). **Document type:** *Newsletter, Trade.* **Description:** Covers developments that have critical implications for M&A practitioners. Includes analysis of recent case studies; IRS revenue rulings; spinoffs and other transactions; IRS regulations; proposed regulations; IRS announcements and notices: and private letter rulings.
Related titles: Online - full text ed.: (from ProQuest Information & Learning).
—CCC.
Published by: Aspen Publishers, Inc. (Subsidiary of: Wolters Kluwer N.V.), 5301 Buckeystown Pike, Ste. 400, Frederick, MD 21704-8319. TEL 800-638-8437, customer.service@aspenpubl.com, http://www.aspenpub.com. Ed. Robert W Wood. **Dist. by:** Distribution Center, 7201 McKinney Circle, Frederick, MD 21701. TEL 301-698-7100, FAX 301-417-7550.

336.2 NLD ISSN 0005-8335
K13
MAANDBLAD BELASTING BESCHOUWINGEN; onafhankelijk maandblad voor belastingrecht en belastingpraktijk. Text in Dutch. 1973 (vol.42). m. adv. bk.rev. abstr.; bibl. index.
—IE, Infotrieve.
Published by: Koninklyke Vermande, PO Box 20, Lelystad, 8200 AA, Netherlands. TEL 31-320-237723. Ed. Dr. H P A M van Arendonk. Circ: 3,000.

336.2 341 NLD
MAASTRICHTSE FISCALE SYMPOSIA. Text in Dutch. 1992. a. price varies. back issues avail. **Document type:** *Proceedings.*
Published by: Kluwer B.V. (Subsidiary of: Wolters Kluwer N.V.), Postbus 23, Deventer, 7400 GA, Netherlands. TEL 31-570-673449, FAX 31-570-691555.

MAGAZINE AFFAIRES PLUS. see *BUSINESS AND ECONOMICS—Investments*

336 IND ISSN 0076-2555
MAHARASHTRA STATE BUDGET IN BRIEF. Text in English, Marathi. 1960. a. free.
Published by: Directorate of Economics and Statistics, MHADA Bldg., Kalanagar Bandra (E), Mumbai, Maharashtra 400 051, India. TEL 91-22-6438781, FAX 91-22-6438781. Ed. B M Nagrale. Circ: (controlled).

336.2 USA ISSN 1055-5498
KF6289
MAJOR TAX PLANNING; proceedings of University of Southern California's Institute on Federal Taxation. Text in English. 1945. irreg. **Document type:** *Proceedings.*
Former titles (until 1955): Major Tax Problems (1055-5501); (until 1954): Proceedings of the Tax Institute (1055-551X)
Indexed: CLI, ILP, LRI.
—CCC.
Published by: (University of Southern California, Institute on Federal Taxation), LexisNexis (Subsidiary of: Reed Elsevier plc), 9443 Springboro Pike, Miamisburg, OH 45342. TEL 800-227-9597, http://www.lexisnexis.com.

336 MWI ISSN 0076-3020
MALAWI. ACCOUNTANT GENERAL. REPORT. Text in English. a. **Document type:** *Government.*
Published by: (Malawi. Accountant General), Government Printer, PO Box 37, Zomba, Malawi.

336 MWI
MALAWI. DEPARTMENT OF TAXES. ANNUAL REPORT OF THE COMMISSIONER OF TAXES. Text in English. a. **Document type:** *Government.*
Published by: Department of Taxes, PO Box 162, Blantyre, Malawi. TEL 265-620277. **Orders to:** Government Printer, PO Box 37, Zomba, Malawi. TEL 265-50-523155.

MALAWI. ECONOMIC PLANNING DIVISION. MID-YEAR ECONOMIC REVIEW. see *PUBLIC ADMINISTRATION*

336 MWI ISSN 0076-3195
HJ83.2
MALAWI. MINISTRY OF FINANCE. BUDGET STATEMENT. Text in English. a. **Document type:** *Government.*
Related titles: ♦ Series: Malawi. Ministry of Finance. Financial Statement.
Published by: Ministry of Finance, PO Box 30049, Lilongwe, Malawi. TEL 265-782199. **Orders to:** Government Printer, PO Box 37, Zomba, Malawi. TEL 265-50-523155.

336 MWI
MALAWI. MINISTRY OF FINANCE. FINANCIAL STATEMENT. Text in English. a. **Document type:** *Government.*
Related titles: ♦ Series of: Malawi. Ministry of Finance. Budget Statement. ISSN 0076-3195.
Published by: Ministry of Finance, PO Box 30049, Lilongwe, Malawi. TEL 265-782199. **Orders to:** Government Printer, PO Box 37, Zomba, Malawi. TEL 265-50-523155.

MALAWI. NATIONAL STATISTICAL OFFICE. BALANCE OF PAYMENTS. see *BUSINESS AND ECONOMICS—Abstracting, Bibliographies, Statistics*

336 MWI ISSN 0076-3314
MALAWI. OFFICE OF THE AUDITOR GENERAL. REPORT. Text in English. a. MWK 2. **Document type:** *Government.*
Published by: (Malawi. Office of the Auditor General), Government Printer, PO Box 37, Zomba, Malawi.

MALAYSIA. DEPARTMENT OF STATISTICS. BALANCE OF PAYMENTS REPORT, MALAYSIA/MALAYSIA. JABATAN PERANGKAAN. LAPORAN IMBANGAN PEMBAYARAN, MALAYSIA. see *BUSINESS AND ECONOMICS—Abstracting, Bibliographies, Statistics*

336.2 GBR
MALAYSIA TAX REVIEW✶. Text in English. 10/yr. HKD 2,500 in Hong Kong; USD 350 elsewhere. **Document type:** *Newsletter.* **Description:** Provides advice on tax planning measures on areas including taxation of foreign-sourced income, double taxation avoidance treaties, expatriate personnel remuneration, the practical difficulties surrounding the recent schedular tax payment and developments in real property gains tax.
Published by: Euromoney Institutional Investor Plc., Nestor House, Playhouse Yard, London, EC4V 5EX, United Kingdom. TEL 44-20-7779-8888, information@euromoneyplc.com, http://www.euromoneyplc.com/.

336.2 CAN
MANITOBA AND SASKATCHEWAN TAX REPORTER. Text in English. m. looseleaf. CND 582 (effective 2005). index. **Document type:** *Trade.* **Description:** Covers every aspect of provincial taxation in Manitoba and Saskatchewan.
Related titles: CD-ROM ed.: CND 531 (effective 2005); Online - full text ed.: CND 515 (effective 2005).
Published by: C C H Canadian Ltd., 90 Sheppard Ave E, Ste 300, North York, ON M2N 6X1, Canada. TEL 416-224-2248, 800-268-4522, FAX 416-224-2243, cservice@cch.ca, http://www.cch.ca.

B

336 CAN ISSN 0380-4488
MANITOBA BUDGET ADDRESS. Text in English. irreg.
Former titles (until 1971): Manitoba Budget Address and Economic Review (0713-1917); (until 1965): Manitoba Budget and Economic Review (0713-1909); (until 1958): Budget Speech (0713-1895)
—CISTI.
Published by: Manitoba. Department of Finance, 103 Legislative Bldg, Winnipeg, MB R3C 0U8, Canada. TEL 204-945-4261, FAX 204-945-4261, mgi@gov.mb.ca, http://www.gov.mb.ca/finance.

336.2 DEU
MANNHEIMER BEITRAEGE ZUM OEFFENTLICHEN RECHT UND STEUERRECHT. Text in German. 1994. irreg., latest vol.28, 2003. EUR 46.80 per vol. (effective 2003). **Document type:** *Magazine, Academic/Scholarly.*
Published by: Peter Lang GmbH Europaeischer Verlag der Wissenschaften, Eschborner Landstr 42-50, Frankfurt Am Main, 60489, Germany. TEL 49-69-7807050, FAX 49-69-78070543, zentrale.frankfurt@peterlang.com, http://www.peterlang.de. Ed. Hans-Wolfgang Arndt.

336.2 USA
KF6450.A15
MANUFACTURERS' TAX ALERT. Text in English. m. USD 310; USD 465 combined subscription print & online eds. (effective 2004). **Document type:** *Newsletter.* **Description:** Provides concise coverage of all major taxation issues that affect manufacturing firms, plus tips for reducing compliance headaches, dealing with auditors and reducing company's tax expenses.
Related titles: Online - full text ed.: USD 410 (effective 2004).
Published by: C C H Inc., 2700 Lake Cook Rd, Riverwoods, IL 60015. TEL 847-267-7000, 800-449-6439, cust_serv@cch.com, http://www.cch.com.

336.2 CAN ISSN 0047-5971
MARITIMES TAX REPORTER NEWSLETTER. Text in English. m. looseleaf. CND 217 (effective 2005). **Document type:** *Newsletter, Trade.* **Description:** Contains information on the newest tax changes in New Brunswick, Newfoundland, Nova Scotia and Prince Edward Island.
Published by: C C H Canadian Ltd., 90 Sheppard Ave E, Ste 300, North York, ON M2N 6X1, Canada. TEL 416-224-2248, 800-268-4522, FAX 416-224-2243, 800-461-4131, cservice@cch.ca, http://www.cch.ca.

345 336.2 USA
MARYLAND TAX COURT SERVICE. Text in English. 1990. m. looseleaf. USD 390. cum.index. **Document type:** *Abstract/Index.*
Published by: Hawkins Publishing Co., Inc., PO Box 480, Mayo, MD 21106-0480. TEL 410-798-1677, FAX 410-798-1098. Ed. Carl R Eyler. Circ: 50.

336 USA ISSN 0732-0825
KFM2870
MASSACHUSETTS APPELLATE TAX BOARD REPORTER. Text in English. 1982. q. looseleaf. USD 179 (effective 2003). cum.index. back issues avail. **Description:** Includes full-text opinions of the Tax Board with case abstracts.
Published by: Michie Company (Subsidiary of: LexisNexis North America), 701 E Water St, Charlottesville, VA 22902-5389. TEL 434-972-7600, 800-446-3410, FAX 434-972-7677, http://www.michie.com. Ed. Stephen M Politi.

336.2 USA
MASSACHUSETTS PRACTICE SERIES. TAXATION. Text in English. latest vol.4, 2002, 4th Ed., base vol. plus a. updates. USD 245 base vol(s). (effective 2004). **Document type:** *Monographic series, Academic/Scholarly.* **Description:** Covers Massachusetts taxes: income, corporate, estate, sales, property and miscellaneous taxes. Controlling cases, statutes and regulations are analyzed and explained.
Related titles: ♦ Series of: Massachusetts Practice Series.

Published by: Thomson West (Subsidiary of: Thomson Corporation, The), 610 Opperman Dr, Eagan, MN 55123-1396. TEL 651-687-7000, 800-328-4880, http://west.thomson.com/product/16757057/product.asp.

MAURITIUS. CENTRAL STATISTICAL OFFICE. DIGEST OF PUBLIC FINANCE STATISTICS. see *BUSINESS AND ECONOMICS—Abstracting, Bibliographies, Statistics*

MAURITIUS. CENTRAL STATISTICAL OFFICE. NATIONAL ACCOUNTS OF MAURITIUS. see *BUSINESS AND ECONOMICS—Abstracting, Bibliographies, Statistics*

336   MUS   ISSN 0543-1565
MAURITIUS. DIRECTOR OF AUDIT. REPORT. Text in English. 1912. a. MUR 75. **Document type:** *Government.*
Published by: Audit Department, Port Louis, Mauritius. Circ: 500.

336   MUS
MAURITIUS. MINISTRY OF FINANCE. UNIFIED REVENUE BOARD. REPORT. Text in English. a.
Published by: Ministry of Finance, Unified Revenue Board, Port Louis, Mauritius. Ed. M Baguant.

336   MUS   ISSN 0076-5562
MAURITIUS. PUBLIC ACCOUNTS COMMITTEE. REPORT. Text in English. irreg., latest 1987-88. price varies. **Document type:** *Government.*
Published by: Government Printing Office, Elizabeth II Ave, Port Louis, Mauritius. TEL 230-2345330, FAX 230-2345322.
Subscr. to: La Tour Koenig, Pointe-aux-sables, Mauritius.

MCGOLDRICK'S CANADIAN CUSTOMS GUIDE "HARMONIZED SYSTEM". see *BUSINESS AND ECONOMICS—International Commerce*

MEDICAL AND DISABILITY APPEAL TRIBUNALS: THE LEGISLATION. see *SOCIAL SERVICES AND WELFARE*

336.2   NLD   ISSN 1389-5656
MEMO BELASTINGCONTROLE. Text in Dutch. 1986. a. EUR 27.50 (effective 2003). **Document type:** *Trade.* **Description:** Presents reference information relating to taxation and fiscal control.
Formerly (until 1998): Zakboekje voor de Belastingcontrole (0923-5531)
Published by: Kluwer B.V. (Subsidiary of: Wolters Kluwer N.V.), Postbus 23, Deventer, 7400 GA, Netherlands. TEL 31-570-673449, FAX 31-570-691555, juridisch@kluwer.nl, http://www.kluwer.nl. Eds. H L Haxe, R N J Kamerling.

340 336   USA   ISSN 0279-9286
MERTENS CURRENT TAX HIGHLIGHTS. Text in English. 1982. latest 2002, base vol. plus m. updates. USD 439.50 base vol(s). (effective 2004). **Document type:** *Newsletter, Trade.* **Description:** Timely resource for the latest information and developments in the ever-changing fields of tax law and regulation. Designed to address the issues affecting your practice, this ongoing series of newsletters, magazines, and alerts keep you informed of significant legal changes.
Published by: Thomson West (Subsidiary of: Thomson Corporation, The), 610 Opperman Dr, Eagan, MN 55123-1396. TEL 651-687-8000, 800-328-4880, FAX 651-687-7302, http://west.thomson.com/product/13515745/product.asp. Ed. Jim Fegen.

MERTENS FEDERAL TAX REGULATIONS. see *LAW*

MERTENS LAW OF FEDERAL INCOME TAXATION; treatise and rulings. see *LAW*

MERTENS TAXLINK, LAWDESK. see *LAW*

MERTENS TREATISE ON THE LAW OF FEDERAL INCOME TAXATION. see *LAW*

336.2 657.6   USA
MICHAEL GRAY CPA'S BOTTOM LINE. Text in English. 1998. m. bk.rev. back issues avail. **Document type:** *Newsletter.* **Description:** Features financial tips, tax planning advice and new tax laws.
Related titles: E-mail ed.; Fax ed.; Online - full text ed.
Address: 1265 S Bascom Ave, Ste 106, San Jose, CA 95128. TEL 408-918-3161, FAX 408-998-2766, dawn@taxtrimmers.com, mgray@innetix.com, http://taxtrimmers.com/news.htm, http://www.innetix.com/~mgraycpa/news.htm. Ed. Dawn Gray. Pub., R&P Michael Gray. Circ: 2,600 (controlled).

MICHIGAN CORPORATION LAW WITH FEDERAL TAX ANALYSIS. see *LAW—Corporate Law*

MICHIGAN TAX LAWYER. see *LAW*

336   USA   ISSN 1555-2071
HJ9777.A1
▼ **MILLER LOCAL GOVERNMENT AUDITS AND SINGLE AUDITS.** Text in English. 2004. a. USD 169 per vol. (effective 2005).

Formed by the merger of (1992-2003): Single Audit Guide (1060-1864); Miller Local Government Audits (1535-3761)
Published by: C C H Inc., 2700 Lake Cook Rd, Riverwoods, IL 60015. TEL 847-267-7000, cust_serv@cch.com, http://www.cch.com.

336.776   USA
HJ11
MINNESOTA. DEPARTMENT OF REVENUE. BIENNIAL REPORT. Text in English. 1940. biennial. stat. **Document type:** *Government.*
Former titles: Minnesota. Department of Revenue. Annual Report (0095-0645); Supersedes: Minnesota. Department of Taxation. Biennial Report
Published by: Department of Revenue, Communications Division, MS 3310, St. Paul, MN 55146. TEL 612-296-3781.

MINNESOTA. DEPARTMENT OF REVENUE. PETROLEUM DIVISION. ANNUAL REPORT. see *PETROLEUM AND GAS*

MINNESOTA LEGAL REGISTER: MINNESOTA TAX COURT DECISIONS. see *LAW—Judicial Systems*

336.2   USA
MINNESOTA SALES AND USE TAX ANNUAL REPORT BULLETIN. Text in English. 1971. a. charts; stat. **Document type:** *Bulletin, Government.* **Description:** Summary of data reported on state sales and tax returns, broken down by major industry and geographic area.
Formerly: Minnesota Sales and Use Tax Quarterly Report Bulletin
Published by: Department of Revenue, MS 2230, St. Paul, MN 55146.

336   ISR
MISSIM. Text in Hebrew. 1987. bi-m.
Published by: Ronen Publishing Company, P O Box 36665, Tel Aviv, 61366, Israel. TEL 03-375912, FAX 03-615460.

366.778   USA
MISSOURI. DEPARTMENT OF REVENUE. COMPREHENSIVE ANNUAL FINANCIAL REPORT. Text in English. 1919. a. price varies. stat. **Document type:** *Government.*
Former titles: Missouri. Department of Revenue. Component Unit Financial Report; Missouri. Department of Revenue. Annual Combined Financial Report
Related titles: Microfiche ed.: (from CIS).
Indexed: SRI.
Published by: Department of Revenue, Financial and General Services, PO Box 475, Jefferson City, MO 65105. TEL 314-751-3530, FAX 314-751-8405. Ed. Nancy Holtschneider. Circ: 300. **Co-sponsor:** Missouri State Treasurer.

MONETARY REFORM. see *POLITICAL SCIENCE*

336   POL   ISSN 1231-1855
MONITOR PODATKOWY. Text in Polish. 1994. m. EUR 191 foreign (effective 2005). **Document type:** *Journal, Trade.*
Published by: Wydawnictwo C.H. Beck, ul Gen. Zajaczka 9, Warsaw, 01518, Poland. TEL 48-22-3377600, FAX 48-22-3377601, redakcja@beck.pl, http://www.monitorpodatkowy.pl, http://wydawnictwo.beck.pl. **Dist. by:** Ars Polona, Krakowskie Przedmiescie 7, Warsaw, Poland. TEL 48-22-9263914, FAX 48-22-9265334, arspolona@arspolona.com.pl, http://www.arspolona.com.pl. **Co-publisher:** Verlag C.H. Beck.

336.2   USA   ISSN 0027-0385
K13
MONTHLY DIGEST OF TAX ARTICLES. Text in English. 1950. m. USD 60. abstr. **Document type:** *Academic/Scholarly.* **Description:** Covers federal income, estate and gift taxes.
Published by: Newkirk Products, Inc., 15 Corporate Circle, Albany, NY 12203. TEL 518-862-3200. Ed., R&P Sonia G Maloney. Pub. Peter Newkirk. Circ: 9,000 (paid).

336.2   GBR
MOORES ROWLAND'S ORANGE TAX GUIDE. Text in English. 1978. a. GBP 47.95 (effective 1999). **Document type:** *Trade.* **Description:** Deals with inheritance tax, national insurance contribution, stamp duty and value added tax.
Former titles: Moores and Rowland's Tax Guide (0267-8829); Rowland's Tax Guide (0143-280X)
Published by: Butterworths Tolley (Subsidiary of: LexisNexis UK (Scottish Office)), Halsbury House, 35 Chancery Ln, London, Mddx WC2A 1EL, United Kingdom. TEL 44-20-74002500, FAX 44-20-7400-2842, order.line@butterworths.co.uk, http://www.butterworths.co.uk/. Ed. Nigel Eastaway.

336   GBR
MOORES ROWLAND'S YELLOW TAX GUIDE. Text in English. a. GBP 47.95. **Document type:** *Trade.* **Description:** Deals with income tax, corporation tax and capital gains tax.
Formerly: Moores Rowland's Orange and Yellow Tax Guides
Published by: Butterworths Tolley (Subsidiary of: LexisNexis UK (Scottish Office)), Halsbury House, 35 Chancery Ln, London, Mddx WC2A 1EL, United Kingdom. TEL 44-20-74002500, FAX 44-20-7400-2842, order.line@butterworths.co.uk, http://www.butterworths.co.uk/. Ed. Colin Davis.

336.2   USA
MORE THAN A PAYCHECK. Text in English. 1984. bi-m. USD 10 (effective 2000). 8 p./no.; back issues avail. **Document type:** *Newsletter.* **Description:** Contains information and news for tax resisters, mainly in the U.S.
Formerly: Network News
Related titles: Online - full text ed.
Published by: National War Tax Resistance Coordinating Committee, Box 6512, Ithaca, NY 14851. FAX 800-269-7464, http://www.nonviolence.org/wtr. Ed. Mary Loehr. Circ: 500.

336   USA   ISSN 1065-5972
MULTI-STATE SALES TAX GUIDE. Text in English. 1940. m. USD 1,565 (effective 2004). **Description:** Leads us through all aspects of the sales and use taxes levied by all U.S. states, plus the District of Columbia. It's a great resource to help avoid costly tax mistakes.
Former titles: Multi-State Sales Tax Reports; All State Sales Tax Reports (0414-0109)
Media: Online - full text. **Related titles:** CD-ROM ed.: USD 1,719 (effective 2004).
Published by: C C H Inc., 2700 Lake Cook Rd, Riverwoods, IL 60015. TEL 847-267-7000, 800-449-6439, cust_serv@cch.com, http://www.cch.com. Pub. Kevin Robert.

343.7305   USA   ISSN 1051-1555
(YEAR) MULTISTATE CORPORATE TAX GUIDE. Text in English. 1984. a. (in 2 vols.), latest 2003. USD 460 (effective 2003). **Document type:** *Trade.* **Description:** Compilation of easy-to-access charts that summarize each state's answers to key issues in income, sales, and use taxation from the top state officials who interpret and apply the rules.
Formerly (until 1989): Multistate Corporate Tax Almanac (0747-718X)
Related titles: CD-ROM ed.
Indexed: ATI.
—CCC.
Published by: Panel Publishers, Inc. (Subsidiary of: Aspen Publishers, Inc.), 1185 Ave of the Americas, 37th Fl, New York, NY 10036. TEL 212-597-0200, 800-638-8437, FAX 212-597-0331, customer.service@aspenpubl.com, http://www.aspenpublishers.com. Eds. John C Healy, Karen J Boucher. **Dist. by:** Aspen Publishers, Inc., Distribution Center, 7201 McKinney Circle, Frederick, MD 21701. TEL 301-698-7100, FAX 301-417-7550.

336   USA
MULTISTATE TAX COMMISSION REVIEW. Text in English. 1981. irreg. USD 35. bk.rev. **Document type:** *Newsletter, Government.* **Description:** Covers policy issues and current developments in state taxation of multijurisdictional business activity.
Published by: Multistate Tax Commission, 444 N Capitol St, N W, Ste 425, Washington, DC 20001. TEL 202-624-8699, FAX 202-624-8819. Ed. Michael Mazerov. Circ: 2,200.

352.14   USA   ISSN 0199-6134
HJ9103
MUNICIPAL FINANCE JOURNAL. Text in English. 1980. q. USD 295 (effective 2005). back issues avail.; reprint service avail. from WSH. **Document type:** *Journal, Trade.* **Description:** Articles and columns covering recent tax and legal trends affecting large and small municipalities.
Related titles: Microfiche ed.: (from WSH); Microform ed.: (from PQC, WSH); Online - full text ed.: (from Florida Center for Library Automation, Gale Group, ProQuest Information & Learning).
Indexed: ABIn, ATI, BLI, BPIA, CLI, ILP, LegCont, ManagCont, PAIS.
—CCC.
Published by: Civic Research Insitute, 4490 US Route 27, PO Box 585, Kingston, NJ 08528. TEL 609-683-4450, FAX 609-683-7291, order@civicresearchinstitute.com, http://www.civicresearchinstitute.com/tax7.html. Ed. Bartley Hildreth.

336.2   DEU
MUSTERGUELTIGE VORDRUCKE, CHECKLISTEN UND ARBEITSHILFEN FUER STEUERBERATER VON A-Z. Text in German. base vol. plus updates 6/yr. EUR 99.70 base vol(s). (effective 2004). **Document type:** *Trade.*
Published by: Verlag fuer Deutsche Steuerberater AG (Subsidiary of: Wolters Kluwer Deutschland GmbH), Marlener Str 2, Offenburg, 77656, Germany. TEL 49-781-9900646, FAX 49-781-9900644, info@steuern-online.de, http://www.steuern-online.de.

332.5   USA
N C B A REPORTS. Text in English. 1979. m. USD 70 (effective 2001). index. 14 p./no.; **Document type:** *Newsletter.* **Description:** Covers government abuse of citizens, IRS abuses, how to defend yourself against the IRS, and issues pertaining to the abolition of the IRS and the Federal Reserve system and money and tax reform.
Published by: National Commodity & Barter Association, PO Box 2255, Longmont, CO 80502. TEL 303-833-3333, ncbarpls@earthnet.net, http://www.earthnet.net/ncba. Ed. John Voss.

336.2   USA
N T A FORUM. Text in English. q.
Indexed: PAIS.

Published by: National Tax Association, 725 15th St, N W, Ste 600, Washington, DC 20005-2109. TEL 202-737-3325, FAX 202-737-7308, natltax@aol.com, http://www.ntanet.org.

336.2 DEU ISSN 0171-8185
N W B - DOKUMENTATION STEUERRECHT; Erlasse, Schreiben, Verfuegungen und Rechtsprechung. (Neue Wirtschafts-Briefe) Text in German. 1949. s-m. looseleaf. adv. bk.rev. bibl. index cum.index. **Document type:** *Abstract/Index.*
Formerly (until 1976): Aktuelle Sammlung der Verfuegungen und Erlasse des Bundesfinanzministeriums, der Laenderfinanzministerium, der Oberfinanzdirektionen und der Steuerrechtsprechung (0002-3841)
Published by: Verlag Neue Wirtschafts-Briefe GmbH & Co., Eschstr 22, Herne, 44629, Germany. TEL 49-2323-141900, FAX 49-2323-141123, info@nwb.de, http://www.nwb.de. Circ: 1,100 (paid).

336.2 RUS
NALOGI. Text in Russian. 24/yr. USD 172 in United States.
Indexed: RASB.
Published by: Gosudarstvennaya Nalogovaya Inspektsiya po G. Moskve, Ul Yablochkova 5, Moscow, 127254, Russian Federation. TEL 7-095-2103308, FAX 7-095-2102221. Ed. V M Ionov. **US dist. addr.:** East View Information Services, 3020 Harbor Ln. N., Minneapolis, MN 55447. TEL 612-550-0961.

336.2 RUS ISSN 1606-1462
NALOGI I BIZNES. Text in Russian. 1999. w. free (effective 2004). **Document type:** *Consumer.*
Media: Online - full text.
Published by: Al'yans Midiya, Bolotnaya ul 12, str 3, Moscow, 115035, Russian Federation. TEL 7-095-2345380, FAX 7-095-2345363, allmedia@allmedia.ru, http://www.businesspress.ru, http://allmedia.ru.

336.2 RUS
NALOGI I EKONOMIKA; ezhemesyachnyi informatsionno-analiticheskii zhurnal po ekonomike Rossii i o nalogoblozhenii. Text in Russian. m. **Document type:** *Journal, Government.*
Description: Includes official answers to reader questions on taxation issues, coverage of topics in accounting methodology, regional legislation and analysis of local economic conditions, and finance and taxation problems.
Published by: (Rossiiskaya Federatsiya. Upravleniya Federal'noi Sluzhby Nalogovoi Politsii), Gosudarstvennaya Nalogovaya Inspektsiya po Novosibirskoi Oblasti, Ul Belinskogo 127, Novosibirsk, 630008, Russian Federation. TEL 7-3832-666471, http://www.nalog.sinor.ru.

336.2 RUS
NALOGOVAYA POLITSIYA. Text in Russian. 24/yr. USD 199.95 in United States.
Published by: Departament Nalogovoi Politsii Rossiiskoi Federatsii, Ul Maroseika 12, Moscow, 101000, Russian Federation. TEL 7-095-2069846. **US dist. addr.:** East View Information Services, 3020 Harbor Ln. N., Minneapolis, MN 55447. TEL 612-550-0961.

336.2 RUS
NALOGOVOE PLANIROVANIE. Text in Russian. q. USD 150 in United States.
Indexed: RASB.
Published by: Invest Ekspert Konsalting, Ozernaya ul 42, Moscow, 119361, Russian Federation. TEL 7-095-4370188, FAX 7-095-4370222. Ed. O V Volkova. **US dist. addr.:** East View Information Services, 3020 Harbor Ln. N., Minneapolis, MN 55447. TEL 612-550-0961.

336 CHN
NASHUI REN. Text in Chinese. m.
Published by: Hubei Sheng Shuiwu Ju, Hongshan Lu, Wuchang-qu, Wuhan, Hubei 430071, China. TEL 712970. Ed. Liu Xiaohui.

NATIONAL ACCOUNTANT. see *BUSINESS AND ECONOMICS—Accounting*

336 FRA
NATIONAL ACCOUNTS OF O E C D COUNTRIES. VOLUME 4, GENERAL GOVERNMENT ACCOUNTS/COMPTES NATIONAUX DES PAYS DE L'O C D E. VOLUME IV, COMPTES DES ADMINISTRATIONS PUBLIQUES. (Organization for Economic Cooperation and Development) Text in English. a. price varies.
Related titles: ♦ Series of: National Accounts of O E C D Countries.
Published by: Organization for Economic Cooperation and Development, 2 Rue Andre Pascal, Paris, 75775 Cedex 16, France. TEL 33-1-45248200, FAX 33-1-45248500, http://www.oecd.org. **Dist. by:** O E C D Turpin North America, PO Box 194, Downingtown, PA 19335-0194. TEL 610-524-5361, 800-456-6323, FAX 610-524-5417, bookscustomer@turpinna.com.

NATIONAL ACCOUNTS OF THE MALTESE ISLANDS. see *BUSINESS AND ECONOMICS—Abstracting, Bibliographies, Statistics*

NATIONAL CUSTOMS TARIFF GUIDEBOOK - ISRAEL. see *BUSINESS AND ECONOMICS—International Commerce*

336.2 USA ISSN 0069-8687
HJ10.3
NATIONAL TAX ASSOCIATION. PROCEEDINGS OF ANNUAL CONFERENCE ON TAXATION AND MINUTES OF THE ANNUAL MEETING. Text in English. 1907. a. USD 70 domestic to individuals; USD 75 foreign to individuals; USD 90 domestic to libraries; USD 95 foreign to libraries; USD 85 membership; USD 100 membership Libraries; USD 130 membership Corporations (effective 2000); membership also includes National Tax Journal. Index. **Document type:** *Proceedings, Trade.* **Description:** Publishes papers from the annual conference on the theory and practice of federal, state and local taxation.
Former titles (until 1996): National Tax Association - Tax Institute of America. Proceedings of the Annual Conference on Taxation (1066-8608); Annual Conference on Taxation. Proceedings
Related titles: Online - full text ed.: (from EBSCO Publishing, H.W. Wilson, O C L C Online Computer Library Center, Inc., ProQuest Information & Learning).
Indexed: ABIn, ATI, ILP.
—CCC.
Published by: National Tax Association, 725 15th St, N W, Ste 600, Washington, DC 20005-2109. TEL 202-737-3325, FAX 202-737-7308, natltax@aol.com, http://www.ntanet.org. R&P Joan Casey. Circ: 3,300.

336.2 USA ISSN 0028-0283
CODEN: NTXJAC
➤ **NATIONAL TAX JOURNAL.** Text in English. 1916. q. USD 90 domestic to individuals; USD 100 foreign to individuals; USD 155 domestic to libraries; USD 165 foreign to libraries (effective 2005); includes Proceedings of the Annual Conference on Taxation. abstr.; bibl.; charts; illus. Index. back issues avail.; reprint service avail. from WSH. **Document type:** *Journal, Academic/Scholarly.* **Description:** Articles on taxation and public finance in the United States and foreign countries.
Formerly (until 1947): National Tax Association. Bulletin
Related titles: Microfiche ed.: (from WSH); Microform ed.: (from PQC); Online - full text ed.: (from EBSCO Publishing, Florida Center for Library Automation, Gale Group, H.W. Wilson, Northern Light Technology, Inc., O C L C Online Computer Library Center, Inc., ProQuest Information & Learning).
Indexed: ABIn, ASCA, ATI, AgeL, BLI, BPI, BPIA, BusI, CJA, CLI, CREJ, CurCont, FamI, IBR, IBSS, IBZ, ILP, IPSA, JEL, LRI, LegCont, PAIS, PCI, RASB, SPAA, SSCI, T&II, WBA.
—BLDSC (6033.115000), IDS, IE, Infotrieve, ingenta. **CCC.**
Published by: National Tax Association, 725 15th St, N W, Ste 600, Washington, DC 20005-2109. TEL 202-737-3325, FAX 202-737-7308, natltax@aol.com, http://ntj.tax.org/, http://www.ntanet.org. Eds. Rosanne Altshuler, Therese J McGuire. R&P Joan Casey. Circ: 3,300.

340 336 CAN
NATIONAL TRADE AND TARIFF SERVICE. Text in English. 6/yr. looseleaf. CND 825 (effective 2001). index. **Description:** Contains legislation and full text of cases decided in the area of trade and tariffs, customs and exercise taxes and special import measures.
Formerly (until 1990): Canadian Customs and Excise Reports (0228-3409)
Published by: LexisNexis Butterworths Canada Inc. (Subsidiary of: LexisNexis North America), 123 Commerce Valley Dr E, Ste 700, Markham, ON L3T 7W8, Canada. TEL 905-479-2665, FAX 905-479-2826, http://www.nationaltradeandtariffservice.htm. Ed. Robin A Ritchie.

336 NLD ISSN 1570-9159
▼ **DE NEDERLANDSCHE BANK. OCCASIONAL STUDIES.** Text in English. 2003. irreg. price varies. **Document type:** *Monographic series.*
Formed by the merger of (1984-2003): Monetary Monographs (0924-4956); (1984-2003): Monetaire Monografieen (0924-4964)
Published by: Nederlandsche Bank N.V., Postbus 98, Amsterdam, 1000 AB, Netherlands. TEL 31-20-5249111, http://www.dnb.nl.

336.2 NLD
NEDERLANDSE JURISPRUDENTIE INZAKE INTERNATIONAAL BELASTINGRECHT; directe belastingen van internationaal opererende ondernemingen. Text in Dutch. 1993. 1-2/yr.), base vol. plus irreg. updates. looseleaf. USD 125 (effective 2000). **Document type:** *Trade.* **Description:** Provides basic analysis of Dutch jurisprudence relating to the taxation of international firms.
Published by: (Juridische Faculteit, Vakgroep Belastingrecht), I B F D Publications BV, H J E Wenckebachweg 210, PO Box 20237, Amsterdam, 1000 HE, Netherlands. TEL 31-20-554-0100, FAX 31-20-620-8626, http://www.ibfd.nl. Ed. A Nooteboom. **Co-sponsor:** International Bureau of Fiscal Documentation.

NELSON A. ROCKEFELLER INSTITUTE OF GOVERNMENT. BULLETIN. see *PUBLIC ADMINISTRATION*

NELSON A. ROCKEFELLER INSTITUTE OF GOVERNMENT. STATE FISCAL BRIEF. see *PUBLIC ADMINISTRATION*

NETHERLANDS. CENTRAAL BUREAU VOOR DE STATISTIEK. NATIONALE REKENINGEN/NETHERLANDS. CENTRAL BUREAU OF STATISTICS. NATIONAL ACCOUNTS. see *BUSINESS AND ECONOMICS—Abstracting, Bibliographies, Statistics*

336.2 CHE ISSN 0028-338X
KKW3546.7
NEUE STEUERPRAXIS. Text in German. 1946. m. CHF 67; CHF 10 newsstand/cover (effective 2003). adv. bk.rev. charts.
Document type: *Government.*
—CCC.
Published by: (Bern. Kantonale Steuerverwaltung), Paul Haupt AG, Falkenplatz 14, Bern, 3001, Switzerland. TEL 41-31-3012434, FAX 41-31-3015469, druckerei@haupt.ch, http://www.haupt.ch.de/druck/fdruck.htm. Circ: 600.

336.2 DEU
DIE NEUE UMSATZSTEUER-PRAXIS VON A-Z. Text in German. 3 base vols. plus updates 14/yr. EUR 149 (effective 2004).
Document type: *Directory, Trade.*
Published by: Verlag Praktisches Wissen GmbH (Subsidiary of: Wolters Kluwer Deutschland GmbH), Marlener Str 2, Offenburg, 77656, Germany. TEL 49-781-605300, FAX 49-781-59825, info@praktisches-wissen.de, http://www.praktisches-wissen.de.

336.2 DEU
DAS NEUE VERTRAGS-HANDBUCH FUER STEUERBERATER; Muster-Vertraege mit Checklisten von A-Z. Text in German. base vol. plus updates 5/yr. EUR 124.90 base vol(s). (effective 2004). **Document type:** *Directory, Trade.*
Published by: Verlag fuer Deutsche Steuerberater AG (Subsidiary of: Wolters Kluwer Deutschland GmbH), Marlener Str 2, Offenburg, 77656, Germany. TEL 49-781-9900646, FAX 49-781-9900644, info@steuern-online.de, http://www.steuern-online.de.

336.1 340 DEU ISSN 0028-3460
NEUE WIRTSCHAFTS-BRIEFE; Zeitschrift fuer Steuer- und Wirtschaftsrecht. Abbreviated title: N W B. Text in German. 1947. w. looseleaf. EUR 228 per month; EUR 171 per month to students; EUR 6 newsstand/cover (effective 2002). adv. bk.rev. abstr.; bibl.; charts; stat. index, cum.index. **Document type:** *Journal, Trade.*
Related titles: CD-ROM ed.: 1997.
Indexed: CERDIC.
—CCC.
Published by: Verlag Neue Wirtschafts-Briefe GmbH & Co., Eschstr 22, Herne, 44629, Germany. TEL 49-2323-141900, FAX 49-2323-141123, info@nwb.de, http://www.nwb.de. Circ: 69,000.

336 USA
NEW ENGLAND WAR TAX RESISTANCE. ANNUAL REPORT. Text in English. a. **Document type:** *Corporate.* **Description:** Information and news on financial affairs, activities and events of the organization.
Published by: New England War Tax Resistance, PO Box 397174, Cambridge, MA 02139. TEL 617-859-0662.

NEW HAMPSHIRE PRACTICE SERIES: MUNICIPAL FINANCE AND TAXATION, VOLUME 16. see *PUBLIC ADMINISTRATION—Municipal Government*

NEW IN DUTY FREE. see *BUSINESS AND ECONOMICS—International Commerce*

NEW JERSEY ADMINISTRATIVE CODE. TREASURY - GENERAL. see *LAW*

NEW JERSEY ADMINISTRATIVE CODE. TREASURY - TAXATION. see *LAW*

336 USA ISSN 0733-1584
HJ11
NEW JERSEY. DEPARTMENT OF THE TREASURY. DIVISION OF TAXATION. ANNUAL REPORT. Text in English. 1945. a. free. 100 p./no. 2 cols./p.; **Document type:** *Government.*
Description: Contains detailed descriptions of the division organization and taxes administered by the division, with various tax statistical tables.
Indexed: SRI.
Published by: (Technical Services , Informational and Publications Branch), Department of the Treasury, Division of Taxation, PO Box 281, Trenton, NJ 08695-0281. TEL 609-633-8426, FAX 609-777-4319, http://www.state.nj.us/treasury/taxation/. Circ: 2,000.

336.2 USA ISSN 1073-6808
HJ2422
NEW JERSEY STATE TAX NEWS. Text in English. 1972. q. free. charts; stat. **Document type:** *Newsletter, Government.*
Description: Information for tax practitioners.
Published by: (New Jersey. Technical Services T S B - O C E), Department of the Treasury, Division of Taxation, PO Box 281, Trenton, NJ 08695-0281. TEL 609-633-8426, FAX 609-777-4319, http://www.state.nj.us/treasury/taxation/. Ed. Linda B Hickey. Circ: 5,000.

336 USA ISSN 0279-6481
NEW JERSEY TAX COURT REPORTS. Text in English. 1980. (in 20 vols.), 3 base vols. plus bi-m. updates. USD 648.25 base vol(s). (effective 2005). **Document type:** *Trade.* **Description:** Contains court cases and decisions from the New Jersey Tax Court, 1981 to date. Provides table of cases, case synopses, and headnotes for each point of law. Includes topics and key number system and search by words and phrases.
Incorporates: Reports of Cases Argued and Determined in the Tax Court of New Jersey (0731-2954)
Published by: Thomson West (Subsidiary of: Thomson Corporation, The), 610 Opperman Dr, Eagan, MN 55123-1396. TEL 651-687-8000, FAX 651-687-7302, customer.service@westgroup.com, http://west.thomson.com/product/22078158/product.asp.

336 USA
NEW YORK (CITY). COMPTROLLERS REPORT. Text in English. 1976. m. free. charts; stat. **Document type:** *Government.*
Published by: Comptrollers Office, Municipal Building, New York, NY 10007. TEL 212-566-7231. Ed. Henry Walter. Circ: 29,000.

336 333.33 USA
NEW YORK CITY. REAL PROPERTY TAX. ANNUAL REPORT. Text in English. a. **Description:** Covers New York City's property market and property tax policy.
Published by: City of New York, Department of Finance, Municipal Bldg, New York, NY 10007. TEL 212-669-4855.

336.2 USA
NEW YORK UNIVERSITY ANNUAL CONFERENCE ON TAX PLANNING FOR 501(C)(3) ORGANIZATIONS. Text in English. a. looseleaf. USD 110 (effective 1999). reprint service avail. from WSH.
Related titles: Microfilm ed.: (from WSH).
Indexed: ATI, CLI, LRI.
Published by: (New York University, School of Continuing Education), Matthew Bender & Co., Inc. (Subsidiary of: LexisNexis North America), 1275 Broadway, Albany, NY 12204. international@bender.com, http://bender.lexisnexis.com.

336 NZL ISSN 0545-7572
NEW ZEALAND CURRENT TAXATION. Text in English. 52/yr. NZD 432. **Description:** Tax intelligence service offering up-to-date information in the taxation field.
—CCC.
Published by: Butterworths of New Zealand Ltd. (Subsidiary of: LexisNexis Asia Pacific), P.O. Box 472, 203-207 Victoria St, Wellington, New Zealand. TEL 64-4-3851479, FAX 64-4-385-1598. Ed. Stephen Gibbs.

NEW ZEALAND GAZETTE. SUPPLEMENT. TAX EVADERS. see *BUSINESS AND ECONOMICS—Trade And Industrial Directories*

NEW ZEALAND. HOUSE OF REPRESENTATIVES. BUDGET. see *PUBLIC ADMINISTRATION*

NEW ZEALAND. HOUSE OF REPRESENTATIVES. ESTIMATES. see *PUBLIC ADMINISTRATION*

336.2 NZL ISSN 1322-4417
K14
➤ **NEW ZEALAND JOURNAL OF TAXATION LAW AND POLICY.** Text in English. 1994. q. NZD 198.91. **Document type:** *Academic/Scholarly.* **Description:** Carries articles dealing with all aspects of taxation law and policy.
Related titles: CD-ROM ed.
Indexed: ILP.
Published by: Brooker's Limited, Level 1 - Telecom Networks House, 68-86 Jervois Quay, Wellington, New Zealand. TEL 64-4998178, FAX 64-4-4998173, service@brookers.co.nz. Eds. Christopher Ohms, Garth Harris. R&P Nigel Royfee.

330 NZL
NEW ZEALAND. STATISTICS NEW ZEALAND. PUBLIC HEALTH FINANCIAL STATISTICS. Text in English. q. stat. **Document type:** *Government.* **Description:** Describes the financial performance and financial position of Hospital and Health Service providers.
Published by: Statistics New Zealand/Te Tari Tatau, PO Box 2922, Wellington, New Zealand. TEL 64-4-495-4600, FAX 64-4-473-2626, info@stats.govt.nz, http://www.stats.govt.nz.

NIGERIA FINANCE YEARBOOK. see *BUSINESS AND ECONOMICS—Banking And Finance*

336.2 USA ISSN 1066-1018
KF6449.A73
NON-PROFIT LEGAL & TAX LETTER. Text in English. 1991. 18/yr. looseleaf. USD 235 (effective 2005). bk.rev. bibl. back issues avail. **Document type:** *Newsletter, Trade.* **Description:** Provides up-to-date information for non-profit organizations and their professional advisors on legal and tax issues affecting the tax-exempt sector.
Incorporates (197?-1996): NonProfit Insight (1056-4594); Which was formerly (until 1991): Tax-Exempt News (0194-228X); Formed by the merger of (1962-1991): Non-Profit Organization Tax Letter (0550-8401); (1989-1991): Membership Organizations Newsletter (1051-7391)
—CCC.
Published by: Organization Management Inc., PO Box 342730, Bethsda, MD 20827-2730. TEL 301-469-8507, FAX 301-469-7271, taxletter@aol.com, http://www.taxexemptresources.com. Eds. Hugh K Webster, Jay Rotz. Pub. Ellis E Meredith.

336 USA
NONPRIVATE FOUNDATIONS: A TAX GUIDE FOR CHARITABLE ORGANIZATIONS. Text in English. 1978. base vol. plus a. updates. USD 115. Supplement avail. **Document type:** *Trade.* **Description:** Defines current tax law as it applies to public charities and publicly supported organizations.
Related titles: Series of: Taxation Series.
Published by: Shepard's (Subsidiary of: LexisNexis North America), 555 Middle Creek Pkwy, Colorado Springs, CO 80921. TEL 800-743-7393, customer_service@shepards.com, http://www.shepards.com, http://www.lexisnexis.com/shepards/. Ed. David R Gray.

336 NOR ISSN 0333-1423
KKN3543.6
NORSK SKATTELOVSAMLING. Text in Norwegian. 1954. a. NOK 788 (effective 2000). **Document type:** *Journal, Trade.*
Related titles: CD-ROM ed.
Published by: Jacob Jaroey, Vraagst 18, Skien, 3701, Norway. TEL 47-35-59-92-26. Ed. Erik Friis Faehn. Pub. Jacob Jaroey.

336.2 USA
NORTH CAROLINA. DEPARTMENT OF REVENUE. FRANCHISE TAX AND CORPORATE INCOME TAX RULES AND BULLETINS. Text in English. 1964. irreg., latest 1995. free. **Document type:** *Bulletin, Government.* **Description:** Guide in the interpretation and administration of the corporate income and franchise tax laws, covering the major provisions and the laws relating to corporate income and franchise taxes.
Former titles (until 1992): North Carolina. Department of Revenue. Franchise Tax and Corporate Income Tax Rules and Regulations; (until 1976): North Carolina. Department of Revenue. Franchise Tax and Corporate Income Tax Bulletins for Taxable Years (0078-138X)
Published by: Department of Revenue, Corporate Income and Franchise Tax Division, PO Box 871, Raleigh, NC 27602-0871. TEL 919-733-8510, FAX 919-733-1821. Circ: 7,500.

336 GBR
NORTHERN IRELAND. DEPARTMENT OF FINANCE AND PERSONNEL. NORTHERN IRELAND ESTIMATES (YEAR); for services under the Government of Northern Ireland. Text in English. a. GBP 15.40 per issue (effective 1999).
Formerly (until 1987): Northern Ireland. Department of Finance and Personnel. Estimates for Services under the Government of Northern Ireland (Year)
Published by: Department of Finance and Personnel, The Stationery Office, Stormont, Belfast, BT4 3SS, United Kingdom. Ed. James M Aleer. R&P Hmso Norwich TEL 44-1603-723005. **Subscr. to:** H.M.S.O., 80 Chichester St, Belfast, Co Antrim BT1 4JY, United Kingdom. TEL 0232-238451.

336 GBR
NORTHERN IRELAND. DEPARTMENT OF FINANCE AND PERSONNEL. SPRING SUPPLEMENTARY ESTIMATES (YEARS). Text in English. bi-m. **Document type:** *Government.*
Formerly: (Years) Northern Ireland. Department of Finance and Personnel. Spring Supplementary Estimates for services under the Government of Northern Ireland
—BLDSC (6151.013275).
Published by: Department of Finance and Personnel, The Stationery Office, Stormont, Belfast, BT4 3SS, United Kingdom.

336 NOR
NORWAY. ROYAL NORWEGIAN MINISTRY OF FINANCE. REVISED NATIONAL BUDGET (YEAR). Text in English, Norwegian. 1947. a. free. **Document type:** *Government.*
Supersedes in part (in 1986): National Budget of Norway (0077-3573)
Published by: Finansdepartementet/Royal Norwegian Ministry of Finance, Aakusgata 40, PO Box 8008, Dep, Oslo, 0030, Norway. TEL 47-22-24-90-90, FAX 47-22-24-95-10, http://www.finans.dep.no. Circ: 1,700.

336 NOR ISSN 0803-5962
NORWAY. ROYAL NORWEGIAN MINISTRY OF FINANCE. THE NATIONAL BUDGET (YEAR). Text in English, Norwegian. 1947. a. free. **Document type:** *Government.*
Supersedes in part (in 1986): National Budget of Norway (0077-3573)
Published by: Finansdepartementet/Royal Norwegian Ministry of Finance, Aakusgata 40, PO Box 8008, Dep, Oslo, 0030, Norway. TEL 47-22-24-90-90, FAX 47-22-24-95-10.

336 336.2 BGR
NOVOTO DANUCHNO ZAKONODATELSTVO. Text in Bulgarian. a.
Published by: Izdatelski Kompleks Trud i Pravo/Labour and Law Publishing House, Pl. Makedonia 1, Fl. 7, Sofia, 1040, Bulgaria. TEL 359-2-9875110, FAX 359-2-9870612, office@trudipravo.bg, http://www.trudipravo.bg.

336.3 MEX
NUEVO CONSULTORIO FISCAL; juridico, laboral y contable-financiero. Text in Spanish. 1987. 5/yr. MXP 415; MXP 18 newsstand/cover (effective 2000). **Description:** Disseminates Mexican fiscal law procedures in the private and public sector.
Formerly: Consultorio Fiscal (0187-6724)
Published by: Universidad Nacional Autonoma de Mexico, Facultad de Contaduria y Administracion, Edificio de la Direccion, 2o. Piso, Cub. 21, Circuito Exterior, Ciudad Universitaria, Apartado Postal 70-287, Mexico City, DF 04510, Mexico. TEL 52-5-6228396, FAX 52-5-6161355, http://server.contad.unam.mx/. Ed. Ma Antonieta Martin Granados.

332 USA
O C C BULLETINS. (Office of the Comptroller of the Currency) Text in English. m. USD 150 (effective 2000). **Document type:** *Bulletin, Government.* **Description:** Provides information of continuing concern regarding O.C.C. or O.C.C.-supported policies and guidelines; informs readers of pending regulation changes and other general information.
Published by: U.S. Office of the Comptroller of the Currency, Administrator of National Banks, 250 E St, S W, Washington, DC 20219. FAX 202-874-5263, http://www.occ.treas.gov.

O E C D EXTERNAL DEBT STATISTICS. see *BUSINESS AND ECONOMICS—Abstracting, Bibliographies, Statistics*

336 FRA ISSN 1608-7143
HJ2005
O E C D JOURNAL ON BUDGETING. Text in English. 199?. q. GBP 197; USD 226, GBP 129, JPY 26,600 updates (effective 2005). **Document type:** *Journal.* **Description:** Provides insight on leading-edge institutional arrangements, systems and instruments for the effective and efficient allocation and management of resources in the public sector.
Related titles: Online - full content ed.: ISSN 1681-2336. 2001. EUR 140, USD 161, GBP 92, JPY 18,900 (effective 2005); Online - full text ed.: (from EBSCO Publishing, Gale Group, IngentaConnect, O C L C Online Computer Library Center, Inc., Swets Information Services); ◆ French ed.: Revue de l'O C D E sur la Gestion Budgetaire. ISSN 1608-7151.
Indexed: ABIn, PAIS.
—BLDSC (6235.254520), CISTI, IE, Infotrieve, ingenta.
Published by: Organization for Economic Cooperation and Development, 2 Rue Andre Pascal, Paris, 75775 Cedex 16, France. TEL 33-1-45248200, FAX 33-1-45248500, http://www.oecd.org. **Dist. by:** Extenza - Turpin, Pegasus Dr, Stratton Business Park, Biggleswade, Beds SG18 8TQ, United Kingdom. TEL 44-1462-687552, FAX 44-1462-480947, subscriptions@extenza-turpin.com; O E C D Turpin North America, PO Box 194, Downingtown, PA 19335-0194. TEL 610-524-5361, FAX 610-524-5417, journalscustomer@turpinna.com.

336 CHE ISSN 1013-5774
OEFFENTLICHE FINANZEN DER SCHWEIZ/FINANCES PUBLIQUES EN SUISSE. Text in French, German. 1972. a. CHF 22 (effective 2001). **Document type:** *Government.*
Published by: Bundesamt fuer Statistik, Espace de l'Europe 10, Neuchatel, 2010, Switzerland. TEL 41-32-7136011, FAX 41-32-7136012, information@bfs.admin.ch, http://www.admin.ch/bfs.

336 DNK ISSN 1602-0928
OEKONOMISK REDEGOERELSE. Text in Danish. 1970. a. **Document type:** *Government.*
Formerly (until 2002): Oekonomisk Oversigt (0106-5580)
Published by: Finansministeriet/Ministry of Finance, Christiansborg Slotsplads, Copenhagen K, 1218, Denmark. TEL 45-33-923333, fm@fm.dk, http://www.fm.dk/1024/visPublikation.asp?artikelID=6748. **Dist. by:** Schultz Information A-S.

336.2 AUT ISSN 0029-9529
OESTERREICHISCHE STEUERZEITUNG. Text in German. 1948. s-m. EUR 198; EUR 11.30 newsstand/cover (effective 2005). bk.rev. index. 24 p./no.; **Document type:** *Magazine, Trade.*
Published by: LexisNexis Verlag ARD Orac GmbH & Co. KG (Subsidiary of: LexisNexis Europe and Africa), Marxergasse 25, Vienna, W 1030, Austria. TEL 43-1-534520, FAX 43-1-53452141, verlag@orac.at, http://www.lexisnexis.at/. Adv. contact Malgorzata Leitliner TEL 43-1-534521115. Circ: 6,300.

336 341 AUT ISSN 0379-4407
K15
OESTERREICHISCHE ZEITSCHRIFT FUER WIRTSCHAFTSRECHT. Text in German. 1974. q. EUR 54 in Europe; EUR 60 elsewhere (effective 2006). adv. **Document type:** *Journal, Trade.*
Indexed: IBR, IBZ.
Published by: (Institut fuer Angewandte-, Sozial-, und Wirtschaftsforschung), Wilhelm Braumueller Universitaets-Verlagsbuchhandlung GmbH, Servitengasse 5, Vienna, 1092, Austria. TEL 43-1-3191159, FAX 43-1-3102805, office@braumueller.at, http://www.braumueller.at. Eds. Karl Korinek, Karl Wenger. Adv. contact Susanne Mondl. Circ: 1,500.

336.2 AUT ISSN 0029-9685
OESTERREICHISCHE ZOLL UND STEUER NACHRICHTEN; Informationen fuer Zoll und Wirtschaft. Text in German. 1956. m. EUR 135; EUR 14 newsstand/cover (effective 2005). adv. bk.rev. abstr.; bibl.; stat.; tr.mk. index, cum.index. **Document type:** *Journal, Trade.*
Published by: Grenz Verlag, Flossgasse 6, Vienna, W 1025, Austria. TEL 43-1-2141715, FAX 43-1-214171530, office@grenzverlag.at, http://www.grenzverlag.at. Ed. Peter Takacs. R&P Martin Baumgartner TEL 43-1-214171541. Adv. contact Gertrude Hauder.

336 CAN ISSN 0843-4050
OFFICE OF THE PROVINCIAL AUDITOR. ANNUAL REPORT. Text in English. 1909. a.
Former titles: Provincial Auditor of Ontario. Annual Report (0711-9380); (until 1979): Provincial Auditor to the Legislative Assembly . Report (0316-4098); (until 1972): Provincial Auditor' Report (0316-4101)
Published by: Office of the Provincial Auditor of Ontario, 20 Dundas St West, Ste 1530, Toronto, ON M5G 2C2, Canada. TEL 416-327-2381, FAX 416-327-9862, comments@opa.gov.on.ca, http://www.auditor.on.ca/english/reports/reports_frame.htm.

336 USA
OFFICIAL I R S PUBLICATIONS. Text in English. 1991. w. (Dec.-Mar.; m. , Apr.-Nov.). looseleaf. USD 260. **Description:** Consists of more than 140 taxpayer information publications.
Published by: R I A (Subsidiary of: Thomson Corporation), 395 Hudson St, New York, NY 10014. TEL 212-367-6300, RIA.CustomerServices@Thomson.com, http://ria.thomson.com/

344.1034 GBR ISSN 1472-3336
THE OFFSHORE & INTERNATIONAL TAXATION REVIEW. Text in English. 1990. 3/yr. GBP 140 (effective 1998). **Document type:** *Bulletin.*
Former titles (until 1999): Offshore Taxation Review (1366-7564); (until 1997): Offshore Tax Planning Review (0961-1363)
—BLDSC (6244.215190).
Published by: Key Haven Publications plc., 7 Crescent Stables, 139 Upper Richmond Rd, London, SW15 2TN, United Kingdom. TEL 44-20-8780-2522, FAX 44-20-8780-1693.

OFFSHORE INVESTMENT. see *BUSINESS AND ECONOMICS—Banking And Finance*

OFFSHORE TAX STRATEGIES. see *LAW—International Law*

336.278 665 USA ISSN 1096-9195
OIL, GAS AND ENERGY QUARTERLY. Text in English. 1951. q. USD 223 (effective 2003). bibl. index. reprint service avail. from WSH,PQC. **Description:** A clearinghouse for the latest tax ideas, techniques and practice pointers in oil and gas taxation and accounting.
Formerly (until 1997): Oil and Gas Tax Quarterly (0030-1396)
Related titles: Microfilm ed.: (from WSH); Microform ed.: (from PQC, WSH).
Indexed: ATI, CLI, FamI, ILP, LRI.
—CCC.
Published by: Matthew Bender & Co., Inc. (Subsidiary of: LexisNexis North America), 1275 Broadway, Albany, NY 12204. international@bender.com, http://bender.lexisnexis.com. Ed. Larry Crumbley.

336.2 USA
OKLAHOMA. AD VALOREM TAX DIVISION. (YEAR) PROGRESS REPORT TO THE LEGISLATURE ON PROPERTY REVALUATION. Text in English. 1968. a. free. stat. **Document type:** *Government.*
Published by: Tax Commission, Ad Valorem Tax Division, 2501 Lincoln Blvd, Oklahoma City, OK 73194. TEL 405-521-3178, FAX 405-521-3991. Ed. Jeff Spelman. Circ: 500.

336.2 USA
ONEDISC; professional research library. Text in English. m. USD 149 starting price. **Description:** Features collection of full texts of all the vital federal tax documents and compiled them into seven individual CD-ROMs follows: Basic OnceDisc Disc, Chief Counsel Advice Disc, Court Opinions Discs, Internal Revenus Manual Disc, FormsDisc, US Tax Treaties Disc and Legislative History Disc.
Media: CD-ROM. **Related titles:** Alternate Frequency ed(s).: m.; q.; a.
Published by: Tax Analysts, 6830 N Fairfax Dr, Arlington, VA 22213. TEL 703-553-4400, 800-955-3444, FAX 703-533-4444.

ONTARIO BUDGET. BUDGET PAPERS. see *PUBLIC ADMINISTRATION*

336.2 CAN ISSN 1189-9131
ONTARIO INCOME TAX WITH RELATED TAXES. Text in English. 1960. irreg., latest 2001, 28th ed. USD 55 per vol. (effective 2005).
Former titles (until 1988): Ontario Corporation and Income Tax Legislation, including Mining Taxes and Small Business Development Corporations (0225-1795); (until 1979): Ontario Corporation and Income Tax Legislation including Mining Taxes (0319-6291); Which superseded in part (in 1975): Ontario and Quebec Corporation and Income Tax (0316-6023)
Published by: C C H Canadian Ltd., 90 Sheppard Ave E, Ste 300, North York, ON M2N 6X1, Canada. TEL 416-224-2248, 800-268-4522, FAX 416-224-2243, 800-461-4131, cservice@cch.ca, http://www.cch.ca.

336.2 CAN ISSN 0048-1866
ONTARIO TAX REPORTER. Text in English. 1950. m. looseleaf. CND 582 (effective 2005). index. **Document type:** *Trade.* **Description:** Current reporting covers every aspect of taxation.
Related titles: CD-ROM ed.: CND 531 (effective 2005); Online - full text ed.: CND 515 (effective 2005).
Indexed: CBCABus.
Published by: C C H Canadian Ltd., 90 Sheppard Ave E, Ste 300, North York, ON M2N 6X1, Canada. TEL 416-224-2248, 800-268-4522, FAX 416-224-2243, cservice@cch.ca, http://www.cch.ca.

336 DNK ISSN 0108-9722
OPGAVESAMLING I SKAT 1. Cover title: Opgavesamling i Skatteret I. Text in Danish. 1980. a. DKK 160.
Published by: Alternativ Revisions Forlag, Riddergade 7, Naestved, 4700, Denmark.

336 DNK ISSN 0108-9730
OPGAVESAMLING I SKAT 2 OG ERHVERVSJURA. Cover title: Opgavesamling i Skatteret II og Erhvervsjura. Text in Danish. 1980. a. DKK 160.
Published by: Alternativ Revisions Forlag, Riddergade 7, Naestved, 4700, Denmark.

336 USA
OREGON. DEPARTMENT OF REVENUE. INCOME, INHERITANCE AND GIFT TAX LAW BOOK. Text in English. biennial. USD 22. **Document type:** *Government.* **Description:** Oregon laws and administrative rules on personal income taxes, corporation income and excise taxes, inheritance and gift taxes.
Published by: Department of Revenue, Revenue Bldg, Salem, OR 97310. TEL 503-945-8636, FAX 503-945-8672.

336 USA
OREGON. DEPARTMENT OF REVENUE. INCOME TAX AND PROPERTY TAX LAWS AND ADMINISTRATIVE RULES. Text in English. a. USD 5. **Document type:** *Government.*
Published by: Department of Revenue, Revenue Bldg, Salem, OR 97310. TEL 503-945-8636, FAX 503-945-8672.

336 USA
OREGON. DEPARTMENT OF REVENUE. PROPERTY ASSESSMENT AND TAXATION ADMINISTRATIVE RULE BOOK. Text in English. biennial. **Document type:** *Government.* **Description:** Contains Oregon property tax administrative rules.
Formerly: Oregon. Department of Revenue. Property Assessment and Taxation Law Book
Published by: Department of Revenue, Revenue Bldg, Salem, OR 97310. TEL 503-945-8636, FAX 503-945-8672.

336 USA
OREGON. DEPARTMENT OF REVENUE. SUMMARY OF OREGON TAXES. Text in English. a. **Document type:** *Government.*
Published by: Department of Revenue, Revenue Bldg, Salem, OR 97310. TEL 503-945-8636, FAX 503-945-8672.

OREGON PERSONAL INCOME TAX STATISTICS. see *BUSINESS AND ECONOMICS—Abstracting, Bibliographies, Statistics*

OREGON PROPERTY TAX STATISTICS. see *BUSINESS AND ECONOMICS—Abstracting, Bibliographies, Statistics*

336.2 POL ISSN 1641-7968
ORZECZNICTWO PODATKOWE. PRZEGLAD. Text in Polish. 2001. bi-m. PLZ 150 (effective 2003).
Published by: Wydawnictwo Prawnicze LexisNexis Sp. z o.o. (Subsidiary of: LexisNexis Europe and Africa), ul Gen K Sosnkowskiego 1, Warsaw, 02-495, Poland. TEL 48-22-6677543, FAX 48-22-7230739, biuro@LexisNexis.pl, http://sklep.lexpolonica.pl.

336.2 JPN ISSN 0078-7094
OUTLINE OF JAPANESE TAX. Text in Japanese. 1953. a., latest 1997. JPY 3,000. **Document type:** *Government.*
Published by: Ministry of Finance, Printing Bureau, 2-2-4 Toranomon, Minato-ku, Tokyo, 105-0001, Japan. **Dist. by:** Government Publications Service Center, 2-1 Kasumigaseki 1-chome, Chiyoda-ku, Tokyo 100-0013, Japan.

336 USA ISSN 1059-2032
P B C FEDERAL TAX GUIDE✶ . Text in English. 1991. q. USD 29.99. **Document type:** *Consumer.*
Published by: Publishing & Business Consultants, 4427 W Slauson Ave, Los Angeles, CA 90043-2717. TEL 213-732-3477, FAX 213-732-9123. Ed. Andeson Napoleon Atia.

336 GBR ISSN 1363-0377
P F I INTELLIGENCE BULLETIN. (Private Finance Initiative) Text in English. 1996. m. GBP 450 domestic; GBP 490 foreign (effective 2001). back issues avail. **Document type:** *Bulletin, Trade.* **Description:** Provides up-to-date information on all aspects of Private Finance Initiative legislation, regulations, working procedures, and market potential.
Published by: SMi Publishing, 1 New Concordia Wharf, Mill St, London, SE1 2BB, United Kingdom. TEL 44-207-827-6000, FAX 44-207-827-6001, pfi@smipublishing.co.uk, ordering@smipublishing.co.uk, http://www.smipublishing.co.uk.

336 PAK
P.T.D. ANNUAL TAX DIGEST. (Pakistan Tax Decisions) Text in English. 1991. a., latest 1997. PKR 1,250 domestic (effective 2001). back issues avail.
Published by: P.L.D. Publishers, 35 Nabha Rd., Lahore 1, Pakistan. TEL 92-42-7356228, FAX 92-42-7238113, pld@brain.net.pk. Ed., Pub. Malik Muhammad Saeed.

336.2 USA ISSN 0160-9912
KF6289.A355
PACKAGE X; reference copies of federal tax forms and instructions. Text in English. a. free (effective 2004).
Published by: U.S. Internal Revenue Service, 1111 Constitution Ave, N W, Washington, DC 20224. TEL 800-829-1040, http://www.irs.gov.

B

336 PAK ISSN 0078-7892
HC440.5.A1
PAKISTAN BASIC FACTS. Text in English. a. PKR 5.
Formerly: Pakistan. Ministry of Finance. Basic Facts About the Budget (0078-8295)
Published by: Office of the Economic Adviser, Islamabad, Pakistan.

PAKISTAN CUSTOMS TARIFF. see *BUSINESS AND ECONOMICS—International Commerce*

336 PAK ISSN 0304-6478
HJ67.5
PAKISTAN. FINANCE DIVISION. ANNUAL BUDGET STATEMENT (FINAL). Text in English. a. stat.
Published by: Finance Division, Islamabad, Pakistan.

336 PAK
PAKISTAN. FINANCE DIVISION. BUDGET IN BRIEF. Text in English. 1964. a. free to qualified personnel.
Formerly: Pakistan. Ministry of Finance. Budget in Brief (0078-8309)
Published by: Finance Division, Islamabad, Pakistan.

336 PAK ISSN 0376-9208
HJ67.5
PAKISTAN. FINANCE DIVISION. ECONOMIC ANALYSIS OF THE BUDGET. Text in English. a. free to qualified personnel. **Document type:** *Government.*
Formerly (until 1973): Pakistan. Ministry of Finance. Economic Analysis of the Central Government (0078-8325)
Published by: Finance Division, Islamabad, Pakistan.

338.9 PAK ISSN 0376-9011
HC440.5
PAKISTAN. FINANCE DIVISION. ESTIMATES OF FOREIGN ASSISTANCE. Text in English. 1976. irreg.
Supersedes (in 1977): Pakistan. Ministry of Finance. Estimates of Foreign Assistance (0555-8786)
Published by: Finance Division, Islamabad, Pakistan.

336 PAK
PAKISTAN. FINANCE DIVISION. SUPPLEMENTARY DEMANDS FOR GRANTS AND APPROPRIATIONS. Text in English. 1973. irreg. free to qualified personnel. charts; stat.
Published by: Finance Division, Islamabad, Pakistan. Circ: (controlled).

336.2 PAK ISSN 0031-0115
PAKISTAN TAX DECISIONS; a comprehensive monthly journal of Pakistan on taxation. Text in English. 1959. m. PKR 2,028, USD 82 (effective 2001). back issues avail.; reprint service avail. from PQC. **Description:** Reports relevant tax law, Federal Government legislation and case decisions in the Supreme Court of Pakistan and the High Courts.
Published by: P.L.D. Publishers, 35 Nabha Rd., Lahore 1, Pakistan. TEL 92-42-7356228, FAX 92-42-7238113, pld@brain.net.pk. Ed., Pub. Malik Muhammad Saeed.

336 382 PAK ISSN 0078-852X
PAKISTAN'S BALANCE OF PAYMENTS (ANNUAL). Text in English. 1948. a. PKR 50, USD 8 (effective 2000). **Document type:** *Government.*
Published by: State Bank of Pakistan, Central Directorate, Public Relations Department, I.I. Chundrigar Rd, PO Box 4456, Karachi, Pakistan. TEL 92-21-9212400, FAX 92-21-9212436, TELEX 21774 SBPK PK.

382 PAK
PAKISTAN'S BALANCE OF PAYMENTS (QUARTERLY). Text in English. q. **Document type:** *Government.*

Published by: State Bank of Pakistan, Central Directorate, Public Relations Department, I.I. Chundrigar Rd, PO Box 4456, Karachi, Pakistan. TEL 92-21-9212400, FAX 92-21-9212436, TELEX 21774 SBPK PK.

336.2 PAN
PANAMA. CONTRALORIA GENERAL. INFORME TRIMESTRAL DE RENTAS Y GASTOS. Cover title: Panama. Contraloria General. Boletin de Contabilidad. Text in Spanish. 1965. q. free. stat. **Document type:** *Government.* **Description:** Provides statistics on the revenue and expenditures of Panama.
Published by: Contraloria General, Direccion de Contabilidad, Apdo. 5213, Panama City, 5, Panama. Circ: 1,000.

PARTNERSHIP AND S CORPORATION COORDINATOR. see *BUSINESS AND ECONOMICS—Investments*

336 USA
PARTNERSHIP TAX PLANNING & PRACTICE. Text in English. 1987. 2 base vols. plus m. updates. looseleaf. USD 578 base vol(s). (effective 2004); includes Partnership Tax Watch Newsletter.. **Document type:** *Newsletter.* **Description:** Includes explanations, tax planning, and choice of entity considerations, sample agreements and compliance forms. Sample partnership agreements allow us to customize the appropriate documents for our clients.
Formerly (until 1993): Partnership Tax Reporter
Related titles: CD-ROM ed.: USD 419 (effective 2000).
Published by: C C H Inc., 2700 Lake Cook Rd, Riverwoods, IL 60015. TEL 847-267-7000, 800-449-6439, FAX 800-224-8299, cust_serv@cch.com, http://www.cch.com. Pub. Kevin Robert.

336 USA
PARTNERSHIP TAXATION. Text in English. 1989. latest 4th ed., 4 base vols. plus q. updates. looseleaf. USD 240 base vol(s).. **Document type:** *Trade.* **Description:** Covers income shifting, 704b regulations, passive loss rules, gift tax consequences, at risk rules, the investment tax credit and appreciation and recapture.
Published by: Shepard's (Subsidiary of: LexisNexis North America), 555 Middle Creek Pkwy, Colorado Springs, CO 80921. TEL 800-743-7393, customer_service@shepards.com, http://www.shepards.com, http://www.lexisnexis.com/shepards/.

336.2 343.4 USA
PATRIOT CANNON; booming for the tax patriot community. Text in English. 1980. bi-m. USD 25. **Document type:** *Newsletter.* **Description:** Covers taxpayers' rights, tax issues, governmental corruption and legal issues.
Address: PO Box 2368, Anderson, SC 29622. Circ: 500.

344 USA ISSN 0895-7975
PAYROLL MANAGER'S LETTER. Text in English. 1984. s-m. USD 232 to individuals (effective 2004). s-a. index. **Document type:** *Newsletter.* **Description:** Provides payroll professionals with everything they need to comply with IRS and SAA (and other relevant governement agencies) rules and regulations. Reports on landmark court cases and their impact on payroll, features relevant technology updates, and keeps readers up on what's new and what to expect in their field.
Related titles: Online - full text ed.: (from EBSCO Publishing, Florida Center for Library Automation, Gale Group).
Indexed: ATI.
—CCC.
Published by: Bureau of Business Practice (Subsidiary of: Aspen Publishers, Inc.), 1185 Avenue of the Americas, 37th Fl, New York, NY 10036. TEL 860-442-4365, 800-243-0876, FAX 860-437-3555, rebecca_armitage@prenhall.com, http://www.bbpnews.com. Ed. Julia Muino Russell. Pub. Peter Garabedian. R&P Kathryn Mennone.

PAYROLL PRACTITIONER'S COMPLIANCE HANDBOOK; year-end and quarterly reporting. see *BUSINESS AND ECONOMICS—Accounting*

343 USA ISSN 1529-2290
PAYROLL PRACTITIONER'S STATE TAX ALERT. Variant title: State Tax Alert. Text in English. m. USD 279 (effective 2003). **Document type:** *Newsletter, Trade.* **Description:** Provides managers with up-to-date news and analysis of state and local payroll developments.
Related titles: Online - full text ed.: (from ProQuest Information & Learning).
Indexed: ATI.
Published by: Institute of Management & Administration, Inc., 3 Park Ave, New York, NY 10016-5902. TEL 212-244-0360, FAX 212-564-0465, subserve@ioma.com, http://www.ioma.com.

343 USA
PAYROLL TAX ALERT. Text in English. 2000. w. USD 240 (effective 2006). **Document type:** *Newsletter, Trade.* **Description:** Provides updates on changes to federal and state payroll policy (wage-hour rules, industrial orders, new posting requirements and tax issues) from every agency that has a hand in corporate payroll & benefits administration.
Formerly: Payroll Tax Fax
Published by: Institute of Management & Administration, Inc., 3 Park Ave, New York, NY 10016-5902. TEL 212-244-0360, FAX 212-564-0465, subserve@ioma.com, http://www.ioma.com/products/prod_detail.php?prodid=125.

PEACE TAX FUND NEWSLETTER. see *POLITICAL SCIENCE—Civil Rights*

336 340 USA
PENNSYLVANIA CHAMBER OF BUSINESS AND INDUSTRY. TAX BULLETIN✶. Text in English. fortn. USD 215 to non-members; USD 165 to members. **Description:** Covers Pennsylvania business tax developments.
Published by: Pennsylvania Chamber of Business and Industry, 417 Walnut St, Harrisburg, PA 17101. TEL 800-326-3252, FAX 717-255-3298.

336 USA
PENNSYLVANIA. STATE TAX EQUALIZATION BOARD. ANNUAL CERTIFICATION✶. Text in English. 1975 (vol.28). a.
Published by: State Tax Equalization Board, Fulton Bldg, 5th Fl, 200 N 3rd St, Harrisburg, PA 17101. TEL 717-787-5950.

336 USA
PENNSYLVANIA TAXATION. Text in English. 1987. base vol. plus a. updates. looseleaf. USD 135. Supplement avail. **Document type:** *Trade.* **Description:** Encompasses all of Pennsylvania's state and local taxes and their governing rules.
Related titles: Series of: Taxation Series.
Published by: Shepard's (Subsidiary of: LexisNexis North America), 555 Middle Creek Pkwy, Colorado Springs, CO 80921. TEL 800-743-7393, customer_service@shepards.com, http://www.shepards.com, http://www.lexisnexis.com/shepards/. Ed. Joseph C Bright Jr.

336 362.6 USA
PENSION AND BENEFITS UPDATE. Text in English. bi-m. USD 50 to non-members; USD 35 to members. **Document type:** *Newsletter.* **Description:** Covers current topics in the areas of public pension and benefits.
Published by: Government Finance Officers Association, 203 N LaSalle St, Ste 2700, Chicago, IL 60601-1210. Subscriptions@gfoa.org, http://www.gfoa.org.

336 GBR ISSN 0964-6744
PERSONAL TAX PLANNING REVIEW. Text in English. 1991. 3/yr. GBP 99 (effective 1998). **Document type:** *Bulletin.*
Published by: Key Haven Publications plc., 7 Crescent Stables, 139 Upper Richmond Rd, London, SW15 2TN, United Kingdom. TEL 44-20-8780-2522, FAX 44-20-8780-1693. Ed. Andrew Hitchmough.

336 USA
PEYRON TAX ACCOUNTANT'S COMMUNIQUE. Text in English. 1978. m. USD 56 domestic; USD 86 foreign (effective 2001). 4 p./no.; back issues avail. **Document type:** *Newsletter.* **Description:** Offers tax preparation advice for accountants, including relevant tax cases, tax code changes, IRS and state tax audits and tips on operating tax preparation offices.
Published by: Peyron Associates Inc., 3212 Preston St, Louisville, KY 46213. TEL 502-637-7483. Ed., R&P Dan Peyron. Circ: 1,500 (paid).

336 340 USA
PEYRON TAX LETTER & SOCIAL SECURITY REPORT. Text in English. 1980. m. USD 44 (effective 1999). **Document type:** *Newsletter.* **Description:** Offers tax savings advice for income and social security taxes.
Published by: Peyron Associates Inc., 3212 Preston St, Louisville, KY 46213. TEL 502-637-7483. Ed., R&P Dan Peyron. Circ: 1,000.

336 PHL
HC451
➤ **PHILIPPINE JOURNAL OF DEVELOPMENT.** Text in English. 1974. s-a., latest vol.29, 2002. USD 55, PHP 900; PHP 400 per issue (effective 2005). adv. bk.rev. 150 p./no.; back issues avail. **Document type:** *Journal, Academic/Scholarly.* **Description:** Studies economics in business, sociology, politics, public administration and foreign relations as they relate to the development of the Philippines.
Former titles (until 2002): Journal of Philippine Development (0115-9143); N E D A Journal of Development
Related titles: Online - full text ed.
Indexed: APEL, BAS, IPP, PAIS, RASB.
Published by: Philippine Institute for Development Studies, NEDA sa Makati Bldg, 106 Amorsolo St, Legaspi Village, Makati Mm, 1229, Philippines. TEL 632-893-5705, FAX 632-816-1091, http://www3.pids.gov.ph/ris/journalindex.htm, http://www.pids.gov.ph. Ed. Jennifer P T Liguton. Circ: 800 (controlled).

336 PHL ISSN 0116-3426
PHILIPPINE REVENUE JOURNAL. Text in English. 1963. m. free. bk.rev.
Indexed: IPP.
Published by: Bureau of Internal Revenue, National Office Bldg, 1st Fl., Quezon City, Philippines. Ed. Manuel F Almario. Circ: 6,000.

336.2 PHL ISSN 0031-7845
PHILIPPINE TAX JOURNAL✶; the magazine for lawyers, accountants and businessmen. Text in English. 1956. m. PHP 24, USD 24. index.
Address: R-203 University Center Bldg, 1985 Recto Ave, Manila, Philippines. Ed. Cirilo G Montejo. Circ: 1,000.

336 USA
PLANNING TAX-EXEMPT ORGANIZATIONS. Text in English. 1983. base vol. plus a. updates. looseleaf. USD 210. Supplement avail. **Document type:** *Trade.* **Description:** Provides information on the planning, formation and continuing representation of tax-exempt organizations—from outlining to drafting documents.
Related titles: Series of: Taxation Series.
Published by: Shepard's (Subsidiary of: LexisNexis North America), 555 Middle Creek Pkwy, Colorado Springs, CO 80921. TEL 800-743-7393, customer_service@shepards.com, http://www.shepards.com, http://www.lexisnexis.com/shepards/. Eds. Robert J Desiderio, Scott A Taylor.

336 332.63 004.678 USA
PLUNKETT'S ON-LINE TRADING, FINANCE & INVESTMENT WEB SITES ALMANAC. Text in English. 1999. biennial. USD 149.99 (effective 2005); includes diskette. **Document type:** *Directory, Trade.* **Description:** Presents a complete profile of the 500 most vital web sites for investors and financial professionals.
Supersedes (in 1999): Plunkett's Almanac of Finance and Investment Web Sites
Published by: Plunkett Research, Ltd, PO Drawer 541737, Houston, TX 77254-1737. TEL 713-932-0000, FAX 713-932-7080, info@plunkettresearch.com, http://www.plunkettresearch.com. Ed., Pub. Jack W Plunkett.

PODATKI I PRAWO GOSPODARCZE UNII EUROPEJSKIEJ. see *LAW*

336 PRT ISSN 0079-4201
PORTUGAL. MINISTERIO DAS FINANCAS. RELATORIO DO ORCAMENTO GERAL DO ESTADO✶. Text in Portuguese. a. price varies.
Published by: Ministerio das Financas, Rua da Alfandega, Lisbon Codex, 1100, Portugal.

343.05 USA
POST MORTEM TAX PLANNING. Text in English. 1982. base vol. plus a. updates. looseleaf. USD 195. Supplement avail. **Document type:** *Trade.* **Description:** Covers income tax and various elections in the estate planning and probate fields.
Related titles: Series of: Tax and Estate Planning Series.
Published by: Shepard's (Subsidiary of: LexisNexis North America), 555 Middle Creek Pkwy, Colorado Springs, CO 80921. TEL 800-743-7393, customer_service@shepards.com, http://www.shepards.com, http://www.lexisnexis.com/shepards/. Ed. Jerry A Kasner.

336 340 GBR
POTTER & MONROE'S TAX PLANNING WITH PRECEDENTS. Text in English. 1988. base vol. plus updates 2/yr. looseleaf. GBP 450 (effective 2005). **Document type:** *Trade.*
Published by: Sweet & Maxwell Ltd., 100 Avenue Road, London, NW3 3PF, United Kingdom. TEL 44-20-74491111, FAX 44-20-74491144, customer.services@sweetandmaxwell.co.uk, http://www.sweetandmaxwell.co.uk. **Subscr. to:** Cheriton House, North Way, Andover, Hants SP10 5BE, United Kingdom.

343 USA ISSN 1531-6122
PRACTICAL ASIAN TAX STRATEGIES. Text in English. 2000. m. USD 786 domestic; USD 836 foreign (effective 2005). adv. **Document type:** *Newsletter, Trade.* **Description:** Provides international tax practitioners, executives and financial professionals with practical advice and actionable plans to achieve maximum tax efficiency for international companies with Asian operations.
Published by: WorldTrade Executive, Inc., 2250 Main St, Ste 100, PO Box 761, Concord, MA 01742. TEL 978-287-0301, FAX 978-287-0302, smahapatra@wtexec.com, info@wtexec.com, http://www.wtexec.com/asiatax.html. Pub. Gary A Brown. Adv. contact Jay Stanley.

343 USA ISSN 1531-6130
PRACTICAL EUROPEAN TAX STRATEGIES; report on tax planning for international tax companies operating in Europe. Text in English. 1999. m. USD 787 domestic; USD 837 foreign (effective 2005). **Document type:** *Newsletter, Trade.* **Description:** Provides international tax practitioners, executives and financial professionals with practical advice and actionable plans to achieve maximum tax efficiency for international companies with operations in Europe.
Published by: WorldTrade Executive, Inc., 2250 Main St, Ste 100, PO Box 761, Concord, MA 01742. TEL 978-287-0301, FAX 978-287-0302, info@wtexec.com, http://www.wtexec.com/eurotax.html. Ed. David R Cooper. Pub. Gary A Brown. Adv. contact Jay Stanley.

382 USA ISSN 1523-2611
PRACTICAL LATIN AMERICAN TAX STRATEGIES. Text in English. 1998. m. USD 784 domestic; USD 834 foreign (effective 2005). **Document type:** *Newsletter, Trade.* **Description:** Contains information on how leading-edge companies are reacting to changes and developments in Latin American tax practice.

Published by: WorldTrade Executive, Inc., 2250 Main St, Ste 100, PO Box 761, Concord, MA 01742. TEL 978-287-0301, FAX 978-287-0302, smahapatra@wtexec.com, info@wtexec.com, http://www.wtexecutive.com/cms/content.jsp?id=com.tms.cms.section.Section_1021, http://www.wtexec.com. Pub. Gary A Brown. Adv. contact Jay Stanley.

338 USA ISSN 1557-3680
KGF4582
PRACTICAL MEXICAN TAX STRATEGIES. Text in English. 2001 (Mar./Apr.). bi-m. USD 698 domestic; USD 748 foreign (effective 2005). **Document type:** *Newsletter, Trade.* **Description:** Contains information on how major companies are reacting to changes and developments in Mexico tax practice.
Published by: WorldTrade Executive, Inc., 2250 Main St, Ste 100, PO Box 761, Concord, MA 01742. TEL 978-287-0301, FAX 978-287-0302, smahapatra@wtexec.com, info@wtexec.com, http://www.wtexec.com/mextax.html. Pub. Gary A Brown. Adv. contact Jay Stanley.

THE PRACTICAL TAX LAWYER. see *LAW*

336.2 657 USA ISSN 1523-6250
HF5681.T3
PRACTICAL TAX STRATEGIES. Text in English. 1998. m. USD 185 (effective 2004). adv. illus. Index. reprints avail. **Document type:** *Trade.* **Description:** Covers current tax developments and their implications and offers solutions to tax problems that arise frequently in general accounting practice.
Formed by the merger of (1966-1998): Taxation for Accountants (0040-0165); (1972-1998): Taxation for Lawyers (0161-178X)
Related titles: Microform ed.: (from PQC); Online - full text ed.: (from O C L C Online Computer Library Center, Inc.).
Indexed: ABIn, ATI, BPI, BPIA, BusI, CLI, FamI, LII, LRI, ManagCont, PAIS.
—IE. **CCC.**
Published by: W G & L Financial Reporting & Management Research (Subsidiary of: R I A), 90 Fifth Ave, New York, NY 10011. TEL 212-645-4800, FAX 212-337-4280, http://www.wgl.com/tax/txac.html. Ed. Sandra K Lewis. Circ: 8,544.

343 USA
PRACTICAL U.S. - DOMESTIC TAX STRATEGIES. Variant title: Practical U.S. / Domestic Tax Strategies. Text in English. m. USD 614 domestic; USD 664 foreign (effective 2005). adv. **Document type:** *Newsletter, Trade.* **Description:** Provides information and advice on all aspects of U.S. domestic tax transactions and practice.
Published by: WorldTrade Executive, Inc., 2250 Main St, Ste 100, PO Box 761, Concord, MA 01742. TEL 978-287-0301, FAX 978-287-0302, smahapatra@wtexex.com, info@wtexec.com, http://www.wtexec.com/usdtax.html. Ed. David R Cooper. Pub. Gary A Brown. Adv. contact Jay Stanley.

343 USA ISSN 1523-2638
PRACTICAL U.S. / INTERNATIONAL TAX STRATEGIES. Variant title: Practical U.S. - International Tax Strategies. Text in English. 1997. 2/m. USD 614 domestic; USD 664 foreign (effective 2005). adv. **Document type:** *Newsletter, Trade.* **Description:** Provides practical guidance covering all aspects of international tax transactions and practice.
Published by: WorldTrade Executive, Inc., 2250 Main St, Ste 100, PO Box 761, Concord, MA 01742. TEL 978-287-0301, FAX 978-287-0302, smahapatra@wtexec.com, info@wtexec.com, http://www.wtexec.com/pusits.html. Ed. David R Cooper. Pub. Gary A Brown. Adv. contact Jay Stanley.

336 340 USA ISSN 1056-9952
KF6369
PRACTITIONERS 1040 DESKBOOK. Text in English. 1989. a. USD 135.
Indexed: ATI.
Published by: Practitioners Publishing Co., PO Box 966, Fort Worth, TX 76101-0966. Ed. Jim Reeves.

336 CAN ISSN 1193-1701
PRACTITIONER'S INCOME TAX ACT. Text in English. 1992. a.
Published by: Canada Federal Publications, 165 University Ave, Toronto, ON M5H 3B8, Canada. TEL 416-860-1611, FAX 800-433-3782, info@fedpubs.com.

336.2 RUS
PRAVOVYE SPOSOBY SNIZHENIYA NALOGOVYKH PLATEZHEI. Text in Russian. q. USD 99.95 in United States.
Address: Profsoyuznaya 3, Moscow, 117036, Russian Federation. TEL 7-095-1299555, FAX 7-095-1246809. Ed. A G Mordukhovich. **US dist. addr.:** East View Information Services, 3020 Harbor Ln. N., Minneapolis, MN 55447. TEL 612-550-0961.

332.6 DEU
PRAXIS-HANDBUCH BETRIEBSPRUEFUNG UND STEUERFAHNDUNG. Text in German. base vol. plus updates 6/yr. EUR 149 base vol(s). (effective 2004). **Document type:** *Trade.*
Published by: Verlag fuer Deutsche Steuerberater AG (Subsidiary of: Wolters Kluwer Deutschland GmbH), Marlener Str 2, Offenburg, 77656, Germany. TEL 49-781-9900646, FAX 49-781-9900644, info@steuern-online.de, http://www.steuern-online.de.

336.2 DEU ISSN 1438-8375
PRAXIS INTERNATIONALE STEUERBERATUNG. Text in German. m. EUR 198 (effective 2004). **Document type:** *Journal, Trade.*
Published by: (Institut fuer Wirtschaftspublizistik), Vogel Verlag und Druck GmbH & Co. KG, Max-Planck-Str 7-9, Wuerzburg, 97064, Germany. TEL 49-931-4180, FAX 49-931-4182100, marliese_bernhardt@vogel-medien.de, http://www.vogel-medien.de. **Subscr. to:** DataM-Services GmbH, Fichtestr 9, Wuerzburg 97074, Germany. TEL 49-931-417001, FAX 49-931-4170499, swestenberger@datam-services.de, http://www.datam-services.de.

336.2 DEU ISSN 1435-0122
PRAXIS STEUERSTRAFRECHT. Text in German. 1998. m. EUR 174 (effective 2004). **Document type:** *Journal, Trade.*
Published by: (Institut fuer Wirtschaftspublizistik), Vogel Verlag und Druck GmbH & Co. KG, Max-Planck-Str 7-9, Wuerzburg, 97064, Germany. TEL 49-931-4180, FAX 49-931-4182100, marliese_bernhardt@vogel-medien.de, http://www.vogel-medien.de. **Subscr. to:** DataM-Services GmbH, Fichtestr 9, Wuerzburg 97074, Germany. TEL 49-931-417001, FAX 49-931-4170499, swestenberger@datam-services.de, http://www.datam-services.de.

336 DEU ISSN 1437-4730
PRAXISHANDBUCH GELDANLAGE. Text in German. 1992. bi-m. looseleaf. **Document type:** *Magazine, Trade.*
Formerly (until 1999): Geld und Steuern (0941-1976)
Published by: W R S Verlag GmbH & Co. KG (Subsidiary of: Rudolf Haufe Verlag GmbH & Co. KG), Fraunhoferstr 5, Planegg, 82152, Germany. TEL 49-89-895170, FAX 49-89-89517250, info@wrs.de, http://www.wrs.de.

336 USA
PRESIDENT'S FISCAL YEAR (YEAR) BUDGET. Text in English. 1991. a. USD 5. **Description:** Discusses the current administration's budget.
Published by: Tax Foundation, 2001 L St NW, Ste. 1050, Washington, DC 20036-4971. tf@taxfoundation.org, http://www.taxfoundation.org.

336 ESP ISSN 0210-5977
HJ60
PRESUPUESTO Y GASTO PUBLICO. Text in Spanish. 1979. 3/yr.
Related titles: Online - full text ed.
Published by: Instituto de Estudios Fiscales, Avda Cardenal Herrera Oria, 378, Madrid, 28035, Spain. TEL 34-91-3398800, FAX 34-91-3398964, http://www.ief.es/. **Subscr. to:** Ministerio de Economia y Hacienda, Centro de Publicaciones, Pz Campillo del Mundo Nuevo, 3, Madrid 28005, Spain. TEL 91-527-1437.

343 USA ISSN 1056-7690
KF6297.Z9
THE PRICE WATERHOUSE INVESTOR'S TAX ADVISER. Text in English. 1991. a.
Published by: (Price Waterhouse GBR), Pocket Books, 1230 Ave of the Americas, New York, NY 10020.

336 GBR ISSN 0967-229X
PRIVATE CLIENT BUSINESS. Text in English. 1992. bi-m. GBP 370, EUR 557 in Europe; GBP 390, USD 709 elsewhere; GBP 185, EUR 279 in Europe to students; GBP 195, USD 355 elsewhere to students (effective 2006). adv. **Document type:** *Bulletin, Trade.* **Description:** Concerns inheritance tax, capital gains tax, foreign affairs, succession, trusts and charities with analysis of issues by financial commentators.
Formerly: Capital Taxes and Estate Planning Quarterly
Indexed: ELJI, LJI.
—**CCC.**
Published by: Sweet & Maxwell Ltd., 100 Avenue Road, London, NW3 3PF, United Kingdom. TEL 44-20-74491111, FAX 44-20-74491144, customer.services@sweetandmaxwell.co.uk, http://www.sweetandmaxwell.co.uk. Ed. Jeanette Culleton. Adv. contact Jackie Wood. **Subscr. outside the UK to:** Cheriton House, North Way, Andover, Hants SP10 5BE, United Kingdom. TEL 44-1264-342706.

336 GBR ISSN 1366-199X
PRIVATE FINANCE INITIATIVE JOURNAL. Text in English. 1996. bi-m. GBP 250 (effective 1999). adv. bk.rev. charts; illus.; stat. back issues avail. **Document type:** *Trade.* **Description:** Focuses on private finance initiatives and public - private partnerships.
Related titles: Online - full text ed.
Published by: Public Sector Information Ltd., Peters Gate House, St Petersgate, Stockport, SK1 1HE, United Kingdom. TEL 44-161-480-2469, FAX 44-161-292-3003, mailbox@psigroup.co.uk, http://www.psigroup.co.uk. Ed., R&P Philip Cunliffe. Pub. Stephen Tucker. Adv. contact Richard Town. B&W page GBP 2,995, color page GBP 4,995. Circ: 1,000 (paid); 7,500 (controlled).

336.22 USA ISSN 1088-291X
PROPERTY TAX ALERT. Text in English. 1995. m. USD 255; USD 415 combined subscription print & online eds. (effective 2004). **Document type:** *Newsletter, Trade.* **Description:** Focuses on providing proven tips and strategies for reducing property tax bills and staying on to of the latest trends in valuation and assessment.
Related titles: Online - full content ed.: USD 360 includes archive issues (effective 2004).
Published by: C C H Inc., 2700 Lake Cook Rd, Riverwoods, IL 60015. TEL 847-267-7000, 800-449-6439, FAX 800-224-8299, cust_serv@cch.com, http://www.cch.com.

336 USA
PROPERTY TAX BULLETIN. Text in English. 1951. irreg., latest no.135, 2004, Sept. price varies. **Document type:** *Bulletin.* **Description:** Addresses issues of interest to local and state government employees and officials.
Published by: University of North Carolina at Chapel Hill, Institute of Government, Knapp Bldg, CB 3330, Chapel Hill, NC 27599-3330. TEL 919-966-4119, FAX 919-962-2707, sales@iogmail.iog.unc.edu, khunt@iogmail.iog.unc.edu, https://iogpubs.iog.unc.edu/products.asp?page=other&category=Property%20Tax%20Bulletin. Ed. Shea Riggsbe Denning. R&P Katrina W Hunt.

B

336.71 352.439 CAN ISSN 1704-6610
PROVINCIAL AUDITOR SASKATCHEWAN. REPORT OF THE PROVINCIAL AUDITOR TO THE LEGISLATIVE ASSEMBLY OF SASKATCHEWAN. Text in English. 1966. a.
Former titles (until 1999): Saskatchewan. Provincial Auditor Saskatchewan. Report (1484-8961); (until 1997): Saskatchewan. Provincial Auditor. Report of the Provincial Auditor (0581-8214)
Published by: Provincial Auditor Saskatchewan, 1500-1920 Broad St, Regina, SK S4P 3V7, Canada. TEL 306-787-6398, FAX 306-787-6383, info@auditor.sk.ca, http://www.auditor.sk.ca.

336 POL ISSN 0867-7514
PRZEGLAD PODATKOWY. Text in Polish. 1991. m. **Description:** Covers Polish and foreign taxation, foreign capital, banking, customs duties.
Address: 20a Bracka St., Warsaw, 00028, Poland. TEL 48-22-6222260, FAX 48-22-6222250. Ed. Witold Konieczny. Circ: 20,000.

PUBLIC BUDGETING AND FINANCE. see *PUBLIC ADMINISTRATION*

PUBLIC FINANCE/FINANCES PUBLIQUES. see *BUSINESS AND ECONOMICS—Banking And Finance*

336 USA ISSN 1523-9721
➤ **PUBLIC FINANCE AND MANAGEMENT.** Text in English. 2000. q. USD 25 to individuals; USD 175 to institutions (effective 2003). adv. bk.rev. back issues avail. **Document type:** *Journal, Academic/Scholarly.* **Description:** Increases knowledge of public finance and administration through policy analysis, empirical research, and theoretical inquiry.
Media: Online - full text.
Indexed: JEL.
—**CCC.**
Published by: Southern Public Administration Education Foundation, Inc., 2103 Fairway Ln, Harrisburg, PA 17112. TEL 717-540-5477, FAX 717-893-1763, spaef@spaef.com, http://www.spaef.com/. Ed. M Peter van der Hoek. Adv. contact Jack Rabin.

336 USA ISSN 1091-1421
HJ101 CODEN: PFQADD
➤ **PUBLIC FINANCE REVIEW.** Text in English. 1973. bi-m. USD 690, GBP 445 to institutions; USD 718, GBP 464 combined subscription to institutions print & online eds. (effective 2006). adv. bk.rev. abstr.; charts; illus. back issues avail.; reprint service avail. from PQC,PSC. **Document type:** *Journal, Academic/Scholarly.* **Description:** Explores the theory, policy, and institutions related to the allocation, distribution, and stabilization functions within the public sectors of the economy.
Formerly (until 1997): Public Finance Quarterly (0048-5853)
Related titles: Microfilm ed.: (from PQC); Online - full text ed.: ISSN 1552-7530. USD 683, GBP 441 to institutions (effective 2006) (from EBSCO Publishing, Florida Center for Library Automation, Gale Group, O C L C Online Computer Library Center, Inc., Sage Publications, Inc., Swets Information Services).
Indexed: ABIn, ASCA, ASG, ATI, AgeL, BPIA, BusI, CREJ, CurCont, ESPM, FamI, IBSS, JEL, MEA&I, ManagCont, PAIS, PSA, RiskAb, SPAA, SSCI, SUSA, T&II.
—BLDSC (6963.500500), IDS, IE, ingenta. **CCC.**
Published by: Sage Publications, Inc., 2455 Teller Rd, Thousand Oaks, CA 91320. TEL 805-499-0721, 800-818-7243, FAX 805-499-8096, 800-583-2665, info@sagepub.com, http://www.sagepub.com/journal.aspx?pid=25. Ed. James Alm. Pub. Sara Miller McCune. R&P Tanya Udin TEL 805-499-0721 ext 7716. Adv. contact Kirsten Beaulieu TEL 805-499-0721 ext 7160. page USD 350. Circ: 800 (paid). **Subscr. in Asia to:** Sage Publications India Pvt. Ltd., M-32 Market, Greater Kailash-I, PO Box 4215, New Delhi 110 048, India; **Subscr. in Europe to:** Sage Publications Ltd., 1 Oliver's Yard, 55 City Rd, London EC1 1SP, United Kingdom. TEL 44-20-73740645, FAX 44-20-73748741, subscription@sagepub.co.uk.

336 GBR
PUBLIC MANAGEMENT AND POLICY ASSOCIATION REPORTS. Text in English. 1985. 6/yr. adv. back issues avail.
Document type: *Monographic series.*
Supersedes: Chartered Institute of Public Finance and Accountancy. Public Finance Foundation. Discussion Papers
Published by: (Public Management and Policy Association), Chartered Institute of Public Finance and Accountancy, 3 Robert St, London, WC2N 6RL, United Kingdom. TEL 44-20-7895-5600, FAX 44-20-7895-5700, publications@cipfa.org, http://www.cipfa.org.uk. R&P Michaela Lavender TEL 44-171-543-5702. Adv. contact Victoria Littler.

336 GBR
PUBLIC MONEY. Text in English. w. **Description:** Directed to all public finance professionals.
Address: Saint Giles House, 50 Poland St, London, W1V 4AX, United Kingdom. TEL 071-287-9800, FAX 071-287-8873. Ed. J Jackson.

PUBLIC-PRIVATE FINANCE. see *BUSINESS AND ECONOMICS—Banking And Finance*

PUBLIC SECTOR. see *PUBLIC ADMINISTRATION*

PUBLIC SERVICES YEARBOOK. see *PUBLIC ADMINISTRATION*

336 332.6 GBR ISSN 1350-2697
PUBLIC TREASURER. Text in English. 1993. m. GBP 35. adv. back issues avail. **Document type:** *Trade.* **Description:** Addresses the multi-billion pound commercial partnerships between local government and the City. News, analysis and in-depth features examine all aspects of investment and treasury management—the local authority pension fund investment market, cash fund management, the money markets and borrowing, insurance and risk management.
Related titles: Online - full text ed.
Indexed: Emerald.
Published by: L G C Communications Ltd. (Subsidiary of: Emap Business Communications Ltd.), 33-39 Bowling Green Ln, London, EC1R 0DA, United Kingdom. TEL 44-171-505-8400, FAX 44-171-837-2725, http://www.emap.com/lgc. Ed. Belinda Fowler. Pub. Crispin Derby. Adv. contact Lisa Edwards. B&W page GBP 1,450, color page GBP 2,325; trim 220 x 300. Circ: 10,256 (paid). **Subscr. to:** 196 High St, Tonbridge, Kent TN9 1BE, United Kingdom.

336 340 USA
PUERTO RICO TAX REPORTER. Text in English, Spanish; Summaries in English. 1964. 2 base vols. plus m. updates. looseleaf. USD 630 base vol(s). (effective 2004). **Description:** Contains the text and explanations of the Puerto Rico Internal Revenue Code, including the important Commonwealth Industrial Incentives Acts. The Reporter includes English translations of the Puerto Rico Internal Revenue Code, General Corporations Act, Municipal License Tax Act, Municipal Property Tax Act, Municipal Revenues Collection Center Act, regulations, and selected cases and rulings.
Formerly: Puerto Rico Tax Reports
Indexed: ATI.
Published by: C C H Inc., 2700 Lake Cook Rd, Riverwoods, IL 60015. TEL 847-267-7000, 800-449-6439, FAX 800-224-8299, cust_serv@cch.com, http://www.cch.com. Pub. Kevin Robert.

336 USA ISSN 0735-7893
PUERTO RICO TAXES. Text in English. 1983. 3 base vols. plus m. updates. USD 775 print or online (effective 2005).
Document type: *Trade.* **Description:** Contains explanations of the law, regulations and court decisions, including coverage of: initial taxes; doing business fees; corporation taxes; income taxes; property taxes; payroll taxes; insurance company taxes; estate and gift taxes; excise taxes; special local taxes; tax incentives and exemptions; and federal taxes, Internal Revenue Code Sections 30A and 936.
Related titles: Online - full content ed.
—CCC.
Published by: R I A (Subsidiary of: Thomson Corporation), 395 Hudson St, New York, NY 10014. TEL 212-367-6300, RIA.CustomerServices@Thomson.com, http://ria.thomson.com/EStore/detail.aspx?ID=WPRTX.

336 FRA ISSN 0257-7801
HC79.I5
QUARTERLY NATIONAL ACCOUNTS. Text in French. q. EUR 136, USD 156, GBP 91, JPY 18,400 (effective 2005). stat.
Document type: *Government.* **Description:** Presents, in standard tables, the components of GDP by expenditure, cost structure and type of activity, the financing and composition of gross capital formation and the components of private final consumption expenditure for member countries.
Formerly (until 1983): O E C D Quarterly National Accounts Bulletin / Bulletin des Comptes Nationaux Trimestriels (0304-3738)
Related titles: CD-ROM ed.: ISSN 1726-9326; Online - full content ed.: ISSN 1609-7629. USD 100 (effective 2004); Online - full text ed.: (from EBSCO Publishing, Gale Group, IngentaConnect, O C L C Online Computer Library Center, Inc., Swets Information Services).
Indexed: IIS, RASB.
—CISTI, Infotrieve.
Published by: Organization for Economic Cooperation and Development, 2 Rue Andre Pascal, Paris, 75775 Cedex 16, France. TEL 33-1-45248200, FAX 33-1-45248500, http://www.oecd.org. **U.S. orders to:** O E C D Turpin North America, PO Box 194, Downingtown, PA 19335-0194. TEL 610-524-5361, 800-456-6323, FAX 610-524-5417, journalscustomer@turpinna.com.

336.2 CAN ISSN 0048-6299
QUEBEC TAX REPORTER. Text in English. 1950. m. looseleaf. CND 582 (effective 2005). index. **Document type:** *Trade.*
Description: Current reporting covers every aspect of consumer and income taxes in Quebec.
Related titles: CD-ROM ed.: CND 531 (effective 2005); Online - full text ed.: CND 515 (effective 2005).
Published by: C C H Canadian Ltd., 90 Sheppard Ave E, Ste 300, North York, ON M2N 6X1, Canada. TEL 416-224-2248, 800-268-4522, FAX 416-224-2243, cservice@cch.ca, http://www.cch.ca.

336.200711 AUS
QUESTION BOOK, INCOME TAX LAW PRINCIPLES, INCOME TAX LAW APPLICATIONS. Text in English. 1985. a., latest 2003. AUD 24 (effective 2003). **Document type:** *Academic/Scholarly.* **Description:** Provides questions on taxation for students taking taxation as part of an accounting or law course.
Former titles: Question Book, Income Tax Law for Accountants, Income Tax Law for Tax Agents (1440-0278); (until 1998): Question Budget, Income Tax Law for Accountants, Income Tax Law for Tax Agents (1325-2135); (until 1996): Question Budget, Taxation Law and Practice (Year) (1034-5159)
Published by: Alan Kirby, Ed. & Pub., PO Box 632, Hurstville, NSW 2232, Australia. TEL 61-2-95794959.

336 DEU ISSN 0481-4142
DIE QUINTESSENZ DES STEUERRECHTS. Abbreviated title: St Q. Text in German. 1967. m. EUR 219; EUR 22.30 newsstand/cover (effective 2004). **Document type:** *Journal, Trade.*
—CCC.
Published by: Stollfuss Verlag GmbH & Co. KG, Dechenstr 7, Bonn, 53115, Germany. TEL 49-228-7240, FAX 49-228-72491181, info@stollfuss.de, http://www.stollfuss.de.

336 USA
R I A ANALYSIS OF FEDERAL TAXES: EXCISE. Text in English. 1991. base vol. plus bi-w. updates. looseleaf. USD 275.
Published by: R I A (Subsidiary of: Thomson Corporation), 395 Hudson St, New York, NY 10014. TEL 212-367- 6300, 212-367-6300.

336 USA
R I A ANALYSIS OF FEDERAL TAXES: INCOME. Text in English. 1991. 14 base vols. plus bi-w. updates. looseleaf. USD 650; includes Weekly Alert, Special Studies, R I A Federal Tax Handbook.
Published by: R I A (Subsidiary of: Thomson Corporation), 395 Hudson St, New York, NY 10014. TEL 212-367- 6300, 212-367-6300.

336 USA
R I A COMPLETE FEDERAL TAX FORMS. Text in English. 1991. 3 base vols. plus bi-w. updates. looseleaf. USD 300.
Published by: R I A (Subsidiary of: Thomson Corporation), 395 Hudson St, New York, NY 10014. TEL 212-367- 6300, 212-367-6300.

336 USA
R I A FEDERAL TAX HANDBOOK. Text in English. 1975. a. looseleaf. USD 25.
Formerly: Master Federal Tax Manual
Indexed: ATI.
Published by: R I A (Subsidiary of: Thomson Corporation), 395 Hudson St, New York, NY 10014. TEL 212-367-6300, RIA.CustomerServices@Thomson.com, http://ria.thomson.com/.

336 340 USA ISSN 1076-2280
KF6276.99
R I A FEDERAL TAX REGULATIONS. Text in English. 1957. and m. Report Bulletins), 5 base vols. plus irreg. updates. looseleaf. USD 310. reprint service avail. from WSH.
Description: Presents full text of income tax regulations and details regulatory activity following tax reform legislation.
Related titles: Microfiche ed.: (from WSH); Online - full text ed.
Indexed: ATI.
Published by: R I A (Subsidiary of: Thomson Corporation), 395 Hudson St, New York, NY 10014. TEL 212- 367-6300.

336 USA
R I A INTERNAL REVENUE CODE AND REGULATIONS. Text in English. 1991. 7 base vols. plus bi-w. updates. looseleaf. USD 275. **Description:** Presents the full text of the Internal Revenue Code and all final, temporary and proposed regulations.
Published by: R I A (Subsidiary of: Thomson Corporation), 395 Hudson St, New York, NY 10014. TEL 212-367- 6300, 212-367-6300.

336 USA
HJ2425
R I A TAX GUIDE. Text in English. 1966. 2 base vols. plus m. updates. looseleaf. USD 350; includes Weekly Alert newsletter.
Formerly: Tax Guide
Related titles: CD-ROM ed.
Published by: R I A (Subsidiary of: Thomson Corporation), 395 Hudson St, New York, NY 10014. TEL 212-367-6300, RIA.CustomerServices@Thomson.com, http://ria.thomson.com/.

RACHUNKOWOSC. see *BUSINESS AND ECONOMICS—Accounting*

RACHUNKOWOSC. PORADNIK PRAKTYCZNY. see *BUSINESS AND ECONOMICS—Accounting*

336 IND ISSN 0079-9556
HJ66.R3
RAJASTHAN, INDIA. DIRECTORATE OF ECONOMICS AND STATISTICS. BUDGET STUDY. Text in English, Hindi. 1959. a. free. **Document type:** *Government.*
Published by: Directorate of Economics and Statistics, Tilak Marg, Jaipur, Rajasthan, India.

336.2 ITA ISSN 0033-9458
RASSEGNA DELLA STAMPA. Text in Italian. 1955. m. looseleaf. bk.rev. abstr.; bibl. index.
Related titles: Cards ed.
Published by: Associazione fra le Societa Italiane per Azioni, Piazza Venezia, 11, Rome, RM 00187, Italy.

336 ITA ISSN 0393-4098
RASSEGNA MENSILE DELLA IMPOSTE DIRETTE. Text in Italian. 1952. m. adv.
Address: c/o Antonino La Mattina, Ed., Via Fregene, 14, Rome, RM 00183, Italy.

336.2 ITA ISSN 1590-749X
RASSEGNA TRIBUTARIA. Text in Italian. 1958. m. adv. bk.rev. abstr.; bibl. index.
Former titles (until 1977): Imposte Dirette Erariali e l'Iva (1590-7228); (until 1973): Le Imposte Erariali (1590-721X)
Published by: E T I SpA, Viale Giuseppe Mazzini, 25, Rome, RM 00195, Italy. FAX 350108. Ed. Dr. Gianni Carbone. Circ: 6,000.

REAL ESTATE PROFESSIONAL'S TAX GUIDE. see *REAL ESTATE*

REAL ESTATE TAX IDEAS. see *REAL ESTATE*

REAL ESTATE TAXATION. see *REAL ESTATE*

336.2 DEU
RECHT UND STEUERN INTERNATIONAL. Text in German. m. EUR 65 (effective 2004). **Document type:** *Journal, Trade.*
Published by: Bundesagentur fuer Aussenwirtschaft, Agrippastr 87-93, Cologne, 50676, Germany. TEL 49-221-20570, FAX 49-221-2057212, info@bfai.de, http://www.bfai.com.

336 SYR ISSN 0080-0309
RECUEIL COMPLET DES BUDGETS DE LA SYRIE. Text in Arabic. a. USD 140 (effective 2001). Index. back issues avail.
Document type: *Yearbook, Corporate.*
Published by: Office Arabe de Presse et de Documentation, 67, Place Chahbandar, PO Box 3550, Damascus, Syria. TEL 963-11-3318237, FAX 963-11-4426021. Ed. Raghda Bittar. Circ: 500 (paid).

REGIONAL LEVIES SERVICE. see *LAW*

336 LSO ISSN 0085-2740
REPORT BY THE AUDITOR GENERAL ON THE ACCOUNTS OF LESOTHO. Text in English. 1966. a., latest 1972-73. USD 0.50.
Published by: Auditor General, PO Box 502, Maseru, Lesotho.

336 TTO
REPORT OF THE AUDITOR GENERAL ON THE PUBLIC ACCOUNTS OF THE REPUBLIC OF TRINIDAD AND TOBAGO. Text in English. 1962. a. USD 1.80. stat.
Published by: (Trinidad and Tobago. Auditor General of Trinidad and Tobago), Government Printery, Sales Section, 48 St Vincent St, Port-of-Spain, Trinidad, Trinidad & Tobago. Circ: 500.

363.3 CAN ISSN 0839-9131
REPORT TO PARLIAMENT BY THE MINISTER OF FISHERIES AND OCEANS RESPECTING THE ADMINISTRATION OF THE ATLANTIC FISHERIES RESTRUCTURING ACT. Cover title: Atlantic Fisheries Restructuring Act. Annual Report. Variant title: Rapport Depose au Parlement par le Ministre des Peches et des Oceans Concernant l'Administration de la Loi sur la Restructuration du Secteur des Peches de l'Atlantique pour l'Annee Financiere. Text in English, French. 1984. a.
Indexed: ESPM.

Published by: Department of Fisheries and Oceans, Communications Directorate, 200 Kent St, 13th Fl, Sta 13228, Ottawa, ON K1A 0E6, Canada. TEL 613-993-0999, FAX 613-990-1866, info@dfo-mpo.gc.ca, http://www.ncr.dfo.ca.

336.2 340 USA ISSN 8755-6294
REPORTS OF THE U.S. TAX COURTS. Text in English. s-a.
Formerly (until 1970): Reports of the Tax Court of the United States (8755-6111)
Related titles: ♦ Alternate Frequency ed(s).: United States Tax Court Reports. ISSN 0040-0017. m.
Published by: U.S. Tax Court, 400 Second St, N W, Washington, DC 20217. TEL 202-606-8704, FAX 202-783-3238.

336 SYC
REPUBLIC OF SEYCHELLES. TRADES TAX REGULATIONS (YEAR). Text in English. a.?. **Document type:** *Government.*
Published by: Ministry of Finance and Information, Trade and Commerce Section, Victoria, Mahe, Seychelles.

RESEARCH INSTITUTE OF AMERICA. SPECIAL STUDIES. see *BUSINESS AND ECONOMICS—Accounting*

RETIREMENT AND BENEFIT PLANNING; strategy and design for businesses and tax-exempt organizations. see *BUSINESS AND ECONOMICS—Personnel Management*

REVENUE LAW JOURNAL. see *LAW*

REVIEW OF REGIONAL STUDIES; the official journal of the Southern regional science association. see *HOUSING AND URBAN PLANNING*

343.48904 657 DNK ISSN 0108-9196
REVISOR POSTEN. Text in Danish. 1983. 4/yr. **Document type:** *Trade.*
Published by: (Foreningen af Statsautoriserede Revisorer/Institute of State Authorized Public Accountants in Denmark), Forlaget Thomson S/A, Nytorv 5, Copenhagen K, 1450, Denmark. TEL 45-33-740700, FAX 45-33-121636, thomson@thomson.dk, http://www/thomson.dk.

REVISTA DE ADMINISTRACAO MUNICIPAL. see *PUBLIC ADMINISTRATION—Municipal Government*

REVISTA DE DERECHO FINANCIERO Y DE HACIENDA PUBLICA. see *LAW*

REVISTA DE INFORMACION FISCAL. see *LAW*

336 MOZ
REVISTA FISCAL. Text in Portuguese. 1989-1992; resumed 1996. q.
Published by: Ministerio das Financas, C P 272, Av 25 de Setembro 1008 5 o, Maputo, Mozambique. TEL 20982. Circ: 2,000.

REVISTA TECNICA TRIBUTARIA. see *LAW*

REVUE BELGE DE SECURITE SOCIALE/BELGIAN SOCIAL SECURITY JOURNAL. see *PUBLIC ADMINISTRATION*

REVUE DE DROIT FRISCAL. see *LAW*

336 FRA ISSN 1608-7151
REVUE DE L'O C D E SUR LA GESTION BUDGETAIRE. (Organisation de Cooperation et de Developpement Economiques) Text in French. q. EUR 197, USD 226, GBP 129, JPY 26,600 (effective 2005). **Description:** Provides insight on leading-edge institutional arrangements, systems and instruments for the effective and efficient allocation and management of resources in the public sector.
Related titles: Online - full content ed.: ISSN 1684-3525. EUR 140, USD 161, GBP 92, JPY 18,900 (effective 2005); Online - full text ed.: (from EBSCO Publishing, Gale Group, IngentaConnect, Swets Information Services); ♦ English ed.: O E C D Journal on Budgeting. ISSN 1608-7143.
Published by: Organization for Economic Cooperation and Development, 2 Rue Andre Pascal, Paris, 75775 Cedex 16, France. TEL 33-1-45248200, FAX 33-1-45248500, http://www.oecd.org. **Dist. by:** Extenza - Turpin, Pegasus Dr, Stratton Business Park, Biggleswade, Beds SG18 8TQ, United Kingdom. TEL 44-1462-687552, FAX 44-1462-480947, subscriptions@extenza-turpin.com; O E C D Turpin North America, PO Box 194, Downingtown, PA 19335-0194. TEL 610-524-5361, 800-456-6323, FAX 610-524-5417, journalscustomer@turpinna.com.

LA REVUE DU TRESOR; organe d'etudes et d'informations professionnelles. see *BUSINESS AND ECONOMICS—Accounting*

336 FRA ISSN 0294-0833
REVUE FRANCAISE DE FINANCES PUBLIQUES. Text in French. 1983. q. bk.rev. reprints avail. **Description:** For professors, finance professionals, public administrators, private business managers.
Indexed: ELLIS.
—IE, Infotrieve.

Published by: (Librairie Generale de Droit et de Jurisprudence), Editions Juridiques Associees, 14 rue Pierre et Marie Curie, Paris, 75005, France. TEL 33-1-44273349, FAX 33-1-43547821. Eds. Marie Christine Esclassan, Michel Bouvier.

REVUE MAROCAINE DE FINANCES PUBLIQUES ET D'ECONOMIE. see *BUSINESS AND ECONOMICS—Banking And Finance*

341.4844 USA
RHOADES & LANGER, U S INTERNATIONAL TAXATION AND TAX TREATIES. Text in English. 1971. irreg. (in 6 vols.). looseleaf. USD 1,316 base vol(s). (effective 2002).
Formerly: U S International Taxation and Tax Treaties
Related titles: CD-ROM ed.: USD 1,412 (effective 2002).
Published by: Matthew Bender & Co., Inc. (Subsidiary of: LexisNexis North America), 1275 Broadway, Albany, NY 12204. international@bender.com, http://bender.lexisnexis.com. Eds. Marshall Langer, Rufus Rhoades.

336 ITA ISSN 0035-595X
RIVISTA DELLA GUARDIA DI FINANZA. Text in Italian. 1952. bi-m. EUR 25.82 domestic; EUR 36.15 foreign (effective 2004). bibl.; illus.; stat. index. **Document type:** *Magazine, Trade.*
Formerly (until 1955): Rivista Tecnico - Professionale e di Cultura del Corpo della Guardia di Finanza (1594-0357)
Indexed: ELLIS, PAIS.
Published by: (Guardia di Finanza), Comando Generale della Guardia di Finanza, Ufficio Stampa, Viale XX1 Aprile 55, Rome, RM 00162, Italy. FAX 39-06-4404762. Ed. Luciano Carta. Circ: 7,500.

336 USA ISSN 1040-2241
KF6272
RUXTON REPORT✶. Text in English. 1982. m. USD 75. adv. bk.rev. back issues avail. **Description:** Covers tax planning and compliance for small business and tax practitioners.
Formerly: B M E Tax Newsletter (0740-2376)
Published by: Ruxton Company, PO Box 20090, Santa Barbara, CA 93120. TEL 303-481-4389. Ed. Jack Kennedy Sr. Circ: 900.

336 340 ZAF ISSN 1019-8474
S A TAX REVIEW. Text in English. q. ZAR 460, USD 100. charts; stat. **Document type:** *Academic/Scholarly.* **Description:** Provides in depth coverage of international tax developments relevant to Southern African readers, and Southern African tax matters relevant to foreign investors.
Media: CD-ROM. **Related titles:** Diskette ed.; ♦ Issued with: InfoTax.
Indexed: ISAP.
Published by: InfoMedia Technologies (Pty) Ltd., PO Box 44597, Claremont, Cape Town 7735, South Africa. TEL 27-21-689 5075, FAX 27-21-689-5025, infomedia@iafrica.com, http://www.pix.za/taxfax/taxfax.html. Ed. Ray Eskinazi. Circ: 360.

336 USA ISSN 0738-2448
S CORPORATIONS (NEW YORK, 1983). Text in English. 1983. report bulletins), base vol. plus m. updates. looseleaf. USD 395. **Description:** Provides in-depth explanations and new ideas from experts in the field. Includes updates on latest developments, official documents and relevant legislative history.
Published by: W G & L Financial Reporting & Management Research (Subsidiary of: R I A), 90 Fifth Ave, New York, NY 10011. TEL 212-645-4800, FAX 212-337-4280. Ed. Robert W Wood.

336 USA
S CORPORATIONS: TAX PRACTICE AND ANALYSIS. Text in English. 1983. w. looseleaf. USD 99 1-4 copies (effective 2004). back issues avail. **Description:** Designed to help practitioners understand and manage individual S corps election, compliance, tax planning and life-cycle needs.
Related titles: CD-ROM ed.: USD 621 (effective 2003).
Published by: C C H Inc., 2700 Lake Cook Rd, Riverwoods, IL 60015. TEL 847-267-7000, 800-449-6439, FAX 800-224-8299, cust_serv@cch.com, http://www.cch.com. Pub. Kevin Robert.

343.48904 DNK ISSN 0904-5139
S R - SKAT. (Statsautoriserede Revisorer) Text in Danish. 1987. 6/yr. DKK 770; DKK 123 per issue (effective 2004). adv. **Document type:** *Trade.*
Formerly (until 1989): F S R Skattedokumentation (0902-3186)
Published by: (Foreningen af Statsautoriserede Revisorer/Institute of State Authorized Public Accountants in Denmark), Forlaget Thomson S/A, Nytorv 5, Copenhagen K, 1450, Denmark. TEL 45-33-740700, FAX 45-33-121636, thomson@thomson.dk, http://www/thomson.dk. Adv. contact Per Christensen TEL 45-33-778875. page DKK 4,900; 145 x 220. Circ: 4,000.

336.2 USA
SALES AND USE TAX ALERT. Text in English. m. USD 310; USD 465 combined subscription print & online eds. (effective 2004). **Document type:** *Newsletter.* **Description:** Provides journalistic approach to gathering and reporting the laws and regulations relevant to coping with sales and use tax compliance for multistate organizations.

Related titles: Online - full text ed.: USD 410 includes archive issues (effective 2004).
Published by: C C H Inc., 2700 Lake Cook Rd, Riverwoods, IL 60015. TEL 847-267-7000, 800-449-6439, cust_serv@cch.com, http://www.cch.com.

336.2 USA ISSN 1543-9895
▼ **SALES & USE TAX MONITOR.** Text in English. 2003 (Mar.). s-m. USD 247 (effective 2003).
Related titles: Online - full text ed.: (from LexisNexis).
Published by: Strafford Publications, Inc., 590 Dutch Valley Rd, N E, Postal Drawer 13729, Atlanta, GA 30324-0729. TEL 404-881-1141, FAX 404-881-0074, editors@straffordpub.com, http://www.straffordpub.com.

336 USA
SALES AND USE TAX REVIEW. Text in English. 1991. m. looseleaf. USD 195. bk.rev. **Document type:** *Newsletter.*
Published by: Corporate Tax Publishers, Inc., PO Box 261, Leonia, NJ 07605. TEL 201-461-6619, FAX 201-461-6619. Eds. Jonathan Skiba, Michael Fishbein.

336.271 IND ISSN 0036-3472
SALES TAX ADVICES. Text in English. 1969. m. INR 400, USD 40 (effective 1999). bk.rev. index. **Document type:** *Consumer.*
Media: Duplicated (not offset).
Published by: Nahar Sales Tax Advices Private Limited, 20-1 Maharshi Debendra Rd., 2nd Fl., Kolkata, West Bengal 700 007, India. TEL 91-33-3997218. Ed. M L Nahar. Pub. Rakesh Kumar Nahar. R&P Sandeep Nahar. Circ: 1,000.

336 DEU ISSN 0342-197X
SAMMLUNG DER ENTSCHEIDUNGEN DES BUNDESFINANZHOFS. Text in German. 1950. 18/yr. EUR 315.30 (effective 2004). **Document type:** *Journal, Trade.*
Published by: Stollfuss Verlag GmbH & Co. KG, Dechenstr 7, Bonn, 53115, Germany. TEL 49-228-72401 FAX 49-228-72491181, info@stollfuss.de, http://www.stollfuss.de/programm/products/0400140.htm.

SAMSOM ACTUALITE COMPTABLE; lettre bimensuelle a l'usage des experts-comptables, reviseurs d'enterprises, directeurs financiers et administratifs. see *BUSINESS AND ECONOMICS—Accounting*

336 BEL ISSN 0776-1465
SAMSOM FISCALE WENKEN. Text in Flemish. 1988. s-m. **Description:** Gives financial advice for those not in the accounting or finance field.
Related titles: French ed.: Samsom Signaux Fiscaux. ISSN 0776-1473.
Published by: C E D Samsom (Subsidiary of: Wolters Samsom Belgie n.v.), Kouterveld 14, Diegem, 1831, Belgium. TEL 32-2-7231111.

336 CAN ISSN 0842-6902
SASKATCHEWAN ASSESSMENT MANAGEMENT AGENCY. ANNUAL REPORT (YEAR). Text in English. 1987. a.
Published by: Saskatchewan Assessment Management Agency, 200 - 2201 - 11th Ave, Regina, SK S4P 0J8, Canada. TEL 306-924-8000, 800-667-7262, FAX 306-924-8070, info.request@sama.sk.ca, http://www.sama.sk.ca/sama/24.html.

332.1 SAU ISSN 0558-7220
HG1213
SAUDI ARABIAN MONETARY AGENCY. ANNUAL REPORT. Text in English. 1961. a. charts. **Document type:** *Government.* **Description:** Reviews economic developments and major trends of the past year.
Related titles: Arabic ed.: At-Taqrir as-Sanawi - S A M A. ISSN 1319-1845.
Published by: Saudi Arabian Monetary Agency, Research and Statistics Department, PO Box 2992, Riyadh, 11169, Saudi Arabia. TEL 966-1-463-3000.

336.2 DEU ISSN 0582-0235
SCHRIFTEN ZUM STEUERRECHT. Text in German. 1965. irreg., latest vol.76, 2003. price varies. **Document type:** *Monographic series, Academic/Scholarly.*
Published by: Duncker und Humblot GmbH, Carl-Heinrich-Becker-Weg 9, Berlin, 12165, Germany. TEL 49-30-7900060, FAX 49-30-79000631, info@duncker-humblot.de, http://www.duncker-humblot.de.

SECURITIES HANDBOOK SERIES. TAX-ADVANTAGED SECURITIES HANDBOOK. see *BUSINESS AND ECONOMICS—Investments*

DER SELBSTAENDIGE. see *BUSINESS AND ECONOMICS—Small Business*

336 USA ISSN 1075-9832
KF6335.A29
SELECTED FEDERAL TAXATION STATUTES AND REGULATIONS. Text in English. 1975. a. USD 38 per vol. (effective 2004). **Document type:** *Trade.* **Description:** Includes edited provisions of the Internal Revenue Code, Treasury Regulations, and various materials prepared by the Internal Revenue Service.

Published by: Thomson West (Subsidiary of: Thomson Corporation, The), 610 Opperman Dr, Eagan, MN 55123-1396. TEL 651-687-8000, 800-328-9352, FAX 651-687-7302, http://west.thomson.com/product/22016101/product.asp.

336 NLD ISSN 0924-4654
SERIES ON INTERNATIONAL TAXATION. Text in Dutch. 1979. irreg., latest 2002, Oct. price varies. back issues avail. **Document type:** *Monographic series, Academic/Scholarly.* **Description:** Discusses specific countries' tax policies, theoretical issues in tax law and tax treaty negotiation.
—BLDSC (8250.161600).
Published by: Kluwer Law International (Subsidiary of: Aspen Publishers, Inc.), Laan van Meerdervoort 70, PO Box 85889, The Hague, 2508 CN, Netherlands. TEL 31-70-3081500, FAX 31-70-3081515, sales@kluwerlaw.com, http://www.kluwerlaw.com.

SEYCHELLES. MINISTRY OF FINANCE. BUDGET ADDRESS. see *PUBLIC ADMINISTRATION*

336 CHN
SHANGHAI CAISHUI/SHANGHAI FINANCIAL TAXATION. Text in Chinese. m.
Published by: Shanghai Caizheng Kexue Yanjiusuo/Shanghai Institute of Financial Science, 60 Jiujiang Rd, Room 518, Shanghai, 200002, China. TEL 3233208.

336 USA ISSN 0732-7714
KF6280.5
SHEPARD'S FEDERAL TAX CITATIONS. Text in English. 1980. base vol. plus bi-m. updates. USD 450. Supplement avail.
Published by: Shepard's (Subsidiary of: LexisNexis North America), 555 Middle Creek Pkwy, Colorado Springs, CO 80921. TEL 719-488-3000, 800-833-9844, FAX 719-481-7621, customer_service@shepards.com, http://www.lexisnexis.com/shepards/.

SHEPARD'S FEDERAL TAX CITATOR. see *LAW—Judicial Systems*

336.2 USA
SHEPARD'S (YEAR) TAX DICTIONARY. Text in English. a. USD 45. **Document type:** *Trade.*
Published by: Shepard's (Subsidiary of: LexisNexis North America), 555 Middle Creek Pkwy, Colorado Springs, CO 80921. TEL 800-743-7393, customer_service@shepards.com, http://www.shepards.com, http://www.lexisnexis.com/shepards/. Ed. Richard A Westin.

336.2 CHN ISSN 1006-3056
SHEWAI SHUIWU/INTERNATIONAL TAXATION IN CHINA. Text in Chinese. 1988. m. CNY 12.50 newsstand/cover (effective 2005). **Document type:** *Journal, Academic/Scholarly.*
Related titles: Online - full text ed.: (from WanFang Data Corp.).
Address: Taxation Building, No.28, Futian Road, Shenzhen, 518033, China. TEL 86-755-83336333 ext 1411, FAX 86-755-83337545, szitctax@public.szptt.net.cn, http://swsw.periodicals.net.cn/, http://www.intertax.cn/.

336 CHN ISSN 1003-448X
SHUIWU YANJIU/TAXATION RESEARCH. Text in Chinese. 1985. m. CNY 60; USD 26 foreign. **Document type:** *Government.*
Related titles: Online - full text ed.: (from East View Information Services).
Published by: (Guojia Shuiwu-ju/State Taxation Bureau), Zhongguo Shuiwu Zazhishe, 5 Yangfangdian Xilu, Haidian District, Beijing, 100038, China. TEL 86-10-6356-6046, FAX 86-10-6356-6042. Ed., R&P Zhang Musheng. Circ: 12,000.

336 GBR
SIMON'S DIRECT TAX SERVICE. Text in English. 12 base vols. plus m. updates. GBP 850. **Document type:** *Trade.* **Description:** Features detailed explanation to the law and practice relating to UK income tax, corporate tax and capital-gains tax, inheritance tax, and international taxation.
Formerly: Simon's Taxes
Related titles: CD-ROM ed.
Published by: Butterworths Tolley (Subsidiary of: LexisNexis UK (Scottish Office)), Halsbury House, 35 Chancery Ln, London, Mddx WC2A 1EL, United Kingdom. TEL 44-20-74002500, FAX 44-20-7400-2842, order.line@butterworths.co.uk, http://www.butterworths.co.uk/.

336.2 GBR ISSN 0308-8030
SIMON'S TAX CASES. Variant title: Simon's Weekly Tax Service: Cases. Text in English. 1973. w. looseleaf. GBP 255 (effective 2000). **Document type:** *Trade.* **Description:** Provides record of changes in the law and practice affecting the major UK taxes. Includes full reports of all tax cases decided in the High Court, the Court of Appeal, the Court of Session in Scotland, the Court of Appeal in Northern Ireland, the House of Lords, and selected European cases.
Related titles: Series of: Simon's Weekly Tax Service.
Published by: Butterworths Tolley (Subsidiary of: LexisNexis UK (Scottish Office)), Halsbury House, 35 Chancery Ln, London, Mddx WC2A 1EL, United Kingdom. TEL 44-20-74002500, FAX 44-20-74002583, order.line@butterworths.co.uk, http://www.butterworths.co.uk/.

336.2 GBR ISSN 1357-7905
SIMON'S WEEKLY TAX INTELLIGENCE. Variant title: Simon's Weekly Tax Service: Intelligence. Text in English. 1973. w. looseleaf. GBP 199 (effective 2000). **Document type:** *Trade.* **Description:** Provides a record of changes in the law and practice affecting the major UK taxes. Covers statutory instruments, Inland Revenue press releases, VAT press releases, official concessions and statements of practice, Parliamentary proceedings, EU material, notes and news, tax case digests, VAT tribunal decisions, budget tax coverage, Finance Bill summaries and reports on progress.
Formerly (until 1994): Simon's Tax Intelligence (0308-8049)
Related titles: CD-ROM ed.: Books on Screen.
Published by: Butterworths Tolley (Subsidiary of: LexisNexis UK (Scottish Office)), Halsbury House, 35 Chancery Ln, London, Mddx WC2A 1EL, United Kingdom. TEL 44-20-74002500, FAX 44-20-7400-2842, order.line@butterworths.co.uk, http://www.butterworths.co.uk/.

336.2 GBR
SINGAPORE TAX REVIEW✶ **.** Text in English. 10/yr. HKD 2,500 in Hong Kong; USD 350 elsewhere. **Document type:** *Newsletter.* **Description:** Provides advice on complicated tax issues and developments for all companies operating in Singapore.
Published by: Euromoney Institutional Investor Plc., Nestor House, Playhouse Yard, London, EC4V 5EX, United Kingdom. TEL 44-20-7779-8888, information@euromoneyplc.com, http://www.euromoneyplc.com/.

336.2 DNK ISSN 1600-8332
SKAT. Text in Danish. 2000. 3/yr. **Document type:** *Journal, Government.*
Related titles: Online - full text ed.: ISSN 1600-8340.
Published by: Skatteministeriet/Danish Ministry of Taxation, Nicolai Eigtveds Gade 28, Copenhagen K, 1402, Denmark. TEL 45-33-923392, FAX 45-33-149105, skm@skm.dk, http://www.skat.dk/publikationer/skat/, http://www.skm.dk.

336.2 DNK ISSN 0905-443X
SKAT UDLAND. Text in Danish. 1990. m. DKK 2,295 (effective 2004). **Description:** International tax laws from a Danish perspective.
Published by: Magnus Informatik AS (Subsidiary of: Wolters Kluwer N.V.), Palaegade 4, PO Box 9026, Copenhagen K, 1022, Denmark. TEL 45-70-203314, FAX 45-33-960161, magnus@magnus.dk, http://www.magnus.dk. Ed. Birgitte Voss TEL 45-33-960177.

SKATTE- OCH TAXERINGSFOERFATTNINGARNA. see *LAW*

336.2 343.04 SWE ISSN 0280-5014
SKATTEFRAGOR KRING BOKSLUTET; handbok i foeretagsbeskattning. Text in Swedish. 1956. a. SEK 170 (effective 1998).
Formerly (until 1992): Skattefraagor Kring ... Aars Bokslut
Published by: S-E Banken, Stockholm, 10640, Sweden. TEL 46-8-763-50-00, FAX 46-8-21-24-57. Circ: 6,000.

336.2 SWE ISSN 1103-3037
SKATTEHANDBOK FOER CHEFER. Text in Swedish. 1991. a. SEK 640 (effective 1992).
Published by: Liber Ekonomi, Malmo, 20510, Sweden.

SKATTELAGSTIFTNING; lagar och andra foerfattningar som de lyder den ... see *LAW*

336 DNK ISSN 0106-8024
SKATTEN✶ **.** Text in Danish. 1946. a. DKK 38.
Published by: Aktuelle Boeger, Birkedammervej 31, Copenhagen Nv, 2400, Denmark.

336 DNK ISSN 0107-3885
SKATTEN. ERHVERV. Text in Danish. 1981. a. DKK 36.
Formerly: Afskrivning
Published by: Aktuelle Boeger, c/o Danske Boghendleres Kommissionsanstalt, Siljangade 6, Copenhagen S, 2300, Denmark. Ed. Jens Stubkjaer.

336 SWE ISSN 1652-7925
SKATTENYHETER. Text in Swedish. 1985. irreg. back issues avail. **Document type:** *Newsletter, Government.*
Former titles (until 2005): S K V -Nytt (1652-1463); (until 2004): R S V -Nytt (0283-5088)
Related titles: Online - full text ed.
Published by: Skatteverket/Swedish National Tax Board (Subsidiary of: Skattefoervaltningen), Solna Strandvaeg 6, Solna, 17194, Sweden. TEL 46-771-778778, huvudkontoret@skatteverket.se, http://www.skatteverket.se. Ed. Egon Vikstroem. **Dist. by:** Fritzes Kundtjaenst.

336.2 SWE ISSN 0346-1254
SKATTENYTT. Variant title: S N. Text in English, Swedish. 1951. m. SEK 678 (effective 2003); SEK 1,251 with yearbook; SEK 212 to students; SEK 85 per issue. bk.rev. bibl.; tr.lit. index: 1968-1997. back issues avail. **Document type:** *Academic/Scholarly.*
Indexed: RASB.
Published by: Iustus Foerlag, Oestra Aagatan 9, Uppsala, 75322, Sweden. TEL 46-18-693091, FAX 46-18-693099, sn@iustus.se, http://www.skattenyt.se, http://www.iustus.se. Eds. Christer Silfverberg, Robert Paahlsson TEL 46-31-7731532.

343.48904 DNK ISSN 0108-6049
SKATTEPOLITISK OVERSIGT. Text in Danish. 1946. 8/yr. DKK 735; DKK 136 per issue (effective 2004). adv. bk.rev. back issues avail. **Document type:** *Journal, Academic/Scholarly.* **Description:** Highlights tax policies for lawyers and auditors.
Published by: Forlaget Thomson S/A, Nytorv 5, Copenhagen K, 1450, Denmark. TEL 45-33-740700, FAX 45-33-121636, thomson@thomson.dk, http://www/thomson.dk. Ed. Henrik Dam. Adv. contact Claus Hansen TEL 45-33-78893. Circ: 2,000.

SKATTERETT; tidsskrift for skatt og avgift. see *LAW*

343.04 SWE ISSN 1652-8964
SKATTEVERKET INFORMERAR. Text in Swedish. 1979. 6/yr. **Document type:** *Government.* **Description:** Information and explanations of current tax laws in Sweden.
Former titles (until 2005): S K V Info (1652-1455); (until 2004): R S V Info (0348-5692)
Published by: Skatteverket/Swedish National Tax Board (Subsidiary of: Skattefoervaltningen), Solna Strandvaeg 6, Solna, 17194, Sweden. TEL 46-771-778778, huvudkontoret@skatteverket.se, http://www.skatteverket.se. **Dist. by:** Fritzes Kundtjaenst, c/o Norstedts Juridik AB, Stockholm 10647, Sweden. TEL 46-8-6909190, FAX 46-8-6909191, order.fritzes@nj.se, http://www.fritzes.se.

336 SWE ISSN 1652-1420
SKATTEVERKETS FOERFATTNINGSSAMLING. Text in Swedish. 1977. irreg., latest 2005. back issues avail. **Document type:** *Government.*
Formerly (until 2004): Riksskatteverkets Foerfattningssamling (0347-3023); Which was formed by the merger of (1972-1976): Riksskatteverkets Meddelanden. Serie Al (0346-0037); (1973-1976): Riksskatteverkets Meddelanden. Serie Dt (0346-0061); (1971-1976): Riksskatteverkets Meddelanden. Serie Du (0346-007X); (1971-1976): Riksskatteverkets Meddelanden. Serie Ex (0346-010X); (1975-1976): Riksskatteverkets Meddelanden. Serie Ff (0346-5896); (1973-1976): Riksskatteverkets Meddelanden. Serie Im (0346-0088); (1972-1976): Riksskatteverkets Meddelanden. Serie Ip (0346-0096)
Published by: Skatteverket/Swedish National Tax Board (Subsidiary of: Skattefoervaltningen), Solna Strandvaeg 6, Solna, 17194, Sweden. TEL 46-771-778778, huvudkontoret@skatteverket.se, http://www.skatteverket.se.

336 USA
SMALL BUSINESS TAX PLANNER. Text in English. 1986. m. looseleaf. USD 215. **Description:** Publishes tax planning articles geared to the small business.
Indexed: ATI.
Published by: R I A (Subsidiary of: Thomson Corporation), 395 Hudson St, New York, NY 10014. TEL 212-367-6300, RIA.CustomerServices@Thomson.com, http://ria.thomson.com/.

336 USA ISSN 0276-5322
KF6491.A15
SMALL BUSINESS TAX REVIEW. Text in English. 1980. m. looseleaf. USD 84 (effective 1999). back issues avail. **Document type:** *Newsletter.* **Description:** Focuses on federal taxes and recent developments aimed at small businesses and individuals.
Related titles: Online - full text ed.
Published by: A-N Group, Inc., PO Box 895, Melville, NY 11747-0895. TEL 516-549-4090, angroup@pb.net, http://www.smbiz.com. Ed., Pub. Steven A Hopfenmuller.

THE SOCIAL FUND: LAW AND PRACTICE. see *SOCIAL SERVICES AND WELFARE*

336.2 FRA ISSN 1683-2434
SOURCE O C D E. FISCALITE. (Organisation de Cooperation et de Developpement Economiques) Text in French. irreg. EUR 771, USD 886, GBP 488, JPY 104,000 (effective 2005).
Related titles: Online - full content ed.: ISSN 1684-3088. EUR 540, USD 621, GBP 356, JPY 72,900 (effective 2005); Online - full text ed.: (from EBSCO Publishing, Gale Group, IngentaConnect, Swets Information Services).
Published by: Organization for Economic Cooperation and Development, 2 Rue Andre Pascal, Paris, 75775 Cedex 16, France. TEL 33-1-45248200, FAX 33-1-45248500, http://www.oecd.org. **Dist. by:** Extenza - Turpin, Pegasus Dr, Stratton Business Park, Biggleswade, Beds SG18 8TQ, United Kingdom. TEL 44-1462-687552, FAX 44-1462-480947; O E C D Turpin North America, PO Box 194, Downingtown, PA 19335-0194. TEL 610-524-5361, 800-456-6323, FAX 610-524-5417, journalscustomer@turpinna.com.

352.4 ZAF
SOUTH AFRICA. OFFICE OF THE AUDITOR-GENERAL. REPORT OF THE AUDITOR-GENERAL. Text in Afrikaans, English. 1993. a. **Document type:** *Government.*

Published by: (South Africa. Office of the Auditor-General), Government Printing Works, 149 Bosman St, Private Bag X85, Pretoria, 0001, South Africa.

SOUTH AFRICA. STATISTICS SOUTH AFRICA. FINANCIAL STATISTICS OF LOCAL GOVERNMENTS. see *PUBLIC ADMINISTRATION—Abstracting, Bibliographies, Statistics*

SOUTH AFRICA. STATISTICS SOUTH AFRICA. STATISTICAL RELEASE. ACTUAL AND ANTICIPATED CAPITAL EXPENDITURE OF THE PUBLIC SECTOR. see *BUSINESS AND ECONOMICS—Abstracting, Bibliographies, Statistics*

SOUTH AFRICA. STATISTICS SOUTH AFRICA. STATISTICAL RELEASE. CENTRAL GOVERNMENT: REVENUE OF THE STATE REVENUE AND OTHER REVENUE ACCOUNTS. see *PUBLIC ADMINISTRATION—Abstracting, Bibliographies, Statistics*

SOUTH AFRICA. STATISTICS SOUTH AFRICA. STATISTICAL RELEASE. EXPENDITURE BY THE GENERAL GOVERNMENT. see *PUBLIC ADMINISTRATION— Abstracting, Bibliographies, Statistics*

SOUTH AFRICA. STATISTICS SOUTH AFRICA. STATISTICAL RELEASE. EXPENDITURE OF THE CENTRAL GOVERNMENT. see *PUBLIC ADMINISTRATION— Abstracting, Bibliographies, Statistics*

SOUTH AFRICA. STATISTICS SOUTH AFRICA. STATISTICAL RELEASE. FINANCIAL STATISTICS OF EXTRABUDGETARY ACCOUNTS AND FUNDS. see *BUSINESS AND ECONOMICS—Abstracting, Bibliographies, Statistics*

SOUTH AFRICA. STATISTICS SOUTH AFRICA. STATISTICAL RELEASE. FINANCIAL STATISTICS OF LOCAL AUTHORITIES AND REGIONAL SERVICES COUNCILS AND JOINT SERVICES BOARDS. see *PUBLIC ADMINISTRATION—Abstracting, Bibliographies, Statistics*

336   USA
SOUTH CAROLINA MONTHLY REVENUE LETTER. Text in English. m. free. **Document type:** *Government.*
Published by: Budget and Control Board, Board of Economic Advisors, Ste 442, Rembert Dennis Bldg, 1000 Assembly St, Columbia, SC 29201. TEL 803-734-3805, FAX 803-734-4719. Ed. M Greg Dibiase. R&P Greg Dibiase TEL 803-734-4604.

336   ESP
SPAIN. MINISTERIO DE ECONOMIA Y HACIENDA. DIRECCION GENERAL DE SEGUROS. BALANCES Y CUENTAS; seguros privados. Text in Spanish. a. charts. **Document type:** *Government.*
Media: Magnetic Tape.
Published by: Ministerio de Economia y Hacienda, Direccion General de Seguros, Paseo Castellana, 44, Madrid, 28046, Spain. TEL 34-1-3397000, FAX 34-1-3397113.

336   USA   ISSN 0194-8237
SPIDELL'S CALIFORNIA TAXLETTER. Text in English. 1979. m. looseleaf. USD 97. back issues avail. **Document type:** *Newsletter.*
Published by: Spidell Publishing, Inc., 1158 N Gilbert St, Anaheim, CA 92801-1401. TEL 714-776-7850, FAX 714-776-9906. Ed., Pub. Robert A Spidell. Circ: 7,000.

336.26   POL   ISSN 0038-7746
SPOLEM. Text in Polish. 1906. s-m. PLZ 72. bk.rev. illus.
Published by: Krajowy Zwiazek Rewizyjny Spoldzielni Spozywcow - Spolem/National Supervision Committee of Consumer Cooperatives, Grazyny 13, Warsaw, 02548, Poland. TEL 48-22-452323, FAX 48-22-452581, TELEX 817611. Circ: 55,000.

340 336   AUS
STAMP DUTIES SOUTH AUSTRALIA. Text in English. 1991. base vol. plus irreg. updates. looseleaf. AUD 575 (effective 2004). **Document type:** *Trade.* **Description:** Features comprehensive coverage of all stamp duties legislation and Stamp Duties Office practice in South Australia.
Published by: Lawbook Co. (Subsidiary of: Thomson Legal & Regulatory Ltd.), PO Box 3502, Rozelle, NSW 2039, Australia. TEL 61-2-85877000, FAX 61-2-85877100, LRA.Service@thomson.com, http:// onlineecom01.thomson.com.au/thomson/Catalog.asp? EES_CMD=SI&EES_ID=100410, http:// www.lawbookco.com.au/. Eds. Jeremy Schultz, Michael Quinlan.

336 340   AUS
STAMP DUTIES W.A. Text in English. 1992. base vol. plus unknown updates. looseleaf. AUD 575 (effective 2004). **Document type:** *Trade.* **Description:** Features comprehensive coverage of all stamp duties legislation and Stamp Duties Office practice in Western Australia.

Published by: Lawbook Co. (Subsidiary of: Thomson Legal & Regulatory Ltd.), PO Box 3502, Rozelle, NSW 2039, Australia. TEL 61-2-85877000, FAX 61-2-85877100, LRA.Service@thomson.com, http:// onlineecom01.thomson.com.au/thomson/Catalog.asp? EES_CMD=SI&EES_ID=100415, http:// www.lawbookco.com.au/. Eds. Ian G Peek, Michael Quinlan.

336   USA
STANDARD FEDERAL TAX REPORTER. Text in English. 25 base vols. plus w. updates. looseleaf. USD 2,528 base vol(s). (effective 2004). **Description:** It is a comprehensive and current federal income tax authority in the industry, providing with a complete and up-to-date picture of federal income tax law organized in the way most logical to many practitioners.
Formerly: Standard Federal Tax Reports (0162-3494)
Related titles: CD-ROM ed.: ISSN 1083-8252. USD 1,626 (effective 2004); Online - full text ed.
Indexed: ATI.
—CCC.
Published by: C C H Inc., 2700 Lake Cook Rd, Riverwoods, IL 60015. TEL 847-267-7000, 800-449-6439, FAX 800-224-8299, cust_serv@cch.com, http://www.cch.com. Pub. Kevin Robert.

336   ZAF
STANDARD TRUST INCOME TAX GUIDE. Text in English. a. ZAR 60. **Description:** Reference guide for the layman and specialist, covering the Income Tax Act, relevant tax legislation, principles and practical advice for tax planning.
Published by: LexisNexis Butterworths South Africa (Subsidiary of: LexisNexis Europe and Africa), PO Box 792, Durban, KwaZulu-Natal 4000, South Africa. TEL 27-31-2683111, FAX 27-31-2683110.

336   CAN   ISSN 0576-3851
STANDING SENATE COMMITTEE ON NATIONAL FINANCE. PROCEEDINGS/DELIBERATIONS DU COMITE SENATORIAL PERMANENT DES FINANCES NATIONALES. Text in English, French. 1969. irreg.
Related titles: Online - full content ed.: ISSN 1498-5772; ISSN 1498-5780.
Published by: Senate of Canada, Standing Senate Committee on National Finance, Ottawa, ON K1A 0A4, Canada. TEL 613-990-0088, FAX 613-990-6666, comsen@sen.parl.gc.ca.

336.2   NZL
STAPLES' GUIDE TO NEW ZEALAND TAX PRACTICE. Text in English. 1936. a. NZD 99. adv.
Former titles: Staples' Guide to New Zealand Income Tax Practice (0111-9370); Guide to New Zealand Income Tax Practice (0072-8616)
Related titles: CD-ROM ed.
Published by: Brooker's Limited, Level 1 - Telecom Networks House, 68-86 Jervois Quay, Wellington, New Zealand. TEL 64-4-4998178, FAX 64-4-4998173, service@brookers.co.nz. Eds. Clifford Mancer, John Veal. Circ: 8,200.

336   USA   ISSN 1042-6027
HJ10.3
STATE FISCAL CAPACITY AND EFFORT. Text in English. 1986. biennial. **Document type:** *Government.*
Published by: U.S. Advisory Commission on Intergovernmental Relations, 800 K St, N W, Ste 450 South Bldg, Washington, DC 20575. TEL 202-653-5640.

336.24   USA
STATE INCOME TAX ALERT. Text in English. bi-w. USD 255; USD 415 combined subscription print & online eds. (effective 2004). **Document type:** *Newsletter.* **Description:** Features late-breaking income tax news with related case material and interviews with well-known income tax practitioners that provide "how to" information and interpretation of news events. Quick-reading charts, case summaries, compliance tips and strategies are among the features that make the State Income Tax Alert attractive to readers short on time.
Related titles: Online - full text ed.: USD 360 includes archive issues (effective 2004).
Published by: C C H Inc., 2700 Lake Cook Rd, Riverwoods, IL 60015. TEL 847-267-7000, 800-449-6439, cust_serv@cch.com, http://www.cch.com.

336.2 343.05   USA   ISSN 1551-1162
▼ **STATE INCOME TAX MONITOR.** Text in English. 2004 (Jul). 20/yr. USD 297 domestic; USD 327 in Canada; USD 352 elsewhere (effective 2005).
Related titles: Online - full text ed.: (from LexisNexis).
Published by: Strafford Publications, Inc., 590 Dutch Valley Rd, N E, Postal Drawer 13729, Atlanta, GA 30324-0729. TEL 404-881-1141, FAX 404-881-0074, custserv@straffordpub.com, http://www.straffordpub.com. Ed. Jon McKenna.

336.3   USA
STATE OF NEBRASKA. ANNUAL BUDGETING REPORT. Cover title: State of Nebraska Annual Budgetary Report. Text in English. 1966. a. free. illus.; stat. **Document type:** *Government.*
Former titles: Nebraska. Department of Administrative Services. Annual Fiscal Report; Nebraska. Accounting Division. Annual Fiscal Report; Nebraska. Accounting Division. Annual Report of Receipts and Disbursements (0090-628X)

Published by: Department of Administrative Services, State Capitol, R, 1315, Lincoln, NE 68509. TEL 402-471-2581. Ed. Bruce Snyder. Circ: 350.

336.3   USA
STATE OF NEBRASKA. COMPREHENSIVE ANNUAL FINANCIAL REPORT. Text in English. 1984. a. free.
Published by: Department of Administrative Services, State Capitol, R, 1315, Lincoln, NE 68509. TEL 402-471-2581. Circ: 350.

STATE TAX ACTION COORDINATOR. see *BUSINESS AND ECONOMICS—Accounting*

336   USA
STATE TAX CASES REPORTS - ALL STATES. Text in English. base vol. plus m. updates. USD 654 base vol(s). (effective 2004). **Description:** Analyzes trends in state tax law as developed by the U.S. Supreme Court and high state courts. Leading decisions that are pertinent for multistate citation are published promptly in monthly reports, and supplemented by accounts of all new developments in the weekly State Tax Review newsletter.
Published by: C C H Inc., 2700 Lake Cook Rd, Riverwoods, IL 60015. TEL 847-267-7000, 800-449-6439, FAX 800-224-8299, cust_serv@cch.com, http://www.cch.com. Pub. Kevin Robert.

336   USA
STATE TAX COLLECTIONS AND RATES. Text in English. 1991. a. USD 10 per issue (effective 2004). **Description:** Details the trends in state tax collections by type of tax and provides major tax rates for each state.
Formerly: Survey of State Tax and Collections
Indexed: SRI.
Published by: Tax Foundation, 2001 L St NW, Ste. 1050, Washington, DC 20036-4971. tf@taxfoundation.org, http://www.taxfoundation.org/publications.specialreport.html. Ed. Bill Ahern.

336   USA   ISSN 0162-1777
STATE TAX GUIDE. Text in English. 1937. 3 base vols. plus s-m. updates. looseleaf. USD 1,278 base vol(s). (effective 2004). **Description:** Contains state tax summaries, organized by state and by tax, so you can quickly find answers to all of your everyday questions and assess the cost of doing business in each state. It's packed with helpful features, including an extensive compilation of quick-reference charts that list tax rates, due dates, tax treatments and more for each state.
Related titles: CD-ROM ed.: USD 1,273 (effective 2004); Online - full text ed.
—CCC.
Published by: C C H Inc., 2700 Lake Cook Rd, Riverwoods, IL 60015. TEL 847-267-7000, 800-449-6439, FAX 800-224-8299, cust_serv@cch.com, http://www.cch.com. Pub. Kevin Robert.

336   USA   ISSN 1057-8404
KF6750
STATE TAX NOTES. Text in English. 1991. w. USD 949 (effective 1999). back issues avail. **Document type:** *Trade.*
Description: Covers state and local tax developments in all 50 states, the District of Columbia, and all governing territories.
Related titles: CD-ROM ed.; Microfiche ed.; Online - full text ed.: (from LexisNexis, The Dialog Corporation).
—CCC.
Published by: Tax Analysts, 6830 N Fairfax Dr, Arlington, VA 22213. TEL 703-553-4400, 800-955-3444, FAX 703-533-4444.

343.043   USA
STATE TAX ONEDISC. Text in English. 1996. m. (q., and a. versions avail.). USD 499 for m ed.; USD 399 for q. ed.; USD 299 for a. ed.. **Description:** Contains complete tax statutes and regulations for all fifty states and DC. Also all U.S. Supreme court decisions concerning state and local taxes, plus many state supreme court decisions and an archive of special reports published in State Tax Notes magazine.
Media: CD-ROM.
Published by: Tax Analysts, 6830 N Fairfax Dr, Arlington, VA 22213. TEL 703-553-4400, 800-955-3444, FAX 703-533-4444. Ed. David Brunori.

336.2   USA   ISSN 0162-1750
KF6750.A15
STATE TAX REVIEW. Text in English. 1941. w. USD 181 (effective 2004). **Document type:** *Newsletter.* **Description:** State Tax Review notes changes in laws, pertinent court decisions, and administrative rulings and offers expert articles from the CCH State Tax Advisory Board and contributing editors.
Related titles: Microform ed.: (from PQC); Online - full text ed.: (from Factiva, Northern Light Technology, Inc., ProQuest Information & Learning).
Indexed: ATI.
—CCC.
Published by: C C H Inc., 2700 Lake Cook Rd, Riverwoods, IL 60015. TEL 847-267-7000, 800-449-6439, FAX 800-224-8299, cust_serv@cch.com, http://www.cch.com. Pub. Kevin Robert.

336   DEU   ISSN 0172-7214
DAS STEUER A B C. Text in German. 1979. bi-m. looseleaf.
Document type: *Bulletin.*

Published by: W R S Verlag GmbH & Co. KG (Subsidiary of: Rudolf Haufe Verlag GmbH & Co. KG), Fraunhoferstr 5, Planegg, 82152, Germany. info@wrs.de, http://www.wrs.de.

336 DEU ISSN 0179-0161
STEUER AKTUELL. Text in German. 1986. s-m. EUR 65; EUR 2 newsstand/cover (effective 2005). adv. **Document type:** *Journal, Trade.* **Description:** Covers legal and taxation issues pertaining to business administration.
Published by: Erich Fleischer Verlag GmbH & Co. KG, Postfach 1264, Achim, 28818, Germany. TEL 49-4202-5170, FAX 49-4202-51741, info@efv-online.de, http://www.efv-online.de. Ed. Thomas Holzer. Adv. contact Manfred Becker.

336.2 AUT
STEUER-AUSLANDDIENST. Text in German. 1973. 4/yr. membership. **Document type:** *Bulletin.*
Published by: Institut fuer Finanzwissenschaft und Steuerrecht, Seilerstaette 24, Vienna, W 1010, Austria. TEL 01-5129910. Ed. Anton Matzinger.

336.2 DEU ISSN 1610-4064
DIE STEUER-BERATER-WOCHE. Text in German. 2002. fortn. EUR 151.20; EUR 7.60 newsstand/cover (effective 2005). **Document type:** *Journal, Trade.*
Related titles: Online - full text ed.
Published by: Verlag Dr. Otto Schmidt KG, Gustav-Heinemann-Ufer 58, Cologne, 50968, Germany. TEL 49-221-93738460, FAX 49-221-93738943, info@otto-schmidt.de, http://www.steuer-berater-center.de, http://www.otto-schmidt.de.

STEUER-BRIEF FUER AERZTE UND ZAHNAERZTE. see *MEDICAL SCIENCES*

STEUER-BRIEF FUER ARCHITEKTEN UND INGENIEURE. see *ENGINEERING*

STEUER-BRIEF FUER DAS BAU- UND BAUNEBENGEWERBE. see *BUILDING AND CONSTRUCTION*

STEUER-BRIEF FUER DAS HOTEL- UND GASTSTAETTENGEWERBE. see *HOTELS AND RESTAURANTS*

STEUER-BRIEF FUER DAS KFZ-GEWERBE. see *TRANSPORTATION—Automobiles*

STEUER-BRIEF FUER DAS PERSONALBUERO. see *BUSINESS AND ECONOMICS—Personnel Management*

STEUER-BRIEF FUER DEN GMBH-GESCHAEFTSFUEHRER. see *BUSINESS AND ECONOMICS—Management*

STEUER-BRIEF FUER HANDELS- UND VERSICHERUNGSVERTRETER. see *INSURANCE*

STEUER-BRIEF FUER HAUS- UND GRUNDBESITZER. see *REAL ESTATE*

STEUER-BRIEF FUER PERSONENGESELLSCHAFTEN. see *CLUBS*

STEUER-BRIEF FUER VEREINE. see *CLUBS*

336.2 DEU ISSN 0937-1680
STEUER-EILDIENST. Text in German. 1913. w. EUR 20.40 per month; EUR 5.90 newsstand/cover (effective 2005). charts; illus. index. back issues avail. **Document type:** *Journal, Trade.*
Former titles: Deutsche Steuer-Zeitung. Eildienst (0724-553X); Deutsche Steuer-Zeitung. Ausgabe B (0012-0782)
—CCC.
Published by: (Germany. Bundesministerium der Finanzen), Stollfuss Verlag GmbH & Co. KG, Dechenstr 7, Bonn, 53115, Germany. TEL 49-228-7240, FAX 49-228-72491181, info@stollfuss.de, http://www.stollfuss.de/programm/products/0400130.htm. Ed. H Hoellig. Circ: 1,300.

STEUER-ERFAHRUNGSAUSTAUSCH KRAFTFAHRZEUGGEWERBE. see *TRANSPORTATION—Automobiles*

336 DEU ISSN 0177-9818
STEUER LEXICON. TEIL I-R. RICHTLINIEN. Text in German. 2 base vols. plus irreg. updates. EUR 20.50 base vol(s). (effective 2005). **Document type:** *Bulletin, Trade.*
Published by: Erich Fleischer Verlag GmbH & Co. KG, Postfach 1264, Achim, 28818, Germany. TEL 49-4202-5170, FAX 49-4202-51741, info@efv-online.de, http://www.efv-online.de.

336 DEU ISSN 0177-9672
STEUER-LEXICON. TEIL III. B F H RECHTSPRECHUNG. Text in German. 5 base vols. plus q. updates. EUR 46 base vol(s).; EUR 18.50 updates per issue (effective 2005). **Document type:** *Bulletin, Trade.*
Published by: Erich Fleischer Verlag GmbH & Co. KG, Postfach 1264, Achim, 28818, Germany. TEL 49-4202-5170, FAX 49-4202-51741, info@efv-online.de, http://www.efv-online.de.

336 DEU ISSN 0177-980X
STEUER-LEXIKON. TEIL I-G. GESETZE, VERORDNUNGEN. Text in German. 2 base vols. plus irreg. updates. EUR 21.50 base vol(s). (effective 2005). **Document type:** *Bulletin, Trade.*
Published by: Erich Fleischer Verlag GmbH & Co. KG, Postfach 1264, Achim, 28818, Germany. TEL 49-4202-5170, FAX 49-4202-51741, info@efv-online.de, http://www.efv-online.de.

336 DEU ISSN 0944-1204
STEUER-LEXIKON. TEIL II. AUFSAETZE, VERFUEGUNGEN, ERLASSE, EINZELFRAGEN, FG-RECHTSPRECHUNG. Text in German. 1954. m. EUR 65 base vol(s). per vol.; EUR 10.50 updates per issue (effective 2005). adv. index. **Document type:** *Bulletin, Trade.* **Description:** Contains essays, commentary, and decrees concerning financial administration and related legal issues.
Formerly (until 1991): Steuer-Lexikon Teil II. Aufsaetze, Verfuegungen, Erlasse, Einzelfragen (0177-9664)
Published by: Erich Fleischer Verlag GmbH & Co. KG, Postfach 1264, Achim, 28818, Germany. TEL 49-4202-5170, FAX 49-4202-51741, info@efv-online.de, http://www.efv-online.de. Ed. Thomas Holzer. Adv. contact Manfred Becker.

336 CHE ISSN 1424-0025
KKW3541.2
STEUER REVUE/REVUE FISCALE. Text in French, German. 1946. m. CHF 220 (effective 2001). adv. bk.rev. back issues avail. **Document type:** *Bulletin, Consumer.*
Indexed: DIP, IBR, IBZ.
Published by: Cosmos Verlag AG, Kraeyigenweg 2, Postfach 425, Muri B. Bern, 3074, Switzerland. TEL 41-31-9506464, FAX 41-31-9506460, info@steuerrevue.ch, http://www.steuerrevue.ch. Ed. R.M. Aeberli. Adv. contact P Schmutz. Circ: 3,500.

336 DEU ISSN 0177-9656
STEUER SEMINAR; praktische Faelle des Steuerrechts. Text in German. 1955. m. EUR 3.80 newsstand/cover (effective 2005). adv. index. **Document type:** *Bulletin, Trade.* **Description:** Covers legal issues related to business administration.
Published by: Erich Fleischer Verlag GmbH & Co. KG, Postfach 1264, Achim, 28818, Germany. TEL 49-4202-5170, FAX 49-4202-51741, info@efv-online.de, http://www.efv-online.de. Ed. Thomas Holzer. Adv. contact Manfred Becker.

336.2 DEU ISSN 0170-7620
STEUER TELEX; Spezialdienst fuer den Steuerfachmann. Text in German. 1960. w. EUR 169.20 (effective 2005). bk.rev. index. **Document type:** *Journal, Trade.*
Formerly (until 1974): Aktuelle Steuer-Informationen (0002-385X)
Published by: Deubner Verlag GmbH & Co. KG, Oststr 11, Cologne, 50996, Germany. TEL 49-221-9370180, FAX 49-221-93701890, kundenservice@deubner-verlag.de, http://www.vrp.de.

STEUER UND STUDIUM; Zeitschrift fuer die Aus- und Fortbildung im Steuerrecht. see *LAW*

336.2 DEU ISSN 0341-2954
STEUER UND WIRTSCHAFT; Zeitschrift fuer die gesamte Steuerwissenschaft. Text in German. 1924. q. EUR 184; EUR 49.80 newsstand/cover (effective 2005). adv. bk.rev. reprint service avail. from SCH. **Document type:** *Journal, Trade.*
Indexed: CERDIC, ELLIS, IBR.
—IE, Infotrieve. **CCC.**
Published by: Verlag Dr. Otto Schmidt KG, Gustav-Heinemann-Ufer 58, Cologne, 50968, Germany. TEL 49-221-93738460, FAX 49-221-93738943, info@otto-schmidt.de, http://www.otto-schmidt.de. Ed. Dr. Wissinger. adv.: B&W page EUR 1,085, color page EUR 1,898.75. Circ: 1,110 (paid and controlled).

DIE STEUER-WARTE. see *PUBLIC ADMINISTRATION*

336.2 DEU
STEUERANWALTSMAGAZIN. Text in German. 1999. q. EUR 39; EUR 9.20 newsstand/cover (effective 2004). adv. **Document type:** *Journal, Trade.*
Published by: Deutscher Anwaltverlag GmbH, Wachsbleiche 7, Bonn, 53111, Germany. TEL 49-228-919110, FAX 49-228-9191123, kontakt@anwaltverlag.de, http://www.anwaltverlag.de. adv.: B&W page EUR 550, color page EUR 1,240. Circ: 1,100 (paid and controlled).

336.2 CHE ISSN 1423-4688
STEUERBELASTUNG IN DER SCHWEIZ - KANTONSHAUPTORTE, KANTONSZIFFERN/CHARGE FISCALE EN SUISSE - CHEFS-LIEUX DES CANTONS, NOMBRES CANTONAUX. Text in French, German. a. CHF 13 (effective 2001). **Document type:** *Government.*
Formerly (until 1986): Steuerbelastung in der Schweiz (0259-6105)
Published by: Bundesamt fuer Statistik, Espace de l'Europe 10, Neuchatel, 2010, Switzerland. TEL 41-32-7136011, FAX 41-32-7136012, information@bfs.admin.ch, http://www.admin.ch/bfs.

336.2 DEU ISSN 0049-223X
K23
DER STEUERBERATER; Zeitschrift fuer Beruf und Praxis. Text in German. 1949. m. EUR 108 domestic; EUR 132 foreign; EUR 10 newsstand/cover (effective 2005). adv. bk.rev. index. reprint service avail. from SCH. **Document type:** *Magazine, Trade.*
Indexed: DIP, IBR, IBZ.
—CCC.
Published by: Verlag Recht und Wirtschaft GmbH, Mainzer Landstr 251, Frankfurt am Main, 60326, Germany. TEL 49-69-759501, FAX 49-69-75952780, verlag@ruw.de, http://www.ruw.de/ruw/zeitschriften/sb/index.html, http://www.ruw-ruw.de. Ed. Thomas Wegerich. Adv. contact Iris Biesinger. B&W page EUR 1,200, color page EUR 2,100; trim 180 x 257. Circ: 3,000 (paid and controlled).

336.2 DEU ISSN 0081-5519
STEUERBERATER-JAHRBUCH; zugleich Bericht ueber den jaehrlich stattfindenden Fachkongress der Steuerberater der BRD. Text in German. 1950. a. EUR 78.80 (effective 2005). **Document type:** *Journal, Trade.*
Published by: (Fachinstitut der Steuerberater), Verlag Dr. Otto Schmidt KG, Gustav-Heinemann-Ufer 58, Cologne, 50968, Germany. TEL 49-221-9373801, FAX 49-221-93738943, info@otto-schmidt.de, http://www.otto-schmidt.de. Circ: 1,500.

336.2 DEU
STEUERBERATER PLUS. Text in German. base vol. plus updates 5/yr. EUR 198; EUR 49 updates per issue (effective 2004). **Document type:** *Trade.*
Media: CD-ROM.
Published by: Verlag fuer Deutsche Steuerberater AG (Subsidiary of: Wolters Kluwer Deutschland GmbH), Marlener Str 2, Offenburg, 77656, Germany. TEL 49-781-9900646, FAX 49-781-9900644, info@steuern-online.de, http://www.steuern-online.de.

336.2 DEU ISSN 0936-434X
STEUERBERATER-, STEUERBEVOLLMACHTIGTEN HANDBUCH. Variant title: StB, StBv Handbuch. Text in German. 1970. 2 base vols. plus irreg. updates. price varies. **Document type:** *Monographic series, Trade.*
Published by: Erich Schmidt Verlag GmbH & Co. (Berlin), Genthiner Str 30G, Berlin, 10785, Germany. TEL 49-30-250085-0, FAX 49-30-25008511, esv@esvmedien.de, http://www.erich-schmidt-verlag.de.

336 DEU ISSN 0490-9658
DIE STEUERBERATUNG. Text in German. 1958. m. **Document type:** *Bulletin.*
Indexed: IBR, IBZ.
—CCC.
Published by: Stollfuss Verlag GmbH & Co. KG, Dechenstr 7, Bonn, 53115, Germany. TEL 49-228-724-0, FAX 49-228-659223, http://www.stollfuss.de.

STEUERBRIEF TOURISTIK. see *TRAVEL AND TOURISM*

336.2 DEU ISSN 1433-1845
DIE STEUERFACHANGESTELLTEN. Text in German. 1966. m. EUR 43.80 (effective 2005). adv. bk.rev. **Document type:** *Magazine, Trade.*
Former titles (until 1996): Steuerfachgehilfen (0936-6164); (until 1989): Briefe fuer Junge Steuerfachleute (0007-0009)
—CCC.
Published by: Friedrich Kiehl Verlag GmbH, Pfaustr 13, Ludwigshafen, 67063, Germany. TEL 49-621-635020, FAX 49-621-6350222, info@kiehl.de, http://www.kiehl.de/zeitschr/steuer/start.htm. Ed. Torsten Hahn. adv.: page EUR 1,580; trim 186 x 260. Circ: 24,500.

336 DEU ISSN 0943-5735
DIE STEUERGESETZE. Text in German. 1949. irreg. looseleaf. price varies. **Document type:** *Monographic series, Trade.*
Published by: Erich Schmidt Verlag GmbH & Co. (Berlin), Genthiner Str 30G, Berlin, 10785, Germany. TEL 49-30-250085-0, FAX 49-30-25008521, vertrieb@esvmedien.de, http://www.erich-schmidt-verlag.de.

336 DEU ISSN 0340-9503
DIE STEUERLICHE BETRIEBSPRUEFUNG; Fachorgan fuer die Wirtschafts- und Pruefungspraxis. Text in German. m. EUR 105.60; EUR 9.80 newsstand/cover (effective 2006). adv. **Document type:** *Journal, Trade.*
Indexed: IBR, IBZ.
—IE, Infotrieve. **CCC.**
Published by: Erich Schmidt Verlag GmbH & Co. (Berlin), Genthiner Str 30G, Berlin, 10785, Germany. TEL 49-30-2500850, FAX 49-30-250085305, esv@esvmedien.de, http://www.esv.info. adv.: page EUR 1,400; trim 171 x 248. Circ: 2,194 (paid and controlled).

336.1 DEU ISSN 1615-8024
STEUERN UND BILANZEN; Zeitschrift fuer das Steuerrecht und die Rechnungslegung der Unternehmen. Text in German. 1999. s-m. EUR 189 per month; EUR 144.60 per month to students; EUR 10 newsstand/cover (effective 2002). **Document type:** *Journal, Trade.*
Published by: Verlag Neue Wirtschafts-Briefe GmbH & Co., Eschstr 22, Herne, 44629, Germany. TEL 49-2323-141900, FAX 49-2323-141123, info@nwb.de, http://www.nwb.de. Circ: 4,800 (paid).

336.2 DEU ISSN 0936-1081
STEUERPRAXIS FUER KREDITINSTITUTE. Text in German. 1949. irreg. price varies. **Document type:** *Monographic series, Trade.*
Published by: Erich Schmidt Verlag GmbH & Co. (Berlin), Genthiner Str 30G, Berlin, 10785, Germany. TEL 49-30-250085-0, FAX 49-30-25008511, esv@esvmedien.de, http://www.erich-schmidt-verlag.de.

336.2 DEU ISSN 1616-6663
STEUERRECHT IN FORSCHUNG UND PRAXIS. Text in German. 2001. irreg., latest vol.9, 2005. price varies. **Document type:** *Monographic series, Academic/Scholarly.*
Published by: Verlag Dr. Kovac, Arnoldstr 49, Hamburg, 22763, Germany. TEL 49-40-3988800, FAX 49-40-39888055, info@verlagdrkovac.de, http://www.verlagdrkovac.de/12-8.htm.

336 DEU
STEUERVERANLAGUNGEN CD-ROM. Text in German. a. EUR 171.80 (effective 2003). **Document type:** *Abstract/Index.*
Media: CD-ROM.
Published by: Verlag C.H. Beck oHG, Wilhelmstr 9, Munich, 80801, Germany. TEL 49-89-38189338, FAX 49-89-38189398, abo.service@beck.de, http://www.beck.de.

336 DEU ISSN 0490-9690
DER STEUERZAHLER. Text in German. 1950. m. adv. 20 p./no. 4 cols./p.; **Document type:** *Magazine, Consumer.*
Published by: Steuerzahler Service GmbH, Postfach 1427, Wiesbaden, 65004, Germany. TEL 49-611-3083688, FAX 49-611-3082599, presse@steuerzahler.de, http://www.steuerzahler.de. Ed. Karl Heinz Daeke. Pub. Karl-Heinz Daeke. Adv. contact Volker Stern. B&W page EUR 8,450, color page EUR 10,990; trim 180 x 268. Circ: 454,735 (controlled).

336.2 DEU
STEUERZAHLER-TIP; Steuertips fuer den privaten Bereich. Text in German. m. **Document type:** *Newsletter, Consumer.* **Description:** Provides tips and advice on tax issues for private concerns.
Published by: V S R W Verlag Dr. Hagen Pruehs GmbH, Rolandstr 48, Bonn, 53179, Germany. TEL 49-228-95124-0, FAX 49-228-9512490, vsrw@vsrw.de, http://www.vsrw.de/Informationsdienste/Steuerzahler_Tip/Steuerzahler-Tip.shtml.

STRUCTURING BUY - SELL AGREEMENTS; tax and legal analysis with forms. see *LAW—Corporate Law*

336 USA
STUDIES IN FEDERAL TAXATION. Text in English. 1969. irreg., latest 1990. price varies. **Document type:** *Trade.*
Published by: American Institute of Certified Public Accountants, Harborside Financial Ctr., 201 Plaza Three, 3rd Fl, Jersey City, NJ 07311-9801. TEL 888-777-7077, FAX 800-302-5766, journal@aicpa.org, http://www.aicpa.org.

336 GBR
STUDIES IN LEASING LAW & TAX. Text in English. a. GBP 20, USD 35 (effective 1998). **Description:** Provides in-depth reviews of the legal and taxation implications of various asset financing and leasing structures.
Related titles: ♦ Supplement to: World Leasing Yearbook (Year). ISSN 0264-0732.
Published by: Euromoney Publications plc, Nestor House, Playhouse Yard, London, EC4V 5EX, United Kingdom. TEL 44-207-7798673, FAX 44-20-77798541.

336.1 SWE ISSN 0039-5455
SUNT FOERNUFT. Text in Swedish. 1921. 8/yr. SEK 300 (effective 2005). adv. bk.rev. illus. index. back issues avail. **Document type:** *Magazine, Consumer.*
Related titles: Audio cassette/tape ed.
Published by: Skattebetalarnas Foerening/Swedish Taxpayers' Association, Baldersgatan 5, Stockholm, 11495, Sweden. TEL 46-8-6131700, FAX 46-8-6131727, info@skattebetalarna.se, http://www.skattebetalarna.se. Ed. Aake Jungdalen. Adv. contact Lars-Bjoern Dorfh TEL 46-8-7952870. Circ: 148,000.

336.2 NLD ISSN 0039-5927
SUPPLEMENTARY SERVICE TO EUROPEAN TAXATION. Text in English. 1963. 24 base vols. plus m. updates. looseleaf. USD 1,935 base vol(s).; USD 1,210 updates (effective 2002). bk.rev. bibl.; charts. **Document type:** *Trade.* **Description:** Summarizes the taxation of individuals and corporations in the majority of European countries, followed by full texts of most double taxation treaties concluded by European countries with others.
Published by: (International Bureau of Fiscal Documentation), I B F D Publications BV, H J E Wenckebachweg 210, PO Box 20237, Amsterdam, 1000 HE, Netherlands. TEL 31-20-554-0100, FAX 31-20-620-8626, info@ibfd.nl, http://www.ibfd.nl. Ed. Juhani Kesti.

336 SWE ISSN 0039-6575
SVENSK HANDELSTIDNING JUSTITIA; ett magasin fraan D & B. Text in Swedish. 1893. 8/yr. SEK 1,295 Online ed. Includes Kreditinformation fraan D&B; SEK 1,695 Paper ed. Includes Kreditinformation fraan D&B (effective 2004). adv.
Formerly (until 1941): Justitia, Svensk Handelstidning
Related titles: Online - full text ed.
Published by: Svensk Handelstidning Justitia A-B (Subsidiary of: Dun & Bradstreet Corporation), Sveavaegen 151, Stockholm, 11346, Sweden. TEL 46-8-6955424, FAX 46-8-6193535, http://www.shj.se. Ed. Thomas Pettersson. Pub. Anna Ericsson. Adv. contact Jan Soederstrand TEL 46-8-6226202. page SEK 18,500; 185 x 250. Circ: 13,500.

336 SWE ISSN 1403-011X
SVENSK HANDELSTIDNING JUSTITIA. AARSFAKTA. Text in Swedish. 1979. q. adv. bk.rev. Supplement avail. **Document type:** *Journal, Trade.*
Former titles (until 1996): Svensk Handelstidning Justita - Kvartal (1101-3540); (until vol. 2, 1990): Justitia Kreditregister (0349-974X); (until 1981): Svensk Handelstidning Justitia - Aarsbok (0349-9316)
Published by: Svensk Handelstidning Justitia A-B (Subsidiary of: Dun & Bradstreet Corporation), Sveavaegen 151, Stockholm, 11346, Sweden. TEL 46-8-6955424, FAX 46-8-6193535, info.shj@dnb.com, http://www.shj.se.

336.2 SWE ISSN 0346-2218
➤ **SVENSK SKATTETIDNING.** Text in Swedish. 1934. 10/yr. SEK 2,335 includes CD (effective 2005). bk.rev. Index. **Document type:** *Magazine, Trade.*
Published by: Norstedts Juridik AB (Subsidiary of: Wolters Kluwer N.V.), Stockholm, 10647, Sweden. TEL 46-8-6909190, FAX 46-8-6909191, kundservice@nj.se, http://www.nj.se. Eds. Anders Koehlmark, Cecilia Gunne.

336.2 SWE ISSN 0282-4108
SVENSK TULL. Text in Swedish. 1946. 10/yr. **Document type:** *Newspaper, Consumer.*
Former titles (until 1985): Generaltullstyrelsens Meddelanden; (until 1968): Kungl. General Tullstyrelsens Meddelanden
Media: Online - full text.
Published by: Generaltullstyrelsen, Fack 2267, Stockholm, 10317, Sweden. http://www.tullverket.se. **Subscr. to:** C.E. Fritzes AB, Stockholm 10647, Sweden.

336.39 SWZ
SWAZILAND. MINISTRY OF FINANCE. RECURRENT ESTIMATES OF PUBLIC EXPENDITURE. Text in English. a. **Document type:** *Government.* **Description:** Includes estimates of public revenue and expenditure.
Formerly: Swaziland. Central Statistical Office. Recurrent Estimates of Public Expenditure
Published by: Ministry of Finance Office, PO Box 443, Mbabane, Swaziland. TEL 268-4048145-9, FAX 268-404-3187. Circ: 600.

336 SWE ISSN 1100-9403
SWEDEN. MINISTRY OF FINANCE. REVISED BUDGET STATEMENT. Text in English. 1975. a. stat.
Former titles (until 1988): Revised Finance Bill (0282-4841); (until 1982): Swedish Economy (0347-5646); (until 1977): Svenska Ekonomin
Published by: Ministry of Finance, Roedbodgatan 6, Stockholm, 10333, Sweden.

336 SWE ISSN 0347-7312
SWEDEN. RIKSREVISIONSVERKET. STATENS FINANSER; Riksrevisionsverkets aarsbok. Text in Swedish. 1921. a. free. **Document type:** *Government.*
Former titles (until 1971): Sweden. Riksrevisionsverket. Riksrevisionsverkets Aarsbok; (until 1962): Sweden. Riksraekenskapsverket. Riksraekenskapsverkets Aarsbok; (until 1930): Sweden. Riksraekenskapsverket. Riksraekenskapsverkets Revisionsberaettelse
Published by: Riksrevisionsverket/National Audit Bureau, Fack 45070, Stockholm, 10430, Sweden. Ed. Tina Granath. Circ: 5,200.

T M A TOBACCO BAROMETER. see *TOBACCO*

T M A TOBACCO WEEKLY. see *TOBACCO*

336.2 346 640 FIN ISSN 0788-9135
TALOUSTAITO. Text in Finnish. 1948. m. EUR 45 (effective 2005). adv. bk.rev. **Document type:** *Magazine, Trade.*
Formerly (until 1989): Veronmaksaja (0356-4703)
Published by: Verotieto Oy/Taxpayers' Association of Finland, Kalevankatu 4, Helsinki, 00100, Finland. TEL 358-9-618871, FAX 358-9-608087, http://www.veronmaksajat.fi. Ed. Antti Marttinen. Adv. contact Ulla Johansson TEL 358-9-222-4636. color page EUR 4,000; 210 x 285. Circ: 191,818.

TAMOZHENNAYA STATISTIKA VNESHNEI TORGOVLI ROSSIISKOI FEDERATSII. see *BUSINESS AND ECONOMICS—Abstracting, Bibliographies, Statistics*

336 RUS
TAMOZHENNYE VEDOMOSTI. BYULLETEN' TAMOZHENNOI INFORMATSII. Text in Russian. m. USD 195 in United States. **Document type:** *Bulletin.*
Published by: Gosudarstvennyi Tamozhennyi Komitet Rossiiskoi Federatsii, Tsentr Ekonomiki i Marketinga, Prechistenka 9, Moscow, 119034, Russian Federation. TEL 7-095-9179236, FAX 7-095-9160229. **US dist. addr.:** East View Information Services, 3020 Harbor Ln. N., Minneapolis, MN 55447. TEL 612-550-0961.

TARIF AKTUELL; Informationsdienst zum Tarifrecht im oeffentlichen Dienst. see *PUBLIC ADMINISTRATION*

336 DEU ISSN 0934-3229
TASCHENLEXIKON STEUERRECHTLICHER ENTSCHEIDUNGEN. Text in German. 1960. irreg. price varies. **Document type:** *Monographic series, Trade.*
Published by: Erich Schmidt Verlag GmbH & Co. (Berlin), Genthiner Str 30G, Berlin, 10785, Germany. TEL 49-30-250085-0, FAX 49-30-25008511, esv@esvmedien.de, http://www.erich-schmidt-verlag.de.

336.946 AUS
TASMANIA. DEPARTMENT OF THE TREASURY. BUDGET PAPERS; summary of estimated expenditure (including expenditure reserved by law) and estimated revenue. Text in English. irreg. AUD 55; AUD 65 foreign (effective 1999). stat. **Document type:** *Government.*
Formerly: Tasmania. Department of the Treasury. Consolidated Revenue Fund
Published by: (Australia. Department of the Treasury), Printing Authority of Tasmania, GPO Box 307 C, Hobart, TAS 7001, Australia. TEL 61-3-6233-3168, FAX 61-3-6233-2460, bookshop@pat.tas.gov.au.

TAX ACCOUNTING. see *BUSINESS AND ECONOMICS—Accounting*

336 USA
TAX ACTION COORDINATOR. Text in English. 10 base vols. plus bi-w. updates. looseleaf. USD 575. **Description:** Provides tax planning guidance and compliance tools.
Indexed: ATI.
Published by: R I A (Subsidiary of: Thomson Corporation), 395 Hudson St, New York, NY 10014. TEL 212-367-6300, RIA.CustomerServices@Thomson.com, http://ria.thomson.com/.

336 ARG
TAX ADMINISTRATION REVIEW✶. Text in English, Spanish. 1985. a. USD 20.
Published by: Inter-American Center of Tax Administrators/Centro Interamericano de Administradores Tributarios, San Jose 83, 2do piso, Buenos Aires, Argentina. **Co-sponsor:** Institute of Fiscal Studies of Spain.

336.2 USA ISSN 0039-9949
HJ2360
TAX ADMINISTRATORS NEWS. Text in English. 1937. m. USD 35 (effective 2000). bk.rev. illus.; stat. **Document type:** *Newsletter.*
Published by: Federation of Tax Administrators, 444 N Capitol St, N W, Ste 348, Washington, DC 20001. TEL 202-624-5890, http://www.taxadmin.org. Ed. Audrey Maynard. Circ: 2,000.

TAX-ADVANTAGED SECURITIES LAW REPORT. see *LAW—Corporate Law*

336 GBR ISSN 1472-4502
➤ **TAX ADVISER.** Text in English. 1976. m. GBP 64 to non-members (effective 2000). adv. bk.rev. **Document type:** *Academic/Scholarly.*
Formerly (until 2000): Taxation Practitioner (1367-3246)
Indexed: ELJI, LJI.
—BLDSC (8611.566500).
Published by: Croner.C C H Group Ltd. (Subsidiary of: Wolters Kluwer N.V.), 145 London Rd, Kingston, Surrey KT2 6SR, United Kingdom. TEL 44-20-85473333, FAX 44-20-85472637, info@croner.co.uk, http://www.croner.cch.co.uk. Circ: 23,000.

336.2 USA ISSN 0039-9957
CODEN: TAADDJ
THE TAX ADVISER; a magazine of tax planning, trends and techniques. Text in English. 1970. m. USD 98 to non-members; USD 71 to members (effective 1999). adv. illus. cum.index. reprint service avail. from PQC,WSH. **Document type:** *Trade.*
Related titles: Microfiche ed.: (from WSH); Microform ed.: (from PQC, WSH); Online - full text ed.: (from EBSCO Publishing, Florida Center for Library Automation, Gale Group, H.W. Wilson, O C L C Online Computer Library Center, Inc., ProQuest Information & Learning).
Indexed: ABIn, ATI, BPI, BPIA, BusI, CLI, FamI, ILP, IPARL, LRI, ManagCont, PSI, T&II.
—BLDSC (8611.566000), IE, ingenta. **CCC.**
Published by: American Institute of Certified Public Accountants, Harborside Financial Ctr., 201 Plaza Three, 3rd Fl, Jersey City, NJ 07311-9801. TEL 888-777-7077, FAX 800-302-5766, journal@aicpa.org, http://www.aicpa.org. Ed. Nick Fiore. Pub. Colleen Katz. Adv. contact Richard Flynn. Circ: 30,000.

336 USA
TAX ANALYST MICROFICHE DATABASE. Text in English. w. USD 2,249 (effective 1999). **Document type:** *Trade.* **Description:** Contains all pages of Tax Notes, State Tax Notes, and Tax Notes International magazines, and all the supporting full-text documents cited.
Formerly: Tax Notes Microfiche Database (0730-8604); Incorporates (1992-1996): State Tax Notes Microfiche Database (1060-491X); Tax Notes International Microfiche Database (0887-5626)
Media: Microfiche. **Related titles:** CD-ROM ed.

▼ new title ➤ refereed ✶ unverified ♦ full entry avail.

Published by: Tax Analysts, 6830 N Fairfax Dr, Arlington, VA 22213. TEL 703-553-4400, 800-955-3444, FAX 703-533-4444.

TAX & BUSINESS ADVISER. see *BUSINESS AND ECONOMICS—Accounting*

343.05   USA
TAX AND BUSINESS PLANNING OF LIMITED LIABILITY COMPANIES. Text in English. 1993. base vol. plus s-a. updates. USD 215 (effective 1999). **Document type:** *Trade.* **Description:** Analyzes all aspects of tax law as it applies to limited-liability corporations and includes annotated sample forms.
Published by: W G & L Financial Reporting & Management Research (Subsidiary of: R I A), 90 Fifth Ave, New York, NY 10011. TEL 212-645-4800, FAX 212-337-4280. Eds. Carter G Bishop, Daniel S Kleinberger.

336   GBR   ISSN 0265-9417
TAX & INSURANCE LETTER∗ . Text in English. 1974. m. GBP 143. **Document type:** *Newsletter.*
Published by: Fleet Street Publications Ltd., 271 Regent St, London, WIR 7PAU, United Kingdom. TEL 44-20-7447-4040, FAX 44-20-7447-4041. Ed. George Littlejohn.

TAX ASPECTS OF BANKRUPTCY LAW AND PRACTICE. see *LAW*

336   USA
TAX ASPECTS OF BUYING AND SELLING CORPORATE BUSINESSES. Text in English. 1983. base vol. plus a. updates. looseleaf. USD 135. Supplement avail. **Document type:** *Trade.* **Description:** For lawyers, accountants and specialists involved in the acquisition and sale of corporate businesses.
Related titles: Series of: Tax and Estate Planning Series.
Published by: Shepard's (Subsidiary of: LexisNexis North America), 555 Middle Creek Pkwy, Colorado Springs, CO 80921. TEL 800-743-7393, customer_service@shepards.com, http://www.shepards.com, http://www.lexisnexis.com/shepards/. Ed. Clifton J Fleming Jr.

336   ZAF
TAX BREAKS. Text in English. 1986. m. USD 190. **Document type:** *Newsletter.* **Description:** Tax advice and opportunities for individuals.
Indexed: ApMecR.
Published by: Prescon Publishing Corporation (Pty) Ltd., PO Box 84004, Greenside, Johannesburg 2034, South Africa. TEL 27-11-7829229, FAX 27-11-7822025, prescon@iafrica.com. Ed. Kathy Thersby.

336   GBR   ISSN 0262-7639
TAX CASE ANALYSIS. Text in English. 1980. m. GBP 245, USD 375. **Document type:** *Bulletin.* **Description:** Tax case decisions and their impact on tax planning.
—CCC.
Published by: Longman Group UK Ltd., Law Tax and Finance Division, 21-27 Lambs Conduit St, London, WC1N 3NJ, United Kingdom. TEL 44-20-7242-2548, FAX 44-207-831-8119. Ed. Peter White.

336   GBR
TAX CASE REPORT. Text in English. irreg. GBP 70 (effective 1998). **Document type:** *Government.*
Published by: Stationery Office, 51 Nine Elms Ln, London, SW8 5DA, United Kingdom. TEL 44-20-7873-0011, FAX 44-20-7873-8463, book.orders@theso.co.uk, http://www.national-publishers.co.uk, http://www.national-publishing.co.uk. Circ: 5,250. **Subscr. to:** PO Box 276, London SW8 5DT, United Kingdom. TEL 44-20-7873-9090, FAX 44-207-873-8200.

336   USA
TAX COURT DECISIONS. Text in English. 1924. 2 base vols. plus w. updates. looseleaf. USD 949 base vol(s). (effective 2004).
Formerly: Tax Court Reports (Decisions Edition) (0162-1823)
Related titles: CD-ROM ed.: USD 555 (effective 2004).
Published by: C C H Inc., 2700 Lake Cook Rd, Riverwoods, IL 60015. TEL 847-267-7000, 800-449-6439, FAX 800-224-8299, cust_serv@cch.com, http://www.cch.com. Pub. Kevin Robert.

336   USA   ISSN 0162-1815
TAX COURT REPORTS. Text in English. 3 base vols. plus w. updates. USD 1,299 base vol(s). (effective 2004). reprint service avail. from WSH. **Description:** Offers full-text reporting of Tax Court Regular and Memorandum decisions, providing you with current, complete access to decisions of the nation's specialized tax tribunal.
Related titles: CD-ROM ed.: (from WSH); Online - full text ed.
—CCC.
Published by: C C H Inc., 2700 Lake Cook Rd, Riverwoods, IL 60015. TEL 847-267-7000, 800-449-6439, FAX 800-224-8299, cust_serv@cch.com, http://www.cch.com. Pub. Kevin Robert.

336.22   USA   ISSN 1527-2311
TAX CREDIT HOUSING MANAGEMENT INSIDER. Text in English. m. USD 347; USD 475 combined subscription print & online eds. (effective 2004). **Document type:** *Newsletter, Trade.*

Published by: Brownstone Publishers, Inc., 149 Fifth Ave, 16th Fl, New York, NY 10010-6801. TEL 212-473-8200, FAX 212-473-8786. Ed. Ronald Leshnower.

336   USA   ISSN 0888-1243
HJ9
THE TAX DIRECTORY. Text in English. 1984. a. (plus q. updates). USD 299 for print or CD-ROM; USD 399 for both print and CD-ROM. back issues avail. **Document type:** *Directory.* **Description:** Lists names, addresses, and telephone information for 45,000 tax officials at the state, federal, and international levels, plus worldwide listings of private tax professionals and corporate tax managers.
Related titles: CD-ROM ed.; Online - full text ed.: (from The Dialog Corporation).
—CCC.
Published by: Tax Analysts, 6830 N Fairfax Dr, Arlington, VA 22213. TEL 703-553-4400, 800-955-3444, FAX 703-533-4444. Ed. Tamera Wells Lee.

336.2   USA   ISSN 0040-0025
K24
THE TAX EXECUTIVE. Text in English. 1944. bi-m. USD 120 in US & Canada; USD 144 foreign (effective 2004). adv. bk.rev. charts; illus.; stat. index. back issues avail.; reprint service avail. from WSH,PQC. **Document type:** *Journal, Trade.* **Description:** Publishes and reprints position papers reflecting innovative, creative thinking; sets forth proposals for change and improvement in tax systems and unique solutions to problems; critically analyzes recent legislation and regulations; and explores means by which the professionalism of corporate tax operations can be enhanced.
Related titles: CD-ROM ed.; Microform ed.: (from PQC); Online - full text ed.: (from EBSCO Publishing, Florida Center for Library Automation, Gale Group, Northern Light Technology, Inc., O C L C Online Computer Library Center, Inc., ProQuest Information & Learning).
Indexed: ABIn, ABRCLP, ATI, BPIA, BusI, CLI, IBR, IBZ, ILP, IPARL, LRI, PAIS, T&II.
—BLDSC (8611.600000), IE, ingenta.
Published by: Tax Executives Institute, Inc., 1200 G St N W, 300, Washington, DC 20005-3814. TEL 202-638-5601, FAX 202-638-5607, http://www.tei.org/. Ed. Fred F Murray. Pub., R&P Timothy J McCormally. Adv. contact Richard Skippon. Circ: 5,500. **Subscr. to:** PO Box 96129, Washington, DC 20090-6129.

336   USA   ISSN 1536-4704
TAX-EXEMPT ORGANIZATION ALERT!. Text in English. 1993. m. USD 175 (effective 2005). **Description:** Covers the latest accounting, audit, tax and other financial news affecting nonprofit organizations.
Related titles: Online - full content ed.
Published by: Nonprofit Resource Center, 1700 Rockville Pike, Ste. 400, Rockville, MD 20852. TEL 301-987-0287, FAX 301-987-0988, questions@nonprofitresource.com, http://www.nonprofitresource.com/alert.htm.

336.2   USA   ISSN 1069-711X
TAX FEATURES. Text in English. 1957. bi-m. USD 15 to non-members (effective 2004). charts; illus.; stat. Supplement avail. **Document type:** *Newsletter.* **Description:** Reports on Tax Foundation analyses, studies, and seminars. Includes columns by leading policymakers.
Former titles: Tax Foundation's Tax Features (0883-1335); (until 1983): Monthly Tax Features (0736-1319); (until 1976): Tax Foundation's Monthly Tax Features (0047-8040)
Related titles: Microfiche ed.: (from CIS); Online - full text ed.: (from ProQuest Information & Learning).
Indexed: ABIn, ATI, PAIS, SRI.
Published by: Tax Foundation, 2001 L St NW, Ste. 1050, Washington, DC 20036-4971. tf@taxfoundation.org, http://www.taxfoundation.org. Ed., R&P Bill Ahern. Circ: 4,000.

TAX FILE. see *BUSINESS AND ECONOMICS—Accounting*

336   USA   ISSN 1527-0408
KF6289.A1
TAX FOUNDATION. BACKGROUND PAPERS. Text in English. 4/yr. USD 60; USD 25 per issue (effective 2004). **Description:** Each issue studies an economic issue in depth.
Published by: Tax Foundation, 2001 L St NW, Ste. 1050, Washington, DC 20036-4971. tf@taxfoundation.org, http://www.taxfoundation.org/publications.background.html. Ed., R&P Bill Ahern. Circ: 1,200.

336   USA
TAX FOUNDATION. FEDERAL TAX BURDENS AND EXPENDITURES BY STATE. Text in English. a. USD 10 per issue (effective 2004). **Description:** Computes the percentage of federal taxes each state bears, and compares this with federal spending in each state.
Former titles: Tax Foundation. Federal Tax Burdens by State; Tax Foundation. Memorandum on the Allocation of the Federal Tax Burden and Federal Grants-in-Aid by State; Tax Foundation. Annual Memorandum
Indexed: SRI.
Published by: Tax Foundation, 2001 L St NW, Ste. 1050, Washington, DC 20036-4971. tf@taxfoundation.org, http://www.taxfoundation.org/publications.specialreport.html. Ed. Bill Ahern.

336   USA   ISSN 1068-0306
TAX FOUNDATION. SPECIAL REPORTS. Text in English. 1991. irreg. (approx. 10/yr). USD 50; USD 10 per issue (effective 2004). **Description:** Each report provides an economic analysis of a topical issue in taxation. Topics include state tax rates, federal spending, President's budget and Tax Freedom Day, among others. Each report contains charts and graphs.
Related titles: Online - full text ed.: (from ProQuest Information & Learning).
Published by: Tax Foundation, 2001 L St NW, Ste. 1050, Washington, DC 20036-4971. tf@taxfoundation.org, http://www.taxfoundation.org/publications.html. Ed. Bill Ahern. R&Ps Alicia Hansen, Bill Ahern. Circ: 1,200.

350   USA
TAX FRAUD AND EVASION. Text in English. a. (in 2 vols.). USD 265. **Document type:** *Trade.*
Indexed: ATI.
Published by: W G & L Financial Reporting & Management Research (Subsidiary of: R I A), 90 Fifth Ave, New York, NY 10011. TEL 212-645-4800, FAX 212-337-4280.

336.2 343.04   USA
TAX FRAUD: AUDITS, INVESTIGATIONS, PROSECUTIONS. Text in English. 1980. 2 base vols. plus irreg. updates. looseleaf. USD 439 base vol(s). (effective 2002). **Description:** Guide to all stages of a tax examination, investigation, litigation and prosecution civil or criminal.
Published by: Matthew Bender & Co., Inc. (Subsidiary of: LexisNexis North America), 1275 Broadway, Albany, NY 12204. international@bender.com, http://bender.lexisnexis.com. Eds. Elliott Silverman, Robert Fink.

336.2   USA   ISSN 0190-7522
KF6369.8.E3
TAX GUIDE FOR COLLEGE TEACHERS AND OTHER COLLEGE PERSONNEL. Text in English. irreg., latest 1998.
Indexed: ATI.
Published by: Academic Information Service, Inc., PO Box 30499, Bethesda, MD 20824-0499. FAX 301-985-2009.

336   ZAF
TAX HANDBOOK. Text in English. a. ZAR 85. **Description:** Provides practitioners with compact and accessible information on tax legislation currently in force.
Formerly (until 1991): Income Tax Handbook
Published by: LexisNexis Butterworths South Africa (Subsidiary of: LexisNexis Europe and Africa), PO Box 792, Durban, KwaZulu-Natal 4000, South Africa. TEL 27-31-2683111, FAX 27-31-2683110.

332.6   BHS
TAX HAVEN REPORTER NEWSLETTER. Text in English. 1985. m. USD 200 (effective 2001). adv. **Document type:** *Newsletter.* **Description:** Covers various popular tax havens, including the Bahamas, Cayman Islands and Panama.
Published by: New Providence Press, PO Box CB 11552, Nassau, Bahamas. TEL 242-327-7359, FAX 242-327-7359, taxman@batelnet.bs, http://www.bahamasbahamas.com. Ed. Thomas P Azzara. Adv. contact Linda Veri. Circ: 1,000.

332.6   BHS
TAX HAVENS OF THE WORLD. Text in English. 1987. a., latest vol.7, 1998. USD 80 (effective 2001). back issues avail. **Document type:** *Bulletin.* **Description:** Covers over 28 tax havens used by businesspeople to cut and eliminate taxes.
Related titles: Online - full text ed.
Published by: New Providence Press, PO Box CB 11552, Nassau, Bahamas. TEL 242-327-7359, FAX 242-327-7359, taxman@batelnet.bs, http://www.bahamasbahamas.com. Ed. Thomas P Azzara. Circ: 7,000.

336.2   USA
TAX HAVENS OF THE WORLD. Text in English. 1974. 3 base vols. plus updates 4/yr. looseleaf. USD 552 base vol(s). (effective 2005). **Description:** Examines tax havens in more than 60 areas around the world.
Published by: Matthew Bender & Co., Inc. (Subsidiary of: LexisNexis North America), 1275 Broadway, Albany, NY 12204. TEL 518-487-3575, 800-252-9257, FAX 518-462-3788, international@bender.com, http://bender.lexisnexis.com. Eds. Dorothy Diamond, Walter Diamond.

336.2 640.75   USA   ISSN 0279-4446
                                                    CODEN: THAOAU
TAX HOTLINE; the inside report for people who need to be on top of every tax break the law allows. Text in English. 1981. m. looseleaf. USD 59 (effective 2004). 16 p./no. 3 cols./p.; back issues avail.; reprints avail. **Document type:** *Newsletter, Consumer.* **Description:** Offers consumers valuable money-saving insider tips from the experts to minimize their tax bill and maximize their ability to deal with the ever-changing IRS laws and loopholes.
Published by: Boardroom, Inc, 281 Tresser Blvd, 8th Fl., Stamford, CT 06901-3246. TEL 203-973-5900, FAX 203-967-3086, http://www.boardroom.com. Ed. David Ellis. Pub. Martin Edelston. R&P Bradley Velardo TEL 203-973-6204. Circ: 165,000. **Subscr. to:** Subscriber Service Center.

336   USA   ISSN 0279-2109
TAX IDEAS. Text in English. base vol. plus updates 13/yr. looseleaf. USD 595 (effective 1999). **Document type:** *Trade.* **Description:** Compiles the most important ideas and strategies.
Published by: W G & L Financial Reporting & Management Research (Subsidiary of: R I A), 90 Fifth Ave, New York, NY 10011. TEL 212-645-4800, FAX 212-337-4280.

336.2   USA   ISSN 1540-8302
TAX INCENTIVES ALERT. Text in English. 2002 (Jul.). m. USD 467 (effective 2005). **Document type:** *Newsletter.*
Related titles: Online - full text ed.: (from LexisNexis).
Published by: Strafford Publications, Inc., 590 Dutch Valley Rd, N E, Postal Drawer 13729, Atlanta, GA 30324-0729. TEL 404-881-1141, FAX 404-881-0074, editors@straffordpub.com, http://www.straffordpub.com/products/tia/index.html. Ed. Jon McKenna. Pub. Richard M Ossoff.

336   GBR   ISSN 0263-9076
TAX INSIGHT. Text in English. 1982. m. GBP 120. back issues avail.
Published by: Templegate Press Ltd., PO Box 3, Woking, Surrey GU21 1AA, United Kingdom. TEL 09323-51991. Ed. Alan Rook. Circ: 1,000.

336 340   GBR   ISSN 0954-7274
K24
THE TAX JOURNAL. Text in English. 1988. w. GBP 188 in British Isles; GBP 290.40 elsewhere (effective 2000). reprint service avail. from WSH. **Document type:** *Trade.* **Description:** Examines and comments on tax cases and explores their wider implications, providing details on transcripts for tax specialists in practice, commerce and public service.
Related titles: Microform ed.: (from PQC).
Indexed: ELJI, HongKongiana, LJI.
—BLDSC (8611.604980). **CCC.**
Published by: Butterworths Tolley (Subsidiary of: LexisNexis UK (Scottish Office)), Halsbury House, 35 Chancery Ln, London, Mddx WC2A 1EL, United Kingdom. TEL 44-20-74002500, FAX 44-20-7400-2842, order.line@butterworths.co.uk, http://www.butterworths.co.uk/.

TAX LAW DICTIONARY. see *LAW*

TAX LAW REVIEW. see *LAW*

TAX LAWS OF THE WORLD. see *LAW*

343.04   ZAF   ISSN 1017-1193
TAX LIBRARY/BELASTINGBIBLIOTEEK. Text in English. 1989. q. ZAR 1,630. **Description:** Presents all relevant South African statutes and reports pertaining to taxation and revenue.
Media: CD-ROM.
Published by: Juta & Company Ltd., Law and Professional Publishing Division, PO Box 14373, Kenwyn, 7790, South Africa. TEL 27-21-7975101, FAX 27-21-7970121, law@juta.co.za, http://www.juta.co.za.

336   USA
TAX MANAGEMENT COMPENSATION PLANNING. Text in English. 1973. m. USD 961 (effective 1999); includes Compensation Planning Journal. adv. bibl. back issues avail. **Document type:** *Trade.* **Description:** Covers the areas of pensions, employee benefits, profit sharing and welfare plans, and deferred compensation planning.
Formerly: Tax Management Executive Compensation
Related titles: CD-ROM ed.; Online - full text ed.: (from Thomson West); ◆ Series of: Tax Management Compensation Planning Journal. ISSN 0747-8607.
Published by: Tax Management Inc. (Subsidiary of: The Bureau of National Affairs, Inc.), 1231 25th St, N W, Washington, DC 20037. TEL 202-452-4200, 800-372-1033, http://www.bnatax.com. Ed., R&P Glenn B Davis. Adv. contact Barbara Patrick.

336 382   GBR
TAX MANAGEMENT COUNTRY PORTFOLIOS. Text in English. 1972. irreg. GBP 456. back issues avail. **Document type:** *Bulletin.* **Description:** Each portfolio covers an individual country, with complete tax planning guidance on conducting successful business operations in that country.
Formerly: Tax Management International Portfolios
Related titles: CD-ROM ed.; Series of: Tax Management International Series.
Published by: Tax Management Inc. (Subsidiary of: The Bureau of National Affairs, Inc.), Heron House, 10 Dean Farrar St, London, SW1H 0DX, United Kingdom. TEL 44-171-222-8831, FAX 44-171-222-5550.

336.2   USA   ISSN 1087-2922
KF6415.A15
TAX MANAGEMENT FINANCIAL PRODUCTS REPORT. Text in English. 1996. s-m. USD 1,022. back issues avail. **Document type:** *Trade.* **Description:** Focuses on the taxation of financial products.
Related titles: Online - full text ed.
Published by: Tax Management Inc. (Subsidiary of: The Bureau of National Affairs, Inc.), 1231 25th St, N W, Washington, DC 20037. TEL 202-452-4200, 800-372-1033, http://www.bnatax.com. Ed. Glenn B Davis.

336   USA
TAX MANAGEMENT FOREIGN INCOME PORTFOLIOS. Text in English. 1964. bi-m. USD 1,395 (effective 1999); includes Tax Management International Journal. bibl. back issues avail. **Document type:** *Trade.* **Description:** Portfolio service covering tax and related corporate problems arising from the U.S. taxation of foreign income and the conduct of business in selected countries around the world.
Related titles: CD-ROM ed.; Online - full text ed.: (from Thomson West); ◆ Series: Tax Management International Journal. ISSN 0090-4600.
Published by: Tax Management Inc. (Subsidiary of: The Bureau of National Affairs, Inc.), 1231 25th St, N W, Washington, DC 20037. TEL 202-452-4200, 800-372-1033, http://www.bnatax.com. Ed. Glenn B Davis.

336   USA
TAX MANAGEMENT I R S FORMS. Text in English. 1988. base vol. plus irreg. updates. looseleaf. USD 392 (effective 1999). back issues avail.
Related titles: CD-ROM ed.
Published by: Tax Management Inc. (Subsidiary of: The Bureau of National Affairs, Inc.), 1231 25th St, N W, Washington, DC 20037. TEL 202-452-4200, 800-372-1033, http://www.bnatax.com. Ed. Glenn B Davis.

336   USA
TAX MANAGEMENT I R S PRACTICE AND POLICY. Text in English. 1990. m. USD 515 (effective 1999); includes Adviser Reporter. back issues avail. **Document type:** *Trade.* **Description:** Comprehensive discussion of IRS practice from audits through collections. Covers IRS directories and industry specific handbooks that help facilitate dealings with the IRS.
Media: CD-ROM.
Published by: Tax Management Inc. (Subsidiary of: The Bureau of National Affairs, Inc.), 1231 25th St, N W, Washington, DC 20037. TEL 202-452-4200, 800-372-1033, http://www.bnatax.com. Ed. Glenn B Davis.

336   USA
TAX MANAGEMENT I R S PRACTICE & POLICY ADVISER REPORTER. Text in English. 1990. m. USD 515; includes Tax Management I R S Practice and Policy on CD-Rom. back issues avail. **Document type:** *Newsletter, Trade.*
Formerly (until 1997): Tax Management I R S Practice and Policy Bulletin
Published by: Tax Management Inc. (Subsidiary of: The Bureau of National Affairs, Inc.), 1231 25th St, N W, Washington, DC 20037. TEL 202-452-4200, 800-372-1033, http://www.bnatax.com. Ed. Glenn B Davis.

336   GBR   ISSN 0143-7941
K4456.2
TAX MANAGEMENT INTERNATIONAL FORUM. Text in English. 1980. q. EUR 725 in eurozone; USD 725 in US & Canada; GBP 450 elsewhere (effective 2005). index. back issues avail. **Document type:** *Newsletter, Trade.* **Description:** Practioners in major industrial nations discuss problems in international tax law.
Related titles: Online - full text ed.: (from The Bureau of National Affairs, Inc.); ◆ Series of: Tax Planning International. ISSN 0309-7900; ◆ Supplement to: Tax Planning International. ISSN 0309-7900.
—IE. **CCC.**
Published by: B N A International Inc. (Subsidiary of: The Bureau of National Affairs, Inc.), 29th Fl, Millbank Tower, 21-24 Millbank, London, SW1P 4QP, United Kingdom. TEL 44-20-75594800, FAX 44-20-75594848, http://www.bnai.com/templates/products.aspx?cat=10&obj=119&country=1. Ed. Melanie Bond.

336.2   USA   ISSN 0090-4600
K24
TAX MANAGEMENT INTERNATIONAL JOURNAL; a monthly professional review of current international tax developments. Text in English. 1972. m. USD 426 (effective 1999). bk.rev. s-a. index. back issues avail.; reprints avail. **Document type:** *Trade.* **Description:** Review of current international tax, fiscal, and economic developments affecting worldwide business operations.
Related titles: Online - full text ed.: ISSN 1544-0761 (from Northern Light Technology, Inc., O C L C Online Computer Library Center, Inc., ProQuest Information & Learning, The Bureau of National Affairs, Inc.); ◆ Series of: Tax Management Foreign Income Portfolios.
Indexed: ABIn, ATI, BPIA, BusI, CLI, FLP, LRI, RASB.
—CCC.
Published by: Tax Management Inc. (Subsidiary of: The Bureau of National Affairs, Inc.), 1231 25th St, N W, Washington, DC 20037. TEL 202-452-4200, 800-372-1033, http://www.bna.com. Ed. Glenn B Davis.

336   USA   ISSN 0148-8295
KF6289.A1
TAX MANAGEMENT MEMORANDUM. Text in English. 1979. bi-w. USD 335 (effective 1999). index. back issues avail. **Document type:** *Trade.* **Description:** Contains discussion and analysis of a current tax development by Tax Management's Advisory Board.

Related titles: Online - full text ed.: ISSN 1544-077X (from Northern Light Technology, Inc., ProQuest Information & Learning, The Bureau of National Affairs, Inc., Thomson West).
Indexed: ATI, CLI, FamI, LRI.
—CCC.
Published by: Tax Management Inc. (Subsidiary of: The Bureau of National Affairs, Inc.), 1231 25th St, N W, Washington, DC 20037. TEL 202-452-4200, 800-372-1033, http://www.bnatax.com. Ed. Glenn B Davis.

336   USA   ISSN 0738-5285
TAX MANAGEMENT PRIMARY SOURCES. Text in English. 1982. m. looseleaf. USD 1,744 (effective 2005); includes Washington Tax Review. Not available to new subscribers.. back issues avail. **Document type:** *Trade.* **Description:** Covers legislative history of the Internal Revenue Code.
Related titles: Online - full text ed.: (from The Bureau of National Affairs, Inc.); ◆ Series: Tax Management Primary Sources Washington Tax Review. ISSN 0887-2562.
—CCC.
Published by: Tax Management Inc. (Subsidiary of: The Bureau of National Affairs, Inc.), 1231 25th St, N W, Washington, DC 20037. TEL 202-452-4200, 800-372-1033, FAX 202-785-7195, http://www.bnatax.com. Ed. Glenn B Davis.

336   USA   ISSN 0887-2562
KF6272
TAX MANAGEMENT PRIMARY SOURCES WASHINGTON TAX REVIEW. Text in English. 1979. m. USD 219 (effective 1998). index. back issues avail. **Document type:** *Trade.* **Description:** Analysis of tax legislative developments.
Formerly: Washington Tax Review (0737-5875)
Related titles: Online - full text ed.: (from The Bureau of National Affairs, Inc.); ◆ Series of: Tax Management Primary Sources. ISSN 0738-5285.
Indexed: BusI.
—CCC.
Published by: Tax Management Inc. (Subsidiary of: The Bureau of National Affairs, Inc.), 1231 25th St, N W, Washington, DC 20037. TEL 202-452-4200, 800-372-1033, http://www.bnatax.com. Ed. Glenn B Davis.

336   USA
KF6352
TAX MANAGEMENT TAX PRACTICE PLUS AND ALL STATES TAXES PLUS. Text in English. 1990. w. USD 1,385. back issues avail. **Document type:** *Trade.* **Description:** Covers the spectrum of taxation, including U.S. income, foreign income, estates, gifts, and trusts, with hundreds of practice applications, includes "IRS Practice Adviser", a procedural service to assist tax practitioners when dealing with the IRS.
Incorporates (1998-1999): I R S Practice Adviser Report (1097-6574); Former titles: Tax Management Tax Practice Plus for Windows (1097-8569); (until 1997): Tax Management Tax Practice Series for Windows (1096-7737)
Media: CD-ROM. **Related titles:** Online - full text ed.: (from The Bureau of National Affairs, Inc.).
—CCC.
Published by: Tax Management Inc. (Subsidiary of: The Bureau of National Affairs, Inc.), 1231 25th St, N W, Washington, DC 20037. TEL 202-452-4200, 800-372-1033, http://www.bnatax.com. Ed. Glenn B Davis.

336   USA   ISSN 1083-7345
TAX MANAGEMENT TAX PRACTICE SERIES BULLETIN. Text in English. 1989. bi-w. USD 113 (effective 1999). back issues avail. **Document type:** *Newsletter.*
Formerly (until 1990): Tax Practice Bulletin (1044-7261)
Related titles: Online - full text ed.: ISSN 1544-4724 (from The Bureau of National Affairs, Inc.).
—CCC.
Published by: Tax Management Inc. (Subsidiary of: The Bureau of National Affairs, Inc.), 1231 25th St, N W, Washington, DC 20037. TEL 202-452-4200, 800-372-1033, http://www.bnatax.com. Ed. Glenn B Davis.

336   USA   ISSN 0494-8270
KF6289.A1
TAX MANAGEMENT TRANSFER PRICING PORTFOLIO SERIES. Text in English. 1995. bi-w. USD 2,068 (effective 1999). back issues avail.
Related titles: Online - full text ed.: (from The Bureau of National Affairs, Inc.).
—CCC.
Published by: Tax Management Inc. (Subsidiary of: The Bureau of National Affairs, Inc.), 1231 25th St, N W, Washington, DC 20037. TEL 202-452-4200, 800-372-1033, http://www.bnatax.com. Ed. Glenn B Davis.

336   GBR   ISSN 1063-2069
KF6461.5
TAX MANAGEMENT TRANSFER PRICING REPORT; a biweekly update on transfer pricing and related issues. Text in English. 1992. bi-w. USD 1,472 (effective 2004). back issues avail. **Document type:** *Magazine, Trade.* **Description:** Focuses exclusively on transfer pricing. Includes regulatory activity, legislative developments, court cases and analysis with practical insight into developments in the area of transfer pricing.
Related titles: Online - full text ed.: ISSN 1521-7760 (from The Bureau of National Affairs, Inc.).

▼ *new title*   ➤ *refereed*   ✳ *unverified*   ◆ *full entry avail.*

—CCC.
Published by: B N A International Inc. (Subsidiary of: The Bureau of National Affairs, Inc.), 29th Fl, Millbank Tower, 21-24 Millbank, London, SW1P 4QP, United Kingdom. TEL 44-20-75594800, FAX 44-20-75594848, bnai@bna.com, http://www.bnai.com.

336 USA
TAX MANAGEMENT U S INCOME. Text in English. 1959. bi-w. USD 2,592; includes Tax Management Weekly Report, Tax Management Revenue Forms Service and Tax Management Memorandum. bibl. back issues avail. **Document type:** *Trade.* **Description:** Portfolio and journal service covering tax planning problems related to federal taxation of domestic income.
Related titles: CD-ROM ed.; Online - full text ed.: (from Thomson West).
Published by: Tax Management Inc. (Subsidiary of: The Bureau of National Affairs, Inc.), 1231 25th St, N W, Washington, DC 20037. TEL 202-452-4200, 800-372-1033, http://www.bnatax.com. Ed. Glenn B Davis.

336 USA ISSN 0884-6057
KF6272
TAX MANAGEMENT WEEKLY REPORT. Text in English. 1982. w. USD 1,073 (effective 1999). back issues avail. **Document type:** *Trade.* **Description:** Reports developments affecting taxation and the tax aspects of accounting. Covers summaries of federal cases including the U.S. Tax Court, synopses of the I.R.S. general counsel and technical advice memoranda, analysis of noteworthy I.R.S. revenue ruling, procedures and private letter ruling, and status reports of Treasury Department actions on pending regulations.
Formerly: B N A's Weekly Tax Report (0733-0405)
Related titles: Online - full text ed.: (from The Bureau of National Affairs, Inc., Thomson West).
Indexed: ATI.
—CCC.
Published by: Tax Management Inc. (Subsidiary of: The Bureau of National Affairs, Inc.), 1231 25th St, N W, Washington, DC 20037. TEL 202-452-4200, 800-372-1033, http://www.bnatax.com. Ed. Glenn B Davis.

336.2 USA ISSN 1534-1550
TAX MANAGEMENT WEEKLY STATE TAX REPORT. Text in English. 1997. w. USD 647 (effective 1999). back issues avail. **Document type:** *Newsletter, Trade.* **Description:** Provides state-by-state analysis of state code and regulations, state administrative and judicial court decisions, and state administrative pronouncements.
Formerly (until 2000): Tax Management Multistate Tax Electronic Weekly Report (1521-9895)
Media: Online - full text (from The Bureau of National Affairs, Inc.).
—CCC.
Published by: Tax Management Inc. (Subsidiary of: The Bureau of National Affairs, Inc.), 1231 25th St, N W, Washington, DC 20037. TEL 202-452-4200, 800-372-1033, http://www.bnatax.com. Ed. George R Farrah.

336 USA ISSN 1083-2289
TAX MANAGEMENT'S MULTISTATE TAX PORTFOLIO SERIES. Text in English. 1994. m. USD 1,455 (effective 2005). back issues avail. **Description:** Provides a comprehensive multi-state discussion of all aspects of a particular state tax planning problems. Also contains detailed citations to state code and regulations, state administrative and judicial court decisions, and state administrative pronouncements.
Related titles: CD-ROM ed.; Online - full text ed.: (from The Bureau of National Affairs, Inc.).
—CCC.
Published by: Tax Management Inc. (Subsidiary of: The Bureau of National Affairs, Inc.), 1231 25th St, N W, Washington, DC 20037. TEL 202-452-4200, 800-372-1033, http://www.bnatax.com. Ed. Glenn B Davis.

336 343.05 USA ISSN 0279-0211
TAX NEWS. Text in English. 2/yr. membership. back issues avail. **Document type:** *Newsletter.*
Published by: (Taxation Section), State Bar of Wisconsin, 5302 Eastpark Blvd, Madison, WI 53718. FAX 608-257-5502, service@wisbar.org. Circ: 850.

336.2 NLD ISSN 0040-0076
K4456.2
TAX NEWS SERVICE. Text in English. 1965. w. looseleaf. USD 470 for print or online edition (effective 2002). q. index, cum.index. back issues avail. **Document type:** *Newsletter.* **Description:** Covers current developments in international taxation.
Related titles: Online - full text ed.: Tax News Service Online. USD 470 (effective 2002) (from Swets Information Services).
Indexed: RASB.
Published by: (International Bureau of Fiscal Documentation), I B F D Publications BV, H J E Wenckebachweg 210, PO Box 20237, Amsterdam, 1000 HE, Netherlands. TEL 31-20-554-0100, FAX 31-20-620-8626, info@ibfd.nl, http://www.ibfd.nl.

336 320 USA ISSN 0270-5494
KF6272
TAX NOTES; the weekly tax service. Text in English. 1972. w. USD 2,000 (effective 2005). index. **Document type:** *Journal, Academic/Scholarly.* **Description:** Provides in-depth coverage of tax news from all federal sources, together with summaries of all tax documents and decisions released each week, and analytical articles and commentary.
Related titles: CD-ROM ed.; Online - full text ed.: (from LexisNexis, The Dialog Corporation).
Indexed: ATI, BusI, CLI, FamI, LRI, LegCont, T&II.
—CCC.
Published by: Tax Analysts, 6830 N Fairfax Dr, Arlington, VA 22213. TEL 703-553-4400, 800-955-3444, FAX 703-533-4444, http://www.taxanalysts.com/www/website.nsf/Web/TaxNotes?OpenDocument. Ed. Christopher Bergin. Circ: (controlled).

336 USA ISSN 1048-3306
K4471.2
TAX NOTES INTERNATIONAL. Text in English. 1979. w. USD 949 (effective 1999). back issues avail. **Description:** Features international tax news and commentary from a worldwide reporting staff along with summaries of statutes, regulations, rulings, court decisions and tax treaties.
Formerly (until 1989): Taxes International (0142-6877)
Related titles: Online - full text ed.: (from The Dialog Corporation).
Indexed: CLI, FamI, LRI.
—BLDSC (8611.608100), ingenta. **CCC.**
Published by: Tax Analysts, 6830 N Fairfax Dr, Arlington, VA 22213. TEL 703-553-4400, 800-955-3444, FAX 703-533-4444. Ed., R&P Susan M Lyons. Pub. Thomas F Field.

336.2 USA ISSN 1058-3971
TAX NOTES INTERNATIONAL WEEKLY NEWS. Text in English. 1991. w.
Related titles: Online - full text ed.: (from LexisNexis).
—BLDSC (8611.608100), IE. **CCC.**
Published by: Tax Analysts, 6830 N Fairfax Dr, Arlington, VA 22213. TEL 703-553-4400, 800-955-3444, FAX 703-533-4444, http://www.taxanalysts.com.

TAX PENALTIES AND INTEREST. see *LAW*

336 USA
TAX PENALTIES AND INTEREST HANDBOOK. Text in English. 1991. base vol. plus a. updates. looseleaf. USD 80. **Description:** Covers all federal and state penalty and interest sections of the Internal Revenue Code.
Published by: LexisNexis (Subsidiary of: LexisNexis North America), PO Box 7587, Charlottesville, VA 22906-7587. TEL 804-972-7600, 800-562-1197, FAX 804-972-7666, llp.customer.support@lexis-nexis.com, http://www.lexislawpublishing.com. Eds. David Minars, Howard Davidoff.

336.2 IND
TAX PLANNING. Text in English, Gujarati. 1975. m. INR 250. adv.
Published by: Swati Prakashan, Purvalaya Building, 14-15 Ramkrishna Nagar, Rajkot, Gujarat 360 002, India. Ed. P C Parekh.

336 346.066 USA
TAX PLANNING FOR CORPORATE ACQUISITIONS✶ . Text in English. 1988. base vol. plus irreg. updates. **Document type:** *Trade.*
Published by: R I A (Subsidiary of: Thomson Corporation), 395 Hudson St, New York, NY 10014. TEL 212-367- 6300, 212-367-6300. Ed. George Brode.

336.2 USA
TAX PLANNING FOR CORPORATIONS AND SHAREHOLDERS. Text in English. 1974. base vol. plus irreg. updates. looseleaf. USD 241 base vol(s). (effective 2002). **Description:** Offers attorneys, accountants and corporate management the most thorough coverage and practical guidance. Covers all vital areasufrom accumulated earnings to corporate reorganizations; from deferred compensation agreements to stock dividends; from going public to professional corporations and limited liability companies; from purchase and sale of businesses to trusts.
Related titles: CD-ROM ed.
Indexed: ATI.
Published by: Matthew Bender & Co., Inc. (Subsidiary of: LexisNexis North America), 1275 Broadway, Albany, NY 12204. international@bender.com, http://bender.lexisnexis.com. Ed. Zolman Cavitch.

TAX PLANNING FOR CORPORATIONS AND SHAREHOLDERS: FORMS. see *LAW—Corporate Law*

336.2 USA
TAX PLANNING FOR THE ALTERNATIVE MINIMUM TAX. Text in English. 1989. base vol. plus s-a. updates. looseleaf. USD 266 base vol(s). (effective 2005). **Description:** covers the ACE and book income adjustments, AMT depreciation rules, AMT treatment of net operating losses, the minimum tax credit, AMT treatment of passive activity losses and Trust and estate issues.
Related titles: CD-ROM ed.
Published by: Matthew Bender & Co., Inc. (Subsidiary of: LexisNexis North America), 1275 Broadway, Albany, NY 12204. TEL 518-487-3575, 800-252-9257, FAX 518-462-3788, international@bender.com, http://bender.lexisnexis.com. Ed. Lance Rook.

336.2 USA ISSN 0040-0092
KF6296.A15
TAX PLANNING IDEAS✶ . Text in English. 1970 (vol.17). s-m. (in 3 vols.). USD 66. adv. bk.rev. charts. reprint service avail. from PQC.
Related titles: Microform ed.: 1970 (vol.17) (from PQC).
Indexed: LII.
Published by: Macmillan Information Company Inc., 90 Fifth Ave, New York, NY 10011-7629. TEL 800-562-0245, FAX 201-816-3569.

336 GBR ISSN 0309-7900
K4464.A13
TAX PLANNING INTERNATIONAL; a monthly journal of international tax planning, development and opportunities. Text in English. 1981. m. index. back issues avail. **Document type:** *Academic/Scholarly.* **Description:** Covers international tax-planning developments and opportunities, including country surveys and tax treaty developments.
Incorporated: Tax Haven Review
Related titles: Online - full text ed.: (from The Bureau of National Affairs, Inc.); ♦ Series: Tax Management International Forum. ISSN 0143-7941; ♦ Supplement(s): Tax Management International Forum. ISSN 0143-7941; Tax Planning International Taxgram. ISSN 0141-8939. 1978; Asia - Pacific Focus. ISSN 1460-7050. 1997.
Indexed: ATI.
—IE, Infotrieve. **CCC.**
Published by: B N A International Inc. (Subsidiary of: The Bureau of National Affairs, Inc.), 29th Fl, Millbank Tower, 21-24 Millbank, London, SW1P 4QP, United Kingdom. TEL 44-20-75594800, FAX 44-20-75594848, bnai@bna.com, http://www.bnai.com. Ed. Deborah Russell.

336 GBR
TAX PLANNING INTERNATIONAL ASIA-PACIFIC FOCUS. Text in English. q. **Document type:** *Newsletter, Trade.* **Description:** Contains tax news and feature articles for those trading within or into Asia-Pacific jurisdictions.
Related titles: Online - full text ed.
Published by: (The Bureau of National Affairs, Inc. USA), B N A International Inc. (Subsidiary of: The Bureau of National Affairs, Inc.), 29th Fl, Millbank Tower, 21-24 Millbank, London, SW1P 4QP, United Kingdom. TEL 44-20-75594800, FAX 44-20-75594848, taxeditorial@bna.com, marketing@bnai.com, http://www.bnai.com. Ed. Lillian Adams. Pub. Deborah Russell.

336 GBR
TAX PLANNING INTERNATIONAL E-COMMERCE. Text in English. m. **Document type:** *Trade.* **Description:** Contains detailed, expert analysis of the latest developments in the taxation of electronic commerce worldwide.
Related titles: Online - full text ed.
Published by: (The Bureau of National Affairs, Inc. USA), B N A International Inc. (Subsidiary of: The Bureau of National Affairs, Inc.), 29th Fl, Millbank Tower, 21-24 Millbank, London, SW1P 4QP, United Kingdom. TEL 44-20-75594800, FAX 44-20-75594848, taxeditorial@bna.com, marketing@bnai.com, http://www.bnai.com. Ed. Lillian Adams. Pub. Deborah Russell.

336 GBR ISSN 1464-8911
KJE7128.A15
TAX PLANNING INTERNATIONAL EUROPEAN UNION FOCUS. Text in English. 2001. 10/yr. USD 895 print & online eds. (effective 2004). **Document type:** *Journal, Trade.* **Description:** Contains detailed, expert analysis of planning issues arising from the implementation of European Union tax developments.
Related titles: Online - full text ed.: (from The Bureau of National Affairs, Inc.).
—CCC.
Published by: (The Bureau of National Affairs, Inc. USA), B N A International Inc. (Subsidiary of: The Bureau of National Affairs, Inc.), 29th Fl, Millbank Tower, 21-24 Millbank, London, SW1P 4QP, United Kingdom. TEL 44-20-75594800, FAX 44-20-75594848, taxeditorial@bna.com, marketing@bnai.com, http://www.bnai.com. Ed. Melanie Bond. Pub. Deborah Russell.

336 GBR
TAX PLANNING INTERNATIONAL TRANSFER PRICING. Text in English. 2001. m. **Document type:** *Trade.* **Description:** Contains detailed, expert analysis of legislative developments in the growing world of transfer pricing regulation.
Published by: (The Bureau of National Affairs, Inc. USA), B N A International Inc. (Subsidiary of: The Bureau of National Affairs, Inc.), 29th Fl, Millbank Tower, 21-24 Millbank, London, SW1P 4QP, United Kingdom. TEL 44-20-75594800, FAX 44-20-75594848, taxeditorial@bna.com, marketing@bnai.com, http://www.bnai.com. Ed., Pub. Deborah Russell.

336.2 USA ISSN 1541-8871
KF6297.Z9
TAX PLANNING STRATEGIES. Text in English. a. USD 24 newsstand/cover (effective 2002).

Former titles (until 2001): Year-End Tax Strategies; (until 1991): Year-End Tax Planning for Returns to be Filed in
Published by: C C H Inc., 2700 Lake Cook Rd, Riverwoods, IL 60015. TEL 800-248-3248, http://www.tax.cch.com.

336 USA ISSN 0892-8649
HJ10.3
TAX POLICY AND THE ECONOMY. Text in English. 1987. a., latest vol.17. price varies. 190 p./no.; back issues avail.; reprint service avail. from PQC. **Document type:** *Monographic series, Academic/Scholarly.* **Description:** Covers issues in the current tax debate, focusing on the economic effects of tax policies. Geared toward policymakers, corporate managers, lawyers and economists.
Related titles: Online - full text ed.: ISSN 1537-2650 (from EBSCO Publishing, Gale Group, IngentaConnect, O C L C Online Computer Library Center, Inc., Swets Information Services).
Indexed: JEL.
—BLDSC (8611.611000), IE, Infotrieve, ingenta. **CCC.**
Published by: (National Bureau of Economic Research), M I T Press, 55 Hayward St, Cambridge, MA 02142-1493. TEL 617-253-5646, FAX 617-258-6779, journals-info@mit.edu, http://mitpress.mit.edu. Ed. James M Poterba. Pub. Paul Dzus.

336 USA ISSN 1086-0088
KF6300.A15
TAX PRACTICE✶. Text in English. 1993. w. USD 199 (effective 1999). q. index. back issues avail. **Document type:** *Journal, Trade.* **Description:** Provides a weekly guide to tax developments including IRS rulings and regulations, tax developments in congress and tax decisions from the courts. Ideal for the busy tax practitioner needing to keep up on all new developments.
Formerly (until 1995): Tax Practice and Controversies (1074-5858); Which was formed by the merger of (1991-1993): I R S Tax Practice Insider (1063-4932); (1991-1993): Tax-Related Documents (1062-9106); Which was formerly (until 1992): Tax-Related Administrative Documents (1060-9865)
Related titles: Online - full text ed.: (from LexisNexis).
—CCC.
Published by: Tax Analysts, 6830 N Fairfax Dr, Arlington, VA 22213. TEL 703-553-4400, 800-955-3444, FAX 703-533-4444. Ed. Robert Manning. Pub. Thomas Field.

350 USA
TAX PRACTICE DESKBOOK. Text in English. base vol. plus a. updates. USD 105. Supplement avail. **Document type:** *Trade.*
Formerly: Freeman and Freeman's Tax Practice Deskbook (Supplement)
Published by: W G & L Financial Reporting & Management Research (Subsidiary of: R I A), 90 Fifth Ave, New York, NY 10011. TEL 212-645-4800, FAX 212-337-4280.

336.2 GBR ISSN 0269-3720
TAX PRACTITIONER'S DIARY. Text in English. a. GBP 21.95. **Document type:** *Trade.* **Description:** Covers income including corporate, inheritance, and value-added taxes, as well as national insurance contributions and stamp duties. Also included is a comprehensive list of tax district addresses and collection offices throughout the U.K.
Published by: Butterworths Tolley (Subsidiary of: LexisNexis UK (Scottish Office)), Halsbury House, 35 Chancery Ln, London, Mddx WC2A 1EL, United Kingdom. TEL 44-20-74002500, FAX 44-20-74002583, order.line@butterworths.co.uk, http://www.butterworths.co.uk/.

336 CAN ISSN 0827-3677
KE5662
TAX PROFILE. Text in English. m. looseleaf. CND 398 (effective 2005). **Document type:** *Trade.* **Description:** Comments on items of interest regarding federal income tax and other federal and provincial taxes.
Related titles: CD-ROM ed.: CND 366 (effective 2005); Online - full text ed.: CND 356 (effective 2005) (from QuickLaw Inc.).
Published by: C C H Canadian Ltd., 90 Sheppard Ave E, Ste 300, North York, ON M2N 6X1, Canada. TEL 416-224-2248, 800-268-4522, FAX 416-224-2243, cservice@cch.ca, http://www.cch.ca.

343.04 AUS ISSN 1441-7596
TAX RATES AND TABLES (PYRMONT). Text in English. 1988. a. looseleaf. AUD 180 (effective 2003). **Document type:** *Trade.* **Description:** Covers Australian tax rates, tax calendars, depreciation rates, and other useful information.
Former titles (until 1998): Australian Tax Rates & Tables (1327-8738); (until 1996): Tax Rates and Tables (Sydney) (1034-8131)
Related titles: CD-ROM ed.; Diskette ed.
Published by: Australian Tax Practice (Subsidiary of: Thomson Legal & Regulatory Ltd.), PO Box 3502, Rozelle, NSW 2039, Australia. ATPOnlineService@thomson.com.au, http://onlineecom01.thomson.com.au/thomson/Catalog.asp?EES_CMD=SI&EES_ID=100196, http://www.atp-online.com.au/.

336.2 USA
TAX RESOURCES TAX TIPS EMAIL UPDATE. Text in English. bi-w. **Description:** Keeps readers current with what is important in the tax world, including money-saving tax tips.
Media: Online - full text.
Published by: Tax Resources, 310 Ultimo Ave, Long Beach, CA 90814-3209. http://www.taxaudit.com/.

336.2 USA ISSN 1059-6356
CODEN: CTLAA8
TAX RETURN PREPARER'S LETTER. Text in English. m. USD 211 (effective 2004). **Document type:** *Newsletter.* **Description:** Covers new tax developments, and critical information on new tax forms and procedures.
Related titles: Online - full text ed.: (from Florida Center for Library Automation, Gale Group).
Indexed: ATI.
Published by: Aspen Publishers, Inc. (Subsidiary of: Wolters Kluwer N.V.), 111Eighth Ave., 7th Fl, New York, NY 10011. TEL 212-771-0600, FAX 212-771-0885, customer.service@aspenpubl.com, http://www.aspenpublishers.com. Ed. Terrence Myers. **Subscr. to:** Customer Care, 7201 McKinney Circle, Frederick, MD 21704. TEL 800-234-1660, FAX 800-901-9075.

336 USA
TAX SAVINGS REPORT. Text in English. 1982. 10/yr. looseleaf. USD 29 (effective 1999 & 2000). index. back issues avail. **Document type:** *Newsletter.* **Description:** Provides income tax advice for individuals and small business owners, including filing and deduction strategies, recordkeeping, and dealing with audits.
Published by: National Taxpayers Union, 108 N Alfred St, Alexandria, VA 22314. TEL 703-683-5700, FAX 703-683-5722. Ed., R&P Ellen Katz TEL 703-560-9129. Circ: 22,000 (paid).

336.2 AUS
➤ **TAX SPECIALIST.** Text in English. 1991. 5/yr. AUD 265 to members (effective 2002). index. back issues avail. **Document type:** *Academic/Scholarly.* **Description:** Provides academic and specialist articles on taxation.
Formerly: Taxation in Australia (Red Edition) (1039-2572)
Indexed: AusPAIS.
Published by: Taxation Institute of Australia, 9th Fl., 64 Castlereagh St, Sydney, NSW 2000, Australia. TEL 61-2-92323422, FAX 61-2-92216953, publications@taxinstitute.com.au, http://www.taxinstitute.com.au/. R&P Alex Moham. Adv. contact Deborah Patison. Circ: 1,500 (paid).

336.2 USA
TAX TALK. Text in English. q. free to members. **Document type:** *Newsletter, Trade.*
Published by: Indiana Manufacturers Association, Inc., One American Sq., Ste 2400, Indianapolis, IN 46282. TEL 317-632-2474, FAX 317-231-2320, ima@imaweb.com, http://www.imaweb.com. Ed. Charlene Hickey. Adv. contact Scott Ford.

336.2 IND ISSN 0040-0122
TAX TIMES. Text in Hindi. 1965. w. looseleaf. INR 45, USD 2. adv. bk.rev. illus.
Published by: Tax Times Trust/Nathoo Rem Jain, Sarafa, Jhansi, Uttar Pradesh, India. Circ: 2,000.

336 USA
TAX TREATIES (NEW YORK); federal income taxation of corporations and shareholders. Text in English. 1969. 3/yr. **Document type:** *Trade.* **Description:** Provides up-to-date analysis of international tax agreements. Includes full official text of every treaty and protocol relating to income, gift and estate taxes.
Media: CD-ROM.
Published by: W G & L Financial Reporting & Management Research (Subsidiary of: R I A), 90 Fifth Ave, New York, NY 10011. TEL 212-645-4800, FAX 212-337-4280. **Subscr. to:** 117 E Stevens Ave,, Valhalla, NY 10595.

538 USA ISSN 0414-0176
TAX TREATIES (RIVERWOODS). Text in English. 4 base vols. plus m. updates. looseleaf. USD 693 base vol(s). (effective 2004). **Description:** Reproduces the full text of U.S. bilateral income, estate and gift tax treaties, exchange of information, totalization (social security), shipping/aircraft tax treaties, protocols, and other related documents on taxation agreements—all arranged alphabetically by country.
Related titles: CD-ROM ed.: USD 654 (effective 2004); Online - full text ed.
—CCC.
Published by: C C H Inc., 2700 Lake Cook Rd, Riverwoods, IL 60015. TEL 847-267-7000, 800-449-6439, FAX 800-224-8299, cust_serv@cch.com, http://www.cch.com. Pub. Kevin Robert.

336.2 NLD
TAX TREATIES DATA BASE ON CD-ROM. Text in English. q. USD 1,520 (effective 2002). **Document type:** *Trade.* **Description:** Provides full text of tax treaties and protocols, including OECD and UN draft and model conventions, in searchable format.
Media: CD-ROM. **Related titles:** Diskette ed.; Online - full text ed.
Published by: (International Bureau of Fiscal Documentation), I B F D Publications BV, H J E Wenckebachweg 210, PO Box 20237, Amsterdam, 1000 HE, Netherlands. TEL 31-20-554-0100, FAX 31-20-620-8626, http://www.ibfd.nl.

336 NLD
TAX TREATMENT OF CROSS-BORDER DONATIONS; including the tax status of charities and foundations. Text in English. 1994. base vol. plus a. updates. looseleaf. USD 185 base vol(s).; USD 70 updates (effective 2002). **Document type:** *Trade.* **Description:** Studies the treatment of charitable non-governmental organizations in over 25 countries, covering tax status and the taxation of donations, and international aspects such as the relevant provisions of tax treaties.
Published by: (International Bureau of Fiscal Documentation), I B F D Publications BV, H J E Wenckebachweg 210, PO Box 20237, Amsterdam, 1000 HE, Netherlands. TEL 31-20-554-0100, FAX 31-20-620-8626, info@ibfd.nl, http://www.ibfd.nl. Ed. Paul Bater.

336 NLD
THE TAX TREATMENT OF TRANSFER PRICING. Text in English. 1987. 6 base vols. plus s-a. updates. looseleaf. USD 1,360 base vol(s).; USD 585 updates (effective 2002). **Document type:** *Trade.* **Description:** Provides in-depth, country-by-country surveys of transfer pricing compiled by leading international tax experts for 20 nations.
Published by: (International Bureau of Fiscal Documentation), I B F D Publications BV, H J E Wenckebachweg 210, PO Box 20237, Amsterdam, 1000 HE, Netherlands. TEL 31-20-554-0100, FAX 31-20-620-8626, info@ibfd.nl, http://www.ibfd.nl. Ed. Rijkele Betten.

336.2 340 ZAF
TAX UPDATE. Text in English. irreg. free.
Related titles: Online - full text ed.
Published by: Deneys Reitz Attorneys, PO Box 61334, Marshalltown, Johannesburg 2107, South Africa. TEL 27-11-8335600, FAX 27-11-8387444, jhb@deneysreitz.co.za, http://www.deneysreitz.co.za. Ed. Patrick Bracher. R&P Jacqui Hampton.

336.2 IND
TAX-VYAPAR; periodical devoted to problems of commerce and taxes. Text in English. 1968. m. INR 200. adv. index.
Related titles: Gujarati ed.; Hindi ed.
Published by: Swati Prakashan, Purvalaya Building, 14-15 Ramkrishna Nagar, Rajkot, Gujarat 360 002, India. Ed. P C Parekh.

336.205 USA
TAX WATCH. Text in English. 1992 (vol.5, no.2). q. membership. **Document type:** *Newsletter.* **Description:** Covers issues relating to tax reform and citizen initiatives.
Published by: South Carolina Association of Taxpayers, PO Box 50799, Columbia, SC 29250. TEL 803-782-6913.

336.2 GBR ISSN 0040-0149
HJ2600
TAXATION; leading authority on tax law practice and administration in the UK. Text in English. 1927. w. GBP 242 (effective 2005). adv. bk.rev. stat. s-a. index. **Document type:** *Magazine, Trade.* **Description:** Provides news and comment on legal decisions for all those engaged in tax work. Changes in legislation and items affecting tax practice are presented in a manageable and digestible format.
Related titles: Online - full text ed.
Indexed: CLI, ELJI, FamI, LJI, LRI, RICS.
—BLDSC (8611.650000), IE, ingenta.
Published by: Butterworths Tolley (Subsidiary of: LexisNexis UK (Scottish Office)), 2 Addiscombe Rd, Croydon, Surrey CR9 5AF, United Kingdom. TEL 44-20-8686-9141, FAX 44-20-8686-3155, sales@tolley.co.uk, http://www.taxation.co.uk/, http://www.butterworths.co.uk. Ed. Mike Truman TEL 44-20-82121949. Adv. contact Zoe Kray TEL 44-20-82121925. Circ: 13,000.

336.2 PAK ISSN 0040-0157
TAXATION. Text and summaries in English. 1959. m. PKR 110. charts.
Indexed: LRI.
Published by: Taxation Publishers, 6 Liaqat Rd., Lahore 6, Pakistan. Ed. S M Raza Nqvi.

336.2 IND
TAXATION. Text in English. 1948. m. INR 425. adv. bk.rev.
Address: 174 Jorbagh, New Delhi, 110 003, India. Ed. B B Bhargava. Circ: 6,000.

336.2 NLD
TAXATION & INVESTMENT IN CANADA. Text in English. 2 base vols. plus s-a. updates. looseleaf. USD 350 base vol(s).; USD 150 updates (effective 2002). **Document type:** *Trade.* **Description:** Outlines and clarifies the laws and systems of both federal and provincial governments.
Formerly: Taxes and Investment in Canada and the U S A
Published by: (International Bureau of Fiscal Documentation), I B F D Publications BV, H J E Wenckebachweg 210, PO Box 20237, Amsterdam, 1000 HE, Netherlands. TEL 31-20-554-0100, FAX 31-20-620-8626, info@ibfd.nl, http://www.ibfd.nl.

B

336 NLD
TAXATION & INVESTMENT IN MEXICO. Text in English. 1994. base vol. plus s-a. updates. looseleaf. USD 320 base vol(s).; USD 150 updates (effective 2002). **Document type:** *Trade.* **Description:** Covers taxation of resident and non-resident individuals and businesses in Mexico, including taxation of capital and capital transfers.
Published by: (International Bureau of Fiscal Documentation), I B F D Publications BV, H J E Wenckebachweg 210, PO Box 20237, Amsterdam, 1000 HE, Netherlands. TEL 31-20-554-0100, FAX 31-20-620-8626, info@ibfd.nl, http://www.ibfd.nl.

336.2 332.6 NLD
TAXATION & INVESTMENT IN SOUTH AFRICA. Text in English. 1994. 2 base vols. plus a. updates. looseleaf. USD 320 base vol(s).; USD 150 updates (effective 2002). **Document type:** *Trade.* **Description:** Provides detailed information on business and taxation in South Africa, including income tax, VAT, capital transfer taxes and exchange controls.
Published by: (International Bureau of Fiscal Documentation), I B F D Publications BV, H J E Wenckebachweg 210, PO Box 20237, Amsterdam, 1000 HE, Netherlands. TEL 31-20-554-0100, FAX 31-20-620-8626, info@ibfd.nl, http://www.ibfd.nl.

336.2 NLD
TAXATION & INVESTMENT IN THE CARIBBEAN. Text in English. 6 base vols. plus s-a. updates. looseleaf. USD 1,090 base vol(s).; USD 420 updates (effective 2002). **Document type:** *Trade.* **Description:** Provides a description of the economic situation in each country, a detailed account of the income tax systems and the incentives available for investment.
Published by: (International Bureau of Fiscal Documentation), I B F D Publications BV, H J E Wenckebachweg 210, PO Box 20237, Amsterdam, 1000 HE, Netherlands. TEL 31-20-554-0100, FAX 31-20-620-8626, info@ibfd.nl, http://www.ibfd.nl. Ed. Elizabeth de Brauw.

336.2 NLD
TAXATION & INVESTMENT IN THE PEOPLE'S REPUBLIC OF CHINA. Text in English. base vol. plus updates 3/yr. looseleaf. USD 320 base vol(s).; USD 150 updates (effective 2002). **Document type:** *Trade.* **Description:** Provides an in-depth analysis of the economy and of the various openings for economic development and business expansion. Allows opportunities and risks to be calculated, potential problems to be identified and provides necessary background information to formulate investment strategies.
Incorporates: Foreign - Related Tax Laws and Regulations of the People's Republic of China
Published by: (International Bureau of Fiscal Documentation), I B F D Publications BV, H J E Wenckebachweg 210, PO Box 20237, Amsterdam, 1000 HE, Netherlands. TEL 31-20-554-0100, FAX 31-20-620-8626, info@ibfd.nl, http://www.ibfd.nl. Ed. Peter Hann.

354.8 USA
TAXATION AND REVENUE POLICIES - STATE CAPITALS. Cover title: State Capitals Newsletters. Taxation and Revenue Policies. Text in English. 1943. 48/yr. USD 365 (effective 2005). back issues avail. **Document type:** *Newsletter.* **Description:** Reports on court rulings and decisions relating to efforts of states to generate revenue. Covers such activities as sales and excise taxes; business, occupation, inheritance, gasoline, bank, and capital gains taxes; and lotteries.
Former titles: From the State Capitals. Taxation and Revenue Policies (0749-2820); (until 1985): From the State Capitals. Taxation and Revenue (0741-3556); (until 1984): From the State Capitals. Taxes: Non-Property (0734-0915); (until 1982): From the State Capitals. Taxes: Local Non-Property (0734-1180)
Related titles: Online - full text ed.: USD 325 per issue (effective 2001) (from Thomson West).
—CCC.
Published by: State Capitals Newsletters, PO Box 7376, Alexandria, VA 22307-7376. TEL 703-768-9600, FAX 703-768-9690, newsletters@statecapitals.com, http://www.statecapitals.com. Pub. Keyes Walworth.

336.2 GBR
TAXATION FOR EMPLOYMENT SPECIALISTS. Text in English. 2000 (June). irreg. GBP 76.95 (effective 2000). **Document type:** *Academic/Scholarly.* **Description:** Deals with the complex field of tax on employment earnings.
Published by: Butterworths Tolley (Subsidiary of: LexisNexis UK (Scottish Office)), Halsbury House, 35 Chancery Ln, London, Mddx WC2A 1EL, United Kingdom. TEL 44-20-74002500, FAX 44-20-7400-2848, order.line@butterworths.co.uk, http://www.butterworths.co.uk/. Eds. Jonathan Maugham, Jonathan Peacock.

336.2 AUS ISSN 0494-8343
K24
➤ **TAXATION IN AUSTRALIA.** Text in English. 1963. m. c/w membership. adv. bk.rev. index. back issues avail. **Document type:** *Academic/Scholarly.* **Description:** Provides tax information for members of the institute including tax rulings, determinations and cases.
Related titles: Online - full text ed.: (from R M I T Publishing).
Indexed: ATI, AusPAIS.
Published by: Taxation Institute of Australia, 9th Fl., 64 Castlereagh St, Sydney, NSW 2000, Australia. TEL 61-2-92323422, FAX 61-2-92216953, publications@taxinstitute.com.au, http://www.taxinstitute.com.au/cda/journals/1,1314,1,00.html. Ed. Robert Allerdie. R&P Alex Moham. Adv. contact Deborah Patison. Circ: 10,000 (controlled).

336.1 NLD
TAXATION IN LATIN AMERICA. Text in English. 4 base vols. plus q. updates. looseleaf. USD 1,060 base vol(s).; USD 600 updates (effective 2002). bibl. **Document type:** *Trade.* **Description:** Documents the legal and taxation systems in full, includes practical, detailed sections on investment.
Formerly: Corporate Taxation in Latin America
Related titles: CD-ROM ed.
Published by: (International Bureau of Fiscal Documentation), I B F D Publications BV, H J E Wenckebachweg 210, PO Box 20237, Amsterdam, 1000 HE, Netherlands. TEL 31-20-554-0100, FAX 31-20-620-8626, info@ibfd.nl, http://www.ibfd.nl. Ed. David Hughes.

336.2 IND
TAXATION LAW REPORTS. Text in English. 1971. m. INR 1,260, USD 74 (effective 2000). adv. bk.rev. bibl.
Published by: All India Reporter Ltd., Congress Nagar, P O Box 209, Nagpur, Maharastra 440 012, India. TEL 91-712-534321, FAX 91-712-526283. Ed. V R Manohar. Circ: 1,500.

336.2 340 GBR
TAXATION OF COMPANIES AND COMPANY RECONSTRUCTIONS. Text in English. 2002. 2 base vols. plus updates 2/yr. looseleaf. GBP 308 base vol(s).; GBP 235, EUR 354 updates in Europe; GBP 245, USD 445 updates elsewhere (effective 2006). **Document type:** *Trade.*
Published by: Sweet & Maxwell Ltd., 100 Avenue Road, London, NW3 3PF, United Kingdom. TEL 44-20-74491111, FAX 44-20-74491144, customer.services@sweetandmaxwell.co.uk, http://www.sweetandmaxwell.co.uk. **Subscr. to:** Cheriton House, North Way, Andover, Hants SP10 5BE, United Kingdom.

336 ZAF
TAXATION OF EMPLOYEES. Text in English. base vol. plus a. updates. looseleaf. ZAR 228. Supplement avail. **Description:** Comprehensive guide to planning tax-effective remuneration packages for employers, employees and the self-employed. Provides practical advice on matters including different approaches to providing fringe benefits, as well as share incentive schemes, deferred compensation and other retirement benefits.
Published by: LexisNexis Butterworths South Africa (Subsidiary of: LexisNexis Europe and Africa), PO Box 792, Durban, KwaZulu-Natal 4000, South Africa. TEL 27-31-2683111, FAX 27-31-2683110.

336.2 USA
TAXATION OF EXEMPTS. Text in English. bi-m. USD 215 domestic (effective 2002). adv. **Document type:** *Journal.* **Description:** Covers intermediate sanctions, combinations and joint ventures, health care organizations, exemption and compliance, private foundations, political and lobbying activity, the unrelated business income tax, charitable giving, compensation, and other topics.
Related titles: Online - full content ed.
Published by: R I A (Subsidiary of: Thomson Corporation), 395 Hudson St, New York, NY 10014. Eds. Joseph Lundy, Robert Boisture. Adv. contact Terry Storholm.

336.2 332.1 USA
TAXATION OF FINANCIAL INSTITUTIONS. Text in English. 1983. 3 base vols. plus s-a. updates. looseleaf. USD 848 base vol(s). (effective 2005). **Description:** covers integrated analysis of the most recent legislative changes and service rulings, tax rules for commercial banks:bad debt reserves, foreclosures, common true holding companies, tax exempt obligations, taxation of banks as securities, tax rules for thrift institutions and tax rules common to both commercial banks and thrift institutions.
Related titles: CD-ROM ed.
Published by: Matthew Bender & Co., Inc. (Subsidiary of: LexisNexis North America), 1275 Broadway, Albany, NY 12204. TEL 518-487-3575, 800-252-9257, FAX 518-462-3788, international@bender.com, http://bender.lexisnexis.com.

TAXATION OF INTELLECTUAL PROPERTY: TAX PLANNING GUIDE. see *PATENTS, TRADEMARKS AND COPYRIGHTS*

336.2 338.2 USA
TAXATION OF MINING OPERATIONS. Text in English. 1981. base vol. plus a. updates. looseleaf. USD 242 base vol(s). (effective 2003). **Description:** Thorough, in-depth treatment, expert analysis of the issues, laws, regulations, cases and rulings that govern federal income taxation of operations involving minerals other than oil and gas.
Published by: Matthew Bender & Co., Inc. (Subsidiary of: LexisNexis North America), 1275 Broadway, Albany, NY 12204. international@bender.com, http://bender.lexisnexis.com. Ed. Peter C Maxfield.

336 NLD
THE TAXATION OF PERMANENT ESTABLISHMENTS. Text in English. 1993. 3 base vols. plus bi-m. updates. looseleaf. USD 780 base vol(s).; USD 210 updates (effective 2002). **Document type:** *Trade.* **Description:** Provides a systematic analysis of the role of permanent establishments in international tax law, including commentary on Articles 5, 7 and 24 of the OECD Model Tax Convention, and the influence of the EU.
Published by: (International Bureau of Fiscal Documentation), I B F D Publications BV, H J E Wenckebachweg 210, PO Box 20237, Amsterdam, 1000 HE, Netherlands. TEL 31-20-554-0100, FAX 31-20-620-8626, info@ibfd.nl, http://www.ibfd.nl. Ed. Irene J J Burgers.

336.2 USA
TAXATION OF PUBLIC UTILITIES. Text in English. 1993. base vol. plus a. updates. looseleaf. USD 283 base vol(s). (effective 2005). **Description:** covers normalization rules, contributions in aid of construction, accounting for income taxes, customer deposits, consolidated tax savings from nonregulated affiliates, the alternative minimum tax and the uniform capitalization rules.
Published by: Matthew Bender & Co., Inc. (Subsidiary of: LexisNexis North America), 1275 Broadway, Albany, NY 12204. TEL 518-487-3575, 800-252-9257, FAX 518-462-3788, international@bender.com, http://bender.lexisnexis.com.

336.2 332.6 USA
TAXATION OF SECURITIES TRANSACTIONS. Text in English. 1971. base vol. plus s-a. updates. looseleaf. USD 353 base vol(s). (effective 2005). **Description:** covers notional principal contracts-financial derivatives, stocks and bonds, stock options, puts and calls, short sales, corporate and government bonds, bailouts, dividend distributions, stock redemptions, partnerships and S corporations, real estate investment trusts, taxable mortgage pools, annuity contracts, foreign sales corporations and foreign currency.
Published by: Matthew Bender & Co., Inc. (Subsidiary of: LexisNexis North America), 1275 Broadway, Albany, NY 12204. TEL 518-487-3575, 800-252-9257, FAX 518-462-3788, international@bender.com, http://bender.lexisnexis.com. Ed. Martin Fried.

350 USA
TAXATION OF THE CLOSELY HELD CORPORATION (SUPPLEMENT). Text in English. base vol. plus biennial updates. USD 155 domestic; USD 218.95 foreign (effective 1999). **Document type:** *Trade.*
Formerly: Taxation of Closely Held Corporations (Supplement)
Published by: W G & L Financial Reporting & Management Research (Subsidiary of: R I A), 90 Fifth Ave, New York, NY 10011. TEL 212-645-4800, FAX 212-337-4280.

336.2 PAK
TAXATION STRUCTURE OF PAKISTAN. Text in English. 1974. a.
Published by: Finance Division, Islamabad, Pakistan.

336 USA
TAXBASE; complete online tax news and reference service. Text in English. 1993. d. back issues avail. **Document type:** *Trade.* **Description:** Covers latest and most comprehensive daily tax news and analysis at the federal, state and international levels, plus in-depth tax research libraries, all in one convenient location on the Internet.
Media: Online - full text.
Address: 6830 N Fairfax Dr, Arlington, VA 22213. TEL 703-533-4400, FAX 703-533-4444, cservice@tax.org, webmaster@tax.org, http://www.tax.org. Circ: 20,000 (paid).

336 USA ISSN 1532-5229
TAXCORE. Text in English. 1997. d. **Description:** Provides access to important tax-related documents from Congress, the IRS, and dozens of other sources, reproduced verbatim on a BNA-administered website.
Media: Online - full text (from The Bureau of National Affairs, Inc.).
—CCC.
Published by: The Bureau of National Affairs, Inc., 1231 25th St., NW, Washington, DC 20037. TEL 800-372-1033, FAX 800-253-0332, bnaplus@bna.com, http://www.bna.com.

336 USA
TAXES (MADISON). Text in English. a. USD 2.25. **Description:** Contains information on all federal, state, and local taxes paid by Wisconsin taxpayers. Includes federal and state income tax filing guides.
Published by: Wisconsin Taxpayers Alliance, 401 North Lawn Ave., Madison, WI 53704-5033. TEL 608-255-4581. Ed. Craig Svoboda.

336 NLD
TAXES AND INVESTMENT IN ASIA AND THE PACIFIC. Text in English. 1978. 15 base vols. plus m. updates. looseleaf. USD 1,875 base vol(s).; USD 1,170 updates (effective 2002). **Document type:** *Trade.* **Description:** Offers information on tax policies and systems for foreign and intraregional investors, governments and policy makers.

Published by: (International Bureau of Fiscal Documentation), I B F D Publications BV, H J E Wenckebachweg 210, PO Box 20237, Amsterdam, 1000 HE, Netherlands. TEL 31-20-554-0100, FAX 31-20-620-8626, info@ibfd.nl, http://www.ibfd.nl. Ed. Peter Hann.

336 NLD
TAXES AND INVESTMENT IN THE MIDDLE EAST. Text in Dutch. 1977. 4 base vols. plus q. updates. looseleaf. USD 875 base vol(s).; USD 470 updates (effective 2002).
Document type: *Trade.* **Description:** Outlines background information on the economy and political structure, and provides the relevant legal, administrative, economic and tax measures.
Published by: (International Bureau of Fiscal Documentation), I B F D Publications BV, H J E Wenckebachweg 210, PO Box 20237, Amsterdam, 1000 HE, Netherlands. TEL 31-20-554-0100, FAX 31-20-620-8626, info@ibfd.nl, http://www.ibfd.nl. Ed. Peter Hann.

336 USA ISSN 0162-3486
KF6272
TAXES ON PARADE. Text in English. w. USD 153 (effective 2004).
Related titles: Online - full text ed.: (from Factiva, ProQuest Information & Learning).
Indexed: ATI.
—CCC.
Published by: C C H Inc., 2700 Lake Cook Rd, Riverwoods, IL 60015. TEL 847-267-7000, 800-449-6439, FAX 800-224-8299, cust_serv@cch.com, http://www.cch.com. Pub. Kevin Robert.

336.22 USA
TAXES - PROPERTY - STATE CAPITALS. Cover title: State Capitals Newsletters. Taxes - Property. Text in English. 1943. 48/yr. looseleaf. USD 365 (effective 2005). index. back issues avail. **Document type:** *Newsletter.* **Description:** Follows trends in state property tax laws and regulations. Emphasizes school financing.
Formerly: From the State Capitals. Taxes - Property (0734-1121); Which incorporated: From the State Capitals. School Financing (0734-0907)
Related titles: Online - full text ed.: USD 325 (effective 2001).
—CCC.
Published by: State Capitals Newsletters, PO Box 7376, Alexandria, VA 22307-7376. TEL 703-768-9600, FAX 703-768-9690, newsletters@statecapitals.com, http://www.statecapitals.com. Pub. Keyes Walworth.

336.2 USA
KF6272 CODEN: TAXSA6
TAXES - THE TAX MAGAZINE. Text in English. 1923. m. USD 245 (effective 2005). bk.rev. charts; illus. index. reprint service avail. from WSH. **Document type:** *Magazine, Academic/Scholarly.* **Description:** Provides thorough, accurate, and insightful analysis of current tax issues, trends, and legislative developments. It features succinct coverage of hot topics in legal, accounting, and economic aspects of federal and state tax—and alerts practitioners of planning opportunities and pitfalls, and rules being developed in Washington.
Former titles: Taxes (Riverwoods) (0040-0181); (until 1939): Tax Magazine (8755-2221); (until 1931): National Tax Magazine (8755-223X); (until 1930): National Income Tax Magazine (8755-2248)
Related titles: Microform ed.: (from PQC); Online - full text ed.: USD 271 (effective 2004) (from bigchalk, ProQuest Information & Learning).
Indexed: ASCA, ATI, AgeL, BPI, BPIA, BusI, CLI, CurCont, FamI, ILP, LII, LRI, LegCont, PAIS, PCI, SSCI, T&II.
—CASDDS, IE. **CCC.**
Published by: C C H Inc., 2700 Lake Cook Rd, Riverwoods, IL 60015. TEL 847-267-7000, cust_serv@cch.com, http://www.cch.com. Pub. Kevin Robert. **Subscr. to:** 4025 W. Peterson Ave., Chicago, IL 60646-6085. TEL 773-866-6000, 800-835-5224, FAX 773-866-3895.

336 FRA
TAXING WAGES/SITUATION DES OUVRIERS AU REGARD DE L'IMPOT ET DES TRANSFERTS SOCIAUX. Text in French. 198?. a. price varies.
Former titles (until 1998): Tax - Benefit Position of Employees (1560-4802); (until 1996): Tax - Benefit Position of Production Workers (1011-4688)
Related titles: Diskette ed.: USD 145; Ed.
Indexed: IIS.
Published by: Organization for Economic Cooperation and Development, 2 Rue Andre Pascal, Paris, 75775 Cedex 16, France. TEL 33-1-45248200, FAX 33-1-45248500, http://www.oecd.org. **U.S. orders to:** O E C D Turpin North America, PO Box 194, Downingtown, PA 19335-0194. TEL 610-524-5361, 800-456-6323, FAX 610-524-5417, bookscustomer@turpinna.com.

336 CAN ISSN 0821-3704
THE TAXLETTER. Text in English. 1983. m. CND 89 (effective 1999). adv. index. **Document type:** *Newsletter.* **Description:** Tax planning strategies and consumer news on personal tax planning.
Published by: Hume Publishing Company Ltd., 604 2200 Yonge St, Toronto, ON M4S 2C6, Canada. TEL 800-733-4863, FAX 416-440-8268, customerservice@humepublishing.com, humenewsletters@mindspring.com, http://www.humepublishing.com. Ed. A Micheal Keerma. Adv. contact Barbara Ritchie.

336.24 ZAF ISSN 0040-0270
K24 CODEN: UNTSAK
TAXPAYER; a monthly journal devoted to the law, practice and incidence of income tax and other revenue laws. Text in English. 1952. m. ZAR 410.40 (effective 1993). adv. bk.rev. charts. index.
Indexed: ISAP.
Published by: Taxpayer C C, 4 Church Sq, PO Box 3191, Cape Town, 8000, South Africa. TEL 21-21-452592, FAX 27-21-4617488. Circ: 2,000.

336 USA
TAXPRO MONTHLY. Text in English. 1979. m. USD 29.95 (effective 2001). back issues avail. **Document type:** *Newsletter, Trade.* **Description:** Tax preparation information for accountants, attorneys and CPAs.
Formerly (until May 2001): 1040 Report (0897-4306)
Published by: National Association of Tax Professionals, 720 Association Dr, PO Box 8002, Appleton, WI 54914. TEL 920-749-1040, FAX 920-749-1062, natp@natptax.com, http://www.natptax.com. R&P David Mellem TEL 920-749-1040 ext 143. Circ: 16,000.

332.6 USA
TAXPRO QUARTERLY JOURNAL. Text in English. 1994. q. USD 39.95 (effective 2004). adv. 48 p./no.; back issues avail. **Document type:** *Journal, Trade.* **Description:** Tax preparation for EAs, CPAs, CFPs, and attorneys.
Formerly (until 2001): Tax Practitioners Journal (1075-5780)
Published by: National Association of Tax Professionals, 720 Association Dr, PO Box 8002, Appleton, WI 54914. TEL 800-558-3402, FAX 800-747-0001, natp@natptax.com, http://www.natptax.com/tax_pro_quarterly_journal.html. Ed., R&P, Adv. contact Cindy Van Beckum TEL 920-749-1040 ext 119. B&W page USD 1,380, color page USD 2,030; trim 8.375 x 10.875. Circ: 19,500 (paid and controlled).

336.22 ESP ISSN 1576-5032
TEMAS TRIBUTARIOS DE ACTUALIDAD FISCAL. Text in Spanish. 2000. m. back issues avail.
Related titles: Online - full text ed.
Published by: Asociacion Espanola de Asesores Fiscales, C. Montalban, 3 6o. derecha, Madrid, 28014, Spain. TEL 34-91-5325154, FAX 34-91-5323794, sedecentral@aedaf.es, http://www.aedaf.es/.

336 USA ISSN 0742-0757
HJ11
TENNESSEE TAX GUIDE. Text in English. 1982. a. USD 25 per issue (effective 2005). **Description:** Comprehensive survey of major Tennessee state and local taxes.
Published by: M. Lee Smith Publishers LLC, PO Box 5094, Brentwood, TN 37024. TEL 615-373-7517, 800-274-6774, FAX 615-373-5183, custserv@mleesmith.com, http://www.mleesmith.com/tenn/ttg.shtml. Ed. Bradford N Forrister. Pub. M Lee Smith.

336 USA
TENNESSEE TAX SERVICE. Text in English. 1989. m. USD 485 (effective 2005). **Description:** Updates developments in Tennessee state and local taxes.
Formerly (until 1992): Tennessee Tax Review (1044-0798)
Published by: M. Lee Smith Publishers LLC, PO Box 5094, Brentwood, TN 37024. TEL 615-373-7517, 800-274-6774, FAX 615-373-5183, custserv@mleesmith.com, http://www.mleesmith.com. Ed. Bradford N Forrister. Pub. M Lee Smith.

336 THA
THAILAND'S BUDGET IN BRIEF. Text in English. 1962. irreg. free. **Document type:** *Government.*
Related titles: Thai ed.: 1960.
Published by: Bureau of the Budget, Bangkok, Thailand. FAX 66-2-271-3662. Circ: 1,500.

343.489 DNK ISSN 0908-8431
TIDSSKRIFT FOR SKATTER OG AFGIFTER; lovgivning, domme og afgoerelser, debat og ny litteratur. Text in Danish. 1994. w. DKK 2,835 per quarter (effective 2004). adv. **Description:** Presents a complete set of Danish tax court decisions, rulings and decisions from the National Tax Tribunal and the administration. Also features articles on current tax topics.
Formed by the merger of (1984-1994): Tidsskrift for Skatteret (0109-2383); (1991-1994): Told Skat Nyt (0906-1517); Which was formerly (until 1991): Skat (0900-0178); Which incorporates (1939-1986): Meddelelser fra Landsskatteretten (0108-5751); (1967-1985): Meddelelser fra Skattedepartementet (0108-576X)
Related titles: Online - full text ed.
Published by: (Denmark. Skatteministeriet/Danish Ministry of Taxation, Denmark. Told- og Skattestyrelsen), Magnus Informatik AS (Subsidiary of: Wolters Kluwer N.V.), Palaegade 4, PO Box 9026, Copenhagen K, 1022, Denmark. TEL 45-70-203314, FAX 45-33-960161, magnus@magnus.dk, http://www.magnus.dk. Ed. Henrik Buhl.

336.2 340 BEL
TIJDSCHRIFT VOOR FISCAAL RECHT. Text in Dutch; Summaries in Dutch, French. m. (except July-Aug.). EUR 475 print & online eds. (effective 2004). back issues avail.
Document type: *Trade.* **Description:** Presents doctrine and commentary on Belgian tax law and publishes court decisions and jurisprudential issues on tax law.
Related titles: Online - full text ed.
Published by: Larcier, Fond Jean-Paques 4, Louvain-la-Neuve, 1348, Belgium. TEL 32-10-482500, FAX 32-10-482519, lawbooks@larcier.be, http://www.editions.larcier.com/revues. Ed. H Dubois.

336 GBR
TILEY AND COLLISON'S U K TAX GUIDE. Text in English. a. GBP 59.95 (effective 2000). **Document type:** *Trade.*
Description: Examines in detail the workings of income tax, corporation tax, capital gains tax, inheritance tax, VAT, stamp duty, and national insurance contributions, showing how they work and the policy behind the statutory provisions.
Formerly (until 1998): Butterworths U K Tax Guide (0264-2174)
Published by: Butterworths Tolley (Subsidiary of: LexisNexis UK (Scottish Office)), Halsbury House, 35 Chancery Ln, London, Mddx WC2A 1EL, United Kingdom. TEL 44-20-74002500, FAX 44-20-7400-2842, order.line@butterworths.co.uk, http://www.butterworths.co.uk/.

B

336 GBR ISSN 0143-1633
TOLLEY'S CAPITAL GAINS TAX. Text in English. 1978. a. GBP 62.95 (effective 2003). Supplement avail. **Document type:** *Journal, Trade.* **Description:** Comprehensive first point of reference guide to all relevant laws and practices.
Published by: Butterworths Tolley (Subsidiary of: LexisNexis UK (Scottish Office)), Halsbury House, 35 Chancery Ln, London, Mddx WC2A 1EL, United Kingdom. TEL 44-20-74002500, FAX 44-20-74002583, TELEX DX Chancery Lane 1023, sales@tolley.co.uk, http://www.butterworths.co.uk. Pub. Gary Mackley-Smith.

336 GBR ISSN 0305-8921
TOLLEY'S CORPORATION TAX. Text in English. a. GBP 62.95 (effective 2003). Supplement avail. **Document type:** *Journal, Trade.* **Description:** Comprehensive first point of reference guide to all relevant laws and practices.
Formerly: Tolley's Profits Tax
Published by: Butterworths Tolley (Subsidiary of: LexisNexis UK (Scottish Office)), Halsbury House, 35 Chancery Ln, London, Mddx WC2A 1EL, United Kingdom. TEL 44-20-74002500, FAX 44-20-74002583, TELEX DX Chancery Lane 1023, sales@tolley.co.uk, http://www.butterworths.co.uk. Pub. Gary Mackley-Smith.

336.2 GBR ISSN 0305-893X
KD5429
TOLLEY'S INCOME TAX. Text in English. 1915. a. GBP 62.95 (effective 2004). Supplement avail. **Document type:** *Journal, Trade.* **Description:** Offers concise, expert advice on income tax matters.
Published by: Butterworths Tolley (Subsidiary of: LexisNexis UK (Scottish Office)), Halsbury House, 35 Chancery Ln, London, Mddx WC2A 1EL, United Kingdom. TEL 44-20-74002500, FAX 44-20-74002583, TELEX DX Chancery Lane 1023, sales@tolley.co.uk, http://www.butterworths.co.uk.

336.2 GBR ISSN 0952-0791
TOLLEY'S INHERITANCE TAX. Text in English. 1979. a. GBP 62.95 (effective 2004). Supplement avail. **Document type:** *Journal, Trade.* **Description:** Provides concise, expert guidance in the area of the inheritance tax in the UK.
Formerly (until 1986): Tolley's Capital Transfer Tax (0144-4042)
—BLDSC (8863.686517).
Published by: Butterworths Tolley (Subsidiary of: LexisNexis UK (Scottish Office)), Halsbury House, 35 Chancery Ln, London, Mddx WC2A 1EL, United Kingdom. TEL 44-20-74002500, FAX 44-20-74002583, TELEX DX Chancery Lane 1023, sales@tolley.co.uk, http://www.butterworths.co.uk.

TOLLEY'S NATIONAL INSURANCE CONTRIBUTIONS. see *INSURANCE*

336.2 GBR
TOLLEY'S PRACTICAL TAX SERVICE; your fortnightly guide to the latest tax developments. Text in English. 1940. fortn. GBP 123; GBP 144 foreign (effective 2000). bk.rev. **Document type:** *Newsletter.* **Description:** Provides updates on all forms of taxes in the United Kingdom.
Former titles (until 1997): Tolley's Practical Tax Newsletter (0143-294X); Fiscal Press (0956-3954); Tax Partner (0954-6537); Income Tax Digest and Accountants' Review (0308-7883)
Indexed: ELJI, LJI.
—BLDSC (8863.686549).
Published by: Butterworths Tolley (Subsidiary of: LexisNexis UK (Scottish Office)), 2 Addiscombe Rd, Croydon, Surrey CR9 5AF, United Kingdom. TEL 44-20-8686-9141, FAX 44-20-8686-3155, andrew_wotton@tolley.co.uk, http://www.tolley.co.uk. Ed. Andrew Wotton.

336.2 GBR ISSN 0951-175X
TOLLEY'S PRACTICAL V A T. (Value Added Tax) Text in English. 1987. m. GBP 170; GBP 129 foreign (effective 2000).
Document type: *Bulletin.*

Indexed: ELJI, LJI.
Published by: Butterworths Tolley (Subsidiary of: LexisNexis UK (Scottish Office)), 2 Addiscombe Rd, Croydon, Surrey CR9 5AF, United Kingdom. TEL 44-20-8686-9141, FAX 44-20-8686-3155, http://www.tolley.co.uk. Ed. Debbie Russell. Circ: 1,200.

336 GBR
TOLLEY'S TAX CASES (YEAR). Text in English. a. GBP 75 per vol. (effective 2003). **Document type:** *Journal, Trade.* **Description:** Compiles brief, concise reports of more than 2,500 essential court and special commissioners' decisions that apply to UK tax legislation from 1875 to the present.
Published by: Butterworths Tolley (Subsidiary of: LexisNexis UK (Scottish Office)), Halsbury House, 35 Chancery Ln, London, Mddx WC2A 1EL, United Kingdom. TEL 44-20-74002500, FAX 44-20-74002583, TELEX DX Chancery Lane 1023, http://www.butterworths.co.uk. Eds. Alan Dolton, Glyn Saunders.

336.2 GBR ISSN 0262-4583
TOLLEY'S TAX DATA (YEAR). Text in English. 1981. s-a. GBP 23.95 (effective 2000 & 2001). **Document type:** *Trade.* **Description:** Contains reference material an all the main UK taxes.
Published by: Butterworths Tolley (Subsidiary of: LexisNexis UK (Scottish Office)), 2 Addiscombe Rd, Croydon, Surrey CR9 5AF, United Kingdom. TEL 44-20-8686-9141, FAX 44-20-8686-3155, http://www.butterworths.co.uk. Eds. David Smailes, Kevin Walton, Robert Wareham.

336.2 GBR ISSN 0950-9267
TOLLEY'S TAX GUIDE. Text in English. a. GBP 64.95 (effective 2004). **Document type:** *Bulletin, Trade.* **Description:** Provides objective, unbiased guidance across the full range of U.K. taxes.
Formerly (until 1984): Tolley's Practical Tax Guide
—BLDSC (8863.686660).
Published by: Butterworths Tolley (Subsidiary of: LexisNexis UK (Scottish Office)), 2 Addiscombe Rd, Croydon, Surrey CR9 5AF, United Kingdom. TEL 44-20-8686-9141, FAX 44-20-8686-3155, http://www.butterworths.co.uk. Eds. Arnold Homer, Rita Burrows.

336.2 GBR ISSN 0307-6687
TOLLEY'S TAX TABLES (YEAR). Text in English. 1922. a., latest 2000-2001. GBP 20.50 (effective 2000). stat.
Published by: Butterworths Tolley (Subsidiary of: LexisNexis UK (Scottish Office)), 2 Addiscombe Rd, Croydon, Surrey CR9 5AF, United Kingdom. TEL 44-20-8686-9141, FAX 44-20-8686-3155. Ed. Gina Antczak.

336 341.57 GBR
TOLLEY'S TAXATION IN THE REPUBLIC OF IRELAND. Text in English. 1973-1992; resumed 199?. a. GBP 48.95 (effective 2000 & 2001). back issues avail. **Document type:** *Trade.* **Description:** Provides a comprehensive review of all the important legislative provisions across the wide range of taxes in Ireland.
Formerly: Tolley's Republic of Ireland Taxation (0308-1184)
Published by: Butterworths Tolley (Subsidiary of: LexisNexis UK (Scottish Office)), 2 Addiscombe Rd, Croydon, Surrey CR9 5AF, United Kingdom. TEL 44-20-8686-9141, FAX 44-20-8686-3155, http://www.butterworths.co.uk. Ed. Glyn Saunders.

336 GBR
TOLLEY'S TAXATION OF EMPLOYMENTS. Text in English. 1990. a., latest 7th Ed. GBP 55.95 (effective 2000). **Document type:** *Bulletin.*
Formerly: Tolley's Taxation of Employments. Schedule E (0968-400X)
Published by: Butterworths Tolley (Subsidiary of: LexisNexis UK (Scottish Office)), 2 Addiscombe Rd, Croydon, Surrey CR9 5AF, United Kingdom. TEL 44-20-8686-9141, FAX 44-20-8686-3155, http://www.tolley.co.uk. Ed. Robert Maas.

336 GBR ISSN 0962-0044
TOLLEY'S V A T CASES (YEAR). (Value Added Tax) Text in English. a. GBP 99 per vol. (effective 2004). **Document type:** *Journal, Trade.* **Description:** Provides more than 3,500 essential court and VAT Tibunal decisions dating back to 1973 that are relevant to current legislation.
—BLDSC (8863.686965).
Published by: Butterworths Tolley (Subsidiary of: LexisNexis UK (Scottish Office)), Halsbury House, 35 Chancery Ln, London, Mddx WC2A 1EL, United Kingdom. TEL 44-20-74002500, FAX 44-20-74002583, TELEX DX Chancery Lane 1023, http://www.butterworths.co.uk. Eds. Alan Dolton, Robert Wareham.

336.2 GBR ISSN 0957-2651
TOLLEY'S V A T PLANNING (YEAR). (Value Added Tax) Text in English. 1986. a. GBP 89.95 per vol. (effective 2004). **Document type:** *Journal, Trade.* **Description:** Offers a practical guide on all aspects of taxation and related financial planning.
Published by: Butterworths Tolley (Subsidiary of: LexisNexis UK (Scottish Office)), Halsbury House, 35 Chancery Ln, London, Mddx WC2A 1EL, United Kingdom. TEL 44-20-74002500, FAX 44-20-74002583, TELEX DX Chancery Lane 1023, http://www.butterworths.co.uk.

336 GBR ISSN 0957-2643
TOLLEY'S VALUE ADDED TAX. Text in English. 1984. a. GBP 105 (effective 2004). Supplement avail. **Document type:** *Journal, Trade.* **Description:** Comprehensive first point of reference guide to all relevant laws and practices.
—BLDSC (8863.686960).
Published by: Butterworths Tolley (Subsidiary of: LexisNexis UK (Scottish Office)), Halsbury House, 35 Chancery Ln, London, Mddx WC2A 1EL, United Kingdom. TEL 44-20-74002500, FAX 44-20-74002583, TELEX DX Chancery Lane 1023, sales@tolley.co.uk, http://www.butterworths.co.uk. Pub. Gary Mackley-Smith.

336 USA ISSN 0743-5010
HD9743.U5
TOP FIVE CONTRACTORS RECEIVING THE LARGEST DOLLAR VOLUME OF PRIME CONTRACT AWARDS IN EACH STATE. Text in English. a.
Published by: U.S. Department of Defense, Washington Headquarters Services, The Pentagon, Washington, DC 20301-1155. TEL 703-545-6700, http://www.dior.whs.mil.

346.082 USA ISSN 1526-7512
KFN5882
TRANSFER AND MORTGAGE RECORDING TAXES IN NEW YORK TITLE CLOSINGS. Text in English. 1994. a. (in 1 vol.), latest 2003. USD 142 base vol(s). (effective 2003). **Description:** Describes how to anticipate taxes when structuring the sale or purchasing of an interest in reality. Summarizes the law and analyzes statutes, regulations, and decisions.
Published by: Michie Company (Subsidiary of: LexisNexis North America), 701 E Water St, Charlottesville, VA 22902-5389. TEL 434-972-7600, 800-446-3410, FAX 434-972-7677, http://www.michie.com. Ed. David M Goldberg.

336.2 USA
▼ **TRANSFER PRICING REPORT.** Text in English. 2004. fortn. **Document type:** *Journal, Trade.* **Description:** Provides news and analysis on tax policies regarding intercompany transfer pricing and helps companies structure their operations to avoid double taxation.
Published by: B N A Inc. (Subsidiary of: The Bureau of National Affairs, Inc.), 1250 23rd St, N W, Washington, DC 20037-1166. TEL 800-223-7270, FAX 202-785-7195, customercare@bna.com, http://www.bnatax.com/tm/transferpricing_details.htm, http://www.bnabooks.com.

TRENDS, TIPS AND TAX. see *BUSINESS AND ECONOMICS—Management*

336 VEN
TRIBUTUM. Text in English, Spanish. 1996. s-a. USD 35 (effective 1998).
Published by: (Universidad Catolica del Tachira), Editorial Ucat, Carrera 14 con calle 14, Apdo 366, San Cristobal, Tachira 5001, Venezuela. TEL 58-76-432080, FAX 58-76-446183. Ed. Andres Eloy Leon Rojas. Circ: 1,000 (paid).

TRUSTS & ESTATES. see *BUSINESS AND ECONOMICS—Investments*

336.2 USA ISSN 0564-4402
KF6289.A1
TULANE TAX INSTITUTE. Key Title: Proceedings of the Annual Tulane Tax Institute. Text in English. 1951. a. USD 479. adv. back issues avail.; reprint service avail. from WSH. **Document type:** *Proceedings.*
Related titles: Audio cassette/tape ed.; Microfiche ed.: (from PMC, WSH); Microfilm ed.: (from PMC, WSH); Online - full text ed.
Indexed: CLI, ILP.
Published by: Bisk - Totaltape Publishing Co., 9417 Princess Palm Ave, Ste 400, Tampa, FL 33619. TEL 800-874-7877, FAX 800-345-8273, bisk@bisk.com, http://www.bisk.com. Ed. Steve Galloway. Pub. Nathan M Bisk. R&P Andrew Titen. Adv. contact Sandy Levine.

336.2 SWE ISSN 0346-2854
TULLINFORMATION; tidskrift. Text in Swedish. 1974. 25/yr. SEK 380 (effective 2000). **Document type:** *Newsletter.*
Published by: Generaltullstyrelsen, Fack 2267, Stockholm, 10317, Sweden. http://www.tullverket.se. **Subscr. to:** C.E. Fritzes AB, Stockholm 10647, Sweden.

336 TUN ISSN 0082-6820
TUNISIA. MINISTERE DU PLAN. BUDGET ECONOMIQUE. Text in French. a. free. **Document type:** *Government.*
Published by: Ministere du Plan, Tunis, Tunisia.

U.S. BUREAU OF THE CENSUS. ANNUAL CAPITAL EXPENDITURES. see *BUSINESS AND ECONOMICS—Abstracting, Bibliographies, Statistics*

336 USA
U.S. DEPARTMENT OF THE TREASURY. BUREAU OF PUBLIC DEBT. TABLES OF REDEMPTION VALUES FOR UNITED STATES SERIES E SAVINGS BOND AND SAVINGS NOTES. Text in English. s-a. USD 5 (effective 2001).
Formerly: Tables of Redemption Values for U.S. Savings Bonds, Series A-E (0039-8829)
Published by: U.S. Department of the Treasury, Bureau of Public Debt, 999 E St Ste 501, Washington, DC 20239-0001. TEL 304-480-6112, FAX 304-480-7959, OAdmin@bpd.treas.gov, http://www.publicdebt.treas.gov/. **Dist. by:** U.S. Government Printing Office, Superintendent of Documents, PO Box 371954, Pittsburgh, PA 15250-7954. TEL 202-512-1800, FAX 202-512-2250, orders@gpo.gov, http://www.access.gpo.gov.

336 USA ISSN 0145-0239
HJ10
U.S. DEPARTMENT OF THE TREASURY. FINANCIAL MANAGEMENT SERVICE. DAILY TREASURY STATEMENT. Text in English. d. (weekdays only). USD 855 domestic; USD 1,068.75 foreign (effective 2001). **Document type:** *Government.* **Description:** Summarizes data on the cash and debt operations of the Treasury based on reporting of the Treasury account balances of the Federal Reserve banks.
Related titles: Online - full content ed.
Indexed: AmStI.
Published by: U.S. Department of the Treasury, Financial Management Service, 401 14th St, S W, Washington, DC 20227. TEL 202-874-9790, DTS.Questions@fms.treas.gov, http://www.fms.treas.gov/dts/. **Subscr. to:** U.S. Government Printing Office, Superintendent of Documents, PO Box 371954, Pittsburgh, PA 15250-7954. TEL 202-512-1800, FAX 202-512-2250.

336 USA ISSN 0884-1063
HJ10
U.S. DEPARTMENT OF THE TREASURY. FINANCIAL MANAGEMENT SERVICE. UNITED STATES GOVERNMENT ANNUAL REPORT AND APPENDIX. Text in English. a. **Document type:** *Government.*
Former titles (until 1983): U.S. Department of the Treasury. Bureau of Government Financial Operations. Treasury Combined Statement of Receipts, Expenditures and Balances of the United States (0191-2062); (until 1977): U.S. Department of the Treasury. Combined Statement of Receipts, Expenditures and Balances of the United States (0098-9096)
Published by: (Budget Reports Branch), U.S. Department of the Treasury, Financial Management Service, 3700 East West Highway, Rm 515C, Hyattsville, MD 20782. TEL 202-874-9910, FAX 202-874-9966, Budget.Reports@fms.sprint.com, http://www.fms.treas.gov/. **Subscr. to:** U.S. Government Printing Office, Superintendent of Documents, PO Box 371954, Pittsburgh, PA 15250-7954. TEL 202-512-1800, FAX 202-512-2250, orders@gpo.gov, http://www.access.gpo.gov.

336.2 USA ISSN 0020-5761
KF6282.A2
U.S. INTERNAL REVENUE SERVICE. BULLETIN. (Semiannual Cummulative Bulletins avail.) Text in English. 1919. w. USD 247 (effective 2004). back issues avail.; reprint service avail. from PQC. **Document type:** *Bulletin, Government.* **Description:** Announces official I.R.S. rulings, Treasury Decisions, Executive Orders, legislation, and court decisions pertaining to internal revenue matters.
Related titles: ◆ CD-ROM ed.: I R S Federal Tax Products CD-ROM; Microform ed.: 1919 (from PMC, PQC); Online - full text ed.: ISSN 1554-9984 (from ProQuest Information & Learning); Cumulative ed(s).
Indexed: ATI, BLI, RASB.
Published by: U.S. Internal Revenue Service, IRS Bulletin Unit, W:CAR:MP:FP, Washington, DC 20224. TEL 309-229-7111, 800-876-1715, http://www.irs.gov/irb/. Circ: 25,057. **Subscr. to:** U.S. Government Printing Office, Superintendent of Documents, PO Box 371954, Pittsburgh, PA 15250-7954. TEL 202-512-1800, FAX 202-512-2250, orders@gpo.gov, http://www.access.gpo.gov.

U.S. INTERNAL REVENUE SERVICE. STATISTICS OF INCOME BULLETIN. see *BUSINESS AND ECONOMICS—Abstracting, Bibliographies, Statistics*

336 USA
U.S. INTERNAL REVENUE SERVICE. TAX MANAGEMENT PORTFOLIOS. Text in English. irreg., latest vol.384, 1992. price varies. **Document type:** *Government.*
Published by: U.S. Internal Revenue Service, 1111 Constitution Ave, N W, Washington, DC 20224. TEL 800-829-1040, http://www.irs.gov. **Dist. by:** Bernan Press, 4611-F Assembly Dr, Lanham, MD 20706-4391. http://www.bernan.com.

336 USA
U.S. INTERNAL REVENUE SERVICE. TAX RULES OF PRACTICE. Text in English. a. **Document type:** *Government.*
Published by: U.S. Internal Revenue Service, 1111 Constitution Ave, N W, Washington, DC 20224. TEL 800-829-1040, http://www.irs.gov. **Dist. by:** Bernan Press, 4611-F Assembly Dr, Lanham, MD 20706-4391. http://www.bernan.com.

336 USA ISSN 1069-8914
KF6419.A65
U S INTERNATIONAL TAX FORMS MANUAL. Text in English. base vol. plus a. updates. looseleaf. USD 255 (effective 1998). **Document type:** *Trade.* **Description:** Provides a comprehensive guide to U.S. international tax reporting and compliance.

Published by: W G & L Financial Reporting & Management Research (Subsidiary of: R I A), 90 Fifth Ave, New York, NY 10011. TEL 212-645-4800, FAX 212-337-4280. Ed. Stuart Singer.

U S INTERNATIONAL TRANSFER PRICING. see *BUSINESS AND ECONOMICS—Banking And Finance*

336.2 USA
U.S. MASTER EXCISE TAX GUIDE. Text in English. a. USD 55 1-4 copies (effective 2004). **Description:** Provides in-depth explanation of all federal excise taxes and serves as a one-stop resource for the thousands of accountants and tax professionals who work with this complex area.
Formerly: U.S. Excise Tax Guide (0083-0534)
Published by: C C H Inc., 2700 Lake Cook Rd, Riverwoods, IL 60015. TEL 847-267-7000, 800-449-6439, cust_serv@cch.com, http://www.cch.com.

336.2 USA ISSN 0083-1700
KF6369.A1
U.S. MASTER TAX GUIDE. Text in English. irreg. looseleaf. USD 57.50 1-4 copies, softbound; USD 75 1-4 copies, hardbound; USD 125 combined subscription print & online eds., 1-4 copies, softbound (effective 2004). **Description:** Reflects all pertinent federal tax law changes, to date of publication, that affect 2002 returns and provides fast and reliable answers to tax questions affecting individuals and business income tax.
Related titles: CD-ROM ed.: USD 99 1-4 copies (effective 2004); Online - full text ed.: USD 199 Federal intenet (effective 2004).
—CCC.
Published by: C C H Inc., 2700 Lake Cook Rd, Riverwoods, IL 60015. TEL 847-267-7000, 800-449-6439, cust_serv@cch.com, http://www.cch.com. Pub. Kevin Robert.

336 USA
HD2753.U6
U.S. MULTISTATE CORPORATE TAX GUIDE. Text in English. 1985. m. looseleaf. USD 75 1-4 copies (effective 2004). **Document type:** *Trade.* **Description:** Provides explanations of major corporate state tax topics for tax professionals who work with multiple state tax jurisdictions.
Formerly: Multistate Corporate Income Tax Guide
Related titles: CD-ROM ed.: USD 1,685 (effective 2003); Online - full text ed.
Published by: C C H Inc., 2700 Lake Cook Rd, Riverwoods, IL 60015. TEL 847-267-7000, 800-449-6439, FAX 800-224-8299, cust_serv@cch.com, http://www.cch.com. Pub. Kevin Robert.

332 USA
U.S. OFFICE OF THE COMPTROLLER OF THE CURRENCY. INTERPRETATIONS AND ACTIONS. Text in English. base vol. plus m. updates. USD 175 (effective 2000). **Document type:** *Trade.* **Description:** Includes legal staff interpretations, trust interpretive letters, securities letters, and bank accounting advisory series. Announces final enforcement actions against national banks and public evaluation, as well as final decisions under the Community Reinvestment Act.
Published by: U.S. Office of the Comptroller of the Currency, Administrator of National Banks, 250 E St, S W, Washington, DC 20219. TEL 202-874-5000, FAX 202-874-5263, http://www.occ.treas.gov.

332 USA ISSN 0738-2146
HG2543
U.S. OFFICE OF THE COMPTROLLER OF THE CURRENCY. QUARTERLY JOURNAL. Text in English. 1981. q. USD 100 (effective 2000). stat. back issues avail.; reprint service avail. from CIS,WSH. **Document type:** *Government.* **Description:** Records the most important O.C.C. actions and policies. Includes policy statements, decisions on banking structure, selected speeches, testimony, material released in the interpretive letters series, summaries of enforcement actions, and other information of interest to administrators of national banks.
Related titles: Microfiche ed.: (from CIS); Online - full text ed.: (from ProQuest Information & Learning).
Indexed: AmStI, BLI.
Published by: U.S. Office of the Comptroller of the Currency, Administrator of National Banks, 250 E St, S W, Washington, DC 20219. FAX 202-874-5263, http://www.occ.treas.gov. Circ: 6,000. **Subscr. to:** PO Box 70004, Chicago, IL 60673-0004.

336.2 USA ISSN 0277-402X
KF6280.A2
U.S. TAX CASES. Text in English. 1935. s-a. USD 75 per vol. (effective 2005).
—CCC.
Published by: C C H Inc., 2700 Lake Cook Rd, Riverwoods, IL 60015. TEL 847-267-7000, 800-449-6439, cust_serv@cch.com, http://www.cch.com. **Subscr. to:** 4025 W. Peterson Ave., Chicago, IL 60646-6085. TEL 773-866-6000, 800-835-5224.

336 USA ISSN 0745-8894
U S TAXATION OF INTERNATIONAL OPERATIONS. Text in English. 1973. report bulletins and articles), base vol. plus s-m. updates. looseleaf. USD 665. **Description:** Examines special concerns of U.S. corporations and American citizens operating or investing abroad.

Published by: W G & L Financial Reporting & Management Research (Subsidiary of: R I A), 90 Fifth Ave, New York, NY 10011. TEL 212-645-4800, FAX 212-337-4280.

340 DEU ISSN 1439-6777
DER UMSATZ-STEUER-BERATER. Text in German. 2000. m. EUR 134; EUR 13.40 newsstand/cover (effective 2005). adv. **Document type:** *Journal, Trade.*
Related titles: Online - full text ed.
Published by: Verlag Dr. Otto Schmidt KG, Gustav-Heinemann-Ufer 58, Cologne, 50968, Germany. TEL 49-221-93738460, FAX 49-221-93738943, info@otto-schmidt.de, http://www.ustb.de, http://www.otto-schmidt.de. Ed. Monika Neu. Adv. contact Renate Becker. B&W page EUR 1,125, color page EUR 1,969. Circ: 3,860 (paid and controlled).

336 DEU ISSN 0937-387X
UMSATZSTEUER-KARTEI. Text in German. 1968. irreg. looseleaf. price varies. **Document type:** *Monographic series, Trade.*
Published by: Erich Schmidt Verlag GmbH & Co. (Berlin), Genthiner Str 30G, Berlin, 10785, Germany. TEL 49-30-250085-0, FAX 49-30-25008521, vertrieb@esvmedien.de, http://www.erich-schmidt-verlag.de.

336.2 DEU ISSN 0341-8669
KK7290.A13
UMSATZSTEUER-RUNDSCHAU. Text in German. 1952. m. EUR 189; EUR 18.90 newsstand/cover (effective 2005). adv. reprints avail. **Document type:** *Journal, Trade.*
—IE, Infotrieve. **CCC.**
Published by: Verlag Dr. Otto Schmidt KG, Gustav-Heinemann-Ufer 58, Cologne, 50968, Germany. TEL 49-221-93738460, FAX 49-221-93738943, info@otto-schmidt.de, http://www.otto-schmidt.de. adv.: B&W page EUR 1,125, color page EUR 1,969. Circ: 3,864 (paid and controlled).

336 DEU ISSN 0935-7998
UMSATZSTEUER- UND VERKEHRSTEUER-RECHT. Text in German. 1909. m. EUR 174.80; EUR 18.10 newsstand/cover (effective 2004). adv. bk.rev. index. **Document type:** *Journal, Trade.*
Formerly: Deutsche Verkehrsteuer-Rundschau (0341-8766)
Indexed: IBR, IBZ.
—CCC.
Published by: Stollfuss Verlag GmbH & Co. KG, Dechenstr 7, Bonn, 53115, Germany. TEL 49-228-7240, FAX 49-228-72491181, info@stollfuss.de, http://www.stollfuss.de/programm/products/0400110.htm. Ed. Friedrich Klenk. adv.: B&W page EUR 1,125, color page EUR 1,740. Circ: 1,300 (paid and controlled).

336 DEU ISSN 0940-8738
UMSATZSTEUERGESETZ. Text in German. 1967. irreg. looseleaf. price varies. **Document type:** *Monographic series, Trade.*
Formerly (until 1991): Umsatzsteuergesetz, Mehrwertsteuer (0935-4476)
Published by: Erich Schmidt Verlag GmbH & Co. (Berlin), Genthiner Str 30G, Berlin, 10785, Germany. TEL 49-30-250085-0, FAX 49-30-25008521, vertrieb@esvmedien.de, http://www.erich-schmidt-verlag.de.

336 CAN ISSN 0838-8393
UNDERSTANDING INCOME TAX; for practitioners. Text in English. a., latest 2004-2005. CND 110 per issue domestic; USD 93.22 per issue foreign (effective 2005). **Description:** Straightforward, non-technical guide to Canadian federal income tax law for the non-specialist.
Published by: Carswell (Subsidiary of: Thomson Corporation), One Corporate Plaza, 2075 Kennedy Rd, Toronto, ON M1T 3V4, Canada. TEL 416-609-8000, 800-387-5164, FAX 416-298-5094, carswell.customerrelations@thomson.com, http://www.carswell.com. Ed. John R Mott.

330.9 UAE
UNITED ARAB EMIRATES. AL-MASRAF AL-MARKAZI. AL-TAQRIR AL-SANAWI/UNITED ARAB EMIRATES. CENTRAL BANK. ANNUAL REPORT. Text in Arabic, English. 1974. a. **Description:** Examines economic, financial and banking trends in the U.A.E. and in the international business climate.
Published by: Central Bank, P O Box 854, Abu Dhabi, United Arab Emirates. TEL 652220, FAX 668483, TELEX 24173 MARKAZI EM. Circ: (controlled).

336.2 340 USA ISSN 0040-0017
HJ10 CODEN: KSLSA7
UNITED STATES TAX COURT REPORTS. Text in English. 1924. m. USD 37 domestic (effective 2001). index. back issues avail.; reprint service avail. from WSH. **Document type:** *Government.* **Description:** Presents judicial decisions on points of law in cases heard in open court, for subsequent citation as precedent.
Formerly: Board of Tax Appeals Reports
Related titles: Microfiche ed.: (from BHP, WSH); Microform ed.: (from BHP, PMC, PQC); Online - full text ed.: (from Thomson West); ◆ Alternate Frequency ed(s).: Reports of the U.S. Tax Courts. ISSN 8755-6294. s-a.
Indexed: ATI, LII.

Published by: U.S. Tax Court, 400 Second St, N W, Washington, DC 20217. TEL 202-606-8704, FAX 202-783-3238. Ed. John T Fee. Circ: 2,663. **Subscr. to:** U.S. Government Printing Office, Superintendent of Documents, PO Box 371954, Pittsburgh, PA 15250-7954. TEL 202-512-1800, FAX 202-512-2250, orders@gpo.gov, http://www.access.gpo.gov.

336.2 DEU ISSN 1436-2945
UNTERNEHMER-TIP; Informationsdienst fuer Einzelunternehmer in Handel, Handwerk und Dienstleistung. Text in German. 1998. m. **Document type:** *Newsletter, Trade.*
Published by: V S R W Verlag Dr. Hagen Pruehs GmbH, Rolandstr 48, Bonn, 53179, Germany. TEL 49-228-95124-0, FAX 49-228-9512490, vsrw@vsrw.de, http://www.vsrw.de/Informationsdienste/Unternehmer_Tip/Unternehmer-Tip.shtml.

UNTERNEHMERBRIEF BAUWIRTSCHAFT. see *BUILDING AND CONSTRUCTION*

V A T T NYT. (Valtion Taloudellinen Tutkimuskeskus) see *BUSINESS AND ECONOMICS*

VADE MECUM: BEGROTING VAN DE SOCIALE BESCHERMING (YEAR)/SOCIAL PROTECTION BUDGET. see *PUBLIC ADMINISTRATION*

336.2 NLD ISSN 0042-2258
VAKSTUDIE NIEUWS; dokumentatie op het gebied van het fiscaal recht. Text in Dutch. 1945. fortn. looseleaf. adv. bk.rev. index.
—IE, Infotrieve.
Published by: Kluwer B.V. (Subsidiary of: Wolters Kluwer N.V.), Postbus 23, Deventer, 7400 GA, Netherlands. TEL 31-570-673449, FAX 31-570-691555, juridisch@kluwer.nl, http://www.kluwer.nl. Circ: 9,000.

336.2 USA ISSN 1557-2919
HG4028.V3
VALUATION STRATEGIES. Text in English. 1997 (Sept./Oct.). bi-m. adv. 48 p./no.; **Document type:** *Journal.*
Published by: R I A (Subsidiary of: Thomson Corporation), 395 Hudson St, New York, NY 10014. TEL 212-367-6300, 800-950-1216, http://www.riahome.com. Ed. John Bogdanski. Adv. contact Terry Storholm.

336.2 GBR
VALUE ADDED TAX AND DUTIES TRIBUNALS REPORTS. Text in English. m. GBP 85. **Document type:** *Government.*
Formerly (until 1996): Value Added Tax and Duties Reports
—BLDSC (9142.059450).
Published by: (Great Britain. V A T and Duties Tribunal), Stationery Office, 51 Nine Elms Ln, London, SW8 5DA, United Kingdom. TEL 44-20-7873-9090, FAX 44-20-7873-8200. **Subscr. to:** Publications Centre, PO Box 276, London SW8 5DT, United Kingdom. TEL 44-171-873-8466, FAX 44-171-873-8222.

336 USA ISSN 0735-9004
K26
➤ **VIRGINIA TAX REVIEW.** Text in English. 1981. q. USD 54 (effective 2005). adv. back issues avail.; reprint service avail. from WSH. **Document type:** *Journal, Academic/Scholarly.* **Description:** Focuses on tax and tax-related matters; written by legal academics and practioners from scholarly and practical perspectives. Notes and comments by students.
Related titles: Online - full text ed.: (from Gale Group, LexisNexis, Thomson West).
Indexed: ABIn, ATI, CLI, FamI, ILP, LRI.
Published by: Virginia Tax Review Association, University of Virginia School of Law, 580 Massie Rd, Charlottesville, VA 22901. TEL 434-924-4726, FAX 434-243-8753, vtra@virginia.edu, http://www.student.virginia.edu/~vtra/. Ed. Krisanne Schlachter. Adv. contact Lorie Helmuth. Circ: 750.

336.2 RUS
VOPROSY NALOGOOBLOZHENIYA. Text in Russian. q. USD 85 foreign (effective 2001).
Indexed: RASB.
Published by: ID FBK-PRESS, Myasnitskaya ul 44-1, Moscow, 101000, Russian Federation. TEL 7-095-7375353, FAX 7-095-7375347, fbk@fbk.ru. Ed. S M Shapigoozov. R&P, Adv. contact Elena Biriukova. Circ: 4,000. **US dist. addr.:** East View Information Services, 3020 Harbor Ln. N., Minneapolis, MN 55447. TEL 612-550-0961.

336 IND
VYAPARI-MITRA. Text in Marathi. 1950. m. INR 120 (effective 1998). adv. bk.rev. bibl. **Document type:** *Trade.*
Address: 106-9 Parashram Kuti, Erandawana J, Pune, Maharashtra 4, India. TEL 637200. Ed. G D Sharma. Circ: 36,500.

336 USA
W G & L TAX AUDIO ALERT. (Warren, Gorham and Lamont) Text in English. m. USD 315; includes Audio Alert Quizzer. **Document type:** *Trade.* **Description:** Provides tax and tax law reports, analysis, and commentary.
Media: Audio cassette/tape.
Published by: W G & L Financial Reporting & Management Research (Subsidiary of: R I A), 90 Fifth Ave, New York, NY 10011. TEL 212-645-4800, FAX 212-337-4280.

▼ new title ➤ refereed ✶ unverified ◆ full entry avail.

336 USA ISSN 1075-0223
W G & L TAX JOURNAL DIGEST. (Warren, Gorham and Lamont) Text in English. 1981. base vol. plus a. updates. USD 127 (effective 2005). **Document type:** *Journal, Trade.*
Description: Summarizes articles on federal taxation from other W.G.L. publications published during the previous year.
Formerly (until 1993): The Journal of Taxation Digest (8755-6049)
—CCC.
Published by: W G & L Financial Reporting & Management Research (Subsidiary of: R I A), 90 Fifth Ave, New York, NY 10011. TEL 212-645-4800, FAX 212-337-4280, http://ria.thomson.com/EStore/detail.asp?ID=JTD5.

336.2 DEU ISSN 0948-0625
W I S O STEUERBRIEF. Text in German. 1995. m. EUR 114 (effective 2004). **Document type:** *Journal, Trade.*
Indexed: PAIS.
Published by: (Institut fuer Wirtschaftspublizistik), Vogel Verlag und Druck GmbH & Co. KG, Max-Planck-Str 7-9, Wuerzburg, 97064, Germany. TEL 49-931-4180, FAX 49-931-4182100, marliese_bernhardt@vogel-medien.de, http://www.vogel-medien.de. **Subscr. to:** DataM-Services GmbH, Fichtestr 9, Wuerzburg 97074, Germany. TEL 49-931-417001, FAX 49-931-4170499, swestenberger@datam-services.de, http://www.datam-services.de.

336.2 634.9 USA
WASHINGTON (STATE). DEPARTMENT OF REVENUE. FOREST TAX SECTION. FOREST TAX ANNUAL REPORT. Text in English. 1973. a. free. **Document type:** *Government.*
Former titles: Washington (State). Department of Revenue. Forest Tax Annual Report; Washington (State). Department of Revenue. Forest Tax Report (0362-7462)
Published by: Department of Revenue, PO Box 47472, Olympia, WA 98504-7472. TEL 360-753-7086, FAX 360-664-8438. Ed. Bill Justis.

336.2 USA
WASHINGTON (STATE). DEPARTMENT OF REVENUE. RESEARCH DIVISION. COMPARATIVE STATE - LOCAL TAXES. Text in English. 1970. a. stat. 34 p./no.; **Document type:** *Government.*
Formerly: Washington (State). Department of Revenue. Research and Information Division. Comparative State-Local Taxes
Published by: Department of Revenue, Research Division, PO Box 47459, Olympia, WA 98504-7459. TEL 360-570-6070, FAX 360-664-0972, http://dor.wa.gov/index.asp?/menu/stats.htm.

WASHINGTON (STATE). DEPARTMENT OF REVENUE. RESEARCH DIVISION. PROPERTY TAX STATISTICS. see *BUSINESS AND ECONOMICS—Abstracting, Bibliographies, Statistics*

WASHINGTON (STATE). DEPARTMENT OF REVENUE. RESEARCH DIVISION. TAX STATISTICS. see *BUSINESS AND ECONOMICS—Abstracting, Bibliographies, Statistics*

336 USA
WASHINGTON TAX DECISIONS; excise tax bulletins. Text in English. 1987. latest 1993, 2 base vols. plus a. updates. looseleaf. USD 160. **Document type:** *Trade.*
Published by: LexisNexis (Subsidiary of: LexisNexis North America), PO Box 7587, Charlottesville, VA 22906-7587. TEL 804-972-7600, 800-562-1197, FAX 804-972-7666, llp.customer.support@lexis-nexis.com, http://www.lexislawpublishing.com.

336 346 USA
WASHINGTON TAXES; a taxpayer's manual for practice before the Department of Revenue. Text in English. 1992. base vol. plus irreg. updates. looseleaf. USD 95. **Description:** Problem solving guide for accountants, attorneys and small business owners, covering current policies and practices of the Washington State Department of Revenue.
Published by: LexisNexis (Subsidiary of: LexisNexis North America), PO Box 7587, Charlottesville, VA 22906-7587. TEL 804-972-7600, 800-562-1197, FAX 804-972-7666, llp.customer.support@lexis-nexis.com, http://www.lexislawpublishing.com. Ed. Martin Silver.

343.04 AUS
WEEKLY TAX BULLETIN. Text in English. w. looseleaf. AUD 725 for print, CD-ROM, E-mail or Online ed. (effective 2003). **Document type:** *Bulletin.* **Description:** Covers tax issues and related news.
Related titles: CD-ROM ed.; E-mail ed.; Online - full content ed.
Published by: Australian Tax Practice (Subsidiary of: Thomson Legal & Regulatory Ltd.), PO Box 3502, Rozelle, NSW 2039, Australia. ATPOnlineService@thomson.com.au, http://onlineecom01.thomson.com.au/thomson/Catalog.asp?EES_CMD=SI&EES_ID=100203, http://www.atp-online.com.au/

THE WELFARE REPORTER (ARLINGTON). see *SOCIAL SERVICES AND WELFARE*

336 USA
WEST VIRGINIA TAX CALENDAR. Text in English. 1950. a. USD 10. **Document type:** *Trade.*
Published by: West Virginia Chamber of Commerce, PO Box 2789, Charleston, WV 25330. TEL 304-342-1115.

336 USA ISSN 1081-0390
KF6287
WEST'S TAX LAW DICTIONARY. Text in English. 1992. a. USD 85 per issue (effective 2004). **Document type:** *Trade.*
Description: Focuses on the general meaning of tax terms, words, and phrases commonly used in modern American tax law.
Published by: Thomson West (Subsidiary of: Thomson Corporation, The), 610 Opperman Dr, Eagan, MN 55123-1396. TEL 651-687-8000, 800-328-9352, FAX 651-687-7302, http://west.thomson.com/product/14545296/product.asp.

343.055 BEL
WETBOEK FISCAAL RECHT - B.T.W./CODE DE DROIT FISCAL - TAXE SUR LA VALEUR AJOUTEE. Text in Dutch, French. 7 base vols. plus updates 3/yr. looseleaf. EUR 513 (effective 2003). **Document type:** *Trade.* **Description:** Covers value added taxation (VAT) in Belgium.
Published by: Kluwer Uitgevers (Subsidiary of: Wolters Kluwer Belgique), Ragheno Business Park, Motstraat 30, Mechelen, B-2800, Belgium. TEL 32-15-800-94571, info@kluwer.be, http://www.kluwer.be.

343.052 BEL ISSN 0774-7640
WETBOEK FISCAAL RECHT - INKOMSTENBELASTING. Variant title: Wetboek Inkomstenbelastingen. Text in Dutch, French. 1985. 5 base vols. plus updates 3/yr. looseleaf. EUR 589 (effective 2003). **Document type:** *Trade.*
Published by: Kluwer Uitgevers (Subsidiary of: Wolters Kluwer Belgique), Ragheno Business Park, Motstraat 30, Mechelen, B-2800, Belgium. TEL 32-15-800-94571, info@kluwer.be, http://www.kluwer.be.

336.2 GBR ISSN 0260-3926
WHILLANS'S TAX TABLES. Text in English. 1948. s-a. GBP 11.95 (effective 2000 & 2001). charts. **Document type:** *Trade.*
Description: Covers income tax, inheritance tax, capital gains tax, corporation tax, and related subjects.
Formerly: Whillans's Tax Tables and Tax Reckoner (0308-7948)
Published by: Butterworths Tolley (Subsidiary of: LexisNexis UK (Scottish Office)), Halsbury House, 35 Chancery Ln, London, Mddx WC2A 1EL, United Kingdom. TEL 44-20-74002500, FAX 44-20-74002583, TELEX DX Chancery Lane 1023, order.line@butterworths.co.uk, http://www.butterworths.co.uk. Eds. Gina Antczak, Sheila Parrington. Circ: 24,000.

336 CAN
WINDOW ON CANADIAN TAX. Text in English. 1991. m. looseleaf. CND 984 (effective 2005). **Document type:** *Trade.*
Description: Summarizes and comments on the most important Revenue Canada income tax documents obtained under the Access to Information Act.
Related titles: CD-ROM ed.: CND 900 (effective 2005); Online - full text ed.: CND 875 (effective 2005).
Published by: C C H Canadian Ltd., 90 Sheppard Ave E, Ste 300, North York, ON M2N 6X1, Canada. TEL 416-224-2248, 800-268-4522, FAX 416-224-2243, cservice@cch.ca, http://www.cch.ca.

336 AUT
WIR STEUERZAHLER. Text in German. q. EUR 40 membership (effective 2004). **Document type:** *Magazine, Consumer.*
Published by: V Oe S - Bund der Steuerzahler, Eschenbachgasse 11, Vienna, W 1010, Austria. TEL 43-1-5810333, FAX 43-1-5856157, office@steuerzahler.at, http://www.steuerzahler.at/steuerzahler.htm. Circ: 10,000.

THE WISCONSIN TAXPAYER. see *PUBLIC ADMINISTRATION*

336 DEU ISSN 0942-7228
WOHNEN-ZEITSCHRIFT FUER DAS WOHNUNGSWESEN IN BAYERN. Key Title: Wohnen (Muenchen). Text in German. 1903. m. adv. bk.rev. **Document type:** *Consumer.*
Formerly: Zeitschrift fuer das Gemeinnuetzige Wohnungswesen in Bayern
Published by: Verband Bayerischer Wohnungsunternehmen e.V., Stollbergstr 7, Munich, 80539, Germany. TEL 49-89-29002032, FAX 49-89-2285940. Ed. Xaver Kroner. R&P, Adv. contact Hedi Dreimueller. Circ: 2,000.

336 GBR
WORLD DIRECTORY OF TAX ADVISERS (YEAR). Text in English. 1993. a. **Document type:** *Trade.*
Published by: Euromoney Institutional Investor Plc., Nestor House, Playhouse Yard, London, EC4V 5EX, United Kingdom. TEL 44-20-7779-8673, FAX 44-20-7779-8541. Ed. Matt Morgan. Pub. Dominic Carman.

336 GBR
WORLD TAX NEWS. Text in English. 6/yr. **Document type:** *Newsletter, Trade.*
Formerly: International Tax News
Published by: Deloitte & Touche (Subsidiary of: Deloitte Touche Tohmatsu International), Hill House, 1 Little New St, London, EC4A 3TR, United Kingdom. TEL 44-171-936-3000, FAX 44-171-583-8517. Ed. E G Tomsett.

336 USA
WORLD TAX PLANNING SERVICE. Text in English. 2001. s-a. **Document type:** *Newsletter.*
Published by: The Bureau of National Affairs, Inc., 1231 25th St., NW, Washington, DC 20037. TEL 800-372-1033, http://www.bna.com. **Subscr. to:** 9435 Key West Ave, Rockville, MD 20850.

336 USA
WORLDWIDE COST OF LIVING; city comparisons. Text in English. s-a. charts. **Document type:** *Trade.* **Description:** Provides detailed information on the cost of more than 160 items in 129 cities across 86 countries.
Media: Online - full content.
Published by: Economist Intelligence Unit, 111 W 57th St, New York, NY 10019. http://store.eiu.com/index.asp?layout=product_home_page&product_id=1990000199&country_id=&ref=product_detail_list_by_title_home_title.

336 GBR
WORLDWIDE LIVING COSTS. Text in English. 1973. 2/yr. GBP 650 (effective 1998). **Document type:** *Corporate.*
Formerly: International Taxation & Cost of Living
Published by: P-E Inbucon Ltd., Brooks House, 34 Paradise Rd, Richmond-upon-Thames, Surrey TW9 1SE, United Kingdom. TEL 44-181-334-5727, FAX 44-181-334-5739, meis@easynet.co.uk.

336.2 USA ISSN 1089-8921
WORLDWIDE TAX TREATIES ON CD-ROM. Text in English. m. (q., and a. versions avail.). price varies. **Description:** Contains the full text of more than 4,000 U.S. and non U.S. tax treaties, from over 180 countries legislative histories of U.S. treaties, and treaty-related news and commentary. Every treaty is published in English and its original language.
Media: CD-ROM.
—CCC.
Published by: Tax Analysts, 6830 N Fairfax Dr, Arlington, VA 22213. TEL 703-533-4400, 800-955-3444, FAX 703-533-4444, http://www.taxanalysts.com/www/website.nsf/Web/WorldwideTaxTreaties?OpenDocument.

336.2 USA
HJ11
WYOMING. DEPARTMENT OF REVENUE. ANNUAL REPORT. Text in English. 1973. a. USD 4. stat. **Document type:** *Government.*
Formerly: Wyoming. Department of Revenue and Taxation. Annual Report (0094-9019)
Indexed: SRI.
Published by: Department of Revenue, Herschler Bldg, Cheyenne, WY 82002-0110. TEL 307-777-7961. Circ: 150.

336 ISR ISSN 0333-5666
YEDA LEMEDA; journal on taxation, law and economics. Text in Hebrew. 1977. m.
Published by: Raayonote Ltd., P O Box 26051, Tel Aviv, 61260, Israel. TEL 03-295749.

336 CAN ISSN 0844-6709
YUKON TERRITORY, DEPARTMENT OF FINANCE. BUDGET ADDRESS. Text in English. a.
Formerly (until 1989): Yukon Territory, Department of Finance. Operation and Maintenance Budget (0842-4985)
Related titles: French ed.: Yukon Territory. Department of Finance. Discours du Budget. ISSN 1482-9452. 1998.
—CISTI.
Published by: Yukon Territory, Department of Finance, Box 2703, Whitehorse, YT Y1A 2C6, Canada. TEL 867-667-5343, FAX 867-393-6217, fininfo@gov.yk.ca, http://www.gov.yk.ca/depts/finance/general/publications.html, http://www.gov.yk.ca/depts/finance/index.html.

▼ **Z ST - ZEITSCHRIFT ZUM STIFTUNGSWESEN.** see *BUSINESS AND ECONOMICS—Investments*

336 DEU ISSN 1439-5908
Z T R. (Zeitschrift fuer Tarifrecht) Text in German. 1987. m. EUR 192; EUR 18 newsstand/cover (effective 2004). **Document type:** *Magazine, Trade.*
Formerly (until 1993): Z T R - Zeitschrift fuer Tarifrecht (0931-8577)
Indexed: DIP, IBR, IBZ.
Published by: Verlagsgruppe Huethig Jehle Rehm GmbH (Subsidiary of: Sueddeutscher Verlag GmbH), Emmy-Noether-Str 2, Munich, 80992, Germany. TEL 49-89-5485206, FAX 49-89-548528230, info@hjr-verlag.de, http://www.huethig-jehle-rehm.de/journals/journal.html?id=17. Ed. Winrich Bolck.

336 CHE
ZAHLUNGSBILANZ DER SCHWEIZ. Text in German. a. **Document type:** *Bulletin, Government.*
Formerly: Ertragsbilanz der Schweiz
Related titles: French ed.: Balance Suisse des Paiements.
Published by: Schweizerische Nationalbank/Banque Nationale Suisse, Boersenstr. 15, Postfach, Zurich, 8022, Switzerland. TEL 41-1-6313111, FAX 41-1-6313911, snb@snb.ch, http://www.snb.ch.

336 COD
ZAIRE. DIRECTION GENERALE DES FINANCES. BULLETIN DES FINANCES. Text in French. 1975 (no.9). bi-m. illus.; stat. **Document type:** *Bulletin.*

Published by: Direction Generale des Finances, B.P. 12997, Kinshasa, Congo, Dem. Republic.

336 ZMB
ZAMBIA. DEPARTMENT OF CUSTOMS AND EXCISE. ANNUAL REPORT OF THE CONTROLLER OF CUSTOMS AND EXCISE. Text in English. a. **Document type:** *Government.* **Description:** Reports on imposition, collection and management of customs, excise and other duties in Zambia.
Published by: (Zambia. Department of Customs and Excise), Government Printing Department, PO Box 30136, Lusaka, Zambia.

336.2 ZMB ISSN 0084-4675
ZAMBIA. DEPARTMENT OF TAXES. ANNUAL REPORT OF THE COMMISSIONER OF TAXES. Text in English. 1964. a. ZMK 150. **Document type:** *Government.* **Description:** Covers collecting of income taxes in Zambia.
Published by: (Zambia. Department of Taxes), Government Printing Department, PO Box 30136, Lusaka, Zambia.

336 ZMB ISSN 0084-4683
ZAMBIA. DEPARTMENT OF THE ADMINISTRATOR-GENERAL AND OFFICIAL RECEIVER. REPORT. Text in English. 1964. a. ZMK 100. **Document type:** *Government.*
Published by: (Zambia. Department of the Administrator-General and Official Receiver), Government Printing Department, PO Box 30136, Lusaka, Zambia.

336 ZMB ISSN 0303-2760
ZAMBIA. OFFICE OF THE AUDITOR-GENERAL. REPORT OF THE AUDITOR-GENERAL. Text in English. 1963. a. ZMK 100. **Document type:** *Government.* **Description:** Reports on government accounting principles.
Published by: (Zambia. Office of the Auditor-General), Government Printing Department, PO Box 30136, Lusaka, Zambia.

336.2 JPN
ZEIMU TOKEI KARA MITA HOJIN KIGYO NO JITTAI. Short title: Hojin Kigyo no Jittai. Text in Japanese. 1963. irreg., latest 1997. JPY 1,740. **Document type:** *Government.*
Published by: Ministry of Finance, Printing Bureau, 2-2-4 Toranomon, Minato-ku, Tokyo, 105-0001, Japan. **Dist. by:** Government Publications Service Center, 2-1 Kasumigaseki 1-chome, Chiyoda-ku, Tokyo 100-0013, Japan.

ZEITSCHRIFT FUER ERBRECHT UND VERMOEGENSNACHFOLGE; Erbrecht - Gesellschaftsrecht - Steuerrecht. see *LAW—Civil Law*

336 DEU ISSN 1432-8933
KKA6076.A13
ZEITSCHRIFT FUER VERMOEGENS- UND IMMOBILIENRECHT; das Recht in den neuen Bundeslaendern. Abbreviated title: V I Z. Text in German. 1991. m. EUR 246 domestic; EUR 266.50 foreign; EUR 23 newsstand/cover (effective 2005). back issues avail. **Document type:** *Journal, Trade.*
Formerly: Zeitschrift fuer Vermoegens- und Investitionsrecht (0940-6867); Incorporates (1990-200?): Deutsch - Deutsche Rechts Zeitschrift (0937-9371)
Related titles: CD-ROM ed.
Indexed: IBR, IBZ.
Published by: Verlag C.H. Beck oHG, Wilhelmstr 9, Munich, 80801, Germany. TEL 49-89-38189338, FAX 49-89-38189398. Circ: 3,000.

336 DEU ISSN 0342-3484
ZEITSCHRIFT FUER ZOELLE UND VERBRAUCHSTEUERN; Aussenwirtschaft, Finanzpolitik, Marktordnung. Text in German. 1925. m. EUR 215.40; EUR 22.30 newsstand/cover (effective 2004). adv. **Document type:** *Journal, Trade.*
Indexed: ELLIS, IBR, IBZ, PHN&I, VITIS, WAE&RSA.
—BLDSC (9496.400000), IE, ingenta. **CCC.**
Published by: Stollfuss Verlag GmbH & Co. KG, Dechenstr 7, Bonn, 53115, Germany. TEL 49-228-7240, FAX 49-228-72491181, info@stollfuss.de, http://www.stollfuss.de/programm/products/0400090.htm. Eds. Arendt, Hampel. adv.: B&W page EUR 1,230, color page EUR 1,845. Circ: 1,300 (paid and controlled).

336 CHN ISSN 1003-4471
ZHONGGUO SHUIWU/CHINA TAXATION. Text in Chinese. m. CNY 78 domestic; USD 31.20 foreign (effective 1999). **Document type:** *Trade.* **Description:** Covers Chinese policies and regulations on taxation.
Related titles: Online - full text ed.: (from East View Information Services).
Indexed: RASB.
Published by: (Guojia Shuiwu-ju/State Taxation Bureau), Zhongguo Shuiwu Zazhishe, 68 Zaolin Qianjie, Beijing, 100053, China. TEL 86-10-6356-6046, FAX 86-10-6356-6042. Ed. Zhang Musheng. **Dist. in US by:** China Books & Periodicals Inc, 360 Swift Ave., Ste. 48, S San Fran, CA 94080-6220. TEL 415-282-2994; **Dist. overseas by:** China International Book Trading Corp, 35 Chegongzhuang Xilu, Haidian District, PO Box 399, Beijing 100044, China. TEL 86-10-68412045, FAX 86-10-68412023, cibtc@mail.cibtc.com.cn, http://www.cibtc.com.cn.

336.2 CHN
ZHONGGUO SHUIWU BAO/CHINA TAXATION NEWS. Text in Chinese. 1991. 4/w. CNY 95.64. **Document type:** *Newspaper.*
Published by: (Guojia Shuiwu Ju), Zhongguo Shuiwu Bao Bianjibu, Ganshiqiao Guang'anmen Wai, Xuanwu-qu, Beijing, 100055, China. TEL 86-10-3269646. Ed. Yang Youjun. Pub. Guan Yongning. **Dist. overseas by:** China International Book Trading Corp, 35 Chegongzhuang Xilu, Haidian District, PO Box 399, Beijing 100044, China.

343.04 CHN ISSN 1007-6174
KNQ3558.A32
ZHONGHUA RENMIN GONGHEGUO SHUISHOU FAGUI GONGGAO/TAX LAWS AND REGULATIONS OF PEOPLE'S REPUBLIC OF CHINA. Text in Chinese. 1996. m. CNY 72 (effective 2004). **Document type:** *Journal, Academic/Scholarly.*
Related titles: Online - full text ed.: (from WanFang Data Corp.).
Published by: Falu Chubanshe/Law Press, Fengtai-qu, Lianhuachi Xili, Zonghe Yewu Lou, Beijing, 100073, China. TEL 86-10-63939680, FAX 86-10-63939681, info@lawpress.com.cn, http://zhrmghgssfggg.periodicals.net.cn/default.html, http://www.lawpress.com.cn/. **Dist. by:** China International Book Trading Corp, 35 Chegongzhuang Xilu, Haidian District, PO Box 399, Beijing 100044, China. TEL 86-10-68412045, FAX 86-10-68412023, cibtc@mail.cibtc.com.cn, http://www.cibtc.com.cn.

336 ZWE
ZIMBABWE. MINISTRY OF FINANCE. BUDGET ESTIMATES. Text in English. 1940. a. ZWD 12. **Document type:** *Government.*
Former titles (until 1995): Zimbabwe. Ministry of Finance. Estimates of Expenditure; (until 1992): Zimbabwe. Ministry of Finance. Financial Statement; Rhodesia. Ministry of Finance. Budget Statement
Published by: Ministry of Finance, Causeway, Private Bag 7705, Harare, Zimbabwe. TEL 263-4-722101, FAX 263-4-796563. Circ: 1,200. **Subscr. to:** Government Printer, Causeway, PO Box CY 341, Harare, Zimbabwe.

350.724 382.7 DNK ISSN 0105-8355
ZISE; told- og skattehistorisk tidsskrift. Text in Danish. 1978. 3/yr. DKK 60 (effective 2001). bk.rev. index. 40 p./no.; back issues avail. **Document type:** *Journal.* **Description:** Customs and tax history.
Indexed: BHA.
Published by: Told- og Skattehistorisk Selskab, Oestbanegade 123, Copenhagen Oe, 2100, Denmark. TEL 45-35-29-73-00, FAX 45-35-43-47-20. Ed. Mikael Venge. R&P Gunnar Jakobsen. Circ: 2,200.

350.724 CHE ISSN 0586-2361
ZOLL - RUNDSCHAU/REVUE DES DOUANES/RIVISTA DELLE DOGANE; Fachzeitschrift der Eidgenoessischen Zollverwaltung. Text in German, French, Italian. 1956. 4/yr. illus. **Document type:** *Journal, Government.*
Indexed: PAIS.
Published by: Directorate General of Customs, Section Information, Monbijoustr 40, Bern, 3003, Switzerland. TEL 41-31-3226743, FAX 41-31-3224294, TELEX 911100-OZD-CH, roger.gauderon@ezv.admin.ch, http://www.zoll.admin.ch. Ed. Roger Gauderon.

336 DEU ISSN 0939-2165
ZOLLRECHT. Text in German. 1977. irreg. looseleaf. price varies. **Document type:** *Monographic series, Trade.*
Published by: Erich Schmidt Verlag GmbH & Co. (Berlin), Genthiner Str 30G, Berlin, 10785, Germany. TEL 49-30-250085-0, FAX 49-30-25008521, vertrieb@esvmedien.de, http://www.erich-schmidt-verlag.de.

336 USA ISSN 1069-4331
KF6449
ZONDERVAN CHURCH AND NONPROFIT ORGANIZATION TAX AND FINANCIAL GUIDE. Text in English. 1991. a. USD 11.99. **Document type:** *Consumer.* **Description:** A complete tax and financial guide for churches and other organizations to help prepare their tax returns each year.
Published by: Zondervan Publishing House, 5300 Patterson Ave S E, Grand Rapids, MI 49530. TEL 616-698-6900, 800-727-3480, FAX 616-698-3439, zpub@zph.com, http://www.zondervan.com. Ed. Stan Gundry. Pub. Scott Bolinder. R&P Carolyn Weidmayer. Circ: 20,000.

336 USA
ZONDERVAN MINISTER'S TAX & FINANCIAL GUIDE. Text in English. 1991. a. USD 14.99. **Description:** A complete guide to help ministers prepare their tax returns each year and plan their financial futures.
Published by: Zondervan Publishing House, 5300 Patterson Ave S E, Grand Rapids, MI 49530. TEL 616-698-6900, 800-727-3480, FAX 616-698-3439, zpub@zph.com, http://www.zondervan.com. Ed. Stan Gundry. R&P Carolyn Weidmayer. Circ: 20,000.

BUSINESS AND ECONOMICS—Small Business

305.412 338.642 USA ISSN 1053-9107
A B C DIALOGUE. Text in English. 1981. bi-m. USD 24 to members (effective 2001). adv. bk.rev. 32 p./no. 3 cols./p.; **Document type:** *Newsletter, Trade.* **Description:** Information related to weddings and wedding business, especially consultants.
Published by: Association of Bridal Consultants, 200 Chestnutland Rd, New Milford, CT 06776-2521. TEL 860-355-0464, FAX 860-354-1404, bridalassn@aol.com, http://www.bridalassn.com. Ed., R&P, Adv. contact Gerard J Monaghan. Circ: 2,800 (controlled).

338.642 346.066 USA
A S B A TODAY. Text in English. bi-m. USD 18 membership. bk.rev. 32 p./no.; **Description:** Includes articles on legislation affecting small business, technology, marketing, getting loans, taxes, trade shows, managing employees, accounting, and all other topics of interest to small business owners.
Published by: American Small Businesses Association, 206 E. College St., Ste. 201, Grapevine, TX 76051-5381. TEL 202-628-6316. Ed., R&P Kristin Liercke. Circ: 30,000 (controlled).

B

THE A S P A JOURNAL. (American Society of Pension Actuaries) see *INSURANCE*

ACCOUNTING FORUM. see *BUSINESS AND ECONOMICS—Accounting*

658.041 USA
ACHIEVE USA HOME BUSINESS JOURNAL. Text in English. 1998. m. back issues avail. **Document type:** *Trade.* **Description:** Covers topics related to small home business owners.
Media: Online - full text.
Address: 13948 Oleander St, Ste 201, Woodbridge, VA 22193. TEL 703-583-8088, editor@achieveusa.com, http://www.achieveusa.com/journal.htm. Ed. Glen Palo.

AGENDA. see *ART*

ALASKA BUSINESS MONTHLY. see *BUSINESS AND ECONOMICS*

ALL ABOUT MAKING MONEY; your guide to financial success. see *BUSINESS AND ECONOMICS—Marketing And Purchasing*

AMERICAN OSTRICH. see *AGRICULTURE*

AMERICAN SWEEPER MAGAZINE. see *ENVIRONMENTAL STUDIES—Waste Management*

AMERICAN WASTE DIGEST. see *ENVIRONMENTAL STUDIES—Waste Management*

AMERICAN WINDOW CLEANER; voice of the professional window cleaner. see *OCCUPATIONS AND CAREERS*

338.642 BGR
ANALIZ NA SEKTORA NA MALKITE I SREDNITE PREDPRIATIA V STRANATA. Text in Bulgarian. a. USD 16 foreign (effective 2002). **Description:** Presents basic economic indexes about the activities of small and average business.
Published by: Natsionalen Statisticheski Institut/National Statistical Institute, ul P Volov, # 2, Sofia, 1038, Bulgaria. FAX 359-2-9803319, publikacii@nsi.bg, http://www.nsi.bg. **Dist. by:** Sofia Books, ul Silivria 16, Sofia 1404, Bulgaria. TEL 359-2-9586257, info@sofiabooks-bg.com, http://www.sofiabooks-bg.com.

338.642 USA
AQUENT MAGAZINE. Text in English. 1999. m. free. adv. illus. back issues avail. **Description:** Dedicated for and about small-business and self-employed professionals.
Media: Online - full text.
Published by: Aquent Partners, 71 W 23rd St, Ste 1608, New York, NY 10010. TEL 212-228-8002, FAX 877-727-8637, site_support@aquent.com, http://www.aquent.com/.

338.642 ITA ISSN 1125-9116
ARGOMENTI. Text in Italian. 1978. 3/yr. EUR 36 domestic; EUR 52 foreign (effective 2003). **Document type:** *Journal.*
Published by: Franco Angeli Edizioni, Viale Monza 106, Milan, 20127, Italy. TEL 39-02-2837141, FAX 39-02-26144793, redazioni@francoangeli.it, http://www.francoangeli.it.

658.8 338.642 USA ISSN 1068-9753
THE ART OF SELF PROMOTION; nuts and bolts for manageable marketing. Text in English. 1990. q. USD 30 domestic; USD 40 foreign (effective 2000). adv. bk.rev. back issues avail. **Document type:** *Newsletter, Trade.* **Description:** Offers practical, inexpensive marketing ideas for self-employed professionals and small business owners.
Related titles: E-mail ed.; Fax ed.; Online - full text ed.

▼ new title ➤ refereed ✶ unverified ◆ full entry avail.

Published by: Ilise Benun, Ed & Pub, PO Box 23, Hoboken, NJ 07030. TEL 201-653-0783, 800-737-0783, FAX 201-222-2494, info@artofselfpromotion.com, http://www.artofselfpromotion.com. R&P, Adv. contact Ilise Benun. Circ: 2,000 (paid).

650 ITA ISSN 0004-3737
ARTIGIANO MODENESE. Text in Italian. 1960. m.
Published by: Libero Artigianato e Piccole Aziende Modenesi, Via Emilia Ouest, 101, Modena, MO 41100, Italy. Ed. Jacobbe Giovanni. Circ: 6,000.

338.642 FRA ISSN 0153-2006
ARTISANAT BATIMENT 34. Text in French. 1975. q. adv.
Published by: Syndicat des Artisans et des Petites Entreprises du Batiment de l, 44 av. Saint-Lazare, Montpellier, 34000, France. Ed. Jose Maldonado.

338.642 USA ISSN 1521-2939
ASIAN ENTERPRISE. Text in English. 1993. m. USD 30 domestic; USD 50 foreign; USD 2.95 newsstand/cover (effective 1999). adv. bk.rev. charts; stat. back issues avail. **Document type:** *Consumer.* **Description:** Focuses on Asian-American small business.
Published by: Asian Business Ventures, Inc., PO Box 2135, Walnut, CA 91788. TEL 909-860-3316, FAX 909-865-4915, asianent@yahoo.com. Ed. Ryan Montez. Pub., R&P, Adv. contact Gelly Borromeo. B&W page USD 2,500, color page USD 3,300; trim 8.37 x 10.87. Circ: 33,000. **Subscr. to:** WSB Group, 1242 S Diamond Bar Blvd D, Diamond Bar, CA 91765. TEL 909-449-1073. **Dist. by:** Ingram Periodicals 1240 Heil Quaker Blvd, La Vergne, TN 37086-7000.

338.642 USA ISSN 1082-6386
ATLANTA SMALL BUSINESS MONTHLY. Text in English. 1987. 12/yr. USD 15 (effective 1998). adv. bk.rev. **Document type:** *Newspaper.* **Description:** Provides "how to" information for owners of small to mid-size businesses; presents such topics as advertising, marketing, finance management, selling and customer service.
Formerly: Atlanta Small Business Journal
Published by: Media 3 Publications, Inc., 4721 Chamblee Dunwoody Rd 100 B, Atlanta, GA 30338-6000. TEL 404-394-2811, FAX 404-394-2719, media@mindspring.com, http://www.media3pub.com. Ed. Millann Funk. Circ: 25,000 (controlled).

AUSTRALIA. BUREAU OF STATISTICS. CHARACTERISTICS OF SMALL BUSINESS, AUSTRALIA. see *BUSINESS AND ECONOMICS—Abstracting, Bibliographies, Statistics*

AUSTRALIA. BUREAU OF STATISTICS. SMALL BUSINESS IN AUSTRALIA. see *BUSINESS AND ECONOMICS—Abstracting, Bibliographies, Statistics*

AUSTRALIAN SMALL BUSINESS LAW JOURNAL. see *LAW—Corporate Law*

AZIENDITALIA; mensile per gli enti locali e le loro aziende. see *BUSINESS AND ECONOMICS—Management*

338 GBR
B R A V E. Text in English. 3/yr.
Address: Small Business Centre, Coach House, 2 Upper York St, Bristol, Glos BS2 8QN, United Kingdom. TEL 44-272-272222, FAX 44-272-445661. Ed. Neil Pickford. Circ: 4,000.

338.642 BGD
BANGLADESH SMALL AND COTTAGE INDUSTRIES CORPORATION. BULLETIN. Text in Bengali. m. **Document type:** *Bulletin.*
Published by: Bangladesh Small and Cottage Industries Corporation, 137-138, Motijheel Commercial Area, Dhaka, 2, Bangladesh.

BANQUES DES PROFESSIONNELS. see *BUSINESS AND ECONOMICS—Banking And Finance*

338.642 USA ISSN 0736-1904
BARTER UPDATE. Text in English. 1983. a. looseleaf. USD 10 newsstand/cover (effective 2005). bibl. **Document type:** *Newsletter.* **Description:** Ideas and possibilities on barter.
Related titles: Microfiche ed.
—CCC.
Published by: Prosperity and Profits Unlimited, PO Box 416, Denver, CO 80201-0416. TEL 303-575-5676, FAX 303-575-1187, starsuccess@excite.com, http://www.curriculumresourceonline.com. Ed., R&P A Doyle TEL 303-575-5676. Circ: 1,000 (paid and controlled).

338.6 BEL ISSN 0067-5393
BELGIUM. CONSEIL SUPERIEUR DES CLASSES MOYENNES. RAPPORT ANNUEL. Text in French. 1951. a. free. **Document type:** *Government.*
Formerly: Belgium. Conseil Superieur des Classes Moyennes. Rapport Annuel du Secretaire General
Related titles: ◆ Dutch ed.: Belgium. Hoge Raad voor de Middenstand. Jaarverslag.

Published by: Conseil Superieur des Classes Moyennes, WTC Tower III, 2nd Fl, Bd Emile Jacqmain 158, Brussels, 1000, Belgium. TEL 32-2-2083404, FAX 32-2-2083405. Ed., R&P Marc Hoogmartens.

338 GBR
BETTER BUSINESS; for all tiny businesses and the self employed. Text in English. 1992. 10/yr. GBP 62 (effective 2004). adv. bk.rev. index. back issues avail. **Document type:** *Newsletter.* **Description:** Contains practical articles on small-business marketing, office management and personnel development for people working from home. Also covers tax law and technology updates.
Formerly: Home Run (0968-2066)
Published by: Active Information, Cribau Mill, Llanvair Discoed, Chepstow, NP16 6RD, United Kingdom. TEL 44-1291-641222, FAX 44-1291-641777, info@better-business.co.uk, http://www.better-business.co.uk. Ed., R&P Sophie Chalmers. Pub., Adv. contact Andrew James.

338.642 371.42 CAN ISSN 1198-8819
BIG DREAMS. Text in English. 1994. m. USD 20. back issues avail.
Related titles: Online - full text ed.: ISSN 1200-5460.
Address: 2202 Haversley Ave, Coquitlam, BC V3J 1W4, Canada. TEL 604-760-1631, FAX 604-931-2135, duncans@wimsey.com, http://www.wimsey.com/~duncans/BigDreams. Ed. Duncan Stickings.

650 IND ISSN 0006-2219
BIHAR INDUSTRIES; quarterly bulletin for small industries. Text in English, Hindi. 1962. q. INR 5. adv. bk.rev. charts; pat.; stat. **Document type:** *Bulletin.*
Published by: Directorate of Industries, Department of Industries and Technical Education, Patna, Bihar, India. Ed. S Krishnan. Circ: 2,500.

BIZ TIPS NEWSLETTER. see *COMPUTERS—Internet*

658.041 USA
BIZLINKS HOMEBASED BUSINESS NEWS. Variant title: BizLinks Weekly Ezine. Text in English. 1997. w. free. adv. **Document type:** *Newsletter.* **Description:** For homebased and small business owners, including marketing reports.
Media: Online - full text.
Address: PO Box 09654, Columbus, OH 43209-0654. TEL 614-237-0846, uonline@3wave.com, http://youonline.net/bizlinks/index.htm. Pub. Victoria Ring. Circ: 11,149.

338 USA
BIZNET ENEWS. Text in English. 1997. w. free. **Document type:** *Newsletter.* **Description:** Devoted to home based and small businesses that are marketing on and off the Internet.
Media: Online - full text.
Address: rlbrye@gate.net. Ed. Rick Brye.

338.642 USA
BIZSUCCESS BREAKTHROUGHS. Text in English. s-m. free. **Description:** Presents reports with practical information, ideas, tips and techniques on how to get real breakthroughs in your business and personal life.
Media: Online - full text.
Address: TEL 800-272-1575, FAX 760-325-9608, gary@bizsuccess.com, http://www.bizsuccess.com/newsletter.htm. Pub. Gary Lockwood.

658.041 USA
THE BIZY MOM NEWSLETTER. Text in English. 1997. w. free. adv. **Document type:** *Newsletter.* **Description:** A resource guide for women with children who want to work at home and for those who already do. Includes business opportunities.
Media: Online - full text.
Published by: Bizy Moms, PO Box 451, Mnt Shasta, CA 96067. TEL 530-938-3050, bizymommy@aol.com, http://www.bizymoms.com. Ed., R&P Liz Folger.

338.642 USA ISSN 1063-3561
BOOTSTRAPPIN' ENTREPRENEUR; the newsletter for individuals with great ideas and a little bit of cash. Text in English. 1992. q. looseleaf. USD 30 (effective 2000). **Document type:** *Newsletter.* **Description:** Covers starting and building a business on a mini-budget, including low-cost marketing strategies, management ideas, success stories.
Related titles: Online - full text ed.
Published by: Research Done Write, 6308 W 89th St, pmb 306 Ul, Los Angeles, CA 90045. TEL 310-568-9861, subscribe@kimberlystansell.com, http://www.kimberlystansell.com. Ed. Kimberly Stansell.

338.642 FRA ISSN 0755-1541
BULLETIN DES METIERS ET DE L'ARTISANAT. Text in French. 1940. 11/yr. **Document type:** *Bulletin.*
Address: 62 rue la Boetie, Paris, 75008, France. TEL 45-61-04-61, FAX 45-63-95-43. Ed. Jean Etienne. Circ: 25,000.

338
BUSINESS DIGEST OF DELAWARE VALLEY✱. Text in English. 1977. 12/yr. USD 20. adv. **Description:** Focuses on small business.
Related titles: Online - full text ed.: 1977 (from The Dialog Corporation).

Indexed: BusDate.
Published by: Business Digest of Philadelphia Inc., PO Box 324, Bala Cynwyd, PA 19004-0324. TEL 215-477-8620. Circ: 25,000.

338 CAN
BUSINESS EXECUTIVE. Text in English. 1994. m. CND 48 (effective 1999). bk.rev.; software rev. 20 p./no. 4 cols./p.; **Document type:** *Newspaper.* **Description:** Contains local business news coverage, columns on human resources, law, computers, finance, and physical fitness submitted by local business people. Features automobile column and local government pages.
Published by: Business Executive Inc., 466 Speers Rd, Ste 220, Oakville, ON L6K 3W9, Canada. TEL 905-845-8300, FAX 905-845-9086, wendyp@interlog.com, http://www.busexec.com. Ed. Wendy Peters. Pub., R&P, Adv. contact Thomas Peters. B&W page CND 2,305; trim 14 x 10. Circ: 25,800 (controlled).

338.642 GBR ISSN 0955-789X
BUSINESS FRANCHISE; create your own commercial success. Text in English. 10/yr. GBP 25; GBP 2.60 newsstand/cover (effective 2000). adv. **Document type:** *Magazine, Consumer.* **Description:** News and views from the world of franchising.
Related titles: Online - full text ed.: (from EBSCO Publishing, Gale Group).
Published by: C M P Information Ltd. (Subsidiary of: United Business Media), 630 Chiswick High Rd, London, W4 5BG, United Kingdom. TEL 44-20-8742-7828, FAX 44-20-8742-0387. Ed. Lynne Lister. Adv. contact Anna Wales. Circ: 20,000. **Dist. by:** Seymour Distribution Ltd, 86 Newman St, London W1T 3EX, United Kingdom. FAX 44-207-396-8002, enquiries@seymour.co.uk.

338.642 346.066 USA ISSN 0274-8991
BUSINESS FRANCHISE GUIDE. Text in English. 2 base vols. plus m. updates. looseleaf. USD 1,175 base vol(s).; USD 1,798 combined subscription print, online & CD-ROM eds. (effective 2004). **Document type:** *Consumer.* **Description:** Contains hundreds of pages of FTC and UFOC guidelines that aid franchisers in developing a uniform format for use under various state laws that require disclosure and registration prior to the sale of franchises.
Related titles: CD-ROM ed.: USD 1,182 (effective 2004); Online - full content ed.: USD 1,305 (effective 2004).
—CCC.
Published by: C C H Inc., 2700 Lake Cook Rd, Riverwoods, IL 60015. TEL 847-267-7000, 800-449-6439, cust_serv@cch.com, http://www.cch.com. Pub. Stacey Caywood.

BUSINESS GAZETTE. see *BUSINESS AND ECONOMICS—Management*

338 USA
BUSINESS HOTLINE ONLINE. Text in English. m. **Description:** Covers topics facing today's small and home based businesses: accounting and finance, legal issues, direct mail, public speaking, personal finance, marketing tips, import & export, business opportunities, franchising information and marketing on the internet.
Media: Online - full text.
Address: webmaster@bizhotline.com, http://www.bizhotline.com.

338.642 USA ISSN 1082-3778
BUSINESS IN BROWARD. Text in English. 1987. 7/yr. USD 32 (effective 2000). adv. bk.rev. **Document type:** *Trade.* **Description:** Covers local business and features local people.
Related titles: Microform ed.: (from PQC); Online - full text ed.: (from O C L C Online Computer Library Center, Inc., ProQuest Information & Learning).
Indexed: ABIn, BusDate.
Published by: Lauderdale Publishing, 500 S.E. 17th St., Ste. 101, Box 460669, Ft. Lauderdale, FL 33346. TEL 954-763-3338, FAX 954-763-4481, SFBIZ@mindspring.com. Ed. Cathy Duber. Pub. Sherry Friedlander. adv.: B&W page USD 1,900, color page USD 2,400; trim 11 x 8.5. Circ: 30,000.

338.642 GBR ISSN 0266-8297
BUSINESS INFORMER. Text in English. 1984. bi-m. GBP 24; GBP 29 foreign. bk.rev. back issues avail. **Description:** Digests UK and EU business legislation and provides associated business information for small- and medium-sized businesses, trade bodies, and business-support groups.
Related titles: Diskette ed.
Published by: Denholme Publishing, PO Box 39, Hartlepool, Cleveland TS24 1SJ, United Kingdom. TEL 44-191-518-4281. Ed., Pub. Alan K Roxborough. Circ: 70,000 (paid).

338.642 USA ISSN 1056-6244
BUSINESS INSIGHT (RICHLAND). Text in English. 1985. m. USD 24. adv. bk.rev. back issues avail. **Document type:** *Trade.* **Description:** Provides local small and medium business executives with information to help them effectively participate in the local business community.
Formerly (until 1991): Business Digest (0897-5221)
Published by: B C O-Marketing Communications, Inc., PO Box 347, Richland, MI 49083-0347. TEL 269-629-3131, FAX 269-629-0803. Ed. Thea Lapham. Pub., R&P Robert Beardsley. Adv. contact R Beardsley. Circ: 15,000 (controlled).

338.642 382 658 USA ISSN 1091-9597
BUSINESS INTELLIGENCE REPORT; strategies and trends for the successful business. Text in English. 1997. m. looseleaf. USD 89 (effective 2000). bk.rev. abstr.; stat. **Document type:** *Newsletter.* **Description:** A fast-read, 3 page fax report that provides business owners and managers with the latest trends, news, tips and strategies in business. Each issue includes a short book excerpt and information analyzed from up to 150 sources.
Related titles: E-mail ed.; Fax ed.
Published by: D B H Communications, Inc., 22337, Kansas City, MO 64113-0337. TEL 816-523-1111, FAX 816-363-3433, dbhcomm@aol.com. Ed. Rebecca Spencer. Pub. John Holsen. Circ: 35,050 (paid); 4,000 (controlled). **Subscr. to:** PO Box 22337, Kansas City, MO 64113.

THE BUSINESS JOURNAL (LIMA); West Central Ohio's leading business publication. see *BUSINESS AND ECONOMICS—Domestic Commerce*

338 USA
THE BUSINESS MONTHLY; the business to business newspaper of Howard County, Laurel & BWI business district. Text in English. 1993. m. USD 25 (effective 2000). adv. illus. **Document type:** *Newspaper, Trade.* **Description:** Covers news and developments in Howard County, Laurel, and Baltimore-Washington International (BWI) business district business, education, technology, banking, construction, finace, and health.
Formerly (until Jan. 1997): Howard County Business Monthly
Published by: Business Monthly, 5550 Sterrett Pl, Ste 214, Columbia, MD 21044-2626. TEL 410-740-7300, FAX 410-992-9754, BizMonthly@aol.com, http://www.bizmonthly.com. Ed. Judith Tripp. Pub., R&P, Adv. contact Carole Pickett. B&W page USD 1,296, color page USD 1,696. Circ: 27,000.

338.642 GBR
BUSINESS NEWS (SOUTH EAST HAMPSHIRE). Text in English. 1987. m. (except January & August). GBP 40 (effective 2000).
Published by: Bishops Printers, Baltic House 4 Fl, Kingston Crescent, Portsmouth, PO2 2QL, United Kingdom. TEL 44-023-9266-6622, FAX 44-023-9269-6666, sehants@chamber.org.uk. Circ: 3,000.

338.642 USA ISSN 0279-4276
HC107.N8
BUSINESS NORTH CAROLINA. Text in English. 1981. m. USD 30 (effective 2005). adv. back issues avail. **Document type:** *Magazine, Trade.* **Description:** Provides cutting edge information about trends and players that can make or break your business.
Related titles: Microform ed.: (from PQC); Online - full text ed.: (from EBSCO Publishing, Florida Center for Library Automation, Gale Group, Northern Light Technology, Inc., O C L C Online Computer Library Center, Inc., ProQuest Information & Learning, The Dialog Corporation).
Indexed: ABIn, Agr, BusDate, PAIS, T&II.
—CCC.
Published by: Red Hand Media, Llc., 5435 77 Center Dr, Ste 50, Charlotte, NC 28217-0711. TEL 704-523-6987, FAX 704-523-4211, bnc@businessnc.com, http://www.businessnc.com. Ed. David Kinney. Pub. Ben Kinney. adv.: B&W page USD 2,575, color page USD 3,865. Circ: 28,500 (paid and controlled).

338.642 USA ISSN 1042-6175
HF5429.235.U5
BUSINESS OPPORTUNITIES HANDBOOK. Text in English. q. USD 22.95; USD 6.99 newsstand/cover (effective 2005). **Document type:** *Directory.* **Description:** Contains detailed listings on over 2,500 companies selling franchises and other business opportunities.
Related titles: Online - full text ed.
Published by: Enterprise Magazines, Inc., 1020 N Broadway, Ste 111, Milwaukee, WI 53202. TEL 800-272-0246, info@busop1.com, http://www.busop1.com. Eds. Mr. Michael McDermott, Ms. Maria Lahm. Pub. Mrs. Betsy L Green. R&P Ms. Maria Lahm. Adv. contacts Ms. Barbara Yelmene, Ms. Kristin Over, Ms. Maria Lahm.

338 USA
BUSINESS ORGANIZATIONS: FRANCHISING. Text in English. 1969. 4 base vols. looseleaf. USD 995 (effective 1999). **Description:** Synthesizes legal, business and tax considerations of modern franchising.
Related titles: CD-ROM ed.
Published by: Matthew Bender & Co., Inc. (Subsidiary of: LexisNexis North America), 1275 Broadway, Albany, NY 12204. international@bender.com, http://www.bender.com, http://bender.lexisnexis.com. Ed. Gladys Glickman.

338.642 USA ISSN 0190-4914
HF5001
THE BUSINESS OWNER. Text in English. 1977. bi-m. USD 199 (effective 2005). 16 p./no. 2 cols./p.; back issues avail.; reprints avail. **Document type:** *Newsletter, Trade.* **Description:** Covers how to value a business, how to save taxes, and selling and buying businesses.
Incorporates (1982-199?): You and Your Business (0736-4865)
Related titles: Online - full text ed.
Indexed: ABIn, ATI, BPIA, BusI, T&II.
Published by: D.L. Perkins, LLC, 7010 S Yale, Ste 120, Tulsa, OK 74136. TEL 918-493-4900, FAX 918-493-4924, 800-634-0605, renae@thebusinessowner.com, http://www.thebusinessowner.com. Ed., Pub. David L Perkins Jr. R&P, Adv. contact Renae Williams TEL 918-493-4900.

338.642 USA ISSN 1084-4473
HD62.7
BUSINESS PLANS HANDBOOK. Text in English. 1994. a., latest vol.9. USD 160 (effective 2005). **Document type:** *Trade.* **Description:** Contains a collection of actual business plans compiled by entrepreneurs seeking funding for small businesses throughout North America.
Published by: Gale Group (Subsidiary of: Thomson Corporation), 27500 Drake Rd, Farmington Hills, MI 48331-3535. TEL 248-699-8061, 800-877-4253, FAX 248-699-4253, galeord@gale.com, http://www.gale.com. Ed. Angela Shupe.

338 GBR
BUSINESS SERVICES RESEARCH MONOGRAPH. Text in English. 1994. irreg. GBP 15 per issue (effective 2002). **Document type:** *Monographic series, Academic/Scholarly.*
Published by: Small Enterprise Research Team, Open University Business School, Open University Business School, Michael Young Building, Walton Hall, Milton Keynes, Bucks MK7 6AA, United Kingdom. TEL 44-1908-655831, FAX 44-1908-655898, oubs-sbrt@open.ac.uk, http://www.sbrt.co.uk. Ed., R&P Dr. Colin Gray.

BUSINESS THEME E-ZINE. see *BUSINESS AND ECONOMICS—Marketing And Purchasing*

658.041 USA
THE BUSINESS WOMAN'S ADVANTAGE NEWSLETTER. Text in English. m. **Document type:** *Newsletter.* **Description:** Covers marketing, finance and business for women.
Media: Online - full text.
Published by: Business Woman's Advantage Newsletter shrigley85@aol.com, http://www.womansadvantage.com/bwa. Ed., Pub. Mershon Shrigley.

338 GBR
C B I - PANNEL KERR FORSTER - S M E TRENDS REPORT. Text in English. 1994. q. GBP 90 to non-members; GBP 45 to members. adv. **Description:** Provides details, analysis and commentary for around 900 small to medium (SME) firms involved in manufacturing in the UK. Aims to present the type of information present in the Industrial Trends Survey for companies with under 500 employees. Includes analysis of optimism, orders, employment, investment, costs, prices, output as well as historical data and a fact file with current statistics.
Published by: Confederation of British Industry, Centre Point, 103 New Oxford St, London, WC1A 1DU, United Kingdom. TEL 44-171-395-8164, FAX 44-171-240-1578. Ed. Sudhair Junankar. R&P Wendy Hayes TEL 44-171-395-8036. Adv. contact Frances Hughes.

C C A NEWS. see *BUSINESS AND ECONOMICS—Banking And Finance*

C P A CLIENT BULLETIN. see *BUSINESS AND ECONOMICS—Accounting*

338.9 COL
CAJA DE CREDITO AGRARIO, INDUSTRIAL Y MINERO. FINANCIAMIENTO DE LA PEQUENA Y MEDIANA INDUSTRIA. Text in Spanish. 1973. a. charts; stat.
Published by: Caja de Credito Agrario Industrial y Minero, Bogota, CUND, Colombia.

338.642 USA ISSN 0883-6159
CALIFORNIA BROKER. Text in English. 1982. m. USD 42 (effective 2005). adv. back issues avail. **Document type:** *Magazine, Trade.*
Formerly: Calunderwriter
Published by: McGee Publishers, Inc., 217 E Alameda Ave, Ste 301, Burbank, CA 91502-2622. TEL 818-848-2957, FAX 818-843-3489, http://www.calbrokermag.com. Ed. Kate Kinkade. Pub. Ric Madden. Adv. contact Scott Halverson. B&W page USD 4,101, color page USD 4,986; trim 8.375 x 10.875. Circ: 25,000 (paid).

338 CAN ISSN 1495-9704
CANADA. INDUSTRY CANADA. CANADA SMALL BUSINESS FINANCING ACT AND SMALL BUSINESS LOAN ACT. ANNUAL REPORT. Text in English, French. 1961. a.
Formerly (until 2000): Canada. Department of Finance. Small Business Loans Act. Annual Report (0527-687X)
Published by: Industry Canada/Industrie Canada, Distribution Services, Communications & Marketing Branch, Rm 268D, West Tower, C.D. Howe Bldg, 235 Queen St, Ottawa, ON K1A 0H5, Canada. Circ: 7,800.

CANADIAN OFFICE GUIDE. see *BUSINESS AND ECONOMICS—Economic Situation And Conditions*

338 CAN
CANADIAN SMALL BUSINESS MANAGEMENT MANUAL. Text in English. bi-m. CND 520 (effective 2003). **Document type:** *Trade.* **Description:** Provides a handy, practical reference for owners and administrators of businesses in Canada. Covers finance, marketing and personnel.
Formerly (until 1995): Canadian Small Business Guide
Published by: C C H Canadian Ltd., 90 Sheppard Ave E, Ste 300, North York, ON M2N 6X1, Canada. TEL 416-224-2248, 800-268-4522, FAX 416-224-2243, cservice@cch.ca, http://www.cch.ca.

338 USA
CASHFLOW. Text in English. 1996. bi-m. adv. **Document type:** *Trade.*
Published by: MarketLynx, 462 Boston St, Topsfield, MA 01983. TEL 508-887-7900. Ed. Barry Harrigan. Circ: (controlled).

CELLULAR SALES & MARKETING; cell the world!. see *COMMUNICATIONS—Telephone And Telegraph*

CHIEF EXECUTIVE OFFICERS NEWSLETTER; for the entrepreneurial manager and the professionals who advise him. see *BUSINESS AND ECONOMICS—Management*

CLEANER. see *HEATING, PLUMBING AND REFRIGERATION*

658 338 USA ISSN 1092-7964
CLEANING BUSINESS; published monthly for the self-employed cleaning & maintenance professional. Text in English. 1996. q. free to qualified personnel (effective 2005). adv. bk.rev. Index. back issues avail. **Document type:** *Magazine, Trade.* **Description:** Provides information for small cleaning and maintenance contractors. Covers janitorial, house cleaning, fire restoration, high pressure washing, carpet and upholstery cleaning, window washing and commercial buildings.
Formerly: Service Business (0736-5764)
Related titles: Online - full text ed.
Published by: Cleaning Consultant Services, Inc., 3693 E. Marginal Way S., Seattle, WA 98134. TEL 206-682-9748, FAX 206-622-6876, wgriffin@cleaningconsultants.com, http://www.cleaningbusiness.com/, http://www.cleaningconsultants.com. Pub. William R Griffin. Adv. contact Nanette Bordner. B&W page USD 400; trim 10.88 x 8.25. Circ: 5,000 (paid and free).

338.642 613.7 USA ISSN 1043-9692
CLUB BUSINESS INTERNATIONAL. Variant title: C B I Magazine. Text in English. 1982. m. USD 72 domestic; USD 120 foreign; free to members (effective 2005). adv. **Document type:** *Magazine, Trade.* **Description:** Concerned with the quality and profitability of racquet and fitness clubs. Includes club profiles, how-to articles and product information.
Related titles: Supplement(s): F I T Equipment Buyers Guide.
Indexed: SportS.
Published by: International Health, Racquet & Sportsclub Association, 263 Summer St, Boston, MA 02210-1114. TEL 617-951-0055, FAX 617-951-0056, cbi@ihrsa.org, http://www.ihrsa.org. Ed. Craig Waters. Pub. Jay Ablondi. Circ: 24,000.

338.642 USA
COACHING TIP OF THE WEEK. Text in English. w. bk.rev. back issues avail. **Document type:** *Newsletter.* **Description:** Designed for business owners, entrepreneurs, and professionals.
Media: Online - full text.
Address: PO Box 2930, Silverdale, WA 98383. TEL 360-308-0760, coachtip@jackienagel.com, http://www.jackienagel.com/coachtip.html/. Ed. Jackie Nagel.

338.642 741.5 USA ISSN 1534-4606
PN6714
COMICS & GAMES RETAILER. Text in English. 1992. m. USD 29.95; USD 5 newsstand/cover; free to qualified personnel (effective 2004). adv. **Document type:** *Magazine, Trade.* **Description:** Covers managing a comics shop and creating profit.
Formerly (until 2001): Comics Retailer (1059-9401)
Published by: Krause Publications, Inc. (Subsidiary of: F & W Publications, Inc.), 700 E State St, Iola, WI 54990-0001. TEL 715-445-2214, 800-258-0929, FAX 715-445-4087, info@krause.com, http://www.krause.com/comics/cr/. Ed. John Jackson Miller Jr. TEL 715-445-2214 ext 360. Pub. Mark Williams TEL 715-445-2214 ext 884. Adv. contact Norma Jean Fochs. B&W page USD 1,547, color page USD 2,346; trim 7.75 x 10.5. Circ: 5,201 (controlled and free).

338 FRA
COMMERCANT. Text in French. bi-m. adv.
Published by: Confederation des Commercants-Detaillants de France et d'Outre Mer, 21 rue du Chateau d'Eau, Paris, 75010, France. Ed. Roger Stoll.

338 GBR
COMMUNITY FUND RESEARCH. Text in English. irreg.
Published by: Community Fund, St Vincent House, 16 Suffolk St, London, SW1Y 4NL, United Kingdom. TEL 44-20-7747-5299, enquiries@community-fund.org.uk, http://www.community-fund.org.uk.

B

658.041 USA
COMPLETE ENTREPRENEUR. Text in English. fortn. free.
Document type: *Newsletter.* **Description:** Provides a wide array of business resources, marketing tools, and feature articles to help small or home businesses expand.
Media: Online - full text.
Address: joan@complete-entrepreneur.com, http://www.complete-entrepreneur.com.

658.156029 USA ISSN 1089-2664
THE COMPLETE GIFT BASKET INDUSTRY REFERENCE DIRECTORY. Text in English. 1996. a. USD 30 (effective 2000). **Document type:** *Directory, Trade.* **Description:** Contains categories of service-related resources for gift basket businesses in all stages of development.
Published by: Sweet Survival, PO Box 31, River Street Sta, Paterson, NJ 07544-0031. TEL 973-279-2799, FAX 973-742-0700, survival@sweetsurvival.com, http://www.sweetsurvival.com. Ed., Pub., R&P, Adv. contact Shirley Frazier. Circ: 850 (paid).

338.642 USA
A CONCISE OVERVIEW; business valuation of small and midsize private companies. Text in English. irreg. USD 24 per issue domestic (effective 2004). adv. **Document type:** *Trade.*
Published by: D.L. Perkins, LLC, 7010 S Yale, Ste 120, Tulsa, OK 74136. TEL 918-493-4900, FAX 918-493-4924, 800-634-0605, renae@thebusinessowner.com, http://www.thebusinessowner.com/mini_reports.php. Pub., R&P David L Perkins Jr. Adv. contact Renae Williams TEL 918-493-4900.

338.642 USA ISSN 1089-5825
CONTRACT PROFESSIONAL; the magazine for IT contractors and consultants. Text in English. 1996. m. USD 30; USD 45 in Canada; USD 60 elsewhere. adv. illus.; tr.lit. **Document type:** *Trade.*
Indexed: CompLI.
Published by: Skinner - James Publishing, 125 Walnut St, Watertown, MA 02172. http://www.cpuniverse.com. Ed. Tony Bogar. Pub. Bob Ziegel. R&P Kathy Kenny. Adv. contact Michael Lamattina. Circ: 50,000.

338 USA
COTTAGE CONNECTION (CHICAGO). Text in English. 1982. bi-m. USD 45. adv. bk.rev. charts; illus.; stat.; tr.lit. back issues avail. **Document type:** *Newsletter.* **Description:** Profiles home-based businesses; articles on legal, accounting, and zoning issues.
Published by: National Association for the Cottage Industry, PO Box 14850, Chicago, IL 60614. TEL 773-472-8116. Ed. Virginia McCullough. Pub. Caralee Smith Kern. Circ: 8,000.

338.642 IND ISSN 0970-7387
COTTAGE INDUSTRIES; an industrial monthly journal. Text in English. 1967. m. INR 100, USD 25 (effective 1999). bk.rev. back issues avail. **Document type:** *Proceedings.*
Description: Features industrial technical projects for entrepreneurs.
Published by: Small Industry Research Institute, 4-43 Roop Nagar, P O Box 2106, New Delhi, 110 007, India. TEL 91-11-2910805, FAX 91-11-2923955, TELEX 031 61028 SIRI IN. Ed. D C Gupta. Circ: 10,000.

COUNTRY SAMPLER'S COUNTRY BUSINESS. see *GIFTWARE AND TOYS*

338.642 USA ISSN 0149-6956
HC107.I3
CRAIN'S CHICAGO BUSINESS. Text in English. 1978. w. (Mon.). USD 94.95 domestic IL, IN, MI & WI; USD 109 domestic other states; USD 148 in Canada; USD 148 elsewhere (effective 2005). adv. reprint service avail. from PQC. **Document type:** *Newspaper, Consumer.* **Description:** Publishes news stories in the metropolitan Chicago market. Includes articles on executive travel, telecommunications, health care, and international business.
Incorporates (1993-1997?): Crain's Small Business (Chicago ed.) (1078-3296)
Related titles: Microfiche ed.: (from PQC); Online - full text ed.: Chicago Business. ISSN 1557-7902 (from bigchalk, EBSCO Publishing, Florida Center for Library Automation, Gale Group, H.W. Wilson, Northern Light Technology, Inc., O C L C Online Computer Library Center, Inc., ProQuest Information & Learning, The Dialog Corporation).
Indexed: ABIn, B&I, BPI, BusDate, LRI, T&II.
—CCC.
Published by: Crain Communications, Inc., 1155 Gratiot Ave, Detroit, MI 48207-2997. TEL 313-446-6000, editor@chicagobusiness.com, http://www.chicagobusiness.com/mag/, http://www.crain.com. Ed. Jeff Bailey. Pub. David Blake. adv.: B&W page USD 13,580, color page USD 16,940. Circ: 50,528.

CREATIVE OUTLETS. see *ARTS AND HANDICRAFTS*

338 686.2 USA
THE CROUSER REPORT. Text in English. 1986. m. (online ed. w.). USD 195 (effective 2000). bk.rev.; software rev. stat. back issues avail. **Document type:** *Newsletter.*
Related titles: Online - full text ed.
Published by: Crouser & Associates, Inc., 235 Dutch Rd, Charleston, WV 25302. TEL 304-342-5100, FAX 304-342-5187, office@crouser.com, http://www.crouser.com. Ed., Pub. Thomas P Crouser. Circ: 1,000 (paid).

338.642 ESP ISSN 1131-6985
CUADERNOS DE ESTUDIOS EMPRESARIALES. Text in Spanish. 1991. a., latest vol.11, 2001. EUR 21 in the European Union; EUR 25 elsewhere (effective 2004). back issues avail. **Document type:** *Journal, Academic/Scholarly.*
Description: Promotes university and business relationships.
—CINDOC.
Published by: (Universidad Complutense de Madrid, Escuela Universitaria de Estudios Empresariales), Universidad Complutense de Madrid, Servicio de Publicaciones, C Isaac Peral s/n, Ciudad Universitaria, Madrid, 28040, Spain. TEL 34-91-3946934, FAX 34-91-3946978, castand@emp.ucm.es, servicio@publicaciones.ucm.es, http://www.ucm.es/publicaciones. Ed. Jose Maria Munoz Yusta.

DAILY JOURNAL OF COMMERCE (PORTLAND). see *BUSINESS AND ECONOMICS—Domestic Commerce*

338 USA
DATA; national newsletter for campground buyers & owners. Text in English. 1983. bi-m. USD 30 (effective 1999). **Document type:** *Newsletter.*
Formerly: Campgroundata
Published by: Campground Data, 1004 Tequesta Trl., Lake Wales, FL 33898-6546. TEL 863-676-0009, db@campground-data.com, http://www.campground-data.com. Ed. Dale S Bourdette. Circ: 4,000.

338.642 USA ISSN 1533-6395
DAYTON BUSINESS JOURNAL. Text in English. 1990. w. (Fri.). USD 77 (effective 2005). adv. bk.rev. charts. back issues avail.; reprints avail. **Document type:** *Newspaper, Trade.*
Former titles: The Business News (Dayton) (1098-3619); Miami Valley Business News
Related titles: Online - full text ed.
Published by: American City Business Journals, Inc. (Dayton), 137 N Main St, 400, Dayton, OH 45402-1772. TEL 937-222-6900, FAX 937-222-9967, dayton@bizjournals.com, trpedmore@amcity.com, http://www.bizjournals.com/dayton/, http://ww.amcity.com/dayton. Circ: 10,000.

338.642 RUS ISSN 1561-7637
DELOVAYA MOSKVA. Text in Russian. 1993. w. RUR 528 for 6 mos. (effective 2005). **Document type:** *Newspaper, Trade.*
Related titles: Online - full text ed.: ISSN 1606-1438.
Published by: (Meriya Moskvy/Moscow Mayor's Office), Izdatel'skii Dom Delovaya Pressa, Staromonetnyi per 10, Moscow, 109180, Russian Federation. TEL 7-095-9508360, sales@delpressa.ru, http://www.delpressa.ru. Ed. Evgenii Seryi. Circ: 54,000. **Co-sponsor:** Fond Podderzhki Malogo i Srednego Biznesa.

338 IND
DEVELOPMENT AND POLICY RESEARCH. Text in English. 1973. bi-m. INR 250, USD 100. **Document type:** *Abstract/Index.*
Formerly: S E N D O C Bulletin. Part 2: Economics and Development (0970-8723)
Published by: National Institute of Small Industry Extension Training, Small Enterprises National Documentation Centre, Yousufguda, Hyderabad, Andhra Pradesh 500 045, India. TEL 91-40-238544, FAX 91-40-238547, TELEX 425-6381-SIET-IN. Ed. G U K Rao.

DIGITAL IMAGING DIGEST. see *PHOTOGRAPHY*

THE DIGITAL WOMAN ONLINE; women with their modems running. see *BUSINESS AND ECONOMICS—Management*

338.642 384.33 USA ISSN 1529-3203
DOCTOR EBIZ; helping small business succeed online. Text in English. 2000. w. adv. back issues avail. **Document type:** *Newsletter, Trade.* **Description:** Provides answers to e-business questions submitted by small business owners.
Media: Online - full content (from Florida Center for Library Automation). **Related titles:** E-mail ed.; Online - full text ed.: (from Gale Group).
Published by: Wilson Internet Services, P O Box 308, Rocklin, CA 95677-0308. TEL 916-652-4659, rfwilson@wilsonweb.com, http://www.doctorebiz.com/, http://www.wilsonweb.com. Ed., Pub. Ralph F. Wilson.

DORADCA PODATNIKA. see *BUSINESS AND ECONOMICS—Public Finance, Taxation*

658.2 USA ISSN 0279-4039
DYNAMIC BUSINESS✶ ; image building for small business. Text in English. 1945. 10/yr. USD 15 to members; USD 25 to non-members (effective 2004). adv. bk.rev. 40 p./no. 3 cols./p.; **Document type:** *Magazine, Trade.* **Description:** Helping small business owners enhance and promote their operations.
Formerly: Smaller Manufacturer
Related titles: Online - full text ed.
Indexed: IHD.
Published by: S M C Business Councils, 1382 Beulah Rd #801, Pittsburgh, PA 15235-5068. TEL 412-371-1500, FAX 412-371-0460, mary@smc.org, http://www.smc.org. Ed., R&P Mary L Heindl. Adv. contact Carol Winterhalter. B&W page USD 1,075, color page USD 1,675. Circ: 10,000 (controlled).

338 AUS ISSN 1322-6398
DYNAMIC SMALL BUSINESS. Cover title: D S B. Text in English. 1993. bi-m. AUD 68 for 2 yrs. (effective 2005). adv.
Document type: *Magazine, Trade.* **Description:** Covers all the issues concerning small business owners from finance, tax, HR, through to finding the best technology for the best price.
Published by: Dynamic Small Business Magazine Plc., Level 11, 80 Mount St, North Sydney, NSW 2060, Australia. TEL 61-2-99556311, FAX 61-2-99547994, http://www.dsbmag.com.au/. adv.: B&W page AUD 3,010, color page AUD 4,010; trim 210 x 275. Circ: 35,170.

E B; Handbuch fuer Selbstaendige und Unternehmer. see *BUSINESS AND ECONOMICS*

338 AUS
E F I C ASSIST NEWS. Text in English. 1992. q. **Document type:** *Newsletter, Trade.* **Description:** Covers issues of particular interest to smaller companies.
Formerly (until 2000): Export Active; Which superseded in part (1977-1999): E F I C; Which was formerly (until 1991): Export Finance & Insurance Review; (until 1990): Export Finance and Insurance Quarterly; (until 1986): E F I C Quarterly (0314-7568)
Related titles: Online - full content ed.
Published by: Export Finance and Insurance Corporation, 22 Pitts St, Sydney, NSW 2000, Australia. TEL 800-685-109, FAX 61-2-9201-5222, info@efic.gov.au, http://www.efic.gov.au/pdfs/EFICAssist%20News.pdf.

338.642 NLD ISSN 0928-222X
E I M IN DE MARKT. (Economisch Instituut voor het Midden- en Kleinbedrijf) Text in Dutch. 1962. q. bk.rev. abstr.; charts; stat.
Formerly (until 1992): E I M Mededelingen (0012-768X)
Indexed: KES.
Published by: Research Institute for Small & Medium Sized Businesses/Economisch Instituut voor het Midden- en Kleinbedrijf, Postbus 7001, Zoetermeer, 2701 AA, Netherlands. TEL 31-79-413634, FAX 31-79-415024. Circ: 2,500.

338.7 NLD ISSN 0070-8836
E I M YEAR REPORT. Text in Dutch. 1961. a. free.
Published by: Economisch Instituut voor het Midden- en Kleinbedrijf/Research Institute for Small & Medium Sized Businesses, Postbus 7001, Zoetermeer, 2701 AA, Netherlands. TEL 31-79-3413634, FAX 31-79-3425786.

338.642 USA ISSN 1531-0612
HF5548.32
E-MERGING BUSINESS; taking your business to the next level. Text in English. 2000. 2/yr. USD 3.99 newsstand/cover (effective 2000). adv. **Document type:** *Magazine, Trade.*
Description: Dedicated to providing small business owners with practical articles and information that helps them to grow and operate their businesses more profitably.
Published by: Image Publishing, LLC, 11925 Wilshire Blvd., Flr. 3, Los Angeles, CA 90025-6605. TEL 310-284-6800, FAX 310-284-6878, inquiries@imagz.com, http://www.imagz.com. Ed. Daniel Kehrer. Pub., Adv. contact Sunil Patel. R&P Doreen DeRose. page USD 57,880. Circ: 250,000 (controlled).

ENRICH!; information bank briefings for network members. see *BUSINESS AND ECONOMICS—Chamber Of Commerce Publications*

330 GBR
ENTERPRISE. Text in English. bi-m. GBP 33 domestic; EUR 75 in Europe; GBP 60, USD 86 foreign (effective 2003). adv.
Document type: *Magazine, Trade.* **Description:** Targets the owners, directors and managers of fast growing, forward thinking small to medium sized enterprises.
Published by: Reed Business Information Ltd. (Subsidiary of: Reed Business), Quadrant House, The Quadrant, Brighton Rd, Sutton, Surrey SM2 5AS, United Kingdom. TEL 44-20-86523500, FAX 44-20-86528932, http://www.reedbusiness.co.uk/rb2_products/rb2_products_enterprise.htm. Ed. Penny Wilson. Adv. contact Vic Bunby TEL 44-20-8652-4030. Circ: 45,000 (paid and controlled). **Subscr. to:** Quadrant Subscription Services, Rockwood House, 9-17 Perrymount Rd, Haywards Heath, W. Sussex RH16 3DH, United Kingdom. TEL 44-20-8652-3500, FAX 44-20-8652-8932, rbi.subscriptions@qss-uk.com.

338.642 IND ISSN 0013-8673
ENTERPRISE. Text in English. 1967. m. INR 18, USD 3. adv. bk.rev. charts; illus.; stat.
Published by: Vidarbha Industries Association, Bank of Maharashtra Bldg. 2nd Fl., Sitabuldi, Nagpur, Maharashtra 440 012, India. Ed. B G Dave. Circ: 2,000.

338.642 USA ISSN 0163-3341
HF5001
ENTREPRENEUR (IRVINE). Text in English. 1973. m. USD 19.97 domestic; USD 31.97 foreign; USD 4.99 newsstand/cover (effective 2005). adv. bk.rev.; software rev. illus. back issues avail.; reprints avail. **Document type:** *Magazine, Consumer.* **Description:** Provides information on running a small business.
Formerly (until 1977): Insider's Report (0098-4353)
Related titles: Microfiche ed.; ♦ Online - full text ed.: Entrepreneur.com; Spanish ed.: Entrepreneuer en Espanol.
Indexed: BPI, MagInd, PAIS, PMR.
—IE, Infotrieve.
Published by: Entrepreneur Media, Inc., 2445 McCabe Way, Ste 400, Irvine, CA 92614. TEL 949-261-2325, 949-261-2325, FAX 949-261-0234, 949-752-1180, 949-261-0234, entmag@entrepreneur.com, http://www.entrepreneur.com. Ed. Rieva Lesonsky. Pub., Adv. contact Carrie Fitzmaurice TEL 212-563-8080. R&P Peggy Castillo Johnson. B&W page USD 45,245, color page USD 60,550; trim 7.25 x 10. Circ: 556,831 (paid). **Subscr. to:** PO Box 50368, Boulder, CO 80321-0368. TEL 800-274-6229, FAX 850-682-7644.

338 USA
ENTREPRENEUR EN ESPANOL. Text in Spanish. m. USD 80 domestic; USD 22 in Mexico; USD 96 elsewhere (effective 2001). adv. **Document type:** *Magazine, Trade.*
Published by: Entrepreneur Media, Inc., 2445 McCabe Way, Ste 400, Irvine, CA 92614. TEL 949-261-2325, FAX 949-261-0234, http://www.soyentrepreneur.com/, http://www.entrepreneur.com. Ed. Mildred Ramo. Pub. Guillermo Perez-Vargas. adv.: B&W page USD 4,536, color page USD 5,032.

338 306.8 USA
ENTREPRENEURIAL COUPLES SUCCESS LETTER. Text in English. bi-w. free. **Document type:** *Newsletter.* **Description:** Dedicated to helping small business owners build a thriving business while enjoying a rewarding intimate relationship with their spouse and family.
Related titles: E-mail ed.; Online - full text ed.
Published by: Anchored Dreams, 793 Sumter Dr., Yardley, PA 19067-4336. TEL 215-321-5269, az@azriela.com, http://www.isquare.com/az/az4.htm, http://www.isquare.com/az4.htm. Ed. Azriela Jaffe.

338.642 CAN ISSN 1188-8997
THE ENTREPRENEURIAL SPIRIT. Text in English. m. **Document type:** *Newsletter.* **Description:** Provides advice, information and company profiles while building a network of small businesses throughout North America.
Published by: A F A B Publishing, 339 10th Ave, S E, Ste 125, Calgary, AB T2G 0W2, Canada. TEL 403-255-9387, FAX 403-264-2540. Ed. Doug Kipp.

338.642 USA ISSN 1533-743X
HD62.5
ENTREPRENEUR'S BE YOUR OWN BOSS. Text in English. 1986. a. USD 3.95 newsstand/cover domestic; CND 5.99 newsstand/cover in Canada (effective 2002). **Document type:** *Magazine, Consumer.* **Description:** Comprehensive listings of franchise and business opportunities and information on starting a business.
Former titles: Entrepreneur's Franchise Special; Entrepreneur's Guide to Franchise and Business Opportunities; Entrepreneur's Franchise Yearbook (0889-4310)
Published by: Entrepreneur Media, Inc., 2445 McCabe Way, Ste 400, Irvine, CA 92614. TEL 949-261-2325, FAX 949-752-1180, entmag@entrepreneur.com, http://www.entrepreneur.com. Pub. Jim Kahn. R&P Peggy Castillo Johnson. Adv. contact Judy Reichman. Circ: 120,000 (paid).

338 USA
ENTREPRENEUR'S DIGEST ✶ . Text in English. 8/yr.
Address: 515 Frances Ave, Loves Park, IL 61111-5908. TEL 414-233-2674. Ed. Raymond Hipp.

338 USA
ENTREPRENEUR'S HOME OFFICE. Text in English. 1997. bi-m. free. tr.lit. back issues avail.; reprints avail. **Document type:** *Trade.* **Description:** Covers all aspects of operating and managing home-based businesses.
Media: Online - full content. **Related titles:** Online - full text ed.
Published by: Entrepreneur Media, Inc., 2445 McCabe Way, Ste 400, Irvine, CA 92614. TEL 949-261-2325, FAX 949-261-0234, homeoffice@enterpreneurmag.com, subscribe@enterpreneurmag.com, http://www.entrepreneur.com. R&P Peggy Castillo Johnson. Adv. contact Russell Palmer.

ENTREPRENEUR'S NETPRENEUR. see *COMPUTERS—Internet*

338.642 USA ISSN 1042-2587
HD2346.U5
ENTREPRENEURSHIP: THEORY AND PRACTICE. Text in English. 1976. bi-m. USD 106 combined subscription in the Americas to individuals print & online eds.; EUR 150 combined subscription in Europe to individuals & Caribbean (print & online eds.); GBP 100 combined subscription elsewhere to individuals print & online eds.; USD 331 combined subscription in the Americas to institutions & Caribbean (print & online eds.); GBP 255 combined subscription elsewhere to institutions print & online eds. (effective 2006). charts; stat.; illus. index. back issues avail.; reprint service avail. from PQC. **Document type:** *Journal, Academic/Scholarly.* **Description:** Publishes results of research in entrepreneurship, small business, and family business.
Formerly (until vol.12): American Journal of Small Business (0363-9428)
Related titles: CD-ROM ed.; Microform ed.: (from PQC); Online - full text ed.: ISSN 1540-6520. USD 96 in the Americas to individuals & Caribbean; EUR 136 in Europe to individuals; GBP 91 elsewhere to individuals; USD 314 in the Americas to institutions & Caribbean; GBP 242 elsewhere to institutions (effective 2006) (from Blackwell Synergy, EBSCO Publishing, Gale Group, H.W. Wilson, IngentaConnect, O C L C Online Computer Library Center, Inc., Swets Information Services).
Indexed: ABIn, ADPA, ASEANManA, ATI, BPI, BPIA, BusI, CPM, CurCont, Emerald, IBSS, Inspec, ManagCont, PAIS, RefZh, SSCI, T&II.
—BLDSC (3790.548000), IE, Infotrieve, ingenta. **CCC.**
Published by: (United States Association for Small Business and Entrepreneurship), Blackwell Publishing, Inc. (Subsidiary of: Blackwell Publishing Ltd.), Commerce Place, 350 Main St, Malden, MA 02148. TEL 781-388-8206, FAX 781-388-8232, subscrip@blackwellpub.com, http://www.blackwellpublishing.com/journals/ETAP. Ed. D Bagby. Circ: 1,600 (paid).

338 SWE ISSN 1104-8891
ENTREPRENOER; magasinet om entreprenoerskap och foeretagende. Text in Swedish. 1994. 11/yr. SEK 520 (effective 2004).
Incorporates in part (1997-2001): Nyhetsbrev. S A F Tidningen Naeringsliv (1651-5080)
Related titles: Online - full content ed.: ISSN 1402-4519; Supplement(s): Entreprenoer.se. ISSN 1651-5110.
Published by: (Svenskt Naeringsliv/Confederation of Swedish Enterprise), Tidningen Entreprenoer, c/o Svenskt Naeringsliv, Storgatan 19, Stockholm, 11482, Sweden. TEL 46-8-7626000. Ed., Pub. Staffan Aakerlund.

338 AUT
ERFOLG IM BERUF. Text in German. q.
Address: Matzleinsdorfer Hochhaus 12-67, Vienna, W 1050, Austria. TEL 01-551351, FAX 01-544458. Ed. Elvira Fischhof. Circ: 4,000.

338.021 PRT ISSN 0872-7570
HD5809
ESTATISTICAS DO EMPREGO. Text in Portuguese. 1985. q. EUR 9.60 (effective 2005).
Formerly (until 1990): Portugal. Instituto Nacional de Estatistica. Inquerito ao Emprego (0870-2640)
Published by: Instituto Nacional de Estatistica, Ave. Antonio Jose de Almeida 2, Lisbon, 1000-043, Portugal. TEL 351-21-8426100, FAX 351-21-8426380, ine@ine.pt, http://www.ine.pt/.

338.7 NLD
EUROPEAN OBSERVATORY FOR S M ES. ANNUAL REPORT. Text in English. 1993. a. price varies. **Document type:** *Corporate.* **Description:** Studies the structure, developments, and determinants of success of SMEs.
Related titles: French ed.; German ed.
—BLDSC (7463.930000).
Published by: E I M, PO Box 7001, Zoetermeer, 2701 AA, Netherlands. TEL 31-79-3413634, FAX 31-79-3425786, ruh@eim.nl. Ed. Rob van der Horst.

338.642 GBR ISSN 0014-4460
EXCHANGE AND MART. Text in English. 1868. w. GBP 82 domestic; GBP 130 in Europe; GBP 225 elsewhere; GBP 30 newsstand/cover (effective 2000). adv. **Document type:** *Consumer.* **Description:** Contains advertisements for automobiles and other products.
Published by: United Advertising Publications plc., Link House, 25 West St, Poole, Dorset BH15 1LL, United Kingdom. TEL 44-1202-445000, FAX 44-1202-445189, market@unitedadvertising.co.uk, http://www.exchangeandmart.co.uk. R&P Michael Peden. Adv. contact Michael James. Circ: 106,581. **Subscr. to:** Garrard House, Garrard House 2-6, Homesdale Rd, Bromley, Dorset BR2 9WL, United Kingdom. TEL 44-20-8402-8181, FAX 44-20-8402-8383.

EXHIBITOR MAGAZINE; the magazine for trade show and event marketing management. see *BUSINESS AND ECONOMICS—Marketing And Purchasing*

338 GBR
F P B QUARTERLY REPORT. Text in English. 1988. q. **Document type:** *Academic/Scholarly.*
Formerly: F P B Action Report
Published by: Forum of Private Business, Ruskin Chambers, Drury Ln, Knutsford, Ches WA16 6HA, United Kingdom. TEL 44-1565-634467, FAX 44-1565-650059. Ed. James Redman.

338.642 USA ISSN 1047-255X
HD62.25
FAMILY BUSINESS; the guide for family companies. Text in English. 1989. q. USD 95 domestic; USD 105 in Canada & Mexico; USD 125 elsewhere (effective 2005). adv. 80 p./no.; back issues avail.; reprints avail. **Document type:** *Magazine, Consumer.* **Description:** Guide for building and managing family companies.
Related titles: Online - full text ed.
Published by: Family Business Publishing Company (Subsidiary of: M L R Holdings), 1845 Walnut St, Ste 900, Philadelphia, PA 19103. TEL 215-405-6084, FAX 215-405-6078, bspector@familybusinessmagazine.com, http://www.familybusinessmagazine.com. Ed., R&P Barbara Spector. Adv. contact Sadye Vogel. B&W page USD 1,920, color page USD 3,000; trim 7 x 10. Circ: 6,000 (paid).

B

338.642 USA ISSN 0894-4865
➤ **FAMILY BUSINESS REVIEW.** Text in English. 1988. q. USD 105 combined subscription in the Americas to individuals & Caribbean (print & online eds.); EUR 125 combined subscription in Europe to individuals print & online eds.; GBP 83 combined subscription elsewhere to individuals print & online eds.; USD 207 combined subscription in the Americas to institutions & Caribbean (print & online eds.); GBP 159 combined subscription elsewhere to institutions print & online eds. (effective 2006). bk.rev. illus. Index. back issues avail.; reprints avail. **Document type:** *Journal, Academic/Scholarly.* **Description:** For professionals and scholars who work with family businesses, the latest ideas and strategies for effectively answering the needs of today's family-run businesses.
Related titles: Online - full text ed.: ISSN 1741-6248. USD 197 in the Americas to institutions & Caribbean; GBP 151 elsewhere to institutions (effective 2006) (from Blackwell Synergy, EBSCO Publishing, Florida Center for Library Automation, Gale Group, IngentaConnect, O C L C Online Computer Library Center, Inc., ProQuest Information & Learning, Swets Information Services).
Indexed: ABIn.
—BLDSC (3865.559220), IE, ingenta. **CCC.**
Published by: (Family Firm Institute), Blackwell Publishing, Inc. (Subsidiary of: Blackwell Publishing Ltd.), Commerce Place, 350 Main St, Malden, MA 02148. TEL 781-388-8206, FAX 781-388-8232, subscrip@blackwellpub.com, http://www.blackwellpublishing.com/journals/FABR. Ed. Joseph H Astrachan. R&P Chris Watson TEL 617-789-4200. Circ: 1,300.

➤ **THE FAMILY CONNECTION.** see *HOME ECONOMICS*

338 USA
▼ **FEMALE ENTREPRENEUR.** Text in English. 2003. bi-m. USD 24.95; USD 4.99 newsstand/cover (effective 2003). adv. **Document type:** *Magazine, Trade.* **Description:** Provides business management information female entrepreneurs need and want to know.
Related titles: Online - full text ed.; Regional ed(s).: Female Entrepreneur Texas. 2004; Female Entrepreneur New York. 2004.
Published by: e-Spirit Holdings, 738 S. Boulder Hwy., Ste. 250, Henderson, NV 89015. TEL 888-363-2574, FAX 702-568-7357, marketing@female-entrepreneur.com, http://www.female-entrepreneur.com. Ed., R&P, Adv. contact Keli Swenson. page USD 1,500; trim 8 x 10.75. Circ: 100,000 (paid and controlled).

THE FINANCING NEWS. see *BUSINESS AND ECONOMICS—Banking And Finance*

338.642 GBR ISSN 0959-8375
FIRST VOICE. Key Title: First Voice of Small Business. Text in English. bi-m. membership. adv. **Document type:** *Trade.* **Description:** Contains articles of interest to small businesses. Includes updates on all campaigns and issues that the federation is fighting in the UK and Europe.
Published by: (Federation of Small Businesses), N F S E Sales Ltd., 2 Catherine Pl, Westminster, London, SW1E 6HF, United Kingdom. TEL 44-171-233-7900, FAX 44-171-233-7899, London@fsb.org.uk, http://www.businessworld.co.uk. Ed. Sarah Beevers. Adv. contact James Parker. B&W page GBP 2,150, color page GBP 2,750. Circ: 63,262.

FLORIDA COUNTY MIGRATION FLOWS 1981-1996. see *BUSINESS AND ECONOMICS—Economic Situation And Conditions*

658 USA ISSN 1554-835X
HD2346.F6
FLORIDA SMALL BUSINESS. Text in English. 1999. irreg. USD 4.95 newsstand/cover. **Document type:** *Consumer.* **Description:** Deals with the small business trends in Florida. Also shares tips and information on starting a small business, including how to find the money, buy technologies, hire workers and more.

Published by: Trend Magazine, Inc., 490 First Avenue S., St. Petersburg, FL 33701. TEL 727-821-5800, http://www.floridasmallbusiness.com.

338.642 SWE ISSN 1403-6592
FOERETAGAREN. Text in Swedish. 1991. 10/yr. SEK 295 (effective 2001). adv. **Document type:** *Magazine, Trade.*
Formerly (until 1998): Tidningen Foeretagarna (1101-7872); Which was formed by the merger of (1936-1991): Smaafoertagartidningen Hantverck och Industri (0283-9652); (1898-1991): Foeretagaren (0015-5276)
Published by: Foeretagarna, Regeringsgatan 52, Stockholm, 10667, Sweden. TEL 46-8-4061700, FAX 46-8-245526, foretagaren@spoon.se, info@foretagarna.se, http://www.foretagarna.se. Ed. Christina Baecker TEL 46-8-4429630. Pub. Gunvor Engstroem. Adv. contact Ninni Westerlund TEL 46-8-7479500. B&W page SEK 34,600, color page SEK 43,900; trim 250 x 340. Circ: 60,000 (controlled).

338.642 USA ISSN 1547-3171
HD62.7
FORTUNE SMALL BUSINESS. Abbreviated title: F S B. Text in English. 1990. m. USD 5.95 newsstand/cover (effective 2004). adv. reprints avail. **Document type:** *Magazine, Trade.* **Description:** Provides information on running small businesses more effectively.
Formerly (until 1999): Your Company (1064-2544)
Related titles: Online - full text ed.: (from EBSCO Publishing, Gale Group).
Published by: Time Inc., Business Information Group (Subsidiary of: Time Warner, Inc.), 1271 Ave of the Americas, New York, NY 10020. TEL 212-522-1212, 800-777-1444, FAX 212-522-0970, editor@fsb.com, http://www.fsb.com/fortunesb. Ed. John Huey. Pubs. Kathleen Kayse, Michael Federle. adv.: B&W page USD 55,000, color page USD 75,000. Circ: 1,250,000 (controlled). **Co-publisher:** American Express Publishing Corp.

338.642 USA ISSN 1551-3114
▼ ➤ **FOUNDATIONS AND TRENDS IN ENTREPRENEURSHIP.** Text in English. 2005. 4/yr. USD 300, EUR 300; USD 340, EUR 340 combined subscription print & online eds. (effective 2006). **Document type:** *Journal, Academic/Scholarly.*
Related titles: Online - full text ed.: ISSN 1551-3122. 2005. USD 300, EUR 300 (effective 2005).
Published by: Now Publishers Inc., PO Box 1024, Hanover, MA 02339. TEL 781-871-0245, FAX 781-871-6172, sales@nowpublishers.com, http://www.nowpublishers.com/ent. Eds. David Autresch, Zoltan Acs. Pub. Zac Rolnik. R&P Mike Casey.

338.642 USA ISSN 0882-5505
HF5429.235.U5
THE FRANCHISE HANDBOOK. Text in English. 1985. q. USD 22.95; USD 6.99 newsstand/cover (effective 2005). **Document type:** *Consumer.* **Description:** Contains information on more than 1700 franchises currently being marketed, as well as articles and expert advice.
Related titles: Online - full text ed.
Published by: Enterprise Magazines, Inc., 1020 N Broadway, Ste 111, Milwaukee, WI 53202. TEL 800-272-0246, info@franchisehandbook.com, info@franchise1.com, http://www.franchisehandbook.com, http://www.franchise1.com. Eds. Mr. Michael McDermott, Ms. Maria Lahm. Pub. Mrs. Betsy L Green. R&P Ms. Maria Lahm. Adv. contacts Ms. Barbara Yelmene, Ms. Kristin Over, Ms. Maria Lahm.

338 USA
FRANCHISE OPPORTUNITIES GUIDE. Text in English. 1962. 2/yr. USD 42 (effective 2001). adv. **Document type:** *Directory.*
Related titles: Online - full content ed.
Published by: International Franchise Association, 1350 New York Ave, N W, Ste 900, Washington, DC 20005. TEL 202-628-8000, FAX 202-628-0812, advertise@franchise.org, http://www.franchise.org/. Ed., R&P Terry Hill TEL 202-628-8000. Pub. Don DeBolt. Adv. contact Guy Mitchell TEL 202-628-8000. Circ: 62,000 (paid).

338.642 GBR ISSN 0144-0543
FRANCHISE WORLD. Text in English. 1978. q. GBP 20. adv. illus.
Indexed: AgeL.
Published by: Franchise Publications, James House, 37 Nottingham Rd, London, SW17 7EA, United Kingdom. Ed. Robert Riding.

338.642 AUS ISSN 1321-408X
FRANCHISING; and own your own business magazine. Text in English. 1987. bi-m. AUD 45 domestic; AUD 120 foreign (effective 2004). adv. back issues avail. **Document type:** *Magazine, Trade.*
Formerly (until 1991): Australasian Franchising
Related titles: Online - full text ed.
Published by: (Franchise Council of Australia), Niche Media Pty Ltd (Subsidiary of: Waivcom Worldwide Ltd.), 165 Fitzroy St, St Kilda, VIC 3182, Australia. TEL 61-3-95255566, FAX 61-3-95255628, subscription@niche.com.au, http://www.niche.com.au/fr/general.html. Eds. Pamella Oddy, Ros O'Sullivan. Adv. contact Gusto Simandjuntak. B&W page AUD 1,875, color page AUD 2,475; trim 205 x 275. Circ: 13,000.

338 DEU
FRANCHISING.MAG. Text in German. 2000. q. EUR 3.40 newsstand/cover (effective 2003). adv. **Document type:** *Magazine, Trade.*
Published by: M M Vg - Management Medien Verlagsgesellschaft, Luederichstr 2-4, Cologne, 51105, Germany. TEL 49-221-82958613, FAX 49-221-82958615. adv.: color page EUR 3,450. Circ: 23,994 (paid and controlled).

338 GBR
THE FUTURAT BUSINESS; the magazine for small and homebased businesses. Text in English. 1998. m. USD 24; USD 2.45 newsstand/cover (effective 1998). adv. **Document type:** *Trade.* **Description:** Aims to meet the needs of the small-business community, particularly people who work from home.
Published by: FuturAt Business Publishing, 27 Collingwood Rd., Redland, Bristol BS6 6PD, United Kingdom. TEL 44-117-903-0204, FAX 44-117-903-0205, fb@lineone.net. Ed. Simon Hargreaves. Adv. contact Molly Crofton.

381.147 USA
G A C S TODAY. (Georgia Association of Convenience Stores) Text in English. 1997. q. free membership (effective 2004). adv. **Document type:** *Magazine, Trade.* **Description:** Covers industry issues, government regulations, and highlights association members and events.
Published by: (Georgia Association of Convenience Stores), Naylor Publications, Inc., 5950 NW 1st Pl, Gainesville, FL 32607-6018. TEL 800-369-6220, http://www.naylor.com. Pub. Shane Holt. adv.: B&W page USD 1,189.50; trim 5.75 x 8.5. Circ: 1,368.

388.642 JPN ISSN 0285-8460
GEKKAN CHUSHO-KIGYO/MONTHLY SMALLER BUSINESSES. Key Title: Chusho Kigyo. Text in Japanese. 1976. m. JPY 3,600.
Published by: Diamond Inc., 4-2 Kasumigaseki 1-chome, Chiyoda-ku, Tokyo, 100-0013, Japan. Ed. Yoshizumi Saito.

338.642 659.1 DEU ISSN 0344-2292
DIE GESCHAEFTSIDEE; Fachmagazin fuer Unternehmensgruendung und neue Maerkte. Text in German. 1976. bi-m. bk.rev. back issues avail. **Document type:** *Bulletin.* **Description:** Market studies, franchise news, new products and how-to articles for German entrepreneurs.
Related titles: French ed.
Published by: V N R Verlag fuer die Deutsche Wirtschaft AG, Theodor-Heuss-Str 2-4, Bonn, 53095, Germany. TEL 49-228-8205-0, FAX 49-228-364411, TELEX 17228309. Ed. Norman Rentrop.

338 DEU
GEWERBE REPORT. Text in German. 1964. 5/yr. EUR 2.56 newsstand/cover (effective 2003). adv. bk.rev. abstr.; illus.; stat. index. back issues avail. **Document type:** *Newspaper, Corporate.*
Published by: Europaverband der Selbstaendigen, Bundesverband Deutschland e.V., Huettenbergstr 38-40, Neunkirchen, 66538, Germany. TEL 49-6821-306240, FAX 49-6821-306241, info@bvd-cedi.de, http://www.bvd-cedi.de. Ed. Karl Kunrath. Adv. contact Doris Hahn. B&W page EUR 1,053, color page EUR 1,368.90. Circ: 20,000 (controlled).

GOVERNMENT PROGRAMS. see *EDUCATION—School Organization And Administration*

GUIDE TO CHOOSING RETIREMENT PLANS FOR SMALL BUSINESSES. see *BUSINESS AND ECONOMICS—Labor And Industrial Relations*

658.041 USA ISSN 1522-7731
THE HOME BUSINESS FILES. Text in English. 1998. w. free. adv. **Document type:** *Newsletter.* **Description:** Provides news and resources for small- and home-based business owners.
Media: Online - full text.
Published by: K. Williams Resources kwilliams@thenett.com, http://www.kwresources.com. Ed. Kelley Williams.

338.642 371.42 651 USA ISSN 1092-4779
HD62.38
HOME BUSINESS MAGAZINE; the home-based entrepreneur's magazine. Text in English. 1993. bi-m. (6 issues per volume). USD 15 domestic; USD 50 in Canada; USD 70 foreign; USD 3.99 newsstand/cover domestic; USD 5.50 newsstand/cover in Canada (effective 2003). adv. bk.rev.; software rev.; Website rev. charts; tr.lit.; illus.; stat. 120 p./no. 3 cols./p.; back issues avail.; reprints avail. **Document type:** *Magazine, Consumer.* **Description:** Provides information on home business opportunities and how to better manage and profit from a home based business. Includes a directory, case histories, and articles on getting started, creating a home office, franchising, mail order, network marketing, and the Internet.
Formerly: National Home Business
Related titles: E-mail ed.; Online - full text ed.
Published by: United Marketing & Research Company, Inc., 9582 Hamilton Ave, PMB 368, Huntington Beach, CA 92646. TEL 714-968-0331, FAX 714-962-7722, henderso@ix.netcom.com, http://www.homebusinessmag.com. Ed., R&P Stacy Ann Henderson. Pub. Richard Henderson. Adv. contact Tom Valline TEL 714-577-0431. B&W page USD 1,980; trim 10.88 x 8.38. Circ: 100,000. **Subscr. to:** National Subscription Fulfillment Services, PO Box, Anaheim, CA 92817. TEL 714-693-1866. **Dist. by:** Curtis Circulation Co., 730 River Road, New Milford, NJ 07646. TEL 201-634-7400, FAX 201-634-7499, new.business@curtiscirc.com.

658.041 USA
HOME BUSINESS NEWSLETTER. Text in English. irreg. (every 2-3 mos.). **Document type:** *Newsletter.* **Description:** Provides articles, tips and news on how to operate a profitable home-based enterprise.
Media: Online - full text.
Address: esimpson@zoomnet.net, http://www.homebiznews.com. Pub. Ed Simpson.

338.942 USA ISSN 1097-2420
HD2333
HOMEBUSINESS JOURNAL. Text in English. 199?. bi-m. USD 18.96 domestic; USD 34 foreign (effective 2002). adv. **Description:** Covers topics of interest to home business owners.
Related titles: Online - full content ed.
Published by: Steffen Publishing, 9584 Main St, Holland Patent, NY 13354. TEL 315-865-4100, FAX 315-865-4000, customerservice@homebusinessjournal.net, http://www.homebizjour.com.

HOW TO BE YOUR OWN PUBLISHER UPDATE. see *PUBLISHING AND BOOK TRADE*

338 746.5 HRV
HRVATSKI OBRTNIK. Text in Croatian. 1947. m. USD 26. back issues avail. **Document type:** *Magazine, Trade.*
Former titles: Obrtnicki Vjesnik; (until Nov., 1990): Zanatski List
Published by: (Savez Udruzenja Samostalnih Privrednika Hrvatske), Magos d.o.o., Alagoviceva 5, Zagreb, 10000, Croatia. TEL 385-1-330815, FAX 385-1-4683218. Ed. Pavao Kurtek. Circ: 15,000. **Subscr. to:** Trg Ivana Mazuranica 5-II, Zagreb 41000, Croatia.

I D A DOWNTOWN NEWSBRIEFS. see *HOUSING AND URBAN PLANNING*

338.642 USA
I G P C NEWSLETTER. (International Guild of Professional Consultants) Text in English. 1999. bi-m. **Document type:** *Newsletter.* **Description:** Includes articles on consulting, marketing, and small business development.
Media: Online - full text.
Published by: I G P C, 1422 Challenger Ave, Davenport, FL 33837. TEL 888-844-1029, FAX 941-420-0516, directcr@igpc.org, http://www.igpc.org/igpclist.htm.

I'M TOO BUSY TO READ MARKETING REPORT SERVICE. see *BUSINESS AND ECONOMICS—Marketing And Purchasing*

338.642 USA ISSN 0190-2458
HF5001 CODEN: INBSD5
IN BUSINESS (EMMAUS); the magazine for environmental entrepreneuring. Text in English. 1979. bi-m. USD 33 domestic; USD 51 foreign (effective 2005). adv. bk.rev. illus. index. back issues avail.; reprints avail. **Document type:** *Magazine, Trade.* **Description:** Discusses methods of incorporating environmentally sound processes and products into business practice.
Related titles: Microfilm ed.; Online - full text ed.: (from bigchalk, EBSCO Publishing, O C L C Online Computer Library Center, Inc., ProQuest Information & Learning).
Indexed: ABIn, BPIA, BusI, EPB, Inspec, T&II.
—BLDSC (4371.696000), IE, ingenta. **CCC.**
Published by: J G Press, Inc., 419 State Ave, Emmaus, PA 18049. TEL 610-967-4135, FAX 610-967-1345, advert@jgpress.com, http://www.jgpress.com/inbusine.htm. Ed., Pub. Jerome Goldstein. Circ: 3,000 (paid and controlled).

338.642 USA ISSN 0162-8968
HD2346.U5 CODEN: INCCDU
INC.; the magazine for growing companies. Text in English. 1979. 18/yr. USD 14 domestic; USD 31 in Canada; USD 50 elsewhere (effective 2005). adv. bk.rev. illus. Index. reprint service avail. from PQC. **Document type:** *Magazine, Trade.*
Incorporates (1995-1998): Self-Employed Professional (1083-7019)
Related titles: Microfiche ed.: (from CIS); Online - full text ed.: (from bigchalk, EBSCO Publishing, Factiva, Florida Center for Library Automation, Gale Group, H.W. Wilson, LexisNexis, O C L C Online Computer Library Center, Inc., ProQuest Information & Learning, The Dialog Corporation); ◆ Supplement(s): Inc. Office Guide. ISSN 0898-1809.
Indexed: ABIn, ATI, Agr, BPI, BRI, BusI, CADCAM, CBRI, CCR, CISA, CurCont, EnvAb, Inspec, LRI, LogistBibl, MASUSE, MagInd, PROMT, PSI, RehabLit, SRI, SoftBase, T&II, TOM, TelAb.
—BLDSC (4374.760000), AskIEEE, CIS, IDS, IE, Infotrieve, ingenta.

Address: 38 Commercial Wharf, Boston, MA 02110. TEL 617-248-8000, FAX 617-248-8090, editors@inc.com, http://www.inc.com. Pub., Adv. contact Gary Mirkin. R&P Diana Bernsee TEL 617-248-8145. Circ: 650,000 (paid).

338.642 USA ISSN 0898-1809
INC. OFFICE GUIDE. Text in English. 1987. a. **Document type:** *Magazine, Trade.*
Related titles: ♦ Supplement to: Inc.. ISSN 0162-8968.
Published by: Inc. (Subsidiary of: Gruner + Jahr U.S.A. Publishing), 38 Commercial Wharf, Boston, MA 02110. TEL 617-248-8000, FAX 617-248-8090.

338.642 USA ISSN 0147-5924
INFO FRANCHISE NEWSLETTER. Text in English. 1977. m. USD 120 in North America; USD 135 out of North America (effective 2000). adv. **Document type:** *Newsletter.* **Description:** Covers business format franchising: list of new franchises, recent legislation and litigation, trends and forecasts.
Published by: Info Franchise News Inc., PO Box 826, Lewiston, NY 14092-7926. TEL 716-754-4669, FAX 905-688-7728, infopress@infonews.com, http://infonews.com/franchise. Ed., Pub. Ted Dixon.

338.642 FRA ISSN 0292-4765
INFORMATIONS ENTREPRISE✶. Text in French. 10/yr.
Published by: Publimag, 22 rue Jasmin, Paris, 75016, France. TEL 45-75-21-21, FAX 45-75-12-77. Ed. Antoine Silber. Circ: 37,000.

338.642 USA ISSN 1087-4054
INSIDE SELF-STORAGE. Text in English. 1991. m. USD 95 domestic; USD 110 in Canada; USD 145 elsewhere (effective 2005). adv. **Document type:** *Magazine, Trade.* **Description:** Covers aspects of the self-storage industry for owners, operators, managers, the self investors, vendors and lenders.
Published by: Virgo Publishing, Inc., 3300 N. Central Ave., Ste 300, Phoenix, AZ 85012. TEL 480-990-1101, FAX 480-990-0819, issmag@vpico.com, cs@vpico.com, http://www.insideselfstorage.com, http://www.vpico.com. Ed. Teri Lanza. Pub. Troy Bix. adv.: B&W page USD 3,290, color page USD 4,575; 7 x 10. Circ: 20,000 (paid and controlled).

INSTITUTE OF CHARTERED ACCOUNTANTS IN ENGLAND AND WALES. ADDING VALUE: FOR THE GENERAL PRACTITIONER SUPPORTING SMALL BUSINESS. see *BUSINESS AND ECONOMICS—Accounting*

338.642 GBR ISSN 1355-2554
HB615
➤ **INTERNATIONAL JOURNAL OF ENTREPRENEURIAL BEHAVIOUR & RESEARCH.** Text in English. 1995. bi-m. EUR 1,479.33 in Europe; USD 1,379 in North America; AUD 1,859 in Australasia; GBP 1,032.83 in UK & elsewhere (effective 2006). reprint service avail. from PSC. **Document type:** *Journal, Academic/Scholarly.*
Related titles: Online - full text ed.: (from EBSCO Publishing, Emerald Group Publishing Limited, Gale Group, IngentaConnect, O C L C Online Computer Library Center, Inc., ProQuest Information & Learning, Swets Information Services).
Indexed: ABIn, EmerIntel, Emerald, e-psyche.
—BLDSC (4542.240400), IE, Infotrieve, ingenta. **CCC.**
Published by: Emerald Group Publishing Limited, 60-62 Toller Ln, Bradford, W Yorks BD8 9BY, United Kingdom. TEL 44-1274-777700, FAX 44-1274-785200, infomation@emeraldinsight.com, http://www.emeraldinsight.com/ijebr.htm. Ed. Oswald Jones.

338.642 GBR ISSN 1479-3059
▼ ➤ **INTERNATIONAL JOURNAL OF GLOBALISATION AND SMALL BUSINESS.** Text in English. 2004. q. USD 450 to institutions; USD 545 combined subscription to institutions print & online eds. (effective 2005). **Document type:** *Journal, Academic/Scholarly.*
Related titles: Online - full text ed.: ISSN 1479-3067. USD 450 (effective 2005) (from EBSCO Publishing).
Indexed: Inspec.
—BLDSC (4542.267800).
Published by: Inderscience Publishers, IEL Editorial Office, PO Box 735, Olney, Bucks MK46 5WB, United Kingdom. TEL 44-1234-240519, FAX 44-1234-240515, ijgsb@inderscience.com, info@inderscience.com, http://www.inderscience.com/ijgsb. **Subscr. to:** World Trade Centre Bldg, 29 route de Pre-Bois, Case Postale 896, Geneva 15 1215, Switzerland. FAX 41-22-7910885, subs@inderscience.com.

338.642 GBR ISSN 0266-2426
HD2341
➤ **INTERNATIONAL SMALL BUSINESS JOURNAL.** Text in English. 1982. bi-m. GBP 567, USD 992 to institutions; GBP 590, USD 1,033 combined subscription to institutions print & online eds. (effective 2006). bk.rev. illus. reprints avail. **Document type:** *Journal, Academic/Scholarly.* **Description:** Provides a forum and a focus for the discussion and dissemination of views and research on the small business sector throughout the world with an emphasis on systematic studies which help to improve the general understanding of small business and contribute to more effective policies for and management of small business.
Incorporates: European Small Business Journal
Related titles: Online - full text ed.: ISSN 1741-2870. GBP 561, USD 981 to institutions (effective 2006) (from bigchalk, C S A, EBSCO Publishing, Florida Center for Library Automation, Gale Group, H.W. Wilson, Northern Light Technology, Inc., O C L C Online Computer Library Center, Inc., Sage Publications, Inc., Swets Information Services).
Indexed: ABIn, BPI, CJA, CPM, CurCont, ESPM, Emerald, IBSS, Inspec, PAIS, RiskAb, SCIMP, SSCI.
—BLDSC (4549.406500), IE, Infotrieve, ingenta, **CCC.**
Published by: Sage Publications Ltd. (Subsidiary of: Sage Publications, Inc.), 1 Oliver's Yard, 55 City Rd, London, EC1 1SP, United Kingdom. TEL 44-20-73248500, FAX 44-20-73248600, info@sagepub.co.uk, http://www.sagepub.co.uk/journal.aspx?pid=105603. Ed. Dr. Robert Blackburn. **Subscr. in the Americas to:** Sage Publications, Inc., 2455 Teller Rd, Thousand Oaks, CA 91320. TEL 805-499-0721, FAX 805-499-0871, journals@sagepub.com.

650 DEU ISSN 0935-4794
INTERNATIONALES GEWERBEARCHIV. SONDERHEFT. Text in German. 1986. irreg., latest vol.5, 2002. price varies. **Document type:** *Monographic series, Trade.*
Related titles: ♦ Supplement to: Z f K E - Zeitschrift fuer K M U und Entrepreneurship. ISSN 1860-4633.
Published by: Duncker und Humblot GmbH, Carl-Heinrich-Becker-Weg 9, Berlin, 12165, Germany. TEL 49-30-7900060, FAX 49-30-79000361, info@duncker-humblot.de, http://www.duncker-humblot.de. Ed. G Besier.

338.642 USA
▼ ➤ **THE INTERNET JOURNAL OF ENTREPRENEURSHIP.** Text in English. 2004. irreg. free to individuals; USD 500 to institutions (effective 2005). **Document type:** *Journal, Academic/Scholarly.*
Media: Online - full content.
Published by: Internet Scientific Publications, L.L.C., 23 Rippling Creek Dr, Sugar Land, TX 77479. TEL 832-443-1193, FAX 281-240-1533, wenker@ispub.com, http://www.ispub.com/ostia/index.php?xmlFilePath=journals/ijes/front.xml.

338 659.1 USA
INTRODUCTION TO MAIL ORDER. Text in English. 1976. q. USD 10 domestic; USD 25 foreign (effective 2001). adv. **Document type:** *Newspaper, Trade.*
Published by: G & B Records, PO Box 10150, Terra Bella, CA 93270-0150. TEL 559-784-5722, gbrecords@ocsnet.net. Ed. Glenn C Bridgeman. Circ: 5,000.

IOWA HOME-BASED BUSINESS DIRECTORY. see *BUSINESS AND ECONOMICS—Trade And Industrial Directories*

ISRAEL. CENTRAL BUREAU OF STATISTICS. INDUSTRY AND CRAFTS SURVEY. see *BUSINESS AND ECONOMICS—Abstracting, Bibliographies, Statistics*

338.6 IND ISSN 0447-2500
JAGRITI; fortnightly news magazine on rural reconstruction. Text in English. 195?. fortn. INR 10. bk.rev. illus.
Related titles: Hindi ed.: ISSN 0970-7018.
Published by: Khadi and Village Industries Commission, Directorate of Publicity, Gramodaya Irla Rd., Vile Parle (West), Mumbai, Maharashtra 400 056, India. Ed. M P Sharma.

333.642 DEU ISSN 0938-7056
JAHRBUCH FRANCHISING. Text in German. 1990. biennial. **Document type:** *Journal, Trade.*
Published by: (Deutscher Franchise Verband e.V.), Deutscher Fachverlag GmbH, Mainzer Landstr 251, Frankfurt Am Main, 60326, Germany. TEL 49-69-759501, FAX 49-69-75952999, info@dfv.de, http://www.dfv.de.

JOURNAL OF BUSINESS (SPOKANE). see *BUSINESS AND ECONOMICS—Banking And Finance*

JOURNAL OF BUSINESS VENTURING. see *BUSINESS AND ECONOMICS*

338.642 SGP ISSN 1084-9467
HB615
➤ **JOURNAL OF DEVELOPMENTAL ENTREPRENEURSHIP**; an international publication devoted to issues of microenterprise development. Text in English. 1996. q. SGD 77, USD 45, EUR 39 to individuals; SGD 326, USD 190, EUR 168 combined subscription to institutions print & online eds. (effective 2006). **Document type:** *Journal, Academic/Scholarly.* **Description:** Provides a forum for the dissemination of descriptive, empirical, and theoretical research that focuses on issues concerning microenterprise and small business development, especially under conditions of adversity.
Related titles: Online - full text ed.: (from EBSCO Publishing, O C L C Online Computer Library Center, Inc., ProQuest Information & Learning).
Indexed: ABIn.
—BLDSC (4969.292000), IE, ingenta.
Published by: (Norfolk State University, Center for Entrepreneurship USA, Miami University, School of Business Administration USA), World Scientific Publishing Co. Pte. Ltd., 5 Toh Tuck Link, Singapore, 596224, Singapore. TEL 65-466-5775, FAX 65-467-7667, wspc@wspc.com.sg, http://www.worldscinet.com/jde/jde.shtml, http://www.worldscientific.com. Ed. Peter Koveos.

338.642 GBR ISSN 1462-6004
JOURNAL OF SMALL BUSINESS AND ENTERPRISE DEVELOPMENT. Text in English. 1995. q. GBP 716.66 in Europe; USD 669 in North America; AUD 1,029 in Australasia; GBP 499.16 in the UK & elsewhere (effective 2006). adv. back issues avail.; reprint service avail. from PSC. **Document type:** *Journal, Academic/Scholarly.* **Description:** Publishes detailed advice, research and opinion on topics of direct use to small and medium-sized businesses.
Formerly (until 1998): Business, Growth and Profitability (1355-6347)
Related titles: Online - full text ed.: (from EBSCO Publishing, Emerald Group Publishing Limited, Gale Group, IngentaConnect, O C L C Online Computer Library Center, Inc., ProQuest Information & Learning, Swets Information Services).
Indexed: ABIn, CPM, Emerald.
—BLDSC (5064.706000), IE, Infotrieve, ingenta. **CCC.**
Published by: Emerald Group Publishing Limited, 60-62 Toller Ln, Bradford, W Yorks BD8 9BY, United Kingdom. TEL 44-1274-777700, FAX 44-1274-785200, editorial@emeraldinsight.com, infomation@emeraldinsight.com, http://www.emeraldinsight.com/jsbed.htm. Ed. Dr. Harry Matlay. Circ: 500 (paid). **Subscr. addr. in N America:** Emerald Group Publishing Ltd., 44 Brattle St, 4th Fl, Cambridge, MA 02138. TEL 617-497-2175, 888-622-0075, FAX 617-354-6875.

338.642 CAN ISSN 0827-6331
JOURNAL OF SMALL BUSINESS AND ENTREPRENEURSHIP✶. Text in English; Summaries in French. 1983. q. CND 80 (effective 1996). back issues avail.
Formerly (until 1985): Journal of Small Business - Canada (0820-957X)
Related titles: Microform ed.: 1983 (from MML).
Indexed: CBCARef, JEL.
—BLDSC (5064.707000), IE, ingenta. **CCC.**
Published by: International Council for Small Business, 350 Victoria St, Ste B725, Toronto, ON M5B 3K3, Canada. TEL 416-289-4724, FAX 416-430-1219. Ed. Raymond W Y Kao. Circ: 1,200. **Subscr. to:** JSBE Secretariat, Centre of Entrepreneurship, Centennial College, P O Box 631, Sta A, Scarborough, ON M1K 5E9, Canada.

658 USA ISSN 0047-2778
HD69.S6 CODEN: JSBMAU
➤ **JOURNAL OF SMALL BUSINESS MANAGEMENT.** Text in English. 1963. q. USD 83 combined subscription in the Americas to individuals & Caribbean (print & online eds.); EUR 105 combined subscription in Europe to individuals print & online eds.; GBP 70 combined subscription elsewhere to individuals print & online eds.; USD 216 combined subscription in the Americas to institutions & Caribbean (print & online eds.); GBP 170 combined subscription elsewhere to institutions print & online eds. (effective 2006). adv. bibl.; illus. index. reprint service avail. from PQC. **Document type:** *Journal, Academic/Scholarly.* **Description:** Articles, features and editorials on small business and entrepreneurship.
Related titles: Microform ed.; Online - full text ed.: ISSN 1540-627X. USD 205 in the Americas to institutions & Caribbean; GBP 162 elsewhere to institutions (effective 2006) (from bigchalk, Blackwell Synergy, EBSCO Publishing, Gale Group, H.W. Wilson, IngentaConnect, Northern Light Technology, Inc., O C L C Online Computer Library Center, Inc., ProQuest Information & Learning, Swets Information Services).
Indexed: ABIn, ADPA, ASCA, ASEANManA, AgeL, BLI, BPI, BPIA, BusI, CJA, CPM, CurCont, ESPM, Emerald, FamI, LRI, MagInd, ManagCont, PAIS, PMA, RASB, RefZh, RiskAb, SSCI, T&II.
—BLDSC (5064.710000), IDS, IE, Infotrieve, ingenta. **CCC.**
Published by: (West Virginia University, Bureau of Business and Economic Research), Blackwell Publishing, Inc. (Subsidiary of: Blackwell Publishing Ltd.), Commerce Place, 350 Main St, Malden, MA 02148. TEL 781-388-8206, FAX 781-388-8232, subscrip@blackwellpub.com, http://www.blackwellpublishing.com/journals/JSBM. Eds. Chandra S Mishra, Daniel L McConaughy. Circ: 3,500. **Co-sponsor:** International Council for Small Business.

338.642 USA ISSN 1081-8510
HD62.7
➤ **JOURNAL OF SMALL BUSINESS STRATEGY**✶. Text in English. 1990. s-a. USD 20 domestic; USD 25 foreign (effective 2004). illus. index. **Document type:** *Journal, Trade.*
Published by: Small Business Institute Directors' Association, Millersville University, Dept of Business Admin, Millersville, PA 17551. TEL 717-972-3842, FAX 717-871-2464, http://www.smallbusinessinstitute.org. Ed. Pam Schinder.

338 IND
K V I C ANNUAL REPORT. Text in English. 1957. a. charts; illus.; stat.
Formerly: India. Khadi and Village Industries Commission. Report (0073-6198)
Related titles: Hindi ed.
Published by: Khadi and Village Industries Commission, Directorate of Publicity, Gramodaya Irla Rd., Vile Parle (West), Mumbai, Maharashtra 400 056, India.

B

386.42 USA ISSN 1068-2422
KANSAS CITY SMALL BUSINESS MONTHLY. Text in English. 1991. m. USD 19.99 (effective 1999). **Document type:** *Trade.* **Description:** Covers new ideas in management, marketing, legal matters, finance, human resources, and office technology.
Related titles: Online - full text ed.
Published by: Kansas City Small Business Monthly, Inc., 10000 W 75th St, Ste 200A, Shawnee Mission, KS 66204. TEL 913-432-6690, FAX 913-980-5928, editor@kcsmallbiz.com, http://www.kcsmallbiz.com. Pub. Kelly Scanlon.

KEY NOTE MARKET ASSESSMENT. COMMERCIAL INSURANCE FOR SMALL BUSINESS. see *INSURANCE*

338 GBR
KEY NOTE MARKET ASSESSMENT. SMALL BUSINESSES & BANKS. Variant title: Small Businesses & Banks Market Assessment. Text in English. 2002. irreg., latest 2002, Jan. GBP 730 per issue (effective 2002). **Description:** Provides an in-depth strategic analysis across a broad range of industries and contains an examination on the scope, dynamics and shape of key UK markets in the consumer, financial, lifestyle and business to business sectors.
Published by: Key Note Ltd., Field House, 72 Oldfield Rd, Hampton, Mddx TW12 2HQ, United Kingdom. TEL 44-20-8481-8750, FAX 44-20-8783-0049, info@keynote.co.uk, http://www.keynote.co.uk. Ed. Simon Taylor.

338 GBR
KEY NOTE MARKET ASSESSMENT. SMALL OFFICE HOME OFFICE (SOHO) - CONSUMER. Text in English. 2001. irreg., latest 2001, May. GBP 730 per issue (effective 2002). **Description:** Provides an in-depth strategic analysis across a broad range of industries and contains an examination on the scope, dynamics and shape of key UK markets in the consumer, financial, lifestyle and business to business sectors.
Published by: Key Note Ltd., Field House, 72 Oldfield Rd, Hampton, Mddx TW12 2HQ, United Kingdom. TEL 44-20-8481-8750, FAX 44-20-8783-0049, info@keynote.co.uk, http://www.keynote.co.uk.

338 651.2 GBR
KEY NOTE MARKET ASSESSMENT. SMALL OFFICE HOME OFFICE (SOHO) - PRODUCT. Text in English. 2001. irreg., latest 2001, Mar. GBP 730 per issue (effective 2002). **Description:** Provides an in-depth strategic analysis across a broad range of industries and contains an examination on the scope, dynamics and shape of key UK markets in the consumer, financial, lifestyle and business to business sectors.
Published by: Key Note Ltd., Field House, 72 Oldfield Rd, Hampton, Mddx TW12 2HQ, United Kingdom. TEL 44-20-8481-8750, FAX 44-20-8783-0049, info@keynote.co.uk, http://www.keynote.co.uk.

338 658 GBR
KEY NOTE MARKET REPORT: EQUIPMENT LEASING. Variant title: Equipment Leasing Market Report. Text in English. irreg., latest 1999, Aug. GBP 340 per issue (effective 2002). **Document type:** *Trade.* **Description:** Provides an overview of the UK equipment leasing market, including industry structure, market size and trends, developments, prospects, and major company profiles.
Formerly (until 1995): Key Note Report: Equipment Leasing (0954-4526)
Related titles: CD-ROM ed.; Online - full text ed.
—CCC.
Published by: Key Note Ltd., Field House, 72 Oldfield Rd, Hampton, Mddx TW12 2HQ, United Kingdom. TEL 44-20-8481-8750, FAX 44-20-8783-0049, info@keynote.co.uk, http://www.keynote.co.uk. Ed. Jenny Baxter.

338.642 GBR ISSN 1460-8316
KEY NOTE MARKET REPORT: FRANCHISING. Variant title: Franchising. Text in English. irreg., latest 2000, July. GBP 340 per issue (effective 2002). **Document type:** *Trade.* **Description:** Provides and overview of a specific UK market segment and includes executive summary, market definition, market size, industry background, competitor analysis, current issues, forecasts, company profiles, and more.
Formerly (until 1997): Key Note Report. Franchising (0954-4712)
Published by: Key Note Ltd., Field House, 72 Oldfield Rd, Hampton, Mddx TW12 2HQ, United Kingdom. TEL 44-20-8481-8750, FAX 44-20-8783-0049, info@keynote.co.uk, http://www.keynote.co.uk. Ed. Nick Bardsley.

338.642 658 POL ISSN 1230-9427
➤ **KOBIETA I BIZNES/WOMEN & BUSINESS;** akademicko-gospodarcze forum. Text in English, Polish. 1993. q. adv. back issues avail. **Document type:** *Journal, Academic/Scholarly, Trade.* **Description:** Presents studies on small and medium businesses run by women.
Related titles: Diskette ed.
Published by: Szkola Glowna Handlowa, Kolegium Gospodarki Swiatowej, Al Niepodleglosci 162, Warsaw, 02554, Poland. TEL 48-22-8495084, FAX 48-22-6466115, ewael@sgh.waw.pl, http://www.kobiety.pl/mfk/kobibiznes.html, http://www.kobiety.pl/mfk.htm. Ed., Pub., Adv. contact Ewa Lisowska. **Co-sponsor:** Miedzynarodowe Forum Kobiet - International Forum for Women.

338 DEU
KREISHANDWERKERSCHAFT MOENCHENGLADBACH. MITTEILUNGSBLATT. Text in German. 1968. m. membership. back issues avail.
Published by: Kreishandwerkerschaft Moenchengladbach, Pescher Str 111-119, Moenchengladbach, 41065, Germany. TEL 02161-45021-23. Circ: 4,000.

338 ITA ISSN 1125-2529
L'IMPRENDITORE. Text in Italian. 1948. m. adv. **Document type:** *Trade.*
Formerly (until 1994): Gazzetta della Piccola Industria (0391-6138)
Indexed: RefZh.
Published by: Servizio Italiano Pubblicazioni Internazionali, Viale Pasteur 6, Rome, 00144, Italy. TEL 39-06-5903601, FAX 39-06-5903339. Ed. Paolo Mazzanti. Circ: 54,000.

338.642 FRA ISSN 1275-7349
LAMY ASSOCIATIONS. Text in French. 1992. 2 base vols. plus irreg. updates. looseleaf. EUR 488.47 print & CD-ROM eds. (effective 2004). Supplement avail. **Description:** Aids in daily management and development of partnerships.
Supersedes (in 1996): Lettres des Associations (1166-5955)
Related titles: CD-ROM ed.; Online - full text ed.: EUR 143 (effective 2003).
Published by: Lamy S.A. (Subsidiary of: Wolters Kluwer France), 21/23 rue des Ardennes, Paris, 75935 Cedex 19, France. TEL 33-1-825080800, FAX 33-1-44721388, lamy@lamy.fr, http://www.lamy.fr.

338.642 690 USA ISSN 1091-109X
LEASING PROFESSIONAL NEWSLETTER. Text in English. 1984. m. looseleaf. USD 195; USD 295 foreign (effective 1999). back issues avail. **Document type:** *Newsletter.* **Description:** Deals with negotiating and drafting strategies for commercial real estate leases. It contains several sample clauses with comment and analyzes both pro-tenant and pro-landlord leasing strategies.
Published by: Leasing Professional, 12486, Scottsdale, AZ 85267-2486. TEL 602-905-8554, FAX 602-905-8554, mail@leasingprofessional.com, http://www.leasingprofessional.com. Ed., Pub. Michael P Chemodurow.

338.642 USA ISSN 1071-0426
LEGACIES; family business newsletter. Text in English. 1989. q. USD 15.95 out of state. bk.rev. 8 p./no.; **Document type:** *Newsletter.* **Description:** Looks at family business forums, conferences, awards, succession problems.
Related titles: Online - full text ed.: (from EBSCO Publishing).
Published by: Baylor University, Institute for Family Business, PO Box 98011, Waco, TX 76798-8011. TEL 254-755-2265, FAX 254-755-2271, Doris_Sandberg@baylor.edu, http://hsb.baylor.edu/html/cel/ifb/ifb_home.htm. Ed. Doris Sandberg. Circ: 7,000.

338.642 FRA ISSN 1143-8894
LA LETTRE SOCIALE DE NOTE D'INFOS FISCALES, SOCIALES ET JURIDIQUES. Text in French. 1989. m.
Related titles: ◆ Supplement to: Note d'Infos. ISSN 1639-6634.
Published by: S I D Communications, BP 1119, Poitiers 9, Cedex 86061, France. TEL 33-5-49-60-20-60, FAX 33-5-49-01-87-08.

LEWIS & CLARK LAW REVIEW. see *LAW*

338 USA
M K JOURNEY. Text in English. free. **Description:** For women who want to start a home-based business. Presents ideas, tips, marketing on how to start-up a new business.
Media: Online - full text.
Address: mkjourney@mailexcite.com, nj@ccat.sas.upenn.edu. Ed. Vance Bell.

687.0688 GBR ISSN 0968-4638
MACHINE KNIT TODAY (UK EDITION). Text in English. 1988. m. GBP 21.60; GBP 31 foreign. adv. **Document type:** *Consumer.* **Description:** Informs and instructs how to run a knitting machine business at home.
Formerly (until 1993): Profitable Machine Knitting (0954-5468)
Related titles: ◆ Regional ed(s).: Machine Knit Today (South African edition). ISSN 1019-7508.
Published by: Aspen Litharne Publishing (Subsidiary of: Aspen Communications plc), PO Box 9, Stratford-upon-Avon, Warks CV37 8RS, United Kingdom. FAX 44-1789-720888. Ed. Carol Chambers. Adv. contact Maggie Michaells. Circ: 20,000.

338.642 DEU ISSN 0177-7491
MAERKTE IM SAARLAND. Text in German. 1947. a. **Document type:** *Bulletin.*
Published by: Statistisches Amt des Saarland, Postfach 103044, Saarbruecken, 66030, Germany. Circ: 600.

658.041 USA
THE MAIL ORDER SECRETS NEWSLETTER. Text in English. 1998. m. free. back issues avail. **Document type:** *Newsletter.* **Description:** Designed for people interested in starting a home business.
Related titles: Online - full text ed.

Published by: Plateau Publishing Co., 4320 196 St, S W, B 444, Lynnwood, WA 98036. TEL 425-750-4727, plateau@plateaubiz.com, http://plateaubiz.com. Pub. Michael Johnson.

MALOE PREDPRINIMATEL'STVO V ROSSII (YEAR). see *BUSINESS AND ECONOMICS—Abstracting, Bibliographies, Statistics*

338.642 DNK ISSN 0107-8305
MARKEDS-BOG. Text in Danish. 1982. a. DKK 100 (effective 1993). illus.
Formerly: Markedskalender
Published by: Dixit, Industrivej 12, Them, 8653, Denmark. TEL 86-84-70-22, FAX 86-84-71-15. Ed. Torben Kahr.

338.642 NLD ISSN 1387-4942
MARKT & HANDEL. Text in Dutch. 1997. m. EUR 51 (effective 2005). adv. bk.rev. charts; illus.; mkt. back issues avail. **Description:** For ambulatory businesses and market vendors.
Formed by the 1997 merger of: Het Marktblad (1385-0253); Handelaar (1387-4950)
Published by: Reed Business Information bv (Subsidiary of: Reed Business), Planetenbaan 80-99, Maarssen, 3606 AK, Netherlands. TEL 31-346-575777, info@reedbusiness.nl, http://www.marktenhandel.nl/, http://www.reedbusiness.nl. Ed. Roland Klaverstijn TEL 31-346-577810. Pub., R&P Sander Bouten. Adv. contact Ben Kleine TEL 31-346-577805. B&W page EUR 942, color page EUR 1,370; trim 210 x 297. Circ: 5,945.

338.642 USA ISSN 0025-6137
MAY TRENDS; marketing and economic trends for business executives. Text in English. 1967. s-a. free. **Document type:** *Consumer.* **Description:** Emphasizes economic, marketing, government trends which affect small business operations. Presents ideas and viewpoints of leading authorities familiar with the field.
Published by: George S. May International Company, Management Consultants, 303 S Northwest Hwy, Park Ridge, IL 60068-4265. TEL 847-825-8806, FAX 847-825-8806. Ed., R&P Roz Angell. Circ: 30,000 (controlled).

MESTER TIDENDE. see *BUILDING AND CONSTRUCTION*

363 320.6 USA ISSN 1541-3268
THE MICROENTERPRISE JOURNAL. Text in English. 2002 (Aug.). w. USD 49.95; USD 5.95 per month (effective 2004). **Document type:** *Journal, Trade.* **Description:** Contains business news for microbusinesses (fewer than five employees) covering politics economic analysis, market research and other timely information.
Incorporates (2002-2003): The MicroEnterprise Monthly (1541-3276)
Media: E-mail.
Published by: Wahmpreneur Publishing, Inc., PO Box 41, Sidney, NY 13838. TEL 607-428-0521, editor@microenterprisejournal.com, info@wahmpreneur.com, http://www.microenterprisejournal.com. Ed. Ms. Dawn Rivers Baker.

338 381 USA
MID-MISSOURI BUSINESS JOURNAL. Text in English. 1992. s-m. USD 31.50 (effective 1998). adv. back issues avail. **Document type:** *Newspaper, Trade.*
Published by: Garte L.L.C., 4250 E Broadway, Ste 1043, Columbia, MO 65201-9093. TEL 573-443-1311, FAX 573-875-1149, midmobiz@mmbj.com. Ed. Bonnie Osborn. Pub. Thomas E Garner. Adv. contact Jeanne Merritt. Circ: 5,000.

MINI LAB FOCUS. see *PHOTOGRAPHY*

338.642 USA ISSN 1048-0919
MINORITY BUSINESS ENTREPRENEUR. Text in English. 1984. bi-m. USD 18 (effective 2005). adv. illus. Index. back issues avail.; reprints avail. **Document type:** *Magazine, Trade.* **Description:** Covers opportunities for minority and women owned businesses to do business with majority-owned businesses and government.
Related titles: Online - full text ed.: (from bigchalk, Northern Light Technology, Inc., SoftLine Information).
Indexed: ENW.
Address: 3528 Torrance Blvd, Ste 101, Torrance, CA 90503-4803. TEL 310-540-9398, FAX 310-792-8263, mbewbe@ix.netcom.com, http://www.mbemag.com. Pub., R&P Ginger Conrad. adv.: B&W page USD 4,200, color page USD 5,200; trim 8 x 10.875. Circ: 28,000.

338 USA
MINORITY SUPPLIER NEWS. Text in English. q. membership. **Document type:** *Newsletter.* **Description:** Contains articles, trends and issues, and current data for corporations and other buying institutions to begin, expand and promote their minority supplier development programs. Aims primarily at purchasing professional and minority business owners.
Published by: National Minority Supplier Development Council, 1040 Avenue Of The Americas., # 2, New York, NY 10018-3703. TEL 212-944-2430, FAX 212-719-9611, info@tmsde.net. Ed. Donna Long. Circ: 30,000 (controlled).

338.642 USA ISSN 0195-0002
MISSISSIPPI BUSINESS JOURNAL. Text in English. 1979. m. USD 49 in state; USD 69 out of state (effective 2005). adv. **Document type:** *Magazine, Trade.*
Related titles: Online - full text ed.: (from EBSCO Publishing, Florida Center for Library Automation, Gale Group, O C L C Online Computer Library Center, Inc., ProQuest Information & Learning, The Dialog Corporation).
Indexed: ABIn, BusDate, LRI, T&II.
—CCC.
Published by: Venture Publishing Co., 5120 Galaxie Dr, Jackson, MS 39206. TEL 601-364-1000, FAX 601-364-1007, mbj@msbusiness.com, http://www.msbusiness.com/. Ed. Jim Laird. Adv. contact Karen Gilder. Circ: 10,500 (controlled).

338.642 USA ISSN 1050-5652
MONEY MAKER'S MONTHLY. Text in English. 1986. m. USD 19.95 domestic; USD 36 in Canada; USD 46 elsewhere (effective 2000). adv. bk.rev. **Document type:** *Trade.*
Description: Devoted to direct sales, network and multilevel marketing.
Address: 1632 E. Cass St., Joliet, IL 60432-2706. TEL 708-633-8888, FAX 708-633-8889, sales@mmmonthly.com, http://www.mmmonthly.com. Pub., R&P Keith B Laggos. Adv. contact Marvin Bohannan. B&W page USD 3,600, color page USD 5,760; trim 15.88 x 10.25. Circ: 100,000.

338.642 USA ISSN 0192-9399
MONEY MAKING OPPORTUNITIES. Text in English. 1960. 5/yr. USD 16 (effective 2005). adv. charts; illus.; tr.lit. **Document type:** *Magazine, Consumer.*
Published by: Success Publishing Co. Inc., 11071 Ventura Blvd, Studio City, CA 91604. TEL 818-980-9166, FAX 818-980-7829, mmomag@aol.com, http://www.moneymakingopps.com. Ed., Pub. Donald H Perry. Adv. contact Roger Perry. Circ: 180,000 (paid).

069.1 USA
MUSEUMS & MORE; specialty shop product news. Text in English. m. free to qualified personnel. adv. **Document type:** *Magazine, Trade.* **Description:** Offers the latest information on new trends, products and industry news relating to specialty gift shops.
Published by: Great American Publishing Co., 75 Applewood Dr, Ste A, Sparta, MI 49345. http://www.museumsandmore.com. Ed. Julie McCallum.

338 USA
MYBUSINESS. Text in English. bi-m. adv. **Document type:** *Magazine, Trade.* **Description:** Provides the knowledge, tools and resources to help small business owners succeed.
Published by: (National Federation of Independent Business), Hammock Publishing, Inc., 3322 W End Ave, Ste 700, Nashville, TN 37203. TEL 615-690-3400, FAX 615-690-3401, info@hammock.com, http://www.mybusinessmag.com, http://www.hammock.com. adv.: B&W page USD 35,931, color page USD 53,897; trim 8 x 10.5.

N A P L ECONOMIC EDGE. see *PRINTING*

338.642 USA ISSN 0196-3171
HF5429.3
N A R D A'S COST OF DOING BUSINESS SURVEY. Text in English. 1947. a. USD 295 (effective 2001). **Document type:** *Trade.*
Indexed: SRI.
Published by: North American Retail Dealers Association, 10 E 22nd St, Ste 310, Lombard, IL 60148-6191. TEL 630-953-8950, FAX 630-953-8957, nardahdq@aol.com, nardahdq@narda.com. Circ: 1,000.

N A S B I C NEWS. see *BUSINESS AND ECONOMICS—Investments*

338 USA
N F D A NOW. Text in English. 1968. q. USD 30 (effective 1999). adv. back issues avail. **Document type:** *Newsletter, Trade.* **Description:** Covers news about the fastener industry and management topics.
Published by: National Fastener Distributors Association, 1717 E Ninth St, Ste 1185, Cleveland, OH 44114. TEL 219-579-1571, FAX 216-579-1531, nfda@nfda-fastener.org, cmcvicker@nfda-fastener.org. Ed. Carolyn Fox. R&P David Merrifield. Adv. contact Connie McVicker. Circ: 900.

338.642 USA ISSN 0195-1513
N F I B. Text in English. m. charts; illus.
Published by: National Federation of Independent Business, 53 Century Blvd, Ste 205, Nashville, TN 37214. Ed. David Cullen.

NATIONAL ACCOUNTANT. see *BUSINESS AND ECONOMICS—Accounting*

NATIONAL DIPPER; the magazine for ice cream retailers. see *FOOD AND FOOD INDUSTRIES*

NATIONAL DIRECTORY OF MINORITY - OWNED BUSINESS FIRMS. see *BUSINESS AND ECONOMICS—Trade And Industrial Directories*

658 GBR
NATWEST / S E R TEAM QUARTERLY SURVEY OF SMALL BUSINESS IN BRITAIN. (Small Enterprise Research Team) Text in English. 1985. q. GBP 140; GBP 40 per issue (effective 2005). **Document type:** *Trade.* **Description:** Consists of a one-stop-shop for research knowledge-SMEs.
Former titles: NatWest Quarterly Survey of Small Business in Britain; (until 2003): NatWest S B R T Quarterly Survey of Small Business in Britain (1479-9669); (until 1993): NatWest Quarterly Survey of Small Business in the UK (0961-4222); (until 1990): Quarterly Survey of Small Business in Britain (0952-1534)
—BLDSC (6054.564500).
Published by: Small Enterprise Research Team, Open University Business School, Open University Business School, Michael Young Building, Walton Hall, Milton Keynes, Bucks MK7 6AA, United Kingdom. TEL 44-1908-655831, FAX 44-1908-655898, oubs-sbrt@open.ac.uk, http://www.serteam.co.uk/d-commerce/Natwest_Survey.html. Ed., R&P Dr. Colin Gray. Adv. contact Mrs. Julie Sullivan.

THE NETWORK JOURNAL; black professional and small business magazine. see *ETHNIC INTERESTS*

338.642 USA ISSN 0279-4527
NEW ORLEANS CITYBUSINESS. Text in English. 1943. w. (Mon.). USD 69; USD 1.50 newsstand/cover (effective 2005). adv. bk.rev. charts; stat.; maps; illus. 4 cols./p.; back issues avail. **Document type:** *Newspaper, Trade.* **Description:** Provides in-depth coverage of local business news.
Former titles: Citybusiness (Metairie); Citybusiness; Supersedes (in 1980): New Orleans Business (0094-3622); Which was formerly: Jefferson Business - New Orleans; Jefferson Business
Related titles: Microfiche ed.: (from PQC); Online - full text ed.: (from EBSCO Publishing, Gale Group, O C L C Online Computer Library Center, Inc., ProQuest Information & Learning, The Dialog Corporation).
Indexed: ABIn, BusDate, T&II.
Published by: New Orleans City Business, 111 Veterans Memorial Blvd, Ste 1440, Metairie, LA 70005-3050. TEL 504-834-9292, FAX 504-832-3550, http://www.neworleanscitybusiness.com. Ed. Terry O'Connor. Pub. Mark Singletary. Adv. contact Lisa Blossman. Circ: 17,000 (paid). **Subscr. to:** PO Box 19308, New Orleans, LA 70179.

338 USA ISSN 1549-8387
HD2346.U52
▼ **THE NEW YORK ENTERPRISE REPORT.** Text in English. 2003. m. free. **Document type:** *Magazine, Trade.* **Description:** Features articles written by leading business experts specifically for small and midsize businesses, with an emphasis on businesses in the New York metro area.
Related titles: Online - full text ed.: ISSN 1549-8395.
Published by: R S L Media LLC, 30 Lincoln Plaza, Ste 18L, New York, NY 10023. TEL 212-307-6760, FAX 212-937-2430, info@nyreport.com, http://www.nyreport.com. Ed., Pub. Robert S Levin.

NEW ZEALAND RETAIL; New Zealand's leading retail magazine. see *BUSINESS AND ECONOMICS—Marketing And Purchasing*

338.642 JPN ISSN 0289-6516
NIKKEI VENTURE. Text in Japanese. 1984. m. JPY 12,840 (effective 2000). adv. **Document type:** *Trade.* **Description:** Focuses on small and medium-sized growth business, with practical information on management, risks, and opportunities.
Published by: Nikkei Business Publications Inc. (Subsidiary of: Nihon Keizai Shimbun, Inc.), 2-7-6 Hirakawa-cho, Chiyoda-ku, Tokyo, 102-8622, Japan. TEL 81-3-5210-8311, FAX 81-3-5210-8530, info@nikkeibpnyc.com, info@nikkeibp-america.com, http://www.nikkeibp.com. Ed. Yasushi Takano. Pub. Katsutoshi Kimura. Adv. contact Tatsuo Ito. B&W page JPY 483,000, color page JPY 725,000; trim 208 x 280. Circ: 77,968. **Dist. in America by:** Nikkei Business Publications America Inc., 575 Fifth Ave, 20th Fl, New York, NY 10017.

338.642 FRA ISSN 1639-6634
NOTE D'INFOS. Text in French. 12/yr. **Document type:** *Magazine, Consumer.*
Former titles (until 2003): Note d'Infos Fiscales, Sociales et Juridiques (0988-6400); (until 1988): Note d'Infos (0992-3144)
Related titles: ♦ Supplement(s): La Lettre Sociale de Note d'Infos Fiscales, Sociales et Juridiques. ISSN 1143-8894.
Published by: S I D Communications, BP 1119, Poitiers 9, Cedex 86061, France. TEL 33-5-49-60-20-60, FAX 33-5-49-01-87-08, sid@sid-editions.fr, http://www.sid-editions.fr/mens_fr.htm. Ed. Laurent David. Circ: 200,000.

658.041 USA
NOTEWORTHY SMALL BUSINESS E-ZINE. Text in English. m. free. **Document type:** *Trade.* **Description:** Covers tips and news about home-based business.
Media: Online - full text.
Published by: C.E.S. Business Consultants, 514 Old Hickory Ln, Ringgold, GA 30736. TEL 706-866-2295, noteworthy@pwgroup.com, http://www.pwgroup.com/ezine. Ed. Marnie Pehrson.

338.642 388.321 GBR ISSN 0260-8294
NOTTINGHAM LICENSED TAXI OWNERS & DRIVERS ASSOCIATION. NEWSLETTER. Text in English. 1980. q.
Published by: Nottingham Licensed Taxi Owners & Drivers Association, 63a Derby Rd, Nottingham, United Kingdom.

658.041 USA
NOVA NEWS; business solutions e-zine. Text in English. m. free. **Document type:** *Newsletter.* **Description:** Designed for small and home-based business owners.
Media: Online - full text.
Address: colden@novaplaza.com, http://www.novaplaza.com/newsletter.shtml. Ed. Colleen Shimkoski.

338.642 CAN ISSN 0820-2737
NOVA SCOTIA BUSINESS JOURNAL. Text in English. 1986. m. CND 27.60 domestic; CND 38.52 foreign (effective 2003). adv. bk.rev. **Document type:** *Journal, Trade.*
Related titles: Microform ed.: 1986 (from PQC).
Indexed: CBCARef.
Published by: Transcontinental Specialty Publications (Subsidiary of: Transcontinental Media, Inc.), 11 Thornhill Dr, Dartmouth, NS B3B 1R9, Canada. TEL 902-468-8027, 800-565-2601, FAX 902-468-2322, nsbj@hfxnews.ca. Pub. Don Brander TEL 902-468-8027 ext 116. Adv. contact Peter Coleman TEL 902-468-8027 ext 108. page CND 3,050. Circ: 10,000.

B

NOVOGRADISKI GLASNIK. see *AGRICULTURE*

338.642 RUS ISSN 1606-1535
NOVOSTI MALOGO BIZNESA. Text in Russian. 1999. w. free (effective 2004). **Document type:** *Consumer.*
Media: Online - full text.
Published by: Al'yans Midiya, Bolotnaya ul 12, str 3, Moscow, 115035, Russian Federation. TEL 7-095-2345380, FAX 7-095-2345363, allmedia@allmedia.ru, http://www.businesspress.ru, http://allmedia.ru.

O P A S T C O ROUNDTABLE; the magazine of ideas for small telephone companies. see *COMMUNICATIONS—Telephone And Telegraph*

338 USA
ON BUYING OR SELLING A BUSINESS. Text in English. 1993. q. free. **Document type:** *Newsletter.* **Description:** Provides a listing and searching service in the Chicago area for those interested in acquiring or selling a manufacturing business.
Published by: F.W. Robbins Co., 2451 N. Clybourn Ave., Apt. 5, Chicago, IL 60614-1949. TEL 773-327-9393, FAX 773-327-6055, frobbins@mcs.com, http://www.mcs.net/~frobbins. Ed., R&P Frank Robbins. Circ: 1,500 (controlled).

338 658 USA ISSN 1097-4377
HF5469.23.U6
OPERATING RESULTS OF INDEPENDENT SUPERMARKETS✶. Text in English. a. USD 75 to non-members; USD 30 to members. **Document type:** *Trade.* **Description:** Managerial tool for independent supermarket retailers to evaluate their own store's operating results.
Indexed: SRI.
Published by: Food Marketing Institute, 655 15th St NW, Suite 700, Washington, DC 20005-5701. TEL 202-452-8444.

338 USA ISSN 0736-2129
OPERATING SMALL BUSINESS INVESTMENT COMPANIES. DIRECTORY. Text in English. irreg.
Published by: U.S. Small Business Administration, 409 Third St, S W, MC 3114, Washington, DC 20416. TEL 800-827-5722, http://www.sba.gov/gils/SBA1997Dec18.134030.html.

346 USA ISSN 1092-2628
OPINION DIGEST. Text in English. 1955. irreg. **Document type:** *Government.* **Description:** Digest of legal opinions rendered by the staff of the administration.
Related titles: Microfiche ed.
Published by: (Office of General Counsel), U.S. Small Business Administration, 409 Third St, S W, MC 3114, Washington, DC 20416. TEL 202-205-6531. **Subscr. to:** National Technical Information Service, Government Research Center, 5285 Port Royal Rd, Springfield, VA 22161. TEL 703-605-6060, 800-363-2068, http://www.ntis.gov.

338 531.54 USA
OPPORTUNITY HOT - LINE. Text in English. 1986. bi-m. USD 125 (effective 2001). adv. **Document type:** *Newsletter, Consumer.* **Description:** Directed to small business owners interested in getting funding from private investors, acquiring government contracts, and networking with other businesses, also investors seeking high-yield investments. Finding investing partners.
Formerly: Networker (Cleveland)
Published by: Business Network, 5420 Mayfield Rd, Ste 205, Cleveland, OH 44124. Ed., R&P, Adv. contact Irwin Friedman. B&W page USD 395; trim 1 x 8.5. Circ: 685.

338 USA
OPPORTUNITYWORLD; the ultimate survival magazine for small businesses and entrepreneurs. Text in English. 1997. bi-m. USD 11.97 domestic; USD 41.97 foreign; USD 2.99 newsstand/cover (effective 2001). adv. 128 p./no. 3 cols./p.; **Document type:** *Trade.* **Description:** For entrepreneurs interested in starting small businesses.

▼ *new title* ➤ *refereed* ✶ *unverified* ♦ *full entry avail.*

Published by: United Communications, 28 Vesey St, 257, New York, NY 10007-2701. TEL 212-785-9080, FAX 212-785-8007, editor@oppworld.com, oppworld@aol.com, http://www.oppworld.com. Ed. Gia Minetta. Pub. Gary Ng TEL 212-785-9080. adv.: page USD 2,485; trim 10.75 x 8. Circ: 125,000.

338 USA
P A T C A DIRECTORY OF CONSULTANTS. Text in English. a. USD 15 per vol. (effective 2000 & 2001). **Document type:** *Directory, Trade.* **Description:** Offers a detailed listing of consultants and subcontractors in a wide variety professional and technical fields.
Related titles: Online - full content ed.: P A T C A Online Directory of Consultants. free.
Published by: Professional and Technical Consultants Association, 849 B Independence Ave, Mountain View, CA 94043. TEL 650-903-8305, FAX 650-967-0995, office@patca.org, info@patca.org, http://www.patca.org/directory/index.html.

338 USA
P A T C A NEWSLETTER. Text in English. q. free. back issues avail. **Document type:** *Newsletter, Trade.* **Description:** Discusses news and issues of interest to a wide audience of business and technical consultants.
Media: Online - full content.
Published by: Professional and Technical Consultants Association, 849 B Independence Ave, Mountain View, CA 94043. TEL 650-903-8305, FAX 650-967-0995, office@patca.org, info@patca.org, http://www.patca.org/newsletter/newsletter.html.

338 GBR
P B W NEWS. Text in English. 1951. fortn. GBP 24 in United Kingdom; GBP 30 in Europe; GBP 40 elsewhere (effective 2001). adv. **Document type:** *Magazine, Trade.* **Description:** Contains news, new products, industry profiles and features.
Former titles (until 199?): Pet Business World (1350-5017); (until 1992): Pet Store Trader
Published by: Plantagenet Publications, Station House, Station Rd., Buckinghamshire, MK16 0AG, United Kingdom. TEL 44-1908-614477, FAX 44-1908-616441, pbwnews@commerce.co.uk, http://www.pbwnews.co.uk. Adv. contact Jason Mayor.

338.642 CAN ISSN 1491-221X
HD2346.C2
P M E; le magazine de l'entrepreneurship du Quebec. (Petites et Moyennes Entreprises) Text in English. 1984. m. (10/yr.). CND 22.95 domestic; CND 55 in United States (effective 2005). adv. **Document type:** *Magazine, Trade.*
Former titles (until 1999): Magazine P M E (1208-5308); (until 1996): P M E (Laval) (0828-8089)
Indexed: PdeR.
Published by: Transcontinental Media, Inc. (Subsidiary of: Transcontinental, Inc.), 1100 Blvd Rene Levesque W, 24th Fl, Montreal, PQ H3B 4X9, Canada. TEL 514-392-9000, FAX 514-392-1489, info@transcontinental.ca, http://www.transcontinental-gtc.com/en/home.html. Ed. Pierre Duhamel. Adv. contact Laurianne Adam. Circ: 34,195 (paid).

338.642 ITA ISSN 1128-7594
P M I; il mensile della piccola e media impresa. (Piccola Media Impresa) Text in Italian. 1994. m. EUR 120 (effective 2005). **Document type:** *Magazine, Consumer.*
Published by: IPSOA Editore (Subsidiary of: Wolters Kluwer Italia Srl), Strada 1, Palazzo F6, Milanofiori, Assago, MI 20090, Italy. TEL 39-02-82476888, FAX 39-02-82476436, http://www.ipsoa.it.

338 FRA
P M I FRANCE✶. Text in French. 5/yr. **Description:** Provides general economic information relevant to small and medium sized industrial enterprises.
Address: 30 rue des Jeuneurs, Paris, 75002, France. TEL 45-08-91-88. Ed. Lazaro Gecsges. Circ: 10,000.

P R C NEWS; a monthly news in brief for the video industry. (Pre Recorded Cassette) see *COMMUNICATIONS—Video*

PARTNERSHIP TAXATION. see *BUSINESS AND ECONOMICS—Public Finance, Taxation*

338.642 GBR ISSN 0961-2602
PARTY TIMES. Text in English. 1991. bi-m. GBP 22.50 (effective 1997). adv. **Document type:** *Trade.* **Description:** Provides an effective communications link between manufacturers, wholesalers and retailers of all products and services for the party industry.
Formerly (until 1997): BalloonWorld
Published by: Plaza Publishing Ltd, 3 Rectory Grove, London, SW4 0DX, United Kingdom. TEL 44-171-819-1200, FAX 44-171-819-1210. Ed. Daniel Phelan. Pub. Andrew Maiden. Adv. contact Alice Frackelton. B&W page GBP 1,095, color page GBP 1,295.

658.041 USA
THE PAY DAY NEWS. Text in English. 1983. m. USD 12; USD 46 foreign (effective 1998). adv. bk.rev. **Document type:** *Trade.* **Description:** Homebased business connection for budget conscious entrepreneurs and internet marketers.
Formerly: Pay Day Tabloid
Related titles: Online - full text ed.: 1983.
Published by: YouOnLine.Net, Innovative Marketing Group, PO Box 724, Sister Bay, WI 54234-0724. TEL 920-854-4360, payday2@bellatlantic.net, webmaster@youonline.net, http://www.youonline.net/payday. Ed., R&P, Adv. contact John Mason. Pub. Victoria Ring. page USD 550. Circ: 15,000.

338.642 BRA ISSN 0104-2297
HD2346.B7
PEQUENAS EMPRESAS GRANDES NEGOCIOS. Text in Portuguese. 1988. m. BRL 87 (effective 2005). adv. illus. back issues avail. **Document type:** *Magazine, Trade.* **Description:** Covers such themes as: business opportunities, how to set up new businesses, new products and services, administration techniques and marketing.
Incorporates (1993-199?): Franchising (0104-8597)
Related titles: Supplement(s): Guia do Empreendedor.
Published by: Editora Globo S.A., Av. Jaguare, 1487, Sao Paulo, SP 05346 902, Brazil. TEL 55-11-37677852, FAX 55-11-37677771, atendimento@edglobo.com.br, http://empresas.globo.com/, http://editoraglobo.globo.com/. Pub. Jose Francisco Queiroz. adv.: color page USD 46,000; trim 274 x 208. Circ: 144,000 (paid).

338 USA
PERSPECTIVES (ALEXANDRIA). Text in English. 1990. q. looseleaf. membership only. charts; illus.; stat.; tr.lit. back issues avail. **Document type:** *Newsletter.* **Description:** Covers governmental relations issues on Capitol Hill affecting the on-premise sign industry.
Published by: International Sign Association, 707 N St Asaph St, Alexandria, VA 22314-1911. TEL 703-836-4012, FAX 703-836-8353, shane@signs.org, http://www.signs.org. Ed. Shane Artim. Circ: 1,200 (paid).

PEST CONTROL TECHNOLOGY. see *ENGINEERING—Chemical Engineering*

PET SERVICES JOURNAL. see *PETS*

338.642 ITA ISSN 0394-7947
PICCOLA IMPRESA/SMALL BUSINESS. Text in Italian. 1988. 3/yr.
Published by: Ins-Edit, Viale Sauli, 49, Genoa, GE 16121, Italy. TEL 39-010-541302. Ed. R Cafferata.

658.041 USA
THE PINNACLE PERSPECTIVE. Text in English. bi-m. free. **Document type:** *Newsletter.* **Description:** Designed for entrepreneurs, home-based business owners, professionals and corporate managers.
Media: Online - full text.
Published by: Pinnacle Perspective, 4529 Angeles Crest Hwy., Ste. 306, La Canada, CA 91011. TEL 818-952-6310, FAX 818-952-3241, ucc2000@aol.com, http://www.uncommoncourtesy.com. Ed., Pub., R&P Susan C. Rempel. Adv. contact Linda Garrison.

338.642 USA
PINNACLE - TEEN BUSINESS!. Text in English. 1999. s-w. free. **Document type:** *Newsletter.* **Description:** Designed for all teens interested in finding out how the Web has opened up the world of business for a whole new generation.
Media: Online - full text.
Published by: Soda Mail, LLC, PO Box 750246, Petaluma, CA 94975. TEL 707-794-1289, laure@sodamail.com, http://www.sodamail.com/site/pinnacle.shtml. Ed. Lauren Elliott.

338.642 USA ISSN 1099-9345
PROFESSIONAL RETAIL STORE MAINTENANCE. Text in English. 1998. m. **Document type:** *Magazine, Trade.*
Published by: France Publications, Inc., 3500 Piedmont Rd, Ste 415, Atlanta, GA 30305. TEL 404-832-8262, FAX 404-832-8260, info@prsm.com, http://www.prsm.com/publications.asp, http://www.francepublications.com. Pub. Jerrold France TEL 404-832-8262 ext 111. Adv. contact Scott France.

338 USA
PROFITS. Text in English. 1970. bi-m. free. bk.rev. charts; illus.
Published by: (School of Business & Public Administration), Howard University, Small Business Development Center, 2600 6th St, N W, Box 748, Washington, DC 20059. TEL 202-806-1550. Ed. Emma J O'Neal. Circ: 2,000.

338.04 CAN ISSN 0711-0316
PROFITS; essential information for entrepreneurs. Text in English, French. 1980. 3/yr. free. bk.rev. charts; illus.; stat.; tr.lit. back issues avail. **Document type:** *Newspaper, Government.* **Description:** Provides owners of small and medium-sized businesses with information of interest and informs them about the Business Development Bank of Canada's products and services.
Related titles: Online - full text ed.
Indexed: CBCARef, CPerl.
Published by: Business Development Bank of Canada, 5 Place Ville Marie, Ste 400, Montreal, PQ H3B 5E7, Canada. TEL 888-463-6232, FAX 877-329-9232, bus-service-center@bdc.ca, bus-service-center@bdc.x400.gc.ca, http://www.bdc.ca. Ed. Sylvain Masse. Circ: 1,000,000 (free).

338.642 658 GBR ISSN 1464-1038
PROSPER; your complete guide to making money. Text in English. m. GBP 7.50 for 3 mos.; GBP 2.10 newsstand/cover. adv. back issues avail. **Document type:** *Consumer.* **Description:** Presents information for people seeking business opportunities and start-up advice.
Former titles (until 1998): Business Opportunity World (1356-1723); (until 1994): Home Business (0967-3288)
Published by: Archant Specialist Ltd. (Subsidiary of: Archant), The Mill, Bearwalden Business Park, Royston Rd, Wendens Ambo, Essex CB11 4GB, United Kingdom. TEL 44-1799-544200, john.moulding@marketlink.co.uk, farine.clarke@archant.co.uk, http://www.archant.co.uk/. Ed. John Moulding. adv.: color page GBP 1,645; trim 210 x 297. Circ: 40,000 (paid).

PUMPER. see *HEATING, PLUMBING AND REFRIGERATION*

658.8 GBR ISSN 0969-1162
Q E D. (Quarterly Enterprise Digest) Text in English. 198?. m. illus. **Document type:** *Journal, Trade.* **Description:** Fosters discussion of issues in business growth and enterprise in small, independent businesses.
—BLDSC (7163.591480).
Published by: 3 i plc, 91 Waterloo Rd, London, SE1 8XP, United Kingdom. Ed. Morrison Halcrow. Pub. Adam Quarry.

QIYE GUANLI/ENTERPRISE MANAGEMENT. see *BUSINESS AND ECONOMICS—Management*

338 CHN ISSN 1671-8119
QIYE YANJIU/CORPORATION RESEARCH. Text in Chinese. 1985. m. CNY 120 (effective 2004). **Document type:** *Journal, Academic/Scholarly.*
Address: 39-1, Dongfeng Dajie, Changchun, 130011, China. TEL 86-431-5903526, FAX 86-431-5974677, chycf@sohu.com, http://www.aphr.org/chycf/. **Dist. outside of China by:** China International Book Trading Corp, 35 Chegongzhuang Xilu, Haidian District, PO Box 399, Beijing 100044, China. TEL 86-10-68412045, FAX 86-10-68412023, cibtc@mail.cibtc.com.cn, http://www.cibtc.com.cn/; **Dist. by:** China Books & Periodicals Inc, 360 Swift Ave., Ste. 48, S San Fran, CA 94080-6220. TEL 415-282-2994.

338 330 USA
QUICK SOLUTIONS. Text in English. 1993. 3/yr. **Document type:** *Trade.* **Description:** Provides small business information and computer guidance.
Media: Online - full text.
Address: vince14@aol.com, http://www.idsonline.com/quick/. Ed. Vince Shelton.

RAZVITIE NA CHASTNIA SEKTOR. see *STATISTICS*

338 GBR
REFERENDUM. Text in English. q. members.
Indexed: RASB.
Address: Ruskin Chambers, Drury Ln, Knutsford, Ches WA16 6HA, United Kingdom. TEL 44-1565-634467, FAX 44-1565-650059, fpbltd@fpb.co.uk, http://www.fpb.co.uk. Ed. Craig McGinty. Circ: 18,278.

REGIONAL DIRECTORY OF MINORITY- AND WOMEN-OWNED BUSINESS FIRMS: CENTRAL EDITION. see *BUSINESS AND ECONOMICS—Trade And Industrial Directories*

REGIONAL DIRECTORY OF MINORITY- AND WOMEN-OWNED BUSINESS FIRMS: EASTERN EDITION. see *BUSINESS AND ECONOMICS—Trade And Industrial Directories*

REGIONAL DIRECTORY OF MINORITY- AND WOMEN-OWNED BUSINESS FIRMS: WESTERN EDITION. see *BUSINESS AND ECONOMICS—Trade And Industrial Directories*

REP TALK. see *BUSINESS AND ECONOMICS—Management*

338.642 USA ISSN 0893-4347
RESEARCH RECOMMENDATIONS; business briefing and tax production report. Text in English. 1937. w. USD 125. **Document type:** *Newsletter.* **Description:** Advises small business owners on economic, political, and management trends, and tax reduction.
—CCC.
Published by: National Institute of Business Management, PO Box 9286, Mclean, VA 22102-0286. TEL 703-905-8000. Ed. Patrick Di Domenico. Circ: 20,000.

338 380.1 USA
RESOURCE GUIDE FOR STARTING AND GROWING A SMALL BUSINESS. Text in English. 1987. a. looseleaf. USD 29.95 domestic; USD 34.95 foreign (effective 2001). bk.rev. **Document type:** *Directory.* **Description:** Lists small business books, magazines, websites, associations, directories and other resources for small business.
Related titles: Diskette ed.; E-mail ed.
Published by: Richard Siedlecki Consulting Inc., 4767 Lake Forrest Dr, N E, Atlanta, GA 30342-2539. TEL 404-303-9900, FAX 404-303-9939, sied@mindspring.com. Ed., R&P Richard Siedlecki.

338 USA
RETAILERS FORUM MAGAZINE. Text in English. 1981. m. USD 30. adv. bk.rev. 200 p./no.; **Document type:** *Magazine, Trade.* **Description:** For owners of retail stores who buy goods for resale through retail outlets.
Formerly: Marketers Forum Magazine (0888-3327)
Published by: Forum Publishing Co., 383 E Main St, Centerport, NY 11721-1538. TEL 631-754-5000, TELEX 804294. Ed., Pub., Adv. contact Martin Stevens. page USD 575; 7 x 10. Circ: 70,000.

338.642 ESP ISSN 1137-8484
REVISTA DE ESTUDIOS EMPRESARIALES. Text in Spanish; Abstracts in English. 1997. a., latest vol.3, 1998. **Document type:** *Academic/Scholarly.*
—CINDOC.
Published by: Universidad de Murcia, Servicio de Publicaciones, Edificio Saavedra Fajardo, C/ Actor Isidoro Maiquez 9, Murcia, 30007, Spain. TEL 34-968-363887, FAX 34-968-363414, servpubl@um.es, http://www.um.es/spumweb. Ed. Maria del Pilar Aguado Jimenez. Circ: 84.

338.642 CAN ISSN 0776-5436
REVUE INTERNATIONALE P M E. (Petite et Moyenne Entreprise) Summaries in English, French, Spanish. 1977. q. CND 54 domestic to individuals; CND 36 foreign to students; CND 86 to institutions (effective 2004).
Formerly (until 1988): P M E: Revue de la Petite et Moyenne Entreprise (0705-0674)
Indexed: PdeR.
Published by: (Universite du Quebec a Trois Rivieres), Presses de l'Universite du Quebec, Delta 1, 2875 boul Laurier, Bureau 450, Ste Foy, PQ G1V 2M2, Canada. TEL 418-657-4399, FAX 418-657-2096, puq@puq.uquebec.ca, http://www.puq.uquebec.ca. Ed. Pierre Andre Julien.

RISK MANAGEMENT FOR EXECUTIVE WOMEN. see *INSURANCE*

338 USA
THE ROTHMAN REPORT✶. Text in English. 1996. fortn. **Document type:** *Trade.* **Description:** Reportage and analysis of current ideas, news and tools of interest to wired small business owners and operators.
Published by: Rothman Report, 1280 E Easter Ave, Littleton, CO 80122. hrothman@ecentral.com, http://www.ecentral.com/business/rothman/. Ed. Howard Rothman.

338 GBR
ROUTLEDGE STUDIES IN SMALL BUSINESS. Text in English. 1996. irreg., latest vol.8, 2002, Oct. price varies. **Document type:** *Monographic series, Academic/Scholarly.*
—BLDSC (8026.519900).
Published by: Routledge (Subsidiary of: Taylor & Francis Group), 4 Park Square, Milton Park, Abingdon, Oxon OX14 4RN, United Kingdom. TEL 44-1235-828600, FAX 44-1235-829000, info@routledge.co.uk, http://www.tandf.co.uk, http://www.routledge.co.uk. Ed. Kevin McNally.

338.642 USA ISSN 8750-3158
S B A N E ENTERPRISE. Text in English. 1984. m. USD 49; USD 95 foreign. adv. bk.rev. charts; illus.; stat. **Document type:** *Newsletter.*
Published by: Smaller Business Association of New England, 204 Second Ave, Waltham, MA 02154. TEL 617-890-9070, FAX 617-890-4567. Ed., R&P Julie Scofield. Adv. contact Jean Peckham. Circ: 2,700.

338 USA
S B I C DIRECTORY AND HANDBOOK OF SMALL BUSINESS FINANCE. Text in English. 1970. a. USD 15 (effective 2000). adv. **Document type:** *Directory.* **Description:** Lists over 400 SBIC's including name, address, types of preferred financing, details of their capital structure.
Published by: International Wealth Success, Inc., 24 Cantebury Rd, Rockville Centre, NY 11570-1310. TEL 516-766-5850, FAX 516-766-5919. Pub. Tyler G Hicks.

658 IND ISSN 0970-8464
HD69.S6
S E D M E. (Small Enterprises Development, Management and Extension) Text in English. 1966. q. INR 300, USD 100. bk.rev. charts; stat. **Document type:** *Academic/Scholarly.*
Formerly: S I E T Studies (0036-1518)
Indexed: ILD.
Published by: National Institute of Small Industry Extension Training, Yousufguda, Hyderabad, Andhra Pradesh 500 045, India. TEL 91-40-238544, FAX 91-40-238547, TELEX 425-6381-SIET-IN. Ed. U B Raju. Circ: 400.

338 GBR
S M E RESEARCH DATABASE. Text in English. 1998 (Sept.). irreg., latest 1998. looseleaf. GBP 150 per vol.; GBP 90 per vol. to students (effective 2002). 453 p./no.; **Description:** Contains a collection of highly condensed summaries of key pieces of research.
Published by: Small Enterprise Research Team, Open University Business School, Open University Business School, Michael Young Building, Walton Hall, Milton Keynes, Bucks MK7 6AA, United Kingdom. TEL 44-1908-655831, FAX 44-1908-655898, OUBS-SBRT@open.ac.uk, http://www.sbrt.co.uk/d-commerce/page9.html. R&P Dr. Colin Gray.

338 IND
S S I. (Small Scale Industries) Text in English. 1976. m. INR 80, USD 30. adv. bk.rev.
Published by: Eastern Trade Press Co., 43 Sunder Mahal, Churchgate, Mumbai, Maharashtra 400 020, India. Ed. Bhojan Krishnan. Circ: 10,000.

338.642 USA ISSN 0278-5048
SALES REP'S ADVISOR. Text in English. 1981. s-m. USD 199 domestic (effective 2005). bk.rev. 6 p./no.; back issues avail.; reprints avail. **Document type:** *Newsletter, Corporate.* **Description:** Provides information on handling crises with power buyers. Includes tax information and strategies, business management, partnering with principals, sales management, legal issues and more.
Published by: Alexander Communications Group, Inc., 28 W 25th St, 8th Fl, New York, NY 10010. TEL 212-228-0246, FAX 212-228-0376, info@repsadvisor.com, info@alexcommgrp.com, http://www.repsadvisor.com, http://www.alexcommgrp.com. Ed. Bill Keenan. Pub. Margaret Dewitt. R&P Mary Dalessandro.

338.642 USA ISSN 1053-1696
HF5482.4
THE SAN FRANCISCO ALMANAC. Text in English. 1990. bi-m. USD 18. adv. bk.rev. **Document type:** *Consumer.* **Description:** Contains general-interest articles about local people, places, and opportunities.
Published by: San Francisco Almanac, 1657 Waller St, Ste A, San Francisco, CA 94117. TEL 415-751-0357. Ed. Walter Biller.

SELBSTAENDIG IN DER WIRTSCHAFT. see *BUSINESS AND ECONOMICS—Economic Situation And Conditions*

338.642 DEU ISSN 0939-0081
DER SELBSTAENDIGE. Text in German. 1962. 5/yr. EUR 2 newsstand/cover (effective 2002). adv. bk.rev. **Document type:** *Magazine, Trade.*
Published by: Bundesverband der Selbstaendigen Deutscher Gewerbeverband e.V., Platz vor dem Neuen Tor 4, Berlin, 10115, Germany. TEL 49-30-280491-0, FAX 49-30-28049111, info@bds-dgv.de, http://www.bds-dgv.de. adv.: B&W page EUR 6,240, color page EUR 6,760; trim 210 x 280. Circ: 63,140 (controlled).

338.642 USA ISSN 1041-8741
SELF-EMPLOYED AMERICA. Text in English. 1989. bi-m. USD 12 to non-members; USD 2 to members (effective 2005). adv. **Document type:** *Magazine, Trade.* **Description:** Presents how-to articles, an analysis of legislative news, and how it affects the self-employed. Also includes tax tips, business advice, profiles of NASE members, and association news.
Related titles: Online - full text ed.
Published by: National Association for the Self-Employed, PO Box 612067, Dallas, TX 75261-2067. TEL 800-232-6273, FAX 800-551-4446, http://www.nase.org. Ed. Suzanne Martin. Circ: 300,000 (controlled).

630 338 USA
SELF-EMPLOYED COUNTRY; communicating for agriculture and the self-employed. Text in English. 1977. q. USD 12 to non-members; free to members (effective 2001). 16 p./no.; back issues avail. **Document type:** *Magazine.* **Description:** Covers rural issues, including legislative news, technological trends, agricultural business news, exchange opportunities, as well as member-related association news.
Formerly (until 2000): C A Highlights
Published by: C A for the Self-Employed, 112 E Lincoln, Box 677, Fergus Falls, MN 56538. TEL 218-739-3241, FAX 218-739-3832, editor@selfemployedcountry.org, http://www.selfemployedcountry.org. Ed. Colleen McGuire-Klemme. Circ: 33,900.

338.642 USA ISSN 0736-1912
SELF-EMPLOYMENT UPDATE. Text in English. 1983. a. USD 6 (effective 2005). **Document type:** *Newsletter.* **Description:** Possibilities and ideas for the self employed.
—CCC.
Published by: Prosperity and Profits Unlimited, PO Box 416, Denver, CO 80201-0416. TEL 303-575-5676, FAX 303-575-1187, starsuccess@excite.com, http://www.sayyesmarketing.com, http://businessidearesource.bigstep.com. Ed., R&P A Doyle TEL 303-575-5676. Circ: 1,500 (paid and controlled).

SELF PUBLISHING UPDATE. see *COMMUNICATIONS*

338.642 USA ISSN 1044-9590
SELF STORAGE JOURNAL. Text in English. m. **Document type:** *Trade.*
Formerly: Self-Service Storage (0892-5062)
Published by: Self Storage Association, 60 Revere Dr, Ste 500, Northbrook, IL 60062-1577. TEL 312-480-9627, FAX 312-480-9282. Ed. Charles Laughlin. Circ: 1,043.

338 USA
SERENDIPITY. Text in English. bi-m. USD 12 domestic. adv. 4 cols./p.; **Document type:** *Newspaper, Trade.* **Description:** Reports on franchises and other small-business opportunities.
Published by: (Inter-Tab), R & S Publications, PO Box 17813, Fountain Hills, AZ 85269-7813.

338 USA
A SERIOUS BUSINESS✶. Text in English. 1996. bi-w. USD 15 (effective 1997 & 1998). bk.rev. **Document type:** *Newsletter.* **Description:** Contains new marketing ideas, how-tos, common problem solutions, valuable resources, tips and tricks by and for successful business people in over 70 countries.
Media: Online - full text.
Published by: Gabriel Publishing Co., Inc., PO Box 1080, Salida, CO 81201-1080. TEL 216-428-6163, 800-359-5166, FAX 216-428-5509, editor@earthone.com, http://earthone.com. Ed. Ray Gabriel. Circ: 4,000.

338 USA ISSN 1094-6853
SHOP OWNER; the manufacturing marketplace of new products and technology. Text in English. q. USD 25 domestic; USD 30 in Canada; USD 40 elsewhere; USD 8 newsstand/cover domestic; USD 12 newsstand/cover in Canada; USD 14 newsstand/cover elsewhere (effective 2000); Free within the United States to qualified individuals. adv. **Document type:** *Trade.*
Published by: Penton Media, Inc. (Subsidiary of: Pittway Company), 1300 E 9th St, Cleveland, OH 44114-1503. TEL 216-696-7000, FAX 216-931-9524, http://www.penton.com. Ed. Thomas J Grasson TEL 216-931-9240. Pub. Joseph Fristik. Adv. contact Louise Bouhasin. B&W page USD 6,565, color page USD 8,100. Circ: 12,000.

338 USA
SIGNALS. Text in English. 1944. bi-m. looseleaf. membership only. bk.rev. charts; illus.; stat.; tr.lit. **Document type:** *Newsletter.* **Description:** Covers issues of importance to small business owners in the on-premise sign industry.
Published by: International Sign Association, 707 N St Asaph St, Alexandria, VA 22314-1911. TEL 703-836-4012, FAX 703-836-8353, shane@signs.org, http://www.signs.org. Ed. Shane Artim. Circ: 1,600.

SMALL BIZ NEWS. see *BUSINESS AND ECONOMICS—Banking And Finance*

338.642 GBR ISSN 0262-3102
SMALL BUSINESS. Text in English. 1976. 4/yr. GBP 115 domestic; GBP 150 foreign (effective 2000). adv. bk.rev. **Document type:** *Newspaper.*
Incorporates: S B B Tax News (0263-3817)
Related titles: Microform ed.: (from PQC).
Published by: Small Business Bureau, Curzon House, Church Rd, Windlesham, Surrey GU20 6BH, United Kingdom. TEL 44-1276-452010, FAX 44-1276-451602, info@sbb.org.uk, http://www.smallbusinessbureau.org.uk. Ed. John Burley. Circ: 6,000.

338.642 USA ISSN 1069-9619
SMALL BUSINESS ADVISOR. Text in English. 1993. m. USD 45 (effective 2004). bk.rev. 16 p./no. 3 cols./p.; back issues avail. **Document type:** *Newsletter, Trade.* **Description:** Allows small-business owners easy access to specialized information their growing companies need; topics include finance and cash flow, human resources management, insurance, law, marketing, technology, and taxation.
Published by: Small Business Advisors, Inc., PO Box 436, Woodmere, NY 11598. TEL 516-374-1387, 800-295-1325, FAX 516-374-1175, smalbusadv@aol.com, http://www.smallbusinessadvice.com. Ed. Ann Liss. Pub. Joseph Gelb. R&P Arthur Vandam TEL 516-374-1387. Circ: 2,000 (paid).

THE SMALL BUSINESS ADVISOR: SOFTWARE NEWS. see *BUSINESS AND ECONOMICS—Computer Applications*

338 363.728 USA
THE SMALL BUSINESS ADVOCATE (AUSTIN). Text in English. bi-m. Free to subscribers in Texas.. back issues avail. **Document type:** *Bulletin, Government.* **Description:** Covers compliance issues and regulatory concerns that affect small businesses in Texas.
Related titles: Online - full content ed.
Published by: Texas Natural Resource Conservation Commission, Small Business and Environmental Assistance Division, Mail Code 106, P O Box 13087, Austin, TX 78711-3087. TEL 512-239-3100, 800-447-2827, FAX 512-239-3165, http://www.tnrcc.state.tx.us/exec/sbea/smallbus.html.

338 USA
SMALL BUSINESS ADVOCATE (BROOKLYN). Text in English. m.
Published by: Brooklyn Journal Publications, Inc., 129 Montague St, Brooklyn, NY 11201. TEL 718-624-6033, FAX 718-875-5302.

338.642 USA ISSN 1045-7658
HD62.7
SMALL BUSINESS ADVOCATE (WASHINGTON). Text in English. 1982. 10/yr. looseleaf. free (effective 2005). bk.rev. stat. **Document type:** *Newsletter, Government.* **Description:** Covers regulatory and legislative issues pertaining to small business with economic research and other items of interest.
Formerly (until 1988): Advocacy Notes
Related titles: Microfiche ed.

Published by: (Office of Advocacy), U.S. Small Business Administration, 409 Third St, S W, MC 3114, Washington, DC 20416. TEL 202-205-6533 202-6533, 800-827-5722, FAX 202-205-6928, advocacy@sba.gov, http://www.sba.gov/advo/newsletter.html. Circ: 11,000 (controlled).

338 332 USA
SMALL BUSINESS BANKING NEWS. Text in English. m. USD 329 (effective 2004). **Document type:** *Newsletter, Trade.* **Description:** Covers profit-making, insider tips and info on products and services aimed at small businesses nationwide.
Published by: Royal Media Group, 1359 Broadway, Ste 1512, New York, NY 10018. TEL 212-564-8972, 800-320-4418, FAX 212-564-8973, info@royalmedia.com, http://www.royalmedia.com/newsletter.cfm?pub=105.

SMALL BUSINESS BIBLIOGRAPHY. see *BUSINESS AND ECONOMICS—Abstracting, Bibliographies, Statistics*

338.642 USA ISSN 0893-8326
HF5001
SMALL BUSINESS BULLETIN (WORCESTER). Text in English. 1978. 6/yr. USD 85. bk.rev. illus. **Document type:** *Bulletin, Trade.*
Former titles: Small Business Report; Small Business
Published by: Small Business Service Bureau, Inc., 554 Main St, PO x 1441, Worcester, MA 01601. TEL 508-756-3513, FAX 508-791-4709. Ed. Bernard Weiss. Circ: 35,000 (controlled).

338.642 CAN ISSN 1481-7357
SMALL BUSINESS CANADA MAGAZINE. Text in English. 1999. bi-m. CND 20 domestic; CND 35 in United States; CND 50 elsewhere (effective 2002). adv. **Description:** Covers news and events of interest to small business owners.
Related titles: E-mail ed.
Address: P O Box 31010, Barrie, ON L4N 0B3, Canada. TEL 705-722-9692, FAX 705-722-7268, editor@smallbusinesscanada.ca, info@smallbusinesscanada.ca, http://www.smallbusinesscanada.ca. Pub. Hayden Bradshaw.

338.642 GBR ISSN 0265-8399
SMALL BUSINESS CONFIDENTIAL✶. Text in English. 1983. m. GBP 118. bk.rev.
Published by: Fleet Street Publications Ltd., 271 Regent St, London, WIR 7PAU, United Kingdom. TEL 44-20-7447-4040, FAX 44-20-7447-4041. Ed. Gillian Clegg.

338.642 USA ISSN 0921-898X
HD2341 CODEN: SBECEX
➤ **SMALL BUSINESS ECONOMICS;** an international journal. Text in English. 1989. 10/yr. EUR 948, USD 968, GBP 585 combined subscription to institutions print & online eds. (effective 2005). adv. bk.rev. illus. Index. back issues avail.; reprint service avail. from PSC. **Document type:** *Journal, Academic/Scholarly.* **Description:** Provides a forum for the economic analysis of the role of small business.
Related titles: Microform ed.: (from PQC); Online - full text ed.: ISSN 1573-0913 (from EBSCO Publishing, Gale Group, IngentaConnect, Kluwer Online, O C L C Online Computer Library Center, Inc., ProQuest Information & Learning, Springer LINK, Swets Information Services).
Indexed: ABIn, APEL, ASCA, BibLing, CurCont, FamI, IBR, IBSS, IBZ, JEL, RefZh, SSCI.
—BLDSC (8309.975880), IDS, IE, Infotrieve, ingenta. **CCC.**
Published by: Springer-Verlag New York, Inc. (Subsidiary of: Springer Science+Business Media), 233 Spring St, New York, NY 10013. TEL 212-460-1500, FAX 212-460-1575, service@springer-ny.com, http://springerlink.metapress.com/openurl.asp?genre=journal&issn=0921-898X, http://www.springer-ny.com. Eds. David B Audretsch, Zoltan J Acs. **Subscr. to:** Journal Fulfillment, PO Box 2485, Secaucus, NJ 07096-2485. TEL 201-348-4033, FAX 201-348-4505, journals@springer-ny.com.

➤ **SMALL BUSINESS ENVIRONMENTAL ADVOCATE.** see *ENVIRONMENTAL STUDIES*

338 USA
SMALL BUSINESS EXECUTIVE REPORT. Text in English. m. USD 52 (effective 1997). **Document type:** *Trade.*
Published by: Charles Moore Associates, Inc., Stump Rd, Box 6, Southampton, PA 18966-0006. TEL 215-355-6084, FAX 215-364-2212. Ed. Fred Bird.

338.642 USA
SMALL BUSINESS INSIGHTS. Text in English. q. free domestic to customers (effective 2005). **Document type:** *Magazine.*
Published by: Mutual of Omaha Companies, Mutual of Omaha Plz., 3301 Dodge St., Omaha, NE 68175. TEL 402-351-7600, FAX 402-351-2775, http://www.mutualofomaha.com. Circ: 50,000 (free).

338 GBR
SMALL BUSINESS ISSUES. Text in English. 1982. q. GBP 80 for membership to individuals; GBP 375 for membership to corporations (effective 2003). adv. bk.rev. **Document type:** *Newsletter, Trade.*
Related titles: Online - full content ed.
Published by: Institute for Small Business Affairs, 1st Fl, 397 Harrogate Rd, LEEDS, LS17 6DJ, United Kingdom. TEL 44-113-3930241, FAX 44-113-3930132, info@isbauk.org, http://www.isbauk.org/public/index.htm. Ed. H Churchill Semple. Circ: 25,000.

338 USA
THE SMALL BUSINESS JOURNAL (CINCINNATI). Text in English. 1994. m. USD 15 domestic; USD 25 foreign; USD 3.50 newsstand/cover (effective 2000). adv. bk.rev.; software rev. stat.; tr.lit. **Document type:** *Consumer.* **Description:** Contains articles on sales and marketing, finance, technology, franchising, tax law, human resources, strategic planning, and home office time management.
Related titles: Online - full text ed.
Published by: Glaser Publishing Co., 407 Vine St, Dept 189, Cincinnati, OH 45202. TEL 513-736-4751, FAX 508-629-0599, tsbj@tsbj.com, http://www.tsbj.com. Ed. Chris Hollis. Pub. Robert J Glaser Jr. Adv. contact Doug Campbell. B&W page USD 1,705, color page USD 3,500; trim 10.88 x 8.38. Circ: 50,000.

338.642 340 USA ISSN 1084-3639
SMALL BUSINESS JOURNAL (LANSING). Text in English. 1995. bi-m. USD 165 membership (effective 2005). adv. charts; illus. **Document type:** *Newsletter, Trade.* **Description:** Focuses on trends and issues which affect small businesses in Michigan. Includes coverage of state government initiatives.
Formerly: Journal of Small Business
Related titles: Online - full text ed.
Published by: Small Business Association of Michigan, P.O. Box 16158, Lansing, MI 48901. TEL 517-482-8788, FAX 517-482-4205, sbam@sbam.org, http://www.sbam.org. Ed. Paul Bukowski. adv.: page USD 935; trim 11 x 8.5. Circ: 8,300.

658.041 USA
SMALL BUSINESS LEADER. Text in English. 1999. m. free. **Description:** Designed for small business owners providing suggestions, ideas and insights that can be applied to business.
Media: Online - full text.
Published by: Prime Strategies, 333 E 23rd St, New York, NY 10010. TEL 212-679-1209, FAX 212-679-8247, sbl@primestrategies.com, http://primestrategies.com/form.htm. Ed., Pub. Marian Banker.

338 USA
SMALL BUSINESS MAGAZINE. Text in English. 1979. m. USD 60. adv. bk.rev.
Published by: Richboro Press, PO Box 947, Southampton, PA 18966-0947. TEL 215-355-6084, FAX 215-364-2212. Ed. George Moore. Pub. Charles Moore.

338.642 USA ISSN 0279-8395
SMALL BUSINESS NEWS. Text in English. m. Free to qualified subscribers. 12 p./no.; **Document type:** *Newsletter, Trade.* **Description:** Covers news and issues of interest to the members of Small Business Hawaii.
Published by: Small Business Hawaii, Incorporated, 6600 Kalanianaole Hwy., Suite 212, Honolulu, HI 92825. TEL 808-396-1724, FAX 808-396-1726, http://www.hotspotshawaii.com/smallbusinesshawaii/.

338 USA
SMALL BUSINESS NEWS - AKRON. Text in English. 1991. m. USD 20 to qualified personnel; USD 2 newsstand/cover (effective 2001). adv. **Document type:** *Newspaper.* **Description:** Provides ideas for owners and managers of growing companies in the Akron region.
Related titles: Microform ed.: (from PQC); Online - full text ed.
Indexed: BusDate.
Published by: Small Business News, Inc. (Akron), 175 Montrose W, Ste 160, Akron, OH 44321. TEL 800-988-4726, FAX 216-529-8924, alarm@sbnnet.com, mmarzec@sbn-online.com, http://www.sbnpub.com. Ed. Connie Swenson. Pub., R&P Michael Marzec TEL 716-228-6397. Adv. contact Dana Edman. Circ: 12,000 (controlled).

338 658 USA
SMALL BUSINESS NEWS - DAYTON. Text in English. 1993. m. USD 20; USD 2 newsstand/cover (effective 1997). adv. bk.rev. **Document type:** *Trade.* **Description:** Covers small business and management news.
Related titles: Online - full text ed.
Indexed: BusDate.
Published by: Small Business News, Inc. (Cleveland), 14725 Detroit Ave, Ste 300, Cleveland, OH 44107-4103. TEL 216-228-6397, FAX 216-529-8924, http://www.sbnpub.com, http://www.sbn-online.com. Ed. Fred Koury. Adv. contact Deborah Jackson. Circ: 16,000 (controlled).

338.642 658 USA ISSN 1096-6897
SMALL BUSINESS NEWS. PHILADELPHIA/SOUTH JERSEY. Text in English. 199?. m. **Description:** Provides presidents, owners and senior decision makers of middle-market companies with news, information and smart ideas for growing their companies. The goal is to provide decision-makers with the knowledge and the tools to build stronger businesses.
Related titles: Online - full text ed.: (from ProQuest Information & Learning).
Indexed: ABIn.
Published by: Small Business News, Inc., 2186 Frankstown Rd, No. 313, Pittsburgh, PA 15212. TEL 412-371-0451, FAX 412-364-2302, pittsburgh@sbnonline.com, http://www.sbnpub.com/.

338 USA
SMALL BUSINESS NEWS REPORT. Text in English. 1992. bi-m. USD 14. adv. bk.rev. **Document type:** *Newsletter.*
Formerly (until 1999): Homebased Business News Report (1067-0300)
Published by: Home Office Management Services, 1151 N.E. Todd George Rd., Lee's Summit, MO 64086-5332. TEL 816-525-4484, FAX 816-525-4484. Ed., R&P, Adv. contact Beth Smith. Circ: 1,000.

338 658 USA
SMALL BUSINESS NEWS - WASHINGTON D C. Variant title: Washington D C - Small Business News. Text in English. m. **Document type:** *Trade.*
Indexed: BusDate.
Published by: Small Business News, Inc. (Cleveland), 14725 Detroit Ave, Ste 300, Cleveland, OH 44107-4103. FAX 216-529-8924, http://www.sbnpub.com, http://www.sbn-online.com.

338.642 USA ISSN 1071-8087
SMALL BUSINESS OPPORTUNITIES. Text in English. 1988. bi-m. USD 11.97 domestic; USD 15.56 in Canada; USD 23.94 elsewhere; USD 3.25 newsstand/cover (effective 2001). adv. illus. reprints avail. **Document type:** *Trade.* **Description:** Provides how-to information on starting and operating a business. Includes profiles on successful entrepreneurs.
Published by: Harris Publications, Inc., 800 Kennesaw Ave, Ste 220, Marietta, GA 30060. TEL 212-807-7100, FAX 212-627-4678, editor@sbomag.com, http://www.sbomag.com/. Ed. Susan Rakowski. Pub. Stanley R Harris. Adv. contact Maura DeLuca. B&W page USD 9,002, color page USD 11,255; 7 x 10. Circ: 250,000.

338 USA
SMALL BUSINESS OR ENTREPRENEURIAL RELATED NEWSLETTERS, PUBLICATIONS & PERIODICALS, ETC.; an updating reference. Text in English. 1990. biennial. USD 11.95 domestic; USD 12.95 in Canada; USD 14.95 elsewhere (effective 2001). **Document type:** *Newsletter.*
Published by: Prosperity and Profits Unlimited, PO Box 416, Denver, CO 80201-0416. TEL 303-575-5676, FAX 970-292-2136, starsuccess@excite.com, http://businessidearesource.bigstep.com. Ed., R&P A Doyle TEL 303-575-5676.

338.642 USA ISSN 1076-8483
HD2346.U5
SMALL BUSINESS PROFILES. Text in English. 1994. a., latest 1995, 2nd ed. USD 140 (effective 2004).
Published by: Gale Group (Subsidiary of: Thomson Corporation), 27500 Drake Rd, Farmington Hills, MI 48331-3535. TEL 248-699-8061, 800-877-4253, FAX 248-699-4253, galeord@gale.com, http://www.gale.com. Ed. Susan M Bourgoin.

658 USA ISSN 1066-646X
SMALL BUSINESS PROFILES (WASHINGTON, D.C.). Text in English. 1991. a.
Published by: U.S. Small Business Administration, 409 Third St, S W, MC 3114, Washington, DC 20416. http://www.sba.gov.

338 CAN ISSN 1205-9099
SMALL BUSINESS QUARTERLY. Text in English. 4/yr. CND 30 (effective 1997). **Document type:** *Government.*
Supersedes: Business Formations and Failures (1184-9223)
Published by: Ministry of Finance and Corporate Relations, B C Stats, Sta Prov Govt, P O Box 9410, Victoria, BC V8W 9V1, Canada. TEL 250-387-0359, FAX 250-387-0380, bcstats@fincc04.fin.gov.bc.ca, http://www.bcstats.gov.bc.ca.

338.642 USA ISSN 0883-3397
HD2346.U5
SMALL BUSINESS SOURCEBOOK. Text in English. 1983. biennial, latest 2004, 19th ed. USD 430 (effective 2004). **Description:** Highlights live and basic print sources of information such as associations, federal and state government agencies, and consulting firms.
Published by: Gale Group (Subsidiary of: Thomson Corporation), 27500 Drake Rd, Farmington Hills, MI 48331-3535. TEL 248-699-8061, 800-877-4253, FAX 248-699-4253, galeord@gale.com, http://www.gale.com. Ed. Carol A Schwartz.

338 USA
SMALL BUSINESS TAX NEWS. Text in English. 1970. m. USD 175 (effective 2000). **Document type:** *Newsletter.* **Description:** Tax guide designed to assist small business owners in preparing their taxes and staying abreast of major issues which could affect their companies' operations.
Formerly: Small Business Tax Control (0162-8658)
Published by: Inside Mortgage Finance Publications, PO Box 42387, Washington, DC 20015. TEL 301-951-1240, FAX 301-656-1709, http://www.imfpubs.com. Ed. David Cooper. Pub. Guy D Cecala. R&P Didi Parks. Circ: 2,900.

SMALL BUSINESS TAX PLANNER. see *BUSINESS AND ECONOMICS—Public Finance, Taxation*

SMALL BUSINESS TAX REVIEW. see *BUSINESS AND ECONOMICS—Public Finance, Taxation*

650 USA ISSN 0898-4972
SMALL BUSINESS U S A. Text in English. 1937. bi-m. USD 250 membership (effective 2004). adv. bk.rev. illus. **Document type:** *Newsletter.* **Description:** Information on wages and benefits, employee quality, healthcare and financing. Focuses on legislation affecting small business.
Former titles (until 1987): Voice of Small Business (0037-7198); Small Business Bulletin
Published by: National Small Business United, 1156 15th St, N W, Ste 1100, Washington, DC 20005-1704. TEL 202-293-8830, nsbu@nsbu.org, http://www.nsba.biz. Ed. David D'Onofrio. Circ: 11,000 (paid).

338 ZAF ◆
SMALL BUSINESS WORLD; committed to small business growth. Text in English. 1993. m. ZAR 28.80. adv. illus. **Document type:** *Trade.*
Indexed: ISAP.
Published by: Damont Publishers, PO Box 490, Newtown, Johannesburg 2113, South Africa.

338.642 CAN ISSN 0835-4251
SMALL BUSINESS WORLD MAGAZINE. Text in English. 1987. bi-m. CND 10, USD 15. adv. bk.rev. back issues avail.
Address: 2433 Southvale Crescent, Ottawa, ON K1B 4T8, Canada. TEL 613-733-4260. Ed. Astrid Robinson. Circ: 10,000.

338.642 GBR ISSN 0957-1329
➤ **SMALL ENTERPRISE DEVELOPMENT**; an international journal. Text in English. 1990. q. GBP 100, USD 150, EUR 150 combined subscription to institutions print & online (effective 2005). adv. bk.rev. abstr. 72 p./no. 1 cols./p.; back issues avail. **Document type:** *Journal, Academic/Scholarly.* **Description:** Provides a forum for those involved in the design and administration of small entertprise devlopments programmes in devloping countries.
Related titles: Online - full content ed.; Online - full text ed.: (from EBSCO Publishing, Gale Group, IngentaConnect, Swets Information Services).
Indexed: ARDT, AgrForAb, ForAb, GEOBASE, HortAb, I&DA, IBR, IBSS, PHN&I, RDA, RRTA, RiceAb, S&F, SWA, WAE&RSA. —BLDSC (8309.983800), IE, Infotrieve, ingenta. **CCC.**
Published by: Intermediate Technology Publications Ltd., 103-105 Southampton Row, London, WC1B 4HL, United Kingdom. TEL 44-20-7436-9761, FAX 44-20-7436-2013, marketing@itpubs.org.uk, http://www.itdgpublishing.org.uk/sed.htm. Ed. Claire Tawney. R&P Helen Marsden. Adv. contact Toby Harry. Circ: 1,000. **Subscr. to:** Portland Customer Services, Commerce Way, Colchester CO2 8HP, United Kingdom. TEL 44-1206-796351, FAX 44-1206-799331, sales@portland-services.com, http://www.portland-services.com. **Dist. by:** Portland Press Ltd., Commerce Way, Colchester CO2 8HP, United Kingdom.

330 GBR ISSN 1742-9773
SMALL ENTERPRISE RESEARCH REPORT; Lloyds / T S B/ S E R Team - triannual report. Text in English. 1993 (Oct.). 3/yr. GBP 100; GBP 40 per vol. (effective 2005). **Document type:** *Academic/Scholarly.* **Description:** Key management problems and practices of smaller businesses are monitored for these reports. They are based on surveys of companies primarily in manufacturing, retail, and business services.
Former titles (until 2005): Lloyds T S B - Small Business Research Team Small Business Management Report; (until 2003): Lloyds T S B - Small Business Research Trust Small Business Management Report; Lloyds Bank - Small Business Research Trust Quarterly Small Business Management Report (0968-6444)
Published by: Small Enterprise Research Team, Open University Business School, Open University Business School, Michael Young Building, Walton Hall, Milton Keynes, Bucks MK7 6AA, United Kingdom. TEL 44-1908-655831, FAX 44-1908-655898, b.porter-blake@open.ac.uk, oubs-sbrt@open.ac.uk, http://www.serteam.co.uk, http://www.sbrt.co.uk/. Ed., R&P J Stanworth. Adv. contact Mrs. Julie Sullivan.

338.6 USA ISSN 1552-3470
▼ **SMALL FIRM BUSINESS.** Text in English. 2004. q. USD 49.95 domestic; USD 79.95 foreign (effective 2005). **Document type:** *Journal, Trade.* **Description:** Provides news, information and advice from industry experts and practitioners to help legal professionals manage the "business side" of running a law firm.
Published by: A L M, 345 Park Ave., S, New York, NY 10010. TEL 212-313-9000, 800-888-8300, FAX 212-481-8255, apress@amlaw.com, http://www.law.com/jsp/law/sfb/index.jsp, http://www.alm.com.

338 TZA
SMALL INDUSTRIES DEVELOPMENT ORGANIZATION. ANNUAL REPORT. Text in English. 1975. a. **Document type:** *Corporate.*
Related titles: Swahili ed.
Published by: Small Industries Development Organization (SIDO), PO Box 2476, Dar Es Salaam, Tanzania. Circ: 1,000.

338 IND
SMALL INDUSTRIES GUIDE✶. Text in English. irreg., latest vol.2, 1969. INR 2 per issue. charts; stat.
Published by: Ministry of Industrial Development, Development Commissioner-Small Scale Industries, Internal Trade and Company Affairs, New Delhi, India.

381 IND
SMALL SCALE INDUSTRIES ENVOY. Text in English. 1972. m. INR 10. adv. bk.rev.
Published by: Maharashtra Small Scale Industries Association, 0-10 Bhavana Prabhadevi, Mumbai, Maharashtra 400 025, India. Ed. Samuel Valiyaparampil. Circ: 5,000.

338 NGA
SMALL-SCALE INDUSTRIES: SOUTH EASTERN AND BENUE PLATEAU STATES OF NIGERIA. Text in English. a.
Published by: University of Nigeria, Department of Economics, Nsukka, Enugu State, Nigeria. Eds. A E Okorafor, E C Iwuji.

338 USA
SMALL TIME OPERATOR; how to start your own small business, keep your books, pay your taxes and stay out of trouble. Text in English. 1976. a. USD 19.95 (effective 2004). bk.rev. **Document type:** *Trade.*
Published by: Bell Springs Publishing, PO Box 1240, Willits, CA 95490. TEL 707-459-6372, 800-515-8050, FAX 707-459-8614, sto@bellsprings.com, info@bellsprings.com, http://www.bellsprings.com. Ed. Bernard Kamoroff. Pub. Sam Leandro. Circ: 40,000.

338 USA
SMALLOFFICE.COM. Text in English. irreg. illus.
Media: Online - full content.
Published by: Freedom Technology Media Group, 156 W 56th St, 3rd Fl, New York, NY 10019. nsullivan@smalloffice.com, http://www.smalloffice.com. Ed. Karen Gujarathi.

338.642 USA ISSN 1544-869X
SMART BUSINESS CLEVELAND. Text in English. 1989. m. USD 20; USD 2 newsstand/cover. adv. back issues avail. **Document type:** *Newspaper.* **Description:** Contains ideas for owners and managers of growing companies in Cuyahoga, Lake, Geauga and Lorain Ca, Lake, Geauga and Lorain counties.
Former titles: S B N Cleveland (1532-494X); Small Business News Cleveland (1080-4803)
Related titles: Microform ed.: (from PQC); Online - full text ed.: (from O C L C Online Computer Library Center, Inc.).
Indexed: BusDate.
Published by: Small Business News, Inc. (Cleveland), 14725 Detroit Ave, Ste 300, Cleveland, OH 44107-4103. TEL 216-228-6397, FAX 216-529-8924, cleveland@sbnnet.com, http://www.sbn-online.com. Ed. Dustin S Klein. R&P Michael Marzec. Adv. contact Melissa Gottleib. Circ: 29,000 (controlled).

338.642 USA ISSN 1544-8703
SMART BUSINESS COLUMBUS. Text in English. m.
Former titles (until 2003): S B N Columbus (1532-4923); Small Business News Columbus (1087-7452)
Related titles: Online - full text ed.: (from O C L C Online Computer Library Center, Inc.).
Published by: Small Business News, Inc. (Cleveland), 14725 Detroit Ave, Ste 300, Cleveland, OH 44107-4103.

338.642 USA ISSN 1544-8711
SMART BUSINESS PITTSBURGH. Text in English. m. free to qualified personnel. adv.
Former titles: S B N Pittsburgh (1532-4931); Small Business News. Pittsburgh (1097-1017)
Related titles: Online - full text ed.: (from O C L C Online Computer Library Center, Inc.).
Published by: Small Business News, Inc., 2186 Frankstown Rd, No. 313, Pittsburgh, PA 15212. TEL 412-371-0451, FAX 412-364-2302, pittsburgh@sbnonline.com, http://www.sbnpub.com/index.asp. Eds. Connie Swenson, Ray Marano.

338.642 RUS ISSN 1813-6966
▼ ➤ **SOBSTVENNOST' I RYNOK.** Text in Russian. 2004. m. **Document type:** *Journal, Academic/Scholarly.*
Published by: Nauka i Tekhnologii, Stromynskii per, 4/1, Moscow, 107076, Russian Federation. admin@nait.ru, http://www.nait.ru. Ed. V I Busov.

338 658 340.56 BGR
SOBSTVENOST I PRAVO. Text in Bulgarian. m. BGL 88.80 (effective 2002). **Description:** Covers public and private properties, property of foreigners, intellectual property and privatization.
Related titles: CD-ROM ed.
Published by: Izdatelski Kompleks Trud i Pravo/Labour and Law Publishing House, Pl. Makedonia 1, Fl. 7, Sofia, 1040, Bulgaria. TEL 359-2-9875110, FAX 359-2-9870612, office@trudipravo.bg, http://www.trudipravo.bg.

338 GBR
SOHO LIFE AND TECHNOLOGY TODAY; the magazine for the changing world of small business. Text in English. m. GBP 24.95 domestic; GBP 30.95 in Europe; GBP 36.95 elsewhere. adv. back issues avail. **Document type:** *Consumer.*
Published by: Dixie Publishing Ltd., Station House, Bunbury Way, Epsom Downs, Surrey KT17 4JP, United Kingdom. TEL 44-1372-747401, FAX 44-1372-747402, editorial@sohoiife.com, http://www.sohoiife.com. Ed. Kristen Bowditch. Pub. Robin Johnson. Adv. contact Paul Kitchen. **Dist. by:** M M C Ltd., Octagon House, White Hart Meadows, Ripley, Woking, Surrey GU23 6HR, United Kingdom.

SOMERSET BUSINESS; the magazine for the Somerset business community. see *BUSINESS AND ECONOMICS—Economic Situation And Conditions*

THE SOURCE (ABINGTON). see *FOOD AND FOOD INDUSTRIES—Grocery Trade*

338 USA
SOUTHEAST ALASKA BUSINESS JOURNAL✶. Text in English. 1990. m. USD 15.60. adv. back issues avail. **Document type:** *Trade.* **Description:** Informs owners of southeastern Alaska businesses on bankruptcies, liens, and business licences.
Published by: Summit Services, Inc., 33102, Juneau, AK 99803-3102. TEL 907-789-0829, FAX 907-789-0987. Ed. Renda Heimbinger. Adv. contact Kristen Hammond. Circ: 5,000.

338.642 USA ISSN 0735-1437
HD2346.U5
THE STATE OF SMALL BUSINESS: A REPORT OF THE PRESIDENT TRANSMITTED TO THE CONGRESS. Text in English. a. price varies. charts; stat. **Document type:** *Government.* **Description:** Compiles statistics on small businesses in the U.S. in an annual report to Congress.
Related titles: CD-ROM ed.; Microfiche ed.: (from NTI).
Published by: U.S. Small Business Administration, 409 Third St, S W, MC 3114, Washington, DC 20416. TEL 800-553-6847, http://www.sba.gov/ADVO/stats/state.html. R&P John Ward. **Subscr. to:** U.S. Government Printing Office, Superintendent of Documents.

338.642 CAN ISSN 1193-3550
STATE OF SMALL BUSINESS AND ENTREPRENEURSHIP IN ATLANTIC CANADA. Text in English. 1991. a.
Related titles: Online - full text ed.: ISSN 1701-2864. 1996; French ed.: Etat de la Petite Entreprise at de l'Entrepreneuriat dans la Region de l'Atlantique. ISSN 1193-3542. 1991.
Published by: Atlantic Canada Opportunities Agency, Blue Cross Centre, 3rd Fl, 644 Main St, Moncton, NB E1C 9J8, Canada. TEL 506-851-2271, FAX 506-851-7403, http://www.acoa.ca/.

338.642 USA ISSN 0742-843X
HD2346.U5
THE STATES AND SMALL BUSINESS: A DIRECTORY OF PROGRAMS AND ACTIVITIES. Text in English. 1979. s-a. price varies. **Document type:** *Directory, Government.* **Description:** Lists more than 1,000 state programs for help in financing a small-business venture.
Formerly: States and Small Business: Programs and Activities
Related titles: Microfiche ed.
Published by: (Office of Advocacy), U.S. Small Business Administration, 409 Third St, S W, MC 3114, Washington, DC 20416. TEL 202-205-6531. Circ: 2,500 (paid). **Subscr to:** U.S. Government Printing Office, Superintendent of Documents.

338.642 NOR ISSN 0803-4028
STIFTELSEN FOR SAMFUNNS- OG NAERINGSLIVSFORSKNING. ARBEIDSNOTAT/CENTER FOR RESEARCH IN ECONOMICS AND BUSINESS ADMINISTRATION. WORKING PAPER. Text in English, Norwegian. 1991. irreg.
Formed by the merger of (1984-1990): Senter for Anvendt Forskning. Arbeidsnotat (0800-6253); (1988-1990): Naeringsokonomisk Institutt. Notat (0802-4766)
Indexed: ASFA, ESPM, WAE&RSA. —ingenta.
Published by: Samfunns- og Naeringslivsforskning A/S/Institute for Research in Economics and Business Administration, Breiviksveien 40, Bergen, 5045, Norway. TEL 47-55-95-95-00, FAX 47-55-95-94-39, publikasjon@snf.no, http://www.snf.no/.

338 USA
SUCCESS MAGAZINE'S WORKING AT HOME. Text in English. 2000. a. USD 4.99 newsstand/cover (effective 2001). adv. **Document type:** *Consumer.*
Published by: National Publisher Services, Inc., 150 Fayetteville St, Ste 1110, Raleigh, NC 27601. TEL 919-807-1100, FAX 919-807-1200, http://www.workingathomeonline.com. Ed. Ripley Hotch. Pub. Victoria I Conte.

SUCCESS ONLINE WEEKLY. see *COMPUTERS—Internet*

381.109489 DNK ISSN 0903-868X
SUPERMARKEDSHAANDBOGEN (YEAR)/SUPERMARKETS AND OTHER LARGE GROCERY STORES. Text in Danish. 1965. a. DKK 1,495 (effective 2004). **Document type:** *Trade.* **Description:** Contains up-to-date information about the Danish everyday commodities market.
Formerly (until 1995): Supermarkeder og Andre Store Daglivarebutikker (Year); Formed by the merger of (1965-1988): Supermarkeder (0586-9005); (1982-1988): Discountbutikker (0108-5255); Formerly (1980-1982): Lavprisbutikker (0107-4342)

Published by: Stockmann-Gruppen A-S, Falkoner Alle 1, 4, Frederiksberg, 2000, Denmark. TEL 45-38-169730, FAX 45-38-169703, stockmann@stockmann.dk, http://www.stockmann.dk. Ed. Henning Bahr.

338.642 USA ISSN 1083-6691
SVOBODA'S BUSINESS MAGAZINE∗; the magazine for the independent business professional. Text in English. 1993. m. (except July-Aug.). USD 20 (effective 2000). adv. bk.rev.; software rev. charts; illus.; stat.; tr.lit. back issues avail. **Document type:** *Trade.* **Description:** Includes hands-on business management articles for entrepreneurs located in the greater Chicago area.
Former titles (until 1996): Svoboda's Home and Small Business; (until 1994): Svoboda's Home and Small Business Reporter; Home and Small Business Reporter
Related titles: Online - full text ed.: 1993.
Published by: American Business Communicators, 1440 W Pratt Blvd, Apt 1, Chicago, IL 60626-4277. TEL 773-381-7741, FAX 773-381-7743, jcs@svobodamag.com, http://www.svobodamag.com. Ed. Jill V Cleary-Svoboda. Pub., Adv. contact Albert J Svoboda. B&W page USD 1,350; trim 15 x 11.5. Circ: 30,000.

338 USA
SWAP MEET MAGAZINE. Text in English. 1990. m. USD 30 (effective 2001). adv. bk.rev. 160 p./no.; **Document type:** *Magazine, Trade.* **Description:** Connects wholesalers and flea market vendors. Provides merchandise sources.
Published by: Forum Publishing Co., 383 E Main St, Centerport, NY 11721-1538. TEL 631-754-5000, FAX 631-754-0630. Ed. Raymond Lawrence. Pub., Adv. contact Martin Stevens. page USD 575; 7 x 10. Circ: 70,000.

338.642 677 USA ISSN 1053-6493
T-SHIRT BUSINESS INFO MAPPING NEWSLETTER. Text in English. 1990. biennial. looseleaf. USD 6.50 domestic; USD 8 foreign (effective 2000). 4 p./no.; **Document type:** *Newsletter.* **Description:** Provides information on the t-shirt business.
—CCC.
Published by: Continnuus, c/o Prosperity & Profits Unlimited Distribution Services, P O Box 416, Denver, CO 80201-0416. TEL 303-575-5676, mail@coursesmith.com. Ed., R&P A C Doyle. Circ: 1,500.

TABAK PLUS GEMAK; vakblad voor de tabaksdetailhandel. see *TOBACCO*

338 GBR
TAKING UP A FRANCHISE; the Daily Telegraph guide. Text in English. a. GBP 9.99. adv. **Document type:** *Trade.*
Published by: Kogan Page Ltd., 120 Pentonville Rd, London, N1 9JN, United Kingdom. FAX 44-20-7837-6348. R&P Caroline Gromm. Adv. contact Linda Batham.

386.42 USA ISSN 0885-1522
TANNING TRENDS; the news journal for the indoor tanning industry. Text in English. 1985. 10/yr. USD 60 domestic; USD 80 foreign (effective 2000). adv. back issues avail. **Document type:** *Trade.*
Published by: Tanning Trends Inc., 3101 Page Ave, Jackson, MI 49203. TEL 517-784-1772, FAX 517-787-3940, tantrends@voyager.net. Ed. Jan Bellamy. Pub., R&P Matt D Russell. Adv. contact Victoria Moss. B&W page USD 1,635, color page USD 2,315; trim 10.75 x 8.25. Circ: 20,000 (controlled). **Subscr. to:** PO Box 1630, Jackson, MI 49204.

TECHNO - BIZ DIGEST. see *COMPUTERS—Internet*

TELEMARKETER. see *BUSINESS AND ECONOMICS—Marketing And Purchasing*

338.642 330.9 USA ISSN 0735-1135
HC107.T3
TENNESSEE'S BUSINESS. Text in English. 1974. 3/yr. free. adv. **Document type:** *Magazine, Consumer.* **Description:** Provides a forum for exchange of ideas in the field of economics and business among businesspersons, academicians, and government officials.
Formerly (until 1990): Tennessee Business and Economic Review
Indexed: PAIS.
Published by: Middle Tennessee State University, College of Business, 1301 E Main St, MTSU Box 102, Murfreesboro, TN 37132. TEL 615-898-2610, FAX 615-898-5045, sgovan@mtsu.edu, http://www.mtsu.edu/~berc/, http://www.mtsu.edu/~berc/publications.html. Ed. Horace E Johns. R&P Sally Govan. Adv. contact Albert E De Prince. Circ: 4,500.

TEXAS PETROLEUM AND C-STORE JOURNAL. see *PETROLEUM AND GAS*

363.7282 338 USA
TEXAS RECYCLER MARKET NEWS. Text in English. m. Free to Texas subcribers.. back issues avail. **Document type:** *Bulletin, Government.* **Description:** Covers recycling markets and current prices on recyclables.
Related titles: Online - full content ed.
Published by: Texas Natural Resource Conservation Commission, Small Business and Environmental Assistance Division, Mail Code 106, P O Box 13087, Austin, TX 78711-3087. TEL 512-239-3100, 800-447-2827, FAX 512-239-3165, recycle@tnrcc.state.tx.us, http://www.tnrcc.state.tx.us/admin/topdoc/pd/008/.

338.6421 CAN ISSN 0834-3497
THUNDER BAY BUSINESS. Text in English. 1984. m. CND 25. adv. back issues avail. **Document type:** *Trade.*
Published by: North Superior Publishing Inc., 1145 Barton St, Thunder Bay, ON P7B 5N3, Canada. TEL 807-623-2348, FAX 807-623-7515. Ed., Pub. Scott A Sumnr. Circ: 10,000.

TIME MANAGEMENT. see *BUSINESS AND ECONOMICS—Personnel Management*

TOLLEY'S PRACTICAL AUDIT & ACCOUNTING. see *BUSINESS AND ECONOMICS—Accounting*

338.642 CAN ISSN 0831-4160
TORONTO BUSINESS MAGAZINE. Text in English. 1975. s-a. CND 65. adv. **Document type:** *Trade.*
Published by: Zanny Publications Ltd., 11966 Woodbine Ave, Gormley, ON L0H 1G0, Canada. TEL 905-887-5048, FAX 905-479-4839. Ed. Amy Margaret. Pub., R&P Janet Gardiner. Adv. contact B Baker. B&W page CND 3,017, color page CND 3,960; trim 10.75 x 8.25. Circ: 41,000.

658.041 USA
TRADE SECRETS. Text in English. irreg. free. **Document type:** *Newsletter.* **Description:** Provides tips to start and grow a business successfully.
Media: Online - full text.
Published by: Gracefield Enterprises, 5 Coach House Dr, Owings Mills, MD 21117. TEL 410-581-3430, nkbelle@gracefield.com, http://www.gracefield.com/gg/news-nl.htm. Ed., Pub. Nancy Belle.

338 388.324 USA
TRUCKSTOP TRAVEL PLAZA. Text in English. 1987. q. USD 20; USD 5 newsstand/cover (effective 2004). adv. **Document type:** *Magazine, Trade.* **Description:** Contains articles and information for the people who own, operate and make the purchasing decisions for the nation's truckstops, fuel stops, interstate travel centers and turnpike plazas.
Formerly (until 1995): Truckstop World (0894-962X)
—CCC.
Published by: Newport Communications (Irvine) (Subsidiary of: H.I.C. Corporation), 38 Executive Pk, Ste 300, Irvine, CA 92614. TEL 949-261-1636, FAX 949-261-2904, ttfeedback@heavytruck.com, http://www.truckstoptravelplaza.com, http://www.heavytruck.com. Ed. Jim Beach. Pub. Richard Faxquhar. adv.: B&W page USD 2,160; trim 8.5 x 10. Circ: 6,100 (controlled).

338.642 USA ISSN 0083-3274
HC106.5
U.S. SMALL BUSINESS ADMINISTRATION. ANNUAL REPORT. Text in English. 1953. a. free. **Document type:** *Government.* **Description:** Summary of activities and accomplishments of the Small Business Administration's numerous program areas.
Related titles: Microfiche ed.: (from NTI).
Published by: U.S. Small Business Administration, 409 Third St, S W, MC 3114, Washington, DC 20416. TEL 202-205-6744. R&P John Ward. Circ: 2,000 (controlled).

338.642 USA ISSN 0742-3802
HD2346.U5
U.S. SMALL BUSINESS ADMINISTRATION. OFFICE OF THE INSPECTOR GENERAL. SEMI-ANNUAL REPORT. Text in English. 1978. s-a. free. **Document type:** *Government.*
Published by: (Office of the Inspector General), U.S. Small Business Administration, 409 Third St, S W, MC 3114, Washington, DC 20416. FAX 202-205-7382. Circ: 300.

U S TRANSACTIONS SMALL BUSINESS QUARTERLY. see *BUSINESS AND ECONOMICS—Banking And Finance*

338 BEL
UNION AND ACTIONS. Text in French. 1948. w. (Fri.). EUR 110; EUR 55 to qualified personnel (effective 2005). **Document type:** *Newspaper.* **Description:** Covers news, issues and problems affecting the self-employed, professionals and entrepreneurs with small to medium-sized businesses.
Formerly: La Voix de l'Union
Published by: (Union des Classes Moyennes), Ediclam asbl, Secretariat National, Avenue A. Lacomble 29, Brussels, 1030, Belgium. TEL 32-2-743-8390, FAX 32-2-743-8395, http://www.ucm.be/ucm/ewcm.nsf/_/B2B4997481B47515C1256C8500338AA6?opendocument. Circ: 28,000.

UNITED STATES HOUSE OF REPRESENTATIVES. COMMITTEE ON SMALL BUSINESS. LEGISLATIVE CALENDAR. see *LAW—Constitutional Law*

UNIVERSITY OF NEW ENGLAND. DEPARTMENT OF ACCOUNTING & FINANCIAL MANAGEMENT. WORKING PAPERS. see *BUSINESS AND ECONOMICS—Accounting*

UPDATE (VIRGINIA). see *FOOD AND FOOD INDUSTRIES—Grocery Trade*

338 630 USA
THE UPRIGHT OSTRICH∗. Text in English. 10/yr. USD 25; USD 35 foreign. **Description:** Supports independent farmers, small business, and the return to a sound money system.
Published by: Order of the Upright Ostrich, 3585 County Rd O, Milwaukee, WI 53080-1435. TEL 414-332-5075. Ed. Peggy Poor.

VENTURE CAPITAL JOURNAL; the only financial analyst of small business investment companies and venture capital companies. see *BUSINESS AND ECONOMICS—Investments*

338.642 332.6 GBR ISSN 0265-6248
VENTURE CAPITAL REPORT. Text in English. 1978. m. GBP 350 (effective 1999). adv. bk.rev. charts; illus. index, cum.index. back issues avail. **Document type:** *Bulletin.*
Published by: Venture Capital Report Ltd., The Magdalen Centre, Oxford Science Park, Oxford, OX4 4GA, United Kingdom. TEL 44-1865-784411, FAX 44-1865-784412, vcr@vcr1978.com, modwenna@vcrdirectory.co.uk, http://www.ver1978.com, http://www.vcr1978.com. Ed. Jonathan Church. Circ: 700.

338 GBR
VENTURE CAPITAL REPORT GUIDE (YEAR) : PRIVATE EQUITY AND VENTURE CAPITAL IN THE U K AND EUROPE. Text in English. 1983. a. GBP 225 (effective 1999). **Document type:** *Trade.*
Former titles: Venture Capital Report Guide to Venture Capital in the U K and Europe; Venture Capital Report Guide to Venture Capital in Europe
Related titles: CD-ROM ed.
Published by: Venture Capital Report Ltd., The Magdalen Centre, Oxford Science Park, Oxford, OX4 4GA, United Kingdom. TEL 44-1865-784411, FAX 44-1865-784412, vcr@vcr1978.com, modwenna@vcrdirectory.co.uk, http://www.vcr1978.com. Ed. Patrick Angier. Circ: 7,800.

338 305.906 USA
▼ **VETERAN'S BUSINESS JOURNAL.** Text in English. 2004. bi-m. USD 12.97; USD 2.95 newsstand/cover (effective 2005). adv. **Document type:** *Magazine, Trade.* **Description:** Provides information and advice to veterans starting a business or seeking to grow an existing one through government sales.
Published by: Victory Media, Inc., PO Box 26, Sewickley, PA 15143. TEL 412-269-1663, FAX 412-291-2772, info@victorymediainc.com, http://www.vetbizjournal.com, http://www.victorymediainc.com. Pub. Chris Hale. Adv. contact Scott Shaw TEL 717-832-3038. B&W page USD 2,990; trim 8.375 x 10.875. Circ: 90,000.

338.642 636.089 USA ISSN 0042-4862
➤ **VETERINARY ECONOMICS**; business solutions for practicing veterinarians. Text in English. 1960. m. USD 42 domestic; USD 59 in Canada & Mexico; USD 83 elsewhere; USD 10 newsstand/cover domestic; USD 15 newsstand/cover foreign (effective 2005). adv. bk.rev. charts; illus.; stat.; tr.lit. Index. reprints avail. **Document type:** *Journal, Academic/Scholarly.* **Description:** Covers all aspects of veterinary practice management and finance.
Related titles: Microform ed.: (from PQC); Online - full text ed.: (from Northern Light Technology, Inc.).
Indexed: ASCA, ATI, FoVS&M, IndVet, SRI, VetBull.
—BLDSC (9227.070000), CISTI, IDS, IE, ingenta. **CCC.**
Published by: (Advanstar Medical Economics Healthcare Communications), Advanstar Communications, Inc., One Park Ave, 2nd Fl, New York, NY 10016. TEL 212-951-6600, FAX 212-951-6604, ve@vetmedpub.com, info@advanstar.com, http://www.vetmedpub.com/ve/index.html, http://www.advanstar.com. Circ: 50,000 (controlled).

338.642 CAN ISSN 0830-8713
VICTORIA'S BUSINESS REPORT. Text in English. 1983. 18/yr. CND 18. adv. **Document type:** *Consumer.*
Published by: Monday Publications Ltd., 818 Broughton St, Victoria, BC V8W 1E4, Canada. TEL 604-382-6188, FAX 604-381-2662. Ed. Gery Lemon. Adv. contact John Meloche. B&W page CND 750. Circ: 14,000.

338 FRA
VOLONTE∗. Text in French. 11/yr.
Published by: Societe d'Edition et de Publication des Petites et Moyennes Entreprises, 30 rue des Jeuneurs, Paris, 75002, France. TEL 45-08-91-88. Ed. Lucien Rebuffel. Circ: 45,000.

VOWS; the bridal and wedding business journal. see *MATRIMONY*

338 RUS
VY I VASH MAGAZIN. Text in Russian. 1998. s-m.
Address: Olimpicheskii pr 16, Biznes-Tsentr Olimpik, 15, Moscow, 129010, Russian Federation. TEL 7-095-9334076, 7-095-9334078, FAX 7-095-9334081. Eds. Alla Knyazeva, Elena Romanova. Circ: 20,000.

W A H M. (Work at Home Moms) see *WOMEN'S INTERESTS*

338 621.38 USA
W E S A NEWSLETTER. Text in English. 1973. bi-m. free to qualified personnel. adv. **Document type:** *Newsletter.*
Published by: Wisconsin Electronic Sales and Service Association, PO Box 531, Butler, WI 53007-0531. TEL 414-761-0888. Ed., Adv. contact Larry Neuens. page USD 50. Circ: 250 (controlled).

WEBPROFESSIONS MONTHLY UPDATE. see *COMPUTERS—Internet*

WHAT'S BREWING. see *BEVERAGES*

338 GBR
WILTSHIRE IN BUSINESS. Text in English. 1996. q. GBP 20 (effective May. 1999). adv. software rev.; video rev.; bk.rev. bibl.; mkt.; stat.; tr.lit. back issues avail. **Document type:** *Magazine, Government.*
Published by: Phoenix 2, Lantern House, Lodge Drove, Woodfalls, Salisbury, SP5 2NH, United Kingdom. TEL 44-1725-512200, FAX 44-1725-511819, walker@phoenix2.prestel.co.uk. Ed., Pub. Amanda Walker. Adv. contact Barbara Hatchett. B&W page GBP 400, color page GBP 550;. Circ: 3,700. **Subscr. to:** Business Link, 22 Bedwin St., Salisbury, Wilts SP1 3UT, United Kingdom. TEL 44-1722-411052.

338 ZAF
WOMEN ENTREPRENEURS IN SOUTH AFRICA. Text in English. 1993. a. illus.
Published by: Dictum Publishers, PO Box 40704, Cleveland, 2022, South Africa.

WOMEN'S BUSINESS JOURNAL. see *WOMEN'S INTERESTS*

WORCESTER BUSINESS JOURNAL. see *BUSINESS AND ECONOMICS—Domestic Commerce*

658.041 USA ISSN 1529-3009
WORK AT HOME PARENTS E-ZINE. Text in English. 1996. 2/w. (Monday & Wednesday). free. adv. back issues avail. **Document type:** *Newsletter.* **Description:** Dedicated to parents who wish to start a home-based business.
Media: Online - full text.
Address: 241 Worthington Ln, Warner Robins, GA 31088. FAX 888-353-3129, michelle@workathomeparents.com, http://www.workathomeparents.com/ezineorder.html. Ed. Michelle Mendez-McCullers. Pub., R&P, Adv. contact Michelle Cruz TEL 954-827-0895. Circ: 78,200.

WORK-AT-HOME SOURCEBOOK; how to find "at-home" work that's right for you. see *OCCUPATIONS AND CAREERS*

338 GBR
WORKING FOR YOURSELF. Text in English. a. GBP 9.99. adv. **Document type:** *Bulletin, Trade.* **Description:** Provides tried and tested guidance for anyone thinking of becoming self-employed.
Published by: Kogan Page Ltd., 120 Pentonville Rd, London, N1 9JN, United Kingdom. FAX 44-20-7837-6348. Ed. Godfrey Golzen. R&P Caroline Gromm. Adv. contact Linda Batham.

338 GBR
WORKS MANAGEMENT SPECIAL REPORT FOR SMALLER COMPANIES. Text in English. q.
Address: Franks Hall, Horton Kirby, Dartford, Kent DA4 9LL, United Kingdom. TEL 44-322-222222, FAX 44-322-289577. Ed. John Dwyer.

338 658 USA
WORLDPROFIT ONLINE MAGAZINE. Text in English. 1996. m. free. bk.rev. **Description:** Aimed primarily at businesses worldwide which want to increase online profits now.
Media: Online - full text.
Published by: Worldprofit, Inc., 50 Follen St, Ste 507, Cambridge, MA 02138. TEL 617-547-6372, FAX 617-547-0061, drjlant@worldprofit.com, http://www.worldprofit.com, http://www.trafficcenter.com. Ed., Pub. Jeffrey Lant. Circ: 200,000.

338.7 658 CHN ISSN 1009-1610
XIANGZHEN QIYE, MINYING JINGJI/TOWNSHIP ENTERPRISES AND CIVILIAN MANAGED ECONOMY. Text in Chinese. 1994. m. CNY 93.60 (effective 2004). 96 p./no.; **Document type:** *Journal, Academic/Scholarly.*
Formerly (until 1999): Xiangzhen Qiye yu Nongchang Guanli (1005-4340)
Indexed: RASB.
Published by: Zhongguo Renmin Daxue, Shubao Zilio Zhongxin/Renmin University of China, Information Center for Social Server, Dongcheng-qu, 3, Zhangzizhong Lu, Beijing, 100007, China. TEL 86-10-64039458, FAX 86-10-64015080, kyes@163.net, http://www.confucius.cn.net/bkdetail.asp?fzt=F22. **Dist. in US by:** China Publications Service, PO Box 49614, Chicago, IL 60649. TEL 312-288-3291, FAX 312-288-8570; **Dist. by:** China International Book Trading Corp, 35 Chegongzhuang Xilu, Haidian District, PO Box 399, Beijing 100044, China. TEL 86-10-68412045, FAX 86-10-68412023, cibtc@mail.cibtc.com.cn, http://www.cibtc.com.cn.

254 USA ISSN 0049-8394
BV652.A1
YOUR CHURCH; helping you with the business of ministry. Text in English. 1955. bi-m. free to qualified personnel (effective 2005). adv. bk.rev. back issues avail.; reprint service avail. from PQC. **Document type:** *Magazine, Trade.* **Description:** Pertains solely to church business administration matters, not general religious topics. Includes reviews and descriptions of products and services necessary for churches to do ministry.
Related titles: Microform ed.: (from PQC); Online - full text ed.: (from EBSCO Publishing).
Indexed: AIAP, CCR.
Published by: Christianity Today International, 465 Gundersen Dr, Carol Stream, IL 60188. TEL 630-260-6200, FAX 630-260-0114, yceditor@aol.com, http://www.yourchurch.net. Ed. Michael Schreiter. Pub. Paul Robbins. R&P Cynthia Thomas. Adv. contacts Brian Ondracek TEL 630-260-6202, Kiernan Mack, Walter Hegel, Joyce Bardin. B&W page USD 7,447, color page USD 8,529. Circ: 150,000 (controlled). **Subscr. to:** Your Church, PO Box 901013, Fort Worth, TX 76101. TEL 800-632-2738.

338.642 ZAF ISSN 1023-5213
YOUR OWN BUSINESS. Text in English. 1994. m. ZAR 76.45. adv. illus. **Document type:** *Consumer.*
Address: PO Box 16557, Vlaeberg, Cape Town 8018, South Africa.

650 DEU ISSN 1860-4633
HD2341.A1
➤ **Z F K E - ZEITSCHRIFT FUER K M U UND ENTREPRENEURSHIP.** Text in German. 1953. q. EUR 48; EUR 38.40 to students; EUR 14 newsstand/cover (effective 2006). adv. bk.rev. index. reprints avail. **Document type:** *Journal, Academic/Scholarly.*
Former titles (until 2004): Zeitschrift fuer Klein- und Mittelunternehmen (1435-6015); (until 1996): Internationales Gewerbearchiv (0020-9481)
Related titles: ♦ Supplement(s): Internationales Gewerbearchiv. Sonderheft. ISSN 0935-4794.
Indexed: DIP, IBR, IBSS, IBZ, KES.
—BLDSC (9467.783000). **CCC.**
Published by: (Schweizerisches Institut fuer Gewerbliche Wirtschaft an der Universitaet St. Gallen CHE), Duncker und Humblot GmbH, Carl-Heinrich-Becker-Weg 9, Berlin, 12165, Germany. TEL 49-30-7900060, FAX 49-30-79000631, info@duncker-humblot.de, http://www.duncker-humblot.de. Ed. Thierry Volery. adv.: page EUR 550; trim 115 x 185. Circ: 1,000 (paid and controlled). **Co-sponsor:** Hochschule St. Gallen fuer Wirtschafts-und Sozialwissenschaft.

338 BEL ISSN 0779-3804
Z O. (Zelfstandig Ondernemen) Text in Dutch. 1921. 21/yr. EUR 132 (effective 2005). adv. **Document type:** *Magazine, Consumer.* **Description:** Provides information on trade management for small businesses.
Formerly (until 1992): Zelfstandig Ondernemen (0779-3790)
Published by: U N I Z O, Spastraat 8, Brussels, 1040, Belgium. TEL 32-2-238-0511, FAX 32-2-238-0596, 32-2-231-1622, redactie@unizo.be, info@unizo.be, http://www.kmonet.be/viewobj.jsp?id=389. Ed. Ronny Lannoo. adv.: B&W page BEF 87,400, color page BEF 129,000; trim 410 x 280. Circ: 28,000.

338 CHN ISSN 1003-5087
ZHONGGUO QIYEJIA/CHINESE ENTREPRENEUR. Text in Chinese. 1985. m. CNY 240 (effective 2004). **Document type:** *Newspaper, Trade.*
Related titles: Online - full text ed.: (from East View Information Services, WanFang Data Corp.).
Published by: Jingji Ribao Baoye Jituan/Economic Daily Newspaper Group, Zhaoyang-qu Anhuili Si-qu, Zhongguo Wukuang Building, no.15, 8th Fl, Beijing, 010-64923461, China. TEL 86-10-64923793, FAX 86-10-64923795, ce@cnemag.com, http://www.cnemag.com.cn/. **Dist. in US by:** China Books & Periodicals Inc, 360 Swift Ave., Ste. 48, S San Fran, CA 94080-6220; **Dist. by:** China International Book Trading Corp, 35 Chegongzhuang Xilu, Haidian District, PO Box 399, Beijing 100044, China. TEL 86-10-68412045, FAX 86-10-68412023, cibtc@mail.cibtc.com.cn, http://www.cibtc.com.cn.

338 CHN
ZHONGGUO XIANGZHEN QIYE/CHINA'S TOWNSHIP ENTERPRISES NEWS. Text in Chinese. m. **Document type:** *Newspaper, Government.*
Published by: Nongye Bu, Xiangzhen Qiye Ju/Ministry of Agriculture, Bureau of Township Enterprises, No 11 Nongzhanguan Nanli, Beijing, 100026, China. TEL 5003366. Ed. Zhang Yi. **Dist. in US by:** China Books & Periodicals Inc, 360 Swift Ave., Ste. 48, S San Fran, CA 94080-6220. TEL 415-282-2994; **Dist. by:** China International Book Trading Corp, 35 Chegongzhuang Xilu, Haidian District, PO Box 399, Beijing 100044, China. TEL 86-10-68412045, FAX 86-10-68412023, cibtc@mail.cibtc.com.cn, http://www.cibtc.com.cn.

658.041 USA
THE 6-FIGURE PRACTICE NEWSLETTER. Text in English. irreg. free. **Document type:** *Newsletter.* **Description:** Offers strategies, methods and resources for building a very high income based on small business, while still living a balanced life.
Media: E-mail.
Published by: Eastern College, 1300 Eogle Rd., St. Davids, PA 19087-3696. TEL 610-341-1595, FAX 610-341-1585, editor@6figurepractice.com, http://www.6figurepractice.com.

338 USA
422 TAX DEDUCTIONS FOR BUSINESSES AND SELF-EMPLOYED INDIVIDUALS. Text in English. 1998. a. USD 22.80 per issue (effective 2004).
Published by: Bell Springs Publishing, PO Box 1240, Willits, CA 95490. TEL 707-459-6372, 800-515-8050, FAX 707-459-8614, taxbook@bellsprings.com, http://www.bellsprings.com. Ed. Bernard Kamoroff. Pub. Sam Leandro. Circ: 5,000.

BUSINESS AND ECONOMICS—Trade And Industrial Directories

B

380.1029 USA ISSN 1043-0121
A 2 L A (YEAR) ANNUAL REPORT✶. Text in English. 1987. a. **Document type:** *Corporate.*
Published by: American Association for Laboratory Accreditation, 5301 Buckeystown Pike 350, Frederick, MD 21704-8370. TEL 301-644-2974, FAX 301-662-2974. Ed. Theresa Adams. Pub. Peter Unger.

380.1029 USA ISSN 1040-9181
TA416.5.U6
A 2 L A (YEAR) DIRECTORY OF ACCREDITED LABORATORIES✶. Text in English. 1980. a. free. index. **Document type:** *Directory, Corporate.* **Description:** Provides scope of testing capability for 1300 laboratories found competent to perform specific tests or types of tests.
Published by: American Association for Laboratory Accreditation, 5301 Buckeystown Pike 350, Frederick, MD 21704-8370. TEL 301-644-3248, FAX 301-662-2974. Ed. Theresa Adams. Pub. Peter Unger.

380.1029 USA ISSN 1040-9157
A 2 L A NEWS✶. Text in English. 1980. q. free. **Document type:** *Newsletter.* **Description:** Presents updating information on accredited labs.
Formerly: A 2 L A Update
Published by: American Association for Laboratory Accreditation, 5301 Buckeystown Pike 350, Frederick, MD 21704-8370. TEL 301-644-3248, FAX 301-662-2974. Ed. Percy Pan. Pub. Peter Unger.

338.0029 USA
A B A JOURNAL ANNUAL BUYERS GUIDE. Text in English. 1993. a. **Document type:** *Directory.*
Published by: American Bar Association, 321 N Clark St, Chicago, IL 60610. TEL 312-988-5000, FAX 312-988-6014. adv.: B&W page USD 3,000, color page USD 4,500; trim 10.75 x 8.19. Circ: 38,000.

338.0029 BEL ISSN 0775-6178
A B C BELGE POUR LE COMMERCE ET L'INDUSTRIE. Text in Dutch, French; Summaries in English, German. 1981. a. **Document type:** *Directory.* **Description:** Presents business information on Belgian companies, including manufacturers and producers, importers, and professional services.
Related titles: CD-ROM ed.; Diskette ed.; Online - full text ed.
Published by: A B C pour le Commerce et l'Industrie C.V., Doornveld 1B28, Asse, 1730, Belgium. TEL 32-2-4630213, FAX 32-2-4630885, http://www.abc-d.be. Ed. Daniel Labbeke.

380.1029 DEU
A B C DER DEUTSCHEN WIRTSCHAFT - QUELLENWERK FUR EINKAUF-VERKAUF. Text in German. a. USD 147 (effective 1999). **Document type:** *Directory.*
Related titles: CD-ROM ed.; Online - full text ed.: (from F I Z Technik).
Published by: A B C Publishing Group, Postfach 100262, Darmstadt, 64202, Germany. TEL 49-6151-3892-0, FAX 49-6151-33164. Ed., R&P Margit Selka. Circ: 27,000. **Dist. in US by:** Western Hemisphere Publishing Corp., PO Box 847, Hillsboro, OR 97123.

338.0029 BEL ISSN 0776-9954
A B C LUXEMBOURGEOIS POUR LE COMMERCE ET L'INDUSTRIE. Text in French. 1989. a. adv. **Document type:** *Directory.* **Description:** Provides information on businesses in Luxembourg in the manufacturing and service sectors.
Related titles: CD-ROM ed.; Diskette ed.; Magnetic Tape ed.; Online - full text ed.
Published by: A B C pour le Commerce et l'Industrie C.V., Doornveld 1B28, Asse, 1730, Belgium. TEL 32-2-4630213, FAX 32-2-4630885, http://www.abc-d.lu. Circ: 3,000.

A B H I DIRECTORY. see *MEDICAL SCIENCES*

381.029 JPN
A C C J DIRECTORY. Text in English. 1950. a. (plus 3 updates). JPY 5,000, USD 45 to members; JPY 10,000, USD 95 to non-members. adv. **Document type:** *Directory.* **Description:** Listing of Chamber members, member firms, supporting associates and companies of the American Chamber of Commerce in Japan.
Related titles: Diskette ed.
Published by: American Chamber of Commerce in Japan, Masonic 39 MT Bldg. 10F, 2-4-5 Azabudai, Minato-ku, Tokyo, 106-0041, Japan. TEL 03-3433-5381, FAX 03-3436-1446, info@accj.or.jp. R&P Jeanmarie Todd.

338.0029 AUS
A D M'S DEFENCE BUSINESS DIRECTORY. Abbreviated title: A D M's A N Z Defence Business Directory. Text in English. s-a. AUD 70 domestic; AUD 90 in New Zealand; AUD 105 in Asia; AUD 140 elsewhere (effective 2005). adv. **Document type:** *Directory, Trade.* **Description:** Lists experienced defense suppliers by category.
Formerly: A D M's Australia New Zealand Defence Business Directory
Published by: Yaffa Publishing Group Pty Ltd., 17-21 Bellevue St, Surry Hills, NSW 2010, Australia. TEL 61-2-92812333, FAX 61-2-92812750, yaffa@yaffa.com.au, http://www.yaffa.com.au. adv.: B&W page AUD 2,045, color page AUD 2,370; trim 210 x 297.

B

338.0029 USA
A D S C MEMBERSHIP DIRECTORY. Text in English. a. USD 95; USD 125 foreign (effective 1998). adv. bk.rev. **Document type:** *Directory.* **Description:** Listings of all contractor, supplier and technical members involved in drilled shaft and anchored earth retention construction and design throughout the world.
Published by: Association of Drilled Shaft Contractors, 14180 Dallas Pkwy, Ste 510, Dallas, TX 75254. TEL 214-343-2091, FAX 214-343-2384. Ed. Scot Litke. Circ: 2,000.

338.0025 USA
A E S C DIRECTORY✶. Text in English. 1963. a. USD 60 to non-members; USD 30 to members. adv. back issues avail. **Document type:** *Directory.*
Formerly (until 1997): Association of Oilwell Servicing Contractors. Directory
Published by: Association of Energy Service Companies, 10200 Richmond Ave, Ste 275, Houston, TX 77042. TEL 214-692-0771. Ed. Polly Fisk. R&P Robert Key. Adv. contact Kristin Van Veen. Circ: 1,000.

658.0029 USA
A F I BUYING DIRECTORY. Text in English. a. USD 35 (effective 1999). adv. **Document type:** *Trade.*
Formerly: A F I Buying Directory and Who's Who
Published by: (National Association of Federally Licensed Firearms Dealers), P G R A Inc., 2400 E Las Olas, Ste 397, Fort Lauderdale, FL 33301. TEL 954-467-9994, FAX 954-463-2501, http://www.amfire.com. Ed. Clint Vander Pool. Pub., R&P Andrew Molchan. Adv. contact Jim Hatfield. B&W page USD 2,200; 10 x 7. Circ: 45,000.

338.0029 USA
A I C P MEMBERSHIP DIRECTORY. Text in English. 1995. a. USD 55 (effective 1999). adv. **Document type:** *Directory.* **Description:** Provides listing of member companies, names, address, phone, fax and contacts. along with general information, including guidelines and production-related forms.
Published by: Association of Independent Commercial Producers, 3 W, 18th St., 5th Fl, New York, NY 10011-4610. TEL 212-929-3000, FAX 212-929-3359, mattm@aicp.com, davids@aicp.com, http://www.aicp.com. R&P Renee Paley. Adv. contact David Stewart. color page USD 7,000; trim 9 x 6.75.

530.81029 USA
A M S A SCALE DIRECTORY; United States and Canada. Text in English. biennial. USD 21 (effective 1999). **Document type:** *Directory, Trade.* **Description:** Contains listing of 1700 scales for weighing trucks in U.S. and Canada.
Formerly: American Movers Conference Scale Directory (Years)
Published by: American Moving and Storage Association, 1611 Duke St, Alexandria, VA 22314. TEL 703-683-7410, FAX 703-683-7527.

338.476292 USA
A P R A (YEAR) MEMBERSHIP DIRECTORY. Text in English. a. USD 900 (effective 2001). back issues avail. **Document type:** *Directory, Trade.* **Description:** Lists rebuilders and suppliers within the automotive aftermarket industry that are members of APRA.
Formerly: A P R A Membership Roster and Trade Directory
Published by: Automotive Parts Rebuilders Association, 4215 Lafayette Center Dr., Ste. 3, Chantilly, VA 20151-1243. Ed. Judith W Chandler. Circ: 2,100.

A P R O DIRECTORY. see *TRAVEL AND TOURISM*

A P T YEARBOOK. (Asia - Pacific Telecommunity) see *COMMUNICATIONS—Telephone And Telegraph*

670.29 USA
A S A MEMBERSHIP DIRECTORY. Text in English. 1980. a. USD 95 to non-members; USD 60 to members (effective 2000). adv. **Document type:** *Directory.*
Published by: American Supply Association, 222 Merchandise Mart Pl, Ste 1400, Chicago, IL 60654-1202. TEL 312-464-0090, FAX 312-464-0091, asa@asa.net, info@asa.net. Pub. Maurice Desmarais. Adv. contact Molly Frank Stewart. Circ: 3,200.

380.1029 368 SGP
A S E A N INSURANCE DIRECTORY. (Association of Southeast Asian Nations) Text in English. a. USD 90 in Singapore & Malaysia; USD 110 elsewhere (effective 2005). **Document type:** *Directory, Trade.* **Description:** Contains more than 500 entires of insurance companies, agencies, associations, personnel, related educational and training institutes.
Related titles: CD-ROM ed.
Published by: Ins Communications Pte. Ltd., 57A Amoy St., Singapore, 069 883, Singapore. TEL 65-62245583, FAX 65-62241091, http://www.asiainsurancereview.com/EStore/asia-insurance-dir.asp.

643.16029 365.34 USA
A S I S SECURITY INDUSTRY BUYERS GUIDE. Text in English. 1987. a., latest 2003. USD 99 to members; USD 179 to non-members (effective 2004). adv. **Document type:** *Directory, Trade.* **Description:** Consolidates purchasing information on industrial-commercial security products, services and systems.
Formerly (until 2000): Security Industry Buyers Guide
Published by: American Society for Industrial Security, 1625 Prince St, Alexandria, VA 22314-2818. TEL 703-519-6200, FAX 703-519-6299, buyersguide@asisonline.org, asis@asisonline.org, http://www.asisonline.org. Ed. Mike Moran. adv.: B&W page USD 4,800; trim 10.88 x 8.25.

380.1029 GBR
A S K HOLLIS - THE DIRECTORY OF U K ASSOCIATIONS. (Associations, Sources, Knowledge) Variant title: The Directory of U K Associations. Text in English. 2001. a., latest 2003, 3rd Ed. GBP 195 per vol. (effective 2005). **Document type:** *Directory, Consumer.* **Description:** Contains over 5,000 associations, pressure groups, unions, institutes, societies and more are profiled, representing every interest area from abrasives through to zoos, from industrial, professional and business sectors to government, charities and the consumer.
Published by: Hollis Publishing Ltd., Harlequin House, 7 High St, Teddington, Middx TW11 8EL, United Kingdom. TEL 44-20-8977-7711, FAX 44-20-8977-1133, orders@hollis-pr.co.uk, http://www.hollis-pr.com/publications/ask.htm, http://www.hollis-pr.co.uk/.

A S T D BUYERS GUIDE AND CONSULTANTS DIRECTORY. see *BUSINESS AND ECONOMICS—Personnel Management*

A T & T NATIONAL TOLL-FREE DIRECTORY - BUSINESS BUYER'S GUIDE - BUSINESS EDITION. see *COMMUNICATIONS—Telephone And Telegraph*

A V M A DIRECTORY AND RESOURCE MANUAL. see *VETERINARY SCIENCE*

658.0029 USA
A W M A BUYING GUIDE & ANNUAL MEMBERSHIP DIRECTORY. Text in English. a. USD 200 (effective 2000). **Document type:** *Directory.* **Description:** Complete guide to the wholesale candy, tobacco and snack food distribution industry.
Published by: American Wholesale Marketers Association, Inc., 2750 Prosperity Ave, Ste 530, Fairfax, VA 22031. TEL 202-463-2124, FAX 202-467-0559. Ed. Ronda Jenkins. Pub., Adv. contact Joyce O'Brien. R&P Joan Fay.

382.029 UAE
A - Z: UNITED ARAB EMIRATES BUSINESS LOCATIONS GUIDE. Text in Arabic. 1988. a.
Published by: Al- Saqr Publishing House, P O Box 198, Ajman, United Arab Emirates. TEL 425135, FAX 421876.

ACCESS (SEATTLE); a guide to the visual arts in Washington State. see *ART*

690.029 USA
ACCESS CONTROL & SECURITY INTEGRATION BUYERS' GUIDE. Text in English. 1958. a. USD 59.95. adv. **Document type:** *Trade.*
Former titles: Access Control Buyers' Guide; Fence Industry - Access Control Directory; Fence Industry Directory
Published by: Primedia Business Magazines & Media, Inc. (Subsidiary of: Primedia, Inc.), 6151 Powers Ferry Rd Ste 200, Atlanta, GA 30339. TEL 770-955-2500, FAX 770-618-0204, inquiries@primediabusiness.com, http://www.primediabusiness.com.

380.1029 AUS ISSN 1329-1130
AD NEWS PROMOTIONAL PRODUCTS DIRECTORY. Text in English. a. **Description:** Presents a variety of promotional ideas for companies looking at new ways to promote themselves.
Published by: Yaffa Publishing Group Pty Ltd., 17-21 Bellevue St, Surry Hills, NSW 2010, Australia. TEL 61-2-9281-2333, FAX 61-2-9281-2750, yaffa@yaffa.com.au, http://www.yaffa.com.au. adv.: B&W page AUD 1,030, color page AUD 1,160; trim 210 x 297. Circ: 8,000.

ADAM FILM WORLD GUIDE DIRECTORY OF ADULT FILM. see *MOTION PICTURES*

ADBRIEF REGISTER: AGENCIES & MARKETERS. see *ADVERTISING AND PUBLIC RELATIONS*

380.1029 570 NLD ISSN 0924-2872
ADRESBOEK VOOR BIOLOGEN. Text in Dutch. 1979. biennial. EUR 34.03 (effective 2001). **Document type:** *Directory.*
Published by: Nederlands Instituut voor Biologie, Postbus 19245, Utrecht, 3501 DE, Netherlands. TEL 31-30-2369244, FAX 31-30-2332877, nibi@nibi.nl, http://www.nibi.nl.

ADRESSBUCH FUER DEN DEUTSCHSPRACHIGEN BUCHHANDEL CD-ROM. see *PUBLISHING AND BOOK TRADE*

005.3029 USA ISSN 0749-4874
T12.3.W2
ADVANCED TECHNOLOGY IN WASHINGTON STATE. Text in English. 1984. a. USD 48 (effective 2000). bk.rev. **Document type:** *Directory.* **Description:** Provides information on over 1500 technology based firms, including address, size by sales and employees, key personnel, market areas, and product data. Includes general information on the technology and software industry in Washington State.
Media: Diskette.
Published by: Commerce Publishing Corp. (Seattle), PO Box 9805, Seattle, WA 98109-0805. TEL 206-286-1498, compub@worldnet.att.net. Ed., Pub., R&P Glenn Avery. Circ: 12,500 (paid).

659.1029 USA
HF5805
ADWEEK DIRECTORY. Text in English. a. USD 399 combined subscription print & CD-ROM eds. (effective 2003). **Document type:** *Directory.* **Description:** Directory of US advertising agencies, public relations firms, and media buying services, providing key facts and personnel.
Formerly: Adweek Agency Directory (1055-8950)
Related titles: CD-ROM ed.; Online - full content ed.: USD 700 (effective 2003); ♦ Supplement to: The Brandweek Directory.
Published by: V N U Business Publications (Subsidiary of: V N U Business Media), 770 Broadway, 7th Fl, New York, NY 10003. FAX 646-654-5518, adweek@adweek.com, bmcomm@vnuinc.com, http://www.adweek.com/adweek/directories/index.jsp, http://www.vnubusinessmedia.com/. Ed. Michael Battaglia. Pub. Mitch Tego. Adv. contact Julie Azous TEL 646-654-5308.

AEROSPACE INTERNATIONAL DIRECTORY OF WORLD AIRLINES. see *TRANSPORTATION—Air Transport*

380.1029 USA
AFFILIATED WAREHOUSE COMPANIES DIRECTORY. Text in English. 1953. biennial. free. **Document type:** *Directory, Trade.* **Description:** Lists third-party warehouses, contacts, phone and fax numbers, location and size, and what type of storage each warehouse has. For organizations seeking public warehouse space or outsource warehousing.
Published by: Affiliated Warehouse Companies, Inc., PO Box 295, Hazlet, NJ 07730. TEL 732-739-2323, sales@awco.com, http://www.awco.com. Ed. Jim McBride. Circ: 16,000 (controlled).

780.29 ESP
AGENDA CLAVE; guia practica de la industria musical y del espectaculo. Text in Spanish. 1993. a. USD 120. adv. **Document type:** *Directory.* **Description:** Provides about 15000 addresses of organizations and professionals in the music and show business industries in Spain and Spanish-speaking countries.
Published by: Clave Profesional, Ave Gaudi, 10 Piso 2, Barcelona, 08025, Spain. TEL 34-93-4575036, FAX 34-93-4561729, clave@revistaclave.com, http://www.espectacularia.com/webs/clave/. Pub., R&P Jordi Rueda. Adv. contact Antonio More. B&W page USD 1,000, color page USD 1,400.

630.29 GBR ISSN 1466-500X
HD1920.7
AGRAFOOD EAST EUROPE. Text in English. m. GBP 810 domestic; GBP 906 in Europe; GBP 1,006 elsewhere (effective 2005). s-a. index. **Document type:** *Newsletter, Trade.* **Description:** Covers production, policy, prices, trade and investment from the former U.S.S.R and Eastern Europe.
Former titles (until 1998): East Europe Agriculture and Food; East Europe and U S S R Agriculture and Food; East Europe and China Agriculture and Food; East Europe Agriculture (0263-3205)
Related titles: Online - full text ed.: (from Gale Group).
Indexed: DSA, MaizeAb, PotatoAb, RefZh, S&F, TriticAb, WAE&RSA.
—CISTI, IE, Infotrieve.

Published by: Agra Europe (London) Ltd. (Subsidiary of: T & F Informa plc), 80 Calverley Rd, Tunbridge Wells, Kent TN1 2UN, United Kingdom. TEL 44-1892-533813, FAX 44-1892-544895, marketing@agra-net.com, http://www.agra-net.com.

AIR FREIGHT DIRECTORY. see *TRANSPORTATION—Air Transport*

380.1029　　　　　USA
ALABAMA BUSINESS CREDIT DIRECTORY. Text in English. a. USD 1,100 combined subscription print, online & CD-ROM eds. (effective 2004 & 2005). back issues avail. **Document type:** *Directory.* **Description:** Contains credit ratings and other valuable information on all businesses within Alabama. Includes company name & address, phone & fax numbers, key executive names & titles, lines of business, years in business, number of employees, estimated annual sales, volume credit rating code, and corporate linkage information.
Related titles: CD-ROM ed.; Online - full text ed.
Published by: American Business Directories (Subsidiary of: American Business Information, Inc.), 5711 S 86th Circle, P O Box 27347, Omaha, NE 68127. TEL 402-593-4600, 888-946-9377, 877-708-3844, FAX 402-331-5481, sales@directoriesusa.com, http://www.directoriesusa.com.

338.0029　　　　　USA　　　　　ISSN 1043-7924
HF5065.A37
ALABAMA BUSINESS DIRECTORY. Text in English. 1988. a. USD 1,100 combined subscription print, online & CD-ROM eds. (effective 2004 & 2005). index. back issues avail. **Document type:** *Directory.* **Description:** Includes all businesses in the state compiled from the yellow pages and telephone-verified. Each listing includes company name, complete address, phone number, name of owner, manager, and employee size, sales volume codes, credit rating codes.
Related titles: CD-ROM ed.; Online - full text ed.
Published by: American Business Directories (Subsidiary of: American Business Information, Inc.), 5711 S 86th Circle, P O Box 27347, Omaha, NE 68127. TEL 402-593-4600, 888-946-9377, 877-708-3844, FAX 402-331-5481, karen.peters@infousa.com, sales@directoriesusa.com, http://www.directoriesusa.com.

ALABAMA COUNCIL A I A DIRECTORY. see *ARCHITECTURE*

670.29　　　　　USA　　　　　ISSN 1061-9585
T12
ALABAMA INDUSTRIAL DIRECTORY. Text in English. 1976. biennial. USD 55 (effective 2000). adv. index. **Document type:** *Directory, Government.* **Description:** Provides basic information on Alabama's mining and manufacturing industries. Each listing contains the company name, address, a contact name, telephone number, SIC code, product descriptions, number of employees and the year the firm was established.
Formerly (until 1991): Alabama Directory of Mining and Manufacturing (0145-4048); Supersedes (in 1976): Industrial Alabama (0073-7321)
Published by: Alabama Development Office, Attn: Alabama Industrial Directory, Alabama Center for Commerce, 401 Adams Ave, Ste 624, Montgomery, AL 36130. TEL 334-242-0400, 800-248-0033, FAX 334-242-2414, 334-353-1212. Ed. Rita Whittington. R&P Wanda Chrietzberg TEL 334-242-0445. Circ: 5,000.

670.29　　　　　USA　　　　　ISSN 1045-2664
HF5065.A37
ALABAMA MANUFACTURERS REGISTER. Text in English. a. USD 83 (effective 2000). adv. **Document type:** *Directory.* **Description:** Profiles 6,759 manufacturers, listed five ways: by product, alphabetically, by city, by S.I.C. and by parent company. Complete addresses, phone numbers and flags for new businesses in city, alphabetical and SIC sections.
Related titles: CD-ROM ed.: USD 445 (effective 2000); Diskette ed.: USD 445.
Published by: Manufacturers' News, Inc., 1633 Central St, Evanston, IL 60201. TEL 847-864-7000, 888-752-5200, FAX 847-332-1100, info@mninfo.com, info@manufacturersnews.com, sales@mninfo.com, http://www.manufacturersnews.com. Ed. Frank Lambing. Adv. contact Charles Scherer. B&W page USD 1,843.

380.1029　　　　　USA　　　　　ISSN 1060-7943
HF5065.C2
ALAMEDA COUNTY COMMERCE AND INDUSTRY DIRECTORY∗ . Text in English. a. USD 75 (effective 1999). **Document type:** *Directory.* **Description:** Lists 3,800 manufacturers, wholesalers and service companies besides 8,900 owners and key executives.
Related titles: CD-ROM ed.; Diskette ed.
Published by: Database Publishing Company, 701 E Ball Rd Ste 100, Anaheim, CA 92805-5962. TEL 714-778-6400, FAX 714-778-6811. R&P Vera Roldan. Circ: 500 (paid).

338.0029　　　　　USA　　　　　ISSN 1048-7069
HF5065.A4
ALASKA BUSINESS DIRECTORY. Text in English. 1990. a. USD 1,100 combined subscription print, online & CD-ROM eds. (effective 2004 & 2005). index. back issues avail. **Document type:** *Directory.* **Description:** Includes all businesses in the state compiled from the yellow pages and telephone-verified. Each listing includes company name, complete address, phone number, name of owner, manager, and employee size and sales volume codes, and credit rating codes.
Related titles: CD-ROM ed.; Online - full text ed.
Published by: American Business Directories (Subsidiary of: American Business Information, Inc.), 5711 S 86th Circle, P O Box 27347, Omaha, NE 68127. TEL 402-593-4600, 888-946-9377, 877-708-3844, FAX 402-331-5481, karen.peters@infousa.com, sales@directoriesusa.com, http://www.directoriesusa.com.

ALASKA BUSINESS MONTHLY. see *BUSINESS AND ECONOMICS*

670.29　　　　　USA　　　　　ISSN 1085-746X
HF5065.A4
ALASKA MANUFACTURERS DIRECTORY. Text in English. 1994. a. USD 51 (effective 2001). adv. 104 p./no.; **Document type:** *Directory.* **Description:** Profiles 841 companies.
Supersedes in part (in 1996): Alaska - Hawaii Manufacturers Directory (1074-2468)
Related titles: CD-ROM ed.: USD 175 (effective 2001); Diskette ed.: USD 195.
Published by: Manufacturers' News, Inc., 1633 Central St, Evanston, IL 60201. TEL 847-864-7000, 888-752-5200, FAX 847-332-1100, info@mninfo.com, info@manufacturersnews.com, sales@mninfo.com, http://www.manufacturersnews.com. Ed. Steve Garland.

061　　　　　CAN　　　　　ISSN 1195-8332
ALBERTA ASSOCIATIONS DIRECTORY ON-LINE. Text in English. 2000. a. **Document type:** *Directory, Trade.* **Description:** Contains detailed information on certification, licensing, professional development, specialized training, workshops, membership requirements, and general association information.
Related titles: Online - full content ed.
Published by: Remington Research, 11428 - 79 Ave., Edmonton, AB T6G 0P6, Canada. FAX 780-435-4636, http://www.associationsdirectory.com/, info@trainthebrain.net.

380.1029 071.1　　　　　USA　　　　　ISSN 1203-5149
HF5072.A4
ALBERTA BUSINESS DIRECTORY. Text in English. 1996. a. USD 1,100 print, online & CD-ROM eds. (effective 2004 & 2005).
Related titles: CD-ROM ed.; Online - full text ed.
Published by: American Business Directories (Subsidiary of: American Business Information, Inc.), 5711 S 86th Circle, P O Box 27347, Omaha, NE 68127. TEL 402-593-4600, 888-946-9377, 877-708-3844, FAX 402-331-5481, sales@directoriesusa.com, http://www.directoriesusa.com.

338.4769　　　　　CAN　　　　　ISSN 1498-6728
ALBERTA CONSTRUCTION SERVICE & SUPPLY DIRECTORY. Text in English. 1992. a. **Document type:** *Government.*
Formerly (until 1999): Canadian Construction Service and Supply Directory, Alberta (1191-9639)
Published by: JuneWarren Publishing, 9915-56 Ave NW, Edmonton, AB T6E 5L7, Canada. TEL 780-944-9333, FAX 780-944-9500, http://www.junewarren.com/.

381.029　　　　　CAN　　　　　ISSN 0823-2350
ALBERTA LEGAL TELEPHONE DIRECTORY. Text in English. 1982. a. looseleaf. CND 27 per issue (effective 2005). adv. 424 p./no.; **Document type:** *Directory.*
Published by: Canada Law Book Inc., 240 Edward St#, Aurora, ON L4G 3S9, Canada. b.loney@canadalawbook.ca, http://www.canadalawbook.ca. Ed. Judy Antoniadis. Adv. contact Colleen Austin TEL 905-841-6472.

665.5029　　　　　CAN　　　　　ISSN 0831-019X
ALBERTA OIL & GAS DIRECTORY. Text in English. 1980. a. CND 95. adv. tr.lit. back issues avail. **Document type:** *Directory.*
Published by: Armadale Publications Inc., Box 1193, MPO, Edmonton, AB T5J 2M4, Canada. TEL 403-429-1073, FAX 403-425-5844. Ed. Winston Mohabir. Circ: 7,000.

338.0029　　　　　IND
ALL INDIA INDUSTRIAL YELLOW PAGES∗ . Short title: A I I T P. Text in English. 1991. irreg. INR 500, USD 80. adv. **Document type:** *Directory.* **Description:** Directory on various Indian industries with name, addresses, telephone, and products.
Published by: (Kanishka Industrial Consultants Pvt. Ltd.), Kanishka Publishing House, IX-2325 Ste.12, Kailash Nagar, New Delhi, 110 031, India. Ed. R K Verma.

338.0029　　　　　ZAF
AMANZIMTOTI BUYER'S GUIDE. Text in English. 1981. a. USD 25 (effective 2001). **Document type:** *Directory.*
Formerly: Amanzimtoti Directory (1016-6327)

Published by: Braby's (Subsidiary of: Associated Industries), Attn: Sue Pearson, PO Box 1426, Pinetown, 3600, South Africa. TEL 27-31-7017021, FAX 27-31-7017036, booksales@brabys.co.za.

AMERICAN ART DIRECTORY. see *ART*

338.0029　　　　　USA　　　　　ISSN 1069-8442
HF5035
AMERICAN BIG BUSINESSES DIRECTORY. Text in English. a. USD 1,100 combined subscription print, online & CD-ROM eds. (effective 2004 & 2005). back issues avail. **Document type:** *Directory.* **Description:** Lists over 177,000 companies with 100 or more employees, alphabetically and by city. Includes company name, complete address and phone number, executive names and titles, up to 3 SIC codes, number of employees and sales volume, and credit rating codes.
Former titles (until 1993): Big Businesses Directory (1061-2173); (until 1990): Blue Chip Companies Directory
Related titles: CD-ROM ed.; Online - full text ed.
Published by: American Business Directories (Subsidiary of: American Business Information, Inc.), 5711 S 86th Circle, P O Box 27347, Omaha, NE 68127. TEL 402-593-4600, 888-946-9377, 877-708-3844, FAX 402-331-5481, sales@directoriesusa.com, http://www.directoriesusa.com.

614.6029　　　　　USA　　　　　ISSN 0065-7565
THE AMERICAN BLUE BOOK OF FUNERAL DIRECTORS. Text in English. 1932. a. USD 75 (effective 1999). adv. bk.rev. back issues avail. **Document type:** *Directory, Trade.* **Description:** Primary directory and reference guide in funeral homes across the US and throughout the world.
Related titles: Online - full text ed.
Published by: F C S Worldwide (Subsidiary of: United Communications Group), 11300 Rockville Pike, Ste 1100, Rockville, MD 20852. TEL 800-500-4585, FAX 301-287-2150, http://www.fcsworldwide.com/index.aspx. adv.: B&W page USD 1,150, color page USD 1,925; trim 11 x 8.25. Circ: 10,000 (paid).

AMERICAN BOOK TRADE DIRECTORY. see *PUBLISHING AND BOOK TRADE*

338.0029　　　　　USA　　　　　ISSN 1062-5119
HF5035
THE AMERICAN BUSINESS DISK. Text in English. base vol. plus s-a. updates. USD 1,995 (effective 2005). **Document type:** *Directory, Trade.* **Description:** Lists 14 million U.S. businesses by name, S.I.C. code, yellow page heading, and geographic location.
Media: CD-ROM.
Published by: InfoUSAGov, 5711 S 86th Circle, PO Box 27347, Omaha, NE 68127. TEL 800-555-5211, FAX 402-537-6199, government@infousa.com, http://www.infousagov.com/ABD_Bus.htm.

380.1029　　　　　ARG
AMERICAN CHAMBER OF COMMERCE IN ARGENTINA. DIRECTORY. Text in English. 1974. a. USD 100. adv. illus. **Document type:** *Directory.* **Description:** Lists American businesses in Argentina. Contains information on the authorities, committees and companies which are members.
Former titles (until 1993): American Business in Argentina; (until 1977): Directory of American Business in Argentina
Published by: American Chamber of Commerce in Argentina, Viamonte, 1133 Piso 8, Capital Federal, Buenos Aires 1053, Argentina. TEL 54-114-3714500, FAX 54-114-3718400. Adv. contact Mariana Urrestarazu. page USD 1,000.

380.102 382　　　　　UKR
AMERICAN CHAMBER OF COMMERCE IN UKRAINE. MEMBERSHIP DIRECTORY. Text in Ukrainian. a. membership. **Document type:** *Directory.* **Description:** Contains information on more than 200 international businesses operating in Ukraine, as well as analysis of key industries.
Published by: American Chamber of Commerce in Ukraine, Shovkovychna vul 42-44 LL 2, Kiev, 252004, Ukraine. TEL 380-44-2476816, FAX 380-44-2476898. Ed. Jorge Zukoski.

AMERICAN COMPANIES: GUIDE TO SOURCES OF INFORMATION/AMERICANISCHE HANDELSGESELLSCHAFTEN: HANDBUCH DER INFORMATIONSQUELLEN/SOCIETES AMERICAINES: REPERTOIRE DES SOURCES DE DOCUMENTATION. see *BUSINESS AND ECONOMICS—Abstracting, Bibliographies, Statistics*

AMERICAN DROP-SHIPPERS DIRECTORY. see *BUSINESS AND ECONOMICS—Marketing And Purchasing*

AMERICAN FINANCIAL DIRECTORY. see *BUSINESS AND ECONOMICS—Banking And Finance*

620.199029　　　　　USA
AMERICAN FLOCK ASSOCIATION DIRECTORY. Text in English. 1987. biennial. free. **Document type:** *Directory.* **Description:** Lists companies which are flock users, flock producers, raw material suppliers, adhesive manufacturers, machinery suppliers, and consultants to the industry.

▼ *new title*　　➤ *refereed*　　∗ *unverified*　　◆ *full entry avail.*

Published by: American Flock Association, 6 Beacon St Ste 1125, Boston, MA 02108-3812. TEL 617-542-8220, FAX 617-542-2199, amerflock@aol.com, http://www.flocking.org. Ed. David Trumbull.

382.029 GRC ISSN 0065-8537
AMERICAN - HELLENIC CHAMBER OF COMMERCE. BUSINESS DIRECTORY. SPECIAL ISSUE. Text in English. 1960. a. USD 250. adv. **Document type:** *Directory, Trade.*
Related titles: ◆ Supplement to: American - Hellenic Chamber of Commerce. Business Directory. ISSN 0065-8529.
Published by: American - Hellenic Chamber of Commerce, 16 Kanari St, Athens, 106 74, Greece. TEL 363-6407. Pub. Sotiris Yannopoulos. Circ: 5,000.

AMERICAN INSTITUTE OF CERTIFIED PUBLIC ACCOUNTANTS. DIRECTORY OF MEMBER FIRMS. see *BUSINESS AND ECONOMICS—Accounting*

670.29 USA ISSN 1061-219X
HD9723
AMERICAN MANUFACTURERS DIRECTORY. Text in English. 1989. a. USD 1,100 combined subscription print, online & CD-ROM eds. (effective 2004 & 2005). index. back issues avail. **Document type:** *Directory.* **Description:** Includes all manufacturers across the US with 25 or more employees compiled from surveys. Each listing includes company name, complete address, phone number, name of owner and/or manager, and employee size and sales volume codes, credit rating codes.
Formerly (until 1991): U S Manufacturers Directory (1042-1742)
Related titles: CD-ROM ed.; Diskette ed.; E-mail ed.; Fax ed.; Magnetic Tape ed.; Online - full text ed.
Published by: American Business Directories (Subsidiary of: American Business Information, Inc.), 5711 S 86th Circle, P O Box 27347, Omaha, NE 68127. TEL 402-593-4600, 888-946-9377, 877-708-3844, FAX 402-331-5481, sales@directoriesusa.com, http://www.directoriesusa.com.

AMERICAN RECOVERY ASSOCIATION. NEWS AND VIEWS. see *BUSINESS AND ECONOMICS—Banking And Finance*

AMERICAN RECYCLING MARKET; annual directory and reference manual. see *ENVIRONMENTAL STUDIES—Waste Management*

AMERICAN SHOEMAKING DIRECTORY OF SHOE MANUFACTURERS. see *SHOES AND BOOTS*

746.92029 USA
AMERICAN SPORTSWEAR & KNITTING TIMES BUYERS' GUIDE (YEAR)✶; and knitwear apparel directory. Text in English. a. USD 25. **Document type:** *Directory, Trade.*
Former titles: Knitting Times Buyers' Guide (Year); Knitting Times Buyers' Guide and Knitwear Apparel Directory; Knitting Times Buyers' Guide and Knitwear Directory; Knitting Times Buyers' Guide Directory; Knitted Outerwear Times Buyer's Guide Directory
Indexed: TTI.
Published by: National Knitwear and Sportswear Association, PO Box 230, Summit, NJ 07902-0230. TEL 212-683-7520, FAX 212-532-0766. Pub. Michael Colangelo.

380.1029 USA ISSN 1061-2114
HF5421
AMERICAN WHOLESALERS AND DISTRIBUTORS DIRECTORY. Text in English. 1992. irreg., latest vol.13, 2004. USD 275 (effective 2004). **Document type:** *Directory, Trade.* **Description:** Contains information on more than 27,000 large and small wholesalers and distributors throughout the U.S and Puerto Rico.
Published by: Gale Group (Subsidiary of: Thomson Corporation), 27500 Drake Rd, Farmington Hills, MI 48331-3535. TEL 248-699-8061, 800-877-4253, FAX 248-699-4253, galeord@gale.com, http://www.gale.com. Ed. Holly Selden.

382.029 USA ISSN 0740-4018
HG4057
AMERICA'S CORPORATE FAMILIES AND INTERNATIONAL AFFILIATES. Text in English. a. (in 3 vols.). USD 1,020 to corporations; USD 895 to libraries (effective 2000). **Description:** Links U.S. parent companies with their foreign subsidiaries and foreign parent companies and their U.S. subsidiaries.
Published by: Dun & Bradstreet (Subsidiary of: Dun & Bradstreet Corporation), c/o Ethan Chazin, Director, Reference Services, Murray Hill, NJ 07094-1218. TEL 973-605-6000.

380.1029 USA ISSN 1080-1227
HG4057
AMERICA'S CORPORATE FINANCE DIRECTORY. Text in English. 1983. a. USD 575 (effective 1999). **Document type:** *Directory.* **Description:** Lists 5,000 leading companies and 17,600 subsidiaries. Entries include information on sales, earnings, assets, liabilities, pension plan and assets, contact information, and US subsidiaries. Each entry also lists up to 23 financial service firms, including insurance brokers, insurers, pension managers, auditors, legal counsel, and master trustees.
Formerly (until 1994): Corporate Finance Bluebook (0740-2546)
Related titles: Magnetic Tape ed.

Published by: LexisNexis (Subsidiary of: LexisNexis North America), PO Box 7587, Charlottesville, VA 22906-7587. TEL 434-972-7600, 800-446-3410, llp.customer.support@lexis-nexis.com, http://www.lexislawpublishing.com.

338.0029 USA ISSN 1057-5642
HG4915
AMERICA'S FINEST COMPANIES✶. Text in English. 1991. a. USD 39.95. stat. **Description:** Lists all US companies with 10 or more straight years of higher earnings and dividends. Provides quality ratings, addresses and other valuable investment information.
Published by: Staton Institute Inc., 2431 Hartmill Ct, Charlotte, NC 28226-6463. TEL 704-365-2122, FAX 704-365-1910, http://www.statoninstitute.com. Ed. Bill Staton. Circ: 33,000.

AMERICA'S PAY-PER-CALL DIRECTORY; a billion dollar baby. see *COMMUNICATIONS—Telephone And Telegraph*

380.1029 USA
AMERICA'S PREMIER COMMUNITY NEWSPAPERS. Text in English. a. USD 110 (effective 2000). **Document type:** *Directory.*
Published by: Business Research Services, Inc., 4701 Sangamore Rd., Ste. S155, Bethesda, MD 20816-2532. TEL 800-845-8420, FAX 202-686-3228. Ed., Pub., R&P Thomas D Johnson.

670.29 FRA
ANNUAIRE FOURNI-LABO PHARMACIE (YEAR); cosmetique et alimentaire. Text in French. a. index. **Description:** For researchers, technicians, laboratory managers and pharmacy industry executives.
Published by: Moreux, 190 bd. Haussmann, Paris, 75008, France. TEL 33-1-44959950, FAX 33-1-49539016, moreux@club-internet.fr.

ANNUARIO DEL PESCE E DELLA PESCA. see *FISH AND FISHERIES*

681.4029 ITA
ANNUARIO OTTICO ITALIANO. Text in Italian. 1970. a. adv. **Document type:** *Directory, Trade.* **Description:** Provides addresses of suppliers and retail sellers of optics, frame, and optical instrument industries in Italy.
Related titles: CD-ROM ed.
Published by: Edizioni Ariminum, Via Negroli 51, Milan, MI 20133, Italy. TEL 39-02-730091, FAX 39-02-717346, welcome@vedere.it, http://www.vedere.it. adv.: color page EUR 1,300. Circ: 15,000 (controlled and free).

ANTIBACTERIAL PRODUCTS AND MARKETS. see *PHARMACY AND PHARMACOLOGY*

670.29 BRA ISSN 0100-9745
ANUARIO DAS INDUSTRIAS. Text in Portuguese. 1952. a. **Document type:** *Directory.*
Published by: Editora Pesquisa e Industria Ltda., Rua Martins Fontes, 230 Andar 1, Centro, Sao Paulo, SP 01050-000, Brazil. TEL 011-259-0333, FAX 011-256-8681.

688.8029 COL ISSN 0121-7968
ANUARIO DEL EMPAQUE. Text in Spanish. 1977. a. free. adv. **Document type:** *Trade.*
Related titles: CD-ROM ed.; Online - full text ed.
Published by: Publicar S.A., Ave. 68, 75-A-50 of. 314,, Apartado Aereo 8010, Santa Fe de Bogota, CUND, Colombia. TEL 57-1-225-5555, FAX 57-1-3115645, colombiaexport@publicor.com, http://www.colombiaexport.com. R&P, Adv. contact Jaime Concha. page USD 2,400. Circ: 18,000.

ANUARIO ESPANOL DE SEGUROS. see *INSURANCE*

338.0029 DEU ISSN 0944-212X
KK64
ANWALT- UND NOTARVERZEICHNIS. Text in German. a. (in 2 vols.). EUR 29.80 (effective 2005). **Document type:** *Directory, Trade.*
Former titles (until 1992): Anwalts- und Notarverzeichnis der Bundesrepublik Deutschland (0172-7621); (until 1978): Anwalts- und Notarverzeichnis der Bundesrepublik (0341-2547)
Related titles: CD-ROM ed.
Published by: Verlag Dr. Otto Schmidt KG, Gustav-Heinemann-Ufer 58, Cologne, 50968, Germany. TEL 49-221-93738460, FAX 49-221-93738943, info@otto-schmidt.de, http://www.otto-schmidt.de.

391.029 NZL ISSN 1175-1681
APPAREL TRADE DIRECTORY. Text in English. 1969. a. NZD 58 (effective 2000). adv. **Document type:** *Directory, Trade.*
Formerly: Apparel Buyers Guide Year Book
Published by: Apparel Publishing Ltd., Dominion Rd, PO Box 56071, Auckland 3, New Zealand. TEL 64-9-3065860, FAX 64-9-3030414, apparel@iprolink.co.nz. Ed. Val Blomfield. Pub., R&P, Adv. contact Paul Blomfield. Circ: 2,000.

380.1029 USA
APPLIANCE MANUFACTURER BUYERS GUIDE. Text in English. 1953. a. USD 25. adv. **Document type:** *Directory.*

Published by: B N P Media, 755 W Big Beaver Rd, Ste 1000, Troy, MI 48084-4903. TEL 248-362-3700, FAX 248-362-0317, http://www.bnp.com, http://www.bnpmedia.com/. Ed. Norman C Remich. Pub. Linda Calkins. Adv. contact Tim Johnson. Circ: 35,200.

381.029 USA ISSN 1553-3441
AQUATICS INTERNATIONAL DIRECTORY. Text in English. a. adv. charts; illus.; tr.lit. back issues avail. **Document type:** *Directory.* **Description:** Contains a buyer's guide and listing by type of product, manufacturers' brand names, key executives and Web sites. Company listings provide addresses, phone and fax numbers, e-mail addresses, number of employees and contact names.
Related titles: ◆ Supplement to: Aquatics International. ISSN 1058-7039.
Published by: Hanley-Wood, LLC (Subsidiary of: J.P. Morgan Chase & Co.), 6222 Wilshire Blvd., Ste. 600, Los Angeles, CA 90048-5100. TEL 323-801-4900, FAX 323-801-4902, tjackson@hanleywood.com, http://www.aquaticsintl.com, http://www.hanleywood.com. Ed. P Lakbawalla. Pub., R&P Jules Field. Adv. contact Karen Cavallo.

382.029 GBR ISSN 0958-2339
ARAB BUYERS' GUIDE TO BRITISH INDUSTRY. Text in Arabic. 1951. a. adv. **Document type:** *Directory.* **Description:** Promotes British and other products or services in the Middle East and North Africa.
Published by: Exact Communications Ltd., First Floor Chambers, 1101 Warwick Rd, Acocks Green, Birmingham, Worcs B27 6RA, United Kingdom. TEL 44-121-707-7272, FAX 44-121-707-2288. Ed. Jonathan Hunt. Pub. Vitek Aukstolis. Adv. contact Michael Burgess.

381.029 GBR
ARAB TRADE DIRECTORY. Text in Arabic, English, French. biennial. USD 120. adv. **Document type:** *Directory.*
Published by: New Product Newsletter Co. Ltd., 1a Chesterfield St, London, W1X 7HF, United Kingdom.

720.29 USA
ARCHITECTS CATALOG. Text in English. 1993. a. free. adv. **Document type:** *Directory.* **Description:** Lists over 6200 national and international building product manufacturers organized by product type and firm name.
Published by: Architects Catalog, Inc., 1275 Post Rd, Ste 200A, Fairfield, CT 06430. TEL 203-256-1600, FAX 203-254-8166, arcat@arcat.com, http://arcat.com. Ed. Leslie Jannott. Circ: 40,000 (controlled).

381.029 BRA
ARGENTINA COMPANY HANDBOOK. Text in Portuguese. a. **Document type:** *Directory.*
Published by: I M F Editora Ltda., Av Erasmo Braga, 227, Grupo 404, Centro, Rio De Janeiro, RJ 20020-000, Brazil. TEL 55-21-240-4347, FAX 55-21-262-7570.

380.1029 USA
ARIZONA BUSINESS CREDIT DIRECTORY. Text in English. a. USD 1,100 combined subscription print, online & CD-ROM eds. (effective 2004 & 2005). back issues avail. **Document type:** *Directory.* **Description:** Contains credit ratings and other valuable information on all businesses within Arizona. Includes company name & address, phone & fax numbers, key executive names & titles, lines of business, years in business, number of employees, estimated annual sales, volume credit rating code, and corporate linkage information.
Related titles: CD-ROM ed.; Diskette ed.; E-mail ed.; Fax ed.; Magnetic Tape ed.; Online - full text ed.
Published by: American Business Directories (Subsidiary of: American Business Information, Inc.), 5711 S 86th Circle, P O Box 27347, Omaha, NE 68127. TEL 402-593-4600, 888-946-9377, 877-708-3844, FAX 402-331-5481, sales@directoriesusa.com, http://www.directoriesusa.com.

338.0029 USA ISSN 1046-3011
HC107.A6
ARIZONA BUSINESS DIRECTORY. Text in English. 1988. a. USD 1,100 combined subscription print, online & CD-ROM eds. (effective 2004 & 2005). index. back issues avail. **Document type:** *Directory.* **Description:** Includes all businesses in the state compiled from the yellow pages and telephone-verified. Each listing includes company name, complete address, phone number, name of owner, manager, and employee size, sales volume codes, credit rating codes.
Related titles: CD-ROM ed.; Diskette ed.; E-mail ed.; Fax ed.; Magnetic Tape ed.; Online - full text ed.
Published by: American Business Directories (Subsidiary of: American Business Information, Inc.), 5711 S 86th Circle, P O Box 27347, Omaha, NE 68127. TEL 402-593-4600, 888-946-9377, 877-708-3844, FAX 402-331-5481, karen.peters@infousa.com, sales@directoriesusa.com, http://www.directoriesusa.com.

670.29 USA ISSN 1071-3514
T12
ARIZONA INDUSTRIAL DIRECTORY; manufacturers, wholesalers. Text in English. 1982. a., latest 2001. USD 123 (effective 2001). **Document type:** *Directory.* **Description:** Provides information on over 8,400 manufacturers in Arizona.
Formerly (until 1988): Arizona Directory of Manufacturers

B

Related titles: CD-ROM ed.: USD 503 (effective 2000); Diskette ed.
Published by: Greater Phoenix Chamber of Commerce, 201 N Central Ave 2700, Phoenix, AZ 85073. TEL 602-254-5521, FAX 602-495-8913, http://www.phoenixchamber.com. Circ: 5,000.

670   USA   ISSN 1525-4070
HF5065.A6
ARIZONA MANUFACTURERS DIRECTORY. Text in English. USD 90 (effective 2000). **Document type:** *Directory.*
Related titles: CD-ROM ed.: USD 355 (effective 2000).
Published by: Manufacturers' News, Inc., 1633 Central St, Evanston, IL 60201. TEL 847-864-7000, 888-752-5200, FAX 847-332-1100, info@manufacturersnews.com, sales@mninfo.com, http://www.manufacturersnews.com. Ed. Frank Lambing.

338.0029   USA   ISSN 1048-7190
HF5065.A8
ARKANSAS BUSINESS DIRECTORY. Text in English. 1988. a. USD 1,100 combined subscription print, online & CD-ROM eds. (effective 2004 & 2005). index. back issues avail. **Document type:** *Directory.* **Description:** Includes all businesses in the state compiled from the yellow pages and telephone-verified. Each listing includes company name, complete address, telephone number, name of owner, manager, and employee size, sales volume codes, and credit rating codes.
Related titles: CD-ROM ed.; Diskette ed.; E-mail ed.; Fax ed.; Magnetic Tape ed.; Online - full text ed.
Published by: American Business Directories (Subsidiary of: American Business Information, Inc.), 5711 S 86th Circle, P O Box 27347, Omaha, NE 68127. TEL 402-593-4600, 888-946-9377, 877-708-3844, FAX 402-331-5481, karen.peters@infousa.com, sales@directoriesusa.com, http://www.directoriesusa.com.

670.29   USA
ARKANSAS DIRECTORY OF MANUFACTURERS. Text in English. 1955. a. USD 75 (effective 1999). adv. illus. **Document type:** *Directory.* **Description:** Profiles approximately 2,600 manufacturers. Includes alphabetical, geographical, exporters, product index, SIC and parent company sections.
Formerly: Directory of Manufacturers in Arkansas (0361-2996)
Related titles: CD-ROM ed.
Published by: Industrial Development Foundation, PO Box 1784, Little Rock, AR 72203. TEL 501-682-7341. Ed. Patricia F Brown. Circ: 5,400. **Dist. by:** Manufacturers' News, Inc., 1633 Central St, Evanston, IL 60201. TEL 847-864-7000.

670.29   USA   ISSN 1082-0264
HF5065.A8
ARKANSAS MANUFACTURERS REGISTER. Text in English. a. USD 74 (effective 2001). adv. **Document type:** *Directory.* **Description:** Profiles 4077 companies in five sections: by product, alphabetically, by city, by SIC, and by parent company.
Related titles: CD-ROM ed.: USD 310 (effective 2001); Diskette ed.: USD 345.
Published by: Manufacturers' News, Inc., 1633 Central St, Evanston, IL 60201. TEL 847-864-7000, 888-752-5200, FAX 847-332-1100, info@manufacturersnews.com, sales@mninfo.com, http://www.manufacturers.com, http://www.manufacturersnews.com. Ed. Steve Garland.

ARKANSAS PRESS ASSOCIATION DIRECTORY. see *JOURNALISM*

381.029 720   PRT
ARQUITOP; directory of architects in Portugal. Text in Portuguese. 1990. a. adv. **Document type:** *Directory.* **Description:** Provides names and addresses of 5000 active architects and planners, and a summary of the activity of the top 1000 architects with their ranking.
Related titles: Diskette ed.
Published by: Construdata S.A., Rua Eira, 1, Alges de Cima, Lisbon, 1495, Portugal. TEL 351-1-4103435, FAX 351-1-4109677, construdata@mail.telpac.pt. Pub. Jose Geada. Adv. contact Margarida Arauyo. color page GBP 1,000. Circ: 10,000.

670.29   GBR
ASIA-PACIFIC GUIDE TO MACHINE TOOL TECHNOLOGY. Text in English. 1996. a. GBP 84; GBP 89 foreign. **Document type:** *Directory, Trade.*
Formerly: Asia Pacific Directory of World Machine Tool Technology (1366-9753)
Published by: Turret R A I plc, Armstrong House, 38 Market Sq, Uxbridge, Middx UB8 1TG, United Kingdom. TEL 44-1895-454545, FAX 44-1895-454647.

670.29   GBR
ASIA-PACIFIC GUIDE TO SURFACE TREATMENT TECHNOLOGY. Text in English. 199?. a. GBP 84; GBP 89 foreign. **Document type:** *Directory, Trade.*
Formerly: Asia Pacific Guide to World Surface Treatment Technology (1365-943X)
Published by: Turret R A I plc, Armstrong House, 38 Market Sq, Uxbridge, Middx UB8 1TG, United Kingdom. TEL 44-1895-454545, FAX 44-1895-454647.

ASIA - PACIFIC MARKETS; a guide to company and industry information sources. see *BUSINESS AND ECONOMICS— International Commerce*

ASIA PACIFIC SHIPPING DIRECTORY. see *TRANSPORTATION—Ships And Shipping*

ASIAN AND AUSTRALASIAN COMPANIES. see *BUSINESS AND ECONOMICS—Abstracting, Bibliographies, Statistics*

381.029   GBR   ISSN 0961-7132
ASIAN TRADER. Text in English, Gujarati, Urdu. 1985. fortn. GBP 50; GBP 3 newsstand/cover (effective 1999). adv. back issues avail. **Document type:** *Trade.* **Description:** Magazine for independent, Asian-owned retail outlets; carries trade and information, supported by all major manufacturers in UK.
Published by: (Garavi Gujarat Group), Asian Trade Publications Ltd., Garavi Gujarat House, 1-2 Silex St, London, SE1 0DW, United Kingdom. TEL 44-171-928-1234, FAX 44-171-261-0055, marl@gujarat.co.uk. Ed. K R Solanki. Adv. contact Mark Borland. Circ: 45,713 (controlled).

380.1029   SLV
ASOCIACION SALVADORENA DE INDUSTRIALES DIRECTORIO DE ASOCIADOS. Text in Spanish. a. **Document type:** *Directory.*
Published by: Asociacion Salvadorena de Industriales, Apartado Postal No. (06) 48, Calles Roma y Liverpool, Colonia Roma, San Salvador, El Salvador.

338.0029   IRL
ASPECT TOP 2500 IRISH COMPANIES. Text in English. 1982. a. adv. back issues avail. **Document type:** *Corporate.*
Former titles: Private Research Top 2000 Irish Companies; Aspect Top 2000 Irish Companies
Related titles: Diskette ed.
Published by: Private Research Ltd., Coliemore House, Coliemore Rd., Dalkey, Co. Dublin, Ireland. TEL 353-1-2848911, FAX 353-1-2048177, info@privateresearch.ie, http://www.privateresearch.ie.

381.029   GBR   ISSN 0260-2474
ASPIS; the classified Greek commercial directory. Text in English, Greek. 1980. a. illus. **Document type:** *Directory.*
Published by: Aspis Publications, 89 Tottenham Ln, London, N8 9BE, United Kingdom.

380.1029   IND
ASSAM DIRECTORY & TEA AREAS HANDBOOK. Text in English. 1928. a., latest vol.66, 2000. INR 1,850, USD 50 (effective 2001). adv. bk.rev. **Document type:** *Directory.* **Description:** Directory of tea producing gardens, tea companies, and tea exporters of India, Bangladesh, Sri Landa, Kenya, and Nepal.
Formerly: Assam Directory of Tea Areas
Published by: Assam Review Publishing Co., 27-A Waterloo St., Kolkata, West Bengal 700 069, India. TEL 33-248-2251, teknokom@satyam.net.in. Ed. G.L. Banerjee. Pub. G L Banerjee. Adv. contact U Bhattacharjee. B&W page USD 150; trim 245 x 180. Circ: 7,500.

338.0029   MWI
ASSOCIATED CHAMBERS OF COMMERCE AND INDUSTRY OF MALAWI. INDUSTRIAL AND TRADE DIRECTORY. Text in English. 1974. biennial (6th 1982). MWK 5. adv. **Document type:** *Directory, Trade.*
Formerly: Industrial Directory and Brand Names Index of Malawi
Published by: Associated Chamber of Commerce and Industry of Malawi, PO Box 258, Blantyre, Malawi. TEL 265-671988, FAX 265-671147, TELEX 43992, mcci@eomw.net. Circ: 1,000.

ASSOCIATION OF M B AS ADDRESS BOOK. see *BUSINESS AND ECONOMICS—Management*

668.4029   FRA
ASSOCIATION POUR LA PROMOTION DE LA PROFESSION DU CAOUTCHOUC ET DE PLASTIQUES. GUIDE. Text in French. 1978. biennial.
Former titles: Union des industries et de la Distribution des Plastiques et du Caoutchouc. Guide; Syndicat General des Commerces et Industries du Caoutchouc et des Plastiques. Guide (0224-2435)
Published by: Association pour la Promotion de la Profession du Caoutchouc et de Plastiques, 37-39 rue de Pommard, Paris, 75012, France. TEL 33-1-55782898, FAX 33-1-55782899. Circ: 3,000.

338.0029   CAN   ISSN 1186-9798
ASSOCIATIONS CANADA; the directory of associations in Canada. Text in English. 1991. a. CND 325 to libraries (effective 2005); for foreign subscr. rates, please contact publisher. **Document type:** *Directory.* **Description:** Lists 19,000 Canadian trade, professional and special-interest organizations and 1800 international groups with Canadian interests.
Incorporates (1973-1998): Directory of Associations in Canada (0316-0734)
Related titles: CD-ROM ed.: ISSN 1209-3726. CND 339; Online - full content ed.; Online - full text ed.

Published by: Micromedia ProQuest (Subsidiary of: ProQuest Information & Learning), 20 Victoria St, Toronto, ON M5C 2N8, Canada. TEL 416-362-5211, 800-387-2689, FAX 416-362-6161, info@micromedia.ca, http://www.micromedia.ca/Directories/Associations.htm. Ed. Mrs. Beata Matlok.

380.1029   USA   ISSN 1054-4070
HD2425
ASSOCIATIONS YELLOW BOOK; who's who at the leading U.S. trade and professional associations. Text in English. 1991. s-a. USD 295; USD 280 renewals (effective 2005). illus. index. **Document type:** *Directory, Trade.* **Description:** Lists 44,000 key management personnel at the leading US trade and professional associations.
Related titles: CD-ROM ed.; Online - full text ed. —CCC.
Published by: Leadership Directories, Inc, 104 Fifth Ave, 2nd Fl, New York, NY 10011. TEL 212-627-4140, FAX 212-645-0931, info@leadershipdirectories.com, http://www.leadershipdirectories.com/ayb.htm. Ed. Chris Muntone. Pub. David J Hurvits.

384.63029   CAN   ISSN 0826-2896
ATLANTIC LEGAL TELEPHONE DIRECTORY. Text in English. 1985. a. CND 25 per issue (effective 2005). adv. 328 p./no.; **Document type:** *Directory.*
Published by: Canada Law Book Inc., 240 Edward St, Aurora, ON L4G 3S9, Canada. TEL 905-841-6472, 800-263-3269, FAX 905-841-5085, b.loney@canadalawbook.ca, http://www.canadalawbook.ca. Adv. contact Colleen Austin TEL 905-841-6472.

380.1029 071.1   USA   ISSN 1203-5157
HF5072.A85
ATLANTIC PROVINCES BUSINESS DIRECTORY. Text in English. 1996. a. USD 1,100 combined subscription print, online & CD-ROM eds. (effective 2004 & 2005). back issues avail. **Document type:** *Directory.* **Description:** Canadian business directory for the Atlantic Provinces of Newfoundland, Nova Scotia, New Brunswick and Prince Edward.
Related titles: CD-ROM ed.; Diskette ed.; E-mail ed.; Fax ed.; Magnetic Tape ed.; Online - full text ed.
Published by: American Business Directories (Subsidiary of: American Business Information, Inc.), 5711 S 86th Circle, P O Box 27347, Omaha, NE 68127. TEL 402-593-4600, 888-946-9377, 877-708-3844, FAX 402-331-5481, sales@directoriesusa.com, http://www.directoriesusa.com.

AUDARENA STADIUM INTERNATIONAL GUIDE & FACILITY BUYERS GUIDE. see *THEATER*

AUDIOTEX DIRECTORY & BUYER'S GUIDE. see *COMMUNICATIONS—Telephone And Telegraph*

684.0029   AUS
AUSTRALASIAN FURNISHING DIRECTORY (YEAR). Text in English. a. AUD 55 in Australia & New Zealand; AUD 60 elsewhere. adv. **Document type:** *Directory, Trade.* **Description:** Provides information on Australasian furniture, soft furnishings and floorcoverings, retailers, manufacturers, suppliers, and interior designers. Provides the names of key people, addresses, and phone numbers.
Published by: Furnishing Publications Pty. Ltd., Courtyard Monash Homaker Centre, 1207 Prices Hwy, Clayton, VIC 3168, Australia. TEL 61-3-9562-9177, FAX 61-3-9562-9477. Ed., Pub., R&P, Adv. contact Keith Dunn.

665.5029   AUS
AUSTRALASIAN OIL & GAS EXPLORERS DIRECTORY. Text in English. 1991. s-a. AUD 60 for 6 mos. for 1 ed.; AUD 95 for 2 eds. (effective 2000). **Document type:** *Directory.* **Description:** Provides contact details for oil and gas explorers and technical service companies involved in Australia, New Zealand and Papua New Guinea.
Related titles: Diskette ed.: AUD 200 for 6 mos. (effective 2000).
Published by: Business Intelligence (W.A.), PO Box 210, Claremont, W.A. 6010, Australia. TEL 61-8-9448-7665, FAX 61-8-9447-5011, kaskade@compuserve.com, busint@wantree.com.au. Ed., Pub. Steve Whitfield. R&P, Adv. contact Gabi Keast. Circ: 300.

629.1029   AUS   ISSN 1321-4012
AUSTRALIAN AEROSPACE INDUSTRY CAPABILITY DIRECTORY∗ . Text in English. 1994. irreg. AUD 10. **Document type:** *Directory.* **Description:** Comprehensive reference on Australian companies offering products and services to the aerospace industry. Originally designed for display at international air shows.
Published by: (Australia. Department of Industry, Science and Technology), A P N Business Information Group (Subsidiary of: A P N News & Media Ltd), 46-50 Porter St, Prahran, VIC 3181, Australia. TEL 61-3-9245-7777, FAX 61-3-9529-2391, info@apnbig.com.au, http://www.apnbig.com.au/.

AUSTRALIAN AND NEW ZEALAND WINE INDUSTRY DIRECTORY. see *BEVERAGES*

B

380.1029   AUS
THE AUSTRALIAN DIRECT MARKETING DIRECTORY. Text in English. a. AUD 149 (effective 2000). **Document type:** *Directory, Abstract/Index.* **Description:** Contains entries of industry companies including company name, address, telephone, fax, key personnel, activity description, major clients, primary market served and E-mail address.
Related titles: Online - full content ed.: AUD 95 (effective 2000).
Published by: Bookman Press Pty Ltd, Lu 10, 227 Collins St, Melbourne, VIC 3000, Australia. TEL 61-3-96542000, FAX 61-3-96542290, bookman@bookman.com.au, http://www.bookman.com.au.

610.29   AUS   ISSN 1444-4399
AUSTRALIAN HEALTH AND MEDICAL EXPORTS✱. Text in English. 1992. a. AUD 85 (effective 2000). **Document type:** *Directory.* **Description:** Outlines exporters of Australian health and medical equipment and services. Indicates areas of expertise, contact details, where they export to, etc.
Formerly: (until 1997): Australian Health and Medical Industry Guide (1323-0824)
Published by: (Austrade), A P N Business Information Group (Subsidiary of: A P N News & Media Ltd), Level 1, 28 Riddell Pde, Elsternwick, VIC 3185, Australia. TEL 61-3-92457800, FAX 61-3-92457840, info@apnbig.com.au, http://www.apnbig.com.au/. Circ: 8,000.

340.029   AUS   ISSN 0155-297X
AUSTRALIAN LEGAL DIRECTORY. Text in English. 1977. a. AUD 105; AUD 150 foreign. **Document type:** *Directory.*
Published by: (Law Council of Australia), Australian Document Exchange Pty. Ltd., 153 Phillip St. 1st Fl., Sydney, NSW 2000, Australia. TEL 61-2-2212677, FAX 61-2-2212372. Ed. Bruce Rose. Circ: 2,000 (paid).

AUSTRALIAN MARKET GUIDE. see *BUSINESS AND ECONOMICS—Investments*

658.8029   AUS
THE AUSTRALIAN WRITER'S MARKETPLACE. Text in English. a. AUD 39.95 for both Print & Online eds. (effective 2000). **Document type:** *Directory, Bibliography.* **Description:** Contains contact names of editors, Tips and hints, guide to Australian literary agents, 215 literary awards and competitions; markets for books, poetry, articles, short stories, reviews, interviews, interviews, fillers and scriptwriters.
Related titles: Online - full content ed.
Published by: Bookman Press Pty Ltd, Lu 10, 227 Collins St, Melbourne, VIC 3000, Australia. TEL 61-3-96542000, FAX 61-3-96542290, bookman@bookman.com.au, http://www.bookman.com.au. Ed. Rhonda Whitton.

338.3475029   TWN   ISSN 1560-7380
AUTO PARTS & ACCESSORIES BUYERS' GUIDE. Text in Chinese. a. USD 25 per issue (effective 2005). **Document type:** *Directory, Trade.* **Description:** Covers suppliers of automobile and motorcycle parts and accessories in Taiwan and elsewhere in East and Southeast Asia.
Formerly: Auto and Motorcycle Parts Buyers' Guide (1027-7854)
Related titles: CD-ROM ed.
Published by: Interface Global Taiwan Co., Ltd., PO Box 173-12, Taipei, 116, Taiwan. TEL 886-2-29180500, FAX 886-2-89119381, service@asiatrademart.com, http://www.tradewinds.com.tw/05_pro_05.htm#3, http://www.asiatrademart.com. Ed. Daniel Foong. Pub. Herbert Chen. R&P Donald Shapiro. Adv. contact Melody Lin TEL 886-2-2351-3180. Circ: 8,000. **Subscr. in U.S. to:** Trade Winds Inc., PO Box 820519, Dallas, TX 75382. TEL 877-861-1188, FAX 972-699-1189, twinds8888@aol.com.

338.4762922   USA
AUTOMOTIVE RECYCLERS ASSOCIATION. MEMBERSHIP DIRECTORY AND BUYER'S GUIDE. Text in English. a. USD 150 to non-members (effective 2000). adv. back issues avail. **Document type:** *Directory.*
Former titles: Automotive Recyclers Buyers Guide. Membership Roster; Automotive Dismantlers and Recyclers. Buyers Guide - Membership Roster
Published by: Automotive Recyclers Association, 3975 Fair Ridge Dr, Ste 20 N, Fairfax, VA 22033-2924. TEL 703-385-1001, FAX 703-385-1494, http://www.a-r-a.org/. Ed. Tammy Haire. Circ: 1,600.

AUTOPART; a directory of companies supplying the motor trade. see *TRANSPORTATION—Automobiles*

AUTOTRADE. see *TRANSPORTATION—Automobiles*

AVIATION BUYERS DIRECTORY. see *AERONAUTICS AND SPACE FLIGHT*

380.1029   USA
B B I A MEMBERSHIP AND PRODUCT INFORMATION GUIDE. Text in English. a. free.
Published by: Billiard and Bowling Institute of America, 200 Castlewood Dr, North Palm Beach, FL 33408. TEL 407-840-1120. Ed. Sebastian Dicasoli. Circ: 2,000.

338.0029   SGP
B C A DIRECTORY OF REGISTERED CONTRACTORS (YEAR). Text in English. a., latest 2000. SGD 46.20 domestic; USD 100 foreign; SGD 41.20 newsstand/cover domestic (effective 2001). **Document type:** *Directory, Government.* **Description:** Includes a comprehensive listing of contractors and suppliers registered with CIDB, the Expenditure and Procurement Policies Unit and the Pharmaceutical Department.
Formerly: C I D B Directory of Registered Contractors (Year)
Published by: Building and Construction Authority, 5 Maxwell Rd, No 08-00 MND Complex Tower Block, Singapore, 069110, Singapore. TEL 65-3257720, FAX 65-3254800, http://www.bca.gov.sg/.

380.1029   CAN   ISSN 0843-8021
B C DAIRY DIRECTORY. Text in English. 1982. a. CND 20 (effective 1998 & 1999). adv. **Document type:** *Directory.* **Description:** Edited for commercial and purebred dairy producers and the dairy industry in British Columbia.
—CISTI.
Address: RR 1, Boothe Rd, Naramata, BC V0H 1N0, Canada. TEL 250-496-5707, FAX 250-496-5132. Ed. Karin W McCarty. Pub. Mike McCarty. Circ: 1,400 (controlled).

B C LABOUR DIRECTORY. see *BUSINESS AND ECONOMICS—Labor And Industrial Relations*

380.1029   GBR
B F S S COUNTRY SPORTS HANDBOOK AND TRADE DIRECTORY. Text in English. 1978. a. adv. bk.rev. illus. **Document type:** *Directory.* **Description:** Supplies information on country sports.
Former titles: Country Sports Directory; (until 1989): B F S S Members Handbook; (until 1988): B F S S Reference Book; British Field Sports Society. Annual Journal
Published by: British Field Sports Society, Old Town Hall, 367 Kennington Rd, London, SE11 4PT, United Kingdom. TEL 44-171-928-4742, FAX 44-171-928-4742, info@bfss.org, http://www.bfss.org. Ed. Derek Bingham. Circ: 80,000.

B H A B INFORMATION HANDBOOK. see *AERONAUTICS AND SPACE FLIGHT*

380.1029   GBR
B H F DIRECTORY. Text in English. a. free. adv. **Document type:** *Directory, Trade.* **Description:** Lists members, officers, products, and services.
Published by: British Hardware Federation, Edgbaston, British Hardware Federation, 225 Bristol Rd, Birmingham, Warks B5 7UB, United Kingdom. TEL 44-121-446-6688, FAX 44-121-446-5215. Ed. John Morgan. Pub., R&P Michael I Weedon. Adv. contact Kevin Toole. Circ: 10,000.

B M A MEMBERSHIP DIRECTORY AND RESOURCE GUIDE. see *ADVERTISING AND PUBLIC RELATIONS*

B M R A RUBBER AND POLYURETHANE DIRECTORY. see *RUBBER*

B N A'S DIRECTORY OF STATE & FEDERAL COURTS, JUDGES, AND CLERKS. see *LAW*

BABY SHOP; the magazine for independent juvenile product retailers. see *GIFTWARE AND TOYS*

BACON'S INTERNET MEDIA DIRECTORY. see *COMPUTERS—Internet*

070.5029   USA   ISSN 1089-098X
Z6951
BACON'S MEDIA CALENDAR DIRECTORY. Variant title: Media Calendar Directory. Text in English. 1982. a. USD 395 (effective 2005). **Document type:** *Directory, Trade.* **Description:** Editorial calendars and profiles of major newspapers and magazines.
Formerly: (until 1993): Bacon's Media Alerts (0736-4644)
Published by: Bacon's Information, Inc., 332 S Michigan Ave, Ste 900, Chicago, IL 60604. TEL 312-922-2400, 800-621-0561, FAX 312-987-9773, directories@bacons.com, http://www.bacons.com. Pub. Ruth McFarland. R&P Ruth Cox McFarland TEL 312-986-2728. Circ: 2,000.

070.5029   USA
BACON'S NEWSPAPER - MAGAZINE DIRECTORY. Text in English. 1952. a. (in 2 vols.). USD 395 (effective 2005). **Document type:** *Directory, Trade.* **Description:** Directory of print media in US, Canada, Mexico and the Caribbean.
Formerly: (until 1992): Bacon's Publicity Checker (0162-3125)
Published by: Bacon's Information, Inc., 332 S Michigan Ave, Ste 900, Chicago, IL 60604. TEL 312-922-2400, 800-621-0561, FAX 312-987-9773, directories@bacons.com, http://www.bacons.com. Pub. Ruth McFarland. R&P Ruth Cox McFarland TEL 312-986-2728. Circ: 10,200.

BACON'S RADIO - T V - CABLE DIRECTORY. see *COMMUNICATIONS—Television And Cable*

799.2029   GBR   ISSN 0067-2947
BAILY'S HUNTING DIRECTORY. Text in English. 1897. a. GBP 34.95 in Europe (effective 2003). adv. bk.rev. 576 p./no.; **Document type:** *Directory.* **Description:** Contains details on hunts and hunting throughout the U.K., Europe, the U.S., and Canada.
Published by: Pearson Publishing Group, Chesterton Mill, French's Rd, Cambridge, CB4 3NP, United Kingdom. TEL 44-1223-350555, FAX 44-1223-356484, bailys@pearson.co.uk, info@pearson.co.uk. Eds. Karen Alexander, Maura Rutter. Pub. Mark Pearson. R&P Maura Rutter. Adv. contact Barney White Spunner. Circ: 1,750.

BAKING INDUSTRY DIRECTORY. see *FOOD AND FOOD INDUSTRIES—Bakers And Confectioners*

BAKING, SNACK DIRECTORY & BUYERS GUIDE. see *AGRICULTURE—Feed, Flour And Grain*

380.1029   RUS
BALTIC FINANCIAL DIRECTORY. Text in English. a. **Document type:** *Directory, Trade.* **Description:** Contains profiles and performance data for all major banks, brokers and listed companies in the Baltics; also includes contact information in background information, country profiles with recent macro-economic indicators, sector overviews, privatization information and specialist chapters on regulatory affairs.
Published by: (Baltic News Service EST), Interfax Ltd., 1-ya Tverskaya-Yamskaya 2, Moscow, 127006, Russian Federation. TEL 7-095-2509840, FAX 7-095-2509727. **Dist. by:** Interfax Deutschland GmbH, Industriestraße 6, Kronberg/Tx 61476 , Germany. TEL 49-61-7361369, FAX 49-61-7361206; Interfax Europe Ltd., 1st Fl, 50 Hans Crescent, Knightsbridge, London SW1X 0N, United Kingdom. TEL 44-20-7581-5550, FAX 44-20-7581-4490; Interfax America, Inc., 3025 S Parker Rd, Ste 737, Aurora, CO 80014-2925. TEL 303-825-1510, 852-2537-2262, FAX 303-825-1513, 852-2537-2264, america@interfax.com, http://www.interfax.com.

381.029   IND
BANGLADESH DIRECTORY AND YEAR BOOK. Text in English. 1976. a. INR 75, USD 15. **Document type:** *Directory.*
Published by: Associated Book Promoters, 9-2 A Ekbalpur Ln., Kolkata, West Bengal 700 023, India.

382.029   BRB
BARBADOS. EXPORT DIRECTORY. Text in English. 1982. irreg. free. adv. **Document type:** *Directory.*
Published by: Export Promotion Corporation, Pelican Industrial Park, St Michael, Barbados. TEL 246-427-5752, FAX 246-427-5867.

HET BELGISCH A G F ADRESBOEK. (Aardappelen - Groenten - Fruit) see *AGRICULTURE—Agricultural Economics*

BENN'S MEDIA: EUROPE. see *JOURNALISM*

BENN'S MEDIA: U K. see *JOURNALISM*

BENN'S MEDIA: WORLD. see *JOURNALISM*

382.029   DEU   ISSN 0935-3771
BERLINER STADTADRESSBUCH. BAND 3: HANDELSREGISTER-VERZEICHNIS✱. Text in German. 1968. a. adv. index. **Document type:** *Directory, Trade.* Berliner Handelsregister Verzeichnis (0067-6063)
Published by: Adressbuch-Gesellschaft Berlin mbH, Schloßstr 127, Olching, 82140, Germany. TEL 49-8142-30734, FAX 49-8142-40391.

380.1029   USA
BEST 900 NUMBERS. Text in English. 1991. a. USD 3.50; USD 4.50 in Canada. **Description:** Guide to "900" (dial-it, pay-per-call, audiotex) services in the United States. Explains the types of 900 services, how they work, who operates them, and typical charges.
Published by: (Philip Leif Group), St. Martin's Press (Subsidiary of: Holtzbrink Publishers), 175 Fifth Ave, New York, NY 10010.

THE BEVERAGE MARKETING DIRECTORY (YEAR). see *BEVERAGES*

BIG BOAT. see *SPORTS AND GAMES—Boats And Boating*

306.446029   USA
BILINGUAL SERVICES DIRECTORY. Text in English. 1989. a. free. adv. **Document type:** *Directory.* **Description:** Features display ads and listings of commercial, social and professional services organizations in the Fox Valley area that employ one or more Spanish speaking employees.
Address: 1135 Sunbury Rd, South Elgin, IL 60177. TEL 708-697-3533, FAX 708-697-3533. Ed. Laura Carillo Barth. adv.: B&W page USD 500; trim 10 x 7. Circ: 10,000.

338.0029　　　　USA
BILLBOARD INTERNATIONAL DISC - TAPE DIRECTORY. (No issue in 2002) Text in English. a. (May). USD 90 (effective 2001). reprint service avail. from PQC. **Document type:** *Directory.* **Description:** Professional services and supplies for CD, record and video manufacturers, audio and videotape manufacturers, video program suppliers and buyers, video music producers and production facilities.
Former titles: Billboard's International Directory of Manufacturing and Packaging; Billboard's Audio-Video-Tape Sourcebook; Billboard International Tape Directory (0090-645X)
Related titles: Microfilm ed.
Published by: Billboard Directories (Subsidiary of: V N U Business Publications), 575 Prospect Street, Lakewood, NJ 08701. TEL 732-363-4156, 800-344-7119, FAX 732-363-0338, ndavis@bpicomm.com, http://orderbillboard.com/moreinfo.cfm?Product_ID=32, http://www.billboard.com.

658.8029　　　　USA　　　　ISSN 1098-3791
ML18
BILLBOARD RECORD RETAILING DIRECTORY. Text in English. 1991. a. (Mar.). USD 216 (effective 2003). adv. **Document type:** *Directory, Trade.* **Description:** Contains more than 7,000 updated listings of independent and chain record stores, chain headquarters, e-retailers, audio book retailers.
Published by: Billboard Directories (Subsidiary of: V N U Business Publications), 575 Prospect Street, Lakewood, NJ 08701. TEL 732-363-4156, 800-344-7119, FAX 732-363-0338, ndavis@bpicomm.com, http://orderbillboard.com/cgi-bin/F4F253E0/mac/additmdtl.mac/showItemDetail?item=BLBDD23&qtyA=0&phsO=N&desc=2003%20Record%20Retailing%20Directory&drps, http://www.billboard.com. adv.: B&W page USD 1,100; trim 9 x 6. Circ: 1,150. **Subscr. to:** V N U Business Publications, PO Box 2011, Marion, OH 43306-811137202. TEL 800-745-8922.

338.0029　　　　GBR
BINSTED'S BOTTLING DIRECTORY (YEAR). Text in English. a. GBP 95 per vol. includes CD-ROM (effective Sep. 2002); GBP 100 per vol. includes CD-ROM (effective Sep. 2003). adv. **Document type:** *Directory, Trade.*
Related titles: CD-ROM ed.
Published by: Binsted Group Plc, Attwood House, Mansfield Park, Four Marks, Alton, Hants GU34 5PZ, United Kingdom. TEL 44-1420-568900, FAX 44-1420-565994, info@binstedgroup.com, http://www.binstedpublications.com/html/directoriesandspecials/bottlingdirectory.asp, http://www.binsteadgroup.com/. Ed., Pub. Edward C Binsted. Adv. contact Andrew Flew.

BINSTED'S DIRECTORY OF FOOD TRADE MARKS AND BRAND NAMES. see *FOOD AND FOOD INDUSTRIES*

BIOCOMMERCE DATA'S BUSINESS PROFILE SERIES. VOLUME 1: THE U S BIOTECHNOLOGY DIRECTORY. see *BIOLOGY—Biotechnology*

BIOCOMMERCE DATA'S BUSINESS PROFILE SERIES. VOLUME 2. THE EUROPEAN BIOTECHNOLOGY DIRECTORY. see *BIOLOGY—Biotechnology*

BIOCOMMERCE DATA'S BUSINESS PROFILE SERIES. VOLUME 3: THE INTERNATIONAL BIOTECHNOLOGY DIRECTORY. see *BIOLOGY—Biotechnology*

BIOCOMMERCE DATA'S BUSINESS PROFILE SERIES. VOLUME 4: THE U K BIOTECHNOLOGY DIRECTORY. see *BIOLOGY—Biotechnology*

338.76302571　　　　CAN
BIOPRODUCTS CANADA. Text in English. 1999. a. CND 149 (effective 2003). **Document type:** *Directory, Trade.*
Formerly (until 2003): New Uses Industry Guide (Year) (1490-571X)
Related titles: CD-ROM ed.: CND 299.99 (effective 2003).
Published by: Contact Canada, 390 Goward Rd, Victoria, BC V9E 2J5, Canada. TEL 250-708-0427, 888-502-6666, FAX 250-708-0429, ccinfo@contactcanada.com, http://www.contactcanada.com/new_uses/.

BIOSCAN; the worldwide biotech industry reporting service. see *BIOLOGY—Biotechnology*

679.29 660.6　　　　DEU
DAS BIOTECHNOLOGIE JAHR- UND ADRESSBUCH. Text in German. 1987. a. EUR 32.80 (effective 2004). adv. **Document type:** *Directory, Trade.*
Published by: Biocom AG, Stralsunder Str 58-59, Berlin, 13355, Germany. TEL 49-30-2649210, FAX 49-30-26492111, service@biocom.de, http://www.biocom.de. Ed. Michael Kuhrt. Adv. contact Oliver Schnell. B&W page EUR 1,680; trim 120 x 175. Circ: 3,000 (paid and controlled).

BIOTECHNOLOGY INTERNATIONAL YEARBOOK (YEAR). see *BIOLOGY—Biotechnology*

658.8029　　　　USA
BLACK BOOK. C P I VALUE GUIDE. (Cars of Particular Interest) Text in English. bi-m. USD 48 (effective 2003). **Document type:** *Trade.* **Description:** Contents cover the fair, good, and excellent retail values for older used cars and light duty trucks from 1946. Also contains values for collectible, luxury, exotic, and highline cars and light trucks from 1946-present.
Published by: Black Book National Auto Research (Subsidiary of: Hearst Corporation), 2620 Barrett Rd, PO Box 758, Gainesville, GA 30503. TEL 770-532-4111, 888-760-2667, http://www.blackbookusa.com/cpi.asp.

658.8029　　　　USA
BLACK BOOK. HEAVY DUTY TRUCK GUIDE. Text in English. m. USD 95 (effective 2003). **Document type:** *Trade.* **Description:** Covers class 4 through class 8 medium & heavy duty trucks; average and rough wholesale; average retail; add/deduct for equipment; mileage charts; model number identifiers.
Published by: Black Book National Auto Research (Subsidiary of: Hearst Corporation), 2620 Barrett Rd, PO Box 758, Gainesville, GA 30503. TEL 770-532-4111, 888-760-2667, http://www.blackbookusa.com.

658.8029　　　　USA
BLACK BOOK. HISTORICAL USED CAR XPRESS. Text in English. w. **Document type:** *Trade.* **Description:** Contains original MSRP, current loan, wholesale, retail and trade-in values for vehicles from May 1999 to current model. Values may be seen as weekly or monthly data. Retrieves data by VIN or by year, make and model.
Media: Online - full content.
Published by: Black Book National Auto Research (Subsidiary of: Hearst Corporation), 2620 Barrett Rd, PO Box 758, Gainesville, GA 30503. TEL 770-532-4111, 888-760-2667, http://www.blackbookusa.com.

658.8029　　　　USA
BLACK BOOK. HISTORY XPRESS. Text in English. m. **Document type:** *Trade.* **Description:** Allows comparison of average wholesale values for up to three vehicles at a time. Includes graphs showing value trends on either monthly or quarterly basis. Allows for mileage and equipment adjustments. Includes original MSRP. Data may be e-mailed.
Media: Online - full content.
Published by: Black Book National Auto Research (Subsidiary of: Hearst Corporation), 2620 Barrett Rd, PO Box 758, Gainesville, GA 30503. TEL 770-532-4111, 888-760-2667, http://www.blackbookusa.com.

658.8029　　　　USA
BLACK BOOK. MONTHLY USED CAR XPRESS. Text in English. m. USD 195 (effective 2003). **Document type:** *Academic/Scholarly.*
Media: Online - full content. **Related titles:** ◆ Print ed.: Black Book. Official Used Car Market Guide Monthly. ISSN 0191-7498.
Published by: Black Book National Auto Research (Subsidiary of: Hearst Corporation), 2620 Barrett Rd, PO Box 758, Gainesville, GA 30503. TEL 770-532-4111, 888-760-2667, http://www.blackbookusa.com.

658.8029　　　　USA
BLACK BOOK. MOTORCYCLE XPRESS. Text in English. m. USD 159 (effective 2003). **Document type:** *Trade.* **Description:** Retrieves by year, make & model; shows average retail, clean trade, fair trade; current loan value; original MSRP; engine displacement; number of cylinders.
Media: Online - full content. **Related titles:** ◆ Print ed.: Black Book. Official Motorcycle Value Guide. ISSN 1520-0345.
Published by: Black Book National Auto Research (Subsidiary of: Hearst Corporation), 2620 Barrett Rd, PO Box 758, Gainesville, GA 30503. TEL 770-532-4111, 888-760-2667, http://www.blackbookusa.com.

658.8029　　　　USA
BLACK BOOK. NEW CAR XPRESS. Text in English. w. USD 239.40; USD 24 per month (effective 2003). **Document type:** *Trade.* **Description:** Provides information by year, make & model; get base invoice & MSRP with percentage markup; interior & exterior colors; major changes for model year; standard and optional equipment with pricing; picture if available.
Media: Online - full content.
Published by: Black Book National Auto Research (Subsidiary of: Hearst Corporation), 2620 Barrett Rd, PO Box 758, Gainesville, GA 30503. TEL 770-532-4111, 888-760-2667, http://www.blackbookusa.com.

658.8029　　　　USA　　　　ISSN 1534-5637
BLACK BOOK. OFFICIAL DOLLAR RESIDUAL VALUE GUIDE. Text in English. bi-m. USD 77 (effective 2003). **Document type:** *Trade.* **Description:** Provides information on the dollar residuals for new vehicles at 12, 24, 36, 48, and 60 months; dollar residual projections for 12-48 months for used vehicles; domestic & import cars and light duty trucks; mileage adjustment charts; add/deduct adjustments for optional equipment.
Published by: Black Book National Auto Research (Subsidiary of: Hearst Corporation), 2620 Barrett Rd, PO Box 758, Gainesville, GA 30503. TEL 770-532-4111, 888-760-2667, http://www.blackbookusa.com.

658.8029　　　　USA　　　　ISSN 1520-0345
BLACK BOOK. OFFICIAL MOTORCYCLE VALUE GUIDE. Text in English. 1998. m. USD 72 (effective 2003). **Document type:** *Trade.* **Description:** Covers the average retail, clean trade and fair trade values for motorcycles, ATVs, snowmobiles and personal watercraft; 14 model years; original MSRP; current loan value; engine displacement; number of cylinders.
Related titles: ◆ Online - full content ed.: Black Book. Motorcycle XPRESS
Published by: Black Book National Auto Research (Subsidiary of: Hearst Corporation), 2620 Barrett Rd, PO Box 758, Gainesville, GA 30503. TEL 770-532-4111, 888-760-2667, http://www.blackbookusa.com.

658.8029　　　　USA　　　　ISSN 1063-6080
BLACK BOOK. OFFICIAL OLD CAR MARKET GUIDE. Text in English. m. USD 75 (effective 2003). **Document type:** *Trade.* **Description:** Includes the wholesale values for domestic & import cars and trucks more than seven years old; eight model years; current loan value; optional equipment values.
Formerly: Black Book. Old Car Market Guide (0747-4393)
Published by: Black Book National Auto Research (Subsidiary of: Hearst Corporation), 2620 Barrett Rd, PO Box 758, Gainesville, GA 30503. TEL 770-532-4111, 888-760-2667, http://www.blackbookusa.com.

658.8029　　　　USA　　　　ISSN 1062-4635
BLACK BOOK. OFFICIAL RESIDUAL VALUE GUIDE. Text in English. bi-m. USD 77 (effective 2003). **Document type:** *Trade.* **Description:** Covers the percentage residuals for new vehicles at 12, 24, 36, 48, and 60 months; dollar residual projections for 12-48 months for used vehicles; domestic & import cars and light duty trucks; mileage adjustment charts; add/deduct adjustments for optional equipment.
Published by: Black Book National Auto Research (Subsidiary of: Hearst Corporation), 2620 Barrett Rd, PO Box 758, Gainesville, GA 30503. TEL 770-532-4111, 888-760-2667, http://www.blackbookusa.com.

629　　　　USA　　　　ISSN 0191-7498
BLACK BOOK. OFFICIAL USED CAR MARKET GUIDE MONTHLY. Text in English. m. **Document type:** *Trade.* **Description:** Covers wholesale and retail values for domestic and import cars, light duty trucks, vans & conversions and sport utility vehicles; original MSRP; current loan value; VIN model numbers.
Related titles: ◆ Online - full content ed.: Black Book. Monthly Used Car XPRESS
Published by: Black Book National Auto Research (Subsidiary of: Hearst Corporation), 2620 Barrett Rd, PO Box 758, Gainesville, GA 30503. TEL 770-532-4111, 888-760-2667, http://www.blackbookusa.com.

658.8029　　　　USA
BLACK BOOK. TRUCK AND VAN GUIDE. Text in English. s-m. USD 88 (effective 2003). **Document type:** *Trade.* **Description:** Covers regionalized wholesale values for domestic & import light duty trucks; sport utility vehicles; full-sized, mini, and commercial vans; wheelbase; adjustment charts for mileage; price adjustments for equipment.
Published by: Black Book National Auto Research (Subsidiary of: Hearst Corporation), 2620 Barrett Rd, PO Box 758, Gainesville, GA 30503. TEL 770-532-4111, 888-760-2667, http://www.blackbookusa.com.

658.8029　　　　USA
BLACK BOOK. TRUCK XPRESS. Text in English. m. USD 159 (effective 2003). **Document type:** *Trade.* **Description:** Contains wholesale, retail and loan values for class 4 through class 8 tractors and straight trucks; adjustments for equipment and mileage.
Media: Online - full content.
Published by: Black Book National Auto Research (Subsidiary of: Hearst Corporation), 2620 Barrett Rd, PO Box 758, Gainesville, GA 30503. TEL 770-532-4111, 888-760-2667, http://www.blackbookusa.com.

658.8029　　　　USA
BLACK BOOK. USED CAR XPRESS. Text in English. w. USD 395 (effective 2003). **Document type:** *Trade.* **Description:** Covers the retail and wholesale pricing for past 15 model years of domestic and import vehicles; retail, wholesale and trade-in values; price adjustments for mileage and equipment; retrieve vehicle by year/make/model or by VIN; calculation of finance and lease payments; used car residuals; prints appraisals.
Media: Online - full content.
Published by: Black Book National Auto Research (Subsidiary of: Hearst Corporation), 2620 Barrett Rd, PO Box 758, Gainesville, GA 30503. TEL 770-532-4111, 888-760-2667, http://www.blackbookusa.com.

658.8029　　　　USA
BLACK BOOK. VEHICLE IDENTIFICATION GUIDE. Text in English. a. USD 60 per issue (effective 2003). **Document type:** *Trade.* **Description:** Contains VIN interpretation charts for model years 1981 to present; model number; body styles; number of cylinders; weight; tire size; wheelbase; taxable horsepower; original MSRP.
Related titles: Online - full content ed.: Black Book. XPRESS Vehicle Identification System. USD 159 (effective 2003).

B

B

Published by: Black Book National Auto Research (Subsidiary of: Hearst Corporation), 2620 Barrett Rd, PO Box 758, Gainesville, GA 30503. TEL 770-532-4111, 888-760-2667, http://www.blackbookusa.com.

658.8029   USA
BLACK BOOK. WEEKLY USED CAR GUIDE. Text in English. w. USD 105 to qualified personnel (effective 2003). **Document type:** *Trade.* **Description:** Four regionalized wholesale values for domestic and import passenger cars and light duty trucks; current loan value; VIN model #; adjustment charts for mileage; price adjustments for equipment.
Published by: Black Book National Auto Research (Subsidiary of: Hearst Corporation), 2620 Barrett Rd, PO Box 758, Gainesville, GA 30503. TEL 770-532-4111, 888-760-2667, http://www.blackbookusa.com.

658.8029   USA   ISSN 1099-629X
BLACK BOOK XPRESS. Variant title: Black Book. Retail Used Car Market Guide. Text in English. 199?. m. USD 80 (effective 2003). **Document type:** *Trade.* **Description:** Covers the retail values for past 15 model years of domestic & import vehicles; price adjustments for equipment; mileage adjustment charts.
Published by: Black Book National Auto Research (Subsidiary of: Hearst Corporation), 2620 Barrett Rd, PO Box 758, Gainesville, GA 30503. TEL 770-532-4111, 888-760-2667, http://www.blackbookusa.com.

658.8029   USA
BLACK BOOK. XPRESS FOR EXOTIC AND OLDER CARS. Text in English. bi-m. USD 159 (effective 2003). **Document type:** *Trade.* **Description:** Includes exotic and older vehicles for years 1946 - present; retrieves by year, make & model; shows excellent, good and fair retail values.
Media: Online - full content.
Published by: Black Book National Auto Research (Subsidiary of: Hearst Corporation), 2620 Barrett Rd, PO Box 758, Gainesville, GA 30503. TEL 770-532-4111, 888-760-2667, http://www.blackbookusa.com.

658.8029   USA
BLACK BOOK XPRESS FOR NEW CARS. Text in English. m. USD 388 (effective 2003). **Document type:** *Trade.* **Description:** Contains the retail and invoice pricing for new domestic & import vehicles; standard & optional equipment; calculation of finance & lease payments; new vehicle residuals.
Media: CD-ROM.
Published by: Black Book National Auto Research (Subsidiary of: Hearst Corporation), 2620 Barrett Rd, PO Box 758, Gainesville, GA 30503. TEL 770-532-4111, 888-760-2667, http://www.blackbookusa.com.

658.8029   USA
BLACK BOOK XPRESS FOR USED VEHICLES. Text in English. m. USD 388 (effective 2003). **Document type:** *Trade.* **Description:** Covers the retail and wholesale pricing for past 15 model years of domestic and import vehicles; retail, wholesale and trade-in values; price adjustments for mileage and equipment; retrieve vehicle by year/make/model or by VIN; calculation of finance and lease payments; used car residuals; prints window stickers and buyer's guides; prints appraisals.
Media: CD-ROM.
Published by: Black Book National Auto Research (Subsidiary of: Hearst Corporation), 2620 Barrett Rd, PO Box 758, Gainesville, GA 30503. TEL 770-532-4111, 888-760-2667, http://www.blackbookusa.com.

338.0029   USA
BLACK PAGES - CHICAGO. Text in English. a. free. adv. **Document type:** *Directory.* **Description:** Profiles and lists black-owned business establishments and services in Chicago.
Address: 400 W 76th St, 200, Chicago, IL 60620. TEL 312-808-1800, FAX 312-952-8329. Pub. Arnette French. Circ: 500,000.

BLACK'S GUIDE: ATLANTA INDUSTRIAL. see *REAL ESTATE*

BLACK'S GUIDE: ATLANTA OFFICE. see *REAL ESTATE*

BLACK'S GUIDE: BOSTON. see *REAL ESTATE*

BLACK'S GUIDE: CHICAGO. see *REAL ESTATE*

BLACK'S GUIDE: CONNECTICUT - NEW YORK SUBURBS - OUTER BOROUGHS. see *REAL ESTATE*

BLACK'S GUIDE: DALLAS - FORT WORTH INDUSTRIAL MARKET. see *REAL ESTATE*

BLACK'S GUIDE: DALLAS - FORT WORTH OFFICE MARKET. see *REAL ESTATE*

BLACK'S GUIDE: DENVER. see *REAL ESTATE*

BLACK'S GUIDE: GREATER PHILADELPHIA, SOUTH NEW JERSEY, DELAWARE & LEHIGH VALLEY INDUSTRIAL. see *REAL ESTATE*

BLACK'S GUIDE: GREATER PHILADELPHIA, SOUTH NEW JERSEY, DELAWARE & LEHIGH VALLEY OFFICE. see *REAL ESTATE*

BLACK'S GUIDE: HOUSTON INDUSTRIAL. see *REAL ESTATE*

BLACK'S GUIDE: LOS ANGELES - ORANGE COUNTY - INLAND EMPIRE. see *REAL ESTATE*

BLACK'S GUIDE: METRO ORLANDO. see *REAL ESTATE*

BLACK'S GUIDE: MICHIGAN. see *REAL ESTATE*

BLACK'S GUIDE: NEW JERSEY INDUSTRIAL MARKET. see *REAL ESTATE*

BLACK'S GUIDE: NEW JERSEY OFFICE MARKET. see *REAL ESTATE*

BLACK'S GUIDE: SAN DIEGO. see *REAL ESTATE*

BLACK'S GUIDE: SAN FRANCISCO BAY AREA. see *REAL ESTATE*

BLACK'S GUIDE: SOUTH FLORIDA FLEX - INDUSTRIAL MARKET. see *REAL ESTATE*

BLACK'S GUIDE: SOUTH FLORIDA - OFFICE MARKET. see *REAL ESTATE*

BLACK'S GUIDE: TAMPA BAY - SOUTHWEST FLORIDA. see *REAL ESTATE*

BLACK'S GUIDE: WASHINGTON D.C. METROPOLITAN AREA. see *REAL ESTATE*

BLACK'S METRO RICHMOND GUIDE. see *REAL ESTATE*

621.388   GBR   ISSN 0960-5142
BLUE BOOK OF BRITISH BROADCASTING. Text in English. 1974. a. GBP 75. adv. **Document type:** *Directory.*
—BLDSC (2114.003000).
Published by: Tellex Monitors Ltd., Communications House, 210 Old St, London, EC1V 9UN, United Kingdom. TEL 44-20-75663100, FAX 44-20-75663152, sales@tellex.press.net, http://www.tellex.press.net. Ed. Robin Mann. R&P. Adv. contact Joanne Ferris. page GBP 750. Circ: 2,000 (paid); 500 (controlled).

BLUE BOOK: THE DIRECTORY OF THE LAW SOCIETY OF SCOTLAND. see *LAW*

381.029   THA
BOARD OF TRADE OF THAILAND. TRADE DIRECTORY. Text in English. a. **Document type:** *Directory.* **Description:** Lists the top 50 Thai importers and exporters of the top 50 important products to about 40 countries of destination.
Published by: Board of Trade of Thailand, 150 Rajbopit Rd, Bangkok, 10200, Thailand. TEL 66-2-221-0555, FAX 66-2-225-3995. Ed. Rachanee Watchareewong.

BOAT & MOTOR DEALER. see *SPORTS AND GAMES—Boats And Boating*

BOAT GUIDE. see *SPORTS AND GAMES—Boats And Boating*

387.0029   USA
BOATING INDUSTRY MARINE BUYERS' GUIDE. Text in English. 1937. a. reprint service avail. from PQC. **Document type:** *Directory, Trade.* **Description:** Comprehensive recreational marine industry sourcebook, including directories of suppliers' addresses, distributors, marine manufacturers' representatives, stock boatbuilders (classified by type), marine product manufacturers and services.
Related titles: Microform ed.: (from PQC); ♦ Supplement to: Boating Industry. ISSN 1543-4400.
Published by: Ehlert Publishing Group, Inc. (Subsidiary of: Affinity Group Inc.), 6420 Sycamore Ln. N. Ste 100, Maple Grove, MN 55369-6003. Ed. Matt Gruhn. Circ: 31,334.

338.0029   GBR
BODYSHOP BUYER'S GUIDE. Text in English. 1991. a. GBP 39.95 domestic; GBP 59.95 foreign (effective 2001). adv. tr.lit. back issues avail. **Document type:** *Directory, Trade.* **Description:** Directed at managers of bodyshops, factors, insurers and distributors.
Related titles: Fax ed.; Online - full text ed.: free qualified subscribers.
Published by: Plenham Ltd., Castle Mill, Lower Kings Rd, Berkhamsted, Herts HP4 2AA, United Kingdom. TEL 44-1442-285300, FAX 44-1442-870740, bodyshop@bodyshopmag.com, http://www.autorefinish.com. Ed. Heather Grant. Pub. Chris Mann. R&P David Young. Adv. contact Cecily Hughes. B&W page GBP 1,200, color page GBP 1,950; trim 190 x 275. Circ: 10,500.

382.029   BOL
BOLIVIA EXPORT DIRECTORY/BOLIVIA DIRECTORIO DE EXPORTADORES. Text in Spanish. a. **Document type:** *Directory.* **Description:** Guide book for producing and exporting firms.
Published by: Instituto Nacional de Promocion de la Exportaciones (INPEX), Casilla 10871, Ave. Arce Esq Goitia, 2021, La Paz, Bolivia. TEL 378000, FAX 391226, TELEX 3643 INPEX BV.

332.6029   USA   ISSN 1053-8658
HG4907
THE BOND BUYER'S MUNICIPAL MARKETPLACE. Text in English. a. USD 425 per issue (effective 2005). adv. **Document type:** *Directory, Trade.*
Formerly: Directory of Municipal Bond Dealers of the United States (0094-100X)
Related titles: Online - full text ed.
—CCC.
Published by: Source Media, Inc., One State St Plaza, 27th Fl, New York, NY 10004. TEL 212-803-6077, 800-221-1809, FAX 212-747-1154, custserv@sourcemedia.com, http://www.munimarketplace.com/mmo/index.jsp, http://www.sourcemedia.com.

380.1029   PRI
THE BOOK OF LISTS. Text in English. 1988. a. USD 15 (effective 2003). charts. 224 p./no.; **Description:** The annual industry-by-industry ranking directory of Perto Rico's top companies.
Published by: Casiano Communications Inc., 1700 Fernandez Juncos Ave, San Juan, 00909-2999, Puerto Rico. TEL 787-728-3000, FAX 787-268-5058, wpedit@casiano.com, cservice@casiano.com, http://www.casiano.com. Ed. Lorelei Albanese. R&P Dianne Pacheco. Adv. contact Enid Rivera. Circ: 35,000.

BOOK PUBLISHING RESOURCE GUIDE. see *PUBLISHING AND BOOK TRADE*

658.0029   DEU
BOOKING. Text in German. 1993. a. EUR 64 (effective 2004). adv. **Document type:** *Directory, Trade.*
Published by: Maerkte und Medien Verlagsgesellschaft mbH (Subsidiary of: Sueddeutscher Verlag GmbH), Karlstr 41, Munich, 80333, Germany. TEL 49-89-5485205, FAX 49-89-54852520, kontakt@kontakter.de, http://www.kontakter.de. adv. B&W page EUR 1,415, color page EUR 2,315. Circ: 2,500 (paid and controlled).

380.1029   AUS
THE BOOKMAN MEDIA GUIDE. Text in English. s-a. AUD 95 for 6 mos. for both Online & CD-ROM editions; AUD 312 for both Online & CD-ROM editions (effective 2000). **Document type:** *Directory, Abstract/Index.* **Description:** Provides a directory of Australia's media organisations and personnel.
Media: CD-ROM. **Related titles:** Online - full content ed.: AUD 95 (effective 2000).
Published by: Bookman Press Pty Ltd, Lu 10, 227 Collins St, Melbourne, VIC 3000, Australia. TEL 61-3-96542000, FAX 61-3-96542290, bookman@bookman.com.au, http://www.bookman.com.au.

338.0029   ZAF
BOTSWANA BUSINESS DIRECTORY. Text in English. 1981. a. USD 80 (effective 2001). adv. **Document type:** *Directory.*
Published by: Braby's (Subsidiary of: Associated Industries), Attn: Sue Pearson, PO Box 1426, Pinetown, 3600, South Africa. TEL 27-31-7017021, FAX 27-31-7017036, booksales@brabys.co.za.

670.29   BWA
BOTSWANA MANUFACTURING DIRECTORY. Text in English. 1984. biennial. free. **Document type:** *Directory, Government.* **Description:** Gives information about manufacturers and the range of manufactured products in Botswana.
Published by: Ministry of Commerce and Industry, Department of Trade and Investment Promotion (T I P A), Private Bag 00367, Gaborone, Botswana. TEL 267-351790, FAX 267-305375. Ed. Mukram Sheikh. Circ: 10,000.

381.029   BWA
BOTSWANA TRADE DIRECTORY. Text in English. 1982. biennial. free. **Document type:** *Directory, Government.* **Description:** Gives information about importers, exporters and service organizations of Botswana.
Published by: Ministry of Commerce and Industry, Department of Trade and Investment Promotion (T I P A), Private Bag 00367, Gaborone, Botswana. TEL 267-351790, FAX 267-305375. Ed. Mukram Sheikh. Circ: 10,000.

338.0029   FRA   ISSN 0299-5921
BOTTIN ENTREPRISES. Text in French; Summaries in English. 1895. a. (3 vols.). USD 500. index. **Description:** Classifies the 100,000 most important French companies by departments and towns, with addresses, telephone, fax, number of employees, capital, executives, and activity.

Formed by the 1987 merger of: Bottin Professions. Liste Alphabetique Nationale des Entreprises (0759-383X); Which was formerly (until 1983): Bottin. Liste Alphabetique Nationale des Entreprises (0294-9997); (1976-1981): Bottin Professions. Liste Alphabetique Nationale des Entreprises (0294-9989); And: Bottin Professions. Rubriques Professionelles (0759-3848); Which was formerly (until 1983): Bottin. Produits et Services (0752-7012); (1976-1980): Bottin Professions. Rubriques (0752-7004)
Related titles: Online - full text ed.
Published by: Bottin S A, 4 rue Andre Boulle, Cretil, Cedex 9 94961, France. TEL 49-81-56-56, FAX 49-81-56-76, TELEX 262 407.

BOXWOOD BUYER'S GUIDE. see *GARDENING AND HORTICULTURE*

BOXWOOD HANDBOOK; a practical guide to knowing and growing boxwood. see *GARDENING AND HORTICULTURE*

338.0029 ZAF
BRABY'S BORDER DIRECTORY AND SURROUNDING AREAS. Variant title: Border Directory. Text in English. a. USD 30 (effective 2001). **Document type:** *Directory.*
Formed by the 1993 merger of: Braby's King William's Town Directory; Braby's Queenstown Directory; Braby's Ciskei Buyer's Guide
Published by: Braby's (Subsidiary of: Associated Industries), Attn: Sue Pearson, PO Box 1426, Pinetown, 3600, South Africa. TEL 27-31-7017021, FAX 27-31-7017036, booksales@brabys.co.za.

338.0029 ZAF ISSN 0378-9217
BRABY'S EAST LONDON DIRECTORY. Text in English. 1961. a. USD 45 (effective 2001). **Document type:** *Directory.*
Related titles: Diskette ed.
Published by: Braby's (Subsidiary of: Associated Industries), Attn: Sue Pearson, PO Box 1426, Pinetown, 3600, South Africa. TEL 27-31-7017021, FAX 27-31-7017036, booksales@brabys.co.za. Ed. A Stagg.

338.0029 ZAF
BRABY'S FREE STATE DIRECTORY. Text in English. a. USD 90 (effective 2001). adv. **Document type:** *Directory.*
Former titles: Braby's Free State - Northern Cape Directory; Braby's Orange Free State Northern Cape Directory; Braby's Orange Free State Directory (0378-9292)
Published by: Braby's (Subsidiary of: Associated Industries), Attn: Sue Pearson, PO Box 1426, Pinetown, 3600, South Africa. TEL 27-31-7017021, FAX 27-31-7017036, booksales@brabys.co.za. Ed. A Stagg.

338.0029 ZAF ISSN 0378-9241
BRABY'S GREYTOWN DIRECTORY. Text in English. 1974. a. USD 30 (effective 2001). **Document type:** *Directory.*
Published by: Braby's (Subsidiary of: Associated Industries), Attn: Sue Pearson, PO Box 1426, Pinetown, 3600, South Africa. TEL 27-31-7017021, FAX 27-31-7017036, booksales@brabys.co.za.

338.0029 ZAF ISSN 0259-4692
BRABY'S HIGHWAY DIRECTORY. Text in English. 1977. a. USD 36 (effective 2001). **Document type:** *Directory.*
Published by: Braby's (Subsidiary of: Associated Industries), Attn: Sue Pearson, PO Box 1426, Pinetown, 3600, South Africa. TEL 27-31-7017021, FAX 27-31-7017036, booksales@brabys.co.za.

338.0029 ZAF ISSN 0378-925X
BRABY'S HOWICK DIRECTORY. Text in English. 1973. a. USD 25 (effective 2001). **Document type:** *Directory.*
Published by: Braby's (Subsidiary of: Associated Industries), Attn: Sue Pearson, PO Box 1426, Pinetown, 3600, South Africa. TEL 27-31-7017021, FAX 27-31-7017036, booksales@brabys.co.za.

338.0029 ZAF
BRABY'S NAMIBIA BUSINESS DIRECTORY. Text in English. 1969. a. USD 95 (effective 2001). adv. **Document type:** *Directory.*
Formerly: Braby's South West Africa Directory (0378-9322)
Published by: Braby's (Subsidiary of: Associated Industries), Attn: Sue Pearson, PO Box 1426, Pinetown, 3600, South Africa. TEL 27-31-7017021, FAX 27-31-7017036, booksales@brabys.co.za.

338.0029 ZAF
BRABY'S NEWCASTLE - DUNDEE - VRYHEID DIRECTORY. Text in English. 1965. a. USD 50 (effective 2001). **Document type:** *Directory.*
Formed by the merger of: Braby's Dundee Directory (0378-9209); Braby's Newcastle Directory (0378-9284); Braby's Vryheid Directory (0378-9330)
Published by: Braby's (Subsidiary of: Associated Industries), Attn: Sue Pearson, PO Box 1426, Pinetown, 3600, South Africa. TEL 27-31-7017021, FAX 27-31-7017036, booksales@brabys.co.za.

338.0029 ZAF
BRABY'S NORTH COAST AND ZULULAND DIRECTORY. Variant title: North Coast and Zululand Directory. Text in English. 1958. a. USD 70 (effective 2001). **Document type:** *Directory.*
Formerly (until 1994): Braby's Natal North Coast and Zululand Directory (0520-7037)
Published by: Braby's (Subsidiary of: Associated Industries), Attn: Sue Pearson, PO Box 1426, Pinetown, 3600, South Africa. TEL 27-31-7017021, FAX 27-31-7017036, booksales@brabys.co.za.

338.0029 ZAF
BRABY'S NORTHERN PROVINCE DIRECTORY. Text in English. irreg. USD 60 (effective 2001).
Published by: Braby's (Subsidiary of: Associated Industries), Attn: Sue Pearson, PO Box 1426, Pinetown, 3600, South Africa. TEL 27-31-7174141, FAX 27-31-7173011, sue@brabys.co.za.

338.0029 ZAF ISSN 0378-9306
BRABY'S PIETERMARITZBURG DIRECTORY. Text in English. 1957. a. USD 70 (effective 2001). **Document type:** *Directory.*
Related titles: Diskette ed.
Published by: Braby's (Subsidiary of: Associated Industries), Attn: Sue Pearson, PO Box 1426, Pinetown, 3600, South Africa. TEL 27-31-7017021, FAX 27-31-7017036, booksales@brabys.co.za. Ed. A Stagg.

338.0029 ZAF ISSN 0378-9314
BRABY'S PRETORIA DIRECTORY. Text in English. 1974. a. USD 70 (effective 2001). **Document type:** *Directory.*
Published by: Braby's (Subsidiary of: Associated Industries), Attn: Sue Pearson, PO Box 1426, Pinetown, 3600, South Africa. TEL 27-31-7017021, FAX 27-31-7017036, booksales@brabys.co.za.

338.0029 ZAF
BRABY'S RED INDEX ON CD-ROM - BRABY'S RED INDEX. Text in English. 1993. q. USD 995 (effective 2001). **Document type:** *Directory.* **Description:** Lists businesses within the nine provinces: Kwa Zulu-Natal, Gauteng, West Cape, North Cape, Free State, Northwest Province, Northern Province, East Cape, and Mpumalanga.
Formerly: Braby's Directory on Disk
Media: CD-ROM.
Published by: Braby's (Subsidiary of: Associated Industries), Attn: Sue Pearson, PO Box 1426, Pinetown, 3600, South Africa. TEL 27-31-7017021, FAX 27-31-7017036, booksales@brabys.co.za.

338.0029 ZAF
BRABY'S S A D C COMMERCIAL DIRECTORY. (Southern African Development Coordination Conference) Text in English. 1924. a. (in 2 vols.). USD 350 (effective 2001). adv. **Document type:** *Directory.* **Description:** Provides alphabetical and classified listings of all businesses in Southern Africa.
Incorporates: S A D C Trade Directory; Which was formerly: S A D C C Directory; Former titles: Braby's Commercial Directory of Southern Africa; Braby's Commercial Directory of South, East and Central Africa (0378-9187); Which incorporates: Cape Times Directory of Southern Africa (0379-4601)
Published by: Braby's (Subsidiary of: Associated Industries), Attn: Sue Pearson, PO Box 1426, Pinetown, 3600, South Africa. TEL 27-31-7017021, FAX 27-31-7017036, booksales@brabys.co.za. Ed. A Stagg. Circ: 20. **Dist. by:** Current Pacific Ltd., PO Box 36-536, Northcote, Auckland, New Zealand. TEL 64-9-480-1388, FAX 64-9-480-1387, info@cplnz.com, http://www.cplnz.com.

338.0029 ZAF ISSN 1016-6378
BRABY'S SOUTH COAST AND SOUTHERN NATAL DIRECTORY. Text in English. 1957. a. USD 70 (effective 2001). **Document type:** *Directory.*
Published by: Braby's (Subsidiary of: Associated Industries), Attn: Sue Pearson, PO Box 1426, Pinetown, 3600, South Africa. TEL 27-31-7017021, FAX 27-31-7017036, booksales@brabys.co.za.

659.1029 USA
HF6182.U5
THE BRANDWEEK DIRECTORY. Text in English. 1988. a. USD 399 combined subscription print & CD-ROM eds. (effective 2003). adv. **Document type:** *Directory.* **Description:** Directory of US brand-name products and services and the organizations that market them. Provides key facts and personnel.
Formerly: Adweek Client - Brand Directory (1049-7064)
Related titles: Online - full content ed.; ♦ Supplement(s): Adweek Directory.
Published by: V N U Business Publications (Subsidiary of: V N U Business Media), 770 Broadway, New York, NY 10003-9595. TEL 646-654-5870, FAX 646-654-5518, adweek@adweek.com, bmcomm@vnuinc.com, http://www.adweek.com/adweek/directories/index.jsp, http://www.vnubusinessmedia.com/.

BRAZILIAN AMERICAN CHAMBER OF COMMERCE NEWS BULLETIN. see *BUSINESS AND ECONOMICS—Chamber Of Commerce Publications*

BRAZILIAN EXPORT MARKET. see *BUSINESS AND ECONOMICS—International Commerce*

380.1029 ISL
BREF TIL STORKAUPMANNA. Text in Icelandic. 1969 (vol.5, no.1). irreg. (approx. 6/yr.). membership.
Formerly: F I S Frettabref
Published by: Felag Islenskra Storkaupmanna/Association of Icelandic Importers, Exporters and Wholesale Merchants, Hus Verslunarinnar, Reykjavik, 103, Iceland. TEL 354-552-7066, FAX 354-568-8441. Ed. Arni Reynisson. Circ: 700 (controlled).

BREWERS DIGEST ANNUAL BUYERS GUIDE AND BREWERY DIRECTORY. see *BEVERAGES*

BREWERS GUILD DIRECTORY. see *BEVERAGES*

BREWERY MANUAL & WHO'S WHO IN BRITISH BREWING & SCOTCH WHISKY DISTILLING INDUSTRIES. see *BEVERAGES*

659.1029 GBR
BRITAIN'S ADVERTISING INDUSTRY (YEAR). Text in English. 1988. irreg., latest 2002. GBP 190 per issue; GBP 250 combined subscription print & CD-ROM or disc (effective 2003). stat. **Description:** Over 1,600 companies are profiled. The report contains 3 years of financial data, tables on key performance criteria, business activities, contact information and details of major acquisitions during the last five years.
Related titles: CD-ROM ed.; Diskette ed.
Published by: Jordan Publishing Ltd., 21 St Thomas St, Bristol, BS1 6JS, United Kingdom. TEL 44-117-9230600, FAX 44-117-9250486, andy_delderfield@jordanpublishing.co.uk, http://www.jordanpublishing.co.uk.

658.0029 GBR
BRITAIN'S TOP 10,000 PRIVATELY OWNED COMPANIES (YEAR). Text in English. a. (in 5 vols., 1 no./vol.), latest 2002. GBP 450 per issue for 5 vol. set; GBP 150 per issue per vol. (effective 2003). **Document type:** *Trade.*
Related titles: CD-ROM ed.; Diskette ed.
Published by: Jordans Ltd. (Subsidiary of: Jordan Publishing Ltd.), 21 Thomas St, Bristol, BS1 6JS, United Kingdom. TEL 44-117-9230600, FAX 44-207-4003333, customersupport@jordans.co.uk, http://www.jordans.co.uk/.

658.0029 GBR
BRITAIN'S TOP FOREIGN OWNED COMPANIES (YEAR). Text in English. a. (in 2 vols., 1 no./vol.), latest 2002, 17th Ed. GBP 230 per issue vols.1 & 2; GBP 145 per issue vol.1 or 2 (effective 2003). **Document type:** *Trade.*
Related titles: Diskette ed.
Published by: Jordans Ltd. (Subsidiary of: Jordan Publishing Ltd.), 21 Thomas St, Bristol, BS1 6JS, United Kingdom. TEL 44-117-9230600, FAX 44-207-4003333, customersupport@jordans.co.uk, http://www.jordans.co.uk/.

658 615 GBR
BRITAIN'S TOP PHARMACEUTICAL COMPANIES. Text in English. irreg., latest 2001. GBP 170 per vol. (effective 2003). stat. **Document type:** *Trade.* **Description:** Over 1,000 companies are profiled. Contains financial data, tables in key performance criteria, activity details, contacts, major acquisitions and associated companies.
Related titles: Diskette ed.: GBP 199.75 per issue (effective 2003).
Published by: Jordans Ltd. (Subsidiary of: Jordan Publishing Ltd.), 21 Thomas St, Bristol, BS1 6JS, United Kingdom. TEL 44-117-9230600, FAX 44-207-4003333, customersupport@jordans.co.uk, http://www.jordans.co.uk/.

658.0029 667.6 GBR
BRITIAN'S PAINT INDUSTRY (YEAR). Text in English. a., latest 2002, 7th Ed. GBP 295 per vol. for print, CD-ROM or disc; GBP 395 combined subscription per vol. for print & CD-ROM or disc (effective 2003). stat. **Document type:** *Trade.*
Related titles: CD-ROM ed.; Diskette ed.
Published by: Jordans Ltd. (Subsidiary of: Jordan Publishing Ltd.), 21 Thomas St, Bristol, BS1 6JS, United Kingdom. TEL 44-117-9230600, FAX 44-207-4003333, customersupport@jordans.co.uk, http://www.jordans.co.uk/.

380.1029 071.1 USA ISSN 1203-5165
HF5072.B75
BRITISH COLUMBIA BUSINESS DIRECTORY. Text in English. a. USD 1,100 combined subscription print, online & CD-ROM eds. (effective 2004 & 2005). back issues avail. **Document type:** *Directory.*
Related titles: CD-ROM ed.; Diskette ed.; E-mail ed.; Fax ed.; Magnetic Tape ed.; Online - full text ed.
Published by: American Business Directories (Subsidiary of: American Business Information, Inc.), 5711 S 86th Circle, P O Box 27347, Omaha, NE 68127. TEL 402-593-4600, 888-946-9377, 877-708-3844, FAX 402-331-5481, sales@directoriesusa.com, http://www.directoriesusa.com.

384.63029 CAN ISSN 0521-0585
BRITISH COLUMBIA LEGAL TELEPHONE DIRECTORY. Text in English. 1965. a. CND 28 per issue (effective 2005). adv. 548 p./no.; **Document type:** *Directory.*
Formerly (until 1958): British Columbia Legal Directory and Telephone List (0317-3305)

B

▼ new title ➤ refereed ✶ unverified ♦ full entry avail.

Published by: Canada Law Book Inc., 240 Edward St#, Aurora, ON L4G 3S9, Canada. b.loney@canadalawbook.ca, http://www.canadalawbook.ca/catalogue.cfm?DSP=Detail&ProductID=119. Adv. contact Colleen Austin TEL 905-841-6472.

BRITISH CONFERENCE DESTINATIONS DIRECTORY (YEAR). see *MEETINGS AND CONGRESSES*

670.29 GBR
BRITISH CONSTRUCTION EQUIPMENT AND CRANES. DIRECTORY. Text in Arabic, English, French, Spanish. a. free. adv. **Document type:** *Directory, Trade.*
Published by: Federation of Manufacturers of Construction Equipment and Cranes, Ambassador House, Brigstock Rd, Thornton Heath, Surrey CR7 7JG, United Kingdom. fmcec@admin.co.uk, http://www.fmcec.org.uk. Circ: 10,000.

382.029 GBR ISSN 1472-3018
HF3503
BRITISH EXPORTS/BRITISCHER EXPORT/EXPORTACIONES BRITANICAS/EXPORTATIONS BRITANNIQUES. Text in English. 1969. a. GBP 195 (effective 2001); free to purchasers & specifiers outside U.K.. adv. **Document type:** *Directory, Corporate.* **Description:** Directory of UK companies with specific interests in exporting outside the UK.
Former titles (until 1999): Kompass British Exports (1472-300X); (until 1993): British Exports (1350-6986)
Related titles: CD-ROM ed.; Online - full text ed.: 1998. free (from Reed Information Services Ltd.).
—BLDSC (2300.040000).
Published by: Kompass (Subsidiary of: Reed Business Information Ltd.), Windsor Court, East Grinstead House, East Grinstead, W Sussex RH19 1XA, United Kingdom. TEL 44-1342-326972, FAX 44-1342-335747, http://www.kompass.co.uk. Ed. Dawn Ingram. Pub. Derek Barley. Adv. contact Julie Mason. Circ: 10,000 (controlled).

BRITISH THEATRE DIRECTORY. see *THEATER*

332.6029 GBR ISSN 0968-2716
BRITON'S INDEX: FINANCIAL INSTITUTIONS. Text in English. 1993. 3/yr. GBP 199 (effective 2000). **Document type:** *Directory.*
Published by: P R Newswire (Europe) Ltd, Communications House, 210 Old St, London, EC1V 9UN, United Kingdom. TEL 44-20-7490-8111, FAX 44-20-7490-1255. Ed. Mary-anne Edmonds.

332.6029 GBR ISSN 0968-2708
BRITON'S INDEX: INVESTMENT RESEARCH ANALYSTS. Text in English. 1989. 3/yr. GBP 199 (effective 2000). **Document type:** *Directory.*
Published by: P R Newswire (Europe) Ltd, Communications House, 210 Old St, London, EC1V 9UN, United Kingdom. TEL 44-20-7490-8111, FAX 44-20-7490-1255. Ed. Mary-anne Edmonds.

BROADCAST PRODUCTION GUIDE. see *COMMUNICATIONS—Television And Cable*

BROADCASTING & CABLE YEARBOOK. see *COMMUNICATIONS—Television And Cable*

THE (YEAR) BROKERS 1000. see *BUSINESS AND ECONOMICS—Investments*

381.029 USA
BUFFALO NIAGARA PARTNERSHIP MEMBERSHIP DIRECTORY. Text in English. a. USD 75 (effective 2000). **Document type:** *Directory, Trade.*
Former titles: Greater Buffalo Partnership Membership Directory; Greater Buffalo Business Directory; Western New York Business Directory; Western New York Buyer's Guide and Roster; Directory-Metropolitan Buffalo; Buffalo Area Chamber of Commerce Buyer's Guide
Related titles: Diskette ed.
Published by: Buffalo Niagara Partnership, 665 Main St., Ste 200, Buffalo, NY 14203-1487. TEL 716-852-7100, FAX 716-852-2761, jhazzan@buffniag.org, http://www.thepartnership.org. Ed. Julie Hazzan. Adv. contact Charlene Janiga. Circ: 6,000.

BUILDERS JOURNAL. see *BUILDING AND CONSTRUCTION*

BUILDING MATERIALS DIRECTORY. see *BUILDING AND CONSTRUCTION*

690.029 USA
BUILDING PRODUCTS FILE. Text in English. 1970. bi-m. USD 495. adv. **Description:** Provides vendor, brand name and CSI 16-division subject access to major manufacturers of construction-related products.
Published by: I H S Energy (Subsidiary of: I H S Energy Group), 15 Inverness Way East, Englewood, CO 80112. FAX 303-799-4085, http://ihsenergy.com. Ed. Liz Maynard Prigge. Circ: 780.

380.1029 GBR ISSN 1464-0155
BULK HANDLING INTERNATIONAL DIRECTORY. Text in English. a. GBP 84; GBP 89 foreign. **Document type:** *Directory, Trade.* **Description:** Offers a guide to the world's suppliers of loose materials handling, storage and distribution equipment and their individual products.
Published by: Turret R A I plc, Armstrong House, 38 Market Sq, Uxbridge, Middx UB8 1TG, United Kingdom. TEL 44-1895-454545, FAX 44-1895-454647.

338.54029 GBR ISSN 1365-9677
BURGUNDY BOOK OF EUROPEAN BROADCASTING. Text in English. 1996. a. GBP 95 (effective 1997). **Document type:** *Directory.*
Published by: Tellex Monitors Ltd., Communications House, 210 Old St, London, EC1V 9UN, United Kingdom. TEL 44-20-75663100, FAX 44-20-75663152, sales@tellex.press.net, http://www.tellex.press.net. Ed. Robin Mann. R&P Joanne Ferris. adv.: page GBP 750. Circ: 1,000 (paid).

338.0029 CAN ISSN 1205-0431
BURNABY B O A R D. Text in English. irreg. CND 10. **Document type:** *Directory.* **Description:** Provides business-to-business references in the area.
Formerly: Burnaby Centennial B O A R D (1188-8075)
Published by: (Burnaby Chamber of Commerce), DoMac Publications Ltd., 108 10721 139 St, Surrey, BC V3T 4L8, Canada. TEL 604-582-7288, FAX 604-583-3000. adv.: B&W page CND 1,795, color page CND 2,295; trim 10.88 x 8.25. Circ: 7,000.

302.23 USA
BURRELLE'S CHESAPEAKE BAY MEDIA DIRECTORY (YEAR); DE, MD, VA, DC. Text in English. a. USD 125 (effective 2001). adv. **Document type:** *Directory, Trade.*
Published by: Burrelle's Media Directories, 75 E Northfield Rd, Livingston, NJ 07039. TEL 973-992-6600, 800-876-3342, FAX 800-898-6677, directory@burrelles.com, info@burrelles.com, http://www.burrelles.com.

BURRELLE'S MEDIA DIRECTORY (CD-ROM EDITION). see *COMMUNICATIONS*

BURRELLE'S MEDIA DIRECTORY. VOL 1, NEWSPAPERS & RELATED MEDIA. see *COMMUNICATIONS*

BURRELLE'S MEDIA DIRECTORY. VOL 2, MAGAZINES & NEWSLETTERS. see *COMMUNICATIONS*

BURRELLE'S MEDIA DIRECTORY. VOL 3, BROADCAST & RELATED MEDIA. see *COMMUNICATIONS*

302.23 USA
BURRELLE'S MIDWEST MEDIA DIRECTORY (YEAR); IL, WI, IN, MI, OH. Text in English. a. USD 125 (effective 2001). adv. **Document type:** *Directory, Trade.*
Published by: Burrelle's Media Directories, 75 E Northfield Rd, Livingston, NJ 07039. TEL 973-992-6600, 800-876-3342, FAX 800-898-6677, directory@burrelles.com, info@burrelles.com, http://www.burrelles.com.

302.23 USA
BURRELLE'S MINNESOTA MEDIA DIRECTORY (YEAR). Text in English. a. USD 100 (effective 2001). adv. **Document type:** *Directory, Trade.*
Published by: Burrelle's Media Directories, 75 E Northfield Rd, Livingston, NJ 07039. TEL 973-992-6600, 800-876-3342, FAX 800-898-6677, directory@burrelles.com, info@burrelles.com, http://www.burrelles.com.

659.1029 USA ISSN 0883-9999
BURRELLE'S NEW ENGLAND MEDIA DIRECTORY (YEAR). Text in English. 1975. a. USD 125 (effective 2001). adv. **Document type:** *Directory.*
Incorporates (1979-1986): Maine Media Directory; Former titles: New England Media Directory; Directory of New England Newspapers, College Publications, Periodicals, and Radio and Television Stations (0195-7619)
Published by: Burrelle's Media Directories, 75 E Northfield Rd, Livingston, NJ 07039. TEL 973-992-6600, 800-876-3342, FAX 800-898-6677, http://www.burrelle.com. Ed., Adv. contact James L Hayes. Circ: 3,000. **Affiliate:** New England Newsclip Agency, Inc.

302.23 USA
BURRELLE'S SOUTHEAST MEDIA DIRECTORY (YEAR); FL, GA, NC, SC, TN. Text in English. a. USD 125 (effective 2001). adv. **Document type:** *Directory, Trade.*
Published by: Burrelle's Media Directories, 75 E Northfield Rd, Livingston, NJ 07039. TEL 973-992-6600, 800-876-3342, FAX 800-898-6677, directory@burrelles.com, info@burrelles.com, http://www.burrelles.com.

302.23 USA
BURRELLE'S TEXAS MEDIA DIRECTORY (YEAR). Text in English. a. USD 100 (effective 2001). **Document type:** *Directory, Trade.*
Published by: Burrelle's Media Directories, 75 E Northfield Rd, Livingston, NJ 07039. TEL 973-992-6600, 800-876-3342, FAX 800-898-6677, directory@burrelles.com, info@burrelles.com, http://www.burrelles.com.

302.23 USA
BURRELLE'S WEST MEDIA DIRECTORY (YEAR); CA, OR, WA, AZ. Text in English. a. USD 125 (effective 2001). adv. **Document type:** *Directory, Trade.*
Published by: Burrelle's Media Directories, 75 E Northfield Rd, Livingston, NJ 07039. TEL 973-992-6600, 800-876-3342, FAX 800-898-6677, directory@burrelles.com, info@burrelles.com, http://www.burrelles.com.

BUS GARAGE INDEX. see *TRANSPORTATION*

BUS INDUSTRY DIRECTORY. see *TRANSPORTATION*

387.029 USA
BUSINESS AND REGIONAL AEROSPACE DIRECTORY. Text in English. a. USD 89 per issue (effective 2004). **Document type:** *Directory, Trade.* **Description:** Up-to-date facts and figures in the U.S. and international commuter regional airline industries, including airlines, manufacturers, consultants, attorneys, air taxi operators, suppliers, trade associations, and more.
Formerly (until 2004): Regional Airline Directory
Published by: Access Intelligence, LLC (Subsidiary of: Veronis, Suhler & Associates Inc.), 1201 Seven Locks Rd, Ste 300, Potomac, MD 20854. TEL 301-354-2000, FAX 301-424-2058, clientservices@accessintel.com, http://www.pbimedia.com.

338.0025 AUT
BUSINESS CLASS. Text in German. a. EUR 19.99 (effective 2005). adv. **Document type:** *Directory, Trade.* **Description:** Contains data on over 120,000 Austrian business-to-business companies.
Formerly: Roter Herold
Published by: Herold Business Data GmbH & Co. KG, Guntramsdorferstr 105, Moedling, N 2340, Austria. TEL 43-2236-401133, FAX 43-2236-4018, kundendienst@herold.co.at, http://www.herold.co.at. Ed. Bettina Schoen. Adv. contacts Manfred Gansch, Martin Kargl.

382.029 FIN ISSN 0355-0346
HD9735.F49
BUSINESS CONTACTS IN FINLAND. Text in Finnish. 1974. irreg. free. adv.
Published by: Yritystieto Oy, PL 148, Helsinki, 00181, Finland. Ed. Borje Thilman. Circ: 15,000.

338.0029 AUT
BUSINESS DATA HUNGARY✶. Text in Hungarian, English, German. 1994. a. HUF 5,200. adv. **Document type:** *Directory.*
Formerly: Company Data Hungary
Published by: Herold Business Data GmbH, Guntramsdorferstrasse 105, Moedling, N 2340, Austria. Ed. Martina Bedi. Adv. contact Karin Schumach. Circ: 25,000.

BUSINESS DESK REFERENCE. see *BUSINESS AND ECONOMICS—Chamber Of Commerce Publications*

338.0029 HKG
BUSINESS DIRECTORY OF HONG KONG. Text in English. 1977. a. HKD 900 domestic; USD 160 foreign. adv. **Document type:** *Trade.* **Description:** Provides information on general business facilities in Hong Kong. Lists over 2900 manufacturers, 3600 importers and exporters, and 5500 services, professional firms and government departments. Includes personnel names, and telephone and fax numbers.
Published by: Current Publications Ltd., GPO Box 9848, Hong Kong, Hong Kong. FAX 852-2543-4702, info@current.com.hk. adv.: B&W page USD 1,200, color page USD 2,000; trim 7 x 10. **Dist. by:** Current Pacific Ltd., PO Box 36-536, Northcote, Auckland, New Zealand. TEL 64-9-480-1388, FAX 64-9-480-1387, info@cplnz.com, http://www.cplnz.com.

338.0029 FIN ISSN 0785-5540
HC340.2
BUSINESS FINLAND. Text in English. 1988. a. FIM 170 (effective 1999). adv. **Document type:** *Directory, Trade.* **Description:** Covers business, economy, and trade in Finland. Includes a list of major Finnish exporters.
Related titles: CD-ROM ed.: ISSN 1239-6494.
Published by: (Central Chamber of Commerce of Finland), Helsinki Media Company Oy, Special Magazines, PL 2, Helsinki Media, 00040, Finland. TEL 358-9-120-5911, FAX 358-0-120-5988. Ed. Veijo Kayhty. R&P Anneli Italvoma Alanen. Adv. contact Anneli Italuoma Alanen. Circ: 30,000.
Co-sponsor: Finnish Foreign Trade Association.

338.0029 IDN
BUSINESS GUIDE BOOK TO JAKARTA✶. Text in English. 1969. a. adv. illus.
Formerly: Djakarta Business Guide Book
Published by: Gabungan Importir Nasional Seluruh Indonesia/National Importers Association of Indonesia, Wisma Nusantara Bldg., Jalan Majapahit No. 1, Jakarta, Indonesia. TEL 021-360-643, FAX 62-021-367269. Circ: 10,000.

338.0029 DEU
BUSINESS INFORMATION BASICS. Text in English. a. GBP 95 (effective 2001). **Document type:** *Directory, Trade.* **Description:** Includes an up-to-date directory of basic business information sources.
Former titles (until 1992): Business Information Yearbook (0953-9263); (until 1988): Business Information Sourcebook
Published by: (Headland Business Information GBR), K.G. Saur Verlag GmbH (Subsidiary of: Gale Group), Ortlerstr 8, Munchen, 81373, Germany. TEL 49-89-769020, FAX 49-89-76902150, info@saur.de, http://www.saur.de.

338.0029 DEU ISSN 0966-2138
BUSINESS INFORMATION FROM GOVERNMENT. Text in English. 1992. biennial. GBP 95 (effective 2001). **Document type:** *Directory, Trade.* **Description:** Comprehensive guide to business information available from government departments and official bodies.
Published by: (Headland Business Information GBR), K.G. Saur Verlag GmbH (Subsidiary of: Gale Group), Ortlerstr 8, Munchen, 81373, Germany. TEL 49-89-769020, FAX 49-89-76902150, info@saur.de, http://www.saur.de.

380.1029 GBR ISSN 0266-3821
HF54.5 CODEN: BIREEY
BUSINESS INFORMATION REVIEW. Text in English. 1984. q. GBP 527, USD 921 to institutions; GBP 548, USD 959 combined subscription to institutions print & online eds. (effective 2006). adv. bk.rev. abstr.; bibl.; charts; stat. index. back issues avail.; reprints avail. **Document type:** *Journal, Academic/Scholarly.* **Description:** Includes articles written by field experts about business information sources, print and electronic. Analyzes information sources in specific industry sectors and countries, and the use of business information.
Related titles: Online - full text ed.: ISSN 1741-6450. GBP 521, USD 912 to institutions (effective 2006) (from EBSCO Publishing, Gale Group, O C L C Online Computer Library Center, Inc., Sage Publications, Inc., Swets Information Services).
Indexed: ABIn, BibInd, BrCerAb, C&ISA, CerAb, CorrAb, CurCont, E&CAJ, EMA, Emerald, IAA, Inspec, LISA, M&MA, M&TEA, MBF, METADEX, PAIS, WAA.
—BLDSC (2933.805000), AskIEEE, IE, Infotrieve, ingenta. **CCC.**
Published by: Sage Publications Ltd. (Subsidiary of: Sage Publications, Inc.), 1 Oliver's Yard, 55 City Rd, London, EC1 1SP, United Kingdom. TEL 44-20-73248500, FAX 44-20-73248600, info@sagepub.co.uk, http://www.sagepub.co.uk/journal.aspx?pid=105827. Ed. Tim Buckley Owen. **Subscr. in the Americas to:** Sage Publications, Inc., 2455 Teller Rd, Thousand Oaks, CA 91320. TEL 805-499-0721, FAX 805-499-0871, journals@sagepub.com.

670.29 USA
BUSINESS JOURNAL'S DIRECTORY OF MANUFACTURING✶. Text in English. a. USD 115. **Document type:** *Directory.* **Description:** Lists over 10,000 manufacturing firms in New Jersey. Provides address, telephone and fax numbers, year founded, sales or revenues, number of employees, SIC code, description, and names and titles of key executives. Includes indexes grouped by industry, geographically, by annual revenues, and by number of employees.
Published by: Corfacts, Business Information Division, c/o Business Journal of New Jersey, Box 920, Morristown, NJ 07751. Ed. Kathleen Barbarello.

380.1029 USA ISSN 0888-1413
HF3010
BUSINESS ORGANIZATIONS, AGENCIES, AND PUBLICATIONS DIRECTORY. Text in English. 1980. biennial, latest 2002. USD 535 (effective 2004). **Document type:** *Directory, Trade.* **Description:** Comprehensive guide to business-related resources.
Formerly: Business Organizations and Agencies Directory (0749-0801)
Related titles: Online - full text ed.
Published by: Gale Group (Subsidiary of: Thomson Corporation), 27500 Drake Rd, Farmington Hills, MI 48331-3535. TEL 248-699-8061, 800-877-4253, FAX 248-699-4253, galeord@gale.com, http://www.gale.com.

BUSINESS REVIEW - DIRECTORY. see *BUSINESS AND ECONOMICS—Chamber Of Commerce Publications*

338.0029 USA ISSN 1091-5508
HG4028.V3
BUSINESS VALUATION BY INDUSTRY REVIEW SERIES. Text in English. 1997. a. (in 5 vols.). USD 595 (effective 2005). adv. back issues avail. **Document type:** *Trade.* **Description:** Contains innumerable studies of actual businesses sold, their price information, financial statements and financial forecasts.
Related titles: CD-ROM ed.: USD 695 (effective 2001).
Published by: N V S T.com, Inc., 14450 N E 29th Pl., Ste.108, Bellevue, WA 98007. TEL 425-702-9733, 800-910-6878, FAX 425-702-9753, http://www.nvst.com/pubs/bvindustry-pub.asp. adv.: B&W page USD 900, color page USD 1,200; trim 10.75 x 7.5. Circ: 10,000.

658.0029 AUS ISSN 0068-4503
HF5292
THE BUSINESS WHO'S WHO OF AUSTRALIA. Text in English. 1964. a. AUD 795. adv. **Document type:** *Directory.* **Description:** Alphabetical listings of major Australian companies. Listings include company names and addresses, affiliated and subsidiary company names, key personnel, products and services, and annual sales figures.
Formerly: Business Who's Who of Australia and Australian Purchasing Yearbook
Related titles: CD-ROM ed.
—CCC.
Published by: Dun & Bradstreet Marketing Pty. Ltd., 19 Havilah St, Chatswood, NSW 2067, Australia. TEL 61-2-9352700, FAX 61-2-9352777. Pub., R&P Sue Francis. Circ: 5,700. **Dist. by:** Current Pacific Ltd., PO Box 36-536, Northcote, Auckland, New Zealand. TEL 64-9-480-1388, FAX 64-9-480-1387, info@cplnz.com, http://www.cplnz.com.

380.1029 TWN
BUSINESSMAN'S DIRECTORY, THE REPUBLIC OF CHINA. Text in Chinese, English. 1971. a. USD 80. adv. bk.rev. **Document type:** *Directory.*
Published by: Taiwan Enterprise Press, Ltd., PO Box 73-4, Taipei, Taiwan. Ed. Henry K C Lee. Circ: 30,000.

380.1 IRL ISSN 0791-5446
BUY & SELL. Text in English. 1990. 2/w. EUR 1.71 newsstand/cover (effective 2002). adv. **Document type:** *Newspaper, Consumer.*
Formerly (until 1991): B & S - Buy and Sell (0791-5039)
Related titles: Regional ed(s).: Buy & Sell (Munster ed.). ISSN 1393-2616. 1995.
Address: Buy & Sell House, Argyle Sq., Donnybrook, Dublin, 4, Ireland. TEL 353-1-6080700, FAX 353-1-6080701, tradeads@buyandsell.ie. Adv. contact Sarah-Jane Donnelly. page EUR 1,960.98. Circ: 78,282 (paid and controlled).

382.029 IND ISSN 0304-968X
HF3783
BUY FROM INDIA; world trade directory & handbook. Text in English. 1974. biennial. INR 300, USD 50 per issue. adv. illus. **Document type:** *Directory.*
Address: 10 Mangal Baugh, Pushpa Park, Daftary Rd., Malad (East), Mumbai, Maharashtra 400 097, India. TELEX 011-4220. Ed. S L Varma. Circ: 4,000.

380.1029 KOR
BUYERS' GUIDE✶. Text in Korean. 1973. a. USD 90.
Published by: Buyers Guide Corp., Korea World Trade Center, 159-1 Samsung-dong, Kangnam-gu, Seoul, 135729, Korea, S. TEL 02-551-2376, FAX 02-551-2377. Circ: 30,000. **Subscr. to:** C.P.O. Box 4922, Seoul, Korea, S.

BUYERS GUIDE FOR THE HEALTH CARE MARKET; a directory of products and service for health care institutions. see *HEALTH FACILITIES AND ADMINISTRATION*

380.1029 USA
BUYER'S GUIDE TO THE NEW YORK MARKET. Text in English. 1930. a. included with Earnshaw's magazine. adv.
Published by: Earnshaw Publications, Inc., 112 W 34th St, New York, NY 10120. Ed. Thomas W Hudson Jr. Circ: 10,000.

025.344 ITA ISSN 1122-8636
C D GUIDA MONACI. (Compact Disc) Text in Italian. s-a. **Document type:** *Directory, Consumer.* **Description:** Complete business data bank of the Italian industrial and service sectors.
Media: CD-ROM.
Published by: Guida Monaci SpA, Via Salaria 1319, Rome, 00138, Italy. TEL 39-06-8887777, FAX 39-06-8889996, guida.monaci@italybygm.it, http://www.italybygm.it.

C E D ANNUAL BUYER'S GUIDE. (Communications, Engineering and Design) see *COMMUNICATIONS—Television And Cable*

C F I INTERNATIONAL DIRECTORY. see *CLOTHING TRADE*

C I DIRECTORY. (Cosmetics International) see *BEAUTY CULTURE—Perfumes And Cosmetics*

C P I PRODUCT PROFILES. see *CHEMISTRY*

384 621.319 GBR ISSN 1350-9888
CABLING WORLD. Text in English. 1991. m. (10/yr.). free to qualified personnel. adv. **Document type:** *Directory, Trade.* **Description:** Provides information on suppliers and solutions for installation and maintenance projects.
Published by: Nexus Media Ltd. (Subsidiary of: Highbury House Communications PLC), Nexus House, Azalea Dr, Swanley, Kent BR8 8HU, United Kingdom. TEL 44-1322-660070, FAX 44-1322-616311, http://www.cabling-world.co.uk/, http://www.hhc.co.uk/. Ed. Robert Riggs TEL 44-1322-660070 ext 2272. Adv. contact Raif Hassan TEL 44-1322-660070 ext 2446. B&W page GBP 2,035, color page GBP 2,665; trim 210 x 297. Circ: 7,564.

380.1029 USA
CALIFORNIA BUSINESS CREDIT DIRECTORY. Text in English. a. USD 1,100 print, online & CD-ROM eds. (effective 2004 & 2005). back issues avail. **Document type:** *Directory.* **Description:** Contains credit ratings and other valuable information on all businesses within California. Includes company name & address, phone & fax numbers, key executive names & titles, lines of business, years in business, number of employees, estimated annual sales, volume credit rating code, and corporate linkage information.
Related titles: CD-ROM ed.; Diskette ed.; E-mail ed.; Fax ed.; Magnetic Tape ed.; Online - full text ed.
Published by: American Business Directories (Subsidiary of: American Business Information, Inc.), 5711 S 86th Circle, P O Box 27347, Omaha, NE 68127. TEL 402-593-4600, 888-946-9377, 877-708-3844, FAX 402-331-5481, sales@directoriesusa.com, http://www.directoriesusa.com.

338.0029 USA
CALIFORNIA BUSINESS DIRECTORY. Text in English. 1992. a. USD 1,100 combined subscription print, online & CD-ROM eds. (effective 2004 & 2005). back issues avail. **Document type:** *Directory.* **Description:** Includes all businesses in the state compiled from the yellow pages and telephone-verified. Each listing includes company name, complete address, phone number, name of owner or manager, employee size, sales volume codes, and credit rating codes.
Related titles: CD-ROM ed.; Diskette ed.; E-mail ed.; Fax ed.; Magnetic Tape ed.; Online - full text ed.
Published by: American Business Directories (Subsidiary of: American Business Information, Inc.), 5711 S 86th Circle, P O Box 27347, Omaha, NE 68127. TEL 402-593-4600, 888-946-9377, 877-708-3844, FAX 402-331-5481, karen.peters@unfousa.com, sales@directoriesusa.com, http://www.directoriesusa.com.

382.029 USA ISSN 0270-4862
HF5065.C2
CALIFORNIA INTERNATIONAL TRADE REGISTER✶. Text in English. 1980-1981; resumed 1989. a. USD 135 (effective 1999). adv. **Document type:** *Directory.* **Description:** Provides key facts on 7,600 California importers and exporters.
Related titles: Diskette ed.: USD 395 (effective 1999).
Published by: (California Trade and Commerce Agency), Database Publishing Company, 701 E Ball Rd Ste 100, Anaheim, CA 92805-5962. TEL 714-778-6400, FAX 714-778-6811. Ed. Sarah Fraser. R&P Vera Roldan. Circ: 750.

670.29 USA ISSN 0068-5739
T12
CALIFORNIA MANUFACTURERS REGISTER✶. Text in English. 1948. a. USD 175 (effective 1999). adv. tr.lit. **Document type:** *Directory.* **Description:** Provides information on over 35,000 manufacturers. Includes products and services, alphabetical and geographical sections, address, phone and SIC in all three sections.
Related titles: CD-ROM ed.: USD 645 (effective 1999); Diskette ed.
Published by: (California Manufacturers Association), Database Publishing Company, 701 E Ball Rd Ste 100, Anaheim, CA 92805-5962. TEL 714-778-6400, FAX 714-778-6811. Ed. Sarah Fraser. R&P Vera Roldan. Circ: 3,500. **Subscr. to:** PO Box 70024, Anaheim, CA 92625-0024. **Dist. by:** Current Pacific Ltd., PO Box 36-536, Northcote, Auckland, New Zealand. TEL 64-9-480-1388, FAX 64-9-480-1387, info@cplnz.com, http://www.cplnz.com.

770.29 JPN
CAMERART PHOTO TRADE DIRECTORY. Text in Japanese. 1958. a. USD 88.50 (effective 1999). illus. **Document type:** *Directory.*
Published by: Intercontinental Marketing Corp., I.P.O. Box 5056, Tokyo, 100-3191, Japan. TEL 81-3-3661-7458, tc9w-ball@asahi-net.or.jp.

796.7099405 AUS ISSN 1441-6417
CAMPERVAN & MOTORHOME TRADER. Text in English. m. AUD 54 (effective 2003). **Document type:** *Magazine, Trade.*
Published by: A C P Trader International Group (Subsidiary of: A C P Publishing Pty. Ltd.), 54-58 Park St, Sydney, NSW 1028, Australia. TEL 61-2-92828000, FAX 61-2-92674361, http://www.acp.com.au/magazinetitles/action/Campervan%20and%20Motorhome%20Trader/, http://www.tradergroup.com.au/. Ed. Ros Bromwich. Adv. contact Rick Smith. **Subscr. to:** Magshop, Reply Paid 4967, Sydney, NSW 2001, Australia. TEL 61-2-92828000, magshop@acp.com.au, http://magshop.com.au.

665.5029 CAN ISSN 0824-4766
CANADA A-Z; oil, gas, mining directory. Text in English. 1980. a. CND 95. adv. tr.lit. back issues avail. **Description:** Lists oil, gas and mining companies in Canada, geographically by cities and by types of activity.
Published by: Armadale Publications Inc., Box 1193, MPO, Edmonton, AB T5J 2M4, Canada. TEL 403-429-1073, FAX 403-425-5844. Ed. Winston Mohabir. Circ: 7,000.

B

670.29 CAN ISSN 1486-732X
CANADA'S GAS PLANT DIRECTORY. Text in English. 1993. a. CND 280 per issue (effective 2005). **Document type:** *Directory, Trade.* **Description:** Covers over 800 gas processing plants and compression facilities in Canada, including information on design capacity, capacity utilization, key personnel, location information, main contractors, operation pressures, pipeline interconnection information, plant processes, products and capacities turnarounds, special interest groups and working interest owners.
Formerly (until 1996): Alberta Gas Plant Directory (1195-4329)
Published by: Northern Star Communications, 900 6th Ave S W, 5th Fl, Calgary, AB T2P 3K2, Canada. TEL 403-263-6881, 800-526-4177, FAX 403-263-6886, nstar@northernstar.ab.ca, http://www.northernstar.ab.ca/channels/northernstar/canadagasplantdirectory.htm, http://www.northernstar.ab.ca/channels/northernstar/home.htm.

639.3 CAN ISSN 1490-9405
CANADIAN AQUACULTURE DIRECTORY, PRODUCER & SUPPLIERS GUIDE. Text in English. 1997. a. CND 199.95 (effective 2003). **Document type:** *Directory, Trade.*
Related titles: CD-ROM ed.: CND 299.95 (effective 2003).
Published by: Contact Canada, 390 Goward Rd, Victoria, BC V9E 2J5, Canada. TEL 250-708-0427, 888-502-6666, FAX 250-708-0429, ccinfo@contactcanada.com, http://www.contactcanada.com/canaqua/.

660.602571 CAN ISSN 1700-8492
CANADIAN BIOTECHNOLOGY. Text in English. 1999. a. CND 199.95 (effective 2003). **Document type:** *Directory, Trade.* **Description:** Contains over 1,100 profiles of biotech companies, research groups, service and supply companies.
Formerly (until 2001): Canadian Biotechnology Directory, Industry and Suppliers Guide (1490-7852)
Related titles: CD-ROM ed.: CND 299.95 (effective 2003).
Published by: Contact Canada, 390 Goward Rd, Victoria, BC V9E 2J5, Canada. TEL 250-708-0427, 888-502-6666, FAX 250-708-0429, ccinfo@contactcanada.com, http://www.contactcanada.com/biotech/.

670.29 CAN
CANADIAN CHEMICAL DIRECTORY. Text in English. 1917. a. CND 150, USD 110 (effective 2000). **Document type:** *Directory.*
Formerly: Chemical Buyer's Guide (0069-2891)
—Linda Hall.
Published by: Camford Information Services Inc., 38 Groomsport Cres, Scarborough, ON M1T 2K9, Canada. TEL 416-291-3215. Pub. Bob Douglas.

670.29 CAN ISSN 0068-8452
HD9655.C2
CANADIAN CHEMICAL, PHARMACEUTICAL AND PRODUCT DIRECTORY. Text in English. 1948. a. CND 35, USD 45. adv. index. **Document type:** *Directory.* **Description:** Listing of Canadian manufacturers, distributors and services for chemical raw materials, products, pharmaceuticals, and equipment. Contains three sections arranged alphabetically by name, products and trade names.
Formerly (until 1967): Canadian Chemical Directory (0381-5749)
Published by: Lloyd Publications of Canada, 66 Falby Ct, Ste 1603, Ajax, ON L1S 3L2, Canada. TEL 416-619-0421. Ed. J Lloyd. Circ: 7,000.

617.6002571 CAN ISSN 1203-2832
CANADIAN DENTAL DIRECTORY. Text in English. 1996. biennial. CND 209 per issue (effective 2005). **Document type:** *Directory, Trade.* **Description:** Lists 15,000 Canadian dentists, dental suppliers and other industry professionals; also includes contact information.
Related titles: CD-ROM ed.
Published by: Business Information Group, 12 Concorde Pl, Ste 800, Toronto, ON M3C 4J2, Canada. TEL 416-442-5600, 800-668-2374, FAX 416-442-2191, http://www.businessinformationgroup.ca/dental/cnddentaldir.asp.

CANADIAN ENVIRONMENTAL DIRECTORY; complete guide to the business of environmental management. see *ENVIRONMENTAL STUDIES*

338.47664 CAN ISSN 0068-8754
CANADIAN FOOD AND PACKAGING DIRECTORY. Text in English. 1924. a. CND 35, USD 45. adv. index. **Document type:** *Directory.* **Description:** Listing of Canadian manufacturers, distributors and wholesalers of foods, packaging, and equipment. Contains three sections arranged alphabetically by name, products and trade names.
Published by: Lloyd Publications of Canada, 66 Falby Ct, Ste 1603, Ajax, ON L1S 3L2, Canada. TEL 416-619-0421. Ed. J Lloyd. Circ: 8,500.

685.31029 CAN ISSN 0068-8762
CANADIAN FOOTWEAR & LEATHER DIRECTORY. Text in English. 1924. a. CND 30, USD 40. adv. index. **Document type:** *Directory.* **Description:** Listing of Canadian manufacturers, distributors and wholesalers of footwear, leather goods, and equipment. Contains three sections arranged alphabetically by name, products and trade names.
Published by: Lloyd Publications of Canada, 66 Falby Ct, Ste 1603, Ajax, ON L1S 3L2, Canada. TEL 416-619-0421. Ed. J Lloyd. Circ: 5,500.

381.029 CAN
CANADIAN FORCES BASE KINGSTON OFFICIAL DIRECTORY. Text in English, French. a. adv. **Document type:** *Directory.* **Description:** Published for exclusive distribution to all military personnel of C.F.B. Kingston and its associated units. Provides correct information on the area phone numbers, shops, services, accommodations, entertainment and restaurants.
Published by: Kingston Publications, P O Box 1352, Kingston, ON K7L 5C6, Canada. TEL 613-549-8442. Ed. Mary Laflamme. Adv. contact Ruth Kirkby.

749.029 CAN ISSN 0068-8789
CANADIAN FURNITURE & FURNISHINGS DIRECTORY. Text in English. 1924. a. CND 30, USD 40. adv. index. **Document type:** *Directory.* **Description:** Listing of Canadian manufacturers, distributors and wholesalers of furniture, and house furnishings. Contains three sections arranged alphabetically by name, products and trade names.
Published by: Lloyd Publications of Canada, 66 Falby Ct, Ste 1603, Ajax, ON L1S 3L2, Canada. TEL 416-619-0421. Ed. J Lloyd. Circ: 5,700.

380.1029 CAN ISSN 0456-3867
TS26
CANADIAN HARDWARE, ELECTRICAL & BUILDING SUPPLY DIRECTORY. Text in English. 1949. a. CND 35, USD 45. adv. index. **Document type:** *Directory.* **Description:** Listing of Canadian manufacturers, wholesalers and distributors of hardware, electrical and building products. Contains three sections: alphabetical by name, product and trade name.
Published by: Lloyd Publications of Canada, 66 Falby Ct, Ste 1603, Ajax, ON L1S 3L2, Canada. TEL 416-619-0421. Ed. J Lloyd. Circ: 8,500.

647.9029 CAN ISSN 0381-5765
CANADIAN HOTEL, RESTAURANT, INSTITUTION & STORE EQUIPMENT DIRECTORY. Text in English. 1925. a. CND 35, USD 45. adv. index. **Document type:** *Directory.* **Description:** Listing of Canadian manufacturers, distributors and wholesalers of hotel, restaurant, institution and store equipment. Contains three sections: alphabetical by name, products and trade names.
Published by: Lloyd Publications of Canada, 66 Falby Ct, Ste 1603, Ajax, ON L1S 3L2, Canada. TEL 416-619-0421. Ed. J Lloyd. Circ: 8,300.

382.029 CAN ISSN 1180-0828
CANADIAN INTERNATIONAL TRADE DIRECTORY. Text in English. 1990. q. CND 200 (effective 2000). **Document type:** *Directory.* **Description:** Examines the world trade scene from a Canadian perspective.
Published by: Intratech (Subsidiary of: E.L. LittleJohn and Associates), P O Box 56067, Minto Place Postal Outlet, Ottawa, ON K1R 7Z1, Canada. TEL 613-235-9183, FAX 613-594-3857. Ed. Edward L Littlejohn. Circ: 200.

391.7029 CAN ISSN 0068-9041
CANADIAN JEWELLERY & GIFTWARE DIRECTORY. Text in English. 1924. a. CND 35, USD 45. adv. index. **Document type:** *Directory.* **Description:** Listing of Canadian manufacturers, distributors and wholesalers of jewellery, giftware, equipment and supplies. Contains three sections arranged alphabetically by name, products and trade name.
Published by: Lloyd Publications of Canada, 66 Falby Ct, Ste 1603, Ajax, ON L1S 3L2, Canada. TEL 416-619-0421. Ed. J Lloyd. Circ: 7,000.

338.1029 CAN ISSN 0315-0879
HF3223
CANADIAN KEY BUSINESS DIRECTORY. Text in English. 1974. a. USD 450. **Document type:** *Directory.*
—CISTI.
Published by: D & B Companies of Canada Ltd., 5770 Hurontario St, Mississauga, ON L5R 3GH, Canada. TEL 416-568-6147, FAX 416-568-6197. Ed. Raymond Martin. Circ: 2,500.

780.29 CAN ISSN 0381-5730
CANADIAN MUSIC DIRECTORY. Text in English. 1926. a. CND 30, USD 40. adv. index. **Document type:** *Directory.* **Description:** Listing of Canadian manufacturers, distributors and wholesalers of music, musical instruments, supplies and more. Contains three sections: alphabetical by name, products and trade names.
Published by: Lloyd Publications of Canada, 66 Falby Ct, Ste 1603, Ajax, ON L1S 3L2, Canada. TEL 416-619-0421. Ed. J Lloyd. Circ: 5,300.

CANADIAN PETROLEUM INDUSTRY. see *PETROLEUM AND GAS*

382.029 CAN ISSN 1183-1677
CANADIAN R & D DIRECTORY. Text in English. 1990. base vol. plus q. updates. CND 200 (effective 2000). **Document type:** *Directory.* **Description:** Lists R&D facilities in Canada, government, universities. Includes R&D tax incentives, government R&D funding programs.
Published by: Intratech (Subsidiary of: E.L. LittleJohn and Associates), P O Box 56067, Minto Place Postal Outlet, Ottawa, ON K1R 7Z1, Canada. TEL 613-235-9183, FAX 613-594-3857. Ed. E L Littlejohn. Circ: 300.

THE CANADIAN RECYCLING HANDBOOK AND DIRECTORY; a guide to waste reduction and recycling for the institutional, commercial and industrial sectors. see *ENVIRONMENTAL STUDIES—Waste Management*

CANADIAN RECYCLING MARKET. see *ENVIRONMENTAL STUDIES—Waste Management*

796.029 CAN ISSN 0316-7771
CANADIAN SPORTING GOODS & PLAYTHINGS. DIRECTORY. Text in English. 1949. a. CND 35, USD 45. adv. index. **Document type:** *Directory.* **Description:** Listing of Canadian manufacturers, distributors and wholesalers of sporting goods, playthings, and recreational equipment. Contains three sections arranged alphabetically by name, products and trade names.
Published by: Lloyd Publications of Canada, 66 Falby Ct, Ste 1603, Ajax, ON L1S 3L2, Canada. TEL 416-619-0421. Ed. J Lloyd. Circ: 8,000.

677.0029 CAN ISSN 0068-9858
CANADIAN TEXTILE DIRECTORY. Text in English. 1924. a. CND 35, USD 45. adv. index. **Document type:** *Directory.*
Published by: Lloyd Publications of Canada, 66 Falby Ct, Ste 1603, Ajax, ON L1S 3L2, Canada. TEL 416-619-0421. Ed. J Lloyd. Circ: 7,500.

688.72029 CAN ISSN 1209-6083
CANADIAN TOY & DECORATION FAIR GUIDE & MEMBERSHIP DIRECTORY. Text in English, French. 1941. a. CND 16.05 (effective 2000). adv. **Document type:** *Newspaper, Trade.*
Former titles (until 1994): Canadian Toy & Decoration Fair (0834-2202); (until 1983): Toy and Decoration Fair Directory (0317-9443); (until 1974): Canadian Toy and Decoration Fair (0833-5222); (until 1973): Canadian Toy Fair (0068-9890); (until 1970): Canadian Toy Fair. Official Directory (0833-5214); (until 196?): Canadian Toy Fair. Directory (0833-5206)
Published by: Canadian Toy Association, P O Box 294, Kleinburg, ON L0J 1C0, Canada. TEL 416-893-1689, FAX 416-893-2392, http://www.cdntoyassn.com. Ed. Sheila Edmondson. Circ: 3,500.

380.1029 CAN ISSN 0068-9904
HF3223
CANADIAN TRADE INDEX. Text in English. 1900. a. CND 249 per issue (effective 2005). adv. index. **Document type:** *Directory, Abstract/Index.*
Related titles: CD-ROM ed.: CND 249 per issue.
—CISTI. **CCC.**
Published by: Canadian Manufacturers & Exporters, Canadian Trade Index, c/o MacRae's Blue Book Ltd, 2085 Hurontario St, Ste 208, Mississauga, ON L5A 4G1, Canada. TEL 905-290-1818, 877-463-6284, FAX 905-290-1760, info@owen-media.com, http://www.ctidirectory.com. Ed. Hugh Owen. Adv. contact Robert Dunford. Circ: 13,000.

338.0029 CAN ISSN 0068-9955
CANADIAN VARIETY MERCHANDISE DIRECTORY. Text in English. 1924. a. CND 35, USD 45. adv. index. **Document type:** *Directory.* **Description:** Listing of Canadian manufacturers, distributors and wholesalers of toys, notions, stationery, and office equipment. Contains three sections arranged alphabetically by name, products and trade names.
Formerly: Canadian Toy, Notion and Stationery Directory
Published by: Lloyd Publications of Canada, 66 Falby Ct, Ste 1603, Ajax, ON L1S 3L2, Canada. TEL 416-619-0421. Ed. J Lloyd. Circ: 6,000.

380.1029 USA
CANDY BUYERS' DIRECTORY. (Includes: Directory of Candy Brokers) Text in English. 1932. a. USD 80 per issue domestic; USD 83 per issue in Canada & Mexico; USD 95 per issue elsewhere (effective 2003). adv. **Document type:** *Directory, Trade.* **Description:** Lists manufacturers, sellers and importers of these items including brand names and products.
Published by: Manufacturing Confectioner Publishing Company, 711 W Water St, PO Box 266, Princeton, WI 54968. TEL 920-295-6969, FAX 920-295-6843, mccutcheons@gomc.com, http://www.gomc.com/sup_file/cb_index.html, http://www.gomc.com/display.asp?pageId=home. Circ: 12,000.

796.54029 AUS
CARAVAN CAMPING DIRECTORY. Text in English. a. membership. adv. **Document type:** *Directory.*
Published by: (National Roads and Motorists Association), N R M A Ltd., 151 Clarence St, Sydney, NSW 2000, Australia. TEL 64-2-2922631, FAX 64-2-2922639. R&P Stephen Salter. Adv. contact Vicky Syrace.

CARAVAN INDUSTRY SUPPLIES & SERVICES DIRECTORY. see *SPORTS AND GAMES—Outdoor Life*

388.3 AUS
CARAVAN TRADER. Text in English. m. AUD 54 (effective 2003). **Document type:** *Magazine, Trade.*

Published by: A C P Trader International Group (Subsidiary of: A C P Publishing Pty. Ltd.), 54-58 Park St, Sydney, NSW 1028, Australia. TEL 61-2-92828000, FAX 61-2-92674361, http://www.acp.com.au/magazinetitles/action/Caravan%20Trader/, http://www.tradergroup.com.au/. Ed. Ros Bromwich. Adv. contact Rick Smith. **Subscr. to:** Magshop, Reply Paid 4967, Sydney, NSW 2001, Australia. TEL 61-2-92828000, magshop@acp.com.au, http://magshop.com.au.

CARD INDUSTRY DIRECTORY. see *BUSINESS AND ECONOMICS—Banking And Finance*

338.0029 USA
CARIBBEAN BUSINESS TO BUSINESS YELLOW PAGES. Text in English. 1980. a. **Document type:** *Directory.* **Description:** Business-to-business import/export directory lists 50,000 businesses from the Caribbean and 1400 US companies which do business in the region, classed by product or service.
Formerly: Caribbean Yellow Pages
Published by: Caribbean Publishing Co. Ltd., 815 NW 57th Ave., Ste. 125, Miami, FL 33126-2068. TEL 305-442-4505, FAX 305-442-8329. Ed., Adv. contact Mary Weinberg. Circ: 50,000.

382.029 USA
CARIBBEAN - LATIN AMERICAN PROFILE. Text in English. 1979. a. USD 95 (effective 2002). adv. maps; stat. **Document type:** *Trade.* **Description:** Covers economy, tourism, government, politics, and business climate.
Former titles: Caribbean Basin Profile; Caribbean Basin Commercial Profile; Caribbean Business Directory; Caribbean Directory
Published by: Caribbean Publishing Co. Ltd., 815 NW 57th Ave., Ste. 125, Miami, FL 33126-2068. TEL 305-442-4205, FAX 305-442-8329. Ed. Mark Ercolin. R&P Benoit Parent. Adv. contact Mary Weinberg. Circ: 10,000.

CARROLL'S DEFENSE INDUSTRY CHARTS. see *MILITARY*

CARROLL'S FEDERAL DIRECTORY; executive, legislative, and judicial. see *PUBLIC ADMINISTRATION*

CARROLL'S FEDERAL REGIONAL DIRECTORY. see *PUBLIC ADMINISTRATION*

CARROLL'S STATE DIRECTORY. see *PUBLIC ADMINISTRATION—Municipal Government*

CARROLL'S STATE DIRECTORY (YEAR) ANNUAL. see *PUBLIC ADMINISTRATION—Municipal Government*

CASTING DIRECTORY/LIMELIGHT ROLVERDELINGSGIDS. see *THEATER*

CASTING SOURCE DIRECTORY. see *METALLURGY*

338.0029 USA ISSN 1042-6167
HF5465.5
CATALOG HANDBOOK; catalog of catalogs. Text in English. 1989. q. USD 22.95; USD 6.99 newsstand/cover (effective 2005). **Document type:** *Directory, Consumer.* **Description:** Directory of retail mail-order catalogs.
Published by: Enterprise Magazines, Inc., 1020 N Broadway, Ste 111, Milwaukee, WI 53202. TEL 800-272-0246. Ed., R&P Ms. Maria Lahm. Pub. Mrs. Betsy L Green. Adv. contacts Ms. Barbara Yelmene, Ms. Kristin Over.

363.75029 USA ISSN 1054-2426
THE CATALOG OF FUNERAL HOME SUPPLIES. Text in English. 1988. a., latest 2001. USD 20 (effective 2005). 150 p./no.; **Document type:** *Directory, Trade.* **Description:** Covers funeral and cemetary services and includes a list of supply firms.
Related titles: Online - full text ed.; ♦ Supplement to: The National Yellow Book of Funeral Directors. ISSN 1054-8238.
Published by: Nomis Publications, Inc., PO Box 5159, Youngstown, OH 44514. TEL 330-965-2380, 800-321-7479, FAX 330-965-2381, info@yelobk.com, http://www.yelobk.com. Ed., Pub., R&P, Adv. contact Margaret Rouzzo. Circ: 3,000 (paid); 18,000 (free).

670.29 USA
CATALOG OF U.S. VALVES. Text in English. triennial. free to qualified personnel. tr.lit. **Document type:** *Trade.* **Description:** Reference to valve and actuator products and services offered by industrial valve manufacturers in the United States for end users and purchasers.
Published by: Valve Manufacturers Association of America, 1050 17th St, N W, Ste 280, Washington, DC 20036. TEL 202-331-8105, FAX 202-296-0378, vma@vma.org, http://www.vma.org. Ed. Lisa Cherubini. Circ: 20,000.

CATALOGO MOTORISTICO. see *TRANSPORTATION—Automobiles*

380.1029 MEX
CATALOGO PRODUCTOS Y SERVICIOS DEL ESTADO DE MEXICO. Text in Spanish. 1973. a.
Published by: Asociacion de Industriales del Estado de Mexico, Diagonal Jose T. Cuellar 99 A, Mexico City 8, DF, Mexico.

338.0029 CYM
CAYMAN ISLANDS YEARBOOK AND BUSINESS DIRECTORY. Text in English. 1987. a. KYD 34 (effective 2000). adv. **Document type:** *Directory.*
Published by: Cayman Free Press Ltd., P O Box 1365, Grand Cayman, Cayman Isl. TEL 345-949-5111, FAX 345-949-7033. Ed. Colleen Webb. Pub., R&P Brian Uzzell. Adv. contact Valerie Simon. Circ: 5,000.

382.029 ANT
CENTRAL BUREAU OF STATISTICS. QUARTERLY TRADE REPORT OF CURACAO AND BONAIRE. Text and summaries in English. 1954. q. ANG 35. **Document type:** *Government.*
Former titles (until 1992): Im- and Export Quarterly Statistics of Curacao and Bonaire by Commodity - Country; (until 1987): Kwartaalstatistiek van de In- en Uitvoer per Land - Goederensoort van Curacao en Bonaire
Published by: Central Bureau of Statistics, Fort Amsterdam z/n, Willemstad, Curacao, Netherlands Antilles. TEL 599-9-611031, FAX 599-9-611696, ank0004@ibm.net. Circ: 250.

CENTRE RANKINGS. see *BUSINESS AND ECONOMICS—Abstracting, Bibliographies, Statistics*

001.4029 GBR ISSN 1365-4322
CENTRES, BUREAUX & RESEARCH INSTITUTES; the directory of UK concentrations of effort, information, and expertise. Text in English. 1987. irreg., latest vol.4, 2000. GBP 125, USD 250 (effective 2001). **Document type:** *Directory.* **Description:** Lists 2,000 centers of research and expertise in the U.K.
Formerly (until 1993): Centres and Bureaux (1352-3228) —BLDSC (3113.170110).
Published by: C.B.D. Research Ltd., 15 Wickham Rd, Beckenham, Kent BR3 5JS, United Kingdom. TEL 44-20-86507745, FAX 44-20-86500768, cbd@cbdresearch.com, http://www.glen.co.uk/cbd, http://www.cbdresearch.com. Ed. C.M. Edwards.

666.029 GBR
CERAMIC INDUSTRIES INTERNATIONAL DIRECTORY. Text in English. 197?. a. GBP 58; GBP 63 foreign. **Document type:** *Directory, Trade.*
Formerly: Ceramic Industries International Buyer's Guide & Directory (0957-3194)
Published by: Turret R A I plc, Armstrong House, 38 Market Sq, Uxbridge, Middx UB8 1TG, United Kingdom. TEL 44-1895-454545, FAX 44-1895-454647.

631.587029 USA
CERTIFIED IRRIGATION SPECIALISTS AND TECHNICIANS DIRECTORY. Text in English. a. free. **Document type:** *Directory.* **Description:** Lists certified landscape irrigation auditors, designers, contractors and managers.
Published by: Irrigation Association, 8260 Willow Oaks Corp Dr, Ste 120, Fairfax, VA 22031-4513. TEL 703-573-3551, FAX 703-573-1913, http://www.irrigation.org. Circ: 1,000.

380.1029 PAK
CHAMBER'S TRADE DIRECTORY. Text in English. irreg. PKR 150. **Document type:** *Directory.*
Published by: Karachi Chamber of Commerce and Industry, Aiwan-e-Tijarat Rd., Shahrah-e-Liaquat, Karachi, 74000, Pakistan.

540.29 USA
CHEM SOURCES INTERNATIONAL. Text in English. 1987. s-a. USD 995 per issue (effective 2005). adv. stat. **Document type:** *Directory, Trade.* **Description:** Lists chemical compounds and distributors produced by foreign firms.
Related titles: CD-ROM ed.: USD 995 per issue (effective 2005); Online - full content ed.: USD 995 per issue (effective 2005).
Published by: Chemical Sources International, Inc., PO Box 1824, Clemson, SC 29633-1824. TEL 864-646-7840, FAX 864-646-9938, info@chemsources.com, http://www.chemsources.com. R&P Krohn Dale. Adv. contacts Michael Thornton, Mike Desing TEL 804-646-7840. B&W page USD 3,500, color page USD 5,000; trim 9.5 x 7.5.

540.29 USA ISSN 0094-6567
TP12
CHEM SOURCES U S A. Text in English. 1958. a. USD 450 per vol. (effective 2003). adv. 1000 p./no. 2 cols./p.; **Document type:** *Catalog, Corporate.* **Description:** Chemical source directory listing compounds of US chemical firms.
Related titles: CD-ROM ed.: USD 495 per vol. (effective 2003); Online - full text ed.
Published by: Chemical Sources International, Inc., PO Box 1824, Clemson, SC 29633-1824. TEL 864-646-7840, FAX 864-646-9938, info@chemsources.com, http://www.chemsources.com. R&Ps Dale Krohn, Krohn Dale. Adv. contacts Michael Thornton, Mike Desing TEL 804-646-7840.

540.29 DEU
CHEMCOMPASS. Text in German. 1953. a. **Document type:** *Directory, Trade.* **Description:** Handbook of the chemical industry in Germany listing 13,000 products, 2,000 manufacturers, and 800 brand names.
Formerly (until 2000): Firmenhandbuch Chemische Industrie (0428-478X)
Media: Online - full content. **Related titles:** CD-ROM ed.
Published by: Verband der Chemischen Industrie, Karlstr 21, Frankfurt am Main, 60329, Germany. TEL 49-69-25560, FAX 49-69-25561471, info@chemcompass.de, internetinfo@vci.de, http://www.chemcompass.de, http://www.vci.de. Circ: 3,000.

540.29 GBR
CHEMICAL ENGINEERING AND CONSTRUCTION DIRECTORY. Text in English. every 2 yrs. GBP 140, USD 215; GBP 190, USD 295 with diskette. adv. **Document type:** *Directory.* **Description:** Contains information on regional contacts, key technology licenses, reference projects worldwide, and relevant contractors in your sector.
Related titles: Diskette ed.
Published by: Reed Business Information Ltd. (Subsidiary of: Reed Business), Quadrant House, The Quadrant, Brighton Rd, Sutton, Surrey SM2 5AS, United Kingdom. TEL 44-208-652-3500, FAX 44-208-652-8977, rbi.subscriptions@qss-uk.com, http://www.reedbusiness.co.uk/. Ed. Alan Tyler TEL 44-20-8652-8126. Adv. contact Anne Martin. **Subscr. to:** Quadrant Subscription Services, PO Box 302, Haywards Heath, W Sussex RH16 3YY, United Kingdom. TEL 44-1444-445566, FAX 44-1444-445447.

CHEMICAL ENGINEERING BUYERS' GUIDE. see *CHEMISTRY*

CHEMICAL INDUSTRY EUROPE. see *ENGINEERING—Chemical Engineering*

CHEMICAL YELLOW PAGES DIRECTORY. see *CHEMISTRY*

CHEMICALS. see *CHEMISTRY*

540.29 JPN
CHEMINDEX; chemical buyers' guide for Japan. Text in Japanese. 1988. a. JPY 26,250 (effective 2005). 900 p./no.; **Document type:** *Abstract/Index.* **Description:** Lists over 16,000 chemical products, major manufacturers, code numbers, addresses, and traders.
Published by: Chemical Daily Co. Ltd., 16-8, Nihonbashi-Hamacho 3-Chome, Chuo-ku, Tokyo, 103-8485, Japan. TEL 81-3-36637932, FAX 81-3-36637275, info@jcw-online.com, http://www.chemicaldaily.co.jp/.

CHEMIST & DRUGGIST DIRECTORY. see *PHARMACY AND PHARMACOLOGY*

338.0029 USA ISSN 1048-7239
HF5068.C4
CHICAGO AREA BUSINESS DIRECTORY. Text in English. 1985. a. USD 1,100 combined subscription print, online & CD-ROM eds. (effective 2004 & 2005). back issues avail. **Document type:** *Directory.* **Description:** Includes all businesses in the Chicago area compiled from the yellow pages and telephone-verified. Each listing includes company name, complete address, name of owner or manager, employer size, sales volume rating codes.
Related titles: CD-ROM ed.; Diskette ed.; E-mail ed.; Fax ed.; Magnetic Tape ed.; Online - full text ed.
Published by: American Business Directories (Subsidiary of: American Business Information, Inc.), 5711 S 86th Circle, P O Box 27347, Omaha, NE 68127. TEL 402-593-4600, 888-946-9377, 877-708-3844, FAX 402-331-5481, karen.peters@infousa.com, sales@directoriesusa.com, http://www.directoriesusa.com.

CHICAGO AREA H I V SERVICES & PROFESSIONALS DIRECTORY. see *MEDICAL SCIENCES—Communicable Diseases*

380.1029 688 USA
CHICAGO SHOPS. Text in English. 2001. a. USD 4.99 per issue (effective 2005). adv. **Document type:** *Directory, Consumer.* **Description:** Guide to shopping in Chicago. Features more than 800 shops in catagories ranging from women's fashions to home accessories, stationary, gifts, food and wine.
Published by: Chicago Tribune Company, 435 N Michigan Ave, Ste 1100, Chicago, IL 60611. TEL 312-222-8999, FAX 312-222-0287, http://www.chicagomag.com. Pub. Randy Hano. Adv. contact Jen Ullrich Eveslage. B&W page USD 4,485, color page USD 6,165; trim 8 x 10.5.

384.14029 HKG
CHINA FAX & TELEX DIRECTORY. Text in English. 1989. a. HKD 345 in Hong Kong; USD 97 elsewhere. **Document type:** *Directory.* **Description:** Lists over 19,000 major organizations in China alphabetically, geographically, numerically by fax and telex, and by industry.
Published by: China Phone Book Company Ltd., 24-F Citicorp Centre, 18 Whitfield Rd, GPO Box 11581, Hong Kong, Hong Kong. FAX 852-2503-1526, cpb@feer.com.

381.029 CHN
CHINA LEADING COMPANIES. Text in English, Chinese. 1992. a. USD 70. adv. **Document type:** *Directory.*
Published by: China Statistical Information and Consultancy Service Center, 38 Yuetan Nanjie, Sanlihe, Beijing, 100826, China. TEL 86-10-8015074, FAX 86-10-8015078.

CHINA LEATHER. see *LEATHER AND FUR INDUSTRIES*

B

338.0029 HKG ISSN 0250-4170
HF5260.A3
CHINA PHONE BOOK & ADDRESS DIRECTORY. Text in Chinese, English. a. back issues avail. **Document type:** *Directory.*
Published by: China Phone Book Company Ltd., 24-F Citicorp Centre, 18 Whitfield Rd, GPO Box 11581, Hong Kong, Hong Kong. TEL 852-508-4405, FAX 852-503-1526. Ed. Mary Ng Wai Yuen.

338.0029 HKG
CHINA PHONE BOOK & BUSINESS DIRECTORY. Text in Chinese, English. 1978. s-a. HKD 750, USD 79 per issue in Hong Kong; USD 97 per issue elsewhere. adv. **Document type:** *Directory.* **Description:** Over 19,000 listings of significant organizations in China with full contact details. Classified by provinces and by major industry groups.
—BLDSC (3180.219000).
Published by: China Phone Book Company Ltd., 24-F Citicorp Centre, 18 Whitfield Rd, GPO Box 11581, Hong Kong, Hong Kong. FAX 852-2503-1526. Adv. contact Vincci Yu. B&W page USD 4,800, color page USD 6,700; trim 276 x 200. Circ: 15,000.

677.0029 GBR
CHINA TEXTILE & GARMENT DIRECTORY. Text in English. 1995. a., latest 2004. GBP 380 per issue (effective 2005). **Document type:** *Directory, Trade.*
Formerly: Chinese Textile Industry Directory
Published by: World Textile Publications Ltd., Perkin House, 1 Longlands St, Bradford, W Yorks BD1 2TP, United Kingdom. TEL 44-1274-378800, FAX 44-1274-378811, info@world-textile.net, http://www.world-textile.net/contact.html.

380.1029 SGP
CHINESE YELLOW PAGES. Text in English. a.
Related titles: Chinese ed.
Published by: Integrated Information Pte. Ltd. (Subsidiary of: Singapore Telecom), Orchard P.O. Box 389, Singapore, Singapore. adv.: B&W page USD 17,600, color page USD 21,725; 260 x 188. Circ: 175,000.

791.43029 USA ISSN 0894-8674
PN1998.A1
CINEMATOGRAPHERS, PRODUCTION DESIGNERS, COSTUME DESIGNERS & FILM EDITORS GUIDE. Text in English. 1988. a. USD 55 (effective 1996). adv. **Document type:** *Directory.* **Description:** Lists film craftspeople and technicians in the motion picture industry.
Published by: IFILM, 1024 N Orange Dr, Hollywood, CA 90038. TEL 323-308-FILM, http://www.ifilm.com. Circ: 2,500.

338.0029 GBR ISSN 0142-5072
DA679
CITY OF LONDON DIRECTORY & LIVERY COMPANIES GUIDE. Text in English. 1863. a. GBP 20.50 (effective 2000). adv. **Document type:** *Directory.* **Description:** Lists names and addresses of liverymen of London, by company.
Published by: City Press Ltd., 42 North Sta. Rd, Colchester, Essex CO1 1RB, United Kingdom. TEL 44-1206-545121, FAX 44-1206-545190, TELEX 98517 DISOP G. Ed., Pub. Patricia M Hetherington. R&P Christopher Hayman. Adv. contact Annabel Palmer. Circ: 1,500 (paid).

CITYFILE. see *BUSINESS AND ECONOMICS—Banking And Finance*

382.029 HKG
CLASSIFIED INTERNATIONAL BUSINESS DIRECTORY FOR CHINA. Text in Chinese. 1981. biennial. HKD 180. adv. bk.rev. **Document type:** *Directory.*
Published by: China Council for the Promotion of International Trade, GPO Box 3724, Hong Kong, Hong Kong. Ed. Richard L C Wong. Circ: 40,000.

CO-OP ADVERTISING PROGRAM SOURCEBOOK (YEAR). see *ADVERTISING AND PUBLIC RELATIONS*

622.029 USA ISSN 1045-6430
TN805.A4
COAL MINE DIRECTORY. Text in English. 1972. a. USD 149 in North America; USD 184 elsewhere (effective 1999). adv. **Document type:** *Directory.* **Description:** Lists all operating coal mines and processing plants in the United States and Canada, including names, addresses, phone and fax numbers, production tonnages, mining types and personnel.
Published by: Primedia Business Magazines & Media, Inc. (Subsidiary of: Primedia, Inc.), 330 N Wabash Ave, Ste 2300, Chicago, IL 60611. inquiries@primediabusiness.com, http://www.primediabusiness.com. Ed. Arthur P Sanda. Pub. Larry Greenberger. R&P, Adv. contact Scott Reynolds TEL 312-609-4352. Circ: 800 (paid).

COFFEE INTERNATIONAL DIRECTORY. see *FOOD AND FOOD INDUSTRIES*

COLE'S REGISTER OF BRITISH ANTIQUARIAN & SECONDHAND BOOKDEALERS. see *PUBLISHING AND BOOK TRADE*

COLLEGE - UNIVERSITY FOODSERVICE WHO'S WHO. see *FOOD AND FOOD INDUSTRIES*

380.1029 USA
COLORADO BUSINESS CREDIT DIRECTORY. Text in English. a. USD 1,100 combined subscription print, online & CD-ROM eds. (effective 2004 & 2005). back issues avail. **Document type:** *Directory.* **Description:** Contains credit ratings and other valuable information on all businesses within Colorado. Includes company name & address, phone & fax numbers, key executive names & titles, lines of business, years in business, number of employees, estimated annual sales, volume credit rating code, and corporate linkage information.
Related titles: CD-ROM ed.; Diskette ed.; E-mail ed.; Fax ed.; Magnetic Tape ed.; Online - full text ed.
Published by: American Business Directories (Subsidiary of: American Business Information, Inc.), 5711 S 86th Circle, P O Box 27347, Omaha, NE 68127. TEL 402-593-4600, 888-946-9377, 877-708-3844, FAX 402-331-5481, sales@directoriesusa.com, http://www.directoriesusa.com.

338.0029 USA ISSN 1048-7204
HF3161.C6
COLORADO BUSINESS DIRECTORY. Text in English. 1987. a. USD 1,100 combined subscription print, online & CD-ROM eds. (effective 2004 & 2005). index. back issues avail. **Document type:** *Directory.* **Description:** Includes all businesses in the state compiled from the yellow pages and telephone-verified. Each listing includes company name, complete address, phone number, name of owner, manager, and employee size, sales volume code and credit rating codes.
Related titles: CD-ROM ed.; Diskette ed.; E-mail ed.; Fax ed.; Magnetic Tape ed.; Online - full text ed.
Published by: American Business Directories (Subsidiary of: American Business Information, Inc.), 5711 S 86th Circle, P O Box 27347, Omaha, NE 68127. TEL 402-593-4600, 888-946-9377, 877-708-3844, FAX 402-331-5481, karen.peters@infousa.com, sales@directoriesusa.com, http://www.directoriesusa.com.

COLORADO BUSINESS RESOURCE DIRECTORY. see *BUSINESS AND ECONOMICS—Chamber Of Commerce Publications*

670.29 USA ISSN 1524-9999
HF5065.C6
COLORADO MANUFACTURERS DIRECTORY. Text in English. 1995. a. USD 81 (effective 2002). adv. 392 p./no.; **Document type:** *Directory.* **Description:** Publishes complete profiles of 5564 manufacturing, mining and selected service firms.
Formerly: Colorado Manufacturers Register (1081-3942)
Related titles: CD-ROM ed.: USD 349 (effective 2002).
Published by: Manufacturers' News, Inc., 1633 Central St, Evanston, IL 60201. TEL 847-864-7000, 888-752-5200, FAX 847-332-1100, info@mninfo.com, info@manufacturersnews.com, sales@mninfo.com, http://www.manufacturersnews.com. Ed. Steve Garland. Circ: 500 (paid).

COMBINED INDEPENDENTS HOLDINGS DIRECTORY. see *BUSINESS AND ECONOMICS—International Commerce*

381.029 GBR ISSN 1368-6100
COMMERCE BUSINESS DIRECTORIES. BLACK COUNTRY. Text in English. 1988. a. GBP 20. adv. **Document type:** *Directory.* **Description:** Lists and describes companies in the Midlands region of England and provides contact persons.
Formed by the merger of (1990-1997): Commerce Business Directories. Black Country South; Which was formerly: Black Country South Business Directory (0963-133X); (1990-1997): Commerce Business Directories. Black Country North (0966-0542); Which was formerly: Black Country North Business Directory (0963-1348); Both of which superseded in part (in 1989): Black Country Business Directory (0957-1035)
Related titles: Diskette ed.: GBP 150.
Published by: Commerce Directories Ltd., Milton Keynes, Station House, Station Rd, Newport Pagnell, Bucks MK16 0AG, United Kingdom. TEL 44-1908-614477, FAX 44-1908-616441. Ed. Karen Pickwick. R&P Steve Williams. Adv. contact Jessica Lamb. Circ: 7,000.

380.1029 GBR ISSN 0957-1051
COMMERCE BUSINESS DIRECTORIES. MILTON KEYNES. Text in English. 1981. a. GBP 30. adv. **Document type:** *Directory.* **Description:** Lists businesses and contact persons in Milton Keynes and the surrounding area.
Related titles: Diskette ed.: GBP 150.
Published by: Commerce Directories Ltd., Milton Keynes, Station House, Station Rd, Newport Pagnell, Bucks MK16 0AG, United Kingdom. TEL 44-1908-614477, FAX 44-1908-616441. Ed. Karen Pickwick. R&P Steve Williams. Adv. contact Jessica Lamb. Circ: 7,500.

381.029 GBR ISSN 0966-0550
COMMERCE BUSINESS DIRECTORIES. NORTHAMPTON. Text in English. 1988. a. GBP 25. adv. **Document type:** *Directory.* **Description:** Lists businesses and contact persons for the Northamptonshire region of England.
Related titles: Diskette ed.: GBP 150.
Published by: Commerce Directories Ltd., Milton Keynes, Station House, Station Rd, Newport Pagnell, Bucks MK16 0AG, United Kingdom. TEL 44-1908-614477, FAX 44-1908-616441. Ed. Karen Pickwick. R&P Steve Williams. Adv. contact Jessica Lamb. Circ: 3,000.

381.029 GBR ISSN 0963-1356
COMMERCE BUSINESS DIRECTORIES. OXFORD. Text in English. 1991. a. GBP 25. adv. **Document type:** *Directory.* **Description:** Lists companies and contact persons for Oxford and the surrounding area.
Related titles: Diskette ed.: GBP 150.
Published by: Commerce Directories Ltd., Milton Keynes, Station House, Station Rd, Newport Pagnell, Bucks MK16 0AG, United Kingdom. TEL 44-1908-614477, FAX 44-1908-616441. Ed. Karen Pickwick. R&P Steve Williams. Adv. contact Jessica Lamb.

338.0029 GBR
COMMERCE BUSINESS DIRECTORIES. PETERBOROUGH AND DISTRICT. Text in English. 1985. a. GBP 25. adv. **Document type:** *Directory.* **Description:** Lists businesses and contact persons in Peterborough and the surrounding area.
Formerly: Commerce Business Directories. Peterborough (0957-1078)
Related titles: Diskette ed.: GBP 150.
Published by: Commerce Directories Ltd., Milton Keynes, Station House, Station Rd, Newport Pagnell, Bucks MK16 0AG, United Kingdom. TEL 44-1908-614477, FAX 44-1908-616441. Ed. Karen Pickwick. R&P Steve Williams. Adv. contact Jessica Lamb. Circ: 3,000.

381.029 GBR
COMMERCE BUSINESS DIRECTORIES. READING AND DISTRICT. Text in English. 1989. a. GBP 25. **Document type:** *Directory.* **Description:** Lists businesses and contact persons in Reading and the surrounding area.
Formerly: Commerce Business Directories. Reading (1355-1582); Which supersedes (in 1991): Reading Business Directory (0957-1086)
Related titles: Diskette ed.: GBP 150.
Published by: Commerce Directories Ltd., Milton Keynes, Station House, Station Rd, Newport Pagnell, Bucks MK16 0AG, United Kingdom. TEL 44-1908-614477, FAX 44-1908-616441. Ed. Karen Pickwick. Circ: 5,000.

381.029 GBR
COMMERCE BUSINESS DIRECTORIES. REDDITCH AND BROMSGROLE. Text in English. 1986. a. GBP 23. adv. **Document type:** *Directory.* **Description:** Lists businesses and contact persons in Redditch and the surrounding area.
Formerly: Commerce Business Directories. Redditch; Which supersedes (in 1990): Redditch and District Business Directory (0964-8585)
Related titles: Diskette ed.: GBP 150.
Published by: Commerce Directories Ltd., Milton Keynes, Station House, Station Rd, Newport Pagnell, Bucks MK16 0AG, United Kingdom. TEL 44-1908-614477, FAX 44-1908-616441. Ed. Karen Pickwick. R&P Steve Williams. Adv. contact Jessica Lamb. Circ: 4,000.

381.029 GBR
COMMERCE BUSINESS DIRECTORIES. TELFORD AND DISTRICT. Text in English. 1985. a. GBP 28. adv. **Document type:** *Directory.* **Description:** Lists businesses and contact persons in Telford and the surrounding area.
Formerly: Commerce Business Directories. Telford (0957-1116)
Related titles: Diskette ed.: GBP 150.
Published by: Commerce Directories Ltd., Milton Keynes, Station House, Station Rd, Newport Pagnell, Bucks MK16 0AG, United Kingdom. TEL 44-1908-614477, FAX 44-1908-616441. R&P Steve Williams. Adv. contact Jessica Lamb. Circ: 6,500.

381.029 GBR ISSN 0967-1501
COMMERCE BUSINESS DIRECTORIES. WATFORD & HEMEL HEMPSTEAD. Text in English. 1992. a. GBP 25. adv. **Document type:** *Directory.* **Description:** Lists businesses and contact persons in Watford and Hemel Hempstead.
Formed by the merger of (1988-1992): Hemel Hempstead Business Directory (0957-1043); (1989-1992): Watford Business Directory (0957-1124)
Related titles: Diskette ed.: GBP 150.
Published by: Commerce Directories Ltd., Milton Keynes, Station House, Station Rd, Newport Pagnell, Bucks MK16 0AG, United Kingdom. TEL 44-1908-614477, FAX 44-1908-616441. Ed. Karen Pickwick. R&P Steve Williams. Adv. contact Jessica Lamb. Circ: 3,000.

338.0029 SGP
COMMERCIAL & INDUSTRIAL GUIDE. Text in English. a.
Published by: Integrated Databases India Ltd., c/o Orchard P.O. Box 389, Singapore, Singapore. adv.: B&W page USD 17,600, color page USD 21,725; trim 275 x 210. Circ: 200,000.

380.1029 ETH
COMMERCIAL BANK OF ETHIOPIA. TRADE DIRECTORY. Text in English. irreg. free. **Document type:** *Directory.*
Published by: Commercial Bank of Ethiopia, PO Box 255, Addis Ababa, Ethiopia.

670.29 GBR
THE COMMERCIAL VEHICLE GUIDE. Variant title: C V Guide. Text in English. 1990. a. GBP 35 domestic; GBP 55 foreign (effective 2001). adv. tr.lit. back issues avail. **Document type:** *Directory, Trade.*
Formerly: Commerical Vehicle Bodybuilders and Repairers Guide
Related titles: Fax ed.; Online - full text ed.
Published by: Plenham Ltd., Castle Mill, Lower Kings Rd, Berkhamsted, Herts HP4 2AA, United Kingdom. TEL 44-1442-285300, FAX 44-1442-870740, bodyshop@bodyshopmag.com, http://www.autorefinish.com. Ed. Heather Grant. Pub., R&P Chris Mann. Adv. contact Cecily Hughes. B&W page GBP 1,000, color page GBP 1,950; trim 190 x 275. Circ: 12,000.

380.1029 ZAF
COMMUNICATION PAGES. Text in English. a. ZAR 150 (effective 2001). adv. **Document type:** *Directory.*
Former Titles: Fax Directory of Southern Africa; Communications (Fax) Directory
Published by: Braby's (Subsidiary of: Associated Industries), Attn: Sue Pearson, PO Box 1426, Pinetown, 3600, South Africa. TEL 27-31-7017021, FAX 27-31-7017036, booksales@brabys.co.za.

670.29 USA ISSN 1047-6393
T223.V4
COMPANIES AND THEIR BRANDS. Text in English. a., latest vol.26, 2004. USD 665 in 2 vols. (effective 2004). Supplement avail. **Description:** Lists over 47,000 company entries including the brand-name products they manufacture or distribute.
Formerly: Trade Names Dictionary: Company Index (0277-0369)
Related titles: Online - full text ed.: (from The Dialog Corporation).
Published by: Gale Group (Subsidiary of: Thomson Corporation), 27500 Drake Rd, Farmington Hills, MI 48331-3535. TEL 248-699-8061, 800-877-4253, FAX 248-699-4253, galeord@gale.com, http://www.gale.com. Ed. Susan Stetler.

338.0029 AUT
DER COMPASS - BAND HANDEL UND DIENSTLEISTUNGEN. Text in German. 1867. a. adv. **Document type:** *Directory, Trade.* **Description:** Describes business structure of Austrian trading and services industry enterprises.
Formerly: Handels - Compass (0253-7087)
Published by: Compass Verlag, Matznergasse 17, Vienna, W 1141, Austria. TEL 43-1-98116-0, FAX 43-1-98116148, office@compass.at, http://www.compass.at. Ed. Karin Schraml. R&P Nikolaus Futter. Adv. contact Michael Bayer TEL 43-1-98116160.

670.29 AUT
DER COMPASS - BAND INDUSTRIE. Text in German. 1867. a. adv. **Document type:** *Directory, Trade.* **Description:** Provides description of business structure of approximately 18,000 manufacturing enterprises of any corporative type classified in lines of production and, within these categories, grouped according to location.
Formerly: Industrie-Compass Oesterreich (0073-7712)
Published by: (Austrian Chamber of Commerce), Compass Verlag, Matznergasse 17, Vienna, W 1141, Austria. TEL 43-1-98116-0, FAX 43-1-98116148, office@compass.at, http://www.compass.at. Ed. Karin Schraml. R&P Nikolaus Futter. Adv. contact Michael Bayer TEL 43-1-98116160.

380.01029 USA
COMPLETE COMMODITY FUTURES DIRECTORY. Text in English. 1980. irreg. looseleaf. USD 245 domestic; USD 395 foreign (effective 2001). adv. **Document type:** *Directory.* **Description:** Contains the names, addresses and telephone numbers of all registered futures and commodity option professionals.
Related titles: Diskette ed.; E-mail ed.; Fax ed.; Magnetic Tape ed.
Published by: Christopher Resources, Inc., PO Box 488, Frankfort, IL 60423-0488. TEL 815-485-8399, 800-332-3441, FAX 815-485-2499, completefutures@cs.com. Ed., Adv. contact M C Marasco. R&P Marty Fabish. Circ: 3,500 (paid).

THE COMPLETE GIFT BASKET INDUSTRY REFERENCE DIRECTORY. see *BUSINESS AND ECONOMICS—Small Business*

COMPOSITE CATALOG OF OIL FIELD EQUIPMENT & SERVICES. see *PETROLEUM AND GAS*

COMPUTER FEATURES DIRECTORY. see *COMPUTERS—Computer Industry Directories*

COMPUTER-GRAPHIK-MARKT. see *COMPUTERS—Computer Graphics*

COMPUTER LISTING SERVICE'S MACHINERY & EQUIPMENT GUIDE. see *MACHINERY*

COMPUTER SECURITY BUYER'S GUIDE. see *COMPUTERS—Computer Security*

380.1029 ZWE
CONFEDERATION OF ZIMBABWE INDUSTRIES. REGISTER & BUYERS GUIDE. Variant title: C Z I Register and Buyer's Guide. Text in English. 1980. a. ZWD 115; ZWD 131.20 foreign. **Document type:** *Directory.*
Published by: (Confederation of Zimbabwe Industries), Thomson Publications Zimbabwe (Pvt) Ltd., Thomson House, PO Box 1683, Harare, Zimbabwe. TEL 263-4-736835, FAX 263-4-752390.

338.0029 USA ISSN 1048-7212
HC107.C8
CONNECTICUT BUSINESS DIRECTORY. Text in English. 1988. a. USD 1,100 combined subscription print, online & CD-ROM eds. (effective 2004 & 2005). index. back issues avail. **Document type:** *Directory.* **Description:** Includes all businesses in the state compiled from the yellow pages and telephone-verified. Each listing includes company name, complete address, phone number, name of owner, manager, and employee size, sales volume codes and credit rating codes.
Related titles: CD-ROM ed.; Diskette ed.; E-mail ed.; Fax ed.; Magnetic Tape ed.; Online - full text ed.
Published by: American Business Directories (Subsidiary of: American Business Information, Inc.), 5711 S 86th Circle, P O Box 27347, Omaha, NE 68127. TEL 402-593-4600, 888-946-9377, 877-708-3844, FAX 402-331-5481, karen.peters@infousa.com, sales@directoriesusa.com, http://www.directoriesusa.com.

670.29 USA ISSN 1091-9600
CONNECTICUT MANUFACTURERS REGISTER. Text in English. 1997. a. USD 78 (effective 2001). adv. charts; illus.; stat. **Document type:** *Directory.* **Description:** Profiles 5,582 manufacturers in five sections: company name, product, S.I.C., city, and parent company.
Related titles: CD-ROM ed.: USD 355 (effective 2001); Diskette ed.; Online - full text ed.
Published by: Manufacturers' News, Inc., 1633 Central St, Evanston, IL 60201. TEL 847-864-7000, 888-752-5200, FAX 847-332-1100, info@mninfo.com, info@manufacturersnews.com, sales@mninfo.com, http://www.manufacturersnews.com. Ed. Frank Lambing. Adv. contact Charles Scherer. B&W page USD 1,843.

CONNECTICUT - RHODE ISLAND TELEPHONE TICKLER FOR INSURANCE MEN & WOMEN. see *INSURANCE*

690.029 USA
CONSTRUCCION PAN-AMERICANA INTERNATIONAL BUYER'S GUIDE. Text in Spanish. 1981. a. **Document type:** *Directory, Trade.* **Description:** Lists manufacturers of construction equipment, accessories and supplies from all over the world.
Published by: International Construction Publishing Inc., 4913 S W 75th Ave, Miami, FL 33155. TEL 305-668-4999, FAX 305-668-7774, info@cpa-mpa.com, http://www.cpa-mpa.com. Ed. Juan Escalante. Circ: 11,780.

CONSTRUCTION EQUIPMENT BUYERS' GUIDE. see *BUILDING AND CONSTRUCTION*

690.029 USA
CONSTRUCTION INDUSTRIES OF MASSACHUSETTS DIRECTORY; a directory and catalog of highway and heavy construction in New England. Text in English. 1948. a. USD 15 (effective 1998). **Document type:** *Directory.*
Formerly: Construction Directory (0099-8281)
Published by: Construction Industries of Massachusetts, Inc., 1500 Providence Highway, Ste 14, Norwood, MA 02062.

620.0029 GBR
CONSULTANT ENGINEERS AND TECHNOLOGIES 500. Variant title: C E T 500. CET500. Text in English. 1991. a., latest 2002. GBP 37.50 (effective 2003). adv. illus.; tr.lit. 150 p./no.; back issues avail.; reprints avail. **Document type:** *Directory, Trade.* **Description:** Guide to the learning engineering consultancies in the UK and Europe.
Formerly: Consultant Engineers 500
Related titles: CD-ROM ed.; Online - full content ed.: free (effective 2001).
Indexed: IMMAb.
Published by: Anchorage Press Ltd., 275 St Margarets Rd, Twickenham, TW1 1PN, United Kingdom. TEL 44-20-8892-9905, FAX 44-20-8891-2462, mail@cet500.com, http://www.cet500.com. Ed., Pub., R&P, Adv. contact Simon Fullalove TEL 44-20-87442028. Circ: 1,500 (controlled).

CONSULTANTS & CONSULTING ORGANIZATIONS DIRECTORY; a reference guide to concerns and individuals engaged in consultation for business, industry and government. see *BUSINESS AND ECONOMICS—Management*

CONTACTS. see *THEATER*

THE CONTAINERSHIP REGISTER (LONDON, 2002). see *TRANSPORTATION—Ships And Shipping*

070.5 GBR
CONTINUUM, PUBLISHERS ASSOCIATION AND THE FEDERATION OF EUROPEAN PUBLISHERS ASSOCIATIONS. DIRECTORY OF PUBLISHING IN CONTINENTAL EUROPE. Text in English. 1991. a. GBP 65. **Document type:** *Directory.*
Published by: Continuum International Publishing Group, The Tower Building, 11 York Rd, London, SE1 7NX, United Kingdom. TEL 44-20-79220880, FAX 44-20-79220881. **Dist. in the U.S. by:** Cassell and Continuum, PCS Data Processing Inc, 360 W 31st St, New York, NY 10001. **Co-sponsors:** Publishers Association; Federation of European Publishers Associations.

380.1029 USA ISSN 1059-7093
CONTRA COSTA COUNTY COMMERCE AND INDUSTRY DIRECTORY✶. Text in English. 1992. a. USD 75. **Document type:** *Directory.* **Description:** Covers 2,700 manufacturing, wholesale, and service firms; and 5,300 top executives.
Related titles: CD-ROM ed.: USD 215; Diskette ed.
Published by: Database Publishing Company, 701 E Ball Rd Ste 100, Anaheim, CA 92805-5962. TEL 714-778-6400, FAX 714-778-6811. R&P Sarah Fraser.

331.11029 USA ISSN 1063-9268
CONTRACT EMPLOYMENT WEEKLY. Text in English. 1969. w. USD 65 (effective 1998). adv. **Document type:** *Trade.*
Formerly: Contract Engineer Weekly
Published by: C.E. Publications, Inc., PO Box 3006, Bothell, WA 98041. TEL 425-806-5200, FAX 425-806-5585. Ed. Janice Erickson. Pub., R&P Jerry Erickson. Adv. contact Carol McDaniel.

CONTRACT FURNISHING DIRECTORY. see *INTERIOR DESIGN AND DECORATION—Furniture And House Furnishings*

CONTROL ENGINEERING AUTOMATION INTEGRATOR GUIDE. see *COMPUTERS—Automation*

CONTROL ENGINEERING BUYERS GUIDE. see *COMPUTERS—Automation*

CONVERTER DIRECTORY; suppliers and services to the U.K. converting industry. see *PAPER AND PULP*

CONVERTING MAGAZINE MANUFACTURERS DIRECTORY. see *PAPER AND PULP*

COOPERATIVE TRADE DIRECTORY FOR SOUTHEAST ASIA. see *BUSINESS AND ECONOMICS—Cooperatives*

659.1029 USA
CORPORATE AFFILIATIONS PLUS. Text in English. q. USD 1,995 (effective 1999). **Description:** Includes the entire Corporate Affiliations Library (public, private, and international), as well as America's Corporate Finance Directory. Allows for the research of corporate statistics and current financials for over 15,000 domestic and foreign companies and their 100,000 subsidiaries, affiliates, divisions, and joint ventures; review profiles of more than 190,000 influential decision makers; locate solid sales leads; discover new investment opportunities.
Media: CD-ROM.
Published by: LexisNexis (Subsidiary of: LexisNexis North America), PO Box 7587, Charlottesville, VA 22906-7587. TEL 434-972-7600, 800-446-3410, info@reedref.com, llp.customer.support@lexis-nexis.com, http://www.reedref.com, http://www.lexislawpublishing.com.

380.1029 USA ISSN 0589-7920
CORPORATE REPORT FACT BOOK; a directory of publicly held companies in the Ninth Federal Reserve District. Text in English. 1967. a. USD 127. **Document type:** *Directory.*
Incorporates: Corporate Report Who's Who in Upper Midwest Business
—CCC.
Published by: American City Business Journals, Inc. (Austin), 505 Powell St, Austin, TX 78703-5121. Ed. Tom Smith. adv.: B&W page USD 1,450. Circ: 3,200 (paid).

670.29 USA
HG4057
CORPTECH DIRECTORY OF TECHNOLOGY COMPANIES✶. Text in English. 1986. a. (in 4 vols.). USD 745 softcover ed.; USD 795 hardcover ed. (effective 1999). **Document type:** *Directory.* **Description:** Comprehensive source of company information on America's 50,000 emerging manufacturers and developers of technology products and services.
Formerly: Corporate Technology Directory (0887-1930)
Related titles: Online - full text ed.: (from Questel Orbit Inc.).
Published by: Corporate Technology Information Services Inc., 300 Baker Ave #3, Concord, MA 01742-2131. TEL 781-932-3100, FAX 781-932-6335, sales@corptech.com, http://www.corptech.com. Ed. Steven W Parker. R&P Steven Parker. Circ: 45,000.

(YEAR) CORRECTIONAL FOODSERVICE WHO'S WHO. see *FOOD AND FOOD INDUSTRIES*

COUNTY GUIDE TO MARINE COMPANIES. see *SPORTS AND GAMES—Boats And Boating*

COVER NOTE INSURANCE DIRECTORY. see *INSURANCE*

CRAWFORD'S DIRECTORY OF CITY CONNECTIONS. see *BUSINESS AND ECONOMICS—Banking And Finance*

381.029 ANT
CURACAO PROFESSIONAL GUIDE. Text in English. a.
Document type: *Directory.*
Published by: Know How Group N.V., Schottegatweg Oost 56, PO Box 473, Willemstad, Curacao, Netherlands Antilles. TEL 367079, FAX 367080.

381.029 ANT
CURACAO TRADE AND INDUSTRY DIRECTORY* . Text in Dutch, English, Spanish. a. illus.
Published by: (Curacao Trade and Industry Association), Citroen-Daal, Pietermaai 21, PO Box 49, Willemstad, Curacao, Netherlands Antilles.

380.1029 GBR ISSN 0070-1858
CURRENT BRITISH DIRECTORIES. Text in English. 1953. irreg., latest vol.13, 2000. GBP 165, USD 330 (effective 2001). adv. index. **Document type:** *Directory.* **Description:** Lists alphabetically some 4,000 directories published in the U.K. —BLDSC (3494.670000), Linda Hall.
Published by: C.B.D. Research Ltd., 15 Wickham Rd, Beckenham, Kent BR3 5JS, United Kingdom. TEL 44-20-86507745, FAX 44-20-86500768, cbd@cbdresearch.com, http://www.cbdresearch.com. Ed. C Ward. Circ: 4,000.

CURRENT DIRECTORY OF INTERNATIONAL CHAMBERS OF COMMERCE AND INDUSTRY. see *BUSINESS AND ECONOMICS—Chamber Of Commerce Publications*

380.1029 GBR ISSN 0070-1955
CURRENT EUROPEAN DIRECTORIES/HANDBUCH DER EUROPAEISCHEN ADRESSBUECHER/REPERTOIRE DES ANNUAIRES EUROPEENS. Text in English. 1969-198?; resumed. irreg., latest vol.3, 1994. GBP 140, USD 280 (effective 2001). adv. index. **Document type:** *Directory.* **Description:** Lists 3,000 directories printed in European countries, along with extensive descriptions and an index of publishers with full addresses.
Published by: C.B.D. Research Ltd., 15 Wickham Rd, Beckenham, Kent BR3 5JS, United Kingdom. TEL 44-20-86507745, FAX 44-20-86500768, cbd@cbdresearch.com, http://www.glen.co.uk/cbd, http://www.cbdresearch.com. Circ: 2,000. **Dist. in U.S. by:** Gale Research Co., 220 Book Tower, Detroit, MI 48226.

540.29 GBR ISSN 1362-4563
CUSTOM TOLL AND CONTRACT SERVICES DIRECTORY. Text in English. 1996. every 2 yrs. GBP 135, USD 199; GBP 160, USD 239 with CD-ROM. adv. **Document type:** *Directory.* **Description:** Guide to the global chemical industry.
Related titles: CD-ROM ed.
Published by: Reed Business Information Ltd. (Subsidiary of: Reed Business), Quadrant House, The Quadrant, Brighton Rd, Sutton, Surrey SM2 5AS, United Kingdom. TEL 44-208-652-3500, FAX 44-208-652-8977, rbi.subscriptions@qss-uk.com, http://www.reedbusiness.co.uk/. Ed. Alan Tyler TEL 44-20-8652-8126. Adv. contact Anne Martin. **Subscr. to:** Quadrant Subscription Services, PO Box 302, Haywards Heath, W Sussex RH16 3YY, United Kingdom. TEL 44-1444-445566, FAX 44-1444-445447.

CYCLISTS' YELLOW PAGES. see *SPORTS AND GAMES—Bicycles And Motorcycles*

381.029 CYP ISSN 0070-2331
CYPRUS CHAMBER OF COMMERCE AND INDUSTRY DIRECTORY* ; guide to commerce, industry, tourism and agriculture. Text in English. 1967. irreg., latest vol.2, 1970. USD 25. **Document type:** *Directory.*
Published by: D. Couvas & Sons Ltd., Box 35, Limassol, Cyprus. **Dist. by:** International Publications Service, 114 E. 32nd St., New York, NY 10016.

380.1029 USA
HG4057
D & B BUSINESS RANKINGS. (Dun & Bradstreet) Text in English. 1982. a. **Description:** Ranks the top 25000 public and private U.S. companies according to both sales volume and number of employees within 67 industry categories, within each state, by size, and by public and private designation.
Formerly (until 1997): Dun's Business Rankings (0734-2845)
Published by: Dun & Bradstreet (Subsidiary of: Dun & Bradstreet Corporation), c/o Ethan Chazin, Director, Reference Services, Murray Hill, NJ 07094-1218. TEL 973-605-6000.

658.0029 USA ISSN 1524-9743
HD69.C6
D & B CONSULTANTS DIRECTORY. (Dun & Bradstreet) Text in English. 1986. a.
Formerly (until 1998): Dun's Consultants Directory (0884-3724)
Published by: Dun & Bradstreet Corporation, 103 J F K Pkwy, Short Hills, NJ 07078. custserv@dnb.com, http://www.dnb.com.

380.1029 USA
HD9981.3
D & B DIRECTORY OF SERVICE COMPANIES. (Dun & Bradstreet) Text in English. 1989. a.
Formerly (until 1998): Dun's Directory of Service Companies (1040-6395)
Published by: Dun & Bradstreet Corporation, 103 J F K Pkwy, Short Hills, NJ 07078. custserv@dnb.com, http://www.dnb.com.

D C C TRADE DIRECTORY. see *BUSINESS AND ECONOMICS—Chamber Of Commerce Publications*

070.5 GBR
D P A MEMBERSHIP BOOK. Text in English. 1989. a. free. adv. stat. index. **Document type:** *Directory, Trade.* **Description:** Lists and provides information on members and publications. Compiles statistics and contains the Code of Professional Practice.
Related titles: CD-ROM ed.: 1989.
Published by: (Directory & Database Publishers Association), Emap Media Ltd. (Subsidiary of: Emap Business Communications Ltd.), 33-39 Bowling Green Ln, London, EC1R 0DA, United Kingdom. TEL 44-20-7505-8000, FAX 44-20-7505-8504, http://www.directory-publisher.co.uk. Ed. Rosemary Pettit. Adv. contact Anthony Margolis. page GBP 300; trim 135 x 195. Circ: 3,000.

070.5 GBR ISSN 1351-251X
D P A NEWS. Text in English. 1992. q. **Document type:** *Newsletter.*
Published by: Directory & Database Publishers Association, Box 23034, London, W11 2WZ, United Kingdom. TEL 44-171-221-9089, http://www.directory-publisher.co.uk. Ed. Rosemary Pettit.

DAIRY FOODS MARKET DIRECTORY. see *FOOD AND FOOD INDUSTRIES*

DALIL AL-MUSADDIRIN/DIRECTORY OF EXPORTERS. see *BUSINESS AND ECONOMICS—International Commerce*

338.0029 USA
DALTON'S ALLENTOWN, BETHLEHEM, LANCASTER READING METROPOLITAN DIRECTORY: BUSINESS - INDUSTRY. Text in English. 1991. a. USD 85. **Document type:** *Directory.* **Description:** Lists over 5,000 companies with company names, addresses, phone and fax numbers, names and titles of key executives.
Related titles: Diskette ed.: USD 325.
Published by: Dalton Directory, 410 Lancaster Ave, Haverford, PA 19041. TEL 800-221-1050, FAX 610-649-3596. Ed. Dot Fisher.

338.0029 USA
DALTON'S BALTIMORE - WASHINGTON METROPOLITAN DIRECTORY: BUSINESS - INDUSTRY. Text in English. a. USD 95. **Document type:** *Directory.* **Description:** Lists more than 8,000 companies with addresses, phone and fax numbers, names and titles of key executives.
Related titles: Diskette ed.: USD 350.
Published by: Dalton Directory, 410 Lancaster Ave, Haverford, PA 19041. TEL 800-221-1050, FAX 610-649-3596. Ed. Dot Fisher.

338.0029 USA ISSN 1052-6609
HF5068.N5
DALTON'S NEW YORK METROPOLITAN DIRECTORY: BUSINESS - INDUSTRY. Text in English. 1984. a. USD 135. **Document type:** *Directory.* **Description:** Lists over 14,000 companies with addresses, phone and fax numbers, names and titles of key executives.
Related titles: Diskette ed.: USD 475.
Indexed: ExcerpMed.
Published by: Dalton Directory, 410 Lancaster Ave, Haverford, PA 19041. TEL 800-221-1050, FAX 610-649-3596. Ed. Dot Fisher.

338.0029 USA ISSN 1053-685X
HF3163.P5
DALTON'S PHILADELPHIA METROPOLITAN DIRECTORY: BUSINESS - INDUSTRY. Text in English. 1964. a. USD 159. **Description:** Lists more than 14,000 companies with addresses, phone and fax numbers, names and titles of key executives.
Former titles (until 1986): Dalton's Delaware Valley Directory (0733-2416); (until 1982): Dalton's Directory of Business and Industry (0732-6955)
Related titles: CD-ROM ed.: USD 289 (effective 1999); Diskette ed.
Published by: Dalton Directory, 410 Lancaster Ave, Haverford, PA 19041. TEL 800-221-1050, FAX 610-649-3596. Ed. David Greenebaum. Pub. John Greenbaum.

338 NZL
THE DATA BOOK; New Zealand film, television, video, photographic stills and theatre. Text in English. a. (plus updates). NZD 191.25 base vol(s). domestic plus first set of updates; NZD 215 base vol(s). in Australia plus first set of updates; NZD 280 base vol(s). elsewhere plus first set of updates; NZD 100 updates domestic; NZD 115 updates in Australia; NZD 125 updates elsewhere (effective 2000). adv. **Document type:** *Trade.* **Description:** Contains three main sections: Aotearoa/New Zealand: the land, the people, and the country as a filming location. It outlines relevant policies and rules and it gives a guide to industry organisations. Listings section: Gives contact details for people and companies in film, television, video and stills photography and professional theatre. Casting sections: begins with listings relating to casting and performance, eg actors agents, choreographers etc - but the main part of this section contains photographs of actors and models along with their major credits and skills.
Published by: Profile Publishing Ltd., Wellesley St, PO Box 5544, Auckland, New Zealand. TEL 64-9-6301040, FAX 64-9-630-1046, info@profile.co.nz, http://www.profile.co.nz/.

DATA ENTRY - DATA CONVERSION SERVICES DIRECTORY. see *COMPUTERS—Electronic Data Processing*

380.1029 USA
DATABASE/DIRECTORY PUBLISHING MARKET FORECAST (YEAR). Text in English. a. USD 495 (effective 2003 & 2004).
Published by: SIMBA Information (Subsidiary of: R.R. Bowker LLC), 60 Long Ridge Rd., Ste 300, Stamford, CT 06902. TEL 203-325-8193, 800-307-2529, FAX 203-325-8915, info@simbanet.com, http://www.simbanet.com.

336.278 GBR ISSN 1358-8974
DATAPACK; buyer's directory for the tax and duty free industry. Text in English. 1993. s-a. GBP 130 (effective 1999).
Document type: *Directory.*
Published by: Wilmington Publishing, 6-8 Underwood St, London, N1 7JQ, United Kingdom. TEL 44-20-7549-2548, FAX 44-20-7549-2550. Ed. Veronica Simpson. Pub. Chris Mitchell. Circ: 3,000 (controlled).

DAVISON'S GOLD BOOK. see *TEXTILE INDUSTRIES AND FABRICS—Abstracting, Bibliographies, Statistics*

DAVISON'S SALESMAN'S BOOK. see *TEXTILE INDUSTRIES AND FABRICS*

DAVISON'S TEXTILE BLUE BOOK. see *TEXTILE INDUSTRIES AND FABRICS*

338.0029 USA ISSN 1048-7085
HF5065.D3
DELAWARE BUSINESS DIRECTORY. Text in English. 1990. a. USD 1,100 combined subscription print, online & CD-ROM eds. (effective 2004 & 2005). index. back issues avail.
Document type: *Directory.* **Description:** Includes all businesses in the state compiled from the yellow pages and telephone-verified. Each listing includes company name, complete address, phone number, name of owner, manager, and employee size, sales volume codes and credit rating codes.
Related titles: CD-ROM ed.; Diskette ed.; E-mail ed.; Fax ed.; Magnetic Tape ed.; Online - full text ed.
Published by: American Business Directories (Subsidiary of: American Business Information, Inc.), 5711 S 86th Circle, P O Box 27347, Omaha, NE 68127. TEL 402-593-4600, 888-946-9377, 877-708-3844, FAX 402-331-5481, karen.peters@infousa.com, sales@directoriesusa.com, http://www.directoriesusa.com.

380.1029 USA ISSN 0272-8117
HD9727.D3
DELAWARE DIRECTORY OF COMMERCE AND INDUSTRY. Text in English. 1950. a. USD 75. adv. **Document type:** *Directory.* **Description:** Company profiles of more than 6,000 firms; includes five sections — alphabetically by company name, SIC, geographical, alphabetical listing of manufacturing and manufacturing industries.
Formerly: Delaware Manufacturers Directory
Related titles: Diskette ed.
Published by: Delaware State Chamber of Commerce, 1201 N Orange St, Box 671, Wilmington, DE 19899. TEL 302-655-7221, FAX 302-654-0691. **Dist. by:** Manufacturers' News, Inc., 1633 Central St, Evanston, IL 60201. TEL 847-864-7000.

670.29 USA ISSN 1087-1896
HF5065.D3
DELAWARE MANUFACTURERS REGISTER. Text in English. a. USD 52 (effective 2002). adv. 104 p./no.; **Document type:** *Directory.* **Description:** Profiles 831 companies in five sections: by product, alphabetically, by city, by SIC, and by parent company.
Related titles: CD-ROM ed.: USD 179 (effective 2002); Diskette ed.
Published by: Manufacturers' News, Inc., 1633 Central St, Evanston, IL 60201. TEL 847-864-7000, 888-752-5200, FAX 847-332-1100, info@mninfo.com, info@manufacturersnews.com, sales@mninfo.com, http://www.manufacturersnews.com. Ed. Steve Garland.

380.1029 USA
DEPARTMENT OF DEFENSE BUYERS GUIDE. Text in English. 2002. a. adv. **Document type:** *Directory, Trade.* **Description:** Contains contact information along with a listings of products and services of more than 850 DOD suppliers.
Published by: Federal Buyers Guide, Inc., 718-B State St, PO Box 22507, Santa Barbara, CA 93101. TEL 805-963-7470, FAX 805-963-7478, stuart@onlibe-info.com, http://www.dodworld.com, http://www.gov-world.com/. Adv. contact David Minor TEL 805-963-7470 ext 18. color page USD 6,595, B&W page USD 3,995; trim 8.5 x 11. Circ: 10,000 (controlled).

THE DESIGN FIRM DIRECTORY - GRAPHIC DESIGN EDITION; a listing of firms and consultants in graphic design in the U.S. see *ADVERTISING AND PUBLIC RELATIONS*

THE DESIGN FIRM DIRECTORY - INTERIOR DESIGN EDITION. see *INTERIOR DESIGN AND DECORATION*

741.6029 USA ISSN 1094-8686
TS171.A1
THE DESIGN FIRM DIRECTORY - PRODUCT DESIGN EDITION; a listing of U.S. firms and consultants in product design and development. Text in English. 1979. a. USD 47 (effective 1998). **Document type:** *Directory.*
Supersedes in part (in 1997): Design Firm Directory - Graphic and Industrial Design Edition (0889-7611); Which supersedes in part (in 1986): Design Directory (0195-4326)
Published by: Wefler & Associates, Inc., 6 Milburn Park., Evanston, IL 60201-1744. TEL 847-475-1866. Pub. W Daniel Wefler. Circ: 600.

DESIGN NEWS O E M DIRECTORY. (Original Equipment Manufacturer) see *MACHINERY*

338.0029 USA ISSN 1084-9971
DESIGNMART. Text in English. 1995. bi-m. USD 30 domestic; USD 40 in Canada; USD 50 elsewhere; USD 7 newsstand/cover domestic; USD 9 newsstand/cover in Canada; USD 11 newsstand/cover elsewhere (effective 2000); Free to qualified personnel. **Document type:** *Trade.*
Published by: Penton Media, Inc. (Subsidiary of: Pittway Company), 1300 E 9th St, Cleveland, OH 44114-1503. http://www.penton.com.

663.2029 USA ISSN 1056-523X
TP548.5.A6
DESKTOP PRODUCTS GUIDE. Key Title: Vineyard & Winery Management. Desktop Products Guide. Text in English. 1970. a. USD 25. adv. **Document type:** *Directory, Trade.* **Description:** Lists suppliers for the wine and grape industry. Includes universities, research centers, seminars, competitions, and wineries by state, including Canada.
Formerly: Vineyard and Winery Management's Desktop Products Guide (1057-5510)
Published by: Vineyard & Winery Services, Inc., PO Box 231, Watkins Glen, NY 14891. TEL 607-535-7133, FAX 607-535-2998. Ed. J William Moffett. R&P J. William Moffett. Adv. contact Rob Merletti. Circ: 2,000.

380.1029 DEU
DEUTSCHER VERSAND-EINKAUFSFUEHRER; erstes und einziges Versandfirmenregister in Deutschland. Text in German. 1984. a. USD 30. adv. **Description:** Presents all kinds of mail order products.
Published by: Horst Ludwig Verlag, Jenseitsstr 10, Bergheim, 50127, Germany. TEL 02271-92791. Circ: 1,500.

384.14029 USA ISSN 1046-7262
DIAL-A-FAX DIRECTORY; world's largest resource of fax services. Text in English. 1987. a. USD 385. **Document type:** *Directory.*
Formerly (until 1989): Fax Phone Book (0896-9434)
Published by: Dial-A-Fax Directories, Benjamin Fox Pavilion, Ste 930, Jenkintown, PA 19046. TEL 215-887-5700, FAX 215-887-7076. Ed., Pub. Beryl Wolk.

338 AUS
DIAL INFO-LINK DIRECTORY. Text in English. a. AUD 105.11 (effective 2001). **Document type:** *Directory, Trade.* **Description:** Covers the the Manufacturing & Technology Industries in Australasia.
Related titles: CD-ROM ed.: AUD 56.60 (effective 2001); Online - full content ed.
Published by: Reed Business Information Pty Ltd (Subsidiary of: Reed Business Information International), Locked Bag 2999, Chatswood, NSW 2067, Australia. customerservice@reedbusiness.com.au, http://www.dialinfolink.com.au/, http://www.reedbusiness.com.au.

790.1 ESP
DIFFUSION SPORT DIRECTORY. Text in Spanish. 1982. a. adv. back issues avail. **Document type:** *Directory.*
Related titles: CD-ROM ed.
Published by: Difusion Ediciones S.L., Rosellon 102, Entlo. 1a, Barcelona, 08029, Spain. TEL 34-93-235702, FAX 34-93-236080, mail@diffusionsport.com, http://www.diffusionsport.com. Ed., Pub. Manuel Freixas. Adv. contact Alicia Casals. Circ: 5,500.

381.029 PAN
DIRECTORIO COMERCIAL E INDUSTRIAL DE PANAMA/COMMERCIAL AND INDUSTRIAL DIRECTORY OF PANAMA. Text in Spanish. 1958. a. USD 20 (effective 1998). adv. **Document type:** *Directory.*
Published by: Camara de Comercio, Industrias y Agricultura de Panama, P.O. Box 74, Panama City, 1, Panama. cciap@panama.phoenix.net, http://www.panacamara.com. Ed. Dinora de Nino. R&P Jorge Carney. Adv. contact Victor A Ortiz. Circ: 2,000.

020.62029 MEX
DIRECTORIO DE CENTROS DE INFORMACION. Text in Spanish. 1973. irreg., latest vol.17, 2000. USD 490 (effective 2001). **Document type:** *Directory.* **Description:** Lists 1,835 associations, government agencies, universities, embassies, information publishers, specialized libraries, and other sources of information for business research. Indexed by topic.
Published by: Ibcon S.A., Gutemberg 224, Col Anzures, Mexico City, DF 11590, Mexico. TEL 52-5-2554577, FAX 52-5-2554577, ibcon@infosel.net.mx, http://www.ibcon.com.mx. Ed. Gabriel Zaid.

382.029 MEX
DIRECTORIO DE CLIENTES PARA EXPORTAR A LOS ESTADOS UNIDOS. Text in English. 1981. irreg., latest vol.14, 2000. USD 380 (effective 2001). **Document type:** *Directory.* **Description:** Lists American, Puerto Rican, and Canadian importers interested in Mexican products. Indexed by product.
Published by: Ibcon S.A., Gutemberg 224, Col Anzures, Mexico City, DF 11590, Mexico. TEL 52-5-2554577, FAX 52-5-2554577, ibcon@infosel.net.mx, http://www.ibcon.com.mx. Ed. Gabriel Zaid.

DIRECTORIO DE COMPUTO. see *COMPUTERS—Computer Industry Directories*

351.092 MEX
DIRECTORIO DE EJECUTIVAS. Text in Spanish. 1996. irreg., latest vol.5, 2000. USD 330 (effective 2001). **Document type:** *Directory.* **Description:** Lists more than 6.051 women executives in business, government and charities in Mexico City.
Published by: Ibcon S.A., Gutemberg 224, Col Anzures, Mexico City, DF 11590, Mexico. TEL 52-5-2554577, FAX 52-5-2554577, ibcon@infosel.net.mx, http://www.ibcon.com.mx. Ed. Gabriel Zaid.

381.029 MEX
DIRECTORIO DE EMPRESAS - DIRECTORIO DE PROVEEDORES - DIRECTORIO POR COLONIAS - DIRECTORIO DE EMPRESARIOS. Text in Spanish. 1992. irreg., latest vol.8, 2001. USD 1,100 for 4 vol. set (effective 2001). **Document type:** *Directory.* **Description:** Lists 15,000 incorporated companies located in Mexico City and greater Mexico City. Provides address, phone and fax numbers, trade area, industry code, and the name and position of the top executive.
Related titles: CD-ROM ed.: CD-ROM de Ejecutivos. 1999. USD 830 (effective 2001).
Published by: Ibcon S.A., Gutemberg 224, Col Anzures, Mexico City, DF 11590, Mexico. TEL 52-5-2554577, FAX 52-5-2554577, ibcon@infosel.net.mx, http://www.ibcon.com.mx. Ed. Gabriel Zaid.

382.029 CUB ISSN 1606-9269
DIRECTORIO DE EXPORTADORES DE LA REPUBLICA DE CUBA (YEAR). Text in English, Spanish. 1996. a. **Document type:** *Directory.* **Description:** Lists exporters and their products and services.
Published by: Ministry of Foreign Trade, Center for Export Promotion of Cuba, Infanta No. 16, esq. 23,, Vedado, La Habana, Cuba. TEL 537-550405, FAX 537-662220, TELEX 51-1174, cepecdir@infocex.cu, http://www.infocex.cu/cepec. Circ: 1,500.

380.1029 URY
DIRECTORIO DE FAX DEL URUGUAY. Text in Spanish. 1991 (3rd ed.). a. **Document type:** *Directory.*
Published by: Urufax s.r.l., Rio Branco, 1358 Of 308, Montevideo, 11103, Uruguay. TEL 98-54-19.

381.029 MEX
DIRECTORIO DE FUNCIONARIOS. Text in Spanish. 1995. irreg., latest vol.12, 2001. USD 430 (effective 2001). **Document type:** *Directory.* **Description:** Lists over 7,981 government officers with address, phone, fax and e-mail.
Related titles: CD-ROM ed.: CD-ROM de Funcionarios. 2000. USD 930 (effective 2001).
Published by: Ibcon S.A., Gutemberg 224, Col Anzures, Mexico City, DF 11590, Mexico. TEL 52-5-2554577, FAX 52-5-2554577, ibcon@infosel.net.mx, http://www.ibon.com.mx. Ed. Gabriel Zaid.

381.029 MEX
DIRECTORIO DE GRANDES COMPRADORES. Text in Spanish. 1982. irreg., latest vol.16, 2001. USD 430 (effective 2001). **Document type:** *Directory.* **Description:** Lists the top Mexican purchasing departments (business and government). Includes executives, titles, addresses, phone and fax numbers, and e-mail and Web site addresses, indexed by products bought.
Published by: Ibcon S.A., Gutemberg 224, Col Anzures, Mexico City, DF 11590, Mexico. TEL 52-5-2554577, FAX 52-5-2554577, ibcon@infosel.net.mx, http://www.ibcon.com.mx. Ed. Gabriel Zaid.

382.029 MEX
DIRECTORIO DE IMPORTADORES. Text in Spanish. 1991. irreg., latest vol.9, 2001. USD 330 (effective 2001). **Document type:** *Directory.* **Description:** Lists Mexican companies importing at least one million dollars per year. Includes executive name, address, phone, fax, e-mail, Web site, and products imported, indexed by products imported.
Published by: Ibcon S.A., Gutemberg 224, Col Anzures, Mexico City, DF 11590, Mexico. TEL 52-5-2554577, FAX 52-5-2554577, ibcon@infosel.net.mx, http://www.ibcon.com.mx. Ed. Gabriel Zaid.

664.92029 MEX ISSN 0187-7631
DIRECTORIO DE LA INDUSTRIA CARNICA. Text in Spanish. 1987. a. USD 25; USD 55 foreign. adv. **Document type:** *Directory.* **Description:** Lists 520 producers and 230 suppliers in the meat industry.
Published by: Alfa Editores Tecnicos S.A., Cumbres de Acultzingo 83, Col. Narvarte, Mexico City, DF 03020, Mexico. TEL 525-579-3333, FAX 525-582-3342, alfotec@telmex.net.mx, http://www.industria-alimentaria.com. adv.: B&W page USD 572, color page USD 800; 280 x 215. Circ: 5,000 (controlled).

663.029 MEX ISSN 0187-764X
DIRECTORIO DE LA INDUSTRIA MEXICANA DE BEBIDAS. Text in Spanish. 1987. a. USD 25; USD 55 foreign. adv. **Document type:** *Directory.* **Description:** Lists 1900 beverage producers and 740 goods and services suppliers.
Published by: Alfa Editores Tecnicos S.A., Cumbres de Acultzingo 83, Col. Narvarte, Mexico City, DF 03020, Mexico. TEL 525-579-3333, FAX 525-582-3342, alfotec@telmex.net.mx, http://www.industria-alimentaria.com. adv.: B&W page USD 572, color page USD 800; trim 280 x 215. Circ: 5,000 (controlled).

DIRECTORIO DE LA MADERA. see *FORESTS AND FORESTRY—Lumber And Wood*

637.1029 MEX ISSN 0187-7623
DIRECTORIO DE LACTEOS MEXICANOS. Text in Spanish. 1988. a. USD 25; USD 55 foreign. adv. **Document type:** *Directory.* **Description:** Lists 550 manufacturers and 300 goods and services suppliers in the dairy industry.
Published by: Alfa Editores Tecnicos S.A., Cumbres de Acultzingo 83, Col. Narvarte, Mexico City, DF 03020, Mexico. TEL 525-579-3333, FAX 525-582-3342, alfotec@telmex.net.mx, http://www.industria-alimentaria.com. adv.: B&W page USD 572, color page USD 800; trim 280 x 215. Circ: 5,000 (controlled).

361.0029 MEX
DIRECTORIO DE OBRAS SOCIALES. Text in Spanish. 1984. irreg., latest vol.8, 1999. USD 60 (effective 2000). **Document type:** *Directory.* **Description:** Lists private charities in Mexico City looking for company patrons. Briefly describes their social work and needs.
Published by: Ibcon S.A., Gutemberg 224, Col Anzures, Mexico City, DF 11590, Mexico. TEL 52-5-2554577, FAX 52-5-2554577, ibcon@infosel.net.mx, http://www.ibcon.com.mx. Ed. Gabriel Zaid.

381.029 MEX
DIRECTORIO DE POBLACIONES. Text in Spanish. 1984. irreg., latest vol.5, 2000. USD 870 (effective 2001). **Document type:** *Directory.* **Description:** List 221 cities and 15,871 towns in alphabetical order, by phone number (if only one in town), zip code, symbols (airport, port, post office), latitude N. and longitude W. (rough), population. Also lists zip codes for neighborhoods (colonias) in cities, and for every street in Mexico City (not including greater Mexico City).
Published by: Ibcon S.A., Gutemberg 224, Col Anzures, Mexico City, DF 11590, Mexico. TEL 52-5-2554577, FAX 52-5-2554577, ibcon@infosel.net.mx, http://www.ibcon.com.mx.

613.029 COL ISSN 0121-800X
DIRECTORIO DE PROVEEDORES DE LA SALUD. Text in Spanish. 1992. a. free. adv. **Description:** Lists suppliers for clinics and hospitals.
Published by: Publicar S.A., Ave. 68, 75-A-50 of. 314,, Apartado Aereo 8010, Santa Fe de Bogota, CUND, Colombia. TEL 57-1-225-5555, FAX 57-1-3115645, colombiaexport@publicor.com, http://www.colombiaexport.com. R&P, Adv. contact Jaime Concha. page USD 2,400. Circ: 20,000.

382.029   MEX

DIRECTORIO DE SERVICIOS PARA EL EXPORTADOR. Text in Spanish. 1980. irreg., latest vol.14, 2000. USD 180 (effective 2001). **Document type:** *Directory.* **Description:** Lists companies, associations and government agencies offering every kind of service needed by exporters in Mexico City, indexed by service.
Published by: Ibcon S.A., Gutemberg 224, Col Anzures, Mexico City, DF 11590, Mexico. TEL 52-5-2554577, FAX 52-5-2554577, ibcon@infosel.net.mx, http://www.ibcon.com.mx. Ed. Gabriel Zaid.

DIRECTORIO DEL AGUA. see *WATER RESOURCES*

DIRECTORIO DEL METAL. see *METALLURGY*

338.0029 333.91 363.728   COL

DIRECTORIO DEL SECTOR DE AGUA POTABLE Y SANEAMIENTO AMBIENTAL. Text in Spanish. a. stat. **Document type:** *Directory.* **Description:** Lists companies and associations in the water and environmental health sectors. Includes statistics of interest on the industry.
Published by: Asociacion Colombiana de Ingenieria Sanitaria y Ambiental, Carretera 15 78-48 Of. 401, Bogota, CUND, Colombia. TEL 2366886, http://www.acodal.org.co. Ed. Nelly Estrada Lopez. Circ: 5,000.

332.6029   COL   ISSN 0123-1162

DIRECTORIO DEL SECTOR FINANCIERO. Text in Spanish. s-a. USD 350 (effective 1998). **Document type:** *Directory.* **Description:** Provides financial information as well as 7450 CEO's and VIP's names and addresses.
Published by: Asociacion Bancaria y de Entidades Financieras, Apartado Aereo 13994, Bogota, CUND, Colombia. TEL 57-1-2114811, FAX 57-1-2119915, info@asobancaria.com, http://www.asobancaria.com.

380.1029   ECU

DIRECTORIO ECUATORIANO; industrial y comercial. Text in Spanish. a. **Document type:** *Directory.*
Published by: O M C Publicaciones, Edif. Johnson, 4o piso, Foch 635 y Reina Victoria, Quito, Ecuador. TEL 548432. Ed. Rocio Gonzalez de Moreno.

380.1029   USA

DIRECTORIO HISPANO; the Hispanic yellow page directory. Text in English. 1988. a. USD 5 (effective 1999). adv. maps. 278 p./no.; **Document type:** *Directory.* **Description:** Offers a business telephone directory and source of information for the Hispanic community.
Address: 685 S Hwy 427, Longwood, FL 32750-6403. TEL 407-767-0070, FAX 407-767-5478. Ed. Dora Casanova de Toro. Pub., Adv. contact Manuel A Toro. B&W page USD 4,800, color page USD 5,200. Circ: 75,000 (controlled).

338.0029   GTM

DIRECTORIO INDUSTRIAL, CENTROAMERICA- PANAMA. Text in Spanish. 1973. irreg.
Published by: Secretaria Permanente del Tratado General de Integracion Economica Centroamericana, 4a Avda. 10-25, ZONA, 14, PO Box 1237, Guatemala City, 01901, Guatemala. TEL 502-3682151, FAX 502-3681071, sieca@pronet.net.gt.

670.29 ·   CHL

DIRECTORIO INDUSTRIAL DE CHILE; fabricantes, productos y servicios. Text in Spanish. 198?. biennial. **Document type:** *Directory.*
Published by: (Sociedad de Fomento Fabril), Publicaciones Lo Castillo S.A., Perez Valenzuela, 1620, Santiago, Chile. TEL 223-8031.

380.1029   COL   ISSN 0122-0217

DIRECTORIO INDUSTRIAL Y COMERCIAL; de America Latina. Text in Spanish. 1966. a. USD 50. **Document type:** *Directory.*
Formerly: Directorio Industrial de Colombia
Published by: Legis S.A., Ave. Eldorado, 81-10, Apartado Aereo 98888, Bogota, CUND, Colombia. TEL 57-1-263-2990, FAX 57-1-410-0628, TELEX 43300 LEGIS CO. Ed., R&P Roberto Escobar. Circ: 50,000 (controlled).

639.3029   MEX

DIRECTORIO INTERNACIONAL DE LA INDUSTRIA PESQUERA Y LA AQUACULTURA. Text in Spanish. a. USD 25; USD 55 foreign. adv. **Document type:** *Directory.* **Description:** Lists over 1350 companies and individuals devoted to fishing and aquaculture activities and over 300 suppliers of equipment, goods and services.
Published by: Alfa Editores Tecnicos S.A., Cumbres de Acultzingo 83, Col. Narvarte, Mexico City, DF 03020, Mexico. TEL 525-579-3333, FAX 525-582-3342, alfotec@telmex.net.mx, http://www.industria-alimentaria.com. adv.: B&W page USD 572, color page USD 800; trim 280 x 215. Circ: 5,000 (controlled).

658.878029   CHL

DIRECTORIO NACIONAL DE ABASTECIMIENTO E INSUMOS PARA SUPERMERCADOS. Text in Spanish. 1992. a. **Document type:** *Directory.*
Published by: (Asociacion Gremial de Supermercados y Autoservicios de Chile), Publicaciones Lo Castillo S.A., Perez Valenzuela, 1620, Santiago, Chile. TEL 2352606, FAX 2352007. Ed. Alberto Gana D.

338.0029   NIC

DIRECTORIO NACIONAL DE EMPRESAS. Text in Spanish. biennial. **Document type:** *Directory.*
Published by: Vistazo Economico, Camino de Oriente Contiguo Rest., Las Brasas, Managua, Nicaragua. TEL 70738.

DIRECTORIO NACIONAL DE ENTIDADES COOPERATIVOS. see *BUSINESS AND ECONOMICS—Cooperatives*

380.1029   LBR

DIRECTORY AND WHO'S WHO IN LIBERIA∗ . Text in English. 1971. irreg. adv. illus.
Published by: A & A Enterprises Inc., P O Box 103, Monrovia, Liberia.

DIRECTORY IN RUSSIAN OF BRITISH FIRMS INTERESTED IN TRADE WITH THE F S U. (Former Soviet Union) see *BUSINESS AND ECONOMICS—International Commerce*

DIRECTORY IRON AND STEEL PLANTS. see *METALLURGY*

DIRECTORY MARKETPLACE. see *PUBLISHING AND BOOK TRADE*

659.1029   GBR

DIRECTORY OF ADVERTISING AGENCIES. Text in English. s-a. GBP 75 newsstand/cover (effective 2000). adv. **Document type:** *Directory, Trade.*
Published by: Pharmaceutical Marketing Limited, Vincent House, Vincent Ln, Dorking, Surrey RH4 3JD, United Kingdom. TEL 44-1306-740777, FAX 44-1306-741069, info@pharmark.co.uk. Ed. Andy Rice. Pub. Mark Savage. R&P Keith Shilson. Adv. contact Zoe Almeida.

DIRECTORY OF ALBERTA'S AGRICULTURAL PROCESSING INDUSTRY. see *AGRICULTURE—Agricultural Economics*

DIRECTORY OF ALTERNATIVE INVESTMENT PROGRAMS. see *BUSINESS AND ECONOMICS—Investments*

DIRECTORY OF AMERICAN FIRMS OPERATING IN FOREIGN COUNTRIES. see *BUSINESS AND ECONOMICS— International Commerce*

381.45687   USA   ISSN 1092-4442
HD9940.U3

DIRECTORY OF APPAREL SPECIALITY STORES (YEAR); includes: family wear, sporting goods, and activewear retailers. Text in English. a. USD 260 (effective 1999). **Document type:** *Directory.* **Description:** Details over 5,000 women's, men's, family, and sporting goods retailers operating approximately 52,000 stores. Listings identify sales volume, number of stores, price lines, product lines, resident buyers, and over 17,000 key executive, buying, merchandising, and administrative personnel.
Formed by the merger of: Directory of Women's and Children's Wear Speciality Stores (Year) (0277-9617); Which was formerly: Directory of Apparel Speciality Stores. Women's and Children's (0272-1104); Directory of Men's and Boys' Wear Speciality Stores (Year) (0277-9625); Which was formerly: Directory of Men's and Boys' Speciality Stores (0272-1112)
Related titles: Diskette ed.; Magnetic Tape ed.
Published by: C S G Information Services (Subsidiary of: Lebhar-Friedman, Inc.), 3922 Coconut Palm Dr, Tampa, FL 33619. TEL 813-664-6800, FAX 813-664-6882. Ed. Keisha Rutledge.

DIRECTORY OF APPLIANCES, EQUIPMENT, CONSTRUCTION MATERIALS, AND COMPONENTS EVALUATED IN ACCORDANCE WITH INTERNATIONAL PUBLICATIONS. see *BUSINESS AND ECONOMICS—Production Of Goods And Services*

720.29   USA

DIRECTORY OF ARCHITECTS IN METROPOLITAN WASHINGTON. Text in English. 1991. biennial. price varies. adv. **Document type:** *Directory.*
Formerly (until 1991): D C - A I A Member Handbook
Published by: American Institute of Architects, Washington Chapter, 1777 Church St, N W, Washington, DC 20036. TEL 202-667-1798, FAX 202-667-4327. R&P Julienne Nelson. Circ: 3,500.

382.029   USA

DIRECTORY OF ARIZONA EXPORTERS. Text in English. 1977. q. USD 35 (effective 1999). adv. **Document type:** *Directory, Government.* **Description:** Lists Arizona companies that currently export or would like to export their products or services.
Formerly: Arizona U S A International Trade Directory
Related titles: Diskette ed.: USD 65 (effective 1999).
Published by: Department of Commerce, 3800 N Central Ave, Ste 1500, Phoenix, AZ 85012. TEL 602-280-1371, FAX 602-280-1305. Ed., Adv. contact Sally Spray. Circ: 5,000.

DIRECTORY OF ASSOCIATION MEETING PLANNERS & CONFERENCE - CONVENTION DIRECTORS. see *MEETINGS AND CONGRESSES*

060   AUS   ISSN 0110-666X

DIRECTORY OF AUSTRALIAN ASSOCIATIONS. Text in English. 1978. bi-m. AUD 395; AUD 650 print & online eds. (effective 2004). adv. Supplement avail. **Document type:** *Directory.*
Related titles: Online - full content ed.: AUD 495 (effective 2004).
Published by: Crown Content, Level 1, 141 Capel St, Nth Melbourne, VIC 3051, Australia. TEL 6-13-93299800, FAX 6-13-93299698, scott@crowncontent.com.au, http://www.australianassociations.com.au, http://www.crowncontent.com.au.

660.6029   AUS   ISSN 1327-1482

DIRECTORY OF AUSTRALIAN BIOTECHNOLOGY COMPANIES. Text in English. 1989. biennial. AUD 25. adv. back issues avail. **Document type:** *Directory, Trade.* **Description:** Provides full-page company profiles of 38 biotech companies and listings of companies serving the industry.
Formerly: Australian and New Zealand Biotechnology Directory (1032-8068)
Media: Online - full text.
Published by: Ausbiotech Ltd., 576 Swan St, Richmond, VIC 3121, Australia. TEL 61-3-9208-4200, FAX 61-3-9208-4201, admin@ausbiotech.org, http://www.ausbioinfo.com/, http://www.ausbiotech.org/. Eds. Barbara Arnold, Martin Playne. Adv. contact Gary Dolder. Circ: 3,000.

381.029   USA   ISSN 0736-0452
HD9710.3.U5

DIRECTORY OF AUTOMOTIVE AFTERMARKET SUPPLIERS (YEAR). Text in English. 1973. a. USD 300 (effective 1999). **Document type:** *Directory.* **Description:** Profiles approximately 1,900 jobber-retailers operating over 23,000 two-or-more unit stores; approximately 1,100 warehouse distributors-branch offices serving over 1.8 million accounts; 17 major buying-programming distribution groups serving over 45,000 members; names and titles of over 10,000 key personnel and decision makers.
Former titles: Directory of Auto Supply Chains (0730-2533); Supersedes in part: Directory: Home Centers and Hardware Chains, Auto Supply Chains (0094-8667); Directory-Hardware and Home Improvement Center Chains, Auto Supply Chains (0092-1483); Directory-Auto Supplies and Hardware Chains
Related titles: Diskette ed.; Magnetic Tape ed.
Published by: C S G Information Services (Subsidiary of: Lebhar-Friedman, Inc.), 3922 Coconut Palm Dr, Tampa, FL 33619. TEL 813-664-6800, FAX 813-664-6882. Ed. Arthur Rosenberg.

DIRECTORY OF BOOK PRINTERS (YEAR). see *PUBLISHING AND BOOK TRADE*

026.34   GBR

DIRECTORY OF BRITISH AND IRISH LAW LIBRARIES. Text in English. irreg., latest vol.6, 1998. GBP 39 to members; GBP 77 to non-members. adv. **Document type:** *Directory.*
Published by: (British and Irish Association of Law Libraries), Sweet & Maxwell Ltd., The Hatchery, Hall Bank Ln, Mytholmroyd, Hebden Bridge, W Yorks HX7 5HQ, United Kingdom. TEL 44-1422-888000, FAX 44-1422-888001, pauline.fothergill@smlawpub.co.uk, customer.services@sweetandmaxwell.co.uk, http://www.smlawpub.co.uk, http://www.sweetandmaxwell.co.uk. Ed. Pauline Fothergill.

380.1029   GBR   ISSN 0309-5487

DIRECTORY OF BRITISH ASSOCIATIONS & ASSOCIATIONS IN IRELAND. Text in English. 1965. biennial (16th ed), latest 2002. GBP 180 (effective 2004). index. **Document type:** *Directory.* **Description:** Lists 7,200 national organizations in the U.K. and Ireland.
Formerly (until 1974): Directory of British Associations (0070-5152)
Related titles: CD-ROM ed.: GBP 250, USD 465 (effective 2001). —BLDSC (3592.766000), CISTI.
Published by: C.B.D. Research Ltd., 15 Wickham Rd, Beckenham, Kent BR3 5JS, United Kingdom. TEL 44-20-86507745, FAX 44-20-86500768, cbd@cbdresearch.com, http://www.cbdresearch.com. Eds. A J W Henderson, S P A Henderson. Circ: 7,000.

DIRECTORY OF BRITISH AVIATION (YEARS). see *TRANSPORTATION—Air Transport*

690.029   USA   ISSN 1085-259X
HD9745.U4

DIRECTORY OF BUILDING PRODUCTS & HARDLINES DISTRIBUTORS. Text in English. a. USD 280 (effective 1999). **Document type:** *Directory.* **Description:** Profiles over 3,100 houseware, paint, electrical, heating, cooling, plumbing, and lumber companies, building supplies distributors (minimum $2 million annual sales), serving over 6.9 million retailers, contractors and commercial accounts. Listings identify sales volume, product lines, markets served, distribution centers, buying/marketing groups and more. Also includes names and titles of over 11,200 key executives and decision makers.
Formerly: Directory of Hardlines Distributors (Year); Incorporates: Directory of Hardware and Housewares Distributors (0882-536X)
Related titles: Diskette ed.; Magnetic Tape ed. —CCC.

Published by: C S G Information Services (Subsidiary of: Lebhar-Friedman, Inc.), 3922 Coconut Palm Dr, Tampa, FL 33619. TEL 813-664-6800, FAX 813-664-6882. Ed. William Larned.

338.0029 USA ISSN 1549-7224
HF54.52.U5
THE DIRECTORY OF BUSINESS INFORMATION RESOURCES. Text in English. a. USD 250 (effective 2004). **Document type:** *Directory, Trade.* **Description:** Provides information on associations, newsletters, magazines, trade shows, directories, databases and web sites organized by major industries.
Related titles: Diskette ed.
Published by: Grey House Publishing, 185 Millerton Rd, PO Box 860, Millerton, NY 12546. TEL 518-789-8700, 800-562-2139, FAX 518-789-0556, http://www.greyhouse.com/businessinfo.htm. Pub. Leslie E Mackenzie. R&P Leslie Mackenzie. **Dist. by:** Current Pacific Ltd., PO Box 36-536, Northcote, Auckland, New Zealand. TEL 64-9-480-1388, FAX 64-9-480-1387, info@cplnz.com, http://www.cplnz.com.

338.0029 USA ISSN 1549-7216
HF5421
DIRECTORY OF BUSINESS TO BUSINESS CATALOGS. Text in English. a. USD 165 (effective 2000). **Document type:** *Directory, Trade.* **Description:** Lists over 6000 business catalog companies in 40 different product areas.
Related titles: Diskette ed.
Published by: Grey House Publishing, Pocket Knife Sq, Lakeville, CT 06039. TEL 518-789-8700, 800-562-2139, FAX 518-789-0556. Pub. Leslie E Mackenzie.

332.6029 USA ISSN 1066-9736
HG65
DIRECTORY OF BUYOUT FINANCING SOURCES. Text in English. 1982. a. USD 325. **Document type:** *Directory.*
Former titles (until 1992): Buyouts Directory of L B O Financing Sources (1050-4915); (until 1990): Buyouts Directory of Financing Sources (1040-5739); (until 1989): Directory of Financing Sources for Buyouts and Acquisitions (0898-1108)
—CCC.
Published by: Securities Data Publishing (Subsidiary of: Thomson Financial / I M G Media), 195 Broadway, New York, NY 10007. TEL 212-333-9202, http://www.thomsonfinancial.com. Ed. Daniel Bokser.

670 USA
DIRECTORY OF CALIFORNIA MANUFACTURERS. Text in English. USD 179 (effective 2000). **Document type:** *Directory.*
Related titles: CD-ROM ed.: USD 869 (effective 2000).
Published by: Manufacturers' News, Inc., 1633 Central St, Evanston, IL 60201. TEL 847-864-7000, 888-752-5200, FAX 847-332-1100, info@manufacturersnews.com, sales@mninfo.com, http://www.manufacturersnews.com. Ed. Frank Lambing.

670.29 USA ISSN 1094-0235
HF5065.C2
DIRECTORY OF CALIFORNIA TECHNOLOGY COMPANIES✶ . Text in English. a. USD 150. **Document type:** *Directory.* **Description:** Identifies 12,100 manufacturers, R & D firms, research laboratories, telecommunications companies, distributors of technology components and products, and aerospace and defense companies in California that utilize medium and high technologies in the operation of their business.
Formerly (until 199?): California Technology Register (1059-7085)
Related titles: CD-ROM ed.: USD 450.
Published by: Database Publishing Company, 701 E Ball Rd Ste 100, Anaheim, CA 92805-5962. TEL 714-778-6400, FAX 714-778-6811. R&P Sarah Fraser.

338.0029 USA
HD9981.7.C2
DIRECTORY OF CALIFORNIA WHOLESALERS AND SERVICE COMPANIES✶ . Text in English. 1979. a. USD 169. **Document type:** *Directory.* **Description:** Provides information on 36,000 California service businesses, including distributors, wholesalers, transportation, finance, and business services companies.
Formerly: California Services Register (0271-6615)
Related titles: Diskette ed.: USD 295 (effective 1999).
Published by: Database Publishing Company, 701 E Ball Rd Ste 100, Anaheim, CA 92805-5962. TEL 714-778-6400, FAX 714-778-6811. Ed. Ken Gregory. R&P Sarah Fraser. Circ: 750. **Subscr. to:** PO Box 70024, Anaheim, CA 92625-0024. **Dist. by:** Current Pacific Ltd., PO Box 36-536, Northcote, Auckland, New Zealand. TEL 64-9-480-1388, FAX 64-9-480-1387, info@cplnz.com, http://www.cplnz.com.

DIRECTORY OF CANADIAN CHARTERED ACCOUNTANTS. see *BUSINESS AND ECONOMICS—Accounting*

DIRECTORY OF CARTOONISTS - GAGWRITERS - SHORT HUMOR MARKETS. see *ART*

381.12029 USA ISSN 0411-7085
TX907
DIRECTORY OF CHAIN RESTAURANT OPERATORS (YEAR); includes: leading chain hotel companies operating foodservice units. Text in English. a. USD 335 per issue; USD 975 combined subscription per issue print & CD eds. (effective 2005). **Document type:** *Directory, Trade.* **Description:** Profiles over 4,000 three-or-more unit chain restaurant companies operating or franchising more than 350,000 restaurants, drive-ins, cafeterias, hotels, motels, contract feeders, industrial feeders, as well as food units in drug chains, general merchandise chains, and discount stores. Identifies sales volume, national franchise headquarter location, number of units operated, primary wholesaler, type of liquor menu and foodservice offered, trading area, and more.
Related titles: CD-ROM ed.: USD 775 per issue (effective 2005); Diskette ed.; Magnetic Tape ed.
Published by: C S G Information Services (Subsidiary of: Lebhar-Friedman, Inc.), 3922 Coconut Palm Dr, Tampa, FL 33619. TEL 813-627-6800, 800-778-9794, FAX 813-627-6882, info@csgis.com, http://www.csgis.com. Ed. Linda Helman.

DIRECTORY OF CHEMICAL PRODUCERS - CANADA. see *CHEMISTRY*

DIRECTORY OF CHEMICAL PRODUCERS - CHINA. see *CHEMISTRY*

DIRECTORY OF CHEMICAL PRODUCERS - EAST ASIA. see *CHEMISTRY*

DIRECTORY OF CHEMICAL PRODUCERS - EUROPE. see *CHEMISTRY*

DIRECTORY OF CHEMICAL PRODUCERS - INDIA. see *CHEMISTRY*

DIRECTORY OF CHEMICAL PRODUCERS - MEXICO. see *CHEMISTRY*

DIRECTORY OF CHEMICAL PRODUCERS - MIDDLE EAST. see *CHEMISTRY*

DIRECTORY OF CHEMICAL PRODUCERS - SOUTH AMERICA. see *CHEMISTRY*

DIRECTORY OF CHEMICAL PRODUCERS - UNITED STATES. see *CHEMISTRY*

DIRECTORY OF CHEMICAL PRODUCTS & BUYERS GUIDE. see *CHEMISTRY*

DIRECTORY OF CHEMICAL PRODUCTS AND PRODUCERS IN CHINA (YEAR). see *ENGINEERING—Chemical Engineering*

540.29 DEU ISSN 0943-7967
DIRECTORY OF CHEMICALS AND THEIR SUPPLIERS - EUROPE✶ . Text in English. 1993. biennial. **Document type:** *Directory, Trade.*
Published by: E C O N Verlag GmbH, Friedrichstr 126, Berlin, 10117, Germany. TEL 49-30-23456300, FAX 49-30-23456303, sabine.kahl@ullstein-buchverlage.de, http://www.econ-verlag.de. Adv. contact Iris Schlimm. Circ: 6,000.

380.1029 CHN
DIRECTORY OF CHINESE ENTERPRISES FOR FOREIGN ECONOMIC RELATIONS AND TRADES. Text in Chinese, English. 1993. biennial. USD 165. **Document type:** *Directory.* **Description:** Lists import and export corporations and enterprises subordinate to Chinese ministries and commissions at the national level.
Published by: Han Consultants Inc., P.O. Box 71006, Wuhan, Hubei 430071, China. TEL 86-27-783-8532, FAX 86-27-787-8343. Circ: 7,000.

381.029 HKG ISSN 0259-1146
DIRECTORY OF CHINESE EXTERNAL ECONOMIC ORGANIZATIONS & INDUSTRIAL - COMMERCIAL ENTERPRISES. Text in Chinese. 1982. irreg. HKD 450, USD 78. **Document type:** *Directory.*
Published by: Economic Information & Agency, 342 Hennessy Rd 10th Fl, 10 th Fl, Wanchai, Hong Kong. TEL 852-573-8217, FAX 852-838-8304.

641.3461029 IDN
DIRECTORY OF COCONUT TRADERS AND EQUIPMENT MANUFACTURERS. Text in English. irreg. **Document type:** *Directory.* **Description:** Lists more than 800 exporters, 400 importers and 60 equipment manufacturers including name of companies, addresses, contact numbers and products they are dealing with.
Formed by the merger of: Directory of Coconut Processing Machinery, Equipment, Manufacturers and Suppliers; Directory of Coconut Products Importers; Directory of Coconut Products Exporters
Published by: Asian and Pacific Coconut Community, 3rd Fl., Lina Bldg., Jl H R Rasuna Said Kav B 7, Kuningan, Jakarta, 12920, Indonesia. TEL 62-21-5221712, FAX 62-21-5221714, TELEX 62863 APCC IA, apcc@indo.net.id, http://www.idrc.org.sg./pan/apcc.

338.0029 USA ISSN 0084-9898
T12
DIRECTORY OF COLORADO MANUFACTURERS. Text in English. 1948. every 18 mos. USD 80 (effective 2001). **Document type:** *Directory.* **Description:** Lists 6,500 manufacturers in alphabetic, geographic and S.I.C. sections. Phone number, top marketing official's name and title, area of distribution and product description in geographical and S.I.C. sections.
Published by: University of Colorado, Business Research Division, Campus Box 420, Boulder, CO 80309-0420. TEL 303-492-8227, FAX 303-492-3620. Ed. Gin S Hayden. Circ: 2,500.

380.1029 SYR
DIRECTORY OF COMMERCE & INDUSTRY. Text in Arabic. 1979. a. USD 60. adv. **Document type:** *Directory.*
Published by: Arab Advertising Organization, 28, Mountanabbi St., P O Box 2842-3034, Damascus, Syria. TEL 225219, TELEX 411923. Ed. Mouhammed Qatian. Circ: 20,000.

332.6029 USA ISSN 1045-0041
HG4028.D5
DIRECTORY OF COMPANIES OFFERING DIVIDEND REINVESTMENT PLANS. Text in English. 1982. a. USD 34.95 (effective 2000). **Document type:** *Directory, Consumer.*
Indexed: ATI.
Published by: Evergreen Enterprises, PO Box 763, Laurel, MD 20725-0763. Ed. S Kinoshita.

DIRECTORY OF COMPOSITE MANUFACTURERS, SUPPLIERS, AND SERVICES (YEAR). see *ENGINEERING—Engineering Mechanics And Materials*

380.1029 USA
HD9696.C63
DIRECTORY OF COMPUTER V A R'S & SYSTEM INTEGRATORS (YEAR). Variant title: Directory of V A Rs. Text in English. a. USD 290 (effective 1999). **Document type:** *Directory.* **Description:** Profiles nearly 5,300 VARs, including value-added dealers, non-storefront VARs, system houses, and system integrators serving a wide variety of end users. Listings identify type of applications, sales volume, percentage of sales in hardware, software, and peripherals, operating systems, products resold, services provided, ability to network, and more. Includes nearly 30,000 key executive, buying, and administrative personnel.
Formerly: Directory of Value Added Resellers (Year) (0884-8300)
Related titles: CD-ROM ed.; Diskette ed.; Magnetic Tape ed.
Published by: C S G Information Services (Subsidiary of: Lebhar-Friedman, Inc.), 3922 Coconut Palm Dr, Tampa, FL 33619. TEL 813-664-6800, 800-927-9292, FAX 813-664-6882. Ed. Ashley Valdes. Pub. William Larned.

DIRECTORY OF CONNECTICUT LIBRARIES AND MEDIA CENTERS; a quick reference to libraries and media centers in Connecticut. see *LIBRARY AND INFORMATION SCIENCES*

DIRECTORY OF CONSULTING ENGINEERING SERVICES IN NORTH CAROLINA. see *ENGINEERING*

670.29 USA
DIRECTORY OF CONTRACT ELECTRONICS MANUFACTURERS. NORTH AMERICAN EDITION (ONLINE EDITION). Text in English. irreg.
Media: Online - full content. **Related titles:** Diskette ed.: USD 345.
Published by: C M P Media LLC (Subsidiary of: United News & Media), 600 Community Dr, Manhasset, NY 11030. http://www.cmp.com. **Subscr. to:** PO Box 1291, Skokie, IL 60076-1291.

380.1029 USA ISSN 0736-9778
HG4057
DIRECTORY OF CORPORATE AFFILIATIONS. Text in English. 1981. a. (in 5 vols.). USD 1,599 per issue (effective 2005). adv. stat. index. 11000 p./no.; **Document type:** *Directory.* **Description:** Five-volume corporate reference tool comprising of three distinct titles and a comprehensive master index.
Incorporates: International Directory of Corporate Affiliations (0730-9465); Former titles (until 1992): Directory of Leading Private Companies, Including Corporate Affiliations (1066-9779); (until 1991): Macmillan Directory of Leading Private Companies (1041-5572)
Related titles: CD-ROM ed.; Magnetic Tape ed.; Online - full text ed.
—CCC.
Published by: LexisNexis (Subsidiary of: LexisNexis North America), PO Box 7587, Charlottesville, VA 22906-7587. TEL 434-972-7600, 800-446-3410, http://www.corporateaffiliations.com, http://www.lexislawpublishing.com. Circ: 2,500.

DIRECTORY OF CREMATORIA. see *FUNERALS*

DIRECTORY OF CUSTOM COASTERS (YEAR). see *ENGINEERING—Engineering Mechanics And Materials*

658.8029   USA   ISSN 1097-7023
HF5465.U3
DIRECTORY OF DEPARTMENT STORES; includes: resident buyers, mail order firms. Text in English. a. USD 290 (effective 1999). **Document type:** *Directory.* **Description:** Provides complete profiles on more than 140 department store companies, 1,100 shoe retailers, 150 jewelry retailers, and 25 leather companies. Includes more than 10,000 names and titles of key executives and buyers. Listings identify sales volume, trading area, private label, products line, store location types, furniture styles and price lines, and resident buyers.
Former titles: Directory of Department Stores and Mail Order Firms (Year) (1090-4921); Directory of Department Stores (Year) (0419-2508)
Related titles: CD-ROM ed.; Diskette ed.; Magnetic Tape ed.
Published by: C S G Information Services (Subsidiary of: Lebhar-Friedman, Inc.), 3922 Coconut Palm Dr, Tampa, FL 33619. TEL 813-664-6800, 800-927-9292, FAX 813-664-6882. Ed. Rick Cordier. Pub. William Larned.

658.0029   USA   ISSN 1084-533X
HF5035
DIRECTORY OF DISCOUNT AND GENERAL MERCHANDISE STORES (YEAR). Text in English. 1961. a. USD 300 (effective 1999). **Document type:** *Directory.* **Description:** Provides complete company profiles on approximately 4,400 total retailers operating over 65,000 stores. Identifies sales volume, square footage, store locations, speciality departments, and more than 29,000 key executives, buying and administrative personnel are included.
Former titles: Directory of Discount Department Stores (Year) (0897-5442); Directory of Discount Department Stores, Catalog Showrooms (Year) (0897-1765); Directory of Discount Department Stores (0736-931X); Directory of Discount Centers (0070-5446)
Related titles: CD-ROM ed.; Diskette ed.; Magnetic Tape ed.
Published by: C S G Information Services (Subsidiary of: Lebhar-Friedman, Inc.), 3922 Coconut Palm Dr, Tampa, FL 33619. TEL 813-664-6800, 800-927-9292, FAX 813-664-6810. Ed. Janice Backer. Pub. William Larned.

338.0029   IND
DIRECTORY OF ECONOMIC RESEARCH CENTRES IN INDIA. Text in English. 1972. irreg., latest vol.2, 1975. INR 500, USD 45 per vol. (effective 2004). adv. Supplement avail. **Document type:** *Directory.* **Description:** List of 250 major economic research institutes in India.
Published by: Information Research Academy, 37 Syed Amir Ali Ave, Flat #9, Kolkata, West Bengal 700 019, India. TEL 91-33-22402681, psguha@vsnl.net, http://www.irakol.net. Ed. Partha Subir Guha. Circ. 2,500.

DIRECTORY OF ELECTRIC UTILITY INDUSTRY. see
ENERGY—Electrical Energy

333.7932   USA   ISSN 1530-1133
HD9697.A3
DIRECTORY OF ELECTRICAL WHOLESALE DISTRIBUTORS. Text in English. 1930. biennial. USD 695 per issue (effective 2003). adv. **Document type:** *Directory, Trade.* **Description:** Contains complete and independent compilation of electrical wholesalers of more than 10,000 headquarters and branch locations, arranged alphabetically by city within state.
Related titles: CD-ROM ed.: USD 2,085 per issue (effective 2001).
Published by: Primedia Business Magazines & Media, Inc. (Subsidiary of: Primedia, Inc.), 9800 Metcalf Ave, Overland Park, KS 66212-2216. TEL 913-341-1300, FAX 913-967-1898, inquiries@primediabusiness.com, http://www.primediabusiness.com.

338.0029   GBR
DIRECTORY OF ENGINEERING CAPACITY. Text in English. 1958. a. GBP 25 (effective 1999). adv. **Document type:** *Directory.* **Description:** Lists plants, capacity and contract machining facilities.
Published by: Coventry and Warwickshire Chamber of Commerce Training and Enterprise, Oak Tree Court, Binley Business Park, Harry Weston Rd, Coventry, CV3 2UN, United Kingdom. Ed. Mark Eatonn. Circ. 5,000.

667.2029   GBR   ISSN 0965-6030
DIRECTORY OF EUROPEAN DYERS, PRINTERS AND FINISHERS. Text in English. 1987. biennial, latest 2002, 8th ed. GBP 50 per issue domestic; GBP 60 per issue foreign (effective 2005). **Document type:** *Directory, Trade.*
Formerly (until 1992): Directory of U K Dyers and Finishers (0951-4074)
Published by: World Textile Publications Ltd., Perkin House, 1 Longlands St, Bradford, W Yorks BD1 2TP, United Kingdom. TEL 44-1274-378800, FAX 44-1274-378811, info@world-textile.net, http://www.world-textile.net/contact.html.

670.29   GBR   ISSN 0952-3626
HD2429.E87
DIRECTORY OF EUROPEAN INDUSTRIAL & TRADE ASSOCIATIONS. Text in English. 1971. irreg., latest vol.6, 1997. GBP 195, USD 390 (effective 2001). **Document type:** *Directory.* **Description:** Lists 6,000 European national trade and industrial organizations outside the U.K.

Formerly: Directory of European Associations. Part 1: National Industrial Trade and Professional Associations (0070-5500) —BLDSC (3593.528000), CASDDS.
Published by: C.B.D. Research Ltd., 15 Wickham Rd, Beckenham, Kent BR3 5JS, United Kingdom. TEL 44-20-86507745, FAX 44-20-86500768, cbd@cbdresearch.com, http://www.cbdresearch.com. Ed. Francis Knott. Circ. 4,000.

658.0029   USA   ISSN 0090-6484
HF5549.5.R44
DIRECTORY OF EXECUTIVE RECRUITERS (STANDARD ED.). Variant title: Directory of Executive Recruiters (Personal Ed.). Text in English. 1971. a. USD 47.95 per vol. (effective 2002). 1180 p./no.; **Document type:** *Directory, Trade.* **Description:** Lists 14,200 recruiters at 5,700 search firms in the U.S., Canada, and Mexico.
Published by: Kennedy Information Inc., One Kennedy Place, Rte 12 S, Fitzwilliam, NH 03447. TEL 603-585-6544, 800-531-0007, FAX 603-585-9555, bookstore@kennedyinfo.com, http://www.kennedyinfo.com/js/der.html.

338.0029   GBR   ISSN 0968-0152
DIRECTORY OF FIRMS. Text in English. 1992. a. GBP 60. adv. **Document type:** *Directory.* **Description:** Lists firms of consulting structural engineers in the U.K.
Published by: Structural Engineers Trading Organisation Ltd., 11 Upper Belgrave St, London, SW1X 8BH, United Kingdom. TEL 44-20-7235-4535, FAX 44-20-7235-4294. Circ. 5,000 (controlled).

338.0029   USA   ISSN 1076-3694
T12
DIRECTORY OF FLORIDA INDUSTRIES. Text in English. 1935. a. USD 106.10 (effective 1998). adv. **Document type:** *Directory.*
Related titles: CD-ROM ed.
Published by: (Florida Chamber of Commerce Management Corp., Inc.), Harris InfoSource International, 2057 2 E Aurora Rd, Twinsburg, OH 44087-1999. TEL 216-425-9000, 800-888-5900, FAX 216-425-7150, catknapp@aol.com. Ed. Gary Cliett. Circ. 5,000 (controlled).

380.1029   USA   ISSN 0271-7662
HD9321.3
DIRECTORY OF FOODSERVICE DISTRIBUTORS (YEAR); includes: full-line food, equipment, supplies, specialty distributors. Text in English. 1973. a. USD 290 (effective 1999). **Document type:** *Directory.* **Description:** Companion to the restaurant database. Profiles 5,000 distributors (with minimum annual sale of $500,000). Identifies sales volume, product lines carried, buying and marketing group affiliations, number of accounts served; type of restaurants and institutions served, trading area and more. Names and titles of over 24,000 key personnel and decision makers.
Formerly: Chain Store Guide Directory: Food Service Distributors (0091-9152)
Related titles: CD-ROM ed.; Magnetic Tape ed. —CISTI.
Published by: C S G Information Services (Subsidiary of: Lebhar-Friedman, Inc.), 3922 Coconut Palm Dr, Tampa, FL 33619. TEL 813-664-6800, FAX 813-664-6882. Ed. Sam Sadler.

658.0029   USA   ISSN 0070-5543
HG4057
DIRECTORY OF FOREIGN FIRMS OPERATING IN THE UNITED STATES. Text in English. 1969. irreg., latest vol.11, 2001. USD 250 (effective 2001). **Document type:** *Directory, Consumer.* **Description:** Lists more than 2,100 foreign firms and 5,700 U.S. affiliates.
Related titles: CD-ROM ed.: USD 675 domestic; USD 1,000 for 2 yrs. domestic (effective 2001); individual country/region editions available upon request. Price from $29.00 - $159.00.
Published by: Uniworld Business Publications, 257 Central Park West, New York, NY 10017-4110. TEL 212-496-2448, FAX 212-592-1000, uniworldbp@aol.com, http://www.unitedworld.com. Ed. Barbara Fiorito. Pub. Debra Lipian.

613.029   USA   ISSN 1049-9253
R712.A1
DIRECTORY OF HEALTH CARE PROFESSIONALS. Text in English. 1990. a. **Document type:** *Directory.*
Published by: American Hospital Association, One N Franklin, Chicago, IL 60606-3421. TEL 312-422-3000, http://www.aha.org.

613.029   USA   ISSN 1064-8496
RA971.33
DIRECTORY OF HEALTHCARE GROUP PURCHASING ORGANIZATIONS. Text in English. 1983. a. USD 325 (effective 2000). adv. **Document type:** *Directory.* **Description:** Provides information on over 500 group purchasing organizations.
Related titles: Online - full text ed.: (from The Dialog Corporation).
Published by: Advanstar Medical Economics Healthcare Communications (Subsidiary of: Advanstar Communications, Inc.), 5 Paragon Dr, Montvale, NJ 07645-1742. TEL 201-358-7657, 800-745-2601, FAX 201-722-2662, mdr@medec.com. Ed. Bill Shaughnessy.

615.1029   USA   ISSN 1054-3082
HD9666.3
DIRECTORY OF HIGH VOLUME INDEPENDENT DRUG STORES (YEAR). Text in English. 1992. a. USD 290 (effective 1999). **Document type:** *Directory.* **Description:** Profiles approximately 8,800 one-unit drug retailers and the names and titles of over 16,500 key executives within those companies (including owner, president, head pharmacist and general buyer). Company listings provide sales volume, product lines carried, square footage, indicates computerized Rx, year founded and more.
Related titles: Diskette ed.; Magnetic Tape ed.
Published by: C S G Information Services (Subsidiary of: Lebhar-Friedman, Inc.), 3922 Coconut Palm Dr, Tampa, FL 33619. TEL 813-664-6800, FAX 813-664-6882. Ed. Debbie Scruggs.

647.95029   USA   ISSN 0888-0166
TX907
DIRECTORY OF HIGH VOLUME INDEPENDENT RESTAURANTS (YEAR). Text in English. 1987. a. USD 335 per issue; USD 975 combined subscription per issue print & CD eds. (effective 2005). **Document type:** *Directory.* **Description:** Provides complete information on over 8,000 one-or-two unit independents, each with a minimum $1 million in annual sales. Listings identify type of foodservice, liquor served, type of menu, sales volume, number of seats, and more. Also includes names and titles of over 22,000 key decision makers.
Related titles: CD-ROM ed.: USD 775 per issue (effective 2005); Diskette ed.; Magnetic Tape ed.
Published by: C S G Information Services (Subsidiary of: Lebhar-Friedman, Inc.), 3922 Coconut Palm Dr, Tampa, FL 33619. TEL 813-627-6800, 800-778-9794, FAX 813-627-6882, info@csgis.com, http://www.csgis.com.

380.1029   USA   ISSN 0272-0167
HD9745.U4
DIRECTORY OF HOME CENTER OPERATORS & HARDWARE CHAINS (YEAR); includes: home center warehouses, lumber/building material outlets, farm & home stores & specialty paint chains. Text in English. 1948. a. USD 300 (effective 1999). **Document type:** *Directory.* **Description:** Details over 5,400 home centers, warehouses, and lumber-building material companies (minimum $1 million in annual sales); and 20 buying groups serving over 100,000 accounts. Listings identify sals volume, product lines carried, distribution centers, percentage of sales to D-I-Y consumers buying-marketing groups and more. Also includes names and titles over 21,000 key executives and buyers.
Supersedes in part: Directory: Home Centers and Hardware Chains, Auto Supply Chains (0094-8667)
Related titles: CD-ROM ed.; Diskette ed.; Magnetic Tape ed.
Published by: C S G Information Services (Subsidiary of: Lebhar-Friedman, Inc.), 3922 Coconut Palm Dr, Tampa, FL 33619. TEL 813-664-6800, FAX 813-664-6882. Ed. Arthur Rosenberg.

749.029   USA   ISSN 0888-0158
HD9773.U4
DIRECTORY OF HOME FURNISHINGS RETAILERS (YEAR); includes: full-line home furnishing stores, and wholesalers. Text in English. 1987. a. USD 290 (effective 1999). **Document type:** *Directory.* **Description:** Provides selling information on approximately 5,100 furniture and home furnishings retail companies, and nearly 430 major wholesalers, each with minimum $1 million annual sales. Includes information on sales volume, price lines, furniture styles, distribution centers, number of stores operated, year founded, and names and titles of over 17,000 key decision makers.
Related titles: Diskette ed.; Magnetic Tape ed.
Published by: C S G Information Services (Subsidiary of: Lebhar-Friedman, Inc.), 3922 Coconut Palm Dr, Tampa, FL 33619. TEL 813-664-6800, FAX 813-664-6882. Ed. Ashley Valdes.

382.029   HKG
DIRECTORY OF HONG KONG IMPORT & EXPORT TRADE∗. Text in Chinese. a. HKD 200. **Document type:** *Directory.*
Published by: Hong Kong Trade and Industry Promotion Centre, 23/F, Wu Sang House, 655 Nathan Rd, Mong Kok, Kowloon, Hong Kong. TEL 852-2399-3100, FAX 852-2381-2492.

338.0029   HKG
DIRECTORY OF HONG KONG INDUSTRIAL SUPPLIERS (YEAR). Text in Chinese, English. 1996. a. HKD 600; USD 115 in S.E. Asia; USD 130 elsewhere. **Document type:** *Directory.* **Description:** Lists over 3,000 industrial suppliers in Hong Kong; contains essential information for sourcing raw materials, semi-manufactures, parts and components, machinery, equipment and tools.
Published by: Hong Kong Productivity Council, HKPC Bldg, 78 Tat Chee Ave, Kowloon, Hong Kong. TEL 852-2788-5814, FAX 852-2788-5959, isd@hkpc.org, http://www.hkpc.org. Circ. 5,000.

338.0029 HKG
DIRECTORY OF HONG KONG INDUSTRIES. Text in English. 1976. a. HKD 750 domestic; HKD 155 in Asia; HKD 170 elsewhere. adv. **Document type:** *Directory.* **Description:** Lists about 6,400 major manufacturing companies in Hong Kong as well as relevant government departments and major industrial and trade associations.
Published by: Hong Kong Productivity Council, HKPC Bldg, 78 Tat Chee Ave, Kowloon, Hong Kong. TEL 852-788-5821, FAX 852-788-5959, TELEX 32842 HKPC HX, isd@hkpc.org, http://www.hkpc.org. Circ: 3,000. **Dist. by:** Current Pacific Ltd., PO Box 36-536, Northcote, Auckland, New Zealand. TEL 64-9-480-1388, FAX 64-9-480-1387, info@cplnz.com, http://www.cplnz.com.

381.029 HKG
DIRECTORY OF HONG KONG TRADE AND INDUSTRY✶ . Text in Chinese, English. 1978. a. HKD 1,180; HKD 420 per vol.. stat. **Document type:** *Directory.*
Published by: Hong Kong Trade and Industry Promotion Centre, 23/F, Wu Sang House, 655 Nathan Rd, Mong Kok, Kowloon, Hong Kong. TEL 852-2399-3100, FAX 852-2381-2492. Ed. Eddie Lam.

362.11029 USA ISSN 0885-9671
RA977
DIRECTORY OF HOSPITAL PERSONNEL. Text in English. 1986. a. USD 275 (effective 2001). **Document type:** *Directory, Trade.*
Related titles: Online - full text ed.: (from The Dialog Corporation).
Published by: Grey House Publishing, 185 Millerton Rd, PO Box 860, Millerton, NY 12546. TEL 518-789-8700, 800-562-2139, FAX 518-789-0556, books@greyhouse.com, http://www.greyhouse.com. Ed. Laura Mars. Pub. Leslie E Mackenzie.

382.029 IND ISSN 0417-5964
DIRECTORY OF INDIAN ENGINEERING EXPORTERS. Text in English. 1957. irreg., latest vol.11, 1995. INR 300, USD 10. adv. illus. **Document type:** *Directory.*
Published by: Engineering Export Promotion Council, World Trade Centre, 3rd Fl., 14-1 B Ezra St., Kolkata, West Bengal 700 001, India. TEL 91-33-250442, FAX 91-33-2319968. Circ: 3,000.

338.0029 PAK
DIRECTORY OF INDUSTRIAL ESTABLISHMENTS IN PUNJAB. Text in English. 1975. a. PKR 40. **Document type:** *Directory.*
Published by: Directorate of Industries and Mineral Development, Lahore, Punjab, Pakistan.

381.029 UAE
DIRECTORY OF INDUSTRIAL PRODUCTS: SHARJAH, UNITED ARAB EMIRATES/DALEEL AL MONTAJAT AL SINA'IAH: AL SHARIQAH. Text in Arabic, English. 1988. a., latest vol.4, 1996-1997. free. adv. **Document type:** *Directory.* **Description:** Provides names, addresses, and activities for Sharjah's industrial firms. Also includes information about development of the industrial sector of Sharjah.
Formerly (until 1998): Directory of Industrial Products: Made in Sharjah, United Arab Emirates
Related titles: CD-ROM ed.; Online - full text ed.
Published by: Sharjah Chamber of Commerce and Industry, P O Box 580, Sharjah, United Arab Emirates. TEL 971-6-5088600, FAX 971-6-5541119, scci@sharjah.gov.ae, http://www.sharjah.gov.ae. Circ: 5,000 (paid).

338.6029 USA ISSN 1050-3218
JK791
DIRECTORY OF INSTITUTIONAL INVESTMENT FUNDS. Text in English. 1989. a. **Document type:** *Directory.* **Description:** Covers two broad categories of institutional investment funds: employee benefit - pension, savings, and deferred compensation; non-employee benefit funds - endowment, specific-purpose, board-designated and foundation.
Published by: Corporate Profiles, Inc., Database Services Group, 27 Janci St, Metuchen, NJ 08840. TEL 908-321-0708.

641.3461029 IDN
DIRECTORY OF INTERNATIONAL COCONUT RESEARCH WORKERS. Text in English. irreg. USD 25. **Document type:** *Directory.* **Description:** Lists more than 255 experts in Asia, Pacific and other regions, which are classified under 24 disciplines and countries.
Published by: Asian and Pacific Coconut Community, 3rd Fl., Lina Bldg., Jl H R Rasuna Said Kav B 7, Kuningan, Jakarta, 12920, Indonesia. TEL 510073, FAX 0062-21-5205160.

669.14 USA
DIRECTORY OF IRON AND STEEL PLANTS. Text in English. triennial. price varies.
Formerly: Directory of Iron and Steel Works of the United States and Canada
Published by: American Iron and Steel Institute, 1133 15th St, N W, Ste 300, Washington, DC 20005. TEL 202-452-7100.

380.1029 ISR
DIRECTORY OF ISRAEL. Text in English. 1953. a. USD 80. adv. bk.rev. **Description:** Lists manufacturers, exporters, and importers of all types of goods.
Formerly: Directory of Israeli Merchants and Manufacturers (0070-5705)
Published by: N.A. Etrogy Publishing Company, P O Box 815, Tel Aviv, 61007, Israel. TEL 972-3-6293451, FAX 972-3-5256155. Ed. A Etrogy. **Dist. by:** International Publications Inc., 303 Park Ave S, New York, NY 10010.

382.029 DEU
DIRECTORY OF JAPANESE ADDRESSES IN EUROPE. Text in German. a. **Document type:** *Directory.*
Published by: Japaninfo Verlag, Bismarckring 40, Ulm, 89077, Germany. TEL 0731-68093, FAX 0731-68095.

382.029 JPN
DIRECTORY OF JAPANESE AFFILIATED COMPANIES IN ASIA (YEAR). Text in Japanese. 1982. triennial. USD 165 (effective 2001); incl. CD-ROM. **Document type:** *Directory.* **Description:** Lists 3,574 Japanese-affiliated companies in Asian countries in alphabetical order and by type of products or business.
Formerly: Directory of Japanese Affiliated Companies in A S E A N Countries (Year)
Published by: (Publications Department), Japan External Trade Organization, 2-5 Toranomom 2-chome, Minato-ku, Tokyo, 105-8466, Japan. TEL 03-3582-3518, FAX 03-3587-2485. **Dist. by:** Current Pacific Ltd., PO Box 36-536, Northcote, Auckland, New Zealand. TEL 64-9-480-1388, FAX 64-9-480-1387, info@cplnz.com, http://www.cplnz.com.

382.029 JPN
DIRECTORY OF JAPANESE AFFILIATED COMPANIES IN THE E U (YEAR). Text in Japanese. triennial. USD 240 (effective 2001). **Document type:** *Directory.* **Description:** Lists 2,988 Japanese-affiliated companies in the EU, alphabetically grouped by country and city, and by the type of products or businesses.
Published by: (Publications Department), Japan External Trade Organization, 2-5 Toranomom 2-chome, Minato-ku, Tokyo, 105-8466, Japan. TEL 03-3582-3518, FAX 03-3587-2485.

382.029 JPN
DIRECTORY OF JAPANESE AFFILIATED COMPANIES IN THE U S A AND CANADA. Text in Japanese. 1969. triennial. JPY 30,000 (effective 2001); incl. CD-ROM. adv. **Document type:** *Directory.* **Description:** Lists 7,900 Japanese-affiliated enterprises in alphabetical order by country and state or province.
Former titles (until 1986): Directory of Japanese Firms, Offices and Other Organizations in the United States; Directory of Japanese Firms, Offices and Subsidiaries in the United States
Published by: (Publications Department), Japan External Trade Organization, 2-5 Toranomom 2-chome, Minato-ku, Tokyo, 105-8466, Japan. TEL 03-3582-3518, FAX 03-3587-2485, TELEX J24378 JETRO.

DIRECTORY OF JAPANESE PUBLISHING INDUSTRY. see *PUBLISHING AND BOOK TRADE*

670.29 USA
T12
DIRECTORY OF KANSAS BUSINESSES. Text in English. 1940. a. USD 50. **Document type:** *Directory.* **Description:** Profiles Kansas businesses including service-oriented companies and manufacturers.
Former titles: Directory of Kansas Manufacturers and Products (0070-5721); (until 1954): Made in Kansas (0415-9586); (until 1953): It's Made in Kansas (0198-8336)
Related titles: Diskette ed.
Published by: Kansas Department of Commerce, 1000 SW Jackson St, Ste 100, Topeka, KS 66612-1354. FAX 913-296-5055, http://kdoch.state.ks.us/public/index.jsp. Ed. Rhonda Egans. Circ: 2,000. **Dist. by:** Manufacturers' News, Inc., 1633 Central St, Evanston, IL 60201. TEL 847-864-7000.

670.29 USA ISSN 0275-1089
T12
DIRECTORY OF LOUISIANA MANUFACTURERS. Text in English. 1942. a. USD 57. index. **Document type:** *Directory.*
Formerly: Louisiana Directory of Manufacturers (0076-1028)
Related titles: CD-ROM ed.: USD 299; Diskette ed.
Published by: Harris InfoSource International, 2057 2 E Aurora Rd, Twinsburg, OH 44087-1999. TEL 216-425-9000, 800-888-5900, FAX 216-425-7150, catknapp@aol.com. Ed. Frances L Carlsen. Circ: 3,500.

380.1029 USA ISSN 1066-9744
HD2746.5
DIRECTORY OF M & A INTERMEDIARIES. Text in English. 1987. a. USD 595 per issue (effective 2005). adv. index. **Document type:** *Directory.* **Description:** Lists corporate acquirers and their criteria, as well as professional service firms and their services.
Formerly: Merger Directory
Published by: Source Media, Inc., One State St Plaza, 27th Fl, New York, NY 10004. TEL 212-803-6077, 800-221-1809, FAX 212-747-1154, custserv@sourcemedia.com, http://www.sourcemedia.com.

658.872029 USA ISSN 0899-5710
HF5465.5
DIRECTORY OF MAIL ORDER CATALOGS. Text in English. 1981. a. USD 250 (effective 2001). **Document type:** *Directory, Trade.* **Description:** Lists over 11000 catalog companies, their presidents, production managers, marketing managers, buyers, and list managers, as well as catalog information.
Related titles: Diskette ed.
Published by: Grey House Publishing, 185 Millerton Rd, PO Box 860, Millerton, NY 12546. TEL 518-789-8700, 800-562-2139, FAX 518-789-0556, books@greyhouse.com, http://www.greyhouse.com. Ed. Laura Mars. Pub. Leslie E Mackenzie. **Dist. by:** Current Pacific Ltd., PO Box 36-536, Northcote, Auckland, New Zealand. TEL 64-9-480-1388, FAX 64-9-480-1387, info@cplnz.com, http://www.cplnz.com.

DIRECTORY OF MAILING LIST COMPANIES. see *ADVERTISING AND PUBLIC RELATIONS*

659.1029 USA ISSN 1045-6201
HF5465.5
DIRECTORY OF MAJOR MAILERS & WHAT THEY MAIL (YEAR). Text in English. 1990. a. USD 495 (effective 1997). adv. index. **Document type:** *Directory.* **Description:** Directory of 6,000 major mailers (names, addresses, phone numbers, list sizes) plus descriptions of 18,000 mailings in 200 categories.
Related titles: CD-ROM ed.; Magnetic Tape ed.
Published by: North American Publishing Co., 1500 Spring Garden St., Ste 1200, Philadelphia, PA 19130-4094. TEL 215-238-5300, FAX 215-238-5457, http://www.napco.com. Ed. Paul Bobrakch. Circ: 1,000.

DIRECTORY OF MANAGEMENT CONSULTANTS IN THE UK. see *BUSINESS AND ECONOMICS—Management*

690.029 IND
DIRECTORY OF MANUFACTURERS & DEALERS OF BUILDING INDUSTRY. Text in English. 1994. irreg. USD 15. adv. **Document type:** *Directory, Trade.* **Description:** Alphabetical listing of manufacturers and dealers of building products and materials in India, including name, address, phone number, details of products, and annual sales.
Published by: Architects Publishing Corp. of India, 51 Sujata, Ground Fl., Rani Sati Marg, Malad East, Mumbai, Maharashtra 400 097, India. TEL 91-22-883-4442. Ed. A K Gupta. Circ: 5,000.

381.029 MEX
DIRECTORY OF MEXICAN CORPORATIONS. Text in English. 1992. irreg., latest vol.8, 2001. USD 330 (effective 2001). **Document type:** *Directory.* **Description:** Lists corporations selling at least ten million US dollars per year. Indexed by CEO, SIC code, foreign associates, location, and products imported and exported.
Published by: Ibcon S.A., Gutemberg 224, Col Anzures, Mexico City, DF 11590, Mexico. TEL 52-5-2554577, FAX 52-5-2554577, ibcon@infosel.net.mx, http://www.ibcon.com.mx. Ed. Gabriel Zaid.

DIRECTORY OF MUSEUMS AND SPECIAL COLLECTIONS IN THE UNITED KINGDOM. see *MUSEUMS AND ART GALLERIES*

670.29 USA ISSN 0070-5926
T12
DIRECTORY OF NEBRASKA MANUFACTURERS. Text in English. 1960. biennial. USD 50 (effective 2000). **Document type:** *Directory.* **Description:** Comprehensive information on over 1,900 manufacturer; includes alphabetical, geographical and SIC sections, plus alphabetical index to product classification.
Published by: Nebraska Department of Economic Development, PO Box 94666, Lincoln, NE 68509. TEL 402-471-3111, FAX 708-322-1100. Ed. Darrell William. R&P Tammy Corby. Circ: 5,000.

670.29 USA ISSN 0889-0382
HD9723
DIRECTORY OF NEW ENGLAND MANUFACTURERS; CT, ME, MA, NH, RI, VT. Text in English. a. USD 128. **Document type:** *Directory.* **Description:** Profiles 22,000 manufacturers in Connecticut, Maine, Massachusetts, New Hampshire, Rhode Island and Vermont; includes alphabetical, geographical and product sections.
Published by: Harris InfoSource International, 2057 2 E Aurora Rd, Twinsburg, OH 44087-1999. TEL 216-425-9000, 800-888-5900, FAX 216-425-7150, catknapp@aol.com, http://www.harrisinfo.com. **Dist. by:** Manufacturers' News, Inc., 1633 Central St, Evanston, IL 60201. TEL 847-864-7000.

B

381.029 USA ISSN 1521-1304
T391
DIRECTORY OF NORTH AMERICAN FAIRS, FESTIVALS AND EXPOSITIONS. Variant title: Fairs, Festivals and Expositions. North America Fairs, Festivals and Expositions. Text in English. 1888. a. (Jan.). USD 70 newsstand/cover (effective 2005). **Document type:** *Directory, Trade.* **Description:** Lists almost 5,000 state and county fairs, festivals and public expositions in the US and Canada that run three days or more. Contains general and statistical data, plus chronological cross-references.
Former titles (until 1986): Directory of North American Fairs, & Expositions (0361-4255); (until 1972): Cavalcade and Directory of Fairs (0069-1291)
Published by: V N U Business Publications (Subsidiary of: V N U Business Media), 770 Broadway, 7th Fl, New York, NY 10003. TEL 646-654-5117, FAX 646-654-5351, bmcomm@vnuinc.com, http://www.vnubusinessmedia.com/. Ed. James Zoltak TEL 323-525-2318. Adv. contact Scott Partridge. Circ: 1,700 (paid). **Subscr. to:** PO Box 2011, Marion, OH 43306-811137202. TEL 800-745-8922.

670.29 USA
HD9727.N9
DIRECTORY OF NORTH DAKOTA MANUFACTURERS AND FOOD PROCESSORS. Text in English. 1959. biennial. USD 50 (effective 1999). **Document type:** *Directory.* **Description:** Lists approximately 790 manufacturers in three color-coded sections: product (by SIC), alphabetical, and geographic.
Former titles: Directory of North Dakota Manufacturers (0090-5577); Directory of North Dakota Industrial and Manufacturing Plants
Media: Online - full text. **Related titles:** Diskette ed.
Published by: Department of Economic Development and Finance, 1833 E Bismarck Expressway, Bismarck, ND 58504. TEL 701-328-5300, FAX 701-328-5320, ccmail.ndef@ranch.state.nd.us, http://www.growingnd.com. Ed. Jody Link. Circ: 2,500. **Dist. by:** Manufacturers' News, Inc., 1633 Central St, Evanston, IL 60201. TEL 847-864-7000.

331.1029 GBR ISSN 0070-6051
HD6270
DIRECTORY OF OVERSEAS SUMMER JOBS; your complete guide to thousands of summer employment opportunities abroad. Variant title: Overseas Summer Jobs. Vacation Work's Overseas Summer Jobs. Text in English. 1969. a. USD 16.95 (effective 2000). **Document type:** *Directory.* **Description:** Lists jobs outside the UK and offers advice on landing one of them.
Published by: Vacation Work Publications, 9 Park End St, Oxford, OX1 1HJ, United Kingdom. TEL 44-1865-241978, FAX 44-1865-790885, vacationwork@vacationwork.co.uk, http://www.vacationwork.co.uk. Ed. David Woodworth. **Dist. in U.S. by:** Peterson's Guides, 202 Carnegie Ctr, Princeton, NJ 08543. TEL 800-338-3282.

DIRECTORY OF PREMIUM, INCENTIVE & TRAVEL BUYERS. see *BUSINESS AND ECONOMICS—Investments*

338.0029 USA ISSN 0887-4042
DIRECTORY OF PRIMES. Text in English. 1983. a. **Document type:** *Directory, Trade.*
Published by: Government Data Publications, Inc., 2300 M St, N W, Washington, DC 20037. TEL 800-275-4688, FAX 718-998-5960, gdp@govdata.com, http://www.govdata.com.

381.029 USA
DIRECTORY OF PRODUCTS AND SERVICES FOR THE VACUUM INDUSTRY. Text in English. 1994. a. USD 10 domestic; USD 15 foreign (effective 2003). adv. **Document type:** *Directory, Trade.* **Description:** Describes products and services of the major vacuum equipment manufacturers.
Published by: Association of Vacuum Equipment Manufacturers, 71 Pinon Hill Place NE, Albuquerque, NM 87122. TEL 505-856-6924, FAX 505-856-6716, aveminfo@avem.org, http://www.avem.org. Ed., R&P, Adv. contact Vivienne Harwood Mattox. Circ: 1,000.

DIRECTORY OF PROFESSIONAL APPRAISERS. see *REAL ESTATE*

332.6029 AUS
DIRECTORY OF PROPERTY INVESTORS AND DEVELOPERS. Text in English. irreg. **Document type:** *Directory.*
Published by: Davies and Dalziel Investment Service, GPO Box 1392 M, Melbourne, VIC 3001, Australia.

DIRECTORY OF QUARRIES, PITS AND QUARRY EQUIPMENT. see *MINES AND MINING INDUSTRY*

200.29 USA
BV655
DIRECTORY OF RELIGIOUS MEDIA. Text in English. 1972. a. USD 89.95 (effective 2000). adv. index. **Document type:** *Directory.* **Description:** Covers the worldwide Christian religious broadcasting industry, listing more than 4500 radio and television stations, program producers, manufacturers, and related suppliers and services.
Formerly: Directory of Religious Broadcasting (0731-0331)
Indexed: ChrPI.
Published by: National Religious Broadcasters, Inc., 9510 Technology Dr., Manassas, VA 20110-4167. TEL 703-330-7000, FAX 703-330-7100, http://www.nrb.org. Ed. Karen M Hawkins. Pub. E Brandt Gustavson. Adv. contact Steve Cross TEL 703-330-7000. B&W page USD 975, color page USD 1,575; trim 10.88 x 8.38. Circ: 2,000 (paid).

DIRECTORY OF RESTAURANT & FAST FOOD CHAINS IN CANADA (YEAR). see *FOOD AND FOOD INDUSTRIES*

658.8029 CAN ISSN 0225-9443
DIRECTORY OF RETAIL CHAINS IN CANADA. Text in English. 1975. a. CND 250. **Document type:** *Directory, Trade.*
Published by: Rogers Media Publishing Ltd, One Mount Pleasant Rd, 11th Fl, Toronto, ON M4Y 2Y5, Canada. TEL 416-764-2000, FAX 416-764-3941, http://www.retailinfonet.com, http://www.rogers.com.

678.2029 GBR
DIRECTORY OF RUBBER ORGANIZATIONS (YEAR). Text in English. 1995. a. GBP 150 per vol. (effective 2003 & 2004). **Document type:** *Directory, Trade.* **Description:** Lists over 220 trade, research and development and government-related organizations worldwide concerned with natural and synthetic rubber or with the manufacture of end products such as tires and general rubber goods.
Related titles: Diskette ed.: GBP 36 non-member companies (effective 2000); E-mail ed.
Published by: International Rubber Study Group, 1st Fl, Heron House, 109/115 Wembley Hill Rd, Wembley, Mddx HA9 8DA, United Kingdom. TEL 44-20-8903-7727, FAX 44-20-8903-2848, irsg@rubberstudy.com, http://www.rubberstudy.com.

380.1029 SGP
DIRECTORY OF SERVICE PROVIDERS TO THE INSURANCE INDUSTRY IN ASIA. Text in English. a. USD 80 in Singapore & Malaysia; USD 110 elsewhere (effective 2005). **Document type:** *Directory, Trade.* **Description:** Lists 18 supporting-value-added services available to the insurance companies and professionals: Legal advisors; auditors; management consultants; banks rating agencies; claims/loss adjusters; recruitment brokers; debt recovery specialist; reinsurance brokers; disaster recovery specialist; risk assessors & risk managers; insurance brokers; run-off service providers; investment, portfolio, & fund managers; security consultants; it service provider; training institutions.
Published by: Ins Communications Pte. Ltd., 57A Amoy St., Singapore, 069 883, Singapore. TEL 65-62245583, FAX 65-62241091, http://www.asiainsurancereview.com/EStore/Dir-of-service-providers.asp.

387.029 SGP ISSN 0218-4400
DIRECTORY OF SINGAPORE SHIPBUILDING & OFFSHORE INDUSTRIES (YEAR). Text in English. a. USD 50. adv. **Document type:** *Directory.* **Description:** Lists marine and offshore industries. Provides information on shipbuilders and repairers, oil rig builders, marine equipment and supplies, offshore equipment and supplies, and other marine-related products and services.
Published by: Times Media Pte Ltd, Directories Division, 1 New Industrial Rd, Times Centre, Singapore, 536196, Singapore. TEL 65-2848844, FAX 65-2850161. Pub., R&P Leslie Lim. Adv. contact Joseph Liang.

381.148029 USA ISSN 0896-2162
HF5469.23.U6
DIRECTORY OF SINGLE UNIT SUPERMARKET OPERATORS (YEAR). Text in English. a. USD 290 (effective 1999). **Document type:** *Directory.* **Description:** Provides selling information on single unit supermarket operators, identifies sales volume, square footage, type of store operated, whether scanning equipment is used, type of specialty departments operated, etc.
Related titles: Diskette ed.; Magnetic Tape ed.
Published by: C S G Information Services (Subsidiary of: Lebhar-Friedman, Inc.), 3922 Coconut Palm Dr, Tampa, FL 33619. TEL 813-664-6800, FAX 813-664-6882. Ed. Sam Sadler.

338.0029 USA ISSN 1538-3458
TS229
DIRECTORY OF STEEL FOUNDRIES AND BUYER'S GUIDE. Text in English. 1930. biennial. USD 95. adv. **Document type:** *Directory.*
Formerly (until 1994): Directory of Steel Foundries in the United States, Canada and Mexico
Related titles: Diskette ed.: USD 200.
Published by: Steel Founders' Society of America, 780 Mcardle Dr., Ste. G, Crystal Lake, IL 60014-8155. TEL 847-382-8240, FAX 847-382-8287, http://www.sfsa.org. Ed. Kathleen J Reese. Adv. contact Kathleen Reese. Circ: 1,500.

331.1029 GBR ISSN 0308-7123
DIRECTORY OF SUMMER JOBS ABROAD. Text in English. 1970. a. GBP 9.99 (effective 2000). **Document type:** *Directory.* **Description:** Geared toward British citizens.
Published by: Vacation Work Publications, 9 Park End St, Oxford, OX1 1HJ, United Kingdom. TEL 44-1865-241978, FAX 44-1865-790885, vacationwork@vacationwork.co.uk, http://www.vacationwork.co.uk. Ed. David Woodworth.

650.14029 GBR ISSN 0143-3490
HF5382.5.G7
DIRECTORY OF SUMMER JOBS IN BRITAIN. Text in English. 1970. a. USD 16.95 (effective 2000). **Document type:** *Directory.*
Published by: Vacation Work Publications, 9 Park End St, Oxford, OX1 1HJ, United Kingdom. TEL 44-1865-241978, FAX 44-1865-790885, vacationwork@vacationwork.co.uk, http://www.vacationwork.co.uk. Ed. David Hatchell. **Dist. in U.S. by:** Peterson's Guides, 202 Carnegie Ctr, Princeton, NJ 08543. TEL 800-338-3282.

658.8029 USA ISSN 0196-1845
HD9321.3
DIRECTORY OF SUPERMARKET, GROCERY & CONVENIENCE STORE CHAINS (YEAR); includes: market share. Text in English. a. USD 300 (effective 1999). **Document type:** *Directory.* **Description:** Profiles approximately 2,200 two-or-more supermarkets and grocery store chains (minimum $2 million annual sales) operating nearly 30,000 units including superstores, warehouse, combo stores; nearly 1,600 convenience store chains operating over 70,000 stores. Listings identify sales volume, store location type, type of store operated, specialty departments, scanning equipment and more. Also includes names and titles of over 26,000 executives and buyers.
Related titles: CD-ROM ed.; Diskette ed.; Magnetic Tape ed. —CISTI.
Published by: C S G Information Services (Subsidiary of: Lebhar-Friedman, Inc.), 3922 Coconut Palm Dr, Tampa, FL 33619. TEL 813-664-6800, FAX 813-664-6882. Ed. Andy Erickson.

DIRECTORY OF SURGICAL SPECIALISTS. see *MEDICAL SCIENCES—Surgery*

382.029 TWN
(YEAR) DIRECTORY OF TAIWAN'S LEADING MANUFACTURERS AND EXPORTERS. Variant title: TAIMEX. Text in Chinese. a. USD 90 in Americas, Europe & Africa; USD 80 in Middle East & Asia; USD 30 elsewhere (effective 2000). adv. **Document type:** *Directory.* **Description:** Provides the latest information on major suppliers in most consumer industries in Taiwan.
Former titles: Directory of Taiwan's Leading Exporters; Directory of Exhibitors Taipei International Trade Fairs
Related titles: CD-ROM ed.
Published by: China Economic News Service, 555 Chunghsiao E. Rd Sec 4, Taipei, 110, Taiwan. TEL 886-2-2642-2629, FAX 886-2-2642-7422, webmaster@www.cens.com, http://www.cens.com. adv.: B&W page TWD 35,000, color page TWD 40,000. **Dist. by:** Current Pacific Ltd., PO Box 36-536, Northcote, Auckland, New Zealand. TEL 64-9-480-1388, FAX 64-9-480-1387, info@cplnz.com, http://www.cplnz.com.

380.1029 CAN ISSN 0845-1656
DIRECTORY OF THE CANADIAN TRADE COMMISSIONER SERVICE. Text in English. 1975. a.
Former titles (until 1989): Canadian Trade Representatives Abroad (0837-6247); (until 1987): Business Directory of Canadian Trade Representation Abroad (0831-5655); (until 1983): Businessmen's Directory of Canadian Trade Representation Abroad (0822-1820); (until 1982): Canada's Trade and Tourism Officers Abroad (0822-1812); (until 1981): Canada's Trade Commissioners and Commercial Officers (0822-1804)
—CISTI.
Published by: (International Trade Canada, Trade Commissioner Service), International Trade Canada, 125 Sussex Drive, Ottawa, ON K1A 0G2, Canada. TEL 613-944-4000, FAX 613-996-9709, http://www.infoexport.gc.ca/ie-en/Directory.jsp, http://www.itcan-cican.gc.ca/menu-en.asp.

DIRECTORY OF THE CANNING, FREEZING, PRESERVING INDUSTRIES. see *FOOD AND FOOD INDUSTRIES*

DIRECTORY OF THE REFRACTORIES INDUSTRY (YEAR). see *CERAMICS, GLASS AND POTTERY*

DIRECTORY OF THE SPANISH COTTON-SYSTEM TEXTILE ENTERPRISES/DIRECTOIRE ENTERPRISES TEXTILES DE PROCESSUS COTONNIER/DIRECTORI EMPRESES TEXTILS DE PROCES COTONER/DIRECTORIO EMPRESAS TEXTILES DE PROCESO ALGODONERO. see *TEXTILE INDUSTRIES AND FABRICS*

380.1029 MYS ISSN 0126-6330
HD9766.M3
DIRECTORY OF TIMBER TRADE. Text in English. 1970. biennial. MYR 342, USD 90 per issue. **Document type:** *Directory.* **Description:** Lists names, addresses, certificate numbers, end colors and shipping marks of timber exporters, sawmillers and manufacturers of timber products in Malaysia. Also includes timber graders, packers, timber preservation and kiln-dry operators.
Published by: Malaysian Timber Industry Board/Lembaga Perindustrian Kayu Malaysia, PO Box 10887, Kuala Lumpur, 50728, Malaysia. TEL 60-3-982-2235, FAX 60-3-9851477, mtib@po.jaring.my. Circ: 5,000.

382.029   BEL
DIRECTORY OF TRADE AND PROFESSIONAL ASSOCIATIONS IN THE EUROPEAN UNION - THE BLUE BOOK. Text in English, French. 199?. a., latest vol.5, 2001. EUR 146 per issue (effective 2004). **Document type:** *Directory.* **Description:** Lists address, telephone and fax numbers, chairman and contact person, and working languages of 700 European Union associations and 8600 national member associations.
Formerly: Directory of E U Trade and Professional Associations and Their Information - The Blue Book
Published by: Euroconfidentiel s.a., Rue de Rixensart 18, Genval, 1332, Belgium. TEL 32-2-6520284, FAX 32-2-6530180, nigel.hunt @infoboard.be. Ed. Christiane Mauwel. Dist. by: Current Pacific Ltd., PO Box 36-536, Northcote, Auckland, New Zealand. TEL 64-9-480-1388, FAX 64-9-480-1387, info@cplnz.com, http://www.cplnz.com.

338.47004   USA   ISSN 1061-9623
QA76
DIRECTORY OF U.S. GOVERNMENT DATAFILES FOR MAINFRAMES AND MICROCOMPUTERS. Text in English. a.
Published by: U.S. Department of Commerce, National Technical Information Service, 5285 Port Royal Rd, Springfield, VA 22161. http://www.ntis.gov.

641.36029   USA
DIRECTORY OF U.S. MEAT SUPPLIERS✱. Text in English. a. **Document type:** *Directory.*
Published by: United States Meat Export Federation, 1050 17th St, 2200, Denver, CO 80265-2073. TEL 303-399-7151, FAX 303-321-7075.

DIRECTORY OF UNITED STATES EXPORTERS. see *BUSINESS AND ECONOMICS—International Commerce*

DIRECTORY OF UNITED STATES IMPORTERS. see *BUSINESS AND ECONOMICS—International Commerce*

384.558029   USA
HD9697.V543
DIRECTORY OF VIDEO DEALERS. Text in English. 1990. a. USD 175. **Document type:** *Directory.* **Description:** Lists 100,000 US retailers of video hardware and software.
Formerly: Directory of Video Retailers (1053-9069)
Published by: Talent & Booking Online, PO Box 14265, Palm Desert, CA 92255. TEL 760-779-8056, FAX 760-773-3568, info@talentandbooking.com, http://www.talentandbooking.com. Ed. Steve Tolin.

380.1029   USA   ISSN 1068-7157
HD9321.3
DIRECTORY OF WHOLESALE GROCERS (YEAR); includes: service merchandisers. Text in English. a. USD 300 (effective 1997). **Document type:** *Directory.* **Description:** Companion to supermarket database. Profiles over 2,000 headquarters, divisions and branches for over 40 coops; 40 voluntary groups; 950 non-sponsoring wholesalers; 45 cash-and-carry warehouse operations; over 220 service merchandisers. Identifies sales volume, product line carried, number of accounts and store served, location, distribution centers, and warehouse type. Also includes 13,000 names and titles of key executives and buyers.
Former titles: Directory of Cooperatives, Voluntaries and Wholesale Grocers (0277-1969); Directory of Retailer Owned Cooperative Chains, Wholesaler Sponsored Voluntary Chains, Wholesale Grocers (0271-8006); Retailer Owned Cooperative Chains, Voluntary Chains and Wholesale Grocers (0196-1810)
Related titles: CD-ROM ed.; Diskette ed.; Magnetic Tape ed.
Published by: C S G Information Services (Subsidiary of: Lebhar-Friedman, Inc.), 3922 Coconut Palm Dr, Tampa, FL 33619. TEL 813-664-6800, FAX 813-664-6882. Ed. Sam Sadler.

338.0029   USA
DIRECTORY OF WIRE COMPANIES OF NORTH AMERICA. Text in English. 1973. a. USD 119 domestic; USD 150 foreign (effective 2000). adv. **Document type:** *Directory.* **Description:** Profiles over 1500 wire companies, ferrous-nonferrous and insulated wire, principal personnel, supplier data and fiber optic firms.
Published by: C R U International, 6305 Ivy Ln., Ste. 422, Greenbelt, MD 20770-6339. TEL 301-441-8997, FAX 301-441-9091. Ed. Florence Kauffman. Adv. contact Carol Calini TEL 203-481-9321. Circ: 5,000.

DIRECTORY OF WORKERS' COMPENSATION MANAGED CARE ORGANIZATIONS. see *LAW—Corporate Law*

DIRECTORY OF WORLD CHEMICAL PRODUCERS (STANDARD EDITION). see *CHEMISTRY*

DIRECTORY TO THE FURNITURE & FURNISHING INDUSTRY. see *INTERIOR DESIGN AND DECORATION—Furniture And House Furnishings*

338.0029   USA
DIRECTORY WORLD'S YELLOW PAGES INDUSTRY SOURCE BOOK. Text in English. 1988. a. USD 149.95 (effective 2000). **Document type:** *Directory.* **Description:** Lists key officers, revenues, leading books, major accounts, sales offices, and suppliers for more than 500 firms involved in all aspects of yellow pages publishing.
Formerly (until 1995): Yellow Pages Industry Source Book
Published by: SIMBA Information (Subsidiary of: R.R. Bowker LLC), 60 Long Ridge Rd., Ste 300, Stamford, CT 06902. TEL 203-325-8193, 800-307-2529, 888-269-5372, FAX 203-325-8915, info@simbanet.com, http://www.simbanet.com. Ed. David Goddard.

670.29   USA
DOCUMENTATION SERVICES INDEX. Text in English. 1964. bi-m. (in 3 vols.). USD 695. adv. **Document type:** *Abstract/Index.* **Description:** Provides vendor and Brand-Trade name access to OEMs servicing aerospace and design engineering fields.
Published by: I H S Energy (Subsidiary of: I H S Energy Group), 15 Inverness Way East, Englewood, CO 80112. FAX 303-799-4085, TELEX 4322083 IHS UI, http://ihsenergy.com. Ed. Liz Maynard Prigge. Circ: 889.

338.0029   USA
DOING BUSINESS IN BOSTON; complete yearbook of business for the greater Boston area. Text in English. 1994. biennial. USD 65 (effective 2001). adv. **Document type:** *Directory, Trade.* **Description:** Profiles 1,274 major public, private, foreign, mutual, nonprofit and subsidiary companies with headquarters in the Boston metropolitan area, encompassing Essex, Middlesex, Norfolk, Plymouth and Suffolk counties in Massachusetts, or companies with significant operations in the region.
Published by: Boston Business Journal, Inc., 10531 Cedar Lake Rd, No 512, Minnetonka, MN 55305. jpl_mn@hotmail.com. Ed. Jeffrey P Levine. Pub. James C Menneto. R&P Jeffrey Levine. adv.: B&W page USD 1,995. Circ: 5,000 (paid).

338.0029   USA   ISSN 1048-7247
HF5065.I3
DOWNSTATE ILLINOIS BUSINESS DIRECTORY. Text in English. 1985. a. USD 1,100 combined subscription print, online & CD-ROM eds. (effective 2004 & 2005). back issues avail. **Document type:** *Directory.* **Description:** Includes all businesses in downstate Illinois compiled from the yellow pages and telephone-verified. Includes company name, complete address, employee size and sales volume, name of owner or manager and credit rating codes.
Related titles: CD-ROM ed.; Diskette ed.; E-mail ed.; Fax ed.; Magnetic Tape ed.; Online - full text ed.
Published by: American Business Directories (Subsidiary of: American Business Information, Inc.), 5711 S 86th Circle, P O Box 27347, Omaha, NE 68127. TEL 402-593-4600, 888-946-9377, 877-708-3844, FAX 402-331-5481, karen.peters@infousa.com, sales@directoriesusa.com, http://www.directoriesusa.com.

DRILLING & WELL SERVICING CONTRACTORS; drilling & well servicing contractors, equipment manufacturers & supply companies. see *PETROLEUM AND GAS*

387.544029   USA
DROP SHIPPING SOURCE DIRECTORY OF MAJOR CONSUMER PRODUCT LINES. Text in English. 1977. a. USD 15 (effective 2003). adv. **Document type:** *Directory, Trade.* **Description:** Lists over 700 supply sources for over 200,000 consumer dropshipped products for mail order and other middlemen.
Published by: Drop Shipping News (Subsidiary of: Consolidated Marketing Services, Inc.), PO Box 7838, New York, NY 10150. TEL 212-688-8797, nscheel@drop-shipping-news.com, http://www.drop-shipping-news.com. Ed.; Pub., Adv. contact Nicholas T Scheel.

338.0029   USA
DUN & BRADSTREET STANDARD REGISTER. Variant title: Dun and Bradstreet - Seyd's Register. Text in English. 1965. a. (in 5 vols.). HNL 1.24.
Former titles: Dun and Bradstreet Register (0070-7635); Bradstreet's Register; Incorporates: Seyd's Commercial Lists (0080-911X)
Published by: Dun's Marketing Services (Subsidiary of: Dun & Bradstreet, Inc.), 3 Sylvan Way, Parsippany, NJ 07054-3896. TEL 201-455-0900.

384.54029   USA   ISSN 0743-7498
HF6146.R3
DUNCAN'S RADIO MARKET GUIDE. Text in English. 1984. a. USD 335.
Published by: Duncan's American Radio, 50 E. Rivercenter Blvd., Ste. 1200, Covington, KY 41011-1654. TEL 513-731-1800. Ed. James H Duncan.

DUNDEE AND TAYSIDE CHAMBER OF COMMERCE AND INDUSTRY. BUYER'S GUIDE AND TRADE DIRECTORY. see *BUSINESS AND ECONOMICS—Chamber Of Commerce Publications*

671.0029   USA   ISSN 0278-8799
TS203
DUN'S INDUSTRIAL GUIDE - THE METALWORKING DIRECTORY. Text in English. 1961. a. USD 795 to institutions; USD 485 to libraries. **Document type:** *Directory.* **Description:** Data on over 71,000 equipment manufacturers and metal distributors.
Formerly: Dun and Bradstreet Metalworking Directory (0070-7597)
Related titles: Magnetic Tape ed.
Published by: Dun & Bradstreet (Subsidiary of: Dun & Bradstreet Corporation), c/o Ethan Chazin, Director, Reference Services, Murray Hill, NJ 07094-1218. TEL 973-605-6000.

338.0029   USA   ISSN 1061-0723
HG4057.A6
DUN'S REGIONAL BUSINESS DIRECTORY. ALABAMA AREA. Text in English. a. USD 575 to corporations; USD 465 to libraries (effective 2000). **Document type:** *Directory.* **Description:** Provides information on the service, performance and operations of companies in Alabama.
Published by: Dun & Bradstreet (Subsidiary of: Dun & Bradstreet Corporation), c/o Ethan Chazin, Director, Reference Services, Murray Hill, NJ 07094-1218. TEL 973-605-6000.

338.7029   USA   ISSN 1051-3876
HG4058.A85
DUN'S REGIONAL BUSINESS DIRECTORY. ATLANTA AREA. Text in English. 1990. a. USD 575 to corporations; USD 465 to libraries (effective 2000). **Document type:** *Directory.* **Description:** Provides information on the services, performance and operations of Atlanta companies.
Published by: Dun & Bradstreet (Subsidiary of: Dun & Bradstreet Corporation), c/o Ethan Chazin, Director, Reference Services, Murray Hill, NJ 07094-1218. TEL 973-605-6000.

338.0029   USA   ISSN 1051-1326
HG4058.B7
DUN'S REGIONAL BUSINESS DIRECTORY. BOSTON AREA. Text in English. 1990. a. USD 575 to corporations; USD 465 to libraries (effective 2000). **Document type:** *Directory.* **Description:** Provides information on the services, performance and operations of Boston area businesses.
Published by: Dun & Bradstreet (Subsidiary of: Dun & Bradstreet Corporation), c/o Ethan Chazin, Director, Reference Services, Murray Hill, NJ 07094-1218. TEL 973-605-6000.

338.0029   USA   ISSN 1061-1126
HG4057.I6
DUN'S REGIONAL BUSINESS DIRECTORY. CENTRAL INDIANA AREA. Text in English. 1991. a. USD 575 to corporations; USD 465 to libraries (effective 2000). **Document type:** *Directory.* **Description:** Provides information on the services, performance and operations of companies in central Indiana.
Published by: Dun & Bradstreet (Subsidiary of: Dun & Bradstreet Corporation), c/o Ethan Chazin, Director, Reference Services, Murray Hill, NJ 07094-1218. TEL 973-605-6000.

338.0029   USA   ISSN 1061-0820
HG4057.P4
DUN'S REGIONAL BUSINESS DIRECTORY. CENTRAL PENNSYLVANIA AREA. Text in English. 1991. a. USD 575 to corporations; USD 465 to libraries (effective 2000). **Document type:** *Directory.* **Description:** Provides information on the services, performance and operations of companies in central Pennsylvania.
Published by: Dun & Bradstreet (Subsidiary of: Dun & Bradstreet Corporation), c/o Ethan Chazin, Director, Reference Services, Murray Hill, NJ 07094-1218. TEL 973-605-6000.

338.0029   USA   ISSN 1061-1134
HG4058.C27
DUN'S REGIONAL BUSINESS DIRECTORY. CHARLOTTE - GREENSBORO AREA. Text in English. 1991. a. USD 575 to corporations; USD 465 to libraries (effective 2000). **Document type:** *Directory.* **Description:** Provides information on the services, performance and operations of companies in and around Charlotte and Greensboro.
Published by: Dun & Bradstreet (Subsidiary of: Dun & Bradstreet Corporation), c/o Ethan Chazin, Director, Reference Services, Murray Hill, NJ 07094-1218. TEL 973-605-6000.

338.0029   USA   ISSN 1061-074X
HG4058.C5
DUN'S REGIONAL BUSINESS DIRECTORY. CHICAGO METROPOLITAN AREA. Text in English. 1990. a. USD 575 to corporations; USD 465 to libraries (effective 2000). **Document type:** *Directory.* **Description:** Provides information on the services, performance and operations of companies in the Chicago metropolitan area.
Published by: Dun & Bradstreet (Subsidiary of: Dun & Bradstreet Corporation), c/o Ethan Chazin, Director, Reference Services, Murray Hill, NJ 07094-1218. TEL 973-605-6000.

338.7029   USA   ISSN 1051-161X
HG4058.C5
DUN'S REGIONAL BUSINESS DIRECTORY. CHICAGO SUBURBAN AREA. Text in English. 1990. a. USD 575 to corporations; USD 465 to libraries (effective 2000). **Document type:** *Directory.* **Description:** Provides information on the services, performance and operations of suburban Chicago businesses.
Published by: Dun & Bradstreet (Subsidiary of: Dun & Bradstreet Corporation), c/o Ethan Chazin, Director, Reference Services, Murray Hill, NJ 07094-1218. TEL 973-605-6000.

338.7029   USA   ISSN 1051-1288
HG4058.C55
DUN'S REGIONAL BUSINESS DIRECTORY. CINCINNATI AREA. Text in English. 1990. a. USD 575 to corporations; USD 465 to libraries (effective 2000). **Document type:** *Directory.* **Description:** Provides information on the services, performance and operations of companies in Cincinnati.
Published by: Dun & Bradstreet (Subsidiary of: Dun & Bradstreet Corporation), c/o Ethan Chazin, Director, Reference Services, Murray Hill, NJ 07094-1218. TEL 973-605-6000.

338.7029   USA   ISSN 1051-1083
HG4058.C6
DUN'S REGIONAL BUSINESS DIRECTORY. CLEVELAND. Text in English. 1989. a. USD 575 to corporations; USD 465 to libraries (effective 2000). **Document type:** *Directory.* **Description:** Provides information on the services, performance and operations of Cleveland businesses.
Published by: Dun & Bradstreet (Subsidiary of: Dun & Bradstreet Corporation), c/o Ethan Chazin, Director, Reference Services, Murray Hill, NJ 07094-1218. TEL 973-605-6000.

338.0029   USA   ISSN 1061-0758
HG4058.C64
DUN'S REGIONAL BUSINESS DIRECTORY. COLUMBUS AREA. Text in English. 1992. a. USD 575 to corporations; USD 465 to libraries (effective 2000). **Document type:** *Directory.* **Description:** Provides information on the services, performance and operations of companies in the Columbus, Ohio area.
Published by: Dun & Bradstreet (Subsidiary of: Dun & Bradstreet Corporation), c/o Ethan Chazin, Director, Reference Services, Murray Hill, NJ 07094-1218. TEL 973-605-6000.

338.7029   USA   ISSN 1051-1180
HG4058.D2
DUN'S REGIONAL BUSINESS DIRECTORY. DALLAS - FORT WORTH AREA. Text in English. 1990. a. USD 575 to corporations; USD 465 to libraries (effective 2000). **Document type:** *Directory.* **Description:** Provides information on the services, performance and operations of Dallas and Fort Worth area businesses.
Published by: Dun & Bradstreet (Subsidiary of: Dun & Bradstreet Corporation), c/o Ethan Chazin, Director, Reference Services, Murray Hill, NJ 07094-1218. TEL 973-605-6000.

338.0029   USA   ISSN 1061-1142
HG4058.D46
DUN'S REGIONAL BUSINESS DIRECTORY. DENVER AREA. Text in English. 1990. a. USD 575 to corporations; USD 465 to libraries (effective 2000). **Document type:** *Directory.* **Description:** Provides information on the services, performance and operations of companies in the Denver area.
Published by: Dun & Bradstreet (Subsidiary of: Dun & Bradstreet Corporation), c/o Ethan Chazin, Director, Reference Services, Murray Hill, NJ 07094-1218. TEL 973-605-6000.

338.7029   USA   ISSN 1051-1628
HG4058.D6
DUN'S REGIONAL BUSINESS DIRECTORY. DETROIT. Text in English. a. USD 575 to corporations; USD 465 to libraries (effective 2000). **Document type:** *Directory.* **Description:** Provides information on the services, performance and operations of Detroit businesses.
Published by: Dun & Bradstreet (Subsidiary of: Dun & Bradstreet Corporation), c/o Ethan Chazin, Director, Reference Services, Murray Hill, NJ 07094-1218. TEL 973-605-6000.

338.0029   USA   ISSN 1061-1207
HG4057.G4
DUN'S REGIONAL BUSINESS DIRECTORY. GEORGIA (EXCLUDING ATLANTA) AREA. Text in English. 1992. a. USD 575 to corporations; USD 465 to libraries (effective 2000). **Document type:** *Directory.* **Description:** Provides information on the services, performance and operations of Georgia companies outside Atlanta.
Published by: Dun & Bradstreet (Subsidiary of: Dun & Bradstreet Corporation), c/o Ethan Chazin, Director, Reference Services, Murray Hill, NJ 07094-1218. TEL 973-605-6000.

338.7029   USA   ISSN 1051-2586
HG4057.C8
DUN'S REGIONAL BUSINESS DIRECTORY. HARTFORD, NEW HAVEN, SPRINGFIELD AREA. Text in English. 1990. a. USD 575 to corporations; USD 465 to libraries (effective 2000). **Document type:** *Directory.* **Description:** Provides information on the services, performance and operations of Connecticut businesses.

Published by: Dun & Bradstreet (Subsidiary of: Dun & Bradstreet Corporation), c/o Ethan Chazin, Director, Reference Services, Murray Hill, NJ 07094-1218. TEL 973-605-6000.

338.7029   USA   ISSN 1051-1172
HG4058.H68
DUN'S REGIONAL BUSINESS DIRECTORY. HOUSTON AREA. Text in English. 1990. a. USD 575, USD 465 (effective 2000). **Document type:** *Directory.* **Description:** Provides information on the services, performance and operations of Houston area businesses.
Published by: Dun & Bradstreet (Subsidiary of: Dun & Bradstreet Corporation), c/o Ethan Chazin, Director, Reference Services, Murray Hill, NJ 07094-1218. TEL 973-605-6000.

338.0029   USA   ISSN 1061-1150
HG4057.I8
DUN'S REGIONAL BUSINESS DIRECTORY. IOWA METROS AND OMAHA, NEBRASKA AREA. Text in English. 1990. a. USD 575 to corporations; USD 465 to libraries (effective 2000). **Document type:** *Directory.* **Description:** Provides information on the services, performance and operations of companies in the Iowa and Omaha areas.
Published by: Dun & Bradstreet (Subsidiary of: Dun & Bradstreet Corporation), c/o Ethan Chazin, Director, Reference Services, Murray Hill, NJ 07094-1218. TEL 973-605-6000.

338.0029   USA   ISSN 1061-0766
HG4057.K2
DUN'S REGIONAL BUSINESS DIRECTORY. KANSAS CITY AREA. Text in English. 1992. a. USD 575 to corporations; USD 465 to libraries (effective 2000). **Document type:** *Directory.* **Description:** Provides information on the services, performance and operations of companies in the Kansas City area.
Published by: Dun & Bradstreet (Subsidiary of: Dun & Bradstreet Corporation), c/o Ethan Chazin, Director, Reference Services, Murray Hill, NJ 07094-1218. TEL 973-605-6000.

338.0029   USA   ISSN 1061-1169
HG4057.K4
DUN'S REGIONAL BUSINESS DIRECTORY. KENTUCKY METROS (INCLUDING EVANSVILLE, IN). Text in English. 1989. a. USD 575 to corporations; USD 465 to libraries (effective 2000). **Document type:** *Directory.* **Description:** Provides information on the services, performance and operations of companies in Kentucky's metropolitan areas.
Published by: Dun & Bradstreet (Subsidiary of: Dun & Bradstreet Corporation), c/o Ethan Chazin, Director, Reference Services, Murray Hill, NJ 07094-1218. TEL 973-605-6000.

338.7029   USA   ISSN 1051-1202
HG4057.N7
DUN'S REGIONAL BUSINESS DIRECTORY. LONG ISLAND, NEW YORK. Text in English. 1990. a. USD 575 to corporations; USD 465 to libraries (effective 2000). **Document type:** *Directory.* **Description:** Provides information on the services, performance and operations of companies on Long Island.
Published by: Dun & Bradstreet (Subsidiary of: Dun & Bradstreet Corporation), c/o Ethan Chazin, Director, Reference Services, Murray Hill, NJ 07094-1218. TEL 973-605-6000.

338.7029   USA   ISSN 1051-158X
HG4057.C2
DUN'S REGIONAL BUSINESS DIRECTORY. LOS ANGELES COUNTY AREA. Text in English. 1990. a. USD 575 to corporations; USD 465 to libraries (effective 2000). **Document type:** *Directory.* **Description:** Provides information on the services, performance and operations of Los Angeles businesses.
Published by: Dun & Bradstreet (Subsidiary of: Dun & Bradstreet Corporation), c/o Ethan Chazin, Director, Reference Services, Murray Hill, NJ 07094-1218. TEL 973-605-6000.

338.7029   USA   ISSN 1051-2594
HG4058.L67
DUN'S REGIONAL BUSINESS DIRECTORY. LOS ANGELES SUBURBAN AREA. Text in English. 1990. a. **Document type:** *Directory.* **Description:** Provides information on the services, performance and operations of businesses in suburban Los Angeles.
Published by: Dun & Bradstreet (Subsidiary of: Dun & Bradstreet Corporation), c/o Ethan Chazin, Director, Reference Services, Murray Hill, NJ 07094-1218. TEL 201-455-0900.

338.7029   USA   ISSN 1051-256X
HG4058.M45
DUN'S REGIONAL BUSINESS DIRECTORY. MEMPHIS AREA. Text in English. 1990. a. USD 575 to corporations; USD 465 to libraries (effective 2000). **Document type:** *Directory.* **Description:** Provides information on the services, performance and operations of Memphis businesses.
Published by: Dun & Bradstreet (Subsidiary of: Dun & Bradstreet Corporation), c/o Ethan Chazin, Director, Reference Services, Murray Hill, NJ 07094-1218. TEL 973-605-6000.

338.7029   USA   ISSN 1051-2551
DUN'S REGIONAL BUSINESS DIRECTORY. MIAMI - FORT LAUDERDALE - WEST PALM BEACH. Text in English. 1990. a. USD 575 to corporations; USD 465 to libraries (effective 2000). **Document type:** *Directory.* **Description:** Provides information on the services, performance and operations of businesses in the greater Miami area.
Published by: Dun & Bradstreet (Subsidiary of: Dun & Bradstreet Corporation), c/o Ethan Chazin, Director, Reference Services, Murray Hill, NJ 07094-1218. TEL 973-605-6000.

338.0029   USA   ISSN 1061-1177
HG4057.M5
DUN'S REGIONAL BUSINESS DIRECTORY. MICHIGAN METROS (EXCLUDING DETROIT) AREA. Text in English. 1991. a. USD 575 to corporations; USD 465 to libraries (effective 2000). **Document type:** *Directory.* **Description:** Provides information on the services, performance and operations of Michigan companies outside Detroit.
Published by: Dun & Bradstreet (Subsidiary of: Dun & Bradstreet Corporation), c/o Ethan Chazin, Director, Reference Services, Murray Hill, NJ 07094-1218. TEL 973-605-6000.

338.7029   USA   ISSN 1051-130X
HG4058.M6
DUN'S REGIONAL BUSINESS DIRECTORY. MILWAUKEE - MADISON AREA. Text in English. 1990. a. USD 575 to corporations; USD 465 to libraries (effective 2000). **Document type:** *Directory.* **Description:** Provides information on the services, performance and operations of Milwaukee and Madison businesses.
Published by: Dun & Bradstreet (Subsidiary of: Dun & Bradstreet Corporation), c/o Ethan Chazin, Director, Reference Services, Murray Hill, NJ 07094-1218. TEL 973-605-6000.

338.7029   USA   ISSN 1051-2535
HG4058.M63
DUN'S REGIONAL BUSINESS DIRECTORY. MINNEAPOLIS - ST. PAUL AREA. Text in English. 1990. a. USD 575 to corporations; USD 465 to libraries (effective 2000). **Document type:** *Directory.* **Description:** Provides information on the services, performance and operations of companies in the Twin Cities.
Published by: Dun & Bradstreet (Subsidiary of: Dun & Bradstreet Corporation), c/o Ethan Chazin, Director, Reference Services, Murray Hill, NJ 07094-1218. TEL 973-605-6000.

338.0029   USA   ISSN 1061-0774
HG4057.N35
DUN'S REGIONAL BUSINESS DIRECTORY. NEW ENGLAND AREA. Text in English. a. USD 575 to corporations; USD 465 to libraries (effective 2000). **Document type:** *Directory.* **Description:** Provides information on the services, performance and operations of New England companies.
Published by: Dun & Bradstreet (Subsidiary of: Dun & Bradstreet Corporation), c/o Ethan Chazin, Director, Reference Services, Murray Hill, NJ 07094-1218. TEL 973-605-6000.

338.7029   USA   ISSN 1051-1318
HG4058.N4
DUN'S REGIONAL BUSINESS DIRECTORY. NEW ORLEANS AREA. Text in English. 1990. a. USD 575 to corporations; USD 465 to libraries (effective 2000). **Document type:** *Directory.* **Description:** Provides information on the services, performance and operations of New Orleans businesses.
Published by: Dun & Bradstreet (Subsidiary of: Dun & Bradstreet Corporation), c/o Ethan Chazin, Director, Reference Services, Murray Hill, NJ 07094-1218. TEL 973-605-6000.

338.7029   USA   ISSN 1051-2543
HG4058.N56
DUN'S REGIONAL BUSINESS DIRECTORY. NEW YORK METROPOLITAN AREA. Text in English. 1990. a. USD 575 to corporations; USD 465 to libraries (effective 2000). **Document type:** *Directory.* **Description:** Provides information on the services, performance and operations of businesses in the New York metropolitan area.
Published by: Dun & Bradstreet (Subsidiary of: Dun & Bradstreet Corporation), c/o Ethan Chazin, Director, Reference Services, Murray Hill, NJ 07094-1218. TEL 973-605-6000.

338.7029   USA   ISSN 1051-2608
HG4058.N57
DUN'S REGIONAL BUSINESS DIRECTORY. NEW YORK SUBURBAN AREA. Text in English. 1990. a. USD 575 to corporations; USD 465 to libraries (effective 2000). **Document type:** *Directory.* **Description:** Provides information on the services, performance and operations of suburban New York businesses.
Published by: Dun & Bradstreet (Subsidiary of: Dun & Bradstreet Corporation), c/o Ethan Chazin, Director, Reference Services, Murray Hill, NJ 07094-1218. TEL 973-605-6000.

338.0029   USA   ISSN 1061-0782
HG4058.N67
DUN'S REGIONAL BUSINESS DIRECTORY. NORFOLK - RICHMOND AREA. Text in English. a. USD 575 to corporations; USD 465 to libraries (effective 2000). **Document type:** *Directory.* **Description:** Provides information on the services, performance and operations of companies in the Norfolk - Richmond area.

Published by: Dun & Bradstreet (Subsidiary of: Dun & Bradstreet Corporation), c/o Ethan Chazin, Director, Reference Services, Murray Hill, NJ 07094-1218. TEL 973-605-6000.

338.0029 USA ISSN 1061-1185
HG4057.C2
DUN'S REGIONAL BUSINESS DIRECTORY. NORTHERN CALIFORNIA AREA. Text in English. 1991. a. USD 575 to corporations; USD 465 to libraries (effective 2000). **Document type:** *Directory.* **Description:** Provides information on the services, performance and operations of businesses in Northern California.
Published by: Dun & Bradstreet (Subsidiary of: Dun & Bradstreet Corporation), c/o Ethan Chazin, Director, Reference Services, Murray Hill, NJ 07094-1218. TEL 973-605-6000.

338.0029 USA ISSN 1051-1296
HG4057.N5
DUN'S REGIONAL BUSINESS DIRECTORY. NORTHERN NEW JERSEY AREA. Text in English. 1990. a. USD 575 to corporations; USD 465 to libraries (effective 2000). **Document type:** *Directory.* **Description:** Provides information on the services, performance and operations of companies in northern New Jersey.
Published by: Dun & Bradstreet (Subsidiary of: Dun & Bradstreet Corporation), c/o Ethan Chazin, Director, Reference Services, Murray Hill, NJ 07094-1218. TEL 973-605-6000.

338.0029 USA ISSN 1061-0804
HF5065.N7
DUN'S REGIONAL BUSINESS DIRECTORY. NORTHERN NEW YORK STATE AREA. Text in English. 1991. a. USD 575 to corporations; USD 465 to libraries (effective 2000). **Document type:** *Directory.* **Description:** Provides information on the services, performance and operations of businesses in northern New York State.
Published by: Dun & Bradstreet (Subsidiary of: Dun & Bradstreet Corporation), c/o Ethan Chazin, Director, Reference Services, Murray Hill, NJ 07094-1218. TEL 973-605-6000.

338.0029 USA ISSN 1061-0790
HG4057.O5
DUN'S REGIONAL BUSINESS DIRECTORY. OKLAHOMA - ARKANSAS AREA. Text in English. 1991. a. USD 575 to corporations; USD 465 to libraries (effective 2000). **Document type:** *Directory.* **Description:** Provides information on the services, performance and operations of companies in Arkansas and Oklahoma.
Published by: Dun & Bradstreet (Subsidiary of: Dun & Bradstreet Corporation), c/o Ethan Chazin, Director, Reference Services, Murray Hill, NJ 07094-1218. TEL 973-605-6000.

338.0029 USA ISSN 1061-1347
HG4057.O7
DUN'S REGIONAL BUSINESS DIRECTORY. OREGON AREA. Text in English. 1991. a. USD 575 to corporations; USD 465 to libraries (effective 2000). **Document type:** *Directory.* **Description:** Provides information on the services, performance and operations of Oregon businesses.
Published by: Dun & Bradstreet (Subsidiary of: Dun & Bradstreet Corporation), c/o Ethan Chazin, Director, Reference Services, Murray Hill, NJ 07094-1218. TEL 973-605-6000.

338.0029 USA ISSN 1061-1193
HG4058.O74
DUN'S REGIONAL BUSINESS DIRECTORY. ORLANDO - JACKSONVILLE AREA. Text in English. 1991. a. USD 575 to corporations; USD 465 to libraries (effective 2000). **Document type:** *Directory.* **Description:** Provides information on the services, performance and operations of businesses in the Orlando and Jacksonville area.
Published by: Dun & Bradstreet (Subsidiary of: Dun & Bradstreet Corporation), c/o Ethan Chazin, Director, Reference Services, Murray Hill, NJ 07094-1218. TEL 973-605-6000.

338.7029 USA ISSN 1051-2519
HG4058.P542
DUN'S REGIONAL BUSINESS DIRECTORY. PHILADELPHIA AREA. Text in English. 1990. a. USD 575 to corporations; USD 465 to libraries (effective 2000). **Document type:** *Directory.* **Description:** Provides information on the services, performance and operations of Philadelphia area businesses.
Published by: Dun & Bradstreet (Subsidiary of: Dun & Bradstreet Corporation), c/o Ethan Chazin, Director, Reference Services, Murray Hill, NJ 07094-1218. TEL 973-605-6000.

338.7029 USA ISSN 1051-1571
HG4058.P545
DUN'S REGIONAL BUSINESS DIRECTORY. PHOENIX - TUCSON. Text in English. 1990. a. USD 575 to corporations; USD 465 to libraries (effective 2000). **Document type:** *Directory.* **Description:** Provides information on the services, performance and operations of Phoenix and Tucson area businesses.
Published by: Dun & Bradstreet (Subsidiary of: Dun & Bradstreet Corporation), c/o Ethan Chazin, Director, Reference Services, Murray Hill, NJ 07094-1218. TEL 973-605-6000.

338.7029 USA ISSN 1051-1210
HG4058.P6
DUN'S REGIONAL BUSINESS DIRECTORY. PITTSBURGH AREA. Text in English. 1990. a. USD 575 to corporations; USD 465 to libraries (effective 2000). **Document type:** *Directory.* **Description:** Provides information on the services, performance and operations of Pittsburgh businesses.
Published by: Dun & Bradstreet (Subsidiary of: Dun & Bradstreet Corporation), c/o Ethan Chazin, Director, Reference Services, Murray Hill, NJ 07094-1218. TEL 973-605-6000.

338.7029 USA ISSN 1051-2578
HG4058.R34
DUN'S REGIONAL BUSINESS DIRECTORY. RALEIGH - DURHAM - FAYETTEVILLE AREA. Text in English. 1990. a. USD 575 to corporations; USD 465 to libraries (effective 2000). **Document type:** *Directory.* **Description:** Provides information on the services, performance and operations of North Carolina companies in the Durham, Raleigh and Fayetteville areas.
Published by: Dun & Bradstreet (Subsidiary of: Dun & Bradstreet Corporation), c/o Ethan Chazin, Director, Reference Services, Murray Hill, NJ 07094-1218. TEL 973-605-6000.

338.0029 USA ISSN 1061-1355
HG4058.S24
DUN'S REGIONAL BUSINESS DIRECTORY. ST. LOUIS AREA. Text in English. 1991. a. USD 575 to corporations; USD 465 to libraries (effective 2000). **Document type:** *Directory.* **Description:** Provides information on the services, performance and operations of companies in the St. Louis area.
Published by: Dun & Bradstreet (Subsidiary of: Dun & Bradstreet Corporation), c/o Ethan Chazin, Director, Reference Services, Murray Hill, NJ 07094-1218. TEL 973-605-6000.

338.0029 USA ISSN 1061-0812
HG4058.S26
DUN'S REGIONAL BUSINESS DIRECTORY. SAN ANTONIO AREA. Text in English. 1991. a. USD 575 to corporations; USD 465 to libraries (effective 2000). **Document type:** *Directory.* **Description:** Provides information on the services, performance and operations of companies in the San Antonio area.
Published by: Dun & Bradstreet (Subsidiary of: Dun & Bradstreet Corporation), c/o Ethan Chazin, Director, Reference Services, Murray Hill, NJ 07094-1218. TEL 973-605-6000.

338.7029 USA ISSN 1051-1563
HG4057.C2
DUN'S REGIONAL BUSINESS DIRECTORY. SAN DIEGO AREA. Text in English. 1990. a. USD 575 to corporations; USD 465 to libraries (effective 2000). **Document type:** *Directory.* **Description:** Provides information on the services, performance and operations of businesses in San Diego.
Published by: Dun & Bradstreet (Subsidiary of: Dun & Bradstreet Corporation), c/o Ethan Chazin, Director, Reference Services, Murray Hill, NJ 07094-1218. TEL 973-605-6000.

338.7029 USA ISSN 1051-1598
HG4058.S4
DUN'S REGIONAL BUSINESS DIRECTORY. SAN FRANCISCO AREA. Text in English. 1990. a. USD 575 to corporations; USD 465 to libraries (effective 2000). **Document type:** *Directory.* **Description:** Provides information on the services, performance and operations of businesses in San Francisco and its environs.
Published by: Dun & Bradstreet (Subsidiary of: Dun & Bradstreet Corporation), c/o Ethan Chazin, Director, Reference Services, Murray Hill, NJ 07094-1218. TEL 973-605-6000.

338.7029 USA ISSN 1051-2527
HG4058.S53
DUN'S REGIONAL BUSINESS DIRECTORY. SEATTLE AREA. Text in English. 1990. a. USD 575 to corporations; USD 465 to libraries (effective 2000). **Document type:** *Directory.* **Description:** Provides information on the services, performance and operations of Seattle businesses.
Published by: Dun & Bradstreet (Subsidiary of: Dun & Bradstreet Corporation), c/o Ethan Chazin, Director, Reference Services, Murray Hill, NJ 07094-1218. TEL 973-605-6000.

338.0029 USA ISSN 1061-1215
HG4057.S6
DUN'S REGIONAL BUSINESS DIRECTORY. SOUTH CAROLINA AREA. Text in English. 1990. a. USD 575 to corporations; USD 465 to libraries (effective 2000). **Document type:** *Directory.* **Description:** Provides information on the services, performance and operations of companies in South Carolina.
Published by: Dun & Bradstreet (Subsidiary of: Dun & Bradstreet Corporation), c/o Ethan Chazin, Director, Reference Services, Murray Hill, NJ 07094-1218. TEL 973-605-6000.

338.7029 USA ISSN 1051-1199
HG4058.T35
DUN'S REGIONAL BUSINESS DIRECTORY. TAMPA - ST. PETERSBURG AREA. Text in English. 1990. a. USD 575 to corporations; USD 465 to libraries (effective 2000). **Document type:** *Directory.* **Description:** Provides information on the services, performance and operations of businesses in the Tampa - St. Petersburg area.
Published by: Dun & Bradstreet (Subsidiary of: Dun & Bradstreet Corporation), c/o Ethan Chazin, Director, Reference Services, Murray Hill, NJ 07094-1218. TEL 973-605-6000.

338.0029 USA ISSN 1061-0731
HG4057.T2
DUN'S REGIONAL BUSINESS DIRECTORY. TENNESSEE METROS AREA. Text in English. 1992. a. USD 575 to corporations; USD 465 to libraries (effective 2000). **Document type:** *Directory.* **Description:** Provides information on the services, performance and operations of companies in Tennessee.
Published by: Dun & Bradstreet (Subsidiary of: Dun & Bradstreet Corporation), c/o Ethan Chazin, Director, Reference Services, Murray Hill, NJ 07094-1218. TEL 973-605-6000.

338.7029 USA ISSN 1051-1601
HG4058.W3
DUN'S REGIONAL BUSINESS DIRECTORY. WASHINGTON D.C. - BALTIMORE AREA. Text in English. 1990. a. USD 575 to corporations; USD 465 to libraries (effective 2000). **Document type:** *Directory.* **Description:** Provides information on the services, performance and operations of businesses in Baltimore and Washington, DC.
Published by: Dun & Bradstreet (Subsidiary of: Dun & Bradstreet Corporation), c/o Ethan Chazin, Director, Reference Services, Murray Hill, NJ 07094-1218. TEL 973-605-6000.

338.0029 ZAF
DURBAN BUSINESS DIRECTORY. Text in English. 1953. a. free. adv. **Document type:** *Directory.*
Former titles: Durban Metropolitan Directory; Durban Corporation Directory (0378-9195)
Related titles: Diskette ed.
Published by: Braby's (Subsidiary of: Associated Industries), Attn: Sue Pearson, PO Box 1426, Pinetown, 3600, South Africa. TEL 27-31-7017021, FAX 27-31-7017036, booksales@brabys.co.za. Ed. A Stagg.

381.029 ZAF
DURBAN CHAMBER OF COMMERCE AND INDUSTRY. MEMBERSHIP DIRECTORY. Text in English. 1926. a. ZAR 30. adv. **Document type:** *Directory.*
Former titles: Durban Regional Chamber of Business. Membership Directory; Natal Chamber of Industries. Yearbook and Directory; Natal Chamber of Industries. Annual Report; Natal Manufacturers Association. Annual Report
Published by: Durban Chamber of Commerce and Industry, PO Box 1506, Durban, KwaZulu-Natal 4000, South Africa. TEL 27-31-335-1000, FAX 27-31-3321288. Ed. N. Thomson. Pub. Graham Cleveland. R&P N Thomson. Adv. contact Colleen Grant. Circ: 7,500.

380.1029 CAN
DURHAM BUSINESS DIRECTORY & CONSUMERS' GUIDE. Text in English. 1976. a. CND 30, USD 40. adv. index. **Description:** Complete listing of all businesses and services within the Durham Region of Ontario arranged in three sections, i.e. alphabetically by company name, products and postal codes.
Former titles: Durham Classified Business Directory and Consumers' Guide; Durham Yellow Directory
Published by: Lloyd Local Directory (Subsidiary of: Lloyd Publications of Canada), 66 Falby Ct, Ste 1603, Ajax, ON L1S 3L2, Canada. TEL 416-619-0421. Ed. J Lloyd. Circ: 30,000.

540.29 NLD
DUTCH CHEMICAL INDUSTRY HANDBOOK/HANDBOEK VOOR DE NEDERLANDSE CHEMISCHE INDUSTRIE. Text in Dutch, English, French, German. 1977. a. looseleaf. **Document type:** *Directory.* **Description:** Directory of all chemical and pharmaceutical producers in the Netherlands, with product registers.
Published by: (Vereniging van de Nederlandse Chemische Industrie/Association of the Dutch Chemical Industry), Samsom H.D. Tjeenk Willink B.V. (Subsidiary of: Wolters Kluwer N.V.), Postbus 316, Alphen aan den Rijn, 2400 AH, Netherlands. TEL 31-1720-66822, FAX 31-1720-66639. Circ: 2,000.

E & B GUIDE. (Estimators & Buyers') see *PRINTING*

E F Y DIRECTORY. (Electronics For You) see *ELECTRONICS*

338.0029 USA
E G S A BUYERS GUIDE AND MEMBER SERVICES DIRECTORY. Text in English. a. free. **Document type:** *Directory.*
Published by: Electrical Generating Systems Association, 1650 S Dixie Hwy, Boca Raton, FL 33432-7462. TEL 561-750-5575, FAX 561-750-5316. Ed. Jim McMullen.

380.1 NZL
E.OFFICE (YEAR); NZ Office Products News annual buyers guide to products & services. Text in English. a., latest 2000. NZD 24.95 domestic; NZD 39.95 foreign (effective 2000). **Document type:** *Directory, Trade.* **Description:** Contains suppliers index to products and services, editorial-style product and service profiles, advice pages and corporate profiles, and updates.
Related titles: ◆ Special ed. of: E.Office.

E

Published by: Profile Publishing Ltd., Wellesley St, PO Box 5544, Auckland, New Zealand. TEL 64-9-6301040, FAX 64-9-630-1046, info@profile.co.nz, http://www.profile.co.nz/.

382.029   BEL   ISSN 1029-4147
THE E U INSTITUTIONS' REGISTER; the orange book. (European Union) Text in English. 1997. a., latest vol.4, 2000. **Document type:** *Directory.* **Description:** Lists key personnel responsibilities and direct telephone numbers of 4500 officials from the major institutions of the European Union.
Formerly (until 1997): E U Institutions' Yellow Pages (1029-4155)
Published by: Euroconfidentiel s.a., Rue de Rixensart 18, Genval, 1332, Belgium. TEL 32-2-6520284, FAX 32-2-6530180, nigel.hunt @infoboard.be. Ed. Christiane Mauwel. **Dist. by:** Current Pacific Ltd., PO Box 36-536, Northcote, Auckland, New Zealand. TEL 64-9-480-1388, FAX 64-9-480-1387, info@cplnz.com, http://www.cplnz.com.

677.0029   GBR
EAST EUROPEAN CLOTHING & TEXTILE INDUSTRY DIRECTORY. Text in English. 1999. biennial, latest 2004, 5th ed. GBP 195 per issue domestic; GBP 205 per issue foreign (effective 2005). **Document type:** *Directory, Trade.*
Formed by the merger of (1996-1999): East European Clothing Industry Directory (1461-443X); (1995-1999): East European Textile Industry Directory
Published by: World Textile Publications Ltd., Perkin House, 1 Longlands St, Bradford, W Yorks BD1 2TP, United Kingdom. TEL 44-1274-378800, FAX 44-1274-378811, info@world-textile.net, http://www.world-textile.net/contact.html.

381.029   ECU
ECUADOR. MINISTERIO DE INDUSTRIAS, COMERCIO E INTEGRACION. DIRECTORIO INDUSTRIAL DE LAS EMPRESAS ACOGIDAS A LA LEY DE FOMENTO INDUSTRIAL. Text in Spanish. 1957. irreg. **Document type:** *Directory, Government.*
Published by: Ministerio de Industrias Comercio e Integracion, Quito, Pichincha, Ecuador.

EDITOR & PUBLISHER MARKET GUIDE. see *BUSINESS AND ECONOMICS—Marketing And Purchasing*

371.67029   USA   ISSN 0193-1067
EDUCATIONAL DEALER. Text in English. 1974. 5/yr. USD 15; free to qualified personnel (effective 2005). adv. bk.rev. back issues avail. **Document type:** *Magazine, Trade.* **Description:** For school supply dealers or distributors. Covers warehousing, merchandising, catalog publishing, etc.
Published by: Fahy - Williams Publishing, Inc., PO Box 1080, Geneva, NY 14456-8080. TEL 315-789-0458, 800-344-0559, FAX 315-789-4263, tmanzer@fwpi.com, http:// www.eddealermagazine.com. Ed. Tina Manzer. Pub. Kevin J Fahy. adv.: B&W page USD 1,470, color page USD 1,985. Circ: 10,500 (paid and controlled).

ELECTRICAL APPLIANCE AND UTILIZATION EQUIPMENT DIRECTORY. see *ELECTRONICS*

ELECTRICAL CONSTRUCTION MATERIALS DIRECTORY. see *ENGINEERING—Electrical Engineering*

ELECTRICAL WORLD DIRECTORY OF ELECTRIC UTILITIES IN CANADA. see *ENERGY—Electrical Energy*

ELECTRICAL WORLD DIRECTORY OF ELECTRIC UTILITIES IN LATIN AMERICA, BERMUDA AND THE CARIBBEAN ISLANDS. see *ENERGY—Electrical Energy*

ELECTROMECHANICAL BENCH REFERENCE. see *ENGINEERING—Electrical Engineering*

621.381029   USA
ELECTRONIC DISTRIBUTION SHOW DIRECTORY. Text in English. 1937. a. adv. illus. back issues avail. **Document type:** *Catalog, Trade.* **Description:** Lists electronic distributors, show exhibitions and program of events.
Published by: Electronic Industry Show Corp, 222 S Riverside Plaza, Ste 2160, Chicago, IL 60606. TEL 312-648-1140, FAX 312-648-4282. Ed., Pub., R&P, Adv. contact Gretchen Ole Weghorst. B&W page USD 1,620, color page USD 2,270; trim 11.25 x 8.5. Circ: 6,000.

621.381029   USA   ISSN 0422-9053
HD9696.A3
ELECTRONIC INDUSTRY TELEPHONE DIRECTORY (YEAR). Abbreviated title: E I T D. Text in English. 1963. a. USD 75 per vol. (effective 2004). adv. **Document type:** *Directory.* **Description:** Industry phone book that contains phone, fax and World Wide Web listings for more than 30,000 company locations and 3,000 product types in the electronics marketplace.
Related titles: Online - full text ed.
Published by: Reed Business Information (Subsidiary of: Reed Business), 100 Enterprise Dr, Ste 600, PO Box 912, Rockaway, NJ 07866-0912. TEL 973-920-7000, 800-222-0289, http://www.eitd.com, http://www.reedbusiness.com. Ed. Aimee Kalnoskas TEL 973-292-5100 x490. Pub. Steve Wirth TEL 973-292-5100 x380. adv.: B&W page USD 6,550, color page USD 8,190; trim 10.88 x 8.25. Circ: 125,000.

380.1029   USA   ISSN 0070-7589
ELECTRONIC MARKETING DIRECTORY. Text in English. 1959. a. **Document type:** *Directory.*
Formerly: Dun and Bradstreet Electronic Marketing Directory
Published by: (National Credit Office), Dun's Marketing Services (Subsidiary of: Dun & Bradstreet, Inc.), 3 Sylvan Way, Parsippany, NJ 07054-3896. TEL 201-455-0900.

621.3029   GBR
ELECTRONICS 150. Text in English. 1979; N.S. 1995. a. USD 630. abstr. index. back issues avail. **Document type:** *Directory.* **Description:** Provides full corporate information on the world's top 150 electronics manufacturers.
Incorporates (in 1988): World Electronics Bulletin (0954-1268); Former titles (until 1995): World Electronics Companies File (0951-5747); (until 1988): European Electronics Companies File; Mackintosh European Electronics Companies File (0142-9671); Which incorporated: Mackintosh European Electronics Companies Bulletin (0143-0696); Mackintosh Yearbook of European Electronics Companies
—CCC.
Published by: Pergamon (Subsidiary of: Elsevier Science & Technology), The Boulevard, Langford Ln, East Park, Kidlington, Oxford OX5 1GB, United Kingdom. TEL 44-1865-843000, FAX 44-1865-843010. Ed. A Fletcher. Circ: 250. **Subscr. to:** Elsevier BV, PO Box 211, Amsterdam 1000 AE, Netherlands. TEL 31-20-485-3757, FAX 31-20-485-3432, nlinfo-f@elsevier.nl, http://www.elsevier.nl.

670.29   GBR   ISSN 1466-0849
THE ELECTRONICS & ELECTRICAL BUYERS GUIDE. Text in English. 1995. a., latest vol.8, 2002/2003. GBP 104 (effective 2002). adv. **Document type:** *Directory, Trade.* **Description:** Comprehensive directory to the UK electonics and electrical industries.
Formerly (until 1999): Electronics Buyers' Guide (1360-6999); **Incorporates:** Electrical & Electronics Trade Directory
Related titles: Online - full content ed.
Published by: C M P Information Ltd. (Subsidiary of: United Business Media), Sovereign House, Sovereign Way, Tonbridge, Kent TN9 1RW, United Kingdom. TEL 44-1732-377391, FAX 44-1732-377552, industry @cmpinformation.com, enquiries @cmpinformation.com, http://www.electronics-electrical.com, http://www.cmpinformation.com. Ed. Philip Dury TEL 44-1732-377542. Pub. Elaine Soni TEL 44-1732-377423. R&P Rachel Wichall TEL 44-1732-377627. Adv. contact Sarah Thompson TEL 44-1732-377576. page GBP 1,155. Circ: 4,000.

338.0029   USA   ISSN 1060-2100
HD9696.A3
ELECTRONICS MANUFACTURERS DIRECTORY; a marketer's guide to manufacturers in the United States and Canada. Text in English. 1949. a. USD 245. adv. index. **Document type:** *Directory.*
Former titles: U S Electronic Industry Directory (1047-5583); (until 1990): Who's Who in Electronics (1047-6709)
Related titles: Diskette ed.: USD 595.
Published by: Harris InfoSource International, 2057 2 E Aurora Rd, Twinsburg, OH 44087-1999. TEL 216-425-9000, 800-888-5900, FAX 216-425-7150, catknapp@aol.com. Ed. Frances L Carlsen. Pub. Mark Sabourin. Circ: 2,000.

621.381029   USA
THE ELECTRONICS SOURCE BOOK. (Avail. in 10 regional editions) Text in English. 1983. a. USD 39.99 (effective 2003). **Document type:** *Directory, Trade.* **Description:** Lists thousands of component manufacturers, service providers and distributors.
Related titles: Online - full text ed.
Published by: Primedia Business Magazines & Media, Inc. (Subsidiary of: Primedia, Inc.), 2121 Alton Pkwy Ste 200, Irvine, CA 92606. TEL 949-252-1146, FAX 949-252-0556, inquiries @primediabusiness.com, http://www.the-esb.com, http://www.primediabusiness.com.

657.029   USA
EMERSON'S DIRECTORY OF LEADING U.S. ACCOUNTING FIRMS. Text in English. 1988. biennial. USD 195; USD 250 foreign. adv. index. **Document type:** *Directory.* **Description:** Provides comprehensive information on the top CPA firms.
Former titles: Emerson's Directory of Leading Accounting Firms Worldwide; Emerson's Directory of Leading U.S. Accounting Firms
Related titles: Diskette ed.: USD 395 domestic; USD 495 foreign.
Published by: Emerson Company, 12356 Northup Way, Ste 103, Bellevue, WA 98005. TEL 425-869-0655, FAX 425-869-0746. Ed., Pub., R&P, Adv. contact James C Emerson.

338.0029   ZAF   ISSN 0259-868X
EMPANGENI - RICHARDS BAY DIRECTORY. Text in English. 1987. a. USD 40 (effective 2001). **Document type:** *Directory.*
Published by: Braby's (Subsidiary of: Associated Industries), Attn: Sue Pearson, PO Box 1426, Pinetown, 3600, South Africa. TEL 27-31-7017021, FAX 27-31-7017036, booksales@brabys.co.za.

EMPLOYMENT LAW DESK BOOK FOR TENNESSEE EMPLOYERS. see *LAW*

382.029   BRA
EMPRESAS JAPONESAS DO BRASIL. ANNUARIO/BURAJIRU NIKKEI KIGYO NENKAN. Text in Japanese, Portuguese. a.
Published by: Selecoes Economicas, Av Paulista, 807, B Vista, Sao Paulo, SP 01311-100, Brazil.

ENCORE DIRECTORY. see *MOTION PICTURES*

ENCYCLOPAEDIA OF HONG KONG TRADE & INDUSTRY (YEAR). see *ENCYCLOPEDIAS AND GENERAL ALMANACS*

338.0029   USA   ISSN 1086-4768
ENCYCLOPEDIA OF BUSINESS. Text in English. 1995. triennial (in 2 vols.), latest 1999. USD 450 (effective 2004). **Document type:** *Trade.*
Published by: Gale Group (Subsidiary of: Thomson Corporation), 27500 Drake Rd, Farmington Hills, MI 48331-3535. TEL 248-699-8061, 800-877-4253, FAX 248-699-4253, galeord@gale.com, http://www.gale.com.

382.029   USA   ISSN 1084-8614
HD2324
ENCYCLOPEDIA OF GLOBAL INDUSTRIES. Text in English. 1996. triennial, latest 2002. USD 460 (effective 2004). **Document type:** *Directory.*
Published by: Gale Group (Subsidiary of: Thomson Corporation), 27500 Drake Rd, Farmington Hills, MI 48331-3535. TEL 248-699-4253, 800-347-4253, FAX 248-699-8035, gale.galeord@thomson.com, http://www.galegroup.com. Ed. Diane M Maniaci.

796.029   USA
ENCYCLOPEDIA OF SPORTS BUSINESS CONTACTS; the sports networking reference guide. Text in English. 1996. a. USD 59.95 domestic; USD 69.95 foreign (effective 2000). **Document type:** *Directory, Trade.* **Description:** Provides a business and sports administration view of the field of sports management, sports media, sports event management and sponsorships, sports marketing and public relations. Includes a directory of contacts from sports facilities, professional, amateur, collegiate, scholastic and international sports.
Formerly (until March 1999): Encyclopedia of Sports Contacts
Published by: Global Sports Productions Ltd., 1223 Broadway, Ste 102, Santa Monica, CA 90404-2707. TEL 310-454-9480, FAX 310-454-6590. Ed. Barbara Boldtmann. Pub. Edward T Kobak Jr. R&P Greg Andrews. Adv. contact Tina Evans. Circ: 7,500 (paid).

333.7916029   GBR   ISSN 0263-9971
ENERGY-SAVING MARKETGUIDE. Text in English. 1982. biennial. GBP 17.50 (effective 2001). adv. **Document type:** *Directory.*
Published by: Aydee Marketing Ltd., Nithsdale House, 159 Cambridge St, Aylesbury, Bucks HP20 1BQ, United Kingdom. TEL 44-1296-434381, FAX 44-1296-436936, info@aydee.com, http://www.aydee.com. Ed., Pub. Richard Salmon. Adv. contact Muriel Scutt. page GBP 1,195; trim 184 x 260. Circ: 6,000.

669.029   GBR
ENGINEERED MATERIALS DIRECTORY OF CONSULTANTS & TRANSLATORS. Text in English. 1988. biennial. USD 70 in the Americas; USD 80 elsewhere. **Document type:** *Directory.*
Published by: (Institute of Materials, Minerals and Mining), Maney Publishing, Hudson Rd, Leeds, W Yorks LS9 7DL, United Kingdom. TEL 44-113-2497481, FAX 44-113-2486983, maney@maney.co.uk, http://www.maney.co.uk.

005.5   USA   ISSN 1043-6944
TA345
ENGINEERING & INDUSTRIAL SOFTWARE DIRECTORY. Text in English. 1985. irreg.
Published by: Elsevier Engineering Information, Inc. (Subsidiary of: Elsevier Science & Technology), 1 Castle Point Ter, Hoboken, NJ 07030-5906. TEL 201-216-8500, 800-221-1044, FAX 201-356-6801, eicustomersupport@elsevier.com, http://www.ei.org.

ENGINEERING INDUSTRIES ASSOCIATION. CLASSIFIED DIRECTORY AND BUYERS GUIDE. see *ENGINEERING*

ENGINEERING INDUSTRY BUYERS' GUIDE. see *ENGINEERING*

620.0029   NZL   ISSN 0110-3571
ENGINEERING REFERENCE HANDBOOK. Text in English. 1976. irreg. (approx. 18/yr). NZD 99. back issues avail. **Document type:** *Directory.* **Description:** Listings of workshop engineering and related companies, including machine capacities, products made, maintenance and design areas.
Published by: Engineering Handbook Ltd., P.O. Box 26-269, Epsom, Auckland, New Zealand. TEL 64-9-3582749, FAX 64-9-3582741. Ed., R&P Des Snell. adv.: page NZD 720; trim 297 x 210. Circ: 500 (paid).

658.8029   DEU
ENTERTAINMENTMARKT GUIDE. Text in German. a. EUR 39.90 (effective 2004). **Document type:** *Directory, Trade.* **Description:** Contains trade information on companies and personnel in the entertainment business.

Published by: Entertainment Media Verlag GmbH und Co. oHG, Einsteinring 24, Dornach, 85609, Germany. TEL 49-89-45114-0, FAX 49-89-45114444, emv@e-media.de, http://www.mediabiz.de.

670.29   IND   ISSN 0971-7463
ENTREPRENEUR INDIA; an industrial monthly journal on industrial development, technologies & project opportunities. Text in English. 1995. m. INR 220 domestic; USD 50 foreign; INR 20 newsstand/cover domestic; USD 5 newsstand/cover foreign (effective 2002).
Published by: National Institute of Industrial Research, 106-E Kamla Nagar, Near Delhi University, 2162, New Delhi, 110 007, India. TEL 91-11-3923955, FAX 91-11-2941561, niir@ndb.vsnl.net.in, http://www.niir.org. Ed., Pub. Ajay Kumar Gupta.

380.1029   USA
ENTREPRENEURS DIRECTORY. Text in English. a. USD 1,100 combined subscription print, online & CD-ROM eds. (effective 2004 & 2005). back issues avail. **Document type:** *Directory.* **Description:** Contains 4.5 Million small business owners and 671,000 entrepreneurs! Features owner's name, company name, address, type of business, etc.
Related titles: CD-ROM ed.; Diskette ed.; E-mail ed.; Fax ed.; Magnetic Tape ed.; Online - full text ed.
Published by: American Business Directories (Subsidiary of: American Business Information, Inc.), 5711 S 86th Circle, P O Box 27347, Omaha, NE 68127. TEL 402-593-4600, 888-946-9377, 877-708-3844, FAX 402-331-5481, sales@directoriesusa.com, http://www.directoriesusa.com.

ENVIRONMENT BUSINESS DIRECTORY. see *ENVIRONMENTAL STUDIES*

ENVIRONMENTAL KEY CONTACTS AND INFORMATION SOURCES. see *ENVIRONMENTAL STUDIES*

ESTATES GAZETTE DIRECTORY. see *REAL ESTATE*

338.0029   ZAF
ESTCOURT - MOOI RIVER SURROUNDS DIRECTORY. Text in English. a. ZAR 30 domestic; USD 30 foreign (effective 2001). **Document type:** *Directory.*
Former titles: KwaZulu - Natal Midlands Directory; Natal Midlands Directory
Published by: Braby's (Subsidiary of: Associated Industries), Attn: Sue Pearson, PO Box 1426, Pinetown, 3600, South Africa. TEL 27-31-7017021, FAX 27-31-7017036, booksales@brabys.co.za.

380.1029   ETH
HF3889.A48
ETHIOPIAN TRADE DIRECTORY. Text in English. 1954. a., latest 1990. reprint service avail. from ISI. **Document type:** *Directory.*
Supersedes: Trade Directory and Guide Book to Ethiopia (0564-0490)
Published by: Ethiopian Chamber of Commerce, PO Box 517, Addis Ababa, Ethiopia. **Co-sponsor:** Addis Ababa Chamber of Commerce.

ETHNIC MEDIA & MARKETS. see *ADVERTISING AND PUBLIC RELATIONS*

382.029   BEL
EURO-LOBBYING: DIRECTORY OF EUROPEAN UNION TRADE AND PROFESSIONAL ASSOCIATIONS/EURO-LOBBYING REPERTOIRE DES ORGANISATIONS PROFESSIONNELLES DE L'UNION EUROPEENNE/EURO-LOBBYING VERZEICHNIS DER VERBAENDE IN DER EUROPAEISCHEN UNION. Text in English, French, German. 1980. biennial, latest 2003, 7th ed. USD 185 per vol. (effective 2005). 500 p./no.; **Document type:** *Directory.* **Description:** Lists more than 600 lobbies at the European Union level in the following sectors of activity: industry, small- and medium-sized enterprises, trade, transport, professions, other activities, trade unions, and consumer organizations; also lists 7,800 member organization addresses, telephone and fax numbers, e-mail and Web addresses.
Formerly: Directory of European Community Trade and Professional Associations (0771-7865)
Published by: Editions Delta, Rue Scailquin 55, Brussels, 1210, Belgium. TEL 32-2-217-5555, FAX 32-2-217-9393, editions.delta@skynet.be, http://www.bernan.com/ Online_Catalog/Title_Page.aspx?TitleID=29000015. Ed. Georges Francis Seingry. **Dist. by:** Bernan Associates, Bernan, 4611-F Assembly Dr., Lanham, MD 20706-4391. TEL 301-459-2255, 800-274-4447, FAX 301-459-0056, query@bernan.com, http://www.bernan.com.

338.0029   DEU   ISSN 0946-3666
EURO PHARMA. Text in German. 1991. a. EUR 212.50 (effective 2003). **Document type:** *Directory, Trade.*
Published by: B. Behr's Verlag GmbH & Co. KG, Averhoffstr. 10, Hamburg, 22085, Germany. TEL 49-40-2270080, FAX 49-40-2201091, info@behrs.de, http://www.behrs.de.

EURO - WHO'S WHO; who is who in the institutions of the European Union and in the other European organizations. see *BIOGRAPHY*

382.029   FRA   ISSN 0982-3360
EUROPAGES. Text in French. 1982. a. USD 66 (effective 2000). **Document type:** *Directory.* **Description:** Lists over 500,000 European companies covering 30 countries and all industries.
Related titles: CD-ROM ed.: USD 66 (effective 2000); Online - full text ed.
Published by: Euredit S.A., 47 rue Louis Blanc, Paris La Defense, Cedex 92984, France. TEL 33-1-41164900, FAX 33-1-41164950, comments@europages.com, http://www.europages.com. Ed. Edouard Prisse. R&P Claudine Leprince. **Dist. by:** Current Pacific Ltd., PO Box 36-536, Northcote, Auckland, New Zealand. TEL 64-9-480-1388, FAX 64-9-480-1387, info@cplnz.com, http://www.cplnz.com.

382   GBR   ISSN 1461-4014
EUROPE REVIEW. Text in English. 1998. q.
Published by: Times Publications Ltd., 30-32 Tabard St., London, SE1 4JU, United Kingdom. TEL 44-20-7089-8830, FAX 44-20-7089-8831, http://www.times-publications.com/ mediadata/EuropeReview.htm. Ed. Darien Graham-Smith.

EUROPEAN ADHESIVES & SEALANTS YEARBOOK AND DIRECTORY. see *PAINTS AND PROTECTIVE COATINGS*

THE EUROPEAN BIOTECHNOLOGY DIRECTORY (YEAR). see *BIOLOGY—Biotechnology*

338.0029   GBR   ISSN 0964-8550
EUROPEAN BUSINESS INFORMATION SOURCEBOOK. Text in English. biennial. GBP 160 (effective 1999). bk.rev. **Document type:** *Directory.* **Description:** Covers European business information sources in the EU, as well as the members of EFTA and in Eastern Europe.
Published by: Headland Business Information, Windsor Ct, East Grinstead House, East Grinstead, W Sussex RH19 1XA, United Kingdom. TEL 44-1342-326972, FAX 44-1342-336198, custserv@bowker-saur.co.uk, http://www.bowker.co.uk. **Subscr. to:** World Wide Subscription Service, Unit 6, Gibbs Reed Farm, Ticehurst, E Sussex TN5 7HE, United Kingdom. TEL 44-1580-200657, FAX 44-1580-200616.

EUROPEAN COIL COATING ASSOCIATION DIRECTORY. see *PAINTS AND PROTECTIVE COATINGS*

EUROPEAN COMPANIES; guide to sources of information. see *BUSINESS AND ECONOMICS—Abstracting, Bibliographies, Statistics*

THE EUROPEAN DIRECTORY OF MANAGEMENT CONSULTANTS. see *BUSINESS AND ECONOMICS— Management*

338.0029   GBR
EUROPEAN DIRECTORY OF WORLD SURFACE TECHNOLOGY. Text in English. a. GBP 84; GBP 89 foreign. **Document type:** *Directory, Trade.*
Published by: Turret R A I plc, Armstrong House, 38 Market Sq, Uxbridge, Middx UB8 1TG, United Kingdom. TEL 44-1895-454545, FAX 44-1895-454647.

EUROPEAN ELECTRONIC PRODUCTION DIRECTORY - SMART GROUP YEARBOOK. see *ELECTRONICS*

EUROPEAN GENERATING SET DIRECTORY. see *ENGINEERING—Electrical Engineering*

EUROPEAN GLASS DIRECTORY AND BUYER'S GUIDE. see *CERAMICS, GLASS AND POTTERY*

THE EUROPEAN HOSPITALS DATABASE ON CD-ROM. see *HEALTH FACILITIES AND ADMINISTRATION*

677.02862   GBR
EUROPEAN INDEX OF YARNS AND FIBRES. Text in English. 1995. biennial, latest 2003, 5th ed. GBP 50 per issue domestic; GBP 60 per issue foreign (effective 2005). **Document type:** *Directory, Trade.* **Description:** Guide to the wide range of natural and man-made fibers and yarns available to European textile manufacturers.
Published by: World Textile Publications Ltd., Perkin House, 1 Longlands St, Bradford, W Yorks BD1 2TP, United Kingdom. TEL 44-1274-378800, FAX 44-1274-378811, info@world-textile.net, http://www.world-textile.net/contact.html.

338.0029 340   GBR
EUROPEAN LEGAL 500. Text in English. 1990. a. GBP 99 (effective 1999). **Document type:** *Directory, Trade.* **Description:** A guide to law firms and lawyers throughout Europe and the Middle East. The directory details the legal system in place in each country, plus a guide to top law firms and areas of best practice. It is used most often commercially by corporate counsel and in-house lawyers to identify legal expertise in other jurisdictions.
Related titles: CD-ROM ed.
Published by: Legalease Ltd., Kensington Square House, 12-14 Ansdell St, London, W8 5BN, United Kingdom. TEL 44-20-7396-9292, FAX 44-20-7396-9300, legalease@link.org, info@legalease.co.uk, http://www.legalease.co.uk.

338.0029   GBR   ISSN 1367-8841
EUROPEAN LOGISTICS DIRECTORY. Text in English. 1997. a. GBP 63; GBP 68 foreign. **Document type:** *Directory, Trade.* **Description:** Reviews the marketplace supplying services and equipment to allow for efficient movement of the fast-growing cross-border trade within Europe.
Published by: Turret R A I plc, Armstrong House, 38 Market Sq, Uxbridge, Middx UB8 1TG, United Kingdom. TEL 44-1895-454545, FAX 44-1895-454647.

EUROPEAN MARKETS: A GUIDE TO COMPANY AND INDUSTRY INFORMATION SOURCES. see *BUSINESS AND ECONOMICS—International Commerce*

302.23029   GBR   ISSN 0968-2694
EUROPEAN MEDIA DIRECTORY. Text in English. 1991. s-a. GBP 459 (effective 2000). **Document type:** *Directory.*
Published by: P R Newswire (Europe) Ltd, Communications House, 210 Old St, London, EC1V 9UN, United Kingdom. TEL 44-20-7490-8111, FAX 44-20-7490-1255. Ed. Paul Chessman.

070.5   GBR
EUROPEAN SPECIALIST PUBLISHERS DIRECTORY. Text in English. 1992. irreg. GBP 48 (effective 1998). **Document type:** *Directory.*
Published by: Gale Research International Ltd., Cheriton House, North Way, PO Box 699, Andover, Hants SP10 5YE, United Kingdom. Ed. Sarah M Hall.

EUROPEAN STAINLESS STEEL DIRECTORY. see *METALLURGY*

380.029   BEL   ISSN 1561-9273
EUROPEAN VENTURE CAPITAL ASSOCIATION. DIRECTORY. Text in English. 1996. a. free. —BLDSC (3830.765710).
Published by: European Venture Capital Association, Minervastraat 4, Zaventem, 1930, Belgium. TEL 32-2-7150020, FAX 32-2-7250704, evca@evca.com, http://www.evca.com.

EVANDALE'S DIRECTORY OF WORLD UNDERWRITERS; the comprehensive directory of non-life insurance worldwide. see *INSURANCE*

380.1029   NLD
EVENTLINE; an international database of conferences, symposia, trade fairs & exhibitions. Text in Dutch. m. price varies. **Document type:** *Directory, Bibliography.* **Description:** Provides a full geographic listing of future events held worldwide, by country, state and city, with a contact address.
Media: Diskette. **Related titles:** Online - full text ed.: (from Data-Star, The Dialog Corporation).
Published by: Elsevier BV (Subsidiary of: Elsevier Science & Technology), Radarweg 29, Amsterdam, 1043 NX, Netherlands. TEL 31-20-4853911, FAX 31-20-4852457, nlinfo-f@elsevier.nl, http://www.elsevier.nl.

338.0029   USA   ISSN 1082-2011
HF5428
EXCLUSIVE BRANDS SOURCEBOOK (YEAR). Text in English. 1994. a. USD 155; USD 165 in Canada; USD 180 elsewhere. bk.rev. **Document type:** *Directory.*
Published by: Exclusive Brands Publications, 167 Madison Ave, Rm 606, New York, NY 10016-5430. TEL 212-213-1007, FAX 212-213-6927, excbrands@aol.com, http://www.pl-eb.com. Ed., R&P Philip Fitzell. Pub. William Fitzell.

EXECUTIVE MANAGED CARE DIRECTORY. see *HEALTH FACILITIES AND ADMINISTRATION*

670.29   USA
EXHIBIT BUILDER SOURCE BOOK DIRECTORY (YEAR). Text in English. 1983. a. USD 50. adv. **Document type:** *Directory.*
Published by: Exhibit Builder, Inc., PO Box 4144, Woodland, CA 91365. TEL 818-225-0100, FAX 818-225-0138. Ed. Judy Pomerantz. Pub., R&P, Adv. contact Jill Brookman. Circ: 20.

EXHIBITIONS ROUND THE WORLD. see *MEETINGS AND CONGRESSES*

387.029   USA
(YEAR) EXPEDITED CARRIERS NETWORK GUIDE. Text in English. a. USD 30 to non-members. **Document type:** *Directory.* **Description:** Provides the user with a complete listing of the expedited services provided by members of the conference and the airports they serve.
Published by: Air and Expedited Motor Carriers Conference, 1600 Duke St., Ste. 220, Alexandria, VA 22314-3421. TEL 703-838-7978, FAX 703-519-1866, dosiecki@trucking.org. Ed. Dave Osiecki. Circ: 400.

380.1029   DNK   ISSN 0908-9659
HF3643
EXPORT DENMARK - KONGERIGET DANMARKS HANDELSKALENDER. Text in Multiple languages. 1883. a. **Description:** Information on 10,000+ export companies in Denmark, the Faroe Islands, Greenland, and Sweden.

▼ *new title*   ➤ *refereed*   ✴ *unverified*   ◆ *full entry avail.*

B

Former titles (until 1993): Kongeriget Danmarks Handelskalender (0302-5403); (until 1962): Kongeriget Danmarks Handels-Kalender med Postadresse-Register (0105-0230); (until 1936): Kongeriget Danmarks Officielle Post- og Telegraf-Adressebog samt Handels-Kalender
Related titles: Online - full content ed.
Published by: Export Denmark Kongeriget Danmarks Handels & Exportkalender, Gammel Koege Landevej 264 C, Hvidovre, 2650, Denmark. TEL 45-70-20-20-23, FAX 45-70-20-20-65, info@export-denmark.dk, http://www.export-denmark.dk.

382.029 GBR
EXPORT DIRECTORY; members and buyers guide. Text in English. a.?. GBP 5. **Document type:** *Directory.*
Published by: Association of Suppliers to the Furniture Industry Export Club, PO Box 10, Epping, Essex CM16 7RR, United Kingdom. TEL 44-992-578873, FAX 44-992-572217.

381.029 CHL ISSN 0717-005X
EXPORT DIRECTORY CHILE/DIRECTORIO DE LA EXPORTACION. Text in English, French, German, Spanish. 1976. a. free. adv. **Document type:** *Directory.* **Description:** Contains background material on exporters, and includes companies that have exported over US$30,000 in the previous year.
Published by: Ministerio de Relaciones Exteriores, Direccion de Promocion de Exportaciones, Alameda Bernardo O Higgins, 1315 Piso 2, Santiago, Chile. FAX 56-2-6960639, TELEX 340120 PROCH CL. Circ: 15,000.

382.029 IRN
EXPORT DIRECTORY, ISLAMIC REPUBLIC OF IRAN. Text in Persian, Modern. a. **Document type:** *Directory.*
Published by: Export Promotion Centre of Iran, Tadjrish, P O Box 11-48, Tehran, Iran.

382.029 BRA
EXPORT DIRECTORY OF BRAZIL/GUIA BRASILEIRO DE EXPORTACAO. Text in English, French, Portuguese, Spanish. 1964. a. BRL 50. bk.rev. illus. **Document type:** *Directory.*
Formerly: G B E: Export Directory of Brazil
Published by: Banco do Brasil S.A., Setor Bancario Sul, Quadra 4, Bloco C, Lote 32, Brasilia, DF 70089900, Brazil. Ed. Gilberto Huber. Circ: 25,000. **Co-sponsor:** Emprendimentos Brasileiros de Informacoes Dirigidas Ltda.

EXPORT REFERENCE GUIDE. see *BUSINESS AND ECONOMICS—International Commerce*

382.029 IRN
EXPORTS DIRECTORY OF IRAN INDUSTRIES. Text in Persian, Modern. biennial. IRR 100,000 (effective 2000). adv. **Document type:** *Directory.* **Description:** Provides information about Iranian industries, agriculture and the economy, with classified listing of Iranian industrial companies.
Published by: Iran Exports Publication Co. Ltd., P O Box 14335 746, Tehran, 15956, Iran. TEL 98-21-8801999, FAX 98-21-8900547.

EXTEL ANNUAL REGISTRARS SERVICE. see *BUSINESS AND ECONOMICS—Investments*

EXTEL ANNUAL REGISTRARS SERVICE SUPPLEMENT. see *BUSINESS AND ECONOMICS—Investments*

620.029 GBR
F I D I C INTERNATIONAL DIRECTORY OF CONSULTING ENGINEERS. Text in English. 1979. a. GBP 75 (effective 2002). adv. **Document type:** *Directory.* **Description:** Lists international consulting engineering firms.
Related titles: Online - full text ed.
Published by: (Federation Internationale des Ingenieurs Conseils), Rhys Jones Publishing Ltd., 5th Floor, 9 Matton Street, London, NW8 8PL, United Kingdom. TEL 44-20-7724-6735, FAX 44-20-7262-0486, fidicdirect@rhysjones.com, http://www.fidicdirect.com. Ed., Adv. contact Dorota Butters. Pub., R&P Rod Rhys Jones. Circ: 5,000.

338.0029 GBR
F M YEARBOOK. (Facilities Management) Text in English. 1992. a. GBP 45; GBP 52 foreign. adv. **Document type:** *Directory.* **Description:** Reference guide for buyers and services in the facilities management profession.
Published by: Faversham House Group Ltd., Faversham House, 232a Addington Rd, South Croydon, Surrey CR2 8LE, United Kingdom. TEL 44-20-86517100, FAX 44-20-86517117. Adv. contact Mark Houghton.

F T BIOTECHNOLOGY & PHARMACEUTICAL COMPANIES DATABASE CD-ROM (YEARS). (Financial Times) see *BIOLOGY—Biotechnology*

F Y I DIRECTORIO ANUAL DE LA GASTRONOMIA. see *FOOD AND FOOD INDUSTRIES*

FABRIC BUYER'S DIRECTORY; the global sourcing guide for fashion fabrics, trimmings and garment accessories. see *TEXTILE INDUSTRIES AND FABRICS*

FAIRPLAY CONTAINER OPERATORS DIRECTORY (YEAR). see *TRANSPORTATION—Ships And Shipping*

687.0688 USA
FASHION MARKET MAGAZINE. Text in English. 1986. m. USD 59 (effective 2000). adv. **Document type:** *Trade.* **Description:** Aimed at the trade apparel market in New York; combined with a collection of original photos of apparel items currently offered on the wholesale market. Includes women's, ready-to-wear, sportwear. Articles include industry news, company profiles. Financial, technology and real estate news and roundtables; everything that pertains to the garment industry in New York City.
Formerly (until 1999): Fashion Market Directory
Published by: Fashion Market Magazine Group, Inc., 617 W 46th St #2, New York, NY 10036-1906. TEL 212-760-5100, FAX 212-760-5112, fashionmmg@aol.com. Ed., Pub., R&P, Adv. contact Nicolas Monjo. Circ: 21,000.

338.0029 USA ISSN 1075-7112
HE7771
FAX U S A; a directory of facsimile numbers for business and organizations nationwide. Text in English. 1993. a., latest 2002, 9th ed. USD 155 (effective 2001). **Document type:** *Directory, Trade.* **Description:** Provides more than 124,000 fax numbers for businesses and organizations nationwide. Includes complete addresses and telephone numbers.
Published by: Omnigraphics, Inc., 615 Griswold St, Detroit, MI 48226. TEL 313-961-1341, 800-234-1340, FAX 313-961-1383, 800-875-1340, info@omnigraphics.com, http://www.omnigraphics.com. Ed. Jennifer Perkins. Pub. Frederick G Ruffner Jr.

380.1029 USA ISSN 1043-7568
HD9715.25.U6
FEDERAL BUYERS GUIDE. Text in English. 1987. 2/yr. bk.rev. **Document type:** *Directory, Trade.* **Description:** Assists federal government buyers in locating businesses wanting to contract to the federal government.
Published by: Federal Buyers Guide, Inc., 718-B State St, PO Box 22507, Santa Barbara, CA 93101. TEL 805-963-7470, FAX 805-963-7478, http://www.federalbuyersguideinc.com/. Ed. Rick Flores. Circ: 10,128.

660.029 BEL
FEDERATIE DER CHEMISCHEN NYVERHEID VAN BELGIE. Text in Dutch. irreg.
Related titles: ♦ Dutch ed.: Federation des Industries Chimiques de Belgique. Annuaire. ISSN 0425-9076.
Published by: Federation des Industries Chimiques de Belgique, Sq Marie Louise 49, Brussels, 1000, Belgium.

660.029 BEL ISSN 0425-9076
FEDERATION DES INDUSTRIES CHIMIQUES DE BELGIQUE. ANNUAIRE/FEDERATIE DER CHEMISCHE NYVERHEID VAN BELGIE. DIRECTORY. Text in Dutch, French. a., latest 1996. free (effective 2005). adv. **Document type:** *Directory.* **Description:** Alphabetical list of the members of the Federation of Industries Chimiques de Belgique and index to their products.
Related titles: ♦ Dutch ed.: Federatie der Chemischen Nyverheid van Belgie.
Published by: Federation des Industries Chimiques de Belgique, Sq Marie Louise 49, Brussels, 1000, Belgium. TEL 32-2-238-9778, FAX 32-2-231-1301, bruxelles@fedichem.be, http://www.fedichem.be/fr/publications/annual_report. Ed. J M Biot. Circ: 2,000.

382.029 PAK
FEDERATION OF PAKISTAN CHAMBERS OF COMMERCE AND INDUSTRY. DIRECTORY OF EXPORTERS. Text in English. 1977. a. PKR 150, USD 20. **Document type:** *Directory.*
Published by: Federation of Pakistan Chambers of Commerce and Industry, Sharea Firdousi, Main Clifton, PO Box 13875, Karachi, 75600, Pakistan.

380.1029 LKA
FERGUSON'S SRI LANKA DIRECTORY (YEAR). Text in English. 1859. biennial. USD 24 (effective 2000). adv. stat. **Document type:** *Directory.*
Formerly: Ferguson's Ceylon Directory
Published by: The Associated Newspapers of Ceylon Ltd., Lake House, D.R. Wijewardena Mawatha, Colombo, 10, Sri Lanka. TEL 94-1-421181, FAX 94-1-449069. Circ: 10,000.

FERRO ALLOY DIRECTORY AND DATABOOK. see *METALLURGY*

380.1029 USA
FIBEROPTIC PRODUCT NEWS BUYER'S GUIDE. Text in English. a. (Sep.). USD 60.50 per issue domestic; USD 70.60 per issue in Canada; USD 68.20 per issue in Mexico; USD 88 per issue elsewhere (effective 2004). **Document type:** *Trade.*
Related titles: Online - full content ed.
Published by: Reed Business Information (Subsidiary of: Reed Business), 100 Enterprise Dr, Ste 600, PO Box 912, Rockaway, NJ 07866-0912. TEL 973-920-7000, 800-222-0289, http://www.fpnmag.com/scripts/categories.asp?dbsec=pd, http://www.reedbusiness.com. Ed. Diane Himes TEL 973-292-5100 ext 330.

FIJI CLASSIFICATION & DICTIONARY OF OCCUPATIONS. see *BUSINESS AND ECONOMICS—Labor And Industrial Relations*

FILM CANADA YEARBOOK. see *MOTION PICTURES*

778.53029 USA ISSN 1055-081X
ML128.M7
FILM COMPOSERS GUIDE. Text in English. 1990. a. USD 50 (effective 1996). adv. **Document type:** *Directory.* **Description:** Lists film composers, their motion picture credits, contact information, releasing company and year.
Published by: IFILM, 1024 N Orange Dr, Hollywood, CA 90038. TEL 323-308-FILM, http://www.ifilm.com. Circ: 2,500.

778.53029 USA ISSN 0740-2872
PN1998.A2
FILM DIRECTORS: A COMPLETE GUIDE. Text in English. 1983. a. USD 65 (effective 1996). adv. **Document type:** *Directory.* **Description:** Lists over 4500 motion picture directors, their credits, contact information, Oscar awards and nominations, and includes interviews. 41,000 film listings.
Published by: IFILM, 1024 N Orange Dr, Hollywood, CA 90038. TEL 323-308-FILM, http://www.ifilm.com. Circ: 5,000.

778.53029 USA ISSN 1058-2630
PN1998.A1
FILM PRODUCERS, STUDIOS, AGENTS AND CASTING DIRECTORS GUIDE. Text in English. 1989. a. USD 55. adv. **Document type:** *Directory.* **Description:** Film industry credit and contact directory. Lists film producers, studios, production companies, casting directors, managers and agents.
Formerly (until 1990): Film Producers, Studios and Agents Guide (0894-8666)
Published by: IFILM, 1024 N Orange Dr, Hollywood, CA 90038. TEL 323-308-FILM, http://www.ifilm.com. Circ: 3,000. **Dist. in Europe by:** Gazelle Book Services, Falcon Hse. Queen Sq, LA1 1RN, Lancaster LA1 1RN, United Kingdom.

778.53029 USA ISSN 0894-864X
PN1996
FILM WRITERS GUIDE. Text in English. 1989. a. USD 60. adv. **Document type:** *Directory.* **Description:** Lists over 7300 screenwriters, their contact information, credits and companies. Includes interviews. Lists 2,000 film titles and listings of unproduced screenplays.
Published by: IFILM, 1024 N Orange Dr, Hollywood, CA 90038. TEL 323-308-FILM, http://www.ifilm.com. Circ: 3,000.

THE FINANCE DIRECTOR'S YEARBOOK. see *BUSINESS AND ECONOMICS—Banking And Finance*

630.29 GBR
FINANCIAL SURVEY. AGRICULTURAL GROWERS & MERCHANTS; company data for success. Text in English. 1986. a. GBP 249 (effective 2001). charts; stat. **Document type:** *Directory, Trade.* **Description:** Contains financial information and contact data for companies in the industry.
Formed by the 1998 merger of: Financial Survey. Agricultural Growers & Merchants. London & South; Which was formerly (until 1991): Financial Survey Company Directory. Agricultural Growers and Merchants. London and South (0952-0015); and: Financial Survey. Agricultural Growers & Merchants. Midlands & North; Which was formerly (until 1991): Financial Survey Company Directory. Agricultural Growers and Merchants. Midlands and North (0952-0112)
Related titles: Diskette ed.: GBP 424 (effective 2001).
Published by: The Prospect Shop Ltd., Field House, 72 Oldfield Rd, Hampton, Middx TW12 2HQ, United Kingdom. TEL 44-20-8461-8730, 44-20-8481-8720, FAX 44-20-8783-1940, info@theprospectshop.co.uk.

623.82029 GBR
FINANCIAL SURVEY. BOAT & MARINE INDUSTRY; company data for success. Text in English. a. charts; stat. **Document type:** *Directory, Trade.* **Description:** Contains financial information and contact data for companies in the industry.
Former titles (until 199?): Financial Survey. Boat Builders & Marine Engineers; (until 1990): Financial Survey Company Directory. Boat Builders and Marine Engineers (0952-5289)
Related titles: Diskette ed.
Published by: The Prospect Shop Ltd., Field House, 72 Oldfield Rd, Hampton, Middx TW12 2HQ, United Kingdom. TEL 44-20-8461-8730, 44-20-8481-8720, FAX 44-20-8783-1940, info@theprospectshop.co.uk.

666.737029 GBR ISSN 1358-8117
FINANCIAL SURVEY. BRICK & TILE MANUFACTURERS AND DISTRIBUTORS. Text in English. a. GBP 249 (effective 2001). **Document type:** *Directory.*
Former titles (until 1995): I C C Financial Survey. Brick and Tile Manufacturers; Financial Survey Company Directory. Brick and Tile Manufacturers (0953-1866)
Related titles: Diskette ed.: GBP 424 (effective 2001).
Published by: The Prospect Shop Ltd., Field House, 72 Oldfield Rd, Hampton, Middx TW12 2HQ, United Kingdom. TEL 44-20-8461-8730, 44-20-8481-8720, FAX 44-20-8783-1940, info@theprospectshop.co.uk.

690.029 GBR
FINANCIAL SURVEY. BUILDERS MERCHANTS. Text in English. a. GBP 249 (effective 2001). **Document type:** *Directory.*

Formed by the merger of: Financial Survey. Builders Merchants. London and South; Which was formerly: Financial Survey Company Directory. Builders Merchants. London and South; Financial Survey. Builders Merchants. Midlands and North; Which was formerly: Financial Survey Company Directory. Builders Merchants. Midlands and North
Related titles: Diskette ed.: GBP 424 (effective 2001).
Published by: The Prospect Shop Ltd., Field House, 72 Oldfield Rd, Hampton, Middx TW12 2HQ, United Kingdom. TEL 44-20-8461-8730, 44-20-8481-8720, FAX 44-20-8783-1940, info@theprospectshop.co.uk.

390.029 GBR
FINANCIAL SURVEY. BUILDING CONTRACTORS; company data for success. Text in English. a., latest vol.44, 2001, Feb. GBP 249 per report (effective 2001). **Document type:** *Directory.*
Formed by the merger of: Financial Survey. Building Contractors. London and South; Which was formerly: Financial Survey Company Directory. Building Contractors. London and South (0952-1356); I C C Financial Survey and Directory. Building Contractors. London and South; Financial Survey. Building Contractors. Midlands and North; Which was formerly: Financial Survey Company Directory. Building Contractors. Midlands and North (0952-1348); I C C Financial Survey and Directory. Building Contractors. Midlands and North
Related titles: Diskette ed.
Published by: The Prospect Shop Ltd., Field House, 72 Oldfield Rd, Hampton, Middx TW12 2HQ, United Kingdom. TEL 44-20-8481-8720, FAX 44-20-8783-1940, info@theprospectshop.co.uk.

677.643029 GBR
FINANCIAL SURVEY. CARPET MANUFACTURERS & WHOLESALE DISTRIBUTORS; company data for success. Variant title: The Carpet Industry. Text in English. a. GBP 249 (effective 2001). charts; stat. **Document type:** *Directory, Trade.* **Description:** Contains financial information and contact data.
Formerly (until 1991): Financial Survey Company Directory. Carpet Manufacturers and Wholesale Distributors (0952-0090)
Related titles: Diskette ed.: GBP 424 (effective 2001).
Published by: The Prospect Shop Ltd., Field House, 72 Oldfield Rd, Hampton, Middx TW12 2HQ, United Kingdom. TEL 44-20-8461-8730, 44-20-8481-8720, FAX 44-20-8783-1940, info@theprospectshop.co.uk.

642.4029 GBR
FINANCIAL SURVEY. CATERING EQUIPMENT INDUSTRY AND DISTRIBUTORS; company data for success. Variant title: The Catering Equipment Industry. Text in English. 1979. a. GBP 249 (effective 2001). **Document type:** *Directory.* **Description:** Contains financial information and contact data for companies in the industry.
Formerly (until 199?): Financial Survey. Catering Equipment Manufacturers and Distributors
Related titles: Diskette ed.: GBP 424 (effective 2001).
Published by: The Prospect Shop Ltd., Field House, 72 Oldfield Rd, Hampton, Middx TW12 2HQ, United Kingdom. TEL 44-20-8461-8730, 44-20-8481-8720, FAX 44-20-8783-1940, info@theprospectshop.co.uk.

332.6029 GBR
FINANCIAL SURVEY. COMMODITY BROKERS. ENGLAND AND WALES; company data for success. Variant title: Commodity & Futures Brokers. Text in English. 1978. a. GBP 249 (effective 2001). **Document type:** *Directory.* **Description:** Contains financial information and contact data for companies in the industry.
Formerly (until 1995): Financial Survey. Commodity and Futures Brokers. England and Wales (0261-5819)
Related titles: Diskette ed.: GBP 424 (effective 2001).
Published by: The Prospect Shop Ltd., Field House, 72 Oldfield Rd, Hampton, Middx TW12 2HQ, United Kingdom. TEL 44-20-8461-8730, 44-20-8481-8720, FAX 44-20-8783-1940, info@theprospectshop.co.uk.

621.3021 GBR
FINANCIAL SURVEY. ELECTRONIC MANUFACTURERS & DISTRIBUTORS; company data for success. Text in English. a. charts; stat. **Document type:** *Directory, Trade.* **Description:** Contains financial information and contact data for companies in the industry.
Formerly (until 1990): Financial Company Directory. Electronic Manufacturers and Distributors (0952-5025)
Related titles: Diskette ed.
Published by: I C C Financial Surveys Ltd, Field House, 72 Oldfield Rd, Hampton, Mddx TW12 2HQ, United Kingdom. TEL 44-181-783-0922, FAX 44-181-783-1940.

338.19 GBR ISSN 1361-4827
FINANCIAL SURVEY. FOOD PROCESSORS; company data for success. Text in English. 1995. a. GBP 249 (effective 2001). **Document type:** *Directory.* **Description:** Contains financial information and contact data for companies in the industry.
Related titles: Diskette ed.: GBP 424 (effective 2001).
Published by: The Prospect Shop Ltd., Field House, 72 Oldfield Rd, Hampton, Middx TW12 2HQ, United Kingdom. TEL 44-20-8461-8730, 44-20-8481-8720, FAX 44-20-8783-1940, info@theprospectshop.co.uk.

641.6153029 GBR
THE FINANCIAL SURVEY. FROZEN FOOD INDUSTRY; company data for success. Text in English. a. GBP 249 (effective 2001). **Document type:** *Directory, Trade.* **Description:** Contains financial information and contact data for companies in the industry.
Former titles (until 1996): Financial Survey. Company Data for Success: Frozen Food Processors, Distributors and Centres (0952-9454); (until 1986): I C C Financial Survey and Directory. Frozen Food Processors, Distributors, and Centres
Related titles: Diskette ed.: GBP 424 (effective 2001).
Published by: The Prospect Shop Ltd., Field House, 72 Oldfield Rd, Hampton, Middx TW12 2HQ, United Kingdom. TEL 44-20-8461-8730, 44-20-8481-8720, FAX 44-20-8783-1940, info@theprospectshop.co.uk.

664.8029 GBR ISSN 1363-8912
FINANCIAL SURVEY. FRUIT, FLOWER & VEGETABLE MERCHANTS. Text in English. 1995. a. GBP 249 (effective 2001). charts; stat. **Document type:** *Directory, Trade.* **Description:** Contains financial information and contact data for companies in the industry.
Formerly (until 1996): I C C Financial Survey. Fruit, Flower and Vegetable Merchants (1363-8661); Which was formed by the 1995 merger of: I C C Financial Survey. Fruit, Flower and Vegetable Merchants. London and South; Which was formerly: Financial Survey Company Directory. Fruit, Flower, and Vegetable Merchants. London and South (0953-5896); I C C Financial Survey. Fruit, Flower, and Vegetable Merchants. Midlands and North; Which was formerly: Financial Survey Company Directory. Fruit, Flower, and Vegetable Merchants. Midlands and North (0953-4733)
Related titles: Diskette ed.: GBP 424 (effective 2001).
Published by: The Prospect Shop Ltd., Field House, 72 Oldfield Rd, Hampton, Middx TW12 2HQ, United Kingdom. TEL 44-20-8461-8730, 44-20-8481-8720, FAX 44-20-8783-1940, info@theprospectshop.co.uk.

332.6029 GBR
FINANCIAL SURVEY. INSTALLMENT, CREDIT, AND FINANCE; company data for success. Text in English. a. GBP 249 (effective 2001). **Document type:** *Directory.* **Description:** Contains financial information and contact data for companies in the industry.
Formerly: Financial Survey Company Directory. Installment, Credit and Finance (0952-7273)
Related titles: Diskette ed.: GBP 424 (effective 2001).
Published by: The Prospect Shop Ltd., Field House, 72 Oldfield Rd, Hampton, Middx TW12 2HQ, United Kingdom. TEL 44-20-8461-8730, 44-20-8481-8720, FAX 44-20-8783-1940, info@theprospectshop.co.uk.

641.36029 GBR
FINANCIAL SURVEY. MEAT, EGG & POULTRY INDUSTRY; company data for success. Text in English. a. GBP 249 (effective 2001). charts; stat. **Document type:** *Directory, Trade.* **Description:** Contains financial information and contact data for companies in the industry.
Former titles: Financial Survey. Meat and Poultry. Scotland; (until 1990): Financial Company Directory. Meat and Poultry. Scotland (0952-5017)
Published by: The Prospect Shop Ltd., Field House, 72 Oldfield Rd, Hampton, Middx TW12 2HQ, United Kingdom. TEL 44-20-8461-8730, 44-20-8481-8720, FAX 44-20-8783-1940, info@theprospectshop.co.uk.

332.6322029 GBR
FINANCIAL SURVEY. METAL STOCKHOLDERS. Text in English. 1986. a. GBP 249 (effective 2001). **Document type:** *Directory.* **Description:** Contains financial information and contact data for companies in the industry.
Formerly: Financial Survey Company Directory. Metal Stockholders (0953-4687)
Related titles: Diskette ed.: GBP 424 (effective 2001).
Published by: The Prospect Shop Ltd., Field House, 72 Oldfield Rd, Hampton, Middx TW12 2HQ, United Kingdom. TEL 44-20-8461-8730, 44-20-8481-8720, FAX 44-20-8783-1940, info@theprospectshop.co.uk.

690.029 GBR
FINANCIAL SURVEY. PLANT HIRE; company data for success. Text in English. a. charts; stat. **Document type:** *Directory, Trade.* **Description:** Contains financial information and contact data for companies in industry.
Formed by the 1995 merger of: Financial Survey. Company Data for Success: Plant Hire. London and South; Which was formerly: Financial Survey Company Directory: Plant Hire. London and South (0953-1963); Financial Survey. Company Data for Success: Plant Hire. Midlands and North; Which was formerly: Financial Survey Company Directory. Plant Hire. Midlands and North (0953-1939)
Related titles: Diskette ed.
Published by: The Prospect Shop Ltd., Field House, 72 Oldfield Rd, Hampton, Middx TW12 2HQ, United Kingdom. TEL 44-20-8461-8730, 44-20-8481-8720, FAX 44-20-8783-1940, info@theprospectshop.co.uk.

332.029 GBR ISSN 1363-5409
FINANCIAL SURVEY. PRINTERS. Text in English. 1996. a. GBP 249 (effective 2001).
Formed by the merger of (1992-1996): Financial Survey. Printers. London and South; Which was formerly: Financial Survey Company Directory (0959-3187); (1992-1996): Financial Survey. Printers. Midlands and North; Which was formerly (1986-1992): Financial Survey Company Directory. Printers. Midlands and North (0953-1769)
Related titles: Diskette ed.: GBP 424 (effective 2001).
Published by: The Prospect Shop Ltd., Field House, 72 Oldfield Rd, Hampton, Middx TW12 2HQ, United Kingdom. TEL 44-20-8461-8730, 44-20-8481-8720, FAX 44-20-8783-1940, info@theprospectshop.co.uk.

684.1029 GBR
FINANCIAL SURVEY. SIGN & STREET FURNITURE MANUFACTURERS & DISTRIBUTORS; company data for success. Variant title: Sign & Street Furniture Industry. Text in English. a. GBP 249 (effective 2001). charts; stat. **Document type:** *Directory, Trade.* **Description:** Contains financial information and contact data for companies in the industry.
Formerly (until 1991): Financial Survey Company Directory. Sign and Street Furniture Manufacturers and Distributors (0952-0147)
Related titles: Diskette ed.; GBP 424 (effective 2001).
Published by: The Prospect Shop Ltd., Field House, 72 Oldfield Rd, Hampton, Middx TW12 2HQ, United Kingdom. TEL 44-20-8461-8730, 44-20-8481-8720, FAX 44-20-8783-1940, info@theprospectshop.co.uk.

B

667.3 GBR ISSN 1363-8947
FINANCIAL SURVEY. TEXTILE RENTAL, LAUNDERERS AND DRY CLEANERS. Text in English. a. GBP 249 (effective 2001).
Formerly (until 1995): I C C Financial Survey. Textile Rental, Launderers and Dry Cleaners (1363-8696); Which was formed by the 1994 merger of: I C C Financial Survey. Laundry and Textile Rental Industry. London and South; I C C Financial Survey. Laundry and Textile Rental Industry. Midlands and North
Related titles: Diskette ed.: GBP 424 (effective 2001).
Published by: The Prospect Shop Ltd., Field House, 72 Oldfield Rd, Hampton, Middx TW12 2HQ, United Kingdom. TEL 44-20-8461-8730, 44-20-8481-8720, FAX 44-20-8783-1940, info@theprospectshop.co.uk.

629.82029 GBR
FINANCIAL SURVEY. THE AUTOMATIC VENDING INDUSTRY; company data for success. Text in English. 1986. a. GBP 249 (effective 2001). charts; stat. **Document type:** *Directory, Trade.* **Description:** Contains financial information and contact data.
Former titles (until 199?): Financial Survey. Automatic Vending; (until 1989): Financial Survey Company Directory. Automatic Vending (0952-0163)
Related titles: Diskette ed.: GBP 424 (effective 2001).
Published by: The Prospect Shop Ltd., Field House, 72 Oldfield Rd, Hampton, Middx TW12 2HQ, United Kingdom. TEL 44-20-8461-8730, 44-20-8481-8720, FAX 44-20-8783-1940, info@theprospectshop.co.uk.

664.752029 GBR
FINANCIAL SURVEY. THE BAKING INDUSTRY; company data for success. Text in English. a. GBP 249 (effective 2001). charts; stat. **Document type:** *Directory, Trade.*
Former titles (until 199?): Financial Survey. Bakery Products Manufacturers; Formerly (until 1991): Financial Survey Company Directory. Bakery Products Manufacturers (0952-0058); Financial Survey and Directory. Bakery Product Manufacturers
Related titles: Diskette ed.; GBP 424 (effective 2001).
Published by: The Prospect Shop Ltd., Field House, 72 Oldfield Rd, Hampton, Middx TW12 2HQ, United Kingdom. TEL 44-20-8461-8730, 44-20-8481-8720, FAX 44-20-8783-1940, info@theprospectshop.co.uk.

332.6029 GBR ISSN 1358-7897
FINANCIAL SURVEY. THE FISH INDUSTRY; company data for success. Text in English. a. GBP 249 (effective 2001). **Document type:** *Directory.*
Formerly: Financial Survey. Fish Trawling, Processing and Merchanting
Related titles: Diskette ed.: GBP 424 (effective 2001).
Published by: The Prospect Shop Ltd., Field House, 72 Oldfield Rd, Hampton, Middx TW12 2HQ, United Kingdom. TEL 44-20-8461-8730, 44-20-8481-8720, FAX 44-20-8783-1940, info@theprospectshop.co.uk.

332.029 GBR ISSN 1363-9056
FINANCIAL SURVEY. THE HAND AND SMALL TOOL INDUSTRY. Text in English. a. GBP 249 (effective 2001). charts; stat.
Former titles (in 1995): I C C Financial Survey. Hand and Small Tool Industry (1359-2629); (until 1994): I C C Financial Survey. Engineers Hand and Small Tool Industry
Related titles: Diskette ed.: GBP 424 (effective 2001).
Published by: The Prospect Shop Ltd., Field House, 72 Oldfield Rd, Hampton, Middx TW12 2HQ, United Kingdom. TEL 44-20-8461-8730, 44-20-8481-8720, FAX 44-20-8783-1940, info@theprospectshop.co.uk.

621.32029 GBR
FINANCIAL SURVEY. THE LIGHTING EQUIPMENT INDUSTRY. Text in English. a. GBP 249 (effective 2001). **Document type:** *Directory.* **Description:** Contains financial information and contact data for companies in the industry.
Formerly: Financial Survey. Lighting Devices and Systems
Related titles: Diskette ed.: GBP 424 (effective 2001).
Published by: The Prospect Shop Ltd., Field House, 72 Oldfield Rd, Hampton, Middx TW12 2HQ, United Kingdom. TEL 44-20-8461-8730, 44-20-8481-8720, FAX 44-20-8783-1940, info@theprospectshop.co.uk.

615.19029 GBR
FINANCIAL SURVEY. THE PHARMACEUTICAL INDUSTRY. Text in English. a. GBP 249 (effective 2001). charts; stat. **Document type:** *Directory, Trade.* **Description:** Contains financial information and contact data for companies in the industry.
Former titles (until 199?): Financial Survey. Pharmaceutical Manufacturers & Distributors; (until 1991): Financial Survey Company Directory. Pharmaceutical Manufacturers and Distributors (0952-4819)
Related titles: Diskette ed.: GBP 424 (effective 2001).
Published by: The Prospect Shop Ltd., Field House, 72 Oldfield Rd, Hampton, Middx TW12 2HQ, United Kingdom. TEL 44-20-8461-8730, 44-20-8481-8720, FAX 44-20-8783-1940, info@theprospectshop.co.uk.

B

770.29 GBR
FINANCIAL SURVEY. THE PHOTOGRAPHIC INDUSTRY; company data for success. Text in English. a. GBP 249 (effective 2001). charts; stat. **Document type:** *Directory, Trade.* **Description:** Contains financial information and contact data for companies in the industry.
Former titles (until 199?): Financial Survey. Photographic Equipment Manufacturers & Distributors; (until 1991): Financial Survey Company Directory. Photographic Equipment Manufacturers and Distributors (0951-7065)
Related titles: Diskette ed.: GBP 424 (effective 2001).
Published by: The Prospect Shop Ltd., Field House, 72 Oldfield Rd, Hampton, Middx TW12 2HQ, United Kingdom. TEL 44-20-8461-8730, 44-20-8481-8720, FAX 44-20-8783-1940, info@theprospectshop.co.uk.

691.1029 GBR
FINANCIAL SURVEY. TIMBER TRADE; company data for success. Text in English. a. GBP 249 (effective 2001). charts; stat. **Document type:** *Directory, Trade.* **Description:** Contains financial information and contact data for companies in the industry.
Former title (until 199?): Financial Survey. Timber Merchants; (until 1991): Financial Survey Company Directory. Timber Merchants (0953-5934)
Related titles: Diskette ed.: GBP 424 (effective 2001).
Published by: The Prospect Shop Ltd., Field House, 72 Oldfield Rd, Hampton, Middx TW12 2HQ, United Kingdom. TEL 44-20-8461-8730, 44-20-8481-8720, FAX 44-20-8783-1940, info@theprospectshop.co.uk.

696.182029 GBR
FINANCIAL SURVEY. TOILETRIES AND COSMETICS INDUSTRY; company data for success. Text in English. a. GBP 249 (effective 2001). charts; stat. **Document type:** *Directory, Trade.* **Description:** Contains financial information and contact data for companies in the industry.
Former titles (until 1994): Financial Survey. Company Data for Success: Toiletry and Cosmetic Industry; (until 1991): Financial Survey Company Directory. Toiletry and Cosmetic Manufacturers and Distributors (0953-5918)
Related titles: Diskette ed.: GBP 424 (effective 2001).
Published by: The Prospect Shop Ltd., Field House, 72 Oldfield Rd, Hampton, Middx TW12 2HQ, United Kingdom. TEL 44-20-8461-8730, 44-20-8481-8720, FAX 44-20-8783-1940, info@theprospectshop.co.uk.

621.3897029 GBR
FINANCIAL SURVEY. VIDEO AND AUDIO VISUAL INDUSTRY; company data for success. Text in English. a. GBP 249 (effective 2001). charts; stat. **Document type:** *Directory, Trade.* **Description:** Contains financial information and contact data for companies in the industry.
Formerly: Financial Survey Company Directory. Audio Visual
Related titles: Diskette ed.: GBP 424 (effective 2001).
Published by: The Prospect Shop Ltd., Field House, 72 Oldfield Rd, Hampton, Middx TW12 2HQ, United Kingdom. TEL 44-20-8461-8730, 44-20-8481-8720, FAX 44-20-8783-1940, info@theprospectshop.co.uk.

380.1029 GBR ISSN 1460-1540
FINANCIAL TIMES FIVE HUNDRED. Key Title: F T 500. Text in English. 1993. a.
—BLDSC (3927.001310).
Published by: Financial Times Group, One Southwark Bridge, London, SE1 9HL, United Kingdom. TEL 44-20-78733000, http://www.pearson.com.

382.029 GBR
HG3851
FINCAREER EUROMONEY CAPITAL MARKETS DIRECTORY (YEAR). Variant title: Paine Webber Euromoney Directory. Text in English. 1973. a., latest 2001. GBP 370, USD 575 (effective 2001). **Document type:** *Directory.* **Description:** Provides a guide to the international capital markets. For bankers, traders, corporate finance executives and all those who need to know who does what in international finance.
Former titles: The PaineWebber Euromoney Directory; S B C Warburg Euromoney Directory; Merrill Lynch - Euromoney Directory (0953-1181); (until 1987): Hambro Euromoney Directory (0306-3933)
Related titles: Regional ed(s).: Euromoney Capital Markets Directory (US & Canada Edition).
—CCC.
Published by: Euromoney Institutional Investor Plc., Nestor House, Playhouse Yard, London, EC4V 5EX, United Kingdom. TEL 44-20-7779-8673, FAX 44-20-7779-8541, http://www.euromoney.com.

338.0029 GBR ISSN 1464-0171
TS653.A1
FINISHING INDUSTRY DIRECTORY. Text in English. 1991. a. GBP 35; GBP 42 foreign. **Document type:** *Directory, Trade.*
Published by: Turret R A I plc, Armstrong House, 38 Market Sq, Uxbridge, Middx UB8 1TG, United Kingdom. TEL 44-1895-454545, FAX 44-1895-454647.

FIRE DIRECTORY (YEAR). see *FIRE PREVENTION*

FIRE PROTECTION EQUIPMENT DIRECTORY. see *FIRE PREVENTION*

FIRE RESISTANCE DIRECTORY. see *FIRE PREVENTION*

FITECH INTERNATIONAL; the international equipment guide for the emergency services. see *FIRE PREVENTION*

THE FITZHUGH DIRECTORY OF INDEPENDENT HEALTHCARE AND LONG TERM CARE. FINANCIAL INFORMATION. see *MEDICAL SCIENCES*

FLEET ASSOCIATION DIRECTORY. see *BUSINESS AND ECONOMICS—Marketing And Purchasing*

380.1029 USA
FLORIDA BUSINESS CREDIT DIRECTORY. Text in English. a. USD 1,100 combined subscription print, online & CD-ROM eds. (effective 2004 & 2005). back issues avail. **Document type:** *Directory.* **Description:** Contains credit ratings and other valuable information on all businesses within Florida. Includes company name & address, phone & fax numbers, key executive names & titles, lines of business, years in business, number of employees, estimated annual sales, volume credit rating code, and corporate linkage information.
Related titles: CD-ROM ed.; Diskette ed.; E-mail ed.; Fax ed.; Magnetic Tape ed.; Online - full text ed.
Published by: American Business Directories (Subsidiary of: American Business Information, Inc.), 5711 S 86th Circle, P O Box 27347, Omaha, NE 68127. TEL 402-593-4600, 888-946-9377, 877-708-3844, FAX 402-331-5481, sales@directoriesusa.com, http://www.directoriesusa.com.

338.0029 USA ISSN 1048-7093
HC107.F6
FLORIDA BUSINESS DIRECTORY. Text in English. 1989. a. USD 1,100 combined subscription print, online & CD-ROM eds. (effective 2004 & 2005). index. back issues avail. **Document type:** *Directory.* **Description:** Includes all businesses in the state compiled from the yellow pages and telephone verified. Each listing includes company name, complete address, phone number, name of owner, manager, and employee size and sales volume codes and credit rating codes.
Formed by the 1990 merger of: Tampa and North Florida Business Directory (1047-2703); Miami and South Florida Business Directory (1047-1804)
Related titles: CD-ROM ed.; Diskette ed.; E-mail ed.; Fax ed.; Magnetic Tape ed.; Online - full text ed.
Published by: American Business Directories (Subsidiary of: American Business Information, Inc.), 5711 S 86th Circle, P O Box 27347, Omaha, NE 68127. TEL 402-593-4600, 888-946-9377, 877-708-3844, FAX 402-331-5481, karen.peters@infousa.com, sales@directoriesusa.com, http://www.directoriesusa.com.

670.29 USA ISSN 0882-9438
HD9727.F6
FLORIDA MANUFACTURERS REGISTER. Text in English. a. USD 154 (effective 2000). adv. illus. **Document type:** *Directory.* **Description:** Profiles 20,500 manufacturers; five different sections list companies by product, alphabetically, by city, by SIC, and by parent company.
Related titles: CD-ROM ed.: USD 670 (effective 2000); Diskette ed.: USD 745 (effective 1999).
Published by: Manufacturers' News, Inc., 1633 Central St, Evanston, IL 60201. TEL 847-864-7000, 888-752-5200, FAX 847-332-1100, info@mninfo.com, info@manufacturersnews.com, sales@mninfo.com, http://www.manufacturersnews.com. Ed. Frank Lambing. Adv. contact Charles Scherer. B&W page USD 1,843.

620.106029 USA
FLUID POWER CERTIFICATION BOARD. CERTIFICATION DIRECTORY; accredited fluid power educational institutions and instructors and certified fluid power mechanics, technicians, specialists and engineers. Text in English. 1991. a. **Document type:** *Directory.*
Published by: (Fluid Power Certification Board), Fluid Power Society, 1420, Cherry Hill, NJ 08034-0054. TEL 414-257-0910, FAX 414-257-4092. Circ: 3,200.

FLUID POWER HANDBOOK & DIRECTORY. see *ENGINEERING—Engineering Mechanics And Materials*

670.29 GBR ISSN 1465-4512
FLUIDS & AIR TECHNOLOGY DIRECTORY. Text in English. 1997. a. GBP 53; GBP 58 foreign. **Document type:** *Directory, Trade.* **Description:** Detailed and comprehensive categorized listing of the products of over 3,500 suppliers to this key industrial sector.
Published by: Turret R A I plc, Armstrong House, 38 Market Sq, Uxbridge, Middx UB8 1TG, United Kingdom. TEL 44-1895-454545, FAX 44-1895-454647.

658.0029 610 USA
FOCUS CARDIO-RESPIRATORY & SLEEP MEDICINE BUYER'S GUIDE. Text in English. a. **Document type:** *Trade.* **Description:** Contains standardized company profiles and index of products and services in the industry.
Published by: FOCUS Publications, Inc., 22 S. Parsonage St., Rhinebeck, NY 12572. TEL 845-876-2936, 800-661-5690, FAX 845-876-2940, http://www.foocus.com/. Pub., Adv. contact Bob Miglino.

FONDO DE PROMOCION DE EXPORTACIONES. DIRECTORIO DE EXPORTADORES/EXPORT DIRECTORY. see *BUSINESS AND ECONOMICS—International Commerce*

338.19029 USA
FOOD INDUSTRY DIRECTORY. Text in English. 1974. a. **Document type:** *Directory.*
Published by: Phoenix Media, PO Box 811768, Boca Raton, FL 33481-1768. Eds. James E Prevor, Kenneth L Whitacre. R&P Fran Ruskin. Circ: 30,000.

FOOD MASTER (PRINT EDITION). see *FOOD AND FOOD INDUSTRIES*

664.09029 GBR
FOOD PACKER INTERNATIONAL DIRECTORY (YEAR). Variant title: Food Packer & Processor Directory (Year). Text in English. a. GBP 95 per vol. includes CD-ROM (effective Aug. 2002); GBP 100 per vol. includes CD-ROM (effective Aug. 2003). adv. **Document type:** *Directory, Trade.*
Published by: Binsted Group Plc, Attwood House, Mansfield Park, Four Marks, Alton, Hants GU34 5PZ, United Kingdom. TEL 44-1420-568900, FAX 44-1420-565994, info@binstedgroup.com, http://www.binstedpublications.com/html/directoriesandspecials/foodpacker.asp, http://www.binsteadgroup.com/. Ed., Pub. Edward C Binsted. Adv. contact Andrew Flew.

664.028029 USA
FOOD PROCESSING GUIDE & DIRECTORY. Text in English. 1977. a. free domestic to qualified personnel; USD 160 foreign (effective 2003). adv. **Document type:** *Directory, Trade.*
Formerly: Food Processing Food Processors' Resource
Published by: Putman Media, 555 W Pierce Rd, Ste 301, Itasca, IL 60143-2649. TEL 630-467-1300, FAX 630-467-1109, ckappel@putman.net, http://www.putmanmedia.com. Ed. Michael Pehanich. Pub., Adv. contact James Powers. B&W page USD 2,710; trim 10.88 x 8. Circ: 66,033.

664.52029 GBR
FOOD RESEARCH & ANALYSIS DIRECTORY. Text in English. a. **Document type:** *Directory, Trade.*
Published by: Turret R A I plc, Armstrong House, 38 Market Sq, Uxbridge, Middx UB8 1TG, United Kingdom. TEL 44-1895-454545, FAX 44-1895-454647.

643.6029 USA
FOODSERVICE GAS EQUIPMENT CATALOG. Text in English. 1946. biennial. USD 15 (effective 1999). illus. **Document type:** *Catalog.* **Description:** A comprehensive guide to gas foodservice equipment in the industry. Contains over 40 categories of commercial equipment from broilers, fryers and ovens to ranges and water heaters.
Published by: C P Publishing, Inc., PO Box 267, Fond du Lac, WI 54936-0267. TEL 920-923-3700, FAX 920-923-6805. Pub. Colleen A Phalen.

363.8029 USA ISSN 1062-7324
FOODSERVICE YEARBOOK INTERNATIONAL. Text in English. 1991. a. USD 65. adv. **Document type:** *Directory, Trade.* **Description:** Lists products, suppliers, associations, exhibitions, publications and country data.
Published by: Keller International Publishing Corp., 150 Great Neck Rd, Great Neck, NY 11021. TEL 516-829-9210, FAX 516-824-5414, http://www.kellerpubs.com. Ed. Howard Stone. Adv. contact Jennifer Zepnick. Circ: 15,700.

330.982 GBR ISSN 1463-0931
FOREIGN COMPANIES IN ARGENTINA YEARBOOK. Text in English. 1998. a. GBP 240, USD 390 (effective 2001). **Document type:** *Trade.* **Description:** Provides extensive corporate data, including contact details, senior executive personnel, indexed company listings, competitor data, and company subsidiaries.
Related titles: CD-ROM ed.: GBP 390, USD 670 (effective 2001).
—CCC.
Published by: Business Monitor International Ltd., Commercial Intelligence Service, 179 Queen Victoria St, London, EC4V 4DU, United Kingdom. TEL 44-20-7248-0468, FAX 44-20-7248-0467, busmon@dial.pipex.com, http://www.businessmonitor.com.

330.981 GBR ISSN 1463-094X
FOREIGN COMPANIES IN BRAZIL YEARBOOK. Text in English. 1998. a. GBP 240, USD 390 (effective 2001). **Document type:** *Trade.* **Description:** Provides extensive corporate data, including contact details, senior executive personnel, indexed company listings, competitor data, and company subsidiaries.
Related titles: CD-ROM ed.: GBP 390, USD 670 (effective 2001).
—CCC.
Published by: Business Monitor International Ltd., Commercial Intelligence Service, 179 Queen Victoria St, London, EC4V 4DU, United Kingdom. TEL 44-20-7248-0468, FAX 44-20-7248-0467, busmon@dial.pipex.com, http://www.businessmonitor.com.

330.983 GBR ISSN 1465-0274
FOREIGN COMPANIES IN CHILE YEARBOOK. Text in English. 1998. a. GBP 240, USD 390 (effective 2001). **Document type:** *Trade.* **Description:** Provides extensive corporate data, including contact details, senior executive personnel, indexed company listings, competitor data, and company subsidiaries.
Related titles: CD-ROM ed.: GBP 390, USD 670 (effective 2001).
—CCC.
Published by: Business Monitor International Ltd., Commercial Intelligence Service, 179 Queen Victoria St, London, EC4V 4DU, United Kingdom. TEL 44-20-7248-0468, FAX 44-20-7248-0467, busmon@dial.pipex.com, http://www.businessmonitor.com.

330.951 GBR ISSN 1463-0958
FOREIGN COMPANIES IN CHINA YEARBOOK. Text in English. 1998. a. GBP 240, USD 390 (effective 2000). **Description:** Provides extensive corporate data, including contact details, senior executive personnel, indexed company listings, competitor data, and company subsidiaries.
Related titles: CD-ROM ed.
—CCC.
Published by: Business Monitor International Ltd., Commercial Intelligence Service, 179 Queen Victoria St, London, EC4V 4DU, United Kingdom. TEL 44-20-7248-0468, FAX 44-20-7248-0467, subs@businessmonitor.com, http://www.businessmonitor.com.

330.9861 GBR ISSN 1465-0282
FOREIGN COMPANIES IN COLOMBIA YEARBOOK. Text in English. 1998. a. GBP 240, USD 390 (effective 2001). **Document type:** *Trade.* **Description:** Provides extensive corporate data, including contact details, senior executive personnel, indexed company listings, competitor data, and company subsidiaries.
Related titles: CD-ROM ed.: GBP 390, USD 670 (effective 2001).
—CCC.
Published by: Business Monitor International Ltd., Commercial Intelligence Service, 179 Queen Victoria St, London, EC4V 4DU, United Kingdom. TEL 44-20-7248-0468, FAX 44-20-7248-0467, busmon@dial.pipex.com, http://www.businessmonitor.com.

330.94371 GBR ISSN 1465-5543
FOREIGN COMPANIES IN CZECH REPUBLIC YEARBOOK. Text in English. 1998. a. GBP 240, USD 390 (effective 2001). **Document type:** *Trade.* **Description:** Provides extensive data on corporations, including contact details, senior executive personnel, indexed company listings, competitor data, and company subsidiaries.
Related titles: CD-ROM ed.: GBP 390, USD 670 (effective 2001).
—CCC.
Published by: Business Monitor International Ltd., Commercial Intelligence Service, 179 Queen Victoria St, London, EC4V 4DU, United Kingdom. TEL 44-20-7248-0468, FAX 44-20-7248-0467, busmon@dial.pipex.com, http://www.businessmonitor.com.

330.962 GBR ISSN 1463-0966
FOREIGN COMPANIES IN EGYPT YEARBOOK. Text in English. 1998. a. GBP 240, USD 390 (effective 2001). **Document type:** *Trade.* **Description:** Provides extensive corporate data, including contact details, senior executive personnel, indexed company listings, competitor data, and company subsidiaries.
Related titles: CD-ROM ed.: GBP 390, USD 670 (effective 2001).
Published by: Business Monitor International Ltd., Commercial Intelligence Service, 179 Queen Victoria St, London, EC4V 4DU, United Kingdom. TEL 44-20-7248-0468, FAX 44-20-7248-0467, busmon@dial.pipex.com, http://www.businessmonitor.com.

330.95215 GBR ISSN 1463-0974
FOREIGN COMPANIES IN HONG KONG YEARBOOK. Text in English. 1998. a. GBP 240, USD 390 (effective 2001). **Description:** Provides extensive information on corporations, including contact details, senior executive personnel, listing by index, competitor data, and company subsidiaries.
Related titles: CD-ROM ed.: GBP 390, USD 670 (effective 2001).
—CCC.
Published by: Business Monitor International Ltd., Commercial Intelligence Service, 179 Queen Victoria St, London, EC4V 4DU, United Kingdom. TEL 44-20-7248-0468, FAX 44-20-7248-0467, busmon@dial.pipex.com, http://www.businessmonitor.com.

330.9439 GBR ISSN 1465-5551
FOREIGN COMPANIES IN HUNGARY YEARBOOK. Text in English. 1998. a. GBP 240, USD 390 (effective 2001). **Document type:** *Trade.* **Description:** Provides detailed information on corporations, including contact details, senior executive personnel, indexed company listings, competitor data, and company subsidiaries.
Related titles: CD-ROM ed.: GBP 390, USD 670 (effective 2001).
—CCC.
Published by: Business Monitor International Ltd., Commercial Intelligence Service, 179 Queen Victoria St, London, EC4V 4DU, United Kingdom. TEL 44-20-7248-0468, FAX 44-20-7248-0467, busmon@dial.pipex.com, http://www.businessmonitor.com.

330.9595 GBR ISSN 1463-0990
HF3800.6.A48
FOREIGN COMPANIES IN MALAYSIA YEARBOOK. Text in English. 1998. a. GBP 240, USD 390 (effective 2000). **Document type:** *Trade.* **Description:** Provides a listing of foreign company operations in Malaysia.
Related titles: CD-ROM ed.: GBP 390, USD 670 (effective 2000).
—CCC.
Published by: Business Monitor International Ltd., Commercial Intelligence Service, 179 Queen Victoria St, London, EC4V 4DU, United Kingdom. TEL 44-20-7248-0468, FAX 44-20-7248-0467, busmon@dial.pipex.com, http://www.businessmonitor.com.

330.972 GBR ISSN 1463-1008
HG4092.Z65
FOREIGN COMPANIES IN MEXICO YEARBOOK. Text in English. 1998. a. GBP 240, USD 390 (effective 2001). **Document type:** *Trade.* **Description:** Provides extensive information on corporations, including contact details, senior executive personnel, indexed company listings, competitor data, and company subsidiaries.
Related titles: CD-ROM ed.: GBP 390, USD 670 (effective 2001).
—CCC.
Published by: Business Monitor International Ltd., Commercial Intelligence Service, 179 Queen Victoria St, London, EC4V 4DU, United Kingdom. TEL 44-20-7248-0468, FAX 44-20-7248-0467, busmon@dial.pipex.com, http://www.businessmonitor.com.

330.985 GBR ISSN 1465-0290
FOREIGN COMPANIES IN PERU YEARBOOK. Text in English. 1998. a. GBP 240, USD 390 (effective 2001). **Document type:** *Trade.* **Description:** Provides extensive information on corporations, including contact details, senior executive personnel, indexed companies, competitor data, and company subsidiaries.
Related titles: CD-ROM ed.: GBP 390, USD 670 (effective 2001).
—CCC.
Published by: Business Monitor International Ltd., Commercial Intelligence Service, 179 Queen Victoria St, London, EC4V 4DU, United Kingdom. TEL 44-20-7248-0468, FAX 44-20-7248-0467, busmon@dial.pipex.com, http://www.businessmonitor.com.

330.9438 GBR ISSN 1465-0258
FOREIGN COMPANIES IN POLAND YEARBOOK. Text in English. 1998. a. GBP 240, USD 390 (effective 2001). **Document type:** *Trade.* **Description:** Provides detailed information on corporations, including contact details, senior executive personnel, indexed company listings, competitor data, and company subsidiaries.
Related titles: CD-ROM ed.: GBP 390, USD 670 (effective 2001).
—CCC.
Published by: Business Monitor International Ltd., Commercial Intelligence Service, 179 Queen Victoria St, London, EC4V 4DU, United Kingdom. TEL 44-20-7248-0468, FAX 44-20-7248-0467, busmon@dial.pipex.com, http://www.businessmonitor.com.

330.947 GBR ISSN 1463-1016
FOREIGN COMPANIES IN RUSSIA YEARBOOK. Text in English. 1998. a. GBP 240, USD 390 (effective 2001). **Document type:** *Trade.* **Description:** Provides detailed information on corporations, including contact details, senior executive personnel, indexed company listings, competitor data, and company subsidiaries.
Related titles: CD-ROM ed.: GBP 390, USD 670 (effective 2001).
—CCC.
Published by: Business Monitor International Ltd., Commercial Intelligence Service, 179 Queen Victoria St, London, EC4V 4DU, United Kingdom. TEL 44-20-7248-0468, FAX 44-20-7248-0467, busmon@dial.pipex.com, http://www.businessmonitor.com.

330.9538 GBR ISSN 1463-1024
FOREIGN COMPANIES IN SAUDI ARABIA YEARBOOK. Text in English. 1998. a. GBP 240, USD 390 (effective 2001). **Document type:** *Trade.* **Description:** Provides extensive information on foreign corporations in Saudi Arabia, including contact details, senior executive personnel, indexed company listings, competitor data, and company subsidiaries.
Related titles: CD-ROM ed.: GBP 390, USD 670 (effective 2001).
Published by: Business Monitor International Ltd., Commercial Intelligence Service, 179 Queen Victoria St, London, EC4V 4DU, United Kingdom. TEL 44-20-7248-0468, FAX 44-20-7248-0467, busmon@dial.pipex.com, http://www.businessmonitor.com.

330.95957 GBR ISSN 1463-1032
FOREIGN COMPANIES IN SINGAPORE YEARBOOK. Text in English. 1998. a. GBP 240, USD 390 (effective 2001). **Document type:** *Trade.* **Description:** Provides extensive information on corporations, including contact details, senior executive personnel, indexed company listings, competitor data, and company subsidiaries.
Related titles: CD-ROM ed.: GBP 390, USD 670 (effective 2001).
—CCC.
Published by: Business Monitor International Ltd., Commercial Intelligence Service, 179 Queen Victoria St, London, EC4V 4DU, United Kingdom. TEL 44-20-7248-0468, FAX 44-20-7248-0467, busmon@dial.pipex.com, http://www.businessmonitor.com.

330.968 GBR ISSN 1463-1040
FOREIGN COMPANIES IN SOUTH AFRICA YEARBOOK. Text in English. 1998. a. GBP 240, USD 390 (effective 2001). **Document type:** *Trade.* **Description:** Provides corporate data on foreign companies in South Africa, including contact details, senior executive personnel, indexed company listings, competitor data, and company subsidiaries.
Related titles: CD-ROM ed.: GBP 390, USD 670 (effective 2001).
—CCC.
Published by: Business Monitor International Ltd., Commercial Intelligence Service, 179 Queen Victoria St, London, EC4V 4DU, United Kingdom. TEL 44-20-7248-0468, FAX 44-20-7248-0467, busmon@dial.pipex.com, http://www.businessmonitor.com.

330.9593 GBR ISSN 1465-0304
FOREIGN COMPANIES IN THAILAND YEARBOOK. Text in English. 1998. a. GBP 240, USD 390 (effective 2001). **Document type:** *Trade.* **Description:** Provides extensive information on corporations, including contact details, senior executive personnel, indexed company listings, competitor data, and company subsidiaries.
Related titles: CD-ROM ed.: GBP 390, USD 670 (effective 2001).
—CCC.
Published by: Business Monitor International Ltd., Commercial Intelligence Service, 179 Queen Victoria St, London, EC4V 4DU, United Kingdom. TEL 44-20-7248-0468, FAX 44-20-7248-0467, busmon@dial.pipex.com, http://www.businessmonitor.com.

330.9561 GBR ISSN 1465-0312
FOREIGN COMPANIES IN TURKEY YEARBOOK. Text in English. 1998. a. GBP 240, USD 390 (effective 2001). **Document type:** *Trade.* **Description:** Provides detailed information on corporations, including contact details, senior executive personnel, indexed company listings, competitor data, as well as company subsidiaries.
Related titles: CD-ROM ed.: GBP 390, USD 670 (effective 2001).
—CCC.
Published by: Business Monitor International Ltd., Commercial Intelligence Service, 179 Queen Victoria St, London, EC4V 4DU, United Kingdom. TEL 44-20-7248-0468, FAX 44-20-7248-0467, busmon@dial.pipex.com, http://www.businessmonitor.com.

330.95357 GBR ISSN 1463-1059
FOREIGN COMPANIES IN UNITED ARAB EMIRATES YEARBOOK. Text in English. 1998. a. GBP 240, USD 390 (effective 2001). **Document type:** *Trade.* **Description:** Provides detailed information on foreign corporations, including contact details, senior executive personnel, indexed company listings, competitor data, and company subsidiaries.
Related titles: CD-ROM ed.: GBP 390, USD 670 (effective 2001).
Published by: Business Monitor International Ltd., Commercial Intelligence Service, 179 Queen Victoria St, London, EC4V 4DU, United Kingdom. TEL 44-20-7248-0468, FAX 44-20-7248-0467, busmon@dial.pipex.com, http://www.businessmonitor.com.

330.987 GBR ISSN 1465-0320
FOREIGN COMPANIES IN VENEZUELA YEARBOOK. Text in English. 1998. a. GBP 240, USD 390 (effective 2001). **Document type:** *Trade.* **Description:** Provides extensive information on corporations, including contact details, senior executive personnel, indexed companies, competitor data, and company subsidiaries.
Related titles: CD-ROM ed.: GBP 390, USD 670 (effective 2001).

—CCC.
Published by: Business Monitor International Ltd., Commercial Intelligence Service, 179 Queen Victoria St, London, EC4V 4DU, United Kingdom. TEL 44-20-7248-0468, FAX 44-20-7248-0467, busmon@dial.pipex.com, http://www.businessmonitor.com.

FORMER SOVIET UNION MARKETING, MEDIA & ADVERTISING DIRECTORY. see *BUSINESS AND ECONOMICS—Marketing And Purchasing*

671.2029 GBR ISSN 0264-5319
FOUNDRY YEARBOOK AND CASTINGS BUYERS' DIRECTORY (YEAR). Text in English. 1972. a. (issued in December). GBP 132 domestic; GBP 141 foreign (effective 2000). **Document type:** *Directory, Trade.* **Description:** Contains the names, addresses, and telephone and fax numbers of U.K. operators of foundries and forges. Lists suppliers of materials and equipment.
Formerly (until 1982): Foundry Year Book (0306-4212)
Indexed: CoppAb.
Published by: D M G World Media Ltd. (Subsidiary of: Daily Mail and General Trust PLC), Queensway House, 2 Queensway, Redhill, Surrey RH1 1QS, United Kingdom. TEL 44-1737-768611, FAX 44-1737-855475, http://www.dmg.co.uk, http://www.dmgworldmedia.com.

B

338.0029 FRA ISSN 1270-8054
HF3553
FRANCE TELEXPORT. Text in English, French, German, Spanish. 1979. a. EUR 182.94 (effective 2001). adv. **Document type:** *Directory.* **Description:** Lists 40,000 French firms doing business abroad, classified by the products they export or import.
Formerly (until 1995): Francexport (0244-710X)
Related titles: CD-ROM ed.
Published by: Telexport, CCIP Direct, 2 rue de Viarmes, Paris, Cedex 1 75040, France. TEL 33-1-55653565, FAX 33-1-55653610, contact@telexport.tm.fr, http://www.telexport.tm.fr. Circ: 15,000 (paid).

338.0029 USA ISSN 0318-8752
HF5429.3
FRANCHISE ANNUAL; complete handbook and directory. Text in English. 1969. a. USD 39.95 in North America; USD 44.95 out of North America. bk.rev. index. **Document type:** *Directory.*
Published by: Info Franchise News Inc., PO Box 826, Lewiston, NY 14092-7926. TEL 716-754-4669, FAX 905-688-7728, infopress@infonews.com, http://infonews.com/franchise. Ed. Ted Dixon. Circ: 15,000.

FRANCO-BRITISH CHAMBER OF COMMERCE AND INDUSTRY. TRADE DIRECTORY. see *BUSINESS AND ECONOMICS—Chamber Of Commerce Publications*

382.029 GBR ISSN 0071-917X
FRANCO-BRITISH TRADE DIRECTORY. Text in English. 1883. a. GBP 70 (effective 2000). **Document type:** *Directory.* **Description:** Annual publication of the French Chamber of Commerce, with a directory of members, activities and useful Franco-British information.
Published by: French Chamber of Commerce in Great Britain, 21 Dartmouth St, London, SW1H 9BP, United Kingdom. Ed. Annie Lavnois. Circ: 2,000.

380.1029 CAN ISSN 0071-9277
HF3223
FRASER'S CANADIAN TRADE DIRECTORY. Text in English. 1913. a. CND 195; CND 220 print & CD-ROM eds. combined (effective 2001). **Document type:** *Directory, Trade.*
Related titles: CD-ROM ed.: CND 195 (effective 2001).
—CISTI.
Published by: Rogers Media Publishing Ltd, One Mount Pleasant Rd, 11th Fl, Toronto, ON M4Y 2Y5, Canada. TEL 416-764-2000, FAX 416-764-3941, http://www.frasers.com, http://www.rogers.com.

338.0029 USA
FREE IN AMERICA CATALOG; the First Coast's business guide for free and inexpensive items. Text in English. 1991. q. free in United States. adv. bk.rev. **Document type:** *Catalog, Consumer.* **Description:** Lists Jacksonville-area businesses, hotels, and resorts; contains news pertaining to free and inexpensive consumer items.
Formerly: Jaguar
Published by: Vaughan Publishing Co., 3478 Fairbanks Rd, PO Box 23401, Jacksonville, FL 32241. TEL 904-260-9198, FAX 904-260-9198, freestuff@aol.com. Ed. Nan Ramey. Adv. contact C H Taylor. B&W page USD 275; trim 10.5 x 8. Circ: 20,000.

FREEDOM OF INFORMATION AND PRIVACY BRANCH. DIRECTORY OF INSTITUTIONS, ONTARIO. see *PUBLIC ADMINISTRATION*

381.029 FRA ISSN 0759-3694
FRENCH COMPANY HANDBOOK; for evaluating key listed French companies. Text in English. 1981. a. USD 75. adv. **Document type:** *Directory.* **Description:** Guide to over 130 major French companies, published with the Paris stock exchange. Offers detailed financial, economic and commercial profile of each company, key facts on doing business in France, and the operations of the Paris financial markets.
Published by: International Business Development, 181 av. Charles-de-Gaulle, Neuilly, Cedex 92125, France. TEL 33-1-41439494, FAX 33-1-41439393. Ed. Bruce Singer. Pub. Richard McClean. R&P Karen Diot. Adv. contact Patricia Goupy. Circ: 17,000. **U.S. subscr. to:** Reference Press Inc., 6448 Hwy 290 E, Ste E 104, Austin, TX 78723. TEL 800-486-8666. **Co-publishers:** Bloomberg; International Herald Tribune.

FROZEN & CHILLED FOODS EUROPE YEARBOOK. see *FOOD AND FOOD INDUSTRIES*

382.029 DEU ISSN 0344-0079
FRUCHTHANDEL ADRESSBUCH. Text in German. 1951. a. EUR 64.50 (effective 2005). adv. **Document type:** *Directory, Trade.* **Description:** Directory of import and wholesale trade in fruit, vegetables, dried fruit and potatoes in Germany, Austria, Belgium, Switzerland and Eastern Europe.
Formerly (until 1962): Adressbuch des Deutschen Frucht-Import und -Grosshandels (0400-552X)
Published by: Dr. Rolf Wolf Verlag GmbH, Postfach 105551, Duesseldorf, 40046, Germany. TEL 49-211-991040, FAX 49-211-663162, info@fruchthandel.de, http://www.fruchthandel.de. Ed. Eva Schmeiss. Pub., R&P Robert Broadfoot. Adv. contact Thomas Gloge. B&W page EUR 1,560, color page EUR 2,640; trim 125 x 210. Circ: 2,500 (paid).

380.1029 GMB
GAMBIA. CENTRAL STATISTICS DEPARTMENT. DIRECTORY OF ESTABLISHMENTS. Text in English. a. GMD 8. **Document type:** *Directory, Government.*
Published by: Central Statistics Department, Wellington St., Banjul, Gambia.

796.029 USA
GAMING SYSTEMS SOURCE DIRECTORY. Text in English. 1983. s-a. USD 10 (effective 2000). adv. **Document type:** *Directory, Consumer.*
Published by: Gibbs Publishing Company, PO Box 97, Sylva, NC 28779-0097. Ed. James Calvin Gibbs. Circ: 200,000.

GAS AND OIL EQUIPMENT DIRECTORY. see *HEATING, PLUMBING AND REFRIGERATION*

GAS INDUSTRY DIRECTORY (YEAR). see *PETROLEUM AND GAS*

GAS UTILITY INDUSTRY. see *PETROLEUM AND GAS*

GAS UTILITY REPORT. see *PETROLEUM AND GAS*

338.0029 ZAF
GAUTENG DIRECTORY. Text in English. a. USD 230 (effective 2001). adv. **Document type:** *Directory.*
Former titles (until 1995): P W V Directory; (until 1994): Rand - Pretoria Directory; Incorporates: Johannesburg - West Rand Directory; Which was formerly: Braby's Business Directory of Johannesburg
Related titles: Diskette ed.
Published by: Braby's (Subsidiary of: Associated Industries), Attn: Sue Pearson, PO Box 1426, Pinetown, 3600, South Africa. TEL 27-31-7017021, FAX 27-31-7017036, booksales@brabys.co.za.

380.1029 USA ISSN 0097-8175
P88.8
GEBBIE PRESS ALL-IN-ONE DIRECTORY. Text in English. 1972. a. USD 100 (effective 2000). index. **Document type:** *Directory.* **Description:** Lists of all public relations outlets in the United States, including daily, weekly, Black and Hispanic newspapers, radio and television stations, general consumer magazines, business papers, trade press, Black press and radio, Hispanic press and radio, farm publications, and news syndicates.
Related titles: Diskette ed.
Published by: Gebbie Press, PO Box 1000, New Paltz, NY 12561. TEL 914-255-7560, FAX 914-256-1239, gebbie@pipeline.com, http://www.gebbieinc.com. Ed. Amalia Gebbie.

GENERAL MEDICAL COUNCIL. MEDICAL REGISTER. see *MEDICAL SCIENCES*

670.29 USA ISSN 0743-4502
HD9981.7.C8
GEORGE D. HALL'S CONNECTICUT SERVICE DIRECTORY. Text in English. 1984. every 18 mos. USD 64. **Document type:** *Directory.* **Description:** Provides specific information for more than 9,200 service-oriented businesses; includes alphabetical, geographical and service by SIC sections.
Related titles: Diskette ed.; Magnetic Tape ed.
Published by: Harris InfoSource International, 2057 2 E Aurora Rd, Twinsburg, OH 44087-1999. TEL 216-425-9000, 800-888-5900, FAX 216-425-7150, catknapp@aol.com, http://www.harrisinfo.com. **Dist. by:** Manufacturers' News, Inc., 1633 Central St, Evanston, IL 60201. TEL 847-864-7000.

670.29 USA ISSN 0889-0390
T12
GEORGE D. HALL'S DIRECTORY OF CENTRAL ATLANTIC STATES MANUFACTURERS; Maryland, Delaware, Virginia, West Virginia, North Carolina, South Carolina. Text in English. every 18 mos. USD 83. **Document type:** *Directory.* **Description:** Profiles over 14,000 manufacturers in Maryland, Delaware, Virginia, West Virginia, and North and South Carolina; includes alphabetical, geographical, and product sections.
Published by: Harris InfoSource International, 2057 2 E Aurora Rd, Twinsburg, OH 44087-1999. TEL 216-425-9000, 800-888-5900, FAX 216-425-7150, catknapp@aol.com, http://www.harrisinfo.com. **Dist. by:** Manufacturers' News, Inc., 1633 Central St, Evanston, IL 60201. TEL 847-864-7000.

670.29 USA ISSN 0196-8270
HD9727.C8
GEORGE D. HALL'S DIRECTORY OF CONNECTICUT MANUFACTURERS. Text in English. every 18 mos. USD 60. **Document type:** *Directory.* **Description:** Profiles over 6,500 manufacturers; includes alphabetical, geographical and product sections.
Published by: Harris InfoSource International, 2057 2 E Aurora Rd, Twinsburg, OH 44087-1999. TEL 216-425-9000, 800-888-5900, FAX 216-425-7150, catknapp@aol.com, http://www.harrisinfo.com. **Dist. by:** Manufacturers' News, Inc., 1633 Central St, Evanston, IL 60201. TEL 847-864-7000.

670.29 USA ISSN 0149-6913
HD9727.M4
GEORGE D. HALL'S DIRECTORY OF MASSACHUSETTS MANUFACTURERS. Text in English. a. USD 60. **Document type:** *Directory.* **Description:** Profiles over 8,000 manufacturers listed alphabetically, geographically, and by product.
Published by: Harris InfoSource International, 2057 2 E Aurora Rd, Twinsburg, OH 44087-1999. TEL 216-425-9000, 800-888-5900, FAX 216-425-7150, catknapp@aol.com, http://www.harrisinfo.com. **Dist. by:** Manufacturers' News, Inc., 1633 Central St, Evanston, IL 60201. TEL 847-864-7000.

670.29 USA ISSN 0892-8282
HD9727.N8
GEORGE D. HALL'S DIRECTORY OF NORTH CAROLINA MANUFACTURERS. Text in English. irreg., latest 1990. USD 49. **Document type:** *Directory.* **Description:** Profiles over 5,700 manufacturers; includes alphabetical, geographical, and product sections.
Published by: Harris InfoSource International, 2057 2 E Aurora Rd, Twinsburg, OH 44087-1999. TEL 216-425-9000, 800-888-5900, FAX 216-425-7150, catknapp@aol.com, http://www.harrisinfo.com. **Dist. by:** Manufacturers' News, Inc., 1633 Central St, Evanston, IL 60201. TEL 847-864-7000.

670.29 USA ISSN 0196-7185
HD9981.7.M4
GEORGE D. HALL'S MASSACHUSETTS SERVICE DIRECTORY. Text in English. a. USD 68. **Document type:** *Directory.* **Description:** Provides information on about 11,800 service-oriented companies; includes alphabetical, geographical and service by SIC sections.
Published by: Harris InfoSource International, 2057 2 E Aurora Rd, Twinsburg, OH 44087-1999. TEL 216-425-9000, 800-888-5900, FAX 216-425-7150, catknapp@aol.com, http://www.harrisinfo.com. **Dist. by:** Manufacturers' News, Inc., 1633 Central St, Evanston, IL 60201. TEL 847-864-7000.

380.1029 USA
GEORGIA BUSINESS CREDIT DIRECTORY. Text in English. a. USD 1,100 combined subscription print, online & CD-ROM eds. (effective 2004 & 2005). back issues avail. **Document type:** *Directory.* **Description:** Contains credit ratings and other valuable information on all businesses within Georgia. Includes company name & address, phone & fax numbers, key executive names & titles, lines of business, years in business, number of employees, estimated annual sales, volume credit rating code, and corporate linkage information.
Related titles: CD-ROM ed.; Diskette ed.; E-mail ed.; Fax ed.; Magnetic Tape ed.; Online - full text ed.
Published by: American Business Directories (Subsidiary of: American Business Information, Inc.), 5711 S 86th Circle, P O Box 27347, Omaha, NE 68127. TEL 402-593-4600, 888-946-9377, 877-708-3844, FAX 402-331-5481, sales@directoriesusa.com, http://www.directoriesusa.com.

338.0029 USA ISSN 1048-7220
HF5065.G4
GEORGIA BUSINESS DIRECTORY. Text in English. 1988. a. USD 1,100 combined subscription print, online & CD-ROM eds. (effective 2004 & 2005). index. back issues avail.
Document type: *Directory.* **Description:** Includes all businesses in the state compiled from the yellow pages and telephone-verified. Each listing includes company name, complete address, phone number, name of owner, manager, and employee size and sales volume codes and credit rating codes.
Related titles: CD-ROM ed.; Diskette ed.; E-mail ed.; Fax ed.; Magnetic Tape ed.; Online - full text ed.
Published by: American Business Directories (Subsidiary of: American Business Information, Inc.), 5711 S 86th Circle, P O Box 27347, Omaha, NE 68127. TEL 402-593-4600, 888-946-9377, 877-708-3844, FAX 402-331-5481, karen.peters@infousa.com, sales@directoriesusa.com, http://www.directoriesusa.com.

670.29 USA ISSN 0896-4009
HD9727.G4
GEORGIA MANUFACTURERS REGISTER. Text in English. a. USD 111 (effective 2001). adv. **Document type:** *Directory.*
Description: Profiles 11,362 manufacturers listed in product, alphabetical, geographical, SIC and by parent company.
Related titles: CD-ROM ed.: USD 535 (effective 2001); Diskette ed.: USD 545.
Published by: Manufacturers' News, Inc., 1633 Central St, Evanston, IL 60201. TEL 847-864-7000, 888-752-5200, FAX 847-332-1100, info@mninfo.com, info@manufacturersnews.com, sales@mninfo.com, http://www.manufacturersnews.com. Ed. Frank Lambing. Adv. contact Charles Scherer.

670.29 USA ISSN 0435-5482
HC107.G4
GEORGIA MANUFACTURING DIRECTORY. Text in English. a. USD 55. **Document type:** *Directory.*
Published by: Department of Industry, Trade and Tourism, Marquis II Tower, Ste 1100, 285 Peachtree Center Ave, Box 1776, Atlanta, GA 30301. TEL 404-656-3607, FAX 404-656-3567, TELEX 211988 GAINTL ATL. Ed. Deborah Battle. Circ: 3,500.

GERMAN-THAI CHAMBER OF COMMERCE HANDBOOK AND DIRECTORY. see *BUSINESS AND ECONOMICS—Chamber Of Commerce Publications*

GERMANY'S TOP 500; a handbook of Germany's largest corporations. see *BUSINESS AND ECONOMICS—Banking And Finance*

GHANA NATIONAL CHAMBER OF COMMERCE. BUSINESS DIRECTORY. see *BUSINESS AND ECONOMICS—Chamber Of Commerce Publications*

338.0029 USA ISSN 1099-8349
GIFT BASKET PRODUCTS GUIDE. Text in English. 1998. a. USD 30 (effective 2000). **Document type:** *Directory.*
Description: Lists over 300 manufacturers and distributors of gift basket products located throughout the U.S.
Published by: Sweet Survival, PO Box 31, River Street Sta, Paterson, NJ 07544-0031. TEL 973-742-0700, FAX 973-742-0700, survival@sweetsurvival.com, http://www.sweetsurvival.com. Ed., Pub., R&P, Adv. contact Shirley Frazier. Circ: 928 (paid).

380.1029 TWN
GIFTS & HOUSEWARES BUYERS' GUIDE. Text in English. 1980. a. USD 30 (effective 2001). adv. **Document type:** *Directory.* **Description:** Covers giftware products and housewares produced in Taiwan.
Formerly: Taiwan Gifts & Housewares Buyers' Guide (1024-8951)
Published by: Interface Global Taiwan Co., Ltd., PO Box 173-12, Taipei, 116, Taiwan. TEL 886-2-2393-2718, FAX 886-2-2395-2901, tradwind@ms2.hinet.net, service@asiatrademart.com, http://www.giftwareb2b.com, http://www.asiatrademart.com. Ed. Daniel Foong. Pub. Herbert Chen. R&P Donald Shapiro. Adv. contact Melody Lin TEL 886-2-2351-3180. Circ: 8,000. **Subscr. in U.S. to:** Trade Winds Inc., PO Box 820519, Dallas, TX 75382. TEL 877-861-1188, FAX 972-699-1189, twinds8888@aol.com.

666.1029 GBR
GLASS AGE DIRECTORY. Text in English. 1986. a. GBP 55 (effective 2000). adv. back issues avail. **Document type:** *Directory, Trade.*
Published by: C M P Information Ltd. (Subsidiary of: United Business Media), City Reach, 5 Greenwich View Pl, Millharbour, London, E14 9NN, United Kingdom. TEL 44-20-7861-6137, FAX 44-20-7861-6552, enquiries@cmpinformation.com, http://www.cmpinformation.com. Ed. Richard Schwarz. Pub. Bob Andrew. Adv. contact Dave Broxton. Circ: 8,000.

666.1029 USA ISSN 1057-5405
TP847
GLASS FACTORY DIRECTORY OF NORTH AMERICA AND U.S. INDUSTRY FACTBOOK. Text in English. 1912. a. USD 30 print ed.; USD 100 CD-ROM or floppy disk eds. (effective 2005). adv. charts; illus.; mkt. **Document type:** *Directory, Corporate.* **Description:** Lists glass factories in the US, Canada, and Mexico, with information on personnel, equipment, and product lines.
Former titles: Glass News Directory; Glass News (0890-3743); (until 1985): National Glass Budget (0027-9390)
Related titles: CD-ROM ed.; Diskette ed.
Indexed: ChemAb, PROMT.
—Linda Hall.
Published by: (National Glass Budget), L J V, Inc., PO Box 2267, Hempstead, NY 11551-2267. TEL 516-481-2188, manager@glassfactorydir.com, http://www.glassfactorydir.com. Ed., R&P Liz Scott. Adv. contact Liiz Scott. Circ: 1,000 (paid).

363.8029 USA ISSN 1529-1189
GLOBAL FOODSERVICE. Text in English. bi-m. adv.
Related titles: Spanish ed.: Global Foodservice en Espanol.
Published by: Keller International Publishing Corp., 150 Great Neck Rd, Great Neck, NY 11021. TEL 516-829-9210, FAX 516-824-5414, http://www.kellerpubs.com. Circ: 20,095.

338.0029 GBR
GLOBAL MARKET SHARE PLANNER. Text in English. 2000. irreg. (in 6 vols.), latest 2002. GBP 3,675 domestic; EUR 5,900 in Europe; USD 5,900 elsewhere (effective Jul. 2002); Includes: Major Market Share Tracker (vol.1), Major Performance Rankings (vol.2), World Leading Global Brand Owners (vol.3), Major Market Share Companies: Americas (vol.4), Major Market Share Companies: Europe (vol.5), and Major Market Share Companies: Asia-Pacific (vol.6).
Document type: *Directory, Trade.* **Description:** Contains information on the performance, activities and positioning of the top national and international consumer brand owning companies.
Related titles: ♦ Series: Major Market Share Companies: Asia Pacific; ♦ Major Market Share Companies: Europe & South Africa; ♦ Major Market Share Companies: The Americas; ♦ Major Performance Rankings; ♦ Market Share Tracker; ♦ World Leading Global Brand Owners.
Published by: Euromonitor, 60-61 Britton St, London, EC1 5UX, United Kingdom. TEL 44-20-7251-8024, FAX 44-20-7608-3149, info@euromonitor.com, http://www.euromonitor.com.

381.029 USA
GOLD BOOK MEMBERSHIP DIRECTORY & BUYER'S GUIDE. Text in English. s-a. USD 95 to non-members (effective 2001); free to members. **Document type:** *Directory.* **Description:** Lists location of members: meat businesses, products and suppliers.
Former titles: American Association of Meat Processors. Gold Book Members; American Association of Meat Processors. Directory of Suppliers and Wholesalers
Published by: American Association of Meat Processors, PO Box 269, Elizabethtown, PA 17022. TEL 717-367-1168, FAX 717-367-9096, aamp@aamp.com, http://www.aamp.com. Ed. Debbie B Sinex. Circ: 2,300.

GOLDEN STATES FINANCIAL DIRECTORY. see *BUSINESS AND ECONOMICS—Banking And Finance*

GOLF COURSE BUILDERS ASSOCIATION OF AMERICA. DIRECTORY. see *BUILDING AND CONSTRUCTION*

GOLF'S YELLOW PAGE DIRECTORY. see *SPORTS AND GAMES—Ball Games*

GOVERNMENT OPPORTUNITIES. see *PUBLIC ADMINISTRATION*

338.0029 USA
HD3861.U6
GOVERNMENT PRIME CONTRACTORS DIRECTORY. Text in English. 1966. a. USD 89.50 (effective 2004). **Document type:** *Directory, Trade.*
Former titles: Government Production Prime Contractors Directory (0887-4107); Directory of Government Production Prime Contractors (0070-5594)
Published by: Government Data Publications, Inc., 2300 M St, N W, Washington, DC 20037. TEL 800-275-4688, FAX 718-998-5960, gdp@govdata.com, http://www.govdata.com. Ed. Siegfried Lobel.

658.0029 USA ISSN 0072-520X
JK3
GOVERNMENTAL RESEARCH ASSOCIATION DIRECTORY; directory of organizations and individuals professionally engaged in governmental research and related activities. Text in English. 1938. a. USD 75 (effective 2000). index.
Document type: *Directory, Trade.*
—CISTI.
Published by: Governmental Research Association, Inc., 402 Samford Hall, Samford University, Birmingham, AL 35229-7017. TEL 205-726-2482. Circ: 700.

GRAIN & MILLING ANNUAL. see *AGRICULTURE—Feed, Flour And Grain*

382.029 338.1 USA ISSN 1076-3929
HD9030.1
GRAIN: WORLD MARKETS AND TRADE. Text in English. 1994. m.
Formed by the merger of (1987-1993): World Grain Situation and Outlook (0898-3399); (1987-1993): Export Markets for U.S. Grain and Products (0896-0216)
Related titles: Online - full text ed.: (from Gale Group).
Published by: U.S. Department of Agriculture, Economic Research Service, Foreign Agricultural Trade of the United States, 1800 M Street NW, Washington, DC 20036-5831. TEL 202-694-5110.

GRAPHIC ARTS BLUE BOOK. DELAWARE VALLEY - OHIO EDITION; directory of graphic arts operating firms and suppliers in Ohio, Pennsylvania, Delaware, Maryland, District of Columbia, and its Virginia suburbs. see *PRINTING*

GRAPHIC ARTS BLUE BOOK. METRO NEW YORK - NEW JERSEY EDITION; directory of graphic arts operating firms and suppliers in metropolitan New York and New Jersey. see *PRINTING*

GRAPHIC ARTS BLUE BOOK. MIDWESTERN EDITION; directory of graphic arts operating firms and suppliers in Illinois, Indiana, Michigan, Wisconsin, Iowa, Minnesota and North and South Dakota. see *PRINTING*

GRAPHIC ARTS BLUE BOOK. NORTHEASTERN EDITION; directory of graphic arts operating firms and suppliers in New England and upstate New York and the Eastern Provinces of Canada. see *PRINTING*

GRAPHIC ARTS BLUE BOOK. PACIFIC NORTHWESTERN EDITION. see *PRINTING*

GRAPHIC ARTS BLUE BOOK. SOUTHERN CALIFORNIA - SOUTHWESTERN EDITION; directory of graphic arts operating firms and suppliers in southern California, Arizona, southern Nevada, and Hawaii. see *PRINTING*

GRAPHIC ARTS BLUE BOOK. TEXAS - CENTRAL EDITION; directory of firms operating equipment graphic arts and suppliers in Texas, New Mexico, Colorado, Kansas, Nebraska, Oklahoma, Louisiana, Arkansas, and Missisuri. see *PRINTING*

GREAT YARMOUTH PORT AND INDUSTRY HANDBOOK. see *TRANSPORTATION—Ships And Shipping*

338.0029 USA
GREATER BATON ROUGE MANUFACTURERS DIRECTORY. Text in English. biennial. USD 25. **Document type:** *Directory.*
Published by: The Chamber of Greater Baton Rouge, 564 Laurel St, Box 3217, Baton Rouge, LA 70821. TEL 504-381-7125. Circ: 5,000.

381.029 USA
GREATER ORLANDO CHAMBER OF COMMERCE MEMBERSHIP DIRECTORY. Text in English. a. USD 15.
Published by: Greater Orlando Chamber of Commerce, PO Box 1234, Orlando, FL 32802. TEL 407-425-1234, FAX 407-839-5020.

387.029 USA
GREATER WASHINGTON - MARYLAND SERVICE STATION AND AUTOMOTIVE REPAIR ASSOCIATION. MEMBERSHIP DIRECTORY & BUYER'S GUIDE. Text in English. 1985. a. **Document type:** *Directory.*
Published by: Greater Washington - Maryland Service Station & Automotive Repair Association, 9420 Annapolis Rd, Ste 307, Lanham, MD 20706-3021. TEL 301-577-2875. Circ: 7,000.

382.029 EGY
THE GREEN BUSINESS GUIDE. Text in English, Arabic. 1981. a. USD 169 (effective 2002). **Document type:** *Directory.*
Description: Features legal & economic information, general & practical information, law, regulations, Egypt's general & economic statistics, general & administrative information, services, industrial, agricultural and trade companies, import - export companies, free zones and industrial zones.
Published by: I T C C O, 22 El Gaber St., From Nasr El Sawra St, Madkoor, Pyramids, Giza, Egypt. TEL 202-585-4450, 202-585-6958, FAX 202-585-4450, ittco@link.com.eg, http://www.green.guide.online.fr/. R&P Dr. Maher Abdel Hady.
Dist. by: Current Pacific Ltd., PO Box 36-536, Northcote, Auckland, New Zealand. TEL 64-9-480-1388, FAX 64-9-480-1387, info@cplnz.com, http://www.cplnz.com.

631.8029 USA
GREEN MARKETS WORLD DIRECTORY OF THE FERTILIZER INDUSTRY. Text in English. a. USD 135; USD 150 foreign (effective 1999). **Document type:** *Directory.* **Description:** Comprehensive information for purchasing or marketing fertilizer worldwide, including names and addresses of organizations, management personnel, production capacities, fertilizer and related products produced and purchased.
Published by: Pike & Fischer, Inc. (Subsidiary of: The Bureau of National Affairs, Inc.), 1010 Wayne Ave, Ste 1400, Silver Spring, MD 20910. TEL 301-562-1530, FAX 301-562-1521.

▼ new title ➤ refereed ✶ unverified ♦ full entry avail.

380.1029 DNK ISSN 0901-6201
HC351
GREENS; haandbogen om dansk erhvervsliv. Text in Danish. 1884. a. DKK 3,996 (effective 1999). **Document type:** *Directory.*
Address: Falkoner Alle 1-4, Frederiksberg, 2000, Denmark. TEL 45-38-16-97-60. Ed., Pub. Steen Hansen. Circ: 3,000.

658.0029 DEU
GRIEPHAN BERLIN KONTAKT; Informationen zum Geschaeft mit dem Staat. Text in German. a. EUR 314.58 (effective 2005). **Document type:** *Directory, Trade.*
Published by: Griephan Verlag GmbH und Co. KG, Nordkanalstr 36, Hamburg, 20097, Germany. TEL 49-40-2371404, FAX 49-40-23714259, info@griephan.de, http://www.griephan.de/de/katalog/zeitschrift_ausgabe.php?objektkode=gri&id=30. Ed. Heinz Schulte.

338.0029 DEU ISSN 1436-9893
DIE GROSSEN 500. Text in German. 1976. a. looseleaf. EUR 15 (effective 2004). **Document type:** *Directory, Trade.*
Related titles: CD-ROM ed.: EUR 99 (effective 2003).
Published by: Hermann Luchterhand Verlag GmbH (Subsidiary of: Wolters Kluwer Deutschland GmbH), Heddesdorfer Str 31, Neuwied, 56564, Germany. TEL 49-2631-8012222, FAX 49-2631-8012223, info@luchterhand.de, http://www.luchterhand.de. Ed. Ernst Schmacke.

338.0029 DEU
GROSSUNTERNEHMEN DER TSCHECHISCHEN REPUBLIK. Text in English, German. 1994. a. EUR 761.83. **Document type:** *Directory.* **Description:** Provides information on 11,000 major companies in the Czech Republic.
Media: CD-ROM.
Published by: Hoppenstedt Bonnier Zeitschriften GmbH, Havelstr. 9, Darmstadt, 64295, Germany. TEL 49-6151-380-0, FAX 49-6151-380-360. Circ: 12,000.

620.0029 GBR ISSN 0959-9959
TA715
GROUND ENGINEERING YEARBOOK. Text in English. 1990. a. GBP 66 domestic (effective 1999); GBP 81 foreign. adv. **Document type:** *Directory, Trade.* **Description:** Directory of addresses and information on suppliers of materials and machinery for geotechnical engineering. Including addresses for major contractors and geotechnical engineers mainly in UK and Europe.
Published by: Emap Construct Ltd. (Subsidiary of: Emap Business Communications Ltd.), 151 Rosebery Ave, London, EC1R 4GB, United Kingdom. TEL 44-20-7505-6600, FAX 44-20-7505-3535, http://www.emapconstruct.co.uk. Ed. Diane McKenzie. R&P Russell Blackmore. Adv. contact Sue Boyle.

380.1029 USA
GUIA; Chicagoland's Spanish Yellow Pages. Text in Spanish. 1980. a. free. **Description:** Contains over 800 classifications and cross references, display ads of local and national advertisers plus facts about Chicago, government offices information, lists of Latino services and advocacy organizations.
Published by: Cinco Estrellas Internacional, Inc., 5104 N. Ravenswood Ave., Chicago, IL 60640-2713. guia@chicagoguia.com, http://www.chicagoguia.com.

382.029 COL ISSN 0121-8018
GUIA DE COMERCIO EXTERIOR EXPORTADORES/GUIDE TO FOREIGN TRADE EXPORTERS. Text in Spanish. 1992. a. free. adv. **Document type:** *Directory.*
Published by: (Analdex), Publicar S.A., Ave. 68, 75-A-50 of. 314,, Apartado Aereo 8010, Santa Fe de Bogota, CUND, Colombia. TEL 57-1-222-5555 ext. 1665, FAX 57-1-3115645, colombiaexport@publicor.com, http://www.colombiaexport.com. R&P, Adv. contact Jaime Concha. page USD 3,500. Circ: 22,000.

686.2029 COL
GUIA DE LA COMUNICACION GRAFICA Y CREATIVA. Text in Spanish. 1992. a. free. adv.
Formerly: Guia del Sector Grafico (0121-7976)
Published by: Publicar S.A., Ave. 68, 75-A-50 of. 314,, Apartado Aereo 8010, Santa Fe de Bogota, CUND, Colombia. TEL 57-1-225-5555, FAX 57-1-3115645, colombiaexport@publicor.com, http://www.colombiaexport.com. R&P, Adv. contact Jaime Concha. page USD 2,400. Circ: 15,000.

015.46 ESP
GUIA DE LA DISTRIBUCION EN ESPANA; libros y publicaciones. Text in Spanish. 1981. a. USD 40. adv. **Document type:** *Directory.* **Description:** Lists distributors of books and periodicals in Spain.
Related titles: CD-ROM ed.: USD 100.
Published by: Federacion de Asociaciones Nacionales de Distribuidores de Ediciones, Santiago Rusinol, 8, Madrid, 28040, Spain. TEL 34-1-5335149, FAX 34-1-5531273.

GUIA DE LA INDUSTRIA ALIMENTARIA/MEXICAN FOOD & FEED INDUSTRY GUIDE. see *FOOD AND FOOD INDUSTRIES*

GUIA DE LA INDUSTRIA: EQUIPO Y APARATOS/PLANT AND LABORATORY EQUIPMENT GUIDE; para laboratorios y plantas. see *MACHINERY*

GUIA DE LA INDUSTRIA QUIMICA/MEXICAN CHEMICAL INDUSTRY GUIDE; productos quimicos-chemicals. see *ENGINEERING—Chemical Engineering*

381.029 PRY
GUIA DE LA INDUSTRIA: REPUBLICA DEL PARAGUAY. Text in Spanish. irreg., latest vol.2, 1983.
Published by: Editora Guia de la Industria, Alberdi, 454, Piso 1, Of. 10, Edif. Cardinal, Asuncion, Paraguay.

GUIA DEL ENVASE Y EMBALAJE/CONTAINER AND PACKAGING GUIDE. see *PACKAGING*

GUIA DOS EDITORES ASSOCIADOS. see *PUBLISHING AND BOOK TRADE*

666.029 ESP
GUIA GENERAL DE LAS INDUSTRIAS CERAMICAS Y AFINES DE ESPANA. Text in Spanish. a. **Document type:** *Directory.*
Formerly: Guia General de las Industrias Azulejeras y Auxiliares de Espana
Published by: Faenza Editrice Iberica S.L., Pol. Ind Sur Nave 39, Castellon, 12006, Spain. TEL 34-964-216570, FAX 34-964-241010, info@faenza.es.

670.29 MEX
GUIA INDUSTRIAL MEXICANA. Text in Spanish. 1967. s-a. **Document type:** *Directory.*
Address: Augustan Melgar, No. 44-5, Mexico, Condesa, Mexico City, DF 06140, Mexico. Ed. Jose Flores Sedano. Circ: 10,000.

623.87029 VEN ISSN 1315-5792
GUIA MARITIMA, PORTUARIA Y DE LA INDUSTRIA NAVAL DE VENEZUELA/MARITIME, PORT AND NAVAL INDUSTRY GUIDE OF VENEZUELA. Text in English, Spanish. a. VEB 10,000 (effective 1998). adv. **Document type:** *Directory.*
Formerly: Derrotero de los Puertos y Costas de Venezuela
Published by: Guia Maritima Portuaria y de la Industria Naval de Venezuela, Quinta Maria Teresa, Urbanizacion Vista Alegre, Calle 11, Vista Alegre, Caracas, DF 1020, Venezuela. TEL 58-02-4724885, FAX 58-02-4723711, ajguzman@etheron.net. Ed. Perdo J Guzman Quevedo. Adv. contact Enrique Andreiny Guzman. B&W page VEB 150,000, color page VEB 400,000.

381.029 PER
GUIA VERDE INDUSTRIAL Y COMERCIAL. Text in Spanish. 1994 (vol.53). a.
Published by: Sirob Ediciones, Urb. Corpac, Ave. Del Parque Norte, 299 Of 02 3o, San Isidro, Lima 27, Peru. TEL 51-14-422980.

659.1029 ITA ISSN 1123-4148
LA GUIDA AGENZIE. Text in Italian. 1990. a. price varies. **Document type:** *Directory, Trade.*
Published by: Marketing Finanza Italia s.r.l., Via Alessandro Stradella, 3, Milan, MI 20129, Italy. TEL 39-02-9400554, FAX 39-02-29401816, http://www.pubblicitaitalia.it. Ed. Lillo Perri. Circ: 4,500.

658.8029 ITA ISSN 1123-4156
GUIDA MARKETING. Text in Italian. 1990. a. price varies. **Document type:** *Directory, Trade.*
Published by: Marketing Finanza Italia s.r.l., Via Alessandro Stradella, 3, Milan, MI 20129, Italy. TEL 39-02-9400554, FAX 39-02-29401816, http://www.pubblicitaitalia.it. Ed. Lillo Perri. Circ: 4,500.

338.0029 TUN ISSN 0330-9290
GUIDE ECONOMIQUE DE LA TUNISIE. Text in French. 1976. a. USD 150 (effective 2000). illus. **Document type:** *Directory.* **Description:** Covers all aspects of the Tunisian economy, including government ministries, commercial legislation, the banking system, and detailed information on more than 8,000 Tunisian companies.
Indexed: PAIS.
Published by: Societe I E A, 16 rue de Rome, Tunis, 1015, Tunisia. TEL 216-1-347441, FAX 216-1-353172, iea@planet.tn.

674.142029 USA
GUIDE FOR BUYERS OF QUALITY HARDWOODS✱. Text in English. 1960. a. free.
Published by: Hardwood Manufacturers Association, 400 Penn Center Blvd, Ste 530, Pittsburgh, PA 15235-5605. Ed. Susan M Regan. Circ: 10,000.

668.55029 FRA ISSN 1766-2826
GUIDE INTERNATIONAL DES FOURNISSEURS DE LA BEAUTE/GENERAL DIRECTORY OF THE PERFUME AND COSMETIC INDUSTRY. Text in English, French. 1948. biennial. adv. index in English and French. **Document type:** *Directory.*
Incorporates in part: Guide International de la Parfumerie (0072-7989)
Published by: Editions Publi-Guid, 195 quai de la Gourdine, Lagny, 77400, France. FAX 33-1-64-02-48-81. Ed. Gilbert Hieblot. Circ: 3,000.

GUIDE OF CONSUMER GOODS IN GREECE/ODEGOS PROIONTON EUREIAS KATANALOSEOS. see *BUSINESS AND ECONOMICS—Marketing And Purchasing*

GUIDE STRATEGIES MULTIMEDIA. see *ADVERTISING AND PUBLIC RELATIONS*

GUIDE TO ELECTRONICS INDUSTRY IN INDIA. see *ELECTRONICS*

338.002 COL
GUIDE TO FOREIGN TRADE: COLOMBIAN EXPORTERS. Text and summaries in English, Spanish. 1968. a., latest vol.30, 1999. free for importers. adv. stat.; tr.lit. **Document type:** *Directory.* **Description:** Colombian exporters directory. Includes more than 3,000 Colombian companies providing products and services.
Media: Diskette.
Published by: Publicar S.A., Ave. 68, 75-A-50 of. 314,, Apartado Aereo 8010, Santa Fe de Bogota, CUND, Colombia. TEL 57-1-225-5555, FAX 57-1-3115645, colombiaexport@publicor.com, http://www.colombiaexport.com. Circ: 17,500.

338.0029 OMN
GUIDE TO INDUSTRY (SULTANATE OF OMAN). Text in English, Arabic. 1981. a. USD 50 (effective 2000). adv. stat.; tr.lit. back issues avail. **Document type:** *Directory, Trade.* **Description:** Covers the expanding manufacturing sector in Oman.
Published by: Apex Publishing, Ruwi, P O Box 2616, Muscat, 112, Oman. TEL 968-799388, FAX 968-793316, apexoman@gto.net.om. Ed. Brent D McKean. Pub. Saleh al Zakwani. Circ: 30,000.

380.1029 USA
GUIDE TO KEY BRITISH ENTERPRISES I AND II. Text in English. a. **Document type:** *Directory.*
Formerly: British Middle Market Directory (0068-2268)
Published by: Dun's Marketing Services (Subsidiary of: Dun & Bradstreet, Inc.), 3 Sylvan Way, Parsippany, NJ 07054-3896. TEL 201-455-0900.

380.1029 576.5 USA
GUIDE TO STEM CELL COMPANIES. Text in English. a. USD 179 per issue (effective 2003). 188 p./no.; **Document type:** *Directory, Trade.* **Description:** Contains listings of 61 companies currently conducting stem cell research. Including complete contact information, senior management, corporate mission, research focus, recent financial reports, and recent news.
Media: E-mail.
Published by: DataTrends Publications, Inc., PO Box 4460, Leesburg, VA 20177-8541. TEL 703-779-0574, FAX 703-779-2267, info@datatrendspublications.com, http://www.datatrendspublications.com/Company_Guide.htm, http://www.datatrendspublications.com/default.htm.

332.6029 CAN ISSN 0827-0864
HG2701
GUIDE TO THE CANADIAN FINANCIAL SERVICES INDUSTRY. Text in English. a. CND 349.95. **Document type:** *Directory.* **Description:** Provides essential facts and figures on over 900 financial services industries.
Related titles: Online - full text ed.
Published by: Globe Information Services, 444 Front St W, Toronto, ON M5V 2S9, Canada. TEL 416-585-5250, FAX 416-585-5249. Ed. Alan Husdal. Pub. Michael J Ryan.

665.5029 USA ISSN 0739-3547
HD9567.A13
GULF COAST OIL DIRECTORY. Text in English. 1952. a. USD 65. adv. back issues avail. **Document type:** *Directory.* **Description:** Contains listings of oil related companies within the 5 state Gulf Coast area, plus listings of PEMEX offices and personnel within Mexico.
Related titles: Diskette ed.
Published by: Atlantic Communications, 1635 W Alabama, Houston, TX 77006. TEL 713-529-1616, FAX 713-529-0936. Ed. Janis Johnson. Pub. Shawn Wymes. Adv. contact Rob Garza. Circ: 9,500.

338.0029 BHR
GULF DIRECTORY. Text in English. 1977. a. BHD 15, USD 85 (effective 2000). adv. **Document type:** *Directory.* **Description:** Reference for businesses in the Gulf region, covering virtually every commercial, industrial, and service company in the six gulf states, including importers and manufacturers agents, and other commercial data.
Formerly: Gulf Telephone Directory
Published by: Tele-Gulf Directory Publications W L L, Bahrain Tower 3rd Fl., PO Box 2738, Manama, Bahrain. TEL 973-213301, FAX 973-210503. Ed. Manuel Fernandes. Adv. contact Caroline Vailshery. B&W page USD 4,100, color page USD 7,049; trim 188 x 260. Circ: 43,000.

690.029   USA   ISSN 1056-3105
HG4235.53.Z65
GULF RECONSTRUCTION BUSINESS GUIDE∗ . Text in English. 1990. bi-m.
Published by: MacQueen & Associates, 316 Saint Peters Church Rd, Chapin, SC 29036-9363.

380.1029   USA
▼ **THE GULF STATE MARINE DIRECTORY.** Text in English. 2004. a. free. adv. **Document type:** *Directory, Trade.* **Description:** Yellow pages for the commercial marine industry in the gulf states.
Published by: Davison Publishing Co., Inc., 3452 Lake Lynda Dr, Ste 363, Orlando, FL 32817. TEL 407-380-8900, FAX 407-380-5222, info@davisonpublishing.com, http://www.davisonpublishing.com. adv.: color page USD 2,232;.

382.029   GBR
GUYANA TRADE DIRECTORY. Text in English. 1981. a. GBP 1. **Document type:** *Directory.*
Published by: Arthur H. Thrower Ltd., 44-46 S Ealing Rd, London, W5, United Kingdom.

H C B INTERNATIONAL DRUM AND I B C GUIDE. (Hazardous Cargo Bulletin) see *PACKAGING*

H I D A MANUFACTURERS DIRECTORY. see *MEDICAL SCIENCES*

362.1   USA   ISSN 0887-4484
RA413.5.U5
H M O - P P O DIRECTORY. (Health Maintenance Organization - Preferred Provider Organization) Text in English. 1986. a. USD 600 combined subscription print & online eds. (effective 2003). **Document type:** *Directory, Trade.* **Description:** Provides comprehensive information on over 1,600 health maintenance and preferred provider organizations arranged alphabetically.
Related titles: CD-ROM ed.; Online - full text ed.: USD 495 (effective 2003).
Published by: Grey House Publishing, 185 Millerton Rd, PO Box 860, Millerton, NY 12546. TEL 518-789-8700, 800-562-2139, FAX 518-789-0556, books@greyhouse.com, http://www.greyhouse.com. Ed. Laura Mars. Pub. Leslie E Mackenzie.

332.6029   GBR
HAMBROS DEALERS DIRECTORY (YEAR); foreign exchange treasury and bullion. Text in English. a. adv. **Document type:** *Directory.* **Description:** Lists banks which are reasonably active in quoting two way prices in the international foreign exchange market, the deposit market, or both. These dealers are members of the Association Cambiste Internationale.
Published by: Hambros, 41 Tower Hill, London, EC3N 4HA, United Kingdom. TEL 44-20-7676-7235, FAX 44-20-7265-0800. Ed., Pub., R&P, Adv. contact Ms. Andrea Nicolson.

HANDBUCH FUER DAS GESUNDHEITSWESEN IN SCHLESWIG-HOLSTEIN. see *MEDICAL SCIENCES*

HANDBUCH MILCH. see *AGRICULTURE—Dairying And Dairy Products*

380.1029   KOR   ISSN 0073-0335
HAPDONG YONGAM. Text in Korean. 1963. a.
Related titles: ◆ English ed.: Korea Annual. ISSN 1225-0147.
Published by: Yonhap News Agency, 85-1 Soosong-Dong, Chongro-ku, PO Box Kwangwhamoon 1039, Seoul, Korea, S.

380.1029   TWN
HARDWARE AND BUILDING MATERIAL BUYERS' GUIDE. Text in English. 1982. a. USD 30 (effective 2001). adv. **Document type:** *Directory, Catalog.* **Description:** Includes building materials, locks, tools, fasteners, and other hardware.
Formerly: Taiwan Hardware Buyers' Guide (1024-8986)
Published by: Interface Global Taiwan Co., Ltd., PO Box 173-12, Taipei, 116, Taiwan. TEL 886-2-2393-2718, FAX 886-2-2395-2901, tradwind@ms2.hinet.net, http://www.hardwareb2b.com, http://www.hardware-guide.com. Ed. Daniel Foong. Pub. Herbert Chen. R&P Donald Shapiro. Adv. contact Melody Lin TEL 886-2-2351-3180. Subscr. in U.S. to: Trade Winds Inc., PO Box 820519, Dallas, TX 75382. TEL 972-699-1188, FAX 972-699-1189, twinds8888@aol.com.

HARPERS GUIDE TO SPORTS TRADE. see *SPORTS AND GAMES*

380.1029   USA   ISSN 1538-4977
HD9981.7.A6
HARRIS ARIZONA SERVICES DIRECTORY. Text in English. 2002. a. USD 99 (effective 2005). **Document type:** *Directory, Trade.*
Published by: Harris InfoSource, 2057 E Aurora Rd, Twinsburg, OH 44087. TEL 800-888-5900, 330-425-9000, FAX 330-425-7150, http://www.harrisinfo.com. Ed. Frances L. Carlsen.

670.29   USA   ISSN 1080-2614
HF5065.C8
HARRIS CONNECTICUT MANUFACTURERS DIRECTORY. Text in English. 1995. a. USD 65. **Document type:** *Directory.*
Related titles: CD-ROM ed.: USD 349; Diskette ed.
Published by: Harris InfoSource International, 2057 2 E Aurora Rd, Twinsburg, OH 44087-1999. TEL 216-425-9000, 800-888-5900, FAX 800-643-5997, catknapp@aol.com. Ed. Frances L Carlsen.

380.1029   USA   ISSN 1536-5727
HD9981.7.C8
HARRIS CONNECTICUT SERVICES DIRECTORY. Text in English. 2002. a. USD 79 (effective 2005). **Document type:** *Directory, Trade.*
Published by: Harris InfoSource, 2057 E Aurora Rd, Twinsburg, OH 44087. TEL 800-888-5900, 330-425-9000, FAX 330-425-7150, http://www.harrisinfo.com. Ed. Frances L. Carlsen.

670.29   USA   ISSN 1080-2592
HARRIS DELAWARE MANUFACTURERS DIRECTORY. Text in English. 1995. a. USD 29. **Document type:** *Directory.*
Related titles: CD-ROM ed.: USD 149; Diskette ed.
Published by: Harris InfoSource, 2057 2 E Aurora Rd, Twinsburg, OH 44087-1999. TEL 216-425-9000, 800-888-5900, FAX 216-425-7150, catknapp@aol.com. Ed. Frances L Carlsen.

380.1029   USA   ISSN 1536-5603
HF5065.D3
HARRIS DIRECTORY OF DELAWARE BUSINESSES. Text in English. 2002. a. USD 99 (effective 2005). **Document type:** *Directory, Trade.*
Published by: Harris InfoSource, 2057 E Aurora Rd, Twinsburg, OH 44087. TEL 800-888-5900, 330-425-9000, FAX 330-425-7150, http://www.harrisinfo.com. Ed. Frances L. Carlsen.

380.1029   USA   ISSN 1538-3059
HF5065.K2
HARRIS DIRECTORY OF KANSAS BUSINESSES. Text in English. 2002. a. USD 129 (effective 2005). **Document type:** *Directory, Trade.*
Published by: Harris InfoSource, 2057 E Aurora Rd, Twinsburg, OH 44087. TEL 800-888-5900, 330-425-9000, FAX 330-425-7150, http://www.harrisinfo.com. Ed. Frances L. Carlsen.

380.1029   USA   ISSN 1536-5611
HF5065.M2
HARRIS DIRECTORY OF MAINE BUSINESSES. Text in English. 2002. a. USD 99 (effective 2005). **Document type:** *Directory, Trade.*
Published by: Harris InfoSource, 2057 E Aurora Rd, Twinsburg, OH 44087. TEL 800-888-5900, 330-425-9000, FAX 330-425-7150, http://www.harrisinfo.com. Ed. Frances L. Carlsen.

380.1029   USA   ISSN 1536-5689
HF5065.M9
HARRIS DIRECTORY OF MONTANA BUSINESSES. Text in English. 2002. a. USD 109 (effective 2005). **Document type:** *Directory, Trade.*
Published by: Harris InfoSource, 2057 E Aurora Rd, Twinsburg, OH 44087. TEL 800-888-5900, 330-425-9000, FAX 330-425-7150, http://www.harrisinfo.com. Ed. Frances L. Carlsen.

380.1029   USA   ISSN 1535-9190
HF5065.N3
HARRIS DIRECTORY OF NEVADA BUSINESSES. Text in English. 2002. a. USD 129 (effective 2005). **Document type:** *Directory, Trade.*
Published by: Harris InfoSource, 2057 E Aurora Rd, Twinsburg, OH 44087. TEL 800-888-5900, 330-425-9000, FAX 330-425-7150, http://www.harrisinfo.com. Ed. Frances L. Carlsen.

380.1029   USA   ISSN 1536-5638
HF5065.N4
HARRIS DIRECTORY OF NEW HAMPSHIRE BUSINESSES. Text in English. 2002. a. USD 99 (effective 2005). **Document type:** *Directory, Trade.*
Published by: Harris InfoSource, 2057 E Aurora Rd, Twinsburg, OH 44087. TEL 800-888-5900, 330-425-9000, FAX 330-425-7150, http://www.harrisinfo.com. Ed. Frances L. Carlsen.

380.1029   USA   ISSN 1536-5646
HF5065.N9
HARRIS DIRECTORY OF NORTH DAKOTA BUSINESSES. Text in English. 2002. a. USD 89 (effective 2005). **Document type:** *Directory, Trade.*
Published by: Harris InfoSource, 2057 E Aurora Rd, Twinsburg, OH 44087. TEL 800-888-5900, 330-425-9000, FAX 330-425-7150, http://www.harrisinfo.com. Ed. Frances L. Carlsen.

380.1029   USA   ISSN 1536-5654
HF5065.S8
HARRIS DIRECTORY OF SOUTH DAKOTA BUSINESSES. Text in English. 2002. a. USD 89 (effective 2005). **Document type:** *Directory, Trade.*
Published by: Harris InfoSource, 2057 E Aurora Rd, Twinsburg, OH 44087. TEL 800-888-5900, 330-425-9000, FAX 330-425-7150, http://www.harrisinfo.com. Ed. Frances L. Carlsen.

380.1029   USA   ISSN 1536-5662
HF5068.W3
HARRIS DIRECTORY OF WASHINGTON, D.C. BUSINESSES. Text in English. 2002. a. USD 89 (effective 2005). **Document type:** *Directory, Trade.*
Published by: Harris InfoSource, 2057 E Aurora Rd, Twinsburg, OH 44087. TEL 800-888-5900, 330-425-9000, FAX 330-425-7150, http://www.harrisinfo.com. Ed. Frances L. Carlsen.

380.1029   USA   ISSN 1532-3846
HARRIS FLORIDA SERVICES DIRECTORY. Text in English. 2001. a. USD 175 (effective 2005). **Document type:** *Directory, Trade.*
Published by: Harris InfoSource, 2057 E Aurora Rd, Twinsburg, OH 44087. TEL 800-888-5900, 330-425-9000, FAX 330-425-7150, http://www.harrisinfo.com.

670.29   USA   ISSN 1065-4755
HF5065.G4
HARRIS GEORGIA MANUFACTURERS DIRECTORY. Text in English. 1994. a. USD 89. **Document type:** *Directory.*
Related titles: CD-ROM ed.: USD 395; Diskette ed.
Published by: Harris InfoSource International, 2057 2 E Aurora Rd, Twinsburg, OH 44087-1999. TEL 216-425-9000, 800-888-5900, FAX 800-643-5997, catknapp@aol.com. Ed. Frances L Carlsen.

380.1029   USA   ISSN 1534-3650
HARRIS GEORGIA SERVICES DIRECTORY. Text in English. 2002. a. USD 159 (effective 2005). **Document type:** *Directory, Trade.*
Published by: Harris InfoSource, 2057 E Aurora Rd, Twinsburg, OH 44087. TEL 800-888-5900, 330-425-9000, FAX 330-425-7150, http://www.harrisinfo.com.

380.1029   USA   ISSN 1532-1606
HARRIS ILLINOIS BUSINESS SERVICE DIRECTORY. Text in English. 2001. a. USD 199 (effective 2005). **Document type:** *Directory, Trade.*
Published by: Harris InfoSource, 2057 E Aurora Rd, Twinsburg, OH 44087. TEL 800-888-5900, 330-425-9000, FAX 330-425-7150, http://www.harrisinfo.com.

381.029   USA   ISSN 1550-1973
HD9727.I3
HARRIS ILLINOIS INDUSTRIAL DIRECTORY (YEAR). Text in English. a. USD 154. **Document type:** *Directory.*
Former titles (until 2001): Illinois Industrial Directory (Year) (1550-1981); (until 2000): Harris Illinois Industrial Directory (Year); Harris Illinois Marketers Industrial Directory (0734-3256)
Related titles: CD-ROM ed.: USD 695; Diskette ed.: USD 695.
Published by: Harris InfoSource International, 2057 2 E Aurora Rd, Twinsburg, OH 44087-1999. TEL 216-425-9000, 800-888-5900, FAX 216-425-7150, catknapp@aol.com.

670.29   USA   ISSN 1549-5795
T12
HARRIS INDIANA INDUSTRIAL DIRECTORY (YEAR). Text in English. 1924. a. USD 99. **Document type:** *Directory.*
Former titles (until 2002): Indiana Industrial Directory (1549-5809); (until 2001): Harris Indiana Industrial Directory (0888-8175); (until 1984): Harris Indiana Marketers Industrial Directory (0734-855X); Indiana Industrial Directory (0073-6910)
Related titles: CD-ROM ed.: USD 549; Diskette ed.
Published by: Harris InfoSource International, 2057 2 E Aurora Rd, Twinsburg, OH 44087-1999. TEL 216-425-9000, 800-888-5900, FAX 216-425-7150, catknapp@aol.com. Ed. Frances L Carlsen.

380.1029   USA   ISSN 1532-1584
HARRIS INDIANA SERVICES DIRECTORY. Text in English. 2001. a. USD 159 (effective 2005). **Document type:** *Directory, Trade.*
Published by: Harris InfoSource, 2057 E Aurora Rd, Twinsburg, OH 44087. TEL 800-888-5900, 330-425-9000, FAX 330-425-7150, http://www.harrisinfo.com.

381.029   USA   ISSN 0887-4255
HD9727.K4
HARRIS KENTUCKY INDUSTRIAL DIRECTORY (YEAR). Text in English. a. USD 76. **Document type:** *Directory.*
Related titles: CD-ROM ed.: USD 325; Diskette ed.: USD 325.
Published by: Harris InfoSource International, 2057 2 E Aurora Rd, Twinsburg, OH 44087-1999. TEL 216-425-9000, 800-888-5900, FAX 216-425-7150, catknapp@aol.com.

B

380.1029 USA ISSN 1533-550X
HARRIS KENTUCKY MANUFACTURERS DIRECTORY. Text in English. 1998. a. USD 99 (effective 2005). **Document type:** *Directory, Trade.*
Formerly (until 2001): Harris Kentucky Directory of Manufacturers (1096-9470)
Published by: Harris InfoSource, 2057 E Aurora Rd, Twinsburg, OH 44087. TEL 800-888-5900, 330-425-9000, FAX 330-425-7150, http://www.harrisinfo.com.

380.1029 USA ISSN 1532-1592
HARRIS KENTUCKY SERVICES DIRECTORY. Text in English. 2001. a. USD 99 (effective 2005). **Document type:** *Directory, Trade.*
Published by: Harris InfoSource, 2057 E Aurora Rd, Twinsburg, OH 44087. TEL 800-888-5900, 330-425-9000, FAX 330-425-7150, http://www.harrisinfo.com.

670.29 USA ISSN 1065-7231
HF5065.M25
HARRIS MARYLAND MANUFACTURERS DIRECTORY (YEAR). Text in English. 1963. a. USD 65. **Document type:** *Directory.*
Former titles (until 1993): Harris Maryland Industrial Directory (1055-5617); (until 1990): Maryland Manufacturers Directory (1050-2718); (until 1989): Directory, Maryland Manufacturers (0070-5802)
Related titles: Diskette ed.: USD 325.
Published by: (Maryland. Department of Economic and Employment Development), Harris InfoSource International, 2057 2 E Aurora Rd, Twinsburg, OH 44087-1999. TEL 216-425-9000, 800-888-5900, FAX 216-425-7150, catknapp@aol.com.

670.29 USA ISSN 1078-6341
HF5065.M3
HARRIS MASSACHUSETTS MANUFACTURERS DIRECTORY. Text in English. 1995. a. USD 70. **Document type:** *Directory.*
Related titles: CD-ROM ed.: USD 395; Diskette ed.
Published by: Harris InfoSource International, 2057 2 E Aurora Rd, Twinsburg, OH 44087-1999. TEL 216-425-9000, 800-888-5900, FAX 216-425-7150, catknapp@aol.com. Ed. Frances L Carlsen.

380.1029 USA ISSN 1536-7452
HD9981.7.M4
HARRIS MASSACHUSETTS SERVICES DIRECTORY. Text in English. 2002. a. USD 139 (effective 2005). **Document type:** *Directory, Trade.*
Published by: Harris InfoSource, 2057 E Aurora Rd, Twinsburg, OH 44087. TEL 800-888-5900, 330-425-9000, FAX 330-425-7150, http://www.harrisinfo.com. Ed. Frances L. Carlsen.

670.29 USA ISSN 0888-8167
HD9727.M5
HARRIS MICHIGAN INDUSTRIAL DIRECTORY (YEAR). Text in English. 1974. a. USD 159. **Document type:** *Directory.*
Former titles: Harris Michigan Marketers Industrial Directory; Harris Michigan Manufacturers Industrial Directory (0363-1869)
Related titles: CD-ROM ed.; Diskette ed.: USD 725.
Published by: Harris InfoSource International, 2057 2 E Aurora Rd, Twinsburg, OH 44087-1999. TEL 330-425-9000, 800-888-5900, FAX 216-425-7150, KevinH@harisinfo.com, http://www.harrisinfo.com.

380.1029 USA ISSN 1532-1614
HARRIS MICHIGAN SERVICES DIRECTORY. Text in English. 2000. a. USD 175 (effective 2005). **Document type:** *Directory, Trade.*
Published by: Harris InfoSource, 2057 E Aurora Rd, Twinsburg, OH 44087. TEL 800-888-5900, 330-425-9000, FAX 330-425-7150, http://www.harrisinfo.com.

670.29 USA ISSN 1096-9489
T12
HARRIS MINNESOTA DIRECTORY OF MANUFACTURERS. Text in English. 1955. a. USD 139 (effective 2005). **Document type:** *Directory, Trade.*
Formerly (until 1998): Minnesota Directory of Manufacturers (0364-1570)
Published by: Harris InfoSource, 2057 E Aurora Rd, Twinsburg, OH 44087. TEL 800-888-5900, 330-425-9000, FAX 330-425-7150, http://www.harrisinfo.com. Circ: 3,500.

338.0029 USA ISSN 0895-2469
T12
HARRIS MISSOURI DIRECTORY OF MANUFACTURERS. Text in English. 1947. a. USD 99. **Document type:** *Directory.*
Formerly: Missouri Directory of Manufacturing and Mining (0076-9584)
Related titles: CD-ROM ed.: USD 549; Diskette ed.
Published by: Harris InfoSource International, 2057 2 E Aurora Rd, Twinsburg, OH 44087-1999. TEL 216-425-9000, 800-888-5900, FAX 216-425-7150, catknapp@aol.com.

670.29 USA ISSN 1061-2076
HF5035
HARRIS NATIONAL MANUFACTURERS DIRECTORY (YEAR). Text in English. 1993. a. USD 725 (effective 2005). **Document type:** *Directory, Trade.*
Related titles: CD-ROM ed.: USD 3,900; Diskette ed.
Published by: Harris InfoSource International, 2057 2 E Aurora Rd, Twinsburg, OH 44087-1999. TEL 216-425-9000, 800-888-5900, FAX 216-425-7150, catknapp@aol.com. Ed. Frances L Carlsen.

670.29 USA ISSN 1061-2025
HF5047
HARRIS NATIONAL MANUFACTURERS DIRECTORY. MIDWEST EDITION (YEAR). Text in English. 1993. a. USD 249 (effective 2005). **Document type:** *Directory, Trade.*
Related titles: CD-ROM ed.: USD 1,695; Diskette ed.: USD 1,695.
Published by: Harris InfoSource International, 2057 2 E Aurora Rd, Twinsburg, OH 44087-1999. TEL 216-425-9000, 800-888-5900, FAX 216-425-7150, catknapp@aol.com.

670.29 USA ISSN 1061-2041
HF5041
HARRIS NATIONAL MANUFACTURERS DIRECTORY. NORTHEAST EDITION (YEAR). Text in English. 1993. a. USD 249 (effective 2005). **Document type:** *Directory, Trade.*
Related titles: CD-ROM ed.: USD 1,295; Diskette ed.: USD 1,295.
Published by: Harris InfoSource International, 2057 2 E Aurora Rd, Twinsburg, OH 44087-1999. TEL 216-425-9000, 800-888-5900, FAX 216-425-7150, catknapp@aol.com.

670.29 USA ISSN 1061-2033
HF5044
HARRIS NATIONAL MANUFACTURERS DIRECTORY. SOUTHEAST EDITION (YEAR). Text in English. 1993. a. USD 249 (effective 2005). **Document type:** *Directory, Trade.*
Related titles: CD-ROM ed.: USD 1,195; Diskette ed.
Published by: Harris InfoSource International, 2057 2 E Aurora Rd, Twinsburg, OH 44087-1999. TEL 216-425-9000, 800-888-5900, FAX 216-425-7150, catknapp@aol.com.

670.29 USA ISSN 1080-3467
HF5041
HARRIS NEW ENGLAND MANUFACTURERS DIRECTORY. Text in English. 1995. a. USD 168. **Document type:** *Directory.*
Related titles: CD-ROM ed.: USD 895; Diskette ed.
Published by: Harris InfoSource International, 2057 2 E Aurora Rd, Twinsburg, OH 44087-1999. TEL 216-425-9000, 800-888-5900, FAX 216-425-7150, catknapp@aol.com. Ed. Frances L Carlsen.

670.29 USA ISSN 1551-742X
HF5065.N5
HARRIS NEW JERSEY MANUFACTURERS DIRECTORY. Text in English. 1995. a. USD 139 per issue (effective 2005). **Document type:** *Directory, Trade.* **Description:** Profiles over 11,400 manufacturers arranged alphabetically, geographically and by product sections.
Former titles (until 2005): Official New Jersey Manufacturers Directory (1086-6299); (until 1996): Harris New Jersey Manufacturers Directory (1078-6325); Which was formed by the merger of (19??-1995): George D. Hall's Directory of New Jersey Manufacturers (1069-5176); Which was formerly (until 1994): George D. Hall's New Jersey Manufacturers Directory (0278-9124); (1959-1995): MacRae's State Industrial Directory. New Jersey (0891-2629); Which was formerly (until 1985): MacRAE's Industrial Directory New Jersey (0739-8492); (until 1983): MacRAE's New Jersey State Industrial Directory (0733-3684); (until 1982): New Jersey State Industrial Directory (0098-6224)
Published by: Harris InfoSource International, 2057 2 E Aurora Rd, Twinsburg, OH 44087-1999. TEL 216-425-9000, 800-888-5900, FAX 216-425-7150, catknapp@aol.com, http://www.harrisinfo.com. **Dist. by:** Manufacturers' News, Inc., 1633 Central St, Evanston, IL 60201. TEL 847-864-7000.

380.1029 USA ISSN 1533-6964
HARRIS NORTH CAROLINA SERVICES DIRECTORY. Text in English. 2002. a. USD 159 (effective 2005). **Document type:** *Directory, Trade.*
Published by: Harris InfoSource, 2057 E Aurora Rd, Twinsburg, OH 44087. TEL 800-888-5900, 330-425-9000, FAX 330-425-7150, http://www.harrisinfo.com.

670.29 USA ISSN 0888-8140
HD9727.O3
HARRIS OHIO INDUSTRIAL DIRECTORY (YEAR). Text in English. 1918. a. USD 149. **Document type:** *Directory.*
Former titles: Harris Ohio Marketers Industrial Directory (0733-4664); Ohio Industrial Directory (0161-4878); Ohio Manufacturers Industrial Directory; Directory of Ohio Manufacturers (0070-5985)
Related titles: CD-ROM ed.: USD 695; Diskette ed.: USD 695.
Published by: Harris InfoSource International, 2057 2 E Aurora Rd, Twinsburg, OH 44087-1999. TEL 216-425-9000, 800-888-5900, FAX 216-425-7150, catknapp@aol.com.

382 USA ISSN 0734-8541
HC107.P4
HARRIS PENNSYLVANIA INDUSTRIAL DIRECTORY (YEAR). Text in English. 1913. a. USD 149. **Document type:** *Directory.*
Former titles (until 1982): Pennsylvania Industrial Directory; Harris Pennsylvania Marketing Directory; Industrial Directory of the Commonwealth of Pennsylvania
Related titles: Diskette ed.: USD 695.
Published by: Harris InfoSource International, 2057 2 E Aurora Rd, Twinsburg, OH 44087-1999. TEL 216-425-9000, 800-888-5900, FAX 216-425-7150, catknapp@aol.com.

670.29 USA ISSN 1078-6333
HF5065.R5
HARRIS RHODE ISLAND MANUFACTURERS DIRECTORY. Text in English. 1995. a. USD 49. **Document type:** *Directory.*
Related titles: CD-ROM ed.: USD 249; Diskette ed.
Published by: Harris Publishing Co. (Twinsburg), 2057 2 Aurora Rd, Twinsburg, OH 44087. TEL 216-425-9000, 800-888-5900, FAX 800-643-5997, catknapp@aol.com. Ed. Frances L Carlsen.

670.29 USA ISSN 1065-4747
HD9727.S6
HARRIS SOUTH CAROLINA MANUFACTURERS DIRECTORY. Text in English. 1994. a. USD 60. **Document type:** *Directory.*
Related titles: CD-ROM ed.: USD 299; Diskette ed.
Published by: Harris InfoSource International, 2057 2 E Aurora Rd, Twinsburg, OH 44087-1999. TEL 216-425-9000, 800-888-5900, FAX 216-425-7150, catknapp@aol.com. Ed. Frances L Carlsen.

380.1029 USA ISSN 1533-6948
HARRIS SOUTH CAROLINA SERVICES DIRECTORY. Text in English. 2002. a. USD 99 (effective 2005). **Document type:** *Directory, Trade.*
Published by: Harris InfoSource, 2057 E Aurora Rd, Twinsburg, OH 44087. TEL 800-888-5900, 330-425-9000, FAX 330-425-7150, http://www.harrisinfo.com.

380.1029 USA ISSN 1065-4739
HARRIS TENNESSEE MANUFACTURERS DIRECTORY. Text in English. 1998. a. USD 99 (effective 2005). **Document type:** *Directory, Trade.*
Published by: Harris InfoSource, 2057 E Aurora Rd, Twinsburg, OH 44087. TEL 800-888-5900, 330-425-9000, FAX 330-425-7150, http://www.harrisinfo.com.

670.29 USA ISSN 1076-5123
HF5065.T4
HARRIS TEXAS MANUFACTURERS DIRECTORY. Text in English. 1995. a. USD 135. **Document type:** *Directory.*
Related titles: CD-ROM ed.: USD 695; Diskette ed.
Published by: Harris InfoSource International, 2057 2 E Aurora Rd, Twinsburg, OH 44087-1999. TEL 216-425-9000, 800-888-5900, FAX 216-425-7150, catknapp@aol.com. Ed. Frances L Carlsen.

670.29 USA ISSN 1531-8311
HF5050
HARRIS U S MANUFACTURERS DIRECTORY. WEST EDITION. Text in English. a. USD 299 (effective 2005). **Document type:** *Directory, Trade.*
Former titles (until 2001): Harris Manufacturers Directory. West Edition (1526-9183); Harris National Manufacturers Directory (West and Southwest Edition) (1061-205X)
Media: Diskette.
Published by: Harris InfoSource International, 2057 2 E Aurora Rd, Twinsburg, OH 44087-1999. TEL 216-425-9000, 800-888-5900, FAX 216-425-7150, catknapp@aol.com.

380.1029 USA ISSN 1533-6972
HARRIS VIRGINIA SERVICES DIRECTORY. Text in English. 2001. a. USD 99 (effective 2005). **Document type:** *Directory, Trade.*
Published by: Harris InfoSource, 2057 E Aurora Rd, Twinsburg, OH 44087. TEL 800-888-5900, 330-425-9000, FAX 330-425-7150, http://www.harrisinfo.com.

670.29 USA ISSN 0887-4247
HD9727.W4
HARRIS WEST VIRGINIA MANUFACTURING DIRECTORY (YEAR). Text in English. 1980. a. USD 49. **Document type:** *Directory.*
Related titles: CD-ROM ed.: USD 249; Diskette ed.: USD 249.
Published by: Harris Publishing Co. (Twinsburg), 2057 2 Aurora Rd, Twinsburg, OH 44087. TEL 216-425-9000, 800-888-5900, FAX 216-425-7150, catknapp@aol.com.

HAVEN GENT. JAARBOEK/GHENT PORT ANNUAL/HAFEN VON GENT. JAHRBUCH/PORT DE GAND. ANNUAIRE. see *TRANSPORTATION—Ships And Shipping*

HAVENS ZEEBRUGGE EN OOSTENDE. JAARBOEK/HAVEN VON ZEEBRUGGE UND OSTENDE. JAHRBUCH/PORTS DE ZEEBRUGGE ET D'OSTENDE. ANNUAIRE/ZEEBRUGGE AND OSTEND PORTS. ANNUAL. see *TRANSPORTATION—Ships And Shipping*

338.0029 USA ISSN 1048-7107
HF5065.H3
HAWAII BUSINESS DIRECTORY. Text in English. 1990. a. USD 1,100 combined subscription print, online & CD-ROM eds. (effective 2004 & 2005). index. back issues avail. **Document type:** *Directory.* **Description:** Includes all businesses in the state. Each listing includes company name, complete address, name of owner, and employee size and sales volume codes and credit rating codes.
Related titles: CD-ROM ed.; Diskette ed.; E-mail ed.; Fax ed.; Magnetic Tape ed.; Online - full text ed.

Published by: American Business Directories (Subsidiary of: American Business Information, Inc.), 5711 S 86th Circle, P O Box 27347, Omaha, NE 68127. TEL 402-593-4600, 888-946-9377, 877-708-3844, FAX 402-331-5481, karen.peters@infousa.com, sales@directoriesusa.com, http://www.directoriesusa.com.

380.1029 USA
HAWAII BUYER'S GUIDE; an authoritative guide to industrial products and services in Hawaii. Text in English. a. **Document type:** *Directory.*
Published by: Pacific Basin Communications Inc., PO Box 913, Honolulu, HI 96808. TEL 808-946-3978. Ed. Jeff Barrus. Pub. Kim Jacobsen. R&P Ethel Murphy.

670.29 USA ISSN 1085-7451
HF5065.H3
HAWAII MANUFACTURERS DIRECTORY. Text in English. 1994. a. USD 58 (effective 2001). adv. 128 p./no.; **Document type:** *Directory.* **Description:** Profiles 1190 companies.
Supersedes in part (in 1996): Alaska - Hawaii Manufacturers Directory (1074-2468)
Related titles: CD-ROM ed.: USD 175 (effective 2000); Diskette ed.
Published by: Manufacturers' News, Inc., 1633 Central St, Evanston, IL 60201. TEL 847-864-7000, 888-752-5200, FAX 847-332-1100, info@mninfo.com, info@manufacturersnews.com, sales@mninfo.com, http://www.manufacturersnews.com. Ed. Steve Garland.

HAZARDOUS LOCATIONS EQUIPMENT. see *ENVIRONMENTAL STUDIES—Waste Management*

338.0029 USA ISSN 1531-2909
E154.5
HEADQUARTERS U S A. Text in English. 1977. a. (in 2 vols.), latest 2002, 24th ed. USD 175 (effective 2001). **Document type:** *Directory, Trade.* **Description:** Lists contact data for more than 139,000 verified listings for US and Canadian businesses, government offices, associations, educational institutions and other organizations. Includes e-mail and Internet addresses, toll-free and fax numbers, and complete mailing addresses and telephone numbers.
Former titles (until 2000): Business Phone Book U S A (1091-3955); (until 1997): National Directory of Addresses and Telephone Numbers (0740-7203)
Published by: Omnigraphics, Inc., 615 Griswold St, Detroit, MI 48226. TEL 313-961-1341, 800-234-1340, FAX 313-961-1383, 800-875-1340, info@omnigraphics.com, http://www.omnigraphics.com. Pub. Frederick G Ruffner Jr.

613.029 GBR
HEALTH & SAFETY MARKETGUIDE. Text in English; Summaries in French, German, Italian, Spanish. 1981. a. GBP 45 (effective 2001). adv. back issues avail. **Document type:** *Directory.*
Former titles (until Dec. 2000): European Health & Safety Marketguide (0962-385X); (until 1990): Health and Safety Marketguide (0261-8036)
Published by: Aydee Marketing Ltd., Nithsdale House, 159 Cambridge St, Aylesbury, Bucks HP20 1BQ, United Kingdom. TEL 44-1296-434381, FAX 44-1296-436936, info@aydee.com, http://www.aydee.com. Ed., Pub. Richard Salmon. Adv. contact Muriel Scutt. page GBP 1,195; trim 184 x 260. Circ: 6,000 (paid).

HEALTH DATA DIRECTORY. see *MEDICAL SCIENCES—Computer Applications*

HEALTHCARE FOODSERVICE WHO'S WHO. see *FOOD AND FOOD INDUSTRIES*

362.1 USA
HEALTHCARE GROUP PURCHASING ORGANIZATIONS. Text in English. a. USD 325; USD 650 print & online eds. (effective 2002). **Document type:** *Directory, Trade.* **Description:** Provides comprehensive information on over 550 group healthcare purchasing organizations.
Related titles: Online - full text ed.
Published by: Grey House Publishing, 185 Millerton Rd, PO Box 860, Millerton, NY 12546. TEL 518-789-8700, 800-562-2139, FAX 518-789-0556, books@greyhouse.com, http://www.greyhouse.com. Ed. Laura Mars. Pub. Leslie E Mackenzie.

380.1029 USA
HISPANIC YELLOW PAGES (ATLANTA)/PAGINAS AMARILLAS HISPANAS; la guia del hispano para el hispano. Text in Spanish. 1989. a. free. adv. **Document type:** *Directory.* **Description:** Includes Hispanic and non-Hispanic businesses and professionals in the Atlanta metro area.
Published by: Casablanca Publications, Inc., PO Box 191033, Atlanta, GA 31119-1033. TEL 404-321-5211, FAX 404-321-6612, info@paginasamarillas-atl.com, http://www.paginasamarillas-atl.com. Ed. Zaida Gonzalez. adv.: B&W page USD 1,350. Circ: 50,000.

380.1029 USA
HISPANIC YELLOW PAGES (FAIRFAX). Variant title: Paginas Amarillas. Text in Spanish. 1986. a. free. adv. **Document type:** *Directory.* **Description:** A yellow page directory which includes public service information such as the location and telephone numbers of airports, public libraries, schools, hospitals, 24-hour pharmacies, entertainment, etc.
Published by: Vega and Associates, 3040 Williams Dr, Ste 404, Fairfax, VA 22031. TEL 703-908-9600, FAX 703-908-9400, vegahyp@aol.com, http://www.vegahyp.com. Ed. Martha Loque. Pub. Francisco Vega Jr. Adv. contact Robert Kershaw. B&W page USD 1,700. Circ: 100,000 (controlled).

HOLLIS EUROPE; the directory of European public relations & PR networks. see *ADVERTISING AND PUBLIC RELATIONS*

HOLLIS SPONSORSHIP & DONATIONS YEARBOOK. see *ADVERTISING AND PUBLIC RELATIONS*

HOLLIS SPONSORSHIP NEWSLETTER. see *ADVERTISING AND PUBLIC RELATIONS*

HOLLIS UK PRESS & PUBLIC RELATIONS ANNUAL. see *ADVERTISING AND PUBLIC RELATIONS*

380.1029 USA
▼ **HOMELAND SECURITY BUYERS GUIDE.** Text in English. 2003. a. adv. **Document type:** *Directory, Trade.* **Description:** Contains contact informatiomn with a listing of products and services of more than 850 homland security suppliers, Used by more 250 military, industrial and government buyers for purchasing information.
Published by: Federal Buyers Guide, Inc., 718-B State St, PO Box 22507, Santa Barbara, CA 93101. TEL 805-963-7470, FAX 805-963-7478, http://www.homelandbuyer.com/, http://www.gov-world.com/. Adv. contact David Minor TEL 805-963-7470 ext 18. B&W page USD 3,995, color page USD 6,495; trim 8.5 x 11. Circ: 10,000 (controlled).

005.3029 HKG
HONG KONG COMPUTER DIRECTORY (YEAR). Text in English. 1992. a. HKD 550; USD 95 in S.E. Asia; USD 105 elsewhere. **Document type:** *Directory.* **Description:** Lists over 2,000 software products and about 1,100 IT related companies.
Published by: Hong Kong Productivity Council, HKPC Bldg, 78 Tat Chee Ave, Kowloon, Hong Kong. TEL 852-2788-5963, FAX 852-2788-5959, isd@hkpc.org, http://www.hkpc.org. Circ: 5,000.

382.029 HKG
HONG KONG IMPORTERS' DIRECTORY (YEAR). Text in Chinese, English. 1993. a. HKD 250; USD 80 in S.E. Asia; USD 100 elsewhere. **Document type:** *Directory.* **Description:** Lists major importers in Hong Kong with full address, telephone, telex and fax numbers, number of employees, sales turnover, major products and brand names. Covers over 8,000 products and 7,000 brand names.
Published by: Hong Kong Productivity Council, HKPC Bldg, 78 Tat Chee Ave, Kowloon, Hong Kong. TEL 582-2788-5814, FAX 852-2788-5959, isd@hkpc.org, http://www.hkpc.org. Circ: 5,000.

338.0029 HKG
HONG KONG LINKAGE INDUSTRY DIRECTORY (YEAR). Text in Chinese, English. 1989. a. HKD 500; USD 90 in S.E. Asia; USD 100 elsewhere. **Document type:** *Directory.* **Description:** Lists of major workshops and suppliers in Hong Kong in various metal sectors including: mould and tool making, surface finishing, industrial machinery repair and maintenance, and more.
Published by: Hong Kong Productivity Council, HKPC Bldg, 78 Tat Chee Ave, Kowloon, Hong Kong. TEL 852-2788-5954, FAX 852-2788-5959, isd@hkpc.org, http://www.hkpc.org. Circ: 5,000.

382.029 HKG ISSN 0073-3245
HONG KONG MANUFACTURERS AND EXPORTERS REGISTER. Text in Chinese. 1963. irreg., latest vol.8, 1975. USD 18. adv. **Document type:** *Directory.*
Published by: Oriental Publicity Service, PO Box 4366, NP, Hong Kong, Hong Kong. Ed. Anthony Leung. Circ: 5,000.

629.8029 HKG
HONG KONG MECHATRONICS DIRECTORY (YEAR). Text in Chinese, English. 1988. a. HKD 150; USD 33 in S.E. Asia; USD 38 elsewhere. **Document type:** *Directory.* **Description:** Lists major local manufacturers, sales agents and retailers engaged in the field of mechatronics.
Published by: Hong Kong Productivity Council, HKPC Bldg, 78 Tat Chee Ave, Kowloon, Hong Kong. TEL 852-2788-5954, FAX 852-2788-5959, isd@hkpc.org, http://www.hkpc.org. Circ: 5,000.

338.0029 USA ISSN 1055-7202
HG4057
HOOVER'S HANDBOOK OF AMERICAN BUSINESS; profiles of 750 major US companies. Text in English. 1991. a., latest 2001. price varies. **Document type:** *Directory, Trade.* **Description:** Profiles 750 major US companies, including histories, financial data, pertinent names and addresses.
Supersedes in part (in 1991): Hoover's Handbook (1056-6279)
Related titles: Online - full text ed.
Published by: Hoover's Inc., 5800 Airport Blvd, Austin, TX 78752-3824. TEL 512-374-4500, FAX 512-374-4501, orders@hoovers.com, http://www.hoovers.com. R&P Dana Smith TEL 512-374-4528.

338.0029 USA ISSN 1069-7519
HG4057
HOOVER'S HANDBOOK OF EMERGING COMPANIES; profiles of America's most exciting grown enterprises. Text in English. 1993. a. USD 99.95 (effective 2002). **Document type:** *Directory, Trade.* **Description:** Profiles 300 growth companies, including high-profile and lesser-known companies. Contains financial data, an overview of operations and pertinent names and addresses.
Related titles: Online - full text ed.
Published by: Hoover's Inc., 5800 Airport Blvd, Austin, TX 78752-3824. TEL 512-374-4500, FAX 512-374-4501, orders@hoovers.com, http://www.hoovers.com. R&P Dana Smith TEL 512-374-4528.

338.0029 USA ISSN 1555-3744
HG4057
HOOVER'S HANDBOOK OF PRIVATE COMPANIES; profiles of major US private enterprises. Text in English. 1994. a. USD 139.95 (effective 2002). **Document type:** *Directory, Trade.* **Description:** Covers the 800 largest privately owned companies in the US, including histories, financial data, and pertinent names and addresses.
Formerly (until 1997): Hoover's Guide to Private Companies (1073-6433)
Related titles: Online - full text ed.
Published by: Hoover's Inc., 5800 Airport Blvd, Austin, TX 78752-3824. TEL 512-374-4500, FAX 512-374-4501, orders@hoovers.com, http://www.hoovers.com. R&P Dana Smith TEL 512-374-4528.

338.0029 USA ISSN 1055-7199
HG4009
HOOVER'S HANDBOOK OF WORLD BUSINESS; profiles of major global enterprises. Text in English. 1992. a. price varies. **Document type:** *Directory, Trade.* **Description:** Profiles 300 major non-US public, private and state-owned companies, including histories, financial data, and pertinent names and addresses.
Supersedes in part (in 1991): Hoover's Handbook (1056-6279)
Related titles: Online - full text ed.
Published by: Hoover's Inc., 5800 Airport Blvd, Austin, TX 78752-3824. TEL 512-374-4500, FAX 512-374-4501, orders@hoovers.com, http://www.hoovers.com. R&P Dana Smith TEL 512-374-4528.

338.009 USA ISSN 1534-8806
HD2755.5
HOOVER'S MASTERLIST OF MAJOR INTERNATIONAL COMPANIES (YEAR). Text in English. 1998. a. USD 149.95 (effective 2002). **Document type:** *Directory, Trade.*
Published by: Hoover's Inc., 5800 Airport Blvd, Austin, TX 78752-3824. TEL 512-374-4500, FAX 512-374-4501, orders@hoovers.com, http://www.hoovers.com. R&P Dana Smith TEL 512-374-4528.

338.0029 USA ISSN 1549-6457
HF5035
HOOVER'S MASTERLIST OF U S COMPANIES (YEAR). Text in English. 1993. a., latest 2002. USD 285 (effective 2004). **Document type:** *Directory, Trade.* **Description:** Covers more than 5,400 US public and private companies and includes basic contact information, sales, number of employees and more.
Formerly (until 2003): Hoover's MasterList of Major U S Companies (Year) (1066-291X)
Related titles: Online - full text ed.
Published by: Hoover's Inc., 5800 Airport Blvd, Austin, TX 78752-3824. TEL 512-374-4500, FAX 512-374-4501, orders@hoovers.com, http://www.hoovers.com. R&P Dana Smith TEL 512-374-4528.

338.0029 635 GBR
HORTICULTURAL DIRECTORY. Text in English. a. GBP 15 per issue (effective 2003). adv. **Document type:** *Directory, Trade.* **Description:** Contains over 300 industry addresses, key contacts, list of industry organizations, index to over 1,500 brand names and a calendar of major events.
Formerly: The Horticulture Directory
Published by: Nexus Media Ltd. (Subsidiary of: Highbury House Communications PLC), Nexus House, Azalea Dr, Swanley, Kent BR8 8HU, United Kingdom. TEL 44-1322-660070, FAX 44-1322-616311, info@nexusmedia.com, http://www.hhc.co.uk/horticulturaldirectory. Ed. Peter Rogers. Adv. contact Keith Dalton. B&W page GBP 1,150, color page GBP 1,300; trim 210 x 297.

362.11029 GBR
HOSPITALS AND TRUSTS DIRECTORY (YEAR). Text in English. 1987. a. GBP 90; USD 144 in United States. adv. **Document type:** *Directory.* **Description:** Provides an up-to-date reference guide to the key practitioners and professionals in the UK health service.
Former titles (until 2002): Directory of Hospitals and Trusts (Year) (1472-1945); (until 2000): Directory of Hospitals and N H S Trusts (Year) (1365-9391); (until 1993): Directory of Hospitals (Year) (0963-6099)

—BLDSC (4333.460000).
Published by: Informa Publishing, 69-77 Paul St, London, EC2A 4IQ, United Kingdom. TEL 44-20-7553-1000, FAX 44-20-7553-1593, liz@pearson-pro.com, http://www.fthealthcare.com.

HOUSTON PETROLEUM INDUSTRY. see *PETROLEUM AND GAS*

HOUSTON - TEXAS OIL DIRECTORY. see *PETROLEUM AND GAS*

HOW TO FIND INFORMATION ABOUT COMPANIES; the corporate intelligence source book. see *BUSINESS AND ECONOMICS*

HUDSON VALLEY TELEPHONE TICKLER. see *INSURANCE*

620.82029   USA
HUMAN FACTORS AND ERGONOMICS SOCIETY DIRECTORY AND YEARBOOK. Text in English. 1958. a. USD 75 to non-members (effective 2003). adv. **Document type:** *Directory, Academic/Scholarly.* **Description:** Contains descriptions of activities that took place among the Society's major committees, local and student chapters and technical interest groups during the previous year; member listings; geographical member index.
Formerly: Human Factors Society. Directory and Yearbook (0270-5311)
—Linda Hall.
Published by: Human Factors and Ergonomics Society, PO Box 1369, Santa Monica, CA 90406-1369. TEL 310-394-1811, FAX 310-394-2410, lois@hfes.org, http://hfes.org. Adv. contact Lois Smith. Circ: 5,000 (paid).

380.1029   HUN   ISSN 1217-2898
HUNGARIAN BUSINESS BOOK∗ ; magyar nyelven. Text in Hungarian. 1993. a. **Document type:** *Trade.*
Related titles: English ed.: ISSN 1217-3045.
Published by: Planetwork Kft., c/o Magyar ISBN Iroda, Orszagos Szechenyi Konutar, Budapest, 1827, Hungary.

I C ALTERNATE SOURCES & REPLACEMENTS D.A.T.A. DIGEST. (Integrated Circuits) see *ELECTRONICS*

I D SYSTEMS BUYERS GUIDE. see *BUSINESS AND ECONOMICS—Computer Applications*

I F L A DIRECTORY. see *LIBRARY AND INFORMATION SCIENCES*

I M INDUSTRIAL MINERALS DIRECTORY. see *MINES AND MINING INDUSTRY*

I N A S P HEALTH DIRECTORY (YEAR). see *MEDICAL SCIENCES*

665.5029   USA
I O G C C MEMBERS AND OIL AND GAS AGENCIES DIRECTORY. Text in English. a. USD 15 (effective 2003). **Document type:** *Directory, Trade.*
Published by: Interstate Oil and Gas Compact Commission, PO Box 53127, Oklahoma City, OK 73152-3127. TEL 405-525-3556, FAX 405-525-3592, iogcc@iogcc.state.ok.us, http://www.iogcc.state.ok.us.

338.0029   USA
I Q DIRECTORY; interactive resources. Text in English. a. (Sep.). USD 359 (effective 2002). **Document type:** *Directory, Trade.* **Description:** Contains listings of more than 2100 organizations, including advertising agencies, brand marketers, media, telecommunications, CD-ROM designers, online content providers, POP/kiosk designers and multimedia video/graphic/audio designers. Provides address, phone, fax, e-mail, URL, services, company profile, accounts, personnel and ad specs.
Related titles: CD-ROM ed.; Online - full content ed.
Published by: V N U Business Publications (Subsidiary of: V N U Business Media), 770 Broadway, New York, NY 10003-9595. TEL 800-468-2395, http://www.vnubusinessmedia.com/box/bp/div_mmr_dir_iq.html.

338   TWN
I S O; Directory of ISO Certified Companies in Taiwan. Text in English. a. USD 25 (effective 2000). **Document type:** *Directory, Trade.* **Description:** Contains more than 2000 Taiwan-based companies with ISO certifications.
Published by: China Economic News Service, 561 Chunghsiao E. Rd Sec 4, Taipei, 10516, Taiwan. TEL 886-2-642-2629, FAX 886-2-2642-7422, TELEX 27710-CENSPC, webmaster@www.cens.com, http://www.cens.com.

I S O 9000 REGISTERED FIRMS DIRECTORY. (International Organization for Standardization) see *BUSINESS AND ECONOMICS—Production Of Goods And Services*

338.0029   USA   ISSN 1048-3357
HF5065.I2
IDAHO BUSINESS DIRECTORY. Text in English. 1989. a. USD 1,100 combined subscription print, online & CD-ROM eds. (effective 2004 & 2005). index. back issues avail. **Document type:** *Directory.* **Description:** Includes all businesses in the state, listing addresses, phone numbers, key personnel, with employee size and sales volume codes and credit rating codes.
Related titles: CD-ROM ed.; Diskette ed.; E-mail ed.; Fax ed.; Magnetic Tape ed.; Online - full text ed.
Published by: American Business Directories (Subsidiary of: American Business Information, Inc.), 5711 S 86th Circle, P O Box 27347, Omaha, NE 68127. TEL 402-593-4600, 888-946-9377, 877-708-3844, FAX 402-331-5481, karen.peters@infousa.com, sales@directoriesusa.com, http://www.directoriesusa.com.

670.29   USA   ISSN 1525-4054
IDAHO MANUFACTURERS DIRECTORY. Text in English. USD 65 (effective 2000). **Document type:** *Directory.*
Related titles: CD-ROM ed.: USD 310 (effective 2000).
Published by: Manufacturers' News, Inc., 1633 Central St, Evanston, IL 60201. TEL 847-864-7000, 888-752-5200, FAX 847-332-1100, info@manufacturersnews.com, sales@mninfo.com, http://www.manufacturersnews.com. Ed. Frank Lambing.

670   USA   ISSN 1081-3950
HF5065.I2
IDAHO MANUFACTURERS REGISTER∗ . Text in English. 1995. a. USD 65. **Document type:** *Directory.* **Description:** Provides detailed profiles of 3,100 manufactures and high tech companies.
Related titles: CD-ROM ed.: USD 185.
Published by: Database Publishing Company, 701 E Ball Rd Ste 100, Anaheim, CA 92805-5962. TEL 714-778-6400, FAX 714-778-6811. Ed., R&P Sarah Fraser. Pub. James H Holly.

380.1029   USA
ILLINOIS BUSINESS CREDIT DIRECTORY. Text in English. a. USD 1,100 combined subscription print, online & CD-ROM eds. (effective 2004 & 2005). back issues avail. **Document type:** *Directory.* **Description:** Contains credit ratings and other valuable information on all businesses within Illinois. Includes company name & address, phone & fax numbers, key executive names & titles, lines of business, years in business, number of employees, estimated annual sales, volume credit rating code, and corporate linkage information.
Related titles: CD-ROM ed.; Diskette ed.; E-mail ed.; Fax ed.; Magnetic Tape ed.; Online - full text ed.
Published by: American Business Directories (Subsidiary of: American Business Information, Inc.), 5711 S 86th Circle, P O Box 27347, Omaha, NE 68127. TEL 402-593-4600, 888-946-9377, 877-708-3844, FAX 402-331-5481, sales@directoriesusa.com, http://www.directoriesusa.com.

338.0029   USA   ISSN 1048-504X
HF5065.I3
ILLINOIS BUSINESS DIRECTORY. Text in English. 1985. a. USD 1,100 combined subscription print, online & CD-ROM eds. (effective 2004 & 2005). index. back issues avail. **Document type:** *Directory.* **Description:** Includes all businesses in the state, listing addresses and phone numbers, key personnel, with employee size and sales volume codes, and credit rating codes.
Related titles: CD-ROM ed.; Diskette ed.; E-mail ed.; Fax ed.; Magnetic Tape ed.; Online - full text ed.
Published by: American Business Directories (Subsidiary of: American Business Information, Inc.), 5711 S 86th Circle, P O Box 27347, Omaha, NE 68127. TEL 402-593-4600, 888-946-9377, 877-708-3844, FAX 402-331-5481, karen.peters@infousa.com, sales@directoriesusa.com, http://www.directoriesusa.com.

670.29   USA   ISSN 0160-3302
T12
ILLINOIS MANUFACTURERS DIRECTORY. Text in English. 1912. a. USD 174 (effective 2000). adv. illus. **Document type:** *Directory.* **Description:** Profiles 23,229 manufacturers listed in six sections: product, alphabetical, geographical, SIC, parent company and Chicago zip code. Published in cooperation with the Illinois chamber of commerce.
Related titles: CD-ROM ed.: USD 670 (effective 2000); Diskette ed.; Magnetic Tape ed.
Published by: Manufacturers' News, Inc., 1633 Central St, Evanston, IL 60201. TEL 847-864-7000, 888-752-5200, FAX 847-332-1100, info@mninfo.com, info@manufacturersnews.com, sales@mninfo.com, http://www.manufacturersnews.com. Ed. Frank Lambing. Adv. contact Charles Scherer. B&W page USD 1,843.

670.29   USA   ISSN 0092-3818
HC107.I3
ILLINOIS SERVICES DIRECTORY. Text in English. a. USD 184 (effective 2001). adv. 1864 p/no.; **Document type:** *Directory.* **Description:** Profiles 28,330 non-manufacturing firms; includes product-service, alphabetical, geographical, SIC, and parent company. Sections published in cooperation with the Illinois Chamber of Commerce.
Related titles: CD-ROM ed.: USD 760 (effective 2000); Diskette ed.

Published by: Manufacturers' News, Inc., 1633 Central St, Evanston, IL 60201. TEL 847-864-7000, 888-752-5200, FAX 847-332-1100, info@mninfo.com, info@manufacturersnews.com, sales@mninfo.com, http://www.manufacturersnews.com. Ed. Steve Garland.

IMMEDIATE ARTS - WRITERS' DIRECTORY; independent & small press publishers. see *PUBLISHING AND BOOK TRADE*

663.2029   USA
HD9350.3
IMPACT WORLD DIRECTORY; leading spirits, wine & beer companies; who's who of industry executives. Text in English. 1990. a. USD 310. adv. index. **Document type:** *Directory.* **Description:** Lists more than 750 suppliers, agents and importers, distributors and wholesalers, and duty free operators in the wine, beer and spirits industry.
Formerly: Impact International Directory (1048-2253)
Published by: Marvin R. Shanken Communications, Inc., 387 Park Ave S, New York, NY 10016. TEL 212-684-4224, FAX 212-684-5424. Ed. Marvin R Shanken.

INDEPENDENT LIQUID TERMINALS ASSOCIATION. DIRECTORY OF BULK LIQUID TERMINAL AND ABOVEGROUND STORAGE TANK EQUIPMENT AND SERVICES: SUPPLIERS OF EQUIPMENT & SERVICES. see *PETROLEUM AND GAS*

INDEPENDENT LIQUID TERMINALS ASSOCIATION. DIRECTORY OF BULK LIQUID TERMINAL AND STORAGE FACILITIES. see *PETROLEUM AND GAS*

INDEPENDENT WOMEN'S SPECIALTY STORES & BOUTIQUES. see *CLOTHING TRADE*

380.1029   USA
INDEPENDENT YELLOW PAGES MARKET (YEAR). Text in English. biennial. USD 2,295 (effective 2005). **Document type:** *Directory, Trade.* **Description:** Contains complete, detailed and up-to-date research data on the independent yellow pages market.
Published by: SIMBA Information (Subsidiary of: R.R. Bowker LLC), 60 Long Ridge Rd., Ste 300, Stamford, CT 06902. TEL 203-325-8193, 800-307-2529, FAX 203-325-8915, info@simbanet.com, http://www.simbanet.com/publications/report_iypm.htm.

INDIAN ARCHITECTS DIRECTORY & REFERENCE BOOK. see *ARCHITECTURE*

INDIAN HOSIERY DIRECTORY. see *CLOTHING TRADE*

382.029   IND
INDIAN IMPORT EXPORT DIRECTORY∗ . Text in English. irreg. USD 50. **Document type:** *Directory.*
Published by: (Reed Information Services), Tele Direct (Informatics) India Pvt. Ltd., A-30, Kailash Colony, New Delhi, 110 048, India. TELEX 031-62746 TEDI IN.

338.0029   IND   ISSN 0971-7234
INDIAN INDUSTRIAL SOURCES. Text in English. 1985. m. INR 250. adv. **Document type:** *Trade.*
Published by: Industrial Magazines (Bombay) Pvt. Ltd., S309 Vasan Udyog Bhavan, Senapati Bapat Marg, Lower Parel, Mumbai, Maharashtra 400 013, India. TEL 91-22-4937718, FAX 91-22-4930514, iisource@giasbm01.vsnl.net.in. Ed., Pub., R&P Deepak Sule. Adv. contact T N Hariharan. B&W page USD 500, color page USD 1,000; trim 20.5 x 27.5. Circ: 17,000.

380.1029   USA
INDIANA BUSINESS CREDIT DIRECTORY. Text in English. a. USD 1,100 combined subscription print, online & CD-ROM eds. (effective 2004 & 2005). back issues avail. **Document type:** *Directory.* **Description:** Contains credit ratings and other valuable information on all businesses within Indiana. Includes company name & address, phone & fax numbers, key executive names & titles, lines of business, years in business, number of employees, estimated annual sales, volume credit rating code, and corporate linkage information.
Related titles: CD-ROM ed.; Diskette ed.; E-mail ed.; Fax ed.; Magnetic Tape ed.; Online - full text ed.
Published by: American Business Directories (Subsidiary of: American Business Information, Inc.), 5711 S 86th Circle, P O Box 27347, Omaha, NE 68127. TEL 402-593-4600, 888-946-9377, 877-708-3844, FAX 402-331-5481, sales@directoriesusa.com, http://www.directoriesusa.com.

338.0029   USA   ISSN 1048-7255
HF5065.I6
INDIANA BUSINESS DIRECTORY. Text in English. 1987. a. USD 1,100 combined subscription print, online & CD-ROM eds. (effective 2004 & 2005). index. back issues avail. **Document type:** *Directory.* **Description:** Includes all businesses in the state, listing address and phone numbers, key personnel, with employee size and sales volume codes, and credit rating codes.
Related titles: CD-ROM ed.; Diskette ed.; E-mail ed.; Fax ed.; Magnetic Tape ed.; Online - full text ed.

Published by: American Business Directories (Subsidiary of: American Business Information, Inc.), 5711 S 86th Circle, P O Box 27347, Omaha, NE 68127. TEL 402-593-4600, 888-946-9377, 877-708-3844, FAX 402-331-5481, karen.peters@infousa.com, sales@directoriesusa.com, http://www.directoriesusa.com.

670.29 USA ISSN 0735-2417
HD9727.I6
INDIANA MANUFACTURERS DIRECTORY. Text in English. a. USD 114 (effective 2000). adv. illus. **Document type:** *Directory.* **Description:** Profiles 11,945 manufacturers listed in five sections: product, alphabetical, geographical, SIC and parent company. Sections published in cooperation with the Indiana Manufacturers Association.
Related titles: CD-ROM ed.: USD 580 (effective 2000); Diskette ed.
Published by: Manufacturers' News, Inc., 1633 Central St, Evanston, IL 60201. TEL 847-864-7000, 888-752-5200, FAX 847-332-1100, info@mninfo.com, info@manufacturersnews.com, sales@mninfo.com, http://www.minfo.com, http://www.manufacturersnews.com. Ed. Frank Lambing. Adv. contact Charles Scherer.

382.029 IDN ISSN 0216-1052
INDONESIAN IMPORTERS DIRECTORY* . Text in English. 1978. biennial. USD 100. charts; stat.; tr.lit. **Document type:** *Directory.* **Description:** General information and lists importers in Indonesia.
Related titles: Supplement(s): List of Goods Allocated.
Published by: Gabungan Importir Nasional Seluruh Indonesia/National Importers Association of Indonesia, Wisma Nusantara Bldg., Jalan Majapahit No. 1, Jakarta, Indonesia. TEL 021-360-643, FAX 62-021-367269. Eds. S Hoesin, Zahri Achmad. Circ: 3,000.

749.029 DNK ISSN 0106-7346
INDRETNINGSHAANDBOGEN; idebog for indretning af virksomheder, institutioner og offentligt miljoe. Text in Danish. 1980. a. DKK 100 (effective 2001). adv. illus. **Document type:** *Directory.* **Description:** Lists furniture and furnishing suppliers, interior designers and architects.
Published by: NOVA Kommunikation A-S, Solvang 23, PO Box 146, Allerod, 3450, Denmark. TEL 45-48-17-00-78, FAX 45-48-17-13-65, info@nova-media.dk, http://www.indret.dk. Ed., Pub., Adv. contact Poul Jacobsen. color page DKK 18,800; trim 180 x 240. Circ: 12,000 (controlled).

380.1029 KEN
INDUSTRIAL & TRADE DIRECTORY. Text in English. a. KES 200. adv. bk.rev. **Document type:** *Directory.*
Formerly (until 1981): Kenya Enterprise
Published by: Translinkers Publishing Co., PO Box 44169, Nairobi, Kenya. Ed. George C Kimani. Circ: 60,000.

338.0029 JPN
INDUSTRIAL GOODS DISTRIBUTION IN JAPAN. Text in English. irreg., latest Oct.1991. USD 750 per issue. index. **Document type:** *Directory.* **Description:** Directory featuring chemical, electronic and other industrial material distributors and trade associations in Japan.
Published by: Dodwell Marketing Consultants, Kowa no 35 Bldg, 14-14 Akasaka 1-chome, Minato-ku, Tokyo, 107-0052, Japan. TEL 03-3589-0207, FAX 03-5570-7132.

INDUSTRIAL MARKET PLACE. see *MACHINERY*

INDUSTRIAL MINERALS DIRECTORY - WORLD GUIDE TO PRODUCERS AND PROCESSORS. see *MINES AND MINING INDUSTRY*

380.1029 IND ISSN 0970-6895
INDUSTRIAL PRODUCTS FINDER. Text in English. 1972. m. INR 525, USD 67 (effective 2000). adv. bk.rev. abstr.; charts; illus. **Document type:** *Trade.* **Description:** Covers new products and news briefs.
Indexed: CRIA.
Published by: IPFonline Ltd., 33 D'Silva Rd, Mylapore, Chennai, 600 004, India. TEL 91-44-4661698, 91-44-4661588, FAX 91-44-4661617, ipf@md4.vsnl.net.in, http://www.industrialproductsfind.com, http://www.ipfonline.com. Ed. Milton D'Silva. Adv. contact Shashie Kumar. color page USD 900. Circ: 24,000.

362.11029 AUS
INFO-LINK THE HOSPITALITY BOOK. Text in English. a. adv. **Document type:** *Directory, Trade.* **Description:** Lists hospitality products and suppliers.
Published by: Reed Business Information Pty Ltd (Subsidiary of: Reed Business Information International), Locked Bag 2999, Chatswood, NSW 2067, Australia. TEL 61-2-9422-2850, FAX 61-2-9422-2844, http://www.infolink.com.au. Ed. Po Ling Fleisher. Adv. contact Angela Higgins.

380.1029 USA ISSN 1045-3652
INFORMATION CATALOG. Text in English. bi-m. free. **Document type:** *Catalog.*
—CCC.
Published by: F I N D - S V P, Inc., 625 Avenue of the Americas, New York, NY 10011-2002. TEL 212-807-2657, 800-346-3787, FAX 212-807-2676, catalog@find/svp.com, http://www.findsvp.com. Ed. Lynn Christie. Pub. Michael Shor.

INFORMATION MARKETPLACE DIRECTORY. see *PUBLISHING AND BOOK TRADE*

INLAND WATERWAYS GUIDE. see *TRANSPORTATION—Ships And Shipping*

INSTITUTE OF CHARTERED ACCOUNTANTS OF SCOTLAND. OFFICIAL DIRECTORY. see *BUSINESS AND ECONOMICS—Accounting*

INSURANCE ALMANAC: WHO, WHAT, WHEN AND WHERE IN INSURANCE. see *INSURANCE*

380.1029 SGP
INSURANCE DIRECTORY OF ASIA. Text in English. a. USD 248 in Singapore & Malaysia; USD 330 elsewhere (effective 2005). **Document type:** *Directory, Trade.* **Description:** Provides a reference guide to 1375 insurance companies in Asia.
Published by: Ins Communications Pte. Ltd., 57A Amoy St., Singapore, 069 883, Singapore. TEL 65-62245583, FAX 65-62241091, http://www.asiainsurancereview.com/EStore/insurance-dir-asia.asp.

INTERACTIVE RESOURCES DIRECTORY. see *COMPUTERS*

INTERIOR DESIGN BUYERS GUIDE. see *INTERIOR DESIGN AND DECORATION*

INTERNATIONAL AIRLINE GUIDE. see *TRANSPORTATION—Air Transport*

639.2029 GBR ISSN 1464-018X
INTERNATIONAL AQUAFEED DIRECTORY & BUYERS GUIDE. Text in English. 1997. a. GBP 89; GBP 95 foreign. **Document type:** *Directory, Trade.* **Description:** Provides topical and relevant information for nutritionists, formulators, production staff, fish scientists and others involved in producing feeds for freshwater and marine species of fish and crustacea worldwide.
Published by: Turret R A I plc, Armstrong House, 38 Market Sq, Uxbridge, Middx UB8 1TG, United Kingdom. TEL 44-1895-454545, FAX 44-1895-454647.

382.029 USA
INTERNATIONAL BUSINESS AND TRADE DIRECTORIES. Text in English. 1996. a. USD 185 (effective 2000). **Document type:** *Directory, Trade.* **Description:** Lists over 8000 worldwide industry-specific business directories.
Related titles: Diskette ed.
Published by: Grey House Publishing, Pocket Knife Sq, Lakeville, CT 06039. TEL 518-789-8700, 800-562-2139, FAX 518-789-0556. **Dist. by:** Current Pacific Ltd., PO Box 36-536, Northcote, Auckland, New Zealand. TEL 64-9-480-1388, FAX 64-9-480-1387, info@cplnz.com, http://www.cplnz.com.

382.029 USA
INTERNATIONAL COMPANIES IN SOUTH CAROLINA. Text in English. base vol. plus a. updates. USD 45 (effective 2001). adv. **Document type:** *Directory.* **Description:** Gives information on companies in South Carolina owned entirely or partially by non-U.S. companies. Provides a section on international capital investment, a parent company section and three indices.
Published by: Department of Commerce, Research and Communications, PO Box 927, Columbia, SC 29202. TEL 803-737-0400, FAX 803-737-1652, http://www.callsouthcarolina.com. R&P Susan Turkopuls. Adv. contact Dennis Craighead.

658.8029 USA ISSN 1095-161X
HF5419
INTERNATIONAL DIRECTORY OF AGENTS, DISTRIBUTORS & WHOLESALERS. Text in English. 1998. a. (in 2 vols.), latest 2002. USD 385 (effective 2004). **Document type:** *Directory, Trade.* **Description:** Alphabetical country section lists over 20,000 international business firms. The classified section includes 65,000 product and company listings.
Published by: Interdata, 1741 Kekamek, Poulsbo, WA 98370. TEL 360-779-1511, 800-818-0140, FAX 360-697-4696, http://www.importersnet.com. **Dist. by:** Current Pacific Ltd., PO Box 36-536, Northcote, Auckland, New Zealand. TEL 64-9-480-1388, FAX 64-9-480-1387, info@cplnz.com, http://www.cplnz.com.

382.029 USA
INTERNATIONAL DIRECTORY OF AGRICULTURAL MACHINERY AND IMPLEMENTS IMPORTERS. Text in English. 1978. a., latest 2001. looseleaf. USD 260 print or CD-ROM ed.; USD 310 combined subscription print & CD-ROM eds. (effective 2004). **Document type:** *Directory, Trade.* **Description:** Provides information for manufacturers, exporters and trading firms; includes complete name and address; name of contact person; email address; year established; number of employees; telephone and fax numbers, bank reference, as well as a listing of agricultural machinery and implements currently being imported. In addition, the directory features a comprehensive classified section where importers are listed by product.
Related titles: CD-ROM ed.
Published by: Interdata, 1741 Kekamek, Poulsbo, WA 98370. TEL 360-779-1511, 800-818-0140, FAX 360-697-4696, http://www.importersnet.com. **Dist. by:** Current Pacific Ltd., PO Box 36-536, Northcote, Auckland, New Zealand. TEL 64-9-480-1388, FAX 64-9-480-1387, info@cplnz.com, http://www.cplnz.com.

382.029 USA
INTERNATIONAL DIRECTORY OF AIRCRAFT AND AVIATION EQUIPMENT & ACCESSORIES IMPORTERS. Text in English. 1978. a., latest 2001. looseleaf. USD 200 print or CD-ROM ed.; USD 250 combined subscription print & CD-ROM eds. (effective 2004). **Document type:** *Directory, Trade.* **Description:** Provides information for manufacturers, exporters and trading firms; includes complete name and address; name of contact person; email address; year established; number of employees; telephone and fax numbers, bank reference, as well as a listing of aircraft and aviation equipment and accessories currently being imported. In addition, the directory features a comprehensive classified section where importers are listed by product.
Related titles: CD-ROM ed.
Published by: Interdata, 1741 Kekamek, Poulsbo, WA 98370. TEL 360-779-1511, 800-818-0140, FAX 360-697-4696, http://www.importersnet.com. **Dist. by:** Current Pacific Ltd., PO Box 36-536, Northcote, Auckland, New Zealand. TEL 64-9-480-1388, FAX 64-9-480-1387, info@cplnz.com, http://www.cplnz.com.

B

382.029 USA
INTERNATIONAL DIRECTORY OF APPAREL AND CLOTHING IMPORTERS. Text in English. 1978. a., latest 2002. looseleaf. USD 320 print or CD-ROM ed.; USD 370 combined subscription print & CD-ROM eds. (effective 2004). **Document type:** *Directory, Trade.* **Description:** Provides information for manufacturers, exporters and trading firms; includes complete name and address; name of contact person; email address; year established; number of employees; telephone and fax numbers, bank reference, as well as a listing of apparel and clothing currently being imported. In addition, the directory features a comprehensive classified section where importers are listed by product.
Related titles: CD-ROM ed.
Published by: Interdata, 1741 Kekamek, Poulsbo, WA 98370. TEL 360-779-1511, 800-818-0140, FAX 360-697-4696, http://www.importersnet.com. **Dist. by:** Current Pacific Ltd., PO Box 36-536, Northcote, Auckland, New Zealand. TEL 64-9-480-1388, FAX 64-9-480-1387, info@cplnz.com, http://www.cplnz.com.

382.029 USA
INTERNATIONAL DIRECTORY OF AUTOMOTIVE EQUIPMENT, PARTS AND ACCESSORIES IMPORTERS. Text in English. 1978. a., latest 2002. looseleaf. USD 320 print or CD-ROM ed.; USD 370 combined subscription print & CD-ROM eds. (effective 2004). **Document type:** *Directory, Trade.* **Description:** Provides information for manufacturers, exporters and trading firms; includes complete name and address; name of contact person; email address; year established; number of employees; telephone and fax numbers, bank reference, as well as a listing of automotive equipment, parts and accessories currently being imported. In addition, the directory features a comprehensive classified section where importers are listed by product.
Related titles: CD-ROM ed.
Published by: Interdata, 1741 Kekamek, Poulsbo, WA 98370. TEL 360-779-1511, 800-818-0140, FAX 360-697-4696, http://www.importersnet.com. **Dist. by:** Current Pacific Ltd., PO Box 36-536, Northcote, Auckland, New Zealand. TEL 64-9-480-1388, FAX 64-9-480-1387, info@cplnz.com, http://www.cplnz.com.

INTERNATIONAL DIRECTORY OF AUTOMOTIVE SUPPLIERS & VEHICLE MANUFACTURERS. see *TRANSPORTATION—Automobiles*

382.029 USA
INTERNATIONAL DIRECTORY OF BEAUTY SUPPLIES, COSMETICS AND TOILETRIES IMPORTERS. Text in English. 1978. a., latest 2002. looseleaf. USD 295 print or CD-ROM ed.; USD 345 combined subscription print & CD-ROM eds. (effective 2004). **Document type:** *Directory, Trade.* **Description:** Provides information for manufacturers, exporters and trading firms; includes complete name and address; name of contact person; email address; year established; number of employees; telephone and fax numbers, bank reference, as well as a listing of beauty supplies, cosmetics and toiletries currently being imported. In addition, the directory features a comprehensive classified section where importers are listed by product.
Related titles: CD-ROM ed.
Published by: Interdata, 1741 Kekamek, Poulsbo, WA 98370. TEL 360-779-1511, 800-818-0140, FAX 360-697-4696, http://www.importersnet.com. **Dist. by:** Current Pacific Ltd., PO Box 36-536, Northcote, Auckland, New Zealand. TEL 64-9-480-1388, FAX 64-9-480-1387, info@cplnz.com, http://www.cplnz.com.

▼ new title ➤ refereed ✶ unverified ♦ full entry avail.

382.029 USA
INTERNATIONAL DIRECTORY OF BICYCLES, MOPEDS AND MOTORCYCLES IMPORTERS. Text in English. 1978. a., latest 2001. looseleaf. USD 200 print or CD-ROM ed.; USD 250 combined subscription print & CD-ROM eds. (effective 2004). **Document type:** *Directory, Trade.* **Description:** Provides information for manufacturers, exporters and trading firms; includes complete name and address; name of contact person; email address; year established; number of employees; telephone and fax numbers, bank reference, as well as a listing of bicycles, mopeds and motorcycles currently being imported. In addition, the directory features a comprehensive classified section where importers are listed by product.
Related titles: CD-ROM ed.
Published by: Interdata, 1741 Kekamek, Poulsbo, WA 98370. TEL 360-779-1511, 800-818-0140, FAX 360-697-4696, http://www.importersnet.com. **Dist. by:** Current Pacific Ltd., PO Box 36-536, Northcote, Auckland, New Zealand. TEL 64-9-480-1388, FAX 64-9-480-1387, info@cplnz.com, http://www.cplnz.com.

B

382.029 USA
INTERNATIONAL DIRECTORY OF BUILDING AND CONSTRUCTION MATERIALS & SUPPLIES IMPORTERS. Text in English. 1978. a., latest 2001. looseleaf. USD 320 print or CD-ROM ed.; USD 370 combined subscription print & CD-ROM eds. (effective 2004). **Document type:** *Directory, Trade.* **Description:** Provides information for manufacturers, exporters and trading firms; includes complete name and address; name of contact person; email address; year established; number of employees; telephone and fax numbers, bank reference, as well as a listing of building and construction materials & supplies currently being imported. In addition, the directory features a comprehensive classified section where importers are listed by product.
Related titles: CD-ROM ed.
Published by: Interdata, 1741 Kekamek, Poulsbo, WA 98370. TEL 360-779-1511, 800-818-0140, FAX 360-697-4696, http://www.importersnet.com. **Dist. by:** Current Pacific Ltd., PO Box 36-536, Northcote, Auckland, New Zealand. TEL 64-9-480-1388, FAX 64-9-480-1387, info@cplnz.com, http://www.cplnz.com.

THE INTERNATIONAL DIRECTORY OF BUSINESS INFORMATION SOURCES & SERVICES. see *BUSINESS AND ECONOMICS—International Commerce*

382.029 USA
INTERNATIONAL DIRECTORY OF CHEMICALS AND ALLIED PRODUCTS IMPORTERS. Text in English. 1978. a., latest 2001. USD 320 print or CD-ROM ed.; USD 370 combined subscription print & CD-ROM eds. (effective 2004). **Document type:** *Directory, Trade.* **Description:** Provides information for manufacturers, exporters and trading firms; includes complete name and address; name of contact person; email address; year established; number of employees; telephone and fax numbers, bank reference, as well as a listing of chemicals and allied products currently being imported. In addition, the directory features a comprehensive classified section where importers are listed by product.
Related titles: CD-ROM ed.
Published by: Interdata, 1741 Kekamek, Poulsbo, WA 98370. TEL 360-779-1511, 800-818-0140, FAX 360-697-4696, http://www.importersnet.com. **Dist. by:** Current Pacific Ltd., PO Box 36-536, Northcote, Auckland, New Zealand. TEL 64-9-480-1388, FAX 64-9-480-1387, info@cplnz.com, http://www.cplnz.com.

382.029 USA
INTERNATIONAL DIRECTORY OF COMMUNICATIONS EQUIPMENT AND SUPPLIES IMPORTERS. Text in English. 1978. a., latest 2001. looseleaf. USD 295 print or CD-ROM ed.; USD 345 combined subscription print & CD-ROM eds. (effective 2004). **Document type:** *Directory, Trade.* **Description:** Provides information for manufacturers, exporters and trading firms; includes complete name and address; name of contact person; email address; year established; number of employees; telephone and fax numbers, bank reference, as well as a listing of communications equipment and supplies currently being imported. In addition, the directory features a comprehensive classified section where importers are listed by product.
Related titles: CD-ROM ed.
Published by: Interdata, 1741 Kekamek, Poulsbo, WA 98370. TEL 360-779-1511, 800-818-0140, FAX 360-697-4696, http://www.importersnet.com. **Dist. by:** Current Pacific Ltd., PO Box 36-536, Northcote, Auckland, New Zealand. TEL 64-9-480-1388, FAX 64-9-480-1387, info@cplnz.com, http://www.cplnz.com.

382.029 USA
INTERNATIONAL DIRECTORY OF COMPUTERS AND DATA PROCESSING EQUIPMENT AND SUPPLIES IMPORTERS. Text in English. 1978. a., latest 2001. looseleaf. USD 320 print or CD-ROM ed.; USD 370 combined subscription print & CD-ROM eds. (effective 2004). **Document type:** *Directory, Trade.* **Description:** Provides information for manufacturers, exporters and trading firms; includes complete name and address; name of contact person; email address; year established; number of employees; telephone and fax numbers, bank reference, as well as a listing of computers and data processing equipment and supplies currently being imported. In addition, the directory features a comprehensive classified section where importers are listed by product.
Related titles: CD-ROM ed.: USD 320 (effective 2001).
Published by: Interdata, 1741 Kekamek, Poulsbo, WA 98370. TEL 360-779-1511, 800-818-0140, FAX 360-697-4696, http://www.importersnet.com. **Dist. by:** Current Pacific Ltd., PO Box 36-536, Northcote, Auckland, New Zealand. TEL 64-9-480-1388, FAX 64-9-480-1387, info@cplnz.com, http://www.cplnz.com.

382.029 USA
INTERNATIONAL DIRECTORY OF CONSTRUCTION AND BUILDING EQUIPMENT IMPORTERS. Text in English. 1978. a., latest 2002. looseleaf. USD 260 print or CD-ROM ed.; USD 310 combined subscription print & CD-ROM eds. (effective 2004). **Document type:** *Directory, Trade.* **Description:** Provides information for manufacturers, exporters and trading firms; includes complete name and address; name of contact person; email address; year established; number of employees; telephone and fax numbers, bank reference, as well as a listing of construction and building equipment currently being imported. In addition, the directory features a comprehensive classified section where importers are listed by product.
Related titles: CD-ROM ed.
Published by: Interdata, 1741 Kekamek, Poulsbo, WA 98370. TEL 360-779-1511, 800-818-0140, FAX 360-697-4696, http://www.importersnet.com. **Dist. by:** Current Pacific Ltd., PO Box 36-536, Northcote, Auckland, New Zealand. TEL 64-9-480-1388, FAX 64-9-480-1387, info@cplnz.com, http://www.cplnz.com.

382.029 USA
INTERNATIONAL DIRECTORY OF CONSUMER ELECTRONICS, AUDIO / VIDEO, T V AND C D'S IMPORTERS. Text in English. 1978. a., latest 2001. looseleaf. USD 260 print or CD-ROM ed.; USD 310 combined subscription print & CD-ROM eds. (effective 2004). **Document type:** *Directory, Trade.* **Description:** Provides information for manufacturers, exporters and trading firms; includes complete name and address; name of contact person; email address; year established; number of employees; telephone and fax numbers, bank reference, as well as a listing of consumer electronics, audio/video, TV & CD's currently being imported. In addition, the directory features a comprehensive classified section where importers are listed by product.
Related titles: CD-ROM ed.
Published by: Interdata, 1741 Kekamek, Poulsbo, WA 98370. TEL 360-779-1511, 800-818-0140, FAX 360-697-4696, http://www.importersnet.com. **Dist. by:** Current Pacific Ltd., PO Box 36-536, Northcote, Auckland, New Zealand. TEL 64-9-480-1388, FAX 64-9-480-1387, info@cplnz.com, http://www.cplnz.com.

382.029 USA
INTERNATIONAL DIRECTORY OF CONTROL EQUIPMENT AND SWITCHES IMPORTERS. Text in English. 1978. a., latest 2001. looseleaf. USD 200 print or CD-ROM ed.; USD 250 print and CD-ROM eds. (effective 2004). **Document type:** *Directory, Trade.* **Description:** Provides information for manufacturers, exporters and trading firms; includes complete name and address; name of contact person; email address; year established; number of employees; telephone and fax numbers, bank reference, as well as a listing of control equipment and switches currently being imported. In addition, the directory features a comprehensive classified section where importers are listed by product.
Related titles: CD-ROM ed.
Published by: Interdata, 1741 Kekamek, Poulsbo, WA 98370. TEL 360-779-1511, 800-818-0140, FAX 360-697-4696, http://www.importersnet.com. **Dist. by:** Current Pacific Ltd., PO Box 36-536, Northcote, Auckland, New Zealand. TEL 64-9-480-1388, FAX 64-9-480-1387, info@cplnz.com, http://www.cplnz.com.

382.029 USA
INTERNATIONAL DIRECTORY OF DRUGS AND PHARMACEUTICALS IMPORTERS. Text in English. 1978. a., latest 2002. looseleaf. USD 260 print or CD-ROM ed.; USD 310 combined subscription print & CD-ROM eds. (effective 2004). **Document type:** *Directory, Trade.* **Description:** Provides information for manufacturers, exporters and trading firms; includes complete name and address; name of contact person; email address; year established; number of employees; telephone and fax numbers, bank reference, as well as a listing of drugs and pharmaceuticals currently being imported. In addition, the directory features a comprehensive classified section where importers are listed by product.
Related titles: CD-ROM ed.
Published by: Interdata, 1741 Kekamek, Poulsbo, WA 98370. TEL 360-779-1511, 800-818-0140, FAX 360-697-4696, http://www.importersnet.com. **Dist. by:** Current Pacific Ltd., PO Box 36-536, Northcote, Auckland, New Zealand. TEL 64-9-480-1388, FAX 64-9-480-1387, info@cplnz.com, http://www.cplnz.com.

INTERNATIONAL DIRECTORY OF ELECTRIC POWER PRODUCERS AND DISTRIBUTORSS. see *ENERGY—Electrical Energy*

382.029 USA
INTERNATIONAL DIRECTORY OF ELECTRICAL EQUIPMENT AND SUPPLIES IMPORTERS. Text in English. 1978. a., latest 2001. looseleaf. USD 295 print or CD-ROM ed.; USD 345 combined subscription print and CD-ROM eds. (effective 2004). **Document type:** *Directory, Trade.* **Description:** Provides information for manufacturers, exporters and trading firms; includes complete name and address; name of contact person; email address; year established; number of employees; telephone and fax numbers, bank reference, as well as a listing of electrical equipment and supplies and supplies currently being imported. In addition, the directory features a comprehensive classified section where importers are listed by product.
Related titles: CD-ROM ed.
Published by: Interdata, 1741 Kekamek, Poulsbo, WA 98370. TEL 360-779-1511, 800-818-0140, FAX 360-697-4696, http://www.importersnet.com. **Dist. by:** Current Pacific Ltd., PO Box 36-536, Northcote, Auckland, New Zealand. TEL 64-9-480-1388, FAX 64-9-480-1387, info@cplnz.com, http://www.cplnz.com.

382.029 USA
INTERNATIONAL DIRECTORY OF ELECTRONIC AND COMPUTER COMPONENTS & PARTS IMPORTERS. Text in English. 1978. a., latest 2001. looseleaf. USD 320 print or CD-ROM ed.; USD 370 print & CD-ROM eds. (effective 2004). **Document type:** *Directory, Trade.* **Description:** Provides information for manufacturers, exporters and trading firms; includes complete name and address; name of contact person; email address; year established; number of employees; telephone and fax numbers, bank reference, as well as a listing of electronic and computer components and parts currently being imported. In addition, the directory features a comprehensive classified section where importers are listed by product.
Related titles: CD-ROM ed.
Published by: Interdata, 1741 Kekamek, Poulsbo, WA 98370. TEL 360-779-1511, 800-818-0140, FAX 360-697-4696, http://www.importersnet.com. **Dist. by:** Current Pacific Ltd., PO Box 36-536, Northcote, Auckland, New Zealand. TEL 64-9-480-1388, FAX 64-9-480-1387, info@cplnz.com, http://www.cplnz.com.

382.029 USA
INTERNATIONAL DIRECTORY OF ENVIRONMENTAL PROTECTION EQUIPMENT IMPORTERS. Text in English. 1978. a., latest 2001. looseleaf. USD 200 print or CD-ROM ed.; USD 250 combined subscription print and CD-ROM ed. (effective 2004). **Document type:** *Directory, Trade.* **Description:** Provides information for manufacturers, exporters and trading firms; includes complete name and address; name of contact person; email address; year established; number of employees; telephone and fax numbers, bank reference, as well as a listing of environmental protection equipment and supplies currently being imported. In addition, the directory features a comprehensive classified section where importers are listed by product.
Related titles: CD-ROM ed.
Published by: Interdata, 1741 Kekamek, Poulsbo, WA 98370. TEL 360-779-1511, 800-818-0140, FAX 360-697-4696, http://www.importersnet.com. **Dist. by:** Current Pacific Ltd., PO Box 36-536, Northcote, Auckland, New Zealand. TEL 64-9-480-1388, FAX 64-9-480-1387, info@cplnz.com, http://www.cplnz.com.

382.029 USA
INTERNATIONAL DIRECTORY OF FLOOR COVERINGS, CARPETS AND RUGS IMPORTERS. Text in English. 1978. a., latest 2002. looseleaf. USD 200 print or CD-ROM ed.; USD 250 combined subscription print & CD-ROM eds. (effective 2004). **Document type:** *Directory, Trade.* **Description:** Provides information for manufacturers, exporters and trading firms; includes complete name and address; name of contact person; email address; year established; number of employees; telephone and fax numbers, bank reference, as well as a listing of floor coverings, carpets and rugs currently being imported. In addition, the directory features a comprehensive classified section where importers are listed by product.
Related titles: CD-ROM ed.
Published by: Interdata, 1741 Kekamek, Poulsbo, WA 98370. TEL 360-779-1511, 800-818-0140, FAX 360-697-4696, http://www.importersnet.com. **Dist. by:** Current Pacific Ltd., PO Box 36-536, Northcote, Auckland, New Zealand. TEL 64-9-480-1388, FAX 64-9-480-1387, info@cplnz.com, http://www.cplnz.com.

382.029 USA
INTERNATIONAL DIRECTORY OF FOOD AND BEVERAGES IMPORTERS. Text in English. 1978. a., latest 2002. looseleaf. USD 320 print or CD-ROM ed.; USD 370 combined subscription print & CD-ROM eds. (effective 2004). **Document type:** *Directory, Trade.* **Description:** Provides information for manufacturers, exporters and trading firms; includes complete name and address; name of contact person; email address; year established; number of employees; telephone and fax numbers, bank reference, as well as a listing of food and beverages currently being imported. In addition, the directory features a comprehensive classified section where importers are listed by product.
Related titles: CD-ROM ed.
Published by: Interdata, 1741 Kekamek, Poulsbo, WA 98370. TEL 360-779-1511, 800-818-0140, FAX 360-697-4696, http://www.importersnet.com. **Dist. by:** Current Pacific Ltd., PO Box 36-536, Northcote, Auckland, New Zealand. TEL 64-9-480-1388, FAX 64-9-480-1387, info@cplnz.com, http://www.cplnz.com.

382.029 USA
INTERNATIONAL DIRECTORY OF FURNITURE AND HOME FURNISHINGS IMPORTERS. Text in English. 1978. a., latest 2001. looseleaf. USD 320 print or CD-ROM ed.; USD 370 combined subscription print & CD-ROM eds. (effective 2004). **Document type:** *Directory, Trade.* **Description:** Provides information for manufacturers, exporters and trading firms; includes complete name and address; name of contact person; email address; year established; number of employees; telephone and fax numbers, bank reference, as well as a listing of furniture and home furnishings currently being imported. In addition, the directory features a comprehensive classified section where importers are listed by product.
Related titles: CD-ROM ed.
Published by: Interdata, 1741 Kekamek, Poulsbo, WA 98370. TEL 360-779-1511, 800-818-0140, FAX 360-697-4696, http://www.importersnet.com. **Dist. by:** Current Pacific Ltd., PO Box 36-536, Northcote, Auckland, New Zealand. TEL 64-9-480-1388, FAX 64-9-480-1387, info@cplnz.com, http://www.cplnz.com.

382.029 USA
INTERNATIONAL DIRECTORY OF GARDEN, LAWN AND PATIO EQUIPMENT AND SUPPLIES IMPORTERS. Text in English. 1978. a., latest 2001. looseleaf. USD 295 print or CD-ROM ed.; USD 345 print & CD-ROM eds. (effective 2004). **Document type:** *Directory, Trade.* **Description:** Provides information for manufacturers, exporters and trading firms; includes complete name and address; name of contact person; email address; year established; number of employees; telephone and fax numbers, bank reference, as well as a listing of garden, lawn and patio equipment and supplies currently being imported. In addition, the directory features a comprehensive classified section where importers are listed by product.
Related titles: CD-ROM ed.
Published by: Interdata, 1741 Kekamek, Poulsbo, WA 98370. TEL 360-779-1511, 800-818-0140, FAX 360-697-4696, http://www.importersnet.com. **Dist. by:** Current Pacific Ltd., PO Box 36-536, Northcote, Auckland, New Zealand. TEL 64-9-480-1388, FAX 64-9-480-1387, info@cplnz.com, http://www.cplnz.com.

382.029 USA
INTERNATIONAL DIRECTORY OF HAND TOOLS AND POWER TOOLS IMPORTERS. Text in English. 1978. a., latest 2001. looseleaf. USD 260 print or CD-ROM ed.; USD 310 combined subscription print & CD-ROM eds. (effective 2004). **Document type:** *Directory, Trade.* **Description:** Provides information for manufacturers, exporters and trading firms; includes complete name and address; name of contact person; email address; year established; number of employees; telephone and fax numbers, bank reference, as well as a listing of hand tools and power tools currently being imported. In addition, the directory features a comprehensive classified section where importers are listed by product.
Related titles: CD-ROM ed.
Published by: Interdata, 1741 Kekamek, Poulsbo, WA 98370. TEL 360-779-1511, 800-818-0140, FAX 360-697-4696, http://www.importersnet.com. **Dist. by:** Current Pacific Ltd., PO Box 36-536, Northcote, Auckland, New Zealand. TEL 64-9-480-1388, FAX 64-9-480-1387, info@cplnz.com, http://www.cplnz.com.

382.029 USA
INTERNATIONAL DIRECTORY OF HOUSEHOLD AND KITCHEN APPLIANCES IMPORTERS. Text in English. 1978. a., latest 2001. looseleaf. USD 220 print or CD-ROM ed.; USD 270 combined subscription print & CD-ROM eds. (effective 2004). **Document type:** *Directory, Trade.* **Description:** Provides information for manufacturers, exporters and trading firms; includes complete name and address; name of contact person; email address; year established; number of employees; telephone and fax numbers, bank reference, as well as a listing of household and kitchen appliances currently being imported. In addition, the directory features a comprehensive classified section where importers are listed by product.
Related titles: CD-ROM ed.
Published by: Interdata, 1741 Kekamek, Poulsbo, WA 98370. TEL 360-779-1511, 800-818-0140, FAX 360-697-4696, http://www.importersnet.com. **Dist. by:** Current Pacific Ltd., PO Box 36-536, Northcote, Auckland, New Zealand. TEL 64-9-480-1388, FAX 64-9-480-1387, info@cplnz.com, http://www.cplnz.com.

382.029 USA
INTERNATIONAL DIRECTORY OF HOUSEWARES AND HOME ACCESSORIES IMPORTERS. Text in English. 1978. a., latest 2001. looseleaf. USD 320 print or CD-ROM ed.; USD 370 combined subscription print & CD-ROM eds. (effective 2004). **Document type:** *Directory, Trade.* **Description:** Provides information for manufacturers, exporters and trading firms; includes complete name and address; name of contact person; email address; year established; number of employees; telephone and fax numbers, bank reference, as well as a listing of housewares and home accessories currently being imported. In addition, the directory features a comprehensive classified section where importers are listed by product.
Related titles: CD-ROM ed.
Published by: Interdata, 1741 Kekamek, Poulsbo, WA 98370. TEL 360-779-1511, 800-818-0140, FAX 360-697-4696, http://www.importersnet.com. **Dist. by:** Current Pacific Ltd., PO Box 36-536, Northcote, Auckland, New Zealand. TEL 64-9-480-1388, FAX 64-9-480-1387, info@cplnz.com, http://www.cplnz.com.

382.029 USA ISSN 1050-5520
HF3873.I58
INTERNATIONAL DIRECTORY OF IMPORTERS: AFRICA. Text in English. 1978. irreg., latest vol.13, 2002. looseleaf. USD 250; USD 1,870 combined subscription for complete 9 vol. set (effective 2001). 479 p./no.; **Document type:** *Directory, Trade.* **Description:** Features more than 11,000 importing firms from 42 different countries in Africa - from Algeria to Zimbabwe. Contains detailed company information, as well as a comprehensive commodity index.
Related titles: CD-ROM ed.: USD 285 (effective 2001).
Published by: Interdata, 1741 Kekamek, Poulsbo, WA 98370. TEL 360-779-1511, 800-818-0140, FAX 360-697-4696, http://www.importersnet.com. **Dist. by:** Current Pacific Ltd., PO Box 36-536, Northcote, Auckland, New Zealand. TEL 64-9-480-1388, FAX 64-9-480-1387, info@cplnz.com, http://www.cplnz.com.

382.029 USA ISSN 1050-5539
HF3751.8
INTERNATIONAL DIRECTORY OF IMPORTERS: ASIA - PACIFIC. Text in English. a. (in 2 vols.), latest vol.13, 2001. looseleaf. USD 385; USD 1,870 combined subscription for complete 9 vol. set (effective 2001). 1122 p./no.; **Document type:** *Directory, Trade.* **Description:** Covers Australia, Bangladesh, China, Hong Kong, India, Indonesia, Japan, Kazakhstan, Malaysia, Mautitius, Nepal, New Zealand, Pakistan, Philippines, Singapore, South Korea, South Pacific Islands, Sri Lanka, Taiwan Thailand, Uzbekistan and Vietnam. Includes a comprehensive index and details company information; over 30,000 entries.
Related titles: CD-ROM ed.: USD 455 (effective 2001).
Published by: Interdata, 1741 Kekamek, Poulsbo, WA 98370. TEL 360-779-1511, 800-818-0140, FAX 360-697-4696, http://www.importersnet.com. **Dist. by:** Current Pacific Ltd., PO Box 36-536, Northcote, Auckland, New Zealand. TEL 64-9-480-1388, FAX 64-9-480-1387, info@cplnz.com, http://www.cplnz.com.

382.029 USA ISSN 1050-5555
HF3493
INTERNATIONAL DIRECTORY OF IMPORTERS: EUROPE. Text in English. a. (in 3 vols.), latest vol.13, 2002. looseleaf. USD 485; USD 1,870 combined subscription for complete 9 vol. set (effective 2001). 1664 p./no.; **Document type:** *Directory, Trade.* **Description:** Covers over 54,000 importers in 36 countries in Western and Eastern Europe. Details company information and contains a comprehensive commodity index.
Related titles: CD-ROM ed.: USD 585 (effective 2001).
Published by: Interdata, 1741 Kekamek, Poulsbo, WA 98370. TEL 360-779-1511, 800-818-0140, FAX 360-697-4696, http://www.importersnet.com. **Dist. by:** Current Pacific Ltd., PO Box 36-536, Northcote, Auckland, New Zealand. TEL 64-9-480-1388, FAX 64-9-480-1387, info@cplnz.com, http://www.cplnz.com.

382.029 USA ISSN 1050-5563
HF3756.A48
INTERNATIONAL DIRECTORY OF IMPORTERS: MIDDLE EAST. Text in English. a., latest vol.13, 2001. looseleaf. USD 250; USD 1,870 combined subscription for complete 9 vol. set (effective 2001). 646 p./no.; **Document type:** *Directory, Trade.* **Description:** Covers Armenia, Azerbaijan, Bahrain, Iran, Israel, Jordan, Kuwait, Lebanon, Malta, Oman, Qatar, Saudi Arabia, Syria, Turkey, United Arab Emirates and Yemen. Lists over 14,000 importers, providing detailed company information and an index.
Related titles: CD-ROM ed.: USD 285 (effective 2001).
Published by: Interdata, 1741 Kekamek, Poulsbo, WA 98370. TEL 360-779-1511, 800-818-0140, FAX 360-697-4696, http://www.importersnet.com. **Dist. by:** Current Pacific Ltd., PO Box 36-536, Northcote, Auckland, New Zealand. FAX 64-9-480-1387, info@cplnz.com, http://www.cplnz.com.

382.029 USA ISSN 1050-5466
HF3012
INTERNATIONAL DIRECTORY OF IMPORTERS: NORTH AMERICA. Text in English. 1982. a., latest vol.12, 2002. looseleaf. USD 250; USD 1,870 combined subscription for complete 9 vol. set (effective 2001). 566 p./no.; **Document type:** *Directory, Trade.* **Description:** Covers the North American continent, featuring 20,000 entries from importing firms in the United States and Canada. Details company information and includes a commodity index.
Related titles: CD-ROM ed.: USD 285 (effective 2001).
Published by: Interdata, 1741 Kekamek, Poulsbo, WA 98370. TEL 360-779-1511, 800-818-0140, FAX 360-697-4696, http://www.importersnet.com. **Dist. by:** Current Pacific Ltd., PO Box 36-536, Northcote, Auckland, New Zealand. TEL 64-9-480-1388, FAX 64-9-480-1387.

382.029 USA ISSN 1050-5547
HF3230.5.A48
INTERNATIONAL DIRECTORY OF IMPORTERS: SOUTH - CENTRAL AMERICA. Text in English. a., latest vol.13, 2002. looseleaf. USD 385; USD 1,870 combined subscription for complete 9 vol. set (effective 2001). 1122 p./no.; **Document type:** *Directory, Trade.* **Description:** Covers Argentina,Belize, Bolivia, Brazil, Chile, Colombia, Costa Rica, Ecuador, El Salvador, Guatemala, Guyana, Honduras, Mexico, Nicaragua, Panama, Paraguay, Peru, Uruguay, Venezuela and the West Indies. Details company information for over 22,000 importers, and includes an index.
Related titles: CD-ROM ed.: USD 455 (effective 2001).
Published by: Interdata, 1741 Kekamek, Poulsbo, WA 98370. TEL 360-779-1511, 800-818-0140, FAX 360-697-4696, http://www.importersnet.com. **Dist. by:** Current Pacific Ltd., PO Box 36-536, Northcote, Auckland, New Zealand. TEL 64-9-480-1388, FAX 64-9-480-1387, info@cplnz.com, http://www.cplnz.com.

B

382.029 USA
INTERNATIONAL DIRECTORY OF JEWELRY AND COSTUME JEWELRY IMPORTERS. Text in English. 1978. a. looseleaf. USD 220 print or CD-ROM ed.; USD 270 combined subscription print or CD-ROM eds. (effective 2004). **Document type:** *Directory, Trade.* **Description:** Provides information for manufacturers, exporters and trading firms; includes complete name and address; name of contact person; email address; year established; number of employees; telephone and fax numbers, bank reference, as well as a listing of jewelry and costume jewelry currently being imported. In addition, the directory features a comprehensive classified section where importers are listed by product.
Related titles: CD-ROM ed.
Published by: Interdata, 1741 Kekamek, Poulsbo, WA 98370. TEL 360-779-1511, 800-818-0140, FAX 360-697-4696, http://www.importersnet.com. **Dist. by:** Current Pacific Ltd., PO Box 36-536, Northcote, Auckland, New Zealand. TEL 64-9-480-1388, FAX 64-9-480-1387, info@cplnz.com, http://www.cplnz.com.

382.029 USA
INTERNATIONAL DIRECTORY OF KITCHENWARE, TABLEWARE AND GLASSWARE IMPORTERS. Text in English. 1978. a., latest 2001. looseleaf. USD 260 print or CD-ROM ed.; USD 310 combined subscription print & CD-ROM eds. (effective 2004). **Document type:** *Directory, Trade.* **Description:** Provides information for manufacturers, exporters and trading firms; includes complete name and address; name of contact person; email address; year established; number of employees; telephone and fax numbers, bank reference, as well as a listing of kitchenware, tableware and glassware currently being imported. In addition, the directory features a comprehensive classified section where importers are listed by product.
Related titles: CD-ROM ed.
Published by: Interdata, 1741 Kekamek, Poulsbo, WA 98370. TEL 360-779-1511, 800-818-0140, FAX 360-697-4696, http://www.importersnet.com. **Dist. by:** Current Pacific Ltd., PO Box 36-536, Northcote, Auckland, New Zealand. TEL 64-9-480-1388, FAX 64-9-480-1387, info@cplnz.com, http://www.cplnz.com.

382.029 USA
INTERNATIONAL DIRECTORY OF LEATHER GOODS, FOOTWEAR AND TRAVEL ACCESSORIES IMPORTERS. Text in English. 1978. a., latest 2002. looseleaf. USD 260 print or CD-ROM ed.; USD 310 combined subscription print & CD-ROM eds. (effective 2004). **Document type:** *Directory, Trade.* **Description:** Provides information for manufacturers, exporters and trading firms; includes complete name and address; name of contact person; email address; year established; number of employees; telephone and fax numbers, bank reference, as well as a listing of leather goods, footwear and travel accessories currently being imported. In addition, the directory features a comprehensive classified section where importers are listed by product.
Related titles: CD-ROM ed.
Published by: Interdata, 1741 Kekamek, Poulsbo, WA 98370. TEL 360-779-1511, 800-818-0140, FAX 360-697-4696, http://www.importersnet.com. **Dist. by:** Current Pacific Ltd., PO Box 36-536, Northcote, Auckland, New Zealand. TEL 64-9-480-1388, FAX 64-9-480-1387, info@cplnz.com, http://www.cplnz.com.

▼ *new title* ➤ *refereed* ✶ *unverified* ♦ *full entry avail.*

382.029 USA
INTERNATIONAL DIRECTORY OF LIGHTING EQUIPMENT, LAMPS AND ACCESSORIES IMPORTERS. Text in English. 1978. a., latest 2001. looseleaf. USD 220 print or CD-ROM ed.; USD 270 combined subscription print & CD-ROM eds. (effective 2004). **Document type:** *Directory, Trade.* **Description:** Provides information for manufacturers, exporters and trading firms; includes complete name and address; name of contact person; email address; year established; number of employees; telephone and fax numbers, bank reference, as well as a listing of lighting equipment, lamps & accessories currently being imported. In addition, the directory features a comprehensive classified section where importers are listed by product.
Related titles: CD-ROM ed.
Published by: Interdata, 1741 Kekamek, Poulsbo, WA 98370. TEL 360-779-1511, 800-818-0140, FAX 360-697-4696, http://www.importersnet.com. **Dist. by:** Current Pacific Ltd., PO Box 36-536, Northcote, Auckland, New Zealand. TEL 64-9-480-1388, FAX 64-9-480-1387, info@cplnz.com, http://www.cplnz.com.

382.029 USA
INTERNATIONAL DIRECTORY OF MACHINE TOOLS AND ACCESSORIES IMPORTERS. Text in English. 1978. a., latest 2001. looseleaf. USD 220 print or CD-ROM ed.; USD 270 combined subscription print & CD-ROM eds. (effective 2004). **Document type:** *Directory, Trade.* **Description:** Provides information for manufacturers, exporters and trading firms; includes complete name and address; name of contact person; email address; year established; number of employees; telephone and fax numbers, bank reference, as well as a listing of machine tools and accessories currently being imported. In addition, the directory features a comprehensive classified section where importers are listed by product.
Related titles: CD-ROM ed.
Published by: Interdata, 1741 Kekamek, Poulsbo, WA 98370. TEL 360-779-1511, 800-818-0140, FAX 360-697-4696, http://www.importersnet.com. **Dist. by:** Current Pacific Ltd., PO Box 36-536, Northcote, Auckland, New Zealand. TEL 64-9-480-1388, FAX 64-9-480-1387, info@cplnz.com, http://www.cplnz.com.

382.029 USA
INTERNATIONAL DIRECTORY OF MARINE AND BOATING EQUIPMENT AND SUPPLIES IMPORTERS. Text in English. 1978. a., latest 2001. looseleaf. USD 260 print or CD-ROM ed.; USD 310 combined subscription print & CD-ROM eds. (effective 2004). **Document type:** *Directory, Trade.* **Description:** Provides information for manufacturers, exporters and trading firms; includes complete name and address; name of contact person; email address; year established; number of employees; telephone and fax numbers, bank reference, as well as a listing of marine and boating equipment and supplies currently being imported. In addition, the directory features a comprehensive classified section where importers are listed by product.
Related titles: CD-ROM ed.
Published by: Interdata, 1741 Kekamek, Poulsbo, WA 98370. TEL 360-779-1511, 800-818-0140, FAX 360-697-4696, http://www.importersnet.com. **Dist. by:** Current Pacific Ltd., PO Box 36-536, Northcote, Auckland, New Zealand. TEL 64-9-480-1388, FAX 64-9-480-1387, info@cplnz.com, http://www.cplnz.com.

382.029 USA
INTERNATIONAL DIRECTORY OF MEASURING EQUIPMENT AND SCALES IMPORTERS. Text in English. 1978. a., latest 2001. looseleaf. USD 220 print or CD-ROM ed.; USD 270 combined subscription print & CD-ROM eds. (effective 2004). **Document type:** *Directory, Trade.* **Description:** Provides information for manufacturers, exporters and trading firms; includes complete name and address; name of contact person; email address; year established; number of employees; telephone and fax numbers, bank reference, as well as a listing of measuring equipment and scales currently being imported. In addition, the directory features a comprehensive classified section where importers are listed by product.
Related titles: CD-ROM ed.
Published by: Interdata, 1741 Kekamek, Poulsbo, WA 98370. TEL 360-779-1511, 800-818-0140, FAX 360-697-4696, http://www.importersnet.com. **Dist. by:** Current Pacific Ltd., PO Box 36-536, Northcote, Auckland, New Zealand. TEL 64-9-480-1388, FAX 64-9-480-1387, info@cplnz.com, http://www.cplnz.com.

382.029 USA
INTERNATIONAL DIRECTORY OF MEDICAL, HOSPITAL AND SURGICAL EQUIPMENT IMPORTERS. Text in English. a., latest 2001. looseleaf. USD 320 print or CD-ROM ed.; USD 370 combined subscription print & CD-ROM eds. (effective 2004). **Document type:** *Directory, Trade.* **Description:** Provides information for manufacturers, exporters and trading firms; includes complete name and address; name of contact person; email address; year established; number of employees; telephone and fax numbers, bank reference, as well as a listing of medical, hospital and surgical equipment currently being imported. In addition, the directory features a comprehensive classified section where importers are listed by product.
Related titles: CD-ROM ed.
Published by: Interdata, 1741 Kekamek, Poulsbo, WA 98370. TEL 360-779-1511, 800-818-0140, FAX 360-697-4696, http://www.importersnet.com. **Dist. by:** Current Pacific Ltd., PO Box 36-536, Northcote, Auckland, New Zealand. TEL 64-9-480-1388, FAX 64-9-480-1387, info@cplnz.com, http://www.cplnz.com.

INTERNATIONAL DIRECTORY OF NEW AND RENEWABLE ENERGY INFORMATION SOURCES AND RESEARCH CENTRES. see *ENERGY*

382.029 USA
INTERNATIONAL DIRECTORY OF OFFICE EQUIPMENT, STATIONERY AND SUPPLIES IMPORTERS. Text in English. 1978. a., latest 2002. looseleaf. USD 320 print or CD-ROM ed.; USD 370 combined subscription print & CD-ROM eds. (effective 2004). **Document type:** *Directory, Trade.* **Description:** Provides information for manufacturers, exporters and trading firms; includes complete name and address; name of contact person; email address; year established; number of employees; telephone and fax numbers, bank reference, as well as a listing of office equipment, stationery and supplies currently being imported. In addition, the directory features a comprehensive classified section where importers are listed by product.
Related titles: CD-ROM ed.
Published by: Interdata, 1741 Kekamek, Poulsbo, WA 98370. TEL 360-779-1511, 800-818-0140, FAX 360-697-4696, http://www.importersnet.com. **Dist. by:** Current Pacific Ltd., PO Box 36-536, Northcote, Auckland, New Zealand. TEL 64-9-480-1388, FAX 64-9-480-1387, info@cplnz.com, http://www.cplnz.com.

382.029 USA
INTERNATIONAL DIRECTORY OF OPTICAL GOODS AND INSTRUMENTS IMPORTERS. Text in English. 1978. a., latest 2001. looseleaf. USD 220 print or CD-ROM ed.; USD 270 combined subscription print & CD-ROM eds. (effective 2004). **Document type:** *Directory, Trade.* **Description:** Provides information for manufacturers, exporters and trading firms; includes complete name and address; name of contact person; email address; year established; number of employees; telephone and fax numbers, bank reference, as well as a listing of optical goods and instruments currently being imported. In addition, the directory features a comprehensive classified section where importers are listed by product.
Related titles: CD-ROM ed.
Published by: Interdata, 1741 Kekamek, Poulsbo, WA 98370. TEL 360-779-1511, 800-818-0140, FAX 360-697-4696, http://www.importersnet.com. **Dist. by:** Current Pacific Ltd., PO Box 36-536, Northcote, Auckland, New Zealand. TEL 64-9-480-1388, FAX 64-9-480-1387, info@cplnz.com, http://www.cplnz.com.

382.029 USA
INTERNATIONAL DIRECTORY OF PAINT, PAINT SUPPLIES AND ALLIED PRODUCTS IMPORTERS. Text in English. 1978. a., latest 2001. looseleaf. USD 220 print or CD-ROM ed.; USD 270 combined subscription print & CD-ROM eds. (effective 2004). **Document type:** *Directory, Trade.* **Description:** Provides information for manufacturers, exporters and trading firms; includes complete name and address; name of contact person; email address; year established; number of employees; telephone and fax numbers, bank reference, as well as a listing of paint, paint supplies and allied products currently being imported. In addition, the directory features a comprehensive classified section where importers are listed by product.
Related titles: CD-ROM ed.
Published by: Interdata, 1741 Kekamek, Poulsbo, WA 98370. TEL 360-779-1511, 800-818-0140, FAX 360-697-4696, http://www.importersnet.com. **Dist. by:** Current Pacific Ltd., PO Box 36-536, Northcote, Auckland, New Zealand. TEL 64-9-480-1388, FAX 64-9-480-1387, info@cplnz.com, http://www.cplnz.com.

382.029 USA
INTERNATIONAL DIRECTORY OF PAPER, PAPER GOODS AND STATIONERY PRODUCTS IMPORTERS. Text in English. 1978. a., latest 2002. looseleaf. USD 295 print or CD-ROM ed.; USD 345 combined subscription print & CD-ROM eds. (effective 2004). **Document type:** *Directory, Trade.* **Description:** Provides information for manufacturers, exporters and trading firms; includes complete name and address; name of contact person; email address; year established; number of employees; telephone and fax numbers, bank reference, as well as a listing of paper, paper goods and stationery products currently being imported. In addition, the directory features a comprehensive classified section where importers are listed by product.
Related titles: CD-ROM ed.
Published by: Interdata, 1741 Kekamek, Poulsbo, WA 98370. TEL 360-779-1511, 800-818-0140, FAX 360-697-4696, http://www.importersnet.com. **Dist. by:** Current Pacific Ltd., PO Box 36-536, Northcote, Auckland, New Zealand. TEL 64-9-480-1388, FAX 64-9-480-1387, info@cplnz.com, http://www.cplnz.com.

382.029 USA
INTERNATIONAL DIRECTORY OF PHOTOGRAPHIC EQUIPMENT AND SUPPLIES IMPORTERS. Text in English. 1978. a., latest 2001. looseleaf. USD 200 print or CD-ROM ed.; USD 250 combined subscription print & CD-ROM eds. (effective 2004). **Document type:** *Directory, Trade.* **Description:** Provides information for manufacturers, exporters and trading firms; includes complete name and address; name of contact person; email address; year established; number of employees; telephone and fax numbers, bank reference, as well as a listing of photographic equipment and supplies currently being imported. In addition, the directory features a comprehensive classified section where importers are listed by product.
Related titles: CD-ROM ed.
Published by: Interdata, 1741 Kekamek, Poulsbo, WA 98370. TEL 360-779-1511, 800-818-0140, FAX 360-697-4696, http://www.importersnet.com. **Dist. by:** Current Pacific Ltd., PO Box 36-536, Northcote, Auckland, New Zealand. TEL 64-9-480-1388, FAX 64-9-480-1387, info@cplnz.com, http://www.cplnz.com.

382.029 USA
INTERNATIONAL DIRECTORY OF PLASTIC AND PLASTIC PRODUCTS IMPORTERS. Text in English. 1978. a., latest 2001. looseleaf. USD 295 print or CD-ROM ed.; USD 345 combined subscription print & CD-ROM eds. (effective 2004). **Document type:** *Directory, Trade.* **Description:** Provides information for manufacturers, exporters and trading firms; includes complete name and address; name of contact person; email address; year established; number of employees; telephone and fax numbers, bank reference, as well as a listing of plastic and plastic products currently being imported. In addition, the directory features a comprehensive classified section where importers are listed by product.
Related titles: CD-ROM ed.
Published by: Interdata, 1741 Kekamek, Poulsbo, WA 98370. TEL 360-779-1511, 800-818-0140, FAX 360-697-4696, http://www.importersnet.com. **Dist. by:** Current Pacific Ltd., PO Box 36-536, Northcote, Auckland, New Zealand. TEL 64-9-480-1388, FAX 64-9-480-1387, info@cplnz.com, http://www.cplnz.com.

382.029 USA
INTERNATIONAL DIRECTORY OF PLUMBING SUPPLIES, SANITARY WARE, PIPES & FITTINGS IMPORTERS. Text in English. 1978. a., latest 2001. looseleaf. USD 260 print or CD-ROM ed.; USD 310 combined subscription print & CD-ROM eds. (effective 2004). **Document type:** *Directory, Trade.* **Description:** Provides information for manufacturers, exporters and trading firms; includes complete name and address; name of contact person; email address; year established; number of employees; telephone and fax numbers, bank reference, as well as a listing of plumbing supplies, sanitary ware, pipes & fittings currently being imported. In addition, the directory features a comprehensive classified section where importers are listed by product.
Related titles: CD-ROM ed.
Published by: Interdata, 1741 Kekamek, Poulsbo, WA 98370. TEL 360-779-1511, 800-818-0140, FAX 360-697-4696, http://www.importersnet.com. **Dist. by:** Current Pacific Ltd., PO Box 36-536, Northcote, Auckland, New Zealand. TEL 64-9-480-1388, FAX 64-9-480-1387, info@cplnz.com, http://www.cplnz.com.

338.0029 GBR ISSN 1354-2400
INTERNATIONAL DIRECTORY OF POWER GENERATION. Text in English. 1994. a. GBP 85; GBP 90 foreign. **Document type:** *Directory, Trade.* **Description:** Provides a comprehensive guide to world suppliers of electricity generating plant, including nuclear and gas turbine technology, along with alternative sources such as wind, geothermal and wave power.
Published by: Turret R A I plc, Armstrong House, 38 Market Sq, Uxbridge, Middx UB8 1TG, United Kingdom. TEL 44-1895-454545, FAX 44-1895-454647.

382.029 USA
INTERNATIONAL DIRECTORY OF PRINTING AND GRAPHIC ARTS EQUIPMENT AND SUPPLIES IMPORTERS. Text in English. 1978. a., latest 2001. looseleaf. USD 220 print or CD-ROM ed.; USD 270 combined subscription print & CD-ROM eds. (effective 2004). **Document type:** *Directory, Trade.* **Description:** Provides information for manufacturers, exporters and trading firms; includes complete name and address; name of contact person; email address; year established; number of employees; telephone and fax numbers, bank reference, as well as a listing of printing and graphic arts equipment and supplies currently being imported. In addition, the directory features a comprehensive classified section where importers are listed by product.
Related titles: CD-ROM ed.
Published by: Interdata, 1741 Kekamek, Poulsbo, WA 98370. TEL 360-779-1511, 800-818-0140, FAX 360-697-4696, http://www.importersnet.com. **Dist. by:** Current Pacific Ltd., PO Box 36-536, Northcote, Auckland, New Zealand. TEL 64-9-480-1388, FAX 64-9-480-1387, info@cplnz.com, http://www.cplnz.com.

380.1029 USA ISSN 0894-7104
Z231.5.P7
INTERNATIONAL DIRECTORY OF PRIVATE PRESSES. Text in English. 1978. a., latest vol.7, 1995. USD 50. back issues avail. **Document type:** *Directory.*
Published by: Educators Research Service, 2443 Fair Oaks Blvd, Ste 316, Sacramento, CA 95825. TEL 916-924-1151. Ed., Pub. Budd Westreich.

382.029 USA
INTERNATIONAL DIRECTORY OF PUMPS AND COMPRESSORS IMPORTERS. Text in English. 1978. a., latest 2001. looseleaf. USD 220 print or CD-ROM ed.; USD 270 combined subscription print & CD-ROM eds. (effective 2004). **Document type:** *Directory, Trade.* **Description:** Provides information for manufacturers, exporters and trading firms; includes complete name and address; name of contact person; email address; year established; number of employees; telephone and fax numbers, bank reference, as well as a listing of pumps and compressors currently being imported. In addition, the directory features a comprehensive classified section where importers are listed by product.
Related titles: CD-ROM ed.
Published by: Interdata, 1741 Kekamek, Poulsbo, WA 98370. TEL 360-779-1511, 800-818-0140, FAX 360-697-4696, http://www.importersnet.com. **Dist. by:** Current Pacific Ltd., PO Box 36-536, Northcote, Auckland, New Zealand. TEL 64-9-480-1388, FAX 64-9-480-1387, info@cplnz.com, http://www.cplnz.com.

382.029 USA
INTERNATIONAL DIRECTORY OF REFRIGERATION, VENTILATION AND HEATING EQUIPMENT IMPORTERS. Text in English. 1978. a., latest 2001. looseleaf. USD 260 print or CD-ROM ed.; USD 310 combined subscription print & CD-ROM eds. (effective 2004). **Document type:** *Directory, Trade.* **Description:** Provides information for manufacturers, exporters and trading firms; includes complete name and address; name of contact person; email address; year established; number of employees; telephone and fax numbers, bank reference, as well as a listing of refrigeration, ventilation and heating equipment currently being imported. In addition, the directory features a comprehensive classified section where importers are listed by product.
Related titles: CD-ROM ed.
Published by: Interdata, 1741 Kekamek, Poulsbo, WA 98370. TEL 360-779-1511, 800-818-0140, FAX 360-697-4696, http://www.importersnet.com. **Dist. by:** Current Pacific Ltd., PO Box 36-536, Northcote, Auckland, New Zealand. TEL 64-9-480-1388, FAX 64-9-480-1387, info@cplnz.com, http://www.cplnz.com.

382.029 USA
INTERNATIONAL DIRECTORY OF SAFETY, SECURITY AND FIRE FIGHTING EQUIPMENT IMPORTERS. Text in English. 1978. a., latest 2001. looseleaf. USD 260 print or CD-ROM ed.; USD 310 combined subscription print & CD-ROM eds. (effective 2004). **Document type:** *Directory, Trade.* **Description:** Provides information for manufacturers, exporters and trading firms; includes complete name and address; name of contact person; email address; year established; number of employees; telephone and fax numbers, bank reference, as well as a listing of safety, security and fire fighting equipment currently being imported. In addition, the directory features a comprehensive classified section where importers are listed by product.
Related titles: CD-ROM ed.
Published by: Interdata, 1741 Kekamek, Poulsbo, WA 98370. TEL 360-779-1511, 800-818-0140, FAX 360-697-4696, http://www.importersnet.com. **Dist. by:** Current Pacific Ltd., PO Box 36-536, Northcote, Auckland, New Zealand. TEL 64-9-480-1388, FAX 64-9-480-1387, info@cplnz.com, http://www.cplnz.com.

382.029 USA
INTERNATIONAL DIRECTORY OF SCREWS, NUTS, BOLTS AND FASTENERS IMPORTERS. Text in English. 1978. a., latest 2001. looseleaf. USD 200 print or CD-ROM ed.; USD 250 combined subscription print & CD-ROM eds. (effective 2004). **Document type:** *Directory, Trade.* **Description:** Provides information for manufacturers, exporters and trading firms; includes complete name and address; name of contact person; email address; year established; number of employees; telephone and fax numbers, bank reference, as well as a listing of screws, nuts, bolts and fasteners currently being imported. In addition, the directory features a comprehensive classified section where importers are listed by product.
Related titles: CD-ROM ed.
Published by: Interdata, 1741 Kekamek, Poulsbo, WA 98370. TEL 360-779-1511, 800-818-0140, FAX 360-697-4696, http://www.importersnet.com. **Dist. by:** Current Pacific Ltd., PO Box 36-536, Northcote, Auckland, New Zealand. TEL 64-9-480-1388, FAX 64-9-480-1387, info@cplnz.com, http://www.cplnz.com.

382.029 USA
INTERNATIONAL DIRECTORY OF SPORTING GOODS AND TOYS IMPORTERS. Text in English. 1978. a. looseleaf. USD 295 print or CD-ROM ed.; USD 345 combined subscription print & CD-ROM eds. (effective 2004). **Document type:** *Directory, Trade.* **Description:** Provides information for manufacturers, exporters and trading firms; includes complete name and address; name of contact person; email address; year established; number of employees; telephone and fax numbers, bank reference, as well as a listing of sporting goods and toys currently being imported. In addition, the directory features a comprehensive classified section where importers are listed by product.
Related titles: CD-ROM ed.
Published by: Interdata, 1741 Kekamek, Poulsbo, WA 98370. TEL 360-779-1511, 800-818-0140, FAX 360-697-4696, http://www.importersnet.com/comdir/comdir13d.htm. **Dist. by:** Current Pacific Ltd., PO Box 36-536, Northcote, Auckland, New Zealand. TEL 64-9-480-1388, FAX 64-9-480-1387, info@cplnz.com, http://www.cplnz.com.

INTERNATIONAL DIRECTORY OF TESTING LABORATORIES. see *PHYSICS—Mechanics*

382.029 USA
INTERNATIONAL DIRECTORY OF TEXTILES AND FABRICS IMPORTERS. Text in English. 1978. a., latest 2001. looseleaf. USD 260 print or CD-ROM ed.; USD 310 combined subscription print & CD-ROM eds. (effective 2004). **Document type:** *Directory, Trade.* **Description:** Provides information for manufacturers, exporters and trading firms; includes complete name and address; name of contact person; email address; year established; number of employees; telephone and fax numbers, bank reference, as well as a listing of textiles and fabrics currently being imported. In addition, the directory features a comprehensive classified section where importers are listed by product.
Related titles: CD-ROM ed.
Published by: Interdata, 1741 Kekamek, Poulsbo, WA 98370. TEL 360-779-1511, 800-818-0140, FAX 360-697-4696, http://www.importersnet.com. **Dist. by:** Current Pacific Ltd., PO Box 36-536, Northcote, Auckland, New Zealand. TEL 64-9-480-1388, FAX 64-9-480-1387, info@cplnz.com, http://www.cplnz.com.

382.029 USA
INTERNATIONAL DIRECTORY OF TIRES AND TUBES IMPORTERS. Text in English. 1978. a., latest 2001. looseleaf. USD 200 print or CD-ROM ed.; USD 250 combined subscription print & CD-ROM eds. (effective 2004). **Document type:** *Directory, Trade.* **Description:** Provides information for manufacturers, exporters and trading firms; includes complete name and address; name of contact person; email address; year established; number of employees; telephone and fax numbers, bank reference, as well as a listing of tires and tubes currently being imported. In addition, the directory features a comprehensive classified section where importers are listed by product.
Related titles: CD-ROM ed.
Published by: Interdata, 1741 Kekamek, Poulsbo, WA 98370. TEL 360-779-1511, 800-818-0140, FAX 360-697-4696, http://www.importersnet.com. **Dist. by:** Current Pacific Ltd., PO Box 36-536, Northcote, Auckland, New Zealand. TEL 64-9-480-1388, FAX 64-9-480-1387, info@cplnz.com, http://www.cplnz.com.

382.029 USA
INTERNATIONAL DIRECTORY OF WATCHES AND CLOCKS IMPORTERS. Text in English. 1978. a., latest 2002. looseleaf. USD 200 print or CD-ROM ed.; USD 250 combined subscription print & CD-ROM eds. (effective 2004). **Document type:** *Directory, Trade.* **Description:** Provides information for manufacturers, exporters and trading firms; includes complete name and address; name of contact person; email address; year established; number of employees; telephone and fax numbers, bank reference, as well as a listing of watches and clocks currently being imported. In addition, the directory features a comprehensive classified section where importers are listed by product.
Related titles: CD-ROM ed.
Published by: Interdata, 1741 Kekamek, Poulsbo, WA 98370. TEL 360-779-1511, 800-818-0140, FAX 360-697-4696, http://www.importersnet.com. **Dist. by:** Current Pacific Ltd., PO Box 36-536, Northcote, Auckland, New Zealand. TEL 64-9-480-1388, FAX 64-9-480-1387, info@cplnz.com, http://www.cplnz.com.

382.029 USA
INTERNATIONAL DIRECTORY OF WELDING AND SOLDERING EQUIPMENT IMPORTERS. Text in English. 1978. a., latest 2001. looseleaf. USD 200 print or CD-ROM ed.; USD 250 combined subscription print & CD-ROM eds. (effective 2004). **Document type:** *Directory, Trade.* **Description:** Provides information for manufacturers, exporters and trading firms; includes complete name and address; name of contact person; email address; year established; number of employees; telephone and fax numbers, bank reference, as well as a listing of welding and soldering equipment currently being imported. In addition, the directory features a comprehensive classified section where importers are listed by product.
Related titles: CD-ROM ed.
Published by: Interdata, 1741 Kekamek, Poulsbo, WA 98370. TEL 360-779-1511, 800-818-0140, FAX 360-697-4696, http://www.importersnet.com. **Dist. by:** Current Pacific Ltd., PO Box 36-536, Northcote, Auckland, New Zealand. TEL 64-9-480-1388, FAX 64-9-480-1387, info@cplnz.com, http://www.cplnz.com.

382.029 USA
INTERNATIONAL DIRECTORY OF WOODWORKING EQUIPMENT AND TOOLS IMPORTERS. Text in English. 1978. a., latest 2001. looseleaf. USD 220 print or CD-ROM ed.; USD 270 combined subscription print & CD-ROM eds. (effective 2004). **Document type:** *Directory, Trade.* **Description:** Provides information for manufacturers, exporters and trading firms; includes complete name and address; name of contact person; email address; year established; number of employees; telephone and fax numbers, bank reference, as well as a listing of woodworking equipment and tools currently being imported. In addition, the directory features a comprehensive classified section where importers are listed by product.
Related titles: CD-ROM ed.
Published by: Interdata, 1741 Kekamek, Poulsbo, WA 98370. TEL 360-779-1511, 800-818-0140, FAX 360-697-4696, http://www.importersnet.com. **Dist. by:** Current Pacific Ltd., PO Box 36-536, Northcote, Auckland, New Zealand. TEL 64-9-480-1388, FAX 64-9-480-1387, info@cplnz.com, http://www.cplnz.com.

INTERNATIONAL ENVIRONMENTAL TECHNOLOGY. ANNUAL BUYERS DIRECTORY. see *ENVIRONMENTAL STUDIES—Pollution*

551.3029 USA ISSN 1074-0104
INTERNATIONAL EROSION CONTROL ASSOCIATION. PRODUCTS & SERVICES DIRECTORY. Text in English. 1990. a. USD 19 to non-members; USD 15 to members. **Document type:** *Directory.* **Description:** Lists 500 manufacturers, suppliers, consultants, contractors, organizations, and government agencies specializing in erosion control.
Published by: International Erosion Control Association, PO Box 4904, Steamboat Springs, CO 80477-4904. TEL 970-879-3010, 800-455-4322, FAX 970-879-8563, ecinfo@ieca.org, http://www.ieca.org.

INTERNATIONAL FOOD DIRECTORY. see *FOOD AND FOOD INDUSTRIES*

664.52029 GBR ISSN 1464-0082
INTERNATIONAL FOOD INGREDIENTS & ANALYSIS DIRECTORY. Text in English. a. GBP 89 domestic; GBP 100 foreign (effective 2000). **Document type:** *Directory, Trade.* **Description:** Provides a comprehensive international guide to suppliers of ingredients and additives for food manufacturers and processors.
—BLDSC (4540.301700).
Published by: Turret R A I plc, Armstrong House, 38 Market Sq, Uxbridge, Middx UB8 1TG, United Kingdom. TEL 44-1895-454545, FAX 44-1895-454647. Pub. Antigone Theoharris.

INTERNATIONAL GUIDE TO THE COALFIELDS. see *MINES AND MINING INDUSTRY*

382.029 USA ISSN 1040-6921
HG4509
INTERNATIONAL INVESTOR'S DIRECTORY; sourcebook for international investor. Text in English. 1988. a. (in 6 vols.). USD 75 per vol.. adv. back issues avail. **Document type:** *Directory.*
Related titles: Diskette ed.
—CCC.
Published by: Asset International, Inc., 125 Greenwich Ave, Greenwich, CT 06830. TEL 203-629-5014, FAX 203-629-5024. Ed. Eric Laursen. Circ: 2,000.

INTERNATIONAL KEY PERSONNEL LIST. see *ENGINEERING—Engineering Mechanics And Materials*

340.029 GBR ISSN 0309-0825
THE INTERNATIONAL LAW LIST. Text in English. 1866. a. GBP 54, USD 85 (effective 1997). **Document type:** *Directory.*
Former titles (until 1936): Reference Register and International Law List; (until 1911): Reference Register
Published by: L. Corper-Mordaunt & Co., 57 Fitzhardinge House, 14 Portman Sq, London, W1H 9HB, United Kingdom. TEL 44-171-935-3853, FAX 44-171-487-3836.

INTERNATIONAL LEATHER GUIDE. see *LEATHER AND FUR INDUSTRIES*

INTERNATIONAL LITERARY MARKET PLACE; the directory of the international book publishing industry. see *PUBLISHING AND BOOK TRADE*

665.5029 USA
INTERNATIONAL OIL SCOUTS ASSOCIATION DIRECTORY. Text in English. 1956. a. USD 35 (effective 2000). **Document type:** *Directory.*

B

B

Published by: International Oil Scouts Association, 940310, Houston, TX 77094-7310. Circ: 400.

INTERNATIONAL PESTICIDE DIRECTORY. see *AGRICULTURE—Crop Production And Soil*

INTERNATIONAL PETROLEUM INDUSTRY. see *PETROLEUM AND GAS*

338.0029   GBR
INTERNATIONAL POWER GENERATION DIRECTORY OF EQUIPMENT MANUFACTURERS (1999). Text in English. 1995. a. GBP 64; GBP 73 foreign (effective 2000). **Description:** Provides detailed information for power industry specifiers and purchasers.
Published by: D M G World Media Ltd. (Subsidiary of: Daily Mail and General Trust PLC), Queensway House, 2 Queensway, Redhill, Surrey RH1 1QS, United Kingdom. TEL 44-1737-768611, FAX 44-1737-855475, http://www.dmg.co.uk, http://www.dmgworldmedia.com.

380.1029   USA
HD999.L173
INTERNATIONAL PRIVATE LABEL DIRECTORY (YEAR). Text in English. 1981. a. USD 75; USD 125 foreign (effective 1999). adv. bk.rev. **Document type:** *Directory.* **Description:** Lists suppliers to private and generic labels. Reaches food, drug and general merchandise buyers.
Formerly: Private Label Directory (1047-2266)
Published by: E.W. Williams Publications Co., 2125 Center Ave, Ste 305, Fort Lee, NJ 07024-5898. TEL 201-592-7007, FAX 201-592-7171. Ed. Olga Gudal. Pub. Andrew H Williams. R&P Tony Faber. Adv. contact Charles Loomer. Circ: 10,000.

INTERNATIONAL RADIATION CURING YEARBOOK & DIRECTORY (YEAR). see *ENGINEERING—Chemical Engineering*

INTERNATIONAL REFRACTORIES HANDBOOK & DIRECTORY. see *CERAMICS, GLASS AND POTTERY*

INTERNATIONAL RELATIONS RESEARCH DIRECTORY. see *POLITICAL SCIENCE—International Relations*

INTERNATIONAL SCRAP DIRECTORY. see *METALLURGY*

380.1029 745.1   USA   ISSN 8755-4356
INTERNATIONAL SOCIETY OF APPRAISERS. MEMBERSHIP DIRECTORY. Text in English. 1983. a., latest 2001. USD 15 (effective 2000 - 2001). adv. illus.; maps; tr.lit. Index. back issues avail. **Document type:** *Directory.* **Description:** Includes a membership roster and several indexes for locating qualified personal property appraisers.
Related titles: E-mail ed.; Online - full text ed.
Published by: International Society of Appraisers, 1131 SW 7th St., Ste. 105, Renton, WA 98055-1229. TEL 206-241-0359, FAX 206-241-0436, isahq@isa-appraisers.org, http://www.isa-appraisers.org. Ed. Christian A Coleman. adv.: page USD 300. Circ: 2,000.

381.029   LKA
INTERNATIONAL TRADE DIRECTORY OF SRI LANKA AND MALDIVES. Text in English. 1989. a. USD 50 (effective 1999). adv. **Document type:** *Directory.*
Published by: Trans Publishing House, 39 Canal Rd., P O Box 489, Fort Colombo 1, Sri Lanka. TEL 94-72-330964, FAX 94-72-575599, TELEX 22082 XPOINT CE. Ed. M. Faizer Mackeen. Pub. M Faizer Mackeen. Adv. contact M B M Nawaz.

380.1029   DEU
INTERNATIONAL TRADESHOW DIRECTORY. Text in English. 1985. s-a. EUR 251; EUR 271 foreign (effective 2000). adv. back issues avail. **Document type:** *Directory, Trade.* **Description:** Schedule of fairs and exhibitions worldwide listing approximately 9,000 trade fair and exhibition dates in 114 countries.
Related titles: CD-ROM ed.
Published by: M + A Verlag fuer Messen, Ausstellungen und Kongresse GmbH (Subsidiary of: Deutscher Fachverlag GmbH), Postfach 200128, Frankfurt Am Main, 60605, Germany. TEL 49-69-759502, FAX 49-69-75951280, int-tradeshow-dir@dfv.de, http://www.m-a.com. Ed. Dorit Vogel Seib. Adv. contact Jutta Fautz. B&W page EUR 2,290.59, color page EUR 3,057.53; trim 280 x 210. Circ: 2,732 (paid). **Dist. by:** Current Pacific Ltd., PO Box 36-536, Northcote, Auckland, New Zealand. TEL 64-9-480-1388, FAX 64-9-480-1387, info@cplnz.com, http://www.cplnz.com.

INTERNATIONAL VENDING BUYER'S GUIDE AND DIRECTORY. see *BUSINESS AND ECONOMICS—Marketing And Purchasing*

380.1029   DEU   ISSN 0094-1611
HD2421
INTERNATIONALES VERZEICHNIS DER WIRTSCHAFTSVERBAENDE/WORLD GUIDE TO TRADE ASSOCIATIONS. Text in German. irreg. (in 2 vols.), latest vol.5, 1998. USD 650 in North America (effective 2001). **Document type:** *Directory, Trade.* **Description:** Provides over 31,000 names and addresses of national and international trade associations, arranged according to category (commercial, economic, industrial and professional).
Published by: K.G. Saur Verlag GmbH (Subsidiary of: Gale Group), Ortlerstr 8, Munchen, 81373, Germany. TEL 49-89-76902-0, FAX 49-89-76902150, customerservice_saur@csi.com, http://www.saur.de. Ed. Michael Zils.

INTERNET YELLOW PAGES (YEAR): BUSINESS MODELS AND MARKET OPPORTUNITIES. see *BUSINESS AND ECONOMICS—Computer Applications*

338.0029   USA
HC107.A11
INTERSTATE MANUFACTURERS & INDUSTRIAL CLASSIFIED DIRECTORY & BUYERS GUIDE. Text in English. 1936. a. adv. **Document type:** *Directory.*
Former titles: Interstate Manufacturers and Industrial Directory Buyers Guide (0193-8541); (until 1977): Eastern Manufacturers and Industrial Directory Buyers Guide (0731-9223)
Published by: Interstate Publishers Corp., 1841 Broadway, Ste 713, New York, NY 10023-5876. TEL 212-246-8484, FAX 212-246-8821. Ed. Frank Masorano. Pub. Ralph Kass. R&P Syl Magid. Adv. contact Paul Levine. page USD 3,600. Circ: 25,000.

338.0029   GBR   ISSN 1465-8976
INTERTRAFFIC INTERNATIONAL DIRECTORY. Text in English. a. **Document type:** *Directory, Trade.*
Published by: Turret R A I plc, Armstrong House, 38 Market Sq, Uxbridge, Middx UB8 1TG, United Kingdom. TEL 44-1895-454545, FAX 44-1895-454647.

INVESTIGATOR'S INTERNATIONAL ALL-IN-ONE DIRECTORY OF THE INVESTIGATIVE INDUSTRY. see *CRIMINOLOGY AND LAW ENFORCEMENT*

338.0029   NGA
INVESTMENTS AND CREDIT CORPORATION OF OYO STATE. INDUSTRIAL DIRECTORY. Text in English. 1970. irreg. **Document type:** *Directory.*
Formerly: Western Nigeria Development Corporation. Industrial Directory
Published by: Investments and Credit Corporation of Oyo State, PMB 5085, Ibadan, Oyo, Nigeria.

338.0029   USA   ISSN 1048-7263
HF5065.I8
IOWA BUSINESS DIRECTORY. Text in English. 1984. a. USD 1,100 combined subscription print, online & CD-ROM eds. (effective 2004 & 2005). index. back issues avail. **Document type:** *Directory.* **Description:** Includes all businesses in the state compiled from the yellow pages and telephone verified. Each listing includes company name, address, name of owner, employee size, sales volume codes, and credit rating codes.
Related titles: CD-ROM ed.; Diskette ed.; E-mail ed.; Fax ed.; Magnetic Tape ed.; Online - full text ed.
Published by: American Business Directories (Subsidiary of: American Business Information, Inc.), 5711 S 86th Circle, P O Box 27347, Omaha, NE 68127. TEL 402-593-4600, 888-946-9377, 877-708-3844, FAX 402-331-5481, karen.peters@infousa.com, sales@directoriesusa.com, http://www.directoriesusa.com.

338.0029   USA
IOWA HOME-BASED BUSINESS DIRECTORY∗. Text in English. 1994. a. USD 15. **Document type:** *Directory.*
Related titles: Diskette ed.: 1994.
Published by: Integrity Communications, 535 Hayward Ave, Ames, IA 50014-7345. FAX 515-292-7154. Ed. Clare Bills. adv.: B&W page USD 250. Circ: 2,000 (paid).

338.4767   USA   ISSN 0737-7940
HD9727.I8
IOWA MANUFACTURERS REGISTER. Text in English. 1983. a. USD 82 (effective 2000). adv. illus. **Document type:** *Directory.* **Description:** Lists 6,686 manufacturers in company name, location, SIC, product and parent company sections published in cooperation with the Iowa association of business and industry.
Related titles: CD-ROM ed.: USD 399 (effective 2000); Diskette ed.; Magnetic Tape ed.
Published by: Manufacturers' News, Inc., 1633 Central St, Evanston, IL 60201. TEL 847-864-7000, 888-752-5200, FAX 847-332-1100, info@mninfo.com, info@manufacturersnews.com, sales@mninfo.com, http://www.manufacturersnews.com. Ed. Frank Lambing. Adv. contact Charles Scherer. B&W page USD 1,843.

IRAN CHAMBER OF COMMERCE, INDUSTRIES AND MINES. DIRECTORY. see *BUSINESS AND ECONOMICS—Chamber Of Commerce Publications*

IRON AND STEEL INTERNATIONAL DIRECTORY (YEAR). see *METALLURGY*

IRRIGATION ASSOCIATION. MEMBERSHIP DIRECTORY AND BUYERS' GUIDE. see *AGRICULTURE—Agricultural Equipment*

338.0029   JPN   ISSN 1341-6162
IRYO KIKI GYOSHA NENKAN/JAPANESE MEDICAL INDUSTRY DIRECTORY. Text in English, Japanese. 1995. biennial. USD 50 newsstand/cover (effective 2001). 128 p./no.; **Document type:** *Trade.* **Description:** Lists approximately 1,300 medical industry companies operating in Japan: makers, importers, exporters, distributors, associations, etc.
Published by: Genyosha Publications Inc., 4-7 Shibuya 2-chome, Shibuya-ku, Tokyo, 150-0002, Japan. TEL 81-3-3407-7521, FAX 81-3-3407-7902, info@genyosha.co.jp, http://www.genyosha.com. Ed., Pub. K Eda. Circ: 7,000.

380.1029   ISL   ISSN 1011-5323
ISLENSK FYRIRTAEKI/ICELANDIC FIRMS. Text in Icelandic. 1983. a. **Description:** Contains information about firms and institutions in Iceland.
Published by: Frodi Ltd., Seljavegur 2, Reykjavik, 101, Iceland. TEL 354-515-5630, FAX 354-515-5599, islenskf@frodi.is. Ed. Berghildur Erla Bernhardsdottir.

ISRAEL CONVENTIONS, TRADE SHOWS, FESTIVALS & SPECIAL EVENTS. see *MEETINGS AND CONGRESSES*

ISRAEL DIAMOND BUYER'S GUIDE. see *JEWELRY, CLOCKS AND WATCHES*

658.564   ISR
ISRAEL INSTITUTE OF PACKAGING. PACKAGING DIRECTORY. Text in English. 1976. a. free. adv. **Document type:** *Directory.*
Published by: Israel Center for Packaging and Product Design, P O Box 20038, Tel Aviv, Israel. TEL 03-5614431, packdes@netvision.net.il. Ed. Varda Stern. Adv. contact Nira Koren. Circ: 5,000.

338.0029   EGY
ITTIHAD AL-SINAAT AL-MISRIYAH. YEAR BOOK/FEDERATION OF EGYPTIAN INDUSTRIES. YEAR BOOK. Text in English. 1961. a. EGP 5. adv. stat. **Document type:** *Directory.*
Published by: Federation of Egyptian Industries/Ittihad al-Sinaat al-Misriyah, 26A Sharia Sherif Pasha, P O Box 251, Cairo, Egypt. TEL 02-3928317, FAX 02-3928075. Ed. Darwish M Darwish. Circ: 900.

332.6029   DEU
J & W BANKING INTERNATIONAL. INTERNATIONAL BANKING AND FINANCE COMMUNICATIONS DIRECTORY. Text in German. 1993. a. USD 150. **Document type:** *Directory, Trade.*
Related titles: CD-ROM ed.
Published by: Telex - Verlag Jaeger & Waldmann GmbH, Postfach 111454, Darmstadt, 64229, Germany. TEL 49-6151-3302-0, FAX 49-6151-3302-50, TELEX 419389-JWLX-D, jwemail@aol.com, http://www.jaeger-waldmann.com. Ed. W Lucius. Pub. W Lich. **Dist. by:** J & W Universal Media Inc., PO Box 637, Commack, NY 11725.

382.029   JPN
J B I A DIRECTORY. Text in English, Japanese. 1972. a. JPY 8,000. **Document type:** *Directory.*
Published by: Japan Book Importers Association, Chiyoda Kaikan, 21-4 Nihonbashi 1-chome, Chuo-ku, Tokyo, 103-0027, Japan. TEL 81-3-3271-6901, FAX 81-3-3271-6920. Ed. Makoto Kobayashi. Circ: 2,000.

658.0029   IDN   ISSN 0215-8590
JAKARTA BUSINESS DIRECTORY. Text in English, Indonesian. 1974. irreg. illus. **Document type:** *Directory.*
Published by: Kamar Dagang dan Industri Jakarta, Jalan W. Jakarta Fair, Tromol Post 3077, Jakarta, Indonesia.

380.1029   IDN
JAKARTA METROPOLITAN BUYERS' GUIDE. Text in English. a.
Published by: C.V. Taro & Co., Jalan Samanhudi ZB, PO Box 3472, Jakarta, Indonesia.

JAPAN CHEMICAL DIRECTORY (YEAR). see *ENGINEERING—Chemical Engineering*

338.0029   JPN   ISSN 0288-9307
HC461
JAPAN COMPANY HANDBOOK. FIRST SECTION. Text in English. 1974. q. JPY 18,800, USD 222 (effective 1999). adv. **Description:** Covers all comapnies listed on first seconds of Japan's 3 major stock exchanges; provides corporate names, addresses, telephone numbers, business descriptions, names and titles of senior officers,shareholders' equities and major stockholders, and overseas offices andsubsidiaries. Includes financial analyses and historical data.
Supersedes: Japan Company Directory (Tokyo, 1974) (0075-3211)
Related titles: Microform ed.: (from MIS).

Published by: Toyo Keizai Inc., 1-2-1 Nihonbashihongoku-cho, Chuo-ku, Tokyo, 1030021, Japan. TEL 81-3-3246-5621, FAX 81-3-3241-5543, jch@toyokeizai.co.jp, http://www.mediagalxy.co.jp/toyokeizai/jch/jch.html. Ed. Fusakazu Lzumura. **Dist. by:** Japan Publications Trading Co., Ltd., Book Export II Dept, PO Box 5030, Tokyo International, Tokyo 101-3191, Japan. TEL 81-3-32923753, FAX 81-3-32920410, infoserials@jptco.co.jp, http://www.jptco.co.jp; **Dist. in US by:** Toyo Keizai America Inc., 450 Fashion Ave., Ste. 1008, New York, NY 10123-1008; **Dist. by:** Current Pacific Ltd., PO Box 36-536, Northcote, Auckland, New Zealand. TEL 64-9-480-1388, FAX 64-9-480-1387, info@cplnz.com, http://www.cplnz.com.

380.1029 JPN
T12.5.J3
JAPAN COMPANY HANDBOOK. SECOND SECTION. (The Japan Company Profile Service provides d. & w. electronic updates on the handbook through Reuters Monitor.) Text in English. 1982. q. JPY 18,800, USD 222. adv. bk.rev.
Description: Covers all companies listed on the second second section of the Japan's 3 major stock exchanges. Provides corporate names, addresses, telephone numbers, business descriptions, names and titles of senior officers, shareholders' equities and major stockholders; including financial analysese and historical data.
Formerly: Second Section Firms (0288-9315)
Related titles: Microform ed.: (from MIS).
Published by: Toyo Keizai Inc., 1-2-1 Nihonbashihongoku-cho, Chuo-ku, Tokyo, 1030021, Japan. TEL 81-3-3246-5655, FAX 81-3-3241-5543. Ed. Fusakazu Izumura. Circ: 15,000. **Dist. in US by:** Toyo Keizai America Inc., 450 Fashion Ave., Ste. 1008, New York, NY 10123-1008; **Dist. by:** Japan Publications Trading Co., Ltd., Book Export II Dept, PO Box 5030, Tokyo International, Tokyo 101-3191, Japan. TEL 81-3-32923753, FAX 81-3-32920410, infoserials@jptco.co.jp, http://www.jptco.co.jp.

382.029 JPN
HC461
JAPAN DIRECTORY. Text in English. 1931. a. JPY 48,000 domestic; JPY 60,000 in Asia; JPY 66,000 in Europe; JPY 63,000 in North America (effective 2000). adv. **Document type:** *Directory.* **Description:** Contains comprehensive information on foreign firms and related organs, foreign residents in Japan, hotels, restaurants, schools, hospitals, clubs, embassies, consulates, government agencies, and classified telephone and fax directories.
Formerly: Japan Directory: Business and Society; Which was formed by the merger of: Japan Business Directory (Year) (0910-1780); Japan Society Directory (0075-322X)
Published by: Japan Press, Ltd., Japan Directory Division, C.P.O. Box 6, Tokyo, 100-8691, Japan. TEL 81-3-3404-5161, FAX 81-3-3404-5152. Ed., Pub. Yoshio Wada. Circ: 15,000.

380.1029 JPN
JAPAN ELECTRONICS BUYERS' GUIDE. Short title: E B G. Text in Japanese. 1968. a. USD 220. adv. **Document type:** *Directory.* **Description:** Directory of Japanese manufacturers and trading firms and product listing classified by 24 product categories.
Media: CD-ROM.
Published by: Dempa Publications Inc., 1-11-15 Higashi Gotanda, Shinagawa-Ku, Tokyo, 141-8715, Japan. TEL 81-3-34456111, FAX 81-3-34447515, http://www.dempa.net/.

381.029 JPN
JAPAN TRADE DIRECTORY (YEAR)/NIHON BOEKI SHINKOKAI. Text in English. 1982. a., latest 2001-2002. JPY 33,000 (effective 2001); incl. CD-ROM. adv. **Document type:** *Directory.* **Description:** Provides detailed information on Japanese companies in export, import and service trades and international transactions.
Published by: (Publication Department), Japan External Trade Organization, 2-5 Toranomom 2-chome, Minato-ku, Tokyo, 105-8466, Japan. TEL 03-3582-3518, FAX 03-3587-2485, TELEX J24378, syuppan@jetro.go.jp, http://www.jetro.go.jp. Circ: 10,000. **Dist. in US by:** Business Network Corporation, 245 Peach Tree Center Ave, Ste 2206, Atlanta, GA 30303; **Dist. by:** Current Pacific Ltd., PO Box 36-536, Northcote, Auckland, New Zealand. TEL 64-9-480-1388, FAX 64-9-480-1387, info@cplnz.com, http://www.cplnz.com.

384.6021 USA
JAPANESE TELEPHONE DIRECTORY AND GUIDE OF SOUTHERN CALIFORNIA. Text in English, Japanese. 1981. a. free. adv. **Document type:** *Directory.*
Published by: Japan Publicity, 19300 S Hamilton Ave, Ste 110, Gardena, CA 90248-4408. TEL 310-515-7100, FAX 310-515-7188, info@japanpub.com, http://www.japanpub.com. Ed., Adv. contact Paul M Whitney. Pub. Chieko Mori. B&W page USD 2,490, color page USD 5,600; trim 10.69 x 8.38. Circ: 65,000 (controlled).

739.27029 HKG
JEWELLERY AND SUPPLIES DIRECTORY FOR ASIA'S JEWELLERY INDUSTRY. Text in English. 1997. a. free. **Document type:** *Directory.* **Description:** Lists equipment and supplies companies and agencies in jewellery and gemstone trade.
Published by: C M P Asia Ltd. (Subsidiary of: United News & Media), 17/F China Resources Bldg, 26 Harbour Rd, Wanchai, Hong Kong. TEL 852-2827-6211, FAX 852-2827-7831. Ed. Brigitte Sheung. Pub. Letitia Chow. adv.: B&W page USD 2,170, color page USD 2,970; 281 x 212.

796.54029 USA
K O A DIRECTORY. Text in English. 1964. a. (Jan.). USD 4 in North America; USD 7 elsewhere (effective 2005). adv. maps. 156 p./no.; **Document type:** *Directory, Consumer.* **Description:** Features product and service-related information on camping. Lists KOA facilities.
Former titles: K O A Directory Road Atlas and Kampground Guide; K O A Directory Road Atlas and Camping Guide; K O A Handbook and Directory for Campers
Published by: Kampgrounds of America, Inc., 550 N. 31st St., Billings, MT 59101. TEL 406-248-7444, FAX 406-248-7414, http://www.koa.com, http://koa.com/. Pub. Jim Rogers. adv.: B&W page USD 21,375, color page USD 26,725; 8.31 x 10.88. Circ: 1,100,000 (controlled).

338.0029 USA ISSN 1048-7271
HF5065.K2
KANSAS BUSINESS DIRECTORY. Text in English. 1983. a. USD 1,100 combined subscription print, online & CD-ROM eds. (effective 2004 & 2005). index. back issues avail. **Document type:** *Directory.* **Description:** Includes all businesses in the state compiled from the yellow pages and telephone verified. Each listing includes company name, address, phone number, name of owner, and employee size and sales volume codes, and credit rating codes.
Related titles: CD-ROM ed.; Diskette ed.; E-mail ed.; Fax ed.; Magnetic Tape ed.; Online - full text ed.
Published by: American Business Directories (Subsidiary of: American Business Information, Inc.), 5711 S 86th Circle, P O Box 27347, Omaha, NE 68127. TEL 402-593-4600, 888-946-9377, 877-708-3844, FAX 402-331-5481, karen.peters@infousa.com, sales@directoriesusa.com, http://www.directoriesusa.com.

670.29 USA
HF5065.K2
KANSAS MANUFACTURERS DIRECTORY. Text in English. 1996. a. USD 75 (effective 2001). adv. 400 p./no.; **Document type:** *Directory.* **Description:** Profiles 4,805 companies in five sections: company name, S.I.C., product, city, and parent company.
Formerly: Kansas Manufacturers Register (1082-0256)
Related titles: CD-ROM ed.: USD 310 (effective 2000); Diskette ed.
Published by: Manufacturers' News, Inc., 1633 Central St, Evanston, IL 60201. TEL 847-864-7000, 888-752-5200, FAX 847-332-1100, info@mninfo.com, info@manufacturersnews.com, sales@mninfo.com, http://www.manufacturersnews.com. Ed. Steve Garland.

KASHRUTH DIRECTORY. see *FOOD AND FOOD INDUSTRIES*

670.29 GBR ISSN 1467-1220
HF54.G7
KELLY'S INDUSTRIAL DIRECTORY. Text in English. 1877. a., latest 2001. GBP 285 (effective 2001). adv. **Document type:** *Directory.* **Description:** Contains information on over 74,000 UK industrial companies.
Former titles (until 1999): Kelly's Directory (1350-4150); (until 1993): Kelly's Business Directory (0269-9265); (until 1986): Kelly's Manufacturers and Merchants Directory (0075-5370)
Related titles: CD-ROM ed.; Online - full text ed.: (from Reed Information Services Ltd.).
—BLDSC (5089.261425). **CCC.**
Published by: Kelly's Directories (Subsidiary of: Reed Business Information Ltd.), Windsor Court, E Grinstead House, E Grinstead, W Sussex RH19 1XA, United Kingdom. TEL 44-1342-326972, FAX 44-1342-335612, kellys.mktg@reedinfo.co.uk, http://www.kellysearch.com. Ed. Denise White. Pub. Brian Gallagher. Adv. contact Claire Crossfield. Circ: 3,200. **Dist. by:** Current Pacific Ltd., PO Box 36-536, Northcote, Auckland, New Zealand. TEL 64-9-480-1388, FAX 64-9-480-1387, info@cplnz.com, http://www.cplnz.com.

380.1029 GBR ISSN 1467-1239
KELLY'S INDUSTRIAL PAGES. Text in English. 1987. a., latest 2001. free. adv. **Document type:** *Directory.* **Description:** Contains information on over 74,000 Uk industrial companies.
Former titles (until 1998): Kelly's Link (1350-4169); (until 1993): Kelly's Business Link (0269-9281)
Related titles: CD-ROM ed.; Online - full text ed.: (from Reed Information Services Ltd.).
Published by: Kelly's Directories (Subsidiary of: Reed Business Information Ltd.), Windsor Court, E Grinstead House, E Grinstead, W Sussex RH19 1XA, United Kingdom. TEL 44-1342-326972, FAX 44-1342-335612, kellys.mktg@reedinfo.co.uk, http://www.kellysearch.com. Ed. Denise White. Pub. Brian Gallagher. Adv. contact Claire Crossfield. Circ: 150,000 (controlled).

338.0029 USA ISSN 1048-728X
HF5065.K4
KENTUCKY BUSINESS DIRECTORY. Text in English. 1985. a. USD 1,100 combined subscription print, online & CD-ROM eds. (effective 2004 & 2005). index. back issues avail. **Document type:** *Directory.* **Description:** Includes all businesses in the state compiled from the yellow pages and telephone-verified. Each listing includes company name, address, phone number, name of owner, and employee size and sales volume code, and credit rating codes.
Related titles: CD-ROM ed.; Diskette ed.; E-mail ed.; Fax ed.; Magnetic Tape ed.; Online - full text ed.
Published by: American Business Directories (Subsidiary of: American Business Information, Inc.), 5711 S 86th Circle, P O Box 27347, Omaha, NE 68127. TEL 402-593-4600, 888-946-9377, 877-708-3844, FAX 402-331-5481, karen.peters@infousa.com, sales@directoriesusa.com, http://www.directoriesusa.com.

670.29 USA ISSN 0075-5494
T12
KENTUCKY DIRECTORY OF MANUFACTURERS. Text in English. 1948. a. USD 84. **Document type:** *Directory.* **Description:** Includes company name and address, parent company and home office name and address, chief executive at plant location, employment, products and SIC codes.
Formerly: Kentucky Industrial Directory (0075-5516)
Published by: Harris Info Source, 2057 E Aurora Rd, Twinsburg, OH 44087. TEL 800-888-5900, FAX 800-643-5997, http://www.harrisinfo.com. Ed. Fran Carlson. Circ: 3,000.

670.29 USA ISSN 0741-9031
T12.3.K4
KENTUCKY MANUFACTURERS REGISTER. Text in English. a. USD 80 (effective 2000). adv. illus. **Document type:** *Directory.* **Description:** Lists 5,850 manufacturers by product, alphabetically, geographically, by SIC, and by parent company.
Related titles: CD-ROM ed.: USD 355 (effective 2000); Diskette ed.: USD 395 (effective 1999).
Published by: Manufacturers' News, Inc., 1633 Central St, Evanston, IL 60201. TEL 847-864-7000, 888-752-5200, FAX 847-332-1100, info@mninfo.com, info@manufacturersnews.com, sales@mninfo.com, http://www.manufacturersnews.com. Ed. Frank Lambing. Adv. contact Charles Scherer. B&W page USD 1,843.

KENTUCKY STATE AGENT HANDBOOK. see *INSURANCE*

KENYA ASSOCIATION OF MANUFACTURERS. MEMBERS LIST AND INTERNATIONAL STANDARD INDUSTRIAL CLASSIFICATION. see *BUSINESS AND ECONOMICS—Production Of Goods And Services*

338.0029 KEN ISSN 0376-8481
HD9737.K4
KENYA. CENTRAL BUREAU OF STATISTICS. DIRECTORY OF INDUSTRIES. Key Title: Directory of Industries. Text in English. irreg., latest 1986. KES 120. stat. **Document type:** *Directory, Government.*
Supersedes: Kenya. Ministry of Finance and Economic Planning. Statistics Division. Register of Manufacturing Firms
Published by: Ministry of Finance and Planning, Central Bureau of Statistics, PO Box 30266, Nairobi, Kenya. **Subscr. to:** Government Press, Haile Selaissie Ave., PO Box 30128, Nairobi, Kenya. TEL 254-2-334075.

KENYA EXPORT DIRECTORY. see *BUSINESS AND ECONOMICS—International Commerce*

KENYA NATIONAL CHAMBER OF COMMERCE AND INDUSTRY. TRADE AND INDUSTRY GUIDE. see *BUSINESS AND ECONOMICS—Chamber Of Commerce Publications*

338.0029 SGP
KEY BUSINESS DIRECTORY OF INDONESIA - THAILAND. Text in English. a. **Document type:** *Directory.*
Published by: Dun & Bradstreet (Singapore) Pte. Ltd., Publications Department, Park Mall, 9 Penang Rd 09-20, Singapore, 238459, Singapore.

338.0029 SGP
KEY BUSINESS DIRECTORY OF MALAYSIA. Text in English. a. **Document type:** *Directory.*
Published by: Dun & Bradstreet (Singapore) Pte. Ltd., Publications Department, Park Mall, 9 Penang Rd 09-20, Singapore, 238459, Singapore.

338.0029 SGP
KEY BUSINESS DIRECTORY OF SINGAPORE. Text in English. a. **Document type:** *Directory.*
Published by: Dun & Bradstreet (Singapore) Pte. Ltd., Publications Department, Park Mall, 9 Penang Rd 09-20, Singapore, 238459, Singapore.

KEY NOTE MARKET REVIEW: BUSINESS INFORMATION IN THE U K. see *BUSINESS AND ECONOMICS—Production Of Goods And Services*

B

338.0029 GBR ISSN 1357-0463
KEY NOTE MARKET REVIEW: CORPORATE SERVICES IN THE U K. Variant title: Corporate Services in the U K. Corporate Services in the United Kingdom. Text in English. 1994. irreg., latest 1994, July. GBP 340 per issue (effective 2002). **Document type:** *Trade.* **Description:** Provides an overview of corporate services in the UK, including industry structure, market size and trends, developments, prospects, and major company profiles.
Related titles: CD-ROM ed.; Online - full text ed.
Published by: Key Note Ltd., Field House, 72 Oldfield Rd, Hampton, Mddx TW12 2HQ, United Kingdom. TEL 44-20-8481-8750, FAX 44-20-8783-0049, info@keynote.co.uk, http://www.keynote.co.uk.

622.334029 USA
KEYSTONE COAL INDUSTRY MANUAL. Text in English. 1918. a. USD 275 in North America; USD 310 out of North America (effective 1999). adv. **Document type:** *Directory.* **Description:** Lists all operating coal mines and processing plants in the US and Canada. Also includes essential information on coal sales, coal exporters, coal transportation companies, users of coal and coal seam geology.
Published by: Primedia Business Magazines & Media, Inc. (Subsidiary of: Primedia, Inc.), 330 N Wabash Ave, Ste 2300, Chicago, IL 60611. inquiries@primediabusiness.com, http://www.primediabusiness.com. **Subscr. to:** PO Box 12993, Overland Park, KS 66282-2993. TEL 800-441-0294, FAX 913-967-1331.

687.0688 USA
KIDS MARKET. Text in English. 1986. 10/yr. USD 59 (effective 2000). adv. **Document type:** *Trade.* **Description:** Aimed at the trade apparel market in New York. Contains a collection of original photos of apparel items currently offered on the wholesale market. Includes children's ready-to-wear sportswear. Articles include news on the industry, company profiles, real estate news, financial and technology news, and roundtables pertaining to everything in the garment industry in New York City.
Published by: Fashion Market Magazine Group, Inc., 617 W 46th St #2, New York, NY 10036-1906. TEL 212-760-5100, FAX 212-760-5112, fashionmmg@aol.com. Ed., Pub., R&P, Adv. contact Nicolas Monjo. Circ: 18,000.

791.43029 DEU
KINOHANDBUCH. Text in German. 1983. a. EUR 45.50 (effective 2002). **Document type:** *Directory, Trade.* **Description:** Directory of the German film industry and retailers.
Published by: Entertainment Media Verlag GmbH und Co. oHG, Einsteinring 24, Dornach, 85609, Germany. TEL 49-89-45114-0, FAX 49-89-45114444, emv@e-media.de, http://www.mediabiz.de. Ed. Ulrich Hoecherl. Pub. Ulrich Scheele. R&P Otto Bachmeier. Adv. contact Rita Behrendt. Circ: 2,700 (controlled).

380.1029 DNK ISSN 0075-661X
HF3643
KOMPASS; indeks over Danmarks industri og naegringsliv. Variant title: Kompass Danmark. Text in Danish; Summaries in Danish, English, German. 1961. s-a. DKK 1,375 (effective 2000). adv. bk.rev. **Document type:** *Directory.*
Related titles: CD-ROM ed.
—BLDSC (5105.601000).
Published by: Forlaget Kompass Danmark, Oeveroedvej 5, Holte, 2840, Denmark. TEL 45-45-46-09-10, FAX 45-45-46-09-11. Circ: 6,000.

659.1029 GBR
KOMPASS ADVERTISING EXTRACTS. Variant title: U K Kompass Buyers Guides. Text in English. 1978. a. (in 5 vols.). **Document type:** *Directory.*
Former titles: Kompass Industrial Sections; Kompass Buyers Guides; Euro Kompass U K Buyers Guides; Euro Kompass U K Industrial Sections
Published by: Kompass (Subsidiary of: Reed Business Information Ltd.), Windsor Court, East Grinstead House, East Grinstead, W Sussex RH19 1XA, United Kingdom. TEL 44-1342-326972, FAX 44-1342-335992, TELEX 95127-INSFER-G. Ed. Dawn Ingram. Circ: 6,000.

670.29 AUS
KOMPASS AUSTRALIA. Text in English. 1970. a. AUD 900 (effective 2005). adv. **Document type:** *Directory, Trade.* **Description:** Lists products and services in Australia, with cross-references to the companies that supply them.
Former titles: Kompass Register; Kompass Australia (0075-6628)
Related titles: CD-ROM ed.: AUD 1,700 (effective 2005).
—BLDSC (5105.603000). **CCC.**
Published by: (Associated Chambers of Manufacturers of Australia), A P N Business Information Group (Subsidiary of: A P N News & Media Ltd), Level 1, 28 Riddell Pde, Elsternwick, VIC 3185, Australia. TEL 61-3-92457800, FAX 61-3-92457840, info@apnbig.com.au, http://www.apnbig.com.au/.

670.29 BEL ISSN 0778-4147
HF5181.B3
KOMPASS BELGIUM; repertoire de l'economie de la Belgique. Text in Dutch, French; Summaries in Dutch, English, French, German. 1961. a. free. adv. **Document type:** *Directory.*
Formerly (until 1990): Kompass Belgium - Luxembourg (0075-6636)
Related titles: CD-ROM ed.; Online - full text ed.
—BLDSC (5105.606000).
Published by: (Foundation for Promoting International Economic Information CHE), Editus Belgium S.A., Av Moliere 256, Brussels, 1060, Belgium. TEL 32-2-3459070, FAX 32-2-3473340, TELEX 62903 KMPSS B. Ed. C Somville. Circ: 4,700. **Dist. in the U.S. and Canada by:** Croner Publications, 211 03, Jamaica, NY 11428.

338.0029 AUS
KOMPASS BUSINESS SERVICES AND TRANSPORT✶. Text in English. 1996. a. AUD 85. **Document type:** *Directory.* **Description:** Lists companies in Australia that provide products and services to businesses in the transport industry.
Formed by the merger of (1994-1996): Kompass Logistic Services and Equipment (1322-2821); (1993-1996): Kompass Business and Commercial Services (1320-5404)
Published by: Peter Isaacson Publications, 46-50 Porter St, Prahran, VIC 3181, Australia. TEL 61-3-9245-7777, FAX 61-3-9245-7840, isaacson@interconnect.com. Adv. contact Joseph Dagher. Circ: 3,000.

338.0029 GBR ISSN 1353-1069
KOMPASS. COMPANY INFORMATION. Variant title: U K Kompass Register Company Information. Text in English. 1962. a. GBP 470 for volumes 1 & 2; GBP 1,145 for 4 volume set (effective 2001); Vols. 1 & 2 sold together. **Document type:** *Directory.*
Supersedes in part (in 1994): Kompass. United Kingdom (0959-6976); Which was formerly: Kompass United Kingdom - C B I (0075-6733)
Related titles: CD-ROM ed.: Kompass Register C Ds. GBP 424 per issue for Kompass Register CD; GBP 779 per issue for Kompass Register CD Plus (effective 2001).
—CCC.
Published by: Kompass (Subsidiary of: Reed Business Information Ltd.), Windsor Court, East Grinstead House, East Grinstead, W Sussex RH19 1XA, United Kingdom. TEL 44-1342-326972, FAX 44-1342-335612, kompass.sales@reedinfo.co.uk, http://www.kompass.co.uk. Ed. Ann Hayes. Pub. Peter Snook. Adv. contact David Foster TEL 44-1342-335951.

670.29 DEU
KOMPASS DEUTSCHLAND/KOMPASS GERMANY; informationswerk ueber ausgewaehlte Deutsche firmen/register of selected German industry and commerce. Text in English, French, German. 1971. a. bk.rev. **Document type:** *Directory, Trade.*
Related titles: CD-ROM ed.
Published by: Kompass Deutschland Verlags- und Vertriebsgesellschaft mbH, Jechtinger Str 13, Freiburg Im Breisgau, 79111, Germany. Ed. Peter Villa.

621.381029 AUS ISSN 1325-8761
KOMPASS ELECTRICAL AND ELECTRONIC PRODUCTS✶. Text in English. 1993. a. AUD 85. **Document type:** *Directory.* **Description:** Details Australian electronics and electrical products suppliers and their associated companies who service the industry. Full contact details are also provided.
Formerly (until 1995): Kompass Electronic and Electrical Products (1320-5412)
Related titles: Online - full text ed.
Published by: Peter Isaacson Publications, 46-50 Porter St, Prahran, VIC 3181, Australia. TEL 61-3-9245-7777, FAX 61-3-9245-7840, isaacson@interconnect.com. Ed. Joseph Dagher. Circ: 1,000.

670.29 FRA ISSN 0759-5689
HC272
KOMPASS FRANCE. Variant title: La France de l'Industrie et ses Services. Text in French; Summaries in English, French, German, Spanish. 1960. a. FRF 2,790 (effective 2000). adv. illus. **Document type:** *Directory.*
Former titles: Repertoire General de la Production Francaise (0337-5714); Annuaire Industriel. Repertoire General de la Production Francaise (0075-6652)
Related titles: Magnetic Tape ed.
Address: 66 quai du Marechal Joffre, Courbevoie, Cedex 92415, France. TEL 33-1-41165100, FAX 33-1-41165156, infos@kompass-france.com, http://www.kompass.fr. Ed., Pub., R&P Bertrand Macabeo. Adv. contact Philippe Leroux. Circ: 10,000.

670.29 NLD ISSN 0075-6660
KOMPASS HOLLAND; informatiewerk over het Nederlandse Bedrijfsleven. Text in Dutch; Summaries in Dutch, English, German, French, Spanish. 1964. a. adv. bk.rev. **Document type:** *Directory, Trade.*
Related titles: CD-ROM ed.
Published by: (Foundation for Promoting International Economic Information CHE), Kompass Nederland, Hogehilweg 15, Amsterdam (ZO), 1101 CB, Netherlands. TEL 31-20-6974041, FAX 31-20-6914404, info@kompass.nl, http://www.kompass.nl. Circ: 8,600. **Subscr. to:** Croner Publications.

670.29 GBR
KOMPASS. INDUSTRIAL TRADE NAMES. Variant title: U K Kompass Register Industrial Trade Names. Text in English. 1966. a. GBP 350 per vol.; GBP 1,145 for 4 volume set (effective 2001). **Document type:** *Directory, Corporate.*
Supersedes in part (in 1992): Kompass. United Kingdom (0959-6976); Which was formerly: Kompass United Kingdom - C B I (0075-6733); Formerly: U K Trade Names (0082-7142)
Related titles: Online - full text ed.: (from Reed Information Services Ltd.).
Published by: Kompass (Subsidiary of: Reed Business Information Ltd.), Windsor Court, East Grinstead House, East Grinstead, W Sussex RH19 1XA, United Kingdom. TEL 44-1342-326972, FAX 44-1342-335612, kompass.sales@reedinfo.co.uk, http://www.kompass.co.uk. Ed. Ann Hayes. Pub. Peter Snook. Adv. contact David Foster TEL 44-1342-335951. Circ: 2,200.

338.0029 IRL ISSN 1393-9289
KOMPASS IRELAND (YEAR); register of industry & commerce. Text in English. 1988. a. EUR 210 (effective 2005). adv. **Document type:** *Directory.*
Related titles: CD-ROM ed.: Irish Kompass On Disk. 1990. IEP 395 (effective 2001); Online - full content ed.
Published by: (Irish Business and Employers Confederation), Kompass Ireland Publishers Ltd., Kompass House, Parnell Ct., 1 Granby Row, Dublin, 1, Ireland. TEL 353-1-8728800, FAX 353-1-8733711, info@kompass.ie, http://www.kompass.ie. Ed. Una Hogan. Adv. contact Patrick Cody. Circ: 2,000.

670.29 MAR ISSN 0075-6695
KOMPASS MAROC; register of Moroccan industry and commerce. Text in English. 1966. a. USD 150. adv. **Document type:** *Directory.*
Related titles: Diskette ed.
Published by: (Foundation for Promoting International Economic Information CHE), Kompass Maroc-Veto, MA, B P 11100, Casablanca, Morocco. FAX 2-266056. Ed. Eric Verdavainne. Circ: 7,000. **Affiliate:** Kompass International AG, Zurich.

338.0029 NOR ISSN 0075-6709
HC362.2
KOMPASS NORGE; indeks over Norges industri og naeringsliv. Text in English, French, German, Norwegian, Spanish; Summaries in English, German, Norwegian. 1970. a. NOK 1,460. adv. back issues avail. **Document type:** *Directory, Trade.*
Incorporates (19??-1972): Norges Industri- og Eksportkalender (0805-1313); Which was formerly (until 1961): Norwegian Export Directory (0805-1305)
Related titles: CD-ROM ed.; E-mail ed.; Fax ed.; Online - full text ed.
Published by: (Export Council of Norway), Kompass Norge A-S, Loekkeveien 87, Stavanger, 4001, Norway. www.kompass.com, http://www.kompass.no, firmapost@kompass.no. Ed. Irene Fjelde Asboernsen. Pub. Per Suanes. Adv. contact Jan Helge Bleuken. Circ: 6,000.

380.1029 GBR ISSN 1353-1085
KOMPASS. PARENTS AND SUBSIDIARIES. Variant title: U K Kompass Register Parents and Subsidiaries. Text in English. 1991. a. GBP 325 per vol.; GBP 1,145 for 4 volume set (effective 2002). **Document type:** *Directory, Trade.*
Supersedes in part (in 1991): Kompass. United Kingdom (0959-6976); Which was formerly: Kompass United Kingdom - C B I (0075-6733)
Published by: Kompass (Subsidiary of: Reed Business Information Ltd.), Windsor Court, East Grinstead House, East Grinstead, W Sussex RH19 1XA, United Kingdom. TEL 44-1342-326972, FAX 44-1342-335612, kompass.sales@reedinfo.co.uk, http://www.kompass.co.uk. Ed. Ann Hayes. Pub. Peter Snook. Adv. contact David Foster TEL 44-1342-335951.

381.029 PHL
KOMPASS PHILIPPINES; register of industry and commerce of the Republic of the Philippines. Text in English. 1990. a. USD 130 (effective 1996). **Document type:** *Directory.* **Description:** Lists 15500 companies and 50000 products and services.
Published by: Belgosa Business Communication Inc., 6-F, PDCP Bank Center, Alfaro cor. Herrera Sts., Salcedo Village, Makati Mm, 1227, Philippines. TEL 632-8925462, FAX 632-8136837, kompass@globe.com.ph. Circ: 500.

380.1029 PRT ISSN 0872-0223
KOMPASS PORTUGAL. Variant title: Reportorio da Industria, Comercio e Servicos de Portugal. Text in English, Portuguese. 1992. a. adv. **Document type:** *Directory.* **Description:** Contains an alphabetical list of companies, trade names, trademark lists, and a list of products and services.
Related titles: CD-ROM ed.; Online - full text ed.
Published by: Interpropo - Sociedade de Propaganda Internacional de Produtos Portugueses Ltda., Rua Coronel Bento Roma, 28, Lisbon, 1700-122, Portugal. TEL 351-218-402150, FAX 351-218-409658, portugal@kompass.pt, http://www.kompass.com. Ed. Henrique Cerqueira.

670.29 GBR ISSN 1353-1050
KOMPASS. PRODUCTS AND SERVICES. Variant title: U K Kompass Register Products and Services. Text in English. 1962. a. (in 2 vols.), latest 2001, June. GBP 470 for volumes 1 & 2; GBP 1,145 for 4 volume set (effective 2001); (vols. 1 & 2 sold together). adv. **Document type:** *Directory.*
Supersedes in part (in 1994): Kompass. United Kingdom (0959-6976); Which was formerly: Kompass United Kingdom - C B I (0075-6733)
Related titles: CD-ROM ed.: 1994. GBP 424 for Kompass Register CD; GBP 779 for Kompass Register CD Plus (effective 2001); Online - full text ed.: (from Reed Information Services Ltd.).
—BLDSC (5105.635000), Linda Hall. **CCC.**
Published by: Kompass (Subsidiary of: Reed Business Information Ltd.), Windsor Court, East Grinstead House, East Grinstead, W Sussex RH19 1XA, United Kingdom. TEL 44-1342-326972, FAX 44-1342-335612, kompass.sales@reedinfo.co.uk, http://www.kompass.co.uk. Ed. Ann Hayes. Pub. Peter Snook. Adv. contact David Foster TEL 44-1342-335951. Circ: 8,500.

630.29 FRA ISSN 0299-6154
KOMPASS PROFESSIONNEL. AGRICULTURE, ALIMENTATION. Text in French. 1960. a. adv. **Document type:** *Directory.*
Former titles (until 1986): Kompass. L'Alimentation Francaise (0337-5242); (until 1973): Annuaire Industriel. L'Alimentation Francaise (0337-5234)
Published by: Kompass France, 66 quai du Marechal Joffre, Courbevoie, Cedex 92415, France. TEL 33-1-41165100, FAX 33-1-41165156, infos@kompass-france.com, http://www.kompass.fr. Ed., Pub., R&P Bertrand Macabeo. Adv. contact Philippe Leroux.

624.029 FRA ISSN 0299-6162
KOMPASS PROFESSIONNEL. BATIMENT ET GENIE CIVIL, MANUTENTION - LEVAGE, BOIS - MEUBLES. Text in French. 1960. a. adv. **Document type:** *Directory.*
Former titles (until 1986): Kompass. Genie Civil, Manutention - Levage, Stockage (0396-0021); (until 1976): Kompass. Equipements de Genie Civil, Manutention, Levage (0337-5498); (until 1975): Kompass. Batiment, Travaux Publics, Manutention Levage (0337-548X); (until 1973): Annuaire Industriel. Batiment, Travaux Publics, Manutention, Levage (0337-5471)
Published by: Kompass France, 66 quai du Marechal Joffre, Courbevoie, Cedex 92415, France. TEL 33-1-41165100, FAX 33-1-41165156, infos@kompass-france.com, http://www.kompass.fr. Ed., Pub., R&P Bertrand Macabeo. Adv. contact Philippe Leroux.

540.29 FRA ISSN 0299-6111
KOMPASS PROFESSIONNEL. CHIMIE, PLASTIQUES, CAOUTCHOUC, PRODUITS MINERAUX. Text in French. 1960. a. adv. **Document type:** *Directory.*
Former titles (until 1987): Kompass. Chimie, Petrole, Plastiques, Caoutchouc (0337-5285); (until 1974): Annuaire Industriel. Chimie, Petrole, Plastique, Caoutchouc (0337-5277)
Published by: Kompass France, 66 quai du Marechal Joffre, Courbevoie, Cedex 92415, France. TEL 33-1-41165100, FAX 33-1-41165156, infos@kompass-france.com, http://www.kompass.fr. Ed., Pub., R&P Bertrand Macabeo. Adv. contact Philippe Leroux.

338.0029 FRA ISSN 0990-8536
KOMPASS PROFESSIONNEL. DISTRIBUTION, COMMERCE DE GROS. Text in French. 1960. a. adv. **Document type:** *Directory.*
Published by: Kompass France, 66 quai du Marechal Joffre, Courbevoie, Cedex 92415, France. TEL 33-1-41165100, FAX 33-1-41165156, infos@kompass-france.com, http://www.kompass.fr. Pub., R&P Bertrand Macabeo. Adv. contact Philippe Leroux.

621.3029 FRA ISSN 0299-612X
KOMPASS PROFESSIONNEL. ELECTRICITE, ELECTRONIQUE, INFORMATIQUE. Text in French. 1960. a. adv. **Document type:** *Directory.*
Former titles (until 1987): Kompass. Electricite, Electronique, Nucleaire (0337-5307); (until 1974): Annuaire Industriel. Electricite, Electronique, Nucleaire (0337-5293)
Published by: Kompass France, 66 quai du Marechal Joffre, Courbevoie, Cedex 92415, France. TEL 33-1-41165100, FAX 33-1-41165156, infos@kompass-france.com, http://www.kompass.fr. Ed., Pub., R&P Bertrand Macabeo. Adv. contact Philippe Leroux.

669.029 FRA ISSN 0299-6138
KOMPASS PROFESSIONNEL. PRODUITS DU METAL. Text in French. 1960. a. adv. **Document type:** *Directory.*
Former titles (until 1987): Kompass. Petite Metallurgie, Composants Mecaniques (0337-5323); (until 1975): Annuaire Industriel. Petite Metallurgie (0337-5315)
Published by: Kompass France, 66 quai du Marechal Joffre, Courbevoie, Cedex 92415, France. TEL 33-1-41165100, FAX 33-1-41165156, infos@kompass-france.com, http://www.kompass.fr. Ed., Pub. Bertrand Macabeo. R&P Bertand Macabeo. Adv. contact Philippe Leroux.

380.1029 FRA ISSN 0299-609X
KOMPASS PROFESSIONNEL. SERVICES, INDUSTRIES GRAPHIQUES. Text in French. 1960. a. adv. **Document type:** *Directory.*
Former titles (until 1987): Kompass. Special Services (0337-5366); (until 1975): Annuaire Industriel. Special Services (0337-5358)
Published by: Kompass France, 66 quai du Marechal Joffre, Courbevoie, Cedex 92415, France. TEL 33-1-41165100, FAX 33-1-41165156, infos@kompass-france.com, http://www.kompass.fr. Ed., Pub., R&P Bertrand Macabeo. Adv. contact Philippe Leroux.

669.029 FRA ISSN 0299-6170
KOMPASS PROFESSIONNEL. SIDERURGIE, METALLURGIE, FONDERIE. Text in French. 1960. a. adv. **Document type:** *Directory.*
Former titles (until 1987): Kompass. Siderurgie, Metallurgie, Fonderie, Travail des Metaux (0337-534X); (until 1975): Annuaire Industriel. Siderurgie, Metallurgie, Fonderie, Travail des Metaux (0337-5331)
Published by: Kompass France, 66 quai du Marechal Joffre, Courbevoie, Cedex 92415, France. TEL 33-1-41165100, FAX 33-1-41165156, infos@kompass-france.com, http://www.kompass.fr. Ed., Pub., R&P Bertrand Macabeo. Adv. contact Philippe Leroux.

627.029 FRA ISSN 0299-6197
KOMPASS PROFESSIONNEL. TECHNIQUES HYDRAULIQUES ET PNEUMATIQUES, CLIMATISATION. Text in French. 1960. a. adv. **Document type:** *Directory.*
Formerly (until 1986): Kompass. Techniques Hydrauliques et Pneumatiques (0396-003X)
Published by: Kompass France, 66 quai du Marechal Joffre, Courbevoie, Cedex 92415, France. TEL 33-1-41165100, FAX 33-1-41165156, infos@kompass-france.com, http://www.kompass.fr. Ed., Pub., R&P Bertrand Macabeo. Adv. contact Philippe Leroux.

670.0029 FRA ISSN 0299-6146
KOMPASS PROFESSIONNEL. TEXTILE, HABILLEMENT, CUIRS ET PEAUX. Text and summaries in English, French, German, Spanish. 1960. a. adv. illus. **Document type:** *Directory.*
Former titles (until 1987): Kompass. Le Textile et l'Habillement (0396-1931); (until 1975): Kompass. L'Industrie Francaise du Textile, de l'Habillement, de la Chaussure (0396-1923)
Published by: Kompass France, 66 quai du Marechal Joffre, Courbevoie, Cedex 92415, France. TEL 33-1-41165100, FAX 33-1-41165156, infos@kompass-france.com, http://www.kompass.fr. Ed., Pub., R&P Bertrand Macabeo. Adv. contact Philippe Leroux.

388.029 FRA ISSN 0990-8552
KOMPASS PROFESSIONNEL. TRANSPORTS, MOYENS DE TRANSPORTS. Text in French. 1960. a. adv. **Document type:** *Directory.*
Published by: Kompass France, 66 quai du Marechal Joffre, Courbevoie, Cedex 92415, France. TEL 33-1-41165100, FAX 33-1-41165156, infos@kompass-france.com, http://www.kompass.fr. Ed., Pub., R&P Bertrand Macabeo. Adv. contact Philippe Leroux.

670.0029 FRA
KOMPASS PROFESSIONNELS. (In 9 sections: Agriculture, Alimentation; Batiment et Genie Civil, Manutention-Levage, Bois-Meubles; Chimie, Plastiques, Caoutchouc, Produits Mineraux; Distribution, Commerce de Gros; Electricite, Electronique, Informatique; Produits du Metal; Services, Industries Graphiques; Textile, Habillement, Cuirs et Peaux; Transports, Moyens de Transports) Text and summaries in English, French, German, Spanish. 1960. a. adv. illus. **Document type:** *Directory.* **Description:** Fifteen sectional directories covering whole French industry.
Published by: Kompass France, 66 quai du Marechal Joffre, Courbevoie, Cedex 92415, France. TEL 33-1-41165100, FAX 33-1-41165156, infos@kompass-france.com, http://www.kompass.fr. Ed., Pub., R&P Bertrand Macabeo. Adv. contact Philippe Leroux.

670.29 CHE ISSN 0075-6717
KOMPASS SCHWEIZ - LIECHTENSTEIN; Informationswerk der schweizerischen Wirtschaft. Text in French, German, Italian; Summaries in English, French, German. 1947. a. USD 150. adv. **Document type:** *Directory.*
Published by: Schweiz Verlag AG, In Grosswiesen 14, Zuerich, 8044, Switzerland. Circ: 10,000. **Dist. in the U.S. and Canada by:** Croner Publications, 211 03, Jamaica, NY 11428.

338.0029 SGP ISSN 0217-0604
HF3800.6.Z8
KOMPASS SINGAPORE. Text in English. 1971. a., latest vol.15, 1992.
—BLDSC (5105.627000).
Published by: Kompass South East Asia Ltd., 326C King George's Ave, Singapore, 208567, Singapore. TEL 296-9684, FAX 296-2561, TELEX RS 20013 KMPSS. **Dist. by:** Current Pacific Ltd., PO Box 36-536, Northcote, Auckland, New Zealand. TEL 64-9-480-1388, FAX 64-9-480-1387, info@cplnz.com, http://www.cplnz.com.

338.0029 ZAF ISSN 1022-3568
KOMPASS SOUTH AFRICA. Text in English. 1993. a. ZAR 900 (effective 1999). adv. **Document type:** *Directory.* **Description:** Lists information on more than 22,000 South African businesses and manufacturers, including addresses, telephone and fax numbers, and their products and services.
Related titles: CD-ROM ed.; Online - full text ed.
Indexed: ISAP.
Published by: Reed Business Information South Africa (Pty) Ltd (Subsidiary of: Reed Business Information International), PO Box 653207, Benmore, 2010, South Africa. TEL 27-11-886-2636, FAX 27-11-886-5424. Adv. contact Rohini Bawa.

670.29 SWE ISSN 0075-6725
HF3673
KOMPASS SVERIGE; handbok oever Sveriges industri och Naeringsliv. Text in Swedish; Summaries in Swedish, English, German. 1958. a. SEK 1,825 (effective 1998). adv. **Document type:** *Directory.*
Related titles: CD-ROM ed.; Online - full text ed.: (from The Dialog Corporation).
Published by: Kompass Sverige AB, Torsgatan 21, Stockholm, 11321, Sweden. FAX 46-8-7363022, http://www.kompass.se, http://www.kompass.com. Circ: 4,000.

B

338.0029 TWN ISSN 0259-4021
HC430.5.A1
KOMPASS TAIWAN. Text in English. 1991. a. (in 2 vols.). USD 300 (effective 2001). adv. **Document type:** *Directory.* **Description:** Provides information on 25,000 companies in Taiwan and their products or services.
Published by: Interface Global Taiwan Co., Ltd., PO Box 173-12, Taipei, 116, Taiwan. TEL 886-2-2393-2718, FAX 886-2-2395-2901, kompass@tpts1.seed.net.tw, tradwind@ms2.hinet.net, http://www.trade-winds.net, http://www.asiatrademart.com. Ed. Don Shapiro. R&P Donald Shapiro. Adv. contact Helen Sun. Circ: 20,000. **Subscr. in U.S. to:** Trade Winds Inc., PO Box 820519, Dallas, TX 75382. TEL 877-861-1188, FAX 972-699-1189, twinds8888@aol.com. **Dist. by:** Current Pacific Ltd., PO Box 36-536, Northcote, Auckland, New Zealand. TEL 64-9-480-1388, FAX 64-9-480-1387, info@cplnz.com, http://www.cplnz.com.

338.1029 PHL ISSN 0117-5718
KONTAKS PHILIPPINES (YEAR). Text in English. 1977. biennial. PHP 950 domestic; USD 70 foreign. adv. reprints avail. **Document type:** *Directory.* **Description:** Provides marketing guide, marketing indices, business profiles and marketing insights of leading opinion writers and business people.
Formerly: Kontaks (0115-513X)
Related titles: ◆ Supplement to: Philippines Business Directory.
Published by: Massmark Philippines, P.O. Box 3333, Manila, 1073, Philippines. TEL 805-0955. Ed. J C Borja. adv.: B&W page USD 250.

381.029 DEU ISSN 0935-0241
KONZERNE IN SCHAUBILDERN. Text in German. 1974. 8/yr. looseleaf. **Document type:** *Directory.* **Description:** Information on 700 international holding companies and their relation to over 85,000 affiliated companies.
Related titles: CD-ROM ed.; Diskette ed.; Online - full text ed.
Published by: Hoppenstedt Bonnier Zeitschriften GmbH, Havelstr. 9, Darmstadt, 64295, Germany. TEL 49-6151-380-267, FAX 49-6151-380131.

380.1029 KOR ISSN 1225-0147
DS901
KOREA ANNUAL; comprehensive handbook on Korea. Text in English. 1963. a. USD 42. adv. charts; stat. **Document type:** *Trade.* **Description:** Reviews major events occurring during the past year, including government activities, economic indices and statistics, education and social affairs.
Related titles: ◆ Korean ed.: Hapdong Yongam. ISSN 0073-0335.
Indexed: RASB.
—BLDSC (5113.450000).
Published by: Yonhap News Agency, 85-1 Soosong-Dong, Chongro-ku, PO Box Kwanghwamoon 1039, Seoul, Korea, S. TEL 82-2-398-3590, FAX 82-2-398-3631, TELEX YONHAP K23618. Ed. Young Il Kim. Pub. So Whan Hyon. Circ: 30,000. **Dist. in the US by:** Western Publications Service, 1359 20th Ave, San Francisco, CA 94122. TEL 415-566-3550.

621.381029 KOR ISSN 1227-5336
KOREA BUYERS GUIDE ELECTRONICS. Text in English. m. USD 70 in Asia; USD 95 elsewhere.
Published by: (Korea Foreign Trade Association), Buyers Guide Corp., Korea World Trade Center, 159-1 Samsung-dong, Kangnam-gu, Seoul, 135729, Korea, S. TEL 82-2-551-2376, FAX 82-2-551-2377. Ed. Sung Hwan Park. **Subscr. to:** Trade Center, P.O. Box 8, Seoul, Korea, S. **Dist. in US by:** Charles Lee, Korea Buyers Guide of America Ltd, 612 S Wheeling Rd, Wheeling, IL 60090. TEL 800-732-3572, 708-459-0995.

380.1029 KOR ISSN 1225-4401
KOREA DIRECTORY. Text in English. 1967. a., latest 2003, 36th Edition. USD 110 in Hong Kong, Japan, Macao, Taiwan, China; USD 120 in South East Asia; USD 130 in North America, Europe, Oceania, Middle East (effective 2005). adv.
Document type: *Directory.* **Description:** Lists manufacturers, business firms and trading companies in Korea.
Published by: Korea Directory Corp., 2nd Fl, KD Center, 8-15, Sinsa 1 Dong, Eunpyeong-gu, Seoul, 122-879, Korea, S. TEL 82-2-389-1595, FAX 82-2-389-4357, koreadirectory@koreadirectory.co.kr, http://www.koreadirectory.co.kr. Adv. contact Y J Kim. page KRW 700; trim 188 x 257. **Dist. by:** Current Pacific Ltd., PO Box 36-536, Northcote, Auckland, New Zealand. TEL 64-9-480-1388, FAX 64-9-480-1387, info@cplnz.com, http://www.cplnz.com.

338.0029 KOR
KOREA YELLOW PAGES (YEAR). Text in English. 1983. a. USD 50. adv. **Document type:** *Directory.* **Description:** Lists major Korean businesses and services.
Published by: Korea Yellow Pages Ltd., PO Box 1525, Seoul, 110615, Korea, S. TEL 82-2-332-5942, FAX 82-2-333-5264. Ed. M E Chong. **Dist. by:** Current Pacific Ltd., PO Box 36-536, Northcote, Auckland, New Zealand. TEL 64-9-480-1388, FAX 64-9-480-1387, info@cplnz.com, http://www.cplnz.com.

B

380.1029 KOR
KOREAN BUSINESS DIRECTORY. Text in English. 1970. a. KRW 65,000 domestic; USD 120 foreign (effective 1999). adv.
Document type: *Directory.* **Description:** Lists about 9,700 of Korea's manufacturers, traders, service industries, economic organizations. Also provides a thorough guide book for conducting profitable business with Korea.
Published by: Korea Chamber of Commerce and Industry, 45 Namdaemunno 4 ga Chung gu, PO Box 25, Seoul, 100743, Korea, S. TEL 82-2-316-3536, FAX 82-2-757-9475, trade@kcci.or.kr, http://www.kcci.or.kr. Ed. Kim Hyo Sung. Pub. Kim Song Ho.

338.0029 KOR
KOREAN SOURCES (YEAR). Text in Korean. s-a. USD 66.
Document type: *Directory.* **Description:** Covers major export industries.
Address: C.P.O. Box 3955, Seoul, Korea, S. TEL 737-9451.

382.029 KOR
KOREAN TRADE DIRECTORY. Text in English. 1959. biennial. KRW 30,000, USD 40 (effective 1991). **Document type:** *Directory.* **Description:** Covers Korean company information indexed by products and import and export items.
Published by: Korea Foreign Trade Association, 159-1 Samsung dong, Dang-nam-ku, Seoul, 135729, Korea, S. TEL 02-551-5267, FAX 02-551-5161, TELEX KOTRASO K 24265. Ed. Yong Hak Park. Circ: 5,000.

338.0029 IND
KOTHARI'S INDUSTRIAL DIRECTORY OF INDIA. Text in English. 1936. every 18 mos., latest vol.40, 1996. USD 225. adv. **Document type:** *Directory.* **Description:** Covers economic, financial, industrial and business decision makers in India and all over the world.
Formerly: Kothari's Economic and Industrial Guide of India; Continues: Kothari's Economic Guide and Investor's Handbook of India
Published by: Kothari Enterprises, Kothari Bldgs., 144 Mahatma Gandhi Salai, Chennai, Tamil Nadu 600 034, India. TEL 91-44-8272131, FAX 91-44-8256464, TELEX 041-8325 KS IN. Ed. S Arokiasamy. Circ: 5,000.

380.1029 DNK ISSN 0900-2243
HF3643
KRAK; industrial and trade directory for Denmark. Text in Danish. 1770. a. (in 4 vols.). DKK 3,025. adv. **Document type:** *Directory.*
Published by: Kraks Forlag AS, Virumgaardsvej 21, Virum, 2830, Denmark. TEL 45-45-83-45-83, FAX 45-45-83-10-11. Circ: 30,000.

382.029 SWE ISSN 1400-1489
KRITISKA EUFAKTA. Text in Swedish. 1989. q. SEK 100 (effective 2002).
Formerly (until 1994): Kritiska Europafakta (1100-8040)
Published by: Nej til E U, Heurlins Plats 11, PO Box 31124, Goeteborg, 40032, Sweden. TEL 46-031-701 01 77, FAX 46-031-13 16 03, http://www.nejtilleu.se. Ed. Goesta Torstensson TEL 68-08-771 43 79.

338.0029 ZAF
KWAZULU - NATAL BUSINESS REGISTER. Text in English. 1983. a. USD 175 (effective 2001). adv. **Document type:** *Directory.*
Former titles (until 1994): Natal - KwaZulu Business Register (0259-2304); (until 1987): Natal Business Register (0258-5006)
Published by: Braby's (Subsidiary of: Associated Industries), Attn: Sue Pearson, PO Box 1426, Pinetown, 3600, South Africa. TEL 27-31-7017021, FAX 27-31-7017036, booksales@brabys.co.za.

381.029 UKR
KYIVSKII DILOVII DOVIDNIK/KIEV BUSINESS DIRECTORY. Text in English, Ukrainian. 1996. m. USD 10 (effective 1999). adv.
Document type: *Directory.* **Description:** Serves as a sourcebook for Ukrainian business information.
Published by: K P Publications, Bul L Ukrainki 34/606, Kiev, Ukraine. TEL 380-44-5738353, FAX 380-44-2543113. Ed. Vitaly Kit. Pub. Jed Sunden. Adv. contact Pieter Kinds. Circ: 50,000.

338.0029 681 GBR
LABORATORY ACTIONFILE. Text in English. 8/yr. looseleaf. free to qualified personnel. adv. **Document type:** *Trade.*
Description: Contains product information for over 12,000 key laboratory specifiers.
Media: Cards.
Published by: Nexus Media Ltd. (Subsidiary of: Highbury House Communications PLC), Nexus House, Azalea Dr, Swanley, Kent BR8 8HU, United Kingdom. TEL 44-1322-660070, FAX 44-1322-616311, info@nexusmedia.com, http://www.hhc.co.uk/labaction. Ed. Alexandra Bailey TEL 44-1322-660070 ext 2349. Adv. contact Justine Smartxxxx. B&W page GBP 590, color page GBP 680; bleed 166 x 91. Circ: 12,000.

670.29 CAN
LABORATORY YELLOW PAGES. Text in English. 1990. a. CND 40. adv. **Document type:** *Directory.*
Published by: Jesmar Communications Inc., 30 E Beaver Creek Rd, Ste 220, Richmond, ON L4B 1J2, Canada. TEL 416-886-5040, FAX 416-886-6615. Ed. Kathleen Hurd. Circ: 32,140.

LACES & EMBROIDERY DIRECTORY ANNUAL. see *TEXTILE INDUSTRIES AND FABRICS*

338.0029 ZAF ISSN 0378-9268
LADYSMITH DIRECTORY. Text in English. a. ZAR 30 (effective 2001). **Document type:** *Directory.*
Published by: Braby's (Subsidiary of: Associated Industries), Attn: Sue Pearson, PO Box 1426, Pinetown, 3600, South Africa. TEL 27-31-7017021, FAX 27-31-7017036, booksales@brabys.co.za. Ed. A Stagg.

LASER FOCUS WORLD BUYERS' GUIDE. see *PHYSICS—Optics*

382.029 CRI
LATIN AMERICAN IMPORT - EXPORT DIRECTORY. Text in English, Spanish. 1983. a. USD 23.50. **Document type:** *Directory.*
Published by: International Trade Council, Apdo 73, San Jose, 1007, Costa Rica. TEL 33-8697.

LAW BOOKS AND SERIALS IN PRINT; a multimedia sourcebook. see *LAW—Abstracting, Bibliographies, Statistics*

LAW FIRMS YELLOW BOOK; who's who in the management of the leading U.S. law firms. see *LAW*

658.0029 USA
THE LEADERSHIP LIBRARY. Text in English. 1994. 38/yr. (comprises 5 q vols and 9 s-a vols). USD 2,750; USD 2,650 renewals (effective 2005). **Document type:** *Directory, Trade.*
Description: Contact information for the 400,000 individuals who constitute the institutional leadership of the United States.
Formerly: Leadership Directories on C D -R O M (1075-3869)
Related titles: CD-ROM ed.: 1997. USD 2,300 single user; includes Internet ed; USD 2,765 renewals single user; includes Internet ed (effective 2001) (from Chadwyck-Healey Inc.); Online - full text ed.: 1999. USD 3,065; USD 2,765 renewals (effective 2001).
Published by: Leadership Directories, Inc, 104 Fifth Ave, 2nd Fl, New York, NY 10011. TEL 212-627-4140, FAX 212-645-0931, info@leadershipdirectories.com, http://www.leadershipdirectories.com/llip.htm. Pub. David J Hurvits.

LEASING SOURCEBOOK; the directory of the U S capital equipment leasing industry. see *BUSINESS AND ECONOMICS—Banking And Finance*

THE LEATHER MANUFACTURER DIRECTORY. see *LEATHER AND FUR INDUSTRIES*

670.29 LBN ISSN 0075-8353
LEBANESE INDUSTRIAL AND COMMERCIAL DIRECTORY/ANNUAIRE DES PROFESSIONS AU LIBAN. Text in French. 1953. biennial. USD 30. adv. **Document type:** *Directory.*
Published by: Middle East Commercial Information Center, P O Box 6466, Beirut, Lebanon. Ed. Charles G Gedeon. Circ: 10,000. **Dist. by:** UNIPUB, 345 Park Ave S, New York, NY 10010.

338.19029 CHE
DIE LEBENSMITTEL- UND GETRAENKE-INDUSTRIE DER SCHWEIZ/L'INDUSTRIE DES PRODUITS ALIMENTAIRES ET DES BOISSONS EN SUISSE. Text in French, German. 1982. a. CHF 89 (effective 2000). **Document type:** *Directory, Trade.*
Published by: Orell Fuessli Verlag, Dietzingerstr 3, Zuerich, 8036, Switzerland. TEL 41-1-4667711, FAX 41-1-4667412. **Dist. by:** BD Buecherdienst AG, Postfach, Einsiedeln 8840, Switzerland. TEL 41-55-4188958, 41-55-4188959.

320.531 USA ISSN 1090-7211
HS2321
THE LEFT GUIDE; a guide to liberal, progressive, and left-of-center organizations. Text in English. 1996. s-a. USD 74.95 (effective 2001). **Document type:** *Directory.*
Description: Profiles over 2,000 think tanks, lobbying groups, publishers, and public-interest litigation organizations. Includes financial information on organizations including revenues, salaries, lobbying expenditures and sources of funding.
Published by: Economics America, Inc., 612 Church St, Ann Arbor, MI 48104. TEL 734-995-0865, FAX 734-747-7258, wilcoxdl@aol.com. Ed. Derk Arend Wilcox.

338.0029 340 GBR
THE LEGAL 500; the clients guide to UK law firms. Variant title: UK Legal 500. Text in English. 1998. a. GBP 99 (effective 1999). **Document type:** *Directory, Trade.* **Description:** A client reference to UK commercial law firms and barristers' chambers.
Related titles: CD-ROM ed.
—BLDSC (5181.414500).
Published by: Legalease Ltd., Kensington Square House, 12-14 Ansdell St, London, W8 5BN, United Kingdom. TEL 44-20-7396-9292, FAX 44-20-7396-9300, legalease@link.org, info@legalease.co.uk, http://www.legalease.co.uk.

387.029 USA ISSN 1068-686X
HE5623
LEONARD'S GUIDE. NATIONAL CONTRACT CARRIERS DIRECTORY. Text in English. 1989. a. USD 110 (effective 2002). **Document type:** *Directory.*
Published by: Leonard Guide, 115 E University Dr, Arlington Heights, IL 60004. TEL 847-797-8101, info@leonardsguide.com, http://www.leonardsguide.com. Circ: 13,000.

658.8029 USA
LEONARD'S GUIDE. NATIONAL THIRD PARTY LOGISTICS DIRECTORY. Text in English. a. USD 110 (effective 2002).
Formerly: Leonard's Guide. National Transportation Brokers Directory
Published by: Leonard Guide, 115 E University Dr, Arlington Heights, IL 60004. TEL 847-797-8101, info@leonardsguide.com, http://www.leonardsguide.com. Circ: 13,000.

658.8029 USA
LEONARD'S GUIDE. NATIONAL WAREHOUSE AND DISTRIBUTION DIRECTORY. Text in English. a. USD 110 (effective 2002). **Document type:** *Directory.*
Published by: Leonard Guide, 115 E University Dr, Arlington Heights, IL 60004. TEL 847-797-8101, info@leonardsguide.com, http://www.leonardsguide.com. Circ: 13,000.

338.0029 ZAF ISSN 1016-3999
LESOTHO BUSINESS DIRECTORY. Text in English. 1973. a. USD 68 (effective 2001). adv. **Document type:** *Directory.*
Published by: Braby's (Subsidiary of: Associated Industries), Attn: Sue Pearson, PO Box 1426, Pinetown, 3600, South Africa. TEL 27-31-7017021, FAX 27-31-7017036, booksales@brabys.co.za.

338 ZAF
LESOTHO GOVERNMENT TELEPHONE DIRECTORY. Text in English. irreg. ZAR 135 (effective 2001). **Document type:** *Directory.*
Published by: Braby's (Subsidiary of: Associated Industries), Attn: Sue Pearson, PO Box 1426, Pinetown, 3600, South Africa. TEL 27-31-7174141, FAX 27-31-7173011, sue@brabys.co.za.

338.0029 USA
LESSONS OF YELLOW PAGES COMPETITION. Text in English. 1993. irreg. USD 1,495 domestic; USD 1,555 in Canada & Mexico; USD 1,535 elsewhere (effective 2000). **Document type:** *Trade.* **Description:** Analyzes the successes and failures among yellow pages directories launched during the previous five years.
Published by: SIMBA Information (Subsidiary of: R.R. Bowker LLC), 60 Long Ridge Rd., Ste 300, Stamford, CT 06902. TEL 203-325-8193, 800-307-2529, 888-269-5372, FAX 203-325-8915, info@simbanet.com, http://www.simbanet.com.

382.029 LBR
LIBERIAN TRADE DIRECTORY∗; basic trade information, exporters & importers. Text in English. irreg. **Document type:** *Directory.*
Published by: (Liberia. Director of Foreign Trade), Ministry of Commerce Industry and Transportation, PO Box 9041, Monrovia, Liberia.

LIGHTWAVE BUYERS GUIDE. see *COMMUNICATIONS*

658.8029 AUS
THE LIST OF LISTS. Text in English. 1985. a., latest 8th ed. AUD 149 for both Print & Online eds. (effective 2000). **Document type:** *Directory.* **Description:** Provides mailing list information for the direct market industry.
Related titles: Online - full content ed.: AUD 95 (effective 2000).
Published by: Bookman Press Pty Ltd, Lu 10, 227 Collins St, Melbourne, VIC 3000, Australia. TEL 61-3-96542000, FAX 61-3-96542290, bookman@bookman.com.au, http://www.bookman.com.au.

LIST OF SHIPOWNERS, MANAGERS AND MANAGING AGENTS. see *TRANSPORTATION—Ships And Shipping*

LITERARY MARKET PLACE; the directory of the book publishing industry. see *PUBLISHING AND BOOK TRADE*

LITERARYMARKETPLACE.COM; the world-wide resource for the book publishing industry. see *PUBLISHING AND BOOK TRADE*

687.029 GBR ISSN 1358-7501
THE LITTLE BLACK BOOK✶. Text in English. 1995. bi-m. **Document type:** *Directory.* **Description:** Portable pocket guide giving the contact details of over 1,500 organizations in the fashion and beauty industries.
Published by: Profile Group (UK) Ltd., 6/7 St Cross St, London, EC1N 8UA, United Kingdom. TEL 44-171-405-4455, FAX 44-171-430-1089. Ed. Sam Allen.

LLOYD'S A S E A N SHIPPING DIRECTORY. (Association of South East Asian Nations) see *TRANSPORTATION—Ships And Shipping*

LLOYD'S MARINE EQUIPMENT BUYERS' GUIDE. see *TRANSPORTATION—Ships And Shipping*

LLOYD'S MARITIME DIRECTORY (YEAR); international shipping & shipbuilding directory. see *TRANSPORTATION—Ships And Shipping*

658.8029 USA
THE LOCATOR. Text in English. 1957. m. USD 48 domestic; USD 4.25 newsstand/cover (effective 2005). 128 p./no. 3 cols./p.; **Document type:** *Magazine, Trade.*
Published by: John Holmes Publishing, PO Box 286, Whiting, IA 51063. TEL 712-458-2213, FAX 712-458-2687, sales@partslocator.com, http://www.partslocator.com. Ed. Wendy Lloyd. Pub. John Holmes. Circ: 18,500 (controlled and free).

LOCATOR OF USED MACHINERY, EQUIPMENT & PLANT SERVICES. see *MACHINERY*

LOCKSMITH LEDGER - INTERNATIONAL DIRECTORY. see *CRIMINOLOGY AND LAW ENFORCEMENT—Security*

676 381.029 USA
TS1088
LOCKWOOD - POST'S DIRECTORY AMERICAN TRAVELER'S EDITION. Variant title: Lockwood Post Pulp & Paper Directory. Text in English. 1873. a., latest 2001. USD 245 per issue (effective 2005). adv. index. reprint service avail. from PQC. **Document type:** *Directory.* **Description:** Covers listing service for the pulp and paper industry; provides indexes of executive offices, industry mills, mill officials, converters, and general paper merchants.
Former titles (until Jun. 2005): Lockwood - Post's Directory North America; Lockwood - Post's Directory of the Pulp, Paper and Allied Trades (1046-5359); (until 1988): Lockwood's Directory of the Paper and Allied Trades (0076-0277)
Related titles: CD-ROM ed.: USD 1,395 newsstand/cover (effective 2002).
—CCC.
Published by: Paperloop, 55 Hawthorne, Ste 600, San Francisco, CA 94105. TEL 415-947-3600, 800-565-9226, FAX 415-947-3700, info@paperloop.com, http://www.pponline.com. Circ: 4,600.

676 382.029 USA
LOCKWOOD - POST'S DIRECTORY ASIAN TRAVELER'S EDITION. Text in English. a. USD 245 per issue (effective 2005). **Document type:** *Directory, Trade.*
Supersedes in part (in Jun. 2005): Lockwood - Post's Directory International; Which was formerly: International Pulp & Paper Directory (0097-2509)
Published by: Paperloop, 55 Hawthorne, Ste 600, San Francisco, CA 94105. TEL 415-947-3600, 800-565-9226, FAX 415-947-3700, info@paperloop.com, http://www.pponline.com.

676 382.029 USA
HD9820.3
LOCKWOOD - POST'S DIRECTORY EUROPEAN TRAVELER'S EDITION. Text in English. a., latest 2001. USD 245 per issue (effective 2005). adv. back issues avail. **Document type:** *Directory, Trade.* **Description:** Contains detailed information on contact, equipment and production of every pulp and paper mill in the world.
Supersedes in part (in Jun. 2005): Lockwood - Post's Directory International; Which was formerly: International Pulp & Paper Directory (0097-2509)
Published by: Paperloop, 55 Hawthorne, Ste 600, San Francisco, CA 94105. TEL 415-947-3600, 800-565-9226, FAX 415-947-3700, info@paperloop.com, http://store.paperloop.com/cgi-bin/paperloop/105-l.html?id=3octnsTc, http://www.pponline.com. adv.: page USD 4,000; trim 11 x 8.5. Circ: 6,000.

676 382.029 USA
LOCKWOOD - POST'S DIRECTORY GLOBAL EDITION. Text in English. a. USD 445 per issue (effective 2005). **Document type:** *Directory, Trade.*
Published by: Paperloop, 55 Hawthorne, Ste 600, San Francisco, CA 94105. TEL 415-947-3600, 800-565-9226, FAX 415-947-3700, info@paperloop.com, http://www.pponline.com.

LONDON PORT HANDBOOK (YEAR). see *TRANSPORTATION—Ships And Shipping*

LONG ISLAND TELEPHONE TICKLER FOR INSURANCE MEN & WOMEN. see *INSURANCE*

380.1029 USA
LOUISIANA BUSINESS CREDIT DIRECTORY. Text in English. a. USD 1,100 combined subscription print, online & CD-ROM eds. (effective 2004 & 2005). back issues avail. **Document type:** *Directory.* **Description:** Contains credit ratings and other valuable information on all businesses within Louisiana. Includes company name & address, phone & fax numbers, key executive names & titles, lines of business, years in business, number of employees, estimated annual sales, volume credit rating code, and corporate linkage information.
Related titles: CD-ROM ed.; Diskette ed.; E-mail ed.; Fax ed.; Magnetic Tape ed.; Online - full text ed.
Published by: American Business Directories (Subsidiary of: American Business Information, Inc.), 5711 S 86th Circle, P O Box 27347, Omaha, NE 68127. TEL 402-593-4600, 888-946-9377, 877-708-3844, FAX 402-331-5481, sales@directoriesusa.com, http://www.directoriesusa.com.

338.0029 USA ISSN 1048-7298
HF5065.L8
LOUISIANA BUSINESS DIRECTORY. Text in English. 1988. a. USD 1,100 combined subscription print, online & CD-ROM eds. (effective 2004 & 2005). index. back issues avail. **Document type:** *Directory.* **Description:** Includes all businesses in the state compiled from the yellow pages and telephone-verified. Each listing includes company name, address, phone number, name of owner, and employee size and sales volume codes, and credit rating codes.
Related titles: CD-ROM ed.; Diskette ed.; E-mail ed.; Fax ed.; Magnetic Tape ed.; Online - full text ed.
Published by: American Business Directories (Subsidiary of: American Business Information, Inc.), 5711 S 86th Circle, P O Box 27347, Omaha, NE 68127. TEL 402-593-4600, 888-946-9377, 877-708-3844, FAX 402-331-5481, karen.peters@infousa.com, sales@directoriesusa.com, http://www.directoriesusa.com.

670.29 USA ISSN 1053-8992
HF5065.L8
LOUISIANA MANUFACTURERS REGISTER. Text in English. 1991. a. USD 74 (effective 2000). adv. **Document type:** *Directory.* **Description:** Lists 5,307 Louisiana manufacturers by their industrial product or service, by SIC, alphabetically by name, geographically by city, and by parent company.
Related titles: CD-ROM ed.: USD 355 (effective 2000); Diskette ed.: USD 395.
Published by: Manufacturers' News, Inc., 1633 Central St, Evanston, IL 60201. TEL 847-864-7000, 888-752-5200, FAX 847-332-1100, info@mninfo.com, info@manufacturersnews.com, sales@mninfo.com, http://www.manufacturersnews.com. Ed. Frank Lambing. Adv. contact Charles Scherer.

LOUISIANA - MISSISSIPPI STATE AGENT HANDBOOK. see *INSURANCE*

670.29 DEU ISSN 0932-3317
M + A - MESSEPLANER INTERNATIONAL; schedule for fairs and exhibitions worldwide. Text in German. 1919. s-a. EUR 143.38; EUR 166 in Europe; EUR 176 elsewhere (effective 2000). adv. **Document type:** *Directory, Trade.* **Description:** Contains basic data on over 9,000 fairs and exhibitions worldwide.
Formerly: M und A Kalender
Related titles: CD-ROM ed.; Online - full text ed.
Published by: M + A Verlag fuer Messen, Ausstellungen und Kongresse GmbH (Subsidiary of: Deutscher Fachverlag GmbH), Postfach 200128, Frankfurt Am Main, 60605, Germany. TEL 49-69-759502, FAX 49-69-75951280, muamesseplaner-redaktion@dfv.de, http://www.m-a.com. Ed. Dorit Vogel Seib. Adv. contact Jutta Fautz. B&W page EUR 2,566.69, color page EUR 3,226.76; trim 297 x 210. Circ: 7,720 (controlled).

380 USA
M H M (YEAR) DIRECTORY. (Material Handling Management) Text in English. a. USD 50 per issue domestic; USD 65 per issue in Canada; USD 95 per issue elsewhere (effective 2000). **Document type:** *Directory, Trade.*
Published by: Penton Media, Inc. (Subsidiary of: Pittway Company), 1300 E 9th St, Cleveland, OH 44114-1503. TEL 216-696-7000, FAX 216-696-8208.

338.0029 GBR
M H N DIRECTORY. (Materials Handling News) Text in English. a. free to qualified personnel. adv. **Document type:** *Directory, Trade.* **Description:** Publishes information on over 10,000 suppliers and their products.
Published by: Nexus Media Ltd. (Subsidiary of: Highbury House Communications PLC), Nexus House, Azalea Dr, Swanley, Kent BR8 8HU, United Kingdom. TEL 44-1322-660070, FAX 44-1322-616311, info@nexusmedia.com, http://www.hhc.co.uk/mhndirectory. Adv. contact Nick Singer. Circ: 12,000.

380 USA
MACHINE DESIGN PRODUCT LOCATOR. Text in English. a. USD 25 per issue domestic; USD 35 per issue in Canada; USD 45 per issue elsewhere (effective 2000). **Document type:** *Trade.*
Published by: Penton Media, Inc. (Subsidiary of: Pittway Company), 1300 E 9th St, Cleveland, OH 44114-1503. http://www.penton.com.

B

338.0029 USA ISSN 0886-9189
T12
MACRAE'S BLUE BOOK✶; serving the original equipment market. Text in English. 1893. a. USD 170. **Document type:** *Directory, Trade.* **Description:** Provides buyers and specifiers with quick and easy access to approximately 45,000 leading manufacturers and their products.
Former titles (until 1985): MacRae's Industrial Directory (0749-5986); (until 1984): MacRae's Blue Book (0076-2067)
Related titles: Diskette ed.
Published by: (MacRae's Blue Book), Business Research Publications, Inc., 210 E 39th St, New York, NY 10016-2754. TEL 800-673-4700, FAX 212-475-1790, http://www.d-net.com/macraes. Ed., R&P Mary O'Hara Smith. **Dist by:** Manufacturers' News, Inc., 1633 Central St, Evanston, IL 60201. TEL 847-864-7000.

338.0029 BHR
MADE IN THE ARAB WORLD. Text in Arabic, English. a. **Document type:** *Directory.* **Description:** Provides statistical and detailed information on the industrial sector in the Arab countries.
Published by: Falcon Publishing, PO Box 5028, Manama, Bahrain. TEL 253162, FAX 259694. Ed. V N Gopalakrishnan. Circ: 22,000.

674.029 CAN ISSN 0316-6414
MADISON'S CANADIAN LUMBER DIRECTORY. Text in English. 1952. a. CND 134.99 (effective 2000). adv. charts; stat. **Document type:** *Directory.*
Published by: Madison's Canadian Lumber Reporter (1973) Ltd., P O Box 2486, Vancouver, BC V6B 3W7, Canada. TEL 604-984-6839, FAX 604-984-6572, madrep@direct.ca, http://www.madisonsreport.com. Ed., Adv. contact Brenna Wong. Pub., R&P Laurence Cater.

615.1029 HUN ISSN 1218-1927
MAI PIAC; a sikeres kereskedo lapja/a magazine of a successful retailer. Text in German, Hungarian; Summaries in English, German, Hungarian. 1994. m. EUR 195 foreign (effective 2005). adv. bk.rev. **Document type:** *Magazine, Trade.* **Description:** Presents information about food and drug market, mainly for retail and wholesale traders.
Published by: Magyar Szakkiado Kft. (Subsidiary of: Deutscher Fachverlag Gmbh), Lovohaz utca 30, Budapest, 1024, Hungary. TEL 36-1-3362480, FAX 36-1-3362488, szakkiado@szakkiado.hu, http://www.maipiac.hu, http://www.szakkiado.hu. Ed. Katalin Nagy. Adv. contact Krisztina Torma. B&W page HUF 350,000, color page HUF 570,000; trim 210 x 297. Circ: 16,500.

658.0029 USA ISSN 0085-2953
HF5466
MAIL ORDER BUSINESS DIRECTORY. Text in English. 1955. a. USD 85 (effective 2000). **Document type:** *Directory.*
Published by: B. Klein Publications, PO Box 6578, Delray Beach, FL 33482. TEL 407-496-3316, FAX 407-496-5546. Ed. Bernard Klein.

MAIL ORDER PRODUCT GUIDE. see *ADVERTISING AND PUBLIC RELATIONS*

338.0029 USA ISSN 1048-7115
HF5065.M2
MAINE BUSINESS DIRECTORY. Text in English. 1990. a. USD 1,100 combined subscription print, online & CD-ROM eds. (effective 2004 & 2005). index. back issues avail. **Document type:** *Directory.* **Description:** Includes all businesses in the state compiled from the yellow pages and telephone verified. Each listing includes company name, address, phone number, name of owner, and employee size and sales volume codes, and credit rating codes.

Related titles: CD-ROM ed.; Diskette ed.; E-mail ed.; Fax ed.; Magnetic Tape ed.; Online - full text ed.
Published by: American Business Directories (Subsidiary of: American Business Information, Inc.), 5711 S 86th Circle, P O Box 27347, Omaha, NE 68127. TEL 402-593-4600, 888-946-9377, 877-708-3844, FAX 402-331-5481, karen.peters@infousa.com, sales@directoriesusa.com, http://www.directoriesusa.com.

670.29 USA ISSN 1522-2012
HF5065.M2
MAINE MANUFACTURERS REGISTER. Text in English. 1999. a. USD 63 (effective 2000). adv. charts; illus.; stat. **Document type:** *Directory.* **Description:** Profiles 2,300 manufacturers listed five ways: by product, company name, S.I.C., city, and parent company.
Related titles: CD-ROM ed.: USD 265 (effective 2000); Diskette ed.; Online - full text ed.
Published by: Manufacturers' News, Inc., 1633 Central St, Evanston, IL 60201. TEL 847-864-7000, 888-752-5200, FAX 847-332-1100, info@mninfo.com, info@manufacturersnews.com, sales@mninfo.com, http://www.manufacturersnews.com. Ed. Frank Lambing. Adv. contact Charles Scherer. B&W page USD 1,843.

MAINE MANUFACTURING DIRECTORY. see *BUSINESS AND ECONOMICS—Production Of Goods And Services*

670.29 USA ISSN 0197-1220
T12
MAINE, VERMONT AND NEW HAMPSHIRE DIRECTORY OF MANUFACTURERS. Text in English. 1979. a. USD 62.50. **Document type:** *Directory.* **Description:** Profiles about 4000 manufacturers; includes alphabetical, geographical and product line by SIC sections, as well as a key executive list.
Related titles: Diskette ed.: USD 295; Magnetic Tape ed.
Published by: Commerce Register, Inc., 190 Godwin Ave, Midland Park, NJ 07432. TEL 201-445-3000, FAX 201-445-5806.

658.0029 661.804 GBR
MAJOR CHEMICAL & PETROCHEMICAL COMPANIES OF EUROPE (YEAR). Text in English. a. GBP 285 (effective 2001). **Document type:** *Directory, Trade.* **Description:** Details over 3,000 of the largest chemical and petrochemical companies in 20 countries of Western Europe.
Published by: Graham & Whiteside Ltd (Subsidiary of: Gale Group), Tuition House, 5-6 Francis Grove, London, SW19 4DT, United Kingdom. TEL 44-20-8947-1011, FAX 44-20-8947-1163, galeord@gale.com, http://www.galegroup.com/graham&whiteside/.

658.0029 661 661.804 GBR
MAJOR CHEMICAL & PETROCHEMICAL COMPANIES OF THE FAR EAST & AUSTRALASIA (YEAR). Text in English. a. GBP 260 (effective 2001). **Document type:** *Directory, Trade.* **Description:** Details more than 1,500 of the largest chemical and petrochemical companies throughout the Asia/Pacific region.
Published by: Graham & Whiteside Ltd (Subsidiary of: Gale Group), Tuition House, 5-6 Francis Grove, London, SW19 4DT, United Kingdom. TEL 44-20-8947-1011, FAX 44-20-8947-1163, galeord@gale.com, http://www.galegroup.com/graham&whiteside/. **Dist. by:** Current Pacific Ltd., PO Box 36-536, Northcote, Auckland, New Zealand. TEL 64-9-480-1388, FAX 64-9-480-1387, info@cplnz.com, http://www.cplnz.com.

658.0029 661.804 GBR
MAJOR CHEMICAL & PETROCHEMICAL COMPANIES OF THE WORLD (YEAR). Text in English. a. GBP 490 (effective 2001). **Document type:** *Directory, Trade.* **Description:** Includes 7,500 of the biggest companies in general chemicals, petrochemicals, industrial gases, agricultural chemicals, specialty chemicals, fertilisers, oil refining and chemical plant.
Published by: Graham & Whiteside Ltd (Subsidiary of: Gale Group), Tuition House, 5-6 Francis Grove, London, SW19 4DT, United Kingdom. TEL 44-20-8947-1011, FAX 44-20-8947-1163, galeord@gale.com, http://www.galegroup.com/graham&whiteside/. **Dist. by:** Current Pacific Ltd., PO Box 36-536, Northcote, Auckland, New Zealand. TEL 64-9-480-1388, FAX 64-9-480-1387, info@cplnz.com, http://www.cplnz.com.

658.0029 GBR ISSN 1365-4845
HF3873
MAJOR COMPANIES OF AFRICA SOUTH OF THE SAHARA (YEAR). Text in English. 1996. a., latest vol.6. GBP 295, USD 530 per vol. (effective 2001). **Document type:** *Directory, Trade.* **Description:** Contains current and comprehensive information on 6,200 companies in the region, including 38,000 named senior executives.
Related titles: CD-ROM ed.: 1997. GBP 575, USD 1,035 (effective 2001).
Published by: Graham & Whiteside Ltd (Subsidiary of: Gale Group), Tuition House, 5-6 Francis Grove, London, SW19 4DT, United Kingdom. TEL 44-20-8947-1011, FAX 44-20-8947-1163, galeord@gale.com, http://www.galegroup.com/graham&whiteside/. Ed. D Butler. **Dist. by:** Current Pacific Ltd., PO Box 36-536, Northcote, Auckland, New Zealand. TEL 64-9-480-1388, FAX 64-9-480-1387, info@cplnz.com, http://www.cplnz.com.

658.0029 GBR
MAJOR COMPANIES OF CENTRAL & EASTERN EUROPE & THE C I S (YEAR). (Commonwealth of the Independent States) Text in English. a. GBP 610 (effective 2001). **Document type:** *Directory, Trade.* **Description:** Includes over 9,750 of the most important business organizations with 92,000 named contacts and 27 countries covered. Features the largest trade organizations, privatized companies, manufacturers, financial institutions and key government organizations throughout this region.
Related titles: CD-ROM ed.: GBP 975 (effective 2001).
Published by: Graham & Whiteside Ltd (Subsidiary of: Gale Group), Tuition House, 5-6 Francis Grove, London, SW19 4DT, United Kingdom. TEL 44-20-8947-1011, FAX 44-20-8947-1163, galeord@gale.com, http://www.galegroup.com/graham&whiteside/. **Dist. by:** Current Pacific Ltd., PO Box 36-536, Northcote, Auckland, New Zealand. TEL 64-9-480-1388, FAX 64-9-480-1387, info@cplnz.com, http://www.cplnz.com.

332.6029 GBR ISSN 1365-0831
HF5154.7.A3
MAJOR COMPANIES OF CENTRAL & EASTERN EUROPE AND THE COMMONWEALTH OF INDEPENDENT STATES. Text in English. 1991. a. USD 1,100 per vol. (effective 2003). **Document type:** *Directory.* **Description:** Provides data on the most important business organizations in the Baltic Republics, Commonwealth of Independent States and other nations in Central Europe.
Former titles (until 1996): Major Business Organisations of Eastern Europe and the Commonwealth of Independent States (0966-0372); (until 1992): Major Business Organisations of Eastern Europe and the Soviet Union (0963-052X)
Published by: Graham & Whiteside Ltd (Subsidiary of: Gale Group), Tuition House, 5-6 Francis Grove, London, SW19 4DT, United Kingdom. TEL 44-20-8947-1011, FAX 44-20-8947-1163, galeord@gale.com, http://www.galegroup.com/graham&whiteside/. Ed. C Tapster.

658.0029 GBR ISSN 1356-2533
MAJOR COMPANIES OF EUROPE (YEAR). Text in English. a. GBP 1,015 For six vol. set; GBP 205 Per single vol. (effective 2001). **Document type:** *Directory, Trade.* **Description:** Provides essential data on the major public and private companies throughout all 20 countries of western Europe. Lists 35,000 of Europe's largest companies, with 392,000 named senior executives.
Related titles: CD-ROM ed.: GBP 1,795 (effective 2001); Microfiche ed.
—BLDSC (5353.603950).
Published by: Graham & Whiteside Ltd (Subsidiary of: Gale Group), Tuition House, 5-6 Francis Grove, London, SW19 4DT, United Kingdom. TEL 44-20-8947-1011, FAX 44-20-8947-1163, galeord@gale.com, http://www.galegroup.com/graham&whiteside/. **Dist. by:** Current Pacific Ltd., PO Box 36-536, Northcote, Auckland, New Zealand. TEL 64-9-480-1388, FAX 64-9-480-1387, info@cplnz.com, http://www.cplnz.com.

658.0029 GBR ISSN 1369-5428
MAJOR COMPANIES OF LATIN AMERICA & THE CARIBBEAN (YEAR). Text in English. 1996. a. GBP 445, USD 795 per vol. (effective 2001). **Document type:** *Directory, Trade.* **Description:** Provides vital data on over 9,200 of the largest companies in Latin America and the Caribbean, including over 42,000 named senior executives.
Formerly (until 1997): Major Companies of Latin America (1365-4659)
Related titles: CD-ROM ed.: GBP 875, USD 1,575 (effective 2001).
Published by: Graham & Whiteside Ltd (Subsidiary of: Gale Group), Tuition House, 5-6 Francis Grove, London, SW19 4DT, United Kingdom. TEL 44-20-8947-1011, FAX 44-20-8947-1163, galeord@gale.com, http://www.galegroup.com/graham&whiteside/. Ed. D Shave. **Dist. by:** Current Pacific Ltd., PO Box 36-536, Northcote, Auckland, New Zealand. TEL 64-9-480-1388, FAX 64-9-480-1387, info@cplnz.com, http://www.cplnz.com.

658.0029 GBR ISSN 0956-8662
MAJOR COMPANIES OF SCANDINAVIA (YEAR). Text in English. 1985. a. GBP 340 per vol. (effective 2001). **Document type:** *Directory, Trade.* **Description:** Provides current and comprehensive information on the top 3,800 Scandinavian companies - Denmark (1000), Finland (650), Norway (900) and Sweden (1,200).
Published by: Graham & Whiteside Ltd (Subsidiary of: Gale Group), Tuition House, 5-6 Francis Grove, London, SW19 4DT, United Kingdom. TEL 44-20-8947-1011, FAX 44-20-8947-1163, galeord@gale.com, http://www.galegroup.com/graham&whiteside/. **Dist. by:** Current Pacific Ltd., PO Box 36-536, Northcote, Auckland, New Zealand. TEL 64-9-480-1388, FAX 64-9-480-1387, info@cplnz.com, http://www.cplnz.com.

658.0029 GBR ISSN 1365-084X
MAJOR COMPANIES OF SOUTH WEST ASIA (YEAR). Text in English. 1997. a. GBP 295, USD 530 per vol. (effective 2001). **Document type:** *Directory, Trade.* **Description:** An authoritative reference tool for information on South West Asia's major companies. Essential data is provided on 4,500 companies, including 3,600 major companies in India. Includes 39,000 named senior executives.
Related titles: CD-ROM ed.: GBP 550, USD 990 (effective 2001).
Published by: Graham & Whiteside Ltd (Subsidiary of: Gale Group), Tuition House, 5-6 Francis Grove, London, SW19 4DT, United Kingdom. TEL 44-20-8947-1011, FAX 44-20-8947-1163, galeord@gale.com, http://www.galegroup.com/graham&whiteside/. Ed. S James. **Dist. by:** Current Pacific Ltd., PO Box 36-536, Northcote, Auckland, New Zealand. TEL 64-9-480-1388, FAX 64-9-480-1387, info@cplnz.com, http://www.cplnz.com.

658.0029 GBR ISSN 0144-0594
HF3866
MAJOR COMPANIES OF THE ARAB WORLD (YEAR). Text in English. a. GBP 510 (effective 2001). **Document type:** *Directory, Trade.* **Description:** Contains 8,000 of the Arab world's largest companies, 77,500 named senior executives, and details on 26 countries.
Related titles: CD-ROM ed.: GBP 900 (effective 2001); Microfiche ed.
—BLDSC (5353.603600).
Published by: Graham & Whiteside Ltd (Subsidiary of: Gale Group), Tuition House, 5-6 Francis Grove, London, SW19 4DT, United Kingdom. TEL 44-20-8947-1011, FAX 44-20-8947-1163, galeord@gale.com, http://www.galegroup.com/graham&whiteside/. **Dist. by:** Current Pacific Ltd., PO Box 36-536, Northcote, Auckland, New Zealand. TEL 64-9-480-1388, FAX 64-9-480-1387, info@cplnz.com, http://www.cplnz.com.

338.0029 GBR
HG4244.6
MAJOR COMPANIES OF THE FAR EAST AND AUSTRALASIA. Variant title: Major Companies of the Far East. Text in Dutch. 1983. a. (in 3 vols., 1 no./vol.). GBP 330 per vol. for vol. 1, 2 or 3; GBP 850 for complete 3 vol. set (effective 2001). adv. **Document type:** *Directory.*
Formerly (until 1990): Major Companies of the Far East. Volume 1. South East Asia (0267-2251)
Related titles: CD-ROM ed.: GBP 1,385 (effective 2001); Microform ed.: (from PQC).
Published by: Graham & Whiteside Ltd (Subsidiary of: Gale Group), Tuition House, 5-6 Francis Grove, London, SW19 4DT, United Kingdom. TEL 44-20-8947-1011, FAX 44-20-8947-1163, galeord@gale.com, http://www.galegroup.com/graham&whiteside/.

658.0029 GBR
MAJOR COMPANIES OF THE WORLD. Text in English. a. GBP 3,500 (effective 2001). **Document type:** *Directory, Trade.* **Description:** Provides detailed information on 85,000 companies and gives access to over 500,000 named senior executives.
Related titles: CD-ROM ed.: GBP 6,585 (effective 2001).
Published by: Graham & Whiteside Ltd (Subsidiary of: Gale Group), Tuition House, 5-6 Francis Grove, London, SW19 4DT, United Kingdom. TEL 44-20-8947-1011, FAX 44-20-8947-1163, galeord@gale.com, http://www.galegroup.com/graham&whiteside/.

338.0029 USA
MAJOR CORPORATIONS DIRECTORY: CENTRAL PUGET SOUND. Text in English. biennial. USD 39.50. **Document type:** *Directory.* **Description:** Lists companies of 100 or more employees in King, Pierce and Snohomish counties. Includes address, phone, fax, key contacts, number of employees and products-service description.
Formerly: Major Employers Directory: Central Puget Sound
Related titles: Diskette ed.
Published by: Greater Seattle Chamber of Commerce, 1301 Fifth Ave, Ste 2400, Seattle, WA 98101-2603. TEL 206-389-7200, FAX 206-389-7288, http://www.seattlechamber.com. Ed. Gina Morales.

658.0029 GBR
MAJOR EMPLOYERS OF EUROPE (YEAR) - THE JOB FINDER'S DIRECTORY. Text in English. a. GBP 165 (effective 2001). **Document type:** *Directory, Trade.* **Description:** Provides summary information on Western Europe's largest employers and identifies the top 10,000 companies in Europe by number of employees.

Published by: Graham & Whiteside Ltd (Subsidiary of: Gale Group), Tuition House, 5-6 Francis Grove, London, SW19 4DT, United Kingdom. TEL 44-20-8947-1011, FAX 44-20-8947-1163, galeord@gale.com, http://www.galegroup.com/graham&whiteside/. **Dist. by:** Current Pacific Ltd., PO Box 36-536, Northcote, Auckland, New Zealand. TEL 64-9-480-1388, FAX 64-9-480-1387, info@cplnz.com, http://www.cplnz.com.

658.0029 GBR
MAJOR ENERGY COMPANIES OF EUROPE (YEAR). Text in English. 1985. a. GBP 285 (effective 2001). **Document type:** *Directory.* **Description:** Contains authoritative data on more than 1,300 of the largest energy companies in 20 European countries.
Published by: Graham & Whiteside Ltd (Subsidiary of: Gale Group), Tuition House, 5-6 Francis Grove, London, SW19 4DT, United Kingdom. TEL 44-20-8947-1011, FAX 44-20-8947-1163, galeord@gale.com, http://www.galegroup.com/graham&whiteside/. **Dist. by:** Current Pacific Ltd., PO Box 36-536, Northcote, Auckland, New Zealand. TEL 64-9-480-1388, FAX 64-9-480-1387, info@cplnz.com, http://www.cplnz.com.

658.0029 GBR
MAJOR ENERGY COMPANIES OF THE FAR EAST & AUSTRALASIA (YEAR). Text in English. a. GBP 260 (effective 2001). **Document type:** *Directory.* **Description:** Contains essential information on more than 500 of the leading energy companies in the Asia/Pacific region.
Published by: Graham & Whiteside Ltd (Subsidiary of: Gale Group), Tuition House, 5-6 Francis Grove, London, SW19 4DT, United Kingdom. TEL 44-20-8947-1011, FAX 44-20-8947-1163, galeord@gale.com, http://www.galegroup.com/graham&whiteside/. **Dist. by:** Current Pacific Ltd., PO Box 36-536, Northcote, Auckland, New Zealand. TEL 64-9-480-1388, FAX 64-9-480-1387, info@cplnz.com, http://www.cplnz.com.

MAJOR ENERGY COMPANIES OF THE WORLD (YEAR). see *ENERGY*

382.029 GBR ISSN 1364-9035
MAJOR FINANCIAL INSTITUTIONS OF EUROPE. Text in Dutch. 1985. a., latest 2002. USD 510 per vol. (effective 2003). **Document type:** *Directory, Trade.* **Description:** Provides detailed coverage of 2,350 of the top financial institutions of Europe, including contact names of 30,000 senior executives.
Former titles (until 1995): Major Financial Institutions of Continental Europe (Year) (0268-232X); Major Banks, Finance and Investment Companies of Continental Europe
Published by: Graham & Whiteside Ltd (Subsidiary of: Gale Group), Tuition House, 5-6 Francis Grove, London, SW19 4DT, United Kingdom. TEL 44-20-8947-1011, FAX 44-20-8947-1163, galeord@gale.com, http://www.galegroup.com/graham&whiteside/.

658.0029 GBR
MAJOR FINANCIAL INSTITUTIONS OF EUROPE (YEAR). Text in English. a. GBP 285 (effective 2001). **Document type:** *Directory.* **Description:** Collects together quality data on over 2,350 of the largest institutions in the finance industry across Europe.
—BLDSC (5353.604920).
Published by: Graham & Whiteside Ltd (Subsidiary of: Gale Group), Tuition House, 5-6 Francis Grove, London, SW19 4DT, United Kingdom. TEL 44-20-8947-1011, FAX 44-20-8947-1163, galeord@gale.com, http://www.galegroup.com/graham&whiteside/. **Dist. by:** Current Pacific Ltd., PO Box 36-536, Northcote, Auckland, New Zealand. TEL 64-9-480-1388, FAX 64-9-480-1387, info@cplnz.com, http://www.cplnz.com.

658.0029 GBR
MAJOR FINANCIAL INSTITUTIONS OF THE ARAB WORLD (YEAR). Text in English. a. GBP 280 (effective 2001). **Document type:** *Directory.* **Description:** Includes 1,000 commercial and investment banks and major foreign bank branches in Arab countries.
Published by: Graham & Whiteside Ltd (Subsidiary of: Gale Group), Tuition House, 5-6 Francis Grove, London, SW19 4DT, United Kingdom. TEL 44-20-8947-1011, FAX 44-20-8947-1163, galeord@gale.com, http://www.galegroup.com/graham&whiteside/. **Dist. by:** Current Pacific Ltd., PO Box 36-536, Northcote, Auckland, New Zealand. TEL 64-9-480-1388, FAX 64-9-480-1387, info@cplnz.com, http://www.cplnz.com.

658.0029 GBR
MAJOR FINANCIAL INSTITUTIONS OF THE FAR EAST & AUSTRALASIA (YEAR). Text in English. a. GBP 270 (effective 2001). **Document type:** *Directory.* **Description:** Contains information on over 1,500 of the largest institutions in the finance industry in the Asia/Pacific region. Over 12,000 named directors and senior executives.
Published by: Graham & Whiteside Ltd (Subsidiary of: Gale Group), Tuition House, 5-6 Francis Grove, London, SW19 4DT, United Kingdom. TEL 44-20-8947-1011, FAX 44-20-8947-1163, galeord@gale.com, http://www.galegroup.com/graham&whiteside/. **Dist. by:** Current Pacific Ltd., PO Box 36-536, Northcote, Auckland, New Zealand. TEL 64-9-480-1388, FAX 64-9-480-1387, info@cplnz.com, http://www.cplnz.com.

658.0029 GBR ISSN 1369-5436
HG64
MAJOR FINANCIAL INSTITUTIONS OF THE WORLD (YEAR). Text in English. 1998. a. (in 2 vols.). GBP 490 (effective 2001). **Document type:** *Directory, Trade.* **Description:** Provides essential data on over 9,000 of the largest institutions in the finance industry worldwide. Including banks, investment, insurance and leasing companies, with named contacts for over 7,000 senior executives.
Published by: Graham & Whiteside Ltd (Subsidiary of: Gale Group), Tuition House, 5-6 Francis Grove, London, SW19 4DT, United Kingdom. TEL 44-20-8947-1011, FAX 44-20-8947-1163, galeord@gale.com, http://www.galegroup.com/graham&whiteside/. Eds. C Oddy, D Shave, S Hornig. **Dist. by:** Current Pacific Ltd., PO Box 36-536, Northcote, Auckland, New Zealand. TEL 64-9-480-1388, FAX 64-9-480-1387, info@cplnz.com, http://www.cplnz.com.

658.0029 GBR
MAJOR FOOD & DRINK COMPANIES OF EUROPE (YEAR). Text in English. a. GBP 285 (effective 2001). **Document type:** *Directory.* **Description:** Contains vital data on over 3,800 of the largest companies in the food, alcoholic and non-alcoholic drinks industries in 20 countries of Western Europe.
Published by: Graham & Whiteside Ltd (Subsidiary of: Gale Group), Tuition House, 5-6 Francis Grove, London, SW19 4DT, United Kingdom. TEL 44-20-8947-1011, FAX 44-20-8947-1163, galeord@gale.com, http://www.galegroup.com/graham&whiteside/. **Dist. by:** Current Pacific Ltd., PO Box 36-536, Northcote, Auckland, New Zealand. TEL 64-9-480-1388, FAX 64-9-480-1387, info@cplnz.com, http://www.cplnz.com.

658.0029 GBR
MAJOR FOOD & DRINK COMPANIES OF THE FAR EAST & AUSTRALASIA (YEAR). Text in English. a. GBP 270 (effective 2001). **Document type:** *Directory.* **Description:** Contains information on over 1,100 leading food, alcoholic and non-alcoholic drinks firms throughout the Asia/Pacific region.
Published by: Graham & Whiteside Ltd (Subsidiary of: Gale Group), Tuition House, 5-6 Francis Grove, London, SW19 4DT, United Kingdom. TEL 44-20-8947-1011, FAX 44-20-8947-1163, galeord@gale.com, http://www.galegroup.com/graham&whiteside/. **Dist. by:** Current Pacific Ltd., PO Box 36-536, Northcote, Auckland, New Zealand. TEL 64-9-480-1388, FAX 64-9-480-1387, info@cplnz.com, http://www.cplnz.com.

658.0029 GBR
MAJOR FOOD & DRINK COMPANIES OF THE WORLD (YEAR). (vol. one: Africa (South of the Sahara), Arab World, Central & Eastern Europe & CIS, Europe (Western); vol. two: Latin America, North America, South East Asia, The Far East & Australasia, South West Asia) Text in English. a. (in 2 vols.), latest 2000. GBP 490 (effective 2001). **Document type:** *Directory.* **Description:** Contains detailed, up-to-date company profiles compiled for the top 9,200 food, alcoholic and non-alcoholic drink companies from around the globe.
Published by: Graham & Whiteside Ltd (Subsidiary of: Gale Group), Tuition House, 5-6 Francis Grove, London, SW19 4DT, United Kingdom. TEL 44-20-8947-1011, FAX 44-20-8947-1163, galeord@gale.com, http://www.galegroup.com/graham&whiteside/. **Dist. by:** Current Pacific Ltd., PO Box 36-536, Northcote, Auckland, New Zealand. TEL 64-9-480-1388, FAX 64-9-480-1387, info@cplnz.com, http://www.cplnz.com.

338.0029 GBR
MAJOR MARKET SHARE COMPANIES: ASIA PACIFIC. Variant title: Major Market Share Companies: Asia Pacific, Vol.6. Text in English. 2000. irreg., latest 2002, July. GBP 625 per vol. domestic; EUR 990 per vol. in Europe; USD 990 per vol. elsewhere (effective Jul. 2002). **Document type:** *Directory, Trade.* **Description:** Contains information on market share performance and detailed financial profiles of leading regional and national companies.
Related titles: ♦ Series of: Global Market Share Planner.
Published by: Euromonitor, 60-61 Britton St, London, EC1 5UX, United Kingdom. TEL 44-20-7251-8024, FAX 44-20-7608-3149, info@euromonitor.com, http://www.euromonitor.com. **Dist. by:** Current Pacific Ltd., PO Box 36-536, Northcote, Auckland, New Zealand. TEL 64-9-480-1388, FAX 64-9-480-1387, info@cplnz.com, http://www.cplnz.com.

338.0029 GBR
MAJOR MARKET SHARE COMPANIES: EUROPE & SOUTH AFRICA. Text in English. 2000. irreg., latest 2002, July. GBP 625 per vol. domestic; EUR 990 per vol. in Europe; USD 990 per vol. elsewhere (effective Jul. 2002). **Document type:** *Directory, Trade.* **Description:** Contains information on market share performance and detailed financial profiles of leading regional and national companies.
Related titles: ♦ Series of: Global Market Share Planner.
Published by: Euromonitor, 60-61 Britton St, London, EC1 5UX, United Kingdom. TEL 44-20-7251-8024, FAX 44-20-7608-3149, info@euromonitor.com, http://www.euromonitor.com.

338.0029 GBR
MAJOR MARKET SHARE COMPANIES: THE AMERICAS. Text in English. 2000. irreg. GBP 625 per vol. domestic; EUR 990 per vol. in Europe; USD 990 per vol. elsewhere (effective Jul. 2002). **Document type:** *Directory, Trade.* **Description:** Contains information on market share performance and detailed financial profiles of leading regional and national companies.
Related titles: ♦ Series of: Global Market Share Planner.
Published by: Euromonitor, 60-61 Britton St, London, EC1 5UX, United Kingdom. TEL 44-20-7251-8024, FAX 44-20-7608-3149, info@euromonitor.com, http://www.euromonitor.com.

338.0029 GBR
MAJOR PERFORMANCE RANKINGS. Text in English. 2000. irreg., latest 2002, July. GBP 745 per vol. domestic; EUR 1,190 per vol. in Europe; USD 1,190 per vol. elsewhere (effective Jul. 2002). **Document type:** *Directory, Trade.* **Description:** Provides rankings by commercial and financial criteria of companies owning leading consumer brands.
Related titles: ♦ Series of: Global Market Share Planner.
Published by: Euromonitor, 60-61 Britton St, London, EC1 5UX, United Kingdom. TEL 44-20-7251-8024, FAX 44-20-7608-3149, info@euromonitor.com, http://www.euromonitor.com.

658.0029 GBR
MAJOR PHARMACEUTICAL COMPANIES OF THE WORLD (YEAR). Text in English. a. GBP 490 (effective 2001). **Document type:** *Directory.* **Description:** Provides essential business profiles for 2,500 of the largest pharmaceutical companies worldwide in the pharmaceutical industry. Over 12,500 named senior executives.
Published by: Graham & Whiteside Ltd (Subsidiary of: Gale Group), Tuition House, 5-6 Francis Grove, London, SW19 4DT, United Kingdom. TEL 44-20-8947-1011, FAX 44-20-8947-1163, galeord@gale.com, http://www.galegroup.com/graham&whiteside/. **Dist. by:** Current Pacific Ltd., PO Box 36-536, Northcote, Auckland, New Zealand. TEL 64-9-480-1388, FAX 64-9-480-1387, info@cplnz.com, http://www.cplnz.com.

658.0029 384 GBR
MAJOR TELECOMMUNICATIONS COMPANIES OF EUROPE (YEAR). Text in English. a. GBP 285 (effective 2001). **Document type:** *Directory.* **Description:** Contains facts and contacts for 1,300 of the largest telecommunications companies and equipment suppliers and internet companies in Europe.
Published by: Graham & Whiteside Ltd (Subsidiary of: Gale Group), Tuition House, 5-6 Francis Grove, London, SW19 4DT, United Kingdom. TEL 44-20-8947-1011, FAX 44-20-8947-1163, galeord@gale.com, http://www.galegroup.com/graham&whiteside/. **Dist. by:** Current Pacific Ltd., PO Box 36-536, Northcote, Auckland, New Zealand. TEL 64-9-480-1388, FAX 64-9-480-1387, info@cplnz.com, http://www.cplnz.com.

658.0029 384 GBR
MAJOR TELECOMMUNICATIONS COMPANIES OF THE FAR EAST & AUSTRALASIA (YEAR). Text in English. a. GBP 270 (effective 2001). **Document type:** *Directory.* **Description:** Contains 1,000 of the largest telecommunications and internet companies and their equipment suppliers in the Asia/Pacific region.
Published by: Graham & Whiteside Ltd (Subsidiary of: Gale Group), Tuition House, 5-6 Francis Grove, London, SW19 4DT, United Kingdom. TEL 44-20-8947-1011, FAX 44-20-8947-1163, galeord@gale.com, http://www.galegroup.com/graham&whiteside/. **Dist. by:** Current Pacific Ltd., PO Box 36-536, Northcote, Auckland, New Zealand. TEL 64-9-480-1388, FAX 64-9-480-1387, info@cplnz.com, http://www.cplnz.com.

690.029 SGP
MALAYSIA CONSTRUCTION EQUIPMENT CATALOGUE (YEAR). Text in English. 1995. a. USD 50 (effective 2000). adv. **Document type:** *Catalog.* **Description:** A comprehensive buying guide for the construction, marine and timber industries.
Formerly: Malaysia Construction and Industrial Equipment Catalogue (Year) (1394-1313)
Published by: Times Media Pte Ltd, Directories Division, 1 New Industrial Rd, Times Centre, Singapore, 536196, Singapore. TEL 65-285-0161, FAX 65-2881186, ttdmktg@cop.tpl.com.sg. Pub., R&P Leslie Lim. Adv. contact Joseph Liang.

▼ new title ➤ refereed ✶ unverified ♦ full entry avail.

720.29 SGP ISSN 1394-1291
MALAYSIA SOURCE BOOK FOR ARCHITECTS AND DESIGNERS (YEAR). Text in English. a. USD 50. adv. **Document type:** *Directory.* **Description:** Guide for the building and furnishing industries. Offers the widest range of products, materials and services available in Malaysia.
Published by: Times Media Pte Ltd, Directories Division, 1 New Industrial Rd, Times Centre, Singapore, 536196, Singapore. TEL 65-2848844, FAX 65-2850161, ttdmktg@cop.tpl.com.sg, http://www.timesbiz.com.sg. Pub., R&P Leslie Lim. Adv. contact Joseph Liang.

381.029 MLT
MALTA TRADE DIRECTORY (YEAR). Text in English. 1968. a. USD 48. adv. bk.rev. **Document type:** *Directory, Trade.* **Description:** Lists of members, economic information on Malta, and tourist and trade statistics.
Former titles: Trade Directory (Year); Malta Chamber of Commerce. Trade Directory; Malta Trade Directory (0076-3446); Malta Chamber of Commerce Classified Directory
Published by: Malta Chamber of Commerce, The Exchange, Republic St., Valletta, VLT 05, Malta. FAX 356-245223. Ed. Anthony Borg Cardona. R&P Anthony Borg Cardonna. Circ: 1,500.

MANAGED HEALTH CARE DIRECTORY. see *HEALTH FACILITIES AND ADMINISTRATION*

380.1029 071.1 USA ISSN 1203-522X
MANITOBA BUSINESS DIRECTORY. Text in English. 1996. a. USD 1,100 combined subscription print, online & CD-ROM eds. (effective 2004 & 2005). back issues avail. **Document type:** *Directory.*
Related titles: CD-ROM ed.; Diskette ed.; E-mail ed.; Fax ed.; Magnetic Tape ed.; Online - full text ed.
Published by: American Business Directories (Subsidiary of: American Business Information, Inc.), 5711 S 86th Circle, P O Box 27347, Omaha, NE 68127. TEL 402-593-4600, 888-946-9377, 877-708-3844, FAX 402-331-5481, sales@directoriesusa.com, http://www.directoriesusa.com.

670.29 SGP ISSN 0218-1983
MANUFACTURERSLINK; a mini directory. Text in English. 1993. biennial. SGD 15. **Document type:** *Directory, Trade.* **Description:** Names and addresses of manufacturers and companies in the service industry.
Published by: Singapore Confederation of Industries, S.M.A. House, 20 Orchard Rd, Singapore, 238830, Singapore. TEL 65-3388787, FAX 65-3365385, scihq@sci.org.sg, http://www.sci.org.sg/sci. Ed. Charlie Chan. Circ: 8,000.

381.147 941 GBR ISSN 1476-8720
MARDEK GUIDE TO U K CONVENIENCE RETAILING. Text in English. 2002 (Mar.). irreg. GBP 495 per issue (effective 2003). **Document type:** *Directory, Trade.* **Description:** Contains market overview, industry trends, outlook, company profiles.
Published by: William Reed Directories (Subsidiary of: William Reed Publishing Ltd.), Broadfield Park, Brighton Rd, Pease Pottage, Crawley, W Sussex RH11 9RT, United Kingdom. TEL 44-1293-610488, FAX 44-1293-610310, directories@william-reed.co.uk, http://www.william-reed.co.uk/directories/mardek_ukcon.htm.

302.23029 AUS ISSN 1036-9201
P88.8
MARGARET GEE'S AUSTRALIAN MEDIA GUIDE. Text in English. 1978. 3/yr. AUD 395; AUD 650 print & online eds. (effective 2004). **Document type:** *Directory, Trade.* **Description:** Directory of Australian media: newspapers, magazines, newsletters, radio, television, and internet publications.
Formerly (until 1992): Margaret Gee's Media Guide (0158-0779)
Related titles: Online - full content ed.: AUD 495 (effective 2004).
Published by: Crown Content, Level 1, 141 Capel St, Nth Melbourne, VIC 3051, Australia. TEL 6-13-93299800, FAX 6-13-93299698, scott@crowncontent.com.au, http://www.crowncontent.com.au/prod/directories/mediaguide.htm. Ed. Jeremy Rann. R&P Michael Wilkinson.

MARINE PRODUCTS DIRECTORY. see *SPORTS AND GAMES—Boats And Boating*

658.0029 GBR
MARKET RESEARCH SOURCEBOOK. Text in English. 1984. a. GBP 175 (effective 2001). **Description:** Provides an up-to-date information source for market researchers, business librarians, business information users and information producers.
Incorporates (in 1997): Market Information (0966-212X)
Published by: Headland Business Information, Windsor Ct, East Grinstead House, East Grinstead, W Sussex RH19 1XA, United Kingdom. TEL 44-1342-326972, FAX 44-1342-336198, http://www.bowker.co.uk. Ed. David Mort. **Subscr. to:** World Wide Subscription Service, Unit G, Gibbs Reed Farm, Ticehurst, E Sussex Tn5 7he, United Kingdom. TEL 44-1580-200657, FAX 44-1580-200616.

MARKET SCOPE. see *FOOD AND FOOD INDUSTRIES*

338.0029 GBR
MARKET SHARE TRACKER. Text in English. 2000. irreg. GBP 745 per vol. domestic; EUR 1,190 per vol. in Europe; USD 1,190 per vol. elsewhere (effective Jan. 2002). **Document type:** *Directory, Trade.* **Description:** Provides market share information on the top companies in fifteen consumer sectors covering thirty countries.
Related titles: ♦ Series of: Global Market Share Planner.
Published by: Euromonitor, 60-61 Britton St, London, EC1 5UX, United Kingdom. TEL 44-20-7251-8024, FAX 44-20-7608-3149, info@euromonitor.com, http://www.euromonitor.com.

338.0029 AUT
MARKETING C D. Text in German. 2/yr. adv. **Document type:** *Directory, Trade.* **Description:** Presents a powerful marketing tool with data on over 306,000 Austrian companies.
Formerly: Company Database C D
Media: CD-ROM.
Published by: (Kreditschutz von 1870), Herold Business Data GmbH & Co. KG, Guntramsdorferstr 105, Moedling, N 2340, Austria. TEL 43-2236-401-133, FAX 43-2236-4018, kundendienst@herold.co.at, http://www.herold.co.at. Ed. Gerhard Krejei. Adv. contact Harald Kasperowski.

658.8029 AUT
MARKETING C D BUSINESS. Text in English. 2/yr. EUR 1,608 (effective 2005). adv. **Document type:** *Directory, Trade.*
Formerly: Marketing Adress Data C D
Media: CD-ROM.
Published by: Herold Business Data GmbH & Co. KG, Guntramsdorferstr 105, Moedling, N 2340, Austria. TEL 43-2236-401133, FAX 43-2236-4018, kundendienst@herold.co.at, http://www.herold.co.at. Ed. Gerhard Krejeier. Adv. contact Vincent Maessen.

MARKETING WITH HONORS; directory of awards competitions. see *BUSINESS AND ECONOMICS—Marketing And Purchasing*

MARKETONS I T DATABANK. see *COMPUTERS—Information Science And Information Theory*

MARTINDALE-HUBBELL CANADIAN LAW DIRECTORY. see *LAW*

MARTINDALE-HUBBELL CORPORATE LAW DIRECTORY. see *LAW*

MARTINDALE-HUBBELL DISPUTE RESOLUTION DIRECTORY. see *LAW*

MARTINDALE-HUBBELL INTERNATIONAL DISPUTE RESOLUTION DIRECTORY (YEAR). see *LAW*

MARTINDALE-HUBBELL INTERNATIONAL LAW DIRECTORY (YEAR). see *LAW*

MARTINDALE-HUBBELL LAW DIRECTORY ON CD-ROM. see *LAW*

380.1029 USA
MARYLAND BUSINESS CREDIT DIRECTORY. Text in English. a. USD 1,100 combined subscription print, online & CD-ROM eds. (effective 2004 & 2005). back issues avail. **Document type:** *Directory.* **Description:** Contains credit ratings and other valuable information on all businesses within Maryland. Includes company name & address, phone & fax numbers, key executive names & titles, lines of business, years in business, number of employees, estimated annual sales, volume credit rating code, and corporate linkage information.
Related titles: CD-ROM ed.; Diskette ed.; E-mail ed.; Fax ed.; Magnetic Tape ed.; Online - full text ed.
Published by: American Business Directories (Subsidiary of: American Business Information, Inc.), 5711 S 86th Circle, P O Box 27347, Omaha, NE 68127. TEL 402-593-4600, 888-946-9377, 877-708-3844, FAX 402-331-5481, sales@directoriesusa.com, http://www.directoriesusa.com.

338.0029 USA ISSN 1048-7123
HF5065.M25
MARYLAND BUSINESS DIRECTORY. Text in English. 1990. a. USD 1,100 combined subscription print, online & CD-ROM eds. (effective 2004 & 2005). index. back issues avail. **Document type:** *Directory.* **Description:** Includes all businesses in the state compiled from the yellow pages and telephone verified. Listings include company name, complete address, phone number, name of owner or manager, employee size and sales volume, and credit rating codes.
Related titles: CD-ROM ed.; Diskette ed.; E-mail ed.; Fax ed.; Magnetic Tape ed.; Online - full text ed.
Published by: American Business Directories (Subsidiary of: American Business Information, Inc.), 5711 S 86th Circle, P O Box 27347, Omaha, NE 68127. TEL 402-593-4600, 888-946-9377, 877-708-3844, FAX 402-331-5481, karen.peters@infousa.com, sales@directoriesusa.com, http://www.directoriesusa.com.

670.29 USA ISSN 1065-2507
HF5065.M25
MARYLAND - D.C. MANUFACTURERS DIRECTORY. Text in English. 1994. a. USD 83 (effective 2002). adv. 464 p./no.; **Document type:** *Directory.* **Description:** Profiles 5,656 companies.
Related titles: CD-ROM ed.: USD 369 (effective 2002); Diskette ed.
Published by: Manufacturers' News, Inc., 1633 Central St, Evanston, IL 60201. TEL 847-864-7000, 888-752-5200, FAX 847-332-1100, info@mninfo.com, info@manufacturersnews.com, sales@mninfo.com, http://www.manufacturersnews.com. Ed. Steve Garland.

670.29 USA
MARYLAND - DELAWARE DIRECTORY OF MANUFACTURERS. Text in English. 1993. a. USD 62.50. **Document type:** *Directory.* **Description:** Profiles about 4000 companies alphabetically, geographically, and by product line. Contains listings of all key executives.
Published by: Commerce Register, Inc., 190 Godwin Ave, Midland Park, NJ 07432. TEL 201-445-3000, FAX 201-445-5806.

380.1029 USA
MASSACHUSETTS BUSINESS CREDIT DIRECTORY. Text in English. a. USD 1,100 combined subscription print, online & CD-ROM eds. (effective 2004 & 2005). back issues avail. **Document type:** *Directory.* **Description:** Contains credit ratings and other valuable information on all businesses within Massachusetts. Includes company name & address, phone & fax numbers, key executive names & titles, lines of business, years in business, number of employees, estimated annual sales, volume credit rating code, and corporate linkage information.
Related titles: CD-ROM ed.; Diskette ed.; E-mail ed.; Fax ed.; Magnetic Tape ed.; Online - full text ed.
Published by: American Business Directories (Subsidiary of: American Business Information, Inc.), 5711 S 86th Circle, P O Box 27347, Omaha, NE 68127. TEL 402-593-4600, 888-946-9377, 877-708-3844, FAX 402-331-5481, sales@directoriesusa.com, http://www.directoriesusa.com.

338.0029 USA ISSN 1048-7131
HF5065.M3
MASSACHUSETTS BUSINESS DIRECTORY. Text in English. 1990. a. USD 1,100 combined subscription print, online & CD-ROM eds. (effective 2004 & 2005). index. back issues avail. **Document type:** *Directory.* **Description:** Includes all businesses in the state compiled from the yellow pages and telephone-verified. Each listing includes company name, address, phone number, name of owner or manager, and employee size-sales volume codes and credit rating codes.
Related titles: CD-ROM ed.; Diskette ed.; E-mail ed.; Fax ed.; Magnetic Tape ed.; Online - full text ed.
Published by: American Business Directories (Subsidiary of: American Business Information, Inc.), 5711 S 86th Circle, P O Box 27347, Omaha, NE 68127. TEL 402-593-4600, 888-946-9377, 877-708-3844, FAX 402-331-5481, karen.peters@infousa.com, sales@directoriesusa.com, http://www.directoriesusa.com.

670.29 USA ISSN 0195-5810
HD9727.M4
MASSACHUSETTS DIRECTORY OF MANUFACTURERS. Text in English. 1975. a. USD 72.50. adv. **Document type:** *Directory.* **Description:** Profiles over 6000 manufacturers listed alphabetically, geographically, and by product line, and SIC. Also lists key executives.
Related titles: Diskette ed.; Magnetic Tape ed.
Published by: Commerce Register, Inc., 190 Godwin Ave, Midland Park, NJ 07432. TEL 201-445-3000, FAX 201-445-5806.

338.0029 USA
MASSACHUSETTS DIRECTORY OF TECHNOLOGY COMPANIES. Text in English. 1983. a. USD 265 (effective 2000). adv. **Document type:** *Directory.*
Formerly: Mass High Tech Directory
Published by: Mass Tech Communications, 200 High St, 4th Fl, Boston, MA 02110-3036. TEL 617-478-0630, http://www.masshightech.com. Ed. Paula Marggraf. R&P Mike Olivieri. Adv. contact Jill Cohen. B&W page USD 2,500. Circ: 1,000 (paid).

670 USA
MASSACHUSETTS MANUFACTURERS REGISTER. Text in English. USD 104 (effective 2001).
Related titles: CD-ROM ed.: USD 490 (effective 2001).
Published by: Manufacturers' News, Inc., 1633 Central St, Evanston, IL 60201. TEL 847-864-7000, 888-752-5200, FAX 847-332-1100, info@manufacturersnews.com, sales@mninfo.com, http://www.manufacturersnews.com. Ed. Frank Lambing.

MASSACHUSETTS TELEPHONE TICKLER FOR INSURANCE MEN & WOMEN. see *INSURANCE*

338.0029   ZAF
MAURITIUS, REUNION & SEYCHELLES DIRECTORY. Text in English. 1969. a. USD 75 (effective 2001). adv. **Document type:** *Directory.*
Published by: Braby's (Subsidiary of: Associated Industries), Attn: Sue Pearson, PO Box 1426, Pinetown, 3600, South Africa. TEL 27-31-7017021, FAX 27-31-7017036, booksales@brabys.co.za.

332.6029   ZAF   ISSN 1350-1143
MCGREGOR'S WHO OWNS WHOM; in South Africa. Text in Dutch. 1980. a., latest vol.23, 2003. ZAR 490 per vol. (effective 2003). 1216 p./no.; **Document type:** *Directory.*
Description: Comprises a summary of annual reports of every company listed on the Johannesburg Securities Exchange, as well as significant details on about 500 South African unlisted companies.
Published by: Who Owns Whom (PTY) Ltd, PO Box 2034, Florida Hills, 1716, South Africa. TEL 27-11-6700500, FAX 27-11-6700506, andrewm@whoownswhom.co.za, http://www.whoownswhom.co.za. Ed. Carla Soares. Pub. Andrew McGregor. Dist. by: African & Caribbean Imprint Library Services, PO Box 2780, South Portland, ME 04116-2780. TEL 207-767-5333, FAX 207-767-5335, ailscils@msn.com, http://www.africanbooks.com/.

791.43029   AUT
MEDIA BIZ BRANCHENFUEHRER; film - tv - radio - video - audio. Text in German. 1992. a. EUR 20 domestic; EUR 26 foreign (effective 2005). adv. 64 p./no.; **Document type:** *Directory, Trade.*
Related titles: CD-ROM ed.
Published by: Bergmayer und Partner Producer OEG, Kalvarienberggasse 67, Vienna, W 1170, Austria. TEL 43-1-40335830, FAX 43-1-403358330, redaktion@mediabiz.at, http://www.mediabiz.at/branche.htm. Ed. Wolfgang Ritzberger. Pub., Adv. contact Sylvia Bergmayer. Circ: 4,000 (controlled).

659.1029   DEU   ISSN 0943-1764
MEDIA-DATEN: DEUTSCHLAND OST. Text in German. 1991. 2/yr. EUR 150; EUR 96 newsstand/cover (effective 2003). adv. **Document type:** *Directory, Trade.*
Published by: Media-Daten Verlag GmbH (Subsidiary of: Springer Science+Business Media), Postfach 1546, Wiesbaden, 65173, Germany. TEL 49-611-78780, FAX 49-611-7878465, info@media-daten.de, http://www.media-daten.de. adv.: B&W page EUR 2,150, color page EUR 3,380. Circ: 800 (paid).

MEDIA DETAIL; vakblad voor de detailhandelaren in de consumentenelectronica. see *ELECTRONICS*

MEDIA MAP OF EASTERN EUROPE. see *COMMUNICATIONS—Television And Cable*

MEDIA MAP OF WESTERN EUROPE. see *BUSINESS AND ECONOMICS—Marketing And Purchasing*

MEDIA MAP YEARBOOK. see *COMMUNICATIONS—Television And Cable*

338.0029   USA
MEDIAWEEK DIRECTORY (CD-ROM EDITION). Text in English. 1996. a. USD 399 (effective 2003). **Document type:** *Directory, Trade.* **Description:** Provides information on local media in the top 100 markets, in addition to reports on national media networks, syndicators, sales representatives and associations.
Former titles: Mediaweek Directory (Print Edition) (1530-6844); (until 1999): Adweek Major Media Directory (1083-6217)
Published by: V N U Business Publications (Subsidiary of: V N U Business Media), 770 Broadway, New York, NY 10003-9595. TEL 646-654-5870, FAX 646-654-5518, http://www.adweek.com/adweek/directories/index.jsp, http://www.vnubusinessmedia.com/.

616.07   CAN   ISSN 1702-6601
MEDICAL & ASSISTIVE DEVICES & DIAGNOSTICS CANADA INDUSTRY & BUYERS GUIDE. Text in English. 1999. a. CND 199.95 (effective 2003). **Document type:** *Directory, Trade.* **Description:** Contains information and profiles on diagnostic companies, service and supply companies, and research groups.
Former titles (until 2002): Diagnostics Canada B2B Industry Guide (1497-9101); (until 2001): Diagnostics Canada Directory, Industry & Suppliers Guide (1493-1044)
Related titles: CD-ROM ed.: CND 299.95 (effective 2003).
Published by: Contact Canada, 390 Goward Rd, Victoria, BC V9E 2J5, Canada. TEL 250-708-0427, 888-502-6666, FAX 250-708-0429, ccinfo@contactcanada.com, http://www.contactcanada.com/diagnostic/.

613.029   TWN
MEDICAL & HEALTH EQUIPMENT BUYERS' GUIDE. Text in English. 1995. s-a. USD 30 per vol. (effective 2001). **Document type:** *Catalog, Trade.* **Description:** Product catalogs and supplier directories for all kinds of medical and health-related equipment and supplies.
Formerly: Taiwan Medical & Health Equipment Buyers' Guide (1025-7799)
Related titles: CD-ROM ed.: USD 20 (effective 2000).

Published by: Interface Global Taiwan Co., Ltd., PO Box 173-12, Taipei, 116, Taiwan. TEL 886-2-2393-2718, FAX 886-2-2395-2901, tradwind@ms2.hinet.net, http://www.medequipb2b.com, http://www.medical-equip-guide.com. Ed. Daniel Foong. Pub. Herbert Chen. R&P Donald Shapiro. Adv. contact Melody Lin TEL 886-2-2351-3180. **Subscr. in US to:** Trade Winds Inc., PO Box 820519, Dallas, TX 75382. TEL 877-861-1188, FAX 972-699-1189, twinds8888@aol.com.

658   USA
MEDICAL INDUSTRY CONFERENCE CALENDAR NEWSLETTER. Text and summaries in English. 2001. bi-m. USD 199 (effective 2002). back issues avail. **Document type:** *Newsletter, Trade.* **Description:** E-mail delivered calendar newsletter lists and profiles key upcoming medical meetings, seminars, symposiums, conferences, courses and trade shows in over 100 countries.
Media: E-mail.
Published by: Biomedical Market Newsletter, Inc., 3237 Idaho Pl, Costa Mesa, CA 92626-2207. TEL 714-434-9500, FAX 714-434-9755, info@biomedical-market-news.com, http://www.biomedical-market-news.com. Ed., Pub. David G Anast.

MEDICAL PRODUCTS OF JAPAN; medical equipment directory. see *MEDICAL SCIENCES*

MEDITERRANEAN SHIPPING DIRECTORY. see *TRANSPORTATION—Ships And Shipping*

387.029   AUS   ISSN 0267-7350
MELBOURNE PORT AND SHIPPING HANDBOOK. Text in English. 1985. a. **Document type:** *Trade.*
Published by: Charter Pacific Publications Pty. Ltd., PO Box 356, Mount Martha, VIC 3934, Australia. TEL 61-3-59771668, FAX 61-3-59771670, charpac@ozemail.com.au. Ed. Gerry Cansdale. Circ: 6,000.

MERCHANDISE MART RESOURCE GUIDE. see *BUSINESS AND ECONOMICS—Marketing And Purchasing*

METALS SOURCING GUIDE. see *METALLURGY*

METRO CALIFORNIA MEDIA. see *ADVERTISING AND PUBLIC RELATIONS*

670.29   USA   ISSN 0317-252X
METRO NEW YORK DIRECTORY OF MANUFACTURERS. Text in English. 1955. a. USD 92.50. adv. **Document type:** *Directory.* **Description:** Profiles more than 8,000 manufacturers and key executives from Manhattan, Bronx, Queens, Brooklyn, Staten Island, and Nassau, Suffolk, Westchester, Rockland, Orange and Putnam counties; includes alphabetical, geographical, and product line by SIC sections.
Related titles: Diskette ed.: USD 395 (effective 1999); Magnetic Tape ed.
Published by: Commerce Register, Inc., 190 Godwin Ave, Midland Park, NJ 07432. TEL 201-445-3000, FAX 201-445-5806.

338.0029   USA
METROPOLITAN MILWAUKEE ASSOCIATION OF COMMERCE. MEMBERSHIP DIRECTORY & BUYERS' GUIDE (YEAR). Text in English. a. USD 10 to members; USD 55 to non-members. **Document type:** *Directory.* **Description:** Lists Milwaukee companies' names, products, services, addresses, phones, contact names and range of employees.
Published by: Metropolitan Milwaukee Association of Commerce, Council of Small Business Executives, 756 N Milwaukee St, Milwaukee, WI 53202. TEL 414-287-4100.

381.029   USA   ISSN 1055-9124
HF3233
MEXICAN PRODUCT GUIDE. Text in English. 1990. a.
Published by: De Paula Publishing and Services Corp., 421 Seventh Ave, Ste 1206, New York, NY 10001. TEL 212-629-4541.

MIAMI MODEL AGENCY DIRECTORY. see *CLOTHING TRADE—Fashions*

380.1029   USA
MICHIGAN BUSINESS CREDIT DIRECTORY. Text in English. a. USD 1,100 combined subscription print, online & CD-ROM eds. (effective 2004 & 2005). back issues avail. **Document type:** *Directory.* **Description:** Contains credit ratings and other valuable information on all businesses within Michigan. Includes company name & address, phone & fax numbers, key executive names & titles, lines of business, years in business, number of employees, estimated annual sales, volume credit rating code, and corporate linkage information.
Related titles: CD-ROM ed.; Diskette ed.; E-mail ed.; Fax ed.; Magnetic Tape ed.; Online - full text ed.
Published by: American Business Directories (Subsidiary of: American Business Information, Inc.), 5711 S 86th Circle, P O Box 27347, Omaha, NE 68127. TEL 402-593-4600, 888-946-9377, 877-708-3844, FAX 402-331-5481, sales@directoriesusa.com, http://www.directoriesusa.com.

338.0029   USA   ISSN 1047-1790
HC107.M5
MICHIGAN BUSINESS DIRECTORY. Text in English. 1987. a. USD 1,100 combined subscription print, online & CD-ROM eds. (effective 2004 & 2005). index. back issues avail. **Document type:** *Directory.* **Description:** Includes all businesses in the state compiled from the yellow pages and telephone verified. Listings include company name, complete address, phone number, name of owner or manager, employee sizes and sales volume, and credit rating codes.
Related titles: CD-ROM ed.; Diskette ed.; E-mail ed.; Fax ed.; Magnetic Tape ed.; Online - full text ed.
Published by: American Business Directories (Subsidiary of: American Business Information, Inc.), 5711 S 86th Circle, P O Box 27347, Omaha, NE 68127. TEL 402-593-4600, 888-946-9377, 877-708-3844, FAX 402-331-5481, karen.peters@infousa.com, sales@directoriesusa.com, http://www.directoriesusa.com.

670.29   USA   ISSN 0736-2889
HD9723
MICHIGAN MANUFACTURERS DIRECTORY. Text in English. 1937. a. USD 157 (effective 2000). adv. **Document type:** *Directory.* **Description:** Provides a complete list of company profiles.
Formerly: Directory of Michigan Manufacturers (0070-5845)
Related titles: CD-ROM ed.: USD 670 (effective 2000); Diskette ed.: USD 795 (effective 1999); Magnetic Tape ed.
—CCC.
Published by: Pick Publications, Inc., 24293 Telegraph Rd. Ste 140, Southfield, MI 48034-7924. TEL 810-827-7111, FAX 810-443-5191, pickinc1@aol.com, http://www.pick-inc.com. Ed. P S Pickell. Circ: 4,000. **Dist. by:** Manufacturers' News, Inc., 1633 Central St, Evanston, IL 60201. TEL 847-864-7000, 888-752-5200, FAX 847-332-1100, info@manufacturersnews.com, http://www.manufacturersnews.com.

MICROCOMPUTER MARKET PLACE (YEAR); the complete guide to PC software and hardware vendors, service providers, and information sources. see *COMPUTERS—Microcomputers*

MIDCONTINENT PETROLEUM INDUSTRY. see *PETROLEUM AND GAS*

MIDDLE EAST AND WORLD WATER DIRECTORY. see *WATER RESOURCES*

332.6029   USA
MIDWEST CLEARING CORPORATION AND MIDWEST SECURITIES TRUST COMPANY. DIRECTORY OF PARTICIPANTS. Text in English. bi-m. **Document type:** *Directory.*
Published by: Midwest Clearing Corporation, One Financial Place, 440 S LaSalle St, Chicago, IL 60605. TEL 312-663-2278. **Co-sponsor:** Midwest Securities Trust Co.

338.0029 670.29   USA
MIDWEST MANUFACTURERS & INDUSTRIAL CLASSIFIED DIRECTORY & BUYERS GUIDE. Text in English. 1937. a. adv. **Document type:** *Directory, Trade.*
Published by: Industrial Directory Publishers, 185 Bridge Plaza, N, Fort Lee, NJ 07024. TEL 201-592-5000, FAX 201-592-7119. Ed. Susan Michael. Pub. Rebecca Kass. Adv. contact R R Kass. B&W page USD 3,600; trim 8.5 x 11. Circ: 19,450.

381.029   COL   ISSN 0121-9030
LAS MIL EMPRESAS MAS GRANDES DE COLOMBIA/ THOUSAND BIGGEST COMPANIES IN COLOMBIA. Text in Spanish. 1986. a. COP 20,000, USD 30 (effective 2000). adv. bk.rev. charts; mkt.; tr.lit. **Document type:** *Corporate.* **Description:** Lists the largest companies in the country. Provides a short economic analysis of the last year.
Related titles: CD-ROM ed.; Diskette ed.
Published by: Confederacion Colombiana de Camaras de Comercio, Carrera 13 no. 27-47 of. 502, Santa Fe de Bogota, CUND, Colombia. TEL 57-1-3467055, FAX 57-1-3467517, confecamaras@inter.net.co, http://www.confecamaras.org.co. adv.: B&W page COP 1,600,000, B&W page USD 800, color page COP 2,000,000, color page USD 1,000; 215 x 280. Circ: 20,000 (paid and controlled).

MINING DIRECTORY: MINING AND MINE EQUIPMENT COMPANIES WORLDWIDE; the standard reference work for the mining industry. see *MINES AND MINING INDUSTRY*

380.1029   USA
MINNESOTA BUSINESS CREDIT DIRECTORY. Text in English. a. USD 1,100 combined subscription print, online & CD-ROM eds. (effective 2004 & 2005). back issues avail. **Document type:** *Directory.* **Description:** Contains credit ratings and other valuable information on all businesses within Minnesota. Includes company name & address, phone & fax numbers, key executive names & titles, lines of business, years in business, number of employees, estimated annual sales, volume credit rating code, and corporate linkage information.
Related titles: CD-ROM ed.; Diskette ed.; E-mail ed.; Fax ed.; Magnetic Tape ed.; Online - full text ed.

B

Published by: American Business Directories (Subsidiary of: American Business Information, Inc.), 5711 S 86th Circle, P O Box 27347, Omaha, NE 68127. TEL 402-593-4600, 888-946-9377, 877-708-3844, FAX 402-331-5481, sales@directoriesusa.com, http://www.directoriesusa.com.

338.0029 USA ISSN 1047-3181
HC107.M6
MINNESOTA BUSINESS DIRECTORY. Text in English. 1984. a. USD 1,100 combined subscription print, online & CD-ROM eds. (effective 2004 & 2005). index. back issues avail. **Document type:** *Directory.* **Description:** Includes all businesses in the state compiled from the yellow pages and telephone verified. Listings include company name, complete address, phone number of owner or manager, employee size and sales volume, and credit rating codes.
Related titles: CD-ROM ed.; Diskette ed.; E-mail ed.; Fax ed.; Magnetic Tape ed.; Online - full text ed.
Published by: American Business Directories (Subsidiary of: American Business Information, Inc.), 5711 S 86th Circle, P O Box 27347, Omaha, NE 68127. TEL 402-593-4600, 888-946-9377, 877-708-3844, FAX 402-331-5481, en.peters@infousa.com, sales@directoriesusa.com, http://www.directoriesusa.com.

B

670.29 USA ISSN 0738-1514
HD9727.M6
MINNESOTA MANUFACTURERS REGISTER. Text in English. a. USD 111 (effective 2000). adv. illus. **Document type:** *Directory.* **Description:** Profiles 11,248 manufacturers in five different sections; listings by product, alphabetical, geographical by city, SIC and parent company.
Related titles: CD-ROM ed.: USD 535 (effective 2000); Diskette ed.
Published by: Manufacturers' News, Inc., 1633 Central St, Evanston, IL 60201. TEL 847-864-7000, 888-752-5200, FAX 847-332-1100, info@mninfo.com, info@manufacturersnews.com, sales@mninfo.com, http://www.manufacturersnews.com. Ed. Frank Lambing. Adv. contact Charles Scherer. B&W page USD 1,843.

MINNESOTA WOMEN'S DIRECTORY. see *WOMEN'S INTERESTS*

658.0029 USA
MINORITY BUSINESS INFORMATION RESOURCES DIRECTORY. Text in English. a. USD 45 (effective 1999). adv. **Document type:** *Directory.* **Description:** Lists legislation and compliance regulations, S.B.A., M.B.D.A. and other federal programs; local minority business directories; and a calendar of trade fairs and conferences.
Supersedes (in 1994): Guide to Obtaining Minority Business Directories; Formerly: Guide to Minority Business Directories (0362-3459)
Published by: Try Us Resources, Inc., 2105 Central Ave, N E, Minneapolis, MN 55418. TEL 612-781-6819, FAX 612-781-0109. Pub. Leslie Smith Bonds. Adv. contact Janice L Anderson.

338.0029 USA
MINORITY - OWNED HIGH TECH BUSINESSES. Text in English. 1992. a. **Document type:** *Directory.* **Description:** Lists over 6,000 minority-owned companies in high technology industries.
Media: Diskette. **Related titles:** CD-ROM ed.
Published by: Business Research Services, Inc., 4701 Sangamore Rd., Ste. S155, Bethesda, MD 20816-2532. TEL 202-364-6473, FAX 202-686-3228.

338.0029 USA ISSN 1046-056X
HF5065.M7
MISSISSIPPI BUSINESS DIRECTORY. Text in English. 1988. a. USD 1,100 combined subscription print, online & CD-ROM eds. (effective 2004 & 2005). index. back issues avail. **Document type:** *Directory.* **Description:** Includes all businesses in the state compiled from the yellow pages and telephone verified. Listings include company name, complete address, phone number of owner of manager, employee size and sales volume, and credit rating codes.
Related titles: CD-ROM ed.; Diskette ed.; E-mail ed.; Fax ed.; Magnetic Tape ed.; Online - full text ed.
Published by: American Business Directories (Subsidiary of: American Business Information, Inc.), 5711 S 86th Circle, P O Box 27347, Omaha, NE 68127. TEL 888-946-9377, 877-708-3844, FAX 402-331-5481, en.peters@infousa.com, sales@directoriesusa.com, http://www.directoriesusa.com.

670.29 USA
MISSISSIPPI MANUFACTURERS - CROSS-MATCH DIRECTORY. Text in English. 1964. biennial. USD 99 (effective 2005). **Document type:** *Directory, Government.* **Description:** Company profiles of 3,100 manufacturers listed alphabetically, geographically and by product.
Formerly: Mississippi Manufacturers Directory
Related titles: Diskette ed.
Published by: Harris InfoSource, 2057 E Aurora Rd, Twinsburg, OH 44087. TEL 800-888-5900, 330-425-9000, FAX 330-425-7150, http://www.harrisinfo.com.

670.29 USA ISSN 1078-2249
HF5065.M7
MISSISSIPPI MANUFACTURERS REGISTER. Text in English. 1995. a. USD 75 (effective 2001). **Document type:** *Directory.* **Description:** Profiles 3,814 companies in product, companyname, SIC, city and parent company sections.
Related titles: CD-ROM ed.: Mississippi Manufacturers Register for Windows 95/98, Windows N T. ISSN 1550-0942. USD 310 (effective 2000); Diskette ed.
Published by: Manufacturers' News, Inc., 1633 Central St, Evanston, IL 60201. TEL 847-864-7000, 888-752-5200, FAX 847-332-1100, info@mninfo.com, info@manufacturersnews.com, sales@mninfo.com, http://www.manufacturersnews.com. Ed. Steve Garland.

380.1029 USA
MISSOURI BUSINESS CREDIT DIRECTORY. Text in English. a. USD 1,100 combined subscription print, online & CD-ROM eds. (effective 2004 & 2005). back issues avail. **Document type:** *Directory.* **Description:** Contains credit ratings and other valuable information on all businesses within Missouri. Includes company name & address, phone & fax numbers, key executive names & titles, lines of business, years in business, number of employees, estimated annual sales, volume credit rating code, and corporate linkage information.
Related titles: CD-ROM ed.; Diskette ed.; E-mail ed.; Fax ed.; Magnetic Tape ed.; Online - full text ed.
Published by: American Business Directories (Subsidiary of: American Business Information, Inc.), 5711 S 86th Circle, P O Box 27347, Omaha, NE 68127. TEL 402-593-4600, 888-946-9377, 877-708-3844, FAX 402-331-5481, sales@directoriesusa.com, http://www.directoriesusa.com.

338.0029 USA ISSN 1048-7301
HF5065.M8
MISSOURI BUSINESS DIRECTORY. Text in English. 1983. a. USD 1,100 combined subscription print, online & CD-ROM eds. (effective 2004 & 2005). index. back issues avail. **Document type:** *Directory.* **Description:** Includes all businesses in the state compiled from the yellow pages and telephone verified. Listings include company name, complete address, phone number, name of owner or manager, employee size and sales volume, and credit rating codes.
Related titles: CD-ROM ed.; Diskette ed.; E-mail ed.; Fax ed.; Magnetic Tape ed.; Online - full text ed.
Published by: American Business Directories (Subsidiary of: American Business Information, Inc.), 5711 S 86th Circle, P O Box 27347, Omaha, NE 68127. TEL 402-593-4600, 888-946-9377, 877-708-3844, FAX 402-331-5481, en.peters@infousa.com, sales@directoriesusa.com, http://www.directoriesusa.com.

670.29 USA ISSN 0893-2816
HD9727.M8
MISSOURI MANUFACTURERS REGISTER. Text in English. a. USD 108 (effective 2001). adv. illus. **Document type:** *Directory.* **Description:** Lists 9,509 manufacturers by product, alphabetically, geographically, by SIC, and parent company. Published in cooperation with the Missouri chamber of commerce.
Related titles: CD-ROM ed.: USD 490 (effective 2001); Diskette ed.
Published by: Manufacturers' News, Inc., 1633 Central St, Evanston, IL 60201. TEL 847-864-7000, 888-752-5200, FAX 847-332-1100, info@mninfo.com, info@manufacturersnews.com, sales@mninfo.com, http://www.manufacturersnews.com. Ed. Frank Lambing. Adv. contact Charles Scherer. B&W page USD 1,843.

338.0029 USA
MIX ANNUAL DIRECTORY OF RECORDING INDUSTRY FACILITIES AND SERVICES. Short title: Master Directory. Variant title: Mix Annual Recording Industry Directory. Text in English. a. USD 24.95 (effective 1998). adv. **Document type:** *Directory, Trade.*
Published by: Cardinal Business Media, Inc., 6400 Hollis, Ste 12, Emeryville, CA 94608. TEL 510-653-3307, FAX 510-653-5142. Ed. Blair Jackson. Pub. Jeffrey Turner. R&P Phil Semler. Adv. contact Brad Borkhart.

658.8029 USA
MODERN GROCER INDUSTRY DIRECTORY. Text in English. biennial. USD 125 (effective 2000). **Document type:** *Directory, Trade.* **Description:** Directory of retailers, vendors, brokers, wholesalers and distributors serving New York, New Jersey and lower Connecticut. Includes cross reference indexes linking products by brand to corporate company names.
Published by: G C Publishing Company, 744 Main St, PO Box 2010, Dennis, MA 02638. TEL 508-385-7700, FAX 580-385-0089, sgriffin@griffcomm.net, http://www.griffcomm.net/.

MODERN MATERIALS HANDLING CASEBOOK DIRECTORY. see *MACHINERY*

MODERN PAINT & COATINGS PAINT RED BOOK; directory of the paint and coatings industry. see *PAINTS AND PROTECTIVE COATINGS*

338.0029 USA ISSN 1048-731X
HF5065.M9
MONTANA BUSINESS DIRECTORY. Text in English. 1989. a. USD 1,100 combined subscription print, online & CD-ROM eds. (effective 2004 & 2005). index. back issues avail. **Document type:** *Directory.* **Description:** Lists all businesses in the state; includes company name, complete address, phone number, name of owner, manager, and employee size, sale volume codes, and credit rating codes.
Related titles: CD-ROM ed.; Diskette ed.; E-mail ed.; Fax ed.; Magnetic Tape ed.; Online - full text ed.
Published by: American Business Directories (Subsidiary of: American Business Information, Inc.), 5711 S 86th Circle, P O Box 27347, Omaha, NE 68127. TEL 402-593-4600, 888-946-9377, 877-708-3844, FAX 402-331-5481, sales@directoriesusa.com, http://www.directoriesusa.com.

670.29 USA ISSN 1057-6681
HD9727.M9
MONTANA MANUFACTURERS DIRECTORY. Text in English. 1955. irreg. USD 60 (effective 2001). stat. **Document type:** *Directory, Government.* **Description:** Profiles over 1,250 manufacturers comprising a $2 billion industrial market.
Former titles: Montana Manufacturers and Products Directory; Directory of Montana Manufacturers (0544-8794)
Related titles: CD-ROM ed.: USD 265 (effective 2001).
Published by: Manufacturers' News, Inc., 1633 Central St, Evanston, IL 60201. TEL 847-864-7000, 888-752-5200, FAX 847-332-1100, info@mninfo@.com, info@manufacturersnews.com, sales@mninfo.com, http://www.manufacturersnews.com. Circ: 3,000.

382.029 MSR ISSN 0303-447X
MONTSERRAT. STATISTICS OFFICE. OVERSEAS TRADE REPORT. Key Title: Overseas Trade (Plymouth). Text in English. irreg. **Document type:** *Government.*
Published by: Statistics Office, Government Headquarters, Plymouth, Montserrat.

332.6029 GBR
MORGAN STANLEY CENTRAL BANK DIRECTORY (YEAR). Text in English. 1991. a. GBP 130; GBP 140 foreign. **Document type:** *Directory.* **Description:** Comprehensive guide to the world's central banks and the people who run them. For each of the 173 banks, the directory offers a run-down of its recent history, and information about the bank's current concerns and duties.
Published by: Central Banking Publications Ltd., Fifth Fl, Tavistock House, Tavistock Sq, London, WC1H 9JZ, United Kingdom. TEL 44-20-73880006, FAX 44-20-73889040, info@centralbanking.co.uk, http://www.centralbanking.co.uk, http://www.centralbanking.co.uk/. Ed., R&P Robert Pringle.

380.1029 USA ISSN 1061-8546
HG4655
MORTGAGE MARKET STATISTICAL ANNUAL. Text in English. 1987. a. USD 469 (effective 2005). charts; stat. **Document type:** *Directory, Trade.* **Description:** Compilation of mortgage- and securities statistics.
Published by: Inside Mortgage Finance Publications, PO Box 42387, Washington, DC 20015. TEL 301-951-1240, FAX 301-656-1709, http://www.imfpubs.com. Ed., Pub. Guy D Cecala. R&P Didi Parks.

791.43025 USA ISSN 0580-0412
MOTION PICTURE, T V & THEATRE DIRECTORY; for services & products. Text in English. 1960. s-a. USD 15.20. adv. back issues avail. **Document type:** *Directory.* **Description:** Directory of the motion picture and television industries. Primarily concerns pre-production, production and post-production (products, services, equipment) of film and video.
Published by: M.P.E. Publications, Inc., PO Box 276, Tarrytown, NY 10591. TEL 212-245-0969, FAX 212-245-0974. Ed. John Low. Adv. contact Michael Graves. Circ: 80,300.

387.029 USA
MOTOR FREIGHT DIRECTORY. (In regional eds.: Southeast, Central States, Chicago, Western States, New England, New York, Mid-Atlantic, Southwest) Text in English. a. USD 110 (effective 2002). **Document type:** *Directory.*
Published by: Leonard Guide, 115 E University Dr, Arlington Heights, IL 60004. TEL 847-797-8101, info@leonardsguide.com, http://www.leonardsguide.com. Circ: 13,000.

388.3475029 USA
MOTORCYCLE PRODUCT NEWS TRADE DIRECTORY. Text in English. 1973. a. adv. **Document type:** *Directory.*
Published by: Athletic Business Publications, Inc., 4130 Lien Rd, Madison, WI 53704-3602. TEL 608-249-0186, FAX 608-249-1153.

380.1 382 TWN ISSN 1029-8711
MOTORCYCLES, PARTS & ACCESSORIES BUYERS' GUIDE. Text in English. 1998. a. USD 30 domestic; USD 30 foreign (effective 2001).
Related titles: CD-ROM ed.; Online - full text ed.

Published by: Interface Global Taiwan Co., Ltd., PO Box 173-12, Taipei, 116, Taiwan. FAX 886-2-2395-2901, tradwind@ms2.hinet.net, http://www.motorcyclesb2b.com, http://www.motorcycle-guide.com. Ed. Daniel Foong. Pub. Herbert Chen. R&P Donald Shapiro. Adv. contact Melody Lin TEL 886-2-2351-3180. Circ: 8,000. **Subscr. to:** Trade Winds Inc., PO Box 820519, Dallas, TX 75382. TEL 877-861-1188, FAX 972-699-1189, twinds8888@aol.com.

338.0029 ZAF
MPUMALANGA DIRECTORY. Text in English. 1976. a. USD 60 (effective 2001). **Document type:** *Directory.*
Former titles: Eastern Transvaal Buyer's Guide; Lowveld - Nelspruit Buyer's Guide; Supersedes: Buyers' Guide, Directory. Lowveld (1016-4006)
Published by: Braby's (Subsidiary of: Associated Industries), Attn: Sue Pearson, PO Box 1426, Pinetown, 3600, South Africa. TEL 27-31-7017021, FAX 27-31-7017036, booksales@brabys.co.za.

MUIR'S ORIGINAL LOG HOME GUIDE FOR BUILDERS & BUYERS. see *BUILDING AND CONSTRUCTION*

MUSIC BUSINESS DIRECTORY. see *MUSIC*

670.29 USA
THE N A F T A REGISTER. (North American Free Trade Agreement) Text in English. a. USD 150 (effective 2000). adv. **Document type:** *Directory.* **Description:** Directory of companies located within the NAFTA region that have a specific interest in exporting their products and services.
Published by: Global Contact, Inc., 16 W. Main St., Marlton, NJ 08053-2092. TEL 609-482-2011, FAX 609-482-2066, globalc@ix.netcom.com. Ed., Pub., R&P, Adv. contact Michael A Ruccolo.

THE N D A PIPELINE. (New Drug Approval) see *PHARMACY AND PHARMACOLOGY*

338.002 630 USA
N G F A DIRECTORY - YEARBOOK (YEAR). Text in English. 1896. a. USD 25 (effective 1999). **Document type:** *Directory.* **Description:** Constitutes a membership directory for NGFA.
Published by: National Grain and Feed Association, 1250 Eye St N W, Ste 1003, Washington, DC 20005. TEL 202-289-0873, FAX 202-289-5388, ngfa@ngfa.org, http://www.ngfa.org. Ed. David Poulas.

338.002 630 USA
N G F A NEWSLETTER. Text in English. 1948. bi-m. USD 450 (effective 1999). tr.lit. **Document type:** *Newsletter.* **Description:** Contains issues involving national food source production, storage, purchase, sale or transport of grain, seed and feed products.
Published by: National Grain and Feed Association, 1250 Eye St N W, Ste 1003, Washington, DC 20005. TEL 202-289-0873, FAX 202-289-5388, ngfa@ngfa.org, http://www.ngfa.org. Ed. Randall C Gordon. Circ: 2,000.

338.0029 USA ISSN 1053-8305
TH2430
N R C A MEMBERSHIP DIRECTORY. Text in English. 1949. a. USD 55 to non-members; USD 5 to members (effective 1999). **Document type:** *Directory.* **Description:** Lists roofing contractors, associate members, international members, and architects as well as engineers and consultants who belong to NRCA.
Published by: National Roofing Contractors Association, O'Hare International Center, 10255 W Higgins Rd, Ste 600, Rosemont, IL 60018-5607. TEL 847-299-9070, FAX 847-299-1183, nrca@nrca.net, http://www.narca.net. Ed. Alison Lavalley. Circ: 5,500.

N S S E A MEMBERSHIP DIRECTORY. see *EDUCATION—School Organization And Administration*

381.029 NAM ISSN 1028-0839
NAMIBIA TRADE DIRECTORY; a review of Namibian trade and industry. Text in English. 1991. a. NAD 60 (effective 2001). adv. illus. back issues avail. **Document type:** *Directory, Trade.* **Description:** Provides a guide to Namibia's facts and figures, ministries, parastals, and institutions. Also includes names and addresses of role-players in the private and public sectors.
Related titles: Online - full text ed.
Published by: Namibia Trade Directory CC, PO Box 21593, Windhoek, Namibia. TEL 264-61-225665, FAX 264-61-220410, sandra@mac.com.na, http://www.tradedirectory.com.na. Ed. Amy Schoeman. Pub. Paul van Schalkwyk. R&P, Adv. contact Sandra van Rooyen. color page NAD 11,990. Circ: 10,000.
Dist. by: Current Pacific Ltd., PO Box 36-536, Northcote, Auckland, New Zealand. TEL 64-9-480-1388, FAX 64-9-480-1387, info@cplnz.com, http://www.cplnz.com.

340.029 USA ISSN 1078-0564
KF316.5.A15
NATHAN'S LEGAL MARKETS✶ ; the definitive resource for marketing to legal professionals. Text in English. 1994. a. USD 159.95 (effective 1998). **Document type:** *Directory.* **Description:** Contains data on advertising and marketing for legal vendors and media planners.
Published by: Dolan Media Co., 706 2nd Ave S., Ste. 1200, Minneapolis, MN 55402-3012. TEL 612-935-9793, 888-534-2863, FAX 612-935-9711.

NATIONAL BIOTECH REGISTER. see *BIOLOGY—Biotechnology*

338.0029 ZAF
HF3901.A48
NATIONAL CLASSIFIED DIRECTORY OF SOUTH AFRICA. Text in English. 1972. a. USD 250 (effective 2001). adv. **Document type:** *Directory.*
Formerly: Commercial and Industrial Register of South Africa (0379-9816)
Published by: Braby's (Subsidiary of: Associated Industries), Attn: Sue Pearson, PO Box 1426, Pinetown, 3600, South Africa. TEL 27-31-7017021, FAX 27-31-7017036, booksales@brabys.co.za.

671.73029 USA
NATIONAL COIL COATING ASSOCIATION. PRODUCT CAPABILITY DIRECTORY (ONLINE EDITION). Text in English. irreg. **Document type:** *Directory, Trade.*
Media: Online - full content.
Published by: National Coil Coating Association, 1300 Sumner Ave, Cleveland, OH 44115-2851. TEL 216-241-7333, FAX 216-241-0105, ncaa@coilcoating.org, http://www.coilcoating.org.

389.6029 USA
NATIONAL CONFERENCE OF STANDARDS LABORATORIES. DIRECTORY OF STANDARDS LABS. Text in English. biennial. USD 120 to non-members; USD 30 to members (effective 2000). **Document type:** *Directory.*
Published by: National Conference of Standards Laboratories, 2995 Wilderness Pl., Ste. 107, Boulder, CO 80301-5404. TEL 303-440-3339, FAX 303-440-3384, ncsl-staff@ncsl-hq.org, http://www.NCSL-Hq.org.

332.62029 USA ISSN 1049-4995
HJ6685
NATIONAL CUSTOMS BROKERS & FORWARDERS ASSOCIATION OF AMERICA. MEMBERSHIP DIRECTORY. Text in English. a. USD 25. adv. **Document type:** *Directory.*
Published by: National Customs Brokers & Forwarders Association of America, Inc., 1200 18th St, N W, Ste 901, Washington, DC 20036. TEL 202-466-0222, FAX 202-466-0226, http://www.ncbfaa.org. Circ: 4,000.

615.534029 USA
NATIONAL DIRECTORY OF CHIROPRACTIC. Text in English. 1989. a., latest 12th ed. USD 45. adv. **Document type:** *Directory.* **Description:** Provides information on the chiropractic profession: lists providers of chiropractic supplies and services; chiropractic colleges; information on chiropractors; state by state information on licensing, examination, societies and organizations.
Related titles: Diskette ed.
Published by: National Directory of Chiropractic Foundation, PO Box 10056, Olathe, KS 66051. TEL 800-888-7914, FAX 913-780-0658, directory@sprintmail.com, http://www.chirodirectory.com, http://www.nationaldirectoryofchiro.com. Ed., R&P Larry Glavas. Pub. Ross S Trivas. Adv. contact Scott Fletcher. page USD 1,995. Circ: 6,800 (paid); 31,200 (controlled).

320.029 USA ISSN 0749-9736
HD59
NATIONAL DIRECTORY OF CORPORATE PUBLIC AFFAIRS. Abbreviated title: C P A. Text in English. 1983. a. USD 109 (effective 2000). adv. **Document type:** *Directory.* **Description:** Comprehensive overview of corporate civic responsibility and public relations carried out by 15,000 leaders in 2,000 companies, with lists by corporation including the office and officers responsible for public and community relations, policy formulation, advocacy advertising, state and federal lobbying, political action, and corporate contributions.
Published by: Columbia Books Inc., 1825 Connecticut Ave NW #625, Washington, DC 20009-5724. TEL 202-898-0662, 888-265-0600, FAX 202-898-0775, info@columbiabooks.com, http://www.columbiabooks.com. Ed. J Valerie Steele. Pub., Adv. contact Michael Goldman.

NATIONAL DIRECTORY OF FIRE CHIEFS & E M S ADMINISTRATORS. see *FIRE PREVENTION*

659.1029 USA
NATIONAL DIRECTORY OF MAILING LISTS. Text in English. 1990. a. USD 695 single CD-ROM user; USD 1,095 CD-ROM network (effective 2000). adv. **Document type:** *Directory.* **Description:** Contains information on more than 15000 responder and subscriber mailing lists.
Media: CD-ROM. **Related titles:** Online - full text ed.

Published by: Oxbridge Communications, Inc., 186 Fifth Ave., New York, NY 10010. TEL 212-741-0231, FAX 212-633-2938. Pub. Fay Shapiro. Adv. contact Kerry Murphy.

338.4 USA ISSN 0094-9663
NATIONAL DIRECTORY OF MINORITY MANUFACTURERS. Text in English. irreg. **Document type:** *Directory, Consumer.*
Published by: Office of Minority Business Enterprises, City of Richmond, Department of Economic Development, 501 East Franklin St, Ste 800, Richmond, VA 23219. TEL 804-646-5633, FAX 804-646-6793, http://www.ci.richmond.va.us.

338.0029 USA ISSN 0886-3881
HD2346.U5
NATIONAL DIRECTORY OF MINORITY - OWNED BUSINESS FIRMS. Text in English. 1985. a. USD 275 (effective 2000). **Document type:** *Directory.* **Description:** Lists over 25,000 minority-owned firms. Organized by SIC code and geographical location. Includes owner's name, telephone, line of business, certification status, start date and sales volume.
Related titles: CD-ROM ed.; Diskette ed.
—CCC.
Published by: Business Research Services, Inc., 4701 Sangamore Rd., Ste. S155, Bethesda, MD 20816-2532. TEL 202-364-6473, FAX 202-686-3228. Ed. Thomas D Johnson.

658.0029 USA ISSN 0886-389X
HD2346.U5
NATIONAL DIRECTORY OF WOMAN - OWNED BUSINESS FIRMS. Text in English. 1986. a. USD 275 (effective 2000). **Document type:** *Directory.* **Description:** Lists over 10,000 woman-owned firms, nationwide, arranged by SIC code, geographical area, with owner's name, telephone, line of business, and certification status noted.
Related titles: CD-ROM ed.; Diskette ed.
—CCC.
Published by: Business Research Services, Inc., 4701 Sangamore Rd., Ste. S155, Bethesda, MD 20816-2532. TEL 202-364-6473, FAX 202-686-3228. Ed., R&P Thomas D Johnson.

381.029 USA ISSN 1520-040X
TK6710
NATIONAL E-MAIL AND FAX DIRECTORY. Text in English. 1989. a., latest 2004. USD 180 (effective 2004). **Document type:** *Directory.* **Description:** Provides the fax numbers of over 180,000 of the nation's most important companies and organizations.
Formerly (until 1999): National Fax Directory (1045-9499)
Published by: Gale Group (Subsidiary of: Thomson Corporation), 27500 Drake Rd, Farmington Hills, MI 48331-3535. TEL 248-699-8061, 800-877-4253, FAX 248-699-4253, galeord@gale.com, http://www.gale.com. Ed. Karin E Koek.

725.5029 USA
NATIONAL FITNESS TRADE JOURNAL. Text in English. 1982. q. USD 25; USD 72 foreign. adv. charts; illus.; stat.; tr.lit. back issues avail. **Document type:** *Trade.*
Published by: (National Health Club Association), Wally Boyko Productions, Inc., PO Box 2378, Corona, CA 91718-2378. TEL 909-371-0606, FAX 909-371-0608. Ed. Greta Blackburn. R&P, Adv. contact Wally Boyko. Circ: 20,000.

380.1029 USA
NATIONAL HARDWOOD LUMBER ASSOCIATION MEMBERSHIP DIRECTORY. Text in English. 1912. a. USD 85. **Document type:** *Directory.* **Description:** Includes products, species, facilities, salesmen.
Formerly: National Hardwood Lumber Association Yearbook
Published by: National Hardwood Lumber Association, PO Box 34518, Memphis, TN 38184-0518. TEL 901-377-1818. Ed. Rebecca Stevens. Circ: 2,000.

NATIONAL LIST OF ADVERTISERS. see *ADVERTISING AND PUBLIC RELATIONS*

NATIONAL ORGANIC DIRECTORY. see *AGRICULTURE*

659.2 USA
THE NATIONAL P R PITCH BOOK. BUSINESS & CONSUMER EDITION. Text in English. a. USD 550 (effective 2003). adv. **Document type:** *Directory, Trade.* **Description:** Contains complete contact information, plus thousands of placement tips from top reporters, editors, producers, and bookers — in their own words — on exactly how (and how not) to approach their media.
Published by: InfoCom Group, 5900 Hollis St, Ste L, Emeryville, CA 94608-2008. TEL 510-596-9300, 800-959-1059, FAX 510-596-9331, webmgr@infocomgroup.com, http://www.infocomgroup.com/npr.html. Ed. Meghan Collins.

659.2 USA
THE NATIONAL P R PITCH BOOK. COMPUTERS & TECHNOLOGY EDITION. Text in English. a. USD 500 (effective 2003). **Document type:** *Directory, Trade.* **Description:** Contains contact information, plus thousands of placement tips from top reporters, editors, producers, and bookers — in their own words — on exactly how (and how not) to approach computer and technology related media.

B

Published by: InfoCom Group, 5900 Hollis St, Ste L, Emeryville, CA 94608-2008. TEL 510-596-9300, 800-959-1059, FAX 510-596-9331, webmgr@infocomgroup.com, http://www.infocomgroup.com/npr.html.

659.2 USA
THE NATIONAL P R PITCH BOOK. HEALTH, FITNESS & MEDICINE EDITION. Text in English. a. USD 500 (effective 2003). **Document type:** *Directory, Trade.* **Description:** Contains contact information, plus thousands of placement tips from top reporters, editors, producers, and bookers — in their own words — on exactly how (and how not) to approach the medical and health media.
Published by: InfoCom Group, 5900 Hollis St, Ste L, Emeryville, CA 94608-2008. TEL 510-596-9300, 800-959-1059, FAX 510-596-9331, webmgr@infocomgroup.com, http://www.infocomgroup.com/npr.html.

659.2 USA
THE NATIONAL P R PITCH BOOK. INVESTMENT, BANKING & FINANCIAL SERVICES EDITION. Text in English. a. USD 500 (effective 2003). **Document type:** *Directory, Trade.* **Description:** Contains contact information, plus thousands of placement tips from top reporters, editors, producers, and bookers — in their own words — on exactly how (and how not) to approach the business and financial media.
Published by: InfoCom Group, 5900 Hollis St, Ste L, Emeryville, CA 94608-2008. TEL 510-596-9300, 800-959-1059, FAX 510-596-9331, webmgr@infocomgroup.com, http://www.infocomgroup.com/npr.html.

659.2 USA
THE NATIONAL P R PITCH BOOK. ISSUES, POLICY & POLITICS EDITION. Text in English. a. USD 550 (effective 2003). **Document type:** *Directory, Trade.* **Description:** Contains contact information, plus thousands of placement tips from top reporters, editors, producers, and bookers — in their own words — on exactly how (and how not) to approach their media.
Published by: InfoCom Group, 5900 Hollis St, Ste L, Emeryville, CA 94608-2008. TEL 510-596-9300, 800-959-1059, FAX 510-596-9331, webmgr@infocomgroup.com, http://www.infocomgroup.com/npr.html.

659.2 USA
THE NATIONAL P R PITCH BOOK. TRAVEL, HOSPITALITY & DESTINATIONS EDITION. Text in English. a. USD 450 (effective 2001). **Document type:** *Directory, Trade.* **Description:** Contains contact information, plus thousands of placement tips from top reporters, editors, producers, and bookers — in their own words — on exactly how (and how not) to approach their media.
Published by: InfoCom Group, 5900 Hollis St, Ste L, Emeryville, CA 94608-2008. TEL 510-596-9300, 800-959-1059, FAX 510-596-9331, webmgr@infocomgroup.com, http://www.infocomgroup.com/npr.html.

NATIONAL PRECAST CONCRETE ASSOCIATION. MEMBERSHIP DIRECTORY & BUYER'S GUIDE. see *BUILDING AND CONSTRUCTION*

NATIONAL REFERRAL ROSTER; the nation's directory of real estate firms. see *REAL ESTATE*

NATIONAL SPORTING GOODS ASSOCIATION BUYING GUIDE. see *SPORTS AND GAMES*

380.1029 USA ISSN 0734-354X
HD2425
NATIONAL TRADE AND PROFESSIONAL ASSOCIATIONS OF THE UNITED STATES. Abbreviated title: N T P A Directory. Text in English. 1966. a. USD 99 paperback ed. (effective 2000). adv. **Document type:** *Directory.* **Description:** Compiles more than 7,500 trade associations, professional societies, and labor unions, with information on the names of executive officers; memberships, staff and budget size; periodic publications; future events, and historical background, primary index alphabetically by organization name, subsidiary indexes by subject, budget, region, executive name, and acronym.
Former titles: National Trade and Professional Association of the United States and Labor Unions; (until 1982): National Trade and Professional Associations of the United States and Canada and Labor Unions (0094-8284); (until 1975): Directory of National Trade and Professional Associations of the United States (0070-5918); (until 1974): National Trade and Professional Associations of the United States and Labor Unions (0090-5038)
—CISTI.
Published by: Columbia Books Inc., 1825 Connecticut Ave NW #625, Washington, DC 20009-5724. TEL 202-898-0662, 888-265-0600, FAX 202-898-0775, info@columbiabooks.com, http://www.columbiabooks.com. Ed. Buck Downs. Pub., Adv. contact Michael Goldman.

363.75029 USA ISSN 1054-8238
HD9999.U53
THE NATIONAL YELLOW BOOK OF FUNERAL DIRECTORS. Text in English. 1974. a. USD 100 (effective 2005). adv. illus. 1200 p./no.; **Document type:** *Directory, Trade.*
Former titles (until 1988): Yellow Book of Funeral Directors and Suppliers (1054-822X); (until 1984): Yellow Book of Funeral Directors and Services (0098-3322)
Related titles: Online - full text ed.; ♦ Supplement(s): The Catalog of Funeral Home Supplies. ISSN 1054-2426.
Published by: Nomis Publications, Inc., PO Box 5159, Youngstown, OH 44514. TEL 330-965-2380, 800-321-7479, FAX 330-965-2381, 800-321-9040, info@yelobk.com, http://www.yelobk.com. Ed., R&P, Adv. contact Kim Graham. Pub. Margaret Rouzzo. Circ: 23,000.

NATIONWIDE DIRECTORY OF CORPORATE MEETING PLANNERS. see *MEETINGS AND CONGRESSES*

NATIONWIDE DIRECTORY OF GIFT, HOUSEWARES & HOME TEXTILE BUYERS. see *GIFTWARE AND TOYS*

NATIONWIDE DIRECTORY OF MEN'S AND BOYS' WEAR BUYERS. see *CLOTHING TRADE*

NATIONWIDE DIRECTORY OF SPORTING GOODS BUYERS. see *SPORTS AND GAMES*

NATIONWIDE DIRECTORY OF WOMEN'S AND CHILDREN'S WEAR BUYERS. see *CLOTHING TRADE*

NATIONWIDE MAJOR MASS MARKET MERCHANDISERS. see *CLOTHING TRADE*

NATIONWIDE OVERNIGHT STABLING DIRECTORY & EQUESTRIAN VACATION GUIDE. see *SPORTS AND GAMES—Horses And Horsemanship*

338.4 CAN ISSN 1700-8476
NATURAL HEALTH PRODUCTS CANADA B2B INDUSTRY GUIDE. Text in English. 2001. a. CND 149 (effective 2003). **Document type:** *Directory, Trade.*
Formerly (until 2002): Natural Health Products Canada Guide (1497-6315)
Published by: Contact Canada, 390 Goward Rd, Victoria, BC V9E 2J5, Canada. TEL 250-708-0427, 888-502-6666, FAX 250-708-0429, ccinfo@contactcanada.com, http://www.contactcanada.com/natural_health/.

338 660.6029 GBR
TP248.3
NATURE BIOTECHNOLOGY DIRECTORY (YEAR). Text in English. 1983. a. USD 325 per issue in United States; GBP 195 per issue elsewhere (effective 2004). adv. **Document type:** *Directory.* **Description:** Provides information on companies, research centers, and academic institutions involved in new and established technologies.
Former titles (until 2003): Biotechnology Directory (Year) (1059-7352); (until 1985): International Biotechnology Directory (0265-3877)
—BLDSC (6046.258500), CISTI, GNLM. **CCC.**
Published by: Nature Publishing Group (Subsidiary of: Macmillan Publishers Ltd.), The MacMillan Building, 4 Crinan St, London, N1 9XW, United Kingdom. TEL 44-20-78334000, FAX 44-20-78433601, subscriptions@nature.com, NatureReviews@nature.com, http://guide.nature.com/, http://www.nature.com. Ed. Louise Baynes TEL 44-20-73242349. Adv. contact Paula Pusey TEL 44-20-75498643. **Subscr. addr outside the US:** Nature Publishing Group Reference, c/o Ebony Bennett, 4 Crinan St, London N1 9XW, United Kingdom. TEL 44-20-7843-4734, npgref@natureny.com; **Subscr. addr. in the US:** N P G Reference, 345 Park Ave S, New York, NY 10010. TEL 800-336-0055, FAX 212-689-9108.

338.0029 USA ISSN 1048-7328
HF5065.N2
NEBRASKA BUSINESS DIRECTORY. Text in English. 1981. a. USD 1,100 combined subscription print, online & CD-ROM eds. (effective 2004 & 2005). index. back issues avail. **Document type:** *Directory.* **Description:** Lists all businesses in the state; includes company name, complete address, phone number, name of owner, manager, and employee size, sales volume codes, and credit rating codes.
Related titles: CD-ROM ed.; Diskette ed.; E-mail ed.; Fax ed.; Magnetic Tape ed.; Online - full text ed.
Published by: American Business Directories (Subsidiary of: American Business Information, Inc.), 5711 S 86th Circle, P O Box 27347, Omaha, NE 68127. TEL 402-593-4600, 888-946-9377, 877-708-3844, FAX 402-331-5481, sales@directoriesusa.com, http://www.directoriesusa.com.

670.29 USA ISSN 1059-7727
HF5065.N2
NEBRASKA MANUFACTURERS REGISTER. Text in English. 1993. a. USD 70 (effective 2001). adv. 280 p./no.; **Document type:** *Directory.* **Description:** Profiles 2996 companies by name, SIC, city, product, and parent company.
Related titles: CD-ROM ed.: USD 269 (effective 2001); Diskette ed.
Published by: Manufacturers' News, Inc., 1633 Central St, Evanston, IL 60201. TEL 847-864-7000, 888-752-5200, FAX 847-332-1100, info@mninfo.com, info@manufacturersnews.com, sales@mninfo.com, http://www.manufacturersnews.com. Ed. Steve Garland.

338.0029 NLD ISSN 0923-6902
NEDERLANDS A B C DIENSTVERLENERS. Text in Dutch. 1987. a. adv. **Document type:** *Directory, Trade.* **Description:** Provides information on more than 23,000 professional service firms in the Netherlands, including branch offices of foreign firms.
Related titles: Online - full text ed.: (from Data-Star).
Published by: A B C voor Handel en Industrie C.V., PO Box 190, Haarlem, 2000 AD, Netherlands. TEL 31-23-5533533, FAX 31-23-5327033, info@abc-d.nl, http://www.abc-d.nl. Ed. F Droog. Adv. contact T Vlot. Circ: 7,000.

338.0029 NLD
NEDERLANDS A B C VOOR HANDEL EN INDUSTRIE. Text in Dutch. 1952. a. adv. **Document type:** *Directory, Trade.* **Description:** Provides business information on producers, importers and merchandisers.
Related titles: Online - full text ed.: (from Data-Star).
Published by: A B C voor Handel en Industrie C.V., PO Box 190, Haarlem, 2000 AD, Netherlands. TEL 31-23-5533533, FAX 31-23-5327033, info@abc-d.nl, http://www.abc-d.nl. Ed. F Droog. Adv. contact T Vlot. Circ: 19,250.

332.6029 USA ISSN 1553-2755
HG4907
NELSON INFORMATION'S DIRECTORY OF INVESTMENT RESEARCH. Text in English. 1975. a. USD 750 per issue (effective 2005). adv. stat. **Document type:** *Directory, Trade.* **Description:** Comprehensive guide to stock research, including corporate profiles, securities analysts covering each stock, and key executives for over 12000 companies worldwide.
Former titles (until 2002): Nelson's Directory of Investment Research (0896-0135); (until 1988): Nelson's Directory of Wall Street Research (0896-3851); Investment Decisions Directory of Wall Street Research (0897-5388); Nelson's Directory of Wall Street Research (0740-8714); Nelson Directory of Securities Research (0272-5355); Directory of Securities Research (0277-8343); National Directory of Wall Street Research
Published by: Nelson Information, 195 Broadway, New York, NY 10007-3100. TEL 800-333-6357, info@nelnet.com, http://www.nelnet.com.

658.325 USA ISSN 1553-3565
HG4907
NELSON INFORMATION'S DIRECTORY OF PENSION FUND CONSULTANTS. Text in English. 1990. a. USD 335 (effective 1999). **Document type:** *Directory.* **Description:** Provides descriptions of more than 350 professional investment consulting firms serving sponsors of employee benefit funds, foundations, and endowments.
Former titles (until 2002): Nelson's Directory of Pension Fund Consultants (1553-3573); (until 1995): Nelson's Guide to Pension Fund Consultants (1053-2536)
Published by: Nelson Information, 195 Broadway, New York, NY 10007-3100. TEL 646-822-2000, http://www.nelsoninformation.com.

333.33029 USA ISSN 1060-5789
HD251
NELSON'S DIRECTORY OF INSTITUTIONAL REAL ESTATE. Text in English. 1992. a. USD 335 (effective 1999). **Document type:** *Directory.* **Description:** Information for pension fund, institutional and foundation investors, sponsors and consultants on institutional real estate investors, real estate investment management services and related support services.
Published by: Nelson Information, 195 Broadway, New York, NY 10007-3100. TEL 914-937-8400, FAX 914-937-8590.

332.6029 USA ISSN 0896-0143
HG4907
NELSON'S DIRECTORY OF INVESTMENT MANAGERS. Text in English. 1988. a. USD 750 per issue; USD 1,295 per issue print and CD-ROM eds. (effective 2005). adv. stat. **Document type:** *Directory, Trade.* **Description:** Contains information on over 2,600 money management firms, including company profiles, investment executives, fees, performance statistics.
Incorporates: Nelson's Guide to Investment Consultants (1049-5630)
Related titles: CD-ROM ed.: USD 995 per issue (effective 2005).
Published by: Nelson Information, 195 Broadway, New York, NY 10007-3100. TEL 800-333-6357, info@nelnet.com, http://www.nelnet.com. Circ: 3,000.

381.029 USA
HD7105.45.U6
NELSON'S DIRECTORY OF PLAN SPONSORS. Text in English. 1990. a. USD 545 (effective 1999). **Document type:** *Directory.* **Description:** Profiles the investments of more than 10,000 sponsors of pension and endowment funds.
Formerly: Nelson's Directory of Plan Sponsors and Tax Exempt Funds (1053-0312)
Published by: Nelson Information, 195 Broadway, New York, NY 10007-3100. TEL 914-937-8400, FAX 914-937-8590.

NETHERLANDS-AMERICAN TRADE DIRECTORY. see *BUSINESS AND ECONOMICS—Chamber Of Commerce Publications*

382.029 GBR ISSN 0308-1273
NETHERLANDS-BRITISH TRADE DIRECTORY. Text in English. 1961. a. GBP 15 to non-members. adv. **Document type:** *Directory.*
Published by: Netherlands-British Chamber of Commerce, Netherlands British Chamber Of Commerce, The Dutch House 307-308, High Holborn, London, WC1V 7LS, United Kingdom. Circ: 5,000.

384.504065 USA ISSN 1093-3859
NETWORKING IN NEW JERSEY; a guide to trade and professional associations in New Jersey. Text in English. 1996. a. USD 49.95; USD 199 floppy disk database. (effective 2001). 213 p./no.; **Document type:** *Directory.* **Description:** Lists 819 trade and professional associations in New Jersey with addresses, fax numbers, web page addresses, and publications.
Related titles: Diskette ed.
Published by: Research Communications Inc, 3724 Jefferson St, 318, Austin, TX 78732. TEL 512-458-2021, 800-331-5076, FAX 512-458-2059, researchcomm@austin.rr.com, http://www.austintx.net/Researchcomm. Eds. Craig Gowen, Matthew Buchanan. Pub. Jeanne Graves. Circ: 500.

NEUMANN; Handbuch fuer den Pressevertrieb. see *PUBLISHING AND BOOK TRADE*

338.0029 USA ISSN 1048-7336
HF5065.N3
NEVADA BUSINESS DIRECTORY. Text in English. 1989. a. USD 1,100 combined subscription print, online & CD-ROM eds. (effective 2004 & 2005). index. back issues avail. **Document type:** *Directory.* **Description:** Includes all businesses in the state compiled from the yellow pages and telephone-verified. Each listing includes company name, complete address, phone number, name of owner, manager, and employee size, sales volume codes, and credit rating codes.
Related titles: CD-ROM ed.; Diskette ed.; E-mail ed.; Fax ed.; Magnetic Tape ed.; Online - full text ed.
Published by: American Business Directories (Subsidiary of: American Business Information, Inc.), 5711 S 86th Circle, P O Box 27347, Omaha, NE 68127. TEL 402-593-4600, 888-946-9377, 877-708-3844, FAX 402-331-5481, sales@directoriesusa.com, http://www.directoriesusa.com.

670.29 USA ISSN 1057-5243
CODEN: ICJREY
NEVADA INDUSTRIAL DIRECTORY. Text in English. 1974. a. USD 99. adv. **Document type:** *Directory.* **Description:** Provides information on over 6,500 companies arranged alphabetically, geographically, and by SIC.
Former titles (until 1987): Compleat Nevada Industrial Directory (0898-8226); Nevada Industrial Directory (1047-1766); Directory of Nevada Businesses (0098-0501)
Related titles: Diskette ed.
Published by: Gold Hill Publishing Co., Drawer F, Virginia City, NV 89440. TEL 702-847-0222. Ed. Max Winthrop. Pub. David W Toll. R&P, Adv. contact David Toll. Circ: 3,500.

670.29 USA ISSN 1083-317X
HF5065.N3
NEVADA MANUFACTURERS REGISTER✶. Text in English. 1996. a. USD 59 (effective 2000). **Document type:** *Directory.* **Description:** Provides complete profiles of 2300 manufacturing, mining and selected service firms.
Related titles: CD-ROM ed.: USD 265 (effective 2000).
Published by: Database Publishing Company, 701 E Ball Rd Ste 100, Anaheim, CA 92805-5962. TEL 714-778-6400, FAX 714-778-6811. R&P Sarah Fraser. **Dist. by:** Manufacturers' News, Inc., 1633 Central St, Evanston, IL 60201. TEL 847-864-7000, 888-752-5200, FAX 847-332-1100, info@manufacturersnews.com, sales@mninfo.com, http://www.manufacturersnews.com.

338.0029 USA ISSN 1048-714X
HF5065.N4
NEW HAMPSHIRE BUSINESS DIRECTORY. Text in English. 1990. a. USD 1,100 combined subscription print, online & CD-ROM eds. (effective 2004 & 2005). index. back issues avail. **Document type:** *Directory.* **Description:** Lists all businesses in the state; includes company name, complete address, phone number, name of owner, manager, and employee size, sales volume codes, and credit rating codes.
Related titles: CD-ROM ed.; Diskette ed.; E-mail ed.; Fax ed.; Magnetic Tape ed.; Online - full text ed.
Published by: American Business Directories (Subsidiary of: American Business Information, Inc.), 5711 S 86th Circle, P O Box 27347, Omaha, NE 68127. TEL 402-593-4600, 888-946-9377, 877-708-3844, FAX 402-331-5481, sales@directoriesusa.com, http://www.directoriesusa.com.

670.29 USA ISSN 1522-1997
HF5065.N4
NEW HAMPSHIRE MANUFACTURERS REGISTER. Text in English. 1998. a. USD 65 (effective 2000). adv. charts; illus.; stat. **Document type:** *Directory.* **Description:** Profiles 2,830 manufacturers in five sections: company name, product, S.I.C., city, and parent company.
Related titles: CD-ROM ed.: USD 265 (effective 2000); Online - full text ed.
Published by: Manufacturers' News, Inc., 1633 Central St, Evanston, IL 60201. TEL 847-864-7000, 888-752-5200, FAX 847-332-1100, info@mninfo.com, info@manufacturersnews.com, sales@mninfo.com, http://www.manufacturersnews.com. Ed. Frank Lambing. Adv. contact Charles Scherer. B&W page USD 1,843.

NEW HAMPSHIRE MANUFACTURING DIRECTORY. see *BUSINESS AND ECONOMICS—Production Of Goods And Services*

380.1029 USA
NEW JERSEY BUSINESS CREDIT DIRECTORY. Text in English. a. USD 1,100 combined subscription print, online & CD-ROM eds. (effective 2004 & 2005). back issues avail. **Document type:** *Directory.* **Description:** Contains credit ratings and other valuable information on all businesses within New Jersey. Includes company name & address, phone & fax numbers, key executive names & titles, lines of business, years in business, number of employees, estimated annual sales, volume credit rating code, and corporate linkage information.
Related titles: CD-ROM ed.; Diskette ed.; E-mail ed.; Fax ed.; Magnetic Tape ed.; Online - full text ed.
Published by: American Business Directories (Subsidiary of: American Business Information, Inc.), 5711 S 86th Circle, P O Box 27347, Omaha, NE 68127. TEL 402-593-4600, 888-946-9377, 877-708-3844, FAX 402-331-5481, sales@directoriesusa.com, http://www.directoriesusa.com.

338.0029 USA ISSN 1048-7158
NEW JERSEY BUSINESS DIRECTORY. Text in English. 1990. a. USD 1,100 combined subscription print, online & CD-ROM eds. (effective 2004 & 2005). index. back issues avail. **Document type:** *Directory.* **Description:** Lists all businesses in the state; includes complete address, phone number, name of owner, manager, and employee size, sales volume codes, and credit rating codes.
Related titles: CD-ROM ed.; Diskette ed.; E-mail ed.; Fax ed.; Magnetic Tape ed.; Online - full text ed.
Published by: American Business Directories (Subsidiary of: American Business Information, Inc.), 5711 S 86th Circle, P O Box 27347, Omaha, NE 68127. TEL 402-593-4600, 888-946-9377, 877-708-3844, FAX 402-331-5481, sales@directoriesusa.com, http://www.directoriesusa.com.

338.0029 USA ISSN 1049-2879
HF5065.N5
NEW JERSEY BUSINESS SOURCE BOOK. Text in English. 1987. a. (in 2 vols.). USD 149.95 (effective 2000). 353 p./no. 2 cols./p.; **Document type:** *Directory.* **Description:** Lists larger corporations, all professional and trade associations, local and international assistance programs for New Jersey businesses, Business press in NJ and New Jersey chambers of commerce.
Related titles: Diskette ed.: USD 495 (effective 2000).
Published by: Research Communications Inc, 3724 Jefferson St, 318, Austin, TX 78732. TEL 512-458-2021, 800-331-5076, FAX 512-458-2059, researchcomm@austin.rr.com, http://www.austintx.net/ResearchComm. Eds. Craig Gowen, Matthew Buchanan. Pub. Jeanne Graves. Circ: 800.

670.29 USA ISSN 0195-9352
HD9727.N5
NEW JERSEY DIRECTORY OF MANUFACTURERS. Text in English. 1979. a. USD 92.50. adv. **Document type:** *Directory.* **Description:** Profiles approximately 9,000 manufacturers and their key executives; includes alphabetical, geographical and product line sections.
Related titles: CD-ROM ed.: USD 495 (effective 1999); Diskette ed.: USD 495 (effective 1999); Magnetic Tape ed.
Published by: Commerce Register, Inc., 190 Godwin Ave, Midland Park, NJ 07432. TEL 201-445-3000, FAX 201-446-5806. Circ: 3,000.

331.80029 USA ISSN 1081-9134
NEW JERSEY LABOR UNIONS. Text in English. 1992. a., latest 2001. USD 49.95 (effective 2000). 100 p./no. 2 cols./p.; **Document type:** *Directory.* **Description:** Lists personnel in all unions in New Jersey. Indexed by county and municipality.
Related titles: Diskette ed.: USD 199 (effective 2000).
Published by: Research Communications Inc, 3724 Jefferson St, 318, Austin, TX 78732. TEL 512-458-2021, 800-331-5076, FAX 512-458-2059, researchcomm@austin.rr.com, rcg@austintx.net, http://www.austintx.net/ResearchComm, http://www.austintx.net/ResourceComm. Eds. Craig Gowen, Jeanne Graves. Circ: 300.

670.29 USA ISSN 1094-1010
HF5065.N5
NEW JERSEY MANUFACTURERS REGISTER. Text in English. 1998. a. USD 111 (effective 2000). adv. charts; illus.; stat. **Document type:** *Directory.* **Description:** Profiles 11,169 manufacturers in five sections: company name, product, S.I.C., city, and parent company.
Related titles: CD-ROM ed.: USD 535 (effective 2000); Online - full text ed.
Published by: Manufacturers' News, Inc., 1633 Central St, Evanston, IL 60201. TEL 847-864-7000, 888-752-5200, FAX 847-332-1100, info@mninfo.com, info@manufacturersnews.com, sales@mninfo.com, http://www.manufacturersnews.com. Ed. Frank Lambing. Adv. contact Charles Scherer. B&W page USD 1,843.

070.5 USA ISSN 1054-5190
P88.8
NEW JERSEY MEDIA GUIDE. Text in English. 1989. a. USD 94.95 (effective 2001). 325 p./no. 2 cols./p.; **Document type:** *Directory.* **Description:** Details all media in the state: newspapers, radio and TV stations, publications, news bureaus and syndicates. Includes details on staffing, address, fax and e-mail addresses.
Related titles: Diskette ed.: USD 295 (effective 2001).
Published by: Research Communications Inc, 3724 Jefferson St, 318, Austin, TX 78732. TEL 512-458-2021, 800-331-2059, FAX 512-458-2059, rcg@austintx.net, http://www.austintx.net/ResourceComm. Ed. Michael Graham. Circ: 500.

NEW JERSEY STATE AGENT HANDBOOK. see *INSURANCE*

338.0029 USA ISSN 1048-7344
HF5065.N6
NEW MEXICO BUSINESS DIRECTORY. Text in English. 1989. a. USD 1,100 combined subscription print, online & CD-ROM eds. (effective 2004 & 2005). index. back issues avail. **Document type:** *Directory.* **Description:** Lists all businesses in the state; includes company name, complete address, phone number, name of owner, manager, and employee size, sale volume codes, and credit rating codes.
Related titles: CD-ROM ed.; Diskette ed.; E-mail ed.; Fax ed.; Magnetic Tape ed.; Online - full text ed.
Published by: American Business Directories (Subsidiary of: American Business Information, Inc.), 5711 S 86th Circle, P O Box 27347, Omaha, NE 68127. TEL 402-593-4600, 888-946-9377, 877-708-3844, FAX 402-331-5481, sales@directoriesusa.com, http://www.directoriesusa.com.

670.29 USA
NEW MEXICO MANUFACTURERS DIRECTORY. Text in English. 1992. biennial. USD 50. stat.; tr.lit. back issues avail. **Document type:** *Directory.* **Description:** Lists manufacturers located in New Mexico. Includes company name, address, phone number, year established, contact person, up to 4 products, and SIC codes.
Related titles: Diskette ed.
Published by: Center for Economic Development, Research, and Assistance, PO Box 30001, Dept 3CR, Las Cruces, NM 88003-8001. TEL 505-646-6315, FAX 505-646-7037. Ed., R&P Heidi Young TEL 505-646-5868.

670.29 USA ISSN 1088-7601
HF5065.N5
NEW MEXICO MANUFACTURERS REGISTER. Text in English. 1997. a. USD 65 (effective 2000). adv. charts; illus.; stat. **Document type:** *Directory.* **Description:** Profiles 2,103 manufacturers listed in five sections: company name, product, S.I.C., city, and parent company.
Related titles: CD-ROM ed.: USD 265 (effective 2000); Diskette ed.; Online - full text ed.
Published by: Manufacturers' News, Inc., 1633 Central St, Evanston, IL 60201. TEL 847-864-7000, FAX 847-332-1100, info@mninfo.com, info@manufacturersnews.com, http://www.manufacturersnews.com. Ed. Frank Lambing. Adv. contact Charles Scherer. B&W page USD 1,843.

658.87029 AUS ISSN 0817-024X
NEW SOUTH WALES & AUSTRALIAN CAPITAL TERRITORY RETAIL DIRECTORY. Text in English. a. AUD 125. **Document type:** *Directory.*
Published by: Jared Publishing, PO Box 51, Mitcham, VIC 3132, Australia. TEL 61-3-8742415, FAX 61-3-8735951. Ed. Bruce Atkinson.

387.029 AUS ISSN 0266-0652
NEW SOUTH WALES PORTS HANDBOOK. Text in English. 1985. a. **Document type:** *Directory, Trade.*
Published by: Charter Pacific Publications Pty. Ltd., PO Box 356, Mount Martha, VIC 3934, Australia. TEL 61-3-59771668, FAX 61-3-59771670, charpac@ozemail.com.au. Ed. Gerry Cansdale. Circ: 6,000.

380.1029 USA
NEW YORK BUSINESS CREDIT DIRECTORY. Text in English. a. USD 1,100 combined subscription print, online & CD-ROM eds. (effective 2004 & 2005). back issues avail. **Document type:** *Directory.* **Description:** Contains credit ratings and other valuable information on all businesses within New York. Includes company name & address, phone & fax numbers, key executive names & titles, lines of business, years in business, number of employees, estimated annual sales, volume credit rating code, and corporate linkage information.
Related titles: CD-ROM ed.; Diskette ed.; E-mail ed.; Fax ed.; Magnetic Tape ed.; Online - full text ed.
Published by: American Business Directories (Subsidiary of: American Business Information, Inc.), 5711 S 86th Circle, P O Box 27347, Omaha, NE 68127. TEL 402-593-4600, 888-946-9377, 877-708-3844, FAX 402-331-5481, sales@directoriesusa.com, http://www.directoriesusa.com.

▼ new title ➤ refereed ✶ unverified ◆ full entry avail.

338.0029 USA
NEW YORK BUSINESS DIRECTORY. Text in English. 1993. a. USD 1,100 combined subscription print, online & CD-ROM eds. (effective 2004 & 2005). index. back issues avail.
Document type: *Directory.* **Description:** Lists all businesses in the state; includes company name, complete address, phone number, name of owner, manager, and employee size, sales volume codes, and credit rating codes.
Related titles: CD-ROM ed.; Diskette ed.; E-mail ed.; Fax ed.; Magnetic Tape ed.; Online - full text ed.
Published by: American Business Directories (Subsidiary of: American Business Information, Inc.), 5711 S 86th Circle, P O Box 27347, Omaha, NE 68127. TEL 402-593-4600, 888-946-9377, 877-708-3844, FAX 402-331-5481, sales@directoriesusa.com, http://www.directoriesusa.com.

NEW YORK DIAMOND BUYER'S GUIDE. see *JEWELRY, CLOCKS AND WATCHES*

670.29 USA ISSN 0070-5942
NEW YORK IMPORTERS. DIRECTORY. Text in English. 1949. irreg.
Published by: Commerce and Industry Association of New York, Church St, New York, NY 10007.

670.29 USA ISSN 1078-6384
HF5065.N7
NEW YORK MANUFACTURERS DIRECTORY. Text in English. 1995. a. USD 109. **Document type:** *Directory.*
Related titles: CD-ROM ed.: USD 695; Diskette ed.
Published by: Harris InfoSource International, 2057 2 E Aurora Rd, Twinsburg, OH 44087-1999. TEL 216-425-9000, 800-888-5900, FAX 216-425-7150, catknapp@aol.com. Ed. Frances L Carlsen.

670.29 USA ISSN 1096-6102
HF5065.N7
NEW YORK MANUFACTURERS REGISTER. Text in English. 1998. a. USD 149 (effective 2001). adv. charts; illus.; stat.
Document type: *Directory.* **Description:** Profiles 17,074 manufacturers in five sections: company name, product, S.I.C., city, and parent company.
Related titles: CD-ROM ed.: USD 670 (effective 2001); Diskette ed.; Online - full text ed.
Published by: Manufacturers' News, Inc., 1633 Central St, Evanston, IL 60201. TEL 847-864-7000, 888-752-5200, FAX 847-332-1100, info@mninfo.com, info@manufacturersnews.com, sales@mninfo.com, http://www.manufacturersnews.com. Ed. Frank Lambing. Adv. contact Charles Scherer. B&W page USD 1,843.

338.0029 USA ISSN 1083-9992
NEW YORK METRO BUSINESS DIRECTORY. Text in English. 1993. a. USD 1,100 combined subscription print, online & CD-ROM eds. (effective 2004 & 2005). back issues avail.
Document type: *Directory.* **Description:** Includes all businesses in the New York City metropolitan area compiled from the yellow pages and telephone-verified. Listings include company name, complete address, phone number, name of owner or manager, employee size and sales volume and credit rating codes.
Related titles: CD-ROM ed.; Diskette ed.; E-mail ed.; Fax ed.; Magnetic Tape ed.; Online - full text ed.
Published by: American Business Directories (Subsidiary of: American Business Information, Inc.), 5711 S 86th Circle, P O Box 27347, Omaha, NE 68127. TEL 402-593-4600, 888-946-9377, 877-708-3844, FAX 402-331-5481, sales@directoriesusa.com, http://www.directoriesusa.com.

NEW YORK PUBLICITY OUTLETS. see *ADVERTISING AND PUBLIC RELATIONS*

NEW YORK STATE AGENT HANDBOOK. see *INSURANCE*

NEW YORK TELEPHONE TICKLER FOR INSURANCE MEN AND WOMEN. see *INSURANCE*

658.0029 NZL ISSN 0077-9571
NEW ZEALAND BUSINESS WHO'S WHO. Text in English. 1935. a. (Mar.). NZD 331.88 domestic for print or CD-ROM ed.; NZD 363 to Australia & the S Pacific for print or CD-ROM ed.; NZD 410 elsewhere for print or CD-ROM ed.; NZD 444.38 combined subscription domestic for both print & CD-ROM eds.; NZD 463 combined subscription to Australia & the S Pacific for both print & CD-ROM eds.; NZD 510 combined subscription elsewhere for both print & CD-ROM eds. (effective 2001). adv. **Document type:** *Directory.* **Description:** Provides up-to-date facts and all the communication data needed to reach New Zealand manufactures, trade suppliers, importers and exporters.
Related titles: CD-ROM ed.
Published by: Liberty Holdings, PO Box 1881, Auckland 1, New Zealand. TEL 64-9-307-1287, 800-658-765, FAX 64-9-373-2634. Circ: 5,000.

380 363.6 NZL
NEW ZEALAND GAZETTE. SUPPLEMENT. POWER COMPANY DISCLOSURE INFORMATION. Text in English. irreg.
Document type: *Government.*
Related titles: ◆ Supplement to: New Zealand Gazette. ISSN 0111-5650.
Published by: Department of Internal Affairs, New Zealand Gazette Office, Level 13, Prime Property Tower, 86-90 Lambton Quay, PO Box 805, Wellington, New Zealand. TEL 64-4-4702930, FAX 64-4-4702932, gazette@parliament.govt.nz, http://www.gazette.govt.nz/diawebsite.nsf.

381 336.2 NZL
NEW ZEALAND GAZETTE. SUPPLEMENT. TAX EVADERS. Text in English. irreg. NZD 261 combined subscription inclds. Gazette, supplements & special eds. (effective 2005).
Document type: *Government.*
Related titles: ◆ Supplement to: New Zealand Gazette. ISSN 0111-5650.
Published by: Department of Internal Affairs, New Zealand Gazette Office, Level 13, Prime Property Tower, 86-90 Lambton Quay, PO Box 805, Wellington, New Zealand. TEL 64-4-4702930, FAX 64-4-4702932, gazette@parliament.govt.nz, http://www.gazette.govt.nz/diawebsite.nsf.

380 306.81 NZL
NEW ZEALAND GAZETTE TRADE LISTS. MARRIAGE CELEBRANTS. Text in English. irreg. NZD 15 newsstand/cover (effective 2006). **Document type:** *Government.*
Published by: Department of Internal Affairs, New Zealand Gazette Office, Level 13, Prime Property Tower, 86-90 Lambton Quay, PO Box 805, Wellington, New Zealand. TEL 64-4-4702930, FAX 64-4-4702932, gazette@parliament.govt.nz, http://www.gazette.govt.nz/diawebsite.nsf.

381.029 351 NZL
NEW ZEALAND GAZETTE TRADE LISTS. PUBLIC VALUERS. Text in English. irreg. NZD 15 (effective 2005). **Document type:** *Government.*
Published by: Department of Internal Affairs, New Zealand Gazette Office, Level 13, Prime Property Tower, 86-90 Lambton Quay, PO Box 805, Wellington, New Zealand. TEL 64-4-4702930, FAX 64-4-4702932, gazette@parliament.govt.nz, http://www.gazette.govt.nz/diawebsite.nsf.

381.029 620 NZL
NEW ZEALAND GAZETTE TRADE LISTS. REGISTER OF ENGINEERS. Text in English. irreg. **Document type:** *Government.*
Published by: Department of Internal Affairs, New Zealand Gazette Office, Level 13, Prime Property Tower, 86-90 Lambton Quay, PO Box 805, Wellington, New Zealand. TEL 64-4-4702930, FAX 64-4-4702932, gazette@parliament.govt.nz, http://www.gazette.govt.nz/diawebsite.nsf.

380 615 NZL
NEW ZEALAND GAZETTE TRADE LISTS. REGISTER OF PHARMACIES. Text in English. irreg. NZD 15 newsstand/cover (effective 2005). **Document type:** *Government.*
Published by: Department of Internal Affairs, New Zealand Gazette Office, Level 13, Prime Property Tower, 86-90 Lambton Quay, PO Box 805, Wellington, New Zealand. TEL 64-4-4702930, FAX 64-4-4702932, gazette@parliament.govt.nz, http://www.gazette.govt.nz/diawebsite.nsf.

NEW ZEALAND NURSERY REGISTER. see *GARDENING AND HORTICULTURE—Florist Trade*

381.029 NZL ISSN 1175-0219
NEW ZEALAND TRADE DIRECTORY. Text in English. 1994. a., latest 5th Edition, 2000-2001. USD 120 foreign (effective 2001). 528 p./no.; **Document type:** *Directory, Trade.*
Description: Lists a cross-section of businesses in New Zealand involved in domestic and international commerce. Also lists schools, government agencies, and chambers of commerce and trade organizations.
Published by: Current Pacific Ltd., PO Box 36-536, Northcote, Auckland, New Zealand.

670.29 NZL ISSN 1173-907X
NEW ZEALAND TRAVEL INDUSTRY DIRECTORY. Text in English. 1968. a. NZD 50; NZD 90 includes Traveltrade (effective 2000). adv. **Document type:** *Directory.* **Description:** Contains listings of all key travel suppliers and their products.
Formerly (until 1996): Travel Executives of New Zealand (1172-3084)
Published by: (Travel Agents Association of New Zealand), T.P.L. Media (Trade Publications), 308 Great South Rd, Greenlane, Auckland, New Zealand. TEL 64-9-5293000, FAX 64-9-529-3001. Ed. Alan Titchall.

338.0029 USA ISSN 1071-8931
PN4899.W304
NEWS MEDIA YELLOW BOOK; who's who among reporters, writers, editors and producers in the leading national news media. Text in English. 1990. q. USD 400; USD 380 renewals (effective 2005). Index. **Document type:** *Directory, Trade.*
Description: Contact information for over 34,000 journalists at over 2,700 news services, networks, newspapers, television and radio stations, as well as independent journalists and syndicated columnists. Includes assignment, program, periodical, geographic, personnel and major indexes.
Formerly (until 1994): News Media Yellow Book of Washington and New York (1043-2620)
Related titles: CD-ROM ed.: (from Chadwyck-Healey Inc.); Online - full text ed.
—CCC.
Published by: Leadership Directories, Inc, 104 Fifth Ave, 2nd Fl, New York, NY 10011. TEL 212-627-4140, FAX 212-645-0931, info@leadershipdirectories.com, http://www.leadershipdirectories.com/nmyb.htm. Ed. Laura Gibbons. Pub. David J Hurvits.

338.0029 NGA ISSN 1116-1027
HC1055.A1
NIGERIA INDUSTRIAL DIRECTORY. Text in English. 1975. irreg. NGN 200. adv. **Document type:** *Directory.*
Formerly: Manufacturers Association of Nigeria. Industrial Directory
Published by: Malthouse Press Ltd., 8 Amore St off Toyin St, PO Box 8917, Ikeja, Lagos, Nigeria. Circ: 5,000 (controlled).

NIGERIAN YELLOW PAGES. see *BUSINESS AND ECONOMICS—Office Equipment And Services*

338.0029 JPN
NIKKEI CORPORATE GUIDE. Text in Japanese. a. **Description:** Provides detailed data and analysis on 2,600 companies, as well as information on securities and life insurance companies.
Published by: Nihon Keizai Shimbun Inc., 1-9-5 Ote-Machi, Chiyoda-ku, Tokyo, 100-0004, Japan. TEL 81-3-32700251, FAX 81-3-52552661.

380.1029 USA ISSN 1520-9148
HD2769.2.U6
NONPROFIT SECTOR YELLOW BOOK; who's who in the management of the leading foundations, universities, museums and other nonprofit organizations. Text in English. 1999. s-a. USD 295; USD 280 renewals (effective 2005). illus. Index. **Document type:** *Directory, Trade.* **Description:** Offers detailed contact and biographical information for more than 50,000 executives and trustees, at over 1,300 nonprofit institutions, in eight areas of the nonprofit sector.
Related titles: CD-ROM ed.; Online - full text ed.
—CCC.
Published by: Leadership Directories, Inc, 104 Fifth Ave, 2nd Fl, New York, NY 10011. TEL 212-627-4140, FAX 212-645-0931, info@leadershipdirectories.com, http://www.leadershipdirectories.com/nsyb.htm. Pub. David J Hurvits.

677.6029 GBR ISSN 0963-701X
NONWOVENS REPORT YEARBOOK. Text in English. 1978. a. GBP 95 per issue domestic; GBP 105 per issue foreign (effective 2005). **Document type:** *Directory, Trade.*
Description: Annual industry review and directory of companies involved in the European nonwovens industries.
Published by: World Textile Publications Ltd., Perkin House, 1 Longlands St, Bradford, W Yorks BD1 2TP, United Kingdom. TEL 44-1274-378800, FAX 44-1274-378811, info@world-textile.net, http://www.world-textile.net/contact.html.

NORDDEUTSCHER MOLKEREI- UND KAESEREI-ADRESSKALENDER; Milchwirtschaft zum Nachschlagen. see *AGRICULTURE—Dairying And Dairy Products*

NORDIC NETWORK. see *SPORTS AND GAMES—Outdoor Life*

663.3029 USA
NORTH AMERICAN BREWERS RESOURCE DIRECTORY. Text in English. 1986. a. USD 100. adv.
Published by: (Institute for Brewing Studies), Association of Brewers, Brewers Publications, PO Box 1679, Boulder, CO 80306-1679. TEL 303-447-0816, FAX 303-447-2825, http://beertown.org/bp.

332.1029 USA ISSN 1529-1367
HG1536
NORTH AMERICAN FINANCIAL INSTITUTIONS DIRECTORY. Text in English. 1894. 2/yr. USD 380 per issue (effective 2001). adv. bk.rev. **Document type:** *Directory, Trade.*
Former titles (until 2000): Polk North American Financial Institutions Directory (1528-8862); (until 1998): Polk's Bank Directory. North American Edition (1058-0611); (until 1982): Polk's World Bank Directory. North American Edition
Related titles: Diskette ed.: 1894; Magnetic Tape ed.: 1894.
Published by: Thomson Financial Services Company, 4709 W Golf Rd, Skokie, IL 60076-1256. TEL 847-676-9600, 800-321-3373, FAX 847-933-8101, prodinfo@tfp.com, customerservice@tfp.com, http://www.tfp.com/banks. Circ: 18,500.

NORTH AMERICAN SUPPLY, DISTRIBUTION, MANUFACTURING AND SERVICE. see *PETROLEUM AND GAS*

380.1029 USA
NORTH CAROLINA BUSINESS CREDIT DIRECTORY. Text in English. a. USD 1,100 combined subscription print, online & CD-ROM eds. (effective 2004 & 2005). back issues avail. **Document type:** *Directory.* **Description:** Contains credit ratings and other valuable information on all businesses within North Carolina. Includes company name & address, phone & fax numbers, key executive names & titles, lines of business, years in business, number of employees, estimated annual sales, volume credit rating code, and corporate linkage information.
Related titles: CD-ROM ed.; Diskette ed.; E-mail ed.; Fax ed.; Magnetic Tape ed.; Online - full text ed.
Published by: American Business Directories (Subsidiary of: American Business Information, Inc.), 5711 S 86th Circle, P O Box 27347, Omaha, NE 68127. TEL 402-593-4600, 888-946-9377, 877-708-3844, FAX 402-331-5481, sales@directoriesusa.com, http://www.directoriesusa.com.

338.0029 USA ISSN 1046-9060
HC107.N8
NORTH CAROLINA BUSINESS DIRECTORY. Text in English. 1988. a. USD 1,100 combined subscription print, online & CD-ROM eds. (effective 2004 & 2005). index. back issues avail. **Document type:** *Directory.* **Description:** Includes all businesses in the state compiled from the yellow pages and telephone-verified. Each listing includes company name, complete address, phone number, name of owner, manager, and employee size, sales volume codes, and credit rating codes.
Related titles: CD-ROM ed.; Diskette ed.; E-mail ed.; Fax ed.; Magnetic Tape ed.; Online - full text ed.
Published by: American Business Directories (Subsidiary of: American Business Information, Inc.), 5711 S 86th Circle, P O Box 27347, Omaha, NE 68127. TEL 402-593-4600, 888-946-9377, 877-708-3844, FAX 402-331-5481, sales@directoriesusa.com, http://www.directoriesusa.com.

380.1029 USA
NORTH CAROLINA DIRECTORY OF TRADE AND PROFESSIONAL ASSOCIATIONS. Text in English. 1976. biennial. USD 64.50 (effective 2000). **Document type:** *Directory.*
Published by: University of North Carolina at Greensboro, Center for Applied Research, 301 Bryan Bldg, Greensboro, NC 27402-6165. TEL 336-334-3088, FAX 336-334-4272, john_redmond@uncg.edu, http://www.uncg.edu/bae/car. Ed. John G Redmond. R&P Pattie Hollinger.

670.29 USA
HF5065.N8
NORTH CAROLINA MANUFACTURERS DIRECTORY. Text in English. 1993. a. USD 75. **Document type:** *Directory.*
Formerly: Directory of North Carolina Manufacturing Firms (1065-4720)
Related titles: CD-ROM ed.: USD 395; Diskette ed.
Published by: Harris InfoSource International, 2057 2 E Aurora Rd, Twinsburg, OH 44087-1999. TEL 216-425-9000, 800-888-5900, FAX 216-425-7150, catknapp@aol.com. Ed. Frances L Carlsen.

670.29 USA ISSN 1073-2128
HF5065.N8
NORTH CAROLINA MANUFACTURERS REGISTER. Text in English. 1994. a. USD 115 (effective 2001). 992 p./no.; **Document type:** *Directory.* **Description:** Profiles 12,472 companies in five sections: by name, SIC, city, product and parent company.
Related titles: CD-ROM ed.: USD 580 (effective 2000); Diskette ed.
Published by: Manufacturers' News, Inc., 1633 Central St, Evanston, IL 60201. TEL 847-864-7000, 888-752-5200, FAX 847-332-1100, info@mninfo.com, info@manufacturersnews.com, sales@mninfo.com, http://www.manufacturersnews.com. Ed. Steve Garland.

(YEAR) NORTH CAROLINA METAL PROCESSORS DIRECTORY. see *MACHINERY*

338.0029 USA ISSN 1046-8129
HF5065.N9
NORTH DAKOTA BUSINESS DIRECTORY. Text in English. 1984. a. USD 1,100 combined subscription print, online & CD-ROM eds. (effective 2004 & 2005). index. back issues avail. **Document type:** *Directory.* **Description:** Lists all businesses in the state; company name, complete address, phone number, name of owner, manager, and employee size, sales volume codes, and credit rating codes.
Related titles: CD-ROM ed.; Diskette ed.; E-mail ed.; Fax ed.; Magnetic Tape ed.; Online - full text ed.
Published by: American Business Directories (Subsidiary of: American Business Information, Inc.), 5711 S 86th Circle, P O Box 27347, Omaha, NE 68127. TEL 402-593-4600, 888-946-9377, 877-708-3844, FAX 402-331-5481, sales@directoriesusa.com, http://www.directoriesusa.com.

670.29 USA ISSN 1087-8343
HF5065.N9
NORTH DAKOTA MANUFACTURERS REGISTER. Text in English. a. USD 58 (effective 2002). 136 p./no.; **Document type:** *Directory.* **Description:** Profiles1,106 companies.
Related titles: CD-ROM ed.: North Dakota Manufacturers Register for Windows 95 & Up, Windows N T. ISSN 1550-0853. USD 179 (effective 2001); Diskette ed.
Published by: Manufacturers' News, Inc., 1633 Central St, Evanston, IL 60201. TEL 847-864-7000, 888-752-5200, FAX 847-332-1100, info@mninfo.com, info@manufacturersnews.com, sales@mninfo.com, http://www.manufacturersnews.com. Ed. Steve Garland.

NORTH - SOUTH CAROLINA STATE AGENT HANDBOOK. see *INSURANCE*

380.1029 GBR
NORTH WEST ENGLAND DIRECTORY OF INDUSTRY & COMMERCE. Text in English. a. GBP 49 (effective 2001). **Document type:** *Directory.*
Published by: Kemps Publishing Ltd., 11 Swan Courtyard, Charles Edward Rd, Birmingham, W Mids B26 1BU, United Kingdom. TEL 44-121-765-4144, FAX 44-121-706-6210.

NORTHEAST STATES PETROLEUM INDUSTRY. see *PETROLEUM AND GAS*

338.0029 USA ISSN 1063-4177
HF5065.C2
NORTHERN CALIFORNIA BUSINESS DIRECTORY. Text in English. 1992. a. USD 1,100 combined subscription print, online & CD-ROM eds. (effective 2004 & 2005). index. back issues avail. **Document type:** *Directory.* **Description:** Includes all businesses in the Northern California area compiled from the yellow pages and telephone-verified. Each listing includes company name, complete address, phone number, name of owner, manager, and employee size, sales volume codes, and credit rating codes.
Related titles: CD-ROM ed.; Diskette ed.; E-mail ed.; Fax ed.; Magnetic Tape ed.; Online - full text ed.
Published by: American Business Directories (Subsidiary of: American Business Information, Inc.), 5711 S 86th Circle, P O Box 27347, Omaha, NE 68127. TEL 402-593-4600, 888-946-9377, 877-708-3844, FAX 402-331-5481, karen.peters@infousa.com, sales@directoriesusa.com, http://www.directoriesusa.com.

338.0029 USA ISSN 1052-8822
HF5065.C2
NORTHERN CALIFORNIA BUSINESS DIRECTORY AND BUYERS GUIDE✶. Text in English. 1991. a. USD 169. **Document type:** *Directory.* **Description:** Contains profiles of 26,000 manufacturers, wholesalers, distributors and service companies in Northern California.
Related titles: CD-ROM ed.: USD 595.
Published by: Database Publishing Company, 701 E Ball Rd Ste 100, Anaheim, CA 92805-5962. TEL 714-778-6400, FAX 714-778-6811. Ed., R&P Sarah Fraser. Circ: 750.

381.029 GBR
NORTHERN IRELAND TRADE DIRECTORY. Text in English. 1997. biennial. USD 150. adv. **Document type:** *Directory.* **Description:** Contains company names, addresses, telephone and fax numbers, contact names, number of employees, products, services, and quality assurance certificates for each company listed.
Related titles: CD-ROM ed.
Published by: Business to Business Publications, The King Bldg, 152 Albertbridge Rd, Belfast, BT5 4GS, United Kingdom. TEL 44-1232-455775, FAX 44-1232-461924, nitradededirectory@unite.co.uk. Ed. J V Herron. Adv. contact Lorna Thomson. page GBP 1,900. Circ: 5,000 (controlled).

NORTHWEST HIGH TECH DATABASE. see *COMPUTERS—Computer Industry Directories*

NORTHWESTERN LUMBER ASSOCIATION DEALER REFERENCE MANUAL AND BUYER'S GUIDE. see *FORESTS AND FORESTRY—Lumber And Wood*

631.52029 USA
O A N DIRECTORY & BUYER'S GUIDE. Text in English. 1961. a. USD 7.50 (effective 1999). adv. illus. **Document type:** *Directory, Trade.* **Description:** Provides more than 20000 listings of plants, products and services for the national nursery, greenhouse and landscape gardening trades.
Published by: Oregon Association of Nurseries, 2780 S.E. Harrison, Ste. 102, Milwaukie, OR 97222. TEL 503-653-8733, FAX 503-653-3956. Ed. Don Grey. Adv. contact Geoff Horning. Circ: 6,500 (controlled).

540.29 USA ISSN 0276-539X
TP12 CODEN: OCBDDH
O P D CHEMICAL BUYERS DIRECTORY. Text in English. 1913. a. included in Chemical Market Reporter. **Document type:** *Directory.*
Formerly: Chemical Buyers Directory
—BLDSC (6265.850000), CASDDS, CISTI, IE, Infotrieve. **CCC.**
Published by: Schnell Publishing Co., Inc. (Subsidiary of: Reed Business Information), Two Rector St, 26th Fl, New York, NY 10006. TEL 212-791-4200, FAX 212-791-4321, http://www.opdsearch.com/. Ed. Helga Tilton TEL 212-791-4231. Pub. Trevor Goodman. Circ: 17,000.

382.029 GBR
O P M A OVERSEAS MEDIA GUIDE. Text in English. 1965. a. GBP 50 (effective 2000). adv. **Document type:** *Directory.*
Formerly (until 1987): Overseas Media Guide (0078-7132)
Published by: Overseas Press and Media Association, c/o Richard Anthony & Co, 13 Station Rd, Finchley, London, N3 2SB, United Kingdom. TEL 44-1223-512631, http://www.opma.co.uk. Ed., Pub., R&P, Adv. contact Jackie Dunn. Circ: 5,000 (controlled).

OCCUPATIONAL HEALTH & SAFETY NEWS. see *OCCUPATIONAL HEALTH AND SAFETY*

338.0029 USA ISSN 0149-1091
HD59
O'DWYER'S DIRECTORY OF CORPORATE COMMUNICATIONS. Text in English. 1975. a. USD 130 (effective 2001). adv. stat. index. **Document type:** *Directory, Trade.*
Published by: J.R. O'Dwyer Co., Inc., 271 Madison Ave, Ste 600, New York, NY 10016. TEL 212-679-2471, john@odwyerpr.com, http://www.odwyerpr.com. Ed. Jack O'Dwyer. Adv. contact Michael Rose.

659.1029 USA ISSN 0191-0051
HD59
O'DWYER'S DIRECTORY OF PUBLIC RELATIONS EXECUTIVES. Text in English. 1979. triennial. USD 120 (effective 2001). **Document type:** *Directory, Trade.*
Published by: J.R. O'Dwyer Co., Inc., 271 Madison Ave, Ste 600, New York, NY 10016. TEL 212-679-2471, john@odwyerpr.com, http://www.odwyerpr.com. Ed. Jack O'Dwyer.

659.1029 USA ISSN 0078-3374
HM263
O'DWYER'S DIRECTORY OF PUBLIC RELATIONS FIRMS. Text in English. 1969. a. USD 175 (effective 2001). adv. **Document type:** *Directory, Trade.*
Published by: J.R. O'Dwyer Co., Inc., 271 Madison Ave, Ste 600, New York, NY 10016. TEL 212-679-2471, john@odwyerpr.com, http://www.odwyerpr.com. Ed. Jack O'Dwyer. Adv. contact Michael Rose. Circ: 2,000.

659.1029 USA
O'DWYER'S NEW YORK PUBLIC RELATIONS DIRECTORY. Text in English. triennial. USD 50 (effective 2001). adv. **Document type:** *Directory, Trade.* **Description:** Contains extensive information on the public relations industry in New York.
Published by: J.R. O'Dwyer Co., Inc., 271 Madison Ave, Ste 600, New York, NY 10016. TEL 212-679-2471, john@odwyerpr.com, http://www.odwyerpr.com. Ed. Jack O'Dwyer. Adv. contact Michael Rose.

OFF-PRICE RETAIL DIRECTORY. see *BUSINESS AND ECONOMICS—Marketing And Purchasing*

OFFICE DEALER; updating the office products industry. see *BUSINESS AND ECONOMICS—Office Equipment And Services*

OFFICIAL BRITISH THEATRE DIRECTORY SEATING PLAN GUIDE. see *THEATER*

OFFICIAL DIRECTORY OF NEW JERSEY LIBRARIES AND MEDIA CENTERS; a quick reference to libraries and media centers in NJ. see *LIBRARY AND INFORMATION SCIENCES*

658.0029 USA
OFFICIAL DISTRIBUTION AND WAREHOUSE DIRECTORY. Text in English. s-a. USD 50.50. **Description:** Includes profiles on warehouse, distribution, logistic, and third-party firms.
Published by: Official Motor Freight Guide, Inc., 1700 W Cortland St, Chicago, IL 60622-1150. TEL 773-278-2454, FAX 773-489-0482. Circ: 6,500.

380.1029 USA
OFFICIAL INTERMODAL GUIDE; directory of intermodal services, facilities and personnel. Text in English. 1983. 2/yr. USD 261 (effective 1998). adv. **Document type:** *Directory.* **Description:** Profiles most intermodal facilities. Company names, contact personnel, addresses and phone numbers are provided.
Published by: Commonwealth Business Media, Inc., 400 Windsor Corporate Ctr, 50 Millstone Rd, Ste 200, East Windsor, NJ 08520-1415. TEL 609-371-7700, FAX 609-371-7883. Ed. Teri Schneider. Pub., R&P, Adv. contact John G John III. Circ: 2,200.

670.29 USA ISSN 1056-6872
T12
OFFICIAL IOWA MANUFACTURERS DIRECTORY. Text in English. 1994. a. USD 67. **Document type:** *Directory.*
Related titles: CD-ROM ed.: USD 325; Diskette ed.

B

Published by: Harris InfoSource International, 2057 2 E Aurora Rd, Twinsburg, OH 44087-1999. TEL 216-425-9000, 800-888-5900, FAX 216-425-7150, catknapp@aol.com. Ed. Frances L Carlsen.

384.558029 USA ISSN 0890-782X
HD9696.V533
OFFICIAL VIDEO DIRECTORY & BUYER'S GUIDE. Text in English. 1987. a. USD 125. adv. **Document type:** *Directory.* **Description:** Sourcebook of suppliers and manufacturers of video hardware and software.
Published by: Talent & Booking Online, PO Box 14265, Palm Desert, CA 92255. TEL 760-779-8056, FAX 760-773-3568, info@talentandbooking.com, http://www.talentandbooking.com. Ed. Steve Tolin. Circ: 6,000.

380.1029 USA
OHIO BUSINESS CREDIT DIRECTORY. Text in English. a. USD 1,100 combined subscription print, online & CD-ROM eds. (effective 2004 & 2005). back issues avail. **Document type:** *Directory.* **Description:** Contains credit ratings and other valuable information on all businesses within Ohio. Includes company name & address, phone & fax numbers, key executive names & titles, lines of business, years in business, number of employees, estimated annual sales, volume credit rating code, and corporate linkage information.
Related titles: CD-ROM ed.; Diskette ed.; E-mail ed.; Fax ed.; Magnetic Tape ed.; Online - full text ed.
Published by: American Business Directories (Subsidiary of: American Business Information, Inc.), 5711 S 86th Circle, P O Box 27347, Omaha, NE 68127. TEL 402-593-4600, 888-946-9377, 877-708-3844, FAX 402-331-5481, sales@directoriesusa.com, http://www.directoriesusa.com.

338.0029 USA ISSN 1048-7360
HF5065.O3
OHIO BUSINESS DIRECTORY. Text in English. 1989. a. USD 1,100 combined subscription print, online & CD-ROM eds. (effective 2004 & 2005). index. back issues avail. **Document type:** *Directory.* **Description:** Includes all business in the state compiled from the yellow pages and telephone-verified. Each listing includes company name, complete address, phone number, name of owner, manager, and employee size, sales volume codes, and credit rating codes.
Related titles: CD-ROM ed.; Diskette ed.; E-mail ed.; Fax ed.; Magnetic Tape ed.; Online - full text ed.
Published by: American Business Directories (Subsidiary of: American Business Information, Inc.), 5711 S 86th Circle, P O Box 27347, Omaha, NE 68127. TEL 402-593-4600, 888-946-9377, 877-708-3844, FAX 402-331-5481, sales@directoriesusa.com, http://www.directoriesusa.com.

670.29 USA ISSN 0737-7495
HD9727.O3
OHIO MANUFACTURERS DIRECTORY. Text in English. 1983. a. USD 167 (effective 2000). adv. **Document type:** *Directory.* **Description:** Lists 22,760 manufacturers by product, alphabetically, geographically by SIC and parent co.
Related titles: CD-ROM ed.: USD 670 (effective 2000); Diskette ed.: USD 745.
Published by: Manufacturers' News, Inc., 1633 Central St, Evanston, IL 60201. TEL 847-864-7000, 888-752-5200, FAX 847-332-1100, info@mninfo.com, info@manufacturersnews.com, sales@mninfo.com, http://www.manufacturersnews.com. Ed. Frank Lambing. Adv. contact Charles Scherer. B&W page USD 1,843.

670.29 USA ISSN 0884-173X
HD9727.O3
OHIO REGISTER OF MANUFACTURERS. Text in English. 1983. a. USD 92.50. adv. illus. **Document type:** *Directory.* **Description:** Profiles over 12,000 manufacturers and their key executives in five different sections: alphabetically, geographically by city, by SIC.
Formerly: Ohio Directory of Manufacturers (0738-3711)
Related titles: Diskette ed.; Magnetic Tape ed.
Published by: Commerce Register, Inc., 190 Godwin Ave, Midland Park, NJ 07432. TEL 201-445-3000, FAX 201-445-5806.

OIL & GAS DIRECTORY. see *PETROLEUM AND GAS*

OILS AND FATS INTERNATIONAL DIRECTORY. see *CHEMISTRY—Organic Chemistry*

338.0029 IND
OKHLA & NEHRU PLACE DIRECTORY; the authentic industrial & business intelligence. Text in English. 1986. irreg., latest vol.4, 1995. INR 225, USD 15. **Document type:** *Directory, Trade.*
Published by: Businesslinks, 3, DSIDC Complex, Okhla Phase-1, New Delhi, 110 020, India. TEL 6819111. Ed. A Azim Siddigui. adv.: page INR 3,000; 210 x 160. Circ: 10,000.

338.0029 USA ISSN 1048-7379
HF5065.O5
OKLAHOMA BUSINESS DIRECTORY. Text in English. 1987. a. USD 1,100 combined subscription print, online & CD-ROM eds. (effective 2004 & 2005). index. back issues avail. **Document type:** *Directory.* **Description:** Includes all businesses in the state compiled from the yellow pages and telephone-verified. Each listing includes company name, complete address, phone number, name of owner, manager, and employee size, sales volume codes and credit rating codes.
Related titles: CD-ROM ed.; Diskette ed.; E-mail ed.; Fax ed.; Magnetic Tape ed.; Online - full text ed.
Published by: American Business Directories (Subsidiary of: American Business Information, Inc.), 5711 S 86th Circle, P O Box 27347, Omaha, NE 68127. TEL 402-593-4600, 888-946-9377, 877-708-3844, FAX 402-331-5481, sales@directoriesusa.com, http://www.directoriesusa.com.

338.0029 USA ISSN 1051-919X
HD9727.O5
OKLAHOMA DIRECTORY OF MANUFACTURERS AND PROCESSORS. Text in English. 1957. a. USD 69. **Document type:** *Directory, Government.*
Published by: Department of Commerce, PO Box 26980, Oklahoma City, OK 73126-0980. TEL 405-815-6552, FAX 405-815-5199. Circ: 4,000.

670.29 USA ISSN 1059-4523
HF5065.O5
OKLAHOMA MANUFACTURERS REGISTER. Text in English. 1992. a. USD 77 (effective 2000). adv. **Document type:** *Directory.* **Description:** Lists 5,993 manufacturers by industrial product, alphabetically, by SIC code and geographically and by parent company.
Related titles: CD-ROM ed.: USD 399 (effective 2000); Diskette ed.: USD 395.
Published by: Manufacturers' News, Inc., 1633 Central St, Evanston, IL 60201. TEL 847-864-7000, 888-752-5200, FAX 847-332-1100, info@mninfo.com, info@manufacturersnews.com, sales@mninfo.com, http://www.manufacturersnews.com. Ed. Frank Lambing. Adv. contact Charles Scherer. B&W page USD 1,843. Circ: 1,429.

011.3 DEU
HF54.5
ONLINE - CD-ROM BUSINESS SOURCEBOOK. Text in English. 1986. a. GBP 175 (effective 2001). **Document type:** *Directory, Trade.* **Description:** Provides a one-stop guide to more than 700 business databases and 59 leading hosts.
Formerly (until 1993): Online Business Sourcebook (0953-5055)
Published by: K.G. Saur Verlag GmbH (Subsidiary of: Gale Group), Ortlerstr 8, Munchen, 81373, Germany. TEL 49-89-769020, FAX 49-89-76902150, info@saur.de, http://www.saur.de. Ed. Pamela Foster.

380.1029 071.1 USA ISSN 1203-5246
HF5072.O58
ONTARIO BUSINESS DIRECTORY. Text in English. 1996. a. USD 1,100 combined subscription print, online & CD-ROM eds. (effective 2004 & 2005). back issues avail. **Document type:** *Directory.*
Related titles: CD-ROM ed.; Diskette ed.; E-mail ed.; Fax ed.; Magnetic Tape ed.; Online - full text ed.
Published by: American Business Directories (Subsidiary of: American Business Information, Inc.), 5711 S 86th Circle, P O Box 27347, Omaha, NE 68127. TEL 402-593-4600, 888-946-9377, 877-708-3844, FAX 402-331-5481, sales@directoriesusa.com, http://www.directoriesusa.com.

338.0029 CAN ISSN 1483-2615
KE214
ONTARIO LEGAL DIRECTORY. Text in English. 1925. a. USD 53 per issue (effective 2005). adv. **Document type:** *Directory, Trade.* **Description:** Contains a list of the lawyers, practising in Ontario, along with a 'blue pages' section of courts, related government, and paralegal information, with contact information.
Formerly: Toronto Legal Directory (0317-588X)
Related titles: CD-ROM ed.: ISSN 1481-4064.
Published by: University of Toronto Press, Reference Division, 10 St Mary St, Ste 700, Toronto, ON M4Y 2W8, Canada. TEL 416-978-2239, FAX 416-978-4738, utpbooks@utpress.utoronto.ca, http://www.utppublishing.com/reference/old.html, http://www.utpress.utoronto.ca. Eds. Gillian Holmes, Lynn Burdon.

OPERA AMERICA. DIRECTORY OF PRODUCTION MATERIALS FOR RENT (YEAR). see *MUSIC*

670.29 GBR
OPUS DESIGN FILE. Text in English. 1984. a. GBP 55 domestic; GBP 65 overseas. **Document type:** *Trade.*
Formerly: Opus Building Services Design File (0266-1063)
—CISTI. **CCC.**
Published by: Builder Group plc., Exchange Tower, 2 Harbour Exchange Sq, London, E14 9GE, United Kingdom. TEL 44-20-7560-4000, FAX 44-20-7560-4404. Circ: 13,900. **Subscr. to:** Building, Freepost (LE6522), Leicstter LE87 4DH, United Kingdom. TEL 01858-468811.

338.0029 USA ISSN 1059-7077
HF5065.C2
ORANGE COUNTY BUSINESS AND INDUSTRIAL DIRECTORY✶. Text in English. a. USD 75. **Document type:** *Directory.* **Description:** Lists 6,500 companies including 3,000 manufacturing firms and 15,250 top executives.
Former titles: Orange County Business Directory; Orange County Commerce and Industry Directory
Published by: Database Publishing Company, 701 E Ball Rd Ste 100, Anaheim, CA 92805-5962. TEL 714-778-6400, FAX 714-778-6811. R&P Sarah Fraser.

338.0029 USA ISSN 1047-8809
HF5065.O7
OREGON BUSINESS DIRECTORY. Text in English. 1989. a. USD 1,100 combined subscription print, online & CD-ROM eds. (effective 2004 & 2005). index. back issues avail. **Document type:** *Directory.* **Description:** Includes all businesses in the state compiled from the yellow pages and telephone-verified. Each listing includes company name, complete address, phone number, name of owner, manager, and employee size, sales volume codes and credit rating codes.
Related titles: CD-ROM ed.; Diskette ed.; E-mail ed.; Fax ed.; Magnetic Tape ed.; Online - full text ed.
Published by: American Business Directories (Subsidiary of: American Business Information, Inc.), 5711 S 86th Circle, P O Box 27347, Omaha, NE 68127. TEL 402-593-4600, 888-946-9377, 877-708-3844, FAX 402-331-5481, sales@directoriesusa.com, http://www.directoriesusa.com.

670.29 USA ISSN 1525-4097
HF5065.O7
OREGON MANUFACTURERS REGISTER✶. Text in English. 1994. a. USD 110 (effective 2000). adv. **Document type:** *Directory.* **Description:** Profiles 7,300 manufacturing and high tech firms and 16,300 CEO's and key executives.
Formerly: Oregon Manufacturers Directory (1071-6890)
Related titles: CD-ROM ed.: USD 445 (effective 2000).
Published by: (Oregon. Department of Economic Development), Database Publishing Company, 701 E Ball Rd Ste 100, Anaheim, CA 92805-5962. TEL 714-778-6400, FAX 714-778-6811, info@mninfo.com, http://www.manufacturersnews.com. Ed., R&P Sarah Fraser. Adv. contact Sheila Mallough. Circ: 1,600. **Dist. by:** Manufacturers' News, Inc., 1633 Central St, Evanston, IL 60201. TEL 847-864-7000, 888-752-5200, FAX 847-332-1100, info@manufacturersnews.com, sales@mninfo.com, http://www.manufacturersnews.com.

ORGANIC PAGES; (Year) North American Resource Directory. see *FOOD AND FOOD INDUSTRIES*

613.029 GBR
ORGANISATIONS CONCERNED WITH HEALTH AND SAFETY INFORMATION. Text in English. a. **Document type:** *Directory.* **Description:** Contains details of organizations concerned with health and safety and related areas.
Formerly (until 1998): Directory of Organisations Concerned with Health and Safety Information
Published by: Health and Safety Executive, Rose Ct, 2 Southwark Bridge, London, SE1 9HS, United Kingdom. TEL 44-1541-545500, FAX 44-114-2892333, http://www.open.gov.uk/hse/org/org98.htm. Ed. Anne Darvill.

OUTLET PROJECT DIRECTORY. see *BUSINESS AND ECONOMICS—Marketing And Purchasing*

OUTLET RETAIL DIRECTORY. see *BUSINESS AND ECONOMICS—Marketing And Purchasing*

382.029 GBR
OVERSEAS TRADE DIRECTORIES; who's who, press guides, year books. Text in English. 1947. irreg. GBP 38, USD 50. adv. **Document type:** *Directory.*
Related titles: Microfilm ed.: (from PQC).
Published by: New Product Newsletter Co. Ltd., 1a Chesterfield St, London, W1X 7HF, United Kingdom. Ed. H R Vaughan. Circ: 5,000.

P A T C A DIRECTORY OF CONSULTANTS. see *BUSINESS AND ECONOMICS—Small Business*

P C P C I MEMBERSHIP DIRECTORY AND PRODUCT LISTING. see *ENGINEERING—Electrical Engineering*

658.0029 USA
P M A DIRECTORY. Text in English. 1968. a. USD 50 (effective 2000). adv. **Document type:** *Directory.* **Description:** Provides a listing of members and property management resources.
Published by: Property Management Association, 7900 Wisconsin Ave, Ste 204, Bethesda, MD 20814-3601. TEL 301-657-9200. Ed. Thomas B Cohn. Adv. contact Sharla V Warren. Circ: 2,500.

665.5029 USA ISSN 1042-4865
HD9567.A17
PACIFIC - MOUNTAIN OIL DIRECTORY. Text in English. 1988. a. adv. back issues avail. **Document type:** *Directory.*
Related titles: Special ed(s).: Pacific - Mountain Oil Directory. Buyer's Guide.

Published by: Atlantic Communications, 1635 W Alabama, Houston, TX 77006. TEL 713-529-1616, FAX 713-520-0936. Ed. Janis Johnson. Pub. Shawn Wymes. Adv. contact Rob Garza. Circ: 7,750.

380.1029   USA   ISSN 0555-8581
PACIFIC SOUTHWEST DIRECTORY. Text in English. 1951. a. USD 60; USD 60 foreign (effective 1999). adv. back issues avail. **Document type:** *Directory.* **Description:** Includes names of representatives from firm, address, types of business, phone and fax numbers. The listing are members and nonmembers alike in the grain and feed industry.
Published by: California Grain & Feed Association, 1521 I St, Sacramento, CA 95814-2016. TEL 916-441-2272, FAX 916-446-1063. Ed. D J Gutierrez. adv.: B&W page USD 260; trim 3.5 x 4.13. Circ: 900 (paid).

910.029   AUS   ISSN 0311-0826
PACIFIC TRAVEL DIRECTORY. Text in English. 1973. a. AUD 7.50. **Document type:** *Directory.*
Address: c/o Pacific Airlines News, PO Box 1, Surfers Paradise, QLD 4217, Australia. Ed. A H McRobbie.

PACKAGING DIGEST MACHINERY - MATERIALS GUIDE. see *PACKAGING*

PACKAGING INDUSTRY DIRECTORY. see *PACKAGING*

PAINT & DECORATING RETAILER'S DECORATING REGISTRY. see *INTERIOR DESIGN AND DECORATION*

PAINT & DECORATING RETAILER'S DIRECTORY OF THE WALLCOVERING INDUSTRY; the gold book. see *INTERIOR DESIGN AND DECORATION*

382.029   PAK
PAKISTAN TRADE DIRECTORY - EXPORTERS AND MANUFACTURERS. Text in English. 1952. irreg. PKR 400, USD 42. adv. **Document type:** *Directory.*
Former titles: Directory of Exporters and Manufacturers; Directory of Pakistan Exporters
Published by: Publishers International, Bandukwala Bldg., No. 4, I.I. Chundrigar Rd., Karachi, Pakistan. Ed. Kamaluddin Ahmed. Circ: 10,000.

338.0029   USA
PAPERBOARD PACKAGING BUYER'S GUIDE. Text in English. a. USD 35 (effective 2004). back issues avail.; reprints avail. **Document type:** *Directory, Trade.* **Description:** Complete listing of US and Canadian equipment, material, and service suppliers serving board converters of corrugated solid fibre, fibre cans and tubes, fibre drums, folding cartons, and rigid boxes.
Published by: Advanstar Communications, Inc., 7500 Old Oak Blvd, Cleveland, OH 44130-3369. TEL 440-891-2767, FAX 440-891-2727. info@advanstar.com, http://www.container-directory.com, http://www.advanstar.com. Ed. Jackie Schultz. Pub. Jill Trupo. R&P Maureen Cannon TEL 440-891-2742. Adv. contact Owen Cleary TEL 440-891-3153. Circ: 100 (paid); 12,000 (controlled). **Subscr. to:** Advanstar Marketing Services, Customer Service Department, 131 West, First St, Duluth, MN 55802. TEL 218-723-9200, 800-598-6008, FAX 218-723-9437.

338.0029   FRA
PARIS-ANGLOPHONE. Text in French. 1989. a. USD 14.95. **Document type:** *Directory, Trade.* **Description:** Provides a complete listing of English-speaking commercial, professional companies and organizations, and cultural activities in France. Also includes doing business in France and housing in France features.
Related titles: Online - full text ed.
Published by: Anglophone S.A., 107 rue de Paris, Montreuil, 93100, France. TEL 33-1-48596658, FAX 33-1-48596668, http://www.paris-anglo.com. Pub. R&P David Applefield. Circ: 10,000 (controlled).

338.0029   USA   ISSN 1048-7395
HF5065.P4
PENNSYLVANIA BUSINESS DIRECTORY. Text in English. 1989. a. USD 1,100 combined subscription print, online & CD-ROM eds. (effective 2004 & 2005). index. back issues avail. **Document type:** *Directory.* **Description:** Includes all businesses in the state compiled from the yellow pages and telephone-verified. Each listing includes company name, complete address, phone number, name of owner, manager, and employee size, sales volume codes, and credit rating codes.
Related titles: CD-ROM ed.; Diskette ed.; E-mail ed.; Fax ed.; Magnetic Tape ed.; Online - full text ed.
Published by: American Business Directories (Subsidiary of: American Business Information, Inc.), 5711 S 86th Circle, P O Box 27347, Omaha, NE 68127. TEL 402-593-4600, 888-946-9377, 877-708-3844, FAX 402-331-5481, sales@directoriesusa.com, http://www.directoriesusa.com.

670.29   USA   ISSN 0733-5237
HD9727.P4
PENNSYLVANIA DIRECTORY OF MANUFACTURERS. Text in English. 1980. a. USD 92.50. adv. **Document type:** *Directory.* **Description:** Profiles approximately 12,000 companies alphabetically, geographically, and by product line. Also lists key executives.
Related titles: Diskette ed.; Magnetic Tape ed.
Published by: Commerce Register, Inc., 190 Godwin Ave, Midland Park, NJ 07432. TEL 201-445-3000, FAX 201-445-5806.

670.29   USA   ISSN 0887-3682
HD9727.P4
PENNSYLVANIA MANUFACTURERS REGISTER. Text in English. a. USD 166 (effective 2001). adv. illus. **Document type:** *Directory.* **Description:** Profiles 20,106 manufacturers; includes product, alphabetical, geographical by city, SIC, and parent company sections.
Related titles: CD-ROM ed.: USD 670 (effective 2001); Diskette ed.
Published by: Manufacturers' News, Inc., 1633 Central St, Evanston, IL 60201. TEL 847-864-7000, 888-752-5200, FAX 847-332-1100, info@mninfo.com, info@manufacturersnews.com, sales@mninfo.com, http://www.manufacturersnews.com. Ed. Frank Lambing. Adv. contact Charles Scherer. B&W page USD 1,843.

PERMIAN BASIN PETROLEUM INDUSTRY. see *PETROLEUM AND GAS*

PETERHEAD PORT HANDBOOK. see *TRANSPORTATION—Ships And Shipping*

PETERSON'S HIDDEN JOB MARKET. see *OCCUPATIONS AND CAREERS*

PETROCHEMICAL INDUSTRY; petrochemical plants, engineering, construction, equipment manufactures & supply companies. see *PETROLEUM AND GAS*

338.7616151902   CAN   ISSN 1490-8689
PHARMA, BIOPHARMA & NUTRACEUTICALS CANADA DIRECTORY, INDUSTRY & SUPPLIERS GUIDE. Text in English. 1996. a. CND 199.95 (effective 2003). **Document type:** *Directory, Trade.*
Related titles: CD-ROM ed.: CND 299.95 (effective 2003).
Published by: Contact Canada, 390 Goward Rd, Victoria, BC V9E 2J5, Canada. TEL 250-708-0427, 888-502-6666, FAX 250-708-0429, ccinfo@contactcanada.com, http://www.contactcanada.com/pharma/.

615.1029   JPN
PHARMACEUTICAL MANUFACTURERS OF JAPAN. Text in Japanese. 1981. biennial. JPY 15,000. **Description:** Addresses and research figures of Japanese pharmaceutical companies.
Published by: Jiho, Inc., Hitotsubashi Bldg. 5F, Hitotsubashi 2-6-3, Chiyoda-ku, Tokyo, 101-8421, Japan. TEL 81-3-32657751, FAX 81-3-32657769, pj@jiho.co.jp, http://www.jiho.co.jp/. **Subscr. to:** ORIOX Japan, Ltd., 3-4-25, Shimomeguro, Meguro-ku, Tokyo 153-0064, Japan. TEL 81-3-3792-5600, FAX 81-3-3792-7500, orioxj@gol.com.

PHARMACEUTICALS (YEAR): INTERNATIONAL YEARBOOK. see *PHARMACY AND PHARMACOLOGY*

PHELON'S DISCOUNT - JOBBING TRADE. see *BUSINESS AND ECONOMICS—Marketing And Purchasing*

PHELON'S WOMEN'S APPAREL AND ACCESSORY SHOPS. see *CLOTHING TRADE—Fashions*

332.1029   USA
PHILADELPHIA STOCK EXCHANGE GUIDE. Text in English. 1965. base vol. plus m. updates. looseleaf. USD 535 base vol(s). (effective 2004). **Description:** Provides members and registered representatives of the Exchange with complete, up-to-date information concerning all Exchange operations.
Related titles: CD-ROM ed.: USD 450 (effective 2004); Online - full text ed.: USD 450 (effective 2004).
Published by: C C H Inc., 2700 Lake Cook Rd, Riverwoods, IL 60015. TEL 847-267-7000, 800-449-6439, cust_serv@cch.com, http://www.cch.com. Pub. Stacey Caywood.

380.1029   PHL
PHILIPPINES BUSINESS DIRECTORY. Text in English. a. PHP 300, USD 75. adv. **Document type:** *Directory.*
Related titles: ◆ Supplement(s): Kontaks Philippines (Year). ISSN 0117-5718.
Published by: Massmark Philippines, P.O. Box 3333, Manila, 1073, Philippines. TEL 805-0955.

PHILIPPINES YEARBOOK OF THE FOOKIEN TIMES. see *BUSINESS AND ECONOMICS—Banking And Finance*

PHILLIPS' INTERNATIONAL PAPER DIRECTORY. see *PAPER AND PULP*

770.29   AUS   ISSN 1327-0710
PHOTOGRAPHERS DIRECTORY. Text in English. a. adv. **Document type:** *Directory, Trade.*
Published by: (Society of Advertising, Commercial and Magazine Photographers), Yaffa Publishing Group Pty Ltd., 17-21 Bellevue St, Surry Hills, NSW 2010, Australia. TEL 61-2-9281-2333, FAX 61-2-9281-2750, yaffa@yaffa.com.au, http://www.yaffa.com.au. adv.: page AUD 1,820; trim 210 x 297. Circ: 9,000.

PHOTOIMAGING YEARBOOK. see *PHOTOGRAPHY*

PHOTONICS DIRECTORY. see *PHYSICS—Optics*

380.1029   USA   ISSN 1528-8552
PHYSICIANS & SURGEONS DIRECTORY. Text in English. 1998. a. USD 1,100 combined subscription print, online & CD-ROM eds. (effective 2004 & 2005). back issues avail.
Related titles: CD-ROM ed.; Diskette ed.; E-mail ed.; Fax ed.; Magnetic Tape ed.; Online - full text ed.
Published by: American Business Directories (Subsidiary of: American Business Information, Inc.), 5711 S 86th Circle, P O Box 27347, Omaha, NE 68127. TEL 402-593-4600, 888-946-9377, 877-708-3844, FAX 402-331-5481, sales@directoriesusa.com, http://www.directoriesusa.com.

017.8   GBR   ISSN 0953-7597
PIMS EUROPEAN TRADE & TECHNICAL DIRECTORY. Text in English. 1988. 2/yr. GBP 185 (effective 1997). **Document type:** *Directory.* **Description:** Directory of European trade and technical presses indexed by subject and publication.
Formerly: Pims European Directory
Published by: P I M S (UK) Ltd., PIMS House, Mildmay Ave, London, N1 4RS, United Kingdom. TEL 44-20-7226-1000, FAX 44-20-7354-7053.

PIMS U K A-Z TOWNS. see *PUBLISHING AND BOOK TRADE*

PIPELINE & GAS JOURNAL ANNUAL DIRECTORY OF PIPELINES AND EQUIPMENT. see *PETROLEUM AND GAS*

PIPELINE INDUSTRY (TULSA); transmission. see *PETROLEUM AND GAS*

338.0029   USA
PITTSBURGH BUSINESS DIRECTORY. Text in English. 1996. a. USD 68.95 (effective 2000). **Document type:** *Directory.* **Description:** Contains profiles of 1345 public, private, nonprofit, subsidiary and other companies, that are either headquartered or maintain significant operations within the Pittsburgh seven-county metropolitan area. Hundreds of other companies are referenced within these profiles including divisions, subsidiaries and affiliates. Also contains biographies of all public company CEOs & the names and titles of more than 6,400 corporate officers.
Published by: Pittsburgh Business Times, 2313 E Carson St, Ste 200, Pittsburgh, PA 15203-2109. TEL 412-481-6397, FAX 412-481-9956. Circ: 3,500 (paid).

PIXEL - THE COMPUTER ANIMATION DICTIONARY; a compilation of new media terms. see *ART—Computer Applications*

PIXEL - THE COMPUTER ANIMATION DIRECTORY. see *ART—Computer Applications*

338.0029   USA   ISSN 0895-4682
AS29.N5
PLACES: A DIRECTORY OF PUBLIC PLACES FOR PRIVATE EVENTS AND PRIVATE PLACES FOR PUBLIC FUNCTIONS. Text in English. 1978. biennial. USD 28.95 (effective 2000). adv. **Document type:** *Directory.* **Description:** Lists close to 1,000 public and private facilities in New York and its environs.
Published by: Tenth House Enterprises, Inc., PO Box 810, Gracie Sta, New York, NY 10028. TEL 212-737-7536, FAX 212-737-9469. Ed. Hannelore Hahn. Pubs. Hannelore Hahn, Tatiana Stoumen. Adv. contact Peter Doncso. Circ: 15,000.

PLANT ENGINEERING PRODUCT SUPPLIER GUIDE. see *ENGINEERING*

678.2029   GBR
PLASTICS, RUBBER & CHEMICAL PRODUCTS; an advertising extract from Kompass. Text in English. a. (in 5 vols.). **Document type:** *Directory.*
Formerly (until 1995): Buyer's Guide. Plastics, Rubber and Chemical Products (Year)
Published by: Kompass (Subsidiary of: Reed Business Information Ltd.), Windsor Court, East Grinstead House, East Grinstead, W Sussex RH19 1XA, United Kingdom. TEL 44-1342-326972, FAX 44-1342-317241.

PLATT'S (YEAR) DIRECTORY OF ELECTRIC POWER PRODUCERS AND DISTRIBUTORS. see *ENERGY—Electrical Energy*

PLAYER'S GUIDE. see *MOTION PICTURES*

▼ *new title*   ➤ *refereed*   ✳ *unverified*   ◆ *full entry avail.*

696.1029 USA
PLUMBING AND MECHANICAL DIRECTORY. Text in English. 1992. a. USD 25. adv. **Document type:** *Directory.* **Description:** For the plumbing - pipe, valves, fittings - hydronic heating industry.
Related titles: Online - full text ed.
Published by: B N P Media, 755 W Big Beaver Rd, Ste 1000, Troy, MI 48084-4903. TEL 248-362-3700, FAX 248-362-0317, http://www.bnpmedia.com/. Ed. Jim Olsztynski. Pub. George Zebrowski. Adv. contact Patty Podboy. B&W page USD 1,885, color page USD 1,935; trim 8.5 x 5.38. Circ: 41,000.

PLUNKETT'S E-COMMERCE & INTERNET BUSINESS ALMANAC. see *COMPUTERS—Internet*

PLUNKETT'S EMPLOYERS' INTERNET SITES WITH CAREERS INFORMATION. see *BUSINESS AND ECONOMICS—Labor And Industrial Relations*

PLUNKETT'S ENERGY INDUSTRY ALMANAC. see *ENERGY*

PLUNKETT'S ENGINEERING AND RESEARCH INDUSTRY ALMANAC. see *ENGINEERING*

PLUNKETT'S ENTERTAINMENT AND MEDIA INDUSTRY ALMANAC. see *COMMUNICATIONS—Television And Cable*

338.0029 USA ISSN 1533-5895
PLUNKETT'S FINANCIAL SERVICES INDUSTRY ALMANAC. Text in English. 1996. a. USD 249.99 (effective 2005); includes CD-ROM. **Document type:** *Directory, Trade.* **Description:** Complete guide to the size, scope and potential of every segment of the financial services industry.
Related titles: CD-ROM ed.
Published by: Plunkett Research, Ltd, PO Drawer 541737, Houston, TX 77254-1737. TEL 713-932-0000, FAX 713-932-7080, info@plunkettresearch.com, http://www.plunkettresearch.com. Ed., Pub. Jack W Plunkett.

613.029 USA ISSN 1099-2928
PLUNKETT'S HEALTH CARE INDUSTRY ALMANAC. Text in English. 1985. a. USD 249.99 (effective 2005); includes CD-ROM. **Document type:** *Directory, Trade.* **Description:** Complete reference guide to the American health care industry and its leading corporations.
Related titles: CD-ROM ed.
Published by: Plunkett Research, Ltd, PO Drawer 541737, Houston, TX 77254-1737. TEL 713-932-0000, FAX 713-932-7080, info@plunkettresearch.com, http://www.plunkettresearch.com. Ed., Pub. Jack W Plunkett.

PLUNKETT'S INFOTECH INDUSTRY ALMANAC. see *COMPUTERS—Microcomputers*

PLUNKETT'S ON-LINE TRADING, FINANCE & INVESTMENT WEB SITES ALMANAC. see *BUSINESS AND ECONOMICS—Public Finance, Taxation*

PLUNKETT'S RETAIL INDUSTRY ALMANAC. see *BUSINESS AND ECONOMICS—Marketing And Purchasing*

PLUNKETT'S TELECOMMUNICATIONS INDUSTRY ALMANAC. see *COMMUNICATIONS—Telephone And Telegraph*

382.029 USA
POCKET BUSINESS GUIDE TO SWITZERLAND. Text in English. 2/yr. adv. **Document type:** *Directory, Trade.* **Description:** Provides information on business travel in Switzerland.
Published by: Pyramid Media Group, 666 Fifth Ave, Ste 230, New York, NY 10103. TEL 212-332-0909, FAX 212-315-1534, info@pyramid.ch, http://www.pyramid.ch. Ed., Pub. Aram Gesar. Adv. contact Martin Brennan.

POLICY PUBLISHERS AND ASSOCIATIONS DIRECTORY. see *POLITICAL SCIENCE*

332.6029 USA
POLK'S FINANCIAL INSTITUTIONS BUYER'S GUIDE AND SERVICES DIRECTORY✶. Text in English. 1991. a. USD 95. adv. **Document type:** *Directory.* **Description:** Categorizes the products and services useful for executives in banking, credit card and securities industries.
Published by: R.L. Polk Co., 4709 Golf Rd, 6th Fl, Skokie, IL 60076-1231. Ed. Jerry Eimbinder. Circ: 15,000.

POLLUTION ENGINEERING PRODUCT - SERVICE LOCATOR. see *ENVIRONMENTAL STUDIES—Waste Management*

POLYMERS PAINT COLOR YEAR BOOK (YEAR). see *PAINTS AND PROTECTIVE COATINGS*

714.029 USA ISSN 0194-5351
HD9993.S953
POOL & SPA NEWS; the national trade magazine for the swimming pool & spa industry. Text in English. 1961. s-m. USD 19.97 (effective 2005). adv. tr.lit. **Document type:** *Magazine, Trade.* **Description:** Carries international, national and regional news of the swimming pool, spa and hot tub industry. News items cover company, association and government-regulatory activities and general industry trends.
Formerly: Pool News (0032-4280)
Related titles: Online - full text ed.: (from Florida Center for Library Automation, Gale Group).
Published by: Hanley-Wood, LLC (Subsidiary of: J.P. Morgan Chase & Co.), 6222 Wilshire Blvd., Ste. 600, Los Angeles, CA 90048-5100. TEL 323-801-4900, FAX 323-801-4902, poolspanews@hanley-wood.com, tjackson@hanleywood.com, http://www.poolspanews.com, http://www.hanleywood.com. Eds. Erika Taylor, P Lakbawalla. Pub. Dick Coleman. adv.: B&W page USD 1,745, color page USD 2,470. Circ: 16,000 (paid and controlled).

728.029 USA
POOL AND SPA NEWS DIRECTORY. Text in English. 1968. a. USD 49.50 (effective 1999). adv. **Document type:** *Directory, Trade.* **Description:** Contains manufacturer-suppliers such as: product listings, a catalog and brochure section, listings of manufacturers' brand names, and an alphabetical section of manufacturers that gives their number of employees, name of chief executive, length of time in business and phone number.
Former titles: Pool and Spa News Source Book; Pool and Spa News Directory; Pool News Directory (0194-1380)
Published by: Leisure Publications, Inc., 4160 Wilshire Blvd, Los Angeles, CA 90010. TEL 323-964-4800, FAX 323-964-4838. Ed. Carolyn Cerbin. Pub., R&P Jules Field. Circ: 16,000.

338.0029 ZAF
PORT ELIZABETH - UITENHAGE DIRECTORY. Text in English. a. USD 35 (effective 2001). **Document type:** *Directory.*
Former titles: Donaldson's Port Elizabeth, Uitenhage and Despatch Directory; Donaldson's Port Elizabeth Directory (0416-2706)
Related titles: Diskette ed.
Published by: Braby's (Subsidiary of: Associated Industries), Attn: Sue Pearson, PO Box 1426, Pinetown, 3600, South Africa. TEL 27-31-7017021, FAX 27-31-7017036, booksales@brabys.co.za. Ed. A Stagg.

PORT OF ANTWERP YEARBOOK. see *TRANSPORTATION—Ships And Shipping*

PORTFOLIO OF BLACK BUSINESS IN SOUTHERN AFRICA. see *BUSINESS AND ECONOMICS*

POWDER COATINGS DIRECTORY. see *ENGINEERING—Chemical Engineering*

PREPARED FOODS FOOD INDUSTRY SOURCEBOOK. see *FOOD AND FOOD INDUSTRIES*

PRINT BUYERS DIRECTORY. see *PRINTING*

338.4 CAN ISSN 1481-9309
PRINTACTION NATIONAL DIRECTORY OF SERVICES & EQUIPMENT FOR THE TRADE. Text in English. 1995. a.
Related titles: ◆ Supplement to: Print Action. ISSN 1481-9287.
Published by: Youngblood Publishing Ltd., 4580 Dufferin St, Ste 404, Toronto, ON M3H 5Y2, Canada. TEL 416-665-7333, 800-363-3261, FAX 416-665-7226.

PRINTING TRADES DIRECTORY. see *PRINTING*

332.6029 USA ISSN 0094-3134
HG4907
PROBE DIRECTORY OF FOREIGN DIRECT INVESTMENT IN THE UNITED STATES✶. Text in English. 1974. irreg., latest 1989. USD 250. **Document type:** *Directory.* **Description:** Lists U.S. manufacturers which are partly or wholly foreign-owned and lists foreign owners by country. Includes addresses, telephone numbers, key product line and key executives.
Published by: Probe International, Inc., 1047 Sunset Rd, Stamford, CT 06903-2429. TEL 203-329-9595, FAX 203-329-8054. Ed. Evalyn Weiner.

664.0029 IND
PROCESSED FOODS & BEVERAGES DIRECTORY (YEAR). Text in English. biennial. INR 700 domestic; USD 50 foreign (effective 2001). **Document type:** *Directory.* **Description:** Covers food & beverage manufacturers, raw materials suppliers, food and beverage processing and packaging machinery suppliers, importers and exporters of processed food, food associations and institutes.
Published by: Amalgamated Press, Narang House, 2nd Fl, 41 Ambalal Doshi Marg Fort, Mumbai, Maharashtra 400 001, India. TEL 91-22-2650268, 91-22-2654184, FAX 91-22-264-1275. Ed., Pub. Norman J Da Silva.

670.29 ESP ISSN 0079-5836
PRODEI; catalogue of Spanish manufacturers, exporters and importers. Text and summaries in English, French, German, Spanish. 1945. biennial. USD 167 (effective 2000). adv. **Document type:** *Directory.* **Description:** Provides information on the Spanish market. All sectors of the Spanish economy from the most qualified precision enterprise to the modest craftsman.
Published by: Capel Editorial Distribuidora S.A., Almirante, 21, Apartado 562, Madrid, 28004, Spain. TEL 34-91-3080644, FAX 34-91-3105141, pcyc@mad.servicom.es. Ed. Esmeralda Capel. Circ: 15,000.

PRODUCCION QUIMICA LATINOAMERICANA/LATIN AMERICAN CHEMICAL PRODUCTION. see *ENGINEERING—Chemical Engineering*

PRODUCCION QUIMICA MEXICANA/MEXICAN CHEMICAL PRODUCTION. see *ENGINEERING—Chemical Engineering*

PRODUCER'S MASTERGUIDE; the international production manual for broadcast-television, feature films, television, commercials, cable, digital and videotape industries in the United States, Canada, the United Kingdom, Bermuda, the Caribbean Islands, Mexico, South America, Europe, Israel, the Far East, Australia and New Zealand. see *MOTION PICTURES*

745.2029 NLD
PRODUCT JAARBOEK. Text in Dutch. a. adv. **Document type:** *Directory.* **Description:** Provides product and company information in the industrial design sector.
Published by: Wyt Uitgeefgroep B.V., Postbus 6438, Rotterdam, 3002 AK, Netherlands. TEL 31-10-425-5944, FAX 31-10-478-0904, wyt-uitgeefgroep@compuserve.com.

PRODUCTS CERTIFIED FOR CANADA DIRECTORY. see *BUSINESS AND ECONOMICS—Production Of Goods And Services*

338.0029 JPN
PRODUCTS GUIDE. Text in Japanese. 1996 (Sep). s-a. included with subscription to Nikkei Electronics, Nikkei Mechanical & Nikkei Microdevices. adv. **Document type:** *Trade.* **Description:** Provides information for electrical and mechanical engineers.
Published by: Nikkei Business Publications Inc. (Subsidiary of: Nihon Keizai Shimbun, Inc.), 2-7-6 Hirakawa-cho, Chiyoda-ku, Tokyo, 102-8622, Japan. TEL 81-3-5210-8311, FAX 81-3-5210-8530, info@nikkeibp-america.com, http://www.nikkeibp.com. adv.: B&W page JPY 560,000, color page JPY 700,000; trim 208 x 280. Circ: 80,000 (paid and controlled).

338.0029 USA
PRODUTOS E SERVICOS. Abbreviated title: P S. Text in Portuguese. 1975. m. free to qualified personnel. **Description:** New industrial products are described and illustrated for export.
Published by: Keller International Publishing Corp., 150 Great Neck Rd, Great Neck, NY 11021. TEL 516-829-9210, FAX 516-824-5414. Ed. Bryan DeLuca. Pub. Terry Beirne. Circ: 22,028 (controlled).

PROF I T DATENBANK CD-ROM. see *COMPUTERS—Information Science And Information Theory*

380.1029 IND ISSN 0079-5925
PROFESSIONAL AND TRADE ORGANISATIONS IN INDIA. Text in English. 1963. irreg. INR 5 domestic; USD 10 foreign (effective 2000). adv. **Document type:** *Directory.* **Description:** Provides information about leading professional and scientific employers, cultural, and trade organizations in India.
Published by: Kothari Publications, 12 India Exchange Pl., Kolkata, West Bengal 700 001, India. TEL 91-33-220-9563. Ed. H Kothari.

PUBLIC RELATIONS OFFICE OF THE SUGAR INDUSTRY. ANNUAIRE. see *FOOD AND FOOD INDUSTRIES*

659.1029 USA
PUBLIC RELATIONS SOCIETY OF AMERICA DIRECTORY. Variant title: Public Relations Journal Register Issue. Text in English. 1945. a. USD 100 domestic; USD 110 in Canada; USD 120 elsewhere (effective 1999). adv. bibl. **Document type:** *Directory.*
Formerly: Public Relations Register
Indexed: PAIS.
Published by: The Public Relations Society of America, Inc., 33 Maiden Ln, 11th Fl, New York, NY 10038-5150. TEL 212-460-1468. Circ: 11,800.

070.5029 USA ISSN 0000-0671
Z475 CODEN: PDWSEG
PUBLISHERS, DISTRIBUTORS & WHOLESALERS OF THE UNITED STATES; a directory of publishers, distributors, associations, wholesalers, software producers and manufacturers listing editorial and ordering addresses, and an ISBN publisher prefix index. Text in English. 1979. a. (in 2 vols.). USD 349 (effective 2004); USD 369 (effective 2005). 4000 p./no.; **Document type:** *Directory, Trade.* **Description:** Includes subsidiaries, imprints and divisions, inactive mergers and acquisitions and out-of-business companies, and specialized publishers. Lists ISBN prefixes and toll-free phone and fax numbers, e-mail and Web addresses. Also includes discount schedule, and returns policies.
Formerly (until 1980): Publishers and Distributors of the United States (0000-0620)
Related titles: Magnetic Tape ed.; Online - full text ed.
—BLDSC (7156.068000), CASDDS, CISTI.

Published by: R.R. Bowker LLC (Subsidiary of: Cambridge Information Group), 630 Central Ave., New Providence, NJ 07974. TEL 908-286-1090, 800-526-9537, FAX 908-219-0098, info@bowker.com, http://www.bowker.com. **Subscr. to:** Order Dept., PO Box 32, New Providence, NJ 07974-9903. TEL 800-521-8110.

338.0029 PRI ISSN 0090-3612
HC157.P8
PUERTO RICO OFFICIAL INDUSTRIAL DIRECTORY. Text in English. 1966. a. USD 129 (effective 1997). adv. stat.
Document type: *Directory.* **Description:** Contains information on more than 8,000 manufacturers, distributors, wholesalers and service firms. Covers the business environment, economic trends, key industry profiles, market and industrial sector statistics, government programs, and industrial parks.
Published by: (Puerto Rico. U.S. Department of Commerce, Economic Development Administration USA), Direct Marketing and Media Group, Inc., P O Box 9024182, San Juan, 00902-4182, Puerto Rico. TEL 787-268-1111, FAX 787-268-7044, dmmg@caribe.net, http://www.prid.com. Ed., R&P Howard G Patterson. Pub. Lilia Molina Ruiz. Adv. contact Diana Lopez. B&W page USD 5,475, color page USD 6,200. Circ: 5,000 (paid). **Dist. in the U.S. by:** Manufacturers' News, Inc., 1633 Central St, Evanston, IL 60201. TEL 847-864-7000.

PULP & PAPER BUYERS GUIDE. see *PAPER AND PULP*

PULP & PAPER COMPANY PROFILES (YEAR). see *PAPER AND PULP*

PULSE BUYERS GUIDE. see *ELECTRONICS*

338.0029 GBR
Q A REGISTER; the United Kingdom register of quality assessed companies. Text in English. 1983. a. GBP 199 (effective 1998). **Document type:** *Directory, Government.*
Former titles (until 1998): D T I - Q A Register (0958-8574); Which superseded in part (in 1989): Register of Quality Assessed United Kingdom Companies (0267-8683); Which was formerly (until 1984): Register of Quality Assessed United Kingdom Manufacturers (0264-7710)
Related titles: CD-ROM ed.: ISSN 1354-6635.
Published by: Stationery Office, 51 Nine Elms Ln, London, SW8 5DA, United Kingdom. TEL 44-20-7873-0011, book.orders@theso.co.uk, http://www.national-publishing.co.uk.

910.029 ITA
Q T DIRECTORY. (Quality Travel) Text in English, Italian. 1988. a. adv. 432 p./no.; **Document type:** *Magazine, Trade.*
Description: Lists the best convention venues in Italy and Europe. Distributed to meeting planners and corporate decision makers.
Published by: Promos Edizioni srl, Via Giacomo Watt 32, Milan, 20143, Italy. TEL 39-02-89151814, FAX 39-02-89151830, promos@qualitytravel.it, http://www.qualitytravel.it. Ed., Pub., R&P Roberto Angri. Adv. contact Claudia Fossati. Circ: 16,000 (paid).

380.1029 071.1 USA
QUEBEC BUSINESS DIRECTORY. Text in English. a. USD 1,100 combined subscription print, online & CD-ROM eds. (effective 2004 & 2005). back issues avail. **Document type:** *Directory.*
Related titles: CD-ROM ed.; Diskette ed.; E-mail ed.; Fax ed.; Magnetic Tape ed.; Online - full text ed.
Published by: American Business Directories (Subsidiary of: American Business Information, Inc.), 5711 S 86th Circle, P O Box 27347, Omaha, NE 68127. TEL 402-593-4600, 888-946-9377, 877-708-3844, FAX 402-331-5481, sales@directoriesusa.com, http://www.directoriesusa.com.

338.0029 BRA ISSN 0102-7115
QUEM E QUEM NA ECONOMIA BRASILEIRA. Text in Portuguese. 1967. a. USD 10. adv.
Published by: Editora Visao Ltda., Rua Alvaro de Carvalho, 354, Centro, Sao Paulo, SP 01050-070, Brazil. TEL 55-11-256-5011, FAX 55-11-258-1919. Ed. Hamilton Lucas de Oliveira. Circ: 140,000.

QUICK GUIDE TO THE NEW TELECOM LINGO. see *COMMUNICATIONS—Telephone And Telegraph*

382.029 ESP
QUIEN VENDE EN ESPANA LOS PRODUCTOS EXTRANJEROS/WHO SELLS FOREIGN PRODUCTS IN SPAIN. Text in Spanish. 1966. biennial.
Published by: Prointer-Ediciones, Pz Puerta del Sol, 11, Madrid, 28013, Spain.

R & D PRODUCT SOURCE TELEPHONE DIRECTORY. (Research & Development) see *TECHNOLOGY: COMPREHENSIVE WORKS*

338.0029 USA
R & I BLUE BOOK. (Recognition & Identification) Text in English. 1991. a.
Published by: Engravers Journal, Inc., PO Box 318, Brighton, MI 48116. TEL 810-229-5725, FAX 810-229-8320. Eds. James J Farrell, Michael J Davis.

338.0029 USA
HF5068.S3
R C G A ROSTER AND MEMBERSHIP SERVICES DIRECTORY✶. Text in English. 1983. a. USD 50 to non-members.
Formerly: Buyer's Guide of Products and Services in St. Louis Region (0741-8205)
Published by: St. Louis Regional Chamber & Growth Association, One Metropolitan Sq, Ste 1300, Commerce, MO 63102. Ed. Laura Barlow.

658.8029 USA
R C G A'S DIRECTORY OF ST. LOUIS LARGE EMPLOYERS✶. Text in English. 1957. biennial. USD 20. **Document type:** *Directory.* **Description:** Lists companies with 100 or more employees located in the St. Louis metropolitan area by groupings, SIC codes, employee size, alpha-order, and zip code.
Formerly: Large Employers Directory of Metropolitan St. Louis
Related titles: Diskette ed.: 1957.
Published by: St. Louis Regional Chamber & Growth Association, One Metropolitan Sq, Ste 1300, Commerce, MO 63102. Ed. Laura Barlow. Circ: 3,600.

R N AND W P L ENCYCLOPEDIA. (Registered Number & Wool Products Label) see *BUSINESS AND ECONOMICS—Production Of Goods And Services*

741.6029 USA
R S V P: THE DIRECTORY OF ILLUSTRATION AND DESIGN. Text in English. 1975. a. USD 20 (effective 2002). adv. illus. 300 p./no.; back issues avail. **Document type:** *Directory.* **Description:** National illustrated directory of illustration and design.
Formerly (until 1991): R S V P: The Directory of Creative Talent
Address: 253 Washington Ave, Box 050314, Brooklyn, NY 11205-0314. TEL 718-857-9267, FAX 718-783-2376, RSVPdirectory@worldnet.att.net, info@rsvpdirectory.com, http://www.RSVPdirectory.com. Ed. Kathleen Creighton. Pubs. Kathleesn Creighton, Richard Lebenson TEL 718-857-9267. R&P, Adv. contact Richard Lebenson TEL 718-857-9267. Circ: 18,000.

338.0029 USA
R VERS GUIDE TO FLORIDA. (Recreational Vehicle) Text in English. 1992. a. **Document type:** *Directory.* **Description:** Lists members, their addresses, phone numbers and products and services.
Formerly: F R V T A Membership Directory
Published by: Florida Recreational Vehicle Trade Association, 10510 Gibsonton Dr, Riverview, FL 33569. TEL 813-741-0488, FAX 813-741-0688, frtva@frvta.org, http://www.frvta.org. Ed. David Kelly. Circ: 50,000.

RADIO CO-OP SOURCES. see *COMMUNICATIONS—Radio*

338.0029 384.5 USA ISSN 1098-3783
ML18
RADIO POWER BOOK. Text in English. a. (Oct.). USD 139 (effective 2003). **Document type:** *Directory, Trade.*
Description: Contains listings of radio stations in 183 organized by format, including listings of record label promotion personnel, radio consultants & syndicators, & Arbitron rankings for the TOP 100 markets.
Published by: Billboard Directories (Subsidiary of: V N U Business Publications), 575 Prospect Street, Lakewood, NJ 08701. TEL 732-363-4156, 800-344-7119, FAX 732-363-0338, ndavis@bpicomm.com, http://orderbillboard.com/cgi-bin/CB7046F3/mac/additmdtl.mac/showItemDetail?item=BLBDD25&qtyA=0&phsO=N&desc=2003%20Radio%20Powerbook&drpshp=N&alOrd=Y&, http://www.billboard.com.
Subscr. to: V N U Business Publications, PO Box 2011, Marion, OH 43306-811137202. TEL 800-745-8922.

381.45687 AUS
RAGTRADER FASHION DIRECTORY. Text in English. a. AUD 95 (effective 1999). adv. **Document type:** *Directory, Trade.*
Description: Lists supplier and agent contact details for labels in Australia. Covers women's, men's, and children's clothing, underwear, accessories and footwear.
Published by: Yaffa Publishing Group Pty Ltd., 17-21 Bellevue St, Surry Hills, NSW 2010, Australia. TEL 61-2-92812333, FAX 61-2-92812750, yaffa@yaffa.com.au, http://www.yaffa.com.au/mags/ragmag.htm. Circ: 5,500.

RAW MATERIALS FOR THE REFRACTORIES INDUSTRY. see *METALLURGY*

691.029 NZL ISSN 0813-5207
RAWLINSONS NEW ZEALAND CONSTRUCTION HANDBOOK. Text in English. 1986. a. NZD 144 domestic; NZD 194 foreign. adv. bk.rev. back issues avail. **Document type:** *Trade.*
Description: A comprehensive guide to building construction costs in New Zealand.
Related titles: CD-ROM ed.
Published by: Rawlinsons New Zealand Construction Handbook Ltd., Rawlinson House, 4th Fl., 25-27 Broadway, Newmarket, Auckland, New Zealand. TEL 64-9-5290061, FAX 64-9-5244977. Ed., R&P Cathy Giddens TEL 64-9-5240874. Circ: 1,200.

RECRUITING AND SEARCH REPORT; executive search - headhunter directories. see *BUSINESS AND ECONOMICS—Personnel Management*

RECYCLED PRODUCTS GUIDE. see *ENVIRONMENTAL STUDIES—Waste Management*

338.0029 DEU ISSN 1434-0712
RED BOX. Text in English, German. 1970. a. EUR 150 (effective 2005). **Document type:** *Directory, Trade.*
Published by: Red Box Verlag GmbH, Hansastr 52, Hamburg, 20144, Germany. TEL 49-40-4501500, FAX 49-40-45015099, info@redbox.de, http://www.redbox.de. Ed., Pub. Margit Bethge. Circ: 10,000 (paid).

070.5 DEU ISSN 0173-959X
REDAKTIONS ADRESS. Text in German. 1979. 2/yr. EUR 208; EUR 162 newsstand/cover (effective 2003). adv. cum.index.
Document type: *Directory, Trade.* **Description:** Contains editorial addresses and information on German media, including approximately 12,000 publications.
Published by: Media-Daten Verlag GmbH (Subsidiary of: Springer Science+Business Media), Postfach 1546, Wiesbaden, 65173, Germany. TEL 49-611-78780, FAX 49-611-7878465, info@media-daten.de, http://www.media-daten.de. adv.: B&W page EUR 2,150, color page EUR 3,380. Circ: 804 (paid).

THE REEFER REGISTER. see *TRANSPORTATION—Ships And Shipping*

382.029 USA
REFERENCE BOOK FOR WORLD TRADERS. Text in English. base vol. plus m. updates. looseleaf. USD 179.95 base vol(s). domestic; USD 208 base vol(s). foreign (effective 2005).
Document type: *Directory.* **Description:** Basic information on and for those participating in international trade.
Published by: Croner Publications, Inc., 10951 Sorrento Valley Rd, Ste 1D, San Diego, CA 92121-1613. TEL 800-441-4033, 800-441-4033, FAX 800-809-0334, paul@croner.com, http://www.croner.com. Ed. Elizabeth Duffy.

332.1029 GBR ISSN 0080-0538
REGENCY INTERNATIONAL DIRECTORY; of private investigators, process servers, private detectives & debt collecting agencies. Text in English. 1967. a. USD 50. adv.
Published by: Regency International Publications Ltd., 325 Canterbury Rd, Densole, Folkestone, Kent CT18 7BB, United Kingdom. TEL 0303-893488, FAX 0303-893488. Ed. Alan L Valle. Circ: (controlled).

338.0029 USA ISSN 1047-7799
HD2346.U52
REGIONAL DIRECTORY OF MINORITY- AND WOMEN-OWNED BUSINESS FIRMS: CENTRAL EDITION. Text in English. s-a. USD 175 (effective 2000). **Document type:** *Directory.*
—CCC.
Published by: Business Research Services, Inc., 4701 Sangamore Rd., Ste. S155, Bethesda, MD 20816-2532. TEL 800-325-8720, FAX 202-686-3228.

338.0029 USA ISSN 1047-7802
HD2346.U52
REGIONAL DIRECTORY OF MINORITY- AND WOMEN-OWNED BUSINESS FIRMS: EASTERN EDITION. Text in English. s-a. USD 175 (effective 2000). **Document type:** *Directory, Trade.*
Published by: Business Research Services, Inc., 4701 Sangamore Rd., Ste. S155, Bethesda, MD 20816-2532. TEL 800-845-8420, FAX 202-686-3228. Ed., R&P Thomas D Johnson.

338.0029 USA ISSN 0886-3946
HD2346.U52
REGIONAL DIRECTORY OF MINORITY- AND WOMEN-OWNED BUSINESS FIRMS: WESTERN EDITION. Text in English. s-a. USD 175 (effective 2000). **Document type:** *Directory.*
—CCC.
Published by: Business Research Services, Inc., 4701 Sangamore Rd., Ste. S155, Bethesda, MD 20816-2532. TEL 800-845-8420, FAX 202-686-3228. Ed., Pub., R&P Thomas D Johnson.

380.1029 USA ISSN 1063-5424
HF5065.C2
REGIONAL INDUSTRIAL BUYING GUIDE. SOUTHERN CALIFORNIA. Variant title: Southern California Regional Industrial Buying Guide. Text in English. 1992. a. **Document type:** *Directory, Trade.*
Published by: Thomas Regional Directory Co. (Subsidiary of: Thomas Publishing Company), 5 Penn Plaza, New York, NY 10001.

670.29 USA ISSN 1070-5600
HF5047
REGIONAL TECHNOLOGY GUIDE - CENTRAL U S✶ . Cover title: Central U S Regional Technology Guide. Text in English. s-a. USD 225 (effective 1999). **Document type:** *Directory.* **Description:** Profiles thousands of technology manufacturers and developers in OH, IN, KY and WV. Covers 17 different high-tech industries, offering detailed information on each company, including key contacts, a description of products manufactured, and employment growth.
Formed by the 1994 merger of: Sales Guide to High Tech Companies - South Central Region (1040-0532); Sales Guide to High Tech Companies - North Central Region (1040-0540)
Published by: Corporate Technology Information Services Inc., 300 Baker Ave #3, Concord, MA 01742-2131. TEL 781-932-3100, FAX 781-932-6335, sales@corptech.com, http://www.corptech.com. R&P Steven Parker.

670.29 USA ISSN 1070-5597
HF5041
REGIONAL TECHNOLOGY GUIDE - EASTERN LAKES✶ . Cover title: Eastern Lakes Regional Technology Guide. Text in English. s-a. USD 225 (effective 1999). **Document type:** *Directory.* **Description:** Profiles thousands of technology manufacturers and developers in upstate NY and PA excluding Philadelphia. Covers 17 different high-tech industries, offering detailed information on each company, including key contacts, a description of products manufactured, and employment growth.
Formerly (until 1994): Sales Guide to High Tech Companies - Eastern Great Lakes (1040-0559)
Published by: Corporate Technology Information Services Inc., 300 Baker Ave #3, Concord, MA 01742-2131. TEL 781-932-3100, FAX 781-932-6335, sales@corptech.com, http://www.corptech.com. R&P Steven Parker.

670.29 USA ISSN 1070-5589
HF5047
REGIONAL TECHNOLOGY GUIDE - GREAT LAKES✶ . Cover title: Great Lakes Regional Technology Guide. Text in English. 1994. s-a. USD 225 (effective 1999). **Document type:** *Directory.* **Description:** Profiles thousands of technology manufacturers and developers in WI, MI and IL. Covers 17 different high-tech industries, offering detailed information on each company, including key contacts, a description of products manufactured, and employment growth.
Published by: Corporate Technology Information Services Inc., 300 Baker Ave #3, Concord, MA 01742-2131. TEL 781-932-3100, FAX 781-932-6335, sales@corptech.com, http://www.corptech.com. R&P Steven Parker.

670.29 USA ISSN 1070-5554
HF5041
REGIONAL TECHNOLOGY GUIDE - MID-ATLANTIC✶ . Cover title: Mid-Atlantic Regional Technology Guide. Text in English. 1988. s-a. USD 225 (effective 1999). **Document type:** *Directory.* **Description:** Profiles thousands of technology manufacturers and developers in DC, VA, and MD. Covers 17 different high-tech industries, offering detailed information on each company, including key contacts, a description of products manufactured, and employment growth.
Formerly (until 1994): Sales Guide to High Tech Companies - Mid Atlantic Region (1040-0575)
Published by: Corporate Technology Information Services Inc., 300 Baker Ave #3, Concord, MA 01742-2131. TEL 781-932-3100, FAX 781-932-6335, sales@corptech.com, http://www.corptech.com. R&P Steven Parker.

670.29 USA ISSN 1070-5570
HF5047
REGIONAL TECHNOLOGY GUIDE - MIDWEST✶ . Cover title: Mid-West Regional Technology Guide. Text in English. 1994. s-a. USD 225 (effective 1999). **Document type:** *Directory.* **Description:** Profiles thousands of technology manufacturers and developers in MN, IA, MO, KS, ND, SD and NE. Covers 17 different high-tech industries, offering detailed information on each company, including key contacts, description of products manufactured, and employment growth.
Published by: Corporate Technology Information Services Inc., 300 Baker Ave #3, Concord, MA 01742-2131. TEL 781-932-3100, FAX 781-932-6335, sales@corptech.com, http://www.corptech.com. R&P Steven Parker.

670.29 USA ISSN 1070-552X
HF5041
REGIONAL TECHNOLOGY GUIDE - NEW ENGLAND✶ . Cover title: New England Regional Technology Guide. Text in English. 1988. s-a. USD 225 (effective 1999). **Document type:** *Directory.* **Description:** Profiles thousands of technology manufacturers and developers in MA, NH, RI, VT and ME. Covers 17 different high-tech industries, offering detailed information on each company, including key contacts, a description of products manufactured, and employment growth.
Formerly (until 1994): Sales Guide to High Tech Companies - New England Region (1040-0591)
Published by: Corporate Technology Information Services Inc., 300 Baker Ave #3, Concord, MA 01742-2131. TEL 781-932-3100, FAX 781-932-6335, sales@corptech.com, http://www.corptech.com. R&P Steven Parker.

670.29 USA ISSN 1070-5546
HF5065.N5
REGIONAL TECHNOLOGY GUIDE - NEW JERSEY AND DELAWARE VALLEY✶ . Cover title: New Jersey & Delaware Valley Regional Technology Guide. Text in English. 1992. s-a. USD 225. **Document type:** *Directory.* **Description:** Profiles thousands of technology manufacturers and developers in NJ, DE and Philadelphia. Covers 17 different high-tech industries, offering detailed information on each company, including key contacts, a description of products manufactured, and employment growth.
Formerly (until 1994): New Jersey Technology Resource Guide (1060-1589)
Published by: Corporate Technology Information Services Inc., 300 Baker Ave #3, Concord, MA 01742-2131. TEL 781-932-3100, FAX 781-932-6335, sales@corptech.com, http://www.corptech.com. R&P Steven Parker.

670.29 USA ISSN 1070-5538
HC108.N72
REGIONAL TECHNOLOGY GUIDE - NEW YORK METRO✶ . Cover title: New York Metro Regional Technology Guide. Text in English. 1988. s-a. USD 225 (effective 1999). **Document type:** *Directory.* **Description:** Profiles thousands of technology manufacturers and developers in New York City, Long Island, Westchester County and CT. Covers 17 different high-tech industries, offering detailed information on each company, including key contacts, a description of products manufactured, and employment growth.
Formerly (until 1994): Sales Guide to High Tech Companies - New York Metro (1040-0583)
Published by: Corporate Technology Information Services Inc., 300 Baker Ave #3, Concord, MA 01742-2131. TEL 781-932-3100, FAX 781-932-6335, sales@corptech.com, http://www.corptech.com. R&P Steven Parker.

670.29 USA ISSN 1070-5635
HF5065.C2
REGIONAL TECHNOLOGY GUIDE - NORTHERN CALIFORNIA✶ . Cover title: Northern California Regional Technology Guide. Text in English. s-a. USD 225 (effective 1999). **Document type:** *Directory.* **Description:** Profiles thousands of technology manufacturers and developers in Greater San Francisco and Silicon Valley. Covers 17 different high-tech industries, offering detailed information on each company, including key contacts, a description of products manufactured, and employment growth.
Supersedes in part (in 1994): Sales Guide to High Tech Companies - California (1041-0260)
Published by: Corporate Technology Information Services Inc., 300 Baker Ave #3, Concord, MA 01742-2131. TEL 781-932-3100, FAX 781-932-6335, sales@corptech.com, http://www.corptech.com. R&P Steven Parker.

670.29 USA ISSN 1070-5619
HF5050
REGIONAL TECHNOLOGY GUIDE - NORTHWEST U S✶ . Cover title: Northwest U S Regional Technology Guide. Text in English. s-a. USD 225 (effective 1999). **Document type:** *Directory.* **Description:** Profiles thousands of technology manufacturers and developers in OR, WA, MT, AK, NV, WY and ID. Covers 17 different high-tech industries, offering detailed information on each company, including key contacts, a description of products manufactured and employment growth.
Formerly (until 1994): Sales Guide to High Tech Companies - Northwest Region (1040-0516)
Published by: Corporate Technology Information Services Inc., 300 Baker Ave #3, Concord, MA 01742-2131. TEL 781-932-3100, FAX 781-932-6335, sales@corptech.com, http://www.corptech.com. R&P Steven Parker.

670.29 USA ISSN 1070-5562
HF5044
REGIONAL TECHNOLOGY GUIDE - SOUTHEAST U S✶ . Cover title: Southeast U S Regional Technology Guide. Text in English. s-a. USD 225 (effective 1999). **Document type:** *Directory.* **Description:** Profiles thousands of technology manufacturers and developers in MS, LA, AR, AL, GA, TN, NC, SC, FL and Puerto Rico. Covers 17 different high-tech industries, offering detailed information on each company, including key contacts, a description of products manufactured, and employment growth.
Formerly (until 1994): Sales Guide to High Tech Companies - Southeast Region (1040-0567)
Published by: Corporate Technology Information Services Inc., 300 Baker Ave #3, Concord, MA 01742-2131. TEL 781-932-3100, FAX 781-932-6335, sales@corptech.com, http://www.corptech.com. R&P Steven Parker.

670.29 USA ISSN 1070-5627
HF5065.C2
REGIONAL TECHNOLOGY GUIDE - SOUTHERN CALIFORNIA✶ . Cover title: Southern California Regional Technology Guide. Text in English. s-a. USD 225 (effective 1999). **Document type:** *Directory.* **Description:** Profiles thousands of technology manufacturers and developers in Los Angeles, Orange County, San Diego and Hawaii. Covers 17 different high-tech industries, offering detailed information on each company, including key contacts, a description of products manufactured, and employment growth.
Supersedes in part (in 1994): Sales Guide to High Tech Companies - California (1041-0260)
Published by: Corporate Technology Information Services Inc., 300 Baker Ave #3, Concord, MA 01742-2131. TEL 781-932-3100, FAX 781-932-6335, sales@corptech.com, http://www.corptech.com. R&P Steven Parker.

670.29 USA ISSN 1070-5643
HF5050
REGIONAL TECHNOLOGY GUIDE - SOUTHWEST U S✶ . Cover title: Southwest U S Regional Technology Guide. Text in English. s-a. USD 225 (effective 1999). **Document type:** *Directory.* **Description:** Profiles thousands of technology manufacturers and developers in UT, CO, NM, AZ, TX and OK. Covers 17 different high-tech industries, offering detailed information on each company, including key contacts, a description of products manufactured and employment growth.
Formerly (until 1994): Sales Guide to High Tech Companies - Southwest Region (1040-0524)
Published by: Corporate Technology Information Services Inc., 300 Baker Ave #3, Concord, MA 01742-2131. TEL 781-932-3100, FAX 781-932-6335, sales@corptech.com, http://www.corptech.com. R&P Steven Parker.

670.29 USA
REGISTRO INDUSTRIAL MEXICANO✶ . Text in English. 1986. a. **Document type:** *Trade.*
Published by: Keller International Publishing Corp., 150 Great Neck Rd, Great Neck, NY 11021. http://www.kellerpubs.com. Circ: 10,000.

380.1029 SGP
REINSURANCE DIRECTORY OF ASIA. Text in English. a. USD 32 in Singapore & Malaysia; USD 50 elsewhere (effective 2005). **Document type:** *Directory, Trade.* **Description:** Contains listing of reinsurers, including full details such as corporate, management and financial data of each reinsurer and reinsurance broker in Asia .
Published by: Ins Communications Pte. Ltd., 57A Amoy St., Singapore, 069 883, Singapore. TEL 65-62245583, FAX 65-62241091, http://www.asiainsurancereview.com/EStore/reinsurance-dir-asia.asp.

338.0029 621.32 USA ISSN 1540-0638
RENTAL AND STAGING SYSTEMS. Text in English. 11/yr. USD 54 domestic; USD 78.50 in Canada; USD 92.50 elsewhere; USD 6 newsstand/cover (effective 2005). adv. back issues avail. **Document type:** *Magazine, Trade.*
Related titles: Online - full text ed.: (from Gale Group, ProQuest Information & Learning).
Indexed: CompD.
Published by: C M P Information, Inc., Entertainment Technology Group (Subsidiary of: C M P Information Ltd.), 460 Park Ave South, 9th Fl, New York, NY 10016. TEL 212-378-0400, FAX 212-378-2160, http://www.rentalandstaging.com/, http://www.uemedia.com. Ed. David Keene. Pub. Adam Goldstein. adv.: B&W page USD 4,030, color page USD 5,185; trim 8.125 x 10.875. Circ: 25,000.

380.1029 CAN ISSN 1184-9916
HD9734.C3
REPERTOIRE DES PRODUITS DISPONIBLES AU QUEBEC. Text in French; Prefatory materials in English, French. 1978. a. CND 179 (effective 2001). adv. **Document type:** *Directory, Trade.* **Description:** Directory of Quebec industries. Lists products and services, trade marks, manufacturers, distributors and business-to-business services.
Formerly (until 1991): Repertoire des Produits Fabriques au Quebec (0704-7940)
Related titles: Online - full text ed.
—CISTI.
Published by: Centre de Recherche Industrielle du Quebec, 333 rue Franquet, Sainte Foy, PQ G1P 4C7, Canada. TEL 418-652-2234, FAX 418-652-2212, http://www.criq.qc.ca/directory/, http://www.icriq.com. Ed. Bernard Turgeon. R&P Francois Lauziere. Adv. contact Louise Lajeunesse. Circ: 5,000.

338.0029 CAN ISSN 1707-1445
REPERTOIRE INDUSTRIEL DU QUEBEC/QUEBEC INDUSTRIAL DIRECTORY. Text in French. 1963. a. CND 319 per issue (effective 2003). **Document type:** *Directory, Trade.* **Description:** Contains detailed information on over 23,600 Quebec manufacturers, wholesalers, distributors and manufacturers' agents.
Former titles (until 2002): Repertoires Scott's, Fabricants du Quebec/Scott's Directories, Quebec Manufacturers (1204-3516); (until 1990): Scott's Repertoires, Fabricants du Quebec/Scott's Directories, Quebec Manufacturers (0829-2221); (until 1983): Scott's Quebec Industrial Directory (0582-3080)
Related titles: CD-ROM ed.: Quebec Industrial Select. PinPointer. CND 319 per issue (effective 2003); Quebec Industrial Select. Profiler. CND 579 per issue (effective 2003); Quebec Industrial Select. Prospector. CND 1,095 per issue (effective 2003).
Published by: Business Information Group, 12 Concorde Pl, Ste 800, Toronto, ON M3C 4J2, Canada. TEL 416-442-5600, 800-668-2374, FAX 416-442-2191, http://www.businessinformationgroup.ca.

REPERTORIO DE LA INDUSTRIA QUIMICA ESPANOLA/ DIRECTORY OF THE SPANISH CHEMICAL INDUSTRY. see *CHEMISTRY*

669.029 CHL
REPERTORIO SIDERURGICO LATINOAMERICANO. Text in Spanish. 1960. biennial. USD 120 in the Americas to members; USD 150 elsewhere to members; USD 155 in the Americas to non-members; USD 170 elsewhere to non-members (effective 2002); (effective 1995). **Document type:** *Directory.* **Description:** Provides data on companies in the sector: addresses, personnel, products and services.
Published by: Instituto Latinoamericano del Fierro y el Acero, Calle Benjamin 2944, 5o piso - Las Condes, Santiago, 9, Chile. TEL 56-2-2330545, FAX 56-2-2330768, ilafa@entelchile.net.

670.29 USA
REPORTERO INDUSTRIAL MEXICANO. Text in Spanish. 1980. m. free to qualified personnel. adv.
Published by: Keller International Publishing Corp., 150 Great Neck Rd, Great Neck, NY 11021. Ed. Felicia Morales. Pub. Terry Beirne. Circ: 22,028 (controlled).

RESOURCE GUIDE FOR STARTING AND GROWING A SMALL BUSINESS. see *BUSINESS AND ECONOMICS—Small Business*

RETAIL DIRECTORY OF EUROPE (YEAR). see *BUSINESS AND ECONOMICS—Marketing And Purchasing*

RETAIL DIRECTORY OF THE UK (YEAR). see *BUSINESS AND ECONOMICS—Marketing And Purchasing*

RETAIL INFO SYSTEMS NEWS DIRECTORY. see *BUSINESS AND ECONOMICS—Computer Applications*

RETIREMENT HOUSING FOODSERVICE WHO'S WHO. see *FOOD AND FOOD INDUSTRIES*

338.0029 USA ISSN 1048-7166
HF5065. R5
RHODE ISLAND BUSINESS DIRECTORY. Text in English. 1990. a. USD 1,100 combined subscription print, online & CD-ROM eds. (effective 2004 & 2005). index. back issues avail. **Document type:** *Directory.* **Description:** Includes all businesses in the state compiled from the yellow pages and telephone-verified. Each listing includes company name, complete address, phone number, name of owner, manager, and employee size, sales volume codes, and credit rating codes.
Related titles: CD-ROM ed.; Diskette ed.; E-mail ed.; Fax ed.; Magnetic Tape ed.; Online - full text ed.
Published by: American Business Directories (Subsidiary of: American Business Information, Inc.), 5711 S 86th Circle, P O Box 27347, Omaha, NE 68127. TEL 402-593-4600, 888-946-9377, 877-708-3844, FAX 402-331-5481, sales@directoriesusa.com, http://www.directoriesusa.com.

670.29 USA ISSN 0361-5103
RHODE ISLAND DIRECTORY OF MANUFACTURERS. Text in English. 1951. a. USD 45 (effective 1996). **Document type:** *Directory.* **Description:** Profiles over 2,500 firms; includes SIC section, as well as alphabetic and geographical indexes.
Formerly: Rhode Island Directory of Manufacturers and List of Commercial Establishments (0080-2743)
Published by: Department of Economic Development, 1 W Exchange St, Providence, RI 02903-1058. TEL 401-277-2601, FAX 401-277-2102. Circ: 3,000. **Dist. by:** Manufacturers' News, Inc., 1633 Central St, Evanston, IL 60201. TEL 847-864-7000.

670.29 USA ISSN 1088-761X
HF5065.R5
RHODE ISLAND MANUFACTURER'S REGISTER. Text in English. 1979. a. USD 59 (effective 2000). adv. charts; illus.; stat. **Document type:** *Directory.* **Description:** Profiles 2,393 manufacturers listed five ways: by company name, product, S.I.C., city and parent company.
Supersedes (in 1997): Connecticut - Rhode Island Directory of Manufacturers (0193-5909)
Related titles: CD-ROM ed.: Rhode Island Manufacturers Register for Windows 95/98, Windows N T. ISSN 1550-0934. USD 265 (effective 2000); Diskette ed.; Magnetic Tape ed.; Online - full text ed.
Published by: Manufacturers' News, Inc., 1633 Central St, Evanston, IL 60201. TEL 847-864-7000, 888-752-5200, FAX 847-332-1100, info@mninfo.com, info@manufacturersnews.com, sales@mninfo.com, http://www.manufacturersnews.com. Adv. contact Charles Scherer. B&W page USD 1,843.

320.52 USA ISSN 1064-7414
HS2321
THE RIGHT GUIDE; a guide to conservative, free-market, and traditional organizations. Text in English. 1992. s-a. USD 74.95 (effective 2001). **Document type:** *Directory.* **Description:** Profiles over 2,000 think tanks, lobbying groups, publishers, and public-interest litigation organizations. Includes financial information on organizations including revenues, salaries, lobbying expenditures and sources of funding.
Published by: Economics America, Inc., 612 Church St, Ann Arbor, MI 48104. TEL 313-995-0865, FAX 313-747-7258, wilcoxdl@aol.com. Ed. Derk Arend Wilcox.

(YEAR) ROANOKE METROPOLITAN AREA INDUSTRIAL DIRECTORY. see *BUSINESS AND ECONOMICS—Chamber Of Commerce Publications*

338.4767029 USA ISSN 0883-8046
T12.3.W47
ROCKY MOUNTAIN HIGH TECHNOLOGY DIRECTORY. Text in English. 1985. a. USD 159 (effective 2001). **Document type:** *Directory.* **Description:** Lists profiles of about 5,400 manufacturers and research and development firms in Arizona, Colorado, Montana, Nevada, New Mexico, Utah and Wyoming engaged in high-technology activities.
Published by: Leading Edge Communications, Inc., 1121 Old Siskiyou Hwy, Ashland, OR 97520. TEL 541-482-4990, FAX 541-482-4993. Eds. Kimberley Boesche, Philip Boesche. Circ: 1,500.

ROCKY MOUNTAIN STATES PETROLEUM INDUSTRY. see *PETROLEUM AND GAS*

ROLLADEN & SONNENSCHUTZ; Fachzeitschrift fuer das Rolladen- und Jalousiebauer-Handwerk. see *ARTS AND HANDICRAFTS*

ROOFING MATERIALS AND SYSTEMS DIRECTORY. see *BUILDING AND CONSTRUCTION*

380.1029 NGA
ROTA TRADE AND INDUSTRIAL DIRECTORY. NORTH CENTRAL STATE✶ . Text in English. s-a. NGN 50. adv.
Published by: Rota Publishing Co. Ltd., A.C. 5 Lagos St., 2nd Fl., PO Box 497, Kaduna, Kaduna State, Nigeria.

ROYAL AERONAUTICAL DIRECTORY OF EUROPEAN AVIATION. see *TRANSPORTATION—Air Transport*

620.0021 ZAF
S A A C E DIRECTORY OF FIRMS/S A V R I FIRMAGIDS. Text in Afrikaans, English. 1967. a., latest 2001. ZAR 150 (effective 2001). adv. **Document type:** *Directory.*
Former titles: South African Association of Consulting Engineers. Directory of Registered Firms; South African Association of Consulting Engineers. Directory of Members' Firms - Suid-Afrikaanse Vereniging van Raadgewende Ingenieurs. Gids van Lede Se Firmas
Published by: South African Association of Consulting Engineers/Suid-Afrikaanse Vereniging van Raadgewende Ingenieurs, PO Box 68482, Bryanston, 2021, South Africa. TEL 27-11-4632022, FAX 27-11-4637383, general@saace.co.za, http://www.saace.co.za. Ed., Adv. contact Pieter Roux. Circ: 3,000.

338.0029 ZAF
S A DIRECTORY OF BLACK MANAGERS. Text in English. 1994. a. ZAR 25. adv. illus. **Document type:** *Directory.*
Published by: Black Enterprise Publishing and Marketing, PO Box 2185, Houghton, Johannesburg 2041, South Africa. Ed. Thami Mazwai.

S A ELECTRONICS BUYER'S GUIDE. (South Africa) see *ELECTRONICS*

S & V TRADE DIRECTORY. see *SHOES AND BOOTS*

332.6029 USA
S I A DIRECTORY & GUIDE. Text in English. a. free. **Document type:** *Directory.* **Description:** Provides a guide to the membership, organization and services of the association.
Published by: Securities Industry Association, 120 Broadway, 35th Fl, New York, NY 10271. TEL 212-608-1500. Ed. Rosalie Pepe.

S I E INVESTMENT ADVISORY GUIDE. see *BUSINESS AND ECONOMICS—Investments*

S P I MEMBERSHIP DIRECTORY AND BUYER'S GUIDE. (Society of the Plastics Industry) see *PLASTICS*

380.1029 USA ISSN 1536-9420
SAN DIEGO COUNTY COMMERCE AND INDUSTRY DIRECTORY. Text in English. 1990. a. USD 99 (effective 2005). **Document type:** *Directory, Trade.* **Description:** Profiles over 4700 manufacturers, wholesalers, importers, exporters, and service companies.
Formerly (until 1999): San Diego County Business Directory (1047-9619)
Related titles: CD-ROM ed.: USD 215 (effective 1999).
Published by: (San Diego Economic Development Corporation), Harris InfoSource, 2057 E Aurora Rd, Twinsburg, OH 44087. TEL 800-888-5900, 330-425-9000, FAX 330-425-7150, http://www.harrisinfo.com.

659.1029 USA ISSN 1063-9144
SAN DIEGO CREATIVE DIRECTORY✶ . Text in English. 1981. every 18 mos. USD 44.50; USD 49.95 newsstand/cover (effective 2000). adv. back issues avail. **Document type:** *Directory.* **Description:** Portfolio of creative services by San Diego area advertisers, plus a directory of those and related services provided by the communications and creative community.
Published by: Blue Book Publishers, Inc., 7777 Fay Ave, Ste G, La Jolla, CA 92037-4325. TEL 858-454-7939, FAX 858-454-5984. Ed., Adv. contact Susan Davidson. Pub. Richard L Levin. R&P Stephen F Milne TEL 858-454-7939 ext 314. color page USD 4,500; trim 11 x 8.5. Circ: 5,000.

380.1029 USA
SAN FRANCISCO COUNTY COMMERCE AND INDUSTRY DIRECTORY✶ . Text in English. a. USD 75. **Document type:** *Directory.* **Description:** Lists 3,700 companies; profiles 770 large companies (2500 plus employees) in the 5-county San Francisco Bay area.
Related titles: CD-ROM ed.: USD 215.
Published by: (San Francisco Chamber of Commerce), Database Publishing Company, 701 E Ball Rd Ste 100, Anaheim, CA 92805-5962. TEL 714-778-6400, FAX 714-778-6811. R&P Sarah Fraser.

SAN JOSE FILM & VIDEO PRODUCTION HANDBOOK - DIRECTORY. see *MOTION PICTURES*

338.0029 USA ISSN 1060-7951
SAN MATEO COUNTY COMMERCE AND INDUSTRY DIRECTORY✶ . Text in English. a. USD 75. **Document type:** *Directory.* **Description:** Lists 2,800 companies, and 7,000 executives, managers and owners. Profiles 770 large companies (250 plus employees) in the 5-county San Francisco Bay area.
Related titles: CD-ROM ed.: USD 215.
Published by: (San Mateo Chamber of Commerce), Database Publishing Company, 701 E Ball Rd Ste 100, Anaheim, CA 92805-5962. TEL 714-778-6400, FAX 714-778-6811. R&P Sarah Fraser.

338.0029 USA
SANTA CLARA COUNTY COMMERCE AND INDUSTRY DIRECTORY✶ . Text in English. a. USD 75. **Document type:** *Directory.* **Description:** Contains 4,900 manufacturers, wholesalers, and high tech firms.
Related titles: CD-ROM ed.: USD 215.
Published by: Database Publishing Company, 701 E Ball Rd Ste 100, Anaheim, CA 92805-5962. TEL 714-778-6400, FAX 714-778-6811. R&P Sarah Fraser.

380.1029 071.1 USA ISSN 1203-5238
HF5072.S2
SASKATCHEWAN BUSINESS DIRECTORY. Text in English. 1996. a. USD 1,100 combined subscription print, online & CD-ROM eds. (effective 2004 & 2005). back issues avail. **Document type:** *Directory.*
Related titles: CD-ROM ed.; Diskette ed.; E-mail ed.; Fax ed.; Magnetic Tape ed.; Online - full text ed.
Published by: American Business Directories (Subsidiary of: American Business Information, Inc.), 5711 S 86th Circle, P O Box 27347, Omaha, NE 68127. TEL 402-593-4600, 888-946-9377, 877-708-3844, FAX 402-331-5481, sales@directoriesusa.com, http://www.directoriesusa.com.

SATELLITE INDUSTRY DIRECTORY. see *COMMUNICATIONS*

SCHOOL FOODSERVICE WHO'S WHO. see *FOOD AND FOOD INDUSTRIES*

687.0688 USA
SCHOOL UNIFORMS. Text in English. 1997. 6/yr. USD 45 (effective 2000). adv. **Document type:** *Trade.* **Description:** Aimed at private, parochial and public schools with school uniforms. For school directors, principals and school boards and districts, as well as for school uniform manufacturers, retailers and distributors. Contains news on the industry, company profiles, show coverage, public and private school sections, website reviews and statistics.
Published by: Fashion Market Magazine Group, Inc., 617 W 46th St #2, New York, NY 10036-1906. TEL 212-541-9350, FAX 212-541-9340, fashionmmg@aol.com. Ed., Pub., R&P, Adv. contact Nicolas Monjo.

658.0029 GBR
SCOTLAND'S TOP COMPANIES (YEAR). Text in English. a., latest 2002/3, 21st Ed. GBP 230 per vol. for vols.1 & 2; GBP 145 per vol. for vol.1 or 2 (effective 2003). **Document type:** *Trade.* **Description:** Provides detailed profiles of the top 2,000 companies.
Related titles: CD-ROM ed.; Diskette ed.
Published by: Jordans Ltd. (Subsidiary of: Jordan Publishing Ltd.), 21 Thomas St, Bristol, BS1 6JS, United Kingdom. TEL 44-117-9230600, FAX 44-207-4003333, customersupport@jordans.co.uk, http://www.jordans.co.uk/.

338.0029 ZAF
SCOTTBURGH DIRECTORY - BUYERS' GUIDE. Text in English. 1984. a. ZAR 30 (effective 2001). **Document type:** *Directory.*
Supersedes: Scottburgh Directory (1016-6874)

Published by: Braby's (Subsidiary of: Associated Industries), Attn: Sue Pearson, PO Box 1426, Pinetown, 3600, South Africa. TEL 27-31-7174141, FAX 27-31-7173011.

615.102571 CAN ISSN 1706-9637
SCOTT'S CANADIAN PHARMACISTS DIRECTORY. Text in English. 1996. biennial. CND 209 per issue (effective 2005). **Document type:** *Directory, Trade.* **Description:** Contains information on over 18,000 Canadian pharmacists.
Formerly (until 2001): Canadian Pharmacists Directory (1203-2840)
Related titles: CD-ROM ed.: National Pharmacists Select Pinpointer. CND 199 per issue (effective 2004); National Pharmacists Select Profiler. CND 449 per issue (effective 2004); National Pharmacists Select Prospector. CND 995 per issue (effective 2004).
Published by: Business Information Group, 12 Concorde Pl, Ste 800, Toronto, ON M3C 4J2, Canada. TEL 416-442-5600, 800-668-2374, FAX 416-442-2191, http://www.businessinformationgroup.ca/medical/cndpharmdirect.asp.

338.0029 CAN ISSN 1204-7619
SCOTT'S DIRECTORIES - ATLANTIC INDUSTRIAL MANUFACTURERS. Text in English. 1977. a. (in May). CND 199 per issue (effective 2004). **Document type:** *Directory, Trade.* **Description:** Accesses information on 5,500 manufacturing, wholesale and distribution companies and 10,081 executives and agents in New Brunswick, Nova Scotia, P.E.I. and Newfoundland.
Former titles (until 1995): Scott's Directories - Atlantic Manufacturing (0831-1854); (until 1985): Scott's Industrial Directory - Atlantic Manufacturers (0706-5167)
Related titles: CD-ROM ed.: CND 199 per issue (effective 2004). —CISTI.
Published by: Business Information Group, 12 Concorde Pl, Ste 800, Toronto, ON M3C 4J2, Canada. TEL 416-442-5600, 800-668-2374, FAX 416-442-2191, http://www.businessinformationgroup.ca.

338.0029 CAN ISSN 0830-9272
HC117.O6
SCOTT'S DIRECTORIES - ONTARIO MANUFACTURERS. Text in English. 1957. a. CND 349 per issue domestic; CND 361 per issue foreign (effective 2004). **Document type:** *Directory, Trade.* **Description:** Complete compilation of information on Canadian manufacturers, wholesalers, distributors and agents.
Former titles (until 1984): Scott's Industrial Directory - Ontario Manufacturers (0316-7879); (until 1972): Scott's Industrial Directory - Ontario Section (0316-7860)
Related titles: CD-ROM ed.: USD 349 per issue (effective 2004).
Published by: Business Information Group, 12 Concorde Pl, Ste 800, Toronto, ON M3C 4J2, Canada. TEL 416-442-5600, 800-668-2374, FAX 416-442-2191, http://www.businessinformationgroup.ca.

338.0029 CAN ISSN 1200-8540
T12.5.C2 S35
SCOTT'S DIRECTORIES - WESTERN INDUSTRIAL MANUFACTURERS. Text in English. 1969. a. (in July). CND 279 per issue (effective 2004). **Document type:** *Directory, Trade.* **Description:** Profiles 17,250 companies and 29,645 executives in British Columbia, Alberta, Saskatchewan and Manitoba.
Former titles (until 1994): Scott's Directories - Western Manufacturers (0829-2248); (until 1986): Scott's Industrial Directory. Western Manufacturers (0317-879X); Scott's Industrial Directory. Western Section (0317-8781)
Related titles: CD-ROM ed.: CND 279 per issue (effective 2004). —CISTI.
Published by: Business Information Group, 12 Concorde Pl, Ste 800, Toronto, ON M3C 4J2, Canada. TEL 416-442-5600, 800-668-2374, FAX 416-442-2191, http://www.businessinformationgroup.ca.

380.1029 CAN
SCOTT'S TORONTO BUSINESS DIRECTORY. Variant title: Greater Toronto (Metro & Boundary). Text in English. 1980. a. (Apr.) (in 2 vols.). CND 429 per vol. (effective 2004). adv. **Document type:** *Directory, Trade.* **Description:** Consists of two volumes: the Metro Edition contains information on 17,250 industrial and industry support companies located in Metro Toronto while the Boundary Edition lists 18,500 companies and 34,400 executives.
Former titles: Scott's Directories. Greater Toronto Business Directory (1199-7494); (until 1993): Scott's Directories, Metropolitan Toronto and Toronto Vicinity Trade (0828-914X); (until 1985): Scott's Trade Directory (0228-6920)
Related titles: CD-ROM ed.: Greater Toronto Business Select. PinPointer. CND 399 per issue (effective 2003); Greater Toronto Business Select. Profiler. CND 799 per issue (effective 2003); Greater Toronto Business Select. Prospector. CND 1,495 per issue (effective 2003).
Published by: Business Information Group, 12 Concorde Pl, Ste 800, Toronto, ON M3C 4J2, Canada. TEL 416-442-5600, 800-668-2374, FAX 416-442-2191, http://www.businessinformationgroup.ca, http://www.scottsinfo.com.

668.4029 USA
SCRAP PLASTICS MARKETS DIRECTORY. Text in English. a. USD 53 domestic; USD 60 foreign (effective 2001). adv. charts. **Document type:** *Directory, Trade.* **Description:** Provides information on more than 425 plastics scrap reclaimers, with company addresses, contact names, and specific scrap plastic preferences. Also includes information on manufacturers of plastics recycling equipment.
Formerly: Directory of U S and Canadian Scrap Plastics Processors and Buyers
Published by: Resource Recycling, Inc., PO Box 42270, Portland, OR 97242-0270. TEL 503-203-1305, FAX 503-203-1356, plasticss@resource-recycling.com, publisher@resource-recycling.com, http://www.resource-recycling.com. Ed. Jerry Powell. Pub. Mary Lynch. R&P Judy Roumpf. Adv. contact Rick Downing TEL 440-257-6453.

381.029 USA ISSN 1079-3712
HF5482
SECONDARY MARKET GUIDE. Text in English. 1994. a. USD 100 (effective 2000). **Document type:** *Directory.*
Published by: Penton Media, Inc. (Hasbrouck Heights) (Subsidiary of: Pittway Company), 611 Rte 46 W, Hasbrouck Heights, NJ 07604. TEL 201-393-9553, 800-526-6052, FAX 201-393-9558.

SECURITECH; the international guide to security equipment. see *CRIMINOLOGY AND LAW ENFORCEMENT*

380.1029 USA ISSN 0080-8512
SEEKER'S GUIDE; a directory of unusual organizations. Text in English. 1961. irreg., latest 1970. USD 5.60.
Published by: Aurea Publications, 207 Allen Ave, Allenhurst, NJ 07711. TEL 908-531-4535. Ed. Alex Sandri White.

338.0029 DEU ISSN 0723-3159
SEIBT INDUSTRIEKATALOG. Text in German. 1921. a. adv. **Document type:** *Directory, Trade.*
Related titles: CD-ROM ed.; Online - full text ed.: (from G B I); English ed.: Seibt Directory of German Industries. ISSN 0940-9831; French ed.: Seibt Repertoire de l'industrie Allemande. ISSN 0940-984X; Multiple languages ed.: Seibt Catalogo de la Industria Alemana. ISSN 0940-9823.
Published by: Seibt Verlag GmbH, Leopoldstr 208, Munich, 80804, Germany. TEL 49-89-360903-0, FAX 49-89-364317, http://www.seibt.com. Adv. contact Brita Graef. Circ: 20,000.

SELL'S MARINE INDUSTRY BUYERS' GUIDE. see *SPORTS AND GAMES—Boats And Boating*

338.0029 GBR ISSN 0261-5584
T12.5.G7
SELL'S PRODUCTS & SERVICES DIRECTORY. Text in English. 1885. a., latest vol.116, 2001/2002. GBP 104 per vol. for print ed.; GBP 166 combined subscription for both print & CD-ROM ed. (effective 2001). adv. bk.rev. **Document type:** *Directory, Trade.* **Description:** Contains comprehensive coverage of the manufacturing and industrial business service sectors in easy to use formats. Provides detailed information on over 60,000 companies, it is the complete A-Z purchasing guide.
Incorporates (1935-1997): Government and Municipal Buyers Guide (0967-3873); Which was formerly: Government and Municipal Contractors (0140-5764); (until 1977): Sell's Government and Municipal Contractors Register (0072-5129); (until 1972): Government and Municipal Contractors Register; Incorporates (1984-1993): Sell's Scottish Directory; Which was formerly: Scottish National Register of Classified Trades (0080-8148); Sell's Directory of Products and Services (0080-8725); Sell's Directory of British Industry and Commerce
Related titles: CD-ROM ed.
Published by: C M P Information Ltd. (Subsidiary of: United Business Media), Sovereign House, Sovereign Way, Tonbridge, Kent TN9 1RW, United Kingdom. TEL 44-1732-377391, FAX 44-1732-377552, industry@unitedbusinessmedia.com, http://www.ubminfo.com/productview.asp?id=14, http://www.cmpinformation.com, http://www.look4industry.co.uk, http://www.ubminfo.com/main.asp. Ed. Philip Dury TEL 44-1732-377542. Pub. Elaine Soni TEL 44-1732-377423. R&P Rachel Wichall TEL 44-1732-377627. Adv. contact Sarah Thompson TEL 44-1732-377576. page GBP 1,155. Circ: 10,500.

SEMICONDUCTOR INDUSTRY ASSOCIATION. (YEAR) ANNUAL REPORT & DIRECTORY. see *ELECTRONICS*

SEMISOURCE. see *ELECTRONICS*

SETTING UP ENTERPRISES IN JAPAN. see *BUSINESS AND ECONOMICS—Investments*

382.029 UAE
SHARJAH COMMERCIAL DIRECTORY/DALIL AL-SHARQAH AL-TIJARI. Text in Arabic, English. 1980. a. USD 45 in the Middle East; USD 75 elsewhere (effective 2001). adv. **Document type:** *Directory.* **Description:** Provides general information on economic development in the U.A.E. and more detailed information on Sharjah, including current projects, commercial, trade and industrial activity. Lists Sharjah-based and other U.A.E. firms by activity type and company name.
Published by: Sharjah Chamber of Commerce and Industry, P O Box 580, Sharjah, United Arab Emirates. TEL 971-6-5088600, FAX 971-6-5541119, scci@sharjah.gov.ae, http://www.sharjah.gov.ae. Ed. Ahmed Mohamed Al-Midfa'a. R&P Saeed O Al Jarwan. Adv. contact Saeed Al Najjar. Circ: 30,000 (paid); 20,000 (controlled).

382.029 UAE
SHARJAH EXPORTER - IMPORTER DIRECTORY/DALEEL AL SARIQAH LIL MOSADDIREEN WA AL-MOSTAWRIDEEN. Text in Arabic, English. 1995. a. free. **Document type:** *Directory.* **Description:** Includes names, addresses, activities, and other information for Sharjah's exporters and importers. Also presents information about ports and customs.
Published by: Sharjah Chamber of Commerce and Industry, P O Box 580, Sharjah, United Arab Emirates. TEL 971-6-5088600, FAX 971-6-5541119, scci@sharjah.gov.ae, http://www.sharjah.gov.ae.

SHELDON'S MAJOR STORES & CHAINS. see *BUSINESS AND ECONOMICS—Marketing And Purchasing*

SHEPHARD'S UNMANNED VEHICLES HANDBOOK. see *AERONAUTICS AND SPACE FLIGHT*

380.1029 ISR
SHERUT MEDA ISKI. Text in Hebrew. m.
Published by: Dun & Bradstreet (Israel) Ltd., P O Box 20001, Tel Aviv, 61200, Israel. TEL (03)216121.

THE SHOE FACTORY BUYER'S GUIDE; directory of suppliers to the shoe manufacturing industry. see *SHOES AND BOOTS*

380.1029 JPN
SHOKURYO KEIZAI NENKAN✶ /FOOD ECONOMICS YEARBOOK. Text in Japanese. a. JPY 2,500. illus.
Formerly: Sogo Keizai Nenkan
Published by: Shokuryo Keizai Shinbun Sha, 35-12 Ishigatsuji-cho, Tennoji-ku, Osaka-shi, 543-0031, Japan.

380.1029 USA ISSN 0037-4210
HF5035
SHOPPING CENTER DIRECTORY✶ . Text in English. 1957. a. USD 765; includes Top Contacts. **Document type:** *Directory.* **Description:** Provides descriptive information regarding U.S. shopping centers, including ownership, leasing information, anchor stores, tenant listings, and more.
Related titles: CD-ROM ed.: 1957.
Published by: National Research Bureau, Inc. (Chicago), 200 W Jackson Blvd no.2700, Chicago, IL 60606-6910. TEL 312-541-0100, FAX 312-541-1492. Ed. Patricia Kelly. Pub. Nancy Veatch. **Orders to:** National Research Bureau, 263 Tresser Blvd., Flr. 9, Stamford, CT 06901-3236. TEL 800-456-4555, FAX 203-563-3131.

SHORTLINER. see *AGRICULTURE—Agricultural Equipment*

658.8029 051 USA
SHOWCASE (ACTON); the luxury emporium. Text in English. 1999 (Jun.). m. USD 29.99 domestic; USD 39.99 in Canada; USD 69.99 elsewhere (effective 2001). adv. **Document type:** *Magazine, Consumer.* **Description:** Contains listings of dealer-owned and pre-owned luxury items for buyers and sellers of luxury items and services, including automobiles, boats, aircraft, real estate and other goods.
Formerly (until 2001): Luxury Media's Showcase (1526-4807)
Published by: CurtCo Media Labs, One Acton Pl, Acton, MA 01720. TEL 800-229-7622, FAX 978-795-3261.

SHOWCASE ILLUSTRATION. see *ART*

380.1029 GBR
SHOWDATES. Text in English. 1981. a. GBP 27.50 (effective 2000); includes Showman's Directory. adv. **Document type:** *Directory.* **Description:** Examines shows such as: agricultural, county, town, air, dog shows, steam engine rallies, and festivals.
Related titles: ◆ Supplement to: Showman's Directory.
Published by: Lance Publications, 45 Bridge St, Godalming, Surrey GU7 1HL, United Kingdom. TEL 44-1483-422184, FAX 44-1483-425697, lanpub@showmans-directory.co.uk, http://www.showmans-directory.co.uk. Ed. Valerie Wright. Pub., Adv. contact Stephen Lance. Circ: 3,500.

380.1029 GBR
SHOWMAN'S DIRECTORY. Text in English. 1968. a. GBP 17 (effective 2000). adv. **Document type:** *Directory.*
Related titles: ◆ Supplement(s): Showdates.
Published by: Lance Publications, 45 Bridge St, Godalming, Surrey GU7 1HL, United Kingdom. TEL 44-1483-422184, FAX 44-1483-425697, lanpub@showmans-directory.co.uk, http://www.showmans-directory.co.uk. Ed. Valerie Wright. Pub., Adv. contact Stephen Lance. Circ: 6,500.

SHOWS & EXHIBITIONS. see *MEETINGS AND CONGRESSES*

SIGNMAKERS AND SUPPLIERS DIRECTORY. see *ADVERTISING AND PUBLIC RELATIONS*

380.1029　　　SGP　　　ISSN 0218-2831
SINGAPORE CONTRACTORS' EQUIPMENT CATALOGUE. Text in English. 1990. a. USD 40. adv. **Document type:** *Catalog.* **Description:** Caters to the building, marine and oil field industry.
Published by: Times Media Pte Ltd, Directories Division, 1 New Industrial Rd, Times Centre, Singapore, 536196, Singapore. TEL 65-285-0161, FAX 65-2881186. Pub., R&P Leslie Lim. Adv. contact Joseph Liang. Circ: 20,000 (controlled).

382.029　　　SGP　　　ISSN 0217-5428
SINGAPORE EXPORTERS∗ . Text in English. 1984. a. SGD 50. **Document type:** *Trade.*
Published by: (Trade Development Board), Singapore Information Services Pte. Ltd., c/o Trade Development Board, 230 Victoria Street, 07-00 Bugis Junction Office Tower, Singapore, 188024, Singapore. TEL 2723390, FAX 2783391.

382.029　　　SGP
SINGAPORE INDIAN CHAMBER OF COMMERCE. ANNUAL REPORT & DIRECTORY. Text in English. 1948. a. SGD 20, USD 25.
Formerly: Singapore Indian Chamber of Commerce. Directory
Published by: Singapore Indian Chamber of Commerce, 101 Cecil St, 23-01 Tong Eng Bldg, Singapore, 069533, Singapore. FAX 65-223-1707, TELEX RS 22336 SINDCC. Circ: 700.

338.0029　　　USA　　　ISSN 0887-4050
SMALL BUSINESS PREFERENTIAL SUBCONTRACTS OPPORTUNITIES MONTHLY. Text in English. m. USD 84 (effective 2005). **Document type:** *Magazine, Trade.*
Published by: Government Data Publications, Inc., 2300 M St, N W, Washington, DC 20037. TEL 800-275-4688, FAX 718-998-5960, gdp@govdata.com, http://www.govdata.com. Ed. Siegfried Lobel.

338.0029　　　PAK
SMAR'S INDUSTRIAL DIRECTORY OF PAKISTAN. Text in English. 1971. a. PKR 25, USD 20. adv. **Document type:** *Directory.*
Published by: Smar International, 6 Afshan Chambers, Tariq Rd., P.E.C.H.S., Karachi 29, Pakistan. Ed. Mahmud-Ul-Hassan. Circ: 5,000.

SOCIETY OF GLASS AND CERAMIC DECORATORS. MEMBERSHIP DIRECTORY. see *CERAMICS, GLASS AND POTTERY*

382.029　　　SLB
SOLOMON ISLANDS TRADE DIRECTORY (YEAR). Text in English. a.?. **Document type:** *Directory, Trade.*
Published by: Ministry of Commerce and Primary Industries, Foreign Investment Board, PO Box G26, Honiara, Solomon Isl. TEL 677-23015, FAX 677-21651.

338.0029　　　FRA　　　ISSN 1166-6609
SONOVISION QUI FAIT QUOI?. Variant title: Qui Fait Quoi?. Text in French. 1990. a. EUR 70 domestic; EUR 95 foreign (effective 2004). **Document type:** *Directory, Trade.*
Published by: Groupe Studio Press (Subsidiary of: Roularta Media Group), 11, rue Charles Schmidt, St Ouen, 93400, France. TEL 33-8-20200959, info@pveditions.com, http://www.pveditions.com.

SORKINS DIRECTORY OF BUSINESS & GOVERNMENT (CHICAGO EDITION). see *BUSINESS AND ECONOMICS—Production Of Goods And Services*

338.0029　　　USA
THE SOURCE (PRINCETON). Text in English. a. adv. **Document type:** *Directory.*
Published by: Construction Financial Management Association, 29 Emmons Dr, Ste F 50, Princeton, NJ 08540-1413. TEL 609-452-8000, FAX 609-452-0417. Ed. Susan A Dunham. R&P Pat Gillette. adv.: B&W page USD 1,565. Circ: 7,000 (controlled).

384　　　CAN　　　ISSN 0700-480X
SOURCES. Text in English, French. 1977. s-a. CND 45; CND 29.95 newsstand/cover (effective 2003). adv. bk.rev. bibl. back issues avail. **Document type:** *Directory.* **Description:** Helps journalists, editors, producers and researchers find expert contacts.
Related titles: Online - full text ed.
—CISTI.
Published by: Sources Publishing, 489 College St, Ste 305, Toronto M6G 1A5, ON M6G 1A5, Canada. TEL 416-964-7799, FAX 416-964-8763, sources@sources.com, http://www.sources.com. Ed. Tracey Parn. Pub. Barrie Zwicker. R&P Ulli Diemer. Adv. contact Michelle Hernandez. B&W page CND 2,100, color page CND 2,500; trim 8.13 x 10.75. Circ: 14,000.

671.52　　　ZAF
SOUTH AFRICAN INSTITUTE OF WELDING. NATIONAL REGISTER/SUID-AFRIKAANSE INSTITUUT VIR SWEIWESE. NASIONALE REGISTER. Text in Afrikaans, English. 1994. a. illus. **Document type:** *Directory.*

Published by: South African Institute of Welding/Suid-Afrikaanse Instituut vir Sweiwese, PO Box 527, Crown Mines, 2025, South Africa.

338.0029　　　USA　　　ISSN 1046-0934
HF5065.S6
SOUTH CAROLINA BUSINESS DIRECTORY. Text in English. 1988. a. USD 1,100 combined subscription print, online & CD-ROM eds. (effective 2004 & 2005). index. back issues avail. **Document type:** *Directory.* **Description:** Includes all businesses in the state compiled from the yellow pages and telephone-verified. Each listing includes company name, complete address, phone number, name of owner, manager, and employee size, sales volume codes, and credit rating codes.
Related titles: CD-ROM ed.; Diskette ed.; E-mail ed.; Fax ed.; Magnetic Tape ed.; Online - full text ed.
Published by: American Business Directories (Subsidiary of: American Business Information, Inc.), 5711 S 86th Circle, P O Box 27347, Omaha, NE 68127. TEL 402-593-4600, 888-946-9377, 877-708-3844, FAX 402-331-5481, sales@directoriesusa.com, http://www.directoriesusa.com.

380.1029　　　USA
SOUTH CAROLINA COMPUTER AND SOFTWARE SERVICES DIRECTORY. Text in English. 1998. a. USD 20 (effective 2000). stat. **Document type:** *Directory, Trade.* **Description:** Provides information on software and computer companies in South Carolina.
Published by: South Carolina Department of Commerce, 1201 Main St., Ste 1600, Columbia, SC 29201-3200. TEL 803-737-0400, FAX 803-737-1652, http://www.callsouthcarolina.com. Ed. Melissa McLeod.

670.29　　　USA
SOUTH CAROLINA INDUSTRIAL DIRECTORY. Text in English. a. USD 85 (effective 2001). adv. stat. **Document type:** *Directory, Government.* **Description:** Provides information on 4,100 manufacturing and business firms in 5 sections and through various statistical data sections.
Related titles: CD-ROM ed.: USD 199.
Published by: Department of Commerce, Research and Communications, PO Box 927, Columbia, SC 29202. TEL 803-737-0400, FAX 803-737-1652, http://www.state.sc.us/commerce. Ed., R&P Susan Turkopuls. Adv. contact Dennis Craighead.

670.29　　　USA　　　ISSN 1074-2476
HF5065.S6
SOUTH CAROLINA MANUFACTURERS REGISTER. Text in English. 1995. a. USD 74 (effective 2001). adv. 488 p./no.; **Document type:** *Directory.* **Description:** Profiles 5,661 companies in five sections by: company name, SIC, city, product and parent company.
Related titles: CD-ROM ed.: USD 355 (effective 2001); Diskette ed.
Published by: Manufacturers' News, Inc., 1633 Central St, Evanston, IL 60201. TEL 847-864-7000, 888-752-5200, FAX 847-332-1100, info@mninfo.com, info@manufacturersnews.com, sales@mninfo.com, http://www.mninfo.com, http://www.manufacturersnews.com. Ed. Steve Garland.

670.29　　　USA　　　ISSN 1090-5073
SOUTH CENTRAL HIGH TECHNOLOGY DIRECTORY. Text in English. 1996. a. USD 90 (effective 2001). **Document type:** *Directory.* **Description:** Lists profiles of about 2,200 manufacturers and research and development firms in Arkansas, Louisiana and Oklahoma engaged in high-technology activities.
Published by: Leading Edge Communications, Inc., 1121 Old Siskiyou Hwy, Ashland, OR 97520. TEL 541-482-4990, FAX 541-482-4993. Eds. Kimberley Boesche, Philip Boesche. Circ: 300.

338.0029　　　ZAF
SOUTH COAST DIRECTORY. Text in English. 1979. a. USD 70 (effective 2001). **Document type:** *Directory.* **Description:** Covers the area south of Dubau along the Kiwa Zulu-Natal coast.
Incorporates: Scottburgh Directory - Buyer's Guide; Port Shepstone - Margate Directory; Which was formerly: Port Shepstone Directory (1016-6823)
Published by: Braby's (Subsidiary of: Associated Industries), Attn: Sue Pearson, PO Box 1426, Pinetown, 3600, South Africa. TEL 27-31-7017021, FAX 27-31-7017036, booksales@brabys.co.za.

338.0029　　　USA　　　ISSN 1048-7409
HF5065.S8
SOUTH DAKOTA BUSINESS DIRECTORY. Text in English. 1984. a. USD 1,100 combined subscription print, online & CD-ROM eds. (effective 2004 & 2005). index. back issues avail. **Document type:** *Directory.* **Description:** Includes all businesses in the state compiled from the yellow pages and telephone-verified. Each listing includes company name, complete address, phone number, name of owner, manager, and employee size, sales volume codes, and credit rating codes.
Related titles: CD-ROM ed.; Diskette ed.; E-mail ed.; Fax ed.; Magnetic Tape ed.; Online - full text ed.

Published by: American Business Directories (Subsidiary of: American Business Information, Inc.), 5711 S 86th Circle, P O Box 27347, Omaha, NE 68127. TEL 402-593-4600, 888-946-9377, 877-708-3844, FAX 402-331-5481, sales@directoriesusa.com, http://www.directoriesusa.com.

338.0029　　　USA　　　ISSN 1088-7628
HF5065.S8
SOUTH DAKOTA MANUFACTURERS REGISTER. Text in English. 1975. a. USD 58 (effective 2000). adv. **Document type:** *Directory.* **Description:** Profiles approximately 1,351 manufacturers; includes SIC, geographical, alphabetical by company name, and parent company sections.
Former titles (until 1997): South Dakota Manufacturers and Processors Directory (1075-6825); (until 1994): Manufacturers and Processors Directory. South Dakota (1049-3050); (until 1990): Directory of Manufacturers and Processors (0743-5940); (until 1984): Manufacturers and Processors Directory (0094-2758)
Related titles: CD-ROM ed.: USD 175 (effective 2000); Diskette ed.: USD 195.
Published by: Manufacturers' News, Inc., 1633 Central St, Evanston, IL 60201. TEL 847-864-7000, 888-752-5200, FAX 847-332-1100, info@mninfo.com, info@manufacturersnews.com, sales@mninfo.com, http://www.manufacturersnews.com. Ed. Frank Lambing. Adv. contact Charles Scherer. B&W page USD 1,843.

SOUTHEAST STATES PETROLEUM INDUSTRY. see *PETROLEUM AND GAS*

910.029　　　ZAF
SOUTHERN AFRICAN TOURISM UPDATE'S BUYERS' GUIDE & WHO'S WHO FOR SOUTHERN AFRICAN TOURISM PRODUCTS. Text in English. 1994. a. adv. illus.; maps. **Document type:** *Directory.*
Published by: (Southern African Tourism and Safari Association), Travel and Trade Publishing (Pty) Ltd., PO Box 662, Auckland Park, Johannesburg 2006, South Africa.

338.0029　　　USA　　　ISSN 1061-2181
HF5065.C2
SOUTHERN CALIFORNIA BUSINESS DIRECTORY. Text in English. 1992. a. USD 1,100 combined subscription print, online & CD-ROM eds. (effective 2004 & 2005). index. back issues avail. **Document type:** *Directory.* **Description:** Includes all businesses in the Southern California area compiled from the yellow pages and telephone-verified. Each listing includes company name, complete address, phone number, name of owner, manager, and employee size, sales volume codes, and credit rating codes.
Related titles: CD-ROM ed.: ISSN 1551-4021; Diskette ed.; E-mail ed.; Fax ed.; Magnetic Tape ed.; Online - full text ed.
Published by: American Business Directories (Subsidiary of: American Business Information, Inc.), 5711 S 86th Circle, P O Box 27347, Omaha, NE 68127. TEL 402-593-4600, 888-946-9377, 877-708-3844, FAX 402-331-5481, karen.peters@infousa.com, sales@directoriesusa.com, http://www.directoriesusa.com.

380.1029　　　USA　　　ISSN 0093-3090
HF5065.C2
SOUTHERN CALIFORNIA BUSINESS DIRECTORY AND BUYERS GUIDE∗ . Text in English. 1964. a. USD 169. adv. illus. **Document type:** *Directory.* **Description:** Details profiles of 31,000 manufacturers, wholesalers, and service companies in 13 Southern California counties. Lists 78000 CEO's owners and key executives.
Related titles: CD-ROM ed.: USD 598 (effective 1999).
Published by: (Los Angeles Area Chamber of Commerce), Database Publishing Company, 701 E Ball Rd Ste 100, Anaheim, CA 92805-5962. TEL 714-778-6400, FAX 714-778-6811. Ed., R&P Sarah Fraser. Circ: 2,500.

SOUTHWESTERN FINANCIAL DIRECTORY. see *BUSINESS AND ECONOMICS—Banking And Finance*

380.1029　　　USA
SPANISH YELLOW PAGES. Text in Spanish. 1986. a. free. adv. **Document type:** *Consumer.* **Description:** Lists services and products for the Hispanic market.
Published by: Spanish Publications, Inc., 6601 Tarnef Dr, Houston, TX 77074. TEL 713-774-4652, FAX 713-774-4666. Ed., Adv. contact Alvaro Duenas. Pub. Mario Duenas. R&P Raul Alonso. Circ: 150,000.

338.0029　　　DEU　　　ISSN 0471-1858
SPEDITEUR ADRESSBUCH. Text in German. 1950. a. EUR 111 (effective 2005). **Document type:** *Directory, Trade.*
Published by: Deutscher Verkehrs Verlag GmbH, Nordkanalstr 36, Hamburg, 20097, Germany. TEL 49-40-2371401, FAX 49-40-23714205, info@dvv-gruppe.de, http://www.dvv-gruppe.de.

796.029　　　USA
SPORT SUMMIT SPORTS BUSINESS DIRECTORY. Text in English. 1995. a. USD 209 domestic; USD 239 foreign (effective 2000). **Document type:** *Directory.* **Description:** Supplies a comprehensive resource guide providing information on over 9,000 companies in every aspect of the sports business industry.

▼ *new title*　　➤ *refereed*　　∗ *unverified*　　◆ *full entry avail.*

Related titles: Online - full content ed.: USD 249 (effective 2000).
Published by: International Sport Summit, 6550 Rock Spring Dr, Ste 500, Bethesda, MD 20817-1126. TEL 301-493-5500, FAX 301-493-0536, ejksports@ejkrause.com, http://www.sportsummit.com. Circ: 9,500.

SPORTS MARKET PLACE. see *SPORTS AND GAMES*

659   DEU   ISSN 0933-4947
SPOTS PLANUNGSDATEN HOERFUNK - FERNSEHEN. Text in German. 1988. q. EUR 210; EUR 74 newsstand/cover (effective 2004). adv. **Document type:** *Directory, Trade.*
Published by: Maerkte und Medien Verlagsgesellschaft mbH (Subsidiary of: Sueddeutscher Verlag GmbH), Karlstr 41, Munich, 80333, Germany. TEL 49-89-5485205, FAX 49-89-54852520, kontakt@kontakter.de, http://www.kontakter.de. adv.: B&W page EUR 1,250, color page EUR 2,200; trim 210 x 297. Circ: 2,000 (paid and controlled).

338   ZAF   ISSN 1016-6904
SPRINGS BUYERS' GUIDE. Text in English. 1990. a. ZAR 30 (effective 2001). **Document type:** *Directory.*
Published by: Braby's (Subsidiary of: Associated Industries), Attn: Sue Pearson, PO Box 1426, Pinetown, 3600, South Africa. TEL 27-31-7174141, FAX 27-31-7173011.

STAFFING INDUSTRY SUPPLIER DIRECTORY. see *BUSINESS AND ECONOMICS—Personnel Management*

STAINLESS STEEL BUYER'S GUIDE (YEAR). see *METALLURGY*

659.1029   USA
HF5805
STANDARD DIRECTORY OF ADVERTISERS (ADVERTISING AGENCIES). Text in English. 1915. a. USD 899 per issue (effective 2005). adv. **Document type:** *Directory, Trade.* **Description:** Lists advertisers alphabetically by industry or by state and city; listings include address and telephone numbers, advertising appropriations and agencies.
Formerly: Standard Directory of Advertisers (Geographic Edition) (0081-4229)
Related titles: CD-ROM ed.; Magnetic Tape ed.; ◆ Special ed. of: Standard Directory of Advertisers (Business Classifications Edition). ISSN 1048-2415.
Published by: Marquis Who's Who, 562 Central Ave, New Providence, NJ 07964. TEL 908-673-1001, 800-473-7020, FAX 908-673-1189, http://www.marquiswhoswho.com. Circ: 25,000.

659.1029   USA   ISSN 1048-2415
HF5805
STANDARD DIRECTORY OF ADVERTISERS (BUSINESS CLASSIFICATIONS EDITION). Text in English. 1964. a. USD 899 per issue (effective 2005). **Document type:** *Directory, Trade.* **Description:** Lists advertisers alphabetically by industry or by state and city; listings include address and telephone numbers, advertising appropriations and agencies.
Related titles: Online - full text ed.; ◆ Special ed(s).: Standard Directory of Advertisers (Advertising Agencies).
—CCC.
Published by: Marquis Who's Who, 562 Central Ave, New Providence, NJ 07964. TEL 908-673-1001, 800-473-7020, FAX 908-673-1189, http://www.marquiswhoswho.com. Circ: 25,000.

659.1029   USA   ISSN 0085-6614
HF5805
STANDARD DIRECTORY OF ADVERTISING AGENCIES; the agency red book. Text in English. 1917. 2/yr. adv. **Document type:** *Directory, Trade.* **Description:** Lists current facts on over 9,500 advertising agencies in the USA. Includes key management, creative, account, and production people.
Related titles: CD-ROM ed.; Magnetic Tape ed.
—CCC.
Published by: LexisNexis (Subsidiary of: LexisNexis North America), PO Box 7587, Charlottesville, VA 22906-7587. TEL 434-972-7600, 800-446-3410, llp.customer.support@lexis-nexis.com, http://web.nexis.com/sources/scripts/info.pl?151201, http://www.lexislawpublishing.com. Circ: 9,200.

659.1029   USA
STANDARD DIRECTORY OF INTERNATIONAL ADVERTISERS AND AGENCIES; the international red book. Text in English. 1984. a. USD 565 (effective 1999). adv. **Document type:** *Directory.* **Description:** In-depth profiles of over 1,700 international advertisers and some 2,000 international advertising agencies from more than 90 countries.
Former titles (until 1991): Macmillan Directory of International Advertisers and Agencies (1056-0947); (until 1990): Standard Directory of Worldwide Marketing (0895-514X); Standard Directory of International Advertisers and Advertising Agencies
Related titles: CD-ROM ed.; Magnetic Tape ed.
Published by: LexisNexis (Subsidiary of: LexisNexis North America), PO Box 7587, Charlottesville, VA 22906-7587. TEL 434-972-7600, 800-446-3410, llp.customer.support@lexis-nexis.com, http://www.lexislawpublishing.com.

338.0029   GBR   ISSN 1367-9279
STAR PERFORMERS. Text in English. 1995. a. GBP 45. adv. **Document type:** *Directory, Trade.* **Description:** Lists Britain's fastest-growing companies.
Related titles: CD-ROM ed.; Diskette ed.
Published by: Commerce Directories Ltd., Milton Keynes, Station House, Station Rd, Newport Pagnell, Bucks MK16 0AG, United Kingdom. TEL 44-1908-616441, FAX 44-1908-614477. Ed. Karen Pickwick. Adv. contact Jessica Lamb.

690.029 338   GBR
STAR PERFORMERS BUILDING & CONSTRUCTION. Text in English. 1997. a. GBP 35. adv. **Document type:** *Directory, Trade.* **Description:** Lists Britain's top 500 building and construction companies.
Related titles: CD-ROM ed.; Diskette ed.
Published by: Commerce Directories Ltd., Milton Keynes, Station House, Station Rd, Newport Pagnell, Bucks MK16 0AG, United Kingdom. TEL 44-1908-614477, FAX 44-1908-616441. Ed. Karen Pickwick. Adv. contact Jessica Lamb.

380.1029   USA   ISSN 1044-324X
HD2425
STATE AND REGIONAL ASSOCIATIONS OF THE UNITED STATES. Abbreviated title: S R A Directory. Text in English. 1988. a. USD 79 (effective 2000). adv. **Document type:** *Directory.* **Description:** Compilation of 7,300 major state and regional societies and labor organizations in the US. Includes information on names and titles of executive officers, membership, staff and budget size, future membership meetings, and historical background.
Published by: Columbia Books Inc., 1825 Connecticut Ave NW #625, Washington, DC 20009-5724. TEL 202-898-0662, 888-265-0600, FAX 202-898-0775, info@columbiabooks.com, http://www.columbiabooks.com. Ed. Buck Downs. Pub., Adv. contact Michael Goldman.

332.6029   IND   ISSN 0971-3808
STOCK EXCHANGE OFFICIAL DIRECTORY. Text in English. 1966. w. INR 3,000. adv. charts; stat. **Document type:** *Corporate.*
Published by: Stock Exchange Foundation, Dalal St. Fort, Mumbai, Maharashtra 400 001, India. TEL 22-274170, FAX 22-2028121, TELEX 011-5925-STEXIN. Ed. R R Nair.

STOCK PHOTO DESKBOOK. see *PHOTOGRAPHY*

STONE FEDERATION HANDBOOK. see *BUILDING AND CONSTRUCTION*

SUEDDEUTSCHER MOLKEREI- UND KAESEREI-ADRESSKALENDER; Milchwirtschaft zum Nachschlagen. see *AGRICULTURE—Dairying And Dairy Products*

SULPHUR RECOVERY DATABOOK. see *ENGINEERING—Chemical Engineering*

SULPHURIC ACID DATABOOK. see *ENGINEERING—Chemical Engineering*

381.029   OMN
SULTANATE OF OMAN BUSINESS DIRECTORY (YEAR). Text in English. 1978. a. USD 50 (effective 1999). adv. stat.; tr.lit. index. back issues avail. **Document type:** *Directory.* **Description:** Business directory covering the entire country and detailing company information.
Published by: Apex Publishing, Ruwi, P O Box 2616, Muscat, 112, Oman. TEL 968-799388, FAX 968-793316, apexoman@gto.net.om. Circ: 40,000.

338.0029   OMN
SULTANATE OF OMAN TELEPHONE DIRECTORY. Text in English. a. free. adv. **Document type:** *Directory.*
Published by: Tele-Gulf Directory Publications, Ruwi, P O Box 3030, Muscat, 112, Oman. TEL 968-605815, FAX 968-605825. Ed. Sreekumar Nair. Circ: 156,000.

SUPPLY, DISTRIBUTION, MANUFACTURING & SERVICE; supply and service companies & equipment manufacturers. see *PETROLEUM AND GAS*

667.9029   GBR   ISSN 0268-9766
SURFACE COATING & RAW MATERIAL DIRECTORY∗. Text in English. 1986. a. index. back issues avail. **Document type:** *Directory, Trade.*
Published by: (Oil & Colour Chemists' Association), Industrial Trade Journals Ltd., Stakes House, Quebec Sq, Westerham, Kent TN16 1TD, United Kingdom. FAX 0959-62325, 0959-62325. Ed. Arthur Potter. Circ: 3,000.

381.029   SWE   ISSN 0282-5813
SVERIGES STOERSTA FOERETAG/LARGEST COMPANIES IN SWEDEN; med nyckeltal foer naeringslivet under (aar); with financial data for Sweden's 10,000 largest companies. Text in Swedish. 1968. a. SEK 1,280 (effective 2000). adv. **Document type:** *Directory, Corporate.*

Former titles (until 1984): Sveriges 4000 Stoersta Foeretag; (until 1983): Sveriges 3000 Stoersta Foeretag; (until 1982): Sveriges 2000 Stoersta Foeretag; (until 1980): Sveriges 1000 Stoersta Foeretag; (until 1973): Sveriges 500 Stoersta Foeretag
Related titles: Diskette ed.
Published by: Ekonomisk Litteratur AB, Fack 14113, Bromma, 16714, Sweden. TEL 46-8-566-22-900, FAX 46-8-566-22-910, info@ekolitt.se, http://www.ekolitt.se. Ed. Krister Wellros. R&P Berit Vonsydow. Adv. contact Gunnar Larsson.

338.0029   ZAF   ISSN 1016-7072
HF5280.A3
SWAZILAND BUYERS' GUIDE. Text in English. 1986. a. USD 50 (effective 2001). **Document type:** *Directory.*
Published by: Braby's (Subsidiary of: Associated Industries), Attn: Sue Pearson, PO Box 1426, Pinetown, 3600, South Africa. TEL 27-31-7017021, FAX 27-31-7017036, booksales@brabys.co.za.

382.029   CHE
SWISS EXPORT DIRECTORY; products and services of Switzerland. Text in English, French, German, Spanish. biennial. USD 35 (effective 2000). **Document type:** *Directory, Trade.*
Published by: Swiss Office for Trade Promotion, Stampfenbachstr 85, Zuerich, 8035, Switzerland. TEL 41-1-3655151, FAX 41-1-3655221, info.zurich@osec.ch, http://www.osec.ch.

SYSTEM SAFETY SOCIETY. DIRECTORY OF CONSULTANTS. see *BUSINESS AND ECONOMICS—Production Of Goods And Services*

T C S & D - U K INDUSTRY BUYERS GUIDE. (Temperature Controlled Storage and Distribution) see *FOOD AND FOOD INDUSTRIES*

333.79029   IND
T E R I ENERGY DATA DIRECTORY AND YEARBOOK; a comprehensive resource on energy, environment and economy. Short title: T E D D Y. Text in English. a. INR 1,375, USD 129 (effective 2001). **Document type:** *Directory.* **Description:** Contains the latest information on energy supply and demand, costs and prices, and sales and consumption.
Published by: Tata Energy Research Institute, Darbari Seth Block, Habitat Place, Lodhi Road, New Delhi, 110 003, India. TEL 91-11-4682100, FAX 91-11-4682144, outreach@teri.res.in. Circ: 4,000.

670.29   USA
TK6011
T I A - M M T A DIRECTORY AND DESK REFERENCE. Text in English. 1976. a. USD 199 (effective 1999). adv. **Document type:** *Directory.* **Description:** Constitutes a buyer's guide to companies that manufacture and distribute business and public communications systems, with company profiles, market reviews and forecasts for the U.S. telecommunications marketplace. Lists products and services provided by each company.
Former titles (until 1998): Multimedia Telecommunications Sourcebook; Telecommunications Sourcebook (0730-9872)
Indexed: SRI.
Published by: Telecommunications Industry Association, 2500 Wilson Blvd, Ste 300, Arlington, VA 22201-3834. TEL 703-907-7472, FAX 703-907-7478, info@mmta.org, tia@tiaonline.org, http://www.mmta.org, http://www.tiaonline.org. Ed. Maryann Lesso. Adv. contact Mary Bradshaw. Circ: 10,000.

T M A DIRECTORY OF CIGARETTE BRANDS. see *TOBACCO*

382.029   TWN
TAIPEI TRADERS INFORMATION SYSTEM. Text in English. 1963. a. USD 60.
Formerly (until 1991): Taiwan Trade Directory
Media: Diskette.
Published by: Importers & Exporters Association of Taipei, 5th Fl, 350 Sungkiang Rd, Taipei, 104, Taiwan. TEL 02-581-3521, FAX 02-542-3704, TELEX 23339.

380.1029   TWN   ISSN 1024-8943
TAIWAN BICYCLES & PARTS GUIDE (YEAR). Text in English. 1982. a. USD 50 (effective 2001). adv. **Description:** Covers bicycles, parts, accessories and machines.
Related titles: CD-ROM ed.: USD 20 (effective 2001).
Published by: Interface Global Taiwan Co., Ltd., PO Box 173-12, Taipei, 116, Taiwan. TEL 886-2-2393-2718, FAX 886-2-2395-2901, tradwind@ms2.hinet.net, http://www.bicyclesb2b.com, http://www.bicycle-guide.com. Pub. Herbert Chen. R&P Donald Shapiro. Adv. contact Melody Lin TEL 886-2-2351-3180. page USD 1,400. Circ: 12,000.
Subscr. in U.S. to: Trade Winds Inc., PO Box 820519, Dallas, TX 75382. TEL 877-861-1188, FAX 972-699-1189, twinds8888@aol.com.

658.0029   TWN
TAIWAN BUYERS' GUIDE (CD-ROM EDITION). Text in Chinese, English. a. adv. **Document type:** *Directory, Trade.*
Media: CD-ROM.

Published by: China Productivity Center, PO Box 769, Taipei, Taiwan. TEL 886-2-6982989, FAX 886-2-6982976. Ed., R&P. Adv. contact Jung-Lien Ma TEL 886-2-26985895.

TAIWAN CHEMICAL IMPORTERS' DIRECTORY (YEAR). see *ENGINEERING—Chemical Engineering*

TAIWAN CHEMICAL PRODUCERS' DIRECTORY (YEAR). see *ENGINEERING—Chemical Engineering*

686.72029   TWN   ISSN 1024-8978
TAIWAN HAND TOOLS BUYERS' GUIDE. Text in English. 1994. a. USD 30 (effective 2001). adv. 250 p./no.; **Document type:** *Directory, Catalog.* **Description:** Product catalogs and supplier directories for all kinds of tools and related products.
Related titles: CD-ROM ed.: USD 20 (effective 2000).
Published by: Interface Global Taiwan Co., Ltd., PO Box 173-12, Taipei, 116, Taiwan. TEL 886-2-2393-2718, FAX 886-2-2395-2901, tradwind@ms2.hinet.net, http://www.handtoolsb2b.com, http://www.handtools-guide.com. Ed. Daniel Foong. Pub. Herbert Chen. R&P Donald Shapiro. Adv. contact Melody Lin TEL 886-2-2351-3180. **Subscr. in U.S. to:** Trade Winds Inc., PO Box 820519, Dallas, TX 75382. TEL 877-861-1188, FAX 972-699-1189, twinds8888@aol.com.

380.1029   TWN
TAIWAN INDUSTRIAL SUPPLIERS; a buyer's best resource. Text in Chinese. 1992. a. USD 60 in Americas, Europe & Africa; USD 50 in Middle East & Asia; USD 30 elsewhere (effective 2000). adv. **Description:** Lists manufacturers of rubber and plastics, transportation equipment, electrical appliances, machinery, hardware parts and components and accessories.
Published by: China Economic News Service, 555 Chunghsiao E. Rd Sec 4, Taipei, 110, Taiwan. TEL 886-2-2642-2629, FAX 886-2-2642-7422, webmaster@www.cens.com, http://www.cens.com. adv.: B&W page TWD 30,000, color page TWD 40,000.

380.1029   USA   ISSN 1055-9116
HF3846.8
TAIWAN PRODUCT GUIDE (YEAR). Text in English. 1990. a.
Published by: De Paula Publishing and Services Corp., 421 Seventh Ave, Ste 1206, New York, NY 10001. TEL 212-629-4541. Ed. Carlos de Paula.

338.0029   TWN
TAIWAN TELECOM DIRECTORY. Text in Chinese. a. adv.
Description: Contains a list of Taiwan telecom suppliers that provides telecommunication regulations and complete lists of products suppliers by alphabetical and product categories.
Published by: Arco Publications Inc., 4F, No. 5, Sec. 1, Pa-Te Rd, Taipei, Taiwan. adv.: page USD 2,200. Circ: 20,000.

TAIWAN TEXTILE INDUSTRY GUIDE. see *TEXTILE INDUSTRIES AND FABRICS*

381.029   TWN   ISSN 0379-7910
TAIWAN YELLOW PAGES. Text in Chinese. a. TWD 1,200, USD 110. adv. **Document type:** *Trade.* **Description:** Lists over 65,000 entries on Taiwan manufacturers and traders.
Related titles: CD-ROM ed.: USD 55.
Published by: Taiwan Yellow Pages Corp., Chouwoo House 2F, 57 Tunhwa S. Rd, Sec 1, P.O. Box 84-84, Taipei, Taiwan. TEL 886-2-2570-9966, FAX 886-2-2578-2739, http://www.twn-online.com.tw. Ed. Lee Chung. Pub. Kingman Sheih. R&P, Adv. contact Gary Man. **Dist. by:** Current Pacific Ltd., PO Box 36-536, Northcote, Auckland, New Zealand. TEL 64-9-480-1388, FAX 64-9-480-1387, info@cplnz.com, http://www.cplnz.com.

791.446029   USA
TALK SHOW HOST DIRECTORY AND RESOURCE GUIDE. Text in English. 1995. a. USD 12.95 (effective 2000). **Document type:** *Directory.*
Published by: Nashe Group, 566 Commonwealth Ave, Boston, MA 02215. TEL 617-437-9757, FAX 617-437-0797, nashe@priority1.net, http://www.talkshowhosts.com. Ed. Carol Nashe. Circ: 3,500 (paid).

TANZANIA IMPORT AND EXPORT DIRECTORY. see *BUSINESS AND ECONOMICS—International Commerce*

670.29   AUS   ISSN 0314-8696
TASMANIAN MANUFACTURERS DIRECTORY. Text in English. 1978. irreg. AUD 25. **Document type:** *Directory, Government.*
Related titles: Diskette ed.: AUD 150.
Published by: Development and Resources, GPO Box 646, Hobart, TAS 7001, Australia. TEL 61-03-62335888, FAX 61-03-62335800, http://www.tdr.tas.gov.au. Circ: 10,000.

THE TECHNOLOGY DIRECTORY OF AUSTRALIA. see *TECHNOLOGY: COMPREHENSIVE WORKS*

658.564029   GBR
TECHNOMARK REGISTER. CONTRACT PACKAGERS & MANUFACTURERS - EUROPE. Text in English. a. GBP 320, USD 576. adv. **Document type:** *Directory.* **Description:** Listing organizations which undertake, as a primary objective, medical, scientific or technical work on a commercial basis involving packaging and manufacturing in the European pharmaceutical and healthcare industries.
Related titles: CD-ROM ed.: GBP 475.
Published by: Technomark Consulting Services Ltd., King House, 5-11 Westbourne Grove, London, W2 4UA, United Kingdom. TEL 44-20-7229-9239, FAX 44-20-7792-2587, info@technomark.com, http://www.technomark.co.uk. Ed. R G Hughes. R&P Marianne Searle. Adv. contact Allan Tappenden.

690.029   GBR
TECHNOMARK REGISTER. CONTRACT RESEARCH ORGANISATIONS - NORTH AMERICA. Text in English. a. GBP 400, USD 720. adv. **Document type:** *Directory.* **Description:** Listing organizations which undertake, as a primary objective, medical, scientific or technical work on a commercial basis in the North American pharmaceutical or healthcare industries.
Published by: Technomark Consulting Services Ltd., King House, 5-11 Westbourne Grove, London, W2 4UA, United Kingdom. TEL 44-20-7229-9239, info@technomark, http://www.technomark.co.uk. Ed. R G Hughes. R&P Marianne Searle. Adv. contact Allan Tappenden.

615.9029   GBR
TECHNOMARK REGISTER. EUROPEAN CONTRACT RESEARCH ORGANISATIONS. CLINICAL RESEARCH. Text in English. 1988. a. GBP 400 (effective 1999); USD 720. adv. **Document type:** *Directory.* **Description:** Listing organizations which undertake, as a primary objective, medical, scientific or technical work on a commercial basis.
Related titles: CD-ROM ed.: GBP 600, USD 1,080.
Published by: Technomark Consulting Services Ltd., King House, 5-11 Westbourne Grove, London, W2 4UA, United Kingdom. TEL 44-20-7229-9239, FAX 44-20-7792-2587, info@technomark.com, http://www.technomark.co.uk. Ed. R G Hughes. R&P Marianne Searle. Adv. contact Allan Tappenden. Circ: 400.

571.95029   GBR
TECHNOMARK REGISTER. EUROPEAN CONTRACT RESEARCH ORGANISATIONS. TOXICOLOGY & ANALYSIS. Text in English. a. GBP 320, USD 576. adv. **Document type:** *Directory.* **Description:** Listing organizations which undertake, as a primary objective, medical, scientific or technical work on a commercial basis in the pharmaceutical or healthcare industries.
Related titles: CD-ROM ed.: GBP 475.
Published by: Technomark Consulting Services Ltd., King House, 5-11 Westbourne Grove, London, W2 4UA, United Kingdom. TEL 44-20-7229-9239, FAX 44-20-7792-2587, info@technomark.com, http://www.technomark.co.uk. Ed. R G Hughes. R&P Marianne Searle. Adv. contact Allen Tappenden.

TELECOM SOURCEBOOK. see *COMMUNICATIONS—Telephone And Telegraph*

621.382029   USA   ISSN 1055-8454
TK5102.5   CODEN: TDIREL
TELECOMMUNICATIONS DIRECTORY; an international descriptive guide to approximately 4,300 telecommunications organizations, systems, and services. Text in English. 1983. biennial, latest 2004, 14th edition. USD 650 per vol. (effective 2004). **Document type:** *Directory, Trade.*
Formerly (until 1993): Telecommunications Systems and Services Directory (0738-3045)
Related titles: Diskette ed.; Magnetic Tape ed.
Published by: Gale Group (Subsidiary of: Thomson Corporation), 27500 Drake Rd, Farmington Hills, MI 48331-3535. TEL 248-699-8061, 800-877-4253, FAX 248-699-4253, galeord@gale.com, http://www.gale.com. Ed. Ellen Pare.

384.55029   USA   ISSN 1055-0828
PN1992
TELEVISION DIRECTORS GUIDE. Text in English. 1990. a. USD 45 (effective 1996). adv. **Document type:** *Directory.* **Description:** Covers network, syndication, cable, MOWs, comedy, drama and specials.
Published by: IFILM, 1024 N Orange Dr, Hollywood, CA 90038. TEL 323-308-FILM, http://www.ifilm.com. Circ: 2,500.

384.554029   USA   ISSN 0049-3317
TELEVISION SPONSORS DIRECTORY; product cross-reference directory. Cover title: Television Sponsors Product Cross-Reference Directory. Text in English. 1970. q. USD 19.40.
Media: Duplicated (not offset).
Published by: Everglades Publishing Co., Drawer Q, Everglades, FL 33929. Ed. Roger C Foss. Circ: 1,200.

384.55029   USA   ISSN 0894-8658
TELEVISION WRITERS GUIDE. Text in English. a. USD 50 (effective 1996). adv. **Document type:** *Directory.* **Description:** Lists people who write for television. Includes contacts, credits, networks and genres.

Published by: IFILM, 1024 N Orange Dr, Hollywood, CA 90038. TEL 323-308-FILM, http://www.ifilm.com. Circ: 3,000.

338.0029   USA   ISSN 1042-8801
HF5065.T2
TENNESSEE BUSINESS DIRECTORY. Text in English. 1987. a. USD 1,100 combined subscription print, online & CD-ROM eds. (effective 2004 & 2005). index. back issues avail. **Document type:** *Directory.* **Description:** Includes all businesses in the state compiled from the yellow pages and telephone-verified. Each listing includes company name, complete address, phone number, name of owner, manager, and employee size, sales volume codes, and credit rating codes.
Related titles: CD-ROM ed.; Diskette ed.; E-mail ed.; Fax ed.; Magnetic Tape ed.; Online - full text ed.
Published by: American Business Directories (Subsidiary of: American Business Information, Inc.), 5711 S 86th Circle, P O Box 27347, Omaha, NE 68127. TEL 402-593-4600, 888-946-9377, 877-708-3844, FAX 402-331-5481, sales@directoriesusa.com, http://www.directoriesusa.com.

670.29   USA   ISSN 1082-0248
HF5065.T2
TENNESSEE MANUFACTURERS REGISTER. Text in English. 1996. a. USD 77 (effective 2000). adv. **Document type:** *Directory.* **Description:** Profiles 6,320 manufacturers in five sections: company name, product, S.I.C., city, and parent company.
Related titles: CD-ROM ed.: USD 445 (effective 2000); Diskette ed.; Online - full text ed.
Published by: Manufacturers' News, Inc., 1633 Central St, Evanston, IL 60201. TEL 847-864-7000, 888-752-5200, FAX 847-332-1100, info@mninfo.com, info@manufacturersnews.com, sales@mninfo.com, http://www.manufacturersnews.com. Ed. Frank Lambing. Adv. contact Charles Scherer. B&W page USD 1,843.

TENNESSEE STATE AGENT HANDBOOK. see *INSURANCE*

670.29   FIN   ISSN 0781-6987
TEOLLISUUDEN KESKUSLIITTO. JASENLUETTELO/ CONFEDERATION OF FINNISH INDUSTRIES. LIST OF MEMBERS/FINLANDS INDUSTRIFOERBUND. MEDLEMSFOERTECKNING. Text in Finnish. biennial. membership.
Formerly: Suomen Teollisuusliittoo. Jasenluettelo
Published by: Teollisuusden Keskusliitto, Etelaranta 10, PL 220, Helsinki, 00131, Finland. Circ: 5,000.

381.029   USA   ISSN 1053-6698
HF5065.T4
TEXAS BUSINESS DIRECTORY. (Texas (Northwest) and Texas (South/Gulf Coast) Editions also available.) Text in English. 1991. a. USD 1,100 combined subscription print, online & CD-ROM eds. (effective 2004 & 2005). index. **Document type:** *Directory.* **Description:** Includes all businesses in the state compiled from the yellow pages and telephone-verified. Each listing includes company name, complete address, phone number, name of owner or manager, and employee size and sales volume codes, and credit rating codes.
Related titles: CD-ROM ed.; Diskette ed.; E-mail ed.; Fax ed.; Magnetic Tape ed.; Online - full text ed.
Published by: American Business Directories (Subsidiary of: American Business Information, Inc.), 5711 S 86th Circle, P O Box 27347, Omaha, NE 68127. TEL 402-593-4600, 888-946-9377, 877-708-3844, FAX 402-331-5481, sales@directoriesusa.com, http://www.directoriesusa.com.

670.29   USA   ISSN 0896-9779
TEXAS HIGH TECHNOLOGY DIRECTORY. Text in English. 1988. a. USD 149 (effective 2001). **Document type:** *Directory.* **Description:** Lists profiles of about 5,000 manufacturers and research and development firms in Texas engaged in high-technology activities.
Published by: Leading Edge Communications, Inc., 1121 Old Siskiyou Hwy, Ashland, OR 97520. TEL 541-482-4990, FAX 541-482-4993. Eds. Kimberley Boesche, Philip Boesche. Circ: 800.

670.29   USA   ISSN 0743-1163
HD9727.T4
TEXAS MANUFACTURERS REGISTER. Text in English. a. USD 161 (effective 2000). adv. illus. **Document type:** *Directory.* **Description:** Profiles 23,292 manufacturers listed in five sections by product, alphabetically, geographically, by SIC, and by parent company.
Related titles: CD-ROM ed.: USD 670 (effective 2000); Diskette ed.: USD 745 (effective 1999).
Published by: Manufacturers' News, Inc., 1633 Central St, Evanston, IL 60201. TEL 847-864-7000, 888-752-5200, FAX 847-332-1100, info@mninfo.com, info@manufacturersnews.com, sales@mninfo.com, http://www.manufacturersnews.com. Ed. Frank Lambing. Adv. contact Charles Scherer. B&W page USD 1,843.

▼ *new title*   ➤ *refereed*   ✱ *unverified*   ◆ *full entry avail.*

780.29 USA ISSN 1062-6646
ML14.T3
THE TEXAS MUSIC INDUSTRY DIRECTORY. Text in English. 1991. a. USD 20 per issue (effective 2003). **Document type:** *Directory, Government.* **Description:** Lists more than 14,000 Texas music businesses cross-referenced among 86 categories. Also lists classical music organizations, schools, songwriters, and events.
Published by: Office of the Governor, Texas Music Office, PO Box 13246, Austin, TX 78711. TEL 512-463-6666, FAX 512-463-4114, music@governor.state.tx.us, http://www.govenor.state.tx.us/music. Eds. Jodi Jenkins, Casey Monahan. Circ: 15.

TEXAS PETROLEUM INDUSTRY. see *PETROLEUM AND GAS*

TEXAS STATE AGENT HANDBOOK. see *INSURANCE*

690.029 THA
THAI BUILDERS DIRECTORY. Text in English. 1970. a. adv. **Document type:** *Directory.* **Description:** Information on the Thai building and construction industry.
Published by: Advertising and Media Consultants Ltd., Silom Condominium 12th Fl, 52-38 Soi Saladaeng 2, Bangkok, 10500, Thailand. TEL 266-9040, FAX 236-6764. Ed. Asha Narula Sehgal. Adv. contact Ravi Sehgal. B&W page THB 22,000, color page THB 45,000; trim 254 x 190. Circ: 20,000.

THAI CHAMBER OF COMMERCE. DIRECTORY (YEAR). see *BUSINESS AND ECONOMICS—Chamber Of Commerce Publications*

684.1029 THA
THAI FURNITURE INDUSTRIES ASSOCIATION DIRECTORY. Text in Thai. 1992. a. USD 24 per issue. **Document type:** *Directory.* **Description:** Covers furniture and timber industries.
Published by: (Thai Furniture Industries Association), Cosmic Group of Companies, 4th Fl Phyathai Bldg, Rajthevi, 31 Phyathai Rd, Bangkok, 10400, Thailand. TEL 245-3850, FAX 246-4737. adv.: color page USD 1,200. Circ: 5,000 (controlled).

381.029 THA ISSN 0857-1155
THAI INDUSTRIAL DIRECTORY. Text in English, Thai. 1970. a. adv. **Document type:** *Directory.*
Published by: Advertising and Media Consultants Ltd., Silom Condominium 12th Fl, 52-38 Soi Saladaeng 2, Bangkok, 10500, Thailand. TEL 2-333401, FAX 236-6764, TELEX 82463 LOOKEAS TH. Ed. Arthit Sehgal. Adv. contact Satish Sehgal. Circ: 15,000.

THAI-KOREAN CHAMBER OF COMMERCE HANDBOOK & DIRECTORY. see *BUSINESS AND ECONOMICS—Chamber Of Commerce Publications*

THAILAND COMPANY INFORMATION (YEAR). see *BUSINESS AND ECONOMICS—Domestic Commerce*

380.1029 THA ISSN 0857-2984
HF3800.55.A46
THAILAND INDUSTRIAL BUYER'S GUIDE. Text in Thai. 1981. a. USD 85. **Document type:** *Directory.* **Description:** Lists Thai manufacturers, exporters, products, and export-related services.
Published by: Business Publications (1985) Co. Ltd., 9-42 Soi Kingpetch, Petchburi Rd, PO Box 2729, Bangkok, 10400, Thailand. TEL 662-2150926-9, FAX 662-2156865.

382.029 IND
THAPAR'S INDIAN INDUSTRIAL DIRECTORY AND IMPORT AND EXPORT DIRECTORY OF THE WORLD. Text in English. 1960. a. USD 120. adv. **Document type:** *Directory.*
Formerly: Calcutta Market
Published by: Sunderdas Gianchand, 644 Jss Rd., Mumbai, Maharashtra 400 002, India. TEL 22-310518. Ed. Ramesh Shetty. Circ: 50,000.

641.3029 USA ISSN 1544-6344
THOMAS FOOD AND BEVERAGE MARKET PLACE. Text in English. 2001. a. (in 3 vols.). USD 495; USD 895 print & CD-ROM eds. (effective 2002). adv. **Document type:** *Directory, Trade.* **Description:** Provides comprehensive food and beverage industry information on over 40,000 companies and 100,000 executives.
Formed by the merger of (1996-2001): Food and Beverage Market Place (1089-4578); (1898-2001): Thomas Food Industry Register (1061-284X); Which was formerly (until 1991): Thomas Grocery Register (0082-4151)
Related titles: CD-ROM ed.: 2001. USD 695 (effective 2002).
Published by: Grey House Publishing, 185 Millerton Rd, PO Box 860, Millerton, NY 12546. TEL 518-789-8700, 800-562-2139, FAX 518-789-0556, books@greyhouse.com, http://www.greyhouse.com/food.htm. adv.: B&W page USD 8,250. Circ: 5,000 (paid).

THOMAS REGISTER OF AMERICAN MANUFACTURERS. see *BUSINESS AND ECONOMICS—Marketing And Purchasing*

381.029 IRL ISSN 0082-4224
THOM'S COMMERCIAL DIRECTORY. Text in English. 1844. a. USD 250. **Document type:** *Directory.*
Published by: Thom's Directories Ltd., Unit 22, Greenmount Industrial Estate, Harold's Cross Rd, Dublin, 6W, Ireland. TEL 353-1-4539050, FAX 353-1-4539104. Ed. J L Wootton.

332.1029 USA ISSN 1529-1375
HG2441
THOMSON BANK DIRECTORY. Text in English. 1876. a. USD 335. adv. stat. **Document type:** *Directory.* **Description:** Provides a comprehensive listing of more than 130,000 banks, covering North American and international banks and their branches.
Former titles (until 2000): Thomson/Polk Bank Directory (1096-228X); (until 1997): Thomson Bank Directory (1057-8986); (until 1991): Rand McNally Bankers Directory (0895-4623); (until 1986): Rand McNally International Bankers Directory (0360-7445)
Related titles: Online - full text ed.: (from LexisNexis).
—CCC.
Published by: Thomson Financial Services Company, 4709 W Golf Rd, Skokie, IL 60076-1256. TEL 847-676-9600, 800-321-3373, FAX 847-933-8101. Ed., R&P Beth Swann. Adv. contact Hugh Boyd.

380.1029 USA ISSN 1062-1717
HG2150
THOMSON SAVINGS DIRECTORY. Text in English. 1982. s-a. USD 255 domestic (effective 2001). adv. **Document type:** *Directory, Trade.* **Description:** Supplies up-to-date information on all U.S. savings institutions and their branches, with addresses, key officers, and comparative financial data.
Former titles (until 1991): U S Savings Institutions Directory (1045-8883); (until 1989): U S Savings and Loan Directory (0734-9203)
Related titles: Online - full text ed.: (from LexisNexis).
—CCC.
Published by: (United States League of Savings Institutions), Thomson Financial Services Company, 4709 W Golf Rd, Skokie, IL 60076-1256. TEL 847-676-9600, 800-321-3373, FAX 847-933-8101, prodinfo@tfp.com, customerservice@tfp.com, http://www.tfp.com/banks. Ed., R&P Beth Swann. Adv. contact Hugh Boyd.

380.1029 USA ISSN 1538-0920
HG1536
THOMSON WORLD BANK DIRECTORY. 1-VOL EDITION✶ . Text in English. 1894. a. USD 243. adv. bk.rev. charts; stat. **Document type:** *Directory.*
Former titles (until 2002): Thomson Bank Directory. 1-Vol Edition (1529-1359); (until 2001): Thomson/Polk Bank Directory. 1-Vol Edition (1094-6691); (until 1997): Polk World Bank Directory. International Edition (1090-6746); (until 1995): Polk Bank Directory. International Edition (1058-0603); (until 1986): Polk's World Bank Directory. International Edition (0085-4999)
Published by: R.L. Polk & Co., Bank Services Division, 4709 Golf Rd, Skokie, IL 60076-1231. Circ: 17,500.

666.029 ITA
TILE BOOK; Italian repertory of ceramic firms. Text in Italian. 1973. a. price varies. **Document type:** *Directory, Trade.*
Formerly: Annuario delle Ceramiche Italiane per l'Edilizia
Published by: Gruppo Editoriale Faenza Editrice SpA, Via Pier de Crescenzi 44, Faenza, RA 48018, Italy. TEL 39-0546-670411, FAX 39-0546-660440, info@faenza.com, http://www.faenza.com. Ed. Franco Rossi. Circ: 5,000.

645.4029 ITA
TILE BRICKS REFRACTORIES SUPPLIERS BOOK. Text in Italian. 1976. a. price varies. **Document type:** *Catalog, Trade.*
Former titles: Suppliers Ceramics Book; Annuario de Fornitori
Published by: Gruppo Editoriale Faenza Editrice SpA, Via Pier de Crescenzi 44, Faenza, RA 48018, Italy. TEL 39-0546-670411, FAX 39-0546-660440, info@faenza.com, http://www.faenza.com. Ed. Franco Rossi. Circ: 5,000.

TIMBER TRADES ADDRESS BOOK. see *FORESTS AND FORESTRY—Lumber And Wood*

338.0029 SGP ISSN 1394-1321
TIMES BUSINESS DIRECTORY OF MALAYSIA (YEAR). Text in English. a. USD 80 (effective 2000). adv. **Document type:** *Directory.* **Description:** Contains comprehensive listings of key local and foreign companies operating in Malaysia.
Published by: Times Media Pte Ltd, Directories Division, 1 New Industrial Rd, Times Centre, Singapore, 536196, Singapore. TEL 65-2848844, FAX 65-2850161, ttdmktg@cop.tpl.com.sg, http://www.timesbiz.com.sg. Pub., Adv. contact Leslie Lim. **Dist. by:** Current Pacific Ltd., PO Box 36-536, Northcote, Auckland, New Zealand. TEL 64-9-480-1388, FAX 64-9-480-1387, info@cplnz.com, http://www.cplnz.com.

338.0029 SGP ISSN 0217-6009
TIMES BUSINESS DIRECTORY OF SINGAPORE. Text in English. 1880. a. USD 120 (effective 2000). adv. bk.rev. **Document type:** *Directory.* **Description:** Provides information on nature of business, contact telephone, fax, addresses, and key personnel for each company listed.
Formerly: Straits Times Directory of Singapore; Supersedes in part: Straits Times Directory of Malaysia and Singapore (0585-3931)
Published by: Times Media Pte Ltd, Directories Division, 1 New Industrial Rd, Times Centre, Singapore, 536196, Singapore. TEL 65-2848844, FAX 65-2850161, ttdmktg@cop.tpl.com.sg, http://www.timesbiz.com.sg. Pub., R&P Leslie Lim. Adv. contact Joseph Liang. **Dist. by:** Current Pacific Ltd., PO Box 36-536, Northcote, Auckland, New Zealand. TEL 64-9-480-1388, FAX 64-9-480-1387, info@cplnz.com, http://www.cplnz.com.

380.1029 NGA
TIMES TRADE AND INDUSTRIAL DIRECTORY. Text in English. 1972. irreg. price varies. illus. **Document type:** *Directory.*
Published by: Daily Times of Nigeria Ltd., Publications Division, New Isheri Rd., PMB 21340, Ikeja, Agidingbi, Lagos, Nigeria. TEL 234-64-900850-9, FAX 234-64-21333. Ed. James O Ojiako.

338.0029 USA
TODAY'S ARIZONA WOMAN BUSINESS DIRECTORY; a directory of women's businesses and businesses interested in reaching the women's market. Text in English. 1975. a. USD 12. adv. index. **Document type:** *Directory.* **Description:** Serves as a guide of services and products. Lists women's businesses, and other businesses and professions providing services to women.
Former titles: Women's Yellow Pages Arizona (1042-8488); (until 1989): Women's Pages Arizona (0894-0703)
Published by: Publishers West, Inc., 4425 N Saddlebag Tr, Scottsdale, AZ 85251. TEL 602-945-5000, FAX 602-941-5196. Ed. Becky Kistler. Pub. Eleanore Klein. Adv. contact Kelli Fawcett. page USD 1,790; trim 10.38 x 8.38. Circ: 30,000.

338.0029 USA ISSN 0363-2962
HE8811
TOLL-FREE DIGEST✶ . Text in English. 1976. a. USD 17.95.
Published by: Toll-Free Digest Co., Inc., PO Box 291, Kinderhook, NY 12106-0291. FAX 518-828-9635. Ed. Paul R Montana.

338.0029 USA ISSN 1092-0285
HE8811
TOLL - FREE PHONE BOOK U S A (YEAR). Text in English. 1997. a., latest 2002, 6th ed. USD 145 (effective 2001). **Document type:** *Directory, Trade.* **Description:** Directory of more than 44,000 toll-free numbers for top companies, organizations, and institutions nationwide. Individual entries also include complete mailing address, regular phone and fax number, and e-mail and Web address. Presented in three arrangements: alphabetical, geographic, and classified.
Published by: Omnigraphics, Inc., 615 Griswold St, Detroit, MI 48226. TEL 313-961-1341, 800-234-1340, FAX 313-961-1383, 800-875-1340, info@omnigraphics.com, http://www.omnigraphics.com. Ed. Jennifer Perkins. Pub. Frederick G Ruffner Jr.

TOOLING AND MANUFACTURING ASSOCIATION. PURCHASING GUIDE. see *BUSINESS AND ECONOMICS—Production Of Goods And Services*

TOOLROOM DIRECTORY. see *MACHINERY*

TOP 400 CONTRACTORS SOURCEBOOK. see *BUILDING AND CONSTRUCTION*

THE TOP 500 DESIGN FIRMS SOURCEBOOK. see *ENGINEERING*

658.0029 GBR
THE TOP 5000 EUROPEAN COMPANIES (YEAR). Text in English. a. GBP 650 (effective 2001). **Document type:** *Directory.* **Description:** Provides key details on Western Europe's largest 5,000 manufacturing and service companies by size of sales revenue, as well as the largest 500 banks by size of assets and the largest 100 insurance companies by size of premium income. Includes league tables and detailed company profiles.
Published by: Graham & Whiteside Ltd (Subsidiary of: Gale Group), Tuition House, 5-6 Francis Grove, London, SW19 4DT, United Kingdom. TEL 44-20-8947-1011, FAX 44-20-8947-1163, galeord@gale.com, http://www.galegroup.com/graham&whiteside/. **Dist. by:** Current Pacific Ltd., PO Box 36-536, Northcote, Auckland, New Zealand. TEL 64-9-480-1388, FAX 64-9-480-1387, info@cplnz.com, http://www.cplnz.com.

658.0029 GBR
THE TOP 5000 GLOBAL COMPANIES (YEAR). Text in English. a. GBP 405 (effective 2001). **Document type:** *Directory.* **Description:** Provides key details on the world's largest 5,000 manufacturing and service companies by size of sales revenue, as well as, the largest 500 banks by size of assets and the largest 100 insurance companies by size of premium income. Includes league tables and detailed company profiles.

Published by: Graham & Whiteside Ltd (Subsidiary of: Gale Group), Tuition House, 5-6 Francis Grove, London, SW19 4DT, United Kingdom. TEL 44-20-8947-1011, FAX 44-20-8947-1163, galeord@gale.com, http://www.galegroup.com/graham&whiteside/. **Dist. by:** Current Pacific Ltd., PO Box 36-536, Northcote, Auckland, New Zealand. TEL 64-9-480-1388, FAX 64-9-480-1387, info@cplnz.com, http://www.cplnz.com.

690.029   USA

TOP CONTACTS✱ . Variant title: Shopping Center Directory's Top Contacts. (Vol. 5 of: Shopping Center Directory) Text in English. 1988. a. USD 305. **Document type:** Directory. **Description:** Provides headquarters information on the top 1500 owners, leasing agents and management companies who control three or more shopping centers in the U.S.
Formerly (until 1994): Shopping Center Developer Directory (1040-1911)
Published by: National Research Bureau, Inc. (Chicago), 200 W Jackson Blvd no.2700, Chicago, IL 60606-6910. TEL 312-541-0100, FAX 312-541-1492. **Orders to:** National Research Bureau, 263 Tresser Blvd., Flr. 9, Stamford, CT 06901-3236. TEL 800-456-4555, FAX 203-563-3131.

332.72029   USA

TOP MORTGAGE MARKET PLAYERS. Text in English. 1990. a. USD 375 (effective 2000). **Document type:** Directory. **Description:** Features more than 5,000 lenders that originate, service or hold over four- to four-family residential mortgages.
Former titles: Mortgage Industry 5000; Mortgage Lender Directory
Related titles: Diskette ed.
Published by: Inside Mortgage Finance Publications, PO Box 42387, Washington, DC 20015. TEL 301-951-1240, FAX 301-656-1709, http://www.imfpubs.com. Ed., Pub. Guy D Cecala. R&P Didi Parks.

338.0029   AUS

TOP SUPER FUNDS. Text in English. a. (May). AUD 3,850 (effective 2000). adv. **Document type:** Directory, Trade. **Description:** Information on Australia's 1,500 largest superannuation funds including contact details, data on fund type, assets under management, service providers and the percentage allocation of funds to investment managers.
Formerly: Super Review Top 1500 Directory
Media: CD-ROM. **Related titles:** Diskette ed.
Published by: Reed Business Information Pty Ltd (Subsidiary of: Reed Business Information International), Locked Bag 2999, Chatswood, NSW 2067, Australia. julia.newbould@reedbusiness.co.au, http://www.superreview.com.au/, http://www.reedbusiness.com.au. Ed. Julia Newbould. Pub. Jeremy Knibbs TEL 61-2-9422-2930. Adv. contact Brad Lawson.

380.1029   RUS

TORGOVAYA GAZETA. Text in Russian. 1991. s-w. USD 229.95 in United States.
Formerly (until 1990): Sovetskaya Torgovlya
Related titles: Microfilm ed.: (from EVP, PQC).
Address: Ul Varvarka 14, Moscow K-12, 103012, Russian Federation. TEL 7-095-2984848, FAX 7-095-2984941, tg@centro.ru. Eds. A A Shandybo, V Ya Pushkarev. Circ: 96,000. **US dist. addr.:** East View Information Services, 3020 Harbor Ln. N., Minneapolis, MN 55447. TEL 612-550-0961.

382.029   ZAF

TOURISM TRADE DIRECTORY: SOUTH AFRICA. Text in English. 1994. a. **Document type:** Directory.
Published by: Satour, Private Bag X164, Pretoria, 0001, South Africa. Ed. Jill Archer.

380.1029   USA

TRADE AND CUSTOMS WORLD DIRECTORY. Text in English. a. USD 499 per issue (effective 2005). **Document type:** Directory, Consumer.
Published by: C Q Press, Inc. (Subsidiary of: Congressional Quarterly, Inc.), 1255 22nd St., N.W., Ste. 400, Washington, DC 20037. TEL 202-729-1800, 800-432-2250, FAX 800-380-3810, customerservice@cq.com, http://www.cqpress.com/gethome.asp.

670.29   USA

TRADE AND PROFESSIONAL ASSOCIATIONS IN CALIFORNIA; a directory. Text in English. 1979. irreg., latest vol.7, 1999. USD 50 to individuals; USD 25 to libraries (effective 2001). **Document type:** Directory. **Description:** Lists of the addresses and telephone numbers of over 2,200 business and professional organizations in the state, alphabetized, numbered, and indexed by subject and key words.
Published by: California Institute of Public Affairs, PO Box 189040, Sacramento, CA 95818. TEL 916-442-CIPA, FAX 916-442-2478, cipa@cipahg.org, http://www.cipahg.org.

658.0029   GBR

TRADE ASSOCIATIONS AND PROFESSIONAL BODIES OF THE CONTINENTAL EUROPEAN UNION. Text in English. a. GBP 155 (effective 2001). **Document type:** Directory. **Description:** Provides essential data on over 4,000 trade associations and professional bodies of the Continental European Union.

Published by: Graham & Whiteside Ltd (Subsidiary of: Gale Group), Tuition House, 5-6 Francis Grove, London, SW19 4DT, United Kingdom. TEL 44-20-8947-1011, FAX 44-20-8947-1163, galeord@gale.com, http://www.galegroup.com/graham&whiteside/. **Dist. by:** Current Pacific Ltd., PO Box 36-536, Northcote, Auckland, New Zealand. TEL 64-9-480-1388, FAX 64-9-480-1387, info@cplnz.com, http://www.cplnz.com.

658.0029   GBR

TRADE ASSOCIATIONS & PROFESSIONAL BODIES OF THE UK. Text in English. irreg. GBP 150 (effective 2001). **Document type:** Directory. **Description:** Provides essential information on over 3,500 trade associations and professional bodies in the UK in the following sectors: trade, business, commercial, environmental and agricultural, legal, government, public administration and military, engineering, technological, natural and social sciences, educational, health and medical, public affairs, labor union associations, federations.
Published by: Graham & Whiteside Ltd (Subsidiary of: Gale Group), Tuition House, 5-6 Francis Grove, London, SW19 4DT, United Kingdom. TEL 44-20-8947-1011, FAX 44-20-8947-1163, galeord@gale.com, http://www.galegroup.com/graham&whiteside/. **Dist. by:** Current Pacific Ltd., PO Box 36-536, Northcote, Auckland, New Zealand. TEL 64-9-480-1388, FAX 64-9-480-1387, info@cplnz.com, http://www.cplnz.com.

TRADE DIMENSIONS' DIRECTORY OF CONVENIENCE STORES; the book of c-store market facts. see FOOD AND FOOD INDUSTRIES

380.1029   USA
HF5429.3

TRADE DIMENSIONS' DIRECTORY OF MASS MERCHANDISERS; the guide to fast-turn, high-volume retailers. Text in English. a. USD 255 (effective 2001). charts; maps. **Document type:** Directory. **Description:** Profiles retail mass merchandising companies, with information on chains, including product lines, names of buyers and other key personnel.
Formerly: Progressive Grocer's Directory of Mass Merchandisers (0890-7986)
Published by: Trade Dimensions, 45 Danbury Rd, Wilton, CT 06897-4445. TEL 203-563-3040, 203-563-3100, FAX 203-563-3131, http://www.tradedimensions.com. Ed. Justin Margitay-Balogh. Pub. Garrett Van Siclen. R&P Garett Van Siclen.

381.029   USA   ISSN 0564-0482

TRADE DIRECTORIES OF THE WORLD. Text in English. base vol. plus m. updates. looseleaf. USD 109.95 base vol(s). domestic; USD 135 base vol(s). foreign (effective 2005). **Document type:** Directory. **Description:** Lists trade, industrial and professional directories.
Published by: Croner Publications, Inc., 10951 Sorrento Valley Rd, Ste 1D, San Diego, CA 92121-1613. TEL 800-441-4033, 800-441-4033, FAX 800-809-0334, paul@croner.com, http://www.croner.com. Ed. Elizabeth Duffy.

380.1029   DNK   ISSN 0109-467X
T12.5.D4

TRADE DIRECTORY FOR DENMARK/ANNUAIRE DE L'EXPORTATION DU DANEMARK/ANUARIO DE LA EXPORTACION DE DINAMARCA/DAENISCHER HANDELSKALENDER. Text in English, French, German, Spanish. 1956. biennial. illus.
Formerly (until 1984): Udenrigshandelskalenderen for Danmark (0532-1360)
Published by: Information Office of the Danish Foreign Trade, Hellerupvej 78, Hellerup, 2900, Denmark. **Dist. by:** Current Pacific Ltd., PO Box 36-536, Northcote, Auckland, New Zealand. TEL 64-9-480-1388, FAX 64-9-480-1387, info@cplnz.com, http://www.cplnz.com.

TRADE DIRECTORY OF MEXICO. see BUSINESS AND ECONOMICS—International Commerce

382   NZL

TRADE NEWS. Text in English. m.
Published by: Lifestyle Publishing Ltd, 51a Riverlea Ave, Pakuranga, P.O. Box 14109, Panmure, Auckland, New Zealand. TEL 64-9-5702658, FAX 64-9-5702684.

TRADE OPPORTUNITY. see BUSINESS AND ECONOMICS—Chamber Of Commerce Publications

382   BLZ

TRADE REPORT ON DISKETTE. Text in English. 1992. a. USD 25 (effective 1999). **Document type:** Government.
Related titles: Diskette ed.
Published by: Ministry of Finance, Central Statistical Office, Belmopan, Belize. TEL 501-8-22352, FAX 501-8-23206, csogob@btl.net.

380.1029   USA

TRADE SHOWS & EXHIBITS SCHEDULE. Text in English. 1925. s-a. USD 217.50 (effective 1999). adv. **Document type:** Directory, Trade. **Description:** Directory listing of trade shows and exhibits scheduled for the published and following year.
Formerly (until 1954): Exhibits Schedule (0531-5360)

—CCC.

Published by: V N U Business Publications (Subsidiary of: V N U Business Media), 770 Broadway, New York, NY 10003-9595. TEL 646-654-7604, bmcomm@vnuinc.com, http://www.vnubusinessmedia.com/. Circ: 2,500.

382.029   TWN

TRADE YELLOW PAGES (YEAR). Text in Chinese. 1990. a. TWD 1,200, USD 65 domestic; USD 90 in North America. **Description:** Lists 30,000 suppliers under 604 product categories in 20 main industrial groups.
Published by: Taiwan Trade Pages Corp., P.O. Box 72-50, Taipei, Taiwan. TEL 02-3053960, FAX 02-3071000. Ed. Valerie Liu. **Dist. by:** Current Pacific Ltd., PO Box 36-536, Northcote, Auckland, New Zealand. TEL 64-9-480-1388, FAX 64-9-480-1387, info@cplnz.com, http://www.cplnz.com.

382.029   SGP

TRADELINK - CHINESE. Text in English. a. USD 50 (effective 2000). adv. **Document type:** Directory. **Description:** Lists Singapore companies engaged in exporting Singapore-manufactured products and services to China.
Published by: Times Media Pte Ltd, Directories Division, 1 New Industrial Rd, Times Centre, Singapore, 536196, Singapore. TEL 65-2848844, FAX 65-2850161, ttdmktg@cop.tpl.com.sg. Pub., R&P Leslie Lim. Adv. contact Joseph Liang.

382.029   SGP

TRADELINK - ENGLISH. Text in English. a. USD 90 (effective 2000). adv. **Document type:** Directory. **Description:** Lists Singapore companies engaged in the exporting of Singapore-manufactured products and services to the world market.
Published by: Times Media Pte Ltd, Directories Division, 1 New Industrial Rd, Times Centre, Singapore, 536196, Singapore. TEL 65-2848844, FAX 65-2850161, ttdmktg@cop.tpl.com.sg, http://www.timesbiz.com.sg. Pub., R&P Leslie Lim. Adv. contact Joseph Liang.

670.29   SGP

TRADELINK - S C I ANNUAL DIRECTORY (YEAR). Text in English. 1960. a. SGD 60 (effective 2000). adv. **Document type:** Directory, Trade. **Description:** Names and addresses of manufacturers as well as names and addresses of companies in the service industry.
Former titles: Tradelink - S M A Annual Directory (Year) (0217-7447); (until 1986): Singapore Manufacturers' Association Directory (0129-9867); Directory of Singapore Manufacturers (0070-6337)
Published by: (Singapore Confederation of Industries), Times Media Pte Ltd, Directories Division, 1 New Industrial Rd, Times Centre, Singapore, 536196, Singapore. TEL 65-2848844, FAX 65-2850161, scihq@sci.org.sg, ttdmktg@cop.tpl.com.sg, http://www.sci.org.sg/sci, http://www.timesbiz.com.sg. Ed. Charlie Chan. Circ: 10,000.

380.1029   USA

TRADESHOW DIRECTORY. Text in English. a. USD 80; USD 110 foreign (effective 1999). adv. tr.lit. back issues avail. **Document type:** Directory, Trade.
Formerly: Tradeshow and Exhibit Manager Buyers Guide (0898-7114)
Related titles: ♦ Supplement(s): Tradeshow and Exhibit Manager. ISSN 0893-2662.
Published by: Goldstein and Associates, 1150 Yale St, Ste 12, Santa Monica, CA 90403-4738. TEL 310-828-1309. Ed. Les Plesko. Pub. Steve Goldstein. Circ: 12,000.

382.029   IND   ISSN 0082-5824

TRADO: ASIAN - AFRICAN DIRECTORY OF EXPORTERS, IMPORTERS AND MANUFACTURERS✱ . Text in English. 1956. a. USD 115. adv. index.
Published by: Trado Publications Pvt. Ltd., c/o Bansi Hse, 1/24 Asaf Ah Rd., New Delhi, 110 001, India. Ed. J K Chug. Circ: 10,000.

796.54029   USA

TRAILER LIFE CAMPGROUND AND R V SERVICES DIRECTORY. Variant title: Campground & R V Services Guide. Text in English. 1971. a. USD 24.95 per issue to non-members; USD 14.95 per issue to members (effective 2005). adv. illus. **Document type:** Directory. **Description:** Lists 25,000 private and public campgrounds, recreational vehicle service and accessory centers, and liquid propane gas locations in North America.
Former titles: Good Sam Club's Recreational Vehicle Owners Directory (0090-3256); Trailer Life's Recreational Vehicle Campground and Services Guide (0093-4283)
Related titles: Online - full text ed.
Published by: (Good Sam Club), Affinity Group Inc., 2575 Vista Del Mar Dr, Ventura, CA 93001-3920. TEL 805-234-3450, 805-667-4100, 800-766-1674, FAX 805-667-4419, info@trailerlife.com, http://www.rv.net. Eds. Ken Freund, Maxye Henry. Pub. Joe Daquino. adv.: B&W page USD 5,020, color page USD 13,125. Circ: 300,000. **Subscr. to:** PO Box 10236, Des Moines, IA 50382-0236.

TRAINING AND ENTERPRISE DIRECTORY. see EDUCATION

THE TRAINING MANAGER'S YEARBOOK. see BUSINESS AND ECONOMICS—Management

▼ *new title*   ➤ *refereed*   ✱ *unverified*   ♦ *full entry avail.*

388.029 GBR
TRANSPORT E-MAIL DIRECTORY. Text in English. a. GBP 20 (effective 2000). **Document type:** *Directory.*
Published by: P T R C Education and Research Services Ltd., Glenthorne House, 5-17 Hammersmith Grove, London, W6 0LG, United Kingdom. TEL 44-20-8741-1516, FAX 44-20-8741-5993.

380.1029 USA ISSN 0447-9181
TRANSPORTATION TELEPHONE TICKLER. Text in English. 1949. a. (in 4 vols.). USD 99.95 (effective 2003). adv. index. **Document type:** *Directory, Trade.* **Description:** Provides the latest names, addresses, telephone/fax numbers, and personnel titles for 24,000 transportation services and suppliers in the United States and Canada.
Related titles: CD-ROM ed.; Online - full text ed.
—CCC.
Published by: Journal of Commerce, Inc. (Subsidiary of: Commonwealth Business Media, Inc.), 33 Washington St, 13th Fl, Newark, NJ 07102. TEL 973-848-7000, 800-215-6084, FAX 609-371-7883, customersvs@joc.com, http://www.tickleronline.com/, http://www.joc.com. Circ: 11,000. **Subscr. to:** Commonwealth Business Media, Inc., 400 Windsor Corporate Ctr, 50 Millstone Rd, Ste 200, East Windsor, NJ 08520-1415. TEL 888-215-6084, FAX 609-371-7883.

910.029 USA
TRAVELODGE/THRIFTLODGE TRAVEL DIRECTORY. Text in English. 1963. a., latest 2001. free (effective 2005). maps. **Document type:** *Directory, Consumer.* **Description:** Provides maps and listings of Travelodge & Thriftlodge locations in United States, including address, telephone, fax, number of rooms available, directions, hotel services and rates.
Former titles: Travelodge North American - International Travel Directory; Travelodge and Viscount Hotels North American Travel Directory; Travelodge - Forte Viscount Hotels Travel Directory; TraveLodge - Viscount Hotels Vacation Travel Directory
Published by: Cendant Corporation, Hotel Division, 1 Sylvan Way, Parsippany, NJ 07054. TEL 973-428-9700, FAX 973-496-7307, internet.services@rsd.cendant.com, http://www.cendant.com/. Ed. Jill Gatyas. Circ: 550,000.

TRAVELTRADE VISA GUIDE. see *BUSINESS AND ECONOMICS—International Commerce*

380.1029 AUS
TRAVELTRADE YEARBOOK. Text in English. 1966. s-a. AUD 60.06 per issue (effective 2001). adv. **Document type:** *Directory, Trade.* **Description:** Comprehensive manual of travel industry suppliers, principals and retailers.
Published by: Reed Business Information Pty Ltd (Subsidiary of: Reed Business Information International), Locked Bag 2999, Chatswood, NSW 2067, Australia. customerservice@reedbusiness.com.au, http://www.reedbusiness.com.au. Ed. Doug Kujovic. Pub. Barrie Parsons. Adv. contact John McGaulley. B&W page AUD 2,500, color page AUD 3,400; trim 210 x 297. Circ: 4,065.

910.029 USA
TRAVELWARE RESOURCES DIRECTORY. Text in English. a. USD 20 (effective 1999). illus. **Document type:** *Directory, Trade.*
Former titles: Luggage and Travelware Directory and Market Guide; Luggage and Travelware Directory; Luggage and Leather Goods Directory
Published by: Business Journals, 50 Day St, Norwalk, CT 06856. TEL 203-853-6015.

381.029 TTO
TRINIDAD AND TOBAGO EXPORT DIRECTORY. Text in English, French, Portuguese, Spanish. 1997. a. **Document type:** *Directory, Trade.* **Description:** Contains listings of Trinidad and Tobago export products and services.
Published by: Media & Editorial Projects Ltd., 6 Prospect Ave, Maraval, Port of Spain, Trinidad & Tobago. TEL 868-622-3821, FAX 868-628-0639, mep@wow.net, http://www.readcaribbean.com. Ed., Pub. Jeremy Taylor. Circ: 8,000 (controlled).

TRINIDAD AND TOBAGO TRADE DIRECTORY. see *BUSINESS AND ECONOMICS—International Commerce*

TRUCKING TIMES AND SPORT UTILITY NEWS. see *TRANSPORTATION—Trucks And Trucking*

658.0029 USA ISSN 0191-6106
HD2346.U5
TRY US; national minority business directory. Text in English. 1969. a. USD 65 (effective 1999). adv. **Document type:** *Directory.* **Description:** Provides names of contact personnel and information on company capabilities, years in business, certifications held, number of employees, previous year's sales and more.
Formerly: National Minority Business Directory (0077-5231)
Published by: Try Us Resources, Inc., 2105 Central Ave, N E, Minneapolis, MN 55418. TEL 612-781-6819, FAX 612-781-0109. Ed., R&P Leslie Smith-Bonds. Pub. Leslie Smith Bonds. Adv. contact Janice L Anderson.

U K A S DIRECTORY OF ACCREDITED LABORATORIES. (United Kingdom Accreditation Service) see *METROLOGY AND STANDARDIZATION*

U K BROADCAST MEDIA. see *COMMUNICATIONS—Television And Cable*

U K BUSINESS & PROFESSIONAL MAGAZINES DIRECTORY. see *BUSINESS AND ECONOMICS*

384.555 GBR
THE U K CABLE REPORT (YEAR). Text in English. a.
Formerly: Who's Who Cable Yearbook (Year)
—BLDSC (9082.652100).
Published by: The Phillips Group, Forum Chambers, Stevenage, Herts SG1 1EL, United Kingdom. TEL 44-1438-742424, FAX 44-1438-780154. Ed. Roger Wilson.

U K FREELANCE DIRECTORY. see *JOURNALISM*

380.1029 GBR
U K KOMPASS REGIONAL SALES GUIDE. Text in English. a. (in 4 vols.), latest 2003. GBP 175; GBP 194 per vol. (effective 2003). **Document type:** *Directory.*
Former titles: Kompass U.K. Regional Sales Guide (Year); Kompass U.K. Management Register
—BLDSC (9082.660400).
Published by: Kompass (Subsidiary of: Reed Business Information Ltd.), Windsor Court, East Grinstead House, East Grinstead, W Sussex RH19 1XA, United Kingdom. TEL 01342-326972, FAX 44-1342-335612, http://www.kompass.co.uk/info/products/rsg.htm. Ed. Ann Hayes. Pub. Peter Snook. Adv. contact David Foster TEL 44-1342-335951. Circ: 16,000.

070.5029 659 GBR ISSN 0968-2678
U K MEDIA DIRECTORY. Text in English. 1983. bi-m. GBP 268 (effective 1999). **Document type:** *Directory.*
Former titles: P N A Media Guide (0955-503X); P N A Medialink (0953-6914); (until 1986): Media Information - U K (0264-8296)
Published by: P R Newswire (Europe) Ltd, Communications House, 210 Old St, London, EC1V 9UN, United Kingdom. TEL 44-20-7490-8111, FAX 44-20-7490-1255. Ed. Paul Chessman.

U K MEDIA TOWN BY TOWN. see *JOURNALISM*

U K NEWSPAPER DIRECTORY. see *JOURNALISM*

U K PLASTICS RECYCLING DIRECTORY. see *PLASTICS*

387.029 GBR ISSN 1463-9092
HE823
U K SHIPPING CONTACTS. Text in English. 1976. a. USD 65. adv. bk.rev. index. back issues avail. **Document type:** *Directory.*
Former titles (until 1997): Lloyd's Shipping Connections (0960-6017); (until 1990): Lloyd's U K Shipping Contacts (0268-3261); (until 1985): London Shipping Contacts (0260-9525)
Related titles: Diskette ed.
Published by: Informa U K Limited (Subsidiary of: T & F Informa plc), Customer Service Dept, Sheepen Pl, Colchester, Essex CO3 3LP, United Kingdom. TEL 44-1206-772223, FAX 44-1206-772771, enquiries@informa.com, http://www.llplimited.com. Ed. Suzanne Hooke. Pub. Alan Condron. Adv. contact Ian Armstrong TEL 44-20-7553-1000. page GBP 590; trim 147 x 210. Circ: 1,000 (controlled). **Subscr. addr. in the US:** L L P Inc, Customer Service, PO Box 1017, Westborough, MA 01581-6017. TEL 1-800-493-4080, FAX 508-231-0856, enquiries.usa@informa.com.

U K SPACE INDEX. see *AERONAUTICS AND SPACE FLIGHT*

677.0029 GBR
U K TEXTILE INDUSTRY DIRECTORY. Text in English. 1970. biennial. GBP 200 per issue (effective 2005). **Document type:** *Directory, Trade.* **Description:** Guide to the world's textile machinery makers and their representatives in the UK.
Supersedes in part: Deskbook of U K Agents (0951-3930)
Published by: World Textile Publications Ltd., Perkin House, 1 Longlands St, Bradford, W Yorks BD1 2TP, United Kingdom. TEL 44-1274-378800, FAX 44-1274-378811, info@world-textile.net, http://www.world-textile.net/contact.html.

U K - U S TRADE DIRECTORY (YEAR). see *BUSINESS AND ECONOMICS—Chamber Of Commerce Publications*

305.5234 GBR ISSN 1356-6369
THE U K WEALTH DIRECTORY✶ . Text in English. 1994. biennial. GBP 81; GBP 86 foreign. **Document type:** *Directory.* **Description:** List the names, addresses, and assets of multi-millionaires in the UK, most owning major quantities of shares in public and private companies.
Published by: (Rowland Lybrand of London), LORD de Chanson Limited, 4 Waterloo Ln, Pocklington, York YO42 2AG, United Kingdom. TEL 44-1759-304390, FAX 44-1759-306377, sales@lord.dechanson.co.uk, http://www.lord.dechanson.co.uk.

381.029 USA
U S 1 DIRECTORY. Text in English. a. adv. **Document type:** *Directory.*
Published by: U S 1 Publishing Co., 12 Roszel Rd, No C 205, Princeton, NJ 08540-6234. TEL 609-452-7000, FAX 609-452-0033. adv.: B&W page USD 955; trim 11 x 8.5. Circ: 5,000.

338.0029 USA
U S A TODAY SOURCE GUIDE. Text in English. a. **Document type:** *Directory.* **Description:** Lists trade and professional organizations, colleges and other institutions, social service and advocacy groups, and a wide range of public and private companies.
Published by: U S A Today (Subsidiary of: Gannett Newspapers), 1000 Wilson Blvd, Arlington, VA 22229. TEL 703-854-3400, FAX 703-854-2034.

380.1029 USA
THE U S BUSINESS DIRECTORY. Variant title: BusinessUSA. Text in English. a. USD 1,100 combined subscription print, online & CD-ROM eds. (effective 2004 & 2005). back issues avail.
Related titles: CD-ROM ed.; Diskette ed.; E-mail ed.; Fax ed.; Magnetic Tape ed.; Online - full text ed.
Published by: American Business Directories (Subsidiary of: American Business Information, Inc.), 5711 S 86th Circle, P O Box 27347, Omaha, NE 68127. TEL 402-593-4600, 888-946-9377, 877-708-3844, FAX 402-331-5481, sales@directoriesusa.com, http://www.directoriesusa.com.

658.0029 339.0029 791.43 384.55 USA ISSN 1079-6797
PN1580
U.S. DIRECTORY OF ENTERTAINMENT EMPLOYERS. Text in English. 1995. a. USD 59.95 per vol. in United States (effective 2003). **Document type:** *Directory, Trade.*
Related titles: Online - full content ed.: EntertainmentEmployers.com.
Published by: Studiolot Publishing, PO Box 72599, Corpus Christi, TX 78472-2599. TEL 800-335-4335, sales@studiolot.com, http://www.entertainmentemployers.com. Eds. Greg Carbajal, Lawrence Haberman. Pub. Greg Carbajal.

380.1029 DEU ISSN 0946-1477
U S E M A C NEWSLETTER. Text in English, German. 10/yr. adv. bk.rev. charts; illus.; pat.; stat. **Document type:** *Newsletter, Trade.*
Formerly: Exporama (0176-540X)
Published by: Verlag Dr. Grueb Nachf., Oelbergweg 8, Bollschweil, 79283, Germany. TEL 49-7633-7025, FAX 49-7633-82129, usemacworldwide@aol.com, http://www.usemac.de. Ed. Rainer Grueb. Circ: 10,000.

U.S. EXPORT DIRECTORY. see *BUSINESS AND ECONOMICS—International Commerce*

382.029 USA
U S FIRMS IN GERMANY/AMERIKANISCHE UNTERNEHMEN IN DEUTSCHLAND. Text in English. a. adv. **Document type:** *Directory, Trade.* **Description:** Provides information on subsidiaries of U.S. owned firms active in Germany.
Related titles: Diskette ed.
Published by: German American Chamber of Commerce, 12 E 49th St, 24th Fl, New York, NY 10017. TEL 212-974-8830, FAX 212-974-8867, info@gaccny.com, http://www.gaccny.com. Ed. Ulrich Hoppe. Adv. contact Benigna Kirsten.

338.4 USA ISSN 0095-7046
U.S. INDUSTRIAL DIRECTORY. Text in English. 1970. a.
—CCC.
Published by: Reed Business Information (Subsidiary of: Reed Business), 360 Park Ave South, New York, NY 10010. TEL 212-519-7265, FAX 617-558-4327.

U S KEY PERSONNEL LIST. see *ENGINEERING—Engineering Mechanics And Materials*

U S - MEXICO BORDER ENVIRONMENTAL DIRECTORY. see *ENVIRONMENTAL STUDIES*

338.0029 USA
UNDERGROUND CONSTRUCTION. ANNUAL DIRECTORY. Text in English. 1952. a. USD 75 (effective 1999). **Document type:** *Directory.*
Former titles: Pipeline and Utilities Construction. Annual Directory; Pipeline and Underground Utilities Construction. Annual Directory
Indexed: AESIS.
Published by: Oildom Publishing Co. of Texas, Inc., PO Box 941669, Houston, TX 77094-8669. TEL 281-558-6930, FAX 281-558-7029. Ed. Robert Carpenter. Pub. Oliver C Klinger III TEL 281-558-6930, ext. 212. Circ: 34,500.

338.0029 UAE
UNITED ARAB EMIRATES. BUSINESS DIRECTORY. Text in Arabic. 1986. a. USD 150. **Document type:** *Directory.*
Published by: Frontline Advertising & Marketing, P O Box 5151, Sharjah, United Arab Emirates. TEL 971-6-735533, FAX 971-6-715552, TELEX 68844 UNIGET EM. Ed. Saeed Saif Al Tonaiji. Circ: 24,000.

382.029   USA   ISSN 1062-8339
HF3012
UNITED STATES IMPORTERS PRODUCT GUIDE. Text in English. a. **Document type:** *Directory*.
Published by: De Paula Publishing and Services Corp., 421 Seventh Ave, Ste 1206, New York, NY 10001. TEL 212-629-4541. Ed. Carlos de Paula.

381.029   USA   ISSN 0502-5842
UNITED STATES - ITALY TRADE DIRECTORY. Text in English. 1950. a. USD 150 (effective 2000). adv. **Document type:** *Directory*.
Media: CD-ROM.
Published by: Italy - America Chamber of Commerce, Inc., 730 Fifth Ave, New York, NY 10019. TEL 212-459-0044, FAX 212-459-0090. Pub., Adv. contact Franco De Angelis. Circ: 5,000.

658.0029   AUS
UNIVERSAL BUSINESS DIRECTORIES. ADELAIDE BUSINESS TO BUSINESS DIRECTORY. Text in English. 1942. a. AUD 40. adv. **Document type:** *Directory*.
Former titles: Universal Business Directories. Adelaide Business and Street Directory; Universal Business Directories. Adelaide and South Australia Country Trade and Business Directory (0083-3797)
Published by: Universal Press Pty. Ltd., 64 Talavera Rd, Macquarie Park, NSW 2113, Australia. TEL 02-8881877, FAX 02-8889850.

658.0029   AUS
UNIVERSAL BUSINESS DIRECTORIES. BRISBANE BUSINESS TO BUSINESS DIRECTORY. Text in English. 1934. a. AUD 40. adv. **Document type:** *Directory*.
Former titles: Universal Business Directories, Brisbane and Suburban Business and Street Directory; Universal Business Directories, Brisbane and Suburban Business and Trade Directory (0083-369X)
Published by: Universal Press Pty. Ltd., 64 Talavera Rd, Macquarie Park, NSW 2113, Australia. TEL 02-8881877, FAX 02-8889850.

658.0029   AUS
UNIVERSAL BUSINESS DIRECTORIES. MELBOURNE BUSINESS TO BUSINESS DIRECTORY. Text in English. 1948. a. AUD 70. adv. **Document type:** *Directory*.
Formerly: Universal Business Directories, Melbourne and Suburban Business and Trade Directory (0083-3746)
Published by: Universal Press Pty. Ltd., 64 Talavera Rd, Macquarie Park, NSW 2113, Australia. TEL 02-8881877, FAX 02-8889850.

658.0029   AUS
UNIVERSAL BUSINESS DIRECTORIES. NEW SOUTH WALES. CENTRAL WEST BUSINESS TO BUSINESS DIRECTORY. Text in English. a. **Document type:** *Directory*.
Published by: Universal Press Pty. Ltd., 64 Talavera Rd, Macquarie Park, NSW 2113, Australia. TEL 02-8881877, FAX 02-8889850.

658.0029   AUS
UNIVERSAL BUSINESS DIRECTORIES. NEW SOUTH WALES. HUNTER REGION BUSINESS TO BUSINESS DIRECTORY. Text in English. a. **Document type:** *Directory*.
Published by: Universal Press Pty. Ltd., 64 Talavera Rd, Macquarie Park, NSW 2113, Australia. TEL 02-8881877, FAX 02-8889850.

658.0029   AUS
UNIVERSAL BUSINESS DIRECTORIES. NEW SOUTH WALES. ILLAWARRA REGION BUSINESS TO BUSINESS DIRECTORY. Text in English. a. **Document type:** *Directory*.
Published by: Universal Press Pty. Ltd., 64 Talavera Rd, Macquarie Park, NSW 2113, Australia. TEL 02-8881877, FAX 02-8889850.

658.0029   AUS
UNIVERSAL BUSINESS DIRECTORIES. NEW SOUTH WALES. NEW ENGLAND REGION BUSINESS TO BUSINESS DIRECTORY. Text in English. a. **Document type:** *Directory*.
Published by: Universal Press Pty. Ltd., 64 Talavera Rd, Macquarie Park, NSW 2113, Australia. TEL 02-8881877, FAX 02-8889850.

658.0029   AUS
UNIVERSAL BUSINESS DIRECTORIES. NEW SOUTH WALES. NORTH COAST REGION BUSINESS TO BUSINESS DIRECTORY. Text in English. a. **Document type:** *Directory*.
Published by: Universal Press Pty. Ltd., 64 Talavera Rd, Macquarie Park, NSW 2113, Australia. TEL 02-8881877, FAX 02-8889850.

658.0029   AUS
UNIVERSAL BUSINESS DIRECTORIES. NEW SOUTH WALES. RIVERINA REGION BUSINESS TO BUSINESS DIRECTORY. Text in English. a. **Document type:** *Directory*.
Published by: Universal Press Pty. Ltd., 64 Talavera Rd, Macquarie Park, NSW 2113, Australia. TEL 02-8881877, FAX 02-8889850.

658.0029   AUS
UNIVERSAL BUSINESS DIRECTORIES. NEW SOUTH WALES. SOUTH EASTERN REGION BUSINESS TO BUSINESS DIRECTORY. Text in English. a. **Document type:** *Directory*.
Published by: Universal Press Pty. Ltd., 64 Talavera Rd, Macquarie Park, NSW 2113, Australia. TEL 02-8881877, FAX 02-8889850.

658.0029   AUS
UNIVERSAL BUSINESS DIRECTORIES. NORTHERN TERRITORY BUSINESS TO BUSINESS DIRECTORY. Text in English. a. AUD 30. **Document type:** *Directory*.
Published by: Universal Press Pty. Ltd., 64 Talavera Rd, Macquarie Park, NSW 2113, Australia. TEL 02-8881877, FAX 02-8889850.

658.0029   AUS
UNIVERSAL BUSINESS DIRECTORIES. PAPUA NEW GUINEA BUSINESS TO BUSINESS DIRECTORY. Text in English. a. AUD 30. **Document type:** *Directory*.
Published by: Universal Press Pty. Ltd., 64 Talavera Rd, Macquarie Park, NSW 2113, Australia. TEL 02-8881877, FAX 02-8889850.

658.0029   AUS
UNIVERSAL BUSINESS DIRECTORIES. PERTH BUSINESS TO BUSINESS DIRECTORY. Text in English. 1960. a. AUD 40. **Document type:** *Directory*.
Formerly: Universal Business Directories, Perth and Fremantle and Suburbs Business and Trade Directory (0083-3789)
Published by: Universal Press Pty. Ltd., 64 Talavera Rd, Macquarie Park, NSW 2113, Australia. TEL 02-8881877, FAX 02-8889850.

658.0029   AUS
UNIVERSAL BUSINESS DIRECTORIES. QUEENSLAND. BUNDABERG BUSINESS TO BUSINESS DIRECTORY. Text in English. a. **Document type:** *Directory*.
Published by: Universal Press Pty. Ltd., 64 Talavera Rd, Macquarie Park, NSW 2113, Australia. TEL 02-8881877, FAX 02-8889850.

658.0029   AUS
UNIVERSAL BUSINESS DIRECTORIES. QUEENSLAND. CAIRNS BUSINESS TO BUSINESS DIRECTORY. Text in English. a. **Document type:** *Directory*.
Published by: Universal Press Pty. Ltd., 64 Talavera Rd, Macquarie Park, NSW 2113, Australia. TEL 02-8881877, FAX 02-8889850.

658.0029   AUS
UNIVERSAL BUSINESS DIRECTORIES. QUEENSLAND. GLADSTONE BUSINESS TO BUSINESS DIRECTORY. Text in English. a. **Document type:** *Directory*.
Published by: Universal Press Pty. Ltd., 64 Talavera Rd, Macquarie Press, NSW 2113, Australia. TEL 02-881877, FAX 02-8889850.

658.0029   AUS
UNIVERSAL BUSINESS DIRECTORIES. QUEENSLAND. GYMPIE BUSINESS TO BUSINESS DIRECTORY. Text in English. a. **Document type:** *Directory*.
Published by: Universal Press Pty. Ltd., 64 Talavera Rd, Macquarie Park, NSW 2113, Australia. TEL 02-8881877, FAX 02-8889850.

658.0029   AUS
UNIVERSAL BUSINESS DIRECTORIES. QUEENSLAND. MACKAY BUSINESS TO BUSINESS DIRECTORY. Text in English. a. **Document type:** *Directory*.
Published by: Universal Press Pty. Ltd., 64 Talavera Rd, Macquarie Park, NSW 2113, Australia. TEL 02-8881877, FAX 02-8889850.

658.0029   AUS
UNIVERSAL BUSINESS DIRECTORIES. QUEENSLAND. MARYBOROUGH BUSINESS TO BUSINESS DIRECTORY. Text in English. a. **Document type:** *Directory*.
Published by: Universal Press Pty. Ltd., 64 Talavera Rd, Macquarie Park, NSW 2113, Australia. TEL 02-8881877, FAX 02-8889850.

658.0029   AUS
UNIVERSAL BUSINESS DIRECTORIES. QUEENSLAND. REDCLIFFE BUSINESS TO BUSINESS DIRECTORY. Text in English. a. **Document type:** *Directory*.
Published by: Universal Press Pty. Ltd., 64 Talavera Rd, Macquarie Park, NSW 2113, Australia. TEL 02-8881877, FAX 02-8889850.

658.0029   AUS
UNIVERSAL BUSINESS DIRECTORIES. QUEENSLAND. ROCKHAMPTON BUSINESS TO BUSINESS DIRECTORY. Text in English. a. **Document type:** *Directory*.
Published by: Universal Press Pty. Ltd., 64 Talavera Rd, Macquarie Park, NSW 2113, Australia. TEL 02-8881877, FAX 02-8889850.

658.0029   AUS
UNIVERSAL BUSINESS DIRECTORIES. QUEENSLAND. SUNSHINE COAST BUSINESS TO BUSINESS DIRECTORY. Text in English. a. **Document type:** *Directory*.
Published by: Universal Press Pty. Ltd., 64 Talavera Rd, Macquarie Park, NSW 2113, Australia. TEL 02-8881877, FAX 02-8889850.

658.0029   AUS
UNIVERSAL BUSINESS DIRECTORIES. QUEENSLAND. TOOWOOMBA BUSINESS TO BUSINESS DIRECTORY. Text in English. a. **Document type:** *Directory*.
Published by: Universal Press Pty. Ltd., 64 Talavera Rd, Macquarie Park, NSW 2113, Australia. TEL 02-8881877, FAX 02-8889850.

658.0029   AUS
UNIVERSAL BUSINESS DIRECTORIES. QUEENSLAND. TOWNSVILLE BUSINESS TO BUSINESS DIRECTORY. Text in English. a. **Document type:** *Directory*.
Published by: Universal Press Pty. Ltd., 64 Talavera Rd, Macquarie Park, NSW 2113, Australia. TEL 02-881877, FAX 02-8889850.

658.0029   AUS
UNIVERSAL BUSINESS DIRECTORIES. SOUTH AUSTRALIA BUSINESS TO BUSINESS DIRECTORY. Text in English. a. AUD 30. **Document type:** *Directory*.
Published by: Universal Press Pty. Ltd., 64 Talavera Rd, Macquarie Park, NSW 2113, Australia. TEL 02-8881877, FAX 02-8889850.

658.0029   AUS
UNIVERSAL BUSINESS DIRECTORIES. SYDNEY BUSINESS TO BUSINESS DIRECTORY. Text in English. 1948. a. AUD 70. adv. **Document type:** *Directory*.
Former titles: Universal Business Directories, Sydney and Suburban Business and Street Directory; Universal Business Directories, Sydney and Suburban Business and Trade Directory (0083-3819)
Published by: Universal Press Pty. Ltd., 64 Talavera Rd, Macquarie Park, NSW 2113, Australia. TEL 02-8881877, FAX 02-8889850.

658.0029   AUS
UNIVERSAL BUSINESS DIRECTORIES. TASMANIA BUSINESS TO BUSINESS DIRECTORY. Text in English. 1950. a. AUD 17. adv. **Document type:** *Directory*.
Former titles: Universal Business Directories. Tasmania Business and Street Directory; Universal Business. Tasmania Business and Trade Directory (0083-3827)
Published by: Universal Press Pty. Ltd., 64 Talavera Rd, Macquarie Park, NSW 2113, Australia. TEL 02-8881877, FAX 02-8889850.

658.0029   AUS
UNIVERSAL BUSINESS DIRECTORIES. VICTORIA. BALLARAT BUSINESS TO BUSINESS DIRECTORY. Text in English. a. **Document type:** *Directory*.
Published by: Universal Press Pty. Ltd., 64 Talavera Rd, Macquarie Park, NSW 2113, Australia. TEL 02-8881877, FAX 02-8889850.

658.0029   AUS
UNIVERSAL BUSINESS DIRECTORIES. VICTORIA. BENDIGO BUSINESS TO BUSINESS DIRECTORY. Text in English. a. **Document type:** *Directory*.
Published by: Universal Press Pty. Ltd., 64 Talavera Rd, Macquarie Park, NSW 2113, Australia. TEL 02-8881877, FAX 02-8889850.

658.0029   AUS
UNIVERSAL BUSINESS DIRECTORIES. VICTORIA. GEELONG BUSINESS TO BUSINESS DIRECTORY. Text in English. a. **Document type:** *Directory*.
Published by: Universal Press Pty. Ltd., 64 Talavera Rd, Macquarie Park, NSW 2113, Australia. TEL 02-8881877, FAX 02-8889850.

658.0029   AUS
UNIVERSAL BUSINESS DIRECTORIES. VICTORIA. GOULBURN VALLEY BUSINESS TO BUSINESS DIRECTORY. Text in English. a. **Document type:** *Directory*.
Published by: Universal Press Pty. Ltd., 64 Talavera Rd, Macquarie Park, NSW 2113, Australia. TEL 02-8881877, FAX 02-8889850.

658.0029   AUS
UNIVERSAL BUSINESS DIRECTORIES. VICTORIA. LATROBE VALLEY BUSINESS TO BUSINESS DIRECTORY. Text in English. a. **Document type:** *Directory*.
Published by: Universal Press Pty. Ltd., 64 Talavera Rd, Macquarie Park, NSW 2113, Australia. TEL 02-8881877, FAX 02-8889850.

658.0029   AUS
UNIVERSAL BUSINESS DIRECTORIES. VICTORIA. NORTH EAST VICTORIA BUSINESS TO BUSINESS DIRECTORY. Text in English. a. **Document type:** *Directory*.

Published by: Universal Press Pty. Ltd., 64 Talavera Rd, Macquarie Park, NSW 2113, Australia. TEL 02-8881877, FAX 02-8889850.

658.0029   AUS
UNIVERSAL BUSINESS DIRECTORIES. VICTORIA. SUNRAYSIA-MALLEE BUSINESS TO BUSINESS DIRECTORIES. Text in English. a. **Document type:** *Directory.*
Published by: Universal Press Pty. Ltd., 64 Talavera Rd, Macquarie Park, NSW 2113, Australia. TEL 02-8881877, FAX 02-8889850.

658.0029   AUS
UNIVERSAL BUSINESS DIRECTORIES. VICTORIA. WEST DISTRICT BUSINESS TO BUSINESS DIRECTORY. Text in English. a. **Document type:** *Directory.*
Published by: Universal Press Pty. Ltd., 64 Talavera Rd, Macquarie Park, NSW 2113, Australia. TEL 02-8881877, FAX 02-8889850.

658.0029   AUS
UNIVERSAL BUSINESS DIRECTORIES. VICTORIA. WIMMERA BUSINESS TO BUSINESS DIRECTORY. Text in English. a. **Document type:** *Directory.*
Published by: Universal Press Pty. Ltd., 64 Talavera Rd, Macquarie Park, NSW 2113, Australia. TEL 02-8881877, FAX 02-8889850.

UP-DATE. see *BUSINESS AND ECONOMICS—Chamber Of Commerce Publications*

338.0029   USA   ISSN 1084-0001
UPSTATE NEW YORK BUSINESS DIRECTORY. Text in English. 1993. a. USD 1,100 combined subscription print, online & CD-ROM eds. (effective 2004 & 2005). back issues avail. **Document type:** *Directory.* **Description:** Includes all businesses in the upstate New York area compiled from the yellow pages and telephone-verified. Listings include company name, complete address, phone number, name of owner or manager, employee size, sales volume, and credit rating codes.
Related titles: CD-ROM ed.; Diskette ed.; E-mail ed.; Fax ed.; Magnetic Tape ed.; Online - full text ed.
Published by: American Business Directories (Subsidiary of: American Business Information, Inc.), 5711 S 86th Circle, P O Box 27347, Omaha, NE 68127. TEL 402-593-4600, 888-946-9377, 877-708-3844, FAX 402-331-5481, sales@directoriesusa.com, http://www.directoriesusa.com.

670.29   USA   ISSN 0732-2860
HD9727.N7
UPSTATE NEW YORK DIRECTORY OF MANUFACTURERS. Text in English. 1981. a. USD 62.50. adv. **Document type:** *Directory.* **Description:** Profiles approximately 5,100 manufacturers; features alphabetical, geographical, and product line by SIC sections.
Related titles: Diskette ed.: USD 295; Magnetic Tape ed.
Published by: Commerce Register, Inc., 190 Godwin Ave, Midland Park, NJ 07432. TEL 201-445-3000, FAX 201-445-5806.

USED EQUIPMENT DIRECTORY. see *MACHINERY*

338.0029   USA   ISSN 1048-7417
HF5065.U8
UTAH BUSINESS DIRECTORY. Text in English. 1989. a. USD 1,100 combined subscription print, online & CD-ROM eds. (effective 2004 & 2005). index. back issues avail. **Document type:** *Directory.* **Description:** Includes all businesses in the state compiled from the yellow pages and telephone-verified. Each listing includes company name, complete address, phone number, name of owner, manager, and employee size, sales volume codes, and credit rating codes.
Related titles: CD-ROM ed.; Diskette ed.; E-mail ed.; Fax ed.; Online - full text ed.
Published by: American Business Directories (Subsidiary of: American Business Information, Inc.), 5711 S 86th Circle, P O Box 27347, Omaha, NE 68127. TEL 402-593-4600, 888-946-9377, 877-708-3844, FAX 402-331-5481, sales@directoriesusa.com, http://www.directoriesusa.com.

670.29   USA   ISSN 8755-2841
HD9727.U8
UTAH DIRECTORY OF BUSINESS AND INDUSTRY. Text in English. 1951. a. USD 34. **Document type:** *Directory, Government.* **Description:** Includes standard industrial code, county and alphabetical listing of all manufacturing firms and nonmanufacturing firms with 20 or more employees.
Formerly: Directory of Utah Manufacturers (0070-6566)
Related titles: Diskette ed.
Published by: Department of Employment Security, Division of Economic Development, 324 S State St, Ste 500, Salt Lake City, UT 84111. TEL 801-538-8700, 800-848-0688, FAX 801-538-8773. Circ: 2,500. **Dist. by:** Manufacturers' News, Inc., 1633 Central St, Evanston, IL 60201. TEL 847-864-7000.

670   USA   ISSN 1525-4119
HF5065.U8
UTAH MANUFACTURERS DIRECTORY. Text in English. USD 75 (effective 2001). **Document type:** *Directory.*
Related titles: CD-ROM ed.: USD 310 (effective 2001).

Published by: Manufacturers' News, Inc., 1633 Central St, Evanston, IL 60201. TEL 847-864-7000, 888-752-5200, FAX 847-332-1100, info@manufacturersnews.com, sales@mninfo.com, http://www.manufacturersnews.com. Ed. Frank Lambing.

UTILITY WEEK DIRECTORY. see *ENERGY*

658.8029   GBR   ISSN 1358-7927
V A R WORLD. (Value Added Reselling) Text in English. 1992. m. GBP 24; GBP 50 foreign. **Document type:** *Trade.*
Related titles: Online - full text ed.: (from Factiva).
Published by: V N U Business Publications Ltd., 32-34 Broadwick St, London, W1A 2HG, United Kingdom. TEL 44-207-4394242, FAX 44-20-7437-7001.

VADEMEKUM DER GESCHICHTSWISSENSCHAFTEN. see *HISTORY—History Of Europe*

670.29   USA
VENDOR CATALOG SERVICES INDEX. Text in English. 1979. bi-m. USD 1,165. adv. **Description:** Provides vendor, brand name and subject access to major manufacturers in all fields including aerospace and engineering components and products.
Formerly: Master Catalog Services Index
Related titles: CD-ROM ed.
Published by: I H S Energy (Subsidiary of: I H S Energy Group), 15 Inverness Way East, Englewood, CO 80112. FAX 303-799-4085, http://ihsenergy.com. Ed. Liz Maynard Prigge. Circ: 2,500.

VENDOR PRODUCT COMPARISON (DESIGN ENGINEERING). see *BUSINESS AND ECONOMICS—Marketing And Purchasing*

338.0029   USA   ISSN 1048-7174
HF5065.V5
VERMONT BUSINESS DIRECTORY. Text in English. 1990. a. USD 1,100 combined subscription print, online & CD-ROM eds. (effective 2004 & 2005). index. back issues avail. **Document type:** *Directory.* **Description:** Includes all businesses in the state compiled from the yellow pages and telephone-verified. Each listing includes company name, address, phone number, name of owner or manager, and employee size and sales volume codes, and credit rating codes.
Related titles: CD-ROM ed.; Diskette ed.; E-mail ed.; Fax ed.; Magnetic Tape ed.; Online - full text ed.
Published by: American Business Directories (Subsidiary of: American Business Information, Inc.), 5711 S 86th Circle, P O Box 27347, Omaha, NE 68127. TEL 402-593-4600, 888-946-9377, 877-708-3844, FAX 402-331-5481, sales@directoriesusa.com, http://www.directoriesusa.com.

670.29   USA
VERMONT BUYER'S GUIDE. Text in English. a. adv. **Document type:** *Consumer.*
Formerly: Vermont Directory of Manufacturers
Published by: Agency of Development and Community Affairs, Pavilion Office Bldg. Montpelier, VT 05602. TEL 802-828-3211, FAX 802-828-3339. Ed. Lori McAllister. Adv. contact Geriame Smart. Circ: 15,000.

380.1029   USA   ISSN 1526-9175
VERMONT MANUFACTURERS DIRECTORY. Text in English. 2000. a. USD 79 (effective 2005). **Document type:** *Directory, Trade.*
Published by: Harris InfoSource, 2057 E Aurora Rd, Twinsburg, OH 44087. TEL 800-888-5900, 330-425-9000, FAX 330-425-7150, http://www.harrisinfo.com.

670   USA   ISSN 1522-2004
HF5065.V5
VERMONT MANUFACTURERS REGISTER. Text in English. USD 55 (effective 2000).
Related titles: CD-ROM ed.: USD 175 (effective 2000).
Published by: Manufacturers' News, Inc., 1633 Central St, Evanston, IL 60201. TEL 847-864-7000, 888-752-5200, FAX 847-332-1100, info@manufacturersnews.com, sales@mninfo.com, http://www.manufacturersnews.com. Ed. Frank Lambing.

VERMONT MANUFACTURING & WHOLESALE - DISTRIBUTOR DIRECTORY. see *BUSINESS AND ECONOMICS—Production Of Goods And Services*

354.6   USA   ISSN 0083-5781
JK3030
VERMONT YEAR BOOK. Text in English. 1818. a. USD 32.85 (effective 1999). adv. maps. **Document type:** *Directory.* **Description:** Comprehensive directory of federal, state, and local government departments and officials in Vermont, with additional listings of businesses, manufacturing, travel and media companies, organizations and professionals.
Formerly: Walton's Register
Published by: National Survey, Inc., School St, PO Box 1040, Chester, VT 05143. TEL 802-875-2121, FAX 802-875-2123. Ed. Aili Farrar. R&P Vincent P Crocker. Adv. contact Sandra Muse Neronsky. B&W page USD 450. Circ: 2,000.

658.0029   DEU
VERZEICHNIS DER VERSANDHANDELS. Text in German. 1996. a. EUR 298 (effective 2005). bk.rev. charts; stat.; tr.lit. back issues avail. **Document type:** *Directory, Trade.* **Description:** Directory of mail order houses in Germany, Austria and Switzerland.
Related titles: CD-ROM ed.; E-mail ed.; Fax ed.; Online - full text ed.
Published by: F I D Verlag GmbH, Koblenzer Str 99, Bonn, 53177, Germany. TEL 49-228-9550333, FAX 49-228-82055756, info@fid-verlag.de, http://www.fid-verlag.de/verzeichnis_des_versandhandels.php. Circ: 1,000.

380.1029   DEU
VERZEICHNIS LIEFERBARER KAUFMEDIEN. Abbreviated title: V L K. Text in German. 1988. s-a. EUR 94.75 (effective 2002). **Document type:** *Directory, Trade.*
Published by: Entertainment Media Verlag GmbH und Co. oHG, Einsteinring 24, Dornach, 85609, Germany. TEL 49-89-45114-0, FAX 49-89-45114444, emv@e-media.de, http://www.mediabiz.de. Ed. Harald Hesse. Pub. Ulrich Scheele. R&P Otto Bachmeier. Adv. contact Stefan Lessmeier.

658.8029   AUS   ISSN 0812-2970
VICTORIAN TASMANIAN RETAIL DIRECTORY. Text in English. 1982. a. AUD 165 (effective 1998). **Document type:** *Directory.* **Description:** Lists leasing managers, shopping centers, retailers and suppliers to retail industry.
Published by: Jared Publishing, PO Box 51, Mitcham, VIC 3132, Australia. TEL 61-3-8742415, FAX 61-3-8735951. Ed. Bruce Atkinson. Circ: 1,000.

VIDEO BUSINESS. see *COMMUNICATIONS—Video*

380.1 384.55029   USA
VIDEO DUPLICATION DIRECTORY. Text in English. 1992. a., latest 9th ed. USD 257 (effective 2001). tr.lit. 100 p./no.; back issues avail.; reprints avail. **Document type:** *Directory.* **Description:** Complete guide to video duplicators in the United States and Canada.
Related titles: Online - full content ed.
Published by: Corbell Publishing Company, 11500 W Olympic Blvd, Ste 400, Los Angeles, CA 90064. TEL 310-444-3048, FAX 310-312-4551, mhealy@corbell.com, http://www.corbell.com. Pub. Maureen Healy.

338.0029   USA   ISSN 1047-2711
HC107.V8
VIRGINIA BUSINESS DIRECTORY. Text in English. 1988. a. USD 1,100 combined subscription print, online & CD-ROM eds. (effective 2004 & 2005). index. back issues avail. **Document type:** *Directory.* **Description:** Includes all businesses in the state compiled from the yellow pages and telephone-verified. Each listing includes company name, complete address, phone number, name of owner or manager, and employee size and sales volume codes, and credit rating codes.
Related titles: CD-ROM ed.; Diskette ed.; E-mail ed.; Fax ed.; Magnetic Tape ed.; Online - full text ed.
Published by: American Business Directories (Subsidiary of: American Business Information, Inc.), 5711 S 86th Circle, P O Box 27347, Omaha, NE 68127. TEL 402-593-4600, 888-946-9377, 877-708-3844, FAX 402-331-5481, sales@directoriesusa.com, http://www.directoriesusa.com.

381.029   USA   ISSN 0882-3219
HC107.V8
VIRGINIA INDUSTRIAL DIRECTORY. Text in English. 1940. a. USD 75 to non-members; USD 60 to members (effective 1999). **Document type:** *Directory.* **Description:** Provides a resource for locating sales contacts, products and services in Virginia.
Formerly (until 1980): Directory of Virginia Manufacturing and Mining (0070-6574)
Related titles: CD-ROM ed.; Diskette ed.
Published by: Virginia Chamber of Commerce, 9 S Fifth St, Richmond, VA 23219. TEL 800-477-7682, FAX 804-783-6112. Ed. Lou Ann Ladin. Circ: 7,000.

670.29   USA   ISSN 1065-2493
HF5065.V8
VIRGINIA MANUFACTURERS DIRECTORY. Text in English. 1993. a. USD 85 (effective 2000). adv. **Document type:** *Directory.* **Description:** Profiles 7,168 manufacturers listed 5 different ways; by product, alphabetically, geographically, by SIC and parent company.
Media: Diskette. **Related titles:** CD-ROM ed.: USD 445 (effective 2000).
Published by: Manufacturers' News, Inc., 1633 Central St, Evanston, IL 60201. TEL 847-864-7000, 888-752-5200, FAX 847-332-1100, info@mninfo.com, info@manufacturersnews.com, sales@mninfo.com, http://www.manufacturersnews.com. Ed. Frank Lambing. Adv. contact Charles Scherer. B&W page USD 1,843. Circ: 1,000.

VIRGINIA STATE AGENT HANDBOOK. see *INSURANCE*

WALDEN'S A B C GUIDE. see *PAPER AND PULP*

WALDEN'S A B C PERSONNEL DIRECTORY. see *PAPER AND PULP*

347.73029 USA ISSN 0742-1095
KF8700.A19
WANT'S FEDERAL - STATE COURT DIRECTORY (YEAR). Text in English. 1984. a. USD 45 (effective 2003). **Document type:** *Directory.* **Description:** Lists federal and state judges and court clerks, with explanations of each state's court system.
—CCC.
Published by: Want Publishing Co., 420 Lexington Ave, Rm 300, New York, NY 10170-0399. TEL 212-687-3774, FAX 212-687-3779, rwant@courts.com, http://www.courts.com. Ed. Robert S Want. Circ: 5,000.

380.1029 USA ISSN 1542-3301
HF5074
WARD'S BUSINESS DIRECTORY OF PRIVATE AND PUBLIC COMPANIES IN CANADA AND MEXICO. Text in English. 2002. a., latest 2002. USD 550 per vol. (effective 2004).
Published by: Gale Group (Subsidiary of: Thomson Corporation), 27500 Drake Rd, Farmington Hills, MI 48331-3535. TEL 248-699-4253, 800-347-4253, FAX 248-699-8035, http://www.galegroup.com.

380.1029 USA ISSN 1048-8707
HG4057
WARD'S BUSINESS DIRECTORY OF U S PRIVATE AND PUBLIC COMPANIES. Text in English. 1989. a. (in 8 vols.), latest 2004, 47th ed. USD 3,075 for entire 8 vol. set (effective 2005).
Formed by the 1989 merger of: Ward's Business Directory of U S Private and Public Companies. Vol.1; Over 11.5 Million Dollars in Sales (1042-816X); Ward's Business Directory of U S Private and Public Companies. Vol.2; From .5 to 11.5 Million Dollars (1042-9190); Ward's Business Directory of U S Private and Public Companies. Vol.3; Ranked by Sales within Industry (1042-9204); Vol.1 was formerly (until 1989): Ward's Business Directory, Vol.1, U S Private Companies, Largest Private Plus Selected Public (0897-1633); (until 1987): Ward's Directory of Largest U S Companies (0882-7990); (until 1984): Ward's Directory of Largest U S Corporations (0730-3122); (1961-1980): Leading U S Corporations (0270-1804); Vol.2 was formerly (until 1989): Ward's Business Directory, Vol.2, U S Private Companies up to 11 Million Dollars in Sales (0897-1641); (until 1987): Ward's Business Directory of Major U S Private Companies (0882-8008); (1984-1985): Ward's Directory of Private U S Companies (0737-4445); Vol.3 was formerly (1988-1989): Ward's Business Directory of U S Private Companies by Industry (0897-1625)
Related titles: Diskette ed.
Published by: Gale Group (Subsidiary of: Thomson Corporation), 27500 Drake Rd, Farmington Hills, MI 48331-3535. TEL 248-699-8061, 800-877-4253, FAX 248-699-4253, galeord@gale.com, http://www.gale.com. Ed. Julie E Towell.

380.1029 POL ISSN 1506-4883
THE WARSAW VOICE I S O ALMANAC (YEAR). Text in English, Polish. 1999. a. PLZ 34 (effective 1999). adv. **Document type:** *Directory, Trade.* **Description:** Presents companies holding I S O certificates.
Published by: Warsaw Voice S.A., Ksiecia Janusza 65, Warsaw, 01452, Poland. TEL 48-22-366377, FAX 48-22-371995, specialprojects@warsawvoice.com.pl, http://www.warsawvoice.com.pl. Ed. Magda Sowinska. Adv. contact Dariusz Gibert. page PLZ 10,860.

338.0029 USA ISSN 1043-9781
HF5065.W2
WASHINGTON BUSINESS DIRECTORY. Text in English. 1988. a. USD 1,100 combined subscription print, online & CD-ROM eds. (effective 2004 & 2005). index. back issues avail. **Document type:** *Directory.* **Description:** Includes all businesses in the state compiled from the yellow pages and telephone-verified. Each listing includes company name, complete address, phone number, name of owner, manager, and employee size, sales volume codes, and credit rating codes.
Related titles: CD-ROM ed.; Diskette ed.; E-mail ed.; Fax ed.; Magnetic Tape ed.; Online - full text ed.
Published by: American Business Directories (Subsidiary of: American Business Information, Inc.), 5711 S 86th Circle, P O Box 27347, Omaha, NE 68127. TEL 402-593-4600, 888-946-9377, 877-708-3844, FAX 402-331-5481, sales@directoriesusa.com, http://www.directoriesusa.com.

338.0029 USA ISSN 1048-7077
HF5068.W3
WASHINGTON D.C. AREA BUSINESS DIRECTORY. Text in English. 1990. a. USD 1,100 combined subscription print, online & CD-ROM eds. (effective 2004 & 2005). index. back issues avail. **Document type:** *Directory.* **Description:** Includes all businesses in the DC metro area compiled from the yellow pages and telephone-verified. Each listing includes company name, complete address, phone number, name of owner, manager, and employee size, sales volume codes, and credit rating codes.
Related titles: CD-ROM ed.; Diskette ed.; E-mail ed.; Fax ed.; Magnetic Tape ed.; Online - full text ed.
Published by: American Business Directories (Subsidiary of: American Business Information, Inc.), 5711 S 86th Circle, P O Box 27347, Omaha, NE 68127. TEL 402-593-4600, 888-946-9377, 877-708-3844, FAX 402-331-5481, sales@directoriesusa.com, http://www.directoriesusa.com.

670 USA ISSN 1525-4100
WASHINGTON MANUFACTURERS DIRECTORY. Text in English. USD 110 (effective 2000).
Related titles: CD-ROM ed.: USD 490 (effective 2000).
Published by: Manufacturers' News, Inc., 1633 Central St, Evanston, IL 60201. TEL 847-864-7000, 888-752-5200, FAX 847-332-1100, info@manufacturersnews.com, sales@mninfo.com, http://www.manufacturersnews.com. Ed. Frank Lambing.

670.29 USA ISSN 0148-5687
T12
WASHINGTON MANUFACTURERS REGISTER✶. Text in English. 1965. a. USD 99. adv. **Document type:** *Directory.* **Description:** Provides updated profiles on 8,051 manufacturers, wood products and high tech companies in Washington state.
Former titles: Directory of Washington Manufacturers (0148-3641); Directory of Washington State Manufacturers, Products, Industry, Location (0419-3857)
Related titles: CD-ROM ed.: USD 295.
Published by: (Washington. Department of Community, Trade and Economic Development), Database Publishing Company, 701 E Ball Rd Ste 100, Anaheim, CA 92805-5962. TEL 714-778-6400, FAX 714-778-6811. Ed., R&P Sarah Fraser. Circ: 1,800.

382.029 USA
WASHINGTON STATE INTERNATIONAL TRADE DIRECTORY. Text in English. a.
Published by: Newman-Burrows Publishing, 1710 S Norman St, Seattle, WA 98144-2819. TEL 206-709-1840, FAX 206-324-8939. R&P Mike Daigle.

WASHINGTON TELECOM DIRECTORY. see *COMMUNICATIONS—Telephone And Telegraph*

338.0029 GBR ISSN 1471-5716
HG4135.5
WATERLOW'S UNQUOTED COMPANIES (YEAR). Text in English. 1985. a. GBP 350. **Document type:** *Directory.* **Description:** Keeps readers up to date with key developments among the top 20,000 unquoted U.K. companies.
Formerly (until 2000): Macmillan's Unquoted Companies (Year) (0267-4378)
—BLDSC (9279.455695).
Published by: Waterlow Specialist Information Publishing Ltd, 6-14 Underwood St, London, N1 7JQ, United Kingdom. TEL 44-171-324-2353, FAX 44-171-324-2312. Adv. contact Samantha Taylor.

338.0029 DEU
WER GEHOERT ZU WEM (ONLINE EDITION. Text in German. irreg. **Document type:** *Directory, Trade.*
Formerly (until 2005): Wer Gehoert zu Wem (Print Edition) (0171-9688)
Media: Online - full content. **Related titles:** CD-ROM ed.: EUR 199 (effective 2005).
Published by: Commerzbank AG, Frankfurt Am Main, 60261, Germany. TEL 49-69-13623615, FAX 49-69-13623422, https://www.commerzbank.de/research/economic_research/d_eur/werzuwem1/, http://www.commerzbank.com.

670.29 DEU
WER LIEFERT WAS?; the cd-rom for purchasing and business professionals. Text in Dutch, English, French, German, Italian, Spanish. 1993. q. EUR 79, USD 68 (effective 2001). adv. **Document type:** *Directory, Trade.* **Description:** Business-to-business directory in six languages covering national and international companies located in Germany, Austria and Switzerland.
Media: CD-ROM. **Related titles:** Online - full text ed.: (from F I Z Technik, G B I, The Dialog Corporation).
Published by: Wer Liefert Was? GmbH, Normannenweg 16-20, Hamburg, 20537, Germany. TEL 49-40-25440-0, FAX 49-40-25440100, info@wlw.de, http://www.wlw.de. Circ: 100,000.

338.0029 DEU
WER LIEFERT WAS? CD - MARKETING; the business database for exact target group marketing. Text in Croatian, Czech, Dutch, English, French, German, Italian, Slovenian, Spanish. 1986. 2/yr. EUR 920, USD 905 per issue (effective 2001). **Document type:** *Directory, Trade.* **Description:** Covers approximately 285,000 companies located in Germany, Austria, Switzerland, Belgium, Luxembourg, the Netherlands, the Czech Republic, Slovenia, Slovakia and Croatia.
Media: CD-ROM.
Published by: Wer Liefert Was? GmbH, Normannenweg 16-20, Hamburg, 20537, Germany. TEL 49-40-25440-0, FAX 49-40-25440100, info@wlw.de, http://www.wlw.de.

670.29 DEU
WER LIEFERT WAS? CENTRAL EUROPE; CD-ROM for new markets. Text in Croatian, Czech, English, French, German, Italian, Slovenian. 1992. a. EUR 49, USD 42 (effective 2001). **Document type:** *Directory, Trade.* **Description:** Business-to-business directory covering approximately 45,000 companies and their products and services in The Czech Republic, Slovenia, Slovakia, and Croatia.
Media: CD-ROM.
Published by: Wer Liefert Was? GmbH, Normannenweg 16-20, Hamburg, 20537, Germany. TEL 49-40-25440-0, FAX 49-40-25440100, info@wlw.de, http://www.wlw.de.

381.029 DEU
WER LIEFERT WAS? EURO CD BOOK; the CD-ROM for purchasing and acquiring new business contacts in Europe. Text in Multiple languages. 1999. a. EUR 119, USD 102 (effective 2001). **Document type:** *Directory, Trade.* **Description:** Features products and services from international companies in 13 European countries: Germany, Austria, Switzerland, Great Britain, France, Italy, Belgium, Luxembourg, Netherlands, Czech Republic, Slovakia, Slovenia, and Croatia.
Media: CD-ROM.
Published by: Wer Liefert Was? GmbH, Normannenweg 16-20, Hamburg, 20537, Germany. TEL 49-40-25440-0, info@wlw.de, http://www.wlw.de. Circ: 80,000.

658.8029 DEU ISSN 1618-0526
WER UND WAS - BACKGEWERBE. Text in German. a. EUR 127.50 (effective 2003). **Document type:** *Directory, Trade.*
Former titles (until 2001): Wer und Was im Deutschen Backgewerbe (1433-1977); (until 199?): Wer und Was in den Deutschen Grossbaeckereien (0939-2610); (until 1990): Wer und Was in der Deutschen Brot-Industrie und den Grossbaeckereien (0936-8108); (until 1980): Wer und Was in der Deutschen Brotindustrie (0171-435X)
Published by: B. Behr's Verlag GmbH & Co. KG, Averhoffstr. 10, Hamburg, 22085, Germany. TEL 49-40-2270080, FAX 49-40-2201091, info@behrs.de, http://www.behrs.de.

658.8029 DEU ISSN 1619-9081
WER UND WAS - OBST-, GEMUESE-, KARTOFFEL- UND NAEHRMITTEL-INDUSTRIE. Text in German. 197?. a. EUR 122 (effective 2003). **Document type:** *Directory, Trade.*
Former titles (until 2002): Wer und Was in der Deutschen Obst-, Gemuese-, Kartoffel- und Naehrmittel-Industrie (1610-0476); (until 1985): Wer und Was in der Deutschen Obst-, Gemuese- und Kartoffelverarbeitenden Industrie (0170-7930)
Published by: B. Behr's Verlag GmbH & Co. KG, Averhoffstr. 10, Hamburg, 22085, Germany. TEL 49-40-2270080, FAX 49-40-2201091, info@behrs.de, http://www.behrs.de.

338.0029 DEU
WER UND WAS - SUESSWAREN-INDUSTRIE. Text in German. 1949. a. EUR 319.50 (effective 2003). **Document type:** *Directory, Trade.*
Former titles: Wer und Was in der Deutschen Suesswarenindustrie (0171-4368); (until 1974): Suesswaren Jahrbuch (0448-1380)
Published by: B. Behr's Verlag GmbH & Co. KG, Averhoffstr. 10, Hamburg, 22085, Germany. TEL 49-40-2270080, FAX 49-40-2201091, info@behrs.de, http://www.behrs.de. Adv. contact Frau Wahlers.

658.8029 DEU ISSN 1618-4793
WER UND WAS - TIEFKUEHL- UND CONVENIENCE-INDUSRIE. Text in German. 1994. irreg. EUR 79.50 (effective 2003). **Document type:** *Directory, Trade.*
Formerly (until 2001): Wer und Was in der Deutschen Tiefkuehlwirtschaft (0948-2814)
Published by: B. Behr's Verlag GmbH & Co. KG, Averhoffstr. 10, Hamburg, 22085, Germany. TEL 49-40-2270080, FAX 49-40-2201091, info@behrs.de, http://www.behrs.de.

338.0029 USA ISSN 1047-9007
HC107.W5
WEST VIRGINIA BUSINESS DIRECTORY. Text in English. 1988. a. USD 1,100 combined subscription print, online & CD-ROM eds. (effective 2004 & 2005). index. back issues avail. **Document type:** *Directory.* **Description:** Includes all businesses in the state compiled from the yellow pages and telephone-verified. Each listing includes company name, complete address, phone number, name of owner, manager, and employee size, sales volume codes, and credit rating codes.
Related titles: CD-ROM ed.; Diskette ed.; E-mail ed.; Fax ed.; Magnetic Tape ed.; Online - full text ed.
Published by: American Business Directories (Subsidiary of: American Business Information, Inc.), 5711 S 86th Circle, P O Box 27347, Omaha, NE 68127. TEL 402-593-4600, 888-946-9377, 877-708-3844, FAX 402-331-5481, sales@directoriesusa.com, http://www.directoriesusa.com.

670.29 USA ISSN 0893-2824
HD9727.W4
WEST VIRGINIA MANUFACTURERS REGISTER. Text in English. 1987. a. USD 64 (effective 2001). adv. **Document type:** *Directory.* **Description:** Profiles 2,340 manufacturers by product, geographically by city, by SIC code, and alphabetically and by parent company.
Related titles: CD-ROM ed.: USD 265 (effective 2001); Diskette ed.
Published by: Manufacturers' News, Inc., 1633 Central St, Evanston, IL 60201. TEL 847-864-7000, 888-752-5200, FAX 847-332-1100, info@mninfo.com, info@manufacturersnews.com, sales@mninfo.com, http://www.manufacturersnews.com. Ed. Frank Lambing. Adv. contact Charles Scherer. B&W page USD 1,843.

▼ new title ➤ refereed ✶ unverified ♦ full entry avail.

338.0029   ZAF
WESTERN CAPE BUSINESS REGISTER. Text in English. 1964.
a. USD 230 (effective 2001). adv. **Document type:** *Directory.*
Former titles: Cape Peninsula Directory; Cape Times Peninsula
Directory (0379-461X)
Related titles: Diskette ed.
Published by: Braby's (Subsidiary of: Associated Industries), Attn:
Sue Pearson, PO Box 1426, Pinetown, 3600, South Africa.
TEL 27-31-7017021, FAX 27-31-7017036,
booksales@brabys.co.za. Ed. A Stagg.

WESTERN STATES PETROLEUM INDUSTRY. see *PETROLEUM
AND GAS*

658.045029   USA   ISSN 1090-7564
WHAT'S NEW FOR FAMILY FUN CENTERS. Text in English.
1993. 9/yr. USD 24; USD 27 in Canada; USD 50 elsewhere.
Document type: *Magazine, Consumer.* **Description:** New
products and services for owners and managers of family
entertainment businesses.
Published by: Adams Business Media, 2101 S Arlington Heights
Rd, 150, Arlington, IL 60005. TEL 847-427-9512, FAX
847-882-6842, http://www.abm.net. Ed. Galynn Nordstrom.

670.29   GBR   ISSN 0142-4971
WHAT'S NEW IN INDUSTRY. Text in English. m. free to qualified
personnel (effective 2005). adv. **Document type:** *Magazine,
Trade.* **Description:** Provides readers with the latest in new
product development and innovation by and for manufacturing.
Related titles: Online - full text ed.: (from Gale Group,
LexisNexis).
Indexed: BrCerAb, IPackAb.
Published by: Centaur Communications Ltd., Sugar Brook Court,
Aston Rd, Bromsgrove, Worcs B60 3EX, United Kingdom.
TEL 44-1527-834400, FAX 44-1527-578548,
customer.service@centaur.co.uk, http://www.wnii.co.uk/,
http://www.centaur.co.uk/. Circ: 41,037.

WHAT'S NEW IN INTERIORS. see *INTERIOR DESIGN AND
DECORATION*

WHERE TO BUILD & WHERE TO REPAIR. see
TRANSPORTATION—Ships And Shipping

338.025   DEU   ISSN 0967-6406
                       CODEN: IJWNAU
WHERE TO BUY BUSINESS INFORMATION. Text in English.
1990. a. **Document type:** *Directory, Trade.* **Description:**
Provides in-depth survey and directory of organizations
offering business information services in U.K.
Published by: K.G. Saur Verlag GmbH (Subsidiary of: Gale
Group), Ortlerstr 8, Munchen, 81373, Germany. TEL
49-89-769020, FAX 49-89-76902150, info@saur.de,
http://www.saur.de.

WHERE TO BUY CHEMICALS, PLANT AND SERVICES. see
BUSINESS AND ECONOMICS—Marketing And Purchasing

THE WHITE BOOK. see *LEISURE AND RECREATION*

338.0029   USA
WHITE PAGES & DIRECTORY LISTINGS (YEAR). Text in
English. 1993. irreg., latest vol.3, July 1997. USD 1,995
(effective 2000). **Document type:** *Trade.* **Description:** Aims
to provide insight into the regulatory and legislative changes
surrounding white pages listings, and data on the policies and
prices of the major telephone companies.
Published by: SIMBA Information (Subsidiary of: R.R. Bowker
LLC), 60 Long Ridge Rd., Ste 300, Stamford, CT 06902. TEL
203-325-8193, 800-307-2529, 888-269-5372, FAX
203-325-8915, info@simbanet.com, http://www.simbanet.com.

382.029   PRI   ISSN 1555-9327
HF5110
THE WHITE PAGES BUSINESS DIRECTORY. Text in English.
1988. a. USD 28.70 per vol. (effective 2005). **Document
type:** *Directory.* **Description:** Complete study of all business
areas, backed up with a compendium of tables and charts.
Former titles (until 200?): Caribbean Business White Pages
(1520-5398); Caribbean Business - to - Business Guide, the
Source; (until 1989): Puerto Rico Business - to - Business
Executive Guide
Published by: Casiano Communications Inc., 1700 Fernandez
Juncos Ave, San Juan, 00909-2999, Puerto Rico. TEL
787-728-3000, FAX 787-268-5058, cservice@casiano.com,
http://www.casiano.com. Ed. Manuel Casiano Jr. Circ: 35,000.

658.0029   USA   ISSN 0149-0281
HF5616.U5
WHO AUDITS AMERICA; a directory of publicly held corporations
and the accounting firms who audit them. Text in English.
1976. s-a. USD 125. back issues avail.
Indexed: ATI.
Published by: Data Financial Press, PO Box 668, Menlo Park,
CA 94026. TEL 415-321-4553. Ed. S P Harris. Circ: 2,500.

338.0029   CHE
WHO OWNS WHOM; der schweizerische Beteiligungsatlas. Text
in German. a. CHF 178 (effective 2000). **Document type:**
Directory, Trade.

Published by: Orell Fuessli Verlag, Dietzingerstr 3, Zuerich, 8036,
Switzerland. TEL 41-1-4667711, FAX 41-1-4667412. **Dist. by:**
BD Buecherdienst AG, Postfach, Einsiedeln 8840, Switzerland.
TEL 41-55-4188959.

338.0029   GBR
HD2927   CODEN: WOWFET
**WHO OWNS WHOM. AUSTRALASIA, ASIA, MIDDLE EAST &
AFRICA.** Text in English. 1971. a. (in 2 vols.). GBP 295
(effective 2000). index. **Document type:** *Directory.*
Former titles: Who Owns Whom. Australasia and Far East
(0302-4091); Who Owns Whom. Australia and Japan
International
Related titles: Online - full text ed.
Indexed: RASB.
—BLDSC (9311.918500). **CCC.**
Published by: Dun & Bradstreet Ltd., 50-100 Holmers Farm Way,
High Wycombe, Bucks HP12 4UL, United Kingdom. TEL
44-1494-423689, FAX 44-1494-422332.

658.0029   GBR   ISSN 1460-7204
HG4135.Z5   CODEN: WOWREV
WHO OWNS WHOM. UNITED KINGDOM AND IRELAND. Text in
English. 1958. a. (in 2 vols.). GBP 375 (effective 2000). index.
Document type: *Directory.*
Former titles (until 1997): Who Owns Whom. United Kingdom
and Republic of Ireland (0140-4040); Who Owns Whom.
United Kingdom (0083-9329)
Related titles: Online - full text ed.
—BLDSC (9311.948000), CISTI. **CCC.**
Published by: Dun & Bradstreet Ltd., 50-100 Holmers Farm Way,
High Wycombe, Bucks HP12 4UL, United Kingdom. TEL
44-1494-423689, FAX 44-1494-422332. Ed. Laura Morel.

700.29   USA
WHOLE ARTS DIRECTORY. Text in English. 1987. irreg. (approx.
triennial). USD 12.95 (effective 2001). **Document type:**
Directory.
Published by: Midmarch Arts Press, 300 Riverside Dr, New York,
NY 10025. TEL 212-666-6990. Ed. Sylvia Moore. R&P Cynthia
Navaretta.

WHO'S WHO; The M F S A blue ribbon buyers' guide to mailing
and fulfillment companies. see *ADVERTISING AND PUBLIC
RELATIONS*

670.29   GBR   ISSN 1464-0163
WHO'S WHO IN BULK HANDLING. Text in English. 1992. a.
GBP 36; GBP 43 foreign. **Document type:** *Directory, Trade.*
Description: A comprehensive directory of Britain's loose
materials handling and storage industry, with complete buyer's
guide listings of products supplied.
Published by: Turret R A I plc, Armstrong House, 38 Market Sq,
Uxbridge, Middx UB8 1TG, United Kingdom. TEL
44-1895-454545, FAX 44-1895-454647.

WHO'S WHO IN CORRUGATED. see *PAPER AND PULP*

658.8   GBR
WHO'S WHO IN DIRECT MARKETING. Text in English. 1996. a.
Document type: *Directory, Trade.* **Description:** Provides a
guide for those responsible for making direct marketing
decisions.
Published by: (Direct Marketing Association), Premier Magazines
Ltd., Haymarket House 1a, 1 Oxendon St, London, SW1Y
4EE, United Kingdom. TEL 44-171-925-2544, FAX
44-207-839-4491, andrew_marsh@premiermags.co.uk,
http://www.premiermags.co.uk, http://www.premiermp.com. Ed.
Andrew Marsh. adv.: B&W page GBP 1,340, color page GBP
1,890.

WHO'S WHO IN INSURANCE. see *INSURANCE*

332.3029   GBR   ISSN 0962-9017
WHO'S WHO IN MORTGAGE FINANCE∗ . Text in English.
1949. biennial. GBP 50. **Document type:** *Directory.*
Former titles: Who's Who in Housing Finance; Building Societies
Who's Who
Published by: Franey and Co. Ltd., 100 Avenue Rd, London,
N14 4EA, United Kingdom.

WHO'S WHO IN RISK MANAGEMENT. see *INSURANCE*

658.0029 576.5   USA
WHO'S WHO IN STEM CELL RESEARCH. (in PDF format) Text
in English. a. USD 179 per issue (effective 2003). **Document
type:** *Directory, Academic/Scholarly.* **Description:** Contains
listings of the world's top stem cell scientists, researchers,
corporate execs, legislators, advocates, etc. Including mailing
addresses, phone numbers, fax numbers, e-mail addresses,
Web addresses, and thumbnail sketches of stem cell-related
research.
Media: E-mail.
Published by: DataTrends Publications, Inc., PO Box 4460,
Leesburg, VA 20177-8541. TEL 703-779-0574, FAX
703-779-2267, info@datatrendspublications.com,
http://www.datatrendspublications.com/Whos_Who.htm,
http://www.datatrendspublications.com/default.htm.

363.70029   GBR
WHO'S WHO IN THE ENVIRONMENT: U K. Text in English. a.
GBP 75 per issue (effective 2000). **Document type:** *Directory,
Trade.* **Description:** Guide for all who are concerned about
the environment in Scotland.
Formerly: Who's Who in the Environment: Scotland
Media: Diskette.
Published by: Environment Council, 212 High Holborn, London,
WC1V 7BW, United Kingdom. TEL 44-20-7836-2626, FAX
44-20-7242-1180, http://www.the-environment-council.org.uk.

338.0029 340   GBR
WHO'S WHO IN THE LAW. Text in English. 1998. a. GBP 35
(effective 1999). **Document type:** *Directory, Trade.*
Description: Provides profiles of the UK's leading
practitioners, barristers and in-house lawyers within
geographical regions. There is also a section on partners of
UK law firms working in overseas offices. The profiles provide
details of work undertaken, career and education histories and
contact information.
Published by: Legalease Ltd., Kensington Square House, 12-14
Ansdell St, London, W8 5BN, United Kingdom. TEL
44-20-7396-9292, FAX 44-20-7396-9300, legalease@link.org,
info@legalease.co.uk, http://www.legalease.co.uk.

WHO'S WHO IN THE MOTION PICTURE INDUSTRY; directors,
producers, writers, & studio executives. see *MOTION
PICTURES*

380.1029   GBR
WHO'S WHO IN THE TACKLE TRADE. Text in English. a. GBP
38 in United Kingdom; GBP 56, EUR 90 rest of Europe; GBP
67, EUR 107, USD 114, JPY 14,000 rest of world rest of
Europe (effective 2000); includes Tackle Talk International.
adv. **Document type:** *Directory.*
Published by: Pendragon Publishing, The Red House, 74-76
High St, Bushey, Watford, Herts WD2 3DE, United Kingdom.
TEL 44-20-8950-6360, FAX 44-20-8420-4163,
tacklint@pendragonpub.com, http://www.pendragonpub.com.
Ed., Pub., R&P Ron Sorkin. Adv. contact Alex Paul.

661.804029   GBR
WHO'S WHO IN WORLD PETROCHEMICALS AND PLASTICS.
Text in English. a. USD 175; USD 240 with CD-ROM.
Document type: *Directory.* **Description:** Lists the vital
commercial contacts who have the authority to conduct
business in the international petrochemical and plastics arena.
Provides vital information to help readers compete in this
dynamic sector.
Related titles: CD-ROM ed.: USD 160.
Published by: Reed Business Information Ltd. (Subsidiary of:
Reed Business), Quadrant House, The Quadrant, Brighton
Rd, Sutton, Surrey SM2 5AS, United Kingdom. TEL
44-20-86523500, FAX 44-20-86528932, http://
www.reedbusiness.co.uk/rb2_products/
rb2_products_who_petrochem_plastics.htm,
http://www.reedinfo.co.uk. **Subscr. to:** Quadrant Subscription
Services, Rockwood House, 9-17 Perrymount Rd, Haywards
Heath, W. Sussex RH16 3DH, United Kingdom. TEL
44-20-8652-3500, FAX 44-20-8652-8932,
rbi.subscriptions@qss-uk.com.

338.0029   NLD   ISSN 0928-7930
WIE LEVERT MERKEN. Text in Dutch. 1984. a. adv. illus.
Document type: *Directory.*
Supersedes in part (in 1992): Merkenwijzer (0921-9285)
Related titles: ♦ Supplement to: Vraag & Aanbod. ISSN
0165-3954.
Published by: Wolters Kluwer N.V., Leewunburg 101, Deventer,
7411 TH, Netherlands. TEL 31-570-648705, FAX
31-570-643015.

338.0029   NLD   ISSN 0928-7949
WIE LEVERT PRODUKTEN EN DIENSTEN. Text in Dutch. 1937.
a. adv. back issues avail. **Document type:** *Directory.*
Supersedes in part (in 1993): Wie Levert (Year) (0922-4718)
Related titles: ♦ Supplement to: Vraag & Aanbod. ISSN
0165-3954.
Published by: Wolters Kluwer N.V., Leewunburg 101, Deventer,
7411 TH, Netherlands. TEL 31-570-648705, FAX
31-570-643015.

338.0029   NLD
WIE LEVERT REGIO. Text in Dutch. a. adv. illus. **Document
type:** *Directory.*
Supersedes in part (in 1993): Wie Levert (Year) (0922-4718)
Related titles: ♦ Supplement to: Vraag & Aanbod. ISSN
0165-3954.
Published by: Wolters Kluwer N.V., Leewunburg 101, Deventer,
7411 TH, Netherlands. TEL 31-570-648705, FAX
31-570-643015.

WIE WERKT WAAR IN DE MEDIA (GEDRUKTE VERSIE). see
BUSINESS AND ECONOMICS—Marketing And Purchasing

WIE WERKT WAAR IN DE RECLAME. see *ADVERTISING AND
PUBLIC RELATIONS*

WINE AND SPIRIT INTERNATIONAL YEAR BOOK. see
BEVERAGES

WINE & SPIRITS INDUSTRY MARKETING. see *BEVERAGES*

663.1029 USA
WINES AND VINES: DIRECTORY OF THE WINE INDUSTRY IN NORTH AMERICA. Text in English. 1941. a. USD 85 domestic; USD 95 in Canada & Mexico; USD 105 elsewhere (effective 2001). adv. **Document type:** *Directory.*
Supersedes: Wines and Vines - Annual Directory of the Wine Industry (0084-0351)
Related titles: CD-ROM ed.
Published by: Hiaring Co., 1800 Lincoln Ave, San Rafael, CA 94901-1298. TEL 415-453-9700, FAX 415-453-2517. Ed. Philip E Hiaring. Adv. contact Dottie Kubota-Cordery. color page USD 2,395; 8.375 x 11.125. Circ: 4,500.

338.0029 USA ISSN 1048-7433
HF5065.W6
WISCONSIN BUSINESS DIRECTORY. Text in English. 1985. a. USD 1,100 combined subscription (effective 2004 & 2005). index. back issues avail. **Document type:** *Directory.* **Description:** Includes all businesses in the state compiled from the yellow pages and telephone-verified. Each listing includes company name, complete address, phone number, name of owner, manager, and employee size, sales volume codes, and credit rating codes.
Related titles: CD-ROM ed.; Diskette ed.; E-mail ed.; Fax ed.; Magnetic Tape ed.; Online - full text ed.
Published by: American Business Directories (Subsidiary of: American Business Information, Inc.), 5711 S 86th Circle, P O Box 27347, Omaha, NE 68127. TEL 402-593-4600, 888-946-9377, 877-708-3844, FAX 402-331-5481, sales@directoriesusa.com, http://www.directoriesusa.com.

670.29 USA ISSN 1520-8133
T12
WISCONSIN MANUFACTURERS DIRECTORY. Text in English. 1921. a. USD 139 (effective 2005). adv. index. **Document type:** *Directory, Trade.*
Formerly (until 1999): Classified Directory of Wisconsin Manufacturers (0069-4525)
Published by: (Wisconsin Manufacturers & Commerce), Harris InfoSource, 2057 E Aurora Rd, Twinsburg, OH 44087. TEL 800-888-5900, 330-425-9000, FAX 330-425-7150, http://www.harrisinfo.com.

670.29 USA ISSN 0738-0070
HD9727.W6
WISCONSIN MANUFACTURERS REGISTER. Text in English. a. USD 118 (effective 2001). adv. illus. **Document type:** *Directory.* **Description:** Profiles 12,658 manufacturers; includes product, alphabetical, geographical, SIC, and parent company.
Related titles: CD-ROM ed.: USD 580 (effective 2001); Diskette ed.
Published by: Manufacturers' News, Inc., 1633 Central St, Evanston, IL 60201. TEL 847-864-7000, 888-752-5200, FAX 847-332-1100, info@mninfo.com, info@manufacturersnews.com, sales@mninfo.com, http://www.manufacturersnews.com. Ed. Frank Lambing. Adv. contact Charles Scherer. B&W page USD 1,843.

677.31029 GBR ISSN 0268-3601
WOOL TRADE DIRECTORY OF THE WORLD. Text in English. 1985. biennial, latest 2004, 10th ed. GBP 175 per issue domestic; GBP 205 per issue foreign (effective 2005). **Document type:** *Directory, Trade.*
Related titles: CD-ROM ed.: GBP 175.
Published by: World Textile Publications Ltd., Perkin House, 1 Longlands St, Bradford, W Yorks BD1 2TP, United Kingdom. TEL 44-1274-378800, FAX 44-1274-378811, info@world-textile.net, http://www.world-textile.net/contact.html.

382.029 USA ISSN 1062-1172
HF54.U5
WORLD BUSINESS DIRECTORY. Text in English. 1992. irreg., latest 2002, Ed. 11. USD 720 per vol. (effective 2005). **Document type:** *Directory, Trade.* **Description:** Compiles information on over 100,000 companies in 190 countries.
Published by: (World Trade Centers Association), Gale Research Co. (Subsidiary of: Gale Group), 27500 Drake Rd, Farmington, MI 48331-3535. TEL 248-699-4253, FAX 248-699-8035, 800-414-5043, gale.galeord@thomson.com, http://www.gale.com/servlet/BrowseSeriesServlet?region=9&imprint=000&titleCode=WBD&edition=. Eds. Kimberley A Peterson, Meghan A O'Meara.

338.0029 GBR
WORLD CONSUMER INCOME AND EXPENDITURE PATTERNS. Text in English. irreg. (in 1 vol., 2 nos./vol.), latest 2002, July. GBP 675 per vol. domestic; EUR 1,090 per vol. in Europe; USD 1,090 per vol. elsewhere (effective Jul. 2002). **Document type:** *Directory, Trade.* **Description:** Contains detailed information on income and earnings as well as consumer spending across 71 countries.
Published by: Euromonitor, 60-61 Britton St, London, EC1 5UX, United Kingdom. TEL 44-20-7251-8024, FAX 44-20-7608-3149, info@euromonitor.com, http://www.euromonitor.com.

338.0029 GBR
WORLD CONSUMER MARKETS; on the internet. Text in English. a., latest 2003, Apr. GBP 3,900, EUR 6,000, USD 6,000 (effective 2003). **Document type:** *Directory, Trade.* **Description:** Contains statistics and information on over 330 consumer products distributed in 52 countries.
Media: CD-ROM. **Related titles:** Online - full text ed.: GBP 1,695, EUR 3,390, USD 3,390.
Published by: Euromonitor, 60-61 Britton St, London, EC1 5UX, United Kingdom. TEL 44-20-7251-8024, FAX 44-20-7608-3149, info@euromonitor.com, http://www.euromonitor.com.

WORLD DATABASE OF BUSINESS INFORMATION SOURCES. see *BUSINESS AND ECONOMICS—Abstracting, Bibliographies, Statistics*

WORLD DIRECTORY OF BUSINESS INFORMATION LIBRARIES. see *LIBRARY AND INFORMATION SCIENCES*

WORLD DIRECTORY OF BUSINESS INFORMATION WEBSITES. see *COMPUTERS—Internet*

387.029 GBR ISSN 0951-5879
WORLD DIRECTORY OF LINER SHIPPING AGENTS*. Text in English. 1987. a. GBP 50, USD 85. adv. back issues avail. **Document type:** *Directory.* **Description:** A shippers' guide to who-represents-whom in the intermodal shipping industry.
Published by: Informa Publishing, 69-77 Paul St, London, EC2A 4IQ, United Kingdom. TEL 44-20-7553-1000, 44-1206-772061, FAX 44-20-7553-1593, 44-1206-772563, enquiries@informa.com. Ed. Jane Degerlund TEL 44-20-7553-1726. Pub. Nick Morgan. Adv. contact Ed Andrews. Circ: 1,000.

WORLD DIRECTORY OF MARKETING INFORMATION SOURCES. see *BUSINESS AND ECONOMICS—Marketing And Purchasing*

WORLD DIRECTORY OF NON-OFFICIAL STATISTICAL SOURCES. see *BUSINESS AND ECONOMICS—Abstracting, Bibliographies, Statistics*

382.029 GBR
WORLD DIRECTORY OF TRADE AND BUSINESS ASSOCIATIONS. Text in English. 1996. biennial, latest vol.4, 2002, Oct. GBP 395, EUR 650, USD 650 per issue (effective 2003). 500 p./no.; **Document type:** *Directory.* **Description:** Provides contacts and details on important trade associations and named contacts operating across all business areas.
Published by: Euromonitor, 60-61 Britton St, London, EC1 5UX, United Kingdom. TEL 44-20-7251-8024, FAX 44-20-7608-3149, info@euromonitor.com, http://www.euromonitor.com. **Dist. by:** Current Pacific Ltd., PO Box 36-536, Northcote, Auckland, New Zealand. TEL 64-9-480-1388, FAX 64-9-480-1387, info@cplnz.com, http://www.cplnz.com.

WORLD DRINKS DATABOOK. see *BEVERAGES*

333.7916 FRA
WORLD ENERGY CONFERENCE. DIRECTORY OF ENERGY INFORMATION CENTRES IN THE WORLD. Text in English, French. 1976. triennial. **Document type:** *Directory.*
Published by: Institut Francais de l'Energie, 3 rue Henri Heine, Paris, 75016, France. FAX 40-50-07-54, TELEX IFENERG 615867.

WORLD FOOD DATA & STATISTICS. see *FOOD AND FOOD INDUSTRIES*

666.1029 ITA ISSN 1129-3969
WORLD GLASSWARE INDUSTRY DIRECTORY. Text in English; Summaries in Italian, English, French, Spanish, German. 1990. a., latest vol.11, 2000. USD 30 domestic; USD 45 foreign (effective 2005). **Document type:** *Directory, Trade.* **Description:** Provides company profiles, addresses, officers, plants, number of employees, capital, trademarks, areas of activity, and innovations.
Published by: Artech Publishing Srl, Via Gramsci 63, Cormano, MI 20032, Italy. TEL 39-02-6630-2904, FAX 39-02-6630-2914, artech@glassonline.com, http://www.glassonline.com. Ed. Marco Pinetti.

WORLD JEWELERY MACHINERY DIRECTORY & YEARBOOK (YEAR). see *JEWELRY, CLOCKS AND WATCHES*

WORLD JEWELOGUE (YEAR). see *JEWELRY, CLOCKS AND WATCHES*

338.0029 GBR
WORLD LEADING GLOBAL BRAND OWNERS. (Vol.3 in Global Market Share Planner Series) Text in English. 2000. irreg., latest 2002, July. GBP 745 per vol. domestic; EUR 1,190 per vol. in Europe; USD 1,190 per vol. elsewhere (effective Jul. 2002). **Document type:** *Directory, Trade.* **Description:** Provides detailed and extensive information on leading multi-national corporations.
Formerly: World's Major Multinationals
Related titles: ♦ Series of: Global Market Share Planner.
Published by: Euromonitor, 60-61 Britton St, London, EC1 5UX, United Kingdom. TEL 44-20-7251-8024, FAX 44-20-7608-3149, info@euromonitor.com, http://www.euromonitor.com. **Dist. by:** Current Pacific Ltd., PO Box 36-536, Northcote, Auckland, New Zealand. TEL 64-9-480-1388, FAX 64-9-480-1387, info@cplnz.com, http://www.cplnz.com.

WORLD LEASING YEARBOOK (YEAR). see *BUSINESS AND ECONOMICS—Economic Situation And Conditions*

338.0029 GBR
WORLD MARKETING DATA AND STATISTICS. Variant title: World Marketing Data and Statistics on the Internet. Text in English. irreg., latest 2003, Jan. GBP 3,225, EUR 5,250, USD 5,250 per vol. (effective 2003). **Document type:** *Directory, Trade.* **Description:** Provides economic and demographic marketing data on over 209 countries.
Media: CD-ROM. **Related titles:** Online - full text ed.: GBP 1,295, EUR 2,590, USD 2,590.
Published by: Euromonitor, 60-61 Britton St, London, EC1 5UX, United Kingdom. TEL 44-20-7251-8024, FAX 44-20-7608-3149, info@euromonitor.com, http://www.euromonitor.com.

338.0029 GBR
WORLD MARKETING FORECASTS; on the internet. Text in English. 1998. a., latest 2003, Jan. GBP 3,900, EUR 6,000, USD 6,000 (effective 2003). **Document type:** *Directory, Trade.* **Description:** Provides data on consumer market and socio-economic forecasts from 52 countries.
Media: CD-ROM. **Related titles:** Online - full text ed.: GBP 1,695, EUR 3,390, USD 3,390.
Published by: Euromonitor, 60-61 Britton St, London, EC1 5UX, United Kingdom. TEL 44-20-7251-8024, FAX 44-20-7608-3149, info@euromonitor.com, http://www.euromonitor.com.

WORLD PHARMACEUTICAL DIRECTORY. see *PHARMACY AND PHARMACOLOGY*

381.1025 GBR ISSN 0953-0274
WORLD RETAIL DIRECTORY AND SOURCEBOOK. Text in English. 1991. irreg., latest 2003, Feb. GBP 775 per vol. domestic; EUR 1,250 per vol. in Europe; USD 1,250 per vol. elsewhere (effective 2003). **Document type:** *Directory, Trade.* **Description:** Contains statistical information on over 2,600 retailers in more than 90 countries.
Published by: Euromonitor, 60-61 Britton St, London, EC1 5UX, United Kingdom. TEL 44-20-7251-8024, FAX 44-20-7608-3149, http://www.euromonitor.com. **Dist. by:** Current Pacific Ltd., PO Box 36-536, Northcote, Auckland, New Zealand. TEL 64-9-480-1388, FAX 64-9-480-1387, info@cplnz.com, http://www.cplnz.com.

THE WORLD SATELLITE ANNUAL. see *COMMUNICATIONS*

WORLD TIME CATALOGUE (YEAR). see *JEWELRY, CLOCKS AND WATCHES*

WORLD TOBACCO DIRECTORY. see *TOBACCO*

381.029 USA
WORLD TRADE CENTERS ASSOCIATION. DIRECTORY. Text in English. 1972. s-a. USD 450 to non-members; USD 150 to members. **Document type:** *Directory.*
Published by: World Trade Centers Association, 1 World Trade Center, Ste 7701, New York, NY 10048. TEL 212-432-7626. Ed. J Squasoni. Circ: 10,000.

338.0029 USA ISSN 1058-5818
HD69.C6
WORLDWIDE DIRECTORY OF CONSULTANTS AND CONTRACTORS. Text in English. 1992. biennial. USD 110 domestic; USD 115 foreign (effective 2000). **Document type:** *Directory.* **Description:** Lists architects, consulting engineers, planners and contractors engaged in construction activities, urban and rural development, and environmental engineering.
Related titles: CD-ROM ed.
Published by: Projects Research, Inc., PO Box 2558, Falls Church, VA 22042. TEL 703-698-9330, FAX 703-698-9837, worldwidedirectory@erols.com, http://www.casmediagroup.com/pri. Ed. Joe Lill.

338.0029 355.4 USA
WORLDWIDE DIRECTORY OF DEFENCE AUTHORITIES. Text in English. s-a. USD 616 per issue (effective 2005). **Document type:** *Directory, Consumer.*
Published by: C Q Press, Inc. (Subsidiary of: Congressional Quarterly, Inc.), 1255 22nd St., N.W., Ste. 400, Washington, DC 20037. TEL 202-729-1800, 800-432-2250, FAX 800-380-3810, customerservice@cq.com, http://www.cqpress.com/gethome.asp.

B

▼ new title ➤ refereed * unverified ♦ full entry avail.

B

621.381029   USA
WORLDWIDE DIRECTORY OF MULTICHIP MODULE VENDORS AND RELATED COMPANIES. Text in English. a. **Document type:** *Directory.* **Description:** Lists up-to-date compilation of finished module and substrate suppliers, MCM design houses, CAD tool vendors, base substrate suppliers, thin film dielectric materials, contract assembly services, bare die sources, testing and inspection services and equipments, and selected academic and research organizations.
Published by: International Society for Hybrid Microelectronics, 1850 Centennial Park Dr, Ste 105, Reston, VA 22091-1517. TEL 703-758-1060, FAX 703-758-1066.

346.048   USA
WORLDWIDE TRADE SECRETS. Text in English. 3 base vols. plus a. updates. looseleaf. USD 440 base vol(s). (effective 2004). **Document type:** *Trade.* **Description:** Describes and analyzes the law of trade secrets in the US and 30 other countries.
Published by: Thomson West (Subsidiary of: Thomson Corporation, The), 610 Opperman Dr, Eagan, MN 55123-1396. TEL 800-328-4880, FAX 651-687-7302, http://west.thomson.com/product/13517906/product.asp. Ed. Terrence F MacLaren.

338.0029   USA
WORLDWIDE YELLOW PAGES MARKETS (YEAR). Text in English. biennial. USD 8,195 (effective 2005 & 2006). **Document type:** *Trade.* **Description:** Assesses the opportunities and pitfalls in the global yellow pages marketplace.
Former titles: Worldwide Yellow Pages Opportunities (Year); (until 1995): New Opportunities in Talking Yellow Pages (Year)
Published by: SIMBA Information (Subsidiary of: R.R. Bowker LLC), 60 Long Ridge Rd., Ste 300, Stamford, CT 06902. TEL 203-325-8193, 800-307-2529, FAX 203-325-8915, info@simbanet.com, http://www.simbanet.com/publications/report_wypm.htm.

338.0029   USA   ISSN 1048-7425
HF5065.W8
WYOMING BUSINESS DIRECTORY. Text in English. 1989. a. USD 1,100 combined subscription print, online & CD-ROM eds. (effective 2004 & 2005). index. back issues avail. **Document type:** *Directory.* **Description:** Includes all businesses in the state compiled from the yellow pages and telephone-verified. Each listing includes company name, complete address, phone number, name of owner, manager, and employee size, sales volume codes, and credit rating codes.
Related titles: CD-ROM ed.; Diskette ed.; E-mail ed.; Fax ed.; Magnetic Tape ed.; Online - full text ed.
Published by: American Business Directories (Subsidiary of: American Business Information, Inc.), 5711 S 86th Circle, P O Box 27347, Omaha, NE 68127. TEL 402-593-4600, 888-946-9377, 877-708-3844, FAX 402-331-5481, sales@directoriesusa.com, http://www.directoriesusa.com.

670   USA   ISSN 1525-4062
WYOMING MANUFACTURERS DIRECTORY. Text in English. a. USD 56 (effective 2001). **Document type:** *Directory.* **Description:** Profiles approximately 1200 manufacturing firms.

Related titles: CD-ROM ed.: USD 175 (effective 2001).
Published by: Manufacturers' News, Inc., 1633 Central St, Evanston, IL 60201. TEL 847-864-7000, 888-752-5200, FAX 847-332-1100, info@manufacturersnews.com, sales@mninfo.com, http://www.manufacturersnews.com. Ed. Frank Lambing.

YEARBOOK OF EUROPEAN TELECOMMUNICATIONS. see *COMMUNICATIONS*

YEARBOOK OF EXPERTS, AUTHORITIES & SPOKESPERSONS; an encyclopedia of sources. see *COMMUNICATIONS—Television And Cable*

YEARBOOK OF SCANDINAVIAN SHIPOWNERS AND SHIP MANAGEMENT COMPANIES/YEARBOOK OF SCANDINAVIAN SHIPOWNERS. see *TRANSPORTATION—Ships And Shipping*

338.0029   USA   ISSN 1071-2461
YELLOW PAGES & DIRECTORY REPORT; the newsletter for the yellow page & directory publishing industry. Text in English. 1985. 22/yr. USD 715; USD 1,378 combined subscription print & online eds. (effective 2005). adv. **Document type:** *Newsletter, Trade.* **Description:** Covers the activities of utility and independent yellow pages publishers, certified marketing representatives, sales agents, and yellow pages associations.
Related titles: Online - full text ed.: USD 689 (effective 2005) (from Factiva, Florida Center for Library Automation, Gale Group, Northern Light Technology, Inc.).
—CCC.
Published by: SIMBA Information (Subsidiary of: R.R. Bowker LLC), 60 Long Ridge Rd., Ste 300, Stamford, CT 06902. TEL 203-325-8193, 800-307-2529, FAX 203-325-8915, info@simbanet.com, http://www.simbanet.com/publications/news_ypdr.htm. Ed. David Goddard.

338.0029   USA
YELLOW PAGES MARKET FORECAST (YEAR). Text in English. 1986. a. USD 2,390 (effective 2006). **Document type:** *Directory, Trade.* **Description:** Reviews the significant developments in the yellow pages market, and provides revenue and market share statistics, analysis on new media products and international ventures, litigation, acquisitions, and divestitures at leading companies.
Former titles (until 2005): Yellow Pages Publishing Market Forecast (Year); Yellow Pages Market Forecast (Year)
Related titles: Online - full text ed.: USD 2,295 (effective 2005).
Published by: SIMBA Information (Subsidiary of: R.R. Bowker LLC), 60 Long Ridge Rd., Ste 300, Stamford, CT 06902. TEL 203-325-8193, 800-307-2529, FAX 203-325-8915, info@simbanet.com, http://www.simbanet.com/publications/report_ypmf.htm. Ed. David Goddard.

658.8029   USA
YELLOW PAGES SALES & MARKETING. Text in English. irreg., latest vol.2, 1996. USD 2,495 domestic; USD 2,535 in Canada & Mexico (effective 2000). **Document type:** *Trade.* **Description:** Analyzes the sales and marketing of yellow pages directories as well as technological developments in the industry.

Published by: SIMBA Information (Subsidiary of: R.R. Bowker LLC), 60 Long Ridge Rd., Ste 300, Stamford, CT 06902. TEL 203-325-8193, 800-307-2529, 888-269-5372, FAX 203-325-8915, info@simbanet.com, http://www.simbanet.com. Ed. David Goddard.

382.029   ZAF
ZAMBIA TRADE DIRECTORY. Text in English. a. USD 100 (effective 2001). adv. **Document type:** *Directory.*
Published by: Braby's (Subsidiary of: Associated Industries), Attn: Sue Pearson, PO Box 1426, Pinetown, 3600, South Africa. TEL 27-31-7017021, FAX 27-31-7017036, booksales@brabys.co.za.

382.029   ZWE
ZIMBABWE EXPORT DIRECTORY. Variant title: C Z I Zimbabwe Export Directory. Text in English. 1983. a. ZWD 115; ZWD 131.20 foreign (effective 1999). **Document type:** *Directory.* **Description:** Includes alphabetical listings of local manufacturing companies and products, as well as all matters related to import and export in the Zimbabwean context.
Published by: (Confederation of Zimbabwe Industries), Thomson Publications Zimbabwe (Pvt) Ltd., Thomson House, PO Box 1683, Harare, Zimbabwe. TEL 263-4-736835, FAX 263-4-752390. Circ: 2,500.

381.029   ZWE
ZIMBABWE NATIONAL CHAMBER OF COMMERCE DIRECTORY. Abbreviated title: Z N C C Directory. Text in English. 1983. a. ZWD 105; ZWD 121.20 foreign (effective 1999). adv. **Document type:** *Directory.* **Description:** Gives alphabetical and classified index of products and services offered by the ZNCC and its members, as well as procedural information on all aspects of local commercial business activity.
Published by: (Zimbabwe National Chamber of Commerce), Thomson Publications Zimbabwe (Pvt) Ltd., Thomson House, PO Box 1683, Harare, Zimbabwe. TEL 263-4-736835, FAX 263-4-752390. Circ: 1,800.

381.029   CAN
1000 PLUS TRADE AND PROFESSIONAL ASSOCIATIONS IN THE TORONTO REGION. Text in English. 1987. irreg. CND 50 to non-members; CND 40 to members. **Document type:** *Directory.* **Description:** Lists 1,200 local, provincial, national and international associations serving the interests of the business community in the Toronto region.
Former titles: Directory of Trade and Professional Associations in the Toronto Region; Directory of Trade and Professional Association in Metropolitan Toronto (0836-4958); Directory of Local and National Business, Trade and Professional Associations in Metropolitan Toronto
Published by: Toronto Board of Trade, 1 First Canadian Place, P O Box 60, Toronto, ON M5X 1C1, Canada. TEL 416-366-6811, http://www.bot.com. Ed. Mary de Reus.

CALCULATING MACHINES

see COMPUTERS—Calculating Machines

CARDIOVASCULAR DISEASES

see MEDICAL SCIENCES—Cardiovascular Diseases

CARPENTRY AND WOODWORK

see BUILDING AND CONSTRUCTION—Carpentry And Woodwork

CERAMICS, GLASS AND POTTERY

see also ART ; ARTS AND HANDICRAFTS

666.1 629.26 USA
A G R R: AUTO GLASS REPLACEMENT & REPAIR; the magazine driving the auto glass industry. Text in English. 1999. bi-m. free to qualified personnel; USD 35 domestic; USD 40 foreign (effective 2005). adv. mkt.; stat. back issues avail. **Document type:** *Magazine, Trade.*
Published by: Key Communications, Inc., PO Box 569, Garrisonville, VA 22463. TEL 540-720-5584, FAX 540-720-5687, info@glass.com, http://www.agrrmag.com/, http://www.key-com.com/. Eds. Brigid O'Leary, Charles Cumpston. Pub. Debra A Levy. Adv. contact Penny Stacey. B&W page USD 2,000, color page USD 3,450. Circ: 15,010 (paid and controlled).

666 GBR ISSN 0268-9847
ADVANCED CERAMICS REPORT; an international newsletter. Text in English. 1986. m. GBP 457, USD 797 (effective 2006). bk.rev. charts; stat. 12 p./no.; back issues avail. **Document type:** *Newsletter, Trade.* **Description:** Reports on technological and business opportunities in advanced ceramics for engineering and electronics.
Related titles: E-mail ed.; Online - full text ed.: (from Factiva, Gale Group, Northern Light Technology, Inc.).
Indexed: BrCerAb, C&ISA, CerAb, CivEngAb, CorrAb, E&CAJ, EMA, IAA, M&TEA, MBF, METADEX, SolStAb, WAA.
—BLDSC (0696.836000), IE, Infotrieve, Linda Hall. **CCC.**
Published by: International Newsletters, 9 A Victoria Sq., Droitwich, Worcs WR9 8DE, United Kingdom. TEL 44-870-1657210, FAX 44-870-1657212, in@intnews.com, http://www.intnews.com/acr.htm. Ed. Nick Dellow.

ADVANCED COMPOSITES BULLETIN; an international newsletter. see *PLASTICS*

666 SGP
ADVANCED SERIES IN CERAMICS. Text in English. 1993. irreg., latest vol.2. price varies. **Document type:** *Monographic series, Academic/Scholarly.*
Published by: World Scientific Publishing Co. Pte. Ltd., 5 Toh Tuck Link, Singapore, 596224, Singapore. TEL 65-466-5775, FAX 65-467-7667, wspc@wspc.com.sg, series@wspc.com.sg, http://www.wspc.com.sg/books/series/asc_series.shtml, http://www.worldscientific.com. Eds. D Niesz, M Mclaren. **Dist. by:** World Scientific Publishing Co., Inc., 1060 Main St, River Edge, NJ 07661. TEL 201-487-9655, FAX 201-487-9656, 888-977-2665; World Scientific Publishing Ltd., 57 Shelton St, London WC2H 9HE, United Kingdom. TEL 44-20-78360888, FAX 44-20-78362020, sales@wspc.co.uk.

666 USA ISSN 0730-9546
ADVANCES IN CERAMICS. Text in English. 1981. irreg., latest vol.28, 1990. price varies. **Document type:** *Monographic series.*
—CISTI. **CCC.**
Published by: American Ceramic Society Inc., 735 Ceramic Pl., # 100, Westerville, OH 43081-8719. info@ceramics.org, http://www.ceramics.org.

AIRBRUSH ACTION. see *ART*

AIRBRUSH-ZEITUNG. see *ART*

AMERICAN ASSOCIATION FOR CRYSTAL GROWTH NEWSLETTER. see *CHEMISTRY—Crystallography*

666.1 USA ISSN 0738-3290
AMERICAN CARNIVAL GLASS NEWS. Text in English. 1966. q. USD 15 to members (effective 1998). adv. back issues avail. **Document type:** *Newsletter.*
Published by: American Carnival Glass Association, c/o Dolores Wagner, Sec, 5951 Fredericks Burg Rd, Wooster, OH 44691. TEL 513-439-0697. Ed. Joan Anderson. Circ: 900.

666 USA ISSN 0002-7812
TP785 CODEN: ACSBA7
AMERICAN CERAMIC SOCIETY. BULLETIN. Variant title: Ceramic Bulletin. Text in English. 1922. m. USD 75 in North America to non-members; USD 131 elsewhere to non-members (effective 2005). adv. bk.rev. charts; illus.; tr.lit. Index. back issues avail.; reprints avail. **Document type:** *Bulletin, Trade.* **Description:** The World Resource for ceramic manufacturing and technology.
Incorporates in part (in Jan. 2004): Glass Researcher (1086-8747)
Related titles: Online - full text ed.: (from EBSCO Publishing, H.W. Wilson, O C L C Online Computer Library Center, Inc., ProQuest Information & Learning).
Indexed: A&ATA, AESIS, AS&TI, ASCA, BrCerAb, C&ISA, CIN, CRIA, CRICC, Cadscan, CerAb, ChemAb, CivEngAb, ConcrAb, CorrAb, CurCont, E&CAJ, EIA, EMA, EngInd, EnvAb, ExcerpMed, F&EA, IAA, ISR, Inspec, LeadAb, M&TEA, MBF, METADEX, MSCI, PCI, PROMT, RefZh, SCI, SSCI, SolStAb, WAA, Zincscan.
—BLDSC (0812.000000), AskIEEE, CASDDS, CINDOC, CISTI, Ei, IDS, IE, Infotrieve, ingenta, Linda Hall. **CCC.**
Published by: American Ceramic Society Inc., 735 Ceramic Pl, Ste 100, Westerville, OH 43081-8720. TEL 614-794-5890, FAX 614-794-5892, info@ceramics.org, http://www.ceramicbulletin.org, http://www.ceramics.org. Ed. Patricia Janeway TEL 614-794-5826. Pub., R&P Marcus A Bailey. Adv. contact Debbie Plummer. B&W page USD 3,725; trim 7 x 10. Circ: 15,500.

666 016 USA ISSN 0002-7820
TP785 CODEN: JACTAW
➤ **JOURNAL OF THE AMERICAN CERAMIC SOCIETY.** Text in English. 1899. m. USD 795 in North America to non-members; USD 880 elsewhere to non-members; USD 160 in North America to members; USD 245 elsewhere to members (effective 2004); USD 1,312 combined subscription in the Americas to institutions print & online eds; GBP 731 combined subscription elsewhere to institutions print & online eds (effective 2006). charts; illus. index. back issues avail.; reprint service avail. from PQC. **Document type:** *Journal, Academic/Scholarly.* **Description:** Contains records of original research that provide or lead to fundamental principles of ceramics. Papers explore mechanisms, structures, and behaviors as they relate to ceramic materials.
Incorporates (1986-1988): Advanced Ceramic Materials (0883-5551); Formerly (until 1918): American Ceramic Society. Transactions (0096-7394)
Related titles: CD-ROM ed.; Microform ed.: (from PMC, PQC); Online - full text ed.: ISSN 1551-2916. USD 1,246 in North America to institutions; GBP 695 elsewhere to institutions (effective 2006) (from Blackwell Synergy, EBSCO Publishing, Gale Group, H.W. Wilson, IngentaConnect, O C L C Online Computer Library Center, Inc., ProQuest Information & Learning, Swets Information Services).
Indexed: A&ATA, AESIS, AS&TI, ASCA, ApMecR, B&BAb, BrCerAb, BullT&T, C&ISA, CCI, CEABA, CIN, CIS, CMCI, CRIA, CRICC, CerAb, ChemAb, ChemInfo, ChemTitl, CivEngAb, ConcrAb, CorrAb, CurCont, E&CAJ, EIA, EMA, EngInd, EnvAb, ExcerpMed, IAA, IBR, INIS AtomInd, ISR, Inspec, LeadAb, M&TEA, MBF, METADEX, MSB, MSCI, MinerAb, PCI, RCI, RefZh, SCI, SolStAb, WAA, Zincscan.
—BLDSC (4684.000000), AskIEEE, CASDDS, CINDOC, CIS, CISTI, Ei, IDS, IE, Infotrieve, ingenta, Linda Hall. **CCC.**
Published by: (American Ceramic Society Inc.), Blackwell Publishing, Inc. (Subsidiary of: Blackwell Publishing Ltd.), Commerce Place, 350 Main St, Malden, MA 02148. TEL 781-388-8206, FAX 781-388-8232, http://www.ceramicjournal.org, http://www.blackwellpublishing.com. Eds. David J Green, David W Johnson Jr. Pub. Glenn Harvey. R&Ps Jeffrey Couts TEL 614-794-5836, Russ Jordan. Circ: 2,100 (paid).

➤ **AMERICAN CLAY EXCHANGE.** see *ANTIQUES*

666 ITA ISSN 0391-5816
ANDAR PER CERAMICHE NEL MONDO. Text in English, French, German, Italian, Portuguese, Spanish. 1969. a. adv. index, cum.index.
Formerly: Andar per Ceramiche (0003-2891)
Address: Via Statutaria, 46-C, Casalgrande, RE 42013, Italy. TEL 0522-846239, FAX 0522-841063. Ed. Mirko A Montanari. Circ: 8,000 (controlled).

666 FRA ISSN 1265-616X
ANNUAIRE - CONFEDERATION DES INDUSTRIES CERAMIQUES DE FRANCE. Text in French. 1953. irreg., latest 1998. adv. **Document type:** *Directory.* **Description:** Lists more than 1,000 addresses of ceramics industry manufacturers and suppliers, and others.
Formerly: Confederation des Industries Ceramiques de France. Annuaire (0069-830X)
Published by: (Confederation des Industries Ceramiques de France), Septima, 14 rue Falguiere, Paris, 75015, France. TEL 33-01-44384800, FAX 33-01-44384809, abo@septima.fr, http://www.batiactu.com.

ANNUAL BOOK OF A S T M STANDARDS. VOLUME 15.01. REFRACTORIES, ACTIVATED CARBON; ADVANCED CERAMICS. see *ENGINEERING—Engineering Mechanics And Materials*

666 621.9 ITA
ANNUARIO A N D I L (YEAR). (Associazione Nazionale degli Industriali dei Laterizi) Text in Italian. 1990. a. price varies. adv. **Document type:** *Directory, Trade.* **Description:** Publishes news about the brick industry.
Published by: (Associazione Nazionale degli Industriali dei Laterizi), Gruppo Editoriale Faenza Editrice SpA, Via Pier de Crescenzi 44, Faenza, RA 48018, Italy. TEL 39-0546-670411, FAX 39-0546-660440, info@faenza.com, http://www.faenza.com. Ed. Franco Rossi. Circ: 5,000.

666 ITA ISSN 0066-4472
ANNUARIO CERAMICA. Text in Italian. 1970. a. USD 20. adv.
Published by: Casa Editrice Palazzo Vecchio, Via Vittorio Emanuele II, 155, Florence, FI 50134, Italy.

ANTIQUES AND COLLECTIBLES NEWSLETTER. see *ANTIQUES*

APPLIED CLAY SCIENCE. see *EARTH SCIENCES—Geology*

ARCHITECTS' GUIDE TO GLASS, METAL & GLAZING. see *ARCHITECTURE*

ARS CERAMICA. see *ANTIQUES*

ART CALENDAR; the business magazine for visual artists. see *ART*

666 ITA ISSN 1124-8572
ARTEREGALO (MILAN); rivista bimestrale della cristalleria, porcellana, ceramica, articoli da regalo e di qualita per la casa. Text in English, Italian. 1966. bi-m. adv. illus. **Document type:** *Magazine, Trade.* **Description:** For dealers of ceramics, porcelain, crystalware, silverware, gift items and high-quality goods for the home.
Published by: Publiemme International s.r.l., Via Francesco Caracciolo, 77, Milan, MI 20155, Italy. TEL 39-02-33100954, FAX 39-02-313864, pubbliemme@pubbliemme.it, info@publiemme.it, http://www.publiemme.it. Ed. Federica Serva. Pub. Massimo Martini. R&P Nello Martini TEL 39-02-33600639. Adv. contact Graziella Giobbi Martini. Circ: 23,000.

ARTSFOCUS. see *MUSEUMS AND ART GALLERIES*

666.1 JPN ISSN 0004-4210
TP194.J3 CODEN: AGKHAD
ASAHI GARASU KENKYU HOKOKU. Text in English, Japanese; Summaries in English. 1950. s-a. exchange basis. adv. cum.index. **Document type:** *Corporate.*
Indexed: BrCerAb, C&ISA, CIN, CerAb, ChemAb, ChemTitl, CivEngAb, CorrAb, E&CAJ, EMA, IAA, INIS AtomInd, JCT, JTA, M&TEA, MBF, METADEX, RefZh, SolStAb, WAA.
—BLDSC (7592.420000), CASDDS, Linda Hall.
Published by: Asahi Glass Co. Ltd., Research Center/Asahi Garasu K.K. Chuoh-Kenkyusho, 1-12-1, Yurakucho, Chiyoda-ku, Tokyo, 100-8405, Japan. http://www.agc.co.jp/rd/library.html. Circ: 1,000.

666 GBR ISSN 1470-0344
ASIAN CERAMICS AND GLASS. Text in English. 1997. m. **Document type:** *Magazine, Trade.* **Description:** Covers production, technology, trade, and markets for floor and wall tile, sanitaryware, porcelain, technical ceramics, and refractories.
Formerly (until 2000): Asian Ceramics (1369-684X)
Indexed: C&ISA, CerAb, CorrAb, E&CAJ, EMA, SolStAb, WAA.
Published by: Industrial Minerals Information Ltd. (Subsidiary of: Metal Bulletin plc), 1 Park House, Park Terr, Worcester Park, Surrey KT4 7HY, United Kingdom. TEL 44-20-78275284, FAX 44-20-78275253, http://www.asianceramics.com, http://www.indmin.com/. Ed. Andy Skillen.

666.1 NLD ISSN 0589-2546
ASSOCIATION INTERNATIONALE POUR L'HISTOIRE DU VERRE. ANNALES DES CONGRES. Text in Dutch. 1958. triennial. price varies. back issues avail. **Document type:** *Proceedings, Academic/Scholarly.* **Description:** Publishes papers presented on the history of glass.
Published by: Association Internationale pour l'Histoire du Verre/International Association for the History of Glass, AIHV Secretariat, PO Box 177, Lochem, 7240 AD, Netherlands. TEL 31-573-256272, FAX 31-573-256272, aihv@wxs.nl. Ed. Annet van Wiechen.

666 NLD ISSN 0447-9823
ASSOCIATION INTERNATIONALE POUR L'HISTOIRE DU VERRE. BULLETIN. Text in English, French, German. 1962. irreg. price varies. bk.rev. **Document type:** *Bulletin, Academic/Scholarly.*
Indexed: BHA, BrArAb.
Published by: Association Internationale pour l'Histoire du Verre/International Association for the History of Glass, AIHV Secretariat, PO Box 177, Lochem, 7240 AD, Netherlands. TEL 31-573-256272, FAX 31-573-256272, aihv@wxs.nl. Ed. Annet van Wiechen. Circ: 200.

C

666 AUS ISSN 1018-6689
TP785 CODEN: JAUSEL
➤ **AUSTRALASIAN CERAMIC SOCIETY. JOURNAL.** Text in English. 1965. s-a. AUD 330 foreign (effective 2002). adv. bk.rev. charts; illus. cum.index. back issues avail.; reprint service avail. from ISI. **Document type:** *Journal, Academic/Scholarly.* **Description:** Covers the fields of ceramic technology, basic science and related materials, including new advances in ceramic materials.
Formerly (until 1992): Australian Ceramic Society. Journal (0004-881X)
Related titles: Microfiche ed.; Microfilm ed.
Indexed: AESIS, BrCerAb, C&ISA, CIN, CRIA, Cadscan, CerAb, ChemAb, ChemTitl, CorrAb, CurCont, E&CAJ, EMA, IAA, INIS AtomInd, Inspec, LeadAb, METADEX, SolStAb, WAA, Zincscan.
—AskIEEE, CASDDS, CISTI, IDS, IE, Linda Hall. **CCC.**
Published by: Australasian Ceramic Society, c/o ANSTO, Private Mail Box 1, Menai, NSW 2234, Australia. TEL 61-2-9717-3997, FAX 61-2-9543-7179, erv@ansto.gov.au, MLC@ansto.gov.au. R&P Lou Vance. Circ: 700.

666.3 AUS
AUSTRALIAN CERAMICS & POTTERY. Text in English. 1996. bi-m. AUD 53.94; AUD 8.99 newsstand/cover (effective 2004). adv. **Document type:** *Magazine, Consumer.*
Formerly (until 1998): Australian Pottery and Ceramics (1325-8397)
Published by: Express Publications Pty. Ltd., 2 Stanley St, Locked Bag 111, Silverwater, NSW 2128, Australia. TEL 61-2-97480599, 800-801-647, FAX 61-2-97481956, subs@magstore.com.au, http://www.magstore.com.au/magdetails.php?id=6.

388.3 USA ISSN 0005-0717
AUTO AND FLAT GLASS JOURNAL. Text in English. 1953. m. USD 39; USD 75 foreign (effective 1999). adv. bk.rev. **Document type:** *Trade.* **Description:** Step-by-step installation procedures for current model cars with business and tax advice, product information, and industry news.
Published by: B K B Publications Inc, 98 Greenwich Ave, 1st Fl, New York, NY 10011-7743. TEL 212-807-7933. Ed. Charlene Komar Stoley. Adv. contact Brian K Burkart TEL 212-807-7933. Circ: 5,700 (paid).

C

666.1 629.286 USA ISSN 1047-2061
HD9710.3.A1
AUTOGLASS. Variant title: Auto Glass Magazine. Text in English. 1990. 7/yr. USD 24.95 domestic; USD 34.95 foreign (effective 2004). adv. **Document type:** *Magazine, Trade.* **Description:** Serving the automotive glass industry, both OEM and aftermarket segments. Reports the latest industry news, insurance and legislative regulations, installation methods, and new product information.
—CISTI.
Published by: National Glass Association, 8200 Greensboro Dr, Ste 302, McLean, VA 22102-3881. TEL 703-442-4890, 866-342-5642, FAX 703-442-0630, nga@glass.org, editorialinfo@glass.org, http://www.glass.org/autoglass/. Ed. Charles Cumpston. R&P Nicole Harris. Adv. contact Mike Gribbin. Circ: 9,327 (paid).

666 690 ESP ISSN 0211-7967
AZULEJO; ceramica noble. Text in English, Spanish. 1979. 4/yr. EUR 117.08 in Europe; EUR 122.50 elsewhere (effective 2004). adv. **Document type:** *Trade.* **Description:** Covers the industry of ceramic tiles.
Indexed: BHA.
—CINDOC.
Published by: Publica S.A., Calle Ecuador, 75, Barcelona, 08029, Spain. TEL 34-933-215045, FAX 34-933-221972, publica@publica.es, http://www.publica.es. Ed. Carlos Romagosa. Circ: 10,000.

666 DEU ISSN 0341-3608
BAUKERAMIK; Information des Fachhandels ueber fein- und grobkeramische Erzeugnisse. Text in German. 1973. q. adv. bk.rev. **Document type:** *Magazine, Trade.*
Published by: Gert Wohlfarth GmbH, Stresemannstr 20-22, Duisburg, 47051, Germany. TEL 49-203-305270, FAX 49-203-30527820, info@wohlfarth.de, http://www.wohlfarth.de. Ed. Gerd Rottstegge. Pub. Gert Wohlfarth. adv.: B&W page EUR 1,980, color page EUR 2,880. Circ: 21,000 (controlled).

666.1 GBR ISSN 0967-3121
BLUE BOOK (YEAR). Text in English. a. adv. **Document type:** *Directory.*
Formerly (until 1990): Flat Glass International Blue Book (0960-9296)
Published by: T B B Publications Ltd., 4 Simon Campion Ct, High St, Epping, Essex CM16 4AU, United Kingdom. TEL 01992-560215, FAX 01992-560216. Adv. contact Simon Edwards. B&W page GBP 890, color page GBP 1,520.

666 CHN ISSN 1000-2871
TP859.5 CODEN: BYTAE8
➤ **BOLI YU TANGCI/GLASS & ENAMEL.** Text in Chinese. 1971. bi-m. CNY 15 per issue domestic (effective 2000). adv. bk.rev. back issues avail. **Document type:** *Academic/Scholarly.* **Description:** Covers glass and enamel research and experiments, production technology, and more.
Related titles: Online - full content ed.: (from WanFang Data Corp.); Online - full text ed.: (from East View Information Services).
Indexed: CIN, ChemAb, ChemTitl.
—BLDSC (4190.421000), CASDDS, IE, ingenta.
Published by: Zhongguo Qinggong Zonghui, Boli Tangci Yanjiusuo, No 6, Lane 365, Xinhua Lu, Shanghai, 200052, China. TEL 86-21-62803142. Ed. Wang Nanning. Pub. Zhang Bin. Adv. contact Pan Yukun. Circ: 5,000 (paid).

666 GBR ISSN 0268-4373
CODEN: BCPREL
BRITISH CERAMIC PROCEEDINGS. Text in English. 1964. a., latest vol.63, 2003. price varies. **Document type:** *Proceedings, Academic/Scholarly.*
Supersedes (in 1984): British Ceramic Society. Proceedings (0524-5141)
Related titles: ♦ Series: Special Ceramics. ISSN 0082-0954.
Indexed: BrCerAb, C&ISA, CIN, CerAb, ChemAb, ChemTitl, CivEngAb, CorrAb, E&CAJ, EMA, IAA, Inspec, M&TEA, MBF, METADEX, SolStAb, WAA.
—AskIEEE, CASDDS, CISTI, IE, Infotrieve, Linda Hall. **CCC.**
Published by: (Institute of Materials, Minerals and Mining), Maney Publishing, Hudson Rd, Leeds, W Yorks LS9 7DL, United Kingdom. TEL 44-113-2497481, FAX 44-113-2486983, maney@maney.co.uk, http://www.maney.co.uk.

666 GBR ISSN 0144-2147
CODEN: SBCRDX
BRITISH CERAMIC RESEARCH. SPECIAL PUBLICATIONS. Text in English. 1948. irreg. (2-3/yr.), latest vol.140, 1998. bibl.; charts.
Indexed: ChemAb.
—BLDSC (8373.930000), CASDDS, CISTI, Linda Hall.
Published by: British Ceramic Research Ltd., Penkhull, Queens Rd, Stoke-on-Trent, Staffs ST4 7LQ, United Kingdom.

666.1 GBR
BRITISH GLASS MANUFACTURERS CONFEDERATION. ANNUAL REVIEW. Text in English. 1955. a. per issue exchange basis. **Document type:** *Corporate.*
Formerly (until 1987): British Glass Industry Research Association. Annual Report (0068-2020)
Published by: British Glass Manufacturers Confederation, Northumberland Rd, Sheffield, S Yorks S10 2UA, United Kingdom. Ed. T L Green. Circ: 500.

666.1 GBR ISSN 0962-032X
BRITISH GLASS MANUFACTURERS CONFEDERATION. DIGEST OF INFORMATION AND PATENT REVIEW. Text in English. 1956. q. GBP 100 to non-members. **Document type:** *Abstract/Index.*
Former titles (until 1988): British Glass Industry Research Association Review; (until 1987): British Glass Industry Research Association. Digest of Information and Patent Review
Indexed: IPackAb.
—BLDSC (3587.630000).
Published by: British Glass Manufacturers Confederation, Northumberland Rd, Sheffield, S Yorks S10 2UA, United Kingdom.

666.1 GBR
BRITISH SOCIETY OF SCIENTIFIC GLASSBLOWERS. JOURNAL. Text in English. q.
—Linda Hall.
Published by: British Society of Scientific Glassblowers, 15 Crompton St, Chelmsford, Essex CM1 3BW, United Kingdom. TEL 44-1245-355981, FAX 44-1245-453783, bssg@kevic.demon.co.uk, http://www.bssg.co.uk.

666 658.8 GBR ISSN 1467-4556
BUSINESS RATIO. CERAMIC MANUFACTURERS. Text in English. 1974. a. GBP 275 (effective 2001). charts; stat. **Document type:** *Trade.*
Former titles (until 1999): Business Ratio Plus: Ceramic Manufacturers (1356-6040); (until 1994): Business Ratio Report. Ceramic Manufacturers (0261-7579)
Published by: The Prospect Shop Ltd., Field House, 72 Oldfield Rd, Hampton, Middx TW12 2HQ, United Kingdom. TEL 44-20-8461-8730, 44-20-8481-8720, FAX 44-20-8783-1940, info@theprospectshop.co.uk.

666.1 SWE ISSN 0280-7076
BYGGGLAS; tidskrift om glas i funktion, yta och miljoe. Text in Swedish. 1933. 6/yr. SEK 390 (effective 2001). adv. **Document type:** *Magazine, Trade.*
Formerly (until 1982): Svensk Glasmaestaretidning (0346-0649)
Published by: Glasbranschfoereningen, Skeppsbron 40, Box 16286, Stockholm, 10325, Sweden. TEL 46-8-4539070, FAX 46-8-4539071, byggg-glas@gbf.se, info@gbf.se, http://www.gbf.se/t_bygg.htm. Ed. Mikael Oedesjoe. Pub. Per Sjoehult. Adv. contact Helene Ulvander. B&W page SEK 9,000, color page SEK 14,500; trim 185 x 265. Circ: 1,300 (paid and controlled).

666 USA
C A C T ADVANCES. Text in English. s-a. back issues avail. **Document type:** *Newsletter, Trade.*
Related titles: Online - full text ed.
Published by: New York State Center for Advanced Ceramic Technology, 2 Pine St, Alfred, NY 14802. TEL 607-871-2486, FAX 607-871-3469, famarakoo@alfred.edu.

CAHIERS DE LA CERAMIQUE EGYPTIENNE. see *ARCHAEOLOGY*

666 CAN ISSN 1486-0945
CODEN: JCCSA9
CANADIAN CERAMICS. Text in English. 1985. a. CND 40 domestic; CND 45 in United States; CND 50 elsewhere. adv. **Document type:** *Newsletter, Trade.*
Formerly (until 1997): Canadian Ceramics Quarterly (0831-2974); Which incorporated (1932-1986): Canadian Ceramics Society. Journal (0068-8444); Which was formed by the merger of (1978-1985): Ceramic Hobbyist (0707-5197); (19??-1985): Canadian Clay and Ceramics Quarterly (0824-2658); Which was formerly (until 1981): Canadian Clay and Ceramics (0009-8566); (until 1965): Clay Products News and Ceramic Record
Related titles: Microfilm ed.: (from PMC).
Indexed: ASCA, B&BAb, BrCerAb, C&ISA, CIN, Cadscan, CerAb, ChemAb, ChemTitl, CorrAb, CurCont, E&CAJ, EMA, EngInd, LeadAb, MSCI, SolStAb, WAA, Zincscan.
—CASDDS, CISTI, IDS, Linda Hall. **CCC.**
Published by: Canadian Ceramic Society, 2175 Sheppard Ave E, Ste 310, Willowdale, ON M2J 1W8, Canada. TEL 416-491-2886, FAX 416-491-1670. Ed. M Sayer. Adv. contact B L Howell. Circ: 800.

666.1 USA
THE CARNIVAL PUMP. Text in English. 1967. q. USD 20 domestic membership; USD 25 foreign membership (effective 2004). **Document type:** *Newsletter, Consumer.* **Description:** Provides information for individuals interested in collecting, trading, and learning about antique carnival glass.
Published by: International Carnival Glass Association, PO Box 306, Mentone, IN 46539. TEL 219-353-7678, bookercgbr@aol.com. Ed. Carl Booker.

666 IND ISSN 0008-9397
CODEN: CGCRAP
CENTRAL GLASS AND CERAMIC RESEARCH INSTITUTE. BULLETIN. Text in English; Summaries in English, French, German. 1954. q. INR 35, USD 24. adv. bk.rev. charts; illus.; stat. index. reprint service avail. from PQC.
Indexed: BrCerAb, C&ISA, CIN, CerAb, ChemAb, ChemTitl, CorrAb, CurCont, E&CAJ, EMA, SolStAb, WAA.
—CASDDS, Linda Hall.
Published by: Central Glass and Ceramic Research Institute, 196, Raja S C Mullick Rd., Kolkata, West Bengal 700 032, India. TEL 33-463496. Circ: 650. **Affiliate:** Council of Scientific and Industrial Research.

666 ITA ISSN 0392-6842
CER; il giornale dell'Assopiastrelle. Text in Italian. 1974. 6/yr. EUR 42 domestic; EUR 78 in Europe; EUR 109 elsewhere (effective 2005). bk.rev. **Document type:** *Magazine, Trade.*
Related titles: English ed.: Cer International. free.
Published by: (Associazione Nazionale dei Produttori di Piastrelle di Ceramica e di Materiali Refrattari), Edi. Cer. SpA (Subsidiary of: Assopiastrelle), Viale Monte Santo 40, Sassuolo, MO 41049, Italy. TEL 39-0536-818111, FAX 39-0536-807935, info@assopiastrelle.it, http://www.assopiastrelle.it. Eds. Angelo Borelli, Marisa Cavatorti. Circ: 10,000.

666 ITA ISSN 0392-6834
CER ANNUARIO. Text in English, Italian. a. EUR 42 (effective 2005). stat. **Document type:** *Directory, Trade.* **Description:** Directory containing statistical information on manufacturing establishments, type of production, and number of employees.
Published by: (Associazione Nazionale dei Produttori di Piastrelle di Ceramica e di Materiali Refrattari), Edi. Cer. SpA (Subsidiary of: Assopiastrelle), Viale Monte Santo 40, Sassuolo, MO 41049, Italy. TEL 39-0536-818111, FAX 39-0536-807935, info@assopiastrelle.it, http://www.assopiastrelle.it. Circ: 10,000.

666 ITA ISSN 0392-6850
CER FORNITORI. Text in English, Italian. 1980. a. EUR 42 (effective 2005). **Document type:** *Directory, Trade.* **Description:** Lists suppliers to the ceramic tile industry.
Related titles: CD-ROM ed.
Published by: (Associazione Nazionale dei Produttori di Piastrelle di Ceramica e di Materiali Refrattari), Edi. Cer. SpA (Subsidiary of: Assopiastrelle), Viale Monte Santo 40, Sassuolo, MO 41049, Italy. TEL 39-0536-818111, FAX 39-0536-807935, info@assopiastrelle.it, http://www.assopiastrelle.it. Circ: 7,000.

666.42 GBR
CERAM PROGRESS. Text in English. 1999. q. back issues avail. **Document type:** *Newsletter, Corporate.*
Formerly: Progress Newsletter
Media: Online - full text. **Related titles:** Print ed.
Published by: Ceram Research Ltd., Queens Rd, Penkhull, Stoke-on-Trent, Staffs ST4 7LQ, United Kingdom. TEL 44-1762-764444, FAX 44-1762-412331, info@ceram.co.uk, http://www.ceram.co.uk. Ed. Ann Pace TEL 44-1782-764241. Circ: 1,000 (controlled).

CERAMAGAZINE; le magazine des professionnels du carreau et de la pierre naturelle. see *ARCHITECTURE*

666 DEU
CERAMIC DICTIONARY. Text in English, German. 1997. irreg. EUR 53 (effective 2000). **Document type:** *Directory, Trade.* **Description:** Focuses the field of ceramics and all of its niches. It incuides technical terms which have been meticulously collected and added to over decades; covers scientific branches such as chemistry, physics, raw material technology, powder metallurgy, engineering, etc.
Media: CD-ROM.
Published by: Verlag Schmid GmbH, Postfach 6609, Freiburg Im Breisgau, 79042, Germany. FAX 49-761-8960990, ceramic@ceramic-journals.com, http://www.ceramic-journals.com.

666 USA ISSN 0196-6219
TP785 CODEN: CESPDK
CERAMIC ENGINEERING AND SCIENCE PROCEEDINGS. Abbreviated title: C E S P. Text in English. 1980. 9/yr. USD 295 in North America to members; USD 335 elsewhere to members (effective 2005). charts; illus. back issues avail.; reprint service avail. from PQC. **Document type:** *Proceedings, Academic/Scholarly.* **Description:** Covers recent advancements in ceramics manufacturing and processing.
Related titles: Online - full text ed.: (from bigchalk, ProQuest Information & Learning).
Indexed: ABIn, BrCerAb, C&ISA, CIN, CRIA, CRICC, CerAb, ChemAb, ChemTitl, CivEngAb, CorrAb, E&CAJ, EMA, EngInd, IAA, ISMEC, Inspec, LHB, M&TEA, MBF, METADEX, SolStAb, WAA.
—BLDSC (3115.240000), CASDDS, CISTI, Ei, IE, Infotrieve, ingenta, Linda Hall. **CCC.**
Published by: American Ceramic Society Inc., 735 Ceramic Pl., # 100, Westerville, OH 43081-8719. info@ceramics.org, http://www.ceramics.org/publications/cesp.asp. Pub. Glenn Harvey. R&P Mark J Mecklenborg TEL 614-794-5829. Circ: 950 (paid).

666 DEU ISSN 0173-9913
CODEN: CCFDD7
CERAMIC FORUM INTERNATIONAL; journal for the ceramic industries and ceramic research. Text in English, German. 1923. 10/yr. EUR 186.50 domestic; EUR 196.35 foreign; EUR 17 newsstand/cover (effective 2004). adv. bk.rev. abstr.; bibl.; charts; illus.; pat. index. **Document type:** *Magazine, Trade.* **Description:** Trade publication for the ceramics industry. Covers the latest information on research in ceramic materials. Includes abstracts of scientific papers.
Formerly (until 1980): Deutsche Keramische Gesellschaft. Berichte (0365-9542)
Related titles: ◆ Supplement(s): Deutsche Keramische Gesellschaft. Fortschrittsberichte. ISSN 0177-6983.
Indexed: A&ATA, BrCerAb, C&ISA, CCI, CEABA, CIN, CerAb, ChemAb, ChemTitl, CivEngAb, CorrAb, CurCont, E&CAJ, EMA, EngInd, IAA, INIS AtomInd, ISMEC, Inspec, M&TEA, MBF, METADEX, MSCI, SSCI, SolStAb, WAA.
—BLDSC (3115.502000), AskIEEE, CASDDS, CISTI, Ei, IDS, IE, Infotrieve, ingenta, Linda Hall. **CCC.**
Published by: (Deutsche Keramische Gesellschaft e.V.), Goeller Verlag GmbH, Aschmattstr 8, Baden-Baden, 76532, Germany. TEL 49-7221-502200, FAX 49-7221-502222, verlag@goeller-verlag.de, http://www.cfi-web.de/index.php3, http://www.goeller-verlag.de. Ed. Karin Scharrer. Pub. Ulrich Goeller. Adv. contact Branka Di Stefano. B&W page EUR 2,250, color page EUR 2,700; trim 186 x 270. Circ: 5,182 (paid and controlled).

CERAMIC INDUSTRIES INTERNATIONAL DIRECTORY. see *BUSINESS AND ECONOMICS—Trade And Industrial Directories*

666 USA ISSN 0009-0220
TP785 CODEN: CEINAT
CERAMIC INDUSTRY; the magazine for refractories, traditional & advanced ceramic manufacturers. Text in English. 1923. 13/yr. USD 86 domestic; USD 8 newsstand/cover; free to qualified personnel (effective 2005). adv. bk.rev. charts; illus.; tr.lit. index. **Document type:** *Magazine, Trade.* **Description:** Serves manufacturers in the refractories, traditional, and advanced ceramic markets with industry news, technology, equipment and market trends coverage.
Related titles: Online - full text ed.: (from EBSCO Publishing, Florida Center for Library Automation, Gale Group, Northern Light Technology, Inc., O C L C Online Computer Library Center, Inc., ProQuest Information & Learning).
Indexed: ABIn, AESIS, AS&TI, B&I, BrCerAb, C&ISA, CerAb, ChemAb, CivEngAb, CorrAb, E&CAJ, EMA, EngInd, ExcerpMed, IAA, ISR, M&TEA, MBF, METADEX, PROMT, RefZh, SolStAb, WAA.
—BLDSC (3116.000000), CISTI, Ei, IE, Infotrieve, ingenta, Linda Hall. **CCC.**
Published by: B N P Media, 2401 W Big Beaver Rd, 7th Fl., Troy, MI 48084. TEL 248-362-3700, FAX 248-244-6429, grahlk@bnpmedia.com, http://www.ceramicindustry.com, http://www.bnpmedia.com/. Ed. Christine Grahl. Pub. Susan Love. Adv. contact Carol Lawrence. Circ: 15,130 (controlled).

666 USA
CERAMIC INDUSTRY DATA BOOK BUYERS GUIDE. Text in English. 1922. a. USD 25. adv. charts. **Document type:** *Directory.*
Formerly (until 1984): Ceramic Data Book (0162-5330)
—Linda Hall.
Published by: B N P Media, 755 W Big Beaver Rd, Ste 1000, Troy, MI 48084-4903. TEL 248-362-3700, FAX 248-362-0317, http://www.bnpmedia.com/. Ed. Pat Janeway. Circ: 13,000.

666 DEU ISSN 1432-4717
CERAMIC NEWS - SPECIAL ISSUES. Text in German. 1994. 3/yr. EUR 180 per issue (effective 2000). adv. **Document type:** *Trade.* **Description:** Information for manufacturers and suppliers in all ceramic sectors with a special focus on progressive international markets.
—Linda Hall.
Published by: Verlag Schmid GmbH, Postfach 6609, Freiburg Im Breisgau, 79042, Germany. TEL 49-761-8960940, FAX 49-761-8960990, ceramic@ceramic-journals.com, http://www.ceramic-journals.com. Ed. Hagen Dettmer. adv.: B&W page EUR 3,300, color page EUR 4,700;. Circ: 10,000 (paid).

666 DEU ISSN 1617-9684
CERAMIC NEWS. SPECIAL REFRACTORIES. Text in Multiple languages. irreg.
Indexed: BrCerAb, C&ISA, CerAb, CorrAb, E&CAJ, EMA, IAA, M&TEA, MBF, METADEX, SolStAb, WAA.
Published by: Verlag Schmid GmbH, Postfach 6609, Freiburg Im Breisgau, 79042, Germany. FAX 49-761-8960940, http://www.ceramic-journals.com.

666 GBR ISSN 0144-1825
TP808
CERAMIC REVIEW. Text in English. 1970. bi-m. GBP 32; GBP 37 overseas. adv. bk.rev. illus.; tr.lit. index. reprints avail. **Document type:** *Trade.*
Related titles: Online - full text ed.: (from H.W. Wilson, O C L C Online Computer Library Center, Inc.).
Indexed: ABM, ArtInd, BrCerAb, DAAI, PCI, Pinpoint.
—BLDSC (3116.400000), IE, Infotrieve, ingenta. **CCC.**
Published by: Ceramic Review Publishing Ltd., 21 Carnaby St, London, W1V 1PH, United Kingdom. TEL 44-171-439-3377, FAX 44-171-287-9954, http://www.gold.net/users/dj94/creview.html. Ed. Emmanuel Cooper. Adv. contact Daphne Matthews. Circ: 8,300.

666 JPN
CERAMIC SOCIETY OF JAPAN. ANNUAL MEETING. Text in English, Japanese. a. **Document type:** *Academic/Scholarly.*
—BLDSC (1087.713000).
Published by: Nippon Seramikkusu Kyokai/Ceramic Society of Japan, 22-17 Hiyakunin-cho 2-chome, Shinjuku-ku, Tokyo, 169-0073, Japan.

666 USA ISSN 8756-8187
TP785 CODEN: CESOEI
CERAMIC SOURCE. Text in English. 1985. a. USD 25 in North America to non-members; USD 31 elsewhere to non-members (effective 2003). adv. charts; illus. reprint service avail. from PQC. **Document type:** *Directory, Trade.*
Related titles: Online - full text ed.
Indexed: CRIA, CRICC, Inspec.
—CISTI. **CCC.**
Published by: American Ceramic Society Inc., 735 Ceramic Pl, Ste 100, Westerville, OH 43081-8720. TEL 614-794-5890, FAX 614-794-5892, info@ceramics.org, http://www.ceramicsource.org, http://www.ceramics.org. Ed., R&P Patricia Janeway TEL 614-794-5826. Pub. Paul Holbrook. Adv. contact John Krzysiak TEL 614-794-5845. Circ: 8,000.

738 AUS
➤ **CERAMIC STUDY GROUP. NEWSLETTER.** Text in English. 1960. 10/yr. AUD 40. adv. bk.rev. **Document type:** *Newsletter.*
Published by: Ceramic Study Group Inc., Sydney, PO Box 1528, Macquarie Centre, NSW 2113, Australia. TEL 61-2-98692195, FAX 61-2-98694722, http://www.zip.com.au/~bobf. Ed. Jo Ane Fuller. R&P Paquita Farmer. Adv. contact P Farmer. Circ: 600.

666 ITA ISSN 1121-0796
CERAMIC WORLD REVIEW. Text in Multiple languages. 1991. q.
Published by: Tile Italia, Via Carlo Zucchi 21-b, Modena, 41100, Italy. TEL 39-059-827780, FAX 39-059-827319, redazione@ceramicworldweb.com/, http://www.ceramicworldweb.it/, http://www.tileitali.it/.

666 ITA ISSN 0366-5801
CODEN: CERMA3
CERAMICA. Text in Italian. 1948. bi-m. USD 70. adv.
Indexed: ABM, BrCerAb, ChemAb.
—CASDDS, CISTI.
Published by: Casa Editrice Palazzo Vecchio, Via Vittorio Emanuele II, 155, Florence, FI 50134, Italy. Ed. Carlo Voltolini. Circ: 3,000.

666 BRA ISSN 0366-6913
CODEN: CMCAAG
CERAMICA. Text in Portuguese. 1954. bi-m. USD 90. adv. bk.rev. illus.; tr.lit. **Document type:** *Trade.* **Description:** Publishes original articles in the entire field of ceramic science and technology.
Related titles: Online - full text ed.: free (effective 2005) (from SciELO).
Indexed: BrCerAb, C&ISA, CerAb, ChemAb, CivEngAb, CorrAb, E&CAJ, EMA, IAA, INIS AtomInd, M&TEA, MBF, METADEX, SolStAb, WAA.
—BLDSC (3117.200000), CASDDS, CISTI, IE, ingenta, Linda Hall.
Published by: Associacao Brasileira de Ceramica, Caixa Postal 8326, Sao Paulo, SP 01065-970 , Brazil. TEL 55-11-268-4284, FAX 55-11-268-7101, rmuccill@net.ipen.br. Circ: 7,000.

666 ESP ISSN 0210-010X
CERAMICA; keramos. Text in Spanish. 1978. q. USD 21 foreign (effective 2001). adv. bk.rev.; software rev. bibl.; tr.lit. index. **Document type:** *Academic/Scholarly.*
Indexed: ABM.
Address: Paseo Acacias, 9, Madrid, 28005, Spain. TEL 34-91-8843073, FAX 34-91-8843073, revistaceramica@terra.es. Ed., Pub. Antonio Vivas. adv.: page USD 380; trim 175 x 240. Circ: 10,000.

666 ITA ISSN 1121-6093
CERAMICA ACTA. Text in English, Italian. 1989. bi-m. adv. bk.rev. **Document type:** *Magazine, Trade.* **Description:** Covers traditional ceramics, advanced technical ceramics, glass, bioceramics, energy and processes and quality.
Indexed: BrCerAb, C&ISA, CerAb, CorrAb, E&CAJ, EMA, IAA, M&TEA, MBF, METADEX, MinerAb, SolStAb, WAA.
—BLDSC (3117.250000), IE, ingenta.
Published by: Centro Ceramico Bologna, Via Tommaso Martelli 26, Bologna, BO 40138, Italy. TEL 39-051-534015, FAX 39-051-530085, centro.ceramico@cencerbo.it, http://www.cencerbo.it. Ed. Giorgio Timellini.

666 BRA ISSN 1413-4608
CERAMICA INDUSTRIAL. Text in Portuguese. 1996. bi-m.
—CISTI.
Published by: Associacao Brasileira de Ceramica, Av Prof Almeida Prado, 532, Cidade Universitaria, Predio 36, 2 andar, sala 3, Sao Paulo, 05508-901, Brazil. TEL 55-11-37687101, FAX 55-11-37684284, abceram@abceram.org.br, http://www.ceramicaindustrial.org.br/, http://www.abceram.org.br.

666 ESP ISSN 0392-8098
CERAMICA INFORMACION. Text in Spanish. 1974. m. (11/yr.). bk.rev. **Document type:** *Magazine, Trade.*
Related titles: ◆ Italian ed.: Ceramica Informazione. ISSN 0009-0271; Portuguese ed.: Ceramica Informacao. EUR 124 (effective 2004); Chinese ed.: Ceramica Informazione (Chinese Edition). EUR 38 (effective 2004).
Indexed: BrCerAb, IECT.
—CINDOC.
Published by: Faenza Editrice Iberica S.L., Pol. Ind Sur Nave 39, Castellon, 12006, Spain. TEL 34-964-216570, FAX 34-964-241010, info@faenza.es. Ed. B Cervera Carceller. Circ: 3,350.

666 ITA ISSN 0009-0271
CODEN: CINFDR
CERAMICA INFORMAZIONE; periodico tecnico specializzato. Text in Italian. 1966. m. (9/yr). EUR 55 domestic; EUR 105 foreign (effective 2005). bk.rev. abstr.; bibl.; charts; illus.; tr.lit. index. **Document type:** *Magazine, Trade.* **Description:** Covers the ceramic sector in Italy. Includes articles about tiles, raw materials and equipment.
Related titles: Online - full content ed.: ISSN 1593-2303. 2001; ◆ Spanish ed.: Ceramica Informacion. ISSN 0392-8098; Portuguese ed.: Ceramica Informacao. EUR 124 (effective 2004); Chinese ed.: Ceramica Informazione (Chinese Edition). EUR 38 (effective 2004).
Indexed: BrCerAb, C&ISA, CIN, CerAb, ChemAb, ChemTitl, CorrAb, E&CAJ, EMA, SolStAb, WAA.
—BLDSC (3117.300000), CASDDS, IE, ingenta.
Published by: (Societa Italiana per la Ceramica), Gruppo Editoriale Faenza Editrice SpA, Via Pier de Crescenzi 44, Faenza, RA 48018, Italy. TEL 39-0546-670411, FAX 39-0546-660440, info@faenza.com, http://www.faenza.com. Ed. Giovanni Biffi. R&P Luisa Teston. Adv. contact Elvio Meri.

747 ARG ISSN 0325-0229
CODEN: CECRBC
➤ **CERAMICA Y CRISTAL.** Text in Spanish. 1961. 4/yr. ARS 20, USD 120 (effective 2002). adv. bk.rev. illus. back issues avail. **Document type:** *Journal, Academic/Scholarly.*
Former titles (until 1965): Estilo (0014-133X); (until 1961): Ceramica y Cristal (0325-0210)
Indexed: BrCerAb, C&ISA, CIN, CerAb, ChemAb, ChemTitl, CorrAb, E&CAJ, EMA, INIS AtomInd, SolStAb, WAA.
—CASDDS.
Published by: Editorial Ciclo, Esteban de Luca 2252 dto.2, Buenos Aires, 1246, Argentina. FAX 54-11-49435799, ciclo@tournet.com.ar, http://www.ceramicaycristal.com.ar. Ed. Arnoldo Alonso Ibanez. Pub. Marcelo Alonso Marasco. R&P Luis Alonso Ibanez. Adv. contact Carla Alonso Marasco. B&W page USD 500, color page USD 750; trim 280 x 200. Circ: 2,500.

C

666 ITA ISSN 1121-6956
CERAMICANTICA; mensile sull'arte della maiolica, dell porcellana e del vetro. Text in Italian; Summaries in English, French, Spanish. 1991. m. (11/yr.). EUR 73 domestic; EUR 110 in Europe; EUR 150 elsewhere (effective 2005). adv. bk.rev.
Document type: *Magazine, Consumer.* **Description:** Specializes in pottery, majolica, porcelain and glass.
Related titles: Online - full text ed.
Published by: Casa Editrice Belriguardo, Via Montebello 18, Ferrara, FE 44100, Italy. TEL 39-0532-247450, FAX 39-0532-205332, info@belriguardo.it, http://www.ceramicantica.it, http://www.belriguardo.it. Pub. Romolo Magnani. R&P, Adv. contact Anna Rossi Guzzetti.

666 PRT ISSN 0872-1912
CERAMICAS. Text in Portuguese. 1998. q. **Document type:** *Magazine, Trade.* **Description:** Trade review of the industrial and artistic ceramics industry.
Published by: Centro de Formacao Profissional para a Industria Ceramica, Rua Luis Caldas, Apartado 39, Caldas da Rainha, 2504-909, Portugal. TEL 351-262-840110, FAX 351-262-842224, geral@cencal.pt, http://www.cencal.pt.

666 700 AUS ISSN 1035-1841
NK3700
CERAMICS; art and perception. Text in English. 1990. q. AUD 55 domestic; NZD 76 in New Zealand; GBP 34 in United Kingdom; EUR 55 in Europe; USD 60 in United States; CND 76 in Canada (effective 2005). adv. bk.rev. illus. back issues avail. **Document type:** *Magazine, Academic/Scholarly.* **Description:** Covers contemporary ceramics, along with trends and stimulating events. Discusses the history of ceramics in various cultures and the persons involved.
Related titles: E-mail ed.; Fax ed.; Online - full text ed.: (from H.W. Wilson, O C L C Online Computer Library Center, Inc., R M I T Publishing).
Indexed: ABM, ArtHuCI, ArtInd, CurCont, DAAI.
—BLDSC (3118.200000), IE, ingenta.
Published by: Ceramic Art & Perception, 120 Glenmore Rd, Paddington, NSW 2021, Australia. TEL 61-2-93615286, FAX 61-2-93615402, ceramics@ceramicart.com.au, http://www.ceramicart.com.au. Ed., Pub., R&P Janet Mansfield TEL 61-2-9361-5286. Adv. contact Jim Johnston TEL 61-2-98802352. color page AUD 1,028; trim 185 x 260. Circ: 11,500 (controlled).

C

666 USA ISSN 1533-7154
CERAMICS IN AMERICA (YEAR). Text in English. 2001. a. **Description:** Examines the role of historical ceramics in the American context.
Published by: Chipstone Foundation, 7820 N Club Circle, Milwaukee, WI 53217. TEL 414-352-0073, http://www.chipstone.org. Ed. Robert Hunter. **Dist. by:** University Press of New England, 1 Court St, Ste 250, Hanover, NH 03755-2048.

666 GBR ISSN 0272-8842
TP785 CODEN: CINNDH
➤ **CERAMICS INTERNATIONAL.** Text and summaries in English. 1974. 8/yr. EUR 1,771 in Europe to institutions; JPY 235,100 in Japan to institutions; USD 1,981 to institutions except Europe and Japan (effective 2006). adv. bk.rev. abstr. back issues avail. **Document type:** *Journal, Academic/Scholarly.* **Description:** Deals with the fundamental aspects of ceramic science and its application to the development of improved traditional and non-traditional ceramic products.
Formerly (until 1981): Ceramurgia International (0390-5519)
Related titles: Online - full text ed.: (from EBSCO Publishing, Gale Group, IngentaConnect, ScienceDirect, Swets Information Services).
Indexed: ASCA, ApMecR, B&BAb, BrCerAb, C&ISA, CCI, CIN, CerAb, ChemAb, ChemTitl, CivEngAb, CorrAb, CurCont, E&CAJ, EMA, EngInd, IAA, ISR, Inspec, M&TEA, MBF, METADEX, MSCI, RefZh, SCI, SolStAb, WAA.
—BLDSC (3119.015000), AskIEEE, CASDDS, CISTI, Ei, IDS, IE, Infotrieve, ingenta, Linda Hall. **CCC.**
Published by: Pergamon (Subsidiary of: Elsevier Science & Technology), The Boulevard, Langford Ln, East Park, Kidlington, Oxford OX5 1GB, United Kingdom. TEL 44-1865-843000, FAX 44-1865-843010, http://www.elsevier.com/locate/ceramint. Ed. Pietro Vincenzini. Circ: 450. **Subscr. to:** Elsevier BV, PO Box 211, Amsterdam 1000 AE, Netherlands. nlinfo-f@elsevier.nl, http://www.elsevier.nl.

666 JPN ISSN 0009-031X
CODEN: SERAA7
CERAMICS JAPAN/SERAMIKKUSU. Text in Japanese. 1966. m. free to members. adv. bk.rev. illus. **Document type:** *Bulletin, Academic/Scholarly.*
Indexed: BrCerAb, C&ISA, CIN, CerAb, ChemAb, ChemTitl, CivEngAb, CorrAb, E&CAJ, EMA, IAA, INIS AtomInd, JCT, JTA, M&TEA, MBF, METADEX, SolStAb, WAA.
—BLDSC (3119.030000), CASDDS, CISTI, IE, ingenta, Linda Hall. **CCC.**
Published by: Nippon Seramikkusu Kyokai/Ceramic Society of Japan, 22-17 Hiyakunin-cho 2-chome, Shinjuku-ku, Tokyo, 169-0073, Japan. TEL 81-3-3362-5231, FAX 81-3-3362-5714, http://www.ceramic.or.jp/ihensyub/index_j.html. Ed. Hideo Hosono. Pub., R&P, Adv. contact Keisuke Shimada TEL 81-3-3362-5234. Circ: 6,000.

666 USA
CERAMICS: LATIN AMERICAN INDUSTRIAL REPORT✶. (Avail. for each of 22 Latin American countries) Text in English. 1985. a. USD 435; per country report.
Published by: Aquino Productions, P O Box 15760, Stamford, CT 06901-0760. Ed. Andres C Aquino.

666 USA ISSN 0009-0328
TP785
CERAMICS MONTHLY. Text in English. 1953. 10/yr. USD 32 domestic to non-members; USD 34.24 in Canada to non-members; USD 57 elsewhere to non-members; USD 26 domestic to members; USD 27.82 in Canada to members; USD 51 elsewhere to members (effective 2005). adv. bk.rev. illus. index. back issues avail.; reprint service avail. from PQC. **Document type:** *Magazine, Trade.* **Description:** Serves potters, ceramic sculptors, schools, craft centers, galleries, collectors and others with interest in ceramics.
Related titles: Microfiche ed.: (from NBI, PQC); Online - full text ed.: (from EBSCO Publishing, H.W. Wilson, O C L C Online Computer Library Center, Inc., ProQuest Information & Learning).
Indexed: A&ATA, ABM, ABS&EES, ASIP, ArtInd, BAS, BHA, BRI, C&ISA, CBRI, DAAI, E&CAJ, IAA, IHTDI, MagInd, Pinpoint.
—BLDSC (3119.050000), IE, Infotrieve, ingenta. **CCC.**
Published by: American Ceramic Society Inc., 735 Ceramic Pl, Ste 100, Westerville, OH 43081-8720. TEL 614-794-5890, FAX 614-794-5892, editorial@ceramicsmonthly.org, info@ceramics.org, http://www.ceramicsmonthly.org, http://www.ceramics.org. Ed. Sherman Hall. Pub., R&P Mark J Mecklenborg TEL 614-794-5829. Adv. contact Steve Hecker TEL 614-794-5809. B&W page USD 8,100, color page USD 2,425. Circ: 40,000 (paid).

CERAMICS-SILIKATY. see *CHEMISTRY—Physical Chemistry*

666 AUS ISSN 1324-4175
CERAMICS TECHNICAL. Text in English. 1995. biennial. AUD 35 domestic; EUR 35 in Europe; GBP 22 in United Kingdom; NZD 46 in New Zealand; USD 35 in United States; CND 50 in Canada (effective 2005). adv. bk.rev. **Document type:** *Magazine, Academic/Scholarly.* **Description:** Promotes the highest quality work in ceramics throughout Australia and worldwide, with articles sourced internationally covering technical developments in contemporary ceramics, trends, and stimulating events. Also discusses the history of ceramics in various cultures and the people involved.
Related titles: Online - full text ed.: (from H.W. Wilson, O C L C Online Computer Library Center, Inc.).
Indexed: ArtHuCI, ArtInd, CurCont, DAAI.
Published by: Ceramic Art & Perception, 120 Glenmore Rd, Paddington, NSW 2021, Australia. TEL 61-2-93615286, FAX 61-2-93615402, ceramics@ceramicart.com.au, http://www.ceramicart.com.au/technical.htm. Pub. Janet Mansfield TEL 61-2-9361-5286. adv.: page AUD 1,028; trim 260 x 185. Circ: 8,500 (paid).

666 FRA ISSN 0009-0336
LA CERAMIQUE MODERNE. Text in French. 1959. m. (except Jul.-Aug. combined). bk.rev. bibl.; charts; illus.; stat. index. **Description:** Devoted to the materials and accessories, as well as the fashioning, baking, enamelling and decoration of ceramics.
Published by: Editions Techniques et Artistiques, 22 rue Le Brun, Paris, 75013, France. TEL 33-1-45871748. Ed. Milutin Krstic. Circ: 3,700.

666 ITA ISSN 0045-6152
TP785 CODEN: CRGIAR
➤ **CERAMURGIA.** Text in Italian; Summaries in English, Italian. 1971. 3/yr. EUR 380 foreign (effective 2002). adv. bk.rev. abstr.; bibl.; illus.; pat. **Document type:** *Trade.*
Indexed: BrCerAb, CIN, ChemAb, ChemTitl, CivEngAb, EngInd, F&EA.
—BLDSC (3119.305000), CASDDS, CISTI, Ei, IE, ingenta, Linda Hall.
Published by: Techna s.r.l., Casella Postale, 174, Faenza, RA 48018, Italy. TEL 39-546-22461, FAX 39-546-664138. Ed. Pietro Vincenzini. Adv. contact Gianantonio Bertoni. B&W page EUR 900, color page EUR 1,200. Circ: 2,100.

666 ROM ISSN 1221-5503
CERCETARI METALURGICE SI DE NOI MATERIALE. Text in Multiple languages. 1960. q.
Formerly (until 1990): Cercetari Metalurgice (0524-8140); Which superseded in part (in 1963): Cercetari Metalurgice si Miniere (1220-1707)
Indexed: BrCerAb, C&ISA, CerAb, CorrAb, E&CAJ, EMA, IAA, M&TEA, MBF, METADEX, SolStAb, WAA.
—BLDSC (5699.098900), IE, ingenta, Linda Hall.
Published by: Institutul de Cercetari Metalurgice, Str Mehadia 39, Bucharest, 77769, Romania.

666 ROM ISSN 0577-3385
CERCETARI MINIERE. Text in English. 1960. a.
Supersedes in part (in 1963): Cercetari Metalurgice si Miniere (1220-1707); Which was formed by the merger of (1958-1959): Cercetari de Metalurgie (1220-1693); (1957-1959): Annarul Institutului de Cercetari Miniere (1220-1685)
Published by: Institutul de Cercetari Metalurgice, Str Mehadia 39, Bucharest, 77769, Romania.

CLAY SCIENCE. see *MINES AND MINING INDUSTRY*

666 GBR ISSN 0954-6146
CLAY TECHNOLOGY. Text in English. bi-m. GBP 25 in United Kingdom; GBP 28 elsewhere (effective 2001). adv. 4 cols./p.; back issues avail. **Document type:** *Journal, Trade.*
Indexed: BrCerAb.
Published by: (Institute of Clay Technology), Newton Mann Ltd., The Derwent Business Centre, Clarke Street, Derby, DE1 2BU, United Kingdom. TEL 44-1332-290460, FAX 44-1332-345680, ct@claytechnology.com, admin@newtonmann.co.uk, http://www.newtonmann.co.uk. adv.: B&W page GBP 460, color page GBP 750; trim 210 x 297. Circ: 2,000.

666 FRA ISSN 0763-0018
COMPOSITES ET NOUVEAUX MATERIAUX (PARIS, 1980). Text in French. 1984. 18/yr. FRF 2,200.
Published by: A Jour (Subsidiary of: Groupe Tests), 26 Rue d'Oradour-sur-Glane, Paris, 75504, France. TEL 33-1-44253500, redac.ajour@groupe-tests.fr, http://www.01net.com, http://www.ajour.fr. Ed. Juliette Fauchet.

666 690 GBR
CONSERVATORY INDUSTRIES. Text in English. q. GBP 73; GBP 82 foreign. **Document type:** *Trade.* **Description:** Covers the manufacture, fabrication and installation of all types of conservatory for both domestic and commercial use.
Published by: Turret R A I plc, Armstrong House, 38 Market Sq, Uxbridge, Middx UB8 1TG, United Kingdom. TEL 44-1895-454545, FAX 44-1895-454647.

CORPUS VASORUM ANTIQUORUM. ITALIA. see *CLASSICAL STUDIES*

738.12 USA
➤ **CRITICAL CERAMICS.** Text in English. 1999. w. free. adv. bk.rev. **Document type:** *Academic/Scholarly.* **Description:** For discussion of contemporary ceramic art.
Media: Online - full text.
Address: Bennington College, Route 67A, Bennington, VT 05201. editor@criticalceramics.org, http://www.criticalceramics.org. Ed., R&P, Adv. contact Forrest Snyder. Circ: 4,000.

666.1 DEU ISSN 1618-8721
TP845
D G G JOURNAL. Text in German. 2002. bi-m. **Document type:** *Journal, Trade.*
Related titles: ♦ English ed.: Glass Science and Technology.
Indexed: BrCerAb, C&ISA, CerAb, CorrAb, E&CAJ, EMA, IAA, M&TEA, MBF, METADEX, WAA.
—Linda Hall.
Published by: Deutsche Glastechnische Gesellschaft e.V., Siemensstr 45, Offenbach, 63071, Germany. TEL 49-69-9758610, FAX 49-69-97586199, dgg@hvg-dgg.de, http://www.hvg-dgg.de.

666 ITA ISSN 1120-5822
D'A; artigianato tra arte e design. Text in Italian. 1990. q. EUR 24 (effective 2005). **Document type:** *Magazine, Trade.*
Published by: Edizioni Imago International Srl, Corso Indipendenza 6, Milan, 20129, Italy. TEL 39-02-70009474, FAX 39-02-70009480, edizionimago@tin.it. Circ: 12,300.

666.1 748 USA ISSN 0895-3961
THE DAZE INC.; the nation's market place for glass and china. Text in English. 1971. m. USD 36; USD 42 foreign (effective 2000). adv. bk.rev.
Formerly (until 1984): Depression Glass Daze (0270-8485)
Published by: Daze Inc., PO Box 57, Otisville, MI 48463. TEL 810-631-4593, FAX 810-631-4567. Ed., R&P Teri Steele. Pub. Teresa Cox. Adv. contact Pam Hetzer. Circ: 20,000.

666 DEU ISSN 0070-4199
CODEN: DKGFBF
DEUTSCHE KERAMISCHE GESELLSCHAFT. FACHAUSSCHUSSBERICHTE. Text in German. 1953. irreg., latest vol.32. price varies. **Document type:** *Journal, Trade.*
Indexed: ChemAb.
—CASDDS.
Published by: Deutsche Keramische Gesellschaft e.V., Am Grott 7, Cologne, 51147, Germany. TEL 49-2203-966480, FAX 49-2203-69301, info@dkg.de, http://www.dkg.de.

666 DEU ISSN 0177-6983
CODEN: FDKGFF
DEUTSCHE KERAMISCHE GESELLSCHAFT. FORTSCHRITTSBERICHTE. Text in German. 1985. irreg. price varies. **Document type:** *Monographic series, Trade.*
Related titles: ♦ Supplement to: Ceramic Forum International. ISSN 0173-9913.
Indexed: BrCerAb, C&ISA, CEABA, CerAb, CorrAb, E&CAJ, EMA, IAA, M&TEA, MBF, METADEX, SolStAb, WAA.
—BLDSC (4024.036300), CASDDS, CISTI, Linda Hall. **CCC.**
Published by: Deutsche Keramische Gesellschaft e.V., Am Grott 7, Cologne, 51147, Germany. TEL 49-2203-966480, FAX 49-2203-69301, info@dkg.de, http://www.dkg.de.

666.1 DEU
DEUTSCHER GLASERKALENDER; Ratgeber und Helfer fuer Glaser und Fensterbauer. Text in German. 1950. a. adv. stat. **Document type:** *Trade.*
Published by: Verlag Karl Hofmann, Postfach 1360, Schorndorf, 73603, Germany. TEL 49-7181-402125, FAX 49-7181-402111. Circ: 5,500.

666 DEU ISSN 0171-399X
DIGEST. Variant title: Messe Digest. Text in German. 1972. 6/yr. adv. **Document type:** *Magazine, Trade.*
Indexed: Englnd.
Published by: Konradin Verlag Robert Kohlhammer GmbH, Ernst Mey Str 8, Leinfelden-Echterdingen, 70771, Germany. TEL 49-711-75940, FAX 49-711-7594390, produktion@digest-online.de, info@konradin.de, http://www.digest-online.de, http://www.konradin.de. Ed. Kirsten Dittmar. Adv. contact Idiko Schiller TEL 49-211-51604915. color page EUR 3,920, B&W page EUR 2,450; trim 184 x 260. Circ: 7,326 (controlled).

666.029 USA
DIRECTORY OF THE REFRACTORIES INDUSTRY (YEAR). Text in English. 1954. quadrennial. USD 85 to non-members; USD 45 to members. **Document type:** *Directory.*
Formerly: Product Directory of the Refractories Industry of the United States (0196-2388)
Published by: Refractories Institute, 650 Smithfield St, Ste 1160, Pittsburgh, PA 15222-3907. TEL 412-281-6787, FAX 412-281-6881. R&P Robert W Crolius. Circ: 1,500.

▼ **DOLLS BEAUTIFUL.** see *ARTS AND HANDICRAFTS*

666 DEU
EHRENPREIS DEUTSCHE KERAMIK. Text in German. 1983. irreg. **Document type:** *Catalog, Academic/Scholarly.*
Published by: Verlag der Museen des Westerwaldkreises, Peter Altmeier Platz 1, Montabaur, 56410, Germany. TEL 49-2602-124226, FAX 49-2602-124542, TELEX 869619-KVMO-D, museen-gmbh@westerwald.rlp.de, http://www.westerwaldkreis.rlp.de.

666.2 HRV ISSN 0350-3607
CODEN: EKESDN
EMAJL, KERAMIKA, STAKLO. Text in Serbo-Croatian; Summaries in English, German. 1964. q. USD 20. adv. bk.rev.
Formerly (until 1969): Emajl (0013-6506)
Indexed: ChemAb.
—CASDDS, Linda Hall.
Published by: Udruzenje Emajliraca Jugoslavije/Yugoslavian Enamellers Association, Srebrnjak 169, Zagreb, 41000, Croatia. Ed. Robert Laslo. Circ: 1,000 (controlled).

666 GBR ISSN 0071-0547
ENGLISH CERAMIC CIRCLE. TRANSACTIONS. Text in English. 1927. a. price varies. cum.index. **Document type:** *Proceedings, Academic/Scholarly.*
Indexed: A&ATA, BHA, BrArAb, NumL.
—BLDSC (8931.523000).
Published by: English Ceramic Circle, c/o Mrs. J. Bennett, Secy, 5 The Dr, Beckenham, Kent BR3 1EE, United Kingdom. Ed. Tom Walford. Circ: 500.

666 DEU
EUROPAISCHE KERAMIK. Text in English, German. 1973. every 5 yrs. EUR 20.45 (effective 2001). **Document type:** *Catalog, Academic/Scholarly.* **Description:** Exhibits the works of artists using various forms and types of ceramics.
Formerly (until 1999): Deutsche Keramik
Published by: (Kreisverwaltung des Westerwaldkreises in Montabaur), Verlag der Museen des Westerwaldkreises, Peter Altmeier Platz 1, Montabaur, 56410, Germany. TEL 49-2602-124226, FAX 49-2602-124542, TELEX 869619-KVMO-D, museen-gmbh@westerwald.rlp.de, http://www.westerwaldkreis.rlp.de. **Dist. by:** Keramikmuseum Westerwald, Lindenstr, Hoehr-Grenzhausen 56203, Germany. TEL 49-2624-946010, FAX 49-2624-9460120.

620.14 GBR ISSN 0955-2219
TA455.C3 CODEN: JECSER
➤ **EUROPEAN CERAMIC SOCIETY. JOURNAL.** Key Title: Journal of the European Ceramic Society. Text in English. 1985. 16/yr. EUR 3,063 in Europe to institutions; JPY 406,800 in Japan to institutions; USD 3,427 elsewhere to institutions (effective 2006). adv. back issues avail. **Document type:** *Journal, Academic/Scholarly.* **Description:** Publishes the results of original research relating to the structure, properties and processing of ceramic materials.
Formerly (until 1989): International Journal of High Technology Ceramics (0267-3762)
Related titles: Online - full text ed.: (from EBSCO Publishing, Gale Group, IngentaConnect, ScienceDirect, Swets Information Services).
Indexed: ASCA, ApMecR, BrCerAb, C&ISA, CCI, CIN, CerAb, ChemAb, ChemTitl, CivEngAb, CorrAb, CurCont, E&CAJ, EMA, Englnd, FLUIDEX, IAA, ISR, Inspec, M&TEA, MBF, METADEX, MSCI, RefZh, SCI, SolStAb, WAA, WTA.
—BLDSC (4741.629000), AskIEEE, CASDDS, CISTI, Ei, IDS, IE, Infotrieve, ingenta, Linda Hall. **CCC.**
Published by: (European Ceramic Society), Elsevier Ltd. (Subsidiary of: Elsevier Science & Technology), The Boulevard, Langford Ln, Kidlington, Oxford, OX5 1GB, United Kingdom. TEL 44-1865-843000, FAX 44-1865-843010, http://www.elsevier.com/locate/jeurceramsoc. Ed. Richard J. Brook. **Subscr. to:** Elsevier BV, PO Box 211, Amsterdam 1000 AE, Netherlands. TEL 31-20-485-3757, FAX 31-20-485-3432, nlinfo-f@elsevier.nl, http://www.elsevier.nl.

666.1029 GBR ISSN 0306-204X
HD9623.E8
EUROPEAN GLASS DIRECTORY AND BUYER'S GUIDE. Text in English. 1970. a. (issued in Jan.). GBP 160 domestic; GBP 168 foreign (effective 2000). adv. **Document type:** *Directory.* **Description:** Provides detailed, up-to-date information on manufacturers, processors, and manipulators of glass products and materials in Europe.
Formerly: Glass Directory and Buyer's Guide
Published by: D M G World Media Ltd. (Subsidiary of: Daily Mail and General Trust PLC), Queensway House, 2 Queensway, Redhill, Surrey RH1 1QS, United Kingdom. TEL 44-1737-768611, FAX 44-1737-855475, http://www.dmg.co.uk, http://www.dmgworldmedia.com. Ed. K Tolley.

666 USA
EXPANDED SHALE, CLAY AND SLATE INSTITUTE. SPECIAL BULLETINS. Text in English. irreg. **Document type:** *Consumer.*
Published by: Expanded Shale, Clay and Slate Institute, 2225 E Murray Holladay Rd, Ste 102, Salt Lake City, UT 84117. TEL 801-272-7070, FAX 801-272-3377.

666 GBR ISSN 0964-6779
FABRICATION & GLAZING INDUSTRIES. Text in English. 1981. m. GBP 25; GBP 40 in Europe; GBP 75 elsewhere. adv. bk.rev. illus. **Document type:** *Trade.* **Description:** Contains articles and industry news of interest to glazing contractors, specifiers, glaziers, and window and door fabricators, installers, and architects.
Formerly (until 1991): Flat Glass International (0262-3315)
Published by: T B B Publications Ltd., 4 Simon Campion Ct, High St, Epping, Essex CM16 4AU, United Kingdom. TEL 01992-560215, FAX 01992-560216. Ed. John Roper. Adv. contact Gerald Batt. Circ: 8,329 (controlled).

666 738 ITA ISSN 0014-679X
NK3700
FAENZA; rivista di studi di storia e di tecnica dell'arte ceramica. Text in Italian; Summaries in English, French, German. 1913. 6/yr. EUR 42 domestic; EUR 58 foreign (effective 2004). adv. bk.rev. bibl.; charts; illus. index. **Document type:** *Bulletin, Academic/Scholarly.*
Indexed: A&ATA, ABM, BHA, DIP, IBR, IBZ, Indlslam.
Published by: Museo Internazionale delle Ceramiche, Viale Baccarini 19, Faenza, RA 48018, Italy. TEL 39-0546-697311, FAX 39-0546-27141, micfaenza@provincia.ra.it, http://www.micfaenza.org. Ed. Gian Carlo Bojani. Circ: 1,000.

666 ITA ISSN 1123-8135
FASHION CERAMIC TILES. Variant title: Ceramic Tile Fashion. Text in Italian. 1983. s-a. price varies. adv. **Document type:** *Catalog, Trade.*
Related titles: ♦ Supplement to: Ceramica per l'Edilizia International. ISSN 0392-4890.
Published by: Gruppo Editoriale Faenza Editrice SpA, Via Pier de Crescenzi 44, Faenza, RA 48018, Italy. TEL 39-0546-670411, FAX 39-0546-660440, info@faenza.com, http://www.faenza.com. Ed. Rolando Giovannini. R&P Luisa Teston. Adv. contact Elvio Neri.

666 JPN ISSN 0911-5269
FINE CERAMICS REPORT. Key Title: F C Report. Text in Japanese. m. **Document type:** *Journal, Academic/Scholarly.*
—BLDSC (3901-202000).
Published by: Nihon Fain Seramikkusu Kyokai/Japan Fine Ceramics Association, 6th Fl, Halifax Onarimon Bldg, 24-10 Nishi Shinbashi 3-chome Minato-ku, Tokyo, 105, Japan. TEL 81-3-34373781, FAX 81-3-34373790, komaki@jfca-net.or.jp, http://www.jfca-net.or.jp/.

666.1 RUS ISSN 0132-6651
TP845 CODEN: FKSTD5
➤ **FIZIKA I KHIMIYA STEKLA.** Text in Russian. 1975. bi-m. RUR 1,150 for 6 mos. domestic (effective 2004). back issues avail. **Document type:** *Journal, Academic/Scholarly.* **Description:** Documents advances in the understanding of the structure, physical and chemical properties, and nature of inorganic glasses and glass-forming melts.
Related titles: Microfilm ed.: (from PQC); ♦ Russian Translation: Glass Physics and Chemistry. ISSN 1087-6596.
Indexed: Englnd, Inspec, RefZh.
—CASDDS, CISTI, East View, KNAW, Linda Hall. **CCC.**
Published by: (Rossiskaya Akademiya Nauk), Izdatel'stvo Nauka, Profsoyuznaya ul 90, Moscow, 117864, Russian Federation. TEL 7-095-3347151, FAX 7-095-4202220, secret@naukaran.ru, http://www.maik.ru/journals/physglas.htm, http://www.naukaran.ru.

666.122 USA ISSN 0016-3155
FUSION. Text in English. 1954. q. free to members (effective 2005). adv. bk.rev. abstr.; illus. **Description:** Educational material pertaining to the field of scientific glassblowing.
Indexed: CPerI, ChemAb, T&II.
—CISTI.
Published by: The American Scientific Glassblowers Society, PO Box 778, Madison, NC 27025. TEL 336-882-0174, FAX 336-882-0172, http://www.asgs-glass.org/asgs2/ASGS_MAIN/Fusion.html. Ed., R&P Marilyn Brown. Adv. contact Dawn Hodgkins. Circ: 1,200.

666 CAN ISSN 0832-9656
FUSION MAGAZINE. Text in English. 1985. 3/yr. CND 55 to individuals; CND 75 to institutions (effective 2002). adv. bk.rev. back issues avail. **Document type:** *Magazine, Trade.* **Description:** Provides a range of subject matter on ceramics and glass from reviews, exhibitions and listings to technical articles and profiles.
Indexed: DAAI.
Published by: Ontario Clay and Glass Association, Gardener s Cottage, 225 Confederation Dr, Toronto, ON M1G 1B2, Canada. TEL 416-438-8946, FAX 416-438-0192, 2fusion@interlog.com. Ed., R&P Helen Rudin TEL 416-533-5798. Pub. Victor Levin. Adv. contact John Durrant TEL 416-977-4099. Circ: 900.

666 745.5 AUS ISSN 1322-5103
FUSIONS. Text in English. 1968. q. AUD 45 to members. adv. bk.rev. **Document type:** *Newsletter.* **Description:** Reports on the association's exhibitions, workshops and coming events. Includes technical notes.
Formerly: Q P A News (1038-2240)
Published by: Queensland Potters Association, Cnr. Malt & Brunswick Sts., Fortitude Valley, QLD 4006, Australia. TEL 61-7-33585122, FAX 61-7-33584540. Ed., R&P Bernice Gerrand. Circ: 850.

666.1 DEU ISSN 1432-6264
TP845
G F F - ZEITSCHRIFT FUER GLAS, FENSTER, FASSADE. Text in German. 1950. m. EUR 84; EUR 62 to students; EUR 9 newsstand/cover (effective 2002). adv. bk.rev. charts; illus.; tr.lit. **Document type:** *Journal, Trade.*
Former titles: Glas und Rahmen (0342-5142); St. Lucas Allgemeine Glaserzeitung (0036-3065)
Indexed: RefZh.
—BLDSC (4165.960000). **CCC.**
Published by: Verlag Karl Hofmann, Postfach 1360, Schorndorf, 73603, Germany. TEL 49-7181-402127, FAX 49-7181-402111, info@hofmann-verlag.de, http://www.hofmann-verlag.de. Ed. Klauspeter Schroeder. Circ: 7,200.

666 NLD
GEMENGDE BRANCHE; vakblad voor de handel in huishoudelijke en luxe artikelen, glas, porselein, aardewerk en kunstnijverheidsartikelen. Text in Dutch. 1948. m. (11/yr.). adv. bk.rev. illus.; tr.lit.
Former titles (until 1978): Vakblad Gemengde Branche; Gemengde Branche (0016-6235)
Indexed: KES.
Published by: Stichting Vakbladen Gemengde en Gespecialiseerde Branches, Postbus 7105, Zoetermeer, 2701 AC, Netherlands. TEL 31-79-321-9251, FAX 31-79-351-4811, stiva@wxs.nl. Eds. Aad van Veldhoven, Rob Antonissen. Adv. contact John Reijpert. B&W page EUR 905.29; bleed 21.4 x 30.1. Circ: 4,587.

GIFTS & DECORATIVE ACCESSORIES; your guide to retaility success. see *GIFTWARE AND TOYS*

666.1 AUT
GLAS. Text in German. 1970 (vol.23). m. EUR 30 domestic; EUR 42 foreign (effective 2005). adv. bk.rev. illus. **Document type:** *Magazine, Trade.*
Former titles: Glas - Oesterreichische Glaserzeitung; Oesterreichische Glaserzeitung (0029-9162)
Published by: (Bundes- und Landesinnungen der Glaser), Oesterreichischer Wirtschaftsverlag GmbH (Subsidiary of: Sueddeutscher Verlag GmbH), Wiedner Hauptstr 120-124, Vienna, W 1051, Austria. TEL 43-1-546640, FAX 43-1-54664406, office@wirtschaftsverlag.at, http://www.wirtschaftsverlag.at. Ed. Birgit Tegtbauer. Adv. contact Hannes Forstner. B&W page EUR 1,582, color page EUR 2,260; trim 185 x 255. Circ: 1,650 (paid and controlled).

GLAS; Architektur und Technik. see *ARCHITECTURE*

666.1 666.5 SWE ISSN 0017-078X
GLAS OCH PORSLIN. Text in Swedish. 1930. bi-m. adv. illus. **Document type:** *Trade.*
Published by: Sveriges Glas- och Porslinshandlarefoerbund (SGPF), Gitarrvaegen, Moelnlycke, 43544, Sweden. TEL 46-31-172640, FAX 46-31-885274, sgpf@tripnet.se, http://www.glasochporslin.se. Eds. Kristian Haneson, Goeran Eklund. Pub. Goeran Eklund. Circ: 800.

666.122 CHE ISSN 0017-0836
GLASBLAESER✶. Text in German. 1947. bi-m. CHF 12, USD 2.80. adv. bk.rev. illus. **Document type:** *Trade.*
Published by: Glasblaeser-Vereinigung, Schuetzenrainweg 10, Riehen, 4125, Switzerland. Ed. Alfred Zollinger. Circ: 200.

666.1 DNK ISSN 0907-1423
GLASMAGASINET. Text in Danish. 1917. q. free to qualified personnel. adv. bk.rev. illus. index. **Document type:** *Bulletin.*

C

Formerly (until 1992): Glarmestertidende (0017-0755)
Published by: (Danish Flat Glass Association), Glasbranche Foreningen, Naverland 2, Glostrup, DK 2600, Denmark. TEL 45-33-322311, FAX 45-33-136560. Ed., R&P, Adv. contact Poul Thorsen TEL 45-43-466323. Circ: 7,500.

666 USA ISSN 1064-900X
GLASS. Text in English. 1979. q. USD 28 domestic; USD 33 in Canada & Mexico; USD 7 newsstand/cover domestic; USD 7.95 newsstand/cover in Canada (effective 2005). adv. **Document type:** *Journal.* **Description:** Provides critical context for glass art within the contemporary art world, including reviews of local, national and international exhibitions, installations, and public art.
Former titles (until 1990): New Glass Work (0898-591X); New Work (0889-6550)
Related titles: Online - full text ed.
Indexed: ArtInd, DAAI.
Published by: Urban Glass, 647 Fulton St, Brooklyn, NY 11217. TEL 718-625-3685, FAX 718-625-3889, urbanglass@aol.com, magazine@urbanglass.org, http://www.urbanglass.org/glass.htm. Ed. Kate Fogarty. Pub. Annette Rose-Shapiro. adv.: B&W page USD 1,576, color page USD 1,888; trim 8.5 x 11.

666.1 GBR ISSN 0017-0984
TP845 CODEN: GLASAT
GLASS (REDHILL); monthly journal of the European glass industry. Text in English. 1923. m. GBP 148 domestic; GBP 180, USD 328 foreign; GBP 26 newsstand/cover (effective Oct. 2004); subscr. includes Glass Directory. adv. **Document type:** *Journal, Trade.* **Description:** Informs professionals in the European glass manufacturing industry. Covers the container, flat, domestic, and specialty glassware sectors.
Related titles: Microform ed.: (from PQC); Online - full text ed.: (from Florida Center for Library Automation, Gale Group); ♦ Supplement(s): Glass Directory (Year).
Indexed: C&ISA, CIN, CerAb, ChemAb, ChemTitl, CorrAb, E&CAJ, EMA, ExcerpMed, IPackAb, ISMEC, Inspec, PST, RefZh, SolStAb, WAA.
—BLDSC (4190.000000), CASDDS, CISTI, Ei, IE, Infotrieve, ingenta, Linda Hall. **CCC.**
Published by: D M G Business Media Ltd. (Subsidiary of: D M G World Media Ltd.), Queensway House, 2 Queensway, Redhill, Surrey RH1 1QS, United Kingdom. TEL 44-1737-768611, FAX 44-1737-855477, info@uk.dmgworldmedia.com, http://www.glassmediaonline.com/, http://www.dmgworldmedia.com/BusinessMediaPublications.html. Ed. John Towers TEL 44-1737-855151. adv.: B&W page GBP 1,296, color page GBP 2,058; trim 210 x 297.

GLASS AGE DIRECTORY. see *BUSINESS AND ECONOMICS—Trade And Industrial Directories*

666 USA ISSN 0361-7610
TP845 CODEN: GLCEAV
➤ **GLASS AND CERAMICS.** Text in English. 1956. m. EUR 3,185, USD 3,245, GBP 1,988 combined subscription to institutions print & online eds. (effective 2005). adv. back issues avail. **Document type:** *Journal, Academic/Scholarly.* **Description:** Reports advances in basic and applied research in glass and ceramic engineering from outstanding Russian scientists.
Related titles: Microfilm ed.: (from PQC); Online - full text ed.: ISSN 1573-8515 (from EBSCO Publishing, Gale Group, IngentaConnect, Kluwer Online, O C L C Online Computer Library Center, Inc., Springer LINK, Swets Information Services); ♦ Translation of: Steklo i Keramika. ISSN 0131-9582.
Indexed: ASCA, AcoustA, BibLing, BrCerAb, C&ISA, Cadscan, CerAb, ChemTitl, CivEngAb, CorrAb, CurCont, E&CAJ, EMA, EngInd, ExcerpMed, IAA, Inspec, LeadAb, M&TEA, MBF, METADEX, MSCI, SolStAb, WAA, Zincscan.
—BLDSC (0412.000000), CASDDS, CISTI, IDS, IE, Infotrieve, ingenta, Linda Hall. **CCC.**
Published by: (Rossiiskaya Akademiya Nauk/Russian Academy of Sciences RUS), Consultants Bureau (Subsidiary of: Springer-Verlag New York, Inc.), 233 Spring St, New York, NY 10013. TEL 212-460-1500, FAX 212-460-1575, service@springer-ny.com, http://springerlink.metapress.com/openurl.asp?genre=journal&issn=0361-7610, http://www.springeronline.com. Ed. L V Sokolova.

666.1 GBR ISSN 0260-6321
GLASS AND GLAZING NEWS. Text in English. 1980. irreg. (3-4/yr.). free. illus. **Document type:** *Newsletter.*
Published by: Glass and Glazing Federation, 44-48 Borough High St, London, SE1 1XB, United Kingdom. TEL 44-171-403-7177. Ed. Catherine Hogan. Circ: 36,500.

666 693 GBR ISSN 0269-0659
GLASS & GLAZING PRODUCTS. Text in English. 1985. m. GBP 30 (effective 1999). back issues avail. **Document type:** *Trade.* **Description:** Contains product updates in glass products for doors and windows.
Indexed: BrCerAb, C&ISA, CerAb, CivEngAb, CorrAb, E&CAJ, EMA, M&TEA, MBF, METADEX, SolStAb, WAA.
Published by: Unity Media Communications Ltd., Stakes House, Quebec Sq, Westerham, Kent TNB16 1UN, United Kingdom. TEL 44-1959-565690, FAX 44-1959-564390, http://www.ggp.co.uk. Ed. Jonathan Brind. Pub. Colin Wilkinson. Circ: 9,300.

GLASS ART SOCIETY JOURNAL. see *ART*

666.1 GBR ISSN 0951-3108
GLASS ASSOCIATION. JOURNAL. Key Title: Journal of the Glass Association. Text in English. biennial. membership. **Document type:** *Trade.* **Description:** Reflects the breadth of interest of current glass studies in the design, social, industrial, and economic contexts of glass, as well as its aesthetic and art historical aspects.
Indexed: DAAI.
Published by: Glass Association, c/o Roger Dodsworth, Broadfield House Glass Museum, Barnett Ln, Kingswinford, W Mids DY6 9QA, United Kingdom. TEL 44-1384-273011, FAX 44-1384-453576. Eds. Ian Wolfenden, Richard Gray.

666.1 CAN ISSN 0843-7041
GLASS CANADA. Text in English. 1989. 6/yr. CND 39 domestic; CND 54 in United States; CND 62 elsewhere (effective 2005). adv. **Document type:** *Magazine, Trade.* **Description:** Serves the needs of Canadian glass, metal, fenestration and autoglass industries.
—CISTI.
Published by: Annex Publishing & Printing, Inc., 222 Argyle Ave, Delhi, ON N4B 2Y2, ON N4B 2Y2, Canada. TEL 519-582-2513, 800-265-2827, FAX 519-582-4040, sfredericks@annexweb.com, http://www.annexweb.com. Circ: 4,742.

666.1 GBR ISSN 0265-9654
NK5100
GLASS CONE. Text in English. s-a. membership.
Published by: Glass Association, c/o Roger Dodsworth, Broadfield House Glass Museum, Barnett Ln, Kingswinford, W Mids DY6 9QA, United Kingdom. TEL 0384-273011, FAX 0384-453576. Ed. Charles Hajdamach.

666 380.1 USA ISSN 0017-1018
TP845 CODEN: GLDIAE
GLASS DIGEST; trade magazine serving the flat glass, architectural metal and allied products industry. Text in English. 1922. 13/yr. USD 50 domestic (effective 2005). adv. charts; illus.; mkt.; stat.; tr.lit. reprint service avail. from PQC. **Document type:** *Magazine, Trade.* **Description:** Aims at flat glass, architectural metal and allied product industry.
Formerly: Glaziers Journal
Related titles: Microform ed.: (from PQC).
Indexed: CIN, ChemAb, ChemTitl, EngInd.
—CASDDS, CISTI, Ei. **CCC.**
Published by: Ashlee Publishing Co., Inc., 18 E 41st St, 20th Fl, New York, NY 10017-6222. FAX 212-376-7723, http://www.glassdigestmagazine.com, http://www.ashlee.com. Ed. Julian Phillips. Pub. Jordan Wright. adv.: B&W page USD 1,815, color page USD 3,215. Circ: 15,500 (paid).

666 669 USA
GLASS DIGEST BUYER'S GUIDE. Text in English. 1958. a. USD 35 (effective 2000); included with Glass Digest. adv. **Document type:** *Catalog, Trade.*
Former titles: International Glass - Metal Catalog (0147-300X); (until 1973): Glass-Metal Catalog (0072-4645); Glass-Metal Directory
Published by: Ashlee Publishing Co., Inc., 18 E 41st St, 20th Fl, New York, NY 10017-6222. TEL 212-376-7722, FAX 212-376-7723. Ed. Julian Phillips. Circ: 15,000.

666.1 GBR
GLASS DIRECTORY (YEAR). Text in English. a. (Feb.). GBP 174 per issue domestic; GBP 183, USD 330 per issue foreign (effective 2005). **Document type:** *Directory, Trade.*
Related titles: ♦ Supplement to: Glass (Redhill). ISSN 0017-0984; ♦ Supplement to: Glass International. ISSN 0143-7836.
Published by: D M G Business Media Ltd. (Subsidiary of: D M G World Media Ltd.), Queensway House, 2 Queensway, Redhill, Surrey RH1 1QS, United Kingdom. TEL 44-1737-768611, FAX 44-1737-855477, info@uk.dmgworldmedia.com, http://www.dmgworldmedia.com/BusinessMediaPublications.html.

GLASS FACTORY DIRECTORY OF NORTH AMERICA AND U.S. INDUSTRY FACTBOOK. see *BUSINESS AND ECONOMICS—Trade And Industrial Directories*

666 USA ISSN 0017-1026
TP845 CODEN: GLINAK
GLASS INDUSTRY. Text in English. 1920. m. USD 50 in North America; USD 60 elsewhere (effective 1999 - 2000). adv. bk.rev. illus.; pat.; stat. index. Supplement avail.; reprint service avail. from PQC. **Document type:** *Trade.* **Description:** Contains news about the glass industry.
Related titles: Microform ed.: (from PQC); Online - full text ed.: (from Florida Center for Library Automation, Gale Group, H.W. Wilson, O C L C Online Computer Library Center, Inc.).
Indexed: AS&TI, BrCerAb, C&ISA, CerAb, CorrAb, E&CAJ, EMA, EngInd, IPackAb, ISMEC, ISR, PROMT, SolStAb, WAA.
—BLDSC (4191.000000), CASDDS, CISTI, Ei, IE, Infotrieve, Linda Hall. **CCC.**
Published by: Ashlee Publishing Co., Inc., 18 E 41st St, 20th Fl, New York, NY 10017-6222. TEL 212-376-7722, FAX 212-376-7723. Ed. Julian Phillips. Circ: 2,700 (paid).

666.1 330 ITA ISSN 1129-3403
GLASS INDUSTRY AGENTS & REPRESENTATIVES WORLD GUIDE. Text in Italian. 1995. a., latest vol.7, 2001. **Document type:** *Directory, Trade.* **Description:** Gives a complete overview of international agents and representatives working in the glass industry, both alphabetically and by country. Includes full address, officers' names, annual sales volume, number of employees, percentage of turnover from glass, company founded, capital, address of local branches, companies represented, and countries where acting as an agent.
Published by: Artech Publishing Srl, Via Gramsci 63, Cormano, MI 20032, Italy. TEL 39-02-6630-2904, FAX 39-02-6630-2914, artech@glassonline.com, http://www.glassonline.com.

666 GBR ISSN 0143-7836
CODEN: GLINDN
GLASS INTERNATIONAL. Text in English. 1978. bi-m. GBP 121 domestic; GBP 172, USD 313 foreign; GBP 36 newsstand/cover (effective Oct. 2004); subscr. includes Glass Directory. adv. **Document type:** *Magazine, Trade.* **Description:** Covers the glass manufacturing industry worldwide.
Related titles: Online - full text ed.: (from Florida Center for Library Automation, Gale Group); ♦ Supplement(s): Glass Directory (Year).
Indexed: EngInd, IPackAb, Inspec.
—BLDSC (4191.150000), CASDDS, IE, Infotrieve, ingenta. **CCC.**
Published by: D M G Business Media Ltd. (Subsidiary of: D M G World Media Ltd.), Queensway House, 2 Queensway, Redhill, Surrey RH1 1QS, United Kingdom. TEL 44-1737-768611, FAX 44-1737-855477, info@uk.dmgworldmedia.com, http://www.glassmediaonline.com/, http://www.dmgworldmedia.com/BusinessMediaPublications.html. Ed. John Towers TEL 44-1737-855151. adv.: B&W page GBP 2,799, color page GBP 3,753; trim 210 x 297.

666 USA
GLASS: LATIN AMERICAN INDUSTRIAL REPORT✶. (Avail. for each of 22 Latin American countries) Text in English. 1985. a. USD 435; per country report.
Published by: Aquino Productions, P O Box 15760, Stamford, CT 06901-0760. Ed. Andres C Aquino.

666.1 USA
GLASS LINE NEWSLETTER. Text in English. 1987 (Apr.). bi-m. USD 25 domestic; USD 35 in Canada & Mexico; USD 45 elsewhere (effective 2005). **Document type:** *Newsletter, Trade.* **Description:** Covers topics for hot glass artists.
Related titles: Online - full content ed.
Published by: Glass Line, PO Box 847, Hungtington Beach, CA 92648-0847. TEL 714-520-0121, FAX 714-520-4370, editor@hotglass.com, http://www.hotglass.com. Ed. Jim Thingwold.

666.1 ITA ISSN 0394-9893
GLASS MACHINERY PLANTS & ACCESSORIES; bi-monthly glass industry international magazine. Text in English. 1988. bi-m. EUR 62 domestic; EUR 130 foreign (effective 2005). adv. illus. back issues avail. **Document type:** *Magazine, Trade.* **Description:** For glassworkers involved in production and processing of hollow and pressed glass: bottles and containers, household, lighting, technical, scientific, medical and industrial glassware.
—BLDSC (4191.230000), IE, ingenta.
Published by: Artech Publishing Srl, Via Gramsci 63, Cormano, MI 20032, Italy. TEL 39-02-6630-2904, FAX 39-02-6630-2914, artech@glassonline.com, http://www.glassonline.com. Ed. Marco Pinetti. Adv. contact Steven Trow.

338.4 666.1 USA ISSN 0747-4261
HD9623.U44
GLASS MAGAZINE. Text in English. 1948. m. USD 34.95 domestic; USD 44.95 foreign (effective 2004). adv. **Document type:** *Magazine, Trade.* **Description:** Serves the architectural glass industry, architectural metal, building, remodeling, and related architectural industries. Reports the latest industry developments, technical information, management strategies, and new product information.
Formerly: Glass Dealer (0094-3746)
Related titles: Online - full text ed.
Indexed: ArtInd, DAAI.
—CISTI, IE.
Published by: National Glass Association, 8200 Greensboro Dr, Ste 302, McLean, VA 22102-3881. TEL 703-442-4890, FAX 703-442-0630, editorialinfo@glass.org, http://www.glass.org. Ed. Charles Cumpston. Pub., R&P Nicole Harris. Adv. contact Jeff Smith. B&W page USD 2,965, color page USD 4,490. Circ: 21,000 (paid and controlled).

666.1 USA
GLASS NEW ENGLAND. Text in English. 1980. q. USD 16. adv. bk.rev. charts; illus.; pat.; stat.; tr.lit. **Document type:** *Magazine, Trade.* **Description:** Covers news for companies engaged in the manufacture, sale, installation, distribution, fabrication, replacement and repair of glass products in the architectural, window, automotive and speciality glass industry.
Formerly (until 1999): The Glass Scene

Published by: Glass Quality Installers Cooperative, PO Box 389, Franklin, MA 02038-0389. TEL 508-528-6211, FAX 508-528-6211. Ed. J A Kruza. adv.: B&W page USD 750; trim 11 x 8.5. Circ: 1,000 (paid).

666.1 NOR ISSN 0802-295X
GLASS OG FASADE. Text in Norwegian. 1974. q. NOK 360 (effective 2002). adv.
Formerly (until 1987): Glassmesteren (0802-2968)
Published by: Glassbransjeforbundet i Norge, c/o Per Pettersen, Vitaminveien 9, Oslo, 0485, Norway. TEL 47-22-09-17-00, FAX 47-22-09-17-09, http://www.gbf.as/glasogfas/glasofa.htm. Eds. Boerre Lund TEL 47-67-58-20-37, Per Pettersen TEL 47-22-09-17-00. Adv. contact Geir Berntsen TEL 47-62-94-10-33. Circ: 4,205.

738.4 USA ISSN 1083-6888
NK4997
➤ **GLASS ON METAL**; the enamelist's magazine. Text in English. 1982. 5/yr. USD 45 domestic; USD 52 in Canada & Mexico; USD 59.10 in Europe; USD 62.50 elsewhere. adv. bk.rev. illus.; tr.lit. cum. index: vols. 1-14. 24 p./no.; back issues avail.; reprints avail. **Document type:** *Magazine, Academic/Scholarly.* **Description:** Covers the history of enameling, contemporary uses, people and places, techniques, technology, and research on new products.
Indexed: ABM, ArtInd.
Published by: Enamelist Society, PO Box 310, Newport, KY 41072. TEL 606-291-3800, FAX 606-291-1849, http://www.craftweb.com/org/enamel/enamel.htm. Ed., R&P, Adv. contact Tom Ellis. B&W page USD 600, color page USD 1,000. Circ: 1,100 (paid).

➤ **GLASS PATTERNS QUARTERLY.** see *ARTS AND HANDICRAFTS*

666.1 RUS ISSN 1087-6596
TP845 CODEN: GPHCEE
➤ **GLASS PHYSICS AND CHEMISTRY.** Text in Russian. 1975. bi-m. EUR 2,058, USD 1,880, GBP 1,285 combined subscription to institutions print & online eds. (effective 2005). back issues avail. **Document type:** *Journal, Academic/Scholarly.* **Description:** Documents advances in the understanding of the structure, physical and chemical properties, and nature of inorganic glasses and glass-forming melts.
Formerly (until 1994): Soviet Journal of Glass Physics and Chemistry (0360-5043)
Related titles: Microfilm ed.: (from PQC); Online - full text ed.: ISSN 1608-313X (from EBSCO Publishing, IngentaConnect, Kluwer Online, O C L C Online Computer Library Center, Inc., Springer LINK, Swets Information Services); ◆ Translation of: Fizika i Khimiya Stekla. ISSN 0132-6651.
Indexed: ASCA, BibLing, CCI, CIN, ChemAb, ChemTitl, EngInd, Inspec, MSB, MSCI.
—BLDSC (0412.012000), AskIEEE, CASDDS, CISTI, Ei, IDS, IE, Infotrieve, ingenta, Linda Hall. **CCC.**
Published by: (Rossiiskaya Akademiya Nauk/Russian Academy of Sciences), M A I K Nauka - Interperiodica, Profsoyuznaya ul 90, Moscow, 117997, Russian Federation. TEL 7-095-3347420, FAX 7-095-3360666, compmg@maik.ru, http://www.maik.ru/journals/physglas.htm. Ed. Vladimir Ya Shevchenko. **Subscr. to:** Springer-Verlag Dordrecht, Journals Department, PO Box 322, Dordrecht, Netherlands. TEL 31-78-6576392, FAX 31-78-6576474.

666.1 USA ISSN 1077-517X
GLASS REFLECTIONS. Text in English. 1983. q. USD 20 domestic; USD 40 foreign (effective 2000). **Document type:** *Newsletter, Consumer.*
Published by: Glass Association of North America, 2945 S W Wanamaker Dr, Ste A, Topeka, KS 66611-5321. TEL 785-266-7013, FAX 785-266-0272. Ed. Kimberly Gerlach. R&P Alice Birch. Adv. contact Joan Anderson. Circ: 500.

666.1 DEU
TP845 CODEN: GLBEAQ
➤ **GLASS SCIENCE AND TECHNOLOGY.** Text in English. 1923. bi-m. EUR 299 (effective 2005). adv. bk.rev. abstr.; bibl.; charts; illus.; pat. index, cum.index: vols.1-30, 31-40, 41-50. 50 p./no. 2 cols./p.; back issues avail. **Document type:** *Journal, Academic/Scholarly.* **Description:** News about glass science and technology.
Former titles (until 2001): Glass Science and Technology - Glastechnische Berichte (0946-7475); (until 1994): Glastechnische Berichte (0017-1085)
Related titles: ◆ German ed.: D G G Journal. ISSN 1618-8721.
Indexed: A&ATA, ASCA, B&BAb, BrCerAb, C&ISA, CCI, CIN, CISA, CerAb, ChemAb, ChemTitl, CivEngAb, CorrAb, CurCont, E&CAJ, EMA, EngInd, IAA, INIS AtomInd, IPackAb, ISMEC, ISR, Inspec, M&TEA, MBF, METADEX, MSCI, RefZh, SCI, SolStAb, WAA.
—BLDSC (4192.060000), AskIEEE, CASDDS, CISTI, Ei, IDS, IE, ingenta, Linda Hall. **CCC.**
Published by: Deutsche Glastechnische Gesellschaft e.V., Siemensstr 45, Offenbach, 63071, Germany. TEL 49-69-9758610, FAX 49-69-97586199, dgg@hvg-dgg.de, gtb@hvg-dgg.de, http://www.hvg-dgg.de/en/dgg/zeitschr.htm. Ed. H A Schaeffer. adv.: B&W page EUR 956.12, color page EUR 1,661.70; trim 171 x 250. Circ: 2,000.

666.1 NLD ISSN 0927-4472
CODEN: GSTEEX
➤ **GLASS SCIENCE AND TECHNOLOGY.** Text in English. 1977. irreg., latest vol.14, 1993. price varies. **Document type:** *Monographic series, Academic/Scholarly.* **Description:** Examines research and topics in glass science and technology, along with other areas of ceramic engineering.
Indexed: CIN, ChemAb, ChemTitl, Inspec.
—CASDDS.
Published by: Elsevier BV (Subsidiary of: Elsevier Science & Technology), Radarweg 29, Amsterdam, 1043 NX, Netherlands. TEL 31-20-4853911, FAX 31-20-4852457, nlinfo-f@elsevier.nl, http://www.elsevier.nl.

666.1 ITA ISSN 1129-3950
GLASS STYLE. Text in English. 1998. s-a. EUR 26 domestic; EUR 44 foreign (effective 2005). illus. back issues avail. **Document type:** *Magazine, Trade.* **Description:** Covers the art, design, industry and sale and marketing of glass and crystal products. Includes information about product collections from all over the world, the use of glass throughout history, glass in paintings, news regarding glassworks, books, exhibitions, competitions, designer profiles, showrooms, innovations, glass projects and new applications. Aimed at producers, decorators, distributors, buyers, architects, and designers.
Published by: Artech Publishing Srl, Via Gramsci 63, Cormano, MI 20032, Italy. TEL 39-02-6630-2904, FAX 39-02-6630-2914, artech@glassonline.com, http://www.glassonline.com.

666.1 ITA ISSN 1126-8573
GLASS TECHNOLOGY INTERNATIONAL. Text in English. 1989. bi-m. EUR 62 domestic; EUR 130 foreign (effective 2005). adv. back issues avail. **Document type:** *Magazine, Trade.* **Description:** For people involved in the flat and bent glass industry. Covers technology, new products, company life, and all innovations in the world of flat glass. Includes a supplier's guide.
Former titles (until 1993): Glasstech International (1128-7233); (until 1992): Automotive Glass (1120-6748)
—BLDSC (4192.150000), IE, ingenta.
Published by: Artech Publishing Srl, Via Gramsci 63, Cormano, MI 20032, Italy. TEL 39-02-6630-2904, FAX 39-02-6630-2914, artech@glassonline.com, http://www.glassonline.com. Ed. Marco Pinetti. Adv. contact Steven Trow.

GLASS WORKSHOP. see *ARTS AND HANDICRAFTS*

666.1 330 ITA
GLASSONLINE WEEKLY WORLD NEWS & FINANCIAL REPORTS. Text in English. 1996. w. USD 120 (effective 2001); Includes World Yellow Pages. **Document type:** *Bulletin, Trade.*
Media: Online - full text.
Published by: Artech Publishing Srl, Via Gramsci 63, Cormano, MI 20032, Italy. TEL 39-02-6630-2904, FAX 39-02-6630-2914, artech@glassonline.com, http://www.glassonline.com.

666.1 330 ITA
GLASSONLINE WORLD YELLOW PAGES. Text in English. 1996. irreg. USD 120 (effective 2001); Includes Weekly World News & Financial Reports. **Document type:** *Directory, Trade.* **Description:** Provides a comprehensive list of glass companies throughout the world.
Media: Online - full text.
Published by: Artech Publishing Srl, Via Gramsci 63, Cormano, MI 20032, Italy. TEL 39-02-6630-2904, FAX 39-02-6630-2914, artech@glassonline.com, http://www.glassonline.com.

666 SWE
▼ **GLASTEKNISK TIDSKRIFT.** Text in English, Swedish. 2003. irreg. **Document type:** *Trade.*
Media: Online - full content.
Published by: Glasforskningsinstitutet (Glafo)/Glass Research Institute, PO Box 3093, Vaexjoe, 35033, Sweden. TEL 46-470-10090, FAX 46-470-40063, info@glafo.se, http://www.glafo.se/bibliotek/glasteknisk_tidskrift.htm.

666.1 DEU ISSN 0017-1107
GLASWELT; Fachmagazin fuer Glas, Fenster, Fassade und Bauelemente. Text in German. 1947. m. EUR 104.40; EUR 13 newsstand/cover (effective 2005). adv. bk.rev. charts; illus.; pat.; tr.lit. index. **Document type:** *Magazine, Trade.*
Formerly: Glaswelt
Related titles: Online - full text ed.
Indexed: ChemAb, IBR.
—CISTI. **CCC.**
Published by: Gentner Verlag Stuttgart, Forststr 131, Stuttgart, 70193, Germany. TEL 49-711-636720, FAX 49-711-63672747, gentner@gentnerverlag.de, http://www.glaswelt-net.de, http://www.gentnerverlag.de. Ed. Hilmar Dueppel. Adv. contact Angela Gruessner. B&W page EUR 1,590, color page EUR 2,520. Circ: 5,748 (paid and controlled).

666 GBR ISSN 0261-0329
GLAZED EXPRESSIONS. Text in English. 1981. 2/yr. GBP 18 in United Kingdom to individuals; GBP 24 elsewhere to individuals; GBP 24 in United Kingdom to institutions; GBP 30 elsewhere to institutions (effective Jul. 2001). bk.rev. illus. **Document type:** *Bulletin.* **Description:** News, research and features pertaining to tiles and architectural ceramics.
Indexed: ABM, AIAP, BrCerAb, C&ISA, CerAb, CorrAb, DAAI, E&CAJ, EMA, SolStAb, WAA.
Published by: Tiles & Architectural Ceramics Society, Liverpool Museum, William Brown St, Liverpool, Merseyside L3 8EN, United Kingdom. TEL 44-151-2070001. Ed. Hans van Lemmen. Circ: 500.

666 GBR ISSN 1368-0099
GLOBAL CERAMIC REVIEW. Text in English. 1966. q. GBP 60 domestic; GBP 88 foreign (effective 2001). adv. bk.rev.; software rev.; Website rev. charts; illus.; pat.; tr.lit. 56 p./no. 2 cols./p.; back issues avail.; reprints avail. **Document type:** *Journal, Trade.* **Description:** Concentrates on ceramic production technology for all sectors of the industry. Features articles on applied technology, case histories, personnel moves, a calendar of events, a quarterly round-up of ceramic industry patents, and information on suppliers.
Formerly (until 1991): British Ceramic Review (0306-7076)
Indexed: BrCerAb, C&ISA, CerAb, CivEngAb, CorrAb, E&CAJ, EMA, M&TEA, MBF, METADEX, RefZh, SolStAb, WAA.
—BLDSC (4195.358300), CISTI, IE, Linda Hall.
Published by: Write Angle Press, 44 Kingsway, Stoke-on-Trent, Staffs ST4 1JH, United Kingdom. TEL 44-1782-411433, FAX 44-1782-747061, sales@global-ceramic.com, charles.wallin@btclick.com, http://www.global-ceramic.com. Ed. Charles R Wallin. R&P Charles Wallin. adv.: B&W page GBP 710, color page GBP 1,330; trim 210 x 297. Circ: 5,000 (paid and controlled).

GROUPE INTERNATIONAL D'ETUDE DE LA CERAMIQUE EGYPTIENNE. BULLETIN DE LIAISON. see *ARCHAEOLOGY*

GUIA GENERAL DE LAS INDUSTRIAS CERAMICAS Y AFINES DE ESPANA. see *BUSINESS AND ECONOMICS—Trade And Industrial Directories*

HANDBOOK FOR CERAMIC TILE INSTALLATION. see *BUILDING AND CONSTRUCTION*

666 KOR
HAN'GUG YO'EOB HAGHOE YOEOB/KOREAN CERAMIC SOCIETY. BULLETIN. Text in Korean. q. **Document type:** *Bulletin, Academic/Scholarly.*
Published by: Han'gug Yo'eob Haghoe/Korean Ceramic Society, Meorijae Bldg., Suite # 403, 984-1, Bangbae-3dong, Seocho-gu, Seoul, 137-849, Korea, S. TEL 82-2-5840185, FAX 82-2-5864582, http://www.ceramics.or.kr/, http://www.ceramics.or.kr/main.jsp.

666 CHN ISSN 1003-319X
HEBEI TAOCI/HEBEI CERAMICS. Text in Chinese. 1973. q. USD 15.
Published by: Hebei Taoci Gongye Keji Qingbaozhan/Hebei Scientific and Technical Information Centre of Ceramic Industry, Taoci Yanjiusuo, Tangshan, Hebei 063020, China. TEL 71414. Ed. Liu Deli. adv.: B&W page USD 1,000, color page USD 1,500. Circ: 1,200.

HEISEY NEWS. see *ANTIQUES*

666 USA ISSN 1045-2397
HIGH TECH CERAMICS NEWS. Text in English. 1989 (Jan.). m. USD 500 domestic; USD 550 foreign; USD 45 newsstand/cover domestic; USD 50 newsstand/cover foreign (effective 2005). back issues avail.; reprints avail. **Document type:** *Newsletter, Trade.* **Description:** Provides current analysis of new products, patents and industry trends. Written for materials companies and materials scientists.
Related titles: Online - full text ed.: (from bigchalk, Data-Star, Factiva, Gale Group, LexisNexis, Northern Light Technology, Inc., The Dialog Corporation).
Indexed: BrCerAb, C&ISA, CerAb, CivEngAb, CorrAb, E&CAJ, EMA, IAA, M&TEA, MBF, METADEX, SolStAb, WAA.
—BLDSC (4307.361055), Linda Hall. **CCC.**
Published by: Business Communications Co., Inc., 25 Van Zant St, Ste 13, Norwalk, CT 06855-1781. TEL 203-853-4266, FAX 203-853-0348, info@bccresearch.com, http://www.buscom.com/letters/htcnpromo/htcnpromo.html, http://www.bccresearch.com. Eds. Thomas Abraham, Alan Hall. Pub. Louis Naturman.

HISTORIC ILLINOIS POTTERIES CIRCULAR SERIES. see *ARCHAEOLOGY*

HOBSTAR. see *ANTIQUES*

I G B C E MAGAZIN. see *ENGINEERING—Chemical Engineering*

I M F NEWSLETTER. (Industrial Materials for the Future) see *ENGINEERING—Industrial Engineering*

I M M E BOLETIN. see *ENGINEERING—Civil Engineering*

IBIDEN COMPANY. ANNUAL REPORT. see *CHEMISTRY*

C

▼ *new title* ➤ *refereed* ✶ *unverified* ◆ *full entry avail.*

666 IND ISSN 0371-750X
TP785 CODEN: TICSAP
➤ **INDIAN CERAMIC SOCIETY. TRANSACTIONS.** Text in English. 1942. q. INR 400, USD 50 (effective 2003). adv. bk.rev. bibl.; charts; illus. reprint service avail. from PQC. **Document type:** *Journal, Academic/Scholarly.* **Description:** Devoted to the advancement of ceramic science, arts and technologies.
Related titles: Microfiche ed.: (from PQC).
Indexed: AnalAb, BrCerAb, C&ISA, CRIA, CRICC, CerAb, ChemAb, CivEngAb, CorrAb, E&CAJ, EMA, IAA, INIS AtomInd, M&TEA, MBF, METADEX, SolStAb, WAA.
—BLDSC (8937.000000), CASDDS, CISTI, IE, ingenta, Linda Hall.
Published by: Indian Ceramic Society, c/o Central Glass and Ceramic Research Institute, Kolkata, West Bengal 700 032, India. TEL 91-33-473-3496, FAX 91-33-413-8878, incers@cal2.vsnl.net.in. Ed., R&P B N Samaddar. Adv. contact Tapan Chakraborty. Circ: 1,500.

666 IND ISSN 0019-4492
NK3700 CODEN: IDCMAL
INDIAN CERAMICS. Text in English. 1938-1988 (Aug.); resumed 1994. q. INR 450, USD 100. bk.rev. abstr.; charts; tr.lit.; stat. index. **Document type:** *Academic/Scholarly.* **Description:** Covers glass, cement, refractory, pottery, oxides, abrasive, fine ceramics and special ceramics.
Indexed: BrCerAb, C&ISA, CIN, CRIA, CRICC, CerAb, ChemAb, ChemTitl, CorrAb, E&CAJ, EMA, M&TEA, METADEX, SolStAb, WAA.
—CASDDS, CISTI, Linda Hall.
Address: 10 Sourin Roy Rd., Behala, Kolkata, West Bengal 700 034, India. TEL 91-33-478-9101, FAX 91-33-468-2612. Ed., R&P Ambar Roy. adv.: page USD 100; 180 x 220. Circ: 500.

C

666 ITA ISSN 1121-7588
TP785 CODEN: INCEE3
➤ **INDUSTRIAL CERAMICS.** Text in English. 1981. 3/yr. EUR 430 (effective 2002). adv. bk.rev. pat.; stat.; tr.lit.; illus. back issues avail. **Document type:** *Newsletter, Trade.* **Description:** Covers fine ceramics, heavy clay products and refractories. Includes activities of research labs throughout the world.
Formerly (until 1986): C I News (0392-2960)
Related titles: Online - full text ed.
Indexed: ASCA, BrCerAb, C&ISA, CBNB, CIN, CerAb, ChemAb, ChemTitl, CivEngAb, CorrAb, E&CAJ, EMA, EngInd, IAA, Inspec, M&TEA, MBF, METADEX, MSCI, SolStAb, WAA.
—BLDSC (4447.080000), AskIEEE, CASDDS, CISTI, Ei, IDS, IE, Infotrieve, ingenta, Linda Hall.
Published by: Techna s.r.l., Casella Postale, 174, Faenza, RA 48018, Italy. TEL 39-546-22461, FAX 39-546-664138. Ed. Pietro Vincenzini. Adv. contact Gianantonio Bertoni. B&W page EUR 1,300, color page EUR 1,600; trim 297 x 210. Circ: 4,000.

666 FRA ISSN 1169-873X
CODEN: INCVEK
L'INDUSTRIE CERAMIQUE ET VERRIERE. Text in English, French. 1903. m. (except Aug.). EUR 149 domestic; EUR 189 foreign (effective 2005). adv. bk.rev. abstr.; bibl.; charts; illus.; stat.; tr.lit. index. **Document type:** *Trade.* **Description:** Covers the fields of ceramic and glass-works.
Formerly (until 1993): Industrie Ceramique (0019-9044); Incorporating (1948-1981): Societe Francaise de Ceramique. Bulletin (0037-931X); (1972-1981): Societe Francaise de Ceramique. Traductions Brevets
Indexed: BrCerAb, C&ISA, CIN, CISA, Cadscan, CerAb, ChemAb, ChemTitl, CivEngAb, CorrAb, E&CAJ, EMA, EngInd, ExcerpMed, IAA, INIS AtomInd, Inspec, LeadAb, M&TEA, MBF, METADEX, MSB, RefZh, SolStAb, WAA, Zincscan.
—BLDSC (4465.050000), CASDDS, CISTI, Ei, IE, Infotrieve, ingenta, Linda Hall. **CCC.**
Published by: Septima, 14 rue Falguiere, Paris, 75015, France. TEL 33-01-44384800, FAX 33-01-44384809. Ed. Catherine Boisaubert. Adv. contact Claire Grau. B&W page EUR 719.56, color page EUR 1,428.45; trim 185 x 270. Circ: 2,500.

666 DEU ISSN 0020-5214
TP785 CODEN: ITCRAC
INTERCERAM; international ceramic review. Text in English; Abstracts in French, German, Spanish. 1951. 6/yr. EUR 218.50 (effective 2004). adv. **Document type:** *Magazine, Trade.* **Description:** Focuses on research and development, innovative technology, new products, market analyses, company profiles, and information about conferences, symposiums and fairs.
Indexed: BrCerAb, C&ISA, CRIA, CerAb, ChemAb, CivEngAb, CorrAb, E&CAJ, EMA, EngInd, IAA, M&TEA, MBF, METADEX, RefZh, SolStAb, WAA.
—BLDSC (4532.000000), CASDDS, CISTI, Ei, IE, Infotrieve, ingenta, Linda Hall. **CCC.**
Published by: D V S Verlag GmbH, Aachener Str 172, Duesseldorf, 40223, Germany. TEL 49-211-15910, FAX 49-211-1591150, verlag@dvs-hg.de, http://www.dvs-verlag.de/de/zeit/ic/. Ed. Paul-Eberhard Keilbar. Adv. contact Iris Jansen. B&W page EUR 2,772, color page EUR 3,772; trim 185 x 261. Circ: 9,500 (paid and controlled).

666 GBR ISSN 1474-4996
INTERNATIONAL CEMENT AND LIME JOURNAL. Text in English. s-a. GBP 50 combined subscription domestic print & online eds.; USD 95 combined subscription foreign print & online eds. (effective 2004). **Document type:** *Journal.*
Formerly (until 2000): International Cement Journal (1365-9219)
Related titles: Online - full text ed.: (from Gale Group).
—CCC.
Published by: Euromoney Institutional Investor Plc., Nestor House, Playhouse Yard, London, EC4V 5EX, United Kingdom. TEL 44-20-7779-8673, FAX 44-20-7779-8541, http://www.euromoneyplc.com. Ed. Juliet Hoskins TEL 44-20-77798261. Adv. contact John Threlfall TEL 44-20-77798664. **Subscr. to:** Eclipse, The In-house Fulfillment Bureau, PO Box 18083, London EC4V 5JS, United Kingdom. TEL 44-20-7779-8610, FAX 44-20-7779-8602, CustomerService@euromoneyplc.com.

666 GBR ISSN 0266-9374
INTERNATIONAL CERAMIC DIRECTORY. Text in English. 1984. quinquennial. GBP 88. **Document type:** *Directory.* **Description:** Lists all ceramic manufacturers from brick and tile to pottery worldwide, containing descriptions, directions and products. Does not include refractory manufacturers.
Published by: London and Sheffield Publishing Co. Ltd., 291 Cricklewood Ln, Childs Hill, London, NW2 2JL, United Kingdom. TEL 44-181-455-9962, FAX 44-181-209-1231.

666 GBR ISSN 1361-7605
INTERNATIONAL CERAMICS. Text in English. s-a. GBP 50 combined subscription domestic print & online eds.; USD 95 combined subscription elsewhere print & online eds. (effective 2004). **Document type:** *Journal, Academic/Scholarly.*
Related titles: Online - full text ed.: (from Gale Group, ProQuest Information & Learning).
Indexed: ABIn.
—CCC.
Published by: Euromoney Institutional Investor Plc., Nestor House, Playhouse Yard, London, EC4V 5EX, United Kingdom. TEL 44-20-7779-8673, FAX 44-20-7779-8541, http://www.international-ceramics.com, http://www.euromoneyplc.com. Ed. Roger Kent TEL 44-114-2365461. Adv. contact John Salt TEL 44-20-77798111. **Subscr. to:** Eclipse, The In-house Fulfillment Bureau, PO Box 18083, London EC4V 5JS, United Kingdom. TEL 44-20-7779-8610, FAX 44-20-7779-8602, CustomerService@euromoneyplc.com.

666 ITA ISSN 1123-8216
INTERNATIONAL CERAMICS JOURNAL. Text in English. 1978. 6/yr. EUR 46 domestic; EUR 89 foreign (effective 2004). adv. **Document type:** *Magazine, Trade.* **Description:** Disseminates information on traditional and new Italian technology in the area of plant, machinery, equipment, raw materials and products for the ceramic sector.
Related titles: Online - full text ed.: ISSN 1593-2060. 1998.
Indexed: BrCerAb, RefZh.
Published by: Gruppo Editoriale Faenza Editrice SpA, Via Pier de Crescenzi 44, Faenza, RA 48018, Italy. TEL 39-0546-670411, FAX 39-0546-660440, info@faenza.com, http://www.faenza.com. Ed. Franco Rossi. Adv. contact Elvio Neri. Circ: 3,297.

INTERNATIONAL DIRECTORY OF DESIGN. see *ART*

666.1 ITA ISSN 1123-5063
INTERNATIONAL GLASS JOURNAL. Text in English. 1937. q. EUR 62 domestic; EUR 76 foreign (effective 2004). **Document type:** *Magazine, Trade.*
Formerly (until 1993): Vetro Informazione (0392-8241)
Indexed: EngInd.
—CINDOC, Ei, Linda Hall.
Published by: Gruppo Editoriale Faenza Editrice SpA, Via Pier de Crescenzi 44, Faenza, RA 48018, Italy. TEL 39-0546-670411, FAX 39-0546-660440, info@faenza.com, http://www.faenza.com. Ed. Franco Roni. Circ: 3,750.

666.1 GBR ISSN 1359-4974
TP845 CODEN: IGREFU
INTERNATIONAL GLASS REVIEW. Text in English. 1995. s-a. GBP 50 combined subscription domestic print & online eds.; USD 95 combined subscription foreign print & online eds. (effective 2004). adv. **Document type:** *Magazine, Trade.*
Related titles: Online - full text ed.: (from Florida Center for Library Automation, Gale Group, O C L C Online Computer Library Center, Inc., ProQuest Information & Learning).
Indexed: ABIn, CIN, ChemAb, ChemTitl.
—CASDDS. **CCC.**
Published by: Euromoney Institutional Investor Plc., Nestor House, Playhouse Yard, London, EC4V 5EX, United Kingdom. TEL 44-20-77798888, FAX 44-20-77798760, http://www.internationalglassreview.com, http://www.euromoney.com. Ed. Matt MacAllan TEL 44-20-77798106. **Dist. in US by:** American Educational Systems, PO Box 246, New York, NY 10024-0246. TEL 800-431-1579.

671.72029 GBR
INTERNATIONAL REFRACTORIES HANDBOOK & DIRECTORY. Text in English. 1976. triennial. GBP 86 (effective 1999). **Document type:** *Directory.* **Description:** Comprehensive list of names, addresses, telephone and fax numbers, and products of all refractory manufacturers and engineers worldwide.
Published by: London and Sheffield Publishing Co. Ltd., 291 Cricklewood Ln, Childs Hill, London, NW2 2JL, United Kingdom. TEL 44-181-455-9962, FAX 44-181-209-1231.

ISENKRAMBRANCHEN. see *INTERIOR DESIGN AND DECORATION—Furniture And House Furnishings*

666 JPN ISSN 0916-4553
JAPAN FINE CERAMICS CENTER REVIEW. Abbreviated title: J F C C Review. Text in Japanese. 1989. a. **Document type:** *Academic/Scholarly.*
Indexed: C&ISA, CerAb, CorrAb, E&CAJ, EMA, SolStAb, WAA.
—BLDSC (4668.387200).
Published by: Fain Seramikkusu Senta/Japan Fine Ceramics Center, 2-4-1 Mutsuno Atsuka-ku, Nagoya, Aichi-ken 456-8587, Japan. TEL 81-52-871-3500, FAX 81-52-871-3505, http://www.jfcc.or.jp/.

666.5 CHN ISSN 1001-9545
JINGDEZHEN TAOCI/JINGDEZHEN CERAMICS. Text in Chinese. q.
Related titles: Online - full text ed.: (from East View Information Services).
Published by: Jiangxi Sheng Taoci Yanjiusuo/Jiangxi Ceramics Research Institute, Zhangshusha, Jingdezhen Dongjiao (East Suburb), Jiangxi 333001, China. TEL 225514. Ed. Wang Deji. **Co-sponsor:** Jiangxi Sheng Taoci Keji Qingbao Zhan.

666.5 CHN ISSN 1000-2278
JINGDEZHEN TAOCI XUEYUAN XUEBAO/JINGDEZHEN CERAMICS INSTITUTE. JOURNAL. Text in Chinese; Abstracts in English. 1980. q. CNY 10. adv. bk.rev. **Document type:** *Academic/Scholarly.* **Description:** Contains research papers and reviews on silicate engineering, ceramics machinery, art & design for ceramics and ceramics history.
Related titles: Online - full text ed.: (from East View Information Services).
—BLDSC (4955.103000), IE, ingenta.
Published by: Jingdezhen Taoci Xueyuan/Jingdezhen Ceramic Institute, Jingdezhen, Jiangxi 333001, China. TEL 0798-441845, FAX 0798-441837. Ed. Lin Yunwan. Circ: 2,000.

666 GBR ISSN 0449-5713
JOURNAL OF CERAMIC HISTORY. Text in English. 1968. a. **Document type:** *Journal.*
—BLDSC (4955.100000).
Published by: Stoke-on-Trent Potteries Museum & Art Gallery, Bethesda St., Hanley, Stoke-On-Trent, ST1 3DW, United Kingdom. TEL 44-1782-202173, museums@stoke.gov.uk.

666 KOR ISSN 1229-9162
➤ **JOURNAL OF CERAMIC PROCESSING RESEARCH.** Text in English. 2000. q. KRW 500 domestic to individuals; USD 50 foreign to individuals; KRW 100,000 domestic to institutions; USD 100 foreign to institutions (effective 2004). **Document type:** *Journal, Academic/Scholarly.* **Description:** Covers the influence of processing routes on the microstructure and properties of ceramics and ceramic-based materials.
Indexed: MSCI.
—BLDSC (4955.101000), IE.
Published by: Hanyang University Ceramic, Processing Research Center, 17 Haengdang-dong, Seongdong-gu, Seoul, 133-791, Korea, S. TEL 82-2-2290-1828, FAX 82-2-2290-2884, jcpr@hanyang.ac.kr, http://journal.hanyang.ac.kr/jcpr/info.htm. Eds. Brian Ralph, Keun Auh Ho. **Subscr. to:** Korean Association of Crystal Growth, Inc., PO Box 27, Sungdong Post Office, Seoul 133-600 , Korea, S.

➤ **JOURNAL OF ELECTROCERAMICS.** see *ENGINEERING—Engineering Mechanics And Materials*

➤ **JOURNAL OF ROMAN POTTERY STUDIES.** see *CLASSICAL STUDIES*

666.1 IND ISSN 0971-3751
CODEN: GLUDDJ
KANCH. Text in English. 1972. q. adv. **Document type:** *Trade.*
Formerly (until 1992): Glass Udyog (0379-0460)
—BLDSC (5085.324500), CASDDS.
Published by: All India Glass Manufacturers' Federation, 812 New Delhi House, 27 Barakhamba Rd., New Delhi, 110 001, India. Ed. N D Shetty.

KERAMICA. see *BUILDING AND CONSTRUCTION*

666 738 DEU ISSN 0023-0561
TP785 CODEN: KERZAS
KERAMISCHE ZEITSCHRIFT. Text in German; Abstracts in English. 1948. m. EUR 210 (effective 2004). adv. **Document type:** *Magazine, Trade.* **Description:** Focuses on research and development, innovative technology, new products, market analyses, company portraits, and information on congresses, symposiums and trade fairs for the complete ceramics industry.

Incorporates (1996-2000): Ziegel-Zeitschrift (1434-2081)
Related titles: German ed.
Indexed: A&ATA, BrCerAb, C&ISA, CISA, CerAb, ChemAb, ChemTitl, CivEngAb, CorrAb, E&CAJ, EMA, Englnd, ExcerpMed, F&EA, IAA, IBZ, ISMEC, M&TEA, MBF, METADEX, RefZh, SolStAb, WAA.
—BLDSC (5089.725000), CASDDS, CISTI, Ei, IE, Infotrieve, ingenta, Linda Hall. **CCC.**
Published by: D V S Verlag GmbH, Aachener Str 172, Duesseldorf, 40223, Germany. TEL 49-211-15910, FAX 49-211-1591150, verlag@dvs-hg.de, http://www.dvs-verlag.de/de/zeit/kera/. Eds. Paul-Eberhard Keilbar, Rainer Humbach. Adv. contact Iris Jansen. B&W page EUR 1,636, color page EUR 2,636. Circ: 5,000 (paid and controlled).

KEY ENGINEERING MATERIALS. see *METALLURGY*

666 338 GBR
KEY NOTE MARKET REPORT: CHINA & EARTHENWARE. Variant title: China & Earthenware Market Report. Text in English. a., latest 2002, Jan. GBP 340 per issue (effective 2002). **Document type:** *Trade.* **Description:** Provides an overview of the UK china & earthenware market, including industry structure, market size and trends, developments, prospects, and major company profiles.
Formerly: Key Note Report: China and Earthenware
Related titles: CD-ROM ed.; Online - full text ed.
Published by: Key Note Ltd., Field House, 72 Oldfield Rd, Hampton, Mddx TW12 2HQ, United Kingdom. TEL 44-20-8481-8750, FAX 44-20-8783-0049, info@keynote.co.uk, http://www.keynote.co.uk. Ed. Emma Wiggin.

666.1 658 GBR ISSN 1460-3918
KEY NOTE MARKET REPORT: GLASSWARE. Variant title: Glassware. Text in English. irreg. (10th Edition), latest 1999, Sept. GBP 340 per issue (effective 2002). **Document type:** *Trade.* **Description:** Provides and overview of a specific UK market segment and includes executive summary, market definition, market size, industry background, competitor analysis, current issues, forecasts, company profiles, and more.
Formerly (until 1997): Key Note Report: Glassware (0954-5220)
Related titles: CD-ROM ed.; Online - full text ed.
Published by: Key Note Ltd., Field House, 72 Oldfield Rd, Hampton, Mddx TW12 2HQ, United Kingdom. TEL 44-20-8481-8750, FAX 44-20-8783-0049, info@keynote.co.uk, http://www.keynote.co.uk. Ed. Nick Bardsley.

KEY NOTE MARKET REPORT: PACKAGING (GLASS). see *PACKAGING*

666 NLD ISSN 0167-5001
CODEN: KLEIDW
KLEI, GLAS, KERAMIEK. Text in Dutch. 1909. 11/yr. EUR 65 to non-members (effective 2005); includes Keramisch Jaarboek. adv. bk.rev. charts; illus. index. **Document type:** *Trade.*
Former titles (until 1980): Klei en Keramiek (0023-2041); (until 1962): Klei (0368-6116)
Indexed: BrCerAb, ChemAb, ExcerpMed, KES.
—BLDSC (5099.076000), CASDDS, CISTI, IE, Infotrieve, Linda Hall.
Published by: Pressofoon Uitgeverij bv, Postbus 2093, Heemskerk, 1960 GB, Netherlands. TEL 31-251-207400, FAX 31-251-207401, kgk@pressofoon.nl. Circ: 1,500.

666 KOR ISSN 1225-9381
TA455.C43
KOREAN JOURNAL OF CERAMICS. Text in Korean. 1995. q. **Document type:** *Journal, Academic/Scholarly.*
Indexed: BrCerAb, C&ISA, CerAb, CorrAb, E&CAJ, EMA, Inspec, SolStAb, WAA.
—BLDSC (5113.524000).
Published by: Han'gug Yo'eob Haghoe/Korean Ceramic Society, Meorijae Bldg., Suite # 403, 984-1, Bangbae-3dong, Seocho-gu, Seoul, 137-849, Korea, S. TEL 82-2-5840185, FAX 82-2-5864582, http://www.ceramics.or.kr/main.jsp. Ed. Sang Heul Choi.

KOVELS ON ANTIQUES AND COLLECTIBLES; the newsletter for dealers, collectors and investors. see *ANTIQUES*

666.3 DEU
LANDESINNUNG DER BAYERISCHEN TOEPFER. MITTEILUNGEN. Text in German. irreg. (3-4/yr.).
Published by: Landesinnung der Bayerischen Toepfer, Toepferweg 16, Sonthofen, 87527, Germany.

666 688 ITA
MAGAZINE PREMIERE. Text in English, Italian. 1987. 4/yr. USD 100 in Europe; USD 160 elsewhere. **Document type:** *Magazine, Consumer.*
Formerly: Premiere
Published by: Eva Rutter Editore s.r.l., Via Emilia, 98, Santa Giuletta, PV 27046, Italy. TEL 0383-899774, FAX 0383-899054. Ed. Eva Rutter. Circ: 9,000.

666 913 DEU ISSN 0076-5171
MATERIALIEN ZUR ROEMISCH-GERMANISCHEN KERAMIK. Text in German. 1914. irreg., latest vol.13, 1998. price varies. **Document type:** *Monographic series, Academic/Scholarly.*
Indexed: AnthLit.
Published by: (Deutsches Archaeologisches Institut, Roemisch-Germanische Kommission), Dr. Rudolf Habelt GmbH, Am Buchenhang 1, Bonn, 53115, Germany. TEL 49-228-9238322, FAX 49-228-9238323, info@habelt.de, http://www.habelt.de.

MINES, MINERALS, ENERGY, ECOLOGY, POLLUTION, CERAMICS, REFRACTORY, CEMENT, GLASS. see *MINES AND MINING INDUSTRY*

338.47666 BRA
MUNDO CERAMICO. Text in Portuguese. 10/yr. USD 100 (effective 2000). adv. back issues avail. **Document type:** *Trade.* **Description:** Covers trade subjects and technological issues that affect the ceramics industry.
Related titles: Special ed(s).: Mundo Ceramico. Buyers Guide.
Published by: Menasce Comunicacoes Ltda., Rua Leopoldo Costo de Magallhaes Jr. 551, Sao Paulo, SP 04542-010, Brazil. TEL 55-11-829-3677, FAX 55-11-820-6147, menasce@originet.com.br. Ed. Maiat Juliboni. Pub., Adv. contact Lazzaro Menasce. page USD 2,200; trim 280 x 210. Circ: 3,000.

MUR; arkitektur og byggeteknikk. see *ARCHITECTURE*

666 DEU
NEMO. Text in German. 1981. a. EUR 400. adv. **Document type:** *Directory.*
Former titles (until 199?): Ceramic Suppliers International (Year) (0944-9825); (until 1993): International Buyers' Guide (0935-6444)
Media: CD-ROM. **Related titles:** English ed.
Published by: Verlag Schmid GmbH, Postfach 6609, Freiburg Im Breisgau, 79042, Germany. FAX 49-761-8960990, ceramic@ceramic-journals.com, http://www.ceramic-journals.com.

666 DEU ISSN 0933-2367
NK3930
NEUE KERAMIK/NEW CERAMICS. Text in German, English. 1987. bi-m. EUR 36 domestic; EUR 48 in Europe; USD 48 elsewhere (effective 2002). adv. bk.rev. 64 p./no.; back issues avail. **Document type:** *Magazine, Trade.* **Description:** Covers articles on ceramic art, science and technology for artists and collectors.
Published by: Verlag Neue Keramik GmbH, Unter den Eichen 90, Berlin, 12205, Germany. TEL 49-30-84109216, FAX 49-30-84109217, info@neue-keramik.de, http://www.ceramics.de. Ed. Gustav Weiss. adv.: B&W page EUR 920, color page EUR 5,146; trim 184 x 248. Circ: 8,000.

666 JPN ISSN 0914-5400
TP785 CODEN: NSKRE2
➤ **NIPPON SERAMIKKUSU KYOKAI GAKUJUTSU RONBUNSHI.** Text in English, Japanese. 1891. m. free to members. adv. bk.rev. **Document type:** *Journal, Academic/Scholarly.* **Description:** Contributes to the development of basic science, application, technology and industry of ceramics-related materials.
Former titles (until 1988): Yogyo Kyokaishi (0009-0255); (until 1950): Yogyo Kyokai Zasshi (0372-7769)
Related titles: Online - full text ed.: ISSN 1348-6535. free (effective 2005) (from J-Stage).
Indexed: ASCA, BrCerAb, C&ISA, CCI, CerAb, ChemAb, CivEngAb, CorrAb, CurCont, E&CAJ, EMA, Englnd, IAA, INIS AtomInd, ISMEC, ISR, Inspec, JTA, M&TEA, MBF, METADEX, MSCI, RefZh, SCI, SolStAb, WAA.
—BLDSC (4725.100000), AskIEEE, CASDDS, CISTI, Ei, IDS, IE, ingenta, Linda Hall. **CCC.**
Published by: Nippon Seramikkusu Kyokai/Ceramic Society of Japan, 22-17 Hiyakunin-cho 2-chome, Shinjuku-ku, Tokyo, 169-0073, Japan. TEL 81-3-3362-5231, FAX 81-3-3362-5714, http://www.ceramic.or.jp/ihensyuj/journal.html. Ed. Hideo Hosono. Circ: 6,000.

666 CHE
OFENBAU PLATTENBELAEGE. Text in German. m. (11/yr.). **Document type:** *Newspaper, Trade.*
Indexed: RefZh.
Published by: Verband Schweizerischer Hafner- und Plattengeschaefte, Solothurnerstr 236, Olten, 4603, Switzerland. TEL 41-62-2059080, FAX 41-62-2059089, info@vhp.ch, http://www.vhp.ch. Eds. Heidi Staeheli, Rene Hayoz. adv.: B&W page CHF 575, color page CHF 975; trim 266 x 182. Circ: 875.

666 RUS
CODEN: OGNPA2
OGNEUPORY I TEKHNICHESKAYA KERAMIKA. Text in Russian; Summaries in English, Russian. 1933. m. USD 165 in United States. adv. bk.rev. back issues avail. **Document type:** *Academic/Scholarly.*
Formerly (until May 1995): Ogneupory (0369-7290)
Related titles: Russian Translation: Ogneupory i Technicheskaya Keramika; ♦ English Translation: Refractories and Industrial Ceramics. ISSN 1083-4877.
Indexed: ChemAb, ChemTitl, Englnd, Inspec, RASB, RefZh.
—BLDSC (0127.002000), AskIEEE, CASDDS, CINDOC, CISTI, Linda Hall. **CCC.**
Address: Staropimenovskii per 8, pod 2, Moscow, 103006, Russian Federation. TEL 7-095-7559038, FAX 7-095-7559040. Ed. A V Serafinovich. **US dist. addr.:** East View Information Services, 3020 Harbor Ln. N., Minneapolis, MN 55447. TEL 612-550-0961.

666 HKG
ORIENTAL CERAMIC SOCIETY OF HONG KONG. BULLETIN. Text in English. 1972. biennial, latest no.12, 1998-2001. price varies. bk.rev. illus. back issues avail. **Document type:** *Monographic series, Academic/Scholarly.* **Description:** Contains articles on Chinese ceramics and other forms of art, reports on activities of the society, and lists members.
Indexed: BAS.
Published by: Oriental Ceramic Society of Hong Kong, PO Box 6202, Central Post Office, Hong Kong, Hong Kong. TEL 852-2527-0696, FAX 852-2527-0271, ocshk@hotmail.com, http://www.orientalceramics.org.hk/. **Dist. by:** Hong Kong University Press, 14-F, Hing Wai Centre, 7 Tin Wan Praya Rd, Aberdeen, Hong Kong. TEL 852-2550-2703, 852-2875-0734, hkupress@hkucc.hku.hk, http://www.hkupress.org.

666 GBR ISSN 0306-0926
THE ORIENTAL CERAMIC SOCIETY. TRANSACTIONS. Text in English. 1921. a. **Document type:** *Monographic series, Academic/Scholarly.*
—**CCC.**
Published by: The Oriental Ceramic Society, 30B Torrington Square, London, WC1E 7JL, United Kingdom. TEL 44-20-7636-7985, FAX 44-20-7580-6749.

PERCORSI IN CERAMICA; rivista di segni e immagini magazine di Casalgrande - Padana. see *ARCHITECTURE*

PERSPECTIVE. see *BUILDING AND CONSTRUCTION—Hardware*

666 POL ISSN 0079-3264
CODEN: PPKCBN
POLSKA AKADEMIA NAUK. ODDZIAL W KRAKOWIE. KOMISJA CERAMICZNA. PRACE: CERAMIKA. Text in Polish; Summaries in English, Russian. 1964. irreg., latest vol.40, 1992. price varies. **Document type:** *Monographic series.*
Indexed: CIN, ChemAb, ChemTitl, Englnd.
—BLDSC (6588.013000), CASDDS, CISTI, Linda Hall.
Published by: (Komisja Ceramiczna), Polska Akademia Nauk, Oddzial w Krakowie, ul sw Jana 28, Krakow, 31018, Poland. TEL 48-12-224853, FAX 48-12-222791. Ed. Roman Pampuch. Circ: 520.

POLYTECHNICAL UNIVERSITY OF BUCHAREST. SCIENTIFIC BULLETIN. SERIES B: CHEMISTRY AND MATERIALS SCIENCE. see *CHEMISTRY*

666 USA ISSN 0032-4477
TP785
POPULAR CERAMICS. Text in English. 1949. 6/yr. USD 27.95 domestic; USD 42.95 foreign; USD 3.95 newsstand/cover (effective 2005). adv. bk.rev. illus. index. **Document type:** *Magazine, Consumer.* **Description:** Provides information for people who truly enjoy creating unique ceramic pieces. A variety of color projects offered for all skill levels.
Incorporates (197?-198?): Plastercrafts (0164-4017)
Related titles: Microform ed.: (from PQC).
Indexed: IHTDI.
Published by: Jones Publishing, Inc., N 7450 Aanstad Rd, PO Box 5000, Iola, WI 54945. TEL 715-445-5000, 800-331-0038, FAX 715-445-4053, jonespub@jonespublishing.com, http://www.popularceramics.com, http://www.jonespublishing.com. Ed., Pub., R&P Mike Harbridge. Adv. contact Alissa Metge. Circ: 8,000 (paid and controlled).

666 DEU ISSN 0942-850X
PORZELLAN UND GLAS; das Branchenmagazin fuer Handel und Industrie. Text in German. 1963. m. adv. charts; illus.; tr.lit. **Document type:** *Magazine, Trade.*
Indexed: KES.
Published by: Krammer Verlag Duesseldorf AG, Hermannstr 3, Duesseldorf, 40233, Germany. TEL 49-211-91493, FAX 49-211-9149450, krammer@krammerag.de, http://www.porzellan-online.de, http://www.krammerag.de. adv.: page EUR 2,150; trim 184 x 260. Circ: 8,200 (controlled).

666 USA ISSN 1096-830X
NK4225
POTTERY MAKING ILLUSTRATED. Text in English. 1998. bi-m. USD 22 in North America to non-members; USD 40 elsewhere to non-members; USD 18 in North America to members; USD 36 elsewhere to members; USD 5 newsstand/cover (effective 2005). adv. illus. back issues avail.; reprints avail. **Document type:** *Magazine, Consumer.* **Description:** Provides practical information on all aspects of making pottery. Features well-illustrated techniques and easy-to-follow instructions on throwing, hand-building, firing, clays, glasses, kilns, tools and equipment.
Related titles: Online - full text ed.: (from EBSCO Publishing, H.W. Wilson, O C L C Online Computer Library Center, Inc., ProQuest Information & Learning).
Indexed: ArtInd, C&ISA, E&CAJ, IAA.
—**CCC.**

C

Published by: American Ceramic Society Inc., 735 Ceramic Pl, Ste 100, Westerville, OH 43081-8720. TEL 614-794-5890, FAX 614-794-5892, potterymaking@acers.org, info@ceramics.org, http://www.potterymaking.org, http://www.ceramics.org. Ed. Bill Jones. Pub. Mark J Mecklenborg TEL 614-794-5829. Adv. contact Steve Hecker TEL 614-794-5809. B&W page USD 1,225, color page USD 1,850. Circ: 13,000 (paid).

POTTERY SOUTHWEST; news, queries & views on archaeological ceramics by Southwesternists. see *ARCHAEOLOGY*

POWDER METALLURGY AND METAL CERAMICS. see *METALLURGY*

PREVISIONS GLISSANTES DETAILLEES EN PERSPECTIVES SECTORIELLES (VOL.24): INDUSTRIE DU VERRE. see *BUSINESS AND ECONOMICS—Economic Situation And Conditions*

666 POL ISSN 1232-9703
PRZEGLAD DOKUMENTACYJNY MATERIALOW OGNIOTRWALYCH I CERAMIKI SPECJALNEJ. Text in Polish. 1963. m. USD 220 (effective 2002). adv. bk.rev. abstr. index. 48 p./no.; reprints avail. **Document type:** *Journal.* **Description:** Covers heat technology, preparation of raw materials, instumental analysis, corrosion, ceramic bobies, special ceramic, composites, filters, application of refractories.
Formerly (until 1994): Przeglad Dokumentacyjny Materialow Ogniotrwalych (0033-2046)
Published by: Instytut Materialow Ogniotrwalych/Institute of Refractory Materials, Ul Toszecka 99, Gliwice, 44101, Poland. TEL 48-32-2701801, FAX 48-32-2701934, TELEX 036172 JMO PL, ointe@imo.gliwice.pl, http://www.imo.gliwice.pl/. Ed. Jerzy Czechowski. Adv. contact Maria Nosek. page USD 300; 120 x 200. Circ: 300.

666 AUS ISSN 0728-0858
QUEENSLAND POTTERS ASSOCIATION. ANNUAL REPORT OF THE DIRECTORS. Text in English. 1979. a. **Document type:** *Corporate.*
Published by: Queensland Potters Association, Cnr. Malt & Brunswick Sts., Fortitude Valley, QLD 4006, Australia. TEL 61-7-33585122, FAX 61-7-33854540. Ed. Bernice Gerrand.

666 668.4 GBR ISSN 0955-212X
RAW MATERIALS FOR PIGMENTS, FILLERS AND EXTENDERS. Text in English. 1988. irreg., latest vol.2, 1995. GBP 87, USD 164 (effective 1998). adv. charts; mkt. **Document type:** *Trade.*
Published by: Industrial Minerals Information Ltd. (Subsidiary of: Metal Bulletin plc), 1 Park House, Park Terr, Worcester Park, Surrey KT4 7HY, United Kingdom. TEL 44-2078-279977, FAX 44-2083-378943, http://www.mineralnet.co.uk.

666 USA ISSN 1083-4877
TN677.A1 CODEN: RICEFY
➤ **REFRACTORIES AND INDUSTRIAL CERAMICS.** Text in English. 1960. 6/yr. EUR 2,958, USD 3,008, GBP 1,845 combined subscription to institutions print & online eds. (effective 2005). adv. charts; illus. index. back issues avail.; reprints avail. **Document type:** *Journal, Academic/Scholarly.* **Description:** Discusses the latest discoveries and developments in the field of refractory materials and ceramics, with attention to the practical aspects of their production and use.
Formerly (until 1996): Refractories (0034-3102)
Related titles: Microfilm ed.: (from PQC); Online - full text ed.: ISSN 1573-9139 (from EBSCO Publishing, Gale Group, IngentaConnect, Kluwer Online, O C L C Online Computer Library Center, Inc., Springer LINK, Swets Information Services); ♦ Translation of: Ogneupory i Tekhnicheskaya Keramika.
Indexed: BibLing, BrCerAb, C&ISA, CerAb, ChemTitl, CivEngAb, CorrAb, CurCont, E&CAJ, EMA, EnerRA, EngInd, IAA, Inspec, M&TEA, MBF, METADEX, MSCI, SolStAb, WAA.
—BLDSC (0420.726800), CASDDS, CISTI, Ei, IDS, IE, Infotrieve, ingenta, Linda Hall. **CCC.**
Published by: (Russia. Ministerstvo Chernoi Metallurgii RUS), Consultants Bureau (Subsidiary of: Springer-Verlag New York, Inc.), 233 Spring St, New York, NY 10013. TEL 212-460-1500, FAX 212-460-1575, service@springer-ny.com, http://springerlink.metapress.com/openurl.asp?genre=journal&issn=1083-4877, http://www.springeronline.com. Ed. S V Kolpakov. **Co-sponsors:** American Institute of Mining, Metallurgical and Petroleum Engineers; American Society for Testing and Materials.

666 USA ISSN 1537-6443
TP838 CODEN: RANECU
REFRACTORIES APPLICATIONS AND NEWS; technology bimonthly for the global refractories industries. Text in English. 1996 (Sept.). bi-m. free. adv.
—BLDSC (7332.977000). **CCC.**
Published by: (Refractories Institute, American Ceramic Society Inc.), University of Missouri-Rolla, Department of Ceramic Engineering, 222 McNutt Hall, 1870 Miner Circle Dr., Rolla, MO 65409-0330. TEL 573-341-6561, FAX 573-341-6934, editor@ranews.info, http://www.ranews.info/. Ed. Robert E. Moore. Adv. contact Dwight Whittemore.

666 GBR ISSN 1362-4547
REFRACTORIES ENGINEER. Text in English. 1972. q. GBP 23.50 to non-members. adv. **Document type:** *Trade.*
Formerly (until 1996): Institute of Refractories Engineers. Journal (0269-6924)
Indexed: BrCerAb, C&ISA, CerAb, CivEngAb, CorrAb, E&CAJ, EMA, IAA, M&TEA, MBF, METADEX, SolStAb, WAA.
—Linda Hall.
Published by: (Institute of Refractories Engineers), Poulton Ltd., Station House, Hednesford, Poulton Ltd, Cannock Rd, Cannock, Staffs WS12 4AF, United Kingdom. TEL 44-1543-422217, FAX 44-1453-877725, 101364.61@compuserve.com. Ed. J.B. Traynor. Adv. contact J B Traynor.

666.1 CHN ISSN 1000-985X
CODEN: RJXUEN
RENGONG JINGTI XUEBAO/JOURNAL OF SYNTHETIC CRYSTALS. Text in Chinese. 1972. q. USD 56.50. 82 p./no.; **Document type:** *Academic/Scholarly.* **Description:** Reports the recent researches and developments in the field of crystal growth and synthetic crystal materials in China.
Formerly (until 1989): Rengong Jingti (1001-0904)
Related titles: Online - full text ed.: (from East View Information Services).
Indexed: CIN, ChemAb, ChemTitl, Inspec, RefZh.
—BLDSC (5068.040000), CASDDS, IE, ingenta.
Published by: (Chinese Ceramic Society, Committee on Crystal Growth and Materials), Chemical Industry Press/Huaxue Gongye Chubanshe, 3 Huixinli, Chaoyang-qu, Beijing, 100029, China. TEL 86-10-4918318, FAX 86-10-4918318. **Co-sponsor:** Research Institute of Synthetic Crystals.

666.1 721.823 USA
LA REVISTA DEL VIDRIO, FACHADAS Y VENTANAS. Abbreviated title: V F V. Text in Spanish. 1997. s-a. free. tr.lit. back issues avail. **Document type:** *Magazine, Trade.* **Description:** Devoted exclusively to the Latin American auto and flat glass, metal and fenestration markets.
Published by: Key Communications, Inc., PO Box 569, Garrisonville, VA 22463. TEL 540-720-5584, http://www.key-com.com/. Pub. Debra Levy. Adv. contact Janeen Cipriani.

666.1 ESP
REVISTA DEL VIDRIO HUECO. Text in Spanish. 4/yr. includes Anuario.
Related titles: Supplement(s): Anuario Espanol del Vidrio Hueco.
Published by: Proporcion 3 S.A., Bruc, 48 2o, Barcelona, 08010, Spain. TEL 3-412-07-64, FAX 3-412-49-25. Ed. Agustin Calvo.

666.1 ESP
REVISTA DEL VIDRIO PLANO. Text in Spanish. 6/yr. includes Anuario. **Description:** Covers plate glass industry and machinery.
Related titles: Supplement(s): Anuario Espanol del Vidrio Plano.
Published by: Proporcion 3 S.A., Bruc, 48 2o, Barcelona, 08010, Spain. TEL 3-412-07-64, FAX 3-412-49-25. Ed. Agustin Calvo.

666 FRA ISSN 0758-3389
LA REVUE DE LA CERAMIQUE ET DU VERRE. Text in French; Summaries in English. 1981. bi-m. EUR 55.64 domestic; EUR 62.50 in Europe (effective 2003). adv. bk.rev. 64 p./no.; back issues avail. **Document type:** *Magazine, Trade.* **Description:** Deals with every feature of ceramics and glass from archeology to contemporary art and techniques.
Formerly (until 1982): Revue de la Ceramique (0294-202X)
Indexed: DAAI.
Published by: Revue de la Ceramique et du Verre, 61 rue Marconi, BP 3, Vendin le Vieil, 62880, France. TEL 33-3-21794444, FAX 33-3-21794445, revue.ceramique.verre@wanadoo.fr, http://www.perso.wanadoo.fr/revue.ceramique.verre. Ed., Pub., Adv. contact Sylvie Girard. B&W page EUR 655.53, color page EUR 1,006.16; 220 x 300. Circ: 6,200 (paid).

666.1 ITA
RIVISTA DEL VETRO. Text in Italian. 8/yr. EUR 35 domestic; EUR 53 foreign (effective 2003). adv. **Document type:** *Consumer.*
Published by: Reed Business Information Spa (Subsidiary of: Reed Business Information International), Viale G. Richard 1/A, Milan, 20143, Italy. TEL 39-02-818301, FAX 39-02-81830406, info@reedbusiness.it, http://www.reedbusiness.it. Circ: 10,000.

SANITARY TABLEWARE, ARTISTIC CERAMICS SUPPLIERS BOOK. see *HEATING, PLUMBING AND REFRIGERATION*

666.1 DEU ISSN 1615-7389
SCHOTT-INFO (DEUTSCHE AUSG.). Text in German. 1976. q. 28 p./no. 3 cols./p.; back issues avail. **Document type:** *Magazine, Trade.*
Formerly (until 1998): Schott-Information (Deutsche Ausg.) (0170-5733)
Related titles: Online - full text ed.: 2001; English ed.: Schott-Info (English Edition). ISSN 1615-7397. 1976; French ed.: Schott-Info (Edition Francaise). ISSN 1615-9799. 1976; Spanish ed.: Schott-Info (Edicion Espanola). ISSN 1615-9802. 1976.
Indexed: BrCerAb, C&ISA, CerAb, CivEngAb, CorrAb, E&CAJ, EMA, IAA, M&TEA, MBF, METADEX, SolStAb, WAA.
Published by: Schott Glas, Hattenbergstr 10, Mainz, 55122, Germany. TEL 49-6131-664321, FAX 49-6131-664011, http://www.schott.com/english/news/publications/schott_info.html. Ed. Christine Fuhr. Pub. Klaus Hofmann. Circ: 7,000 (controlled).

666.1 DEU ISSN 0343-9445
SCHOTT INTERN. Text in German. 1953. m. **Document type:** *Newsletter, Corporate.*
Related titles: English ed.: ISSN 0720-1087; French ed.: ISSN 0936-2878.
Published by: Schott Glas, Hattenbergstr 10, Mainz, 55122, Germany. TEL 49-6131-664321, FAX 49-6131-664011, http://www.schott.com.

666 KOR
SCIENCE & TECHNOLOGY OF CERAMIC MATERIALS. Text in Korean. 3/yr.
Published by: Han'gug Yo'eob Haghoe/Korean Ceramic Society, Meorijae Bldg., Suite # 403, 984-1, Bangbae-3dong, Seocho-gu, Seoul, 137-849, Korea, S. TEL 82-2-5840185, FAX 82-2-5864582, http://www.ceramics.or.kr/paper/, http://www.ceramics.or.kr/main.jsp.

SCIENCE OF SINTERING. see *METALLURGY*

666.1 HUN ISSN 0237-2169
SCIENTIFIC SOCIETY OF THE SILICATE INDUSTRY. CONFERENCE ON SILICATE INDUSTRY AND SILICATE SCIENCE. Text in English, German, Hungarian, Russian. 1973. quadrennial. USD 64.
Related titles: Microfiche ed.
Published by: (Scientific Society of the Silicate Industry), OMIKK Technoinform, Muzeum utca 17, Budapest 8, Hungary. Ed. Maria Palocz. **Subscr. to:** PO Box 12, Budapest 1428, Hungary.

666.3 GBR ISSN 0260-7972
SCOTTISH POTTERY STUDIES. Text in English. 1982. irreg. GBP 1.95.
Published by: Scottish Pottery Society, c/o Mr. Graeme Cruickshank, 21 Warrender Park Terr, Edinburgh, United Kingdom. Circ: 1,000.

666 KOR ISSN 1226-976X
SE'RA'MISEUTEU. Text in Korean. 1998. q.
—BLDSC (3119.250000).
Published by: Han'gug Yo'eob Haghoe/Korean Ceramic Society, Meorijae Bldg., Suite # 403, 984-1, Bangbae-3dong, Seocho-gu, Seoul, 137-849, Korea, S. TEL 82-2-5840185, FAX 82-2-5864582, http://www.ceramics.or.kr/main.jsp.

SEVRES. see *ARTS AND HANDICRAFTS*

666 BEL ISSN 0037-5225
TP785 CODEN: SIINAT
SILICATES INDUSTRIELS; ceramic science and technology. Text in English, French, German. 1930. bi-m. EUR 130 domestic; EUR 175 foreign (effective 2005). adv. bk.rev. abstr.; bibl.; charts; illus.; tr.lit. index. **Document type:** *Bulletin.*
Indexed: ASCA, BrCerAb, C&ISA, CRIA, CRICC, CerAb, ChemAb, ChemTitl, CivEngAb, CorrAb, E&CAJ, EMA, EngInd, HRIS, IAA, M&TEA, MBF, METADEX, MSCI, RefZh, SolStAb, WAA.
—BLDSC (8279.000000), CASDDS, CISTI, Ei, IDS, IE, ingenta, Linda Hall.
Published by: Belgian Ceramic Society, Av Gouverneur Cornez 4, Mons, 7000, Belgium. TEL 32-65-403434, FAX 32-65-348005, si@bcrc.be, info@bcrc.be, http://www.bcrc.be/si.html. R&P, Adv. contact Dr. Jacques Tirlocq. Circ: 1,000.

666 CZE ISSN 0037-637X
TP845 CODEN: SKKEAQ
SKLAR A KERAMIK✶ /GLASS AND CERAMICS MAKER; odborny casopis pro prumysl skla, keramiky a bizuterie. Text in Czech; Summaries in English, French, German, Russian. 1951. m. CZK 400 (effective 1999). adv. bk.rev. stat.; tr.lit. index. back issues avail. **Description:** Consists of original articles, branch news, economic information and social events.
Indexed: BrCerAb, CIN, CISA, ChemAb, ChemTitl, F&EA, RASB.
—CASDDS, CISTI, Linda Hall.
Published by: Ceska Sklarska Spolecnost, Sloupska 666, Novy Bor, 43901, Czech Republic. TEL 42-424-34617, FAX 42-417-255-45. Adv. contact Sazavova. Circ: 3,400. **Dist. by:** Artia, Ve Smeckach 30, Prague 1 111 27, Czech Republic.

666 ESP ISSN 0366-3175
TP785 CODEN: BSCVB9
SOCIEDAD ESPANOLA DE CERAMICA Y VIDRIO. BOLETIN. Text in Spanish; Abstracts in English. 1961. bi-m. EUR 150 (effective 2005). bk.rev.; Website rev. abstr.; bibl.; charts; illus.; pat.; tr.lit. index. 80 p./no.; back issues avail. **Document type:** *Bulletin.*
Formerly (until 1972): Sociedad Espanola de Ceramica. Boletin (0037-8550)
Related titles: Microform ed.
Indexed: BrCerAb, C&ISA, CIN, CerAb, ChemAb, ChemTitl, CivEngAb, CorrAb, CurCont, E&CAJ, EMA, IAA, IECT, INIS AtomInd, M&TEA, MBF, METADEX, MSCI, SolStAb, WAA.
—BLDSC (2191.520000), CASDDS, CINDOC, CISTI, IDS, IE, ingenta, Linda Hall. **CCC.**

C

Published by: Sociedad Espanola de Ceramica y Vidrio/Spanish Company of Ceramics and Glass, Camino Valdelatas s/n, Despacho 176, Madrid, 28049, Spain. TEL 34-91-7355840, FAX 34-91-7355843, secv@icv.csic.es, http://www.secv.es/. Ed. Emilio Criado Herrero. Circ: 1,500 (controlled).

748.029 USA
SOCIETY OF GLASS AND CERAMIC DECORATORS. MEMBERSHIP DIRECTORY. Text in English. 1964. a. USD 250 to non-members (effective 2001). **Document type:** *Directory.* **Description:** Lists companies and individuals involved in all aspects of decorating glass and ceramicware worldwide. Decorators are identified by type of product and by decorating technique through 350 indexes, which also list suppliers.
Formerly: Society of Glass Decorators. Membership Directory
Published by: Society of Glass and Ceramic Decorators, 4340 East-West Hwy, 200, Bethesda, MD 20814. TEL 301-951-3933, FAX 301-951-3801, sgcd@sgcd.org, http://www.sgcd.org. Eds. Andrew Bopp, Caroline Struggs. Pubs. Andrew Bopp, Sandra Spence. Circ: 800.

748 USA
SOCIETY OF GLASS AND CERAMIC DECORATORS. TECHNOTEBOOK. Text in English. 1964. a. USD 495 to non-members; USD 195 to members (effective 1999). **Document type:** *Proceedings.* **Description:** Serves as a technical and regulatory manual for the decorating industry. Includes sections on inks, colors and pigments, drying, firing and annealing, precious metals, screen printing, ceramic decorating and other subjects. Articles are compiled from SGCD seminar presentations and other sources.
Former titles (until 1994): Society of Glass and Ceramic Decorators. Seminar Proceedings; Society of Glass Decorators. Seminar Proceedings; Society of Glass Decorators. Papers Presented at Annual Seminar (0081-1602)
Published by: Society of Glass and Ceramic Decorators, 4340 East-West Hwy, 200, Bethesda, MD 20814. TEL 301-951-3933, FAX 301-951-3801, sgcd@sgcd.org. Ed., R&P Andrew Bopp. Pub. Sandra Spence. Circ: 800.

666.1 645 GBR ISSN 1357-4752
SPECCHECK. Text in English. q. **Document type:** *Directory.*
Published by: T B B Publications Ltd., 4 Simon Campion Ct, High St, Epping, Essex CM16 4AU, United Kingdom. TEL 01992-560215, FAX 01992-560216. adv.: page GBP 995; trim 210 x 297. Circ: 10,000.

666.1 ITA ISSN 0391-4259
CODEN: RSSVDT
STAZIONE SPERIMENTALE DEL VETRO. RIVISTA. Text in Italian. 1971. bi-m. EUR 39.25 domestic; EUR 53.19 foreign (effective 2005). adv. bk.rev. abstr.; bibl.; pat. index. **Document type:** *Magazine, Trade.*
Indexed: ChemAb, ChemTitl.
—BLDSC (7978.800000), CASDDS, CISTI, IE, ingenta, Linda Hall.
Published by: (Stazione Sperimentale del Vetro), Mazzanti Editori Srl, Via delle Industrie 19B, Marghera, VE 30175, Italy. TEL 39-041-5385565, FAX 39-041-2529525. Circ: 1,500.

666 666.1 RUS ISSN 0131-9582
CODEN: STKRAQ
STEKLO I KERAMIKA. Text in Russian. 1944. m. USD 215 (effective 2004). bk.rev. abstr.; charts; illus.; stat. index. **Document type:** *Magazine, Trade.* **Description:** Publishes reports about exhibitions, fairs and conferences, raw materials, equipment and manufactured items ads, training of personnel.
Related titles: ♦ English Translation: Glass and Ceramics. ISSN 0361-7610.
Indexed: BrCerAb, C&ISA, CIN, CerAb, ChemAb, ChemTitl, CivEngAb, CorrAb, E&CAJ, EMA, EngInd, Inspec, M&TEA, MBF, METADEX, RASB, RefZh, SolStAb, WAA.
—BLDSC (0169.000000), AskIEEE, CASDDS, CINDOC, CISTI, East View, Linda Hall. **CCC.**
Published by: Stroiizdat, Dolgorukovskaya ul 23-a, Moscow, 111442, Russian Federation. TEL 7-095-4953976. Ed. L V Sokolova. Circ: 7,160. **US dist. addr.:** East View Information Services, 3020 Harbor Ln. N., Minneapolis, MN 55447. TEL 800-477-1005, FAX 800-800-3839, eastview@eastview.com, http://www.eastview.com.

666.1 USA ISSN 1555-6026
TP859 CODEN: PSAGB6
SYMPOSIUM ON THE ART OF SCIENTIFIC GLASSBLOWING. PROCEEDINGS. Text in English. 1956. a. price varies. adv. bibl.; illus. **Document type:** *Proceedings, Trade.* **Description:** Technical papers presented at the annual ASGS symposium.
Former titles (until 199?): Symposium and Exhibition on the Art of Scientific Glassblowing. Proceedings (1554-8198); (until 1991): Symposium and Exhibition on the Art of Glassblowing. Proceedings (0743-409X); (until 1981): Symposium on the Art of Scientific Glassblowing Proceedings (0569-7468)
Published by: The American Scientific Glassblowers Society, PO Box 778, Madison, NC 27025. TEL 336-427-2406, FAX 336-427-2496, http://www.asgs-glass.org. Ed., R&P Marilyn Brown. Adv. contact Dawn Hodgkins. Circ: 1,000.

666 POL ISSN 0039-8144
TP785 CODEN: SZKCAN
SZKLO I CERAMIKA. Text in Polish; Summaries in English, French, Russian. 1935. bi-m. PLZ 84; PLZ 14 per issue (effective 2004). adv. bk.rev. 48 p./no.; **Document type:** *Trade.*
Indexed: BrCerAb, C&ISA, CIN, CerAb, ChemAb, ChemTitl, CorrAb, E&CAJ, EMA, F&EA, Inspec, RefZh, SolStAb, WAA.
—CASDDS, CISTI, Linda Hall.
Published by: Wydawnictwo SIGMA - N O T Sp. z o.o., ul Ratuszowa 11, PO Box 1004, Warsaw, 00950, Poland. TEL 48-22-8180918, FAX 48-22-6192187, informacja@sigma-not.pl, http://www.sigma-not.pl. Ed. Danuta Biernacka Pruszkowska TEL 48-22-8437421 ext248. adv.: B&W page PLZ 1,200, color page PLZ 2,700. Circ: 600.

TABLE ET CADEAU. see *INTERIOR DESIGN AND DECORATION—Furniture And House Furnishings*

666 GBR ISSN 0143-7755
TP785
TABLEWARE INTERNATIONAL. Text in English. 1877. m. (11/yr.). GBP 86.92 domestic; USD 181.79 foreign (effective 2005). bk.rev. **Document type:** *Magazine, Trade.* **Description:** Contains news, views and reviews on all aspects of the tabletop, quality gifts and housewares industries .
Former titles: Tableware International and Pottery Gazette (0039-8853); Pottery Gazette and Glass Trade Review
Indexed: ABM, BrCerAb, C&ISA, CerAb, CorrAb, E&CAJ, EMA, KES, SolStAb, WAA.
—IE, Infotrieve.
Published by: D M G World Media Ltd. (Subsidiary of: Daily Mail and General Trust PLC), Queensway House, 2 Queensway, Redhill, Surrey RH1 1QS, United Kingdom. TEL 44-1737-768611, FAX 44-1737-855469, info@uk.dmgworldmedia.com, http://www.tablewareinternational.com/, http://www.dmgworldmedia.com. Ed. Peter Tipthorp TEL 44-1737-855223. Pub. Robin Beaman TEL 44-1737-855211. Adv. contact Patrick Horne TEL 44-20-85152093. Circ: 10,500.

666 CHN ISSN 1000-9892
TAOCI YANJIU/CERAMICS STUDIES JOURNAL. Text in Chinese. q. CNY 18.
Related titles: Online - full text ed.: (from East View Information Services).
—BLDSC (3116.655000).
Published by: Jiangxi Sheng Taoci Yanjiusuo/Jiangxi Ceramics Research Institute, Zhangshusha, Jingdezhen Dongjiao (East Suburb), Jiangxi 333001, China. TEL 443186. Ed. Tai Xilin. **Dist. outside China by:** China International Book Trading Corp, 35 Chegongzhuang Xilu, Haidian District, PO Box 399, Beijing 100044, China. **Co-sponsor:** Jiangxi Sheng Taoci Keji Qingbao Zhan.

666 ESP ISSN 0211-7290
TECNICA CERAMICA. Text in Spanish. 1971. 10/yr. EUR 109.08 in Europe; EUR 119.08 elsewhere (effective 2004). adv. bk.rev. bibl.; charts; illus. **Document type:** *Trade.*
Indexed: BrCerAb, C&ISA, CerAb, CivEngAb, CorrAb, E&CAJ, EMA, IAA, IECT, M&TEA, MBF, METADEX, RefZh, SolStAb, WAA.
—CINDOC.
Published by: Publica S.A., Calle Ecuador, 75, Barcelona, 08029, Spain. TEL 34-933-215045, FAX 34-933-221972, publica@publica.es, http://www.publica.es. Ed. Juan Balague Castella. Circ: 3,000.

666 DEU ISSN 0938-9806
TILE & BRICK INTERNATIONAL. Text in English; Summaries in French, German, Spanish. 1984. bi-m. EUR 189 (effective 2005). adv. **Document type:** *Magazine, Trade.* **Description:** Focuses on research and development, innovative technology, new products, market analyses, company profiles, and information about conferences, symposiums and fairs.
Formerly (until 1989): Interbrick (0178-2223)
Indexed: BrCerAb, C&ISA, CerAb, CorrAb, E&CAJ, EMA, RefZh, SolStAb, WAA.
—BLDSC (8845.620000), CISTI, Ei, IE, ingenta. **CCC.**
Published by: D V S Verlag GmbH, Aachener Str 172, Duesseldorf, 40223, Germany. TEL 49-211-15910, FAX 49-211-1591150, verlag@dvs-verlag.de, http://www.dvs-verlag.de. Ed. Rosemarie Vocht-Mields. Adv. contact Iris Jansen. B&W page EUR 2,125, color page EUR 3,280. Circ: 7,500.

666 691.4 USA ISSN 0192-9550
TILE & DECORATIVE SURFACES; the voice of America's tile market. Text in English. 1950. m. USD 50 domestic; USD 55 in Canada & Mexico; USD 60 overseas. adv. bk.rev. illus. index. **Document type:** *Magazine, Trade.* **Description:** Provides timely, topical editorial content to be used daily as a reference source by key buyers and decision-makers who comprise the highly qualified readership of the publication.
Formerly: Tile and Architectural Ceramics (0040-7666)
Indexed: BrCerAb, C&ISA, CerAb, CorrAb, E&CAJ, EMA, SolStAb, WAA.
—CCC.
Published by: Ashlee Publishing Co., Inc., 18 E 41st St, 20th Fl, New York, NY 10017-6222. TEL 212-376-7722, FAX 212-376-7723, publisher@ashlee.com, http://www.tilemagazine.com/, http://www.ashlee.com. Ed. Joel Bruinooge. Pub. Jordon Wright. Adv. contact Hazel Cristan. B&W page USD 2,000, color page USD 2,900; trim 11.13 x 16.88. Circ: 20,042.

TILE BOOK; Italian repertory of ceramic firms. see *BUSINESS AND ECONOMICS—Trade And Industrial Directories*

TILE BRICKS REFRACTORIES SUPPLIERS BOOK. see *BUSINESS AND ECONOMICS—Trade And Industrial Directories*

666 USA ISSN 1077-6974
CODEN: ARADFX
TILE DESIGN & INSTALLATION. Text in English. 1987. q. USD 55 domestic; USD 70.85 in Canada; USD 91 elsewhere. adv. **Document type:** *Trade.* **Description:** For professionals who design, specify, distribute, install and buy quality tile products.
Formerly (until 1994): Tile World (1074-455X)
Indexed: BrCerAb, C&ISA, CerAb, CorrAb, E&CAJ, EMA, SolStAb, WAA.
Published by: B N P Media, 755 W Big Beaver Rd, Ste 1000, Troy, MI 48084-4903. TEL 248-362-3700, FAX 248-362-0317, http://www.bnp.com, http://www.bnpmedia.com/. Ed. John Maynard. Pub., Adv. contact Myra Smitley. Circ: 17,530.

738 USA ISSN 1078-5655
TILE HERITAGE; a review of American tile history. Text in English. 1994. irreg. USD 12 per issue in United States to non-members; USD 9.60 per issue in United States to members (effective 2003). **Document type:** *Trade.* **Description:** Contains informative articles by selected scholars on ceramic tile history in the U.S. and beyond.
Published by: Tile Heritage Foundation, PO Box 1850, Healdsburg, CA 95448. TEL 707-431-8453, FAX 707-431-8455, foundation@tileheritage.org, http://www.tileheritage.org. Ed. Joseph A Taylor.

TILE ITALIA. see *INTERIOR DESIGN AND DECORATION*

666 690 USA
TILE NEWS. Text in English. 1980. 2/yr. free. **Document type:** *Magazine, Trade.* **Description:** Presents new uses, ideas and designs for the Italian tile industry in the U.S.
Related titles: Online - full text ed.
Published by: (Italian Tile Center), Italian Trade Commission, 33 E. 67th St., New York, NY 10021. TEL 212-980-1500, FAX 212-758-1050, tileinfo@italtrade.com, http://www.italytile.com. R&P Jacqueline Greaves. Circ: 21,000 (controlled and free).

666 GBR ISSN 1363-948X
TILE U K. Text in English. 1996. q. GBP 15 (effective 2000). adv. **Document type:** *Magazine, Trade.* **Description:** Covers ceramic wall and floor tiles, natural stone, terrazzo and glass tiles, tiling tools and machinery.
Indexed: BrCerAb, C&ISA, CerAb, CorrAb, E&CAJ, EMA, SolStAb, WAA.
Published by: C M P Information Ltd. (Subsidiary of: United Business Media), Oliver's Pl, Eastway, Fulwood, P O Box 18, Preston, Lancs PR2 9GU, United Kingdom. enquiries@cmpinformation.com, http://www.cmpinformation.com. Ed. Joe Simpson TEL 44-1580-752404. Pub. Bob Andrew. Adv. contact John French TEL 44-161-488-4362. Circ: 6,000.

666 GBR ISSN 0264-5157
TILES & ARCHITECTURAL CERAMICS SOCIETY JOURNAL. Text in English. biennial. back issues avail. **Document type:** *Journal, Academic/Scholarly.* **Description:** Illustrated articles of original research.
Indexed: ABM, AIAP, BHA, BrCerAb, C&ISA, CerAb, CorrAb, DAAI, E&CAJ, EMA, SolStAb, WAA.
Published by: Tiles & Architectural Ceramics Society, 3 Castle View, Leeds, LS17 5BY, United Kingdom. TEL 44-113-2685117, juanlem@netcomuk.co.uk. Ed. Hans van Lemmen.

666 GBR ISSN 1355-6738
TILES & ARCHITECTURAL CERAMICS SOCIETY NEWSLETTER. Text in English. 1985. q. bk.rev. back issues avail. **Document type:** *Newsletter, Consumer.*
Indexed: BrCerAb.
Published by: Tiles & Architectural Ceramics Society, 24 Beacon Dr, West Kirby, Wirrall CH48 7ED, United Kingdom. TEL 44-151-6259953, theparkers@lineone.net. Ed. Penny Beckett.

666 ZAF
TILING NEWS. Text in English. 1993. bi-m. membership. illus. **Document type:** *Newsletter.*
Published by: (South African Ceramic Tile Manufacturers Association), Association Services, PO Box 19139, Fisher's Hill, 1408, South Africa.

666.1 GBR
TOPICAL ISSUES IN GLASS. Text in English. 1992. irreg., latest vol.3. price varies.
—BLDSC (8867.395000).

Published by: Society of Glass Technology, Don Valley House, Savile St. East, Sheffield, S Yorks S4 7UQ, United Kingdom. TEL 44-114-2634455, FAX 44-114-2634411, sgt@glass.demon.co.uk, http://www.sgt.org.

U.S. GLASS, METAL & GLAZING. see *BUILDING AND CONSTRUCTION*

UMSCHAU. see *ENGINEERING—Chemical Engineering*

666.2 GBR ISSN 0042-7519
CODEN: VITEAM

VITREOUS ENAMELLER. Text in English. 1969. q. GBP 47 in Europe; USD 101.19, GBP 54 elsewhere (effective 2005). adv. bk.rev. **Document type:** *Journal, Academic/Scholarly.* **Description:** Covers every aspect of the science and technology of Vitreous Enamel.
Formerly (until 1968): Institute of Vitreous Enamellers. Bulletin and Proceedings (0537-9709)
Indexed: BrCerAb, C&ISA, CerAb, ChemAb, CivEngAb, CorrAb, E&CAJ, EMA, IAA, M&TEA, MBF, METADEX, RefZh, SolStAb, WAA.
—BLDSC (9244.200000), CASDDS, CISTI, Linda Hall.
Published by: Institute of Vitreous Enamellers, 39 Sweetbriar Way, Heath Hayes, Cannock, Staffs WS12 2US, United Kingdom. TEL 44-1543-450596, FAX 44-8700-941237, info@ive.org.uk, http://www.ive.org.uk/publications-ve.htm. Circ: 300.

VJESNIK ZA ARHEOLOGIJU I HISTORIJU DALMATINSKU. see *ARCHAEOLOGY*

666.152 USA
WINDOW FILM MAGAZINE. Text in English. 1999. bi-m. USD 40 (effective 2005). adv. tr.lit. back issues avail. **Document type:** *Magazine, Trade.* **Description:** Dedicated to the window tinting industry.
Published by: Key Communications, Inc., PO Box 569, Garrisonville, VA 22463. TEL 540-720-5584, FAX 540-720-5687, http://www.windowfilmmag.com, http://www.key-com.com/. Ed. Brigid O'Leary. Pub. Debra A Levy. Adv. contact Penny Stacey. page USD 1,995, color page USD 3,465. Circ: 6,000 (controlled).

C

666 690 GBR ISSN 0263-1784
WINDOW INDUSTRIES. Text in English. 1975. m. GBP 78; GBP 99 foreign (effective 1999). adv. bk.rev. **Document type:** *Trade.*
Formerly (until 1982): Double Glazing (0306-3879)
Indexed: METADEX.
Published by: Turret R A I plc, Armstrong House, 38 Market Sq, Uxbridge, Middx UB8 1TG, United Kingdom. TEL 44-1895-454545, FAX 44-1895-454647. Circ: 2,500.

WINDOW TRADE NEWS. see *BUILDING AND CONSTRUCTION*

666 POL ISSN 1429-9089
WOKOL PLYTEK CERAMICZNYCH. Text in Polish. 1998. q. PLZ 48; PLZ 12 per issue (effective 2004). adv. **Document type:** *Trade.*
Published by: Wydawnictwo SIGMA - N O T Sp. z o.o., ul Ratuszowa 11, PO Box 1004, Warsaw, 00950, Poland. TEL 48-22-8180918, FAX 48-22-6192187, informacja@sigma-not.pl, http://www.sigma-not.pl. Ed. Krystyna Wisniewska TEL 48-22-8262027. adv.: color page PLZ 6,400.

666 GBR ISSN 0959-6127
TP785 CODEN: WCREEJ
WORLD CERAMICS & REFRACTORIES. Text in English. 1990. bi-m. GBP 148; GBP 170 foreign (effective 1999). adv. bk.rev. abstr.; illus.; tr.lit. **Document type:** *Trade.* **Description:** Trade publication covering all aspects of ceramics, refractories, heavy clay, brick, pipe and tile and industrial ceramic industries, from manufacturers to suppliers.
Formed by the 1990 merger of: Euroclay (0306-1841); Refractories Journal (0034-3110); Incorporates (in 1988): Metals and Minerals International (0265-0983); Formerly (until 1973): Claycraft (0009-8582)
Indexed: AESIS, BrCerAb, C&ISA, CRIA, CRICC, CerAb, ChemAb, CivEngAb, CorrAb, E&CAJ, EMA, IAA, IMMAb, M&TEA, MBF, METADEX, RefZh, SolStAb, WAA.
—BLDSC (9353.132000), CASDDS, CISTI, IE, Infotrieve, ingenta, Linda Hall.
Published by: London and Sheffield Publishing Co. Ltd., 291 Cricklewood Ln, Childs Hill, London, NW2 2JL, United Kingdom. TEL 44-181-455-9962, FAX 44-181-209-1231. Ed. B G R Lohan. Circ: 3,280.

WORLD GLASSWARE INDUSTRY DIRECTORY. see *BUSINESS AND ECONOMICS—Trade And Industrial Directories*

666 KOR ISSN 1225-1372
YO'EOB HAGHOEJI/KOREAN CERAMIC SOCIETY. JOURNAL. Text in Korean. 1964. m. **Document type:** *Journal, Academic/Scholarly.*
Supersedes in part (in 1974): Yoeob Hoeji (0372-7807)
Published by: Han'gug Yo'eob Haghoe/Korean Ceramic Society, Meorijae Bldg., Suite # 403, 984-1, Bangbae-3dong, Seocho-gu, Seoul, 137-849, Korea, S. TEL 82-2-5840185, FAX 82-2-5864582, http://www.ceramics.or.kr/paper/, http://www.ceramics.or.kr/main.jsp.

666 624 DEU ISSN 0341-0552
TP785 CODEN: ZIIND7
Z I INTERNATIONAL; journal for the brick and tile, structural ceramics, refractory and clay pipe industries. (Ziegelindustrie) Text in English, German; Summaries in French, Italian, Spanish. 1948. 11/yr. EUR 214.20 domestic; EUR 240 foreign; EUR 22.50 newsstand/cover (effective 2005). adv. bk.rev. charts; illus.; pat.; stat.; tr.lit. index, cum.index. **Document type:** *Journal, Trade.* **Description:** Trade publication for the brick and tile, structural ceramics, refractory and clay pipe industries. Includes calendar of events, industry and company news, topical news, preview of events, and positions available.
Formerly (until 1976): Z I: Ziegelindustrie (0044-4693)
Indexed: BrCerAb, C&ISA, CIN, CISA, CerAb, ChemAb, ChemTitl, CorrAb, E&CAJ, EMA, EngInd, F&EA, ISMEC, Inspec, RefZh, SolStAb, WAA.
—BLDSC (9512.950000), CASDDS, CISTI, EI, IE, ingenta, Linda Hall. **CCC.**
Published by: (Bundesverband der Deutschen Ziegelindustrie e.V.), Bauverlag BV GmbH (Subsidiary of: Springer Science+Business Media), Avenwedderstr 55, Guetersloh, 33311, Germany. TEL 49-5241-802119, FAX 49-5241-809582, ulrike.mattern@springer-sbm.com, http://www.zi-online.info, http://www.bauverlag.de. adv.: color page EUR 3,290, B&W page EUR 2,210. Circ: 4,654 (paid and controlled).

666 CHN ISSN 1001-9642
ZHONGGUO TAOCI/CHINESE CERAMICS. Text in Chinese. 1959. bi-m. CNY 24. adv. **Document type:** *Academic/Scholarly.*
Related titles: Online - full text ed.: (from East View Information Services).
—BLDSC (3180.125650).
Published by: Qinggong Zhonghui, Taoci Kexue Yanjiusuo/Ministry of Light Industry, Research Institute of Ceramics, 203 Xinchang Xilu, Jingdezhen, Jiangxi 333001, China. TEL 86-798-443138, FAX 86-798-442642. Ed., R&P Fanhao Zeng. Adv. contact Ziyin Xu. Circ: 3,500 (paid).

663.737 620.142 CHN ISSN 1001-6945
ZHUANWA/BRICK - TILE. Text in Chinese. 1971. bi-m. back issues avail. **Document type:** *Academic/Scholarly.*
Related titles: Online - full content ed.: (from WanFang Data Corp.); Online - full text ed.: (from East View Information Services).
Published by: (Zuojia Jianzhu Cailiao Gongye Ju), Zhuanwa, 954 Chan-An Nan Lu, Xi'an, 710061, China. TEL 86-29-5221486, 86-29-5224572, FAX 86-29-5244644, 86-29-5235744, btagency@pub.online.xa.sn.cn. Ed. Hui Xiao. **Co-sponsor:** Xi'an Ducai Yanjiu Shjiyuan.

CERAMICS, GLASS AND POTTERY—Abstracting, Bibliographies, Statistics

666 016 GBR ISSN 1743-6753
TP785 CODEN: BCTRE7
➤ **ADVANCES IN APPLIED CERAMICS**; structural, functional and bioceramics. Text in English. 1971. bi-m. USD 498 in North America to institutions; GBP 308 elsewhere to institutions (effective 2005). adv. bk.rev. abstr.; bibl.; charts; illus.; pat. index. back issues avail. **Document type:** *Journal, Academic/Scholarly.* **Description:** Covers all aspects of ceramic science and technology, including industrial production.
Former titles (until 2005): British Ceramic Transactions (0967-9782); (until 1994): British Ceramic. Transactions and Journal (0266-7606); (until 1984): British Ceramic Society. Tranactions and Journal (0307-7357); Which was formed by the merger of (1963-1971): British Ceramic Society. Journal (0524-5133); (1939-1971): British Ceramic Society. Transactions (0371-5469); Which was formerly: Ceramic Society. Transactions (0371-5655); (until 1917): English Ceramic Society. Transactions (0371-6236); (until 1903): North Staffordshire Ceramic Society. Transactions
Related titles: Online - full text ed.: ISSN 1743-6761 (from EBSCO Publishing, Gale Group, IngentaConnect, Swets Information Services).
Indexed: AESIS, ASCA, BrCerAb, BrTechI, C&ISA, CCI, CIN, CRIA, CRICC, CerAb, ChemAb, ChemTitl, CivEngAb, CorrAb, CurCont, E&CAJ, EMA, EngInd, F&EA, IAA, IBR, ISMEC, ISR, Inspec, M&TEA, MBF, METADEX, MSCI, SCI, SSCI, SolStAb, WAA.
—BLDSC (2293.460000), AskIEEE, CASDDS, CISTI, IDS, IE, Infotrieve, ingenta, Linda Hall. **CCC.**
Published by: (Institute of Materials, Minerals and Mining), Maney Publishing, Hudson Rd, Leeds, W Yorks LS9 7DL, United Kingdom. TEL 44-113-2497481, FAX 44-113-2486983, bct@materials.org.uk, maney@maney.co.uk, http://www.ingenta.com/journals/browse/maney/bct, http://www.maney.co.uk. Ed. Mohan J Edirisinghe. R&P Mark Hull TEL 44-20-74517312. Adv. contact Bob Stanton TEL 44-1527-404295. B&W page GBP 500, color page GBP 1,100; trim 210 x 297. Circ: 3,000.

540 666 USA ISSN 0895-5948
CODEN: CSCMEU
C A SELECTS. CERAMIC MATERIALS (JOURNALS). Text in English. 1988. s-w. USD 315 to non-members; USD 95 to members (effective 2005). **Document type:** *Abstract/Index.* **Description:** Covers the chemistry, production, and use of oxide and nonoxide ceramics and glass ceramics as structural and building materials, refractories, thermal and electrical insulators, membranes, solid electrolytes, cutting tools, and dishware.
Published by: Chemical Abstracts Service (C A S) (Subsidiary of: American Chemical Society), 2540 Olentangy River Rd., Columbus, OH 43210-0012. TEL 614-447-3600, FAX 614-447-3713, help@cas.com, http://www.cas.org, http://caselects.cas.org. **Subscr. to:** PO Box 3012, Columbus, OH 43210. TEL 800-753-4227, FAX 614-447-3751.

666.0272 USA ISSN 0885-0100
CODEN: CSCPE5
C A SELECTS. CERAMIC MATERIALS (PATENTS). Text in English. s-w. USD 315 to non-members; USD 95 to members (effective 2005). **Document type:** *Abstract/Index.* **Description:** Covers patents on the chemistry and technology of the ceramic industry, including cermets.
Published by: Chemical Abstracts Service (C A S) (Subsidiary of: American Chemical Society), 2540 Olentangy River Rd., Columbus, OH 43210-0012. TEL 614-447-3600, FAX 614-447-3713, help@cas.com, http://www.cas.org, http://caselects.cas.org. **Subscr. to:** PO Box 3012, Columbus, OH 43210. TEL 800-753-4227, FAX 614-447-3751.

016.666 USA ISSN 1555-6409
C S A WORLD CERAMIC ABSTRACTS. Text in English. m. USD 380 includes access to full back-file (effective 2006). **Description:** Provides comprehensive coverage of all aspects of ceramics manufacture, processing and applications.
Media: Online - full text (from Questel Orbit Inc.). **Related titles:** CD-ROM ed.: ISSN 1056-3490. USD 895 (effective 2000) (from National Information Services Corp. (N I S C)); ♦ Print ed.: Ceramic Abstracts. ISSN 0095-9960.
Published by: C S A Journal Division (Subsidiary of: Cambridge Information Group), 7200 Wisconsin Ave, Ste 715, Bethesda, MD 20814. TEL 301-961-6798, 800-843-7751, FAX 301-961-6799, journals@csa.com, http://www.csa.com.
Co-publisher: Ceram Research Ltd.

016.666 USA ISSN 0095-9960
TP785 CODEN: CEAUAA
CERAMIC ABSTRACTS. Text in English. 1922. 5/yr. USD 245 combined subscription to individuals print & online eds.; USD 510 combined subscription to institutions print & online eds. (effective 2006). adv. index. back issues avail.; reprints avail. **Document type:** *Journal, Abstract/Index.* **Description:** Includes over 200,000 abstracts and patents on ceramics and related fields.
Supersedes in part (in 1922): American Ceramic Society. Journal (0002-7820); Which was formerly (until 1917): American Ceramic Society. Transactions (0096-7394)
Related titles: CD-ROM ed.: ISSN 1056-3490. USD 895 (effective 2000) (from National Information Services Corp. (N I S C)); ♦ Online - full text ed.: C S A World Ceramic Abstracts. ISSN 1555-6409.
Indexed: CRIA.
—CISTI, Linda Hall. **CCC.**
Published by: (American Ceramic Society Inc.), C S A Journal Division (Subsidiary of: Cambridge Information Group), 7200 Wisconsin Ave, Ste 715, Bethesda, MD 20814. TEL 301-961-6798, 800-843-7751, FAX 301-961-6799, journals@csa.com, http://www.csa.com. Eds. Jennifer R Griffiths, Kathleen Hickman. Pub. Fred Durr. R&P Barbara Inkellis TEL 301-961-6718. Circ: 2,000 (paid).

666.1 FRA
FRANCE. SERVICE D'ETUDE DES STRATEGIES ET DES STATISTIQUES INDUSTRIELLES. RESULTATS MENSUELS DES ENQUETES DE BRANCHE. INDUSTRIE DU VERRE. Text in French. m. stat. **Description:** Follows developments in the glass industry through the performance of selected indicators.
Published by: Service d'Etude des Strategies et des Statistiques Industrielles (SESSI), 85 bd. du Montparnasse, Paris, Cedex 6 75270, France. TEL 45-56-42-34, FAX 45-56-40-71.

666.1 FRA
FRANCE. SERVICE D'ETUDE DES STRATEGIES ET DES STATISTIQUES INDUSTRIELLES. RESULTATS TRIMESTRIELS DES ENQUETES DE BRANCHE. INDUSTRIE DU VERRE. Text in French. q. stat. **Description:** Provides detailed industry-wide performance statistics for comparative evaluations.
Published by: Service d'Etude des Strategies et des Statistiques Industrielles (SESSI), 85 bd. du Montparnasse, Paris, Cedex 6 75270, France. TEL 45-56-42-34, FAX 45-56-40-71.

666.1 016 GBR ISSN 0017-1050
TP845 CODEN: GLSTAK
➤ **GLASS TECHNOLOGY.** Text in English. 1960. bi-m. GBP 195 domestic; GBP 216 foreign (effective 2005). adv. bk.rev. abstr. index. 40 p./no. 2 cols./p.; **Document type:** *Journal, Academic/Scholarly.* **Description:** Discusses the use of applied science in the production and manipulation of glasses of every kind. Peer reviewed reports on the physics of inorganic glasses and the glassy state.
Formerly (until 1960): Society of Glass Technology. Journal (0368-4105)
Related titles: Microform ed.: (from PMC); Online - full text ed.: (from EBSCO Publishing, Gale Group, H.W. Wilson, IngentaConnect, O C L C Online Computer Library Center, Inc.); Series: Society of Glass Technology. Journal. Section A.
Indexed: AS&TI, ASCA, BrArAb, BrCerAb, BrTechl, C&ISA, CCI, CIN, Cadscan, CerAb, ChemAb, ChemTitl, CorrAb, CurCont, E&CAJ, EMA, EngInd, ExcerpMed, IPackAb, ISMEC, ISR, Inspec, LeadAb, MSCI, RefZh, SCI, SolStAb, WAA, Zincscan.
—BLDSC (4192.100000), AskIEEE, CASDDS, CISTI, Ei, IE, Infotrieve, ingenta, Linda Hall. **CCC.**
Published by: Society of Glass Technology, Don Valley House, Savile St. East, Sheffield, S Yorks S4 7UQ, United Kingdom. TEL 44-114-2634455, FAX 44-114-2634411, gt@sgt.org, sgt@glass.demon.co.uk, http://www.sgt.org. Ed., Adv. contact David Moore. R&P Jenny Lawless. Circ: 1,250 (paid).

658.8 USA
INTERNET MARKETING TIPS. Text in English. m. free.
Description: Contains tips for marketers on putting the Internet to one's advantage.
Media: Online - full text.
Published by: Internet Marketing Center feri@marketingtips.com, http://www.marketingtips.com/. Ed. Corey Rudl.

666.1 016 GBR ISSN 0031-9090
TA450 CODEN: PCGLA6
➤ **PHYSICS AND CHEMISTRY OF GLASSES.** Text in English. 1960. bi-m. GBP 214 domestic; GBP 235 foreign (effective 2005). bk.rev. abstr.; charts; illus.; pat. index. **Document type:** *Journal, Academic/Scholarly.*
Related titles: Online - full text ed.: (from EBSCO Publishing, Gale Group, IngentaConnect).
Indexed: ASCA, BrCerAb, BrTechl, C&ISA, CCI, CIN, Cadscan, CerAb, ChemAb, ChemTitl, CorrAb, CurCont, E&CAJ, EMA, EngInd, ISR, Inspec, LeadAb, MSCI, PhysBer, RefZh, SCI, SolStAb, WAA, Zincscan.
—BLDSC (6478.100000), AskIEEE, CASDDS, CISTI, Ei, IE, Infotrieve, ingenta, Linda Hall. **CCC.**
Published by: Society of Glass Technology, Don Valley House, Savile St. East, Sheffield, S Yorks S4 7UQ, United Kingdom. TEL 44-114-2634455, FAX 44-114-2634411, pc@sgt.org, sgt@glass.demon.co.uk, http://www.sgt.org. Ed. David Moore. R&P Jenny Lawless. Circ: 1,000 (paid).

016.666 GBR ISSN 0957-8897
WORLD CERAMICS ABSTRACTS. Text in English. 1958. m. abstr. back issues avail. **Document type:** *Journal, Abstract/Index.*
Formerly (until 1989): British Ceramic Abstracts (0300-4570)
—Linda Hall. **CCC.**
Published by: Ceram Research Ltd., Queens Rd, Penkhull, Stoke-on-Trent, Staffs ST4 7LQ, United Kingdom. TEL 44-1762-764444, FAX 44-1762-412331, info@ceram.co.uk, http://www.ceram.co.uk. Ed. Ann Pace TEL 44-1782-764241. Circ: 500.

CHAMBER OF COMMERCE PUBLICATIONS

see BUSINESS AND ECONOMICS—Chamber Of Commerce Publications

CHEMICAL ENGINEERING

see ENGINEERING—Chemical Engineering

CHEMISTRY

see also CHEMISTRY—Analytical Chemistry ; CHEMISTRY—Computer Applications ; CHEMISTRY—Crystallography ; CHEMISTRY—Electrochemistry ; CHEMISTRY—Inorganic Chemistry ; CHEMISTRY—Organic Chemistry ; CHEMISTRY—Physical Chemistry

540 USA ISSN 1554-8929
▼ **A C S CHEMICAL BIOLOGY.** (American Chemical Society) Abbreviated title: Chemical Digest. Text in English. forthcoming 2006 (Jan.). m. USD 1,950 in North America to institutions; USD 2,034 elsewhere to institutions; USD 120 in North America to members; USD 204 elsewhere to members; USD 75 in North America to students; USD 159 elsewhere to students (effective 2006).
Related titles: Online - full text ed.: ISSN 1554-8937. forthcoming 2006 (Jan.). USD 70 (effective 2006).
Published by: American Chemical Society, 1155 16th St, N W, Washington, DC 20036. TEL 202-872-4600, 800-227-5558, service@acs.org, http://www.acs.org.

540 USA ISSN 0065-7719
CODEN: ACMOAG
A C S MONOGRAPH SERIES. Text in English. 1924. irreg., latest vol.191, 1998. price varies. **Document type:** *Monographic series, Academic/Scholarly.*
Formerly: American Chemical Society Monographs (0065-7751)
Indexed: BIOSIS Prev, BiolAb, ChemAb.
—CASDDS, CISTI. **CCC.**
Published by: (American Chemical Society), Oxford University Press (Subsidiary of: Oxford University Press), 2001 Evans Rd, Cary, NC 27513. TEL 919-677-0977, 800-852-7323, FAX 919-677-1714, jnlorders@oup-usa.org, http://www.oup.com/us/catalog/general/series/ACSMonographSeries/?view=usa, http://www.us.oup.com. Ed. M Joan Comstock.

540 USA ISSN 0097-6156
CODEN: ACSMC8
➤ **A C S SYMPOSIUM SERIES.** Text in English. 1974. irreg., latest vol.518, 1993. price varies. reprint service avail. from ISI. **Document type:** *Proceedings, Academic/Scholarly.*
Indexed: APIAb, APICat, APIH&E, APIOC, APIPR, APIPS, APITS, ASCA, ASFA, Agr, BIOSIS Prev, BiolAb, CCI, CIN, CTFA, ChemAb, ChemInfo, ChemTitl, CivEngAb, DSA, ESPM, EngInd, FS&TA, IMMAb, ISR, Inspec, MSB, MaizeAb, PGrRegA, RiceAb, SCI, SIA, SoyAb, TriticAb, VITIS, WeedAb.
—BLDSC (0578.895000), CASDDS, CISTI, Ei, IDS, IE, Infotrieve, ingenta, KNAW. **CCC.**
Published by: American Chemical Society, 1155 16th St, N W, Washington, DC 20036. TEL 202-872-4614, 800-227-5558, FAX 202-776-8264, service@acs.org, http://pubs.acs.org. Ed. M Joan Comstock.

540 USA ISSN 1424-6376
A R K I V O C. (Archives of Organic Chemistry) Text in English. 2000. bi-m. free (effective 2005). back issues avail.
Description: Publishes full papers describing sound original work that is of interest to organic chemists, including bio-organic and organometallic chemists.
Media: Online - full text. **Related titles:** Online - full text ed.: 2000. free (effective 2005).
Published by: Arkat USA, Inc. http://www.arkat-usa.org/. Ed. Dr. Eric Scriven.

A S B C NEWSLETTER. see *BEVERAGES*

ACADEMIA DE STIINTE A REPUBLICII MOLDOVA. BULETINUL. STIINTE BIOLOGICE SI CHIMICE/AKADEMIYA NAUK RESPUBLIKI MOLDOVA. IZVESTIYA. BIOLOGICHESKIE I KHIMICHESKIE NAUKI. see *BIOLOGY*

540 TWN ISSN 0001-3927
➤ **ACADEMIA SINICA. INSTITUTE OF CHEMISTRY. BULLETIN.** Text in English; Abstracts in Chinese. 1959. a. (in 2 vols.). exchange basis. charts; illus. **Document type:** *Bulletin, Academic/Scholarly.* **Description:** The Bulletin has two parts. Part A presents original articles, review articles and notes in all fields of chemistry. Part B is a collection of abstracts of the articles published in previous year by principal investigators in the Institute of Chemistry. The scope of the journal extends from classical organic and inorganic chemistry through materials chemistry and biophysical studies, covering all aspects in chemistry and related fields.
Indexed: CIN, ChemAb, ChemTitl, PBA.
—BLDSC (2580.200000), CISTI, ingenta.
Published by: Academia Sinica, Institute of Chemistry/Chung Yang Yen Chiu Yuan, Hua Hsueh Yen Chiu So, Nankang, Taipei, 11529, Taiwan. TEL 866-2-2782-2009, FAX 866-2-2783-1237, TELEX 17414 ACADSINA. Ed. Ling Kang Liu. Circ: 1,000.

540 USA
ACADEMIC DIGEST. Text in English. 3/yr. **Document type:** *Academic/Scholarly.*
Published by: American Chemical Society, 1155 16th St, N W, Washington, DC 20036. TEL 202-872-4614, 800-227-5558, FAX 202-776-8264, service@acs.org, http://pubs.acs.org.

540 660 FRA ISSN 1631-0748
QD1 CODEN: CRCOCR
➤ **ACADEMIE DES SCIENCES. COMPTES RENDUS. CHIMIE.** Text and summaries in English, French. 1836. 12/yr. EUR 354.50 domestic to institutions; EUR 420 in Europe to institutions; JPY 50,400 in Japan to institutions; USD 526 elsewhere to institutions (effective 2006). charts; illus. index. **Document type:** *Journal, Academic/Scholarly.* **Description:** Publishes research in all areas of applied and experimental chemistry.
Formerly (until 2001): Academie des Sciences. Comptes Rendus. Serie 2c. Chimie (1387-1609); Which superseded in part (in 1994): Academie des Sciences. Comptes Rendus. Serie 2. Mecanique, Physique, Chimie, Sciences de la Terre, Sciences de l'Univers (0764-4450); Which was formerly (until 1984): Academie des Sciences. Comptes Rendus des Seances. Serie 2: Mechanique - Physique, Chimie, Sciences de l'Univers, Sciences de la Terre (0750-7623); (until 1981): Academie des Sciences. Comptes Rendus des Seances. Serie 2: Mecanique, Physique, Chimie, Sciences de la Terre, Sciences de l'Univers (0249-6305); Which was formed by the 1981 merger of: Academie des Sciences. Comptes Rendus Hebdomadaires des Seances. Serie B: Sciences Physiques (0335-5993); Academie des Sciences. Comptes Rendus Hebdomadaires des Seances. Serie C. Sciences Chimiques (0567-6541)
Related titles: Microform ed.: (from PMC); Online - full text ed.: (from EBSCO Publishing, Gale Group, IngentaConnect, ScienceDirect, Swets Information Services); Abridged ed.
Indexed: CCI, ChemAb, CurCR, CurCont, INIS AtomInd, ISR, IndChem, Inspec, MSB, RCI, RefZh, SCI.
—BLDSC (3384.515600), AskIEEE, CASDDS, CISTI, IDS, IE, ingenta, KNAW, Linda Hall. **CCC.**
Published by: (Academie des Sciences), Elsevier France, Editions Scientifiques et Medicales (Subsidiary of: Elsevier Science & Technology), 23 Rue Linois, Paris, 75724, France. TEL 33-1-71724600, FAX 33-1-71724650, http://www.elsevier.com/locate/crci. Ed. P. Braunstein. **Subscr. to:** Elsevier BV, PO Box 211, Amsterdam 1000 AE, Netherlands. TEL 31-20-485-3757, FAX 31-20-485-3432, http://www.elsevier.nl.

➤ **ACADEMIE SERBE DES SCIENCES ET DES ARTS. CLASSE DES SCIENCES MATHEMATIQUES ET NATURELLES. BULLETIN SCIENCES NATURELLES.** see *SCIENCES: COMPREHENSIVE WORKS*

540 660 USA ISSN 0001-4478
ACCELERATOR NEWSLETTER. Text in English. 1916. m. (Sep.-May). USD 5. adv. bk.rev. illus. **Document type:** *Bulletin.* **Description:** Newsletter of the Indiana section of the ACS. Covers local section events and speakers as well as regional events. Intended to be of interest to local chemists, chemistry teachers, students, professors.
Published by: American Chemical Society, Indiana Section, PO Box 1291, Indianapolis, IN 46206-1291. TEL 317-247-8141. Ed. Wendy Hager. Circ: 1,400.

540 USA ISSN 0001-4842
QD1 CODEN: ACHRE4
➤ **ACCOUNTS OF CHEMICAL RESEARCH.** Text in English. 1968. m. USD 568 in North America to institutions; USD 618 elsewhere to institutions; USD 71 in North America to members; USD 121 elsewhere to members; USD 53 in North America to students; USD 103 elsewhere to students (effective 2006). illus. index. back issues avail.; reprints avail. **Document type:** *Journal, Academic/Scholarly.* **Description:** Contains information on major advances in basic research and applications. Brief, critical articles cover diverse areas of chemical research.
Related titles: Microfiche ed.: USD 408 in North America; USD 426 elsewhere (effective 2002); Microfilm ed.: USD 408 in North America; USD 413 elsewhere (effective 2002); Online - full text ed.: ISSN 1520-4898. USD 70 (effective 2006) (from EBSCO Publishing, Swets Information Services).
Indexed: ABIPC, ASCA, CCI, CIN, CTE, Cadscan, ChemAb, ChemInfo, ChemTitl, CurCR, CurCont, DSA, EIA, EnvAb, ExcerpMed, GSI, INIS AtomInd, ISR, IndMed, Inpharma, LeadAb, MEDLINE, MOS, MSB, MSCI, NPU, NutrAb, ProtozoAb, RA&MP, RCI, Reac, RefZh, SCI, Zincscan.
—BLDSC (0573.529660), CASDDS, CINDOC, CISTI, IDS, IE, Infotrieve, ingenta, KNAW, Linda Hall. **CCC.**
Published by: American Chemical Society, 1155 16th St, N W, Washington, DC 20036. TEL 202-872-4614, 800-227-5558, FAX 202-776-8264, service@acs.org, http://pubs.acs.org/journals/achre4/about.html. Ed. Joan Selverstone Valentine. Circ: 6,920 (paid).

540 660 SVN ISSN 1318-0207
QD1 CODEN: ACSLE7
ACTA CHIMICA SLOVENICA. Text in English; Summaries in English, Slovenian. 1954. q. EUR 110 foreign (effective 2005). adv. bk.rev. index. **Document type:** *Journal, Academic/Scholarly.*
Formerly (until 1993): Slovensko Kemijsko Drustvo. Vestnik (0560-3110)
Related titles: Online - full text ed.: ISSN 1580-3155. free (effective 2005) (from EBSCO Publishing).
Indexed: CCI, CIN, ChemAb, ChemTitl, CurCont, RefZh, VITIS.
—BLDSC (0611.015000), CASDDS, CISTI, IE, ingenta, Linda Hall.
Published by: Slovensko Kemijsko Drustvo/Slovenian Chemical Society, Hajdrihova 19, Ljubljana, 1000, Slovenia. TEL 386-1-4760252, chem.soc@ki.si, http://acta.chem-soc.si. Ed. Janez Kosmrlj. Circ: 1,400.

540 POL ISSN 1233-2356
QD79.C4
ACTA CHROMATOGRAPHICAE. Text in English. 1992. irreg.
Description: Publishes papers on all aspects of theory and practice of chromatography.
Related titles: Online - full text ed.: free (effective 2005).
Indexed: AnalAb, CCI, MSB, RefZh.
—BLDSC (0611.310000), IE, ingenta.
Published by: Uniwersytet Slaski w Katowicach, Instytut Chemii, Ul Szkolna, 9, Katowice, 40006, Poland. TEL 48-32-599978, http://www.us.edu.pl/uniwersytet/jednostki/wydzialy/chemia/acta/tekst/.

C

540 IND ISSN 0253-7338
QD1 CODEN: ACICDV
ACTA CIENCIA INDICA. CHEMISTRY. Text in English. 1974. q. USD 100 (effective 2006). adv. bk.rev. **Document type:** *Academic/Scholarly.*
Supersedes in part (in 1979): Acta Ciencia Indica (0379-5411)
Indexed: CIN, ChemAb, ChemTitl, EngInd, Inspec.
—BLDSC (0611.371000), CASDDS, CISTI, Ei, IE, ingenta, Linda Hall.
Published by: (Society for the Progress of Science), Pragati Prakashan, c/o K.K. Mittal, Business Manager, P O Box 62, Meerut, Uttar Pradesh 250 001, India. TEL 91-121-640642, FAX 91-121-663838. Circ: 1,000 (paid). **Subscr. to:** I N S I O Scientific Books & Periodicals, P O Box 7234, Indraprastha HPO, New Delhi 110 002, India. info@insio.com, http://www.insio.com.

ACTA PHARMACEUTICA TURCICA. see *PHARMACY AND PHARMACOLOGY*

ACTA PHYSICA ET CHIMICA DEBRECINA. see *PHYSICS*

669 540 FIN ISSN 1239-0518
CODEN: ASCMA4
ACTA POLYTECHNICA SCANDINAVICA. C H. CHEMICAL TECHNOLOGY SERIES. Text and summaries in English. 1958. irreg. (5-7/yr.). price varies. index, cum.index: 1958-1994. back issues avail.; reprint service avail. from PQC. **Document type:** *Monographic series, Academic/Scholarly.* **Description:** Presents research results in chemical engineering.
Former titles (until 1995): Acta Polytechnica Scandinavica. Chemical Technology and Metallurgy Series (0781-2698); (until 1983): Acta Polytechnica Scandinavica. Chemistry and Metallurgy Series (0001-6853)
Related titles: Microfilm ed.: (from PQC).
Indexed: ASCA, B&BAb, BrCerAb, C&ISA, CIN, Cadscan, CerAb, ChemAb, ChemTitl, CivEngAb, CorrAb, CurCont, E&CAJ, EMA, EngInd, IAA, IMMAb, Inspec, LeadAb, M&TEA, MBF, METADEX, RefZh, SolStAb, WAA, Zincscan.
—BLDSC (0661.255100), AskIEEE, CASDDS, CISTI, IE, Linda Hall. **CCC.**
Published by: Finnish Academies of Technology, Mariankatu 8 B 11, Helsinki, 00170, Finland. TEL 358-9-2782400, FAX 358-9-2782177, facte@facte.com. Ed. Seppo Palosaari. Circ: 500.

540.7 POL ISSN 0208-6182
CODEN: AULCD2
ACTA UNIVERSITATIS LODZIENSIS: FOLIA CHIMICA. Text in Polish; Summaries in Multiple languages. 1955-1974; N.S. 1982. irreg. **Document type:** *Academic/Scholarly.* **Description:** Provides scientific research papers on physical, organic, inorganic and general chemistry.
Supersedes in part: Uniwersytet Lodzki. Zeszyty Naukowe. Seria 2: Nauki Matematyczno-Przyrodnicze (0076-0366)
Indexed: CIN, ChemAb, ChemTitl.
—CASDDS, CISTI, KNAW, Linda Hall.
Published by: Wydawnictwo Uniwersytetu Lodzkiego/Lodz University Press, ul Jaracza 34, Lodz, 90262, Poland. TEL 331671. **Dist. by:** Ars Polona, Krakowskie Przedmiescie 7, Warsaw, Poland.

540 CZE ISSN 0232-0061
ACTA UNIVERSITATIS PALACKIANAE OLOMUCENSIS. FACULTAS RERUM NATURALIUM. CHEMICA. Text in Czech. 1973. irreg.
Formerly (until 1981): Univerzita Palackeho v Olomouci. Prirodovedecka Fakulta. Sbornik Praci. Chemica (0231-6099)
Indexed: RefZh.
—BLDSC (0585.420000), Linda Hall.
Published by: Univerzita Palackeho v Olomouci, Prirodovedecka Fakulta, tr Svobody 26, c.p.686, Olomouc, 77146, Czech Republic. TEL 420-68-5634060, FAX 420-68-5225737, dekanprf@risc.upd.cz, http://www.upd.cz.

540 FRA ISSN 0151-9093
CODEN: ACCHDG
➤ **ACTUALITE CHIMIQUE.** Text in French. 1973. 11/yr. FRF 1,100; FRF 1,367 foreign (effective 1998). adv. bk.rev. bibl.; charts; illus. back issues avail. **Document type:** *Academic/Scholarly.*
Indexed: ASCA, CCI, CIN, CISA, ChemAb, ChemInfo, ChemTitl, EngInd, ExcerpMed, INIS AtomInd, SSCI, VITIS.
—BLDSC (0677.102000), CASDDS, CISTI, Ei, IDS, IE, Infotrieve, ingenta, Linda Hall. **CCC.**
Published by: Societe Francaise de Chimie, 250 rue Saint-Jacques, Paris, 75005, France. TEL 33-1-40467160, FAX 33-1-40467161. Circ: 2,378 (controlled). **Co-sponsor:** Societe de Chimie Industrielle.

➤ **ADHAESION - KLEBEN & DICHTEN;** Klebstoffe, Dichtstoffe, Geraete- und Anlagentechnik, Anwendungen. see *PLASTICS*

540 JPN ISSN 0917-9917
ADSORPTION NEWS★. Text in English, Japanese. 1987. q. **Document type:** *Newsletter.*
Published by: Nihon Kyuchaku Gakkai/Japan Society on Adsorption, Department of Molecular and Material Sciences, Graduate School of Engineering Sciences, Kyushu University, Kasuga-shi, Fukuoka 816-8580, Japan. TEL 81-92-5837526, FAX 81-92-5730342, jsad@mm.kyushu-u.ac.jp, http://www.chem.kumamoto-u.ac.jp/~jsad/index_j.html. Ed. Katsumi Kaneko.

ADVANCED BATTERY TECHNOLOGY. see *ENGINEERING—Electrical Engineering*

ADVANCED FUEL CELL TECHNOLOGY. see *ENGINEERING—Chemical Engineering*

660 DEU ISSN 1615-4150
QD1 CODEN: ASCAF7
➤ **ADVANCED SYNTHESIS & CATALYSIS.** Abbreviated title: A S C. Text in English. 1992. 18/yr. EUR 1,258 in Europe; CHF 1,928 in Switzerland & Liechtenstein; USD 1,468 elsewhere; EUR 1,384 combined subscription in Europe print & online eds.; CHF 2,121 combined subscription in Switzerland & Liechtenstein, for print & online eds.; USD 1,615 combined subscription elsewhere print & online eds. (effective 2006). bk.rev. charts; illus. index. 100 p./no.; reprint service avail. from PQC. **Document type:** *Journal, Academic/Scholarly.* **Description:** Scientific journal covering all fields of applied organic chemistry using catalytic methods.
Former titles (until 2001): Journal fuer Praktische Chemie - Practical Applications and Applied Chemistry (1436-9966); (until 1999): Journal fuer Praktische Chemie. Chemiker-Zeitung (0941-1216); Which was formed by the merger of (1828-1992): Journal fuer Praktische Chemie (0021-8383); Which was formerly (until 1954): Journal fuer Makromolekulaere Chemie (0368-301X); (1878-1992): Chemiker-Zeitung (0009-2894); Which was formerly (until 1970): Chemiker-Zeitung, Chemische Apparatur, Verfahrenstechnik (0942-7686); (until 1968): Chemiker-Zeitung, Chemische Apparatur (0375-8710); (until 1959): Chemiker-Zeitung (0942-7678)
Related titles: Microfiche ed.: (from BHP); Microfilm ed.: (from PMC, PQC); Online - full text ed.: ISSN 1615-4169. EUR 1,258 in Europe to institutions; CHF 1,928 to institutions in Switzerland & Liechtenstein; USD 1,468 elsewhere to institutions (effective 2006) (from EBSCO Publishing, Swets Information Services, Wiley InterScience).
Indexed: ASCA, ASFA, CCI, CEABA, CIN, Cadscan, ChemAb, ChemInfo, ChemTitl, CurCR, CurCont, DBA, ExcerpMed, FS&TA, ISR, IndChem, Inspec, LeadAb, RCI, RefZh, SCI.
—BLDSC (0696.931980), AskIEEE, CASDDS, CINDOC, CISTI, IDS, IE, ingenta, Linda Hall. **CCC.**
Published by: Wiley - V C H Verlag GmbH & Co. KGaA (Subsidiary of: John Wiley & Sons, Inc.), Boschstr 12, Weinheim, 69469, Germany. TEL 49-6201-6060, FAX 49-6201-117, 49-6201-606328, asc@wiley-vch.de, subservice@wiley-vch.de, http://www.wiley-vch.de. Eds. J Richmond, R Noyori. R&P Claudia Rutz. Adv. contact Simone Tremmel TEL 49-6201-606562. Circ: 600.

540 512 MEX ISSN 0188-7009
➤ **ADVANCES IN APPLIED CLIFFORD ALGEBRAS.** Text in Spanish. 1991. 3/yr. bk.rev. **Document type:** *Journal, Academic/Scholarly.* **Description:** Covers Clifford Algebras and their applications to other branches of mathematics and physics.
Related titles: Online - full text ed.; Supplement(s): Advances in Applied Clifford Algebras. Proceedings Supplement.
Indexed: Inspec, MathR, MathSciNet.
—BLDSC (0698.937000), IE, ingenta.
Published by: Universidad Nacional Autonoma de Mexico, Facultad de Quimica, Apartado Postal 70-197, Mexico, D.F., 04510 , Mexico. TEL 52-5-6223439, FAX 52-5-6223711, andoni@servidor.unam.mx, http://www.clifford.org/~clf-alg.

540 ISR
ADVANCES IN DYNAMIC STEREOCHEMISTRY. Text in English. 1985. a. (2 vols.). USD 60 (effective 1999). **Document type:** *Academic/Scholarly.*
Published by: Freund Publishing House, Ltd., P O Box 35010, Tel Aviv, 61350, Israel. TEL 972-3-5628540, FAX 972-3-5628538, h_freund@netvision.net.il, http://www.freundpublishing.com. Ed. Marcel Gielen.

660 USA ISSN 1075-1629
QD921 CODEN: AMCLEV
ADVANCES IN METAL AND SEMICONDUCTOR CLUSTERS. Text in English. 1992. irreg., latest vol.5, 2001. price varies. **Document type:** *Monographic series, Academic/Scholarly.* **Description:** Focuses on spectroscopic measurements of molecular structure, kinetic and dynamic measurements of cluster chemistry, quantum theoretical models of cluster bonding, synthesis of new materials from clusters, and attempts to synthesize and isolate clusters in macroscopic quantities.
Indexed: CIN, ChemAb, ChemTitl, MSB.
—BLDSC (0709.404000), CASDDS, CISTI. **CCC.**
Published by: J A I Press Inc. (Subsidiary of: Elsevier Science & Technology), 360 Park Ave S, New York, NY 10010-1710. TEL 212-989-5800, FAX 212-633-3990, usinfo-f@elsevier.com, http://www.elsevier.com/wps/find/bookdescription.cws_home/BS_AMSCC/description#description. Ed. Michael A Duncan.

540 GBR
ADVANCES IN PROCESS CONTROL 5. Text in English. 1985. **Document type:** *Proceedings.*
—BLDSC (0710.902000).
Published by: Institution of Chemical Engineers, George E Davis Bldg, 165-189 Railway Terr, Rugby, Warks CV21 3HQ, United Kingdom. TEL 44-1788-578214, FAX 44-1788-560833, http://www.icheme.org/learning/.

541.28 USA ISSN 0065-3276
QD453 CODEN: AQCHA9
➤ **ADVANCES IN QUANTUM CHEMISTRY.** Text in English. 1964. irreg., latest vol.41, 2002. USD 175 per vol. vol.46 (effective 2004). index. reprint service avail. from ISI. **Document type:** *Academic/Scholarly.* **Description:** Presents surveys of current developments in this rapidly developing field that falls between the historically established areas of mathematics, physics, and chemistry.
Related titles: Online - full text ed.: (from ScienceDirect).
Indexed: ASCA, CCI, CIN, ChemAb, ChemTitl, ISR, Inspec, PhysBer, SCI.
—CASDDS, CISTI, IE, Linda Hall. **CCC.**
Published by: Academic Press (Subsidiary of: Elsevier Science & Technology), 525 B St, Ste 1900, San Diego, CA 92101-4495. TEL 619-231-6616, 800-894-3434, apsubs@acad.com, http://www.academicpress.com. Ed. Per Olov Lowdin.

540 USA ISSN 1068-7459
QD380 CODEN: ASUCEY
ADVANCES IN SUPRAMOLECULAR CHEMISTRY. Text in English. 1990. irreg., latest vol.7, 2000. price varies. back issues avail. **Document type:** *Monographic series, Academic/Scholarly.* **Description:** Presents a variety of articles that encompass the broad scope of supramolecular chemistry.
Indexed: CIN, ChemAb, ChemTitl.
—BLDSC (0711.593950), CASDDS, Linda Hall. **CCC.**
Published by: J A I Press Inc. (Subsidiary of: Elsevier Science & Technology), 360 Park Ave S, New York, NY 10010-1710. TEL 212-989-5800, FAX 212-633-3990, usinfo-f@elsevier.com, http://www.elsevier.com/wps/find/bookdescription.cws_home/BS_ASC/description#description. Ed. George Gokel.

540 USA ISSN 0278-6826
TP244.A3 CODEN: ASTYDQ
➤ **AEROSOL SCIENCE AND TECHNOLOGY.** Text in English. 1982. m. GBP 683, USD 1,127 combined subscription to institutions print & online eds. (effective 2006). bk.rev. reprint service avail. from PSC. **Document type:** *Journal, Academic/Scholarly.* **Description:** Covers theoretical and experimental investigations of aerosol and closely related phenomena.
Incorporates (1985-1988): Atomisation and Spray Technology (0266-3481)
Related titles: Microform ed.: (from PQC); Online - full text ed.: ISSN 1521-7388. GBP 649, USD 1,071 to institutions (effective 2006) (from EBSCO Publishing, Gale Group, IngentaConnect, O C L C Online Computer Library Center, Inc., ScienceDirect, Swets Information Services).
Indexed: ASCA, ASFA, ApMecR, BrCerAb, C&ISA, CCI, CEA, CEABA, CIN, CMCI, CerAb, ChemAb, ChemTitl, CivEngAb, CorrAb, CurCont, E&CAJ, EIA, EMA, EPB, ESPM, EnerInd, EnerRev, EngInd, EnvEAb, ExcerpMed, FLUIDEX, GEOBASE, IAA, INIS AtomInd, ISR, Inspec, M&GPA, M&TEA, MBF, METADEX, MSB, PollutAb, SCI, SolStAb, TCEA, WAA.
—BLDSC (0729.835400), AskIEEE, CASDDS, CISTI, Ei, IDS, IE, Infotrieve, ingenta, Linda Hall. **CCC.**
Published by: (American Association for Aerosol Research), Taylor & Francis Inc. (Subsidiary of: Taylor & Francis Group), 325 Chestnut St, Ste 800, Philadelphia, PA 19106. TEL 215-625-8900, 800-354-1420, FAX 215-625-2940, info@taylorandfrancis.com, http://www.tandf.co.uk/journals/titles/02786826.asp, http://www.taylorandfrancis.com. Ed. Richard C Flagan. **Subscr. addr. in Europe:** Taylor & Francis Ltd, Journals Customer Service, Rankine Rd, Basingstoke, Hants RG24 8PR, United Kingdom. TEL 44-1256-813000, FAX 44-1256-330245, enquiry@tandf.co.uk.

541 660 ESP ISSN 0001-9704
TP1 CODEN: AFINAE
➤ **AFINIDAD;** revista de quimica teorica y aplicada. Text in English, Spanish; Summaries in Catalan, English, Spanish. 1921. bi-m. EUR 36.06 domestic; EUR 36.06 in Portugal; EUR 36.06 in Latin America; USD 80 elsewhere (effective 2003). adv. bk.rev. charts; illus. index. **Document type:** *Academic/Scholarly.*
Indexed: ASCA, CCI, CEABA, CIN, Cadscan, ChemAb, ChemTitl, CurCont, IECT, ISR, LeadAb, MSB, RCI, RefZh, SCI, SIA, VITIS, WSCA, WeedAb, Zincscan.
—BLDSC (0732.000000), CASDDS, CINDOC, CISTI, IDS, IE, Infotrieve, ingenta, Linda Hall. **CCC.**
Published by: Asociacion de Quimicos e Ingenieros, Instituto Quimico de Sarria, Via Augusta, 390, Barcelona, 08017, Spain. TEL 34-93-2672000, FAX 34-93-2804276, aiqs@iqs.es, afin@iqs.es, http://www.aiqs.es. Ed. Jaume Arboles. Adv. contact Anton Ma Sitjes TEL 34-93-2672000. B&W page EUR 401, color page EUR 802; 210 x 297. Circ: 5,000 (controlled).

➤ **AG-CHEM AGE/NOYAKU JIDAI.** see *AGRICULTURE*

➤ **AGROCHEMIA/AGRICULTURAL CHEMICALS.** see *AGRICULTURE*

C

➤ **AGROCHIMICA**; rivista internazionale di chimica vegetale, pedologia e fertilizzazione del suolo. see *AGRICULTURE*

➤ **AGROTECHNIKA**; poradnik nawozenia i ochrony roslin. see *AGRICULTURE*

➤ **AKADEMIA ROLNICZA, POZNAN. ROCZNIKI. FIZYKA, CHEMIA.** see *PHYSICS*

540 GEO
QD1 CODEN: IGSKDH
➤ **AKADEMIYA NAUK GRUZII. IZVESTIYA. SERIYA KHIMICHESKAYA.** Text in Georgian, Russian, English. 1975. q. USD 180 foreign (effective 2003). abstr.; bibl.; charts; illus. reprints avail. **Document type:** *Journal, Academic/Scholarly.*
Formerly: Akademiya Nauk Gruzinskoi S.S.R. Izvestiya. Seriya Khimicheskaya (0132-6074)
Indexed: AnalAb, ChemAb, MaizeAb, RefZh.
—CASDDS, CISTI, Linda Hall. **CCC.**
Published by: Georgian Academy of Sciences, Rustaveli pr 52, Tbilisi, 380008, Georgia. TEL 995-32-995480, FAX 995-32-998823. Circ: 100 (paid).

➤ **AKADEMIYA NAUK TURKMENISTANA. IZVESTIYA. SERIYA FIZIKO-TEKHNICHESKIKH, KHIMICHESKIKH I GEOLOGICHESKIKH NAUK.** see *PHYSICS*

540 GBR ISSN 1369-7048
QD1
ALCHEMIST. Text in English. 199?. w. free. adv. bk.rev. **Document type:** *Newsletter.* **Description:** Summariezes current news stories with links to about each story. Readers can access research news, links to selected web sites, topics currently discussed on chemistry lists and newsgroups, and a conference diary.
Media: Online - full text.
Published by: ChemWeb Inc., 50 New Bond St, London, W1Y 9HA, United Kingdom. TEL 44-171-499-4748, FAX 44-171-499-4102, info@chemweb.com, http://chemweb.com./alchem/home.html. Adv. contact Hugh Jenkins.

ALMANAK NUKLIR BIOLOGI DAN KIMIA. see *ENERGY—Nuclear Energy*

540.1 GBR ISSN 0002-6980
QD1 CODEN: AMBXAO
➤ **AMBIX.** Text in English. 1937. 3/yr. (in 1 vol., 3 nos./vol.). USD 69 in North America to individuals; GBP 38 elsewhere to individuals; USD 144 in North America to institutions; GBP 84 elsewhere to institutions (effective 2005). adv. bk.rev. illus. index, cum.index. **Document type:** *Journal, Academic/Scholarly.* **Description:** Facilitate the publication of high-quality research and discussion in all aspects of the history of alchemy and chemistry, including the chemical industry, as well as the history of pharmacy and environmental studies of the chemical industry.
Related titles: Online - full text ed.: (from EBSCO Publishing, IngentaConnect).
Indexed: AmH&L, CIN, ChemAb, ChemTitl, HistAb, IndIslam, PCI.
—BLDSC (0809.000000), CASDDS, CISTI, IE, Infotrieve, ingenta, Linda Hall. **CCC.**
Published by: (Society for the History of Alchemy and Chemistry), Maney Publishing, Hudson Rd, Leeds, W Yorks LS9 7DL, United Kingdom. TEL 44-113-2497481, FAX 44-113-2486983, maney@maney.co.uk, http://www.maney.co.uk/search?fwaction=show&fwid=468. Ed. Dr. Peter J T Morris. Circ: 500.

540.71025 USA ISSN 0193-5011
Z5525.U5
AMERICAN CHEMICAL SOCIETY. DIRECTORY OF GRADUATE RESEARCH. Text in English. 1955. biennial. USD 60. back issues avail. **Document type:** *Directory, Academic/Scholarly.*
Related titles: Online - full text ed.
—BLDSC (3593.800000), CASDDS. **CCC.**
Published by: (Committee on Professional Training), American Chemical Society, 1155 16th St, N W, Washington, DC 20036. TEL 202-872-4614, 800-227-5558, FAX 202-776-8264, service@acs.org, http://pubs.acs.org. **Subscr. to:** Member & Subscriber Services, PO Box 3337, Columbus, OH 43210. TEL 614-447-3776, 800-333-9511, FAX 614-447-3671.

540 USA ISSN 0002-7863
QD1 CODEN: JACSAT
➤ **AMERICAN CHEMICAL SOCIETY. JOURNAL.** Text in English. 1879. w. USD 3,418 in North America to institutions; USD 3,773 elsewhere to institutions; USD 425 in North America to members; USD 780 elsewhere to members; USD 319 in North America to students; USD 674 elsewhere to students (effective 2006). adv. bk.rev. charts; illus. index. back issues avail.; reprints avail. **Document type:** *Journal, Academic/Scholarly.* **Description:** Documents advances in all areas of chemical research. Publishes papers across a wide range of chemistry, presenting new methodologies applied to important problems, new synthetic methods, novel theoretical advances and significant new results on structures and reactions.
Supersedes in part (in 1914): American Chemical Journal (0096-4085); (in 1893): Journal of Analytical and Applied Chemistry
Related titles: CD-ROM ed.; Microfiche ed.: USD 2,457 in North America to institutions; USD 2,534 elsewhere to institutions (effective 2002) (from PMC); Microfilm ed.: USD 2,457 in North America to institutions; USD 2,552 elsewhere to institutions (effective 2002); Online - full text ed.: ISSN 1520-5126. USD 100 (effective 2006) (from EBSCO Publishing, Swets Information Services).
Indexed: ABIPC, AESIS, AS&TI, ASCA, ASFA, ApMecR, ApicAb, BIOBASE, BIOSIS Prev, BPRC&P, BiolAb, BrCerAb, BullT&T, CCI, CIN, CPA, CTE, Cadscan, ChemAb, ChemInfo, ChemTitl, CurCR, CurCont, DBA, DSA, ESPM, EngInd, ExcerpMed, FS&TA, GSI, HortAb, IABS, INIS AtomInd, ISR, IndChem, IndMed, Inpharma, Inspec, LeadAb, MEDLINE, MOS, MSB, MSCI, NPU, NRN, NucAcAb, NutrAb, OrnHort, PetrolAb, ProtozoAb, RA&MP, RAPRA, RCI, RM&VM, Reac, RefZh, S&F, SCI, SIA, VITIS, Zincscan.
—BLDSC (4685.000000), AskIEEE, CASDDS, CINDOC, CISTI, Ei, IDS, IE, Infotrieve, ingenta, Linda Hall. **CCC.**
Published by: American Chemical Society, 1155 16th St, N W, Washington, DC 20036. TEL 202-872-4614, 800-227-5558, FAX 202-776-8264, jacs.aus@cm.utexas.edu, service@acs.org, http://pubs.acs.org/journals/jacsat/index.html. Eds. Charlotte Steigers Sauer, Peter J Stang. Circ: 13,000 (paid). **Subscr. to:** Member & Subscriber Services, PO Box 3337, Columbus, OH 43210. TEL 614-447-3776, 800-333-9511, FAX 614-447-3671.

540 CAN
AMERICAN CHEMISTRY. Text in English. bi-m. **Document type:** *Magazine, Trade.* **Description:** Targets chemical industry executives, regulatory officials and consultants who make and influence the decisions and policies that govern the business of chemistry in the U.S.
Published by: (American Chemistry Council USA), Kenilworth Media Inc., 710 -15 Wertheim Court, Richmond Hill, ON L4B 3H7, Canada. TEL 905-771-7333, 877-738-7624, FAX 905-771-7336, publisher@kenilworth.com, http://www.kenilworth.com. Circ: 14,000 (controlled).

540 USA
AMERICAN INSTITUTE OF CHEMISTS. PROFESSIONAL DIRECTORY. Text in English. 1969. a. USD 75 to non-members; USD 20 to members (effective 2000). adv. **Document type:** *Newsletter, Trade.*
Formerly: American Institute of Chemists. Membership Directory (0084-6376)
—**CCC.**
Published by: American Institute of Chemists, Inc., 1620 I St NW, Ste. 615, Washington, DC 20006-4005. TEL 703-836-2090. Ed., Pub., R&P, Adv. contact Sharon Dobson. Circ: 5,000.

AMERICAN LEATHER CHEMISTS ASSOCIATION. JOURNAL. see *LEATHER AND FUR INDUSTRIES*

AMERICAN SOCIETY OF BREWING CHEMISTS. JOURNAL. see *BEVERAGES*

542 ZAF ISSN 1017-317X
ANALYTICAL REPORTER. Text in English. 1988. ZAR 275 domestic; ZAR 356 foreign (effective 2003).
Published by: Primedia Publishing, 366 Pretoria Ave, Ferndale, Randburg, Transvaal 2194, South Africa. TEL 27-11-787-5725, FAX 27-11-787-5776, http://www.primemags.co.za.

543 JPN ISSN 0910-6340
CODEN: ANSCEN
➤ **ANALYTICAL SCIENCES.** Text in English. 1985. m. USD 120 to individuals; USD 240 to institutions (effective 2004). back issues avail. **Document type:** *Journal, Academic/Scholarly.* **Description:** Publishes papers on all aspects of the theory and practice of analytical sciences, including fundamental and applied, inorganic and organic, wet chemical and instrumental methods.
Related titles: Online - full text ed.: ISSN 1348-2246. free (effective 2005) (from EBSCO Publishing, J-Stage).
Indexed: ASCA, AnalAb, CCI, CIN, ChemAb, ChemTitl, ChromAb, CurCont, FCA, HortAb, INIS AtomInd, ISR, MSB, NutrAb, RCI, RefZh, SCI, SIA, VITIS.
—BLDSC (0897.139500), CASDDS, CISTI, IDS, IE, Infotrieve, ingenta, Linda Hall. **CCC.**
Published by: Japan Society for Analytical Chemistry/Nihon Bunseki Kagaku Kai, 1-26-2 Nishigotanda, Shinagawa, Tokyo, 141-0031, Japan. TEL 81-3-34903351, FAX 81-3-34903572, analytsci@jsac.or.jp, http://wwwsoc.nii.ac.jp/jsac/analsci.html. Ed. H Watarai. Circ: 3,600. **Subscr. to:** Royal Society of Chemistry, Journals Subscription Dept, Distribution Centre, Blackhouse Rd, Letchworth, Herts SG6 1HN, United Kingdom. FAX 44-1462-480947; Maruzen Co., Ltd., Export Dept., PO Box 5050, Tokyo International 100-3191, Japan. FAX 81-3-3278-9256.

540 DEU ISSN 0044-8249
QD1 CODEN: ANCEAD
ANGEWANDTE CHEMIE. Text in German. 1888. 48/yr. EUR 3,498 in Europe to institutions; CHF 6,038 to institutions in Switzerland & Liechtenstein; USD 4,798 elsewhere to institutions; EUR 3,848 combined subscription in Europe to institutions print & online eds.; CHF 6,642 combined subscription to institutions in Switzerland & Liechtenstein, for print and online eds.; USD 5,278 combined subscription elsewhere to institutions print & online eds. (effective 2006). adv. bk.rev. illus. back issues avail. **Document type:** *Journal, Academic/Scholarly.*
Incorporates (1960-1990): Zeitschrift fuer Chemie (0044-2402); Former titles (until 1949): Angewandte Chemie. A, Wissenschaftlicher Teil (0170-9046); (until 1947): Die Chemie (0932-2159); (until 1942): Angewandte Chemie (0932-2140); (until 1932): Zeitschrift fuer Angewandte Chemie (0932-2132); (until 1921): Zeitschrift fuer Angewandte Chemie. Ausgabe A
Related titles: Microfilm ed.: (from PQC, VCI); Online - full text ed.: ISSN 1521-3757. EUR 3,498 in Europe to institutions; CHF 6,038 to institutions in Switzerland & Liechtenstein; USD 4,798 elsewhere to institutions (effective 2006) (from EBSCO Publishing, Swets Information Services, Wiley InterScience); ♦ International ed.: Angewandte Chemie (International Edition). ISSN 1433-7851; ♦ Supplement(s): Chemistry. ISSN 0947-6539.
Indexed: A&ATA, ABIPC, ASCA, ASFA, BPRC&P, BiolAb, CEABA, Cadscan, ChemAb, ChemInfo, CivEngAb, CurCR, CurCont, ExcerpMed, ISR, IndChem, IndIslam, IndMed, LeadAb, NutrAb, ProtozoAb, RM&VM, RefZh, SCI, SSCI, Zincscan.
—BLDSC (0902.000000), CASDDS, CINDOC, CISTI, IE, ingenta, Linda Hall. **CCC.**
Published by: (Gesellschaft Deutscher Chemiker), Wiley - V C H Verlag GmbH & Co. KGaA (Subsidiary of: John Wiley & Sons, Inc.), Boschstr 12, Weinheim, 69469, Germany. TEL 49-6201-6060, FAX 49-6201-606328, subservice@wiley-vch.de, http://www.angewandte.de, http://www.wiley-vch.de. Ed. Peter Goelitz. R&P Claudia Rutz. Adv. contact Simone Tremmel TEL 49-6201-606562. B&W page EUR 2,800, color page EUR 4,250. Circ: 3,620 (paid). **Subscr. in the Americas to:** John Wiley & Sons, Inc., 111 River St, Hoboken, NJ 07030-5774. TEL 201-748-6645, FAX 201-748-6088, subinfo@wiley.com; **Subscr. outside Germany, Austria & Switzerland to:** John Wiley & Sons Ltd., The Atrium, Southern Gate, Chichester, West Sussex PO19 8SQ, United Kingdom. TEL 44-1243-779777, FAX 44-1243-775878.

540 DEU ISSN 1433-7851
QD1 CODEN: ACIEF5
➤ **ANGEWANDTE CHEMIE (INTERNATIONAL EDITION).** Text in English. 1961. 48/yr. EUR 3,748 in Europe; CHF 6,388 in Switzerland & Liechtenstein; USD 5,168 elsewhere; EUR 4,123 combined subscription in Europe print & online eds.; CHF 7,027 combined subscription in Switzerland & Liechtenstein, for print and online eds.; USD 5,685 combined subscription elsewhere print & online eds. (effective 2006). adv. bk.rev. illus. Index. reprints avail. **Document type:** *Journal, Academic/Scholarly.*
Formerly (until 1998): Angewandte Chemie: International Edition in English (0570-0833)
Related titles: Microfilm ed.: (from VCI); Online - full text ed.: ISSN 1521-3773. EUR 3,748 in Europe to institutions; CHF 6,388 to institutions in Switzerland & Liechtenstein; USD 5,168 elsewhere to institutions (effective 2006) (from EBSCO Publishing, Swets Information Services, Wiley InterScience); ♦ International ed. of: Angewandte Chemie. ISSN 0044-8249.
Indexed: ABIPC, ASCA, BIOBASE, CCI, CIN, ChemAb, ChemInfo, ChemTitl, CurCR, CurCont, DBA, EngInd, FS&TA, HelmAb, HortAb, IABS, ISR, IndChem, IndVet, Inpharma, Inspec, MEDLINE, MOS, MSCI, NPU, OrnHort, PE&ON, ProtozoAb, RCI, Reac, RefZh, SCI, VITIS, VetBull.
—BLDSC (0902.000500), AskIEEE, CASDDS, CINDOC, CISTI, Ei, IE, ingenta, Linda Hall. **CCC.**
Published by: Wiley - V C H Verlag GmbH & Co. KGaA (Subsidiary of: John Wiley & Sons, Inc.), Boschstr 12, Weinheim, 69469, Germany. TEL 49-6201-606-0, FAX 49-6201-606-328, subservice@wiley-vch.de, http://www3.interscience.wiley.com/cgi-bin/home. Ed. Peter Goelitz. Adv. contact Marion Schulz TEL 49-6201-606565. B&W page EUR 2,800, color page EUR 4,250. Circ: 3,390. **Subscr. in the Americas to:** John Wiley & Sons, Inc., 111 River St, Hoboken, NJ 07030-5774. TEL 201-748-6645, FAX 201-748-6088, uscs-wis@wiley.com; **Subscr. outside Germany, Austria & Switzerland to:** John Wiley & Sons Ltd., The Atrium, Southern Gate, Chichester, West Sussex PO19 8SQ, United Kingdom. TEL 44-1243-779777, FAX 44-1243-775878.

540 CHN ISSN 1006-8376
ANJISUAN HE SHENGWU ZIYUAN/AMINO ACIDS AND BIOTIC RESOURCES. Text in Chinese. q. CNY 5 domestic (effective 2000).
Related titles: Online - full content ed.: (from WanFang Data Corp.); Online - full text ed.: (from East View Information Services).
Published by: (Wuhan Shi Kexue Jieshu Qingbao Yanjiusuo), Wuhan Daxue, Luojiashan, Wuchang-qu, Wuhan, Hubei 430072, China. TEL 86-27-87664846. Ed. Guang-cun He.

C

540.1 USA ISSN 0172-4967
ANLEITUNG FUER DIE CHEMISCHE LABORATORIUMSPRAXIS - CHEMICAL LABORATORY PRACTICE. Text in English. 1970. irreg., latest vol.24, 1989. price varies. reprint service avail. from ISI. **Document type:** *Monographic series.*
Formerly: Anleitung fuer die Chemische Laboratoriumspraxis (0066-1910)
Published by: Springer-Verlag New York, Inc. (Subsidiary of: Springer Science+Business Media), 233 Spring St, New York, NY 10013. TEL 212-460-1500, FAX 212-473-6272. Ed. H Mayer-Kaupp.

540 FIN ISSN 1239-6311
QD1 CODEN: AAFCAX
ANNALES ACADEMIAE SCIENTIARUM FENNICAE. CHEMICA. Text in English, French, German. 1909. irreg. price varies. back issues avail. **Document type:** *Academic/Scholarly.*
Formerly (until 1995): Annales Academiae Scientiarum Fennicae. Series A, II: Chemica (0066-1961); Which superseded in part (in 1941): Annales Academiae Scientiarum Fennicae. Series A (0365-673X)
Related titles: Microform ed.
Indexed: AnalAb, BibAg, BiolAb, ChemAb, ExcerpMed, HortAb, INIS AtomInd, IndMed, Inspec.
—AskIEEE, CASDDS, CISTI, KNAW, Linda Hall.
Published by: Suomalainen Tiedeakatemia/Academia Scientiarum Fennica, Mariankatu 5, Helsinki, 00170, Finland. TEL 358-9-636800, FAX 358-9-660117, acadsci@acadsci.fi, http://www.acadsci.fi. Ed. Lauri Niinistoe. Circ: 330. **Dist. by:** Bookstore Tiedekirja, Kirkkokatu 14, Helsinki 00170, Finland. TEL 358-9-635177, FAX 358-9-635017, tiedekirja@pp.kolumbus.fi, http://www.tsv.fi/tkirja/tiekirj.html.

540 FRA ISSN 0151-9107
QD1 CODEN: ANCPAC
➤ **ANNALES DE CHIMIE: SCIENCE DES MATERIAUX.** Text and summaries in English, French. 1789. 6/yr. EUR 402 in Europe to institutions; USD 483 elsewhere to institutions (effective 2003). adv. bk.rev. illus. index. back issues avail.; reprint service avail. from ISI. **Document type:** *Journal, Academic/Scholarly.* **Description:** Publishes original reports and developments in the fields of metal manufacturing, solid mineral compounds, macromolecular organic compounds, thermodynamic properties, reactivity, reactive kinetics, and geochemistry.
Supersedes in part (in 1914): Annales de Chimie et de Physique (0365-1444); Which was formerly (until 1816): Annales de Chimie (0003-3936)
Related titles: Microform ed.: (from PMC, PQC); Online - full text ed.: (from EBSCO Publishing, Gale Group, IngentaConnect, ScienceDirect, Swets Information Services).
Indexed: ASCA, AnalAb, BrCerAb, C&ISA, CCI, CIN, Cadscan, CerAb, ChemAb, ChemInfo, ChemTitl, CivEngAb, CorrAb, CurCR, CurCont, E&CAJ, EMA, EngInd, ExcerpMed, IAA, INIS AtomInd, ISR, IndChem, Inspec, LeadAb, M&TEA, MBF, METADEX, MSCI, RCI, RefZh, S&F, SCI, SolStAb, WAA, Zincscan.
—BLDSC (0970.000000), AskIEEE, CASDDS, CISTI, IDS, IE, ingenta, Linda Hall. **CCC.**
Published by: (International Union of Testing and Research Laboratories for Materials and Structures), Lavoisier, 11 rue Lavoisier, Paris, 75008, France. TEL 33-1-42653995, FAX 33-1-42650246, info@lavoisier.fr, http://www.elsevier.com/locate/anncsm, http://www.lavoisier.fr. Circ: 1,160.

540 POL ISSN 0137-6853
QC1 CODEN: AUMCD7
ANNALES UNIVERSITATIS MARIAE CURIE-SKLODOWSKA. SECTIO AA. CHEMIA. Text in English, French, Polish; Summaries in English, Polish. 1946. a. price varies. **Document type:** *Academic/Scholarly.*
Indexed: CIN, ChemAb, ChemTitl.
—CASDDS, CISTI, Linda Hall.
Published by: Uniwersytet Marii Curie-Sklodowskiej w Lublinie, Wydawnictwo, pl M Curie Sklodowskiej 5, Lublin, 20031, Poland. TEL 48-81-375304, FAX 48-81-336699. Ed. Kazimierz Sykut. Circ: 550.

540 DEU ISSN 0003-4592
CODEN: ANCRAI
➤ **ANNALI DI CHIMICA**; journal of analytical and environmental chemistry. Text in English. 1914. m. EUR 384 in Europe; CHF 598 in Switzerland & Liechtenstein; USD 518 elsewhere; EUR 423 combined subscription in Europe print & online eds.; CHF 658 combined subscription in Switzerland & Liechtenstein for print & online eds.; USD 570 combined subscription elsewhere print & online eds. (effective 2006). **Document type:** *Journal, Academic/Scholarly.* **Description:** Covers analytical and environmental chemistry, applied chemistry, mass spectrometry and electrochemistry.
Formerly (until 1950): Annali di Chimica Applicata (0365-1037)
Related titles: Microfiche ed.: (from BHP); Online - full text ed.: ISSN 1612-8877. EUR 384 in Europe to institutions; CHF 598 to institutions in Switzerland & Liechtenstein; USD 518 elsewhere to institutions (effective 2006) (from EBSCO Publishing, Wiley InterScience).
Indexed: ASCA, AnalAb, BIOSIS Prev, BiolAb, CCI, CIN, Cadscan, ChemAb, ChemInfo, ChemTitl, CurCR, CurCont, DSA, EngInd, ExcerpMed, ISR, IndChem, IndMed, LeadAb, MEDLINE, MSB, RCI, RefZh, SCI, VITIS, Zincscan.
—BLDSC (1012.000000), CASDDS, CISTI, Ei, IDS, IE, Infotrieve, ingenta, Linda Hall. **CCC.**
Published by: (Societa Chimica Italiana ITA), Wiley - V C H Verlag GmbH & Co. KGaA (Subsidiary of: John Wiley & Sons, Inc.), Boschstr 12, Weinheim, 69469, Germany. TEL 49-6201-6060, FAX 49-6201-606328, info@wiley-vch.de, http://www3.interscience.wiley.com/cgi-bin/jabout/107636969/2294_info.html, http://www.wiley-vch.de. Ed. Edoardo Mentasti. Circ: 450 (paid and controlled).

540 GBR ISSN 0268-2605
QD410 CODEN: AOCHEX
➤ **APPLIED ORGANOMETALLIC CHEMISTRY.** Text in English. 1987. m. USD 2,440 to institutions; USD 2,684 combined subscription to institutions print & online eds. (effective 2006). adv. back issues avail.; reprint service avail. from PSC. **Document type:** *Journal, Academic/Scholarly.* **Description:** Gives an effective outlet to applied work in the organometallic field.
Related titles: Microform ed.: (from PQC); Online - full content ed.: ISSN 1099-0739. 1997. USD 2,440 to institutions (effective 2006); Online - full text ed.: (from EBSCO Publishing, Swets Information Services, Wiley InterScience).
Indexed: ASCA, BIOSIS Prev, BiolAb, CCI, CIN, ChemAb, ChemInfo, ChemTitl, CurCont, EngInd, ISR, LHB, MOS, MSB, MSCI, RAPRA, RCI, RefZh, SCI.
—BLDSC (1576.270000), CASDDS, CISTI, Ei, IDS, IE, Infotrieve, ingenta. **CCC.**
Published by: John Wiley & Sons Ltd. (Subsidiary of: John Wiley & Sons, Inc.), The Atrium, Southern Gate, Chichester, West Sussex PO19 8SQ, United Kingdom. TEL 44-1243-779777, FAX 44-1243-775878, customer@wiley.co.uk, http://www.interscience.wiley.com/jpages/0268-2605/, http://www.wiley.co.uk. Ed. P J Craig. adv.: B&W page GBP 650, color page GBP 1,550; 170 x 230. Circ: 400. **Subscr. to:** John Wiley & Sons, Inc., 111 River St, Hoboken, NJ 07030-5774. TEL 201-748-6645, 800-225-5945, subinfo@wiley.com.

➤ **ARCHEIA TES PHARMAKEUTIKES (ATHENS).** see *PHARMACY AND PHARMACOLOGY*

➤ **ARCHIMEDES (NEW SERIES)**; new studies in the history and philosophy of science and technology. see *SCIENCES: COMPREHENSIVE WORKS*

➤ **ARCHIVUM COMBUSTIONIS.** see *ENGINEERING*

540 IND ISSN 0971-9822
ASIAN CHEMISTRY LETTERS. Text in English. 1997. q.
—BLDSC (1742.403540).
Published by: Anita Publications, KC-68-1, Old Kavi Nagar, Ghaziabad, Uttar Pradesh 201 002, India. TEL 91-11-840374, FAX 91-11-2413388.

540 IND ISSN 0970-7077
CODEN: AJCHEW
➤ **ASIAN JOURNAL OF CHEMISTRY**; an international quarterly research journal of chemistry. Text in English. 1989. q. INR 550, USD 70 to individuals; INR 1,000, USD 300 to institutions (effective 2004). adv. bk.rev. 400 p./no.; back issues avail. **Document type:** *Journal, Academic/Scholarly.* **Description:** All branches of chemistry.
Related titles: E-mail ed.
Indexed: ASCA, CCI, CIN, ChemAb, ChemTitl, INIS AtomInd, MSB, MSCI.
—BLDSC (1742.473000), CASDDS, IDS, IE, ingenta, Linda Hall.
Published by: Chemic Publishing Co., C/o Himanshu Agarwal, 11/100, Rajendra Nagar, Sector 3, Sahibabad, Ghaziabad, Uttar Pradesh 201 005, India. TEL 91-120-2630138, http://www.geocities.com/ajchem1988/. Ed. R K Agarwal. R&P, Adv. contact Pushpa Agarwal TEL 91-575-630138. Circ: 650. **Dist. by:** H P C Publishers Distributors Pvt. Ltd., 4805 Bharat Ram Rd, 24 Darya Ganj, New Delhi 110 002, India. TEL 91-11-325-4401, FAX 91-11-619-3511.

540 ARG ISSN 0365-0375
CODEN: AAQAAE
➤ **ASOCIACION QUIMICA ARGENTINA. ANALES.** Text in English, Spanish; Abstracts in English, Spanish. 1912. bi-m. abstr. **Document type:** *Academic/Scholarly.*
Indexed: CCI, CIN, ChemAb, ChemTitl, CurCR, CurCont, FS&TA, INIS AtomInd, IndChem, MSB, RCI.
—BLDSC (0870.000000), CASDDS, CINDOC, CISTI, IDS, IE, ingenta, Linda Hall.
Published by: Consejo Nacional de Investigaciones Cientificas y Tecnicas, Centro Argentino de Informacion Cientifica y Tecnologica, Saavedra, 15 Piso 1 O, Capital Federal, Buenos Aires 1083, Argentina. **Co-sponsor:** Asociacion Quimica Argentina.

540 EGY ISSN 1010-2671
ASSIUT UNIVERSITY. FACULTY OF SCIENCE. BULLETIN. SECTION B. CHEMISTRY. Text in English. 1982. s-a. free (effective 2004). **Document type:** *Bulletin, Academic/Scholarly.*
Formerly (until 1982): Assiut University. Faculty of Science. Bulletin. Section B. Biological and Geological Sciences (0254-6256); Which superseded in part (in 1979): Assiut University. Science and Technology. Bulletin (0379-3389)
Published by: Assiut University, Faculty of Science, c/o Dr. Muhammad Bahey, Assiut, Egypt. TEL 20-88-411376, FAX 20-88-342708, science@aun.edu.eg, sup@aun.eun.eg, http://derp.sti.sci.eg/data/0296.htm, http://www.aun.eun.eg. Ed. Dr. Muhammad Bahey-El-Din Hasan Mazen.

540 BRA ISSN 0365-0073
CODEN: AABQAL
ASSOCIACAO BRASILEIRA DE QUIMICA. ANAIS. Text in English, Portuguese. 1942. a.
Formerly (until 1951): Associacao Quimica do Brasil. Anais (0365-0383)
Indexed: INIS AtomInd, RefZh.
—CISTI.
Published by: Associacao Brasileira de Quimica, Rua das Laranjeiras, 371/801, Rio de Janeiro, RJ 22240-001, Brazil. TEL 55-21-22244480, abqnacional@abq.org.br, http://www.abq.org.br/. Ed. Geraldo Vicentini.

540 570 610 BEL ISSN 0770-1578
ASSOCIATION BELGE DES TECHNOLOGUES DE LABORATOIRE. REVUE/BELGISCHE VERENIGING VAN LABORATORIUM TECHNOLOGEN. TIJDSCHRIFT. Text in Multiple languages. 1974. q.
Indexed: RefZh.
Published by: Association Belge des Technologues de Laboratoire/Belgische Vereniging van Laboratorium Technologen, c/o Nicole Arras, Stenemolenstaat 64, Mechelen, 2800, Belgium. FAX 32-15-423496, http://www.bvlt-abtl.be.

ASSOCIATION OF MARINE LABORATORIES OF THE CARIBBEAN. NEWSLETTER. see *EARTH SCIENCES—Oceanography*

ASSOCIATION OF MARINE LABORATORIES OF THE CARIBBEAN. PROCEEDINGS. see *EARTH SCIENCES—Oceanography*

ATELIERS. see *CHILDREN AND YOUTH—For*

540 DEU
AUSBILDER IN DER CHEMISCHEN INDUSTRIE. Text in German. 1970. bi-m. **Document type:** *Magazine, Trade.*
Published by: (Bundesarbeitgeberverband Chemie), Dr. Curt Haefner Verlag GmbH, Bachstr 14-16, Heidelberg, 69121, Germany. TEL 49-6221-64460, FAX 49-6221-644640, info@haefner-verlag.de, http://www.haefner-verlag.de. Circ: 5,500.

540 AUS ISSN 1031-8305
AUSTRALIAN CHEMISTRY RESOURCE BOOK. Text in English. 1982. a. AUD 10, USD 7 (effective 2000). **Document type:** *Academic/Scholarly.* **Description:** Directed to secondary and higher-level teachers of chemistry.
Published by: (Royal Australian Chemical Institute), Charles Stuart University - Mitchell, School of Applied Sciences, Bathurst, NSW 2795, Australia. TEL 61-2-6331-5125, FAX 61-2-6338-4649. Ed. C.L. Fogliani. R&P C L Fogliani. Circ: 2,500.

540 AUS ISSN 0004-9425
QD1 CODEN: AJCHAS
➤ **AUSTRALIAN JOURNAL OF CHEMISTRY**; an international journal for chemical science. Text in English. 1948. m. AUD 800; AUD 870 combined subscription for print & online eds. (effective 2001). adv. bibl.; charts; illus.; abstr. index. back issues avail. **Document type:** *Journal, Academic/Scholarly.* **Description:** Covers all areas of chemical science and technology; e.g., synthesis, structure, new materials, macromolecules, supramolecular chemistry, biological chemistry and nanotechnology.
Supersedes in part (in 1952): Australian Journal of Scientific Research. Series A: Physical Sciences (0365-3676)
Related titles: Microform ed.: (from PQC); Online - full text ed.: USD 800 (effective 2000) (from EBSCO Publishing, Gale Group, O C L C Online Computer Library Center, Inc., Swets Information Services).
Indexed: ABIPC, AESIS, ASCA, ASFA, AgBio, AgrForAb, AnalAb, BPRC&P, BiolAb, BullT&T, CCI, CEABA, CIN, CLL, Cadscan, ChemAb, ChemInfo, ChemTitl, CurCR, CurCont, DBA, DSA, ESPM, EngInd, ExcerpMed, FCA, FPA, FS&TA, ForAb, HelmAb, HerbAb, HortAb, I&DA, INIS AtomInd, ISR, IndChem, IndVet, LHB, LeadAb, MOS, MSB, NPU, NemAb, NutrAb, OrnHort, PBA, PGrRegA, PHN&I, ProtozoAb, RA&MP, RCI, RM&VM, RPP, RefZh, RevApplEntom, S&F, SCI, SIA, TDB, TTI, VetBull, WAE&RSA, WTA, WeedAb, Zincscan, ZooRec.
—BLDSC (1806.000000), CASDDS, CINDOC, CISTI, Ei, IDS, IE, Infotrieve, ingenta, Linda Hall. **CCC.**
Published by: (C S I R O Australia), C S I R O Publishing, 150 Oxford St, PO Box 1139, Collingwood, VIC 3066, Australia. TEL 61-3-96627500, FAX 61-3-96627611, ajc@publish.csiro.au, publishing@csiro.au, http://www.publish.csiro.au/journals/ajc/index.html. Eds. Dr. Alison Green TEL 61-3-96627630, J M Cameron. Pub. Dr. Alison Green TEL 61-3-96627630. Circ: 750.

➤ **AUSZUEGE AUS DEN EUROPAEISCHEN PATENTANMELDUNGEN. TEIL 1A. CHEMIE UND HUETTENWESEN.** see *PATENTS, TRADEMARKS AND COPYRIGHTS*

C

540 GBR
B A M A ANNUAL REPORT. Text in English. a. **Document type:** *Corporate.*
Published by: British Aerosol Manufacturers Association, Kings Bldg, Smith Sq, London, SW1P 3JJ, United Kingdom. TEL 44-171-828-5111, FAX 44-171-834-8436. Ed., R&P Sarah Ross.

660 USA
B A S F INFORMATION. Text in English. m. **Document type:** *Newspaper, Consumer.* **Description:** Covers the products and activities of the BASF corporation for its employees.
Published by: B A S F Corporation, 100 Campus Dr., Florham Park, NJ 07932-1020. falland@basf.com, http://www.basf.com.

540 RUS ISSN 0869-8406
QD1 CODEN: BKZHFU
BASHKIRSKII KHIMICHESKII ZHURNAL. Text in Russian. 1993. q. USD 56 foreign (effective 2004). **Document type:** *Journal, Academic/Scholarly.*
Indexed: RefZh.
Published by: Izdatel'stvo Reaktiv, ul Ul'yanovykh, 75, Ufa, 450029, Russian Federation. TEL 7-3472-431139, FAX 7-3472-431256. Ed. D L Rakhmankulov. **Dist. by:** M K - Periodica, ul Gilyarovskogo 39, Moscow 129110, Russian Federation. TEL 7-095-2845008, FAX 7-095-2813798, info@periodicals.ru, http://www.mkniga.ru.

BAYER REPORT. see *PHARMACY AND PHARMACOLOGY*

BEN-GURION UNIVERSITY OF THE NEGEV. INSTITUTES FOR APPLIED RESEARCH. SCIENTIFIC ACTIVITIES. see *AGRICULTURE*

540 DEU ISSN 0943-3104
DER BENZOLRING. Text in German. 1980. 3/yr. free. **Document type:** *Academic/Scholarly.*
Published by: (Chemischen Instituts Dr. Flad), W E G R A Verlags-Gesellschaft mbH, Breitscheidstr 127, Stuttgart, 70176, Germany. TEL 0711-634760, FAX 0711-634768, TELEX 721779-CHF-D. Circ: 10,000.

540 570 KAZ
BIOLOGIYA ZHENE KHIMIYA. Text in Kazakh. bi-m. USD 139 in United States.
Published by: Ministry of Education, Ul Zhambyla 25, Almaty, 480100, Kazakstan. TEL 3272-616582. Ed. E Sairam. **US dist. addr.:** East View Information Services, 3020 Harbor Ln. N., Minneapolis, MN 55447. TEL 612-550-0961.

BIOLOHIYA I KHIMIYA V SHKOLI. see *BIOLOGY*

BIORESOURCE TECHNOLOGY. see *BIOLOGY—Biotechnology*

660 DEU ISSN 0006-4750
BLICK VOM HOCHHAUS. Text in German. 1960. m. free. bk.rev. **Document type:** *Trade.*
Published by: Huels AG, Marl, 45764, Germany. Ed. Georg Heinze.

540 660 IND ISSN 0067-9925
CODEN: BOTEAE
BOMBAY TECHNOLOGIST. Text in English. 1951. a. INR 50, USD 5. adv. **Document type:** *Academic/Scholarly.*
Indexed: BiolAb, ChemAb.
Published by: Technological Association, University of Bombay, Department of Chemical Technology, N.M. Parekh Marg Matunga, Mumbai, Maharashtra 400 019, India. FAX 91-22-4145614, ssd@udct.ernet.in. Ed. S D Samant. Circ: 1,000.

643 USA
HD9585.B67
BORAX PIONEER. Text in English. 1994. 3/yr. free (effective 2005). **Document type:** *Magazine, Trade.* **Description:** Technical, market and service information from word's leading supplier of refined borates.
Related titles: Online - full text ed.
Published by: U.S. Borax Inc., 26877 Tourney Rd, Valencia, CA 91355. TEL 661-287-5400, FAX 661-287-6259, http://www.borax.com. Ed. Susan Keefe. Circ: 7,000 (free).

BRAGANTIA. see *AGRICULTURE*

540 BRA ISSN 0103-5053
QD1 CODEN: JOCSET
➤ **BRAZILIAN CHEMICAL SOCIETY. JOURNAL.** Variant title: Journal of the Brazilian Chemical Society. Text in English. 1990. bi-m. BRL 47 domestic to members; USD 50 foreign to members; BRL 125 domestic to non-members; USD 50 in Latin America to non-members; USD 100 elsewhere to non-members; BRL 125 domestic to institutions; USD 150 foreign to institutions (effective 2004). abstr. back issues avail.; reprints avail. **Document type:** *Journal, Academic/Scholarly.* **Description:** Devoted to the publication of research papers in all fields of chemistry, except the education, philosophy and history of chemistry.
Related titles: Online - full text ed.: free (effective 2005) (from SciELO).
Indexed: AESIS, AnalAb, CCI, CIN, ChemAb, ChemTitl, CurCR, CurCont, FCA, INIS AtomInd, ISR, IndChem, MSB, RCI, SCI, VITIS.
—BLDSC (4712.050000), CASDDS, CISTI, IDS, IE, ingenta. **CCC.**
Published by: Sociedade Brasileira de Quimica, Ave Prof Lineu Prestes, 748, Bloco 2 - Superior, Sao Paulo, 05508, Brazil. TEL 55-11-3032-2299, FAX 55-11-3814-3602, office@jbcs.sbq.org.br, http://www.sbq.org.br/jbcs. Ed. Dr. Jailson B de Andrade. R&P Dr. Elisabeth Magalhaes. Circ: 500 (paid).

➤ **BROMIDES IN AGRICULTURE.** see *AGRICULTURE*

540 BGR ISSN 0861-9808
QD1 CODEN: BCHCE4
➤ **BULGARIAN CHEMICAL COMMUNICATIONS/IZVESTIYA PO KHIMIYA.** Text in English; Summaries in Bulgarian. 1968. q. USD 213 (effective 2005). adv. index. back issues avail.; reprint service avail. from IRC. **Document type:** *Journal, Academic/Scholarly.* **Description:** Presents original scientific papers submitted by Bulgarian and foreign scientists. Disseminates new information and achievements in the chemical sciences.
Formerly (until 1992): Izvestiia po Khimiia (0324-1130)
Indexed: CIN, ChemAb, ChemTitl, Inspec, MLA-IB, RefZh.
—BLDSC (2366.677550), AskIEEE, CASDDS, CINDOC, CISTI, IE, ingenta, KNAW, Linda Hall.
Published by: Bulgarska Akademiya na Naukite, Institut po Obshcha i Neorganichna Khimia/Bulgarian Academy of Sciences, Institute of General and Inorganic Chemistry, Akad G Bonchev 11, office 105, Blok 11 BAN, Sofia, 1113, Bulgaria. TEL 359-2-7132576, FAX 359-2-720038, TELEX 22729 ECHBAN-BG, bnachem@bgearn.bitnet, http://www.cl.bas.bg/magazines/chemical/default.htm. Ed., Adv. contact Venko N Beschkov. Circ: 700. **Dist. by:** Sofia Books, ul Silivria 16, Sofia 1404, Bulgaria. TEL 359-2-9586257, info@sofiabooks-bg.com, http://www.sofiabooks-bg.com. **Co-sponsor:** Bulgarian Chemical Society.

540 660 BGR ISSN 1311-1663
➤ **BULGARIAN CHEMISTRY AND INDUSTRY.** Text in English. 1922. s-a. USD 354 foreign (effective 2006). **Document type:** *Journal, Academic/Scholarly.* **Description:** Presents original research, new theoretical concepts, applications and critical reviews in the science of industrial practice of all aspects of chemistry, chemical engineering, environmental protection and improved and emerging technologies.
Related titles: ◆ Bulgarian ed.: Khimiya i Industriya. ISSN 1310-6716.
—BLDSC (2366.677570), IE, ingenta.
Published by: (Suiuz na Bulgarskite Khimitsi/Union of Bulgarian Chemists), Union of Chemists in Bulgaria **Dist. by:** Sofia Books, ul Silivria 16, Sofia 1404, Bulgaria. TEL 359-2-9586257, info@sofiabooks-bg.com, http://www.sofiabooks-bg.com.

540.9 USA ISSN 1053-4385
BULLETIN FOR THE HISTORY OF CHEMISTRY. Text in English. 1988. s-a. USD 36 domestic to libraries; USD 40 foreign to libraries (effective 2005). bk.rev. back issues avail.
—Linda Hall.
Published by: American Chemical Society, Division of History of Chemistry, c/o Dr. Vera V. Mainz, School of Chemical Sciences, 142B RAL, Box 34 Noyes Lab, 600 S Mathews Ave, Urbana, IL 61801. mainz@uiuc.edu, http://www.scs.uiuc.edu/~mainzv/HIST/bulletin/index.htm. Ed. Paul R Jones.

BULLETIN OF MAGNETIC RESONANCE. see *PHYSICS*

540 IND ISSN 0970-4620
CODEN: BPAAS:C
➤ **BULLETIN OF PURE & APPLIED SCIENCES. SECTION C: CHEMISTRY.** Text in English. 1982. s-a. INR 300, USD 50 (effective 2005). adv. bk.rev. 80 p./no.; back issues avail.; reprints avail. **Document type:** *Journal, Academic/Scholarly.* **Description:** Research papers related with Chemical Science.
Supersedes in part (in 1983): Bulletin of Pure & Applied Sciences (0970-4604)
Media: Large Type (11 pt.).
—CISTI, Linda Hall. **CCC.**
Published by: A.K. Sharma, Ed. & Pub., 19-A, D D A Flats, Mansarover Park, Shahdara, New Delhi, 110 032, India. TEL 91-11-2117408, bulletin@mantraonline.com, ajaykumarsharma1955@yahoo.com. Ed., Pub., R&P, Adv. contact A K Sharma. B&W page INR 1,000, B&W page USD 50, color page INR 2,000, color page USD 100. Circ: 600.

540 658.8 GBR ISSN 1467-8985
BUSINESS RATIO. CHEMICAL DISTRIBUTORS. Text in English. 1985. a. GBP 275 (effective 2001). charts; stat. **Document type:** *Trade.*
Former titles (until 1999): Business Ratio Plus: Chemical Distributors (1355-8994); (until 1994): Business Ratio Report. Chemical Distributors (0268-4284)
Published by: The Prospect Shop Ltd., Field House, 72 Oldfield Rd, Hampton, Middx TW12 2HQ, United Kingdom. TEL 44-20-8461-8730, 44-20-8481-8720, FAX 44-20-8783-1940, info@theprospectshop.co.uk.

540 338 658.8 GBR ISSN 1472-7706
BUSINESS RATIO REPORT. INDUSTRIAL CHEMICAL MANUFACTURERS. Text in English. 1974. a. GBP 275 (effective 2001). charts; stat. **Document type:** *Trade.*
Formerly (until 2000): Business Ratio. Industrial Chemical Manufacturers (1468-3628); Which was formed by the 1998 merger of: Business Ratio Plus: Industrial Chemical Manufacturers. Major (1356-6482); Which was formerly (until 1994): Business Ratio Report. Industrial Chemical Manufacturers. Major (0267-002X); &: Business Ratio Plus: Industrial Chemical Manufacturers. Intermediate (1357-0439); Which was formerly (until 1994): Business Ratio Report. Industrial Chemical Manufacturers. Intermediate (0267-0011); Both superseded in part (in 1984): Business Ratio Report. Chemical Manufacturers (0261-7587)
Published by: The Prospect Shop Ltd., Field House, 72 Oldfield Rd, Hampton, Middx TW12 2HQ, United Kingdom. TEL 44-20-8461-8730, 44-20-8481-8720, FAX 44-20-8783-1940, info@theprospectshop.co.uk.

540 JPN ISSN 0913-3747
C I C S J BULLETIN. (Chemical Information and Computer Sciences) Text in English, Japanese. 1983. bi-m. **Document type:** *Bulletin.*
Related titles: Online - full content ed.: ISSN 1347-2283; Online - full text ed.: (from J-Stage).
Published by: Chemical Society Of Japan, Division of Chemical Information and Computer Sciences, 1-5, Kanda-Surugadai, Chiyoda-ku, Tokyo, 101-8307, Japan. TEL 81-3-3292-6161, FAX 81-3-3292-6318, info@chemistry.or.jp, http://cicsj.jstage.jst.go.jp/, http://www.chemistry.or.jp/.

540.29 CAN
C P I PRODUCT PROFILES. Text in English. irreg. CND 75, USD 65 domestic; USD 65 foreign (effective 2000). **Document type:** *Trade.* **Description:** Provides basic market information for chemical products.
Published by: Camford Information Services Inc., 38 Groomsport Cres, Scarborough, ON M1T 2K9, Canada. TEL 416-291-3215, FAX 416-291-3406. Ed. George Deligiannis.

C

540 530 USA ISSN 0147-6262
QD65
C R C HANDBOOK OF CHEMISTRY AND PHYSICS. Text in English. 1913. a., latest 84th ed. USD 139.95 (effective 2003). **Document type:** *Academic/Scholarly.* **Description:** Offers a broad coverage of all types of data commonly encountered by physical scientists.
Formerly (until 1977): Handbook of Chemistry and Physics (0363-3055)
Related titles: CD-ROM ed.: C R C Handbook of Chemistry and Physics on CD-ROM. USD 199.95 (effective 2003); Online - full text ed.
—BLDSC (3487.096270), CISTI. **CCC.**
Published by: C R C Press, LLC (Subsidiary of: Taylor & Francis Group), 2000 N W Corporate Blvd, Boca Raton, FL 33431. TEL 800-272-7737, journals@crcpress.com, http://www.crcpress.com/. Ed. David R Lide.

660 USA
C S M A EXECUTIVE NEWSWATCH. Text in English. 1977. w. membership only. **Document type:** *Newsletter.*
Published by: Chemical Specialties Manufacturers Association, 1913 Eye St, N W, Washington, DC 20006. TEL 202-872-8110. Ed. Anastasia Ralph. Pub. Raysh Engel. Circ: 1,000.

C S M C R I NEWSLETTER. see *EARTH SCIENCES—Oceanography*

C Y R I C ANNUAL REPORT. (Cyclotron Radioisotope Center) see *MEDICAL SCIENCES—Radiology And Nuclear Medicine*

540 363.7 GBR ISSN 1359-0243
CAMBRIDGE ENVIRONMENTAL CHEMISTRY SERIES. Text in English. 1991. irreg., latest 2002. price varies. **Document type:** *Monographic series, Academic/Scholarly.*
Indexed: BIOSIS Prev.
—BLDSC (3015.950150).
Published by: Cambridge University Press, The Edinburgh Bldg, Shaftesbury Rd, Cambridge, CB2 2RU, United Kingdom. TEL 44-1223-312393, FAX 44-1223-315052, information@cambridge.org, http://publishing.cambridge.org/series/cecs, http://www.cup.cam.ac.uk/.

540 CAN ISSN 1187-8746
CAMFORD CHEMICAL REPORT. Text in English. 1969. w. (50/yr.). CND 779, USD 669 domestic; CND 799 foreign (effective 2000). **Document type:** *Newsletter.*
Former titles: Corpus Chemical Report (0228-653X); C P I Management Service (0315-257X); Polyfacts (0315-2588)
Indexed: PROMT.
—CISTI. **CCC.**
Published by: Camford Information Services Inc., 38 Groomsport Cres, Scarborough, ON M1T 2K9, Canada. TEL 416-291-3215, FAX 416-291-3406. Ed. Joe Piccione. Circ: 200 (paid).

540 CAN ISSN 0823-5228
CODEN: CCHNEE
CANADIAN CHEMICAL NEWS/L'ACTUALITE CHIMIQUE CANADIENNE. Short title: A C C N. Text in English, French. 1949. 10/yr. CND 55 domestic; CND 65 combined subscription domestic print & online eds; USD 50 foreign; USD 58 combined subscription foreign print & online eds; CND 8 per issue domestic; USD 7 per issue foreign (effective 2005). adv. bk.rev. charts; illus.; tr.lit. index. back issues avail. **Document type:** *Magazine, Trade.*
Formerly (until 1984): Chemistry in Canada (0009-3114)
Related titles: Microfiche ed.: (from MML); Microfilm ed.: (from MML); Microform ed.: (from MML); Online - full text ed.: (from Gale Group).
Indexed: BiolAb, CBCARef, CBPI, CEABA, CIN, CISA, CPerI, ChemAb, ChemTitl, EIA, EngInd, EnvAb, ExcerpMed, RefZh, Telegen.
—BLDSC (3018.990000), CASDDS, CISTI, Ei, IE, ingenta, Linda Hall. **CCC.**
Published by: Chemical Institute of Canada, 130 Slater St, Ste 550, Ottawa, ON K1P 6E2, Canada. TEL 613-232-6252, FAX 613-232-5862, info@accn.ca, http://www.accn.ca. Eds. Dana Munroe, Michelle T Piquette. Circ: 7,000.

540 CAN ISSN 0008-4042
QD1 CODEN: CJCHAG
➤ **CANADIAN JOURNAL OF CHEMISTRY/JOURNAL CANADIEN DE CHIMIE.** Text mainly in English; Text occasionally in French. 1929. m. CND 348 domestic to individuals; USD 523 foreign to individuals; CND 1,067 domestic to institutions; USD 1,242 foreign to institutions (effective 2005). adv. bibl.; illus. index. back issues avail.; reprint service avail. from PQC. **Document type:** *Academic/Scholarly.*
Formerly (until 1951): Canadian Journal of Research. Section B: Chemical Sciences (0366-7391); Which superseded in part (in 1935): Canadian Journal of Research (0366-6581)
Related titles: Microfiche ed.: (from MML); Microform ed.: (from MML, PMC, PQC); Online - full text ed.: ISSN 1480-3291 (from bigchalk, EBSCO Publishing, Gale Group, IngentaConnect, Micromedia ProQuest, O C L C Online Computer Library Center, Inc., ProQuest Information & Learning, Swets Information Services).
Indexed: ABIPC, ASCA, ASFA, BPRC&P, BiolAb, CBCARef, CCI, CIN, CPerI, CTE, Cadscan, ChemAb, ChemInfo, ChemTitl, CurCR, CurCont, DBA, DSA, EngInd, ExcerpMed, FPA, ForAb, GSI, HerbAb, HortAb, INIS AtomInd, ISR, IndChem, IndVet, Inspec, LeadAb, MOS, MSB, MSCI, NPU, NutrAb, PetrolAb, RCI, RefZh, S&F, SCI, WTA, Zincscan.
—BLDSC (3031.000000), AskIEEE, CASDDS, CINDOC, CISTI, Ei, IDS, IE, Infotrieve, ingenta, Linda Hall, PADDS. **CCC.**
Published by: N R C Research Press, Building M 55, Ottawa, ON K1A 0R6, Canada. TEL 613-993-0362, FAX 613-952-7656, pubs@nrc-cnrc.gc.ca, http://pubs.nrc-cnrc.gc.ca/cgi-bin/rp/rp2_desc_e?cjc. Eds. Dr. Dick Puddephatt, Bruce P Dancik. Adv. contact Judy Gorman. B&W page CND 675; trim 11 x 8.5. Circ: 1,488.

C

540 660 NLD ISSN 1566-7367
QD505 CODEN: CCAOAC
CATALYSIS COMMUNICATIONS. Text in English. 2000. 12/yr. EUR 583 in Europe to institutions; JPY 77,500 in Japan to institutions; USD 651 to institutions except Europe and Japan (effective 2006). **Document type:** *Journal, Academic/Scholarly.* **Description:** Provides rapid publication of short papers across the broad spectrum of catalytic research.
Related titles: Online - full text ed.: (from EBSCO Publishing, Gale Group, IngentaConnect, ScienceDirect, Swets Information Services).
Indexed: BiolAb, CCI, ChemAb, CurCR, CurCont, IndChem, RCI, RefZh.
—BLDSC (3090.905000), CISTI, IE, Infotrieve, ingenta. **CCC.**
Published by: Elsevier BV (Subsidiary of: Elsevier Science & Technology), Radarweg 29, Amsterdam, 1043 NX, Netherlands. TEL 31-20-4853911, FAX 31-20-4852457, nlinfo-f@elsevier.nl, http://www.elsevier.com/locate/catcom, http://www.elsevier.nl. Ed. Dr. B Luecke.

540 660 USA ISSN 1011-372X
QD505 CODEN: CALEER
➤ **CATALYSIS LETTERS.** Text in English. 1988. 28/yr. (in 7 vols.). EUR 2,678, USD 2,718, GBP 1,678 combined subscription to institutions print & online eds. (effective 2005). adv. reprint service avail. from PSC. **Document type:** *Journal, Academic/Scholarly.* **Description:** Covers the science of catalysis and subdisciplines.
Related titles: Online - full text ed.: ISSN 1572-879X (from EBSCO Publishing, Gale Group, IngentaConnect, Kluwer Online, O C L C Online Computer Library Center, Inc., Springer LINK, Swets Information Services).
Indexed: APIAb, ASCA, BibLing, CCI, CIN, ChemAb, ChemTitl, CurCont, EngInd, ISR, MSB, MSCI, RCI, RefZh, SCI.
—BLDSC (3090.907000), CASDDS, CISTI, Ei, IDS, IE, Infotrieve, ingenta, Linda Hall. **CCC.**
Published by: Plenum US (Subsidiary of: Springer Science+Business Media), 233 Spring St, New York, NY 10013. TEL 212-460-1500, FAX 212-460-1575, service@springer-ny.com, http://springerlink.metapress.com/openurl.asp?genre=journal&issn=1011-372X, http://www.springeronline.com. Eds. Gabor A Somorjai, John Meurig Thomas.

➤ **CATALYSIS TODAY.** see *ENGINEERING—Chemical Engineering*

540 USA ISSN 0008-767X
QD1 CODEN: CATLAG
CATALYST (PHILADELPHIA). Text in English. 1916. m. (Sep.-Jun.). USD 4.25 domestic to non-members; USD 5.25 foreign to non-members; USD 2 to members (effective 2005). adv. bk.rev. illus. 16 p./no. 2 cols./p.; back issues avail. **Document type:** *Newsletter, Trade.* **Description:** Contains advertising and coming events, letters to the editor and personnel news of interest to members of the Philadelphia section of the American Chemical Society.
Related titles: Online - full text ed.
Indexed: HistAb.
Published by: American Chemical Society, Philadelphia Section, University of Pennsylvania, Department of Chemistry, Philadelphia, PA 19104-6323. TEL 215-382-1589, philaacs@aol.com. Ed. Robin Davis. Adv. contact Vincent Gale. B&W page USD 695; trim 7.1875 x 4.5. Circ: 5,330 (paid and controlled).

540 660 GBR ISSN 1793-1398
➤ **CATALYTIC SCIENCE SERIES.** Text in English. 1999. irreg., latest vol.5, 2005, Winter. price varies. bibl. 300 p./no.; **Document type:** *Monographic series, Academic/Scholarly.*
Former titles: Series In Catalytic Science; Series On Catalytic Science
—BLDSC (3092.323000), ingenta.
Published by: Imperial College Press (Subsidiary of: World Scientific Publishing Co. Pte. Ltd.), 57 Shelton St, London, WC2H 9HE, United Kingdom. TEL 44-20-7836-3954, FAX 44-20-7836-2002, edit@icpress.co.uk, geetha@icpress.co.uk, http://www.wspc.com.sg/books/series/css_series.shtml, http://www.icpress.co.uk/. Ed. Graham J Hutchings. **Dist. by:** World Scientific Publishing Co., Inc., 1060 Main St, River Edge, NJ 07661. TEL 201-487-9655, 800-227-7562, FAX 201-487-9656, 888-977-2665, wspc@wspc.com; World Scientific Publishing Ltd., 57 Shelton St, London WC2H 9HE, United Kingdom. TEL 44-20-78360888, FAX 44-20-78362020, sales@wspc.co.uk.

660 IND ISSN 0008-8579
CAUSTIC. Text in English, Malayalam. 1967. q. free. adv. bk.rev. illus.
Published by: Travancore-Cochin Chemicals Ltd., Udyogamandal, Alwaye, Kerala 683 501, India. Ed. G P C Nayar. Circ: 1,200.

540 POL ISSN 1644-3624
➤ **CENTRAL EUROPEAN JOURNAL OF CHEMISTRY.** Text in English. 2002. q. USD 249, EUR 199 to individuals; USD 900, EUR 800 to institutions (effective 2006). **Document type:** *Journal, Academic/Scholarly.* **Description:** Provides an international medium for the publication of research results and reviews in all areas of chemistry.
Media: Online - full text (from EBSCO Publishing, Gale Group, IngentaConnect, O C L C Online Computer Library Center, Inc.).
Indexed: BrCerAb, C&ISA, CCI, CerAb, CorrAb, E&CAJ, EMA, IAA, M&TEA, MBF, METADEX, WAA.
Published by: Central European Science Journals, 8, Mariensztat St, Warsaw, 00-302, Poland. TEL 48-22-8286020, FAX 48-22-8286024, gm@cesj.com, http://www.cesj.com/chemistry.html. Ed. Prof Mikhail Antipin.

540 CAN ISSN 0703-1157
CHEM 13 NEWS. Text in English. 1968. 9/yr. CND 20 domestic; USD 22 in United States; CND 29 elsewhere (effective 2005 - 2006). adv. bk.rev. illus. back issues avail. **Document type:** *Journal, Academic/Scholarly.* **Description:** Contains teaching ideas, experiments, demonstrations, humor and background articles for high school chemistry teachers.
Indexed: ChemAb, RefZh.
—CISTI. **CCC.**
Published by: University of Waterloo, Chemistry Department, c/o Chem 13 News, Waterloo, ON N2L 3G1, Canada. TEL 519-888-4567 ext 3701, FAX 519-888-9168, lbrubach@uwaterloo.ca, http://www.science.uwaterloo.ca/chem13news. Ed., R&P, Adv. contact Lewis J Brubacher. page CND 480; 19.1 x 24.2. Circ: 4,000 (paid).

CHEM SOURCES INTERNATIONAL. see *BUSINESS AND ECONOMICS—Trade And Industrial Directories*

CHEM SOURCES U S A. see *BUSINESS AND ECONOMICS—Trade And Industrial Directories*

CHEMECOLOGY; covering health, safety and the environment. see *ENVIRONMENTAL STUDIES*

540 371.3 POL ISSN 0411-8634
CODEN: CHSZAY
CHEMIA W SZKOLE. Text in Polish. 1954. 5/yr. EUR 25 foreign (effective 2005). bk.rev.; software rev.; Website rev. bibl.; illus. 64 p./no.; **Document type:** *Journal, Academic/Scholarly.* **Description:** Discusses the latest achievements in chemistry and chemical technology, and presents new concepts in teaching chemistry.
—CASDDS.
Published by: (Poland. Ministerstwo Edukacji Narodowej), Wydawnictwa Szkolne i Pedagogiczne, Pl Dabrowskiego 8, Warsaw, 00950, Poland. TEL 48-22-8279280, wsip@wsip.com.pl, http://www.wsip.com.pl/serwisy/czaschem/index.html. Ed. Andrzej Rubaszkiewicz. Adv. contact Barbara Parcinska-Wywnialek. **Dist.by:** Ars Polona, Krakowskie Przedmiescie 7, Warsaw, Poland. TEL 48-22-9263914, FAX 48-22-9265334, arspolona@arspolona.com.pl, http://www.arspolona.com.pl.

660 IND ISSN 0009-2320
TP1 CODEN: CHAIAT
CHEMICAL AGE OF INDIA. Text in English. 1949. m. INR 600 domestic; USD 95 foreign; INR 75 newsstand/cover domestic (effective 2000). adv. bk.rev. abstr.; charts; illus.; tr.lit. index. **Document type:** *Academic/Scholarly.*
Related titles: Microform ed.: (from PQC).
Indexed: CEA, CLOSS, ChemAb, F&EA, FLUIDEX, S&F, TCEA.
—CASDDS, CISTI, Linda Hall. **CCC.**
Published by: (Chemical Process Industries of India), Technical Press Publications, Eucharistic Congress Bldg. No.1, 5/1 Convent St, Colaba, Mumbai, Maharashtra 400 039, India. TEL 91-22-2021446, FAX 91-22-2871499, TELEX 11-83479 CHEM IN. adv.: B&W page USD 1,750, color page USD 2,250; trim 18 x 23. Circ: 6,400.

540 CAN ISSN 1481-9848
CHEMICAL AND CHEMICAL PRODUCTS INDUSTRIES (ONLINE EDITION). Text in English. 1985. a.
Formerly (until 1997): Chemical and Chemical Products Industries (Print Edition) (0835-0183); Which was formed by the merger of (1970-1985): Miscellaneous Chemical Industries (0700-0464); Which was formed by the merger of (1960-1970): Explosives and Ammunition Manufacturers (0575-8467); (1969-1970): Other Chemical Industries (0829-8475); Which was formerly (in 1968): Other Chemical Industries, N E S (0829-8467); (until 1967): Other Chemical Industries (0575-9250); Which was formed by the merger of (19??-1960): Adhesives Industry (0700-0510); (19??-1960): Inks Industry (0700-0499); (19??-1960): Coal Tar Distillation Industry (0700-0502); (19??-1960): Polishes and Dressings Industry (0700-0480); (1948-1960): Miscellaneous Chemical Products Industry (0700-0472); Which was formerly (until 1948): Miscellaneous Chemical Products in Canada (0829-8408); (until 1947): Miscellaneous Chemical Products Industry in Canada (0829-8394); (until 1945): Miscellaneous Chemical Products Industry (0829-8386); (192?-1936): Miscellaneous Chemical Products Industry in Canada (0829-8378); And (1981-1985): Industrial and Agricultural Chemical Products (0319-907X); Which was formed by the merger of (1960-1981): Manufacturers of Mixed Fertilizers (0090-0397); (1960-1981): Manufacturers of Industrial Chemicals (0527-5539); Which was formed by the merger of (19??-1960): Compressed Gases Industry (0700-0561); (1949-1960): Acids, Alkalies and Salts Industry (0700-0553); Which was formerly (19??-1949): Acids, Alkalies and Salts Industry in Canada; (1950-1960): Fertilizers Industry (0381-0860); Which was formerly (until 1950): Fertilizer Manufacturing Industry; And (1981-1985): Pharmaceuticals, Cleaning Compounds and Toilet Preparations (0319-9061); Which was formed by 1981 the merger of: Manufacturers of Toilet Preparations (0384-3882); Which was formerly (until 1960): Toilet Preparations Industry (0384-3890); (until 1948): Toilet Preparations Industry in Canada (0825-3218); (1960-1981): Manufacturers of Pharmaceuticals and Medicines (0701-7340); Which was formerly (until 1960): Medicinal and Pharmaceutical Preparations Industry (0701-7359); (until 1948): Medicinal & Pharmaceutical Preparations Industry in Canada (0825-3242); (1960-1981): Manufacturers of Soap and Cleaning Compounds (0384-3912); Which was formerly (until 1960): Soaps, Washing Compounds and Cleaning Preparations Industry (0384-3920); (until 1948): Soaps, Washing Compounds and Cleaning Preparations Industry in Canada (0825-3234); (until 1935): Soaps, Cleaning Preparations and Washing Compounds Industry in Canada (0825-3226); (until 1931): Soaps and Washing Compounds Industry in Canada; And (1984-1985): Paint and Varnish Industry (0833-7489); Which was formerly (until 1984): Paint and Varnish Manufacturers (0384-4714); (until 1960): Paints, Varnishes and Lacquers Industry (0410-5699); (until 1950): Paints and Varnishes Industry
Media: Online - full content. **Related titles:** French ed.: Industries Chimiques. ISSN 1481-9856. 1997.
—CISTI.
Published by: Statistics Canada, Manufacturing, Construction and Energy Division, Ste 1500 Main Bldg Holland Ave, Ottawa, ON K1A OT6, Canada. TEL 613-951-8116, 800-263-1136, infostats@statcan.ca.

363.7 IND ISSN 0971-2151
CODEN: CEREEH
➤ **CHEMICAL & ENVIRONMENTAL RESEARCH.** Text in English. 1992. q. INR 450 domestic to individuals; USD 60 foreign to individuals; INR 750 domestic to institutions; USD 100 foreign to institutions (effective 2003). bk.rev. back issues avail. **Document type:** *Journal, Academic/Scholarly.* **Description:** Contains research papers dealing with all aspects of environmental research and research in chemistry.
Indexed: CIN, ChemAb, ChemTitl.
—BLDSC (3138.050000), CASDDS, IE, ingenta.

Published by: Muslim Association for the Advancement of Science, 44 Ahmad Nagar, Dodhpur, Aligarh, Uttar Pradesh 202 001, India. TEL 91-571-2405493, FAX 91-571-2401209, maas1@vsnl.com, http://www.members.rediff.com/maasjis/index.html. Ed., R&P Ali Mohammad. Circ: 300.

540 615 JPN ISSN 0009-2363
RS1.N56 CODEN: CPBTAL
➤ **CHEMICAL & PHARMACEUTICAL BULLETIN.** Text in English. 1953. m. USD 125 combined subscription Incls. Biological & Pharmaceutical Bulletin (effective 2005). adv. charts; tr.mk. Index. 150 p./no.; **Document type:** *Bulletin, Academic/Scholarly.* **Description:** Covers physical and inorganic chemistry, organic chemistry, natural products chemistry, medicinal chemistry, analytical chemistry, pharmacognosy, and physical pharmacy.
Formerly: Pharmaceutical Bulletin
Related titles: Microfilm ed.: (from PMC); Online - full text ed.: ISSN 1347-5223. free (effective 2005) (from EBSCO Publishing, J-Stage).
Indexed: AEA, ASCA, ASFA, AbHyg, AgBio, AgrForAb, AnBrAb, AnalAb, BIOSIS Prev, BioCN&I, BiolAb, CCI, CIN, CPA, ChemAb, ChemInfo, ChemTitl, CurCR, CurCont, DBA, DSA, DentInd, ExcerpMed, FCA, FPA, ForAb, HelmAb, HerbAb, HortAb, INIS AtomInd, IPA, ISR, IndChem, IndMed, IndVet, Inpharma, MBA, MEDLINE, MOS, MSB, MSCI, NPU, NucAcAb, NutrAb, OrnHort, PBA, PE&ON, PGegResA, PGrRegA, PHN&I, PN&I, ProtozoAb, RA&MP, RCI, RM&VM, RPP, Reac, RefZh, RevApplEntom, S&F, SCI, SIA, SeedAb, SoyAb, TDB, TriticAb, VITIS, VetBull, WeedAb.
—BLDSC (3138.800000), CASDDS, CINDOC, CISTI, GNLM, IDS, IE, Infotrieve, ingenta, KNAW, Linda Hall. **CCC.**
Published by: Pharmaceutical Society of Japan/Nihon Yakugakkai, 2-12-15, Shibuya, Shibuya-ku, Tokyo, 150-0002, Japan. TEL 81-3-34063321, FAX 81-3-34981835, ronb@pharm.or.jp, http://cpb.pharm.or.jp, http://www.pharm.or.jp/. Ed. Takehisa Kunieda. Circ: 3,650.

540 570 GBR ISSN 1747-1605
CHEMICAL BIOLOGY VIRTUAL JOURNAL. Text in English. 2002. m. GBP 199, USD 364 combined subscription print & online eds. (effective 2006). bk.rev. **Document type:** *Journal, Academic/Scholarly.* **Description:** Provides an easy-to-use point of access to chemical biology literature in RSC publications. Includes reviews, current awareness, news and opinions articles.
Related titles: Online - full text ed.: ISSN 1747-1613. GBP 179, USD 328 (effective 2006).
Published by: Royal Society of Chemistry, Thomas Graham House, Science Park, Milton Rd, Cambridge, CB4 0WF, United Kingdom. TEL 44-1223-420066, FAX 44-1223-423623, sales@rsc.org, http://www.rsc.org/Publishing/Journals/cb/index.asp. Ed. Dr. Caroline Evans.

540 USA ISSN 0009-2398
CHEMICAL BOND. Text in English. 1950. 9/yr. USD 5. adv. bk.rev. **Document type:** *Newsletter.* **Description:** Lists events and member news.
Published by: American Chemical Society, St. Louis Section, c/o Messenger Printing Co., 125 W. Argonne Dr., St. Louis, MO 63122. Ed. John Bornmann. Circ: 1,850.

540 USA ISSN 0009-2401
CODEN: CHEBAS
CHEMICAL BULLETIN. Text in English. 1914. 10/yr. USD 15 domestic; USD 20 foreign (effective 2005). adv. **Document type:** *Magazine, Trade.* **Description:** Contains organization news.
—Linda Hall.
Published by: American Chemical Society, 1155 16th St, N W, Washington, DC 20036. TEL 202-872-4614, 800-227-5558, FAX 202-776-8264, chicagoacs@ameritech.net, http://www.acs.org. Ed. Cherlyn Bradley. Circ: 5,600 (paid and controlled).

540 GBR ISSN 1359-7345
QD1 CODEN: CHCOFS
➤ **CHEMICAL COMMUNICATIONS.** Variant title: ChemComm. Text in English. 1965. w. ((bi-weekly until 2005)). GBP 1,745, USD 3,193 combined subscription print & online eds. (effective 2006); subscr. includes Chemical Technology. adv. charts; illus. index. reprint service avail. from PQC. **Document type:** *Journal, Academic/Scholarly.* **Description:** Covers developments in all branches of chemistry.
Former titles (until 1996): Journal of the Chemical Society - Chemical Communications (0022-4936); (until 1972): Chemical Communications (0009-241X)
Related titles: E-mail ed.; Microform ed.: (from PQC); Online - full text ed.: ISSN 1364-548X. GBP 1,570, USD 2,874 (effective 2006) (from EBSCO Publishing, O C L C Online Computer Library Center, Inc., Swets Information Services); ◆ Partial English translation(s): Chemical Technology. ISSN 1744-1560; ◆ Includes: Molecular BioSystems. ISSN 1742-206X.
Indexed: ABIPC, AESIS, ASCA, ASFA, AgrForAb, B&BAb, BiolAb, CCI, CIN, CTE, ChemAb, ChemInfo, ChemTitl, CurCR, CurCont, DBA, ESPM, EngInd, ExcerpMed, GenetAb, ISR, IndChem, MOS, MSB, MSCI, NPU, PollutAb, RCI, RefZh, SCI, SIA.
—BLDSC (3139.350000), CASDDS, CINDOC, CISTI, Ei, IDS, IE, Infotrieve, ingenta, Linda Hall. **CCC.**
Published by: Royal Society of Chemistry, Thomas Graham House, Science Park, Milton Rd, Cambridge, CB4 0WF, United Kingdom. TEL 44-1223-420066, FAX 44-1223-423623, chemcomm@rsc.org, sales@rsc.org, http://www.rsc.org/Publishing/Journals/cc/index.asp. Ed. Dr. Sarah Thomas. **Subscr. to:** Portland Press Ltd., R S C Distribution Services, Commerce Way, Whitehall Industrial Estate, Colchester CO2 8HP, United Kingdom. TEL 44-1206-226050, FAX 44-1206-226055, sales@rscdistribution.org.

540 IND ISSN 0970-9525
CHEMICAL DIGEST; industrial trends and opportunities. Text in English. 1971. m. INR 100, USD 40. adv. bk.rev. **Document type:** *Newsletter.* **Description:** Covers the latest developments in economy, business, and technology to apprise entrepreneurs and corporate houses of emerging opportunities.
Published by: Small Business Publications, 4/45 Roop Nagar, P O Box 2131, New Delhi, 110 007, India. TEL 91-11-3973701, FAX 91-11-2947577, sbp-group@usa.net. Ed. R K Gupta. adv.: page INR 7,500, page USD 1,500; 190 x 250. Circ: 15,000.

660 661 KOR ISSN 0304-5277
QD49.K8 CODEN: HWKYDI
CHEMICAL EDUCATION. Text in Korean. 1974. 4/yr. USD 20 to members; USD 30 to non-members; USD 40 to institutions (effective 2001). adv. 130 p./no.; **Document type:** *Magazine, Academic/Scholarly.* **Description:** Provides information related to chemical education.
—CASDDS, Linda Hall.
Published by: Korean Chemical Society/Daehan Hwahak Hoe, 635-4 Yeoksam-dong, Kangnam-gu, Seoul, 135-703, Korea, S. TEL 82-2-34533781, FAX 82-2-34533785, kcschem@neon.kcsnet.or.kr, http://www.kcsnet.or.kr. Ed. Jong Yoon Park. Circ: 1,000.

540.7 USA ISSN 1430-4171
QD40 CODEN: CHEDF5
➤ **THE CHEMICAL EDUCATOR.** Text in English. 1996. bi-m. USD 29.95 to individuals; USD 149.95 to institutions (effective 2005). **Document type:** *Journal, Academic/Scholarly.* **Description:** Provides resources and information for chemical education professionals.
Media: Online - full text (from Springer LINK). **Related titles:** ◆ Supplement(s): Chemical Educator Annual.
Indexed: CIN, ChemAb, ChemTitl, MSB.
—**CCC.**
Published by: Boise State University, 1910 University Dr, Boise, ID 83725. TEL 208-345-8204, 208-385-1011, chedr@tce.boisestate.edu. Ed. Clifford LeMaster.

540.7 USA
CHEMICAL EDUCATOR ANNUAL. Text in English. 1999. a., latest vol.8, 2004. USD 49 per vol. to individuals for B&W edition; USD 79 per vol. to institutions for B&W edition; USD 129 per vol. to individuals for color edition; USD 195 per vol. to institutions for color edition (effective 2004). **Document type:** *Journal, Academic/Scholarly.* **Description:** Provides libraries and individuals with a quick print reference to all articles which appeared in The Chemical Educator in the previous year.
Related titles: ◆ Supplement to: The Chemical Educator. ISSN 1430-4171.
Published by: Boise State University, 1910 University Dr, Boise, ID 83725. TEL 208-345-8204, FAX 208-426-3198, tce@chemeducator.org, http://www.chemeducator.org.

540 USA ISSN 1539-6797
TP158
CHEMICAL ENGINEERING BUYERS' GUIDE. Text in English. 1975. a. adv. **Document type:** *Directory, Trade.*
Former titles (until 1992): Chemical Engineering Equipment Byuers' Guide (0272-4057); (until 1981): Chemical Engineering. Equipment Byuers' Guide Issue (0094-9841)
Related titles: Online - full content ed.; ◆ Supplement to: Chemical Engineering. ISSN 0009-2460.
Published by: Chemical Week Associates, 110 William St 11th Fl, New York, NY 10038. TEL 212-621-4900, FAX 212-621-4690, http://www.che.com/buyersguide/index.php. adv.: B&W page USD 8,050; trim 7.875 x 10.75.

540 IND ISSN 0009-2533
CODEN: CHERDB
CHEMICAL ERA. Text in English. 1964. m. INR 150.
Indexed: ChemAb, ExcerpMed.
—CASDDS, CISTI.
Published by: O. N. Pandeya Ed. & Pub., 105-C Block F, New Alipore, Kolkata, West Bengal 700 053, India. Ed. L K Pandeya.

CHEMICAL GAZETTE. see *LAW—Corporate Law*

540 USA ISSN 1066-5315
CODEN: CHHEEM
CHEMICAL HERITAGE. Text in English. 1982. q. free Donation (effective 2005). adv. bk.rev. bibl.; illus. back issues avail. **Document type:** *Magazine, Academic/Scholarly.* **Description:** Aims at chemists, chemical engineers, teachers, and scholars. Reports on developments in history of the chemical sciences and technologies and on programs of the foundation and its constituent parts:Beckman Center, Othmer Library, and public outreach.
Former titles (until 1993): Beckman Center News and Othmer Library News; (until 1992): Beckman Center for the History of Chemistry. News (1052-0414); (until 1987): C H O C News (0736-4555)
Related titles: Online - full text ed.
Indexed: CIN, ChemAb, ChemTitl, GSI.
—CASDDS, Linda Hall. **CCC.**
Published by: Chemical Heritage Foundation, 315 Chestnut St, Philadelphia, PA 19106. TEL 215-925-2222, FAX 215-925-1954, editor@chemheritage.org, http://www.chemheritage.org. Ed., R&P Frances Coulborn Kohler. Adv. contact Kerry O'Connor. color page USD 1,000, B&W page USD 1,000; trim 7.25 x 9.75. Circ: 25,000.

540 658.8 USA ISSN 1051-9041
CHEMICAL INDUSTRIES NEWSLETTER. Text in English. 1960. bi-m. free. abstr.; stat. **Document type:** *Newsletter.*
Former titles: Chemical Industries Centers Newsletter; Chemical Industries Division Newsletter; Chemical Industries Center Newsletter; Chemical Economics Newsletter
Related titles: Online - full text ed.
Indexed: RAPRA.
—BLDSC (3147.150000), Linda Hall.
Published by: S R I Consulting, Chemical Business Research Division, 333 Ravenswood Ave, Menlo Park, CA 94025. TEL 650-859-3346, http://www.cbrd.sriconsulting.com. Ed. Steven Read.

CHEMICAL INDUSTRY IN (YEAR) - ANNUAL REVIEW. see *BUSINESS AND ECONOMICS—Production Of Goods And Services*

338.4 USA ISSN 1054-4941
HD9651.1
CHEMICAL INDUSTRY SOURCEBOOK AND STRATEGIC OVERVIEW✶. Text in English. a.
Published by: Lavely Associates, 12 Cordis St, No 1, Charlestown, MA 02129-3303.

540 GBR ISSN 0045-6403
CHEMICAL INSIGHT. Text in English. 1972. fortn. GBP 575, USD 862 (effective 2000). bk.rev. index. **Document type:** *Newsletter.* **Description:** Coverage includes mergers and acquisitions, competitor activities, growth trends, and financial performances of the global chemical industry.
Indexed: PROMT.
—**CCC.**
Published by: Reed Business Information Ltd. (Subsidiary of: Reed Business), Quadrant House, The Quadrant, Brighton Rd, Sutton, Surrey SM2 5AS, United Kingdom. TEL 44-20-86523500, FAX 44-208-652-8977, rbi.subscriptions@qss-uk.com, http://www.reedinfo.co.uk/. Ed. Nigel Davis TEL 44-20-8652-3397. **Subscr. to:** Quadrant Subscription Services, PO Box 302, Haywards Heath, W Sussex RH16 3YY, United Kingdom. TEL 44-1444-445566, FAX 44-1444-445447.

540 CHE ISSN 1523-1623
CODEN: CJIHAC
➤ **CHEMICAL JOURNAL ON INTERNET.** Text mainly in English. 1999. m. free. bk.rev. **Document type:** *Journal, Academic/Scholarly.* **Description:** Publishes papers on the latest achievements and breakthroughs in both fundamental research and applied research of chemical sciences both in China and abroad.
Media: Online - full text. **Related titles:** CD-ROM ed.: USD 100 (effective 2000).
Published by: Molecular Diversity Preservation International, MDPI Center, Matthaeusstr 11, Basel, 4057, Switzerland. TEL 41-79-3223379, 41-61-6837734, FAX 41-61-3028918, CJI302@126.com; CJI@mdpi.org, http://mirror.switch.ch/mdpi/cji/, http://www.mdpi.org/. **Co-sponsors:** National Natural Science Foundation of China, Department of Chemical Sciences; Chinese Academy of Sciences, Institute of Chemistry/Zhongguo Kexueyuan, Huaxue Yanjiusuo.

660 667.6 615 USA ISSN 1092-0110
TP1 CODEN: CMKRA5
CHEMICAL MARKET REPORTER. Text in English. 1871. w. USD 199 (effective 2005). adv. bk.rev. charts; mkt.; stat.; illus. reprints avail. **Document type:** *Magazine, Trade.*
Former titles (until 1996): Chemical Marketing Reporter (0090-0907); (until 1972): Oil, Paint and Drug Reporter (0030-1469)
Related titles: Microfilm ed.: (from PMC, PQC); Online - full text ed.: (from EBSCO Publishing, Factiva, Florida Center for Library Automation, Gale Group, H.W. Wilson, Northern Light Technology, Inc., O C L C Online Computer Library Center, Inc., ProQuest Information & Learning, The Dialog Corporation).

▼ *new title* ➤ *refereed* ✶ *unverified* ◆ *full entry avail.*

Indexed: ABIPC, ABIn, B&I, BPI, BPIA, BusI, CBNB, CIN, ChemAb, ChemTitl, EngInd, EnvAb, EnvInd, F&EA, IPA, KES, LHB, PROMT, RAPRA, T&II.
—BLDSC (3148.631000), CASDDS, IE, Linda Hall. **CCC.**
Published by: Schnell Publishing Co., Inc. (Subsidiary of: Reed Business Information), Two Rector St, 26th Fl, New York, NY 10006. TEL 212-791-4200, FAX 212-791-4310, http://icis.com/publications, http://www.chemexpo.com. Pub. Melanie Robson. Adv. contact Jonathan Sismey. B&W page USD 3,247, color page USD 5,102. Circ: 20,000 (paid and controlled).

540 GBR
CHEMICAL MODELLING: APPLICATIONS AND THEORY. (Vol.3 to be puiblished April 2004) Text in English. 2000. irreg., latest vol.2, 2002, May. GBP 249.50 per vol. (effective Jun. 2004). back issues avail. **Document type:** *Monographic series, Academic/Scholarly.* **Description:** Comprises critical literature reviews of molecular modelling, both theoretical and applied. Molecular modelling in this context refers to modelling the structure, properties and reactions of atoms, molecules & materials.
Published by: Royal Society of Chemistry, Thomas Graham House, Science Park, Milton Rd, Cambridge, CB4 0WF, United Kingdom. TEL 44-1223-432360, FAX 44-1223-425017, sales@rsc.org, http://www.rsc.org.

540 USA
CHEMICAL MONOGRAPHS REVIEW★. Text in English. 1985. q. looseleaf. free. bk.rev. back issues avail. **Document type:** *Monographic series.* **Description:** Covers review of new chemistry books and chemistry related books.
Published by: Chemists' Club Library, 40 W 45th St, New York, NY 10036-4203. TEL 212-679-6383, FAX 212-779-0349. Circ: 600.

C

540 SVK ISSN 0366-6352
QD1 CODEN: CHZVAN
➤ **CHEMICAL PAPERS/CHEMICKE ZVESTI.** Text in English. 1947. bi-m. USD 120 foreign (effective 2005). adv. bk.rev. charts; illus.; abstr. index. 68 p./no. 2 cols./p.; reprints avail. **Document type:** *Journal, Academic/Scholarly.* **Description:** Publishes original works from physical, organic, macromolecular and analytical chemistry, biochemistry, chemical engineering, from inorganic and organic technology as well as from technology of wood, cellulose and chemical fibres.
Indexed: ABIPC, ASCA, AnalAb, BiolAb, CCI, CEA, CEABA, CISA, Cadscan, ChemAb, ChemInfo, CurCont, INIS AtomInd, ISR, LeadAb, MSB, MSCI, RAPRA, RCI, RefZh, SCI, TCEA, WSCA, Zincscan.
—BLDSC (3148.770000), CASDDS, CISTI, IDS, IE, ingenta, Linda Hall. **CCC.**
Published by: (Slovenska Chemicka Spolocnost), Slovak Academic Press Ltd., Nam Slobody 6, PO Box 57, Bratislava, 81005, Slovakia. chempap@savba.sk, sap@sappress.sk, http://www.chem.sav.sk/chempap.html, http://www.sappress.sk. Ed. K Babor. adv.: page USD 100. **Dist. by:** Slovart G.T.G. s.r.o., Krupinska 4, PO Box 152, Bratislava 85299, Slovakia. TEL 421-2-63839472, FAX 421-2-63839485, info@slovart-gtg.sk, http://www.slovart-gtg.sk. **Co-sponsor:** Tomas Bata University, Faculty of Technology.

530 USA ISSN 1060-4782
CHEMICAL PROCESS SAFETY REPORT. Text in English. m.
—**CCC.**
Published by: Thompson Publishing Group, 1725 K St, N W, Ste 700, Washington, DC 20006. http://www.thompson.com.

540 USA ISSN 1527-8999
QD1 CODEN: CRHEAK
➤ **THE CHEMICAL RECORD.** Text in English. 2001. bi-m. USD 395 domestic to institutions; USD 467 in Canada & Mexico to institutions; USD 509 elsewhere to institutions; USD 435 combined subscription domestic to institutions print & online eds.; USD 507 combined subscription in Canada & Mexico to institutions print & online eds.; USD 549 combined subscription elsewhere to institutions print & online eds. (effective 2006). **Document type:** *Journal, Academic/Scholarly.* **Description:** Publishes timely and critical overviews of new developments at the cutting edge of chemistry of interest to a wide audience of chemists.
Related titles: Online - full text ed.: ISSN 1528-0691. USD 395 to institutions (effective 2006) (from EBSCO Publishing, Swets Information Services, Wiley InterScience).
Indexed: BBCI, CCI, ChemAb, CurCont.
—BLDSC (3150.342000), CISTI, IE, ingenta.
Published by: (Japan Chemical Forum JPN), John Wiley & Sons, Inc., 111 River St, Hoboken, NJ 07030-5774. TEL 201-748-6000, FAX 201-748-5915, uscs-wis@wiley.com, http://www.wiley.com. Eds. Gerhard Ertl TEL 49-30-8413-5100, Koji Nakanishi TEL 212-854-2169, Yuan T Lee TEL 886-2-2789-9404. **Subscr. addr. outside the Americas:** John Wiley & Sons Ltd., The Atrium, Southern Gate, Chichester, West Sussex PO19 8SQ, United Kingdom. TEL 44-1243-779777, FAX 44-1243-775878.

➤ **CHEMICAL REGULATION REPORTER**; a weekly review of activity affecting chemical users and manufacturers. see *ENVIRONMENTAL STUDIES—Pollution*

540.711 CHN ISSN 1005-9040
CODEN: CRCUED
➤ **CHEMICAL RESEARCH IN CHINESE UNIVERSITIES.** Text in English. 1984. q. CNY 36 domestic (effective 2000). **Document type:** *Academic/Scholarly.* **Description:** Comprehensive academic journal on chemistry. Contains theses, research notes, letters and reviews by teachers, researchers, postgraduates and graduate students.
Formerly (until vol.7, 1991): Chemical Journal of Chinese Universities (1000-9213)
Related titles: Online - full content ed.: (from WanFang Data Corp.); Online - full text ed.: (from East View Information Services).
Indexed: ASCA, CCI, CIN, ChemAb, ChemTitl, CurCont, EngInd, MSB, MSCI, RefZh.
—BLDSC (3150.441000), CASDDS, Ei, IE, ingenta.
Published by: Jilin University, Changchun, 130023, China. cjcu@mail.jlu.edu.cn. Ed. Ao-qing Tang. **Dist. by:** Science Press New York.

540 USA ISSN 0009-2665
QD1 CODEN: CHREAY
➤ **CHEMICAL REVIEWS.** Text in English. 1924. m. USD 1,048 in North America to institutions; USD 1,148 elsewhere to institutions; USD 124 in North America to members; USD 224 elsewhere to members; USD 93 in North America to students; USD 193 elsewhere to students (effective 2006). adv. bibl.; charts; illus. index. back issues avail.; reprints avail. **Document type:** *Journal, Academic/Scholarly.* **Description:** Provides comprehensive critical analyses in all fields of chemistry: organic, inorganic, physical, analytical, theoretical, and biological.
Related titles: Microfiche ed.: USD 753 in North America to institutional members; USD 765 elsewhere to institutional members (effective 2002); Microfilm ed.: USD 753 in North America to institutions; USD 768 elsewhere to institutions (effective 2002); Online - full text ed.: ISSN 1520-6890. USD 70 (effective 2006) (from EBSCO Publishing, Swets Information Services).
Indexed: ABIPC, AS&TI, ASCA, ASFA, ApMecR, BiolAb, CCI, CEABA, CIN, CTE, Cadscan, ChemAb, ChemInfo, ChemTitl, CurCR, CurCont, DBA, DSA, EngInd, ExcerpMed, GSI, INIS AtomInd, ISR, IndChem, IndMed, LeadAb, MEDLINE, MOS, MSB, MSCI, NPU, NutrAb, RAPRA, RCI, RefZh, S&F, SCI, WSCA, WTA, Zincscan.
—BLDSC (3151.000000), CASDDS, CINDOC, CISTI, Ei, IDS, IE, Infotrieve, ingenta, Linda Hall. **CCC.**
Published by: American Chemical Society, 1155 16th St, N W, Washington, DC 20036. TEL 202-872-4614, 800-227-5558, FAX 202-776-8264, service@acs.org, http://pubs.acs.org/cr. Ed. Josef Michl. adv.: color page USD 1,720. Circ: 4,800 (paid). **Subscr. to:** Member & Subscriber Services, PO Box 3337, Columbus, OH 43210. TEL 614-447-3776, 800-333-9511, FAX 614-447-3671.

540 GBR ISSN 1478-6524
CODEN: CSHCBM
▼ **CHEMICAL SCIENCE.** Text in English. 2004. m. GBP 199, USD 364 combined subscription print & online eds. (effective 2006). **Document type:** *Journal, Academic/Scholarly.* **Description:** Contains coverage from all RSC Publications, to provide a 'snapshot' of the latest developments across the chemical sciences.
Related titles: Online - full text ed.: ISSN 1742-2183. GBP 179, USD 328 (effective 2006).
—**CCC.**
Published by: Royal Society of Chemistry, Thomas Graham House, Science Park, Milton Rd, Cambridge, CB4 0WF, United Kingdom. TEL 44-1223-420066, FAX 44-1223-423623, http://www.rsc.org/Publishing/ChemScience/index.asp. Ed. Katie Gibb. Pub. Ms. Janet L Dean. **Subscr. to:** Portland Press Ltd., R S C Distribution Services, Commerce Way, Whitehall Industrial Estate, Colchester CO2 8HP, United Kingdom. TEL 44-1206-226050, FAX 44-1206-226055, sales@rscdistribution.org.

540 ETH ISSN 1011-3924
QD1 CODEN: BCETE6
➤ **CHEMICAL SOCIETY OF ETHIOPIA. BULLETIN.** Text in English. 1987. s-a. (in 1 vol.). free domestic to members; ETB 65 domestic to individuals; USD 45 foreign to individuals; ETB 90 domestic to institutions; USD 60 foreign to institutions (effective 2005). adv. bk.rev. index. 90 p./no.; back issues avail. **Document type:** *Bulletin, Academic/Scholarly.*
Related titles: Online - full text ed.: ISSN 1726-801X. 2001 (from Gale Group, IngentaConnect, International Network for the Availability of Scientific Publications, African Journals Online, Swets Information Services).
Indexed: ASCA, CCI, CIN, ChemAb, ChemTitl, CurCont, EnvAb, MSB.
—BLDSC (2442.950000), CASDDS, IDS.
Published by: Chemical Society of Ethiopia, PO Box 32934, Addis Ababa, Ethiopia. TEL 251-1-121201, FAX 251-1-560276, chemistry.aau@telecom.net.et, http://www.inasp.info/ajol/journals/cse/about.html. Eds. B S Chandravanshi, Taddese Wondimu. Adv. contact Taddese Wondimu. Circ: 500.

540 JPN ISSN 0009-2673
QD1 CODEN: BCSJA8
➤ **THE CHEMICAL SOCIETY OF JAPAN. BULLETIN.** Text in English. 1926. m. JPY 1,500, USD 143 to members; USD 989 in North America to institutions; USD 800 elsewhere to institutions (effective 2004). illus. Index. back issues avail.; reprint service avail. from PQC. **Document type:** *Bulletin, Academic/Scholarly.* **Description:** Publishes original research papers in all chemical research areas, including general and physical, analytical and inorganic, organic and biological and applied chemistry. It features significant completed studies, improved procedures of wide applicability, accounts of novel observations and important data of archival value.
Related titles: Microfilm ed.: (from PMC, PQC); Online - full text ed.: ISSN 1348-0634 (from EBSCO Publishing, J-Stage).
Indexed: ABIPC, APIAb, APICat, APIH&E, APIOC, APIPR, APIPS, APITS, ASCA, ASFA, AgBio, AnalAb, ApMecR, BPRC&P, BiolAb, CCI, CIN, Cadscan, ChemAb, ChemInfo, ChemTitl, CurCR, CurCont, DBA, DSA, EIA, ESPM, EnerInd, EngInd, ExcerpMed, ForAb, HortAb, INIS AtomInd, ISR, IndChem, JCT, JTA, LeadAb, M&GPA, MEDLINE, MOS, MSB, NPU, PBA, PetrolAb, RAPRA, RCI, RefZh, S&F, SCI, SIA, WSCA, Zincscan.
—BLDSC (2443.000000), CASDDS, CINDOC, CISTI, IDS, IE, Infotrieve, ingenta, Linda Hall, PADDS. **CCC.**
Published by: Chemical Society of Japan/Nippon Kagakukai, 1-5, Kanda-Surugadai 1-Chome, Chiyoda-ku, Tokyo, 101-0062, Japan. TEL 81-3-32926169, FAX 81-3-32926317, info@chemistry.or.jp, http://www.chemistry.or.jp/journals/bcsj/index-e.html. Ed. Kohei Tamao. Circ: 3,500. **Subscr. in N. America to:** American Chemical Society; **Subscr. to:** Membership Division, 1,Kanda-Surugadai1-Chome, Chiyoda-ku, Tokyo 101-8307, Japan. TEL 81-3-32926169, FAX 81-3-32926317.

540 JPN
CHEMICAL SOCIETY OF JAPAN. DIVISION OF COLLOID AND SURFACE CHEMISTRY. NEWSLETTER. Text in English, Japanese. bi-m. **Document type:** *Newsletter.*
Published by: (Division of Colloid and Surface Chemistry), Chemical Society of Japan/Nippon Kagakukai, 1-5, Kanda-Surugadai 1-Chome, Chiyoda-ku, Tokyo, 101-0062, Japan.

540 530 616.075 JPN
CHEMICAL SOCIETY OF JAPAN. SYMPOSIUM ON PHYSICAL AND CHEMICAL ASPECTS OF ULTRASOUND. PROCEEDINGS/ONPA NO BUSSEI TO KAGAKU TORONKAI KOEN RONBUNSHU. Text in Japanese. a. **Document type:** *Proceedings.*
Published by: Chemical Society of Japan/Nippon Kagakukai, 1-5, Kanda-Surugadai 1-Chome, Chiyoda-ku, Tokyo, 101-0062, Japan.

540 PAK ISSN 0253-5106
QD1 CODEN: JCSPDF
➤ **CHEMICAL SOCIETY OF PAKISTAN. JOURNAL.** Text in English, French, German; Summaries in English. 1979. q. PKR 100, USD 60.45 (effective 2005). bk.rev. back issues avail. **Document type:** *Academic/Scholarly.*
Indexed: ASCA, AnalAb, CCI, CIN, ChemAb, ChemTitl, CurCR, CurCont, EngInd, FS&TA, INIS AtomInd, IndChem, MSB, RCI.
—BLDSC (4729.082000), CASDDS, CISTI, Ei, IDS, IE, ingenta.
Published by: Chemical Society of Pakistan, H.E.J. Research Institute of Chemistry, University of Karachi, Karachi, 75280, Pakistan. FAX 92-21-466896, TELEX 28095 HEJRI PK. Ed. Atta-Ur-Rahman. Circ: 1,000.

540 GBR ISSN 0306-0012
QD1 CODEN: CSRVBR
➤ **CHEMICAL SOCIETY REVIEWS.** Text in English. 1972. 9/yr. GBP 454, USD 831 combined subscription print & online eds. (effective 2006). bibl.; charts; illus. index, cum.index. reprints avail. **Document type:** *Academic/Scholarly.* **Description:** Provides short, introductory reviews on topics of current interest in the chemical sciences.
Superseded: Chemical Society, London. Quarterly Reviews (0009-2681); Royal Institute of Chemistry Reviews (0035-8940)
Related titles: Online - full text ed.: ISSN 1460-4744. GBP 409, USD 748 (effective 2006) (from EBSCO Publishing, O C L C Online Computer Library Center, Inc., Swets Information Services).
Indexed: ASCA, AnalAb, ApMecR, BIOSIS Prev, BiolAb, BrCerAb, BullT&T, CCI, CIN, CLL, Cadscan, ChemAb, ChemInfo, ChemTitl, CurCR, CurCont, DBA, DSA, EngInd, FS&TA, IMMAb, ISR, IndChem, LeadAb, MSB, MSCI, RCI, RefZh, SCI, WSCA, WTA, Zincscan.
—BLDSC (3151.550000), CASDDS, CINDOC, CISTI, Ei, IDS, IE, Infotrieve, ingenta, Linda Hall. **CCC.**
Published by: Royal Society of Chemistry, Thomas Graham House, Science Park, Milton Rd, Cambridge, CB4 0WF, United Kingdom. TEL 44-1223-432360, FAX 44-1223-423623, csr@rsc.org, sales@rsc.org, http://www.rsc.org/Publishing/Journals/cs/index.asp. Ed. Dr. Robert D Eagling. **Subscr. to:** Portland Press Ltd., R S C Distribution Services, Commerce Way, Whitehall Industrial Estate, Colchester CO2 8HP, United Kingdom. TEL 44-1206-226050, FAX 44-1206-226055, sales@rscdistribution.org.

540 USA ISSN 0411-8871
CHEMICAL SPOTLIGHT. Text in English. 1950. m. USD 227.

Published by: Chemical Spotlight Inc., 203 Oak St, Ridgewood, NJ 07450-2512. TEL 201-444-7810, FAX 201-444-7939. Ed. Harry E Whitmore.

540 660 IND ISSN 0045-6497
CHEMICAL TAKE-OFF; monthly journal of chemical and chemical-based industries. Text in English. 1971. m. INR 40, USD 11. adv. bk.rev. charts. back issues avail.
Address: G-77 Himalaya House, Curzon Rd., New Delhi, India. Ed. S Chopra. Circ: 6,000.

540 GBR ISSN 1744-1560
CHEMICAL TECHNOLOGY. Text in English. m. GBP 199, USD 364 combined subscription print & online eds. (effective 2006). bk.rev. **Document type:** *Journal, Academic/Scholarly.* **Description:** Draws together coverage from RSC publications and provides succinct accounts of the latest industrial applications and technological aspects of research across the broad range of the chemical sciences.
Related titles: Online - full text ed.: GBP 179, USD 328 (effective 2006); ◆ Partial translation of: Chemical Communications. ISSN 1359-7345; ◆ Supplement to: The Analyst. ISSN 0003-2654; ◆ Supplement to: Green Chemistry. ISSN 1463-9262; ◆ Supplement to: Lab On a Chip. ISSN 1473-0197.
—CCC.
Published by: Royal Society of Chemistry, Thomas Graham House, Science Park, Milton Rd, Cambridge, CB4 0WF, United Kingdom. TEL 44-1223-420066, FAX 44-1223-420247, sales@rsc.rg, http://www.rsc.org/Publishing/ChemTech/index.asp. Ed. Niamh O'Conner.

540 USA ISSN 0149-2381
TP1 CODEN: CTTRDY
CHEMICAL TIMES & TRENDS. Text in English. 1977. q. USD 27; USD 39 foreign (effective 1997). adv. bk.rev. charts; illus. **Document type:** *Trade.*
Indexed: CIN, ChemAb, ChemTitl, EngInd, ResCtrInd.
—BLDSC (3151.790000), CASDDS, CISTI, Ei.
Published by: Chemical Specialties Manufacturers Association, 1913 Eye St, N W, Washington, DC 20006. TEL 202-872-8110, http://www.csma.org/. Ed., R&P Connie Neuman. Circ: 7,000.

540 GBR
CHEMICAL WEEK (INTERNATIONAL EDITION). Text in English. 1914. w. USD 419 (effective 1998). adv. bk.rev. **Document type:** *Trade.* **Description:** Provides global news and analysis for the chemical industry.
Indexed: IPackAb, LHB, RAPRA, WSCA.
Address: 24-25 Scala St, London, W1P 1LU, United Kingdom. TEL 44-20-7436-7676, FAX 44-20-7436-3749, http://www.chemweek.com. Ed. David Hunter. Pub. Michael Silber. Adv. contact John Michael. Circ: 33,309; 22,009 (paid).

540 660 IND ISSN 0045-6500
TP1 CODEN: CHWEBQ
CHEMICAL WEEKLY. Text in English. 1957. w. INR 840, USD 175 (effective 2005). adv. bk.rev. pat.; stat.; mkt. 220 p./no. 3 cols./p.; **Document type:** *Newspaper, Abstract/Index.* **Description:** Devoted to the Chemical and Allied Industries.
Related titles: Online - full content ed.
Indexed: CBNB, CIN, ChemAb, ChemTitl.
—BLDSC (3153.030000), CASDDS, IE, ingenta.
Published by: Sevak Publications, G.D. Ambekar Rd., 306 Shri Hanuman Industrial Estate, Wadala, P O Box 7110, Mumbai, Maharashtra 400 031, India. TEL 91-22-4120743, 91-44-827-1659, FAX 91-22-4168612, 91-44-825-5434, chemicalweekly@vsnl.com, sevak@bom2.vsnl.net.in, http://www.chemicalweekly.com. Ed., Pub. Ravi Raghavan. Adv. contact Vijay Raghavan. B&W page USD 300; trim 17.5 x 22.5. Circ: 70,000 (paid).

540 658.8 USA
CHEMICAL YELLOW PAGES DIRECTORY. Text in English. 1984. a. free with subscr. to Purchasing. adv. **Document type:** *Directory, Trade.* **Description:** Lists suppliers, chemical distributors, packaging firms, environmental services, and transportation and storage companies.
Former titles (until 1994): C P I Purchasing Chemicals Yellow Pages Annual Buying Guide; (until 1992): C P I Purchasing Chemicals Directory
Related titles: ◆ Supplement to: Purchasing (Newton). ISSN 0033-4448.
Published by: Reed Business Information (Subsidiary of: Reed Business), 275 Washington St, Newton, MA 02458. TEL 617-558-4291, FAX 617-558-4327, http://www.chemyellowpages.com/, http://www.reedbusiness.com. Circ: 25,000.

540.21 GBR
CHEMICALS. Text in English. 1920. a. GBP 110 domestic; GBP 130 foreign. **Document type:** *Directory.*
Formerly: British Chemicals and Their Manufacturers
Published by: (Chemical Industries Association Ltd.), Hamlet Information Services Ltd., Padlock Rd, West Wratting, Cambridge, CB1 5LS, United Kingdom. TEL 01223-290838, FAX 01223-290687. Ed. C E Freer. Pub. Peter G Lewis. Circ: 13,000.

540 IND ISSN 0009-2746
CHEMICALS - INTERNATIONAL. Text in English. 1965. m. INR 25. adv. charts; illus.; stat.
Published by: Encee Technical Publications Corporation, 1-E-22 Jhandewalan Ext., New Delhi, India. Eds. S K Nanda, V Navin. Circ: 5,760.

540 USA
CHEMICALS: LATIN AMERICAN INDUSTRIAL REPORT✶. (Avail. for each of 22 Latin American countries) Text in English. 1985. a. USD 435; per country report.
Published by: Aquino Productions, P O Box 15760, Stamford, CT 06901-0760. Ed. Andres C Aquino.

CHEMICALS TODAY. see *ENGINEERING—Chemical Engineering*

540 CZE ISSN 0009-2770
CODEN: CHLSAC
➤ **CHEMICKE LISTY.** Text in Czech, Slovak, English; Abstracts and contents page in English. 1876. m. EUR 225 (effective 2005). adv. bk.rev.; software rev.; Website rev. abstr.; charts; illus.; bibl.; maps; stat.; tr.mk.; tr.lit. index. 50 p./no. 2 cols./p.; back issues avail.; reprints avail. **Document type:** *Journal, Academic/Scholarly.* **Description:** Review of articles on progress in chemistry, papers on laboratory techniques and instruments, book reviews, discussions, reports on selected meetings and personal reports.
Related titles: Online - full text ed.: ISSN 1213-7103. free (effective 2005).
Indexed: A&ATA, ASCA, AnalAb, BiolAb, CCI, CEABA, CIN, CISA, CMCI, Cadscan, ChemAb, ChemTitl, CurCont, EngInd, FS&TA, INIS AtomInd, ISR, LeadAb, MSB, MSCI, NutrAb, RCI, RefZh, S&F, SCI, SIA, SSCI, WSCA, Zincscan.
—BLDSC (3154.000000), CASDDS, CISTI, Ei, IDS, IE, ingenta, Linda Hall. **CCC.**
Published by: Ceska Spolecnost Chemicka/Czech Chemical Society, Novotneho lavka 5, Prague, 11668, Czech Republic. TEL 420-2-21082370, FAX 420-2-22220184, chem.listy@csvts.cz, csch@csch.cz, http://chemicke-listy.vscht.cz/cz/index.html, http://www.csch.cz. Ed. Bohumil Prof. Kratochvil. Adv. contact Pavel Drasar. color page USD 800. Circ: 1,000. **Dist. in Western countries by:** Kubon & Sagner Buchexport - Import GmbH, Postfach 340180, Munich 8000, Germany. **Co-sponsor:** Institute of Chemical Technology, Prague.

540 DEU ISSN 0009-2851
QD1 CODEN: CUNZAW
➤ **CHEMIE IN UNSERER ZEIT.** Abbreviated title: C H I U Z. Text in German. 1967. bi-m. EUR 188 in Europe; CHF 298 in Switzerland & Liechtenstein; USD 208 elsewhere; EUR 188 combined subscription in Europe print & online eds.; CHF 328 combined subscription in Switzerland & Liechtenstein for print & online eds.; USD 229 combined subscription elsewhere print & online eds. (effective 2006). adv. bk.rev.; software rev.; Website rev. charts; illus. index. reprint service avail. from ISI. **Document type:** *Journal, Academic/Scholarly.*
Related titles: Online - full text ed.: ISSN 1521-3781. EUR 188 in Europe to institutions; CHF 298 to institutions in Switzerland & Liechtenstein; USD 208 elsewhere to institutions (effective 2006) (from EBSCO Publishing, Swets Information Services, Wiley InterScience).
Indexed: A&ATA, ASCA, BiolAb, CCI, CEABA, CIN, Cadscan, ChemAb, ChemInfo, ChemTitl, CurCont, EngInd, ExcerpMed, FS&TA, ISR, LeadAb, MSB, RCI, SCI, VITIS, Zincscan.
—BLDSC (3157.550000), CASDDS, CISTI, Ei, IDS, IE, Infotrieve, ingenta, Linda Hall. **CCC.**
Published by: (Gesellschaft Deutscher Chemiker), Wiley - V C H Verlag GmbH & Co. KGaA (Subsidiary of: John Wiley & Sons, Inc.), Boschstr 12, Weinheim, 69469, Germany. TEL 49-6201-6060, FAX 49-6201-606328, chiuz@wiley-vch.de, subservice@wiley-vch.de, http://www.wiley-vch.de/home/chiuz. Ed. Doris Fischer-Henningsen. R&P Claudia Rutz. Adv. contact Marion Schulz TEL 49-6201-606565. B&W page EUR 2,600, color page EUR 3,950. Circ: 9,813 (paid and controlled). **Subscr. in the Americas to:** John Wiley & Sons, Inc.. TEL 201-748-6645, FAX 201-748-6088, subinfo@wiley.com; **Subscr. outside Germany, Austria & Switzerland to:** John Wiley & Sons Ltd., The Atrium, Southern Gate, Chichester, West Sussex PO19 8SQ, United Kingdom. TEL 44-1243-779777, FAX 44-1243-775878.

➤ **CHEMIEARBEITER.** see *BUSINESS AND ECONOMICS—Labor And Industrial Relations*

540 POL ISSN 0009-2886
CODEN: CHGLAY
➤ **CHEMIK**; miesiecznik naukowo-techniczny. Text in Polish. 1948. m. EUR 113 foreign (effective 2005). adv. bk.rev. illus. index. 32 p./no. 2 cols./p.; **Document type:** *Newspaper, Academic/Scholarly.* **Description:** Addressed to engineers and economists in the chemical and related industries, as well as to the workers of scientific-research units.
Indexed: CEABA, CIN, ChemAb, ChemTitl, RefZh.
—CASDDS, CISTI, Linda Hall.
Published by: (Poland. Stowarzyszenie Inzynierow i Technikow Przemyslu Chemicznego), Zaklad Wydawniczy Chempress, ul Gornych Walow 25, skr poczt 46a, Gliwice, 44100, Poland. chemik@magsoft.com.pl, http://miesiecznikchemik.webpark.pl. Eds. Anna Bieniecka, Marian Grobelny. Adv. contact Anna Bieniecka. B&W page PLZ 8,000. Circ: 650. **Dist. by:** Ars Polona, Krakowskie Przedmiescie 7, Warsaw, Poland. TEL 48-22-9263914, FAX 48-22-9265334, arspolona@arspolona.com.pl, http://www.arspolona.com.pl.

660 DEU
DER CHEMIKALIENHANDEL. Text in English, German. 1999. q. EUR 40 (effective 2001). adv. bk.rev.; software rev. bibl.; charts; illus.; mkt.; pat.; stat.; tr.lit. **Document type:** *Magazine, Trade.* **Description:** Covers all aspects of the chemical trade industry.
Published by: Zeitungs- und Zeitschriftenverlag Heinrichs, Brueggekamp 1, Barsinghausen, 30890, Germany. TEL 49-5105-2289. Ed., Pub. Gerhard Heinrichs. adv.: B&W page EUR 4,000, color page EUR 6,000; trim 192 x 295.

CHEMINDEX; chemical buyers' guide for Japan. see *BUSINESS AND ECONOMICS—Trade And Industrial Directories*

540 NLD ISSN 1389-0433
CODEN: CHWEFU
CHEMISCH2WEEKBLAD. Text in Dutch. 1999. 20/yr. EUR 206.70 domestic; EUR 210 in Europe; EUR 213 elsewhere (effective 2005). adv. **Document type:** *Trade.* **Description:** Covers developments in chemistry and in the chemical industry, including economic and policy news, and working conditions.
Formed by the merger of (1976-1999): Chemisch Weekblad - Chemische Courant (0378-1887); (1903-1999): Chemisch Magazine (0167-2746); Which was formerly (until 1980): Chemisch Weekblad Magazine (0378-1895); Which superseded in part (in Jan.1976): Chemisch Weekblad (0009-2932)
Related titles: Online - full text ed.
Indexed: CBNB, KES, LHB.
—BLDSC (3164.700000), CISTI, IE, ingenta, Linda Hall.
Published by: (Koninklijke Nederlandse Chemische Vereniging), Beta Publishers, Postbus 249, Leidschendam, 2260 AE, Netherlands. TEL 31-70-4440600, FAX 31-70-3378799, redactie@c2w.nl, info@betapublishers.nl, http://www.c2w.nl/. Ed. Dr. Alexander Duyndam TEL 31-70-4440601. Pub. Dr. Roeland Dobbelaer.

540 660 615 CHE ISSN 0009-2983
CODEN: CHRUAE
CHEMISCHE RUNDSCHAU; Magazin fuer Chemie, Lebensmitteltechnologie, Pharmazie und Biotechnologie. Text in German. 1947. m. CHF 98, EUR 69 (effective 2004). adv. bk.rev. illus.; mkt. **Document type:** *Magazine, Trade.*
Related titles: Online - full text ed.
Indexed: CBNB, CEABA, CIN, CISA, ChemAb, ChemTitl, KES, PROMT.
—CASDDS.
Published by: Vogt-Schild AG, Zuchwilerstr 21, Solothurn 1, 4501, Switzerland. TEL 41-32-6247111, FAX 41-32-6247444, redaktion@chemische-rundschau.ch, a.widmer@vsonline.ch, http://www.chemische-rundschau.ch. Ed. Alfred Widmer. Adv. contact Hansruedi Spiri. B&W page EUR 1,960, color page EUR 2,800; trim 290 x 440. Circ: 11,500 (controlled).

540 USA ISSN 0009-3025
QD1 CODEN: CHESAB
➤ **THE CHEMIST.** Text in English. 1923. 6/yr. USD 75 (effective 2005). adv. bk.rev. charts; illus.; tr.lit. reprint service avail. from PQC. **Document type:** *Journal, Academic/Scholarly.* **Description:** Concerned with the professional, economic and ethical status of chemists and chemical engineers.
Related titles: Microform ed.: (from PQC).
Indexed: ABIPC, ChemAb, EngInd.
—Linda Hall. **CCC.**
Published by: American Institute of Chemists, Inc., 315 Chestnut St., Philadelphia, PA 19106-2702. TEL 215-873-8224, FAX 215-925-1954, publications@theaic.org, http://www.theaic.org. Eds. Edmund S Moka, Jeffrey W Hurst. Pub. Jeffrey W Hurst. adv.: B&W page USD 625; trim 8.5 x 11. Circ: 5,000.

540 DEU ISSN 0947-6539
QD1 CODEN: CEUJED
➤ **CHEMISTRY**; a European journal. Text in English. 1995. 36/yr. EUR 3,298 in Europe; CHF 5,148 in Switzerland & Liechtenstein; USD 4,054 elsewhere; EUR 3,628 combined subscription in Europe print & online eds.; CHF 5,663 combined subscription in Switzerland & Liechtenstein for print & online eds.; USD 4,460 combined subscription elsewhere print & online eds. (effective 2006). adv. illus. Index. 230 p./no. 2 cols./p.; reprints avail. **Document type:** *Journal, Academic/Scholarly.*
Related titles: Online - full text ed.: ISSN 1521-3765. 1998. EUR 3,298 in Europe to institutions; CHF 5,148 to institutions in Switzerland & Liechtenstein; USD 4,054 elsewhere to institutions (effective 2006) (from EBSCO Publishing, Swets Information Services, Wiley InterScience); ◆ Supplement to: Angewandte Chemie. ISSN 0044-8249.
Indexed: BAS, CCI, ChemAb, ChemInfo, CurCR, CurCont, ISR, IndChem, IndMed, Inspec, MEDLINE, RCI, RefZh, SCI.
—BLDSC (3168.860500), CASDDS, CINDOC, CISTI, IDS, IE, Infotrieve, ingenta, Linda Hall. **CCC.**

C

Published by: Wiley - V C H Verlag GmbH & Co. KGaA (Subsidiary of: John Wiley & Sons, Inc.), Boschstr 12, Weinheim, 69469, Germany. TEL 49-6201-606-0, FAX 49-6201-606-328, chemistry@wiley-vch.de, subservice@wiley-vch.de, http://www.wiley-vch.de/home/chemistry, http://www3.interscience.wiley.com/cgi-bin/home. Ed. Neville Compton. Pub. Eva E Wille. R&P Claudia Rutz. Adv. contact Aenne Anders TEL 49-6201-606552. **Subscr. in N., S. & Central America to:** John Wiley & Sons, Inc., 111 River St, Hoboken, NJ 07030-5774. TEL 201-748-6645, FAX 201-748-6088, subinfo@wiley.com; **Subscr. outside Germany, Austria & Switzerland to:** John Wiley & Sons Ltd., The Atrium, Southern Gate, Chichester, West Sussex PO19 8SQ, United Kingdom. TEL 44-1243-779777, FAX 44-1243-775878, cs-journals@wiley.co.uk.

530 DEU ISSN 1612-1872
QH345

▼ ➤ **CHEMISTRY & BIODIVERSITY.** Text in English. 2004. m. EUR 1,044 in Europe; CHF 1,508 in Switzerland & Liechtenstein; USD 1,197 elsewhere; EUR 1,149 combined subscription in Europe print & online eds.; CHF 1,659 combined subscription in Switzerland & Liechtenstein for print & online eds.; USD 1,317 combined subscription elsewhere print & online eds. (effective 2006). **Document type:** *Journal, Academic/Scholarly.* **Description:** Publishes articles on all aspects of biodiversity studied at the molecular and macromolecular levels.

Related titles: Online - full text ed.: ISSN 1612-1880. EUR 1,044 in Europe; CHF 1,508 in Switzerland & Liechtenstein; USD 1,197 elsewhere (effective 2006) (from EBSCO Publishing, Swets Information Services, Wiley InterScience).

Indexed: ASFA, B&BAb, CCI, CurCont, ExcerpMed, RefZh.

—BLDSC (3168.887500), CISTI, IE, Linda Hall. **CCC.**

Published by: Wiley - V C H Verlag GmbH & Co. KGaA (Subsidiary of: John Wiley & Sons, Inc.), Boschstr 12, Weinheim, 69469, Germany. TEL 49-6201-6060, FAX 49-6201-606328, editor@chembiodiv.ch, info@wiley-vch.de, http://www3.interscience.wiley.com/cgi-bin/jhome/106056929, http://www.wiley-vch.de. Eds. Bernard Testa, M. Volkan Kisakurek.

C

540 570 USA ISSN 1074-5521
QP501 CODEN: CBOLE2

➤ **CHEMISTRY & BIOLOGY.** Text in English. 1994. 12/yr. USD 341 in US & Canada to individuals; EUR 406 in Europe to individuals; JPY 42,200 in Japan to individuals; USD 353 elsewhere to individuals; EUR 1,706 in Europe to institutions; JPY 177,200 in Japan to institutions; USD 1,483 elsewhere to institutions (effective 2006). adv. bk.rev. illus. back issues avail. **Document type:** *Journal, Academic/Scholarly.* **Description:** Provides the forum for chemists and biologists for the exchange of information and ideas. Informs its readers of developments in modern chemistry and biology.

Related titles: Online - full text ed.: USD 328 to individuals (effective 2005) (from EBSCO Publishing, Gale Group, IngentaConnect, O C L C Online Computer Library Center, Inc., ScienceDirect, Swets Information Services).

Indexed: AEBA, AIDS&CR, ASCA, ASFA, AbHyg, AgBio, AnBrAb, BBCI, BIOBASE, BIOSIS Prev, BiolAb, BiolDig, CIN, CTA, ChemAb, ChemTitl, ChemoAb, CurCont, ESPM, GenetAb, HGA, ISR, IndMed, IndVet, Inpharma, M&PBA, MBA, MEDLINE, NSA, NucAcAb, NutrAb, OGFA, PBA, ProtozoAb, RA&MP, RM&VM, RPP, Reac, RefZh, RevApplEntom, S&F, SCI, SoyAb, TDB, VetBull, WeedAb.

—BLDSC (3168.890000), CASDDS, CISTI, GNLM, IDS, IE, Infotrieve, ingenta, Linda Hall. **CCC.**

Published by: Cell Press (Subsidiary of: Elsevier Science & Technology), 1100 Massachusetts Ave, Cambridge, MA 02138. TEL 617-661-7057, FAX 617-661-7061, editor@cell.com, http://www.elsevier.com/locate/chembiol, http://www.cellpress.com/. Eds. Michael Famulok, Peter Seeberger, Ronald Breaker. adv.: B&W page USD 1,050, color page USD 2,405; trim 8.5 x 11. Circ: 4,700. **Subscr. to:** Elsevier BV, PO Box 211, Amsterdam 1000 AE, Netherlands. TEL 31-20-485-3757, FAX 31-20-485-3432, nlinfo-f@elsevier.nl, http://www.elsevier.nl; 6277 Sea Harbor Dr, Orlando, FL 32887. TEL 407-345-3000, 866-314-2355, FAX 407-363-9661, subs@cell.com.

540 577 GBR ISSN 0275-7540
QH545.A1 CODEN: CHECDY

➤ **CHEMISTRY AND ECOLOGY.** Text in English. 1982. bi-m. GBP 1,617, USD 2,090 combined subscription to institutions print & online eds. (effective 2006). reprint service avail. from PSC. **Document type:** *Journal, Academic/Scholarly.* **Description:** Publishes original papers, short communications and occasional review articles on the relationship between chemistry and ecological processes.

Related titles: CD-ROM ed.; Microform ed.; Online - full text ed.: ISSN 1029-0370. GBP 1,536, USD 1,986 to institutions (effective 2006) (from EBSCO Publishing, Gale Group, IngentaConnect, O C L C Online Computer Library Center, Inc., Swets Information Services).

Indexed: ASFA, ApEcolAb, ChemAb, ESPM, EnvAb, EnvEAb, FS&TA, GEOBASE, PollutAb, SFA, SWRA, ToxAb, WildRev, ZooRec.

—BLDSC (3169.500000), CISTI, IE, Infotrieve. **CCC.**

Published by: Taylor & Francis Ltd (Subsidiary of: Taylor & Francis Group), 4 Park Sq, Milton Park, Abingdon, OX14 4RN, United Kingdom. TEL 44-1235-828600, FAX 44-1235-829000, info@tandf.co.uk, http://www.tandf.co.uk/journals/titles/02757540.asp. Ed. Roberto Danovaro. **Subscr. in N America to:** Taylor & Francis Inc., Customer Services Dept, 325 Chestnut St, 8th Fl, Philadelphia, PA 19106. TEL 215-625-8900, 800-354-1420, FAX 215-625-8914, customerservice@taylorandfrancis.com; **Subscr. to:** Journals Customer Service, Rankine Rd, Basingstoke, Hants RG24 8PR, United Kingdom. TEL 44-1256-813000, FAX 44-1256-330245, enquiry@tandf.co.uk.

660.6 615.19 GBR ISSN 0009-3068
TP1 CODEN: CHINAG

CHEMISTRY & INDUSTRY. Text in English. 1881. s-m. GBP 200, USD 330 (effective 2004). adv. bk.rev. bibl.; charts; illus.; pat.; stat. index. 36 p./no.; back issues avail.; reprints avail. **Document type:** *Magazine, Trade.*

Related titles: Online - full text ed.: (from EBSCO Publishing, Factiva, Florida Center for Library Automation, Gale Group, H.W. Wilson, O C L C Online Computer Library Center, Inc.); Supplement(s): Supply Line.

Indexed: AEA, APIAb, APICat, APIH&E, APIOC, APIPR, APIPS, APITS, AS&TI, ASCA, AgBio, AnBrAb, AnalAb, BioDAb, BiolAb, BrTechl, CBNB, CBTA, CCI, CEA, CEABA, CIN, CIS, CISA, CRIA, CSNB, CTFA, Cadscan, ChemAb, ChemInfo, ChemTitl, CurCR, CurCont, DBA, DSA, EIA, EngInd, EnvAb, ExcerpMed, F&EA, FCA, FLUIDEX, FPA, FS&TA, HECAB, HerbAb, HortAb, I&DA, IPackAb, ISR, IndChem, IndIslam, IndVet, LHB, LeadAb, MEDLINE, MOS, MSB, MaizeAb, NPU, NutrAb, PBA, PROMT, PST, PetrolAb, ProtozoAb, RA&MP, RAPRA, RCI, RHEA, RM&VM, RPP, RevApplEntom, S&F, SCI, SFA, SSCI, SeedAb, SoyAb, TCEA, Telegen, TriticAb, VetBull, WAE&RSA, WSCA, WTA, WeedAb, Zincscan.

—BLDSC (3170.000000), CASDDS, CINDOC, CISTI, Ei, IDS, IE, Infotrieve, ingenta, Linda Hall. **CCC.**

Published by: Society of Chemical Industry, 14 Belgrave Sq, London, SW1X 8PS, United Kingdom. TEL 44-20-72353681, FAX 44-20-72359410, enquiries@chemind.org, http://www.chemind.org, http://www.soci.org. Ed. Neil Eisberg. Adv. contact Mark Janaway TEL 44-20-75981532. page USD 2,000. Circ: 9,161 (paid). **Subscr. in Japan to:** U S A C O Corp., 2-17-12 Higashi-Azabu, Minato-ku, Tokyo 106-0044, Japan. inquiry@usaco.co.jp, http://www.usaco.co.jp/; **Subscr. to:** Distribution Centre, Blackhorse Rd, Letchworth, Herts SG6 1HN, United Kingdom. **Dist. addr.:** Extenza - Turpin, Pegasus Dr, Stratton Business Park, Biggleswade, Beds SG18 8TQ, United Kingdom. TEL 44-1462-672555, FAX 44-1462-480-947.

540.71 IND ISSN 0970-597X

CHEMISTRY EDUCATION. Text in English. 1984. q. INR 120, USD 40.

Published by: (India. University Grants Commission), New Age International Pvt. Ltd., Journals Division, 4835-24 Ansari Rd., Darya Ganj, New Delhi, 110 002, India. TEL 91-11-3267996, FAX 91-11-326-7437. Circ: 1,000.

340.7 GRC

➤ **CHEMISTRY EDUCATION: RESEARCH AND PRACTICE.** Text in English, French. 2000. q. free (effective 2005). back issues avail. **Document type:** *Journal, Academic/Scholarly.*

Formerly: Chemistry Education: Research and Practice in Europe (1109-4028)

Media: Online - full text.

Indexed: ERA, ETA, MEA, RHEA, SEA, SENA, SOMA, TEA.

Published by: University of Ioannina, Department of Chemistry, GR-451, Ioannina, 10, Greece. TEL 30-2651-098431, FAX 30-2651-098798, gtseper@cc.uoi.gr, http://www.uoi.gr/cerp/. Ed. Georgious Tsaparlis.

540 RUS ISSN 1023-8603

CHEMISTRY FOR SUSTAINABLE DEVELOPMENT. Text in English. 1998. bi-m. free (effective 2005). **Document type:** *Journal, Academic/Scholarly.* **Description:** Aims to integrate all aspects of chemical research on the basis of new economically acceptable processes, making possible harmonious relations between the chemical industry and the environment.

Media: Online - full content. **Related titles:** ◆ Russian ed.: Khimiya v Interesakh Ustoichivogo Razvitiya. ISSN 0869-8538.

—Linda Hall.

Published by: (Rossiiskaya Akademiya Nauk, Institut Khimii Tverdogo Tela i Mekhanokhimii/Russian Academy of Sciences, Institute of the Chemistry of Solid Matter and Mechanochemistry), Izdatel'stvo Sibirskogo Otdeleniya Rossiiskoi Akademii Nauk/Publishing House of the Russian Academy of Sciences, Siberian Branch, Morskoi pr 2, a/ya 187, Novosibirsk, 630090, Russian Federation. TEL 7-3832-300570, FAX 7-3832-333755, csd@ad-sbras.nsc.ru, psb@ad-sbras.nsc.ru, http://www-psb.ad-sbras.nsc.ru/English/CSDE.HTM. Ed. Nikolai Lyakhov.

540 USA

CHEMISTRY FOR THE 21ST CENTURY SERIES. Variant title: I U P A C Chemistry for the 21st Century Series. Text in English. irreg., latest 1994. **Document type:** *Monographic series.*

Published by: (International Union of Pure and Applied Chemistry), C R C Press, LLC (Subsidiary of: Taylor & Francis Group), 2000 N W Corporate Blvd, Boca Raton, FL 33431. TEL 800-272-7737, journals@crcpress.com, http://www.crcpress.com/.

540 AUS ISSN 0314-4240
TP1 CODEN: CHAUDY

➤ **CHEMISTRY IN AUSTRALIA.** Text in English. 1931. m. AUD 170 domestic to institutions; AUD 190 foreign to institutions (effective 2004). bk.rev. charts; illus.; stat. index. **Document type:** *Academic/Scholarly.* **Description:** Provides topical science articles, news conference listings, and reports on new products.

Formerly (until July 1977): Royal Australian Chemical Institute. Proceedings (0035-8746)

Related titles: Microfiche ed.

Indexed: AESIS, ASI, AnalAb, CBNB, CIN, CSNB, Cadscan, ChemAb, ChemTitl, DSA, EngInd, FS&TA, INIS AtomInd, LHB, LeadAb, MSB, RHEA, Zincscan.

—BLDSC (3170.230000), CASDDS, CISTI, Ei, IE, ingenta, Linda Hall. **CCC.**

Published by: Royal Australian Chemical Institute, 21 Vale St, North Melbourne, VIC 3051, Australia. TEL 61-3-93285309, FAX 61-3-93282670, chemaust@raci.org.au, member@raci.org.au, http://www.raci.org.au/ChemAust/. Ed. Sally Woollett. Adv. contact Joanna Dettl TEL 61-7-35116246. Circ: 5,986.

540 NZL ISSN 0110-5566
QD1 CODEN: CMNZAA

CHEMISTRY IN NEW ZEALAND. Text in English. 1936. bi-m. subscr. incld. with membership. adv. bk.rev. **Document type:** *Journal, Academic/Scholarly.* **Description:** Contains articles relating to chemistry and laboratory techniques in research, education and industry both in New Zealand and overseas. Also includes items on political and regulatory developments affecting the science industry in general.

Formerly (until 1967): New Zealand Institute of Chemistry. Journal (0028-8225)

Related titles: Online - full text ed.

Indexed: CIN, ChemAb, ChemTitl, EngInd, MSB.

—BLDSC (3172.070000), CASDDS, CISTI, Ei, IE, ingenta, Linda Hall. **CCC.**

Published by: (New Zealand Institute of Chemistry), Ancat Holdings Ltd., Howick, PO Box 38-546, Auckland, New Zealand. TEL 64-9-5353475, FAX 64-9-5353476, chemistry@ancat.co.nz, ancat@ancat.co.nz, http://www.ancat.co.nz/chemistr.htm. Ed. B W L Graham. Circ: 1,500.

540 660 USA ISSN 0193-6484
QD1 CODEN: CINRDT

CHEMISTRY INTERNATIONAL; the news magazine of IUPAC. Text in English. 1979. bi-m. USD 45 to individuals; USD 99 to institutions (effective 2004). adv. **Document type:** *Journal, Academic/Scholarly.*

Formerly: I U P A C Information Bulletin (0145-5672); Which superseded (1956-1977): International Union of Pure and Applied Chemistry. Information Bulletin (0539-1148)

Related titles: Microform ed.: (from PQC); Online - full text ed.: ISSN 1365-2192 (from EBSCO Publishing).

Indexed: CIN, ChemAb, ChemTitl, ExcerpMed, IndVet, RAPRA, RefZh, WSCA.

—BLDSC (3172.010000), CASDDS, CISTI, IE, Infotrieve, ingenta, Linda Hall. **CCC.**

Published by: International Union of Pure and Applied Chemistry, IUPAC Secretariat, PO Box 13757, Research Triangle Park, NC 27709-3757. edit.ci@iupac.org, http://www.iupac.org/publications/ci/index.html. Circ: 6,665.

540 JPN ISSN 0366-7022
QD1 CODEN: CMLTAG

➤ **CHEMISTRY LETTERS.** Text in English. 1972. m. USD 654 in North America to institutions (effective 2005). back issues avail.; reprint service avail. from PQC. **Document type:** *Academic/Scholarly.* **Description:** Covers all the fields of pure and industrial chemistry.

Related titles: Microfiche ed.; Online - full text ed.: ISSN 1348-0715 (from EBSCO Publishing, J-Stage).

Indexed: ASCA, ASFA, AnalAb, BPRC&P, CCI, CIN, Cadscan, ChemAb, ChemInfo, ChemTitl, CurCR, CurCont, DBA, DSA, ESPM, EngInd, ExcerpMed, INIS AtomInd, ISR, IndChem, JCT, JTA, LeadAb, MOS, MSB, NPU, NucAcAb, RCI, RefZh, S&F, SCI, SIA, SWRA, TTI, Zincscan.

—BLDSC (3172.020000), CASDDS, CISTI, Ei, IDS, IE, Infotrieve, ingenta, Linda Hall. **CCC.**

Published by: Chemical Society of Japan/Nippon Kagakukai, 1-5, Kanda-Surugadai 1-Chome, Chiyoda-ku, Tokyo, 101-0062, Japan. TEL 81-3-32926169, FAX 81-3-32926317, info@chemistry.or.jp, http://www.csj.jp/journals/chem-lett/index-e.html, http://www.chemistry.or.jp/. Ed. Tsutomu Katsuki. Circ: 4,000. **Subscr. in N. America to:** American Chemical Society; **Subscr. to:** Membership Division, 1,Kanda-Surugadai1-Chome, Chiyoda-ku, Tokyo 101-8307, Japan. TEL 81-3-32926169, FAX 81-3-32926317.

540 USA ISSN 0069-3146

➤ **CHEMISTRY OF FUNCTIONAL GROUPS.** Text in English. 1965. irreg., latest 1997. price varies. back issues avail. **Document type:** *Monographic series, Academic/Scholarly.*

Indexed: CCI.

Published by: John Wiley & Sons, Inc., 111 River St, Hoboken, NJ 07030-5774. TEL 201-748-6000, 800-825-7550, FAX 201-748-5915, uscs-wis@wiley.com, http://www.wiley.com/WileyCDA/Section/id-11128.html. Ed. Zvi Rappoport.

540 GBR ISSN 0959-8464
CODEN: CEEVE3
CHEMISTRY REVIEW. Text in English. 1991. 4/yr. GBP 24.95 domestic; GBP 31 in Europe; GBP 36 elsewhere (effective Sep. 2004). adv. **Document type:** *Magazine, Academic/Scholarly.*
Related titles: Online - full text ed.: (from Gale Group).
Indexed: BrTechI, CIN, ChemAb, ChemTitl, M&TEA, MSB.
—BLDSC (3172.155000), CASDDS, IE, ingenta. **CCC.**
Published by: Philip Allan Updates, Market Pl, Deddington, Banbury, Oxon OX15 0SE, United Kingdom. TEL 44-1869-338652, FAX 44-1869-338803, sales@philipallan.co.uk, http://www.philipallan.co.uk. Ed. Shiela Tarrant. R&P Ceri Jenkins.

540 GBR ISSN 1473-7604
QD1 CODEN: CWHOBI
➤ **CHEMISTRY WORLD.** Text in English. 1965. m. GBP 583, USD 1,067 combined subscription print & online eds. (effective 2006). adv. bk.rev. illus. Index. reprints avail. **Document type:** *Magazine, Academic/Scholarly.* **Description:** Contains scientific articles of general chemical interest and keeps the scientist up-to-date on economic, political, and social factors and their effects on the scientific community.
Formerly (until 2004): Chemistry in Britain (0009-3106); Which was formed by the merger of (1950-1964): Royal Institute of Chemistry. Journal (0368-3958); Which was formerly: Royal Institute of Chemistry of Great Britain and Ireland. Journal and Proceedings; (1957-1964): Chemical Society. Proceedings (0369-8718); Which superseded in part (in 1877): Chemical Society. Journal (0368-1769)
Related titles: Online - full text ed.: GBP 525, USD 960 (effective 2006) (from EBSCO Publishing).
Indexed: A&ATA, AESIS, ASCA, AbHyg, AnalAb, BiolAb, BrCerAb, BrTechI, CBNB, CBTA, CCI, CEABA, CIN, CISA, CSNB, Cadscan, ChemAb, ChemInfo, ChemTitl, CurCont, DBA, DSA, ESPM, EngInd, EnvAb, EnvInd, ExcerpMed, FS&TA, HECAB, ISR, LHB, LeadAb, MEDLINE, MOS, MSB, NPU, NutrAb, PROMT, RCI, RHEA, RILM, RefZh, S&F, SCI, SSCI, SWRA, TDB, WSCA, Zincscan.
—BLDSC (3172.205000), CASDDS, CISTI, Ei, IDS, IE, Infotrieve, ingenta, Linda Hall. **CCC.**
Published by: Royal Society of Chemistry, Thomas Graham House, Science Park, Milton Rd, Cambridge, CB4 0WF, United Kingdom. TEL 44-1223-432360, FAX 44-1223-423623, chemistryworld@rsc.org, sales@rsc.org, http://www.rsc.org/chemistryworld/About/index.asp. Ed. Karen Harries-Rees. Circ: 45,000. **Subscr. to:** Portland Press Ltd., R S C Distribution Services, Commerce Way, Whitehall Industrial Estate, Colchester CO2 8HP, United Kingdom. TEL 44-1206-226050, FAX 44-1206-226055, sales@rscdistribution.org.

540 920 NLD ISSN 0921-8629
➤ **CHEMISTS AND CHEMISTRY.** Text in Dutch. 1984. irreg., latest vol.20, 2001. price varies. **Document type:** *Monographic series, Academic/Scholarly.*
—BLDSC (3172.235000), CISTI.
Published by: Springer-Verlag Dordrecht (Subsidiary of: Springer Science+Business Media), Van Godewijckstraat 30, Dordrecht, 3311 GX, Netherlands. TEL 31-78-6576050, FAX 31-78-6576474, http://www.springeronline.com.

540 DEU ISSN 0944-5846
➤ **CHEMKON - CHEMIE KONKRET**; Forum fuer Unterricht und Didaktik. Text in German. 1994. q. EUR 68 in Europe; CHF 144 in Switzerland & Liechtenstein; USD 88 elsewhere; EUR 75 combined subscription in Europe print & online eds.; CHF 159 combined subscription in Switzerland & Liechtenstein for print & online eds.; USD 97 combined subscription elsewhere print & online eds. (effective 2006). adv. **Document type:** *Journal, Academic/Scholarly.* **Description:** Helps teachers and professors make the world of chemistry more tangible to their students.
Related titles: Online - full text ed.: ISSN 1521-3730. EUR 68 in Europe to institutions; CHF 144 to institutions in Switzerland & Liechtenstein; USD 88 elsewhere to institutions (effective 2006) (from EBSCO Publishing, Swets Information Services, Wiley InterScience).
—IE. **CCC.**
Published by: Wiley - V C H Verlag GmbH & Co. KGaA (Subsidiary of: John Wiley & Sons, Inc.), Boschstr 12, Weinheim, 69469, Germany. TEL 49-6201-6060, FAX 49-6201-606328, subservice@wiley-vch.de, http://www.wiley-vch.de. Ed. Dr. Walter Jansen. R&P Claudia Rutz. Adv. contact R Veit. Circ: 1,200. **Subscr. in the Americas to:** John Wiley & Sons, Inc., 111 River St, Hoboken, NJ 07030-5774. TEL 201-748-6645, FAX 201-748-6088, subinfo@wiley.com; **Subscr. outside Germany, Austria & Switzerland to:** John Wiley & Sons Ltd., The Atrium, Southern Gate, Chichester, West Sussex PO19 8SQ, United Kingdom. TEL 44-1243-779777, FAX 44-1243-775878.

540 USA ISSN 0736-4687
CHEMMATTERS. Text in English. 1983. q. USD 12 domestic; USD 16 foreign (effective 2005). **Document type:** *Academic/Scholarly.* **Description:** For first-year chemistry students. Seeks to "demystify the everyday world" by explaining how chemistry works in the world around us.
Related titles: CD-ROM ed.: ChemMatters on CD-ROM. USD 49.95 (effective 2003).
Indexed: CIJE.
—CCC.
Published by: (Office of High School Chemistry), American Chemical Society, 1155 16th St, N W, Washington, DC 20036. TEL 202-872-4614, 800-227-5558, FAX 202-776-8264, service@acs.org, http://www.acs.org/education/curriculum/chemmatt.html, http://pubs.acs.org. Eds. Helen Herlocker, Michael J Tinnesand. R&P Janet Boese TEL 800-227-5558 ext 6164. Circ: 40,000 (paid).

▼ **CHEMMEDCHEM.** see *PHARMACY AND PHARMACOLOGY*

CHEMOSPHERE. see *ENVIRONMENTAL STUDIES—Toxicology And Environmental Safety*

540 CHL ISSN 0717-9324
CODEN: JCCSCB
➤ **THE CHILEAN CHEMICAL SOCIETY. JOURNAL.** Text and summaries in English. 1949. q. USD 40 domestic; USD 100 foreign (effective 2003). adv. bk.rev. bibl.; charts; illus. cum.index. back issues avail. **Document type:** *Journal, Academic/Scholarly.*
Formerly (until Mar. 2003): Sociedad Chilena de Quimica. Boletin (0366-1644)
Related titles: Microfilm ed.; Online - full text ed.: ISSN 0717-9707. 1999. free (effective 2005) (from SciELO).
Indexed: ASCA, BiolAb, CCI, CIN, ChemAb, ChemTitl, CurCont, ISR, LHB, RCI, SCI.
—BLDSC (2190.250000), CASDDS, CISTI, IDS, IE, ingenta, Linda Hall.
Published by: Sociedad Chilena de Quimica, Dpto. 19, Paicavi, 170, Concepcion, Chile. TEL 56-41-227815, FAX 56-41-235819, http://www.schq.cl. Ed., Adv. contact Guillermo Contreras Koder TEL 56-41-227815. Circ: 450.

540 CHE ISSN 0009-4293
TP1 CODEN: CHIMAD
➤ **CHIMIA.** Text in English, French, German. 1923. 10/yr. CHF 220 domestic to individuals; CHF 270 foreign to individuals (effective 2004). adv. bk.rev. abstr.; charts; illus. cum.index every 10 yrs. back issues avail. **Document type:** *Journal, Academic/Scholarly.*
Former titles (until 1947): Schweizer Chemiker-Zeitung und Technik-Industrie (0370-9264); (until 1944): Technik und Industrie und Schweizer Chemiker-Zeitung (0372-1434); Which was formed by the merger of (1917-1923): Schweizerische Chemiker-Zeitung (0370-9051); (1918-1923): Technik und Industrie (1423-1506)
Related titles: Microfilm ed.: (from PMC); Online - full text ed.: (from Gale Group, IngentaConnect).
Indexed: ASCA, AnalAb, BiolAb, CCI, CEA, CEABA, CIN, CISA, ChemAb, ChemInfo, ChemTitl, CurCR, CurCont, DSA, EngInd, ExcerpMed, FS&TA, INIS AtomInd, ISR, IndChem, MOS, MSB, MSCI, NPU, RCI, RefZh, SCI, SSCI, TCEA, VITIS.
—BLDSC (3173.000000), CASDDS, CINDOC, CISTI, Ei, IDS, IE, Infotrieve, ingenta, Linda Hall.
Published by: Schweizerische Chemische Gesellschaft, Baerenplatz 2, Bern, 3011, Switzerland. TEL 41-31-3104090, FAX 41-31-3121678, info@swiss-chem-soc.ch, http://www.chimia.ch, http://www.swiss-chem-soc.ch. Ed., R&P Camille Ganter. Circ: 3,600.

540 TUR ISSN 0379-5896
CODEN: CATUA9
➤ **CHIMICA ACTA TURCICA.** Text in English, French, German; Summaries in English. 1973. 3/yr. USD 30 (effective 1998 & 1999). charts; stat. **Document type:** *Academic/Scholarly.* **Description:** Publishes original research papers and short notes in all fields of pure and applied chemistry and chemical engineering.
Indexed: CIN, ChemAb, ChemTitl, INIS AtomInd.
—BLDSC (3174.030000), CASDDS, CISTI, Linda Hall.
Published by: Istanbul Universitesi, Muhendislik Fakultesi Dekanligi/Istanbul University, Faculty of Engineering, Dean's Office, Avcilar - Istanbul, 34850, Turkey. TEL 90-212-5911998, FAX 90-212-5911997, chimactr@magnet.com.tr. Eds. Murat Orbay, Resat Apak. Circ: 300.

540.71 ITA ISSN 0392-8942
CODEN: CSCUDJ
CHIMICA NELLA SCUOLA. Text in Italian. 1983. 5/yr. USD 40 foreign.
Related titles: ♦ Supplement to: La Chimica e l'Industria. ISSN 0009-4315.
—CASDDS.
Published by: (Societa Chimica Italiana), Editrice di Chimica s.r.l., Viale Liegi, 48, Rome, RM 00198, Italy. TEL 39-6-8549691, FAX 39-6-8548734.

540 ITA ISSN 0392-839X
CODEN: CHOGDS
➤ **CHIMICA OGGI/CHEMISTRY TODAY.** Text in English. 1982. 10/yr. EUR 48 domestic; EUR 99 foreign (effective 2005). adv. bk.rev. Index. back issues avail. **Document type:** *Journal, Academic/Scholarly.*
Related titles: Online - full text ed.: (from EBSCO Publishing).
Indexed: AEA, ASCA, CBNB, CBTA, CCI, CEABA, CIN, ChemAb, ChemTitl, EngInd, FPA, HortAb, IPA, NutrAb, PN&I, RA&MP, RCI, RPP, RevApplEntom, S&F, SIA, WeedAb.
—BLDSC (3175.100000), CASDDS, CISTI, Ei, IDS, IE, ingenta.
Published by: Tekno Scienze s.r.l., Via Aurelio Saffi 23, Milan, MI 20123, Italy. TEL 39-02-4818011, FAX 39-02-4818070, http://www.teknoscienze.com. Ed. Carla Scesa. R&P, Adv. contact Michaela Carmagnola. B&W page USD 2,050; trim 210 x 297. Circ: 8,000.

540 FRA
CODEN: ICHEDI
CHIMIE HEBDO; chimie, parachimie, pharmacie. Text in French; Summaries in English, German. w. (42/yr.). **Description:** Devoted to the chemicals, specialty chemical and pharmaceutical industries in France and throughout the world.
Formerly (until Apr. 1998): Informations Chimie Hebdo (0339-6045)
Related titles: Online - full text ed.; ♦ Supplement to: Info Chimie Magazine. ISSN 1286-0921.
Indexed: CBNB, CIN, ChemAb, ChemTitl, RefZh.
—BLDSC (3179.230000), CASDDS.
Published by: Societe d'Expansion Technique et Economique S.A., 4 rue de Seze, Paris, 75009, France. TEL 33-1-44945060, FAX 33-1-44945075, http://www.infochimie.presse.fr. Ed. Dmitri Savostianoff.

CHINA CHEMICAL MARKET NEWSLETTER. see *BUSINESS AND ECONOMICS—Marketing And Purchasing*

540 CHN ISSN 1001-8417
CODEN: CCLEE7
➤ **CHINESE CHEMICAL LETTERS**; preliminary chemical communications in English. Text in English. 1991. m. CNY 33 newsstand/cover (effective 2005). index. back issues avail. **Document type:** *Academic/Scholarly.* **Description:** Publishes preliminary accounts of important Chinese chemical research not previously published in Chinese literature.
Related titles: Microform ed.: (from PQC); Online - full text ed.: (from East View Information Services, WanFang Data Corp.).
Indexed: ASCA, CCI, CIN, ChemAb, ChemTitl, MSCI, RCI, RefZh.
—BLDSC (3180.274300), CASDDS, IE, ingenta.
Published by: Institute of Materia Medica, 1, Xiannongtan Street, Beijing, 100050 , China. cclbj@imm.ac.cn, http://zghxkb.periodicals.net.cn/, http://www.imm.ac.cn/. Ed. Xiaotian Liang. **Co-sponsor:** National Natural Science Foundation of China.

C

540 TWN ISSN 0009-4536
QD1 CODEN: JCCTAC
➤ **CHINESE CHEMICAL SOCIETY. JOURNAL (TAIPEI).** Text in Multiple languages. 1954. bi-m. USD 56 to non-members; USD 62 in Hong Kong; USD 75 elsewhere (effective 1999). adv. abstr.; bibl.; charts. **Document type:** *Journal, Academic/Scholarly.* **Description:** Contains both experimental and theoretical research on fundamental aspects of chemistry.
Supersedes in part: Chinese Chemical Society. Journal (Peiping) (0375-8745)
Indexed: ASCA, AbHyg, AgBio, AgrForAb, AnalAb, BiolAb, BrCerAb, C&ISA, CCI, CIN, CPA, Cadscan, CerAb, ChemAb, ChemInfo, ChemTitl, CorrAb, CurCont, E&CAJ, EMA, FCA, FPA, ForAb, HortAb, IAA, ISR, LeadAb, M&TEA, MBF, METADEX, MOS, MSB, NPU, NutrAb, OrnHort, PHN&I, ProtozoAb, RA&MP, RCI, RM&VM, RPP, S&F, SCI, SIA, SeedAb, SolStAb, SoyAb, TDB, WAA, WeedAb, Zincscan.
—BLDSC (4729.250000), CASDDS, CINDOC, CISTI, Ei, IDS, IE, ingenta, Linda Hall.
Published by: Chinese Chemical Society/Zhongguo Huaxuehui, Rm.903, 9th Fl, No7 Chungking S. Rd, Sec 1, P.O. Box 609, Taipei, 10099, Taiwan. TEL 886-2-2789-8512, FAX 886-2-2311-8464, http://www.sinica.edu.tw/~ccswww/jccs.htm. Ed. Chun Chen Liao. Circ: 2,000. **Co-sponsor:** National Science Council.

➤ **CHINESE JOURNAL OF CHEMICAL ENGINEERING.** see *ENGINEERING—Chemical Engineering*

540 CHN ISSN 1001-604X
QD1 CODEN: CJOCEV
➤ **CHINESE JOURNAL OF CHEMISTRY.** Text in English. 1983. m. EUR 1,398 in Europe print or online eds. (effective 2005); CHF 2,298 in Switzerland print or online eds.; USD 1,798 elsewhere print or online eds.; EUR 1,538 combined subscription in Europe print & online eds.; CHF 2,528 combined subscription in Switzerland print & online eds.; USD 1,978 combined subscription elsewhere print & online eds. (effective 2006). adv. 96 p./no.; **Document type:** *Journal, Academic/Scholarly.* **Description:** Presents research on organic, inorganic, physical, and analytical chemistry in mainland China.
Formerly (until 1989): Acta Chimica Sinica (English Edition) (0256-7660)
Related titles: Online - full text ed.: ISSN 1614-7065. EUR 1,398 in Europe to institutions; CHF 2,298 to institutions in Switzerland & Liechtenstein; USD 1,978 elsewhere to institutions (effective 2006) (from East View Information Services, EBSCO Publishing, Swets Information Services, WanFang Data Corp., Wiley InterScience); ♦ Chinese ed.: Huaxue Xuebao. ISSN 0567-7351.
Indexed: ASCA, CCI, CEABA, CIN, ChemAb, ChemTitl, CurCR, CurCont, EngInd, ISR, IndChem, MOS, MSCI, NPU, RCI, SCI.
—BLDSC (3180.299500), CASDDS, CISTI, Ei, IDS, IE, ingenta, KNAW, Linda Hall.

Published by: Zhongguo Kexueyuan, Shanghai Youji Huaxue Yanjiusuo/Chinese Academy of Sciences, Shanghai Institute of Organic Chemistry, 345, Fenglin Lu, Shanghai, 200032, China. TEL 86-21-64163300 ext 2655, FAX 86-21-64166128, bianji@mail.sioc.ac.cn, sioc@mail.sioc.ac.cn, http://www.sioc-journal.cn/zghx/index_en.asp, http://www.sioc.ac.cn/. Ed. Guo-Zhen Ji. Circ: 6,000. **Subscr. to:** John Wiley & Sons Ltd., The Atrium, Southern Gate, Chichester, West Sussex PO19 8SQ, United Kingdom. TEL 44-1243-779777, FAX 44-1243-843232. **Co-publisher:** Wiley - V C H Verlag GmbH & Co. KGaA.

➤ **CHINESE JOURNAL OF GEOCHEMISTRY.** see *EARTH SCIENCES—Geology*

➤ **CHINESE MARKETS FOR DIMETHYLFORMAMIDE.** see *BUSINESS AND ECONOMICS—Marketing And Purchasing*

➤ **CHINESE MARKETS FOR METHANOL.** see *BUSINESS AND ECONOMICS—Marketing And Purchasing*

➤ **CLINICA CHIMICA ACTA.** see *MEDICAL SCIENCES*

540 CZE ISSN 0010-0765
QD1 CODEN: CCCCAK

➤ **COLLECTION OF CZECHOSLOVAK CHEMICAL COMMUNICATIONS.** Text in English. 1919. m. EUR 985, USD 1,080 combined subscription to institutions print & online eds. (effective 2005). bk.rev. bibl.; charts; illus. index. back issues avail. **Document type:** *Journal, Academic/Scholarly.*
Description: Publishes theoretical and experimental results achieved at research institutes and universities in the Czech Republic, covering research in all branches of chemistry, including chemical physics, physical, and quantum chemistry.
Indexed: ABIPC, ASCA, AnBrAb, AnalAb, BioDAb, BiolAb, CCI, CEA, CEABA, CIN, CISA, CMCI, CPA, Cadscan, ChemAb, ChemInfo, ChemTitl, CurCR, CurCont, DBA, DSA, EngInd, ExcerpMed, F&EA, FCA, FPA, FS&TA, ForAb, HerbAb, I&DA, INIS AtomInd, ISR, IndChem, LeadAb, MOS, MSB, MSCI, NPU, NutrAb, PBA, PHN&I, RA&MP, RAPRA, RCI, RM&VM, RPP, RefZh, S&F, SCI, SIA, TCEA, VITIS, WSCA, WTA, Zincscan.
—BLDSC (3310.500000), CASDDS, CISTI, Ei, IDS, IE, Infotrieve, ingenta, Linda Hall.
Published by: Akademie Ved Ceske Republiky, Ustav Organicke Chemie a Biochemie/Czech Academy of Sciences, Institute of Organic Chemistry and Biochemistry, Flemingovo nam 2, Prague, 16610, Czech Republic. cccc@uochb.cas.cz, http://cccc.uochb.cas.cz/. Ed. Michal Hocek. Pub. Bohumir Valter. Circ: 2,550. **Subscr. to:** Myris Trade, V Stihlach 1311, PO Box 2, Prague 4 14201, Czech Republic. TEL 420-2-34035200, FAX 420-2-34035207, myris@myris.cz, http://www.myris.cz.

➤ **COLOR.** see *PHYSICS—Optics*

➤ **COLORATION TECHNOLOGY.** see *CLEANING AND DYEING*

540 NLD ISSN 1464-3383
RS419

➤ **COMBINATORIAL CHEMISTRY.** Text in Dutch. 12/yr. back issues avail. **Document type:** *Journal, Academic/Scholarly.*
Description: Contains articles on combinatorial chemistry.
Media: Online - full text (from ScienceDirect). **Related titles:** ♦ Series of: Biotechnology and Bioengineering. ISSN 0006-3592.
—BLDSC (3324.738500), IE, ingenta. **CCC.**
Published by: Elsevier BV (Subsidiary of: Elsevier Science & Technology), Radarweg 29, Amsterdam, 1043 NX, Netherlands. TEL 31-20-4853911, FAX 31-20-4852457, nlinfo-f@elsevier.nl, http://www.elsevier.com/locate/comche, http://www.elsevier.nl. Ed. Jack Baldwin.

540 NLD ISSN 1386-2073
RS419 CODEN: CCHSFU

➤ **COMBINATORIAL CHEMISTRY & HIGH THROUGHPUT SCREENING.** Text in English. 1997. 8/yr. EUR 1,340, USD 1,340 to institutions (academic), print or online; EUR 1,930, USD 1,930 to corporations print or online; EUR 250, USD 250 combined subscription to individuals print & online; EUR 1,470, USD 1,470 combined subscription to institutions (academic), print & online; EUR 2,320, USD 2,320 combined subscription to corporations print & online (effective 2004). adv. **Document type:** *Journal, Academic/Scholarly.*
Description: Publishes original research articles describing various topics in combinatorial chemistry and/or high throughput screening. Ancillary subjects, such as robotics and informatics, are also covered.
Related titles: Online - full text ed.: (from EBSCO Publishing, Gale Group, IngentaConnect, Swets Information Services).
Indexed: ASFA, AbHyg, AgBio, B&BAb, BIOSIS Prev, BioEngAb, BiolAb, CCI, ChemAb, CurCont, ExcerpMed, HelmAb, IndMed, IndVet, M&PBA, MEDLINE, MSB, PHN&I, ProtozoAb, RA&MP, RCI, RM&VM, S&F, SIA.
—BLDSC (3324.739000), CASDDS, CISTI, IDS, IE, Infotrieve, ingenta. **CCC.**
Published by: Bentham Science Publishers Ltd., PO Box 1673, Hilversum, BR 1200, Netherlands. TEL 31-35-6923800, FAX 31-35-6980150, M.Bentham@inter.nl.net, http://www.bentham.org/cchts. Eds. Andrew T Merritt TEL 44-1438-763603, Peter E Nielsen, Takenori Kusumi TEL 81-886-33-7288, Richard B van Breemen TEL 312-996-9353. **Subscr. addr. in the US:** Bentham Science Publishers Ltd., 1400 Pine St, PO Box 640310, San Francisco, CA 94164-0310. FAX 415-775-4503, shidding@worldonline.nl.

540 NLD ISSN 1384-2811

COMBINATORIAL CHEMISTRY AND MOLECULAR DIVERSITY. ANNUAL REPORTS. Text in Dutch. 1997. irreg., latest vol.2, 1999. **Document type:** *Monographic series, Academic/Scholarly.*
Indexed: BIOSIS Prev.
Published by: Wolters Kluwer N.V., Postbus 17, Dordrecht, 3300 AA, Netherlands. services@wkap.nl, http://www.wkap.nl/prod/s/ARCC, http://www.wolters-kluwer.nl/frameset.

660 GBR ISSN 1367-1952

THE COMBINED CHEMICAL DICTIONARY ON CD-ROM; complete reference of over 380,000 compounds. Text in English. 1997. s-a. GBP 8,000; GBP 2,500 renewals.
Description: Provides all entries previously only available on one or more of the following discs: Dictionary of Analytical Reagents, Dictionary of Inorganic Compounds, Dictionary of Organometallic Compounds, Dictionary of Natural Products, Dictionary of Organic Compounds, and Pharmasource.
Media: CD-ROM.
Published by: Chapman & Hall, Electronic Publishing Division, Chapman & Hall, 2-6 Boundary Row, London, SE1 8HN, United Kingdom. TEL 44-20-7865-0066, FAX 44-20-7522-0101, cust.serv@chall.co.uk, http://epd.chapmanhall.com. **Dist. by:** Cheriton House, North Way, Andover, Hamps SP10 5BE, United Kingdom. TEL 44-1264-332424, FAX 44-1264-342787.

COMLINE: CHEMICAL INDUSTRY OF JAPAN. see *ENGINEERING—Chemical Engineering*

COMMENTATIONES PHYSICO-MATHEMATICAE ET CHEMICO-MEDICAE. see *PHYSICS*

549 FRA ISSN 0338-9839

COMPLEMENTS AU NUVEAU TRAITE DE CHIMIE MINERALE. Text in French. 1974. irreg. price varies. **Document type:** *Monographic series, Academic/Scholarly.*
—BLDSC (3364.204000). **CCC.**
Published by: Masson Editeur (Subsidiary of: Groupe Medimedia France), 21 Rue Camille Desmoulins, Issy les Moulineaux, 92789 Cedex 9, France. TEL 33-1-73281634, FAX 33-1-73281649, infos@masson.fr, http://www.masson.fr.

540 620 SGP ISSN 1793-0979

COMPUTATIONAL CHEMISTRY; reviews of current trends. Text in English. 1996. irreg., latest vol.9, 2005, Jun. price varies. **Document type:** *Monographic series, Academic/Scholarly.*
Published by: World Scientific Publishing Co. Pte. Ltd., 5 Toh Tuck Link, Singapore, 596224, Singapore. TEL 65-466-5775, FAX 65-467-7667, wspc@wspc.com.sg, series@wspc.com.sg, http://www.wspc.com.sg/books/series/ccrct_series.shtml, http://www.worldscientific.com. Ed. Jerzy Leszczynski. **Dist. by:** World Scientific Publishing Co., Inc., 1060 Main St, River Edge, NJ 07661. TEL 201-487-9655, 800-227-7562, FAX 201-487-9656, 888-977-2665; World Scientific Publishing Ltd., 57 Shelton St, London WC2H 9HE, United Kingdom. TEL 44-20-78360888, FAX 44-20-78362020, sales@wspc.co.uk.

540 GBR ISSN 1553-3603

▼ **COMPUTATIONAL CHEMISTRY REVIEWS.** Text in English. forthcoming 2006 (Jan.). q.
Related titles: Online - full text ed.: ISSN 1553-376X. forthcoming 2006 (Jan.).
Published by: John Wiley & Sons Ltd. (Subsidiary of: John Wiley & Sons, Inc.), The Atrium, Southern Gate, Chichester, West Sussex PO19 8SQ, United Kingdom. TEL 44-1243-779777, FAX 44-1243-775878, customer@wiley.co.uk, http://www.wiley.co.uk.

540 USA

CONCEPTS IN CHEMISTRY✶. Text in English. irreg. price varies.
Published by: Houghton Mifflin Co., 222 Berkeley St, Boston, MA 02116. TEL 617-725-5000, FAX 617-277-5409.

540 CHE ISSN 1020-6167
RA1190 CODEN: CCADFI

CONCISE INTERNATIONAL CHEMICAL ASSESSMENT DOCUMENTS. Text in English. 1998. irreg.
Indexed: ExcerpMed, HelmAb, HortAb, IndVet, PGrRegA, PoultAb, S&F, WeedAb.
Published by: World Health Organization, International Programme for Chemical Safety, c/o Dr. A Aitio, Geneve 27, CH-1211, Switzerland. TEL 44-22-7913592, FAX 44-22-7914848.

540 SVK ISSN 0139-9535
CODEN: PCCHDB

CONFERENCE ON COORDINATION CHEMISTRY PROCEEDINGS. Text in Slovak. irreg., latest 1976, 6th, Bratislava. price varies.
Indexed: CIN, ChemAb, ChemTitl.
—CASDDS.
Published by: Slovenska Vysoka Skola Technicka, Janska 1, Bratislava, 81237, Slovakia.

540 USA ISSN 1064-2811
TP12

CONSULTING SERVICES. Text in English. 1928. biennial. USD 30 domestic; USD 70 foreign (effective 2000). **Document type:** *Directory.* **Description:** Directory containing a one-page resume for each member and an extensive classified directory listing members by their field of expertise.
Published by: Association of Consulting Chemists and Chemical Engineers, Inc., c/o Linda B Townsend, Exec Sec, Box 297, Sparta, NJ 07871. TEL 973-729-6671, FAX 973-729-7088, http://www.chemconsult.org. Ed. Linda. Circ: 500.

541.224 NLD ISSN 0010-8545
QD475 CODEN: CCHRAM

➤ **COORDINATION CHEMISTRY REVIEWS.** Text in English, French, German. 1966. 24/yr. EUR 4,833 in Europe to institutions; JPY 642,200 in Japan to institutions; USD 5,407 to institutions except Europe and Japan; EUR 431 in Europe to qualified personnel; JPY 56,700 in Japan to qualified personnel; USD 484 to qualified personnel except Europe and Japan (effective 2006). adv. bk.rev. charts; illus. index. back issues avail. **Document type:** *Journal, Academic/Scholarly.*
Description: Offers rapid publication of review articles on topics of current interest and importance in coordination chemistry. Includes aspects on organometallic, theoretical and bioinorganic chemistry.
Related titles: Microform ed.: (from PQC); Online - full text ed.: (from EBSCO Publishing, Gale Group, IngentaConnect, ScienceDirect, Swets Information Services).
Indexed: ASCA, BrCerAb, CCI, CIN, CerAb, ChemAb, ChemInfo, ChemTitl, CorrAb, CurCont, EMA, ISR, M&TEA, MBF, METADEX, MSCI, RefZh, SCI, WAA.
—BLDSC (3465.500000), CASDDS, CISTI, IDS, IE, Infotrieve, ingenta, Linda Hall. **CCC.**
Published by: Elsevier BV (Subsidiary of: Elsevier Science & Technology), Radarweg 29, Amsterdam, 1043 NX, Netherlands. TEL 31-20-4853911, FAX 31-20-4852457, nlinfo-f@elsevier.nl, http://www.elsevier.com/locate/ccr, http://www.elsevier.nl. Ed. Dr. A. B.P. Lever.

➤ **CORROSION ENGINEERING SCIENCE AND TECHNOLOGY.** see *METALLURGY*

540 HRV ISSN 0011-1643
CODEN: CCACAA

➤ **CROATICA CHEMICA ACTA.** Text in English; Abstracts in English, Croatian. 1927. q. USD 80 to institutions; USD 25 to members; USD 10 to students (effective 2002). adv. bk.rev. abstr.; bibl.; illus. index. 300 p./no. 1 cols./p.; reprint service avail. from PQC. **Document type:** *Academic/Scholarly.*
Related titles: Microform ed.: (from PQC); Online - full text ed.: ISSN 1334-417X. 2003. free (effective 2005).
Indexed: ASCA, AnalAb, BiolAb, CCI, CIN, Cadscan, ChemAb, ChemInfo, ChemTitl, CurCont, INIS AtomInd, ISR, LeadAb, MOS, MathSciNet, NPU, PhysBer, RCI, RefZh, SCI, Zincscan.
—BLDSC (3487.500000), CASDDS, CISTI, IDS, IE, ingenta, Linda Hall.
Published by: Hrvatsko Kemijsko Drustvo/Croatian Chemical Society, 19, Marulicev trg, 163, Zagreb, HR-10001, Croatia. TEL 385-1-4895508, FAX 385-1-4829958, trina@rudjer.irb.hr, http://pubwww.srce.hr/ccacaa. Ed. Nenad Trinajstic TEL 385-1-468-0095. Circ: 900.

➤ **CROPLIFE.** see *AGRICULTURE—Crop Production And Soil*

➤ **CRYO-LETTERS.** see *BIOLOGY—Physiology*

540 615 NLD ISSN 1573-4072

▼ **CURRENT BIOACTIVE COMPOUNDS.** Text in English. 2005 (Apr.). 3/yr. USD 570 to corporations print or online; USD 275 academic institutions; print or online; USD 110 combined subscription to individuals print & online; USD 680 combined subscription to corporations print & online; USD 300 combined subscription academic instituions; print & online (effective 2005). **Document type:** *Journal, Academic/Scholarly.*
Description: Aims to provide updates to researchers about new bioactive compounds with proven activities in various biological screenings and pharmacological models.
Related titles: Online - full text ed.: (from Gale Group, IngentaConnect).
—**CCC.**
Published by: Bentham Science Publishers Ltd., PO Box 1673, Hilversum, BR 1200, Netherlands. TEL 31-35-6923800, FAX 31-35-6980150, M.Bentham@inter.nl.net, http://www.bentham.org/cbc/index2.htm. Eds. Atta-ur Rahman TEL 92-21-4969873, M Iqbal Choudhary TEL 92-21-4969873.

C

540 616 NLD ISSN 0929-8673
RS400 CODEN: CMCHE7
➤ **CURRENT MEDICINAL CHEMISTRY.** Text in English. 1994. bi-w. EUR 2,890, USD 2,890 to institutions (academic), print or online; EUR 6,740, USD 6,740 to corporations print or online; EUR 590, USD 590 combined subscription to individuals print & online; EUR 3,180, USD 3,180 combined subscription to institutions (academic), print & online; EUR 8,090, USD 8,090 combined subscription to corporations print & online (effective 2004). adv. back issues avail. **Document type:** *Journal, Academic/Scholarly.* **Description:** Publishes reviews on developments in medicinal chemistry and rational drug design.
Related titles: Online - full text ed.: (from EBSCO Publishing, Gale Group, IngentaConnect, Swets Information Services).
Indexed: ASCA, AbHyg, AgrForAb, B&BAb, BBCI, BIOBASE, BIOSIS Prev, CIN, CPA, ChemAb, ChemTitl, CurCont, DSA, ExcerpMed, FPA, ForAb, HelmAb, HortAb, IABS, ISR, IndMed, IndVet, Inpharma, M&PBA, MEDLINE, MSB, NutrAb, OrnHort, PBA, PE&ON, PGegResA, PHN&I, ProtozoAb, RA&MP, RM&VM, RPP, Reac, SCI, TDB, VetBull.
—BLDSC (3500.304000), CASDDS, CISTI, GNLM, IDS, IE, Infotrieve, ingenta. **CCC.**
Published by: Bentham Science Publishers Ltd., PO Box 1673, Hilversum, BR 1200, Netherlands. TEL 31-35-6923800, FAX 31-35-6980150, M.Bentham@inter.nl.net, http://www.bentham.org/cmc. Ed. Atta-ur Rahman TEL 92-21-4969873. **Subscr. addr. in the US:** Bentham Science Publishers Ltd., 1400 Pine St, PO Box 640310, San Francisco, CA 94164-0310. FAX 415-775-4503, shidding@worldonline.nl.

➤ **CURRENT TOPICS IN MEDICINAL CHEMISTRY.** see *MEDICAL SCIENCES*

➤ **CURRENT TOPICS IN PHYTOCHEMISTRY.** see *BIOLOGY—Botany*

➤ **CUSTOM TOLL AND CONTRACT SERVICES DIRECTORY.** see *BUSINESS AND ECONOMICS—Trade And Industrial Directories*

540 POL
CODEN: CZTEAY
CZASOPISMO TECHNICZNE. SERIA C: CHEMIA. Text in Polish; Contents page in Multiple languages. 1877; N.S. 1992. irreg. PLZ 20 (effective 2000). bk.rev. charts; illus. index. **Document type:** *Academic/Scholarly.*
Supersedes in part: Czasopismo Techniczne (0011-4561); Which was formerly (until 1883): Dzwignia (1230-2791)
—CASDDS, Linda Hall.
Published by: Politechnika Krakowska, Ul Warszawska 24, Krakow, 31155, Poland. TEL 48-12-6374289, FAX 48-12-6374289. Ed. Elzbieta Nachlik. Adv. contact Ewa Malochleb. Circ: 12,000.

DANESHMAND. see *ENGINEERING*

540 DNK ISSN 0011-6335
CODEN: DAKEAT
DANSK KEMI. Text in Danish. 1927. m. DKK 475. adv. bk.rev. reprints avail. **Document type:** *Journal, Trade.*
Formerly (until 1962): Kemisk Maanedsblad og Nordisk Handelsblad for Kemisk Industri (0368-5233); Which was formed by the merger of (1920-1927): Nordisk Handelsblad for Kemisk Industri; (19??-1927): Kemisk Maanedsblad
Related titles: Online - full text ed.
Indexed: CBNB, CISA, ChemAb, INIS AtomInd, MSB.
—CASDDS, CISTI, Linda Hall.
Published by: (Kemisk Forening/Danish Chemical Society), TechMedia A/S, Naverland 35, Glostrup, 2600, Denmark. TEL 45-43-242628, FAX 45-43-242626, info@techmedia.dk, http://www.techmedia.dk/html/medieinfo/dak.asp. Eds. Claus Cornett, Thorvald Pedersen, Katrinee Meyn. Adv. contact Annie Overgaard TEL 45-43-242593. B&W page DKK 17,900, color page DKK 21,500; 265 x 185. Circ: 6,550.

540 CHN ISSN 1000-8438
QD1 CODEN: DAHUEW
➤ **DAXUE HUAXUE/UNIVERSITY CHEMISTRY.** Text in Chinese. 1986. bi-m. USD 36 (effective 1997). **Document type:** *Academic/Scholarly.* **Description:** Provides a forum for issues relating to higher chemical education. Reports new trends in chemistry and related disciplines.
Related titles: Online - full text ed.: (from East View Information Services).
Indexed: CIN, ChemAb, ChemTitl.
—BLDSC (9106.450000), CASDDS.
Published by: Zhongguo Huaxue Xuehui, Daxue Huaxue Bianjibu/Chinese Chemical Society, Editorial Office of University Chemistry, Beijing University Chemistry Bldg., Haidian-qu, Beijing, 100871, China. TEL 861-6275-1721, FAX 861-6275-4096, qiuxb@infoc3.icas.cn. Ed. Tongwen Hua. **Co-sponsor:** Research Center of Higher Chemical Education.

540 USA ISSN 0095-8387
QD1 CODEN: DCBUAC
THE DEL-CHEM BULLETIN. Text in English. 1944. 8/yr. free to members (effective 2004). adv. bk.rev. **Document type:** *Bulletin, Trade.*
—CASDDS.
Published by: American Chemical Society, Delaware Section, PO Box 711, Montchanin, DE 19710. http://membership.acs.org/D/Del/. Ed. Sheree R Gold. Adv. contact Vince Gale TEL 781-837-0424. B&W page USD 465; trim 6 x 9. Circ: 2,400.

DEUTSCHES KUNSTSTOFF-INSTITUT. JAHRESBERICHT. see *PLASTICS*

DICCIONARIO DE ESPECIALIDADES AGROQUIMICAS. see *AGRICULTURE*

540 GBR ISSN 1359-785X
DICTIONARY OF INORGANIC AND ORGANOMETALLIC COMPOUNDS ON CD-ROM. Text in English. 1995. s-a. GBP 3,500; GBP 950 renewals. bibl.; charts. **Document type:** *Directory, Academic/Scholarly.* **Description:** Contains chemical, structural and bibliographic data on over 90,000 compounds.
Media: CD-ROM.
Published by: Chapman & Hall, Electronic Publishing Division, Chapman & Hall, 2-6 Boundary Row, London, SE1 8HN, United Kingdom. TEL 44-20-7865-0066, FAX 44-20-7522-0101, cust.serv@chall.co.uk, http://epd.chapmanhall.com. **Dist. by:** Cheriton House, North Way, Andover, Hamps SP10 5BE, United Kingdom. TEL 44-1264-332424, FAX 44-1264-342787.

DIMENSIO. see *MATHEMATICS*

DIQIU HUAXUE/GEOCHEMICA. see *EARTH SCIENCES—Geology*

540 AUS
DIRECTORY OF AUSTRALIAN AND NEW ZEALAND CHEMICAL MANUFACTURERS & WHOLESALERS. Text in English. 1991. biennial. AUD 125 domestic; USD 85 foreign.
Published by: Chemical Advisory Service, P.O. Box 38, Vermont, VIC 3133, Australia. TEL 61-3-93353208, FAX 61-3-93351750, casgm@ozemail.com.au, http://www.cas.com.au. Ed. Graham Millward.

540.29 USA ISSN 1045-5256
HD9655.C2
DIRECTORY OF CHEMICAL PRODUCERS - CANADA. Text in English. 1988. a. USD 940; USD 605 renewals (effective 2000). stat. **Document type:** *Directory.* **Description:** Lists commercial chemical manufacturers; includes locations and product plants.
Related titles: CD-ROM ed.: USD 1,180 (effective 2000); Online - full text ed.
Published by: S R I Consulting, Chemical Business Research Division, 333 Ravenswood Ave, Menlo Park, CA 94025. TEL 650-859-3627, FAX 650-859-4623. Ed. C Read.

540.29 USA ISSN 1535-2978
TP12
DIRECTORY OF CHEMICAL PRODUCERS - CHINA. Text in English. 1995. a. USD 1,920; USD 1,230 renewals (effective 2000). **Document type:** *Directory.* **Description:** Lists all commercial chemical producers. Includes plant locations and products.
Related titles: CD-ROM ed.: USD 2,400 (effective 2000); Online - full text ed.
Published by: S R I Consulting, Chemical Business Research Division, 333 Ravenswood Ave, Menlo Park, CA 94025. TEL 650-859-3627, FAX 650-859-4623. Ed. C Read.

540.29 USA ISSN 1049-6068
HD9657.E182
DIRECTORY OF CHEMICAL PRODUCERS - EAST ASIA. Text in English. 1989. a. USD 2,560; USD 1,635 renewals (effective 2000). **Document type:** *Directory.*
Related titles: CD-ROM ed.: USD 3,150 (effective 2000); Online - full text ed.
Published by: S R I Consulting, Chemical Business Research Division, 333 Ravenswood Ave, Menlo Park, CA 94025. TEL 650-859-3627, FAX 650-859-4623. Ed. C Read.

660.029 USA ISSN 1520-0558
TP12
DIRECTORY OF CHEMICAL PRODUCERS - EUROPE. Text in English. 1978. a. USD 2,750; USD 1,775 renewals (effective 2000). **Document type:** *Directory.* **Description:** Lists all commercial chemical producers, including product locations and products.
Formerly: Directory of Chemical Producers - Western Europe
Related titles: CD-ROM ed.: USD 3,440 (effective 2000); Online - full text ed.
Published by: S R I Consulting, Chemical Business Research Division, 333 Ravenswood Ave, Menlo Park, CA 94025. TEL 650-859-3627, FAX 650-859-4623, dcp@sric.sri.com, http://www.cbrd.sriconsulting.com. Ed. C Read.

660.029 USA ISSN 1535-296X
TP12
DIRECTORY OF CHEMICAL PRODUCERS - INDIA. Text in English. 1995. a. **Description:** Lists all commercial chemical producers, including plant locations and products.
Related titles: CD-ROM ed.
Published by: S R I Consulting, Chemical Business Research Division, 333 Ravenswood Ave, Menlo Park, CA 94025. TEL 650-859-3627, FAX 650-859-4623, dcp@sric.sri.com, http://www.cbrd.sriconsulting.com. Ed. C Read.

540.29 USA ISSN 1535-2986
TP12
DIRECTORY OF CHEMICAL PRODUCERS - MEXICO. Text in English. 1995. a. USD 1,080; USD 695 renewals (effective 2000). **Document type:** *Directory.* **Description:** Lists all commercial chemical producers, including plant locations and products.
Related titles: CD-ROM ed.: USD 1,350 (effective 2000); Online - full text ed.
Published by: S R I Consulting, Chemical Business Research Division, 333 Ravenswood Ave, Menlo Park, CA 94025. TEL 650-859-3627, FAX 650-859-4623. Ed. C Read.

540.29 USA ISSN 1535-2951
TP12
DIRECTORY OF CHEMICAL PRODUCERS - MIDDLE EAST. Text in English. 1995. a. USD 1,250; USD 805 renewals (effective 2000). **Document type:** *Directory.* **Description:** Lists all commercial chemical producers, including plant locations and products.
Related titles: CD-ROM ed.: USD 1,560 (effective 2000); Online - full text ed.
Published by: S R I Consulting, Chemical Business Research Division, 333 Ravenswood Ave, Menlo Park, CA 94025. TEL 650-859-3627, FAX 650-859-4623. Ed. C Read.

540.29 USA ISSN 1082-1163
DIRECTORY OF CHEMICAL PRODUCERS - SOUTH AMERICA. Text in English. 1995. a. USD 1,520; USD 985 renewals (effective 2000). **Document type:** *Directory.* **Description:** Lists all commercial chemical producers, including plant locations and products.
Related titles: CD-ROM ed.: USD 1,900 (effective 2000); Online - full text ed.
Published by: S R I Consulting, Chemical Business Research Division, 333 Ravenswood Ave, Menlo Park, CA 94025. TEL 650-859-3627, FAX 650-859-4623. Ed. C Read.

660.029 USA ISSN 0012-3277
HD9651.3
DIRECTORY OF CHEMICAL PRODUCERS - UNITED STATES. Text in English. 1961. a. USD 2,030; USD 1,295 renewals (effective 2000). charts; stat. **Document type:** *Directory.* **Description:** Lists all commercial chemical producers, including plant locations and products.
Related titles: CD-ROM ed.: USD 2,540 (effective 2000); Online - full text ed.
Published by: S R I Consulting, Chemical Business Research Division, 333 Ravenswood Ave, Menlo Park, CA 94025. TEL 650-859-3627, FAX 650-859-4623. Ed. C Read.

540.29 GBR ISSN 0961-270X
DIRECTORY OF CHEMICAL PRODUCTS & BUYERS GUIDE. Text in English. a. GBP 110; GBP 130 foreign. **Document type:** *Directory.*
Formerly (until 1991): Chemicals. Text - Intro
—BLDSC (3593.283050).
Published by: (Chemical Industries Association Ltd.), Hamlet Information Services Ltd., Padlock Rd, West Wratting, Cambridge, CB1 5LS, United Kingdom. TEL 01223-290838, FAX 01223-290687. Ed. C E Freer. Pub. Peter G Lewis. Circ: 3,500.

540.29 USA ISSN 1078-0548
TP12
DIRECTORY OF WORLD CHEMICAL PRODUCERS (STANDARD EDITION). Text in English. 1980. triennial. USD 950. adv. **Document type:** *Directory.* **Description:** Contains 56,831 alphabetically listed product titles (including cross-references), manufactured by 7,076 chemical producers in 81 countries on 6 continents.
Supersedes in part (in 1996): Directory of World Chemical Producers (Year) (0196-0555)
Related titles: Diskette ed.: USD 1,800 single user; USD 3,000 network (effective 1999); Special ed(s).: Directory of World Chemical Producers (Limited Edition). ISSN 1078-053X. USD 600.
—CISTI.
Published by: Chemical Information Services, Inc., PO Box 743512, Dallas, TX 75374. TEL 214-349-6200, FAX 214-349-6286, cheminfo@connect.net, info@chemicalinfo.com, http://www.chemicalinfo.com. Ed. Charles M Schwarz. Adv. contact Erica Sims. **Dist. by:** CIS Data Services, Inc., 4111 N Central Expwy, Ste 203, Dallas, TX 75204. TEL 214-520-2680.

DIZHI DIQIU HUAXUE/GEOLOGY - GEOCHEMISTRY. see *EARTH SCIENCES—Geology*

560 RUS ISSN 0012-5008
QD1 CODEN: DKCHAY
➤ **DOKLADY CHEMISTRY.** Text in English. 1933. m. EUR 2,795, USD 2,498, GBP 1,745 combined subscription to institutions print & online eds. (effective 2005). back issues avail. **Document type:** *Journal, Academic/Scholarly.* **Description:** Takes a close look at experimental and theoretical research in all branches of chemical science.

C

Formerly (until 1963): Academy of Sciences of the U S S R. Chemistry Section. Proceedings (0197-8217); Incorporates (1933-2001): Doklady Chemical Technology (0012-4990)
Related titles: Microfilm ed.: (from PQC); Online - full text ed.: ISSN 1608-3113 (from EBSCO Publishing, Gale Group, IngentaConnect, Kluwer Online, O C L C Online Computer Library Center, Inc., Springer LINK, Swets Information Services); ♦ Partial translation of: Rossiiskaya Akademiya Nauk. Doklady. ISSN 0869-5652.
Indexed: BibLing, CCI, CEA, CEABA, ChemAb, ChemTitl, CurCont, EnerRA, ISR, MOS, MSB, NPU, RCI, SCI, TCEA.
—BLDSC (0411.320000), CISTI, IE, Infotrieve, ingenta, Linda Hall. **CCC.**
Published by: (Rossiiskaya Akademiya Nauk/Russian Academy of Sciences), M A I K Nauka - Interperiodica, Profsoyuznaya ul 90, Moscow, 117997, Russian Federation. TEL 7-095-3347420, FAX 7-095-3360666, dan@maik.ru, compmg@maik.ru, http://www.maik.ru. Ed. Victor A. Kabanov. **Subscr. to:** Springer-Verlag Dordrecht, Journals Department, PO Box 322, Dordrecht, Netherlands. TEL 31-78-6576392, FAX 31-78-6576474.

540   IND   ISSN 0012-5792
SB951   CODEN: DOEAAH
DOWN TO EARTH. Text in English. 1944. 3/yr. INR 288 domestic; USD 26 in Bhutan Bangladesh, Nepal, & Pakistan; USD 48 rest of world (effective 2005). back issues avail.
Indexed: AEA, AESIS, BiolAb, ChemAb, FCA, ForAb, HortAb, MaizeAb, RPP, S&F, SFA, SeedAb, WeedAb, WildRev.
—BLDSC (3620.000000), CISTI, Linda Hall.
Published by: Society for Environmental Communications, 41 Tughlakabad Institutional Area, New Delhi, 110062, India. TEL 91-11-26066854, FAX 91-11-29955879, editor@downtoearth.org.in, http://www.downtoearth.org.in/section.asp?sec_id=51&foldername=20030215. Circ: 8,000.

DUPONT MAGAZINE. see *BUSINESS AND ECONOMICS*

DUTCH CHEMICAL INDUSTRY HANDBOOK/HANDBOEK VOOR DE NEDERLANDSE CHEMISCHE INDUSTRIE. see *BUSINESS AND ECONOMICS—Trade And Industrial Directories*

540 530   GBR   ISSN 0143-7208
TP890   CODEN: DYPIDX
➤ **DYES AND PIGMENTS.** Text in English. 1980. 12/yr. EUR 2,259 in Europe to institutions; JPY 299,800 in Japan to institutions; USD 2,527 elsewhere to institutions (effective 2006). adv. bk.rev. charts; illus. Index. back issues avail.
Document type: *Journal, Academic/Scholarly.* **Description:** Covers the scientific and technical aspects of the chemistry and physics of dyes, pigments and their intermediates.
Related titles: Microform ed.: (from PQC); Online - full text ed.: (from EBSCO Publishing, Gale Group, IngentaConnect, ScienceDirect, Swets Information Services).
Indexed: ASCA, B&BAb, C&ISA, CCI, CIN, Cadscan, ChemAb, ChemInfo, ChemTitl, CurCont, E&CAJ, Engind, ISR, Inspec, LeadAb, MSB, MSCI, RCI, RefZh, SCI, SolStAb, TTI, WSCA, WTA, Zincscan.
—BLDSC (3635.600000), CASDDS, CINDOC, CISTI, Ei, IDS, IE, Infotrieve, ingenta, Linda Hall. **CCC.**
Published by: Pergamon (Subsidiary of: Elsevier Science & Technology), The Boulevard, Langford Ln, East Park, Kidlington, Oxford OX5 1GB, United Kingdom. TEL 44-1865-843000, FAX 44-1865-843010, http://www.elsevier.com/locate/dyepig. Eds. B. Glover, Dr. S Burkinshaw, Sung-Hoon Kim. **Subscr. to:** Elsevier BV, PO Box 211, Amsterdam 1000 AE, Netherlands. TEL 31-20-485-3757, FAX 31-20-485-3432, nlinfo-f@elsevier.nl, http://www.elsevier.nl.

➤ **E C N CHEMSCOPE.** see *ENGINEERING—Chemical Engineering*

540   USA
E I N E C S PLUS C D. (European Inventory of Existing Commercial Chemical Substances) Text in English, Multiple languages. 1998. a. USD 1,495. **Description:** Lists more than 100,000 chemical substances from the European List of Notified Chemical Substances and the European Dangerous Substances list.
Related titles: CD-ROM ed.: (from SilverPlatter Information, Inc.); Online - full text ed.: (from SilverPlatter Information, Inc.).
Published by: SilverPlatter Information, Incorporated (Subsidiary of: Ovid Technologies, Incorporated), 100 River Ridge Dr., Norwood, MA 02062. TEL 800-343-0064, info@silverplatter.com, sales@ovid.com, http://www.silverplatter.com, http://www.ovid.com.

EAST-WEST JOURNAL OF MATHEMATICS. see *BIOLOGY*

540 530   BRA   ISSN 0100-4670
                          CODEN: ECQUDX
➤ **ECLETICA QUIMICA.** Text in Portuguese; Summaries in English, Portuguese. 1976. s-a. free (effective 2005). bibl.; charts; abstr. **Document type:** *Journal, Academic/Scholarly.* **Description:** Presents results of chemical research.
Related titles: Online - full content ed.: free (effective 2005) (from SciELO).
Indexed: ASCA, AnalAb, BiolAb, CCI, CIN, ChemAb, ChemTitl, FCA, RefZh, VITIS.
—BLDSC (3647.895000), CASDDS, CISTI, IDS, KNAW.

Published by: Fundacao Editora U N E S P, Praca da Se 108, Sao Paulo, SP 01001-900, Brazil. TEL 55-11-32427171, cgb@marilia.unesp.br, http://www.unesp.br. Ed. Dr. Antonio Tallarico Adorno. Circ: 1,000.

540   MEX   ISSN 0187-893X
                          CODEN: EUQIEM
➤ **EDUCACION QUIMICA.** Text in English, French, Portuguese, Spanish. 1989. q. MXP 80, USD 30 (effective 2000). adv. bk.rev. back issues avail. **Document type:** *Academic/Scholarly.* **Description:** Presents original papers on chemistry. Designed for college teachers.
Related titles: Online - full text ed.
Indexed: CIN, ChemAb, ChemTitl.
—CASDDS.
Published by: Universidad Nacional Autonoma de Mexico, Facultad de Quimica, Apartado Postal 70-197, Mexico, D.F., 04510 , Mexico. TEL 52-5-6223439, FAX 52-5-6223711, andoni@servidor.unam.mx. Ed. Andoni Garritz Ruiz. Circ: 1,300 (paid).

540.71   GBR   ISSN 0013-1350
QD1   CODEN: EDCHAU
EDUCATION IN CHEMISTRY. Text in English. 1964. bi-m. GBP 206, USD 376 (effective 2006). adv. bk.rev.; film rev. charts; illus. index. reprint service avail. from PQC. **Document type:** *Journal, Academic/Scholarly.* **Description:** Devoted to the problems of chemical education at all levels from the secondary school to the university. Covers a broad range of pertinent topics of interest to teachers.
Related titles: Microform ed.: (from PQC).
Indexed: BrEdI, CBTA, CIJE, CIN, CPE, ChemAb, ChemTitl, ERA, ETA, ExcerpMed, HECAB, LHB, MRD, RHEA, RefZh, SWA, TEA.
—BLDSC (3661.226000), CASDDS, CISTI, IE, Infotrieve, ingenta, Linda Hall. **CCC.**
Published by: Royal Society of Chemistry, Thomas Graham House, Science Park, Milton Rd, Cambridge, CB4 0WF, United Kingdom. TEL 44-1223-432360, FAX 44-1223-423623, eic@rsc.org, sales@rsc.org, http://www.rsc.org. Ed. Kathryn Roberts. **Subscr. to:** Portland Press Ltd., R S C Distribution Services, Commerce Way, Whitehall Industrial Estate, Colchester CO2 8HP, United Kingdom. TEL 44-1206-226050, FAX 44-1206-226055, sales@rscdistribution.org.

540   EGY   ISSN 0449-2285
➤ **EGYPTIAN JOURNAL OF CHEMISTRY/AL-MAGALLA AL-MISRIYYA LI-L-KTMIYA'.** Text in English; Summaries in Arabic, English. 1958. bi-m. USD 217 (effective 2003). bibl.; charts. reprint service avail. from IRC. **Document type:** *Journal, Academic/Scholarly.*
Formerly (until 1971): Journal of Chemistry of the United Arab Republic (1011-2863)
Indexed: BiolAb, CIN, ChemAb, ChemInfo, ChemTitl, DSA, FCA, HelmAb, HerbAb, HortAb, IndVet, MSB, NutrAb, ProtozoAb, RM&VM, RPP, RevApplEntom, RiceAb, S&F, SIA.
—BLDSC (3664.350000), CISTI, IE, Infotrieve, ingenta, Linda Hall.
Published by: (Egyptian Chemical Society, Research Department), National Information and Documentation Centre (NIDOC), Tahrir St., Dokki, Awqaf P.O., Giza, Egypt. TEL 20-2-3371696, FAX 20-2-3371746, http://derp.sti.sci.eg/data/0110.htm. Ed. Dr. M Kamel.

➤ **EGYPTIAN JOURNAL OF SOLIDS.** see *PHYSICS*

540   JPN
EKITAI KUROMATOGURAFU KENKYUKAI KOEN YOSHISHU/RESEARCH GROUP OF LIQUID CHROMATOGRAPHY. PROCEEDINGS. Text in English. 1966. a. **Document type:** *Proceedings.*
Published by: Ekitai Kuromatogurafu Kenkyukai/Research Group of Liquid Chromatography, c/o Ms. Iwase, Pasutsuru Kenkyujo, 103-5 Tanaka-Monzencho, Sakyo-ku, Kyoto-shi, 606-0000, Japan.

EKOLOGICHESKAYA KHIMIYA/ECOLOGICAL CHEMISTRY. see *ENVIRONMENTAL STUDIES—Toxicology And Environmental Safety*

541.0421   USA   ISSN 1099-0062
TK7869   CODEN: ESLEF6
➤ **ELECTROCHEMICAL AND SOLID-STATE LETTERS.** Text in English. 1998. m. USD 312 in North America; USD 347 elsewhere (effective 2006). back issues avail. **Document type:** *Journal, Academic/Scholarly.* **Description:** Covers leading edge research and development in the fields of electrochemical and solid-state science and technology.
Related titles: CD-ROM ed.: USD 75 includes Journal of the Electrochemical Society (effective 2000); Microfiche ed.; Online - full text ed.: (from EBSCO Publishing).
Indexed: BrCerAb, C&ISA, CCI, CerAb, CivEngAb, CorrAb, CurCont, E&CAJ, EMA, EngInd, IAA, Inspec, M&TEA, MBF, METADEX, MSB, MSCI, RefZh, SCI, SPINweb, WAA.
—BLDSC (3698.805000), CASDDS, CINDOC, CISTI, IDS, IE, Infotrieve, ingenta, Linda Hall. **CCC.**

Published by: (Institute of Electrical and Electronics Engineers, Inc., I E E E Electron Devices Society), Electrochemical Society, Inc., 65 S Main St, Bldg D, Pennington, NJ 08534-2839. TEL 609-737-1902, FAX 609-737-2743, ecs@electrochem.org, http://scitation.aip.org/ESL/, http://www.electorchem.org/. Ed. Dr. Dennis Hess. R&P Mr. Terry McCloughan. **Subscr. to:** Maruzen Co., Ltd., 3-10 Nihonbashi 2-chome, Chuo-ku, Tokyo 103-0027, Japan. FAX 81-3-3275-0657; Universal Subscription Agency, Pvt. Ltd., 877, Udyog Vihar, V, Gurgoan 122001, India. TEL 91-124-347261, FAX 91-124-342496.

➤ **ELECTRONIC CHEMICALS NEWS.** see *ELECTRONICS*

540   DEU   ISSN 0173-0835
QD79.E44   CODEN: ELCTDN
➤ **ELECTROPHORESIS.** Text in English. 1980. s-m. EUR 3,024 in Europe; CHF 4,478 in Switzerland & Liechtenstein; USD 3,678 elsewhere; EUR 3,327 combined subscription in Europe print & online eds.; CHF 4,926 combined subscription in Switzerland & Liechtenstein for print & online eds.; USD 4,046 combined subscription elsewhere print & online eds. (effective 2006). adv. bk.rev. illus. reprint service avail. from ISI.
Document type: *Journal, Academic/Scholarly.*
Related titles: Microfilm ed.: (from VCI); Online - full text ed.: ISSN 1522-2683. EUR 3,024 in Europe to institutions; CHF 4,478 to institutions in Switzerland & Liechtenstein; USD 3,678 elsewhere to institutions (effective 2006) (from EBSCO Publishing, Swets Information Services, Wiley InterScience).
Indexed: ASCA, ASFA, AbHyg, AgBio, AgrForAb, AnBrAb, AnalAb, BBCI, BIOBASE, BIOSIS Prev, BiolAb, CCI, CIN, CPA, ChemAb, ChemTitl, ChromAb, CurCont, DSA, ExcerpMed, FCA, FPA, FS&TA, ForAb, HelmAb, HerbAb, HortAb, I&DA, IABS, ISR, IndMed, IndVet, Inpharma, Inspec, MEDLINE, MSB, MSCI, MaizeAb, NemAb, NutrAb, OrnHort, PBA, PGegResA, PGrRegA, PHN&I, PN&I, PotatoAb, PoultAb, ProtozoAb, RA&MP, RM&VM, RPP, Reac, RefZh, RevApplEntom, RiceAb, S&F, SCI, SIA, SeedAb, SoyaB, TDB, TriticAb, VITIS, VetBull, WeedAb.
—BLDSC (3706.378000), CASDDS, CINDOC, CISTI, Ei, GNLM, IDS, IE, Infotrieve, ingenta, Linda Hall. **CCC.**
Published by: Wiley - V C H Verlag GmbH & Co. KGaA (Subsidiary of: John Wiley & Sons, Inc.), Boschstr 12, Weinheim, 69469, Germany. TEL 49-6201-6060, FAX 49-6201-606328, subservice@wiley-vch.de, http://www3.interscience.wiley.com/cgi-bin/home. Ed. Bertold J Radola. Circ: 1,250 (paid and controlled). **Subscr. in the Americas to:** John Wiley & Sons, Inc., 111 River St, Hoboken, NJ 07030-5774. TEL 201-748-6645, FAX 201-748-6088, subinfo@wiley.com; **Subscr. outside Germany, Austria & Switzerland to:** John Wiley & Sons Ltd., The Atrium, Southern Gate, Chichester, West Sussex PO19 8SQ, United Kingdom. TEL 44-1243-779777, FAX 44-1243-775878.

➤ **ENERGY & FUELS.** see *ENERGY*

540   NLD   ISSN 1383-8598
ENVIRONMENT & CHEMISTRY. Text in English. 1995. irreg., latest vol.2, 1998. price varies. **Document type:** *Monographic series.*
Indexed: CIN, ChemAb, ChemTitl.
—BLDSC (3791.099050).
Published by: Springer-Verlag Dordrecht (Subsidiary of: Springer Science+Business Media), Van Godewijckstraat 30, Dordrecht, 3311 GX, Netherlands. TEL 31-78-6576050, FAX 31-78-6576474, http://www.springeronline.com.

▼ **ENVIRONMENTAL CHEMISTRY.** see *ENVIRONMENTAL STUDIES*

363.7 660   DEU   ISSN 1610-3653
▼ **ENVIRONMENTAL CHEMISTRY LETTERS.** Text in English. 2003. q. EUR 198 combined subscription to institutions print & online eds. (effective 2005). adv. **Document type:** *Journal, Academic/Scholarly.*
Related titles: Online - full text ed.: ISSN 1610-3661 (from EBSCO Publishing, Springer LINK, Swets Information Services).
—BLDSC (3791.411700), IE. **CCC.**
Published by: Springer-Verlag (Subsidiary of: Springer Science+Business Media), Tiergartenstr 17, Heidelberg, 69121, Germany. TEL 49-6221-3450, FAX 49-6221-345229. Eds. Eric Lichtfouse, Stephanie Dudd. Adv. contact Stephan Kroeck TEL 49-30-827875739. **Subscr. in the Americas to:** Springer-Verlag New York, Inc., Journal Fulfillment, PO Box 2485, Secaucus, NJ 07096-2485. TEL 800-777-4643, 201-348-4033, FAX 201-348-4505, journals@springer-ny.com, http://www.springer-ny.com; **Subscr. to:** Springer GmbH Auslieferungsgesellschaft, Haberstr 7, Heidelberg 69126, Germany. TEL 49-6221-345-0, FAX 49-6221-345-4229, subscriptions@springer.de.

540   EST   ISSN 1406-0124
QD1   CODEN: PESCFO
➤ **ESTONIAN ACADEMY OF SCIENCES. PROCEEDINGS. CHEMISTRY/AKADEMIYA NAUK ESTONII. IZVESTIYA. KHIMIYA/EESTI TEADUSTE AKADEEMIA TOIMETISED. KEEMIA.** Text in English; Summaries in English, Estonian. 1952. q. EUR 85 foreign (effective 2004). adv. abstr.; charts; illus.; maps. 48 p./no.; back issues avail. **Document type:** *Journal, Academic/Scholarly.*

Formerly (until 1990): Akademiya Nauk Estonskoi S.S.R. Izvestiya. Khimiya (0201-8128); Which superseded in part (in 1978): Akademiya Nauk Estonskoi S.S.R. Izvestiya. Khimiya. Geologiya

Related titles: Online - full text ed.: (from EBSCO Publishing).

Indexed: ASFA, BrCerAb, C&ISA, CIN, CerAb, ChemAb, ChemTitl, CivEngAb, CorrAb, E&CAJ, EMA, ESPM, HortAb, IAA, INIS AtomInd, M&TEA, MBF, METADEX, SolStAb, WAA.

—BLDSC (6699.205000), CASDDS, CISTI, IE, ingenta, KNAW, Linda Hall. CCC.

Published by: (Eesti Teaduste Akadeemia), Teaduste Akadeemia Kirjastus/Estonian Academy Publishers, Kohtu 6, Tallinn, 10130, Estonia. TEL 372-6-454504, FAX 372-6-466026, niine@kirj.ee, http://www.kirj.ee. Ed. Hillar Aben. R&P Asta Tikerpae TEL 373-6-454504. Adv. contact Asta Tikerpae TEL 373-6-454106. Circ: 550.

---

660   KAZ   ISSN 1562-3920
TP1

EURASIAN CHEMICO-TECHNOLOGICAL JOURNAL. Text in English. 1999. q. Description: Covers experimental and theoretical investigations in the field of chemistry and chemical technology. Among the subjects emphasized are: production of new materials and technologies; modern problems of organic synthesis technologies; investigation of physical and chemical properties, thermochemistry and thermodynamics, etc.

Indexed: BrCerAb, C&ISA, CerAb, CorrAb, E&CAJ, EMA, IAA, M&TEA, MBF, METADEX, RefZh, WAA.

—BLDSC (3828.088600), CISTI, Linda Hall.

Published by: (International Higher Education Academy of Sciences RUS), Kazakhskii Natsional'nyi Universitet im. al'-Farabi, Institut Novykh Khimicheskikh Tekhnologii i Materialov/Al-Farabi Kazakh State National University, Institute of New Chemical Technologies and Materials, Karasai Batyr St, 95, Almaty, 480012, Kazakstan. TEL 7-3272-927435, FAX 7-3272-472609, mburkit@nursat.kz, http://eurasianchemtech.vub.ac.be. Ed. Z A Mansurov.

EURO COURSES. CHEMICAL AND ENVIRONMENTAL SCIENCE. see ENVIRONMENTAL STUDIES

---

540 341   GBR   ISSN 0967-7844

EUROCHEM MONITOR. Text in English. 10 base vols. plus s-a. updates. looseleaf. GBP 2,100 base vol(s). domestic basic vol. & first year updates; GBP 2,229 base vol(s). in Europe basic vol. & first year updates; GBP 2,369 base vol(s). elsewhere basic vol. & first year updates; GBP 1,645 renewals domestic for 2004 updates (renewals only); GBP 1,746 renewals in Europe for 2004 updates (renewals only); GBP 1,872 renewals elsewhere for 2004 updates (renewals only) (effective 2005). Document type: Newsletter, Trade. Description: Ten volume reference set containing the full and consolidated texts of EU legislation on the marketing and use of dangerous substances and preparations.

Published by: Agra Europe (London) Ltd. (Subsidiary of: T & F Informa plc), 80 Calverley Rd, Tunbridge Wells, Kent TN1 2UN, United Kingdom. TEL 44-1892-533813, FAX 44-1892-544895, marketing@agra-net.com, http://www.agra-europe.co.uk/Publications/Agra-Rep24.html, http://www.agra-net.com.

EUROPOORT KRINGEN. see TRANSPORTATION—Ships And Shipping

F A C E N A. see BIOLOGY

---

540   DEU   ISSN 0933-5927
CODEN: FSFSES

F & S. (Filtrieren und Separieren) Text in German. 1987. bi-m. EUR 50 (effective 2005). adv. bk.rev. Document type: Journal, Academic/Scholarly.

Indexed: CEABA, CIN, ChemAb, ChemTitl.

—CASDDS, CISTI, IE. CCC.

Published by: V D L - Verlag GmbH, Heinrich-Heine-Str 5, Roedermark, 63322, Germany. TEL 49-6074-920880, FAX 49-6074-93334, vdl-verlag@t-online.de, http://www.fs-journal.de. adv.: B&W page EUR 3,100, color page EUR 4,360; trim 176 x 247. Circ: 5,940 (paid and controlled).

FACTA UNIVERSITATIS. SERIES PHYSICS, CHEMISTRY AND TECHNOLOGY. see PHYSICS

FARBE AKTUELL PLUS. see PHARMACY AND PHARMACOLOGY

FARMACI. see PHARMACY AND PHARMACOLOGY

---

540   CHN   ISSN 1000-9035
CODEN: JMOSE7

FENZI KEXUE XUEBAO (CHANGCHUN)/JOURNAL OF MOLECULAR SCIENCE. Text in Chinese. 1981. q. CNY 8 newsstand/cover (effective 2003). charts; abstr. 64 p./no.; Document type: Journal, Academic/Scholarly.

Former titles (until 1985): Fenzi Kexue yu Huaxue Yanjiu (1007-2411); (until 1982): Fenzi Kexue Xuebao (Wuchang) (0253-3677)

Related titles: Online - full content ed.: (from WanFang Data Corp.); Online - full text ed.: (from East View Information Services).

Indexed: Inspec, RefZh.

—BLDSC (5020.731000), CISTI, IE, ingenta.

Published by: Dongbeishi Daxue Shuqikanshe/Northeast Normal University Science & Technology Press, 5268, Renmin Dajie, Changchun, 130024, China. TEL 86-431-5268024, fzxb@nenu.edu.cn, http://fzkxxb.periodicals.com.cn/default.html. Ed. Jiazhong Sun. Dist. by: China International Book Trading Corp, 35 Chegongzhuang Xilu, Haidian District, PO Box 399, Beijing 100044, China. TEL 86-10-68412045, FAX 86-10-68412023, cibtc@mail.cibtc.com.cn, http://www.cibtc.com.cn.

FIREWORKS. see LEISURE AND RECREATION

FIZIKA I KHIMIYA OBRABOTKI MATERIALOV. see ENGINEERING—Engineering Mechanics And Materials

---

540   USA   ISSN 0014-5920

FL A C S✶. (Florida Section of American Chemical Society) Text in English. 1948. m. (except July, Aug., Sep.). USD 2. adv. bk.rev. illus.

Published by: (Florida Section), American Chemical Society, 1155 16th St, N W, Washington, DC 20036. Circ: 2,350 (controlled).

FLAME RETARDANCY OF POLYMERIC MATERIALS PROCEEDINGS (YEAR). see FIRE PREVENTION

---

540   CZE

FOLIA FACULTATIS SCIENTIARUM NATURALIUM UNIVERSITATIS MASARYKIANAE BRUNENSIS: CHEMIA. Text in Czech. a. price varies. Document type: Monographic series, Academic/Scholarly.

Formerly: Folia Facultatis Scientiarum Naturalium Universitatis Purkynianae Brunensis: Chemia (0323-0236)

Indexed: BiolAb.

—CISTI, Linda Hall.

Published by: Masarykova Universita, Prirodovedecka Fakulta/Masaryk University, Faculty of Sciences, Kotlarska 2, Brno, 61137, Czech Republic. Ed. Josef Havel.

FOOD AND CHEMICAL TOXICOLOGY. see ENVIRONMENTAL STUDIES—Toxicology And Environmental Safety

---

664   NLD   ISSN 0308-8146
TX501   CODEN: FOCHDJ

➤ FOOD CHEMISTRY. Text in English. 1976. 24/yr. EUR 3,862 in Europe to institutions; JPY 513,000 in Japan to institutions; USD 4,318 to institutions except Europe and Japan; EUR 174 in Europe to qualified personnel; JPY 23,100 in Japan to qualified personnel; USD 193 to qualified personnel except Europe and Japan (effective 2006). adv. bk.rev. illus. Index. back issues avail.; reprints avail. Document type: Journal, Academic/Scholarly. Description: Concerned with the chemistry and biochemistry of foods, as well as the chemical and biochemical changes occurring in them.

Incorporates (1985-1991): Journal of Micronutrient Analysis (0266-349X)

Related titles: Microform ed.: (from PQC); Online - full text ed.: (from EBSCO Publishing, Gale Group, IngentaConnect, ScienceDirect, Swets Information Services).

Indexed: A&ATA, AEA, ASCA, ASFA, AbHyg, AgBio, Agr, AgrForAb, AnBrAb, AnalAb, ApicAb, B&BAb, BBCI, BIOSIS Prev, BioDAb, BiolAb, CCI, CIN, CPA, ChemAb, ChemTitl, CurCont, CurPA, DSA, ESPM, EngInd, ExcerpMed, FCA, FPA, FS&TA, FaBeAb, ForAb, HerbAb, HortAb, IPackAb, ISR, IndVet, MSB, MaizeAb, NutrAb, OrnHort, PBA, PGegResA, PGrRegA, PHN&I, PN&I, PotatoAb, PoultAb, ProtozoAb, RA&MP, RM&VM, RPP, RefZh, RevApplEntom, RiceAb, S&F, S&MA, SCI, SIA, SeedAb, SoyAb, TDB, TOSA, TriticAb, VITIS, VetBull, WeedAb.

—BLDSC (3977.284000), CASDDS, CISTI, IDS, IE, Infotrieve, ingenta, Linda Hall. CCC.

Published by: Elsevier BV (Subsidiary of: Elsevier Science & Technology), Radarweg 29, Amsterdam, 1043 NX, Netherlands. TEL 31-20-4853911, FAX 31-20-4852457, nlinfo-f@elsevier.nl, http://www.elsevier.com/locate/foodchem, http://www.elsevier.nl. Subscr. in the Americas to: Elsevier, Subscription Customer Service, 6277 Sea Harbor Dr, Orlando, FL 32887-4800. TEL 407-345-4020, 877-839-7126, FAX 407-363-1354.

---

340   ESP   ISSN 1137-4411
QC1

FORMULA. Text in Spanish. 1990. irreg. price varies. Document type: Monographic series, Academic/Scholarly.

Formerly (until 1997): Cuadernos de Seccion. Ciencias Fisico-Quimicas y Matematicas (1130-5282)

Indexed: IECT.

—CINDOC.

Published by: Eusko Ikaskuntza/Sociedad de Estudios Vascos, Palacio Miramar, Miraconcha 48, Donostia, San Sebastian 20007, Spain. TEL 34-943-310855, FAX 34-943-213956, ei-sev@sc.ehu.es, http://www.eusko-ikaskuntza.org/.

---

540   NLD   ISSN 1386-4238
QD6   CODEN: FOCHFL

➤ FOUNDATIONS OF CHEMISTRY; philosophical, historical and interdisciplinary studies of chemistry. Text in English. 1999. 3/yr. EUR 160, USD 160, GBP 100 combined subscription to institutions print & online eds. (effective 2005). adv. bk.rev. reprint service avail. from PSC. Document type: Academic/Scholarly. Description: Provides an interdisciplinary forum for chemists, biochemists, philosophers, historians, educators, and sociologists to discuss conceptual and fundamental issues in chemistry.

Related titles: Online - full text ed.: ISSN 1572-8463 (from EBSCO Publishing, Gale Group, IngentaConnect, Kluwer Online, O C L C Online Computer Library Center, Inc., Springer LINK, Swets Information Services).

Indexed: BibLing, CPE, ERA, ETA, GSI, MEA, PhilInd, RHEA, RefZh, SEA, SENA, SOMA, TEA.

—BLDSC (4025.290200), IE, Infotrieve, ingenta, Linda Hall. CCC.

Published by: Springer-Verlag Dordrecht (Subsidiary of: Springer Science+Business Media), Van Godewijckstraat 30, Dordrecht, 3311 GX, Netherlands. TEL 31-78-6576050, FAX 31-78-6576474, http://springerlink.metapress.com/openurl.asp?genre=journal&issn=1386-4238, http://www.springeronline.com. Ed. Eric R Scerri.

➤ FRESENIUS ENVIRONMENTAL BULLETIN. see ENVIRONMENTAL STUDIES

▼ ➤ FRONTIERS IN DRUG DESIGN AND DISCOVERY. see PHARMACY AND PHARMACOLOGY

▼ ➤ FRONTIERS IN MEDICINAL CHEMISTRY. see MEDICAL SCIENCES

---

540 572   NLD   ISSN 1574-0897

▼ FRONTIERS IN NATURAL PRODUCT CHEMISTRY. Text in English. 2005. a. USD 130 per vol. (effective 2005). Document type: Monographic series, Academic/Scholarly. Description: Covers all aspects of research in the chemistry and biochemistry of naturally occurring compounds including coverage of work on natural substances of land and sea and of plants, microbes and animals.

Related titles: CD-ROM ed.; Online - full content ed.; Online - full text ed.: (from Gale Group, IngentaConnect).

Published by: Bentham Science Publishers Ltd., PO Box 1673, Hilversum, BR 1200, Netherlands. TEL 31-35-6923800, FAX 31-35-6980150, M.Bentham@inter.nl.net, http://www.bentham.org/fnpc/index2.htm. Eds. Atta-ur Rahman TEL 92-21-4969873, Khalid Muhammad Khan, M Iqbal Choudhary TEL 92-21-4969873.

546.731   RUS

FTORNYE ZAMETKI/FLUORINE NOTES. Text in English, Russian. 1998. 6/yr. back issues avail. Document type: Academic/Scholarly. Description: Examines fluorine chemistry.

Media: Online - full text.

Address: Vavilova ul 28, Moscow, 117813, Russian Federation. TEL 7-095-1356494, FAX 7-095-135-6509, nots@fluorine.ru, http://www.fluorine.ru/Notes/fluoronote.html. Ed. Ellia Igoumnova.

GALAXIA. see TEXTILE INDUSTRIES AND FABRICS

---

540   CHN   ISSN 1003-3874
CODEN: GACAFF

➤ GANGUANG CAILIAO/PHOTOSENSITIVE MATERIALS. Text in Chinese. 1973. bi-m. CNY 15; USD 10 foreign. adv. bk.rev. Document type: Academic/Scholarly. Description: Provides information on the development, manufacture and application of photosensitive materials. Covers new products, technologies and trends of the market and industrial circle.

Related titles: Online - full text ed.: (from East View Information Services).

Indexed: CIN, ChemAb, ChemTitl.

—CASDDS.

Published by: Huagong Bu, Ganguang Cailiao Xinxi Zhan/Ministry of Chemical Industry, Information Center for Photographic Materials, c/o Zhongguo Lekai Jiaopian Gongsi, Jianshe Rd, Baoding, Hebei 071054, China. TEL 86-312-3033279, FAX 86-312-3026296, hjbdlkqb@public.sj.hj.cn. Ed. Rongguo Yao. R&P Fengqi Wang. Adv. contact Licheng Du. Circ: 5,000 (paid).

540.711   CHN   ISSN 0251-0790
QD1   CODEN: KTHPDM

➤ GAODENG XUEXIAO HUAXUE XUEBAO/CHEMICAL JOURNAL OF CHINESE UNIVERSITIES. Text in Chinese. 1980. m. CNY 180; CNY 15 newsstand/cover (effective 2005). 192 p./no.; Document type: Journal, Academic/Scholarly. Description: Contains theses, research notes, letters and reviews by teachers, researchers, postgraduates, and graduate students.

Related titles: Online - full text ed.: (from East View Information Services, WanFang Data Corp.).

Indexed: ASCA, CCI, CIN, ChemAb, ChemTitl, CurCont, ISR, MSB, RCI, RefZh, RevApplEntom, SCI, SIA.

—BLDSC (3148.330000), CASDDS, CISTI, Ei, IDS, IE, ingenta.

Published by: Gaodeng Jiaoyu Chubanshu, Jilian University, Qianwei Campus, Changchun, 100023, China. TEL 86-431-8499264, FAX 86-431-8499870, cjcu@mail.jlu.edu.cn, http://www.cjcu.jlu.edu.cn/. Ed. Ao-qing Tang. **Dist. overseas by:** China International Book Trading Corp, 35 Chegongzhuang Xilu, Haidian District, PO Box 399, Beijing 100044, China. TEL 86-10-68412045, FAX 86-10-68412023, cibtc@mail.cibtc.com.cn, http://www.cibtc.com.cn.

547.7 CHN ISSN 1003-3726
CODEN: GATOE5

➤ **GAOFENZI TONGBAO/POLYMER BULLETIN.** Text in Chinese; Abstracts in English. 1988. bi-m. CNY 48 domestic (effective 2004). 80 p./no.; **Document type:** *Journal, Academic/Scholarly.*
Related titles: Online - full content ed.: (from WanFang Data Corp.); Online - full text ed.: (from East View Information Services).
Indexed: CIN, ChemAb, ChemTitl, MSB.
—BLDSC (6547.702400), CASDDS, IE, ingenta.
Published by: Zhongguo Huaxuehui/Chinese Chemical Society, Haidian Zhongguancun, 2, Beiyijie, Beijing, 100080, China. TEL 81-10-62588926, gfztb@iccas.ac.cn, http://gfztb.periodicals.net.cn/default.html. **Dist. by:** China International Book Trading Corp, 35 Chegongzhuang Xilu, Haidian District, PO Box 399, Beijing 100044, China. TEL 86-10-68412045, FAX 86-10-68412023, cibtc@mail.cibtc.com.cn, http://www.cibtc.com.cn.

540 JPN ISSN 0386-961X
QD1 CODEN: GNKGAN

GENDAI KAGAKU/CHEMISTRY TODAY. Text in Japanese. 1971. m. JPY 8,100 (effective 2005). **Document type:** *Journal, Academic/Scholarly.*
Indexed: CIN, ChemAb, ChemTitl, RefZh.
—BLDSC (3172.192000), CASDDS, CISTI.
Published by: Tokyo Kagaku Dojin, 36-7 Sengoku 3-chome, Bunkyo-ku, Tokyo, 112-0011, Japan. TEL 81-3-39465311, FAX 81-3-39465316, info@tkd-pbl.com, http://www.tkd.pbl.com.

540 JPN ISSN 0910-4747
CODEN: GKZOE3

GENDAI KAGAKU. ZOKAN/CHEMISTRY TODAY. SPECIAL NUMBER. Text in Japanese. 1984. bi-m.
Indexed: CIN, ChemAb, ChemTitl.
—CASDDS.
Published by: Tokyo Kagaku Dojin, 36-7 Sengoku 3-chome, Bunkyo-ku, Tokyo, 112-0011, Japan.

GEOCHEMICAL SOCIETY. SPECIAL PUBLICATION. see *EARTH SCIENCES—Geology*

540 USA ISSN 1467-4866
QE514 CODEN: GETRF9

➤ **GEOCHEMICAL TRANSACTIONS.** Text in English. N.S. 2000. irreg. USD 100 to institutions (effective 2005). **Document type:** *Academic/Scholarly.* **Description:** Serves as a medium for the rapid publication of research in all areas of chemistry which relate to materials and processes occurring in the Earth's aquasphere and geosphere.
Media: Online - full text (from EBSCO Publishing, O C L C Online Computer Library Center, Inc.).
Indexed: ASFA, CPI, CurCont, ESPM, Inspec, M&GPA, SWRA, WRCInf.
—Infotrieve, Linda Hall. **CCC.**
Published by: American Institute of Physics, 2 Huntington Quadrangle, Ste 1NO1, Melville, NY 11747-4502. aipinfo@aip.org, http://gt.aip.org/gt/top.jsp, http://www.aip.org. Ed. Scott Wood. **Subscr. to:** Extenza - Turpin, Pegasus Dr, Stratton Business Park, Biggleswade, Beds SG18 8TQ, United Kingdom. **Co-sponsor:** American Chemical Society, Division of Geochemistry.

➤ **THE GEORGE B. PEGRAM LECTURE SERIES.** see *SCIENCES: COMPREHENSIVE WORKS*

540 GHA ISSN 0855-0484

GHANA JOURNAL OF CHEMISTRY. Text in English. 1989. s-a.
Indexed: INIS AtomInd.
—BLDSC (4166.215000), IE, ingenta.
Published by: University of Cape Coast, University Post Office, Cape Coast, Ghana. TEL 233-42-32378, FAX 233-42-32485, ucclib@ucc.gn.apc.org.

540 660 BIH ISSN 0367-4444
CODEN: GHTBAB

GLASNIK HEMICARA I TEHNOLOGA BOSNE I HERCEGOVINE. Text in Serbo-Croatian. irreg.
Related titles: Series of: Documenta Chemica Yugoslavica.
Indexed: ChemAb.
—CASDDS.
Published by: Akademija Nauka i Umjetnosti Bosne i Hercegovine, Hemijski Institut, Vojvode Putnika 43, Sarajevo, Bosnia Herzegovina. Ed. Franjo Krleza.

540 660 MKD ISSN 0350-0136
CODEN: GHTMDD

GLASNIK NA HEMICARITE I TEHNOLOZITE NA MAKEDONIJA/BULLETIN OF THE CHEMISTS AND TECHNOLOGISTS OF MACEDONIA. Text in English, Macedonian. 1974. s-a. **Description:** Publishes reviews, original scientific papers, short communications, and professional papers in all areas of chemistry and technology.
Indexed: INIS AtomInd.
Published by: Sojuz na Hemicarite i Tehnolozite na Makedonija/Society of Chemists and Technologists of Macedonia, c/o Zoran Zdravkovski, Institute of Chemistry, Arhimedova 5, Skopje, Macedonia. TEL 389-2-117055, FAX 389-2-226865, http://www.pmf.ukim.edu.mk/PMF/Chemistry/glasnik/, http://www.pmf.ukim.edu.mk/PMF/Chemistry/sojuz.htm. Ed. Trajce Stafilov.

540 GBR ISSN 0072-6524

GREAT BRITAIN. LABORATORY OF THE GOVERNMENT CHEMIST. ANNUAL REPORT OF THE GOVERNMENT CHEMIST. Text in English. 1959. a. GBP 5.40. reprint service avail. from PQC. **Document type:** *Government.*
Published by: Stationery Office, 51 Nine Elms Ln, London, SW8 5DA, United Kingdom. TEL 44-20-7873-0011, FAX 44-20-7873-8247, book.orders@theso.co.uk, http://www.national-publishing.co.uk.

660 363.72 GBR ISSN 1463-9262
TP155 CODEN: GRCHFJ

➤ **GREEN CHEMISTRY.** Text in English. 1999. m. GBP 859, USD 1,571 combined subscription print & online eds. (effective 2006); subscr. includes Chemical Technology. **Document type:** *Journal, Academic/Scholarly.* **Description:** Covers all chemical aspects of clean technology, and research relating to a reduction in the environmental impact of chemicals.
Related titles: Online - full text ed.: ISSN 1463-9270. GBP 773, USD 1,414 (effective 2006) (from EBSCO Publishing, O C L C Online Computer Library Center, Inc., Swets Information Services); ♦ Supplement(s): Chemical Technology. ISSN 1744-1560.
Indexed: AEA, AgBio, AgrForAb, CCI, CSNB, ChemAb, CurCont, DSA, EnvAb, FCA, FPA, ForAb, HerbAb, HortAb, I&DA, ISR, LHB, OrnHort, PBA, RA&MP, RCI, RefZh, S&F, SCI, SIA, SoyAb, WeedAb.
—BLDSC (4214.935500), CISTI, IE, Infotrieve, ingenta, Linda Hall. **CCC.**
Published by: Royal Society of Chemistry, Thomas Graham House, Science Park, Milton Rd, Cambridge, CB4 0WF, United Kingdom. TEL 44-1223-432360, FAX 44-1223-423623, minhas@rsc.org, sales@rsc.org, advertising@rsc.org, http://www.rsc.org/greenchem. Ed. Harpal Minhas TEL 44-1223-432293. **Dist. by:** Portland Press Ltd., R S C Distribution Services, Commerce Way, Whitehall Industrial Estate, Colchester CO2 8HP, United Kingdom. TEL 44-1206-226050, FAX 44-1206-226055, sales@rscdistribution.org

338.4766 CHN ISSN 1007-1865

GUANGDONG HUAGONG/GUANGDONG CHEMICAL INDUSTRY. Text in Chinese. 1973. q. CNY 60 (effective 2003). **Document type:** *Journal, Trade.*
Related titles: Online - full text ed.: (from East View Information Services).
—BLDSC (4223.858075), IE, ingenta.
Published by: Guangdong-Sheng Zhonghua Gongyeting, 116, Yuehua Road, Guangzhou, 510034, China. TEL 86-20-83336009, FAX 86-20-83380392, gdcic@163.net, http://www.gdchem.com/book1.htm.

540 MEX

GUIA QUIMICA LATINOAMERICANA/LATIN AMERICAN CHEMICAL GUIDE. Text in English, Spanish. 1998. a. USD 150 (effective 1998).
Published by: Informatica Cosmos, S.A. de C.V., Calz. del Hueso 122-A1, Col. Ex-Hacienda Coapa, Mexico City, DF 14300, Mexico. Ed. Raul Macazaga. Circ: 5,000 (paid).

HANDBOOK OF CHEMICAL NEUROANATOMY. see *MEDICAL SCIENCES—Psychiatry And Neurology*

540 DEU

➤ **HANDBOOK OF ENVIRONMENTAL CHEMISTRY.** Text in English. 1980. irreg. price varies. reprint service avail. from ISI. **Document type:** *Monographic series, Academic/Scholarly.* **Description:** Provides a complete description of the environment and of transformations occurring on a local or global scale.
Related titles: Online - full text ed.; Series: Handbook of Environmental Chemistry. Volume 1: The Natural Environment and the Biogeochemical Cycles. ISSN 1433-6820; Handbook of Environmental Chemistry. Volume 2: Reactions and Processes. ISSN 1433-6839; Handbook of Environmental Chemistry. Volume 3: Anthropogenic Compounds. ISSN 1433-6847; Handbook of Environmental Chemistry. Volume 4: Air Pollution. ISSN 1433-6855. 1986; Volume 5: Water Pollution. ISSN 1433-6863. 1991.
Indexed: BIOSIS Prev.
—BLDSC (4250.439000), ingenta.
Published by: Springer-Verlag (Subsidiary of: Springer Science+Business Media), Tiergartenstr 17, Heidelberg, 69121, Germany. TEL 49-6221-3450, FAX 49-6221-345229, subscriptions@springer.de, http://www.springeronline.com/sgw/cda/frontpage/0,0,4-0-69-1190168-0,0.html?referer=www.springeronline.com/series/698, http://www.springer.de. Ed. Otto Hutzinger. **Subscr. to:** Springer-Verlag New York, Inc., 233 Spring St, New York, NY 10013. TEL 800-777-4643, orders@springer-ny.com, http://www.springer-ny.com.

540 JPN

HANDBOOK OF EXISTING & NEW CHEMICAL SUBSTANCES. Text in English. irreg., latest vol.7, 1996. JPY 29,600; USD 303 in Asia; USD 313 elsewhere. 850 p./no.; **Description:** Lists chemical substances based on Chemical Substance Control Law in Japan.
Related titles: Japanese ed.
Published by: (Japan. Ministry of International Trade & Industry, Japan. Basic Industries Bureau, Chemical Products Safety Division), Chemical Daily Co. Ltd., 3-16-8 Nihonbashihama-cho, Chuo-ku, Tokyo, 103-8485, Japan. FAX 81-3-3663-7275, jcsweb@chemicaldaily.co.jp, http://www.chemicaldaily.co.jp/. **Dist. in America by:** Tekno-Info Corp., PO Box 436627, Louisville, KY 40253-6627. TEL 502-245-9628, 502-245-8152.

333.72 NLD

➤ **HANDBOOK OF NATURAL PRODUCTS DATA.** Text in English. 1990. irreg., latest vol.3, 1994. price varies. charts; stat. back issues avail. **Document type:** *Monographic series, Academic/Scholarly.*
Published by: Elsevier BV (Subsidiary of: Elsevier Science & Technology), Radarweg 29, Amsterdam, 1043 NX, Netherlands. TEL 31-20-4853911, FAX 31-20-4852457, nlinfo-f@elsevier.nl, http://www.elsevier.nl. Ed. Atta U Rahman.

➤ **HANDBOOK ON THE PHYSICS AND CHEMISTRY OF RARE EARTHS.** see *PHYSICS*

➤ **HANNENG CAILIAO/ENERGETIC MATERIALS.** see *ENERGY*

540 ARM
QD1.A3515 CODEN: AYKZAN

HAYASTANI CHIMIKAKAN HANDES. Text and summaries in Armenian, English, Russian. 1947. 4/yr. AMD 400. index. **Document type:** *Academic/Scholarly.*
Formerly: Armyanskii Khimicheskii Zhurnal - Aikakan Himiakan Amsagir (0515-9628)
Indexed: CIN, ChemAb, ChemTitl, INIS AtomInd, MSB, RefZh.
—CASDDS, CISTI, Linda Hall. **CCC.**
Published by: Hayastany Guitoutyunnery Azgayin Academia/National Academy of Sciences of the Republic of Armenia, Marshal Bagramyan Ave 24b, Erevan, 375019, Armenia. TEL 78852-524580, FAX 78852-151087. Ed. S A Vartanian.

HAZARD ASSESSMENT OF CHEMICALS. see *ENGINEERING—Chemical Engineering*

540 CHN ISSN 1003-5095

HEBEI HUAGONG/HEBEI CHEMICAL ENGINEERING. Text in Chinese. 1978. q.
Related titles: Online - full text ed.: (from East View Information Services).
Published by: Hebei Sheng Huagong Xuehui/Hebei Society of Chemical Engineering, 1 Jianhuamian Dajie, Shijiazhuang, Hebei 050031, China. TEL 741853. Ed. Rong Wenzhong.

540 CHE ISSN 0018-019X
QD1 CODEN: HCACAV

➤ **HELVETICA CHIMICA ACTA.** Text in German, English, French, Italian. 1918. m. EUR 1,778 in Europe; CHF 2,844 Switzerland & Liechtenstein; USD 2,368 elsewhere; EUR 1,956 combined subscription in Europe print & online eds.; CHF 3,129 combined subscription Switzerland & Liechtenstein for print & online eds.; USD 2,605 combined subscription elsewhere print & online eds. (effective 2006). adv. abstr.; charts. index. **Document type:** *Journal, Academic/Scholarly.*
Related titles: Microfilm ed.: (from PMC); Online - full text ed.: ISSN 1522-2675. EUR 1,778 in Europe; CHF 2,844 in Switzerland & Liechtenstein; USD 2,368 elsewhere (effective 2006) (from EBSCO Publishing, Swets Information Services, Wiley InterScience).
Indexed: ABIPC, ASCA, ASFA, AbHyg, AgrForAb, AnalAb, BiolAb, BullT&T, CCI, CIN, CPA, ChemAb, ChemInfo, ChemTitl, CurCR, CurCont, DBA, DSA, ESPM, EngInd, ExcerpMed, FCA, FPA, FS&TA, ForAb, HortAb, ISR, IndChem, Inpharma, MEDLINE, MOS, MSB, MSCI, NPU, NutrAb, OrnHort, PollutAb, PoultAb, ProtozoAb, RA&MP, RCI, RM&VM, RPP, Reac, RefZh, SCI, SIA, SSCI, SeedAb, SoyAb, TTI, TriticAb, VITIS, WRCInf, WeedAb.
—BLDSC (4287.000000), CASDDS, CINDOC, CISTI, Ei, IDS, IE, Infotrieve, ingenta, Linda Hall. **CCC.**
Published by: (Schweizerische Chemische Gesellschaft/Swiss Chemical Society), Verlag Helvetica Chimica Acta, Hofwiesenstr 26, Zuerich, 8042, Switzerland. TEL 41-1-3602434, vhca@vhca.ch, http://www.wiley-vch.de/publish/en/journals/alphabeticIndex/2217/, http://www.vhca.ch. Ed. Dr. M Volkan Kisakurek. Adv. contact Col. Angela Schimpf TEL 49-6-201606559. B&W page EUR 1,200; trim 125 x 200. Circ: 1,907 (paid and controlled). **Subscr. in the Americas to:**

C

John Wiley & Sons, Inc., 111 River St, Hoboken, NJ 07030-5774. TEL 201-748-6645, FAX 201-748-6088, subinfo@wiley.com; **Subscr. to:** Wiley - V C H Verlag GmbH & Co. KGaA, Boschstr 12, Weinheim 69469, Germany. TEL 49-6201-606147, 49-6201-6060, FAX 49-6201-606117, 49-6201-606328, info@wiley-vch.de, http://www.wiley-vch.de.

540 SCG ISSN 0440-6826
CODEN: HMPGAI
HEMIJSKI PREGLED/CHEMICAL REVIEW. Text in Serbian. 1950. bi-m. USD 30 (effective 2005). **Document type:** *Journal, Academic/Scholarly.*
Indexed: CIN, ChemAb, ChemTitl.
—CASDDS.
Published by: Srpsko Hemijsko Drustvo/Serbian Chemical Society, Karnegijeva 4/III, PO Box 35-08, Belgrade, 11120. TEL 381-11-3303663, shdoffice@tmf.bg.ac.yu, http://www.shd.org.yu. Ed. Stanimir Arsenijevic. Adv. contact Vera Stupljanin. Circ: 750.

540 ISR ISSN 0793-0283
CODEN: HCOMEX
➤ **HETEROCYCLIC COMMUNICATIONS**; an international journal in heterocyclic chemistry. Text in English. 1994. 6/yr., latest vol.8. USD 370 (effective 2006). reprints avail. **Document type:** *Academic/Scholarly.* **Description:** Publishes preliminary research reports and full-length research papers conveying important developments on all phases of heterocyclic chemistry, including inorganic-ring systems.
Indexed: CCI, CIN, ChemAb, ChemTitl, CurCont.
—BLDSC (4301.259000), CASDDS, CISTI, IE, ingenta.
Published by: Freund Publishing House, Ltd., P O Box 35010, Tel Aviv, 61350, Israel. TEL 972-3-5628540, FAX 972-3-5628538, h_freund@netvision.net.il, http://hetcomm.tripod.com/ed_board.html, http:// www.freundpublishing.com. Ed. R R Gupta.

540 USA ISSN 0164-6109
THE HEXAGON. Text in English. 1910. q. USD 5 (effective 2000). bk.rev. illus. **Document type:** *Academic/Scholarly.* **Description:** Covers the history of chemistry.
Published by: Alpha Chi Sigma Fraternity, Department of Chemistry, University of Michigan, Ann Arbar, MI 48109-1055. TEL 734-764-7329, FAX 734-647-4865. Ed. Brian P Coppola. Pub. Maury Boyd. Circ: 30,000. **Subscr. to:** 2114 N Franklin Rd, Indianapolis, IN 46219.

HIGH - TC UPDATE. see *PHYSICS*

HINDUSTAN LATEX. VARSHIKA RIPORTA/HINDUSTAN LATEX. ANNUAL REPORTS. see *PLASTICS*

HIROSHIMA UNIVERSITY. JOURNAL OF SCIENCE. SERIES A. PHYSICS AND CHEMISTRY. see *PHYSICS*

HOKKAIDO KYOIKU DAIGAKU KIYO. DAI-2-BU, A. SUGAKU, BUTSURI, KAGAKU, KOGAKU-HEN/HOKKAIDO UNIVERSITY OF EDUCATION. JOURNAL. SECTION 2 A. MATHEMATICS, PHYSICS, CHEMISTRY, ENGINEERING. see *MATHEMATICS*

540 TWN
HUA HSUEH/CHEMISTRY. Text in Chinese. 4/yr. USD 20 (effective 1999). **Document type:** *Academic/Scholarly.*
—BLDSC (3168.850000).
Published by: Chinese Chemical Society/Zhongguo Huaxuehui, Rm.903, 9th Fl, No7 Chungking S. Rd, Sec 1, P.O. Box 609, Taipei, 10099, Taiwan. TEL 886-2-3313176, FAX 886-2-3118464.

338.4766 660 CHN ISSN 1000-6613
TP1 CODEN: HUJIEK
HUAGONG JINZHAN/CHEMICAL INDUSTRY AND ENGINEERING PROGRESS. Text in Chinese. 1982. bi-m. USD 70. adv. 64 p./no.; **Document type:** *Academic/Scholarly.* **Description:** Features the current developments and advances in the field of chemical industry and engineering. Topics include chemical industry, technology, engineering, machinery, process automation, environmental protection, economy and management.
Related titles: Online - full text ed.: (from East View Information Services).
Indexed: CIN, ChemAb, ChemTitl.
—BLDSC (3148.010000), CASDDS, IE, ingenta.
Published by: (Chemical Industry and Engineering Society of China), Chemical Industry Press/Huaxue Gongye Chubanshe, 3 Huixinli, Chaoyang-qu, Beijing, 100029, China. TEL 86-10-4918318, FAX 86-10-4918318. Ed. Chengwei Shi. Adv. contact Yanhong Dai.

540 662.6 CHN ISSN 1004-0862
HUAGONG ZHI YOU/FRIEND OF CHEMICAL INDUSTRY. Text in Chinese. q. USD 2 per issue. adv. **Document type:** *Academic/Scholarly.*
Published by: Hebei Shiyou Huagong Guihua Shejiyuan/Hebei Institute of Petrochemical Industry, 11 Jichang Lu, Shijiazhuang, Hebei 050071, China. TEL 0312-311486. Ed. Jiang Ximing. Adv. contact Zhao Tina Hong.

363.7 CHN ISSN 0254-6108
QD1 CODEN: HUHUDB
➤ **HUANJING HUAXUE/JOURNAL OF ENVIRONMENTAL CHEMISTRY.** Text in Chinese; Summaries in English. 1982. bi-m. CNY 108 (effective 2004). adv. **Document type:** *Academic/Scholarly.* **Description:** Contains original theses and reviews on environmental analytic chemistry, pollution chemistry, pollution prevention chemistry, and recent research results.
Related titles: Online - full text ed.: (from East View Information Services, WanFang Data Corp.).
Indexed: CIN, ChemAb, ChemTitl, MSB.
—BLDSC (3791.410800), CASDDS, CISTI, IE, ingenta, Linda Hall.
Published by: (Zhongguo Kexueyuan, Shengtai Huanjing Yanjiu Zhongxin/Chinese Academy of Sciences, Research Center for Eco-environmental Sciences), Kexue Chubanshe/Science Press, 16 Donghuang Cheng Genbei Jie, Beijing, 100717, China. TEL 86-10-64000246, FAX 86-10-64030255, http://hjhx.periodicals.net.cn/default.html, http:// www.sciencep.com/. Circ: 21,000. **Dist. by:** China International Book Trading Corp, 35 Chegongzhuang Xilu, Haidian District, PO Box 399, Beijing 100044, China. TEL 86-10-68412045, FAX 86-10-68412023, cibtc@mail.cibtc.com.cn, http://www.cibtc.com.cn.

540 CHN ISSN 1001-7631
TP155 CODEN: HFGGEU
HUAXUE FANYING GONGCHENG YU GONGYI/CHEMICAL REACTION ENGINEERING AND TECHNOLOGY. Text in Chinese. 1985. q. USD 48. **Document type:** *Academic/Scholarly.*
Related titles: Online - full text ed.: (from East View Information Services).
Indexed: APIAb, CEABA, CIN, ChemAb, ChemTitl, EngInd, RefZh.
—BLDSC (3150.332000), CASDDS, CISTI, Ei, IE, ingenta, Linda Hall.
Published by: (Huagong Xi), Zhejiang Daxue, Zheda Lu 38, Hangzhou, Zhejiang 310027, China. TEL 86-571-7951227, FAX 86-571-7951358. Ed. Chen Gantang.

540 CHN ISSN 1005-281X
CODEN: HJINEL
HUAXUE JINZHAN/PROGRESS IN CHEMISTRY. Text in Chinese. 1989. q. USD 60 (effective 2000). **Document type:** *Academic/Scholarly.* **Description:** Reports on the latest development in the field of chemistry.
Related titles: CD-ROM ed.; Online - full text ed.: (from East View Information Services).
Indexed: CCI, CIN, ChemAb, ChemTitl.
—BLDSC (6866.910000), CASDDS, IE, ingenta.
Published by: Zhongguo Kexueyuan, Wenxian Qingbao Zhongxin/Chinese Academy of Sciences, Documentation and Information Center, 8 Kexueyuan Nanlu, Zhongguancun, Beijing, 100080, China. TEL 86-1-6256-2547, FAX 81-1-6256-6846, scinfo@las.ac.cn. Ed. Qian Wenzao.

540 CHN ISSN 0441-3776
QD1 CODEN: HHTPAU
HUAXUE TONGBAO/CHEMICAL BULLETIN. Text in Chinese. 1933. m. CNY 144 (effective 2004). adv. **Document type:** *Bulletin, Academic/Scholarly.* **Description:** Presents trends and developments in pure and applied chemistry in China and abroad. Contains review articles, notes and communications, experimental techniques, basic knowledge, history of chemistry, and academic activities.
Related titles: Online - full text ed.: (from East View Information Services, WanFang Data Corp.).
Indexed: CIN, ChemAb, ChemTitl, EngInd, MSB.
—BLDSC (3168.840000), CASDDS, CISTI, Ei, IE, ingenta, Linda Hall.
Published by: Kexue Chubanshe/Science Press, 16 Donghuang Cheng Genbei Jie, Beijing, 100717, China. TEL 86-10-64000246, FAX 86-10-64030255, hxtb@iccas.ac.cn, http://hxtb.periodicals.net.cn/default.html, http:// www.sciencep.com/. Ed. Liu Yuanyuan. Circ: 41,000. **Dist. by:** China International Book Trading Corp, 35 Chegongzhuang Xilu, Haidian District, PO Box 399, Beijing 100044, China. TEL 86-10-68412045, FAX 86-10-68412023, cibtc@mail.cibtc.com.cn, http://www.cibtc.com.cn.

HUAXUE WULI XUEBAO/CHINESE JOURNAL OF CHEMICAL PHYSICS. see *PHYSICS*

540 CHN ISSN 0567-7351
QD1 CODEN: HHHPA4
➤ **HUAXUE XUEBAO/ACTA CHIMICA SINICA.** Text in Chinese; Summaries in English. 1933. m. CNY 264 (effective 2004). adv. **Document type:** *Journal, Academic/Scholarly.* **Description:** Presents original research on organic, inorganic, physical, and analytical chemistry in mainland China.
Supersedes in part: Chinese Chemical Society. Journal (Peiping) (0375-8745)
Related titles: Online - full text ed.: (from East View Information Services, WanFang Data Corp.); ♦ English ed.: Chinese Journal of Chemistry. ISSN 1001-604X.
Indexed: ASCA, AnalAb, BiolAb, CCI, CIN, ChemAb, ChemTitl, CurCont, EngInd, ISR, MOS, MSB, MSCI, RCI, RefZh, SCI.
—BLDSC (0611.000000), CASDDS, CISTI, Ei, IDS, IE, ingenta, Linda Hall.
Published by: (Zhongguo Kexueyuan, Shanghai Youji Huaxue Yanjiusuo/Chinese Academy of Sciences, Shanghai Institute of Organic Chemistry), Kexue Chubanshe/Science Press, 16 Donghuang Cheng Genbei Jie, Beijing, 100717, China. TEL 86-10-64000246, FAX 86-10-64030255, bcanji@mail.sioc.ac.cn, http://hxxb.periodicals.net.cn/ default.html. Circ: 8,000.

540 CHN ISSN 1004-1656
QD1
HUAXUE YANJIU YU YINGYONG/CHEMICAL RESEARCH AND APPLICATION. Text in Chinese; Abstracts in English. 1989. bi-m. CNY 8, USD 3.40 newsstand/cover (effective 2003). adv. reprints avail. **Document type:** *Journal, Academic/Scholarly.*
Related titles: Online - full content ed.: (from WanFang Data Corp.); Online - full text ed.: (from East View Information Services).
Indexed: MSB.
—BLDSC (3150.440200), IE, ingenta.
Published by: Sichuan Sheng Huaxue Huagong Xuehui/Faculty of Chemistry, Sichuan University, 29, Wangjian Road, Chengdu, 610064, China. TEL 86-28-5418495, FAX 86-28-5412907, suqcp@mail.sc.cninfo.net, http://hxyjyyy.periodicals.com.cn/default.html. Ed. Hua-ming Zhao. **Dist. by:** China International Book Trading Corp, 35 Chegongzhuang Xilu, Haidian District, PO Box 399, Beijing 100044, China. TEL 86-10-68412045, FAX 86-10-68412023, cibtc@mail.cibtc.com.cn, http://www.cibtc.com.cn.

540 570.285 CHN ISSN 1672-5425
HUAXUE YU SHENGWU GONGCHENG/CHEMISTRY & BIOENGINEERING. Text in Chinese. 1984. bi-m. CNY 8 newsstand/cover (effective 2005). **Document type:** *Journal, Academic/Scholarly.*
Formerly: Hubei Huagong (1004-0404)
Related titles: Online - full text ed.: (from East View Information Services).
—BLDSC (4335.494000).
Address: 89, Guanshan Yilu, Wuchang, Wuhan 430073, China. TEL 86-27-87439567, FAX 86-27-87438921, hbci@public.wh.hb.cn; hbhgtg@163.com. Ed. An-qiang Liu.

HUNGARIAN ACADEMY OF SCIENCES. CENTRAL RESEARCH INSTITUTE FOR PHYSICS. YEARBOOK/MAGYAR TUDOMANYOS AKADEMIA. KOZPONTI FIZIKAI KUTATO INTEZET. EVKONYV. see *PHYSICS*

540 338 660 HUN ISSN 0133-0276
TP1 CODEN: HJICAI
➤ **HUNGARIAN JOURNAL OF INDUSTRIAL CHEMISTRY.** Text in English. 1973. a. USD 150 (effective 1999). adv. bk.rev. charts; stat. index. back issues avail. **Document type:** *Journal, Academic/Scholarly.* **Description:** Deals with the results of fundamental and applied research, unit operations, chemical processes, chemical and biochemical engineering, and environmental engineering.
Indexed: APIAb, APICat, APIH&E, APIOC, APIPR, APIPS, APITS, ASCA, C&ISA, CCI, CEA, CEABA, CIN, Cadscan, ChemAb, ChemTitl, CurCont, E&CAJ, EngInd, GasAb, ISMEC, LeadAb, SolStAb, TCEA, Zincscan.
—BLDSC (4337.025000), CASDDS, CISTI, Ei, IDS, IE, Infotrieve, ingenta, Linda Hall.
Published by: University of Veszprem, Research Institute of Chemical Engineering, PO Box 158, Veszprem, 8201, Hungary. TEL 36-88-422-022-4298, FAX 1-908-771-8736, hjic@mukki.richem.hu, http://www.vein.hu/HJIC. Ed. Dr. Endre Bodor. Circ: 1,200. **Subscr. to:** Kultura, PO Box 149, Budapest 1389, Hungary.

660 KOR ISSN 1225-004X
QD1 CODEN: HKKCAZ
HWAHAG SE'GYE/CHEMWORLD. Text in Korean. 1946. m. USD 40 to members; USD 70 to non-members; USD 100 to institutions (effective 2001). adv. 160 p./no.; **Document type:** *Newsletter.*
Formerly (until 1991): Hwahag Gwa Gonneb Nui Jinbo/Progress in Chemistry and Chemical Industry (0439-9838)
—BLDSC (3172.384000), CASDDS, CISTI, Linda Hall.
Published by: Korean Chemical Society/Daehan Hwahak Hoe, 635-4 Yeoksam-dong, Kangnam-gu, Seoul, 135-703, Korea, S. TEL 82-2-34533781, FAX 82-2-34533785, kcchem@neon.kcsnet.or.kr, kcschem@neon.kcsnet.or.kr, http://www.kcsnet.or.kr. Ed. Kyung Soo Paek. Adv. contact Sun Yeoul Lee. B&W page USD 250, color page USD 1,000; trim 258 x 188. Circ: 5,500.

HYLE; international journal for philosophy of chemistry. see *PHILOSOPHY*

HYOMEN KAGAKU KISO KOZA/TEXTBOOK OF LECTURES ON SURFACE SCIENCE. see *PHYSICS*

HYOMEN KAGAKU KOEN TAIKAI KOEN YOSHISHU/SURFACE SCIENCE SOCIETY OF JAPAN. ABSTRACTS OF MEETINGS. see *PHYSICS*

HYOMEN KAGAKU SEMINA/TEXTBOOK OF SEMINAR ON SURFACE SCIENCE. see *PHYSICS*

540 CHE
I A V INFORMATIONEN✶. Text in German. bi-m.

C

▼ new title ➤ refereed ✶ unverified ♦ full entry avail.

Published by: Internationalen Aerosol - Verband/International Aerosol Association, Bahnhofstr 37, Zuerich, 8002, Switzerland.

540 USA CODEN: ICPNDH
I C P INFORMATION NEWSLETTER (ONLINE). (Inductively Coupled Plasma) (in pdf files) Text in English. 1975. m., latest vol.28. USD 67 domestic; USD 92 in Europe; USD 102 elsewhere (effective 2003). adv. back issues avail. **Document type:** *Newsletter, Academic/Scholarly.*
Formerly (until Nov. 2002): I C P Information Newsletter (Print) (0161-6951)
Media: E-mail. **Related titles:** CD-ROM ed.
Indexed: RefZh.
—BLDSC (4362.065400), IE, Infotrieve.
Published by: I C P Information Newsletter, Inc., PO Box 666, Hadley, MA 01035-0666. TEL 413-256-8942, FAX 413-256-3746, icpnews@chem.umass.edu, http://www-unix.oit.umass.edu/~wc2004/ICPnews.htm.

540 JPN ISSN 1342-0321
QD51.5.J3 CODEN: IAREFM
I C R ANNUAL REPORT. Text in English. a. **Document type:** *Academic/Scholarly.*
—BLDSC (4362.066720), CASDDS, IE, ingenta, Linda Hall.
Published by: Kyoto University, Institute for Chemical Research/Kyoto Daigaku Kenkyusho, Gokasho, ICR Library, Uji-shi, Kyoto 611-0011, Japan. TEL 81-774-38-3009, FAX 81-774-38-4370, http://www.kuicr.kyoto-u.ac.jp/. Ed. Misae Hiramoto.

I F S C C MAGAZINE. (International Federation of Societies of Cosmetic Chemists) see *BEAUTY CULTURE—Perfumes And Cosmetics*

I N A VJESNIK INDUSTRIJE NAFTE. see *PETROLEUM AND GAS*

540 ESP
➤ **I.Q.S. TESIS DOCTORALES. TRABAJOS DE FIN DE CARRERA. TESIS DE MASTER.** Text in Spanish. 1971. a. USD 10 (effective 1999). back issues avail. **Document type:** *Academic/Scholarly.*
Formerly (until 1989): I.Q.S. Trabajos de fin de Carrera (0210-508X)
Indexed: ChemAb, IECT.
—CINDOC.
Published by: Institut Quimic de Sarria, Barcelona, 08017, Spain. TEL 34-93-203-8900, FAX 34-93-205-6266, nval@iqs.url.es, http://www.iqs.url.es. Circ: (controlled).

➤ **I T E BATTERY LETTERS ON BATTERIES, NEW TECHNOLOGIES, AND MEDICINE.** see *ENGINEERING—Electrical Engineering*

➤ **I U P A C SERIES ON ANALYTICAL AND PHYSICAL CHEMISTRY OF ENVIRONMENTAL SYSTEMS.** see *ENVIRONMENTAL STUDIES—Toxicology And Environmental Safety*

540 666 JPN
IBIDEN COMPANY. ANNUAL REPORT. Text in Japanese. 1989. a. **Description:** Information on electronics-related products, fine ceramics, and building materials.
Published by: Ibiden Company Ltd., Somubu, 2-1 Kanda-cho, Ogaki-shi, Gifu-ken 503-0917, Japan. TEL 0584-813111, FAX 0584-814574.

THE IMMUNOASSAY KIT DIRECTORY. SERIES A: CLINICAL CHEMISTRY. see *MEDICAL SCIENCES—Allergology And Immunology*

THE IMMUNOASSAY KIT DIRECTORY. SERIES B: INFECTIOUS DISEASES. see *MEDICAL SCIENCES—Allergology And Immunology*

INDIAN CHEMICAL DIRECTORY. see *ENGINEERING—Chemical Engineering*

540 IND ISSN 0019-4522
QD1 CODEN: JICSAH
➤ **INDIAN CHEMICAL SOCIETY. JOURNAL.** Text in English. 1923. m. USD 400 to institutions (effective 2006). adv. bk.rev. index. reprint service avail. from PQC. **Document type:** *Journal, Academic/Scholarly.* **Description:** Publishes original research papers (Articles and Notes) and Reviews in all areas of chemistry.
Incorporates: Indian Journal of Applied Chemistry (0019-5065)
Related titles: Microform ed.: (from PMC, PQC).
Indexed: ASCA, AnalAb, BiolAb, CCI, CIN, CTE, Cadscan, ChemAb, ChemInfo, ChemTitl, CurCR, CurCont, DBA, DSA, EngInd, ExcerpMed, FS&TA, INIS AtomInd, IndChem, LeadAb, MOS, MSB, NPU, NutrAb, RCI, RPP, RefZh, Zincscan.
—BLDSC (4763.000000), CASDDS, CINDOC, CISTI, Ei, IDS, IE, Infotrieve, ingenta, Linda Hall.
Published by: (Indian Chemical Society), Scientific Publishers, 5-A New Pali Rd., Near Hotel Taj Hari Mahal, PO Box 91, Jodhpur, Rajasthan 342 003, India. TEL 91-291-2433323, FAX 91-291-2512580, info@scientificpub.com, journals@scientificpub.com, http://www.scientificpub.com/bookdetails.php?booktransid=337&bookid=333. Ed. B Chakrabarti. adv.: B&W page USD 400, color page USD 800; trim 160 x 210. Circ: 900 (paid).

540 IND ISSN 0971-457X
TP1 CODEN: ICHTEU
➤ **INDIAN JOURNAL OF CHEMICAL TECHNOLOGY.** Text in English. 1963. bi-m. USD 200 to institutions (effective 2006). adv. bibl.; charts; illus. index. back issues avail.; reprint service avail. from PQC. **Document type:** *Journal, Academic/Scholarly.* **Description:** Publishes original research papers related to the theory and practice of all aspects of chemical engineering and applied chemistry.
Supersedes in part (in 1994): Indian Journal of Technology (0019-5669)
Related titles: Microform ed.: (from PQC).
Indexed: ASCA, ASFA, AnalAb, ApMecR, BiolAb, BrCerAb, C&ISA, CADCAM, CEA, CEABA, CIN, CTE, Cadscan, CerAb, ChemAb, ChemTitl, CivEngAb, CorrAb, CurCont, DSA, E&CAJ, EIA, EMA, ESPM, EnerInd, EngInd, EnvAb, EnvEAb, ExcerpMed, FLUIDEX, FS&TA, GasAb, GeotechAb, IAA, INIS AtomInd, Inspec, LeadAb, M&TEA, MBF, METADEX, MinerAb, NutrAb, PollutAb, RefZh, S&F, SIA, SolStAb, TCEA, WAA, WTA, Zincscan.
—BLDSC (4410.595000), AskIEEE, CASDDS, CISTI, IDS, IE, Infotrieve, ingenta, Linda Hall.
Published by: (India. Council of Scientific and Industrial Research, India. Publications & Information Directorate), Scientific Publishers, 5-A New Pali Rd., Near Hotel Taj Hari Mahal, PO Box 91, Jodhpur, Rajasthan 342 003, India. TEL 91-291-2433323, FAX 91-291-2512580, info@scientificpub.com, http://www.scientificpub.com/bookdetails.php?booktransid=315&bookid=311. Ed. G P Phondke. Circ: 1,200.

540 IND ISSN 0376-4710
CODEN: ICACEC
➤ **INDIAN JOURNAL OF CHEMISTRY. SECTION A: INORGANIC, PHYSICAL, THEORETICAL AND ANALYTICAL CHEMISTRY.** Text in English. 1976. m. USD 550 to institutions (effective 2006). adv. charts; illus. index. back issues avail. **Document type:** *Academic/Scholarly.* **Description:** Focuses on Financial Management issues in the context of development of MNC- Parented developed countries vis-a-vis MNC-Controlled Developing countries Based on latest financial management Techniques and case studies.
Supersedes in part (1963-1976): Indian Journal of Chemistry (0019-5103)
Indexed: ASCA, AnalAb, BiolAb, CCI, CIN, CRIA, CRICC, CTE, Cadscan, ChemAb, ChemInfo, ChemTitl, CurCR, CurCont, INIS AtomInd, ISR, IndChem, Inspec, LeadAb, MSB, MSCI, NutrAb, RCI, RefZh, SCI, ST&MA, TTI, WTA.
—BLDSC (4410.601000), CASDDS, CINDOC, CISTI, Ei, IDS, IE, Infotrieve, ingenta, Linda Hall.
Published by: (India. Council of Scientific and Industrial Research, India. Publications & Information Directorate), Scientific Publishers, 5-A New Pali Rd., Near Hotel Taj Hari Mahal, PO Box 91, Jodhpur, Rajasthan 342 003, India. TEL 91-291-2433323, FAX 91-291-2512580, info@scientificpub.com, http://www.scientificpub.com/bookdetails.php?booktransid=313&bookid=309. Ed. S S Saksena. Circ: 1,400. **Co-sponsor:** Indian National Science Academy.

540 IND ISSN 0376-4699
QD1 CODEN: IJSBDB
➤ **INDIAN JOURNAL OF CHEMISTRY. SECTION B: ORGANIC AND MEDICINAL CHEMISTRY.** Text in English. 1976. m. USD 550 to institutions (effective 2006). back issues avail. **Document type:** *Journal, Academic/Scholarly.* **Description:** Focuses on Financial Management issues in the context of development of MNC- Parented developed countries vis-a-vis MNC-Controlled Developing countries Based on latest financial management Techniques and case studies. Publishes results of original experimental and theoretical studies In Inorganic, Bioinorganic, Theoretical and Analytical Chemistry.
Supersedes in part (1963-1976): Indian Journal of Chemistry (0019-5103)
Indexed: ASCA, ASFA, AbHyg, AgrForAb, AnalAb, BiolAb, CCI, CIN, CPA, CTE, ChemAb, ChemInfo, ChemTitl, CurCR, CurCont, DSA, ESPM, FCA, FPA, ForAb, HelmAb, HortAb, INIS AtomInd, ISR, IndChem, IndVet, Inspec, MBA, MOS, MSB, MaizeAb, NPU, NutrAb, OrnHort, PBA, PGegResA, PGrRegA, PHN&I, ProtozoAb, RA&MP, RCI, RM&VM, RPP, RefZh, RevApplEntom, RiceAb, SCI, SIA, SSCI, SeedAb, SoyAb, TDB, TTI, TriticAb, VetBull, WTA, WeedAb.
—BLDSC (4410.610000), CASDDS, CINDOC, CISTI, Ei, IDS, IE, Infotrieve, ingenta, Linda Hall.
Published by: (India. Council of Scientific and Industrial Research, India. Publications & Information Directorate), Scientific Publishers, 5-A New Pali Rd., Near Hotel Taj Hari Mahal, PO Box 91, Jodhpur, Rajasthan 342 003, India. TEL 91-291-2433323, FAX 91-291-2512580, info@scientificpub.com, http://www.scientificpub.com/bookdetails.php?booktransid=314&bookid=310. Ed. S S Saksena. **Co-sponsor:** Indian National Science Academy.

540 IND ISSN 0971-1627
QD399 CODEN: IJCHEI
➤ **INDIAN JOURNAL OF HETEROCYCLIC CHEMISTRY.** Text in English. 1991. q. INR 500, USD 150 (effective 2001). adv. bk.rev. 100 p./no. 2 cols./p.; back issues avail.; reprints avail. **Document type:** *Academic/Scholarly.* **Description:** Publishes review articles and original research papers pertaining to structure and synthesis, mechanism of reactions, spectral studies, biologically active compounds, bio-chemical studies, physicochemical work and phytochemistry.
Indexed: ASCA, CCI, CIN, ChemAb, ChemTitl, CurCont, RCI.
—BLDSC (4414.350000), CASDDS, CISTI, IDS, IE, ingenta.
Address: C-85, Sector B, Aliganj Scheme, Lucknow, Uttar Pradesh 226 024, India. TEL 91-522-323421, profraj@sancharnet.in, http://www.ijhc.com. Ed., Pub., R&P R S Varma. Circ: 250.

540 USA ISSN 0019-6924
THE INDICATOR. Text in English. 1920. m. (Sep.-June). free to members (effective 2005). adv. illus. **Document type:** *Magazine, Trade.*
Published by: American Chemical Society, New York & North Jersey Sections, 1 Cable Court, Montville, NJ 07045. TEL 973-331-5142, FAX 973-331-5143, sturchio@optonline.net, http://theindicator.org/, http://njacs.org. Ed. Malcom Sturchio. Adv. contact Vincent Gale TEL 781-837-0424. B&W page USD 1,025; trim 5.5 x 8.5. Circ: 12,000 (controlled).

540 ARG ISSN 0368-0819
CODEN: IYQBAZ
INDUSTRIA Y QUIMICA. Text in Spanish. 1935. irreg. (4-6/yr.). bibl. back issues avail. **Document type:** *Bulletin, Trade.*
Related titles: Online - full text ed.
—CASDDS, CINDOC.
Published by: Editorial Petroquimica, Talcahuano, 231 1o A, Capital Federal, Buenos Aires 1013, Argentina. TEL 54-114-3835832, FAX 54-114-3836047, info@aqa.org.ar. adv.: page USD 1,200. Circ: 3,000 (controlled).

660 628.5 NLD ISSN 0926-9614
CODEN: ICHLE6
➤ **INDUSTRIAL CHEMISTRY LIBRARY.** Text in English. 1989. irreg., latest vol.10, 2001. price varies. back issues avail. **Document type:** *Monographic series, Academic/Scholarly.* **Description:** Surveys an array of topics in industrial chemistry.
Indexed: CIN, ChemAb, ChemTitl.
—BLDSC (4448.310000), CASDDS, CISTI, IE, ingenta. **CCC.**
Published by: Elsevier BV (Subsidiary of: Elsevier Science & Technology), Radarweg 29, Amsterdam, 1043 NX, Netherlands. TEL 31-20-4853911, FAX 31-20-4852457, nlinfo-f@elsevier.nl, http://www.elsevier.nl.

540 FRA ISSN 1286-0921
CODEN: INFCA8
INFO CHIMIE MAGAZINE. Text in French. 1963. 8/yr. EUR 225 domestic (effective 2005); EUR 245 in Europe; EUR 315 elsewhere (effective 2003). adv. charts; illus.; mkt.; stat. index. back issues avail.
Formed by the merger of (1982-1998): Chimie Magazine (0245-940X); (1963-1998): Informations - Chimie (0020-045X); Which incorporated: Chimie et Industrie (0009-4358); Genie Chimique (0433-3713); Hauts Polymeres
Related titles: Microfilm ed.: (from PMC); ♦ Supplement(s): Chimie Hebdo.
Indexed: A&ATA, APIAb, APICat, APIH&E, APIOC, APIPR, APIPS, APITS, B&I, CBNB, CIN, ChemAb, ChemInfo, ChemTitl, ExcerpMed, INIS AtomInd, KES, RAPRA, RefZh.
—BLDSC (4478.876565), CASDDS, CISTI, Ei, IE, Infotrieve, Linda Hall. **CCC.**
Published by: Societe d'Expansion Technique et Economique S.A., 4 rue de Seze, Paris, 75009, France. TEL 33-1-44945074, FAX 33-1-44945068, diff@sete-edition.fr, http://www.infochimie.presse.fr. Ed. Sylvie Latieule. Circ: 7,500.

540 USA ISSN 1528-9303
TP669 CODEN: IFRMEC
INFORM (CHAMPAIGN). Text in English. 1990. m. USD 135 domestic to individuals; USD 145 foreign to individuals; USD 750 to institutions (effective 2005). adv. bk.rev. charts; illus. back issues avail.; reprints avail. **Document type:** *Magazine, Trade.* **Description:** Contains news and information of interest to professionals involved in the science and technology of fats and oils, surfactants, detergents, proteins, oleochemicals, and related substances.
Formerly (until 2000): I N F O R M: International News on Fats, Oils & Related Materials (0897-8026); Which superseded in part (in 1990): Journal of the American Oil Chemists' Society (0003-021X); Which was formerly (until 1947): Oil & Soap (0095-9510); (until 1932): Oil & Fat Industries (0095-9502); (until 1927): Journal of Oil & Fat Industries (0095-9774)
Related titles: Online - full text ed.: (from O C L C Online Computer Library Center, Inc., ProQuest Information & Learning).
Indexed: ABIPC, AEA, AbHyg, AgBio, Agr, BioCN&I, CIN, CPA, ChemAb, ChemTitl, DSA, EngInd, FCA, FPA, FS&TA, ForAb, HerbAb, HortAb, MaizeAb, NutrAb, OrnHort, PAIS, PBA, PGegResA, PHN&I, RA&MP, RDA, RefZh, S&F, SIA, SeedAb, SoyAb, TDB, TTI, TriticAb, VITIS, WAE&RSA.
—BLDSC (4478.882000), CASDDS, CISTI, Ei, GNLM, IE, ingenta, Linda Hall. **CCC.**

C

Published by: (American Oil Chemists' Society), A O C S Press, 2211 W Bradley Ave, Champaign, IL 61821. publications@aocs.org, http://www.aocs.org/press/inform/. Eds. Catherine Watkins, Jim Rattray. R&P Greg Reed. Adv. contacts Amie Zeigler, Trish Sipes. B&W page USD 1,650, color page USD 2,860; 8.25 x 11. Circ: 7,000 (paid).

540 DEU
INFORMATION SOURCES IN CHEMISTRY. Text in English. irreg., latest vol.5, 2000. USD 100 in North America (effective 2001). bibl. **Document type:** *Directory, Bibliography.*
Description: Evaluates specific materials - professional journals, government publications, gray literature for the pure and industrial chemist. Covers inorganic chemistry to pharmaceuticals.
Related titles: ◆ Series: Information Sources for the Press and Broadcast Media; ◆ Information Sources in Finance and Banking; ◆ Information Sources in the Life Sciences; ◆ Information Sources in Grey Literature; ◆ Information Sources in Physics; ◆ Guides to Information Sources Series; ◆ Information Sources in Architecture and Construction; ◆ Information Sources in Development Studies; ◆ Information Sources in Engineering; ◆ Information Sources in Environmental Protection; ◆ Information Sources in Law; ◆ Information Sources in Official Publications.
Published by: K.G. Saur Verlag GmbH (Subsidiary of: Gale Group), Ortlerstr 8, Munchen, 81373, Germany. TEL 49-89-769020, FAX 49-89-76902150, info@saur.de, http://www.saur.de. Eds. J F Rowland, R T Bottle.

540 DEU
INSTITUT FUER THEORETISCHE CHEMIE. UNIVERSITAET STUTTGART. ARBEITSBERICHT. Text in German. 1966. biennial. **Document type:** *Academic/Scholarly.*
Published by: Universitaet Stuttgart, Institut fuer Theoretische Chemie, Pfaffenwaldring 55, Stuttgart, 70569, Germany. TEL 0711-6854401, FAX 0711-6854442. Ed. H Preuss. Circ: 350.

540 IND ISSN 0020-3254
TP1 CODEN: JOICA7
➤ **INSTITUTION OF CHEMISTS (INDIA). JOURNAL.** Text in English. 1929. bi-m. USD 25. adv. bk.rev. charts; illus. index. back issues avail. **Document type:** *Proceedings, Academic/Scholarly.*
Supersedes in part: Institution of Chemists (India). Journal and Proceedings
Indexed: CIN, ChemAb, ChemTitl, DSA, EngInd, FS&TA.
—BLDSC (4791.300000), CASDDS, CISTI, Ei, IE, ingenta, Linda Hall.
Published by: Institution of Chemists (India), 11-4 Dr. Biresh Guha Rd., Kolkata, West Bengal 700 017, India. TEL 91-33-240-3832. Ed. Debi Chakravarti. R&P Arun K Chakravarti. Adv. contact Hony Secretary. B&W page USD 30; trim 234 x 180. Circ: 1,500.

540 IND ISSN 0369-8599
INSTITUTION OF CHEMISTS (INDIA). PROCEEDINGS. Text in English. q. **Document type:** *Proceedings, Academic/Scholarly.*
Supersedes in part: Institution of Chemists (India). Journal and Proceedings
Indexed: ChemAb.
Published by: Institution of Chemists (India), 11-4 Dr. Biresh Guha Rd., Kolkata, West Bengal 700 017, India. TEL 91-33-240-3832. Ed. Debi Chakravarti. R&P Arun R Chakravarti. Circ: 2,000.

540 ESP
INSTITUTO DE CATALISIS Y PETROLEOQUIMICA. MEMORIA. Text in Spanish. a. back issues avail.
Related titles: Online - full text ed.
—CINDOC.
Published by: Instituto de Catalisis y Petroquimica, Campus de la UAM Cantoblanco, Madrid, 28049esp, Spain. http://www.icp.csic.es/.

540 ROM
INSTITUTUL DE SUBINGINERI ORADEA. LUCRARI STIINTIFICE: SERIA CHIMIE. Text in Romanian; Text occasionally in English, French; Summaries in English, French, German, Romanian. 1967. a. **Document type:** *Academic/Scholarly.*
Formerly: Institutul Pedagogic Oradea. Lucrari Stiintifice: Seria Chimie; Which superseded in part (in 1973): Institutul Pedagogic Oradea. Lucrari Stiintifice: Seria Matematica, Fizica, Chimie; Which superseded in part (in 1971): Institutul Pedagogic Oradea. Lucrari Stiintifice: Seria A si Seria B; Which was formerly (until 1969): Institutul Pedagogic Oradea. Lucrari Stiintifice
Published by: Institutul de Subingineri Oradea, Calea Armatei Rosii 5, Oradea, 3700, Romania.

540 660 ROM ISSN 1223-8147
QD1 CODEN: BPICDV
INSTITUTUL POLITEHNIC DIN IASI. BULETINUL. SECTIA 2: CHIMIE. Text in English, French, German, Italian, Russian, Spanish. 1946. s-a. per issue exchange basis. adv. bk.rev. bibl.
Former titles: Institutul Politehnic din Iasi. Buletinul. Sectia 2: Chimie si Inginerie Chimica (0254-7104); Institutul Politehnic Iasi. Buletinul. Sectia 2: Chimie (0373-3246)
Related titles: Series of: Institutul Politehnic din Iasi. Buletinul.
Indexed: ApMecR, CIN, ChemAb, ChemTitl, Inspec, MathR.
—BLDSC (2366.102500), CASDDS, CISTI, Linda Hall.
Published by: Institutul Politehnic din Iasi "Gh Asachi", Bd Copou 11, Iasi, 6600, Romania. TEL 40-1-46577, FAX 40-81-47923. Eds. Alfred Braier, Hugo Rosman. Circ: 450.

INTERMETALLICS. see *METALLURGY*

540 USA ISSN 1056-9480
TS695
INTERNATIONAL CONFERENCE ON CHEMICAL VAPOR DEPOSITION. PROCEEDINGS. Text in English. 1967. irreg. (vols. 20-40). price varies. back issues avail. **Document type:** *Proceedings.* **Description:** Covers all aspects of CVD technology, including fundamental chemistry studies and microelectronic and photonic applications.
Related titles: Microform ed.: (from PQC); ◆ Series of: Electrochemical Society. Proceedings. ISSN 0161-6374.
—CCC.
Published by: Electrochemical Society, Inc., 65 S Main St, Bldg D, Pennington, NJ 08534-2839. TEL 609-737-1902, FAX 609-737-2743, ecs@electrochem.org, http://www.electorchem.org/. R&P Mary E Yess. **Co-sponsor:** American Nuclear Society, Inc.

540 USA ISSN 1051-2292
➤ **INTERNATIONAL FEDERATION OF CLINICAL CHEMISTRY. JOURNAL.** Text in English. 1989. 4/yr. USD 80 to non-members; free to members. adv. **Document type:** *Journal, Trade.* **Description:** Covers laboratory practices, clinical applications, and the evaluation of advances in technology for laboratory testing.
Indexed: CIN, ChemAb, ChemTitl, MEDLINE.
—Infotrieve.
Published by: International Federation of Clinical Chemistry, PO Box 509, Albany, NY 12201-0509. TEL 518-485-5395, FAX 518-485-5414, ifcc@ifcc.org, http://www.ifcc.org/eJIFCC/. Circ: 26,000.

➤ **INTERNATIONAL GUIDE TO SCIENTIFIC INSTRUMENTS & CHEMICALS.** see *INSTRUMENTS*

➤ **INTERNATIONAL JOURNAL OF OCCUPATIONAL SAFETY AND ERGONOMICS.** see *OCCUPATIONAL HEALTH AND SAFETY*

541.28 USA ISSN 0020-7608
QD462 CODEN: IJQCB2
➤ **INTERNATIONAL JOURNAL OF QUANTUM CHEMISTRY.** Text mainly in English; Text occasionally in French, German; Summaries in English, French; Text in English. 1966. 15/yr. USD 9,850 domestic to institutions; USD 10,030 in Canada & Mexico to institutions; USD 10,135 elsewhere to institutions; USD 10,835 combined subscription domestic to institutions print & online eds.; USD 11,015 combined subscription in Canada & Mexico to institutions print & online eds.; USD 11,120 combined subscription elsewhere to institutions print & online eds. (effective 2006). adv. bk.rev. cum.index. back issues avail. **Document type:** *Journal, Academic/Scholarly.* **Description:** Publishes information on quantam mechanics: fundamental concepts; mathematical structure; applications to atoms, molecules, crystals and molecular biology.
Related titles: Microform ed.: (from PQC); Online - full content ed.: ISSN 1097-461X. 1996. USD 9,850 to institutions (effective 2006); Online - full text ed.: (from EBSCO Publishing, Swets Information Services, Wiley InterScience).
Indexed: ASCA, CCI, CIN, ChemAb, ChemTitl, CurCont, EngInd, ExcerpMed, ISR, Inspec, MSB, MSCI, PhysBer, RCI, RefZh, SCI.
—BLDSC (4542.512000), AskIEEE, CASDDS, CISTI, Ei, IDS, IE, Infotrieve, ingenta, Linda Hall. **CCC.**
Published by: John Wiley & Sons, Inc., 111 River St, Hoboken, NJ 07030-5774. TEL 201-748-6000, 800-825-7550, FAX 201-748-5915, erkki@kvac.uu.se, uscs-wis@wiley.com, http://www.interscience.wiley.com/jpages/0020-7608, http://www.wiley.com. Eds. Erkki J Brandas TEL 46-18-4713263, Ohrn Yngve. adv.: B&W page GBP 640, color page GBP 1,515; trim 165 x 254. Circ: 800 (paid). **Subscr. outside the Americas to:** John Wiley & Sons Ltd., The Atrium, Southern Gate, Chichester, West Sussex PO19 8SQ, United Kingdom. TEL 44-1243-843335, 0800-243407, FAX 44-1243-843232, cs-journals@wiley.co.uk.

540.7 USA ISSN 0306-7696
CODEN: INCECZ
INTERNATIONAL NEWSLETTER ON CHEMICAL EDUCATION. Text in English. 1974. s-a. GBP 6 for 2 yrs. to individuals; GBP 12 for 2 yrs. to institutions. **Document type:** *Newsletter.*
Indexed: HECAB.
—CASDDS, Linda Hall.
Published by: (University of Leeds, School of Education GBR, International Union of Pure and Applied Chemistry, Committee on Teaching and Chemistry GBR), C R C Press, LLC (Subsidiary of: Taylor & Francis Group), 2000 N W Corporate Blvd, Boca Raton, FL 33431. TEL 800-272-7737, journals@crcpress.com, http://www.crcpress.com/. Ed. Peter Towse. Circ: 3,500.

INTERNATIONAL POLYMER SCIENCE AND TECHNOLOGY. see *PLASTICS*

540 GBR ISSN 0958-661X
CODEN: ISMCEE
➤ **INTERNATIONAL SERIES OF MONOGRAPHS ON CHEMISTRY.** Text in English. 1977. irreg., latest vol.33, 1997. price varies. **Document type:** *Monographic series, Academic/Scholarly.*
Indexed: Inspec.
—BLDSC (4549.259600), ingenta.
Published by: Oxford University Press, Great Clarendon St, Oxford, OX2 6DP, United Kingdom. TEL 44-1865-556767, FAX 44-1865-556646, enquiry@oup.co.uk, http://www.oup-usa.org/catalogs/general/series/International_Series_of_Monographs_on_Chemistry.html.

660 USA
INTERNATIONAL U V - E B PROCESSING CONFERENCE AND EXHIBITION. PROCEEDINGS. Text in English. 1988. biennial. USD 150 (effective 1998). back issues avail. **Document type:** *Proceedings.*
—BLDSC (7242.273000).
Published by: RadTech International North America, 60 Revere Dr, Ste 500, Northbrook, IL 60062. TEL 847-480-9576, FAX 847-480-9282, uveb@radtech.org, http://www.radtech.org.

540 GBR ISSN 1362-671X
INTERNET JOURNAL OF VIBRATIONAL SPECTROSCOPY. Text in English. 1996. bi-m.
Media: Online - full text.
Published by: Ventacon Ltd., Gable Cottage, Crawley, Winchester, SO21 2PR, United Kingdom. FAX 44-1962-776390, ijvs@soton.ac.uk, louise@ijvs.demon.co.uk, http://www.ijvs.com/. Ed. Patrick Hendra.

540 USA
INTRODUCTION TO GRAVITATION CHEMISTRY; experimental and theoretical reviews. Text in English. 1974. s-a. free. bk.rev. bibl.; charts; illus. **Document type:** *Corporate.*
Media: Duplicated (not offset).
Published by: Ensanian Physicochemical Institute, PO Box 98, Eldred, PA 16731. TEL 814-225-3296. Ed. Minas Ensanian. Circ: 100 (controlled).

540 660 IRN ISSN 1021-9986
CODEN: IJCEE9
➤ **IRANIAN JOURNAL OF CHEMISTRY AND CHEMICAL ENGINEERING (INTERNATIONAL ENGLISH EDITION).** Text in English. 1981. 2/yr. EUR 150 to individuals Africa, Asia & Europe; EUR 200 to individuals The Americas, Japan & Australia; EUR 200 to institutions Africa, Asia & Europe; EUR 250 to institutions The Americas, Japan & Australia (effective 2005). bk.rev. abstr.; bibl.; charts; illus.; mkt.; pat.; tr.lit. back issues avail. **Document type:** *Academic/Scholarly.*
Description: Publishes original research articles, reviews and short communications on all areas of pure and applied chemistry and chemical engineering (theoretical and experimental). Serves as medium for exchange between Iranian academia and industry and the world scientific community.
Related titles: E-mail ed.; Fax ed.; Persian, Modern ed.: Nashriyyah-i Shimi va-Muhandisi-i Shimi-i Iran. ISSN 1022-7768.
Indexed: ASCA, CCI, CIN, ChemAb, ChemTitl, INIS AtomInd, MLA-IB.
—BLDSC (4567.528830), CASDDS, IDS, ingenta.
Published by: Jihad Danishgahi/Iranian Research Center for Chemical Industries, P O Box 13145-1494, Tehran, Iran. TEL 98-21-6498191, FAX 98-21-6400730, TELEX 214259 DMJD IR, ijcce@jdcord.jd.ac.ir, http://www.ijcce.irdci.ac.ir, http://www.ijcce.ac.ir. Ed. Mohammad N Sarbolouki. Pub., R&P Majid Amidpour. Circ: 1,500; 2,000 (controlled).

541.388 GBR ISSN 1025-6016
CODEN: IEHSF8
➤ **ISOTOPES IN ENVIRONMENTAL AND HEALTH STUDIES.** Text in English, German, Russian. 1966. q. GBP 638, USD 832 combined subscription to institutions print & online eds. (effective 2006). adv. bk.rev. charts; illus. index. reprint service avail. from PSC. **Document type:** *Journal, Academic/Scholarly.* **Description:** Deals with all aspects of isotope application in environmental and health studies, such as: investigations using variations in natural isotope abundance isotope ecology, isotope hydrology, isotope geology.
Formerly (until 1995): Isotopenpraxis (0021-1915)
Related titles: Online - full text ed.: GBP 606, USD 790 to institutions (effective 2006) (from EBSCO Publishing, Gale Group, IngentaConnect, O C L C Online Computer Library Center, Inc., Swets Information Services).
Indexed: ASCA, ASFA, AbHyg, AgrForAb, AnBrAb, AnalAb, BPRC&P, CCI, CPA, ChemAb, CurCont, DSA, EPB, ESPM, EngInd, EnvEAb, ExcerpMed, FCA, FPA, ForAb, GEOBASE, HerbAb, HortAb, I&DA, ISR, IndMed, IndVet, Inspec, M&GPA, NutrAb, PollutAb, PoultAb, RCI, S&F, SCI, SeedAb, SoyAb, VetBull, WRCInf.
—BLDSC (4583.413000), CISTI, IE, Infotrieve, ingenta, Linda Hall. **CCC.**

C

Published by: Taylor & Francis Ltd (Subsidiary of: Taylor & Francis Group), 4 Park Sq, Milton Park, Abingdon, OX14 4RN, United Kingdom. TEL 44-1235-828600, FAX 44-1235-829000, http://www.tandf.co.uk/journals/titles/10256016.asp. Ed. Dr. Peter Krumbiegel. **Subscr. to:** Journals Customer Service, Rankine Rd, Basingstoke, Hants RG24 8PR, United Kingdom. TEL 44-1256-813000, FAX 44-1256-330245, enquiry@tandf.co.uk.

540 ISR ISSN 0021-2148
QD1 CODEN: ISJCAT

➤ **ISRAEL JOURNAL OF CHEMISTRY.** Text in English. 1951. q. USD 450 combined subscription print & online eds. (effective 2003). adv. charts; illus. index. 90 p./no.; back issues avail. **Document type:** *Academic/Scholarly.* **Description:** Publishes current research in chemistry from around the world. Each issues presents papers on a single topic.
Related titles: Microfilm ed.: (from PMC); Online - full text ed.: (from EBSCO Publishing).
Indexed: ASCA, ASFA, AnalAb, BPRC&P, BiolAb, CCI, CEABA, CIN, Cadscan, ChemAb, ChemInfo, ChemTitl, CurCR, CurCont, DBA, DSA, ESPM, EngInd, FCA, ForAb, HortAb, I&DA, ISR, IndChem, Inspec, LeadAb, MOS, MSB, MSCI, NPU, NutrAb, PollutAb, RCI, RM&VM, RPP, RefZh, S&F, SCI, SIA, TriticAb, WeedAb, Zincscan.
—BLDSC (4583.802000), AskIEEE, CASDDS, CINDOC, CISTI, Ei, IDS, IE, Infotrieve, ingenta, Linda Hall. **CCC.**
Published by: Laser Pages Publishing Ltd., P O Box 35409, Jerusalem, 91352, Israel. laserpages@netmedia.net.il, http://www.sciencefromisrael.com. Ed. Haim Levanon. R&P R Lichtensztajn. Adv. contact Elcya Weiss. Circ: 400.

541 615.8 HUN ISSN 0865-0497
TK9400 CODEN: IZDIE2

IZOTOPTECHNIKA, DIAGNOSZTIKA/ISOTOPE TECHNICS, DIAGNOSTICS. Short title: I T D. Text in Hungarian; Summaries in English. 1958. 4/yr. USD 30. adv. bk.rev. **Document type:** *Academic/Scholarly.* **Description:** Covers the application of stable and radio-isotopes in medicine, industry, agriculture and basic research.
Former titles (until 1989): Izotoptechnika (0004-7201); Atomtechnikai Tajekoztato
Indexed: BiolAb, CIN, ChemAb, ChemTitl, Inspec.
—AskIEEE, CASDDS, CISTI.
Published by: Izotop Intezet Kft., PO Box 77, Budapest, 1525, Hungary. TEL 361-169-9499, FAX 361-169-5087, TELEX 225360. Ed. Istvan Mucha. adv.: page USD 100. Circ: 350 (controlled).

IZVESTIYA VYSSHIKH UCHEBNYKH ZAVEDENII. SEVERO-KAVKAZSKII REGION. ESTESTVENNYE NAUKI/NORTH-CAUCASUS SCIENTIFIC CENTER OF HIGH SCHOOL. NATURAL SCIENCES. NEWS. see *MATHEMATICS*

540 JPN ISSN 0388-5186
CODEN: JAFODZ

J A I C I FORUM. Text in Japanese. 1979. a. free. **Document type:** *Newsletter.*
Published by: Japan Association for International Chemical Information/Kagaku Joho Kyokai, 6-25-4 Honkomagome, Bunkyo-ku, Tokyo, 113-0021, Japan. TEL 81-3-5978-3608, FAX 81-3-5978-3600, http://www.jaici.or.jp. Ed. Osamu Suzuki.

540 CHE

JAHRBUCH CHEMISCHE RUNDSCHAU; Jahresausgabe zur Wochenzeitung fuer Chemie, Pharmazie und Lebensmitteltechnik. Text in German. 1961. a. CHF 25 (effective 1998). adv. bk.rev. **Document type:** *Academic/Scholarly.*
Published by: Vogt-Schild AG, Zuchwilerstr 21, Solothurn 1, 4501, Switzerland. TEL 41-32-6247111, FAX 41-32-6247444, a.widmer@vsonline.ch, http://www.vsonline.ch. Ed. Alfred Widmer. Adv. contact Andreas Benz. B&W page CHF 2,750, color page CHF 3,850; trim 260 x 185. Circ: 5,800.

540 JPN ISSN 0914-6415

JAPANESE SYMPOSIUM ON PLASMA CHEMISTRY. NEWS/PURAZUMA KAGAKU GODO SHINPOJUMU. Text in English, Japanese. 1988. s-a.
Published by: Organizing Committee of Japanese Symposium on Plasma Chemistry/Purazuma Kagaku Godo Shinpojumu Soshiki Iinkai, Kyoto Daigaku Kogakubu Denshi Kogakka, Yoshidahon-Machi, Sakyo-ku, Kyoto-shi, 606-8317, Japan.

540 CHN ISSN 0254-5861
QD471 CODEN: JHUADF

➤ **JIEGOU HUAXUE/CHINESE JOURNAL OF STRUCTURAL CHEMISTRY.** Text in Chinese, English. 1982. bi-m. CNY 30 domestic; USD 88 foreign (effective 2000). **Document type:** *Academic/Scholarly.* **Description:** Publishes original research papers on new experimental and theoretical investigations and outstanding achievements in the area of structural chemistry, particularly molecular and crystal structure, quantum chemistry calculations, IR spectroscopy, NMR, EPR and mass spectroscopy.
Related titles: Microfilm ed.; Online - full text ed.: (from East View Information Services).
Indexed: CCI, CIN, ChemAb, ChemTitl, CurCont, RCI.
—BLDSC (3180.678000), CASDDS, IE, ingenta.
Published by: Chinese Academy of Sciences, Fujian Institute of Research on the Structure of Matter, P.O. Box 143, Fuzhou, Fujian 350002, China. TEL 86-591-3711368, FAX 86-591-3714946, TELEX 92219 FIRSM CN, qjxu@ms.fjirsm.ac.cn. Ed. Lu Jia Xi. R&P Lu Jia-xi. Circ: 1,000 (controlled).

540 660 CHN ISSN 1003-5214
TP155

JINGXI HUAGONG/FINE CHEMICALS. Text in Chinese. 1984. m. CNY 8, USD 3.40 per issue (effective 2003). **Document type:** *Journal, Academic/Scholarly.*
Related titles: Online - full text ed.: (from East View Information Services).
Indexed: BrCerAb, C&ISA, CerAb, CorrAb, E&CAJ, EMA, IAA, M&TEA, MBF, METADEX, RefZh, WAA.
—BLDSC (3927.746000), IE, ingenta, Linda Hall.
Published by: Zhongguo Huagong Xuehui/Chemical Industry and Engineering Society of China, PO Box 304, Dalian, 116023, China. TEL 86-411-4357652, http://www.finechemicals.com.cn/. Ed. Shao Yu-chang. **Dist. by:** China International Book Trading Corp, 35 Chegongzhuang Xilu, Haidian District, PO Box 399, Beijing 100044, China. TEL 86-10-68412045, FAX 86-10-68412023, cibtc@mail.cibtc.com.cn, http://www.cibtc.com.cn.

661 CHN ISSN 1009-9212

JINGXI HUAGONG ZHONGJIANTI/FINE CHEMICAL INTERMEDIATES. Text in Chinese. 1971. bi-m. CNY 48 (effective 2004). **Document type:** *Journal, Academic/Scholarly.*
Related titles: Online - full text ed.: (from East View Information Services, WanFang Data Corp.).
Indexed: BrCerAb, C&ISA, CerAb, CorrAb, E&CAJ, EMA, IAA, M&TEA, MBF, METADEX, RefZh, SolStAb, WAA.
—BLDSC (3927.744700), Linda Hall.
Address: 399, Furong Zhonglu, Changsha, 410007, China. j-fci@163.com, http://jxhgzjt.periodicals.net.cn/default.html. **Dist. by:** China International Book Trading Corp, 35 Chegongzhuang Xilu, Haidian District, PO Box 399, Beijing 100044, China. TEL 86-10-68412045, FAX 86-10-68412023, cibtc@mail.cibtc.com.cn, http://www.cibtc.com.cn.

JOURNAL OF ADVANCES IN CHEMICAL PHYSICS. see *PHYSICS*

JOURNAL OF ALLOYS AND COMPOUNDS. see *METALLURGY*

540 NLD ISSN 0165-2370
TP156.P9 CODEN: JAAPDD

➤ **JOURNAL OF ANALYTICAL AND APPLIED PYROLYSIS.** Text in English. 1979. 6/yr. EUR 2,431 in Europe to institutions; JPY 323,100 in Japan to institutions; USD 2,721 to institutions except Europe and Japan (effective 2006). adv. bk.rev. illus. back issues avail. **Document type:** *Journal, Academic/Scholarly.* **Description:** Devoted to the publication of qualitative and quantitative results relating to: controlled thermal degradation and pyrolysis of technical and biological macromolecules; environmental, geochemical, biological and medical applications of analytical pyrolysis; basic studies in high temperature chemistry, reaction kinetics and pyrolysis mechanisms.
Related titles: Microform ed.: (from PQC); Online - full text ed.: (from EBSCO Publishing, Gale Group, IngentaConnect, ScienceDirect, Swets Information Services).
Indexed: A&ATA, AESIS, ASCA, AnalAb, BiolAb, CCI, CIN, CIS, ChemAb, ChemTitl, CurCont, EngInd, GasAb, GeophysAb, ISMEC, ISR, MSB, RCI, SCI.
—BLDSC (4928.100000), CASDDS, CINDOC, CISTI, Ei, IDS, IE, Infotrieve, ingenta, Linda Hall. **CCC.**
Published by: Elsevier BV (Subsidiary of: Elsevier Science & Technology), Radarweg 29, Amsterdam, 1043 NX, Netherlands. TEL 31-20-4853911, FAX 31-20-4852457, nlinfo-f@elsevier.nl, http://www.elsevier.com/locate/jaap, http://www.elsevier.nl. Eds. K. J. Voorhees, M. Blazso. **Subscr. in the Americas to:** Elsevier, Subscription Customer Service, 6277 Sea Harbor Dr, Orlando, FL 32887-4800. TEL 407-345-4020, 877-839-7126, FAX 407-363-1354.

540 551.5 NLD ISSN 0167-7764
QC879.6 CODEN: JATCE2

➤ **JOURNAL OF ATMOSPHERIC CHEMISTRY.** Text in English. 1983. 9/yr. EUR 1,088, USD 1,108, GBP 718 combined subscription to institutions print & online eds. (effective 2005). bk.rev. illus. index. reprint service avail. from PSC. **Document type:** *Journal, Academic/Scholarly.* **Description:** Cover the study of the chemistry of the Earth's atmosphere, the emphasis being laid on the region below about 100 km.
Related titles: Microform ed.: (from PQC); Online - full text ed.: ISSN 1573-0662 (from EBSCO Publishing, Gale Group, IngentaConnect, Kluwer Online, O C L C Online Computer Library Center, Inc., Ovid Technologies, Inc., Springer LINK, Swets Information Services).
Indexed: AESIS, ASCA, ASFA, AgrForAb, BIOBASE, BibLing, CCI, CIN, CPA, ChemAb, ChemTitl, CurCont, EPB, ESPM, EngInd, EnvAb, EnvEAb, EnvInd, ExcerpMed, FLUIDEX, FPA, ForAb, GEOBASE, HerbAb, HortAb, I&DA, IAA, IABS, IBR, IBZ, ISR, M&GPA, M&TEA, MaizeAb, OceAb, OrnHort, PGegResA, PollutAb, RefZh, S&F, SCI, SWRA.
—BLDSC (4949.050000), CASDDS, CIS, CISTI, Ei, IDS, IE, Infotrieve, ingenta, Linda Hall. **CCC.**
Published by: Springer-Verlag Dordrecht (Subsidiary of: Springer Science+Business Media), Van Godewijckstraat 30, Dordrecht, 3311 GX, Netherlands. TEL 31-78-6576050, FAX 31-78-6576474, http://springerlink.metapress.com/openurl.asp?genre=journal&issn=0167-7764, http://www.springeronline.com. Eds. Andreas Wahner, Elliot L Atlas, Hajime Akimoto, Roderic L Jones.

540 330.9 658 DEU ISSN 1613-9615

▼ ➤ **JOURNAL OF BUSINESS CHEMISTRY.** Text in English. 2004. m. **Document type:** *Journal, Academic/Scholarly.* **Description:** Examines issues associated with leadership and management for the chemist or manager in chemical research or industry.
Related titles: Online - full text ed.: ISSN 1613-9623. free (effective 2005) (from EBSCO Publishing).
Published by: Westfaelische Wilhelms-Universitaet Muenster, Faculty of Chemistry and Pharmaceutical Sciences, Schlossplatz 2, Muenster, 48149, Germany. TEL 49-251-830, FAX 49-251-8332090, verwaltung@uni-muenster.de, http://www.businesschemistry.org/.

540 USA ISSN 0732-8303
QD320 CODEN: JCACDM

➤ **JOURNAL OF CARBOHYDRATE CHEMISTRY.** Text in English. 1974. 9/yr. GBP 1,163, USD 1,918 combined subscription to institutions print & online eds. (effective 2006). adv. reprint service avail. from PSC. **Document type:** *Journal, Academic/Scholarly.* **Description:** Serves as an international forum for novel synthetic methods for carbohydrates, mechanistic carbohydrate chemistry and many other topics.
Supersedes in part (in 1982): Journal of Carbohydrates, Nucleosides, Nucleotides (0094-0585)
Related titles: Microform ed.: (from RPI); Online - full text ed.: ISSN 1532-2327. GBP 1,105, USD 1,822 to institutions (effective 2006) (from EBSCO Publishing, O C L C Online Computer Library Center, Inc., Swets Information Services).
Indexed: ABIPC, AEBA, ASCA, AgBio, Agr, AgrForAb, B&BAb, BBCI, BIOSIS Prev, BioEngAb, BiolAb, CCI, CIN, ChemAb, ChemInfo, ChemTitl, CurCR, CurCont, DSA, ESPM, EngInd, ExcerpMed, HelmAb, HortAb, ISR, IndChem, IndVet, Inpharma, M&PBA, MOS, MSB, NPU, NutrAb, RCI, RM&VM, RPP, Reac, RefZh, SCI, SIA, VetBull.
—BLDSC (4954.855000), CASDDS, CISTI, Ei, IDS, IE, Infotrieve, ingenta, Linda Hall. **CCC.**
Published by: Taylor & Francis Inc. (Subsidiary of: Taylor & Francis Group), 325 Chestnut St, Ste 800, Philadelphia, PA 19016. TEL 215-625-8900, 800-354-1420, FAX 215-625-2940, info@taylorandfrancis.com, http://www.tandf.co.uk/journals/titles/07328303.asp, http://www.taylorandfrancis.com. Ed. Peter H Seeberger. Adv. contact Sharon Moran. B&W page USD 600. Circ: 550.

540 USA ISSN 1058-5834
QD502 CODEN: JCBKEI

JOURNAL OF CHEMICAL AND BIOCHEMICAL KINETICS. Text in English. 1991. q. USD 450 (effective 2005). **Document type:** *Journal, Academic/Scholarly.* **Description:** Presents original research on the development and use of kinetic methods, in the study of mechanisms and kinetics of chemical and biochemical processes.
Indexed: CIN, ChemAb, ChemTitl.
—CASDDS, CISTI, Linda Hall.
Published by: Nova Science Publishers, Inc., 400 Oser Ave, Ste 1600, Hauppauge, NY 11788-3619. TEL 631-231-7269, FAX 631-231-8175, novascience@earthlink.net, http://www.novapublishers.com/journals/kinetics.html. Ed. Gennady E Zaikov.

540 660 USA ISSN 0021-9568
CODEN: JCEAAX

➤ **JOURNAL OF CHEMICAL AND ENGINEERING DATA.** Text in English. 1956. bi-m. USD 981 in North America to institutions; USD 1,026 elsewhere to institutions; USD 127 in North America to members; USD 172 elsewhere to members; USD 95 in North America to students; USD 140 elsewhere to students (effective 2006). adv. bibl.; charts; illus. index. back issues avail.; reprints avail. **Document type:** *Journal, Academic/Scholarly.* **Description:** International source for experimental data on pure compounds and their mixtures in the gaseous, liquid, and soild-state, as well as semi-empirical and theoretical correlations for predicting properties of scientific and technological importance.
Formerly (until 1959): Chemical & Engineering Data Series (0095-9146)
Related titles: Microfiche ed.: USD 705 in North America to institutions; USD 714 elsewhere to institutions (effective 2002); Microfilm ed.: USD 705 in North America to institutions; USD 710 elsewhere to institutions (effective 2002); Online - full text ed.: ISSN 1520-5134. USD 40 (effective 2006) (from EBSCO Publishing, Swets Information Services).
Indexed: ABIPC, APIAb, APICat, APIH&E, APIOC, APIPR, APIPS, APITS, AS&TI, ASCA, B&BAb, CCI, CEA, CEABA, CIN, CTE, Cadscan, ChemAb, ChemInfo, ChemTitl, CurCR, CurCont, E&PHSE, EngInd, F&EA, GP&P, GasAb, INIS AtomInd, ISR, IndChem, LeadAb, MOS, OffTech, PetrolAb, RAPRA, RCI, RefZh, S&F, SCI, TCEA, VITIS, Zincscan.
—BLDSC (4955.800000), CASDDS, CINDOC, CISTI, Ei, IDS, IE, Infotrieve, ingenta, Linda Hall, PADDS. **CCC.**

C

Published by: American Chemical Society, 1155 16th St, N W, Washington, DC 20036. TEL 202-872-4614, 800-227-5558, FAX 202-776-8264, marsh@jced.com, service@acs.org, http://pubs.acs.org/jced. Ed. Dr. Kenneth N Marsh. Circ: 1,600 (paid). **Subscr. to:** Member & Subscriber Services, PO Box 3337, Columbus, OH 43210. TEL 614-447-3776, 800-333-9511, FAX 614-447-3671.

➤ **JOURNAL OF CHEMICAL ECOLOGY.** see *ENVIRONMENTAL STUDIES*

540.7 CHN ISSN 1003-3807
JOURNAL OF CHEMICAL EDUCATION. Text in Chinese; Abstracts in English. 1980. bi-m. USD 125 (effective 2001).
Related titles: Online - full text ed.: (from East View Information Services, Northern Light Technology, Inc.).
Published by: Chinese Chemical Society/Zhongguo Huaxuehui, PO Box 2709, Beijing, 100080, China. TEL 86-10-6256-8157, FAX 86-10-6256-8157, qiuxb@infoc3.icas.cn.

540.711 USA ISSN 0021-9584
QD1 CODEN: JCEDA8
➤ **JOURNAL OF CHEMICAL EDUCATION.** Text in English. 1924. m. USD 45 domestic to individuals; USD 60 foreign to individuals; USD 155 combined subscription domestic to institutions print ed. & password access to online ed.; USD 200 combined subscription foreign to institutions print ed. & password access to online ed.; USD 225 combined subscription domestic to institutions print ed. & IP-Number access to online ed.; USD 290 combined subscription foreign to institutions print ed. & IP-Number access to online ed. (effective 2005). adv. bk.rev.; film rev. abstr.; charts; illus.; stat.; tr.lit. index. back issues avail.; reprint service avail. from PQC. **Document type:** *Journal, Academic/Scholarly.*
Description: Publishes articles and notes, surveying the state of the art in such wide ranging areas as computers, thermodynamic engines and cryoscopy.
Related titles: CD-ROM ed.; Microform ed.: (from PMC, PQC); Online - full text ed.: (from EBSCO Publishing, Northern Light Technology, Inc., O C L C Online Computer Library Center, Inc., ProQuest Information & Learning).
Indexed: A&ATA, ABIPC, ABIn, BRI, BiolAb, CBRI, CCI, CIJE, CIN, CISA, CPE, ChemAb, ChemInfo, ChemTitl, CurCont, DSA, ERA, ETA, EduInd, ExcerpMed, GSI, HECAB, ISR, IndIslam, Inspec, LHB, MEDLINE, MSB, MSCI, RASB, RCI, RHEA, RefZh, SCI, SSCI, VITIS.
—BLDSC (4956.000000), CASDDS, CINDOC, CISTI, Ei, GNLM, IDS, IE, Infotrieve, ingenta, Linda Hall. **CCC.**
Published by: (American Chemical Society, Division of Chemical Education, Inc.), American Chemical Society, 1155 16th St, N W, Washington, DC 20036. TEL 202-872-4614, 800-227-5558, FAX 202-776-8264, jce@chem.wisc.edu, service@acs.org, http://jchemed.chem.wisc.edu/, http://www.acs.org. Ed. J W Moore. Circ: 15,000 (paid).

540 GBR
QD40 CODEN: JRPSDC
▼ ➤ **JOURNAL OF CHEMICAL RESEARCH (PRINT EDITION).** Text in English, French, German. 2004. m. GBP 875, USD 1,396 combined subscription to institutions print & online eds. (effective 2006); .. illus. index. reprints avail. **Document type:** *Journal, Academic/Scholarly.* **Description:** Presents papers from all branches of chemistry.
Formed by the merger of (1977-2004): Journal of Chemical Research. Synopses (Print Edition) (0308-2342); (1977-2004): Journal of Chemical Research. Miniprint (Print Edition) (0308-2350)
Related titles: Microfiche ed.: GBP 365, USD 577 (effective 2004); Online - full text ed.: Journal of Chemical Research (Online Edition). 1997. GBP 787, USD 1,258 (effective 2006) (from EBSCO Publishing, Gale Group, IngentaConnect, O C L C Online Computer Library Center, Inc., Swets Information Services).
Indexed: ASCA, AnalAb, BiolAb, CCI, Cadscan, ChemAb, ChemInfo, CurCR, CurCont, ISR, IndChem, LeadAb, MOS, MSB, NPU, RCI, RefZh, SCI, Zincscan.
—BLDSC (4957.005000), CASDDS, CINDOC, CISTI, IDS, IE, Infotrieve, Linda Hall. **CCC.**
Published by: Science Reviews Ltd., PO Box 314, St Albans, Herts AL1 4ZG, United Kingdom. TEL 44-1727-847322, FAX 44-1727-847323, jcr@scilet.com, scilet@scilet.com, http://www.scilet.com/Chemistry/jcr1.htm. Ed. Alwyn G Davies. **Subscr. to:** Extenza - Turpin, Pegasus Dr, Stratton Business Park, Biggleswade, Beds SG18 8TQ, United Kingdom.

540 IND ISSN 0377-8444
JOURNAL OF CHEMICAL SCIENCES (AMRITSAR). Text in English. 1975. irreg. **Document type:** *Journal, Academic/Scholarly.*
—CISTI, Linda Hall.
Published by: Guru Nanak Dev University Press, Press & Publications Department, Amritsar, Punjab 143 005, India. TEL 91-183-258802, FAX 91-183-258819, dcse.gndu@yahoo.com.

540 IND
QD1 CODEN: PIAADM
➤ **JOURNAL OF CHEMICAL SCIENCES (BANGALORE).** Text in English. 1934. bi-m. INR 150 domestic to individuals; USD 40 foreign to individuals; INR 250 domestic to institutions; USD 150 foreign to institutions (effective 2003). bibl.; illus.; abstr. index. 100 p./no. 1 cols./p.; back issues avail.; reprint service avail. from PQC,ISI. **Document type:** *Proceedings, Academic/Scholarly.* **Description:** Research papers, brief reports, rapid communications, review articles.
Formerly (until 2004): Indian Academy of Sciences. Proceedings. Chemical Sciences (0253-4134); Which superseded in part (in 1978): Indian Academy of Sciences. Proceedings. Part A. Physical Sciences (0370-0089)
Related titles: Microfilm ed.: (from PQC).
Indexed: ASCA, B&BAb, CCI, CIN, CTE, ChemAb, ChemInfo, ChemTitl, CurCont, EIA, EnvAb, INIS AtomInd, ISR, Inspec, MSB, PGrRegA, PhysBer, RM&VM, RPP, RefZh, S&F, SCI, SoyAb.
—BLDSC (6709.920000), AskIEEE, CASDDS, CISTI, Ei, IDS, IE, Infotrieve, ingenta, KNAW, Linda Hall.
Published by: Indian Academy of Sciences, C.V. Raman Ave., Sadashivanagar, P O Box 8005, Bangalore, Karnataka 560 080, India. TEL 91-80-23612546, FAX 91-80-23616094, chemsci@ias.ernet.in, http://www.ias.ac.in/chemsci. Ed. S S Krishnamurthy. R&P G Madhavan. Circ: 1,000.

540 USA ISSN 1549-9618
QD462.A1
▼ **JOURNAL OF CHEMICAL THEORY AND COMPUTATION.** Text in English. 2005 (Jan.). bi-m. USD 1,053 in North America to institutions; USD 1,098 elsewhere to institutions; USD 135 in North America to members; USD 180 elsewhere to members; USD 101 in North America to students; USD 146 elsewhere to students (effective 2006).
Related titles: Online - full text ed.: ISSN 1549-9626. 2005 (Jan.). USD 40 (effective 2006) (from EBSCO Publishing).
Indexed: Inspec.
—BLDSC (4957.095000). **CCC.**
Published by: American Chemical Society, 1155 16th St, N W, Washington, DC 20036. TEL 202-872-4614, 800-227-5558, FAX 202-776-8264, service@acs.org, http://www.acs.org, http://pubs.acs.org.

660 IND ISSN 0021-9622
JOURNAL OF CHEMICALS AND ALLIED INDUSTRIES. Text in English. bi-m. USD 30.
Published by: Ad International, Sayajiganj, Baroda, Gujarat 390 005, India. Ed. C M Pandit. Circ: 2,500.

543.8 NLD ISSN 1570-0232
QP519.9.C47 CODEN: JCBADL
➤ **JOURNAL OF CHROMATOGRAPHY. B, ANALYTICAL TECHNOLOGIES IN THE BIOMEDICAL AND LIFE SCIENCES.** Text in English, French, German; Summaries in English. 1977. 32/yr. EUR 5,147 in Europe to institutions; JPY 683,800 in Japan to institutions; USD 5,757 elsewhere to institutions (effective 2006). adv. bk.rev. charts; illus. index. back issues avail.; reprint service avail. from PQC. **Document type:** *Journal, Academic/Scholarly.* **Description:** Addresses developments in and applications of separation science related to drugs and other pharmacologically active compounds, and to research in biomedical sciences.
Former titles: Journal of Chromatography. B, Biomedical Sciences and Applications (1387-2273); (until 1997): Journal of Chromatography - Biomedical Applications (0378-4347)
Related titles: Microform ed.: (from PQC); Online - full text ed.: (from EBSCO Publishing, Gale Group, IngentaConnect, ScienceDirect, Swets Information Services).
Indexed: ASCA, AbHyg, AgBio, AgrForAb, AnBrAb, AnalAb, BBCI, BIOBASE, BIOSIS Prev, BiolAb, CCI, CISA, CLL, CPA, ChemAb, ChemTitl, ChromAb, CurCont, DBA, DSA, EPB, EngInd, ExcerpMed, FCA, FPA, FS&TA, ForAb, HelmAb, HortAb, IABS, IPA, ISR, IndMed, IndVet, Inpharma, MEDLINE, MSB, NSCI, NutrAb, OrnHort, PBA, PGrRegA, PHN&I, PN&I, PoultAb, ProtozoAb, RA&MP, RCI, RM&VM, RPP, Reac, RefZh, S&F, SCI, SIA, SeedAb, SoyAb, TDB, THA, TriticAb, VITIS, VetBull, WeedAb.
—BLDSC (4958.350300), CASDDS, CINDOC, CISTI, GNLM, IDS, IE, ingenta, Linda Hall. **CCC.**
Published by: Elsevier BV (Subsidiary of: Elsevier Science & Technology), Radarweg 29, Amsterdam, 1043 NX, Netherlands. TEL 31-20-4853911, FAX 31-20-4852457, nlinfo-f@elsevier.nl, http://www.elsevier.com/locate/jchromb, http://www.elsevier.nl. Eds. G. Hopfgartner, H T Karnes, R. Bischoff. adv.: B&W page USD 1,020, color page USD 2,205; trim 192 x 262. Circ: 1,500.

540 USA ISSN 1040-7278
QD921 CODEN: JCSCEB
➤ **JOURNAL OF CLUSTER SCIENCE;** including nanoclusters and nanoparticles. Text in English. 1989. q. EUR 670, USD 670, GBP 418 combined subscription to institutions print & online eds. (effective 2005). adv. back issues avail.; reprint service avail. from PSC. **Document type:** *Journal, Academic/Scholarly.* **Description:** Allows for the interdisciplinary exploration of the chemical and physical properties, bonding and structure, mathematics, and molecular biology of clusters.
Related titles: Online - full text ed.: ISSN 1572-8862 (from EBSCO Publishing, Gale Group, IngentaConnect, Kluwer Online, O C L C Online Computer Library Center, Inc., Springer LINK, Swets Information Services).
Indexed: BibLing, BrCerAb, C&ISA, CCI, CIN, CerAb, ChemAb, ChemTitl, CivEngAb, CorrAb, CurCont, E&CAJ, EMA, IAA, ISR, Inspec, M&TEA, MBF, METADEX, MSCI, RCI, RefZh, SCI, SolStAb, WAA.
—BLDSC (4958.792500), AskIEEE, CASDDS, CISTI, IDS, IE, Infotrieve, ingenta, Linda Hall. **CCC.**
Published by: Plenum US (Subsidiary of: Springer Science+Business Media), 233 Spring St, New York, NY 10013. TEL 212-460-1500, FAX 212-460-1575, service@springer-ny.com, http://springerlink.metapress.com/openurl.asp?genre=journal&issn=1040-7278, http://www.springeronline.com. Eds. Boon K Teo, Richard D Adams.

540 USA ISSN 0192-8651
QD39.3.E46 CODEN: JCCHDD
➤ **JOURNAL OF COMPUTATIONAL CHEMISTRY.** Text in English. 1980. 16/yr. USD 2,675 domestic to institutions; USD 2,867 in Canada & Mexico to institutions; USD 2,979 elsewhere to institutions; USD 2,943 combined subscription domestic to institutions print & online eds.; USD 3,135 combined subscription in Canada & Mexico to institutions print & online eds.; USD 3,247 combined subscription elsewhere to institutions print & online eds. (effective 2006). adv. back issues avail.; reprint service avail. from PQC. **Document type:** *Journal, Academic/Scholarly.* **Description:** Covers all aspects of computational chemistry: organic, inorganic, physical, analytical, and molecular mechanics. Also explores quantum chemistry.
Related titles: Microform ed.: (from PQC); Online - full content ed.: ISSN 1096-987X. 1996. USD 2,675 to institutions (effective 2006); Online - full text ed.: (from EBSCO Publishing, Swets Information Services, Wiley InterScience).
Indexed: ABIPC, ASCA, CCI, CIN, Cadscan, ChemAb, ChemTitl, CurCont, EngInd, ISR, Inspec, LeadAb, MSB, MathR, RCI, SCI, Zincscan.
—BLDSC (4963.460000), AskIEEE, CASDDS, CISTI, Ei, IDS, IE, Infotrieve, ingenta, Linda Hall.
Published by: John Wiley & Sons, Inc., 111 River St, Hoboken, NJ 07030-5774. TEL 800-825-7550, FAX 201-748-5915, uscs-wis@wiley.com, http://www3.interscience.wiley.com/cgi-bin/jhome/33822, http://www.wiley.com. Eds. Charles L Brooks, Gernot Frenking, Hiroshi Nakatsuji. adv.: B&W page USD 1,080, color page USD 2,420; trim 8.25 x 11. Circ: 800 (paid). **Subscr. outside the Americas to:** John Wiley & Sons Ltd., The Atrium, Southern Gate, Chichester, West Sussex PO19 8SQ, United Kingdom. TEL 44-1243-779777, FAX 44-1243-775878, cs-journals@wiley.co.uk.

541.224 GBR ISSN 0095-8972
QD471 CODEN: JCCMBQ
➤ **JOURNAL OF COORDINATION CHEMISTRY.** Text in French. 1971. 18/yr. GBP 5,018, USD 6,200 combined subscription to institutions print & online eds. (effective 2006). adv. reprint service avail. from PSC. **Document type:** *Journal, Academic/Scholarly.* **Description:** Publishes the results of original investigations involving the physical and chemical properties, syntheses and structures of coordination compounds of metals.
Related titles: CD-ROM ed.: ISSN 1029-0389. 1996; Microform ed.; Online - full text ed.: ISSN 1026-7441. 1995. GBP 4,767, USD 5,890 to institutions (effective 2006) (from EBSCO Publishing, Gale Group, IngentaConnect, O C L C Online Computer Library Center, Inc., Swets Information Services).
Indexed: ASCA, CCI, Cadscan, ChemAb, CurCont, EngInd, ISR, Inspec, LeadAb, MSB, RCI, SCI, Zincscan.
—BLDSC (4965.320000), CISTI, Ei, IE, Infotrieve, ingenta, Linda Hall. **CCC.**
Published by: Taylor & Francis Ltd (Subsidiary of: Taylor & Francis Group), 4 Park Sq, Milton Park, Abingdon, OX14 4RN, United Kingdom. TEL 44-1235-828600, FAX 44-1235-829000, info@tandf.co.uk, http://www.tandf.co.uk/journals/titles/00958972.asp. Eds. Jim D Atwood, Peter A Williams. **Subscr. to:** Journals Customer Service, Rankine Rd, Basingstoke, Hants RG24 8PR, United Kingdom. TEL 44-1256-813000, FAX 44-1256-330245, enquiry@tandf.co.uk.

540 GBR ISSN 1745-8080
▼ **JOURNAL OF EXPERIMENTAL NANOSCIENCE.** Text in English. forthcoming 2006. q. GBP 175, USD 280 combined subscription to institutions print & online eds. (effective 2006). **Document type:** *Journal, Academic/Scholarly.* **Description:** Provides a showcase for advances in the experimental sciences underlying nanotechnology and nanomaterials.
Related titles: Online - full content ed.: ISSN 1745-8099. forthcoming 2006.
Published by: Taylor & Francis Ltd (Subsidiary of: Taylor & Francis Group), 4 Park Sq, Milton Park, Abingdon, OX14 4RN, United Kingdom. TEL 44-1235-828600, FAX 44-1235-829000, info@tandf.co.uk, http://www.tandf.co.uk/journals/titles/17458080.asp. Eds. Francesco Stellacci, Kwong-Yu Chan, Dr. Molly Stevens.

JOURNAL OF FLUORESCENCE. see *CHEMISTRY—Inorganic Chemistry*

JOURNAL OF FOOD COMPOSITION AND ANALYSIS. see *FOOD AND FOOD INDUSTRIES*

JOURNAL OF INDUSTRIAL TEXTILES. see *TEXTILE INDUSTRIES AND FABRICS*

C

▼ new title ➤ refereed ✶ unverified ♦ full entry avail.

540 USA ISSN 1082-6076
QD79.C454 CODEN: JLCTFC
➤ **JOURNAL OF LIQUID CHROMATOGRAPHY & RELATED TECHNOLOGIES.** Text in English. 1978. 20/yr. GBP 2,247, USD 3,708 combined subscription to institutions print & online eds. (effective 2006). adv. charts; illus. index. back issues avail.; reprint service avail. from PSC. **Document type:** *Journal, Academic/Scholarly.* **Description:** Publishes a selection of critical papers dealing with analytical, preparative and process-scale liquid chromatography of all types and technologies.
Formerly (until 1996): Journal of Liquid Chromatography (0148-3919)
Related titles: Microform ed.: (from RPI); Online - full text ed.: ISSN 1520-572X. GBP 2,135, USD 3,523 (effective 2006) (from EBSCO Publishing, O C L C Online Computer Library Center, Inc., Swets Information Services).
Indexed: ABIPC, ASCA, ASFA, AbHyg, AgBio, Agr, AgrForAb, AnalAb, BIOBASE, BIOSIS Prev, BibAg, BiolAb, C&ISA, CCI, CIN, CPA, ChemAb, ChemTitl, ChromAb, CurCont, DSA, E&CAJ, ESPM, EngInd, ExcerpMed, FCA, FPA, FS&TA, ForAb, HelmAb, HerbAb, HortAb, I&DA, IABS, ISMEC, ISR, IndVet, Inpharma, MSB, MSCI, MaizeAb, NemAb, NutrAb, OrnHort, PBA, PGrRegA, PHN&I, PN&I, PotatoAb, PoultAb, ProtozoAb, RA&MP, RCI, RM&VM, RPP, Reac, RefZh, RevApplEntom, RiceAb, S&F, SAA, SCI, SIA, SWRA, SeedAb, SolStAb, SoyAb, TDB, ToxAb, TriticAb, VITIS, VetBull, WeedAb.
—BLDSC (5010.510500), CASDDS, CINDOC, CISTI, Ei, GNLM, IDS, IE, Infotrieve, ingenta, Linda Hall. **CCC.**
Published by: Taylor & Francis Inc. (Subsidiary of: Taylor & Francis Group), 325 Chestnut St, Ste 800, Philadelphia, PA 19016. TEL 215-625-8900, 800-354-1420, FAX 215-625-8914, info@taylorandfrancis.com, http://www.tandf.co.uk/journals/titles/10826076.asp, http://www.taylorandfrancis.com. Ed. Dr. Jack Cazes. Adv. contact Sharon Moran. B&W page USD 600. Circ: 800.

C

➤ **JOURNAL OF LUMINESCENCE.** see *PHYSICS—Optics*

540 GBR ISSN 0959-9428
TA401 CODEN: JMACEP
➤ **JOURNAL OF MATERIALS CHEMISTRY.** Text in English. 1991. fortn. (weekly from 2005). GBP 1,991, USD 3,644 combined subscription print & online eds. (effective 2006). **Document type:** *Academic/Scholarly.* **Description:** Focuses on areas of materials chemistry associated with advanced technology.
Related titles: Microform ed.: (from PQC); Online - full text ed.: ISSN 1364-5501. GBP 1,792, USD 3,279 (effective 2006) (from EBSCO Publishing, O C L C Online Computer Library Center, Inc., Swets Information Services); ♦ Abridged ed.: Soft Matter. ISSN 1744-683X.
Indexed: ASCA, BrCerAb, C&ISA, CCI, CIN, CTE, CerAb, ChemAb, ChemTitl, CivEngAb, CorrAb, CurCont, E&CAJ, EMA, IAA, ISR, M&TEA, MBF, METADEX, MSB, MSCI, RAPRA, RCI, RefZh, SCI, SolStAb, WAA.
—BLDSC (5012.205000), CASDDS, CINDOC, CISTI, IDS, IE, Infotrieve, ingenta, Linda Hall. **CCC.**
Published by: Royal Society of Chemistry, Thomas Graham House, Science Park, Milton Rd, Cambridge, CB4 0WF, United Kingdom. TEL 44-1223-432360, FAX 44-1223-423623, materials@rsc.org, sales@rsc.org, advertising@rsc.org, http://www.rsc.org/Publishing/Journals/jm/index.asp. Ed. Dr. Graham McCann. **Subscr. to:** Portland Press Ltd., R S C Distribution Services, Commerce Way, Whitehall Industrial Estate, Colchester CO2 8HP, United Kingdom. TEL 44-1206-226050, FAX 44-1206-226055, sales@rscdistribution.org.

➤ **JOURNAL OF MATHEMATICAL CHEMISTRY.** see *MATHEMATICS*

➤ **JOURNAL OF MATHEMATICAL SCIENCES.** see *MATHEMATICS*

541.2 NLD ISSN 0022-2860
QD471 CODEN: JMOSB4
➤ **JOURNAL OF MOLECULAR STRUCTURE.** Text in English, French, German. 1967. 66/yr. EUR 6,749 in Europe to institutions; JPY 895,600 in Japan to institutions; USD 7,549 to institutions except Europe and Japan (effective 2006). adv. bk.rev. charts; illus. **Document type:** *Journal, Academic/Scholarly.* **Description:** Provides new information on molecular structure, regardless of the physical method or methods used in the study.
Related titles: Microform ed.: (from PQC); Online - full text ed.: (from EBSCO Publishing, Gale Group, IngentaConnect, ScienceDirect, Swets Information Services); ♦ Supplement(s): Journal of Molecular Structure: THEOCHEM. ISSN 0166-1280.
Indexed: ASCA, BIOBASE, BullT&T, CCI, Cadscan, ChemAb, ChemInfo, ChemTitl, CurCont, IABS, ISR, Inspec, LeadAb, MSB, MSCI, PhysBer, RCI, RefZh, SCI, Zincscan.
—BLDSC (5020.800000), AskIEEE, CASDDS, CISTI, Ei, IDS, IE, Infotrieve, ingenta, Linda Hall. **CCC.**
Published by: Elsevier BV (Subsidiary of: Elsevier Science & Technology), Radarweg 29, Amsterdam, 1043 NX, Netherlands. TEL 31-20-4853911, FAX 31-20-4852457, nlinfo-f@elsevier.nl, http://www.elsevier.com/locate/molstruc, http://www.elsevier.nl. Eds. A J Barnes, J Laane.

541.2 CHN
JOURNAL OF MOLECULAR STRUCTURE. Text in English. 1985. q. USD 218 (effective 1997).
Published by: Chinese Chemical Society/Zhongguo Huaxuehui, PO Box 2709, Beijing, 100080, China. TEL 86-10-6256-8157, FAX 86-10-6256-8157, qiuxb@infoc3.icas.cn.

540 NLD ISSN 0166-1280
QD471 CODEN: THEODJ
➤ **JOURNAL OF MOLECULAR STRUCTURE: THEOCHEM.** Text in English, French, German. 1981. 72/yr. EUR 7,558 in Europe to institutions; JPY 1,004,400 in Japan to institutions; USD 8,456 elsewhere to institutions (effective 2006). back issues avail. **Document type:** *Journal, Academic/Scholarly.* **Description:** For chemical physicists, chemists, and biochemists concerned with the application of theoretical methods for the resolution of practical chemical problems.
Formerly: Theochem
Related titles: Microform ed.: (from PQC); Online - full text ed.: (from EBSCO Publishing, Gale Group, IngentaConnect, ScienceDirect, Swets Information Services); ♦ Supplement to: Journal of Molecular Structure. ISSN 0022-2860.
Indexed: ASFA, CCI, CIN, CMCI, ChemAb, ChemInfo, ChemTitl, CurCont, ISR, Inspec, MSB, MSCI, RCI, RefZh, SCI.
—AskIEEE, CASDDS, CISTI, IDS, IE, Infotrieve. **CCC.**
Published by: Elsevier BV (Subsidiary of: Elsevier Science & Technology), Radarweg 29, Amsterdam, 1043 NX, Netherlands. TEL 31-20-4853911, FAX 31-20-4852457, nlinfo-f@elsevier.nl, http://www.elsevier.com/locate/theochem, http://www.elsevier.nl. Eds. Dr. C E Dykstra, J. L. Rivail.

➤ **JOURNAL OF NANOSCIENCE AND NANOTECHNOLOGY.** see *PHYSICS*

➤ **JOURNAL OF NATURAL SCIENCES AND MATHEMATICS.** see *SCIENCES: COMPREHENSIVE WORKS*

➤ **JOURNAL OF NON-CRYSTALLINE SOLIDS.** see *PHYSICS*

➤ **JOURNAL OF OIL PALM RESEARCH.** see *AGRICULTURE*

➤ **JOURNAL OF OLEO SCIENCE.** see *ENGINEERING—Chemical Engineering*

541 USA ISSN 0047-2689
Q199 CODEN: JPCRBU
➤ **JOURNAL OF PHYSICAL AND CHEMICAL REFERENCE DATA.** Text in English. 1972. 4/yr. USD 795 combined subscription domestic; USD 815 combined subscription in Canada, Mexico, Central and South America and Caribbean; USD 825 combined subscription in Europe, Asia, Middle East, Africa and Oceania (effective 2005); print & online eds.. charts; illus. index. back issues avail.; reprints avail. **Document type:** *Journal, Academic/Scholarly.* **Description:** Presents compilations of critically evaluated data on physical and chemical properties.
Related titles: CD-ROM ed.: ISSN 1546-5969; Microfiche ed.: (from AIP); Microfilm ed.: (from AIP); Online - full text ed.: ISSN 1529-7845. USD 595 in USA, Canada, Mexico, Central and South America, Caribbean, Europe, Asia, Middle East, Africa and Oceania (effective 2003) (from EBSCO Publishing, Swets Information Services); ♦ Supplement(s): Journal of Physical and Chemical Reference Data. Monograph. ISSN 1063-0651.
Indexed: AS&TI, ASCA, ApMecR, BullT&T, CCI, CEABA, CIN, CPI, Cadscan, ChemAb, ChemTitl, CurCont, GPAA, INIS AtomInd, ISR, Inspec, LeadAb, MSB, PhysBer, RCI, RefZh, S&F, SPINweb, Zincscan.
—BLDSC (5035.700000), AskIEEE, CASDDS, CISTI, IDS, IE, Infotrieve, ingenta, Linda Hall. **CCC.**
Published by: National Institute of Standards and Technology (Subsidiary of: U.S. Department of Commerce), 100 bureau Dr, Stop 2500, Gaithersburg, MD 20899-2500. jpcrd@email.nist.gov, inquiries@nist.gov, http://scitation.aip.org/jpcrd/, http://www.nist.gov. Eds. Malcolm Chase Jr., Robert L Watters. Circ: 220. **Subscr. to:** American Institute of Physics, PO Box 503284, St Louis, MO 63150-3284. TEL 800-344-6902, subs@aip.org, http://librarians.aip.org. **Co-sponsor:** American Chemical Society.

541 USA ISSN 1063-0651
CODEN: JPCMEI
JOURNAL OF PHYSICAL AND CHEMICAL REFERENCE DATA. MONOGRAPH. Text in English. 1989. irreg. price varies.
Related titles: ♦ Supplement to: Journal of Physical and Chemical Reference Data. ISSN 0047-2689.
Indexed: CIN, ChemAb, ChemTitl.
—BLDSC (5035.705000), CASDDS, CISTI, IE. **CCC.**
Published by: American Institute of Physics, 1 Physics Ellipse, College Park, MD 20740-3843. TEL 301-209-3100, FAX 301-209-0843, aipinfo@aip.org, http://www.aip.org.
Co-sponsors: U.S. National Institute for Standards and Technology; American Chemical Society.

JOURNAL OF PHYSICS AND CHEMISTRY OF SOLIDS. see *PHYSICS*

540 FRA ISSN 1088-4246
QD441 CODEN: JPPHFZ
➤ **JOURNAL OF PORPHYRINS AND PHTHALOCYANINES.** Text in English. 1997. 8/yr. EUR 175.49, USD 180 to individuals; EUR 438.72, USD 450 to institutions; EUR 126.74, USD 130 to members (effective 2003). adv. **Document type:** *Journal, Academic/Scholarly.* **Description:** Provides the means for researchers, scientists and engineers interested in exploring the applications of these materials, to publish original research papers and short communications.
Related titles: Online - full text ed.: ISSN 1099-1409 (from EBSCO Publishing, Swets Information Services, Wiley InterScience).
Indexed: CCI, CurCont, ISR, MSB, RefZh, SCI.
—BLDSC (5041.146800), CASDDS, CISTI, IDS, IE, Infotrieve, ingenta. **CCC.**
Published by: Society of Porphyrins & Phthalocyanines, Universite de Bourgogne - Faculte des Sciences Gabriel, LIMSAG (UMR 5633), 6 boulevard Gabriel, Dijon, 21000, France. TEL 33-3-80-39-61-18, FAX 33-3-80-39-68-39, jpp@u-bourgogne.fr, http://www.u-bourgogne.fr/jpp/. Ed. Karl M Karl. adv.: B&W page GBP 650, color page GBP 1,550; trim 210 x 297.

➤ **JOURNAL OF PYROTECHNICS.** see *ENGINEERING—Chemical Engineering*

541.2 RUS ISSN 0022-4766
QD1 CODEN: JSTCAM
➤ **JOURNAL OF STRUCTURAL CHEMISTRY.** Text in English. 1960. 7/yr. EUR 3,215, USD 3,275, GBP 1,938 combined subscription to institutions print & online eds. (effective 2005). back issues avail. **Document type:** *Journal, Academic/Scholarly.* **Description:** Features papers on all aspects of theoretical and practical structural chemistry, with emphasis on new physical techniques and methods. Includes studies on the structure of organic and inorganic compounds in all phases.
Related titles: Microfilm ed.: (from PQC); Online - full text ed.: ISSN 1573-8779 (from EBSCO Publishing, Gale Group, IngentaConnect, Kluwer Online, O C L C Online Computer Library Center, Inc., Springer LINK, Swets Information Services); ♦ Russian ed.: Zhurnal Strukturnoi Khimii. ISSN 0136-7463.
Indexed: ASCA, BibLing, CCI, ChemAb, ChemTitl, CurCont, EnerRA, EngInd, ISR, Inspec, MSB, MSCI, NPU, RCI, SCI.
—BLDSC (0415.360000), AskIEEE, CASDDS, CISTI, Ei, IDS, IE, Infotrieve, ingenta. **CCC.**
Published by: (Rossiiskaya Akademiya Nauk/Russian Academy of Sciences), M A I K Nauka - Interperiodica, Profsoyuznaya ul 90, Moscow, 117997, Russian Federation. TEL 7-095-3347420, FAX 7-095-3360666, compmg@maik.ru, http://www.che.nsk.su/jsc_eng/, http://www.maik.ru. Ed. L N Mazalov. **Subscr. to:** Springer-Verlag Dordrecht, Journals Department, PO Box 322, Dordrecht, Netherlands. TEL 31-78-6576392, FAX 31-78-6576474.

540 GBR ISSN 1741-5993
▼ ➤ **JOURNAL OF SULFUR CHEMISTRY.** Text in English. 2004. bi-m. GBP 1,626, USD 2,429 combined subscription to institutions print & online eds. (effective 2006). **Document type:** *Journal, Academic/Scholarly.* **Description:** Publishes reviews, full papers, and communications in the following areas: organic and inorganic chemistry, industrial chemistry, materials and polymer chemistry, biological chemistry and interdisciplinary studies directly related to sulfur science.
Formed by the merger of (1982-2004): Sulfur Letters (0278-6117); (1980-2004): Sulfur Reports (0196-1772)
Related titles: Online - full text ed.: ISSN 1741-6000. GBP 1,545, USD 2,308 to institutions (effective 2006) (from EBSCO Publishing).
—BLDSC (5067.107500), CISTI, IE.
Published by: Taylor & Francis Ltd (Subsidiary of: Taylor & Francis Group), 4 Park Sq, Milton Park, Abingdon, OX14 4RN, United Kingdom. TEL 44-1235-828600, FAX 44-1235-829000, info@tandf.co.uk, http://www.tandf.co.uk/journals/titles/17415993.asp. Ed. Adrian L Schwan. **Subscr. to:** Journals Customer Service, Rankine Rd, Basingstoke, Hants RG24 8PR, United Kingdom. TEL 44-1256-813000, FAX 44-1256-330245, enquiry@tandf.co.uk.

540 NLD ISSN 1472-7862
QD875 CODEN: JSCOC9
JOURNAL OF SUPRAMOLECULAR CHEMISTRY. Text in English. 2001. bi-m. EUR 435 in Europe to institutions; JPY 57,800 in Japan to institutions; USD 472 elsewhere to institutions (effective 2003). **Document type:** *Journal, Academic/Scholarly.* **Description:** Aims at producing in-depth coverage of all disciplines and sub-disciplines related to the dynamic and widely expanding field of supramolecular chemistry.
Related titles: Online - full text ed.: (from EBSCO Publishing, Gale Group, IngentaConnect, ScienceDirect, Swets Information Services).
Indexed: ChemAb, RefZh.
—BLDSC (5067.290000), IE, ingenta.
Published by: Elsevier BV (Subsidiary of: Elsevier Science & Technology), Radarweg 29, Amsterdam, 1043 NX, Netherlands. TEL 31-20-4853911, FAX 31-20-4852457, nlinfo-f@elsevier.nl, http://www.elsevier.com/locate/jsupra, http://www.elsevier.nl. Eds. Dr. G W Gokel, Dr. J L Atwood.

JOURNAL OF SYNTHETIC LUBRICATION; research, development and application of synthetic lubricants and functional fluids. see *PETROLEUM AND GAS*

540 546 GBR ISSN 0260-8847
JOURNAL OF SYNTHETIC METHODS. Text in English. 1942. m.
Formerly (until 1978): C R D S Abstracts Journal
Related titles: Online - full text ed.: 1942.
Published by: Derwent Information (Subsidiary of: Thomson Corporation), 14 Great Queen St., London, WC2B 5DF, United Kingdom. TEL 44-20-73442800, FAX 44-20-73442900, custserv@derwent.co.uk, http://www.derwent.com. **U.S. subscr. to:** Derwent Information, 1725 Duke St, Ste 250, Alexandria, VA 22314. TEL 800-337-9368, custserv@derwentus.com.

540 IND ISSN 0971-6408
JOURNAL OF TEACHING AND RESEARCH IN CHEMISTRY; an international journal. Text in English. 1994. q. INR 100, USD 20 (effective 2000); includes membership. **Document type:** *Academic/Scholarly.*
Indexed: ChemTitl.
—BLDSC (5068.285580), IE, ingenta.
Published by: Utkal University, Department of Chemistry, Bhubaneswar, Orissa 751 004, India. Eds. B C Singh, U N Dash. Pub. R C Samanta Roy.

540 USA ISSN 1541-6003
QD1 CODEN: JUCRBV
JOURNAL OF UNDERGRADUATE CHEMISTRY RESEARCH. Text in English. 2002. q. USD 50 domestic to individuals; USD 120 domestic to institutions; USD 150 foreign (effective 2004).
—BLDSC (5071.511000).
Published by: Virginia Military Institute, Chemistry Department, 300 Science Bldg., Lexington, VA 24450. TEL 540-464-7244, FAX 540-464-7261, http://academics.vmi.edu/chemistry/Jucr/main.htm, http://academics.vmi.edu/Default.asp?dept=CHEM. Ed. Daniel Y. Pharr.

540 USA ISSN 0277-3813
TS932 CODEN: JWCTDJ
➤ **JOURNAL OF WOOD CHEMISTRY AND TECHNOLOGY.** Text in English. 1981. q. GBP 924, USD 1,526 combined subscription to institutions print & online eds. (effective 2006). reprint service avail. from PSC. **Document type:** *Journal, Academic/Scholarly.* **Description:** Focuses exclusively on the chemistry of wood, wood components, and wood products.
Related titles: Microform ed.: (from RPI); Online - full text ed.: ISSN 1532-2319. GBP 878, USD 1,450 to institutions (effective 2006) (from EBSCO Publishing, O C L C Online Computer Library Center, Inc., Swets Information Services).
Indexed: ABIPC, ASCA, Agr, AgrForAb, BibAg, C&ISA, CCI, CIN, CPA, ChemAb, ChemTitl, CurCont, E&CAJ, EngInd, FCA, FPA, ForAb, HortAb, ISR, MSCI, P&BA, PBA, RA&MP, RefZh, RiceAb, SCI, SIA, SolStAb, TriticAb.
—BLDSC (5072.635500), CASDDS, CISTI, Ei, IDS, IE, Infotrieve, ingenta, Linda Hall. **CCC.**
Published by: Taylor & Francis Inc. (Subsidiary of: Taylor & Francis Group), 325 Chestnut St, Ste 800, Philadelphia, PA 19016. TEL 215-625-8900, 800-354-1420, FAX 215-625-2940, info@taylorandfrancis.com, http://www.tandf.co.uk/journals/titles/02773813.asp, http://www.taylorandfrancis.com. Ed. Leland R Schroeder. Circ: 300.

540 JPN ISSN 0451-1964
TP1 CODEN: KAKYAU
KAGAKU (KYOTO)/CHEMISTRY. Text in Japanese. 1946. m. JPY 800 per issue (effective 2003). adv. **Document type:** *Academic/Scholarly.*
Related titles: ◆ Supplement(s): Kagaku. Zokan. ISSN 0368-5470.
Indexed: ChemAb, ChemTitl, JPI, MSB.
—CASDDS, CISTI, Linda Hall.
Published by: Kagaku Dojin Publishing Co., Inc., Yanaginobanba-Nishiiru, Bukkoji-Dori, Shimogyo-Ku, Kyoto, 600-8074, Japan. TEL 81-75-352-3373, FAX 81-75-351-8301, webmaster@kagakudojin.co.jp, http://www.kagakudojin.co.jp. Ed. Yasuo Matsui. Pub. Ryosuke Sone. R&P Hisashi Hirabayashi. Adv. contact Takahiro Kato.

660 JPN
KAGAKU KOGYO NIPPO/CHEMICAL DAILY. Text in Japanese. 1937. d. JPY 9,990 per month (effective 2005). adv. **Document type:** *Newspaper, Trade.*
Indexed: B&I, ChemAb.
Published by: Chemical Daily Co. Ltd., 16-8, Nihonbashi-Hamacho 3-Chome, Chuo-ku, Tokyo, 103-8485, Japan. TEL 81-3-36637931, FAX 81-3-36637275, subsales@chemicaldaily.co.jp, http://www.chemicaldaily.co.jp/. Circ: 130,000.

660 540 JPN ISSN 0022-7684
CODEN: KAKTAF
KAGAKU TO KOGYO (TOKYO)/CHEMISTRY AND CHEMICAL INDUSTRY. Text in Japanese. 1948. m. free to members. bibl. reprint service avail. from PQC. **Document type:** *Journal, Academic/Scholarly.*
Indexed: ChemAb, ChemTitl, JTA, RefZh.
—CASDDS, CISTI, Linda Hall. **CCC.**
Published by: Chemical Society of Japan/Nippon Kagakukai, 1-5, Kanda-Surugadai 1-Chome, Chiyoda-ku, Tokyo, 101-0062, Japan. TEL 81-3-32926169, FAX 81-3-32926317, info@chemistry.or.jp, http://www.chemistry.or.jp/journals/kakou/. Circ: 33,000. **Subscr. to:** Membership Division, 1,Kanda-Surugadai1-Chome, Chiyoda-ku, Tokyo 101-8307, Japan. TEL 81-3-32926169, FAX 81-3-32926317.

540.7 JPN
CODEN: XIGXE6
KAGAKU TO KYOIKU/CHEMICAL EDUCATION. Text in Japanese. 1952. m. JPY 5,400 to members (effective 2005). **Document type:** *Journal, Academic/Scholarly.*
Former titles: Kagaku Kyoiku (0386-2151); Kagaku Kyoiku Shimpojumu
Indexed: CIN, ChemAb, ChemTitl, RefZh.
—CASDDS. **CCC.**
Published by: Chemical Society of Japan/Nippon Kagakukai, 1-5, Kanda-Surugadai 1-Chome, Chiyoda-ku, Tokyo, 101-0062, Japan. TEL 81-3-32926164, FAX 81-3-32926318, kyoiku@chemistry.or.jp, info@chemistry.or.jp, http://www.chemistry.or.jp/journals/chem-edu/index.html. Ed. Yoshito Takeuchi. Circ: 5,400.

540 JPN ISSN 0368-5470
CODEN: KGZKA3
KAGAKU. ZOKAN/CHEMISTRY, EXTRA NUMBER. Text in Japanese. 1956. irreg. JPY 3,800 per issue (effective 2000). adv. **Document type:** *Academic/Scholarly.*
Related titles: ◆ Supplement to: Kagaku (Kyoto). ISSN 0451-1964.
Indexed: CIN, ChemAb, ChemTitl, JPI.
—CASDDS, CISTI.
Published by: Kagaku Dojin Publishing Co., Inc., Yanaginobanba-Nishiiru, Bukkoji-Dori, Shimogyo-Ku, Kyoto, 600-8074, Japan. TEL 81-75-352-3373, webmaster@kagakudojin.co.jp, http://www.kagakudojin.co.jp. Ed. Yuko Taira. Pub. Ryosuke Sone. R&P Hisashi Hirabayashi. Adv. contact Takahiro Kato.

540 JPN ISSN 0386-9512
QD11 CODEN: KAKEE8
KAGAKUSHU KENKYU (TOKYO, 1974)/JAPANESE SOCIETY FOR THE HISTORY OF CHEMISTRY. JOURNAL. Text in Japanese; Summaries in English. 1974. 4/yr. JPY 2,000 per issue. **Document type:** *Journal, Academic/Scholarly.*
Indexed: ChemAb, JPI.
—BLDSC (4809.447000), CASDDS. **CCC.**
Published by: Kagakushi Gakkai/Japanese Society for the History of Chemistry, c/o Prof. Makoto Ohno, Aichi Prefectural University, Faculty of Foreign Studies, Kumabari, Nagakute, Aichi, 480-1198, Japan. yht01511@nifty.ne.jp, http://members.jcom.home.ne.jp/kagakushi/Table_Content.html, http://members.jcom.home.ne.jp/kagakushi/index.html. **Dist. overseas by:** Maruzen Co., Ltd., Import & Export Dept, PO Box 5050, Tokyo International, Tokyo 100-3191, Japan.

KAIYO KAGAKU KENKYU/RESEARCH INSTITUTE OF OCEANOCHEMISTRY. TRANSACTIONS. see *EARTH SCIENCES—Oceanography*

540 JPN ISSN 0917-2408
CODEN: KKAGEY
KANKYO KAGAKU/JOURNAL OF ENVIRONMENTAL CHEMISTRY. Text in English, Japanese. 1991. q. JPY 4,000 per issue.
Indexed: ChemAb, ChemTitl, FS&TA, MSB.
—BLDSC (4979.359500), CASDDS.
Published by: Kankyo Kagaku Kenkyukai/Japan Society for Environmental Chemistry, Kokuritsu Kankyo Kenkyujo Kaggaku Kankyobu, 16-2 Onogawa, Tsukuba-shi, Ibaraki-ken 305-0053, Japan.

540 JPN
KAO INSTITUTE FOR FUNDAMENTAL RESEARCH. BULLETIN. Text in English. 1985. a. **Document type:** *Bulletin.*
Published by: Kao Corporation, Kao Institute for Fundamental Research, 2606 Akabane, Haga-gun, Ichikai-machi, Tochigi-ken 321-3426, Japan.

KAUCHUK I REZINA. see *RUBBER*

540 KAZ ISSN 1025-9341
QD1 CODEN: IMSKFR
KAZAKSTAN RESPUBLIKASY ULTTYK GYLYM AKADEMIASYNYN HABARLARY. SERIYA KHIMICHESKAYA/NATSIONALNAYA AKADEMIYA NAUK RESPUBLIKI KAZAKHSTAN. IZVESTIYA. SERIYA KHIMICHESKAYA. Text in Russian, Kazakh. 1947. bi-m. charts. index. **Document type:** *Journal, Academic/Scholarly.*
Formerly (until 1992): Akademiya Nauk Kazakhskoi S.S.R. Izvestiya. Seriya Khimicheskaya (0002-3205)
Indexed: AnalAb, ChemAb, INIS AtomInd, MSB.
—CASDDS, CISTI, Linda Hall. **CCC.**
Published by: (Kazakstan Respublikasy Ulttyk Gylym Akademiasy/National Academy of Sciences of the Republic of Kazakhstan), Gylym, Pushkina 111-113, Almaty, 480100, Kazakstan. TEL 3272-611877. Ed. E E Ergozhin. **Subscr. to:** G.R. Kondubayeva.

338.4 660 FIN ISSN 0355-1628
TP1 CODEN: KMKMAA
KEMIA - KEMI/FINNISH CHEMICAL JOURNAL. Text in Finnish, Swedish; Summaries in English. 1973. 9/yr. EUR 73 domestic; EUR 78 in Nordic countries; EUR 118 elsewhere (effective 2005). adv. bk.rev. abstr.; charts; illus.; mkt.; pat.; stat.; tr.lit.; tr.mk. index. reprint service avail. from PQC,ISI. **Document type:** *Magazine, Trade.*
Formed by the merger of (1965-1973): Kemian Teollisuus (0022-9822); Which was formerly (1948-1965): Teknillisen Kemian Aikakausle (0371-8328); (1931-1973): Suomen Kemistilehti A (0371-4098); Supersedes in part (1916-1973): Finska Kemisamfundet. Meddelanden (0015-2498)
Related titles: Online - full text ed.
Indexed: CBNB, CBTA, CEA, CEABA, ChemAb, ChemTitl, DSA, FS&TA, INIS AtomInd, LHB, P&BA, RefZh, S&F, TCEA.
—BLDSC (5089.263500), CASDDS, CISTI, Ei, IE, Infotrieve, ingenta, Linda Hall.
Published by: (Suomen Kemian Seura/Association of Finnish Chemical Societies), Kempulssi Oy, Mariankatu 26 B 9, Helsinki, 00170, Finland. TEL 358-9-6220903, FAX 358-9-62209337, toimitus@kemia-lehti.fi, http://www.kemia-lehti.fi. Eds. Veikko Antila TEL 358-9-62209333, Leena Laitinen TEL 358-9-62209331. Adv. contact Sauli Ilola TEL 358-9-62209335. B&W page EUR 1,700, color page EUR 2,600; 210 x 297. Circ: 5,700. **Co-sponsor:** Chemical Industry Federation of Finland.

540 HUN ISSN 0075-5397
QD1 CODEN: KUERDK
A KEMIA UJABB EREDMENYEI. Text in Hungarian. 1970. irreg., latest vol.95, 2006. price varies. back issues avail. **Document type:** *Monographic series, Academic/Scholarly.*
Indexed: CIN, ChemAb, ChemTitl.
—CASDDS.
Published by: Akademiai Kiado Rt. (Subsidiary of: Wolters Kluwer N.V.), Prielle Kornelia U. 19, Budapest, 1117, Hungary. TEL 36-1-4648282, FAX 36-1-4648221, journals@akkrt.hu, http://www.akkrt.hu. Ed. Bela Csakvari.

540 SWE
KEMIKALIER. Text in Swedish. 1976. biennial. SEK 160 (effective 2001). **Document type:** *Journal, Trade.*
Published by: Plast- och Kemibranscherna, Box 5501, Stockholm, 114 85, Sweden. FAX 46-8-411-45-26, info@plast-kemi.se, http://www.plast-kemi.se.

540 FIN ISSN 0356-7818
KEMISTIN KALENTERI. Text in Finnish, Swedish. 1947. a. adv.
Published by: Luonnontieteiden Akateemisten Liitto/Finnish Union of Experts in Science, Rautatielaeisenkatu 6, Helsinki, 00520, Finland. Adv. contact Irmeli Puntari. Circ: 3,500.

540 SWE ISSN 1650-0725
QD1 CODEN: KETIAL
KEMIVAERLDEN. Text in Swedish. 1993. 12/yr. SEK 1,029 domestic; SEK 1,264 in Scandinavia; SEK 1,274 elsewhere (effective 2003). adv. bk.rev. abstr.; bibl.; charts; illus.; stat. index. **Document type:** *Magazine, Trade.*
Incorporates (in 2000): Kemisk Tidskrift (1650-0733); Supersedes in part (in 2000): Kemisk Tidskrift - Kemivaerlden (1104-2788); Which was formed by the merger of (1992-1993): Kemivaerlden (1102-6650); (1889-1993): Kemisk Tidskrift (0039-6605); Which was formerly (until 1969): Svensk Kemisk Tidskrift (0371-0742); Which incorporated (1985-19??): Bioteknik & Biokemi (0282-9509)
Related titles: Online - full text ed.
Indexed: BiolAb, CBNB, CEABA, CISA, CSNB, ChemAb, ChemInfo, ChemTitl, CurCont, DSA, EngInd, FS&TA, LHB, P&BA.
—BLDSC (5089.358000), CASDDS, CISTI, Ei, IE, ingenta, Linda Hall.
Published by: (Svenska Kemistsamfundet), Mentor Online AB, Tryffelslingan 10, PO Box 72001, Lidingoe, 18172, Sweden. TEL 46-8-6704100, FAX 46-8-6616455, http://www3.mentoronline.se/chemical/kemivarlden. Ed., Pub. Sverker Nyman TEL 46-8-6704270. Adv. contact Stephan Martins TEL 46-8-6704185. B&W page SEK 20,960, color page SEK 26,850; 210 x 297. Circ: 11,500. **Co-sponsor:** Svenska Kemiingenjoerers Riksfoerening.

KEMIVAERLDEN BIOTECH. see *BIOLOGY—Biotechnology*

660 RUS
➤ **KHIMICHESKAYA TEKHNOLOGIYA/CHEMICAL TECHNOLOGY.** Text in Russian. 2000. m. USD 699 foreign (effective 2005). **Document type:** *Journal, Academic/Scholarly.* **Description:** Designed for for industrial production workers, research and design institutes, high school and college students. Brings technical information, analysis, teaching and production methods.
Published by: Nauka i Tekhnologii, Stromynskii per, 4/1, Moscow, 107076, Russian Federation. admin@nait.ru, http://www.nait.dacom.ru/journals/index.php?p_journal_id=1, http://www.nait.ru. Ed. A I Khol'kin. **Dist. by:** East View Information Services, 3020 Harbor Ln. N., Minneapolis, MN 55447. TEL 800-477-1005, FAX 800-800-3839, eastview@eastview.com, http://www.eastview.com.

➤ **KHIMIKO-FARMATSEVTICHESKII ZHURNAL/JOURNAL OF PHARMACEUTICAL CHEMISTRY.** see *PHARMACY AND PHARMACOLOGY*

C

540 BGR ISSN 0861-9255
KHIMIYA. Text in Bulgarian. 1992. bi-m. USD 36 foreign (effective 2002). **Document type:** *Journal, Academic/Scholarly.*
Indexed: RefZh.
—BLDSC (0393.649400).
Published by: Ministerstvo na Obrazovanieto i Naukata na Republika Bulgaria/Ministry of Education and Sciences of the Republic of Bulgaria, 125 Tzarigradsko Shosse Blvd., Bl. 5, PO Box 336, Sofia, 1113, Bulgaria. TEL 359-2-705298, http://www.webspawner.com/users/khimiyachemistry/, http://www.minedu.government.bg. **Dist. by:** Sofia Books, ul Silivria 16, Sofia 1404, Bulgaria. TEL 359-2-9586257, info@sofiabooks-bg.com, http://www.sofiabooks-bg.com.

660 363.7 BGR ISSN 1310-6716
KHIMIYA I INDUSTRIYA. Text in Bulgarian. 1922. s-a. EUR 220 in Europe; USD 220 elsewhere (effective 2005). bk.rev. Index. back issues avail. **Document type:** *Journal, Academic/Scholarly.* **Description:** Issues original research, new theoretical concepts and application and critical reviews in the science or industrial practice of all aspects of chemistry, chemical engineering, applied chemistry, environmental protection, improved and emerging technologies.
Related titles: ♦ English ed.: Bulgarian Chemistry and Industry. ISSN 1311-1663.
Indexed: RASB.
—BLDSC (0393.820000), CISTI.
Published by: (Suiuz na Bulgarskite Khimitsi/Union of Bulgarian Chemists), Scientific Bulgarian Communications, 7 Nezabravka St, PO Box 249, Sofia, 1113, Bulgaria. scibulcom@global.bg. Ed., Pub., Adv. contact Slavi Ivanov.

C

660 UKR ISSN 0204-3556
TD204 CODEN: KTVODL
KHIMIYA I TEKHNOLOHIYA VODY/CHEMISTRY AND TECHNOLOGY OF WATER; nauchno-teoreticheskii zhurnal. Text in Russian; Summaries in English, Russian. 1979. bi-m. USD 242 foreign (effective 2005). **Document type:** *Journal, Academic/Scholarly.* **Description:** Presents articles of theoretical and experimental nature on foundations of water purification and treatment technology, technological procedures of treatment and demineralization of water, natural and mineral waters, ecological and hygiene-related aspects of water purification and water treatment.
Related titles: ♦ English Translation: Journal of Water Chemistry and Technology. ISSN 1063-455X.
Indexed: ASFA, BrCerAb, C&ISA, CIN, CerAb, ChemAb, ChemTitl, CivEngAb, CorrAb, Djerelo, E&CAJ, EMA, ESPM, EngInd, INIS AtomInd, M&TEA, MBF, METADEX, MSB, RefZh, SIA, SolStAb, WAA.
—BLDSC (0393.846500), CASDDS, CISTI, East View, Linda Hall. **CCC.**
Published by: Natsional'na Akademiya Nauk Ukrainy, Instytut Koloyidnoi Khimii ta Khimii Vody, vul Akad Vernadskogo 42, Kyiv, 03680, Ukraine. TEL 380-44-4240196, FAX 380-44-4238224, honch@iccwc.kiev.ua. Ed. V V Goncharuk. **US dist. addr.:** East View Information Services, 3020 Harbor Ln. N., Minneapolis, MN 55447. TEL 763-550-0961, FAX 763-559-2931, eastview@eastview.com, http://www.eastview.com.

540 RUS CODEN: KHZHAZ
KHIMIYA I ZHIZN' - XXI VEK/CHEMISTRY AND LIFE - 21ST CENTURY. Text in Russian. 1965. m. USD 150 foreign (effective 2003). adv. bk.rev. **Description:** Covers a wide range of topics including all aspects of chemistry, biology, medical research. agroscience, food science and related fields.
Formerly: Khimiya i Zhizn' (0130-5972)
Related titles: Online - full text ed.
Indexed: ChemAb, IAA, RefZh.
—CASDDS, CISTI, East View, Linda Hall.
Published by: Kompaniya Khimiya i Zhizn'/Chemistry and Life, Moscow, 107005, Russian Federation. TEL 7-95-267-54-18, FAX 7-95-267-54-18, chelife@glas.apc.org, http://www.courier.com.ru./ch/index.html, http://www.aha.zu/~hj. R&P Strelnikova Lubov. Adv. contact Blagutina Vezonika. color page USD 500. Circ: 5,000. **Dist. by:** M K - Periodica, ul Gilyarovskogo 39, Moscow 129110, Russian Federation. TEL 7-095-2845008, FAX 7-095-2813798, info@periodicals.ru, http://www.mkniga.ru; **US dist. addr.:** East View Information Services, 3020 Harbor Ln. N., Minneapolis, MN 55447. TEL 612-550-0961.

KHIMIYA TVERDOGO TOPLIVA. see *ENGINEERING—Chemical Engineering*

540 UKR ISSN 1606-7304
KHIMIYA UKRAINY/UKRAINIAN CHEMISTRY. Text in Russian. m. UAK 100 per month domestic; USD 15 per month foreign (effective 2003). **Document type:** *Journal.*
Related titles: Online - full content ed.: ISSN 1606-7290. 2000. UAK 720 domestic; USD 120 foreign (effective 2003).
Indexed: RefZh.
Published by: Delovoi Mir/Business World, P.O. Box 127, Dnepropetrovsk, 49000, Ukraine. chemistry@business.dp.ua, http://www.business.dp.ua/chemr/xu.htm.

540 RUS ISSN 0869-8538
TP1 CODEN: KIURFI
KHIMIYA V INTERESAKH USTOICHIVOGO RAZVITIYA. Text in Russian; Summaries in English. 1963. 6/yr. RUR 2,210 for 6 mos. domestic; USD 480 foreign (effective 2005). bk.rev. illus. index. 110 p./no. 2 cols./p.; back issues avail. **Document type:** *Journal, Academic/Scholarly.*
Former titles (until 1993): Sibirskii Khimicheskii Zhurnal; (until 1990): Akademiya Nauk S.S.S.R. Sibirskoe Otdelenie. Izvestiya. Seriya Khimicheskikh Nauk (0002-3426)
Related titles: ♦ English ed.: Chemistry for Sustainable Development. ISSN 1023-8603.
Indexed: CCI, CEABA, CIN, Cadscan, ChemAb, ChemTitl, LeadAb, MSB, MSCI, RefZh, SCI, SIA, Zincscan.
—BLDSC (0394.220000), CASDDS, CISTI, East View, Linda Hall. **CCC.**
Published by: (Rossiiskaya Akademiya Nauk, Institut Khimii Tverdogo Tela i Mekhanokhimii/Russian Academy of Sciences, Institute of the Chemistry of Solid Matter and Mechanochemistry), Izdatel'stvo Sibirskogo Otdeleniya Rossiiskoi Akademii Nauk/Publishing House of the Russian Academy of Sciences, Siberian Branch, Morskoi pr 2, a/ya 187, Novosibirsk, 630090, Russian Federation. TEL 7-3832-300570, FAX 7-3832-333755, csd@ad-sbras.nsc.ru, phsb@ad-sbras.nsc.ru, http://www-psb.ad-sbras.nsc.ru/csdw.htm. Ed. Nikolai Lyakhov. Circ: 1,400. **Dist. by:** M K - Periodica, ul Gilyarovskogo 39, Moscow 129110, Russian Federation. TEL 7-095-2845008, FAX 7-095-2813798, info@periodicals.ru, http://www.mkniga.ru.

540 RUS ISSN 0368-5632
CODEN: KHSHAY
KHIMIYA V SHKOLE. Text in Russian. 7/yr. USD 63 foreign (effective 2000).
Indexed: RefZh.
—CASDDS, CISTI, East View.
Published by: Izdatel'stvo Shkola Press, Rustaveli ul 10-3, Moscow, 127254, Russian Federation. TEL 7-095-2198380, FAX 7-095-2195289. Ed. L S Levina. **US dist. addr.:** East View Information Services, 3020 Harbor Ln. N., Minneapolis, MN 55447. TEL 612-550-0961.

541 RUS ISSN 0023-1193
CODEN: KHVKAO
KHIMIYA VYSOKIKH ENERGII. Text in Russian; Summaries in English. 1967. bi-m. RUR 850 for 6 mos. domestic (effective 2004). **Document type:** *Journal, Academic/Scholarly.* **Description:** Publishes theoretical papers and reports on experimental studies in radiation chemistry, photochemistry, plasma chemistry, laser chemistry, and related areas.
Related titles: Online - full text ed.; ♦ English Translation: High Energy Chemistry. ISSN 0018-1439.
Indexed: ASCA, BPRC&P, CCI, ChemAb, CurCont, MSB, MSCI, RefZh.
—BLDSC (0393.700000), CASDDS, CINDOC, Ei, Linda Hall. **CCC.**
Published by: Izdatel'stvo Nauka, Profsoyuznaya ul 90, Moscow, 117864, Russian Federation. TEL 7-095-3347151, FAX 7-095-4202220, secret@naukaran.ru, http://www.maik.rssi.ru/journals/highen.htm, http://www.naukaran.ru.

540 JPN
KIKAN KAGAKU SOSETSU/SURVEY OF CHEMISTRY. QUARTERLY. Text in Japanese; Summaries in English, Japanese. 1973. q. JPY 5,040 (effective 1999).
Indexed: CIN, ChemAb, ChemTitl, JPI, MSB.
—BLDSC (5095.308960).
Published by: (Nippon Kagakkai/Chemical Society of Japan), Gakkai Shuppan Senta/Japan Scientific Societies Press, 6-2-10 Hongo Bunkyoku, Tokyo, 113-0033, Japan.

540 MYS ISSN 0126-9070
QD1 CODEN: KMIADZ
KIMIA*. Text in English. 1970. a. free to qualified personnel. adv. illus.
Indexed: ChemAb, INIS AtomInd.
—CASDDS.
Published by: Malaysian Institute of Chemistry, c/o Rubber Research Institute of Malaysia, 260 Jalan Ampang, Kuala Lumpur, 50450, Malaysia. Circ: 1,500.

540 PHL ISSN 0115-2130
CODEN: KIMIDH
➤ **KIMIKA.** Text in English. 1961. s-a. PHP 100 domestic; USD 15 foreign (effective 2003). adv. bk.rev. charts; illus. back issues avail. **Document type:** *Academic/Scholarly.* **Description:** Publishes original papers on chemical researches and chemical education, preliminary communications and reviews.
Formerly: Chemists' Quarterly (0045-6527)
Media: Duplicated (not offset).
Indexed: ChemAb, INIS AtomInd.
—CASDDS.
Published by: Kapisanang Kimika ng Pilipinas/Chemical Society of the Philippines, c/o Dr. Florian R del Mundo, Rm 1110 Institute of Chemistry, University of the Philippines, Diliman, Quezon City 1128, Philippines. kkp@info.com.ph, nsri@nicole.upd.edu.ph, http://www.info.com.ph/~pfcs2000/kimika.html, http://luff.latrobe.edu.au/~chejs/chemistry/kkp.html. Ed., R&P Fortunato Sevilla III. Adv. contact Florian Delmundo. B&W page PHP 3,000; 8 x 11. Circ: 750.

540 JPN ISSN 0916-4367
KISO KAGAKU KENKYUJO KOENKAI KOENSHU/PROCEEDINGS FOR THE I F C SYMPOSIUM. Text in English, Japanese. 1985. a. **Document type:** *Proceedings.*
Published by: Kiso Kagaku Kenkyujo/Institute for Fundamental Chemistry, 3-4 Takanonishibiraki-cho, Sakyo-ku, Kyoto-shi, 606-8103, Japan.

540 620 NOR ISSN 0023-1983
QD1 CODEN: KJEMAR
KJEMI. Text in Norwegian. 1913. 10/yr. (10/yr.). NOK 475 in Scandinavia; NOK 615 elsewhere (effective 2003). adv. bk.rev. bibl.; illus.; pat.; stat.; tr.lit. index. reprint service avail. from PQC. **Document type:** *Journal, Academic/Scholarly.* **Description:** Covers a wide area within the chemical field, from scientific works to operative projects and processes.
Former titles (until 1968): Tidsskrift for Kjemi, Bergvesen og Metallurgi (0040-7097); (until 1941): Tidsskrift for Kjemi og Bergvesen (0371-8697)
Related titles: Microform ed.: (from PQC); Online - full text ed.
Indexed: BrCerAb, C&ISA, CBNB, CerAb, ChemAb, ChemInfo, ChemTitl, CivEngAb, CorrAb, E&CAJ, EMA, EngInd, IAA, INIS AtomInd, M&TEA, MBF, METADEX, MSB, SolStAb, WAA.
—BLDSC (5098.430000), CASDDS, CISTI, Linda Hall. **CCC.**
Published by: (Norsk Kjemisk Selskap/Norwegian Chemical Society), Media Oslo As, Storgata 14, Postboks 151, Sentrum, Oslo, 0102, Norway. TEL 47-23-158500, FAX 47-22-171279, kjemi@online.no, http://www.kjemi.com. Ed., R&P Lars Ole Oerjasaeter TEL 47-23-158502. Adv. contact Turid Eidsvaag TEL 47-23-158504. B&W page NOK 1,850, color page NOK 3,950; trim 185 x 260. Circ: 6,677.

KLINISCHE CHEMIE; Mitteilungen. see *MEDICAL SCIENCES*

540 JPN ISSN 0389-0279
QD1 CODEN: KDRKDD
KOCHI UNIVERSITY. FACULTY OF SCIENCE. MEMOIRS. SERIES C, CHEMISTRY/KOCHI DAIGAKU RIGAKUBU KIYO. KAGAKU. Text in English. 1980. a.
Indexed: ChemAb.
—BLDSC (5597.834000), CISTI.
Published by: Kochi University, Faculty of Science/Kochi Daigaku Rigakubu, 5-1 Akebono-cho 2-chome, Kochi-shi, 780-8072, Japan.

KOLORISZTIKAI ERTESITO/COLORISTICAL REVIEW. see *ENGINEERING—Chemical Engineering*

KOMPASS PROFESSIONNEL. CHIMIE, PLASTIQUES, CAOUTCHOUC, PRODUITS MINERAUX. see *BUSINESS AND ECONOMICS—Trade And Industrial Directories*

541.224 RUS ISSN 0132-344X
QD474 CODEN: KOKHDC
➤ **KOORDINATSIONNAYA KHIMIYA.** Text in Russian. 1975. m. RUR 930 for 6 mos. domestic (effective 2004). back issues avail. **Document type:** *Journal, Academic/Scholarly.* **Description:** Explores all aspects of theoretical and experimental coordination chemistry, covering such areas as the synthesis, structure, properties, and quantum chemistry of coordination compounds; the kinetics and mechanisms of chemical reactions involving the formation of complex compunds; catalytic processes; and the development of practical new materials based on coordination compounds.
Related titles: Microfilm ed.: (from PQC); Online - full text ed.; ♦ English Translation: Russian Journal of Coordination Chemistry. ISSN 1070-3284.
Indexed: EngInd, INIS AtomInd, RefZh.
—CASDDS, CISTI, IDS, KNAW, Linda Hall. **CCC.**
Published by: (Rossiiskaya Akademiya Nauk/Russian Academy of Sciences), Izdatel'stvo Nauka, Profsoyuznaya ul 90, Moscow, 117864, Russian Federation. TEL 7-095-3347151, FAX 7-095-4202220, secret@naukaran.ru, http://www.maik.rssi.ru/cgi-bin/list.pl?page=kordkhim, http://www.naukaran.ru.

540 KOR ISSN 0253-2964
QD1 CODEN: BKCSDE
➤ **KOREAN CHEMICAL SOCIETY. BULLETIN.** Text in English. 1980. m. KRW 30,000 combined subscription domestic to members for Bulletin & Journal of Korean Chemical Society; USD 80 foreign to members; USD 130 foreign to non-members; USD 170 foreign to institutions (effective 2005). adv. 120 p./no.; **Document type:** *Journal, Academic/Scholarly.* **Description:** Contains leading research journal of the Korean chemical community, reach out chemical community worldwide through KCSNet, covering the entire chemistry and related fields.
Incorporates (1991-199?, vol.11): Korean Journal of Medicinal Chemistry (1225-0058)
Related titles: Online - full text ed.: ISSN 1229-5949. free (effective 2005).
Indexed: ASCA, CCI, CEABA, CIN, ChemAb, ChemInfo, ChemTitl, CurCont, INIS AtomInd, ISR, LHB, MSB, RCI, SCI.
—BLDSC (2600.359000), CISTI, IE, ingenta, Linda Hall.
Published by: Korean Chemical Society/Daehan Hwahak Hoe, 635-4 Yeoksam-dong, Kangnam-gu, Seoul, 135-703, Korea, S. TEL 82-2-34533781, FAX 82-2-34533785, kcschem@neon.kcsnet.or.kr, http://newjournal.kcsnet.or.kr/, http://www.kcsnet.or.kr. Ed. Su-moon Park. Circ: 3,000.

660 KOR ISSN 1017-2548
QD1 CODEN: JKCSEZ
➤ **KOREAN CHEMICAL SOCIETY. JOURNAL/DAEHAN HWAHAK HOE JEE.** Text in Korean; Text occasionally in English. 1949. s-m. KRW 30,000 combined subscription domestic to members for Bulletin & Journal of Korean Chemical Society; USD 50 foreign to members; USD 30 foreign to non-members; USD 70 foreign to institutions (effective 2005). adv. 110 p./no.; back issues avail. **Document type:** *Journal, Academic/Scholarly.* **Description:** Provides comprehensive coverage of chemistry and chemistry related subjects, including chemical education.
Related titles: Online - full text ed.: free (effective 2005).
Indexed: CIN, ChemAb, ChemTitl, EngInd, INIS AtomInd, MSB.
—BLDSC (4812.200000), CASDDS, CISTI, IE, ingenta, Linda Hall.
Published by: Korean Chemical Society/Daehan Hwahak Hoe, 635-4 Yeoksam-dong, Kangnam-gu, Seoul, 135-703, Korea, S. TEL 82-2-34533781, FAX 82-2-34533785, kcschem@neon.kcsnet.or.kr, http://newjournal.kcsnet.or.kr/, http://www.kcsnet.or.kr. Ed. Burm Kyong Jin TEL 82-032-4005492. Circ: 3,000.

➤ **KORROZIOS FIGYELO/CORROSION OBSERVER.** see *PAINTS AND PROTECTIVE COATINGS*

➤ **KUMAMOTO JOURNAL OF MATHEMATICS.** see *MATHEMATICS*

540 PRK
KWAHAKGWA KWAHAKGONEOP. Text in Korean. bi-m.
Published by: Korean Academy of Sciences, Hamhung Branch, Pyongyang, Korea, N.

KYUSHU DAIGAKU CHUO BUNSEKI SENTA HOKOKU/KYUSHU UNIVERSITY. CENTER OF ADVANCED INSTRUMENTAL ANALYSIS. REPORT. see *INSTRUMENTS*

KYUSHU DAIGAKU CHUO BUNSEKI SENTA NYUSU/KYUSHU UNIVERSITY. CENTER OF ADVANCED INSTRUMENTAL ANALYSIS. NEWS. see *INSTRUMENTS*

540 JPN ISSN 0085-2635
QD1 CODEN: MFKCAL
KYUSHU UNIVERSITY. FACULTY OF SCIENCE. MEMOIRS. SERIES C: CHEMISTRY/KYUSHU DAIGAKU RIGAKUBU KIYO C. KAGAKU. Text in English. 1948. a. per issue exchange basis.
Indexed: ChemAb, Inspec, JCT, JTA, MSB.
—AskIEEE, CASDDS, CISTI, Linda Hall.
Published by: Kyushu University, Faculty of Science, Department of Chemistry, 6-10-1 Hakozaki, Higashi-ku, Fukuoks City, 812-8581, Japan. TEL 81-92-6422521, FAX 81-92-6422522, http://www.scc.kyushu-u.ac.jp/index.html. Circ: 650.

660 GBR ISSN 1365-7623
LAB AFRICA. Text in English. 2/yr. GBP 40 (effective 2000).
Description: Covers the latest in laboratory equipment and chemicals.
Related titles: Special ed(s).: Lab Africa. Annual Buyers Guide.
Published by: International Labmate Ltd., Oak Court, Sandridge Park, Porters Wood, St Albans, Herts AL3 6PH, United Kingdom. TEL 44-1727-855574, FAX 44-1727-841694.

660 GBR ISSN 1355-8625
LAB ASIA. Text in English. 1994. 6/yr. GBP 45 (effective 2000).
Description: Covers the latest in laboratory equipment and chemicals.
Related titles: Special ed(s).: Lab Asia. Annual Buyers Guide.
Published by: International Labmate Ltd., Oak Court, Sandridge Park, Porters Wood, St Albans, Herts AL3 6PH, United Kingdom. TEL 44-1727-855574, FAX 44-1727-841694.

540 570 GBR ISSN 1473-0197
QD53 CODEN: LCAHAM
➤ **LAB ON A CHIP**; miniaturisation for chemistry and biology. Text in English. 2001 (Sept). 6/yr. (monthly from 2005). GBP 870, USD 1,592 combined subscription print & online eds. (effective 2006); subscr. includes Chemcial Technology. adv. **Document type:** *Journal, Academic/Scholarly.* **Description:** Examines miniaturisation research, technology and its applications in chemistry, biology, physics, electronics, clinical chemistry, fabrication, engineering and materials science, aiding communication and collaboration across disciplines.
Related titles: Online - full text ed.: ISSN 1473-0189. GBP 783, USD 1,432 (effective 2006) (from EBSCO Publishing, O C L C Online Computer Library Center, Inc., Swets Information Services); ♦ Supplement(s): Chemical Technology. ISSN 1744-1560.
Indexed: AnalAb, BIOSIS Prev, BiolAb, ChemAb, ExcerpMed, FS&TA, Inspec, MSB, RefZh.
—BLDSC (5137.730000), CISTI, IE, Infotrieve, ingenta, Linda Hall. **CCC.**
Published by: Royal Society of Chemistry, Thomas Graham House, Science Park, Milton Rd, Cambridge, CB4 0WF, United Kingdom. TEL 44-1223-432360, FAX 44-1223-425017, sales@rsc.rg, http://www.rsc.org/loc. adv.: B&W page GBP 685. **Dist. by:** Portland Press Ltd., R S C Distribution Services, Commerce Way, Whitehall Industrial Estate, Colchester CO2 8HP, United Kingdom. TEL 44-1206-226050, FAX 44-1206-226055, sales@rscdistribution.org.

540 CAN ISSN 1486-3197
LABORATORY FOCUS. Text in English. 1998. s-a. free domestic; USD 30 in United States; USD 100 elsewhere (effective 2003).
Related titles: Online - full text ed.; ♦ Supplement(s): Laboratory Focus (Gazette Edition). ISSN 1495-5660.
Published by: Promotive Communications, 4220 Steeles Ave, W Unit C-15, Woodbridge, ON L4L 3S8, Canada. TEL 905-264-2871, FAX 905-264-6265, promo@lab-focus.com, http://www.lab-focus.com/labfocus.html.

540 CAN ISSN 1495-5660
LABORATORY FOCUS (GAZETTE EDITION). Text in English. 1999. bi-m.
Formerly (until 1999): Laboratory Gazette (1495-5679)
Related titles: ♦ Supplement to: Laboratory Focus. ISSN 1486-3197.
Published by: Promotive Communications, 4220 Steeles Ave, W Unit C-15, Woodbridge, ON L4L 3S8, Canada. TEL 905-264-2871, FAX 905-264-6265, promo@lab-focus.com, http://www.lab-focus.com/.

540 USA ISSN 0748-4585
TP151
LANGE'S HANDBOOK OF CHEMISTRY. Text in English. 1934. irreg. USD 150 per issue (effective 2005).
Formerly (until 1973): Handbook of Chemistry (0190-4035)
Related titles: Online - full text ed.: ISSN 1539-2279.
Published by: McGraw-Hill Companies, Inc., 1221 Ave of the Americas, New York, NY 10020. TEL 212-512-2000, customer.service@mcgraw-hill.com, http://www.mcgraw-hill.com.

540 531 ARG ISSN 0327-0793
CODEN: LAARE8
➤ **LATIN AMERICAN APPLIED RESEARCH.** Text in English. 1988. q. USD 100 (effective 1999). adv. bk.rev. **Document type:** *Academic/Scholarly.*
Indexed: CEABA, CIN, ChemAb, ChemTitl, CurCont, INIS AtomInd, VITIS.
—CASDDS, CISTI, IE, Infotrieve, Linda Hall.
Published by: Plapiqui, Universidad Nacional del Sur (UNS) - Consejo Nacional de Investigaciones Cientificas y Tecnicas (CONICET), Casilla de Correo 717, Bahia Blanca, 8000, Argentina. TEL 54-291-486-1700, FAX 54-291-486-1600, TELEX 81758 PPINQ, laar@plapiqui.edu.ar, amolsen@criba.edu.ar. Ed. Dr. Jorge Moiola. R&P Dr. Jorge Moiola. Adv. contact Ana Maria Olsen. Circ: 400.

540 LVA ISSN 0868-8249
QD1 CODEN: LKZUE8
➤ **LATVIJAS KIMIJAS ZURNALS/LATVIAN JOURNAL OF CHEMISTRY.** Text in Latvian, English, Russian. 1961. bi-m. index. **Document type:** *Journal, Academic/Scholarly.* **Description:** Publishes experimental and theoretical papers covering areas of inorganic, physical, analytical, organic, bio-organic, polymer and environmental chemistry in Latvian, English and Russian as well as review papers and short communications - letters.
Formerly (until 1991): Akademiya Nauk Latviiskoi S.S.R. Izvestiya. Seriya Khimicheskaya (0002-3248)
Indexed: ABIPC, CIN, ChemAb, ChemTitl, EngInd, INIS AtomInd, MSB, RefZh.
—BLDSC (0095.410000), CASDDS, CISTI, IE, ingenta, KNAW, Linda Hall. **CCC.**
Published by: Riga Technical University, Institute of Inogranic Chemistry, 34, Miera St, Salaspils-1, Riga, Latvia. TEL 371-7-226032, FAX 371-7-800779, http://www.nki.lv/Eng/Journal.htm. Ed. T Millers.

540 ITA ISSN 1122-4967
LEADER FOR CHEMIST. Text in Italian. 1990. 10/yr. adv.
Address: Via Olmetto, 5, Milan, MI 20123, Italy. TEL 2-87-83-97, FAX 2-86-65-76. Ed. Genina Jacoboni.

LEBENSMITTEL- UND BIOTECHNOLOGIE; die oesterreichische Fachzeitschrift fuer Lebensmittelindustrie und -forschung. see *FOOD AND FOOD INDUSTRIES*

LEBENSMITTELCHEMIE; Zeitschrift des Lebensmittelchemischen Gesellschaft. see *FOOD AND FOOD INDUSTRIES*

540 USA ISSN 0342-4901
CODEN: LNCHDA
LECTURE NOTES IN CHEMISTRY. Text in English. 1976. irreg., latest vol.69, 1998. price varies. reprint service avail. from ISI. **Document type:** *Monographic series.*
Indexed: CCMJ, CIN, ChemAb, ChemTitl, Inspec.
—BLDSC (5180.184600), CASDDS, CISTI, ingenta. **CCC.**
Published by: Springer-Verlag New York, Inc. (Subsidiary of: Springer Science+Business Media), 233 Spring St, New York, NY 10013. TEL 212-460-1500, FAX 212-473-6272.

660 DEU ISSN 0024-2845
TP1101 CODEN: LIBOAM
LICHTBOGEN; Hauszeitschrift der Huels-Gesellschaften. Text in German. 1951. s-a. free. **Document type:** *Trade.*
Indexed: ChemAb, Inspec.
—AskIEEE, CASDDS.
Published by: Huels AG, Marl, 45764, Germany. Ed. Georg Heinze.

540 LTU ISSN 0235-7216
Q4 CODEN: CHMJES
➤ **LIETUVOS MOKSLU AKADEMIJA. CHEMIJA/LITHUANIAN ACADEMY OF SCIENCES. CHEMISTRY/LITOVSKAYA AKADEMIYA NAUK. KHIMIYA.** Text in Russian; Summaries in Lithuanian. 1955. 6/yr. charts; illus. index. **Document type:** *Journal, Academic/Scholarly.* **Description:** Focuses on chemistry, technology and physical geography with a chronicle of the activities of the Lithuanian Academy of Sciences.
Supersedes in part (in 1990): Lietuvos T.S.R. Mokslu Akademijos Darbai. B Serija. Chemija, Technika, Fizine Geografija / Akademiya Nauk Litovskoi S.S.R. Trudy. Seriya B. Khimiya, Tekhnika, Fizicheskaya Geografiya (0132-2729)
Indexed: ApMecR, BiolAb, ChemAb, ChemTitl, HortAb, Inspec, MathR.
—BLDSC (3157.799000), CASDDS, CISTI, Linda Hall. **CCC.**
Published by: Lietuvos Mokslu Akademija/Lithuanian Academy of Sciences, Gedimino pr 3, Vilnius, 2600, Lithuania. TEL 370-2-613651, FAX 370-2-618464, matfizch@ktl.mii.lt, prezidum@ktl.mii.lt, http://neris.mii.lt/LMA/. Circ: 710.

540 634.9 CHN ISSN 0253-2417
LINCHAN HUAXUE YU GONGYE/CHEMISTRY AND INDUSTTY OF FOREST PRODUCTS. Text in Chinese. 1981. q. **Document type:** *Journal, Academic/Scholarly.*
Related titles: Online - full text ed.: (from East View Information Services, WanFang Data Corp.).
Published by: Zhongguo Linye Kexue Yanjiuyuan, Linchan Huaxue Gongye Yanjiusuo, 16, Suojinwucun, Nanjing, 210042, China. TEL 86-25-85482493, FAX 86-25-85413445, lchx@chinajournal.net.cn, http://lchxygy.periodicals.net.cn/.

540 CHN ISSN 1001-5493
QD562.I63 CODEN: LJYXE5
➤ **LIZI JIAOHUAN YU XIFU/ION EXCHANGE AND ADSORPTION**; fanyingxing gaofenzi. Text in Chinese. 1985. bi-m. CNY 8.80 newsstand/cover domestic (effective 2001). adv. software rev. 96 p./no.; back issues avail. **Document type:** *Academic/Scholarly.*
Related titles: Online - full text ed.: (from East View Information Services).
Indexed: CIN, ChemAb, ChemTitl, EngInd.
—BLDSC (4564.320000), CASDDS, IE, ingenta.
Published by: Nankai Daxue, Gaofenzi Huaxue Yanjiusuo/Nankai University, Institute of Polymer Chemistry, Balitai, Nankai-qu, Tianjin 300071, China. pocninth@public.tpt.tj.cn. Ed. He Binglin. Adv. contact Xu Jiayi.

540 FIN ISSN 1457-9936
LUONNONTIETEIDEN AKATEEMISET/KEMISTEN. Text in Finnish, Swedish. 1957. bi-m. adv. charts. **Document type:** *Magazine, Trade.* **Description:** Focuses on professional and social questions concerning chemists, the chemical industry and trade.
Formerly (until 2001): Kemisti (0022-9865)
Published by: Luonnontieteiden Akateemisten Liitto/Finnish Union of Experts in Science, Rautatielaeisenkatu 6, Helsinki, 00520, Finland. TEL 358-207-489400, FAX 358-9-142208, http://www.luonnontieteidenakateemiset.org. Ed. Kirsti Janhunen. Adv. contact Raili Pimia. Circ: 5,000.

540 HUN ISSN 1418-9933
QD1 CODEN: MGKFA3
➤ **MAGYAR KEMIAI FOLYOIRAT, KEMIAI KOZLEMENYEK/HUNGARIAN JOURNAL OF CHEMISTRY, CHEMICAL COMMUNICATIONS.** Text in Hungarian; Summaries in Multiple languages. 1997. m. USD 90 (effective 2000). adv. bk.rev. charts; illus. index. **Document type:** *Bulletin, Academic/Scholarly.*
Formed by the merger of (1895-1997): Magyar Kemiai Folyoirat (0025-0155); (1966-1997): Kemiai Kozlemenyek (0022-9814)
Indexed: ASCA, AnalAb, BiolAb, CCI, ChemAb, ChemInfo, ChemTitl, CurCR, CurCont, EngInd, INIS AtomInd, ISR, IndChem, MOS, MSB, MSCI, NPU, RCI, RefZh, S&F, SCI.
—BLDSC (5342.000000), CASDDS, CISTI, Ei, IDS, IE, ingenta, Linda Hall.
Published by: Magyar Kemikusok Egyesulete/Hungarian Chemical Society, Fo utca 68, Budapest, 1027, Hungary. TEL 36-1-2016883, http://www.kfki.hu/~cheminfo/mkf. Ed. E Pungor. Circ: 1,400.

540 HUN ISSN 0025-0163
QD1 CODEN: MGKLAL
MAGYAR KEMIKUSOK LAPJA. Text in Hungarian. 1946. m. USD 70 (effective 2000). adv. bk.rev. **Document type:** *Bulletin.*
Indexed: A&ATA, AnalAb, CEABA, CIN, ChemAb, ChemInfo, ChemTitl, INIS AtomInd, MSB, RefZh.
—CASDDS, CISTI, Linda Hall.
Published by: Magyar Kemikusok Egyesulete/Hungarian Chemical Society, Fo utca 68, Budapest, 1027, Hungary. TEL 36-1-2016883. Ed. Dr. Laszlo Racz.

546 GBR ISSN 1024-1221
CODEN: MGCHE7
➤ **MAIN GROUP CHEMISTRY.** Text in English. 1995-2002; resumed 2005 (vol.4). 4/yr. GBP 190, USD 305 to institutions (effective 2006). **Document type:** *Journal, Academic/Scholarly.*
Related titles: Online - full text ed.: ISSN 1745-1167. GBP 181, USD 290 to institutions (effective 2006) (from EBSCO Publishing, Gale Group, IngentaConnect).
Indexed: CCI, CurCR, CurCont, IndChem, RCI.

C

—BLDSC (5351.843000).
Published by: Taylor & Francis Ltd (Subsidiary of: Taylor & Francis Group), 4 Park Sq, Milton Park, Abingdon, OX14 4RN, United Kingdom. TEL 44-1235-828600, FAX 44-1235-829000, info@tandf.co.uk, http://www.tandf.co.uk/journals/titles/10241221.asp. Ed. David A Atwood. **Subscr. in N America to:** Taylor & Francis Inc., Customer Services Dept, 325 Chestnut St, 8th Fl, Philadelphia, PA 19106. TEL 215-625-8900, 800-354-1420, FAX 215-625-8914, customerservice@taylorandfrancis.com; **Subscr. outside N America to:** Journals Customer Service, Rankine Rd, Basingstoke, Hants RG24 8PR, United Kingdom. TEL 44-1256-813000, FAX 44-1256-330245, enquiry@tandf.co.uk.

➤ **MAIN GROUP METAL CHEMISTRY.** see *METALLURGY*

540 IRN ISSN 1015-2849
MAJALLAH-I SHIMI/IRANIAN JOURNAL OF CHEMISTRY. Text in Persian, Modern. 1988. 3/yr. IRR 12,000; GBP 18 in the Middle East; GBP 20 in Europe; GBP 25 elsewhere (effective 2001). **Document type:** *Journal, Academic/Scholarly.*
Description: Publishes news and articles on chemistry, including philosophical and historical aspects.
Published by: Markaz-i Nashr-i Danishgahi/Iran University Press, 85 Park Ave., P O Box 15875-4748, Tehran, Iran. TEL 98-21-8713232, FAX 98-21-8725954, pobox@iup-ir.com. Ed. Ali Pourjavady. Circ: 4,000.

MAJOR CHEMICAL AND PETROCHEMICAL COMPANIES OF EUROPE. see *PETROLEUM AND GAS*

540 JPN
MAKU SHINPOJUMU/MEMBRANE SYMPOSIUM. Text in English, Japanese. 1989. a.
Published by: Nihon Maku Gakkai/Membrane Society of Japan, Hongo 5-26-5-702, Bunkyo-ku, Tokyo, 113-0033, Japan. membrane@muu.biglobe.ne.jp, http://wwwsoc.nacsis.ac.jp/membrane/index.html.

C

542 USA ISSN 1082-5878
Q183.A1 CODEN: MMLAF6
MANAGING THE MODERN LABORATORY; the journal of laboratory management. Variant title: M M L. Text in English. 1995. q. USD 145 domestic to individuals; USD 195 foreign to individuals; USD 250 domestic to institutions; USD 300 foreign to institutions (effective 2005). **Document type:** *Magazine.*
Indexed: CSNB, LHB.
—BLDSC (5359.291000), IE, ingenta.
Published by: International Scientific Communications, Inc., 30 Controls Dr, PO Box 670, Shelton, CT 06484-0870. TEL 203-926-9300, FAX 203-926-9310, iscpubs@iscpubs.com, http://www.iscpubs.com. Eds. David W. Green, Susan Messinger.

540 EGY ISSN 1110-4562
MANSOURA SCIENCE BULLETIN. A, CHEMISTRY/NASHRAT KOLIYYAT AL-'LUM A KIMYYAA. Text in English. 1976. bi-m. USD 720; EGP 10 newsstand/cover. **Document type:** *Bulletin, Academic/Scholarly.*
Published by: Mansoura University, Faculty of Science, PO Box 35516, Mansoura - Dakahlia, Egypt. TEL 20-50-2247055, FAX 20-50-2247330, http://derp.sti.sci.eg/data/0173.htm, http-://www.mans.edu.eg.

MARINE CHEMISTRY. see *EARTH SCIENCES*

540 CZE
MASARYK UNIVERSITY. FACULTY OF SCIENCES. SCRIPTA CHEMIA/SCRIPTA FACULTATIS SCIENTIARUM NATURALIUM UNIVERSITATIS MASARYKIANAE BRUNENSIS. CHEMIA. Text in English, French, Russian. a. price varies. illus. **Document type:** *Academic/Scholarly.*
Formerly: Scripta Facultatis Scientiarum Naturalium Universitatis Purkynianae Brunensis. Chemia (0231-5971); Supersedes in part (in 1970): Universita J.E. Purkyne. Prirodovedecka Fakulta. Spisy
Indexed: ForAb.
Published by: Masarykova Universita, Prirodovedecka Fakulta/Masaryk University, Faculty of Sciences, Kotlarska 2, Brno, 61137, Czech Republic. Ed. Jiri Hala.

540 510 SCG ISSN 0340-6253
QD39.3.M3 CODEN: MATCDY
➤ **MATCH**; communications in mathematical and computer chemistry. Text mainly in English; Text occasionally in French, German. 1975. 2/yr. EUR 70 (effective 2003). bk.rev. abstr.; bibl.; charts. index. back issues avail. **Document type:** *Journal, Academic/Scholarly.*
Indexed: CCI, CCMJ, CMCI, ChemAb, MSB, MathR, MathSciNet, RefZh, ZentMath.
—CASDDS, CISTI, IDS, Linda Hall. **CCC.**
Published by: University of Kragujevac, Faculty of Science, PO Box 60, Kragujevac, 34000. TEL 381-34-331876, FAX 381-34-335040, gutman@knez.uis.kg.ac.yu, http://www.pmf.kg.ac.yu/match. Ed., R&P Ivan Gutman. Circ: 200.

➤ **MATERIALS CHEMISTRY AND PHYSICS.** see *ENGINEERING—Engineering Mechanics And Materials*

➤ **MATERIALS RESEARCH SOCIETY SYMPOSIUM PROCEEDINGS.** see *PHYSICS*

540 NLD ISSN 1369-7021
MATERIALS TODAY. Text in English. 1998. 12/yr. EUR 169 in Europe to institutions; JPY 22,500 in Japan to institutions; USD 189 to institutions except Europe and Japan (effective 2006). **Document type:** *Journal, Academic/Scholarly.*
Description: Focuses on the hottest areas of materials research including materials chemistry, electronic and optoelectronic materials, polymers and advanced structural materials.
Related titles: Online - full text ed.: (from EBSCO Publishing, Gale Group, IngentaConnect, ScienceDirect, Swets Information Services).
Indexed: Inspec.
—BLDSC (5396.507000), CISTI, IE, ingenta. **CCC.**
Published by: Elsevier BV (Subsidiary of: Elsevier Science & Technology), Radarweg 29, Amsterdam, 1043 NX, Netherlands. TEL 31-20-4853911, FAX 31-20-4852457, materialstoday@elsevier.com, nlinfo-f@elsevier.nl, http://www.elsevier.com/locate/mattod, http://www.elsevier.nl. Ed. C. Sealy.

540 510 GBR ISSN 1049-2801
CODEN: MCHEET
MATHEMATICAL CHEMISTRY. Text in English. 1991. irreg., latest vol.7, 2003. price varies. **Document type:** *Monographic series, Academic/Scholarly.*
Indexed: ZentMath.
—CISTI. **CCC.**
Published by: Taylor & Francis Ltd (Subsidiary of: Taylor & Francis Group), 4 Park Sq, Milton Park, Abingdon, OX14 4RN, United Kingdom. TEL 44-1235-828600, FAX 44-1235-829000, info@tandf.co.uk, http://www.tandf.co.uk/journals. **Subscr. addr. in US:** International Publishers Direct, PO Box 32160, Newark, NJ 07102. FAX 215-750-6343.

MATSUSHITA TECHNICAL JOURNAL. see *ENGINEERING—Electrical Engineering*

540 USA ISSN 0145-7055
TP992.5
MCCUTCHEON'S EMULSIFIERS AND DETERGENTS (NORTH AMERICAN EDITION). Text in English. 1949. a. USD 80 per issue (effective 2005). adv. **Document type:** *Directory, Trade.*
Description: List of over 4,000 surfactant materials for users and purchasers, categorized by trade name, identity, manufacturer, concentration, type, HLB index, CAS number, and application.
—**CCC.**
Published by: Manufacturing Confectioner Publishing Company, 711 W Water St, PO Box 266, Princeton, WI 54968. TEL 920-295-6969, FAX 920-295-6843, themc@gomc.com, http://www.gomc.com/display.asp?pageId=home. Ed. Kate Allured. Circ: 5,300.

540 USA ISSN 1550-1639
TP992.5
MCCUTCHEON'S VOLUME 1: EMULSIFIERS AND DETERGENTS (INTERNATIONAL EDITION). Text in English. a. USD 80 per issue (effective 2004). **Document type:** *Trade.*
Description: List of over 4,000 surfactant materials for users and purchasers, categorized by trade name, identity, manufacturer, concentration, type, HLB index, CAS number, and application.
Former titles (until 199?): McCutcheon's Emulsifiers and Detergents - International Edition (0734-0567); (until 1981): McCutcheon's Detergents and Emulsifiers - International Edition (0145-7063)
—**CCC.**
Published by: Manufacturing Confectioner Publishing Company, 711 W Water St, PO Box 266, Princeton, WI 54968. TEL 920-295-6969, FAX 920-295-6843, mccutcheons@gomc.com, http://www.gomc.com/mccutcheons. Ed. Kate Allured.

▼ **MEDICINAL CHEMISTRY.** see *MEDICAL SCIENCES*

MEDICINAL CHEMISTRY RESEARCH; an international journal for rapid communications on design and mechanisms of action of biologically active agents. see *MEDICAL SCIENCES*

615.19 NLD ISSN 1567-2034
▼ ➤ **MEDICINAL CHEMISTRY REVIEWS ONLINE.** Text in English. 2004. q. EUR 110, USD 110 to individuals; EUR 610, USD 610 to corporations; EUR 340, USD 340 to institutions (academic) (effective 2004). **Document type:** *Journal, Academic/Scholarly.* **Description:** Publishes reviews in medicinal chemistry and related areas written by leading experts in the field.
Media: Online - full content. **Related titles:** Online - full text ed.: (from Gale Group, IngentaConnect).
—**CCC.**
Published by: Bentham Science Publishers Ltd., PO Box 1673, Hilversum, BR 1200, Netherlands. TEL 31-35-6923800, FAX 31-35-6980150, M.Bentham@inter.nl.net, http://www.bentham.org/. Eds. Atta-ur Rahman TEL 92-21-4969873, Matthew Honan.

➤ **MEISEI DAIGAKU KENKYU KIYO. RIKOGAKUBU/MEISEI UNIVERSITY. RESEARCH BULLETIN. PHYSICAL SCIENCES AND ENGINEERING.** see *ENGINEERING*

540 USA
MEMBRANE PLANNING CONFERENCE (YEAR). Text in English. 1983. a. USD 375 (effective 2005). **Document type:** *Proceedings.*
Published by: Business Communications Co., Inc., 25 Van Zant St, Ste 13, Norwalk, CT 06855-1781. TEL 203-853-4266, FAX 203-853-0348, info@bccresearch.com, http://www.bccresearch.com.

661 GBR ISSN 0958-2118
MEMBRANE TECHNOLOGY. Text in English. 1991. 12/yr. EUR 934 in Europe to institutions; JPY 124,100 in Japan to institutions; USD 1,047 to institutions except Europe and Japan (effective 2006). adv. reprints avail. **Document type:** *Newsletter, Academic/Scholarly.* **Description:** Covers developments in membrane separation and purification technology, research and applications in a wide variety of industries, including pharmaceuticals, food and beverages, electronics, biotechnology and chemicals.
Related titles: Microform ed.: (from PQC); Online - full text ed.: (from EBSCO Publishing, Gale Group, IngentaConnect, ScienceDirect, Swets Information Services).
Indexed: CEABA, FLUIDEX, WTA.
—BLDSC (5548.026600), IE, Infotrieve, ingenta. **CCC.**
Published by: Elsevier Advanced Technology (Subsidiary of: Elsevier Science & Technology), The Boulevard, Langford Ln, Kidlington, Oxon OX5 2BG, United Kingdom. TEL 44-1865-843750, FAX 44-1865-843971, eatsales@elsevier.co.uk, http://www.elsevier.com/locate/membtech. Ed. D Hopwood. **Subscr. to:** Elsevier BV, PO Box 211, Amsterdam 1000 AE, Netherlands. TEL 31-20-485-3757, FAX 31-20-485-3432, nlinfo-f@elsevier.nl, http://www.elsevier.nl.

540 GBR ISSN 0959-9436
QD1 CODEN: MENCEX
➤ **MENDELEEV COMMUNICATIONS.** Text in English. 1991. bi-m. USD 824 in United States to institutions; GBP 503 rest of world to institutions; USD 867 combined subscription in United States to institutions print & online eds.; GBP 529 combined subscription rest of world to institutions print & online eds.; USD 165 per issue in United States to institutions; GBP 101 per issue rest of world to institutions (effective 2005); all subscribers get free archival CD-ROM; all online subscribers have a free access to all available backfile. illus.; abstr.; bibl.; charts. 50 p./no. 2 cols./p.; back issues avail.; reprints avail. **Document type:** *Journal, Academic/Scholarly.* **Description:** Provides immediate access to new work being conducted in Russia and other states of the former Soviet Union.
Related titles: CD-ROM ed.: 1997. free with subscription to print ed.; E-mail ed.; Online - full text ed.: ISSN 1364-551X. USD 729 in United States to institutions; GBP 445 elsewhere to institutions (effective 2004) (from EBSCO Publishing, O C L C Online Computer Library Center, Inc., Swets Information Services).
Indexed: ASCA, CCI, CEABA, CIN, ChemAb, ChemTitl, CurCont, EngInd, MOS, MSB, MSCI, RAPRA, RefZh, SCI.
—BLDSC (5678.442050), CASDDS, CINDOC, CISTI, Ei, IDS, IE, Infotrieve, ingenta, Linda Hall. **CCC.**
Published by: (Royal Society of Chemistry, Rossiiskaya Akademiya Nauk/Russian Academy of Sciences RUS), Turpion Ltd., 207 Brondesbury Park, London, NW2 5JN, United Kingdom. TEL 44-20-84590066, FAX 44-20-84516454, custserv@turpion.ru, info@turpion.org, custserv@ioc.ac.ru, http://www.turpion.org/journal/mc. Eds. A G Davies, O M Nefedov. Pub., Adv. contact Lev Malov. R&P Irina Makhova. **Subscr. addr.:** Extenza - Turpin, Pegasus Dr, Stratton Business Park, Biggleswade, Beds SG18 8TQ, United Kingdom. **Co-publisher:** Turpion - Moscow Ltd.

➤ **LA MER/UMI.** see *BIOLOGY*

540 SGP ISSN 1793-1371
METHODS IN CHROMATOGRAPHY. Text in English. 1996. irreg., latest vol.1. price varies. **Document type:** *Monographic series, Academic/Scholarly.*
Published by: World Scientific Publishing Co. Pte. Ltd., 5 Toh Tuck Link, Singapore, 596224, Singapore. TEL 65-466-5775, FAX 65-467-7667, wspc@wspc.com.sg, series@wspc.com.sg, http://www.wspc.com.sg/books/series/mc_series.shtml, http://www.worldscientific.com. Ed. C K Lim. **Dist. by:** World Scientific Publishing Co., Inc., 1060 Main St, River Edge, NJ 07661. TEL 201-487-9655, 800-227-7562, FAX 201-487-9656, 888-977-2665; World Scientific Publishing Ltd., 57 Shelton St, London WC2H 9HE, United Kingdom. TEL 44-20-78360888, FAX 44-20-78362020, sales@wspc.co.uk.

MICROCHEMICAL JOURNAL. see *BIOLOGY—Microscopy*

540 NLD ISSN 1389-5575
CODEN: MMCIAE
➤ **MINI - REVIEWS IN MEDICINAL CHEMISTRY.** Text in English. 2001 (Jun.). bi-m. EUR 1,470, USD 1,470 to institutions (academic), print or online; EUR 2,600, USD 2,600 to corporations print or online; EUR 350, USD 350 combined subscription to individuals print & online; EUR 1,620, USD 1,620 combined subscription to institutions (academic), print & online; EUR 3,120, USD 3,120 combined subscription to corporations print & online (effective 2004). adv. back issues avail. **Document type:** *Journal, Academic/Scholarly.*
Description: Covers all areas of medicinal chemistry including developments in rational drug design, synthetic chemistry, bioorganic chemistry, high-throughput screening, combinatorial chemistry, drug targets, and natural product research and structure-activity relationship studies.
Related titles: Online - full text ed.: (from EBSCO Publishing, Gale Group, IngentaConnect, Swets Information Services).
Indexed: BIOSIS Prev, ChemAb, ExcerpMed.
—BLDSC (5797.439950), CISTI, IE, Infotrieve. **CCC.**
Published by: Bentham Science Publishers Ltd., PO Box 1673, Hilversum, BR 1200, Netherlands. TEL 31-35-6923800, FAX 31-35-6980150, M.Bentham@inter.nl.net, http://www.bentham.org/mrmc. Eds. Atta-ur Rahman TEL 92-21-4969873, M Iqbal Choudhary TEL 92-21-4969873, Patrice Talaga TEL 32-2-3862727. **Subscr. addr. in the US:** Bentham Science Publishers Ltd., 1400 Pine St, PO Box 640310, San Francisco, CA 94164-0310. FAX 415-775-4503, shidding@worldonline.nl.

540 USA ISSN 0026-5411
MINNESOTA CHEMIST. Text in English. 1942. 8/yr. USD 8 (effective 2005). adv. bk.rev. **Document type:** *Magazine, Trade.*
Published by: American Chemical Society, 1155 16th St, N W, Washington, DC 20036. TEL 202-872-4614, 800-227-5558, FAX 202-776-8264, sue.lee2@genmills.com, http://www.acs.org. Ed. Sue Lee. Circ: 2,800 (paid and free).

540 DEU ISSN 1617-5301
MITTEILUNGEN DER FACHGRUPPE UMWELTCHEMIE UND OKOTOXIKOLOGIE, GESELLSCHAFT DEUTSCHER CHEMIKER. Text in German. 1995. q. EUR 48 in Europe; CHF 74 to Switzerland & Liechtenstein (effective 2006). **Document type:** *Journal, Academic/Scholarly.*
Formerly (until 2000): Mitteilungsblatt - Gesellschaft Deutscher Chemiker, Fachgruppe Umweltchemie und Okotoxikologie (0948-6283)
Related titles: Online - full content ed.: ISSN 1618-3258. 2001.
—**CCC.**
Published by: Wiley - V C H Verlag GmbH & Co. KGaA (Subsidiary of: John Wiley & Sons, Inc.), Boschstr 12, Weinheim, 69469, Germany. TEL 49-6201-6060, FAX 49-6201-606328, subservice@wiley-vch.de, http://www.wiley-vch.de.

540 GBR ISSN 0747-7406
MODERN CHLOR-ALKALI TECHNOLOGY. Text in English. 1980. irreg., latest vol.8, 2001. Price varies. **Document type:** *Monographic series, Academic/Scholarly.*
—BLDSC (5886.027000), CISTI. **CCC.**
Published by: (Society of Chemical Industry), Blackwell Publishing Ltd., 9600 Garsington Rd, Oxford, OX4 2ZG, United Kingdom. TEL 44-1865-776868, FAX 44-1865-714591, customerservices@oxon.blackwellpublishing.com, http://www.blackwellpublishing.com. **Co-sponsor:** Royal Society of Chemistry.

MOESSBAUER EFFECT REFERENCE AND DATA JOURNAL. see *PHYSICS—Optics*

540 CHE ISSN 1422-8599
CODEN: MOLBAI
MOLBANK. Text in English. 2002. irreg. free (effective 2005). **Document type:** *Monographic series, Academic/Scholarly.*
Description: It publishes one-compound-per-paper short notes and communications on synthetic compounds and natural products.
Media: Online - full text.
Published by: Molecular Diversity Preservation International, MDPI Center, Matthaeusstr 11, Basel, 4057, Switzerland. TEL 41-61-6837734, FAX 41-61-3028918, lin@mdpi.org, http://www.mdpi.net/molbank/index.htm, http://www.mdpi.org/.

MOLECULAR AND CELLULAR PROBES. see *MEDICAL SCIENCES—Experimental Medicine, Laboratory Technique*

▼ **MOLECULAR BIOSYSTEMS.** see *BIOLOGY*

540 USA ISSN 1543-8384
RM301.65
▼ **MOLECULAR PHARMACEUTICS.** Text in English. 2004. bi-m. USD 1,280 in North America to institutions; USD 1,320 elsewhere to institutions; USD 135 in North America to members; USD 175 elsewhere to members; USD 101 in North America to students; USD 141 elsewhere to students (effective 2006). **Description:** Focuses on molecular mechanistic approaches to the development of bio-available drugs and delivery systems.
Related titles: Online - full text ed.: ISSN 1543-8392. USD 40 (effective 2006) (from EBSCO Publishing, Swets Information Services).
Indexed: ASFA, B&BAb, BioEngAb, ExcerpMed, M&PBA.
—BLDSC (5900.817995), CISTI, IE, Linda Hall. **CCC.**
Published by: American Chemical Society, 1155 16th St, N W, Washington, DC 20036. TEL 202-872-4614, 800-227-5558, FAX 202-776-8264, service@acs.org, http://pubs.acs.org/journals/mpohbp/index.html, http://www.acs.org.

660 USA ISSN 1436-8269
MOLECULAR SIEVES - SCIENCE AND TECHNOLOGY. Text in English. 1981. irreg., latest vol.4, 2004. price varies. reprint service avail. from ISI. **Document type:** *Monographic series, Academic/Scholarly.* **Description:** Covers all aspects of the rapidly developing science and technology of zeolites and related microporous crystalline materials.
Formerly (until 1996): Catalysis: Science and Technology (0175-9361)
Related titles: Online - full text ed.: ISSN 1616-8569.
—IE, ingenta.
Published by: Springer-Verlag New York, Inc. (Subsidiary of: Springer Science+Business Media), 233 Spring St, New York, NY 10013. TEL 212-460-1500, 800-777-4643, FAX 212-473-6272, http://link.springer.de/link/service/series/3829/, http://www.springer-ny.com. Eds. J R Anderson, M Boudart.

540 GBR ISSN 0892-7022
QC167.5 CODEN: MOSIEA
➤ **MOLECULAR SIMULATION.** Text in English. 15/yr. GBP 3,440, USD 4,475 combined subscription to institutions print & online eds. (effective 2006). reprint service avail. from PSC. **Document type:** *Journal, Academic/Scholarly.* **Description:** Covers all aspects of research related to molecular modelling and simulation.
Related titles: CD-ROM ed.; Microform ed.; Online - full text ed.: ISSN 1029-0435. 1996. GBP 3,268, USD 4,251 to institutions (effective 2006) (from EBSCO Publishing, Gale Group, IngentaConnect, O C L C Online Computer Library Center, Inc., Swets Information Services).
Indexed: ASCA, BrCerAb, C&ISA, CCI, CerAb, ChemAb, CorrAb, CurCont, E&CAJ, EMA, EngInd, IAA, ISMEC, ISR, M&TEA, MBF, METADEX, MSCI, RAPRA, SCI, SolStAb, WAA, ZentMath.
—BLDSC (5900.833000), CISTI, IE, Infotrieve, ingenta, Linda Hall. **CCC.**
Published by: Taylor & Francis Ltd (Subsidiary of: Taylor & Francis Group), 4 Park Sq, Milton Park, Abingdon, OX14 4RN, United Kingdom. TEL 44-1235-828600, FAX 44-1235-829000, info@tandf.co.uk, http://www.tandf.co.uk/journals/titles/08927022.asp. Ed. Nick Quirke. **Subscr. to:** Journals Customer Service, Rankine Rd, Basingstoke, Hants RG24 8PR, United Kingdom. TEL 44-1256-813000, FAX 44-1256-330245, enquiry@tandf.co.uk.

540 AUT ISSN 0026-9247
QD1 CODEN: MOCMB7
➤ **MONATSHEFTE FUER CHEMIE/CHEMICAL MONTHLY;** an international journal of chemistry. Text in English. 1880. m. EUR 1,498 combined subscription to institutions print & online eds. (effective 2005). adv. charts; illus.; abstr. index. back issues avail.; reprint service avail. from PQC. **Document type:** *Journal, Academic/Scholarly.* **Description:** Features recent research results in inorganic, structural, physical, and organic chemistry and biochemistry.
Formerly (until 1967): Monatshefte fuer Chemie und Verwandte Teile Anderer Wissenschaften (0343-7329)
Related titles: Microform ed.: (from PQC); Online - full text ed.: ISSN 1434-4475 (from EBSCO Publishing, Springer LINK, Swets Information Services); ♦ Supplement(s): Monatshefte fuer Chemie. Supplementum. ISSN 0935-8439.
Indexed: BiolAb, BullT&T, CCI, CIN, ChemAb, ChemInfo, ChemTitl, CurCR, CurCont, DBA, EngInd, INIS AtomInd, ISR, IndChem, IndMed, MOS, MSB, NPU, RCI, RefZh, SCI.
—BLDSC (5904.000000), CASDDS, CINDOC, CISTI, Ei, IDS, IE, Infotrieve, ingenta, KNAW, Linda Hall. **CCC.**
Published by: Springer-Verlag Wien (Subsidiary of: Springer Science+Business Media) journals@springer.at, http://link.springer.de/link/service/journals/00706/, http://www.springer.at. R&P Angela Foessl TEL 43-1-3302415517. adv.: B&W page EUR 1,000; 170 x 250. **Subscr. in the Americas to:** Springer-Verlag New York, Inc., Journal Fulfillment, PO Box 2485, Secaucus, NJ 07096-2485. TEL 800-777-4643, 201-348-4033, FAX 201-348-4505, journals@springer-ny.com.

540 AUT ISSN 0935-8439
➤ **MONATSHEFTE FUER CHEMIE. SUPPLEMENTUM.** Text in English. 1989. irreg. price varies. **Document type:** *Monographic series, Academic/Scholarly.*
Related titles: ♦ Supplement to: Monatshefte fuer Chemie. ISSN 0026-9247.
—**CCC.**
Published by: Springer-Verlag Wien (Subsidiary of: Springer Science+Business Media) TEL 43-1-330-2415, FAX 43-1-330-2426, journals@springer.at, http://www.springer.at.

➤ **MONOGRAPHS ON THE PHYSICS AND CHEMISTRY OF MATERIALS.** see *PHYSICS*

540 USA ISSN 0027-1314
QD1
➤ **MOSCOW STATE UNIVERSITY CHEMISTRY BULLETIN.** Text in English. 1966. bi-m. USD 1,965 per vol. in US & Canada; USD 2,265 per vol. elsewhere (effective 2006). charts; illus.; abstr. index. back issues avail. **Document type:** *Bulletin, Academic/Scholarly.* **Description:** Covers general, radiation, analytical, organic, petroleum chemistry and electrochemistry.
Related titles: ♦ Translation of: Moskovskii Gosudarstvennyi Universitet. Vestnik. Seriya 2: Khimiya. ISSN 0579-9384.
Indexed: AnalAb, BullT&T, CurCont.
—BLDSC (0416.238000), CISTI, IE, ingenta, Linda Hall. **CCC.**
Published by: (Moskovskii Gosudarstvennyi Universitet im. M.V. Lomonosova/M.V. Lomonosov Moscow State University RUS), Allerton Press, Inc., 18 W 27th St, New York, NY 10001. TEL 646-424-9686, FAX 646-424-9695, journals@allertonpress.com, http://www.allertonpress.com/journals/muc.htm. Ed. Valerii V Lunin.

540 RUS ISSN 0579-9384
CODEN: VMUKA5
➤ **MOSKOVSKII GOSUDARSTVENNYI UNIVERSITET. VESTNIK. SERIYA 2: KHIMIYA.** Contents page in English. 1960. bi-m. USD 66 foreign (effective 2004). bk.rev. bibl. index. **Document type:** *Journal, Academic/Scholarly.*
Supersedes in part (1956-1959): Moskovskii Gosudarstvennyi Universitet. Vestnik. Seriya Matematiki, Mekhaniki, Astronomii, Fiziki, Khimii (0579-9376)
Related titles: Online - full text ed.: free (effective 2005); ♦ English Translation: Moscow State University Chemistry Bulletin. ISSN 0027-1314.
Indexed: ASCA, CCI, CIN, ChemAb, ChemTitl, CurCont, IAA, MSB, RASB, RCI, RefZh.
—BLDSC (0032.350000), CASDDS, CISTI, East View, IDS, Linda Hall. **CCC.**
Published by: (Moskovskii Gosudarstvennyi Universitet im. M.V. Lomonosova, Khimicheskii Fakul'tet/M.V. Lomonosov Moscow State University, Department of Chemistry), Izdatel'stvo Moskovskogo Gosudarstvennogo Universiteta im. M. V. Lomonosova/Publishing House of Moscow State University, B Nikitskaya 5/7, Moscow, 103009, Russian Federation. TEL 7-095-2295091, FAX 7-095-2036671, kd_mgu@rambler.ru, http://www.chem.msu.su/rus/vmgu, http://www.msu.ru/depts/MSUPubl. **Dist. by:** M K - Periodica, ul Gilyarovskogo 39, Moscow 129110, Russian Federation. TEL 7-095-2845008, FAX 7-095-2813798, info@periodicals.ru, http://www.mkniga.ru.

➤ **MULTINATIONAL CHEMICALS AND PETROCHEMICALS COMPANIES.** see *BUSINESS AND ECONOMICS—International Commerce*

➤ **N A P R A L E R T.** (Natural Products Alert) see *PHARMACY AND PHARMACOLOGY*

➤ **N A T O SCIENCE SERIES. SERIES II, MATHEMATICS, PHYSICS AND CHEMISTRY.** (North Atlantic Treaty Organization) see *MATHEMATICS*

540 ITA ISSN 1592-2286
N C F INTERNATIONAL. (Notiziario Chimico Farmaceutico) Text in English. 1997. q. EUR 41 domestic (effective 2004).
Formerly (until 2000): B C F International (1592-2294)
Published by: Tecniche Nuove SpA, Via Eritrea 21, Milan, MI 201, Italy. TEL 39-02-390901, FAX 39-02-7570364, ncfinternational@tecnichenuove.com, info@tecnichenuove.com, http://www.tecnichenuove.com.

N C F. NOTIZIARIO CHIMICO E FARMACEUTICO. see *PHARMACY AND PHARMACOLOGY*

540 USA ISSN 0896-2367
N O B C CH E. PROCEEDINGS. Text in English. a.
Published by: National Organization for the Professional Advancement of Black Chemists and Chemical Engineers, PO Box 77040, Washington, DC 20013. TEL 800-776-1419, FAX 202-667-1705.

660 DEU ISSN 1439-9598
CODEN: NACHFB
NACHRICHTEN AUS DER CHEMIE. Text in German. 1953. m. EUR 224 domestic; EUR 238 in Europe; EUR 259 elsewhere (effective 2005). adv. bk.rev. index. reprint service avail. from ISI. **Document type:** *Journal, Academic/Scholarly.*
Former titles (until 2000): Nachrichten aus Chemie, Technik und Laboratorium (0341-5163); (until 1977): Nachrichten aus Chemie und Technik (0027-738X)
Related titles: Microfilm ed.: (from VCI); Online - full text ed.
Indexed: ASCA, CCI, CEABA, CIN, ChemAb, ChemInfo, ChemTitl, EngInd, ExcerpMed, MSB, MSCI, SSCI.
—BLDSC (6006.380000), CASDDS, CISTI, Ei, IDS, IE, Infotrieve, ingenta, Linda Hall. **CCC.**
Published by: Gesellschaft Deutscher Chemiker, Varrentrappstr 40-42, Frankfurt am Main, 60486, Germany. TEL 49-69-79170, FAX 49-69-7917463, snachrichten@gdch.de, ms@gdch.de, http://www.gdch.de/taetigkeiten/nch.htm. Ed. Ernst Guggolz. Adv. contact Susanne Beutel. page EUR 4,790; trim 180 x 260. Circ: 25,666 (paid and controlled).

NAGOYA KOGYO DAIGAKU KIYO/NAGOYA INSTITUTE OF TECHNOLOGY. BULLETIN. see *ENGINEERING*

C

▼ **NANOTOXICOLOGY.** see *MEDICAL SCIENCES—Radiology And Nuclear Medicine*

NATIONAL FISHERIES UNIVERSITY OF PUSAN. INSTITUTE OF MARINE SCIENCES. CONTRIBUTIONS. see *BIOLOGY*

540 BLR ISSN 1561-8331
QD1 CODEN: VBSKAK
NATSIYANAL'NAYA AKADEMIYA NAVUK BELARUSI. VESTSI. SERYYA KHIMICHNYKH NAVUK/NATIONAL ACADEMY OF SCIENCES OF BELARUS. PROCEEDINGS. SERIES OF CHEMICAL SCIENCES. Text in Belorussian, Russian; Contents page in English. 1965. q. bibl.; charts; illus. index. **Document type:** *Journal, Academic/Scholarly.* **Description:** Presents papers on analytical, physical, inorganic, organic, bioorganic chemistry, chemistry of high-molecular compounds, applied chemistry and chemical technology.
Former titles (until 1998): Akademiya Navuk Belarusi. Vestsi. Seryya Khimichnykh Navuk (1025-5567); (until 1992): Akademiya Navuk Belarusskai S.S.R. Vestsi. Seryya Khimichnykh Navuk (0002-3590)
Indexed: CoppAb, INIS AtomInd, RefZh.
—BLDSC (0037.835000), CASDDS, CISTI, KNAW, Linda Hall. **CCC.**
Published by: (Natsiyanal'naya Akademiya Navuk Belarusi/National Academy of Sciences of Belarus), Vydavetstvo Belaruskaya Navuka/Publishing House Belaruskaya Navuka, 18 Academician V F Kuprevich St, Minsk, 220141, Belarus. TEL 375-17-2632327, FAX 375-17-2637618, chemistry@presidium.bas-net.by, belnauka@infonet.by, http://ns1.hmti.ac.by/publications/vestich/vestic.html. Ed. I I Lishtvan. Circ: 200.

540 GBR ISSN 1478-6419
CODEN: NPRAAT
➤ **NATURAL PRODUCT RESEARCH.** Text in English. 1992. 14/yr. GBP 2,195, USD 2,947 combined subscription to institutions print & online eds. (effective 2006). reprint service avail. from PSC. **Document type:** *Journal, Academic/Scholarly.* **Description:** Covers all aspects of research in the chemistry and biochemistry of naturally occurring compounds.
Formerly (until 2003): Natural Product Letters (1057-5634)
Related titles: CD-ROM ed.: ISSN 1026-8049. 1995; Microform ed.; Online - full text ed.: ISSN 1478-6427. 2000. GBP 2,085, USD 2,800 to institutions (effective 2006) (from EBSCO Publishing, Gale Group, IngentaConnect, O C L C Online Computer Library Center, Inc., Swets Information Services).
Indexed: ASCA, ASFA, AgBio, AgrForAb, B&BAb, BBCI, BIOBASE, CCI, CPA, ChemAb, ESPM, ExcerpMed, FCA, FPA, ForAb, HortAb, IABS, MBA, NemAb, OrnHort, PBA, PGegResA, PGrRegA, PHN&I, PN&I, ProtozoAb, RA&MP, RM&VM, RPP, S&F, SeedAb, TDB, VITIS, WeedAb, ZooRec.
—BLDSC (6040.738050), CISTI, IE, Infotrieve, ingenta. **CCC.**
Published by: Taylor & Francis Ltd (Subsidiary of: Taylor & Francis Group), 4 Park Sq, Milton Park, Abingdon, OX14 4RN, United Kingdom. TEL 44-1235-828600, FAX 44-1235-829000, info@tandf.co.uk, http://www.tandf.co.uk/journals/titles/14786419.asp. Ed. Atta-ur Rahman. **Subscr. in N America to:** Taylor & Francis Inc., Customer Services Dept, 325 Chestnut St, 8th Fl, Philadelphia, PA 19106. TEL 215-625-8900, 800-354-1420, FAX 215-625-8914, customerservice@taylorandfrancis.com; **Subscr. to:** Journals Customer Service, Rankine Rd, Basingstoke, Hants RG24 8PR, United Kingdom. TEL 44-1256-813000, FAX 44-1256-330245, enquiry@tandf.co.uk.

➤ **NATURE BIOTECHNOLOGY.** see *BIOLOGY—Biotechnology*

540 572 GBR ISSN 1552-4450
▼ ➤ **NATURE CHEMICAL BIOLOGY.** Text in English. 2005 (June). m. EUR 127 in Europe to individuals in Eurozone; USD 149 in the Americas to individuals; GBP 82 to individuals in the UK & elsewhere; EUR 1,291 in Europe to institutions Eurozone; USD 1,500 in the Americas to institutions; GBP 833 to institutions in the UK & elsewhere; EUR 110 in Europe to students Eurozone; USD 130 in the Americas to students; GBP 71 to students in the UK & elsewhere (effective 2006). **Document type:** *Journal, Academic/Scholarly.* **Description:** Publishes research relevant to bioorganic, bioinorganic and biophysical chemists, as well as biologists who seek to understand biological systems at the molecular level.
Related titles: Online - full content ed.: ISSN 1552-4469; Online - full text ed.: (from EBSCO Publishing).
Published by: Nature Publishing Group (Subsidiary of: Macmillan Publishers Ltd.), The MacMillan Building, 4 Crinan St, London, N1 9XW, United Kingdom. TEL 44-20-78334000, FAX 44-20-78433601, NatureReviews@nature.com, http://www.nature.com/naturechemicalbiology. Ed. Terry L Shepherd.

▼ ➤ **NATURE METHODS.** see *SCIENCES: COMPREHENSIVE WORKS*

570 610 USA ISSN 0195-7198
CODEN: PSSBDF
NAUKOVE TOVARYSTVO IMENI SHEVCHENKA. PROCEEDINGS OF THE SECTION OF CHEMISTRY, BIOLOGY AND MEDICINE. Text in English, Ukrainian. 1973 (vol.7). irreg. price varies. **Document type:** *Proceedings.*
Supersedes in part: Naukove Tovarystvo Imeni Shevchenka. Proceedings of the Section of Mathematics, Natural Sciences and Medicine (0470-5017)
Published by: Shevchenko Scientific Society, 63 Fourth Ave, New York, NY 10003. TEL 212-254-5130.

540 NLD ISSN 1570-8306
CODEN: NTKCFX
NEDERLANDS TIJDSCHRIFT VOOR KLINISCHE CHEMIE EN LABORATORIUMGENEESKUNDE. Text in Dutch. 1976. bi-m. bk.rev. index. back issues avail. **Document type:** *Academic/Scholarly.*
Former titles (until 2003): Nederlands Tijdschrift voor Klinische Chemie (1380-3689); (until 1995): Nederlandse Vereniging voor Klinische Chemie. Tijdschrift (0168-8472)
Indexed: BIOBASE, CIN, ChemAb, ChemTitl, ExcerpMed, IABS.
—BLDSC (6071.960000), CASDDS, CISTI, GNLM, IE, Infotrieve, KNAW.
Published by: Nederlandse Vereniging voor Klinische Chemie en Laboratoriumgeneeskunde, Catharijnesingel 49A, Utrecht, 3511 GC, Netherlands. TEL 31-30-2328623, FAX 31-30-2311178, buro@nvkc.nl, http://www.nvkc.nl/publicaties/tijdschrift.php. Circ: 800.

540 RUS ISSN 0203-493X
QP356.3 CODEN: NERODV
NEIROKHIMIYA. Text in Russian. q. RUR 1,400 for 6 mos. domestic (effective 2004). **Document type:** *Journal, Academic/Scholarly.*
Indexed: ChemAb, ChemTitl, RefZh.
—CASDDS, East View, GNLM.
Published by: Izdatel'stvo Nauka, Profsoyuznaya ul 90, Moscow, 117864, Russian Federation. TEL 7-095-3347151, FAX 7-095-4202220, secret@naukaran.ru, http://www.maik.ru/cgi-bin/list.pl?page=neiro, http://www.naukaran.ru.

546 RUS ISSN 0869-5784
CODEN: IVNMAW
NEORGANICHESKIE MATERIALY. Text in Russian. 1965. m. RUR 485 for 6 mos. domestic (effective 2004). bk.rev. abstr.; charts; illus. index. **Document type:** *Journal, Academic/Scholarly.* **Description:** Discusses phase equilibrium, including P-T-X diagrams and the fundamentals of inorganic materials science, which determines preparatory conditions for compounds of various compositions.
Formerly: Akademiya Nauk S.S.S.R. Izvestiya. Seriya Neorganicheskie Materialy (0002-337X)
Related titles: Online - full text ed.; ◆ English Translation: Inorganic Materials. ISSN 0020-1685.
Indexed: BullT&T, ChemAb, INIS AtomInd, Inspec, PhysBer, RefZh.
—BLDSC (0124.160000), CASDDS, CISTI, East View, KNAW, Linda Hall. **CCC.**
Published by: (Rossiiskaya Akademiya Nauk/Russian Academy of Sciences), Izdatel'stvo Nauka, Profsoyuznaya ul 90, Moscow, 117864, Russian Federation. TEL 7-095-3347151, FAX 7-095-4202220, neorganmat@igic.ras.ru, secret@naukaran.ru, http://www.maik.rssi.ru/cgi-bin/list.pl?page=neorgmat, http://www.naukaran.ru.

NEUROCHEMISTRY INTERNATIONAL. see *MEDICAL SCIENCES—Psychiatry And Neurology*

540 GBR ISSN 1144-0546
QD1 CODEN: NJCHE5
➤ **NEW JOURNAL OF CHEMISTRY.** Text in English. 1977. m. GBP 711, USD 1,301 combined subscription print & online eds. (effective 2006). **Document type:** *Journal, Academic/Scholarly.*
Formerly (until 1987): Nouveau Journal de Chimie (0398-9836)
Related titles: Online - full text ed.: ISSN 1369-9261. 1977. GBP 640, USD 1,171 (effective 2006) (from EBSCO Publishing, O C L C Online Computer Library Center, Inc., Swets Information Services).
Indexed: ASCA, BPRC&P, CCI, CIN, CMCI, Cadscan, ChemAb, ChemInfo, ChemTitl, CurCR, CurCont, EngInd, ExcerpMed, INIS AtomInd, ISR, IndChem, Inspec, LeadAb, MOS, MSB, MSCI, NPU, RCI, SCI, Zincscan.
—BLDSC (6084.319900), AskIEEE, CASDDS, CINDOC, CISTI, Ei, IDS, IE, Infotrieve, ingenta, Linda Hall. **CCC.**
Published by: (France. Centre National de la Recherche Scientifique FRA), Royal Society of Chemistry, Thomas Graham House, Science Park, Milton Rd, Cambridge, CB4 0WF, United Kingdom. TEL 44-1223-432360, FAX 44-1223-423623, njc@rsc.org, sales@rsc.org, http://www.rsc.org/njc. Circ: 1,000. **Subscr. to:** Portland Press Ltd., R S C Distribution Services, Commerce Way, Whitehall Industrial Estate, Colchester CO2 8HP, United Kingdom. TEL 44-1206-226050, FAX 44-1206-226055, sales@rscdistribution.org.

➤ **NEW TRENDS IN SYNTHETIC MEDICINAL CHEMISTRY.** see *MEDICAL SCIENCES*

➤ **NICAD (YEAR).** see *METALLURGY*

540 JPN
NIHON BUNSEKI SENTA KOHO/JAPAN CHEMICAL ANALYSIS CENTER. REPORT. Text in Japanese. 1979. s-a. **Document type:** *Bulletin.*
Published by: Nihon Bunseki Senta/Japan Chemical Analysis Center, 295-3 Sanno-cho, Inage-ku, Chiba-shi, 263-0002, Japan. Ed. Yoh Katayama.

540 JPN
NIHON BUNSEKI SENTA NYUSU/JAPAN CHEMICAL ANALYSIS CENTER. NEWS. Text in Japanese. 1985. bi-m. **Document type:** *Newsletter.*
Published by: Nihon Bunseki Senta/Japan Chemical Analysis Center, 295-3 Sanno-cho, Inage-ku, Chiba-shi, 263-0002, Japan. Ed. Yoh Katayama.

540 JPN ISSN 0915-860X
CODEN: NKOGEZ
NIHON ION KOKAN GAKKAISHI/JAPAN ASSOCIATION OF ION EXCHANGE. JOURNAL. Text in English, Japanese; Summaries in English. 1990. s-a. **Document type:** *Academic/Scholarly.*
—BLDSC (5008.057000), CASDDS.
Published by: Nihon Ion Kokan Gakkai/Japan Association of Ion Exchange, Kogyo Daigaku Rigakubu Kagakka Abe Kenkyushitsu, 12-1 Okayama 2-chome, Meguro-ku, Tokyo, 152-0033, Japan.

NIHON RIKAGAKU KYOKAI. KENKYU KIYO. see *PHYSICS*

NIIGATA RIKAGAKU/JOURNAL OF PHYSICS AND CHEMISTRY OF NIIGATA. see *PHYSICS*

540 JPN ISSN 0369-4356
NIIGATA UNIVERSITY. FACULTY OF SCIENCE. SCIENCE REPORTS. SERIES C: CHEMISTRY. Text in Multiple languages. 1964. irreg. per issue exchange basis.
Published by: Niigata Daigaku, Rigakubu/Niigata University, Faculty of Science, 8050 Igarashi Nino-cho, Niigata-shi, Niigata-ken 950-21, Japan.

540 JPN ISSN 0285-7626
QD49.J3
NIPPON KAGAKKAI KOEN YOKOSHU/CHEMICAL SOCIETY OF JAPAN. PREPRINTS OF THE CONFERENCE. Text in Japanese. s-a.
—BLDSC (6112.702000).
Published by: Chemical Society of Japan/Nippon Kagakukai, 1-5, Kanda-Surugadai 1-Chome, Chiyoda-ku, Tokyo, 101-0062, Japan.

NIPPON KAYAKU. ANNUAL REPORT. see *PHARMACY AND PHARMACOLOGY*

540 ESP
NOTICIAS PARA QUIMICOS. Text in Spanish. 11/yr.
Address: Avda. Puerta del Angel 24, 1o, Barcelona, 08002, Spain. TEL 3-179-249, FAX 3-179-299. Ed. Antonio P Gasco. Circ: 4,200.

540 ITA
NOTIZIE DOW. Text in Italian. 1967. bi-m. free. adv. back issues avail.
Formerly: Dow in Italia
Published by: Dow Italia, Via Gioacchino Murat, 23, Milan, MI 20159, Italy. FAX 02-27772710. Circ: 2,500.

NUCLEUS. see *ENERGY—Nuclear Energy*

540 USA ISSN 0362-0026
QD1 CODEN: NCLUA2
➤ **THE NUCLEUS (HARVARD).** Text in English. 1922. m. (except June and Aug.). USD 11 (effective 2003). adv. back issues avail. **Document type:** *Newsletter, Academic/Scholarly.* **Description:** Announces section meetings, section and member news, and articles of general interest to members.
Published by: American Chemical Society, Northeastern Section, 19 Mill Rd, Harvard, MA 01451. TEL 781-837-0424, FAX 781-837-8792, http://www.nesacs.org. Ed., R&P Arno Heyn TEL 617-969-5712. Adv. contact Vincent J Gale. Circ: 7,500 (controlled).

➤ **O P D CHEMICAL BUYERS DIRECTORY.** see *BUSINESS AND ECONOMICS—Trade And Industrial Directories*

540 USA ISSN 0029-8271
THE OCTAGON. Text in English. 1918. 8/yr. USD 1 to non-members (effective 1998). adv. bk.rev. reprint service avail. from PQC. **Document type:** *Newsletter.* **Description:** Contains organization news.
Related titles: Microform ed.: (from PQC).
Indexed: AIAP.
Published by: American Chemical Society, Lehigh Valley Section, 744 N Broad St, Allentown, PA 18104. TEL 610-770-7348, FAX 610-770-7348, gbcmars@enter.net. Ed. Gail Marsella. Circ: 1,000 (controlled).

540 AUT ISSN 0379-5314
QD1 CODEN: OCMZAX
OESTERREICHISCHE CHEMIE ZEITSCHRIFT. Text in German. 1947. bi-m. EUR 55.50 domestic; EUR 74 foreign (effective 2005). adv. bk.rev. illus.; tr.lit. **Document type:** *Journal, Trade.*
Formerly (until 1974): Oesterreichische Chemiker-Zeitung (0258-4336)
Indexed: ChemAb, ChemInfo, ChemTitl, INIS AtomInd, MSB.

C

—BLDSC (6305.700000), CASDDS, CISTI.
Published by: Verlag Lorenz, Ebendorferstr 10, Vienna, W 1010, Austria. TEL 43-1-40566950, FAX 43-1-4068693, chemie@verlag-lorenz.at, office@verlag-lorenz.at, http://www.verlag-lorenz.at/chemie/index.html. Ed. Sepp Fischer. adv.: B&W page EUR 2,300, color page EUR 3,680; trim 184 x 256. Circ: 5,600.

OIL & CHEMICAL WORKER. see *LABOR UNIONS*

660   NLD
ONDERNEMINGSANALYSES CHEMIE. Text in Dutch. a.
Description: Financial and economic information on the chemical industry and related industries in the Netherlands.
Published by: Reed Business Information bv (Subsidiary of: Reed Business), Postbus 16400, Den Haag, 2500 BK, Netherlands. TEL 31-70-3624800, FAX 31-70-3605606.

540   USA   ISSN 0553-0377
ORGANIZATION OF AMERICAN STATES. DEPARTMENT OF SCIENTIFIC AFFAIRS. SERIE DE QUIMICA: MONOGRAFIAS. Text in English. 1965. irreg., latest vol.21, 1979. USD 3.50. **Document type:** *Monographic series.*
Published by: Organization of American States/Organizacion de los Estados Americanos, Department of Publications, 1889 F St, N W, Washington, DC 20006. TEL 703-941-1617. Circ: 3,000.

540   IND   ISSN 0970-020X
            CODEN: OJCHEG
ORIENTAL JOURNAL OF CHEMISTRY. Text in English. 1985. 3/yr. USD 150 to institutions (effective 2006). bk.rev. back issues avail. **Document type:** *Journal, Academic/Scholarly.*
Indexed: ASFA, B&BAb, ChemAb, ESPM, MSB, PollutAb, RefZh, SWRA, ToxAb.
—BLDSC (6291.176550), CISTI, IE, ingenta.
Published by: Scientific Publishers, 5-A New Pali Rd., Near Hotel Taj Hari Mahal, PO Box 91, Jodhpur, Rajasthan 342 003, India. TEL 91-291-2433323, FAX 91-291-2512580, info@scientificpub.com, http://www.scientificpub.com/ bookdetails.php?booktransid=460&bookid=456.

ORIGINS OF LIFE AND EVOLUTION OF THE BIOSPHERE. see *BIOLOGY*

540   GBR   ISSN 1367-109X
OXFORD CHEMISTRY PRIMERS. Text in English. irreg., latest vol.99, 2002. price varies. **Document type:** *Monographic series.*
—BLDSC (6320.679500), IE, ingenta.
Published by: Oxford University Press, Great Clarendon St, Oxford, OX2 6DP, United Kingdom. TEL 44-1865-556767, FAX 44-1865-556646, enquiry@oup.co.uk, http://www.oup-usa.org/ catalogs/general/series/Oxford_Chemistry_Primers.html, http://www.oup.co.uk/. **Orders in N. America to:** Oxford University Press, 2001 Evans Rd, Cary, NC 27513. jnlorders@oup-usa.org.

540   GBR   ISSN 0302-4199
OXFORD CHEMISTRY SERIES. Text in English. irreg., latest vol.35, 1990. price varies. **Document type:** *Monographic series.*
—CISTI.
Published by: Oxford University Press, Great Clarendon St, Oxford, OX2 6DP, United Kingdom. TEL 44-1865-556767, FAX 44-1865-556646, enquiry@oup.co.uk, http://www.oup-usa.org/ catalogs/general/series/Oxford_Chemistry_Series.html, http://www.oup.co.uk/. **Orders in N. America to:** Oxford University Press, 2001 Evans Rd, Cary, NC 27513. jnlorders@oup-usa.org.

540   UZB
QD1   CODEN: UZKZAC
O'ZBEKISTON KIMYO JURNALI/UZBEK JOURNAL ON CHEMISTRY. Text in Russian. 1957. bi-m. USD 215 foreign (effective 2004). charts. index. **Document type:** *Journal, Academic/Scholarly.* **Description:** Presents research papers on the development of chemistry in Uzbekistan and the rest of the world.
Formerly: Uzbekskii Khimicheskii Zhurnal (0042-1707)
Indexed: ABIPC, BiolAb, CIN, ChemAb, ChemTitl, INIS AtomInd.
—BLDSC (0384.100000), CASDDS, CISTI, Linda Hall. **CCC.**
Published by: O'zbekiston Respublikasi Fanlar Akademiyasi/Academy of Sciences of Uzbekistan, 70, Academician Yahyo, Gulamov St, Tashkent, 700047, Uzbekistan. http://www.academy.uz. **Dist. by:** East View Information Services, 3020 Harbor Ln. N., Minneapolis, MN 55447. TEL 800-477-1005, FAX 800-800-3839, eastview@eastview.com, http://www.eastview.com.

PACKAGING TECHNOLOGY AND SCIENCE. see *PACKAGING*

540 330   GBR   ISSN 1469-3011
PERFORMANCE CHEMICALS EUROPE. Text in English. 1986. q. EUR 153 in Europe; GBP 92, USD 160 (effective 2003). adv. charts; illus.; stat. back issues avail. **Document type:** *Trade.* **Description:** Provides news and inside knowledge of all sectors of the international speciality and fine chemicals industry, from pharmaceuticals to paints and coatings, agrochemicals to personal care products.

Former titles (until 1999): Performance Chemicals International (1368-2172); (until 1997): Performance Chemicals (0950-3870)
Related titles: Online - full text ed.: (from ProQuest Information & Learning); ♦ Supplement(s): Performance Chemicals News Bulletin. ISSN 1365-1528.
Indexed: B&I, CBNB, CEABA, CSNB, EngInd, LHB, RAPRA, WSCA.
—CISTI, IE, Infotrieve. **CCC.**
Published by: Reed Business Information Ltd. (Subsidiary of: Reed Business), Quadrant House, The Quadrant, Brighton Rd, Sutton, Surrey SM2 5AS, United Kingdom. TEL 44-20-86523500, FAX 44-20-86528932, http:// www.reedbusiness.co.uk/. Ed. Alan Tyler TEL 44-20-8652-8126. Pub. Les Edwards. Adv. contact John Wright. Circ: 6,582. **Subscr. to:** Quadrant Subscription Services, Rockwood House, 9-17 Perrymount Rd, Haywards Heath, W. Sussex RH16 3DH, United Kingdom. TEL 44-20-8652-3500, FAX 44-20-8652-8932, rbi.subscriptions@qss-uk.com.

540   GBR   ISSN 1365-1528
PERFORMANCE CHEMICALS NEWS BULLETIN. Text in English. 1994. 2/yr. (2/yr.?).
Related titles: ♦ Supplement to: Performance Chemicals Europe. ISSN 1469-3011.
Indexed: B&I.
Published by: Reed Business Information Ltd. (Subsidiary of: Reed Business), Quadrant House, The Quadrant, Brighton Rd, Sutton, Surrey SM2 5AS, United Kingdom. TEL 44-208-652-3500, FAX 44-208-652-8977, rbi.subscriptions@qss-uk.com, http://www.reedbusiness.co.uk/.

PERFUMER & FLAVORIST. see *BEAUTY CULTURE—Perfumes And Cosmetics*

THE PESTICIDE MANUAL. see *AGRICULTURE*

PHARMACEUTICAL CHEMISTRY JOURNAL. see *PHARMACY AND PHARMACOLOGY*

PHARMACHEM. see *PHARMACY AND PHARMACOLOGY*

PHARMACOCHEMISTRY LIBRARY. see *PHARMACY AND PHARMACOLOGY*

540   USA
PHI LAMBDA UPSILON. REGISTER. Text in English. 1925. s-a. USD 3.
Indexed: ChemAb.
Published by: Phi Lambda Upsilon, Honorary Chemical Society, c/o John Zimmerman, Ed, Department of Chemistry, Wabash College, Crawfordsville, IN 47933. Circ: 3,500.

540   GBR   ISSN 1474-905X
QD701   CODEN: PPSHCB
➤ **PHOTOCHEMICAL & PHOTOBIOLOGICAL SCIENCES.** Text in English. 2002. m. GBP 1,089, USD 1,992 combined subscription print & online eds. (effective 2006). adv.
Document type: *Journal, Academic/Scholarly.* **Description:** Contains research on the interaction of the environment with living systems and into areas in which environmental factors affect health or in which light is a cost-effective catalyst or alternative source of energy.
Related titles: Online - full text ed.: ISSN 1474-9092. GBP 980, USD 1,793 (effective 2006) (from EBSCO Publishing, O C L C Online Computer Library Center, Inc., Swets Information Services).
Indexed: BBCI, CCI, ChemAb, CurCR, CurCont, ExcerpMed, IndChem, RCI, RefZh.
—BLDSC (6465.979100), CISTI, IE, Infotrieve, ingenta, Linda Hall. **CCC.**
Published by: (European Photochemistry Association FRA, European Society for Photobiology CHE), Royal Society of Chemistry, Thomas Graham House, Science Park, Milton Rd, Cambridge, CB4 0WF, United Kingdom. TEL 44-1223-420066, FAX 44-1223-423623, pps@rsc.org, sales@rsc.org, http://www.rsc.org/pps. Ed. Dr. Jamie Humphrey. **Subscr. to:** Portland Press Ltd., R S C Distribution Services, Commerce Way, Whitehall Industrial Estate, Colchester CO2 8HP, United Kingdom. TEL 44-1206-226050, FAX 44-1206-226055, sales@rscdistribution.org.

540   GBR   ISSN 0556-3860
QD601.A1   CODEN: PHCYAQ
PHOTOCHEMISTRY. (In five parts: Part I (Physical Aspects of Photochemistry), Part II (Organic Aspects of Photochemistry), Part III (Polymer Photochemistry), Part IV (Photochemical Aspects of Solar Energy Conversion), Part V (Artificial Photosynthesis)) Text in English. 1968. a., latest vol.34, 2004, Jan. GBP 249.95, USD 459 per vol. (effective 2004). charts. index. back issues avail. **Document type:** *Academic/Scholarly.* **Description:** Provides annual reviews of photo-induced processes.
Indexed: BIOSIS Prev, ChemAb, EngInd.
—BLDSC (6465.983000), CASDDS, CISTI, Ei, IE, ingenta, Linda Hall. **CCC.**

Published by: Royal Society of Chemistry, Thomas Graham House, Science Park, Milton Rd, Cambridge, CB4 0WF, United Kingdom. TEL 44-1223-432360, FAX 44-1223-423623, sales@rsc.org, advertising@rsc.org, http://www.rsc.org/ CFbooks/sprindex.cfm?BKC=PC. Ed. I Dunkin. **Subscr. to:** Extenza - Turpin, Pegasus Dr, Stratton Business Park, Biggleswade, Beds SG18 8TQ, United Kingdom.

▼ **PHOTONICS AND NANOSTRUCTURES;** fundamentals and applications. see *PHYSICS*

PHYSICS AND CHEMISTRY OF MATERIALS TREATMENT. see *ENGINEERING—Engineering Mechanics And Materials*

PHYSICS AND CHEMISTRY OF MATERIALS WITH LOW-DIMENSIONAL STRUCTURES. see *PHYSICS—Mechanics*

PLASMA CHEMISTRY & PLASMA PROCESSING. see *ENGINEERING—Chemical Engineering*

PLATINUM METALS REVIEW (ONLINE). see *METALLURGY*

PODSTAWY I METODY OCENY SRODOWISKA PRACY/PRINCIPLES AND METHODS OF ASSESSING THE WORKING ENVIRONMENT. see *PUBLIC HEALTH AND SAFETY*

660   POL   ISSN 0867-8928
TP1   CODEN: PJACE2
POLISH JOURNAL OF APPLIED CHEMISTRY. Text in English. 1957. q. EUR 94 foreign (effective 2005). abstr.; charts; illus. index. 120 p./no.; **Document type:** *Journal, Academic/Scholarly.* **Description:** Publication on chemistry, chemical technology and related areas.
Former titles: Chemia Stosowana (0376-0898); Chemia Stosowana. Seria A: Zagadnienia Technologii Chemicznej (0009-2231)
Indexed: CIN, ChemAb, ChemTitl, INIS AtomInd, RefZh.
—BLDSC (6543.666000), CASDDS, CISTI, IE, ingenta, Linda Hall.
Published by: Polska Akademia Nauk, Centrum Chemii Polimerow/Polish Academy of Sciences, Center of Polymer Chemistry, ul M.Sklodowskiej-Curie 34, Zabrze, 41819, Poland. FAX 48-32-2712969, pjachem@cchp-pan.zabrze.pl, http://www.cchp-pan.zabrze.pl/index_pliki/pjapchem.html. Circ: 700. **Dist. by:** Ars Polona, Krakowskie Przedmiescie 7, Warsaw, Poland. TEL 48-22-9263914, FAX 48-22-9265334, arspolona@arspolona.com.pl, http://www.arspolona.com.pl.

540   POL   ISSN 0137-5083
QD1   CODEN: PJCHDQ
➤ **POLISH JOURNAL OF CHEMISTRY.** Text in English. 1921. m. EUR 395 foreign (effective 2005). bk.rev. charts. index. **Document type:** *Journal, Academic/Scholarly.*
Formerly (until 1978): Roczniki Chemii (0035-7677)
Indexed: ASCA, CCI, Cadscan, ChemAb, ChemInfo, ChemTitl, CurCR, CurCont, EngInd, INIS AtomInd, ISR, IndChem, LeadAb, MOS, MSB, MSCI, NPU, RCI, RefZh, SCI, Zincscan.
—BLDSC (6543.667000), CASDDS, CISTI, Ei, IDS, IE, Infotrieve, ingenta, Linda Hall. **CCC.**
Published by: Polskie Towarzystwo Chemiczne/Polish Chemical Society, Institute of Physical Chemistry, Polish Academy of Sciences, ul Kasprzaka 44/52, Warsaw, 01224, Poland. pjch@ichf.edu.pl, http://malina.ichf.edu.pl/pjch, http://www.ptchem.lodz.pl. Ed. Bogdan Baranowski. Circ: 730. **Dist. by:** Ars Polona, Krakowskie Przedmiescie 7, Warsaw, Poland. TEL 48-22-9263914, FAX 48-22-9265334, arspolona@arspolona.com.pl, http://www.arspolona.com.pl.

540   POL   ISSN 0416-7341
            CODEN: ZNGCAU
POLITECHNIKA GDANSKA. ZESZYTY NAUKOWE. CHEMIA. Text in English, Polish; Summaries in Russian. 1955. irreg. price varies. abstr.; bibl.; charts. **Document type:** *Academic/Scholarly.* **Description:** Deals with organic, analytic and physical chemistry: corrosion protection technology, drugs, fats, food and fish technology.
Indexed: ChemAb.
—CASDDS, Linda Hall.
Published by: Politechnika Gdanska, Ul G Narutowicza 11-12, Gdansk, 80952, Poland. **Dist. by:** Osrodek Rozpowszechniania Wydawnictw Naukowych PAN, Palac Kultury i Nauki, Warsaw 00901, Poland.

540   POL
POLITECHNIKA KRAKOWSKA. MONOGRAFIE. SERIA: INZYNIERIA I TECHNOLOGIA CHEMICZNA. Text in Polish; Summaries in English, French, German, Russian. 1985. irreg. price varies. bibl.; charts; illus. **Document type:** *Monographic series, Academic/Scholarly.*
Related titles: Series of: Politechnika Krakowska. Monografie. ISSN 0860-097X.
Published by: Politechnika Krakowska, Ul Warszawska 24, Krakow, 31155, Poland. TEL 48-12-6374289, FAX 48-12-6374289. Ed. Elzbieta Nachlik. Adv. contact Ewa Malochleb. Circ: 200.

540 POL ISSN 0867-7735
QD1 CODEN: ZNPCB8
POLITECHNIKA KRAKOWSKA. ZESZYTY NAUKOWE. INZYNIERIA I TECHNOLOGIA CHEMICZNA. Text in Polish; Summaries in English, French, German, Russian. 1968. irreg. price varies. bibl.; charts; illus. **Document type:** *Monographic series, Academic/Scholarly.*
Formerly: Politechnika Krakowska. Zeszyty Naukowe. Chemia (0075-7055)
Indexed: CIN, ChemAb, ChemTitl, RefZh.
—CASDDS, CISTI, Linda Hall.
Published by: Politechnika Krakowska, Ul Warszawska 24, Krakow, 31155, Poland. TEL 48-12-6374289, FAX 48-12-6374289. Ed. Elzbieta Nachlik. Adv. contact Ewa Malochleb. Circ: 200.

540 POL ISSN 0458-1555
QD1 CODEN: ZNPLAY
POLITECHNIKA LODZKA. ZESZYTY NAUKOWE. CHEMIA. Text in Polish; Summaries in English, Russian. 1954. irreg. price varies. reprints avail. **Document type:** *Monographic series, Academic/Scholarly.* **Description:** Articles on analytical chemistry, organic chemistry, inorganic chemistry, polymer chemistry and radiation chemistry.
Related titles: Microform ed.
Indexed: ChemAb.
—CASDDS, CISTI, Linda Hall.
Published by: (Politechnika Lodzka/Technical University of Lodz), Wydawnictwo Politechniki Lodzkiej, ul Wolczanska 223, Lodz, 93005, Poland. TEL 48-42-6312087. Ed. Bogdan Ptaszynski TEL 48-42-6840793. Circ: 200. **Dist. by:** Ars Polona, Krakowskie Przedmiescie 7, Warsaw, Poland. TEL 48-22-9263914, FAX 48-22-9265334, arspolona@arspolona.com.pl, http://www.arspolona.com.pl.

540 660 POL ISSN 0372-9494
QD1 CODEN: ZNSCAM
POLITECHNIKA SLASKA. ZESZYTY NAUKOWE. CHEMIA. Text in Polish; Summaries in English, German, Russian. 1957. irreg. price varies. **Document type:** *Academic/Scholarly.*
Indexed: ChemAb.
—BLDSC (9512.325700), CASDDS, IE, ingenta, Linda Hall.
Published by: Politechnika Slaska, ul Akademicka 5, Gliwice, 44100, Poland. wydawnictwo_mark@polsl.pl. Ed. Genowefa Bienkiewicz. Circ: 205. **Dist. by:** Ars Polona, Krakowskie Przedmiescie 7, Warsaw, Poland.

540 POL ISSN 0137-2300
CODEN: PNPWBQ
POLITECHNIKA WARSZAWSKA. PRACE NAUKOWE. CHEMIA. Text in Polish. 1954. irreg., latest no.62, 1999. **Document type:** *Academic/Scholarly.*
Formerly (until 1968): Politechnika Warszawska. Zeszyty Naukowe. Chemia (0372-9478)
—BLDSC (6590.790000), CASDDS, Linda Hall.
Published by: Oficyna Wydawnicza Politechniki Warszawskiej/Publishing House of the Warsaw University of Technology, ul Polna 50, Warsaw, 00644, Poland. bgpw@pg.pw.edu.pl, oficyna@wpw.pw.edu.pl.

668.8 GBR ISSN 0032-3861
TP156.P6 CODEN: POLMAG
➤ **POLYMER.** Text in English. 1960. 26/yr. EUR 6,206 in Europe to institutions; JPY 824,100 in Japan to institutions; USD 6,943 to institutions except Europe and Japan; EUR 472 in Europe to qualified personnel; JPY 62,700 in Japan to qualified personnel; USD 529 to qualified personnel except Europe and Japan (effective 2006). adv. bk.rev. abstr.; bibl.; charts. index. **Document type:** *Journal, Academic/Scholarly.* **Description:** Provides international coverage of the science and technology of polymers.
Incorporates: Computational and Theoretical Polymer Science (1089-3156); Incorporates (in 1991): Polymer Communications (0263-6476)
Related titles: Microfilm ed.: (from PQC); Online - full text ed.: (from EBSCO Publishing, Gale Group, IngentaConnect, ScienceDirect, Swets Information Services).
Indexed: ABIPC, ASCA, B&BAb, BioEngAb, BrCerAb, BrTechI, C&ISA, CCI, CerAb, ChemAb, ChemTitl, CivEngAb, CorrAb, CurCont, CurPA, E&CAJ, EMA, EngInd, FLUIDEX, IAA, ISMEC, ISR, Inspec, M&TEA, MBF, METADEX, MSCI, P&BA, RAPRA, RCI, RefZh, SCI, SIA, SolStAb, TTI, WAA, WSCA, WTA.
—BLDSC (6547.700000), AskIEEE, CASDDS, CISTI, Ei, IDS, IE, Infotrieve, ingenta, Linda Hall. **CCC.**
Published by: Elsevier Ltd. (Subsidiary of: Elsevier Science & Technology), The Boulevard, Langford Ln, Kidlington, Oxford, OX5 1GB, United Kingdom. TEL 44-1865-843000, FAX 44-1865-843010, nlinfo-f@elsevier.nl, http://www.elsevier.com/locate/polymer. Circ: 2,000 (paid). **Subscr. to:** Elsevier BV, PO Box 211, Amsterdam 1000 AE, Netherlands. TEL 31-20-485-3757, FAX 31-20-485-3432, http://www.elsevier.nl.

540 DEU ISSN 0170-0839
QD380 CODEN: POBUDR
➤ **POLYMER BULLETIN.** Text in English. 1978. m. EUR 1,498 combined subscription to institutions print & online eds. (effective 2005). adv. back issues avail.; reprint service avail. from ISI. **Document type:** *Journal, Academic/Scholarly.* **Description:** Offers results in advances in polymer science, including biopolymers polymer engineering.
Related titles: Microfiche ed.: (from PQC); Online - full text ed.: ISSN 1436-2449 (from EBSCO Publishing, Springer LINK, Swets Information Services).
Indexed: ABIPC, CCI, CIN, Cadscan, ChemAb, ChemTitl, CurCont, EngInd, ISR, Inspec, LeadAb, MSCI, PhysBer, RAPRA, RCI, RefZh, SCI, SIA, TTI, Zincscan.
—BLDSC (6547.702500), CASDDS, CISTI, Ei, IDS, IE, Infotrieve, ingenta, Linda Hall. **CCC.**
Published by: Springer-Verlag (Subsidiary of: Springer Science+Business Media), Tiergartenstr 17, Heidelberg, 69121, Germany. TEL 49-6221-3450, FAX 49-6221-345229, http://link.springer.de/link/service/journals/00289/index.htm. Eds. K Muellen, R Faust, Yoshiki Chujo. Adv. contact Stephan Kroeck TEL 49-30-827875739. **Subscr. in the Americas to:** Springer-Verlag New York, Inc., Journal Fulfillment, PO Box 2485, Secaucus, NJ 07096-2485. TEL 800-777-4643, 201-348-4033, FAX 201-348-4505, journals@springer-ny.com, http://www.springer-ny.com; **Subscr. to:** Springer GmbH Auslieferungsgesellschaft, Haberstr 7, Heidelberg 69126, Germany. TEL 49-6221-345-0, FAX 49-6221-345-4229, subscriptions@springer.de.

540 NLD ISSN 0926-9118
CODEN: PSLIF3
➤ **POLYMER SCIENCE LIBRARY.** Text in English. 1979. irreg., latest vol.10, 1996. price varies. back issues avail. **Document type:** *Monographic series, Academic/Scholarly.* **Description:** Reports on research and innovations in polymer development and applications.
—BLDSC (6547.738400), CASDDS.
Published by: Elsevier BV (Subsidiary of: Elsevier Science & Technology), Radarweg 29, Amsterdam, 1043 NX, Netherlands. TEL 31-20-4853911, FAX 31-20-4852457, nlinfo-f@elsevier.nl, http://www.elsevier.nl. Ed. A D Jenkins.

540 RUS ISSN 1560-0904
POLYMER SCIENCE. SERIES B. Text in English. 1995. irreg. USD 4,440 in North America; USD 5,133 elsewhere (effective 2004). **Document type:** *Journal, Academic/Scholarly.* **Description:** Contains reviews on all aspects of fundamental polymer science, basic technological information on polymer synthesis and modification and the processing of polymeric materials and polymer-based composites; and methods of investigation.
Supersedes in part (in 1995): Polymer Science. Series A (0965-545X); Which was formerly (until 1992): Polymer Science U.S.S.R. (0032-3950)
Related titles: ♦ Translation of: Vysokomolekulyarnye Soedineniya. Seriya A i Seriya B. ISSN 1023-3091.
Indexed: BrCerAb, C&ISA, CCI, CerAb, CorrAb, CurCont, E&CAJ, EMA, IAA, ISR, M&TEA, MBF, METADEX, MSCI, RAPRA, RCI, SCI, SolStAb, WAA.
—BLDSC (0416.904200), CISTI, IE, Infotrieve, ingenta, Linda Hall.
Published by: M A I K Nauka - Interperiodica, Profsoyuznaya ul 90, Moscow, 117997, Russian Federation. TEL 7-095-3347420, FAX 7-095-3360666, compmg@maik.ru, http://www.maik.ru/cgi-bin/journal.pl?name=polscib&page=main. Ed. Nikolai A Plate. R&P Vladimir I Vasil'ev. **Subscr. to:** Interperiodica, PO Box 1831, Birmingham, AL 35201-1831. TEL 205-995-1567, 800-633-4931, FAX 205-995-1588.

540 RUS ISSN 1811-2382
➤ **POLYMER SCIENCE. SERIES C.** Text in English. 2000. s-a. **Document type:** *Journal, Academic/Scholarly.*
Related titles: ♦ Translation of: Vysokomolekulyarnye Soedineniya. Seriya C.
Published by: M A I K Nauka - Interperiodica, Profsoyuznaya ul 90, Moscow, 117997, Russian Federation. TEL 7-095-3361600, FAX 7-095-3360666, compmg@maik.ru, http://www.maik.ru.

➤ **POLYMERS FOR ADVANCED TECHNOLOGIES.** see *PLASTICS*

540 660 ROM ISSN 1454-2331
QD1 CODEN: SICSEI
POLYTECHNICAL UNIVERSITY OF BUCHAREST. SCIENTIFIC BULLETIN. SERIES B: CHEMISTRY AND MATERIALS SCIENCE. Text in English, French, German, Spanish; Summaries in Romanian, English. 1929. q. USD 150 (effective 1999). bk.rev. abstr.; bibl.; charts; illus.; maps; stat. back issues avail. **Document type:** *Bulletin, Academic/Scholarly.*
Former titles: Universitatea Politehnica Bucuresti. Buletin Stiintific. Chimie si Stiinta Materialelor; Institutul Politehnic Bucuresti. Buletin Stiintific. Chimie, Metalurgie si Stiinta Materialelor (1220-305X); Which was formed by the 1990 merger of: Institutul Politehnic Bucuresti. Buletin. Seria Chimie (1012-3229); Institutul Politehnic Bucuresti. Buletin. Seria Metalurgia (1012-3210); Seria Metalurgie was formerly (until 1983) : Institutul Politehnic Gheorghe Gheorghiu-Dej Bucuresti. Buletin. Seria Metalurgie (0256-4580); Seria Chimie was formerly (until 1983) : Institutul Politehnic Gheorghe Gheorghiu-Dej Bucuresti. Buletin. Seria Chimie (0257-7798); Which both superseded in part (in 1982) : Institutul Politehnic Gheorghe Gheorghiu-Dej Bucuresti. Buletin. Seria Chimie - Metalurgie (0378-9616); Which was formerly (until 1976) : Institutul Politehnic Gheorghe Gheorghiu-Dej Bucuresti. Buletin (0366-0419); (until 1965): Institutul Politehnic Bucuresti. Buletin (0020-4242); Poltitehnice i din Bucuresti. Buletin
Indexed: BrCerAb, C&ISA, CerAb, ChemAb, ChemTitl, CivEngAb, CorrAb, E&CAJ, EMA, EngInd, IAA, Inspec, M&TEA, MBF, METADEX, RefZh, SolStAb, WAA.
—BLDSC (8177.810000), AskIEEE, CASDDS, CISTI, Ei, Linda Hall.
Published by: Universitatea Politehnica Bucuresti, Biblioteca Centrala, Splaiul Independentei 313, Bucharest, 77206, Romania. TEL 40-4100400, FAX 40-4115365, gabiss@main.rector.pub.ro. Ed. C Berbente. Circ: 1,000. **Subscr. to:** Rodipet S.A.

POWERPLANT CHEMISTRY; the journal of all power plant chemistry areas. see *ENERGY—Electrical Energy*

540.71 DEU ISSN 1617-5638
PRAXIS DER NATURWISSENSCHAFTEN - CHEMIE IN DER SCHULE. Text in German. 2000. 8/yr. EUR 63.20 domestic to individuals; EUR 72 foreign to individuals; EUR 47.20 domestic to students; EUR 54 foreign to students (effective 2006). bk.rev. **Document type:** *Journal, Academic/Scholarly.*
Formed by the merger of (1953-2000): Chemie in der Schule (0009-2843); (1951-2000): Praxis der Naturwissenschaften. Chemie (0177-9516); Which was formerly (until 1980): Praxis der Naturwissenschaften. Chemie im Unterricht der Schulen (0342-8745); (until 1973): Praxis der Naturwissenschaften. Teil 3. Chemie (0342-8737)
Indexed: IBR, IBZ, RefZh.
—BLDSC (6603.175850), CASDDS, CISTI, IE, ingenta.
Published by: Aulis-Verlag Deubner GmbH und Co. KG, Antwerpener Str 6-12, Cologne, 50672, Germany. TEL 49-221-957454-0, FAX 49-221-518443, info@aulis.de, http://www.aulis.de. R&P Wolfgang Deubner. Adv. contact Ulrike Lennertz. Circ: 5,400 (paid).

540 USA ISSN 1547-6391
▼ **PRISTINE PROCESSING.** Text in English. 2003 (Sept.). q. free to qualified personnel (effective 2005). adv. **Document type:** *Magazine, Trade.*
Published by: Chemical Week Associates, 110 William St 11th Fl, New York, NY 10038. TEL 212-621-4674, FAX 212-621-4694, http://www.pristineprocessing.com, http://www.chemweek.com. Ed. Deborah W. Hairston. Adv. contact Doris Deutsch. B&W page USD 5,000; trim 7.875 x 10.75. Circ: 20,000 (controlled).

540 610 NLD ISSN 0079-6468
RM30 CODEN: PMDCAY
➤ **PROGRESS IN MEDICINAL CHEMISTRY.** Text in English. 1961. irreg., latest vol.42, 2004. price varies. back issues avail. **Document type:** *Monographic series, Academic/Scholarly.* **Description:** Explores research and developments in the subspecialty of medicinal chemistry.
Incorporates (1992-2000): Advances in Medicinal Chemistry (1067-5698)
Related titles: Online - full text ed.: (from ScienceDirect).
Indexed: BIOSIS Prev, BiolAb, CIN, ChemAb, ChemTitl, DBA, ISR, IndMed, MEDLINE.
—BLDSC (6868.970000), CASDDS, CISTI, GNLM, IE, Infotrieve, ingenta, KNAW, Linda Hall. **CCC.**
Published by: Elsevier BV (Subsidiary of: Elsevier Science & Technology), Radarweg 29, Amsterdam, 1043 NX, Netherlands. TEL 31-20-4853911, FAX 31-20-4852457, nlinfo-f@elsevier.nl, http://www.elsevier.com/wps/find/bookdescription.cws_home/BS_PMC/description#description, http://www.elsevier.nl. Eds. A W Oxford, F D King, G Lawton.

540 ESP
PROYECTOS QUIMICOS. Text in Spanish. 1976. fortn. EUR 325.38 domestic; EUR 303.84 foreign (effective 2004). adv. stat. **Document type:** *Bulletin, Trade.* **Description:** Covers chemistry, drugs, plastics and paper.
Related titles: Alternate Frequency ed(s).: bi-m.
Published by: Tecnipublicaciones Espana, S.L., Avda de Manoteras 44, 3a Planta, Madrid, 28050, Spain. TEL 34-91-2972000, FAX 34-91-2972154, tp@tecnipublicaciones.com, http://www.tecnipublicaciones.com. adv.: B&W page EUR 887, color page EUR 1,031; bleed 210 x 285. Circ: 3,000 (controlled).

660 POL ISSN 0033-2496
TP1 CODEN: PRCHAB
PRZEMYSL CHEMICZNY. Text in Polish; Summaries in English, Polish, Russian; Contents page in English, French, Polish, Russian. 1917. m. PLZ 240 domestic; USD 180 foreign; PLZ 20 per issue (effective 2004). adv. bk.rev. abstr.; bibl.; charts; illus. index. 44 p./no.; **Document type:** *Trade.*
Indexed: ASCA, CCI, CEA, CEABA, CIN, Cadscan, ChemAb, ChemInfo, ChemTitl, CurCR, CurCont, IndChem, LeadAb, MSCI, RCI, RefZh, S&F, SSCI, TCEA, TTI, WSCA, Zincscan.
—BLDSC (6945.050000), CASDDS, CISTI, Ei, IDS, IE, Infotrieve, ingenta, Linda Hall.
Published by: (Poland. Ministerstwo Przemyslu Chemicznego), Wydawnictwo SIGMA - N O T Sp. z o.o., ul Ratuszowa 11, PO Box 1004, Warsaw, 00950, Poland. TEL 48-22-8180918, FAX 48-22-6192187, pechem@pol.pl, informacja@sigma-not.pl, http://www.sigma-not.pl. Ed. Andrzej Szyprowski. adv.: B&W page PLZ 1,800, color page PLZ 3,950. Circ: 800.
Co-sponsor: Stowarzyszenie Inzynierow i Technikow Przemyslu Chemicznego.

540 660 USA ISSN 0033-4545
QD1 CODEN: PACHAS
➤ **PURE AND APPLIED CHEMISTRY.** Text in English. 1960. m. USD 99 to individuals; USD 1,500 to institutions (effective 2004). adv. abstr.; illus.; stat. Index. back issues avail.; reprints avail. **Document type:** *Journal, Academic/Scholarly.* **Description:** Publishes the text of lectures delivered by scientists at IUPAC symposia and specially commissioned review articles on important topics within the field.
Formerly: International Congress of Pure and Applied Chemistry. Lectures (0074-3925)
Related titles: Microform ed.: (from PQC); Online - full text ed.: ISSN 1365-3075 (from EBSCO Publishing, O C L C Online Computer Library Center, Inc., Swets Information Services).
Indexed: A&ATA, ASCA, AbHyg, AgBio, AgrForAb, AnalAb, ApicAb, BiolAb, BullT&T, CCI, CIN, CIS, CPA, Cadscan, ChemAb, ChemInfo, ChemTitl, CurCont, DSA, EngInd, ExcerpMed, FCA, FPA, FS&TA, ForAb, HortAb, I&DA, ISR, IndMed, Inspec, LeadAb, MEDLINE, MOS, MSCI, MaizeAb, NemAb, NutrAb, OrnHort, PBA, PGegResA, PHN&I, ProtozoAb, RA&MP, RAPRA, RCI, RPP, RefZh, RiceAb, S&F, SCI, SIA, TDB, WeedAb, Zincscan.
—BLDSC (7161.300000), CASDDS, CINDOC, CISTI, Ei, IDS, IE, Infotrieve, ingenta, Linda Hall. **CCC.**
Published by: International Union of Pure and Applied Chemistry, IUPAC Secretariat, PO Box 13757, Research Triangle Park, NC 27709-3757. TEL 919-485-8700, FAX 919-485-8706, secretariat@iupac.org, http://www.iupac.org/publications/pac/. Eds. Bernardo J Harold, James R Bull, John W Lorimer. Circ: 845.

➤ **THE PYROTECHNIC LITERATURE SERIES.** see *ENGINEERING—Chemical Engineering*

➤ **THE PYROTECHNIC REFERENCE SERIES.** see *ENGINEERING—Chemical Engineering*

➤ **PYROTECHNICA**; occasional papers in pyrotechnics. see *ENGINEERING—Chemical Engineering*

540 PRT
CODEN: BSPQES
QUIMICA. Text in Portuguese. 1977. q. back issues avail. **Document type:** *Newsletter, Trade.* **Description:** Quarterly bulletin of the Portuguese Chemical Society.
Formerly (until 1992): Sociedade Portuguesa de Quimica. Boletim (0870-1180)
Indexed: CIN, ChemAb, ChemTitl.
—BLDSC (7216.590000), CASDDS, CISTI.
Published by: Sociedade Portuguesa de Quimica, Av. da Republica 37-4o, Lisbon, 1050-187, Portugal. TEL 351-21-7934637, FAX 351-21-7952349, sede@spq.pt, http://www.spq.pt. Ed. Carlos Pessoa. Circ: 3,800.

540 ESP ISSN 1139-2436
CODEN: RSQCEV
➤ **QUIMICA CLINICA**; revista de la sociedad espanola de bioquimica clinica y patologia molecular. Text in Spanish; Summaries in English. 1982. bi-m. free to members (effective 2005). adv. bk.rev. bibl.; charts; illus. index. **Document type:** *Academic/Scholarly.* **Description:** Contains original articles on research in clinical chemistry.
Formerly (until 1999): Sociedad Espanola de Quimica Clinica. Revista (0213-8514)
Indexed: BIOBASE, ChemAb, ExcerpMed, IABS.
—BLDSC (7216.635000), CASDDS, IE, ingenta. **CCC.**
Published by: (Sociedad Espanola de Quimica Clinica), Ediciones Mayo S.A., Aribau, 185-187 2a Planta, Barcelona, 08021, Spain. TEL 34-93-2090255, FAX 34-93-2020643, edmayo@ediciones.mayo.es, http://www.edicionesmayo.es/. Ed. Jordi Huguet. Adv. contact Jose Mayoral TEL 34-93-2090255. Circ: 2,000 (controlled). **Subscr. to:** S.E.Q.C., Padilla, 323-325, entl. 4a, Barcelona 08013, Spain. TEL 34-3-2269827.

540 BRA ISSN 0481-4118
QUIMICA E DERIVADOS. Text in Portuguese. 1965. m. USD 70 domestic; USD 200 foreign (effective 2000). adv. charts; illus.; tr.lit. **Description:** Deals with the chemical-petrochemical industry. Covers marketing development, researches, chemical and petrochemical sales in Brazil.
Indexed: B&I.
Published by: Editora Q D Ltda., Rua Conselheiro Brotero, 589 Cj 11-1o Andar, B Funda, Sao Paulo, SP 01154-001, Brazil. TEL 55-11-826-6899, FAX 55-11-825-8192, editoraqd@sti.com.br, http://www.qd.com.br. Ed. Denisard Gerila da Silva Pinto. Pubs. Denisard Gerola da Silva Pinto, Emanuel Fairbanks. Adv. contact Rogerio Barbato. B&W page USD 3,950, color page USD 6,350. Circ: 15,000.

540 ESP ISSN 0213-7828
QUIMICA HOY. Text in Spanish. 1983. 10/yr. USD 125 (effective 1999 & 2000). **Description:** Covers technical and business aspects of the chemicals industry in Spain.
Indexed: RefZh.
Published by: Quimitecnia Ediciones S.L., Santiago de Compostela, 64, Madrid, 28034, Spain. TEL 34-1-730-5801, FAX 34-1-738-7266, quimicahoy@retemail.es. Ed. Basilio Ballestin. Adv. contact Mercedes Martin. Circ: 10,500.

540 GBR
QUIMICA LATINOAMERICANA. Text in Spanish, English. 1999. q. free to qualified personnel (effective 2003). **Document type:** *Magazine, Trade.* **Description:** Provides a clear and comprehensive picture of the diverse and complex issues affecting the chemical industry in Latin America.
Published by: Reed Business Information Ltd. (Subsidiary of: Reed Business), Quadrant House, The Quadrant, Brighton Rd, Sutton, Surrey SM2 5AS, United Kingdom. TEL 44-20-86523500, FAX 44-20-86528932, http://www.reedbusiness.co.uk/rb2_products/rb2_products_ql.htm. Ed. Monica Bianchi TEL 44-20-8652-8121. **Subscr. to:** Quadrant Subscription Services, Rockwood House, 9-17 Perrymount Rd, Haywards Heath, W. Sussex RH16 3DH, United Kingdom. TEL 44-20-8652-3500, FAX 44-20-8652-8932, rbi.subscriptions@qss-uk.com.

540 BRA ISSN 0100-4042
QD1 CODEN: QUNODK
➤ **QUIMICA NOVA.** Text in Portuguese, Spanish, English. 1978. every 2 mos., latest vol.24, 2001. BRL 110 domestic to individuals; BRL 150 domestic to institutions; BRL 75 domestic to libraries; USD 120 foreign (effective 2005). abstr. 144 p./no.; back issues avail. **Document type:** *Journal, Academic/Scholarly.* **Description:** Publishes the results of original researches, review articles, notes on new methods and techniques, education and general issues in the area of chemistry.
Related titles: Online - full text ed.: free (effective 2005) (from SciELO).
Indexed: CCI, ChemAb, INIS AtomInd, MSB, RCI, VITIS.
—BLDSC (7216.940000), CISTI, IE, ingenta. **CCC.**
Published by: Sociedade Brasileira de Quimica, Ave Prof Lineu Prestes, 748, Bloco 2 - Superior, Sao Paulo, 05508, Brazil. TEL 55-11-3032-2299, FAX 55-11-3814-3602, office@jbcs.sbq.org.br, http://www.sbq.org.br/jbcs. Ed. Eliezer J. de L. Barreiro. Adv. contact Pricila Gil. Circ: 200 (paid); 2,800 (controlled). **Co-sponsors:** Ministerio da Ciencia e Tecnologia, Programa de Apoio a Publicacoes Cientificas; Conselho Nacional de Desenvolvimento Cientifico e Tecnologico.

➤ **R T E C S.** (Registry of Toxic Effects of Chemical Substances) see *ENVIRONMENTAL STUDIES—Toxicology And Environmental Safety*

➤ **RADIATION PHYSICS AND CHEMISTRY.** see *PHYSICS—Nuclear Physics*

541.3884 JPN ISSN 0033-8303
R895.A1 CODEN: RAISAB
RADIOISOTOPES. Text in English, Japanese; Summaries in English. 1952. m. JPY 11,000 to non-members; JPY 6,000 to members (effective 2004). adv. abstr.; bibl.; charts; illus. index. **Document type:** *Academic/Scholarly.* **Description:** Contains research papers in the basic and applied field of radio- and stable isotopes and radiation research, including biological and medical sciences as well as environmental radioactivity and radiological protection.
Related titles: Online - full content ed.; Online - full text ed.: (from J-Stage).
Indexed: A&ATA, BIOSIS Prev, BiolAb, CIN, ChemAb, ChemTitl, DSA, DentInd, ExcerpMed, FS&TA, INIS AtomInd, IndMed, Inspec, JTA, MEDLINE, MSB, RefZh, VITIS.
—BLDSC (7237.300000), AskIEEE, CASDDS, CISTI, GNLM, IE, Infotrieve, ingenta, Linda Hall. **CCC.**
Published by: Japan Radioisotope Association/Nihon Aisotope Kyokai, 2-28-45 Honkomagome, Bunkyo-ku, Tokyo, 113-0021, Japan. TEL 81-3-53958021, FAX 81-3-53958051, kaiin@jrias.or.jp, http://radioisotopes.jstage.jst.go.jp/, http://www.jrias.or.jp/jrias/. Circ: 5,000.

660 USA ISSN 1056-0793
CODEN: RARPEH
RADTECH REPORT. Text in English. 1988. bi-m. USD 60; USD 95 foreign to libraries. adv. **Document type:** *Trade.* **Description:** Covers research, development, marketing and end-use of UV-EB cured inks, coatings and adhesives.
Indexed: CIN, ChemAb, ChemTitl, RAPRA.
—BLDSC (7242.275000), CASDDS, IE, ingenta, Linda Hall.
Published by: RadTech International North America, 60 Revere Dr, Ste 500, Northbrook, IL 60062. TEL 847-480-9576, FAX 847-480-9282, uveb@radtech.org, http://www.radtech.org. Ed. Kelly Xintaris. R&P Christine Dionne. Adv. contact Don Wink. Circ: 1,038.

540 ESP ISSN 1575-3417
CODEN: ANQUEX
➤ **REAL SOCIEDAD ESPANOLA DE QUIMICA. ANALES.** Text in English; Summaries in English, Spanish. 1990. bi-m. adv. bk.rev. bibl.; charts; illus. index. **Document type:** *Academic/Scholarly.* **Description:** Provides a forum for chemical research in many areas.
Formerly (until 1998): Anales de Quimica (1130-2283); Which was formed by the merger of (1903-1990): Anales de Quimica. Serie A. Quimica Fisica e Ingeniera Quimica (0214-9397); Which was formerly (until 1989): Anales de Quimica. Serie A. Quimica Fisica y Quimica Tecnica (0211-1330); (1903-1990): Anales de Quimica. Serie B. Quimica Inorganica y Quimica Analitica (0211-1349); (1903-1990): Anales de Quimica. Serie C. Quimica Organica y Bioquimica (0211-1357); All of which superseded in part (in 1980): Anales de Quimica (0365-4990); Which was formerly (until 1967): Real Sociedad Espanola de Fisica y Quimica. Anales. Serie B: Quimica (0034-088X); Which superseded in part (in 1948): Anales de Fisica y Quimica (0365-2351); Which was formerly (until 1941): Anales de la Sociedad Espanola de Fisica y Quimica (0365-6675)
Indexed: ASCA, CCI, ChemAb, CurCR, CurCont, IECT, IndChem, MOS, MSB, MSCI, NPU, RCI, SIA, SSCI.
—CASDDS, CINDOC, CISTI, IDS, IE, Linda Hall. **CCC.**
Published by: (Real Sociedad Espanola de Quimica), Springer-Verlag Iberica S.A. (Subsidiary of: Springer Science+Business Media), Provenca, 388 1a planta, Barcelona, 08025, Spain. TEL 34-3-4570227, FAX 34-3-4571502, springer.bcn@springer.es. Ed. Jaume Casabo Gispert. Circ: 1,700 (paid). **Subscr. in N. America to:** Springer-Verlag New York, Inc., Journal Fulfillment, PO Box 2485, Secaucus, NJ 07096-2485. TEL 212-460-1500, FAX 212-473-6272.

540 SGP
RECENT ADVANCES IN COMPUTATIONAL CHEMISTRY. Text in English. 1995. irreg., latest vol.5. price varies. **Document type:** *Monographic series, Academic/Scholarly.* **Description:** The aim of the series is to enable both beginners and experimentalists to read, and to take advantage of, the rapidly growing literature of computational chemistry.
Published by: World Scientific Publishing Co. Pte. Ltd., 5 Toh Tuck Link, Singapore, 596224, Singapore. TEL 65-466-5775, FAX 65-467-7667, wspc@wspc.com.sg, series@wspc.com.sg, http://www.wspc.com.sg/books/series/racc_series.shtml, http://www.worldscientific.com. Ed. Delano P Chong. **Dist. by:** World Scientific Publishing Co., Inc., 1060 Main St, River Edge, NJ 07661. TEL 201-487-9655, 800-227-7562, FAX 201-487-9656, 888-977-2665; World Scientific Publishing Ltd., 57 Shelton St, London WC2H 9HE, United Kingdom. TEL 44-20-78360888, FAX 44-20-78362020.

RECENT ADVANCES IN PHYTOCHEMISTRY. see *BIOLOGY—Botany*

RECENT RESEARCH DEVELOPMENTS IN NON-CRYSTALLINE SOLIDS. see *PHYSICS*

RECENT RESEARCH DEVELOPMENTS IN OIL CHEMISTRY. see *PETROLEUM AND GAS*

541.28 IND
RECENT RESEARCH DEVELOPMENTS IN QUANTUM CHEMISTRY. Text in English. a.
Published by: Transworld Research Network, T C 36-248 (1), Trivandrum, Kerala 695 008, India. http://www.transworldresearch.com.

540.29 ESP
REPERTORIO DE LA INDUSTRIA QUIMICA ESPANOLA/ DIRECTORY OF THE SPANISH CHEMICAL INDUSTRY. Text in Spanish. triennial. **Document type:** *Directory.*
Published by: Federacion Empresarial de la Industria Quimica Espanola, Hermosilla, 31, Madrid, 28001, Spain. TEL 34-91-431-7964, FAX 34-91-576-3381, feique@interbook.net.

RESEARCH (DEUTSCHE AUSG.). see *PHARMACY AND PHARMACOLOGY*

RESEARCH (SPANISH EDITION). see *PHARMACY AND PHARMACOLOGY*

540 NLD ISSN 0922-6168
QD501 CODEN: RCINEE
➤ **RESEARCH ON CHEMICAL INTERMEDIATES**; an international journal. Text in English. 1972. 9/yr. USD 1,313 combined subscription in the Americas print & online eds.; EUR 1,050 combined subscription elsewhere print & online eds. (effective 2006). adv. back issues avail.; reprint service avail. from PSC. **Document type:** *Journal, Academic/Scholarly.* **Description:** Publishes current research and reviews on the properties, structures and reactivities of intermediate species in all the various domains of chemistry and related disciplines.
Former titles (until 1988): Reviews of Chemical Intermediates (0162-7546); (until 1977): Reviews on Reactive Species in Chemical Reactions (0048-7562)
Related titles: Online - full text ed.: ISSN 1568-5675. USD 1,182 in the Americas to institutions; EUR 945 elsewhere to institutions (effective 2006) (from EBSCO Publishing, Gale Group, IngentaConnect, Kluwer Online, O C L C Online Computer Library Center, Inc., Springer LINK, Swets Information Services).
Indexed: ASCA, CCI, CIN, ChemAb, ChemTitl, CurCR, CurCont, EngInd, ISR, IndChem, MSB, RCI, SCI.
—BLDSC (7734.775000), CASDDS, CISTI, Ei, IE, Infotrieve, ingenta, Linda Hall. **CCC.**

C

Published by: V S P (Subsidiary of: Brill Academic Publishers), Brill Academic Publishers, PO Box 9000, Leiden, 2300 PA, Netherlands. TEL 31-71-5353500, FAX 31-71-5317532, vsppub@brill.nl, http://www.brill.nl/ m_catalogue_sub6_id9762.htm, http://www.vsppub.com. Eds. J K S Wan, M C Depew, M Anpo. **Dist. by:** Extenza - Turpin, Pegasus Dr, Stratton Business Park, Biggleswade, Beds SG18 8TQ, United Kingdom. TEL 44-1767-604954, FAX 44-1767-601640, marketing@extenza-turpin.com, http://www.extenza-turpin.com.

➤ **REVIEWS IN CHEMICAL ENGINEERING.** see *ENGINEERING—Chemical Engineering*

542 USA ISSN 1069-3599
QD39.3.E46 CODEN: RCCHEY
➤ **REVIEWS IN COMPUTATIONAL CHEMISTRY.** Text in English. 1990. irreg., latest vol.20, 2004. USD 150 per vol. (effective 2004). back issues avail. **Document type:** *Monographic series, Academic/Scholarly.* **Description:** Brings together renowned experts in the field of computer-aided research.
Indexed: CCI, CIN, ChemAb, ChemTitl, SCI.
—BLDSC (7789.077000), CASDDS, CISTI, IE, ingenta. **CCC.**
Published by: John Wiley & Sons, Inc., 111 River St, Hoboken, NJ 07030-5774. TEL 201-748-6000, 800-825-7550, FAX 201-748-5915, uscs-wis@wiley.com, http://www.wiley.com.

541 USA
REVIEWS OF PLASMA CHEMISTRY. Text in English. 1991. irreg., latest vol.2, 1994. price varies. back issues avail. **Document type:** *Monographic series.* **Description:** English translations of works originally published in Russian.
Published by: Consultants Bureau (Subsidiary of: Springer-Verlag New York, Inc.), 233 Spring St, New York, NY 10013. TEL 212-460-1500, FAX 212-460-1575, service@springer-ny.com, http://www.springeronline.com. Ed. B M Smirnov.

540 JPN ISSN 0915-6151
CODEN: RHCHEZ
➤ **REVIEWS ON HETEROATOM CHEMISTRY.** Text in English. 1988. 2/yr. JPY 28,000 (effective 2001). **Document type:** *Journal, Academic/Scholarly.* **Description:** Covers physical inorganic and organic chemistry, and physical as well as synthetic organic chemistry of sulfur, phosphorous, selenium, boron, and many other elements.
Indexed: ASCA, CCI, CIN, ChemAb, ChemTitl, CurCont, SCI.
—BLDSC (7790.768800), CASDDS, CISTI.
Published by: M Y U, Scientific Publishing Division, 1-23-3-303 Sendagi, Bunkyo-ku, Tokyo, 113-0022, Japan. TEL 81-3-38227374, FAX 81-3-38278547, myukk@kt.rim.or.jp, myukk@myu-inc.jp, http://www.kt.rim.or.jp/~myukk, http://www.myu-inc.jp/myukk/index.html.

C

540 CUB ISSN 1015-8553
QD1 CODEN: RCCQER
REVISTA C E N I C. CIENCIAS QUIMICAS. Text and summaries in English, Spanish. 1969. 3/yr. USD 60 in North America; USD 90 elsewhere (effective 2000). bibl.; charts. back issues avail. **Description:** Presents national and international articles in the chemical sciences; covers organic, inorganic, physical and analytical chemistry.
Formerly (until 1986): Revista de Ciencias Fisicas (0254-0525)
Related titles: Online - full text ed.: (from EBSCO Publishing).
Indexed: ChemAb, ChemTitl, CivEngAb, INIS AtomInd, MSB, SIA.
—BLDSC (7804.765000), CASDDS, CINDOC, CISTI.
Published by: (Cuba. Ministerio de Educacion Superior), Centro Nacional de Investigaciones Cientificas, Ave. 25 y 158, Apdo. 6880 y 6990, Havana, 10600, Cuba. TEL 537-219045, FAX 537-330497, cnic@reduniv.edu.cu. Ed. Juan J Meitin. Circ: 750.

REVISTA COLOMBIANA DE CIENCIAS QUIMICO FARMACEUTICAS. see *PHARMACY AND PHARMACOLOGY*

540 CUB ISSN 0258-5995
CODEN: RCQUE7
REVISTA CUBANA DE QUIMICA. Summaries in English, Spanish. 198?. q. USD 25 in North America; USD 26 in South America; USD 28 elsewhere.
Indexed: CIN, ChemAb, ChemTitl.
—CASDDS, CISTI.
Published by: (Cuba. Ministerio de Educacion Superior), Ediciones Cubanas, Obispo No. 527, Apdo. 605, Havana, Cuba. TEL 32-5556-60.

660 ROM ISSN 0034-7752
CODEN: RCBUAU
➤ **REVISTA DE CHIMIE.** Summaries in English, German; Text in Romanian. 1949. m. ROL 595,000 domestic to individuals; ROL 952,000 domestic to institutions; USD 180 foreign (effective 2003). adv. bk.rev. abstr.; bibl.; illus.; pat. index. 100 p./no.; back issues avail. **Document type:** *Magazine, Academic/Scholarly.*
Indexed: ASCA, AnalAb, CCI, CEA, CEABA, CISA, ChemAb, ChemTitl, CurCont, EngInd, INIS AtomInd, MSB, MSCI, RCI, SSCI, TCEA, VITIS.
—BLDSC (7849.500000), CASDDS, CISTI, Ei, IDS, IE, ingenta, Linda Hall.
Published by: Syscom 18 s.r.l., Calea Plevnei 139B, Bucharest, 77131, Romania. revista@syscom.ro, syscom@syscom.ro, http://www.bch.ro. Ed., Adv. contact Carmen Mihaela Ioan. Pub. Petru Filip. Circ: 1,600.

➤ **REVISTA DE FIZICA SI CHIMIE.** see *PHYSICS*

540 PER ISSN 1012-3946
➤ **REVISTA DE QUIMICA.** Text in Spanish. 1987. s-a. USD 30 (effective 2003). bk.rev. **Document type:** *Academic/Scholarly.*
Published by: Pontificia Universidad Catolica del Peru, Fondo Editorial, Plaza Francia 1164, Cercado de Lima, Lima, 1, Peru. editorial@pucp.edu.pe, feditor@pucp.edu.pe, http://www.pucp.edu.co, http://www.pucp.edu.pe. Ed. Olga Lock de Ugaz.

540 MEX ISSN 0370-5943
QD1 CODEN: RLAQA8
➤ **REVISTA LATINOAMERICANA DE QUIMICA.** Text in English, Spanish; Abstracts occasionally in English. 1970. q. free. bk.rev. illus. **Document type:** *Academic/Scholarly.*
Description: Contains original papers and reviews on organic chemistry, natural products, and phytochemistry.
Indexed: AgBio, BioCN&I, BiolAb, CIN, CPA, ChemAb, ChemTitl, CurCont, EngInd, FPA, FS&TA, ForAb, HortAb, NutrAb, OrnHort, PBA, PGegResA, PHN&I, ProtozoAb, RA&MP, RM&VM, RPP, RevApplEntom, S&F, SeedAb, TDB, WeedAb.
—BLDSC (7863.514500), CASDDS, CISTI, Ei, IE, ingenta, Linda Hall.
Published by: (Universidad Nacional Autonoma de Mexico, Instituto de Quimica), Laboratorios Mixim S.A. de C.V., Jardin Sur No 6, Col Centro, Naucalpan, MEX 53000, Mexico. TEL 52-55-55765800, FAX 52-55-55594512, mixim@labmixim.com, http://www.labmixim.com/. Circ: 800 (controlled).

540 CUB
REVISTA TECNOLOGIA: QUIMICA. Text in Spanish. q. USD 25 in North America; USD 26 in South America; USD 28 in Europe.
Published by: (Cuba. Ministerio de la Industria Basica), Ediciones Cubanas, Obispo No. 527, Apdo. 605, Havana, Cuba. TEL 32-5556-60.

REVUE DES COMPOSITES ET DES MATERIAUX AVANCES. see *ENGINEERING—Engineering Mechanics And Materials*

REVUE EUROPEENNE DES ELEMENTS FINIS. see *ENGINEERING—Engineering Mechanics And Materials*

540 ROM ISSN 0035-3930
QD1 CODEN: RRCHAX
➤ **REVUE ROUMAINE DE CHIMIE/ROMANIAN JOURNAL OF CHEMISTRY.** Text in English, French, German, Russian, Spanish. 1956. m. bk.rev. bibl.; charts; illus. index. **Document type:** *Journal, Academic/Scholarly.*
Indexed: ABIPC, ASCA, AnalAb, BiolAb, CCI, CEA, Cadscan, ChemAb, ChemInfo, ChemTitl, CurCR, CurCont, INIS AtomInd, ISR, IndChem, LeadAb, MOS, MSB, MSCI, NPU, RCI, RefZh, SCI, WSCA, Zincscan.
—BLDSC (7946.200000), CASDDS, CISTI, IDS, IE, Infotrieve, ingenta, KNAW, Linda Hall.
Published by: (Academia Romana), Editura Academiei Romane/Publishing House of the Romanian Academy, Calea 13 Septembrie 13, Sector 5, Bucharest, 76117, Romania. TEL 40-21-4119008, FAX 40-21-4103983, edacad@ear.ro, http://www.ear.ro. Ed. A T Balaban. Circ: 3,000. **Dist. by:** Rodipet S.A., Piata Presei Libere 1, sector 1, PO Box 33-57, Bucharest 3, Romania. TEL 40-21-2224126, 40-21-2226407, rodipet@rodipet.ro.

540 ITA
RICH MAC - CHIMICA NEWS. Text in Italian. 1919. 11/yr. EUR 44 (effective 2005); Included in subscription of Inquinamento. adv. **Document type:** *Magazine, Trade.*
Formerly: La Chimica e l'Industria. Rich-Mac Magazine
Related titles: Online - full text ed.
Published by: V N U Business Publications (Italy), Via Gorki 69, Cinisello Balsamo, MI 20092, Italy. TEL 39-02-660341, FAX 39-02-66034238, http://www.jackson.it/cn/, http://www.vnu.it. adv.: B&W page EUR 1,369, color page EUR 1,999; bleed 210 x 297. Circ: 14,000.

540 JPN ISSN 0913-302X
RIGAKU DENKI JANARU/RIGAKU DENKI JOURNAL. Text in Japanese; Summaries in English. 1959. s-a. **Document type:** *Academic/Scholarly.*
Indexed: ChemAb.
Published by: Rigaku Denki K.K./Rigaku Corp., 3-9-12 Matsubara-cho, Akishima-shi, Tokyo-to 196-0003, Japan. TEL 0425-45-8139, FAX 0425-46-7090. Ed. Tomoya Arai. Pub. Hikaru Shimura.

RIKAGAKKAISHI/JOURNAL OF PHYSICS, CHEMISTRY AND EARTH SCIENCE. see *SCIENCES: COMPREHENSIVE WORKS*

540 USA
ROCHESTER CHEMUNICATIONS. Text in English. 1949. bi-m. USD 6 (effective 1999). adv. charts; illus.; tr.lit. back issues avail. **Document type:** *Newsletter.*
Formerly: Genesee Valley Chemunications (0016-6642)
Published by: American Chemical Society, Rochester Section, Inc., PO Box 15571, Rochester, NY 14615-0571. kschlech@brockport.edu. Ed., Adv. contact Kenneth D Schlecht. Circ: 1,500; 1,400 (controlled).

540 570 550 ROM ISSN 1454-8267
ROMANIAN ACADEMY. PROCEEDINGS. SERIES B: CHEMISTRY, LIFE SCIENCES AND GEOSCIENCES. Text in English. 1999. 3/yr.
Indexed: AbHyg, AnBrAb, BioCN&I, CPA, FCA, ForAb, HerbAb, HortAb, PBA, PotatoAb, RA&MP, RPP, S&F, TriticAb.
—BLDSC (6791.090000), CISTI, IE, Linda Hall.
Published by: (Academia Romana), Editura Academiei Romane/Publishing House of the Romanian Academy, Calea 13 Septembrie 13, Sector 5, Bucharest, 76117, Romania. TEL 40-21-4119008, FAX 40-21-4103983.

540 660 RUS ISSN 1026-3500
AS262 CODEN: IASKEA
ROSSIISKAYA AKADEMIYA NAUK. IZVESTIYA. SERIYA KHIMICHESKAYA. Text in Russian. 1936. m. charts; illus. index. **Document type:** *Journal, Academic/Scholarly.*
Description: Disseminates research into inorganic, organic, biological, physical, and analytical chemistry.
Formerly (until no.2, 1992): Akademiya Nauk S.S.S.R. Izvestiya. Seriya Khimicheskaya (0002-3353)
Related titles: ♦ English Translation: Russian Chemical Bulletin. ISSN 1066-5285.
Indexed: AnalAb, BrCerAb, CEABA, CerAb, ChemAb, CorrAb, EMA, INIS AtomInd, M&TEA, MBF, METADEX, RefZh, WAA, WSCA.
—BLDSC (0082.309000), CASDDS, CINDOC, CISTI, East View, KNAW, Linda Hall. **CCC.**
Published by: (Rossiiskaya Akademiya Nauk/Russian Academy of Sciences), Izdatel'stvo Nauka, Profsoyuznaya ul 90, Moscow, 117864, Russian Federation. TEL 7-095-3347151, FAX 7-095-4202220, secret@naukaran.ru, http://www.naukaran.ru. Circ: 2,750. **Subscr. to:** Springer-Verlag Dordrecht, Journals Department, PO Box 322, Dordrecht, Netherlands. TEL 31-78-6576392, FAX 31-78-6576474. **Dist. by:** M K - Periodica, ul Gilyarovskogo 39, Moscow 129110, Russian Federation. TEL 7-095-2845008, FAX 7-095-2813798, info@periodicals.ru, http:// www.mkniga.ru.

540 660 628 RUS
TP1.V82 CODEN: ZVKOA6
➤ **ROSSIISKII KHIMICHESKII ZHURNAL**; zhurnal Rossiiskogo khimicheskogo obshchestva im. D.I. Mendeleeva. Text in Russian. 1869; N.S. 1956. bi-m. RUR 180 (effective 1999). adv. back issues avail. **Document type:** *Academic/Scholarly.*
Description: Devoted to present-day problems in modern chemistry. Consists of reviews and papers written by leading experts in the field.
Formerly (until 1994): Vsesoyuznoe Khimicheskoe Obshchestvo im. D.I. Mendeleeva. Zhurnal (0373-0247)
Indexed: BrCerAb, C&ISA, CerAb, ChemAb, ChemTitl, CivEngAb, CorrAb, E&CAJ, EMA, FS&TA, M&TEA, MBF, METADEX, MSB, RefZh, SolStAb, WAA.
—BLDSC (0154.059275), CASDDS, CISTI, East View, Linda Hall. **CCC.**
Published by: Rossiiskoe Khimicheskoe Obshchestvo im. D.I. Mendeleeva, Krivokolennyi per 12, Moscow, 101000, Russian Federation. TEL 7-095-921-9810, FAX 7-095-921-5472, lisich@petrol.chem.msu.ru. Ed. G V Lisichkin. Adv. contact N N Gavrilova. B&W page USD 300. Circ: 1,000 (paid). **Subscr. to:** Rospechat', Pr-t Marshala Zhukova 4, Moscow 123995, Russian Federation. TEL 7-095-1956401, FAX 7-095-1951431. **Dist. addr.:** Leninskii pr-t., Leninskii pr-t 19, Moscow 117927, Russian Federation. TEL 7-095-236-0533, FAX 7-095-236-0533.; **US dist. addr.:** East View Information Services, 3020 Harbor Ln. N., Minneapolis, MN 55447. TEL 612-550-0961.

540 660 GBR ISSN 0260-6291
CODEN: SROCDO
ROYAL SOCIETY OF CHEMISTRY. SPECIAL PUBLICATIONS. Text in English. 1956 (vol.4). irreg., latest no.295, 2004, May. price varies. back issues avail. **Document type:** *Monographic series, Academic/Scholarly.* **Description:** Covers advances in all applications of chemistry.
Formerly (until 1980): Chemical Society. Special Publication (0577-618X)
Indexed: BIOSIS Prev, ChemAb, ChemTitl, MSB, S&F.
—BLDSC (8380.510000), CASDDS, CISTI, IE, Infotrieve, ingenta, KNAW. **CCC.**
Published by: Royal Society of Chemistry, Thomas Graham House, Science Park, Milton Rd, Cambridge, CB4 0WF, United Kingdom. TEL 44-1223-420066, FAX 44-1223-423623, sales@rsc.org, http://www.rsc.org/is/books/proceed.htm.

540 660 RUS ISSN 1066-5285
QD1 CODEN: RCBUEY
➤ **RUSSIAN CHEMICAL BULLETIN.** Text in English. 1936. m. EUR 3,498, USD 3,568, GBP 2,185 combined subscription to institutions print & online eds. (effective 2005). back issues avail. **Document type:** *Journal, Academic/Scholarly.*
Description: Disseminates research into inorganic, organic, biological, physical, and analytical chemistry.
Former titles (until 1994): Russian Academy of Sciences. Division of Chemical Sciences. Bulletin (1063-5211); (until 1992): Academy of Sciences of the U S S R. Division of Chemical Sciences. Bulletin (0568-5230)

Related titles: Microfilm ed.: (from PQC); Online - full text ed.: ISSN 1573-9171 (from EBSCO Publishing, Gale Group, IngentaConnect, Kluwer Online, O C L C Online Computer Library Center, Inc., Springer LINK, Swets Information Services); ♦ Translation of: Rossiiskaya Akademiya Nauk. Izvestiya. Seriya Khimicheskaya. ISSN 1026-3500.
Indexed: ASCA, BibLing, CCI, Cadscan, ChemAb, ChemInfo, ChemTitl, CurCont, EnerRA, ISR, LeadAb, MOS, MSB, NPU, RCI, SCI, Zincscan.
—BLDSC (0420.754200), CASDDS, CISTI, IDS, IE, Infotrieve, ingenta, Linda Hall. **CCC.**
Published by: (Rossiiskaya Akademiya Nauk/Russian Academy of Sciences), M A I K Nauka - Interperiodica, Profsoyuznaya ul 90, Moscow, 117997, Russian Federation. TEL 7-095-3347420, FAX 7-095-3360666, compmg@maik.ru, http://www.maik.ru. Ed. O M Nefedov. **Subscr. to:** Springer-Verlag Dordrecht, Journals Department, PO Box 322, Dordrecht, Netherlands. TEL 31-78-6576392, FAX 31-78-6576474.

540 GBR ISSN 0036-021X
QD1 CODEN: RCRVAB
➤ **RUSSIAN CHEMICAL REVIEWS.** Text in English. 1960. m. USD 1,726 in United States to institutions; GBP 1,150 rest of world to institutions; USD 1,817 combined subscription in United States to institutions print & online eds.; GBP 1,211 combined subscription rest of world to institutions print & online eds.; USD 173 newsstand/cover in United States to institutions; GBP 115 newsstand/cover rest of world to institutions (effective 2005); subscr. includes access to 10-year (1995-2004) electronic archive.. bibl.; charts; abstr.; illus. index. 100 p./no. 2 cols./p.; back issues avail. **Document type:** *Journal, Academic/Scholarly.* **Description:** Provides easy access to the achievements of chemists from Russia and the other countries of the former Soviet Union.
Related titles: CD-ROM ed.; E-mail ed.; Online - full text ed.: ISSN 1468-4837. USD 1,635 in United States; GBP 1,090 elsewhere (effective 2005) (from EBSCO Publishing, Swets Information Services); ♦ Translation of: Uspekhi Khimii. ISSN 0042-1308.
Indexed: ChemAb, ChemInfo, CurCont, EngInd, ExcerpMed, MSB, WTA.
—BLDSC (0420.755000), CISTI, Ei, IE, Infotrieve, ingenta, Linda Hall. **CCC.**
Published by: (Royal Society of Chemistry, Rossiiskaya Akademiya Nauk/Russian Academy of Sciences RUS), Turpion Ltd., 207 Brondesbury Park, London, NW2 5JN, United Kingdom. TEL 44-20-84590066, FAX 44-20-84516454, custserv@turpion.ru, info@turpion.org, http://www.turpion.org/journal/rc. Ed. O M Nefedov. Pub., R&P, Adv. contact Lev Malov TEL 7-095-1356417. **Subscr. to:** Extenza - Turpin, Pegasus Dr, Stratton Business Park, Biggleswade, Beds SG18 8TQ, United Kingdom. **Co-publisher:** Turpion - Moscow Ltd.

541.224 RUS ISSN 1070-3284
QD474 CODEN: RJCCEY
➤ **RUSSIAN JOURNAL OF COORDINATION CHEMISTRY.** Text in English. 1975. m. EUR 2,578, USD 2,338, GBP 1,618 combined subscription to institutions print & online eds. (effective 2005). back issues avail. **Document type:** *Journal, Academic/Scholarly.* **Description:** Explores all aspects of theoretical and experimental coordination chemistry, covering such areas as the synthesis, structure, properties, and quantum chemistry of coordination compounds; the kinetics and mechanisms of chemical reactions involving the formation of complex compunds; catalytic processes; and the development of practical new materials based on coordination compounds.
Formerly (until 1994): Soviet Journal of Coordination Chemistry (0364-4626)
Related titles: Microfilm ed.: (from PQC); Online - full text ed.: ISSN 1608-3318 (from EBSCO Publishing, Gale Group, IngentaConnect, Kluwer Online, O C L C Online Computer Library Center, Inc., Springer LINK, Swets Information Services); ♦ Translation of: Koordinatsionnaya Khimiya. ISSN 0132-344X.
Indexed: BibLing, CCI, ChemAb, ChemTitl, CurCont, EngInd, ISR, MSB, RCI, SCI.
—BLDSC (0420.760850), CASDDS, CISTI, IDS, IE, Infotrieve, ingenta. **CCC.**
Published by: (Rossiiskaya Akademiya Nauk/Russian Academy of Sciences), M A I K Nauka - Interperiodica, Profsoyuznaya ul 90, Moscow, 117997, Russian Federation. TEL 7-095-3347420, FAX 7-095-3360666, compmg@maik.ru, http://www.maik.rssi.ru/journals/cochem.htm, http://www.maik.ru. Ed. Nikolai Kuznetsov. **Subscr. to:** Springer-Verlag Dordrecht, Journals Department, PO Box 322, Dordrecht, Netherlands. TEL 31-78-6576392, FAX 31-78-6576474.

540 RUS ISSN 1070-3632
QD1 CODEN: RJGCEK
➤ **RUSSIAN JOURNAL OF GENERAL CHEMISTRY.** Text in English. 1931. m. EUR 3,968, USD 3,568, GBP 2,478 combined subscription to institutions print & online eds. (effective 2005). back issues avail. **Document type:** *Journal, Academic/Scholarly.* **Description:** Examines fundamental problems in chemistry, especially synthesis and organic reactions. Topics covered include biologically active substances, organometallic compounds, and applied spectroscopy.
Former titles (until 1994): Journal of General Chemistry; (until 1993): Journal of General Chemistry of the U S S R (0022-1279)
Related titles: Microfilm ed.: (from PQC); Online - full text ed.: ISSN 1608-3350 (from EBSCO Publishing, Gale Group, IngentaConnect, Kluwer Online, O C L C Online Computer Library Center, Inc., Springer LINK, Swets Information Services); ♦ Translation of: Zhurnal Obshchei Khimii. ISSN 0044-460X.
Indexed: BibLing, CCI, ChemAb, ChemTitl, CurCR, CurCont, EnerRA, EngInd, ISR, IndChem, MOS, MSB, RCI, SCI, SIA.
—BLDSC (0420.760950), CASDDS, CISTI, IE, Infotrieve, ingenta, Linda Hall. **CCC.**
Published by: (Rossiiskaya Akademiya Nauk/Russian Academy of Sciences), M A I K Nauka - Interperiodica, Profsoyuznaya ul 90, Moscow, 117997, Russian Federation. TEL 7-095-3347420, FAX 7-095-3360666, compmg@maik.ru, http://www.maik.rssi.ru/journals/genchem.htm, http://www.maik.ru. Ed. Anatoly I Rusanov. **Subscr. to:** Springer-Verlag Dordrecht, Journals Department, PO Box 322, Dordrecht, Netherlands. TEL 31-78-6576392, FAX 31-78-6576474.

540 JPN ISSN 0370-8047
TP215 CODEN: RYUSAZ
➤ **RYUSAN TO KOGYO/SULPHURIC ACID AND INDUSTRY.** Text in Japanese. 1948. m. JPY 7,200 (effective 2001). adv. bk.rev. index. 36 p./no.; back issues avail. **Document type:** *Bulletin, Academic/Scholarly.*
Indexed: RefZh.
—CASDDS, CISTI, Linda Hall.
Published by: Sulphuric Acid Association of Japan, 21-1 Shinbashi 2-chome, Minato-ku, Tokyo, 105-0004, Japan. TEL 81-3-3572-5498, FAX 81-3-3572-5490, ryusan@oak.ocn.ne.jp. Ed. Seiichi Furuya. adv.: page JPY 35,000; 22.5 x 15. Circ: 1,300.

540 USA
S A C I SLANTS. Text in English. 1952. 3/yr. membership. adv. bk.rev. **Document type:** *Newsletter.*
Published by: Sales Association of the Chemical Industry, Inc., 66 Morris Ave, Ste 2A, Springfield, NJ 07081-1450. TEL 973-379-1100, FAX 973-379-6507. Ed. George Ellas. Adv. contact Dale Nieves. Circ: 300.

540 USA ISSN 0044-7595
S C A L A C S. (Southern California Section of American Chemical Society) Text in English. 1945. 7/yr. free to members; USD 10 to non-members (effective 2005). adv. bk.rev. **Document type:** *Magazine, Trade.*
Indexed: A&ATA, ExcerpMed.
Published by: American Chemical Society, Southern California Section, 14934 S Figueroa St, Gardena, CA 90248. TEL 310-327-1216, FAX 310-538-9965. Ed., Adv. contact Nancy Paradiso. page USD 425. Circ: 2,500 (paid and free).

338.4766 USA
S O C M A CHEMICAL BOND. Text in English. 1966. 10/yr. USD 50 to non-members (effective 1999). reprints avail. **Document type:** *Newsletter.* **Description:** Covers the latest developments affecting the chemical industry; reviews membership activities, including seminars and workshops.
Formerly: S O C M A Newsletter
Media: Duplicated (not offset). **Related titles:** Online - full text ed.
Published by: Synthetic Organic Chemical Manufacturers Association, 1850 M St, N W, S 700, Washington, DC 20036. TEL 202-721-4100, FAX 202-296-8120. Ed. Dawn M Shiley. Circ: 3,000.

SAITAMA MATHEMATICAL JOURNAL. see *MATHEMATICS*

540 RUS
SAMARSKII GOSUDARSTVENNYI UNIVERSITET. VESTNIK. ESTESTVENNONAUCHNAYA SERIYA. KHIMIYA/SAMARA STATE UNIVERSITY. VESTNIK. NATURAL SCIENCE SERIES. CHEMISTRY. Text in Russian; Summaries in English. 1995. a., latest 2003. **Document type:** *Journal, Academic/Scholarly.*
Related titles: Online - full text ed.
Published by: (Samarskii Gosudarstvennyi Universitet), Izdatel'stvo Samarskii Universitet/Publishing House of Samara State University, ul Akademika Pavlova 1, k 209, Samara, 443011, Russian Federation. vestnikNS@ssu.samara.ru, http://www.ssu.samara.ru/~vestnik/content/cheme.html. Ed. Dr. Yu N Radaev.

SANKT-PETERBURGSKII UNIVERSITET. VESTNIK. SERIYA FIZIKA I KHIMIYA. see *PHYSICS*

660 JPN ISSN 0036-4649
CODEN: SAKNBI
SANYO KASEI NEWS. Text in Japanese. 1949. bi-m. free. bk.rev. charts; illus.
—CASDDS.
Published by: Sanyo Chemical Industries Ltd., 11-1 Ikkyo-Nomoto-cho, Higashiyama-ku, Kyoto-shi, 605-0000, Japan. Ed. Yoshizo Takayanagi. Circ: 6,000 (controlled).

540 SAU ISSN 1319-6103
SAUDI CHEMICAL SOCIETY. JOURNAL. Text in English. 1996. s-a. **Document type:** *Journal, Academic/Scholarly.*
Indexed: AbHyg, AgrForAb, CPA, DSA, FCA, FPA, ForAb, HortAb, IndVet, NutrAb, OrnHort, PGrRegA, PHN&I, ProtozoAb, RA&MP, RM&VM, RPP, S&F, SeedAb, TDB, WeedAb.
—BLDSC (4869.562000).
Published by: Saudi Chemical Society, PO Box 2455, Riyadh, 11451, Saudi Arabia.

540 DEU
SAUGFINGER. Text in German. 1999. a. EUR 10 newsstand/cover (effective 2002). **Document type:** *Magazine, Academic/Scholarly.* **Description:** Informs students about the very varied professional opportunities open to chemistry graduates and aims to stimulate interest in studying chemistry.
Published by: G I T Verlag GmbH (Subsidiary of: Wiley - V C H Verlag GmbH & Co. KGaA), Roesslerstr 90, Darmstadt, 64293, Germany. TEL 49-6151-8090-0, FAX 49-6151-8090144, info@gitverlag.com, http://www.saugfinger.de, http://www.gitverlag.com. Circ: 20,000 (controlled).

540 ISR ISSN 0792-1233
CODEN: SCMAE6
SCIENCE AND ENGINEERING OF COMPOSITE MATERIALS. Text in English. 1986. 6/yr., latest vol.10. USD 330 (effective 2006). adv. back issues avail. **Document type:** *Academic/Scholarly.* **Description:** Provides a forum for discussion of all aspects related to the structure and performance under simulated and actual service conditions of composites.
Formerly (until 1992): Composite Materials Science (0334-181X)
Indexed: ASCA, ApMecR, BrCerAb, C&ISA, CIN, CerAb, ChemAb, ChemTitl, CivEngAb, CorrAb, CurCont, E&CAJ, EMA, IAA, M&TEA, MBF, METADEX, MSCI, RAPRA, SolStAb, WAA.
—BLDSC (8133.023000), CASDDS, CISTI, IE, ingenta, Linda Hall.
Published by: Freund Publishing House, Ltd., P O Box 35010, Tel Aviv, 61350, Israel. TEL 972-3-5628540, FAX 972-3-5628538, h_freund@netvision.net.il, http://www.freundpublishing.com/Science_Engineering_Composite%20Materials/Compprev.htm. Eds. M Zako, R Pyrz, S V Hoa, O Rand. Circ: 1,000.

540 CHN ISSN 1006-9291
QD1 CODEN: SCBCFQ
➤ **SCIENCE IN CHINA. SERIES B: CHEMISTRY.** Text in English. 1952. bi-m. CNY 480 (effective 2005). adv. index. back issues avail.; reprints avail. **Document type:** *Journal, Academic/Scholarly.* **Description:** Contains academic papers on scientific work in the field of chemistry.
Supersedes in part (in 1996): Science in China. Series B: Chemistry, Life Sciences and Earth Sciences (1001-652X); Which was formerly (until 1989): Scientia Sinica. Series B: Chemistry, Life Sciences and Earth Sciences (0253-5823); Which superseded in part: Scientia Sinica
Related titles: Microform ed.; Online - full text ed.: USD 50 (effective 2004) (from East View Information Services, WanFang Data Corp.); ♦ Chinese ed.: Zhongguo Kexue. B Ji: Huaxue. ISSN 1006-9240.
Indexed: ASCA, ASFA, CCI, CRFR, Cadscan, ChemAb, ChemTitl, CurCont, EngInd, ISR, LeadAb, MSB, MSCI, RCI, RefZh, RevApplEntom, SCI, SSCI, WSCA, Zincscan.
—BLDSC (8141.669500), CASDDS, CISTI, Ei, GNLM, IDS, IE, Infotrieve, ingenta, Linda Hall. **CCC.**
Published by: (Chinese Academy of Sciences/Zhongguo Kexueyuan), Zhongguo Kexue Zazhishe/Science in China Press, 16 Donghuangchenggen North Street, Beijing, 100717, China. TEL 86-10-64019820, FAX 86-10-64031816, sale@scichina.com, http://www.scichina.com/. Circ: 10,000. **Subscr. to:** Maney Publishing, China Journal Distribution Services, Hudson Rd, Leeds LS9 7DI, United Kingdom. TEL 44-113-2497481, FAX 44-113-2486983, subscriptions@maney.co.uk.

540 SCG ISSN 0352-5139
QD1 CODEN: JSCSEN
SERBIAN CHEMICAL SOCIETY. JOURNAL. Text in English; Abstracts in Serbo-Croatian. 1930. 12/yr. USD 70 (effective 2005). adv. bk.rev. charts; illus. index. **Document type:** *Journal, Academic/Scholarly.*
Formerly (until 1985): Glasnik Hemijskog Drustva-Societe Chimique, Belgrade. Bulletin (0017-0941)
Related titles: Online - full text ed.: free (effective 2005); Series of: Documenta Chemica Yugoslavica.
Indexed: AnalAb, BiolAb, BrCerAb, C&ISA, CCI, CIN, CerAb, ChemAb, ChemTitl, CivEngAb, CorrAb, CurCont, E&CAJ, EMA, EngInd, FS&TA, IAA, INIS AtomInd, M&TEA, MBF, METADEX, MOS, MSB, NPU, RefZh, SIA, SolStAb, WAA.
—BLDSC (4874.638000), CASDDS, CISTI, Ei, IDS, IE, ingenta, KNAW, Linda Hall.
Published by: Srpsko Hemijsko Drustvo/Serbian Chemical Society, Karnegijeva 4/III, PO Box 35-08, Belgrade, 11120. TEL 381-11-3303663, shdoffice@tmf.bg.ac.yu, http://www.shd.org.yu/HtDocs/SHD/JSCS-home.htm. Ed., Adv. contact Dragutin M. Drazic. Circ: 1,500.

SHIYOU HUAGONG/PETROCHEMICAL TECHNOLOGY. see *PETROLEUM AND GAS*

C

540 SGP ISSN 0129-5772
CODEN: SNIBDV

➤ **SINGAPORE NATIONAL INSTITUTE OF CHEMISTRY. BULLETIN.** Cover title: S N I C Bulletin. Text in English. 1972. a. SGD 30 domestic; USD 20 foreign. adv. charts. **Document type:** *Bulletin, Academic/Scholarly.*
Indexed: ChemAb.
—BLDSC (2720.298000), CASDDS.
Published by: Singapore National Institute of Chemistry, c/o Department of Chemistry, Kent Ridge, National University of Singapore, Singapore, 119260, Singapore. TEL 65-772-2914, FAX 65-779-1691, TELEX UNISPO-RS33943, chmlaiyh@leonis.nus.sg. Ed. Yee Hing Lai. Circ: 1,000.

540 MEX ISSN 0583-7693
QD1 CODEN: RSQMAN

➤ **SOCIEDAD QUIMICA DE MEXICO. REVISTA.** Text in Spanish. 1957. bi-m. USD 55 (effective 2005). adv. **Document type:** *Academic/Scholarly.*
Indexed: BiolAb, ChemAb, ChemTitl, INIS AtomInd, MSB, RefZh.
—CASDDS, Linda Hall.
Published by: Sociedad Quimica de Mexico, Mar del Norte 5, Col San Alvaro, Del Azcapotzalco, Mexico City, DF 02090, Mexico. TEL 52-55-53862905, FAX 52-55-53860255. Eds. Federico Garcia Jimenez, Guillermo Delgado Lamas. Adv. contact Rosa Jaime C. Circ: 3,500.

540 PER ISSN 1810-634X
QD1 CODEN: BSQPAQ

SOCIEDAD QUIMICA DEL PERU. REVISTA. Text in Spanish, English. 1934. q. USD 40 domestic; USD 50 foreign (effective 2004). adv. bk.rev. abstr.; bibl. 90 p./no.; **Document type:** *Journal, Academic/Scholarly.*
Formerly (until 2003): Sociedad Quimica del Peru. Boletin (0037-8623)
Indexed: BiolAb, CIN, ChemAb, ChemTitl, INIS AtomInd.
—BLDSC (7833.450000), CASDDS, CISTI, IE, ingenta, Linda Hall.
Published by: (Comision de Publicaciones, Presidente), Sociedad Quimica del Peru, Av. Nicolas de Aranibar 696, Santa Beatriz, Lima, 14-0576, Peru. TEL 51-1-4723925, FAX 51-1-2659049, sqperu@amauta.rcp.net.pe, http://www.pucp.edu.pe/~quimica/sqp.htm. Ed., R&P Leonidas Romero Unzueta. Circ: 1,500.

540 DZA ISSN 1111-4797
CODEN: JSACEX

➤ **SOCIETE ALGERIENNE DE CHIMIE. JOURNAL/ALGERIAN CHEMICAL SOCIETY. JOURNAL.** Short title: J S A C. Text in Arabic, English, French. 1991. s-a. back issues avail. **Document type:** *Academic/Scholarly.* **Description:** Publishes research done in all areas of chemistry.
Indexed: CIN, ChemAb, ChemTitl.
—BLDSC (4876.680000), CASDDS, IE, ingenta.
Published by: Societe Algerienne de Chimie, El Alia, B P 63, Bab Ezzouar, Alger, 16111, Algeria. TEL 213-21-247912, FAX 213-21-247311. Ed., Pub. O Benali Baitich.

540 FRA ISSN 0996-8083

➤ **SOCIETE FRANCAISE DE CHIMIE. ANNUAIRE.** Text in French. 1956. biennial. **Document type:** *Academic/Scholarly.*
Formerly (until 1983): Societe Chimique de France. Annuaire (0996-8091)
Published by: Societe Francaise de Chimie, 250 rue Saint-Jacques, Paris, 75005, France. TEL 33-1-40467160, FAX 33-1-40467161.

➤ **SOCIETE NATIONALE DES SCIENCES NATURELLES ET MATHEMATIQUES DE CHERBOURG. MEMOIRES.** see *SCIENCES: COMPREHENSIVE WORKS*

➤ **SOCIETY OF COSMETIC CHEMISTS OF JAPAN. JOURNAL.** see *BEAUTY CULTURE—Perfumes And Cosmetics*

➤ **SOCIETY OF LEATHER TECHNOLOGISTS AND CHEMISTS. JOURNAL.** see *LEATHER AND FUR INDUSTRIES*

540 BGR ISSN 0584-0317

SOFIISKI UNIVERSITET SV. KLIMENT OHRIDSKI. KHIMICHESKI FAKULTET. GODISHNIK. Text in Bulgarian; Summaries in English. 1963. irreg., latest vol.71, 1976. price varies. reprint service avail. from IRC.
Formerly (until 1970): Sofiiski Universitet. Khimicheski Fakultet. Godishnik (1310-5035)
Indexed: ChemAb, RefZh.
—CISTI, Linda Hall.
Published by: (Sofiiski Universitet Sv. Kliment Ohridski, Khimicheski Fakultet/Sofia University St. Kliment Ohridski, Faculty of Chemistry), Universitetsko Izdatelstvo Sv. Kliment Okhridski/Publishing House of the Sofia University St. Kliment Ohridski, Akad G Bonchev 6, Sofia, 1113, Bulgaria. Circ: 550.

540 530 GBR ISSN 1744-683X

▼ ➤ **SOFT MATTER.** Text in English. 2005. m. GBP 751, USD 1,374 combined subscription print & online eds. (effective 2006). adv. back issues avail. **Document type:** *Journal, Academic/Scholarly.* **Description:** Provides a forum for the communication of generic science underpinning the properties and applications of soft matter.
Related titles: Online - full text ed.: ISSN 1744-6848. GBP 676, USD 1,237 (effective 2006); ◆ Abridged ed. of: Journal of Materials Chemistry. ISSN 0959-9428.
—CCC.
Published by: Royal Society of Chemistry, Thomas Graham House, Science Park, Milton Rd, Cambridge, CB4 0WF, United Kingdom. TEL 44-1223-420066, FAX 44-1223-420247, softmatter@rsc.org, http://www.softmatter.org, http://www.rsc.org. Ed. Carol Stanier. Pub. Ms. Janet L Dean. Adv. contact Ian Swain TEL 44-1223-432310. Circ: 1,000 (paid). **Subscr. addr. in the US:** Portland Customer Services, Commerce Way, Colchester CO2 8HP, United Kingdom. TEL 44-1206-796351, FAX 44-1206-799331, sales@portland-services.com, http://www.portland-services.com.

➤ **SOLID FUEL CHEMISTRY.** see *ENGINEERING—Chemical Engineering*

540 USA ISSN 0191-5622
QD543 CODEN: SDSEDK

➤ **SOLUBILITY DATA SERIES.** Variant title: I U P A C Solubility Data Series. (published in special issues of the Journal of Physical and Chemical Reference Data) Text in English. 1979. q. back issues avail. **Document type:** *Academic/Scholarly.*
Related titles: Microfilm ed.: (from PQC).
Indexed: ChemAb.
—CASDDS, CISTI. **CCC.**
Published by: International Union of Pure and Applied Chemistry, IUPAC Secretariat, PO Box 13757, Research Triangle Park, NC 27709-3757. TEL 919-485-8700, FAX 919-485-8706, secretariat@iupac.org, http://www.iupac.org/publications/sds/.

540 ZAF ISSN 0379-4350
QD1 CODEN: SAJCDG

➤ **SOUTH AFRICAN JOURNAL OF CHEMISTRY/SUID-AFRIKAANSE TYDSKRIF VIR CHEMIE.** Text and summaries in English. 1948. q. ZAR 300 domestic; USD 250 foreign (effective 2004). adv. charts; illus. index. **Document type:** *Journal, Academic/Scholarly.* **Description:** Publishes original theoretical and applied research in molecular, organic, inorganic, and analytic chemistry. Covers general matters affecting the environment, industry, and research.
Incorporates: South African Chemical Institute. Journal (0038-2078)
Related titles: Microform ed.: (from PQC); Online - full text ed.: (from EBSCO Publishing, International Network for the Availability of Scientific Publications, African Journals Online).
Indexed: ASCA, ASFA, CCI, CIN, ChemAb, ChemTitl, CurCont, ESPM, EngInd, INIS AtomInd, ISAP, ISR, MSB, PollutAb, RCI, RefZh, SCI.
—BLDSC (8338.800000), CASDDS, CISTI, Ei, IDS, IE, Linda Hall.
Published by: (South African Chemical Institute), South African Bureau for Scientific Publications, PO Box 11663, Pretoria, Hatfield 0028, South Africa. TEL 27-12-322-6404, FAX 27-12-320-7803, bspman@icon.co.za, http://www.safest.org.za/bsp. Ed., Adv. contact T A Ford. Circ: 1,700.

540 BRA ISSN 0104-5431
CODEN: SBJCEO

SOUTHERN BRAZILIAN JOURNAL OF CHEMISTRY. Short title: Scienco. Text in English; Summaries in Portuguese. 1996 (vol.4, no.4). s-a. USD 35 in Latin America; USD 50 elsewhere. **Description:** Publishes original research articles on chemistry and related interdisciplinary areas. Occasionally includes review papers and articles dealing with chemical education and philosophy and history of science.
Indexed: CIN, ChemAb, ChemTitl.
—BLDSC (8352.921300), CASDDS.
Address: c/o Lavinel G. Ionescu, Editor, 15032 Agronomia, Porto Alegre, RGS, Brazil. TEL 55-51-4851820, FAX 55-51-3391564.

540 GBR

SPECIALTY CHEMICALS; the international magazine for performance, fine and specialty chemicals. Text in English. 10/yr. GBP 166 domestic; GBP 187, USD 340 foreign; GBP 31 newsstand/cover (effective Oct. 2004); subscr. includes Where to Buy Chemicals, Plant and Services directory. adv. **Document type:** *Magazine, Trade.* **Description:** Includes developments in the specialty chemical industry worldwide.
Related titles: Online - full text ed.: Specialty Chemicals Online; ◆ Supplement(s): Where to Buy Chemicals, Plant and Services. ISSN 1367-806X.
Published by: D M G Business Media Ltd. (Subsidiary of: D M G World Media Ltd.), Queensway House, 2 Queensway, Redhill, Surrey RH1 1QS, United Kingdom. TEL 44-1737-768611, FAX 44-1737-855477, info@uk.dmgworldmedia.com, http://www.specchemonline.com/, http://www.dmgworldmedia.com/BusinessMediaPublications.html. Ed. Dr. Andrew Warmington TEL 44-1737-855080. Adv. contact Paul Davis TEL 44-1737-855060. color page GBP 3,486; trim 210 x 297.

540 GBR ISSN 0584-8555
QD95 CODEN: SPIOAD

SPECTROSCOPIC PROPERTIES OF INORGANIC & ORGANOMETALLIC COMPOUNDS. Text in English. 1968. a., latest vol.36, 2004, Feb. GBP 269.50, USD 462 per vol. (effective 2004). charts; illus. index. 520 p./no.; back issues avail. **Document type:** *Academic/Scholarly.* **Description:** Reviews the literature in the field.
Indexed: BIOSIS Prev, CIN, ChemAb, ChemTitl.
—BLDSC (8411.110000), CASDDS, CISTI, IE, Infotrieve, ingenta, Linda Hall. **CCC.**
Published by: Royal Society of Chemistry, Thomas Graham House, Science Park, Milton Rd, Cambridge, CB4 0WF, United Kingdom. TEL 44-1223-432360, FAX 44-1223-423623, sales@rsc.org, http://www.rsc.org/CFbooks/sprindex.cfm?BKC=SP. Ed. G Davidson. **Subscr. to:** Extenza - Turpin, Pegasus Dr, Stratton Business Park, Biggleswade, Beds SG18 8TQ, United Kingdom.

SPECTROSCOPY; an international journal. see *BIOLOGY—Biochemistry*

540 USA ISSN 0172-6323

SPRINGER ADVANCED TEXTS IN CHEMISTRY. Text in English. irreg. price varies. **Document type:** *Monographic series.*
Published by: Springer-Verlag New York, Inc. (Subsidiary of: Springer Science+Business Media), 233 Spring St, New York, NY 10013. TEL 212-460-1500, FAX 212-473-6272. Ed. C Cantor.

660 572 DEU ISSN 1612-7617

▼ **SPRINGER SERIES ON CHEMICAL SENSORS AND BIOSENSORS.** Text in English. 2003. irreg., latest vol.2, 2004. price varies. **Document type:** *Monographic series, Academic/Scholarly.*
—BLDSC (8424.755200), IE.
Published by: Springer-Verlag (Subsidiary of: Springer Science+Business Media), Haber Str 7, Heidelberg, 69126, Germany. TEL 49-6221-3450, FAX 49-6221-229, orders@springer.de, http://www.springer.de.

540 DEU ISSN 1617-1306

SPRINGER SERIES ON FLUORESCENCE. Text in English. 2001. irreg., latest vol.2, 2002. price varies. **Document type:** *Monographic series, Academic/Scholarly.* **Description:** Publishes state-of-the-art articles that can serve as invaluable tools for both practitioners and researchers involved in fluorescence spectroscopy, fluorescence imaging and fluorescent probes.
—BLDSC (8424.763150), CISTI, IE, ingenta.
Published by: Springer-Verlag (Subsidiary of: Springer Science+Business Media), Tiergartenstr 17, Heidelberg, 69121, Germany. TEL 49-6221-3450, FAX 49-6221-345229, subscriptions@springer.de, http://www.springer-sbm.de.

540 USA ISSN 1040-0400
QD471 CODEN: STCHES

➤ **STRUCTURAL CHEMISTRY;** computational and experimental studies of chemical and biological systems. Text in English. 1990. bi-m. EUR 788, USD 818, GBP 508 combined subscription to institutions print & online eds. (effective 2005). adv. bk.rev. back issues avail.; reprint service avail. from PSC. **Document type:** *Journal, Academic/Scholarly.* **Description:** Examines the condensed and gaseous states of matter and discusses various techniques to determine structure and energetics.
Related titles: Online - full text ed.: ISSN 1572-9001 (from EBSCO Publishing, Gale Group, IngentaConnect, Kluwer Online, O C L C Online Computer Library Center, Inc., Springer LINK, Swets Information Services).
Indexed: ASCA, BibLing, CCI, CIN, ChemAb, ChemTitl, CurCont, EngInd, ISR, Inspec, RefZh, SCI.
—BLDSC (8476.380000), AskIEEE, CASDDS, CISTI, Ei, IDS, IE, Infotrieve, ingenta. **CCC.**
Published by: Plenum US (Subsidiary of: Springer Science+Business Media), 233 Spring St, New York, NY 10013. TEL 212-460-1500, FAX 212-460-1575, service@springer-ny.com, http://springerlink.metapress.com/openurl.asp?genre=journal&issn=1040-0400, http://www.springeronline.com. Ed. Istvan Hargittai.

541 DEU ISSN 0081-5993
QD461 CODEN: STBGAG

➤ **STRUCTURE AND BONDING.** Text in English. 1966. irreg., latest vol.119, 2005. price varies. reprint service avail. from ISI. **Document type:** *Monographic series, Academic/Scholarly.*
Related titles: Online - full text ed.: ISSN 1616-8550.
Indexed: ASCA, BIOSIS Prev, BiolAb, CCI, CIN, ChemAb, ChemTitl, EngInd, ISR, MSCI, RCI, SCI.
—BLDSC (8478.700000), CASDDS, CISTI, IDS, IE, Infotrieve, ingenta, Linda Hall. **CCC.**
Published by: Springer-Verlag (Subsidiary of: Springer Science+Business Media), Tiergartenstr 17, Heidelberg, 69121, Germany. TEL 49-6221-3450, FAX 49-6221-345229, subscriptions@springer.de, http://www.springer.de. Circ: 1,500.

➤ **STRUCTURE AND DYNAMICS OF MOLECULAR SYSTEMS.** see *PHYSICS*

540 ESP ISSN 0370-923X
CODEN: SCUSAS

STUDIA CHEMICA. Text in English, Spanish. 1965. a. price varies. **Document type:** *Academic/Scholarly.*
Indexed: CIN, ChemAb, ChemTitl, IECT.
—CASDDS. **CCC.**
Published by: Ediciones Universidad de Salamanca, Apartado 325, Salamanca, 37080, Spain. TEL 34-923-294598, FAX 34-923-262579, http://www3.usal.es/~eus/indexsp.htm. Ed. Julio Casado.

540 ROM ISSN 1224-7154
QD1 CODEN: SUBCAB
STUDIA UNIVERSITATIS "BABES-BOLYAI". CHEMIA. Text in English, French, German, Romanian; Summaries in English, French, German, Romanian. 1958. s-a. per issue exchange basis. bk.rev. abstr.; charts; illus.; bibl. index. **Document type:** *Academic/Scholarly.*
Indexed: AnalAb, CIN, ChemAb, ChemTitl, PsycholAb, RefZh.
—BLDSC (8482.308200), CASDDS.
Published by: Universitatea "Babes-Bolyai", Biblioteca Centrala Universitara/Babes-Bolyai University, Central University Library in Cluj-Napoca, Mihail Kogalniceanu 1B, Cluj-Napoca, 3400, Romania. TEL 40-64-194315, FAX 40-64-191906, staff@staff.ubbcluj.ro, http://www.ubbcluj.ro. Ed. Alina Vesa.

STUDIES IN INTERFACE SCIENCE. see *PHYSICS*

540 NLD ISSN 1572-5995
➤ **STUDIES IN NATURAL PRODUCTS CHEMISTRY.** Text in English. 1988. irreg., latest vol.29, 2003. price varies. back issues avail. **Document type:** *Monographic series, Academic/Scholarly.* **Description:** Investigates all aspects of the experimental and applied chemistry of natural products.
Indexed: CCI, CIN, ChemAb, ChemTitl, CurCont.
—BLDSC (8491.149800), ingenta.
Published by: Elsevier BV (Subsidiary of: Elsevier Science & Technology), Radarweg 29, Amsterdam, 1043 NX, Netherlands. TEL 31-20-4853911, FAX 31-20-4852457, nlinfo-f@elsevier.nl, http://www.elsevier.nl. Ed. Atta U Rahman.

668.42 NLD ISSN 0922-5579
CODEN: SPLSEA
➤ **STUDIES IN POLYMER SCIENCE.** Text in English. 1988. irreg., latest vol.7, 1990. price varies. back issues avail. **Document type:** *Monographic series, Academic/Scholarly.* **Description:** Publishes studies in applied chemistry and chemical engineering of polymer science.
Indexed: CIN, ChemAb, ChemTitl.
—BLDSC (8491.224300), CASDDS, CISTI, ingenta. **CCC.**
Published by: Elsevier BV (Subsidiary of: Elsevier Science & Technology), Radarweg 29, Amsterdam, 1043 NX, Netherlands. TEL 31-20-4853911, FAX 31-20-4852457, nlinfo-f@elsevier.nl, http://www.elsevier.nl.

➤ **STUDIES OF COLOR/SHIKISAI KENKYU.** see *PHYSICS—Optics*

630 JPN ISSN 0387-1312
CODEN: SKTOBY
SUMITOMO KAGAKU TOKUSHUGO/SUMITOMO CHEMICAL REVIEW. Text in Japanese. q. **Document type:** *Journal, Trade.*
Indexed: BrCerAb, C&ISA, CerAb, CorrAb, E&CAJ, EMA, IAA, INIS AtomInd, M&TEA, MBF, METADEX, RefZh, SolStAb, WAA.
—Linda Hall.
Published by: Sumitomo Chemical Co., Ltd, 5-33, Kitahama 4-chome, Chuo-ku, Osaka, 541-8110, Japan. TEL 81-6-62203891, FAX 81-6-62203345, http://www.sumitomo-chem.co.jp/.

SUPERCONDUCTOR SCIENCE & TECHNOLOGY. see *PHYSICS*

540 530 GBR ISSN 0749-6036
QC611.8.S86 CODEN: SUMIEK
➤ **SUPERLATTICES AND MICROSTRUCTURES.** Text in English. 1985. 12/yr. EUR 276 in Europe to individuals; JPY 29,700 in Japan to individuals; USD 244 elsewhere to individuals; EUR 1,141 in Europe to institutions; JPY 123,100 in Japan to institutions; USD 1,014 elsewhere to institutions (effective 2006). adv. abstr. back issues avail.; reprints avail. **Document type:** *Academic/Scholarly.* **Description:** Devoted to the physics, chemistry, materials science, and electrical engineering aspects of submicron structures and the materials from which such structures will be fabricated.
Related titles: Online - full text ed.: ISSN 1096-3677. USD 1,069 (effective 2002) (from EBSCO Publishing, Gale Group, IngentaConnect, O C L C Online Computer Library Center, Inc., ScienceDirect, Swets Information Services).
Indexed: ASCA, BrCerAb, C&ISA, CIN, CerAb, ChemAb, ChemTitl, CivEngAb, CorrAb, CurCont, E&CAJ, EMA, EngInd, IAA, ISR, Inspec, M&TEA, MBF, METADEX, MSCI, RefZh, SCI, SolStAb, WAA.
—BLDSC (8547.076700), AskIEEE, CASDDS, CISTI, Ei, IDS, IE, Infotrieve, ingenta, Linda Hall. **CCC.**
Published by: Academic Press (Subsidiary of: Elsevier Science & Technology), 24-28 Oval Rd, London, NW1 7DX, United Kingdom. TEL 44-20-72674466, FAX 44-20-74822293, apsubs@acad.com, http://www.elsevier.com/locate/superlattices. Ed. H Zabel. R&P Catherine John. Adv. contact Nik Screen.

540 GBR ISSN 1061-0278
QD380 CODEN: SCHEER
➤ **SUPRAMOLECULAR CHEMISTRY.** Text in English. 1992. 8/yr. GBP 1,395, USD 1,765 combined subscription to institutions print & online eds. (effective 2006). reprint service avail. from PSC. **Document type:** *Journal, Academic/Scholarly.* **Description:** Publishes research in the many facets of supramolecular chemistry, including analytical, inorganic, organic and physical chemistry.
Related titles: CD-ROM ed.: ISSN 1026-7816; Microform ed.; Online - full text ed.: ISSN 1029-0478. GBP 1,325, USD 1,674 to institutions (effective 2006) (from EBSCO Publishing, Gale Group, IngentaConnect, O C L C Online Computer Library Center, Inc., Swets Information Services).
Indexed: ASCA, CCI, ChemAb, CurCont, ISR, MSB, SCI.
—BLDSC (8547.638685), CISTI, IE, Infotrieve, ingenta. **CCC.**
Published by: Taylor & Francis Ltd (Subsidiary of: Taylor & Francis Group), 4 Park Sq, Milton Park, Abingdon, OX14 4RN, United Kingdom. TEL 44-1235-828600, FAX 44-1235-829000, info@tandf.co.uk, http://www.tandf.co.uk/journals/titles/10610278.asp. Ed. Jonathan Sessler. **Subscr. to:** Journals Customer Service, Rankine Rd, Basingstoke, Hants RG24 8PR, United Kingdom. TEL 44-1256-813000, FAX 44-1256-330245, enquiry@tandf.co.uk.

570 USA ISSN 0081-9603
CODEN: SFSSA5
➤ **SURFACTANT SCIENCE SERIES.** Text in English. 1966. irreg., latest vol.120, 2004. USD 195 per vol. vol.120 (effective 2004). adv. **Document type:** *Monographic series, Academic/Scholarly.*
Indexed: BIOSIS Prev, BiolAb, CIN, ChemAb, ChemTitl.
—BLDSC (8548.100000), CASDDS, CISTI, IE, ingenta. **CCC.**
Published by: Marcel Dekker Inc. (Subsidiary of: Taylor & Francis Group), 270 Madison Ave, New York, NY 10016-0602. TEL 212-696-9000, FAX 212-685-4540, journals@dekker.com, http://www.dekker.com. R&P Julia Mulligan. Adv. contact Eridania Perez. **Subscr. to:** 6000 Broken Sound Pkwy NW, Ste. 300, Boca Raton, FL 33487-2713. TEL 800-228-1160.

540 USA ISSN 0039-792X
QD1
SYRACUSE CHEMIST. Text in English. 1908. 10/yr. USD 5 to members (effective 2003). bk.rev. **Document type:** *Newsletter.* **Description:** Devoted to the interests and activities of ACS (American Chemical Society) members throughout Greater Syracuse.
Indexed: ChemAb.
Published by: American Chemical Society, Syracuse Section, 220 Carlton Dr, DeWitt, NY 13214-1409. TEL 315-445-9803, FAX 315-445-9803, drsponsl@twcny.rr.com, http://www.esf.edu/acssyr/syrchemist/homesyrchem.html. Ed. Diana Sponsler. Circ: 700.

TAIWAN SUGAR RESEARCH INSTITUTE. ANNUAL REPORT/TAI-WAN TANG YEH YEN CHIU SO NIEN PAO. see *AGRICULTURE—Crop Production And Soil*

662 JPN ISSN 0371-5345
CODEN: TASOA3
TANSO/CARBONS. Text in Japanese. 1949. q. **Document type:** *Journal, Academic/Scholarly.*
Indexed: INIS AtomInd.
—BLDSC (8602.665000), CISTI, IE, Linda Hall. **CCC.**
Published by: Tanso Zairyo Gakkai/Carbon Society of Japan, 3-11-6, Otsuka, Bunkyo-ku, Ohtsuka 3 cho-me Bldg., Tokyo, 112-0012, Japan. TEL 81-3-59407640, FAX 81-3-59407980, tanso-info@r-sipec.jp, http://www.tanso.org/.

TECHNIQUE (SAN DIEGO). see *BIOLOGY*

540 USA ISSN 0082-2531
QD61 CODEN: TQCMAT
➤ **TECHNIQUES OF CHEMISTRY.** Text in English. 1971. irreg., latest vol.22, 1992. price varies. **Document type:** *Monographic series, Academic/Scholarly.*
Incorporates: Technique of Inorganic Chemistry; Technique of Organic Chemistry (0082-240X)
Indexed: CIN, ChemAb, ChemTitl.
—BLDSC (8743.870000), CASDDS, CISTI. **CCC.**
Published by: John Wiley & Sons, Inc., 111 River St, Hoboken, NJ 07030-5774. TEL 201-748-6000, 800-825-7550, FAX 201-748-5915, uscs-wis@wiley.com, http://www.wiley.com. Ed. A Weissberger.

660 CUB ISSN 0253-9276
CODEN: TEQUD8
TECNOLOGIA QUIMICA. Text in Spanish. 1980. 3/yr. USD 15. charts; illus.
Indexed: CEA, CIN, ChemAb, ChemTitl, FS&TA, TCEA.
—CASDDS, CINDOC.
Published by: (Universidad de Oriente), Ediciones Cubanas, Obispo No. 527, Apdo. 605, Havana, Cuba. TEL 32-5556. Ed. Maria Luz Garcia Ferrada. Circ: 1,000. **Co-sponsor:** Sociedad Cubana de Quimica.

540 ITA
TECNORAMA CHIMICA. Text in Italian. 2/yr.
Published by: Pubblicita Edizioni Associati s.r.l., Via Simone D'Orsenigo, 22, Milan, MI 20135, Italy. TEL 2-551-18-42, FAX 2-551-85-263. Ed. Ugo Carutti. Circ: 6,600.

540 UKR ISSN 0497-2627
CODEN: TEKHA4
➤ **TEORETICHESKAYA I EKSPERIMENTAL'NAYA KHIMIYA;** nauchno-teoreticheskii zhurnal. Text in Russian; Abstracts in English, Russian, Ukrainian. 1965. bi-m. USD 148 foreign (effective 2004). **Document type:** *Journal, Academic/Scholarly.* **Description:** Publishes papers concerning theory, kinetics and mechanics of chemical reactions, reactivity, principles of control of chemical processes, influence of various physical factors on these processes, physical-chemical bases for development of newl processes, substances, and materials.
Related titles: Online - full text ed.; ♦ English Translation: Theoretical and Experimental Chemistry. ISSN 0040-5760.
Indexed: ASCA, CCI, CIN, ChemAb, ChemTitl, CurCont, Djerelo, INIS AtomInd, Inspec, MathR, RCI, RefZh, SCI.
—BLDSC (0177.700000), AskIEEE, CASDDS, CISTI, East View, IDS, Linda Hall. **CCC.**
Published by: Natsional'na Akademiya Nauk Ukrainy, Instytut Fizychnoi Khimii im. L.V. Pysarzhevskoho/National Academy of Sciences of Ukraine, L.V. Pysarzhevsky Institute of Physical Chemistry, Pr-kt Nauky 31, Kyiv, 03039, Ukraine. TEL 380-44-2651190, FAX 380-44-2656216, ipcukr@sovam.com, http://www.inphyschem-nas.kiev.ua/?cont=gurnal. Ed. Vitaly D Pokhodenko. Circ: 300 (paid); 50 (controlled). **Dist. by:** East View Information Services, 3020 Harbor Ln. N., Minneapolis, MN 55447. TEL 800-477-1005, FAX 800-800-3839, eastview@eastview.com, http://www.eastview.com.

➤ **THALAMUS AND RELATED SYSTEMS.** see *BIOLOGY*

542 NLD ISSN 1380-7323
THEORETICAL AND COMPUTATIONAL CHEMISTRY. Text in English. 1994. irreg., latest vol.11, 2002. price varies. back issues avail. **Document type:** *Monographic series, Academic/Scholarly.*
Indexed: CIN, ChemAb, ChemTitl.
—BLDSC (8814.552260).
Published by: Elsevier BV (Subsidiary of: Elsevier Science & Technology), Radarweg 29, Amsterdam, 1043 NX, Netherlands. TEL 31-20-4853911, FAX 31-20-4852457, nlinfo-f@elsevier.nl, http://www.elsevier.nl.

541 USA ISSN 0040-5760
QD1 CODEN: TEXCAK
➤ **THEORETICAL AND EXPERIMENTAL CHEMISTRY.** Text in English. 1965. bi-m. EUR 2,835, USD 2,888, GBP 1,765 combined subscription to institutions print & online eds. (effective 2005). adv. back issues avail.; reprint service avail. from PSC. **Document type:** *Journal, Academic/Scholarly.* **Description:** Explores all aspects of chemical theory, particularly quantum chemistry, chemical thermodynamics, theory of solutions, surface phenomena, and chemical physics.
Related titles: Microfilm ed.: (from PQC); Online - full text ed.: ISSN 1573-935X (from EBSCO Publishing, Gale Group, IngentaConnect, Kluwer Online, O C L C Online Computer Library Center, Inc., Springer LINK, Swets Information Services); ♦ Translation of: Teoreticheskaya i Eksperimental'naya Khimiya. ISSN 0497-2627.
Indexed: BibLing, ChemAb, ChemTitl, Inspec.
—BLDSC (0426.200000), AskIEEE, CASDDS, CISTI, IE, Infotrieve, ingenta. **CCC.**
Published by: (Natsional'na Akademiya Nauk Ukrainy UKR), Consultants Bureau (Subsidiary of: Springer-Verlag New York, Inc.), 233 Spring St, New York, NY 10013. TEL 212-460-1500, FAX 212-460-1575, service@springer-ny.com, http://springerlink.metapress.com/openurl.asp?genre=journal&issn=0040-5760, http://www.springeronline.com. Ed. V D Pokhodenko.

541 USA ISSN 0082-3961
➤ **THEORETICAL CHEMISTRY;** a series of monographs. Text in English. 1965. irreg., latest vol.13, 1994. **Document type:** *Monographic series, Academic/Scholarly.*
Indexed: ChemAb.
—**CCC.**
Published by: Academic Press (Subsidiary of: Elsevier Science & Technology), 525 B St, Ste 1900, San Diego, CA 92101-4495. Eds. D P Craig, R McWeeny.

541.2 DEU ISSN 1432-881X
QD1 CODEN: TCACFW
➤ **THEORETICAL CHEMISTRY ACCOUNTS;** theory, computation and modeling. Text in English. 1962. 10/yr. (in 2 vols., 5 nos./vol.). EUR 2,490 combined subscription to institutions print & online eds. (effective 2005). adv. bk.rev. charts; illus. back issues avail.; reprint service avail. from ISI. **Document type:** *Journal, Academic/Scholarly.* **Description:** Covers theoretical chemistry, chemical physics, quantum chemistry, gas phase dynamics, structure and dynamics of condensed phases, statistical mechanics.
Formerly (until 1997): Theoretica Chimica Acta (0040-5744)
Related titles: Microform ed.: (from PQC); Online - full text ed.: ISSN 1432-2234 (from EBSCO Publishing, Springer LINK, Swets Information Services).
Indexed: ASCA, CCI, CIN, CMCI, ChemAb, ChemTitl, CurCont, EngInd, ISR, Inspec, MSB, PhysBer, RCI, RefZh, SCI.
—BLDSC (8814.555750), AskIEEE, CASDDS, CISTI, Ei, IDS, IE, Infotrieve, ingenta, Linda Hall. **CCC.**

C

Published by: Springer-Verlag (Subsidiary of: Springer Science+Business Media), Tiergartenstr 17, Heidelberg, 69121, Germany. TEL 49-6221-3450, FAX 49-6221-345229, http://link.springer.de/link/service/journals/00214/index.htm. Eds. Dr. Christopher J Cramer, Dr. Donald G Truhlar. Adv. contact Stephan Kroeck TEL 49-30-827875739. **Subscr. in the Americas to:** Springer-Verlag New York, Inc., Journal Fulfillment, PO Box 2485, Secaucus, NJ 07096-2485. TEL 800-777-4643, 201-348-4033, FAX 201-348-4505, journals@springer-ny.com, http://www.springer-ny.com; **Subscr. to:** Springer GmbH Auslieferungsgesellschaft, Haberstr 7, Heidelberg 69126, Germany. TEL 49-6221-345-0, FAX 49-6221-345-4229, subscriptions@springer.de.

540 CHN ISSN 1001-6880
QD415.A1 CODEN: TCYKE5

TIANRAN CHANWU YANJIU YU KAIFA/NATURAL PRODUCT RESEARCH AND DEVELOPMENT. Text in Chinese; Abstracts in English. 1989. q. USD 100 (effective 1997). adv. reprints avail. **Document type:** *Journal, Academic/Scholarly.*
Related titles: Online - full text ed.: (from East View Information Services).
Indexed: AgBio, AgrForAb, CIN, CPA, ChemAb, ChemTitl, FPA, ForAb, HortAb, MSB, NutrAb, OrnHort, PBA, PGegResA, PHN&I, RA&MP, RM&VM, RPP, SIA, SeedAb, SoyAb, TriticAb.
—BLDSC (6040.738100), CASDDS, IE, ingenta.
Published by: Zhongguo Kexueyuan, Chengdu Fenyuan/Chinese Academy of Sciences, Chengdu Branch, 9 Renmin Nanlu 4 Duan, Chengdu, Sichuan 610015, China. TEL 86-28-85223853, FAX 86-28-85220439, bj@clas.ac.cn, qkcf@clas.ac.cn, http://www.natureproduct.cn/, http://www.clas.ac.cn/. Ed. Bogang Li. R&P, Adv. contact Yan Wang. Circ: 2,000 (paid). **Co-sponsor:** Chengdu Library of the Chinese Academy of Sciences.

TOHOKU JOURNAL OF AGRICULTURAL RESEARCH. see *AGRICULTURE—Crop Production And Soil*

TOHOKU UNIVERSITY. SCIENCE REPORTS OF THE RESEARCH INSTITUTES. SERIES A: PHYSICS, CHEMISTRY, AND METALLURGY/TOHOKU DAIGAKU KENKYUJO HOKOKU. A-SHU: BUTSURIGAKU, KAGAKU, YAKINGAKU. see *PHYSICS*

TOHOKU UNIVERSITY. SCIENCE REPORTS. SERIES 8: PHYSICS AND ASTRONOMY. see *PHYSICS*

TOKYO DAIGAKU RIGAKUBU CHIKAKU KAGAKU JIKKEN SHISETSU IHO/LABORATORY FOR EARTHQUAKE CHEMISTRY. BULLETIN. see *EARTH SCIENCES*

540 660 USA ISSN 1022-5528
CODEN: TOCAFI

➤ **TOPICS IN CATALYSIS.** Text in English. 1994. 20/yr. (in 4 vols.). EUR 2,178, USD 2,225, GBP 1,348 combined subscription to institutions print & online eds. (effective 2005). adv. back issues avail.; reprint service avail. from PSC. **Document type:** *Journal, Academic/Scholarly.* **Description:** Explores developments in the science of catalysis, offering a forum for seminal ideas and advances among practitioners operating in a wide range of subdisciplines, including heterogeneous, homogeneous, and enzymatic catalysis.
Related titles: Online - full text ed.: ISSN 1572-9028 (from EBSCO Publishing, Gale Group, IngentaConnect, Kluwer Online, O C L C Online Computer Library Center, Inc., Springer LINK, Swets Information Services).
Indexed: APIAb, ASCA, BibLing, CCI, CIN, ChemAb, CurCont, RCI, RefZh.
—BLDSC (8867.432100), CASDDS, CISTI, IDS, IE, Infotrieve, ingenta, Linda Hall. **CCC.**
Published by: Plenum US (Subsidiary of: Springer Science+Business Media), 233 Spring St, New York, NY 10013. TEL 212-460-1500, FAX 212-460-1575, service@springer-ny.com, http://springerlink.metapress.com/openurl.asp?genre=journal&issn=1022-5528, http://www.springeronline.com. Eds. Gabor A Somorjai, John Meurig Thomas.

540 DEU ISSN 0340-1022
QD1 CODEN: TPCCAQ

➤ **TOPICS IN CURRENT CHEMISTRY.** Text in English. 1965. irreg., latest vol.262, 2006. price varies. reprint service avail. from ISI. **Document type:** *Monographic series, Academic/Scholarly.*
Formerly: Fortschritte der Chemischen Forschung (0071-7894)
Related titles: Online - full text ed.: (from EBSCO Publishing).
Indexed: ASCA, BIOSIS Prev, BiolAb, CCI, CIN, ChemAb, ChemInfo, ChemTitl, CurCR, IndChem, Inspec, MEDLINE, RCI, SCI.
—BLDSC (8867.435000), CASDDS, CINDOC, CISTI, IE, Infotrieve, ingenta, Linda Hall. **CCC.**
Published by: Springer-Verlag (Subsidiary of: Springer Science+Business Media), Tiergartenstr 17, Heidelberg, 69121, Germany. TEL 49-6221-3450, FAX 49-6221-345229, subscriptions@springer.de, http://www.springer.de.

➤ **TOPICS IN INORGANIC AND GENERAL CHEMISTRY.** see *CHEMISTRY—Inorganic Chemistry*

541.223 USA ISSN 0082-500X
QD481 CODEN: TOSTBF

➤ **TOPICS IN STEREOCHEMISTRY.** Text in English. 1967. irreg., latest vol.24, 2003. price varies. **Document type:** *Monographic series, Academic/Scholarly.*
Indexed: ASCA, CCI, ChemAb, ChemInfo, ISR, RCI, SCI.
—BLDSC (8867.490000), CASDDS, CISTI, IE, ingenta, Linda Hall.
Published by: John Wiley & Sons, Inc., 111 River St, Hoboken, NJ 07030-5774. TEL 201-748-6000, 800-825-7550, FAX 201-748-5915, uscs-wis@wiley.com, http://www.wiley.com.

➤ **TOXICOLOGICAL AND ENVIRONMENTAL CHEMISTRY.** see *ENVIRONMENTAL STUDIES—Toxicology And Environmental Safety*

➤ **TOYODA KENKYU HOKOKU/TOYODA PHYSICAL AND CHEMICAL RESEARCH INSTITUTE. REPORTS.** see *PHYSICS*

540 530 NLD ISSN 0169-3913
QC173.4.P67 CODEN: TPMEEI

➤ **TRANSPORT IN POROUS MEDIA.** Text in Dutch. 1986. m. EUR 1,498, USD 1,528, GBP 988 combined subscription to institutions print & online eds. (effective 2005). bk.rev. illus. index. back issues avail.; reprint service avail. from PSC. **Document type:** *Journal, Academic/Scholarly.* **Description:** Presents original basic and applied research work on the physical and chemical aspects of transport phenomena in a porous medium, including microscopic and large-scale processes, mathematical and numerical models, in such diverse fields as petroleum engineering and biomedicine.
Related titles: Microform ed.: (from PQC); Online - full text ed.: ISSN 1573-1634 (from EBSCO Publishing, Gale Group, IngentaConnect, Kluwer Online, O C L C Online Computer Library Center, Inc., Springer LINK, Swets Information Services).
Indexed: ABIPC, AEA, ASCA, ApMecR, BibLing, BrCerAb, C&ISA, CCI, CEABA, CIN, CerAb, ChemAb, CorrAb, CurCont, E&CAJ, EMA, EngInd, FLUIDEX, FPA, GEOBASE, GeotechAb, I&DA, IAA, ICEA, ISMEC, ISR, M&TEA, MBF, METADEX, MSCI, MathR, MathSciNet, PetrolAb, RefZh, S&F, SCI, SolStAb, TCEA, TriticAb, WAA.
—BLDSC (9025.871000), CASDDS, CISTI, Ei, IDS, IE, Infotrieve, ingenta, Linda Hall, PADDS. **CCC.**
Published by: Springer-Verlag Dordrecht (Subsidiary of: Springer Science+Business Media), Van Godewijckstraat 30, Dordrecht, 3311 GX, Netherlands. TEL 31-78-6576050, FAX 31-78-6576474, http://springerlink.metapress.com/openurl.asp?genre=journal&issn=0169-3913, http://www.springeronline.com. Ed. Jacob Bear.

540 TUR ISSN 1300-0527
CODEN: TJCHE3

➤ **TURKISH JOURNAL OF CHEMISTRY.** Text in English. 1976. 6/yr. USD 300 (effective 2005). **Document type:** *Journal, Academic/Scholarly.*
Formerly (until 1994): Doga Turkish Journal of Chemistry (1010-7614); Supersedes in part (in 1986): Doga Bilim Dergisi. Serie A: Basic Sciences
Related titles: Online - full text ed.: ISSN 1303-6130. free (effective 2005) (from EBSCO Publishing).
Indexed: ASCA, BioCN&I, BiolAb, CCI, CIN, ChemAb, ChemTitl, CurCont, FS&TA, Inspec, MSCI, S&F.
—BLDSC (9072.468300), CASDDS, CISTI, IDS, IE, ingenta, Linda Hall.
Published by: Scientific and Technical Research Council of Turkey - TUBITAK/Turkiye Bilimsel ve Teknik Arastirma Kurumu, Ataturk Bulvari No. 221, Kavaklidere, Ankara, 06100, Turkey. TEL 90-312-468-5300, FAX 90-312-426-8073, TELEX 43186 BTAK TR, bdym@tubitak.gov.tr, http://journals.tubitak.gov.tr/chem/index.php, http://www.tubitak.gov.tr. Eds. Ayhan S Demir, Bahattin Baysal.

540 UKR ISSN 0041-6045
QD1 CODEN: UKZHAU

➤ **UKRAINSKII KHIMICHESKII ZHURNAL/UKRAINIAN CHEMICAL JOURNAL**; nauchnyi zhurnal. Text in Ukrainian, English, Russian. 1925. bi-m. USD 135 foreign (effective 2004). bk.rev. tr.lit. index. **Document type:** *Journal, Academic/Scholarly.* **Description:** Publishes review articles discussing specific areas of inorganic chemistry, physical chemistry and electrochemistry, organic chemistry and chemistry of polymers.
Related titles: Ukrainian ed.: Ukrains'kyi Khimichnyi Zhurnal. ISSN 0372-4204.
Indexed: ABIPC, AnalAb, BrCerAb, C&ISA, CCI, CEABA, CerAb, ChemAb, ChemInfo, ChemTitl, CivEngAb, CorrAb, Djerelo, E&CAJ, EMA, EngInd, INIS AtomInd, M&TEA, MBF, METADEX, MSB, MSCI, NutrAb, PotatoAb, RefZh, SolStAb, WAA, WeedAb.
—CASDDS, CISTI, East View, Ei, KNAW, Linda Hall. **CCC.**
Published by: Natsional'na Akademiya Nauk Ukrainy, Instytut Zahal'noyi i Neorhanichnoyi Khimii im. V.I.Vernads'koho/National Academy of Sciences of Ukraine, V.I. Vernadskii Institute of General and Inorganic Chemistry, Pr Akad Palladina 32-34, Kyiv, 03680, Ukraine. TEL 380-44-4240322, FAX 380-44-4243070, kazdobin@ionc.kar.net, http://www.ionc.kar.net/journal/index.html, http://www.ionc.kar.net/index.html. Ed. Sergiy Volkov. Circ: 1,624. **US dist. addr.:** East View Information Services, 3020 Harbor Ln. N., Minneapolis, MN 55447. TEL 800-477-1005, FAX 800-800-3839, eastview@eastview.com, http://www.eastview.com.

660 DEU ISSN 1435-6007

ULLMANN'S ENCYCLOPEDIA OF INDUSTRIAL CHEMISTRY. Text in English. irreg., latest vol.6, 2002. EUR 5,990 (effective 2004).
Related titles: CD-ROM ed.; Online - full text ed.
Published by: Wiley - V C H Verlag GmbH & Co. KGaA (Subsidiary of: John Wiley & Sons, Inc.), Boschstr 12, Weinheim, 69469, Germany. TEL 49-6201-6060, FAX 49-6201-606328, ullmanns@wiley-vch.de, info@wiley-vch.de, sales-books@wiley-vch.de, http://www.wiley-vch.de. Eds. Barbara Elvers, Stephen Hawkins, Hubert Pelc TEL 49-6201-606246. Adv. contact Aenne Anders TEL 49-6201-606552.

540 NLD ISSN 0924-6223
CODEN: UCREEV

➤ **UNDERSTANDING CHEMICAL REACTIVITY.** Text in English. 1986. irreg., latest vol.24, 2004. price varies. **Document type:** *Monographic series, Academic/Scholarly.*
Indexed: CIN, ChemAb, ChemTitl, MSB.
—BLDSC (9090.004250), CISTI, IE, ingenta. **CCC.**
Published by: Springer-Verlag Dordrecht (Subsidiary of: Springer Science+Business Media), Van Godewijckstraat 30, Dordrecht, 3311 GX, Netherlands. TEL 31-78-6576050, FAX 31-78-6576474, http://www.springeronline.com. Ed. Paul G Mezey.

540.71 MEX

UNIVERSIDAD NACIONAL AUTONOMA DE MEXICO. FACULTAD DE QUIMICA. GACETA. Text in Spanish. w. free. back issues avail.
Related titles: Online - full text ed.
Published by: Universidad Nacional Autonoma de Mexico, Facultad de Medicina, 3er. Piso, Bloque B, Ciudad Universitaria, Box 70-298, Mexico City DF, 04510, Mexico. TEL 52-5-6223439, FAX 52-5-6223711, fqciqt@servidor.unam.mx, http://www.fquim.unam.mx/.

540 ITA ISSN 0428-240X

UNIVERSITA DI FERRARA. ANNALI. SEZIONE 5: CHIMICA PURA ED APPLICATA. Text in Italian. 1954. a. price varies.
Related titles: Supplement(s): Universita. di Ferrara. Annali. Sezione 5: Chimica Pura ed Applicata. Supplemento. ISSN 0365-785X. 1956.
—Linda Hall.
Published by: (Universita degli Studi di Ferrara), Casa Editrice Leo S. Olschki, Viuzzo del Pozzetto 8, Florence, 50126, Italy. TEL 39-055-6530684, FAX 39-055-6530214, celso@olschki.it, http://www.olschki.it.

540 ROM ISSN 1221-5341
QD1 CODEN: AUZCAZ

UNIVERSITATEA "AL. I. CUZA" DIN IASI. ANALELE STIINTIFICE. CHIMIE. Text in English, French, German, Italian, Romanian, Russian. 1955. a. ROL 20. abstr.
Former titles (until 1992): Universitatea "Al. I. Cuza" din Iasi. Analele Stiintifice. Sectiunea 1c: Chimie (0041-9117); (until 1963): Universitatea "Al. I. Cuza" din Iasi. Analele Stiintifice. Sectiunea I, Matematica. Fizica. Chimie (0448-9039)
Indexed: ChemAb.
—BLDSC (0869.655000), CISTI, Linda Hall.
Published by: Universitatea "Al. I. Cuza" din Iasi/"Alexandru Ioan Cuza" University of Iasi, Carol I Boulevard, Iasi, 6600, Romania. TEL 40-032-201000, FAX 40-032-201201, sysadmin@uaic.ro, http://www.uaic.ro. Ed. Dr. I A Schneider. Circ: 750.

540 GBR ISSN 1369-5614

UNIVERSITY CHEMISTRY EDUCATION. (From January 2001, University Chemistry Education will be available only in electronic format on www.rsc.org, the Royal Society of Chemistry's web site. Access will be free.) Text in English. 1997. s-a. free. **Description:** Covers the teaching of chemistry in higher education.
Media: Online - full text.
—IDS.
Published by: Royal Society of Chemistry, Thomas Graham House, Science Park, Milton Rd, Cambridge, CB4 0WF, United Kingdom. TEL 44-1223-432360, FAX 44-1223-423623, sales@rsc.org, advertising@rsc.org, http://www.rsc.org/uchmed, http://www.rsc.org/pccp. Ed. M J Pilling. **Subscr. to:** Extenza - Turpin, Pegasus Dr, Stratton Business Park, Biggleswade, Beds SG18 8TQ, United Kingdom.

540 660 TUR ISSN 1303-6017

UNIVERSITY OF ANKARA. FACULTY OF SCIENCE. COMMUNICATIONS. SERIES B: CHEMISTRY AND CHEMICAL ENGINEERING. Text in English. 1948. s-a. exchange basis.

C

Formerly: Universite d'Ankara. Faculte des Sciences. Communications. Serie B: Chimie (0570-1414); Which superseded in part (in 1952): Universite d'Ankara. Faculte des Sciences. Communications (0366-6956)
Related titles: Online - full text ed.: (from EBSCO Publishing).
—CISTI.
Published by: Ankara Universitesi, Fen Fakultesi, Dogol Caddesi, Ankara, 06100, Turkey. TEL 90-312-2126720, FAX 90-312-2232395, commun@science.ankara.edu.tr, http://www.ankara.edu.tr/rectorate/kutuphane/Yayinlar/dergiler/communeng.htm, http://www.science.ankara.edu.tr/. Ed. Oner Cakar.

540 POL ISSN 0554-8241
QA1 CODEN: SCUCDH
UNIWERSYTET IM. ADAMA MICKIEWICZA. CHEMIA. Text in Polish; Summaries in English. 1960. irreg., latest vol.64, 1995.
Document type: *Monographic series, Academic/Scholarly.* **Description:** Contains current research results of the university's scholars, their Ph.D. works and monographs. Each volume contains the work of one author.
Formerly (until 1971): Uniwersytet im. Adama Mickiewicza w Poznaniu. Wydzial Matematyki, Fizyki i Chemii. Prace. Seria Chemia (1230-0063)
Indexed: ChemAb, ChemTitl.
—CASDDS, CISTI, Linda Hall.
Published by: Wydawnictwo Naukowe Uniwersytetu im. Adama Mickiewicza/Adam Mickiewicz University Press, Nowowiejskiego 55, Poznan, 61-734, Poland. TEL 48-61-527380, FAX 48-61-527701. Pub. Maria Jankowska. R&P Malgorzata Bis. Circ: 280.

540 POL ISSN 0867-1095
QD1 CODEN: UIACEG
UNIWERSYTET JAGIELLONSKI. ZESZYTY NAUKOWE. ACTA CHIMICA. Variant title: Universitatis Iagellonicae. Acta Chimica. Text in English, Polish; Summaries in English, Polish, Russian. 1959. irreg., latest 1999. price varies. bibl.; illus.
Document type: *Monographic series, Academic/Scholarly.*
Formerly (until 1990): Uniwersytet Jagiellonski. Zeszyty Naukowe. Prace Chemiczne (0083-4319)
Indexed: ChemAb.
—CASDDS, CISTI, Linda Hall.
Published by: (Uniwersytet Jagiellonski, Wydzial Chemii), Wydawnictwo Uniwersytetu Jagiellonskiego/Jagiellonian University Press, ul Grodzka 26, Krakow, 31044, Poland. TEL 48-12-4312364, FAX 48-12-4301995, wydaw@if.uj.edu.pl, http://www.wuj.pl. **Dist. by:** Ars Polona, Krakowskie Przedmiescie 7, Warsaw, Poland. TEL 48-22-9263914, FAX 48-22-9265334, arspolona@arspolona.com.pl, http://www.arspolona.com.pl.

540 POL ISSN 1640-131X
QD1 CODEN: ZWSCDK
UNIWERSYTET OPOLSKI. ZESZYTY NAUKOWE. CHEMIA. Text in Polish; Summaries in English. 1974. irreg., latest 2002. price varies, avail. on exchange basis. **Document type:** *Monographic series, Academic/Scholarly.*
Formerly (until 1994): Wyzsza Szkola Pedagogiczna, Opole. Zeszyty Naukowe. Seria A. Chemia (0324-9034)
Indexed: ChemAb.
—CASDDS.
Published by: Wydawnictwo Uniwersytetu Opolskiego, ul Sienkiewicza 33, Opole, 45037, Poland. TEL 48-77-4410878, wydawnictwo@uni.opole.pl. Ed. Witold Waclawek.

540 DEU
CODEN: NUCHFF
UNTERRICHT CHEMIE. Text in German. 1970. 6/yr. EUR 63; EUR 10 newsstand/cover (effective 2005). adv. **Document type:** *Journal, Academic/Scholarly.*
Formerly: Naturwissenschaften im Unterricht Chemie (0946-2139); Which superseded in part (in 1990): Naturwissenschaften im Unterricht. Physik, Chemie (0342-5479); (in 1978): Naturwissenschaften im Unterricht (0342-5460)
Indexed: IBZ.
—CASDDS. **CCC.**
Published by: Erhard Friedrich Verlag GmbH, Im Brande 17, Seelze, 30926, Germany. TEL 49-511-400040, FAX 49-511-40004170, info@friedrich-verlag.de, http://www.friedrich-verlag.de. adv.: B&W page EUR 1,020, color page EUR 1,530. Circ: 7,000 (paid and controlled).

540 RUS ISSN 0042-1308
QD1 CODEN: USKHAB
➤ **USPEKHI KHIMII.** Text in Russian. 1932. m. USD 298 worldwide (effective 2005). bibl.; charts; illus. index.
Document type: *Journal, Academic/Scholarly.* **Description:** Publishes reviews covering most aspects of modern chemistry.
Related titles: ♦ English Translation: Russian Chemical Reviews. ISSN 0036-021X.
Indexed: ASCA, BiolAb, CCI, CEABA, CIN, ChemAb, ChemTitl, CurCont, EngInd, ISR, MSCI, RASB, RefZh, SCI.
—BLDSC (0388.000000), CASDDS, CINDOC, CISTI, East View, Ei, IDS, KNAW, Linda Hall. **CCC.**
Published by: (Rossiiskaya Akademiya Nauk/Russian Academy of Sciences), Turpion - Moscow Ltd., Leninskii pr-t 47, Moscow, 119991, Russian Federation. TEL 7-095-1356417, FAX 7-095-1358860, ukh@ioc.ac.ru, custserv@turpion.ru, http://rcr.ioc.ac.ru, http://www.turpion.org. Ed. O M Nefedov. Pub., Adv. contact Tatiana Teplova TEL 7-095-1358797. R&P Tatiana Teplova. Circ: 4,225. **US dist. addr.:** East View Information Services, 3020 Harbor Ln. N., Minneapolis, MN 55447. TEL 763-550-0961, FAX 763-559-2931, eastview@eastview.com, http://www.eastview.com; **Dist. by:** M K - Periodica, ul Gilyarovskogo 39, Moscow 129110, Russian Federation. TEL 7-095-2845008, FAX 7-095-2813798, info@periodicals.ru, http://www.mkniga.ru.

➤ **V W D - CHEMIE: KAUTSCHUK.** see *BUSINESS AND ECONOMICS—Investments*

➤ **VEGYIPARI SZAKIRODALMI TAJEKOZTATO/CHEMICAL ENGINEERING ABSTRACTS.** see *CHEMISTRY—Abstracting, Bibliographies, Statistics*

540 NLD ISSN 0924-2031
QD96.I5 CODEN: VISPEK
➤ **VIBRATIONAL SPECTROSCOPY.** Text in Dutch. 1990. 6/yr. EUR 1,447 in Europe to institutions; JPY 192,200 in Japan to institutions; USD 1,619 to institutions except Europe and Japan (effective 2006). bk.rev. illus. Index. back issues avail.
Document type: *Journal, Academic/Scholarly.* **Description:** Publishes original research and short communications in vibrational spectroscopy, review articles, and news dealing with theory, applications, techniques and instrumentation in infrared, near infrared and Raman spectroscopy.
Related titles: Microform ed.: (from PQC); Online - full text ed.: (from EBSCO Publishing, Gale Group, IngentaConnect, ScienceDirect, Swets Information Services); ♦ Series of: Analytica Chimica Acta. ISSN 0003-2670.
Indexed: ABIPC, ASCA, AnalAb, BiolAb, BrCerAb, C&ISA, CCI, CIN, CerAb, ChemAb, ChemTitl, CivEngAb, CorrAb, CurCont, DBA, E&CAJ, EMA, EngInd, ExcerpMed, IAA, ISR, IndMed, Inspec, M&TEA, MBF, METADEX, MSB, MSCI, RefZh, SCI, SolStAb, WAA, WSCA.
—BLDSC (9232.252100), AskIEEE, CASDDS, CISTI, Ei, GNLM, IDS, IE, Infotrieve, ingenta, Linda Hall. **CCC.**
Published by: Elsevier BV (Subsidiary of: Elsevier Science & Technology), Radarweg 29, Amsterdam, 1043 NX, Netherlands. TEL 31-20-4853911, FAX 31-20-4852457, nlinfo-f@elsevier.nl, http://www.elsevier.com/locate/vibspec, http://www.elsevier.nl. Eds. J H van der Maas, M. Diem. Circ: 30,000. **Subscr. to:** PO Box 211, Amsterdam 1000 AE, Netherlands. TEL 31-20-485-3757, FAX 31-20-485-3432.

➤ **VIRTUAL JOURNAL OF ULTRAFAST SCIENCE.** see *PHYSICS*

➤ **VOM WASSER.** see *WATER RESOURCES*

540 570 RUS
VORONEZHSKII GOSUDARSTVENNYI UNIVERSITET. VESTI. KHIMIYA, BIOLOGIYA. Text in Russian. 2000. irreg. (1/2 a year).
Published by: Voronezhskii Gosudarstvennyi Universitet, Universitetskaya pl 1, Voronezh, 394693, Russian Federation. TEL 7-0732-789657, FAX 7-0732-554308, office@main.vsu.ru, http://www.vsu.ru/dept/science/public/vest_vsu/biochem.html.

540 USA ISSN 0506-1083
CODEN: VRTXA6
THE VORTEX. Text in English. 1939. 10/yr. USD 15 to non-members; free to members (effective 2004). adv. bk.rev. back issues avail. **Document type:** *Newsletter, Academic/Scholarly.* **Description:** News of interest to chemists in Northern California.
Related titles: Online - full text ed.
Published by: American Chemical Society, California Section, 49 Quail Court, Ste 315, Walnut Creek, CA 94596. TEL 925-287-8055, FAX 925-287-8056, office@calacs.org, http://www.calacs.org/Vortex.html. Ed. Louis A Rigali TEL 510-763-8771. Adv. contact Gale Vince TEL 781-837-0424. B&W page USD 580; trim 5.5 x 8.5. Circ: 3,500 (controlled).

540 RUS
➤ **VYSOKOMOLEKULYARNYE SOEDINENIYA. SERIYA C.** Text in Russian. s-a. **Document type:** *Journal, Academic/Scholarly.*
Related titles: ♦ English Translation: Polymer Science. Series C. ISSN 1811-2382.
Published by: Izdatel'stvo Nauka, Profsoyuznaya ul 90, Moscow, 117864, Russian Federation. TEL 7-095-3347151, FAX 7-095-4202220, secret@naukaran.ru, http://www.naukaran.ru.

540 DEU
WACKER WERK & WIRKEN. Abbreviated title: W W W. Text in English, German. 1970. m. free. **Document type:** *Magazine, Trade.* **Description:** Reports on company strategies, events, and products such as silicones, polymers, and semiconductor materials.
Related titles: International ed.: Wacker World-Wide.
Published by: Wacker-Chemie GmbH, Hanns-Seidel-Platz 4, Munich, 81737, Germany. TEL 49-89-62791614, FAX 49-89-62791818, http://www.wacker.com. Ed. Doris Wacker. Circ: 39,000.

WASTE MANAGEMENT. see *ENVIRONMENTAL STUDIES—Waste Management*

540 USA ISSN 0557-1588
THE WELCH FOUNDATION. CONFERENCES ON CHEMICAL RESEARCH. PROCEEDINGS. Text in English. 1957. a.
Document type: *Proceedings, Academic/Scholarly.*
Published by: Welch Foundation, 5555 San Felipe, Ste 1900, Houston, TX 77056-2732. TEL 713-961-9884, FAX 713-961-5168, http://www.welch1.org.

WEST AFRICAN JOURNAL OF BIOLOGICAL AND APPLIED CHEMISTRY. see *BIOLOGY—Biochemistry*

WHERE TO BUY CHEMICALS, PLANT AND SERVICES. see *BUSINESS AND ECONOMICS—Marketing And Purchasing*

540 POL ISSN 0043-5104
CODEN: WICHAP
WIADOMOSCI CHEMICZNE. Text in Polish; Summaries in English. 1947. bi-m. USD 20. bk.rev. abstr.; illus. index.
Document type: *Academic/Scholarly.* **Description:** Research reports on theoretical chemistry and practical applications of experimental results.
Indexed: CEABA, CIN, ChemAb, INIS AtomInd, MSB.
—CASDDS, CISTI, Linda Hall.
Published by: (Polskie Towarzystwo Chemiczne/Polish Chemical Society), Wydawnictwo Uniwersytetu Wroclawskiego Spolka z o.o., Pl Uniwersytecki 9-13, Wroclaw, 50-137, Poland. TEL 48-71-441006, FAX 48-71-402735. Ed. Jozef Ziolkowski. Circ: 600. **Subscr. to:** Redakcja Wiadomosci Chemicznych, Ul F Joliot Curie 14, Wroclaw 50383, Poland. TEL 48-71-204389, FAX 48-71-221406.

540 USA
WORLD ETHYLENE AND DERIVATIVES. Text in English. 1973. a. charts; stat. **Document type:** *Trade.*
Formerly: Ethylene and Derivatives
Related titles: CD-ROM ed.
Published by: S R I Consulting, World Petrochemicals Program, 16945 N Chase Dr, Ste 1910, Houston, TX 77060. TEL 281-876-6923, FAX 281-876-6923, pbjacek@sric.sri.com, http://www.wp.sric.sri.com. Ed. J P Bjacek.

540 USA
WORLD PROPYLENE AND DERIVATIVES. Text in English. 1973. a. charts; stat. **Document type:** *Trade.*
Formerly: Propylene and Derivatives
Related titles: CD-ROM ed.
Published by: S R I Consulting, World Petrochemicals Program, 16945 N Chase Dr, Ste 1910, Houston, TX 77060. TEL 281-876-6923, FAX 281-876-6923, pbjacek@sric.sri.com, http://www.wp.sric.sri.com. Ed. J B Bjacek.

540 SGP ISSN 1793-1363
WORLD SCIENTIFIC LECTURE AND COURSE NOTES IN CHEMISTRY. Text in English. 1994. irreg., latest vol.8. price varies. **Document type:** *Monographic series, Academic/Scholarly.* **Description:** It has been developed for courses in Chemistry intended for graduate students and advanced undergraduates. It assumes that the reader is familiar with calculus and basic chemistry and physics. The authors of each volume attempt to structure the lecture material in such a way that a smooth transition comes about from elementary to more complicated matters. It is also be used by researchers who are not familiar with a particular subject, but would like to master it so that it can be used in their research.
Published by: World Scientific Publishing Co. Pte. Ltd., 5 Toh Tuck Link, Singapore, 596224, Singapore. TEL 65-466-5775, FAX 65-467-7667, wspc@wspc.com.sg, series@wspc.com.sg, http://www.wspc.com.sg/books/series/wslcnc_series.shtml, http://www.worldscientific.com. Ed. S H Lin. **Dist. by:** World Scientific Publishing Co., Inc., 1060 Main St, River Edge, NJ 07661. TEL 201-487-9655, 800-227-7562, FAX 201-487-9656, 888-977-2665; World Scientific Publishing Ltd., 57 Shelton St, London WC2H 9HE, United Kingdom. TEL 44-20-78360888, FAX 44-20-78362020.

540 SGP
WORLD SCIENTIFIC LECTURE AND NOTES IN CHEMISTRY. Text in English. 1991. irreg., latest vol.8, 2004. price varies.
Document type: *Monographic series, Academic/Scholarly.*
Description: Provides information to chemistry graduate students and advanced undergraduates already familiar with calculus and basic chemistry and physics.
Published by: World Scientific Publishing Co. Pte. Ltd., 5 Toh Tuck Link, Singapore, 596224, Singapore. TEL 65-466-5775, FAX 65-467-7667, http://www.wspc.com.sg/books/series/wslcnc_series.shtml.

540 SGP ISSN 1793-138X
WORLD SCIENTIFIC SERIES IN 20TH CENTURY CHEMISTRY. Text in English. 1993. irreg., latest vol.13. price varies.
Document type: *Monographic series, Academic/Scholarly.*
Description: Aims to provide a historical perspective on the development and progress of the varied fields now to be found in Chemistry. It achieves this by collecting together all the major papers published by great chemists of this century, in volumes often edited and with commentary by the featured chemist himself/herself. Other volumes in this series may contain histories, or collections of classic papers in a particular area of chemistry. This collection of volumes forms a valuable first-handed record of important discoveries and developments for current and future generations of chemists.

C

Published by: World Scientific Publishing Co. Pte. Ltd., 5 Toh Tuck Link, Singapore, 596224, Singapore. TEL 65-466-5775, FAX 65-467-7667, wspc@wspc.com.sg, series@wspc.com.sg, http://www.wspc.com.sg/books/series/wsscc_series.shtml, http://www.worldscientific.com. Eds. A H Zewail, D H R Barton, F A Cotton, Y T Lee. **Dist. by:** World Scientific Publishing Co., Inc., 1060 Main St, River Edge, NJ 07661. TEL 201-487-9655, 800-227-7562, FAX 201-487-9656, 888-977-2665; World Scientific Publishing Ltd., 57 Shelton St, London WC2H 9HE, United Kingdom. TEL 44-20-78360888, FAX 44-20-78362020.

WORLD SCIENTIFIC SERIES IN CONTEMPORARY CHEMICAL PHYSICS. see *PHYSICS*

XIANWEISU KEXUE YU JISHU/JOURNAL OF CELLULOSE SCIENCE AND TECHNOLOGY. see *PAPER AND PULP*

540 CHN ISSN 1000-0518
TP1 CODEN: YIHUED
YINGYONG HUAXUE/CHINESE JOURNAL OF APPLIED CHEMISTRY. Text in Chinese; Abstracts in English. 1983. m. CNY 9.80 newsstand/cover (effective 2005). **Document type:** *Journal, Academic/Scholarly.*
Related titles: Online - full text ed.: (from East View Information Services).
Indexed: HortAb, RefZh, WeedAb.
—BLDSC (3180.294000), CASDDS, CISTI, IE, ingenta.
Published by: Zhongguo Kexueyuan, Changchun Yingyong Huaxue Yanjiusuo/Chinese Academy of Sciences, Changchun Institute of Applied Chemistry, 5625, Renmin Dajie, Changchun, 130022, China. TEL 86-431-5262016, FAX 86-431-5685653, yyhx@ciac.jl.cn, http://yyhx.periodicals.net.cn/, http://www.ciac.jl.cn/.

ZAOZHI HUAXUE PIN/PAPER CHEMICALS. see *PAPER AND PULP*

540 DEU ISSN 0044-2313
QD1 CODEN: ZAACAB
➤ **ZEITSCHRIFT FUER ANORGANISCHE UND ALLGEMEINE CHEMIE/JOURNAL OF INORGANIC AND GENERAL CHEMISTRY.** Abbreviated title: Z A A C. Text in English, German. 1892. 15/yr. EUR 1,858 in Europe; CHF 2,808 in Switzerland & Liechtenstein; USD 2,298 elsewhere; EUR 2,044 combined subscription in Europe for print & online eds.; CHF 3,089 combined subscription in Switzerland & Liechtenstein for print & online eds.; USD 2,528 combined subscription elsewhere for print & online eds. (effective 2006). illus. index. 242 p./no. 2 cols./p.; reprints avail. **Document type:** *Journal, Academic/Scholarly.* **Description:** Covers all areas of inorganic chemistry, including solid-state, coordination, molecular and inorganic element.
Former titles (until 1950): Zeitschrift fuer Anorganische Chemie (0372-7874); (until 1943): Zeitschrift fuer Anorganische und Allgemeine Chemie (0863-1778); (until 1915): Zeitschrift fuer Anorganische Chemie (0863-1786)
Related titles: Microform ed.: (from PMC); Online - full text ed.: ISSN 1521-3749. EUR 1,858 in Europe; CHF 2,808 in Switzerland & Liechtenstein; USD 2,298 elsewhere (effective 2006) (from EBSCO Publishing, Swets Information Services, Wiley InterScience).
Indexed: ASCA, AnalAb, BrCerAb, BullT&T, CCI, CIN, ChemAb, ChemInfo, ChemTitl, CurCont, EngInd, INIS AtomInd, ISR, Inspec, MSB, RCI, RefZh, SCI.
—BLDSC (9452.000000), AskIEEE, CASDDS, CINDOC, CISTI, Ei, IDS, IE, Infotrieve, ingenta, Linda Hall. **CCC.**
Published by: Wiley - V C H Verlag GmbH & Co. KGaA (Subsidiary of: John Wiley & Sons, Inc.), Boschstr 12, Weinheim, 69469, Germany. TEL 49-6201-6060, FAX 49-6201-606328, subservice@wiley-vch.de, info@wiley-vch.de, http://www.wiley-vch.de. Eds. K Dehnicke, W Bronger, W Hanke. R&P Claudia Rutz. Circ: 750.

540.71 CHN ISSN 1009-2935
ZHONGXUE HUAXUE JIAOYUXUE/TEACHING AND LEARNING OF CHEMISTRY IN MIDDLE SCHOOL. Text in Chinese. 1980. bi-m. CNY 57.60 (effective 2004). 56 p./no.; **Document type:** *Journal, Academic/Scholarly.* **Description:** Covers secondary school chemistry education, teaching methods and curriculum.
Formerly: Zhongxue Huaxue Jiaoxue (1001-2958)
Published by: Zhongguo Renmin Daxue, Shubao Zilio Zhongxin/Renmin University of China, Information Center for Social Server, Dongcheng-qu, 3, Zhangzizhong Lu, Beijing, 100007, China. TEL 86-10-64039458, FAX 86-10-64015080, kyes@163.net, http://www.confucius.cn.net/bkdetail.asp?fzt=G37. **Dist. in US by:** China Publications Service, PO Box 49614, Chicago, IL 60649. TEL 312-288-3291, FAX 312-288-8570; **Dist. by:** China International Book Trading Corp, 35 Chegongzhuang Xilu, Haidian District, PO Box 399, Beijing 100044, China. TEL 86-10-68412045, FAX 86-10-68412023, cibtc@mail.cibtc.com.cn, http://www.cibtc.com.cn.

ZHONGXUESHENG SHU-LI-HUA (GAOZHONG BAN). see *EDUCATION—Teaching Methods And Curriculum*

540 RUS ISSN 0044-460X
CODEN: ZOKHA4
➤ **ZHURNAL OBSHCHEI KHIMII.** Text in Russian. 1931. m. USD 595 foreign (effective 2005). bibl.; charts. index. **Document type:** *Journal, Academic/Scholarly.* **Description:** Examines fundamental problems in chemistry, especially synthesis and organic reactions. Topics covered include biologically active substances, organometallic compounds, and applied spectroscopy.
Related titles: ◆ English Translation: Russian Journal of General Chemistry. ISSN 1070-3632.
Indexed: ABIPC, ASCA, AnalAb, BrCerAb, C&ISA, CCI, CIN, CerAb, ChemAb, ChemInfo, ChemTitl, CivEngAb, CorrAb, CurCR, CurCont, DBA, E&CAJ, EMA, EngInd, ExcerpMed, INIS AtomInd, ISR, IndChem, M&TEA, MBF, METADEX, MSCI, RCI, RefZh, SCI, SIA, SolStAb, WAA, WTA.
—BLDSC (0064.000000), CASDDS, CINDOC, CISTI, East View, Ei, IDS, KNAW, Linda Hall. **CCC.**
Published by: (Rossiiskaya Akademiya Nauk/Russian Academy of Sciences), Izdatel'stvo Nauka, Sankt-Peterburgskoe Otdelenie, Mendeleevskaya liniya 1, St Petersburg, 199034, Russian Federation. TEL 7-812-3286291, chem@thesa.ru. Ed. Anatoly I Rusanov. Circ: 3,335. **Dist. by:** East View Information Services, 3020 Harbor Ln. N., Minneapolis, MN 55447. TEL 800-477-1005, FAX 800-800-3839, eastview@eastview.com, http://www.eastview.com.

➤ **ZHURNAL PRIKLADNOI KHIMII.** see *ENGINEERING—Chemical Engineering*

CHEMISTRY—Abstracting, Bibliographies, Statistics

547 JPN
ABSTRACTS OF THE SYMPOSIUM ON ORGANOMETALLIC CHEMISTRY, JAPAN/YUKI KINZOKU KAGAKU TORONKAI KOEN YOSHISHU. Text in English. a. **Document type:** *Abstract/Index.*
Published by: Kinki Chemical Society/Kinki Kagaku Kyokai, 8-4, Utsubohon-machi 1-chome, Nishi-ku, Osaka 550, Japan.

016.5431 JPN
ABSTRACTS OF THE TOKYO CONFERENCE ON INSTRUMENTAL ANALYSIS AND ANALYTIC SYSTEMS/BUNSEKI KIKI TO KAISEKI SHISUTEMU NI KANSURU TOKYO TORONKAI KOEN YOSHISHU. Text in Japanese. a. **Document type:** *Abstract/Index.*
Published by: Japan Society for Analytical Chemistry/Nihon Bunseki Kagaku Kai, 1-26-2 Nishigotanda, Shinagawa, Tokyo, 141-0031, Japan.

016.5431 JPN
ABSTRACTS ON THE SYMPOSIUM ON MOLECULAR STRUCTURE/BUNSHI KOZO SOGO TORONKAI KOEN YOSHISHU. Text in Japanese. 1973. a. **Document type:** *Abstract/Index.*
Published by: Chemical Society of Japan/Nippon Kagakukai, 1-5, Kanda-Surugadai 1-Chome, Chiyoda-ku, Tokyo, 101-0062, Japan.

540 GBR ISSN 0891-7760
TP967
ADHESIVES ABSTRACTS. Text in English. 1988. m. GBP 305 domestic; USD 490, EUR 490 foreign (effective 2003). **Document type:** *Abstract/Index.* **Description:** Provides references to bibliographic information on all types of adhesives, sealants, bonding agents and technologies.
Related titles: CD-ROM ed.; Online - full text ed.: (from Data-Star, Questel Orbit Inc., The Dialog Corporation).
Indexed: RAPRA.
—CCC.
Published by: R A P R A Technology Ltd., Shawbury, Shrewsbury, Shrops SY4 4NR, United Kingdom. rhondel@rapra.net, http://www.polymerlibrary.com, http://www.rapra.net.

016.548 USA ISSN 0569-4221
QD901 CODEN: ACRABY
AMERICAN CRYSTALLOGRAPHIC ASSOCIATION. PROGRAM & ABSTRACTS. Text in English. 1950. a. USD 15 to members; USD 20 to non-members (effective 2005). **Document type:** *Abstract/Index.*
Indexed: ChemAb, Inspec.
Published by: American Crystallographic Association, c/o Hauptman-Woodward Med Res Inst, 73 High St, PO Box 96, Buffalo, NY 14203. TEL 716-898-8690, FAX 716-898-8695, http://www.hwi.buffalo.edu/aca/. Circ: 2,500. **Distr. by:** Polycrystal Book Service, PO Box 3439, Dayton, OH 45401.

016.543 016 GBR ISSN 0003-2689
QD71 CODEN: AABSAR
ANALYTICAL ABSTRACTS. Text in English. 1954. m. GBP 2,064, USD 3,778 combined subscription print & online eds. (effective 2006). adv. abstr. index. reprints avail. **Document type:** *Journal, Abstract/Index.* **Description:** Provides abstracts of papers, books and application notes of importance and interest to analytical chemists.
Related titles: CD-ROM ed.: Analytical Abstracts On CD-ROM. 1980. USD 1,950 (effective 2002) (from SilverPlatter Information, Inc., The Dialog Corporation); Microform ed.: (from PMC, PQC); Online - full text ed.: Analytical Abstracts Online. ISSN 1471-7107. GBP 1,858, USD 3,400 (effective 2006) (from Data-Star, Questel Orbit Inc.).
Indexed: AESIS.
—BLDSC (0896.000000), CISTI, Linda Hall. **CCC.**
Published by: Royal Society of Chemistry, Thomas Graham House, Science Park, Milton Rd, Cambridge, CB4 0WF, United Kingdom. TEL 44-1223-420066, FAX 44-1223-423623, sales@rsc.org, http://www.rsc.org. Ed. Mike Corkill. **Subscr. to:** Portland Press Ltd., R S C Distribution Services, Commerce Way, Whitehall Industrial Estate, Colchester CO2 8HP, United Kingdom. TEL 44-1206-226050, FAX 44-1206-226055, sales@rscdistribution.org

061.547 DEU
BEILSTEIN ABSTRACTS. Text in English. irreg. free to chemWeb customers. **Description:** Contains articles in organic chemistry published from 1980 to the present. Serves research chemists, biochemists and scientists of many related disciplines in industry and universities throughout the world. Includes critically reviewed and evaluated documents from the Beilstein Handbook of Organic Chemistry as well as data from journals.
Formerly: NetFire
Media: Online - full text.
Published by: M D L Information Systems GmbH (Subsidiary of: Elsevier Science & Technology), Theodor-Heuss-Allee 108, Frankfurt Am Main, 60486, Germany. TEL 49-69-5050-4242, FAX 49-69-5050-4245, info-de@mdl.com, http://www.mdl.com.

540 DEU
BEILSTEIN BRIEF. Text in German. s-a. free. charts; illus. back issues avail. **Document type:** *Bulletin.* **Description:** Informs users of Beilstein chemical database products of enhancements, new-releases, and company news.
Published by: M D L Information Systems GmbH (Subsidiary of: Elsevier Science & Technology), Theodor-Heuss-Allee 108, Frankfurt Am Main, 60486, Germany. TEL 49-69-5050-4242, FAX 49-69-5050-4245, info-de@mdl.com, http://www.beilstein.com/bbrief. Ed. Yvonne Schickel. Pub. Edward Cohen.

540 015 POL ISSN 0137-5040
BIBLIOTEKA CHEMII. Text in Polish. 1977. irreg., latest vol.11, 1987.
Published by: Wydawnictwo Naukowe P W N SA/Polish Scientific Publishers P W N, ul Miodowa 10, Warsaw, 00251, Poland. TEL 48-22-6954321, FAX 48-22-6954288. **Dist. by:** Ars Polona, Krakowskie Przedmiescie 7, Warsaw, Poland.

016.66 016.574 USA
BIOTECHNOLOGY & BIOENGINEERING ABSTRACTS. Text in English. m. USD 7,250 includes access to full back file (effective 2004). **Document type:** *Abstract/Index.* **Description:** Covers research, applications, regulatory developments and new patents across all areas of biotechnology and bioengineering, including medical, pharmaceutical, agricultural, environmental and marine biology.
Media: Online - full text.
Published by: C S A Journal Division (Subsidiary of: Cambridge Information Group), 7200 Wisconsin Ave, Ste 715, Bethesda, MD 20814. TEL 301-961-6798, 800-843-7751, FAX 301-961-6799, journals@csa.com, http://www.csa.com/factsheets/biotclust-set-c.php.

540 016 USA
C A SELECTS. Text in English. 1976. s-w. USD 315 to non-members; USD 95 to members; USD 472 combined subscription print & online eds. (effective 2005). **Document type:** *Abstract/Index.*
Related titles: Online - full text ed.: USD 315 (effective 2005).
Published by: Chemical Abstracts Service (C A S) (Subsidiary of: American Chemical Society), 2540 Olentangy River Rd., Columbus, OH 43210-0012. TEL 614-447-3600, FAX 614-447-3713, help@cas.com, http://www.cas.org, http://caselects.cas.org. Ed. David W Weisgerber. **Subscr. to:** PO Box 3012, Columbus, OH 43210. TEL 800-753-4227, FAX 614-447-3751.

540 011 USA ISSN 1045-8514
CODEN: CAACEY
C A SELECTS. ACTIVATED CARBON. Text in English. s-w. USD 315 to non-members; USD 95 to members (effective 2005). **Document type:** *Abstract/Index.* **Description:** Covers manufacture, properties, and uses of activated carbon including sorption of volatile solvents, purification of aqueous solutions in the refining of sugar and alcohols, water purification, wastewater treatment, immobile phase in gas chromatography, and vacuum technology.
Published by: Chemical Abstracts Service (C A S) (Subsidiary of: American Chemical Society), 2540 Olentangy River Rd., Columbus, OH 43210-0012. TEL 614-447-3600, FAX 614-447-3713, help@cas.com, http://www.cas.org, http://caselects.cas.org. **Subscr. to:** PO Box 3012, Columbus, OH 43210. TEL 800-753-4227, FAX 614-447-3751.

540 011 USA ISSN 1045-8506
CODEN: CSADER
C A SELECTS. ADSORPTION. Text in English. s-w. USD 315 to non-members; USD 95 to members (effective 2005).
Document type: *Abstract/Index.* **Description:** Covers the phenomena of adsorption as well as the properties of adsorbed substances.
Published by: Chemical Abstracts Service (C A S) (Subsidiary of: American Chemical Society), 2540 Olentangy River Rd., Columbus, OH 43210-0012. TEL 614-447-3600, FAX 614-447-3713, help@cas.com, http://www.cas.org, http://caselects.cas.org. **Subscr. to:** PO Box 3012, Columbus, OH 43210. TEL 800-753-4227, FAX 614-447-3751.

540 USA ISSN 0895-5964
CODEN: CSACEO
C A SELECTS. ALKYLATION & CATALYSTS. Text in English. 1988. s-w. USD 315 to non-members; USD 95 to members (effective 2005). **Document type:** *Abstract/Index.*
Description: Covers alkylation of such compounds as alkanes, alkenes, benzenes, and amines with agents such as alcohols and olefins; catalysts used to effect alkylations.
Published by: Chemical Abstracts Service (C A S) (Subsidiary of: American Chemical Society), 2540 Olentangy River Rd., Columbus, OH 43210-0012. TEL 614-447-3600, FAX 614-447-3713, help@cas.com, http://www.cas.org, http://caselects.cas.org. **Subscr. to:** PO Box 3012, Columbus, OH 43210. TEL 800-753-4227, FAX 614-447-3751.

541.37 USA ISSN 0160-8959
CODEN: CSAEDT
C A SELECTS. ANALYTICAL ELECTROCHEMISTRY. Text in English. s-w. USD 315 to non-members; USD 95 to members (effective 2005). **Document type:** *Abstract/Index.*
Description: Covers analytical electrochemistry involving organic and inorganic compounds; amperometric, conductometric, coulometric, and potentiometric titrations; stripping voltammetry, polarographic analysis; and electroanalysis using ion-specific electrodes.
Published by: Chemical Abstracts Service (C A S) (Subsidiary of: American Chemical Society), 2540 Olentangy River Rd., Columbus, OH 43210-0012. TEL 614-447-3600, FAX 614-447-3713, help@cas.com, http://www.cas.org, http://caselects.cas.org. **Subscr. to:** PO Box 3012, Columbus, OH 43210. TEL 800-753-4227, FAX 614-447-3751.

540 USA ISSN 1045-8522
CODEN: CAAAES
C A SELECTS. ANTIBACTERIAL AGENTS. Text in English. s-w. USD 315 to non-members; USD 95 to members (effective 2005). **Document type:** *Abstract/Index.* **Description:** Covers design, synthesis, therapeutic use, mode of action, and structure-activity relationships of antibacterial agents.
Formerly (until 1989): C A Selects. Bactericides, Disinfectants and Antiseptics (0890-1848)
Published by: Chemical Abstracts Service (C A S) (Subsidiary of: American Chemical Society), 2540 Olentangy River Rd., Columbus, OH 43210-0012. TEL 614-447-3600, FAX 614-447-3713, help@cas.com, http://www.cas.org, http://caselects.cas.org. **Subscr. to:** PO Box 3012, Columbus, OH 43210. TEL 800-753-4227, FAX 614-447-3751.

540 USA ISSN 0275-7028
CODEN: CAAODZ
C A SELECTS. ANTIOXIDANTS. Text in English. s-w. USD 315 to non-members; USD 95 to members (effective 2005).
Document type: *Abstract/Index.* **Description:** Covers chemistry of oxidation prevention, as well as manufacture and new uses of antioxidants.
Published by: Chemical Abstracts Service (C A S) (Subsidiary of: American Chemical Society), 2540 Olentangy River Rd., Columbus, OH 43210-0012. TEL 614-447-3600, FAX 614-447-3713, help@cas.com, http://www.cas.org, http://caselects.cas.org. **Subscr. to:** PO Box 3012, Columbus, OH 43210. TEL 800-753-4227, FAX 614-447-3751..

540 011 USA ISSN 1061-5342
CODEN: CABCE5
C A SELECTS. BISMUTH CHEMISTRY. Text in English. 1992. s-w. USD 315 to non-members; USD 95 to members (effective 2005). **Document type:** *Abstract/Index.*
Description: Covers all aspects of the chemistry of bismuth.
Published by: Chemical Abstracts Service (C A S) (Subsidiary of: American Chemical Society), 2540 Olentangy River Rd., Columbus, OH 43210-0012. TEL 614-447-3600, FAX 614-447-3713, help@cas.com, http://www.cas.org, http://caselects.cas.org. **Subscr. to:** PO Box 3012, Columbus, OH 43210. TEL 800-753-4227, FAX 614-447-3751.

547 USA ISSN 0734-8851
CODEN: CASPER
C A SELECTS. BLOCK & GRAFT POLYMERS. Text in English. s-w. USD 315 to non-members; USD 95 to members (effective 2005). **Document type:** *Abstract/Index.*
Description: Covers preparation, properties, uses of block or segmented polymers; compositional block copolymers and stereoblock polymers (additional and, or condensation); synthesis of graft copolymers: catalytic, mechanistic, kinetic aspects.
Published by: Chemical Abstracts Service (C A S) (Subsidiary of: American Chemical Society), 2540 Olentangy River Rd., Columbus, OH 43210-0012. TEL 614-447-3600, FAX 614-447-3713, help@cas.com, http://www.cas.org, http://caselects.cas.org. **Subscr. to:** PO Box 3012, Columbus, OH 43210. TEL 800-753-4227, FAX 614-447-3751.

C A SELECTS. CERAMIC MATERIALS (JOURNALS). see *CERAMICS, GLASS AND POTTERY—Abstracting, Bibliographies, Statistics*

540 USA ISSN 0734-8797
CODEN: CASAEG
C A SELECTS. CHELATING AGENTS. Text in English. s-w. USD 315 to non-members; USD 95 to members (effective 2005).
Document type: *Abstract/Index.* **Description:** Covers chelating agents and complexing agents in analytical procedures, separation processes, isolation of metals, and industrial processes.
Published by: Chemical Abstracts Service (C A S) (Subsidiary of: American Chemical Society), 2540 Olentangy River Rd., Columbus, OH 43210-0012. TEL 614-447-3600, FAX 614-447-3713, help@cas.com, http://www.cas.org, http://caselects.cas.org. **Subscr. to:** PO Box 3012, Columbus, OH 43210. TEL 800-753-4227, FAX 614-447-3751.

540 USA ISSN 1040-712X
CODEN: CASOEO
C A SELECTS. CHEMICAL ENGINEERING OPERATIONS. Text in English. 1989. s-w. USD 315 to non-members; USD 95 to members (effective 2005). **Document type:** *Abstract/Index.*
Description: Covers the theory and technology of unit operations including flow, heat transfer, mass transfer, material handling, size modification, and mixing; separation by absorption, adsorption, crystallization, drying, evaporation, and sedimentation.
Related titles: Online - full text ed.: USD 305 (effective 2004).
Published by: Chemical Abstracts Service (C A S) (Subsidiary of: American Chemical Society), 2540 Olentangy River Rd., Columbus, OH 43210-0012. TEL 614-447-3600, FAX 614-447-3713, help@cas.com, http://www.cas.org, http://caselects.cas.org.

C A SELECTS. CHEMICAL INSTRUMENTATION. see *INSTRUMENTS—Abstracting, Bibliographies, Statistics*

540 USA ISSN 0885-0119
CODEN: CSCDE3
C A SELECTS. CHEMICAL VAPOR DEPOSITION. Abbreviated title: C V D. Text in English. s-w. USD 315 to non-members; USD 95 to members (effective 2005). **Document type:** *Abstract/Index.* **Description:** Covers CVD processes, with emphasis on device fabrications; epitaxial growth of semiconductors; and deposition of thin film for recording and memory devices.
Published by: Chemical Abstracts Service (C A S) (Subsidiary of: American Chemical Society), 2540 Olentangy River Rd., Columbus, OH 43210-0012. TEL 614-447-3600, FAX 614-447-3713, help@cas.com, http://www.cas.org, http://caselects.cas.org. **Subscr. to:** PO Box 3012, Columbus, OH 43210. TEL 800-753-4227, FAX 614-447-3751.

549 USA ISSN 0146-4426
CODEN: CSCCDX
C A SELECTS. COAL SCIENCE AND PROCESS CHEMISTRY. Text in English. s-w. USD 315 to non-members; USD 95 to members (effective 2005). **Document type:** *Abstract/Index.*
Description: Covers coal liquefaction, gasification, coal combustion, and coal mine gases.
Published by: Chemical Abstracts Service (C A S) (Subsidiary of: American Chemical Society), 2540 Olentangy River Rd., Columbus, OH 43210-0012. TEL 614-447-3600, FAX 614-447-3713, help@cas.com, http://www.cas.org, http://caselects.cas.org. **Subscr. to:** PO Box 3012, Columbus, OH 43210. TEL 800-753-4227, FAX 614-447-3751.

540 USA ISSN 0160-8967
CODEN: CSCADR
C A SELECTS. COLLOIDS (APPLIED ASPECTS). Text in English. s-w. USD 315 to non-members; USD 95 to members (effective 2005). **Document type:** *Abstract/Index.*
Description: Covers emulsions, gels, latexes, micellar solutions, sols, and other forms of colloidal dispersions; uses of these materials in cosmetics, foods, fuels, metals, and other products.
Published by: Chemical Abstracts Service (C A S) (Subsidiary of: American Chemical Society), 2540 Olentangy River Rd., Columbus, OH 43210-0012. TEL 614-447-3600, FAX 614-447-3713, help@cas.com, http://www.cas.org, http://caselects.cas.org. **Subscr. to:** PO Box 3012, Columbus, OH 43210. TEL 800-753-4227, FAX 614-447-3751.

540 USA ISSN 0190-9444
CODEN: CCMADX
C A SELECTS. COLLOIDS (MACROMOLECULAR ASPECTS). Text in English. s-w. USD 315 to non-members; USD 95 to members (effective 2005). **Document type:** *Abstract/Index.*
Description: Covers macromolecular emulsions, gels, latexes, micellar solutions, sols, and other forms of colloidal dispersions; uses in coatings, elastomers, plastics, textiles, and other industries.
Published by: Chemical Abstracts Service (C A S) (Subsidiary of: American Chemical Society), 2540 Olentangy River Rd., Columbus, OH 43210-0012. TEL 614-447-3600, FAX 614-447-3713, help@cas.com, http://www.cas.org, http://caselects.cas.org. **Subscr. to:** PO Box 3012, Columbus, OH 43210. TEL 800-753-4227, FAX 614-447-3751.

540 USA ISSN 0160-8975
CODEN: CCPADE
C A SELECTS. COLLOIDS (PHYSICOCHEMICAL ASPECTS). Text in English. s-w. USD 315 to non-members; USD 95 to members (effective 2005). **Document type:** *Abstract/Index.*
Description: Covers the physical chemistry of colloids, suspensions, and dispersions.
Published by: Chemical Abstracts Service (C A S) (Subsidiary of: American Chemical Society), 2540 Olentangy River Rd., Columbus, OH 43210-0012. TEL 614-447-3600, FAX 614-447-3713, help@cas.com, http://www.cas.org, http://caselects.cas.org. **Subscr. to:** PO Box 3012, Columbus, OH 43210. TEL 800-753-4227, FAX 614-447-3751.

540 USA ISSN 0885-0127
CODEN: CSCSEE
C A SELECTS. COLOR SCIENCE. Text in English. s-w. USD 315 to non-members; USD 95 to members (effective 2005).
Document type: *Abstract/Index.* **Description:** Covers photochromic materials, phosphors, and light-emitting substances with respect to color.
Published by: Chemical Abstracts Service (C A S) (Subsidiary of: American Chemical Society), 2540 Olentangy River Rd., Columbus, OH 43210-0012. TEL 614-447-3600, FAX 614-447-3713, help@cas.com, http://www.cas.org, http://caselects.cas.org. **Subscr. to:** PO Box 3012, Columbus, OH 43210. TEL 800-753-4227, FAX 614-447-3751.

540 USA ISSN 1040-7154
CODEN: CAMTE9
C A SELECTS. COMPOSITE MATERIALS (POLYMERIC). Text in English. 1989. s-w. USD 315 domestic to non-members; USD 95 to members (effective 2005). **Document type:** *Abstract/Index.* **Description:** Covers the chemistry, manufacture, and use of composites with plastic (polymeric) matrixes and fibrous, granular, or spherical fillers.
Related titles: Online - full text ed.: USD 305 (effective 2004).
Published by: Chemical Abstracts Service (C A S) (Subsidiary of: American Chemical Society), 2540 Olentangy River Rd., Columbus, OH 43210-0012. TEL 614-447-3600, FAX 614-447-3713, help@cas.com, http://www.cas.org, http://caselects.cas.org.

C

540 USA ISSN 0160-9025
CODEN: CCOCDF
C A SELECTS. COMPUTERS IN CHEMISTRY. Text in English. s-w. USD 315 to non-members; USD 95 to members (effective 2005). **Document type:** *Abstract/Index.*
Description: Covers the online and offline uses of computers in chemistry; data processing, information retrieval; process control, programmed calculations, computer simulation models.
Published by: Chemical Abstracts Service (C A S) (Subsidiary of: American Chemical Society), 2540 Olentangy River Rd., Columbus, OH 43210-0012. TEL 614-447-3600, FAX 614-447-3713, help@cas.com, http://www.cas.org, http://caselects.cas.org. **Subscr. to:** PO Box 3012, Columbus, OH 43210. TEL 800-753-4227, FAX 614-447-3751.

540 USA ISSN 0885-0135
CODEN: CACPEF
C A SELECTS. CONDUCTIVE POLYMERS. Text in English. s-w. USD 315 to non-members; USD 95 to members (effective 2005). **Document type:** *Abstract/Index.* **Description:** Covers the preparation, properties, and uses of conductive polymers.
Published by: Chemical Abstracts Service (C A S) (Subsidiary of: American Chemical Society), 2540 Olentangy River Rd., Columbus, OH 43210-0012. TEL 614-447-3600, FAX 614-447-3713, help@cas.com, http://www.cas.org, http://caselects.cas.org. **Subscr. to:** PO Box 3012, Columbus, OH 43210. TEL 800-753-4227, FAX 614-447-3751.

540 USA ISSN 0146-4434
CODEN: CSCODZ
C A SELECTS. CORROSION. Text in English. s-w. USD 315 to non-members; USD 95 to members (effective 2005).
Document type: *Abstract/Index.* **Description:** Covers the corrosion, rusting, tarnishing of metals and alloys.
Published by: Chemical Abstracts Service (C A S) (Subsidiary of: American Chemical Society), 2540 Olentangy River Rd., Columbus, OH 43210-0012. TEL 614-447-3600, FAX 614-447-3713, help@cas.com, http://www.cas.org, http://caselects.cas.org. **Subscr. to:** PO Box 3012, Columbus, OH 43210. TEL 800-753-4227, FAX 614-447-3751.

540 USA ISSN 0740-0721
CODEN: CSCREB
C A SELECTS. CROSSLINKING REACTIONS. Text in English. s-w. USD 315 to non-members; USD 95 to members (effective 2005). **Document type:** *Abstract/Index.*
Description: Covers the formulation of three-dimensional polymer networks by various means, e.g., polymerization of monomers with functionally greater than two, reaction of functional linear polymers with multifunctional agents, irradiation of linear polymers to generate free radicals.

▼ new title ➤ refereed ✶ unverified ♦ full entry avail.

Published by: Chemical Abstracts Service (C A S) (Subsidiary of: American Chemical Society), 2540 Olentangy River Rd., Columbus, OH 43210-0012. TEL 614-447-3600, FAX 614-447-3713, help@cas.com, http://www.cas.org, http://caselects.cas.org. **Subscr. to:** PO Box 3012, Columbus, OH 43210. TEL 800-753-4227, FAX 614-447-3751.

548 USA ISSN 0162-7740 CODEN: CSCGDB

C A SELECTS. CRYSTAL GROWTH. Text in English. s-w. USD 315 to non-members; USD 95 to members (effective 2005). **Document type:** *Abstract/Index.* **Description:** Covers the growth of crystals, dendrites, whiskers, and crystallites.
Published by: Chemical Abstracts Service (C A S) (Subsidiary of: American Chemical Society), 2540 Olentangy River Rd., Columbus, OH 43210-0012. TEL 614-447-3600, FAX 614-447-3713, help@cas.com, http://www.cas.org, http://caselects.cas.org. **Subscr. to:** PO Box 3012, Columbus, OH 43210. TEL 800-753-4227, FAX 614-447-3751.

540 USA ISSN 1524-5780 CODEN: CADSFU

C A SELECTS. DETERGENTS, SOAPS, & SURFACTANTS. Text in English. s-w. USD 315 to non-members; USD 95 to members (effective 2005). **Document type:** *Abstract/Index.* **Description:** Covers preparation, properties, and uses of soaps and synthetic detergents; formulation; dry-cleaning solvents.
Former titles: C A Selects Plus. Detergents, Soaps, and Surfactants (1083-2807); C A Selects. Detergents, Soaps, and Surfactants (0162-7767)
Published by: Chemical Abstracts Service (C A S) (Subsidiary of: American Chemical Society), 2540 Olentangy River Rd., Columbus, OH 43210-0012. TEL 614-447-3600, FAX 614-447-3713, help@cas.com, http://www.cas.org, http://caselects.cas.org. **Subscr. to:** PO Box 3012, Columbus, OH 43210. TEL 800-753-4227, FAX 614-447-3751.

540 USA ISSN 0275-7052 CODEN: CDITD9

C A SELECTS. DISTILLATION TECHNOLOGY. Text in English. s-w. USD 315 to non-members; USD 95 to members (effective 2005). **Document type:** *Abstract/Index.* **Description:** Covers distillation as a unit process; design of distillation equipment; extractive and molecular distillation; applications of distillation technology.
Published by: Chemical Abstracts Service (C A S) (Subsidiary of: American Chemical Society), 2540 Olentangy River Rd., Columbus, OH 43210-0012. TEL 614-447-3600, FAX 614-447-3713, help@cas.com, http://www.cas.org, http://caselects.cas.org. **Subscr. to:** PO Box 3012, Columbus, OH 43210. TEL 800-753-4227, FAX 614-447-3751.

540 011 USA ISSN 1045-8557 CODEN: CSELE3

C A SELECTS. ELASTOMERS. Text in English. s-w. USD 315 to non-members; USD 95 to members (effective 2005). **Document type:** *Abstract/Index.* **Description:** Covers preparation, properties, reactions, and uses of elastomers.
Published by: Chemical Abstracts Service (C A S) (Subsidiary of: American Chemical Society), 2540 Olentangy River Rd., Columbus, OH 43210-0012. TEL 614-447-3600, FAX 614-447-3713, help@cas.com, http://www.cas.org, http://caselects.cas.org. **Subscr. to:** PO Box 3012, Columbus, OH 43210. TEL 800-753-4227, FAX 614-447-3751.

541.37 USA ISSN 0885-0143 CODEN: CSEOEC

C A SELECTS. ELECTRICALLY CONDUCTIVE ORGANICS. Text in English. s-w. USD 315 to non-members; USD 95 to members (effective 2005). **Document type:** *Abstract/Index.* **Description:** Covers electrical conductors and superconductors based on organic compounds.
Published by: Chemical Abstracts Service (C A S) (Subsidiary of: American Chemical Society), 2540 Olentangy River Rd., Columbus, OH 43210-0012. TEL 614-447-3600, FAX 614-447-3713, help@cas.com, http://www.cas.org, http://caselects.cas.org. **Subscr. to:** PO Box 3012, Columbus, OH 43210. TEL 800-753-4227, FAX 614-447-3751.

547 USA ISSN 0734-8770 CODEN: CAESEY

C A SELECTS. ELECTROCHEMICAL ORGANIC SYNTHESIS. Text in English. s-w. USD 315 to non-members; USD 95 to members (effective 2004). **Document type:** *Abstract/Index.* **Description:** Covers organic synthesis in which the starting material, one or more intermediates, or the final product is prepared by a specific electrochemical process.
Published by: Chemical Abstracts Service (C A S) (Subsidiary of: American Chemical Society), 2540 Olentangy River Rd., Columbus, OH 43210-0012. TEL 614-447-3600, FAX 614-447-3713, help@cas.com, http://www.cas.org, http://caselects.cas.org. **Subscr. to:** PO Box 3012, Columbus, OH 43210. TEL 800-753-4227, FAX 614-447-3751.

541.37 USA ISSN 0146-4442 CODEN: CSERDK

C A SELECTS. ELECTROCHEMICAL REACTIONS. Text in English. s-w. USD 317 to non-members; USD 95 to members (effective 2005). **Document type:** *Abstract/Index.* **Description:** Covers electrolysis, electrooxidation, electroreduction, polarography; electrochemical reactions in biochemistry, organic, macromolecular, applied, and inorganic chemistry.
Published by: Chemical Abstracts Service (C A S) (Subsidiary of: American Chemical Society), 2540 Olentangy River Rd., Columbus, OH 43210-0012. TEL 614-447-3600, FAX 614-447-3713, help@cas.com, http://www.cas.org, http://caselects.cas.org. **Subscr. to:** PO Box 3012, Columbus, OH 43210. TEL 800-753-4227, FAX 614-447-3751.

541.37 USA ISSN 0162-7783 CODEN: CSELD2

C A SELECTS. ELECTRODEPOSITION. Text in English. s-w. USD 315 to non-members; USD 95 to members (effective 2005). **Document type:** *Abstract/Index.* **Description:** Covers electroplating and electroforming.
Published by: Chemical Abstracts Service (C A S) (Subsidiary of: American Chemical Society), 2540 Olentangy River Rd., Columbus, OH 43210-0012. TEL 614-447-3600, FAX 614-447-3713, help@cas.com, http://www.cas.org, http://caselects.cas.org. **Subscr. to:** PO Box 3012, Columbus, OH 43210. TEL 800-753-4227, FAX 614-447-3751.

541.37 USA ISSN 0146-4469 CODEN: CSEAD3

C A SELECTS. ELECTRON SPIN RESONANCE (CHEMICAL ASPECTS). Text in English. s-w. USD 315 to non-members; USD 95 to members (effective 2005). **Document type:** *Abstract/Index.* **Description:** Includes information on electron nuclear double resonance and electron paramagnetic resonance.
Published by: Chemical Abstracts Service (C A S) (Subsidiary of: American Chemical Society), 2540 Olentangy River Rd., Columbus, OH 43210-0012. TEL 614-447-3600, FAX 614-447-3713, help@cas.com, http://www.cas.org, http://caselects.cas.org. **Subscr. to:** PO Box 3012, Columbus, OH 43210. TEL 800-753-4227, FAX 614-447-3751.

541.37 USA ISSN 0885-0151 CODEN: CSEME6

C A SELECTS. ELECTRONIC CHEMICALS & MATERIALS. Text in English. s-w. USD 315 to non-members; USD 95 to members (effective 2005). **Document type:** *Abstract/Index.* **Description:** Covers specialty chemicals, materials, and processes involved in the fabrication of solid-state electronic devices.
Published by: Chemical Abstracts Service (C A S) (Subsidiary of: American Chemical Society), 2540 Olentangy River Rd., Columbus, OH 43210-0012. TEL 614-447-3600, FAX 614-447-3713, help@cas.com, http://www.cas.org, http://caselects.cas.org. **Subscr. to:** PO Box 3012, Columbus, OH 43210. TEL 800-753-4227, FAX 614-447-3751.

540 USA ISSN 0734-8754 CODEN: CAEDEN

C A SELECTS. EMULSIFIERS AND DEMULSIFIERS. Text in English. s-w. USD 315 to non-members; USD 95 to members (effective 2005). **Document type:** *Abstract/Index.* **Description:** Preparation, properties, uses of surface-active agents in formation, stabilization, or destabilization of emulsions.
Published by: Chemical Abstracts Service (C A S) (Subsidiary of: American Chemical Society), 2540 Olentangy River Rd., Columbus, OH 43210-0012. TEL 614-447-3600, FAX 614-447-3713, help@cas.com, http://www.cas.org, http://caselects.cas.org. **Subscr. to:** PO Box 3012, Columbus, OH 43210. TEL 800-753-4227, FAX 614-447-3751.

660.284 USA ISSN 0195-4970 CODEN: CEPOD2

C A SELECTS. EMULSION POLYMERIZATION. Text in English. s-w. USD 315 to non-members; USD 95 to members (effective 2005). **Document type:** *Abstract/Index.* **Description:** Covers polymerizations carried out in emulsion to produce plastics, elastomers, coating materials.
Published by: Chemical Abstracts Service (C A S) (Subsidiary of: American Chemical Society), 2540 Olentangy River Rd., Columbus, OH 43210-0012. TEL 614-447-3600, FAX 614-447-3713, help@cas.com, http://www.cas.org, http://caselects.cas.org. **Subscr. to:** PO Box 3012, Columbus, OH 43210. TEL 800-753-4227, FAX 614-447-3751.

540 USA ISSN 0275-7060 CODEN: CEPRDB

C A SELECTS. EPOXY RESINS. Text in English. s-w. USD 315 to non-members; USD 95 to members (effective 2005). **Document type:** *Abstract/Index.* **Description:** Covers synthesis, curing, properties, uses of macromolecular compounds containing multiple epoxide rings; application as thermosetting resin, coatings, adhesives.
Published by: Chemical Abstracts Service (C A S) (Subsidiary of: American Chemical Society), 2540 Olentangy River Rd., Columbus, OH 43210-0012. TEL 614-447-3600, FAX 614-447-3713, help@cas.com, http://www.cas.org, http://caselects.cas.org. **Subscr. to:** PO Box 3012, Columbus, OH 43210. TEL 800-753-4227, FAX 614-447-3751.

665 USA ISSN 0275-7079 CODEN: CSFODG

C A SELECTS. FATS & OILS. Text in English. s-w. USD 315 to non-members; USD 95 to members (effective 2005). **Document type:** *Abstract/Index.* **Description:** Covers extraction, analysis, properties, uses, synthesis and manufacture of analogs.
Published by: Chemical Abstracts Service (C A S) (Subsidiary of: American Chemical Society), 2540 Olentangy River Rd., Columbus, OH 43210-0012. TEL 614-447-3600, FAX 614-447-3713, help@cas.com, http://www.cas.org, http://caselects.cas.org. **Subscr. to:** PO Box 3012, Columbus, OH 43210. TEL 800-753-4227, FAX 614-447-3751.

540 USA ISSN 0740-0713 CODEN: CSFCEF

C A SELECTS. FERMENTATION CHEMICALS. Text in English. s-w. USD 315 to non-members; USD 95 to members (effective 2005). **Document type:** *Abstract/Index.* **Description:** Covers compounds prepared by fermentation processes; compounds routinely used in fermentation processes.
Published by: Chemical Abstracts Service (C A S) (Subsidiary of: American Chemical Society), 2540 Olentangy River Rd., Columbus, OH 43210-0012. TEL 614-447-3600, FAX 614-447-3713, help@cas.com, http://www.cas.org, http://caselects.cas.org. **Subscr. to:** PO Box 3012, Columbus, OH 43210. TEL 800-753-4227, FAX 614-447-3751.

540 USA ISSN 0162-7805 CODEN: CSFLD7

C A SELECTS. FLAMMABILITY. Text in English. s-w. USD 315 to non-members; USD 95 to members (effective 2005). **Document type:** *Abstract/Index.* **Description:** Covers flammability of materials and test methods for determining it; relationship of chemical structure to flammability; enhancing flammability of combustibles; reducing flammability of materials; synthesis and use of flame retardants and fireproofing agents.
Published by: Chemical Abstracts Service (C A S) (Subsidiary of: American Chemical Society), 2540 Olentangy River Rd., Columbus, OH 43210-0012. TEL 614-447-3600, FAX 614-447-3713, help@cas.com, http://www.cas.org, http://caselects.cas.org. **Subscr. to:** PO Box 3012, Columbus, OH 43210. TEL 800-753-4227, FAX 614-447-3751.

540 USA ISSN 0195-4989 CODEN: CFSTD5

C A SELECTS. FLUIDIZED SOLIDS TECHNOLOGY. Text in English. s-w. USD 315 to non-members; USD 95 to members (effective 2005). **Document type:** *Abstract/Index.* **Description:** Covers apparatus design and engineering; fluidized combustion for energy production and waste disposal.
Published by: Chemical Abstracts Service (C A S) (Subsidiary of: American Chemical Society), 2540 Olentangy River Rd., Columbus, OH 43210-0012. TEL 614-447-3600, FAX 614-447-3713, help@cas.com, http://www.cas.org, http://caselects.cas.org. **Subscr. to:** PO Box 3012, Columbus, OH 43210. TEL 800-753-4227, FAX 614-447-3751.

540 USA ISSN 0895-5921 CODEN: CASFEV

C A SELECTS. FLUOROPOLYMERS. Text in English. 1988. s-w. USD 315 to non-members; USD 95 to members (effective 2005). **Document type:** *Abstract/Index.* **Description:** Covers preparation, properties, and use of organic polymeric substances with a substantial fluorine content.
Published by: Chemical Abstracts Service (C A S) (Subsidiary of: American Chemical Society), 2540 Olentangy River Rd., Columbus, OH 43210-0012. TEL 614-447-3600, FAX 614-447-3713, help@cas.com, http://www.cas.org, http://caselects.cas.org. **Subscr. to:** PO Box 3012, Columbus, OH 43210. TEL 800-753-4227, FAX 614-447-3751.

C A SELECTS. FOOD & FEED ANALYSIS. see *FOOD AND FOOD INDUSTRIES—Abstracting, Bibliographies, Statistics*

664 615.9 USA ISSN 0162-7813 CODEN: CSFTDV

C A SELECTS. FOOD TOXICITY. Text in English. s-w. USD 315 to non-members; USD 95 to members (effective 2005). **Document type:** *Abstract/Index.* **Description:** Covers mutagenicity, teratogenicity, carcinogenicity, toxic side effects, and health hazards of foods and additives; contamination of foods by agrochemicals, nitroso compounds, heavy metals, aromatic hydrocarbons, and other toxicants.
Published by: Chemical Abstracts Service (C A S) (Subsidiary of: American Chemical Society), 2540 Olentangy River Rd., Columbus, OH 43210-0012. TEL 614-447-3600, FAX 614-447-3713, help@cas.com, http://www.cas.org, http://caselects.cas.org. **Subscr. to:** PO Box 3012, Columbus, OH 43210. TEL 800-753-4227, FAX 614-447-3751.

540 USA ISSN 0890-1880 CODEN: CAFCEP

C A SELECTS. FORMULATION CHEMISTRY. Text in English. 1987. s-w. USD 315 to non-members; USD 95 to members (effective 2005). **Document type:** *Abstract/Index.* **Description:** Covers materials used as fillers and inactive agents in processed materials; drugs, cleaning agents, paints, and cosmetics.

C

Published by: Chemical Abstracts Service (C A S) (Subsidiary of: American Chemical Society), 2540 Olentangy River Rd., Columbus, OH 43210-0012. TEL 614-447-3600, FAX 614-447-3713, help@cas.com, http://www.cas.org, http://caselects.cas.org. **Subscr. to:** PO Box 3012, Columbus, OH 43210. TEL 800-753-4227, FAX 614-447-3751.

540 USA ISSN 0895-5972
CODEN: CFRAEC

C A SELECTS. FREE RADICALS (ORGANIC ASPECTS). Text in English. 1987. s-w. USD 315 to non-members; USD 95 to members (effective 2005). **Document type:** *Abstract/Index.*
Description: Covers formation, chemical reactions, and reactivities of organic free radicals.
Published by: Chemical Abstracts Service (C A S) (Subsidiary of: American Chemical Society), 2540 Olentangy River Rd., Columbus, OH 43210-0012. TEL 614-447-3600, FAX 614-447-3713, help@cas.com, http://www.cas.org, http://caselects.cas.org. **Subscr. to:** PO Box 3012, Columbus, OH 43210. TEL 800-753-4227, FAX 614-447-3751.

540 USA ISSN 0195-4997
CODEN: CSFAD8

C A SELECTS. FUEL & LUBRICANT ADDITIVES. Text in English. s-w. USD 315 to non-members; USD 95 to members (effective 2005). **Document type:** *Abstract/Index.*
Description: Covers manufacture, development, and use of additives for fuels and lubricants; petroleum-based and non-petroleum-based products.
Published by: Chemical Abstracts Service (C A S) (Subsidiary of: American Chemical Society), 2540 Olentangy River Rd., Columbus, OH 43210-0012. TEL 614-447-3600, FAX 614-447-3713, help@cas.com, http://www.cas.org, http://caselects.cas.org. **Subscr. to:** PO Box 3012, Columbus, OH 43210. TEL 800-753-4227, FAX 614-447-3751.

540 USA ISSN 0160-9076
CODEN: CSGTD2

C A SELECTS. GASEOUS WASTE TREATMENT. Text in English. s-w. USD 315 to non-members; USD 95 to members (effective 2005). **Document type:** *Abstract/Index.*
Description: Covers treatment and control of gaseous waste products from stationary sources, primarily industrial.
Published by: Chemical Abstracts Service (C A S) (Subsidiary of: American Chemical Society), 2540 Olentangy River Rd., Columbus, OH 43210-0012. TEL 614-447-3600, FAX 614-447-3713, help@cas.com, http://www.cas.org, http://caselects.cas.org. **Subscr. to:** PO Box 3012, Columbus, OH 43210. TEL 800-753-4227, FAX 614-447-3751.

660.284 USA ISSN 0162-7821
CODEN: CSHPDT

C A SELECTS. HEAT-RESISTANT AND ABLATIVE POLYMERS. Text in English. s-w. USD 315 to non-members; USD 95 to members (effective 2005). **Document type:** *Abstract/Index.*
Description: Covers polymers which are stable at high temperatures, e.g., plastic, fibers, rubbers, coatings; polymeric ablative materials; means of increasing thermal stability of polymers, e.g., heat-stabilizer additives.
Published by: Chemical Abstracts Service (C A S) (Subsidiary of: American Chemical Society), 2540 Olentangy River Rd., Columbus, OH 43210-0012. TEL 614-447-3600, FAX 614-447-3713, help@cas.com, http://www.cas.org, http://caselects.cas.org. **Subscr. to:** PO Box 3012, Columbus, OH 43210. TEL 800-753-4227, FAX 614-447-3751.

540 USA ISSN 0895-5891
CODEN: CSHAEJ

C A SELECTS. HOT-MELT ADHESIVES. Text in English. 1988. s-w. USD 315 to non-members; USD 95 to members (effective 2005). **Document type:** *Abstract/Index.*
Description: Covers preparation, composition, properties, and uses of hot-melt adhesives and sealants.
Published by: Chemical Abstracts Service (C A S) (Subsidiary of: American Chemical Society), 2540 Olentangy River Rd., Columbus, OH 43210-0012. TEL 614-447-3600, FAX 614-447-3713, help@cas.com, http://www.cas.org, http://caselects.cas.org. **Subscr. to:** PO Box 3012, Columbus, OH 43210. TEL 800-753-4227, FAX 614-447-3751.

535 USA ISSN 0190-9428
CODEN: CSIADN

C A SELECTS. INFRARED SPECTROSCOPY (ORGANIC ASPECTS). Text in English. s-w. USD 315 to non-members; USD 95 to members (effective 2005). **Document type:** *Abstract/Index.* **Description:** Covers organic, macromolecular, and biochemical aspects of infrared spectroscopy; spectroscopic characterization of substances.
Published by: Chemical Abstracts Service (C A S) (Subsidiary of: American Chemical Society), 2540 Olentangy River Rd., Columbus, OH 43210-0012. TEL 614-447-3600, FAX 614-447-3713, help@cas.com, http://www.cas.org, http://caselects.cas.org. **Subscr. to:** PO Box 3012, Columbus, OH 43210. TEL 800-753-4227, FAX 614-447-3751.

660.284 USA ISSN 0734-8843
CODEN: CAIPEB

C A SELECTS. INITIATION OF POLYMERIZATION. Text in English. s-w. USD 315 to non-members; USD 95 to members (effective 2005). **Document type:** *Abstract/Index.*
Description: Covers preparation of polymerization catalysts or initiators, characterization and use in polymerization; kinetic and mechanistic aspects.
Published by: Chemical Abstracts Service (C A S) (Subsidiary of: American Chemical Society), 2540 Olentangy River Rd., Columbus, OH 43210-0012. TEL 614-447-3600, FAX 614-447-3713, help@cas.com, http://www.cas.org, http://caselects.cas.org. **Subscr. to:** PO Box 3012, Columbus, OH 43210. TEL 800-753-4227, FAX 614-447-3751.

643 546 USA ISSN 0275-7087
CODEN: CSACDN

C A SELECTS. INORGANIC ANALYTICAL CHEMISTRY. Text in English. s-w. USD 315 to non-members; USD 95 to members (effective 2005). **Document type:** *Abstract/Index.*
Description: Covers methods and reagents for detection and determination of elements, radicals, and compounds in inorganic materials; analysis of inorganic coordination compounds; analytical apparatus and techniques; analysis of nuclear materials, water, sewage, wastes, agrochemicals, soils, cement, concrete products.
Published by: Chemical Abstracts Service (C A S) (Subsidiary of: American Chemical Society), 2540 Olentangy River Rd., Columbus, OH 43210-0012. TEL 614-447-3600, FAX 614-447-3713, help@cas.com, http://www.cas.org, http://caselects.cas.org. **Subscr. to:** PO Box 3012, Columbus, OH 43210. TEL 800-753-4227, FAX 614-447-3751.

546 USA ISSN 0195-5012
CODEN: CIOMDJ

C A SELECTS. INORGANIC & ORGANOMETALLIC REACTION SYSTEMS. Text in English. s-w. USD 315 to non-members; USD 95 to members (effective 2005). **Document type:** *Abstract/Index.* **Description:** Covers mechanistic and kinetic aspects of reactions of inorganic, organometallic and organometalloidal compounds.
Published by: Chemical Abstracts Service (C A S) (Subsidiary of: American Chemical Society), 2540 Olentangy River Rd., Columbus, OH 43210-0012. TEL 614-447-3600, FAX 614-447-3713, help@cas.com, http://www.cas.org, http://caselects.cas.org. **Subscr. to:** PO Box 3012, Columbus, OH 43210. TEL 800-753-4227, FAX 614-447-3751.

546 USA ISSN 0275-7095
CODEN: CIRCD4

C A SELECTS. INORGANIC CHEMICALS & REACTIONS. Text in English. s-w. USD 315 to non-members; USD 95 to members (effective 2005). **Document type:** *Abstract/Index.*
Description: Covers synthesis, chemical properties, reactions, nonindustrial preparation and applications of inorganic compounds; properties of metal carbonyls, cyanides, carbides, cyanates, and carbonates.
Published by: Chemical Abstracts Service (C A S) (Subsidiary of: American Chemical Society), 2540 Olentangy River Rd., Columbus, OH 43210-0012. TEL 614-447-3600, FAX 614-447-3713, help@cas.com, http://www.cas.org, http://caselects.cas.org. **Subscr. to:** PO Box 3012, Columbus, OH 43210. TEL 800-753-4227, FAX 614-447-3751.

540 USA ISSN 0890-1899
CODEN: CSICEU

C A SELECTS. ION CHROMATOGRAPHY. Text in English. 1987. s-w. USD 315 to non-members; USD 95 to members (effective 2005). **Document type:** *Abstract/Index.*
Description: Covers the principle and application of ion chromatography in analytical procedures.
Published by: Chemical Abstracts Service (C A S) (Subsidiary of: American Chemical Society), 2540 Olentangy River Rd., Columbus, OH 43210-0012. TEL 614-447-3600, FAX 614-447-3713, help@cas.com, http://www.cas.org, http://caselects.cas.org. **Subscr. to:** PO Box 3012, Columbus, OH 43210. TEL 800-753-4227, FAX 614-447-3751.

540 USA ISSN 0195-5020
CODEN: CSIPDY

C A SELECTS. ION-CONTAINING POLYMERS. Text in English. s-w. USD 315 to non-members; USD 95 to members (effective 2005). **Document type:** *Abstract/Index.*
Description: Covers theoretical and practical aspects; polyelectrolytes.
Published by: Chemical Abstracts Service (C A S) (Subsidiary of: American Chemical Society), 2540 Olentangy River Rd., Columbus, OH 43210-0012. TEL 614-447-3600, FAX 614-447-3713, help@cas.com, http://www.cas.org, http://caselects.cas.org. **Subscr. to:** PO Box 3012, Columbus, OH 43210. TEL 800-753-4227, FAX 614-447-3751.

540 USA ISSN 0146-4493
CODEN: CSIODV

C A SELECTS. ION EXCHANGE. Text in English. s-w. USD 315 to non-members; USD 95 to members (effective 2005). **Document type:** *Abstract/Index.* **Description:** Covers theory and applications including material and equipment for ion exchange.
Published by: Chemical Abstracts Service (C A S) (Subsidiary of: American Chemical Society), 2540 Olentangy River Rd., Columbus, OH 43210-0012. TEL 614-447-3600, FAX 614-447-3713, help@cas.com, http://www.cas.org, http://caselects.cas.org. **Subscr. to:** PO Box 3012, Columbus, OH 43210. TEL 800-753-4227, FAX 614-447-3751.

535.58 USA ISSN 0195-5039
CODEN: CLAPDD

C A SELECTS. LASER APPLICATIONS. Text in English. s-w. USD 315 to non-members; USD 95 to members (effective 2005). **Document type:** *Abstract/Index.* **Description:** Covers interactions of laser radiation with materials; physicochemical and biochemical effects of laser radiation; applications of lasers and laser radiation.
Indexed: Inspec.
Published by: Chemical Abstracts Service (C A S) (Subsidiary of: American Chemical Society), 2540 Olentangy River Rd., Columbus, OH 43210-0012. TEL 614-447-3600, FAX 614-447-3713, help@cas.com, http://www.cas.org, http://caselects.cas.org. **Subscr. to:** PO Box 3012, Columbus, OH 43210. TEL 800-753-4227, FAX 614-447-3751.

540 USA ISSN 0885-0178
CODEN: CSLREM

C A SELECTS. LASER - INDUCED CHEMICAL REACTIONS. Text in English. s-w. USD 315 to non-members; USD 95 to members (effective 2005). **Document type:** *Abstract/Index.*
Description: Covers laser-induced processes; photochemical reactions initiated by laser radiation; thermal reactions induced by laser heating.
Published by: Chemical Abstracts Service (C A S) (Subsidiary of: American Chemical Society), 2540 Olentangy River Rd., Columbus, OH 43210-0012. TEL 614-447-3600, FAX 614-447-3713, help@cas.com, http://www.cas.org, http://caselects.cas.org. **Subscr. to:** PO Box 3012, Columbus, OH 43210. TEL 800-753-4227, FAX 614-447-3751.

548 USA ISSN 0148-2351
CODEN: CSLCDA

C A SELECTS. LIQUID CRYSTALS. Text in English. s-w. USD 315 to non-members; USD 95 to members (effective 2005). **Document type:** *Abstract/Index.* **Description:** Covers application, preparation, properties, and structure of liquid crystals.
Published by: Chemical Abstracts Service (C A S) (Subsidiary of: American Chemical Society), 2540 Olentangy River Rd., Columbus, OH 43210-0012. TEL 614-447-3600, FAX 614-447-3713, help@cas.com, http://www.cas.org, http://caselects.cas.org. **Subscr. to:** PO Box 3012, Columbus, OH 43210. TEL 800-753-4227, FAX 614-447-3751.

540 665 USA ISSN 0734-8738
CODEN: CASLEF

C A SELECTS. LUBRICANTS, GREASES, & LUBRICATION. Text in English. s-w. USD 315 to non-members; USD 95 to members (effective 2005). **Document type:** *Abstract/Index.*
Description: Covers manufacture, properties, and use of lubricants; oils, emulsions, greases, solid lubricants; additives for lubricants.
Published by: Chemical Abstracts Service (C A S) (Subsidiary of: American Chemical Society), 2540 Olentangy River Rd., Columbus, OH 43210-0012. TEL 614-447-3600, FAX 614-447-3713, help@cas.com, http://www.cas.org, http://caselects.cas.org. **Subscr. to:** PO Box 3012, Columbus, OH 43210. TEL 800-753-4227, FAX 614-447-3751.

540 USA ISSN 1040-7197
CODEN: CAMSE6

C A SELECTS. MEMBRANE SEPARATION. Text in English. 1989. s-w. USD 315 to non-members; USD 95 to members (effective 2005). **Document type:** *Abstract/Index.*
Description: Covers theory and technology of dialysis, electrodialysis, electroosmosis, gas separation by membrane permeation and pervaporation.
Published by: Chemical Abstracts Service (C A S) (Subsidiary of: American Chemical Society), 2540 Olentangy River Rd., Columbus, OH 43210-0012. TEL 614-447-3600, FAX 614-447-3713, help@cas.com, http://www.cas.org, http://caselects.cas.org.

661 USA ISSN 0890-1821
CODEN: CSMMEC

C A SELECTS. MEMORY & RECORDING DEVICES & MATERIALS. Text in English. 1987. s-w. USD 315 to non-members; USD 95 to members (effective 2005). **Document type:** *Abstract/Index.* **Description:** Covers materials used for information storage; recording tapes and disks, optical disks, and computer memories.
Published by: Chemical Abstracts Service (C A S) (Subsidiary of: American Chemical Society), 2540 Olentangy River Rd., Columbus, OH 43210-0012. TEL 614-447-3600, FAX 614-447-3713, help@cas.com, http://www.cas.org, http://caselects.cas.org. **Subscr. to:** PO Box 3012, Columbus, OH 43210. TEL 800-753-4227, FAX 614-447-3751.

C

▼ new title ➤ refereed ✶ unverified ♦ full entry avail.

669 USA ISSN 0160-9114
CODEN: CSMCDF

C A SELECTS. METALLO ENZYMES & METALLO COENZYMES. Text in English. s-w. USD 315 to non-members; USD 95 to members (effective 2005).
Document type: *Abstract/Index.* **Description:** Covers preparation, analysis, and biochemical effects of enzymes and coenzymes that contain metals (cobalt, copper, iron, zinc, and molybdenum); metalloproteins, metal-containing vitamins; mechanisms by which metals are bound to enzymes.
Published by: Chemical Abstracts Service (C A S) (Subsidiary of: American Chemical Society), 2540 Olentangy River Rd., Columbus, OH 43210-0012. TEL 614-447-3600, FAX 614-447-3713, help@cas.com, http://www.cas.org, http://caselects.cas.org. **Subscr. to:** PO Box 3012, Columbus, OH 43210. TEL 800-753-4227, FAX 614-447-3751.

540 011 USA ISSN 1059-2784
CODEN: CAMMEM

C A SELECTS. MOLECULAR MODELING (BIOCHEMICAL ASPECTS). Text in English. 1992. s-w. USD 315 to non-members; USD 95 to members (effective 2005).
Document type: *Abstract/Index.* **Description:** Covers the design of pharmaceuticals, agrochemicals, and other bioactive agents; modeling studies on structures of macromolecules; pharmacophores; and quantitative structure-activity relationships.
Published by: Chemical Abstracts Service (C A S) (Subsidiary of: American Chemical Society), 2540 Olentangy River Rd., Columbus, OH 43210-0012. TEL 614-447-3600, FAX 614-447-3713, help@cas.com, http://www.cas.org, http://caselects.cas.org. **Subscr. to:** PO Box 3012, Columbus, OH 43210. TEL 800-753-4227, FAX 614-447-3751.

540 USA ISSN 0740-0691
CODEN: CSNSEZ

C A SELECTS. NATURAL PRODUCT SYNTHESIS. Text in English. s-w. USD 315 to non-members; USD 95 to members (effective 2005). **Document type:** *Abstract/Index.*
Description: Covers laboratory synthesis of known natural products; partial and total synthesis, unsuccessful attempts at synthesis.
Published by: Chemical Abstracts Service (C A S) (Subsidiary of: American Chemical Society), 2540 Olentangy River Rd., Columbus, OH 43210-0012. TEL 614-447-3600, FAX 614-447-3713, help@cas.com, http://www.cas.org, http://caselects.cas.org. **Subscr. to:** PO Box 3012, Columbus, OH 43210. TEL 800-753-4227, FAX 614-447-3751.

540 USA ISSN 0148-2416
CODEN: CSBCDS

C A SELECTS. NEW BOOKS IN CHEMISTRY. Text in English. s-w. USD 315 to non-members; USD 95 to members (effective 2005). **Document type:** *Abstract/Index.*
Description: Covers all new books in chemistry and chemical engineering cited in CA; includes monographs, series publications, and conference proceedings.
Published by: Chemical Abstracts Service (C A S) (Subsidiary of: American Chemical Society), 2540 Olentangy River Rd., Columbus, OH 43210-0012. TEL 614-447-3600, FAX 614-447-3713, help@cas.com, http://www.cas.org, http://caselects.cas.org. **Subscr. to:** PO Box 3012, Columbus, OH 43210. TEL 800-753-4227, FAX 614-447-3751.

016.57 USA ISSN 0734-872X
CODEN: CAPREI

C A SELECTS. NOVEL NATURAL PRODUCTS. Text in English. s-w. USD 315 to non-members; USD 95 to members (effective 2005). **Document type:** *Abstract/Index.*
Description: Covers new natural products; isolation, detection, or discovery of previously unknown natural products; and synthesis of new derivatives or compounds of new or known natural products.
Published by: Chemical Abstracts Service (C A S) (Subsidiary of: American Chemical Society), 2540 Olentangy River Rd., Columbus, OH 43210-0012. TEL 614-447-3600, FAX 614-447-3713, help@cas.com, http://www.cas.org, http://caselects.cas.org. **Subscr. to:** PO Box 3012, Columbus, OH 43210. TEL 800-753-4227, FAX 614-447-3751.

C A SELECTS. NOVEL POLYMERS FROM PATENTS. see *PATENTS, TRADEMARKS AND COPYRIGHTS—Abstracting, Bibliographies, Statistics*

540 011 USA ISSN 0275-7109
CODEN: CSNHDZ

C A SELECTS. NOVEL SULFUR HETEROCYCLES. Text in English. 1981. s-w. USD 315 to non-members; USD 95 to members (effective 2005). **Document type:** *Abstract/Index.*
Description: Covers the synthesis of new sulfur-containing ring systems and new compounds containing known sulfur heterocycles.
Published by: Chemical Abstracts Service (C A S) (Subsidiary of: American Chemical Society), 2540 Olentangy River Rd., Columbus, OH 43210-0012. TEL 614-447-3600, FAX 614-447-3713, help@cas.com, http://www.cas.org, http://caselects.cas.org. **Subscr. to:** PO Box 3012, Columbus, OH 43210. TEL 800-753-4227, FAX 614-447-3751.

016.547042 USA ISSN 1052-1976
CODEN: CSOOES

C A SELECTS. OLEOCHEMICALS CONTAINING NITROGEN. Text in English. 1990. s-w. USD 315 to non-members; USD 95 to members (effective 2005). **Document type:** *Abstract/Index.* **Description:** Covers analysis, preparation, properties, reactions, and uses of amides, amines, betaines, imidazoles, imidazolines, nitriles, and quaternary ammonium compounds derived from fats and oils.
Published by: Chemical Abstracts Service (C A S) (Subsidiary of: American Chemical Society), 2540 Olentangy River Rd., Columbus, OH 43210-0012. TEL 614-447-3600, FAX 614-447-3713, help@cas.com, http://www.cas.org, http://caselects.cas.org. **Subscr. to:** PO Box 3012, Columbus, OH 43210. TEL 800-753-4227, FAX 614-447-3751.

C A SELECTS. OPTICAL AND PHOTOSENSITIVE MATERIALS. see *PHYSICS—Abstracting, Bibliographies, Statistics*

540 USA ISSN 0195-5071
CODEN: COORD8

C A SELECTS. OPTIMIZATION OF ORGANIC REACTIONS. Text in English. s-w. USD 315 to non-members; USD 95 to members (effective 2005). **Document type:** *Abstract/Index.*
Description: Covers parameters and variables that affect reaction selectivity, product yield, and product quality; includes computer-based and other simulation models.
Published by: Chemical Abstracts Service (C A S) (Subsidiary of: American Chemical Society), 2540 Olentangy River Rd., Columbus, OH 43210-0012. TEL 614-447-3600, FAX 614-447-3713, help@cas.com, http://www.cas.org, http://caselects.cas.org. **Subscr. to:** PO Box 3012, Columbus, OH 43210. TEL 800-753-4227, FAX 614-447-3751.

016.54317 USA ISSN 0275-7117
CODEN: COACDT

C A SELECTS. ORGANIC ANALYTICAL CHEMISTRY. Text in English. s-w. USD 315 to non-members; USD 95 to members (effective 2005). **Document type:** *Abstract/Index.*
Description: Covers methods, reagents, apparatus; detection and determination of elements, radicals, and compounds in organic materials; and analysis of organometallic compounds.
Published by: Chemical Abstracts Service (C A S) (Subsidiary of: American Chemical Society), 2540 Olentangy River Rd., Columbus, OH 43210-0012. TEL 614-447-3600, FAX 614-447-3713, help@cas.com, http://www.cas.org, http://caselects.cas.org. **Subscr. to:** PO Box 3012, Columbus, OH 43210. TEL 800-753-4227, FAX 614-447-3751.

540 USA ISSN 0885-0186
CODEN: CSOMEM

C A SELECTS. ORGANIC OPTICAL MATERIALS. Text in English. s-w. USD 315 to non-members; USD 95 to members (effective 2005). **Document type:** *Abstract/Index.*
Description: Covers optical materials based on organic compounds.
Published by: Chemical Abstracts Service (C A S) (Subsidiary of: American Chemical Society), 2540 Olentangy River Rd., Columbus, OH 43210-0012. TEL 614-447-3600, FAX 614-447-3713, help@cas.com, http://www.cas.org, http://caselects.cas.org. **Subscr. to:** PO Box 3012, Columbus, OH 43210. TEL 800-753-4227, FAX 614-447-3751.

540 USA ISSN 0162-7848
CODEN: CSOMDL

C A SELECTS. ORGANIC REACTION MECHANISMS. Text in English. s-w. USD 315 to non-members; USD 95 to members (effective 2005). **Document type:** *Abstract/Index.*
Description: Covers organic reaction pathways; organic reaction intermediates.
Published by: Chemical Abstracts Service (C A S) (Subsidiary of: American Chemical Society), 2540 Olentangy River Rd., Columbus, OH 43210-0012. TEL 614-447-3600, FAX 614-447-3713, help@cas.com, http://www.cas.org, http://caselects.cas.org. **Subscr. to:** PO Box 3012, Columbus, OH 43210. TEL 800-753-4227, FAX 614-447-3751.

540 USA ISSN 0195-508X
CODEN: CORSDQ

C A SELECTS. ORGANIC STEREOCHEMISTRY. Text in English. s-w. USD 315 to non-members; USD 95 to members (effective 2005). **Document type:** *Abstract/Index.*
Description: Covers conformational and configurational analysis; steric factors in organic reactions and properties of organic compounds; asymmetric synthesis, preparation of specific stereoisomers, and stereoselectivity of organic reactions.
Published by: Chemical Abstracts Service (C A S) (Subsidiary of: American Chemical Society), 2540 Olentangy River Rd., Columbus, OH 43210-0012. TEL 614-447-3600, FAX 614-447-3713, help@cas.com, http://www.cas.org, http://caselects.cas.org. **Subscr. to:** PO Box 3012, Columbus, OH 43210. TEL 800-753-4227, FAX 614-447-3751.

540 USA ISSN 0160-9130
CODEN: COMCDL

C A SELECTS. ORGANO-TRANSITION METAL COMPLEXES. Text in English. s-w. USD 315 to non-members; USD 95 to members (effective 2005). **Document type:** *Abstract/Index.*
Description: Covers organic complexes of copper, silver, gold, titanium, zirconium, hafnium, vanadium, niobium, tantalum, chromium, manganese, molybdenum, tungsten, technetium, rhenium, iron, cobalt, nickel, ruthenium, platinum, palladium, osmium, and iridium; compounds with a bond between a transition metal and carbon; complexes with bonds between metals and compounds such as phosphines.
Published by: Chemical Abstracts Service (C A S) (Subsidiary of: American Chemical Society), 2540 Olentangy River Rd., Columbus, OH 43210-0012. TEL 614-447-3600, FAX 614-447-3713, help@cas.com, http://www.cas.org, http://caselects.cas.org. **Subscr. to:** PO Box 3012, Columbus, OH 43210. TEL 800-753-4227, FAX 614-447-3751.

540 USA ISSN 0160-905X
CODEN: CORCDC

C A SELECTS. ORGANOFLUORINE CHEMISTRY. Text in English. s-w. USD 315 to non-members; USD 95 to members (effective 2005). **Document type:** *Abstract/Index.*
Description: Covers synthesis and manufacture of organofluorine compounds; includes properties, reactions, and use of compounds containing a carbon-fluorine bond.
Published by: Chemical Abstracts Service (C A S) (Subsidiary of: American Chemical Society), 2540 Olentangy River Rd., Columbus, OH 43210-0012. TEL 614-447-3600, FAX 614-447-3713, help@cas.com, http://www.cas.org, http://caselects.cas.org. **Subscr. to:** PO Box 3012, Columbus, OH 43210. TEL 800-753-4227, FAX 614-447-3751.

540 USA ISSN 0895-5859
CODEN: COOSEC

C A SELECTS. ORGANOMETALLICS IN ORGANIC SYNTHESIS. Text in English. 1988. s-w. USD 315 to non-members; USD 95 to members (effective 2005).
Document type: *Abstract/Index.* **Description:** Covers uses of organometallic compounds and complexes in the synthesis of organic compounds, generally those containing no carbon-metal bonds.
Published by: Chemical Abstracts Service (C A S) (Subsidiary of: American Chemical Society), 2540 Olentangy River Rd., Columbus, OH 43210-0012. TEL 614-447-3600, FAX 614-447-3713, help@cas.com, http://www.cas.org, http://caselects.cas.org. **Subscr. to:** PO Box 3012, Columbus, OH 43210. TEL 800-753-4227, FAX 614-447-3751.

540 USA ISSN 0162-783X
CODEN: CAOCDZ

C A SELECTS. ORGANOPHOSPHORUS CHEMISTRY. Text in English. s-w. USD 315 to non-members; USD 95 to members (effective 2005). **Document type:** *Abstract/Index.*
Description: Covers preparation, reactions and applications of organophosphorus compounds.
Published by: Chemical Abstracts Service (C A S) (Subsidiary of: American Chemical Society), 2540 Olentangy River Rd., Columbus, OH 43210-0012. TEL 614-447-3600, FAX 614-447-3713, help@cas.com, http://www.cas.org, http://caselects.cas.org. **Subscr. to:** PO Box 3012, Columbus, OH 43210. TEL 800-753-4227, FAX 614-447-3751.

540 USA ISSN 1040-7189
CODEN: CAOCE2

C A SELECTS. ORGANOSULFUR CHEMISTRY (JOURNALS). Text in English. 1989. s-w. USD 315 to non-members; USD 95 to members (effective 2005). **Document type:** *Abstract/Index.* **Description:** Journal literature on the chemistry of organic compounds containing sulfur.
Published by: Chemical Abstracts Service (C A S) (Subsidiary of: American Chemical Society), 2540 Olentangy River Rd., Columbus, OH 43210-0012. TEL 614-447-3600, FAX 614-447-3713, help@cas.com, http://www.cas.org, http://caselects.cas.org. **Subscr. to:** PO Box 3012, Columbus, OH 43210. TEL 800-753-4227, FAX 614-447-3751.

540 USA ISSN 0195-5101
CODEN: COGCDP

C A SELECTS. ORGANOTIN CHEMISTRY. Text in English, s-w. USD 315 to non-members; USD 95 to members (effective 2005). **Document type:** *Abstract/Index.* **Description:** Covers preparation, properties, chemical behavior, and use of compounds containing one or more carbon-tin bonds.
Published by: Chemical Abstracts Service (C A S) (Subsidiary of: American Chemical Society), 2540 Olentangy River Rd., Columbus, OH 43210-0012. TEL 614-447-3600, FAX 614-447-3713, help@cas.com, http://www.cas.org, http://caselects.cas.org. **Subscr. to:** PO Box 3012, Columbus, OH 43210. TEL 800-753-4227, FAX 614-447-3751.

540 USA ISSN 1040-7170
CODEN: COXCE9

C A SELECTS. OXIDATION CATALYSTS. Text in English. 1989. s-w. USD 315 to non-members; USD 95 to members (effective 2005). **Document type:** *Abstract/Index.*
Description: Covers new catalysts for known oxidation processes as well as catalysts for new oxidations.

C

Published by: Chemical Abstracts Service (C A S) (Subsidiary of: American Chemical Society), 2540 Olentangy River Rd., Columbus, OH 43210-0012. TEL 614-447-3600, FAX 614-447-3713, help@cas.com, http://www.cas.org, http://caselects.cas.org. **Subscr. to:** PO Box 3012, Columbus, OH 43210. TEL 800-753-4227, FAX 614-447-3751.

540   USA   ISSN 1040-7219
                                              CODEN: CAOSEG
C A SELECTS. OXIDE SUPERCONDUCTORS. Text in English. 1989. s-w. USD 315 to non-members; USD 95 to members (effective 2005). **Document type:** *Abstract/Index.* **Description:** Covers oxides that are used as or suitable for superconductors.
Published by: Chemical Abstracts Service (C A S) (Subsidiary of: American Chemical Society), 2540 Olentangy River Rd., Columbus, OH 43210-0012. TEL 614-447-3600, FAX 614-447-3713, help@cas.com, http://www.cas.org, http://caselects.cas.org. **Subscr. to:** PO Box 3012, Columbus, OH 43210. TEL 800-753-4227, FAX 614-447-3751.

540   USA   ISSN 0146-4515
                                              CODEN: CSPCDU
C A SELECTS. PAPER & THIN-LAYER CHROMATOGRAPHY. Text in English. s-w. USD 315 to non-members; USD 95 to members (effective 2005). **Document type:** *Abstract/Index.* **Description:** Covers theory and applications; equipment and materials; paper, plate and thin-layer chromatography.
Published by: Chemical Abstracts Service (C A S) (Subsidiary of: American Chemical Society), 2540 Olentangy River Rd., Columbus, OH 43210-0012. TEL 614-447-3600, FAX 614-447-3713, help@cas.com, http://www.cas.org, http://caselects.cas.org. **Subscr. to:** PO Box 3012, Columbus, OH 43210. TEL 800-753-4227, FAX 614-447-3751.

540   USA   ISSN 1040-7200
                                              CODEN: CPCME9
C A SELECTS. PAPER CHEMISTRY. Text in English. 1989. s-w. USD 315 to non-members; USD 95 to members (effective 2005). **Document type:** *Abstract/Index.* **Description:** Covers chemical aspects of paper manufacture including stock preparation, various additives, sizing, and coating.
Published by: Chemical Abstracts Service (C A S) (Subsidiary of: American Chemical Society), 2540 Olentangy River Rd., Columbus, OH 43210-0012. TEL 614-447-3600, FAX 614-447-3713, help@cas.com, http://www.cas.org, http://caselects.cas.org. **Subscr. to:** PO Box 3012, Columbus, OH 43210. TEL 800-753-4227, FAX 614-447-3751.

540   USA   ISSN 0885-0194
                                              CODEN: CSPCEV
C A SELECTS. PHASE TRANSFER CATALYSIS. Text in English. s-w. USD 315 to non-members; USD 95 to members (effective 2005). **Document type:** *Abstract/Index.* **Description:** Covers reactions deliberately carried out in systems containing two or more phases, in the presence of agents that promote contact of materials in the phases.
Published by: Chemical Abstracts Service (C A S) (Subsidiary of: American Chemical Society), 2540 Olentangy River Rd., Columbus, OH 43210-0012. TEL 614-447-3600, FAX 614-447-3713, help@cas.com, http://www.cas.org, http://caselects.cas.org. **Subscr. to:** PO Box 3012, Columbus, OH 43210. TEL 800-753-4227, FAX 614-447-3751.

016.572   USA   ISSN 0148-2335
                                              CODEN: CSPHDB
C A SELECTS. PHOTOBIOCHEMISTRY. Text in English. s-w. USD 315 to non-members; USD 95 to members (effective 2005). **Document type:** *Abstract/Index.* **Description:** Covers photochemistry of biological materials, their constituents, and molecular structure.
Published by: Chemical Abstracts Service (C A S) (Subsidiary of: American Chemical Society), 2540 Olentangy River Rd., Columbus, OH 43210-0012. TEL 614-447-3600, FAX 614-447-3713, help@cas.com, http://www.cas.org, http://caselects.cas.org. **Subscr. to:** PO Box 3012, Columbus, OH 43210. TEL 800-753-4227, FAX 614-447-3751.

540 011   USA   ISSN 1051-3949
                                              CODEN: CPHOE6
C A SELECTS. PHOTOCATALYSTS. Text in English. 1990. s-w. USD 315 to non-members; USD 95 to members (effective 2005). **Document type:** *Abstract/Index.* **Description:** Covers preparation and usage of photocatalysts and photocatalyzed reactions.
Published by: Chemical Abstracts Service (C A S) (Subsidiary of: American Chemical Society), 2540 Olentangy River Rd., Columbus, OH 43210-0012. TEL 614-447-3600, FAX 614-447-3713, help@cas.com, http://www.cas.org, http://caselects.cas.org. **Subscr. to:** PO Box 3012, Columbus, OH 43210. TEL 800-753-4227, FAX 614-447-3751.

547   USA   ISSN 0885-0208
                                              CODEN: CSPSEB
C A SELECTS. PHOTOCHEMICAL ORGANIC SYNTHESIS. Text in English. s-w. USD 315 to non-members; USD 95 to members (effective 2005). **Document type:** *Abstract/Index.* **Description:** Covers preparation and reactions of organic compounds under ultraviolet or other irradiation.

Published by: Chemical Abstracts Service (C A S) (Subsidiary of: American Chemical Society), 2540 Olentangy River Rd., Columbus, OH 43210-0012. TEL 614-447-3600, FAX 614-447-3713, help@cas.com, http://www.cas.org, http://caselects.cas.org. **Subscr. to:** PO Box 3012, Columbus, OH 43210. TEL 800-753-4227, FAX 614-447-3751.

540   USA   ISSN 0885-0216
                                              CODEN: CSPHEC
C A SELECTS. PHOTORESISTS. Text in English. s-w. USD 315 to non-members; USD 95 to members (effective 2005). **Document type:** *Abstract/Index.* **Description:** Covers materials and technology for fabricating and developing photoresists used in photolithography, printing and microelectronics.
Published by: Chemical Abstracts Service (C A S) (Subsidiary of: American Chemical Society), 2540 Olentangy River Rd., Columbus, OH 43210-0012. TEL 614-447-3600, FAX 614-447-3713, help@cas.com, http://www.cas.org, http://caselects.cas.org. **Subscr. to:** PO Box 3012, Columbus, OH 43210. TEL 800-753-4227, FAX 614-447-3751.

540   USA   ISSN 0749-7326
                                              CODEN: CSPPE2
C A SELECTS. PHOTOSENSITIVE POLYMERS. Text in English. s-w. USD 315 to non-members; USD 95 to members (effective 2005). **Document type:** *Abstract/Index.* **Description:** Covers preparation, properties, and uses of light-sensitive polymers, photocurable coatings and sheet material.
Published by: Chemical Abstracts Service (C A S) (Subsidiary of: American Chemical Society), 2540 Olentangy River Rd., Columbus, OH 43210-0012. TEL 614-447-3600, FAX 614-447-3713, help@cas.com, http://www.cas.org, http://caselects.cas.org. **Subscr. to:** PO Box 3012, Columbus, OH 43210. TEL 800-753-4227, FAX 614-447-3751.

540   USA   ISSN 0890-1937
                                              CODEN: CPCHES
C A SELECTS. PLATINUM AND PALLADIUM CHEMISTRY. Text in English. s-w. USD 315 to non-members; USD 95 to members (effective 2005). **Document type:** *Abstract/Index.* **Description:** Covers preparation, properties, reactions, uses, and characterization of compounds that contain platinum or palladium.
Published by: Chemical Abstracts Service (C A S) (Subsidiary of: American Chemical Society), 2540 Olentangy River Rd., Columbus, OH 43210-0012. TEL 614-447-3600, FAX 614-447-3713, help@cas.com, http://www.cas.org, http://caselects.cas.org. **Subscr. to:** PO Box 3012, Columbus, OH 43210. TEL 800-753-4227, FAX 614-447-3751.

540   USA   ISSN 1083-2726
                                              CODEN: CSPEF4
C A SELECTS PLUS. ADHESIVES. Text in English. s-w. USD 315 to non-members; USD 95 to members; USD 472 combined subscription to individuals print & online eds. (effective 2005). **Document type:** *Abstract/Index.* **Description:** Covers adhesives, binders, glues, caulks, sealants, mastics, grouts.
Formerly: C A Selects. Adhesives (0162-7686)
Related titles: Online - full text ed.: USD 315 (effective 2005).
Published by: Chemical Abstracts Service (C A S) (Subsidiary of: American Chemical Society), 2540 Olentangy River Rd., Columbus, OH 43210-0012. TEL 614-447-3600, FAX 614-447-3713, help@cas.com, http://www.cas.org, http://caselects.cas.org. **Subscr. to:** PO Box 3012, Columbus, OH 43210. TEL 800-753-4227, FAX 614-447-3751.

540   USA   ISSN 1084-2306
                                              CODEN: CAPIFQ
C A SELECTS PLUS. ASYMMETRIC SYNTHESIS & INDUCTION. Text in English. s-w. USD 315 to non-members; USD 95 to members (effective 2005). **Document type:** *Abstract/Index.* **Description:** Covers synthetic methods for enantiomeric enrichment of compounds that contain one or more asymmetric centers.
Formerly: C A Selects. Asymmetric Synthesis and Induction (0890-183X)
Published by: Chemical Abstracts Service (C A S) (Subsidiary of: American Chemical Society), 2540 Olentangy River Rd., Columbus, OH 43210-0012. TEL 614-447-3600, FAX 614-447-3713, help@cas.com, http://www.cas.org, http://caselects.cas.org. **Subscr. to:** PO Box 3012, Columbus, OH 43210. TEL 800-753-4227, FAX 614-447-3751.

541.37   USA   ISSN 1083-267X
                                              CODEN: CSPBFT
C A SELECTS PLUS. BATTERIES & FUEL CELLS. Text in English. s-w. USD 315 to non-members; USD 95 to members (effective 2005). **Document type:** *Abstract/Index.* **Description:** Covers design, manufacture, properties, and use of primary and secondary batteries; materials-related and electrochemical aspects; reclamation of materials from spent batteries; and electrodes for batteries and fuel cells.
Formerly: C A Selects. Batteries and Fuel Cells (0162-7708)
Published by: Chemical Abstracts Service (C A S) (Subsidiary of: American Chemical Society), 2540 Olentangy River Rd., Columbus, OH 43210-0012. TEL 614-447-3600, FAX 614-447-3713, help@cas.com, http://www.cas.org, http://caselects.cas.org. **Subscr. to:** PO Box 3012, Columbus, OH 43210. TEL 800-753-4227, FAX 614-447-3751.

547   USA   ISSN 1084-2314
                                              CODEN: CPCCFE
C A SELECTS PLUS. CARBOHYDRATES (CHEMICAL ASPECTS). Text in English. s-w. USD 315 to non-members; USD 95 to members (effective 2005). **Document type:** *Abstract/Index.* **Description:** Characterization, reactions, structure analysis, and nonindustrial synthesis of carbohydrates and their derivatives and polymers.
Formerly: C A Selects. Carbohydrates (Chemical Aspects) (0740-0756)
Published by: Chemical Abstracts Service (C A S) (Subsidiary of: American Chemical Society), 2540 Olentangy River Rd., Columbus, OH 43210-0012. TEL 614-447-3600, FAX 614-447-3713, help@cas.com, http://www.cas.org, http://caselects.cas.org. **Subscr. to:** PO Box 3012, Columbus, OH 43210. TEL 800-753-4227, FAX 614-447-3751.

547   USA   ISSN 1083-2793
                                              CODEN: CSPCFW
C A SELECTS PLUS. CARBON & HETEROATOM N M R. Text in English. s-w. USD 315 to non-members; USD 95 to members (effective 2005). **Document type:** *Abstract/Index.* **Description:** Covers the chemical aspects of nuclear magnetic resonance (NMR) of carbon, fluorine, phosphorus, and other heteroatoms; and chemically-induced dynamic nuclear polarization.
Formerly: C A Selects. Carbon and Heteroatom N M R (0190-9401)
Published by: Chemical Abstracts Service (C A S) (Subsidiary of: American Chemical Society), 2540 Olentangy River Rd., Columbus, OH 43210-0012. TEL 614-447-3600, FAX 614-447-3713, help@cas.com, http://www.cas.org, http://caselects.cas.org. **Subscr. to:** PO Box 3012, Columbus, OH 43210. TEL 800-753-4227, FAX 614-447-3751.

540   USA   ISSN 1083-2777
                                              CODEN: CSPAFQ
C A SELECTS PLUS. CATALYSIS (APPLIED & PHYSICAL ASPECTS). Text in English. s-w. USD 315 to non-members; USD 95 to members (effective 2005). **Document type:** *Abstract/Index.* **Description:** Covers the theory and applications of heterogeneous and homogeneous catalysis and catalysts; and effect of catalysts on reaction kinetics.
Formerly: C A Selects. Catalysis (Applied and Physical Aspects) (0146-440X)
Published by: Chemical Abstracts Service (C A S) (Subsidiary of: American Chemical Society), 2540 Olentangy River Rd., Columbus, OH 43210-0012. TEL 614-447-3600, FAX 614-447-3713, help@cas.com, http://www.cas.org, http://caselects.cas.org. **Subscr. to:** PO Box 3012, Columbus, OH 43210. TEL 800-753-4227, FAX 614-447-3751.

547   USA   ISSN 1083-2785
                                              CODEN: CSPYFU
C A SELECTS PLUS. CATALYSIS (ORGANIC REACTIONS). Text in English. s-w. USD 315 to non-members; USD 95 to members (effective 2005). **Document type:** *Abstract/Index.* **Description:** Covers the theory and applications of heterogeneous and homogeneous catalysis and catalysts in organic chemistry.
Formerly: C A Selects. Catalysis (Organic Reactions) (0146-4396)
Published by: Chemical Abstracts Service (C A S) (Subsidiary of: American Chemical Society), 2540 Olentangy River Rd., Columbus, OH 43210-0012. TEL 614-447-3600, FAX 614-447-3713, help@cas.com, http://www.cas.org, http://caselects.cas.org. **Subscr. to:** PO Box 3012, Columbus, OH 43210. TEL 800-753-4227, FAX 614-447-3751.

540   USA   ISSN 1084-2330
                                              CODEN: CPCTFV
C A SELECTS PLUS. CONTROLLED RELEASE TECHNOLOGY. Text in English. s-w. USD 315 to non-members; USD 95 to members (effective 2005). **Document type:** *Abstract/Index.* **Description:** Covers the science and technology of controlled release of biologically active materials (drugs, agrochemicals).
Formerly: C A Selects. Controlled Release Technology (0740-0748)
Published by: Chemical Abstracts Service (C A S) (Subsidiary of: American Chemical Society), 2540 Olentangy River Rd., Columbus, OH 43210-0012. TEL 614-447-3600, FAX 614-447-3713, help@cas.com, http://www.cas.org, http://caselects.cas.org. **Subscr. to:** PO Box 3012, Columbus, OH 43210. TEL 800-753-4227, FAX 614-447-3751.

541.37   USA   ISSN 1084-0036
                                              CODEN: CPELFH
C A SELECTS PLUS. ELECTROPHORESIS. Text in English. s-w. USD 315 to non-members; USD 95 to members (effective 2005). **Document type:** *Abstract/Index.* **Description:** Covers techniques of electrophoretic processes; cataphoresis, ionophoresis, isolectric focusing.
Formerly: C A Selects. Electrophoresis (0195-4962)
Published by: Chemical Abstracts Service (C A S) (Subsidiary of: American Chemical Society), 2540 Olentangy River Rd., Columbus, OH 43210-0012. TEL 614-447-3600, FAX 614-447-3713, help@cas.com, http://www.cas.org, http://caselects.cas.org. **Subscr. to:** PO Box 3012, Columbus, OH 43210. TEL 800-753-4227, FAX 614-447-3751.

C

▼ *new title*   ▶ *refereed*   ✳ *unverified*   ◆ *full entry avail.*

540 USA ISSN 1084-2357
CODEN: CSEAF5

C A SELECTS PLUS. ENZYME APPLICATIONS. Text in English. 1988. s-w. USD 315 to non-members; USD 95 to members (effective 2005). **Document type:** *Abstract/Index.*
Description: Covers studies in which enzymes are used as catalytic agents for the synthesis of organic compounds; synthetic or artificial enzymes (synzymes, for example:, cyclodextrins, cyclophanes, polyethylenimines, crown ethers) and semisynthetic enzymes such as flavopapains.
Formerly: C A Selects. Enzyme Applications (0895-593X)
Published by: Chemical Abstracts Service (C A S) (Subsidiary of: American Chemical Society), 2540 Olentangy River Rd., Columbus, OH 43210-0012. TEL 614-447-3600, FAX 614-447-3713, help@cas.com, http://www.cas.org, http://caselects.cas.org. **Subscr. to:** PO Box 3012, Columbus, OH 43210. TEL 800-753-4227, FAX 614-447-3751.

614.19 USA ISSN 1084-2365
CODEN: CSFCFG

C A SELECTS PLUS. FORENSIC CHEMISTRY. Text in English. s-w. USD 315 to non-members; USD 95 to members (effective 2005). **Document type:** *Abstract/Index.*
Description: Covers the chemistry of investigative science.
Formerly: C A Selects. Forensic Chemistry (0362-9880)
Published by: Chemical Abstracts Service (C A S) (Subsidiary of: American Chemical Society), 2540 Olentangy River Rd., Columbus, OH 43210-0012. TEL 614-447-3600, FAX 614-447-3713, help@cas.com, http://www.cas.org, http://caselects.cas.org. **Subscr. to:** PO Box 3012, Columbus, OH 43210. TEL 800-753-4227, FAX 614-447-3751.

016.543 USA ISSN 1083-2734
CODEN: CSPGFA

C A SELECTS PLUS. GAS CHROMATOGRAPHY. Text in English. s-w. USD 315 to non-members; USD 95 to members (effective 2005). **Document type:** *Abstract/Index.*
Description: Covers gas chromatography in chemical analysis; gas-liquid and vapor phase chromatography; and instrumentation and apparatus for gas chromatography.
Formerly: C A Selects. Gas Chromatography (0146-4477)
Published by: Chemical Abstracts Service (C A S) (Subsidiary of: American Chemical Society), 2540 Olentangy River Rd., Columbus, OH 43210-0012. TEL 614-447-3600, FAX 614-447-3713, help@cas.com, http://www.cas.org, http://caselects.cas.org. **Subscr. to:** PO Box 3012, Columbus, OH 43210. TEL 800-753-4227, FAX 614-447-3751.

543.8 USA ISSN 1084-290X
CODEN: CSGCFL

C A SELECTS PLUS. GEL PERMEATION CHROMATOGRAPHY. Text in English. s-w. USD 315 to non-members; USD 95 to members (effective 2005). **Document type:** *Abstract/Index.*
Description: Covers theory and application of gel permeation chromatography; high-speed gel chromatography; size exclusion chromatographic techniques; affinity chromatography.
Formerly: C A Selects. Gel Permeation Chromatography (0146-4485)
Published by: Chemical Abstracts Service (C A S) (Subsidiary of: American Chemical Society), 2540 Olentangy River Rd., Columbus, OH 43210-0012. TEL 614-447-3600, FAX 614-447-3713, help@cas.com, http://www.cas.org, http://caselects.cas.org. **Subscr. to:** PO Box 3012, Columbus, OH 43210. TEL 800-753-4227, FAX 614-447-3751.

540 USA ISSN 1083-2815
CODEN: CSPHFD

C A SELECTS PLUS. HIGH PERFORMANCE LIQUID CHROMATOGRAPHY. Text in English. s-w. USD 315 to non-members; USD 95 to members (effective 2005). **Document type:** *Abstract/Index.* **Description:** Covers high speed, high pressure, high performance, and high resolution liquid chromatography.
Formerly: C A Selects. High Performance Liquid Chromatography (0195-5217)
Published by: Chemical Abstracts Service (C A S) (Subsidiary of: American Chemical Society), 2540 Olentangy River Rd., Columbus, OH 43210-0012. TEL 614-447-3600, FAX 614-447-3713, help@cas.com, http://www.cas.org, http://caselects.cas.org. **Subscr. to:** PO Box 3012, Columbus, OH 43210. TEL 800-753-4227, FAX 614-447-3751.

438 USA ISSN 1084-2381
CODEN: CSLTFT

C A SELECTS PLUS. LIQUID WASTE TREATMENT. Text in English. s-w. USD 315 to non-members; USD 95 to members (effective 2005). **Document type:** *Abstract/Index.*
Description: Covers treatment and disposal by physical, chemical, and biological methods; domestic and industrial sewage and wastewater; sludge that results from liquid waste treatment.
Formerly (until 1996): C A Selects. Liquid Waste Treatment (0160-9106)
Published by: Chemical Abstracts Service (C A S) (Subsidiary of: American Chemical Society), 2540 Olentangy River Rd., Columbus, OH 43210-0012. TEL 614-447-3600, FAX 614-447-3713, help@cas.com, http://www.cas.org, http://caselects.cas.org. **Subscr. to:** PO Box 3012, Columbus, OH 43210. TEL 800-753-4227, FAX 614-447-3751.

535 USA ISSN 1083-2742
CODEN: CSPMFS

C A SELECTS PLUS. MASS SPECTROMETRY. Text in English. s-w. USD 315 to non-members; USD 95 to members (effective 2005). **Document type:** *Abstract/Index.*
Description: Covers methodology, apparatus, and experimental results obtained by various spectrometric techniques; structure, thermochemistry, energetics, reaction kinetics and mechanisms, and analytical applications.
Formerly: C A Selects. Mass Spectrometry (0362-9872)
Published by: Chemical Abstracts Service (C A S) (Subsidiary of: American Chemical Society), 2540 Olentangy River Rd., Columbus, OH 43210-0012. TEL 614-447-3600, FAX 614-447-3713, help@cas.com, http://www.cas.org, http://caselects.cas.org. **Subscr. to:** PO Box 3012, Columbus, OH 43210. TEL 800-753-4227, FAX 614-447-3751.

540 USA ISSN 1083-2653
CODEN: CSPOFY

C A SELECTS PLUS. ORGANOSILICON CHEMISTRY. Text in English. s-w. USD 315 to non-members; USD 95 to members (effective 2005). **Document type:** *Abstract/Index.*
Description: Covers compounds containing a silicon-carbon bond, silanes, siloxanes, silocarbonates.
Formerly: C A Selects. Organosilicon Chemistry (0362-9899)
Published by: Chemical Abstracts Service (C A S) (Subsidiary of: American Chemical Society), 2540 Olentangy River Rd., Columbus, OH 43210-0012. TEL 614-447-3600, FAX 614-447-3713, help@cas.com, http://www.cas.org, http://caselects.cas.org. **Subscr. to:** PO Box 3012, Columbus, OH 43210. TEL 800-753-4227, FAX 614-447-3751.

547 USA ISSN 1083-270X
CODEN: CSPTFF

C A SELECTS PLUS. PHOTOCHEMISTRY. Text in English. s-w. USD 315 to non-members; USD 95 to members (effective 2005). **Document type:** *Abstract/Index.* **Description:** Covers fluorescence, luminescence, phosphorescence, photochromism, phosphors, light-induced excited state interactions, photochemical mechanisms.
Formerly: C A Selects. Photochemistry (0362-9856)
Published by: Chemical Abstracts Service (C A S) (Subsidiary of: American Chemical Society), 2540 Olentangy River Rd., Columbus, OH 43210-0012. TEL 614-447-3600, FAX 614-447-3713, help@cas.com, http://www.cas.org, http://caselects.cas.org. **Subscr. to:** PO Box 3012, Columbus, OH 43210. TEL 800-753-4227, FAX 614-447-3751.

540 USA ISSN 1083-2696
CODEN: CSPLFP

C A SELECTS PLUS. POLYURETHANES. Text in English. s-w. USD 315 to non-members; USD 95 to members (effective 2005). **Document type:** *Abstract/Index.* **Description:** Covers preparation, properties, reaction, uses of urethane polymers, that are derived from polyisocyanates and polyols.
Formerly: C A Selects. Polyurethanes (0740-0705)
Published by: Chemical Abstracts Service (C A S) (Subsidiary of: American Chemical Society), 2540 Olentangy River Rd., Columbus, OH 43210-0012. TEL 614-447-3600, FAX 614-447-3713, help@cas.com, http://www.cas.org, http://caselects.cas.org. **Subscr. to:** PO Box 3012, Columbus, OH 43210. TEL 800-753-4227, FAX 614-447-3751.

540 USA ISSN 1084-0087
CODEN: CSPWFO

C A SELECTS PLUS. RECOVERY & RECYCLING OF WASTES. Text in English. s-w. USD 315 to non-members; USD 95 to members (effective 2005). **Document type:** *Abstract/Index.*
Description: Covers processes and equipment used for recycling or recovery of all types of waste materials; inorganic and organic wastes, plastics, oils, industrial effluents, sewage, steel and other metals, ashes, slags, also with conversion and utilization of waste material.
Formerly: C A Selects. Recovery and Recycling of Wastes (0160-9157)
Published by: Chemical Abstracts Service (C A S) (Subsidiary of: American Chemical Society), 2540 Olentangy River Rd., Columbus, OH 43210-0012. TEL 614-447-3600, FAX 614-447-3713, help@cas.com, http://www.cas.org, http://caselects.cas.org. **Subscr. to:** PO Box 3012, Columbus, OH 43210. TEL 800-753-4227, FAX 614-447-3751.

540 USA ISSN 1084-0095
CODEN: CSSTFU

C A SELECTS PLUS. SOLID & RADIOACTIVE WASTE TREATMENT. Text in English. s-w. USD 315 to non-members; USD 95 to members (effective 2005). **Document type:** *Abstract/Index.* **Description:** Covers the chemical and chemical engineering aspects of treatment and disposal.
Formerly: C A Selects. Solid and Radioactive Waste Treatment (0160-9165)
Published by: Chemical Abstracts Service (C A S) (Subsidiary of: American Chemical Society), 2540 Olentangy River Rd., Columbus, OH 43210-0012. TEL 614-447-3600, FAX 614-447-3713, help@cas.com, http://www.cas.org, http://caselects.cas.org. **Subscr. to:** PO Box 3012, Columbus, OH 43210. TEL 800-753-4227, FAX 614-447-3751.

540 USA ISSN 1084-0117
CODEN: CSPUFI

C A SELECTS PLUS. ULTRAFILTRATION. Text in English. s-w. USD 315 to non-members; USD 95 to members (effective 2005). **Document type:** *Abstract/Index.* **Description:** Covers technology and use of hyperfiltration and ultrafiltration; reverse osmosis (biochemical, medical, food technology, water purification, waste treatment).
Formerly: C A Selects. Ultrafiltration (0195-5195)
Published by: Chemical Abstracts Service (C A S) (Subsidiary of: American Chemical Society), 2540 Olentangy River Rd., Columbus, OH 43210-0012. TEL 614-447-3600, FAX 614-447-3713, help@cas.com, http://www.cas.org, http://caselects.cas.org. **Subscr. to:** PO Box 3012, Columbus, OH 43210. TEL 800-753-4227, FAX 614-447-3751.

540 USA ISSN 1084-0109
CODEN: CSWTFG

C A SELECTS PLUS. WATER TREATMENT. Text in English. s-w. USD 315 to non-members; USD 95 to members (effective 2005). **Document type:** *Abstract/Index.* **Description:** Covers chemical and physical purification of water for home and industrial use, also water softening.
Formerly: C A Selects. Water Treatment (0740-073X)
Published by: Chemical Abstracts Service (C A S) (Subsidiary of: American Chemical Society), 2540 Olentangy River Rd., Columbus, OH 43210-0012. TEL 614-447-3600, FAX 614-447-3713, help@cas.com, http://www.cas.org, http://caselects.cas.org. **Subscr. to:** PO Box 3012, Columbus, OH 43210. TEL 800-753-4227, FAX 614-447-3751.

540 USA ISSN 1083-2718
CODEN: CSPZFX

C A SELECTS PLUS. ZEOLITES. Text in English. s-w. USD 315 to non-members; USD 95 to members (effective 2005). **Document type:** *Abstract/Index.* **Description:** Covers preparation of synthetic zeolites; use of synthetic and natural zeolites and molecular sieves in adsorption and drying, catalysis, ion exchange, separation by molecular size.
Formerly: C A Selects. Zeolites (0190-4949)
Published by: Chemical Abstracts Service (C A S) (Subsidiary of: American Chemical Society), 2540 Olentangy River Rd., Columbus, OH 43210-0012. TEL 614-447-3600, FAX 614-447-3713, help@cas.com, http://www.cas.org, http://caselects.cas.org. **Subscr. to:** PO Box 3012, Columbus, OH 43210. TEL 800-753-4227, FAX 614-447-3751.

540 USA ISSN 0890-1945
CODEN: CSPJEI

C A SELECTS. POLYACRYLATES (JOURNALS). Text in English. s-w. USD 315 to non-members; USD 95 to members (effective 2005). **Document type:** *Abstract/Index.*
Description: Covers polymers prepared from acrylic and or methacrylic acid esters.
Published by: Chemical Abstracts Service (C A S) (Subsidiary of: American Chemical Society), 2540 Olentangy River Rd., Columbus, OH 43210-0012. TEL 614-447-3600, FAX 614-447-3713, help@cas.com, http://www.cas.org, http://caselects.cas.org. **Subscr. to:** PO Box 3012, Columbus, OH 43210. TEL 800-753-4227, FAX 614-447-3751.

540 USA ISSN 1045-8549
CODEN: CAPLEY

C A SELECTS. POLYACRYLATES (PATENTS). Text in English. s-w. USD 315 to non-members; USD 95 to members (effective 2005). **Document type:** *Abstract/Index.*
Description: Includes patent literature dealing with preparation, properties, and uses of polymers and copolymers from acrylic acid and - or methacrylic acid esters.
Published by: Chemical Abstracts Service (C A S) (Subsidiary of: American Chemical Society), 2540 Olentangy River Rd., Columbus, OH 43210-0012. TEL 614-447-3600, FAX 614-447-3713, help@cas.com, http://www.cas.org, http://caselects.cas.org. **Subscr. to:** PO Box 3012, Columbus, OH 43210. TEL 800-753-4227, FAX 614-447-3751.

540 011 USA ISSN 0734-8703
CODEN: CAPOE9

C A SELECTS. POLYESTERS. Text in English. s-w. USD 315 to non-members; USD 95 to members (effective 2005). **Document type:** *Abstract/Index.* **Description:** Covers the chemistry of polyesters: preparation, properties, formulation, and use.
Published by: Chemical Abstracts Service (C A S) (Subsidiary of: American Chemical Society), 2540 Olentangy River Rd., Columbus, OH 43210-0012. TEL 614-447-3600, FAX 614-447-3713, help@cas.com, http://www.cas.org, http://caselects.cas.org. **Subscr. to:** PO Box 3012, Columbus, OH 43210. TEL 800-753-4227, FAX 614-447-3751.

540 USA ISSN 0895-5840
CODEN: CSEPEF

C A SELECTS. POLYIMIDES. Text in English. 1988. s-w. USD 315 to non-members; USD 95 to members (effective 2005). **Document type:** *Abstract/Index.* **Description:** Covers preparation, properties, and uses of polymers that contain imide linkages in the main chain.

C

Published by: Chemical Abstracts Service (C A S) (Subsidiary of: American Chemical Society), 2540 Olentangy River Rd., Columbus, OH 43210-0012. TEL 614-447-3600, FAX 614-447-3713, help@cas.com, http://www.cas.org, http://caselects.cas.org. **Subscr. to:** PO Box 3012, Columbus, OH 43210. TEL 800-753-4227, FAX 614-447-3751.

541 USA ISSN 0734-8827
CODEN: CAPBE4

C A SELECTS. POLYMER BLENDS. Text in English. s-w. USD 315 to non-members; USD 95 to members (effective 2005). **Document type:** *Abstract/Index.* **Description:** Covers morphology and physical and mechanical properties of mixtures of polymers.
Published by: Chemical Abstracts Service (C A S) (Subsidiary of: American Chemical Society), 2540 Olentangy River Rd., Columbus, OH 43210-0012. TEL 614-447-3600, FAX 614-447-3713, help@cas.com, http://www.cas.org, http://caselects.cas.org. **Subscr. to:** PO Box 3012, Columbus, OH 43210. TEL 800-753-4227, FAX 614-447-3751.

541 USA ISSN 0734-8835
CODEN: CAPDEA

C A SELECTS. POLYMER DEGRADATION. Text in English. s-w. USD 315 to non-members; USD 95 to members (effective 2005). **Document type:** *Abstract/Index.* **Description:** Covers chemical, photochemical, radiochemical, mechanical, thermal, and oxidative degradation of polymers as well as kinetics and mechanisms of degradative reactions.
Published by: Chemical Abstracts Service (C A S) (Subsidiary of: American Chemical Society), 2540 Olentangy River Rd., Columbus, OH 43210-0012. TEL 614-447-3600, FAX 614-447-3713, help@cas.com, http://www.cas.org, http://caselects.cas.org. **Subscr. to:** PO Box 3012, Columbus, OH 43210. TEL 800-753-4227, FAX 614-447-3751.

541 USA ISSN 0195-5128
CODEN: CAPMD2

C A SELECTS. POLYMER MORPHOLOGY. Text in English. s-w. USD 315 to non-members; USD 95 to members (effective 2005). **Document type:** *Abstract/Index.* **Description:** Covers crystallinity and noncrystalline ordering on a supramolecular level in polymeric materials and their effect on physical and chemical properties of natural and synthetic polymers.
Published by: Chemical Abstracts Service (C A S) (Subsidiary of: American Chemical Society), 2540 Olentangy River Rd., Columbus, OH 43210-0012. TEL 614-447-3600, FAX 614-447-3713, help@cas.com, http://www.cas.org, http://caselects.cas.org. **Subscr. to:** PO Box 3012, Columbus, OH 43210. TEL 800-753-4227, FAX 614-447-3751.

541 USA ISSN 0885-0224
CODEN: CPKCEJ

C A SELECTS. POLYMERIZATION KINETICS & PROCESS CONTROL. Text in English. s-w. USD 315 to non-members; USD 95 to members (effective 2005). **Document type:** *Abstract/Index.* **Description:** Covers kinetic studies on addition, condensation, and other types of polymerization.
Published by: Chemical Abstracts Service (C A S) (Subsidiary of: American Chemical Society), 2540 Olentangy River Rd., Columbus, OH 43210-0012. TEL 614-447-3600, FAX 614-447-3713, help@cas.com, http://www.cas.org, http://caselects.cas.org. **Subscr. to:** PO Box 3012, Columbus, OH 43210. TEL 800-753-4227, FAX 614-447-3751.

540 USA ISSN 0195-5136
CODEN: CLPODH

C A SELECTS. PORPHYRINS. Text in English. s-w. USD 315 to non-members; USD 95 to members (effective 2005). **Document type:** *Abstract/Index.* **Description:** Covers chemical and biochemical aspects of porphyrins.
Published by: Chemical Abstracts Service (C A S) (Subsidiary of: American Chemical Society), 2540 Olentangy River Rd., Columbus, OH 43210-0012. TEL 614-447-3600, FAX 614-447-3713, help@cas.com, http://www.cas.org, http://caselects.cas.org. **Subscr. to:** PO Box 3012, Columbus, OH 43210. TEL 800-753-4227, FAX 614-447-3751.

540 USA ISSN 0148-2343
CODEN: CSEPDE

C A SELECTS. PROSTAGLANDINS. Text in English. s-w. USD 315 to non-members; USD 95 to members (effective 2005). **Document type:** *Abstract/Index.* **Description:** Covers the chemistry of prostaglandins, prostacyclins, thromboxanes, leukotrienes; enzymes of prostaglandin metabolism.
Published by: Chemical Abstracts Service (C A S) (Subsidiary of: American Chemical Society), 2540 Olentangy River Rd., Columbus, OH 43210-0012. TEL 614-447-3600, FAX 614-447-3713, help@cas.com, http://www.cas.org, http://caselects.cas.org. **Subscr. to:** PO Box 3012, Columbus, OH 43210. TEL 800-753-4227, FAX 614-447-3751.

540 USA ISSN 0190-941X
CODEN: CPMRD5

C A SELECTS. PROTON MAGNETIC RESONANCE. Text in English. s-w. USD 315 to non-members; USD 95 to members (effective 2005). **Document type:** *Abstract/Index.* **Description:** Covers the chemical aspects of nuclear magnetic resonance (NMR) of hydrogen, deuterium, and tritium.
Published by: Chemical Abstracts Service (C A S) (Subsidiary of: American Chemical Society), 2540 Olentangy River Rd., Columbus, OH 43210-0012. TEL 614-447-3600, FAX 614-447-3713, help@cas.com, http://www.cas.org, http://caselects.cas.org. **Subscr. to:** PO Box 3012, Columbus, OH 43210. TEL 800-753-4227, FAX 614-447-3751.

540 USA ISSN 0890-1953
CODEN: CSQPE7

C A SELECTS. QUATERNARY AMMONIUM COMPOUNDS. Text in English. 1987. s-w. USD 315 to non-members; USD 95 to members (effective 2005). **Document type:** *Abstract/Index.* **Description:** Covers preparation, properties, reactions, and uses of compounds that contain at least one nitrogen atom covalently bonded to four non-hydrogen atoms.
Published by: Chemical Abstracts Service (C A S) (Subsidiary of: American Chemical Society), 2540 Olentangy River Rd., Columbus, OH 43210-0012. TEL 614-447-3600, FAX 614-447-3713, help@cas.com, http://www.cas.org, http://caselects.cas.org. **Subscr. to:** PO Box 3012, Columbus, OH 43210. TEL 800-753-4227, FAX 614-447-3751.

540 USA ISSN 0146-4523
CODEN: CSRCD6

C A SELECTS. RADIATION CHEMISTRY. Text in English. s-w. USD 315 to non-members; USD 95 to members (effective 2005). **Document type:** *Abstract/Index.* **Description:** Covers radiation chemistry and biochemistry; radiation chemistry in aqueous and non-aqueous systems; energy transfer and ionic reactions.
Related titles: Online - full text ed.: USD 305 (effective 2004).
Published by: Chemical Abstracts Service (C A S) (Subsidiary of: American Chemical Society), 2540 Olentangy River Rd., Columbus, OH 43210-0012. TEL 614-447-3600, FAX 614-447-3713, help@cas.com, http://www.cas.org, http://caselects.cas.org.

540 USA ISSN 0749-7342
CODEN: CSRCE7

C A SELECTS. RADIATION CURING. Text in English. s-w. USD 315 to non-members; USD 95 to members (effective 2005). **Document type:** *Abstract/Index.* **Description:** Covers treatment of polymers with electron beams, gamma rays, and other forms of ionizing radiation.
Published by: Chemical Abstracts Service (C A S) (Subsidiary of: American Chemical Society), 2540 Olentangy River Rd., Columbus, OH 43210-0012. TEL 614-447-3600, FAX 614-447-3713, help@cas.com, http://www.cas.org, http://caselects.cas.org. **Subscr. to:** PO Box 3012, Columbus, OH 43210. TEL 800-753-4227, FAX 614-447-3751.

016.5438 USA ISSN 0148-2432
CODEN: CARSDU

C A SELECTS. RAMAN SPECTROSCOPY. Text in English. s-w. USD 315 to non-members; USD 95 to members (effective 2005). **Document type:** *Abstract/Index.* **Description:** Covers all aspects of Raman spectroscopy; includes methodology, apparatus, experimental results, and theoretical treatments.
Published by: Chemical Abstracts Service (C A S) (Subsidiary of: American Chemical Society), 2540 Olentangy River Rd., Columbus, OH 43210-0012. TEL 614-447-3600, FAX 614-447-3713, help@cas.com, http://www.cas.org, http://caselects.cas.org. **Subscr. to:** PO Box 3012, Columbus, OH 43210. TEL 800-753-4227, FAX 614-447-3751.

540 USA ISSN 0890-1961
CODEN: CSSSEQ

C A SELECTS. SILICAS & SILICATES. Text in English. 1987. s-w. USD 315 to non-members; USD 95 to members (effective 2005). **Document type:** *Abstract/Index.* **Description:** Covers preparation, properties, reaction, and uses of synthetic and naturally occurring inorganic compounds that contain silicon tetrahedrally bonded to oxygen.
Related titles: Online - full text ed.: USD 305 (effective 2004).
Published by: Chemical Abstracts Service (C A S) (Subsidiary of: American Chemical Society), 2540 Olentangy River Rd., Columbus, OH 43210-0012. TEL 614-447-3600, FAX 614-447-3713, help@cas.com, http://www.cas.org, http://caselects.cas.org.

540 USA ISSN 0895-5832
CODEN: CSISEA

C A SELECTS. SILOXANES & SILICONES. Text in English. 1988. s-w. USD 315 to non-members; USD 95 to members (effective 2005). **Document type:** *Abstract/Index.* **Description:** Covers preparation, properties, reactions, and uses of monomeric, oligomeric, and polymeric compounds, the basic structure of which consists of alternating silicon and oxygen atoms.
Published by: Chemical Abstracts Service (C A S) (Subsidiary of: American Chemical Society), 2540 Olentangy River Rd., Columbus, OH 43210-0012. TEL 614-447-3600, FAX 614-447-3713, help@cas.com, http://www.cas.org, http://caselects.cas.org. **Subscr. to:** PO Box 3012, Columbus, OH 43210. TEL 800-753-4227, FAX 614-447-3751.

540 USA ISSN 0895-5824
CODEN: CSSNEB

C A SELECTS. SOLID STATE N M R. (Nuclear Magnetic Resonance) Text in English. 1988. s-w. USD 315 to non-members; USD 95 to members (effective 2005). **Document type:** *Abstract/Index.* **Description:** Covers methodology and apparatus for solid-state NMR studies.
Published by: Chemical Abstracts Service (C A S) (Subsidiary of: American Chemical Society), 2540 Olentangy River Rd., Columbus, OH 43210-0012. TEL 614-447-3600, FAX 614-447-3713, help@cas.com, http://www.cas.org, http://caselects.cas.org. **Subscr. to:** PO Box 3012, Columbus, OH 43210. TEL 800-753-4227, FAX 614-447-3751.

540 USA ISSN 0146-4531
CODEN: CSSEDH

C A SELECTS. SOLVENT EXTRACTION. Text in English. s-w. USD 315 to non-members; USD 95 to members (effective 2005). **Document type:** *Abstract/Index.* **Description:** Covers chemical applications of solvent extraction; solvent properties, solvent recovery, fuel processing.
Published by: Chemical Abstracts Service (C A S) (Subsidiary of: American Chemical Society), 2540 Olentangy River Rd., Columbus, OH 43210-0012. TEL 614-447-3600, FAX 614-447-3713, help@cas.com, http://www.cas.org, http://caselects.cas.org. **Subscr. to:** PO Box 3012, Columbus, OH 43210. TEL 800-753-4227, FAX 614-447-3751.

540 USA ISSN 0885-0232
CODEN: CSANEN

C A SELECTS. SPECTROCHEMICAL ANALYSIS. Text in English. s-w. USD 315 to non-members; USD 95 to members (effective 2005). **Document type:** *Abstract/Index.* **Description:** Covers spectroscopic techniques used in chemical analysis.
Published by: Chemical Abstracts Service (C A S) (Subsidiary of: American Chemical Society), 2540 Olentangy River Rd., Columbus, OH 43210-0012. TEL 614-447-3600, FAX 614-447-3713, help@cas.com, http://www.cas.org, http://caselects.cas.org. **Subscr. to:** PO Box 3012, Columbus, OH 43210. TEL 800-753-4227, FAX 614-447-3751.

C

615 USA ISSN 0160-9181
CODEN: CSASD3

C A SELECTS. STEROIDS (CHEMICAL ASPECTS). Text in English. s-w. USD 315 to non-members; USD 95 to members (effective 2005). **Document type:** *Abstract/Index.* **Description:** Covers isolation and synthesis of steroids, their chemical reactions and transformations.
Published by: Chemical Abstracts Service (C A S) (Subsidiary of: American Chemical Society), 2540 Olentangy River Rd., Columbus, OH 43210-0012. TEL 614-447-3600, FAX 614-447-3713, help@cas.com, http://www.cas.org, http://caselects.cas.org. **Subscr. to:** PO Box 3012, Columbus, OH 43210. TEL 800-753-4227, FAX 614-447-3751.

540 USA ISSN 0895-5816
CODEN: CSSREN

C A SELECTS. STRUCTURE - ACTIVITY RELATIONSHIPS. Text in English. 1988. s-w. USD 315 to non-members; USD 95 to members (effective 2005). **Document type:** *Abstract/Index.* **Description:** Covers structure-activity relationships of therapeutic agents and compounds that have potential therapeutic uses.
Published by: Chemical Abstracts Service (C A S) (Subsidiary of: American Chemical Society), 2540 Olentangy River Rd., Columbus, OH 43210-0012. TEL 614-447-3600, FAX 614-447-3713, help@cas.com, http://www.cas.org, http://caselects.cas.org. **Subscr. to:** PO Box 3012, Columbus, OH 43210. TEL 800-753-4227, FAX 614-447-3751.

540 USA ISSN 0195-5152
CODEN: CSUADF

C A SELECTS. SURFACE ANALYSIS. Text in English. s-w. USD 315 to non-members; USD 95 to members (effective 2005). **Document type:** *Abstract/Index.* **Description:** Covers the analytical chemistry of surface technology.
Published by: Chemical Abstracts Service (C A S) (Subsidiary of: American Chemical Society), 2540 Olentangy River Rd., Columbus, OH 43210-0012. TEL 614-447-3600, FAX 614-447-3713, help@cas.com, http://www.cas.org, http://caselects.cas.org. **Subscr. to:** PO Box 3012, Columbus, OH 43210. TEL 800-753-4227, FAX 614-447-3751.

540 USA ISSN 0146-454X
CODEN: CSSAD5

C A SELECTS. SURFACE CHEMISTRY (PHYSICOCHEMICAL ASPECTS). Text in English. s-w. USD 315 to non-members; USD 95 to members (effective 2005). **Document type:** *Abstract/Index.* **Description:** Covers the physical chemistry and properties of solid surface.
Published by: Chemical Abstracts Service (C A S) (Subsidiary of: American Chemical Society), 2540 Olentangy River Rd., Columbus, OH 43210-0012. TEL 614-447-3600, FAX 614-447-3713, help@cas.com, http://www.cas.org, http://caselects.cas.org. **Subscr. to:** PO Box 3012, Columbus, OH 43210. TEL 800-753-4227, FAX 614-447-3751.

▼ new title ➤ refereed ✶ unverified ♦ full entry avail.

540 USA ISSN 0195-5160
CODEN: CSSYD9
C A SELECTS. SYNFUELS. Text in English. s-w. USD 315 to non-members; USD 95 to members (effective 2005).
Document type: *Abstract/Index.* **Description:** Covers production of fuel from new sources.
Published by: Chemical Abstracts Service (C A S) (Subsidiary of: American Chemical Society), 2540 Olentangy River Rd., Columbus, OH 43210-0012. TEL 614-447-3600, FAX 614-447-3713, help@cas.com, http://www.cas.org, http://caselects.cas.org. **Subscr. to:** PO Box 3012, Columbus, OH 43210. TEL 800-753-4227, FAX 614-447-3751.

541 USA ISSN 0275-7168
CODEN: CSYPDC
C A SELECTS. SYNTHETIC HIGH POLYMERS. Text in English. s-w. USD 315 to non-members; USD 95 to members (effective 2005). **Document type:** *Abstract/Index.*
Description: Covers the organic and physical chemistry of linear and branched synthetic organic and inorganic polymers.
Published by: Chemical Abstracts Service (C A S) (Subsidiary of: American Chemical Society), 2540 Olentangy River Rd., Columbus, OH 43210-0012. TEL 614-447-3600, FAX 614-447-3713, help@cas.com, http://www.cas.org, http://caselects.cas.org. **Subscr. to:** PO Box 3012, Columbus, OH 43210. TEL 800-753-4227, FAX 614-447-3751.

540 USA ISSN 0195-5179
CODEN: CSCPD4
C A SELECTS. SYNTHETIC MACROCYCLIC COMPOUNDS. Text in English. s-w. USD 315 to non-members; USD 95 to members (effective 2005). **Document type:** *Abstract/Index.*
Description: Covers synthesis and applications of macrocyclic compounds and ligands, for example crown ethers and macrocyclic tetramines.
Published by: Chemical Abstracts Service (C A S) (Subsidiary of: American Chemical Society), 2540 Olentangy River Rd., Columbus, OH 43210-0012. TEL 614-447-3600, FAX 614-447-3713, help@cas.com, http://www.cas.org, http://caselects.cas.org. **Subscr. to:** PO Box 3012, Columbus, OH 43210. TEL 800-753-4227, FAX 614-447-3751.

C

536 USA ISSN 0195-5187
CODEN: CSANDM
C A SELECTS. THERMAL ANALYSIS. Text in English. s-w. USD 315 to non-members; USD 95 to members (effective 2005).
Document type: *Abstract/Index.* **Description:** Covers DTA, thermogravimetry, differential scanning calorimetry, evolved-gas analysis, thermodilatometry, thermoelectrometry, thermomagnetometry, thermosonimetry.
Published by: Chemical Abstracts Service (C A S) (Subsidiary of: American Chemical Society), 2540 Olentangy River Rd., Columbus, OH 43210-0012. TEL 614-447-3600, FAX 614-447-3713, help@cas.com, http://www.cas.org, http://caselects.cas.org. **Subscr. to:** PO Box 3012, Columbus, OH 43210. TEL 800-753-4227, FAX 614-447-3751.

536 USA ISSN 0162-7864
CODEN: CSTHDV
C A SELECTS. THERMOCHEMISTRY. Text in English. s-w. USD 315 to non-members; USD 95 to members (effective 2005).
Document type: *Abstract/Index.* **Description:** Covers chemical thermodynamics: heat capacities and thermodynamic functions such as enthalpies, free energies, and entropies for physicochemical and biochemical processes.
Published by: Chemical Abstracts Service (C A S) (Subsidiary of: American Chemical Society), 2540 Olentangy River Rd., Columbus, OH 43210-0012. TEL 614-447-3600, FAX 614-447-3713, help@cas.com, http://www.cas.org, http://caselects.cas.org. **Subscr. to:** PO Box 3012, Columbus, OH 43210. TEL 800-753-4227, FAX 614-447-3751.

540 USA ISSN 0160-919X
CODEN: CSTADA
C A SELECTS. TRACE ELEMENT ANALYSIS. Text in English. s-w. USD 315 to non-members; USD 95 to members (effective 2005). **Document type:** *Abstract/Index.*
Description: Covers detection and determination of trace elements found in solid, liquid, or gaseous environments such as food, rocks, soils, petroleum products, and sewage.
Published by: Chemical Abstracts Service (C A S) (Subsidiary of: American Chemical Society), 2540 Olentangy River Rd., Columbus, OH 43210-0012. TEL 614-447-3600, FAX 614-447-3713, help@cas.com, http://www.cas.org, http://caselects.cas.org. **Subscr. to:** PO Box 3012, Columbus, OH 43210. TEL 800-753-4227, FAX 614-447-3751.

C A SELECTS. X-RAY ANALYSIS & SPECTROSCOPY. see *PHYSICS—Abstracting, Bibliographies, Statistics*

016.547 USA ISSN 1555-6077
TA455.P58
C S A ADVANCED POLYMERS ABSTRACTS. Text in English. 1996. m. USD 1,025 (effective 2006). **Document type:** *Abstract/Index.*
Media: Online - full content.
Published by: C S A Journal Division (Subsidiary of: Cambridge Information Group), 7200 Wisconsin Ave, Ste 715, Bethesda, MD 20814. TEL 301-961-6798, 800-843-7751, FAX 301-961-6799, journals@csa.com, http://www.csa.com. Ed. Mark Furneaux.

016.54 GBR ISSN 1474-9173
QD501 CODEN: CCRACN
CATALYSTS & CATALYSED REACTIONS. Text in English. 2002. m. GBP 625, USD 1,143 combined subscription print & online eds. (effective 2006). **Document type:** *Journal, Abstract/Index.* **Description:** Current awareness publication, containing graphical abstracts of new developments in catalysis selected from over 100 primary journals.
Related titles: Online - full text ed.: ISSN 1474-9181. GBP 562, USD 1,029 (effective 2006) (from EBSCO Publishing).
—BLDSC (3092.284000), Linda Hall. **CCC.**
Published by: Royal Society of Chemistry, Thomas Graham House, Science Park, Milton Rd, Cambridge, CB4 0WF, United Kingdom. TEL 44-1223-420066, FAX 44-1223-423623, sales@rsc.org, http://www.rsc.org. **Subscr. to:** Portland Press Ltd., R S C Distribution Services, Commerce Way, Whitehall Industrial Estate, Colchester CO2 8HP, United Kingdom. TEL 44-1206-226050, FAX 44-1206-226055, sales@rscdistribution.org.

CENTRAL PATENTS INDEX; chemical technology inventions. see *PATENTS, TRADEMARKS AND COPYRIGHTS—Abstracting, Bibliographies, Statistics*

540 USA ISSN 0009-2258
QD1 CODEN: CHABA8
CHEMICAL ABSTRACTS. Text in English. 1907. w. (in 2 vols.). USD 27,200 combined subscription print, microfilm & microfiche eds. (effective 2005); includes CA Index Guide. illus. Index. back issues avail.; reprints avail. **Document type:** *Abstract/Index.* **Description:** Provides summaries and indexes of disclosures in recently published scientific documents. Approximately 8,000 journals, technical reports, dissertations, conference proceedings, and new books, in any of 50 languages, are monitored yearly, as are patent specifications from 27 countries and two international organizations.
Related titles: CD-ROM ed.: USD 30,200 (effective 2005); Microfiche ed.: (from IDC); Microfilm ed.; Online - full text ed.
—BLDSC (3134.000000), CASDDS, CINDOC, CISTI, Linda Hall.
Published by: Chemical Abstracts Service (C A S) (Subsidiary of: American Chemical Society), 2540 Olentangy River Rd., Columbus, OH 43210-0012. TEL 614-447-3600, 800-848-6538, FAX 614-447-3713, help@cas.com, http://www.cas.org/PRINTED/printca.html. **Subscr. to:** PO Box 3012, Columbus, OH 43210. TEL 800-753-4227, FAX 614-447-3751.

540 016 USA ISSN 0090-8363
CODEN: CAAEA2
CHEMICAL ABSTRACTS - APPLIED CHEMISTRY AND CHEMICAL ENGINEERING SECTIONS. Text in English. 1963. s-w. USD 3,355; USD 3,040 to CA subscribers; USD 671 ACS members (effective 2005). charts; pat.; stat. index.
Document type: *Abstract/Index.*
Supersedes: Chemical Abstracts - Applied Chemistry Sections (0009-2266)
Related titles: Online - full text ed.
Published by: Chemical Abstracts Service (C A S) (Subsidiary of: American Chemical Society), 2540 Olentangy River Rd., Columbus, OH 43210-0012. TEL 614-447-3600, FAX 614-447-3713, help@cas.com, http://www.cas.org. Ed. David W Weisgerber. **Subscr. to:** PO Box 3012, Columbus, OH 43210. TEL 800-753-4227, FAX 614-447-3751. **Co-publisher:** American Chemical Society.

540 USA ISSN 0097-6474
CODEN: CACICQ
CHEMICAL ABSTRACTS. COLLECTIVE INDEX. Text in English. 1907. irreg. USD 54,900 15th Collective Index (effective 2005). **Document type:** *Abstract/Index.*
Formerly (until 1961): Decennial Index to Chemical Abstracts (0894-2048)
Related titles: CD-ROM ed.: Collective Index on CD. ISSN 1091-1456. USD 47,300 (effective 2003); Microfilm ed.
—CINDOC, CISTI.
Published by: Chemical Abstracts Service (C A S) (Subsidiary of: American Chemical Society), 2540 Olentangy River Rd., Columbus, OH 43210-0012. TEL 614-447-3600, FAX 614-447-3713, help@cas.com, http://www.cas.org. **Subscr. to:** PO Box 3012, Columbus, OH 43210. TEL 800-753-4227, FAX 614-447-3751.

540 USA ISSN 0093-5719
QD1
CHEMICAL ABSTRACTS. INDEX GUIDE. Text in English. 1968. irreg. USD 19,890; USD 27,200 includes Chemical Abstracts (effective 2005).
—CINDOC, Linda Hall.
Published by: Chemical Abstracts Service (C A S) (Subsidiary of: American Chemical Society), 2540 Olentangy River Rd., Columbus, OH 43210-0012. TEL 614-447-3600, FAX 614-447-3713, help@cas.com, http://www.cas.org. **Subscr. to:** PO Box 3012, Columbus, OH 43210. TEL 800-753-4227, FAX 614-447-3751.

547.7 016 USA ISSN 0009-2274
CODEN: CAMLAF
CHEMICAL ABSTRACTS - MACROMOLECULAR SECTIONS. Text in English. 1963. s-w. USD 3,355; USD 3,040 to CA subscribers; USD 671 ACS members (effective 2005). abstr.; charts; pat.; stat. index. **Document type:** *Abstract/Index.*
Related titles: Online - full text ed.
Indexed: WTA.
Published by: Chemical Abstracts Service (C A S) (Subsidiary of: American Chemical Society), 2540 Olentangy River Rd., Columbus, OH 43210-0012. TEL 614-447-3600, FAX 614-447-3713, help@cas.com, http://www.cas.org. Ed. David W Weisgerber. **Subscr. to:** PO Box 3012, Columbus, OH 43210. TEL 800-753-4227, FAX 614-447-3751.

547 016 USA ISSN 0009-2282
CODEN: CAOCAW
CHEMICAL ABSTRACTS - ORGANIC CHEMISTRY SECTIONS. Text in English. 1963. s-w. USD 3,355; USD 3,040 to CA subscribers; USD 671 ACS members (effective 2005). abstr.; charts; pat.; stat. index. **Document type:** *Abstract/Index.*
Related titles: Online - full text ed.
Published by: Chemical Abstracts Service (C A S) (Subsidiary of: American Chemical Society), 2540 Olentangy River Rd., Columbus, OH 43210-0012. TEL 614-447-3600, FAX 614-447-3713, help@cas.com, http://www.cas.org. Ed. David W Weisgerber. **Subscr. to:** PO Box 3012, Columbus, OH 43210. TEL 800-753-4227, FAX 614-447-3751.

543 016 547 USA ISSN 0278-1832
CODEN: CAISDJ
CHEMICAL ABSTRACTS - PHYSICAL, INORGANIC AND ANALYTICAL CHEMISTRY SECTIONS. Text in English. 1963. s-w. USD 3,355; USD 3,040 to CA subscribers; USD 671 ACS members (effective 2005). abstr.; charts; pat.; stat. index.
Document type: *Abstract/Index.*
Supersedes: Chemical Abstracts - Physical and Analytical Chemistry Sections (0009-2290)
Related titles: Online - full text ed.
Published by: Chemical Abstracts Service (C A S) (Subsidiary of: American Chemical Society), 2540 Olentangy River Rd., Columbus, OH 43210-0012. TEL 614-447-3600, FAX 614-447-3713, help@cas.com, http://www.cas.org. Ed. David W Weisgerber. **Subscr. to:** PO Box 3012, Columbus, OH 43210. TEL 800-753-4227, FAX 614-447-3751.

540 016 USA
QD1 CODEN: CHABA8
CHEMICAL ABSTRACTS - SECTION GROUPINGS. Text in English. 1907. w. USD 3,355 to non-members; USD 3,040 to CA subscibers; USD 671 ACS members (effective 2005).
Document type: *Abstract/Index.*
Related titles: Online - full text ed.
Published by: Chemical Abstracts Service (C A S) (Subsidiary of: American Chemical Society), 2540 Olentangy River Rd., Columbus, OH 43210-0012. TEL 614-447-3600, FAX 614-447-3713, help@cas.com, http://www.cas.org. Ed. David W Weisgerber. **Subscr. to:** PO Box 3012, Columbus, OH 43210. TEL 800-753-4227, FAX 614-447-3751.

540 016 USA ISSN 0001-0634
Z5523 CODEN: CASSI6
CHEMICAL ABSTRACTS SERVICE SOURCE INDEX. Abbreviated title: C A S S I. Text in English. 1969. USD 1,700 (effective 2005). **Document type:** *Abstract/Index.*
Related titles: CD-ROM ed.: C A S Source Index Cumulative. USD 2,510 per vol. (effective 2005); Online - full text ed.; Supplement(s): ISSN 0738-6222. 1970. USD 295 (effective 2001).
—BLDSC (3138.700000), CASDDS, CISTI, GNLM, Linda Hall. **CCC.**
Published by: Chemical Abstracts Service (C A S) (Subsidiary of: American Chemical Society), 2540 Olentangy River Rd., Columbus, OH 43210-0012. TEL 614-447-3600, FAX 614-447-3713, help@cas.com, http://www.cas.org. Ed. David W Weisgerber. **Subscr. to:** PO Box 3012, Columbus, OH 43210. TEL 800-753-4227, FAX 614-447-3751.

016.543 USA
CHEMICAL BUSINESS NEWSBASE. Text in English. 1993. d.
Document type: *Abstract/Index.* **Description:** Product, market and company information for the chemical industry worldwide and its allied sectors. Also contains legislation and environmental issues.
Media: Online - full text. **Related titles:** CD-ROM ed.: Dialog on Disc Chemical Business News Base. USD 2,995 for 18 mos. (effective 2000) (from The Dialog Corporation).
Published by: Elsevier Engineering Information, Inc. (Subsidiary of: Elsevier Science & Technology), 360 Park Ave S, New York, NY 10010. TEL 800-221-1044, FAX 212-633-3680, eicustomersupport@elsevier.com, http://www.ei.org/cbnb.html.
Subscr. to: The Dialog Corp. Plc., OnDisc Europe, 2 Des Roches Sq, Witan Way, Witney, Oxon OX8 6BE, United Kingdom. TEL 44-1993-899300, FAX 44-1993-899333.

CHEMICAL HAZARDS IN INDUSTRY. see *OCCUPATIONAL HEALTH AND SAFETY—Abstracting, Bibliographies, Statistics*

CHEMICAL SAFETY NEWSBASE. see *OCCUPATIONAL HEALTH AND SAFETY—Abstracting, Bibliographies, Statistics*

016.54   DEU   ISSN 0931-7597
QD1   CODEN: CINFES
CHEMINFORM; selected abstracts in chemistry. Text in German. 1972. w. EUR 4,088 in Europe; CHF 6,988 in Switzerland & Liechtenstein; USD 5,308 elsewhere; EUR 4,497 combined subscription in Europe print & online eds.; CHF 7,687 combined subscription in Switzerland & Liechtenstein for print & online eds.; USD 5,839 combined subscription elsewhere print & online eds.; EUR 4,388 combined subscription in Europe print & annual CD; CHF 5,704 combined subscription in Switzerland & Liechtenstein for print & annual CD; USD 7,358 combined subscription elsewhere print & annual CD (effective 2006). adv. index. back issues avail.; reprint service avail. from ISI. **Document type:** *Abstract/Index.*
Formerly (until 1987): Chemischer Informationsdienst (0009-2975); Which was formed by the merger of (1970-1972): Chemischer Informationsdienst. Organische Chemie (0300-5151); (1970-1972): Chemischer Informationsdienst. Anorganische und Physikalische Chemie (0300-5135)
Related titles: CD-ROM ed.: ISSN 1431-5890; Microfilm ed.: (from VCI); Online - full text ed.: ISSN 1522-2667. EUR 4,088 in Europe; CHF 6,988 in Switzerland & Liechtenstein; USD 5,308 elsewhere (effective 2006) (from EBSCO Publishing, Wiley InterScience).
—CASDDS. **CCC.**
Published by: (Gesellschaft Deutscher Chemiker), Wiley - V C H Verlag GmbH & Co. KGaA (Subsidiary of: John Wiley & Sons, Inc.), Boschstr 12, Weinheim, 69469, Germany. TEL 49-6201-6060, FAX 49-6201-606328, cheminform@fiz-chemie.de, subservice@wiley-vch.de, info@wiley-vch.de, http://www3.interscience.wiley.com/cgi-bin/jhome/60500229, http://www.wiley-vch.de. Ed. Helga Lehmann-Seider. Adv. contact Marion Schulz TEL 49-6201-606565. B&W page EUR 990; 115 x 180. Circ: 1,000. **Subscr. in the Americas to:** John Wiley & Sons, Inc., 111 River St, Hoboken, NJ 07030-5774. TEL 201-748-6645, FAX 201-748-6088, subinfo@wiley.com; **Subscr. outside Germany, Austria & Switzerland to:** John Wiley & Sons Ltd., The Atrium, Southern Gate, Chichester, West Sussex PO19 8SQ, United Kingdom. TEL 44-1243-779777, FAX 44-1243-775878. **Co-sponsor:** Fachinformationszentrum Chemie und Bayer AG.

540   USA   ISSN 1057-6088
CHEMISTRY CITATION INDEX. Text in English. 1991. bi-m. USD 1,785 for CD-ROM (effective 2005). **Document type:** *Abstract/Index.* **Description:** Provides bibliographic data, cited references, related records and English-language author abstracts from international scholarly research journals and conference proceedings.
Related titles: CD-ROM ed.: (from Thomson I S I); Magnetic Tape ed.
Published by: Thomson I S I (Subsidiary of: Thomson Corporation), 3501 Market St., Philadelphia, PA 19104. TEL 215-386-0100, 800-336-4474, FAX 215-386-2911, sales@isinet.com, http://scientific.thomson.com/products/cci/, http://www.isinet.com.

540 016   USA   ISSN 1555-6417
QP455
CHEMORECEPTION ABSTRACTS (ONLINE EDITION). Text in English. m. USD 550 (effective 2006). adv. bk.rev. abstr. index on CD-ROM. back issues avail. **Document type:** *Abstract/Index.* **Description:** Covers research into taste, smell, internal chemoreception, chemotaxis, and practical applications.
Media: Online - full content.
Published by: (European Chemoreception Research Organization), C S A Journal Division (Subsidiary of: Cambridge Information Group), 7200 Wisconsin Ave, Ste 715, Bethesda, MD 20814. TEL 301-961-6798, 800-843-7751, FAX 301-961-6799, journals@csa.com, http://www.csa.com/factsheets/chemoreception-set-c.php. Ed. Janet L Padgett. Pub. Ted Caris.

547 011   USA   ISSN 1431-9268
QD1   CODEN: CHEMFW
CHEMTRACTS. Text in English. 1997. m. USD 144 to individuals; USD 645 to institutions (effective 2004). adv. **Document type:** *Journal, Abstract/Index.* **Description:** Provides updates on the newest trends and developments in chemistry by summarizing and commenting on current and past research.
Formed by the merger of (1988-1997): Chemtracts: Organic Chemistry (0895-4445); (1991-1997): Chemtracts: Biochemistry and Molecular Biology (1045-2680); (1990-1997): Chemtracts: Inorganic Chemistry (1051-7227); Which was formerly: Chemtracts: Analytical, Physical and Inorganic Chemistry (1048-7840); (1989-1990): Chemtracts: Analytical and Physical Chemistry (0899-7810)
Indexed: CIN, ChemAb, ChemTitl, ExcerpMed.
—BLDSC (3172.323000), CASDDS, IE, ingenta. **CCC.**
Published by: Data Trace Publishing Company, 110 West Rd, Ste 227, Baltimore, MD 21204. TEL 800-342-0454, info@datatrace.com, http://www.datatrace.com/chemistry/series_journal.htm.

016.544   GBR   ISSN 0268-6287
QD117.C5
CHROMATOGRAPHY ABSTRACTS. Text in English. 1958. m. GBP 1,725, USD 3,157 (effective 2006). adv. index. back issues avail. **Document type:** *Abstract/Index.* **Description:** Provides a rapid update on the latest literature in chromatography and separation science.
Former titles (until 1986): Gas and Liquid Chromatography Abstracts (0301-388X); (until 1973): Gas Chromatography Abstracts (0016-4887)
Related titles: Microform ed.: (from PQC); Online - full text ed. —Linda Hall. **CCC.**
Published by: Royal Society of Chemistry, Thomas Graham House, Science Park, Milton Rd, Cambridge, CB4 0WF, United Kingdom. TEL 44-1223-432360, FAX 44-1223-423623, sales@rsc.org, http://www.rsc.org/chromabs. Ed. Mike Corkill. **Subscr. to:** Portland Press Ltd., R S C Distribution Services, Commerce Way, Whitehall Industrial Estate, Colchester CO2 8HP, United Kingdom. TEL 44-1206-226050, FAX 44-1206-226055, sales@rscdistribution.org. **Co-sponsor:** Chromatographic Society.

547   JPN
CONGRESS OF HETEROCYCLIC CHEMISTRY. BOOK OF ABSTRACTS/FUKUSOKAN KAGAKU TORONKAI KOEN YOSHISHU. Text in English, Japanese. a. JPY 1,800 per issue (effective 2000). **Document type:** *Abstract/Index.*
Published by: Yuki Gosei Kagaku Kyokai/Society of Synthetic Organic Chemistry, Japan, Kagaku-Kaikan 5F, 1-5 Kanda-Surugadai, Chiyoda-ku, Tokyo, 101-0062, Japan. syn.org.chem@tokyo.email.ne.jp, http://wwwsoc.nii.ac.jp/ssocj. Ed. Tsuneo Imamoto.

016.54   DEU
CROSSFIRE. (Comprises 2 databases: Beilstein Database; Gmelin Database) Text in German. 1994. q. **Document type:** *Abstract/Index.* **Description:** Indexes and abstracts articles from more than 180 peer-reviewed chemical journals.
Formerly: CrossFire Abstracts
Media: Online - full text (from The Dialog Corporation).
Published by: M D L Information Systems GmbH (Subsidiary of: Elsevier Science & Technology), Theodor-Heuss-Allee 108, Frankfurt Am Main, 60486, Germany. TEL 49-69-5050-4242, FAX 49-69-5050-4245, info@beilstein.com, info-de@mdl.com, http://www.beilstein.com, http://www.mdl.com.

540   NLD   ISSN 0885-1980
CURRENT ADVANCES IN CLINICAL CHEMISTRY. Text in English. 1974. 12/yr. EUR 1,510 in Europe to institutions; JPY 200,200 in Japan to institutions; USD 1,690 to institutions except Europe and Japan; EUR 141 in Europe to qualified personnel; JPY 19,300 in Japan to qualified personnel; USD 159 to qualified personnel except Europe and Japan (effective 2006). adv. bk.rev. **Document type:** *Abstract/Index.* **Description:** Provides a current awareness service for clinical chemists, research workers, teachers and students in the field of clinical chemistry. Lists titles of papers published throughout the world classified into 29 main areas and provides a comprehensive listing of review articles.
Formerly: Current Clinical Chemistry (0305-0165)
Related titles: Diskette ed.; Microform ed.: (from PQC); Online - full text ed.
—BLDSC (3494.062500), GNLM. **CCC.**
Published by: (Association of Clinical Biochemists GBR), Elsevier BV (Subsidiary of: Elsevier Science & Technology), Radarweg 29, Amsterdam, 1043 NX, Netherlands. TEL 31-20-4853911, FAX 31-20-4852457, nlinfo-f@elsevier.nl, http://www.elsevier.com/locate/caclinchem, http://www.elsevier.nl. Circ: 2,400.

016 540   KOR
CURRENT BIBLIOGRAPHIES ON SCIENCE AND TECHNOLOGY: CHEMISTRY AND CHEMICAL INDUSTRY. Text in Korean. 1962. m. USD 114. reprint service avail. from PQC. **Document type:** *Bibliography.*
Formerly: Current Index to Journals in Science and Technology: Chemistry and Chemical Industry; Supersedes in part: Current Bibliography on Sciences and Technology
Published by: Korea Institute for Economics and Technology, 206-9 Cheongryangri-Dong, Dongdaimun-Ku, P.O. Box 205, Seoul, Korea, S. Circ: 450.

540 660 016   JPN   ISSN 0011-3271
                                  CODEN: KGBHDD
CURRENT BIBLIOGRAPHY ON SCIENCE AND TECHNOLOGY: CHEMISTRY AND CHEMICAL ENGINEERING (FOREIGN)/KAGAKU GIJUTSU BUNKEN SOKUHO. KAGAKU, KAGAKU KOGYO-HEN (GAIKOKU-HEN). Text in Japanese. 1958. 3/m. USD 2,580. index. **Document type:** *Bibliography.*
Related titles: CD-ROM ed.; Online - full text ed.: (from JICST).
Published by: Japan Science and Technology Corporation, Information Center for Science and Technology/Kagaku Gijutsu Shinko Jigyodan, 5-3 Yonban-cho, Chiyoda-ku, Tokyo, 102-0081, Japan. TEL 81-3-3214-8413, FAX 81-3-5214-8410. Circ: 900.

540 660 016   JPN   ISSN 0385-6003
CURRENT BIBLIOGRAPHY ON SCIENCE AND TECHNOLOGY: CHEMISTRY AND CHEMICAL ENGINEERING (JAPANESE)/KAGAKU GIJUTSU BUNKEN SOKUHO KAGAKU. KAGAKU KOGYO-HEN (KOKUNAI-HEN). Text in Japanese. 1958. m. USD 1,020. index. **Document type:** *Bibliography.*
Related titles: CD-ROM ed.; Online - full text ed.: (from JICST).
Published by: Japan Science and Technology Corporation, Information Center for Science and Technology/Kagaku Gijutsu Shinko Jigyodan, 5-3 Yonban-cho, Chiyoda-ku, Tokyo, 102-0081, Japan. TEL 81-3-5214-8413, FAX 81-3-5214-8410. Circ: 1,200.

540 016   USA   ISSN 0163-6278
QD262   CODEN: CCHRDP
CURRENT CHEMICAL REACTIONS. Short title: C C R. Text in English. 1979. m. USD 1,325. **Document type:** *Academic/Scholarly.* **Description:** Indexes new or modified reactions or syntheses reported on in chemistry and pharmaceutical journals.
—BLDSC (3496.005000), CASDDS.
Published by: Thomson I S I (Subsidiary of: Thomson Corporation), 3501 Market St., Philadelphia, PA 19104. TEL 215-386-0100, FAX 215-386-2911.

011   USA
CURRENT CHEMICAL REACTIONS DATABASE. Short title: C C R Database. Text in English. 1986. a. USD 35,000; primary site fee for initial CPU-CPU cluster; additional site fee USD12,500. **Document type:** *Bibliography.* **Description:** Indexes new or modified reactions or syntheses reported in chemistry and pharmaceutical journals.
Formerly: Current Chemical Reactions Inhouse Database for R E A C C S
Media: Online - full content.
Published by: Thomson I S I (Subsidiary of: Thomson Corporation), 3501 Market St., Philadelphia, PA 19104. TEL 215-386-0100, FAX 215-386-2911.

530 540 016   USA   ISSN 0163-2574
Z7143   CODEN: CPCSDQ
CURRENT CONTENTS: PHYSICAL, CHEMICAL & EARTH SCIENCES. Short title: C C: P C & E S. Text in English. 1961. w. USD 730. illus. Index. reprints avail. **Document type:** *Abstract/Index.* **Description:** Tables of contents of important publications covering physical, chemical and earth sciences.
Formerly: Current Contents, Physical and Chemical Sciences (0011-3417); Which was formed by the merger of: Current Contents, Physical Sciences; Current Contents, Chemical Sciences
Related titles: CD-ROM ed.: (from Thomson I S I); Diskette ed.; Magnetic Tape ed.; Online - full text ed.
Indexed: AESIS, AnalAb.
—BLDSC (3496.206300), CASDDS, KNAW.
Published by: Thomson I S I (Subsidiary of: Thomson Corporation), 3501 Market St., Philadelphia, PA 19104. TEL 215-386-0100, FAX 215-386-2911, http://www.isinet.com.

016.66   IND   ISSN 0300-4376
CURRENT TITLES IN ELECTROCHEMISTRY. Text in English. 1969. m. USD 135 to institutions (effective 2006). adv. index. **Document type:** *Abstract/Index.* **Description:** Contains a bibliographic listing of classified titles in electrochemistry.
Incorporates: Electrochemical News
Published by: Scientific Publishers, 5-A New Pali Rd., Near Hotel Taj Hari Mahal, PO Box 91, Jodhpur, Rajasthan 342 003, India. TEL 91-291-2433323, FAX 91-291-2512580, info@scientificpub.com, http://www.scientificpub.com/bookdetails.php?booktransid=303&bookid=299. Ed. M Jayachandran. Circ: 1,000.

540 660   DEU   ISSN 0930-276X
F I Z CHEMIE AKTUELL. (Fachinformationszentrum) Text and summaries in English, German. 1986. s-a. free. 5 p./no. 3 cols./p.; back issues avail. **Document type:** *Newsletter, Academic/Scholarly.*
Published by: Fachinformationszentrum Chemie, Franklinstr 11, Berlin, 10587, Germany. TEL 49-30-39977140, FAX 49-30-39977132, info@fiz-chemie.de, http://www.fiz-chemie.de. Ed. Anthony R Flambard. Circ: 2,200 (controlled). **Dist. by:** Postfach 120337, Berlin 10593, Germany.

540   DEU   ISSN 0949-9342
FACHBUCHVERZEICHNIS MATHEMATIK - PHYSIK - CHEMIE. Text in German. 1900. a. **Document type:** *Trade.*
Formed by the merger of: Fachbuchverzeichnis Chemie (0343-6438); Fachbuchverzeichnis Mathematik - Physik (0343-639X)
Published by: Rossipaul Kommunikation GmbH, Menzinger Str 37, Munich, 80638, Germany. TEL 49-89-179106-0, FAX 49-89-17910622. Ed. Angela Sendlinger. Circ: 30,000.

C

016.541   GBR   ISSN 1351-4180
FOCUS ON CATALYSTS. Text in English. 1994. 12/yr. EUR 841 in Europe to institutions; JPY 111,800 in Japan to institutions; USD 942 to institutions except Europe and Japan (effective 2006). bk.rev. **Document type:** *Newsletter, Academic/Scholarly.* **Description:** Reports on business and technical developments across the catalysis field - heterogeneous, homogeneous and enzymatic - across all applications. Monitors all important developments for catalysts and chemical processing. Each issue starts with a brief editorial and then provides a series of concise summaries on business, market and technical developments from a global perspective.
Related titles: Online - full text ed.: (from EBSCO Publishing, Gale Group, IngentaConnect, ScienceDirect, Swets Information Services).
Indexed: CBNB.
—BLDSC (3964.203885), IE, ingenta. **CCC.**
Published by: Elsevier Advanced Technology (Subsidiary of: Elsevier Science & Technology), The Boulevard, Langford Ln, Kidlington, Oxon OX5 2BG, United Kingdom. TEL 44-1865-843750, FAX 44-1865-843971, eatsales@elsevier.co.uk, http://www.elsevier.com/locate/focat. Ed. A. E. Comyns. **Subscr. to:** Elsevier BV, PO Box 211, Amsterdam 1000 AE, Netherlands. TEL 31-20-485-3757, FAX 31-20-485-3432, nlinfo-f@elsevier.nl, http://www.elsevier.nl.

016.66   GBR   ISSN 1351-4210
FOCUS ON SURFACTANTS. Text in English. 1994. 12/yr. EUR 841 in Europe to institutions; JPY 111,800 in Japan to institutions; USD 942 elsewhere to institutions (effective 2006). bk.rev. **Document type:** *Newsletter, Academic/Scholarly.* **Description:** Covers all developments in the manufacture of surfactants. Features market news, including statistical, e-commerce and administrative reports, company and business news, new product information and news, and environmental issues.
Related titles: Online - full text ed.: (from EBSCO Publishing, Gale Group, IngentaConnect, ScienceDirect, Swets Information Services).
Indexed: CBNB, TTI.
—BLDSC (3964.235750), IE, ingenta. **CCC.**
Published by: Elsevier Advanced Technology (Subsidiary of: Elsevier Science & Technology), The Boulevard, Langford Ln, Kidlington, Oxon OX5 2BG, United Kingdom. TEL 44-1865-843750, FAX 44-1865-843971, eatsales@elsevier.co.uk, http://www.elsevier.com/locate/fos, http://www.elsevier.nl. Ed. C Edser. **Subscr. to:** Elsevier BV, PO Box 211, Amsterdam 1000 AE, Netherlands. TEL 31-20-485-3757, FAX 31-20-485-3432, nlinfo-f@elsevier.nl.

540   FRA
FRANCE. SERVICE D'ETUDE DES STRATEGIES ET DES STATISTIQUES INDUSTRIELLES. RESULTATS MENSUELS DES ENQUETES DE BRANCHE. INDUSTRIE CHIMIQUE DE BASE. Text in French. m. stat. **Document type:** *Government.* **Description:** Follows developments in the chemical industry through the performance of selected indicators.
Published by: Service d'Etude des Strategies et des Statistiques Industrielles (SESSI), 85 bd. du Montparnasse, Paris, Cedex 6 75270, France. TEL 45-56-42-34, FAX 45-56-40-71.

540   FRA
FRANCE. SERVICE D'ETUDE DES STRATEGIES ET DES STATISTIQUES INDUSTRIELLES. RESULTATS MENSUELS DES ENQUETES DE BRANCHE. PARACHIMIE. Text in French. m. stat. **Document type:** *Government.* **Description:** Follows industry developments through the performance of selected indicators.
Published by: Service d'Etude des Strategies et des Statistiques Industrielles (SESSI), 85 bd. du Montparnasse, Paris, Cedex 6 75270, France. TEL 45-56-42-34, FAX 45-56-40-71.

540   FRA
FRANCE. SERVICE D'ETUDE DES STRATEGIES ET DES STATISTIQUES INDUSTRIELLES. RESULTATS TRIMESTRIELS DES ENQUETES DE BRANCHE. INDUSTRIE CHIMIQUE DE BASE. Text in French. q. **Document type:** *Government.* **Description:** Provides detailed industry-wide performance statistics for comparative evaluations.
Published by: Service d'Etude des Strategies et des Statistiques Industrielles (SESSI), 85 bd. du Montparnasse, Paris, Cedex 6 75270, France. TEL 45-56-42-34, FAX 45-56-40-71.

540   FRA
FRANCE. SERVICE D'ETUDE DES STRATEGIES ET DES STATISTIQUES INDUSTRIELLES. RESULTATS TRIMESTRIELS DES ENQUETES DE BRANCHE. PARACHIMIE. Text in French. q. **Document type:** *Government.* **Description:** Provides detailed industry-wide performance statistics for comparative evaluations.
Published by: Service d'Etude des Strategies et des Statistiques Industrielles (SESSI), 85 bd. du Montparnasse, Paris, Cedex 6 75270, France. TEL 45-56-42-34, FAX 45-56-40-71.

FURO INJEKUSHON BUNSEKI KOENKAI KOEN YOSHISHU/ABSTRACTS OF MEETING ON FLOW INJECTION ANALYSIS. see *CHEMISTRY—Analytical Chemistry*

608.7   GBR   ISSN 0533-7526
GERMAN PATENTS GAZETTE. SECTION 1: CHEMICAL. Text in English. 1968. w. USD 1,800. illus. **Document type:** *Abstract/Index.*
Published by: Derwent Information (Subsidiary of: Thomson Corporation), 14 Great Queen St., London, WC2B 5DF, United Kingdom. TEL 44-20-73442800, FAX 44-20-73442900, custserv@derwent.co.uk, http://www.derwent.com. **U.S.** **subscr. to:** Derwent Information, 1725 Duke St, Ste 250, Alexandria, VA 22314. TEL 800-337-9368, custserv@derwentus.com.

HIGH PERFORMANCE LIQUID CHROMATOGRAPHY. see *PHARMACY AND PHARMACOLOGY—Abstracting, Bibliographies, Statistics*

540 016   USA   ISSN 0891-6055
INDEX CHEMICUS. Short title: I C. Text in English. 1960. w. q. and a. index. **Document type:** *Abstract/Index.* **Description:** Abstract reports on the synthesis, isolation and identification of new organic compounds as reported in journals worldwide.
Formerly (until 1987): Current Abstracts of Chemistry and Index Chemicus (0161-455X); Which was formed by the 1977 merger of: Index Chemicus (0160-1482); Current Abstracts of Chemistry (0160-1490); Which both superseded in part: Current Abstracts of Chemistry and Index Chemicus (0011-3158)
Related titles: CD-ROM ed.: (from Thomson I S I).
Published by: Thomson I S I (Subsidiary of: Thomson Corporation), 3501 Market St., Philadelphia, PA 19104. TEL 215-386-0100, 800-336-4474, FAX 215-386-2911, sales@isinet.com, http://www.isinet.com.

344.0424   USA
INDEX TO CHEMICAL REGULATIONS. Text in English. 1980. m. looseleaf. USD 861 (effective 2001). back issues avail. **Document type:** *Abstract/Index.* **Description:** Contains more than 80,000 citations by chemical name to the Code of Federal Regulations and the Federal Register.
Formerly: Index to Government Regulation (0195-9492)
Related titles: ◆ Series of: Chemical Regulation Reporter. ISSN 0148-7973; ◆ Supplement to: Chemical Regulation Reporter. ISSN 0148-7973.
—**CCC.**
Published by: The Bureau of National Affairs, Inc., 1231 25th St., NW, Washington, DC 20037. TEL 202-452-4200, 800-372-1033, 800-452-7773, FAX 202-822-8092, customercare@bna.com, bnaplus@bna.com, http://www.bna.com/. **Pub.** Greg C McCaffery.

016.540   JPN   ISSN 0915-0447
JAPANESE SYMPOSIUM ON PLASMA CHEMISTRY. ABSTRACT PAPERS/PURAZUMA KAGAKU GODO SHINPOJUMU ABUSUTORAK UTOSHU. Text in English, Japanese. 1988. a. **Document type:** *Abstract/Index.*
Published by: Organizing Committee of Japanese Symposium on Plasma Chemistry/Purazuma Kagaku Godo Shinpojumu Soshiki Iinkai, Kyoto Daigaku Kogakubu Denshi Kogakka, Yoshidahon-Machi, Sakyo-ku, Kyoto-shi, 606-8317, Japan.

548   JPN
JINKO KESSHO KOGAKKAI TOKUBETSU KOENKAI KOEN YOSHISHU/ASSOCIATION OF SYNTHETIC CRYSTAL SCIENCE AND TECHNOLOGY. ABSTRACTS OF THE SPECIAL MEETING. Text in Japanese. 1983. a. **Document type:** *Abstract/Index.*
Published by: Jinko Kessho Kogakkai/Association of Synthetic Crystal Science and Technology, Nagoya Daigaku Kogakubu Oyo Kagakka Dai 1 Koza, Furocho, Chikusa-ku, Nagoya-shi, Aichi-ken 462, Japan.

540   JPN
KAGAKU HANNO TORONKAI KOEN YOSHISHU/ABSTRACTS OF THE MEETING ON CHEMICAL REACTION. Text in Japanese. 1984. a. **Document type:** *Abstract/Index.*
Published by: Chemical Society of Japan/Nippon Kagakukai, 1-5, Kanda-Surugadai 1-Chome, Chiyoda-ku, Tokyo, 101-0062, Japan.

016.54 016   JPN   ISSN 0386-2143   CODEN: KASHDM
KAGAKU SHOHO. Text mainly in English. 1973. fortn. JPY 42,000 (effective 2001). adv. bk.rev. **Document type:** *Abstract/Index.*
Indexed: ABIPC.
Published by: Japan Association for International Chemical Information/Kagaku Joho Kyokai, 6-25-4 Honkomagome, Bunkyo-ku, Tokyo, 113-0021, Japan. TEL 81-3-5978-3631, FAX 81-3-5978-3600, http://www.jaici.or.jp. Ed. Ikuko Tanaka. Circ: 50. **Dist. overseas by:** Japan Publications Trading Co., Ltd., Book Export II Dept, PO Box 5030, Tokyo International, Tokyo 101-3191, Japan.

541   JPN
KOKAGAKU TORONKAI KOEN YOSHISHU/ABSTRACTS OF SYMPOSIUM ON PHOTOCHEMISTRY. Text in Japanese. 1953. a.
Published by: Chemical Society of Japan/Nippon Kagakukai, 1-5, Kanda-Surugadai 1-Chome, Chiyoda-ku, Tokyo, 101-0062, Japan.

540   JPN
KOTAI NO HANNOSEI TORONKAI KOEN YOKOSHU/ ABSTRACTS OF THE MEETING ON SOLID REACTIVITY. Text in Japanese; Summaries in English. 1990. a. **Document type:** *Abstract/Index.*
Published by: Chemical Society of Japan/Nippon Kagakukai, 1-5, Kanda-Surugadai 1-Chome, Chiyoda-ku, Tokyo, 101-0062, Japan.

540   JPN
KYUCHAKU SHINPOJUMU ABUSUTORAKUTOSHU∗ /SYMPOSIUM ON ADSORPTION. ABSTRACTS. Text in Japanese. a.
Published by: Nihon Kyuchaku Gakkai/Japan Society on Adsorption, Department of Molecular and Material Sciences, Graduate School of Engineering Sciences, Kyushu University, Kasuga-shi, Fukuoka 816-8580, Japan. TEL 81-92-5837526, FAX 81-92-5730342, jsad@mm.kyushu-u.ac.jp, http://www.chem.kumamoto-u.ac.jp/~jsad/index_j.html.

016.54   GBR   ISSN 0025-4738
QC451   CODEN: MSPBBX
MASS SPECTROMETRY BULLETIN. Text in English. 1966. m. GBP 2,095, USD 3,834 (effective 2006). adv. bk.rev. bibl. index, cum.index. **Document type:** *Abstract/Index.*
Description: Contains titles and bibliographic details of recently published documents dealing with mass spectrometry.
Related titles: Online - full text ed.: price varies.
—Linda Hall. **CCC.**
Published by: Royal Society of Chemistry, Thomas Graham House, Science Park, Milton Rd, Cambridge, CB4 0WF, United Kingdom. TEL 44-1223-432360, FAX 44-1223-423623, sales@rsc.org, http://www.rsc.org/publishing/currentawareness/msb/about.asp. Circ: 500. **Dist. by:** Portland Press Ltd., R S C Distribution Services, Commerce Way, Whitehall Industrial Estate, Colchester CO2 8HP, United Kingdom. TEL 44-1206-226050, FAX 44-1206-226055, sales@rscdistribution.org.

016.547   GBR   ISSN 0265-4245   CODEN: MOSYDN
METHODS IN ORGANIC SYNTHESIS. Text in English. m. GBP 625, USD 1,143 combined subscription print & online eds. (effective 2006). **Document type:** *Abstract/Index.*
Description: Aimed at synthetic organic chemists. Each issue contains about 200 items, including titles, bibliographic details and schematic reaction diagrams. Text is included where necessary to clarify reaction schemes.
Related titles: Online - full text ed.: ISSN 1478-1565. GBP 562, USD 1,029 (effective 2006) (from EBSCO Publishing).
—BLDSC (5748.203300), Linda Hall. **CCC.**
Published by: Royal Society of Chemistry, Thomas Graham House, Science Park, Milton Rd, Cambridge, CB4 0WF, United Kingdom. TEL 44-1223-432360, FAX 44-1223-423623, sales@rsc.org, advertising@rsc.org, http://www.rsc.org/mos. **Dist. by:** Portland Press Ltd., R S C Distribution Services, Commerce Way, Whitehall Industrial Estate, Colchester CO2 8HP, United Kingdom. TEL 44-1206-226050, FAX 44-1206-226055, sales@rscdistribution.org.

540   USA   ISSN 1089-6279   CODEN: NCINF5
NATIONAL CHEMICAL INVENTORIES. Text in English. USD 2,500; USD 1,625 renewals (effective 2005).
Media: CD-ROM.
Published by: Chemical Abstracts Service (C A S) (Subsidiary of: American Chemical Society), 2540 Olentangy River Rd., Columbus, OH 43210-0012. TEL 614-447-3600, FAX 614-447-3713, help@cas.com, http://www.cas.org.

016.547   GBR   ISSN 0950-1711   CODEN: NPUPEP
NATURAL PRODUCT UPDATES. Text in English. m. GBP 625 combined subscription print & online eds. (effective 2005); USD 1,143 combined subscription print & online eds. (effective 2006). **Document type:** *Abstract/Index.*
Description: Includes isolation studies (e.g., new compounds and known compounds from new sources), structure determinations, new properties, total and biosyntheses. Contains six indexes, author plus five subject indexes (source, taxonomic names, biological activity, trivial names, and compound class).
Related titles: Online - full text ed.: ISSN 1478-1557. GBP 562, USD 1,029 (effective 2006) (from EBSCO Publishing).
—Linda Hall. **CCC.**
Published by: Royal Society of Chemistry, Thomas Graham House, Science Park, Milton Rd, Cambridge, CB4 0WF, United Kingdom. TEL 44-1223-432360, FAX 44-1223-423623, sales@rsc.org, advertising@rsc.org, http://www.rsc.org/publishing/currentawareness/npu/index.asp. **Subscr. to:** Portland Press Ltd., R S C Distribution Services, Commerce Way, Whitehall Industrial Estate, Colchester CO2 8HP, United Kingdom. TEL 44-1206-226050, FAX 44-1206-226055, sales@rscdistribution.org.

NETHERLANDS PATENTS REPORT. see *PATENTS, TRADEMARKS AND COPYRIGHTS—Abstracting, Bibliographies, Statistics*

540 JPN
NIHON BUNSEKI KAGAKKAI KOEN YOSHISHU/JAPAN SOCIETY FOR ANALYTICAL CHEMISTRY. ABSTRACTS OF THE ANNUAL MEETING. Text in Japanese. a. **Document type:** *Abstract/Index.*
—BLDSC (2930.654000).
Published by: Nihon Bunseki Kagakkai/Japan Society for Analytical Chemistry, 1-26-2 Nishigotanda, Shinagawa, Tokyo, 141-0031, Japan. TEL 81-3-34903351, FAX 81-3-34903572, analytsci@jsac.or.jp, http://wwwsoc.nii.ac.jp/jsac/.

548 JPN
NIHON KESSHO GAKKAI NENKAI KOEN YOSHISHU∗ /CRYSTALLOGRAPHIC SOCIETY OF JAPAN. ABSTRACTS OF ANNUAL MEETING. Text in English, Japanese. a. **Document type:** *Abstract/Index.*
Published by: Nihon Kessho Gakkai/Crystallographic Society of Japan, Nissei Otuka 3-chome Bldg, Otuka 3-11-6, Bunkyo-ku, Tokyo, 112-0012, Japan. TEL 81-3-59407640, FAX 81-3-59407980, cr-info@rlz.co.jp, http://wwwsoc.nii.ac.jp/crsj/.

540 JPN
NIHON KYUCHAKU GAKKAI KENKYU HAPPYOKAI KOEN YOSHISHU∗ /JAPAN SOCIETY ON ADSORPTION. ABSTRACTS OF THE MEETING. Text in English, Japanese. 1987. a. **Document type:** *Abstract/Index.*
Published by: Nihon Kyuchaku Gakkai/Japan Society on Adsorption, Department of Molecular and Material Sciences, Graduate School of Engineering Sciences, Kyushu University, Kasuga-shi, Fukuoka 816-8580, Japan. jsad@mm.kyushu-u.ac.jp.

540 JPN
NIHON MAKU GAKKAI NENKAI KOEN YOSHISHU/MEMBRANE SOCIETY OF JAPAN. ABSTRACTS OF ANNUAL MEETING. Text in English, Japanese. a. **Document type:** *Abstract/Index.*
Published by: Nihon Maku Gakkai/Membrane Society of Japan, Hongo 5-26-5-702, Bunkyo-ku, Tokyo, 113-0033, Japan. membrane@muu.biglobe.ne.jp, http://wwwsoc.nacsis.ac.jp/membrane/index.html.

541 USA ISSN 0893-6684
POLYMER BLENDS, ALLOYS AND INTERPENETRATING POLYMER NETWORKS ABSTRACTS. Text in English. 1987. m. GBP 493 to institutions in Europe, Middle East, Africa & Australasia; USD 690 elsewhere to institutions; GBP 42 newsstand/cover to institutions in Europe, Middle East, Africa & Australasia; USD 59 newsstand/cover elsewhere to institutions (effective 2003). back issues avail.; reprints avail. **Document type:** *Abstract/Index.* **Description:** Publishes extended abstracts on the research and development of polymer blends and alloys.
Related titles: Online - full content ed.; Online - full text ed.: (from Swets Information Services).
—CCC.
Published by: Sage Publications, Inc., 2455 Teller Rd, Thousand Oaks, CA 91320. TEL 805-499-0721, FAX 805-499-0871, info@sagepub.com, http://www.sagepub.com. Circ: 90 (paid).

POLYMER CONTENTS. see *ENGINEERING—Abstracting, Bibliographies, Statistics*

RARE EARTH BULLETIN. see *METALLURGY—Abstracting, Bibliographies, Statistics*

016.5 540 USA
REACTION CITATION INDEX. Text in English. 1996. m. **Document type:** *Abstract/Index.* **Description:** Provides bibliographic information on new or newly modified synthetic methods with fully searchable cited references.
Related titles: Online - full text ed.
Published by: Thomson I S I (Subsidiary of: Thomson Corporation), 3501 Market St., Philadelphia, PA 19104. TEL 215-386-0100, FAX 215-386-2911, sales@isinet.com, http://www.isinet.com.

016.543 RUS ISSN 0203-6045
REFERATIVNYI ZHURNAL. ANALITICHESKAYA KHIMIYA. OBORUDOVANIE LABORATORII. Text in Russian. 1953. s-m. (24/yr.). USD 559 foreign (effective 2006). **Document type:** *Journal, Abstract/Index.*
Related titles: CD-ROM ed.; Online - full text ed.
Published by: Vserossiiskii Institut Nauchnoi i Tekhnicheskoi Informatsii (VINITI), Ul Usievicha 20, Moscow, 125190, Russian Federation. TEL 7-095-1526441, FAX 7-095-9430060, dir@viniti.ru, http://www.viniti.ru. **Dist. by:** Informnauka Ltd., Ul Usievicha 20, Moscow 125190, Russian Federation. alfimov@viniti.ru.

016.572 RUS
REFERATIVNYI ZHURNAL. BIOORGANICHESKAYA KHIMIYA. MAKROMOLEKULY. Text in Russian. 1982. m. USD 556 foreign (effective 2006). **Document type:** *Journal, Abstract/Index.*
Related titles: CD-ROM ed.; Online - full text ed.
Published by: Vserossiiskii Institut Nauchnoi i Tekhnicheskoi Informatsii (VINITI), Ul Usievicha 20, Moscow, 125190, Russian Federation. TEL 7-095-1526441, FAX 7-095-9430060, dir@viniti.ru, http://www.viniti.ru. **Dist. by:** Informnauka Ltd., Ul Usievicha 20, Moscow 125190, Russian Federation. alfimov@viniti.ru.

016.5413 RUS ISSN 0208-1636
REFERATIVNYI ZHURNAL. FIZICHESKAYA KHIMIYA: KHIMICHESKAYA TERMODINAMIKA, FIZIKOKHIMICHESKII ANALIZ, RASTVORY, ELEKTROKHIMIYA. Text in Russian. 1953. m. USD 511 foreign (effective 2006). **Document type:** *Journal, Abstract/Index.*
Related titles: CD-ROM ed.; Online - full text ed.
Indexed: RefZh.
—East View.
Published by: Vserossiiskii Institut Nauchnoi i Tekhnicheskoi Informatsii (VINITI), Ul Usievicha 20, Moscow, 125190, Russian Federation. TEL 7-095-1526441, FAX 7-095-9430060, dir@viniti.ru, http://www.viniti.ru. **Dist. by:** Informnauka Ltd., Ul Usievicha 20, Moscow 125190, Russian Federation. alfimov@viniti.ru.

016.5413 RUS ISSN 0208-1725
REFERATIVNYI ZHURNAL. FIZICHESKAYA KHIMIYA: KINETIKA, KATALIZ, FOTOKHIMIYA, RADYATSIONNAYA KHIMIYA, PLAZMOKHIMIYA. Text in Russian. 1953. 24/yr. USD 756 foreign (effective 2006). **Document type:** *Journal, Abstract/Index.*
Related titles: CD-ROM ed.; Online - full text ed.
Published by: Vserossiiskii Institut Nauchnoi i Tekhnicheskoi Informatsii (VINITI), Ul Usievicha 20, Moscow, 125190, Russian Federation. TEL 7-095-1526441, FAX 7-095-9430060, dir@viniti.ru, http://www.viniti.ru. **Dist. by:** Informnauka Ltd., Ul Usievicha 20, Moscow 125190, Russian Federation. alfimov@viniti.ru.

016.5413 RUS ISSN 0208-1717
REFERATIVNYI ZHURNAL. FIZICHESKAYA KHIMIYA: KRISTALLOKHIMIYA, KHIMIYA TVERDOGO TELA, GAZY, ZHIDKOSTI, AMORFNYE TELA, POVERKHNOSTNYE YAVLENIYA, KHIMIYA KOLLOIDOV. Text in Russian. 1953. 24/yr. USD 1,064 foreign (effective 2006). **Document type:** *Journal, Abstract/Index.*
Related titles: CD-ROM ed.; Online - full text ed.
Published by: Vserossiiskii Institut Nauchnoi i Tekhnicheskoi Informatsii (VINITI), Ul Usievicha 20, Moscow, 125190, Russian Federation. TEL 7-095-1526441, FAX 7-095-9430060, dir@viniti.ru, http://www.viniti.ru. **Dist. by:** Informnauka Ltd., Ul Usievicha 20, Moscow 125190, Russian Federation. alfimov@viniti.ru.

016.54 RUS ISSN 0486-2325
QD1 CODEN: RZKHAR
REFERATIVNYI ZHURNAL. KHIMIYA. Text in Russian. 1953. 24/yr. USD 8,328 foreign (effective 2006). **Document type:** *Journal, Abstract/Index.*
Related titles: CD-ROM ed.; Online - full text ed.
Indexed: AnalAb, ChemAb.
—BLDSC (0151.000000), CASDDS, East View, Linda Hall. **CCC.**
Published by: Vserossiiskii Institut Nauchnoi i Tekhnicheskoi Informatsii (VINITI), Ul Usievicha 20, Moscow, 125190, Russian Federation. TEL 7-095-1526441, FAX 7-095-9430060, dir@viniti.ru, http://www.viniti.ru. Ed. Vladimir Bondar. **Dist. by:** Informnauka Ltd., Ul Usievicha 20, Moscow 125190, Russian Federation. alfimov@viniti.ru.

016.54 016.553 RUS ISSN 0203-6169
REFERATIVNYI ZHURNAL. KHIMIYA I PERERABOTKA GORYUCHIKH ISKOPAEMYKH I PRIRODNYKH GAZOV. Text in Russian. 1953. m. USD 435 foreign (effective 2006). **Document type:** *Journal, Abstract/Index.*
Related titles: CD-ROM ed.; Online - full text ed.
Published by: Vserossiiskii Institut Nauchnoi i Tekhnicheskoi Informatsii (VINITI), Ul Usievicha 20, Moscow, 125190, Russian Federation. TEL 7-095-1526441, FAX 7-095-9430060, dir@viniti.ru, http://www.viniti.ru. **Dist. by:** Informnauka Ltd., Ul Usievicha 20, Moscow 125190, Russian Federation. alfimov@viniti.ru.

016.54 016.664 RUS ISSN 0235-3156
REFERATIVNYI ZHURNAL. KHIMIYA I TEKHNOLOGIYA PISHCHEVYKH PRODUKTOV. Text in Russian. 1953. m. USD 679 foreign (effective 2006). **Document type:** *Journal, Abstract/Index.*
Related titles: CD-ROM ed.; Online - full text ed.
—East View.
Published by: Vserossiiskii Institut Nauchnoi i Tekhnicheskoi Informatsii (VINITI), Ul Usievicha 20, Moscow, 125190, Russian Federation. TEL 7-095-1526441, FAX 7-095-9430060, dir@viniti.ru, http://www.viniti.ru. **Dist. by:** Informnauka Ltd., Ul Usievicha 20, Moscow 125190, Russian Federation. alfimov@viniti.ru.

016.54 RUS ISSN 0203-6150
REFERATIVNYI ZHURNAL. KHIMIYA VYSOKOMOLEKULIARNYKH SOEDINENII. Text in Russian. 1953. 24/yr. USD 837 foreign (effective 2006). **Document type:** *Journal, Abstract/Index.*
Related titles: CD-ROM ed.; Online - full text ed.
—East View.
Published by: Vserossiiskii Institut Nauchnoi i Tekhnicheskoi Informatsii (VINITI), Ul Usievicha 20, Moscow, 125190, Russian Federation. TEL 7-095-1526441, FAX 7-095-9430060, dir@viniti.ru, http://www.viniti.ru. **Dist. by:** Informnauka Ltd., Ul Usievicha 20, Moscow 125190, Russian Federation. alfimov@viniti.ru.

016.546 RUS ISSN 0234-9639
REFERATIVNYI ZHURNAL. NEORGANICHESKAYA KHIMIYA. KOMPLEKSNYE SOEDINENIYA. RADIOKHIMIYA. Text in Russian. 1953. 24/yr. USD 554 foreign (effective 2006). **Document type:** *Journal, Abstract/Index.*
Related titles: CD-ROM ed.; Online - full text ed.
—CCC.
Published by: Vserossiiskii Institut Nauchnoi i Tekhnicheskoi Informatsii (VINITI), Ul Usievicha 20, Moscow, 125190, Russian Federation. TEL 7-095-1526441, FAX 7-095-9430060, dir@viniti.ru, http://www.viniti.ru. **Dist. by:** Informnauka Ltd., Ul Usievicha 20, Moscow 125190, Russian Federation. alfimov@viniti.ru.

016.54 RUS ISSN 0203-607X
REFERATIVNYI ZHURNAL. OBSHCHIE VOPROSY KHIMICHESKOI TEKHNOLOGII. Text in Russian. 1953. 24/yr. USD 954 foreign (effective 2006). **Document type:** *Journal, Abstract/Index.*
Related titles: CD-ROM ed.; Online - full text ed.
Published by: Vserossiiskii Institut Nauchnoi i Tekhnicheskoi Informatsii (VINITI), Ul Usievicha 20, Moscow, 125190, Russian Federation. TEL 7-095-1526441, FAX 7-095-9430060, dir@viniti.ru, http://www.viniti.ru. **Dist. by:** Informnauka Ltd., Ul Usievicha 20, Moscow 125190, Russian Federation. alfimov@viniti.ru.

016.5413 RUS ISSN 0208-1695
REFERATIVNYI ZHURNAL. OBSHCHIE VOPROSY KHIMII. FIZICHESKAYA KHIMIYA. STROENIE MOLEKUL. Text in Russian. 1953. 24/yr. USD 652 foreign (effective 2006). **Document type:** *Journal, Abstract/Index.*
Related titles: CD-ROM ed.; Online - full text ed.
Published by: Vserossiiskii Institut Nauchnoi i Tekhnicheskoi Informatsii (VINITI), Ul Usievicha 20, Moscow, 125190, Russian Federation. TEL 7-095-1526441, FAX 7-095-9430060, dir@viniti.ru, http://www.viniti.ru. **Dist. by:** Informnauka Ltd., Ul Usievicha 20, Moscow 125190, Russian Federation. alfimov@viniti.ru.

C

016.547 RUS ISSN 0203-6088
REFERATIVNYI ZHURNAL. ORGANICHESKAYA KHIMIYA. Text in Russian. 1953. m. (24/yr.). USD 910 foreign (effective 2006). **Document type:** *Journal, Abstract/Index.*
Related titles: CD-ROM ed.; Online - full text ed.
Published by: Vserossiiskii Institut Nauchnoi i Tekhnicheskoi Informatsii (VINITI), Ul Usievicha 20, Moscow, 125190, Russian Federation. TEL 7-095-1526441, FAX 7-095-9430060, dir@viniti.ru, http://www.viniti.ru. **Dist. by:** Informnauka Ltd., Ul Usievicha 20, Moscow 125190, Russian Federation. alfimov@viniti.ru.

016.572 RUS ISSN 0235-3148
REFERATIVNYI ZHURNAL. PRIRODNYE ORGANICHESKIE SOEDINENIYA I IKH SINTETICHESKIE ANALOGI. Text in Russian. 1953. s-m. USD 714 foreign (effective 2006). **Document type:** *Journal, Abstract/Index.*
Formerly (until 2002): Referativnyi Zhurnal. Bioorganicheskaya Khimiya (0235-3121)
Related titles: CD-ROM ed.; Online - full text ed.
Published by: Vserossiiskii Institut Nauchnoi i Tekhnicheskoi Informatsii (VINITI), Ul Usievicha 20, Moscow, 125190, Russian Federation. TEL 7-095-1526441, FAX 7-095-9430060, dir@viniti.ru, http://www.viniti.ru. **Dist. by:** Informnauka Ltd., Ul Usievicha 20, Moscow 125190, Russian Federation. alfimov@viniti.ru.

016.546 RUS
REFERATIVNYI ZHURNAL. TEKHNOLOGIYA NEORGANICHESKIKH VESHCHESTV I MATERIALOV. Text in Russian. 1953. 24/yr. USD 506 foreign (effective 2006). **Document type:** *Journal, Abstract/Index.*
Formerly (until 2002): Referativnyi Zhurnal. Tekhnologiya Neorganicheskikh Veshchestv i Produktov. Proizvodstvo Udobrenii (0235-2214)
Related titles: CD-ROM ed.; Online - full text ed.
—East View.
Published by: Vserossiiskii Institut Nauchnoi i Tekhnicheskoi Informatsii (VINITI), Ul Usievicha 20, Moscow, 125190, Russian Federation. TEL 7-095-1526441, FAX 7-095-9430060, dir@viniti.ru, http://www.viniti.ru. **Dist. by:** Informnauka Ltd., Ul Usievicha 20, Moscow 125190, Russian Federation. alfimov@viniti.ru.

016.54 016.6151 RUS ISSN 0203-6134
REFERATIVNYI ZHURNAL. TEKHNOLOGIYA ORGANICHESKIKH LEKARSTVENNYKH VESHCHESTV, VETERINARNYKH PREPARATOV I PESTITSIDOV. Text in Russian. 1953. 24/yr. USD 776 foreign (effective 2006). **Document type:** *Journal, Abstract/Index.*
Related titles: CD-ROM ed.; Online - full text ed.
Published by: Vserossiiskii Institut Nauchnoi i Tekhnicheskoi Informatsii (VINITI), Ul Usievicha 20, Moscow, 125190, Russian Federation. TEL 7-095-1526441, FAX 7-095-9430060, dir@viniti.ru, http://www.viniti.ru. **Dist. by:** Informnauka Ltd., Ul Usievicha 20, Moscow 125190, Russian Federation. alfimov@viniti.ru.

▼ new title ➤ refereed ∗ unverified ♦ full entry avail.

016.547 RUS ISSN 0203-6126
REFERATIVNYI ZHURNAL. TEKHNOLOGIYA ORGANICHESKIKH VESHCHESTV. Text in Russian. 1953. 24/yr. USD 526 foreign (effective 2006). **Document type:** *Journal, Abstract/Index.*
Related titles: CD-ROM ed.; Online - full text ed.
—East View.
Published by: Vserossiiskii Institut Nauchnoi i Tekhnicheskoi Informatsii (VINITI), Ul Usievicha 20, Moscow, 125190, Russian Federation. TEL 7-095-1526441, FAX 7-095-9430060, dir@viniti.ru, http://www.viniti.ru. **Dist. by:** Informnauka Ltd., Ul Usievicha 20, Moscow 125190, Russian Federation. alfimov@viniti.ru.

016.54 016.6684 RUS ISSN 0208-1733
REFERATIVNYI ZHURNAL. TEKHNOLOGIYA POLIMERNYKH MATERYALOV: PLASTMASSY, IONOOBMENNYE MATERYALY. Text in Russian. 1953. 24/yr. USD 632 foreign (effective 2006). **Document type:** *Journal, Abstract/Index.*
Related titles: CD-ROM ed.; Online - full text ed.
Published by: Vserossiiskii Institut Nauchnoi i Tekhnicheskoi Informatsii (VINITI), Ul Usievicha 20, Moscow, 125190, Russian Federation. TEL 7-095-1526441, FAX 7-095-9430060, dir@viniti.ru, http://www.viniti.ru. **Dist. by:** Informnauka Ltd., Ul Usievicha 20, Moscow 125190, Russian Federation. alfimov@viniti.ru.

016.54 016.3384 016.685 RUS ISSN 0208-1768
REFERATIVNYI ZHURNAL. TEKHNOLOGIYA POLIMERNYKH MATERYALOV: PRIRODNYE VYSOKOMOLEKULYARNYE SOEDINENIYA. KHIMIYA I PERERABOTKA DREVESINY. KHIMICHESKIE VOLOKNA. TEKSTIL'NYE MATERIALY. BUMAGA. KOZHA. MEKH. Text in Russian. 1953. 24/yr. USD 372 foreign (effective 2006). **Document type:** *Journal, Abstract/Index.*
Related titles: CD-ROM ed.; Online - full text ed.
—East View.
Published by: Vserossiiskii Institut Nauchnoi i Tekhnicheskoi Informatsii (VINITI), Ul Usievicha 20, Moscow, 125190, Russian Federation. TEL 7-095-1526441, FAX 7-095-9430060, dir@viniti.ru, http://www.viniti.ru. **Dist. by:** Informnauka Ltd., Ul Usievicha 20, Moscow 125190, Russian Federation. alfimov@viniti.ru.

C

016.54 RUS ISSN 0208-1741
REFERATIVNYI ZHURNAL. TEKHNOLOGIYA POLIMERNYKH MATERYALOV: REZINA, LAKOKRASOCHNYE MATERIALY I ORGANICHESKIE POKRYTIYA. VSPOMOGATEL'NYE MATERIALY DLIA PROIZVODSTVA POLIMEROV I IZDELII IZ NIKH. Text in Russian. 1953. 24/yr. USD 346 foreign (effective 2006). **Document type:** *Journal, Abstract/Index.*
Related titles: CD-ROM ed.; Online - full text ed.
Published by: Vserossiiskii Institut Nauchnoi i Tekhnicheskoi Informatsii (VINITI), Ul Usievicha 20, Moscow, 125190, Russian Federation. TEL 7-095-1526441, FAX 7-095-9430060, dir@viniti.ru, http://www.viniti.ru. **Dist. by:** Informnauka Ltd., Ul Usievicha 20, Moscow 125190, Russian Federation. alfimov@viniti.ru.

016.54 RUS ISSN 0235-3164
REFERATIVNYI ZHURNAL. TEKHNOLOGIYA PROIZVODSTVA PRODUKTOV BYTOVOI KHIMII. PARFUMERIYA I KOSMETIKA. Text in Russian. 1953. 24/yr. USD 157 foreign (effective 2006). **Document type:** *Journal, Abstract/Index.*
Formerly (until 2002): Referativnyi Zhurnal. Tekhnologiya Proizvodstva Produktov Bytovoi Khimii
Related titles: CD-ROM ed.; Online - full text ed.
—East View.
Published by: Vserossiiskii Institut Nauchnoi i Tekhnicheskoi Informatsii (VINITI), Ul Usievicha 20, Moscow, 125190, Russian Federation. TEL 7-095-1526441, FAX 7-095-9430060, dir@viniti.ru, http://www.viniti.ru. **Dist. by:** Informnauka Ltd., Ul Usievicha 20, Moscow 125190, Russian Federation. alfimov@viniti.ru.

RIKAGAKU KENKYUJO KENKYU NENPO/I P C R ANNUAL REPORTS OF RESEARCH ACTIVITIES. see *PHYSICS—Abstracting, Bibliographies, Statistics*

RIKEN NYUSU/RIKEN NEWS. see *PHYSICS—Abstracting, Bibliographies, Statistics*

540 005 USA ISSN 1040-1229
Z699.5.S3 CODEN: STNWEQ
S T NEWS. (Scientific & Technical Information Network) Text in English. 1985. bi-m. free (effective 2005); only for the STN international subscribers. **Document type:** *Newsletter.*
Description: Informs and educates online users about content, changes, efficient ways to search the more than 200 databases on STN International - chemistry, engineering, health and safety, materials and numeric data, and more.
Related titles: Online - full text ed.
Indexed: Inpharma, PE&ON, Reac.
Published by: Chemical Abstracts Service (C A S) (Subsidiary of: American Chemical Society), 2540 Olentangy River Rd., Columbus, OH 43210-0012. TEL 614-447-3600, FAX 614-447-3713, help@cas.com, http://www.cas.org. Ed. Larry Wade. Circ: (controlled).

540 016 RUS ISSN 0202-8948
SIGNAL'NAYA INFORMATSIYA. KHIMIYA VODY. Text in Russian. 1971. s-m. **Document type:** *Abstract/Index.*
Published by: Vserossiiskii Institut Nauchnoi i Tekhnicheskoi Informatsii (VINITI), Ul Usievicha 20, Moscow, 125190, Russian Federation. **Dist. by:** M K - Periodica, ul Gilyarovskogo 39, Moscow 129110, Russian Federation. TEL 7-095-2845008, FAX 7-095-2813798, info@periodicals.ru, http://www.mkniga.ru.

016.5413 JPN
SYMPOSIUM ON RADIOCHEMISTRY. ABSTRACTS OF PAPERS/HOSHA KAGAKU TORONKAI KOEN YOKOSHU. Text in Japanese; Summaries in English. 1957. a. **Document type:** *Abstract/Index.*
Published by: Chemical Society of Japan/Nippon Kagakukai, 1-5, Kanda-Surugadai 1-Chome, Chiyoda-ku, Tokyo, 101-0062, Japan.

540 665.5 USA CODEN: TCZEFR
TECHNICAL LITERATURE ABSTRACTS: CATALYSTS - ZEOLITES (ONLINE EDITION). Text in English. w. **Document type:** *Abstract/Index.* **Description:** Reports scientific and technical developments, and general news concerning catalysts and zeolites used in the petroleum, energy, and petrochemical industries, including pollution-control catalysts. The information is drawn from trade magazines and scientific journals published world-wide, as well as conference papers.
Media: Online - full text (from Questel Orbit Inc.).
Published by: Elsevier Engineering Information, Inc. (Subsidiary of: Elsevier Science & Technology), 360 Park Ave S, New York, NY 10010. TEL 800-221-1044, FAX 212-633-3680, info@apiencompass.org, eicustomersupport@elsevier.com, http://www.ei.org/encompass.html, http://www.apiencompass.org.

540 665.5 USA ISSN 1087-1454 CODEN: TFREF8
TECHNICAL LITERATURE ABSTRACTS: FUEL REFORMULATION. Text in English. 1994. m. USD 350 to non-members; USD 175 to members. **Document type:** *Abstract/Index.* **Description:** Reports on composition, properties, regulations, blending, preparations of compounds for use in reformulated fules, and related topics.
Formerly: Literature Abstracts: Fuel Reformulation (1074-6854)
Related titles: Online - full text ed.: (from Questel Orbit Inc.).
Published by: Elsevier Engineering Information, Inc. (Subsidiary of: Elsevier Science & Technology), 1 Castle Point Ter, Hoboken, NJ 07030-5906. TEL 212-366-4040, FAX 212-366-4298, info@apiencompass.org, http://www.apiencompass.org.

540 665.5 USA ISSN 1087-1462 CODEN: TTRIFG
TECHNICAL LITERATURE ABSTRACTS: TRIBOLOGY. Text in English. 1994. m. USD 350 to non-members; USD 175 to members. **Document type:** *Abstract/Index.* **Description:** Reports on the tribology of both petroleum-based and synthetic lubricants and industrial oils, including tribology, friction, lubrication and wear.
Formerly: Literature Abstracts: Tribology (1074-6889)
Related titles: Online - full text ed.: (from Questel Orbit Inc.).
Published by: Elsevier Engineering Information, Inc. (Subsidiary of: Elsevier Science & Technology), 1 Castle Point Ter, Hoboken, NJ 07030-5906. TEL 212-366-4040, FAX 212-366-4298, info@apiencompass.org, http://www.apiencompass.org.

540 JPN
TOSHITSU SHINPOJUMU KOEN YOSHISHU✶ /JAPANESE CARBOHYDRATE SYMPOSIUM. ABSTRACTS. Text in Japanese; Summaries in English. 1978. a. JPY 5,000. adv. **Document type:** *Proceedings, Abstract/Index.*
Published by: Nihon Toshitsu Gakkai/Japanese Society for Carbohydrate Research, c/o Gakushin Publishing Co., 1-8, Tarumi-cho 1 chome, Suita, Osaka 564-0062, Japan. TEL 81 6-63300956, FAX 81 6-63301109, jscr@gak.co.jp, http://www.gak.co.jp/jscr/. Ed. Masaki Saito. Pub. Toshisuke Kawasaki. R&P, Adv. contact Yasuhiro Kuratome.

540 USA ISSN 1061-9143
HD9651.1
U S CHEMICAL INDUSTRY STATISTICAL HANDBOOK. Text in English. 1990. a. **Document type:** *Corporate.*
Indexed: SRI.
Published by: Chemical Manufacturers Association, 1300 Wilson Blvd, Arlington, VA 22209. FAX 703-741-6091. R&P Carolyn Dillingham TEL 703-741-5929.

540 016 660 HUN ISSN 0231-0775
VEGYIPARI SZAKIRODALMI TAJEKOZTATO/CHEMICAL ENGINEERING ABSTRACTS. Text in Hungarian. 1949. m. HUF 9,900. index. **Document type:** *Abstract/Index.*
Supersedes (as from 1982): Muszaki Lapszemle. Kemia Vegyipar - Technical Abstracts. Chemistry, Chemical Industry (0027-5026)
Published by: Orszagos Muszaki Informacios Kozpont es Konyvtar/National Technical Information Centre and Library, Muzeum utca 17, PO Box 12, Budapest, 1428, Hungary. Ed. Eszter Molnar. Circ: 520. **Subscr. to:** Kultura, PO Box 149, Budapest 1389, Hungary.

643 JPN
X SEN BUNSEKI TORONKAI KOEN YOSHISHU/ABSTRACTS OF ANNUAL CONFERENCE ON X-RAY CHEMICAL ANALYSIS. Text in Japanese. 1964. a. membership. **Document type:** *Abstract/Index.*
Published by: Nihon Bunseki Kagakkai/Japan Society for Analytical Chemistry, 1-26-2 Nishigotanda, Shinagawa, Tokyo, 141-0031, Japan.

547 JPN
YUKI HANNO KAGAKU TORONKAI KOEN YOKOSHU/ ABSTRACTS OF SYMPOSIUM ON ORGANIC REACTIONS. Text in Japanese; Summaries in English. a.
Published by: Chemical Society of Japan/Nippon Kagakukai, 1-5, Kanda-Surugadai 1-Chome, Chiyoda-ku, Tokyo, 101-0062, Japan.

643 546 CHN
ZHONGGUO WUJI FENXI HUAXUE WENZHAI/CHINESE INORGANIC ANALYTICAL CHEMISTRY ABSTRACTS. Text in Chinese. bi-m. **Document type:** *Abstract/Index.*
Published by: Yejin Gongye Chubanshe, 39 Songzhuyuan Beixiang, Shatan, Beijing, 100009, China. TEL 4015599. Ed. Xu Junduo.

CHEMISTRY—Analytical Chemistry

543 AUS ISSN 1020-5586
➤ **A C G C CHEMICAL RESEARCH COMMUNICATIONS.** Text in English. 1991. irreg. free. illus. back issues avail. **Document type:** *Journal, Academic/Scholarly.* **Description:** Publishes original chemical research conducted in Asia.
—BLDSC (0575.380000), IE, ingenta.
Published by: Asian Coordinating Group for Chemistry, c/o Barry N Noller, Chair ACGC, PO Box 84, Archerfield, QLD 4109, Australia. TEL 61 7 3274 9221, FAX 61 7 3274 9003, b.noller@mailbox.uq.edu.au, http://www.facs-as.org/acgc/acgc-introduction.htm.

543 USA ISSN 1060-3271
S583 CODEN: JAINEE
➤ **A O A C INTERNATIONAL. JOURNAL.** (Association of Analytical Communities) Text in English. 1915. bi-m. USD 303 in US & Canada to members; USD 389 elsewhere to members; USD 418 in US & Canada to non-members (effective 2005). adv. abstr.; charts; illus.; pat.; stat. index. back issues avail. **Document type:** *Journal, Academic/Scholarly.* **Description:** Papers on chemical analytical methodology pertaining to food, agriculture, drugs, forensics, industrial chemicals and the environment.
Former titles (until 1992): Association of Official Analytical Chemists. Journal (0004-5756); (until 1966): Association of Official Agricultural Chemists. Journal (0095-9111)
Related titles: Microform ed.: (from PMC); Online - full text ed.
Indexed: ABIPC, AESIS, ASCA, ASFA, AbHyg, AgBio, Agr, AgrForAb, AnBrAb, AnalAb, ApicAb, B&AI, B&BAb, BIOSIS Prev, BibAg, BiolAb, CCI, CPA, Cadscan, ChemAb, ChromAb, CurCont, DBA, DSA, ESPM, EngInd, EnvAb, EnvEAb, ExcerpMed, FCA, FPA, FS&TA, ForAb, H&SSA, HelmAb, HerbAb, HortAb, I&DA, INIS AtomInd, IPA, IPackAb, ISR, IndMed, IndVet, Inpharma, LHB, LeadAb, MBA, MEDLINE, MSB, MaizeAb, NemAb, NutrAb, OrnHort, PBA, PGegResA, PGrRegA, PHN&I, PN&I, PST, PollutAb, PotatoAb, PoultAb, ProtozoAb, RA&MP, RCI, RM&VM, RPP, Reac, RevApplEntom, RiceAb, S&F, SCI, SFA, SIA, SPPI, SeedAb, SoyAb, TDB, Telegen, ToxAb, TriticAb, VITIS, VetBull, WAE&RSA, WeedAb, Zincscan, ZooRec.
—BLDSC (4698.400000), CASDDS, CINDOC, CIS, CISTI, GNLM, IDS, IE, Infotrieve, ingenta, Linda Hall. **CCC.**
Published by: A O A C International, 481 N Frederick Ave, Ste 500, Gaithersburg, MD 20877-2417. TEL 301-924-7077, 800-379-2622, FAX 301-924-7087, aoac@aoac.org, http://www.aoac.org. Eds. James Tanner, Robert Rathbone. R&P Krystyna McIver. Adv. contacts Randy McClure, Lise Murphy. Circ: 4,200 (paid).

543 USA
➤ **A T - PROCESS;** the journal of process analytical chemistry. (Advanced Technologies) Text in English. q. USD 275 to individuals; USD 675 to institutions (effective 2003). **Document type:** *Journal, Academic/Scholarly.* **Description:** Focuses on the latest developments in instrumentation, applications, regulations, research and new technology within process analytical chemistry, field analytical chemistry, and real-time analysis.
Media: Online - full text.
—BLDSC (1765.363000).
Published by: InfoScience Services, Inc., PO Box 7100, Grayslake, IL 60030-7100. TEL 847-548-1800, FAX 847-548-1811, infoscience@ais.net, http://www.infoscience.com/jpac.

➤ **ABSTRACTS OF THE TOKYO CONFERENCE ON INSTRUMENTAL ANALYSIS AND ANALYTIC SYSTEMS/BUNSEKI KIKI TO KAISEKI SHISUTEMU NI KANSURU TOKYO TORONKAI KOEN YOSHISHU.** see *CHEMISTRY—Abstracting, Bibliographies, Statistics*

➤ **ABSTRACTS ON THE SYMPOSIUM ON MOLECULAR STRUCTURE/BUNSHI KOZO SOGO TORONKAI KOEN YOSHISHU.** see *CHEMISTRY—Abstracting, Bibliographies, Statistics*

543.1 DEU ISSN 0949-1775
CODEN: AQASF3

➤ **ACCREDITATION AND QUALITY ASSURANCE**; journal for quality, comparability and reliability in chemical measurement. Text in English. 1996. m. EUR 298 combined subscription to institutions print & online eds. (effective 2005). reprint service avail. from PSC. **Document type:** *Journal, Academic/Scholarly.* **Description:** Contains research articles on carrying out chemical measurements with reliable analytical results.
Related titles: Online - full text ed.: ISSN 1432-0517 (from EBSCO Publishing, Springer LINK, Swets Information Services).
Indexed: AgBio, AnalAb, CCI, CIN, ChemAb, ChemTitl, CurCont, FCA, HortAb, I&DA, MSB, MaizeAb, PBA, PHN&I, RRTA, S&F, SoyAb, TDB, TriticAb.
—BLDSC (0573.743000), CASDDS, CISTI, IDS, IE, Infotrieve, ingenta. **CCC.**
Published by: Springer-Verlag (Subsidiary of: Springer Science+Business Media), Tiergartenstr 17, Heidelberg, 69121, Germany. TEL 49-6221-3450, FAX 49-6221-345229, http://link.springer.de/link/service/journals/00769/index.htm. Ed. Helmut Guenzler. Adv. contact Stephan Kroeck TEL 49-30-827875739. **Subscr. in the Americas to:** Springer-Verlag New York, Inc., Journal Fulfillment, PO Box 2485, Secaucus, NJ 07096-2485. TEL 800-777-4643, 201-348-4033, FAX 201-348-4505, journals@springer-ny.com, http://www.springer-ny.com; **Subscr. to:** Springer GmbH Auslieferungsgesellschaft, Haberstr 7, Heidelberg 69126, Germany. TEL 49-6221-345-0, FAX 49-6221-345-4229, subscriptions@springer.de.

543.1 USA ISSN 0896-422X
ADVANCED COATINGS & SURFACE TECHNOLOGY. Text in English. 1985. m. USD 1,152 to individuals (effective 2005). **Document type:** *Newsletter, Trade.* **Description:** Reports and puts into perspective significant developments in coatings and surface modification across a broad range of industry lines.
Related titles: E-mail ed.: USD 960 to individuals (effective 2005); Online - full text ed.: (from Factiva, Florida Center for Library Automation, Gale Group).
Indexed: P&BA.
Published by: Technical Insights (Subsidiary of: Frost & Sullivan), 7550 IH 10 West, Ste 400, San Antonio, TX 78229. TEL 212-850-8600, FAX 212-850-8800, technicalinsights@frost.com, http://www.frost.com/prod/servlet/ti-home.pag. Ed. Peter Savage. Pub. Paul Majchrzjk.

543.1 USA
ADVANCES IN ASYMMETRIC SYNTHESIS. Text in English. 1995. irreg., latest vol.3, 1998. price varies. **Document type:** *Monographic series, Academic/Scholarly.*
Indexed: CIN, ChemAb, ChemTitl.
—BLDSC (0699.500000), ingenta.
Published by: J A I Press Inc. (Subsidiary of: Elsevier Science & Technology), 360 Park Ave S, New York, NY 10010-1710. TEL 212-989-5800, FAX 212-633-3990, usinfo-f@elsevier.com, http://www.elsevier.com. Ed. Alfred Hassner.

535.84 USA ISSN 1068-5561
QD96.A8 CODEN: AATSEJ
ADVANCES IN ATOMIC SPECTROSCOPY. Text in English. 1992. irreg., latest vol.6, 2000. price varies. back issues avail. **Document type:** *Monographic series, Academic/Scholarly.* **Description:** Publishes papers on recent developments in the research and application of atomic spectroscopy.
Indexed: CIN, ChemAb, ChemTitl.
—BLDSC (0699.820000), CASDDS. **CCC.**
Published by: J A I Press Inc. (Subsidiary of: Elsevier Science & Technology), 360 Park Ave S, New York, NY 10010-1710. TEL 212-989-5800, FAX 212-633-3990, usinfo-f@elsevier.com, http://www.elsevier.com/wps/find/bookdescription.cws_home/BS_AATOM/description#description. Ed. Joseph Sneddon.

543.8 USA ISSN 0065-2415
QD271 CODEN: ADCYA3
➤ **ADVANCES IN CHROMATOGRAPHY.** Text in English. 1966. irreg., latest vol.42, 2003. price varies. adv. **Document type:** *Monographic series, Academic/Scholarly.*
Indexed: ASCA, Agr, BiolAb, CCI, CIN, ChemAb, ChemTitl, DSA, DentInd, EngInd, FS&TA, ISR, IndMed, MEDLINE, NutrAb, SCI.
—BLDSC (0703.850000), CASDDS, CISTI, GNLM, IDS, IE, Infotrieve, ingenta, Linda Hall. **CCC.**
Published by: Taylor & Francis Inc. (Subsidiary of: Taylor & Francis Group), 325 Chestnut St, Ste 800, Philadelphia, PA 19016. TEL 215-625-8900, 800-354-1420, FAX 215-625-2940, info@taylorandfrancis.com, http://www.taylorandfrancis.com. Ed. Phyllis Brown.

667.205 GBR ISSN 1462-4761
ADVANCES IN COLOUR SCIENCE & TECHNOLOGY. Text in English. 1998. q. **Document type:** *Academic/Scholarly.*
—BLDSC (0704.010000), IE, ingenta.
Published by: University of Leeds, Department of Colour Chemistry and Dyeing, Leeds, W Yorks LS2 9JT, United Kingdom.

547 GBR ISSN 0568-000X
ADVANCES IN MASS SPECTROMETRY. Text in English. 1959. irreg., latest 2001. GBP 509.
—CISTI. **CCC.**
Published by: John Wiley & Sons Ltd. (Subsidiary of: John Wiley & Sons, Inc.), The Atrium, Southern Gate, Chichester, West Sussex PO19 8SQ, United Kingdom. http://www.wiley.co.uk. Ed. Emilio Gelphi.

542.1 USA ISSN 0044-7749
Q184 CODEN: ALBYBL
➤ **AMERICAN LABORATORY.** Text in English. 1968. m. free to qualified personnel (effective 2005). adv. bk.rev. charts; illus.; stat.; tr.lit. Supplement avail.; back issues avail. **Document type:** *Magazine, Academic/Scholarly.* **Description:** Dedicated to chemists and biologists interested in all aspects of laboratory practice and basic research.
Related titles: Microfiche ed.
Indexed: ABIPC, ASCA, Agr, AnalAb, BIOSIS Prev, BiolAb, BrCerAb, C&ISA, CADCAM, CCI, CIN, CINAHL, CSNB, CerAb, ChemAb, ChemTitl, CivEngAb, CorrAb, CurCont, CurPA, E&CAJ, EIA, EMA, EnerInd, EngInd, EnvAb, ExcerpMed, FS&TA, IAA, IHD, ISMEC, ISR, Inspec, LHB, M&TEA, MBF, METADEX, MSB, NutrAb, ORMS, QC&AS, RCI, SCI, SoftBase, SolStAb, TTI, TelAb, Telegen, VITIS, WAA, WRCInf.
—BLDSC (0840.300000), AskIEEE, CASDDS, Ei, GNLM, IE, ingenta, Linda Hall. **CCC.**
Published by: International Scientific Communications, Inc., 30 Controls Dr, PO Box 670, Shelton, CT 06484-0870. TEL 203-926-9300, FAX 203-926-9310, iscpubs@iscpubs.com, http://www.iscpubs.com. Ed., Pub. Brian Howard. adv.: page USD 12,500. Circ: 135,000 (controlled).

643 USA ISSN 0893-8830
CODEN: ALANEK
AMERICAN LABORATORY NEWS. Text in English. 1987. m. USD 260 domestic; USD 295 foreign; free to qualified personnel (effective 2005). adv. **Document type:** *Magazine, Trade.*
Published by: International Scientific Communications, Inc., 30 Controls Dr, PO Box 670, Shelton, CT 06484-0870. TEL 203-926-9300, FAX 203-926-9310, iscpubs@iscpubs.com, http://www.iscpubs.com/. Ed. Brian Howard. Pub. William Wham. adv.: B&W page USD 6,525, color page USD 8,325. Circ: 130,321. **U.K. subscr. to:** I.S.C. House, Progress Business Centre, 5 Whittle Pkwy., Slough, Berks SL1 6OQ, United Kingdom. TEL 44-1628-668881.

AMERICAN SOCIETY FOR MASS SPECTROMETRY. JOURNAL. see *PHYSICS—Optics*

ANALYSES OF HAZARDOUS SUBSTANCES IN BIOLOGICAL MATERIALS. see *ENVIRONMENTAL STUDIES—Toxicology And Environmental Safety*

543 GBR ISSN 0003-2654
QD71 CODEN: ANALAO
➤ **THE ANALYST.** Text in English. 1876. m. GBP 1,089, USD 1,992 combined subscription print & online eds. (effective 2006); subscr. includes Chemical Technology. adv. bk.rev. abstr.; charts; illus. index, cum.index every 10 yrs. (1876-1965). 2 cols./p.; reprints avail. **Document type:** *Journal, Academic/Scholarly.* **Description:** Contains original research papers, critical and tutorial reviews on state-of-the-art techniques and their applications and a rapid communications.
Incorporates (in 2000): Analytical Communications (1359-7337); Which was formerly (until 1996): Analytical Proceedings (0144-557X); Which superseded (in Jan. 1981): Chemical Society. Analytical Division. Proceedings (0306-1396); Which was formerly (1964-1975): Society for Analytical Chemistry. Proceedings (0037-9697); (1994-1995): Analytical Proceedings Including Analytical Communications
Related titles: Microform ed.: (from PQC); Online - full text ed.: ISSN 1364-5528. 1996. GBP 980, USD 1,793 (effective 2006) (from EBSCO Publishing, O C L C Online Computer Library Center, Inc., Swets Information Services); ♦ Supplement(s): Chemical Technology. ISSN 1744-1560.
Indexed: A&ATA, ABIPC, AEA, AESIS, ASFA, AbHyg, AgBio, AgrForAb, AnBrAb, AnalAb, BIOBASE, BiolAb, C&ISA, CCI, CIN, CISA, CPA, CTE, ChemAb, ChemTitl, ChromAb, CivEngAb, CorrAb, CurCont, DBA, DSA, DentInd, E&CAJ, EMA, ExcerpMed, FCA, FPA, FS&TA, ForAb, HelmAb, HerbAb, HortAb, I&DA, IABS, IPA, IPackAb, ISR, IndIslam, IndMed, IndVet, Inspec, M&TEA, MEDLINE, METADEX, MSB, MSCI, MaizeAb, NutrAb, OrnHort, P&BA, PBA, PGrRegA, PHN&I, PN&I, PotatoAb, PoultAb, ProtozoAb, RA&MP, RAPRA, RCI, RM&VM, RPP, RefZh, RevApplEntom, RiceAb, S&F, SCI, SFA, SIA, SeedAb, SolStAb, SoyAb, TDB, TriticAb, VITIS, VetBull, WAA, WAE&RSA, WRCInf, WSCA, WeedAb.
—BLDSC (0893.000000), CASDDS, CINDOC, CISTI, GNLM, IDS, IE, Infotrieve, ingenta, Linda Hall. **CCC.**
Published by: Royal Society of Chemistry, Thomas Graham House, Science Park, Milton Rd, Cambridge, CB4 0WF, United Kingdom. TEL 44-1223-420066, FAX 44-1223-423623, analyst@rsc.org, sales@rsc.org, http://www.rsc.org/analyst. **Dist. by:** Portland Press Ltd., R S C Distribution Services, Commerce Way, Whitehall Industrial Estate, Colchester CO2 8HP, United Kingdom. TEL 44-1206-226050, FAX 44-1206-226055, sales@rscdistribution.org.

543.8 USA ISSN 1545-7532
ANALYTIC SEPARATIONS NEWS. Text in English. 1988. m. USD 500 domestic; USD 50 foreign; USD 45 newsstand/cover domestic; USD 50 newsstand/cover foreign (effective 2005). back issues avail.; reprints avail. **Document type:** *Newsletter, Trade.* **Description:** Covers the fields of high-technology organic separations and biomolecular separations, including benchtop supercritical fluid chromatography, large-scale commercial gel chromatography, affinity technologies, and biosensors.
Formerly (until 2003): High Tech Separations News (1046-039X)
Related titles: Online - full text ed.: (from bigchalk, Data-Star, Factiva, Florida Center for Library Automation, Gale Group, LexisNexis, Northern Light Technology, Inc., The Dialog Corporation).
—**CCC.**
Published by: Business Communications Co., Inc., 25 Van Zant St, Ste 13, Norwalk, CT 06855-1781. TEL 203-853-4266, FAX 203-853-0348, info@bccresearch.com, http://www.buscom.com/letters/asnpromo/asnpromo.html, http://www.bccresearch.com. Ed. Alan Hall. Pub. Louis Naturman.

543.1 669 ZAF ISSN 1022-1123
ANALYTICA. Text in Afrikaans, English. 1958; N.S. 1993. q. membership. adv. illus. **Document type:** *Bulletin.*
Former titles (until Sep. 1993): South African Institute of Assayers and Analysts. Bulletin (0254-1831); (until 1968): Suid-Afrikaanse Instituut van Essaieurs en Analitici. Joernaal (0038-2213)
Indexed: ISAP.
Published by: South African Chemical Institute, Analytical Division/Suid-Afrikaanse Chemiese Instituut, Analitiese Divisie, c/o Ms M Julsing, Spectro-Analytical Instruments, Groenkloof, PO Box 17063, Yeoville, 0027, South Africa.

543 NLD ISSN 0003-2670
QD71 CODEN: ACACAM
➤ **ANALYTICA CHIMICA ACTA.** Text in English, French, German; Summaries in English. 1947. 52/yr. EUR 8,002 in Europe to institutions; JPY 1,062,100 in Japan to institutions; USD 8,952 elsewhere to institutions (effective 2006). adv. bk.rev. charts; illus. cum.index. reprints avail. **Document type:** *Journal, Academic/Scholarly.* **Description:** Publishes research papers, reviews and short communications covering all aspects of analytical science.
Incorporates: Analytica Chimica Acta - Computer Technique and Optimization (0378-4304)
Related titles: Microform ed.: (from PQC); Online - full text ed.: (from EBSCO Publishing, Gale Group, IngentaConnect, ScienceDirect, Swets Information Services); ♦ Series: Vibrational Spectroscopy. ISSN 0924-2031.
Indexed: ABIPC, AEA, AESIS, ASCA, ASFA, AbHyg, AgBio, AgrForAb, AnBrAb, AnalAb, B&BAb, BIOSIS Prev, BioEngAb, BiolAb, BrCerAb, C&ISA, CBTA, CCI, CEABA, CIN, CIS, CMCI, CPA, Cadscan, CerAb, ChemAb, ChemTitl, ChromAb, CivEngAb, CorrAb, CurCont, DBA, DSA, E&CAJ, EMA, ESPM, EngInd, EnvEAb, ExcerpMed, FCA, FPA, FS&TA, ForAb, HelmAb, HerbAb, HortAb, I&DA, IAA, ISR, IndMed, IndVet, Inspec, LeadAb, M&GPA, M&TEA, MBF, MEDLINE, METADEX, MSB, MSCI, MaizeAb, NemAb, NucAcAb, NutrAb, OrnHort, PBA, PGegResA, PGrRegA, PHN&I, PN&I, PollutAb, PotatoAb, PoultAb, ProtozoAb, RA&MP, RAPRA, RCI, RM&VM, RPP, RefZh, RevApplEntom, RiceAb, S&F, SCI, SIA, SWRA, SeedAb, SolStAb, SoyAb, TDB, TriticAb, VITIS, VetBull, WAA, WRCInf, WeedAb, Zincscan.
—BLDSC (0895.000000), CASDDS, CINDOC, CISTI, Ei, IDS, IE, Infotrieve, ingenta, Linda Hall. **CCC.**
Published by: Elsevier BV (Subsidiary of: Elsevier Science & Technology), Radarweg 29, Amsterdam, 1043 NX, Netherlands. TEL 31-20-4853911, FAX 31-20-4852457, nlinfo-f@elsevier.nl, http://www.elsevier.com/locate/aca, http://www.elsevier.nl. Eds. L Buydens, P R Haddad, R P Baldwin.

543 DEU ISSN 1618-2642
CODEN: FJACES
➤ **ANALYTICAL AND BIOANALYTICAL CHEMISTRY.** Text in English. 2001. s-m. EUR 3,760 combined subscription to institutions print & online eds. (effective 2005). adv. bk.rev. abstr.; bibl.; charts. index, cum.index. back issues avail.; reprint service avail. from ISI. **Document type:** *Journal, Academic/Scholarly.* **Description:** Covers all fields of pure and applied analytical chemistry and bioanalysis, including topics at their interfaces with the life and health sciences, the engineering and materials sciences, environmental science, the earth sciences, and others.
Formed by the merger of (1862-2001): Fresenius' Journal of Analytical Chemistry (0937-0633); Which was formerly: Fresenius' Zeitschrift fuer Analytische Chemie (0016-1152); (1999-2001): Analusis Magazine (1293-2701); (1982-2001): Quimica Analitica (0212-0569)
Related titles: Microform ed.: (from PMC, PQC); Online - full text ed.: ISSN 1618-2650 (from EBSCO Publishing, Springer LINK, Swets Information Services); Supplement(s): Mitteilungsblatt - Gesellschaft Deutscher Chemiker, Fachgruppe Analytische Chemie. ISSN 0939-0065.
Indexed: A&ATA, AEA, ASCA, ASFA, AbHyg, AgBio, AgrForAb, AnBrAb, AnalAb, ApicAb, B&BAb, BIOSIS Prev, BioEngAb, BiolAb, BrCerAb, C&ISA, CCI, CEABA, CIN, CMCI, CPA, CerAb, ChemAb, ChemTitl, ChromAb, CivEngAb, CorrAb, CurCont, DBA, DSA, E&CAJ, EMA, ESPM, EngInd, EnvEAb, ExcerpMed, FCA, FPA, FS&TA, ForAb, HelmAb, HerbAb,

C

HortAb, I&DA, IAA, IMMAb, INIS AtomInd, ISR, IndMed, IndVet, Inspec, M&TEA, MBF, MEDLINE, METADEX, MSB, MSCI, MaizeAb, NemAb, NutrAb, OrnHort, PBA, PGegResA, PGrRegA, PHN&I, PN&I, PollutAb, PotatoAb, PoultAb, ProtozoAb, RA&MP, RCI, RM&VM, RPP, RefZh, RevApplEntom, RiceAb, S&F, SCI, SIA, SSCI, SWRA, SeedAb, SolStAb, SoyAb, TDB, ToxAb, TriticAb, VITIS, VetBull, WAA, WAE&RSA, WRCInf, WeedAb.
—BLDSC (0896.320000), AskIEEE, CASDDS, CINDOC, CISTI, Ei, IDS, IE, ingenta, Linda Hall. **CCC.**
Published by: (Gesellschaft Deutscher Chemiker, Fachgruppe Analytische Chemie), Springer-Verlag (Subsidiary of: Springer Science+Business Media), Tiergartenstr 17, Heidelberg, 69121, Germany. TEL 49-6221-3450, FAX 49-6221-345229, http://link.springer.de/link/service/journals/00216/index.htm. adv.: B&W page EUR 680, color page EUR 1,720. Circ: 750 (paid). **Subscr. in the Americas to:** Springer-Verlag New York, Inc., Journal Fulfillment, PO Box 2485, Secaucus, NJ 07096-2485. TEL 800-777-4643, 201-348-4033, FAX 201-348-4505, journals@springer-ny.com, http://www.springer-ny.com; **Subscr. to:** Springer GmbH Auslieferungsgesellschaft, Haberstr 7, Heidelberg 69126, Germany. TEL 49-6221-345-0, FAX 49-6221-345-4229, subscriptions@springer.de.

543 USA ISSN 0003-2700
TP1 CODEN: ANCHAM

➤ **ANALYTICAL CHEMISTRY.** Text in English. 1929. s-m. (plus Review Issue and Labguide). USD 1,484 in North America to institutions; USD 1,664 elsewhere to institutions; USD 152 in North America to members; USD 332 elsewhere to members; USD 114 in North America to students; USD 294 elsewhere to students (effective 2006). adv. bk.rev. abstr.; bibl.; charts; illus.; tr.lit. Index. back issues avail.; reprints avail. **Document type:** *Journal, Academic/Scholarly.* **Description:** Contains scientific articles on both theoretical and applied aspects of analysis, as well as correspondence and laboratory aids.
Formerly (until 1946): Industrial and Engineering Chemistry. Analytical Edition (0096-4484)
Related titles: Microfiche ed.: USD 1,066 in North America; USD 1,102 elsewhere (effective 2002); Microfilm ed.: USD 1,066 in North America; USD 1,086 elsewhere (effective 2002); Online - full text ed.: ISSN 1520-6882. USD 75 to individual members (effective 2005) (from EBSCO Publishing, Swets Information Services); Supplement(s): LabGuide. ISSN 1520-4782. 1973.
Indexed: ABIPC, AEA, AESIS, AIA, APIAb, APICat, APIH&E, APIOC, APIPR, APIPS, APITS, AS&TI, ASCA, ASFA, AbHyg, AgBio, AgrForAb, AnBrAb, AnalAb, ApicAb, B&BAb, BCIRA, BioCN&I, BioEngAb, BiolAb, BrCerAb, CCI, CEABA, CIJE, CIN, CIS, CISA, CJPI, CLL, CPA, CTE, ChemAb, ChemTitl, ChromAb, CivEngAb, CompAb, CurCont, DBA, DSA, DentInd, E&PHSE, EIA, ESPM, EngInd, EnvAb, EnvEAb, EnvInd, ExcerpMed, F&EA, FCA, FPA, FS&TA, ForAb, GP&P, GSI, GasAb, HelmAb, HortAb, I&DA, IHD, INIS AtomInd, IPA, ISMEC, ISR, IndMed, IndVet, Inspec, LeadAb, MEDLINE, METADEX, MSB, MSCI, MaizeAb, MinerAb, NSCI, NemAb, NutrAb, OceAb, OffTech, OrnHort, P&BA, PBA, PGegResA, PGrRegA, PHN&I, PN&I, PetrolAb, PollutAb, PotatoAb, PoultAb, ProtozoAb, RA&MP, RAPRA, RCI, RM&VM, RPP, RefZh, Repind, RevApplEntom, S&F, SCI, SIA, SSCI, SWRA, SoyAb, TDB, THA, TTI, Telegen, TriticAb, VITIS, VetBull, WAE&RSA, WRCInf, WSCA, WTA, WeedAb, Zincscan.
—BLDSC (0897.000000), AskIEEE, CASDDS, CINDOC, CISTI, Ei, GNLM, IDS, IE, Infotrieve, ingenta, KNAW, Linda Hall, PADDS. **CCC.**
Published by: American Chemical Society, 1155 16th St, N W, Washington, DC 20036. TEL 202-872-4600, 800-227-5558, FAX 202-776-8258, analytical@acs.org, service@acs.org, http://pubs.acs.org/ac. Ed. Royce W Murray. adv.: page USD 4,530. Circ: 11,680.

547.7 664.9 USA

ANALYTICAL CHEMISTRY LABORATORY GUIDEBOOK. RESIDUE CHEMISTRY. Text in English. irreg. USD 39 per issue; USD 48.75 per issue foreign. **Document type:** *Government.* **Description:** Provides persons involved with analyzing meat and poultry products for U.S.D.A. regulation compliance with a compendium of analytical methods to ensure quality results in laboratory practice and training.
Published by: U.S. Department of Agriculture, Office of Public Affairs, Administration Bldg, Rm 201A, Independence Ave, between 12th and 14th Sts, S W, Washington, DC 20250. **Subscr. to:** U.S. Government Printing Office, Superintendent of Documents, PO Box 371954, Pittsburgh, PA 15250-7954. TEL 202-512-1800, FAX 202-512-2250, orders@gpo.gov, http://www.access.gpo.gov.

543 USA ISSN 1086-4377

ANALYTICAL CHEMISTRY NEWS & FEATURES (PRINT EDITION). Text in English. 1996. m. USD 1,374 domestic; USD 1,543 foreign (effective 2005).
Related titles: Online - full text ed.: Analytical Chemistry News & Features (Online Edition). ISSN 1520-5843 (from EBSCO Publishing).
Indexed: BiolDig.
—CCC.
Published by: American Chemical Society, 1155 16th St, N W, Washington, DC 20036. service@acs.org, http://www.acs.org.

543 USA ISSN 0003-2719
QD71 CODEN: ANALBP

➤ **ANALYTICAL LETTERS.** Text in English. 1968. 15/yr. USD 3,708, GBP 2,247 combined subscription to institutions print & online eds. (effective 2006). adv. abstr. reprint service avail. from PSC. **Document type:** *Journal, Academic/Scholarly.* **Description:** Provides the information on recent advances in all areas of analytical chemistry.
Supersedes in part: Analytical Letters
Related titles: Microform ed.: (from RPI); Online - full text ed.: ISSN 1532-236X. USD 3,523, GBP 2,135 to institutional members (effective 2006) (from EBSCO Publishing, O C L C Online Computer Library Center, Inc., Swets Information Services).
Indexed: AEA, ASCA, ASFA, AbHyg, AgBio, AnBrAb, AnalAb, ApicAb, BBCI, BIOBASE, BIOSIS Prev, BiolAb, BrCerAb, C&ISA, CCI, CEABA, CPA, Cadscan, CerAb, ChemAb, ChromAb, CivEngAb, CorrAb, CurCont, DSA, E&CAJ, EMA, ESPM, EngInd, ExcerpMed, FCA, FPA, FS&TA, ForAb, HelmAb, HortAb, I&DA, IAA, IABS, ISR, IndVet, Inpharma, LeadAb, M&TEA, MBF, METADEX, MSB, MSCI, MaizeAb, NutrAb, OrnHort, PBA, PGrRegA, PHN&I, PN&I, PotatoAb, PoultAb, ProtozoAb, RA&MP, RCI, RM&VM, RPP, Reac, RefZh, RevApplEntom, S&F, SCI, SIA, SWRA, SeedAb, SolStAb, SoyAb, TDB, TriticAb, VITIS, VetBull, WAA, WeedAb, Zincscan.
—BLDSC (0897.100000), CASDDS, CISTI, Ei, GNLM, IDS, IE, Infotrieve, ingenta, Linda Hall. **CCC.**
Published by: Taylor & Francis Inc. (Subsidiary of: Taylor & Francis Group), 325 Chestnut St, Ste 800, Philadelphia, PA 19016. TEL 215-625-8900, 800-354-1420, FAX 215-625-2940, info@taylorandfrancis.com, http://www.tandf.co.uk/journals/titles/00032719.asp, http://www.taylorandfrancis.com. Ed. George G Guilbault. Adv. contact Sharon Moran. B&W page USD 600. Circ: 550.

543 NLD ISSN 0926-4345
CODEN: ASLIE7

➤ **ANALYTICAL SPECTROSCOPY LIBRARY.** Text in English. 1987. irreg., latest vol.10, 2000. price varies. back issues avail. **Document type:** *Monographic series, Academic/Scholarly.* **Description:** Covers the use of analytical spectroscopy in chemical engineering research.
Indexed: CIN, ChemAb, ChemTitl.
—BLDSC (0897.143700), CASDDS, CISTI, ingenta. **CCC.**
Published by: Elsevier BV (Subsidiary of: Elsevier Science & Technology), Radarweg 29, Amsterdam, 1043 NX, Netherlands. TEL 31-20-4853911, FAX 31-20-4852457, nlinfo-f@elsevier.nl, http://www.elsevier.nl.

➤ **ANNALES DE BIOLOGIE CLINIQUE DU QUEBEC.** see *MEDICAL SCIENCES—Experimental Medicine, Laboratory Technique*

➤ **ANNUAL BOOK OF A S T M STANDARDS. VOLUME 03.05. ANALYTICAL CHEMISTRY FOR METALS, ORES, AND RELATED MATERIALS(I): E32 TO E1724.** see *ENGINEERING—Engineering Mechanics And Materials*

➤ **ANNUAL BOOK OF A S T M STANDARDS. VOLUME 14.01. HEALTHCARE INFORMATICS.** see *ENGINEERING—Engineering Mechanics And Materials*

543 USA ISSN 0003-7028
QD71 CODEN: APSPA4

➤ **APPLIED SPECTROSCOPY.** Text in English. 1946. m. USD 725 combined subscription domestic to institutions print & online eds.; USD 774 combined subscription in Canada & Mexico to institutions print & online eds.; USD 833 combined subscription elsewhere to institutions print & online eds. (effective 2005). adv. bk.rev.; software rev. bibl.; charts; illus.; tr.lit. index. back issues avail.; reprints avail. **Document type:** *Journal, Academic/Scholarly.* **Description:** It covers all areas of spectroscopy and contains up-to-date information on the field via research articles and reviews, includes buyers guides and lists employment opportunities.
Related titles: Online - full content ed.; Online - full text ed.: (from CEDOCAR, EBSCO Publishing, Gale Group, IngentaConnect, O C L C Online Computer Library Center, Inc.).
Indexed: A&ATA, ABIPC, AESIS, ASCA, ASFA, AnalAb, BIOSIS Prev, BiolAb, BrCerAb, C&ISA, CCI, CIN, Cadscan, ChemAb, ChemTitl, CurCont, E&CAJ, ESPM, EngInd, ExcerpMed, INIS AtomInd, ISR, Inspec, LeadAb, MSB, MSCI, NumL, RAPRA, RefZh, SCI, SIA, SPINweb, SSCI, SWRA, SolStAb, WSCA, Zincscan.
—BLDSC (1579.000000), AskIEEE, CASDDS, CISTI, Ei, IDS, IE, Infotrieve, ingenta, Linda Hall. **CCC.**
Published by: Society for Applied Spectroscopy, 201-B Broadway St, Frederick, MD 21701-6501. TEL 301-694-8122, FAX 301-694-6860, http://www.s-a-s.org/journal/on-line_journal.htm. Eds. Paul Farnsworth, Joel Harris. R&P Bonnie Saylor. Adv. contacts Martha Chapin, Matt Bertholf. Circ: 3,100 (paid).

➤ **ASIA-PACIFIC GUIDE TO SURFACE TREATMENT TECHNOLOGY.** see *BUSINESS AND ECONOMICS—Trade And Industrial Directories*

➤ **ASIAN JOURNAL OF SPECTROSCOPY.** see *PHYSICS—Optics*

643 USA ISSN 0195-5373
QC454.A8 CODEN: ASPND7

➤ **ATOMIC SPECTROSCOPY.** Text in English. 1962. bi-m. charts; illus. index. back issues avail.; reprint service avail. from PQC. **Document type:** *Academic/Scholarly.* **Description:** Disseminates information, new applications and analytical data in atomic absorption spectrophotometry and related disciplines.
Supersedes (in 1980): Atomic Absorption Newsletter (0044-9954)
Related titles: Microfilm ed.: (from PQC).
Indexed: ABIPC, AESIS, ASCA, AnalAb, BrCerAb, C&ISA, CCI, CIN, Cadscan, CerAb, ChemAb, ChemTitl, CivEngAb, CorrAb, CurCont, DSA, E&CAJ, EIA, EMA, EngInd, EnvAb, ExcerpMed, IAA, ISR, Inspec, LeadAb, M&TEA, MBF, METADEX, MSB, RefZh, SCI, SolStAb, VITIS, WAA, WSCA, Zincscan.
—BLDSC (1771.080000), AskIEEE, CASDDS, CISTI, Ei, IDS, IE, Infotrieve, ingenta, Linda Hall.
Published by: Perkin - Elmer Corp., 710 Bridgeport Ave., Shelton, CT 06484-4794. TEL 203-761-2532, FAX 203-761-2892, lustan@perkin-elmer.com, http://www.perkin-elmer.com. Ed., R&P Anneliese Lust. Circ: 3,000. **Subscr. to:** PO Box 557, Florham Park, NJ 07932.

543 060 AUS ISSN 1325-1694

AUSTRALIAN CONFERENCE ON NUCLEAR TECHNIQUES OF ANALYSIS. PROCEEDINGS. Text in English. 1976. biennial. **Document type:** *Proceedings.*
Formerly (until 1978): Australian Conference on Nuclear Techniques of Analysis. Summary of Proceedings (0811-9430)
Indexed: Inspec.
Published by: Australian Institute of Nuclear Science and Engineering, New Illawarra Rd, Lucas Heights, NSW 2234, Australia. TEL 61-02-97173376, FAX 61-02-97179268, ainse@ansto.gov.au, http://ansto.gov.au/ainse/.

BEITRAEGE ZUR TABAKFORSCHUNG INTERNATIONAL; contributions to tobacco research. see *TOBACCO*

543.8 GBR ISSN 0269-3879
CODEN: BICHE2

➤ **BIOMEDICAL CHROMATOGRAPHY.** Text in English. 1986. 12/yr. USD 2,495 to institutions; USD 2,745 combined subscription to institutions print & online eds. (effective 2006). adv. reprint service avail. from PSC. **Document type:** *Journal, Academic/Scholarly.* **Description:** Devoted to the publication of original papers on the applications of chromatography and allied techniques in the biological and medical sciences.
Related titles: Microform ed.: (from PQC); Online - full content ed.: ISSN 1099-0801. 1997. USD 2,495 to institutions (effective 2006); Online - full text ed.: (from EBSCO Publishing, Swets Information Services, Wiley InterScience).
Indexed: ASCA, AnalAb, B&BAb, BBCI, BIOBASE, BIOSIS Prev, BioEngAb, BiolAb, CCI, CIN, ChemAb, ChemTitl, ChromAb, CurCont, DSA, EngInd, ExcerpMed, FCA, ForAb, HerbAb, HortAb, IABS, ISR, IndMed, IndVet, Inpharma, MEDLINE, MSB, MaizeAb, NutrAb, OrnHort, PHN&I, PN&I, PoultAb, ProtozoAb, RA&MP, RCI, RM&VM, Reac, S&F, SCI, SIA, TriticAb, VITIS, VetBull, WeedAb.
—BLDSC (2087.758000), CASDDS, CISTI, Ei, GNLM, IDS, IE, Infotrieve, ingenta, Linda Hall. **CCC.**
Published by: John Wiley & Sons Ltd. (Subsidiary of: John Wiley & Sons, Inc.), The Atrium, Southern Gate, Chichester, West Sussex PO19 8SQ, United Kingdom. TEL 44-1243-779777, FAX 44-1243-775878, customer@wiley.co.uk, http://www.interscience.wiley.com/jpages/0269-3879/, http://www.wiley.co.uk. Ed. C K Lim. adv.: B&W page GBP 650, color page GBP 1,550; trim 210 x 297. Circ: 300. **Subscr. in the Americas to:** John Wiley & Sons, Inc., 111 River St, Hoboken, NJ 07030-5774. TEL 201-748-6645, 800-225-5945, subinfo@wiley.com.

543.1 JPN ISSN 0386-2178
CODEN: BUNSD3

BUNSEKI/ANALYTICAL CHEMISTRY. Text in Japanese. 1975. m. free to members. **Document type:** *Journal, Academic/Scholarly.*
Indexed: AESIS, AnalAb, ApicAb, ChemAb, INIS AtomInd, JPI, MSB, S&F.
—CASDDS, CISTI. **CCC.**
Published by: Japan Society for Analytical Chemistry/Nihon Bunseki Kagaku Kai, 1-26-2 Nishigotanda, Shinagawa, Tokyo, 141-0031, Japan. TEL 81-3-34903351, FAX 81-3-34903572, analytsci@jsac.or.jp, http://wwwsoc.nii.ac.jp/jsac/bunseki.html.

543 JPN ISSN 0525-1931
QD71 CODEN: BNSKAK

➤ **BUNSEKI KAGAKU/JAPAN ANALYST.** Text in Japanese; Summaries in English. 1946. m. free to members. adv. back issues avail. **Document type:** *Journal, Academic/Scholarly.*
Formerly (until 1950): Bunseki to Shiyaku (0366-4511)
Related titles: Microfiche ed.; Online - full text ed.: free (effective 2005) (from J-Stage).
Indexed: A&ATA, ASCA, AnalAb, ArtHuCI, CCI, CIN, Cadscan, ChemAb, ChemTitl, CurCont, DSA, EngInd, FS&TA, INIS AtomInd, ISR, JTA, LeadAb, MSB, MSCI, NutrAb, RCI, RefZh, S&F, SCI, SIA, VITIS, WeedAb, Zincscan.
—BLDSC (2930.600000), CASDDS, CISTI, Ei, IDS, IE, ingenta, Linda Hall. **CCC.**

C

Published by: Japan Society for Analytical Chemistry/Nihon Bunseki Kagaku Kai, 1-26-2 Nishigotanda, Shinagawa, Tokyo, 141-0031, Japan. TEL 81-3-34903351, FAX 81-3-34903572, http://bunsekikagaku.jstage.jst.go.jp/. Ed. Yoshimasa Nihei. Circ: 4,400. **Dist. by:** Japan Publications Inc., 2-1 Sarugaku-cho 1-chome, Chiyoda-ku, Tokyo 101-0064, Japan.

543.1   JPN
QD71
                                    CODEN: CACFEJ
C A C S FORUM. (Chemical Analysis Center Saitama University) Text in Japanese. 1981. a.
Indexed: ChemAb.
—BLDSC (2945.395000).
Published by: Saitama University, Chemical Analysis Center/Saitama Daigaku Bunseki Senta, 255 Shimo-Okubo, Urawa-shi, Saitama-ken 338-0825, Japan.

643   DEU   ISSN 0179-9398
C L B MEMORY. (Chemie fur Labor und Betrieb) Text in German. 1950. m. **Document type:** *Journal, Academic/Scholarly.*
Formerly (until 1983): Lernen + Leisten (0341-518X)
Related titles: ◆ Supplement to: Chemie in Labor und Biotechnik. ISSN 0943-6677.
—CCC.
Published by: Rubikon Verlag, Bammentaler Str 6-8, Gaiberg, 69251, Germany.

355.31   USA   ISSN 0899-7047
UG447
C M L ARMY CHEMICAL REVIEW. Text in English. 1985. s-a. USD 12 (effective 2001). **Document type:** *Government.* **Description:** Presents professional information about the Chemical Corps functions related to nuclear, biological, chemical, smoke, flame field expedients, and NBC reconnaissance in combat support.
Related titles: Online - full text ed.: ISSN 1556-4916 (from Gale Group).
Published by: Army Chemical Review, Attn: Mattie Kirby, US Maneuver Support Center, 320 Engineering Loop, Ste 2100, Fort Leonard Wood, MO 65473-8929. TEL 205-848-5725, FAX 205-848-5058. Ed. Mattie Kirby. Circ: 8,600. **Subscr. to:** U.S. Government Printing Office, Superintendent of Documents, PO Box 371954, Pittsburgh, PA 15250-7954. TEL 202-512-1800, FAX 202-512-2250, orders@gpo.gov, http://www.access.gpo.gov.

543   USA
C P A C MONITOR. Text in English. 1983. 2/yr. pat.; tr.lit. back issues avail. **Document type:** *Newsletter.* **Description:** Covers general research topics currently pursued at the center; upcoming conferences; science articles highlighting new technology advances.
Published by: Center for Process Analytical Chemistry, Box 351700, University of Washington, Seattle, WA 98195-1700. TEL 206-685-2326, FAX 206-543-6506, http://www.cpac.washington.edu. Ed. Betsy McGrath. Circ: 1,800 (controlled).

CANADIAN JOURNAL OF ANALYTICAL SCIENCES AND SPECTROSCOPY. see *PHYSICS—Optics*

CERAMICS-SILIKATY. see *CHEMISTRY—Physical Chemistry*

543   POL   ISSN 0009-2223
                                    CODEN: CANWAJ
➤ **CHEMIA ANALITYCZNA.** Text in English; Summaries in English, Polish. 1956. bi-m. EUR 100 domestic; EUR 114 in Europe; EUR 128 in North America; EUR 140 elsewhere (effective 2005). adv. bk.rev. bibl.; charts; illus. index. 160 p./no.; back issues avail.; reprints avail. **Document type:** *Journal, Academic/Scholarly.* **Description:** Publishes original research papers, short communications, laboratory notes, reviews.
Indexed: ASCA, AnalAb, CCI, CIN, Cadscan, ChemAb, ChemTitl, CurCont, DSA, EngInd, F&EA, FS&TA, INIS AtomInd, ISR, LeadAb, MSB, NutrAb, RCI, RefZh, S&F, SCI, VITIS, Zincscan.
—BLDSC (3133.700000), CASDDS, CISTI, Ei, IDS, IE, ingenta, Linda Hall.
Published by: (Polska Akademia Nauk, Komitet Chemii Analitycznej/Polish Academy of Sciences, Committee on Analytical Chemistry), Polskie Towarzystwo Chemiczne/Polish Chemical Society, c/o Editor of Chemia Analityczna, Warsaw University, Faculty of Chemistry, Pasteura 1, Warsaw, 02093, Poland. TEL 48-22-8222393, FAX 48-22-8224889, chemanal@chem.uw.edu.pl, http://www.chem.uw.edu.pl/chemanal, http://www.ptchem.lodz.pl. Ed., R&P Adam Hulanicki TEL 48-22-8221085. Adv. contact Alicja Jedlewska. page PLZ 170; 14 x 21. Circ: 300. **Co-sponsor:** Komitet Badan Naukowych/Committee of Scientific Research.

543   USA   ISSN 0069-2883
                                    CODEN: CAMCBN
➤ **CHEMICAL ANALYSIS;** a series of monographs on analytical chemistry and its applications. Text in English. 1953. irreg., latest 2000. price varies. index. **Document type:** *Monographic series, Academic/Scholarly.*
Indexed: BIOSIS Prev, BiolAb, CIN, ChemAb, ChemTitl, EngInd, MSB.
—BLDSC (3137.500000), CASDDS, CISTI, Ei, IE, Infotrieve, ingenta.

Published by: John Wiley & Sons, Inc., 111 River St, Hoboken, NJ 07030-5774. TEL 201-748-6000, 800-825-7550, FAX 201-748-5915, uscs-wis@wiley.com, http://www.wiley.com. Eds. J D Winefordner, P J Elving.

543 546 547 660   GBR   ISSN 1466-6111
CHEMICALS, CHEMICAL TECHNOLOGY & INSTRUMENTATION WORLD BUYERS' GUIDE; world buyers' guide for chemicals, bulk drugs, chemical equipment, analytical & process control instruments. Text in English. 1999. a. GBP 180, USD 290 (effective 1999). adv. **Document type:** *Directory.* **Description:** Covers manufacturers, importers and process control instruments world wide.
Related titles: Large type ed. 8 pt.
Published by: Global Promotions, 1 Tobin Close, London, NW3 3DY, United Kingdom. TEL 44-171-586-1720, FAX 44-171-483-2684, sang@globalnet.co.uk. Ed., Adv. contact Mr. R.S.C. Iengar. B&W page USD 300, color page USD 450; trim 18 x 26. Circ: 4,500 (paid); 500.

643   DEU   ISSN 0943-6677
                                    CODEN: CHLBAT
CHEMIE IN LABOR UND BIOTECHNIK. Text in German. 1949. m. EUR 99.80 domestic; EUR 110.20 foreign (effective 2005). adv. bk.rev. abstr.; charts; illus.; stat. index. **Document type:** *Journal, Academic/Scholarly.*
Former titles: C L B Chemie fuer Labor und Betrieb (0722-6764); (until 1982): Chemie fuer Labor und Betrieb (0009-2835)
Related titles: ◆ Supplement(s): C L B Memory. ISSN 0179-9398.
Indexed: AESIS, AnalAb, CEABA, CIN, CISA, ChemAb, ChemTitl, ExcerpMed, MSB, RefZh.
—BLDSC (3157.160000), CASDDS, CISTI, IE, ingenta. **CCC.**
Published by: Rubikon Verlag, Bammentaler Str 6-8, Gaiberg, 69251, Germany. TEL 49-6223-970743, FAX 49-6223-970741, redaktion@clb.de, http://www.clb.de. Ed. Rolf Kickuth. Adv. contact Natalia Khilian. page EUR 2,100; trim 177 x 260. Circ: 5,623.

CHEMOMETRICS AND INTELLIGENT LABORATORY SYSTEMS. see *CHEMISTRY—Computer Applications*

543 660   BEL   ISSN 0771-730X
➤ **CHIMIE NOUVELLE.** Text in English, French. 1983. q. EUR 58. bk.rev. stat. back issues avail. **Document type:** *Academic/Scholarly.* **Description:** Deals with several areas of chemistry and industrial chemistry for chemists and researchers.
Indexed: RefZh.
—BLDSC (3179.750000), CISTI, IE, ingenta.
Published by: Societe Royale de Chimie, Av Franlin Roosevelt 50, Brussels, 1050, Belgium. TEL 32-2-6505208, FAX 32-2-6505184, src@ulb.ac.be, http://www.ulb.ac.be/assoc/src. Ed., Pub. Desire Daloze. Adv. contact Colette Jamar. Circ: 1,500 (paid).

543.8   DEU   ISSN 0009-5893
QD79.C4   CODEN: CHRGB7
➤ **CHROMATOGRAPHIA.** Text in English; Summaries in English, French, German. 1968. 24/yr. EUR 1,610 in Europe to institutions (effective 2006). adv. bk.rev. charts; illus. index. **Document type:** *Journal, Academic/Scholarly.*
Related titles: Microfilm ed.: (from PQC); Online - full text ed.: ISSN 1612-1112 (from EBSCO Publishing, ScienceDirect, Springer LINK, Swets Information Services).
Indexed: ASCA, AbHyg, AgBio, AgrForAb, AnalAb, BIOBASE, BioCN&I, BioDAb, BiolAb, CCI, CEABA, CIN, CISA, CPA, Cadscan, ChemAb, ChemTitl, ChromAb, CurCont, DSA, ESPM, ExcerpMed, FCA, FPA, FS&TA, ForAb, HelmAb, HerbAb, HortAb, I&DA, IABS, ISR, IndVet, Inpharma, LeadAb, MSB, MSCI, MaizeAb, NemAb, NutrAb, OrnHort, PBA, PE&ON, PGegResA, PGrRegA, PHN&I, PN&I, PotatoAb, PoultAb, ProtozoAb, RA&MP, RCI, RM&VM, RPP, RRTA, Reac, RevApplEntom, RiceAb, S&F, SCI, SIA, SWRA, SoyAb, TDB, TriticAb, VITIS, VetBull, WRCInf, WeedAb, Zincscan.
—BLDSC (3182.450000), CASDDS, CINDOC, CISTI, GNLM, IDS, IE, Infotrieve, ingenta, Linda Hall. **CCC.**
Published by: Friedr. Vieweg und Sohn Verlagsgesellschaft mbH (Subsidiary of: Springer Science+Business Media), Postfach 5829, Wiesbaden, 65048, Germany. TEL 49-611-7878357, FAX 49-611-7878420, http://www.elsevier.com/locate/chromatographia, http://www.vieweg.de. Circ: 2,000.

543   USA   ISSN 0069-3936
                                    CODEN: CHGSAL
➤ **CHROMATOGRAPHIC SCIENCE SERIES.** Text in English. 1965. irreg., latest vol.88, 2002. price varies. adv. **Document type:** *Monographic series, Academic/Scholarly.*
Indexed: BIOSIS Prev, CIN, ChemAb, ChemTitl, MSB.
—BLDSC (3182.821000), CASDDS, CISTI, IE, ingenta, KNAW. **CCC.**
Published by: Marcel Dekker Inc. (Subsidiary of: Taylor & Francis Group), 270 Madison Ave, New York, NY 10016-0602. TEL 212-696-9000, FAX 212-685-4540, http://www.dekker.com. Ed. J C Giddings. R&P Julia Mulligan. Adv. contact Eridania Perez.

643   JPN   ISSN 1342-8284
                                    CODEN: KUROE9
CHROMATOGRAPHY; journal of separation and detection sciences. Text in English, Japanese. 1989. 3/yr. membership. **Document type:** *Journal, Academic/Scholarly.*

Formerly (until 1996): Kuromatografi (0917-3048)
Indexed: CIN, ChemAb, ChemTitl.
—BLDSC (3182.906000), CASDDS, IE, ingenta.
Published by: Kuromatografi Kagakkai/Society for Chromatographic Sciences, c/o Nobuo Tanaka, Kyoto Institute of Technology, Department of Polymer Science, Matsugasaki, Sakyo-ku, Kyoto, 606-8585, Japan. FAX 82-75-7247710, haginaka@mwu.mukogawa-u.ac.jp, nobuo@ipc.kit.ac.jp, http://www.josai.ac.jp/hkoba/scs_sub/scsJR/scsJV18N03EG.html, http://www.josai.ac.jp/hkoba/scs_sub/scs_mig_jp.html. Ed. Jun Haginaka. R&P Nobui Tanaka.

543   NLD   ISSN 0166-526X
QD75
➤ **COMPREHENSIVE ANALYTICAL CHEMISTRY.** Text in Dutch. 1959. irreg., latest vol.38, 2002. price varies. back issues avail. **Document type:** *Monographic series, Academic/Scholarly.*
Formerly: Wilson and Wilson's Comprehensive Analytical Chemistry (0069-8024)
Related titles: Online - full text ed.: (from ScienceDirect).
—BLDSC (3366.240000), CISTI, IE, Infotrieve.
Published by: Elsevier BV (Subsidiary of: Elsevier Science & Technology), Radarweg 29, Amsterdam, 1043 NX, Netherlands. TEL 31-20-4853911, FAX 31-20-4852457, nlinfo-f@elsevier.nl, http://www.elsevier.nl. Ed. D. Barcelo.

➤ **COSMETIC SCIENCE MONOGRAPHS.** see *BEAUTY CULTURE—Perfumes And Cosmetics*

543   USA   ISSN 1040-8347
QD71   CODEN: CCACBB
➤ **CRITICAL REVIEWS IN ANALYTICAL CHEMISTRY.** Text in English. 1970. q. USD 744, GBP 450 combined subscription to institutions print & online eds. (effective 2006). bibl.; charts; illus. back issues avail.; reprint service avail. from PSC. **Document type:** *Journal, Academic/Scholarly.* **Description:** Provides scholarly reviews of topics within the vast discipline of analytical chemistry.
Formerly: C R C Critical Reviews in Analytical Chemistry (0007-8980)
Related titles: Online - full text ed.: USD 707, GBP 428 to institutions (effective 2006) (from EBSCO Publishing, Gale Group, IngentaConnect, O C L C Online Computer Library Center, Inc., ProQuest Information & Learning, ScienceDirect, Swets Information Services).
Indexed: AESIS, ASCA, ASFA, AnalAb, B&BAb, BiolAb, BrCerAb, C&ISA, CCI, CIN, CerAb, ChemAb, ChemTitl, CorrAb, CurCont, E&CAJ, EMA, EPB, ESPM, EngInd, FLUIDEX, GEOBASE, IAA, ISR, M&TEA, MBF, METADEX, MSB, RefZh, S&F, SCI, SWRA, WAA, WRCInf.
—BLDSC (3487.470000), CASDDS, CISTI, Ei, IDS, IE, Infotrieve, ingenta, Linda Hall. **CCC.**
Published by: Taylor & Francis Inc. (Subsidiary of: Taylor & Francis Group), 325 Chestnut St, Ste 800, Philadelphia, PA 19016. TEL 215-625-8900, 800-354-1420, FAX 215-625-2940, info@taylorandfrancis.com, http://www.tandf.co.uk/journals/titles/10408347.asp, http://www.taylorandfrancis.com. Ed. Charles Lochmuller. Circ: 590. **Subscr. outside N. America to:** Taylor & Francis Ltd, Journals Customer Service, Rankine Rd, Basingstoke, Hants RG24 8PR, United Kingdom. TEL 44-1256-813000, FAX 44-1256-330245, enquiry@tandf.co.uk.

543   NLD   ISSN 1573-4110
▼ **CURRENT ANALYTICAL CHEMISTRY.** Text in English. 2005 (Jan). q. USD 570 to corporations print or online; USD 275 academic institutions; print or online; USD 110 combined subscription to individuals; USD 680 combined subscription to corporations print & online; USD 300 combined subscription academic institutions; print & online (effective 2005). **Document type:** *Journal, Academic/Scholarly.* **Description:** Publishes authoritative reviews on all the most recent advances in analytical chemistry. All aspects of the field are represented including analytical methodology, techniques and instrumentation in both fundamental and applied areas of the field.
Related titles: Online - full text ed.: (from Gale Group, IngentaConnect).
—CCC.
Published by: Bentham Science Publishers Ltd., PO Box 1673, Hilversum, BR 1200, Netherlands. TEL 31-35-6923800, FAX 31-35-6980150, M.Bentham@inter.nl.net, http://www.bentham.org/cac/index2.htm. Ed. Atta-ur Rahman TEL 92-21-4969873.

➤ **CURRENT OPINION IN DRUG DISCOVERY & DEVELOPMENT.** see *PHARMACY AND PHARMACOLOGY*

543 664   USA
CURRENT PROTOCOLS IN FOOD ANALYTICAL CHEMISTRY. Text in English. base vol. plus q. updates. looseleaf. USD 555 (effective 2004). **Document type:** *Academic/Scholarly.* **Description:** Responds to the need for a current and continuously updated source of food chemistry methods and instrumentation.
Related titles: CD-ROM ed.: USD 540 (effective 2003); Online - full content ed.

C

Published by: John Wiley & Sons, Inc., 111 River St, Hoboken, NJ 07030-5774. TEL 201-748-6000, 800-825-7550, FAX 201-748-5915, aboyle@mindspring.com, protocol@wiley.com, http://www.does.org/masterli/cpfac.html, http://www.wiley.com. Ed. Ann Boyle. **Subscr. to:** PO Box 5597, Somerset, NJ 08875. TEL 732-650-4630, FAX 732-650-4623.

543 541.37 USA ISSN 0891-0006
QP519.9.S45 CODEN: CUSEEW
CURRENT SEPARATIONS. Text in English. 1979. q.
Indexed: ChemAb.
—BLDSC (3504.009000), CISTI, IE, Infotrieve.
Published by: Bioanalytical Systems, Inc., 2701 Kent Ave, W. Lafayette, IN 47906. TEL 765-463-4527, 800-845-4246, FAX 765-497-1102, bas@bioanalytical.com, http://www.currentseparations.com, http://www.bioanalytical.com.

542.1 DEU ISSN 0070-315X
CODEN: DMDGAG
DECHEMA MONOGRAPHIEN. Text in German. 1930. irreg., latest vol.137, 2001. price varies. index. reprint service avail. from ISI. **Document type:** *Monographic series, Academic/Scholarly.*
Indexed: CEABA, CIN, ChemAb, ChemTitl, DSA, FS&TA, MSB.
—BLDSC (3535.995000), CASDDS, CISTI, IE, ingenta, Linda Hall. **CCC.**
Published by: (Deutsche Gesellschaft fuer Chemisches Apparatewesen e.V. - DECHEMA), Wiley - V C H Verlag GmbH & Co. KGaA (Subsidiary of: John Wiley & Sons, Inc.), Boschstr 12, Weinheim, 69469, Germany. TEL 49-6201-6060, FAX 49-6201-606328, subservice@wiley-vch.de, http://www.wiley-vch.de. **Subscr. in N. America to:** John Wiley & Sons, Inc., 111 River St, Hoboken, NJ 07030-5774. TEL 201-748-6645, FAX 201-748-6088, subinfo@wiley.com; **Subscr. outside Germany, Austria & Switzerland to:** John Wiley & Sons Ltd., The Atrium, Southern Gate, Chichester, West Sussex PO19 8SQ, United Kingdom. TEL 44-1243-779777, FAX 44-1243-775878.

C

643 MEX
DICCIONARIO DE ESPECIALIDADES EN ANALISIS CLINICOS. Text in Spanish. 1985. a.
Published by: Ediciones P L M S.A. de C.V., San Bernardino 17, Col del Valle, Mexico City, DF 03100, Mexico. TEL 687-1766, FAX 536-5027. Ed. Patricia Calderon. Circ: 5,000.

543 JPN ISSN 0385-1516
CODEN: DONED9
DOJIN NYUSU/DOJIN NEWS. Text in Japanese; Summaries in English. 1976. 6/yr. free. **Document type:** *Newsletter.*
Description: Covers topics in chemistry and their applications in pharmacology.
Indexed: BiolAb, CIN, ChemAb, ChemTitl.
—CASDDS.
Published by: Dojindo Laboratories, Kumamoto Techno Research Park, 2025-5 Tabaru, Kumamoto-gun, Mashiki-machi, Kumamoto-ken 861-2202, Japan. TEL 81-96-286-1515, FAX 81-96-286-1525, info@dojindo.co.jp, order@dojindo.co.jp, http://www.dojindo.co.jp.

615.19 JPN ISSN 0919-9322
DONJINDO NEWSLETTER. Text in English. 1992. 3/yr. free. adv. **Document type:** *Newsletter.* **Description:** Covers topics in chemistry and their application in pharmacology.
Published by: Dojindo Laboratories, Kumamoto Techno Research Park, 2025-5 Tabaru, Kamimashiki-gun, Mashiki-machi, Kumamoto-ken 861-2202, Japan. TEL 096-286-1515, FAX 096-286-1525, info@dojindo.co.jp, order@dojindo.co.jp, http://www.dojindo.co.jp. Ed. Meiko Sato. R&P Mikihiko Saito. Adv. contact Ken'yu Kina.

643 DEU ISSN 1040-0397
QD115 CODEN: ELANEU
➤ **ELECTROANALYSIS.** Text in English. 1989. s-m. EUR 2,548 in Europe; CHF 4,418 in Switzerland & Liechtenstein; USD 3,128 elsewhere; EUR 2,548 combined subscription in Europe print & online eds.; CHF 4,860 combined subscription in Switzerland & Liechtenstein for print & online eds.; USD 3,441 combined subscription elsewhere print & online eds. (effective 2006). adv. **Document type:** *Journal, Academic/Scholarly.*
Description: Covers all fundamental and practical aspects of electroanalysis.
Related titles: Microfilm ed.: (from VCI); Online - full text ed.: ISSN 1521-4109. EUR 2,548 in Europe; CHF 4,418 in Switzerland & Liechtenstein; USD 3,128 elsewhere (effective 2006) (from EBSCO Publishing, Swets Information Services, Wiley InterScience).
Indexed: AESIS, ASCA, AnalAb, BIOSIS Prev, BiolAb, CCI, CEABA, CIN, CTE, ChemAb, ChemTitl, CurCont, DSA, EngInd, ISR, MSB, MSCI, NutrAb, RCI, RefZh, SCI, SIA, VITIS.
—BLDSC (3698.789000), CASDDS, CISTI, Ei, GNLM, IDS, IE, Infotrieve, ingenta, Linda Hall. **CCC.**
Published by: Wiley - V C H Verlag GmbH & Co. KGaA (Subsidiary of: John Wiley & Sons, Inc.), Boschstr 12, Weinheim, 69469, Germany. TEL 49-6201-6060, FAX 49-6201-606328, subservice@wiley-vch.de, http://www3.interscience.wiley.com/cgi-bin/home. Ed. Joseph Wang. R&P Claudia Rutz. Adv. contact P Gregory. **Subscr. in the Americas to:** John Wiley & Sons, Inc., 111 River St, Hoboken, NJ 07030-5774. TEL 201-748-6645, FAX 201-748-6088, subinfo@wiley.com; **Subscr. outside Germany, Austria & Switzerland to:** John Wiley & Sons Ltd., The Atrium, Southern Gate, Chichester, West Sussex PO19 8SQ, United Kingdom. TEL 44-1243-779777, FAX 44-1243-775878.

543 USA ISSN 0070-9778
QD115 CODEN: ELCHAI
ELECTROANALYTICAL CHEMISTRY: A SERIES OF ADVANCES. Text in English. 1966. irreg., latest vol.22. USD 195 per vol. vol.22 (effective 2004). adv. **Document type:** *Monographic series.*
Indexed: ASCA, CCI, CIN, ChemAb, ChemTitl, ISR, MSCI, RCI, SCI.
—BLDSC (3698.795000), CASDDS, CISTI, IDS, IE, ingenta, Linda Hall. **CCC.**
Published by: Marcel Dekker Inc. (Subsidiary of: Taylor & Francis Group), 270 Madison Ave, New York, NY 10016-0602. TEL 212-696-9000, FAX 212-685-4540, http://www.dekker.com/servlet/product/productid/7399-3. Eds. Allen J Bard, I. Rubinstein. R&P Julia Mulligan. Adv. contact Eridania Perez. **Subscr. to:** 6000 Broken Sound Pkwy NW, Ste. 300, Boca Raton, FL 33487-2713. TEL 800-228-1160, jrnlorders@dekker.com.

EUROPEAN DIRECTORY OF WORLD SURFACE TECHNOLOGY. see *BUSINESS AND ECONOMICS—Trade And Industrial Directories*

543 FRA
QD71 CODEN: ANLSCY
➤ **EUROPEAN JOURNAL OF ANALYTICAL CHEMISTRY.** Short title: Eur J A C. Text and summaries in English, French. 1972. 10/yr. adv. bk.rev. abstr.; charts; illus.; pat.; tr.lit. back issues avail.; reprint service avail. from ISI. **Document type:** *Academic/Scholarly.* **Description:** Divided into two sections. The first section publishes only refereed original manuscripts. The second section provides professional information: company news, meetings, application of techniques, new instruments and equipment, catalogues and brochures, a full coverage of all new products and a dossier on a special subject.
Formerly (until 2002): Analusis (0365-4877); Formed by the 1972 merger of: Methodes Physiques d'Analyse (0026-122X); Which was formerly (until 1965): Groupement pour l'Advancement des Methodes Spectographiques. Publications (0369-9390); (1950-1959): Congres du Groupement pour l'Advancement des Methodes d'Analyse Spectrographique des Produits Metallurgiques (0366-5992); And: Chimie Analytique (0009-4331); Which was formerly (until 1947): Annales de Chimie Analytique (0365-1053); (until 1942): Annales de Chimie Analytique et de Chimie Appliquee et Revue de Chimie Analytique Reunies (0365-1010); (until 1919): Annales de Chimie Analytique et de Chimie Appliquee a l'Industrie, a l'Agriculture, a la Pharmacie et la Biologie et Revue de Chimie Analytique Reunies (0365-5016); Which was formed by the merger of (1890-1918): Annales de Chimie Analytique Appliquee a l'Industrie, a l'Agriculture, a la Pharmacie et la Biologie (0398-9828); (1893-1918): Revue de Chimie Analytique Appliquee a l'Industrie, a l'Agriculture, a la Metallurgie, au Commerce, a la Pharmacie et aux Sciences Medicales (0398-981X)
Related titles: Online - full text ed.: European Journal of Analytical Chemistry (EurJAC) Online (from EBSCO Publishing, ScienceDirect, Swets Information Services).
Indexed: AESIS, ASCA, ASFA, AbHyg, AnBrAb, AnalAb, BioCN&I, BiolAb, CCI, CIN, CPA, ChemAb, ChemTitl, CurCont, DSA, ESPM, EngInd, ExcerpMed, FCA, FPA, FS&TA, ForAb, HelmAb, HortAb, I&DA, ISR, IndVet, MSB, MSCI, NumL, NutrAb, OrnHort, PGegResA, PGrRegA, PHN&I, PN&I, RA&MP, RCI, RM&VM, RPP, RevApplEntom, S&F, SCI, SIA, TriticAb, VITIS, VetBull, WeedAb.
—BLDSC (0890.800000), CASDDS, CINDOC, CISTI, Ei, IDS, IE, Linda Hall. **CCC.**
Published by: (Societe Francaise de Chimie), E D P Sciences, 17 Ave du Hoggar, Parc d'Activites de Courtaboeuf, BP 112, Cedex A, Les Ulis, F-91944, France. TEL 33-1-69187575, FAX 33-1-69860678, subscribers@edpsciences.org, http://www.edpsciences.org. Ed. P Arpino. Circ: 3,000.
Co-sponsors: Societe de Chimie Industrielle; Gesellschaft der Deutscher Chemiker, GW.

543.1 GBR ISSN 1469-0667
CODEN: EJMSCL
➤ **EUROPEAN JOURNAL OF MASS SPECTROMETRY.** Text in English. 1995. bi-m. GBP 397 combined subscription domestic for print and online eds.; EUR 600 combined subscription in Europe for print and online eds.; USD 670 combined subscription elsewhere for print and online eds. (effective 2005). **Document type:** *Journal, Academic/Scholarly.*
Description: Disseminates original research concerned with the mass spectrometry of atomic and molecular species.
Formerly (until 1998): European Mass Spectrometry (1356-1049)
Related titles: Online - full text ed.: ISSN 1365-0718. GBP 325 domestic; EUR 487.50 in Europe; USD 585 elsewhere (effective 2005) (from EBSCO Publishing).
Indexed: ASCA, AnalAb, BIOSIS Prev, BiolAb, CCI, ChemAb, CurCont, MSB, VITIS.
—BLDSC (3829.731150), CASDDS, CISTI, IDS, IE, Infotrieve, ingenta. **CCC.**
Published by: I M Publications, 6 Charlton Mill, Charlton, Chichester, W Sussex PO18 0HY, United Kingdom. TEL 44-1243-811334, FAX 44-1243-811711, imp@impub.demon.co.uk, http://www.impub.co.uk/ems.html. Ed. Gill Stockford.

➤ **EXPERIMENTAL AND MOLECULAR PATHOLOGY.** see *MEDICAL SCIENCES*

643 CHN ISSN 0253-3820
QD71 CODEN: FHHHDT
FENXI HUAXUE/CHINESE JOURNAL OF ANALYTICAL CHEMISTRY. Text in Chinese; Abstracts in English. 1972. m. CNY 180 domestic; USD 360 foreign; CNY 15 newsstand/cover domestic; CNY 30 newsstand/cover foreign (effective 2005). adv. **Document type:** *Academic/Scholarly.*
Description: Provides the latest research results concerning all branches of analytical chemistry.
Related titles: Online - full content ed.: (from WanFang Data Corp.); Online - full text ed.: (from East View Information Services).
Indexed: AnalAb, BrCerAb, C&ISA, CCI, CIN, CerAb, ChemAb, ChemTitl, CivEngAb, CorrAb, DSA, E&CAJ, EMA, IAA, M&TEA, MBF, METADEX, MSB, NutrAb, RefZh, SIA, SolStAb, WAA.
—BLDSC (3180.290800), CASDDS, CISTI, IE, ingenta, Linda Hall.
Published by: (Zhongguo Huaxuehui/Chinese Chemical Society), Zhongguo Kexueyuan, Changchun Yingyong Huaxue Yanjiusuo/Chinese Academy of Sciences, Changchun Institute of Applied Chemistry, 5625, Renmin Dajie, Changchun, 130022, China. TEL 86-431-5262017, FAX 86-431-5262018, fxhx@ciac.jl.cn; cywang@ciac.jl.cn, http://www.analchem.cn/, http://www.ciac.jl.cn/. Ed. Er Kang Wang. R&P Lai Ming Li. Adv. contact Bao Ning Wang. page USD 750. Circ: 6,000.
Dist. outside China by: China International Book Trading Corp, 35 Chegongzhuang Xilu, Haidian District, PO Box 399, Beijing 100044, China. TEL 86-10-68412045, FAX 86-10-68412023, cibtc@mail.cibtc.com.cn, http://www.cibtc.com.cn.

FOLIA MICROBIOLOGICA. see *BIOLOGY—Biochemistry*

543 USA ISSN 0887-736X
QD415.A1 CODEN: FCINEI
FOR FORMULATION CHEMISTS ONLY. Abbreviated title: F 2 C O. Text in English. 1989. irreg. USD 285 (effective 1999). adv. bibl.; charts; illus. index, cum.index. back issues avail.
Document type: *Trade.* **Description:** Covers applied research, raw materials, chemical and formulation technology for technicians in the chemical specialty and consumer product industries.
Incorporates (1988-1991): Acta Industria Chimica (1042-2013); (1989-1991): Applied Esthetiques (0896-5056); (1989-1991): C I T A Exam Reviews (1042-8933); (1989-1991): Cosmetech (0895-8718); (1988-1991): Health and Beauty Formulary (0892-4643); And (1989-1991): Technitrivia (0892-4651); (1982-1985): Erde Novus; Which was formerly: Erde International (0735-2840)
—CISTI. **CCC.**
Published by: C I T A International (USA), Industrial Journals Division, 3464 W Earll Dr, Ste E F, Phoenix, AZ 85017-5260. TEL 602-447-0480, FAX 602-447-0305. Ed. E M Morsy. Circ: 2,000.

643 JPN
FURO INJEKUSHON BUNSEKI KOENKAI KOEN YOSHISHU/ABSTRACTS OF MEETING ON FLOW INJECTION ANALYSIS. Text in Japanese. 1984. s-a. JPY 3,000 (effective 1999). **Document type:** *Abstract/Index.*
Published by: Nihon Bunseki Kagakkai, Furo Injekushon Bunseki Kenkyu Kondankai/Japan Society for Analytical Chemistry, Division of Flow Injection Analysis, University Faculty of Science Dept of Chemistry, 3-1-1 Tsushima-Naka, Okayama-shi, 700-0082, Japan. TEL 81-86-251-7846, FAX 8-86-251-7853, motomizu@cc.okayama-u.ac.jp.

543.8 DEU ISSN 0940-032X
G I T SPEZIAL SEPARATION. Text in German. a. EUR 10 in Europe to institutions; USD 14 elsewhere to institutions (effective 2006). adv. **Document type:** *Journal, Trade.*
Formerly: G I T Spezial Chromotagraphie
Indexed: INIS AtomInd, MSB.
—BLDSC (4179.656100), CISTI, IE.
Published by: (Glas-und Instrumenten-Technik), G I T Verlag GmbH (Subsidiary of: Wiley - V C H Verlag GmbH & Co. KGaA), Roesslerstr 90, Darmstadt, 64293, Germany. TEL 49-6151-80900, FAX 49-6151-8090146, info@gitverlag.com, http://www.gitverlag.com/index.html?content=%2Fwj%2Fengine%2Fde%2Fpub%2Fmag%2Fsep. Ed. Margareta Dellert-Ritter. Adv. contact Hubert Schulz TEL 49-6151-8090116. B&W page EUR 6,540; trim 185 x 260. Circ: 25,000.

543 BRA
GUIA DAS ANALISES. Text in Portuguese. 1994. a. BRL 250, USD 250 (effective 2000). adv. back issues avail. **Document type:** *Directory.*

Published by: Editora Q D Ltda., Rua Conselheiro Brotero, 589 Cj 11-1o Andar, B Funda, Sao Paulo, SP 01154-001, Brazil. TEL 55-11-826-6899, FAX 55-11-825-8192, editoraqd@sti.com.br. Ed. Emanoel Fairbanks. Pub. Denisard Gerola S Pinto. Adv. contact Rogerio Barbato. page USD 5,474.13; trim 275 x 205. Circ: 10,000.

543.1 USA
I U P A C HANDBOOK (YEAR). Text in English. irreg. **Document type:** *Academic/Scholarly.*
Published by: (International Union of Pure and Applied Chemistry), C R C Press, LLC (Subsidiary of: Taylor & Francis Group), 2000 N W Corporate Blvd, Boca Raton, FL 33431. TEL 800-272-7737, journals@crcpress.com, http://www.crcpress.com/.

543 616 USA ISSN 1092-2059
CODEN: ILAMF4
INSIDE LABORATORY MANAGEMENT. Text in English. 1997. m. USD 149 to individuals non-members; USD 225 to institutions non-members; USD 100 to members; USD 49 to students (effective 2005). **Document type:** *Academic/Scholarly.* **Description:** Provides the information needed to stay current and knowledgeable about laboratory practices for chemical and microbiological analysis of food, drug, agricultural, and environmental matrices.
Indexed: AESIS, AnalAb.
—BLDSC (4518.152357). **CCC.**
Published by: A O A C International, 481 N Frederick Ave, Ste 500, Gaithersburg, MD 20877-2417. TEL 800-379-2622, FAX 301-924-7089, aoac@aoac.org, http://www.aoac.org/pubs/pubinsidelab.html.

INSTRUMENTA. see *INSTRUMENTS*

543 USA ISSN 1073-9149
QD53 CODEN: ISCTEF
➤ **INSTRUMENTATION SCIENCE & TECHNOLOGY.** Text in English. 1973. bi-m. GBP 963, USD 1,589 combined subscription to institutions print & online eds. (effective 2006). adv. bk.rev. bibl.; charts; illus. reprint service avail. from PSC. **Document type:** *Journal, Academic/Scholarly.* **Description:** Dedicated to publishing papers dealing with instrument design innovations and applications in the areas of chemistry, biotechnology, and environemntal science.
Incorporates (in 2003): Journal of Trace and Microprobe Techniques (0733-4680); Former titles (until 1994): Analytical Instrumentation (0743-5797); (until 1984): Chemical, Biomedical and Environmental Instrumentation (0190-4094); Chemical Instrumentation (0009-2592)
Related titles: Online - full text ed.: ISSN 1525-6030. GBP 915, USD 1,510 to institutions (effective 2006) (from EBSCO Publishing, O C L C Online Computer Library Center, Inc., Swets Information Services).
Indexed: ABIPC, ASCA, AnalAb, B&BAb, BiolAb, CCI, CIN, CTE, ChemAb, ChemTitl, CurCont, EngInd, ExcerpMed, INIS AtomInd, ISR, ISRS, Inspec, MSB, SCI.
—BLDSC (4529.043800), AskIEEE, CASDDS, CISTI, Ei, IDS, IE, Infotrieve, ingenta, Linda Hall. **CCC.**
Published by: Taylor & Francis Inc. (Subsidiary of: Taylor & Francis Group), 325 Chestnut St, Ste 800, Philadelphia, PA 19016. TEL 215-625-8900, 800-354-1420, FAX 215-625-2940, info@taylorandfrancis.com, http://www.tandf.co.uk/journals/titles/10739149.asp, http://www.taylorandfrancis.com. Ed. Dr. Jack Cazes. adv.: B&W page USD 800. Circ: 325.

543 DEU ISSN 1435-6163
➤ **INTERNATIONAL JOURNAL FOR ION MOBILITY SPECTROMETRY.** Text in English. 1998. q. **Document type:** *Journal, Academic/Scholarly.* **Description:** Covers the theory and practice of ion mobility spectrometry, including various ionization and coupling techniques.
—BLDSC (4542.311500).
Published by: International Society for Ion Mobility Spectrometry, c/o Institut fuer Spektrochemie und Angewandte Spektroskopie, Bunsen-Kirchhoff-Str 11, Dortmund, 44139, Germany. TEL 49-231-1392238, FAX 49-231-1392438. Eds. Gary Eiceman, Joerg Ingo Baumbach.

628 GBR ISSN 0306-7319
QD71 CODEN: IJEAA3
➤ **INTERNATIONAL JOURNAL OF ENVIRONMENTAL ANALYTICAL CHEMISTRY.** Text in English. 1972. 15/yr. GBP 2,953, USD 3,690 combined subscription to institutions print & online eds. (effective 2006). adv. bk.rev. bibl.; charts. index. reprint service avail. from PSC. **Document type:** *Journal, Academic/Scholarly.*
Related titles: CD-ROM ed.; Microform ed.; Online - full text ed.: ISSN 1029-0397. GBP 2,805, USD 3,506 to institutions (effective 2006) (from EBSCO Publishing, Gale Group, IngentaConnect, O C L C Online Computer Library Center, Inc., Swets Information Services).
Indexed: ASCA, ASFA, AbHyg, Agr, AgrForAb, AnBrAb, AnalAb, ApicAb, BIOBASE, BiolAb, CCI, CPA, Cadscan, ChemAb, ChromAb, CurCont, DSA, DokArb, EIA, EPB, ESPM, EnerInd, EngInd, EnvAb, EnvEAb, ExcerpMed, FCA, FPA, FS&TA, ForAb, H&SSA, HortAb, I&DA, IABS, ISR, IndMed, LHB, LeadAb, M&GPA, M&TEA, MEDLINE, MSB, MaizeAb, NemAb, NutrAb, OrnHort, PGrRegA, PHN&I, PN&I, PollutAb, PotatoAb, RA&MP, RCI, RPP, RiceAb, S&F, SCI, SWRA, SoyAb, TDB, TriticAb, VITIS, WAE&RSA, WeedAb, Zincscan.
—BLDSC (4542.241000), CINDOC, CISTI, GNLM, IE, Infotrieve, ingenta. **CCC.**
Published by: Taylor & Francis Ltd (Subsidiary of: Taylor & Francis Group), 4 Park Sq, Milton Park, Abingdon, OX14 4RN, United Kingdom. TEL 44-1235-828600, FAX 44-1235-829000, info@tandf.co.uk, http://www.tandf.co.uk/journals/titles/03067319.asp. Ed. Juan Albaiges. **Subscr. in N. America to:** Taylor & Francis Inc., Customer Services Dept, 325 Chestnut St, 8th Fl, Philadelphia, PA 19106. TEL 215-625-8900, 800-354-1420, FAX 215-625-8914, customerservice@taylorandfrancis.com; **Subscr. to:** Journals Customer Service, Rankine Rd, Basingstoke, Hants RG24 8PR, United Kingdom. TEL 44-1256-813000, FAX 44-1256-330245, enquiry@tandf.co.uk.

➤ **INTERNATIONAL JOURNAL OF P I X E.** (Particle-Induced X-ray Emission) see *PHYSICS—Nuclear Physics*

➤ **INTERNATIONAL JOURNAL OF POLYMER ANALYSIS & CHARACTERIZATION.** see *ENGINEERING—Chemical Engineering*

643 USA ISSN 0010-2164
CODEN: ILBYA6
INTERNATIONAL LABORATORY. Text in English. 1971. 6/yr. free to qualified personnel (effective 2004). adv. bk.rev. charts; illus.; stat.; tr.lit. Supplement avail. **Document type:** *Magazine, Trade.*
Indexed: AnalAb, BiolAb, CEABA, CISA, CSNB, ChemAb, CurCont, EngInd, ExcerpMed, IndVet, LHB, MSB, NutrAb, RAPRA, RefZh, VITIS, WSCA, WTA.
—BLDSC (4542.705000), CASDDS, IE, Infotrieve, ingenta.
Published by: International Scientific Communications, Inc., 30 Controls Dr, PO Box 670, Shelton, CT 06484-0870. TEL 203-926-9300, FAX 203-926-9310, iscpubs@iscpubs.com, http://www.iscpubs.com, http://www.iscpubs.com/. Eds. Brian Howard, Susan Messinger. Pub. William Wham. adv.: B&W page USD 7,835, color page USD 10,570. Circ: 52,503 (controlled). **U.K. subscr. to:** I.S.C. House, Progress Business Centre, 5 Whittle Pkwy., Slough, Berks SL1 6QQ, United Kingdom. TEL 44-1628-669199, 55-1628-668881.

INTERNATIONAL LABORATORY BUYERS' GUIDE. see *BIOLOGY—Biotechnology*

643 USA
INTERNATIONAL LABORATORY NEWS. Text in English. m. free domestic to qualified personnel. adv. **Document type:** *Magazine, Trade.*
Published by: International Scientific Communications, Inc., 30 Controls Dr, PO Box 670, Shelton, CT 06484-0870. TEL 203-926-9300, FAX 203-926-9310, webmaster@iscpubs.com, http://www.internationallaboratory.com. Ed., Pub. Brian Howard. adv.: B&W page USD 5,495.

643 USA
INTERNATIONAL LABORATORY. PACIFIC RIM EDITION. Text in English. q. **Document type:** *Trade.*
Formerly: International Laboratory. Asian - Australian Edition (0894-1661)
Published by: International Scientific Communications, Inc., 30 Controls Dr, PO Box 670, Shelton, CT 06484-0870. TEL 203-926-9300, iscpubs@iscpubs.com, http://www.iscpubs.com. Ed. Brian Howard. Pub. William Wham. adv.: B&W page USD 6,315, color page USD 6,885. **U.K. subscr. to:** I.S.C. House, Progress Business Centre, 5 Whittle Pkwy., Slough, Berks SL1 6QQ, United Kingdom. TEL 44-1628-668881.

643 GBR ISSN 0267-9477
QD96.A8 CODEN: JASPE2
➤ **JOURNAL OF ANALYTICAL ATOMIC SPECTROMETRY.** Abbreviated title: J A A S. Text in English. 1986. m. GBP 1,285, USD 2,352 combined subscription print & online eds. (effective 2006). adv. bk.rev. **Document type:** *Journal, Academic/Scholarly.* **Description:** Contains original research papers, short papers, communications and letters concerned with all aspects of the development and analytical applications of spectrometric techniques.
Incorporated (in 1985): Annual Reports on Analytical Atomic Spectroscopy (0306-1353)
Related titles: Online - full text ed.: ISSN 1364-5544. GBP 1,157, USD 2,117 (effective 2006) (from EBSCO Publishing, O C L C Online Computer Library Center, Inc., Swets Information Services).
Indexed: ASCA, AnalAb, ArtHuCI, BIOSIS Prev, BiolAb, CCI, CIN, ChemAb, ChemTitl, CurCont, DSA, EngInd, ExcerpMed, FS&TA, ForAb, HortAb, ISR, M&GPA, MSB, MSCI, MinerAb, NutrAb, RefZh, RiceAb, S&F, SCI, SIA, SoyAb, VITIS, WRCInf.
—BLDSC (4928.200000), CASDDS, CISTI, Ei, IDS, IE, Infotrieve, ingenta, Linda Hall. **CCC.**
Published by: Royal Society of Chemistry, Thomas Graham House, Science Park, Milton Rd, Cambridge, CB4 0WF, United Kingdom. TEL 44-1223-432360, FAX 44-1223-423623, jaas@rsc.org, sales@rsc.rg, advertising@rsc.org, http://www.rsc.org/jaas. **Subscr. to:** Portland Press Ltd., R S C Distribution Services, Commerce Way, Whitehall Industrial Estate, Colchester CO2 8HP, United Kingdom. TEL 44-1206-226050, FAX 44-1206-226055, sales@rscdistribution.org.

543 RUS ISSN 1061-9348
QD71 CODEN: JACTE2
➤ **JOURNAL OF ANALYTICAL CHEMISTRY.** Text in English. 1946. m. EUR 3,698, USD 3,288, GBP 2,312 combined subscription to institutions print & online eds. (effective 2005). back issues avail. **Document type:** *Journal, Academic/Scholarly.* **Description:** Covers theoretical and some applied aspects of analytical chemistry; it informs the reader of new trends in analytical methods, samples, and analytes; new instruments; and reagents.
Formerly (until 1993): Journal of Analytical Chemistry of the U S S R (0021-8766)
Related titles: Microfilm ed.: (from PQC); Online - full text ed.: ISSN 1608-3199 (from EBSCO Publishing, Gale Group, IngentaConnect, Kluwer Online, O C L C Online Computer Library Center, Inc., Springer LINK, Swets Information Services); ♦ Translation of: Zhurnal Analiticheskoi Khimii. ISSN 0044-4502.
Indexed: ASCA, AnalAb, BibLing, CCI, CIN, Cadscan, ChemAb, ChemTitl, CurCont, EngInd, ExcerpMed, FS&TA, ISR, LeadAb, MSB, MSCI, RCI, RM&VM, S&F, SCI, VITIS, WeedAb, Zincscan.
—BLDSC (0412.990000), CASDDS, CISTI, IDS, IE, Infotrieve, ingenta, Linda Hall. **CCC.**
Published by: (Rossiiskaya Akademiya Nauk/Russian Academy of Sciences), M A I K Nauka - Interperiodica, Profsoyuznaya ul 90, Moscow, 117997, Russian Federation. TEL 7-095-3347420, FAX 7-095-3360666, compmg@maik.ru, http://www.maik.rssi.ru/journals/anchem.htm, http://www.maik.ru. Ed. Yu A G Zolotov. **Subscr. to:** Springer-Verlag Dordrecht, Journals Department, PO Box 322, Dordrecht, Netherlands. TEL 31-78-6576392, FAX 31-78-6576474.

➤ **JOURNAL OF APPLIED SPECTROSCOPY.** see *PHYSICS—Optics*

542 USA ISSN 1463-9246
QD75.4.A8 CODEN: JAMCF2
➤ **JOURNAL OF AUTOMATED METHODS & MANAGEMENT IN CHEMISTRY.** Text in English; Summaries in French, German. 1978. bi-m. USD 710 combined subscription to institutions print & online eds. (effective 2005). adv. reprint service avail. from PSC. **Document type:** *Journal, Academic/Scholarly.* **Description:** Covers all aspects of automation and mechanization in analytical, clinical and industrial environments. Contains articles on instrumentation, management economics and the philosophy of automation.
Formerly (until 1999): Journal of Automatic Chemistry (0142-0453)
Related titles: Online - full text ed.: ISSN 1464-5068 (from EBSCO Publishing, Gale Group, IngentaConnect, O C L C Online Computer Library Center, Inc., Swets Information Services).
Indexed: AESIS, ASCA, AnalAb, B&BAb, BIOBASE, BioEngAb, BrRB, C&ISA, CCI, CIN, ChemAb, ChemTitl, CurCont, DSA, E&CAJ, ExcerpMed, FS&TA, IAA, IABS, ISR, Inpharma, Inspec, Reac, SCI.
—BLDSC (4949.557700), AskIEEE, CASDDS, CISTI, Ei, GNLM, IDS, IE, Infotrieve, ingenta, Linda Hall. **CCC.**
Published by: (Royal Society of Chemistry GBR, Automated Methods Group GBR), Hindawi Publishing Corporation, PO Box 1210, Sylvania, OH 43560. FAX 866-446-3294, jammc.ed@hindawi.com, hindawi@hindawi.com, http://www.hindawi.com/journals/jammc/about.html. Ed. Peter Stockwell. **Co-sponsor:** Laboratory Automation Standards Foundation.

543 GBR ISSN 0886-9383
QD39.3.M3 CODEN: JOCHEU
➤ **JOURNAL OF CHEMOMETRICS.** Text in English. 1987. m. USD 1,800 to institutions; USD 1,980 to institutions print & online eds. (effective 2006). adv. bk.rev. back issues avail.; reprint service avail. from PSC. **Document type:** *Journal, Academic/Scholarly.* **Description:** Contains papers on fundamental and applied aspects of chemometrics and provides a forum for the exchange of information on meetings, and such for the international chemometrics research community.
Related titles: Microform ed.: (from PQC); Online - full content ed.: ISSN 1099-128X. 1996. USD 1,800 to institutions (effective 2006); Online - full text ed.: (from EBSCO Publishing, Swets Information Services, Wiley InterScience).
Indexed: ASCA, ASFA, AnalAb, BioEngAb, CCI, CIN, CIS, ChemAb, ChemTitl, CurCont, ESPM, EngInd, FS&TA, ISR, Inspec, MSB, NSA, SCI, ST&MA, VITIS.
—BLDSC (4957.380000), CASDDS, CISTI, Ei, IDS, IE, Infotrieve, ingenta, Linda Hall. **CCC.**
Published by: John Wiley & Sons Ltd. (Subsidiary of: John Wiley & Sons, Inc.), The Atrium, Southern Gate, Chichester, West Sussex PO19 8SQ, United Kingdom. TEL 44-1243-779777, FAX 44-1243-775878, customer@wiley.co.uk, http://www3.interscience.wiley.com/cgi-bin/jhome/4425, http://www.wiley.co.uk. Ed. S D Brown. adv.: B&W page GBP 650, color page GBP 1,550; trim 200 x 260. Circ: 312. **Subscr. in the Americas to:** John Wiley & Sons, Inc., 111 River St, Hoboken, NJ 07030-5774. TEL 201-748-6645, 800-225-5945, subinfo@wiley.com.

543.8 USA ISSN 0021-9665
QD271 CODEN: JCHSBZ

➤ **JOURNAL OF CHROMATOGRAPHIC SCIENCE.** Text in English. 1963. 10/yr. USD 380 domestic; USD 395 foreign (effective 2005). adv. bk.rev.; software rev. charts; illus.; abstr.; bibl.; tr.lit. index. 60 p./no. 2 cols./p.; back issues avail.; reprints avail. **Document type:** *Journal, Academic/Scholarly.*
Formerly: Journal of Gas Chromatography (0096-2686)
Related titles: Microfiche ed.; Microfilm ed.: (from MML); Online - full text ed.: (from EBSCO Publishing, Gale Group, IngentaConnect, Swets Information Services); Print ed.
Indexed: ABIPC, AESIS, APIAb, APICat, APIH&E, APIOC, APIPR, APIPS, APITS, ASCA, ASFA, AbHyg, AnalAb, BIOSIS Prev, BiolAb, CCI, CIN, ChemAb, ChemTitl, ChromAb, CurCont, DBA, DSA, ESPM, ExcerpMed, F&EA, FCA, FS&TA, GasAb, HortAb, I&DA, INIS AtomInd, ISR, IndMed, IndVet, Inpharma, MEDLINE, MSB, NutrAb, OrnHort, PollutAb, RA&MP, RCI, RM&VM, Reac, RefZh, S&F, SCI, SIA, SWRA, TDB, VITIS, VetBull, WRCInf, WSCA, WeedAb.
—BLDSC (4958.300000), CASDDS, CINDOC, CISTI, Ei, GNLM, IDS, IE, Infotrieve, ingenta, Linda Hall. **CCC.**
Published by: Preston Publications, Inc., 6600 W. Touhy Ave., Niles, IL 60714-0312. TEL 847-647-2900, FAX 847-647-1155, http://www.j-chrom-sci.com/, http://www.prestonpub.com. Eds. B M Gordon, Huba Kalasz, Kevin Bailey TEL 847-647-2900 ext 1300. Pub., Adv. contact S Tinsley Preston TEL 847-647-2900 ext 1300. R&P Kevin Bailey TEL 847-647-2900 ext 1300. Circ: 1,600 (paid).

543.8 NLD ISSN 0021-9673
CODEN: JCRAEY

➤ **JOURNAL OF CHROMATOGRAPHY A.** Variant title: Journal of Chromatography A. Text in English, French, German; Summaries in English. 1956. 78/yr. EUR 12,225 in Europe to institutions; JPY 1,623,300 in Japan to institutions; USD 13,674 elsewhere to institutions (effective 2006). adv. bk.rev. bibl.; charts; illus. cum.index. reprints avail. **Document type:** *Journal, Academic/Scholarly.* **Description:** Covers all aspects of electrophoresis, mass spectrometry and other separation and detection methods. Targets analytical chemists, biochemists, clinical chemists and all those who are concerned with the separation and identification of mixtrures or compounds in mixtures.
Incorporates: Chromatographic Reviews (0009-5907); Supersedes (in 1958): Chromatographic Methods (0412-3425)
Related titles: Microform ed.: (from PQC); Online - full text ed.: (from EBSCO Publishing, Gale Group, IngentaConnect, ScienceDirect, Swets Information Services); ♦ Supplement(s): Journal of Chromatography Library. ISSN 0301-4770; Journal of Chromatography. Supplementary Volume. ISSN 0376-737X.
Indexed: ABIPC, AEA, AESIS, ASCA, ASFA, AbHyg, AgBio, Agr, AgrForAb, AnBrAb, AnalAb, ApicAb, BIOBASE, BIOSIS Prev, BibAg, BioCN&I, BioDAb, BiolAb, CCI, CIS, CLL, CPA, Cadscan, ChemAb, ChemTitl, ChromAb, CurCont, DBA, DSA, DentInd, EPB, ESPM, EngInd, ExcerpMed, FCA, FPA, FS&TA, FaBeAb, ForAb, HelmAb, HerbAb, HortAb, I&DA, IABS, ISR, IndMed, IndVet, LeadAb, MEDLINE, MSB, MSCI, MaizeAb, NPU, NSCI, NemAb, NutrAb, OrnHort, P&BA, PBA, PGegResA, PGrRegA, PHN&I, PN&I, PST, PollutAb, PotatoAb, PoultAb, ProtozoAb, RA&MP, RCI, RM&VM, RPP, RRTA, RefZh, RevApplEntom, RiceAb, S&F, SCI, SFA, SIA, SSCI, SeedAb, SoyAb, TDB, THA, TOSA, TriticAb, VITIS, VetBull, WAE&RSA, WRCInf, WeedAb, Zincscan.
—BLDSC (4958.350200), CASDDS, CINDOC, CISTI, GNLM, IDS, IE, Infotrieve, ingenta, Linda Hall. **CCC.**
Published by: Elsevier BV (Subsidiary of: Elsevier Science & Technology), Radarweg 29, Amsterdam, 1043 NX, Netherlands. TEL 31-20-4853911, FAX 31-20-4852457, nlinfo-f@elsevier.nl, http://www.elsevier.com/locate/chroma, http://www.elsevier.nl. Eds. C F Poole, J G Dorsey, R W Giese. adv.: B&W page USD 1,020, color page USD 2,205; trim 192 x 262. Circ: 1,700.

543.8 NLD ISSN 0301-4770
CODEN: JCLIDR

➤ **JOURNAL OF CHROMATOGRAPHY LIBRARY.** Text in English. 1973. irreg., latest vol.66, 2002. price varies. back issues avail. **Document type:** *Monographic series, Academic/Scholarly.* **Description:** Discusses the application of chromatography in research in chemistry and chemical engineering.
Related titles: ♦ Supplement to: Journal of Chromatography A. ISSN 0021-9673.
Indexed: BIOSIS Prev, BiolAb, CIN, ChemAb, ChemTitl, MSB.
—BLDSC (4958.351000), CASDDS, CISTI, IE, ingenta. **CCC.**
Published by: Elsevier BV (Subsidiary of: Elsevier Science & Technology), Radarweg 29, Amsterdam, 1043 NX, Netherlands. TEL 31-20-4853911, FAX 31-20-4852457, nlinfo-f@elsevier.nl, http://www.elsevier.nl.

543.1 USA ISSN 1520-4766
QD262 CODEN: JCCHFF

➤ **JOURNAL OF COMBINATORIAL CHEMISTRY.** Text in English. 1999. bi-m. USD 1,145 in North America to institutions; USD 1,190 elsewhere to institutions; USD 160 in North America to members; USD 205 elsewhere to members; USD 120 in North America to students; USD 165 elsewhere to students (effective 2006). adv. back issues avail. **Document type:** *Journal, Academic/Scholarly.* **Description:** Publishes studies that facilitate the synthesis of chemical research.
Related titles: Online - full text ed.: ISSN 1520-4774. USD 40 (effective 2006) (from EBSCO Publishing, Swets Information Services).
Indexed: B&BAb, BIOSIS Prev, BioEngAb, BiolAb, CCI, ChemAb, ChemInfo, CurCR, CurCont, ISR, IndChem, IndMed, M&PBA, MEDLINE, MSB, RCI, RefZh, SCI.
—BLDSC (4960.200000), CISTI, IE, Infotrieve, ingenta, Linda Hall. **CCC.**
Published by: American Chemical Society, 1155 16th St, N W, Washington, DC 20036. TEL 202-872-4614, 202-872-4600, 800-227-5558, FAX 202-776-8264, 202-872-3727, service@acs.org, http://pubs.acs.org/jcc. Ed. Anthony W Czarnik. adv.: color page USD 5,400.

543.1 CHE ISSN 1572-6657
QD551 CODEN: JECHES

➤ **JOURNAL OF ELECTROANALYTICAL CHEMISTRY.** Text in English. 1960. 26/yr. EUR 9,555 in Europe to institutions; JPY 1,268,300 in Japan to institutions; USD 10,689 elsewhere to institutions; EUR 450 in Europe to qualified personnel; JPY 59,100 in Japan to qualified personnel; USD 503 elsewhere to qualified personnel (effective 2006). adv. bk.rev. illus. index. back issues avail. **Document type:** *Journal, Academic/Scholarly.* **Description:** Examines all aspects of the interdisciplinary subject of electrochemistry, both theoretical and applied.
Former titles (until 1992): Journal of Electroanalytical Chemistry and Interfacial Electrochemistry (0022-0728); (until 1966): Journal of Electroanalytical Chemistry (0368-1874)
Related titles: Microform ed.: (from PQC); Online - full text ed.: (from EBSCO Publishing, Gale Group, IngentaConnect, ScienceDirect, Swets Information Services).
Indexed: AESIS, ASCA, AnalAb, CCI, CEABA, CIN, CTE, Cadscan, ChemAb, ChemTitl, CurCont, EngInd, ExcerpMed, F&EA, IAA, ISR, Inspec, LeadAb, MSB, MSCI, NutrAb, RCI, RefZh, SCI, SIA, VITIS, Zincscan.
—BLDSC (4974.700000), AskIEEE, CASDDS, CINDOC, CISTI, IDS, IE, ingenta, Linda Hall. **CCC.**
Published by: Elsevier S.A., PO Box 564, Lausanne 1, 1001, Switzerland. TEL 41-21-3207381, FAX 41-21-3235444, http://www.elsevier.com/locate/jelechem. Eds. Christian Amatore, H. D. Abruna, J. M. Feliu. **Subscr. to:** Elsevier BV, PO Box 211, Amsterdam 1000 AE, Netherlands. TEL 31-20-485-3757, FAX 31-20-485-3432, nlinfo-f@elsevier.nl, http://www.elsevier.nl.

543 363.7063 GBR ISSN 1464-0325
TD172 CODEN: JEMOFW

➤ **JOURNAL OF ENVIRONMENTAL MONITORING.** Abbreviated title: J E M. Text in English. 1999. bi-m. GBP 1,177, USD 2,154 combined subscription print & online eds. (effective 2006). **Document type:** *Academic/Scholarly.* **Description:** Covers all aspects of contaminant measurement relating to the indoor, outdoor and workplace environments.
Related titles: Online - full text ed.: ISSN 1464-0333. GBP 1,059, USD 1,939 (effective 2006) (from EBSCO Publishing, O C L C Online Computer Library Center, Inc., Swets Information Services).
Indexed: AEA, ASFA, AbHyg, AgBio, AnBrAb, AnalAb, B&BAb, BIOBASE, BIOSIS Prev, BiolAb, CPA, CSNB, ChemAb, CurCont, DBA, DSA, ESPM, EnvAb, EnvEAb, ExcerpMed, FCA, FPA, FS&TA, ForAb, H&SSA, HelmAb, HerbAb, HortAb, I&DA, IABS, ISR, IndVet, LHB, M&GPA, MEDLINE, MSB, MaizeAb, NemAb, NutrAb, PBA, PGegResA, PGrRegA, PHN&I, PollutAb, PotatoAb, ProtozoAb, RDA, RM&VM, RPP, RRTA, RefZh, RevApplEntom, RiceAb, S&F, SCI, SIA, SWRA, TDB, TriticAb, VetBull, WAE&RSA, WeedAb, ZooRec.
—BLDSC (4979.383700), CISTI, IE, Infotrieve, ingenta, Linda Hall. **CCC.**
Published by: Royal Society of Chemistry, Thomas Graham House, Science Park, Milton Rd, Cambridge, CB4 0WF, United Kingdom. TEL 44-1223-432360, FAX 44-1223-423623, sales@rsc.org, advertising@rsc.org, http://www.rsc.org/jem. Ed. Harpal Minhas TEL 44-1223-432293. **Subscr. to:** Portland Press Ltd., R S C Distribution Services, Commerce Way, Whitehall Industrial Estate, Colchester CO2 8HP, United Kingdom. TEL 44-1206-226050, FAX 44-1206-226055, sales@rscdistribution.org.

643 JPN ISSN 0911-775X
CODEN: JFIAEA

JOURNAL OF FLOW INJECTION ANALYSIS/F I A KENKYU KONDANKAI KAISHI. Text in Japanese; Summaries in English. 1984. s-a. JPY 3,000 (effective 2000). **Document type:** *Academic/Scholarly.*
Indexed: AnalAb.
—BLDSC (4984.430000), IE, ingenta.
Published by: Nihon Bunseki Kagakkai, Furo Injekushon Bunseki Kenkyu Kondankai/Japan Society for Analytical Chemistry, Division of Flow Injection Analysis, University Faculty of Science Dept of Chemistry, 3-1-1 Tsushima-Naka, Okayama-shi, 700-0082, Japan. TEL 8-86-251-7846, FAX 8-86-254-7853, motomizu@cc.okayama-u.ac.jp. Ed. Tadao Sakai.

543 USA ISSN 1532-1819
RB46.5 CODEN: JIIOAZ

➤ **JOURNAL OF IMMUNOASSAY AND IMMUNOCHEMISTRY.** Text in English. 1980. q. GBP 735, USD 1,214 combined subscription to institutions print & online eds. (effective 2006). adv. reprint service avail. from PSC. **Document type:** *Journal, Academic/Scholarly.* **Description:** Presents coverage of this rapidly expanding field, providing practical, hands-on information with an emphasis on applications.
Formerly (until 2001): Journal of Immunoassay (0197-1522)
Related titles: Microform ed.: (from RPI); Online - full text ed.: ISSN 1532-4230. GBP 698, USD 1,153 to institutions (effective 2006) (from EBSCO Publishing, O C L C Online Computer Library Center, Inc., Swets Information Services).
Indexed: AEBA, AIDS&CR, ASCA, ASFA, AbHyg, AnalAb, B&BAb, BBCI, BCI, BIOBASE, BIOSIS Prev, BioEngAb, BiolAb, CIN, ChemAb, ChemTitl, CurCont, ESPM, ExcerpMed, IABS, ISR, ImmunAb, IndMed, IndVet, Inpharma, M&PBA, MBA, MEDLINE, ProtozoAb, Reac, RefZh, SCI, Telegen, VetBull, ViroIAbstr.
—BLDSC (5004.570000), CASDDS, CISTI, GNLM, IDS, IE, ingenta, KNAW, Linda Hall. **CCC.**
Published by: Taylor & Francis Inc. (Subsidiary of: Taylor & Francis Group), 325 Chestnut St, Ste 800, Philadelphia, PA 19016. TEL 215-625-8900, 800-354-1420, FAX 215-625-2940, info@taylorandfrancis.com, http://www.tandf.co.uk/journals/titles/15321819.asp, http://www.taylorandfrancis.com. Ed. Dr. Jack Cazes. Adv. contact Sharon Moran. B&W page USD 600. Circ: 350.

547 016 GBR ISSN 0362-4803
QD466 CODEN: JLCRD4

➤ **JOURNAL OF LABELLED COMPOUNDS AND RADIOPHARMACEUTICALS.** Text in English, French, German. 1964. 14/yr. USD 4,070 to institutions; USD 4,477 combined subscription to institutions print & online eds. (effective 2006). adv. bk.rev. bibl.; charts; illus. index. back issues avail.; reprint service avail. from PQC,ISI,PSC. **Document type:** *Journal, Academic/Scholarly.* **Description:** Publishes original scientific manuscripts dealing with all aspects of research and development leading to and resulting in labelled compound preparation.
Formerly: Journal of Labelled Compounds (0022-2135)
Related titles: Microform ed.: (from PQC); Online - full text ed.: ISSN 1099-1344. 1997. USD 4,070 to institutions (effective 2006) (from EBSCO Publishing, Swets Information Services, Wiley InterScience).
Indexed: ASCA, ASFA, AnalAb, BIOSIS Prev, BiolAb, CCI, CIN, ChemAb, ChemTitl, CurCR, CurCont, DBA, DSA, ESPM, EngInd, ExcerpMed, GenetAb, ISR, IndChem, Inpharma, MOS, MSB, NPU, NSCI, NutrAb, PE&ON, ProtozoAb, RCI, RM&VM, Reac, RefZh, RevApplEntom, SCI, SIA, Telegen, WeedAb.
—BLDSC (5009.910000), CASDDS, CISTI, Ei, GNLM, IDS, IE, Infotrieve, ingenta, KNAW, Linda Hall. **CCC.**
Published by: (International Isotope Society), John Wiley & Sons Ltd. (Subsidiary of: John Wiley & Sons, Inc.), The Atrium, Southern Gate, Chichester, West Sussex PO19 8SQ, United Kingdom. TEL 44-1243-779777, FAX 44-1243-775878, customer@wiley.co.uk, http://www3.interscience.wiley.com/cgi-bin/jhome/3209, http://www.wiley.co.uk. Eds. B Langstrom, J R Jones, P G Williams. adv.: B&W page GBP 750, color page GBP 1,650; trim 165 x 248. **Subscr. in the Americas to:** John Wiley & Sons, Inc., 111 River St, Hoboken, NJ 07030-5774. TEL 800-225-5945, subinfo@wiley.com.

547 GBR ISSN 1076-5174
QD272.S6 CODEN: JMSPFJ

➤ **JOURNAL OF MASS SPECTROMETRY.** Text in English. 1968. m. USD 6,120 to institutions; USD 6,732 combined subscription to institutions print & online eds. (effective 2006). adv. bk.rev. index, cum.index. back issues avail.; reprint service avail. from PSC. **Document type:** *Journal, Academic/Scholarly.* **Description:** Promotes mass spectrometry as an international and multidisciplinary field of scientific enquiry.
Formerly: O M S - Organic Mass Spectrometry (0030-493X); Which incorporates (1991-1994): Biological Mass Spectrometry (1052-9306); Which was formerly (until 1991): Biomedical and Environmental Mass Spectrometry (0887-6134); (1974-1986): B M S - Biomedical Mass Spectrometry (0306-042X)
Related titles: Microform ed.: (from PQC); Online - full text ed.: ISSN 1096-9888. 1996. USD 6,120 to institutions (effective 2006) (from EBSCO Publishing, Swets Information Services, Wiley InterScience).
Indexed: AESIS, ASCA, ASFA, AbHyg, AgBio, AnBrAb, AnalAb, B&BAb, BBCI, BIOSIS Prev, BioCN&I, BiolAb, CCI, ChemAb, ChemTitl, CurCR, CurCont, DSA, EPB, ESPM, EngInd, EnvAb, ExcerpMed, FCA, FPA, ForAb, GenetAb, HelmAb, HortAb, ISMEC, ISR, IndChem, IndMed, IndVet, Inpharma, MEDLINE, MSB, MaizeAb, NutrAb, OrnHort, PBA, PGegResA, PGrRegA, PN&I, PollutAb, ProtozoAb, RA&MP, RCI, RM&VM, RPP, Reac, RefZh, S&F, SCI, SIA, SeedAb, SoyAb, TDB, TriticAb, VITIS, VetBull, WeedAb.
—BLDSC (5012.179500), CASDDS, CISTI, Ei, GNLM, IDS, IE, Infotrieve, ingenta, Linda Hall. **CCC.**
Published by: John Wiley & Sons Ltd. (Subsidiary of: John Wiley & Sons, Inc.), The Atrium, Southern Gate, Chichester, West Sussex PO19 8SQ, United Kingdom. TEL 44-1243-779777, FAX 44-1243-775878, customer@wiley.co.uk, http://www3.interscience.wiley.com/cgi-bin/jhome/6043, http://www.wiley.co.uk. Ed. Richard Caprioli. adv.: B&W page GBP 750, color page GBP 1,650; trim 210 x 297. Circ: 1,200. **Subscr. in the Americas to:** John Wiley & Sons, Inc., 111 River St, Hoboken, NJ 07030-5774. TEL 201-748-6645, 800-225-5945, subinfo@wiley.com.

➤ **JOURNAL OF MOLECULAR SPECTROSCOPY.** see *PHYSICS—Optics*

C

543.1 GBR ISSN 0967-0335
CODEN: JNISEI
➤ **JOURNAL OF NEAR INFRARED SPECTROSCOPY.** Text in English. 1993. bi-m. GBP 217, EUR 325 in Europe includes free web access; USD 400 elsewhere includes free web access; GBP 280, EUR 420 combined subscription in Europe includes NIR News; USD 515 combined subscription elsewhere includes NIR News (effective 2005). adv. bk.rev. **Document type:** *Journal, Academic/Scholarly.* **Description:** Covers research and applications of near-infrared spectroscopy.
Related titles: CD-ROM ed.: GBP 500, EUR 775 in Europe; USD 855 elsewhere (effective 2005); Online - full text ed.: ISSN 1364-6575 (from EBSCO Publishing).
Indexed: AEA, AgrForAb, AnBrAb, AnalAb, BioCN&I, CCI, CPA, ChemAb, ChemTitl, CurCont, DSA, FCA, FPA, FS&TA, ForAb, HortAb, I&DA, IndVet, MSB, MaizeAb, NutrAb, PBA, PHN&I, PN&I, PoultAb, S&F, SIA, SeedAb, SoyAb, TTI, TriticAb.
—BLDSC (5021.393500), CASDDS, CISTI, IE, ingenta. **CCC.**
Published by: N I R Publications, 6 Charlton Mill, Charlton, Chichester, W Sussex PO18 0HY, United Kingdom. TEL 44-1243-811334, FAX 44-1243-811711, nir@nirpublications.com, http://www.nirpublications.com/jnirs.html. Ed. Graeme D Batten TEL 61-269-332812. R&P Katie Michael. Adv. contact Jill Stockford. B&W page GBP 395, color page GBP 725; trim 192 x 261.

543.8 HUN ISSN 0933-4173
QD79.C8 CODEN: JPCTE5
➤ **JOURNAL OF PLANAR CHROMATOGRAPHY - MODERN TLC.** (Thin Layer Chromatography) Text in English. 1987. bi-m. USD 296; USD 51 per issue (effective 2003). bk.rev. index. 80 p./no. 2 cols./p.; back issues avail.; reprints avail. **Document type:** *Journal, Academic/Scholarly.* **Description:** Publishes papers on analytical and preparative planar chromatography in the pharmaceutical and chemical industries.
Indexed: ASCA, AnalAb, BIOSIS Prev, BiolAb, CCI, CIN, ChemAb, ChemTitl, ChromAb, CurCont, EngInd, ExcerpMed, ISR, MSB, NutrAb, SCI, SIA, VITIS, WeedAb.
—BLDSC (5073.675000), CASDDS, CISTI, Ei, GNLM, IDS, IE, Infotrieve, ingenta, Linda Hall. **CCC.**
Published by: Research Institute for Medicinal Plants, Jozsef Attila u 38, Budakalasz, 2011, Hungary. rimp@mail.matav.hu. Ed., R&P, Adv. contact Szabolcs Nyiredy. Circ: 1,450 (paid); 220 (controlled).

543.088 HUN ISSN 0236-5731
QD605 CODEN: JRNCDM
➤ **JOURNAL OF RADIOANALYTICAL AND NUCLEAR CHEMISTRY**; an international journal dealing with all aspects and applications of nuclear chemistry. Text in English. 1984. 3/yr. EUR 8,598, USD 8,705, GBP 5,375 combined subscription to institutions print & online eds. (effective 2005). adv. bk.rev. bibl.; charts; illus.; abstr. index. 240 p./no.; back issues avail. **Document type:** *Journal, Academic/Scholarly.* **Description:** Publishes original papers, review papers, and short communications.
Formed by the merger of (1968-1984): Journal of Radioanalytical Chemistry (0134-0719); (1969-1984): Radiochemical and Radioanalytical Letters (0079-9483)
Related titles: Microform ed.: (from PQC); Online - full text ed.: ISSN 1588-2780 (from EBSCO Publishing, Gale Group, IngentaConnect, Kluwer Online, O C L C Online Computer Library Center, Inc., Ovid Technologies, Inc., Springer LINK, Swets Information Services).
Indexed: A&ATA, AESIS, ASCA, ASFA, AnalAb, ApicAb, ArtHuCI, BPRC&P, BibLing, BiolAb, BrCerAb, C&ISA, CCI, CIN, CerAb, ChemAb, ChemTitl, CorrAb, CurCont, DSA, E&CAJ, EMA, EngInd, ExcerpMed, FS&TA, IAA, INIS AtomInd, ISR, Inspec, M&GPA, M&TEA, MBF, METADEX, MSB, MSCI, NutrAb, PhysBer, RCI, RefZh, S&F, SCI, SFA, SIA, SSCI, SolStAb, WAA.
—BLDSC (5043.890000), AskIEEE, CASDDS, CISTI, Ei, IDS, IE, ingenta, Linda Hall. **CCC.**
Published by: (Institute of Inorganic and Analytical Chemistry), Akademiai Kiado Rt. (Subsidiary of: Wolters Kluwer N.V.), Prielle Kornelia U. 19, Budapest, 1117, Hungary. TEL 36-1-4648282, FAX 36-1-4648221, journals@akkrt.hu, http://springerlink.metapress.com/openurl.asp?genre=journal&issn=0236-5731, http://www.akkrt.hu. Ed. Tibor Braun. **Co-publisher:** Plenum US.

540 GBR ISSN 0377-0486
QC454.R36 CODEN: JRSPAF
➤ **JOURNAL OF RAMAN SPECTROSCOPY.** Short title: J R S. Text in English, French, German. 1973. m. USD 5,565 to institutions; USD 6,122 combined subscription to institutions print & online eds. (effective 2006). adv. bk.rev. index. back issues avail.; reprint service avail. from PSC. **Document type:** *Journal, Academic/Scholarly.* **Description:** Provides readers with original work in all aspects of Ramam spectroscopy, including higher-order processes and Brillouin and Rayleigh scattering.
Related titles: Microform ed.: (from PQC); Online - full text ed.: ISSN 1097-4555. USD 5,565 to institutions (effective 2006) (from EBSCO Publishing, Swets Information Services, Wiley InterScience).
Indexed: ABIPC, ASCA, AnalAb, BrCerAb, C&ISA, CCI, CIN, CerAb, ChemAb, ChemTitl, CivEngAb, CorrAb, CurCont, E&CAJ, EMA, EngInd, IAA, ISR, Inspec, M&TEA, MBF, METADEX, MSCI, RefZh, SCI, SolStAb, WAA.
—BLDSC (5045.600000), AskIEEE, CASDDS, CISTI, Ei, IDS, IE, Infotrieve, ingenta, Linda Hall. **CCC.**
Published by: John Wiley & Sons Ltd. (Subsidiary of: John Wiley & Sons, Inc.), The Atrium, Southern Gate, Chichester, West Sussex PO19 8SQ, United Kingdom. TEL 44-1243-779777, FAX 44-1243-775878, JRS@mail.uni-wuerzburg.de, customer@wiley.co.uk, http://www3.interscience.wiley.com/cgi-bin/jhome/3420, http://www.wiley.co.uk. Ed. W Kiefer. adv.: B&W page GBP 650, color page GBP 1,550; trim 210 x 297. **Subscr. in the Americas to:** John Wiley & Sons, Inc., 111 River St, Hoboken, NJ 07030-5774. TEL 800-225-5945, subinfo@wiley.com.

543.8 DEU ISSN 1615-9306
QD79.C4 CODEN: JSSCCJ
➤ **JOURNAL OF SEPARATION SCIENCE.** Text in English. 1978. 18/yr. EUR 1,394 in Europe; CHF 2,298 in Switzerland & Liechtenstein; USD 1,588 elsewhere; EUR 1,534 combined subscription in Europe print & online eds.; CHF 2,528 combined subscription in Switzerland & Liechtenstein for print & online eds.; USD 1,747 combined subscription elsewhere print & online eds. (effective 2006). bk.rev. charts; illus.; abstr.; bibl. index. back issues avail.; reprints avail. **Document type:** *Journal, Academic/Scholarly.* **Description:** Deals with all aspects of the theory and practice of chromatographic science.
Incorporates (1989-2002): Journal of Microcolumn Separations (1040-7685); Former titles (until 2001): H R C - Journal of High Resolution Chromatography (0935-6304); (until 1989): H R C and C C - Journal of High Resolution Chromatography & Chromatography Communications (0344-7138)
Related titles: Online - full text ed.: ISSN 1615-9314. EUR 1,394 in Europe; CHF 2,298 in Switzerland & Liechtenstein; USD 1,588 elsewhere (effective 2006) (from EBSCO Publishing, Swets Information Services, Wiley InterScience).
Indexed: AEA, ASCA, AgBio, AnalAb, BIOSIS Prev, BiolAb, CCI, CEABA, CIN, CISA, CPA, ChemAb, ChemTitl, ChromAb, CurCont, DSA, ExcerpMed, FCA, FPA, FS&TA, ForAb, HelmAb, HortAb, I&DA, ISR, IndVet, Inpharma, MSB, MSCI, MaizeAb, NutrAb, OrnHort, PBA, PE&ON, PHN&I, PN&I, PoultAb, ProtozoAb, RA&MP, RCI, RM&VM, RPP, Reac, RefZh, RevApplEntom, S&F, SCI, SFA, SIA, SeedAb, SoyAb, TDB, TOSA, TriticAb, VITIS, VetBull, WeedAb.
—BLDSC (5063.880000), CASDDS, CISTI, Ei, GNLM, IDS, IE, Infotrieve, ingenta, Linda Hall. **CCC.**
Published by: Wiley - V C H Verlag GmbH & Co. KGaA (Subsidiary of: John Wiley & Sons, Inc.), Boschstr 12, Weinheim, 69469, Germany. TEL 49-6201-6060, FAX 49-6201-606328, subservice@wiley-vch.de, info@wiley-vch.de, http://www.wiley-vch.de/home/jss. Ed. Hartmut Frank. R&P Claudia Rutz. Adv. contact Achim Kraus. Circ: 4,896.

543.1 NLD ISSN 0896-8446
TP156.E8 CODEN: JSFLEH
➤ **THE JOURNAL OF SUPERCRITICAL FLUIDS.** Text in Dutch. 1988. 12/yr. EUR 1,107 in Europe to institutions; JPY 147,200 in Japan to institutions; USD 1,241 elsewhere to institutions; EUR 599 in Europe to qualified personnel; JPY 79,700 in Japan to qualified personnel; USD 672 elsewhere to qualified personnel (effective 2006). adv. bk.rev. back issues avail. **Document type:** *Academic/Scholarly.* **Description:** Devoted to the fundamental and applied aspects of supercritical fluids and processes.
Related titles: Online - full text ed.: (from EBSCO Publishing, Gale Group, IngentaConnect, ScienceDirect, Swets Information Services).
Indexed: ASCA, BrCerAb, C&ISA, CCI, CIN, CerAb, ChemAb, ChemTitl, CivEngAb, CorrAb, CurCont, E&CAJ, EMA, EngInd, FS&TA, IAA, ISR, M&TEA, MBF, METADEX, MSB, SCI, SolStAb, VITIS, WAA.
—BLDSC (5067.119000), CASDDS, CISTI, Ei, IDS, IE, Infotrieve, ingenta, Linda Hall. **CCC.**
Published by: Elsevier BV (Subsidiary of: Elsevier Science & Technology), Radarweg 29, Amsterdam, 1043 NX, Netherlands. TEL 31-20-4853911, FAX 31-20-4852457, nlinfo-f@elsevier.nl, http://www.elsevier.com/locate/supflu, http://www.elsevier.nl. Ed. Erdogan Kiran. Circ: 250.

543.8 541.37 USA
L C G C ASIA PACIFIC; the magazine of separation science. (Liquid Chromatography Gas Chromatography) Text in English. 1998. q. USD 32 in Asia & the Pacific except Japan; USD 40 elsewhere; USD 8 newsstand/cover in Asia & the Pacific (effective 2004). adv. tr.lit.; charts; illus.; stat. back issues avail. **Document type:** *Magazine, Trade.* **Description:** Offers practical solutions-oriented information to help chromatographers in industry and academia. Covers new or improved applications of liquid gaschromatography and electrophoresis.
Published by: Advanstar Communications, Inc., One Park Ave, 2nd Fl, New York, NY 10016. TEL 212-951-6600, FAX 212-951-6793, lcgcedit@lcgcmag.com, info@advanstar.com, http://www.advanstar.com. Ed. Mike MacRae. Pub., Adv. contact Michael Tessalone TEL 732-225-9500. B&W page USD 5,415, color page USD 1,150; trim 10.75 x 8. Circ: 10,000 (controlled).

543.8 USA ISSN 1471-6577
L C G C EUROPE. (Liquid Chromatography Gas Chromatography) Text in English. 1999. m. GBP 90 domestic; GBP 130 in Canada & Mexico; GBP 20 newsstand/cover elsewhere (effective 2004).
Related titles: Online - full text ed.: (from EBSCO Publishing, Gale Group).
Indexed: AnalAb, CCI, MSB, VITIS.
—BLDSC (5162.246003), IE, ingenta. **CCC.**
Published by: Advanstar Communications, Inc., One Park Ave, 2nd Fl, New York, NY 10016. TEL 212-951-6600, FAX 212-951-6793.

543.8 GBR ISSN 0895-5441
L C G C INTERNATIONAL (EUROPEAN ED.); the magazine of separation science. (Liquid Chromatography - Gas Chromatography) Text in English. 1987. m. GBP 90 domestic; GBP 130 foreign (effective 2004). adv. stat.; tr.lit. back issues avail. **Document type:** *Magazine, Trade.* **Description:** Targets users and specifiers of chromatographic equipment in Western Europe. Serves field of agriculture, food, beverage, biotechnology, cosmetic, toiletries, manufacturing, processing, R & D, QA-QC, medical, biological in the field of separation science.
Related titles: ◆ Regional ed(s).: L C G C North America. ISSN 1527-5949.
Indexed: AESIS, AnalAb, CEABA, ChemAb, ChromAb, DSA, ESPM, EngInd, FS&TA, MSB, RAPRA, SWRA, WSCA.
—Ei, Infotrieve. **CCC.**
Published by: Advanstar Communications, Unit C, First Fl., Lamb House, Church St., Chiswick, London, W4 2PD, United Kingdom. TEL 44-208-9870900, FAX 44-208-9870901, lcgc@advanstar.co.uk, info@advanstar.com, http://www.lcgcint-mag.com, http://www.advanstar.com. adv.: B&W page USD 5,620, color page USD 7,255; trim 7 x 10. Circ: 25,917 (controlled).

543.8 USA ISSN 1527-5949
QD79.C454 CODEN: LCGCE7
➤ **L C G C NORTH AMERICA**; the magazine of separation science. (Liquid Chromatography Gas Chromatography) Text in English. 1983. m. USD 67 domestic; USD 87 in Canada & Mexico; USD 129 elsewhere; USD 7.50 newsstand/cover domestic; USD 9.50 newsstand/cover foreign (effective 2005). adv. charts; illus.; stat.; tr.lit. back issues avail. **Document type:** *Journal, Academic/Scholarly.* **Description:** Devoted peer reviewed editorial exclusively to the needs of chromatographers in industry and academia. Highlights concise research papers that examine a wide variety of new or improved applications of liquid, gas, and supercritical chromatography.
Former titles: L C - G C (0888-9090); L C - Liquid Chromatography and H P L C Magazine (0746-0252)
Related titles: Microform ed.: (from PQC); Online - full text ed.: (from EBSCO Publishing, Florida Center for Library Automation, Gale Group); ◆ Regional ed(s).: L C G C International (European Ed.). ISSN 0895-5441.
Indexed: AnalAb, CCI, ChemAb, ChemTitl, ChromAb, CurCont, ESPM, ISR, MSB, RCI, SCI, SWRA, Telegen, VITIS.
—BLDSC (5162.247200), CASDDS, CISTI, Ei, IDS, IE, ingenta, Linda Hall. **CCC.**
Published by: Advanstar Communications, Inc., 275 Grove St., Ste. 2-130, Auburndale, MA 02466-2275. lcgcedit@lcgcmag.com, info@advanstar.com, http://www.chromatographyonline.com, http://www.advanstar.com. Eds. Kristy Aro, Bruce Flickinger. Pub., Adv. contact Michael Tessalone TEL 732-225-9500. Circ: 50,100 (controlled).

543.1 ITA ISSN 1120-8376
CODEN: LABOE4
LABORATORIO 2000; rivista del ricercatore chimico e biologico. Text in Italian. 1987. 9/yr. free to members. bk.rev. **Document type:** *Magazine, Trade.*
Indexed: AnalAb, CIN, ChemAb, ChemTitl.
—BLDSC (5137.955000), CASDDS, IE, ingenta.
Published by: Morgan Edizioni Tecniche Srl, Viale Zara 9, Milan, MI 20124, Italy. TEL 39-02-69001227, FAX 39-02-69001229, lab2000@iol.it, http://www.lab2000.com. Ed., R&P Enrico Boeri. Adv. contact Marcella Meloni. Circ: 10,000.

LUMINESCENCE; journal of biological and chemical luminescence. see *CHEMISTRY—Physical Chemistry*

543.1 GBR ISSN 0749-1581
QD476 CODEN: MRCHEG
➤ **MAGNETIC RESONANCE IN CHEMISTRY.** Text in English. 1969. 13/yr. USD 5,880 to institutions; USD 6,468 combined subscription to institutions print & online eds. (effective 2006). adv. bk.rev. charts. index, cum.index. back issues avail.; reprint service avail. from PSC. **Document type:** *Journal, Academic/Scholarly.* **Description:** Provides comprehensive coverage of magnetic resonance in all branches of chemistry.
Formerly: O M R - Organic Magnetic Resonance (0030-4921)
Related titles: Microform ed.: (from PQC); Online - full text ed.: ISSN 1097-458X. 1996. USD 5,880 to institutions (effective 2006) (from EBSCO Publishing, Swets Information Services, Wiley InterScience).
Indexed: ASCA, CCI, CIN, ChemAb, ChemTitl, CurCR, CurCont, EngInd, ExcerpMed, ISR, IndChem, Inspec, MSB, MSCI, NPU, RCI, RefZh, SCI.
—BLDSC (5337.790000), CASDDS, CISTI, Ei, IDS, IE, Infotrieve, ingenta, Linda Hall. **CCC.**

C

Published by: John Wiley & Sons Ltd. (Subsidiary of: John Wiley & Sons, Inc.), The Atrium, Southern Gate, Chichester, West Sussex PO19 8SQ, United Kingdom. TEL 44-1243-779777, FAX 44-1243-775878, customer@wiley.co.uk, http://www3.interscience.wiley.com/cgi-bin/jhome/3767, http://www.wiley.co.uk. Ed. H Guenther. adv.: B&W page GBP 650, color page GBP 1,550; trim 210 x 297. Circ: 900. **Subscr. in the Americas to:** John Wiley & Sons, Inc., 111 River St, Hoboken, NJ 07030-5774. TEL 201-748-6645, 800-225-5945, subinfo@wiley.com.

643 JPN ISSN 1340-8097
QC454.M3 CODEN: SHIBAK
MASS SPECTROMETRY SOCIETY OF JAPAN. JOURNAL/MASS SPECTROSCOPY. Text in English, Japanese. 1953. bi-m. JPY 8,500 membership (effective 2004). **Document type:** *Journal, Academic/Scholarly.*
Formerly (until 1992): Shitsuryo Bunseki (0542-8645)
Indexed: AnalAb, ChemAb, CurCont, INIS AtomInd, Inspec, JPI, MSB.
—BLDSC (4821.350000), AskIEEE, CASDDS, CISTI, IE, Linda Hall. **CCC.**
Published by: Nihon Shitsuryo Bunseki Gakkai/Mass Spectrometry Society of Japan, c/o International Academic Printing Co., Ltd., 8-8 Takadanobaba 3-chome, Shinjuku-ku, Tokyo, 169-0075, Japan. TEL 81-3-53896076, FAX 81-3-33682822, http://www.mssj.jp.

METALURGIJA/METALLURGY. see *METALLURGY*

543 AUT ISSN 0026-3672
QD71 CODEN: MIACAQ
➤ **MICROCHIMICA ACTA**; an international journal on micro and trace analysis. Text in English. 1938. m. EUR 1,768 combined subscription to institutions print & online eds. (effective 2005). adv. charts; illus.; abstr. index. back issues avail.; reprint service avail. from ISI. **Document type:** *Journal, Academic/Scholarly.* **Description:** Presents latest results from all areas of analytical chemistry.
Former titles (until 1966): Mikrochimica et Ichnoanalytica Acta (0369-0504); (until 1963): Mikrochimica Acta (0344-838X); (until 1953): Mikrochemie Vereinigt mit Mikrochimica Acta (0369-2795); Which was formed by the merger of (1937-1938): Mikrochimica Acta (0344-8436); (1923-1938): Mikrochemie (0369-0261)
Related titles: Microform ed.: (from PQC); Online - full text ed.: ISSN 1436-5073 (from EBSCO Publishing, Springer LINK, Swets Information Services); ♦ Supplement(s): Mikrochimica Acta. ISSN 0076-8642.
Indexed: ASCA, ASFA, AnalAb, BiolAb, BrCerAb, C&ISA, CCI, CIN, CMCI, Cadscan, CerAb, ChemAb, ChemTitl, CivEngAb, CorrAb, CurCont, DSA, E&CAJ, EMA, ESPM, ExcerpMed, FS&TA, IAA, INIS AtomInd, ISR, LeadAb, M&TEA, MBF, MEDLINE, METADEX, MSB, MinerAb, NumL, NutrAb, PollutAb, RCI, SCI, SSCI, SWRA, SolStAb, VITIS, WAA, Zincscan.
—BLDSC (5758.452000), CASDDS, CINDOC, CISTI, IDS, IE, ingenta, Linda Hall. **CCC.**
Published by: Springer-Verlag Wien (Subsidiary of: Springer Science+Business Media) journals@springer.at, http://www.springer.at/mikro. Ed. Otto S Wolfbeis. R&P Angela Foessl TEL 43-1-3302415517. Adv. contact Michael Katzenberger TEL 43-1-3302415220. B&W page EUR 1,000; 170 x 230. **Subscr. in the Americas to:** Springer-Verlag New York, Inc., Journal Fulfillment, PO Box 2485, Secaucus, NJ 07096-2485. TEL 800-777-4643, 201-348-4033, FAX 201-348-4505, journals@springer-ny.com, http://www.springer-ny.com; **Subscr. to:** Springer GmbH Auslieferungsgesellschaft. subscriptions@springer.de.

502.82 USA ISSN 0026-282X
QH201 CODEN: MICRAD
➤ **MICROSCOPE.** Text in English. 1937. q. USD 75 (effective 2004). adv. bk.rev. bibl.; charts; illus.; pat.; stat.; tr.lit. index, cum.index. back issues avail. **Document type:** *Academic/Scholarly.* **Description:** Dedicated to the advancement of all forms of microscopy for the biologist, mineralogist, metallographer or chemist.
Formerly (until 1967): Microscope and Crystal Front (0368-8992); Which incorporated (1958-1962): Crystal Front (0574-5136)
Indexed: A&ATA, ABIPC, BIOSIS Prev, BiolAb, BrCerAb, C&ISA, CerAb, ChemAb, CivEngAb, CorrAb, CurCont, E&CAJ, EMA, ExcerpMed, IAA, Inspec, M&TEA, MBF, METADEX, RefZh, SCI, SolStAb, WAA.
—BLDSC (5760.000000), AskIEEE, CASDDS, CISTI, IE, Infotrieve, ingenta, Linda Hall. **CCC.**
Published by: McCrone Research Institute, 2820 S Michigan Ave, Chicago, IL 60616-3292. TEL 312-842-7100, FAX 312-842-1078, info@mcri.org, http://mcri.org/McRI_products.html#anchor116238, http://www.mcri.org. Ed. Dr. David A Stoney. Adv. contact Nancy Daerr. Circ: 1,200.

543 USA ISSN 0076-8642
CODEN: MKASAK
MIKROCHIMICA ACTA; micro and trace analysis. Text in English. 1966. irreg., latest vol.144, no.4, 2004. price varies. reprint service avail. from ISI. **Document type:** *Monographic series, Academic/Scholarly.*
Related titles: Microform ed.: (from PQC); Online - full text ed.; ♦ Supplement to: Microchimica Acta. ISSN 0026-3672.
Indexed: CIN, ChemAb, ChemTitl, INIS AtomInd.
—BLDSC (5762.010000), CASDDS, CINDOC, CISTI, IE, ingenta, Linda Hall. **CCC.**
Published by: Springer-Verlag New York, Inc. (Subsidiary of: Springer Science+Business Media), 233 Spring St, New York, NY 10013. TEL 212-460-1500, 800-777-4643, FAX 212-473-6272, http://www.springer.at/mikro, http://www.springer-ny.com. **Subscr. outside N. America to:** Springer GmbH Auslieferungsgesellschaft, Haberstr 7, Heidelberg 69126, Germany. TEL 49-6221-345-0, FAX 49-6221-345-4229, subscriptions@springer.de, http://link.springer.de.

543 USA ISSN 1573-4501
➤ **MODERN ANALYTICAL CHEMISTRY.** Text in English. 1976. irreg., latest 2003. USD 125 per vol. (effective 2005); Analytical Advances for Hydrocarbon Research. **Document type:** *Monographic series, Academic/Scholarly.*
Published by: Springer-Verlag New York, Inc. (Subsidiary of: Springer Science+Business Media), 233 Spring St, New York, NY 10013. TEL 212-460-1500, FAX 212-460-1575, service@springer-ny.com, http://www.springer-ny.com.

543.1 GBR ISSN 0960-3360
N I R NEWS. Text in English. 8/yr. GBP 95, EUR 150 in Europe; USD 175 elsewhere; GBP 280, EUR 420 combined subscription in Europe includes Journal of Near Infrared Spectroscopy; USD 515 combined subscription elsewhere includes Journal of Near Infrared Spectroscopy (effective 2005); subscr. includes online access. adv. bk.rev. **Document type:** *Newsletter, Academic/Scholarly.*
Indexed: AESIS, AnalAb, TTI.
—BLDSC (6113.568400), IE, Infotrieve.
Published by: N I R Publications, 6 Charlton Mill, Charlton, Chichester, W Sussex PO18 0HY, United Kingdom. TEL 44-1243-811334, FAX 44-1243-811711, nir@nirpublications.com, http://www.nirpublications.com. Ed. Graeme D Batten TEL 61-269-332812. Adv. contact Ian Michael. B&W page GBP 395, color page GBP 725; trim 210 x 297. Circ: 600.

N M R IN BIOMEDICINE. (Nuclear Magnetic Resonance) see *MEDICAL SCIENCES—Radiology And Nuclear Medicine*

NIGERIAN STORED PRODUCTS RESEARCH INSTITUTE. ANNUAL REPORT. see *AGRICULTURE—Agricultural Equipment*

643 JPN
NIHON BUNSEKI KAGAKKAI GAKUJUTSU KOENKAI/ PROCEEDINGS OF THE LECTURE MEETING ON ANALYTICAL CHEMISTRY. Text in Japanese. a. **Document type:** *Proceedings.*
Published by: Japan Society for Analytical Chemistry/Nihon Bunseki Kagaku Kai, 1-26-2 Nishigotanda, Shinagawa, Tokyo, 141-0031, Japan.

543 USA ISSN 1080-0344
S587
OFFICIAL METHODS OF ANALYSIS OF AOAC INTERNATIONAL. Text in English. 1920. quinquennial (plus 5 a. updates.). looseleaf. USD 449.10 to members; USD 499 to non-members (effective 2005). index. **Description:** Tested and officially adopted chemical and biological methods pertaining to food, agriculture, pharmaceuticals, and the environment.
Former titles (until 1995): A O A C International. Official Methods of Analysis (0066-961X); (until 1970): Association of Official Analytical Chemists. Official Methods of Analysis (0884-0474); (until 1965): Association of Official Analytical Chemists. Official and Tentative Methods of Analysis (0884-0466)
Related titles: CD-ROM ed.: USD 575 in North America; USD 595 elsewhere.
Indexed: B&BAb, ChemAb, RA&MP.
—BLDSC (6240.519000), CISTI. **CCC.**
Published by: A O A C International, 481 N Frederick Ave, Ste 500, Gaithersburg, MD 20877-2417. TEL 800-379-2622, FAX 301-924-7089. Ed. Patricia Cunniff. R&P Krystyna McIver. Circ: 20,000.

543 547 USA ISSN 0078-6136
QC437
➤ **ORGANIC ELECTRONIC SPECTRAL DATA.** Text in English. 1960. irreg., latest vol.31, 1995. price varies. **Document type:** *Monographic series, Academic/Scholarly.*
—CISTI, Linda Hall.
Published by: (Organic Electronic Spectral Data, Inc.), John Wiley & Sons, Inc., 111 River St, Hoboken, NJ 07030-5774. TEL 201-748-6000, 800-825-7550, FAX 201-748-5915, uscs-wis@wiley.com, http://www.wiley.com.

➤ **PESTYCYDY/PESTICIDES.** see *AGRICULTURE—Crop Production And Soil*

➤ **PHOTONICS SPECTRA.** see *PHYSICS—Optics*

543.1 USA ISSN 1084-3124
QC482.D5
POWDER DIFFRACTION FILE. HANAWALT SEARCH MANUAL. INORGANIC PHASES. Text in English. a. USD 325 (effective 2000). index.
Formerly (until 1991): Powder Diffraction File Search Manual. Hanawalt Method. Inorganic (0092-1319)
Related titles: CD-ROM ed.; Magnetic Tape ed.; Microfiche ed.
—CISTI.
Published by: Joint Committee on Powder Diffraction Standards, International Centre for Diffraction Data, Newton Sq. Corp. Camp, 12, Newton Square, PA 19073. TEL 610-325-9810, FAX 610-325-9823, TELEX 847170.

546 USA ISSN 0092-0509
QC482.D5
POWDER DIFFRACTION FILE SEARCH MANUAL. ALPHABETICAL LISTING. INORGANIC. Text in English. a. USD 325 (effective 2000). index.
Published by: Joint Committee on Powder Diffraction Standards, International Centre for Diffraction Data, 12 Campus Blvd, Newtown, PA 19073. TEL 610-325-9814, FAX 610-325-9823, http://www.icdd.com.

543.17 USA ISSN 0148-9054
CODEN: PSPED9
➤ **PRACTICAL SPECTROSCOPY SERIES.** Text in English. 1976. irreg., latest vol.38, 2004. USD 99.75 per vol. vol.38 (effective 2004). adv. **Document type:** *Monographic series, Academic/Scholarly.*
Indexed: BIOSIS Prev, BiolAb, CIN, ChemAb, ChemTitl.
—BLDSC (6595.850000), CASDDS, CISTI, IE, ingenta. **CCC.**
Published by: Marcel Dekker Inc. (Subsidiary of: Taylor & Francis Group), 270 Madison Ave, New York, NY 10016-0602. TEL 212-696-9000, FAX 212-685-4540, journals@dekker.com, http://www.dekker.com. Pub. Russell Dekker. R&P Julia Mulligan. Adv. contact Eridania Perez. **Subscr. to:** 6000 Broken Sound Pkwy NW, Ste. 300, Boca Raton, FL 33487-2713. TEL 800-228-1160.

543.1 NLD ISSN 1385-4100
CODEN: PRHPEU
PROGRESS IN H P L C - H P C E. (High-Performance Liquid Chromatography - High-Performance Capillary Electrophoresis) Text in English. 1985. irreg., latest vol.7, 1998. price varies. back issues avail. **Document type:** *Monographic series, Academic/Scholarly.* **Description:** Publishes basic research and applications of HPLC-HPCE research in the fields of neuroscience, pharmacology, medicine and chemistry.
Formerly (until 1997): Progress in H P L C (0920-9832)
Indexed: CIN, ChemAb, ChemTitl.
—BLDSC (6868.437320), CASDDS, CISTI, ingenta, KNAW.
Published by: V S P (Subsidiary of: Brill Academic Publishers), Brill Academic Publishers, PO Box 9000, Leiden, 2300 PA, Netherlands. TEL 31-71-5353500, FAX 31-71-5317532, vsppub@brill.nl, http://www.vsppub.com/books/bs15.html. **Dist. in US & Canada by:** Books International, PO Box 605, Herndon, VA 20172. TEL 703-661-1500, FAX 703-661-1501.

543.1 NLD ISSN 0079-6565
QC762 CODEN: PNMRAT
➤ **PROGRESS IN NUCLEAR MAGNETIC RESONANCE SPECTROSCOPY.** Text in English. 1966. 8/yr. EUR 1,128 in Europe to institutions; JPY 150,000 in Japan to institutions; USD 1,264 to institutions except Europe and Japan (effective 2006). Index. **Document type:** *Journal, Academic/Scholarly.* **Description:** Publishes review articles covering applications of NMR in chemistry, biochemistry and biological science, as well as fundamental theory and instrumental developments.
Related titles: Microfilm ed.: (from PQC); Online - full text ed.: (from EBSCO Publishing, Gale Group, IngentaConnect, ScienceDirect, Swets Information Services).
Indexed: ASCA, B&BAb, CCI, CIN, ChemAb, ChemTitl, CurCont, EngInd, ISR, Inspec, SCI.
—BLDSC (6870.750000), AskIEEE, CASDDS, CISTI, Ei, GNLM, IDS, IE, Infotrieve, ingenta, Linda Hall. **CCC.**
Published by: Elsevier BV (Subsidiary of: Elsevier Science & Technology), Radarweg 29, Amsterdam, 1043 NX, Netherlands. TEL 31-20-4853911, FAX 31-20-4852457, nlinfo-f@elsevier.nl, http://www.elsevier.com/locate/pnmrs, http://www.elsevier.nl. **Subscr. to:** Elsevier, Subscription Customer Service, 6277 Sea Harbor Dr, Orlando, FL 32887-4800. TEL 407-345-4020, 877-839-7126, FAX 407-363-1354; PO Box 211, Amsterdam 1000 AE, Netherlands. TEL 31-20-485-3757, FAX 31-20-485-3432.

➤ **R & D DIGEST.** (Research & Development) see *ENERGY*

➤ **R L B L NEWSLETTER.** see *BIOLOGY—Biophysics*

543.84 301.16 GBR ISSN 0951-4198
QD96.M3 CODEN: RCMSEF
➤ **RAPID COMMUNICATIONS IN MASS SPECTROMETRY.** Text in English. 1987. 24/yr. USD 5,150 to institutions; USD 5,665 combined subscription to institutions print & online eds. (effective 2006). adv. back issues avail.; reprints avail. **Document type:** *Journal, Academic/Scholarly.* **Description:** Publishes preliminary accounts of recent research in mass spectrometry.
Related titles: Microform ed.: (from PQC); Online - full text ed.: ISSN 1097-0231. 1996. USD 5,150 to institutions (effective 2006) (from EBSCO Publishing, Swets Information Services, Wiley InterScience).
Indexed: ASCA, AnalAb, BIOBASE, BIOSIS Prev, BiolAb, CCI, CIN, CPA, ChemAb, ChemTitl, CurCont, DSA, EngInd, FCA, FPA, HortAb, IABS, ISR, IndMed, IndVet, Inspec, MEDLINE, MSB, OrnHort, PGrRegA, PlantSci, PoultAb, RA&MP, RM&VM, RefZh, S&F, SCI, TDB, VITIS, VetBull, WeedAb.

C

—BLDSC (7254.440000), AskIEEE, CASDDS, CISTI, Ei, GNLM, IDS, IE, Infotrieve, ingenta, Linda Hall. **CCC.**
Published by: John Wiley & Sons Ltd. (Subsidiary of: John Wiley & Sons, Inc.), The Atrium, Southern Gate, Chichester, West Sussex PO19 8SQ, United Kingdom. TEL 44-1243-779777, FAX 44-1243-775878, customer@wiley.co.uk, http://www.interscience.wiley.com/jpages/0951-4198/, http://www.wiley.co.uk. Ed. R K Boyd. Pub. Ray Boucher. R&P Diane Southern TEL 44-1243-770347. adv.: B&W page GBP 750, color page GBP 1,650; trim 210 x 297. **Subscr. in the Americas to:** John Wiley & Sons, Inc., 111 River St, Hoboken, NJ 07030-5774. TEL 201-748-6645, 800-225-5945, subinfo@wiley.com.

543 IND
RECENT RESEARCH DEVELOPMENTS IN ANALYTICAL CHEMISTRY. Text in English. a., latest vol.1, 2001.
Published by: Transworld Research Network, T C 36-248 (1), Trivandrum, Kerala 695 008, India. http:// www.transworldresearch.com.

543.1 IND
RECENT RESEARCH DEVELOPMENTS IN ELECTRO ANALYTICAL CHEMISTRY. Text in English. a., latest vol.1, 1999.
Published by: Transworld Research Network, T C 36-248 (1), Trivandrum, Kerala 695 008, India. http:// www.transworldresearch.com.

543 IND
RECENT RESEARCH DEVELOPMENTS IN PURE & APPLIED ANALYTICAL CHEMISTRY. Text in English. a., latest vol.4, 2002.
Published by: Transworld Research Network, T C 36-248 (1), Trivandrum, Kerala 695 008, India. http:// www.transworldresearch.com.

REFERATIVNYI ZHURNAL. ANALITICHESKAYA KHIMIYA. OBORUDOVANIE LABORATORII. see *CHEMISTRY—Abstracting, Bibliographies, Statistics*

543.1 JPN ISSN 0034-6691
➤ **REVIEW OF POLAROGRAPHY/PORAROGURAFI.** Text in Multiple languages. 1953. bi-m. JPY 4,000 (effective 2000). adv. bk.rev. charts; illus. index. **Document type:** *Newsletter, Academic/Scholarly.*
Indexed: ChemAb.
—BLDSC (7794.100000), CISTI, Linda Hall.
Published by: Polarographic Society of Japan/Nihon Porarogurafu Gakkai, Division of Applied Life Sciences, Graduate School of Agriculture, Kyoto University, Sakyo-ku, Kyoto-shi, 606-8502, Japan. TEL 81-75-753-6393, FAX 81-75-753-6456, kkano@kais.kyoto-u.ac.jp, http://www.bapc.kais.kyoto-u.ac.jp. Ed. Sorin Kihara. Adv. contact Kenji Kano. Circ: 300. **Dist. overseas by:** Japan Publications Trading Co., Ltd., Book Export II Dept, PO Box 5030, Tokyo International, Tokyo 101-3191, Japan. TEL 81-3-32923753, FAX 81-3-32920410, infoserials@jptco.co.jp, http://www.jptco.co.jp.

543 ISR ISSN 0048-752X
QD71 CODEN: RACYAX
➤ **REVIEWS IN ANALYTICAL CHEMISTRY.** Text in English. 1971. q. USD 320 (effective 2006). adv. bk.rev. index. back issues avail. **Document type:** *Academic/Scholarly.*
Description: Consists of two types: One is the classical review of the literature covering a certain period in the development of a particular field. This review is addressed to the expert in the field and brings him up to date in a concise manner. The other kind of review is written for the research worker contemplating entering a new field of endeavor or for the chemist who wishes to examine the applicability of a new technique to his research.
Indexed: ASCA, AnalAb, CCI, CIN, CTE, ChemAb, ChemTitl, ExcerpMed, MSB.
—BLDSC (7786.930000), CASDDS, IE, Infotrieve, ingenta, Linda Hall.
Published by: Freund Publishing House, Ltd., P O Box 35010, Tel Aviv, 61350, Israel. TEL 972-3-5628540, FAX 972-3-5628538, h_freund@netvision.net.il, http://www.freundpublishing.com/MEDIA/Analytical.htm. Ed. I Schechter. Circ: 1,000.

543.1 USA
➤ **SELECTED TOPICS IN MASS SPECTROMETRY.** Text in English. 1994. irreg., latest vol.1, 1994. USD 162 per vol. (effective 2005); for vol.1. **Document type:** *Monographic series, Academic/Scholarly.*
Published by: Springer-Verlag New York, Inc. (Subsidiary of: Springer Science+Business Media), 233 Spring St, New York, NY 10013. TEL 212-460-1500, FAX 212-460-1575, service@springer-ny.com, http://www.springer-ny.com. Ed. D H Russell.

547 CHE ISSN 1424-8220
TA165 CODEN: SENSC9
➤ **SENSORS.** Text in English. 2000. m. free (effective 2005). **Document type:** *Journal, Academic/Scholarly.* **Description:** International and interdisciplinary journal of science and technology, related to sensors and biosensors.
Formerly (until 2001): Diversity (1424-2818)
Media: Online - full text. **Related titles:** Print ed.: ISSN 1424-3210.
Indexed: AnalAb, CCI, MSB.
Published by: Molecular Diversity Preservation International, MDPI Center, Matthaeusstr 11, Basel, 4057, Switzerland. TEL 41-79-3223379, 41-61-6837734, FAX 41-61-3028918, sensors@mdpi.org, lin@mdpi.org, http://www.mdpi.net/sensors, http://www.mdpi.org/. Ed., Pub. Shu-Kun Lin.

543 USA ISSN 1542-2119
TP156.S45 CODEN: SPRECU
➤ **SEPARATION AND PURIFICATION REVIEWS.** Text in English. 1968. q. USD 818, GBP 495 combined subscription to institutions print & online eds. (effective 2006). adv. charts; illus. reprint service avail. from PSC. **Document type:** *Journal, Academic/Scholarly.* **Description:** Provides summaries of significant novel developments in this constantly evolving field.
Former titles (until 2003): Separation and Purification Methods (0360-2540); (until 1971): Progress in Separation and Purification (0079-676X)
Related titles: Microform ed.: (from RPI); Online - full text ed.: ISSN 1542-2127. USD 777, GBP 470 to institutions (effective 2006) (from EBSCO Publishing, O C L C Online Computer Library Center, Inc., Swets Information Services).
Indexed: ASCA, AnalAb, BioEngAb, BiolAb, BrCerAb, C&ISA, CCI, CEA, CEABA, CerAb, ChemAb, ChemTitl, CivEngAb, CorrAb, CurCont, E&CAJ, EMA, EngInd, ExcerpMed, IAA, ISR, M&TEA, MBF, METADEX, RCI, SCI, SolStAb, TCEA, WAA.
—BLDSC (8242.231000), CASDDS, CISTI, IDS, IE, Infotrieve, ingenta, Linda Hall. **CCC.**
Published by: Taylor & Francis Inc. (Subsidiary of: Taylor & Francis Group), 325 Chestnut St, Ste 800, Philadelphia, PA 19016. TEL 215-625-8900, 800-354-1420, FAX 215-625-2940, info@taylorandfrancis.com, http://www.tandf.co.uk/journals/ titles/15422119.asp, http://www.taylorandfrancis.com. Ed. Alain Berthod. Circ: 325.

543 USA ISSN 0149-6395
TP156.S45 CODEN: SSTEDS
➤ **SEPARATION SCIENCE AND TECHNOLOGY.** Text in English. 1966. 16/yr. USD 3,526, GBP 2,137 combined subscription to institutions print & online eds. (effective 2006). adv. charts; illus.; stat. reprint service avail. from PSC. **Document type:** *Journal, Academic/Scholarly.* **Description:** Reviews the newest concepts and techniques for dealing with problems encountered by professionals in this rapidly expanding field.
Formerly (until vol.13, 1978): Separation Science (0037-2366)
Related titles: Microform ed.: (from RPI); Online - full text ed.: ISSN 1520-5754. USD 3,350, GBP 2,030 to institutions (effective 2006) (from EBSCO Publishing, O C L C Online Computer Library Center, Inc., Swets Information Services); ♦ Issued with: Solvent Extraction and Ion Exchange. ISSN 0736-6299.
Indexed: ABIPC, AESIS, ASCA, AnalAb, BioEngAb, BiolAb, BrCerAb, C&ISA, CCI, CEA, CEABA, CerAb, ChemAb, ChemTitl, CivEngAb, CorrAb, CurCont, DSA, E&CAJ, EMA, ESPM, EnvEAb, ExcerpMed, FLUIDEX, IAA, INIS AtomInd, ISMEC, ISR, M&TEA, MBF, METADEX, MSB, MSCI, PollutAb, RCI, RefZh, S&F, SCI, SWRA, SolStAb, TCEA, VITIS, WAA, WTA.
—BLDSC (8242.255000), CASDDS, CINDOC, CISTI, Ei, IDS, IE, Infotrieve, ingenta, Linda Hall. **CCC.**
Published by: Taylor & Francis Inc. (Subsidiary of: Taylor & Francis Group), 325 Chestnut St, Ste 800, Philadelphia, PA 19016. TEL 215-625-8900, 800-354-1420, FAX 215-625-8914, info@taylorandfrancis.com, http://www.tandf.co.uk/journals/ titles/01496395.asp, http://www.taylorandfrancis.com. Ed. Steven Cramer. Adv. contact Sharon Moran. B&W page USD 600. Circ: 600 (paid and free).

543 616.075 GBR ISSN 0926-2040
QC762 CODEN: SSNRE4
➤ **SOLID STATE NUCLEAR MAGNETIC RESONANCE.** Abbreviated title: S S N M R. Text in English. 1992. 8/yr. EUR 579 in Europe to individuals; JPY 60,500 in Japan to individuals; USD 505 elsewhere to individuals; EUR 1,245 in Europe to institutions; JPY 130,100 in Japan to institutions; USD 1,083 elsewhere to institutions; EUR 290 in Europe to students; JPY 30,400 in Japan to students; USD 253 elsewhere to students (effective 2006). back issues avail. **Document type:** *Academic/Scholarly.* **Description:** Covers experimental and theoretical aspects of solid state NMR, including advances in instrumentation, techniques and methodology, simulation and applications.
Related titles: Microform ed.: 1992 (from PQC); Online - full text ed.: ISSN 1527-3326. USD 1,068 (effective 2002) (from EBSCO Publishing, Gale Group, IngentaConnect, O C L C Online Computer Library Center, Inc., ScienceDirect, Swets Information Services).
Indexed: ASCA, B&BAb, BrCerAb, C&ISA, CCI, CIN, CerAb, ChemAb, ChemTitl, CivEngAb, CorrAb, CurCont, E&CAJ, EMA, EngInd, IAA, ISR, IndMed, Inspec, M&TEA, MBF, MEDLINE, METADEX, RefZh, SCI, SolStAb, WAA.
—BLDSC (8327.391000), AskIEEE, CASDDS, CISTI, Ei, GNLM, IDS, IE, Infotrieve, ingenta, Linda Hall. **CCC.**
Published by: Academic Press (Subsidiary of: Elsevier Science & Technology), 24-28 Oval Rd, London, NW1 7DX, United Kingdom. TEL 44-20-72674466, FAX 44-20-74822293, apsubs@acad.com, http://www.elsevier.com/locate/ysnmr. Ed. J Klinowski.

643 USA ISSN 0736-6299
QD63.E88 CODEN: SEIEDB
➤ **SOLVENT EXTRACTION AND ION EXCHANGE.** Text in English. 1983. bi-m. USD 1,912, GBP 1,159 combined subscription to institutions print & online eds. (effective 2006). bibl.; illus.; charts. index. reprint service avail. from PSC. **Document type:** *Journal, Academic/Scholarly.* **Description:** Provides current, comprehensive coverage of advances and developments in all areas of solvent extraction and ion exchange studies.
Related titles: Microform ed.: (from RPI); Online - full text ed.: ISSN 1532-2262. 2001. USD 1,816, GBP 1,101 to institutions (effective 2006) (from EBSCO Publishing, O C L C Online Computer Library Center, Inc., Swets Information Services); ♦ Includes: Separation Science and Technology. ISSN 0149-6395.
Indexed: ASCA, AnalAb, BrCerAb, C&ISA, CCI, CEA, CEABA, CIN, CerAb, ChemAb, ChemTitl, CivEngAb, CorrAb, CurCont, E&CAJ, EMA, EngInd, FLUIDEX, IAA, IMMAb, INIS AtomInd, ISR, M&TEA, MBF, METADEX, MSB, RCI, RefZh, S&F, SCI, SolStAb, TCEA, WAA.
—BLDSC (8327.806500), CASDDS, CINDOC, CISTI, Ei, IDS, IE, Infotrieve, ingenta, Linda Hall. **CCC.**
Published by: Taylor & Francis Inc. (Subsidiary of: Taylor & Francis Group), 325 Chestnut St, Ste 800, Philadelphia, PA 19016. TEL 215-625-8900, 800-354-1420, FAX 215-625-2940, info@taylorandfrancis.com, http://www.tandf.co.uk/journals/ titles/07366299.asp, http://www.taylorandfrancis.com. Eds. Bruce Moyer, Kenneth Nash. Circ: 325.

543 FRA ISSN 1255-2909
CODEN: SPDMDJ
➤ **SPECTRA ANALYSE;** la revue scientifique d'actualite sur les techniques et l'instrumentation d'analyse destinee aux laboratoires industriels a la recherche et a l'enseignement. Text in French; Summaries in English, French. 1972. bi-m. adv. bk.rev. bibl.; illus. **Document type:** *Magazine, Academic/Scholarly.* **Description:** Covers physico-chemistry, physics, optics and biology used in university and research labs, as well as quality control labs.
Former titles (until 2001): Spectra 2000 Analyse (1635-947X); (until 1993): Spectra 2000 (0399-1172)
Indexed: AnalAb, CIN, ChemAb, ChemTitl, MSB, RefZh.
—BLDSC (8408.672500), CASDDS, CISTI, IE, Infotrieve, ingenta. **CCC.**
Published by: P C I, 176 rue du Temple, Paris, 75003, France. TEL 33-1-44593838, FAX 33-1-44593839. Ed. Monique Chevalier. Adv. contact Emmanuelle Arin. Circ: 5,000.

C

535.84 NLD ISSN 1386-1425
QD95 CODEN: SAMCAS
➤ **SPECTROCHIMICA ACTA PART A: MOLECULAR AND BIOMOLECULAR SPECTROSCOPY.** Text in English, French, German. 1939. 15/yr. EUR 3,553 in Europe to institutions; JPY 471,900 in Japan to institutions; USD 3,975 elsewhere to institutions; EUR 285 in Europe to qualified personnel; JPY 37,800 in Japan to qualified personnel; USD 317 elsewhere to qualified personnel (effective 2006). adv. bk.rev. charts; illus. back issues avail.; reprints avail. **Document type:** *Journal, Academic/Scholarly.* **Description:** Publishes original work in molecular spectroscopy and its applications in chemical problems.
Formerly (until 1995): Spectrochimica Acta. Part A: Molecular Spectroscopy (0584-8539); Which superseded in part (in 1967): Spectrochimica Acta (0371-1951)
Related titles: E-mail ed.; Microfiche ed.: (from MIM); Microfilm ed.: (from PQC); Online - full text ed.: (from EBSCO Publishing, Gale Group, IngentaConnect, ScienceDirect, Swets Information Services).
Indexed: ABIPC, ASCA, ASFA, AnalAb, BIOSIS Prev, BiolAb, BrCerAb, BullT&T, CCI, CIN, ChemAb, ChemTitl, CurCont, ESPM, EngInd, FPA, ISR, IndMed, Inspec, MEDLINE, MSB, MSCI, PollutAb, RCI, RefZh, S&F, SCI.
—BLDSC (8410.010000), AskIEEE, CASDDS, CINDOC, CISTI, Ei, IDS, IE, Infotrieve, ingenta, Linda Hall. **CCC.**
Published by: Elsevier BV (Subsidiary of: Elsevier Science & Technology), Radarweg 29, Amsterdam, 1043 NX, Netherlands. TEL 31-20-4853911, FAX 31-20-4852457, nlinfo-f@elsevier.nl, http://www.elsevier.com/locate/saa, http://www.elsevier.nl. Eds. J Steinfeld, J R Durig. Circ: 1,800.

535.84 NLD ISSN 0584-8547
QD95 CODEN: SAASBH
➤ **SPECTROCHIMICA ACTA PART B: ATOMIC SPECTROSCOPY.** Text in English. 1939. 12/yr. EUR 3,262 in Europe to institutions; JPY 433,000 in Japan to institutions; USD 3,647 to institutions except Europe and Japan; EUR 263 in Europe to qualified personnel; JPY 35,000 in Japan to qualified personnel; USD 293 to qualified personnel except Europe and Japan (effective 2006). bk.rev. charts; illus. Index. reprints avail. **Document type:** *Journal, Academic/Scholarly.*
Description: Addresses theory and fundamentals, methodology, development, instrumentation and applications in atomic spectroscopy and mass spectroscopy for inorganic analysis.
Supersedes in part (in 1967): Spectrochimica Acta (0371-1951)
Related titles: Microfiche ed.: (from MIM); Microfilm ed.: (from PQC); Online - full text ed.: (from EBSCO Publishing, Gale Group, IngentaConnect, ScienceDirect, Swets Information Services).

Indexed: ASCA, ASFA, AnalAb, BCIRA, BIOSIS Prev, BiolAb, BrCerAb, C&ISA, CCI, CIN, CerAb, ChemAb, ChemTitl, CivEngAb, CorrAb, CurCont, DSA, E&CAJ, EMA, ESPM, EngInd, ExcerpMed, F&EA, FPA, ForAb, HerbAb, HortAb, IAA, INIS AtomInd, ISR, Inspec, M&GPA, M&TEA, MBF, METADEX, MSB, MSCI, OrnHort, PhysBer, PollutAb, PotatoAb, RefZh, S&F, SCI, SIA, SWRA, SolStAb, TriticAb, VITIS, WAA, WRCInf.
—BLDSC (8410.020000), AskIEEE, CASDDS, CINDOC, CISTI, Ei, IDS, IE, Infotrieve, ingenta, Linda Hall. **CCC.**
Published by: Elsevier BV (Subsidiary of: Elsevier Science & Technology), Radarweg 29, Amsterdam, 1043 NX, Netherlands. TEL 31-20-4853911, FAX 31-20-4852457, nlinfo-f@elsevier.nl, http://www.elsevier.com/locate/sab, http://www.elsevier.nl. Eds. G de Loos-Vollebregt, N Omenetto. Circ: 1,600.

543 USA ISSN 0887-6703
QC450 CODEN: SPECET
SPECTROSCOPY. Text in English. 1985. m. USD 67 domestic; USD 87 in Canada & Mexico; USD 129 elsewhere; USD 7.50 per issue domestic; USD 9.50 per issue foreign (effective 2005). charts; illus.; stat.; tr.lit. back issues avail. **Document type:** *Magazine, Trade.* **Description:** Concise research and applications articles for users and buyers of all types of spectroscopic equipment and related accessories. Combines practical information with principles of modern spectroscopy for analysts in industrial, research and development, or QA/QC, process monitoring, environmental testing, biomedical diagnostics, and chemical research.
Related titles: Online - full text ed.: (from bigchalk, EBSCO Publishing, Florida Center for Library Automation, Gale Group, Northern Light Technology, Inc., ProQuest Information & Learning).
Indexed: ABIPC, AESIS, AnalAb, CCI, CIN, ChemAb, ChemTitl, CurCont, ExcerpMed, ISR, MSB, SCI, Telegen.
—BLDSC (8411.113900), CASDDS, CISTI, Ei, IDS, IE, ingenta. **CCC.**
Published by: Advanstar Communications, Inc., One Park Ave, 2nd Fl, New York, NY 10016. TEL 212-951-6600, FAX 212-951-6793, spec@spectroscopymag.com, info@advanstar.com, http://www.spectroscopyonline.com, http://www.advanstar.com. Ed. Mark L Dlugoss. Circ: 24,300 (controlled). **Subscr. to:** Advanstar Marketing Services, Customer Service Department, 131 West, First St, Duluth, MN 55802. TEL 218-723-9200, 800-598-6008, FAX 218-723-9437.

C

543.1 GBR ISSN 0966-0941
QC450 CODEN: SPEUEF
SPECTROSCOPY EUROPE. Text in English. 1992. bi-m. EUR 130 in Europe to institutions; USD 175 elsewhere to institutions (effective 2006). adv. **Document type:** *Journal, Academic/Scholarly.*
Formed by the merger of (1989-1992): Spectroscopy World (0956-9820); (1989-1992): Spectroscopy International (1040-7669); Which was formerly (1975-1989): European Spectroscopy News (0307-0026)
Related titles: Online - full text ed.: ISSN 1522-2349 (from Wiley InterScience).
Indexed: AnalAb, CIN, ChemAb, ChemTitl, EngInd, FS&TA, Inspec, MSB, RAPRA, WSCA.
—BLDSC (8411.115300), AskIEEE, CASDDS, CISTI, IE, Infotrieve, ingenta. **CCC.**
Published by: (Association of British Spectroscopists), I M Publications, 6 Charlton Mill, Charlton, Chichester, W Sussex PO18 0HY, United Kingdom. TEL 44-1243-811334, FAX 44-1243-811711, imp@impub.demon.co.uk, http://www.spectroscopyeurope.com, http://www.impub.co.uk. Ed., Pub., Adv. contact Ian Michael. page USD 6,205; trim 210 x 297. Circ: 21,000 (controlled). **Subscr. in the Americas to:** John Wiley & Sons, Inc., 111 River St, Hoboken, NJ 07030-5774. TEL 201-748-6645, FAX 201-748-6088, subinfo@wiley.com.

643 NLD ISSN 0168-6461
➤ **STUDIES IN ANALYTICAL CHEMISTRY.** Text in English. 1981. irreg., latest vol.8, 1989. price varies. **Document type:** *Monographic series, Academic/Scholarly.* **Description:** Reviews topics in analytical chemistry.
Indexed: Inspec.
Published by: Elsevier BV (Subsidiary of: Elsevier Science & Technology), Radarweg 29, Amsterdam, 1043 NX, Netherlands. TEL 31-20-4853911, FAX 31-20-4852457, nlinfo-f@elsevier.nl, http://www.elsevier.com/inca/tree/?key=B1SACH, http://www.elsevier.nl.

543.1 CHE ISSN 0257-8972
TS670.A1 CODEN: SCTEEJ
➤ **SURFACE AND COATINGS TECHNOLOGY.** Text in English, French, German. 1973. 24/yr. EUR 6,404 in Europe to institutions; JPY 850,700 in Japan to institutions; USD 7,162 to institutions except Europe and Japan (effective 2006). adv. bk.rev. illus. index. back issues avail.; reprints avail. **Document type:** *Journal, Academic/Scholarly.* **Description:** Provides a forum for the exchange of information on the science, technology and applications of thin and thick coatings and modified surfaces which alter the properties of materials.
Former titles (until 1986): Surface Technology (0376-4583); (until 1976): Electrodeposition and Surface Treatment (0300-9416)
Related titles: Microform ed.: (from PQC); Online - full text ed.: (from EBSCO Publishing, Gale Group, IngentaConnect, ScienceDirect, Swets Information Services).
Indexed: ABIPC, ASCA, B&BAb, BioEngAb, BrCerAb, C&ISA, CCI, CIN, CerAb, ChemAb, ChemTitl, CivEngAb, CoppAb, CorrAb, CurCont, E&CAJ, EMA, EngInd, ExcerpMed, FLUIDEX, IAA, ISMEC, ISR, Inspec, M&TEA, MBF, METADEX, MFA, MSB, MSCI, PhysBer, RefZh, SCI, SolStAb, WAA, WTA, Weldasearch.
—BLDSC (8547.720000), AskIEEE, CASDDS, CISTI, Ei, IDS, IE, Infotrieve, ingenta, Linda Hall. **CCC.**
Published by: Elsevier S.A., PO Box 564, Lausanne 1, 1001, Switzerland. TEL 41-21-3207381, FAX 41-21-3235444, http://www.elsevier.com/locate/surfcoat. Eds. A Matthews, B D Sartwell. **Subscr. to:** Elsevier BV, PO Box 211, Amsterdam 1000 AE, Netherlands. TEL 31-20-485-3757, FAX 31-20-485-3432, nlinfo-f@elsevier.nl, http://www.elsevier.nl.

543 GBR ISSN 0142-2421
QC173.4.S94 CODEN: SIANDQ
➤ **SURFACE AND INTERFACE ANALYSIS.** Abbreviated title: S I A. Text in English. 1972. 13/yr. USD 6,505 to institutions; USD 7,156 combined subscription to institutions print & online eds. (effective 2006). adv. bk.rev. index. back issues avail.; reprints avail. **Document type:** *Journal, Academic/Scholarly.* **Description:** Presents papers on the development and application of characterization techniques for surfaces, interfaces, and thin films.
Related titles: CD-ROM ed.; Microform ed.: (from PQC); Online - full text ed.: ISSN 1096-9918. 1996. USD 6,505 to institutions (effective 2006) (from EBSCO Publishing, Swets Information Services, Wiley InterScience).
Indexed: AESIS, AnalAb, B&BAb, BrCerAb, C&ISA, CCI, CIN, CerAb, ChemAb, ChemTitl, CivEngAb, CorrAb, CurCont, E&CAJ, EMA, EngInd, IAA, ISR, Inspec, M&TEA, MBF, METADEX, MSB, MSCI, RCI, RefZh, SCI, SolStAb, WAA.
—BLDSC (8547.742000), AskIEEE, CASDDS, CISTI, Ei, IDS, IE, Infotrieve, ingenta, Linda Hall. **CCC.**
Published by: John Wiley & Sons Ltd. (Subsidiary of: John Wiley & Sons, Inc.), The Atrium, Southern Gate, Chichester, West Sussex PO19 8SQ, United Kingdom. TEL 44-1243-779777, FAX 44-1243-775878, customer@wiley.co.uk, http://www3.interscience.wiley.com/cgi-bin/jhome/2009, http://www.wiley.co.uk. Ed. John F Watts. Pub. Ray Boucher. R&P Diane Southern TEL 44-1243-770347. adv.: B&W page GBP 650, color page GBP 1,550; trim 210 x 297. Circ: 900. **Subscr. in the Americas to:** John Wiley & Sons, Inc., 111 River St, Hoboken, NJ 07030-5774. TEL 201-748-6645, 800-225-5945, subinfo@wiley.com

543.1 GBR ISSN 1743-4033
▼ **SURFACE WORLD & PRODUCT FINISHING.** Text in English. 2003. m. **Document type:** *Magazine, Trade.*
Formed by the merger of (1948-2003): Product Finishing (London) (0032-9762); (1993-2003): Surface World (1351-0525)
Published by: Hill Media Ltd., 119 High St, Berkhamsted, Herts HP4 2DJ, United Kingdom. TEL 44-1442-878787, FAX 44-1442-870888.

543.17 USA ISSN 1088-1468
T R C SPECTRAL DATA - 1 H NUCLEAR MAGNETIC RESONANCE. (Thermodynamics Research Center) Text in English. 1959. biennial. looseleaf. USD 600. **Document type:** *Academic/Scholarly.*
Former titles (until 1985): Thermodynamics Research Center. Hydrocarbon Project. Selected Values of Properties of Hydrocarbons and Related Compounds. Category F: Selected Nuclear Magnetic Resonance Data; A P I Research Project 44. Selected Values of Properties of Hydrocarbons and Related Compounds. Category F: Selected Nuclear Magnetic Resonance Data (0065-9681)
Published by: Thermodynamics Research Center, Texas Engineering Experiment Station, TEES Headquarters, 3577 TAMU, College Station, TX 77843-3577. TEL 409-845-4940, FAX 409-847-8590, info@trchpl.tamu.edu, mmartell@tamu.edu, http://trcweb.tamu.edu, http://tees.tamu.edu/. Pub. Kenneth N Marsh. Circ: 146.

543.17 USA ISSN 1088-1506
➤ **T R C SPECTRAL DATA - 13 C NUCLEAR MAGNETIC RESONANCE.** (Thermodynamics Research Center) Text in English. 1975. s-a. USD 550. **Document type:** *Academic/Scholarly.*
Former titles (until 1985): Thermodynamics Research Center. Hydrocarbon Project. Selected Values of Properties of Hydrocarbons and Related Compounds. Category G: Selected 13-C Nuclear Magnetic Resonance Spectral Data; A P I Research Project 44. Selected Values of Properties of: Selected 13 C Nuclear Magnetic Resonance Spectral Data
Published by: Thermodynamics Research Center, Texas Engineering Experiment Station, TEES Headquarters, 3577 TAMU, College Station, TX 77843-3577. TEL 409-845-4940, FAX 409-847-8590, info@trchpl.tamu.edu, mmartell@tamu.edu, http://trcweb.tamu.edu, http://tees.tamu.edu/. Pub. Kenneth N Marsh. Circ: 140.

543.1 USA ISSN 1088-7989
➤ **T R C SPECTRAL DATA - INFRARED.** (Thermodynamics Research Center) Text in English. 1943. biennial. looseleaf. USD 600. **Document type:** *Academic/Scholarly.* **Description:** Data sheets include the structure, empirical formula, CAS registry number, Wiswesser line notation, instrumental parameters, and analytical data for each sample.
Former titles (until 1985): Thermodynamics Research Center. Hydrocarbon Project. Selected Values of Properties of Hydrocarbons and Related Compounds. Category B: Selected Infrared Spectral Data; A P I Research Project 44. Selected Values of Properties of Hydrocarbons and Related Compounds. Category B: Selected Infrared Spectral Data (0065-9649)
Published by: Thermodynamics Research Center, Texas Engineering Experiment Station, TEES Headquarters, 3577 TAMU, College Station, TX 77843-3577. TEL 409-845-4940, FAX 409-847-8590, info@trchpl.tamu.edu, mmartell@tamu.edu, http//trcweb.tamu.edu, http://tees.tamu.edu/. Pub. Kenneth N Marsh. Circ: 238.

543.17 USA ISSN 1088-1476
T R C SPECTRAL DATA - MASS. (Thermodynamics Research Center) Text in English. 1947. biennial. looseleaf. USD 600. **Document type:** *Academic/Scholarly.*
Former titles (until 1985): Thermodynamics Research Center. Hydrocarbon Project. Selected Values of Properties of Hydrocarbons and Related Compounds. Category E: Selected Mass Spectral Data; A P I Research Project 44. Selected Values of Properties of Hydrocarbons and Related Compounds. Category E: Selected Mass Spectral Data (0065-9673); Incorporates: Thermodynamics Research Center. Data Project. Selected Values of Properties of Chemical Compounds. Category E. Selected Mass Spectral Data
Published by: Thermodynamics Research Center, Texas Engineering Experiment Station, TEES Headquarters, 3577 TAMU, College Station, TX 77843-3577. TEL 409-845-4940, FAX 409-847-8590, info@trchpl.tamu.edu, mmartell@tamu.edu, http://trcweb.tamu.edu, http://tees.tamu.edu/. Pub. Kenneth N Marsh. Circ: 283.

543.17 USA ISSN 1088-1484
T R C SPECTRAL DATA - RAMAN. (Thermodynamics Research Center) Text in English. 1948. s-a. USD 600. **Document type:** *Academic/Scholarly.*
Former titles (until 1986): Thermodynamics Research Center. Hydrocarbon Project. Selected Values of Properties of Hydrocarbons and Related Compounds. Category D: Selected Raman Spectral Data; A P I Research Project 44. Selected Values of Properties of Hydrocarbons and Related Compounds. Category D: Selected Raman Spectral Data (0065-9665); Incorporates: Thermodynamics Research Center. Data Project. Selected Values of Properties of Chemical Compounds. Category D. Selected Raman Spectral Data (0082-4038)
Published by: Thermodynamics Research Center, Texas Engineering Experiment Station, TEES Headquarters, 3577 TAMU, College Station, TX 77843-3577. TEL 409-845-4940, FAX 409-847-8590, info@trchpl.tamu.edu, mmartell@tamu.edu, http://trcweb.tamu.edu, http://tees.tamu.edu/. Pub. Kenneth N Marsh. Circ: 159.

543.17 USA ISSN 1088-1492
➤ **T R C SPECTRAL DATA - ULTRAVIOLET.** (Thermodynamics Research Center) Text in English. 1945. s-a. looseleaf. USD 600. **Document type:** *Academic/Scholarly.* **Description:** Data sheets include the structure, empirical formula, CAS registry number, Wiswesser line notation, instrumental parameters and analytical data for each sample.
Former titles: Thermodynamics Research Center. Hydrocarbon Project. Selected Values of Properties of Hydrocarbons and Related Compounds. Category C: Selected Ultraviolet Spectral Data; A P I Research Project 44. Selected Values of Properties of Hydrocarbons and Related Compounds. Compound C: Selected Ultraviolet Spectral Data (0065-9657); Incorporating: Thermodynamics Research Center. Data Project. Selected Values of Properties of Chemical Compounds. Category C. Selected Ultraviolet Spectral Data
Published by: Thermodynamics Research Center, Texas Engineering Experiment Station, TEES Headquarters, 3577 TAMU, College Station, TX 77843-3577. TEL 409-845-4940, FAX 409-847-8590, info@trchpl.tamu.edu, mmartell@tamu.edu, http://trcweb.tamu.edu, http://tees.tamu.edu/. Pub. Kenneth N Marsh. Circ: 227.

541 USA
➤ **T R C THERMODYNAMIC TABLES - NON-HYDROCARBONS.** (Thermodynamics Research Center) Text in English. 1955. biennial. looseleaf. USD 1,200. **Document type:** *Academic/Scholarly.*
Formerly: Thermodynamics Research Center. Data Project. Selected Values of Properties of Chemical Compounds. Category A. Tables of Selected Values of Physical and Thermodynamic Properties of Chemical Compounds (0082-4046)
—**CCC.**
Published by: Thermodynamics Research Center, Texas Engineering Experiment Station, TEES Headquarters, 3577 TAMU, College Station, TX 77843-3577. TEL 409-845-4940, FAX 409-847-8590, info@trchpl.tamu.edu, mmartell@tamu.edu, http://trcweb.tamu.edu, http://tees.tamu.edu/. Pub. Kenneth N Marsh. Circ: 230.

543 NLD ISSN 0039-9140
QD71 CODEN: TLNTA2
➤ **TALANTA.** Text in English. 1958. 15/yr. EUR 3,243 in Europe to institutions; JPY 430,700 in Japan to institutions; USD 3,628 to institutions except Europe and Japan (effective 2006). adv. bk.rev. charts; illus. index. back issues avail. **Document type:** *Academic/Scholarly.* **Description:** Publishes papers, reviews, and communications in all branches of pure and applied analytical chemistry, including relevant advances in the study of chemical sensors.
Related titles: Microfiche ed.: (from MIM); Microfilm ed.: (from PQC); Online - full text ed.: (from EBSCO Publishing, Gale Group, IngentaConnect, ScienceDirect, Swets Information Services).
Indexed: ASCA, ASFA, AbHyg, AgBio, AgrForAb, AnBrAb, AnalAb, BIOSIS Prev, BiolAb, CCI, CPA, ChemAb, CurCont, DBA, DSA, ESPM, ExcerpMed, FCA, FPA, FS&TA, ForAb, HelmAb, HerbAb, HortAb, I&DA, IABS, ISR, IndVet, MSB, MSCI, NutrAb, OrnHort, PBA, PGrRegA, PHN&I, PN&I, PoultAb, ProtozoAb, RA&MP, RCI, RM&VM, RPP, RefZh, RiceAb, S&F, SCI, SIA, SWRA, SeedAb, SoyAb, TDB, TriticAb, VITIS, VetBull, WRCInf, WeedAb.
—BLDSC (8601.100000), CASDDS, CINDOC, CISTI, IDS, IE, Infotrieve, ingenta, Linda Hall. **CCC.**
Published by: Elsevier BV (Subsidiary of: Elsevier Science & Technology), Radarweg 29, Amsterdam, 1043 NX, Netherlands. TEL 31-20-4853911, FAX 31-20-4852457, nlinfo-f@elsevier.nl, http://www.elsevier.com/locate/talanta, http://www.elsevier.nl. Eds. E H Hansen, G D Christian, M Kauffmann. Circ: 2,100.

543 NLD ISSN 0167-9244
CODEN: TIACD4
➤ **TECHNIQUES AND INSTRUMENTATION IN ANALYTICAL CHEMISTRY.** Text in English. 1978. irreg., latest vol.24, 2002. price varies. back issues avail. **Document type:** *Monographic series, Academic/Scholarly.* **Description:** Deals with applications of various instrumentation techniques in analytical chemistry, as well as biochemistry laboratory automation, pharmaceutical chemistry, environmental monitoring, and instrumentation.
Indexed: BIOSIS Prev, CIN, ChemAb, ChemTitl.
—BLDSC (8743.280000), CASDDS, CISTI, IE, ingenta. **CCC.**
Published by: Elsevier BV (Subsidiary of: Elsevier Science & Technology), Radarweg 29, Amsterdam, 1043 NX, Netherlands. TEL 31-20-4853911, FAX 31-20-4852457, nlinfo-f@elsevier.nl, http://www.elsevier.nl.

543.1 535 GBR ISSN 0262-8716
CODEN: TVUSD5
TECHNIQUES IN VISIBLE AND ULTRAVIOLET SPECTROMETRY. Text in English. 1981. irreg., latest vol.4, 1993. **Document type:** *Monographic series.*
—CASDDS.
Published by: (U V Spectrometry Group), Chapman & Hall Ltd. (Subsidiary of: International Thomson Publishing Group), Journals Department, 2-6 Boundary Row, London, SE1 8HN, United Kingdom. TEL 44-20-7865-0066, FAX 44-20-7522-9623. **Orders to:** International Thomson Publishing Services Ltd.

543.0858 USA
TOPICS IN FLUORESCENCE SPECTROSCOPY. Text in English. 1991. irreg., latest vol.10, 2005. price varies. back issues avail. **Document type:** *Monographic series.*
Indexed: CIN, ChemAb, ChemTitl.
Published by: Springer-Verlag New York, Inc. (Subsidiary of: Springer Science+Business Media), 233 Spring St, New York, NY 10013. TEL 212-460-1500, FAX 212-460-1575, service@springer-ny.com, http://www.springer-ny.com. Eds. C D Geddes, J R Lakowicz.

543 FRA ISSN 0768-598X
TOXICOLOGIE ANALYTIQUE. ANNALES. Text in French. 1989. q.
Formerly (until 1999): Toxicorama (0996-8423)
Published by: Societe Francaise de Toxicologie Analytique, Laboratoire de Biochimie et de Toxicologie, Centre Hospitalier Universitaire, 350, avenue Jacques Coeur, Poitiers, 86021, France. TEL 33-5-4944-4444, FAX 33-5-4944-3834, http://www.sfta.org.

543 NLD ISSN 0165-9936
QD71 CODEN: TTAEDJ
➤ **TRENDS IN ANALYTICAL CHEMISTRY.** Abbreviated title: Tr A C. Text in English. 1981. 11/yr. EUR 194 in Europe to individuals; JPY 25,900 in Japan to individuals; USD 217 to individuals except Europe and Japan (effective 2006). adv. bk.rev. Supplement avail.; back issues avail. **Document type:** *Academic/Scholarly.* **Description:** Covers analytical chemistry, biotechnology, clinical chemistry, environmental chemistry, pharmaceutical chemistry, toxicology, industrial chemistry, process analytical chemistry, food chemistry and geochemistry.
Related titles: Microform ed.: (from PQC); Online - full text ed.: (from EBSCO Publishing, Gale Group, IngentaConnect, ScienceDirect, Swets Information Services); ♦ Cumulative ed. of: Trends in Analytical Chemistry (Library Edition). ISSN 0167-2940; ♦ Special ed(s).: Trends in Analytical Chemistry (Library Edition). ISSN 0167-2940.
Indexed: AESIS, ASCA, AnalAb, BIOSIS Prev, BiolAb, BrCerAb, CBTA, CCI, CEABA, CIN, CIS, ChemAb, ChemTitl, ChromAb, CurCont, DSA, EngInd, EnvAb, ExcerpMed, FS&TA, IPA, ISR, Inspec, MSB, NutrAb, RCI, RefZh, S&F, SCI.
—BLDSC (9049.529000), AskIEEE, CASDDS, CISTI, Ei, IDS, IE, ingenta. **CCC.**
Published by: Elsevier BV (Subsidiary of: Elsevier Science & Technology), Radarweg 29, Amsterdam, 1043 NX, Netherlands. TEL 31-20-4853911, FAX 31-20-4852457, nlinfo-f@elsevier.nl, http://www.elsevier.com/locate/trac, http://www.elsevier.nl. Pub. M. Purvis. adv.: B&W page USD 1,020, color page USD 2,205; trim 210 x 280. Circ: 650.

543.1 NLD ISSN 0167-2940
QD71 CODEN: TTAEDJ
➤ **TRENDS IN ANALYTICAL CHEMISTRY (LIBRARY EDITION).** Variant title: Tr A C Compendium Series. Trends in Analytical Chemistry (Library Edition). Text in English. 1981. 11/yr. EUR 1,345 in Europe to institutions; JPY 178,600 in Japan to institutions; USD 1,505 to institutions except Europe and Japan (effective 2006). charts. back issues avail.; reprints avail. **Document type:** *Monographic series, Academic/Scholarly.* **Description:** Collects archival material from Trends in Analytical Chemistry.
Related titles: Online - full text ed.: (from Gale Group, IngentaConnect, Swets Information Services); ♦ Cumulative ed(s).: Trends in Analytical Chemistry. ISSN 0165-9936; ♦ Special ed. of: Trends in Analytical Chemistry. ISSN 0165-9936; ♦ Supplement(s): Trends in Analytical Chemistry. Supplement.
Indexed: AnalAb, BiolAb, CCI, ChemAb, CurCont, DSA, EngInd, FS&TA, IPA, MSB, RefZh, SCI.
—CINDOC, CISTI, Infotrieve, Linda Hall. **CCC.**
Published by: Elsevier BV (Subsidiary of: Elsevier Science & Technology), Radarweg 29, Amsterdam, 1043 NX, Netherlands. TEL 31-20-4853911, FAX 31-20-4852457, nlinfo-f@elsevier.nl, http://www.elsevier.com/locate/tracfs, http://www.elsevier.nl. Eds. A Townshend, D Coleman, Y Gohshi.

543 NLD
TRENDS IN ANALYTICAL CHEMISTRY. SUPPLEMENT. Variant title: TrAC Supplement. Text in English. 1994 (vol.2). irreg., latest vol.3, 1996. price varies. back issues avail. **Document type:** *Academic/Scholarly.* **Description:** Highlights research into trends in analytical chemistry.
Related titles: ♦ Supplement to: Trends in Analytical Chemistry (Library Edition). ISSN 0167-2940.
Published by: Elsevier BV (Subsidiary of: Elsevier Science & Technology), Radarweg 29, Amsterdam, 1043 NX, Netherlands. TEL 31-20-4853911, FAX 31-20-4852457, nlinfo-f@elsevier.nl, http://www.elsevier.nl. Ed. D Coleman.

643 USA ISSN 1460-3055
U K LABORATORY. Text in English. bi-m.
Formerly: Laboratory Products Technology
Published by: International Scientific Communications, Inc., 30 Controls Dr, PO Box 670, Shelton, CT 06484-0870. TEL 203-926-9300, FAX 203-926-9310, iscpubs@iscpubs.com, http://www.iscpubs.com/.

UNIVERSIDAD CENTRAL DE VENEZUELA. FACULTAD DE FARMACIA. REVISTA. see *PHARMACY AND PHARMACOLOGY*

543.1 GBR ISSN 0965-6758
V G MONOGRAPHS IN MASS SPECTROMETRY. Text in English. irreg., latest vol.3. **Document type:** *Monographic series, Academic/Scholarly.*
Published by: V G Instruments Ltd., Tudor Rd, Altrincham, Manchester WA14 5RZ, United Kingdom. TEL 0161-929-9666. Ed. R A W Johnstone.

643 USA
VARIAN SAMPLE PREPARATION PRODUCTS. ANNUAL INTERNATIONAL SYMPOSIUM. PROCEEDINGS. Text in English. a. **Document type:** *Proceedings.* **Description:** Brings together scientists who use bonded silica extraction techniques in their sample preparation methodologies.
Formerly: Analytichem International. Annual International Symposium. Proceedings
Published by: Varian Sample Preparation Products, 25200 Commercentre Dr., Lake Forest, CA 92630-8810. R&P Nigel Simpson.

543 JPN
X PAGE. Variant title: X-ray Structure Analysis Online. Text in English. q. free. back issues avail. **Document type:** *Journal, Academic/Scholarly.* **Description:** Reports on unpublished X-ray structure data of all classes of compounds.
Media: Online - full content.
Published by: Japan Society for Analytical Chemistry/Nihon Bunseki Kagaku Kai, 1-26-2 Nishigotanda, Shinagawa, Tokyo, 141-0031, Japan. TEL 81-3-34903351, FAX 81-3-34903572, analytsci@jsac.or.jp, http://wwwsoc.nii.ac.jp/jsac/analscix/.

543 GBR ISSN 0049-8246
QC481 CODEN: XRSPAX
➤ **X-RAY SPECTROMETRY**; an international journal. Variant title: X R S. Text in English. 1972. bi-m. USD 3,080 to institutions; USD 3,388 combined subscription to institutions print & online eds. (effective 2006). adv. bk.rev. bibl.; illus.; tr.lit. back issues avail.; reprints avail. **Document type:** *Journal, Academic/Scholarly.* **Description:** Covers advances in techniques, methods and equipment, news and events, and provides a platform for the discussion of more sophisticated X-ray analytical methods.
Related titles: Microform ed.: (from PQC); Online - full text ed.: ISSN 1097-4539. USD 3,080 to institutions (effective 2006) (from EBSCO Publishing, Swets Information Services, Wiley InterScience).
Indexed: AESIS, ASCA, ASFA, AnalAb, BrCerAb, C&ISA, CCI, CerAb, ChemAb, CivEngAb, CorrAb, CurCont, E&CAJ, EMA, EngInd, IAA, ISR, Inspec, M&TEA, MBF, METADEX, MSB, RCI, SCI, SolStAb, WAA.
—BLDSC (9365.780000), CASDDS, CISTI, Ei, IDS, IE, Infotrieve, ingenta, Linda Hall. **CCC.**
Published by: John Wiley & Sons Ltd. (Subsidiary of: John Wiley & Sons, Inc.), The Atrium, Southern Gate, Chichester, West Sussex PO19 8SQ, United Kingdom. TEL 44-1243-779777, FAX 44-1243-775878, customer@wiley.co.uk, http://www3.interscience.wiley.com/cgi-bin/jhome/1870, http://www.wiley.co.uk. Ed. R van Grieken. R&P Diane Southern TEL 44-1243-770347. adv.: B&W page GBP 750, color page GBP 1,650; trim 210 x 297. Circ: 800. **Subscr. in the Americas to:** John Wiley & Sons, Inc., 111 River St, Hoboken, NJ 07030-5774. TEL 800-225-5945, subinfo@wiley.com.

543.085 JPN ISSN 0911-7806
CODEN: XBNSDA
X SEN BUNSEKI NO SHINPO/ADVANCES IN X-RAY CHEMICAL ANALYSIS. Text in Japanese; Summaries in English, Japanese. 1970. a. JPY 5,775 newsstand/cover (effective 2004). **Document type:** *Journal, Academic/Scholarly.*
Formerly: X-Sen Kogyo Bunseki
Related titles: CD-ROM ed.
Indexed: CIN, ChemAb, ChemTitl, INIS AtomInd.
—BLDSC (0712.205000), CASDDS. **CCC.**
Published by: (National Institute for Materials Science, X-Ray Laboratory), Agune Gijutsu Senta/Agne Gijutsu Center, 1-25 Minami-Aoyama 5-chome, Minato-ku, Tokyo, 107-0062, Japan. TEL 81-3-34095329, FAX 81-3-34098237, http://www.nims.go.jp/xray/xbun/, http://www.agne.co.jp/books/.

X SEN BUNSEKI TORONKAI KOEN YOSHISHU/ABSTRACTS OF ANNUAL CONFERENCE ON X-RAY CHEMICAL ANALYSIS. see *CHEMISTRY—Abstracting, Bibliographies, Statistics*

543 RUS ISSN 0044-4502
QD71 CODEN: ZAKHA8
ZHURNAL ANALITICHESKOI KHIMII. Text in Russian; Abstracts and contents page in English. 1946. m. RUR 990 for 6 mos. domestic (effective 2004). adv. bk.rev. charts. index. **Document type:** *Journal, Academic/Scholarly.* **Description:** Covers theoretical and some applied aspects of analytical chemistry; it informs the reader of new trends in analytical methods, samples, and analytes; new instruments; and reagents.
Related titles: Online - full text ed.; ♦ English Translation: Journal of Analytical Chemistry. ISSN 1061-9348.
Indexed: ABIPC, AnalAb, BrCerAb, C&ISA, CerAb, ChemAb, CivEngAb, CorrAb, DSA, E&CAJ, EMA, EngInd, FS&TA, INIS AtomInd, M&TEA, MBF, METADEX, NutrAb, PotatoAb, RefZh, SolStAb, WAA, WeedAb.
—BLDSC (0060.600000), CASDDS, CINDOC, CISTI, East View, IE, Infotrieve, KNAW, Linda Hall. **CCC.**
Published by: (Rossiiskaya Akademiya Nauk/Russian Academy of Sciences), Izdatel'stvo Nauka, Profsoyuznaya ul 90, Moscow, 117864, Russian Federation. TEL 7-095-3347151, FAX 7-095-4202220, secret@naukaran.ru, http://www.maik.rssi.ru/cgi-bin/list.pl?page=ankhim, http://www.naukaran.ru. Circ: 4,050.

ZHURNAL PRIKLADNOI SPEKTROSKOPII. see *PHYSICS—Optics*

CHEMISTRY—Computer Applications

542.85 006 GBR ISSN 0364-5916
QD503 CODEN: CCCTD6
➤ **C A L P H A D.** (Computer Coupling of Phase Diagrams and Thermochemistry) Text in English. 1977. 4/yr. EUR 1,282 in Europe to institutions; JPY 170,200 in Japan to institutions; USD 1,434 elsewhere to institutions (effective 2006). adv. software rev. abstr. back issues avail. **Document type:** *Journal, Academic/Scholarly.* **Description:** Covers all aspects of calculating and using phase diagrams in thermochemistry and studies of phase equilibrium, including applications in industrial processes.
Related titles: Microfilm ed.: (from PQC); Online - full text ed.: (from EBSCO Publishing, Gale Group, IngentaConnect, ScienceDirect, Swets Information Services).

C

Indexed: ASCA, BiolAb, BrCerAb, C&ISA, CCI, CIN, CerAb, ChemAb, CivEngAb, CompC, CorrAb, CurCont, E&CAJ, EMA, Englnd, IAA, ISMEC, ISR, Inspec, M&TEA, MBF, METADEX, MSCI, RCI, RefZh, SCI, SolStAb, WAA.
—BLDSC (3015.540000), AskIEEE, CASDDS, CISTI, Ei, IDS, IE, Infotrieve, ingenta, Linda Hall. **CCC.**
Published by: Pergamon (Subsidiary of: Elsevier Science & Technology), The Boulevard, Langford Ln, East Park, Kidlington, Oxford OX5 1GB, United Kingdom. TEL 44-1865-843000, FAX 44-1865-843010, http://www.elsevier.com/locate/calphad. Eds. Larry Kaufman, Z.-K. Liu. Circ: 1,025. **Subscr. to:** Elsevier BV, PO Box 211, Amsterdam 1000 AE, Netherlands. nlinfo-f@elsevier.nl, http://www.elsevier.nl.

➤ **C A SELECTS. COMPUTERS IN CHEMISTRY.** see *CHEMISTRY—Abstracting, Bibliographies, Statistics*

542.85 572.8 JPN ISSN 1347-6297
➤ **CHEM-BIO INFORMATICS JOURNAL.** Abbreviated title: C B I Journal. Text in English. 2001. q. back issues avail. **Document type:** *Journal, Academic/Scholarly.*
Related titles: Online - full content ed.: ISSN 1347-0442. free (effective 2005); Online - full text ed.: (from J-Stage).
Indexed: B&BAb, BioEngAb.
Published by: Chem-Bio Informatics Society, IIDA Bldg, Rm 301, Yoga 4-3-16, Setagaya-ku, Tokyo, 158-0097, Japan. TEL 81-3-5491-5423, FAX 81-3-5491-5462, cbistaff@cbi.or.jp, http://cbij.jstage.jst.go.jp/, http://www.cbi.or.jp/index.html.

542.85 USA
TP184
CHEMICAL ENGINEERING PROGRESS SOFTWARE DIRECTORY. Text in English. 1984. a. adv. index. **Document type:** *Directory, Trade.* **Description:** Describes more than 1,700 software programs worldwide in 35 categories, including environmental control, waste management, equipment design, fluid dynamics, particle dynamics, flow analysis, materials, process control and process design.
Formerly: A.I.Ch.E. Applications Software Survey of Personal Computers (0743-0183)
Media: Online - full text.
Published by: American Institute of Chemical Engineers, 3 Park Ave, New York, NY 10016-5901. TEL 212-591-8100, 800-242-4363, FAX 212-591-8888, kares@aiche.org, xpress@aiche.org, http://www.aiche.org. Ed. Karen Lutta Simpson. R&P Karen Simpson TEL 212-591-7337. Adv. contact Gerry Moss.

542.85 NLD ISSN 1572-4778
▼ **CHEMINFORMATICS.** Text in English. 2004. s-a. EUR 176, USD 209 (effective 2006). adv. **Document type:** *Journal, Academic/Scholarly.* **Description:** Features invited reviews and innovations in the rapidly growing and evolving field of computerized chemical information handling. Covers all those fields in which information technology and resources are used to transform chemical data into information and information into knowledge and is of particular interest to chemists, computer scientists and information specialists.
Related titles: Online - full content ed.: EUR 150, USD 170 (effective 2005); Online - full text ed.: (from O C L C Online Computer Library Center, Inc.).
—CCC.
Published by: I O S Press, Nieuwe Hemweg 6B, Amsterdam, 1013 BG, Netherlands. info@iospress.nl, http://www.iospress.nl/html/15724778.php. Ed. Curt M Breneman TEL 518-276-2678. R&P Ms. Carry Koolbergen TEL 31-20-6382189. Adv. contact Ms. Jolijn van Eunen.

542.85 NLD ISSN 0169-7439
QD39.3.S7 CODEN: CILSEN
➤ **CHEMOMETRICS AND INTELLIGENT LABORATORY SYSTEMS.** Text in English. 1987. 10/yr. EUR 2,224 in Europe to institutions; JPY 295,500 in Japan to institutions; USD 2,487 elsewhere to institutions (effective 2006). adv. bk.rev. illus.; stat. index, cum.index. back issues avail. **Document type:** *Journal, Academic/Scholarly.* **Description:** Publishes articles about new developments on laboratory techniques in chemistry and related disciplines which are characterized by the application of statistical and computer methods.
Related titles: Microform ed.: (from PQC); Online - full text ed.: (from EBSCO Publishing, Gale Group, IngentaConnect, ScienceDirect, Swets Information Services).
Indexed: AnalAb, B&BAb, BioEngAb, CCI, CIN, CIS, CMCI, ChemAb, ChemTitl, CurCont, Englnd, ExcerpMed, FS&TA, ISR, Inspec, MSB, SCI, SIA, VITIS.
—BLDSC (3172.264000), AskIEEE, CASDDS, CINDOC, CISTI, Ei, GNLM, IDS, IE, Infotrieve, ingenta, Linda Hall. **CCC.**
Published by: (Chemometrics Society), Elsevier BV (Subsidiary of: Elsevier Science & Technology), Radarweg 29, Amsterdam, 1043 NX, Netherlands. TEL 31-20-4853911, FAX 31-20-4852457, nlinfo-f@elsevier.nl, http://www.elsevier.com/locate/chemometrics, http://www.elsevier.nl. Eds. P. D. Wentzell, P. Minkkinen, R. Tauler.

542.85 USA ISSN 1386-7857
➤ **CLUSTER COMPUTING;** the journal of networks, software tools and applications. Text in Dutch. 1998. q. EUR 384, USD 384, GBP 240 combined subscription to institutions print & online eds. (effective 2005). adv. reprint service avail. from PSC. **Document type:** *Journal, Academic/Scholarly.* **Description:** Supplies a forum for presenting the latest research and technology that unify the fields of parallel processing, distributed computing systems, and computer networks.
Related titles: Online - full text ed.: ISSN 1573-7543 (from EBSCO Publishing, Gale Group, IngentaConnect, Kluwer Online, O C L C Online Computer Library Center, Inc., Springer LINK, Swets Information Services).
Indexed: BibLing, BrCerAb, C&ISA, CerAb, CompLI, CorrAb, E&CAJ, EMA, IAA, Inspec, M&TEA, MBF, METADEX, RefZh, SolStAb, WAA.
—BLDSC (3287.112600), IE, Infotrieve, ingenta, Linda Hall. **CCC.**
Published by: Springer-Verlag New York, Inc. (Subsidiary of: Springer Science+Business Media), 233 Spring St, New York, NY 10013. TEL 212-460-1500, FAX 212-460-1575, service@springer-ny.com, http://springerlink.metapress.com/openurl.asp?genre=journal&issn=1386-7857, http://www.springer-ny.com. Ed. Salim Hariri. **Subscr. to:** Journal Fulfillment, PO Box 2485, Secaucus, NJ 07096-2485. TEL 201-348-4033, FAX 201-348-4505, journals@springer-ny.com.

542.85 GBR ISSN 1476-9271
QD39.3.E46 CODEN: CBCOCH
➤ **COMPUTATIONAL BIOLOGY AND CHEMISTRY.** Text in English. 1977. 6/yr. EUR 1,535 in Europe to institutions; JPY 203,400 in Japan to institutions; USD 1,713 to institutions except Europe and Japan (effective 2006). adv. bk.rev. back issues avail. **Document type:** *Academic/Scholarly.* **Description:** Publishes papers on applications of computer techniques to chemistry and biochemistry.
Formerly: Computers & Chemistry (0097-8485)
Related titles: Microfilm ed.: (from PQC); Online - full text ed.: (from EBSCO Publishing, Gale Group, IngentaConnect, ScienceDirect, Swets Information Services).
Indexed: ABIPC, ASCA, ASFA, AnalAb, B&BAb, BBCI, BioEngAb, BiolAb, CCI, CEA, CEABA, CIN, CMCI, Cadscan, ChemAb, ChemTitl, CompAb, CompC, CompLI, CompR, CurCont, Englnd, HGA, ISR, IndMed, InfoSAb, Inspec, LeadAb, MEDLINE, MSB, RCI, RefZh, SCI, ZentMath, Zincscan.
—BLDSC (3390.576700), AskIEEE, CASDDS, CISTI, Ei, IDS, IE, ingenta, Linda Hall. **CCC.**
Published by: Pergamon (Subsidiary of: Elsevier Science & Technology), The Boulevard, Langford Ln, East Park, Kidlington, Oxford OX5 1GB, United Kingdom. TEL 44-1865-843000, FAX 44-1865-843010, http://www.elsevier.com/locate/cbac. Ed. J. Crabbe. Circ: 1,000. **Subscr. to:** Elsevier BV, PO Box 211, Amsterdam 1000 AE, Netherlands. TEL 31-20-485-3757, FAX 31-20-485-3432, nlinfo-f@elsevier.nl, http://www.elsevier.nl.

➤ **COMPUTER - AIDED CHEMICAL ENGINEERING.** see *ENGINEERING—Computer Applications*

542.85 CHN
COMPUTER CHEMISTRY MONOGRAPH SERIES. Text in English. 1992. irreg., latest vol.3, 1993. **Document type:** *Monographic series.*
Published by: Kexue Chubanshe/Science Press, 16 Donghuang Cheng Genbei Jie, Beijing, 100717, China. TEL 86-10-64000246, FAX 86-10-64030255. Ed. Jianrong Zhang.

660.285 006 GBR ISSN 0098-1354
TP149 CODEN: CCENDW
➤ **COMPUTERS & CHEMICAL ENGINEERING.** Text in English. 1977. 12/yr. EUR 2,466 in Europe to institutions; JPY 327,400 in Japan to institutions; USD 2,759 to institutions except Europe and Japan; EUR 309 in Europe to qualified personnel; JPY 41,100 in Japan to qualified personnel; USD 346 to qualified personnel except Europe and Japan (effective 2006). adv. bk.rev. illus. Supplement avail.; back issues avail.; reprints avail. **Document type:** *Academic/Scholarly.* **Description:** Presents information on developments in computer applications used to solve chemical engineering problems.
Related titles: Microfilm ed.: (from PQC); Online - full text ed.: (from EBSCO Publishing, Gale Group, IngentaConnect, ScienceDirect, Swets Information Services).
Indexed: ABIPC, AIA, APIAb, APICat, APIH&E, APIOC, APIPR, APIPS, APITS, AS&TI, ASCA, C&ISA, CADCAM, CCI, CEA, CEABA, CIN, CMCI, ChemAb, ChemTitl, CivEngAb, CompAb, CompC, CompLI, CurCont, E&CAJ, ESPM, Englnd, ExcerpMed, FLUIDEX, H&SSA, IAA, ISMEC, ISR, Inspec, LHB, SCI, SSCI, SoftAbEng, SolStAb, TCEA, WRCInf.
—BLDSC (3394.664000), AskIEEE, CASDDS, CISTI, Ei, IDS, IE, Infotrieve, ingenta, Linda Hall. **CCC.**
Published by: Pergamon (Subsidiary of: Elsevier Science & Technology), The Boulevard, Langford Ln, East Park, Kidlington, Oxford OX5 1GB, United Kingdom. TEL 44-1865-843000, FAX 44-1865-843010, http://www.elsevier.com/locate/compchemeng. Ed. G V Reklaitis. Circ: 1,000. **Subscr. to:** Elsevier BV, PO Box 211, Amsterdam 1000 AE, Netherlands. TEL 31-20-485-3757, FAX 31-20-485-3432, nlinfo-f@elsevier.nl, http://www.elsevier.nl.

➤ **CURRENT COMPUTER-AIDED DRUG DESIGN.** see *MEDICAL SCIENCES—Computer Applications*

542.85 CHN ISSN 1001-4160
QA75.5 CODEN: JYYHE6
➤ **JISUANJI YU YINGYONG HUAXUE/COMPUTERS AND APPLIED CHEMISTRY.** Text in Chinese. 1984. bi-m. CNY 228 (effective 2004). adv. **Document type:** *Journal, Academic/Scholarly.* **Description:** Covers applied chemistry, chemical mathematics, computer advances in chemometrics, process simulation, control, artificial intelligence, optimization and graphics in chemistry, molecular modeling, structure-property correlation and data processing. Emphasis is on computational chemistry.
Related titles: Online - full text ed.: (from East View Information Services, WanFang Data Corp.).
Indexed: ChemAb.
—BLDSC (3394.647000), CASDDS, IE, ingenta.
Published by: (Zhongguo Kexueyuan, Guocheng Gongcheng Yanjiuyuan/Chinese Academy of Sciences, Institute of Process Engineering), Kexue Chubanshe/Science Press, 16 Donghuang Cheng Genbei Jie, Beijing, 100717, China. TEL 86-10-64000246, FAX 86-10-64030255, hwang@lcc.icm.ac.cn, http://jsjyyyhx.periodicals.net.cn/default.html. Circ: 4,000. **Co-sponsor:** Chinese University of Science and Technology.

540.285071 USA ISSN 1050-4303
CODEN: JEDCEI
➤ **JOURNAL OF CHEMICAL EDUCATION: SOFTWARE. SERIES C;** for Apple Macintosh computers. Text in English. 1989. irreg. back issues avail. **Document type:** *Academic/Scholarly.* **Description:** Publishes instructional software on disk with ancillary printed materials for students and teachers.
Related titles: CD-ROM ed.; Diskette ed.
Indexed: CIN, ChemAb, ChemTitl.
—CASDDS.
Published by: American Chemical Society, 1155 16th St, N W, Washington, DC 20036. TEL 202-872-4614, 800-227-5558, FAX 202-776-8264, jcesoft@chem.wisc.edu, http://jchemed.chem.wisc.edu/, http://www.acs.org. Circ: 1,000.

540.285071 USA ISSN 1066-4157
QD1 CODEN: JESDES
➤ **JOURNAL OF CHEMICAL EDUCATION: SOFTWARE. SERIES D;** for windows. Text in English. 1993. irreg. back issues avail. **Document type:** *Academic/Scholarly.* **Description:** Instructional software published on disk with ancillary printed materials for students and teachers.
Related titles: CD-ROM ed.; Diskette ed.
Indexed: CIN, ChemAb, ChemTitl.
Published by: American Chemical Society, 1155 16th St, N W, Washington, DC 20036. TEL 202-872-4614, 800-227-5558, FAX 202-776-8264, jcesoft@chem.wisc.edu, http://jchemed.chem.wisc.edu/, http://www.acs.org. Circ: 500.

540.285071 USA ISSN 1050-6942
CODEN: JESSE5
➤ **JOURNAL OF CHEMICAL EDUCATION: SOFTWARE. SPECIAL ISSUE SERIES.** Text in English. 1989. irreg. back issues avail. **Document type:** *Academic/Scholarly.*
Related titles: CD-ROM ed.; Diskette ed.; Video ed.
Indexed: CIN, ChemAb, ChemTitl.
—CASDDS.
Published by: American Chemical Society, 1155 16th St, N W, Washington, DC 20036. TEL 202-872-4614, 800-227-5558, FAX 202-776-8264, jcesoft@chem.wisc.edu, http://jchemed.chem.wisc.edu/, http://www.acs.org. Circ: 1,500.

542.85 006 USA ISSN 1549-9596
QD1 CODEN: JCISD8
➤ **JOURNAL OF CHEMICAL INFORMATION AND MODELING.** Text in English. 1960. bi-m. USD 671 in North America to institutions; USD 716 elsewhere to institutions; USD 132 in North America to members; USD 177 elsewhere to members; USD 99 in North America to students; USD 144 elsewhere to students (effective 2006). adv. bk.rev. charts. index. back issues avail. **Document type:** *Journal, Academic/Scholarly.* **Description:** Publishes research papers in all areas of information and computer science relevant to chemistry and chemical technology.
Former titles (until 2005): Journal of Chemical Information and Computer Sciences (0095-2338); (until 1975): Journal of Chemical Documentation (0021-9576)
Related titles: Microfiche ed.: USD 486 in North America to institutions; USD 495 elsewhere to institutions (effective 2002); Online - full text ed.: ISSN 1549-960X. USD 40 (effective 2006) (from EBSCO Publishing, Swets Information Services).
Indexed: ABIPC, ASCA, Agr, AnalAb, B&BAb, BibAg, BiolAb, C&ISA, CCI, CEA, CIN, CMCI, ChemAb, ChemInfo, ChemTitl, CompAb, CompC, CompLI, CurCont, E&CAJ, Englnd, ExcerpMed, ICEA, ISMEC, ISR, IndMed, InfoSAb, Inspec, LISA, MEDLINE, MathSciNet, PROMT, RASB, RCI, RefZh, SCI, SSCI, SoftAbEng, SolStAb, TCEA.
—BLDSC (4956.820500), AskIEEE, CASDDS, CINDOC, CISTI, Ei, GNLM, IDS, IE, Infotrieve, ingenta, Linda Hall. **CCC.**

C

Published by: American Chemical Society, 1155 16th St, N W, Washington, DC 20036. TEL 202-872-4614, 800-227-5558, FAX 202-776-8264, jchim@yale.edu, service@acs.org, http://pubs.acs.org/jcics. Ed. William Jorgensen. adv.: color page USD 3,690. Circ: 2,600 (paid). **Subscr. to:** Member & Subscriber Services, PO Box 3337, Columbus, OH 43210. TEL 614-447-3776, 800-333-9511, FAX 614-447-3671.

542.85 JPN ISSN 1345-8647
JOURNAL OF COMPUTER AIDED CHEMISTRY. Text in English. 2000. irreg. **Document type:** *Journal, Academic/Scholarly.*
Media: Online - full content.
Published by: Chemical Society Of Japan, Division of Chemical Information and Computer Sciences, 1-5, Kanda-Surugadai, Chiyoda-ku, Tokyo, 101-8307, Japan. TEL 81-3-3292-6161, FAX 81-3-3292-6318, jcac@chemistry.or.jp, info@chemistry.or.jp, http://jcac.jstage.jst.go.jp/, http://www.chemistry.or.jp/.

542.85 NLD ISSN 0920-654X
QD480 CODEN: JCADEQ
➤ **JOURNAL OF COMPUTER - AIDED MOLECULAR DESIGN.** Text in English. 1987. m. EUR 2,028, USD 2,068, GBP 1,268 combined subscription to institutions print & online eds. (effective 2005). adv. charts; illus.; stat. reprint service avail. from PSC. **Document type:** *Journal, Academic/Scholarly.*
Description: Disseminates information on both the theory and application of computer-based methods in the analysis and design of molecules. Includes molecular modelling studies in pharmaceutical, polymer, materials, and surface sciences, as well as other molecular based disciplines.
Incorporates (1993-2001): Perspectives in Drug Discovery and Design (0928-2866)
Related titles: Diskette ed.; Online - full text ed.: ISSN 1573-4951 (from EBSCO Publishing, Gale Group, IngentaConnect, Kluwer Online, O C L C Online Computer Library Center, Inc., Springer LINK, Swets Information Services); ♦ Supplement(s): Perspectives in Drug Discovery and Design. ISSN 0928-2866.
Indexed: ASCA, ASFA, B&BAb, BBCI, BIOSIS Prev, BibLing, BioEngAb, BiolAb, CCI, CIN, ChemAb, ChemTitl, CompLI, CurCont, EngInd, ExcerpMed, FS&TA, ISR, IndMed, Inpharma, M&PBA, MEDLINE, PE&ON, RM&VM, Reac, RefZh, SCI.
—BLDSC (4963.580000), CASDDS, CISTI, Ei, GNLM, IDS, IE, Infotrieve, ingenta, Linda Hall. **CCC.**
Published by: Springer-Verlag Dordrecht (Subsidiary of: Springer Science+Business Media), Van Godewijckstraat 30, Dordrecht, 3311 GX, Netherlands. TEL 31-78-6576050, FAX 31-78-6576474, http://springerlink.metapress.com/openurl.asp?genre=journal&issn=0920-654X, http://www.springeronline.com. Eds. Andrew R Leach, Federico Gago, Terry R Stouch.

542.85 JPN ISSN 1347-1767
JOURNAL OF COMPUTER CHEMISTRY, JAPAN. Text in English, Japanese. 2002. q. **Document type:** *Journal, Academic/Scholarly.*
Related titles: Online - full text ed.: ISSN 1347-3824. free (effective 2005) (from J-Stage).
Published by: Society of Computer Chemistry, Japan/Nihon Kompyuta Kagakkai, 2-7-4 Torigoe Taito-ku Taitouku, Tokyo, 111-0054, Japan. TEL 81-3-58250599, FAX 81-3-58250654, office@sccj.net, http://www.sccj.net/publications/index.htm.

541.220285 USA ISSN 1093-3263
QD461 CODEN: JMGMFI
➤ **JOURNAL OF MOLECULAR GRAPHICS AND MODELLING.** Text in English. 1983. 6/yr. EUR 1,042 in Europe to institutions; JPY 138,500 in Japan to institutions; USD 1,166 to institutions except Europe and Japan; EUR 313 in Europe to qualified personnel; JPY 41,600 in Japan to qualified personnel; USD 349 to qualified personnel except Europe and Japan (effective 2006). adv. bk.rev. abstr.; illus. index. back issues avail. **Document type:** *Academic/Scholarly.*
Description: Presents practical and theoretical research on the use of computer graphics for the investigation of molecular structure, function and interaction.
Formerly (until 1997): Journal of Molecular Graphics (0263-7855)
Related titles: Microform ed.: (from PQC); Online - full text ed.: (from EBSCO Publishing, Gale Group, IngentaConnect, ScienceDirect, Swets Information Services).
Indexed: ASFA, Agr, BBCI, BCI, BIOBASE, BIOSIS Prev, BioEngAb, BiolAb, C&ISA, CCI, CIN, ChemAb, ChemTitl, CompC, CurCont, E&CAJ, EngInd, ExcerpMed, GenetAb, IABS, ISR, IndMed, Inspec, MEDLINE, RCI, RefZh, SCI, SolStAb.
—BLDSC (5020.713100), CASDDS, CISTI, Ei, GNLM, IDS, IE, Infotrieve, ingenta, Linda Hall. **CCC.**
Published by: (Molecular Graphics and Modelling Society), Elsevier Inc. (Subsidiary of: Elsevier Science & Technology), 360 Park Ave. S, New York, NY 10010-1710. TEL 212-633-3730, 888-437-4636, usinfo-f@elsevier.com, http://www.elsevier.com/locate/jmgm. Eds. A. J. Holder, Dr. J. W. Essex. **Subscr. outside the Americas to:** Elsevier BV, PO Box 211, Amsterdam 1000 AE, Netherlands. TEL 31-20-485-3757, FAX 31-20-485-3432.

332.1 SGP ISSN 0219-6336
QD450
➤ **JOURNAL OF THEORETICAL AND COMPUTATIONAL CHEMISTRY.** Text in English. 2002. q. SGD 185, USD 109, EUR 101 to individuals; SGD 531, USD 313, EUR 292 combined subscription to institutions print & online eds.; SGD 319, USD 188, EUR 175 combined subscription in developing nations to institutions print & online eds. (effective 2006). back issues avail. **Document type:** *Journal, Academic/Scholarly.*
Description: Publishes original contributions on broad aspects: from both the development of fundamental theoretical methodology and computational algorithm to extensive numerical applications to specific scientific problems ranging from gas-phase to condensed phase, and to biological systems. It covers general research areas broadly defined as quantum chemistry, chemical dynamics, statistical mechanics, and chemical biology.
Related titles: Online - full content ed.; Online - full text ed.: (from EBSCO Publishing, O C L C Online Computer Library Center, Inc., Swets Information Services).
Indexed: BrCerAb, C&ISA, CCI, CerAb, CorrAb, CurCont, E&CAJ, EMA, IAA, M&TEA, MBF, METADEX, SolStAb, WAA.
—BLDSC (5069.074730), CISTI, IE, ingenta, Linda Hall. **CCC.**
Published by: World Scientific Publishing Co. Pte. Ltd., 5 Toh Tuck Link, Singapore, 596224, Singapore. TEL 65-466-5775, FAX 65-467-7667, wspc@wspc.com.sg, http://www.worldscinet.com/jtcc/jtcc.shtml, http://www.worldscientific.com. Ed. John Zeng Hui Zhang TEL 212-998-8412. **Subscr. to:** Farrer Rd, PO Box 128, Singapore 912805, Singapore. sales@wspc.com.sg. **Dist. by:** World Scientific Publishing Co., Inc., 1060 Main St, River Edge, NJ 07661. TEL 201-487-9655, 800-227-7562, FAX 201-487-9656, 888-977-2665.; World Scientific Publishing Ltd., 57 Shelton St, London WC2H 9HE, United Kingdom. TEL 44-20-78360888, FAX 44-20-78362020, sales@wspc.co.uk.

542.85 JPN ISSN 0919-3391
KAGAKU SOFUTOWEA GAKKAI KENKYU TORONKAI KOEN YOSHISHU. Text in Japanese. 1986. a.
Published by: Kagaku Sofutowea Gakkai/Chemical Software Society of Japan, Fukui Kogyo Koto Senmon Gakko, Geshi-cho, Sabae-shi, Fukui-ken 916-8507, Japan. TEL 81-778062-1111, FAX 81-778-62-1108.

542.85 JPN ISSN 0918-0869
CODEN: KASOEA
KAGAKU TO SOFUTOWEA/CHEMISTRY AND SOFTWARE. Text in Japanese; Summaries in English. q. membership.
Indexed: ChemAb.
—BLDSC (3170.150000).
Published by: Kagaku Sofutowea Gakkai/Chemical Software Society of Japan, Fukui Kogyo Koto Senmon Gakko, Geshi-cho, Sabae-shi, Fukui-ken 916-8507, Japan. TEL 81-778-62-1111, FAX 81-778-62-1108.

542.85 USA ISSN 1059-7530
QD39.3.E46 CODEN: MCCHED
➤ **METHODS IN COMPUTATIONAL CHEMISTRY.** Text in English. 1987. irreg., latest 1993, Jan. USD 205 per vol. (effective 2005). back issues avail. **Document type:** *Monographic series, Academic/Scholarly.* **Description:** Providing specialist reviews and analyses of contemporary theories, algorithms, and techniques, this series aims to facilitate the effective exploitation of available computing.
Indexed: CCI, ChemAb, ChemTitl.
—CASDDS, CISTI, KNAW. **CCC.**
Published by: Springer-Verlag New York, Inc. (Subsidiary of: Springer Science+Business Media), 233 Spring St, New York, NY 10013. TEL 212-460-1500, FAX 212-460-1575, service@springer-ny.com, http://www.springer-ny.com. **Dist. by:** Journal Fulfillment, PO Box 2485, Secaucus, NJ 07096-2485.

542.85 JPN ISSN 0919-4894
SAISHIN KAGAKU SOFUTOWEASHU/ANNUAL REPORT OF CHEMICAL SOFTWARES. Text in English, Japanese. 1985. a.
Published by: Kagaku Sofutowea Gakkai/Chemical Software Society of Japan, Fukui Kogyo Koto Senmon Gakko, Geshi-cho, Sabae-shi, Fukui-ken 916-8507, Japan. TEL 81-778-62-1111, FAX 81-778-62-1108.

THEORETICAL AND COMPUTATIONAL CHEMISTRY. see *CHEMISTRY*

CHEMISTRY—Crystallography

548 USA ISSN 1058-9945
A C A NEWSLETTER. (American Crystallographic Association Newsletter) Text in English. 1985. q. free to members (effective 2005).
—CISTI.
Published by: American Crystallographic Association, c/o Hauptman-Woodward Med Res Inst, 73 High St, PO Box 96, Buffalo, NY 14203. TEL 716-898-8690, FAX 716-898-8695, marcia@hwi.buffalo.edu, http://www.hwi.buffalo.edu/aca/.

ACTA BIOPHYSICS SINICA. see *BIOLOGY—Biophysics*

548 DNK ISSN 0108-7673
QD901 CODEN: ACACEQ
➤ **ACTA CRYSTALLOGRAPHICA. SECTION A: FOUNDATIONS OF CRYSTALLOGRAPHY.** Text in English, French, German, Russian. 1948. bi-m. EUR 158 combined subscription in Europe to individuals print & online eds.; USD 176 combined subscription in the Americas to individuals &Caribbean, print & online eds.; GBP 105 combined subscription elsewhere to individuals print & online eds.; USD 558 combined subscription in the Americas to institutions & Caribbean, print & online eds.; GBP 332 combined subscription elsewhere to institutions print & online eds. (effective 2006). adv. bk.rev. illus. Index. reprint service avail. from ISI,PSC. **Document type:** *Journal, Academic/Scholarly.*
Formerly (until 1982): Acta Crystallographica. Section A: Crystal Physics, Diffraction, Theoretical and General Crystallography (0567-7394); Which superseded in part (until 1967): Acta Crystallographica (0365-110X)
Related titles: Microfilm ed.: DKK 2,723 (effective 2001) (from PMC); Online - full text ed.: Acta Crystallographica. Section A: Foundations of Crystallography. Online. ISSN 1600-5724. 1968. EUR 150 in Europe to individuals; USD 168 in the Americas to individuals & Caribben; GBP 100 elsewhere to individuals; USD 575 in the Americas to institutions & Caribbean; GBP 342 elsewhere to institutions (effective 2006) (from Blackwell Synergy, EBSCO Publishing, Gale Group, IngentaConnect, O C L C Online Computer Library Center, Inc., Swets Information Services); ♦ Supplement(s): International Union of Crystallography. Collected Abstracts of the Triennial Congress. ISSN 0731-8561.
Indexed: ASCA, BiolAb, BrCerAb, C&ISA, CCI, CCMJ, CIN, Cadscan, CerAb, ChemAb, ChemTitl, CorrAb, CurCont, E&CAJ, EMA, EngInd, IAA, INIS AtomInd, ISR, IndMed, Inspec, LeadAb, M&TEA, MBF, MEDLINE, METADEX, MSCI, MathR, MathSciNet, RCI, RefZh, S&F, SCI, SolStAb, WAA, Zincscan.
—BLDSC (0612.015000), AskIEEE, CASDDS, CISTI, Ei, IDS, IE, Infotrieve, ingenta, Linda Hall. **CCC.**
Published by: (International Union of Crystallography), Blackwell Munksgaard (Subsidiary of: Blackwell Publishing Ltd.), Rosenoerns Alle 1, PO Box 227, Copenhagen V, 1502, Denmark. TEL 45-77-333333, FAX 45-77-333377, customerservice@munksgaard.dk, http://www.blackwellpublishing.com/journals/AYA, http://www.munksgaard.dk/. Eds. Dieter Schwarzenbach, John R Helliwell. Adv. contact Andrea Sharpe. Circ: 1,500.

548 DNK ISSN 0108-7681
QD901 CODEN: ASBSDK
➤ **ACTA CRYSTALLOGRAPHICA. SECTION B: STRUCTURAL SCIENCE.** Text in English, French, German, Russian. 1983. bi-m. EUR 165 combined subscription in Europe to individuals print & online eds.; USD 185 combined subscription in the Americas to individuals & Caribbean, print & online eds.; GBP 110 combined subscription elsewhere to individuals print & online eds.; USD 591 combined subscription in the Americas to institutions & Caribbean, print & online eds.; GBP 352 combined subscription elsewhere to institutions print & online eds. (effective 2006). adv. bk.rev. reprint service avail. from ISI,PSC. **Document type:** *Journal, Academic/Scholarly.*
Supersedes in part (1968-1983): Acta Crystallographica. Section B: Structural Crystallography and Crystal Chemistry (0567-7408); Which superseded in part (1948-1968): Acta Crystallographica (0001-5520)
Related titles: Microfilm ed.: (from PMC); Online - full text ed.: Acta Crystallographica. Section B: Structural Science. Online. ISSN 1600-5740. 2000. EUR 158 in Europe to individuals; USD 176 in the Americas to individuals & Caribbean; GBP 105 elsewhere to individuals; USD 609 in the Americas to institutions & Caribbean; GBP 363 elsewhere to institutions (effective 2006) (from Blackwell Synergy, EBSCO Publishing, Gale Group, IngentaConnect, O C L C Online Computer Library Center, Inc., Swets Information Services).
Indexed: ABIPC, ASCA, BiolAb, BrCerAb, C&ISA, CCI, CIN, Cadscan, CerAb, ChemAb, CorrAb, CurCont, E&CAJ, EMA, EngInd, IAA, INIS AtomInd, ISR, IndMed, Inspec, LeadAb, M&TEA, MBF, MEDLINE, METADEX, MSCI, MathR, RCI, RefZh, S&F, SCI, SolStAb, WAA, Zincscan.
—BLDSC (0612.020500), AskIEEE, CASDDS, CISTI, Ei, IDS, IE, Infotrieve, ingenta, Linda Hall. **CCC.**
Published by: (International Union of Crystallography), Blackwell Munksgaard (Subsidiary of: Blackwell Publishing Ltd.), Rosenoerns Alle 1, PO Box 227, Copenhagen V, 1502, Denmark. TEL 45-77-333333, FAX 45-77-333377, info@mks.blackwellpublishing.com, http://www.blackwellpublishing.com/journals/AYB, http://www.blackwellmunksgaard.com. Ed. John R Helliwell. Adv. contact Andrea Sharpe. Circ: 1,400.

C

548 DNK ISSN 0108-2701
QD901 CODEN: ACSCEE
➤ **ACTA CRYSTALLOGRAPHICA. SECTION C: CRYSTAL STRUCTURE COMMUNICATIONS.** Text in English, French, German, Russian. 1948. m. EUR 429 combined subscription in Europe to individuals print & online eds.; USD 480 combined subscription in the Americas to individuals & Caribbean, print & online eds.; GBP 286 combined subscription elsewhere to individuals print & online eds.; USD 1,539 combined subscription in the Americas to institutions & Caribbean, print & online eds.; GBP 916 combined subscription elsewhere to institutions print & online eds. (effective 2006). adv. bk.rev. reprint service avail. from ISI,PSC. **Document type:** *Journal, Academic/Scholarly.*
Description: Publishes concise reports on crystal and molecular structures.
Incorporates (1972-1982): Crystal Structure Communications (0302-1742); Supersedes in part (in 1983): Acta Crystallographica. Section B: Structural Crystallography and Crystal Chemistry (0567-7408); Which superseded in part (in 1968): Acta Crystallographica (0365-110X)
Related titles: Online - full text ed.: ISSN 1600-5759. EUR 408 in Europe to individuals; USD 456 in the Americas to individuals & Caribbean; GBP 271 elsewhere to individuals; USD 1,645 in the Americas to institutions & Caribbean; GBP 979 elsewhere to institutions (effective 2006) (from Blackwell Synergy, EBSCO Publishing, Gale Group, IngentaConnect, O C L C Online Computer Library Center, Inc., Swets Information Services).
Indexed: ASCA, B&BAb, BrCerAb, C&ISA, CCI, CIN, CerAb, ChemAb, ChemInfo, ChemTitl, CorrAb, CurCont, E&CAJ, EMA, EngInd, IAA, INIS AtomInd, ISR, IndMed, Inspec, M&TEA, MBF, MEDLINE, METADEX, MSCI, NPU, RCI, RefZh, S&F, SCI, SolStAb, WAA.
—BLDSC (0612.021000), AskIEEE, CASDDS, CISTI, Ei, IDS, IE, Infotrieve, ingenta, Linda Hall. **CCC.**
Published by: (International Union of Crystallography), Blackwell Munksgaard (Subsidiary of: Blackwell Publishing Ltd.), Rosenoerns Alle 1, PO Box 227, Copenhagen V, 1502, Denmark. TEL 45-77-333333, FAX 45-77-333377, info@mks.blackwellpublishing.com, http://www.blackwellpublishing.com/journals/AYC, http://www.munksgaard.dk. Ed. John R Helliwell. Adv. contact Andrea Sharpe. Circ: 1,400.

548 DNK ISSN 0907-4449
QP519.9.X72 CODEN: ABCRE6
➤ **ACTA CRYSTALLOGRAPHICA. SECTION D: BIOLOGICAL CRYSTALLOGRAPHY/BIOLOGICAL CRYSTALLOGRAPHY.** Text in Danish. 1993. 12/yr., latest vol.58, no.12, 2002. EUR 264 combined subscription in Europe to individuals print & online eds.; USD 296 combined subscription in the Americas to individuals & Caribbean, print & online eds.; GBP 176 combined subscription elsewhere to individuals print & online eds.; USD 951 combined subscription in the Americas to institutions & Caribbean, print & online eds.; GBP 566 combined subscription elsewhere to institutions print & online eds. (effective 2006). adv. bk.rev. reprint service avail. from PSC. **Document type:** *Journal, Academic/Scholarly.*
Description: Publishes articles covering any aspect of structural biology with a particular emphasis on the structures of biological macromolecules and the methods used to determine them.
Related titles: Online - full text ed.: ISSN 1399-0047. EUR 251 in Europe to individuals; USD 281 in the Americas to individuals & Caribbean; GBP 168 elsewhere to individuals; USD 980 in the Americas to institutions & Caribbean; GBP 583 elsewhere to institutions (effective 2006) (from Blackwell Synergy, EBSCO Publishing, Gale Group, IngentaConnect, O C L C Online Computer Library Center, Inc., Swets Information Services).
Indexed: ASCA, AbHyg, AgBio, AgrForAb, AnBrAb, BBCI, BIOBASE, BIOSIS Prev, BioCN&I, BiolAb, BrCerAb, C&ISA, CCI, CIN, CPA, CerAb, ChemAb, ChemTitl, CorrAb, CurCont, DSA, E&CAJ, EMA, FCA, FS&TA, ForAb, HelmAb, HerbAb, HortAb, IAA, IABS, ISR, IndMed, IndVet, Inspec, M&TEA, MBF, MEDLINE, METADEX, MaizeAb, NemAb, NutrAb, OrnHort, PBA, PGrRegA, PHN&I, PN&I, PotatoAb, PoultAb, ProtozoAb, RA&MP, RM&VM, RPP, RefZh, RevApplEntom, RiceAb, S&F, SCI, SIA, SeedAb, SolStAb, SoyAb, TDB, TriticAb, VetBull, WAA, WeedAb.
—BLDSC (0612.022000), AskIEEE, CASDDS, CISTI, IDS, IE, Infotrieve, ingenta, Linda Hall. **CCC.**
Published by: (International Union of Crystallography), Blackwell Munksgaard (Subsidiary of: Blackwell Publishing Ltd.), Rosenoerns Alle 1, PO Box 227, Copenhagen V, 1502, Denmark. TEL 45-77-33-3333, FAX 45-77-33-3377, info@mks.blackwellpublishing.com, http://www.blackwellpublishing.com/journals/AYD, http://www.blackwellmunksgaard.com. Ed. John R Helliwell. Adv. contact Andrea Sharpe. Circ: 1,400.

548 DNK ISSN 1600-5368
QD901 CODEN: ACSEBH
➤ **ACTA CRYSTALLOGRAPHICA. SECTION E: STRUCTURE REPORTS ONLINE.** Text in English. 2001. m. USD 93 in the Americas to individuals & Caribbean; EUR 84 in Europe to individuals; GBP 56 elsewhere to individuals; USD 1,599 in the Americas to institutions & Caribbean; GBP 950 elsewhere to institutions (effective 2006). **Document type:** *Journal, Academic/Scholarly.* **Description:** Publishes concise reports on inorganic, metal-organic and organic structures for the needs of the structural sciences community.
Media: Online - full text (from Gale Group, IngentaConnect, O C L C Online Computer Library Center, Inc.).
Indexed: BrCerAb, C&ISA, CCI, CerAb, CorrAb, CurCont, E&CAJ, EMA, IAA, Inspec, M&TEA, MBF, METADEX, SolStAb, WAA.
—Infotrieve. **CCC.**
Published by: Blackwell Munksgaard (Subsidiary of: Blackwell Publishing Ltd.), Rosenoerns Alle 1, PO Box 227, Copenhagen V, 1502, Denmark. TEL 45-77-333333, FAX 45-77-333377, info@mks.blackwellpublishing.com, http://www.blackwellpublishing.com/journals/AYE, http://www.blackwellmunksgaard.com. Ed. John R Helliwell.

548 DNK ISSN 1744-3091
QD901
▼ **ACTA CRYSTALLOGRAPHICA. SERIES F.** Text in English. 2005. m. EUR 213 in Europe to individuals; USD 238 in the Americas to individuals & Caribbean; GBP 142 elsewhere to individuals; USD 911 in the Americas to institutions & Caribbean; GBP 543 elsewhere to institutions (effective 2006).
Description: Provides communications on the crystallization and structure determination of biological macromolecules.
Media: Online - full content. **Related titles:** Online - full text ed.: (from O C L C Online Computer Library Center, Inc.).
—CCC.
Published by: (International Union of Crystallography), Blackwell Munksgaard (Subsidiary of: Blackwell Publishing Ltd.), Rosenoerns Alle 1, PO Box 227, Copenhagen V, 1502, Denmark. TEL 45-77-33-33-33, FAX 45-77-33-33-77, http://www.blackwellpublishing.com/journals/AYF, http://www.munksgaard.dk/.

548 666 USA ISSN 0896-1654
AMERICAN ASSOCIATION FOR CRYSTAL GROWTH NEWSLETTER. Text in English. 1970. 3/yr. USD 35 membership; USD 15 to students (effective 2000). adv. bk.rev. bibl.; charts; illus. back issues avail. **Document type:** *Newsletter.* **Description:** Focuses on crystal growth community activities.
Published by: American Association for Crystal Growth, 25 4th St., Somerville, NJ 08876-3205. TEL 805-492-7047, FAX 805-492-4062, aacg@lafn.org, http://www.crystalgrowth.org. Ed., R&P Patricia A Morris TEL 302-695-2153. Adv. contact John DeCosta. Circ: 600.

548 USA
AMERICAN CRYSTALLOGRAPHIC ASSOCIATION. ANNUAL REPORTS. Text in English. a.
—BLDSC (1087.475000).
Published by: American Crystallographic Association, c/o Hauptman-Woodward Med Res Inst, 73 High St, PO Box 96, Buffalo, NY 14203. TEL 716-898-8690, FAX 716-898-8695, marcia@hwi.buffalo.edu, http://www.hwi.buffalo.edu/aca/.

548 USA ISSN 0514-8863
AMERICAN CRYSTALLOGRAPHIC ASSOCIATION. MONOGRAPHS. Text in English. 1944. irreg., latest vol.8, 1979. price varies. **Document type:** *Monographic series.*
Indexed: ChemAb, Inspec.
Published by: American Crystallographic Association, c/o Hauptman-Woodward Med Res Inst, 73 High St, PO Box 96, Buffalo, NY 14203. TEL 716-898-8690, FAX 716-898-8695, http://www.hwi.buffalo.edu/aca/. Circ: 1,250. **Dist. by:** Polycrystal Book Service, PO Box 3439, Dayton, OH 45401.

AMERICAN CRYSTALLOGRAPHIC ASSOCIATION. PROGRAM & ABSTRACTS. see *CHEMISTRY—Abstracting, Bibliographies, Statistics*

548 USA ISSN 0065-8006
QD901 CODEN: TACAAH
AMERICAN CRYSTALLOGRAPHIC ASSOCIATION. TRANSACTIONS. Text in English. 1965. a. USD 30 domestic to non-members; USD 40 foreign to non-members; USD 20 domestic to members; USD 30 foreign to members (effective 2005). back issues avail. **Document type:** *Proceedings.*
Indexed: CIN, ChemAb, ChemTitl.
—CASDDS, CISTI, Ei, Linda Hall.
Published by: American Crystallographic Association, c/o Hauptman-Woodward Med Res Inst, 73 High St, PO Box 96, Buffalo, NY 14203. TEL 716-898-8690, FAX 716-898-8695, http://www.hwi.buffalo.edu/aca/. Circ: 2,500. **Dist. by:** Polycrystal Book Service, PO Box 3439, Dayton, OH 45401.

AMERICAN MINERALOGIST; an international journal of earth and planetary materials. see *MINES AND MINING INDUSTRY*

548 DEU ISSN 0948-1907
TA401 CODEN: CVDEFX
➤ **CHEMICAL VAPOR DEPOSITION.** Abbreviated title: C V D. Text in English. 1995. m. EUR 908 in Europe (effective 2006); CHF 1,398 in Switzerland & Liechtenstein (effective 2005); USD 1,158 elsewhere; EUR 999 combined subscription in Europe print & online eds.; CHF 1,538 combined subscription in Switzerland & Liechtenstein, for print & online eds.; USD 1,274 combined subscription elsewhere print & online eds. (effective 2006). adv. 48 p./no. 2 cols./p.; back issues avail.; reprints avail. **Document type:** *Journal, Academic/Scholarly.*
Description: Publishes reviews, short communications and full papers on all aspects of chemical vapor deposition and related technologies.
Related titles: Online - full text ed.: ISSN 1521-3862. 1998. EUR 908 in Europe to institutions; CHF 1,398 to institutions in Switzerland & Liechtenstein; USD 1,158 elsewhere to institutions (effective 2006) (from EBSCO Publishing, Swets Information Services, Wiley InterScience); ♦ Supplement to: Advanced Materials. ISSN 0935-9648.
Indexed: BrCerAb, C&ISA, CCI, CIN, CerAb, ChemAb, ChemInfo, ChemTitl, CorrAb, CurCont, E&CAJ, EMA, EngInd, IAA, INIS AtomInd, ISR, Inspec, M&TEA, MBF, METADEX, MSB, MSCI, RCI, RefZh, SCI, SolStAb, WAA.
—BLDSC (3152.800000), AskIEEE, CASDDS, CISTI, IDS, IE, Linda Hall. **CCC.**
Published by: Wiley - V C H Verlag GmbH & Co. KGaA (Subsidiary of: John Wiley & Sons, Inc.), Boschstr 12, Weinheim, 69469, Germany. TEL 49-6201-606-0, FAX 49-6201-606-328, advmat@wiley-vch.de, subservice@wiley-vch.de, http://www.wiley-vch.de. Eds. Esther Levy, Michael Hitchman. R&P Claudia Rutz. Adv. contact P Gregory. page EUR 2,000; trim 180 x 260. **Subscr. in N. America to:** John Wiley & Sons, Inc., 111 River St, Hoboken, NJ 07030-5774. TEL 201-748-6645, FAX 201-748-6088, subinfo@wiley.com; **Subscr. outside Germany, Austria & Switzerland to:** John Wiley & Sons Ltd., The Atrium, Southern Gate, Chichester, West Sussex PO19 8SQ, United Kingdom. TEL 44-1243-779777, FAX 44-1243-775878.

➤ **CONDENSED MATTER THEORIES.** see *PHYSICS*

548 USA ISSN 1528-7483
QD921 CODEN: CGDEFU
CRYSTAL GROWTH & DESIGN. Text in English. 2001. bi-m. USD 2,360 in North America to institutions; USD 2,405 elsewhere to institutions; USD 293 in North America to members; USD 338 elsewhere to members; USD 220 in North America to students; USD 265 elsewhere to students (effective 2006). back issues avail. **Document type:** *Journal, Academic/Scholarly.* **Description:** Dedicated to publishing articles on the physical, chemical and biological phenomena and processes related to crystal growth and design of new materials.
Related titles: Online - full text ed.: ISSN 1528-7505. USD 70 (effective 2006) (from EBSCO Publishing, Swets Information Services).
Indexed: CCI, ChemAb, CivEngAb, CurCR, CurCont, IndChem, Inspec, METADEX, MSCI, RCI, RefZh.
—BLDSC (3490.156850), CISTI, IE, Linda Hall. **CCC.**
Published by: American Chemical Society, 1155 16th St, N W, Washington, DC 20036. TEL 202-872-4614, 800-227-5558, FAX 202-776-8264, service@acs.org, http://pubs.acs.org/crystal. Ed. Robin D Rogers.

548 660 DEU ISSN 0232-1300
QD901 CODEN: CRTEDF
➤ **CRYSTAL RESEARCH AND TECHNOLOGY**; journal of experimental and industrial crystallography. Text in English. 1966. m. EUR 1,748 in Europe; CHF 2,998 in Switzerland & Liechtenstein; USD 2,198 elsewhere; EUR 1,923 combined subscription in Europe print & online eds.; CHF 3,298 combined subscription in Switzerland & Liechtenstein for print & online eds.; USD 2,418 combined subscription elsewhere print & online eds. (effective 2006). bk.rev. charts; illus. index. **Document type:** *Journal, Academic/Scholarly.*
Formerly (until 1981): Kristall und Technik (0023-4753)
Related titles: Online - full text ed.: ISSN 1521-4079. EUR 1,748 in Europe to institutions; CHF 2,998 to institutions in Switzerland & Liechtenstein; USD 2,198 elsewhere to institutions (effective 2006) (from EBSCO Publishing, Swets Information Services, Wiley InterScience).
Indexed: ASCA, BrCerAb, C&ISA, CCI, CIN, Cadscan, CerAb, ChemAb, ChemInfo, ChemTitl, CivEngAb, CorrAb, CurCont, E&CAJ, EMA, EngInd, IAA, INIS AtomInd, ISR, Inspec, LeadAb, M&TEA, MBF, METADEX, MSB, MSCI, PhysBer, RCI, RefZh, S&F, SCI, SolStAb, WAA, Zincscan.
—BLDSC (3490.157500), AskIEEE, CASDDS, CISTI, Ei, IDS, IE, Infotrieve, ingenta, Linda Hall. **CCC.**
Published by: Wiley - V C H Verlag GmbH & Co. KGaA (Subsidiary of: John Wiley & Sons, Inc.), Boschstr 12, Weinheim, 69469, Germany. FAX 49-6201-606-117, adsales@wiley-vch.de, http://www.wiley-vch.de/home/crt, http://www3.interscience.wiley.com/cgi-bin/home. Ed. Wolfgang Neumann. R&P Claudia Rutz. **Subscr. in the Americas to:** John Wiley & Sons, Inc., 111 River St, Hoboken, NJ 07030-5774. TEL 201-748-6645, FAX 201-748-6088, subinfo@wiley.com; **Subscr. outside Germany, Austria & Switzerland to:** John Wiley & Sons Ltd., The Atrium, Southern Gate, Chichester, West Sussex PO19 8SQ, United Kingdom. TEL 44-1243-779777, FAX 44-1243-775878.

548 RUS ISSN 1063-7745
QD901 CODEN: CYSTE3
➤ **CRYSTALLOGRAPHY REPORTS.** Text in English. 1956. bi-m. USD 2,455 combined subscription in United States to institutions; USD 2,475 combined subscription to institutions in Canada, Mexico, Central and South America & Caribbean; USD 2,490 combined subscription to institutions in Europe, Asia, Middle East, Africa & Oceania (effective 2004); print & online eds.. bibl.; charts; illus. index. back issues avail. **Document type:** *Journal, Academic/Scholarly.* **Description:** Contains original papers, short communications and reviews on various aspects of crystallography.
Formerly: Soviet Physics - Crystallography (0038-5638)

C

Related titles: Online - full text ed.: ISSN 1562-689X. USD 1,964 worldwide (effective 2004) (from EBSCO Publishing, Swets Information Services); ♦ Translation of: Kristallografiya. ISSN 0023-4761.
Indexed: CCI, CPI, ChemAb, CurCont, EngInd, GPAA, INIS AtomInd, ISR, Inspec, MSCI, MathR, PhysBer, RCI, SCI, SPINweb, ZentMath.
—BLDSC (0411.083000), AskIEEE, CISTI, IDS, IE, Infotrieve, ingenta, Linda Hall. **CCC.**
Published by: (Rossiiskaya Akademiya Nauk/Russian Academy of Sciences), M A I K Nauka - Interperiodica, Profsoyuznaya ul 90, Moscow, 117997, Russian Federation. TEL 7-095-3347420, FAX 7-095-3360666, compmg@maik.ru, http://www.maik.ru/cgi-bin/journal.pl?name=cryst&page=main. Ed. Lev A Shuvalov. **Subscr. to:** American Institute of Physics, PO Box 503284, St Louis, MO 63150-3284. TEL 516-576-2270, 800-344-6902, FAX 516-349-9704, subs@aip.org.

548 GBR ISSN 0889-311X
QD901 CODEN: CRRVEN
➤ **CRYSTALLOGRAPHY REVIEWS.** Text in English. q. GBP 790, USD 1,043 combined subscription to institutions print & online eds. (effective 2006). reprint service avail. from PSC. **Document type:** *Journal, Academic/Scholarly.* **Description:** publishes English language reviews on topics in crystallography and crystal growth, covering all theoretical and applied aspects of biological, chemical, industrial, mineralogical and physical crystallography.
Related titles: Microform ed.; Online - full text ed.: ISSN 1476-3508. GBP 751, USD 991 to institutions (effective 2006) (from EBSCO Publishing, Gale Group, IngentaConnect, O C L C Online Computer Library Center, Inc., Swets Information Services).
Indexed: BrCerAb, C&ISA, CerAb, CivEngAb, CorrAb, E&CAJ, EMA, EngInd, IAA, M&TEA, MBF, METADEX, SolStAb, WAA.
—BLDSC (3490.162000), CISTI, IE, Infotrieve, Linda Hall. **CCC.**
Published by: Taylor & Francis Ltd (Subsidiary of: Taylor & Francis Group), 4 Park Sq, Milton Park, Abingdon, OX14 4RN, United Kingdom. TEL 44-1235-828600, FAX 44-1235-829000, info@tandf.co.uk, http://www.tandf.co.uk/journals/titles/0889311x.asp. Ed. Moreton Moore. **Subscr. in N. America to:** Taylor & Francis Inc., Customer Services Dept, 325 Chestnut St, 8th Fl, Philadelphia, PA 19106. TEL 215-625-8900, 800-354-1420, FAX 215-625-8914, customerservice@taylorandfrancis.com; **Subscr. to:** Journals Customer Service, Rankine Rd, Basingstoke, Hants RG24 8PR, United Kingdom. TEL 44-1256-813000, FAX 44-1256-330245, enquiry@tandf.co.uk.

540 GBR ISSN 1466-8033
QD901 CODEN: CRECF4
➤ **CRYSTENGCOMM.** Text in English. 1999. irreg. GBP 300, USD 549 (effective 2006). back issues avail. **Document type:** *Journal, Academic/Scholarly.* **Description:** Provides a forum for the publication of peer-reviewed articles and communications from all areas of crystal engineering.
Media: Online - full text (from EBSCO Publishing, O C L C Online Computer Library Center, Inc.).
Indexed: CCI.
—Infotrieve. **CCC.**
Published by: Royal Society of Chemistry, Thomas Graham House, Science Park, Milton Rd, Cambridge, CB4 0WF, United Kingdom. TEL 44-1223-432360, FAX 44-1223-423623, crystengcomm@rsc.org, sales@rsc.org, http://www.rsc.org/crystengcomm. Ed. Dr. Jamie Humphrey. R&P Sharon Bellard. **Subscr. to:** Portland Press Ltd., R S C Distribution Services, Commerce Way, Whitehall Industrial Estate, Colchester CO2 8HP, United Kingdom. TEL 44-1206-226050, FAX 44-1206-226055, sales@rscdistribution.org.

553.82 622.382 CHE ISSN 0925-9635
CODEN: DRMTE3
➤ **DIAMOND AND RELATED MATERIALS.** Text in English. 1991. 12/yr. EUR 2,201 in Europe to institutions; JPY 292,400 in Japan to institutions; USD 2,463 to institutions except Europe and Japan; EUR 74 in Europe to qualified personnel; JPY 9,700 in Japan to qualified personnel; USD 81 to qualified personnel except Europe and Japan (effective 2006). abstr. back issues avail. **Document type:** *Academic/Scholarly.* **Description:** Covers basic and applied research on diamond materials and related substances, including high-temperature high-pressure synthetic materials.
Related titles: Microform ed.: (from PQC); Online - full text ed.: (from EBSCO Publishing, Gale Group, IngentaConnect, ScienceDirect, Swets Information Services).
Indexed: ASCA, BrCerAb, C&ISA, CCI, CIN, CerAb, ChemAb, ChemTitl, CivEngAb, CorrAb, CurCont, E&CAJ, EMA, EngInd, FLUIDEX, IAA, ISR, Inspec, M&TEA, MBF, METADEX, MSB, MSCI, RefZh, SCI, SolStAb, WAA.
—BLDSC (3579.835200), AskIEEE, CASDDS, CISTI, IDS, IE, Infotrieve, ingenta, Linda Hall. **CCC.**
Published by: Elsevier S.A., PO Box 564, Lausanne 1, 1001, Switzerland. TEL 41-21-3207381, FAX 41-21-3235444, http://www.elsevier.com/locate/diamond. Eds. R Messier, Dr. R Nemanich. **Subscr. to:** Elsevier BV, PO Box 211, Amsterdam 1000 AE, Netherlands. TEL 31-20-485-3757, FAX 31-20-485-3432, nlinfo-f@elsevier.nl, http://www.elsevier.nl.

➤ **DISLOCATIONS IN SOLIDS.** see *PHYSICS*

548 JPN
EKISHO DISUPUREI SANGYO NENKAN/ANNUAL OF LIQUID CRYSTAL DISPLAY INDUSTRIES. Text in Japanese. 1992. a. JPY 56,650.
Published by: C M C Co. Ltd., 5-4 Uchikanda 1-chome, Chiyoda-ku, Tokyo, 101-0047, Japan.

548 JPN
EKISHO TORONKAI KOEN YOKOSHU/PREPRINTS OF SYMPOSIUM ON LIQUID CRYSTALS. Text in Japanese. 1975. a.
Published by: Chemical Society of Japan/Nippon Kagakukai, 1-5, Kanda-Surugadai 1-Chome, Chiyoda-ku, Tokyo, 101-0062, Japan.

530.429 USA
➤ **ELECTRONIC LIQUID CRYSTAL COMMUNICATIONS.** Short title: e-LC. Variant title: Liquid Crystal Communications. Text in English. 2002. irreg. free (effective 2005). **Document type:** *Journal, Academic/Scholarly.* **Description:** Provides the liquid crystal community with rapid access to the most recent research results in advance of their publication in journals.
Media: Online - full content.
Published by: Kent State University, Liquid Crystal Institute, PO Box 5190, Kent, OH 44242-0001. TEL 330-672-2654, FAX 330-672-2796, mail@lci.kent.edu, http://e-lc.org/. Ed. A Jakli.

▼ ➤ **ELEMENTS.** see *MINES AND MINING INDUSTRY*

➤ **GEMS & GEMOLOGY.** see *JEWELRY, CLOCKS AND WATCHES*

548 USA
QC173.45
INTERNATIONAL JOURNAL OF CONDENSED MATTER RESEARCH AND INTERNET REVIEWS. Text in English. 1993. q. USD 550 (effective 2005). **Document type:** *Journal, Academic/Scholarly.* **Description:** Provides information on crystal growth, thin film processing, amorphous and disordered systems, magnetism, superfluidity, surfaces, and phase transitions.
Former title: Condensed Matter and Materials Communication (1067-6147)
—CISTI.
Published by: Nova Science Publishers, Inc., 400 Oser Ave, Ste 1600, Hauppauge, NY 11788-3619. TEL 631-231-7269, FAX 631-231-8175, novascience@earthlink.net, http://www.novapublishers.com/journals/condensed.html. Ed. A V Narlikar.

548 DNK ISSN 0731-8561
INTERNATIONAL UNION OF CRYSTALLOGRAPHY. COLLECTED ABSTRACTS OF THE TRIENNIAL CONGRESS. Text in English, French, German. 1960. triennial. back issues avail.; reprint service avail. from ISI. **Document type:** *Proceedings, Academic/Scholarly.*
Related titles: ♦ Supplement to: Acta Crystallographica. Section A: Foundations of Crystallography. ISSN 0108-7673.
Published by: (International Union of Crystallography), Blackwell Munksgaard (Subsidiary of: Blackwell Publishing Ltd.), Rosenoerns Alle 1, PO Box 227, Copenhagen V, 1502, Denmark. TEL 45-77-333333, FAX 45-77-333377, info@mks.blackwellpublishing.com, http://www.blackwellmunksgaard.com.

548 GBR ISSN 0953-3060
INTERNATIONAL UNION OF CRYSTALLOGRAPHY. CRYSTALLOGRAPHIC SYMPOSIA. Text in English. 1987. irreg., latest vol.6, 1993. GBP 35 per vol. (effective 2004). **Document type:** *Monographic series, Academic/Scholarly.*
—BLDSC (4551.557000).
Published by: (International Union of Crystallography), Oxford University Press, Great Clarendon St, Oxford, OX2 6DP, United Kingdom. TEL 44-1865-556767, FAX 44-1865-556646, enquiry@oup.co.uk, http://www.oup.co.uk/isbn/0-19-855788-4.

548 GBR ISSN 1352-7932
INTERNATIONAL UNION OF CRYSTALLOGRAPHY. MONOGRAPHS ON CRYSTALLOGRAPHY. Text in English. 1992. irreg., latest 2002. p;rice varies. **Document type:** *Monographic series, Academic/Scholarly.*
—BLDSC (4588.859500). **CCC.**
Published by: (International Union of Crystallography), Oxford University Press, Great Clarendon St, Oxford, OX2 6DP, United Kingdom, TEL 44-1865-556767, FAX 44-1865-556646, enquiry@oup.co.uk, http://www.oup.co.uk/.

548 USA ISSN 1067-0696
QD901 CODEN: IUCNEB
INTERNATIONAL UNION OF CRYSTALLOGRAPHY. NEWSLETTER. Text in English. 1993. q. free. adv. **Document type:** *Newsletter, Trade.*
Related titles: Online - full text ed.: (from EBSCO Publishing).
Indexed: RefZh.
—**CCC.**
Published by: International Union of Crystallography, Editorial Office, c/o Hauptman Woodward Medical Research Institute, 73 High St, Buffalo, NY 14203-1196. patti@hwi.buffalo.edu, http://www.hwi.buffalo.edu/ACA/. Ed. William L Duax. Adv. contact Patricia Coley.

548 GBR ISSN 0962-7383
INTERNATIONAL UNION OF CRYSTALLOGRAPHY. TEXTS ON CRYSTALLOGRAPHY. Text in English. 1989. irreg., latest 2002. price varies. **Document type:** *Monographic series.*
—BLDSC (4551.557500).
Published by: (International Union of Crystallography), Oxford University Press, Great Clarendon St, Oxford, OX2 6DP, United Kingdom. TEL 44-1865-556767, FAX 44-1865-556646, enquiry@oup.co.uk, http://www.oup-usa.org/catalogs/general/series/International_Union_of_Crystallography_Texts_on_Crystallography.html, http://www.oup.co.uk/. **Orders in N. America to:** Oxford University Press, 2001 Evans Rd, Cary, NC 27513. jnlorders@oup-usa.org.

JINKO KESSHO KOGAKKAI TOKUBETSU KOENKAI KOEN YOSHISHU/ASSOCIATION OF SYNTHETIC CRYSTAL SCIENCE AND TECHNOLOGY. ABSTRACTS OF THE SPECIAL MEETING. see *CHEMISTRY—Abstracting, Bibliographies, Statistics*

548 DNK ISSN 0021-8898
QD901 CODEN: JACGAR
➤ **JOURNAL OF APPLIED CRYSTALLOGRAPHY.** Text in English. 1968. 7/yr. EUR 167 combined subscription in Europe to individuals print & online eds.; USD 187 combined subscription in the Americas to individuals & Caribbean (print & online eds.); GBP 111 combined subscription elsewhere to individuals print & online eds.; USD 608 combined subscription in the Americas to institutions & Caribbean (print & online eds.); GBP 362 combined subscription elsewhere to institutions print & online eds. (effective 2006). adv. bk.rev. charts; illus.; stat. reprint service avail. from ISI. **Document type:** *Journal, Academic/Scholarly.*
Related titles: Online - full text ed.: ISSN 1600-5767. USD 627 in the Americas to institutions & Caribbean; GBP 373 elsewhere to institutions (effective 2006) (from Blackwell Synergy, EBSCO Publishing, Gale Group, IngentaConnect, O C L C Online Computer Library Center, Inc., Swets Information Services).
Indexed: A&ATA, ABIPC, ASCA, ApicAb, BrCerAb, C&ISA, CCI, CIN, Cadscan, CerAb, ChemAb, ChemTitl, CompLI, CorrAb, CurCont, E&CAJ, EMA, EngInd, IAA, INIS AtomInd, ISMEC, ISR, Inspec, LeadAb, M&TEA, MBF, METADEX, MSCI, PhysBer, RCI, RefZh, SCI, SolStAb, WAA, WTA, Zincscan.
—BLDSC (4942.400000), AskIEEE, CASDDS, CISTI, Ei, IDS, IE, Infotrieve, ingenta, Linda Hall. **CCC.**
Published by: (International Union of Crystallography), Blackwell Munksgaard (Subsidiary of: Blackwell Publishing Ltd.), Rosenoerns Alle 1, PO Box 227, Copenhagen V, 1502, Denmark. TEL 45-77-333333, FAX 45-77-333377, fsub@mail.munksgaard.dk, info@mks.blackwellpublishing.com, http://www.blackwellpublishing.com/journals/JCR, http://www.munksgaard.dk/. Ed. G Kostorz. Adv. contact Andrea Sharpe. Circ: 1,250.

548 USA ISSN 1074-1542
QD901 CODEN: JCCYEV
➤ **JOURNAL OF CHEMICAL CRYSTALLOGRAPHY.** Text in English. 1971. m. EUR 1,098, USD 1,118, GBP 685 combined subscription to institutions print & online eds. (effective 2005). adv. bk.rev. index. back issues avail.; reprint service avail. from PSC. **Document type:** *Journal, Academic/Scholarly.* **Description:** Publishes research results in the general area of crystallography and its relation to problems of molecular structure.
Former titles (until 1994): Journal of Crystallographic and Spectroscopic Research (0277-8068); (until 1982): Journal of Crystal and Molecular Structure (0308-4086)
Related titles: Online - full text ed.: ISSN 1572-8854 (from EBSCO Publishing, Gale Group, IngentaConnect, Kluwer Online, O C L C Online Computer Library Center, Inc., Springer LINK, Swets Information Services).
Indexed: ASCA, ASFA, BibLing, CCI, CIN, ChemAb, ChemTitl, CurCont, ISR, Inspec, MSB, PhysBer, RCI, RefZh, SCI.
—BLDSC (4955.840000), AskIEEE, CASDDS, CISTI, IDS, IE, Infotrieve, ingenta, Linda Hall. **CCC.**
Published by: Plenum US (Subsidiary of: Springer Science+Business Media), 233 Spring St, New York, NY 10013. TEL 212-460-1500, FAX 212-460-1575, service@springer-ny.com, http://springerlink.metapress.com/openurl.asp?genre=journal&issn=1074-1542, http://www.springeronline.com. Ed. William T Pennington.

548 NLD ISSN 0022-0248
QD921 CODEN: JCRGAE
➤ **JOURNAL OF CRYSTAL GROWTH.** Text in Dutch. 1967. 24/yr. EUR 10,452 in Europe to institutions; JPY 1,388,200 in Japan to institutions; USD 11,692 elsewhere to institutions; EUR 964 in Europe to qualified personnel; JPY 128,300 in Japan to qualified personnel; USD 1,079 elsewhere to qualified personnel (effective 2006). adv. bk.rev. index. back issues avail.; reprints avail. **Document type:** *Journal, Academic/Scholarly.* **Description:** Offers a common reference and publication source for workers engaged in research on the experimental and theoretical aspects of crystal growth and its applications.
Formerly: International Journal for Crystal Growth
Related titles: Microform ed.: (from PQC); Online - full text ed.: (from EBSCO Publishing, Gale Group, IngentaConnect, ScienceDirect, Swets Information Services).

C

Indexed: ASCA, BrCerAb, C&ISA, CCI, CEA, CIN, Cadscan, CerAb, ChemAb, ChemTitl, CivEngAb, CorrAb, CurCont, E&CAJ, EMA, EngInd, IAA, ISMEC, ISR, Inspec, LeadAb, M&TEA, MBF, METADEX, MSB, MSCI, MinerAb, PhysBer, RCI, RefZh, S&F, SCI, SolStAb, TCEA, WAA, Zincscan.
—BLDSC (4965.800000), AskIEEE, CASDDS, CISTI, Ei, IDS, IE, Infotrieve, ingenta, Linda Hall. **CCC.**
Published by: Elsevier BV, North-Holland (Subsidiary of: Elsevier Science & Technology), Sara Burgerhartstraat 25, Amsterdam, 1055 KV, Netherlands. TEL 31-20-485-3911, FAX 31-20-485-2457, nlinfo-f@elsevier.nl, http://www.elsevier.com/locate/jcrysgro, http://www.elsevier.nl. Ed. T F Kuech. **Subscr. to:** Elsevier BV, PO Box 211, Amsterdam 1000 AE, Netherlands. TEL 31-20-485-3757, FAX 31-20-485-3432, http://www.elsevier.nl.

➤ **JOURNAL OF SUPERHARD MATERIALS.** see *PHYSICS*

548 RUS ISSN 0023-4761
QD901 CODEN: KRISAJ
KRISTALLOGRAFIYA. Text in Russian. 1956. bi-m. RUR 1,490 for 6 mos. domestic (effective 2004). **Document type:** *Journal, Academic/Scholarly.* **Description:** Contains original papers, short communications and reviews on various aspects of crystallography.
Related titles: Online - full text ed.; ♦ English Translation: Crystallography Reports. ISSN 1063-7745.
Indexed: ASCA, BiolAb, BrCerAb, C&ISA, CCI, CIN, Cadscan, CerAb, ChemAb, ChemTitl, CivEngAb, CorrAb, CurCont, E&CAJ, EMA, EngInd, IAA, ISR, Inspec, LeadAb, M&TEA, MBF, METADEX, MSCI, MathSciNet, RefZh, SCI, SolStAb, WAA, ZentMath, Zincscan.
—BLDSC (0093.000000), AskIEEE, CASDDS, CINDOC, CISTI, East View, Ei, IDS, Linda Hall. **CCC.**
Published by: (Rossiiskaya Akademiya Nauk/Russian Academy of Sciences), Izdatel'stvo Nauka, Profsoyuznaya ul 90, Moscow, 117864, Russian Federation. TEL 7-095-3347151, FAX 7-095-4202220, secret@naukaran.ru, http://www.maik.rssi.ru/cgi-bin/list.pl?page=krist, http://www.naukaran.ru.

LANDOLT-BOERNSTEIN: NUMERICAL DATA AND FUNCTIONAL RELATIONSHIPS IN SCIENCE AND TECHNOLOGY. GROUP III, CONDENSED MATTER. see *PHYSICS*

548 GBR ISSN 0267-8292
QD923 CODEN: LICRE6
➤ **LIQUID CRYSTALS**; an international journal in the field of anisotropic fluids. Text in English. 1986. m. GBP 2,771, USD 4,576 combined subscription to institutions print & online eds. (effective 2006). adv. index. back issues avail.; reprint service avail. from PSC. **Document type:** *Journal, Academic/Scholarly.* **Description:** Presents reports of original research of an experimental or a theoretical nature on all liquid-crystalline materials, their synthesis and their applications.
Related titles: Online - full text ed.: ISSN 1366-5855. GBP 2,632, USD 4,347 to institutions (effective 2006) (from EBSCO Publishing, Gale Group, IngentaConnect, O C L C Online Computer Library Center, Inc., Swets Information Services).
Indexed: ASCA, CCI, CIN, ChemAb, ChemTitl, CurCont, EngInd, ISR, Inspec, MSCI, RCI, SCI.
—BLDSC (5221.923000), AskIEEE, CASDDS, CISTI, Ei, IDS, IE, Infotrieve, ingenta, Linda Hall. **CCC.**
Published by: Taylor & Francis Ltd (Subsidiary of: Taylor & Francis Group), 4 Park Sq, Milton Park, Abingdon, OX14 4RN, United Kingdom. TEL 44-1235-828600, FAX 44-1235-829000, info@tandf.co.uk, http://www.tandf.co.uk/journals/titles/02678292.asp. Eds. C T Imrie, Noel Clark. **Subscr. in N. America to:** Taylor & Francis Inc., Customer Services Dept, 325 Chestnut St, 8th Fl, Philadelphia, PA 19106. TEL 800-354-1420, FAX 215-625-8914; **Subscr. to:** Journals Customer Service, Rankine Rd, Basingstoke, Hants RG24 8PR, United Kingdom. TEL 44-1256-813000, FAX 44-1256-330245, enquiry@tandf.co.uk.

548 USA ISSN 0146-5597
QD923 CODEN: LCOFDL
LIQUID CRYSTALS AND ORDERED FLUIDS. Text in English. 1969. irreg., latest vol.4, 1984. price varies.
Indexed: Inspec.
—CISTI. **CCC.**
Published by: Springer-Verlag New York, Inc. (Subsidiary of: Springer Science+Business Media), 233 Spring St, New York, NY 10013. TEL 212-460-1500, FAX 212-460-1575, service@springer-ny.com, http://www.springer-ny.com.

548 GBR ISSN 1358-314X
➤ **LIQUID CRYSTALS TODAY (ONLINE EDITION).** Text in English. 1990. q. free to members (effective 2006); Free with subscription to Liquid Crystals. bk.rev. back issues avail. **Document type:** *Journal, Academic/Scholarly.* **Description:** Provides a link between liquid crystal technology and the more fundamental aspects of liquid crystal science.
Media: Online - full text (from Gale Group, IngentaConnect, O C L C Online Computer Library Center, Inc., Swets Information Services).
Indexed: Inspec.
—CISTI, Infotrieve. **CCC.**

Published by: (International Liquid Crystal Society), Taylor & Francis Ltd (Subsidiary of: Taylor & Francis Group), 4 Park Sq, Milton Park, Abingdon, OX14 4RN, United Kingdom. TEL 44-1235-828600, FAX 44-1235-829000, info@tandf.co.uk, http://www.liquidcrystalstoday.com, http://www.tandf.co.uk/journals. Ed. Alex Seed. **Subscr. to:** Journals Customer Service, Rankine Rd, Basingstoke, Hants RG24 8PR, United Kingdom. TEL 44-1256-813000, FAX 44-1256-330245, enquiry@tandf.co.uk.

548 GBR ISSN 0025-5408
TA404.2 CODEN: MRBUAC
➤ **MATERIALS RESEARCH BULLETIN.** Text in English, French, German, Russian; Summaries in English. 1966. 12/yr. EUR 2,131 in Europe to institutions; JPY 283,000 in Japan to institutions; USD 2,385 to institutions except Europe and Japan (effective 2006). adv. bk.rev. charts; illus. back issues avail. **Document type:** *Bulletin, Academic/Scholarly.* **Description:** Publishes research on crystal growth, materials preparation and characterization, and the structure and properties of electronically, optically or mechanically interesting solids.
Related titles: Microfilm ed.: (from PQC); Online - full text ed.: (from EBSCO Publishing, Gale Group, IngentaConnect, ScienceDirect, Swets Information Services).
Indexed: ASCA, ApMecR, C&ISA, CCI, CTE, Cadscan, ChemAb, ChemTitl, CivEngAb, CurCont, E&CAJ, EngInd, IAA, INIS AtomInd, ISMEC, ISR, Inspec, LeadAb, MSCI, PhysBer, RefZh, SCI, SolStAb, Zincscan.
—BLDSC (5396.410000), AskIEEE, CASDDS, CISTI, Ei, IDS, IE, Infotrieve, ingenta, Linda Hall. **CCC.**
Published by: Pergamon (Subsidiary of: Elsevier Science & Technology), The Boulevard, Langford Ln, East Park, Kidlington, Oxford OX5 1GB, United Kingdom. TEL 44-1865-843000, FAX 44-1865-843010, mrb@rutchem.rutgers.edu, http://www.elsevier.com/locate/matresbu. Ed. M Greenblatt. Circ: 1,400. **Subscr. to:** Elsevier BV, PO Box 211, Amsterdam 1000 AE, Netherlands. TEL 31-20-485-3757, FAX 31-20-485-3432, nlinfo-f@elsevier.nl, http://www.elsevier.nl.

➤ **MICROSCOPE.** see *CHEMISTRY—Analytical Chemistry*

548 USA ISSN 1542-1406
QD901 CODEN: MCLCD8
➤ **MOLECULAR CRYSTALS AND LIQUID CRYSTALS.** Variant title: Molecular Crystals and Liquid Crystals Science and Technology. Section A: Molecular Crystals and Liquid Crystals. Text in English. 1966. 18/yr. GBP 12,306, USD 16,441 combined subscription to institutions print & online eds. (effective 2006). adv. bk.rev. charts; illus. reprint service avail. from PSC. **Document type:** *Journal, Academic/Scholarly.* **Description:** Publishes original research papers of both an experimental and theoretical nature in three areas of specialization: molecular crystals, low-dimensional solids and liquid crystals.
Formed by the 2003 merger of: Molecular Crystals and Liquid Crystals Science and Technology. Section A. Molecular Crystals and Liquid Crystals (1058-725X); Molecular Crystals and Liquid Crystals Science and Technology. Section C. Molecular Materials (1058-7276); Both of which superseded in part (in 1992): Molecular Crystals and Liquid Crystals (1056-8816); Which superseded in part (in 1991): Molecular Crystals and Liquid Crystals Incorporating Nonlinear Optics (1044-1859); Which was formerly (until 1987): Molecular Crystals and Liquid Crystals (0026-8941); (until 1969): Molecular Crystals (0369-1152)
Related titles: Online - full text ed.: ISSN 1543-5318. GBP 11,691, USD 15,619 to institutions (effective 2006) (from EBSCO Publishing, Gale Group, IngentaConnect, O C L C Online Computer Library Center, Inc., Swets Information Services).
Indexed: ASCA, ApMecR, B&BAb, BPRC&P, BiolAb, CCI, Cadscan, ChemAb, CurCont, EngInd, ISR, Inspec, LeadAb, MSCI, RAPRA, RCI, RefZh, SCI, Zincscan.
—BLDSC (5900.817000), AskIEEE, CISTI, IE, Infotrieve, ingenta, Linda Hall. **CCC.**
Published by: Taylor & Francis Inc. (Subsidiary of: Taylor & Francis Group), 325 Chestnut St, Ste 800, Philadelphia, PA 19016. TEL 215-625-8900, 800-354-1420, FAX 215-625-8914, info@taylorandfrancis.com, http://www.tandf.co.uk/journals/titles/15421406.asp, http://www.taylorandfrancis.com. Ed. Mortimer M Labes. **Subsc. outside N. America:** Taylor & Francis Ltd, Journals Customer Service, Rankine Rd, Basingstoke, Hants RG24 8PR, United Kingdom. TEL 44-1256-813000, FAX 44-1256-330245, enquiry@tandf.co.uk.

548 NLD ISSN 0377-2012
➤ **MOLECULAR STRUCTURES AND DIMENSIONS. BIBLIOGRAPHY.** Text in Dutch. 1970. irreg., latest vol.15, 1984. price varies. **Document type:** *Monographic series, Academic/Scholarly.*
Related titles: ♦ Series: Organic and Organometallic Crystal Structures; Bibliography.
Published by: Springer-Verlag Dordrecht (Subsidiary of: Springer Science+Business Media), Van Godewijckstraat 30, Dordrecht, 3311 GX, Netherlands. TEL 31-78-6576050, FAX 31-78-6576474, http://www.springeronline.com.

➤ **NIHON KESSHO GAKKAI NENKAI KOEN YOSHISHU/CRYSTALLOGRAPHIC SOCIETY OF JAPAN. ABSTRACTS OF ANNUAL MEETING.** see *CHEMISTRY—Abstracting, Bibliographies, Statistics*

548 JPN ISSN 0369-4585
QD901 CODEN: NKEGAF
NIHON KESSHO GAKKAISHI/CRYSTALLOGRAPHIC SOCIETY OF JAPAN. JOURNAL. Text in Japanese; Summaries in English. 1959. bi-m. JPY 4,250 membership (effective 2005). **Document type:** *Journal, Trade.*
Indexed: ChemAb, INIS AtomInd, Inspec, JPI, RefZh.
—BLDSC (4732.560000), AskIEEE, CASDDS, CISTI, IE, ingenta, Linda Hall. **CCC.**
Published by: Nihon Kessho Gakkai/Crystallographic Society of Japan, Nissei Otuka 3-chome Bldg, Otuka 3-11-6, Bunkyo-ku, Tokyo, 112-0012, Japan. TEL 81-3-59407640, FAX 81-3-59407980, cr-info@rlz.co.jp, http://wwwsoc.nii.ac.jp/crsj/contents-j.html.

548 JPN ISSN 0385-6275
QD921 CODEN: NKSGDK
NIHON KESSHO SEICHO GAKKAISHI/JAPANESE ASSOCIATION OF CRYSTAL GROWTH. JOURNAL. Text in Japanese; Summaries in English. 1974. 3/yr. membership. **Document type:** *Journal, Academic/Scholarly.*
Indexed: ChemAb, JPI, MinerAb.
—CASDDS. **CCC.**
Published by: Nihon Kessho Seicho Gakkai/Japanese Association of Crystal Growth, c/o Words Publishing House, 2-62-8-507 Higashi Ikebukuro, Toshima-ku, Tokyo, 170-0013, Japan. TEL 81-3-59501290, FAX 81-3-56501292, jacg@jacg.gakushuin.ac.jp, http://wwwsoc.nii.ac.jp/jacg. **Dist. by:** Business Center for Academic Societies Japan, 5-16-19 Honkomagome, Bunkyo-ku, Tokyo 113-0021, Japan. TEL 81-3-5814-5811, FAX 81-3-5814-5822.

548 JPN
NYU DAIYAMONDO/NEW DIAMOND. Text in Japanese. 1985. q. JPY 476 per issue (effective 2003).
—BLDSC (6083.136000).
Published by: (Nyu Daiyamondo Foramu/Japan New Diamond Forum), Ohmsha Ltd, 3-1 Kanda-Nishiki-cho, Chiyoda-ku, Tokyo, 101-0054, Japan. TEL 81-3-32330641, hgcj@ohmsha.co.jp, kaigaika@ohmsha.co.jp, http://www.ohmsha.co.jp/index-e.htm.

PERIODICO DI MINERALOGIA. see *MINES AND MINING INDUSTRY*

548 GBR ISSN 0960-8974
CODEN: PCGMED
➤ **PROGRESS IN CRYSTAL GROWTH AND CHARACTERIZATION OF MATERIALS.** Text in English. 1978. 4/yr. EUR 2,980 in Europe to institutions; JPY 395,700 in Japan to institutions; USD 3,334 to institutions except Europe and Japan (effective 2006); with Journal of Crystal Growth. back issues avail.; reprints avail. **Document type:** *Journal, Academic/Scholarly.* **Description:** Covers all aspects of crystal growth and characterization, including crystals of semiconductors and electronic materials, oxides, synthetic minerals, magnetic and optical crystals, organic crystals, metals and thin films.
Formerly (until 1992): Progress in Crystal Growth and Characterization (0146-3535)
Related titles: Microfilm ed.: (from PQC); Online - full text ed.: (from EBSCO Publishing, Gale Group, IngentaConnect, ScienceDirect, Swets Information Services).
Indexed: ASCA, BrCerAb, C&ISA, CCI, CerAb, ChemAb, ChemTitl, CivEngAb, CorrAb, CurCont, E&CAJ, EMA, EngInd, IAA, ISR, Inspec, M&TEA, MBF, METADEX, MSCI, PhysBer, RCI, SCI, SolStAb, WAA.
—BLDSC (6868.085000), AskIEEE, CASDDS, CISTI, Ei, IDS, IE, Infotrieve, ingenta, Linda Hall. **CCC.**
Published by: Pergamon (Subsidiary of: Elsevier Science & Technology), The Boulevard, Langford Ln, East Park, Kidlington, Oxford OX5 1GB, United Kingdom. TEL 44-1865-843000, FAX 44-1865-843010, http://www.elsevier.com/locate/pcrysgrow. Ed. J B Mullin. **Subscr. to:** Elsevier BV, PO Box 211, Amsterdam 1000 AE, Netherlands. TEL 31-20-485-3757, FAX 31-20-485-3432, nlinfo-f@elsevier.nl, http://www.elsevier.nl.

548 IND
RECENT RESEARCH DEVELOPMENTS IN CRYSTAL GROWTH. Text in English. a., latest vol.3, 2001.
—BLDSC (7305.087340).
Published by: Transworld Research Network, T C 36-248 (1), Trivandrum, Kerala 695 008, India. http://www.transworldresearch.com.

548 SGP
SERIES ON LIQUID CRYSTALS. Text in English. 1995. irreg., latest vol.3, 2000, Nov. price varies. **Document type:** *Monographic series, Academic/Scholarly.*

C

Published by: World Scientific Publishing Co. Pte. Ltd., 5 Toh Tuck Link, Singapore, 596224, Singapore. TEL 65-466-5775, FAX 65-467-7667, wspc@wspc.com.sg, series@wspc.com.sg, http://www.wspc.com.sg/books/series/slc_series.shtml, http://www.worldscientific.com. Ed. H L Ong. **Dist. by:** World Scientific Publishing Co., Inc., 1060 Main St, River Edge, NJ 07661. TEL 201-487-9655, 800-227-7562, FAX 201-487-9656, 888-977-2665; World Scientific Publishing Ltd., 57 Shelton St, London WC2H 9HE, United Kingdom. TEL 44-20-78360888, FAX 44-20-78362020.

548 GBR
WILEY SERIES IN SOLUTION CHEMISTRY. Text in English. irreg., latest 2002. price varies. **Document type:** *Monographic series, Academic/Scholarly.*
—BLDSC (9317.920000), ingenta.
Published by: John Wiley & Sons Ltd. (Subsidiary of: John Wiley & Sons, Inc.), The Atrium, Southern Gate, Chichester, West Sussex PO19 8SQ, United Kingdom. TEL 44-1243-779777, FAX 44-1243-775878, customer@wiley.co.uk, http://www.wiley.co.uk. **Subscr. in the Americas to:** John Wiley & Sons, Inc., 111 River St, Hoboken, NJ 07030-5774. TEL 201-748-6645, FAX 201-748-6088, subinfo@wiley.com.

548 NLD ISSN 0512-2724
WORLD DIRECTORY OF CRYSTALLOGRAPHERS AND OF OTHER SCIENTISTS EMPLOYING CRYSTALLOGRAPHIC METHODS. Text in English. 1960. irreg., latest vol.10, 1997. price varies.
Formerly: World Directory of Crystallographers and Other Persons Working with Crystallographic Methods
Related titles: Online - full content ed.
Published by: (International Union of Crystallography DNK), Springer-Verlag Dordrecht (Subsidiary of: Springer Science+Business Media), Van Godewijckstraat 30, Dordrecht, 3311 GX, Netherlands. TEL 31-78-6576050, FAX 31-78-6576474, wdc@iucr.org, http://www.iucr.org/iucr-top/wdc/index.html, http://www.springeronline.com.

548 DEU ISSN 0044-2968
QD901 CODEN: ZEKRDZ
➤ **ZEITSCHRIFT FUER KRISTALLOGRAPHIE**; international journal for structural, physical, and chemical aspects of crystalline materials. Text and summaries in English, German. 1877. 12/yr. EUR 1,322 domestic print or online ed.; EUR 1,334 foreign print or online ed.; EUR 1,472 combined subscription domestic print & online eds.; EUR 1,484 combined subscription foreign print & online eds.; EUR 208 newsstand/cover print & online eds. (effective 2005). bibl.; charts; illus. index. back issues avail. **Document type:** *Journal, Academic/Scholarly.* **Description:** International coverage of structural, physical, and chemical aspects of crystalline materials.
Related titles: Microform ed.: (from PMC); Online - full text ed.: EUR 1,298 (effective 2005) (from EBSCO Publishing, Gale Group, Swets Information Services); ♦ Supplement(s): Zeitschrift fuer Kristallographie. Supplement Issues. ISSN 0930-486X.
Indexed: ASCA, BrCerAb, CCI, CCMJ, CIN, ChemAb, ChemTitl, CurCont, EngInd, INIS AtomInd, ISR, Inspec, MSCI, MathR, MathSciNet, MinerAb, PhysBer, RCI, RefZh, S&F, SCI, ZentMath.
—BLDSC (9468.000000), AskIEEE, CASDDS, CISTI, Ei, IDS, IE, Infotrieve, ingenta, Linda Hall. **CCC.**
Published by: Oldenbourg Wissenschaftsverlag GmbH, Rosenheimer Str 145, Munich, 81671, Germany. TEL 49-89-450510, FAX 49-89-45051204, zkrist@verlag.oldenbourg.de, vertrieb-zs@verlag.oldenbourg.de, http://www.zkristallogr.de, http://www.oldenbourg.de.

548 DEU ISSN 1433-7266
QD901 CODEN: ZKNSFT
➤ **ZEITSCHRIFT FUER KRISTALLOGRAPHIE - NEW CRYSTAL STRUCTURES.** Text in German. 1997. q. EUR 258; EUR 78 newsstand/cover (effective 2004). **Document type:** *Journal, Academic/Scholarly.* **Description:** Publishes results of determinations of crystal structures without detailed discussion.
Indexed: CCI, CurCont, INIS AtomInd, ISR, Inspec, MSCI, RCI, RefZh, SCI.
—BLDSC (9468.128000), CASDDS, CISTI, IDS, IE, Infotrieve, ingenta, Linda Hall. **CCC.**
Published by: Oldenbourg Wissenschaftsverlag GmbH, Rosenheimer Str 145, Munich, 81671, Germany. TEL 49-89-450510, FAX 49-89-45051204, vertrieb-zs@verlag.oldenbourg.de, http://www.zkristallogr.de, http://www.oldenbourg.de. Eds. H Schulz, H G von Schnering.

548 DEU ISSN 0930-486X
➤ **ZEITSCHRIFT FUER KRISTALLOGRAPHIE. SUPPLEMENT ISSUES.** Text in English. 1984. irreg., latest vol.20, 2003. price varies. **Document type:** *Monographic series, Academic/Scholarly.*
Related titles: ♦ Supplement to: Zeitschrift fuer Kristallographie. ISSN 0044-2968.
—BLDSC (9468.050000), CISTI.
Published by: Oldenbourg Wissenschaftsverlag GmbH, Rosenheimer Str 145, Munich, 81671, Germany. TEL 49-89-45051399, FAX 49-89-45051333, vertrieb-zs@verlag.oldenbourg.de, http://www.oldenbourg.de.

CHEMISTRY—Electrochemistry

541.37 535 DEU ISSN 1616-301X
TK7874.8 CODEN: AFMDC6
➤ **ADVANCED FUNCTIONAL MATERIALS.** Abbreviated title: A F M. Text in English. 1992. 18/yr. EUR 2,458 in Europe to institutions; CHF 3,878 to institutions in Switzerland & Liechtenstein; USD 2,958 elsewhere to institutions; EUR 2,704 combined subscription in Europe to institutions for print & online eds.; CHF 4,266 combined subscription to institutions in Switzerland & Liechtenstein, for print & online eds.; USD 3,254 combined subscription elsewhere to institutions for print & online eds. (effective 2006). adv. bk.rev. index. back issues avail.; reprints avail. **Document type:** *Journal, Academic/Scholarly.* **Description:** Covers all aspects of materials science from an interdisciplinary perspective, with an emphasis on new materials and methods for their preparation, modification and investigation.
Formerly (until 2001): Advanced Materials for Optics and Electronics (1057-9257); Which was formed by the merger of (1986-1991): Chemtronics (0267-5900); (1985-1991): Journal of Molecular Electronics (0748-7991)
Related titles: Microform ed.: (from PQC); Online - full text ed.: ISSN 1616-3028. EUR 2,458 in Europe; CHF 3,878 in Switzerland & Liechtenstein; USD 2,958 elsewhere (effective 2006) (from EBSCO Publishing, Swets Information Services, Wiley InterScience).
Indexed: ASCA, BrCerAb, C&ISA, CCI, CIN, CerAb, ChemAb, ChemTitl, CorrAb, CurCont, E&CAJ, EMA, EngInd, IAA, INIS AtomInd, ISR, Inspec, M&TEA, MBF, METADEX, MSCI, RAPRA, RCI, RefZh, SCI, SolStAb, WAA.
—BLDSC (0696.853900), AskIEEE, CASDDS, CISTI, Ei, IDS, IE, Infotrieve, ingenta, Linda Hall. **CCC.**
Published by: Wiley - V C H Verlag GmbH & Co. KGaA (Subsidiary of: John Wiley & Sons, Inc.), Boschstr 12, Weinheim, 69469, Germany. TEL 49-6201-6060, FAX 49-6201-606328, subservice@wiley-vch.de, http://www.wiley-vch.de/home/afm. Ed., Adv. contact P Gregory. R&P Claudia Rutz. page EUR 2,000; trim 180 x 260. Circ: 450. **Subscr. to:** John Wiley & Sons Ltd., The Atrium, Southern Gate, Chichester, West Sussex PO19 8SQ, United Kingdom. TEL 44-1243-779777, FAX 44-1243-775878.

➤ **ADVANCES IN ELECTROCHEMICAL SCIENCE AND ENGINEERING.** see *ENGINEERING—Chemical Engineering*

541.37 USA ISSN 1071-9687
QD501 CODEN: AGPCER
ADVANCES IN GAS PHASE ION CHEMISTRY. Text in English. 1992. irreg., latest vol.4, 2001. price varies. back issues avail. **Document type:** *Monographic series, Academic/Scholarly.*
Indexed: CCI, CIN, ChemAb, ChemTitl.
—BLDSC (0707.540000), CISTI.
Published by: J A I Press Inc. (Subsidiary of: Elsevier Science & Technology), 360 Park Ave S, New York, NY 10010-1710. TEL 212-989-5800, FAX 212-633-3990, usinfo-f@elsevier.com, http://www.elsevier.com/wps/find/bookseriesdescription.cws_home/BS_AGIC/description. Eds. L M Babcock, N G Adams.

AMERICAN ASSOCIATION FOR FUEL CELLS. NEWSLETTER; Our Energy Future. see *ENERGY—Electrical Energy*

APPLIED SURFACE SCIENCE. see *METALLURGY*

541.37 AUS ISSN 1328-3901
CODEN: COAUDF
AUSTRALASIAN CORROSION ASSOCIATION. ANNUAL CONFERENCE PROCEEDINGS✶. Text in English. 1960. a., latest 2001. AUD 214.50 to non-members; AUD 170.50 to members (effective 2001). bk.rev. **Document type:** *Proceedings.*
Formerly (until 1992): Australasian Corrosion Association. Conference (0729-2341)
Related titles: CD-ROM ed.: ISSN 1442-0139. AUD 181.50 per issue to non-members; AUD 132 per issue to members (effective 2001).
Indexed: CIN, ChemAb, ChemTitl.
—BLDSC (3473.506500).
Published by: Australasian Corrosion Association, c/o ACA Secretariat, PO Box 634, Brentford Square, VIC 3131, Australia. http://www.corrprev.org.au/. Adv. contact S Nugent. Circ: 350.

541.37 IND ISSN 0256-1654
CODEN: BUELE6
➤ **BULLETIN OF ELECTROCHEMISTRY.** Text in English. 1985. m. USD 175 to institutions (effective 2006). adv. bk.rev. 60 p./no.; back issues avail. **Document type:** *Academic/Scholarly.* **Description:** Contains comprehensive coverage of electrochemistry.
Incorporates: Electrometallurgy Bulletin
Indexed: ASCA, ASFA, BioDAb, BrCerAb, C&ISA, CCI, CEABA, CIN, CTE, CerAb, ChemAb, ChemTitl, CivEngAb, CorrAb, E&CAJ, EMA, ESPM, EngInd, GasAb, IAA, INIS AtomInd, Inspec, M&TEA, MBF, METADEX, MSCI, SolStAb, WAA, WSCA.
—BLDSC (2850.500000), CASDDS, CISTI, Ei, IDS, IE, Infotrieve, ingenta, Linda Hall. **CCC.**

Published by: (Central Electrochemical Research Institute), Scientific Publishers, 5-A New Pali Rd., Near Hotel Taj Hari Mahal, PO Box 91, Jodhpur, Rajasthan 342 003, India. TEL 91-291-2433323, FAX 91-291-2512580, info@scientificpub.com, http://www.scientificpub.com/bookdetails.php?booktransid=434&bookid=430. Ed. S K Rangarajan. Circ: 300. **Dist. by:** Scientific Distribution Service, 5-A Bhagat-ko-kothi, P O Box 33, Jodhpur, Rajasthan 342 001, India.

➤ **BUSINESS RATIO REPORT. PRINTED CIRCUIT MANUFACTURERS (YEAR).** see *ELECTRONICS*

541.37 JPN
CHEMICAL SENSORS/KAGAKU SENSA. Text in Japanese; Summaries in English. 1985. 4/yr.
—BLDSC (3151.528000), ingenta.
Published by: Electrochemical Society of Japan, Japan Association of Chemical Sensors/Denki Kagaku Kyokai Kagaku Sensa Kenkyukai, c/o Mr Shimizu, Kyushu Daigaku Daigakuin Sogo Rikogaku Kenkyuka, 6-1 Kasuga-Koen, Kasuga-shi, Fukuoka-ken 816-0811, Japan.

CORROSAO E PROTECCAO DE MATERIAIS. see *METALLURGY*

541.37 AUS ISSN 1326-1932
CODEN: COAUDF
CORROSION AND MATERIALS✶. Text in English. 1976. 6/yr. AUD 55 domestic; AUD 65 foreign (effective 2001). **Document type:** *Academic/Scholarly.*
Formerly (until 1996): Corrosion Australasia (0155-6002)
Indexed: AESIS, BrCerAb, C&ISA, CIN, CerAb, ChemAb, ChemTitl, CivEngAb, CorrAb, E&CAJ, EMA, IAA, M&TEA, MBF, METADEX, RefZh, SolStAb, WAA, WSCA.
—BLDSC (3473.500500), CASDDS, CISTI, Linda Hall.
Published by: Australasian Corrosion Association, c/o ACA Secretariat, PO Box 634, Brentford Square, VIC 3131, Australia. http://www.corrprev.org.au/. Adv. contact S Nugent.
Co-sponsor: Asian Pacific Materials and Corrosion Association.

CORROSION ENGINEERING. see *METALLURGY*

CURRENT SEPARATIONS. see *CHEMISTRY—Analytical Chemistry*

541.37 JPN
DENKAI GIJUTSU TORONKAI SODA KOGYO GIJUTSU TORONKAI KOEN YOSHISHU. Text in Japanese. a. **Document type:** *Proceedings, Academic/Scholarly.*
—BLDSC (3550.647700).
Published by: Denki Kagaku Kyokai, Denki Kagaku Gijutsu Iinkai, 79-5 Tokiwadai, Hodogaya-ku, Yokohama National University, Yokohama, 240-8501, Japan. TEL 81-45-3394021, FAX 81-45-3394024, denkai@electrochem.jp, http://denkai.electrochem.jp/.

541.37 CHN ISSN 1006-3471
CODEN: DIANFX
➤ **DIAN HUAXUE/ELECTROCHEMISTRY.** Text in Chinese; Abstracts in English. 1995. q. CNY 32 domestic; USD 40 foreign (effective 2003). 120 p./no.; **Document type:** *Academic/Scholarly.*
Related titles: Online - full content ed.: (from WanFang Data Corp.); Online - full text ed.: (from East View Information Services).
Indexed: ChemAb.
—BLDSC (3698.905000), CASDDS.
Published by: Zhongguo Huaxuehui/Chinese Chemical Society, Haidian Zhongguancun, 2, Beiyijie, Beijing, 100080, China. xiaodh@xmu.edu.cn, http://www.xmu.edu.cn/library.html. Ed. Wu Tian Tian.

541.37 CHN ISSN 1001-3849
DIANDU YU JINGSHI/PLATING AND FINISHING. Text in Chinese. 1973. bi-m. USD 10 (effective 1992). adv. bk.rev.
Related titles: Online - full text ed.: (from East View Information Services).
Indexed: C&ISA, E&CAJ, EngInd, IAA, RefZh.
—Ei.
Published by: Tianjin Diandu Gongcheng Xuehui/Tianjin Electroplating Engineering Society, Hebei Zhigong Dexue, Xingfu Dao Wangchuanchang, Hebei-qu, Tianjin 300150, China. TEL 661431. Ed. Liang Qimin. Circ: 5,000.

541.37 CHN ISSN 1004-227X
TS670.A1 CODEN: DYTUEM
DIANDU YU TUSHI/ELECTROPLATING & FINISHING. Text in Chinese. 1982. q. USD 20. adv. **Document type:** *Trade.*
Related titles: Online - full text ed.: (from East View Information Services).
Indexed: BrCerAb, C&ISA, CIN, CerAb, ChemAb, ChemTitl, CorrAb, E&CAJ, EMA, IAA, M&TEA, MBF, METADEX, RefZh, WAA.
—BLDSC (3706.950000), CASDDS, IE, ingenta, Linda Hall.

C

▼ new title ➤ refereed ✶ unverified ♦ full entry avail.

Published by: Guangdong Qinggong Diandu Xuehui/ Electroplaters Society of Guangdong Light Industry, No1, En-long Bei, Zhongshan Rd 7, Guangzhou, Guangdong 510170, China. TEL 86-620-8172-6886, FAX 86-620-8170-1214, gslri@public1.guangzhou.gd.cn. Ed., R&P, Adv. contact Xie Suling. Circ: 10,000.

541.37 USA

E C S MONOGRAPH SERIES. Text in English. irreg. **Document type:** *Monographic series.* **Description:** Provides authoritative accounts of specific topics in electrochemistry, solid state science and related disciplines.

Published by: Electrochemical Society, Inc., 65 S Main St, Bldg D, Pennington, NJ 08534-2839. TEL 609-737-1902, FAX 609-737-2743, ecs@electrochem.org, http://www.electorchem.org/. R&P Mary E Yess.

547 GBR ISSN 0963-5637 CODEN: ESTPEA

ELECTROCHEMICAL SCIENCE AND TECHNOLOGY OF POLYMERS. Text in English. 1987. irreg., latest vol.2, 1990. price varies. back issues avail. **Document type:** *Monographic series.*

Indexed: CIN, ChemAb, ChemTitl.

—CASDDS.

Published by: Pergamon (Subsidiary of: Elsevier Science & Technology), The Boulevard, Langford Ln, East Park, Kidlington, Oxford OX5 1GB, United Kingdom. TEL 44-1865-843000, FAX 44-1865-843010. Ed. R G Linford. **Subscr. to:** Elsevier BV, PO Box 211, Amsterdam 1000 AE, Netherlands. TEL 31-20-485-3757, FAX 31-20-485-3432, nlinfo-f@elsevier.nl, http://www.elsevier.nl.

541.37 USA ISSN 1064-8208
TP250 CODEN: ELSIE3

THE ELECTROCHEMICAL SOCIETY INTERFACE. Text in English. 1992. q. USD 47 domestic to non-members; USD 52 foreign to non-members (effective 2005). adv. back issues avail. **Document type:** *Journal, Academic/Scholarly.* **Description:** Contains news, reviews, and articles on technical matters of general interest to Electrochemical Society members.

Supersedes in part (in 1992): Electrochemical Society. Journal (0013-4651); Which incorporated (in 1949): Electrochemical Society. Transactions (0096-4743); Which was formerly (1902-1931): American Electrochemical Society (0096-4786); Electrochemical Society. Journal was formed by the 1948 merger of: Electrochemical Society, Inc. Bulletin (0898-1388); Electrochemical Society. Preprint (0898-1396)

Related titles: Online - full text ed.: (from EBSCO Publishing).

Indexed: BrCerAb, C&ISA, CEABA, CIN, CerAb, ChemAb, ChemTitl, CivEngAb, CorrAb, E&CAJ, EMA, EngInd, IAA, Inspec, M&TEA, MBF, METADEX, RefZh, SolStAb, WAA.

—BLDSC (4533.447500), AskIEEE, CASDDS, CINDOC, CISTI, Ei, IE, Infotrieve, ingenta, Linda Hall. **CCC.**

Published by: Electrochemical Society, Inc., 65 S Main St, Bldg D, Pennington, NJ 08534-2839. TEL 609-737-1902, FAX 609-737-2743, interface@electrochem.org, ecs@electrochem.org, http://www.electrochem.org/publications/interface/interface.htm, http://www.electorchem.org/. Ed. Dr. Krishnan Rajeshwar. R&P Mr. Terry McCloughan. adv.: B&W page USD 917, color page USD 1,670; trim 8.125 x 10.875. Circ: 8,600.

541.37 USA ISSN 0013-4651
TP250 CODEN: JESOAN

➤ **ELECTROCHEMICAL SOCIETY. JOURNAL.** Text in English. 1947. m. USD 833 domestic to non-members; USD 873 foreign to non-members (effective 2005); includes Electrochemical and Solid-State Letters. charts; illus. index. 500 p./no. 2 cols./p.; back issues avail.; reprint service avail. from PQC. **Document type:** *Journal, Academic/Scholarly.* **Description:** Contains technical papers covering basic researches in electrochemical science and technology and solid-state science and technology.

Incorporates (1963-1968): Electrochemical Technology (0424-8090); (1902-1949): Electrochemical Society. Transactions (0096-4743); Which was formerly (until 1931): American Electrochemical Society. Transactions (0096-4786); Formed by the merger of (19??-1947): Electrochemical Society. Preprint (0898-1396); (1931-1947): Electrochemical Society, Inc. Bulletin (0898-1388)

Related titles: CD-ROM ed.: USD 75 includes Electrochemical and Solid-State Letters (effective 2000); Microfilm ed.: (from PMC, PQC); Online - full text ed.: USD 520 (effective 2003) (from EBSCO Publishing).

Indexed: A&ATA, ABIPC, AS&TI, AnalAb, ApMecR, BrCerAb, BullT&T, C&ISA, CCI, CEABA, CIN, CMCI, CTE, Cadscan, CerAb, ChemAb, ChemInfo, ChemTitl, CivEngAb, CoppAb, CorrAb, CurCont, E&CAJ, EMA, EngInd, F&EA, IAA, INIS AtomInd, ISMEC, ISR, Inspec, LeadAb, M&TEA, MBF, METADEX, MSB, MSCI, PhotoAb, RCI, RefZh, S&F, SCI, SPINweb, SolStAb, WAA, Zincscan.

—BLDSC (4737.000000), AskIEEE, CASDDS, CINDOC, CISTI, Ei, IDS, IE, Infotrieve, ingenta, Linda Hall. **CCC.**

Published by: Electrochemical Society, Inc., 65 S Main St, Bldg D, Pennington, NJ 08534-2839. TEL 609-737-1902, FAX 609-737-2743, ecs@electrochem.org, http://ojps.aip.org/JES, http://www.electorchem.org/. Ed. Dr. Paul A Kohl. R&Ps Mary E Yess, Mr. Terry McCloughan. Circ: 6,000 (paid).

541.37 USA ISSN 1091-8213
QD551

ELECTROCHEMICAL SOCIETY. MEETING ABSTRACTS. Text in English. s-a. USD 168 to non-members; USD 140 to members (effective 2005). **Document type:** *Abstract/Index.* **Description:** Contains abstracts of technical papers presented at the Society's spring and fall meetings.

Formerly (until 1996): Electrochemical Society. Extended Abstracts (0160-4619)

Related titles: CD-ROM ed.; Online - full content ed.

Indexed: CTE, Inspec.

—BLDSC (5536.222420), CISTI, Linda Hall. **CCC.**

Published by: Electrochemical Society, Inc., 65 S Main St, Bldg D, Pennington, NJ 08534-2839. TEL 609-737-1902, FAX 609-737-2743, ecs@electrochem.org, http://www.electrochem.org, http://www.electorchem.org/.

541.37 IND ISSN 0013-466X
TP250 CODEN: JESIA5

➤ **ELECTROCHEMICAL SOCIETY OF INDIA. JOURNAL.** Text in English. 1952. q. INR 300 domestic; USD 70 foreign (effective 2000). adv. bk.rev. abstr.; illus. index. **Document type:** *Academic/Scholarly.* **Description:** Publishes papers on all aspects of the science, technology and engineering of electrochemistry and related subjects.

Indexed: CIN, CTE, Cadscan, ChemAb, ChemTitl, CivEngAb, CurCont, EngInd, ISA, Inspec, LeadAb, Zincscan.

—BLDSC (4737.500000), AskIEEE, CASDDS, CISTI, Ei, IE, ingenta, Linda Hall. **CCC.**

Published by: (Electrochemical Society of India), Scientific Publishers, 5-A New Pali Rd., Near Hotel Taj Hari Mahal, PO Box 91, Jodhpur, Rajasthan 342 003, India. TEL 91-291-2433323, FAX 91-291-2512580, info@scientificpub.com, http://www.scientificpub.com. Ed. S K Vijayalakshamma. Circ: 600.

541.37 USA ISSN 0161-6374 CODEN: PESODO

ELECTROCHEMICAL SOCIETY. PROCEEDINGS. Key Title: Proceedings - Electrochemical Society. Text in English. 1967. irreg. back issues avail. **Document type:** *Proceedings.* **Description:** Publishes proceedings of symposia and international conferences sponsored by the Society in such fields as electrodeposition, batteries, corrosion, dielectric science and technology, electronics, compound semiconductors, high temperature materials, physical electrochemistry, industrial electrolysis and electrochemical engineering.

Related titles: Microform ed.: (from PQC); ◆ Series: International Conference on Chemical Vapor Deposition. Proceedings. ISSN 1056-9480.

Indexed: CIN, ChemAb, ChemTitl, Inspec, MSB.

—BLDSC (6695.400000), CASDDS, CISTI, Ei. **CCC.**

Published by: Electrochemical Society, Inc., 65 S Main St, Bldg D, Pennington, NJ 08534-2839. TEL 609-737-1902, FAX 609-737-2743, ecs@electrochem.org, http://www.electorchem.org/. R&P Mary E Yess.

541.37 USA ISSN 0275-0171

ELECTROCHEMICAL SOCIETY SERIES. Text in English. 1948. irreg., latest 1996. price varies. back issues avail. **Document type:** *Monographic series, Academic/Scholarly.*

Indexed: Inspec.

Published by: (Electrochemical Society, Inc.), John Wiley & Sons, Inc., 111 River St, Hoboken, NJ 07030-5774. TEL 201-748-6000, 800-825-7550, FAX 201-748-5915, uscs-wis@wiley.com, http://www.wiley.com.

541.37 JPN ISSN 1344-3542
QD551 CODEN: EECTFA

➤ **ELECTROCHEMISTRY/DENKI KAGAKU OYOBI KOGYO BUTSURI KAGAKU.** Text mainly in Japanese. 1933. m. free to members. adv. bk.rev. abstr.; charts; illus.; stat. index. reprints avail. **Document type:** *Journal, Academic/Scholarly.* **Description:** Contains theses, academic articles, and bulletins.

Formerly (until 1999): Denki Kagaku Oyobi Kogyo Butsuri Kagaku/Electrochemistry and Industrial Physical Chemistry (0366-9297); Which incorporated (1933-1961): Electrochemical Society of Japan. Journal (0013-4678); (until 1961): Denki Kagaku (0366-9440)

Indexed: AnalAb, BrCerAb, C&ISA, CCI, CEABA, CIN, CerAb, ChemAb, ChemTitl, CivEngAb, CorrAb, CurCont, E&CAJ, EMA, IAA, INIS AtomInd, ISR, Inspec, JCT, JTA, M&TEA, MBF, METADEX, MSB, MSCI, RCI, SCI, SolStAb, WAA, WRCInf.

—BLDSC (3698.911000), AskIEEE, CASDDS, CISTI, IDS, IE, ingenta, Linda Hall. **CCC.**

Published by: Electrochemical Society of Japan/Denki Kagaku Kai Kyokai, 4-8-30 Kudan-Minami, Chiyoda-ku, Tokyo, 102-0074, Japan. TEL 81-3-32344213, FAX 81-3-32343599, http://www.electrochem.jp/journal/list.html. Circ: 2,500 (controlled).

541.37 USA ISSN 1388-2481
QD551 CODEN: ECCMF9

ELECTROCHEMISTRY COMMUNICATIONS. Text in English. 1999. 12/yr. EUR 526 in Europe to institutions; JPY 69,900 in Japan to institutions; USD 587 elsewhere to institutions (effective 2006). **Document type:** *Journal, Academic/Scholarly.* **Description:** Provides dissemination of short communications covering the whole field of electrochemistry, including fundamental electrochemistry, electrode reaction mechanisms, computational and theoretical electrochemistry, properties of interfaces, electrochemical surface science, batteries and power sources, organic and organometallic electrochemistry, bioelectrochemistry, spectroelectrochemistry, and sonoelectrochemistry.

Related titles: Online - full text ed.: (from EBSCO Publishing, Gale Group, IngentaConnect, ScienceDirect, Swets Information Services).

Indexed: AESIS, AnalAb, CCI, ChemAb, CurCont, ISR, Inspec, MSCI, RefZh, SCI.

—BLDSC (3698.912000), CASDDS, CINDOC, CISTI, IE, Infotrieve, ingenta, Linda Hall. **CCC.**

Published by: Elsevier Inc. (Subsidiary of: Elsevier Science & Technology), 360 Park Ave. S, New York, NY 10010-1710. TEL 212-633-3730, 888-437-4636, elchem@physchem.ox.ac.uk, usinfo-f@elsevier.com, http://www.elsevier.com/locate/elecom. Eds. Dr. J. F. Rusling, Dr. Kohei Uosaki, R. G. Compton.

541.37 GBR ISSN 0013-4686
TP250 CODEN: ELCAAV

➤ **ELECTROCHIMICA ACTA.** Text in English, French, German. 1959. 28/yr. EUR 4,174 in Europe to institutions; JPY 554,200 in Japan to institutions; USD 4,669 elsewhere to institutions (effective 2006). adv. bk.rev. charts; illus. index. back issues avail.; reprint service avail. from PQC. **Document type:** *Journal, Academic/Scholarly.* **Description:** Publishes original papers and critical reviews in pure and applied electrochemistry.

Related titles: Microfilm ed.: (from PQC); Online - full text ed.: (from EBSCO Publishing, Gale Group, IngentaConnect, ScienceDirect, Swets Information Services).

Indexed: AnalAb, BrCerAb, C&ISA, CCI, CEA, CEABA, CIN, CTE, Cadscan, CerAb, ChemAb, ChemInfo, ChemTitl, CivEngAb, CorrAb, CurCont, E&CAJ, EMA, EngInd, ExcerpMed, IAA, ISMEC, ISR, Inspec, LeadAb, M&TEA, MBF, METADEX, MSB, MSCI, RCI, RefZh, SCI, SolStAb, TCEA, WAA, Zincscan.

—BLDSC (3698.950000), CASDDS, CISTI, Ei, IDS, IE, Infotrieve, ingenta, Linda Hall. **CCC.**

Published by: (International Society of Electrochemistry), Pergamon (Subsidiary of: Elsevier Science & Technology), The Boulevard, Langford Ln, East Park, Kidlington, Oxford OX5 1GB, United Kingdom. TEL 44-1865-843000, FAX 44-1865-843010, EACTA@ncl.ac.uk, http://www.elsevier.com/locate/electacta. Eds. E J Cairns, S Trasatti. Circ: 1,900. **Subscr. to:** Elsevier BV, PO Box 211, Amsterdam 1000 AE, Netherlands. TEL 31-20-485-3757, FAX 31-20-485-3432, nlinfo-f@elsevier.nl, http://www.elsevier.nl.

541.37 RUS ISSN 0424-8570
QD551 CODEN: ELKKAX

ELEKTROKHIMIYA. Text in Russian. 1965. m. RUR 930 for 6 mos. domestic (effective 2004). back issues avail. **Document type:** *Journal, Academic/Scholarly.* **Description:** Reports developments in the sub-disciplines of electrochemistry, including electrochemistry of solid electrolytes, membrane electrolysis, electro-organic chemistry, and theory and application of impedance spectroscopy in electrochemistry.

Related titles: Microfilm ed.: (from PQC); Online - full text ed.; ◆ English Translation: Russian Journal of Electrochemistry. ISSN 1023-1935.

Indexed: BrCerAb, C&ISA, CEABA, CerAb, CivEngAb, CorrAb, CurCont, E&CAJ, EMA, INIS AtomInd, M&TEA, MBF, METADEX, RefZh, SolStAb, WAA.

—BLDSC (0399.123000), CASDDS, CINDOC, CISTI, East View, KNAW, Linda Hall. **CCC.**

Published by: (Rossiiskaya Akademiya Nauk/Russian Academy of Sciences), Izdatel'stvo Nauka, Profsoyuznaya ul 90, Moscow, 117864, Russian Federation. TEL 7-095-3347151, FAX 7-095-4202220, secret@naukaran.ru, http://www.maik.rssi.ru/cgi-bin/list.pl?page=elkhim, http://www.naukaran.ru.

620.112 CHN ISSN 1005-748X

➤ **FUSHI YU FANGHU/CORROSION AND PROTECTION.** Text in Chinese; Summaries in Chinese, English. 1980. m. CNY 72 domestic (effective 2000); USD 80 newsstand/cover foreign; CNY 6 newsstand/cover. adv. index. back issues avail. **Document type:** *Academic/Scholarly.*

Related titles: Fax ed.; Online - full text ed.: (from East View Information Services).

Indexed: FLUIDEX, METADEX.

—BLDSC (3473.512000), IE, ingenta.

Published by: Shanghai Research Institute of Materials, 99 Han Dan Rd, Shanghai, 200437, China. TEL 86-21-6542-0775, FAX 86-21-6542-0554. Eds. Wu Yang, Yunchang Chen. Pub. Ming Wang. R&P Xiaodan Guo TEL 86-21-65449079. Adv. contact Tao Si. B&W page CNY 2,500, B&W page USD 300, color page CNY 6,000, color page USD 800; trim 205 x 286. Circ: 4,000 (paid); 1,000 (controlled). **Dist. overseas by:** China Publication Foreign Trade Company, PO Box 782, Beijing 100011, China. **Co-sponsor:** Shanghai Society of Corrosion Science and Technology.

➤ **GALVANOTEKHNIKA I OBRABOTKA POVERKHNOSTI/ ELECTROPLATING AND SURFACE TREATMENT.** see *ENGINEERING—Electrical Engineering*

➤ **HOKKAIDO UNIVERSITY. CATALYSIS RESEARCH CENTER. ANNUAL REPORT (YEAR)/HOKKAIDO DAIGAKU SHOKUBAI KAGAKU KENKYU CENTER NENPO.** see *CHEMISTRY—Physical Chemistry*

669 JPN ISSN 0915-1869
CODEN: HYGIEX

HYOMEN GIJUTSU/SURFACE FINISHING SOCIETY OF JAPAN. JOURNAL. Text in English. 1950. s-a. free to members. adv. bk.rev. charts; illus. Index. **Document type:** *Journal, Academic/Scholarly.*

Formed by the merger of (1950-1988): Kinzoku Hyomen Gijutsu (0026-0614); (1970-1988): Jitsumu Hyomen Gijutsu (0368-2358); Which was formerly (1954-1970): Kinzoku Hyomen Gijutsu Genba Panfuretto (0368-5527)

Related titles: Online - full text ed.: (from J-Stage).

Indexed: BrCerAb, C&ISA, CIN, CerAb, ChemAb, ChemTitl, CivEngAb, CorrAb, E&CAJ, EMA, EngInd, IAA, INIS AtomInd, Inspec, M&TEA, MBF, METADEX, SolStAb, WAA.

—BLDSC (4904.472000), CASDDS, CISTI, Ei, IE, ingenta, Linda Hall. **CCC.**

Published by: Hyomen Gijutsu Kyokai/Surface Finishing Society of Japan, 2-7-1 Kanda Suda-cho, Chiyoda-ku, Tokyo, 101-0041, Japan. TEL 81-3-32523286, FAX 81-3-32523288, http://wwwsoc.nii.ac.jp/sfj/. Ed. Tetsuya Osaka. Circ: 5,000.

541.37 USA ISSN 0741-1413

INTERNATIONAL ELECTROCHEMICAL PROGRESS✶. Text in English. 1972. m. USD 360; USD 450 foreign. bk.rev. abstr.; bibl.; pat.; stat. back issues avail.

Indexed: ChemAb.

Published by: International Electrochemical Institute, 189 Parsonage Hill Rd, Short Hills, NJ 07078-1523. TEL 201-273-1088. Ed. J A Leduc.

541.37 NLD ISSN 0021-891X
TP250 CODEN: JAELBJ

➤ **JOURNAL OF APPLIED ELECTROCHEMISTRY.** Text in English. 1971. m. EUR 2,148, USD 2,178, GBP 1,345 combined subscription to institutions print & online eds. (effective 2005). adv. reprint service avail. from PQC,ISI,PSC. **Document type:** *Journal, Academic/Scholarly.* **Description:** Publishes articles in fields such as cell design, corrosion, electrochemical reaction engineering, the electrochemical treatment of effluents, hydrometallurgy, molten salt and solid state electrochemistry, new battery systems, solar cells and surface finishing.

Related titles: Online - full text ed.: ISSN 1572-8838 (from EBSCO Publishing, Gale Group, IngentaConnect, Kluwer Online, O C L C Online Computer Library Center, Inc., Springer LINK, Swets Information Services).

Indexed: AESIS, AS&TI, ASCA, ASFA, BibLing, BrCerAb, C&ISA, CCI, CEABA, CIN, CTE, Cadscan, CerAb, ChemAb, ChemTitl, ChemoAb, CivEngAb, CorrAb, CurCont, E&CAJ, EMA, EngInd, ExcerpMed, IAA, ISMEC, ISR, Inspec, LeadAb, M&TEA, MBF, METADEX, MSB, MSCI, RefZh, SCI, SolStAb, VITIS, WAA, Zincscan.

—BLDSC (4942.600000), AskIEEE, CASDDS, CISTI, Ei, IDS, IE, Infotrieve, ingenta, Linda Hall. **CCC.**

Published by: (International Society of Electrochemistry GBR), Springer-Verlag Dordrecht (Subsidiary of: Springer Science+Business Media), Van Godewijckstraat 30, Dordrecht, 3311 GX, Netherlands. TEL 31-78-6576050, FAX 31-78-6576474, http://springerlink.metapress.com/openurl.asp?genre=journal&issn=0021-891X, http://www.springeronline.com. Ed. A A Wragg.

541.37 CAN ISSN 1480-2422

JOURNAL OF NEW MATERIALS FOR ELECTROCHEMICAL SYSTEMS. Text in English. 1998. q. CND 150 to individuals; CND 170 combined subscription to individuals print & online eds; CND 650 to institutions; CND 800 combined subscription to institutions print & online eds (effective 2004). **Description:** Publishes work that is both analytical and experimental, and reviews and commercial aspects related to the field.

Indexed: CCI, CurCont, Inspec, MSCI, RefZh.

—BLDSC (5022.720000), CISTI, IE, ingenta. **CCC.**

Published by: Ecole Polytechnique de Montreal, C P 6079, Succ. Centre-Ville, Montreal, PQ H3C 3A7, Canada. TEL 514-340-4725, FAX 514-340-4466, osavadogo@mailsrv.polymtl.ca, http://www.newmaterials.polymtl.ca, http://www.polymtl.ca/fr/fr/index.php. Ed. O Savadogo.

541.37 DEU ISSN 1432-8488
CODEN: JSSEFS

➤ **JOURNAL OF SOLID STATE ELECTROCHEMISTRY**; current research and development in science and technology. Text in English. 1997. m. EUR 430 combined subscription to institutions print & online eds. (effective 2005). adv. back issues avail. **Document type:** *Journal, Academic/Scholarly.* **Description:** Devoted to all aspects of solid-state chemistry and solid-state physics in electrochemistry.

Related titles: Microform ed.: (from PQC); Online - full text ed.: ISSN 1433-0768 (from EBSCO Publishing, Springer LINK, Swets Information Services).

Indexed: CCI, CTE, ChemAb, CurCont, Inspec, MSCI, RefZh.

—BLDSC (5065.410000), CASDDS, CISTI, IDS, IE, Infotrieve, ingenta. **CCC.**

Published by: Springer-Verlag (Subsidiary of: Springer Science+Business Media), Tiergartenstr 17, Heidelberg, 69121, Germany. TEL 49-6221-3450, FAX 49-6221-345229, http://link.springer.de/link/service/journals/10008/index.htm. Ed. Fritz Scholz. Adv. contact Stephan Kroeck TEL 49-30-827875739. **Subscr. in the Americas to:** Springer-Verlag New York, Inc., Journal Fulfillment, PO Box 2485, Secaucus, NJ 07096-2485. TEL 800-777-4643, 201-348-4033, FAX 201-348-4505, journals@springer-ny.com, http://www.springer-ny.com; **Subscr. to:** Springer GmbH Auslieferungsgesellschaft, Haberstr 7, Heidelberg 69126, Germany. TEL 49-6221-345-0, FAX 49-6221-345-4229, subscriptions@springer.de.

➤ **JOURNAL OF SURFACE SCIENCE AND TECHNOLOGY.** see *PHYSICS—Mechanics*

541.37 621.381 GBR ISSN 1524-511X
TS695 CODEN: JWBMFT

➤ **JOURNAL OF WIDE BANDGAP MATERIALS.** Text in English. 1999. q. GBP 317 combined subscription to institutions print & online eds. in Europe, Middle East, Africa & Australasia; USD 459 combined subscription elsewhere to institutions print & online eds. (effective 2004). **Document type:** *Academic/Scholarly.* **Description:** Reports on the research and development of wide bandgap materials for electronic and opto-electronic applications.

Related titles: E-mail ed.; Online - full content ed.; Online - full text ed.: ISSN 1530-8081 (from EBSCO Publishing, O C L C Online Computer Library Center, Inc., Sage Publications, Inc., Swets Information Services).

Indexed: BrCerAb, C&ISA, CerAb, ChemAb, CivEngAb, CorrAb, E&CAJ, EMA, IAA, Inspec, M&TEA, MBF, METADEX, RAPRA, SolStAb, WAA.

—BLDSC (5072.613000), CISTI, IE, Infotrieve, Linda Hall. **CCC.**

Published by: Sage Publications Ltd. (Subsidiary of: Sage Publications, Inc.), 1 Oliver's Yard, 55 City Rd, London, EC1 1SP, United Kingdom. TEL 44-20-73248500, FAX 44-20-73248600, info@sagepub.co.uk, http://www.sagepub.co.uk/. Circ: 100.

541 JPN
CODEN: KAGSEU

KAGAKU SENSA KENKYU HAPPYOKAI/CHEMICAL SENSOR SYMPOSIUM. PROCEEDINGS. Text in English, Japanese. 1981. s-a. JPY 5,000. adv. **Document type:** *Proceedings.*

Published by: Denki Kagaku Kyokai, Kagaku Sensa Kenkyukai/Electrochemical Society of Japan, Japan Association of Chemical Sensors, Kyushu University, Graduate School of Engineering and Sciences, 6-1 Kasuga-Koen, Kasuga-shi, Fukuoka-ken 816-0811, Japan. TEL 81-92-583-7538, FAX 81-92-583-7539, sensor@mm.kyushu-u.ac.jp, http://chemsens.mase.nagasaki-u.ac.jp. Ed. Denki Kagaku Kai. Adv. contact Norio Miura.

KEY ABSTRACTS - HIGH-TEMPERATURE SUPERCONDUCTORS. see *PHYSICS—Abstracting, Bibliographies, Statistics*

541.37 JPN

KYOKAI RYOIKI NI OKERU DENKI KAGAKU SEMINA/SEMINAR ON ELECTROCHEMISTRY IN BOUNDARY REGION. PROCEEDINGS. Text in Japanese. s-a. **Document type:** *Proceedings.*

Published by: Denki Kagaku Kyokai, Kanto Shibu/ Electrochemical Society of Japan, Kanto Branch, Yamanashi Daigaku Kogakubu, Muki Gosei Kenkyu Shisetsu, 3-11 Takeda 4-chome, Kofu-shi, Yamanashi-ken 400-0016, Japan.

L C G C ASIA PACIFIC; the magazine of separation science. (Liquid Chromatography Gas Chromatography) see *CHEMISTRY—Analytical Chemistry*

641 668 USA ISSN 1068-7440
CODEN: MPFAEU

➤ **METALLIZED PLASTICS**; fundamental and applied aspects. Text in English. 1989. irreg., latest 1992. price varies. back issues avail. **Document type:** *Proceedings, Academic/Scholarly.*

Indexed: ChemAb, ChemTitl, MSCI.

—CASDDS. **CCC.**

Published by: (Electrochemical Society, Inc.), Springer-Verlag New York, Inc. (Subsidiary of: Springer Science+Business Media), 233 Spring St, New York, NY 10013. TEL 212-460-1500, FAX 212-460-1575, service@springer-ny.com, http://www.springer-ny.com. Ed. K L Mittal.

540 USA ISSN 1063-8814
CODEN: MSUCEU

➤ **METHODS OF SURFACE CHARACTERIZATION.** Text in English. 1987. irreg., latest vol.5, 1999. price varies. back issues avail. **Document type:** *Monographic series, Academic/Scholarly.*

Indexed: ChemAb, ChemTitl.

—BLDSC (5748.207500), CASDDS, CISTI. **CCC.**

Published by: Springer-Verlag New York, Inc. (Subsidiary of: Springer Science+Business Media), 233 Spring St, New York, NY 10013. TEL 212-460-1500, FAX 212-460-1575, service@springer-ny.com, http://www.springer-ny.com. Eds. A W Czanderna, C J Powell, D M Hercules, T E Madey. **Dist. by:** Journal Fulfillment, PO Box 2485, Secaucus, NJ 07096-2485.

541.37 USA ISSN 0076-9924
QD552 CODEN: MAECAO

➤ **MODERN ASPECTS OF ELECTROCHEMISTRY.** Text in English. 1964. irreg., latest vol.38, 2005. price varies. **Document type:** *Monographic series, Academic/Scholarly.*

Indexed: CCI, ChemAb, ChemTitl.

—BLDSC (5883.670000), CASDDS, CISTI, IE, ingenta, KNAW. **CCC.**

Published by: Springer-Verlag New York, Inc. (Subsidiary of: Springer Science+Business Media), 233 Spring St, New York, NY 10013. TEL 212-460-1500, FAX 212-460-1575, service@springer-ny.com, http://www.springer-ny.com. Eds. Brian E Conway, Costas G Vayenas, Ralph E White.

➤ **NICAD (YEAR).** see *METALLURGY*

➤ **NIHON KAISUI GAKKAISHI/SOCIETY OF SEA WATER SCIENCE, JAPAN. BULLETIN.** see *EARTH SCIENCES—Oceanography*

660 NOR ISSN 0801-9606

OVERFLATE TEKNIKK. Text in Norwegian. 1958. q. NOK 200.

Former titles: Galvano Teknisk Tidsskrift (0046-5372); Norsk Galvano Teknisk Tidsskrift

Indexed: CISA.

Published by: Norsk Galvanoteknisk Landsforening, Postboks 2608, St Hanshaugen, Oslo, 0131, Norway. TEL 02-865139. Ed. Erik Bang. Circ: 3,700.

541.37 JPN

P E D KENKYUKAI/RESEARCH GROUP OF PASSIVE ELECTROCHEMICAL DEVICES. PROCEEDINGS. Text in Japanese. 1988. s-a. **Document type:** *Proceedings.*

Published by: P E D Research Group, Promissing Surface Science Laboratory, 5-9-2-102 Minami-Osawa, Hachioji-shi, Tokyo-to 192-0364, Japan.

541.37 PRT ISSN 0872-1904

PORTUGALIAE ELECTROCHIMICA ACTA. Text in Multiple languages. 1983. q. EUR 20 (effective 2005).

Indexed: RefZh.

—BLDSC (6556.600000), CISTI, IE, ingenta.

Published by: Sociedade Portuguesa de Electroquimica/ Portuguese Electrochemical Society, c/o Departamento de Quimica, Universidad de Coimbra, Coimbra, 3004-535, Portugal. ajbarros@fc.up.pt, http://www.peacta.qui.uc.pt/, http://www.peacta.qui.uc.pt/page5.htm. Ed. Ana Carreira Lopez. Pub. Victor M.M. Lobo.

541.37 IND

RECENT RESEARCH DEVELOPMENTS IN ELECTROCHEMISTRY. Text in English. a., latest vol.4, 2001.

—BLDSC (7305.087542).

Published by: Transworld Research Network, T C 36-248 (1), Trivandrum, Kerala 695 008, India. http://www.transworldresearch.com.

REVIEW OF POLAROGRAPHY/PORAROGURAFI. see *CHEMISTRY—Analytical Chemistry*

541.37 RUS ISSN 1023-1935
QD551 CODEN: RJELE3

➤ **RUSSIAN JOURNAL OF ELECTROCHEMISTRY.** Text in English. 1965. 13/yr. EUR 3,748, USD 3,388, GBP 2,288 combined subscription to institutions print & online eds. (effective 2005). back issues avail. **Document type:** *Journal, Academic/Scholarly.* **Description:** Reports developments in the sub-disciplines of electrochemistry, including electrochemistry of solid electrolytes, membrane electrolysis, electro-organic chemistry, and theory and application of impedance spectroscopy in electrochemistry.

Former titles (until 1994): Russian Electrochemistry (1070-3276); (until 1993): Soviet Electrochemistry (0038-5387)

Related titles: Microfilm ed.: (from PQC); Online - full text ed.: ISSN 1608-3342 (from EBSCO Publishing, Gale Group, IngentaConnect, Kluwer Online, O C L C Online Computer Library Center, Inc., Springer LINK, Swets Information Services); ♦ Translation of: Elektrokhimiya. ISSN 0424-8570.

Indexed: ASCA, BibLing, CCI, CIN, CTE, ChemAb, ChemTitl, CurCont, ESPM, EngInd, ISR, Inspec, MSCI, RCI, SCI, SIA, SSCI, SWRA, WRCInf.

—BLDSC (0420.760925), CASDDS, CISTI, IDS, IE, Infotrieve, ingenta, Linda Hall. **CCC.**

Published by: (Rossiiskaya Akademiya Nauk/Russian Academy of Sciences), M A I K Nauka - Interperiodica, Profsoyuznaya ul 90, Moscow, 117997, Russian Federation. TEL 7-095-3347420, FAX 7-095-3360666, compmg@maik.ru, http://www.maik.rssi.ru/journals/elchem.htm, http://www.maik.ru. Ed. Boris M Grafov. **Subscr. to:** Springer-Verlag Dordrecht, Journals Department, PO Box 322, Dordrecht, Netherlands. TEL 31-78-6576392, FAX 31-78-6576474.

C

541.37 CHE ISSN 0925-4005
TK7881.2 CODEN: SABCEB
➤ **SENSORS AND ACTUATORS B: CHEMICAL**; international journal devoted to research and development of physical and chemical transducers. Text in English. 1981. 16/yr. EUR 3,420 in Europe to institutions; JPY 454,500 in Japan to institutions; USD 3,827 elsewhere to institutions (effective 2006). back issues avail.; reprints avail. **Document type:** *Academic/Scholarly.* **Description:** Covers all aspects of research and development of sensor elements transforming and transducing chemical signals into information about the chemical composition of the sample analyzed.
Supersedes in part (in 1990): Sensors and Actuators (0250-6874)
Related titles: Microform ed.: (from PQC); Online - full text ed.: (from EBSCO Publishing, Gale Group, IngentaConnect, ScienceDirect, Swets Information Services).
Indexed: AEBA, ASFA, AnalAb, BioEngAb, BrCerAb, C&ISA, CCI, CMCI, CerAb, ChemAb, ChemTitl, ChemoAb, CivEngAb, CorrAb, CurCont, E&CAJ, EMA, ESPM, EngInd, EnvEAb, IAA, ISR, Inspec, M&PBA, M&TEA, MBF, METADEX, MSB, MSCI, NutrAb, PhysBer, PollutAb, RefZh, SCI, SIA, SolStAb, VITIS, WAA.
—BLDSC (8241.785220), AskIEEE, CASDDS, CISTI, Ei, IDS, IE, Infotrieve, ingenta, Linda Hall. **CCC.**
Published by: Elsevier S.A., PO Box 564, Lausanne 1, 1001, Switzerland. TEL 41-21-3207381, FAX 41-21-3235444, http://www.elsevier.com/locate/snb. Ed. M Koudelka-Hep. **Subscr. to:** Elsevier BV, PO Box 211, Amsterdam 1000 AE, Netherlands. TEL 31-20-485-3757, FAX 31-20-485-3432, nlinfo-f@elsevier.nl, http://www.elsevier.nl.

➤ **SILICON CHEMISTRY**; an international journal devoted to all aspects of silicon science and technology. see *CHEMISTRY—Inorganic Chemistry*

➤ **STUDIES IN SURFACE SCIENCE AND CATALYSIS.** see *PHYSICS—Mechanics*

➤ **SURFACE ENGINEERING AND APPLIED ELECTROCHEMISTRY.** see *ENGINEERING—Mechanical Engineering*

541.37 IND ISSN 0036-0678
CODEN: TSETA6
TRANSACTIONS S A E S T. Text in English. 1966. q. INR 100, USD 25 to non-members (effective 2005). adv. bk.rev. bibl.; charts; illus. **Description:** Covering Research Papers, Invited lectures, Papers presented at conferences, Society News, Book Reviews, Symposium announcement etc.
Media: Duplicated (not offset).
Indexed: BrCerAb, C&ISA, CTE, CerAb, ChemAb, ChemTitl, CivEngAb, CorrAb, E&CAJ, EMA, EngInd, IAA, INIS AtomInd, Inspec, M&TEA, MBF, METADEX, SolStAb, WAA.
—BLDSC (9005.200000), CASDDS, CISTI, Ei, IE, ingenta, Linda Hall. **CCC.**
Published by: Society for Advancement of Electrochemical Science and Technology, Secretary, Central Electrochemical Research Institute Campus, Karaikudi, Tamil Nadu 623 006, India. TEL 91-4565-227550, FAX 91-4565-227713, saest@cscecri.ren.nic.in, saestindia@rediffmail.com, saestkkd@yahoo.com, http://www.cecri-india.com/html/Societies/saest.htm. Ed. Dr. V Yegnaraman. Circ: 1,800.

ZAIRYO TO KANKYO/CORROSION ENGINEERING. see *METALLURGY*

CHEMISTRY—Inorganic Chemistry

546 541.38 USA ISSN 0898-8838
QD151 CODEN: AICHEP
➤ **ADVANCES IN INORGANIC CHEMISTRY.** Text in English. 1959. irreg., latest vol.53, 2002. USD 154 per vol. vol.56 (effective 2004). index. reprint service avail. from ISI. **Document type:** *Monographic series, Academic/Scholarly.* **Description:** Presents comprehensive reviews of the current progress in all areas within inorganic chemistry ranging from bio-inorganic to solid state studies.
Formerly (until 1987): Advances in Inorganic Chemistry and Radiochemistry (0065-2792)
Related titles: Online - full text ed.: ISSN 1557-8917 (from ScienceDirect).
Indexed: ASCA, CCI, CIN, ChemAb, ChemInfo, ChemTitl, ISR, SCI.
—BLDSC (0709.197000), CASDDS, CISTI, IE, ingenta, Linda Hall. **CCC.**
Published by: Academic Press (Subsidiary of: Elsevier Science & Technology), 525 B St, Ste 1900, San Diego, CA 92101-4495. TEL 619-231-6616, 800-894-3434, apsubs@acad.com, http://www.academicpress.com. Ed. A G Sykes.

546 USA ISSN 1059-4256
QD181.S6 CODEN: ADSDEO
ADVANCES IN SILICON CHEMISTRY; a research annual. Text in English. irreg. ((vol.4 due 2003)), latest vol.3, 1996. price varies. **Document type:** *Monographic series, Academic/Scholarly.* **Description:** Covers new research in the field.
Indexed: CIN, ChemAb, ChemTitl.
—CASDDS. **CCC.**
Published by: J A I Press Inc. (Subsidiary of: Elsevier Science & Technology), 360 Park Ave S, New York, NY 10010-1710. TEL 212-989-5800, FAX 212-633-3990, usinfo-f@elsevier.com, http://www.elsevier.com. Ed. Gerald L Larson.

AGROW; world crop protection news. see *AGRICULTURE*

546 ISR ISSN 1565-3633
BIOINORGANIC CHEMISTRY AND APPLICATIONS. Text in English. 4/yr. USD 300 (effective 2006). **Document type:** *Academic/Scholarly.* **Description:** Publishes original research in the form of articles, notes, letters and reviews in the general field of bioinorganic chemistry and its applications. Its scope includes all aspects of bioinorganic chemistry, including bioorganometallic chemistry and applied bioinorganic chemistry.
Formerly (until 2003): Advances in Bioinorganic Chemistry
Indexed: CCI.
—BLDSC (2072.351000), IE.
Published by: Freund Publishing House, Ltd., P O Box 35010, Tel Aviv, 61350, Israel. TEL 972-3-5628540, FAX 972-3-5628538, h_freund@netvision.net.il, http://www.freundpublishing.com/Bioinorganic_Chemistry_Applications/bioedboard.htm. Ed. Dr. Nick Hadjiliadis.

CARBON. see *CHEMISTRY—Organic Chemistry*

546 549 USA ISSN 0731-1869
CARBON-GRAPHITE COMPOSITE MATERIAL STUDY. Text in English. 1978. a.
Published by: (United States. Office of Science and Technology Policy), U.S. National Aeronautics and Space Administration, 800 Independence Ave, S W, Washington, DC 20591. help@sti.nasa.gov, http://www.sti.nasa.gov.

CHEMICALS, CHEMICAL TECHNOLOGY & INSTRUMENTATION WORLD BUYERS' GUIDE; world buyers' guide for chemicals, bulk drugs, chemical equipment, analytical & process control instruments. see *CHEMISTRY—Analytical Chemistry*

546 USA ISSN 0260-3594
QD146 CODEN: COICDZ
➤ **COMMENTS ON INORGANIC CHEMISTRY.** Text in English. bi-m. GBP 907, USD 1,252 combined subscription institutions print & online eds. (effective 2006). bk.rev. reprint service avail. from PSC. **Document type:** *Journal, Academic/Scholarly.* **Description:** Intended as a vehicle for concisely and authoritatively written critical discussions of recent important developments in inorganic chemistry.
Related titles: Microform ed.; Online - full text ed.: ISSN 1548-9574. GBP 862, USD 1,189 to institutions (effective 2006) (from EBSCO Publishing, Gale Group, IngentaConnect, O C L C Online Computer Library Center, Inc., Swets Information Services).
Indexed: ASCA, CCI, ChemAb, CurCont.
—BLDSC (3336.028500), CISTI, IE, Infotrieve, ingenta. **CCC.**
Published by: Taylor & Francis Inc. (Subsidiary of: Taylor & Francis Group), 325 Chestnut St, Ste 800, Philadelphia, PA 19016. TEL 215-625-8900, 800-354-1420, FAX 215-625-8914, info@taylorandfrancis.com, http://www.tandf.co.uk/journals/titles/02603594.asp, http://www.taylorandfrancis.com. Ed. John P Fackler Jr. TEL 979-845-0648. **Subscr. outside N. America to:** Taylor & Francis Ltd, Journals Customer Service, Rankine Rd, Basingstoke, Hants RG24 8PR, United Kingdom. TEL 44-1256-813000, FAX 44-1256-330245, enquiry@tandf.co.uk.

546 CHN ISSN 0253-9837
QD505 CODEN: THHPD3
➤ **CUIHUA XUEBAO/JOURNAL OF CATALYSIS.** Text in Chinese; Summaries in English. 1980. bi-m. CNY 15 per issue (effective 2005). adv. **Document type:** *Academic/Scholarly.* **Description:** Covers heterogeneous and homogeneous catalysis, surface chemistry, catalytic kinetics, and biocatalysis. Occasionally presents special review articles.
Related titles: Online - full text ed.: (from East View Information Services, WanFang Data Corp.).
Indexed: ASFA, BrCerAb, C&ISA, CCI, CIN, CerAb, ChemAb, ChemTitl, CivEngAb, CorrAb, CurCont, E&CAJ, EMA, ESPM, EnvEAb, IAA, M&TEA, MBF, METADEX, PollutAb, RefZh, SWRA, SolStAb, WAA.
—BLDSC (3180.298500), CASDDS, CISTI, IE, ingenta, Linda Hall.
Published by: (Zhongguo Huaxuehui/Chinese Chemical Society, Zhongguo Kexueyuan, Dalian Huaxue Wuli Yanjiusuo/Chinese Academy of Sciences, Dalian Institute of Chemical Physics), Kexue Chubanshe/Science Press, 16 Donghuang Cheng Genbei Jie, Beijing, 100717, China. TEL 86-10-64000246, FAX 86-10-64030255, journal@cspg.net, http://www.sciencep.com/GB/content/2001-05/14/content_847.htm. Ed. Li-Wu Lin. Circ: 6,000.

546 GBR ISSN 1477-9226
QD146 CODEN: DTARAF
➤ **DALTON TRANSACTIONS**; an international journal of inorganic chemistry. Text in English. 1972. s-m. GBP 2,154, USD 3,942 combined subscription print & online eds. (effective 2006). adv. charts; illus. index. reprints avail. **Document type:** *Journal, Academic/Scholarly.* **Description:** Contains papers on all aspects of the chemistry of inorganic and organometallic compounds, including bio-inorganic and solid-state inorganic chemistry.
Former titles (until 2003): Journal of the Chemical Society. Dalton Transactions (1472-7773); (until 2001): Dalton (Cambridge) (1470-479X); Incorporates in part (in Jan. 2000): Acta Chemica Scandinavica (0904-213X); Which was formed by the 1989 merger of: Acta Chemica Scandinavica. Series A: Physical and Organic Chemistry (0904-6437); Acta Chemica Scandinavica. Series B: Organic Chemistry and Biochemistry (0904-6445); Which superseded in part (1947-1973): Acta Chemica Scandinavica (0001-5393); Dalton Transactions (0300-9246); Supersedes in part: Chemical Society, London. Journal. Section A: Inorganic, Physical and Theoretical Chemistry (0022-4944)
Related titles: Microform ed.: (from PQC); Online - full text ed.: ISSN 1364-5447. GBP 1,939, USD 3,548 (effective 2006) (from EBSCO Publishing, O C L C Online Computer Library Center, Inc., Swets Information Services).
Indexed: ABIPC, AS&TI, ASCA, ASFA, BiolAb, BrCerAb, BullT&T, CCI, CIN, Cadscan, ChemAb, ChemInfo, ChemTitl, CurCont, DBA, ESPM, ISR, IndChem, LeadAb, MSB, RCI, RefZh, SCI, Zincscan.
—BLDSC (3517.830000), CASDDS, CINDOC, CISTI, Ei, IDS, IE, ingenta, Linda Hall. **CCC.**
Published by: Royal Society of Chemistry, Thomas Graham House, Science Park, Milton Rd, Cambridge, CB4 0WF, United Kingdom. TEL 44-1223-432360, FAX 44-1223-423623, dalton@rsc.org, sales@rsc.org, http://www.rsc.org/dalton. Ed. Dr. Jamie Humphrey. **Subscr. to:** Portland Press Ltd., R S C Distribution Services, Commerce Way, Whitehall Industrial Estate, Colchester CO2 8HP, United Kingdom. TEL 44-1206-226050, FAX 44-1206-226055, sales@rscdistribution.org.

546 USA ISSN 0964-2463
DICTIONARY OF INORGANIC COMPOUNDS. SUPPLEMENT. Text in English. 1993. a. price varies.
Published by: C R C Press, LLC (Subsidiary of: Taylor & Francis Group), 2000 N W Corporate Blvd, Boca Raton, FL 33431. TEL 561-994-0555, FAX 561-989-9732, 800-374-3401, journals@crcpress.com, http://www.crcpress.com/.

546 DEU ISSN 1434-1948
QD146 CODEN: EJICFO
➤ **EUROPEAN JOURNAL OF INORGANIC CHEMISTRY.** Text in English. 1998. s-m. EUR 2,794 in Europe; CHF 4,878 in Switzerland & Liechtenstein; USD 3,738 elsewhere; EUR 3,074 combined subscription in Europe print & online eds.; CHF 5,366 combined subscription print & online eds. in Switzerland & Liechtenstein; USD 4,112 combined subscription elsewhere print & online eds. (effective 2006). adv. illus.; bibl. Index. 270 p./no. 2 cols./p.; reprints avail. **Document type:** *Journal, Academic/Scholarly.* **Description:** Publishes full papers, microreviews, and short communications from the entire spectrum of inorganic, bioinorganic, organometallic and solid state chemistry.
Formed by the merger of (1947-1998): Chemische Berichte (0009-2940); Part of (1907-1998): Societe Chimique de France. Bulletin (0037-8968); Which was formerly (until 1946): Bulletin de la Societe Chimique de France. Memoires (0366-3132); Part of (1945-1998): Societes Chimiques Belges. Bulletin (0037-9646); Part of (1871-1998): Gazzetta Chimica Italiana (0016-5603); Part of (1990-1998): Anales de Quimica (1130-2283); Part of (1905-1998): Revista Portuguesa de Quimica (0035-0419); Part of (1969-1998): Chimika Chronika (0366-693X); Part of (1951-1998): Acta Chimica Hungarica: Models in Chemistry (1217-8969); Part of (1882-1998): Recueil des Travaux Chimiques des Pays-Bas (0165-0513); Which was formerly (until 1920): Recueil des Travaux Chimiques des Pays-Bas et de la Belgique (0370-7539); (until 1897): Recueil des Travaux Chimiques des Pays-Bas (0034-186X)
Related titles: Online - full text ed.: ISSN 1099-0682. EUR 2,794 in Europe to institutions; CHF 4,878 to institutions in Switzerland & Liechtenstein; USD 3,738 elsewhere to institutions (effective 2006) (from EBSCO Publishing, Swets Information Services, Wiley InterScience).
Indexed: ASFA, CCI, CIN, ChemAb, ChemInfo, ChemTitl, CurCR, CurCont, EngInd, ISR, IndChem, Inspec, MEDLINE, MOS, MSB, NPU, RCI, RefZh, SCI.
—BLDSC (3829.730450), CASDDS, CINDOC, CISTI, GNLM, IDS, IE, Infotrieve, ingenta, Linda Hall. **CCC.**
Published by: Wiley - V C H Verlag GmbH & Co. KGaA (Subsidiary of: John Wiley & Sons, Inc.), Boschstr 12, Weinheim, 69469, Germany. TEL 49-6201-6060, FAX 49-6201-606328, ejic-ejoc@wiley-vch.de, subservice@wiley-vch.de, http://www.eurjic.org, http://www3.interscience.wiley.com/cgi-bin/home. Ed. Karen J Hindson. Pub. Eva E Wille. R&P Claudia Rutz. Adv. contact Aenne Anders TEL 49-6201-606552. B&W page EUR 2,100;

180 x 260. **Subscr. in the Americas to:** John Wiley & Sons, Inc., 111 River St, Hoboken, NJ 07030-5774. TEL 201-748-6645, FAX 201-748-6088, subinfo@wiley.com; **Subscr. outside of Germany and Austria to:** John Wiley & Sons Ltd., The Atrium, Southern Gate, Chichester, West Sussex PO19 8SQ, United Kingdom. TEL 44-1243-779777, FAX 44-1243-775878.

546 CHN ISSN 1001-1625
QE389.62 CODEN: GUTOE9
GUISUANYAN TONGBAO/CHINESE SILICATE SOCIETY. BULLETIN. Text in Chinese. bi-m. CNY 1 per issue.
Related titles: Online - full text ed.: (from East View Information Services).
Indexed: CIN, ChemAb, ChemTitl.
—CASDDS.
Published by: Tianjin Guisuanyan Xuehui/Tianjin Silicate Society, 26 Qudian Jie, Hongqiao-qu, Tianjin 300230, China. TEL 250852.

546 CHN ISSN 0454-5648
TP785 CODEN: KSYHA5
➤ **GUISUANYAN XUEBAO/CHINESE CERAMIC SOCIETY. JOURNAL.** Text in Chinese. 1957. bi-m. USD 60. adv. abstr. **Document type:** *Academic/Scholarly.* **Description:** Covers the latest development in research, production and design of cement, glass, ceramics, refractory, artificial crystal and nonmetal mine.
Related titles: Online - full text ed.: (from East View Information Services).
Indexed: A&ATA, BrCerAb, C&ISA, CIN, CerAb, ChemAb, ChemTitl, CivEngAb, CorrAb, E&CAJ, EMA, EngInd, IAA, Inspec, M&TEA, MBF, METADEX, MSB, RefZh, SolStAb, WAA.
—BLDSC (4729.240000), CASDDS, CISTI, IE, ingenta, Linda Hall.
Published by: Chinese Ceramic Society, Guojia Jiancaiju Nei, (Inside National Bureau of Bldg. Materials), Baiwanzhuang, Beijing, 100831, China. TEL 86-10-68352977, FAX 86-10-68342016, cersoc@public3.bta.net.cn, http://www.ceramsoc.com. Ed. Fuxi Gan. R&P, Adv. contact Keshun Shi. B&W page USD 300, color page USD 900; 210 x 260.

➤ **HANDBOOK OF BINARY PHASE DIAGRAMS.** see *ENGINEERING—Mechanical Engineering*

546 USA ISSN 1042-7163
QD399 CODEN: HETCE8
➤ **HETEROATOM CHEMISTRY.** Text in English. 1990. 7/yr. USD 1,475 domestic to institutions; USD 1,559 in Canada & Mexico to institutions; USD 1,608 elsewhere to institutions; USD 1,623 combined subscription domestic to institutions print & online eds.; USD 1,707 combined subscription in Canada & Mexico to institutions print & online eds.; USD 1,756 combined subscription elsewhere to institutions print & online eds. (effective 2006). adv. **Document type:** *Journal, Academic/Scholarly.*
Related titles: Online - full content ed.: ISSN 1098-1071. USD 1,475 to institutions (effective 2006); Online - full text ed.: (from EBSCO Publishing, Swets Information Services, Wiley InterScience).
Indexed: ASCA, CCI, CIN, ChemAb, ChemInfo, ChemTitl, CurCont, EngInd, ISR, RCI, RefZh, SCI.
—BLDSC (4301.230000), CASDDS, CISTI, Ei, IDS, IE, Infotrieve, ingenta. **CCC.**
Published by: John Wiley & Sons, Inc., 111 River St, Hoboken, NJ 07030-5774. TEL 201-748-6000, FAX 201-748-5915, uscs-wis@wiley.com, http://www3.interscience.wiley.com/cgi-bin/jhome/38027, http://www.wiley.com. Ed. Francois Mathey. adv.: B&W page GBP 640, color page GBP 1,515; trim 210 x 279. Circ: 855. **Subscr. outside the Americas to:** John Wiley & Sons Ltd., The Atrium, Southern Gate, Chichester, West Sussex PO19 8SQ, United Kingdom. TEL 44-1243-843335, 0800-243407, FAX 44-1243-843232, cs-journals@wiley.co.uk.

540 CHN ISSN 1008-1011
➤ **HUAXUE YANJIU/CHEMICAL RESEARCHES.** Text in Chinese; Summaries in English. 1987. q. CNY 20 domestic; USD 40 foreign; CNY 5 newsstand/cover domestic (effective 2000). abstr.; charts. back issues avail. **Document type:** *Academic/Scholarly.* **Description:** Contains research reports or brief reports, summaries and progress, introduction of new knowledge and technology, and exchange of research experience.
Related titles: CD-ROM ed.; E-mail ed.; Fax ed.; Online - full text ed.: (from East View Information Services, WanFang Data Corp.).
Indexed: RefZh.
—BLDSC (4335.491500).
Published by: Henan Daxue/Henan University, 85 Minglun Jie, Kaijeng, Henan 475001, China. TEL 86-378-286-6141, FAX 86-378-286-1029, hxyj@public2.zz.ha.cn, http://www.henu.edu.cn. Ed. Ni Jiazuan. Pub. Chen Bosen. Circ: 300 (paid); 1,200 (controlled).

▼ ➤ **HYDROGEN.** see *ENERGY*

546 CZE
I I C. BULLETIN. (Institute of Inorganic Chemistry) Text in Czech. a. **Document type:** *Academic/Scholarly.* **Description:** Covers research at the institute.
Published by: Akademie Ved Ceske Republiky, Ustav Anorganicke Chemie/Czech Academy of Sciences, Institute of Inorganic Chemistry, Rez U Prahy, 250 68, Czech Republic. TEL 42-2-24311458, FAX 42-2-24311881, bludska@iic.cas.cz, http://www.lib.cas.cz/knav/journals/eng/IIC_Bulletin.htm. Ed. Jana Bludska.

546 USA ISSN 0020-1669
QD1 CODEN: INOCAJ
➤ **INORGANIC CHEMISTRY.** Text in English. 1962. bi-w. USD 2,812 in North America to institutions; USD 3,002 elsewhere to institutions; USD 316 in North America to members; USD 506 elsewhere to members; USD 237 in North America to students; USD 427 elsewhere to students (effective 2006). adv. bk.rev. illus. index. back issues avail.; reprints avail. **Document type:** *Journal, Academic/Scholarly.* **Description:** Publishes fundamental studies, both experimental and theoretical, in all phases of inorganic chemistry.
Related titles: Microfiche ed.: USD 2,021 in North America to institutions; USD 2,060 elsewhere to institutions (effective 2002); Microfilm ed.: USD 2,021 in North America to institutions; USD 2,076 elsewhere to institutions (effective 2002); Online - full text ed.: ISSN 1520-510X. USD 85 (effective 2006) (from EBSCO Publishing, Swets Information Services).
Indexed: ASCA, ASFA, BPRC&P, BrCerAb, BullT&T, CCI, CIN, Cadscan, ChemAb, ChemInfo, ChemTitl, CurCont, EngInd, ExcerpMed, GSI, INIS AtomInd, ISR, IndChem, IndMed, LeadAb, MEDLINE, MSB, MSCI, RCI, RefZh, S&F, SCI, Zincscan.
—BLDSC (4515.870000), CASDDS, CINDOC, CISTI, Ei, IDS, IE, Infotrieve, ingenta, Linda Hall. **CCC.**
Published by: American Chemical Society, 1155 16th St, N W, Washington, DC 20036. TEL 202-872-4614, 800-227-5558, FAX 202-776-8264, inorg@chem.rochester.edu, service@acs.org, http://pubs.acs.org/ic. Eds. Arlene Bristol, Richard Eisenberg. adv.: color page USD 4,550. Circ: 4,000 (paid). **Subscr. to:** Member & Subscriber Services, PO Box 3337, Columbus, OH 43210. TEL 614-447-3776, 800-333-9511.

546 NLD ISSN 1387-7003
QD146 CODEN: ICCOFP
➤ **INORGANIC CHEMISTRY COMMUNICATIONS.** Text in English. 1998. 12/yr. EUR 555 in Europe to institutions; JPY 73,600 in Japan to institutions; USD 620 elsewhere to institutions; EUR 135 in Europe to qualified personnel; JPY 18,000 in Japan to qualified personnel; USD 152 elsewhere to qualified personnel (effective 2006). back issues avail. **Document type:** *Journal, Academic/Scholarly.* **Description:** Dedicated to the rapid publication of short communications and preliminary notes in the major areas of inorganic and organometallic chemistry.
Related titles: Online - full text ed.: (from EBSCO Publishing, Gale Group, IngentaConnect, ScienceDirect, Swets Information Services).
Indexed: CCI, ChemAb, CurCR, CurCont, ISR, IndChem, Inspec, MSB, RCI, RefZh, SCI.
—BLDSC (4515.870500), CASDDS, CINDOC, CISTI, IDS, IE, Infotrieve, ingenta. **CCC.**
Published by: Elsevier BV (Subsidiary of: Elsevier Science & Technology), Radarweg 29, Amsterdam, 1043 NX, Netherlands. TEL 31-20-4853911, FAX 31-20-4852457, nlinfo-f@elsevier.nl, http://www.elsevier.com/locate/inoche, http://www.elsevier.nl. Eds. B.-S. Kang, T. E. Bitterwolf, U. Belluco.

546 660 RUS ISSN 0020-1685
TN4 CODEN: INOMAF
➤ **INORGANIC MATERIALS.** Text in English. 1965. m. (Plus one supplement.). EUR 3,948, USD 3,748, GBP 2,398 combined subscription to institutions print & online eds. (effective 2005). charts; illus. index. back issues avail. **Document type:** *Journal, Academic/Scholarly.* **Description:** Examines the composition, structure, disparity, and properties of inorganic substances.
Related titles: Microfilm ed.: (from PQC); Online - full text ed.: ISSN 1608-3172 (from EBSCO Publishing, Gale Group, IngentaConnect, Kluwer Online, O C L C Online Computer Library Center, Inc., Springer LINK, Swets Information Services); ♦ Translation of: Neorganicheskie Materialy. ISSN 0869-5784.
Indexed: BibLing, BrCerAb, C&ISA, CCI, CIN, Cadscan, CerAb, ChemAb, ChemTitl, CivEngAb, CorrAb, CurCont, E&CAJ, EMA, EnerRA, EngInd, IAA, ISR, Inspec, LeadAb, M&TEA, MBF, METADEX, MSB, MSCI, SolStAb, WAA, Zincscan.
—BLDSC (0412.620000), AskIEEE, CASDDS, CISTI, Ei, IDS, IE, Infotrieve, ingenta, Linda Hall. **CCC.**
Published by: (Rossiiskaya Akademiya Nauk/Russian Academy of Sciences), M A I K Nauka - Interperiodica, Profsoyuznaya ul 90, Moscow, 117997, Russian Federation. TEL 7-095-3347420, FAX 7-095-3360666, compmg@maik.ru, http://www.maik.rssi.ru/journals/inorgmat.htm, http://www.maik.ru. Ed. G G Devyatykh. **Subscr. to:** Springer-Verlag Dordrecht, Journals Department, PO Box 322, Dordrecht, Netherlands. TEL 31-78-6576392, FAX 31-78-6576474.

➤ **INORGANIC REACTION MECHANISMS.** see *CHEMISTRY—Physical Chemistry*

546 NLD ISSN 0020-1693
QD146 CODEN: ICHAA3
➤ **INORGANICA CHIMICA ACTA.** Text in English. 1967. 15/yr. EUR 8,121 in Europe to institutions; JPY 1,078,600 in Japan to institutions; USD 9,086 to institutions except Europe and Japan; EUR 431 in Europe to qualified personnel; JPY 56,700 in Japan to qualified personnel; USD 484 to qualified personnel except Europe and Japan (effective 2006). adv. bk.rev. bibl.; stat.; illus. index. reprints avail. **Document type:** *Journal, Academic/Scholarly.* **Description:** Covers various aspects of inorganic chemistry. For inorganic chemists and organometallic chemists.
Incorporates: Chimica Acta Reviews (0073-8085)
Related titles: Microform ed.: (from PQC); Online - full text ed.: (from EBSCO Publishing, Gale Group, IngentaConnect, ScienceDirect, Swets Information Services).
Indexed: AESIS, ASCA, AcoustA, BPRC&P, CCI, CIN, ChemAb, ChemInfo, ChemTitl, CurCont, ExcerpMed, ISR, IndChem, MSB, MSCI, RCI, RefZh, S&F, SCI.
—BLDSC (4515.910000), CASDDS, CINDOC, CISTI, Ei, IDS, IE, Infotrieve, ingenta, Linda Hall. **CCC.**
Published by: Elsevier BV (Subsidiary of: Elsevier Science & Technology), Radarweg 29, Amsterdam, 1043 NX, Netherlands. TEL 31-20-4853911, FAX 31-20-4852457, nlinfo-f@elsevier.nl, http://www.elsevier.com/locate/ica, http://www.elsevier.nl. Eds. R J Puddephat, U. Belluco.

➤ **INSTITUTO NACIONAL DEL CARBON. MEMORIA.** see *CHEMISTRY—Organic Chemistry*

➤ **INTERNATIONAL FIBER JOURNAL.** see *TEXTILE INDUSTRIES AND FABRICS*

546 UKR ISSN 0234-4483
QD189 CODEN: IRTEEE
IONNYE RASPLAVY I TVERDYE ELEKTROLITY; respublikanskii mezhvedomstvennyi sbornik nauchnykh trudov. Text in Ukrainian. 1985. a.
Indexed: CIN, ChemAb, ChemTitl.
—CASDDS, Linda Hall.
Published by: (Institut Obshchei i Neorganicheskoi Khimii), Natsional'na Akademiya Nauk Ukrainy, vul Volodymyrs'ka 54, Kyiv, 01601, Ukraine. TEL 380-44-2352239, FAX 380-44-2343243, prez@nas.gov.ua, http://www.nas.gov.ua. **Dist. by:** M K - Periodica, ul Gilyarovskogo 39, Moscow 129110, Russian Federation. TEL 7-095-2845008, FAX 7-095-2813798, info@periodicals.ru, http://www.mkniga.ru.

ISSLEDOVANIYA V OBLASTI KHIMII REDKOZEMEL'NYKH ELEMENTOV. see *EARTH SCIENCES*

546 DEU ISSN 0949-8257
QP531 CODEN: JBCFA
➤ **JOURNAL OF BIOLOGICAL INORGANIC CHEMISTRY.** Abbreviated title: J B I C. Text in English. 1996. 8/yr. EUR 808 combined subscription to institutions print & online eds. (effective 2005). adv. back issues avail. **Document type:** *Journal, Academic/Scholarly.* **Description:** Covers aspects of chemistry related to biological systems, including enzyme catalysis transport and toxicity, synthetic chemistry, and analytical methods.
Related titles: Online - full text ed.: ISSN 1432-1327 (from EBSCO Publishing, Springer LINK, Swets Information Services).
Indexed: BBCI, BiolAb, CIN, CPA, ChemAb, ChemTitl, CurCont, DSA, ExcerpMed, FCA, ForAb, HortAb, ISR, IndMed, IndVet, Inpharma, MEDLINE, MSB, NutrAb, ProtozoAb, RPP, Reac, RefZh, S&F, SCI, VetBull, WeedAb.
—BLDSC (4663.436500), CASDDS, CISTI, IDS, IE, Infotrieve, ingenta. **CCC.**
Published by: (Society of Biological Inorganic Chemistry), Springer-Verlag (Subsidiary of: Springer Science+Business Media), Tiergartenstr 17, Heidelberg, 69121, Germany. TEL 49-6221-3450, FAX 49-6221-345229, http://link.springer.de/link/service/journals/00775/index.htm. Ed. Lawrence Que TEL 612-626-9405. Adv. contact Stephan Kroeck TEL 49-30-827875739. **Subscr. in the Americas to:** Springer-Verlag New York, Inc., Journal Fulfillment, PO Box 2485, Secaucus, NJ 07096-2485. TEL 800-777-4643, 201-348-4033, FAX 201-348-4505, journals@springer-ny.com, http://www.springer-ny.com; **Subscr. to:** Springer GmbH Auslieferungsgesellschaft, Haberstr 7, Heidelberg 69126, Germany. TEL 49-6221-345-0, FAX 49-6221-345-4229, subscriptions@springer.de.

546 549.125 USA ISSN 1053-0509
QC477 CODEN: JOFLEN
➤ **JOURNAL OF FLUORESCENCE.** Text in English. 1991. bi-m. EUR 758, USD 778, GBP 428 combined subscription to institutions print & online eds. (effective 2005). adv. back issues avail.; reprint service avail. from PSC. **Document type:** *Journal, Academic/Scholarly.* **Description:** Addresses the latest issues in fluourescence spectroscopy, highlighting its rapid growth owing to new light-generation and -detection technologies and the development of modern instrumentation for time-resolved and imaging applications.
Related titles: Online - full text ed.: ISSN 1573-4994 (from EBSCO Publishing, Gale Group, IngentaConnect, Kluwer Online, O C L C Online Computer Library Center, Inc., Springer LINK, Swets Information Services).
Indexed: B&BAb, BibLing, CCI, CIN, ChemAb, ChemTitl, CurCont, EngInd, ISR, Inspec, SCI.

C

—BLDSC (4984.525000), CASDDS, CISTI, Ei, IE, Infotrieve, ingenta, Linda Hall. **CCC.**
Published by: Plenum US (Subsidiary of: Springer Science+Business Media), 233 Spring St, New York, NY 10013. TEL 212-460-1500, FAX 212-460-1575, service@springer-ny.com, http://springerlink.metapress.com/openurl.asp?genre=journal&issn=1053-0509, http://www.springeronline.com. Ed. Chris D Geddes.

546 661 CHE ISSN 0022-1139
QD181.F1 CODEN: JFLCAR
➤ **JOURNAL OF FLUORINE CHEMISTRY.** Text in English, French, German. 1971. 12/yr. EUR 3,762 in Europe to institutions; JPY 499,900 in Japan to institutions; USD 4,207 to institutions except Europe and Japan; EUR 189 in Europe to qualified personnel; JPY 24,900 in Japan to qualified personnel; USD 212 to qualified personnel except Europe and Japan (effective 2006). adv. bk.rev. back issues avail. **Document type:** *Journal, Academic/Scholarly.* **Description:** Contains research data on the chemistry of fluorine and of compounds where halogen is a dominant element. Deals with the fundamental and industrial aspects of fluorine and its components. Serves both pure and applied research in this field.
Related titles: Microform ed.: (from PQC); Online - full text ed.: (from EBSCO Publishing, Gale Group, IngentaConnect, ScienceDirect, Swets Information Services).
Indexed: ASCA, CCI, CIN, ChemAb, ChemInfo, ChemTitl, CurCR, CurCont, EngInd, ISR, IndChem, LHB, MOS, MSB, MSCI, PhysBer, RCI, RefZh, SCI.
—BLDSC (4984.530000), CASDDS, CISTI, Ei, IDS, IE, Infotrieve, ingenta, Linda Hall. **CCC.**
Published by: Elsevier S.A., PO Box 564, Lausanne 1, 1001, Switzerland. TEL 41-21-3207381, FAX 41-21-3235444, http://www.elsevier.com/locate/fluor. Eds. B. Smart, John M. Winfield, T. Nakajima. **Subscr. to:** Elsevier BV, PO Box 211, Amsterdam 1000 AE, Netherlands. TEL 31-20-485-3757, FAX 31-20-485-3432, nlinfo-f@elsevier.nl, http://www.elsevier.nl.

➤ **JOURNAL OF INORGANIC AND ORGANOMETALLIC POLYMERS.** see *CHEMISTRY—Organic Chemistry*

➤ **JOURNAL OF INORGANIC BIOCHEMISTRY.** see *BIOLOGY—Biochemistry*

➤ **JOURNAL OF SYNTHETIC METHODS.** see *CHEMISTRY*

➤ **M I R L REPORTS.** (Mineral Industry Research Laboratory) see *MINES AND MINING INDUSTRY*

➤ **MACROMOLECULAR THEORY AND SIMULATIONS.** see *CHEMISTRY—Organic Chemistry*

546 USA ISSN 0161-5149
QP532 CODEN: MIBSCD
➤ **METAL IONS IN BIOLOGICAL SYSTEMS.** Text in English. 1974. irreg., latest vol.40, 2004. USD 250 per vol. (effective 2004). adv. **Document type:** *Monographic series, Academic/Scholarly.*
Indexed: ASCA, Agr, BBCI, BIOSIS Prev, CCI, CIN, ChemAb, ChemTitl, ISR, IndMed, MEDLINE, SCI, ZooRec.
—BLDSC (5687.100000), CASDDS, CISTI, IDS, IE, Infotrieve, ingenta, KNAW. **CCC.**
Published by: Marcel Dekker Inc. (Subsidiary of: Taylor & Francis Group), 270 Madison Ave, New York, NY 10016-0602. TEL 212-696-9000, FAX 212-685-4540, journals@dekker.com, http://www.dekker.com. Ed. Helmut Sigel. R&P Julia Mulligan. Adv. contact Eridania Perez. **Subscr. to:** 6000 Broken Sound Pkwy NW, Ste. 300, Boca Raton, FL 33487-2713. TEL 800-228-1160.

546 USA ISSN 0891-4540
➤ **MODERN INORGANIC CHEMISTRY.** Text in English. irreg., latest 2002. price varies. back issues avail. **Document type:** *Monographic series, Academic/Scholarly.*
Indexed: Inspec.
—CCC.
Published by: Springer-Verlag New York, Inc. (Subsidiary of: Springer Science+Business Media), 233 Spring St, New York, NY 10013. TEL 212-460-1500, FAX 212-460-1575, service@springer-ny.com, http://www.springer-ny.com.

➤ **MOLTEN SALT FORUM.** see *ENGINEERING—Chemical Engineering*

➤ **NEWSLETTER GOLD, SILVER AND URANIUM FROM SEAS AND OCEANS PROGRESS UPDATE.** see *ENGINEERING—Chemical Engineering*

➤ **NH3 NEWS.** see *HEATING, PLUMBING AND REFRIGERATION*

546.536 JPN ISSN 0388-0664
CODEN: NTRED4
NIPPON TUNGSTEN REVIEW. Text in English. 1968. a., latest vol.35, 2001. free. **Document type:** *Bulletin, Trade.*
Indexed: BrCerAb, C&ISA, CIN, CerAb, ChemAb, ChemTitl, CivEngAb, CorrAb, E&CAJ, EMA, IAA, M&TEA, MBF, METADEX, RefZh, SolStAb, WAA.
—BLDSC (6113.563000), CASDDS, IE, ingenta, Linda Hall. **CCC.**
Published by: Nippon Tungsten Co. Ltd., NT Bldg, 2-8 Minoshima 1-chome, Hakata-ku, Fukuoka-shi, 812-0017, Japan. TEL 81-942-817710, FAX 81-942-817713, http://www.nittan.co.jp/. Ed. T Koumura.

546 USA
NOMENCLATURE SERIES. Variant title: I U P A C Nomenclature Series. Text in English. irreg., latest 1990. **Document type:** *Monographic series.*
Published by: (International Union of Pure and Applied Chemistry), C R C Press, LLC (Subsidiary of: Taylor & Francis Group), 2000 N W Corporate Blvd, Boca Raton, FL 33431. TEL 800-272-7737, journals@crcpress.com, http://www.crcpress.com/.

546 JPN ISSN 0917-9976
CODEN: PLETEJ
PHOSPHORUS LETTER. Text in Japanese. 1986. s-a. JPY 10,000 (effective 2005). **Document type:** *Journal, Academic/Scholarly.*
—BLDSC (6465.311000). **CCC.**
Published by: Nihon Muki Rin Kagakkai/Japanese Association of Inorganic Phosphorus Chemistry, c/o Sakurai Makoto, Chubu University, Department of Applied Chemistry, Matsumoto-cho 1200, Kasugai, 487-8501, Japan. TEL 81-568-511111, FAX 81-568-514545, watanabe@isc.chubu.ac.jp. Ed. Mitsutomo Tsuhako. R&P Makoto Watanabe TEL 81-568-51-2188.

546.7 USA ISSN 1042-6507
QD181.S1 CODEN: PSSLEC
➤ **PHOSPHORUS, SULFUR AND SILICON AND THE RELATED ELEMENTS.** Text in English. 1976. m. GBP 7,533, USD 9,828 combined subscription to institutions print & online eds. (effective 2006). adv. bk.rev. index. back issues avail.; reprint service avail. from PSC. **Document type:** *Journal, Academic/Scholarly.* **Description:** Covers the organic, inorganic and biochemistry of phosphorus (including arsenic, antimony and bismuth), sulfur (including selenium, tellurium), and silicon (including germanium, tin).
Formerly: Phosphorous and Sulfur and the Related Elements (0308-664X); Formed by the merger of: International Journal of Sulfur Chemistry. Part A. Original Articles, Notes and Communications (0094-9337); International Journal of Sulfur Chemistry. Part B. Quarterly Reports (0094-9345); International Journal of Sulfur Chemistry. Part C. Mechanisms of Reactions of Sulfur Compound (0094-9353); Which was formerly: International Journal of Sulfur Chemistry (0047-0775)
Related titles: CD-ROM ed.: ISSN 1026-7719. 1995; Microform ed.; Online - full text ed.: ISSN 1563-5325. GBP 7,156, USD 9,337 to institutions (effective 2006) (from EBSCO Publishing, Gale Group, IngentaConnect, O C L C Online Computer Library Center, Inc., Swets Information Services).
Indexed: ASCA, BiolAb, CCI, Cadscan, ChemAb, CurCR, CurCont, EngInd, ISR, IndChem, Inspec, LeadAb, MOS, MSB, MSCI, NPU, RCI, RefZh, S&F, SCI, Zincscan.
—BLDSC (6465.312000), CISTI, Ei, IE, Infotrieve, ingenta, Linda Hall. **CCC.**
Published by: Taylor & Francis Inc. (Subsidiary of: Taylor & Francis Group), 325 Chestnut St, Ste 800, Philadelphia, PA 19016. TEL 215-625-8900, 800-354-1420, FAX 215-625-8914, info@taylorandfrancis.com, http://www.tandf.co.uk/journals/titles/10426507.asp, http://www.taylorandfrancis.com. Ed. Robert R Holmes. **Subsc. outside N. America:** Taylor & Francis Ltd, Journals Customer Service, Rankine Rd, Basingstoke, Hants RG24 8PR, United Kingdom. TEL 44-1256-813000, FAX 44-1256-330245, enquiry@tandf.co.uk.

546 NLD ISSN 0277-5387
QD1 CODEN: PLYHDE
➤ **POLYHEDRON.** Text in English. 1982. 18/yr. EUR 6,631 in Europe to institutions; JPY 880,600 in Japan to institutions; USD 7,419 to institutions except Europe and Japan; EUR 309 in Europe to qualified personnel; JPY 41,100 in Japan to qualified personnel; USD 346 to qualified personnel except Europe and Japan (effective 2006). illus. Index. reprints avail. **Document type:** *Journal, Academic/Scholarly.* **Description:** Publishes original, fundamental, experimental and theoretical research in major areas of inorganic and organometallic chemistry, as well as review articles and collections of research papers on selected topics.
Incorporated: Journal of Inorganic and Nuclear Chemistry (0022-1902); Inorganic and Nuclear Chemistry Letters (0020-1650)
Related titles: Microfiche ed.: (from MIM); Microfilm ed.: (from PQC); Online - full text ed.: (from EBSCO Publishing, Gale Group, IngentaConnect, ScienceDirect, Swets Information Services).
Indexed: ASCA, BiolAb, BullT&T, CCI, CIN, Cadscan, ChemAb, ChemTitl, CurCR, CurCont, EngInd, ISR, IndChem, Inspec, LeadAb, MSB, MSCI, RCI, RefZh, SCI, Zincscan.
—BLDSC (6547.690000), CASDDS, CINDOC, CISTI, Ei, IDS, IE, Infotrieve, ingenta, Linda Hall. **CCC.**
Published by: Elsevier BV (Subsidiary of: Elsevier Science & Technology), Radarweg 29, Amsterdam, 1043 NX, Netherlands. TEL 31-20-4853911, FAX 31-20-4852457, http://www.elsevier.com/locate/poly, http://www.elsevier.nl.

546 USA ISSN 8756-0127
QC482.D5
POWDER DIFFRACTION FILE ALPHABETIC INDEX. INORGANIC PHASE. Text in English. 1980. a. USD 375 per issue; USD 375 per issue to institutions (effective 2004).
—CISTI.
Published by: International Centre for Diffraction Data, 12 Campus Blvd, Newton Square, PA 19073-3273. TEL 610-325-9814, FAX 610-325-9823, info@icdd.com, http://www.icdd.com.

POWDER DIFFRACTION FILE. HANAWALT SEARCH MANUAL. INORGANIC PHASES. see *CHEMISTRY—Analytical Chemistry*

POWDER DIFFRACTION FILE SEARCH MANUAL. ALPHABETICAL LISTING. INORGANIC. see *CHEMISTRY—Analytical Chemistry*

PREVISIONS GLISSANTES DETAILLEES EN PERSPECTIVES SECTORIELLES (VOL.20): CHIMIE MINERALE. see *BUSINESS AND ECONOMICS—Economic Situation And Conditions*

546 JPN
PROCEEDINGS OF SYMPOSIUM ON HETEROATOM CHEMISTRY/HETERO GENSHI KAGAKU TORONKAI KOEN YOSHISHU. Text in Japanese; Summaries in English. a. **Document type:** *Proceedings.*
Published by: Chemical Society of Japan/Nippon Kagakukai, 1-5, Kanda-Surugadai 1-Chome, Chiyoda-ku, Tokyo, 101-0062, Japan.

546 USA ISSN 0079-6379
QD151 CODEN: PIOCAR
➤ **PROGRESS IN INORGANIC CHEMISTRY.** Text in English. 1959. irreg., latest vol.52, 2004. price varies. **Document type:** *Monographic series, Academic/Scholarly.*
Indexed: ASCA, CCI, ChemAb, ChemTitl, ISR, RCI, SCI.
—BLDSC (6868.600000), CASDDS, CISTI, IE, Infotrieve, ingenta, Linda Hall.
Published by: John Wiley & Sons, Inc., 111 River St, Hoboken, NJ 07030-5774. TEL 201-748-6000, 800-825-7550, FAX 201-748-5915, uscs-wis@wiley.com, http://www.wiley.com.

546 IND
RECENT RESEARCH DEVELOPMENTS IN INORGANIC CHEMISTRY. Text in English. a., latest vol.3, 2001.
Published by: Transworld Research Network, T C 36-248 (1), Trivandrum, Kerala 695 008, India. http://www.transworldresearch.com.

REFERATIVNYI ZHURNAL. NEORGANICHESKAYA KHIMIYA. KOMPLEKSNYE SOEDINENIYA. RADIOKHIMIYA. see *CHEMISTRY—Abstracting, Bibliographies, Statistics*

REFERATIVNYI ZHURNAL. TEKHNOLOGIYA NEORGANICHESKIKH VESHCHESTV I MATERIALOV. see *CHEMISTRY—Abstracting, Bibliographies, Statistics*

546 ISR ISSN 0193-4929
CODEN: RICHD7
➤ **REVIEWS IN INORGANIC CHEMISTRY.** Text in English. q., latest vol.22. USD 390 (effective 2006). adv. bk.rev. index. back issues avail. **Document type:** *Academic/Scholarly.* **Description:** Presents review articles on developments in the various fields of inorganic and organometallic compounds: synthesis, crystal structure, coordination chemistry, solution behavior, thermochemistry, etc.
Indexed: ASCA, CCI, CIN, ChemAb, ChemTitl, CurCont, RCI.
—BLDSC (7790.796000), CASDDS, CISTI, IE, Infotrieve, ingenta, Linda Hall.
Published by: Freund Publishing House, Ltd., P O Box 35010, Tel Aviv, 61350, Israel. TEL 972-3-5628540, FAX 972-3-5628538, h_freund@netvision.net.il, http://www.freundpublishing.com/Reviews_Inorganic_Chemistry/InorgPrev.htm. Ed. M Zangen.

541 546 GBR ISSN 0260-1818
QD1 CODEN: APCCDO
ROYAL SOCIETY OF CHEMISTRY. ANNUAL REPORTS ON THE PROGRESS OF CHEMISTRY. SECTION A: INORGANIC CHEMISTRY. Text in English. 1904. a. GBP 230, USD 378 combined subscription print & online eds. (effective 2006). **Document type:** *Academic/Scholarly.* **Description:** Provides critical coverage of the significant advances in inorganic chemistry for the general reader.
Supersedes: Chemical Society. Annual Reports on the Progress of Chemistry. Section A: Physical and Inorganic Chemistry (0308-6003); Which was formerly: Chemical Society, London. Annual Reports on the Progress of Chemistry. Section A: General, Physical and Inorganic Chemistry (0069-3022)
Related titles: Online - full text ed.: ISSN 1460-4760. GBP 207, USD 378 (effective 2006) (from EBSCO Publishing, O C L C Online Computer Library Center, Inc., Swets Information Services).
Indexed: CIN, ChemAb, ChemTitl, RefZh.
—BLDSC (1513.807000), CASDDS, CINDOC, CISTI, IE, Infotrieve, Linda Hall. **CCC.**

C

Published by: Royal Society of Chemistry, Thomas Graham House, Science Park, Milton Rd, Cambridge, CB4 0WF, United Kingdom. TEL 44-1223-432360, FAX 44-1223-423623, sales@rsc.org, advertising@rsc.org, http://www.rsc.org/Publishing/Journals/ic/. Ed. Dr. Robert D Eagling. Circ: 2,000. **Subscr. to:** Portland Press Ltd., R S C Distribution Services, Commerce Way, Whitehall Industrial Estate, Colchester CO2 8HP, United Kingdom. TEL 44-1206-226050, FAX 44-1206-226055, sales@rscdistribution.org.

546 RUS ISSN 0036-0236
QD1 CODEN: RJICAQ
RUSSIAN JOURNAL OF INORGANIC CHEMISTRY. Text in English. 1956. m. USD 4,348 in North America; USD 5,000 elsewhere (effective 2004). bk.rev. bibl.; charts. index.
Document type: *Journal, Academic/Scholarly.* **Description:** Covers the following topics of research; the synthesis and properties of inorganic compounds, coordination compounds, high-temperature semiconductors, physiochemical analysis of inorganic systems, theoretical inorganic chemistry, physical methods of investigation, and physical chemistry of solutions.
Related titles: Microform ed.: (from PMC); ♦ Russian ed.: Zhurnal Neorganicheskoi Khimii. ISSN 0044-457X; ♦ Translation of: Zhurnal Neorganicheskoi Khimii. ISSN 0044-457X.
Indexed: CCI, CurCont, EngInd, ExcerpMed, ISR, Inspec, MSB, RCI, S&F, SCI.
—BLDSC (0420.761000), AskIEEE, CISTI, IE, Infotrieve, ingenta, Linda Hall.
Published by: M A I K Nauka - Interperiodica, Profsoyuznaya ul 90, Moscow, 117997, Russian Federation. TEL 7-095-3347420, FAX 7-095-3360666, compmg@maik.ru, http://www.maik.rssi.ru/journals/inrgchem.htm, http://www.maik.ru. Ed. Nikolai Kuznetsov. R&P Vladimir I Vasil'ev. **Subscr. to:** Interperiodica, PO Box 1831, Birmingham, AL 35201-1831. TEL 205-995-1567, 800-633-4931, FAX 205-995-1588.

546 NLD ISSN 1569-0660
CODEN: SCIHB4
➤ **SILICON CHEMISTRY**; an international journal devoted to all aspects of silicon science and technology. Text in English. 2002. bi-m. EUR 273, USD 273, GBP 180 combined subscription to institutions print & online eds. (effective 2005). adv. reprint service avail. from PSC. **Document type:** *Journal, Academic/Scholarly.* **Description:** Publishes original research on all aspects of science and engineering, where silicon plays a significant part. Includes research incorporating the element of silicon in the following subject areas: synthetic chemistry, organic and inorganic.
Related titles: Online - full text ed.: ISSN 1572-8994 (from EBSCO Publishing, Gale Group, IngentaConnect, Kluwer Online, O C L C Online Computer Library Center, Inc., Springer LINK, Swets Information Services).
Indexed: BibLing, ChemAb.
—BLDSC (8279.140000), IE, Infotrieve, ingenta. **CCC.**
Published by: Springer-Verlag Dordrecht (Subsidiary of: Springer Science+Business Media), Van Godewijckstraat 30, Dordrecht, 3311 GX, Netherlands. TEL 31-78-6576050, FAX 31-78-6576474, http://springerlink.metapress.com/openurl.asp?genre=journal&issn=1569-0660, http://www.springeronline.com. Ed. Janis Matisons.

666 669 ITA ISSN 1124-4003
TS700 CODEN: NCIPD9
SMALTO PORCELLANATO; tecnologia e mercati. Text in Italian; Summaries in English, Spanish. 1964. 3/yr. free. adv. bk.rev. charts; illus.; stat. cum.index every 3 yrs. back issues avail.
Document type: *Journal, Academic/Scholarly.* **Description:** Covers the field of enamelling, includes research, experiments and the new initiatives taken in this field.
Formerly (until 1994): Smalto (1124-4011); Supersedes (1964-1987): Notiziario Informativo (0392-6648)
Related titles: Online - full text ed.
Indexed: BrCerAb, C&ISA, CIN, CerAb, ChemAb, ChemTitl, CivEngAb, CorrAb, E&CAJ, EMA, IAA, M&TEA, MBF, METADEX, SolStAb, WAA.
—BLDSC (8310.190530), CASDDS.
Published by: Centro Italiano Smalti Porcellanati, Via Olona, 41, Pero, MI 20016, Italy. TEL 39-02-38103333, FAX 39-02-38103288, cispedit@libero.it, http://www.cisp.it. Ed. Silvano Pagliuca. R&P Francesca Perna. Adv. contact Mariella Dell'Anna. B&W page EUR 375, color page EUR 645; 22 x 29.7. Circ: 2,500.

546 FRA ISSN 1293-2558
QD478 CODEN: SSSCFJ
➤ **SOLID STATE SCIENCES.** Text in English. 1964. 12/yr. EUR 884 in Europe to institutions; JPY 117,500 in Japan to institutions; USD 988 to institutions except Europe and Japan (effective 2006). **Document type:** *Academic/Scholarly.*
Description: Covers all areas of solid-state and inorganic chemistry.
Incorporates (1999-2002): International Journal of Inorganic Materials (1466-6049); Which was formerly: Journal of Inorganic Materials (1463-0176); Former titles (until 1999): European Journal of Solid State and Inorganic Chemistry (0992-4361); (until 1988): Revue de Chimie Minerale / Inorganic Chemistry Review / Revue fuer Anorganische Chemie (0035-1032)
Related titles: Microform ed.: (from PQC); Online - full text ed.: (from EBSCO Publishing, Gale Group, IngentaConnect, ScienceDirect, Swets Information Services).
Indexed: ASCA, BrCerAb, C&ISA, CCI, CIN, Cadscan, CerAb, ChemAb, ChemInfo, ChemTitl, CorrAb, CurCont, E&CAJ, EMA, EngInd, IAA, INIS AtomInd, ISR, Inspec, LeadAb, M&TEA, MBF, METADEX, MSCI, RCI, RefZh, SCI, SolStAb, WAA, Zincscan.
—BLDSC (8327.476000), AskIEEE, CASDDS, CISTI, Ei, IDS, IE, Infotrieve, ingenta, Linda Hall. **CCC.**
Published by: Elsevier France, Editions Scientifiques et Medicales (Subsidiary of: Elsevier Science & Technology), 23 Rue Linois, Paris, 75724, France. TEL 33-1-45589110, FAX 33-1-45589419, academic@elsevier-fr.com, http://www.elsevier.com/locate/ssscie. Ed. G Ferey.

546 NLD ISSN 0169-3158
CODEN: SICHEJ
➤ **STUDIES IN INORGANIC CHEMISTRY.** Text in English. 1978. irreg., latest vol.19, 1994. price varies. **Document type:** *Monographic series, Academic/Scholarly.* **Description:** Presents research into the chemical properties of inorganic elements and compounds.
Indexed: CIN, ChemAb, ChemTitl, Inspec.
—BLDSC (8490.739000), CASDDS, IE, ingenta. **CCC.**
Published by: Elsevier BV (Subsidiary of: Elsevier Science & Technology), Radarweg 29, Amsterdam, 1043 NX, Netherlands. TEL 31-20-4853911, FAX 31-20-4852457, nlinfo-f@elsevier.nl, http://www.elsevier.nl.

546 UKR ISSN 0203-3119
TA418.26 CODEN: SVMAD2
➤ **SVERKHTVERDYE MATERIALY**; nauchno-teoreticheskii zhurnal. Text in Russian, English, Ukrainian; Contents page in English, Russian. 1979. bi-m. USD 160 foreign (effective 2004). adv. **Document type:** *Journal, Academic/Scholarly.* **Description:** Publishes papers dealing with the production, structure, and investigation of the properties of diamonds, cubic boron nitride, ceramics, related machining and mining tools, superabrasive powders, and related machining processes.
Formerly: Sinteticheskie Almazy (0586-4534)
Related titles: CD-ROM ed.; Online - full text ed.; ♦ English Translation: Journal of Superhard Materials. ISSN 1063-4576.
Indexed: BrCerAb, C&ISA, CIN, CerAb, ChemAb, ChemTitl, CivEngAb, CorrAb, Djerelo, E&CAJ, EMA, EngInd, INIS AtomInd, Inspec, M&TEA, MBF, METADEX, RefZh, SolStAb, WAA.
—BLDSC (0160.897000), CASDDS, CISTI, East View, Linda Hall. **CCC.**
Published by: Natsional'na Akademiya Nauk Ukrainy, Instytut Nadtverdykh Materialiv im. V.M. Bakulya, vul Avtozavodska 2, Kyiv, 04074, Ukraine. TEL 380-44-4688640, FAX 380-44-4688625, boris@ism.kiev.ua, alcon@ism.kiev.ua, http://www.rql.kiev.ua/almaz_j, http://www.ism.kiev.ua/indexrnf.html. Ed. N V Novikov. R&P A V Shcherbakov. Adv. contact A.V. Shcherbakov. Circ: 350. **US dist. addr.:** East View Information Services, 3020 Harbor Ln. N., Minneapolis, MN 55447. TEL 800-477-1005, FAX 800-800-3839, eastview@eastview.com, http://www.eastview.com.

➤ **TETRAHEDRON: ASYMMETRY.** see *CHEMISTRY—Organic Chemistry*

546 622 667.6 668.4 GBR ISSN 1350-908X
TI02 WORLDWIDE UPDATE. Text in English. 1993. bi-m. USD 2,000 foreign (effective 2001). charts; mkt.; stat.; tr.lit. back issues avail. **Document type:** *Newsletter, Trade.* **Description:** Covering all aspects of the international titanium dioxide pigment & feedstock industries, including supply, demand, prices, new plants & projects, corporate financial news, acquisitions & mergers, and technical innovations.
Published by: Artikol Ltd., 39 Cromwell Rd., Beckenham, BR3 4LL, United Kingdom. TEL 44-20-8658-2621, FAX 44-20-8402-1544, regadams@artikol.com, http://www.theoffice.net/artikol. Ed., Pub. Reg Adams. Circ: 215 (paid).

TOPICS IN BIOLOGICAL INORGANIC CHEMISTRY. see *BIOLOGY—Biochemistry*

546 NLD ISSN 0924-6142
CODEN: TELCEW
➤ **TOPICS IN F-ELEMENT CHEMISTRY.** Text in English. 1985. irreg., latest vol.3, 1995. price varies. **Document type:** *Monographic series, Academic/Scholarly.*
Indexed: ChemAb.
—CASDDS, CISTI. **CCC.**
Published by: Springer-Verlag Dordrecht (Subsidiary of: Springer Science+Business Media), Van Godewijckstraat 30, Dordrecht, 3311 GX, Netherlands. TEL 31-78-6576050, FAX 31-78-6576474, http://www.springeronline.com. Ed. Shyama P Sinha.

546 540 NLD ISSN 0082-495X
➤ **TOPICS IN INORGANIC AND GENERAL CHEMISTRY.** Text in English. 1964. irreg., latest vol.24, 1996. price varies.
Document type: *Monographic series, Academic/Scholarly.*
Description: Describes research and advances in inorganic and general chemistry.
Published by: Elsevier BV (Subsidiary of: Elsevier Science & Technology), Radarweg 29, Amsterdam, 1043 NX, Netherlands. TEL 31-20-4853911, FAX 31-20-4852457, nlinfo-f@elsevier.nl, http://www.elsevier.nl. Ed. P L Robinson.

546 NOR
UNIVERSITETET I TRONDHEIM. NORGES TEKNISKE HOEGSKOLE. INSTITUTT FOR UORGANISK KJEMI. AVHANDLING. Text in Norwegian. 1976. irreg., latest vol.53, 1988. NOK 300.
Indexed: RefZh.
Published by: Norges Teknisk-Naturvitenskapelige Universitet, Institutt for Kjemi/Norwegian University of Science and Technology, Department of Chemistry, Trondheim, 7491, Norway. TEL 47-73-55-08-70, FAX 47-73-55-08-77. Circ: 250.

UNIVERSITY OF ALASKA. MINERAL INDUSTRY RESEARCH LABORATORY. ANNUAL REPORT OF RESEARCH PROGRESS. see *MINES AND MINING INDUSTRY*

546 RUS
VESTNIK MOLODYCH UCHENYCH. NEORGANICHESKAYA KHIMIYA. Text in Russian. 2002. s-a. **Document type:** *Journal, Academic/Scholarly.*
Related titles: Online - full text ed.: ISSN 1609-5456. 2000.
Published by: Redaktsiya Zhurnala Vestnik Molodych Uchenych, 1-ya Krasnoarmeiskaya Ul., dom 1, Sankt-Peterburg, 198005, Russian Federation. alexmosh@mail.ru, vmu@peterlink.ru, http://www.informika.ru/text/magaz/science/vys/CHEMIC/main.html. Ed. A Moshnikov. **Co-sponsors:** Rossiiskaya Akademiya Nauk, Sankt-Peterburgskii Nauchnyi Tsentr; Ministerstvo Obrazovaniya i Nauki Rossiiskoi Federatsii/Ministry of Education and Science of the Russian Federation; Sovet Rektorov Vuzov Sankt-Peterburga.

546 CHN ISSN 1000-324X
TP785 CODEN: WCXUET
➤ **WUJI CAILIAO XUEBAO/JOURNAL OF INORGANIC MATERIALS.** Text in Chinese; Summaries in English. 1986. bi-m. CNY 150 (effective 2004). adv. **Document type:** *Journal, Academic/Scholarly.* **Description:** Covers research on man-made crystals, special glass and ceramics, amorphous semiconductors, inorganic coating materials, and inorganic composites.
Related titles: Online - full text ed.: (from East View Information Services, WanFang Data Corp.).
Indexed: C&ISA, CIN, ChemAb, ChemTitl, E&CAJ, IAA, MSCI.
—BLDSC (5007.300000), CASDDS, IDS, IE, ingenta.
Published by: (Zhongguo Kexueyuan, Shanghai Suanyan Yanjiusuo), Kexue Chubanshe/Science Press, 16 Donghuang Cheng Genbei Jie, Beijing, 100717, China. TEL 86-10-64000246, FAX 86-10-64030255, wjclxb@sunm.shcnc.ac.cn, http://wjclxb.periodicals.net.cn/default.html, http://www.sciencep.com/. Circ: 8,000. **Dist. by:** China International Book Trading Corp, 35 Chegongzhuang Xilu, Haidian District, PO Box 399, Beijing 100044, China. TEL 86-10-68412045, FAX 86-10-68412023, cibtc@mail.cibtc.com.cn, http://www.cibtc.com.cn.

546 CHN ISSN 1001-4861
QD146 CODEN: WHUXEO
WUJI HUAXUE XUEBAO/CHINESE JOURNAL OF INORGANIC CHEMISTRY. Text in Chinese, English. 1985. q. USD 39 (effective 1997).
Related titles: Online - full text ed.: (from East View Information Services).
Indexed: CCI, CIN, ChemAb.
—BLDSC (3180.357000), CASDDS, CISTI, ingenta.
Published by: Chinese Chemical Society/Zhongguo Huaxuehui, PO Box 2709, Beijing, 100080, China. TEL 86-10-6256-8157, FAX 86-10-6256-8157.

546.34 JPN
YOYUEN KAGAKU TORONKAI YOSHISHU/SYMPOSIUM ON MOLTEN SALT CHEMISTRY. Text in English, Japanese; Summaries in English. 1967. a.
Published by: Denki Kagaku Kyokai, Yoyuen Iinkai/Electrochemical Society of Japan, Molten Salt Committee, c/o Osaka Daigaku Kogakubu Zairyo Kaihatsu Kogakka, 2-1 Yamada-Oka, Suita-shi, Osaka-fu 565-0871, Japan.

546.34 JPN ISSN 0916-1589
CODEN: YKKAEG
YOYUEN OYOBI KOON KAGAKU/MOLTEN SALTS. Text in Japanese; Summaries in English. 1989. 3/yr.
Indexed: CIN, ChemAb, INIS AtomInd.
—BLDSC (5901.460000), CASDDS.
Published by: Denki Kagaku Kyokai, Yoyuen Iinkai/Electrochemical Society of Japan, Molten Salt Committee, c/o Osaka Daigaku Kogakubu Zairyo Kaihatsu Kogakka, 2-1 Yamada-Oka, Suita-shi, Osaka-fu 565-0871, Japan.

546 547 DEU ISSN 0932-0776
QD1 CODEN: ZNBSEN
➤ **ZEITSCHRIFT FUER NATURFORSCHUNG. SECTION B: A JOURNAL OF CHEMICAL SCIENCES.** Text in English, German. 1947. m. EUR 721 domestic; EUR 737 foreign (effective 2004). adv. bk.rev. charts; illus. index. 115 p./no.; **Document type:** *Journal, Academic/Scholarly.* **Description:** Publishes original papers, microreviews, and letters from all areas of inorganic chemistry, solid state chemistry, coordination chemistry, molecular chemistry, and organic chemistry.
Former titles (until 1987): Zeitschrift fuer Naturforschung. Section B: Inorganic and Organic Chemistry (0340-5087); (until 1973): Zeitschrift fuer Naturforschung. Ausgabe B. (0044-3174)

Indexed: ASCA, ASFA, BiolAb, BullT&T, CCI, CIN, ChemAb, ChemInfo, ChemTitl, CurCR, CurCont, DBA, EngInd, ExcerpMed, HortAb, INIS AtomInd, ISR, IndChem, Inspec, MEDLINE, MOS, MSB, MSCI, NPU, RCI, RM&VM, SCI, WeedAb.
—BLDSC (9475.000000), AskIEEE, CASDDS, CINDOC, CISTI, IDS, IE, Infotrieve, ingenta, Linda Hall. **CCC.**
Published by: Verlag der Zeitschrift fuer Naturforschung, Postfach 2645, Tuebingen, 72016, Germany. TEL 49-7071-31555, FAX 49-7071-360571, mail@znaturforsch.com, http:// www.znaturforsch.com/b.htm. Ed. Dr. Heide Voelter. R&P Tamina Greifeld. Adv. contact Anneliese Eipper. Circ: 600.

➤ **ZHONGGUO WUJI FENXI HUAXUE WENZHAI/CHINESE INORGANIC ANALYTICAL CHEMISTRY ABSTRACTS.** see *CHEMISTRY—Abstracting, Bibliographies, Statistics*

546   RUS   ISSN 0044-457X
                                CODEN: ZNOKAQ
➤ **ZHURNAL NEORGANICHESKOI KHIMII.** Text in Russian. 1956. m. RUR 366 for 6 mos. domestic (effective 2004). adv. bk.rev. bibl.; charts; illus. index. **Document type:** *Journal, Academic/Scholarly.*
Related titles: Online - full text ed.; ◆ English ed.: Russian Journal of Inorganic Chemistry. ISSN 0036-0236; ◆ English Translation: Russian Journal of Inorganic Chemistry. ISSN 0036-0236.
Indexed: ASCA, BrCerAb, BullT&T, C&ISA, CCI, CIN, CerAb, ChemAb, ChemInfo, ChemTitl, CivEngAb, CorrAb, CurCR, CurCont, E&CAJ, EMA, EngInd, INIS AtomInd, IndChem, Inspec, M&TEA, MBF, METADEX, MSCI, RCI, RefZh, SCI, SolStAb, WAA.
—BLDSC (0062.000000), AskIEEE, CASDDS, CINDOC, CISTI, East View, IDS, KNAW, Linda Hall. **CCC.**
Published by: (Rossiiskaya Akademiya Nauk, Institut Obshchei i Neorganicheskoi Khimii im. N.S. Kurnakova), Izdatel'stvo Nauka, Profsoyuznaya ul 90, Moscow, 117864, Russian Federation. TEL 7-095-3347151, FAX 7-095-4202220, secret@naukaran.ru, http://www.maik.ru/cgi-bin/list.pl?page= nergkhim, http://www.naukaran.ru. Ed. Yurii A Buslaev. Circ: 2,825.

CHEMISTRY—Organic Chemistry

➤ **ABSTRACTS OF THE SYMPOSIUM ON ORGANOMETALLIC CHEMISTRY, JAPAN/YUKI KINZOKU KAGAKU TORONKAI KOEN YOSHISHU.** see *CHEMISTRY—Abstracting, Bibliographies, Statistics*

➤ **ADDITIVES FOR POLYMERS.** see *PLASTICS*

➤ **ADVANCED COMPOSITES MANUFACTURING CENTRE NEWSLETTER.** see *PLASTICS*

543.17   USA   ISSN 1079-350X
QD305.H7   CODEN: ACCHFI
ADVANCES IN CARBENE CHEMISTRY. Text in English. 1994. irreg., latest vol.3, 2001. price varies. back issues avail. **Document type:** *Monographic series, Academic/Scholarly.* **Description:** Provides authoritative and timely contributions addressing a wide range of topics associated with carbene chemistry.
Indexed: CIN, ChemAb, ChemTitl.
—CASDDS, CISTI. **CCC.**
Published by: J A I Press Inc. (Subsidiary of: Elsevier Science & Technology), 360 Park Ave S, New York, NY 10010-1710. TEL 212-989-5800, FAX 212-633-3990, usinfo-f@elsevier.com, http://www.elsevier.com/wps/find/bookdescription.cws_home/ 621952/description#description. Ed. Udo H Brinker.

547.59   USA   ISSN 0065-2725
QD400   CODEN: AHTCAG
➤ **ADVANCES IN HETEROCYCLIC CHEMISTRY.** Text in English. 1963. irreg., latest vol.83, 2002. USD 160 per vol. vol.86 (effective 2004). index. reprint service avail. from ISI. **Document type:** *Monographic series, Academic/Scholarly.* **Description:** For organic chemists, polymer chemists, and many biological scientists.
Related titles: Online - full text ed.: ISSN 1557-8429 (from ScienceDirect).
Indexed: ASCA, CCI, CIN, ChemAb, ChemInfo, ChemTitl, CurCR, ISR, IndChem, MEDLINE, RCI, SCI.
—BLDSC (0709.020000), CASDDS, CISTI, IE, Infotrieve, ingenta, Linda Hall. **CCC.**
Published by: Academic Press (Subsidiary of: Elsevier Science & Technology), 525 B St, Ste 1900, San Diego, CA 92101-4495. TEL 619-231-6616, 800-894-3434, FAX 619-699-6422, apsubs@acad.com, http://www.sciencedirect.com/science/ bookseries/00652725, http://www.academicpress.com. Ed. Alan Katritzky.

547   NLD
➤ **ADVANCES IN INCLUSION SCIENCE.** Text in Dutch. 1983. irreg., latest vol.7, 1992. price varies. **Document type:** *Monographic series, Academic/Scholarly.*
Published by: Springer-Verlag Dordrecht (Subsidiary of: Springer Science+Business Media), Van Godewijckstraat 30, Dordrecht, 3311 GX, Netherlands. TEL 31-78-6576050, FAX 31-78-6576474, http://www.springeronline.com.

547   NLD   ISSN 1574-0870
▼ **ADVANCES IN ORGANIC SYNTHESIS.** Text in English. 2005. irreg. USD 130 per vol. (effective 2005). **Document type:** *Monographic series, Academic/Scholarly.* **Description:** Publishes the latest and most important advances in organic synthesis.
Related titles: CD-ROM ed.; Online - full content ed.; Online - full text ed.: (from Gale Group, IngentaConnect).
Published by: Bentham Science Publishers Ltd., PO Box 1673, Hilversum, BR 1200, Netherlands. TEL 31-35-6923800, FAX 31-35-6980150, M.Bentham@inter.nl.net, http:// www.bentham.org/aos/index2.htm. Ed. Atta-ur Rahman TEL 92-21-4969873.

547.05   USA   ISSN 0065-3055
QD411   CODEN: AOMCAU
➤ **ADVANCES IN ORGANOMETALLIC CHEMISTRY.** Text in English. 1964. irreg., latest vol.48, 2001. USD 170 per vol. vol.51 (effective 2004). index. reprint service avail. from ISI. **Document type:** *Monographic series, Academic/Scholarly.* **Description:** Provides an authoritative, definitive review addressing all aspects of organometallic chemistry.
Related titles: Online - full text ed.: (from ScienceDirect).
Indexed: ASCA, CCI, CIN, ChemAb, ChemInfo, ChemTitl, CurCR, ISR, IndChem, MSB, RCI, SCI.
—BLDSC (0709.561000), CASDDS, CISTI, IE, Infotrieve, ingenta, Linda Hall. **CCC.**
Published by: Academic Press (Subsidiary of: Elsevier Science & Technology), 525 B St, Ste 1900, San Diego, CA 92101-4495. TEL 619-231-6616, 800-894-3434, apsubs@acad.com, http://www.academicpress.com. Eds. F G A Stone, Robert West.

➤ **ADVANCES IN POLYMER BLENDS AND ALLOYS TECHNOLOGY.** see *ENGINEERING—Chemical Engineering*

547   USA   ISSN 0065-3195
QD281.P6   CODEN: APSIDK
➤ **ADVANCES IN POLYMER SCIENCE/FORTSCHRITTE DER HOCHPOLYMEREN-FORSCHUNG.** Text in English, French, German. 1958. irreg., latest vol.196, 2006. price varies. reprint service avail. from ISI. **Document type:** *Monographic series, Academic/Scholarly.* **Description:** Presents critical reviews of the present and future trends in polymer and biopolymer science including chemistry, physical chemistry, physics and materials science.
Related titles: Online - full text ed.: ISSN 1436-5030 (from EBSCO Publishing).
Indexed: ASCA, BiolAb, CCI, CIN, ChemAb, ChemTitl, EngInd, ISR, Inspec, MSCI, RAPRA, SCI, TTI, WTA.
—BLDSC (0710.600000), CASDDS, CISTI, Ei, IDS, IE, Infotrieve, ingenta, Linda Hall. **CCC.**
Published by: Springer-Verlag New York, Inc. (Subsidiary of: Springer Science+Business Media), 233 Spring St, New York, NY 10013. TEL 212-460-1500, 800-777-4643, FAX 212-473-6272, http://www.springer-ny.com.

630   USA
AGRICULTURAL CHEMICAL NEWS. Text in English. 1978. m. USD 80 domestic; USD 100 foreign (effective 2004). stat. back issues avail. **Document type:** *Newsletter.* **Description:** Presents new developments with agricultural chemicals. Features new registrations, use patterns, experimental permits on insecticides, herbicides, fungicides and miscellaneous pesticides used in the U.S.
Formerly: Agricultural Chemical Newsletter
Indexed: CBNB, RPP, WeedAb.
Published by: Thomson Publications, PO Box 9335, Fresno, CA 93791. TEL 559-266-2964, FAX 559-266-0189, susan@agbook.com, http://www.agbook.com. Ed. W T Thomson. R&P Susan Heflin. Circ: 1,000 (paid and controlled)

630   USA
AGRICULTURAL SPRAY ADJUVANTS. Text in English. a. USD 24.95 (effective 2000). **Document type:** *Trade.*
Published by: Thomson Publications, PO Box 9335, Fresno, CA 93791. TEL 559-266-2964, FAX 559-266-0189, http://www.agbook.com. Ed. W T Thomson. R&P Lori Thomson Harvey TEL 209-323-1533.

547   USA   ISSN 0002-5100
QD1   CODEN: ALACBI
➤ **ALDRICHIMICA ACTA.** Text in English. 1967. q. looseleaf. free (effective 2005). adv. charts; illus.; mkt.; pat.; stat.; tr.lit.; tr.mk. **Document type:** *Newsletter, Academic/Scholarly.*
Formerly: Kardinex Sheets
Indexed: ASCA, CCI, CIN, ChemAb, ChemInfo, CurCont, ISR, IndChem, LHB, MOS, RCI, SCI.
—BLDSC (0786.810000), CASDDS, CISTI, Linda Hall.
Published by: Aldrich, 1001 W St Paul Ave, Milwaukee, WI 53233. TEL 414-298-7907, FAX 414-273-4979, aldrich@sial.com, http://www.sigma-aldrich.com. Ed., R&P Alfonse Runquist. Circ: 200,000 (controlled).

➤ **ALKALOIDS: CHEMICAL AND BIOLOGICAL PERSPECTIVES.** see *BIOLOGY—Biochemistry*

547 615.7   USA   ISSN 1099-4831
QD421.A1   CODEN: ALKAAR
➤ **THE ALKALOIDS: CHEMISTRY AND BIOLOGY.** Text in English. 1950. irreg., latest vol.59, 2002. USD 152 per vol. (effective 2003). reprint service avail. from ISI. **Document type:** *Monographic series, Academic/Scholarly.*
Formerly (until 1998): The Alkaloids: Chemistry and Pharmacology (0099-9598)
Related titles: Online - full text ed.: (from ScienceDirect).
Indexed: BIOSIS Prev, CIN, ChemAb, ChemTitl, MSB.
—BLDSC (0788.529000), CASDDS, CISTI, GNLM, IE, Infotrieve, ingenta. **CCC.**
Published by: Academic Press (Subsidiary of: Elsevier Science & Technology), 525 B St, Ste 1900, San Diego, CA 92101-4495. apsubs@acad.com, http://www.academicpress.com.

547.8 665.5   USA   ISSN 0569-3799
TP690.A1   CODEN: ACPCAT
AMERICAN CHEMICAL SOCIETY. PETROLEUM CHEMISTRY DIVISION. PREPRINTS. Text in English. 1956. 4/yr. USD 26 to individuals; USD 96 to libraries (effective 2002). back issues avail. **Description:** Publishes preprints of papers presented at national meetings.
Indexed: ChemAb, PetrolAb.
—BLDSC (6607.900000), CISTI, IE, Infotrieve, ingenta, Linda Hall, PADDS.
Published by: American Chemical Society, Division of Petroleum Chemistry, 1155 Sixteenth St, NW, Washington, DC 20036. TEL 202-872-4600, 800-227-5558, FAX 202-872-4615, help@acs.org, http://www.acs.org. **Subscr. to:** PO Box 3337, Columbus, OH 43210. TEL 614-447-3776, 800-333-9511, service@acs.org.

BEILSTEIN ABSTRACTS. see *CHEMISTRY—Abstracting, Bibliographies, Statistics*

547   DEU   ISSN 1860-5397
▼ ➤ **BEILSTEIN JOURNAL OF ORGANIC CHEMISTRY.** Text in English. 2005. irreg. free (effective 2006). **Document type:** *Journal, Academic/Scholarly.* **Description:** Covers all aspects of organic chemistry.
Media: Online - full text.
Published by: Beilstein - Institut zur Foerderung der Chemischen Wissenschaften, Trakehner Str 7/9, Frankfurt am Main, 60487, Germany. TEL 49-69-716732, FAX 49-69-716732, info@beilstein-institut.de, http://bjoc.beilstein-journals.org, http://www.beilstein-institut.de. Ed. Jonathan Clyden.

547   USA   ISSN 0067-4915
BEILSTEINS HANDBUCH DER ORGANISCHEN CHEMIE. SUPPLEMENT. (The main work was published: 1918-1937; First Supplement: 1928-1938; Second Supplement: 1941-1957; Third Supplement: 1930-1949; Fourth Supplement: 1950-1959; Fifth Supplement: 1960-1979) Text in English. 1972. irreg., latest 1987. price varies. reprint service avail. from ISI. **Document type:** *Academic/Scholarly.*
Related titles: Online - full text ed.
—Linda Hall. **CCC.**
Published by: Springer-Verlag New York, Inc. (Subsidiary of: Springer Science+Business Media), 233 Spring St, New York, NY 10013. TEL 212-460-1500, FAX 212-473-6272.

BIOCHEMICAL PHARMACOLOGY. see *PHARMACY AND PHARMACOLOGY*

547   USA   ISSN 1525-7797
                                CODEN: BOMAF6
BIOMACROMOLECULES. Text in English. 2000. bi-m. USD 1,357 in North America to institutions; USD 1,442 elsewhere to institutions; USD 230 in North America to members; USD 315 elsewhere to members; USD 173 in North America to students; USD 258 elsewhere to students (effective 2006). back issues avail. **Document type:** *Journal, Academic/Scholarly.* **Description:** Publishes original research focused on the integration of knowledge on both polymer and biological sciences. Among the basic areas the journal will cover are monomers and polymers from renewable resources, catabolism of polymer degradation products, biocatalysis, biomacromolecular assembly, biomimetics, biomineralization, bioprocesing, biorecycling and bioremediation.
Related titles: Online - full text ed.: ISSN 1526-4602. 2000. USD 70 (effective 2006) (from EBSCO Publishing, Swets Information Services).
Indexed: AIDS&CR, B&BAb, BBCI, BIOBASE, BIOSIS Prev, BiolAb, CCI, ChemAb, CurCR, CurCont, ESPM, ExcerpMed, ISR, IndChem, M&PBA, RCI, RefZh, SCI, VirolAbstr.
—BLDSC (2087.702000), CISTI, IE, Infotrieve, ingenta, Linda Hall. **CCC.**
Published by: American Chemical Society, 1155 16th St, N W, Washington, DC 20036. TEL 202-872-4600, 800-227-5558, FAX 202-872-3727, service@acs.org, http://pubs.acs.org/ biomac. Ed. Ann-Christine Albertsson TEL 46-8-212646.

547 610 GBR ISSN 0968-0896
QP550 CODEN: BMECEP

➤ **BIOORGANIC & MEDICINAL CHEMISTRY.** Text in English. 1993. 24/yr. EUR 1,926 in Europe to institutions; JPY 255,900 in Japan to institutions; USD 2,155 elsewhere to institutions; EUR 210 in Europe to qualified personnel; JPY 28,000 in Japan to qualified personnel; USD 236 elsewhere to qualified personnel (effective 2006). back issues avail. **Document type:** *Journal, Academic/Scholarly.* **Description:** Publishes full original research papers and critical reviews on biomolecular chemistry, medicinal chemistry and related disciplines.

Related titles: Microfilm ed.: (from PQC); Online - full text ed.: ISSN 1464-3391 (from EBSCO Publishing, Gale Group, IngentaConnect, ScienceDirect, Swets Information Services).

Indexed: BBCI, BIOBASE, BIOSIS Prev, BiolAb, CCI, CIN, ChemAb, ChemInfo, ChemTitl, CurCont, DBA, ExcerpMed, IABS, ISR, IndMed, Inpharma, MEDLINE, MSB, PE&ON, Reac, RefZh, SCI, VITIS.

—BLDSC (2089.325000), CASDDS, CINDOC, CISTI, GNLM, IDS, IE, Infotrieve, ingenta, Linda Hall. **CCC.**

Published by: Pergamon (Subsidiary of: Elsevier Science & Technology), The Boulevard, Langford Ln, East Park, Kidlington, Oxford OX5 1GB, United Kingdom. TEL 44-1865-843000, FAX 44-1865-843010, http://www.elsevier.com/locate/bmc. Eds. Dr. Chi-Huey Wong, H. Waldmann, Yuichi Hashimoto. **Subscr. to:** Elsevier BV, PO Box 211, Amsterdam 1000 AE, Netherlands. TEL 31-20-485-3757, FAX 31-20-485-3432, nlinfo-f@elsevier.nl, http://www.elsevier.nl.

547 610 GBR ISSN 0960-894X
QP501 CODEN: BMCLE8

➤ **BIOORGANIC & MEDICINAL CHEMISTRY LETTERS.** Text in English. 1991. 24/yr. EUR 2,482 in Europe to institutions; JPY 329,500 in Japan to institutions; USD 2,775 elsewhere to institutions; EUR 304 in Europe to qualified personnel; JPY 40,400 in Japan to qualified personnel; USD 340 elsewhere to qualified personnel; EUR 152 in Europe to students; JPY 20,100 in Japan to students; USD 168 elsewhere to students (effective 2006). back issues avail. **Document type:** *Journal, Academic/Scholarly.* **Description:** Publishes preliminary communications and theoretical research results in bioorganic and medicinal chemistry.

Related titles: Microfilm ed.: (from PQC); Online - full text ed.: ISSN 1464-3405 (from EBSCO Publishing, Gale Group, IngentaConnect, ScienceDirect, Swets Information Services).

Indexed: ASCA, AbHyg, AgrForAb, BBCI, BIOBASE, BIOSIS Prev, BiolAb, CCI, CIN, CPA, ChemAb, ChemInfo, ChemTitl, CurCont, DBA, DSA, ExcerpMed, FCA, FPA, ForAb, HelmAb, HortAb, IABS, ISR, IndMed, IndVet, Inpharma, MEDLINE, MOS, MSB, NPU, NSCI, NutrAb, PBA, PE&ON, PGrRegA, PoultAb, ProtozoAb, RA&MP, RCI, RM&VM, RPP, Reac, RefZh, RevApplEntom, RiceAb, S&F, SCI, SIA, SeedAb, TDB, TriticAb, VetBull, WeedAb.

—BLDSC (2089.330000), CASDDS, CINDOC, CISTI, GNLM, IDS, IE, Infotrieve, ingenta, Linda Hall. **CCC.**

Published by: Pergamon (Subsidiary of: Elsevier Science & Technology), The Boulevard, Langford Ln, East Park, Kidlington, Oxford OX5 1GB, United Kingdom. TEL 44-1865-843000, FAX 44-1865-843010, http://www.elsevier.com/locate/bmcl. Eds. Dr. D L Boger, L Ghosez, M. Shibasaki. **Subscr. to:** Elsevier BV, PO Box 211, Amsterdam 1000 AE, Netherlands. TEL 31-20-485-3757, FAX 31-20-485-3432, nlinfo-f@elsevier.nl, http://www.elsevier.nl.

547 USA ISSN 0045-2068
QP501 CODEN: BOCMBM

➤ **BIOORGANIC CHEMISTRY.** Text in English. 1971. 6/yr. EUR 322 in Europe to individuals; JPY 33,600 in Japan to individuals; USD 241 to individuals except Europe and Japan; EUR 691 in Europe to institutions; JPY 72,100 in Japan to institutions; USD 521 to institutions except Europe and Japan; EUR 163 in Europe to students; JPY 17,100 in Japan to students; USD 141 to students except Europe and Japan (effective 2006). adv. bk.rev. charts; illus.; stat. index. back issues avail. **Document type:** *Journal, Academic/Scholarly.* **Description:** Presents articles in which the principles and techniques of organic and physical organic chemistry are used to solve problems of relevance to biology or to chemical studies inspired by biology.

Related titles: Online - full text ed.: ISSN 1090-2120. USD 553 (effective 2002) (from EBSCO Publishing, Gale Group, IngentaConnect, O C L C Online Computer Library Center, Inc., ScienceDirect, Swets Information Services).

Indexed: ABIPC, ASCA, ASFA, AgBio, Agr, BBCI, BIOSIS Prev, BibAg, BiolAb, CCI, CIN, CPA, ChemAb, ChemTitl, CurCont, DBA, ExcerpMed, FCA, ForAb, HortAb, ISR, Inpharma, MEDLINE, MOS, MSB, NPU, NutrAb, OrnHort, PBA, RA&MP, RCI, RM&VM, Reac, SCI, WeedAb.

—BLDSC (2089.350000), CASDDS, CISTI, GNLM, IDS, IE, ingenta, Linda Hall. **CCC.**

Published by: Academic Press (Subsidiary of: Elsevier Science & Technology), 525 B St, Ste 1900, San Diego, CA 92101-4495. TEL 619-231-6616, 800-894-3434, FAX 619-699-6422, apsubs@acad.com, http://www.elsevier.com/locate/bioorg, http://www.academicpress.com. Ed. C.P. Whitman.

547 RUS ISSN 0132-3423
QD415.A1 CODEN: BIKHD7

➤ **BIOORGANICHESKAYA KHIMIYA.** Text in Russian; Summaries in English. 1975. bi-m. RUR 990 for 6 mos. domestic; USD 363 foreign (effective 2004). illus. **Document type:** *Journal, Academic/Scholarly.* **Description:** Publishes reviews and the results of original experimental and theoretical investigations on the structure, structure-activity relationships, and synthesis of biopolymers such as proteins, nucleic acids, polysaccharides, mixed biopolymers and their more highly organized complexes and low molecular mass bioregulators such as peptides, lipids, and antibiotics.

Related titles: Online - full text ed.; ♦ Russian Translation: Russian Journal of Bioorganic Chemistry. ISSN 1068-1620.

Indexed: ASCA, AgBio, BBCI, BIOSIS Prev, BiolAb, CCI, CIN, ChemAb, ChemTitl, CurCont, DBA, DSA, ExcerpMed, HelmAb, ISR, IndMed, IndVet, Inpharma, MEDLINE, MOS, MSB, NPU, NutrAb, PBA, PGrRegA, PN&I, RCI, RM&VM, RPP, Reac, RefZh, RevApplEntom, SCI, SIA, VITIS, VetBull, ZooRec.

—CASDDS, CISTI, East View, GNLM, IDS, KNAW, Linda Hall. **CCC.**

Published by: (Rossiiskaya Akademiya Nauk/Russian Academy of Sciences), Izdatel'stvo Nauka, Profsoyuznaya ul 90, Moscow, 117864, Russian Federation. TEL 7-095-3347151, FAX 7-095-4202220, rjbc@ibch.ru, secret@naukaran.ru, http://www.maik.rssi.ru/cgi-bin/list.pl?page=biokhim, http://www.naukaran.ru. **Dist. by:** M K - Periodica, ul Gilyarovskogo 39, Moscow 129110, Russian Federation. TEL 7-095-2845008, FAX 7-095-2813798, info@periodicals.ru, http://www.mkniga.ru.

547 USA ISSN 0006-3525
QP801.P64 CODEN: BIPMAA

➤ **BIOPOLYMERS**; original research on biological molecules and assemblies. Text in English. 1946. 18/yr. USD 7,625 domestic to institutions; USD 7,913 in Canada & Mexico to institutions; USD 8,081 elsewhere to institutions; USD 8,388 combined subscription domestic to institutions print & online eds.; USD 8,676 combined subscription in Canada & Mexico to institutions print & online eds.; USD 8,844 combined subscription elsewhere to institutions print & online eds. (effective 2006); incl. Peptide Science. adv. index. back issues avail.; reprint service avail. from PQC. **Document type:** *Journal, Academic/Scholarly.* **Description:** Covers organic and physical chemistry, experimental and theoretical research, static and dynamic aspects of structure. Includes an examination of the broad aspects of biospectroscopy.

Incorporates (1995-2000): Biospectroscopy (1075-4261); Supersedes in part (in 1963): Journal of Polymer Science (0022-3832)

Related titles: Microform ed.: (from PQC); Online - full content ed.: ISSN 1097-0282. 1996. USD 7,625 to institutions (effective 2006); Online - full text ed.: (from EBSCO Publishing, Swets Information Services, Wiley InterScience).

Indexed: ABIPC, ASCA, ASFA, AbHyg, AgBio, Agr, AnBrAb, ApMecR, B&BAb, BBCI, BIOBASE, BIOSIS Prev, BioEngAb, BiolAb, C&ISA, CCI, CIN, CPA, ChemAb, ChemTitl, CurCont, DSA, E&CAJ, ESPM, EngInd, ExcerpMed, FCA, FPA, FS&TA, ForAb, HortAb, IABS, ISMEC, ISR, IndMed, IndVet, Inpharma, MEDLINE, MSB, MSCI, NutrAb, OrnHort, PBA, PGegResA, PoultAb, RA&MP, RAPRA, RM&VM, RPP, Reac, RevApplEntom, SCI, SIA, SolStAb, SoyAb, TriticAb, VetBull.

—BLDSC (2089.470000), CASDDS, CISTI, Ei, GNLM, IDS, IE, Infotrieve, ingenta, Linda Hall. **CCC.**

Published by: John Wiley & Sons, Inc., 111 River St, Hoboken, NJ 07030-5774. TEL 800-825-7550, FAX 201-748-5915, uscs-wis@wiley.com, http://www.wiley.com/journals. Ed. Murray Goodman. adv.: B&W page GBP 640, color page GBP 1,515; trim 210 x 279. Circ: 900 (paid). **Subscr. outside the Americas to:** John Wiley & Sons Ltd., The Atrium, Southern Gate, Chichester, West Sussex PO19 8SQ, United Kingdom. TEL 44-1243-779777, FAX 44-1243-775878, cs-journals@wiley.co.uk.

➤ **C A SELECTS. OLEOCHEMICALS CONTAINING NITROGEN.** see *CHEMISTRY—Abstracting, Bibliographies, Statistics*

547 GBR
CODEN: CBHCA4

CARBOHYDRATE CHEMISTRY. Text in English. 1967. a., latest vol.34, 2003. GBP 219.50, USD 379 per vol. (effective 2004). charts; illus. index. back issues avail. **Document type:** *Academic/Scholarly.* **Description:** Provides review coverage of all publications relevant to the chemistry of monosaccharides and oligosaccharides in a given year.

Former titles (until 1998): Carbohydrate Chemistry. Part 1: Monosaccharides, Disaccharides, and Specific Oligosaccharides (0951-8428); (until 1986): Carbohydrate Chemistry. Part 1: Mono-Di-Tri-saccharides and Their Derivatives (0951-8401); Which superseded in part: Carbohydrate Chemistry (0576-7172)

Related titles: Online - full text ed.

Indexed: CIN, ChemAb, ChemTitl, MSB, SIA.

—BLDSC (3050.980000), CASDDS, CISTI, IE, ingenta, Linda Hall. **CCC.**

Published by: Royal Society of Chemistry, Thomas Graham House, Science Park, Milton Rd, Cambridge, CB4 0WF, United Kingdom. TEL 44-1223-420066, FAX 44-1223-423623, sales@rsc.org, http://www.rsc.org/CFbooks/sprindex.cfm?BKC=CB. Ed. R J Ferrier. **Subscr. to:** Extenza - Turpin, Pegasus Dr, Stratton Business Park, Biggleswade, Beds SG18 8TQ, United Kingdom. TEL 44-1462-672555.

547.782 GBR ISSN 0144-8617
QD320 CODEN: CAPOD8

➤ **CARBOHYDRATE POLYMERS.** Text in English. 1981. 16/yr. EUR 2,725 in Europe to institutions; JPY 361,300 in Japan to institutions; USD 3,046 elsewhere to institutions; EUR 158 in Europe to qualified personnel; JPY 20,800 in Japan to qualified personnel; USD 177 elsewhere to qualified personnel (effective 2006). adv. bk.rev. charts; illus.; abstr. back issues avail. **Document type:** *Journal, Academic/Scholarly.* **Description:** Covers the study and exploitation of the industrial PTO applications of carbohydrate polymers in areas such as food, textiles, papers, wood, oil field applications and industrial chemistry.

Related titles: Microform ed.: (from PQC); Online - full text ed.: (from EBSCO Publishing, Gale Group, IngentaConnect, ScienceDirect, Swets Information Services).

Indexed: ABIPC, ASCA, AgBio, Agr, AgrForAb, BIOSIS Prev, BibAg, BiolAb, C&ISA, CCI, CEABA, CIN, CPA, ChemAb, ChemTitl, CurCont, DSA, E&CAJ, EngInd, FCA, FPA, FS&TA, ForAb, HerbAb, HortAb, I&DA, ISR, IndVet, Inpharma, MSCI, MaizeAb, NutrAb, OrnHort, P&BA, PBA, PGegResA, PGrRegA, PHN&I, PN&I, PotatoAb, PoultAb, ProtozoAb, RA&MP, RCI, RM&VM, RPP, Reac, RevApplEntom, RiceAb, S&F, SCI, SIA, SeedAb, SolStAb, SoyAb, TTI, TriticAb, VITIS, VetBull, WeedAb.

—BLDSC (3050.990480), CASDDS, CISTI, Ei, IDS, IE, Infotrieve, ingenta, Linda Hall. **CCC.**

Published by: Pergamon (Subsidiary of: Elsevier Science & Technology), The Boulevard, Langford Ln, East Park, Kidlington, Oxford OX5 1GB, United Kingdom. TEL 44-1865-843000, FAX 44-1865-843010, http://www.elsevier.com/locate/carbpol. Eds. Dr. J F Kennedy, Dr. John R Mitchell, W. J. Orts. **Subscr. to:** Elsevier BV, PO Box 211, Amsterdam 1000 AE, Netherlands. TEL 31-20-485-3757, FAX 31-20-485-3432, nlinfo-f@elsevier.nl, http://www.elsevier.nl.

547 GBR ISSN 0008-6215
QD321 CODEN: CRBRAT

➤ **CARBOHYDRATE RESEARCH.** Text in English, French, German. 1965. 18/yr. EUR 6,770 in Europe to institutions; JPY 898,900 in Japan to institutions; USD 7,572 elsewhere to institutions; EUR 281 in Europe to qualified personnel; JPY 37,400 in Japan to qualified personnel; USD 315 elsewhere to qualified personnel (effective 2006). adv. bk.rev. charts; illus. index. back issues avail. **Document type:** *Journal, Academic/Scholarly.* **Description:** Includes all aspects of carbohydrate chemistry and biochemistry. Covers sugars and their derivatives (including cyclitols and model compounds for carbohydrate reactions), oligo- and polysaccharides, nucleosides, nucleotides, and glycoconjugates.

Related titles: Microform ed.: (from PQC); Online - full text ed.: (from EBSCO Publishing, Gale Group, IngentaConnect, ScienceDirect, Swets Information Services).

Indexed: ABIPC, ASCA, AbHyg, AgBio, Agr, AgrForAb, BIOBASE, BIOSIS Prev, BibAg, BioCN&I, BiolAb, C&ISA, CCI, CIN, CPA, ChemAb, ChemInfo, ChemTitl, CurCR, CurCont, DBA, DSA, E&CAJ, EngInd, ExcerpMed, FCA, FPA, FS&TA, ForAb, HelmAb, HerbAb, HortAb, IABS, ISMEC, ISR, IndChem, IndMed, IndVet, Inpharma, MEDLINE, MOS, MSB, MSCI, MaizeAb, NPU, NutrAb, OrnHort, P&BA, PBA, PGegResA, PHN&I, PN&I, PotatoAb, ProtozoAb, RA&MP, RCI, RM&VM, RPP, Reac, RefZh, RevApplEntom, S&F, SCI, SIA, SeedAb, SolStAb, SoyAb, TDB, TriticAb, VITIS, VetBull, WeedAb.

—BLDSC (3050.990500), CASDDS, CINDOC, CISTI, Ei, IDS, IE, Infotrieve, ingenta, Linda Hall. **CCC.**

Published by: Pergamon (Subsidiary of: Elsevier Science & Technology), The Boulevard, Langford Ln, East Park, Kidlington, Oxford OX5 1GB, United Kingdom. TEL 44-1865-843000, FAX 44-1865-843010, http://www.elsevier.com/locate/carres. Eds. Dr. D C Baker, D. Horton, J Defaye. **Subscr. to:** Elsevier BV, PO Box 211, Amsterdam 1000 AE, Netherlands. nlinfo-f@elsevier.nl, http://www.elsevier.nl.

547 GBR ISSN 0008-6223
QD181.C1 CODEN: CRBNAH

➤ **CARBON.** Text in English, French, German. 1963. 15/yr. EUR 2,779 in Europe to institutions; JPY 368,900 in Japan to institutions; USD 3,106 elsewhere to institutions; EUR 187 in Europe to qualified personnel; JPY 24,800 in Japan to qualified personnel; USD 209 elsewhere to qualified personnel (effective 2006). adv. bk.rev. abstr.; charts; illus. index. back issues avail. **Document type:** *Journal, Academic/Scholarly.* **Description:** Covers topics in the physics and chemistry of substances related to aromatic or tetrahedrally bonded carbonaceous solids, and compounds transformed into them by heat treatment and other means.

Related titles: Microfilm ed.: (from PQC); Online - full text ed.: (from EBSCO Publishing, Gale Group, IngentaConnect, ScienceDirect, Swets Information Services).

Indexed: AESIS, ASCA, BrCerAb, C&ISA, CCI, CEA, CIN, CerAb, ChemAb, ChemTitl, CivEngAb, CorrAb, CurCont, E&CAJ, EMA, EngInd, ExcerpMed, F&EA, IAA, ISMEC, ISR, Inspec, M&TEA, MBF, METADEX, MSB, MSCI, RCI, RefZh, SCI, SolStAb, WAA.

—BLDSC (3050.991000), AskIEEE, CASDDS, CINDOC, CISTI, Ei, IDS, IE, Infotrieve, ingenta, Linda Hall. **CCC.**

C

Published by: (American Carbon Society USA), Pergamon (Subsidiary of: Elsevier Science & Technology), The Boulevard, Langford Ln, East Park, Kidlington, Oxford OX5 1GB, United Kingdom. TEL 44-1865-843000, FAX 44-1865-843010, http://www.elsevier.com/locate/carbon. Ed. Peter A. Thrower. Circ: 1,600. **Subscr. to:** Elsevier BV, PO Box 211, Amsterdam 1000 AE, Netherlands. TEL 31-20-485-3757, FAX 31-20-485-3432, nlinfo-f@elsevier.nl, http://www.elsevier.nl.

547 NLD ISSN 0920-4652
CODEN: CMCOES

CATALYSIS BY METAL COMPLEXES. Text in Dutch. 1976. irreg., latest vol.28, 2005. price varies. **Document type:** *Monographic series, Academic/Scholarly.*
Formerly (until 1980): Homogeneous Catalysis in Organic and Inorganic Chemistry (0920-4393)
Indexed: BiolAb, CIN, ChemAb, ChemTitl.
—BLDSC (3090.910000), CASDDS, CISTI, IE, Infotrieve, ingenta. **CCC.**
Published by: Springer-Verlag Dordrecht (Subsidiary of: Springer Science+Business Media), Van Godewijckstraat 30, Dordrecht, 3311 GX, Netherlands. TEL 31-78-6576050, FAX 31-78-6576474, http://www.springeronline.com. Eds. Brian R James, Piet van Leeuwen.

547 GBR
CATALYSTS FOR FINE CHEMICAL SYNTHESIS. Text in English. 2002 (Sept). irreg., latest vol.3, 2004, Nov. price varies. **Document type:** *Monographic series, Academic/Scholarly.* **Description:** Aims to be a practical help for advanced undergraduate, graduate and postgraduate students, as well as experienced chemists in industry and academia working in organic and organometallic synthesis.
—BLDSC (3092.295000).
Published by: John Wiley & Sons Ltd. (Subsidiary of: John Wiley & Sons, Inc.), The Atrium, Southern Gate, Chichester, West Sussex PO19 8SQ, United Kingdom. TEL 44-1243-779777, FAX 44-1243-775878, cs-journals@wiley.co.uk, http://www.wiley.co.uk. Ed. Stanley M Roberts.

C

CELLULAR POLYMERS. see *PLASTICS*

547 NLD ISSN 0969-0239
TS933.C4 CODEN: CELLE8
➤ **CELLULOSE.** Text in Dutch. 1994. 6/yr. EUR 798, USD 825, GBP 488 combined subscription to institutions print & online eds. (effective 2005). adv. reprint service avail. from PSC. **Document type:** *Journal, Academic/Scholarly.* **Description:** Contains research and review papers relating to scientific progress in the field of cellulose, especially the chemistry, biochemistry, physics, and materials science of cellulose and its derivatives.
Related titles: Online - full text ed.: ISSN 1572-882X (from EBSCO Publishing, Gale Group, IngentaConnect, Kluwer Online, O C L C Online Computer Library Center, Inc., Springer LINK, Swets Information Services).
Indexed: ASCA, BIOSIS Prev, BibLing, BiolAb, CCI, CurCont, DBA, EngInd, FLUIDEX, ISR, MSCI, P&BA, RefZh, SCI, TTI, WTA.
—BLDSC (3098.059800), CASDDS, CISTI, IDS, IE, Infotrieve, ingenta. **CCC.**
Published by: (American Chemical Society USA, Cellulose Division USA), Springer-Verlag Dordrecht (Subsidiary of: Springer Science+Business Media), Van Godewijckstraat 30, Dordrecht, 3311 GX, Netherlands. TEL 31-78-6576050, FAX 31-78-6576474, http://springerlink.metapress.com/openurl.asp?genre=journal&issn=0969-0239, http://www.springeronline.com. Ed. Wolfgang Glasser. **Co-sponsor:** Japanese Cellulose Research Society.

547 ROM ISSN 0576-9787
TS920 CODEN: CECTAH
➤ **CELLULOSE CHEMISTRY AND TECHNOLOGY**; international journal for physics, chemistry and technology of cellulose and lignin. Text and summaries in English, French, German, Russian. 1967. 6/yr. bk.rev. **Document type:** *Academic/Scholarly.*
Indexed: ABIPC, ASCA, CCI, CEABA, CIN, ChemAb, ChemTitl, CurCont, DBA, EngInd, ExcerpMed, ISR, MSB, MSCI, P&BA, SCI, TTI.
—BLDSC (3098.090000), CASDDS, CISTI, Ei, IDS, IE, Infotrieve, ingenta, KNAW, Linda Hall.
Published by: Editura Academiei Romane/Publishing House of the Romanian Academy, Calea 13 Septembrie 13, Sector 5, Bucharest, 76117, Romania. TEL 40-21-4119008, FAX 40-21-4103983, edacad@ear.ro, http://www.ear.ro. Ed. Cristofor I Simionescu. **Dist. by:** Rodipet S.A., Piata Presei Libere 1, sector 1, PO Box 33-57, Bucharest 3, Romania. TEL 40-21-2224126, 40-21-2226407, rodipet@rodipet.ro.

➤ **CHEMICALS, CHEMICAL TECHNOLOGY & INSTRUMENTATION WORLD BUYERS' GUIDE**; world buyers' guide for chemicals, bulk drugs, chemical equipment, analytical & process control instruments. see *CHEMISTRY—Analytical Chemistry*

547 USA ISSN 0069-3138
QD181.C1 CODEN: CPHCAY
➤ **CHEMISTRY AND PHYSICS OF CARBON: A SERIES OF ADVANCES.** Text in English. 1966. irreg., latest vol.28, 2003. USD 225 per vol. (effective 2004). adv. **Document type:** *Monographic series, Academic/Scholarly.*
Indexed: ASCA, CCI, CIN, ChemAb, ChemTitl, ISR, MSCI, SCI.
—BLDSC (3170.050000), CASDDS, CISTI, IDS, IE, ingenta, Linda Hall. **CCC.**
Published by: Marcel Dekker Inc. (Subsidiary of: Taylor & Francis Group), 270 Madison Ave, New York, NY 10016-0602. TEL 212-696-9000, FAX 212-685-4540, http://www.dekker.com. Pub. Russell Dekker. R&P Julia Mulligan. Adv. contact Eridania Perez.

547.59 USA ISSN 0069-3154
QD399 CODEN: CHECAV
➤ **CHEMISTRY OF HETEROCYCLIC COMPOUNDS (NEW YORK, 1951)**; a series of monographs. Text in English. 1951. irreg., latest vol.62, 2004. price varies. index. **Document type:** *Monographic series, Academic/Scholarly.*
Indexed: CIN, ChemAb, ChemTitl.
—BLDSC (3171.300000), CASDDS, CISTI, IE, ingenta.
Published by: John Wiley & Sons, Inc., 111 River St, Hoboken, NJ 07030-5774. TEL 201-748-6000, 800-825-7550, FAX 201-748-5915, uscs-wis@wiley.com, http://www.wiley.com. Ed. Garry M Coppola.

547 USA ISSN 0009-3122
QD400 CODEN: CHCCAL
➤ **CHEMISTRY OF HETEROCYCLIC COMPOUNDS (NEW YORK, 1965).** Text in English. 1965. m. EUR 3,358, USD 3,418, GBP 2,008 combined subscription to institutions print & online eds. (effective 2005). adv. back issues avail. **Document type:** *Journal, Academic/Scholarly.* **Description:** Publishes articles on the synthesis, structure, reactivity and biological activity of heterocyclic compounds, including natural products.
Related titles: Microfilm ed.: (from PQC); Online - full text ed.: ISSN 1573-8353 (from EBSCO Publishing, Gale Group, IngentaConnect, Kluwer Online, O C L C Online Computer Library Center, Inc., Springer LINK, Swets Information Services); ♦ Translation of: Khimiya Geterotsiklicheskikh Soedinenii. ISSN 0132-6244.
Indexed: BibLing, CCI, CIN, ChemAb, ChemInfo, ChemTitl, CurCR, CurCont, IndChem, MOS, MSB, RCI, SCI.
—BLDSC (0410.600000), CASDDS, CISTI, Ei, IE, Infotrieve, ingenta. **CCC.**
Published by: (Latvijas Organiskas Sintezes Instituts/Latvian Institute of Organic Synthesis LVA), Consultants Bureau (Subsidiary of: Springer-Verlag New York, Inc.), 233 Spring St, New York, NY 10013. TEL 212-460-1500, FAX 212-460-1575, service@springer-ny.com, http://springerlink.metapress.com/openurl.asp?genre=journal&issn=0009-3122, http://www.springeronline.com. Ed. E Lukevics. **Subscr. to:** Springer-Verlag Dordrecht, Journals Department, PO Box 322, Dordrecht, Netherlands. TEL 31-78-6576392, FAX 31-78-6576474; Springer-Verlag New York, Inc., Journal Fulfillment, PO Box 2485, Secaucus, NJ 07096-2485. TEL 201-348-4033, FAX 201-348-4505, journals@springer-ny.com.

547 USA ISSN 0009-3130
QD415.A1 CODEN: CHNCA8
➤ **CHEMISTRY OF NATURAL COMPOUNDS.** Text in English. 1965. bi-m. EUR 2,798, USD 2,855, GBP 1,748 combined subscription to institutions print & online eds. (effective 2005). adv. back issues avail. **Document type:** *Journal, Academic/Scholarly.* **Description:** Explores the structures of the various classes of natural compounds - the chemical characteristics of botanical families, genus, and species - to better understand the comparative laws, as well as the coonnection between the structures of substances.
Related titles: Microfilm ed.: (from PQC); Online - full text ed.: ISSN 1573-8388 (from EBSCO Publishing, Gale Group, IngentaConnect, Kluwer Online, O C L C Online Computer Library Center, Inc., Ovid Technologies, Inc., Springer LINK, Swets Information Services); ♦ Translation of: Khimiya Prirodnykh Soedinenii. ISSN 0023-1150.
Indexed: AESIS, AgBio, AgrForAb, AnalAb, BibLing, BioCN&I, BiolAb, CCI, CPA, ChemAb, ChemTitl, CurCR, CurCont, DSA, EngInd, ExcerpMed, FCA, FPA, ForAb, HelmAb, HerbAb, HortAb, I&DA, ISR, IndChem, MSB, MaizeAb, NPU, NutrAb, OrnHort, PBA, PGegResA, PGrRegA, PHN&I, PotatoAb, ProtozoAb, RA&MP, RCI, RM&VM, RPP, RevApplEntom, RiceAb, S&F, SCI, SIA, SeedAb, SoyAb, TDB, TriticAb, WeedAb.
—BLDSC (0410.650000), CASDDS, CISTI, GNLM, IE, Infotrieve, ingenta. **CCC.**
Published by: (Uzbek Academy of Sciences UZB), Consultants Bureau (Subsidiary of: Springer-Verlag New York, Inc.), 233 Spring St, New York, NY 10013. TEL 212-460-1500, FAX 212-460-1575, service@springer-ny.com, http://springerlink.metapress.com/openurl.asp?genre=journal&issn=0009-3130, http://www.springeronline.com. Ed. Kh M Shakhidoyatov.

577 547 CHE ISSN 0937-7409
QH541.15.C44 CODEN: CHMOE9
➤ **CHEMOECOLOGY**; evolutionary, mechanistic and environmental approaches to chemically-mediated interactions. Text in English. 1990-199?; N.S. 1998. q. EUR 358 combined subscription to institutions print & online eds. (effective 2005). back issues avail. **Document type:** *Journal, Academic/Scholarly.* **Description:** Publishes papers dealing with the manifold interactions between organisms (between animals or animal and plant) caused by chemical substances and their interactions.
Related titles: Online - full text ed.: ISSN 1423-0445. N.S. (from EBSCO Publishing, Springer LINK, Swets Information Services).
Indexed: AgBio, AgrForAb, AnBrAb, BBCI, BIOBASE, BIOSIS Prev, BioCN&I, BiolAb, CIN, CPA, ChemAb, ChemTitl, CurCont, FCA, FPA, ForAb, HerbAb, HortAb, MaizeAb, OrnHort, PBA, PGegResA, PGrRegA, PotatoAb, RA&MP, RM&VM, RPP, RefZh, RevApplEntom, RiceAb, S&F, SeedAb, TriticAb, WeedAb, ZooRec.
—BLDSC (3172.258000), CASDDS, CISTI, IE, Infotrieve, ingenta, Linda Hall. **CCC.**
Published by: Birkhaeuser Verlag AG (Subsidiary of: Springer Science+Business Media), Viaduktstr 42, Postfach 133, Basel, 4051, Switzerland. TEL 41-61-2050707, FAX 41-61-2050799, chemoeco@ulb.ac.be, info@birkhauser.ch, http://link.springer.de/link/service/journals/00049/index.htm, http://www.birkhauser.ch/journals. Eds. Desire Daloze TEL 32-2-6503537, Jacques M Pasteels TEL 32-2-6504014. Circ: 400. **Subscr. in the Americas to:** Springer-Verlag New York, Inc., Journal Fulfillment, PO Box 2485, Secaucus, NJ 07096-2485. TEL 800-777-4643, 201-348-4033, FAX 201-348-4505, journals@birkhauser.com; **Subscr. to:** Springer GmbH Auslieferungsgesellschaft, Haberstr 7, Heidelberg 69126, Germany. TEL 49-6221-345-0, FAX 49-6221-345-4229, birkhauser@springer.de.

➤ **CHEMTRACTS.** see *CHEMISTRY—Abstracting, Bibliographies, Statistics*

660.284 SGP ISSN 0256-7679
QD380 CODEN: CJPSEG
➤ **CHINESE JOURNAL OF POLYMER SCIENCE.** Text in English. 1983. bi-m. SGD 234, USD 136, EUR 131 to individuals; SGD 585, USD 340, EUR 327 combined subscription to institutions print & online eds. (effective 2006). adv. 96 p./no.; back issues avail. **Document type:** *Journal, Academic/Scholarly.* **Description:** Studies polymer synthesis, polymer physics, polymer chemistry, specialty polymers.
Related titles: Online - full content ed.: (from WanFang Data Corp.); Online - full text ed.: ISSN 1439-6203 (from EBSCO Publishing); ♦ Chinese ed.: Gaofenzi Xuebao. ISSN 1000-3304.
Indexed: ASCA, BrCerAb, C&ISA, CCI, CIN, CerAb, ChemAb, ChemTitl, CivEngAb, CorrAb, CurCont, E&CAJ, EMA, EngInd, IAA, ISMEC, M&TEA, MBF, METADEX, MSCI, RAPRA, RefZh, SolStAb, TTI, WAA.
—BLDSC (3180.559000), CASDDS, CISTI, Ei, IDS, IE, Infotrieve, ingenta, Linda Hall. **CCC.**
Published by: (Zhongguo Huaxuehui/Chinese Chemical Society CHN), World Scientific Publishing Co. Pte. Ltd., 5 Toh Tuck Link, Singapore, 596224, Singapore. TEL 65-466-5775, FAX 65-467-7667, wspc@wspc.com.sg, http://www.worldscinet.com/cjps/cjps.shtml. Ed. Fo-song Wang. Circ: 6,000.

➤ **CHINESE MARKETS FOR FATTY ACIDS.** see *BUSINESS AND ECONOMICS—Marketing And Purchasing*

➤ **CHINESE MARKETS FOR FATTY ALCOHOL.** see *BUSINESS AND ECONOMICS—Marketing And Purchasing*

547 DEU ISSN 0303-402X
QD549 CODEN: CPMSB6
➤ **COLLOID AND POLYMER SCIENCE**; Kolloid-Zeitschrift und Zeitschrift fuer Polymere. Text in English. 1906. m. EUR 2,598 combined subscription to institutions print & online eds. (effective 2005). adv. bk.rev. abstr.; bibl.; charts; illus. Index. back issues avail. **Document type:** *Journal, Academic/Scholarly.* **Description:** Devoted to colloid and polymer science and its interdisciplinary interactions.
Former titles (until 1973): Kolloid-Zeitschrift und Zeitschrift fuer Polymere (0023-2904); (until 1961): Kolloid-Zeitschrift (0368-6590); Which incorporated: Kolloid-Beihefte (0368-6345); Zeitschrift fur Chemie und Industrie der Kolloide (0372-820X)
Related titles: Microform ed.: (from PMC, PQC); Online - full text ed.: ISSN 1435-1536 (from EBSCO Publishing, Springer LINK, Swets Information Services); ♦ Supplement(s): Progress in Colloid and Polymer Science. ISSN 0340-255X.
Indexed: A&ATA, ABIPC, ASCA, ApMecR, BPRC&P, BiolAb, C&ISA, CCI, CEABA, CIN, ChemAb, ChemTitl, CurCont, DSA, E&CAJ, E&PHSE, EngInd, ExcerpMed, GP&P, ISMEC, ISR, Inspec, MSCI, P&BA, PetrolAb, PhotoAb, RAPRA, RCI, RefZh, S&F, SCI, SIA, SolStAb, TTI, WSCA.
—BLDSC (3313.350000), AskIEEE, CASDDS, CISTI, Ei, IDS, IE, Infotrieve, ingenta, KNAW, Linda Hall, PADDS. **CCC.**
Published by: Springer-Verlag (Subsidiary of: Springer Science+Business Media), Tiergartenstr 17, Heidelberg, 69121, Germany. TEL 49-6221-3450, FAX 49-6221-345229, http://link.springer.de/link/service/journals/00396/index.htm. Eds. Friedrich Kremer, Walter Richtering. Adv. contact Stephan Kroeck TEL 49-30-827875739. Circ: 2,000. **Subscr.**

in the Americas to: Springer-Verlag New York, Inc., Journal Fulfillment, PO Box 2485, Secaucus, NJ 07096-2485. TEL 800-777-4643, 201-348-4033, FAX 201-348-4505, journals@springer-ny.com, http://www.springer-ny.com; **Subscr. to:** Springer GmbH Auslieferungsgesellschaft, Haberstr 7, Heidelberg 69126, Germany. TEL 49-6221-345-0, FAX 49-6221-345-4229, subscriptions@springer.de.

547 USA ISSN 0149-9378
QD262
COMPENDIUM OF ORGANIC SYNTHETIC METHODS. Text in English. 1971. irreg., latest vol.11, 2003. price varies. back issues avail. **Document type:** *Monographic series, Academic/Scholarly.*
Related titles: Online - full text ed.
Published by: John Wiley & Sons, Inc., 111 River St, Hoboken, NJ 07030-5774. TEL 201-748-6000, 800-825-7550, FAX 201-748-5915, uscs-wis@wiley.com, http://www.wiley.com. **Subscr. outside the Americas to:** John Wiley & Sons Ltd., The Atrium, Southern Gate, Chichester, West Sussex PO19 8SQ, United Kingdom. TEL 44-1243-779777, FAX 44-1243-775878.

CONGRESS OF HETEROCYCLIC CHEMISTRY. BOOK OF ABSTRACTS/FUKUSOKAN KAGAKU TORONKAI KOEN YOSHISHU. see *CHEMISTRY—Abstracting, Bibliographies, Statistics*

547 011 USA
CONTROLLED RELEASE NEWSLETTER. Text in English. 1982. irreg. (2-3/yr.). USD 65 to members (effective 1999). bk.rev. **Document type:** *Newsletter.*
Published by: Controlled Release Society, Inc., 13355 10th Ave N, Ste. 108, Minneapolis, MN 55441-5554. TEL 847-808-7071. Ed. T J Roseman. Circ: 3,000.

547 USA
RS201.C64 CODEN: PCRMEY
CONTROLLED RELEASE SOCIETY. PROCEEDINGS. Text in English. 1973. a. USD 85 to members (effective 1999). back issues avail. **Document type:** *Proceedings.*
Formerly (until 2002): Controlled Release Society. International Symposium on Controlled Release of Bioactive Materials. Proceedings (1022-0178)
Related titles: CD-ROM ed.
Indexed: CIN, ChemAb, ExcerpMed.
—BLDSC (6841.422500), CASDDS, IE, ingenta, KNAW.
Published by: (Korean Society for Biomaterials KOR), Controlled Release Society, Inc., 13355 10th Ave N, Ste. 108, Minneapolis, MN 55441-5554. TEL 847-808-7071. Circ: 3,000.

540 ESP ISSN 1132-1369
CROMATOGRAFIA Y TECNICAS AFINES. Text in Spanish. 1973. s-a.
Formerly (until 1989): Grupo de Cromatografia y Tecnicas Afines. Boletin Informativo (0211-0512)
Indexed: IECT.
—CINDOC.
Published by: Instituto de Quimica Organica General, Juan de la Cierva, 3, Madrid, 28006, Spain. TEL 34-91-5622900. Ed. Isabel Martinez Castro.

547 NLD ISSN 1385-2728
QD241 CODEN: CORCFE
➤ **CURRENT ORGANIC CHEMISTRY.** Text in English. 1997. 15/yr. EUR 1,710, USD 1,710 to institutions (academic), print or online; EUR 3,640, USD 3,640 to corporations print or online; EUR 470, USD 470 combined subscription to individuals print & online; EUR 1,890, USD 1,890 combined subscription to institutions (academic), print & online; EUR 4,370, USD 4,370 combined subscription to corporations print & online (effective 2004). adv. **Document type:** *Journal, Academic/Scholarly.* **Description:** Publishes reviews on the current progress in the fields of asymmetric synthesis, organo-metallic chemistry, bioorganic chemistry, heterocyclic chemistry, natural product chemistry, and analytic methods in organic chemistry.
Related titles: Online - full text ed.: (from EBSCO Publishing, Gale Group, IngentaConnect, Swets Information Services).
Indexed: CCI, ChemAb, CurCont, ExcerpMed, ISR, MSB, SCI.
—BLDSC (3500.785000), CASDDS, CISTI, IDS, IE, Infotrieve, ingenta. **CCC.**
Published by: Bentham Science Publishers Ltd., PO Box 1673, Hilversum, BR 1200, Netherlands. TEL 31-35-6923800, FAX 31-35-6980150, M.Bentham@inter.nl.net, http://www.bentham.org/coc. Ed. Atta-ur Rahman TEL 92-21-4969873. **Subscr. addr. in the US:** Bentham Science Publishers Ltd., 1400 Pine St, PO Box 640310, San Francisco, CA 94164-0310. FAX 415-775-4503, shidding@worldonline.nl.

547 NLD ISSN 1570-1794
▼ **CURRENT ORGANIC SYNTHESIS.** Text in English. 2004. q. USD 140 combined subscription to individuals print & online; USD 500 combined subscription to institutions (academic), print & online; USD 970 combined subscription to corporations print & online (effective 2005). **Document type:** *Journal, Academic/Scholarly.* **Description:** Publishes in-depth reviews on all areas of synthetic organic chemistry i.e. asymmetric synthesis, organometallic chemistry, novel synthetic approaches to complex organic molecules, carbohydrates, polymers, protein chemistry, DNA chemistry, supramolecular chemistry, molecular recognition and new synthetic methods in organic chemistry.
Related titles: Online - full content ed.; Online - full text ed.: (from EBSCO Publishing, Gale Group, IngentaConnect, Swets Information Services).
Indexed: CCI, CurCont.
—BLDSC (3500.785500), IE. **CCC.**
Published by: Bentham Science Publishers Ltd., PO Box 1673, Hilversum, BR 1200, Netherlands. TEL 31-35-6923800, FAX 31-35-6980150, M.Bentham@inter.nl.net, http://www.bentham.org/. Ed. Atta-ur Rahman TEL 92-21-4969873. **Subscr. address in the US:** Bentham Science Publishers Ltd., 1400 Pine St, PO Box 640310, San Francisco, CA 94164-0310. FAX 415-775-4503.

547.92 IND ISSN 0972-4788
CURRENT TOPICS IN STEROID RESEARCH. Text in English. 1998. a.
—BLDSC (3504.926000).
Published by: Research Trends, T.C. 17/250(3), Chadiyara Rd, Poojapura, Trivandrum, Kerala 695 012, India.

665 JPN ISSN 0011-5355
CODEN: DKSSAB
DAIICHI KOGYO SEIYAKU. SHAHO/DAIICHI KOGYO SEIYAKU. REVIEW. Text in Japanese. 1931. bi-m. free. adv. bk.rev. charts; illus. **Document type:** *Trade.*
—CASDDS.
Published by: Daiichi Kogyo Seiyaku Co. Ltd., New Kyoto Center Bldg., 614, Higahi-shiokoji-cho, Shimokyo-ku, Kyoto, 600, Japan. TEL 81-75-343-1181, FAX 81-75-343-1421. Ed. Syoichi Haatori. Circ: 4,000.

664 NLD ISSN 0167-4501
CODEN: DFSCDX
➤ **DEVELOPMENTS IN FOOD SCIENCE.** Text in English. 1978. irreg., latest vol.41, 2000. price varies. back issues avail. **Document type:** *Monographic series, Academic/Scholarly.* **Description:** Reports on research and developments in various areas of food science and technology.
Indexed: ASFA, Agr, BIOSIS Prev, CIN, ChemAb, ChemTitl, ESPM, FS&TA, MSB.
—BLDSC (3579.071800), CASDDS, CISTI, IE, ingenta. **CCC.**
Published by: Elsevier BV (Subsidiary of: Elsevier Science & Technology), Radarweg 29, Amsterdam, 1043 NX, Netherlands. TEL 31-20-4853911, FAX 31-20-4852457, nlinfo-f@elsevier.nl, http://www.elsevier.nl.

547.84 GBR ISSN 0264-3022
QD380 CODEN: DOPODF
➤ **DEVELOPMENTS IN ORIENTED POLYMERS.** Text in English. 1982. irreg., latest vol.2, 1987. price varies. back issues avail. **Document type:** *Monographic series, Academic/Scholarly.*
—CASDDS, CISTI. **CCC.**
Published by: Pergamon (Subsidiary of: Elsevier Science & Technology), The Boulevard, Langford Ln, East Park, Kidlington, Oxford OX5 1GB, United Kingdom. TEL 44-1865-843000, FAX 44-1865-843010. Ed. I M Ward. **Subscr. to:** Elsevier BV, PO Box 211, Amsterdam 1000 AE, Netherlands. TEL 31-20-485-3757, FAX 31-20-485-3432, nlinfo-f@elsevier.nl, http://www.elsevier.nl.

547 GBR ISSN 0967-6686
QD246
DICTIONARY OF ORGANIC COMPOUNDS ON CD-ROM. Text in English. 1993. s-a. GBP 3,500; GBP 950 renewals. **Document type:** *Academic/Scholarly.* **Description:** Contains chemical, structural and bibliographic data on more than 152,000 organic compounds with full-text retrieval and substructure searching.
Media: CD-ROM. **Related titles:** Supplement(s): ISSN 0264-1100.
Published by: Chapman & Hall, Electronic Publishing Division, Chapman & Hall, 2-6 Boundary Row, London, SE1 8HN, United Kingdom. TEL 44-20-7865-0066, FAX 44-20-7522-0101, cust.serv@chall.co.uk, http://epd.chapmanhall.com. **Dist. by:** Cheriton House, North Way, Andover, Hamps SP10 5BE, United Kingdom. TEL 44-1264-332424, FAX 44-1264-342787.

547 660 USA
CODEN: KLCBDZ
EASTMAN FINE CHEMICALS NEWS. Text in English. 1927. 3/yr. looseleaf. free to qualified personnel. adv. reprint service avail. from PQC.
Former titles: Kodak Laboratory Chemicals News; (until 1987): Kodak Laboratory Chemicals Bulletin (0270-4986); (until 1980): Eastman Organic Chemical Bulletin (0096-221X); Organic Chemical Bulletin (0012-897X)
Related titles: Microform ed.: (from PQC).
Indexed: ChemAb.
—CASDDS, Linda Hall.
Published by: (Laboratory and Research Products), Eastman Kodak Co., 343 State St, Rochester, NY 14650. TEL 716-724-2207, FAX 716-722-3179, TELEX 68-54148. Ed. Deborah Nippon. Circ: 90,000.

ELECTROCHEMICAL SCIENCE AND TECHNOLOGY OF POLYMERS. see *CHEMISTRY—Electrochemistry*

547 GBR ISSN 1464-4622
QD95 CODEN: EPARF3
ELECTRON PARAMAGNETIC RESONANCE. Text in English. 1973. irreg., latest vol.18, 2004. price varies. charts; illus. index. back issues avail. **Document type:** *Monographic series, Academic/Scholarly.* **Description:** Reviews electron spin resonance literature.
Formerly (until 1998): Electron Spin Resonance. Part A; Which Superseded in part: Electron Spin Resonance (0305-9758)
Related titles: Online - full text ed.
Indexed: BIOSIS Prev, CIN, ChemAb, ChemTitl, SCI.
—BLDSC (3699.761970), CASDDS, CISTI, IE, ingenta. **CCC.**
Published by: Royal Society of Chemistry, Thomas Graham House, Science Park, Milton Rd, Cambridge, CB4 0WF, United Kingdom. TEL 44-1223-432360, FAX 44-1223-423623, sales@rsc.org, http://www.rsc.org/publishing/books/0854043209.asp. Eds. B C Gilbert, D M Murphy, M J Davies. **Subscr. to:** Extenza - Turpin, Pegasus Dr, Stratton Business Park, Biggleswade, Beds SG18 8TQ, United Kingdom.

660.284 547 JPN ISSN 0013-8460
ENBI TO PORIMA/VINYLS AND POLYMERS. Text in Japanese; Summaries in English. 1961. m. JPY 16,000. adv. bk.rev. abstr.; charts; illus.; stat. index. reprint service avail. from PQC.
Media: Duplicated (not offset). **Related titles:** Online - full text ed.
Indexed: ASCA, JTA.
Published by: Institute of Polymer Industry, Inc./Porima Kogyo Kenkyujo, C.P.O. Box 1176, Tokyo, 100-8693, Japan. http://www.rapra.net. Ed. Fumio Miyamoto. Circ: 16,000.

665 ITA ISSN 0014-0902
CODEN: EDAGAH
ESSENZE-DERIVATI AGRUMARI. Text in Italian. 1930. q. adv. bk.rev. abstr.; bibl.; charts; stat. index.
Related titles: Microform ed.
Indexed: ASFA, AnalAb, CIN, ChemAb, ChemTitl, ESPM, FS&TA, HortAb, WeedAb.
—CASDDS.
Published by: Stazione Sperimentale per l'Industria delle Essenze e dei Derivati Agrumari, Corso Vittorio Emanuele 131, Reggio Calabria, RC 89100, Italy. Ed. Angelo Di Giacomo. Circ: 500.

EUROPEAN JOURNAL OF MEDICINAL CHEMISTRY. see *BIOLOGY—Biochemistry*

547 DEU ISSN 1434-193X
QD241 CODEN: EJOCFK
➤ **EUROPEAN JOURNAL OF ORGANIC CHEMISTRY.** Text in English. 1998. s-m. EUR 3,338 in Europe; CHF 5,538 in Switzerland & Liechtenstein; USD 4,484 elsewhere; EUR 3,672 combined subscription in Europe print & online eds.; CHF 6,092 combined subscription in Switzerland & Liechtenstein for print & online eds.; USD 4,933 combined subscription elsewhere print & online eds. (effective 2006). adv. illus.; bibl. Index. 220 p./no. 2 cols./p.; reprints avail. **Document type:** *Journal, Academic/Scholarly.* **Description:** Presents full papers, microreviews, and short communications from the entire spectrum of synthetic organic, bioorganic and physical-organic chemistry.
Formed by the merger of (1818-1998): Liebigs Annalen (0947-3440); Which was formerly (until 1995): Liebigs Annalen der Chemie (0170-2041); (until 1978): Justus Liebigs Annalen der Chemie (0075-4617); (until 1840): Annalen der Pharmacie (0365-5490); (until 1832): Magazin fuer Pharmacie (0369-1462); (until 1825): Magazin fuer die Neuesten Erfahrungen, Entdeckungen und Berichtigungen im Gebiete der Pharmacie (0369-1004); (until 1823): Allgemeine Bordische Annalen der Chemie fuer die Freunde der Naturkunde und Arzneiwissenschaft im Russischen Reiche (0365-4923); Part of (1907-1998): Societe Chimique de France. Bulletin (0037-8968); Which was formerly (until 1946): Bulletin de la Societe Chimique de France. Memoires (0366-3132); Part of (1945-1998): Societes Chimiques Belges. Bulletin (0037-9646); Part of (1871-1998): Gazzetta Chimica Italiana (0016-5603); Part of (1990-1998): Anales de Quimica (1130-2283); Part of (1905-1998): Revista Portuguesa de Quimica (0035-0419); Part of (1969-1998): Chimika Chronika (0366-693X); Part of (1951-1998): Acta Chimica Hungarica: Models in Chemistry (1217-8969); Part of (1882-1998): Recueil des Travaux Chimiques des Pays-Bas (0165-0513); Which was formerly (until 1920): Recueil des Travaux Chimiques des Pays-Bas et la Belgique (0370-7539); (until 1897): Recueil des Travaux Chimiques des Pays-Bas (0034-186X)
Related titles: Online - full text ed.: ISSN 1099-0690. EUR 3,338 in Europe to institutions; CHF 5,538 to institutions in Switzerland & Liechtenstein; USD 4,484 elsewhere to institutions (effective 2006) (from EBSCO Publishing, Swets Information Services, Wiley InterScience).

C

▼ new title ➤ refereed ✶ unverified ♦ full entry avail.

Indexed: ASFA, AbHyg, AgrForAb, BioCN&I, CCI, CIN, ChemAb, ChemInfo, ChemTitl, CurCR, CurCont, DBA, DSA, ESPM, EngInd, ForAb, HelmAb, HortAb, ISR, IndChem, IndVet, Inspec, MOS, MSB, NPU, NemAb, OrnHort, PHN&I, PN&I, PollutAb, PotatoAb, ProtozoAb, RA&MP, RCI, RM&VM, RPP, RefZh, RevApplEntom, SCI, SIA, TDB, VetBull, WeedAb, ZooRec.
—BLDSC (3829.733255), CASDDS, CINDOC, CISTI, IDS, IE, Infotrieve, ingenta, Linda Hall. **CCC.**
Published by: Wiley - V C H Verlag GmbH & Co. KGaA (Subsidiary of: John Wiley & Sons, Inc.), Boschstr 12, Weinheim, 69469, Germany. TEL 49-6201-6060, FAX 49-6201-606328, ejic-ejoc@wiley-vch.de, adsales@wiley-vch.de, http://www.eurjoc.org, http://www3.interscience.wiley.com/cgi-bin/home. Ed. Haymo Ross. Pub. Eva E Wille. R&P Claudia Rutz. Adv. contact Aenne Anders TEL 49-6201-606552. B&W page EUR 2,100; 180 x 260. **Subscr. in the Americas to:** John Wiley & Sons, Inc., 111 River St, Hoboken, NJ 07030-5774. TEL 201-748-6645, FAX 201-748-6088, subinfo@wiley.com; **Subscr. outside of Germany and Austria to:** John Wiley & Sons Ltd., The Atrium, Southern Gate, Chichester, West Sussex PO19 8SQ, United Kingdom. TEL 44-1243-779777, FAX 44-1243-775878, cs-journals@wiley.co.uk.

547 GBR ISSN 0014-3057
QD281.P6 CODEN: EUPJAG
➤ **EUROPEAN POLYMER JOURNAL.** Text in English, French, German, Italian. 1965. 12/yr. EUR 3,315 in Europe to institutions; JPY 440,300 in Japan to institutions; USD 3,708 to institutions except Europe and Japan (effective 2006). adv. bk.rev. abstr.; charts; illus. back issues avail. **Document type:** *Journal, Academic/Scholarly.* **Description:** Publishes results bearing on the physics and chemistry of natural and synthetic macronuclear substances, and review articles covering advances in polymer technology.
Related titles: Microfilm ed.: (from PQC); Online - full text ed.: (from EBSCO Publishing, Gale Group, IngentaConnect, ScienceDirect, Swets Information Services).
Indexed: ASCA, AnalAb, BrCerAb, C&ISA, CCI, CIN, CerAb, ChemAb, ChemTitl, CivEngAb, CorrAb, CurCont, DSA, E&CAJ, EMA, EngInd, ExcerpMed, IAA, ISMEC, ISR, Inspec, M&TEA, MBF, METADEX, MSB, MSCI, RAPRA, RCI, RefZh, SCI, SolStAb, TTI, WAA, WSCA.
—BLDSC (3829.791000), CASDDS, CISTI, Ei, IDS, IE, Infotrieve, ingenta, Linda Hall. **CCC.**
Published by: Pergamon (Subsidiary of: Elsevier Science & Technology), The Boulevard, Langford Ln, East Park, Kidlington, Oxford OX5 1GB, United Kingdom. TEL 44-1865-843000, FAX 44-1865-843010, http://www.elsevier.com/locate/europolj. Ed. D. M. Haddleton. Circ: 1,400. **Subscr. to:** Elsevier BV, PO Box 211, Amsterdam 1000 AE, Netherlands. TEL 31-20-485-3757, FAX 31-20-485-3432, nlinfo-f@elsevier.nl, http://www.elsevier.nl.

547 USA ISSN 0271-616X
QD262 CODEN: FFRSEV
FIESER AND FIESER'S REAGENTS FOR ORGANIC SYNTHESIS. Text in English. 1967. irreg., latest 2000. price varies. **Document type:** *Monographic series, Academic/Scholarly.*
Formerly (until 1980): Reagents for Organic Synthesis (0271-6747)
—CASDDS, CISTI.
Published by: John Wiley & Sons, Inc., 111 River St, Hoboken, NJ 07030-5774. TEL 201-748-6000, 800-825-7550, FAX 201-748-5915, uscs-wis@wiley.com, http://www.wiley.com. Ed. Louis F Fieser. **Subscr. outside the Americas to:** John Wiley & Sons Ltd., The Atrium, Southern Gate, Chichester, West Sussex PO19 8SQ, United Kingdom. TEL 44-1243-779777, FAX 44-1243-775878.

FITOTERAPIA. see *BIOLOGY—Botany*

547 GBR ISSN 0882-5734
CODEN: FFJOED
➤ **FLAVOUR & FRAGRANCE JOURNAL.** Text in English. 1986. bi-m. USD 1,535 to institutions; USD 1,689 combined subscription to institutions print & online eds. (effective 2006). adv. bk.rev. back issues avail.; reprint service avail. from PSC. **Document type:** *Journal, Academic/Scholarly.* **Description:** Covers the rapid publication of scientific and technical papers on essential oils and related products.
Related titles: Online - full content ed.: ISSN 1099-1026. USD 1,535 to institutions (effective 2006); Online - full text ed.: (from EBSCO Publishing, Swets Information Services, Wiley InterScience).
Indexed: AEA, ASFA, AbHyg, AgBio, AgrForAb, AnalAb, BIOBASE, BIOSIS Prev, BiolAb, CIN, CPA, ChemAb, ChemTitl, ChemoAb, CurCont, DSA, EngInd, ExcerpMed, FCA, FPA, FS&TA, ForAb, HortAb, IABS, MSB, NPU, NutrAb, OrnHort, PBA, PGegResA, PGrRegA, PHN&I, PoultAb, RA&MP, RM&VM, RPP, RevApplEntom, S&F, SIA, SeedAb, TDB, VITIS, WeedAb.
—BLDSC (3950.047000), CASDDS, CISTI, Ei, GNLM, IDS, IE, Infotrieve, ingenta. **CCC.**
Published by: John Wiley & Sons Ltd. (Subsidiary of: John Wiley & Sons, Inc.), The Atrium, Southern Gate, Chichester, West Sussex PO19 8SQ, United Kingdom. TEL 44-1243-779777, FAX 44-1243-775878, customer@wiley.co.uk, http://www.interscience.wiley.com/jpages/0882-5734, http://www.wiley.co.uk. Ed. J Piggott. adv.: B&W page GBP 650, color page GBP 1,550; trim 210 x 297. Circ: 500. **Subscr. to:** John Wiley & Sons, Inc., 111 River St, Hoboken, NJ 07030-5774. TEL 201-748-6645, 800-225-5945, subinfo@wiley.com.

➤ **FOLIA MICROBIOLOGICA.** see *BIOLOGY—Biochemistry*

547 AUT ISSN 0071-7886
QD241 CODEN: FCONAA
➤ **FORTSCHRITTE DER CHEMIE ORGANISCHER NATURSTOFFE/PROGRESS IN THE CHEMISTRY OF ORGANIC NATURAL PRODUCTS.** Text in English. 1938. irreg., latest vol.87, 2004. price varies. cum.index: vols.1-20 (1938-1962). reprint service avail. from ISI. **Document type:** *Monographic series, Academic/Scholarly.* **Description:** Contains contributions on various topics related to the origin, distribution, chemistry, synthesis, biochemistry, function or use of various classes of naturally occurring substances ranging from small molecules to biopolymers.
Indexed: AgBio, Agr, BIOSIS Prev, BiolAb, CCI, CPA, ChemAb, ChemInfo, ChemTitl, DBA, ExcerpMed, FPA, ForAb, HortAb, IndMed, MEDLINE, PBA, PGegResA, RA&MP, RM&VM, RPP, VITIS.
—BLDSC (6867.200000), CASDDS, CISTI, IE, Infotrieve, ingenta, Linda Hall. **CCC.**
Published by: Springer-Verlag Wien (Subsidiary of: Springer Science+Business Media) TEL 43-1-3302415-0, FAX 43-1-330242665, books@springer.at, http://www.springeronline.com/sgw/cda/frontpage/0,11855,1-40109-69-1187179-0,00.html, http://www.springer.at. Eds. Heinz Falk, W Herz. R&P Angela Foessl TEL 43-1-3302415517.

547 NLD ISSN 1574-0900
▼ **FRONTIERS IN ORGANIC CHEMISTRY.** Text in English. 2005. a. USD 130 per vol. (effective 2005). **Document type:** *Monographic series, Academic/Scholarly.* **Description:** Publishes the latest and most important advances in organic chemistry.
Related titles: CD-ROM ed.; Online - full content ed.; Online - full text ed.: (from IngentaConnect).
Published by: Bentham Science Publishers Ltd., PO Box 1673, Hilversum, BR 1200, Netherlands. TEL 31-35-6923800, FAX 31-35-6980150, M.Bentham@inter.nl.net, http://www.bentham.org/foc/index2.htm. Ed. Atta-ur Rahman TEL 92-21-4969873.

547 ESP ISSN 0017-3495
CODEN: GRACAN
➤ **GRASAS Y ACEITES.** Text and summaries in English, Spanish. 1950. bi-m. EUR 130.69 domestic; EUR 150,80 foreign (effective 2005). adv. bk.rev. abstr.; bibl.; charts; illus.; pat.; stat. index. **Document type:** *Journal, Academic/Scholarly.* **Description:** Includes articles on seed oil products, proteins, vegetable products, detergents and surfactants, by-products and vegetation water treatment.
Related titles: Online - full text ed.: (from EBSCO Publishing).
Indexed: ASCA, ASFA, ApicAb, B&BAb, BIOSIS Prev, BiolAb, CIN, CLL, CPA, ChemAb, ChemTitl, ChemoAb, CurCont, DSA, ESPM, FCA, FS&TA, H&SSA, HerbAb, HortAb, IECT, ISR, MBA, MaizeAb, NutrAb, OrnHort, PBA, PGegResA, PHN&I, PN&I, PollutAb, PotatoAb, PoultAb, RA&MP, RPP, RefZh, S&F, SCI, SIA, SeedAb, SoyAb, TriticAb, VITIS.
—BLDSC (4213.000000), CASDDS, CINDOC, CISTI, IDS, IE, ingenta. **CCC.**
Published by: Consejo Superior de Investigaciones Cientificas, Instituto de la Grasa, Ave Padre Garcia Tejero, 4, Sevilla, 41012, Spain. TEL 34-95-4611550, FAX 34-95-4616790, igrasa@cica.es, http://www.ig.csic.es/. Circ: 1,000.

547 CHN ISSN 1005-1511
QD156 CODEN: ZGDXFY
HECHENG HUAXUE/CHINESE JOURNAL OF SYNTHETIC CHEMISTRY. Text in Chinese, English. 1993. bi-m. CNY 57, USD 24 (effective 2003). bk.rev. 112 p./no.; **Document type:** *Academic/Scholarly.*
Related titles: Online - full text ed.: (from East View Information Services, WanFang Data Corp.).
Indexed: CIN, ChemAb, ChemTitl, MOS, NPU.
—BLDSC (3180.680200), CASDDS, IE, ingenta.
Published by: Chengdu Yuji Huaxuesuo/Chengdu Organic Chemistry Co., Ltd. (Subsidiary of: Zhongguo Kexueyuan/Chinese Academy of Sciences), No.9 Section 4, Renmin Nan lu, Chengdu, 610041, China. TEL 86-28-85255007, tqs@cioc.ac.cn, http://hchx.periodicals.net.cn/default.html. Circ: 1,000. **Dist. overseas by:** China International Book Trading Corp, 35 Chegongzhuang Xilu, Haidian District, PO Box 399, Beijing 100044, China. TEL 86-10-68412045, FAX 86-10-68412023, cibtc@mail.cibtc.com.cn, http://www.cibtc.com.cn.

547.59 JPN ISSN 0385-5414
QD399 CODEN: HTCYAM
➤ **HETEROCYCLES.** Text in English. 1973. 15/yr. EUR 4,016 in Europe to institutions; USD 4,491 to institutions except Europe and Japan (effective 2006). bk.rev. Index. reprint service avail. from PQC. **Document type:** *Journal, Academic/Scholarly.* **Description:** Publishes accounts of research on the organic chemistry of heterocyclic compounds and natural products having the heterocyclic system.
Related titles: Microform ed.: (from PQC); Online - full text ed.: (from EBSCO Publishing, ScienceDirect).
Indexed: ASCA, CCI, CIN, ChemAb, ChemInfo, ChemTitl, CurCR, CurCont, DBA, ISR, IndChem, MOS, MSB, NPU, RCI, RefZh, SCI, SSCI, VITIS.
—BLDSC (4301.250000), CASDDS, CISTI, IDS, IE, Infotrieve, ingenta, Linda Hall. **CCC.**
Published by: Japan Institute of Heterocyclic Chemistry, 1-7-17 Motoaka-Saka, Minato-ku, Tokyo, 107-0051, Japan. TEL 81-3-3404-5019, FAX 81-3-3497-9370, be3k-kmtn@asahi-net.ov.jp, info@heterocycles.com, www.heterocycles.com, http://www.heterocycles.jp/heterohtml/index.html. Ed. Keiichiro Fukumoto. Circ: 1,100. **Subscr. outside Japan to:** Elsevier BV, PO Box 211, Amsterdam 1000 AE, Netherlands. TEL 31-20-485-3757, FAX 31-20-485-3432.

660.284 547 GBR ISSN 0954-0083
TA455.P58 CODEN: HPPOEX
➤ **HIGH PERFORMANCE POLYMERS.** Text in English. 1989-ceased; resumed 2003. bi-m. GBP 489, USD 757 to institutions; GBP 509, USD 788 combined subscription to institutions print & online eds. (effective 2006). index. **Document type:** *Journal, Academic/Scholarly.* **Description:** Publishes research papers on polymer chemistry. Covers molecular modeling and polymer design, as well as the testing and performance of polymers.
Related titles: Microfiche ed.: USD 395 in North America; GBP 206 elsewhere (effective 2002) (from AIP); Online - full text ed.: ISSN 1361-6412. GBP 483, USD 749 to institutions (effective 2006) (from C S A, EBSCO Publishing, O C L C Online Computer Library Center, Inc., Sage Publications, Inc., Swets Information Services).
Indexed: BrCerAb, C&ISA, CCI, CIN, CerAb, ChemAb, ChemTitl, CivEngAb, CorrAb, CurCont, E&CAJ, EMA, EngInd, IAA, ISR, Inspec, M&TEA, MBF, METADEX, MSCI, RAPRA, SCI, SolStAb, TTI, WAA.
—BLDSC (4307.338660), AskIEEE, CASDDS, CISTI, Ei, IDS, IE, Infotrieve, ingenta, Linda Hall. **CCC.**
Published by: (Institute of Physics), Sage Science Press (UK) (Subsidiary of: Sage Publications, Inc.), 1 Oliver's Yard, 55 City Rd, London, EC1Y 1SP, United Kingdom. TEL 44-20-73248500, FAX 44-20-73248600, info@sagepub.com, http://www.sagepub.co.uk/journal.aspx?pid=105574. Ed. John Connell. Circ: 141. **Subscr. in the Americas to:** Sage Publications, Inc., 2455 Teller Rd, Thousand Oaks, CA 91320. TEL 805-499-0721, FAX 805-499-0871, journals@sagepub.com.

➤ **HUAXUE YANJIU/CHEMICAL RESEARCHES.** see *CHEMISTRY—Inorganic Chemistry*

547.01 USA
HYDROCARBON ONLINE. Text in English. 1997. m. adv. bk.rev. **Document type:** *Newsletter.* **Description:** Serves the needs of engineers, managers, government personnel, and consulting firms involved with hydrocarbon.
Media: Online - full text.
Address: mmcnulty@hydrocarbononline.com, http://news.hydrocarbononline.com/. Ed. Mike Mcnulty Mike Hagan.

547 662.6 USA ISSN 1056-7194
TP360 CODEN: INBOES
INDUSTRIAL BIOPROCESSING; a monthly intelligence service. Text in English. 1979. m. USD 1,152 in North America to institutions (effective 2005). abstr.; bibl.; charts; pat.; stat.; tr.lit. back issues avail. **Document type:** *Newsletter, Trade.* **Description:** Focuses on industrial processes involving biological routes to produce chemicals and energy; reflects the growing interest in bioproducts and the marketplace.
Former titles (until 1991): Bioprocessing Technology (0885-5625); (until 1985): Biomass Digest (0163-6766)
Related titles: Online - full text ed.: (from Factiva, Florida Center for Library Automation, Gale Group).
Indexed: ABIPC, Agr, CBTA, EngInd.
—CISTI.
Published by: Frost & Sullivan, 7550 W Interstate 10, Ste 9, San Antonio, TX 78229. ibinfo@insights.com, http://www.insights.com, http://www.frost.com.

547 ESP ISSN 0490-2602
INSTITUTO NACIONAL DEL CARBON. MEMORIA. Text in Spanish. 1956. a.
—CINDOC.
Published by: Consejo Superior de Investigaciones Cientificas, Instituto Nacional del Carbon, C. Francisco Pintado Fe, No. 26, Oviedo, 33011, Spain. TEL 34-98-5119090, FAX 34-98-5297662, http://www.incar.csic.es/.

INTERNATIONAL DATA SERIES. SELECTED DATA ON MIXTURES. SERIES A. THERMODYNAMIC PROPERTIES OF NON-REACTING BINARY SYSTEMS OF ORGANIC SUBSTANCES. see *CHEMISTRY—Physical Chemistry*

C

547 600 USA ISSN 1073-2136
CODEN: IFSSEZ
➤ **INTERNATIONAL FIBER SCIENCE AND TECHNOLOGY SERIES.** Text in English. 1983. irreg., latest vol.15, 1998. USD 275 per vol. (effective 2004). adv. **Document type:** *Monographic series, Academic/Scholarly.*
Indexed: CIN, ChemAb, ChemTitl.
—BLDSC (4540.186650), CASDDS, CISTI. **CCC.**
Published by: Marcel Dekker Inc. (Subsidiary of: Taylor & Francis Group), 270 Madison Ave, New York, NY 10016-0602. TEL 212-696-9000, FAX 212-685-4540, journals@dekker.com, http://www.dekker.com. Pub. Russell Dekker. R&P Julia Mulligan. Adv. contact Eridania Perez. **Subscr. to:** 6000 Broken Sound Pkwy NW, Ste. 300, Boca Raton, FL 33487-2713. TEL 800-228-1160.

547 USA ISSN 1537-3207
➤ **INTERNATIONAL JOURNAL OF COATINGS SCIENCE.** Text in English. 2002 (Aug.). q. USD 60 to individuals; USD 250 to institutions (effective 2002). **Document type:** *Journal, Academic/Scholarly.*
Media: Online - full content.
Published by: (University of Southern Mississippi, School of Polymers and High Performance Materials), The U S M Polymer Science Press, Box 10076, Hattiesburg, MS 39406-0076. TEL 601-266-5635, FAX 601-266-6868, ijcs@usm.edu, http://www.usm.edu/ijcs. Ed. Marek W. Urban.

➤ **INTERNATIONAL JOURNAL OF CONDENSED MATTER RESEARCH AND INTERNET REVIEWS.** see *CHEMISTRY—Crystallography*

547 CHE ISSN 1422-0067
QH506 CODEN: IJMCFK
INTERNATIONAL JOURNAL OF MOLECULAR SCIENCES. Text in English. 2000. q. free access to selected articles (effective 2005). back issues avail. **Document type:** *Journal, Academic/Scholarly.* **Description:** Provides an advanced forum for chemistry, molecular physics (chemical physics and physical chemistry) and molecular biology.
Media: Online - full text. **Related titles:** ♦ CD-ROM ed.: International Journal of Molecular Sciences CD-ROM. ISSN 1424-6783.
Indexed: CCI, CurCont, ExcerpMed, Inspec.
Published by: Molecular Diversity Preservation International, MDPI Center, Matthaeusstr 11, Basel, 4057, Switzerland. TEL 41-79-3223379, 41-61-6837734, FAX 41-61-3028918, lin@mdpi.org, http://www.mdpi.org/ijms. Ed., Pub., Adv. contact Shu-Kun Lin.

547 CHE ISSN 1424-6783
INTERNATIONAL JOURNAL OF MOLECULAR SCIENCES CD-ROM. Text in English. 2000. a. USD 150 to individuals; USD 300 to institutions (effective 2001). **Document type:** *Academic/Scholarly.*
Media: CD-ROM. **Related titles:** ♦ Online - full text ed.: International Journal of Molecular Sciences. ISSN 1422-0067.
Published by: Molecular Diversity Preservation International, MDPI Center, Matthaeusstr 11, Basel, 4057, Switzerland. TEL 41-79-3223379, 41-61-6837734, FAX 41-61-3028918, http://www.mdpi.org/ijms. Ed.; Pub., Adv. contact Shu-Kun Lin.

INTERNATIONAL JOURNAL OF POLYMERIC MATERIALS. see *ENGINEERING—Chemical Engineering*

540 547 JPN ISSN 0075-2010
ITSUU LABORATORY, TOKYO. ANNUAL REPORT/ITSUU KENKYUJO NENPO. Text in English, German; Summaries in Japanese. 1950. irreg. (a. or biennial). per issue exchange basis.
Related titles: CD-ROM ed.
—CISTI.
Published by: Itsuu Laboratory/Itsuu Kenkyujo, 28-10 Tamagawa 2-chome, Setagaya-ku, Tokyo, 158-0094, Japan. Ed. M Natsume.

665 547.8 USA ISSN 0003-021X
TP1 CODEN: JAOCA7
➤ **J A O C S.** (Journal of the American Oil Chemists' Society) Text in English. 1917. m. USD 102 to members; USD 141 to non-members; USD 414 to non-members institutions; USD 58 to students members (effective 2005). adv. bibl.; charts; illus.; stat. index. back issues avail.; reprint service avail. from PQC. **Document type:** *Journal, Academic/Scholarly.* **Description:** Covers research, production, processing, packaging, and distribution in the field of fats, oils, proteins. and other substances.
Former titles (until 1947): Oil & Soap (0095-9510); (until 1932): Oil & Fat Industries (0095-9502); (until 1927): Journal of Oil & Fat Industries (0095-9774)
Related titles: Microfilm ed.: (from PMC, PQC); Online - full text ed.: (from EBSCO Publishing, O C L C Online Computer Library Center, Inc., ProQuest Information & Learning).
Indexed: A&ATA, ABIPC, AEA, AS&TI, ASCA, ASFA, AbHyg, AgBio, Agr, AgrForAb, AnalAb, BBCI, BIOSIS Prev, BibAg, BiolAb, CCI, CEA, CEABA, CIN, CPA, CTFA, Cadscan, ChemAb, ChemInfo, ChemTitl, ChromAb, CurCont, DSA, ESPM, ExcerpMed, FCA, FPA, FS&TA, ForAb, H&SSA, HerbAb, HortAb, I&DA, ISMEC, ISR, IndVet, LeadAb, MEDLINE, MSB, MaizeAb, NutrAb, OrnHort, PBA, PGegResA, PGrRegA, PHN&I, PN&I, PotatoAb, PoultAb, RA&MP, RCI, RM&VM, RPP, RefZh, RevApplEntom, RiceAb, S&F, SCI, SIA, SWRA, SeedAb, SoyAb, TCEA, TOSA, TTI, TriticAb, VITIS, VetBull, WAE&RSA, WSCA, WTA, WeedAb, Zincscan.
—BLDSC (4689.300000), CASDDS, CINDOC, CISTI, Ei, GNLM, IDS, IE, Infotrieve, ingenta, Linda Hall. **CCC.**
Published by: (American Oil Chemists' Society), A O C S Press, 2211 W Bradley Ave, Champaign, IL 61821. TEL 217-359-2344, FAX 217-351-8091, publications@aocs.org, http://www.aocs.org/press/jaocs.htm. Ed. John Cherry. Pub. Mary Lane. R&P Connie Winslow. Adv. contact Lisa Spencer. Circ: 4,000.

➤ **JOURNAL OF BIOMATERIALS SCIENCE. POLYMER EDITION.** see *BIOLOGY—Biotechnology*

547 USA ISSN 0022-152X
QD400 CODEN: JHTCAD
➤ **JOURNAL OF HETEROCYCLIC CHEMISTRY;** international journal. Abbreviated title: J H C. Text in English. 1964. 6/yr. USD 695; USD 1,110 combined subscription print & online eds. (effective 2005). adv. bk.rev. bibl.; charts; illus. index. reprints avail. **Document type:** *Journal, Academic/Scholarly.* **Description:** Consists of reviews, articles, communications to the editor and notes from chemists worldwide of research in heterocyclic chemistry.
Incorporates: Lectures in Heterocyclic Chemistry (0090-2268)
Related titles: Online - full text ed.: (from EBSCO Publishing).
Indexed: ASCA, BiolAb, CCI, CIN, ChemAb, ChemInfo, ChemTitl, CurCR, CurCont, DBA, EngInd, ExcerpMed, ISR, IndChem, IndVet, MOS, MSB, NPU, RCI, RefZh, SCI.
—BLDSC (4998.200000), CASDDS, CINDOC, CISTI, Ei, IDS, IE, Infotrieve, ingenta, Linda Hall. **CCC.**
Published by: HeteroCorporation, PO Box 170, Provo, UT 84603-0170. TEL 801-400-7373, FAX 801-356-7373, suggest@jhetchem.com, jhetchem@yahoo.com, http://www.jhetchem.com, http://www.jhetchem.com/. Ed., Pub., R&P Lyle Castle. Circ: 1,600 (paid).

660.284 546 USA ISSN 1053-0495
QD196 CODEN: JIOPE4
➤ **JOURNAL OF INORGANIC AND ORGANOMETALLIC POLYMERS.** Text in English. 1991. q. EUR 568, USD 568, GBP 355 combined subscription to institutions print & online eds. (effective 2005). adv. back issues avail.; reprint service avail. from PSC. **Document type:** *Journal, Academic/Scholarly.* **Description:** Addresses the synthesis, characterization, evaluation, and phenomena of inorganic and organometallic polymers.
Related titles: Online - full text ed.: ISSN 1572-8870 (from EBSCO Publishing, Gale Group, IngentaConnect, Kluwer Online, O C L C Online Computer Library Center, Inc., Springer LINK, Swets Information Services).
Indexed: ASCA, BibLing, CCI, CIN, ChemAb, ChemTitl, CurCont, EngInd, MSCI, RAPRA, RefZh.
—BLDSC (5007.100000), CASDDS, CISTI, Ei, IDS, IE, Infotrieve, ingenta, Linda Hall. **CCC.**
Published by: Plenum US (Subsidiary of: Springer Science+Business Media), 233 Spring St, New York, NY 10013. TEL 212-460-1500, FAX 212-460-1575, service@springer-ny.com, http://springerlink.metapress.com/openurl.asp?genre=journal&issn=1053-0495, http://www.springeronline.com. Ed. Martel Zeldin.

547 USA ISSN 1060-1325
QD380 CODEN: JSPCE6
➤ **JOURNAL OF MACROMOLECULAR SCIENCE: PART A - PURE AND APPLIED CHEMISTRY.** Text in English. 1964. m. GBP 2,539, USD 4,190 combined subscription to institutions print & online eds. (effective 2006). adv. reprint service avail. from PSC. **Document type:** *Journal, Academic/Scholarly.* **Description:** Serves as a resource for basic or applied polymer research, including work with natural, synthetic, graft, functional, and specialty polymers, and co-polymers.
Formerly (until 1992): Journal of Macromolecular Science: Part A - Chemistry (0022-233X); Supersedes in part: Journal of Macromolecular Chemistry (0449-2730)
Related titles: Microform ed.: (from RPI); Online - full text ed.: ISSN 1520-5738. GBP 2,412, USD 3,981 (effective 2006) (from EBSCO Publishing, O C L C Online Computer Library Center, Inc., Swets Information Services).
Indexed: ASCA, BiolAb, BrCerAb, C&ISA, CCI, CIN, CLL, CerAb, ChemAb, ChemTitl, CivEngAb, CorrAb, CurCont, E&CAJ, EMA, EngInd, IAA, ISMEC, ISR, M&TEA, MBF, METADEX, MSB, MSCI, RAPRA, RCI, RefZh, SCI, SIA, SolStAb, WAA, WSCA.
—BLDSC (5010.762000), CASDDS, CISTI, Ei, IDS, IE, Infotrieve, ingenta, Linda Hall. **CCC.**
Published by: Taylor & Francis Inc. (Subsidiary of: Taylor & Francis Group), 325 Chestnut St, Ste 800, Philadelphia, PA 19016. TEL 215-625-8900, 800-354-1420, FAX 215-625-8914, info@taylorandfrancis.com, http://www.tandf.co.uk/journals/titles/10601325.asp, http://www.taylorandfrancis.com. Adv. contact Sharon Moran. B&W page USD 600. Circ: 650.

➤ **JOURNAL OF MACROMOLECULAR SCIENCE: PART B - PHYSICS.** see *PHYSICS*

547 USA ISSN 1532-1797
QD380 CODEN: JMSPCG
➤ **JOURNAL OF MACROMOLECULAR SCIENCE: PART C - POLYMER REVIEWS.** Text in English. 1961. q. GBP 963, USD 1,589 combined subscription to institutions print & online eds. (effective 2006). adv. reprint service avail. from PSC. **Document type:** *Journal, Academic/Scholarly.* **Description:** Provides readers with scientific and technical information.
Former titles (until 2000): Journal of Macromolecular Science: Part C - Reviews in Macromolecular Chemistry and Physics (0736-6574); Journal of Macromolecular Science. Part C. Reviews in Macromolecular Chemistry (0022-2356); Reviews in Macromolecular Chemistry
Related titles: Microform ed.: (from RPI); Online - full text ed.: ISSN 1532-9038. GBP 915, GBP 1,510 (effective 2006) (from EBSCO Publishing, O C L C Online Computer Library Center, Inc., Swets Information Services).
Indexed: ASCA, CCI, ChemAb, ChemTitl, CurCR, CurCont, EngInd, ISR, IndChem, Inspec, MSCI, RAPRA, RCI, RefZh, SCI, TTI.
—BLDSC (5010.775000), AskIEEE, CASDDS, CISTI, Ei, IDS, IE, ingenta, Linda Hall. **CCC.**
Published by: Taylor & Francis Inc. (Subsidiary of: Taylor & Francis Group), 325 Chestnut St, Ste 800, Philadelphia, PA 19016. TEL 215-625-8900, 800-354-1420, FAX 215-625-8914, info@taylorandfrancis.com, http://www.tandf.co.uk/journals/titles/15321797.asp, http://www.taylorandfrancis.com. Ed. Elliot P Douglas. Circ: 600.

547 GBR ISSN 0952-3499
QP517.M67 CODEN: JMORE4
➤ **JOURNAL OF MOLECULAR RECOGNITION.** Text in English. 1988. bi-m. USD 1,395 to institutions; USD 1,535 combined subscription to institutions print & online eds. (effective 2006). adv. bk.rev. back issues avail.; reprint service avail. from PSC. **Document type:** *Journal, Academic/Scholarly.* **Description:** Covers the research on the basic principles, characterization, and application of specific molecular interactions in chemistry, biology, biotechnology and medicine.
Related titles: Microform ed.: (from PQC); Online - full text ed.: ISSN 1099-1352. USD 1,395 to institutions (effective 2006) (from EBSCO Publishing, Swets Information Services, Wiley InterScience).
Indexed: ASCA, BBCI, BIOBASE, BIOSIS Prev, BiolAb, ChemAb, ChemTitl, CurCont, EngInd, IABS, IndMed, MEDLINE, RefZh.
—BLDSC (5020.725000), CASDDS, CISTI, Ei, GNLM, IDS, IE, Infotrieve, ingenta, Linda Hall. **CCC.**
Published by: John Wiley & Sons Ltd. (Subsidiary of: John Wiley & Sons, Inc.), The Atrium, Southern Gate, Chichester, West Sussex PO19 8SQ, United Kingdom. TEL 44-1243-779777, FAX 44-1243-775878, customer@wiley.co.uk, http://www3.interscience.wiley.com/cgi-bin/jhome/13149, http://www.wiley.co.uk. Ed. Marc van Regenmortel. adv.: B&W page GBP 650, color page GBP 1,550; trim 210 x 279. **Subscr. in the Americas to:** John Wiley & Sons, Inc., 111 River St, Hoboken, NJ 07030-5774. TEL 800-225-5945, subinfo@wiley.com.

➤ **JOURNAL OF NATURAL GAS CHEMISTRY.** see *PETROLEUM AND GAS*

547 USA ISSN 0022-3263
QD241 CODEN: JOCEAH
➤ **THE JOURNAL OF ORGANIC CHEMISTRY.** Text in English. 1936. bi-w. USD 2,310 in North America to institutions; USD 2,560 elsewhere to institutions; USD 200 in North America to members; USD 450 elsewhere to members; USD 150 in North America to students; USD 400 elsewhere to students (effective 2006). adv. charts; illus. index. back issues avail.; reprints avail. **Document type:** *Journal, Academic/Scholarly.* **Description:** Offers the organic chemist critical accounts of original work in a given field, and interpretative reviews of existing data that present new viewpoints.
Related titles: CD-ROM ed.; Microfiche ed.: USD 1,660 in North America to institutions; USD 1,699 elsewhere to institutions (effective 2002); Microfilm ed.: USD 1,660 in North America to institutions; USD 1,755 elsewhere to institutions (effective 2002); Online - full text ed.: ISSN 1520-6904. USD 85 (effective 2006) (from EBSCO Publishing, Swets Information Services).
Indexed: ABIPC, BIOSIS Prev, BiolAb, CCI, CIN, Cadscan, ChemAb, ChemInfo, ChemTitl, CurCR, CurCont, DBA, DSA, EngInd, ExcerpMed, FS&TA, GSI, HelmAb, HortAb, INIS AtomInd, ISR, IndChem, IndMed, IndVet, Inpharma, LHB, LeadAb, MEDLINE, MOS, MSB, NPU, NutrAb, ProtozoAb, RA&MP, RAPRA, RCI, RM&VM, RPP, Reac, RefZh, RevApplEntom, S&F, SCI, SIA, TDB, VITIS, VetBull, Zincscan.
—BLDSC (5027.000000), CASDDS, CINDOC, CISTI, Ei, GNLM, IDS, IE, Infotrieve, ingenta, Linda Hall. **CCC.**
Published by: American Chemical Society, 1155 16th St, N W, Washington, DC 20036. TEL 202-872-4600, 202-872-4554, FAX 202-776-8264, joc@chem.utah.edu, service@acs.org, http://pubs.acs.org/joc. Ed. C Dale Poulter. adv.: color page USD 2,680. Circ: 9,000 (paid). **Subscr. to:** Member & Subscriber Services, PO Box 3337, Columbus, OH 43210. TEL 614-447-3776, 800-333-9511, FAX 614-447-3671.

C

▼ new title ➤ refereed ✶ unverified ♦ full entry avail.

547.05 669 CHE ISSN 0022-328X
CODEN: JORCAI

➤ **JOURNAL OF ORGANOMETALLIC CHEMISTRY.** Text in English, French, German; Summaries in English. 1963. 26/yr. EUR 10,442 in Europe to institutions; JPY 1,388,000 in Japan to institutions; USD 11,682 elsewhere to institutions; EUR 621 in Europe to qualified personnel; JPY 82,200 in Japan to qualified personnel; USD 696 elsewhere to qualified personnel (effective 2006). adv. bk.rev. illus. index. back issues avail. **Document type:** *Journal, Academic/Scholarly.* **Description:** Deals with theoretical aspects, structural chemistry, synthesis, physical and chemical properties including reaction mechanisms, and practical applications of organo-elements compounds in a sense corresponding essentially to Section 29 of Chemical Abstracts.
Incorporates (1968-1972): Organometallic Chemistry Reviews. Section A: Subject Reviews (0030-5111); (1964-1972): Organometallic Chemistry Reviews. Section B: Annual Surveys (0030-512X); Which was formerly (1964-1966): Annual Survey of Organometallic Chemistry (0570-2682); Section A & B superseded (in 1967): Organometallic Chemistry Reviews (0474-6384)
Related titles: Microform ed.: (from PQC); Online - full text ed.: (from EBSCO Publishing, Gale Group, IngentaConnect, ScienceDirect, Swets Information Services).
Indexed: ASCA, BPRC&P, CCI, CIN, ChemAb, ChemInfo, ChemTitl, CurCR, CurCont, EngInd, ISR, IndChem, MOS, MSB, MSCI, RCI, RefZh, SCI.
—BLDSC (5027.100000), CASDDS, CINDOC, CISTI, Ei, IDS, IE, Infotrieve, ingenta, Linda Hall. **CCC.**
Published by: Elsevier S.A., PO Box 564, Lausanne 1, 1001, Switzerland. TEL 41-21-3207381, FAX 41-21-3235444, http://www.elsevier.com/locate/jorganchem. Eds. G Bertrand, R D Adams, W A Herrmann. **Subscr. to:** Elsevier BV, PO Box 211, Amsterdam 1000 AE, Netherlands. TEL 31-20-485-3757, FAX 31-20-485-3432, nlinfo-f@elsevier.nl, http://www.elsevier.nl.

547 GBR ISSN 1075-2617
QD431.A1 CODEN: JPSIEI

➤ **JOURNAL OF PEPTIDE SCIENCE.** Text in English. 1994. m. USD 1,130 to institutions; USD 1,243 combined subscription to institutions print & online eds. (effective 2006). adv. back issues avail.; reprint service avail. from PSC. **Document type:** *Journal, Academic/Scholarly.*
Related titles: Microform ed.: (from PQC); Online - full text ed.: ISSN 1099-1387. USD 1,130 to institutions (effective 2006) (from EBSCO Publishing, Swets Information Services, Wiley InterScience).
Indexed: BBCI, BIOSIS Prev, BiolAb, CIN, ChemAb, ChemTitl, CurCont, DSA, ExcerpMed, FCA, HortAb, ISR, IndMed, IndVet, Inspec, MEDLINE, MSB, NutrAb, RA&MP, RM&VM, RPP, SCI, SIA, TDB, VetBull.
—BLDSC (5030.530000), CASDDS, CISTI, IDS, IE, Infotrieve, ingenta, Linda Hall. **CCC.**
Published by: (European Peptide Society), John Wiley & Sons Ltd. (Subsidiary of: John Wiley & Sons, Inc.), The Atrium, Southern Gate, Chichester, West Sussex PO19 8SQ, United Kingdom. TEL 44-1243-779777, FAX 44-1243-775878, customer@wiley.co.uk, http://www3.interscience.wiley.com/cgi-bin/jhome/6016, http://www.wiley.co.uk. Ed. J R Jones. adv.: B&W page GBP 650, color page GBP 1,550; trim 210 x 279. **Subscr. in the Americas to:** John Wiley & Sons, Inc., 111 River St, Hoboken, NJ 07030-5774. TEL 201-748-6645, 800-225-5945, subinfo@wiley.com.

668.9 JPN ISSN 0914-9244
QD382.P45 CODEN: JSTEEW

JOURNAL OF PHOTOPOLYMER SCIENCE AND TECHNOLOGY/FOTOPORIMA KONWAKAISHI. Text in English, Japanese. 1988. a. free to members (effective 2005). **Document type:** *Journal, Academic/Scholarly.*
Related titles: Online - full text ed.: ISSN 1349-6336 (from J-Stage).
Indexed: CCI, ChemAb, CurCont, Inspec, MSCI.
—BLDSC (5035.300000), CISTI, IE, Infotrieve, ingenta.
Published by: Technical Association of Photopolymers Japan, c/o Dr. Kenichiro Nakamura, Tokai University, Department of Electro Photo Optics, Kitakaneme, Hiratsuka, Kanagawa 259-1292, Japan. TEL 81-463-502156, FAX 81-463-502408, nakamura@keyaki.cc.u-tokai.ac.jp, http://www.jstage.jst.go.jp/browse/photopolymer, http://www.ao.u-tokai.ac.jp/photopolymer/p.htm.

JOURNAL OF PHYSICAL ORGANIC CHEMISTRY. see *CHEMISTRY—Physical Chemistry*

660.284 IND ISSN 0970-0838
QD380 CODEN: JOPME8

➤ **JOURNAL OF POLYMER MATERIALS**; an international journal. Text in English. 1984. q. USD 150 (effective 2003). adv. bk.rev. **Document type:** *Journal, Academic/Scholarly.* **Description:** Publishes original laboratory findings and research relevant to the field of polymer science and technology, including synthesis, morphology, structure, new analytical techniques, processing and fabrication.
Indexed: ASCA, BrCerAb, C&ISA, CIN, CLL, CTE, CerAb, ChemAb, ChemTitl, CivEngAb, CorrAb, E&CAJ, EMA, EngInd, ExcerpMed, IAA, Inspec, M&TEA, MBF, METADEX, MSCI, RAPRA, SolStAb, WAA.
—BLDSC (5040.998000), CASDDS, CISTI, Ei, IDS, IE, Infotrieve, ingenta, Linda Hall. **CCC.**
Published by: Oxford & I.B.H. Publishing Co. Pvt. Ltd., 66 Janpath, New Delhi, 110 001, India. FAX 91-11-3710090, rajuprim@vsnl.com. Ed. Sukumar Maiti. R&P Raju Primlani.

547 USA ISSN 0887-624X
QD471 CODEN: JPACEC

➤ **JOURNAL OF POLYMER SCIENCE. PART A, POLYMER CHEMISTRY.** Text in English, French, German. 1946. 24/yr. USD 13,690 domestic to institutions; USD 13,978 in Canada & Mexico to institutions; USD 14,146 elsewhere to institutions; USD 15,059 combined subscription domestic to institutions print & online eds.; USD 15,347 combined subscription in Canada & Mexico to institutions print & online eds.; USD 15,515 combined subscription elsewhere to institutions print & online eds. (effective 2006); Incl. Journal of Polymer Science. Part B, Polymer Physics. adv. bk.rev. bibl.; charts; illus. index. back issues avail.; reprint service avail. from PQC. **Document type:** *Journal, Academic/Scholarly.*
Incorporates in part (in 1990): Journal of Polymer Science. Part C, Polymer Letters (0887-6258); Which was formerly (until 1986): Journal of Polymer Science. Polymer Letters Edition (0360-6384); (1963-1972): Journal of Polymer Science. Part B, Polymer Letters (0449-2986); Former titles (until 1986): Journal of Polymer Science. Polymer Chemistry Edition (0360-6376); (until 1972): Journal of Polymer Science. Part A-1, Polymer Chemistry (0449-296X); Which superseded in part (in 1966): Journal of Polymer Science. Part A. General Papers (0449-2951); Which superseded in part (in 1963): Journal of Polymer Science (0022-3832)
Related titles: Microform ed.: (from PQC); Online - full text ed.: ISSN 1099-0518. USD 13,690 to institutions (effective 2006) (from EBSCO Publishing, Swets Information Services, Wiley InterScience).
Indexed: ABIPC, ASCA, AnalAb, ApMecR, B&BAb, BPRC&P, BrCerAb, C&ISA, CCI, CIN, CLL, CerAb, ChemAb, ChemTitl, CivEngAb, CorrAb, CurCont, E&CAJ, EMA, EngInd, IAA, ISMEC, ISR, Inspec, M&TEA, MBF, MEDLINE, METADEX, MSB, MSCI, P&BA, PhotoAb, RAPRA, RCI, RefZh, SCI, SolStAb, TTI, WAA, WSCA, WTA.
—BLDSC (5041.002050), AskIEEE, CASDDS, CISTI, Ei, GNLM, IDS, IE, Infotrieve, ingenta, Linda Hall. **CCC.**
Published by: John Wiley & Sons, Inc., 111 River St, Hoboken, NJ 07030-5774. TEL 201-748-6000, FAX 201-748-5915, uscs-wis@wiley.com, http://www3.interscience.wiley.com/cgi-bin/jhome/36444, http://www.wiley.com. Ed. Mitsuo Sawamoto. adv.: B&W page GBP 640, color page GBP 1,515; trim 216 x 279. Circ: 1,850. **Subscr. outside the Americas to:** John Wiley & Sons Ltd., The Atrium, Southern Gate, Chichester, West Sussex PO19 8SQ, United Kingdom. TEL 44-1243-843335, 0800-243407, FAX 44-1243-843232, cs-journals@wiley.co.uk.

547 USA ISSN 0887-6266
QD471 CODEN: JPBPEM

➤ **JOURNAL OF POLYMER SCIENCE. PART B, POLYMER PHYSICS.** Text in English, French, German. 1946. 24/yr. USD 13,690 domestic to institutions; USD 13,978 in Canada & Mexico to institutions; USD 14,146 elsewhere to institutions; USD 15,059 combined subscription domestic to institutions print & online eds.; USD 15,347 combined subscription in Canada & Mexico to institutions print & online eds.; USD 15,515 combined subscription elsewhere to institutions print & online eds. (effective 2006); includes Part A: Polymer Chemistry & Symposia. adv. bibl.; charts; illus. index. back issues avail. **Document type:** *Proceedings, Academic/Scholarly.*
Incorporates in part (in 1990): Journal of Polymer Science. Part C, Polymer Letters (0887-6258); Which was formerly (until 1986): Journal of Polymer Science. Polymer Letters Edition (0360-6384); (1963- 1972): Journal of Polymer Science. Part B, Polymer Letters (0449-2986); Former titles (until 1986): Journal of Polymer Science. Polymer Physics Edition (0098-1273); (until 1972): Journal of Polymer Science. A-2, Polymer Physics (0449-2978); Which superseded in part (in 1966): Journal of Polymer Science. Part A. General Papers (0449-2951); Which superseded in part (in 1963): Journal of Polymer Science (0022-3832)
Related titles: Microform ed.: (from PQC); Online - full text ed.: ISSN 1099-0488. USD 13,690 to institutions (effective 2006) (from EBSCO Publishing, Swets Information Services, Wiley InterScience).
Indexed: ABIPC, ASCA, ApMecR, B&BAb, BPRC&P, BrCerAb, C&ISA, CCI, CIN, CLL, CerAb, ChemAb, ChemTitl, CivEngAb, CorrAb, CurCont, E&CAJ, EMA, EngInd, IAA, ISMEC, ISR, Inspec, M&TEA, MBF, METADEX, MSCI, P&BA, PhysBer, RAPRA, RCI, RefZh, SCI, SolStAb, TTI, WAA, WSCA, WTA.
—BLDSC (5041.005000), AskIEEE, CASDDS, CISTI, Ei, GNLM, IDS, IE, Infotrieve, ingenta, Linda Hall. **CCC.**
Published by: John Wiley & Sons, Inc., 111 River St, Hoboken, NJ 07030-5774. TEL 201-748-6000, FAX 201-748-5915, uscs-wis@wiley.com, http://www3.interscience.wiley.com/cgi-bin/jhome/36698, http://www.wiley.com. Ed. Robert M Briber. adv.: B&W page GBP 640, color page GBP 1,515; trim 216 x 279. Circ: 1,850. **Subscr. outside the Americas to:** John Wiley & Sons Ltd., The Atrium, Southern Gate, Chichester, West Sussex PO19 8SQ, United Kingdom. TEL 44-1243-843335, 0800-243407, FAX 44-1243-843232, cs-journals@wiley.co.uk.

668.9 572.33 USA ISSN 1566-2543
QP801.P64 CODEN: JPENFW

➤ **JOURNAL OF POLYMERS AND THE ENVIRONMENT.** Text in English. 1994. q. EUR 404, USD 404, GBP 253 combined subscription to institutions print & online eds. (effective 2005). adv. reprint service avail. from PSC. **Document type:** *Journal, Academic/Scholarly.* **Description:** Provides interdisciplinary coverage of the science of polymer degradation, including new materials, natural origin polymers, degradable blends and composites, processing, material property elucidation, and degradation testing.
Formerly: Journal of Environmental Polymer Degradation (1064-7546)
Related titles: Online - full text ed.: ISSN 1572-8900. USD 404 to institutions (effective 2005) (from EBSCO Publishing, Gale Group, IngentaConnect, Kluwer Online, O C L C Online Computer Library Center, Inc., Springer LINK, Swets Information Services).
Indexed: ASCA, ASFA, B&BAb, BIOSIS Prev, BibLing, BiolAb, BrCerAb, C&ISA, CCI, CIN, CerAb, ChemAb, ChemTitl, CivEngAb, CorrAb, CurCont, E&CAJ, EMA, EPB, ESPM, EngInd, EnvEAb, GEOBASE, IAA, M&TEA, MBA, MBF, METADEX, MSCI, PollutAb, RAPRA, RefZh, SolStAb, WAA, WTA.
—BLDSC (5041.030100), CASDDS, CISTI, IDS, IE, Infotrieve, ingenta, Linda Hall. **CCC.**
Published by: Plenum US (Subsidiary of: Springer Science+Business Media), 233 Spring St, New York, NY 10013. TEL 212-460-1500, FAX 212-460-1575, service@springer-ny.com, http://springerlink.metapress.com/openurl.asp?genre=journal&issn=1566-2543, http://www.springeronline.com. Ed. Stephen P McCarthy.

665 USA ISSN 1097-3958
TP994 CODEN: JSDEFL

➤ **JOURNAL OF SURFACTANTS AND DETERGENTS.** Text in English. 1998. q. USD 187 domestic to individuals; USD 202 foreign to individuals; USD 376 domestic to institutions; USD 391 foreign to institutions (effective 2005). adv. back issues avail. **Document type:** *Journal, Academic/Scholarly.* **Description:** Covers industry news related to surfactants, detergents, and soaps.
Related titles: Online - full content ed.; Online - full text ed.: (from EBSCO Publishing, O C L C Online Computer Library Center, Inc.).
Indexed: CCI, ChemAb, CurCont, MSB, RefZh.
—BLDSC (5067.365000), CASDDS, CISTI, IE, Infotrieve, ingenta. **CCC.**
Published by: (American Oil Chemists' Society), A O C S Press, 2211 W Bradley Ave, Champaign, IL 61821. TEL 217-359-2344, FAX 217-351-8091, publications@aocs.org, http://www.aocs.org/press/jaocs-jsd-lipids.asp. Ed. Mark Mac. adv.: B&W page USD 1,660; trim 8.25 x 11. Circ: 750.

547 LVA ISSN 0132-6244

➤ **KHIMIYA GETEROTSIKLICHESKIKH SOEDINENII.** Text in Russian. 1965. m. **Document type:** *Journal, Academic/Scholarly.*
Related titles: ♦ English Translation: Chemistry of Heterocyclic Compounds (New York, 1965). ISSN 0009-3122.
Indexed: CCI, CIN, ChemAb, ChemTitl, CurCR, CurCont, DBA, ISR, IndChem, RCI, RefZh, SCI.
—BLDSC (0393.800000), CISTI, Linda Hall. **CCC.**
Published by: Latvijas Organiskas Sintezes Instituts/Latvian Institute of Organic Synthesis, Aizkraukles iela 21, Riga, 1006, Latvia. TEL 371-7-551822, FAX 371-7-550338, hgs@osi.lv, sinta@osi.lv, http://www.osi.lv/hgs/hgs.html. Ed. E Lukevics.

547 UZB ISSN 0023-1150
CODEN: KPSUAR

➤ **KHIMIYA PRIRODNYKH SOEDINENII.** Text in Russian. 1965. bi-m. USD 160 foreign (effective 2004). index. **Document type:** *Journal, Academic/Scholarly.* **Description:** Publishes academic articles about research results in natural compounds chemistry.
Related titles: ♦ English Translation: Chemistry of Natural Compounds. ISSN 0009-3130.
Indexed: ABIPC, ASCA, ApicAb, BiolAb, CCI, ChemAb, ChemTitl, CurCont, DSA, EngInd, FPA, ForAb, HortAb, ISR, IndChem, PGrRegA, RCI, RPP, RefZh, S&F, SCI, SeedAb, WeedAb, ZooRec.
—BLDSC (0394.300000), CASDDS, CISTI, Ei, IDS, Linda Hall. **CCC.**
Published by: O'zbekiston Respublikasi Fanlar Akademiyasi/Academy of Sciences of Uzbekistan, 70, Academician Yahyo, Gulamov St, Tashkent, 700047, Uzbekistan. http://www.academy.uz. Circ: 816. **Dist. by:** East View Information Services, 3020 Harbor Ln. N., Minneapolis, MN 55447. TEL 800-477-1005, FAX 800-800-3839, eastview@eastview.com, http://www.eastview.com.

660.284 JPN ISSN 0454-1138
QD139.P6 CODEN: KOBUA3

KOBUNSHI/HIGH POLYMERS, JAPAN. Text in Japanese. 1952. m. subscr. incld. with membership. adv. 80 p./no.; **Document type:** *Journal, Academic/Scholarly.* **Description:** Includes reviews, research papers, reports, news, announcements, calendar of meetings, and other information.
Indexed: CIN, ChemAb, ChemTitl, INIS AtomInd, MSB, TTI.
—BLDSC (5100.615000), CASDDS, CISTI, Linda Hall. **CCC.**

C

Published by: Nihon Kobunshi Gakkai/Society of Polymer Science, Japan, Shintomicho-Tokyu Bldg., 3-10-9 Irifune, Chuo-ku, Tokyo, 104-0042, Japan. TEL 81-3-55403771, FAX 81-3-55403737, http://www.spsj.or.jp/c5/kobunshi/kobunshi.htm. Ed. Hachiro Nakanishi. Circ: 14,000.

547 660.284 JPN ISSN 0386-2186
TP1080 CODEN: KBRBA3

➤ **KOBUNSHI RONBUNSHU/JAPANESE JOURNAL OF POLYMER SCIENCE AND ENGINEERING.** Text in Japanese; Abstracts in English. 1944. m. subscr. incld. with membership. abstr.; bibl. Index. 72 p./no.; **Document type:** *Journal, Academic/Scholarly.* **Description:** Contains original papers, notes, short communications, and comprehensive papers on all aspects of polymers; such as polymer synthesis and reactions, structures and physical properties of polymers, functional polymers, and polymer engineering.
Formerly: Kobunshi Kagaku (0023-2556)
Indexed: A&ATA, ASCA, B&BAb, CCI, CIN, ChemAb, ChemTitl, CivEngAb, CurCont, EngInd, FLUIDEX, INIS AtomInd, ISR, Inspec, MSCI, RAPRA, RefZh, SSCI, TTI, WTA.
—BLDSC (4658.130000), CASDDS, CISTI, Ei, IDS, ingenta, Linda Hall. **CCC.**
Published by: Nihon Kobunshi Gakkai/Society of Polymer Science, Japan, Shintomicho-Tokyu Bldg., 3-10-9 Irifune, Chuo-ku, Tokyo, 104-0042, Japan. TEL 81-3-55403771, FAX 81-3-55403737, koron@spsj.or.jp, http://www.spsj.or.jp/c5/koron/koron.htm. Circ: 1,450 (controlled).

547 NLD ISSN 1570-1786

▼ **LETTERS IN ORGANIC CHEMISTRY.** Text in English. 2004. q. USD 280 combined subscription to individuals print & online; USD 920 combined subscription to corporations print & online; USD 1,820 combined subscription to institutions (academic), print & online (effective 2005). **Document type:** *Journal, Academic/Scholarly.* **Description:** Publishes original letters on all areas of organic chemistry including synthesis, bioorganic, medicinal, natural products, organometallic, supramolecular, molecular recognition, and physical organic chemistry.
Related titles: Online - full content ed.; Online - full text ed.: (from EBSCO Publishing, Gale Group, IngentaConnect, Swets Information Services).
Indexed: CCI, CurCont.
—BLDSC (5185.170173), IE. **CCC.**
Published by: Bentham Science Publishers Ltd., PO Box 1673, Hilversum, BR 1200, Netherlands. TEL 31-35-6923800, FAX 31-35-6980150, M.Bentham@inter.nl.net, http://www.bentham.org/. Ed. Atta-ur Rahman TEL 92-21-4969873.

LIANYOU SHEJI/PETROLEUM REFINERY ENGINEERING. see *PETROLEUM AND GAS*

665.4 DEU ISSN 0076-891X

M W V JAHRESBERICHT; Mineraloel-zahlen. Text in German. 1950. a. EUR 4.50 (effective 2003). **Document type:** *Bulletin, Academic/Scholarly.*
Formerly: M W V - A E V Jahresbericht
Published by: Mineraloelwirtschafts Verband e.V., Steindamm 55, Hamburg, 20099, Germany. TEL 49-40-24849-0, FAX 49-40-24849253, mvw@mvw.de, http://www.mwv.de. Circ: 4,500.

547 DEU ISSN 1022-1352
QD471 CODEN: MCHPES

➤ **MACROMOLECULAR CHEMISTRY AND PHYSICS.** Text in English. 1947. 18/yr. price varies; journal only avail. as a part of various subscr. packages. bk.rev. charts; illus. index. **Document type:** *Journal, Academic/Scholarly.* **Description:** Contains research in all current areas of macromolecular science.
Incorporates (1950-1999): Acta Polymerica (0323-7648); Formerly (until 1993): Makromolekulare Chemie (0025-116X)
Related titles: Online - full text ed.: ISSN 1521-3935. 2000 (from EBSCO Publishing, Swets Information Services, Wiley InterScience).
Indexed: ASCA, BiolAb, CCI, CIN, ChemAb, ChemTitl, CurCR, CurCont, EngInd, ISR, IndChem, MSB, MSCI, RAPRA, RCI, RefZh, SCI, TTI, WSCA.
—BLDSC (5330.398000), CASDDS, CINDOC, CISTI, Ei, IDS, IE, Infotrieve, ingenta, Linda Hall. **CCC.**
Published by: Wiley - V C H Verlag GmbH & Co. KGaA (Subsidiary of: John Wiley & Sons, Inc.), Boschstr 12, Weinheim, 69469, Germany. TEL 49-6201-6060, FAX 49-6201-606328, subservice@wiley-vch.de, http://www.wiley-vch.de. Ed. Ingrid Meisel. R&P Claudia Rutz. **Subscr. outside Germany, Austria & Switzerland to:** John Wiley & Sons Ltd., The Atrium, Southern Gate, Chichester, West Sussex PO19 8SQ, United Kingdom. TEL 44-1243-779777, FAX 44-1243-775878, cs-journals@wiley.co.uk.

547 660.284 DEU ISSN 1438-7492
TP1101 CODEN: MMENFA

➤ **MACROMOLECULAR MATERIALS & ENGINEERING.** Text in English, French, German. 1967. m. EUR 1,998 in Europe; CHF 3,148 in Switzerland & Liechtenstein; USD 2,648 elsewhere; EUR 2,198 combined subscription in Europe print & online eds.; CHF 3,463 combined subscription in Switzerland & Liechtenstein for print and online eds.; USD 2,913 combined subscription elsewhere print & online eds. (effective 2006). charts; illus. cum.index every 50 vols. **Document type:** *Journal, Academic/Scholarly.* **Description:** Publishes reviews, feature articles, full papers, and communications covering the entire field of macromolecular materials and engineering.
Formerly (until 2000): Angewandte Makromolekulare Chemie (0003-3146)
Related titles: Online - full text ed.: ISSN 1439-2054. EUR 1,998 in Europe; CHF 3,148 in Switzerland & Liechtenstein; USD 2,648 elsewhere (effective 2006) (from EBSCO Publishing, Swets Information Services, Wiley InterScience).
Indexed: A&ATA, ASCA, AnalAb, CCI, CIN, Cadscan, ChemAb, ChemTitl, CurCR, CurCont, EngInd, ExcerpMed, ISR, IndChem, LeadAb, MSB, MSCI, RAPRA, RCI, RefZh, SCI, TTI, WSCA, WTA, Zincscan.
—BLDSC (5330.398700), CASDDS, CINDOC, CISTI, Ei, IDS, IE, Infotrieve, ingenta, Linda Hall. **CCC.**
Published by: Wiley - V C H Verlag GmbH & Co. KGaA (Subsidiary of: John Wiley & Sons, Inc.), Boschstr 12, Weinheim, 69469, Germany. TEL 49-6201-6060, FAX 49-6201-606328, subservice@wiley-vch.de, http://www.interscience.wiley.com/jpages/0003-3146/, http://www.wiley-vch.de. Ed. Ingrid Meisel. R&P Claudia Rutz. **Subscr. outside Germany, Austria & Switzerland to:** John Wiley & Sons Ltd., The Atrium, Southern Gate, Chichester, West Sussex PO19 8SQ, United Kingdom. TEL 44-1243-779777, FAX 44-1243-775878, cs-journals@wiley.co.uk.

547 DEU ISSN 1022-1336
QD380 CODEN: MRCOE3

➤ **MACROMOLECULAR RAPID COMMUNICATIONS.** Text in English. bi-w. price varies; journal only avail. as a part of subscr. packages. bk.rev. index. **Document type:** *Journal, Academic/Scholarly.* **Description:** Publishes research in all current areas of macromolecular science.
Former titles (until 1994): Makromolekulare Chemie. Rapid Communications (0173-2803); Makromolekulare Chemie. Short Communications
Related titles: Online - full text ed.: ISSN 1521-3927 (from EBSCO Publishing, Swets Information Services, Wiley InterScience).
Indexed: ASCA, CCI, CIN, ChemAb, ChemTitl, CurCR, CurCont, ISR, IndChem, MSCI, RAPRA, RCI, RefZh, SCI, WSCA.
—BLDSC (5330.400000), CASDDS, CINDOC, CISTI, IDS, IE, Infotrieve, ingenta, Linda Hall. **CCC.**
Published by: Wiley - V C H Verlag GmbH & Co. KGaA (Subsidiary of: John Wiley & Sons, Inc.), Boschstr 12, Weinheim, 69469, Germany. TEL 49-6201-6060, FAX 49-6201-606328, subservice@wiley-vch.de, http://www.wiley-vch.de. Ed. Ingrid Meisel. R&P Claudia Rutz. **Subscr. outside Germany, Austria & Switzerland to:** John Wiley & Sons Ltd., The Atrium, Southern Gate, Chichester, West Sussex PO19 8SQ, United Kingdom. TEL 44-1243-779777, FAX 44-1243-775878, cs-journals@wiley.co.uk.

668.9 KOR ISSN 1598-5032
TP156.P6 CODEN: MRAECT

➤ **MACROMOLECULAR RESEARCH.** Text in English. 1993. bi-m. **Document type:** *Journal, Academic/Scholarly.* **Description:** Contains original researches on all aspects of polymer science, engineering, and technology.
Formerly (until 2002): Korea Polymer Journal (1225-5947)
Indexed: ASCA, CCI, CurCont, ISR, MSCI, SCI.
—BLDSC (5330.412500), IE.
Published by: Polymer Society of Korea, Rm. 601 Hatchon Bldg., Kangnam-ku, 831 Yeoksam dong, Seoul, 135792, Korea, S. TEL 02-561-5203, FAX 02-553-6938, http://www.polymer.or.kr. Ed. Iwhan Cho.

547 GBR ISSN 0963-6986

MACROMOLECULAR STRUCTURES. Text in English. 1991. a. USD 411 in North America to individuals; GBP 250 elsewhere to individuals; USD 822 in North America to institutions; GBP 500 elsewhere to institutions. back issues avail. **Document type:** *Academic/Scholarly.*
—BLDSC (5330.416000), GNLM.
Published by: Current Science Ltd, Middlesex House, 34-42 Cleveland St, London, W1P 6LB, United Kingdom. TEL 44-20-73230323, FAX 44-20-75801938, info@cursci.co.uk, http://www.currentsciencegroup.com. Eds. Kurt Wuethrich, Wayne A Hendrickson. Pub. Dave Weedon. **Dist. by:** Extenza - Turpin, Pegasus Dr, Stratton Business Park, Biggleswade, Beds SG18 8TQ, United Kingdom. FAX 44-1462-480947.

547 DEU ISSN 1022-1360
QD380 CODEN: MSYMEC

➤ **MACROMOLECULAR SYMPOSIA.** Text in English. 1987. 14/yr. EUR 1,618 in Europe; CHF 2,548 in Switzerland &Liechtenstein; USD 2,128 elsewhere; EUR 1,780 combined subscription in Europe print & online eds.; CHF 2,803 combined subscription in Switzerland & Liechtenstein for print and online eds.; USD 2,341 combined subscription elsewhere print & online eds. (effective 2006). charts; illus. index. **Document type:** *Journal, Academic/Scholarly.* **Description:** Publishes research and contributions in all areas of macromolecular science.
Formerly (until 1993): Makromolekulare Chemie. Macromolecular Symposia (0258-0322); Which incorporated (1975-1989): Makromolekulare Chemie. Supplementband (0253-5904)
Related titles: Online - full text ed.: ISSN 1521-3900. EUR 1,618 in Europe; CHF 2,548 in Switzerland & Liechtenstein; USD 2,128 elsewhere (effective 2006) (from EBSCO Publishing, Swets Information Services, Wiley InterScience).
Indexed: ASCA, CCI, CIN, ChemAb, ChemTitl, CurCont, MSCI, RAPRA, WSCA.
—BLDSC (5330.416400), CASDDS, CINDOC, CISTI, GNLM, IDS, IE, Infotrieve, ingenta, Linda Hall. **CCC.**
Published by: Wiley - V C H Verlag GmbH & Co. KGaA (Subsidiary of: John Wiley & Sons, Inc.), Boschstr 12, Weinheim, 69469, Germany. TEL 49-6201-6060, FAX 49-6201-606328, subservice@wiley-vch.de, info@wiley-vch.de, http://www.wiley-vch.de/home2/masy/. Ed. Ingrid Meisel. R&P Claudia Rutz. **Subscr. outside Germany, Austria & Switzerland to:** John Wiley & Sons Ltd., The Atrium, Southern Gate, Chichester, West Sussex PO19 8SQ, United Kingdom. TEL 44-1243-779777, FAX 44-1243-775878, cs-journals@wiley.co.uk.

547 546 DEU ISSN 1022-1344
QD380 CODEN: MTHSEK

➤ **MACROMOLECULAR THEORY AND SIMULATIONS.** Text in English. 1992. 9/yr. EUR 598 in Europe; CHF 948 in Switzerland & Liechtenstein; USD 798 elsewhere; EUR 658 combined subscription in Europe print & online eds.; CHF 1,043 combined subscription in Switzerland & Liechtenstein for print and online eds.; USD 878 combined subscription elsewhere print & online eds. (effective 2006). bk.rev. charts; illus. **Document type:** *Journal, Academic/Scholarly.* **Description:** Publishes reviews, feature articles, full papers, and communications on macromolecular theory and computer simulations.
Formerly (until 1994): Makromolekulare Chemie. Theory and Simulations (1018-5054)
Related titles: Online - full text ed.: ISSN 1521-3919. EUR 598 in Europe; CHF 948 in Switzerland & Liechtenstein; USD 798 elsewhere (effective 2006) (from EBSCO Publishing, Swets Information Services, Wiley InterScience).
Indexed: ASCA, CCI, CIN, ChemAb, ChemTitl, CurCont, ISR, Inspec, MSCI, RAPRA, RefZh, SCI, WSCA.
—BLDSC (5330.418000), AskIEEE, CASDDS, CINDOC, CISTI, IDS, IE, Infotrieve, ingenta, Linda Hall. **CCC.**
Published by: Wiley - V C H Verlag GmbH & Co. KGaA (Subsidiary of: John Wiley & Sons, Inc.), Boschstr 12, Weinheim, 69469, Germany. TEL 49-6201-6060, FAX 49-6201-606328, subservice@wiley-vch.de, info@wiley-vch.de, http://www.interscience.wiley.com/jpages/1022-1344/, http://www.wiley-vch.de. Ed. Ingrid Meisel. R&P Claudia Rutz. **Subscr. outside Germany, Austria & Switzerland to:** John Wiley & Sons Ltd., The Atrium, Southern Gate, Chichester, West Sussex PO19 8SQ, United Kingdom. TEL 44-1243-779777, FAX 44-1243-775878, cs-journals@wiley.co.uk.

547 USA ISSN 0024-9297
QD380 CODEN: MAMOBX

➤ **MACROMOLECULES.** Text in English. 1968. bi-m. USD 2,820 in North America to institutions; USD 3,065 elsewhere to institutions; USD 361 in North America to members; USD 606 elsewhere to members; USD 271 in North America to students; USD 516 elsewhere to students (effective 2006). adv. charts; illus. index. back issues avail. **Document type:** *Journal, Academic/Scholarly.* **Description:** Areas covered include synthesis, polymerization mechanisms and kinetics, chemical reactions, solution characteristics, spectroscopy, and bulk properties of organic, inorganic, and biopolymers.
Related titles: Microfiche ed.: USD 2,027 in North America to institutions; USD 2,066 elsewhere to institutions (effective 2002); Microfilm ed.: USD 2,027 in North America to institutions; USD 2,057 elsewhere to institutions (effective 2002); Online - full text ed.: ISSN 1520-5835. USD 85 (effective 2006) (from EBSCO Publishing, Swets Information Services).
Indexed: ABIPC, ASCA, BPRC&P, BrCerAb, C&ISA, CCI, CIN, CMCI, CerAb, ChemAb, ChemTitl, CivEngAb, CorrAb, CurCont, E&CAJ, EMA, EngInd, FS&TA, IAA, ISMEC, ISR, M&TEA, MBF, MEDLINE, METADEX, MSB, MSCI, P&BA, RAPRA, RCI, RefZh, SCI, SolStAb, TTI, WAA, WSCA, WTA.
—BLDSC (5330.420000), CASDDS, CINDOC, CISTI, Ei, GNLM, IDS, IE, Infotrieve, ingenta, Linda Hall. **CCC.**
Published by: American Chemical Society, 1155 16th St, N W, Washington, DC 20036. TEL 202-872-4600, 800-227-5558, FAX 202-872-3727, service@acs.org, http://pubs.acs.org/macromolecules. Ed. Timothy P Lodge. adv.: color page USD 3,920. Circ: 2,800 (paid). **Subscr. to:** Member & Subscriber Services, PO Box 3337, Columbus, OH 43210. TEL 614-447-3776, 800-333-9511, FAX 614-447-3671.

C

▼ new title ➤ refereed ✶ unverified ♦ full entry avail.

547 USA ISSN 1545-438X
QD380
▼ **MACROMOLECULES CONTAINING METAL AND METAL-LIKE ELEMENTS.** Text in English. 2003 (Oct.). s-a. (2-3x/yr). USD 125 per issue (effective 2004).
Related titles: Online - full text ed.: ISSN 1545-4398.
Published by: John Wiley & Sons, Inc., 111 River St, Hoboken, NJ 07030-5774. TEL 201-748-6000, FAX 201-748-5915, http://www.wiley.com.

660 USA ISSN 1058-9937
CODEN: MMIEE2
MCCUTCHEON'S FUNCTIONAL MATERIALS (INTERNATIONAL EDITION). Text in English. 1985. a. USD 80 per issue (effective 2003). adv. **Document type:** *Trade.* **Description:** Comprehensive formulator's guide to over 4000 products used in conjunction with surface active agents which are categorized by trade name identity, physical characteristics and product applications.
—**CCC.**
Published by: Manufacturing Confectioner Publishing Company, 711 W Water St, PO Box 266, Princeton, WI 54968. TEL 920-295-6969, FAX 920-295-6843, mccutcheons@gomc.com, www.gomc.com/mccutcheons. Ed. Kate Allured.

547 USA ISSN 0734-0559
TP202 CODEN: MMNEER
MCCUTCHEON'S FUNCTIONAL MATERIALS (NORTH AMERICAN EDITION). Text in English. a. USD 80 per issue (effective 2005). **Document type:** *Directory.* **Description:** Comprehensive formulator's guide to over 4000 products used in conjunction with surface active agents which are categorized by trade name, identity, physical characteristics and product application.
—CASDDS. **CCC.**
Published by: Manufacturing Confectioner Publishing Company, 711 W Water St, PO Box 266, Princeton, WI 54968. TEL 920-295-6969, FAX 920-295-6843, themc@gomc.com, http://www.gomc.com/display.asp?pageId=home. Ed. Kate Allured.

547 NLD ISSN 1570-193X
▼ **MINI - REVIEWS IN ORGANIC CHEMISTRY.** Text in English. 2004. q. USD 140 combined subscription to individuals print & online; USD 500 combined subscription to institutions (academic), print & online; USD 970 combined subscription to corporations print & online (effective 2005). **Document type:** *Journal, Academic/Scholarly.* **Description:** Publishes original reviews on all areas of organic chemistry including synthesis, bioorganic, medicinal, natural products, organometallic, supramolecular, molecular recognition, and physical organic chemistry.
Related titles: Online - full content ed.; Online - full text ed.: (from EBSCO Publishing, Gale Group, IngentaConnect, Swets Information Services).
Indexed: CCI, CurCont.
—BLDSC (5797.439955), IE. **CCC.**
Published by: Bentham Science Publishers Ltd., PO Box 1673, Hilversum, BR 1200, Netherlands. TEL 31-35-6923800, FAX 31-35-6980150, M.Bentham@inter.nl.net, http://www.bentham.org/. Ed. Atta-ur Rahman TEL 92-21-4969873.

547 CHE ISSN 1420-3049
CODEN: MOLEFW
➤ **MOLECULES;** a journal of synthetic organic and natural product chemistry. Text in English. 1996. m. free access to selected articles (effective 2005). bk.rev. abstr. back issues avail. **Document type:** *Journal, Academic/Scholarly.* **Description:** Covers small- and medium-sized molecules and their preparation (synthesis, biosynthesis, extraction), structural elucidation, properties and applications.
Media: Online - full content. **Related titles:** ◆ Special ed(s).: Molecules (Print Archive Edition).
Indexed: CIN, ChemAb, ChemTitl, CurCont, MSB.
—CISTI, IE, Infotrieve. **CCC.**
Published by: Molecular Diversity Preservation International, MDPI Center, Matthaeusstr 11, Basel, 4057, Switzerland. TEL 41-79-3223379, 41-61-6837734, FAX 41-61-3028918, molinfo@mdpi.org, lin@mdpi.org, http://www.mdpi.org/molecules. Ed., Pub., Adv. contact Shu-Kun Lin.

547 GBR ISSN 0265-0568
QD415.A1 CODEN: NPRRDF
➤ **NATURAL PRODUCT REPORTS;** a journal of current development in bioorganic chemistry. Text in English. 1984. bi-m. GBP 669, USD 1,224 combined subscription print & online eds. (effective 2006). adv. bk.rev. index. back issues avail. **Document type:** *Journal, Academic/Scholarly.* **Description:** Aims to both document and stimulate research into natural products via critical literature reviews on the chemistry and biochemistry of alkaloids, terpenoids, steroids, fatty acids, and O-heterocyclic, aliphatic, aromatic, and alicyclic natural products.
Formed by the merger of (1971-1984): Biosynthesis (0301-0708); (1970-1984): Alkalois (0305-9707); (1971-1984): Terpenoids and Steroids (0300-5992); (1979-1983): Aliphatic and Related Natural Product (0142-7318); Which superseded in part: Aliphatic Chemistry (0305-618X); Which was formerly (1973-1974): Aliphatic, Alicyclic, and Saturated Heterocyclic Chemistry. Part I. Aliphatic Chemistry (0302-4164)
Related titles: Online - full text ed.: ISSN 1460-4752. GBP 602, USD 1,101 (effective 2006) (from EBSCO Publishing, O C L C Online Computer Library Center, Inc., Swets Information Services).
Indexed: ASCA, Agr, BBCI, BIOBASE, BibAg, CCI, CIN, ChemAb, ChemInfo, ChemTitl, CurCR, CurCont, IABS, ISR, IndMed, MEDLINE, MOS, NPU, PlantSci, RCI, RefZh, SCI.
—BLDSC (6040.738000), CASDDS, CISTI, IDS, IE, Infotrieve, ingenta, Linda Hall. **CCC.**
Published by: Royal Society of Chemistry, Thomas Graham House, Science Park, Milton Rd, Cambridge, CB4 0WF, United Kingdom. TEL 44-1223-432360, FAX 44-1223-423623, npr@rsc.org, sales@rsc.org, advertising@rsc.org, http://www.rsc.org/npr. Ed. Dr. Robert D Eagling. R&P Sharon Bellard. Circ: 800. **Subscr. to:** Portland Press Ltd., R S C Distribution Services, Commerce Way, Whitehall Industrial Estate, Colchester CO2 8HP, United Kingdom. TEL 44-1206-226050, FAX 44-1206-226055, sales@rscdistribution.org.

547 GBR
NATURAL PRODUCTS NEWS. Text in English. 1994. 12/yr. GBP 59; GBP 69 in Europe; GBP 79 elsewhere (effective 2001). adv. bk.rev. 80 p./no.; back issues avail. **Document type:** *Magazine, Trade.* **Description:** Aims to inform and entertain health food retailers, suppliers and others in the natural healthcare movement by communicating news, opinions and ideas from all sectors of the industry.
Published by: Full Moon Communications, 58 High St, Steyning, BN44 3RD, United Kingdom. TEL 44-1903-817300, FAX 44-1903-817310, info@naturalproducts.co.uk, http://www.naturalproducts.co.uk. Ed. Jim Manson. Pub. Robin Bines. Adv. contact Philip Daniell TEL 44-1903-817301. color page GBP 2,150; trim 245 x 342. Circ: 5,300 (paid).

NEW CONCEPTS IN POLYMER SCIENCE. see *ENGINEERING—Chemical Engineering*

OILS & FATS INTERNATIONAL. see *FOOD AND FOOD INDUSTRIES*

665.3029 GBR ISSN 0265-6477
OILS AND FATS INTERNATIONAL DIRECTORY. Text in English. 1984. a. GBP 131 domestic; GBP 142 foreign (effective 2000). **Document type:** *Directory.*
—BLDSC, CISTI.
Published by: D M G World Media Ltd. (Subsidiary of: Daily Mail and General Trust PLC), Queensway House, 2 Queensway, Redhill, Surrey RH1 1QS, United Kingdom. TEL 44-1737-768611, FAX 44-1737-855475, http://www.dmg.co.uk, http://www.dmgworldmedia.com.

547 FRA ISSN 1258-8210
CODEN: RFCGAE
➤ **OLEAGINEUX CORPS GRAS LIPIDES.** Abbreviated title: O C L. Text in French. 1954; N.S. 1994. bi-m. EUR 244 combined subscription domestic print & online eds.; EUR 265 combined subscription in the European Union print & online eds.; EUR 276 combined subscription elsewhere print & online eds. (effective 2006). adv. bk.rev. bibl.; charts; pat. index. **Document type:** *Journal, Academic/Scholarly.* **Description:** For scientists, industrialists, producers and advisors in the oilseeds industries.
Supersedes (in 1994): Revue Francaise des Corps Gras (0035-3000)
Related titles: Microform ed.: N.S. (from PMC); Online - full text ed.: (from EBSCO Publishing).
Indexed: AEA, ASCA, AbHyg, AgBio, AgrForAb, ArtHuCI, CBNB, CIN, CISA, CPA, ChemAb, ChemTitl, CurCont, DSA, EngInd, ExcerpMed, FCA, FPA, FS&TA, ForAb, HerbAb, HortAb, IndVet, MaizeAb, NutrAb, OrnHort, PBA, PGegResA, PGrRegA, PHN&I, PN&I, PoultAb, ProtozoAb, RA&MP, RDA, RM&VM, RPP, RefZh, RevApplEntom, S&F, SIA, SSCI, SeedAb, SoyAb, TDB, TriticAb, WAE&RSA, WeedAb.
—BLDSC (6235.135900), CASDDS, CISTI, Ei, IDS, IE, Infotrieve, ingenta, Linda Hall. **CCC.**
Published by: John Libbey Eurotext, 127 Avenue de la Republique, Montrouge, 92120, France. TEL 33-1-46730660, FAX 33-1-40840999, contact@jle.com, http://www.john-libbey-eurotext.fr. Ed. Jean Claude Icart. **Subscr. to:** A T E I, 3 av. Pierre Kerautret, Romainville 92230, France. TEL 33-1-48408686, FAX 33-1-48400731, atei@club-internet.fr.

665 ESP ISSN 1696-8301
OLEO. GUIA DE LA INDUSTRIA Y COMERCIO DE ACEITES Y GRASAS. Text in Spanish. 1961. a. adv. stat.
Former titles (until 2002): Oleo. Anuario de Aceites, Grasas e Industrias Afines (1695-0100); (until 1999): Oleo: Anuario Espanol de Aceites y Grasas e Industrias Auxiliares (1695-0097)
Published by: Tecnipublicaciones Espana, S.L., Avda de Manoteras 44, 3a Planta, Madrid, 28050, Spain. TEL 34-91-2972000, FAX 34-91-2972154, tp@tecnipublicaciones.com, http://www.tecnipublicaciones.com. Circ: 1,500.

547 541 GBR ISSN 1477-0520
QD241 CODEN: OBCRAK
▼ **ORGANIC & BIOMOLECULAR CHEMISTRY.** Text in English. 2003. 24/yr. GBP 2,520, USD 4,612 combined subscription print & online eds. (effective 2006). adv. back issues avail. **Document type:** *Journal, Academic/Scholarly.* **Description:** Brings together molecular design, synthesis, structure, function and reactivity in one journal. It publishes fundamental work on synthetic, physical and biomolecular organic chemistry as well as all organic aspects of: chemical biology, medicinal chemistry, natural product chemistry, supramolecular chemistry, macromolecular chemistry, theoretical chemistry, and catalysis.
Formed by the 2003 merger of: Royal Chemical Society. Journal. Perkin Transactions 1 (1472-7781); Which was formerly (until 2001): Perkin 1 (1470-4358); (until 1999): Royal Society of Chemistry. Journal: Perkin Transactions 1 (0300-922X); (until 1971): Chemical Society, London. Journal. Section C. Organic Chemistry (0022-4952); and of: Royal Chemical Society. Journal. Perkin Transactions 2 (1472-779X); Which was formerly (until 2001): Perkin 2 (1470-1820); (until 1999): Royal Society of Chemistry. Journal: Perkin Transactions 2 (0300-9580); (until 1971): Chemistry Society, London. Journal. Section B. Physical Organic Chemistry (0045-6470); Both of which superseded in part (1848-1877): Chemical Society. Journal (0368-1769); Perkin Transactions 1 incorporated (1994-1998): Contemporary Organic Synthesis (1350-4894); Perkin 1 & Perkin 2 incorporated in part (in Jan. 2000): Acta Chemica Scandinavica (0904-213X); Which was formed by the 1989 merger of: Acta Chemica Scandinavica A: Physical and Inorganic Chemistry (0904-6437); Which was formerly (until 1986): Acta Chemica Scandivavica. Series A: Physical and Inorganic Chemistry (0302-4377); and of: Acta Chemical Scandinavica B: Organic Chemistry and Biochemistry (0904-6445); Which was formerly (until 1986): Acta Chemica Scandinavica. Series B: Organic and Biochemistry (0302-4369); Both of which superseded in part (1947-1973): Acta Chemica Scandinavica (0001-5393)
Related titles: Online - full text ed.: ISSN 1477-0539. GBP 2,268, USD 4,150 (effective 2006) (from EBSCO Publishing, O C L C Online Computer Library Center, Inc., Swets Information Services).
Indexed: CCI, ChemAb, ChemInfo, CurCR, CurCont, ISR, IndChem, RCI, RefZh, SCI.
—BLDSC (6286.350000), CISTI, IE, ingenta, Linda Hall. **CCC.**
Published by: Royal Society of Chemistry, Thomas Graham House, Science Park, Milton Rd, Cambridge, CB4 0WF, United Kingdom. TEL 44-1223-420066, FAX 44-1223-423623, obc@rsc.org, rsc1@rsc.org, http://www.rsc.org/obc. Ed. Dr. Vikki Allen. **Subscr. to:** Portland Press Ltd., R S C Distribution Services, Commerce Way, Whitehall Industrial Estate, Colchester CO2 8HP, United Kingdom. TEL 44-1206-226050, FAX 44-1206-226055, sales@rscdistribution.org.

ORGANIC AND ORGANOMETALLIC CRYSTAL STRUCTURES; BIBLIOGRAPHY. see *BIBLIOGRAPHIES*

547 USA ISSN 0078-611X
CODEN: OCSMBP
➤ **ORGANIC CHEMISTRY;** a series of monographs. Text in English. 1964. irreg., latest vol.48, 1987. reprint service avail. from ISI. **Document type:** *Monographic series, Academic/Scholarly.*
—CASDDS, CISTI. **CCC.**
Published by: Academic Press (Subsidiary of: Elsevier Science & Technology), 525 B St, Ste 1900, San Diego, CA 92101-4495. apsubs@acad.com, http://www.academicpress.com. Ed. Harry W Wasserman.

➤ **ORGANIC ELECTRONIC SPECTRAL DATA.** see *CHEMISTRY—Analytical Chemistry*

560 551.9 GBR ISSN 0146-6380
QE516.5 CODEN: ORGEDE
➤ **ORGANIC GEOCHEMISTRY.** Text in English. 1978. 12/yr. EUR 2,848 in Europe to institutions; JPY 378,200 in Japan to institutions; USD 3,187 to institutions except Europe and Japan (effective 2006). adv. bk.rev. illus. index. back issues avail.; reprints avail. **Document type:** *Journal, Academic/Scholarly.* **Description:** Covers organic chemistry, geology, mineralogy, biogeochemistry, oceanography and hydrology.
Related titles: Microfilm ed.: (from PQC); Online - full text ed.: (from EBSCO Publishing, Gale Group, IngentaConnect, ScienceDirect, Swets Information Services).
Indexed: AESIS, ASCA, ASFA, BIOBASE, C&ISA, CCI, ChemAb, ChemTitl, CurCont, E&CAJ, ESPM, EngInd, ExcerpMed, FCA, FPA, ForAb, GEOBASE, HortAb, I&DA, IABS, IMMAb, ISMEC, ISR, M&GPA, MSB, MaizeAb, PGegResA, PetrolAb, PollutAb, RCI, RPP, RefZh, RevApplEntom, S&F, SCI, SFA, SIA, SWRA, SolStAb, SoyAb, TriticAb, WRCInf, WeedAb.
—BLDSC (6288.200000), CASDDS, CISTI, Ei, IDS, IE, Infotrieve, ingenta, Linda Hall, PADDS. **CCC.**
Published by: (European Association of Organic Geochemists), Pergamon (Subsidiary of: Elsevier Science & Technology), The Boulevard, Langford Ln, East Park, Kidlington, Oxford OX5 1GB, United Kingdom. TEL 44-1865-843000, FAX 44-1865-843010, http://www.elsevier.com/locate/orggeochem. Eds. J R Maxwell, L R Snowden. Circ: 1,100. **Subscr. to:** Elsevier BV, PO Box 211, Amsterdam 1000 AE, Netherlands. TEL 31-20-485-3757, FAX 31-20-485-3432, nlinfo-f@elsevier.nl, http://www.elsevier.nl.

C

547 USA ISSN 1523-7060
QD241 CODEN: ORLEF7
➤ **ORGANIC LETTERS.** Text in English. 1999. fortn. USD 3,630 in North America to institutions; USD 3,790 elsewhere to institutions; USD 360 in North America to members; USD 520 elsewhere to members; USD 270 in North America to students; USD 430 elsewhere to students (effective 2006). adv. back issues avail. **Document type:** *Journal, Academic/Scholarly.* **Description:** Contains reports of fundamental research in all branches of the theory and practice of organic, physical organic, organometallic, medicinal, and bioorganic chemistry.
Related titles: Online - full text ed.: ISSN 1523-7052. USD 85 (effective 2006) (from EBSCO Publishing, Swets Information Services).
Indexed: BIOSIS Prev, BiolAb, CCI, ChemAb, ChemInfo, CurCR, CurCont, ISR, IndChem, IndMed, MEDLINE, MSB, RCI, RefZh, SCI, ZooRec.
—BLDSC (6288.350000), CISTI, IE, Infotrieve, ingenta, Linda Hall. **CCC.**
Published by: American Chemical Society, 1155 16th St, N W, Washington, DC 20036. TEL 202-872-4614, 800-227-5558, FAX 202-776-8264, service@acs.org, http://pubs.acs.org/journals/orlef7/index.html. Ed. Amos B Smith. adv.: color page USD 2,635. Circ: 5,500 (paid).

547 USA ISSN 0030-4948
QD262 CODEN: OPPIAK
➤ **ORGANIC PREPARATIONS AND PROCEDURES INTERNATIONAL**; the new journal for organic synthesis. Text in English. 1969. bi-m. USD 130 to individuals; USD 245 to institutions (effective 2005). adv. bk.rev. index. back issues avail. **Document type:** *Journal, Academic/Scholarly.*
Formerly (until 1971): Organic Preparations and Procedures (0885-6672)
Indexed: ASCA, CCI, CIN, ChemAb, ChemInfo, ChemTitl, CurCR, CurCont, ISR, IndChem, RCI, RefZh, SCI, SSCI.
—BLDSC (6288.875000), CASDDS, CISTI, IDS, IE, Infotrieve, ingenta, Linda Hall. **CCC.**
Published by: Organic Preparations and Procedures, Inc., PO Box 610009, Newton, MA 02461-0009. info@oppint.com, http://www.oppint.com. Ed. J P Anselme. Adv. contact Fabienne Madsen. Circ: 600.

547 USA ISSN 1083-6160
TP155.7 CODEN: OPRDFK
➤ **ORGANIC PROCESS RESEARCH AND DEVELOPMENT.** Text in English. 1997. bi-m. USD 827 in North America to institutions; USD 872 elsewhere to institutions; USD 113 in North America to members; USD 158 elsewhere to members; USD 85 in North America to students; USD 130 elsewhere to students (effective 2006). adv. back issues avail. **Document type:** *Journal, Academic/Scholarly.* **Description:** Contains original research reports on developments relating to batch and semi-batch chemical process industries. Covers relevant aspects of organic chemistry, catalysis, analytical chemistry, and chemical engineering.
Related titles: Online - full text ed.: ISSN 1520-586X. USD 40 (effective 2006) (from EBSCO Publishing, Swets Information Services).
Indexed: CCI, ChemAb, ChemInfo, CurCont, RCI, RefZh.
—BLDSC (6288.880000), CASDDS, CISTI, IDS, IE, Infotrieve, ingenta, Linda Hall. **CCC.**
Published by: American Chemical Society, 1155 16th St, N W, Washington, DC 20036. TEL 202-872-4614, 800-227-5558, FAX 202-776-8264, oprd@scientificupdate.co.uk, service@acs.org, http://pubs.acs.org/journals/oprdfk/index.html, http://www.acs.org. Ed. Trevor Laird. adv.: color page USD 3,840. Circ: 1,300 (paid). **Subscr. in Americas to:** Member & Subscriber Services, PO Box 3337, Columbus, OH 43210. TEL 614-447-3776, 800-333-9511, FAX 614-447-3671.

547 GBR ISSN 0474-4772
ORGANIC REACTION MECHANISMS. Text in English. 1965. a., latest 1999. price varies.
—BLDSC (6288.900000), CISTI, IE, Linda Hall.
Published by: John Wiley & Sons Ltd. (Subsidiary of: John Wiley & Sons, Inc.), The Atrium, Southern Gate, Chichester, West Sussex PO19 8SQ, United Kingdom. TEL 44-1243-779777, FAX 44-1243-775878, http://www3.interscience.wiley.com/cgi-bin/booktoc/107613984.

547 541.39 USA ISSN 0078-6160
➤ **ORGANIC REACTION MECHANISMS. ANNUAL SURVEY.** Text in English. 1966. a., latest 1998. price varies. **Document type:** *Academic/Scholarly.*
Indexed: ChemAb.
Published by: John Wiley & Sons, Inc., 111 River St, Hoboken, NJ 07030-5774. TEL 201-748-6000, FAX 201-748-5915, uscs-wis@wiley.com, http://www.wiley.com.

547 541.39 USA ISSN 0078-6179
CODEN: ORREAW
➤ **ORGANIC REACTIONS.** Text in English. 1942. irreg., latest vol.65, 2005. price varies. **Document type:** *Monographic series, Academic/Scholarly.*
Indexed: BiolAb, CCI, ChemAb, ChemTitl, CurCont, ISR, NutrAb.
—BLDSC (6288.910000), CASDDS, CISTI, IE, Infotrieve, ingenta, Linda Hall.
Published by: John Wiley & Sons, Inc., 111 River St, Hoboken, NJ 07030-5774. TEL 201-748-6000, FAX 201-748-5915, uscs-wis@wiley.com, http://www.wiley.com. Ed. W G Dauben.

547 541.39 USA ISSN 0078-6209
QD262 CODEN: ORSYAT
➤ **ORGANIC SYNTHESES.** Text in English. 1993 (vol.71). a., latest vol.80, 2003. price varies. **Document type:** *Monographic series, Academic/Scholarly.*
Related titles: Microform ed.: (from PMC).
Indexed: ABIPC, ASCA, CCI, ChemAb, ChemTitl, ISR, RCI, SCI.
—BLDSC (6288.950000), CASDDS, CISTI, IE, Infotrieve, ingenta.
Published by: John Wiley & Sons, Inc., 111 River St, Hoboken, NJ 07030-5774. TEL 201-748-6000, 800-825-7550, FAX 201-748-5915, uscs-wis@wiley.com, http://www3.interscience.wiley.com/cgi-bin/mrwhome/104554793/HOME, http://www.wiley.com.

547 541.39 USA ISSN 0078-6217
QD262
ORGANIC SYNTHESES - COLLECTIVE VOLUMES. Text in English. 1941. irreg., latest vol.10, 2004, years 1975-1979. USD 160 per vol. (effective 2005). **Document type:** *Monographic series, Academic/Scholarly.*
—CISTI, IE, Linda Hall.
Published by: John Wiley & Sons, Inc., 111 River St, Hoboken, NJ 07030-5774. TEL 201-748-6000, 800-825-7550, FAX 201-748-5915, uscs-wis@wiley.com, http://www.wiley.com. Ed. Jeremiah P Freeman.

547 USA ISSN 1047-773X
QD262 CODEN: OSTAE7
ORGANIC SYNTHESIS; theory and applications. Text in English. 1989. irreg., latest vol.5, 2001. price varies. back issues avail. **Document type:** *Monographic series, Academic/Scholarly.* **Description:** Covers areas of organic synthesis ranging from the latest developments in enantioselective methodologies to reviews of updated chemical methods.
Indexed: CIN, ChemAb, ChemTitl.
—BLDSC (6288.952000), CASDDS, CISTI, ingenta, KNAW. **CCC.**
Published by: J A I Press Inc. (Subsidiary of: Elsevier Science & Technology), 360 Park Ave S, New York, NY 10010-1710. TEL 212-989-5800, FAX 212-633-3990, usinfo-f@elsevier.com, http://www.elsevier.com/wps/find/bookdescription.cws_home/BS_OSTA/description#description. Ed. Tomas Hudlicky.

547.05 GBR ISSN 0301-0074
QD410 CODEN: OGMCAQ
ORGANOMETALLIC CHEMISTRY. Text in English. 1971. a., latest vol.31, 2004. GBP 249.50 per vol. (effective 2005). charts; illus. index. back issues avail. **Document type:** *Monographic series, Academic/Scholarly.* **Description:** Includes extensive references.
Indexed: BIOSIS Prev, ChemAb, ChemTitl, Englnd.
—BLDSC (6291.080000), CASDDS, CISTI, Ei, IE, ingenta, Linda Hall. **CCC.**
Published by: Royal Society of Chemistry, Thomas Graham House, Science Park, Milton Rd, Cambridge, CB4 0WF, United Kingdom. TEL 44-1223-432360, FAX 44-1223-423623, sales@rsc.org, advertising@rsc.org, http://www.rsc.org/Publishing/Books/0854043381.asp, http://www.rsc.org/spr. Ed. M Green. **Subscr. to:** Extenza - Turpin, Pegasus Dr, Stratton Business Park, Biggleswade, Beds SG18 8TQ, United Kingdom.

547 JPN ISSN 0917-1274
ORGANOMETALLIC NEWS. Text in Japanese. q.
Published by: Kinki Chemical Society, Division of Organometallic Chemistry/Kinki Kagaku Kyokai Yuki Kinzoku Bukai, 8-4 Utsubohon-Machi 1-chome, Nishi-ku, Osaka-shi, 550-0004, Japan. TEL 06-441-5531, FAX 06-443-6685.

547 USA ISSN 0276-7333
QD410 CODEN: ORGND7
➤ **ORGANOMETALLICS.** Text in English. 1982. bi-m. USD 2,650 in North America to institutions; USD 2,830 elsewhere to institutions; USD 273 in North America to members; USD 453 elsewhere to members; USD 205 in North America to students; USD 385 elsewhere to students (effective 2006). adv. charts; illus. index. back issues avail.; reprints avail. **Document type:** *Journal, Academic/Scholarly.* **Description:** Records progress in one of the most active fields for organometallic, inorganic, organic and materials chemists. Articles, communications, mini-reviews and notes detail the synthesis, structure, bonding, chemical reactivity and reaction mechanisms and applications of organometallic and organometalloidal compounds.
Related titles: Microform ed.; Online - full text ed.: ISSN 1520-6041. USD 85 (effective 2006) (from EBSCO Publishing, Swets Information Services).
Indexed: ASCA, CCI, CIN, Cadscan, ChemAb, ChemInfo, ChemTitl, CurCR, CurCont, Englnd, INIS AtomInd, ISR, IndChem, LeadAb, MOS, MSB, MSCI, RCI, RefZh, SCI, Zincscan.
—BLDSC (6291.102500), CASDDS, CINDOC, CISTI, Ei, IDS, IE, Infotrieve, ingenta, Linda Hall. **CCC.**
Published by: American Chemical Society, 1155 16th St, N W, Washington, DC 20036. TEL 202-872-4614, 800-227-5558, FAX 202-776-8264, service@acs.org, http://pubs.acs.org/organometallics. Ed. Dr. Dietmar Seyferth. adv.: color page USD 3,600. Circ: 1,173 (paid).

547 GBR ISSN 0306-0713
QD412.P1 CODEN: OPCMAZ
ORGANOPHOSPHORUS CHEMISTRY. Text in English. 1968. a., latest vol.34, 2005. GBP 249.50 per vol. (effective 2005). charts; illus. index. back issues avail. **Document type:** *Monographic series, Academic/Scholarly.* **Description:** Comprehensive annual review of the literature published on Organophosphorus Chemistry between July 1997 and June 1998.
Indexed: BIOSIS Prev, ChemAb, ChemTitl.
—BLDSC (6291.110000), CASDDS, CISTI, IE, ingenta, Linda Hall. **CCC.**
Published by: Royal Society of Chemistry, Thomas Graham House, Science Park, Milton Rd, Cambridge, CB4 0WF, United Kingdom. TEL 44-1223-432360, FAX 44-1223-423623, sales@rsc.org, advertising@rsc.org, http://www.rsc.org/Publishing/Books/0854043446.asp, http://www.rsc.org/spr. Eds. D W Allen, J C Tebby. **Subscr. to:** Extenza - Turpin, Pegasus Dr, Stratton Business Park, Biggleswade, Beds SG18 8TQ, United Kingdom.

547 BGR ISSN 0209-4541
QD281.O9 CODEN: OXCODW
➤ **OXIDATION COMMUNICATIONS.** Text in English. 1977. q. (in 1 vol., 4 nos./vol.). EUR 380 in Europe; USD 475 elsewhere (effective 2006). adv. bk.rev. 1000 p./no.; **Document type:** *Journal, Academic/Scholarly.* **Description:** Devoted to the global oxy-reduction interactions in nature with an international focus on new fundamental and technological research.
Indexed: ASCA, CCI, ChemAb, ChemTitl, CurCont.
—BLDSC (6321.035000), CASDDS, CISTI, IDS, IE, ingenta, Linda Hall. **CCC.**
Published by: Scientific Bulgarian Communications, 7 Nezabravka St, PO Box 249, Sofia, 1113, Bulgaria. scibulcom@global.bg. Ed., Pub., R&P Slavi Ivanov.

➤ **PESTYCYDY/PESTICIDES.** see *AGRICULTURE—Crop Production And Soil*

668.9 BRA
PLASTICO INDUSTRIAL. Text in Portuguese. 1998. m. USD 100 foreign (effective 2001). adv. bk.rev. back issues avail. **Document type:** *Magazine, Trade.* **Description:** Focuses on the processing of polymeric materials, formulation, application, machines, equipment, and production.
Published by: Aranda Editora Ltda., Al. Olga 315, Perdizes, Sao Paulo,, SP 01155-900, Brazil. TEL 55-11-38245300, FAX 55-11-3662-0103, info@arandanet.com.br, http://www.arandanet.com.br. Eds. Hellen C Souza, Jose R.A. Souza. Adv. contact Jose Roberto Goncalves. B&W page BRL 2,301, color page BRL 3,186; trim 21 x 28.

547 POL ISSN 0032-2725
TP986.A1 CODEN: POLIA4
➤ **POLIMERY/POLYMERS.** Variant title: Polimery Tworzywa Wieloczasteczkowe. Text in English, Polish. 1956. m. EUR 211 foreign (effective 2005). adv. bk.rev. bibl.; pat. reprints avail. **Document type:** *Journal, Academic/Scholarly.* **Description:** Covers such topics as: synthesis, analysis and properties of polymers, technology of plastics, rubbers, synthetic fibers and lacquers, manufacturing processes and apparatuses, processing machinery.
Former titles (until 1961): Tworzywa Wieloczasteczkowe (0372-3364); (until 1960): Towarzywa, Guma, Lakiery (0372-3313); (until 1958): Tworzywa
Indexed: ABIPC, ASCA, BrCerAb, C&ISA, CCI, CEABA, CIN, CerAb, ChemAb, ChemTitl, CivEngAb, CorrAb, E&CAJ, EMA, Englnd, IAA, INIS AtomInd, Inspec, M&TEA, MBF, METADEX, MSCI, RAPRA, RCI, RefZh, SolStAb, TTI, WAA, WSCA.
—BLDSC (6543.398000), CASDDS, CISTI, IDS, IE, Infotrieve, ingenta, Linda Hall.
Published by: Instytut Chemii Przemyslowej/Industrial Chemistry Research Institute, ul Rydygiera 8, Warsaw, 01793, Poland. polimery@ichp.pl, http://www.ichp.pl/polimery. Ed. Barbara Witowska Mocek. **Dist. by:** Ars Polona, Krakowskie Przedmiescie 7, Warsaw, Poland. TEL 48-22-9263914, FAX 48-22-9265334, arspolona@arspolona.com.pl, http://www.arspolona.com.pl.

668.9 610 POL ISSN 0370-0747
CODEN: PMYMAX
➤ **POLIMERY W MEDYCYNIE.** Text in Polish. 1965. 4/yr. EUR 25 foreign (effective 2005). adv. bk.rev. **Document type:** *Journal, Academic/Scholarly.*
Formerly (until 1971): Tworzywa Sztuczne w Medycynie (0372-3356)
Indexed: ChemAb, ChemTitl, IndMed, MEDLINE.
—BLDSC (6547.742600), CASDDS, CISTI, GNLM, IE, Infotrieve, ingenta.
Published by: Akademia Medyczna we Wroclawiu, Katedra Chirurgii Urazowej, Zaklad Chirurgii Eksperymentalnej i Badania Biomaterialow/Wroclaw Medical University, Chair of Traumatology, Department of Experimental Surgery and Biomaterials, ul Poniatowskiego 2, Wroclaw, 50326, Poland. TEL 48-71-3226310, FAX 48-71-3227526, sekr@chekssp.am.wroc.pl. Ed., Adv. contact Roman Rutowski. R&P Urszula Tomczyk. Circ: 800 (paid); 200 (controlled). **Dist. by:** Ars Polona, Krakowskie Przedmiescie 7, Warsaw, Poland. TEL 48-22-9263914, FAX 48-22-9265334, arspolona@arspolona.com.pl, http://www.arspolona.com.pl.

C

547.7 660.6 POL ISSN 1509-7013 CODEN: ZPLSDI

➤ **POLITECHNIKA LODZKA. ZESZYTY NAUKOWE. CHEMIA SPOZYWCZA I BIOTECHNOLOGIA.** Text in Polish; Summaries in English. 1955. irreg. price varies. 120 p./no. 1 cols./p.; **Document type:** *Monographic series, Academic/Scholarly.* **Description:** Analyzes the chemical technology of food, biotechnology, technology of fermentation, bio-inorganic and analytical chemistry.
Former titles: Politechnika Lodzka. Zeszyty Naukowe. Technologia i Chemia Spozywcza (0209-0600); (until 1980): Politechnika Lodzka. Zeszyty Naukowe. Chemia Spozywcza (0528-9254)
Indexed: AgrAg, AgrLib, ChemAb.
—BLDSC (9512.310350), CASDDS, CISTI, Linda Hall.
Published by: (Politechnika Lodzka/Technical University of Lodz), Wydawnictwo Politechniki Lodzkiej, ul Wolczanska 223, Lodz, 93005, Poland. TEL 48-42-6312087, dakal@snack.p.lodz.pl. Ed. Danuta Kalemba TEL 48-42-6313423. Circ: 206. **Dist. by:** Ars Polona, Krakowskie Przedmiescie 7, Warsaw, Poland. TEL 48-22-9263914, FAX 48-22-9265334, arspolona@arspolona.com.pl, http://www.arspolona.com.pl.

547 USA ISSN 1040-6638
QD335 CODEN: PARCEO

➤ **POLYCYCLIC AROMATIC COMPOUNDS**; an international and interdisciplinary journal. Text in English. 1990. 5/yr. (in 4 vols., 4 nos./vol.). GBP 2,922, USD 3,665 combined subscription to institutions print & online eds. (effective 2006). reprint service avail. from PSC. **Document type:** *Journal, Academic/Scholarly.* **Description:** Provides an international and interdisciplinary forum for all aspects of research related to polycyclic aromatic compounds (PAC).
Related titles: CD-ROM ed.: ISSN 1026-7743. 1995; Microform ed.; Online - full text ed.: ISSN 1563-5333. GBP 2,776, USD 3,482 to institutions (effective 2006) (from EBSCO Publishing, Gale Group, IngentaConnect, O C L C Online Computer Library Center, Inc., Swets Information Services).
Indexed: ASCA, CCI, ChemAb, CurCont, FS&TA, RAPRA.
—BLDSC (6547.558000), CISTI, IE, Infotrieve, ingenta. **CCC.**
Published by: Taylor & Francis Inc. (Subsidiary of: Taylor & Francis Group), 325 Chestnut St, Ste 800, Philadelphia, PA 19016. TEL 215-625-8900, 800-354-1420, FAX 215-625-8914, info@taylorandfrancis.com, http://www.tandf.co.uk/journals/titles/10406638.asp, http://www.taylorandfrancis.com. Ed. Phillippe Garrigues. **Subsc. outside N. America:** Taylor & Francis Ltd, Journals Customer Service, Rankine Rd, Basingstoke, Hants RG24 8PR, United Kingdom. TEL 44-1256-813000, FAX 44-1256-330245, enquiry@tandf.co.uk.

660.284 668.4 GBR ISSN 0141-3910 CODEN: PDSTDW

➤ **POLYMER DEGRADATION AND STABILITY.** Text in English. 1979. 12/yr. EUR 3,695 in Europe to institutions; JPY 490,500 in Japan to institutions; USD 4,134 to institutions except Europe and Japan (effective 2006). adv. bk.rev. charts; illus. index. **Document type:** *Journal, Academic/Scholarly.* **Description:** Deals with the degradation reactions and their control which are a major preoccupation of practitioners of the many and diverse aspects of modern polymer technology.
Incorporates: Polymer Photochemistry (0144-2880)
Related titles: Microform ed.: (from PQC); Online - full text ed.: (from EBSCO Publishing, Gale Group, IngentaConnect, ScienceDirect, Swets Information Services).
Indexed: AEA, ASCA, AgrForAb, B&BAb, BioEngAb, BrCerAb, C&ISA, CCI, CerAb, ChemAb, ChemTitl, CivEngAb, CorrAb, CurCont, DSA, E&CAJ, EMA, EngInd, ExcerpMed, FCA, FPA, ForAb, HerbAb, HortAb, IAA, ISR, M&TEA, MBF, METADEX, MSB, MSCI, MaizeAb, OrnHort, RAPRA, RCI, RefZh, S&F, SCI, SIA, SolStAb, TTI, TriticAb, WAA, WSCA.
—BLDSC (6547.704700), CASDDS, CISTI, Ei, IDS, IE, Infotrieve, ingenta, Linda Hall. **CCC.**
Published by: Elsevier Ltd. (Subsidiary of: Elsevier Science & Technology), The Boulevard, Langford Ln, Kidlington, Oxford, OX5 1GB, United Kingdom. TEL 44-1865-843000, FAX 44-1865-843010, nlinfo-f@elsevier.nl, http://www.elsevier.com/locate/polydegstab. Ed. N. C. Billingham. **Subscr. to:** Elsevier BV, PO Box 211, Amsterdam 1000 AE, Netherlands. TEL 31-20-485-3757, FAX 31-20-485-3432, http://www.elsevier.nl.

➤ **POLYMER ENGINEERING AND SCIENCE.** see *ENGINEERING—Chemical Engineering*

547 JPN ISSN 0032-3896
QD380 CODEN: POLJB8

➤ **POLYMER JOURNAL.** Text in English. 1970. m. JPY 13,800 to individual members; JPY 47,000 to institutional members (effective 2004). Index. back issues avail. **Document type:** *Journal, Academic/Scholarly.* **Description:** Provides international coverage of every field of polymers such as polymer chemistry, physics and biopolymers.
Related titles: Online - full text ed.: ISSN 1349-0540 (from J-Stage).
Indexed: ABIPC, ASCA, B&BAb, C&ISA, CCI, CIN, ChemAb, ChemTitl, CurCont, E&CAJ, EngInd, INIS AtomInd, ISMEC, ISR, JCT, JTA, MSCI, RAPRA, RCI, SCI, SolStAb, TTI.
—BLDSC (6547.707000), CASDDS, CISTI, Ei, IDS, IE, Infotrieve, ingenta, Linda Hall. **CCC.**
Published by: Nihon Kobunshi Gakkai/Society of Polymer Science, Japan, Shintomicho-Tokyu Bldg., 3-10-9 Irifune, Chuo-ku, Tokyo, 104-0042, Japan. TEL 81-3-55403771, FAX 81-3-55403737, hpj@spsj.or.jp, kobunshi@spsj.or.jp, http://www.spsj.or.jp/c5/pj/pj.htm. Ed. Mitsuru Ueda. Circ: 2,000.

547 660.084 USA ISSN 0360-2559 CODEN: PPTEC7

➤ **POLYMER-PLASTICS TECHNOLOGY AND ENGINEERING.** Text in English. 1962. m. GBP 1,826, USD 3,013 combined subscription to institutions print & online eds. (effective 2006). adv. abstr. reprint service avail. from PSC. **Document type:** *Journal, Academic/Scholarly.* **Description:** Includes original articles, reviews, notes and letters on various topics.
Incorporates (in 2004): Polymer Reaction Engineering (1054-3414); Polymer Process Engineering (0735-7931); Formerly (until 1972): Journal of Macromolecular Science: Part D - Reviews in Polymer Processing and Technology (0022-2321)
Related titles: Microform ed.: (from RPI); Online - full text ed.: ISSN 1525-6111. GBP 1,735, USD 2,862 to institutions (effective 2006) (from EBSCO Publishing, O C L C Online Computer Library Center, Inc., Swets Information Services); Special ed(s).: Polymer-Plastics Technology and Engineering (Hardcover Edition). ISSN 0092-5012.
Indexed: ASCA, BrCerAb, C&ISA, CCI, CEABA, CIN, CerAb, ChemAb, ChemTitl, CivEngAb, CorrAb, CurCont, E&CAJ, EMA, EngInd, ExcerpMed, FLUIDEX, IAA, ISMEC, ISR, Inspec, M&TEA, MBF, METADEX, MSCI, RAPRA, RCI, RefZh, SCI, SSCI, SolStAb, WAA, WSCA, WTA.
—BLDSC (6547.714500), AskIEEE, CASDDS, CISTI, Ei, IDS, IE, Infotrieve, ingenta, Linda Hall. **CCC.**
Published by: Taylor & Francis Inc. (Subsidiary of: Taylor & Francis Group), 325 Chestnut St, Ste 800, Philadelphia, PA 19016. TEL 215-625-8900, 800-354-1420, FAX 215-625-2940, info@taylorandfrancis.com, http://www.tandf.co.uk/journals/titles/03602559.asp, http://www.taylorandfrancis.com. Ed. Munmaya K Mishra. Circ: 325.

547 USA ISSN 0032-3934 CODEN: ACPPAY

➤ **POLYMER PREPRINTS.** Variant title: American Chemical Society. Division of Polymer Chemistry. Papers Presented at the Meeting. Text in English. 1960. s-a. USD 20 to members; USD 100 to non-members (effective 2004). adv. back issues avail. **Document type:** *Journal, Academic/Scholarly.*
Related titles: CD-ROM ed.
Indexed: BrCerAb, C&ISA, CIN, CerAb, ChemAb, ChemTitl, CivEngAb, CorrAb, E&CAJ, EMA, IAA, M&TEA, MBF, METADEX, MSB, RAPRA, SolStAb, TTI, WAA.
—BLDSC (6547.715000), CASDDS, CINDOC, CISTI, Ei, IE, Infotrieve, ingenta, Linda Hall.
Published by: American Chemical Society, Division of Polymer Chemistry, Inc., c/o Mrs. Neta L. Byerly, Virginia Tech, 410 Davidson Hall, MC 0279, Blacksburg, VA 24061. TEL 540-231-3029, FAX 540-231-2588, http://www.polyacs.org/main/preprintsonline.shtml, http://www.polyacs.org/index.shtml. Ed., R&P Robson F Storey. Adv. contact Kathryn E Uhrich. Circ: 9,000. **Subscr. to:** ACS, PO Box 20453, Newark, NJ 07101.

547 RUS ISSN 0965-545X
QD471 CODEN: PSSAFE

➤ **POLYMER SCIENCE. SERIES A.** Text in English. 1959. m. USD 4,440 in North America; USD 5,133 elsewhere (effective 2004). adv. abstr.; charts; illus. index. reprint service avail. from PQC. **Document type:** *Journal, Academic/Scholarly.* **Description:** Offers a comprehensive view of all multidisciplinary aspects of theoretical and experimental polymer research and application.
Formerly (until 1992): Polymer Science U.S.S.R. (0032-3950)
Related titles: Online - full text ed.: (from ScienceDirect); ♦ Translation of: Vysokomolekulyarnye Soedineniya. Seriya A i Seriya B. ISSN 1023-3091.
Indexed: A&ATA, ApMecR, BrCerAb, C&ISA, CCI, CerAb, CivEngAb, CorrAb, CurCont, E&CAJ, EMA, IAA, ISR, Inspec, M&TEA, MBF, METADEX, MSCI, RAPRA, RCI, SCI, SolStAb, WAA.
—BLDSC (0416.904000), CISTI, IE, Infotrieve, ingenta, Linda Hall. **CCC.**
Published by: (Rossiiskaya Akademiya Nauk, Institut Neftekhimichskogo Sinteza im. A.V. Tonchieva), M A I K Nauka - Interperiodica, Profsoyuznaya ul 90, Moscow, 117997, Russian Federation. TEL 7-095-3347420, FAX 7-095-3360666, compmg@maik.ru, http://www.maik.rssi.ru/journals/polscia.htm, http://www.maik.ru. Ed. Nikolai A Plate. R&P Vladimir I Vasil'ev. Circ: 1,000. **Subscr. to:** Interperiodica, PO Box 1831, Birmingham, AL 35201-1831. TEL 205-995-1567, 800-633-4931, FAX 205-995-1588.

➤ **POLYMER TESTING.** see *PLASTICS*

660.284 USA ISSN 0743-0515
TP935 CODEN: PMSEDG

➤ **POLYMERIC MATERIALS SCIENCE AND ENGINEERING.** Text in English. s-a. USD 100 (effective 2005). back issues avail. **Document type:** *Academic/Scholarly.*
Incorporates: Organic Coatings and Plastics Chemistry Preprints; Which was formerly titled: Coatings and Plastics Preprints
Related titles: CD-ROM ed.: P M S E Preprints. ISSN 1550-6703. USD 50 newsstand/cover (effective 2005).
Indexed: BrCerAb, C&ISA, CIN, CerAb, ChemAb, ChemTitl, CivEngAb, CorrAb, E&CAJ, EMA, EngInd, IAA, IPackAb, M&TEA, MBF, METADEX, MSB, P&BA, SolStAb, TTI, WAA.
—BLDSC (6547.741400), CASDDS, CISTI, Ei, IE, Infotrieve, ingenta, Linda Hall.
Published by: American Chemical Society, 1155 16th St, N W, Washington, DC 20036. TEL 202-872-4600, 800-227-5558, FAX 202-776-8258, service@acs.org, http://www.acs.org. Circ: 4,200.

543.17 USA ISSN 0092-0576
QC482.D5

POWDER DIFFRACTION FILE SEARCH MANUAL. ORGANIC. Cover title: Powder Diffraction File Search Manual (Numerical, Alphabetical, Formulae) Organic Compounds. Text in English. a. USD 325 (effective 2000). index.
Related titles: CD-ROM ed.; Magnetic Tape ed.; Microfiche ed.
Published by: Joint Committee on Powder Diffraction Standards, International Centre for Diffraction Data, 12 Campus Blvd, Newtown, PA 19073. TEL 610-325-9814, FAX 610-325-9823, TELEX 847170, http://www.icdd.com.

PREVISIONS GLISSANTES DETAILLEES EN PERSPECTIVES SECTORIELLES (VOL.21): CHIMIE ORGANIQUE. see *BUSINESS AND ECONOMICS—Economic Situation And Conditions*

PROGRESS IN COLLOID AND POLYMER SCIENCE. see *CHEMISTRY—Physical Chemistry*

547 GBR ISSN 0163-7827
QD301 CODEN: PLIRDW

➤ **PROGRESS IN LIPID RESEARCH.** Text in English. 1952. 6/yr. EUR 1,258 in Europe to institutions; JPY 166,900 in Japan to institutions; USD 1,408 to institutions except Europe and Japan (effective 2006). **Document type:** *Journal, Academic/Scholarly.* **Description:** Includes topics on analysis, properties, chemistry, metabolism, medicine, nutrition, molecular biology, food science and technology related to lipid chemistry.
Formerly: Progress in the Chemistry of Fats and Other Lipids (0079-6832)
Related titles: Microfilm ed.: (from PQC); Online - full text ed.: (from EBSCO Publishing, Gale Group, IngentaConnect, ScienceDirect, Swets Information Services).
Indexed: ASCA, AbHyg, AgBio, AnBrAb, BBCI, BIOBASE, BIOSIS Prev, BiolAb, CIN, CPA, ChemAb, ChemTitl, CurCont, DSA, EngInd, ExcerpMed, FCA, FS&TA, HortAb, IABS, ISR, IndMed, Inpharma, MEDLINE, MaizeAb, NutrAb, PBA, PE&ON, PGrRegA, PoultAb, RM&VM, RPP, Reac, RefZh, SCI, VetBull, WeedAb.
—BLDSC (6868.640000), CASDDS, CISTI, Ei, GNLM, IDS, IE, Infotrieve, ingenta, Linda Hall. **CCC.**
Published by: Pergamon (Subsidiary of: Elsevier Science & Technology), The Boulevard, Langford Ln, East Park, Kidlington, Oxford OX5 1GB, United Kingdom. TEL 44-1865-843000, FAX 44-1865-843010, http://www.elsevier.com/locate/plipres. **Subscr. to:** Elsevier BV, PO Box 211, Amsterdam 1000 AE, Netherlands. TEL 31-20-485-3757, FAX 31-20-485-3432, nlinfo-f@elsevier.nl, http://www.elsevier.nl.

➤ **PROGRESS IN ORGANIC COATINGS.** see *PAINTS AND PROTECTIVE COATINGS*

➤ **PROGRESS IN PHYSICAL ORGANIC CHEMISTRY.** see *CHEMISTRY—Physical Chemistry*

547 660.284 GBR ISSN 0079-6700
QD281.P6 CODEN: PRPSB8

➤ **PROGRESS IN POLYMER SCIENCE.** Text in English. 1967. 12/yr. EUR 2,414 in Europe to institutions; JPY 320,800 in Japan to institutions; USD 2,702 to institutions except Europe and Japan (effective 2006). index. **Document type:** *Academic/Scholarly.* **Description:** Covers developments in polymers in the fields of chemistry, engineering and physics, as well as emerging disciplines such as the study of functional and specialty polymers.
Related titles: Microfilm ed.: (from PQC); Online - full text ed.: (from EBSCO Publishing, Gale Group, IngentaConnect, ScienceDirect, Swets Information Services).
Indexed: ASCA, BrCerAb, C&ISA, CCI, CerAb, ChemAb, ChemTitl, CivEngAb, CorrAb, CurCont, E&CAJ, EMA, EngInd, HRIS, IAA, ISMEC, ISR, Inspec, M&TEA, MBF, METADEX, MSCI, RAPRA, RCI, RefZh, SCI, SolStAb, TTI, WAA.
—BLDSC (6873.570000), CASDDS, CISTI, Ei, IDS, IE, Infotrieve, ingenta, Linda Hall. **CCC.**
Published by: Elsevier Ltd. (Subsidiary of: Elsevier Science & Technology), The Boulevard, Langford Ln, Kidlington, Oxford, OX5 1GB, United Kingdom. TEL 44-1865-843000, FAX 44-1865-843010, nlinfo-f@elsevier.nl, http://www.elsevier.com/locate/ppolysci. Eds. G. C. Berry, K. Matyjaszewski. **Subscr. to:** Elsevier BV, PO Box 211, Amsterdam 1000 AE, Netherlands. TEL 31-20-485-3757, FAX 31-20-485-3432, http://www.elsevier.nl.

547 IND

RECENT RESEARCH DEVELOPMENTS IN ORGANIC & BIOORGANIC CHEMISTRY. Text in English. a., latest vol.4, 2001.

C

Published by: Transworld Research Network, T C 36-248 (1), Trivandrum, Kerala 695 008, India. http://www.transworldresearch.com.

547 IND
RECENT RESEARCH DEVELOPMENTS IN ORGANIC CHEMISTRY. Text in English. a., latest vol.5, 2001.
—BLDSC (7305.087650).
Published by: Transworld Research Network, T C 36-248 (1), Trivandrum, Kerala 695 008, India. http://www.transworldresearch.com.

660.6 IND
RECENT RESEARCH DEVELOPMENTS IN PLASMAS. Text in English. a.
Published by: Transworld Research Network, T C 36-248 (1), Trivandrum, Kerala 695 008, India. http://www.transworldresearch.com.

547 IND
RECENT RESEARCH DEVELOPMENTS IN POLYMER SCIENCE. Text in English. a., latest vol.5, 2001.
Published by: Transworld Research Network, T C 36-248 (1), Trivandrum, Kerala 695 008, India. http://www.transworldresearch.com.

547 IND
RECENT RESEARCH DEVELOPMENTS IN SYNTHETIC ORGANIC CHEMISTRY. Text in English. a., latest vol.3, 2000. USD 40 (effective 2004).
—BLDSC (7305.087720).
Published by: Transworld Research Network, T C 36-248 (1), Trivandrum, Kerala 695 008, India. http://www.transworldresearch.com.

REFERATIVNYI ZHURNAL. BIOORGANICHESKAYA KHIMIYA. MAKROMOLEKULY. see *CHEMISTRY—Abstracting, Bibliographies, Statistics*

REFERATIVNYI ZHURNAL. ORGANICHESKAYA KHIMIYA. see *CHEMISTRY—Abstracting, Bibliographies, Statistics*

REFERATIVNYI ZHURNAL. PRIRODNYE ORGANICHESKIE SOEDINENIYA I IKH SINTETICHESKIE ANALOGI. see *CHEMISTRY—Abstracting, Bibliographies, Statistics*

REFERATIVNYI ZHURNAL. TEKHNOLOGIYA ORGANICHESKIKH VESHCHESTV. see *CHEMISTRY—Abstracting, Bibliographies, Statistics*

REPORTS ON PROGRESS IN POLYMER PHYSICS IN JAPAN. see *PHYSICS*

547 USA ISSN 0742-5996
QD390 CODEN: RSHAEE
RING SYSTEMS HANDBOOK. Text in English. 1960. irreg. USD 610; USD 872 includes annual supplements; USD 480 only supplements (effective 2005). **Document type:** *Abstract/Index.*
Former titles: Parent Compound Handbook; Ring Index: A List of Ring Systems Used in Organic Chemistry. Supplement (0080-309X)
Related titles: Online - full text ed.; Supplement(s): USD 420 (effective 2001).
Indexed: ChemAb.
Published by: Chemical Abstracts Service (C A S) (Subsidiary of: American Chemical Society), 2540 Olentangy River Rd., Columbus, OH 43210-0012. TEL 614-447-3600, FAX 614-447-3713, help@cas.com, http://www.cas.org, http://caselects.cas.org. **Subscr. to:** PO Box 3012, Columbus, OH 43210. TEL 800-753-4227, FAX 614-447-3751.

664 ITA ISSN 0035-6808
TP670.A1 CODEN: RISGAD
RIVISTA ITALIANA DELLE SOSTANZE GRASSE. Text in Italian. 1924. m. EUR 90 domestic; EUR 190 foreign (effective 2005). adv. bk.rev. abstr.; charts; illus.; stat. index. reprints avail. **Document type:** *Magazine, Trade.* **Description:** Publishes original works concerning chemistry, analysis, technology, and problems relating to pollution in fields connected with fats and oils and derivatives.
Indexed: AbHyg, AgBio, AgrForAb, AnBrAb, ApicAb, BiolAb, CEABA, CIN, CPA, ChemAb, ChemTitl, DSA, FCA, FPA, FS&TA, ForAb, HortAb, MSB, MaizeAb, NutrAb, OrnHort, PBA, PGegResA, PHN&I, PotatoAb, PoultAb, RA&MP, RDA, RPP, RefZh, RevApplEntom, S&F, SIA, SeedAb, SoyAb, TDB, TOSA, TriticAb, WAE&RSA, WeedAb.
—BLDSC (7987.650000), CASDDS, CINDOC, IE, Infotrieve, ingenta, Linda Hall.
Published by: Stazione Sperimentale per le Industrie degli Oli e Grassi, Via Giuseppe Colombo 79, Milan, MI 20133, Italy. TEL 39-02-7064971, FAX 39-02-2363953, rivista@ssog.it, info@ssog.it, http://www.ssog.it/risg_indice.php. Ed. Oreste Cozzoli. R&P Fedeli Enzo. Adv. contact Lionello Cariboni. Circ: 4,000.

547 NLD ISSN 0080-3758
➤ **RODD'S CHEMISTRY OF CARBON COMPOUNDS.** Text in Dutch. 1964. irreg. price varies. Supplement avail.; back issues avail. **Document type:** *Monographic series, Academic/Scholarly.* **Description:** Provides a complete reference for the chemistry of organic carbon compounds.
Related titles: ◆ Supplement(s): Rodd's Chemistry of Carbon Compounds. Supplements to the Second Edition.
Published by: Elsevier BV (Subsidiary of: Elsevier Science & Technology), Radarweg 29, Amsterdam, 1043 NX, Netherlands. TEL 31-20-4853911, FAX 31-20-4852457, nlinfo-f@elsevier.nl, http://www.elsevier.nl. Eds. M. F. Ansell, S Coffey.

547 NLD
➤ **RODD'S CHEMISTRY OF CARBON COMPOUNDS. SUPPLEMENTS TO THE SECOND EDITION.** Text in English. 1973. irreg., latest 1995. price varies. back issues avail. **Document type:** *Monographic series, Academic/Scholarly.*
Related titles: ◆ Supplement to: Rodd's Chemistry of Carbon Compounds. ISSN 0080-3758.
Published by: Elsevier BV (Subsidiary of: Elsevier Science & Technology), Radarweg 29, Amsterdam, 1043 NX, Netherlands. TEL 31-20-4853911, FAX 31-20-4852457, nlinfo-f@elsevier.nl, http://www.elsevier.nl. Ed. M Sainsbury.

547 GBR ISSN 0069-3030
QD1 CODEN: CACBB4
ROYAL SOCIETY OF CHEMISTRY. ANNUAL REPORTS ON THE PROGRESS OF CHEMISTRY. SECTION B: ORGANIC CHEMISTRY. Text in English. 1904. a. GBP 230, USD 420 combined subscription print & online eds. (effective 2006). **Document type:** *Academic/Scholarly.* **Description:** Provides for the general reader critical coverage of the important advances in organic chemistry.
Related titles: Online - full text ed.: ISSN 1460-4779. GBP 207, USD 378 (effective 2006) (from EBSCO Publishing, O C L C Online Computer Library Center, Inc., Swets Information Services).
Indexed: BIOSIS Prev, CIN, ChemAb, ChemTitl, RefZh.
—BLDSC (1513.820000), CASDDS, CINDOC, CISTI, IE, Infotrieve, Linda Hall. **CCC.**
Published by: Royal Society of Chemistry, Thomas Graham House, Science Park, Milton Rd, Cambridge, CB4 0WF, United Kingdom. TEL 44-1223-432360, FAX 44-1223-423623, annrep@rsc.org, sales@rsc.org, advertising@rsc.org, http://www.rsc.org/Publishing/Journals/oc/index.asp. Ed. Dr. Robert D Eagling. **Subscr. to:** Portland Press Ltd., R S C Distribution Services, Commerce Way, Whitehall Industrial Estate, Colchester CO2 8HP, United Kingdom. TEL 44-1206-226050, FAX 44-1206-226055, sales@rscdistribution.org.

547 RUS ISSN 1068-1620
QD415.A1 CODEN: RJBCET
➤ **RUSSIAN JOURNAL OF BIOORGANIC CHEMISTRY.** Text in Russian. 1975. bi-m. EUR 2,338, USD 2,148, GBP 1,368 combined subscription to institutions print & online eds. (effective 2005). back issues avail. **Document type:** *Journal, Academic/Scholarly.* **Description:** Disseminates the results of original experimental and theoretical investigations on the structure, structure-activity relationships, and synthesis of biopolymers and low-molecular-mass bioregulators.
Formerly (until 1993): Soviet Journal of Bioorganic Chemistry (0360-4497)
Related titles: Microfilm ed.: (from PQC); Online - full text ed.: ISSN 1608-330X (from EBSCO Publishing, Gale Group, IngentaConnect, Kluwer Online, O C L C Online Computer Library Center, Inc., Springer LINK, Swets Information Services); ◆ Translation of: Bioorganicheskaya Khimiya. ISSN 0132-3423.
Indexed: BBCI, BibLing, BiolAb, CCI, ChemAb, ChemTitl, CurCont, ISR, IndVet, Inpharma, MSB, PE&ON, RCI, RM&VM, Reac, SCI, VITIS.
—BLDSC (0420.760700), CISTI, IE, Infotrieve, ingenta. **CCC.**
Published by: (Rossiiskaya Akademiya Nauk/Russian Academy of Sciences), M A I K Nauka - Interperiodica, Profsoyuznaya ul 90, Moscow, 117997, Russian Federation. TEL 7-095-3347420, FAX 7-095-3360666, rjbc@ibch.ru, compmg@maik.ru, http://www.maik.rssi.ru/journals/biochem.htm, http://www.maik.ru. Ed. Vadim T Ivanov. **Subscr. to:** Springer-Verlag Dordrecht, Journals Department, PO Box 322, Dordrecht, Netherlands. TEL 31-78-6576392, FAX 31-78-6576474.

547 RUS ISSN 1070-4280
QD241 CODEN: RJOCEQ
➤ **RUSSIAN JOURNAL OF ORGANIC CHEMISTRY.** Text in English. 1965. m. EUR 3,888, USD 3,498, GBP 2,428 combined subscription to institutions print & online eds. (effective 2005). back issues avail. **Document type:** *Journal, Academic/Scholarly.* **Description:** Reports on all aspects of modern organic synthesis, theoretical organic chemistry, structure and mechanism, and the application of organometallic compounds in organic synthesis.
Former titles (until 1994): Journal of Organic Chemistry; (until 1993): Journal of Organic Chemistry of the U S S R (0022-3271); Soviet Journal of Organic Chemistry
Related titles: Microfilm ed.: (from PQC); Online - full text ed.: ISSN 1608-3393 (from EBSCO Publishing, Gale Group, IngentaConnect, Kluwer Online, O C L C Online Computer Library Center, Inc., Springer LINK, Swets Information Services); ◆ Translation of: Zhurnal Organicheskoi Khimii. ISSN 0514-7492.
Indexed: ApicAb, BibLing, CCI, ChemAb, ChemInfo, ChemTitl, CurCR, CurCont, ISR, IndChem, MOS, MSB, MSCI, NPU, RCI, SCI.
—BLDSC (0420.762500), CASDDS, CISTI, IE, Infotrieve, ingenta, Linda Hall. **CCC.**
Published by: (Rossiiskaya Akademiya Nauk/Russian Academy of Sciences), M A I K Nauka - Interperiodica, Profsoyuznaya ul 90, Moscow, 117997, Russian Federation. TEL 7-095-3347420, FAX 7-095-3360666, compmg@maik.ru, http://www.maik.rssi.ru/journals/orgchem.htm, http://www.maik.ru. Ed. Irina P Beletskaya. **Subscr. to:** Springer-Verlag Dordrecht, Journals Department, PO Box 322, Dordrecht, Netherlands. TEL 31-78-6576392, FAX 31-78-6576474.

➤ **SCHRIFTENREIHE LEBENSMITTELCHEMIE, LEBENSMITTELQUALITAET.** see *FOOD AND FOOD INDUSTRIES*

➤ **SENJO NI KANSURU SHINPOJUMU/SYMPOSIUM OF CLEANING.** see *ENGINEERING—Chemical Engineering*

547.8 JPN ISSN 1341-7215
CODEN: SERDEK
➤ **SOLVENT EXTRACTION RESEARCH AND DEVELOPMENT, JAPAN.** Text in English. 1994. a. membership. **Document type:** *Academic/Scholarly.* **Description:** Covers pure chemistry and technology related to solvent extraction such as coordination chemistry, analytical chemistry, chemical engineering, metallurgy and pharmaceuticals.
Indexed: AnalAb, CCI, CIN, ChemAb, ChemTitl, CurCont.
—BLDSC (8327.806800), CASDDS.
Published by: Japan Association of Solvent Extraction, Saga University, Faculty of Science & Engineering, Department of Chemistry & Applied Chemistry, 1 Honjo-machi, Saga, 840-8502, Japan. Ed. Kenichi Akiba. Circ: 200.

664.2 547 DEU ISSN 0038-9056
CODEN: STRKA6
➤ **STARCH/STAERKE**; international journal for the investigation, processing and use of carbohydrates and their derivatives. Text in English, German. 1949. m. EUR 1,038 in Europe; CHF 1,668 in Switzerland & Liechtenstein; USD 1,320 elsewhere; EUR 1,142 combined subscription in Europe print & online eds.; CHF 1,835 combined subscription in Switzerland & Liechtenstein for print & online eds.; USD 1,452 combined subscription elsewhere print & online eds. (effective 2006). adv. bk.rev. abstr.; bibl.; charts; illus.; stat.; pat. index. back issues avail.; reprint service avail. from ISI. **Document type:** *Journal, Academic/Scholarly.*
Related titles: Microfilm ed.: (from VCI); Online - full text ed.: ISSN 1521-379X. EUR 1,038 in Europe; CHF 1,668 in Switzerland & Liechtenstein; USD 1,320 elsewhere (effective 2006) (from EBSCO Publishing, Swets Information Services, Wiley InterScience).
Indexed: ABIPC, ASCA, AgBio, AgrForAb, AnalAb, BIOSIS Prev, BiolAb, CCI, CIN, CPA, ChemAb, ChemTitl, CurCont, DBA, EngInd, ExcerpMed, FCA, FS&TA, HerbAb, HortAb, INIS AtomInd, ISR, MSCI, MaizeAb, NutrAb, PBA, PGegResA, PHN&I, PotatoAb, RefZh, RiceAb, SCI, SIA, SeedAb, TriticAb, WTA, WeedAb.
—BLDSC (8434.735000), CASDDS, CINDOC, CISTI, IDS, IE, Infotrieve, ingenta, Linda Hall. **CCC.**
Published by: Wiley - V C H Verlag GmbH & Co. KGaA (Subsidiary of: John Wiley & Sons, Inc.), Boschstr 12, Weinheim, 69469, Germany. TEL 49-6201-6060, FAX 49-6201-606328, adsales@wiley-vch.de, subservice@wiley-vch.de, info@wiley-vch.de, http://www.wiley-vch.de. Ed. Barbara Elvers. R&P Claudia Rutz. Adv. contact Aenne Anders TEL 49-6201-606552. B&W page EUR 1,300, color page EUR 2,620. Circ: 841 (paid and controlled). **Subscr. in the Americas to:** John Wiley & Sons, Inc.. TEL 201-748-6645, FAX 201-748-6088, subinfo@wiley.com; **Subscr. outside Germany, Austria & Switzerland to:** John Wiley & Sons Ltd., The Atrium, Southern Gate, Chichester, West Sussex PO19 8SQ, United Kingdom. TEL 44-1243-779777, FAX 44-1243-775878.

547 NLD ISSN 0165-3253
CODEN: SOCHDQ
➤ **STUDIES IN ORGANIC CHEMISTRY.** Text in English. 1979. irreg., latest vol.53, 1998. price varies. back issues avail. **Document type:** *Proceedings, Academic/Scholarly.* **Description:** Disseminates experimental and applied research on various topics in organic chemistry.
Indexed: BIOSIS Prev, CIN, ChemAb, ChemTitl, CurCont.
—BLDSC (8491.185000), CASDDS, CISTI, ingenta. **CCC.**
Published by: Elsevier BV (Subsidiary of: Elsevier Science & Technology), Radarweg 29, Amsterdam, 1043 NX, Netherlands. TEL 31-20-4853911, FAX 31-20-4852457, nlinfo-f@elsevier.nl, http://www.elsevier.nl.

547 JPN
SYMPOSIUM ON SOLVENT EXTRACTION. PROCEEDINGS. Text in Japanese. 1981. a. JPY 5,000. **Document type:** *Proceedings.*
Indexed: CIN, ChemAb, ChemTitl.
—BLDSC (684+9.632150), ingenta.
Published by: Japanese Association of Solvent Extraction/Nihon Yobai Chushutsu Gakkai, Dept of Chemical Science & Engineering, Osaka University, Toyonaka, 560-8531, Japan. FAX 81-6-850-6273. Ed., R&P, Adv. contact Isao Komasawa.

C

▼ new title ➤ refereed ✶ unverified ◆ full entry avail.

547 DEU ISSN 1861-1958

▼ ➤ **SYNFACTS**; highlights in current synthetic organic chemistry. Text in English. 2005. m. EUR 932.80 domestic; EUR 936.50 in Europe; EUR 956.80 elsewhere; EUR 99 to students (effective 2006). **Document type:** *Journal, Academic/Scholarly.* **Description:** Provides a commented overview of the most interesting current trends in synthetic chemistry.
Related titles: Online - full text ed.: ISSN 1861-194X.
Published by: Georg Thieme Verlag, Ruedigerstr 14, Stuttgart, 70469, Germany. TEL 49-711-8931421, FAX 49-711-8931410, leser.service@thieme.de, http://www.thieme-chemistry.com/thieme-chemistry/journals/info/synfacts/index.shtml, http://www.thieme.de.

547 541.39 DEU ISSN 0936-5214
QD262 CODEN: SYNLES

➤ **SYNLETT**; accounts and rapid communications in synthetic organic chemistry. Text in English. 1989. 20/yr. EUR 253.60 domestic to individuals; EUR 256.80 in Europe to individuals; EUR 297.60 elsewhere to individuals; EUR 993.60 domestic to institutions; EUR 996.80 in Europe to institutions; EUR 1,037.60 elsewhere to institutions; EUR 69 to students (effective 2006). adv. illus. Index. reprints avail. **Document type:** *Journal, Academic/Scholarly.* **Description:** Covers modern synthetic methodology as applied to both traditional and new areas of organic research.
Related titles: Online - full text ed.: ISSN 1437-2096. USD 199 to individuals; USD 702 to institutions; USD 99 to students; USD 52 per issue (effective 2001) (from EBSCO Publishing, O C L C Online Computer Library Center, Inc., Swets Information Services).
Indexed: ABIPC, ASCA, CCI, CIN, ChemAb, ChemInfo, ChemTitl, CurCR, CurCont, DBA, EngInd, ExcerpMed, ISR, IndChem, MOS, NPU, RCI, RefZh, SCI.
—BLDSC (8585.970000), CASDDS, CISTI, Ei, IDS, IE, Infotrieve, ingenta, Linda Hall. **CCC.**
Published by: Georg Thieme Verlag, Ruedigerstr 14, Stuttgart, 70469, Germany. TEL 49-711-8931421, FAX 49-711-8931410, kunden.service@thieme.de, http://www.thieme-chemistry.com/thieme-chemistry/journals/info/synlett/index.shtml, http://www.thieme.de/chemistry. Ed. Dr. K P C Vollhardt. R&P Kristina Kurz. Circ: 2,800. **Subscr. to:** Thieme Medical Publishers, 333 Seventh Ave, New York, NY 10001. custserv@thieme.com, http://www.thieme.com/journals.

C

547 541.39 DEU ISSN 0039-7881
QD262 CODEN: SYNTBF

➤ **SYNTHESIS**; journal of synthetic organic chemistry. Text in English. 1969. 20/yr. EUR 416.50 domestic to individuals; EUR 423.90 in Europe to individuals; EUR 503.40 elsewhere to individuals; EUR 1,465.50 domestic to institutions; EUR 1,472.90 in Europe to institutions; EUR 1,552.40 elsewhere to institutions; EUR 69 to students (effective 2006). adv. bk.rev. abstr.; bibl.; charts; illus.; stat. index. reprint service avail. from PQC. **Document type:** *Journal, Academic/Scholarly.*
Related titles: Microform ed.: (from PQC); Online - full text ed.: ISSN 1437-210X. USD 314 to individuals; USD 1,066 to institutions; USD 75 per issue (effective 2001) (from EBSCO Publishing, O C L C Online Computer Library Center, Inc., Swets Information Services).
Indexed: ABIPC, ASCA, CCI, ChemAb, ChemInfo, CurCR, CurCont, DBA, ExcerpMed, HortAb, ISR, IndChem, Inpharma, MOS, MSB, NPU, RA&MP, RCI, RM&VM, Reac, RefZh, SCI, SIA, WeedAb.
—BLDSC (8586.785000), CASDDS, CISTI, Ei, IDS, IE, Infotrieve, ingenta, Linda Hall. **CCC.**
Published by: Georg Thieme Verlag, Ruedigerstr 14, Stuttgart, 70469, Germany. TEL 49-711-8931421, FAX 49-711-8931410, kunden.service@thieme.de, www.thieme-chemistry.com, http://www.thieme.de. Ed. D Enders. R&P Kristina Kurz. Circ: 3,700. **Subscr. to:** Thieme Medical Publishers, 333 Seventh Ave, New York, NY 10001. custserv@thieme.com, http://www.thieme.com/journals.

547 USA ISSN 0039-7911
QD262 CODEN: SYNCAV

➤ **SYNTHETIC COMMUNICATIONS**; an international journal for rapid communication of synthetic organic chemistry. Text in English. 1971. 24/yr. USD 3,107, GBP 1,883 combined subscription to institutions print & online eds. (effective 2006). adv. reprint service avail. from PSC. **Document type:** *Journal, Academic/Scholarly.* **Description:** Presents coverage on a braod range of topics, ranging from the synthesis of natural products and related intermediates to the synthesis and utilization of new reagents for functional group interconversions.
Related titles: Microform ed.: (from RPI); Online - full text ed.: ISSN 1532-2432. USD 2,952, GBP 1,789 to institutions (effective 2006) (from EBSCO Publishing, O C L C Online Computer Library Center, Inc., Swets Information Services).
Indexed: ASCA, BiolAb, CCI, CIN, ChemAb, ChemInfo, ChemTitl, CurCR, CurCont, DBA, EngInd, ExcerpMed, ISR, IndChem, MOS, NPU, ProtozoAb, RCI, RefZh, RevApplEntom, SCI, WeedAb.
—BLDSC (8586.830000), CASDDS, CINDOC, CISTI, Ei, IDS, IE, Infotrieve, ingenta, Linda Hall. **CCC.**
Published by: Taylor & Francis Inc. (Subsidiary of: Taylor & Francis Group), 325 Chestnut St, Ste 800, Philadelphia, PA 19016. TEL 215-625-8900, 800-354-1420, FAX 215-625-8914, info@taylorandfrancis.com, http://www.tandf.co.uk/journals/titles/00397911.asp, http://www.taylorandfrancis.com. Ed. Michael Kolb. Adv. contact Sharon Moran. B&W page USD 600. Circ: 1,100 (paid and free).

547 ITA

TARGETS IN HETEROCYCLIC SYSTEMS. Text in English. 1997.
Indexed: MSB.
—BLDSC (8606.254340).
Published by: Societa Chimica Italiana, Viale Liegi, 48c, Rome, RM 00198, Italy. TEL 39-06-8549691, FAX 39-06-8548734. Eds. Dominico Spinelli, Orazio A Attanasi.

547 USA ISSN 1080-8914

TECHNIQUES IN PROTEIN CHEMISTRY. Text in English. 1989. a., latest vol.7, 1996. USD 83.95 per vol. (effective 2005). **Document type:** *Academic/Scholarly.*
—BLDSC (8745.331000), IE, ingenta. **CCC.**
Published by: (Protein Society), Academic Press (Subsidiary of: Elsevier Science & Technology), 525 B St, Ste 1900, San Diego, CA 92101-4495.

547 664 IND ISSN 0040-2818

TELHAN PATRIKA/OILSEEDS JOURNAL. Text in English, Hindi. 1969. q. INR 43.50. adv. bk.rev. charts; illus.; stat.
Indexed: FCA, HerbAb, ISAP.
—CISTI.
Published by: Directorate of Oilseeds Development, Telhan Bhavan, Himayatnagar, Hyderabad, Andhra Pradesh 500 029, India. Ed. Dr. G V Ramana Murthy. Circ: 300.

547 JPN

TENNEN YUKI KAGOBUTSU TORONKAI KOEN YOSHISHU/SYMPOSIUM ON THE CHEMISTRY OF NATURAL PRODUCTS. SYMPOSIUM PAPERS. Text in Japanese. 1957. a.
Indexed: CIN, ChemAb, ChemTitl, MSB.
—BLDSC, ingenta.
Published by: Chemical Society of Japan/Nippon Kagakukai, 1-5, Kanda-Surugadai 1-Chome, Chiyoda-ku, Tokyo, 101-0062, Japan.

547 GBR ISSN 0040-4020
QD241 CODEN: TETRAB

➤ **TETRAHEDRON.** Text in English, French, German. 1957. 52/yr. EUR 619 in Europe to individuals; JPY 82,000 in Japan to individuals; USD 694 elsewhere to individuals; EUR 14,980 in Europe to institutions; JPY 1,989,300 in Japan to institutions; USD 16,756 elsewhere to institutions (effective 2006); including Tetrahedron: Asymmetry. adv. bk.rev. illus. index. **Document type:** *Journal, Academic/Scholarly.* **Description:** Covers organic synthesis, natural products chemistry, studies of reaction mechanisms, and various aspects of spectroscopy.
Related titles: Microfiche ed.: (from MIM); Microfilm ed.: (from PQC); Online - full text ed.: (from EBSCO Publishing, Gale Group, IngentaConnect, ScienceDirect, Swets Information Services).
Indexed: ABIPC, ASFA, AgrForAb, ApicAb, BIOSIS Prev, BioCN&I, BiolAb, CCI, CIN, CPA, ChemAb, ChemInfo, ChemTitl, CurCR, CurCont, DBA, DSA, EngInd, ExcerpMed, FCA, FPA, ForAb, HelmAb, HortAb, IAA, ISR, IndChem, Inpharma, MEDLINE, MOS, MSB, MSCI, NPU, NutrAb, OrnHort, PGrRegA, ProtozoAb, RA&MP, RCI, RM&VM, RPP, Reac, RefZh, SCI, SeedAb, SoyAb, VITIS, WeedAb, ZooRec.
—BLDSC (8796.850000), CASDDS, CINDOC, CISTI, Ei, GNLM, IDS, IE, Infotrieve, ingenta, Linda Hall. **CCC.**
Published by: Pergamon (Subsidiary of: Elsevier Science & Technology), The Boulevard, Langford Ln, East Park, Kidlington, Oxford OX5 1GB, United Kingdom. TEL 44-1865-843000, FAX 44-1865-843010, http://www.elsevier.com/locate/tet. Ed. L Ghosez. Circ: 3,000. **Subscr. to:** Elsevier BV, PO Box 211, Amsterdam 1000 AE, Netherlands. TEL 31-20-485-3757, FAX 31-20-485-3432, nlinfo-f@elsevier.nl, http://www.elsevier.nl.

547 546 GBR ISSN 0957-4166
QD481 CODEN: TASYE3

➤ **TETRAHEDRON: ASYMMETRY.** Text in English. 1990. 24/yr. EUR 2,482 in Europe to institutions; JPY 329,500 in Japan to institutions; USD 2,775 to institutions except Europe and Japan; EUR 220 in Europe to qualified personnel; JPY 29,200 in Japan to qualified personnel; USD 245 to qualified personnel except Europe and Japan (effective 2006). abstr. back issues avail. **Document type:** *Journal, Academic/Scholarly.* **Description:** Presents experimental or theoretical research results of outstanding significance and timeliness in the field of organic chemistry and its application to related disciplines, especially bio-organic chemistry.
Related titles: Microfiche ed.: (from MIM); Microfilm ed.: (from PQC); Online - full text ed.: ISSN 1362-511X. 1996 (from EBSCO Publishing, Gale Group, IngentaConnect, ScienceDirect, Swets Information Services).
Indexed: ASCA, CCI, CIN, ChemAb, ChemInfo, ChemTitl, CurCR, CurCont, DBA, EngInd, ExcerpMed, ISR, IndChem, MOS, MSB, NPU, RCI, RefZh, SCI, SIA.
—BLDSC (8796.852000), CASDDS, CINDOC, CISTI, Ei, GNLM, IDS, IE, Infotrieve, ingenta, Linda Hall. **CCC.**
Published by: Pergamon (Subsidiary of: Elsevier Science & Technology), The Boulevard, Langford Ln, East Park, Kidlington, Oxford OX5 1GB, United Kingdom. TEL 44-1865-843000, FAX 44-1865-843010, http://www.elsevier.com/locate/tetasy. Eds. S G Davies, T Hayashi. **Subscr. to:** Elsevier BV, PO Box 211, Amsterdam 1000 AE, Netherlands. TEL 31-20-485-3757, FAX 31-20-485-3432, nlinfo-f@elsevier.nl, http://www.elsevier.nl.

547 GBR ISSN 0040-4039
QD241 CODEN: TELEAY

➤ **TETRAHEDRON LETTERS.** Text in English, French, German. 1959. 52/yr. EUR 10,911 in Europe to institutions; JPY 1,449,000 in Japan to institutions; USD 12,204 to institutions except Europe and Japan; EUR 442 in Europe to qualified personnel; JPY 58,800 in Japan to qualified personnel; USD 495 to qualified personnel except Europe and Japan; EUR 223 in Europe to students; JPY 29,600 in Japan to students; USD 250 to students except Europe and Japan (effective 2006). adv. illus. Index. back issues avail.; reprints avail. **Document type:** *Journal, Academic/Scholarly.* **Description:** Covers developments in techniques, structures, methods and conclusions in experimental and theoretical organic chemistry.
Related titles: Microfiche ed.: (from MIM); Microfilm ed.: (from PQC); Online - full text ed.: EUR 3,128.81 in Europe to institutions; JPY 434,100 in Japan to institutions; USD 3,500 elsewhere to institutions (effective 2001) (from EBSCO Publishing, Gale Group, IngentaConnect, ScienceDirect, Swets Information Services).
Indexed: ASCA, ASFA, Agr, AgrForAb, ApicAb, BIOSIS Prev, BibAg, BiolAb, CCI, CEABA, CIN, CMCI, CPA, ChemAb, ChemInfo, ChemTitl, CurCR, CurCont, DBA, DSA, EngInd, ExcerpMed, FPA, ForAb, HortAb, ISR, IndChem, Inpharma, MEDLINE, MOS, MSB, MSCI, NPU, OrnHort, PGrRegA, ProtozoAb, RA&MP, RCI, RM&VM, RPP, Reac, RefZh, RevApplEntom, SCI, SIA, SeedAb, VITIS, WeedAb, ZooRec.
—BLDSC (8796.860000), CASDDS, CINDOC, CISTI, Ei, GNLM, IDS, IE, Infotrieve, ingenta, Linda Hall. **CCC.**
Published by: Pergamon (Subsidiary of: Elsevier Science & Technology), The Boulevard, Langford Ln, East Park, Kidlington, Oxford OX5 1GB, United Kingdom. TEL 44-1865-843000, FAX 44-1865-843010, http://www.elsevier.com/locate/tetlet. Eds. B Ganem, E J Thomas, J Wood, Lin Guo Qiang, S Z Zard, Y Yamamoto. Circ: 3,380. **Subscr. to:** Elsevier BV, PO Box 211, Amsterdam 1000 AE, Netherlands. TEL 31-20-485-3757, FAX 31-20-485-3432, nlinfo-f@elsevier.nl, http://www.elsevier.nl.

547 541.39 CHE ISSN 0253-200X
QD262

➤ **THEILHEIMER'S SYNTHETIC METHODS OF ORGANIC CHEMISTRY.** Variant title: Synthetic Methods of Organic Chemistry. Text in English. 1948. irreg., latest vol.67, 2005. price varies. **Document type:** *Monographic series, Academic/Scholarly.* **Description:** Contains abstracts describing new reactions and synthetic methods as reported in worldwide scientific literature.
Formerly (until 1982): Synthetic Methods of Organic Chemistry (0082-1136)
Related titles: Online - full text ed.: (from Questel Orbit Inc.).
Indexed: ASCA, BiolAb, ChemAb, CurCont, IndMed.
—CISTI, GNLM, KNAW, Linda Hall. **CCC.**
Published by: S. Karger AG, Allschwilerstr 10, Basel, 4009, Switzerland. TEL 41-61-3061111, FAX 41-61-3061234, karger@karger.ch, http://www.karger.com/THEIL, http://www.karger.ch. Ed. A F Finch.

547 660 NLD ISSN 0923-6732
CODEN: TISCER

➤ **TOPICS IN INCLUSION SCIENCE.** Text in English. 1988. irreg., latest vol.6, 1995. price varies. **Document type:** *Monographic series, Academic/Scholarly.*
Indexed: ChemAb.
—BLDSC (8867.448000), CASDDS.
Published by: Springer-Verlag Dordrecht (Subsidiary of: Springer Science+Business Media), Van Godewijckstraat 30, Dordrecht, 3311 GX, Netherlands. TEL 31-78-6576050, FAX 31-78-6576474, http://www.springeronline.com. Ed. J Eric D Davies.

547 DEU ISSN 1436-6002

➤ **TOPICS IN ORGANOMETALLIC CHEMISTRY.** Text in English. 1998. irreg., latest vol.16, 2005. price varies. **Document type:** *Monographic series, Academic/Scholarly.* **Description:** Provides coverage of a broad range of topics of pure and applied organometallic chemistry.
Related titles: Online - full text ed.: ISSN 1616-8534.
—BLDSC (8867.473500), CISTI. **CCC.**
Published by: Springer-Verlag (Subsidiary of: Springer Science+Business Media), Tiergartenstr 17, Heidelberg, 69121, Germany. TEL 49-6221-3450, FAX 49-6221-345229, subscriptions@springer.de, http://link.springer.de/link/service/series/3418/index.htm, http://www.springer.de.

547 IND

➤ **TRENDS IN CARBOHYDRATE CHEMISTRY.** Text in English. a., latest vol.7, 2001. INR 1,500 domestic; USD 750 foreign (effective 2003). adv. bk.rev. back issues avail.; reprints avail. **Document type:** *Yearbook, Academic/Scholarly.*

Published by: Surya International Publications, 4-B, Nashville Rd, Dehra Dun, Uttaranchal 248 001, India. TEL 91-135-2711936, FAX 91-135-2654173, surya_pub@rediffmail.com, http://www.suryapublication.com. Ed. P L Soni. adv.: B&W page USD 100, color page USD 500; trim 12.5 x 20.

547 JPN ISSN 0915-7352
CODEN: TGGLEE

➤ **TRENDS IN GLYCOSCIENCE AND GLYCOTECHNOLOGY.** Variant title: T I G G. Text and summaries in English, Japanese. 1988. s-m. JPY 5,000 to individuals; JPY 22,000 to institutions. adv. back issues avail. **Document type:** *Academic/Scholarly.*
Indexed: ASCA, BBCI, CIN, ChemAb, ChemTitl.
—BLDSC (9049.610000), CASDDS, CISTI, GNLM, IDS, IE, ingenta.
Published by: (F C C A and J S C R), Gakushin Company Ltd., 1-1-8 Tarumi-cho, Suita-shi, Osaka-fu 564-0062, Japan. TEL 81-6-6330-0956, FAX 81-6-6330-1109, pub@gak.co.jp, http://www.gak.co.jp. Ed., Pub. Tatsuya Yamagata.

➤ **TRIBOLOGIE UND SCHMIERUNGSTECHNIK.** see *ENGINEERING—Chemical Engineering*

➤ **UNIVERSIDAD CENTRAL DE VENEZUELA. FACULTAD DE FARMACIA. REVISTA.** see *PHARMACY AND PHARMACOLOGY*

➤ **V A T I S UPDATE. OZONE LAYER PROTECTION.** (Value Added Technology Information Service) see *ENVIRONMENTAL STUDIES*

547 CHN ISSN 0253-2786
QD241 CODEN: YCHHDX

➤ **YOUJI HUAXUE/CHINESE JOURNAL OF ORGANIC CHEMISTRY.** Text in Chinese; Summaries in English. 1980. m. CNY 180 domestic; USD 180 foreign; CNY 15 newsstand/cover (effective 2005). adv. **Document type:** *Journal, Academic/Scholarly.* **Description:** Publishes research papers, communications and reviews of developments both in China and abroad.
Related titles: Online - full text ed.: (from East View Information Services, WanFang Data Corp.).
Indexed: CCI, CIN, ChemAb, MSB, RefZh.
—CASDDS, IDS, IE, Linda Hall.
Published by: (Zhongguo Kexueyuan, Shanghai Youji Huaxue Yanjiusuo/Chinese Academy of Sciences, Shanghai Institute of Organic Chemistry), Kexue Chubanshe/Science Press, 16 Donghuang Cheng Genbei Jie, Beijing, 100717, China. TEL 86-10-64000246, FAX 86-10-64030255, bianji@mail.sioc.ac.cn, http://www.sciencep.com/gb/content/2001-05/14/content_947.htm. Ed. Qing-Yun Chen. Circ: 12,000. **Dist. by:** China International Book Trading Corp, 35 Chegongzhuang Xilu, Haidian District, PO Box 399, Beijing 100044, China. TEL 86-10-68412045, FAX 86-10-68412023, cibtc@mail.cibtc.com.cn, http://www.cibtc.com.cn.

➤ **YUKAGAKU SANKA SEMINA/SEMINAR ON OXIDATION.** see *ENGINEERING—Chemical Engineering*

547 JPN ISSN 0037-9980
CODEN: YGKKAE

➤ **YUKI GOSEI KAGAKU KYOKAISHI/JOURNAL OF SYNTHETIC ORGANIC CHEMISTRY.** Text in Japanese; Summaries in English. 1943. m. JPY 11,000 per issue membership (effective 2004). adv. abstr.; bibl.; charts. **Document type:** *Journal, Academic/Scholarly.*
Indexed: ASCA, C&ISA, CCI, CIN, ChemAb, ChemInfo, ChemTitl, CurCR, CurCont, E&CAJ, EngInd, ISR, IndChem, JPI, JTA, MOS, MSB, MSCI, NPU, ProtozoAb, RCI, RefZh, SCI, SolStAb, WeedAb.
—BLDSC (5068.050000), CASDDS, CISTI, Ei, IDS, IE, Infotrieve, ingenta, Linda Hall. **CCC.**
Published by: Yuki Gosei Kagaku Kyokai/Society of Synthetic Organic Chemistry, Japan, Kagaku-Kaikan 5F, 1-5 Kanda-Surugadai, Chiyoda-ku, Tokyo, 101-0062, Japan. TEL 81-3-32927621, FAX 81-3-32927622, syn.org.chem@tokyo.email.ne.jp, http://wwwsoc.nii.ac.jp/ssocj/journal/journal.html. Ed. Tsuneo Imamoto.

➤ **YUKI HANNO KAGAKU TORONKAI KOEN YOKOSHU/ABSTRACTS OF SYMPOSIUM ON ORGANIC REACTIONS.** see *CHEMISTRY—Abstracting, Bibliographies, Statistics*

➤ **ZEITSCHRIFT FUER NATURFORSCHUNG. SECTION B: A JOURNAL OF CHEMICAL SCIENCES.** see *CHEMISTRY—Inorganic Chemistry*

547 RUS ISSN 0514-7492
CODEN: ZORKAE

➤ **ZHURNAL ORGANICHESKOI KHIMII.** Text in Russian. 1965. m. RUR 1,070 for 6 mos. domestic (effective 2004). back issues avail. **Document type:** *Journal, Academic/Scholarly.* **Description:** Reports on all aspects of modern organic synthesis, theoretical organic chemistry, structure and mechanism, and the application of organometallic compounds in organic synthesis.
Related titles: Microfilm ed.: (from PQC); ♦ English Translation: Russian Journal of Organic Chemistry. ISSN 1070-4280.
Indexed: CCI, CIN, ChemTitl, CurCR, CurCont, DBA, IndChem, RCI, RefZh, SCI.
—BLDSC (0064.300000), CASDDS, CINDOC, CISTI, IDS, KNAW, Linda Hall. **CCC.**
Published by: (Rossisskaya Akademiya Nauk), Izdatel'stvo Nauka, Profsoyuznaya ul 90, Moscow, 117864, Russian Federation. TEL 7-095-3347151, FAX 7-095-4202220, secret@naukaran.ru, http://www.naukaran.ru.

➤ **ZHURNAL ORHANICHNOI TA FARMATSEVTYCHNOI KHIMII/JOURNAL OF ORGANIC AND PHARMACEUTICAL CHEMISTRY;** naukovyi zhurnal. see *PHARMACY AND PHARMACOLOGY*

CHEMISTRY—Physical Chemistry

523.01 FRA ISSN 1631-0705
QC1 CODEN: CRPOBN

ACADEMIE DES SCIENCES. COMPTES RENDUS. PHYSIQUE. Text in French, English. 1795. 10/yr. EUR 327.96 domestic to institutions; EUR 403 in Europe to institutions; JPY 45,300 in Japan to institutions; USD 470 elsewhere to institutions (effective 2006). back issues avail. **Document type:** *Journal, Academic/Scholarly.* **Description:** Covers the fields of physics and astrophysics, including particles and fields, nuclei, atoms and molecules, condensed matter, gas and plasmas, physical chemistry and biophysics, metrology and instrumentation, celestial mechanics, cosmology, solar systems, Earth Moon systems, interstellar medium, cosmic rays, and physical processes in astronomy.
Formerly (until 2002): Academie des Sciences. Comptes Rendus. Serie 4: Physique, Astrophysique (1296-2147); Which superseded in part (in 2000): Academie des Sciences. Comptes Rendus. Serie 2b: Mecanique, Physique, Astronomie (1287-4620); Which superseded in part (in 1998): Academie des Sciences. Comptes Rendus. Serie 2b: Mecanique, Physique, Chimie, Astronomie (1251-8069); Which superseded in part (in 1994): Academie des Sciences. Comptes Rendus. Serie 2b: Mecanique, Physique, Chimie, Sciences de la Terre, Sciences de l'Univers (0764-4450); Which was formerly (until 1984): Academie des Sciences. Comptes Rendus des Seances. Serie 2: Mecanique - Physique, Chimie, Sciences de l'Univers, Sciences de la Terre (0750-7623); (until 1981): Academie des Sciences. Comptes Rendus des Seances. Serie 2: Mecanique, Physique, Chimie, Sciences de la Terre, Sciences de l'Univers (0249-6305); Which was formed by the 1980 merger of: Academie des Sciences. Comptes Rendus des Hebdomadaires des Seances. Series A et B. Serie B: Sciences Physiques (0335-5993); Which was formerly (until 1975): Academie des Sciences. Comptes Rendus Hebdomadaires des Seances. Serie B: Sciences Physiques (0302-8437); Which superseded in part (in 1974): Academie des Sciences. Comptes Rendus Hebdomadaires des Seances. Series A et B. Sciences Mathematiques et Sciences Physiques (0997-4482); (1965-1980): Academie des Sciences. Comptes Rendus des Hebdomadaires des Seances. Serie C: Sciences Chimiques (0567-6541); Both of which superseded in part (in 1965): Academie des Sciences. Comptes Rendus Hebdomadaires des Seances (0001-4036)
Related titles: Online - full text ed.: (from EBSCO Publishing, Gale Group, IngentaConnect, ScienceDirect, Swets Information Services).
Indexed: BioEngAb, C&ISA, ChemAb, CurCont, E&CAJ, IAA, INIS AtomInd, ISR, Inspec, M&GPA, RefZh, SCI.
—BLDSC (3384.868000), CISTI, IE, ingenta, Linda Hall, PADDS. **CCC.**
Published by: (Academie des Sciences), Elsevier France, Editions Scientifiques et Medicales (Subsidiary of: Elsevier Science & Technology), 23 Rue Linois, Paris, 75724, France. TEL 33-1-71724600, FAX 33-1-71724650, academic@elsevier.fr, http://www.elsevier.com/locate/crhy, http://www.elsevier.fr. Eds. G Laval, J. Villain. **Subscr. to:** Elsevier BV, PO Box 211, Amsterdam 1000 AE, Netherlands. TEL 31-20-485-3757, FAX 31-20-485-3432, http://www.elsevier.nl.

541 SGP ISSN 1793-0766

ADVANCED SERIES IN PHYSICAL CHEMISTRY. Text in English. 1994. irreg., latest vol.16, 2005. price varies. 532 p./no.; **Document type:** *Monographic series, Academic/Scholarly.* **Description:** Publishes selected graduate texts and stand-alone review monographs with specific themes, focusing on modern topics and new developments in experimental and theoretical physical chemistry and chemical physics.
—BLDSC (0696.928730).
Published by: World Scientific Publishing Co. Pte. Ltd., 5 Toh Tuck Link, Singapore, 596224, Singapore. TEL 65-466-5775, FAX 65-467-7667, wspc@wspc.com.sg, series@wspc.com.sg, http://www.wspc.com/books/series/aspc_series.shtml, http://www.worldscientific.com. Ed. C Y Ng. **Dist. by:** World Scientific Publishing Co., Inc., 1060 Main St, River Edge, NJ 07661. TEL 201-487-9655, FAX 201-487-9656, 888-977-2665; World Scientific Publishing Ltd., 57 Shelton St, London WC2H 9HE, United Kingdom. TEL 44-20-78360888, FAX 44-20-78362020, sales@wspc.co.uk.

541.395 USA ISSN 0360-0564
QD501 CODEN: ADCAAX

➤ **ADVANCES IN CATALYSIS.** Text in English. 1948. irreg., latest vol.47, 2002. USD 174 per vol. vol.47 (effective 2004). reprint service avail. from ISI. **Document type:** *Academic/Scholarly.* **Description:** Provides a comprehensive review of all aspects of catalytic research.
Formerly: Advances in Catalysis and Related Subjects (0065-2342)
Related titles: Online - full text ed.: (from ScienceDirect).
Indexed: ASCA, BiolAb, CCI, CIN, ChemAb, ChemInfo, ChemTitl, CurCR, ISR, IndChem, RCI, SCI.
—BLDSC (0702.990000), CASDDS, CISTI, IE, ingenta, Linda Hall. **CCC.**
Published by: Academic Press (Subsidiary of: Elsevier Science & Technology), 525 B St, Ste 1900, San Diego, CA 92101-4495. TEL 619-231-6616, 800-894-3434, FAX 619-699-6422, apsubs@acad.com, http://www.academicpress.com.

➤ **ADVANCES IN CHEMICAL PHYSICS.** see *PHYSICS*

541 NLD ISSN 0001-8686
QD506 CODEN: ACISB9

➤ **ADVANCES IN COLLOID AND INTERFACE SCIENCE.** Text in English, French, German. 1965. 16/yr. EUR 2,098 in Europe to institutions; JPY 278,800 in Japan to institutions; USD 2,344 elsewhere to institutions (effective 2006). adv. bk.rev. charts. back issues avail.; reprints avail. **Document type:** *Journal, Academic/Scholarly.* **Description:** Covers all traditional and other subjects in the realm of colloid and surface science.
Related titles: Microform ed.: (from PQC); Online - full text ed.: (from EBSCO Publishing, Gale Group, IngentaConnect, ScienceDirect, Swets Information Services).
Indexed: ABIPC, AESIS, ASCA, AcoustA, C&ISA, CCI, CIN, ChemAb, ChemTitl, CurCont, DSA, E&CAJ, EngInd, ISMEC, ISR, IndMed, Inspec, MEDLINE, MSCI, PhotoAb, PhysBer, RefZh, SCI, SolStAb, WSCA.
—BLDSC (0703.950000), CASDDS, CISTI, Ei, GNLM, IDS, IE, Infotrieve, ingenta, Linda Hall. **CCC.**
Published by: Elsevier BV (Subsidiary of: Elsevier Science & Technology), Radarweg 29, Amsterdam, 1043 NX, Netherlands. TEL 31-20-4853911, FAX 31-20-4852457, nlinfo-f@elsevier.nl, http://www.elsevier.com/locate/cis, http://www.elsevier.nl. Eds. J Berg, R Miller.

C

547.13 USA ISSN 0065-3152
QD601.A1 CODEN: ADPCA2

➤ **ADVANCES IN PHOTOCHEMISTRY.** Text in English. 1963. irreg., latest vol.28, 2005. price varies. index. **Document type:** *Monographic series, Academic/Scholarly.*
Indexed: CIN, ChemAb, ChemInfo, ChemTitl, MSB.
—BLDSC (0709.780000), CASDDS, CISTI, IE, Infotrieve, ingenta, Linda Hall. **CCC.**
Published by: John Wiley & Sons, Inc., 111 River St, Hoboken, NJ 07030-5774. TEL 201-748-6000, 800-825-7550, FAX 201-748-5915, uscs-wis@wiley.com, http://www.wiley.com.

546.5 USA ISSN 0065-3160
QD476 CODEN: APORAO

➤ **ADVANCES IN PHYSICAL ORGANIC CHEMISTRY.** Text in English. 1963. irreg., latest vol.37. USD 136 per vol. vol.38 (effective 2004). reprint service avail. from ISI. **Document type:** *Academic/Scholarly.* **Description:** Provides the chemical community with authoritative and critical assessments of the many aspects of physical organic chemistry.
Related titles: Online - full text ed.: (from ScienceDirect).
Indexed: ASCA, CCI, CIN, ChemAb, ChemInfo, ChemTitl, ISR, SCI.
—BLDSC (0709.800000), CASDDS, CISTI, IE, Infotrieve, ingenta, Linda Hall. **CCC.**
Published by: Academic Press (Subsidiary of: Elsevier Science & Technology), 525 B St, Ste 1900, San Diego, CA 92101-4495. TEL 619-231-6616, 800-894-3434, apsubs@acad.com, http://www.academicpress.com. Ed. V Gold.

541 USA

ADVANCES IN QUANTITATIVE STRUCTURE-PROPERTY RELATIONSHIPS. Text in English. 1996. irreg., latest vol.3, 2002. price varies. **Document type:** *Monographic series, Academic/Scholarly.* **Description:** Provides interesting and timely reviews covering all aspects of the field.
—BLDSC (0711.143000).
Published by: J A I Press Inc. (Subsidiary of: Elsevier Science & Technology), 360 Park Ave S, New York, NY 10010-1710. TEL 212-989-5800, FAX 212-633-3990, usinfo-f@elsevier.com, http://www.elsevier.com. Ed. Marvin Charton.

ADVANCES IN SOLID STATE TECHNOLOGY. see *PHYSICS*

541 USA ISSN 1569-2868

ADVANCES IN SONOCHEMISTRY. Text in English. 1990. irreg., latest vol.6, 2001. price varies. back issues avail. **Document type:** *Monographic series, Academic/Scholarly.* **Description:** Designed to meet the needs of both researchers and graduate students of the subject.
Indexed: CCI, CIN, ChemAb, ChemTitl.
—BLDSC (0711.455000).
Published by: J A I Press Inc. (Subsidiary of: Elsevier Science & Technology), 360 Park Ave S, New York, NY 10010-1710. TEL 212-989-5800, FAX 212-633-3990, usinfo-f@elsevier.com, http://www.elsevier.com/wps/find/bookseriesdescription.cws_home/BS_ASON/description. Ed. Timothy Mason.

541 GBR

AEROFILL NEWS. Text in English. 1980. s-a.

Published by: Aerofill Ltd., Clayton Rd, Hayes, Middx UB3 1RU, United Kingdom. FAX 44-181-561-3308. Ed. C M Nimmo. Circ: 5,000.

AMERICAN CRYSTALLOGRAPHIC ASSOCIATION. PROGRAM & ABSTRACTS. see *CHEMISTRY—Abstracting, Bibliographies, Statistics*

AMERICAN MINERALOGIST; an international journal of earth and planetary materials. see *MINES AND MINING INDUSTRY*

546.5 541.39 USA ISSN 0066-409X
QD262 CODEN: ARSYEF

➤ **ANNUAL REPORTS IN ORGANIC SYNTHESIS.** Text in English. 1971. irreg., latest 2003. USD 105 per vol. (effective 2004). reprint service avail. from ISI. **Document type:** *Academic/Scholarly.* **Description:** Deals with methods of synthesizing heterocyclic systems, the use of protecting groups and synthetically useful transformations.
—CISTI, Linda Hall. **CCC.**
Published by: Academic Press (Subsidiary of: Elsevier Science & Technology), 525 B St, Ste 1900, San Diego, CA 92101-4495. TEL 619-231-6616, 800-894-3434, apsubs@acad.com, http://www.academicpress.com.

541 USA ISSN 0066-426X
QD1 CODEN: ARPLAP

➤ **ANNUAL REVIEW OF PHYSICAL CHEMISTRY.** Text in English. 1950. a., latest vol.55, 2004. USD 188 to institutions print or online ed.; USD 226 combined subscription to institutions print & online eds. (effective 2006). bibl.; charts; abstr. index, cum.index. back issues avail.; reprint service avail. from PSC. **Document type:** *Academic/Scholarly.* **Description:** Reviews filter and synthesize primary research to identify the principal contributions in the field of physical chemistry.
Related titles: Microfilm ed.: (from PQC); Online - full content ed.: ISSN 1545-1593. USD 183 (effective 2005) (from HighWire Press); Online - full text ed.: (from bigchalk, EBSCO Publishing, H.W. Wilson, O C L C Online Computer Library Center, Inc., ProQuest Information & Learning, Swets Information Services).
Indexed: ABIPC, ASCA, ASFA, CCI, CIN, CMCI, Cadscan, ChemAb, ChemTitl, CurCont, ESPM, EngInd, F&EA, GSI, ISR, IndMed, Inspec, LeadAb, MEDLINE, MRD, SCI, WSCA, Zincscan.
—BLDSC (1526.000000), CASDDS, CINDOC, CISTI, Ei, IDS, IE, Infotrieve, ingenta, KNAW, Linda Hall. **CCC.**
Published by: Annual Reviews, 4139 El Camino Way, Palo Alto, CA 94303-0139. TEL 650-493-4400, 800-523-8635, FAX 650-424-0910, service@annualreviews.org, http://arjournals.annualreviews.org/loi/physchem, http://www.annualreviews.org. Ed. Stephen R Leone. R&P Laura Folkner.

➤ **ARCHIVES OF THERMODYNAMICS.** see *PHYSICS—Heat*

➤ **BOPUXUE ZAZHI/CHINESE JOURNAL OF MAGNETIC RESONANCE.** see *PHYSICS—Optics*

541.36 USA ISSN 0572-6921

BRIGHAM YOUNG UNIVERSITY. CENTER FOR THERMOCHEMICAL STUDIES. CONTRIBUTIONS✱. Text in English. irreg., latest vol.66, 1975. price varies.
Published by: Brigham Young University, Center for Thermochemical Studies, Provo, UT 84602.

C A SELECTS. LASER APPLICATIONS. see *CHEMISTRY—Abstracting, Bibliographies, Statistics*

541 GBR ISSN 0140-0568
QD505 CODEN: CATADK

CATALYSIS. (Vol.16 due early 2002.) Text in English. 1976. irreg., latest vol.16, 2002. GBP 189.50, USD 306 per vol. (effective 2004). charts; illus. Index. 214 p./no.; **Document type:** *Journal, Academic/Scholarly.* **Description:** Provides systematic and detailed reviews of topics of interest to scientists and engineers in the catalysis field.
Indexed: BIOSIS Prev, CCI.
—BLDSC (3090.880000), CASDDS, CISTI, IE, ingenta, Linda Hall. **CCC.**
Published by: Royal Society of Chemistry, Thomas Graham House, Science Park, Milton Rd, Cambridge, CB4 0WF, United Kingdom. TEL 44-1223-420066, FAX 44-1223-423623, sales@rsc.org, http://www.rsc.org/CFbooks/sprindex.cfm?BKC=CA. Ed. J J Spivey. **Dist. by:** Extenza - Turpin, Pegasus Dr, Stratton Business Park, Biggleswade, Beds SG18 8TQ, United Kingdom. FAX 44-1462-480947.

660.299 541.395 USA ISSN 0161-4940
QD501 CODEN: CRSEC9

➤ **CATALYSIS REVIEWS: SCIENCE AND ENGINEERING.** Text in English. 1959. q. USD 1,353, GBP 820 combined subscription to institutions print & online eds. (effective 2006). adv. reprint service avail. from PSC. **Document type:** *Journal, Academic/Scholarly.* **Description:** Offers articles in such areas as advances in technology and theory, reactor design, and other topics.
Formerly: Catalysis Reviews (0008-7645)
Related titles: Microform ed.: (from RPI); Online - full text ed.: ISSN 1520-5703. USD 1,285, GBP 779 to institutions (effective 2006) (from EBSCO Publishing, O C L C Online Computer Library Center, Inc., Swets Information Services).
Indexed: APIAb, APICat, APIH&E, APIOC, APIPR, APIPS, APITS, ASCA, BrCerAb, C&ISA, CCI, CEA, CEABA, CIN, CerAb, ChemAb, ChemInfo, ChemTitl, CorrAb, CurCR, CurCont, E&CAJ, EMA, EngInd, GasAb, IAA, ISR, IndChem, M&TEA, MBF, METADEX, RCI, RefZh, SCI, SolStAb, TCEA, WAA.
—BLDSC (3090.941000), CASDDS, CINDOC, CISTI, Ei, IDS, IE, Infotrieve, ingenta, Linda Hall. **CCC.**
Published by: Taylor & Francis Inc. (Subsidiary of: Taylor & Francis Group), 325 Chestnut St, Ste 800, Philadelphia, PA 19016. TEL 215-625-8900, 800-354-1420, FAX 215-625-2940, info@taylorandfrancis.com, http://www.tandf.co.uk/journals/titles/01614940.asp, http://www.taylorandfrancis.com. Eds. Alexis T Bell, Kamil Klier. Adv. contact Sharon Moran. B&W page USD 800. Circ: 800.

660.299 541.395 USA ISSN 1571-1013
CODEN: CSURFY

CATALYSIS SURVEYS FROM ASIA. Text in Dutch. 1997. 4/yr. EUR 420, USD 420, GBP 262 combined subscription to institutions print & online eds. (effective 2005). reprint service avail. from PSC. **Document type:** *Academic/Scholarly.*
Formerly (until 2002): Catalysis Surveys from Japan (1384-6574)
Related titles: Online - full text ed.: ISSN 1572-8803 (from EBSCO Publishing, Gale Group, IngentaConnect, Kluwer Online, O C L C Online Computer Library Center, Inc., Springer LINK, Swets Information Services).
Indexed: BibLing, CCI, CurCont, ISR, SCI.
—BLDSC (3090.943200), CASDDS, IDS, IE, Infotrieve, ingenta. **CCC.**
Published by: Plenum US (Subsidiary of: Springer Science+Business Media), 233 Spring St, New York, NY 10013. TEL 212-460-1500, FAX 212-460-1575, service@springer-ny.com, http://springerlink.metapress.com/openurl.asp?genre=journal&issn=1571-1013, http://www.springeronline.com. Eds. Ei-ichi Kikuchi, Makato Misono, San Heup Moon, Yoshio Ono.

541 JPN
CODEN: SHKUAJ

CATALYSTS & CATALYSIS✱. Text in English. 1959. 8/yr. JPY 2,000 per issue (effective 2003). **Document type:** *Academic/Scholarly.*
Formerly: Shokubai - Catalyst (0559-8958)
Indexed: ChemAb, INIS AtomInd, JPI, RefZh.
—CASDDS, CISTI, ingenta, Linda Hall. **CCC.**
Published by: Shokubai Gakkai/Catalysis Society of Japan, 1-5-3 Kandasurugadai, Chiyodaku, Tokyo, 101-0062, Japan. TEL 81-3-32918224, FAX 81-3-32918225, catsj@pb3.so-net.ne.jp, http://www.shokubai.org/index.html.

549.6 CZE ISSN 0862-5468
TA455.S46 CODEN: CERSEP

CERAMICS-SILIKATY. Text in Czech, English; Summaries in Czech, English, Russian. 1957. q. bk.rev. charts; illus. index. **Document type:** *Journal, Academic/Scholarly.* **Description:** Original articles covering all branches of silicate research, including chemistry, physical chemistry and engineering.
Formerly (until 1990): Silikaty (0037-5241)
Related titles: Online - full text ed.: free (effective 2005).
Indexed: ABM, ASCA, BrCerAb, C&ISA, CIN, CerAb, ChemAb, ChemTitl, CorrAb, CurCont, DAAI, E&CAJ, EMA, EngInd, IAA, Inspec, MSCI, SCI, SolStAb, WAA.
—BLDSC (3119.058000), AskIEEE, CASDDS, CISTI, Ei, IDS, IE, ingenta, Linda Hall.
Published by: (Vysoka Skola Chemicko Technologicka v Praze), S K Press v.o.s., Masarykovo nam 35, Ricany, 25101, Czech Republic. http://www.ceramics-silikaty.cz/index.htm. Circ: 1,350. **Dist. in Western countries by:** Kubon & Sagner Buchexport - Import GmbH, Postfach 24, Munich 34 8000, Germany.

541 530 NLD ISSN 0301-0104
QD450 CODEN: CMPHC2

➤ **CHEMICAL PHYSICS.** Text in English. 1973. 36/yr. EUR 7,128 in Europe to institutions; JPY 946,100 in Japan to institutions; USD 7,972 elsewhere to institutions (effective 2006). index. back issues avail. **Document type:** *Journal, Academic/Scholarly.* **Description:** Publishes experimental and theoretical papers on all aspects of chemical physics.
Related titles: Microform ed.: (from PQC); Online - full text ed.: (from EBSCO Publishing, Gale Group, IngentaConnect, ScienceDirect, Swets Information Services).
Indexed: ASCA, ApicAb, BPRC&P, CCI, CIN, Cadscan, ChemAb, ChemTitl, CurCont, ISR, Inspec, LeadAb, MSB, MSCI, MathR, PhysBer, RCI, RefZh, SCI, Zincscan.
—BLDSC (3148.820000), AskIEEE, CASDDS, CISTI, IDS, IE, Infotrieve, ingenta, Linda Hall. **CCC.**
Published by: Elsevier BV, North-Holland (Subsidiary of: Elsevier Science & Technology), Sara Burgerhartstraat 25, Amsterdam, 1055 KV, Netherlands. TEL 31-20-485-3911, FAX 31-20-485-2457, nlinfo-f@elsevier.nl, http://www.elsevier.com/locate/chemphys, http://www.elsevier.nl. Eds. H. P. Trommsdorff, R M Hochstrasser, W. Domcke. **Subscr.:** Elsevier BV, PO Box 211, Amsterdam 1000 AE, Netherlands. TEL 31-20-485-3757, FAX 31-20-485-3432, http://www.elsevier.nl.

541 NLD ISSN 0009-2614
CODEN: CHPLBC

➤ **CHEMICAL PHYSICS LETTERS.** Text in Dutch. 1967. 102/yr. EUR 11,635 in Europe to institutions; JPY 1,546,200 in Japan to institutions; USD 13,016 to institutions except Europe and Japan; EUR 561 in Europe to qualified personnel; JPY 73,700 in Japan to qualified personnel; USD 626 to qualified personnel except Europe and Japan (effective 2006). adv. illus. index, cum.index. back issues avail.; reprints avail. **Document type:** *Journal, Academic/Scholarly.* **Description:** Devoted to the analysis of phenomena in the domain of chemical physics.
Related titles: Microform ed.: (from PQC); Online - full text ed.: (from EBSCO Publishing, Gale Group, IngentaConnect, ScienceDirect, Swets Information Services).
Indexed: ASCA, BPRC&P, BullT&T, CCI, CIN, Cadscan, ChemAb, ChemTitl, CurCont, EngInd, IAA, ISR, Inspec, LeadAb, MSB, MSCI, MathR, PhysBer, RCI, RefZh, SCI, Zincscan.
—BLDSC (3148.830000), AskIEEE, CASDDS, CISTI, Ei, IDS, IE, Infotrieve, ingenta, Linda Hall. **CCC.**
Published by: Elsevier BV, North-Holland (Subsidiary of: Elsevier Science & Technology), Sara Burgerhartstraat 25, Amsterdam, 1055 KV, Netherlands. TEL 31-20-485-3911, FAX 31-20-485-2457, nlinfo-f@elsevier.nl, http://www.elsevier.com/locate/cplett, http://www.elsevier.nl/homepage/about/us/regional_sites.htt. Eds. A Zewail, D C Clary, V Sundstroem. **Subscr. to:** Elsevier BV, PO Box 211, Amsterdam 1000 AE, Netherlands. TEL 31-20-485-3757, FAX 31-20-485-3432.

541 NLD

➤ **THE CHEMICAL PHYSICS OF SOLID SURFACES.** Text in English. 1981. irreg., latest vol.11, 2003. price varies. back issues avail. **Document type:** *Monographic series, Academic/Scholarly.* **Description:** Publishes research into the chemical physics of solid surfaces.
Indexed: CIN, ChemAb, ChemTitl, Inspec.
Published by: Elsevier BV (Subsidiary of: Elsevier Science & Technology), Radarweg 29, Amsterdam, 1043 NX, Netherlands. TEL 31-20-4853911, FAX 31-20-4852457, nlinfo-f@elsevier.nl, http://www.elsevier.nl.

541 NLD

CHEMICAL SENSOR TECHNOLOGY. Text in English. 1988. irreg., latest vol.4, 1992. price varies. bk.rev. abstr. back issues avail. **Document type:** *Academic/Scholarly.* **Description:** Examines and publishes research in developments in chemical sensors.
Published by: Elsevier BV (Subsidiary of: Elsevier Science & Technology), Radarweg 29, Amsterdam, 1043 NX, Netherlands. TEL 31-20-4853911, FAX 31-20-4852457, nlinfo-f@elsevier.nl, http://www.elsevier.nl.

CHEMICAL THERMODYNAMICS. see *PHYSICS—Heat*

541 DEU ISSN 1439-4235
QD450 CODEN: CPCHFT

➤ **CHEMPHYSCHEM**; a European journal of chemical physics and physical chemistry. Text in English. 1903. m. EUR 1,248 in Europe; CHF 1,928 in Switzerland & Liechtenstein; USD 1,434 elsewhere; EUR 1,373 combined subscription in Europe print & online eds.; CHF 2,121 combined subscription in Switzerland & Liechtenstein for print & online eds.; USD 1,578 combined subscription elsewhere print & online eds. (effective 2006). adv. bk.rev. abstr.; illus. 60 p./no. 2 cols./p.; back issues avail.; reprints avail. **Document type:** *Journal, Academic/Scholarly.* **Description:** Contains news, comments, papers, reviews, and communications on all aspects of physical chemistry.
Formerly (until 2000): Journal de Chimie Physique (0021-7689); Which incorporated (1923-1930): Revue Generale des Colloides (0370-5048)
Related titles: Online - full text ed.: ISSN 1439-7641. EUR 1,248 in Europe to institutions; CHF 1,928 to institutions in Switzerland & Liechtenstein; USD 1,434 elsewhere to institutions (effective 2006) (from EBSCO Publishing, Swets Information Services, Wiley InterScience).
Indexed: ASFA, CCI, ChemAb, CurCont, GenetAb, ISR, Inspec, RefZh, SCI.
—BLDSC (3172.310500), CISTI, IE, Infotrieve, ingenta, Linda Hall. **CCC.**
Published by: Wiley - V C H Verlag GmbH & Co. KGaA (Subsidiary of: John Wiley & Sons, Inc.), Boschstr 12, Weinheim, 69469, Germany. TEL 49-6201-606-0, FAX 49-6201-606-328, chemphyschem@wiley-vch.de, subservice@wiley-vch.de, http://www.chemphyschem.com, http://www.wiley-vch.de. Ed. Peter Goelitz. R&P Claudia Rutz. Adv. contact Aenne Anders TEL 49-6201-606552. page EUR 2,600; trim 180 x 260.

➤ **COLLOID AND POLYMER SCIENCE**; Kolloid-Zeitschrift und Zeitschrift fuer Polymere. see *CHEMISTRY—Organic Chemistry*

C

541 NLD ISSN 0927-7757
QD549 CODEN: CPEAEH
➤ **COLLOIDS AND SURFACES A: PHYSICOCHEMICAL AND ENGINEERING ASPECTS.** Text in English. 1980. 60/yr. EUR 6,173 in Europe to institutions; JPY 819,300 in Japan to institutions; USD 6,904 to institutions except Europe and Japan (effective 2006). adv. bk.rev. back issues avail. **Document type:** *Journal, Academic/Scholarly.* **Description:** Publishes original papers on basic colloid and surface science and, in particular, its application in engineering and applied science.
Supersedes in part (in 1993): Colloids and Surfaces (0166-6622)
Related titles: Microform ed.: (from PQC); Online - full text ed.: (from EBSCO Publishing, Gale Group, IngentaConnect, ScienceDirect, Swets Information Services).
Indexed: ABIPC, AESIS, ASCA, B&BAb, BioEngAb, BiolAb, BrCerAb, C&ISA, CCI, CIN, ChemAb, ChemTitl, CurCont, DSA, E&CAJ, EngInd, ExcerpMed, FLUIDEX, ISMEC, ISR, Inspec, MSCI, P&BA, PetrolAb, PhotoAb, RAPRA, RCI, SCI, SIA, SSCI, SolStAb, WSCA.
—BLDSC (3313.552010), AskIEEE, CASDDS, CISTI, Ei, IDS, IE, Infotrieve, ingenta, Linda Hall, PADDS. **CCC.**
Published by: Elsevier BV (Subsidiary of: Elsevier Science & Technology), Radarweg 29, Amsterdam, 1043 NX, Netherlands. TEL 31-20-4853911, FAX 31-20-4852457, nlinfo-f@elsevier.nl, http://www.elsevier.com/locate/colsurfa, http://www.elsevier.nl. Eds. D. C. Prieve, D. N. Furlong, Dr. H Moehwald.

541 NLD ISSN 0927-7765
QP517.S87 CODEN: CSBBEQ
➤ **COLLOIDS AND SURFACES B: BIOINTERFACES.** Text in English. 1980. 14/yr. EUR 1,898 in Europe to institutions; JPY 251,900 in Japan to institutions; USD 2,124 elsewhere to institutions (effective 2006). back issues avail. **Document type:** *Journal, Academic/Scholarly.* **Description:** Provides an international forum for fundamental and applied research on colloids and interfacial phenomena in relation to systems of biological origin, with particular attention to the medical, pharmaceutical, biotechnology, food and cosmetics fields.
Supersedes in part (in 1993): Colloids and Surfaces (0166-6622)
Related titles: Microform ed.: (from PQC); Online - full text ed.: (from EBSCO Publishing, Gale Group, IngentaConnect, ScienceDirect, Swets Information Services).
Indexed: ASCA, B&BAb, BBCI, BioEngAb, CCI, CIN, ChemAb, ChemTitl, CurCont, EngInd, ExcerpMed, ISR, Inspec, MEDLINE, MSCI, P&BA, PhotoAb, RAPRA, SCI, SSCI.
—BLDSC (3313.552020), AskIEEE, CASDDS, CISTI, Ei, IDS, IE, Infotrieve, ingenta, Linda Hall. **CCC.**
Published by: Elsevier BV (Subsidiary of: Elsevier Science & Technology), Radarweg 29, Amsterdam, 1043 NX, Netherlands. TEL 31-20-4853911, FAX 31-20-4852457, nlinfo-f@elsevier.nl, http://www.elsevier.com/locate/colsurfb, http://www.elsevier.nl. Eds. Dr. H. J. Busscher, J L Brash, R. M. Leblanc.

➤ **COMBUSTION INSTITUTE. WESTERN STATES SECTION. PAPERS.** see *ENGINEERING—Chemical Engineering*

662 541 USA ISSN 0010-2202
QD516 CODEN: CBSTB9
➤ **COMBUSTION SCIENCE AND TECHNOLOGY.** Text in English. 1969. m. GBP 4,438, USD 6,912 combined subscription to institutions print & online eds. (effective 2006). adv. charts; illus. index. reprint service avail. from PSC. **Document type:** *Journal, Academic/Scholarly.*
Incorporates (in 1975): Pyrodynamics (0555-8344)
Related titles: CD-ROM ed.; Microform ed.; Online - full text ed.: ISSN 1563-521X. GBP 4,216, USD 6,566 to institutions (effective 2006) (from EBSCO Publishing, Gale Group, IngentaConnect, O C L C Online Computer Library Center, Inc., Swets Information Services).
Indexed: AESIS, AS&TI, ASCA, ASFA, ApMecR, CCI, CEA, ChemAb, CivEngAb, CurCont, EPB, EngInd, ExcerpMed, F&EA, GasAb, IAA, ISMEC, ISR, Inspec, METADEX, MSCI, SCI.
—BLDSC (3330.205000), CISTI, IE, Infotrieve, ingenta. **CCC.**
Published by: Taylor & Francis Inc. (Subsidiary of: Taylor & Francis Group), 325 Chestnut St, Ste 800, Philadelphia, PA 19016. TEL 215-625-8900, 800-354-1420, FAX 215-625-2940, 215-625-8914, info@taylorandfrancis.com, http://www.tandf.co.uk/journals/titles/00102203.asp, http://www.taylorandfrancis.com. Eds. Irvin Glassman, Richard A Yetter. **Subscr. outside N. America to:** Taylor & Francis Ltd, Journals Customer Service, Rankine Rd, Basingstoke, Hants RG24 8PR, United Kingdom. TEL 44-1256-813000, FAX 44-1256-330245, enquiry@tandf.co.uk.

541.361 USA ISSN 0883-5519
COMBUSTION SCIENCE AND TECHNOLOGY BOOK SERIES. Text in English. 1975. irreg., latest vol.5, 2002. price varies. **Document type:** *Monographic series, Academic/Scholarly.*
—CISTI. **CCC.**
Published by: Routledge (Subsidiary of: Taylor & Francis Ltd), 270 Madison Ave, New York, NY 10016. TEL 212-216-7800, FAX 212-564-1563, info@routledge-ny.com, http://www.routledge-ny.com.

541 NLD ISSN 0069-8040
➤ **COMPREHENSIVE CHEMICAL KINETICS.** Text in English. 1969. irreg., latest vol.38, 2001. price varies. back issues avail. **Document type:** *Monographic series, Academic/Scholarly.* **Description:** Deals with both the basic theories of developments and applications in the broad field of chemical kinetics.
Indexed: EngInd.
—BLDSC (3366.300000), CISTI, Ei, IE, ingenta.
Published by: Elsevier BV (Subsidiary of: Elsevier Science & Technology), Radarweg 29, Amsterdam, 1043 NX, Netherlands. TEL 31-20-4853911, FAX 31-20-4852457, nlinfo-f@elsevier.nl, http://www.elsevier.nl. Eds. C. F.H. Tipper, R G Compton.

▼ ➤ **CONCEPTS IN MAGNETIC RESONANCE. PART A.** see *MEDICAL SCIENCES—Radiology And Nuclear Medicine*

➤ **CONCEPTS IN MAGNETIC RESONANCE. PART B: MAGNETIC RESONANCE ENGINEERING.** see *MEDICAL SCIENCES—Radiology And Nuclear Medicine*

541.345 GBR ISSN 1359-0294
QD549 CODEN: COCSFL
➤ **CURRENT OPINION IN COLLOID & INTERFACE SCIENCE.** Short title: C O C I S. Text in English. 1996. 6/yr. EUR 296 in Europe to individuals; JPY 39,300 in Japan to individuals; USD 332 elsewhere to individuals; EUR 1,420 in Europe to institutions; JPY 188,700 in Japan to institutions; USD 1,590 elsewhere to institutions; EUR 154 in Europe to students; JPY 20,500 in Japan to students; USD 172 elsewhere to students (effective 2006). **Document type:** *Journal, Academic/Scholarly.* **Description:** Examines the major areas of colloid, interface and polymer science.
Related titles: Online - full text ed.: (from EBSCO Publishing, Gale Group, IngentaConnect, ScienceDirect, Swets Information Services).
Indexed: BrCerAb, C&ISA, CCI, CIN, CerAb, ChemAb, ChemTitl, CivEngAb, CorrAb, CurCont, E&CAJ, EMA, ExcerpMed, FS&TA, IAA, M&TEA, MBF, METADEX, MSCI, SolStAb, WAA.
—BLDSC (3500.773540), CISTI, IDS, IE, Infotrieve, ingenta, Linda Hall. **CCC.**
Published by: Pergamon (Subsidiary of: Elsevier Science & Technology), The Boulevard, Langford Ln, East Park, Kidlington, Oxford OX5 1GB, United Kingdom. TEL 44-1865-843000, FAX 44-1865-843010, http://www.elsevier.com/locate/cocis. Eds. Brian H Robinson, Eric W Kaler, K. H. Holmberg. **Subscr. to:** Elsevier BV, PO Box 211, Amsterdam 1000 AE, Netherlands. TEL 31-20-485-3757, FAX 31-20-485-3432, nlinfo-f@elsevier.nl, http://www.elsevier.nl.

541 NLD ISSN 1568-2366
DEVELOPMENTS IN FULLERENE SCIENCE. Text in English. 2000. irreg., latest vol.5, 2004. price varies. **Document type:** *Monographic series, Academic/Scholarly.*
—BLDSC (3579.071860), CISTI.
Published by: Springer-Verlag Dordrecht (Subsidiary of: Springer Science+Business Media), Van Godewijckstraat 30, Dordrecht, 3311 GX, Netherlands. TEL 31-78-6576050, FAX 31-78-6576474, http://www.springeronline.com.

541 RUS ISSN 0012-5016
QD1 CODEN: DKPCAG
➤ **DOKLADY PHYSICAL CHEMISTRY.** Text in English. 1933. m. EUR 3,765, USD 3,368, GBP 2,348 combined subscription to institutions print & online eds. (effective 2005). back issues avail. **Document type:** *Journal, Academic/Scholarly.* **Description:** Publishes short preliminary accounts of ideas and methods in physical chemistry to study organic and inorganic compounds, materials, and processes.
Related titles: Microfilm ed.: (from PQC); Online - full text ed.: ISSN 1608-3121 (from EBSCO Publishing, Gale Group, IngentaConnect, Kluwer Online, O C L C Online Computer Library Center, Inc., Springer LINK, Swets Information Services); ♦ Partial translation of: Rossiiskaya Akademiya Nauk. Doklady. ISSN 0869-5652.
Indexed: BibLing, CCI, ChemAb, ChemTitl, CurCont, EnerRA, ISR, MSB, RCI, SCI.
—BLDSC (0411.350000), CISTI, Ei, IE, Infotrieve, ingenta, Linda Hall. **CCC.**
Published by: (Rossiiskaya Akademiya Nauk/Russian Academy of Sciences), M A I K Nauka - Interperiodica, Profsoyuznaya ul 90, Moscow, 117997, Russian Federation. TEL 7-095-3347420, FAX 7-095-3360666, compmg@maik.ru, http://www.maik.ru/cgi-bin/journal.pl?name=danpc&page=main. Ed. Victor A. Kabanov. **Subscr. to:** Springer-Verlag Dordrecht, Journals Department, PO Box 322, Dordrecht, Netherlands. TEL 31-78-6576392, FAX 31-78-6576474.

541 USA ISSN 0737-3937
TP363 CODEN: DRTEDQ
➤ **DRYING TECHNOLOGY**; an international journal. Text in English. 1983. m. GBP 1,687, USD 2,783 combined subscription to institutions print & online eds. (effective 2006). adv. bk.rev. charts. reprint service avail. from PSC. **Document type:** *Journal, Academic/Scholarly.* **Description:** Explores in depth, the science technology, and engineering of drying, dewatering, and related topics.
Related titles: Microform ed.: (from RPI); Online - full text ed.: ISSN 1532-2300. GBP 1,603, USD 2,644 to institutions (effective 2006) (from EBSCO Publishing, O C L C Online Computer Library Center, Inc., Swets Information Services).
Indexed: ABIPC, AEA, AESIS, ASCA, Agr, AgrForAb, AnBrAb, ApMecR, C&ISA, CEA, CEABA, CIN, CPA, ChemAb, ChemTitl, CurCont, DSA, E&CAJ, EngInd, ExcerpMed, FCA, FLUIDEX, FPA, FS&TA, ForAb, HerbAb, HortAb, ISMEC, ISR, MSCI, MaizeAb, NutrAb, OrnHort, PBA, PGegResA, PHN&I, PotatoAb, RA&MP, RDA, RefZh, RiceAb, S&F, SCI, SIA, SeedAb, SolStAb, SoyAb, TCEA, TriticAb, WAE&RSA, WTA.
—BLDSC (3630.226500), CASDDS, CISTI, Ei, IDS, IE, Infotrieve, ingenta, Linda Hall. **CCC.**
Published by: Taylor & Francis Inc. (Subsidiary of: Taylor & Francis Group), 325 Chestnut St, Ste 800, Philadelphia, PA 19016. TEL 215-625-8900, 800-354-1420, FAX 215-625-8914, info@taylorandfrancis.com, http://www.tandf.co.uk/journals/titles/07373937.asp, http://www.taylorandfrancis.com. Ed. Arun S Mujumdar. Adv. contact Sharon Moran. page USD 600. Circ: 350 (paid).

547.13 FRA ISSN 1011-4246
CODEN: EPNWDD
E P A NEWSLETTER. Text in English. 1978. 4/yr. CHF 30. bk.rev. abstr. **Document type:** *Newsletter, Trade.* **Description:** Contains research articles, technical reports, local and national photochemistry reports, historical articles, travel reports, association news, reports and announcements of events, abstracts of theses, titles of new photochemistry books and review papers, and positions available.
Indexed: ChemAb.
—BLDSC (3793.301830), CASDDS, IE, ingenta. **CCC.**
Published by: European Photochemistry Association, c/o Dr. Jean Kossanyi, 2-8 rue Henri Dunant, BP 28, Thiais, 94320, France. TEL 33-1-49781323, FAX 33-1-49781243, jean.kossanyi@glvt-cnrs.fr, http://www.unibas.ch/epa/. Ed., R&P, Adv. contact Dr. Jean Kossanyi. Circ: 960.

E-POLYMERS. see *ENGINEERING—Chemical Engineering*

E S R F NEWSLETTER. (European Synchrotron Radiation Facility) see *PHYSICS—Nuclear Physics*

ELECTROCHEMICAL SOCIETY OF INDIA. JOURNAL. see *CHEMISTRY—Electrochemistry*

ENSANIAN PHYSICOCHEMICAL INSTITUTE. JOURNAL. see *PHYSICS*

ENVIRONMENTAL AND CHEMICAL PHYSICS/APLINKOS FIZIKA. see *PHYSICS*

541 USA
EXPERIMENTAL THERMODYNAMICS SERIES. Variant title: I U P A C Experimental Thermodynamics Series. Text in English. irreg., latest vol.4, 1994. **Document type:** *Monographic series.*
Published by: (International Union of Pure and Applied Chemistry, Commission on Thermodynamics), C R C Press, LLC (Subsidiary of: Taylor & Francis Group), 2000 N W Corporate Blvd, Boca Raton, FL 33431. TEL 800-272-7737, journals@crcpress.com, http://www.crcpress.com/.

541 GBR ISSN 1359-6640
QD1 CODEN: FDISE6
➤ **FARADAY DISCUSSIONS.** Text in English. 1946. 3/yr. GBP 470, USD 861 combined subscription print & online eds. (effective 2006). index. **Document type:** *Academic/Scholarly.* **Description:** Designed to cover the broad aspects of physicochemical topics to encourage scientists of various disciplines to contribute their varied viewpoints to a common theme.
Former titles (until 1991): Faraday Discussions of the Chemical Society (0301-7249); (until 1972): Discussions of the Faraday Society (0366-9033); (until 1947): Faraday Society. Discussions (0014-7664)
Related titles: Microfilm ed.: (from PQC); Online - full text ed.: ISSN 1364-5498. 1997. GBP 423, USD 775 (effective 2006) (from EBSCO Publishing, O C L C Online Computer Library Center, Inc., Swets Information Services).
Indexed: ASCA, BPRC&P, BiolAb, BrCerAb, CCI, CIN, CTE, Cadscan, ChemAb, ChemTitl, CurCont, EngInd, ISR, IndMed, Inspec, LeadAb, MEDLINE, MSB, MSCI, MathR, RAPRA, RCI, RefZh, SCI, Zincscan.
—BLDSC (3866.900000), AskIEEE, CASDDS, CINDOC, CISTI, IDS, IE, Infotrieve, ingenta, Linda Hall. **CCC.**
Published by: Royal Society of Chemistry, Thomas Graham House, Science Park, Milton Rd, Cambridge, CB4 0WF, United Kingdom. TEL 44-1223-432360, FAX 44-1223-423623, faraday@rsc.org, sales@rsc.org, http://www.rsc.org/faraday_d. Ed. Dr. Susan Weatherby. **Subscr. to:** Portland Press Ltd., R S C Distribution Services, Commerce Way, Whitehall Industrial Estate, Colchester CO2 8HP, United Kingdom. TEL 44-1206-226050, FAX 44-1206-226055, sales@rscdistribution.org

541 BGR ISSN 0204-5958
TA405 CODEN: FKMEDW
FIZIKO-KHIMICHESKA MEKHANIKA/PHYSICO-CHEMICAL MECHANICS. Text in Bulgarian, German, Russian; Summaries in English, Russian. 1975. irreg. BGL 1.15 per issue. illus. reprint service avail. from IRC.
Indexed: BSLMath, CIN, ChemAb, ChemTitl, RefZh.
—CASDDS, CISTI, Linda Hall.

C

Published by: (Bulgarska Akademiya na Naukite/Bulgarian Academy of Sciences), Universitetsko Izdatelstvo Sv. Kliment Okhridski/Publishing House of the Sofia University St. Kliment Ohridski, Akad G Bonchev 6, Sofia, 1113, Bulgaria. Circ: 480. **Dist. by:** Hemus, 6 Rouski Blvd., Sofia 1000, Bulgaria.

FIZYKO-KHIMICHNA MEKHANIKA MATERIALIV/FIZIKO-KHIMICHESKAYA MEKHANIKA MATERIALOV/ PHYSICOCHEMICAL MECHANICS OF MATERIALS; mizhnarodnyi naukovo-tekhnichnyi zhurnal. see *PHYSICS—Mechanics*

549 541 POL ISSN 0137-1282
CODEN: FPMIDB

FIZYKOCHEMICZNE PROBLEMY MINERALURGII/ PHYSICOCHEMICAL PROBLEMS OF MINERAL PROCESSING. Text in English, Polish. 1967. a. EUR 9 per issue foreign (effective 2005). **Document type:** *Journal, Academic/Scholarly.* **Description:** Publishes original papers dealing with the principles of mineral processing and papers on technological aspects of mineral processing.
Formerly (until 1977): Fizykochemiczne Problemy Przerobki Kopalin (0137-1290)
Indexed: METADEX, RefZh.
—Linda Hall.
Published by: (Politechnika Wroclawska, Instytut Gornictwa, Zaklad Przerobki Kopalin), Oficyna Wydawnicza Politechniki Wroclawskiej, Wybrzeze Wyspianskiego 27, Wroclaw, 50370, Poland. TEL 48-71-3202994, oficwyd@pwr.wroc.pl, http://www.pwr.wroc.pl/~oficwyd/#OFICYNA. **Dist. by:** Ars Polona, Krakowskie Przedmiescie 7, Warsaw, Poland. TEL 48-22-9263914, FAX 48-22-9265334, arspolona@arspolona.com.pl, http://www.arspolona.com.pl.

C

541.392 NLD ISSN 0378-3812
QD504 CODEN: FPEQDT

➤ **FLUID PHASE EQUILIBRIA.** Text in English. 1978. 24/yr. EUR 5,165 in Europe to institutions; JPY 715,000 in Japan to institutions; USD 5,776 to institutions except Europe and Japan (effective 2006). adv. bk.rev. charts; illus. Index. back issues avail.; reprints avail. **Document type:** *Journal, Academic/Scholarly.* **Description:** For researchers and applied scientists, particularly those in chemical and metallurgical engineering, concerned with the properties or applications of fluid-phase equilibria.
Related titles: Microform ed.: (from PQC); Online - full text ed.: (from EBSCO Publishing, Gale Group, IngentaConnect, ScienceDirect, Swets Information Services).
Indexed: APIAb, ASCA, BrCerAb, C&ISA, CCI, CEA, CEABA, CIN, CerAb, ChemAb, ChemTitl, CivEngAb, CorrAb, CurCont, E&CAJ, E&PHSE, EMA, EngInd, FLUIDEX, GP&P, GasAb, IAA, ISMEC, ISR, Inspec, M&TEA, MBF, METADEX, MSCI, OffTech, PetrolAb, RCI, RefZh, SCI, SIA, SolStAb, TCEA, WAA.
—BLDSC (3962.170000), CASDDS, CISTI, Ei, IDS, IE, Infotrieve, ingenta, Linda Hall, PADDS. **CCC.**
Published by: Elsevier BV (Subsidiary of: Elsevier Science & Technology), Radarweg 29, Amsterdam, 1043 NX, Netherlands. TEL 31-20-4853911, FAX 31-20-4852457, nlinfo-f@elsevier.nl, http://www.elsevier.com/locate/fluid, http://www.elsevier.nl. Eds. H Inomata, J O'Connell, P. T. Cummings, T de Loos. **Subscr. in the Americas to:** Elsevier, Subscription Customer Service, 6277 Sea Harbor Dr, Orlando, FL 32887-4800. TEL 407-345-4020, 877-839-7126, FAX 407-363-1354.

541 USA ISSN 1536-383X
QD181.C1 CODEN: FNCNAR

➤ **FULLERENES, NANOTUBES, AND CARBON NANOSTRUCTURES.** Text in English. 1993. q. GBP 1,109, USD 1,831 combined subscription to institutions print & online eds. (effective 2006). adv. bibl.; charts; illus. **Document type:** *Journal, Academic/Scholarly.* **Description:** Provides peer-reviewed, original papers from all fields of scientific inquiry related to fullerene compounds, this sought-after publication provides a worldwide forum for investigators interested in fundamental and applied fullerene science issues.
Formerly (until 2002): Fullerene Science and Technology (1064-122X)
Related titles: Microfilm ed.: (from RPI); Online - full text ed.: ISSN 1536-4046. GBP 1,054, USD 1,739 to institutions (effective 2006) (from EBSCO Publishing, O C L C Online Computer Library Center, Inc., Swets Information Services).
Indexed: ASCA, BrCerAb, C&ISA, CCI, CIN, CerAb, ChemAb, ChemTitl, CivEngAb, CorrAb, CurCont, E&CAJ, EMA, EngInd, IAA, ISR, Inspec, M&TEA, MBF, METADEX, MSB, MSCI, RAPRA, RCI, RefZh, SCI, SolStAb, WAA.
—BLDSC (4055.559980), AskIEEE, CASDDS, CISTI, Ei, IDS, IE, ingenta, Linda Hall. **CCC.**
Published by: Taylor & Francis Inc. (Subsidiary of: Taylor & Francis Group), 325 Chestnut St, Ste 800, Philadelphia, PA 19016. TEL 215-625-8900, 800-354-1420, FAX 215-625-2940, info@taylorandfrancis.com, http://www.tandf.co.uk/journals/titles/1536383x.asp, http://www.taylorandfrancis.com. Ed. Dirk Guldi. Adv. contact Sharon Moran. B&W page USD 600. Circ: 250.

541.393 CHN ISSN 1000-3304
QD380 CODEN: GAXUE9

➤ **GAOFENZI XUEBAO/ACTA POLYMERICA SINICA.** Text in Chinese; Summaries in English. 1957. bi-m. CNY 180 (effective 2004). adv. **Document type:** *Journal, Academic/Scholarly.* **Description:** Includes polymer synthesis, polymer chemistry, polymer physics, and physical chemistry, as well as applied polymer science.
Formerly (until 1986): Gaofenzi Tongxun (0453-2880)
Related titles: Online - full content ed.: (from WanFang Data Corp.); Online - full text ed.: (from East View Information Services); ♦ English ed.: Chinese Journal of Polymer Science. ISSN 0256-7679.
Indexed: CCI, CIN, ChemAb, ChemTitl, MSCI, RCI, RefZh.
—BLDSC (0660.800000), CASDDS, IDS, IE, ingenta, Linda Hall.
Published by: (Zhongguo Huaxuehui/Chinese Chemical Society), Kexue Chubanshe/Science Press, 16 Donghuang Cheng Genbei Jie, Beijing, 100717, China. TEL 86-10-64000246, FAX 86-10-64030255, wangj@iccas.ac.cn, http://gfzxb.periodicals.net.cn/default.html. Ed. Xinde Feng. Circ: 6,000.

541 JPN ISSN 0910-6774

➤ **HANDAI KAGAKU NETSUGAKU REPOTO/OSAKA UNIVERSITY. RESEARCH CENTER FOR MOLECULAR THERMODYNAMICS. ANNUAL REPORT.** Text in English, Japanese; Summaries in English. 1984. a., latest vol.21. 300 p./no.; **Document type:** *Academic/Scholarly.*
—**CCC.**
Published by: Osaka Daigaku, Rigakubu, Fuzoku Bunshi Netsurikigaku/Osaka University, Faculty of Science, Research Center for Molecular Thermodynamics, 1-1 Machikaneyama-cho, Toyonaka-shi, Osaka-fu 560-0043, Japan. TEL 81-6-6850-5523, FAX 81-6-6850-5526, sorai@chem.sci.osaka-u.ac.jp. R&P Michio Sorai. Circ: 1,000.

541 RUS ISSN 0018-1439
QD601.A1 CODEN: HIECAP

➤ **HIGH ENERGY CHEMISTRY.** Text in English. 1967. bi-m. EUR 3,348, USD 2,998, GBP 2,088 combined subscription to institutions print & online eds. (effective 2005). back issues avail. **Document type:** *Journal, Academic/Scholarly.* **Description:** Publishes theoretical papers and reports on experimental studies in radiation chemistry, photochemistry, plasma chemistry, laser chemistry, and related areas.
Related titles: Microfilm ed.: (from PQC); Online - full text ed.: ISSN 1608-3148 (from EBSCO Publishing, Gale Group, IngentaConnect, Kluwer Online, O C L C Online Computer Library Center, Inc., Springer LINK, Swets Information Services); ♦ Translation of: Khimiya Vysokikh Energii. ISSN 0023-1193.
Indexed: BibLing, BiolDig, CCI, CIN, Cadscan, ChemAb, ChemTitl, CurCont, EnerRA, EngInd, ISR, LeadAb, MSB, RCI, SCI, Zincscan.
—BLDSC (0412.086500), CASDDS, CISTI, IDS, IE, Infotrieve, ingenta. **CCC.**
Published by: (Rossiiskaya Akademiya Nauk/Russian Academy of Sciences), M A I K Nauka - Interperiodica, Profsoyuznaya ul 90, Moscow, 117997, Russian Federation. TEL 7-095-3347420, FAX 7-095-3360666, compmg@maik.ru, http://www.maik.rssi.ru/journals/highen.htm, http://www.maik.ru. Ed. Mikhail Alfimov. **Subscr. to:** Springer-Verlag Dordrecht, Journals Department, PO Box 322, Dordrecht, Netherlands. TEL 31-78-6576392, FAX 31-78-6576474.

541.39 USA ISSN 1093-3611
TA417.7.H55 CODEN: HTMPFG

➤ **HIGH TEMPERATURE MATERIAL PROCESSES**; an international journal. Text in English. q. USD 108 to individuals; USD 480 to institutions (effective 2005). **Document type:** *Journal, Academic/Scholarly.* **Description:** Covers the engineering aspects of high-temperature science, chemistry, material science, energy technology, metallurgy, physics, and spectroscopy.
Related titles: Online - full text ed.: (from EBSCO Publishing).
Indexed: ApMecR, BrCerAb, C&ISA, CerAb, CivEngAb, CorrAb, CurCont, E&CAJ, EMA, IAA, M&TEA, MBF, METADEX, MSCI, SolStAb, WAA.
—BLDSC (4307.367600), CISTI, IDS, IE, ingenta, Linda Hall. **CCC.**
Published by: Begell House Inc., 145 Madison Ave, New York, NY 10016-6717. TEL 212-795-1999, FAX 212-213-8368, amouroux@ext.jussieu.fr, begellhouse@worldnet.att.net, http://www.begellhouse.com/htmp/htmp.html. Eds. Jacques Amouroux, Pierre Fauchais. **Subscr. to:** PO Box 176, Congers, NY 10920.

➤ **HIGH TEMPERATURES - HIGH PRESSURES.** see *PHYSICS—Heat*

541.37 JPN ISSN 0915-8170

HOKKAIDO UNIVERSITY. CATALYSIS RESEARCH CENTER. ANNUAL REPORT (YEAR)/HOKKAIDO DAIGAKU SHOKUBAI KAGAKU KENKYU CENTER NENPO. Text in English, Japanese. 1989. a. free. **Description:** Provides information concerning activities of the institute.
Formerly (until 1989): Hokkaido University. Catalysis Research Center. Annual Report (0911-6664)
—BLDSC (1140.870000), Linda Hall.
Published by: Hokkaido University, Catalysis Research Center, Kita-11, Nishi-10, Kita-ku, Sapporo, 060, Japan. TEL 81-11-716-2111, FAX 81-11-709-4748, kyodo@cat.hokudai.ac.jp, http://www.hokudai.ac.jp/catalyl/index.eng.html. Ed. Matsushima Tatsuo. Circ: 1,000.

541 JPN

HOSHASEN KAGAKU TORONKAI KOEN YOSHISHU/ PROCEEDINGS OF SYMPOSIUM ON RADIATION CHEMISTRY. Text in English, Japanese. 1957. a. **Document type:** *Proceedings.*
Published by: Nihon Hoshasen Kagakkai/Japanese Society of Radiation Chemistry, Nihon Genshiryoku Kenkyujo Takasaki Kenkyujo, 1233 Watanuki-Machi, Takasaki-shi, Gunma-ken 370-1207, Japan.

546 541.39 USA ISSN 1028-6624
QD502.5 CODEN: IORMA3

INORGANIC REACTION MECHANISMS. Text in English. q. EUR 95 in Europe to individuals; JPY 15,932 in Japan to individuals; USD 90 elsewhere to individuals; EUR 412 combined subscription in Europe to institutions print & online; JPY 52,286 combined subscription in Japan to institutions print & online; USD 426 combined subscription elsewhere to institutions print & online (effective 2005). charts; illus. index. 80 p./no.; **Document type:** *Journal, Academic/Scholarly.* **Description:** Contains original papers reporting the results of original significant studies in the general area of kinetics and mechanisms of inorganic reactions in solution, and also of studies designed to define reaction pathways or mechanisms via detection and characterisation of intermediates by spectroscopic or structural means.
Related titles: Online - full text ed.: (from EBSCO Publishing, Gale Group, IngentaConnect, O C L C Online Computer Library Center, Inc., Swets Information Services); Print ed.: ISSN 1607-8470. 199?.
Indexed: CCI, ChemAb, CurCont.
—BLDSC (4515.887500), CASDDS, IE, Infotrieve, Linda Hall. **CCC.**
Published by: (Royal Society of Chemistry GBR), Old City Publishing, Inc., 628 N 2nd St, Philadelphia, PA 19123. TEL 215-925-4390, FAX 215-925-4371, info@oldcitypublishing.com, http://www.oldcitypublishing.com/IRM/IRM.html. Eds. Geoffrey A Lawrence TEL 61-2-49215444, Peter Moore TEL 44-2476-523236, Robert I Haines TEL 902-566-0698.

546.5 541.39 USA ISSN 0073-8077
QD156 CODEN: INSYA3

➤ **INORGANIC SYNTHESES SERIES.** Text in English. 1939. irreg., latest vol.33, 2002. USD 105 per vol. (effective 2005). adv. bk.rev. index, cum.index: vols.1-10 in vol.10. **Document type:** *Monographic series, Academic/Scholarly.*
Indexed: ASCA, CCI, CIN, ChemAb, ChemTitl, ISR, RCI, SCI.
—BLDSC (4515.900000), CASDDS, CISTI, IE, ingenta.
Published by: (American Chemical Society), John Wiley & Sons, Inc., 111 River St, Hoboken, NJ 07030-5774. TEL 201-748-6000, 800-825-7550, FAX 201-748-5915, uscs-wis@wiley.com, http://www.wiley.com/WileyCDA/WileyTitle/productCd-0471208256.html. Ed. Dimitri Coucouvanis.

541 USA ISSN 0147-1503
QD541 CODEN: ISDMAT

INTERNATIONAL DATA SERIES. SELECTED DATA ON MIXTURES. SERIES A. THERMODYNAMIC PROPERTIES OF NON-REACTING BINARY SYSTEMS OF ORGANIC SUBSTANCES. Text in English. 1973. q. USD 1,200. **Document type:** *Academic/Scholarly.* **Description:** Data on the thermodynamic properties of organic substances.
Indexed: BrCerAb, C&ISA, CIN, CerAb, ChemAb, ChemTitl, CivEngAb, CorrAb, E&CAJ, EMA, IAA, M&TEA, MBF, METADEX, RefZh, SolStAb, WAA.
—BLDSC (4539.503000), CASDDS, CISTI, IE, ingenta. **CCC.**
Published by: Thermodynamics Research Center, Texas Engineering Experiment Station, TEES Headquarters, 3577 TAMU, College Station, TX 77843-3577. TEL 409-845-4940, FAX 409-847-8590, info@trchpl.tamu.edu, mmartell@tamu.edu, http://trcweb.tamu.edu, http://tees.tamu.edu/. Pub. Kenneth N Marsh. Circ: 128.

541 USA ISSN 0538-8066
QD501 CODEN: IJCKBO

➤ **INTERNATIONAL JOURNAL OF CHEMICAL KINETICS.** Text in English. 1968. m. USD 3,650 domestic to institutions; USD 3,794 in Canada & Mexico to institutions; USD 3,878 elsewhere to institutions; USD 4,015 combined subscription domestic to institutions print & online eds.; USD 4,159 combined subscription in Canada & Mexico to institutions print & online eds.; USD 4,243 combined subscription elsewhere to institutions print & online eds. (effective 2006). adv. bk.rev. index. back issues avail.; reprint service avail. from PQC. **Document type:** *Journal, Academic/Scholarly.* **Description:** Covers quantitative relationships between molecular structure and chemical activity, organic and inorganic chemistry, biochemical kinetics, reaction mechanisms, and surface kinetics.
Formerly: International Board Of Chemical Kinetics
Related titles: Microform ed.: (from PQC); Online - full content ed.: ISSN 1097-4601. 1996. USD 3,650 to institutions (effective 2006); Online - full text ed.: (from EBSCO Publishing, Swets Information Services, Wiley InterScience).

Indexed: AESIS, ASCA, BPRC&P, BiolAb, C&ISA, CCI, CEABA, CIN, ChemAb, ChemInfo, ChemTitl, CurCont, E&CAJ, EngInd, ExcerpMed, ISR, LHB, MSB, RCI, RefZh, SCI, SolStAb.
—BLDSC (4542.165000), CASDDS, CISTI, Ei, IDS, IE, Infotrieve, ingenta, Linda Hall. **CCC.**
Published by: John Wiley & Sons, Inc., 111 River St, Hoboken, NJ 07030-5774. TEL 201-748-6000, FAX 201-748-5915, uscs-wis@wiley.com, http://www3.interscience.wiley.com/cgi-bin/jhome/5000443, http://www.wiley.com. Ed. Wing Tsang. adv.: B&W page USD 1,080, color page USD 2,420; trim 8.25 x 11. Circ: 600 (paid). **Subscr. outside the Americas to:** John Wiley & Sons Ltd., The Atrium, Southern Gate, Chichester, West Sussex PO19 8SQ, United Kingdom. TEL 44-1243-843335, 0800-243407, FAX 44-1243-843232, cs-journals@wiley.co.uk.

541.35 EGY
INTERNATIONAL JOURNAL OF PHOTOENERGY. Text in English. s-a. USD 295 domestic to libraries; USD 334 foreign to libraries; USD 135 combined subscription domestic to individuals print & online eds.; USD 174 combined subscription foreign to individuals print & online eds.; USD 354 combined subscription domestic to libraries print & online eds.; USD 393 combined subscription foreign to libraries print & online eds. (effective 2004). back issues avail. **Document type:** *Journal, Academic/Scholarly.* **Description:** Consolidates research activities in chemistry, physics and technology of photochemistry, photophysics, photobiology and solar energy utilization into a single and unique forum for discussing and sharing knowledge and experience between researchers, scientists and engineers interested in exploring the applications of these state-of-the-art topics and up-to-date research results and news.
Related titles: Online - full text ed.: ISSN 1110-662X. 1999.
—BLDSC (4542.458500).
Published by: Ain Shams University, Faculty of Science, The Photoenergy Center, Abbassia, Cairo, Egypt. TEL 20-22-6347683, FAX 20-22-24845941, ijp@photoenergy.org, http://www.photoenergy.org/ijp.

541 GBR ISSN 0144-235X
QD450 CODEN: IRPCDL
➤ **INTERNATIONAL REVIEWS IN PHYSICAL CHEMISTRY.** Text in English. 1981-1984; resumed 1985. q. GBP 774, USD 1,278 combined subscription to institutions print & online eds. (effective 2006). adv. bk.rev. bibl.; charts; illus. index. back issues avail.; reprint service avail. from PSC. **Document type:** *Journal, Academic/Scholarly.* **Description:** Presents scholarly and critical reviews on important and developing aspects of modern physical chemistry and chemical physics. Provides a means by which to assist specialists and generalists in research, industry and teaching so they can keep abreast of advances in expanding subjects.
Related titles: Online - full text ed.: ISSN 1366-591X. GBP 735, USD 1,214 to institutions (effective 2006) (from EBSCO Publishing, Gale Group, IngentaConnect, O C L C Online Computer Library Center, Inc., Swets Information Services).
Indexed: ASCA, CCI, CIN, ChemAb, ChemTitl, CurCont, EngInd, ISR, RefZh, SCI.
—BLDSC (4547.440000), CASDDS, CISTI, Ei, IDS, IE, Infotrieve, ingenta, Linda Hall. **CCC.**
Published by: Taylor & Francis Ltd (Subsidiary of: Taylor & Francis Group), 4 Park Sq, Milton Park, Abingdon, OX14 4RN, United Kingdom. TEL 44-1235-828600, FAX 44-1235-829000, info@tandf.co.uk, http://www.tandf.co.uk/journals/titles/0144235X.asp. Eds. Jeremy M Hutson, Roger E Miller. **Subscr. in N. America to:** Taylor & Francis Inc., Customer Services Dept, 325 Chestnut St, 8th Fl, Philadelphia, PA 19106. TEL 215-625-8900, 800-354-1420, FAX 215-625-8914, customerservice@taylorandfrancis.com; **Subscr. to:** Journals Customer Service, Rankine Rd, Basingstoke, Hants RG24 8PR, United Kingdom. TEL 44-1256-813000, FAX 44-1256-330245, enquiry@tandf.co.uk.

541 USA
INTERNATIONAL THERMODYNAMIC TABLES OF THE FLUID STATE. Variant title: I U P A C International Thermodynamic Tables of the Fluid State. Text in English. irreg., latest vol.12, 1993. **Document type:** *Monographic series.*
Published by: (International Union of Pure and Applied Chemistry), C R C Press, LLC (Subsidiary of: Taylor & Francis Group), 2000 N W Corporate Blvd, Boca Raton, FL 33431. TEL 800-272-7737, journals@crcpress.com, http://www.crcpress.com/.

547.13 GBR
INTERNET PHOTOCHEMISTRY AND PHOTOBIOLOGY. Text in English. m. bk.rev. **Document type:** *Academic/Scholarly.* **Description:** Aims to promote the use of the Internet in the communication of research and education in all areas of photochemistry and photobiology.
Media: Online - full text.
Published by: North East Wales Institute, N E Wales Institute, 19 Mold Rd, Wrexham, LL11 2AW, United Kingdom. TEL 44-1978-293372, FAX 44-1978-290008, paul@infochem.co.uk, http://www.photobiology.com. Ed. Paul Heelis.

541.372 USA ISSN 0092-0193
QD561 CODEN: IESEBH
➤ **ION EXCHANGE AND SOLVENT EXTRACTION**; a series of advances. Text in English. 1966. irreg., latest vol.16, 2004. USD 235 per vol. (effective 2004). adv. illus. **Document type:** *Monographic series, Academic/Scholarly.*
Formed by the 1973 merger of: Ion Exchange: A Series of Advances (0075-0328); Solvent Extraction Reviews
Related titles: Microform ed.: (from RPI).
Indexed: CCI, CIN, ChemAb, ChemTitl.
—BLDSC (4564.390000), CASDDS, CISTI, Linda Hall. **CCC.**
Published by: Marcel Dekker Inc. (Subsidiary of: Taylor & Francis Group), 270 Madison Ave, New York, NY 10016-0602. TEL 212-696-9000, FAX 212-685-4540, journals@dekker.com, http://www.dekker.com. Eds. Arup K. SenGupta, Yizhak Marcus. R&P Julia Mulligan. Adv. contact Eridania Perez. **Subscr. to:** 6000 Broken Sound Pkwy NW, Ste. 300, Boca Raton, FL 33487-2713. TEL 800-228-1160.

541 NLD ISSN 0924-4875
CODEN: JSQCA7
➤ **JERUSALEM SYMPOSIA ON QUANTUM CHEMISTRY AND BIOCHEMISTRY.** Text in English. 1969. irreg., latest vol.27, 1995. price varies. **Document type:** *Proceedings, Academic/Scholarly.*
Indexed: BiolAb, CIN, ChemAb, ChemTitl, EngInd.
—CASDDS.
Published by: (Israel Academy of Sciences and Humanities ISR, Section on Sciences ISR), Springer-Verlag Dordrecht (Subsidiary of: Springer Science+Business Media), Van Godewijckstraat 30, Dordrecht, 3311 GX, Netherlands. TEL 31-78-6576050, FAX 31-78-6576474, http://www.springeronline.com.

➤ **JOURNAL OF ADHESION.** see *PHYSICS*

541 CAN ISSN 1203-8407
TD192.45 CODEN: JAOTFT
➤ **JOURNAL OF ADVANCED OXIDATION TECHNOLOGIES.** Short title: J A O T s. Text in English. 1996-2000; resumed 2001. s-a. USD 280 (effective 2004). **Document type:** *Journal, Academic/Scholarly.* **Description:** Provides an international forum that accepts papers describing basic research and practical applications of advanced oxidation technologies.
Indexed: CCI.
—BLDSC (4918.947200), CASDDS, CISTI, IE, ingenta. **CCC.**
Published by: Science & Technology Integration, Inc., 34 University Plaza Dr, PO Box 63001, Dundas, ON L9H 4H0, Canada. TEL 905-529-9291, FAX 905-529-9985, info@JAOTs.net, http://www.jaots.net. Ed. Detlef W Bahnemann.

➤ **JOURNAL OF BIOMOLECULAR N M R.** (Nuclear Magnetic Resonance) see *BIOLOGY—Biochemistry*

541.395 660 USA ISSN 0021-9517
QD501 CODEN: JCTLA5
➤ **JOURNAL OF CATALYSIS.** Text in English. 1962. 16/yr. EUR 770 in Europe to individuals; JPY 80,600 in Japan to individuals; USD 596 elsewhere to individuals; EUR 5,587 in Europe to institutions; JPY 583,300 in Japan to institutions; USD 4,390 elsewhere to institutions (effective 2006). adv. bibl.; charts; illus. index. back issues avail. **Document type:** *Journal, Academic/Scholarly.* **Description:** Publishes original studies in heterogeneous and homogeneous catalysis as well as studies relating catalytic properties with chemical processes at surface, studies of the chemistry of surfaces, and engineering studies related to catalysis.
Related titles: Online - full text ed.: ISSN 1090-2694. USD 4,559 (effective 2002) (from EBSCO Publishing, Gale Group, IngentaConnect, O C L C Online Computer Library Center, Inc., ScienceDirect, Swets Information Services).
Indexed: AESIS, APIAb, APICat, APIH&E, APIOC, APIPR, APIPS, APITS, AS&TI, ASCA, BiolAb, CCI, CEA, CEABA, CIN, ChemAb, ChemInfo, ChemTitl, CurCont, EngInd, ExcerpMed, GasAb, INIS AtomInd, ISR, MSB, MSCI, RCI, RefZh, SCI, TCEA.
—BLDSC (4954.890000), CASDDS, CISTI, Ei, IDS, IE, Infotrieve, ingenta, Linda Hall. **CCC.**
Published by: Academic Press (Subsidiary of: Elsevier Science & Technology), 525 B St, Ste 1900, San Diego, CA 92101-4495. TEL 619-231-6616, 800-894-3434, FAX 619-699-6422, apsubs@acad.com, http://www.elsevier.com/locate/jcat, http://www.academicpress.com. Ed. E. Inglesia.

➤ **JOURNAL OF CHEMICAL PHYSICS.** see *PHYSICS*

541.36 GBR ISSN 0021-9614
QD501 CODEN: JCTDAF
➤ **THE JOURNAL OF CHEMICAL THERMODYNAMICS.** Text in English. 1969. 12/yr. EUR 2,183 in Europe to institutions; JPY 236,000 in Japan to institutions; USD 1,942 elsewhere to institutions (effective 2006). adv. reprints avail. **Document type:** *Academic/Scholarly.* **Description:** Reports the results of significant new measurements of thermodynamical and equilibrium quantities for chemical reactions and of thermodynamic properties of pure substances and of mixtures, using calorimetric, (P, V, T), spectroscopic, and other methods.
Related titles: Online - full text ed.: ISSN 1096-3626. USD 2,048 (effective 2002) (from EBSCO Publishing, Gale Group, IngentaConnect, O C L C Online Computer Library Center, Inc., ScienceDirect, Swets Information Services).
Indexed: APIAb, ASCA, BullT&T, CCI, CEABA, CIN, Cadscan, ChemAb, ChemInfo, ChemTitl, CurCont, EngInd, GasAb, INIS AtomInd, ISR, Inspec, LeadAb, MSB, RCI, RefZh, S&F, SCI, Zincscan.
—BLDSC (4957.100000), AskIEEE, CASDDS, CISTI, Ei, IDS, IE, Infotrieve, ingenta, Linda Hall. **CCC.**
Published by: Academic Press (Subsidiary of: Elsevier Science & Technology), 24-28 Oval Rd, London, NW1 7DX, United Kingdom. TEL 44-20-7267-4466, FAX 44-20-7482-2293, apsubs@acad.com, http://www.elsevier.com/locate/jct. Eds. A R H Goodwin, J P M Trusler, R. D. Weir.

541 GBR
JOURNAL OF COLLECTIVE CHEMISTRY AND PHYSICS✶ . Text in English. 1952. s-a. (in double nos.). USD 21. adv. abstr.; bibl.; charts; illus.; pat.
Formerly: Journal of Detergents and Collective Chemistry and Physics (0022-0361)
Address: Drs. L. Zakarias & J. Zakarias, 7 Downside Rd, Bristol, Glos BS8 2XE, United Kingdom.

541.345 USA ISSN 0021-9797
QD549 CODEN: JCISA5
➤ **JOURNAL OF COLLOID AND INTERFACE SCIENCE.** Text in English. 1946. 24/yr. EUR 2,565 in Europe to individuals; JPY 267,800 in Japan to individuals; USD 2,012 to individuals except Europe and Japan; EUR 5,510 in Europe to institutions; JPY 575,400 in Japan to institutions; USD 4,321 to institutions except Europe and Japan (effective 2006). adv. bk.rev. illus. index. back issues avail. **Document type:** *Journal, Academic/Scholarly.* **Description:** Publishes original research on fundamental principles and applications of colloids.
Formerly: Journal of Colloid Science (0095-8522)
Related titles: Online - full text ed.: ISSN 1095-7103. USD 4,493 (effective 2002) (from EBSCO Publishing, Gale Group, IngentaConnect, O C L C Online Computer Library Center, Inc., ScienceDirect, Swets Information Services).
Indexed: ABIPC, AEA, AESIS, APIAb, APICat, APIH&E, APIOC, APIPR, APIPS, APITS, ASCA, ASFA, AbHyg, ApMecR, B&BAb, BibAg, BioCN&I, BioEngAb, BiolAb, BrCerAb, C&ISA, CCI, CEA, CEABA, CIN, CPA, CerAb, ChemAb, ChemTitl, CorrAb, CurCont, DSA, E&CAJ, E&PHSE, EIA, EMA, EngInd, ExcerpMed, FCA, FPA, FS&TA, GP&P, HortAb, I&DA, IAA, INIS AtomInd, ISR, Inspec, MEDLINE, MSCI, NutrAb, OffTech, P&BA, PGrRegA, PetrolAb, PhotoAb, PhysBer, ProtozoAb, RAPRA, RCI, RM&VM, RPP, RefZh, S&F, SCI, SIA, SolStAb, SoyAb, TCEA, TriticAb, WAA, WSCA, WeedAb.
—BLDSC (4958.900000), CASDDS, CINDOC, CISTI, Ei, IDS, IE, Infotrieve, ingenta, Linda Hall, PADDS. **CCC.**
Published by: Academic Press (Subsidiary of: Elsevier Science & Technology), 525 B St, Ste 1900, San Diego, CA 92101-4495. TEL 619-231-6616, 800-894-3434, FAX 619-699-6422, apsubs@acad.com, http://www.elsevier.com/locate/jcis, http://www.academicpress.com. Ed. Darsh T. Wasan.

541 USA ISSN 0193-2691
QD549 CODEN: JDTEDS
➤ **JOURNAL OF DISPERSION SCIENCE AND TECHNOLOGY.** Text in English. 1980. 8/yr. GBP 1,164, USD 1,921 combined subscription to institutions print & online eds. (effective 2006). adv. reprint service avail. from PSC. **Document type:** *Journal, Academic/Scholarly.* **Description:** Deals with dispersions on the technological level.
Related titles: Microform ed.: (from RPI); Online - full text ed.: ISSN 1532-2351. GBP 1,106, USD 1,825 to institutions (effective 2006) (from EBSCO Publishing, O C L C Online Computer Library Center, Inc., Swets Information Services).
Indexed: APIAb, APIOC, ASCA, B&BAb, BIOSIS Prev, BiolAb, CCI, CEA, CEABA, CIN, ChemAb, ChemTitl, CurCont, DSA, EngInd, FLUIDEX, FS&TA, IPA, ISR, MSCI, PetrolAb, PhotoAb, RCI, RefZh, SCI, TCEA, WSCA.
—BLDSC (4969.820000), CASDDS, CISTI, Ei, IDS, IE, Infotrieve, ingenta, Linda Hall, PADDS. **CCC.**
Published by: Taylor & Francis Inc. (Subsidiary of: Taylor & Francis Group), 325 Chestnut St, Ste 800, Philadelphia, PA 19016. TEL 215-625-8900, 800-354-1420, FAX 215-625-2940, info@taylorandfrancis.com, http://www.tandf.co.uk/journals/titles/01932691.asp, http://www.taylorandfrancis.com. Ed. Johan Sjoblom. Adv. contact Sharon Moran. B&W page USD 600. Circ: 400.

541 NLD ISSN 1388-3127
CODEN: JIMCEN
➤ **JOURNAL OF INCLUSION PHENOMENA AND MACROCYCLIC CHEMISTRY.** Text in English. 1983. m. EUR 1,298, USD 1,328, GBP 815 combined subscription to institutions print & online eds. (effective 2005). bk.rev. illus. Index. reprint service avail. from PSC. **Document type:** *Journal, Academic/Scholarly.* **Description:** Publishes primarily reports of original research and preliminary communications, provided the latter represent a significant advance in the understanding of inclusion science. Critical reviews dealing with recent advances in the field are a periodic feature of the journal.
Former titles (until 1999): Journal of Inclusion Phenomena and Molecular Recognition in Chemistry (0923-0750); (until 1989): Journal of Inclusion Phenomena (0167-7861)

C

Related titles: Microform ed.: (from PQC); Online - full text ed.: ISSN 1573-1111 (from EBSCO Publishing, Gale Group, IngentaConnect, Kluwer Online, O C L C Online Computer Library Center, Inc., Ovid Technologies, Inc., Springer LINK, Swets Information Services).
Indexed: ASCA, BibLing, CCI, CIN, ChemAb, ChemTitl, CurCR, CurCont, EngInd, IABS, IBR, IBZ, ISR, IndChem, MSCI, RCI, RefZh, SCI.
—BLDSC (5005.103500), CASDDS, CISTI, Ei, IDS, IE, ingenta, Linda Hall. **CCC.**
Published by: Springer-Verlag Dordrecht (Subsidiary of: Springer Science+Business Media), Van Godewijckstraat 30, Dordrecht, 3311 GX, Netherlands. TEL 31-78-6576050, FAX 31-78-6576474, http://springerlink.metapress.com/openurl.asp?genre=journal&issn=0923-0750, http://www.springeronline.com. Eds. Janusz Lipkowski, John D Lamb.

541 NLD ISSN 0376-7388
TP159.M4 CODEN: JMESDO
➤ **JOURNAL OF MEMBRANE SCIENCE.** Text in Dutch. 1977. 40/yr. EUR 6,359 in Europe to institutions; JPY 844,100 in Japan to institutions; USD 7,115 to institutions except Europe and Japan (effective 2006). bk.rev. illus. Index. reprints avail. **Document type:** *Academic/Scholarly.* **Description:** Presents research on the structure and functions of non-biological membranes, with relevant papers on aspects of biological membranes.
Related titles: Microform ed.: (from PQC); Online - full text ed.: (from EBSCO Publishing, Gale Group, IngentaConnect, ScienceDirect, Swets Information Services).
Indexed: AEBA, ASCA, ASFA, BIOBASE, BioEngAb, BiolAb, C&ISA, CCI, ChemAb, ChemTitl, CivEngAb, CurCont, DSA, E&CAJ, ESPM, EngInd, EnvEAb, ExcerpMed, FLUIDEX, FS&TA, IABS, ISMEC, ISR, Inspec, MSCI, PollutAb, RAPRA, RCI, RefZh, SCI, SIA, SolStAb, VITIS, WRCInf, WTA.
—BLDSC (5017.620000), AskIEEE, CASDDS, CISTI, Ei, GNLM, IDS, IE, Infotrieve, ingenta, Linda Hall. **CCC.**
Published by: Elsevier BV (Subsidiary of: Elsevier Science & Technology), Radarweg 29, Amsterdam, 1043 NX, Netherlands. TEL 31-20-4853911, FAX 31-20-4852457, jms@che.gatech.edu, nlinfo-f@elsevier.nl, http://www.elsevier.com/locate/memsci, http://www.elsevier.nl. Ed. W J Koros.

C

541.395 NLD ISSN 1381-1169
QD505 CODEN: JMCCF2
➤ **JOURNAL OF MOLECULAR CATALYSIS A: CHEMICAL.** Text in English, French, German. 1975. 36/yr. EUR 5,207 in Europe to institutions; JPY 691,900 in Japan to institutions; USD 5,823 elsewhere to institutions (effective 2006). bk.rev. back issues avail. **Document type:** *Journal, Academic/Scholarly.* **Description:** Covers new research in molecular activation in chemical and metal complex catalysis, heterogenous catalysis, and biochemical catalysis.
Supersedes in part (in 1995): Journal of Molecular Catalysis (0304-5102)
Related titles: Microform ed.: (from PQC); Online - full text ed.: (from EBSCO Publishing, Gale Group, IngentaConnect, ScienceDirect, Swets Information Services).
Indexed: APIAb, ASCA, BiolAb, C&ISA, CCI, CEABA, CIN, ChemAb, ChemTitl, CurCont, DSA, E&CAJ, EngInd, ExcerpMed, ISR, MSCI, RCI, RefZh, SCI, SolStAb.
—BLDSC (5020.705050), CASDDS, CISTI, Ei, IDS, IE, Infotrieve, ingenta, Linda Hall. **CCC.**
Published by: Elsevier BV (Subsidiary of: Elsevier Science & Technology), Radarweg 29, Amsterdam, 1043 NX, Netherlands. TEL 31-20-4853911, FAX 31-20-4852457, nlinfo-f@elsevier.nl, http://www.elsevier.com/locate/molcata, http://www.elsevier.nl. Ed. E G Derouane.

541 NLD ISSN 0167-7322
CODEN: JMLIDT
➤ **JOURNAL OF MOLECULAR LIQUIDS.** Text in English, French, German. 1969. 21/yr. EUR 2,584 in Europe to institutions; JPY 343,500 in Japan to institutions; USD 2,890 to institutions except Europe and Japan (effective 2006). adv. bk.rev. illus. back issues avail. **Document type:** *Journal, Academic/Scholarly.* **Description:** Publishes both primary papers and authoritative review articles covering all aspects of molecular liquid processes based on the increasing variety of experimental and theoretical methods now available.
Former titles (until vol.24, 1982): Advances in Molecular Relaxation and Interaction Processes (0378-4487); (until 1976): Advances in Molecular Relaxation Processes (0001-8716)
Related titles: Microform ed.: (from PQC); Online - full text ed.: (from EBSCO Publishing, Gale Group, IngentaConnect, ScienceDirect, Swets Information Services).
Indexed: ASCA, BiolAb, CCI, CIS, ChemAb, ChemTitl, CurCont, EngInd, ISR, Inspec, MSCI, PhysBer, SCI.
—BLDSC (5020.714000), AskIEEE, CASDDS, CISTI, Ei, IDS, IE, Infotrieve, ingenta, Linda Hall. **CCC.**
Published by: Elsevier BV (Subsidiary of: Elsevier Science & Technology), Radarweg 29, Amsterdam, 1043 NX, Netherlands. TEL 31-20-4853911, FAX 31-20-4852457, nlinfo-f@elsevier.nl, http://www.elsevier.com/locate/molliq, http://www.elsevier.nl. Ed. J. Barthel.

541.2 DEU ISSN 1610-2940
CODEN: JMMOFK
➤ **JOURNAL OF MOLECULAR MODELING.** Text in English. 1996. bi-m. EUR 560 combined subscription to institutions print & online eds. (effective 2005). back issues avail. **Document type:** *Journal, Academic/Scholarly.* **Description:** Publishes papers from all areas of molecular modeling, both applications and method development.
Related titles: CD-ROM ed.: Molecular Modeling Annual. ISSN 0949-183X; Online - full text ed.: ISSN 0948-5023 (from EBSCO Publishing, Springer LINK, Swets Information Services).
Indexed: CCI, CurCont, FCA, HelmAb, IndMed, Inpharma, PBA, ProtozoAb, RA&MP, RM&VM, Reac, S&F, TriticAb.
—BLDSC (5020.716480), CASDDS, IDS, IE, Infotrieve. **CCC.**
Published by: (Friedrich-Alexander-Universitaet Erlangen-Nuernberg, Institut fuer Organische Chemie), Springer-Verlag (Subsidiary of: Springer Science+Business Media), Tiergartenstr 17, Heidelberg, 69121, Germany. TEL 49-6221-3450, FAX 49-6221-345229, http://link.springer.de/link/service/journals/00894/index.htm. Ed. Tim Clark. Adv. contact Stephan Kroeck TEL 49-30-827875739. **Subscr. in the Americas to:** Springer-Verlag New York, Inc., Journal Fulfillment, PO Box 2485, Secaucus, NJ 07096-2485. TEL 800-777-4643, 201-348-4033, FAX 201-348-4505, journals@springer-ny.com, http://www.springer-ny.com; **Subscr. to:** Springer GmbH Auslieferungsgesellschaft, Haberstr 7, Heidelberg 69126, Germany. TEL 49-6221-345-0, FAX 49-6221-345-4229, subscriptions@springer.de.

547.13 CHE ISSN 1010-6030
QD701 CODEN: JPPCEJ
➤ **JOURNAL OF PHOTOCHEMISTRY AND PHOTOBIOLOGY, A: CHEMISTRY.** Text in English. 1972. 24/yr. EUR 5,238 in Europe to institutions; JPY 695,500 in Japan to institutions; USD 5,858 elsewhere to institutions; EUR 88 in Europe to qualified personnel; JPY 11,600 in Japan to qualified personnel; USD 100 elsewhere to qualified personnel (effective 2006). adv. bk.rev. illus. index. back issues avail. **Document type:** *Journal, Academic/Scholarly.* **Description:** Concerned with either quantitative or qualitative aspects of photochemistry. Includes papers on applied photochemistry which entails photoinitiation of polymerization, photo cross-linking, photodegradation or photostabilization of polymers, photohalogenation, chemical aspects of photography and the design of photoreactors.
Formerly: Journal of Photochemistry (0047-2670)
Related titles: Microform ed.: (from PQC); Online - full text ed.: (from EBSCO Publishing, Gale Group, IngentaConnect, ScienceDirect, Swets Information Services).
Indexed: ASCA, BPRC&P, CCI, CIN, ChemAb, ChemTitl, CurCont, EngInd, ExcerpMed, GenetAb, ISR, JW-D, MSB, MSCI, PhotoAb, PhysBer, RCI, RefZh, SCI, VITIS.
—BLDSC (5034.840000), CASDDS, CISTI, Ei, IDS, IE, Infotrieve, ingenta, Linda Hall. **CCC.**
Published by: Elsevier S.A., PO Box 564, Lausanne 1, 1001, Switzerland. TEL 41-21-3207381, FAX 41-21-3235444, jphoto@physchem.ox.ac.uk, http://www.elsevier.com/locate/jphotochem. Eds. H. Masuhara, Kazuhito Hashimoto, R. Schmehl. **Subscr. to:** Elsevier BV, PO Box 211, Amsterdam 1000 AE, Netherlands. TEL 31-20-485-3757, FAX 31-20-485-3432, nlinfo-f@elsevier.nl, http://www.elsevier.nl.

547.13 CHE ISSN 1389-5567
QH515 CODEN: JPPCAF
➤ **JOURNAL OF PHOTOCHEMISTRY AND PHOTOBIOLOGY, C: PHOTOCHEMISTRY REVIEWS.** Text mainly in English. 2000. 4/yr. EUR 499 in Europe to institutions; JPY 66,200 in Japan to institutions; USD 558 elsewhere to institutions (effective 2006). back issues avail. **Document type:** *Journal, Academic/Scholarly.* **Description:** Provides a forum for mutual communication among scientists in various fields of photochemistry.
Related titles: Online - full text ed.: (from EBSCO Publishing, Gale Group, IngentaConnect, ScienceDirect, Swets Information Services).
Indexed: CCI, ChemAb, CurCont, JW-D.
—BLDSC (5034.900000), CISTI, IE, Infotrieve, ingenta, Linda Hall. **CCC.**
Published by: Elsevier S.A., PO Box 564, Lausanne 1, 1001, Switzerland. TEL 41-21-3207381, FAX 41-21-3235444, http://www.elsevier.com/locate/jphotochemrev. Ed. Masahiro Irie. **Subscr. to:** Elsevier BV, PO Box 211, Amsterdam 1000 AE, Netherlands. TEL 31-20-485-3757, FAX 31-20-485-3432, nlinfo-f@elsevier.nl, http://www.elsevier.nl.

547.13 KOR ISSN 1225-8555
JOURNAL OF PHOTOSCIENCE. Text in English. 1994. q. **Document type:** *Journal, Academic/Scholarly.*
—BLDSC (5035.330000), IE, ingenta.
Published by: (Prof. Sang Chul /Shim, Ed.), Korean Society of Photoscience, Chungnam National University, Department of Chemistry, 220 Gung-dong, Yuseong-gu, Daejeon, 305-764, Korea, S. http://www.chungnam.ac.kr/english/.

541 USA ISSN 1089-5639
QD450 CODEN: JPCAFH
➤ **THE JOURNAL OF PHYSICAL CHEMISTRY PART A: MOLECULES, SPECTROSCOPY, KINETICS, ENVIRONMENT AND GENERAL THEORY.** Text in English. 1896. w. USD 4,274 in North America to institutions includes Part B; USD 4,964 elsewhere to institutions includes Part B; USD 436 in North America to members; USD 781 elsewhere to members; USD 327 in North America to students; USD 672 elsewhere to students (effective 2006). adv. charts. Index. back issues avail. **Document type:** *Journal, Academic/Scholarly.* **Description:** Reports new experimental and theoretical research dealing with fundamental aspects of physical chemistry and chemical physics.
Supersedes in part (in 1997): Journal of Physical Chemistry (0022-3654); Which was formerly (until 1952): Journal of Physical and Colloid Chemistry (0092-7023); (until 1946): Journal of Physical Chemistry (0092-7325)
Related titles: Microfiche ed.: USD 3,071 in North America to institutions (includes Part B); USD 3,148 elsewhere to institutions (includes Part B) (effective 2002); Microfilm ed.: USD 3,071 in North America to institutions (includes Part B); USD 3,141 elsewhere to institutions (includes Part B) (effective 2002); Online - full text ed.: ISSN 1520-5215. USD 100 includes Part B (effective 2006) (from EBSCO Publishing, Swets Information Services).
Indexed: ABIPC, APIAb, APICat, APIH&E, APIOC, APIPR, APIPS, APITS, AS&TI, ASCA, ASFA, BPRC&P, BrCerAb, CCI, CEA, CIS, CMCI, CTE, Cadscan, ChemAb, ChemInfo, CurCont, DSA, E&PHSE, ESPM, EngInd, FS&TA, GP&P, GSI, IAA, INIS AtomInd, ISR, IndMed, Inspec, LeadAb, M&GPA, MSB, MSCI, OceAb, OffTech, PetrolAb, PhysBer, RAPRA, RCI, RefZh, S&F, SCI, SIA, SWRA, TCEA, WRCInf, Zincscan.
—BLDSC (5036.130000), AskIEEE, CASDDS, CINDOC, CISTI, Ei, IDS, IE, Infotrieve, ingenta, Linda Hall, PADDS. **CCC.**
Published by: American Chemical Society, 1155 16th St, N W, Washington, DC 20036. TEL 202-872-4600, 800-227-5558, FAX 202-776-8264, jphyschm@chem.northwestern.edu, service@acs.org, http://pubs.acs.org/jpca. Ed. George C Schatz. adv.: page USD 1,940. **Subscr. to:** Member & Subscriber Services, PO Box 3337, Columbus, OH 43210. TEL 614-447-3776, 800-333-9511, FAX 614-447-3671.

541 USA ISSN 1520-6106
QD1 CODEN: JPCBFK
➤ **THE JOURNAL OF PHYSICAL CHEMISTRY PART B: CONDENSED MATTER, MATERIALS, SURFACES, INTERFACES & BIOPHYSICAL.** Text in English. 1896. w. USD 4,274 in North America to institutions includes Part A; USD 4,964 elsewhere to institutions includes Part A; USD 512 in North America to members; USD 857 elsewhere to members; USD 384 in North America to students; USD 729 elsewhere to students (effective 2006). adv. charts. index. back issues avail. **Document type:** *Journal, Academic/Scholarly.* **Description:** Reports new and original experimental and theoretical basic research of interest to physical chemists and chemical physicists. Publishes studies on materials, as well as studies on the structure and properties of surfaces and interfaces.
Formerly: The Journal of Physical Chemistry Part B: Materials, Surfaces, Interfaces & Biophysical (1089-5647); Which superseded in part (in 1997): Journal of Physical Chemistry (0022-3654); Which was formerly (until 1952): Journal of Physical and Colloid Chemistry (0092-7023); (until 1946): Journal of Physical Chemistry (0092-7325)
Related titles: Microfiche ed.: USD 3,071 in North America to institutions (includes Part A); USD 3,148 elsewhere to institutions (includes Part A) (effective 2002); Microfilm ed.: USD 3,071 in North America to institutions (includes Part A); USD 3,141 elsewhere to institutions (includes Part A) (effective 2002); Online - full text ed.: ISSN 1520-5207. USD 100 includes Part A (effective 2006) (from EBSCO Publishing, Swets Information Services).
Indexed: APIAb, AS&TI, B&BAb, C&ISA, CCI, CTE, ChemAb, ChemInfo, CurCont, E&CAJ, EngInd, FS&TA, GSI, INIS AtomInd, ISR, Inspec, MSB, PetrolAb, RCI, RefZh, SCI, SolStAb.
—BLDSC (5036.131000), CASDDS, CINDOC, CISTI, IDS, IE, ingenta, Linda Hall, PADDS. **CCC.**
Published by: American Chemical Society, 1155 16th St, N W, Washington, DC 20036. TEL 202-872-4614, 800-227-5558, FAX 202-776-8264, service@acs.org, http://www.pubs.acs.org/jpcb, http://pubs.acs.org. Ed. George C Schatz. **Subscr. to:** Member & Subscriber Services, PO Box 3337, Columbus, OH 43210. TEL 614-447-3776, 800-333-9511, FAX 614-447-3671.

541 547 GBR ISSN 0894-3230
QD476 CODEN: JPOCEE
➤ **JOURNAL OF PHYSICAL ORGANIC CHEMISTRY.** Text in English. 1988. m. USD 2,385 to institutions; USD 2,624 combined subscription to institutions print & online eds. (effective 2006). adv. back issues avail.; reprint service avail. from PSC. **Document type:** *Journal, Academic/Scholarly.* **Description:** Provides an international forum for the rapid publication of original scientific papers dealing with physical organic chemistry in its broadest sense.
Related titles: Microform ed.: (from PQC); Online - full text ed.: ISSN 1099-1395. USD 2,385 to institutions (effective 2006) (from EBSCO Publishing, Swets Information Services, Wiley InterScience).
Indexed: ASCA, CCI, CIN, ChemAb, ChemTitl, CurCont, EngInd, ISR, Inspec, MOS, MSB, RCI, RefZh, SCI.

—BLDSC (5036.211000), AskIEEE, CASDDS, CISTI, Ei, IDS, IE, Infotrieve, ingenta, Linda Hall. **CCC.**
Published by: John Wiley & Sons Ltd. (Subsidiary of: John Wiley & Sons, Inc.), The Atrium, Southern Gate, Chichester, West Sussex PO19 8SQ, United Kingdom. TEL 44-1243-779777, FAX 44-1243-775878, customer@wiley.co.uk, http://www3.interscience.wiley.com/cgi-bin/jhome/4569, http://www.wiley.co.uk. Ed. Joseph B Lambert. adv.: B&W page GBP 595, color page GBP 1,495; trim 200 x 260. Circ. 500. **Subscr. in the Americas to:** John Wiley & Sons, Inc., 111 River St, Hoboken, NJ 07030-5774. TEL 201-748-6645, 800-225-5945, subinfo@wiley.com.

➤ **JOURNAL OF PLANAR CHROMATOGRAPHY - MODERN TLC.** (Thin Layer Chromatography) see *CHEMISTRY—Analytical Chemistry*

541 531   USA   ISSN 0022-4596
QD901   CODEN: JSSCBI
➤ **JOURNAL OF SOLID STATE CHEMISTRY.** Text in English, French, German. 1969. 12/yr. EUR 5,429 in Europe to institutions; JPY 567,100 in Japan to institutions; USD 4,319 elsewhere to institutions; EUR 310 in Europe to qualified personnel; JPY 32,500 in Japan to qualified personnel; USD 248 elsewhere to qualified personnel (effective 2006). adv. bk.rev. abstr.; bibl.; charts. index. back issues avail. **Document type:** *Journal, Academic/Scholarly.* **Description:** Covers developments in the field of solid state chemistry and related areas such as ceramics and amorphous materials. Features studies of chemical, structural, thermodynamic, electronic, magnetic, and optical processes in solids.
Related titles: Online - full text ed.: ISSN 1095-726X. USD 4,458 (effective 2002) (from EBSCO Publishing, Gale Group, IngentaConnect, O C L C Online Computer Library Center, Inc., ScienceDirect, Swets Information Services).
Indexed: AESIS, ASCA, C&ISA, CCI, CIN, Cadscan, CerAb, ChemAb, ChemTitl, CorrAb, CurCont, E&CAJ, EMA, EngInd, INIS AtomInd, ISR, Inspec, LeadAb, MSCI, RCI, RefZh, SCI, SSCI, SolStAb, WAA, Zincscan.
—BLDSC (5065.400000), AskIEEE, CASDDS, CISTI, Ei, IDS, IE, Infotrieve, ingenta, Linda Hall. **CCC.**
Published by: Academic Press (Subsidiary of: Elsevier Science & Technology), 525 B St, Ste 1900, San Diego, CA 92101-4495. TEL 619-231-6616, 800-894-3434, FAX 619-699-6422, apsubs@acad.com, http://www.elsevier.com/locate/jssc, http://www.academicpress.com. Ed. M. G. Kanatzidis.

541.34   USA   ISSN 0095-9782
QD541   CODEN: JSLCAG
➤ **JOURNAL OF SOLUTION CHEMISTRY.** Text in English. 1972. m. EUR 1,395, USD 1,418, GBP 868 combined subscription to institutions print & online eds. (effective 2005). adv. index. back issues avail.; reprint service avail. from PSC. **Document type:** *Journal, Academic/Scholarly.* **Description:** Surveys research on the physical chemistry from several disciplines, including physical chemistry, chemical physics, molecular biology, statistical mechanics, biochemistry, and biophysics.
Related titles: Microfilm ed.: (from PQC); Online - full text ed.: ISSN 1572-8927 (from EBSCO Publishing, Gale Group, IngentaConnect, Kluwer Online, O C L C Online Computer Library Center, Inc., Springer LINK, Swets Information Services).
Indexed: ASCA, BibLing, BiolAb, BrCerAb, C&ISA, CCI, CIN, Cadscan, CerAb, ChemAb, ChemTitl, CivEngAb, CorrAb, CurCont, E&CAJ, EMA, EngInd, IAA, ISR, LeadAb, M&TEA, MBF, METADEX, MSB, PhysBer, RCI, RefZh, S&F, SCI, SolStAb, WAA, Zincscan.
—BLDSC (5065.600000), CASDDS, CISTI, Ei, IDS, IE, Infotrieve, ingenta, Linda Hall. **CCC.**
Published by: Plenum US (Subsidiary of: Springer Science+Business Media), 233 Spring St, New York, NY 10013. TEL 212-460-1500, FAX 212-460-1575, service@springer-ny.com, http://springerlink.metapress.com/openurl.asp?genre=journal&issn=0095-9782, http://www.springeronline.com. Eds. Donald A Palmer, Joseph A Rard.

541.36   HUN   ISSN 1388-6150
QD515   CODEN: JTACF7
➤ **JOURNAL OF THERMAL ANALYSIS AND CALORIMETRY;** an international forum for thermal studies. Text in English, French, German. 1969. m. EUR 4,968, USD 5,058, GBP 3,108 to institutions print or online ed. (effective 2005). adv. bk.rev. abstr.; bibl. index. 350 p./no.; back issues avail.; reprints avail. **Document type:** *Journal, Academic/Scholarly.* **Description:** Papers covering all aspects of thermal analysis, calorimetry and experimental thermodynamics.
Formerly (until 1998): Journal of Thermal Analysis (0368-4466)
Related titles: Microform ed.: (from PQC); Online - full text ed.: ISSN 1572-8943. 1999 (from EBSCO Publishing, Kluwer Online, O C L C Online Computer Library Center, Inc., Springer LINK, Swets Information Services).
Indexed: ASCA, AnalAb, ApMecR, BibLing, BrCerAb, BullT&T, C&ISA, CCI, CIN, Cadscan, CerAb, ChemAb, ChemTitl, CivEngAb, CorrAb, CurCont, E&CAJ, EMA, EngInd, FS&TA, IAA, IBuildSA, ISMEC, ISR, Inspec, LeadAb, M&TEA, MBF, METADEX, MSB, MSCI, RAPRA, RCI, S&F, SCI, SIA, SolStAb, WAA, Zincscan.
—BLDSC (5069.090100), CASDDS, CINDOC, CISTI, Ei, IDS, IE, Infotrieve, ingenta, Linda Hall. **CCC.**

Published by: Akademiai Kiado Rt. (Subsidiary of: Wolters Kluwer N.V.), Prielle Kornelia U. 19, Budapest, 1117, Hungary. TEL 36-1-4648282, FAX 36-1-4648221, journals@akkrt.hu, http://springerlink.metapress.com/openurl.asp?genre=journal&issn=1388-6150, http://www.akkrt.hu. Ed. Judit Simon. adv.: B&W page GBP 595, color page GBP 1,495; trim 169 x 240. **Co-publisher:** Plenum US.

541   RUS   ISSN 0207-401X
QD450   CODEN: KHFID9
KHIMICHESKAYA FIZIKA. Text in Russian. m. RUR 850 for 6 mos. domestic; USD 375 foreign (effective 2004). **Document type:** *Journal, Academic/Scholarly.*
Indexed: ChemAb, ChemTitl, Inspec, MSB, RefZh.
—CASDDS, CISTI, East View, IDS, KNAW, Linda Hall. **CCC.**
Published by: Izdatel'stvo Nauka, Profsoyuznaya ul 90, Moscow, 117864, Russian Federation. TEL 7-095-3347151, FAX 7-095-4202220, secret@naukaran.ru, http://www.maik.ru/cgi-bin/list.pl?page=khimfiz, http://www.naukaran.ru. **US dist. addr.:** East View Information Services, 3020 Harbor Ln. N., Minneapolis, MN 55447. TEL 800-477-1005, FAX 800-800-3839, eastview@eastview.com, http://www.eastview.com.

KHIMIYA VYSOKIKH ENERGII. see *CHEMISTRY*

541   RUS   ISSN 0023-1584
QD501   CODEN: KICAA8
➤ **KINETICS AND CATALYSIS.** Text in English. 1960. bi-m. EUR 3,628, USD 3,298, GBP 2,268 combined subscription to institutions print & online eds. (effective 2005). back issues avail. **Document type:** *Journal, Academic/Scholarly.* **Description:** Presents theoretical and experimental research on heterogeneous and homogeneous kinetics and catalysis.
Related titles: Microfilm ed.: (from PQC); Online - full text ed.: ISSN 1608-3210 (from EBSCO Publishing, IngentaConnect, Kluwer Online, O C L C Online Computer Library Center, Inc., Ovid Technologies, Inc., Springer LINK, Swets Information Services); ◆ Translation of: Kinetika i Kataliz. ISSN 0453-8811.
Indexed: APIAb, ASCA, BibLing, CCI, CEA, CEABA, ChemAb, ChemTitl, CurCont, EnerRA, EngInd, ISR, MSB, MSCI, RCI, SCI, TCEA.
—BLDSC (0415.410000), CASDDS, CISTI, Ei, IDS, IE, Infotrieve, ingenta, Linda Hall. **CCC.**
Published by: (Rossiiskaya Akademiya Nauk/Russian Academy of Sciences), M A I K Nauka - Interperiodica, Profsoyuznaya ul 90, Moscow, 117997, Russian Federation. TEL 7-095-3347420, FAX 7-095-3360666, compmg@maik.ru, http://www.maik.rssi.ru/journals/kincat.htm, http://www.maik.ru. Ed. Vladimir B Kazansky. **Subscr. to:** Springer-Verlag Dordrecht, Journals Department, PO Box 322, Dordrecht, Netherlands. TEL 31-78-6576392, FAX 31-78-6576474.

541   RUS   ISSN 0453-8811
QD501   CODEN: KNKTA4
➤ **KINETIKA I KATALIZ.** Text in Russian. 1960. bi-m. RUR 1,380 for 6 mos. domestic (effective 2004). back issues avail. **Document type:** *Journal, Academic/Scholarly.* **Description:** Presents theoretical and experimental research on heterogeneous and homogeneous kinetics and catalysis.
Related titles: Microfilm ed.: (from PQC); Online - full text ed.: ◆ English Translation: Kinetics and Catalysis. ISSN 0023-1584.
Indexed: ChemTitl, RefZh.
—BLDSC (0088.800000), CASDDS, CISTI, East View, Linda Hall. **CCC.**
Published by: (Rossiiskaya Akademiya Nauk/Russian Academy of Sciences), Izdatel'stvo Nauka, Profsoyuznaya ul 90, Moscow, 117864, Russian Federation. TEL 7-095-3347151, FAX 7-095-4202220, secret@naukaran.ru, http://www.maik.rssi.ru/cgi-bin/list.pl?page=kinkat, http://www.naukaran.ru.

541   JPN   ISSN 0913-4689
KOKAGAKU∗ /PHOTOCHEMISTRY. Text in Japanese; Summaries in English. 1977. a.
Indexed: ChemAb.
—**CCC.**
Published by: Kokagaku Kyokai/Japanese Photochemistry Association, c/o Nagamura Laboratory, Department of Applied Chemistry, Kyushu University, 6-10-1 Hakozaki, Higahi-ku, Fukuoka, 812-8581, Japan. TEL 81-92-6424374, FAX 81-92-6515606, kokagaku@cstf.kyushu-u.ac.jp, http://www.cstf.kyushu-u.ac.jp/jpa/index.html. Ed. Hiroshi Miyasaka.

KOKAGAKU TORONKAI KOEN YOSHISHU/ABSTRACTS OF SYMPOSIUM ON PHOTOCHEMISTRY. see
CHEMISTRY—Abstracting, Bibliographies, Statistics

---

541   USA   ISSN 0743-7463
QD506.A1   CODEN: LANGD5
➤ **LANGMUIR;** the A C S journal of surfaces and colloids. Text in English. 1985. bi-w. USD 3,145 in North America to institutions; USD 3,350 elsewhere to institutions; USD 618 in North America to members; USD 823 elsewhere to members; USD 464 in North America to students; USD 669 elsewhere to students (effective 2006). adv. bk.rev. illus. Index. back issues avail.; reprints avail. **Document type:** *Journal, Academic/Scholarly.* **Description:** Offers broad coverage of all areas of fundamental surface and colloid science. Coverage includes such topics as micelles, visicles, emulsions, gels, surfactants, colloids, crystal growth nucleation, liquid crystals, imaging spectroscopy, electro-chemistry, biological colloids & interfaces, biopolymers, nanostructures, multicomponent systems and materials.
Related titles: Microform ed.; Online - full text ed.: ISSN 1520-5827. USD 85 (effective 2006) (from EBSCO Publishing, Swets Information Services).
Indexed: ABIPC, APICat, APIH&E, APIOC, APIPR, APIPS, APITS, ASCA, B&BAb, C&ISA, CCI, CIN, ChemAb, ChemTitl, CurCont, E&CAJ, EngInd, INIS AtomInd, ISMEC, ISR, Inspec, MSB, MSCI, P&BA, RCI, RefZh, SCI, SIA, SolStAb, VITIS, WSCA.
—BLDSC (5155.686000), CASDDS, CISTI, Ei, IDS, IE, Infotrieve, ingenta, Linda Hall. **CCC.**
Published by: American Chemical Society, 1155 16th St, N W, Washington, DC 20036. TEL 202-872-4600, 800-227-5558, FAX 202-776-8258, service@acs.org, http://pubs.acs.org/langmuir. Ed. David G Whitten. Circ. 1,750. **Subscr. to:** Member & Subscriber Services, PO Box 3337, Columbus, OH 43210. TEL 614-447-3776, 800-333-9511, FAX 614-447-3671.

➤ **LASER FOCUS WORLD BUYERS' GUIDE.** see *PHYSICS—Optics*

541   GBR   ISSN 1522-7235
QH641   CODEN: LUMIFC
➤ **LUMINESCENCE;** journal of biological and chemical luminescence. Text in English. 1987. bi-m. USD 1,560 to institutions; USD 1,716 combined subscription to institutions print & online eds. (effective 2006). adv. back issues avail.; reprint service avail. from PSC. **Document type:** *Journal, Academic/Scholarly.* **Description:** Provides a forum for the publication of original scientific papers, short communications, technical notes and reviews on fundamental and applied aspects of all forms of luminescence.
Formerly (until 1999): Journal of Bioluminescence and Chemiluminescence (0884-3996)
Related titles: Microform ed.: (from PQC); Online - full text ed.: ISSN 1522-7243. USD 1,560 to institutions (effective 2006) (from EBSCO Publishing, Swets Information Services, Wiley InterScience).
Indexed: AEA, AEBA, ASCA, ASFA, AbHyg, AgBio, AnalAb, B&BAb, BBCI, BIOSIS Prev, BioEngAb, BiolAb, CBTA, CEABA, CIN, CPA, CTA, ChemAb, ChemTitl, CurCont, DSA, ESPM, EngInd, FCA, GenetAb, ISR, IndMed, IndVet, Inpharma, Inspec, MEDLINE, NutrAb, PBA, PollutAb, ProtozoAb, RM&VM, Reac, RefZh, RiceAb, SCI, SeedAb, SoyAb, Telegen, VITIS, VetBull, ZooRec.
—BLDSC (5304.782850), AskIEEE, CASDDS, CISTI, Ei, GNLM, IDS, IE, Infotrieve, ingenta, Linda Hall. **CCC.**
Published by: John Wiley & Sons Ltd. (Subsidiary of: John Wiley & Sons, Inc.), The Atrium, Southern Gate, Chichester, West Sussex PO19 8SQ, United Kingdom. TEL 44-1243-779777, FAX 44-1243-775878, customer@wiley.co.uk, http://www3.interscience.wiley.com/cgi-bin/jhome/10009400, http://www.wiley.co.uk. Ed. L J Kricka. adv.: B&W page GBP 650, color page GBP 1,550; trim 210 x 279. **Subscr. in N. America to:** John Wiley & Sons, Inc., 111 River St, Hoboken, NJ 07030-5774. TEL 201-748-6645, 800-225-5945, subinfo@wiley.com.

➤ **MATERIALS CHARACTERIZATION.** see *METALLURGY*

➤ **MATERIALS SCIENCE FORUM.** see *PHYSICS*

541.7 620.1   NLD   ISSN 1387-1811
TP159.M6   CODEN: MIMMFJ
➤ **MICROPOROUS AND MESOPOROUS MATERIALS.** Text in English. 1993. 30/yr. EUR 2,520 in Europe to institutions; JPY 334,800 in Japan to institutions; USD 2,820 elsewhere to institutions; EUR 308 in Europe to qualified personnel; JPY 41,400 in Japan to qualified personnel; USD 344 elsewhere to qualified personnel (effective 2006). pat. back issues avail. **Document type:** *Academic/Scholarly.* **Description:** Publishes research on all aspects of crystalline and amorphous solids such as zeolites, carbon molecular sieves, pillared clays, microporous metal oxides and other related microporous solids, including practical applications of such materials in environmental protection or electronics related processes.
Incorporates (1981-1997): Zeolites (0144-2449); **Formerly:** Microporous Materials (0927-6513)
Related titles: Microform ed.: (from PQC); Online - full text ed.: (from EBSCO Publishing, Gale Group, IngentaConnect, ScienceDirect, Swets Information Services).
Indexed: APIAb, ASCA, C&ISA, CCI, CIN, ChemAb, ChemTitl, CurCont, E&CAJ, EngInd, FLUIDEX, ISR, MSB, MSCI, RCI, RefZh, SCI, SolStAb, WTA.
—BLDSC (5759.731400), CASDDS, CISTI, Ei, IDS, IE, Infotrieve, ingenta, Linda Hall. **CCC.**

C

Published by: (International Zeolite Association), Elsevier BV (Subsidiary of: Elsevier Science & Technology), Radarweg 29, Amsterdam, 1043 NX, Netherlands. TEL 31-20-4853911, FAX 31-20-4852457, nlinfo-f@elsevier.nl, http://www.elsevier.com/locate/micromeso, http://www.elsevier.nl. Ed. M Stocker.

➤ **MOCAXUE XUEBAO/TRIBOLOGY.** see *PHYSICS—Mechanics*

541 GBR ISSN 0026-8976
QC173 CODEN: MOPHAM
➤ **MOLECULAR PHYSICS**; an international journal in the field of chemical physics. Text in English, French, German. 1958. s-m. GBP 3,986, USD 6,575 combined subscription to institutions print & online eds. (effective 2006). adv. bk.rev. bibl.; charts; illus. Index. reprint service avail. from PSC. **Document type:** *Journal, Academic/Scholarly.* **Description:** Contains original research papers on chemical physics, including all aspects of the physics and biophysics of molecules and, particularly, on molecular structure, properties, dynamics and collisions and on the equilibrium, transport and relaxation properties of molecular assemblies.
Related titles: Microform ed.; Online - full text ed.: ISSN 1362-3028. 1996. GBP 3,787, USD 6,246 to institutions (effective 2006) (from EBSCO Publishing, Gale Group, IngentaConnect, O C L C Online Computer Library Center, Inc., Swets Information Services).
Indexed: ASCA, BPRC&P, CCI, CIN, ChemAb, ChemTitl, CurCont, EngInd, IAA, ISR, Inspec, MSB, MSCI, MathR, PhysBer, RefZh, SCI, SSCI.
—BLDSC (5900.820000), AskIEEE, CASDDS, CISTI, Ei, IDS, IE, Infotrieve, ingenta, Linda Hall. **CCC.**
Published by: Taylor & Francis Ltd (Subsidiary of: Taylor & Francis Group), 4 Park Sq, Milton Park, Abingdon, OX14 4RN, United Kingdom. TEL 44-1235-828600, FAX 44-1235-829000, info@tandf.co.uk, http://www.tandf.co.uk/journals/titles/00268976.asp. Eds. Frederic Merkt, Jean-Pierre Hansen, N C Handy, T P Softley. **Subscr. in N. America to:** Taylor & Francis Inc., Customer Services Dept, 325 Chestnut St, 8th Fl, Philadelphia, PA 19106. TEL 800-354-1420, FAX 215-625-8914; **Subscr. to:** Journals Customer Service, Rankine Rd, Basingstoke, Hants RG24 8PR, United Kingdom. TEL 44-1256-813000, FAX 44-1256-330245, enquiry@tandf.co.uk.

541 GBR ISSN 0305-9804
QC762 CODEN: NMRNBE
NUCLEAR MAGNETIC RESONANCE. Text in English. 1972. a., latest vol.32, 2003. GBP 259.50, USD 448 per vol. (effective 2004). charts; illus. index. back issues avail. **Document type:** *Academic/Scholarly.* **Description:** Annual and biennial reports which provides comprehensive coverage of the literature on Nuclear Magnetic Resonance.
Indexed: BIOSIS Prev, CIN, ChemAb, ChemTitl, EngInd.
—BLDSC (6180.902000), CASDDS, CISTI, Ei, IE, ingenta, Linda Hall. **CCC.**
Published by: Royal Society of Chemistry, Thomas Graham House, Science Park, Milton Rd, Cambridge, CB4 0WF, United Kingdom. TEL 44-1223-432360, FAX 44-1223-423623, sales@rsc.org, advertising@rsc.org, http://www.rsc.org/CFbooks/sprindex.cfm?BKC=NM. Ed. G A Webb. **Subscr. to:** Extenza - Turpin, Pegasus Dr, Stratton Business Park, Biggleswade, Beds SG18 8TQ, United Kingdom.

541 JPN ISSN 0078-429X
QD506
OKAYAMA UNIVERSITY. FACULTY OF SCIENCE. RESEARCH LABORATORY FOR SURFACE SCIENCE. REPORTS/OKAYAMA DAIGAKU RIGAKUBU KAIMEN KAGAKU KENKYU SHISETSU HOKOKU. Text in English. 1954. a. free or exchange basis.
Indexed: Inspec.
—AskIEEE, Linda Hall.
Published by: (Research Laboratory for Surface Science), Okayama University, Faculty of Science, 1-1 Tsushima-Naka 3-chome, Okayama-shi, 700-0082, Japan. TEL 0862-52-1111, FAX 0862-52-6601. Ed. M Iwami. Circ: 350.

▼ **ORGANIC & BIOMOLECULAR CHEMISTRY.** see *CHEMISTRY—Organic Chemistry*

ORGANIC REACTION MECHANISMS. ANNUAL SURVEY. see *CHEMISTRY—Organic Chemistry*

ORGANIC REACTIONS. see *CHEMISTRY—Organic Chemistry*

ORGANIC SYNTHESES. see *CHEMISTRY—Organic Chemistry*

ORGANIC SYNTHESES - COLLECTIVE VOLUMES. see *CHEMISTRY—Organic Chemistry*

541 USA ISSN 0030-770X
QD171 CODEN: OXMEAF
➤ **OXIDATION OF METALS**; an international journal of the science of gas-solid reactions. Text in English. 1969. m. EUR 1,678, USD 1,708, GBP 1,048 combined subscription to institutions print & online eds. (effective 2005). adv. back issues avail.; reprint service avail. from PSC. **Document type:** *Journal, Academic/Scholarly.* **Description:** Disseminates research on all aspects of gas-solid reactions.
Related titles: Microfilm ed.: (from PQC); Online - full text ed.: ISSN 1573-4889 (from EBSCO Publishing, Gale Group, IngentaConnect, Kluwer Online, O C L C Online Computer Library Center, Inc., Springer LINK, Swets Information Services).
Indexed: ASCA, BibLing, BrCerAb, C&ISA, CCI, CEABA, CIN, CerAb, ChemAb, ChemTitl, CivEngAb, CorrAb, CurCont, E&CAJ, EMA, ESPM, EngInd, F&EA, IAA, INIS AtomInd, ISR, Inspec, M&TEA, MBF, METADEX, MSB, MSCI, PollutAb, RefZh, SCI, SolStAb, WAA.
—BLDSC (6321.040000), AskIEEE, CASDDS, CISTI, Ei, IDS, IE, Infotrieve, ingenta, Linda Hall. **CCC.**
Published by: Springer-Verlag New York, Inc. (Subsidiary of: Springer Science+Business Media), 233 Spring St, New York, NY 10013. TEL 212-460-1500, FAX 212-460-1575, service@springer-ny.com, http://springerlink.metapress.com/openurl.asp?genre=journal&issn=0030-770X, http://www.springer-ny.com. Ed. D L Douglass. **Subscr. to:** Journal Fulfillment, PO Box 2485, Secaucus, NJ 07096-2485. TEL 201-348-4033, FAX 201-348-4505, journals@springer-ny.com.

541.38 JPN
OYO HOSHASEN KAGAKU SHINPOJUMU KOEN YOSHISHU/PROCEEDINGS OF APPLIED RADIATION CHEMISTRY SYMPOSIUM. Text in Japanese. a. **Document type:** *Proceedings.*
Published by: Nihon Hoshasen Kagakkai/Japanese Society of Radiation Chemistry, Nihon Genshiryoku Kenkyujo Takasaki Kenkyujo, 1233 Watanuki-Machi, Takasaki-shi, Gunma-ken 370-1207, Japan.

547.13 USA ISSN 0031-8655
QD601.A1 CODEN: PHCBAP
➤ **PHOTOCHEMISTRY AND PHOTOBIOLOGY.** Text in English. 1962. 12/yr. (in 2 vols.). USD 605 to institutions; USD 625 combined subscription to institutions print & online eds. (effective 2005). adv. bk.rev. bibl.; charts; illus. back issues avail. **Document type:** *Journal, Academic/Scholarly.* **Description:** Publishes original reports and reviews on current topics in photobiology and in photobiologically relevant photochemistry.
Related titles: CD-ROM ed.; Microfilm ed.: (from PQC); Online - full text ed.: (from bigchalk, BioOne, C S A, EBSCO Publishing, O C L C Online Computer Library Center, Inc., ProQuest Information & Learning).
Indexed: AEA, AMED, ASCA, ASFA, AbHyg, AgBio, Agr, AgrForAb, AnBrAb, B&BAb, BBCI, BIOSIS Prev, BPRC&P, BibAg, BioCN&I, BiolAb, CCI, CPA, ChemAb, ChemTitl, CurCont, DSA, EngInd, ExcerpMed, FCA, FPA, ForAb, GenetAb, HGA, HerbAb, HortAb, IAA, IABS, ISR, IndMed, IndVet, Inpharma, JW-D, MBA, MEDLINE, MS&D, MSB, MaizeAb, NSCI, NemAb, NucAcAb, NutrAb, OrnHort, PBA, PE&ON, PGegResA, PGrRegA, PHN&I, PlantSci, ProtozoAb, RA&MP, RM&VM, RPP, Reac, RefZh, RevApplEntom, RiceAb, S&F, SCI, SIA, SoyAb, TDB, TriticAb, VetBull, WeedAb.
—BLDSC (6465.985000), CASDDS, CISTI, Ei, GNLM, IDS, IE, Infotrieve, ingenta, Linda Hall. **CCC.**
Published by: American Society for Photobiology, BioTech Park, Ste 9, 1021 15th St, Augusta, GA 30901. TEL 706-722-7511, FAX 706-722-7515, phot@allenpress.com, http://phot.allenpress.com/photonline/?request=index-html, http://www.pol-us.net. Ed. J C Scaiano. Adv. contact Sarah A Stephens. Circ: 2,100. **Subscr. to:** Allen Press Inc., PO Box 1897, Lawrence, KS 66044. TEL 785-843-1235, FAX 785-843-1274, orders@allenpress.com, http://www.allenpress.com.

541 MAR ISSN 1114-3800
PHYSICAL & CHEMICAL NEWS. Text in English.
—BLDSC (6475.245000), IE.
Address: 22 Lotissement Dachra, Sidi Moussa, El Jadida, 24000, Morocco. TEL 212-68-504344, FAX 212-23-353454, pcn@iam.net.ma, http://webserver.iam.ma/~pcn/. Ed. Abdelmajid Belafhal.

541 GBR ISSN 1463-9076
QD450 CODEN: PPCPFQ
➤ **PHYSICAL CHEMISTRY CHEMICAL PHYSICS.** Abbreviated title: P C C P. Text in English. 1999. 24/yr. GBP 2,082, USD 3,810 combined subscription print & online eds. (effective 2006). adv. illus. Index. reprints avail. **Document type:** *Journal, Academic/Scholarly.* **Description:** Publishes original work in physical chemistry and chemical physics.
Formed by the merger of (1990-1998): Journal of the Chemical Society. Faraday Transactions (0956-5000); Which was formed by the merger of (1972-1989): Journal of the Chemical Society. Faraday Transactions I (0300-9599); (1972-1989): Journal of the Chemical Society. Faraday Transactions II (0300-9238); Incorporates (1968-1984): Faraday Society. Symposia (0301-5696); Which superseded (1905-1971): Faraday Society Transactions (0014-7672); and (1897-1998): Berichte der Bunsen-Gesellschaft (0940-483X); Which was formerly (until 1980): Berichte der Bunsengesellschaft fur Physikalische Chemie (0005-9021); (until 1962): Zeitschrift fuer Elektrochemie (0372-8382); (until 1951): Zeitschrift fuer Elektrochemie und Angewandte Physikalische Chemie (0372-8323)
Related titles: Online - full text ed.: P C C P Online. ISSN 1463-9084. GBP 1,874, USD 3,429 (effective 2006) (from EBSCO Publishing, O C L C Online Computer Library Center, Inc., Swets Information Services).
Indexed: APIAb, APICat, APIH&E, APIOC, APIPR, APIPS, APITS, ASCA, ASFA, BPRC&P, BiolAb, C&ISA, CCI, CEA, CEABA, CIN, CTE, Cadscan, ChemAb, ChemInfo, ChemTitl, CurCont, E&CAJ, EngInd, ISMEC, ISR, IndChem, Inspec, LeadAb, MSB, RCI, RefZh, S&F, SCI, SIA, SolStAb, Zincscan.
—BLDSC (6475.306000), CINDOC, CISTI, IDS, IE, Infotrieve, ingenta, Linda Hall. **CCC.**
Published by: Royal Society of Chemistry, Thomas Graham House, Science Park, Milton Rd, Cambridge, CB4 0WF, United Kingdom. TEL 44-1223-432360, FAX 44-1223-423623, pccp@rsc.org, sales@rsc.org, advertising@rsc.org, http://www.rsc.org/pccp. Ed. Dr. Susan Weatherby. adv.: page GBP 630. **Subscr. to:** Portland Press Ltd., R S C Distribution Services, Commerce Way, Whitehall Industrial Estate, Colchester CO2 8HP, United Kingdom. TEL 44-1206-226050, FAX 44-1206-226055, sales@rscdistribution.org.

541 USA
➤ **PHYSICAL CHEMISTRY: SCIENCE AND ENGINEERING.** Text in English. 1996. irreg., latest vol.2, 1999. price varies. charts; illus. back issues avail. **Document type:** *Monographic series, Academic/Scholarly.* **Description:** Presents researchers and advanced students in chemistry and chemical engineering with the ideas and results that are most promising for the development of new chemical products and technology.
Published by: Princeton University Press, 41 William St, Princeton, NJ 08540-5237. TEL 609-258-4900, FAX 609-258-6305, http://pup.princeton.edu/catalogs/series/pcse.html. Eds. John M Prausnitz, Leo Brewer. **Subscr. addr. in US:** California - Princeton Fulfillment Services, 1445 Lower Ferry Rd, Ewing, NJ 08618. TEL 800-777-4726, FAX 800-999-1958, orders@cpfs.pupress.princeton.edu. **Dist. addr. in Canada:** University Press Group, 164 Hillsdale Ave E, Toronto, ON M4S 1T5, Canada.; **Dist. addr. in UK:** John Wiley & Sons Ltd., The Atrium, Southern Gate, Chichester, West Sussex PO19 8SQ, United Kingdom.

541 GBR
PHYSICAL ORGANOMETALLIC CHEMISTRY. Text in English. irreg., latest 2002. price varies. **Document type:** *Monographic series, Academic/Scholarly.*
—BLDSC (6475.860000).
Published by: John Wiley & Sons Ltd. (Subsidiary of: John Wiley & Sons, Inc.), The Atrium, Southern Gate, Chichester, West Sussex PO19 8SQ, United Kingdom. TEL 44-1243-779777, FAX 44-1243-775878, customer@wiley.co.uk, http://www.wiley.co.uk. Ed. Marcel Gielen.

PHYSICS AND CHEMISTRY OF LIQUIDS; an international journal. see *PHYSICS—Mechanics*

PLASTICHEM. see *ENGINEERING—Chemical Engineering*

541.36 536 USA ISSN 1540-7489
QD516 CODEN: SYMCAQ
➤ **PROCEEDINGS OF THE COMBUSTION INSTITUTE.** Variant title: International Symposium on Combustion. Proceedings. Text in English. 1928. 2/yr. EUR 638 in Europe to institutions; JPY 84,800 in Japan to institutions; USD 715 to institutions except Europe and Japan (effective 2006). cum.index in 10th and 20th issues. **Document type:** *Proceedings, Academic/Scholarly.* **Description:** Presents papers on applied and theoretical research activities in the industry.
Former titles (until 2000): Symposium (International) on Combustion (0082-0784); (until 1952): Symposium on Combustion and Flame, and Explosion Phenomena (1062-2896); (until 1948): Proceedings of the Symposium on Combustion (1062-2888)
Related titles: Online - full text ed.: (from EBSCO Publishing, ScienceDirect).
Indexed: CIN, ChemAb, ChemTitl, EngInd, ISR, MSB, SCI.
—BLDSC (6681.300000), CASDDS, Ei, IE, ingenta. **CCC.**
Published by: Combustion Institute, 5001 Baum Blvd., Ste. 635, Pittsburgh, PA 15213-1851. TEL 412-387-1366, FAX 412-687-0340, http://www.elsevier.com/locate/proci. Eds. J H Chen, M D Colket, R S Barlow. Circ: 3,500.

541 547 DEU ISSN 0340-255X
QD549 CODEN: PCPSD7
PROGRESS IN COLLOID AND POLYMER SCIENCE. Text in English. 1909. irreg., latest vol.130, 2005. price varies. adv. reprint service avail. from ISI. **Document type:** *Monographic series, Academic/Scholarly.* **Description:** Publishes topic-related volumes in the area of colloid and polymer science and its interdisciplinary interactions.
Formerly (until 1971): Fortschrittsberichte ueber Kolloide und Polymere (0071-8017)
Related titles: Online - full text ed.: ISSN 1437-8027 (from EBSCO Publishing, Swets Information Services); ♦ Supplement to: Colloid and Polymer Science. ISSN 0303-402X.
Indexed: ApicAb, CIN, ChemAb, ChemTitl, CurCont, Inspec, P&BA, RAPRA, WSCA, WTA.
—BLDSC (6867.750000), CASDDS, CISTI, Ei, IE, Infotrieve, ingenta, KNAW, Linda Hall. **CCC.**
Published by: Springer-Verlag (Subsidiary of: Springer Science+Business Media), Haber Str 7, Heidelberg, 69126, Germany. TEL 49-30-82787-448, subscriptions@springer.de, http://www.springer-sbm.de. Ed. Walter Richtering. Circ: 2,000.

C

546.5   USA   ISSN 0079-6662
QD476   CODEN: PPOCA8
➤ **PROGRESS IN PHYSICAL ORGANIC CHEMISTRY.** Text in English. 1963. irreg., latest vol.20, 1993. price varies. **Document type:** *Monographic series, Academic/Scholarly.*
Indexed: CIN, ChemAb, ChemInfo, ChemTitl, ISR.
—CASDDS, CISTI, Linda Hall.
Published by: John Wiley & Sons, Inc., 111 River St, Hoboken, NJ 07030-5774. TEL 201-748-6000, 800-825-7550, FAX 201-748-5915, uscs-wis@wiley.com, http://www.wiley.com. Eds. A Streitwieser Jr., R W Taft.

541.39   GBR   ISSN 1468-6783
QD501   CODEN: PRKNAZ
PROGRESS IN REACTION KINETICS AND MECHANISM. Text in English. 1961. q. GBP 460, USD 733 combined subscription to institutions print & online eds. (effective 2006). index. **Document type:** *Journal, Academic/Scholarly.*
Description: Publishes authoritative review articles on all aspects of chemical kinetics, with particular emphasis on quantitative aspects.
Formerly (until 1999): Progress in Reaction Kinetics (0079-6743)
Related titles: Microfilm ed.: (from PQC); Online - full text ed.: ISSN 1471-406X. GBP 368, USD 586 (effective 2006) (from EBSCO Publishing, Gale Group, IngentaConnect, Swets Information Services).
Indexed: ASCA, BiolAb, CCI, CIN, ChemAb, ChemInfo, ChemTitl, CurCont, EngInd, ISR, MSB, SCI.
—BLDSC (6873.760000), CASDDS, CISTI, Ei, IDS, IE, Infotrieve, ingenta, Linda Hall. **CCC.**
Published by: Science Reviews Ltd., PO Box 314, St Albans, Herts AL1 4ZG, United Kingdom. TEL 44-1727-847322, FAX 44-1727-847323, scilet@scilet.com, http://www.scilet.com/ Chemistry/Kinetics/progress.htm. **Dist. by:** Extenza - Turpin, Pegasus Dr, Stratton Business Park, Biggleswade, Beds SG18 8TQ, United Kingdom. TEL 44-1462-672555, FAX 44-1462-480-947, custservturpin@turpinltd.com, http://www.extenza-turpin.com.

541   GBR   ISSN 0079-6786
QD473   CODEN: PSSTAW
➤ **PROGRESS IN SOLID STATE CHEMISTRY.** Text in English. 1964. 4/yr. EUR 796 in Europe to institutions; JPY 105,500 in Japan to institutions; USD 889 to institutions except Europe and Japan; EUR 86 in Europe to qualified personnel; JPY 11,500 in Japan to qualified personnel; USD 98 to qualified personnel except Europe and Japan (effective 2006). index. **Document type:** *Journal, Academic/Scholarly.* **Description:** Reviews recent advances, with an emphasis on physical properties and structural chemistry.
Related titles: Microfilm ed.: (from PQC); Online - full text ed.: (from EBSCO Publishing, Gale Group, IngentaConnect, ScienceDirect, Swets Information Services).
Indexed: ASCA, CCI, ChemAb, ChemTitl, EngInd, ISR, Inspec, MSB, MSCI, RCI, RefZh, SCI.
—BLDSC (6924.565000), AskIEEE, CASDDS, CISTI, Ei, IDS, IE, Infotrieve, ingenta, Linda Hall. **CCC.**
Published by: Pergamon (Subsidiary of: Elsevier Science & Technology), The Boulevard, Langford Ln, East Park, Kidlington, Oxford OX5 1GB, United Kingdom. TEL 44-1865-843000, FAX 44-1865-843010, http:// www.elsevier.com/locate/pssc. Eds. Armin Reller, M Subramanian. **Subscr. to:** Elsevier BV, PO Box 211, Amsterdam 1000 AE, Netherlands. TEL 31-20-485-3757, FAX 31-20-485-3432, nlinfo-f@elsevier.nl, http://www.elsevier.nl.

541.38   USA   ISSN 1045-845X
QD601.A1   CODEN: RARAE6
➤ **RADIOACTIVITY & RADIOCHEMISTRY;** a journal of applied measurements. Text in English. 1990. q. USD 65 domestic to individuals; USD 115 foreign to individuals; USD 198 foreign to institutions; USD 145 domestic to institutions (effective 2001). adv. 70 p./no. 2 cols./p.; back issues avail. **Document type:** *Journal, Academic/Scholarly.* **Description:** Provides practical information for those working in the field of radioactivity measurements.
Related titles: Online - full text ed.
Indexed: CIN, ChemAb, ChemTitl, EngInd, INIS AtomInd.
—BLDSC (7234.229700), CASDDS, CISTI, Ei, IE, Infotrieve.
Published by: Caretaker Technology, Inc., 1380 Seaboard Industrial Blvd, Atlanta, GA 30318. TEL 404-352-4620, FAX 404-352-0515. Ed., R&P Thetis S McFarland. Adv. contact Cynthia Smith. Circ: 1,200 (paid). **Subscr. to:** PO Box 19656, Atlanta, GA 30325.

541   JPN   ISSN 0441-2516
RADIOACTIVITY SURVEY DATA IN JAPAN. Text in English. 1963. s-a. (in 2 vols.). free. **Document type:** *Government.*
—BLDSC (7234.240000).
Published by: National Institute of Radiological Sciences/Hoshasen Igaku Sogo Kenkyujo, 4-9-1 Anagawa, Chiba, 260, Japan. TEL 043-251-2111, FAX 047-256-9616. Ed. S Sakurai. Circ: 1,300.

541.38   RUS   ISSN 1066-3622
QD601.A1   CODEN: RDIOEO
➤ **RADIOCHEMISTRY.** Text in English. 1959. bi-m. EUR 3,358, USD 3,098, GBP 2,098 combined subscription to institutions print & online eds. (effective 2005). back issues avail.
Document type: *Journal, Academic/Scholarly.* **Description:** Examines the theoretical and applied aspects of radiochemistry.

Formerly (until 1993): Soviet Radiochemistry (0038-576X)
Related titles: Microfilm ed.: (from PQC); Online - full text ed.: ISSN 1608-3288 (from EBSCO Publishing, Gale Group, IngentaConnect, Kluwer Online, O C L C Online Computer Library Center, Inc., Ovid Technologies, Inc., Springer LINK, Swets Information Services); ◆ Translation of: Radiokhimiya. ISSN 0033-8311.
Indexed: BibLing, CCI, ChemAb, ChemTitl, CurCont, ISR, MSB, RCI, SCI.
—BLDSC (0420.716800), CASDDS, CISTI, Ei, IDS, IE, Infotrieve, ingenta. **CCC.**
Published by: (Rossiiskaya Akademiya Nauk/Russian Academy of Sciences), M A I K Nauka - Interperiodica, Profsoyuznaya ul 90, Moscow, 117997, Russian Federation. TEL 7-095-3347420, FAX 7-095-3360666, compmg@maik.ru, http://www.maik.rssi.ru/journals/radchem.htm, http://www.maik.ru. Ed. Boris Myasoedov. **Subscr. to:** Springer-Verlag Dordrecht, Journals Department, PO Box 322, Dordrecht, Netherlands. TEL 31-78-6576392, FAX 31-78-6576474.

541.38   DEU   ISSN 0033-8230
QD601.A1   CODEN: RAACAP
➤ **RADIOCHIMICA ACTA;** international journal for chemical aspects of nuclear science and technology. Text in English. 1962. m. EUR 1,139 domestic; EUR 1,148 foreign; EUR 1,269 combined subscription domestic print & online eds.; EUR 1,278 combined subscription foreign print & online eds.; EUR 108 newsstand/cover (effective 2005). adv. bibl.; charts. back issues avail. **Document type:** *Journal, Academic/Scholarly.*
Description: Publishes original papers and review articles on chemical aspects of nuclear science and technology.
Related titles: Online - full text ed.: (from EBSCO Publishing, Swets Information Services).
Indexed: ASCA, AnalAb, BiolAb, CCI, CIN, ChemAb, ChemTitl, CurCont, EngInd, INIS AtomInd, ISR, Inspec, MSB, MSCI, RCI, RefZh, SCI.
—BLDSC (7234.495000), AskIEEE, CASDDS, CISTI, Ei, IDS, IE, Infotrieve, ingenta, Linda Hall. **CCC.**
Published by: Oldenbourg Wissenschaftsverlag GmbH, Rosenheimer Str 145, Munich, 81671, Germany. TEL 49-89-450510, FAX 49-89-45051204, vertrieb-zs@verlag.oldenbourg.de, http://www.radiochimacta.de, http://www.oldenbourg.de. Circ: 1,000.

541 615.842   RUS   ISSN 0033-8311
QD601.A1   CODEN: RADKAU
➤ **RADIOKHIMIYA.** Text in Russian. 1959. bi-m. USD 289 foreign (effective 2005). index. **Document type:** *Journal, Academic/Scholarly.* **Description:** Examines the theoretical and applied aspects of radiochemistry.
Related titles: ◆ English Translation: Radiochemistry. ISSN 1066-3622.
Indexed: BrCerAb, C&ISA, CIN, CerAb, ChemAb, ChemTitl, CivEngAb, CorrAb, CurCont, E&CAJ, EMA, EngInd, F&EA, INIS AtomInd, M&TEA, MBF, METADEX, RefZh, SolStAb, WAA.
—BLDSC (0139.500000), CASDDS, CISTI, East View, Linda Hall. **CCC.**
Published by: (Rossiiskaya Akademiya Nauk/Russian Academy of Sciences), Izdatel'stvo Nauka, Sankt-Peterburgskoe Otdelenie, Mendeleevskaya liniya 1, St Petersburg, 199034, Russian Federation. TEL 7-812-3286291, bfmyas@pran.ru, http://www.maik.rssi.ru/journals/radchem.htm. Ed. Boris F Myasoedov. **Dist. by:** East View Information Services, 3020 Harbor Ln N., Minneapolis, MN 55447. TEL 800-477-1005, FAX 800-800-3839, eastview@eastview.com, http://www.eastview.com.

➤ **RANLIAO HUAXUE XUEBAO/JOURNAL OF FUEL CHEMISTRY AND TECHNOLOGY.** see *ENGINEERING—Chemical Engineering*

➤ **RANSHAO KEXUE YU JISHU/JOURNAL OF COMBUSTION SCIENCE AND TECHNOLOGY.** see *PHYSICS—Heat*

541   HUN   ISSN 0133-1736
QD502   CODEN: RKCLAU
➤ **REACTION KINETICS AND CATALYSIS LETTERS.** Text in English. 1974. s-a. EUR 1,998, USD 2,038, GBP 1,248 combined subscription to institutions print & online eds. (effective 2005). adv. bk.rev. abstr.; bibl. 200 p./no.; back issues avail. **Document type:** *Journal, Academic/Scholarly.*
Description: Covers kinetics of homogeneous reactions in gas, liquid and solid phase; homogeneous catalysis; heterogeneous catalysis; absorption in heterogeneous catalysis; transport processes related to reaction kinetics and catalysis; preparation and study of catalysts; reactors and apparatus.
Related titles: Microform ed.: (from PQC); Online - full text ed.: ISSN 1588-2837. 1999 (from EBSCO Publishing, Gale Group, IngentaConnect, Kluwer Online, O C L C Online Computer Library Center, Inc., Springer LINK, Swets Information Services).
Indexed: APIAb, ASCA, BibLing, C&ISA, CCI, CIN, ChemAb, ChemTitl, CurCont, E&CAJ, EngInd, ISMEC, ISR, MSCI, RCI, RefZh, SCI, SolStAb.
—BLDSC (7300.268000), CISTI, Ei, IDS, IE, Infotrieve, ingenta, Linda Hall. **CCC.**

Published by: (Magyar Tudomanyos Akademia/Hungarian Academy of Sciences), Akademiai Kiado Rt. (Subsidiary of: Wolters Kluwer N.V.), Prielle Kornelia U. 19, Budapest, 1117, Hungary. TEL 36-1-4648282, FAX 36-1-4648221, journals@akkrt.hu, http://springerlink.metapress.com/ openurl.asp?genre=journal&issn=0133-1736, http://www.akkrt.hu. Ed. L I Simandi. **Co-publisher:** Plenum US.

541   IND
RECENT DEVELOPMENTS IN COLLOIDS & INTERFACE RESEARCH. Text in English. a. **Document type:** *Journal, Academic/Scholarly.*
—BLDSC (7304.112200).
Published by: Transworld Research Network, T C 36-248 (1), Trivandrum, Kerala 695 008, India. http:// www.transworldresearch.com.

541   IND
RECENT RESEARCH DEVELOPMENTS IN CHEMICAL PHYSICS. Text in English. a., latest vol.2, 2001.
—BLDSC (7305.087320).
Published by: Transworld Research Network, T C 36-248 (1), Trivandrum, Kerala 695 008, India. http:// www.transworldresearch.com.

547.13   IND
RECENT RESEARCH DEVELOPMENTS IN PHOTOCHEMISTRY & PHOTOBIOLOGY. Text in English. a., latest vol.5, 2001.
Published by: Transworld Research Network, T C 36-248 (1), Trivandrum, Kerala 695 008, India. http:// www.transworldresearch.com.

541   IND
RECENT RESEARCH DEVELOPMENTS IN PHYSICAL CHEMISTRY. Text in English. a., latest vol.5, 2001.
Indexed: MSB.
—BLDSC (7305.087670).
Published by: Transworld Research Network, T C 36-248 (1), Trivandrum, Kerala 695 008, India.

REFERATIVNYI ZHURNAL. FIZICHESKAYA KHIMIYA: KHIMICHESKAYA TERMODINAMIKA, FIZIKOKHIMICHESKII ANALIZ, RASTVORY, ELEKTROKHIMIYA. see *CHEMISTRY—Abstracting, Bibliographies, Statistics*

REFERATIVNYI ZHURNAL. FIZICHESKAYA KHIMIYA: KINETIKA, KATALIZ, FOTOKHIMIYA, RADYATSIONNAYA KHIMIYA, PLAZMOKHIMIYA. see *CHEMISTRY—Abstracting, Bibliographies, Statistics*

REFERATIVNYI ZHURNAL. FIZICHESKAYA KHIMIYA: KRISTALLOKHIMIYA, KHIMIYA TVERDOGO TELA, GAZY, ZHIDKOSTI, AMORFNYE TELA, POVERKHNOSTNYE YAVLENIYA, KHIMIYA KOLLOIDOV. see *CHEMISTRY—Abstracting, Bibliographies, Statistics*

REFERATIVNYI ZHURNAL. OBSHCHIE VOPROSY KHIMII. FIZICHESKAYA KHIMIYA. STROENIE MOLEKUL. see *CHEMISTRY—Abstracting, Bibliographies, Statistics*

541   NLD   ISSN 1380-6777
QD502   CODEN: RCKIE9
➤ **RESEARCH IN CHEMICAL KINETICS.** Text in English. 1993. irreg., latest vol.3, 1995. price varies. back issues avail. **Document type:** *Monographic series, Academic/Scholarly.* **Description:** Publishes authoritative review articles on a wide range of newly developing topics in the kinetics of both the gaseous and condensed phases.
Indexed: CIN, ChemAb, ChemTitl.
—BLDSC (7734.776000), CISTI, ingenta. **CCC.**
Published by: Elsevier BV (Subsidiary of: Elsevier Science & Technology), Radarweg 29, Amsterdam, 1043 NX, Netherlands. TEL 31-20-4853911, FAX 31-20-4852457, nlinfo-f@elsevier.nl, http://www.elsevier.com/inca/tree/?key= B1RCK, http://www.elsevier.nl. Eds. G Hancock, R G Compton.

➤ **REVIEW OF POLAROGRAPHY/PORAROGURAFI.** see *CHEMISTRY—Analytical Chemistry*

541.345   RUS   ISSN 0023-2912
QD549   CODEN: KOZHAG
ROSSIISKAYA AKADEMIYA NAUK. KOLLOIDNYI ZHURNAL. Text in Russian; Abstracts and contents page in English. 1935. bi-m. RUR 1,300 for 6 mos. domestic (effective 2004). charts; illus. index, cum.index vols. 1-10. **Document type:** *Journal, Academic/Scholarly.* **Description:** Explores the area of chemical science, dealing with the disperse state of matter and surface phenomena.
Related titles: Online - full text ed.; ◆ English Translation: Russian Academy of Sciences. Colloid Journal. ISSN 1061-933X.
Indexed: ABIPC, BrCerAb, CIN, CerAb, ChemAb, ChemTitl, CorrAb, EMA, EngInd, GeotechAb, Inspec, M&TEA, MBF, METADEX, PhysBer, RAPRA, RCI, RefZh, WAA.
—BLDSC (0091.000000), CASDDS, CINDOC, CISTI, East View, IE, Infotrieve, KNAW, Linda Hall. **CCC.**

C

Published by: (Rossiiskaya Akademiya Nauk/Russian Academy of Sciences), Izdatel'stvo Nauka, Profsoyuznaya ul 90, Moscow, 117864, Russian Federation. TEL 7-095-3347151, FAX 7-095-4202220, secret@naukaran.ru, http://www.maik.ru/cgi-bin/list.pl?page=kolzhur, http://www.naukaran.ru. Circ: 2,290.

---

541   GBR   ISSN 0260-1826
QD1   CODEN: ACPCDW
ROYAL SOCIETY OF CHEMISTRY. ANNUAL REPORTS ON THE PROGRESS OF CHEMISTRY. SECTION C: PHYSICAL CHEMISTRY. Text in English. a. GBP 230, USD 420 combined subscription print & online eds. (effective 2006). **Document type:** *Journal, Academic/Scholarly.* **Description:** Provides critical coverage for the general reader of the important advances in physical chemistry.
Supersedes in part: Royal Society of Chemistry. Annual Reports on the Progress of Chemistry. Section A: Physical and Inorganic Chemistry
Related titles: Online - full text ed.: ISSN 1460-4787. GBP 207, USD 378 (effective 2006) (from EBSCO Publishing, O C L C Online Computer Library Center, Inc., Swets Information Services).
Indexed: CIN, ChemAb, ChemTitl, MSB, RefZh.
—BLDSC (1513.850000), CASDDS, CISTI, IE, Infotrieve, Linda Hall. **CCC.**
Published by: Royal Society of Chemistry, Thomas Graham House, Science Park, Milton Rd, Cambridge, CB4 0WF, United Kingdom. TEL 44-1223-432360, FAX 44-1223-423623, sales@rsc.org, advertising@rsc.org, http://www.rsc.org/Publishing/Journals/pc/index.asp. Ed. Dr. Robert D Eagling.
Subscr. to: Portland Press Ltd., R S C Distribution Services, Commerce Way, Whitehall Industrial Estate, Colchester CO2 8HP, United Kingdom. TEL 44-1206-226050, FAX 44-1206-226055, sales@rscdistribution.org.

541.345   RUS   ISSN 1061-933X
QD549   CODEN: CJRSEQ
▶ **RUSSIAN ACADEMY OF SCIENCES. COLLOID JOURNAL.** Key Title: Colloid Journal of the Russian Academy of Sciences. Text in English. 1935. bi-m. EUR 3,278, USD 2,912, GBP 2,048 combined subscription to institutions print & online eds. (effective 2005). back issues avail. **Document type:** *Journal, Academic/Scholarly.* **Description:** Publlishes the results of experimental and theoretical chemical science research into the disperse state of matter and surface phenomena in disperse systems.
Former titles (until 1992): Colloid Journal of the U S S R (0010-1303); (until 1963): Colloid Journal (New York) (0190-4337).
Related titles: Online - full text ed.: ISSN 1608-3067 (from EBSCO Publishing, IngentaConnect, Kluwer Online, O C L C Online Computer Library Center, Inc., Springer LINK, Swets Information Services); ◆ Translation of: Rossiiskaya Akademiya Nauk. Kolloidnyi Zhurnal. ISSN 0023-2912.
Indexed: BibLing, CCI, ChemAb, ChemTitl, CurCont, EngInd, GeotechAb, ISR, Inspec, MSCI, RCI, SCI.
—BLDSC (0410.950000), CASDDS, CISTI, Ei, IDS, IE, Infotrieve, ingenta, Linda Hall. **CCC.**
Published by: (Rossiiskaya Akademiya Nauk/Russian Academy of Sciences), M A I K Nauka - Interperiodica, Profsoyuznaya ul 90, Moscow, 117997, Russian Federation. TEL 7-095-3347420, FAX 7-095-3360666, compmg@maik.ru, http://www.maik.rssi.ru/journals/colljour.htm, http://www.maik.ru. Ed. Nikolai V Churaev. **Subscr. to:** Springer-Verlag Dordrecht, Journals Department, PO Box 322, Dordrecht, Netherlands. TEL 31-78-6576392, FAX 31-78-6576474.

---

541   RUS   ISSN 0036-0244
QD1   CODEN: RJPCAR
RUSSIAN JOURNAL OF PHYSICAL CHEMISTRY. Text in English. 1930. m. USD 4,587 in North America; USD 5,280 elsewhere; USD 5,504 combined subscription in North America print & online eds.; USD 6,336 combined subscription elsewhere print & online eds. (effective 2005). bibl.; charts; illus. **Document type:** *Journal, Academic/Scholarly.* **Description:** Offers a comprehensive review of theoretical and experimental research not only from the Russian Academy of Sciences but also from the entire Commonwealth of Independant States. Articles published concern chemical thermodynamics and thermochemistry, biophysical chemistry, photochemistry and magnetochemistry, materials structure, quantum chemistry, physical chemistry of solutions, and methods and techniques of physicochemical investigations.
Related titles: ◆ Russian ed.: Zhurnal Fizicheskoi Khimii. ISSN 0044-4537; ◆ Translation of: Zhurnal Fizicheskoi Khimii. ISSN 0044-4537.
Indexed: CCI, CEA, CTE, CurCont, EngInd, ISR, Inspec, MSB, PhysBer, RCI, S&F, SCI, TCEA.
—BLDSC (0420.763000), AskIEEE, CISTI, IE, Infotrieve, ingenta, Linda Hall. **CCC.**
Published by: M A I K Nauka - Interperiodica, Profsoyuznaya ul 90, Moscow, 117997, Russian Federation. TEL 7-095-3347420, FAX 7-095-3360666, compmg@maik.ru, http://www.maik.rssi.ru/journals/physchem.htm, http://www.maik.ru. Ed. Valerii V Lunin. R&P Vladimir I Vasil'ev. **Subscr. to:** Interperiodica, PO Box 1831, Birmingham, AL 35201-1831. TEL 205-995-1567, 800-633-4931, FAX 205-995-1588.

---

541   JPN
SEKIGAI RAMAN BUNKENSHU/INFRARED AND RAMAN SPECTROSCOPY. Text in English. 1978. bi-m. JPY 5,000 to individuals; JPY 32,000 to institutions (effective 2000). **Document type:** *Academic/Scholarly.*
Published by: Sekigai Raman Kenkyukai/Raman and Infrared Analysis Committee, c/o Saitama University, Faculty of Science, Dept. of Chemistry, Urawa, Saitama 33-8570, Japan. Ed., R&P, Adv. contact Mitsuo Tasumi. Circ: 200.

---

541   SGP
SERIES ON SYNCHROTRON RADIATION TECHNIQUES AND APPLICATIONS. Text in English. 1995. irreg., latest vol.6. price varies. **Document type:** *Monographic series, Academic/Scholarly.* **Description:** Devoted to techniques using synchrotron light and their applications. Focuses on a particular technique, covering the historical and theoretical background, instrumentation and also giving a comprehensive and up-to-date review of the various applications of the technique.
Published by: World Scientific Publishing Co. Pte. Ltd., 5 Toh Tuck Link, Singapore, 596224, Singapore. TEL 65-466-5775, FAX 65-467-7667, wspc@wspc.com.sg, series@wspc.com.sg, http://www.wspc.com.sg/books/series/ssrta_series.shtml, http://www.worldscientific.com. Eds. D H Bilderback, K O Hodgson, M Kiskinova, R Rosei. **Dist. by:** World Scientific Publishing Co., Inc., 1060 Main St, River Edge, NJ 07661. TEL 201-487-9655, 800-227-7562, FAX 201-487-9656, 888-977-2665; World Scientific Publishing Ltd., 57 Shelton St, London WC2H 9HE, United Kingdom. TEL 44-20-78360888, FAX 44-20-78362020.

---

541   JPN
SHOKUBAI KENKYU KONDANKAI/KANSAI CATALYSIS RESEARCH GROUP. REPORT OF THE MEETING. Text in Japanese. a. membership.
Published by: Shokubai Gakkai, Kansai Chiku/Catalysis Society of Japan, Kansai Branch, Kagaku Gijutsu Senta, 8-4 Utsubohon-Machi 1-chome, Nishi-ku, Osaka-shi, 550-0004, Japan.

---

541   JPN   ISSN 1343-9936
SHOKUBAI TORONKAI, TORONKAI A YOKOSHU∗ . Text in Japanese. 1994. a. JPY 3,500 (effective 2003). **Document type:** *Journal, Academic/Scholarly.*
Formerly (until 1998): Shokubai Kenkyu Happyokai, Shokubai Toronkai A Koen Yokoshu (1342-9620); Which was formed by the merger of (1966-1994): Shokubai Kenkyu Happyokai Koen Yokoshu (0919-6064); (1979-1994): Shokubai Toronkai A Koen Yokoshu
Published by: Shokubai Gakkai/Catalysis Society of Japan, 1-5-3 Kandasurugadai, Chiyodaku, Tokyo, 101-0062, Japan. TEL 81-3-32918224, FAX 81-3-32918225, catsj@pb3.so-net.ne.jp, http://www.shokubai.org/index.html.

SOLID STATE COMMUNICATIONS. see *PHYSICS*

541.35   USA   ISSN 1044-5536
▶ **THE SPECTRUM.** Text in English. 1988. q. **Document type:** *Journal, Academic/Scholarly.* **Description:** Provides scientists with an opportunity to communicate the latest results in the photochemical sciences in an informal format.
Indexed: RefZh.
—BLDSC (8411.158600).
Published by: Bowling Green State University, Center for Photochemical Sciences, 132 Overman Hall, Bowling Green, OH 43403. TEL 419-372-2420, FAX 419-372-0366, http://www.bgsu.edu/departments/photochem/research/spectrum.html, http://www.bgsu.edu/departments/photochem/general/index.html.

▶ **SPRINGER SERIES IN CHEMICAL PHYSICS.** see *PHYSICS*

---

541   NLD   ISSN 0167-6881
    CODEN: SPTCDZ
▶ **STUDIES IN PHYSICAL AND THEORETICAL CHEMISTRY.** Text in Dutch. 1978. irreg., latest vol.87, 2001. price varies. back issues avail. **Document type:** *Monographic series, Academic/Scholarly.* **Description:** Examines research in physical and theoretical chemistry.
Indexed: BIOSIS Prev, BiolAb, CIN, ChemAb, ChemTitl, Inspec.
—BLDSC (8491.222400), CASDDS, CISTI, IE, ingenta. **CCC.**
Published by: Elsevier BV (Subsidiary of: Elsevier Science & Technology), Radarweg 29, Amsterdam, 1043 NX, Netherlands. TEL 31-20-4853911, FAX 31-20-4852457, nlinfo-f@elsevier.nl, http://www.elsevier.nl.

▶ **SULZER TECHNICAL REVIEW.** see *ENGINEERING*

---

541   USA   ISSN 0081-9573
QD506.A1   CODEN: SCOSBX
▶ **SURFACE AND COLLOID SCIENCE.** Text in English. 1969. irreg., latest vol.17, 2004. price varies. **Document type:** *Monographic series, Academic/Scholarly.*
Indexed: ApMecR, CCI, CIN, ChemAb, ChemTitl.
—BLDSC (8547.730000), CASDDS, CISTI, IE, Infotrieve, KNAW, Linda Hall. **CCC.**
Published by: Springer-Verlag New York, Inc. (Subsidiary of: Springer Science+Business Media), 233 Spring St, New York, NY 10013. TEL 212-460-1500, FAX 212-460-1575, service@springer-ny.com, http://www.springer-ny.com. Eds. Egon Matijevic, Michal Borkovec.

▶ **SURFACE SCIENCE.** see *PHYSICS*

▶ **SYMPOSIUM ON RADIOCHEMISTRY. ABSTRACTS OF PAPERS/HOSHA KAGAKU TORONKAI KOEN YOKOSHU.** see *CHEMISTRY—Abstracting, Bibliographies, Statistics*

▼ ▶ **SYNFACTS;** highlights in current synthetic organic chemistry. see *CHEMISTRY—Organic Chemistry*

▶ **SYNLETT;** accounts and rapid communications in synthetic organic chemistry. see *CHEMISTRY—Organic Chemistry*

▶ **SYNTHESIS;** journal of synthetic organic chemistry. see *CHEMISTRY—Organic Chemistry*

541.39 546.1   USA   ISSN 1553-3174
QD156   CODEN: SRIMCN
▶ **SYNTHESIS AND REACTIVITY IN INORGANIC, METAL-ORGANIC, AND NANO-METAL CHEMISTRY.** Text in English. 1971. 10/yr. USD 2,348, GBP 1,423 combined subscription to institutions print & online eds. (effective 2006). adv. reprint service avail. from PSC. **Document type:** *Journal, Academic/Scholarly.* **Description:** Provides dessemination of original research papers of reactions, techniques, and synthetic methods in organic, metal-organic, bio-inorganic and inorganic solid state chemistry.
Former titles (until 2005): Synthesis and Reactivity in Inorganic and Metal-Organic Chemistry (0094-5714); Synthesis in Inorganic and Metalorganic Chemistry (0039-789X)
Related titles: Microform ed.: (from RPI); Online - full text ed.: ISSN 1553-3182. USD 2,231, GBP 1,352 to institutions (effective 2006) (from EBSCO Publishing, O C L C Online Computer Library Center, Inc., Swets Information Services).
Indexed: ASCA, C&ISA, CCi, CIN, ChemAb, ChemTitl, CurCR, CurCont, E&CAJ, EngInd, IAA, ISR, IndChem, MOS, RCI, RefZh, SCI.
—BLDSC (8586.787000), CASDDS, CISTI, IDS, IE, Infotrieve, ingenta, Linda Hall. **CCC.**
Published by: Taylor & Francis Inc. (Subsidiary of: Taylor & Francis Group), 325 Chestnut St, Ste 800, Philadelphia, PA 19016. TEL 215-625-8900, 800-354-1420, FAX 215-625-8914, info@taylorandfrancis.com, http://www.tandf.co.uk/journals/titles/15533174.asp, http://www.taylorandfrancis.com. Ed. Kattesh V Katti. Adv. contact Sharon Moran. B&W page USD 600. Circ: 300 (paid and free).

546.5   USA
▶ **T R C THERMODYNAMIC TABLES - HYDROCARBONS.** (Thermodynamics Research Center) Text in English. 1942. biennial. looseleaf. USD 1,200. charts; stat. **Document type:** *Academic/Scholarly.* **Description:** Includes properties of hydrocarbons and sulfur compounds related to petroleum.
Former titles: Thermodynamics Research Center. Hydrocarbons Project. Selected Values of Properties of Hydrocarbons and Related Compounds. Category A: Tables of Selected Values of Physical and Thermodynamic Properties of Hydrocarbons; A P I Research Project 44. Selected Values of Properties of Hydrocarbons and Related Compounds. Category A: Tables of Selected Values of Physical and Thermodynamic Properties of Hydrocarbons (0065-9630)
—**CCC.**
Published by: Thermodynamics Research Center, Texas Engineering Experiment Station, TEES Headquarters, 3577 TAMU, College Station, TX 77843-3577. TEL 409-845-4940, FAX 409-847-8590, info@trchpl.tamu.edu, mmartell@tamu.edu, http://trcweb.tamu.edu, http://tees.tamu.edu/. Pub. Kenneth N Marsh. Circ: 319.

▶ **T R C THERMODYNAMIC TABLES - NON-HYDROCARBONS.** (Thermodynamics Research Center) see *CHEMISTRY—Analytical Chemistry*

▶ **TALK.** see *HANDICAPPED—Hearing Impaired*

---

668   DEU   ISSN 0932-3414
    CODEN: TSDEES
▶ **TENSIDE SURFACTANTS DETERGENTS;** journal for theory, technology & application of surfactants. Text in English, German. 1964. bi-m. EUR 338; EUR 67.80 newsstand/cover (effective 2006). adv. bk.rev. charts; illus.; pat. index. **Document type:** *Journal, Academic/Scholarly.*
Former titles (until 1986): Tenside - Detergents (0040-3490); (until 1970): Tenside (0497-2546)
Indexed: ASCA, C&ISA, CCI, CEABA, CIN, ChemAb, ChemInfo, ChemTitl, CurCont, E&CAJ, EngInd, ExcerpMed, INIS AtomInd, ISMEC, PROMT, RCI, SolStAb.
—BLDSC (8790.932000), CASDDS, CISTI, Ei, IDS, IE, Infotrieve, ingenta, Linda Hall. **CCC.**
Published by: (Gesellschaft Deutscher Chemiker), Carl Hanser Verlag GmbH & Co. KG, Kolbergerstr 22, Munich, 81679, Germany. TEL 49-89-998300, FAX 49-89-984809, tenside@t-online.de, http://www.hanser.de/zeitschriften/index.asp?fz=ts. Ed. Juergen Bohnen. adv.: B&W page EUR 2,400, color page EUR 3,600. Circ: 1,611 (paid and controlled). **Co-sponsor:** Deutscher Ausschuss fuer Grenzflaechenaktive Stoffe

---

▶ **THEILHEIMER'S SYNTHETIC METHODS OF ORGANIC CHEMISTRY.** see *CHEMISTRY—Organic Chemistry*

541.36 NLD ISSN 0040-6031
CODEN: THACAS
➤ **THERMOCHIMICA ACTA.** Text in Dutch. 1970. 30/yr. EUR 8,507 in Europe to institutions; JPY 1,129,200 in Japan to institutions; USD 9,517 to institutions except Europe and Japan (effective 2006). adv. bk.rev. back issues avail.
Document type: *Journal, Academic/Scholarly.* **Description:** Covers thermal analysis, thermochemistry, and chemical thermodynamics.
Related titles: E-mail ed.; Microform ed.: (from PQC); Online - full text ed.: (from EBSCO Publishing, Gale Group, IngentaConnect, ScienceDirect, Swets Information Services).
Indexed: A&ATA, ASCA, AnalAb, BrCerAb, BullT&T, C&ISA, CCI, CEABA, CerAb, ChemAb, ChemInfo, ChemTitl, CivEngAb, CorrAb, CurCont, E&CAJ, EMA, EngInd, ExcerpMed, IAA, ISR, LHB, M&TEA, MBF, METADEX, MSB, MSCI, RCI, RefZh, S&F, SCI, SIA, SolStAb, WAA.
—BLDSC (8814.820000), CASDDS, CISTI, Ei, IDS, IE, Infotrieve, ingenta, Linda Hall. **CCC.**
Published by: Elsevier BV (Subsidiary of: Elsevier Science & Technology), Radarweg 29, Amsterdam, 1043 NX, Netherlands. TEL 31-20-4853911, FAX 31-20-4852457, nlinfo-f@elsevier.nl, http://www.elsevier.com/locate/tca, http://www.elsevier.nl. Eds. C Schick, L Hansen, S Vyazovkin. **Subscr. to:** Elsevier, Subscription Customer Service, 6277 Sea Harbor Dr, Orlando, FL 32887-4800. TEL 407-345-4020, 877-839-7126, FAX 407-363-1354.

541.36 536.7 USA
➤ **THERMODYNAMICS AT TEXAS A & M.** Text in English. 1973. s-a. free. **Document type:** *Academic/Scholarly.* **Description:** Describes activities, publications and projects at the Thermodynamics Research Center and the Chemical Engineering Department at Texas A & M University.
Formerly: T R C Current Data News
Published by: Thermodynamics Research Center, Texas Engineering Experiment Station, TEES Headquarters, 3577 TAMU, College Station, TX 77843-3577. TEL 409-845-4940, FAX 409-847-8590, info@trchpl.tamu.edu, mmartell@tamu.edu, http://trcweb.tamu.edu, http://tees.tamu.edu/. Pub., R&P Kenneth N Marsh.
Co-sponsor: Chemical Engineering Department.

546.5 ISR
TOPICS IN PHYSICAL ORGANOMETALLIC CHEMISTRY. Text in English. 1985. a. USD 80 for vol. 4; USD 60 for each vol. 1-3. adv. **Document type:** *Academic/Scholarly.*
—BLDSC (8867.473500).
Published by: Freund Publishing House, Ltd., P O Box 35010, Tel Aviv, 61350, Israel. http://www.freundpublishing.com. Ed. Marcel Gielen.

541.38 JPN ISSN 0916-8486
CODEN: KTSSEJ
TOYAMA DAIGAKU SUISO DOITAI KINO KENKYU SENTA KENKYU HOKOKU/TOYAMA UNIVERSITY. HYDROGEN ISOTOPE RESEARCH CENTER. ANNUAL REPORT. Text in English, Japanese; Summaries in English. 1981. a. free.
Indexed: ChemAb, ChemTitl.
—BLDSC (1471.919270), CASDDS.
Published by: Toyama Daigaku, Suiso Doitai Kino Kenkyu Senta, 3190 Gofuku, Toyama-shi, 930-0887, Japan.

ULTRASONICS SONOCHEMISTRY. see *PHYSICS—Sound*

530 NLD ISSN 0090-1911
QC454.V5 CODEN: VBSSBB
➤ **VIBRATIONAL SPECTRA AND STRUCTURE.** Text in Dutch. 1972. irreg., latest vol.24, 1999. price varies. charts; illus. index. back issues avail.; reprint service avail. from ISI.
Document type: *Monographic series, Academic/Scholarly.*
Description: Discusses current research and trends in vibrational spectra and science.
Indexed: CIN, ChemAb, Inspec.
—BLDSC (9232.252000), CASDDS, CISTI, ingenta, Linda Hall. **CCC.**
Published by: Elsevier BV (Subsidiary of: Elsevier Science & Technology), Radarweg 29, Amsterdam, 1043 NX, Netherlands. TEL 31-20-4853911, FAX 31-20-4852457, nlinfo-f@elsevier.nl, http://www.elsevier.nl. Ed. J R Durig.

541 RUS
VYSOKOMOLEKULYARNYE SOEDINENIYA. KRATKIE SOOBSHCHENIYA. Text in Russian; Summaries in English. 1959. m. charts; illus. index.
Indexed: ChemAb.
—BLDSC (0416.904300).
Published by: (Rossiiskaya Akademiya Nauk, Otdelenie Obshchei i Tekhnicheskoi Khimii), Izdatel'stvo Nauka, Profsoyuznaya ul 90, Moscow, 117864, Russian Federation. TEL 7-095-3347151, FAX 7-095-4202220, secret@naukaran.ru, http://www.naukaran.ru. Ed. V A Kargin.

541 RUS ISSN 1023-3091
CODEN: VYSBAI
VYSOKOMOLEKULYARNYE SOEDINENIYA. SERIYA A I SERIYA B. Text in Russian; Summaries in English. 1959. m. USD 536 foreign (effective 2005). charts; illus. index.
Document type: *Journal, Academic/Scholarly.* **Description:** Covers all aspects of macromolecular chemistry and physics, including polymer synthetics and reaction mechanisms, structure and physical properties of polymers, their blends and composites, polymer solutions, and polymer processing.
Formed by the 1993 merger of: Vysokomolekylyarnye Soedineniya. Seriya A (0507-5475); Vysokomolekylyarnye Soedineniya. Seriya B (0507-5483)
Related titles: Online - full text ed.; ♦ English Translation: Polymer Science. Series A. ISSN 0965-545X; ♦ English Translation: Polymer Science. Series B. ISSN 1560-0904.
Indexed: ABIPC, ASCA, C&ISA, CCI, CIN, ChemAb, ChemTitl, CurCont, E&CAJ, EngInd, ISR, Inspec, MSCI, RAPRA, RCI, RefZh, SCI, SolStAb, WTA.
—BLDSC (0046.803000), CASDDS, CINDOC, CISTI, East View, IDS, IE, Linda Hall. **CCC.**
Published by: (Rossiiskaya Akademiya Nauk, Institut Neftekhimichskogo Sinteza im. A.V. Tonchieva), Izdatel'stvo Nauka, Profsoyuznaya ul 90, Moscow, 117864, Russian Federation. TEL 7-095-3347151, FAX 7-095-4202220, secret@naukaran.ru, http://www.maik.ru/cgi-bin/list.pl?page=vms, http://www.naukaran.ru. **Dist. by:** East View Information Services, 3020 Harbor Ln. N., Minneapolis, MN 55447. TEL 800-477-1005, FAX 800-800-3839, eastview@eastview.com, http://www.eastview.com.

541 CHN ISSN 1000-6818
CODEN: WHXUEU
WULI HUAXUE XUEBAO/ACTA PHYSICO - CHIMICA SINICA. Text in Chinese, English. 1985. m. USD 126 (effective 1997).
Related titles: Online - full text ed.: (from East View Information Services).
Indexed: CCI, CIN, ChemAb, Inspec, MSB, RefZh.
—BLDSC (0650.655000), AskIEEE, CASDDS, IE, ingenta.
Published by: (Zhongguo Huaxuehui/Chinese Chemical Society), Beijing Daxue Chubanshe/Beijing University Press, Haidian-qu, Beijing, 100871, China. TEL 86-10-2182998, FAX 86-10-2181051.

541.34 JPN
YOEKI KAGAKU SHINPOJUMU KOEN YOSHISHU/SYMPOSIUM ON SOLUTION CHEMISTRY OF JAPAN. Text in Japanese. 1978. a. **Document type:** *Proceedings.*
Published by: Yoeki Kagaku Kenkyukai/Association of Japanese Solution Chemists, c/o Prof. M. Nakahara, Institute for Chemical Research, Kyoto University, Uji, Kyoto 611-0011, Japan. TEL 81-774-38-3076, FAX 81-774-38-3076, yoeki@nmr.kuicr.kyoto-u.ac.jp. Ed. Masaru Nakahara.

YOYUEN KAGAKU TORONKAI YOSHISHU/SYMPOSIUM ON MOLTEN SALT CHEMISTRY. see *CHEMISTRY—Inorganic Chemistry*

YOYUEN OYOBI KOON KAGAKU/MOLTEN SALTS. see *CHEMISTRY—Inorganic Chemistry*

ZEITSCHRIFT FUER NATURFORSCHUNG. SECTION A: A JOURNAL OF PHYSICAL SCIENCES. see *PHYSICS*

541 DEU ISSN 0942-9352
QD1 CODEN: ZPCFAX
➤ **ZEITSCHRIFT FUER PHYSIKALISCHE CHEMIE/ INTERNATIONAL JOURNAL OF RESEARCH IN PHYSICAL CHEMISTRY AND CHEMICAL PHYSICS.** Text in English, German. 1887. 12/yr. EUR 1,219 domestic print or online ed.; EUR 1,228 foreign print or online ed.; EUR 1,409 combined subscription domestic print & online eds.; EUR 1,418 combined subscription foreign print & online eds.; EUR 164 newsstand/cover (effective 2005). adv. bk.rev. charts; illus. index. **Document type:** *Journal, Academic/Scholarly.*
Description: Contains research articles and short communications.
Formed by the merger of (1954-1990): Zeitschrift fuer Physikalische Chemie. Neue Folge (Munich) (0044-3336); (1940-1990): Zeitschrift fuer Physikalische Chemie (Leipzig) (0323-4479)
Related titles: Microform ed.: (from PMC); Online - full text ed.: (from EBSCO Publishing, Swets Information Services).
Indexed: APIAb, APICat, APIH&E, APIOC, APIPR, APIPS, APITS, ASCA, ApMecR, BiolAb, BullT&T, CCI, CEABA, CIN, ChemAb, ChemInfo, ChemTitl, CurCont, EngInd, ISR, Inspec, MSB, MSCI, RCI, RefZh, SCI.
—BLDSC (9481.800000), CASDDS, CISTI, Ei, IE, Infotrieve, ingenta, Linda Hall. **CCC.**
Published by: Oldenbourg Wissenschaftsverlag GmbH, Rosenheimer Str 145, Munich, 81671, Germany. TEL 49-89-450510, FAX 49-89-45051204, zpc-redaktion@verlag.oldenbourg.de, vertrieb-zs@verlag.oldenbourg.de, http://www.z-phys-chem.de, http://www.oldenbourg.de. Circ: 1,700.

541 RUS ISSN 0044-4537
CODEN: ZFKHA9
ZHURNAL FIZICHESKOI KHIMII. Text in Russian. 1930. m. RUR 1,390 for 6 mos. domestic (effective 2004). bk.rev. bibl.; charts; illus. index. **Document type:** *Journal, Academic/Scholarly.* **Description:** Offers a comprehensive review of theoretical and experimental research not only from the Russian Academy of Sciences but also from the entire Commonwealth of Independant States. Articles published concern chemical thermodynamics and thermochemistry, biophysical chemistry, photochemistry and magnetochemistry, materials structure, quantum chemistry, physical chemistry of solutions, and methods and techniques of physicochemical investigations.
Related titles: ♦ English ed.: Russian Journal of Physical Chemistry. ISSN 0036-0244; ♦ English Translation: Russian Journal of Physical Chemistry. ISSN 0036-0244.
Indexed: ASCA, BullT&T, CCI, CEABA, CIN, ChemAb, ChemInfo, ChemTitl, CurCont, GasAb, INIS AtomInd, ISR, Inspec, MSCI, RAPRA, RefZh, SCI.
—BLDSC (0067.000000), AskIEEE, CASDDS, CINDOC, CISTI, East View, IDS, Linda Hall. **CCC.**
Published by: (Rossiiskaya Akademiya Nauk/Russian Academy of Sciences), Izdatel'stvo Nauka, Profsoyuznaya ul 90, Moscow, 117864, Russian Federation. TEL 7-095-3347151, FAX 7-095-4202220, secret@naukaran.ru, http://www.maik.ru/cgi-bin/list.pl?page=fizkhim, http://www.naukaran.ru. Circ: 3,185.

541 RUS ISSN 0136-7463
QD1 CODEN: ZSTKAI
➤ **ZHURNAL STRUKTURNOI KHIMII.** Text in Russian. 1960. bi-m. RUR 582 for 6 mos. domestic; USD 180 foreign (effective 2005). bk.rev. bibl. index. back issues avail.
Document type: *Journal, Academic/Scholarly.* **Description:** Covers theory of molecular structure and chemical bonding; study of the structure of molecules by physical methods; structure of liquids and solutions; crystal chemistry; questions of methodology; brief communications and reviews.
Related titles: ♦ English ed.: Journal of Structural Chemistry. ISSN 0022-4766.
Indexed: CIN, ChemAb, ChemTitl, INIS AtomInd, Inspec, RAPRA, RefZh.
—BLDSC (0065.500000), CASDDS, CISTI, East View, Linda Hall. **CCC.**
Published by: (Rossiiskaya Akademiya Nauk, Sibirskoe Otdelenie, Institut Neorganicheskoy Khimii), Izdatel'stvo Sibirskogo Otdeleniya Rossiiskoi Akademii Nauk/Publishing House of the Russian Academy of Sciences, Siberian Branch, Morskoi pr 2, a/ya 187, Novosibirsk, 630090, Russian Federation. TEL 7-3832-300570, FAX 7-3832-333755, JSC@che.nsk.su, psb@ad-sbras.nsc.ru, http://www.che.nsk.su/jsc_rus, http://www-psb.ad-sbras.nsc.ru. Ed. L N Mazalov. Circ: 300. **Subscr. to:** Springer-Verlag Dordrecht, Journals Department, PO Box 322, Dordrecht, Netherlands. TEL 31-78-6576392, FAX 31-78-6576474.

CHILDREN AND YOUTH—About

see also EDUCATION ; MEDICAL SCIENCES—Pediatrics

➤ **A A T E NEWSLETTER.** see *THEATER*

362.7 USA
KF479.A59
A B A CHILD LAW PRACTICE. (American Bar Association) Text in English. 1982. m. USD 179 to individuals; USD 209 to institutions (effective 2003). bk.rev. back issues avail.
Document type: *Newsletter.* **Description:** Keeps lawyers, judges and other professionals abreast of case law and legislative developments, particularly in the areas of child maltreatment, adoption, termination of parental rights, civil rights, juvenile justice, and to tort actions involving children and families.
Former titles: A B A Juvenile and Child Welfare Law Reporter (0887-896X); National Juvenile Law Reporter
Indexed: V&AA.
Published by: American Bar Association, Center on Children and the Law, 740 15th St, N W, Washington, DC 20005-1009. TEL 202-662-1743, FAX 202-662-1755, childlawpractice@staff.abanet.org, http://www.abanet.org. Ed. Claire Sandt. R&P Lisa Waxler. Circ: 800.

649 GBR ISSN 1464-2212
A C P C SERIES. Text in English. 1996. irreg. **Document type:** *Monographic series.*
—BLDSC (0578.699630). **CCC.**
Published by: (Area Child Protection Comittee), Department of Health, SD2, Rm 804, Hannibal House, Elephant and Castle, London, SE1 6TE, United Kingdom. TEL 44-171-972-2193.

A C T A C NEWSLETTER. see *COMMUNICATIONS—Television And Cable*

362.7 AUS ISSN 1327-2810
A C W A NEWS. (Association of Childrens Welfare Agencies) Text in English. 1996. m. **Document type:** *Magazine.*
Media: Online - full text.

C

Published by: Association of Childrens Welfare Agencies, Inc., Level 2 Central Sq, 323 Castlereagh St, Sydney, NSW 2000, Australia. TEL 61-2-9281-8822, FAX 61-2-9281-8827, cindyn@acwanet.com, eric.scott@acwa.asn.au, http://www.acwanet.com.

155.4 AUS ISSN 1440-5148
A E C A RESEARCH IN PRACTICE SERIES. Text in English. 1978. q. AUD 42.40 domestic; AUD 44 foreign (effective 2002). bibl.; charts; illus. back issues avail. **Document type:** *Monographic series.* **Description:** Contains practical information to workers in all early childhood settings.
Former titles (until 1997): A E C A Resource Book Series (1320-2170); (until 1992): Australian Early Childhood Resource Booklets (0156-0999)
Indexed: AEI, e-psyche.
Published by: Early Childhood Australia Inc., Knox St, PO Box 105, Watson, ACT 2602, Australia. TEL 61-2-6241-6900, FAX 61-2-6241-5547, national@aeca.org.au, eca@earlychildhood.org.au. R&P Penelope Craswell. Circ: 2,500.

371.3 AUS ISSN 1445-0496
A E C A VOICE. Text in English. 1984. q. looseleaf. free with AECA membership. 3 p./no.; **Document type:** *Newsletter, Academic/Scholarly.* **Description:** Features publications and conferences on early childhood.
Former titles (until 2000): A E C A Newsletter (1320-274X); (until 1993): Australian Early Childhood Newsletter (1030-0236)
Published by: Early Childhood Australia Inc., Knox St, PO Box 105, Watson, ACT 2602, Australia. TEL 61-2-6241-6900, FAX 61-2-6241-5547, publishing@aeca.org.au, http://www.earlychildhood.org.au/. Ed. Pam Cahir. R&P Penelope Craswell. Circ: 7,000.

C

649 RUS
A I F. SEMEINYI SOVET. (Argumenty i Fakty) Text in Russian. 24/yr. USD 45 foreign (effective 2003). **Document type:** *Newspaper, Consumer.* **Description:** The paper for parents about bringing up children and adolescents, tips from teachers, doctors, psychologists, and lawyers; entertaining games.
Related titles: Online - full content ed.; ◆ Supplement to: Argumenty i Fakty. ISSN 0204-0476.
Published by: Redaktsiya Argumenty i Fakty, Myasnitskaya ul 42, Moscow, 101000, Russian Federation. TEL 7-095-9286862, info@aif.ru, http://www.aif.ru/online/ss. **US dist. addr.:** East View Information Services, 3020 Harbor Ln. N., Minneapolis, MN 55447. TEL 763-550-0961, FAX 763-559-2931, eastview@eastview.com, http://www.eastview.com.

A L S C PROGRAM SUPPORT PUBLICATIONS. see *LIBRARY AND INFORMATION SCIENCES*

A L S CONNECT. (Association for Library Service to Children) see *LIBRARY AND INFORMATION SCIENCES*

A TO ZOO; subject access to children's picture books. see *BIBLIOGRAPHIES*

028.5 NZL ISSN 1175-3501
ABOUT KIDS. Text in English. 2000. m. **Document type:** *Magazine, Consumer.*
Published by: A C P New Zealand, 17B Hargreaves St, College Hill, Pasonby, Auckland, 1036, New Zealand. TEL 64-9-3735408, FAX 64-9-3089498.

ACTA MEDICA AUXOLOGICA. see *MEDICAL SCIENCES—Endocrinology*

ACTEENS ACCESSORIES. see *RELIGIONS AND THEOLOGY—Protestant*

618 ESP ISSN 1578-1232
ACTUAL BEBE; revista profesional para puntos de venta especializados. Text in Spanish. 1999. 6/yr. EUR 46 domestic; EUR 81.60 in Europe (effective 2004). **Document type:** *Magazine, Trade.*
Published by: Goodman Business Press S.A., Goya 115, 4to. dcha., Madrid, 28009, Spain. TEL 34-91-3096310, FAX 34-91-4018090, info@goodman-bp.com, http://www.goodman-bp.com.

ADOLESCENCE. see *MEDICAL SCIENCES—Psychiatry And Neurology*

370.15 USA ISSN 0001-8449
HQ793 CODEN: ADOLAO
➤ **ADOLESCENCE (SAN DIEGO)**; an international quarterly devoted to the physiological, psychological, psychiatric, sociological, and educational aspects of the second decade of human life. Text in English. 1966. q. USD 90 to individuals; USD 128 to institutions (effective 2002). adv. bk.rev. bibl.; charts; illus.; stat. cum.index. 256 p./no.; back issues avail.; reprint service avail. from PQC,ISI. **Document type:** *Journal, Academic/Scholarly.* **Description:** Articles cover a variety of viewpoints on topics relating to adolescence.
Related titles: CD-ROM ed.; Microform ed.: (from PQC); Online - full text ed.: (from bigchalk, Chadwyck-Healey Inc., EBSCO Publishing, Florida Center for Library Automation, Gale Group, H.W. Wilson, O C L C Online Computer Library Center, Inc., ProQuest Information & Learning).
Indexed: ABIn, ABS&EES, AC&P, AMHA, ASCA, ASSIA, AbAn, AgeL, Agr, BRI, BibAg, BiolAb, CBRI, CIJE, CINAHL, CJA, CLFP, ChLitAb, CurCont, DIP, EAA, ECER, ERA, ESPM, ETA, EduInd, ExcerpMed, FamI, H&SSA, HEA, IBR, IBZ, IMFL, IndMed, MEA, MEA&I, MEDLINE, PCI, PsySCDP, PsycInfo, PsycholAb, RHEA, RI-1, RI-2, RILM, RefZh, RiskAb, SEA, SENA, SFSA, SOMA, SOPODA, SRRA, SSA, SSCI, SSI, SWA, SWR&A, SociolAb, TEA, THA, V&AA, e-psyche.
—BLDSC (0696.581000), GNLM, IDS, IE, ingenta. **CCC.**
Published by: Libra Publishers, Inc., 3089C Clairemont Dr, PMB 383, San Diego, CA 92117. TEL 858-571-1414. Ed., Adv. contact William Kroll. R&P Jon Kroll. page USD 300. Circ: 3,000.

➤ **ADOLESCENCIA Y SALUD.** see *MEDICAL SCIENCES*

➤ **ADOLESCENT PSYCHIATRY**; annals of the American Society for Adolescent Psychiatry. see *MEDICAL SCIENCES—Psychiatry And Neurology*

362.7 808.81 ROM
➤ **ADOLESCENTA.** Text in Romanian. 1995. m. ROL 5,000, USD 250. illus. **Document type:** *Academic/Scholarly.* **Description:** Contains poems.
Published by: Grupul Salor Industrial Tractorul, Str. Turnului 3, Brasov, 2200, Romania. TEL 40-068164979. Ed. Georgeta Blendea.

649 KOR ISSN 1226-1688
ADONG HAGHOEJI✱. Text in Korean; Contents page in English. 1980. s-a. **Document type:** *Academic/Scholarly.*
—BLDSC (5113.526000).
Published by: Han'gug Adong Haghoe/Korean Association of Child Studies, 11-1, Daehyun-dong, Seodaemun-gu, Ewha Womans University, Seoul, 130-701, Korea, S. TEL 82-2-972-9576, http://www.childkorea.or.kr/.

ADOPTALK. see *SOCIAL SERVICES AND WELFARE*

362.734 USA ISSN 1547-6405
▼ **ADOPTING TODAY.** Text in English. 2003 (Nov.). m. USD 29.95 (effective 2003). **Document type:** *Magazine.*
Published by: E D I X Media Group, 5165 W. Woodmill Dr. Ste. 12, Wilmington, DE 19808. TEL 888-281-1284, FAX 302-225-1287, http://www.adoptingtoday.com. Ed. Deborah Tokarski. Pub. Lance Burris.

362.7 CAN ISSN 1181-845X
ADOPTION HELPER; devoted to helping people adopt. Text in English. 1990. q. CND 32 (effective 2000); USD 32 in United States; USD 48 elsewhere. adv. bk.rev. bibl.; illus. back issues avail. **Document type:** *Consumer.* **Description:** Covers adoption news, adoption processes, domestic and international adoptions, adoption for singles and special needs adoptions.
Published by: Helper Publishing, 185 Panoramic Dr, Sault Ste Marie, ON P6B 6E3, Canada. FAX 705-945-1170, helper@helping.com, http://www.helping.com. Ed., Pub. Mr. Robin Hilborn. Circ: 700 (paid).

649 USA ISSN 1076-1020
ADOPTIVE FAMILIES. Text in English. 1967. bi-m. USD 24.95 domestic; USD 32.95 in Canada; USD 36.95 elsewhere (effective 2005). adv. bk.rev.; film rev.; video rev.; Website rev. illus.; charts; stat. index. 80 p./no.; back issues avail.; reprints avail. **Document type:** *Magazine.* **Description:** Provides personal stories from readers as well as articles written by adoption professionals.
Formerly (until 1994): Ours (Minneapolis) (0899-9333)
Related titles: Supplement(s): Adoption Guide. USD 9.95 domestic; USD 14.95 elsewhere (effective 2000 - 2001).
Published by: Adoptive Families Magazine, 39 W 37th Str, 15th fl, New York, NY 10018. TEL 646-366-0830, FAX 646-366-0842, letters@adoptivefamilies.com, http://www.adoptivefamiliesmagazine.com/. Ed., Pub. Susan Caughman. Circ: 25,000. **Subscr. to:** PO Box 5159, Brentwood, TN 37024. TEL 800-372-3300.

ADULTSPAN JOURNAL. see *PSYCHOLOGY*

ADVANCES IN LEARNING AND BEHAVIORAL DISABILITIES. see *EDUCATION—Special Education And Rehabilitation*

ADVANCES IN MOTOR DEVELOPMENT RESEARCH. see *PHYSICAL FITNESS AND HYGIENE*

ADVOCASEY. see *SOCIAL SERVICES AND WELFARE*

362 USA ISSN 1529-2622
THE AFRICAN CONNECTION. Text in English. 1990. bi-m. **Document type:** *Newsletter.*
Published by: Americans For African Adoptions, Inc., 8910 Timberwood Dr, Indianapolis, IN 46234-1952. TEL 317-271-4567, FAX 317-271-8739, info@africanadoptions.org, http://www.africanadoptions.org/.

AGENDA PARA MAMA. see *MEDICAL SCIENCES—Obstetrics And Gynecology*

AGORA; debats - jeunesse. see *SOCIOLOGY*

369.4 BGD ISSN 0002-1040
AGRADOOT. Text in Bengali. 1950. m. BDT 12. adv. bk.rev. illus. index.
Formerly: East Bengal Scout
Published by: Bangladesh Scout Samity, National Headquarters, 67-A Purana Paltan, Dhaka, 2, Bangladesh. Ed. Abdul Wahab. Circ: 2,000.

AIDS BOOK REVIEW JOURNAL. see *MEDICAL SCIENCES—Communicable Diseases*

AKCENTY. see *RELIGIONS AND THEOLOGY—Protestant*

362.7 DEU ISSN 0720-3551
AKTION JUGENDSCHUTZ. INFORMATIONEN. Short title: A J S Informationen. Text in German. 1965. q. EUR 7.50 (effective 2005). adv. bk.rev. bibl.; charts; illus.; stat. back issues avail. **Document type:** *Magazine, Consumer.*
Published by: Aktion Jugendschutz Landesarbeitsstelle Baden-Wuerttemberg, Stafflenbergstr 44, Stuttgart, 70184, Germany. TEL 49-711-2373711, FAX 49-711-2373730, info@ajs-bw.de, http://www.ajs-bw.de. Ed. Birgit Ebbert. Circ: 20,000.

ALBERTA CHILDREN'S SERVICES ANNUAL REPORT. see *SOCIAL SERVICES AND WELFARE*

028.5 USA
ALL ABOUT BABY & CHILD. Text in English. q. adv. **Description:** Articles cover children and parenting.
Media: Online - full content.
Published by: All About Baby LLC, 621 Nortontown Rd, Guilford, CT 06437. TEL 203-458-3003, http://www.allaboutbaby.com. Adv. contact Gia Schioppo Calistro.

649 USA
ALL ABOUT KIDS. Text in English. 1988. m. free at various distribution points in Greater Cincinnati or Northern Kentucky. adv. bk.rev. **Document type:** *Consumer.*
Published by: Midwest Parenting Publications, 1901 Broad Ripple Ave., Indianapolis, IN 46220-2327. TEL 513-684-0501, 317-722-8500, FAX 513-684-0507, 317-722-8510, all-kids@mindspring.com, http://www.aak.com. Ed. Shelly Bucksot. Pub. Greg Wynne. Adv. contact Mike Hussey. Circ: 50,000 (controlled).

369.4 SWE ISSN 1651-6583
ALLTID SCOUT. Variant title: Scout med Ledarbladet. Text in Swedish. 2002. 6/yr. **Document type:** *Magazine, Consumer.*
Supersedes in part (in 2001): Ledarbladet Samspel (1652-0823); Which superseded in part (in 2000): Scout (0346-0827); Which incorporated (1961-1989): Ledarbladet Samspel (0345-7044); Which was formed by the merger of (1958-1961): Samspel; (1929-1961): Sveriges Flickors Scoutfoerbunds Ledarblads; Incorporated (1912-1964): Scouten; Trekloevern
Published by: Svenska Scoutfoerbundet, PO Box 801, Solna, 16928, Sweden. TEL 46-8-56843200, FAX 46-8-56843203, info@ssf.scout.se, http://www.ssf.scout.se/o.o.i.s/242. Ed. Tobbe Lundell. Pub. Anita Lindqvist.

AMERICAN ACADEMY OF CHILD AND ADOLESCENT PSYCHIATRY. JOURNAL. see *MEDICAL SCIENCES—Psychiatry And Neurology*

649 USA ISSN 0044-7544
HQ750.A2
AMERICAN BABY; for expectant and new parents. Text in English. 1938. m. USD 23.94 domestic; USD 39.94 in Canada; free to qualified personnel (effective 2005). adv. bk.rev. illus. back issues avail.; reprints avail. **Document type:** *Magazine, Consumer.* **Description:** Advises and supports expectant and new parents, providing them with the information they need most.
Formerly: Mothers-to-Be - American Baby (0027-156X)
Related titles: Online - full text ed.; ◆ Includes: First Year of Life. ISSN 1076-1756.
Indexed: Agr, CHNI, CINAHL, HlthInd, MagInd.
Published by: Meredith Corp., 125 Park Ave, 19th Fl, New York, NY 10017. TEL 212-557-6600, FAX 212-455-1345, support@americanbaby.com, http://www.americanbaby.com, http://www.meredith.com. Ed. Judith Nolte. Pub. Robert Davidowitz. adv.: B&W page USD 90,400, color page USD 124,300. Circ: 2,000,000 (controlled).

AMERICAN JOURNAL OF ORTHOPSYCHIATRY. see *PSYCHOLOGY*

649 USA
AMERICAN MOTHER✱. Text in English. q. USD 20 to members (effective 1998). adv. bk.rev. **Document type:** *Magazine, Consumer.* **Description:** Helps strengthen the moral and spiritual foundation of the family - the home. Includes lessons for study chapters of Young Mothers and articles on family life.

Published by: American Mothers, Inc., 15 DuPont Circle, Washington, DC 20036. TEL 402-489-7587, FAX 402-489-7591. Ed., R&P Lois Schwab. Adv. contact Sue Hickenlooper. Circ: 7,500 (paid).

AND BABY. see *HOMOSEXUALITY*

305.23 369.4 SWE
ANGELAEGET; foer ledare bland barn, ungdom och familj. Text in Swedish. 1956. q. adv. **Document type:** *Trade.*
Formerly (until 1997): Ledarkontakt (0345-7052)
Published by: Nybygget-Kristen Samverkan, Olaigatan 4, PO Box 1624, Oerebo, 70116, Sweden. TEL 46-19-16-76-00, FAX 46-19-16-76-11. adv.: B&W page SEK 2,000.

ANGELIC WARFARE DISPATCH. see *RELIGIONS AND THEOLOGY—Roman Catholic*

THE ANN CRAFT TRUST BULLETIN. see *SOCIAL SERVICES AND WELFARE*

ANNUAIRE DES COMMUNAUTES D'ENFANTS. see *EDUCATION*

ANNUAL EDITIONS: CHILD GROWTH & DEVELOPMENT. see *MEDICAL SCIENCES—Pediatrics*

ANNUAL PROGRESS IN CHILD PSYCHIATRY AND CHILD DEVELOPMENT. see *MEDICAL SCIENCES—Psychiatry And Neurology*

APPRENTISSAGE ET SOCIALISATION. see *EDUCATION—Special Education And Rehabilitation*

THE ARC INSIGHT. see *SOCIAL SERVICES AND WELFARE*

649 618.082 USA
ARIZONA PARENTING. Text in English. 1989. m. free at select locations in AZ. adv. illus. **Document type:** *Consumer.* **Description:** Covers parenting topics relating to raising children ages 0 - 12.
Formerly: Arizona Parenting from A to Z
Published by: United Parenting Publications (Subsidiary of: Trader Publishing Co.), 4041 N Central Ave, Ste 1000, Phoenix, AZ 85012. TEL 602-279-7977, http://arizona.parenthood.com/. Ed. Chris Wolfe. Adv. contact Tony Rutledge. Circ: 50,000.

ARTICLE 13; law & policy journal of the National Children's and Youth Law Centre. see *LAW*

367 URY
ASOCIACION. Text in Spanish. 1959-1978; resumed 1979. q. free.
Formerly: Confederacion Sudamericana de Asociaciones Cristianas de Jovenes. Noticias (0010-5503)
Published by: Confederacion Latinoamericana de Asociaciones Cristianas de Jovenes/Latin American Confederation of YMCAs, Colonia, 1884 Piso 1, Montevideo, 11205, Uruguay. Ed. Edgardo G Crovetto.

155.4 616.8 USA ISSN 1077-0305
ASSOCIATION FOR CHILD PSYCHOANALYSIS. NEWSLETTER. Text in English. 1980. q. free. bk.rev. abstr.; bibl. back issues avail. **Document type:** *Newsletter, Academic/Scholarly.* **Description:** Publishes abstracts of scientific meetings and reports on the activities of the members of the association.
Indexed: e-psyche.
Published by: Association for Child Psychoanalysis, Inc., PO Box 253, Ramsey, NJ 07446. TEL 201-825-3138, FAX 201-825-3138, childanalysis@compuserve.com. Eds. Barbara Streeter, Denia Barrett. Circ: 700.

649 USA
AT LARGE. Text in English. m. adv. **Description:** Contains information related to parenting.
Address: 116 Auburn Park, Ste 1, Dallas, GA 30132. TEL 770-443-0314, FAX 770-443-0573. Ed., Pub. N F Cabrini.

647 USA
ATLANTA BABY✶. Text in English. 1992. 6/yr. adv. **Document type:** *Magazine, Consumer.* **Description:** Designed for expectant parents as well as new parents of children up to 18 months old. Covers resources, hospitals, maternity, and new baby issues.
Published by: Cole, Sanford and Whitmire, 2346 Perimeter Park Dr., Atlanta, GA 30341. TEL 770-454-7599, FAX 770-454-7699. Ed., Pub. Liz White. R&P Peggy Middendorf. Adv. contact Nancy McDanie. B&W page USD 1,356; trim 9.75 x 7.5. Circ: 30,000 (controlled).

647 USA
ATLANTA PARENT. Text in English. 1983. m. free in Atlanta; USD 30 subscr - mailed elsewhere (effective 2005). adv. bk.rev. **Document type:** *Magazine, Consumer.* **Description:** Covers all aspects of parenting from birth through teen years with emphasis on local isues and resources.
Published by: Atlanta Parent, Inc., 2346 Perimeter Park Dr, Ste 10, Atlanta, GA 30341-1319. TEL 770-454-7599, FAX 770-454-7699, atlantaparent@atlantaparent.com, http://www.atlantaparent.com. Ed., Pub. Liz White. adv.: B&W page USD 1,820; trim 8.25 x 10.5. Circ: 110,000 (paid and controlled).

ATT ADOPTERA. see *SOCIAL SERVICES AND WELFARE*

AUSTRALIAN EARLY CHILDHOOD ASSOCIATION. VICTORIAN BRANCH. NEWSLETTER. see *EDUCATION*

640 052 AUS
THE AUSTRALIAN FAMILY. Text in English. 1980. q. AUD 25 (effective 1999). bk.rev. stat. back issues avail. **Document type:** *Bulletin.* **Description:** Marketed to individuals and organizations in the community concerned with the strengthening and support of the family.
Formerly: Australian Family Bulletin (0811-3661)
Published by: Australian Family Association, 582 Queensberry, North Melbourne, VIC 3051, Australia. TEL 61-3-9329-5757, FAX 61-3-9328-2877. Ed., R&P Mary Helen Woods. Circ: 2,500.

649 AUS ISSN 0312-5033
➤ **AUSTRALIAN JOURNAL OF EARLY CHILDHOOD.** Text in English. 1960. q. AUD 60 domestic; AUD 64 foreign (effective 2005). adv. bk.rev. abstr.; bibl.; charts; illus.; stat. Index. back issues avail. **Document type:** *Journal, Academic/Scholarly.* **Description:** Addresses theory, research, and opinion concerning early childhood education. The primary emphasis is on early childhood practices and programs in Australia.
Formerly (until 1975): Preschool Quarterly
Related titles: Microfilm ed.: (from PQC); Online - full text ed.: (from Florida Center for Library Automation, Gale Group, R M I T Publishing).
Indexed: AEI, CIJE, CPE, ERA, ETA, Faml, IBSS, MEA, SEA, SENA, SWA, TEA.
—BLDSC (1807.550000), IE, Infotrieve, ingenta.
Published by: Early Childhood Australia Inc., Knox St, PO Box 105, Watson, ACT 2602, Australia. TEL 61-2-62421800, 800-356-900, FAX 61-2-62421818, eca@earlychildhood.org.au, http://www.earlychildhood.org.au/pubs_subs_ajec.htm. Circ: 2,500.

649 367 AUS ISSN 1444-4429
AUSTRALIAN MULTIPLES MAGAZINE. Text in English. 1984. 5/yr. AUD 7.50 to members; AUD 15 to non-members; AUD 20 foreign (effective 2001). bk.rev. **Document type:** *Newsletter.* **Description:** Articles relevant to multiple births: personal experiences, research, information.
Formerly (until Aug.2000): A M B A News (0815-1652)
Published by: Australian Multiple Birth Association, PO Box 105, Coogee, NSW 2034, Australia. TEL 61-3-52561336, amba_national@yahoo.com.au, http://www.amba.org.au. Ed., Pub. Jennifer Allcorn. Circ: 1,800.

AYUDANDO A LOS ESTUDIANTES A APRENDER (ESCUELA INTERMEDIA). see *EDUCATION*

AYUDANDO A LOS ESTUDIANTES A APRENDER (ESCUELA SECUNDARIA). see *EDUCATION*

AYUDANDO A LOS NINOS A APRENDER (ESCUELA PRIMARIA). see *EDUCATION*

AYUDANDO A LOS NINOS A APRENDER (PREPARACION PARALA ESCUELA). see *EDUCATION*

305.23 GBR
B B C PARENTING. Text in English. m. GBP 2.70 newsstand/cover (effective 2003). **Document type:** *Magazine, Consumer.*
Published by: B B C Worldwide Ltd., 80 Wood Ln, London, W12 0TT, United Kingdom. TEL 44-20-84331070, FAX 44-20-84332231, bbcparentingmagazine@bbc.co.uk, bbcworldwide@bbc.co.uk, http://www.bbcmagazines.com/parenting/.

B F H I NEWS. (Baby-Friendly Hospital Initiative) see *SOCIAL SERVICES AND WELFARE*

362.7 800 DEU
B P J M AKTUELL. Text in German. 1993. q. EUR 33; EUR 11 newsstand/cover (effective 2005). **Document type:** *Journal, Trade.*
Formerly: B P J S Aktuell (0943-5638)
Published by: (Bundespruefstelle fuer Jugendgefaehrdende Medien), Forum Verlag Godesberg GmbH, Ferdinandstr 16, Moenchengladbach, 41061, Germany. TEL 49-2161-206669, FAX 49-2161-209183, forumverlaggodesberg.gmbh@t-online.de, http://www.forumvg.de. Circ: 4,500.

B P SPIRIT. see *CLUBS*

362.7 SWE ISSN 1651-3762
B R I S TIDNINGEN BARN OCH UNGDOM. (Barnens Raett i Samhaellet) Text in Swedish. 1974. q. SEK 250 to individual members; SEK 50 to students (effective 2004). adv. back issues avail. **Document type:** *Magazine, Consumer.*
Former titles (until 2002): Barn och Ungdom (1400-108X); (until 1993): Bris-Bladet (0348-0631); Which incorporates (1989-1991): Bris-Bladet Kort och Gott (1101-6744)
Related titles: Online - full text ed.
Published by: Barnens Raet i Samhaellet/Children's Right in Society, Karlavaegen 121, Stockholm, 11526, Sweden. TEL 46-8-59888800, FAX 46-8-59888801, info@briss.se, http://www.bris.se/library/news.asp. Ed. Gunnar Sandelin. Pub. Kerstin Thuresson. Adv. contact Pernilla Thurin TEL 46-31-840494.

649 618.9 USA
BABY (KENNESAW). Text in English. 2001. bi-m. USD 19.99; USD 5.99 newsstand/cover (effective 2002). adv. **Document type:** *Consumer.*
Published by: Highbury House Communications, Inc. (Subsidiary of: Highbury House Communications PLC), Barrett Court, Ste 23, 1925 Vaughn Rd, NW, Kennesaw, GA 30144. TEL 770-422-3225. Ed. Jeanine Cox. Pub. Michael Meyers.

649 GBR
BABY & YOU. Text in English. 1978. m. GBP 2.30 newsstand/cover (effective 2003). adv. **Document type:** *Magazine, Consumer.* **Description:** Covers newborn care though the first year. Every health, emotional, nutritional, and family issue is dealt with, plus we carry product reviews of all the latest baby equipment, as well as great competition and giveaways.
Former titles: New Baby (1469-1418); (until 2000): Baby Magazine (0958-2517)
Published by: Highbury - WV (Subsidiary of: Highbury House Communications PLC), 53-79 Highgate Rd, London, NW5 1TW, United Kingdom. TEL 44-20-73311000, FAX 44-20-73311273, http://www.hhc.co.uk/newbaby. Ed. Claire Davies.

BABY MAGAZINE INFANT CARE GUIDE. see *MEDICAL SCIENCES—Pediatrics*

649 618.92 DEU ISSN 0724-1119
BABY POST. Text in German. bi-m. adv. **Document type:** *Magazine, Consumer.*
Published by: Marken Verlag GmbH, Bonner Str 323, Cologne, 50968, Germany. TEL 49-221-9574270, FAX 49-221-95742777, marken-info@markenverlag.de, http://www.markenverlag.de/babypost_inhalt.html. adv.: page EUR 7,160; trim 210 x 280. Circ: 108,962 (controlled).

649.1 USA ISSN 1529-5389
BABY TALK. Text in English. 1935. 10/yr. USD 19.95; USD 1.95 newsstand/cover (effective 2005); free to qualified personnel. adv. bk.rev. charts; illus.; tr.lit. reprints avail. **Document type:** *Magazine, Consumer.* **Description:** Discusses pregnancy, birth, and parenting from prenatal to 18 months of age. Focuses on heath issues, personal stories and newborn care.
Former titles (until 2000): Parenting's Baby Talk (1092-1869); (until 199?): Baby Talk Magazine (0749-971X); (until 1977): New Baby Talk (0364-1554); (until 1976): Baby Talk (0005-3589)
Related titles: Online - full text ed.: (from EBSCO Publishing, Gale Group, H.W. Wilson, LexisNexis, O C L C Online Computer Library Center, Inc., ProQuest Information & Learning).
Indexed: RGAb, RGPR.
Published by: Time - Warner Inc., 530 5th Ave, New York, NY 10036. TEL 212-522-8989, FAX 212-522-8750, babytalk-letters@time-inc.com, http://www.babytalk.com. Ed. Susan Kane. Pub. Jeff Wellington. adv.: B&W page USD 74,440, color page USD 93,040; trim 10.5 x 7.88. Circ: 1,800,000.

649 DEU ISSN 1619-4349
BABY UNSER GLUECK. Text in German. 1984. 2/yr. EUR 3.20 newsstand/cover (effective 2004). adv. **Document type:** *Magazine, Consumer.*
Published by: Marken Verlag GmbH, Bonner Str 323, Cologne, 50968, Germany. TEL 49-221-9574270, FAX 49-221-95742777, marken-info@markenverlag.de, http://www.markenverlag.de. adv.: page EUR 8,480. Circ: 100,000 (controlled).

649 NLD ISSN 1388-9389
BABY WERELD; vakblad voor het baby- en kleutervak. Text in Dutch. 1981. q. EUR 17.70; EUR 7 newsstand/cover (effective 2005). adv. bk.rev. back issues avail. **Document type:** *Trade.* **Description:** Provides news and information to retailers of baby and toddler furniture, strollers, and accessories.
Formerly (until 1991): Piccolo (0169-6076)
Published by: Uitgeverij Ruiters, Postbus 28017, Hoogland, 3828 ZG, Netherlands. TEL 31-33-4530068, FAX 31-33-4530069, ruiters@baby-wereld.nl. Circ: 800.

649 GBR ISSN 1465-170X
BABYCARE AND PREGNANCY. Text in English. 1994. m. GBP 18; GBP 1.80 newsstand/cover (effective 1999). adv. **Document type:** *Consumer.* **Description:** Provides new mothers and mothers-to-be with the latest medical information and advice on pre-conceptual care, pregnancy, birth and babycare up to age two.
Former titles (until 1997): Babycare and Your Pregnancy (1366-4999); (until 1996): First Steps (1355-6320)

C

Published by: D.C. Thomson & Co. Ltd., 80 Kingsway East, Dundee, Angus, Scotland DD4 8SL, United Kingdom. FAX 44-1382-462097, baby@dcthomson.co.uk, http://www.dcthomson.co.uk/mags/baby. Ed. Irene Duncan. Adv. contact Sharon Mudie. B&W page GBP 2,100, color page GBP 3,255. **Subscr. to:** Babycare and Pregnancy, Freepost, Subscribers. Dept., Albert Sq, Dundee, Angus DD1 9XU, United Kingdom. TEL 44-1382-223131.

BABYCARE BOOK. see *MEDICAL SCIENCES—Pediatrics*

BABYFIRST. see *MEDICAL SCIENCES—Pediatrics*

649 GBR
BABY'S BEST BUYS. Text in English. 1998. s-a. GBP 3.50 newsstand/cover (effective 2003). adv. **Document type:** *Magazine, Consumer.* **Description:** Provides assistance in sorting through all the baby products and services available.
Published by: Highbury - WV (Subsidiary of: Highbury House Communications PLC), 53-79 Highgate Rd, London, NW5 1TW, United Kingdom. TEL 44-20-73311000, FAX 44-20-73311273, http://www.hhc.co.uk/babysbestbuys. Ed. Hannah Rand.

790.019 JPN
BALLOON. Text in Japanese. 1986. m. JPY 7,200 domestic; JPY 13,680 per issue foreign (effective 2001). **Document type:** *Consumer.* **Description:** Contains articles on the physical and emotional aspects of pregnancy, prenatal and postnatal growth and development, nutrition, infant and baby psychology.
Published by: Shufunotomo Co. Ltd., 2-9 Kanda-Surugadai, Chiyoda-ku, Tokyo, 101-8911, Japan. TEL 81-3-5280-7522, FAX 81-3-5280-7422, international@shufunotomo.co.jp, http://www.shufunotomo.co.jp. Ed. Kimiko Ono. Circ: 80,000.

649 USA
BALTIMORE'S CHILD. Text in English. 1984. m. USD 25.20; free newsstand/cover (effective 2004). adv. bk.rev. **Document type:** *Newspaper, Consumer.*
Related titles: Online - full text ed.
Address: 11 Dutton Ct, Baltimore, MD 21228. TEL 410-367-5883, FAX 410-719-9342, info@baltimoreschild.com, http://www.baltimoreschild.com. Eds. Joanne Giza, Sharon Keech. adv.: B&W page USD 2,111; trim 12 x 10.25. Circ: 65,000; 65,000 (controlled).

362.7 ITA ISSN 0393-4209
BAMBINI. Text in Italian. 1984. m. (10/yr.). EUR 44.20 domestic; EUR 72 in Europe; EUR 94 elsewhere (effective 2005). adv. bk.rev. abstr.; bibl. Index. 80 p./no.; back issues avail. **Document type:** *Magazine, Trade.* **Description:** Magazine for childhood educators.
Published by: Edizioni Junior s.r.l., Viale dell'Industria, Azzano San Paolo (BG), 24052, Italy. TEL 39-035-534123, FAX 39-035-534143, bambini@edizionijunior.it, http://www.edizionijunior.it. Ed. Ferruccio Cremaschi. Circ: 14,000 (controlled); 7,000 (paid).

362.7 ITA
➤ **BAMBINI IN EUROPA.** Text in Italian. 2001. m. EUR 31 (effective 2005). adv. bk.rev. abstr.; bibl. back issues avail. **Document type:** *Magazine, Trade.* **Description:** It is published in eight languages in eight European countries (Italy, Spain, France, Germany, Belgium, the Netherlands, Denmark, the UK.) Covers up to date trends, scientific research and good professional practices.
Published by: Edizioni Junior s.r.l., Viale dell'Industria, Azzano San Paolo (BG), 24052, Italy. TEL 39-035-534123, FAX 39-035-534143, bambini@edizionijunior.it, http://www.edizionijunior.it. Ed. Ferruccio Cremaschi. Circ: 5,000 (paid); 8,000 (controlled).

362.7 GBR ISSN 1460-9681
BARNARDO'S TODAY. Text in English. 1985. q. free. **Document type:** *Newsletter.* **Description:** Addresses the changing needs and problems of children in the U.K. today.
Address: Tanners Ln, Barkingside, Ilford, Essex IG6 1QG, United Kingdom. TEL 44-181-550-8822, FAX 44-181-550-0429. Ed. Ali Worthy. Circ: 100,000.

808.068 SWE ISSN 0347-772X
➤ **BARNBOKEN.** Text in Swedish; Summaries in English. 1977. s-a. SEK 105 domestic; SEK 200 foreign; SEK 60 per issue domestic; SEK 100 per issue foreign (effective 2004). bk.rev. bibl.; tr.lit. **Document type:** *Journal, Academic/Scholarly.* **Description:** Articles and essays on children's literature by specialists; information on research in the field.
Indexed: ChLitAb.
Published by: Svenska Barnboksinstitutet/Swedish Institute for Children's Books, Odengatan 61, Stockholm, 11322, Sweden. TEL 46-8-54542050, FAX 46-8-54542054, info@ski.kb.se, http://www.sbi.kb.se. Ed. Eva Nordlinder. Pub. Sonja Svensson. Circ: 1,000.

➤ **BARNLAEKAREN.** see *SOCIAL SERVICES AND WELFARE*

➤ **BAUSTEINE KINDERGARTEN.** see *EDUCATION—Teaching Methods And Curriculum*

649 USA
BAY AREA PARENT. Text in English. 1983. m. free (effective 2005). adv. 84 p./no. 4 cols./p.; **Document type:** *Newspaper, Consumer.*
Formerly: San Francisco Peninsula Parent
Published by: United Advertising Publications, Inc., 1660 S Amphlett Blvd, Ste 335, San Mateo, CA 94402. TEL 650-655-7600, FAX 650-655-7601, cindy.byrnc@parenthood.com, http://sanfrancisco.parenthood.com/. Pub., Adv. contact Cindy Byne. B&W page USD 2,519, color page USD 2,897. Circ: 55,000 (free).

369.4 DEU ISSN 0174-2175
BAYERISCHE LANDJUGEND. Text in German. 1951. bi-m. EUR 15 (effective 2005). adv. bk.rev. abstr.; illus. **Document type:** *Newspaper, Consumer.*
Published by: Bayerische Jungbauernschaft e.V., Aubinger Weg 5, Germering, 82110, Germany. TEL 49-89-8944140, FAX 49-89-89441410, bjb-lgs@t-online.de, http://www.landjugend.de/bayern/zeitschr.htm, http://www.landjugend.de/bayern/index.htm. Ed. Harald Fehde. Circ: 1,800.

BEAR ESSENTIAL NEWS FOR KIDS. see *CHILDREN AND YOUTH—For*

649.1 HRV ISSN 1330-3902
BEBE; mjesecnik za roditelje i trudnice. Text in Croatian. 1992. m. HRK 180 domestic; EUR 44 foreign (effective 2002). adv. **Document type:** *Magazine, Consumer.*
Published by: Bebe d.o.o., Iblerov Trg 2, Zagreb, 10000, Croatia. TEL 385-1-4556268, FAX 385-1-4576810, bebe@bebe.hr, http://www.bebe.hr. Ed. Jasna Sipek. adv.: page HRK 9,200.

649.1 PRT
▼ **BEBE D'HOJE.** Text in Portuguese. 2003. m. EUR 2.50 newsstand/cover (effective 2005). **Document type:** *Magazine, Consumer.*
Published by: Motorpress Lisboa, SA, Rua Policarpio Anjos No. 4, Cruz Quebrada, Dafundo 1495-742, Portugal. TEL 351-21-4154500, FAX 351-21-4154501, bebedhoje@motorpress.pt, buzine@motorpress.pt, http://www.autohoje.com/quiosque.aspx?pub=0cb20267&ano=#l, http://www.mpl.pt/. Adv. contact Filomena Simoes. Circ: 19,156 (paid).

649.1 USA ISSN 1520-7730
BEFORE BIRTH AND BEYOND; community newsletter. Text in English. s-m. free. adv. **Document type:** *Newsletter.* **Description:** Presents articles on pregnancy, infant and child health, reader tips, freebies and information of interest to parents and persons who work in the areas of pregnancy, childbirth, breastfeeding, parenting and pediatrics.
Related titles: Online - full text ed.
Published by: Doerr Consulting, StorkNet, 3702 S Virginia St, No G 12 235, Reno, NV 89502. storknet@storknet.org, http://www.storknet.com/newsletter/index.html. Ed. Maribeth Doerr. Circ: 1,500.

BEGINNING (NASHVILLE). see *RELIGIONS AND THEOLOGY—Protestant*

155.4 367 DEU ISSN 0067-5105
BEITRAEGE ZUR KINDERPSYCHOTHERAPIE. Text in German. 1965. irreg., latest vol.32, 1998. price varies. index. **Document type:** *Monographic series, Academic/Scholarly.* —GNLM.
Published by: Ernst Reinhardt Verlag, Kemnatenstr 46, Munich, 80639, Germany. TEL 49-89-1780160, FAX 49-89-17801630. Eds. Gerd Biermann, Manfred Endres.

649 CAN ISSN 0005-965X
BEST WISHES. Text in English. 1949. s-a. free to new mothers. adv. illus. **Document type:** *Consumer.*
Published by: Family Communications, Inc., 65 The East Mall, Etobicoke, ON M8Z 5W3, Canada. Circ: 170,000 (controlled).

305.23 DEU ISSN 1438-5295
BETRIFFT MAEDCHEN; Zeitschrift fuer parteiliche Maechenarbeit. Text in German. q. EUR 17.50; EUR 6.50 newsstand/cover (effective 2003). adv. **Document type:** *Magazine, Academic/Scholarly.*
Published by: (Institut fuer Soziale Arbeit e.V.), Julius Beltz GmbH & Co. KG, Werderstr 10, Weinheim, 69469, Germany. TEL 49-6201-60070, FAX 49-6201-6007382, info@beltz.de, http://www.betrifftmaedchen.de, http://www.beltz.de. Ed. Monika Weber. Adv. contact Brigitte Bell. page EUR 410; trim 210 x 295. Circ: 1,000 (paid and controlled).

347.63 CZE ISSN 1212-0480
BETYNKA. Text in Czech. 1992. m. CZK 348 domestic; CZK 39 newsstand/cover (effective 2004). adv. **Document type:** *Magazine, Consumer.* **Description:** Contains articles and information about sexuality, pregnancy and birth, infant care and child rearing.
Published by: Burda Praha spol. s.r.o., Uruguayska 17, Prague 2, 120 00, Czech Republic. TEL 420-2-22520618, FAX 420-2-22522648, klincokova@burda.cz, http://www.burda.cz. Adv. contact Pavla Vondrackova. page CZK 130,000; trim 180 x 250. Circ: 70,000 (paid and controlled).

BIBLIOTHEQUE DE TRAVAIL JUNIOR. see *EDUCATION*

790.019 USA
BIG APPLE PARENT. Text in English. 1985. m. USD 29. adv. bk.rev. **Document type:** *Newspaper, Consumer.* **Description:** For parents raising children in New York City.
Published by: Family Communications, 9 E 38th St 4, New York, NY 10016-0003. TEL 212-889-6400, FAX 212-689-4958, parentspaper@parentsknow.com, http://www.parentsknow.com. Ed., R&P Helen Freedman. Pub., Adv. contact Steve Bauman. Circ: 70,000 (controlled).

BIG LITTLE TIMES. see *PUBLISHING AND BOOK TRADE*

649 ITA ISSN 1124-1748
BIMBISANI E BELLI. Text in Italian. 1993. m. EUR 21 domestic (effective 2005). illus. **Document type:** *Magazine, Consumer.* **Description:** Publishes articles of interest to mothers caring for infants and toddlers.
Published by: Unistar Srl (Subsidiary of: Casa Editrice Universo SpA), Corso di Porta Nuova 3A, Milan, 20121, Italy. TEL 39-02-636751, FAX 39-02-252007333, bimbisani@casaeditriceuniverso.com. Circ: 139,901 (paid).

649 USA
BIRMINGHAM FAMILY TIMES. Text in English. m. adv. **Description:** Provides a variety of information and resources to parents of newborns through parents of teens.
Published by: United Parenting Publications (Subsidiary of: Trader Publishing Co.), 2821 2nd Ave South, F, Birmingham, AL 35233. TEL 205-326-0846, FAX 205-326-0139.

362.7 USA
BIRTH TO THREE PARENTING NEWSLETTER. Text in English. 1978. bi-m. looseleaf. USD 15 (effective 2000). adv. bk.rev. illus. **Document type:** *Newsletter, Consumer.* **Description:** Offers parents of children age 3 and under articles about parenting issues and a list of events for children and parents.
Former titles: Birth to Three; Birth to Three and Beyond; Birth to Three Newsletter (0895-6669)
Published by: Birth to Three, 86 Centennial Loop, Eugene, OR 97401-7909. TEL 503-484-5316, FAX 503-484-1449, BirthToThree@birthto3.org, http://www.birthto3.org. Ed., R&P, Adv. contact Sylvia Lee Hanley TEL 541-349-7786. Circ: 1,500.

369.4 FRA ISSN 0980-2371
BIVOUAC. Text in French. 1954. 6/yr. adv. bk.rev. **Description:** Covers scouting and society. For boys and girls 12 to 16 years of age.
Formerly: A.E.I.O.U.
Published by: Eclaireuses et Eclaireurs Unionistes de France, 15 rue Klock, Clichy, 92110, France. TEL 33-1-42705220, FAX 33-1-47304030, sn@eeudf.org. Ed. Michael Schloesing. Circ: 5,000.

649 USA ISSN 0745-8649
BLACK BEAT. Text in English. 1974. m. USD 21.95 domestic; USD 27.95 in Canada; USD 29.95 elsewhere (effective 2003). adv. illus. back issues avail.; reprints avail. **Document type:** *Magazine, Consumer.* **Description:** Contains pictures and features, which is targeted to African-American teens and gives kids the latest on their favorite musicians and music.
Formerly (until 1983): Soul Teen (0277-8114)
Published by: Dorchester Media, 333 Seventh Ave, 11th Fl, New York, NY 10001. TEL 212-979-4800, 800-666-8783, FAX 212-979-7342, http://www.blackbeat.com.

362.7 USA
BLACK CHILD ADVOCATE. Text in English. 1971. 2/yr. USD 16 to non-members (effective 2003); subscr. incl. Child Health Talk. bk.rev. **Document type:** *Newsletter, Academic/Scholarly.* **Description:** For those interested in issues affecting the lives of black children, youth and families. Includes public policy information, and updates of the activities of NBCDI's volunteer affiliate network.
Indexed: V&AA.
Published by: National Black Child Development Institute, 1101 15th St, NW, Ste 900, Washington, DC 20005. TEL 202-833-2220, FAX 202-234-1738, moreinfo@nbcdi.org, http://www.nbcdi.org. Ed., R&P Carla Taylor. Circ: 3,500.

BLACK FAMILY TODAY. see *ETHNIC INTERESTS*

649 USA ISSN 1087-3899
BLACK PARENTING TODAY; information and resources for greater Philadelphia families. Text in English. q. USD 12 to individuals; USD 25 to institutions; USD 3 newsstand/cover (effective 2001).
Related titles: Online - full text ed.: (from ProQuest Information & Learning, SoftLine Information).
Indexed: ENW.
Published by: Black Parenting Today, Inc., P O Box 28663, Philadelphia, PA 19151. bpt@libertynet.org. Ed., Pub. Valerie Harris.

BOERN OG UNGE; dag- og doegninstitutioner i Danmark. see *SOCIAL SERVICES AND WELFARE*

BOERNS HVERDAG; tidsskrift for foraeldre, paedagoger og bestyrelsesmedlemmer. see *EDUCATION*

647 USA
BOISE FAMILY MAGAZINE. Text in English. m. **Description:** Promotes "family fun, education, and parental involvement.".
Published by: Liz Buckingham Publishing, 13191 W Scotfield St, Boise, ID 83713. TEL 208-938-2119, FAX 208-938-2117, boisefamily@cs.com, http://www.boisefamily.com. Pub. Liz Buckingham. Adv. contact Jeane Huff TEL 208-375-2889.

028.5 USA ISSN 1055-4742
Z1037
BOOK LINKS; connecting books, libraries, and classrooms. Text in English. 1991. 6/yr. USD 28.95 domestic; USD 36 foreign; USD 6 per issue (effective 2005). adv. bk.rev. bibl.; illus. index. back issues avail.; reprints avail. **Document type:** *Bibliography.* **Description:** Designed for teachers, librarians, library media specialists, booksellers, parents, and other adults interested in introducing children to books. Responds to the trend of teachers increasingly using quality literature to teach children across all disciplines.
Related titles: Online - full text ed.: (from EBSCO Publishing, Northern Light Technology, Inc., ProQuest Information & Learning).
Indexed: MASUSE, RGYP.
—BLDSC (2248.120000), IE, ingenta. **CCC.**
Published by: American Library Association, 50 E Huron St, Chicago, IL 60611-2795. TEL 800-545-2433, 800-545-2433, FAX 312-944-8741, ltillotson@ala.org, http://www.ala.org/BookLinks/index.html. Ed. Laura Tillotson. Pub. Bill Ott. Circ: 30,000. **Subscr. to:** Kable Fulfillment Services, 308 E Hitt St, Mount Morris, IL 61504. TEL 888-350-0949, FAX 815-734-5858, blnk@kable.com.

371.3 USA
BOOK MARK; children's literature in review with related activities for preschoolers through young adults. Text in English. 1977. 2/yr. USD 10. bk.rev.
Former titles (until 1982): In Review: Books for Children and Young People with Related Activities; Children's Literature in Review
Indexed: BRI, CBRI.
Address: c/o Jane Bingham, Oakland University, School of Human and Educational Services, Rochester, MI 48063. TEL 313-370-3015. Eds. Gloria Blatt, Jane Bingham. Circ: 1,000.

649 GBR
BOUNTY BABY BOOK. Text in English. 1974. a. free. adv. **Document type:** *Magazine, Consumer.*
Published by: Bounty Publications Ltd., 3 Theobald Ct, Theobald St, Borehamwood, Herts WD6 4RN, United Kingdom. TEL 44-181-207-4040, FAX 44-181-207-6966, jbonson@bountysca.co.uk, http://www.bounty.com. Ed. Mary Manning. adv.: color page GBP 27,000; trim 148 x 210. Circ: 700,000.

649 GBR
THE BOUNTY BABYCARE GUIDE. Text in English. 1964. a. adv. **Document type:** *Journal, Consumer.* **Description:** Packed with information on breastfeeding, sleeping and advice on development during baby's early days.
Published by: Bounty Publications Ltd., 3 Theobald Ct, Theobald St, Borehamwood, Herts WD6 4RN, United Kingdom. TEL 44-181-207-4040, 44-181-207-4040.

649 IRL
THE BOUNTY BABYCARE GUIDE. Text in English. 1973. a. adv. **Document type:** *Journal, Consumer.*
Published by: Bounty Services (Ireland) Ltd., Bromhill Rd, Unit 66, Tallaght, Dublin, 24, Ireland. TEL 353-1-4596066, FAX 353-1-4596082.

649 GBR
BOUNTY GUIDE TO FATHERHOOD. Text in English. 2000. 2/yr. free. adv. **Document type:** *Journal, Consumer.*
Published by: Bounty Publications Ltd., 3 Theobald Ct, Theobald St, Borehamwood, Herts WD6 4RN, United Kingdom. TEL 44-181-207-4040, FAX 44-181-207-6966.

649 GBR
BOUNTY TODDLER GUIDE. Text in English. 2/yr. free. adv. **Document type:** *Journal, Consumer.*
Published by: Bounty Publications Ltd., 3 Theobald Ct, Theobald St, Borehamwood, Herts WD6 4RN, United Kingdom. TEL 44-181-207-4040, FAX 44-181-207-6966, http://www.bounty.com.

649 GBR
BOUNTY YOUNG FAMILY GUIDE. Text in English. 1988. a. adv. **Document type:** *Journal, Consumer.* **Description:** Provides essential help in understanding your baby's health and feeding needs.
Published by: Bounty Publications Ltd., 3 Theobald Ct, Theobald St, Borehamwood, Herts WD6 4RN, United Kingdom. TEL 44-181-207-4040, FAX 44-181-207-6966, http://www.bounty.com.

369.4 USA
BOYS & GIRLS CLUBS OF AMERICA BULLETIN✶. Text in English. 1965. 4/yr. free. bk.rev. charts; illus. reprint service avail. from PQC.
Formerly (until 1991): Boys Club Bulletin (0006-8586)
Published by: Boys & Girls Clubs of America, 3 W 35th St, 9th Fl, New York, NY 10001-2204. TEL 212-351-5900. Ed. Glen Slattery. Circ: 25,000.

649 JPN
BOYS RUSH. Text in Japanese. 1998. m. JPY 6,000 domestic; JPY 10,200 foreign; JPY 500 newsstand/cover domestic (effective 2001). adv. **Document type:** *Consumer.* **Description:** Covers fashion and trends for young men in their late teens and early 20s.
Published by: Shufunotomo Co. Ltd., 2-9 Kanda-Surugadai, Chiyoda-ku, Tokyo, 101-8911, Japan. TEL 81-3-5280-7417, international@shufunotomo.co.jp, http://www.shufunotomo.co.jp. Ed. Kazuhiro Hidaki. R&P Yoshiyuki Ogino. Adv. contact Fujio Mano. Circ: 180,000. **Subscr. to:** Nippan IPS, 3-11-6 Tidabashi, Chiyoda-ku, Tokyo, Japan. TEL 81-3-3238-0700, FAX 81-3-3238-0707.

BRAILLE CHESS MAGAZINE. see *SPORTS AND GAMES*

BRAIN, CHILD; the magazine for thinking mothers. see *WOMEN'S INTERESTS*

053.932 BEL
BRIEVEN AAN JONGE OUDERS. Text in Dutch. 1979. a. free. adv. bk.rev. illus. **Document type:** *Magazine, Consumer.* **Description:** For parents who are expecting a baby, or who have young children from 0 to 3 years old.
Former titles: Brieven aan Gezinnen; Brieven aan Jonge Ouders
Published by: Publicarto N.V., Rue de la Poste 111, Bruxelles, 1030, Belgium. TEL 32-02-2203040, 32-02-779-0000, FAX 32-02-2203093, 32-02-779-1616, com@publicarto.be. Ed. Jef Berghmans. Adv. contact Catherine Doolaege. Circ: 62,750 (free).

362.7 USA ISSN 1058-1073
HQ767.8
BROWN UNIVERSITY CHILD AND ADOLESCENT BEHAVIOR LETTER; monthly reports on the problems of children and adolescents growing up. Text in English. 1984. m. USD 995 domestic to institutions; USD 1,043 in Canada & Mexico to institutions; USD 1,061 elsewhere to institutions; USD 1,095 combined subscription domestic to institutions print & online eds.; USD 1,143 combined subscription in Canada & Mexico to institutions print & online eds.; USD 1,161 combined subscription elsewhere to institutions print & online eds. (effective 2006). bk.rev. abstr.; bibl.; stat. 8 p./no.; back issues avail.; reprints avail. **Document type:** *Newsletter, Academic/Scholarly.* **Description:** Offers practical interventions, professional commentary and hands on techniques for working with troubled children and adolescents.
Incorporates (in 1992): Children and Teens Today (0882-942X); Which was formerly (until 1985): Children and Teens in Crisis (0732-7420); Former titles (until 1991): Brown University Child Behavior and Development Letter (0898-2562); (until 1986): The Brown University Human Development Letter (0885-7261)
Related titles: E-mail ed.; Online - full text ed.: ISSN 1556-7575. USD 995 (effective 2006) (from EBSCO Publishing, Florida Center for Library Automation, Gale Group, O C L C Online Computer Library Center, Inc.).
Indexed: CINAHL, e-psyche.
—CCC.
Published by: John Wiley & Sons, Inc., 111 River St, Hoboken, NJ 07030-5774. TEL 201-748-6000, 800-825-7550, FAX 201-748-5915, uscs-wis@wiley.com, http://www.wiley.com.

BROWN UNIVERSITY CHILD & ADOLESCENT PSYCHOPHARMACOLOGY UPDATE; updates on research, use of psychotropic medications and specific interventions with children & adolescents. see *MEDICAL SCIENCES—Pediatrics*

369.4 GBR ISSN 0007-2524
BROWNIE. Text in English. 1962. m. GBP 16.80; GBP 1.10 newsstand/cover (effective 1999). adv. bk.rev. charts; illus. **Description:** Contains games, stories, puzzles, and help for Brownies with badge requirements.
Published by: Guide Association, 17-19 Buckingham Palace Rd, London, SW1W 0PP, United Kingdom. TEL 44-20-7834-6242, FAX 44-20-7828-8317, CHQ@guides.org.uk, http://www.guides.org.uk. Ed., R&P Marion Thompson. Pub. Anne Moffat. Adv. contact Sarah Harrison. Circ: 30,000.

369.4 CAN ISSN 0045-334X
BUFFALO. Text in English. 1946. 6/yr. CND 15 (effective 1999). **Document type:** *Newsletter.*
Published by: Girl Guides of Canada, Manitoba Council, 872 St James St, Winnipeg, MB R3G 3J7, Canada. TEL 204-774-1939, FAX 204-774-9271, info@manitoba.girlguides.ca. Ed., R&P Cheryl Ryan. Circ: 1,474 (controlled).

BUILDING READERS (ELEMENTARY SCHOOL EDITION). see *EDUCATION*

BUILDING READERS (READING READINESS EDITION). see *EDUCATION*

BULLETIN JUGEND UND LITERATUR. see *LIBRARY AND INFORMATION SCIENCES*

C B C FEATURES; containing news of the children's book world. see *PUBLISHING AND BOOK TRADE*

C C B D NEWSLETTER. see *EDUCATION—Special Education And Rehabilitation*

369.4 DNK ISSN 0109-2979
C C ORIENTERING. Text in Danish. 1983. q. free. illus.
Published by: Coordination Committee for Polish - Jewish Youth in Denmark, PO Box 77, Copenhagen K, 1000, Denmark.

362.7 USA ISSN 0276-6531
HV741
C D F REPORTS. Text in English. m. USD 29.95. back issues avail. **Description:** Covers a range of issues concerning child welfare, including poverty, maternal and child health, education, employment, housing and more.
Published by: Children's Defense Fund, 25 E St, N W, Washington, DC 20001. TEL 202-628-8787, FAX 202-662-3530. Circ: 8,000.

649 USA
C F CHILD CARE BULLETIN. Text in English. 1978. bi-m. USD 20 to individuals; USD 30 to institutions (effective 2003). bk.rev. 8 p./no.; back issues avail. **Document type:** *Bulletin.*
Former titles: C F Child; Family Day Care Bulletin; Family Day Care Food Bulletin
Published by: Children's Foundation, 3020 Mt Vernon Ave., Alexandria, VA 22305-2637. TEL 202-347-3300. Ed. Sandra Gellert. Circ: 2,000.

362.76 USA
C H I L D NEWSLETTER. Text in English. 1984. q. USD 25 membership (effective 2003). bk.rev. **Document type:** *Newsletter, Consumer.* **Description:** Seeks to end the child abuse and neglect associated with the practices of certain religious groups.
Published by: (Children's Healthcare Is a Legal Duty), C H I L D, Inc., PO Box 2604, Sioux City, IA 51106. TEL 712-948-3500, FAX 712-948-3704, childinc@netins.net, http://www.childrenshealthcare.org. Ed., R&P Rita Swan. Circ: 440 (controlled).

C S L I PUBLICATION. see *LINGUISTICS*

649 FRA ISSN 0007-9820
CAHIERS DE LA PUERICULTRICE. Text in French. 1964. 10/yr. EUR 99.90 domestic to individuals; EUR 108 in Europe to individuals; JPY 13,800 in Japan to individuals; USD 130 elsewhere to individuals; EUR 100.88 domestic to institutions; EUR 109 in Europe to institutions; JPY 14,000 in Japan to institutions; USD 132 elsewhere to institutions (effective 2006). **Document type:** *Journal, Academic/Scholarly.* **Description:** Deals directly with day-to-day nursery nursing practice, providing the profession with the information it needs to enhance professional skills. Includes news in the therapeutic, pediatric, economic, and public health fields; continuous training updating knowledge on a pediatric pathology nursing practice in areas such as protocol, observance, and relation to the newborn or young baby; and a practical guide with new products, books, and multimedia.
—CISTI. **CCC.**
Published by: Elsevier France, Editions Scientifiques et Medicales (Subsidiary of: Elsevier Science & Technology), 23 Rue Linois, Paris, 75724, France. TEL 33-1-71724600, FAX 33-1-71724650, http://www.elsevier.com/locate/cahpu, http://www.elsevier.fr. Ed. Catherine Killian.

CALDECOTT (YEAR) MEDAL BOOKS. see *BIBLIOGRAPHIES*

649 CAN ISSN 1198-6069
CALGARY'S CHILD. Text in English. bi-m. CND 15 (effective 2005). **Document type:** *Magazine, Consumer.* **Description:** Presents news and information about issues, classes, activities and support for families.
Address: 723, 105-150 Crowfoot Crescent N W, Calgary, AB T3G 3T2, Canada. TEL 403-241-6066, FAX 403-286-9731, calgaryschild@shaw.ca, http://www.calgaryschild.com.

CALL LINK. see *RELIGIONS AND THEOLOGY—Protestant*

790.019 USA ISSN 0740-4131
SK601.A1
CAMPING MAGAZINE. Text in English. 1926. bi-m. USD 24.95 (effective 2005). adv. charts; illus.; stat.; tr.lit. Index. back issues avail.; reprint service avail. from PQC. **Document type:** *Magazine, Consumer.* **Description:** Offers camp directors and counselors practical and professional advice.
Related titles: Microform ed.: (from PQC); Online - full text ed.: (from EBSCO Publishing, Gale Group, Northern Light Technology, Inc., O C L C Online Computer Library Center, Inc., ProQuest Information & Learning).
Indexed: CIJE, MASUSE, MagInd, PEI, RehabLit, SPI, SportS.
—IE, Infotrieve.
Published by: American Camping Association, Inc., 5000 State Rd 67 N, Martinsville, IN 46151-7902. TEL 765-342-8456, 800-428-2267, FAX 765-342-2065, magazine@acacamps.org, msnider@acacamps.org, http://www.acacamps.org. Ed. Harriet Gamble. R&P Teresa Nicodemus. Adv. contact Elaine Kidwell. Circ: 7,000 (paid).

C

362.7 796 CAN ISSN 0300-435X
CANADIAN GUIDER. Text in English. 1932. 5/yr. CND 9 domestic; CND 12.50 foreign; CND 2 newsstand/cover. bk.rev. back issues avail. **Description:** Includes leadership tips and program activities for guide leaders.
Published by: (National Council), Girl Guides of Canada, 50 Merton St, Toronto, ON M4S 1A3, Canada. TEL 416-487-5281, FAX 416-487-7024, ggc@girlguides.ca, http://www.girlguides.ca. Ed. Sharon Jackson Pruner. R&P Barbara Crocker. adv.: B&W page CND 1,600, color page CND 2,200; trim 10.88 x 8.13. Circ: 60,000 (controlled).

CANDLELIGHTERS CHILDHOOD CANCER FOUNDATION YOUTH NEWSLETTER. see *MEDICAL SCIENCES—Oncology*

362.7 USA
CARING FOR THE LITTLE ONES; creating a network of people who work with infants and toddlers. Text in English. m. **Description:** Provides information on how to teach and take care of infants and toddlers.
Address: PO Box 97, Cowdrey, CO 80434-0097. TEL 303-723-4708.

CARNEGIE-MELLON SYMPOSIA ON COGNITION SERIES. see *PSYCHOLOGY*

649 USA
CATCH ONLINE MAGAZINE. Text in English. irreg. **Document type:** *Newsletter.* **Description:** Parent-friendly, across-the-kitchen-table type of chat complimented by original graphics and a casual atmosphere.
Media: Online - full text.
Published by: PageBrothers Professional Services L.L.C. http://www.pagebrothers.com/catch/index.html.

CATHOLIC EDUCATION CIRCULAR. see *EDUCATION*

C

282.085 USA ISSN 1069-4862
CATHOLIC PARENT. Text in English. 1993. bi-m. USD 24 (effective 2003). adv. bk.rev. illus. reprints avail. **Document type:** *Consumer.*
Indexed: CPL.
Published by: Our Sunday Visitor, Inc., 200 Noll Plaza, Huntington, IN 46750. FAX 260-359-9117, 800-348-2440, cparent@osv.com, http://web.fwi.com/osv/periodicals/periodical.cfm?id=CatholicParent, http://www.osv.com. Eds. Greg Erlandson, Woodeen Koenig Bricker. Adv. contact Peter Schownir TEL 800-348-2440. B&W page USD 1,050, color page USD 1,315; trim 10.88 x 8.38. Circ: 34,535.

028.5 USA ISSN 0008-9036
Z1037.A1
CENTER FOR CHILDREN'S BOOKS. BULLETIN. Text in English. 1947. m. (except combined issue July/Aug). USD 50 to individuals; USD 75 to institutions; USD 105 combined subscription to institutions (effective 2006). adv. bk.rev. abstr.; tr.lit.; illus. Index. 48 p./no.; reprint service avail. from PQC,ISI,PSC. **Document type:** *Magazine, Bibliography.* **Description:** Provides summaries and critical evaluations of newly published and forthcoming books for children.
Related titles: Microform ed.: (from PQC); Online - full text ed.: USD 75 to institutions (effective 2006) (from EBSCO Publishing, H.W. Wilson, O C L C Online Computer Library Center, Inc., ProQuest Information & Learning).
Indexed: BRD, BRI, CBRI, RGYP.
—CCC.
Published by: (University of Illinois at Urbana-Champaign, Center for Children's Books), University of Illinois Press, 1325 S Oak St, Champaign, IL 61820-6903. TEL 866-244-0626, FAX 217-244-9910, bccb@alexia.lis.uiuc.edu, journals@uillinois.edu, http://www.lis.uiuc.edu/puboff/bccb/, http://www.press.uillinois.edu. Adv. contact Clyde Wantland TEL 217-244-6496. B&W page USD 395. Circ: 3,000 (paid).

649 USA
CENTRAL FLORIDA FAMILY. Text in English. 1985. m. USD 18 (effective 2001). adv. **Document type:** *Consumer.*
Related titles: Online - full text ed.
Published by: Orlando Sentinel Communications, 633 N Orange Ave, Orlando, FL 32801. TEL 407-420-5680, http://www.centralfloridafamily.com, http://www.floridafamily.com. Ed., Pub. Sue Ross. Adv. contact Mike Lyons. Circ: 70,000 (controlled).

649.1 USA
CENTRAL PENN PARENT. Text in English. 1995. m. free at select locations in central PA. **Document type:** *Consumer.*
Published by: Journal Publications, Inc., 101 N Second St, 2nd Fl., Harrisburg, PA 17101. TEL 717-236-4300, FAX 717-236-6803, http://www.centralpennparent.com/. Ed. Karren Johnson. Pub. David A Schankweiler. Adv. contact Darren Helder. Circ: 35,000.

649 CAN ISSN 0705-3215
C'EST POUR QUAND. Text in English. 1978. s-a. adv. **Document type:** *Consumer.*
Published by: Family Communications, Inc., 65 The East Mall, Etobicoke, ON M8Z 5W3, Canada. Ed. Manon Leymone. Circ: 52,000 (controlled).

286 USA ISSN 0009-1723
CHARITY AND CHILDREN; the voice of child care in North Carolina. Text in English. 1887. m. free. adv. bk.rev. **Document type:** *Newspaper.* **Description:** Provides information to friends and supporters about services.
Published by: Baptist Children's Homes of North Carolina, Inc., PO Box 338, Thomasville, NC 27361-0338. TEL 336-474-1211, FAX 336-472-3802. Ed. Norman Jameson. Pub. Michael C Blackwell. Circ: 55,000.

CHEROKEE BOYS CLUB NEWSLETTER. see *ETHNIC INTERESTS*

649 USA
CHICAGO PARENT. Text in English. m. free (effective 2005). adv. **Document type:** *Magazine, Consumer.* **Description:** Offers information, inspiration, perspective and empathy to parents in the Chicago metropolitan area.
Published by: Wednesday Journal Inc., 141 S Oak Park Ave, Oak Park, IL 60302-2901. TEL 708-386-5555, FAX 708-524-8360, chiparent@wjinc.com, http://www.chicagoparent.com. Ed. Susy Schultz. Circ: 135,000 (free).

CHIEF ADJUDICATION OFFICER. ANNUAL REPORT. see *SOCIAL SERVICES AND WELFARE*

155.4 USA ISSN 0894-7988
CHILD; the essential guide for parents. Text in English. 1986. 10/yr. USD 9.97 domestic; USD 28.94 in Canada; USD 3.50 newsstand/cover (effective 2005). adv. bk.rev. illus. reprints avail. **Document type:** *Magazine, Consumer.* **Description:** Offers information on child rearing and includes articles on child development, behavior, health, nutrition, fitness, and education. Covers new products and services for children and their parents, as well as travel, fashion, food and beauty topics.
Formerly (until 1986): For Today's Children
Related titles: Online - full text ed.
Indexed: RILM, e-psyche.
Published by: Gruner + Jahr U.S.A. Publishing (Subsidiary of: Gruner und Jahr AG & Co.), 375 Lexington Ave, New York, NY 10017. TEL 212-499-2000, FAX 212-499-2038, childmail@childmagazine.com, corpcomm@gjusa.com, http://www.child.com, http://www.gjusa.com. Ed. Miriam Arond. Adv. contact Elisabeth Paredes. Circ: 925,000 (paid). **Subscr. to:** PO Box 3176, Harlan, IA 51593-0367. **Dist. in UK by:** Comag, Tavistock Works, Tavistock Rd, W Drayton, Middx UB7 7QX, United Kingdom. TEL 44-1895-444055, FAX 44-1895-433602.

CHILD ABUSE. see *CRIMINOLOGY AND LAW ENFORCEMENT*

362.76 GBR ISSN 0145-2134
HV713 CODEN: CABND3
➤ **CHILD ABUSE & NEGLECT.** Text in English. 1977. 12/yr. EUR 201 in Europe to individuals; JPY 26,500 in Japan to individuals; USD 224 to individuals except Europe and Japan; EUR 1,485 in Europe to institutions; JPY 197,300 in Japan to institutions; USD 1,662 to institutions except Europe and Japan (effective 2006). adv. bk.rev. illus. index. back issues avail.; reprints avail. **Document type:** *Journal, Academic/Scholarly.* **Description:** Provides an international multidisciplinary forum on all aspects of child abuse and neglect, including sexual abuse, with emphasis on prevention and treatment.
Formerly: International Journal on Child Abuse and Neglect
Related titles: Microfilm ed.: (from PQC); Online - full text ed.: (from EBSCO Publishing, Gale Group, IngentaConnect, ScienceDirect, Swets Information Services).
Indexed: ABIn, AC&P, AMHA, ASCA, ASSIA, BDM&CN, BrEdI, CDA, CIJE, CINAHL, CJA, CurCont, DIP, ECER, ESPM, EduInd, ExcerpMed, FamI, H&SSA, IBR, IBSS, IBZ, INI, IPARL, IPsyAb, IUSGP, IndMed, MEDLINE, PCI, PsycInfo, PsycholAb, RefZh, RiskAb, SFSA, SOPODA, SSA, SSCI, SSI, SWR&A, SociolAb, V&AA, e-psyche.
—BLDSC (3172.912500), GNLM, IDS, IE, Infotrieve, ingenta, KNAW. **CCC.**
Published by: (International Society for Prevention of Child Abuse and Neglect), Pergamon (Subsidiary of: Elsevier Science & Technology), The Boulevard, Langford Ln, East Park, Kidlington, Oxford OX5 1GB, United Kingdom. TEL 44-1865-843000, FAX 44-1865-843010, http://www.elsevier.com/locate/chiabuneg. Ed. Dr. John M. Leventhal. Circ: 1,500. **Subscr. to:** Elsevier BV, PO Box 211, Amsterdam 1000 AE, Netherlands. nlinfo-f@elsevier.nl, http://www.elsevier.nl.

➤ **CHILD ABUSE, CHILD WELFARE & ADOPTION.** see *CHILDREN AND YOUTH—Abstracting, Bibliographies, Statistics*

➤ **CHILD ABUSE PREVENTION**; national child protection clearing house newsletter. see *SOCIAL SERVICES AND WELFARE*

➤ **CHILD ABUSE PREVENTION ISSUES.** see *SOCIAL SERVICES AND WELFARE*

➤ **CHILD & ADOLESCENT HEALTH CARE.** see *MEDICAL SCIENCES—Pediatrics*

▼ ➤ **CHILD & ADOLESCENT MENTAL HEALTH IN PRIMARY CARE**; for professionals working with children & adolescents. see *MEDICAL SCIENCES—Pediatrics*

➤ **CHILD AND ADOLESCENT SOCIAL WORK JOURNAL.** see *SOCIOLOGY*

➤ **CHILD AND FAMILY LAW QUARTERLY.** see *LAW—Family And Matrimonial Law*

➤ **CHILD & FAMILY SOCIAL WORK.** see *SOCIAL SERVICES AND WELFARE*

➤ **CHILD & FAMILY SOCIAL WORK ONLINE.** see *SOCIAL SERVICES AND WELFARE*

155.4 USA ISSN 1053-1890
HV701 CODEN: CYCFEH
➤ **CHILD AND YOUTH CARE FORUM**; an independent journal of day and residential child and youth care practice. Text in English. 1971. bi-m. EUR 698, USD 728, GBP 438 combined subscription to institutions print & online eds. (effective 2005). adv. bk.rev. bibl.; illus. Index. back issues avail.; reprint service avail. from PQC,ISI,PSC. **Document type:** *Journal, Academic/Scholarly.* **Description:** Covers the training of personnel and psychological testing.
Former titles (until 1991): Child and Youth Care Quarterly (0893-0848); (until 1987): Child Care Quarterly (0045-6632)
Related titles: Microform ed.: (from PQC); Online - full text ed.: ISSN 1573-3319 (from EBSCO Publishing, Gale Group, IngentaConnect, Kluwer Online, O C L C Online Computer Library Center, Inc., Ovid Technologies, Inc., Springer LINK, Swets Information Services).
Indexed: ABIn, AC&P, AMHA, ASCA, ASSIA, Agr, BibAg, BibLing, CDA, CIJE, CMHR, CurCont, ECER, ERA, ETA, EduInd, FamI, IMFL, MEA, MEA&I, PsySCDP, PsycInfo, PsycholAb, RHEA, RILM, RefZh, SEA, SENA, SFSA, SOMA, SSA, SSCI, SUSA, SWR&A, TEA, V&AA, e-psyche.
—BLDSC (3172.915800), GNLM, IDS, IE, Infotrieve, ingenta. **CCC.**
Published by: Plenum US (Subsidiary of: Springer Science+Business Media), 233 Spring St, New York, NY 10013. TEL 212-460-1500, FAX 212-460-1575, service@springer-ny.com, http://springerlink.metapress.com/openurl.asp?genre=journal&issn=1053-1890, http://www.springeronline.com. Eds. Doug Magnuson, Sibylle Artz.

➤ **CHILD & YOUTH SERVICES.** see *SOCIAL SERVICES AND WELFARE*

649.1 CAN ISSN 1481-8027
➤ **CHILD CARE BRIDGES.** Text in English. 1976. q. CND 35. adv. bk.rev. **Document type:** *Newsletter, Academic/Scholarly.* **Description:** A regular update of the association's work towards quality care and of issues and developments affecting children, child care programs and early childhood educators in centres and family day care homes.
Formerly (until 1999): Family Day Care Association of Manitoba. Bridges (1483-4596); Which incorporated (1984-199?): Child Care Focus (0847-3234)
Published by: Manitoba Child Care Association, 364 McGregor St, Winnipeg, MB R2W 4X3, Canada. TEL 204-586-8587, FAX 204-589-5613. Ed., R&P Debra Mayer. Adv. contact Claire Funk. Circ: 2,600.

649 362.7 618.92 155.4 GBR ISSN 1357-5279
➤ **CHILD CARE IN PRACTICE.** Text in English. q. GBP 136, USD 224 combined subscription to institutions print & online eds. (effective 2006). reprint service avail. from PSC. **Document type:** *Journal, Academic/Scholarly.* **Description:** Aimed at professionals working in all disciplines in the provision of children's services, including social care, health care, medicine, psychology, education, police and probationary services, and legal services.
Related titles: Online - full text ed.: ISSN 1476-489X. GBP 129, USD 213 to institutions (effective 2006) (from EBSCO Publishing, Gale Group, IngentaConnect, O C L C Online Computer Library Center, Inc., Swets Information Services).
Indexed: FamI, IBSS.
—BLDSC (3172.931000), IE, ingenta. **CCC.**
Published by: (Child Care in Practice Group IRL), Routledge (Subsidiary of: Taylor & Francis Group), 4 Park Sq, Milton Park, Abingdon, Oxon OX14 4RN, United Kingdom. TEL 44-1235-828600, FAX 44-1235-829000, info@routledge.co.uk, http://www.tandf.co.uk/journals/titles/13575279.asp, http://www.routledge.com. Ed. Lynne Peyton. **Subscr. to:** Taylor & Francis Ltd, Journals Customer Service, Rankine Rd, Basingstoke, Hants RG24 8PR, United Kingdom. TEL 44-1256-813000, FAX 44-1256-330245.

➤ **CHILD CARE INFORMATION EXCHANGE.** see *EDUCATION—School Organization And Administration*

649 155.4 USA ISSN 0009-3920
HQ750.A1 CODEN: CHDEAW
➤ **CHILD DEVELOPMENT.** Text in English. 1930. bi-m. USD 429 combined subscription in the Americas to institutions & Caribbean (print & online eds.); GBP 305 combined subscription elsewhere to institutions print & online eds. (effective 2006); subscr. includes 4 issues Society for Research in Child Development. Monographs. adv. bk.rev. illus. index. back issues avail.; reprints avail. **Document type:** *Journal, Academic/Scholarly.* **Description:** Publishes original articles on all aspects of child development, from the prenatal period through adolescence.
Related titles: Microform ed.: (from PQC); Online - full text ed.: ISSN 1467-8624. USD 408 in the Americas to institutions & Caribbean; GBP 290 elsewhere to institutions (effective 2006) (from Blackwell Synergy, EBSCO Publishing, Florida Center for Library Automation, Gale Group, IngentaConnect, JSTOR (Web-based Journal Archive), O C L C Online Computer Library Center, Inc., Swets Information Services).
Indexed: AC&P, AMED, AMHA, ASCA, ASSIA, AbAn, AcaI, AgeL, Agr, BAS, BDM&CN, BMAb, BRI, BibAg, BiolAb, CBRI, CDA, CIJE, CIS, CJA, CPE, ChPerI, CommAb, CurCont, DIP, DSHAb, DentInd, ERA, ESPM, ETA, FamI, H&SSA, HlthInd, IBR, IBSS, IBZ, IMFL, IndMed, L&LBA, LingAb, MEA, MEA&I, MEDLINE, MLA, MLA-IB, NSCI, NutrAb, PCI, PRA, PsyScDP, PsycInfo, PsycholAb, RASB, RHEA, RRTA, SEA, SENA, SFSA, SOMA, SOPODA, SRRA, SSA, SSCI, SSI, SWA, SociolAb, TEA, V&AA, YAE&RB, e-psyche.
—BLDSC (3172.940000), CINDOC, CISTI, GNLM, IDS, IE, Infotrieve, ingenta, KNAW. **CCC.**
Published by: (Society for Research in Child Development), Blackwell Publishing, Inc. (Subsidiary of: Blackwell Publishing Ltd.), Commerce Place, 350 Main St, Malden, MA 02148. TEL 781-388-8206, FAX 781-388-8232, subscrip@blackwellpub.com, http://www.blackwellpublishing.com/journals/CDEV. Ed. Lynn S Liben. Circ: 8,600 (paid).

362.7 USA
CHILD HEALTH TALK. Text in English. 1987. 2/yr. USD 16 to non-members; includes Black Child Advocate. **Document type:** *Newsletter.* **Description:** Provides practical guidance and advice to parents on health issues facing Black children. Covers topics such as nutrition, safety, exercise, and common childhood illnesses.
Published by: National Black Child Development Institute, 1101 15th St, NW, Ste 900, Washington, DC 20005. TEL 202-833-2220, FAX 202-234-1738. Ed. Kim Sanwogou. Circ: 5,000.

331.31 363.1 346.01 USA
HD6228
CHILD LABOR MONITOR (ONLINE). Text in English. 1991. q. free. back issues avail. **Document type:** *Newsletter, Academic/Scholarly.* **Description:** Focuses on state, national, and international efforts to end child labor exploitation, and to ensure the health, education and well being of working minors.
Formerly: Child Labor Monitor (Print) (1060-6661)
Media: Online - full content.
Published by: National Consumers League, Inc., 1701 K St, N W, Ste 1200, Washington, DC 20006. TEL 202-835-3323, FAX 202-835-0747, http://www.stopchildlabor.org/. Ed. Darlene Adkins.

649 410 GBR
CHILD LANGUAGE AND CHILD DEVELOPMENT. Text in English. a. **Document type:** *Journal, Academic/Scholarly.*
—BLDSC (3172.944680).
Published by: Multilingual Matters Ltd., Frankfurt Lodge, Clevedon Hall, Victoria Rd, Clevedon, North Somerset BS21 7HH, United Kingdom. TEL 44-1275-876519, FAX 44-1275-871673, info@multilingual-matters.com, http://www.multilingual-matters.com.

649 USA
CHILD MAGAZINE'S GUIDE TO BABY PRODUCTS✶ ; the resource for new parents. Text in English. 1992. a. USD 4.95 newsstand/cover. adv. **Document type:** *Consumer.*
Published by: New York Times Company, Magazine Group, 375 Lexington Ave, New York, NY 10017-5514. TEL 212-463-1600, FAX 212-463-1383. Pub. Rebecca McPheters. Adv. contact Pam Sigal. B&W page USD 14,025, color page USD 16,900; trim 10.5 x 8. Circ: 600,000 (controlled).

649 USA ISSN 1049-2402
CHILD MAGAZINE'S GUIDE TO HAVING A BABY✶ . Variant title: Having a Baby. Text in English. 1990. a. adv.
Description: Information for expectant parents.
Published by: (Nurses Association for the American College of Obstetricians and Gynecology (NAACOG)), New York Times Company, Magazine Group, 375 Lexington Ave, New York, NY 10017-5514. TEL 212-463-1600, FAX 212-463-1553. Ed. Laura Manske. Circ: 1,200,000 (controlled).

362.7 USA ISSN 1077-5595
RC569.5.C55 CODEN: CMALFA
➤ **CHILD MALTREATMENT.** Text in English. 1996. q. USD 468, GBP 302 to institutions; USD 487, GBP 315 combined subscription to institutions print & online eds. (effective 2006). adv. illus. Index. back issues avail.; reprints avail. **Document type:** *Journal, Academic/Scholarly.* **Description:** Reports the latest scientific information and technical innovations relating to child abuse.
Related titles: Online - full text ed.: ISSN 1552-6119. USD 463, GBP 299 to institutions (effective 2006) (from C S A, EBSCO Publishing, O C L C Online Computer Library Center, Inc., Sage Publications, Inc., Swets Information Services).
Indexed: ASSIA, CDA, CINAHL, CJA, CPE, CurCont, DIP, ERA, ESPM, ETA, FamI, GSS&RPL, H&SSA, IBR, IBZ, IndMed, MEA, MEDLINE, PsycInfo, PsycholAb, RHEA, RiskAb, SEA, SENA, SFSA, SOMA, SOPODA, SSA, SSCI, SWA, SociolAb, TEA, V&AA, e-psyche.
—BLDSC (3172.944770), IE, Infotrieve, ingenta. **CCC.**
Published by: (American Professional Society on the Abuse of Children), Sage Publications, Inc., 2455 Teller Rd, Thousand Oaks, CA 91320. TEL 805-499-0721, FAX 805-499-8096, info@sagepub.com, http://www.sagepub.com/journal.aspx?pid=15. Ed. Steven J Ondersma. Pub. Sara Miller McCune. R&P Tanya Udin TEL 805-499-0721 ext 7716. Adv. contact Kirsten Beaulieu TEL 805-499-0721 ext 7160. page USD 350. Circ: 3,000 (paid). **Subscr. overseas to:** Sage Publications Ltd., 1 Oliver's Yard, 55 City Rd, London EC1 1SP, United Kingdom. TEL 44-20-73740645, FAX 44-20-73748741, subscription@sagepub.co.uk.

362.7 USA ISSN 1554-3684
HV741
CHILD PROTECTION LAW REPORT; the independent newsletter for professionals working with children and youth. Text in English. 1975. m. looseleaf. USD 187 in US & Mexico; USD 191 elsewhere; USD 217 combined subscription print & email eds. (effective 2005). bk.rev. charts; stat. index. 8 p./no. 2 cols./p.; back issues avail. **Document type:** *Newsletter.* **Description:** Offers advice and funding information for managers of child-assistance programs.
Formerly (until Dec. 2004): Child Protection Report (0147-1260)
Related titles: E-mail ed.: ISSN 1554-3692. USD 147 (effective 2005); Online - full text ed.: (from Gale Group).
Indexed: V&AA.
—CCC.
Published by: Business Publishers, Inc., 8737 Colesville Rd., Flr. 10, Silver Spring, MD 20910-3976. TEL 800-274-6737, custserv@bpinews.com, http://www.bpinews.com/hr/pages/cpr.cfm. Ed. Quintin Chatman. Pub. Leonard A Eiserer.

CHILD STUDY JOURNAL. see *EDUCATION*

CHILD SUPPORT PROSECUTORS' BULLETIN. see *LAW—Family And Matrimonial Law*

CHILD WELFARE; journal of policy, practice and program. see *SOCIAL SERVICES AND WELFARE*

CHILD WELFARE REPORT. see *SOCIAL SERVICES AND WELFARE*

CHILD WELFARE REVIEW; the internet journal on child welfare. see *SOCIAL SERVICES AND WELFARE*

305.23 GBR ISSN 0907-5682
HQ767.8 CODEN: CHILFF
➤ **CHILDHOOD**; a global journal of child research. Text in English. 1993. q. GBP 395, USD 691 to institutions; GBP 411, USD 720 combined subscription to institutions print & online eds. (effective 2006). adv. bk.rev. charts; illus. reprints avail. **Document type:** *Journal, Academic/Scholarly.* **Description:** Interdisciplinary forum for research relating to children in contemporary global society that spans divisions between geographical regions, disciplines, social and cultural contexts, and applied and basic research.
Related titles: Online - full text ed.: ISSN 1461-7013. GBP 391, USD 684 to institutions (effective 2006) (from C S A, EBSCO Publishing, O C L C Online Computer Library Center, Inc., Sage Publications, Inc., Swets Information Services).
Indexed: ASSIA, BrNI, CIJE, CINAHL, CurCont, FamI, IBSS, IPsyAb, PsycInfo, PsycholAb, SFSA, SOPODA, SSA, SSCI, SociolAb, V&AA, e-psyche.
—BLDSC (3172.951500), IDS, IE, Infotrieve, ingenta. **CCC.**
Published by: (Norwegian Centre for Child Research), Sage Publications Ltd. (Subsidiary of: Sage Publications, Inc.), 1 Oliver's Yard, 55 City Rd, London, EC1 1SP, United Kingdom. TEL 44-20-73248500, FAX 44-20-73248600, info@sagepub.co.uk, http://www.sagepub.co.uk/journal.aspx?pid=105488. Eds. Chris Jenks, Jens Qvortrup, Olga Nieuwenhuys. Adv. contact Jenny Kirby. page GBP 195; trim 192 x 114. Circ: 700. **Subscr. in the Americas to:** Sage Publications, Inc., 2455 Teller Rd, Thousand Oaks, CA 91320. TEL 805-499-0721, FAX 805-499-0871, journals@sagepub.com.

➤ **CHILDHOOD EDUCATION.** see *EDUCATION—Teaching Methods And Curriculum*

362.7 PHL
CHILDHOPE ASIA NEWSLETTER. Text in English. 1991. q. USD 20. **Document type:** *Newsletter.* **Description:** Aims to raise awareness and knowledge about the situation of street children in Asia through publication of research findings on street children issues.
Indexed: IPP.
Published by: Childhope Asia (Philippines), Inc., 1210 Penafrancia, Paco, Manila, 1007, Philippines. TEL 632-563-4647, FAX 632-563-2242, chsea@vasia.com. Ed., Pub. Teresita L Silva. Circ: 2,000.

649.1 IRL ISSN 1649-0975
CHILDLINKS. Text in English. 1993. q. adv. **Document type:** *Magazine, Consumer.*
Published by: (National Children's Resource Centre), Millennium Publications, 625 N. Circular Rd., Dublin, 1, Ireland. TEL 353-1-8552900, FAX 353-1-8552964, millennium.publications@indigo.ie. adv.: page EUR 1,267; bleed 210 x 297. Circ: 7,000 (controlled).

362.7 GBR
CHILDMINDING. Text in English. 1990. q. GBP 20 for 2 yrs. membership (effective Apr. 2000). adv. bk.rev. **Document type:** *Newsletter.* **Description:** Deals with all aspects of childminding and child care.
Formerly: Scottish Childminding Association Magazine (0959-0145)
Published by: Scottish Childminding Association, Ste 3, 7 Melville Ter, Stirling, FK8 2ND, United Kingdom. TEL 44-1786-445377, FAX 44-1786-449062, childminding@dial.pipex.com, http://www.dialspace.dial.pipex.com/childminding. Ed., R&P Alice McGrath. Adv. contact Karine Lee. Circ: 6,500.

▼ **CHILDREN AND LIBRARIES.** see *LIBRARY AND INFORMATION SCIENCES*

C

649 GBR ISSN 0951-0605
HQ767.8
CHILDREN & SOCIETY. Text in English. 1987. 5/yr. USD 320 to institutions; USD 352 combined subscription to institutions print & online eds. (effective 2005). adv. bk.rev. index. back issues avail. **Document type:** *Journal, Academic/Scholarly.* **Description:** Covers all aspects of child health, education, care and development.
Related titles: Online - full content ed.: USD 320 to institutions (effective 2005); Online - full text ed.: ISSN 1099-0860 (from EBSCO Publishing, Gale Group, IngentaConnect, Swets Information Services, Wiley InterScience).
Indexed: AC&P, ASSIA, BrEdI, CIJE, CJA, CPE, ERA, ETA, IBR, IBSS, IBZ, MEA, PSA, PsycInfo, PsycholAb, RHEA, SEA, SENA, SOMA, SOPODA, SSA, SWA, SWR&A, SociolAb, TEA, e-psyche.
—BLDSC (3172.961300), IE, Infotrieve, ingenta. **CCC.**
Published by: (National Children's Bureau), Blackwell Publishing Ltd., 9600 Garsington Rd, Oxford, OX4 2ZG, United Kingdom. TEL 44-1865-776868, FAX 44-1865-714591, customerservices@oxon.blackwellpublishing.com, http://www.interscience.wiley.com/jpages/0951-0605/, http://www.blackwellpublishing.com. adv.: B&W page GBP 650, color page GBP 1,550; trim 200 x 260. Circ: 700.

340 028.5 USA
KF479.A15
CHILDREN AND THE LAW. Text in English. 1986. s-a. USD 8. **Document type:** *Newsletter.* **Description:** Articles on children's rights, information on current services and resources.
Formerly: Child Advocacy and Protection Newsletter
Indexed: V&AA.
Published by: American Bar Association, Young Lawyers Division, 321 N. Clark St., Ste. 1400, Chicago, IL 60610-7656. TEL 312-988-5555, FAX 312-988-6281.

362.7 GBR ISSN 1465-9522
CHILDREN & VIOLENCE. Text in English. 1998. bi-m. free. **Document type:** *Newsletter.* **Description:** Brings together a wide range of people committed to the creation of a non-violent society.
Indexed: e-psyche.
—CCC.
Published by: National Children's Bureau, 8 Wakley St, London, EC1V 7QE, United Kingdom. TEL 44-20-78436000, FAX 44-20-72789512, http://www.ncb.org.uk. Circ: 1,000.

649 GBR ISSN 0956-3113
CHILDREN AND WAR NEWSLETTER✶ ; a newsletter for adults. Text in English. 1988. a. GBP 5. illus. back issues avail. **Document type:** *Newsletter.* **Description:** Critiques the militarization of children who play with war toys.
Published by: Peace Pledge Union, 1 Peace Passage, London, N7 0BT, United Kingdom. TEL 44-20-74249444. Ed. Jan Melichar. Circ: 400.

649 362.7 GBR
CHILDREN AND YOUNG PEOPLE. Text in English. 2000 (Jan.). m. **Description:** Publishes information for the training of child care professionals.
Media: Online - full content.

Published by: Social Education Trust whbs@childrenandyoungpeople.com, http://www.children.uk.co. **Co-sponsors:** Caring for Children; Institute of Childcare and Social Education.

649   USA   ISSN 1063-892X
HV741
CHILDREN AND YOUTH FUNDING REPORT. Text in English. 1992. s-m. USD 419 (effective 2005). 18 p./no. 2 cols./p.; back issues avail.; reprints avail. **Document type:** *Newsletter.* **Description:** Contains coverage of federal, foundation and private grant opportunities for programs in such areas as public assistance, child welfare, juvenile justice, education, mental health, substance abuse, job training, disability services, health care and other children-related areas.
Incorporated (1994-2003): Family Services Report (1524-9484); Which was formerly (until 1999): Families in Crisis Funding Report (1075-3184)
Related titles: Online - full content ed.
—CCC.
Published by: C D Publications, Inc., 8204 Fenton St, Silver Spring, MD 20910-2889. TEL 301-588-6380, 800-666-6380, FAX 301-588-6385, cyf@cdpublications.com, info@cdpublications.com, http://www.cdpublications.com/pubs/childrenandyouthfunding.php. Ed. Stephen Albright. Pub. Mike Gerecht.

362.7   GBR   ISSN 0190-7409
HV701
➤ **CHILDREN AND YOUTH SERVICES REVIEW.** Text in English. 1979. 12/yr. EUR 1,057 in Europe to institutions; JPY 140,400 in Japan to institutions; USD 1,182 to institutions except Europe and Japan; EUR 171 in Europe to qualified personnel; JPY 22,600 in Japan to qualified personnel; USD 190 to qualified personnel except Europe and Japan (effective 2006). bk.rev. illus. Index. back issues avail.; reprints avail. **Document type:** *Journal, Academic/Scholarly.* **Description:** Provides a forum for the critical analysis and assessment of social service programs designed to serve young people throughout the world, including in-depth coverage of child welfare, foster care, adoptions, child abuse and neglect, income support, mental health services, and social policy.
Related titles: Microfilm ed.: (from PQC); Online - full text ed.: (from EBSCO Publishing, Gale Group, IngentaConnect, ScienceDirect, Swets Information Services).
Indexed: AC&P, AMHA, ASCA, ASG, ASSIA, CDA, CIJE, CJA, ChPerl, CurCont, ECER, ERA, ETA, ExcerpMed, Faml, MEA, PSI, PsycInfo, PsycholAb, RHEA, SEA, SENA, SFSA, SOMA, SOPODA, SPAA, SSA, SSCI, SSI, SWR&A, SociolAb, TEA, V&AA, e-psyche.
—BLDSC (3172.962000), IDS, IE, Infotrieve, ingenta. **CCC.**
Published by: Pergamon (Subsidiary of: Elsevier Science & Technology), The Boulevard, Langford Ln, East Park, Kidlington, Oxford OX5 1GB, United Kingdom. TEL 44-1865-843000, FAX 44-1865-843010, http://www.elsevier.com/locate/childyouth. Ed. Dr. Duncan Lindsey. Circ: 1,200. **Subscr. to:** Elsevier BV, PO Box 211, Amsterdam 1000 AE, Netherlands. TEL 31-20-485-3757, FAX 31-20-485-3432, nlinfo-f@elsevier.nl, http://www.elsevier.nl.

➤ **CHILDREN BEFORE THE COURT**; reflections on legal issues affecting minors. see *LAW—Judicial Systems*

649   USA   ISSN 1538-7895
CHILDREN FAR AND WIDE. Text in English. q. USD 25 domestic; USD 35 in Canada; USD 45 elsewhere (effective 2003). adv. **Description:** Covers abused and neglected children, parenting skills, including stories and photographs.
Related titles: Online - full content ed.
Address: c/o CAFFAR.org, 507 N Sullivan Rd, Ste A-6, Veradale, WA 99037-8531. TEL 509-777-0064, FAX 509-928-2392, info@ChildrenFarandWide.com, http://www.childrenfarandwide.com/. adv.: B&W page USD 135, color 1/2 page USD 595; bleed 8.75 x 11.75.

CHILDREN FIRST!. see *SOCIAL SERVICES AND WELFARE*

364.36   USA   ISSN 0147-9881
HV9103
CHILDREN IN CUSTODY; a report on public juvenile detention and correctional facility census. Text in English. 1971. biennial. free.
Supersedes: U.S. Department of Health, Education and Welfare. Statistics on Public Institutions for Delinquent Children (0082-9935)
Published by: U.S. Department of Justice, Office of Juvenile Justice and Delinquency Prevention, 633 Indiana Ave, N W, Washington, DC 20531. TEL 202-307-5929, FAX 202-514-6384. Circ: 10,000. **Subscr. to:** PO Box 6000, Rockville, MD 20850.

CHILDREN IN FINLAND. see *SOCIAL SERVICES AND WELFARE*

CHILDREN IN FOCUS. see *SOCIAL SERVICES AND WELFARE*

362.7   GBR   ISSN 1465-9360
CHILDREN NOW. Text in English. 1969. q. GBP 43.57 domestic membership to individuals; GBP 38.73 foreign membership to individuals; GBP 45 elsewhere membership to individuals (effective 2000); free with membership. bk.rev. back issues avail. **Document type:** *Bulletin.* **Description:** Contains articles on the latest issues effecting children. Includes news about NCB activities, publications and conferences.
Former titles (until 1999): Children U K (1356-7020); (until 1994): Concern (0591-017X)
Indexed: BrEdl.
—BLDSC (3172.969100), IE, ingenta. **CCC.**
Published by: National Children's Bureau, 8 Wakley St, London, EC1V 7QE, United Kingdom. TEL 44-20-78436000, FAX 44-20-72789512, http://www.ncb.org.uk. Ed. Alison Love. Circ: 2,500.

649   USA
CHILDREN NOW. Text in English. 1996. q.
Media: Online - full content.
—BLDSC (3172.969100).
Address: 1212 Broadway, 5th Fl, Oakland, CA 94612. http://www.childrennow.org/.

649   USA   ISSN 1546-2250
▼ ➤ **CHILDREN, YOUTH AND ENVIRONMENTS.** Abbreviated title: C Y E. Text in English. 2003. s-a. free (effective 2005). **Document type:** *Journal, Academic/Scholarly.* **Description:** This journal and multidisciplinary, international network is dedicated to improving the lives of young people. It targets researchers, policy makers and professionals.
Media: Online - full text.
Indexed: SFSA, SociolAb.
Published by: University of Colorado, Campus Box 226, Boulder, CO 80309. TEL 303-442-7631, FAX 303-492-7272, http://cye.colorado.edu/, http://www.genders.org/.

362.7   USA   ISSN 0739-425X
CHILDREN'S ADVOCATE. Text mainly in English; Text occasionally in Spanish. 1973. bi-m. USD 12 (effective 2003). adv. bk.rev. **Document type:** *Newsletter.* **Description:** Covers California, national, and international policy issues affecting children and families. Written for children's service providers, child advocates, parents, policy makers, and educators.
Published by: Action Alliance for Children, 1201 Martin Luther King, Jr Way, Oakland, CA 94612. TEL 510-444-7136, aac@4children.org, http://www.4children.org. Ed. Jean Tepperman. Adv. contact Jessine Foss. page USD 490. Circ: 14,000.

CHILDREN'S AID SOCIETY. ANNUAL REPORT. see *SOCIAL SERVICES AND WELFARE*

CHILDREN'S AID SOCIETY NEWS. see *SOCIAL SERVICES AND WELFARE*

THE CHILDREN'S BOOK HANDBOOK. see *PUBLISHING AND BOOK TRADE*

CHILDREN'S BOOKWATCH. see *CHILDREN AND YOUTH—Abstracting, Bibliographies, Statistics*

CHILDREN'S BUSINESS. see *CLOTHING TRADE—Fashions*

CHILDREN'S CLOTHING INTERNATIONAL. see *CLOTHING TRADE*

CHILDREN'S COURT OF NEW SOUTH WALES INFORMATION BULLETIN. see *LAW—Criminal Law*

028.5 398   USA   ISSN 0739-5558
GR43.C4
CHILDREN'S FOLKLORE REVIEW. Text in English. 1979. s-a. free to members. bk.rev. cum.index: 1978-1988. back issues avail. **Document type:** *Academic/Scholarly.*
Indexed: ChLitAb, MLA-IB.
Published by: (Department of English), East Carolina University, E Fifth St, Greenville, NC 27858-4353. TEL 252-757-6672, FAX 252-757-4889, http://www.acls.org/afolks.htm. Ed. C W Sullivan III. Circ: 150.

▼ **CHILDREN'S GEOGRAPHIES.** see *PSYCHOLOGY*

649 362.1   USA
CHILDREN'S HEALTH & SAFETY. Text in English. bi-m. **Document type:** *Directory, Consumer.* **Description:** Sourcebook for parents of young children provides key health information.
Address: 103 Glen St, Glen Cove, NY 11542. TEL 516-656-0911, FAX 516-656-0904.

CHILDREN'S HEALTH CARE. see *SOCIAL SERVICES AND WELFARE*

372   USA
CHILDREN'S HOUSE - CHILDREN'S WORLD; a magazine for parents, teachers and professionals about today's children. Text in English. 1966. bi-m. USD 11.95 (effective 1998). adv. bk.rev. abstr.; charts; illus.; stat. **Document type:** *Magazine, Consumer.* **Description:** Discusses education and development of children from ages 3-16.

Formerly (until 1978): Children's House Magazine (0009-4137)
Related titles: Diskette ed.
Indexed: ECER, RehabLit.
Published by: (Montessori-Piaget for Health), Children's House, Inc., PO Box 111, Caldwell, NJ 07006. TEL 973-239-3442, FAX 973-483-1234. Ed. Kenneth Edelson. Pub. Avi Ben Edelson. R&P Sharon Edelson. Adv. contact Margalit Lindman. Circ: 50,000 (paid).

362.7   NZL   ISSN 1174-0477
➤ **CHILDREN'S ISSUES**; journal of the Children's Issues Centre. Text in English. 1997. s-a. NZD 45 (effective 2002). adv. illus. 44 p./no.; back issues avail. **Document type:** *Academic/Scholarly.* **Description:** Features reports on current research, discussion of topical issues, news items and guest columnists, and comments from children.
Indexed: INZP.
Published by: (University Of Otago, Children's Issues Centre), University of Otago Press, 56 Union St, PO Box 56, Dunedin, New Zealand. TEL 64-3-479-8807, FAX 64-3-479-8385, cic@otago.ac.nz, university.press@stonebow.otago.ac.nz. Eds. Anne Smith, Nicola Taylor. R&P Wendy Harrex. Adv. contact Robin Frame. B&W page NZD 255; trim 30 x 21. Circ: 650.

➤ **CHILDREN'S LAW NEWS.** see *LAW—Family And Matrimonial Law*

➤ **CHILDREN'S LEGAL RIGHTS JOURNAL.** see *LAW—Family And Matrimonial Law*

➤ **CHILDREN'S LITERATURE ASSOCIATION QUARTERLY.** see *LIBRARY AND INFORMATION SCIENCES*

808.899282   NLD   ISSN 0045-6713
Z1037.A1   CODEN: CLEDEW
➤ **CHILDREN'S LITERATURE IN EDUCATION;** an international quarterly. Text in English. 1970. q. EUR 368, USD 378, GBP 235 combined subscription to institutions print & online eds. (effective 2005). adv. bk.rev. index. reprint service avail. from PQC,PSC. **Document type:** *Journal, Academic/Scholarly.* **Description:** Provides for librarians, teachers, teachers-in-training, writers and interested parents. Seeks to promote lively discussion of writing for young people.
Related titles: Microform ed.: (from PQC); Online - full text ed.: ISSN 1573-1693. USD 378 to institutions (effective 2005) (from EBSCO Publishing, Gale Group, IngentaConnect, Kluwer Online, O C L C Online Computer Library Center, Inc., Springer LINK, Swets Information Services).
Indexed: ABIn, AES, ASCA, ArtHuCI, BEL&L, BRI, BibLing, BrEdl, CBRI, CIJE, CPE, ChLitAb, CurCont, EduInd, Faml, MLA-IB, PCI, SOPODA.
—BLDSC (3172.991000), IDS, IE, Infotrieve, ingenta. **CCC.**
Published by: Springer-Verlag Dordrecht (Subsidiary of: Springer Science+Business Media), Van Godewijckstraat 30, Dordrecht, 3311 GX, Netherlands. TEL 31-78-6576050, FAX 31-78-6576474, http://springerlink.metapress.com/openurl.asp?genre=journal&issn=0045-6713, http://www.springeronline.com. Eds. Geoff Fox, Margaret Mackey.

369.4 200   USA   ISSN 1054-1144
CHILDREN'S MINISTRY. Text in English. 1991. 6/yr. USD 24.95; USD 29.95 combined subscription print & online eds. (effective 2005). adv. **Document type:** *Journal, Consumer.* **Description:** Provides practical help for Christian adults who work with children from birth to sixth grade.
Indexed: CCR.
Published by: Group Publishing, Inc., PO Box 481, Loveland, CO 80539. TEL 800-447-1070, FAX 970-292-4373, info@grouppublishing.com, http://www.cmmag.com, http://www.grouppublishing.com. Ed. Christine Yount. Pub. Tim Gilmour. R&P Jane Gerk. Adv. contact Sophia Winter. page USD 4,495; trim 8 x 10.75. Circ: 80,000 (paid and controlled).
Subscr. to: PO Box 469081, Escondido, CA 92046-9081.

362.7   USA
CHILDREN'S NEWS✱ . Text in English. 1973. bi-m. USD 10. adv. bk.rev. back issues avail.
Published by: Children's Council of San Francisco, 575 Sutter St, 2nd Fl, San Francisco, CA 94102-1108. TEL 415-864-1881. Ed. Linda Revel. Circ: 20,000.

362.7   GBR
CHILDREN'S RESIDENTIAL CARE UNIT NEWSLETTER. Text in English. 1995. 3/yr. free. bk.rev. **Document type:** *Newsletter.* **Description:** Publicizes the work of the Residential Care Unit's projects in key areas such as education, children's rights and participation, health care and preparation for adulthood.
Formerly: Children's Residential Care Newsletter (1357-7085)
—CCC.
Published by: National Children's Bureau, 8 Wakley St, London, EC1V 7QE, United Kingdom. TEL 44-20-78436000, FAX 44-20-72789512, http://www.ncb.org.uk. Circ: 1,000.

CHILDREN'S TECHNOLOGY REVIEW. see *COMPUTERS—Software*

CHILDREN'S VOICE. see *SOCIAL SERVICES AND WELFARE*

362.7 GBR ISSN 0265-1459
KD735.A13
➤ **CHILDRIGHT.** Text in English. 1983. 10/yr. GBP 32 in United Kingdom to individuals; GBP 42 elsewhere to individuals; GBP 45 in United Kingdom to institutions; GBP 50 in Europe to institutions; GBP 60 elsewhere to institutions (effective 2001). adv. bk.rev. **Document type:** *Bulletin, Academic/Scholarly.* **Description:** Explains and assesses enacted and propose legislation affecting children and young people. discusses research, analyses policy development, carries features from leading experts in the area and representatives of the major UK organisations concerned with children's rights; monitors news, legal cases, parliamentary debates, legislation and publications.
Indexed: ELJI, HRIR, LJI.
—BLDSC (3172.992700), IE, ingenta. **CCC.**
Published by: Children's Legal Centre Ltd., University of Essex, Wivenhoe Park, Colchester, Essex CO4 3SQ, United Kingdom. TEL 44-1206-874026, FAX 44-1206-873428, clc@essex.ac.uk, http://www.childrenslegalcentre.com. Eds. Carolyn Hamilton, Marcus Roberts TEL 44-1206-873483. R&P, Adv. contact Marcus Roberts TEL 44-1206-873483. Circ: 1,500 (paid).

155.4 USA ISSN 0749-8632
CHILD'S PLAY. Text in English. 1984. q. USD 55 domestic membership; USD 60 foreign membership (effective 2003). adv. bk.rev. back issues avail. **Document type:** *Newsletter.* **Description:** Covers toy libraries, toys, play and programs advantageous to the healthy development of children. Also provides a network among professionals who work with children in play settings.
Published by: U S A Toy Library Association, 1326 Wilmette Ave., Wilmette, IL 60091-2560. TEL 847-864-3330, FAX 847-864-3332, usatla@aol.com, http://usatla.deltacollege.org/newsletter.html. Ed., R&P, Adv. contact Judith Iacuzzi. Pub. Judith Q Iacuzzi. Circ: 700.

267 268 USA ISSN 1064-2781
CHILDWORLD. Text in English. 1976. q. free. illus.; abstr. 20 p./no.; **Document type:** *Newsletter, Consumer.* **Description:** Informs donors and sponsors of the activities and programs C.C.F. is conducting worldwide on behalf of needy children.
Formerly (until Aug. 1978): C C F World News
Published by: Christian Children's Fund, Inc., Development Office, Box 85066, Richmond, VA 23286-8912. http://www.christianchildrensfund.org. Ed. Alison Abbitt. Circ: 260,000 (controlled and free).

028.5 USA ISSN 1089-8018
Z1039.S5
CHOICES FOR YOUNG READERS. LIBRARY-TEACHER PROFESSIONAL EDITION. Text in English. 1997. irreg. USD 89.50 per issue (effective 2003). **Document type:** *Academic/Scholarly.* **Description:** Provides reading recommendations for second to sixth graders and is designed for use by teachers, librarians, and reading specialists.
Media: CD-ROM.
Published by: John Gordon Burke Publisher, Inc., PO Box 1492, Evanston, IL 60204-1492. TEL 847-866-8625, FAX 847-866-6639, info@jgburkepub.com, http://www.jgburkepub.com/choices-cd.html, http://jgburkepub.com.

028.5 USA ISSN 1089-8026
Z1039.S5
CHOICES FOR YOUNG READERS PARENT-HOME EDITION. Text in English. 1997. irreg. USD 39.95 per issue (effective 2003). **Description:** Contains 664 book recomendations.
Media: CD-ROM.
Published by: John Gordon Burke Publisher, Inc., PO Box 1492, Evanston, IL 60204-1492. TEL 847-866-8625, FAX 847-866-6639, info@jgburkepub.com, http://www.jgburkepub.com/choices-cd.html, http://jgburkepub.com.

649 268 USA ISSN 0009-5389
CHRISTIAN HOME & SCHOOL. Text in English. 6/yr. USD 13.95 domestic; CND 21.50 in Canada; USD 25 elsewhere (effective 2003). adv. bk.rev. **Description:** Aimed at contemporary Christian families. Focuses on family life and educational and parenting issues.
Published by: Christian Schools International, 3350 E Paris Ave, S E, Grand Rapids, MI 49512-3054. TEL 616-957-1070, 800-635-8288, FAX 616-957-5022, RogerS@csionline.org, info@csionline.org, http://community.gospelcom.net/Brix?pageID=2869. Ed. Gordon L Bordewyk. Adv. contact Lori Feenstra. Circ: 67,000.

649 266 USA ISSN 1065-7215
CHRISTIAN PARENTING TODAY. Text in English. 1988. q. USD 17.95 domestic; USD 22.95 foreign; USD 4.95 newsstand/cover (effective 2005). adv. bk.rev.; music rev.; video rev. back issues avail. **Document type:** *Magazine, Consumer.* **Description:** Encourages and informs parents of children 0-12 who want to build strong families from a positive Christian perspective.
Formerly: Christian Parenting (1040-8088)
Related titles: CD-ROM ed.; Online - full text ed.: ISSN 1551-1839 (from Gale Group).
Indexed: CCR, ChrPI.
—CCC.
Published by: Christianity Today International, 465 Gundersen Dr, Carol Stream, IL 60188. TEL 630-260-6200, FAX 630-260-0114, cpt@christianparenting.net, http://www.christianparenting.net, http://www.christianitytoday.com. Pub. Paul Robbins. R&P Raelynn Eickhoff. Adv. contact Brian Ondracek TEL 630-260-6202. B&W page USD 3,171, color page USD 3,805; trim 10.75 x 8. Circ: 76,000.

CHURCH LADS' AND CHURCH GIRLS' BRIGADE. ANNUAL REPORT. see *RELIGIONS AND THEOLOGY—Protestant*

649 USA
CINCINNATI FAMILY. Text in English. m. free (effective 2004). adv. **Document type:** *Magazine, Consumer.* **Description:** Offers a variety of parenting articles featuring local resources - doctors, teachers, other parents, people you know and trust.
Published by: Radio Cincinnati, Inc., 895 Central Ave, Ste 900, Cincinnati, OH 45202. TEL 513-241-9898, FAX 513-241-6689, http://www.warm98.com/magazine/. Ed. S Landers. Pub. Gary Lewis TEL 513-412-7973. Adv. contact Jennie Shirrell TEL 513-241-9898. B&W page USD 900; trim 8.5 x 10. Circ: 64,800.

CLARKE HALL & MORRISON ON CHILDREN. see *LAW*

649 POL ISSN 1506-9796
CLAUDIA RODZICE. Text in Polish. 1999. bi-m. **Document type:** *Magazine, Consumer.*
Published by: Gruner und Jahr Polska Sp. z o.o. & Co., Ul. Wynalazek 4, Warsaw, 02-677, Poland. TEL 48-22-607-02-00, FAX 48-22-607-02-21, marketing@gjpoland.com.pl, http://www.guj.com.pl.

CLEARING HOUSE. see *EDUCATION*

649 USA
CLEVELAND - AKRON FAMILY; helping families grow since 1989. Text in English. 1989. m. free. adv. bk.rev. 50 p./no.; back issues avail. **Document type:** *Newspaper.* **Description:** Encourages positive family interaction and updates parents on area events, educational trends, entertainment venues and services for families and children.
Formerly: Family Times of Cleveland (1043-836X)
Published by: T N T Publications, LLC, 35475 Vine St, Ste 224, Eastlake, OH 44095. TEL 440-510-2000, FAX 440-510-2001, publisher@tntpublications.com, http://www.clevelandakronfamily.com/, http://www.tntpublications.com. Ed. Frances Richards TEL 410-510-2000 ext 202. Pub. Todd Nighswonger TEL 410-510-2000 ext 207. adv.: B&W page USD 2,300; trim 8.375 x 10.875. Circ: 65,000.

649.1 306.874 USA ISSN 1060-8222
CLEVELAND PARENT MAGAZINE. Text in English. 1989. m. USD 18 (effective 1998). adv. bk.rev.; film rev. illus. **Document type:** *Consumer.*
Related titles: Online - full text ed.
Published by: Midwest Parenting Publications, 20325 Center Ridge Rd, Ste 135, Rocky River, OH 44116. TEL 440-895-9723, FAX 440-895-9753. Ed. Aura Ensley. Adv. contact Sue Wynne. page USD 1,410; trim 13 x 10. Circ: 50,000.

616.8 362 GBR ISSN 1359-1045
RJ499.A1 CODEN: CCPPFR
➤ **CLINICAL CHILD PSYCHOLOGY & PSYCHIATRY.** Text in English. 1996. q. GBP 433, USD 758 to institutions; GBP 451, USD 790 combined subscription to institutions print & online eds. (effective 2006). adv. bk.rev. **Document type:** *Journal, Academic/Scholarly.* **Description:** Publishes papers that focus on clinical and therapeutic aspects of child and adolescent psychology and psychiatry.
Related titles: Online - full text ed.: ISSN 1461-7021. GBP 429, USD 750 to institutions (effective 2006) (from C S A, EBSCO Publishing, O C L C Online Computer Library Center, Inc., Sage Publications, Inc., Swets Information Services).
Indexed: ASG, ASSIA, ExcerpMed, FamI, IPsyAb, PsycInfo, PsycholAb, SFSA, V&AA, e-psyche.
—BLDSC (3286.268400), GNLM, IE, Infotrieve, ingenta. **CCC.**
Published by: Sage Publications Ltd. (Subsidiary of: Sage Publications, Inc.), 1 Oliver's Yard, 55 City Rd, London, EC1 1SP, United Kingdom. TEL 44-20-73248500, FAX 44-20-73248600, info@sagepub.co.uk, http://www.sagepub.co.uk/journal.aspx?pid=105491. Ed. Bernadette Wren. Adv. contact Jenny Kirby. page GBP 250; trim 200 x 125. Circ: 1,150. **Subscr. in the Americas to:** Sage Publications, Inc., 2455 Teller Rd, Thousand Oaks, CA 91320. TEL 805-499-0721, FAX 805-499-0871, journals@sagepub.com.

649 USA
COLORADO PARENT MAGAZINE. Text in English. m. free. adv. bk.rev.; film rev.; music rev.; software rev.; video rev. **Document type:** *Consumer.* **Description:** Contains parenting articles and a calendar of events and activities to inform families and children.
Published by: United Parenting Publications (Subsidiary of: Trader Publishing Co.), 3801 E Florida Ave, Denver, CO 80210. FAX 303-722-2330. Ed. Kerry Arquette. adv.: page USD 1,925; trim 13 x 10. Circ: 100,000.

COMMUNICATION DISORDERS QUARTERLY. see *EDUCATION—Special Education And Rehabilitation*

COMMUNITY CARE REVIEW NEWSLETTER. see *SOCIAL SERVICES AND WELFARE*

THE COMPLEAT MOTHER; the magazine of pregnancy, birth and breastfeeding. see *MEDICAL SCIENCES—Obstetrics And Gynecology*

COMPUKIDS; het computerblad voor kinderen. see *COMPUTERS—Computer Games*

COMUNITA SPORTIVA; settimanale di informazione e orientamento delle attivita CSI. see *CHILDREN AND YOUTH—For*

CONCERN NEWS. see *SOCIAL SERVICES AND WELFARE*

CONNECT; supporting student participation. see *EDUCATION*

649 USA
CONNECTICUT PARENT MAGAZINE. Text in English. 1984. m. USD 24 domestic (effective 2001). adv. bk.rev. illus. 52 p./no.; back issues avail. **Document type:** *Newspaper.* **Description:** Focuses on independent education, healthcare, birthing, family travel, camps and summer programs, and more relating to parents planning to have children, or who have children - newborn through 12.
Published by: Choice Media, LLC, 420 E Main St, Ste 18, Branford, CT 06405. TEL 203-483-1700, FAX 203-483-0522, ctparent@aol.com. Eds. Joel MacClaren, Joseph Zibell. Pub., R&P Joel MacClaren. Adv. contact Kathy Dann. Circ: 50,000.

CONTACT (STOCKPORT); Covies, supporting children and youth. see *RELIGIONS AND THEOLOGY*

C

155.4 GBR ISSN 1463-9491
➤ **CONTEMPORARY ISSUES IN EARLY CHILDHOOD.** Text in English. 2000. 3/yr. USD 19 to individuals; GBP 140 domestic to libraries; USD 205 foreign to libraries (effective 2005). bk.rev. abstr.; illus. **Document type:** *Journal, Academic/Scholarly.* **Description:** Enables researchers and professionals exploring new, emerging, and alternative perspectives in their work with young children.
Media: Online - full text.
—CCC.
Published by: Symposium Journals (Subsidiary of: wwwords Ltd), PO Box 204, Didcot, Oxford, OX11 9ZQ, United Kingdom. TEL 44-1235-818062, FAX 44-1235-817275, info@symposium-journals.co.uk, subscriptions@symposium-journals.co.uk, http://www.wwwords.co.uk/ciec/, http://www.symposium-journals.co.uk/. Eds. Nicola J Yelland, Susan J Grieshaber.

➤ **CONTRIBUTIONS TO RESIDENTIAL TREATMENT.** see *PSYCHOLOGY*

155 USA ISSN 0273-124X
CONTRIBUTIONS TO THE STUDY OF CHILDHOOD AND YOUTH. Text in English. 1982. irreg., latest vol.6, 1990. price varies. **Document type:** *Monographic series, Academic/Scholarly.*
Published by: Greenwood Publishing Group Inc. (Subsidiary of: Harcourt International), 88 Post Rd W, PO Box 5007, Westport, CT 06881. TEL 203-226-3571, FAX 203-226-1502, webmaster@greenwood.com, http://www.greenwood.com.

649 USA ISSN 1556-410X
▼ **COOKIE**; a lifestyle magazine for sophisticated parents. Text in English. forthcoming 2006. **Document type:** *Magazine, Consumer.* **Description:** Covers high-end accessories, clothing, food, beauty tips, and services for upscale parents and children.
—CCC.
Published by: Fairchild Publications, Inc., 7 W 34th St, New York, NY 10001-8191. customerservice@fairchildpub.com, http://www.fairchildpub.com.

COORDINATORS OF CHILDREN'S AND YOUNG ADULT SERVICES IN PUBLIC LIBRARY SYSTEMS SERVING AT LEAST 100,000 PEOPLE. see *LIBRARY AND INFORMATION SCIENCES*

362.7 USA
COUNCIL FOR EARLY CHILDHOOD PROFESSIONAL RECOGNITION. COUNCIL NEWS & VIEWS. Text in English. 1983. 3/yr. free. **Document type:** *Newsletter.* **Description:** Informs the CDA community about the activities occurring nationwide regarding the Child Development Associate credential.
Formerly (until Aug. 1996): Competence
Published by: Council for Early Childhood Professional Recognition, 2460 16th St, N W, Washington, DC 20009-3575. TEL 202-265-9090, FAX 202-265-9161, cda@cdacouncil.org, http://www.cdacouncil.org. Ed., R&P Michael R Bertoochi. Circ: 14,000.

COUNSELING AND HUMAN DEVELOPMENT. see *EDUCATION*

CREATIONS. see *ART*

649 BRA ISSN 0104-3986
CRESCER; em familia. Text in Portuguese. 1993. m. BRL 78 (effective 2005). adv. illus. **Document type:** *Consumer.* **Description:** Covers family development, children's health and education, baby care, pregnancy, and childbirth.
Related titles: Online - full text ed.
Published by: Editora Globo S.A., Rua Domingos Sergio dos Anjos, 277, Pirituba, Jd S Elias, Sao Paulo, SP 05136-170, Brazil. http://revistacrescer.globo.com/, http://editoraglobo.globo.com/. Ed. Alvizio Falcao Filho. Pub. Jose Francisco Queiroz. adv.: color page USD 35,200; trim 274 x 208. Circ: 139,000 (paid).

CRUSADER (ALPHARETTA). see *RELIGIONS AND THEOLOGY—Protestant*

CSALADI LAP; egeszsegmagazin. see *WOMEN'S INTERESTS*

CURRENT POPULATION REPORTS: HOUSEHOLD ECONOMIC STUDIES. A CHILD'S DAY (SELECTED INDICATORS OF CHILD WELL-BEING). see *POPULATION STUDIES*

CURRENT POPULATION REPORTS: POPULATION CHARACTERISTICS. CHILDREN'S LIVING ARRANGEMENTS AND CHARACTERISTICS. see *POPULATION STUDIES*

CYBERMOM DOT COM. see *WOMEN'S INTERESTS*

D D D EXPRESS. (Division on Developmental Disabilities) see *EDUCATION—Special Education And Rehabilitation*

305.23 DEU ISSN 0949-4669
D F V - FAMILIE. Text in German. 1964. bi-m. EUR 12.30 (effective 2003). adv. **Document type:** *Magazine, Consumer.*
Formerly (until 1993): Die Familie (0938-1465)
Published by: Deutscher Familienverband, Luisenstr 48, Berlin, 10117, Germany. TEL 49-30-30882960, FAX 49-30-30882961, redaktion@deutscher-familienverband.de, post@deutscher-familienverband.de, http://www.deutscher-familienverband.de. Ed. Frauke Oblaender-Garlichs. adv.: B&W page EUR 3,170, color page EUR 4,755. Circ: 72,751 (paid and controlled).

C

155.5 DEU ISSN 0947-7012
D J I - BULLETIN. Text in English. 1986. q. (English, French and Spanish editions: a.). free. **Document type:** *Bulletin.*
Related titles: French ed.: ISSN 0947-7004; German ed.: ISSN 0930-7842; Spanish ed.: ISSN 0947-7942.
Indexed: IBZ.
Published by: Deutsches Jugendinstitut e.V./German Youth Institute, Nockherstr 2, Munich, 81541, Germany. keddi@dji.de, http://cgi.dji.de. Ed. Richard Rathgeber. Circ: 8,000.

D J K SPORTMAGAZIN. (Deutsche Jugendkraft) see *SPORTS AND GAMES*

649.1 USA
D P F NEWSLETTER. Text in English. 1981. bi-m. USD 30 (effective 2001). back issues avail. **Document type:** *Newsletter.* **Description:** Aims at an audience interested in adult baby games.
Published by: Diaper Pail Friends, 38 Miller Ave, Ste 127, Mill Valley, CA 94941. Ed. Thomas E Siegel. Circ: 1,500.

649 USA
DAD'S MAGAZINE. Text in English. 2000. q. USD 3.95 newsstand/cover (effective 2001). adv. **Document type:** *Consumer.*
Published by: B X T V, Inc., Box 2323, Glen Ellyn, IL 60138. TEL 630-790-1007, FAX 630-790-3077, dadsmag@aol.com, http://www.dadsmagazine.com. Ed. James Evans. Pub. Jonathan Scott.

649 USA
DALLAS FAMILY MAGAZINE; the magazine for today's parents. Text in English. 1993. m.
Published by: United Advertising Publications, Inc., 2323 Mcdaniel Dr., Ste. 200, Carrollton, TX 75006-8355. TEL 214-233-5131, FAX 214-233-5514. Circ: 80,000.

649 USA
DALLASCHILD. Variant title: Dallas Child. Text in English. 1986. m. free (effective 2004). adv. **Document type:** *Magazine, Consumer.* **Description:** Address the concerns and needs of families, with a special focus on children from prenatal through adolescence. Offer a well-informed, local and relevant perspective on issues affecting families and serve as both a strong voice in the community and a staunch advocate for children.
Related titles: Online - full content ed.
Published by: Lauren Publications, 4275 Kellway Circle, Ste 146, Addison, TX 75001. TEL 972-447-9188, 800-638-4461, FAX 972-447-0633, publisher@dallaschild.com, http://www.dallaschild.com/. Pub. Joylyn Niebes. Adv. contact Alison Davis. B&W page USD 3,045; trim 8.25 x 10.75. Circ: 80,000.

305.234 362.7 USA
DANE COUNTY KIDS. Text in English. 1992. m. free. adv. bk.rev.; film rev.; software rev.; video rev. back issues avail. **Document type:** *Newspaper, Consumer.*
Published by: Erickson Publishing LLC, PO Box 45050, Madison, WI 53744-5050. TEL 608-831-2131, FAX 608-831-2141, http://www.danecountykids.com/. Ed. Jennifer Howard. Pub. Kristin Erickson. Adv. contact Carrie Goddard. page USD 980; trim 13.25 x 10. Circ: 23,000.

305.23 CHN ISSN 1006-1789
DANGDAI QINGNIAN YANJIU/RESEARCH OF MODERN YOUNG PEOPLE. Text in Chinese. 1989. bi-m. CNY 5 newsstand/cover (effective 2005). **Document type:** *Journal, Academic/Scholarly.*
Related titles: Online - full content ed.; Online - full text ed.: (from East View Information Services).
Published by: Shanghai Shehui Kexueyuan, Qingshaonian Yanjiusuo/Shanghai Academy of Social Sciences, Institute of Youth and Juvenile Studies, 7/622 Huaihai Zhonglu, Shanghai, 200020, China. TEL 86-21-53060606 ext 2593, sassqssz@online.net.cn, http://ddqnyj.periodicals.net.cn/.

649 USA ISSN 1521-4273
DAUGHTERS; for parents of girls. Text in English. 1996. bi-m. USD 24.95 (effective 2004). **Document type:** *Newsletter, Consumer.*
Related titles: Online - full text ed.: (from bigchalk, EBSCO Publishing, Gale Group, O C L C Online Computer Library Center, Inc., ProQuest Information & Learning).
Indexed: GendWatch.
Published by: New Moon Publishing, 34 E Superior St, Ste 200, Duluth, MN 55802. TEL 218-728-5507, 888-849-8476, FAX 218-728-0314, http://www.daughters.com, http://www.newmoon.org. Ed. Lynette Lamb. Pub. Joe Kelly.

369.4 FRA ISSN 0751-5812
DEMAIN. Text in French. 1920. m. (7/yr.). bk.rev.; film rev. abstr.; charts; illus.; stat.
Formerly: Chef
Indexed: RASB.
Published by: Editions Scouts de France, 54 av. Jean Jaures, Paris, 75019, France. TEL 33-1-44523737, FAX 33-1-42380987. Ed. Philippe Da Costa. Circ: 40,000.

331.31 USA
THE DEPARTMENT OF LABOR'S (YEAR) FINDINGS ON THE WORST FORMS OF CHILD LABOR. Text in English. a.
Related titles: Online - full content ed.
Published by: U.S. Department of Labor, Bureau of International Labor Affairs, Frances Perkins Bldg, Rm C-4325, 200 Constitution Ave, NW, Washington, DC 20210. TEL 202-693-4770, FAX 202-693-4780, Contact-ILAB@dol.gov, http://www.dol.gov/ilab/.

DESARROLLANDO LA LECTURA (PREPARACIDON PARA LA LECTURA). see *EDUCATION*

028.5 RUS ISSN 0130-3104
PN1009.R8
DETSKAYA LITERATURA. Text in Russian; Summaries in English, French, German. 1966. bi-m. USD 99.95. bk.rev. bibl. **Description:** Publishes children's fiction.
Indexed: ChLitAb, RASB.
—East View. **CCC.**
Address: Dobroslobodskaya ul 6, Moscow, 107066, Russian Federation. TEL 7-095-2650107, FAX 7-095-2650107, http://www.mastak.sitek.ru/home_page/det_lit/. Ed. I G Nagaev. **US dist. addr.:** East View Information Services, 3020 Harbor Ln. N., Minneapolis, MN 55447. TEL 612-550-0961.

301 DEU ISSN 0012-0332
DEUTSCHE JUGEND; Zeitschrift fuer die Jugendarbeit. Text in German. 1953. m. (11/yr.). EUR 49.50, EUR 39.50; EUR 5.50 newsstand/cover (effective 2004). adv. bk.rev.; film rev. index. **Document type:** *Magazine, Consumer.*
Indexed: DIP, IBR, IBZ, RASB.
—IE, Infotrieve. **CCC.**
Published by: Juventa Verlag GmbH, Ehretstr 3, Weinheim, 69469, Germany. TEL 49-6201-90200, FAX 49-6201-902013, juventa@juventa.de, http://www.juventa.de/zeitschriften/deutsche_jugend/deutsche_jugend.html. Eds. Gaby Brenner, Gerd Brenner. Adv. contact Silke Schweim. page EUR 620; trim 149 x 198. Circ: 3,600 (paid and controlled).

DIFFERENT KIND OF PARENTING; a 'zine for parents whose children have died. see *PSYCHOLOGY*

DIGITAL KIDS. see *COMMUNICATIONS*

DIMENSION (BIRMINGHAM). see *RELIGIONS AND THEOLOGY—Protestant*

371.3 USA ISSN 1068-6177
HQ767.8
➤ **DIMENSIONS OF EARLY CHILDHOOD.** Text in English. 1972. q. free to members. adv. bk.rev. index. back issues avail. **Document type:** *Journal, Academic/Scholarly.* **Description:** Focuses on issues concerning people working in early childhood education and care including theory, practice, and public policy. Aims to provide useful articles for teachers.
Formerly: Dimensions (Little Rock) (0160-6425)
Indexed: CIJE, IMFL.
—BLDSC (3588.471300), IE, ingenta. **CCC.**
Published by: Southern Early Childhood Association, PO Box 55930, Little Rock, AR 72215-5930. TEL 501-221-1648, FAX 501-227-5297, secainfo@southernearlychildhood.org, http://www.southernearlychildhood.org/. Ed. Janet Brown McCracken. Adv. contact Adeline Luzader. Circ: 20,000.

➤ **(YEAR) DIRECTORY OF AMERICAN YOUTH ORGANIZATIONS**; a resource guide to 500 clubs, groups, troops, teams, societies, lodges, and more for young people. see *CLUBS*

362.7 028.5 USA
DIRECTORY OF FAMILY CHILD CARE ASSOCIATIONS, SUPPORT GROUPS, & SUPPORT AGENCIES. Text in English. 1984. a. USD 25 (effective 2003). **Document type:** *Directory.*
Former titles: Directory of Family Child Care Associations and Support Groups; Directory of Family Day Care Associations and Support Groups
Published by: Children's Foundation, 3020 Mt Vernon Ave., Alexandria, VA 22305-2637. TEL 202-347-3300, http://www.childrensfoundation.net/publications/natldirectory.htm. Ed. Kay Hollestelle.

DIRECTORY OF SELECTED EARLY CHILDHOOD PROGRAMS. see *EDUCATION—Special Education And Rehabilitation*

DISCOVERY (BIRMINGHAM). see *RELIGIONS AND THEOLOGY—Protestant*

DISCOVERY Y M C A. (Young Men's Christian Association) see *SOCIAL SERVICES AND WELFARE*

028.5 RUS
DLYA SAMYKH-SAMYKH MALENKYKH. Text in Russian. s-a. RUR 160 (effective 2002). **Document type:** *Journal.* **Description:** Covers early child development for parents of children ages 1-3. Examines the role of pictures, speech and emotional development, and instructive games.
Published by: Izdatel'skii Dom Karapuz, Izmailovskoe shosse 48a, Moscow, 105318, Russian Federation. TEL 7-095-9182810, http://www.karapuz.com.

DOCUMENTI DELLA SCUOLA. see *EDUCATION*

649 BGR
DOM, DETE, DETSKA GRADINA. Text in Bulgarian. bi-m. USD 36 foreign (effective 2002).
Published by: Ministerstvo na Obrazovanieto i Naukata na Republika Bulgaria/Ministry of Education and Sciences of the Republic of Bulgaria, 125 Tzarigradsko Shosse Blvd., Bl. 5, PO Box 336, Sofia, 1113, Bulgaria. TEL 359-2-705298, http://www.minedu.government.bg. **Dist. by:** Sofia Books, ul Silivria 16, Sofia 1404, Bulgaria. TEL 359-2-9586257, info@sofiabooks-bg.com, http://www.sofiabooks-bg.com.

649 CHN
DONGFANG WAWA (YINGER BAN)/EASTERN BABIES (AGE 0-3 EDITION). Text in Chinese. 1999. m. CNY 45.60; CNY 3.80 newsstand/cover (effective 2004). **Document type:** *Magazine, Consumer.*
Published by: Jiangsu Shaonian Ertong Chubanshe/Jiangsu Junveniles and Children's Publishing House, 14F Phoenix Palace Hotel, 47 Hunan Rd, Nanjing, Jiangsu 210009, China. TEL 86-25-3242508, FAX 86-25-3242350, sushao@public1.ptt.js.cn, http://www.sushao.com/index.php3.

649 CHN ISSN 1008-3952
DONGFANG WAWA (YOUER BAN)/EASTERN BABIES (AGE 3-7 EDITION). Text in Chinese. m. CNY 60; CNY 5 newsstand/cover (effective 2004). **Document type:** *Journal, Consumer.*
Published by: Jiangsu Shaonian Ertong Chubanshe/Jiangsu Junveniles and Children's Publishing House, 14F Phoenix Palace Hotel, 47 Hunan Rd, Nanjing, Jiangsu 210009, China. TEL 86-25-3242508, FAX 86-25-3242350, sushao@public1.ptt.js.cn, http://www.sushao.com/wawa.php3, http://www.sushao.com/index.php3. **Dist. by:** China International Book Trading Corp, 35 Chegongzhuang Xilu, Haidian District, PO Box 399, Beijing 100044, China. TEL 86-10-68412045, FAX 86-10-68412023, cibtc@mail.cibtc.com.cn, http://www.cibtc.com.cn.

362.7 CAN ISSN 0824-278X
DOUBLE FEATURE. Text in English, French. 1978. q. CND 20 domestic to non-members; CND 28 foreign to non-members; CND 2.95 newsstand/cover. adv. bk.rev. back issues avail. **Document type:** *Consumer.* **Description:** Covers issues relating to multiple birth families, personal accounts, international input, medical information and support networks.
Published by: Parents of Multiple Births Assoc. Inc., P O Box 234, Gormley, ON LOH1GO, Canada. TEL 416-513-7506, office@pomba.org, http://www.pomba.org. Ed. Theresa Cressatti. adv.: page CND 300. Circ: 2,200 (paid).

649 USA
THE DOULA ✶; mothering the mother. Text in English. 1986. q. USD 15; USD 3.95 newsstand/cover. bk.rev. back issues avail. **Document type:** *Consumer.* **Description:** Provides information and support to mothers and fathers who practice responsive parenting, with a special emphasis on supporting full-time mothers.
Published by: Democratic Management Services, 3010 Woodlawn Ave, Falls Church, VA 22042-1826. TEL 408-464-9488, FAX 408-464-9488, thedoula@aol.com. Ed., Pub. Michele Winkler. adv.: page USD 450; trim 11 x 8.5. Circ: 3,000.

DOVETAIL; a journal by and for Jewish/Christian families. see *ETHNIC INTERESTS*

DOWN & UP. see *HANDICAPPED*

649 700 USA ISSN 1097-3508
DREAM/GIRL; the arts magazine for girls. Text in English. 1997. bi-m. USD 22.95 (effective 2004). bk.rev.; dance rev.; film rev.; music rev.; play rev.; video rev. 28 p./no.; back issues avail. **Document type:** *Magazine, Consumer.* **Description:** Encourages creative genius in 9-to 15- year-old girls with writing exercises, art projects, interviews and student contests. Also publishes younger writers.
Published by: Dowell Media, PO Box 51867, Durham, NC 27717. TEL 919-419-0644, sales@dgarts.com, http://www.dgarts.com, http://www.dowellmedia.com. Ed., Pub. Mrs. Frances O Dowell. R&P Mr. Clifton P Dowell TEL 919-676-2694.

649 USA
THE DUKE SERIES IN CHILD DEVELOPMENT & PUBLIC POLICY. Text in English. irreg. price varies. **Document type:** *Monographic series, Academic/Scholarly.*
Published by: Guilford Publications, Inc., 72 Spring St, 4th Fl, New York, NY 10012. TEL 212-431-9800, 800-365-7006, FAX 212-966-6708, info@guilford.com, http://www.guilford.com.

DYNAMITE WRITE CHILDREN'S NEWSPAPER. see *CHILDREN AND YOUTH—For*

DZIECKO. see *WOMEN'S HEALTH*

362.7 GBR ISSN 0300-4430
HQ767.8 CODEN: ECDCAD
➤ **EARLY CHILD DEVELOPMENT AND CARE.** Text in English. 1971. 8/yr. (in 6 vols., 1 no./vol.). GBP 2,163, USD 2,710 combined subscription to institutions print & online eds. (effective 2006). adv. bk.rev. abstr.; charts; illus. index. reprint service avail. from PSC. **Document type:** *Journal, Academic/Scholarly.* **Description:** Serves psychologists, educators, psychiatrists, pediatricians, social workers and other professionals who deal with research, planning, education and care of infants and young children.
Related titles: Microform ed.; Online - full text ed.: ISSN 1476-8275. GBP 2,055, USD 2,575 to institutions (effective 2006) (from EBSCO Publishing, Gale Group, IngentaConnect, O C L C Online Computer Library Center, Inc., Swets Information Services).
Indexed: ABIn, ASSIA, BiolAb, BrEdI, CDA, CIJE, CPE, DIP, ERA, ETA, EduInd, ExcerpMed, IBR, IBSS, IBZ, IPsyAb, MEA, PsycInfo, PsycholAb, RHEA, RILM, RefZh, SEA, SENA, SOMA, SWA, TEA, e-psyche.
—BLDSC (3642.950000), CISTI, IE, Infotrieve, ingenta. **CCC.**
Published by: Routledge (Subsidiary of: Taylor & Francis Group), 4 Park Sq, Milton Park, Abingdon, Oxon OX14 4RN, United Kingdom. TEL 44-1235-828600, FAX 44-1235-829000, info@routledge.co.uk, http://www.tandf.co.uk/journals/titles/03004430.asp, http://www.routledge.com. Ed. Roy Evans. **Subscr. in N. America to:** Taylor & Francis Inc., Customer Services Dept, 325 Chestnut St, 8th Fl, Philadelphia, PA 19106. TEL 215-625-8900, 800-354-1420, FAX 215-625-8914, customerservice@taylorandfrancis.com; **Subscr. to:** Taylor & Francis Ltd, Journals Customer Service, Rankine Rd, Basingstoke, Hants RG24 8PR, United Kingdom. TEL 44-1256-813000, FAX 44-1256-330245, enquiry@tandf.co.uk.

372.87 780 649 USA ISSN 1085-522X
EARLY CHILDHOOD CONNECTIONS. Text in English. 1995. q. **Document type:** *Journal, Academic/Scholarly.* **Description:** Aims to stimulate discussion and application regarding the music, movement, and language development of young children. Broad-based and interdisciplinary in scope. Presents current research, pedagogical viewpoints, and diverse approaches to education reform in a context that increases awareness of the developmental needs of young children while nurturing a lifelong love of learning.
Indexed: MusicInd.
Published by: Foundation for Music-Based Learning, Box 4274, Greensboro, NC 27404-4274. TEL 336-272-5303.

EARLY CHILDHOOD DIGEST; families and teachers as partners. see *EDUCATION—Teaching Methods And Curriculum*

EARLY CHILDHOOD EDUCATION JOURNAL. see *EDUCATION*

▼ **EARLY CHILDHOOD LEARNING**; resources for successful teaching. see *EDUCATION—Teaching Methods And Curriculum*

362.7 649 USA ISSN 1080-3564
EARLY CHILDHOOD NEWS. Text in English. 1989. bi-m. free to qualified personnel (effective 2004). bk.rev. **Document type:** *Magazine, Trade.* **Description:** For owners, directors, principals and administrators of child-care programs serving children from six weeks old to third grade. Provides news, articles and analysis of trends in child care, and product reviews.
Indexed: CIJE.
—BLDSC (3642.958000). **CCC.**
Published by: Peter Li Education Group, 2621 Dryden Rd, Ste 300, Dayton, OH 45439-1661. TEL 937-847-5900, FAX 937-847-5910, http://www.earlychildhoodnews.com. Ed. Megan Shaw. Circ: 24,000.

EARLY CHILDHOOD RESEARCH & PRACTICE; an internet journal on the development, care, and education of young children. see *EDUCATION*

649 USA ISSN 1536-4739
EARLY DEVELOPMENTS. Text in English. 1997. q. **Document type:** *Journal, Academic/Scholarly.*
Related titles: Online - full content ed.
Published by: Frank Porter Graham Child Development Center, Publications Office, CB #8185, Chapel Hill, NC 27599-8185. TEL 919-966-0857, FPGpublications@unc.edu, http://www.fpg.unc.edu/products/product_detail.cfm?apubsID=606.

EARLY INTERVENTION. see *EDUCATION—Special Education And Rehabilitation*

EARNSHAW'S REVIEW. see *CLOTHING TRADE*

155.649 USA ISSN 1065-2655
EASTSIDE PARENT. Text in English. 1986. m. USD 15. adv. bk.rev.; play rev. **Document type:** *Consumer.* **Description:** Guide for parents, educators and child-care providers. Features include a calendar of events, plays, movies, and ideas for outings and restaurants.
Published by: United Parenting Publications (Subsidiary of: Trader Publishing Co.), 123 N W 36th St, Ste 215, Seattle, WA 98107. TEL 206-441-0191, FAX 206-441-4919, http://www.parenthood.com. Circ: 20,000.

370 ITA ISSN 0012-9453
ECO DEGLI ORATORI E DEI CIRCOLI GIOVANILI. Text in Italian. 1907. bi-m. EUR 25 (effective 2004). bk.rev.; film rev. bibl. index. **Document type:** *Magazine, Consumer.*
Published by: Cooperativa Culturale in Dialogo srl, Via Sant' Antonio 5, Milan, MI 20122, Italy. TEL 39-02-58391348, FAX 39-02-58391345, http://www.indialogo.it. Ed. Sergio Gianelli. Circ: 1,100 (controlled).

305.231 FRA ISSN 0424-2238
L'ECOLE DES PARENTS. Text in French. 1949. 5/yr. (plus 2 special issues). adv. bk.rev. **Description:** For parents and educators. Contains information, research and regular chronicles to help families make the best educational choices for their children.
—IE, Infotrieve.
Published by: Federation Nationale des Ecole des Parents et des Educateurs, 5 impasse Bon Secours, Paris, Cedex 11 75543, France. TEL 33-1-44934470, FAX 33-1-44934484, http://www.ecoledesparents.org. Ed. Colette Barroux. Pub. Philippe Gutton. Adv. contact Isabelle Dureault. Circ: 15,000.

362.7 CAN ISSN 0840-4445
THE EDGE. Text in English. 1988. 10/yr. CND 12 domestic; USD 14 foreign (effective 2001). **Document type:** *Consumer.* **Description:** Official youth publication of the Salvation Army in Canada. Includes contemporary social and moral issues, Christian lifestyle and contemporary Christian music.
Related titles: Microform ed.: (from MML).
Published by: Salvation Army, 2 Overlea Blvd, Toronto, ON M4H 1P4, Canada. TEL 416-422-6118, FAX 416-422-6120. Ed., R&P Allison Norton. Circ: 5,000.

EDUCATION AND HEALTH; a quarterly journal. see *EDUCATION*

EDUCATOR'S NOTEBOOK ON FAMILY INVOLVEMENT. see *EDUCATION*

EINHARD INTERN; Schulzeitschrift des staedtischen Einhard-Gymnasiums Aachen. see *EDUCATION*

649 370 DEU ISSN 0046-1849
ELTERN. Text in German. 1960. m. EUR 29.40; EUR 2.60 newsstand/cover (effective 2005). adv. **Document type:** *Magazine, Consumer.*
Incorporates (1992-1998): Mein Kind und Ich (0943-3546); Former titles (until 1996): Eltern-Magazin (0721-0612); (until 1965): Eltern-Magazin Wir Babys (0721-0620); (until 1965): Wir Babys (0721-0590)
Published by: Gruner und Jahr AG & Co., Weihenstephaner Str 7, Munich, 81673, Germany. TEL 49-89-41520, FAX 49-89-4152651, redaktion@eltern.de, guj-redaktion@guj.de, http://www.eltern.de, http://www.guj.de. Ed. Marie-Luise Lewicki. adv.: page EUR 28,400; trim 185 x 250. Circ: 391,353 (paid). **Subscr. to:** P M S GmbH & Co. KG, Grafenberger Allee 100, Duesseldorf 40237, Germany. TEL 49-203-76908-0, FAX 49-203-7690830.

649 370 DEU ISSN 1435-2028
ELTERN FOR FAMILY. Text in German. 1996. m. EUR 22.80; EUR 2.20 newsstand/cover (effective 2003). adv. **Document type:** *Magazine, Consumer.*
Published by: Gruner und Jahr AG & Co., Weihenstephaner Str 7, Munich, 81673, Germany. TEL 49-89-4152-0, FAX 49-89-4152651, http://www.eltern.de/forfamily, http://www.guj.de. Ed. Marie-Luise Lewicki. Adv. contact Thomas Bily. page EUR 11,450. Circ: 155,728 (paid).

649 DEU
ELTERN SONDERHEFT MEIN BABY. Text in German. a. EUR 4.90 newsstand/cover (effective 2003). adv. back issues avail. **Document type:** *Magazine, Consumer.*
Published by: Gruner und Jahr AG & Co., Weihenstephaner Str 7, Munich, 81673, Germany. TEL 49-89-4152-0, FAX 49-89-4152665, guj-redaktion@guj.de. adv.: page EUR 19,850. Circ: 150,000 (controlled).

155.4 DEU
ELTERN UNSER KIND. Text in German. 1980. q. free. **Document type:** *Consumer.*
Formerly: Eltern das Gesunde Kind
Published by: Gruner und Jahr AG & Co., Weihenstephaner Str 7, Munich, 81673, Germany. TEL 49-89-4152-0, FAX 49-89-4152665. Circ: 120,000.

ELTERNRUNDBRIEF. see *EDUCATION—Special Education And Rehabilitation*

362.7 CAN ISSN 0825-7531
EMPATHIC PARENTING. Text in English. 1978. q. CND 10 to members. bk.rev. **Document type:** *Newsletter.* **Description:** Reprint journal that focuses on the long-term emotional consequences of child abuse and neglect.
Former titles: Canadian Society for the Prevention of Cruelty to Children. Journal (0705-6591); Empathic Parenting
Related titles: Microfiche ed.: (from MML); Microform ed.: (from MML); Online - full text ed.: (from Gale Group, Micromedia ProQuest).
Indexed: CBPI, CPerI.
Published by: Canadian Society for the Prevention of Cruelty to Children, 356 First St., P O Box 700, Midland, ON L4R 4P4, Canada. TEL 705-526-5647, FAX 705-526-0214. Ed. Dr. E T Barker. Circ: 2,000.

649.1 USA ISSN 1526-2154
THE EMPOWERED PARENTING EZINE. Text in English. 1999. w. free. bk.rev. back issues avail. **Document type:** *Newsletter.* **Description:** Offers articles on child rearing from birth to adulthood, and encouragement for parents to be their best.
Related titles: Online - full text ed.
Published by: J B Information Station, PO Box 515165, St. Louis, MO 63151. TEL 314-638-3161. Ed., Pub., Adv. contact Joan Bramsch. Circ: 1,000.

155.4 618.92 FRA ISSN 0013-7545
HQ768
ENFANCE; psychologie, pedagogie, neuro-psychiatrie, sociologie. Text in French. 1948. q. EUR 53 domestic to individuals (effective 2005). adv. bk.rev. index. **Document type:** *Journal, Academic/Scholarly.* **Description:** Publishes the works of well-known developmental psychologists.
Indexed: IBR, IBSS, L&LBA, PsycInfo, PsycholAb, SOPODA, e-psyche.
—BLDSC (3747.869000), IE, Infotrieve, ingenta.
Published by: (Laboratoire de Psycho-Biologie de l'Enfant), Presses Universitaires de France, 6 Avenue Reille, Paris, 75685 Cedex 14, France. TEL 33-1-58103100, FAX 33-1-58103182, revue.enfance@free.fr, revues@puf.com, http://revue.enfance.free.fr/enfance.html, http://www.puf.com. Eds. Helene Gratiot Alphandery, Jacqueline Nadel. Circ: 2,000.

155.5 FRA ISSN 1286-5559
ENFANCE & PSY; la revue de tous les professionnels de l'enfance et de l'adolescence. Text in French. 1997. q. EUR 44 domestic to individuals; EUR 55 domestic to institutions; EUR 60 foreign (effective 2003). **Document type:** *Magazine, Trade.*
Published by: Editions Eres, 11 rue des Alouettes, Ramonville Saint-Agne, 31520, France. TEL 33-5-61751576, FAX 33-5-61735289, eres@edition-eres.com, http://www.edition-eres.com. Eds. Didier Lauru, Patrice Huerre, Jean-Louis Le Run. Circ: 1,800.

649.1 FRA ISSN 0397-4820
ENFANT MAGAZINE. Text in French. 1976. m. EUR 20.60 domestic; EUR 28 in the European Union; EUR 30.60 elsewhere (effective 2005). illus. **Document type:** *Magazine, Consumer.* **Description:** Is intended for women at a crucial point in their lives - when they are pregnant or looking after young children.

Published by: Bayard Presse, 3 Rue Bayard, Paris, 75393 Cedex 08, France. TEL 33-1-44356060, FAX 33-1-44356161, redactions@bayard-presse.com, http://www.enfant-magazine.com, http://www.bayardpresse.com. Ed. Carole Renucci. Circ: 1,686,000 (paid and controlled).

362.7 CAN ISSN 1497-312X
ENFANTES QUEBEC. Text in English. 1988. 8/yr. USD 30 (effective 1999). adv. **Document type:** *Newspaper, Consumer.* **Description:** Offers practical information for parents in the Greater Montreal region concerning children's health, leisure activities, and education.
Former titles (until 1998): Magazine Enfants Quebec (1195-2946); (until 1993): Le Magazine Enfants Quebec (1187-435X); (until 1991): Mensuel Enfants (0835-5223)
Published by: Les Editions Heritage, 300 Arran St, St Lambert, PQ J4R 1K5, Canada. TEL 514-875-9612, FAX 450-672-5448, magazines@editionsheritage.com. Ed. Claire Chabot. Pub. Sylvie Payette. Adv. contact Carole Martin. B&W page USD 1,840, color page USD 6,160. Circ: 70,000.

ENFANTS DU MONDE. see *SOCIAL SERVICES AND WELFARE*

ERZIEHUNG HEUTE; Die oesterreichische Zeitschrift fuer Schule, Bildung und Erziehung. see *EDUCATION*

362.7 300 DEU ISSN 1432-0258
ERZIEHUNG, SCHULE, GESELLSCHAFT. Text in German. 1994. irreg., latest vol.19, 1998. **Document type:** *Academic/Scholarly.*
Published by: Ergon Verlag, Grombuehlstr 7, Wuerzburg, 97080, Germany. TEL 49-931-280084, FAX 49-931-282872, ergon-verlag@t-online.de, service@ergon-verlag.de.

ESPERA. see *MEDICAL SCIENCES—Obstetrics And Gynecology*

ESPERANTO U S A. see *LINGUISTICS*

ETABLISSEMENTS MEDICAUX POUR ENFANTS. see *HEALTH FACILITIES AND ADMINISTRATION*

EVANGELIZING TODAY'S CHILD. see *RELIGIONS AND THEOLOGY—Protestant*

EVERY CHILD. see *EDUCATION*

EXCEPTIONAL CHILDREN. see *EDUCATION—Special Education And Rehabilitation*

EXCEPTIONAL PARENT; the magazine for families and professionals caring for people with special needs. see *EDUCATION—Special Education And Rehabilitation*

649 CAN ISSN 0827-6366
EXPECTING. Text in English. s-a.
Published by: Family Communications, Inc., 65 The East Mall, Etobicoke, ON M8Z 5W3, Canada. TEL 416-537-2604, FAX 416-538-1794. Circ: 145,000 (controlled).

EXPENDITURES ON CHILDREN BY FAMILIES. see *HOME ECONOMICS*

649 GBR
THE EXPRESS PARENT. Text in English. 1999. m. adv. **Document type:** *Magazine, Consumer.* **Description:** Contains features on all aspects of parenting.
Published by: United Advertising Publications plc., Link House, 25 West St, Poole, Dorset BH15 1LL, United Kingdom. TEL 44-1202-445000, FAX 44-1202-445612.

EXTRATOUR. see *TRAVEL AND TOURISM*

362.41 GBR ISSN 0967-8719
EYE CONTACT. Text in English. 1991. 3/yr. GBP 12 (effective 2000). bk.rev. **Document type:** *Bulletin.* **Description:** Information about visually impaired children with additional needs.
Related titles: Audio cassette/tape ed.; Braille ed.; Diskette ed.
—BLDSC (3854.590000).
Published by: Royal National Institute for the Blind, Education, Training and Employment Division, 7 Poplar St, Fisher Gate, Nottingham, NG1 1GP, United Kingdom. webmaster@rnib.org.uk, webmaster@rnib.org.uk, http://www.rnib.org.uk. Ed. Karen Porter. Circ: 1,000 (paid). **Subscr. to:** RNIB, PO Box 173, Peterborough, Cambs PE2 6WS, United Kingdom. TEL 44-1733-370777, FAX 44-1733-371555.

362.732 DNK ISSN 0108-2418
F I C E INFORMATION. Text in Danish. 1977. q. DKK 200 (effective 1997). bk.rev. **Document type:** *Bulletin.*
Published by: Federation Internationale des Communautes d'Enfants - Denmark, Sekretariatet, Limosegyden 6, Nr. Aaby, 5580, Denmark. TEL 45-64-42-16-16, FAX 45-64-42-16-12. Ed. Fanni Vibeke Lasson. Circ: 300.

F U N D A M I N D REVISTA. (Fundacion Asistencia Materno-Infantil de Ayuda a Ninos Carenciados y Discapacitados) see *SOCIAL SERVICES AND WELFARE*

362.7 360 GBR
FACTFILE; facts and figures about children in the UK. Text in English. a., latest 2001. GBP 7.50 newsstand/cover (effective 2001). **Document type:** *Bulletin.*
Former titles: N C H Action for Children Factfile; (until 1994): N C H Factfile
Related titles: ◆ Regional ed(s).: Factfile (Scotland).
Indexed: RefZh.
—BLDSC (3863.466970).
Published by: N C H, 85 Highbury Park, London, N5 1UD, United Kingdom. TEL 44-20-7704-7000, FAX 44-20-7226-2537, http://www.nch.org.uk.

362.7 360 GBR
FACTFILE (SCOTLAND); facts and figures about Scotland's children. Text in English. a., latest 2002. GBP 5 newsstand/cover (effective 2002). **Description:** Pulls together information from a wide range of official sources to provide a picture of what is happening today to children and young people in Scotland.
Related titles: ◆ Regional ed(s).: Factfile.
—BLDSC (3863.466950).
Published by: N C H Scotland, 17 Newton Pl, Glasgow, G3 7PY, United Kingdom. TEL 44-141-332-4041, FAX 44-141-332-7002, http://www.nch.org.uk.

FAITH & FAMILY; the magazine of catholic living. see *RELIGIONS AND THEOLOGY—Roman Catholic*

649 FRA ISSN 1246-3299
FAMILI; le magazine tendrement pratique des parents d'aujourd'hui. Text in French. 1993. m. EUR 22 (effective 2005). back issues avail. **Description:** For young parents and mothers-to-be.
Published by: Groupe Marie Claire, 10 Boulevard des Freres Voisins, Issy-les-Moulineaux, 92792 Cedex 9, France. TEL 33-1-41468888, FAX 33-1-41468686, http://www.famili.fr, http://www.groupemarieclaire.com. Circ: 186,642.

FAMILIE & CO. see *MEDICAL SCIENCES—Pediatrics*

649 AUT
FAMILIENMAGAZIN. Text in German, French, English, Chinese. 1957. 10/yr. adv. bk.rev. illus. **Document type:** *Magazine, Consumer.*
Formerly: Elternblatt (0013-6441)
Indexed: e-psyche.
Published by: Kinderfreunde Oesterreich, Rauhensteingasse 5-5, Vienna, W 1010, Austria. TEL 43-1-5121298, FAX 43-1-512129862, kind-und-co@kinderfreunde.at, http://www.kinderfreunde.at. Ed., R&P Gerda Stockhammer TEL 43-1-74095456. Circ: 65,000.

649 GBR ISSN 1354-9553
FAMILIES MAGAZINE. Text in English. 1990. 10/yr. GBP 15.50 (effective 1999). bk.rev.; play rev.; software rev.; video rev.; Website rev. illus. back issues avail. **Document type:** *Magazine, Consumer.* **Description:** Contains information for parents with young children.
Related titles: Online - full text ed.
Address: P.O. Box 4302, London, SW16 1ZS, United Kingdom. TEL 44-20-8696-9680, FAX 44-20-8696-9679, editor@familiesmagazine.co.uk, http://www.familiesmagazine.co.uk. Ed., Adv. contact Mrs. P Gravell. Pub. Mr. J.D. Gravell. Circ: 130,000 (paid); 77,000 (controlled).

649 USA
FAMILIES WITH CHILDREN FROM CHINA. Text in English. irreg. **Document type:** *Magazine, Consumer.*
Address: PO Box 237065, Ansonia Station, NY 10023. TEL 212-579-0115, FAX 212-244-3573, joinfccny@aol.com, http://www.fccny.org.

649 USA
FAMILY (MOUNTAINSIDE). Text in English. 1994. 8/yr. free. adv. 40 p./no. 4 cols./p.; **Document type:** *Newspaper, Consumer.* **Description:** Contains articles on effective child rearing, health, education, child care, and other topics of importance and interest to New Jersey parents, particularly those in Morris County.
Formerly: Morris County Family
Published by: Kids Monthly Publications, Inc., 1122 Rte. 22 W., Mountainside, NJ 07092. TEL 908-232-2913, FAX 908-317-9518, http://www.njcountyfamily.com/editorial/13-05/toc_1305.htm. Ed., R&P Farn Dupre. Pub., Adv. contact Cindy Mironovich. Circ: 130,000.

362.7 DEU ISSN 0944-6982
FAMILY (WITTEN). Text in German. 1992. q. EUR 12.80; EUR 3.70 newsstand/cover (effective 2003). adv. back issues avail. **Document type:** *Magazine, Consumer.*
Published by: Bundes Verlag GmbH, Bodenborn 43, Witten, 58452, Germany. TEL 49-2302-93093-0, FAX 49-2302-9309310, info@bundes-verlag.de, http://www.bundes-verlag.de. Ed. Ulrich Eggers. adv.: B&W page EUR 2,030, color page EUR 2,670; trim 188 x 258. Circ: 48,070 (paid).

649 306.85 USA ISSN 1543-494X
▼ **FAMILY FOCUS (COLORADO SPRINGS).** Text in English. 2003 (Apr./May). bi-m.
Published by: Focus on the Family, Inc., 8605 Explorer Dr, Colorado Springs, CO 80920-1051. TEL 719-531-3400, 800-232-6459, FAX 719-531-3424, http://www.family.org. Eds. Andrea Vinley Jewel, Chuck Johnson.

362.7 028.5 USA
FAMILY GUIDE; resource guide for parents & children. Text in English. 1987. a. free. adv. back issues avail. **Document type:** *Directory, Consumer.* **Description:** Listings of schools, activities, events and health care information in central New Jersey.
Formerly: Family Guide for Parents and Kids
Published by: Media Resources Group, 2248, Huntington, NY 11743-0888. TEL 609-443-6010, FAX 609-443-7140, http://www.insidenj.com/familyguide/. Pubs. John Waters, Laurence B Glasberg. Adv. contact Rhonda Pedowitz. Circ: 25,000.

FAMILY LIFE MATTERS. see *SOCIOLOGY*

649 USA
FAMILY MATTERS!. Text in English. 1999. m. free (effective 2003). **Document type:** *Newsletter, Consumer.* **Description:** A free monthly e-zine with articles on conscientious parenting, child development and the core issues that today's parents face. Includes kidsafe web site links and periodic book reviews on children's books and books on parenting.
Media: Online - full text.
Published by: Kokopellis Treasures, 5231 Rosehill Crt, Reno, NV 89502-7785. TEL 775-856-4288, soulful@aol.com, http://kokopellistreasures.com/soulful/familymatters.html, http://kokopellistreasures.com. Ed., R&P, Adv. contact Laura Ramirez TEL 775-856-4288. Circ: 5,573.

649 USA
FAMILY NEWS. Text in English. m. adv. **Description:** Parenting magazine covers education, environment, entertainment, finance, and computers. Also includes a family calendar of events and a regular section on family wellness.
Published by: A P P L E FamilyWorks, 4 Joseph Ct, San Rafael, CA 94903. TEL 415-492-1022, FAX 415-492-1099, familynews@familyworks.org, http://www.familyworks.org. Ed. Mini Knudsen. Adv. contact Richard Standard.

FAMILY TIMES (EAU CLAIRE); the newspaper for Chippewa Valley parents. see *HOME ECONOMICS*

FAMILY WAYS; education resources for pregnancy to parenthood. see *MEDICAL SCIENCES—Obstetrics And Gynecology*

051 USA ISSN 1056-6333
GV182.8
FAMILYFUN. Text in English. 1991. 10/yr. USD 10 domestic; USD 22 in Canada; USD 30 elsewhere (effective 2005). adv. bk.rev. illus. reprints avail. **Document type:** *Magazine, Consumer.* **Description:** Family-oriented publication directed to parents with children ages 3-12.
Related titles: Online - full text ed.
Published by: Family and Children's Magazine Group (Subsidiary of: Walt Disney Co.), 244 Main St, Northampton, MA 01060. TEL 413-585-0444, 800-289-4849, letters@familyfun.com, FAFcustserv@cdsfulfillment.com, http://familyfun.go.com. Eds. Ann Hallock, Alexandra Kennedy. Pub. Mary Beth Wright. adv.: B&W page USD 78,625, color page USD 104,825. Circ: 1,700,000 (paid).

649 306.874 USA ISSN 1091-5516
FATHERING MAGAZINE; the online magazine for men with families. Text in English. 1995. m. free. adv. bk.rev. illus. reprints avail. **Document type:** *Consumer.* **Description:** Publishes news and articles related to fathering.
Media: Online - full text (from Gale Group).
Published by: Fathering Enterprises, Inc., PO Box 231891, Houston, TX 77223. sheldon@fathermag.com, http://www.fathermag.com/. Ed., R&P Alexander Sheldon. Circ: 1,000,000.

FEDERATION OF CATHOLIC PARENT-TEACHER ASSOCIATIONS OF ONTARIO. NEWSLETTER. see *EDUCATION*

053.1 DEU
FINDEFUCHS; Das Familienmagazin. Text in German. 1988. 8/yr. EUR 80 (effective 2003). adv. **Document type:** *Magazine, Consumer.* **Description:** Contains articles and features of interest to all members of a family.
Address: Heinrich-von Stephan-Str 15, Freiburg, 79100, Germany. TEL 49-761-555331, FAX 49-761-5559271, info@findefuchs.de, http://www.findefuchs.de. adv.: B&W page EUR 1,395, color page EUR 1,953; trim 190 x 270. Circ: 18,500 (paid and controlled).

FIRST LANGUAGE. see *LINGUISTICS*

FIRST STEPS IN MISSIONS. see *RELIGIONS AND THEOLOGY—Protestant*

FIRST TEACHER; for people who care for young children. see *EDUCATION*

348 USA ISSN 1076-1756
FIRST YEAR OF LIFE; a guide to your baby's growth and development month by month. Text in English. 1977. 3/yr. Dist. with The American Baby Basket for New Parents through participating hospitals only. adv. **Document type:** *Magazine, Consumer.* **Description:** Details physical, emotional and social growth of the baby during monthly stages.
Related titles: ♦ Issued with: American Baby. ISSN 0044-7544.
Indexed: CINAHL.
Published by: Meredith Corp., 1716 Locust St, Des Moines, IA 50309-3023. TEL 515-284-3000, FAX 515-284-3657, http://www.meredith.com. adv.: B&W page USD 124,500, color page USD 158,700; trim 10.5 x 7.88. Circ: 3,000,000 (controlled).

808.899282 USA ISSN 0892-6735
➤ **FIVE OWLS**; a publication for readers, personally and professionally involved in children's literature. Text in English. 1986. q. USD 35 domestic; USD 45 in Canada & Mexico; USD 55 elsewhere (effective 2005). adv. bk.rev. bibl.; illus. index. back issues avail.; reprints avail. **Document type:** *Journal, Academic/Scholarly.* **Description:** Each issue contains articles about trends and issues in the field of children's literature, an interview with an author or illustrator, and 12-15 book reviews.
Indexed: BRI, CBRI, ChLitAb.
Published by: The Jara Society dba The Five Owls, PO Box 235, Marathon, TX 79842. TEL 432-386-4257, FAX 432-386-9087, thefiveowls@yahoo.com, http://www.fiveowls.com/. Ed. Dr. Mark I West. Pub., Adv. contact Dan Dailey. B&W page USD 1,150. Circ: 3,000 (paid).

➤ **FOCAL POINT**; a national bulletin on family support and children's mental health. see *HANDICAPPED*

➤ **FOCUS ON EXCEPTIONAL CHILDREN.** see *EDUCATION—Special Education And Rehabilitation*

➤ **FOCUS ON THE FAMILY.** see *RELIGIONS AND THEOLOGY*

649 USA ISSN 1542-393X
▼ **FOCUS ON YOUR CHILD'S DISCOVERY YEARS.** Text in English. 2003 (Jan.). 8/yr.
Published by: Focus on the Family, Inc., 8605 Explorer Dr, Colorado Springs, CO 80920-1051. TEL 719-531-3400, 800-232-6459, FAX 719-531-3424, http://www.family.org. Eds. Annette Bourland, Chuck Johnson.

649 USA ISSN 1542-8990
▼ **FOCUS ON YOUR CHILD'S EARLY STAGES.** Text in English. 2003 (Feb.). 8/yr.
Published by: Focus on the Family, Inc., 8605 Explorer Dr, Colorado Springs, CO 80920-1051. TEL 719-531-3400, 800-232-6459, FAX 719-531-3424, http://www.family.org. Eds. Traci Pedone, Chuck Johnson.

649 USA ISSN 1550-8560
▼ **FOCUS ON YOUR CHILD'S TEEN PHASES.** Text in English. 2004 (Sept.). 8/yr. free (effective 2004).
Published by: Focus on the Family, Inc., 8605 Explorer Dr, Colorado Springs, CO 80920-1051. TEL 719-531-3400, 800-232-6459, FAX 719-531-3424, http://www.family.org. Eds. Traci Pedone, Chuck Johnson.

649 USA ISSN 1542-3948
▼ **FOCUS ON YOUR CHILD'S TWEEN AGES.** Text in English. 2003 (Jan.). 8/yr.
Published by: Focus on the Family, Inc., 8605 Explorer Dr, Colorado Springs, CO 80920-1051. TEL 719-531-3400, 800-232-6459, FAX 719-531-3424, http://www.family.org. Eds. Jesse Florea, Chuck Johnson.

FOEDSEL & FOERAELDRASKAP. see *MEDICAL SCIENCES—Obstetrics And Gynecology*

THE FOREIGN-BORN PARENT NETWORK; the newsletter for Speakers of Other Languages and parents of bilingual smart kids. see *LINGUISTICS*

649 NOR ISSN 0332-513X
FORELDRE OG BARN. Text in Norwegian. 1977. fortn. NOK 230. adv.
Published by: Hjemmet Mortensen Forlag AS, Box 5001, Majorstua, Oslo, 0301, Norway. TEL 47-22-58-55-00, FAX 47-22-58-05-66. Ed. Edda Espeland. adv.: B&W page NOK 11,900, color page NOK 198,000. Circ: 62,000.

649 USA
FORTWORTHCHILD. Variant title: Fort Worth Child. Text in English. m. free (effective 2004). adv. **Document type:** *Magazine, Consumer.* **Description:** Addresses the concerns and needs of families, with a special focus on children from prenatal through adolescence. Offers a well-informed, local and relevant perspective on issues affecting families and serves as both a strong voice in the community and a staunch advocate for children.
Related titles: Online - full content ed.
Published by: Lauren Publications, 4275 Kellway Circle, Ste 146, Addison, TX 75001. TEL 972-447-9188, 800-638-4461, FAX 972-447-0633, publisher@dallaschild.com, http://www.fortworthchild.com/. Pub. Joylyn Niebes. Adv. contact Alison Davis.

FORUM JUGENDHILFE. see *SOCIAL SERVICES AND WELFARE*

362.7 GBR ISSN 0262-8120
FOSTER CARE. Text in English. 1975. q. GBP 8. adv. bk.rev. back issues avail. **Document type:** *Trade.* **Description:** News items and informational articles on the legislative, health care, parenting, and child care issues pertaining to fostering, with advertisements of children to be placed, and announcements of courses and conferences.
Indexed: ASSIA.
—BLDSC (4024.385000), IE, ingenta.
Published by: National Foster Care Association, 87 Blackfriars Rd, London, SE1 8HA, United Kingdom. TEL 44-171-620-6400, FAX 44-171-620-6401, nfca@fostercare.org.uk, http://ourworld.compuserve.com/homepages/fostering. Ed., R&P, Adv. contact Gillian Davies. Circ: 23,000.

305.234 USA
FOX VALLEY KIDS. Text in English. 1994. m. free. adv. bk.rev. back issues avail. **Document type:** *Newspaper, Consumer.*
Published by: Erickson Publishing LLC, PO Box 45050, Madison, WI 53744-5050. TEL 608-831-2131, 800-722-6461, FAX 608-832-2141, writeus@ericksonpublishing.com, http://www.foxvalleykids.com/. Ed. Barbara A Schmitz. Pub. Kristin Erickson. Adv. contact Brenda Peterson. page USD 940; trim 13.25 x 10. Circ: 27,000.

FRIA TIDER. see *LEISURE AND RECREATION*

371 CHE ISSN 1424-8824
FRITZ UND FRAENZI; das Magazin fuer Eltern schulpflichtiger Kinder. Text in German. 2001. bi-m. CHF 24 domestic; CHF 32 foreign; CHF 5 newsstand/cover (effective 2004). **Document type:** *Magazine, Consumer.*
Published by: Zollikofer AG, Fuerstenlandstr 122, Postfach 2362, St. Gallen, 9001, Switzerland. TEL 41-71-2727370, FAX 41-71-2727586, leserservice@zollikofer.ch, http://www.fritz-und-fraenzi.ch, http://www.zollikofer.ch.

028.5 USA
FROST'S SUMMER CAMP GUIDE. Text in English. a. USD 7 newsstand/cover (effective 2003). adv. **Document type:** *Consumer.* **Description:** Helps parents choose an appropriate summer camp for their child.
Published by: Frost Publications, 100 Moore Rd, Wantage, NJ 07461. TEL 201-784-7662, FAX 201-784-7646, info@frosts.com, http://www.gocamps.com/, http://www.frosts.com/. Pub. Don Frost.

305.23 DEU
FRUEHE KINDHEIT. Text in German. 1998. 6/yr. EUR 29.80; EUR 14.90 to students; EUR 4.90 newsstand/cover (effective 2003). adv. **Document type:** *Magazine, Consumer.*
Published by: (Deutsche Liga fuer das Kind in Familie und Gesellschaft e.V.), Rigotti-Klarhorst Medienagentur GmbH, Muffendorfer Hauptstr 26, Bonn, 53177, Germany. TEL 49-228-9359388, FAX 49-228-9359389, verlag@fruehe-kindheit.de, http://www.fruehe-kindheit.de, http://www.rigotti-klarhorst.de. adv.: B&W page EUR 1,095, color page EUR 1,890. Circ: 5,000 (controlled).

649 DEU ISSN 0721-9121
FRUEHFOERDERUNG INTERDISZIPLINAER; Zeitschrift fuer Praxis und Theorie der fruehen Hilfe fuer behinderte und entwicklungsauffaellige Kinder. Text in German. 1982. q. EUR 46; EUR 36.80 to students; EUR 16 newsstand/cover (effective 2005). adv. bk.rev. index. back issues avail. **Document type:** *Journal, Academic/Scholarly.*
Indexed: DIP, IBR, IBZ, PsycholAb, e-psyche.
—GNLM. **CCC.**
Published by: Ernst Reinhardt Verlag, Kemnatenstr 46, Munich, 80639, Germany. TEL 49-89-1780160, FAX 49-89-17801630, webmaster@reinhardt-verlag.de, http://www.reinhardt-verlag.de/db/detail.cfm?tnr=4443. Ed. Otto Speck. adv.: B&W page EUR 550; trim 130 x 200. Circ: 1,800.

649 CHN ISSN 1000-727X
FUMU BIDU/PARENTS MONTHLY. Text in Chinese. m. USD 36.80.
Published by: Beijing Chubanshe/Beijing Publishing House, 6 Beisanhuan Zhonglu, Beijing, 100011, China. TEL 2016699. Ed. Tao Xincheng. **Dist. in US by:** China Books & Periodicals Inc, 360 Swift Ave., Ste. 48, S San Fran, CA 94080-6220. TEL 415-282-2994.

028.5 DEU ISSN 0176-2753
FUNDEVOGEL✶; kritisches Kinder-Medien-Magazin. Text in German. 1984. q. back issues avail. **Document type:** *Magazine, Consumer.*
Indexed: ChLitAb, IBR, IBZ.
Published by: Dipa-Verlag, Nassauer Str 1, Frankfurt am Main, 60439, Germany. TEL 49-69-95732044. Circ: 1,200.

649 USA
THE FUTURE GENERATION; a zine for subculture parents, kids, friends & others. Text in English. 1989. irreg. USD 3 newsstand/cover (effective 2005).
Published by: China Martens, P O Box 4803, Balimore, MD 21211. china410@hotmail.com.

362.7 USA ISSN 1054-8289
HV741 CODEN: FCHIEW
➤ **THE FUTURE OF CHILDREN.** Text in English. 1991. 2/yr. USD 40 to individuals; USD 90 to institutions (effective 2005). illus. reprints avail. **Document type:** *Journal, Academic/Scholarly.* **Description:** Covers child health, education, and welfare public policy issues.
Related titles: Online - full text ed.: ISSN 1550-1558. free (effective 2005) (from Gale Group, Northern Light Technology, Inc., O C L C Online Computer Library Center, Inc., Project MUSE, ProQuest Information & Learning).
Indexed: ASCA, BibInd, CDA, CIJE, CINAHL, CJA, CurCont, ExcerpMed, FamI, IMFL, INI, IndMed, MEDLINE, PsycInfo, PsycholAb, SOPODA, SRRA, SSA, SSCI, SWR&A, SociolAb, e-psyche.
—BLDSC (4060.523000), GNLM, IDS, IE, Infotrieve, ingenta.
Published by: Princeton University, Woodrow Wilson School of Public and International Affairs, Robertson Hall, Princeton, NJ 08544-1013. TEL 609-258-4800, wwswww@princeton.edu, http://www.futureofchildren.org, http://www.wws.princeton.edu. Ed. Sara McLanahan. Circ: 50,000.

649 305.868 USA
EL FUTURO. Text in English. q. **Document type:** *Newsletter.* **Description:** Covers a variety of topics, including increasing Hispanic cultural awareness and Latino values.
Media: Online - full text.
Published by: National Latino Children's Institute, 320 El Paso St., San Antonio, TX 78207-5000. nlca@inetport.com, http://www.nlci.org/press/elfuturo.htm.

C

G A L R O BULLETIN. (Guardians ad Litem and Reporting Officers) see *LAW*

649 USA ISSN 1545-6714
GAY PARENT. Text in English. 1998. bi-m. USD 20 domestic; USD 30 foreign (effective 2004). adv. bk.rev.; film rev.; play rev.; tel.rev.; video rev. 16 p./no.; back issues avail. **Document type:** *Magazine, Consumer.*
Related titles: Online - full text ed.: (from EBSCO Publishing).
Address: Box 750852, Forest Hills, NY 11375-0852. TEL 718-997-0392, http://www.gayparentmag.com. Ed., Adv. contact Angeline Acain.

GAY YOUTH COMMUNITY NEWS. see *HOMOSEXUALITY*

GIFTED CHILD TODAY MAGAZINE; the nation's leading resource for nurturing talented children . see *EDUCATION—Special Education And Rehabilitation*

GIFTED EDUCATION PRESS QUARTERLY. see *EDUCATION—Special Education And Rehabilitation*

GIFTED UNLIMITED. see *EDUCATION—Special Education And Rehabilitation*

155.5 JPN ISSN 0915-4965
GIFU SHISHUNKI KENKYU/GIFU SOCIETY OF ADOLESCENTOLOGY. JOURNAL. Text in Japanese. 1985. a. adv. **Document type:** *Bulletin.*
Indexed: e-psyche.
Published by: (Gifu Shishunki Kenkyukai), Gifuken Seishin Hoken Senta/Gifu Prefectural Mental Health Center, 8-1 Shimonara 2-chome, Gifu-shi, 500-8385, Japan. Ed. Akihiko Shibata. Adv. contact Hiroyuki Koide.

028.5 USA
GIRAFFE NEWS. Text in English. 1982. s-a. USD 35. **Document type:** *Newsletter.* **Description:** Presents stories about heroes and news for members of the Giraffe Project.
Formerly: Giraffe Gazette
Published by: Giraffe Project, 197 Second St, Box 759, Langley, WA 98260. TEL 360-221-7989, FAX 360-2217817, office@giraffe.org, http://www.giraffe.org/giraffe/. Ed. Ann Medlock. Circ: 2,000 (paid).

369.4 USA
GIRL SCOUT NEWS. Text in English. q. free domestic to members. adv. **Document type:** *Newsletter, Trade.*
Formerly: Millwheel
Published by: Girl Scouts of Lake Erie Council, 19201 Villaview Rd., Cleveland, OH 44119-3074. TEL 216-481-1313, FAX 216-692-4060, girlscouts@gslec.org, communications@gslec.org, http://www.gslec.org. adv.: B&W page USD 825.

053.1 DEU
GIRLIESTYLE.DE; das interaktive Maedchenmagazin. Text in German. 2000. m. adv. **Document type:** *Consumer.* **Description:** Provides an interactive forum for the interests of teenage girls.
Media: Online - full text.

Address: Oberschlesierstr 76, Muenster, 48151, Germany. TEL 49-251-97429338, FAX 49-251-97429339, info@girliestyle.de, http://www.girliestyle.de. Ed. Alexandra Mierswa. Adv. contact Philipp Weber. online banner EUR 22.50; 468 x 60.

GLOBAL CHILD HEALTH NEWS & REVIEW. see *MEDICAL SCIENCES—Pediatrics*

649   USA
GRAND RAPIDS FAMILY MAGAZINE. Text in English. 1964. m.
Published by: Gemini Publications, 549 Ottawa Ave N W, Ste 201, Grand Rapids, MI 49503-1444. TEL 616-459-4545, FAX 616-459-4800. Ed. Carole Valade Copenhaver. Pub. John H Zwarensteyn.

649   USA   ISSN 1055-5153
GRAND RAPIDS PARENT. Text in English. 1989. m. USD 12; free to qualified personnel (effective 2005). adv. **Document type:** *Magazine, Consumer.* **Description:** Covers finance, psychology, humor, child development, dining, education, food, new products, healthcare, events and recipes for parents.
Published by: Gemini Publications, 549 Ottawa Ave N W, Ste 201, Grand Rapids, MI 49503-1444. TEL 616-459-4545, FAX 616-459-4800, http://www.grfamily.com. Ed. Carole Valade. Pub. John Vawarensteyn. Adv. contact Randy Prichard. Circ: 24,000 (paid and free).

GRANTS FOR CHILDREN & YOUTH. see *EDUCATION—School Organization And Administration*

649   USA
GREAT LAKES FAMILY; the magazine for Southwest Michigan parents. Text in English. 1988. bi-m. free (effective 2004). adv. **Document type:** *Magazine, Consumer.* **Description:** Local magazine dedicated to providing Southwest Michigan parents with information vital to raising healthy, well-adjusted children.
Related titles: Online - full content ed.
Published by: C L S Communications, PO Box 714, Kalamazoo, MI 490004. TEL 269-382-4530, FAX 269-388-4249, editor@glfamily.com, http://www.glfamily.com/. Ed., Pub. Cynthia L Schrauben. adv.: page USD 990; bleed 8.7 x 11.2. Circ: 19,995.

305.23   BEL   ISSN 1384-7511
GROTER GROEIEN. Text in Dutch. 1984. quadrennial. EUR 22.13 (effective 2003). adv. charts; illus. **Document type:** *Journal, Consumer.* **Description:** Offers mothers articles and advice on child rearing.
Published by: Sanoma Magazines Belgium, Telecomlaan 5-7, Diegem, 1831, Belgium. TEL 32-2-7762211, FAX 32-2-776-2317, http://www.sanoma-magazines.be/HomePage.aspx?flash=1&Language=nl.

369.4 200   USA   ISSN 0163-8971
                                    CODEN: CRCMEN
GROUP (LOVELAND); the youth ministry magazine. Text in English. 1974. 6/yr. USD 24.95 domestic (effective 2005); USD 28.95 foreign (effective 2003). adv. bk.rev.; film rev. index. back issues avail. **Document type:** *Magazine, Consumer.* **Description:** Contains practical help for Christian adults who work with youth.
Former titles (until 1997): Jr. High Ministry Magazine (1055-1409); Group's Jr. High Ministry Magazine (0884-0504)
Related titles: Online - full text ed.: (from ProQuest Information & Learning).
Indexed: BiolAb, CCR, ChrPI, CurCont, SSCI.
Published by: Group Publishing, Inc., PO Box 481, Loveland, CO 80539. TEL 800-447-1070, FAX 970-292-4373, info@grouppublishing.com, http://www.groupmag.com, http://www.grouppublishing.com. Ed. Rick Lawrence. Pub. Tim Gilmour. R&P Jane Gerk. Adv. contact Shelley Richards. Circ: 55,000. **Subscr. to:** PO Box 469080, Escondida, CA 92046-9080.

649   FRA   ISSN 1146-061X
GROUPE DE RECHERCHE ET D'ACTION POUR L'ENFANCE. LETTRE. Key Title: La Lettre du GRAPE. Text in French. 1990. q. EUR 40 domestic; EUR 48 foreign (effective 2003). **Document type:** *Magazine, Consumer.*
Published by: (Groupe de Recherche et d'Action pour l'Enfance (GRAPE), Editions Eres, 11 rue des Alouettes, Ramonville Saint-Agne, 31520, France. TEL 33-5-61751576, FAX 33-5-61735289, enfance.grape@noos.fr, eres@edition-eres.com, http://www.legrape.com, http://www.edition-eres.com. Ed. Francoise Petitot. Circ: 1,100.

649 155.4   USA
GROWING CHILD. Text in English. 1971. m. looseleaf. USD 14.95 (effective 2004). adv. bk.rev. back issues avail. **Document type:** *Newsletter.* **Description:** For parents of children up to age 6.
Related titles: ♦ Supplement(s): Growing Parent Newsletter. ISSN 0193-8037.
Published by: Dunn & Hargitt, Inc., 2336 Northwestern Ave., W Lafayette, IN 47906-1806. TEL 765-423-2624, FAX 765-423-4495, growchild@aol.com, http:// www.growingchild.com. Ed. Nancy Kleckner. Circ: 30,000.

649   USA   ISSN 0193-8037
GROWING PARENT NEWSLETTER. Text in English. 1975. m. included with subscr. to Growing Child. back issues avail. **Document type:** *Newsletter.*

Related titles: ♦ Supplement to: Growing Child.
Published by: Dunn & Hargitt, Inc., 2336 Northwestern Ave., W Lafayette, IN 47906-1806. TEL 765-423-2624, FAX 765-423-4495, growchild@aol.com, http:// www.growingchild.com. Ed. Nancy Kleckner. Circ: 30,000.

155.4   USA
GROWING TOGETHER. Text in English. 1985. m. USD 30 (effective 2000). **Description:** For use by daycare and preschool facilities.
Published by: Dunn & Hargitt, Inc., 2336 Northwestern Ave., W Lafayette, IN 47906-1806. TEL 765-423-2624, FAX 765-423-4495, growchild@aol.com. Ed. Nancy Kleckner. Circ: 2,500.

649   ESP   ISSN 1138-8404
GUIA DE SU PRIMER ANO. Text in Spanish. 1995. s-a. free to qualified personnel. **Document type:** *Consumer.* **Description:** Contains information on baby care for new mothers.
Fromerly (until 1998): Guia de Mi Bebe y Yo (1135-643X)
Published by: Sfera Editores S.L., Pol. Mas Blau Ed. Muntadas, planta baja Esc. B, SOLSONES, 2, El Prat De Llobregat, Barcelona 08820, Spain. TEL 34-93-370-8585, FAX 34-93-370-5060, sfera@intercom.es. Ed. Juan Turu. Circ: 154,803 (controlled).

649   ITA   ISSN 1123-8089
LA GUIDA DI IO E IL MIO BAMBINO. Text in Italian. 1989. s-a. adv. **Document type:** *Directory, Consumer.*
Formerly (until 1993): Avere un Bambino (1123-9336)
Published by: Sfera Editore SpA (Subsidiary of: R C S Mediagroup), Via Angelo Rizzoli 2, Milan, MI 20132, Italy. TEL 39-02-25841. Circ: 439,968.

369.4   GBR
GUIDE ASSOCIATION. EXECUTIVE NEWS. Text in English. m. free. back issues avail. **Document type:** *Bulletin.*
Description: Reports on news of the association.
Media: Online - full text.
Published by: Guide Association, 17-19 Buckingham Palace Rd, London, SW1W 0PP, United Kingdom. TEL 44-20-7834-6242, chq@guides.org.uk, http://www.guides.org.uk/news/.

GUIDE TO TOYS FOR CHILDREN WHO ARE BLIND OR VISUALLY IMPAIRED. see *HANDICAPPED—Visually Impaired*

369.4   GBR   ISSN 0265-2706
GUIDING. Text in English. 1914. m. GBP 15; GBP 1.30 newsstand/cover. adv. bk.rev. charts; illus. index. **Document type:** *Newsletter, Consumer.*
Formerly (until Jan. 1983): Guider (0017-534X)
Published by: Guide Association, 17-19 Buckingham Palace Rd, London, SW1W 0PP, United Kingdom. TEL 44-20-7834-6242, CHQ@guides.org.uk, http://www.guides.org.uk. Ed. Nora Warner. Pub. Anne Moffat. Adv. contact Sarah Harrison. Circ: 27,500.

GUILFORD SCHOOL PRACTITIONER SERIES. see *PSYCHOLOGY*

HACER FAMILIA. see *WOMEN'S INTERESTS*

790.019   CHN   ISSN 1002-4069
➤ **HAIZI TIANDI/CHILDREN'S WORLD.** Text in Chinese. 1989. m. CNY 42 (effective 2004). adv. bk.rev. charts; illus. back issues avail. **Document type:** *Academic/Scholarly.*
Description: Contains information to help the young students study literature, art and other forms of knowlege tools.
Related titles: Fax ed.
Published by: Zhongguo Songqingling Jijinghui/Songqingling Fund Association, 21, Andeli Bei Lu, Beijing, 100011, China. adv.: B&W page CNY 7,000, color page CNY 10,000; trim 140 x 160. **Dist. by:** China International Book Trading Corp, 35 Chegongzhuang Xilu, Haidian District, PO Box 399, Beijing 100044, China. TEL 86-10-68412045, FAX 86-10-68412023, cibtc@mail.cibtc.com.cn, http://www.cibtc.com.cn.

649   DEU
HALLO BABY. Text in German. 1990. 2/yr. adv. **Document type:** *Magazine, Consumer.*
Published by: Junior-Verlag GmbH und Co. KG, Fehlandtstr 41, Hamburg, 20534, Germany. Adv. contact Sabine Raum. color page EUR 18,800; trim 103 x 150. Circ: 300,000 (controlled).

HANDLING CHILD CUSTODY, ABUSE, AND ADOPTION CASES. see *LAW—Family And Matrimonial Law*

362.7   USA
HARLEMLIVE; Harlem's youth internet publication. Text in English. 1996. irreg. **Description:** Promotes training for young people in Harlem.
Media: Online - full text.
Address: 525 W. 120th St., # 144, New York, NY 10027-6625. editor@harlemlive.org, http://www.harlemlive.org. Eds. Justin Young, Nicolle Farrow.

HARO!; en tidning om barn och foeraeldrar. see *SOCIOLOGY*

HAVE CHILDREN WILL TRAVEL. see *TRAVEL AND TOURISM*

649 618   GBR
HAVING A BABY. Text in English. 1994. bi-m. GBP 2.60 newsstand/cover (effective 2000). adv. **Document type:** *Magazine, Consumer.*
Published by: National Magazine Company Ltd., National Magazine House, 72 Broadwick St, London, W1F 9EP, United Kingdom. TEL 44-20-74395000, FAX 44-20-74376886, http://www.natmags.co.uk.

649   GBR   ISSN 1467-4149
HAVING BABIES. Text in English. 1999. w. GBP 1.60 newsstand/cover (effective 2001). **Document type:** *Magazine, Consumer.* **Description:** Provides a guide for parents of babies and young children or those planning to start a family.
Published by: Eaglemoss Publications Ltd., 5 Cromwell Rd, London, SW7 2HR, United Kingdom. TEL 44-20-7590-8300, FAX 44-20-7590-8301, hjames@woodgt.co.uk, http://www.havingbabies.co.uk, http://www.eaglemoss.co.uk.

HAWAII. DEPARTMENT OF HEALTH. MENTAL HEALTH SERVICES FOR CHILDREN AND YOUTH; children's MH services branch. see *SOCIAL SERVICES AND WELFARE*

649   USA   ISSN 1529-2665
HEALTHY KIDS EN ESPANOL. Text in Spanish. q. free (effective 2003); Avail. through participating pediatrician offices only. **Document type:** *Magazine, Consumer.* **Description:** Targets Spanish-speaking parents of children up to 10 years old.
Published by: Meredith Corp., 1716 Locust St, Des Moines, IA 50309-3023. TEL 515-284-3000, 800-556-9184, FAX 515-284-3657, http://www.meredith.com.

158 362.7   GBR   ISSN 1462-8260
HEALTHY MINDS. Text in English. 1998. s-a. free. **Document type:** *Bulletin.* **Description:** Highlights the contributions of voluntary sector initiatives to the mental health and well-being of young people.
Indexed: e-psyche.
Published by: National Children's Bureau, 8 Wakley St, London, EC1V 7QE, United Kingdom. TEL 44-20-78436000, FAX 44-20-72789512, http://www.ncb.org.uk. Circ: 1,000.

305.23   NLD
HELLO BABY. Text in Dutch. a. adv. illus. **Document type:** *Journal, Consumer.* **Description:** Offers new mothers advice on caring for their babies.
Published by: V N U Tijdschriften B.V., Postbus 1900, Hoofddorp, 2130 JH, Netherlands. TEL 31-23-556-6770, FAX 31-23-556-6771, ServiceTeam@tijdschriften.vnu.com, http://www.vnu.nl/vnu/organisatie.

HELPING CHILDREN LEARN (ELEMENTARY SCHOOL EDITION); tips families can use to help children to do better in school. see *EDUCATION*

HELPING CHILDREN LEARN (SCHOOL READINESS ENGLISH EDITION); tips families can use to help children do better in school. see *EDUCATION*

HELPING STUDENTS LEARN (HIGH SCHOOL ENGLISH EDITION); tips families can use to help students do better in school. see *EDUCATION*

HELPING STUDENTS LEARN (MIDDLE SCHOOL ENGLISH EDITION). see *EDUCATION*

HIDDEN CHILD. see *RELIGIONS AND THEOLOGY—Judaic*

362   GBR
HIGHLIGHT (LONDON). Text in English. 1973. bi-m.
—BLDSC (4307.490000).
Published by: National Children's Bureau, 8 Wakley St, London, EC1V 7QE, United Kingdom. TEL 44-20-78436000, FAX 44-20-72789512, http://www.ncb.org.uk.

HIP MAMA; the parenting zine. see *LITERARY AND POLITICAL REVIEWS*

HISPANIC AMERICAN FAMILY MAGAZINE. see *ETHNIC INTERESTS*

HOOFS & HORNS. see *AGRICULTURE—Poultry And Livestock*

HORN BOOK GUIDE TO CHILDREN'S AND YOUNG ADULT BOOKS. see *PUBLISHING AND BOOK TRADE*

THE HORN BOOK MAGAZINE; recommending books for children and young adults. see *PUBLISHING AND BOOK TRADE*

HOT 100; a quick guide to federal programs and services for youth. see *SOCIAL SERVICES AND WELFARE*

HOTLINE (STONY BROOK); news service on the missing children field. see *CRIMINOLOGY AND LAW ENFORCEMENT*

649   USA
HOUSTON FAMILY. Text in English. m. adv.

C

Published by: United Parenting Publications (Subsidiary of: Trader Publishing Co.), 2620 Fountainview, 200, Houston, TX 77057. TEL 713-266-1885, FAX 713-266-1915, http://www.houstonfamily.com, http://www.parenthood.com.

HUMAN STRESS: CURRENT SELECTED RESEARCH. see *PSYCHOLOGY*

HUNYIN YU JIATING/MARRIAGE & FAMILY. see *MATRIMONY*

I C A N COMMUNICATE. see *EDUCATION—Special Education And Rehabilitation*

I C C W JOURNAL. see *SOCIAL SERVICES AND WELFARE*

649 PHL
I M C H NEWSLETTER. Text in English. 1969. m. PHP 10, USD 1.50. abstr.; charts; illus. **Document type:** *Newsletter.*
Published by: Institute of Maternal and Child Health, National Training Center for Maternal Health Services, 11 Banawe St, Quezon City, Philippines. TEL 712-01-49, FAX 712-10-13. Ed. Jose O Obordo. Circ: 4,000.

649.1 USA
I - MOM. Text in English. w. adv. back issues avail. **Document type:** *Newsletter.* **Description:** Includes tips, resources, advice and knowledge needed by work-at-home moms.
Media: Online - full text.
Published by: Moms Network Exchange, PO Box 238, Rosemount, MN 55068. TEL 651-423-4036, FAX 651-322-1702, cyndi@momsnetwork.com, http://www.momsnetwork.com/busdirmore/mnenewsletter.shtml/. Ed., Pub. Cyndi Webb.

I S I S MAGAZINE. see *EDUCATION—Guides To Schools And Colleges*

649 028.5 RUS
IGRA I DETI; zhurnal dlya roditelei i pedagogov. Text in Russian. 2002. bi-m. **Document type:** *Magazine, Consumer.*
Published by: Redaktsiya Zhurnala Igra i Deti, a/ya 69, Moscow, 115551, Russian Federation. TEL 7-095-3928318, FAX 7-095-3927563, linka-press@mtu-net.ru, igra@i-deti.ru, http://www.i-deti.ru. Ed. Yelena Gorbacheva.

303.32 USA
THE IMAGE. Text in English. s-a. free (effective 2005). **Document type:** *Newsletter, Consumer.*
Published by: Big Brothers & Big Sisters of Greater Los Angeles, 1055 Wilshire Blvd, Ste 1950, Los Angeles, CA 90017. TEL 213-481-3611, FAX 323-258-2072. Ed. Keith Padgett. Circ: 8,000 (free).

IMPACT! (SEATTLE). see *BUSINESS AND ECONOMICS—International Development And Assistance*

IMPACT (WESTPORT). see *SOCIAL SERVICES AND WELFARE*

370 GBR ISSN 0962-3507
IN COMMON. Text in English. 1974. s-a. free. bk.rev. **Document type:** *Newsletter.* **Description:** Serves as the magazine of the Commonwealth Youth Programme for those involved in youth affairs in the Commonwealth.
Former titles (until 1989): C Y P News Service; Commonwealth Youth News
Published by: (Commonwealth Youth Programme), Commonwealth Secretariat, Marlborough House, Pall Mall, London, SW1Y 5HX, United Kingdom. TEL 44-2078-393411, FAX 44-2079-300827, http://www.thecommonwealth.org. Ed. Jacqui Kissai. Circ: 4,000.

305.23 618.2 NLD
IN VERWACHTING. Text in Dutch. a. adv. charts; illus. **Document type:** *Magazine, Consumer.* **Description:** Offers expectant mothers important advice on caring for their unborn infants to provide the best chances for having a healthy baby.
Published by: V N U Tijdschriften B.V., Postbus 1900, Hoofddorp, 2130 JH, Netherlands. TEL 31-23-556-6770, FAX 31-23-556-6771, ServiceTeam@tijdschriften.vnu.com, http://www.vnu.nl/vnu/organisatie.

267 USA
INCONTACT. Text in English. 1984. q. free. **Document type:** *Newsletter.* **Description:** Publishes primarily for donors to club and camp ministry for children; covers issues affecting children and youth, stories of children and adult volunteers involved in the program.
Published by: Pioneer Clubs, PO Box 788, Wheaton, IL 60189-0788. TEL 630-293-1600, FAX 630-293-3053. Ed. Gary L Wall. Circ: 6,000.

649 USA ISSN 1072-2084
INDY'S CHILD. Text in English. 1984. m. USD 18. adv. bk.rev. **Document type:** *Consumer.* **Description:** Covers education, women's issues, camps, enrichement, teen issues, computer hardware and software and gives parenting advice.
Published by: Indy's Child, Inc., 250 E. 96th St., Ste. 100, Indianapolis, IN 46240-3730. TEL 317-722-8500, FAX 317-722-8510, editor@indyschild.com, http://www.indyschild.com. Ed., Pub. Tom Wynne. Adv. contact Mike Hussey. B&W page USD 1,400, color page USD 1,800; trim 13.5 x 11.25. Circ: 70,000 (controlled).

362.7 USA ISSN 0797-8375
HV703
INFANCIA. Text in English, French, Portuguese, Spanish. 1927. q. bk.rev. abstr.; charts; illus.; stat.
Former titles (until 1990): Instituto Interamericano del Nino. Boletin (0020-4056); (until 1957): Instituto Internacional Americano de Proteccion a la Infancia. Boletin (0366-1849)
Indexed: PAIS.
Published by: (Instituto Interamericano del Nino), Organization of American States/Organizacion de los Estados Americanos, General Secretariat, Department of Publications, 1889 F St, N W, Washington, DC 20006-4499. TEL 202-458-3527, FAX 202-458-3534. Circ: 2,400. **Dist. by:** Center for Promotion and Distribution of Publications, PO Box 66398, Washington, DC 20035.

362.7 PER ISSN 1024-6363
INFANCIA Y SOCIEDAD. Text in Spanish. 1994. irreg., latest vol.5, 1995. price varies. back issues avail. **Document type:** *Monographic series, Academic/Scholarly.*
Published by: (Instituto de Estudios Peruanos), I E P Ediciones (Subsidiary of: Instituto de Estudios Peruanos), Horacio Urteaga 694, Jesus Maria, Lima, 11, Peru. TEL 51-14-3326194, FAX 51-14-3326173, libreria@iep.org.pe, http://iep.perucultural.org.pe.

305.232 USA ISSN 1525-0008
BF719 CODEN: INFAG8
INFANCY. Text in English. 2000. bi-m. (in 2 vols.). USD 595 in US & Canada to institutions; USD 640 elsewhere to institutions; USD 625 combined subscription in US & Canada to institutions print & online eds.; USD 670 combined subscription elsewhere to institutions print & online eds. (effective 2006). adv. back issues avail.; reprint service avail. from PSC. **Document type:** *Journal, Academic/Scholarly.* **Description:** Provides original research on normal and aberrant infant development in the first two years, including both human and animal research.
Related titles: Online - full text ed.: ISSN 1532-7078. USD 565 worldwide to institutions (effective 2006) (from EBSCO Publishing, Gale Group, O C L C Online Computer Library Center, Inc., Swets Information Services).
Indexed: CurCont, ExcerpMed, FamI, PsycInfo, PsycholAb, SSCI, e-psyche.
—BLDSC (4478.256000), IE, Infotrieve, ingenta. **CCC.**
Published by: (International Society on Infant Studies), Lawrence Erlbaum Associates, Inc., 10 Industrial Ave, Mahwah, NJ 07430-2262. TEL 201-258-2200, 800-926-6579, FAX 201-236-0072, journals@erlbaum.com, http://www.leaonline.com/loi/in. Ed. Richard N Aslin. adv.: page USD 475; trim 5 x 8.

INFANT AND CHILD DEVELOPMENT. see *PSYCHOLOGY*

INFANT PROJECTS. see *EDUCATION—Teaching Methods And Curriculum*

INFANTS AND YOUNG CHILDREN; an interdisciplinary journal of special care practices. see *MEDICAL SCIENCES—Pediatrics*

155.4 ITA ISSN 0390-2420
INFANZIA. Text in Italian. 1973. m. adv. bk.rev.
Indexed: e-psyche.
Published by: La Nuova Italia Editrice S.p.A, Via Ernesto Codignola 1, Florence, 50018, Italy. nib.reviews@lanuovaitalia.it, http://www.lanuovaitalia.it/. Ed. Pietro Bertolini.

INFORMASIAN. see *HANDICAPPED—Visually Impaired*

INFORMATION PLUS REFERENCE SERIES. CHILD ABUSE; betraying a trust. see *SOCIAL SERVICES AND WELFARE*

INFORMATION PLUS REFERENCE SERIES. GROWING UP IN AMERICA. see *SOCIOLOGY*

303.60835 USA
INFORMATION PLUS REFERENCE SERIES. YOUTH VIOLENCE CRIME & GANGS; children at risk. Text in English. biennial, latest 2004. USD 40 per vol. (effective 2005). **Document type:** *Monographic series, Academic/Scholarly.*
Related titles: Online - full content ed.; ♦ Series of: Information Plus Reference Series.
Published by: Gale Group (Subsidiary of: Thomson Corporation), 27500 Drake Rd, Farmington Hills, MI 48331-3535. TEL 248-699-4253, 800-877-4253, FAX 248-699-8035, 800-414-5043, galeord@gale.com, http://www.galegroup.com.

INFORMATION TECHNOLOGY IN CHILDHOOD EDUCATION ANNUAL. see *EDUCATION—Computer Applications*

649 USA
THE INFORMED PARENT; the weekly internet magazine of the 21st century. Text in English. m.
Media: Online - full content.
Published by: Intermag Productions, 23546 Coyote Springs Dr, Diamond Bar, CA 91765. http://www.informedparent.com. Ed. John H Samson.

267 NLD ISSN 0041-2562
INKLUSIEF. Text in Dutch. 1971. 4/yr. adv. bk.rev. **Document type:** *Newsletter, Consumer.*
Incorporates (1977-1982): Binnenste Buiten (0166-2910)
Published by: Y M C A Nederland, Soestdijkerweg 10b, Den Dolder, 3734 MH, Netherlands. TEL 31-35-6668700, FAX 31-35-6668688, info@ymca.nl, http://www.ymca.nl. Circ: 6,000.

649 USA
INLAND EMPIRE FAMILY. Text in English. m. USD 18 (effective 2004). adv. **Description:** Covers parenting issues for parents of infants to teens.
Published by: Churm Publishing, 1451 Quail St, Ste 201, Newport Beach, CA 92660. TEL 949-757-1404, FAX 949-757-1996, info@churmpublishing.com, http://www.churmpublishing.com. Ed. Craig Reem. Pub. Steve Churm.

155.4 649 USA ISSN 1065-1039
INSIDE - OUTSIDE; a guide to positive parenting. Text in English. 1991. q. USD 35 for 15 copies. adv. bk.rev. charts. **Description:** Covers positive parenting issues, self esteem issues, positive interaction and bonding-nurturing with children, and health and safety articles.
Published by: Institute for Women and Children, 4680 Lake Underhill Rd, Orlando, FL 32807. TEL 407-277-1942, FAX 407-381-0907. Ed. Judy Peterson. Circ: 7,000.

268.6 649.7 NLD ISSN 1383-9632
INTERMEZZO; nieuws- en informatieblad over jeugd- en jongerenwerk in en rond de sow-kerken. Text in Dutch. 1958; N.S. 1995. bi-m. bk.rev. **Description:** Features youth projects sponsored by Reformed churches in the Netherlands.
Formerly (until Sep. 1995): Bijblijven (Driebergen) (0006-226X)
Published by: Samen op Weg Jeugdwerk, Postbus 99, Driebergen Rysenberg, 3970 AB, Netherlands. TEL 31-343-523222, FAX 31-343-523250. Ed. Ineke van der Vegt. Circ: 5,000.

C

362.7 155.4 GBR ISSN 0267-3843
➤ **INTERNATIONAL JOURNAL OF ADOLESCENCE AND YOUTH.** Text in English. 1987. 4/yr. **Document type:** *Journal, Academic/Scholarly.* **Description:** Covers psychological growth and development, health and medical care, social policy, education, employment, unemployment, leisure, sex education, family relationships, and homelessness.
Indexed: ASSIA, BrEdI, CINAHL, CJA, CPE, DIP, ERA, ETA, FamI, IBR, IBSS, IBZ, MEA, PsycInfo, PsycholAb, RHEA, RILM, SEA, SENA, SOMA, SOPODA, SSA, SociolAb, TEA, e-psyche.
—BLDSC (4541.562000), IE, Infotrieve, ingenta. **CCC.**
Published by: A B Academic Publishers, PO Box 42, Bicester, Oxon OX26 6NW, United Kingdom. jrnls@abapubl.demon.co.uk. Ed. Roy Evans.

155.4 CAN ISSN 1206-8330
INTERNATIONAL JOURNAL OF CHILDREN & ADOLESCENTS✶. Text in Arabic, English. 1997. q. CND 400 (effective 2000). adv. bk.rev. **Document type:** *Journal, Consumer.* **Description:** Designed for concise, cooperative publication of simple accelerated and safe creative ideas.
Published by: M.I. Ismail, Ed. & Pub., P O Box 98029, Mississauga, ON L5L 3A0, Canada. FAX 516-277-2875.

THE INTERNATIONAL JOURNAL OF CHILDREN'S RIGHTS. see *POLITICAL SCIENCE—Civil Rights*

INTERNATIONAL JOURNAL OF CHILDREN'S SPIRITUALITY. see *PSYCHOLOGY*

INTERNATIONAL JOURNAL OF DISABILITY, COMMUNITY & REHABILITATION. see *EDUCATION—Special Education And Rehabilitation*

372.21 USA ISSN 0020-7187
➤ **INTERNATIONAL JOURNAL OF EARLY CHILDHOOD.** Text in English, French, Spanish. 1969. 2/yr. membership. adv. bk.rev. reprint service avail. from PQC. **Document type:** *Journal, Academic/Scholarly.* **Description:** Keeps readers up to date with OMEP research and papers.
Related titles: Microform ed.: 1969 (from PQC); Online - full text ed.: (from bigchalk, Northern Light Technology, Inc., ProQuest Information & Learning).
Indexed: ABIn, BrEdI, CDA, CIJE, CPE, ERA, ETA, EduInd, FamI, MEA, RASB, RHEA, SEA, SENA, SOMA, SSI, TEA.
—BLDSC (4542.190000), IE, Infotrieve, ingenta.
Published by: World Organization for Early Childhood Education/Organisation Mondiale pour l'Education Prescolaire (OMEP), c/o Dr Margaret Devine, 81 Irving Pl, Apt 16, New York, NY 10003. Ed. Dr. Stephen Graves TEL 813 974-1026. Circ: 2,000.

▼ ➤ **INTERNATIONAL JOURNAL OF PEDIATRIC OBESITY.** see *NUTRITION AND DIETETICS*

155.5 DEU ISSN 1432-4873
➤ **INTERNATIONAL STUDIES ON CHILDHOOD AND ADOLESCENCE.** Text in English. 1995. irreg., latest vol.7, 1999. price varies. **Document type:** *Monographic series, Academic/Scholarly.*
Published by: Walter de Gruyter GmbH & Co. KG, Genthiner Str. 13, Berlin, 10785, Germany. TEL 49-30-260050, FAX 49-30-26005251, wdg-info@degruyter.de, http://www.degruyter.de.

➤ **THE INTERNET GUIDE TO BABY HEALTH.** see *MEDICAL SCIENCES—Pediatrics*

➤ **INTERPLAY.** see *CHILDREN AND YOUTH—For*

649 ITA ISSN 1123-8062
IO E IL MIO BAMBINO. Text in Italian. 1983. m. **Document type:** *Magazine, Consumer.*
Published by: Sfera Editore SpA (Subsidiary of: R C S Mediagroup), Via Angelo Rizzoli 2, Milan, MI 20132, Italy. TEL 39-02-25841. Circ: 200,996.

649 ITA
IO E MIO FIGLIO. Text in Italian. 1978. m. adv.
Published by: Publibaby Srl, Via Enrico Fermi, 18, Cusago, MI 20090, Italy. TEL 39-02-90119700, FAX 39-02-90390464. Ed. Emilio Terzagli. Circ: 185,000.

649 USA
IOWA PARENT. Text in English. m. free. **Description:** A niche publication dedicated to informing, serving and entertaining families in Des Moines and Central Iowa.
Address: PO Box 957, Des Moines, IA 50304. TEL 515-284-8173, FAX 515-286-2597, info@iowaparent.com, http://www.iowaparent.com. Ed. Jan R Walker. Circ: 30,000.

C

362.76 345.025 616.858 USA
HV8079.C48 CODEN: ICCAEG
➤ **ISSUES IN CHILD ABUSE ACCUSATIONS (ONLINE).** Text in English. 1989. biennial. free. bk.rev. back issues avail. **Document type:** *Journal, Academic/Scholarly.* **Description:** Provides a multidisciplinary forum on all aspects of child abuse, with special emphasis on research and commentary that questions the methods and conventional wisdom of the child abuse establishment.
Formerly: Issues in Child Abuse Accusations (Print) (1043-8823)
Media: Online - full content.
Indexed: SOPODA.
—GNLM.
Published by: Institute for Psychological Therapies, 13200 Cannon City Blvd, Northfield, MN 55057. TEL 507-645-8881, FAX 507-645-8883, under006@tc.umn.edu, http://www.ipt-forensics.com/journal/index.htm. Circ: 200 (paid).

362.7 USA
ISSUES IN CHILDREN'S AND FAMILIES' LIVES SERIES. Text in English. irreg., latest vol.2, 1995. price varies. **Document type:** *Monographic series.*
Related titles: Series of: The John & Kelly Hartman Series.
—BLDSC (4584.152000), ingenta.
Published by: Sage Publications, Inc., Books, 2455 Teller Rd, Thousand Oaks, CA 91320. TEL 805-499-0721, FAX 805-499-0871. **Subscr. to:** Sage Publications Ltd., 1 Oliver's Yard, 55 City Rd, London EC1 1SP, United Kingdom; Sage Publications India Pvt. Ltd., M-32 Market, Greater Kailash-I, PO Box 4215, New Delhi 110 048, India.

J D C - BROOKDALE INSTITUTE OF GERONTOLOGY AND HUMAN DEVELOPMENT. ANNUAL REPORT. see *GERONTOLOGY AND GERIATRICS*

J D C - BROOKDALE INSTITUTE OF GERONTOLOGY AND HUMAN DEVELOPMENT. RESEARCH SERIES. see *GERONTOLOGY AND GERIATRICS*

362.7 AUT
J U M - JUGEND UND MEDIEN; Lehrerzeitung des Buchklubs. Text in German. 1990. 4/yr. membership. **Document type:** *Bulletin.*
Published by: Oesterreichischer Buchklub der Jugend, Mayerhofgasse 6, Vienna, W 1041, Austria. TEL 43-1-5051754-0, FAX 43-1-505175450.

JA ZUM BABY; medizinischer Ratgeber fuer werdende und junge Eltern. see *MEDICAL SCIENCES—Pediatrics*

362.7 DEU
JAHRBUCH JUGENDFORSCHUNG. Text in German. 2000. a. EUR 24.90 (effective 2004). **Document type:** *Journal, Academic/Scholarly.*
Published by: V S - Verlag fuer Sozialwissenschaften (Subsidiary of: Springer Science+Business Media), Abraham-Lincoln-Str 46, Wiesbaden, 65189, Germany. TEL 49-611-78780, FAX 49-611-7878400, info@vs-verlag.de, http://www.vs-verlag.de.

JEUGDLITERATUUR IN PRAKTIJK. see *EDUCATION—Teaching Methods And Curriculum*

THE JEWISH PARENT CONNECTION. see *RELIGIONS AND THEOLOGY—Judaic*

362.7 AUT
DAS JOURNAL FUER KINDERGARTEN, HORT UND ELTERNHAUS. Text in German. 4/yr. adv. **Document type:** *Magazine, Consumer.*
Published by: N.J. Schmid Verlag, Leberstr 122, Vienna, 1110, Austria. TEL 43-1-74032735, FAX 43-1-74032750, g.milletich@schmid-verlag.at, http://www.schmid-verlag.at. Ed. Waltraud Rumpl. Adv. contact Monika Steiner. B&W page EUR 2,470, color page EUR 3,640; trim 190 x 275. Circ: 60,000 (controlled).

155.5 GBR ISSN 0140-1971
RJ499.A1
➤ **JOURNAL OF ADOLESCENCE.** Text in English. 1978. 6/yr. EUR 116 in Europe to individuals; JPY 12,600 in Japan to individuals; USD 105 to individuals except Europe and Japan; EUR 546 in Europe to institutions; JPY 59,000 in Japan to institutions; USD 486 to institutions except Europe and Japan (effective 2006). adv. bk.rev. index. reprints avail. **Document type:** *Journal, Academic/Scholarly.* **Description:** International, broadly based, cross-disciplinary journal that addresses itself to issues of professional and academic importance.
Related titles: Online - full text ed.: ISSN 1095-9254. USD 513 (effective 2002) (from Chadwyck-Healey Inc., EBSCO Publishing, Gale Group, IngentaConnect, O C L C Online Computer Library Center, Inc., ScienceDirect, Swets Information Services).
Indexed: AC&P, ASCA, ASSIA, AddicA, Agr, AmH&L, BibAg, BrEdI, BrNI, CIJE, CJA, CurCont, ERA, ESPM, ExcerpMed, FamI, H&SSA, HistAb, HospAb, IPsyAb, IndMed, MEDLINE, PCI, PsycInfo, PsycholAb, RiskAb, SEA, SOMA, SOPODA, SRRA, SSA, SSCI, SSI, SWA, SWR&A, SociolAb, TEA, e-psyche.
—BLDSC (4918.942000), GNLM, IDS, IE, Infotrieve, ingenta, KNAW. **CCC.**
Published by: Academic Press (Subsidiary of: Elsevier Science & Technology), Harcourt Pl, 32 Jamestown Rd, London, NW1 7BY, United Kingdom. TEL 44-20-7424-4200, FAX 44-20-7483-2293, apsubs@acad.com, http://www.elsevier.com/locate/adolescence. Ed. Dr. A. Hagell. R&P Catherine John. Adv. contact Nik Screen. **Subscr. to:** Harcourt Publishers Ltd., Foots Cray High St, Sidcup, Kent DA14 5HP, United Kingdom. TEL 44-208-3085700, FAX 44-20-83090807.

➤ **JOURNAL OF ADOLESCENT HEALTH.** see *MEDICAL SCIENCES*

➤ **JOURNAL OF ADOLESCENT RESEARCH.** see *PSYCHOLOGY*

362.7 896 USA ISSN 0795-4506
JOURNAL OF AFRICAN CHILDREN'S AND YOUTH LITERATURE. Variant title: J A C Y L. Text in English. 1989. a. USD 12 to individuals; USD 25 to libraries. adv. bk.rev. **Document type:** *Academic/Scholarly.* **Description:** Provides a forum in which scholars working in the field of children's literature and youth literature can address a cross-section of those who work with children and books.
Indexed: ChLitAb, MLA-IB.
Address: Department of English and Foreign Languages, Mississippi Valley State University, Itta Bena, MS 38941. TEL 601-254-3453, FAX 601-254-3452, oosa@fielding.mvsu.edu. Ed. Osayimwense Osa.

JOURNAL OF CHILD AND ADOLESCENT PSYCHIATRIC NURSING. see *MEDICAL SCIENCES—Nurses And Nursing*

JOURNAL OF CHILD & ADOLESCENT SUBSTANCE ABUSE. see *DRUG ABUSE AND ALCOHOLISM*

JOURNAL OF CHILD AND FAMILY STUDIES. see *PSYCHOLOGY*

649 USA ISSN 0741-9481
➤ **JOURNAL OF CHILD AND YOUTH CARE WORK.** Text in English. 1984. a. USD 30 to individuals; USD 60 to institutions; free to members (effective 2004). adv. **Document type:** *Journal, Academic/Scholarly.* **Description:** Publishes articles on the practice of child and youth care in public and private institutions, group homes, community based programs, and daycare/preschool settings, as well as the generic practice of child and youth care in other contexts such as home based, street work, and private practice.
Published by: Association for Child & Youth Care Practice, Inc., 161 Wisonsin Ave., Ste. 6000, Milwaukee, WI 53203. TEL 414-227-3356, FAX 414-227-3224, info@acycp.org, http://www.acycp.org/journal.htm. Ed. Varda Mann-Feder. Pub., R&P, Adv. contact John Korsmo. B&W page USD 250. Circ: 2,000 (paid and controlled).

362.7 USA ISSN 1537-9418
JOURNAL OF CHILD CUSTODY; research, issues & practices. Text in English. 2002 (Spring). q. USD 360 combined subscription domestic to institutions print & online eds.; USD 486 combined subscription in Canada to institutions print & online eds.; USD 522 combined subscription elsewhere to institutions print & online eds. (effective 2006). adv. 120 p./no. 1 cols./p.; reprint service avail. from HAW. **Document type:** *Journal, Academic/Scholarly.* **Description:** Addresses both practical and theoretical issues, and provides essential 'How To's.' It is a source for up-to-date information on the issues and challenges facing professionals in this constantly evolving field.
Related titles: Online - full text ed.: ISSN 1537-940X (from EBSCO Publishing, O C L C Online Computer Library Center, Inc., Swets Information Services).
Indexed: DIP, ERA, FamI, IBR, IBZ, RefZh, SFSA.
—Haworth.
Published by: Haworth Press, Inc., 10 Alice St, Binghamton, NY 13904-1580. TEL 607-722-5857, 800-429-6784, FAX 607-722-1424, 800-895-0582, getinfo@haworthpress.com, http://www.haworthpress.com/web/JCC. Ed. Leslie Drozd. R&P Ruth Ann Heath TEL 607-722-5857 ext 316. Adv. contact Rebecca Miller-Baum TEL 607-722-5857 ext 337. B&W page USD 315, color page USD 550; trim 4.375 x 7.125.

155.4 GBR ISSN 0305-0009
P118
➤ **JOURNAL OF CHILD LANGUAGE.** Text in English. 1974. q. GBP 198 to institutions; USD 324 in North America to institutions; GBP 218 combined subscription to institutions print & online eds.; USD 360 combined subscription in North America to institutions print & online eds. (effective 2006). adv. bk.rev. back issues avail.; reprint service avail. from PSC,PQC. **Document type:** *Journal, Academic/Scholarly.* **Description:** Covers all aspects of the scientific study of language behavior in children and the underlying principles, including normal and pathological development of both monolingual and bilingual children.
Related titles: Microform ed.: (from PQC); Online - full text ed.: ISSN 1469-7602. GBP 182 to institutions; USD 302 in North America to institutions (effective 2006) (from EBSCO Publishing, O C L C Online Computer Library Center, Inc., Swets Information Services).
Indexed: ABIn, AMED, ASCA, ASSIA, AbAn, ArtHuCI, BDM&CN, BibLing, BrEdI, CDA, CIJE, CINAHL, CPE, ChLitAb, CommAb, CurCont, DIP, EAA, ERA, ETA, EduInd, FamI, IBR, IBZ, INI, IndMed, L&LBA, LT&LA, LingAb, MEA, MEA&I, MEDLINE, MLA, MLA-IB, PCI, PsySCDP, PsycInfo, PsycholAb, RASB, RHEA, SEA, SENA, SFSA, SOMA, SOPODA, SSCI, SWA, TEA, YAE&RB, e-psyche.
—BLDSC (4957.600000), IDS, IE, Infotrieve, ingenta. **CCC.**
Published by: Cambridge University Press, The Edinburgh Bldg, Shaftesbury Rd, Cambridge, CB2 2RU, United Kingdom. TEL 44-1223-312393, FAX 44-1223-315052, jcl@fs4.psy.man.ac.uk, journals@cambridge.org, http://uk.cambridge.org/journals/jcl. Ed. Elena Lieven. R&P Linda Nicol TEL 44-1223-325757. Adv. contact Rebecca Curtis TEL 44-1223-325757. Circ: 1,850. **Subscr. to:** Cambridge University Press, 100 Brook Hill Dr, West Nyack, NY 10994. TEL 845-353-7500, FAX 845-353-4141, journals_subscriptions@cup.org

➤ **JOURNAL OF CHILD PSYCHOTHERAPY.** see *PSYCHOLOGY*

➤ **JOURNAL OF CHILD SEXUAL ABUSE**; research, treatment & program innovations for victims, survivors & offenders. see *SOCIAL SERVICES AND WELFARE*

➤ **JOURNAL OF CHILDREN & POVERTY.** see *SOCIAL SERVICES AND WELFARE*

028.5 USA ISSN 1521-7779
PN1009.A1
➤ **JOURNAL OF CHILDREN'S LITERATURE.** Text in English. 1994. s-a. USD 20 domestic; USD 22 in Canada; USD 30 elsewhere (effective 2004). adv. bk.rev. bibl. **Document type:** *Journal, Academic/Scholarly.* **Description:** Serves those with a personal and professional interest in children's literature. Includes scholarly and practical articles and booklists.
Formerly (until 1994): Children's Literature Assembly Bulletin
Related titles: Online - full text ed.: (from H.W. Wilson, O C L C Online Computer Library Center, Inc.).
Indexed: ABIn, EduInd.
Published by: Children's Literature Assembly, c/o Dr. Elizabeth Poe, Eastern Connecticut University, 697-C Allen Hall, Box 6122, Morgantown, VA 26501-6122. TEL 860-465-4533, FAX 860-465-5099, ernsts@easternct.edu, http://www.childrensliteratureassembly.org/journal3.htm. Ed., Adv. contact Patricia Austin TEL 504-280-6526. page USD 195; trim 4.5 x 7.5. Circ: 1,000.

➤ **JOURNAL OF CLINICAL CHILD AND ADOLESCENT PSYCHOLOGY.** see *PSYCHOLOGY*

305.235 USA ISSN 0272-4316
HQ796

➤ **JOURNAL OF EARLY ADOLESCENCE.** Text in English. 1981. q. USD 464, GBP 300 to institutions; USD 483, GBP 312 combined subscription to institutions print & online eds. (effective 2006). adv. bk.rev.; film rev. back issues avail.; reprint service avail. from PQC. **Document type:** *Journal, Academic/Scholarly.* **Description:** Takes an interdisciplinary approach through research studies, reviews, and theoretical papers to the need for focus on the characteristics of persons 10-14 years old.
Related titles: Microform ed.; Online - full text ed.: ISSN 1552-5449. USD 459, GBP 297 to institutions (effective 2006) (from bigchalk, C S A, EBSCO Publishing, O C L C Online Computer Library Center, Inc., Sage Publications, Inc., Swets Information Services).
Indexed: AMHA, ASCA, Agr, CDA, CIJE, CJA, CLFP, CurCont, ESPM, FamI, H&SSA, IMFL, MEA, PRA, PsycInfo, PsycholAb, SFSA, SOPODA, SSA, SSCI, SSI, SWR&A, SociolAb, V&AA, e-psyche.
—BLDSC (4970.701000), IDS, IE, Infotrieve, ingenta. **CCC.**
Published by: Sage Publications, Inc., 2455 Teller Rd, Thousand Oaks, CA 91320. TEL 805-499-0721, FAX 805-499-0871, info@sagepub.com, http://www.sagepub.com/journal.aspx?pid=125. Ed. Alexander T Vazsonyi. R&P Tanya Udin TEL 805-499-0721 ext 7716. Adv. contact DeAnna Vega Hammersley. Circ: 1,200. **Subscr. overseas to:** Sage Publications Ltd., 1 Oliver's Yard, 55 City Rd, London EC1 1SP, United Kingdom. TEL 44-20-73740645, FAX 44-20-73748741, subscription@sagepub.co.uk.

▼ ➤ **JOURNAL OF EARLY AND INTENSIVE BEHAVIOR INTERVENTION.** see *PSYCHOLOGY*

▼ ➤ **JOURNAL OF EARLY CHILDHOOD AND INFANT PSYCHOLOGY.** see *PSYCHOLOGY*

➤ **JOURNAL OF EARLY CHILDHOOD LITERACY.** see *EDUCATION*

➤ **JOURNAL OF EARLY INTERVENTION.** see *EDUCATION—Special Education And Rehabilitation*

➤ **JOURNAL OF EXPERIMENTAL CHILD PSYCHOLOGY.** see *PSYCHOLOGY*

➤ **JOURNAL OF HIV - AIDS PREVENTION IN CHILDREN & YOUTH.** see *MEDICAL SCIENCES—Communicable Diseases*

▼ ➤ **JOURNAL OF PUBLIC CHILD WELFARE.** see *SOCIAL SERVICES AND WELFARE*

▼ ➤ **JOURNAL OF RESEARCH IN CHARACTER EDUCATION.** see *EDUCATION—Teaching Methods And Curriculum*

➤ **JOURNAL OF RESEARCH IN CHILDHOOD EDUCATION**; an international journal of research on the education of children. see *EDUCATION*

155.4 USA ISSN 1050-8392
HQ796 CODEN: JRADET

JOURNAL OF RESEARCH ON ADOLESCENCE. Text in English. q. USD 120 combined subscription in the Americas to individuals print & online eds.; EUR 134 combined subscription in Europe to individuals & Caribbean (print & online eds.); GBP 89 combined subscription elsewhere to individuals print & online eds.; USD 471 combined subscription in the Americas to institutions & Caribbean (print & online eds.); GBP 335 combined subscription elsewhere to institutions print & online eds. (effective 2006). **Document type:** *Journal, Academic/Scholarly.*
Related titles: Online - full text ed.: ISSN 1532-7795. 199?. USD 447 in the Americas to institutions & Caribbean; GBP 319 elsewhere to institutions (effective 2006) (from Blackwell Synergy, EBSCO Publishing, Gale Group, IngentaConnect, O C L C Online Computer Library Center, Inc., Ovid Technologies, Inc., Swets Information Services).
Indexed: ASSIA, AddicA, CJA, CurCont, EAA, ERA, ESPM, ETA, FamI, H&SSA, MEA, PsycInfo, PsycholAb, RHEA, SEA, SENA, SFSA, SOMA, SSA, SSCI, SWA, SociolAb, TEA, e-psyche.
—BLDSC (5051.920000), IE, Infotrieve, ingenta. **CCC.**
Published by: (Society for Research on Adolescence), Blackwell Publishing, Inc. (Subsidiary of: Blackwell Publishing Ltd.), Commerce Place, 350 Main St, Malden, MA 02148. TEL 781-388-8206, FAX 781-388-8232, subscrip@blackwellpub.com, http://www.blackwellpublishing.com/journals/JRA. Ed. B Bradford Brown.

JOURNAL OF SOCIAL WORK PRACTICE. see *SOCIAL SERVICES AND WELFARE*

155.4 USA ISSN 0047-2891
HQ796 CODEN: JYADA

➤ **JOURNAL OF YOUTH AND ADOLESCENCE**; a multidisciplinary research publication. Text in English. 1972. bi-m. EUR 858, USD 875, GBP 538 combined subscription to institutions print & online eds. (effective 2005). adv. bibl.; charts; illus. back issues avail.; reprint service avail. from PSC. **Document type:** *Journal, Academic/Scholarly.* **Description:** Enables psychiatrists, psychologists, sociologists, social workers, counsellors, and educators to share ideas relevant to the subject of youth and adolescence.
Related titles: Microfilm ed.: (from PQC); Online - full text ed.: ISSN 1573-6601 (from bigchalk, EBSCO Publishing, Florida Center for Library Automation, Gale Group, IngentaConnect, Kluwer Online, O C L C Online Computer Library Center, Inc., Ovid Technologies, Inc., ProQuest Information & Learning, Springer LINK, Swets Information Services).
Indexed: ABIn, AC&P, AMHA, ASCA, ASSIA, AddicA, AgeL, Agr, BibAg, BibLing, CDA, CERDIC, CIJE, CJA, CLFP, ChPerI, CommAb, CurCont, DIP, EAA, ERA, ETA, EduInd, ExcerpMed, FamI, HEA, IBR, IBZ, IMFL, MEA, MEA&I, PCI, PsySc DP, PsycInfo, PsycholAb, RHEA, RILM, RefZh, SEA, SENA, SFSA, SOMA, SOPODA, SRRA, SSA, SSCI, SSI, SUSA, SWA, SociolAb, TEA, THA, V&AA, e-psyche.
—BLDSC (5072.720000), GNLM, IDS, IE, Infotrieve, ingenta. **CCC.**
Published by: Plenum US (Subsidiary of: Springer Science+Business Media), 233 Spring St, New York, NY 10013. TEL 212-460-1500, FAX 212-460-1575, service@springer-ny.com, http://springerlink.metapress.com/openurl.asp?genre=journal&issn=0047-2891, http://www.springeronline.com. Eds. Daniel Offer, Roger J R Levesque.

305.235 GBR ISSN 1367-6261
JOURNAL OF YOUTH STUDIES. Text in English. 1998. 5/yr. GBP 266, USD 439 combined subscription to institutions print & online eds. (effective 2006). reprint service avail. from PSC. **Document type:** *Journal, Academic/Scholarly.* **Description:** Aims to serve as a multidisciplinary journal devoted to a theoretical and empirical understanding of young people's experiences and life contexts.
Related titles: Online - full text ed.: ISSN 1469-9680. GBP 253, USD 417 to institutions (effective 2006) (from EBSCO Publishing, Gale Group, IngentaConnect, O C L C Online Computer Library Center, Inc., Swets Information Services).
Indexed: CJA, CPE, ERA, ETA, FamI, MEA, PsycInfo, PsycholAb, RHEA, SEA, SENA, SOMA, SRRA, SSA, SWA, SociolAb, TEA, e-psyche.
—BLDSC (5072.725000), IE, Infotrieve, ingenta. **CCC.**
Published by: Routledge (Subsidiary of: Taylor & Francis Group), 4 Park Sq, Milton Park, Abingdon, Oxon OX14 4RN, United Kingdom. TEL 44-1235-828600, FAX 44-1235-829000, info@routledge.co.uk, http://www.tandf.co.uk/journals/titles/13676261.asp, http://www.routledge.co.uk. Ed. Andy Furlong. **Subscr. to:** Taylor & Francis Ltd, Journals Customer Service, Rankine Rd, Basingstoke, Hants RG24 8PR, United Kingdom. TEL 44-1256-813000, FAX 44-1256-330245.

362.7 DEU ISSN 0342-0175
JUGEND BERUF GESELLSCHAFT; Zeitschrift fuer Jugendsozialarbeit. Text in German. 1949. q. EUR 3 newsstand/cover (effective 2003). bk.rev. index. back issues avail. **Document type:** *Magazine, Consumer.*
Indexed: DIP, IBR, IBZ.
Published by: Bundesarbeitsgemeinschaft Jugendsozialarbeit, Hohe Str 73, Bonn, 53119, Germany. TEL 49-228-959680, FAX 49-228-9596830, jbg-redaktion@bagjaw.de, info@bagjaw.de, http://www.bagjaw.de. Ed., R&P Paul Fuelbier. Pub. Henrik von Bothmer. Circ: 2,500.

155.5 DEU ISSN 0943-058X
JUGEND - MEDIEN - SCHUTZ - REPORT. Text in German. 6/yr. EUR 49; EUR 11 newsstand/cover (effective 2004). adv. **Document type:** *Magazine, Academic/Scholarly.*
Former titles (until 1992): J M S - Report (0941-732X); (until 1991): B P S - Report (0170-5067)
Indexed: DIP, IBR, IBZ.
—CCC.
Published by: Nomos Verlagsgesellschaft mbH und Co. KG, Waldseestr 3-5, Baden-Baden, 76530, Germany. TEL 49-7221-20140, FAX 49-7221-210427, nomos@nomos.de, marketing@nomos.de, http://www.nomos.de. Ed. Dirk Nolden. Adv. contact Bettina Kohler. B&W page EUR 1,800, color page EUR 2,925; trim 190 x 277. Circ: 7,000 (paid and controlled).

DAS JUGENDAMT. see *LAW*

JUGENDHILFE. see *SOCIAL SERVICES AND WELFARE*

JUGENDHILFE-NETZ. see *SOCIAL SERVICES AND WELFARE*

028.5 027.62 CHE ISSN 0256-6532
JUGENDLITERATUR. Text in German. 1975. 4/yr. CHF 20. adv. bk.rev. back issues avail. **Document type:** *Bulletin.* **Description:** News and information concerning children's literature. Covers writers, reports of events, honor list, choice of books on various subjects. Includes list of events.
Formerly: Schweizerischer Bund fuer Jugendliteratur. Nachrichten
Indexed: ChLitAb.
Published by: Schweizerischer Bund fuer Jugendliteratur, Gewerbestr 8, Cham, 6330, Switzerland. TEL 41-41-7413140, FAX 41-41-7400159, sbj@bluewin.ch. Adv. contact Iris Wolf. Circ: 4,500.

JUGENDNACHRICHTEN; Zeitschrift des Bayerischen Jugendrings. see *EDUCATION—International Education Programs*

JUGENDWOHL; Zeitschrift fuer Kinder- und Jugendhilfe. see *SOCIAL SERVICES AND WELFARE*

JUNGE FAMILIE; das Baby-Journal. see *MEDICAL SCIENCES—Pediatrics*

649 790.019 GBR
JUNIOR; the world's finest parenting magazine. Text in English. 1998. m. GBP 23.97 in United Kingdom; GBP 40 in Europe; GBP 50 in United States; GBP 64 elsewhere; GBP 2.90 newsstand/cover (effective Sep. 2001). adv. bk.rev.; software rev. 148 p./no.; back issues avail. **Document type:** *Magazine, Consumer.* **Description:** Each issue contains articles on how to better enjoy your children, your home, and personal relationships. Recreational travel activities, and children's fashion are included.
Published by: Beach Magazines and Publishing, 4 Cromwell Pl, London, SW7 2JE, United Kingdom. TEL 44-20-7761-8900, FAX 44-20-7761-8951, info@juniormagazine.co.uk, http://www.juniormagazine.co.uk. Ed. Catherine O'Dolan. Pub. Chris Taggart. Adv. contact Jo Anne Smith TEL 44-20-7761-8950. color page GBP 3,750; 228 x 300. **Dist. by:** Comag, Tavistock Works, Tavistock Rd, W Drayton, Middx UB7 7QX, United Kingdom. TEL 44-1895-433600, FAX 44-189-543-3606.

362.7 USA
JUNIOR CITIZEN. Text in English. 1910. s-a. free to qualified personnel. **Document type:** *Newsletter.*
Published by: Connecticut Junior Republic Association Inc., Goshen Rd, PO Box 161, Litchfield, CT 06759. TEL 860-567-9423. Ed., R&P Hedy L Barton. Circ: 10,000.

JUNIOR EDUCATION. see *EDUCATION*

JUNIOR FOCUS. see *EDUCATION—Teaching Methods And Curriculum*

JUNIORS. see *CLOTHING TRADE—Fashions*

649 USA
JUST KIDS. Text in English. q. free (effective 2005). **Document type:** *Newsletter, Consumer.* **Description:** Provides general health information for kids.
Published by: Children's Hospital (Omaha), Children's Healthcare Services, 8301 Dodge St., Omaha, NE 68114. TEL 402-390-5400, FAX 402-955-6959, mriehart@childrens-omaha.com, http://www.chsomaha.org/images/files/b13_file1_46296.pdf. Ed. Deb Naegele. Circ: 20,000 (free).

JUVENILE AND FAMILY COURT JOURNAL. see *LAW—Family And Matrimonial Law*

JUVENILE AND FAMILY JUSTICE TODAY. see *LAW—Family And Matrimonial Law*

JUVENILE AND FAMILY LAW DIGEST. see *LAW—Family And Matrimonial Law*

JUVENILE CORRECTIONAL MENTAL HEALTH REPORT. see *CRIMINOLOGY AND LAW ENFORCEMENT*

JUVENILE JUSTICE. see *CRIMINOLOGY AND LAW ENFORCEMENT*

369.4 020 USA
JUVENILE MISCELLANY. Text in English. 1970. 2/yr. free.
Related titles: Microform ed.: (from PQC).
Indexed: ChLitAb.
Published by: (De Grummond Children's Literature Research Collection), University of Southern Mississippi, McCain Library, PO Box 5148, Hattiesburg, MS 39406-5148. TEL 601-266-4349. Ed. Dee Jones. Circ: 1,400.

362.7 CUB ISSN 0864-1412
JUVENTUD REBELDE. Text in Spanish. 1965. d. USD 25 in Central America; USD 30 in South America; USD 35 in Europe; USD 40 in Africa; USD 45 in Australia & New Zealand.
Related titles: Online - full text ed.: Cuba Rebelde Digital. ISSN 1563-8340.
Indexed: RASB.
Published by: (Union de Jovenes Comunistas), Ediciones Cubanas, Obispo No. 527, Apdo. 605, Havana, Cuba. TEL 32-5556-60, http://www.jrebelde.cubaweb.cu/.

362.7 DEU ISSN 0946-4824
K I D - KINDERINFORMATIONSDIENST. Text in German. 1991. q. adv. bk.rev. **Document type:** *Academic/Scholarly.*

C

Published by: K I D Verlag, Samansstr 4, Bonn, 53227, Germany. TEL 49-228-443195, FAX 49-228-443195, hanswein@t-online.de. Ed., Pub. Hans Weingartz.

K J R BURG INFO; Jugendpolitik und Jugendarbeit im Landkreis Muenchen. see *SOCIAL SERVICES AND WELFARE*

053.1 DEU
KAENGURU; Stadtmagazin fuer Familien in Koeln. Text in German. 1999. 10/yr. EUR 25 (effective 2005). adv.
Document type: *Magazine, Consumer.*
Published by: Kaenguru - Colonia Verlag, Hansemannstr 17-21, Cologne, 50823, Germany. TEL 49-221-5463790, FAX 49-221-5463811, geiger@kaenguru-colonia.de, http://www.kaenguru-colonia.de. Ed. Christiane Huth-Jelkmann. Adv. contact Susanne Geiger-Krautmacher. B&W page EUR 1,450, color page EUR 2,450; trim 183 x 260. Circ: 57,000 (paid and controlled).

KAKS'PLUS. see *GENERAL INTEREST PERIODICALS—Finland*

796.1 910.4 DEU
DIE KAKTUSBLUETE. Text in German. 1973. 3/yr. EUR 0.50 newsstand/cover (effective 2005). bk.rev.; film rev.; music rev.; play rev. back issues avail. **Document type:** *Bulletin, Consumer.*
Published by: Geschwister-Scholl-Schule, Kapellenstr 38, Hagen, 58099, Germany. TEL 49-2331-61060, FAX 49-2331-61250, Geschwister-Scholl-Hauptschule@web.de, http://www.geschwister-scholl-schule.de. Ed. Oezlem Atasoy. Pub. Friedhelm Kuhl. Circ: 1,600.

649 USA
KANSAS CITY PARENT MAGAZINE. Text in English. m.
Description: Provides a number of resources for Kansas City parents. Includes a family calendar, as well as contests for kids.
Published by: Insight Commnications, 13839 S Mur-Len, N, Olathe, KS 66062. TEL 913-782-3238, FAX 913-782-3338, http://www.kcparent.com/. Pub. L Richard Bruursema. Adv. contact Sheila Bruursema.

C

649 DEU
KARLSRUHER KIND; die regionale Elternzeitung. Text in German. 1987. m. free newsstand/cover. adv. **Document type:** *Magazine, Consumer.*
Published by: Verlag Karl Goerner, Hildebrandstr. 23, Karlsruhe, 76227, Germany. TEL 49-721-43536, FAX 49-721-491995, info@karl-goerner.de, http://www.karlsruher-kind.de, http://www.karl-goerner.de. adv.: B&W page EUR 1,517, color page EUR 2,655; trim 223 x 315. Circ: 27,500 (controlled).

362.7 GBR
KEY NOTE MARKET ASSESSMENT. BABY PRODUCTS. Text in English. irreg., latest 1994, Jan. GBP 730 per issue (effective 2002). **Document type:** *Trade.* **Description:** Provides an overview of a specific UK market segment and includes executive summary, market definition, market size, industry background, competitor analysis, current issues, forecasts, company profiles, and more.
Former titles (until 1999): Key Note Market Report: Baby Products; Key Note Report: Baby Products (0954-433X)
Related titles: CD-ROM ed.; Online - full text ed.
Published by: Key Note Ltd., Field House, 72 Oldfield Rd, Hampton, Mddx TW12 2HQ, United Kingdom. TEL 44-20-8481-8750, FAX 44-20-8783-0049, info@keynote.co.uk, http://www.keynote.co.uk.

362.7 338 GBR
KEY NOTE MARKET ASSESSMENT. CHILDCARE. Variant title: Childcare Market Assessment. Text in English. 1998. irreg., latest 2000, July. GBP 730 per issue (effective 2002).
Description: Provides an overview of a specific UK market segment and includes executive summary, market definition, market size, industry background, competitor analysis, current issues, forecasts, company profiles, and more.
Formerly (until 2000): Key Note Market Report: Childcare (1464-5688)
Published by: Key Note Ltd., Field House, 72 Oldfield Rd, Hampton, Mddx TW12 2HQ, United Kingdom. TEL 44-20-8481-8750, FAX 44-20-8783-0049, info@keynote.co.uk, http://www.keynote.co.uk. Ed. Simon Howitt.

658 GBR
KEY NOTE MARKET ASSESSMENT. MARKETING TO CHILDREN 4-11. Text in English. 2001. irreg., latest 2001, July. GBP 730 per issue (effective 2002). **Description:** Provides an in-depth strategic analysis across a broad range of industries and contains an examination on the scope, dynamics and shape of key UK markets in the consumer, financial, lifestyle and business to business sectors.
Published by: Key Note Ltd., Field House, 72 Oldfield Rd, Hampton, Mddx TW12 2HQ, United Kingdom. TEL 44-20-8481-8750, FAX 44-20-8783-0049, info@keynote.co.uk, http://www.keynote.co.uk. Ed. Simon Taylor.

KEY NOTE MARKET ASSESSMENT. TEENAGE MAGAZINES. see *JOURNALISM*

649 658 GBR ISSN 1478-3932
KEY NOTE MARKET ASSESSMENT. TWEENAGERS. Variant title: Tweenagers Market Assessment. Text in English. 2001 (Aug). irreg., latest 2001, Aug. GBP 730 per issue (effective 2002). **Document type:** *Journal, Trade.* **Description:** Provides an in-depth strategic analysis across a broad range of industries and contains an examination on the scope, dynamics and shape of key UK markets in the consumer, financial, lifestyle and business to business sectors.
Published by: Key Note Ltd., Field House, 72 Oldfield Rd, Hampton, Mddx TW12 2HQ, United Kingdom. TEL 44-20-8481-8750, FAX 44-20-8783-0049, info@keynote.co.uk, http://www.keynote.co.uk. Ed. Simon Taylor.

658 GBR
KEY NOTE MARKET REPORT: THE UNDER-16S MARKET. Text in English. 1998 (June). irreg., latest 1998. GBP 340 per issue (effective 2002). **Description:** Provides an overview of a specific UK market segment and includes executive summary, market definition, market size, industry background, competitor analysis, current issues, forecasts, company profiles, and more.
Published by: Key Note Ltd., Field House, 72 Oldfield Rd, Hampton, Mddx TW12 2HQ, United Kingdom. TEL 44-20-8481-8750, FAX 44-20-8783-0049, info@keynote.co.uk, http://www.keynote.co.uk. Ed. Louis Barfe.

658 GBR
KEY NOTE MARKET REPORT: THE UNDER-5S MARKET. Text in English. 1997 (Oct). irreg., latest 1997. GBP 340 per issue (effective 2002). **Description:** Provides an overview of a specific UK market segment and includes executive summary, market definition, market size, industry background, competitor analysis, current issues, forecasts, company profiles, and more.
Published by: Key Note Ltd., Field House, 72 Oldfield Rd, Hampton, Mddx TW12 2HQ, United Kingdom. TEL 44-20-8481-8750, FAX 44-20-8783-0049, info@keynote.co.uk, http://www.keynote.co.uk. Ed. Phillippa Smith.

658 GBR
KEY NOTE MARKET REPORT: YOUTH MARKET IN THE U.K. Text in English. 1994. irreg., latest 1994. GBP 340 per issue (effective 2002). **Document type:** *Trade.* **Description:** Provides an overview of a specific UK market segment and includes executive summary, market definition, market size, industry background, competitor analysis, current issues, forecasts, company profiles, and more.
Formerly: Key Note Market Review: Youth Market in the U.K.
Related titles: CD-ROM ed.; Online - full text ed.
Published by: Key Note Ltd., Field House, 72 Oldfield Rd, Hampton, Mddx TW12 2HQ, United Kingdom. TEL 44-20-8481-8750, FAX 44-20-8783-0049, info@keynote.co.uk, http://www.keynote.co.uk. Ed. Phillippa Smith.

KIDBITS: N A Y S I YOUTH, SPORT, FACTS & DEMOGRAPHICS. see *SPORTS AND GAMES*

KID'N AROUND. see *CHILDREN AND YOUTH—For*

362.7 USA ISSN 1060-9814
KIDS COUNT DATA BOOK. Text in English. 1990. a.
Published by: Center for the Study of Social Policy, 1575 Eye St NW, Ste 500, Washington, DC 20005. TEL 202-371-1565, FAX 202-371-1472, http://www.cssp.org/.

362.7 USA
KIDS LIB NEWS; natural family resources. Text in English. 1985. q. USD 12. adv. bk.rev. **Document type:** *Magazine, Consumer.* **Description:** Covers holistic parenting instincts and children's rights, with articles on home-birth and midwifery, circumcision, sex education, kiddie porno paranoia, underwater homebirthing, TV violence and advertising.
Published by: Oness Press, PO Box 1064, Kurtistown, HI 96760. Ed. Mycall Sunanda. Circ: 1,000.

649 USA ISSN 1547-5174
KIDS' PAGES. Text in English. 2001. 8/yr.
Published by: Kids' Pages Cares, P O Box 745216, Arvada, CO 80006. TEL 303-277-0053, home@kidspages.org, http://www.kidspages.org. Ed., Pub. Ellen Blair.

028.5 363.3 USA
KIDS TODAY. Text in English. 1997. 10/yr. **Document type:** *Magazine, Trade.*
Related titles: ♦ Supplement to: Furniture / Today. ISSN 0194-360X.
Published by: Reed Business Information (Subsidiary of: Reed Business), 7025 Albert Pick Rd Ste 200, Greensboro, NC 27409. TEL 336-605-0121, FAX 336-605-1143, pcohen@reedbusiness.com, http://www.kidstodayonline.com/, http://www.reedbusiness.com. Ed. Jane Kitchen TEL 336-605-1111. Pub. Peter Cohen TEL 336-605-3799.

649 CAN ISSN 0847-3935
KIDS TRIBUTE. Text in English. q. free (effective 2005). adv. **Document type:** *Consumer.* **Description:** Covers film and general interest magazine for children.
Related titles: Online - full text ed.: (from EBSCO Publishing).
Published by: Tribute Publishing, Inc., 71 Barber Green Rd, Don Mills, ON M3C 2B2, Canada. TEL 416-445-0544, FAX 416-445-2894. Ed. Rise Levy. Pub., R&P Sandra I Stewart. Adv. contact Katherine Bridgman. B&W page USD 17,500, color page USD 19,440. Circ: 300,000.

362.7 AUS ISSN 1038-3409
KIDSAFE. Text in English. 1979. q. AUD 20 (effective 1998). adv. **Document type:** *Journal, Consumer.* **Description:** Information on prevention of children's injuries.
Former titles (until Autumn 1994): Safe Guard (0818-0474); (until 1986): Child Accident Prevention Foundation of Australia. Quarterly Journal (0725-9573); (until 1981): Child Accident Prevention Foundation of Australia. Journal (0728-8778)
Published by: Child Accident Prevention Foundation of Australia, Suite 4, Level 1, 280 Church St, Richmond, VIC 3121, Australia. TEL 61-3-94271008, FAX 61-3-94213831. Ed. Carol Taylor. Adv. contact Janine O'Longhlan. Circ: 3,000.

790.1922 DEU
KIDSHOP; was Kinder wuenschen und Eltern wissen muessen. Text in German. q. adv. **Document type:** *Magazine, Consumer.* **Description:** Provides information and guidelines for parents on a wide variety of consumer goods aimed at children.
Published by: Entertainment Media Verlag GmbH und Co. oHG, Einsteinring 24, Dornach, 85609, Germany. TEL 49-89-45114-0, FAX 49-89-45114444, emv@e-media.de, http://www.mediabiz.de. adv.: B&W page EUR 6,750, color page EUR 8,280. Circ: 340,000 (controlled).

649 USA
KIDZ MAGAZINE✶. Text in English. 1988. m. USD 12. adv. bk.rev.; film rev. **Description:** For parents, doctors and teachers who are involved with children. Includes a calendar of events and medical reviews.
Formerly: Kids, Kids, Kidz
Published by: Kids Production, Inc., 1334 Dodge St, Omaha, NE 68102-1126. TEL 402-391-0441. Ed. Melanie Morrissey Clark. Circ: 50,000.

371.392 DEU ISSN 0945-5582
DAS KIND. Text in German. 1987. s-a. EUR 16; EUR 6.50 newsstand/cover (effective 2004). bk.rev. back issues avail. **Document type:** *Magazine, Trade.*
Published by: Deutsche Montessori Gesellschaft e.V., Butterblumenweg 5, Wiesbaden, 65201, Germany. TEL 49-611-2054871, FAX 49-611-2054872, kontakt@montessori-gesellschaft.de, http://www.montessori-gesellschaft.de. Eds. Ela Eckart, Ingeborg Waldschmidt. Circ: 500.

613.0432 DEU
KIND & GESUNDHEIT. Text in German. 1998. bi-m. EUR 9.60; EUR 1.80 newsstand/cover (effective 2003). adv. **Document type:** *Magazine, Consumer.*
Published by: Medikom Verlagsgesellschaft fuer Medien Infotainment Kommunikation mbH & Co. KG, Am Alten Posthof 3, Cologne, 50667, Germany. TEL 49-221-990330, FAX 49-221-99033550, verlag@medikom.de, http://www.medikom.de. adv.: page EUR 25,150. Circ: 399,000 (paid and controlled).

KIND EN ADOLESCENT. see *MEDICAL SCIENCES—Pediatrics*

362.7 DEU ISSN 0939-4354
➤ **KIND - JUGEND - GESELLSCHAFT**; Zeitschrift fuer Jugendschutz. Text in German. 1956. 4/yr. EUR 35; EUR 10 newsstand/cover (effective 2005). adv. **Document type:** *Journal, Academic/Scholarly.*
Formerly (until 1991): Jugendschutz (0342-6394)
Indexed: DIP, IBR, IBZ.
Published by: (Bundesarbeitsgemeinschaft Kinder- und Jugendschutz e.V.), Hermann Luchterhand Verlag GmbH (Subsidiary of: Wolters Kluwer Deutschland GmbH), Heddesdorfer Str 31, Neuwied, 56564, Germany. TEL 49-2631-8012222, FAX 49-2631-8012223, info@luchterhand.de, http://www.luchterhand.de. Ed. Ingrid Hillebrandt. Adv. contact Gabriele Pannwitz. B&W page EUR 485, color page EUR 1,295.

362.7 305.31 DEU ISSN 0176-8115
KIND UND VATER; Informationen zur aktiven Vaterschaft. Text in German. 1984. irreg. EUR 3.50 newsstand/cover (effective 2003). adv. bk.rev. back issues avail. **Document type:** *Magazine, Consumer.*
Published by: Eltern fuer Aktive Vaterschaft e.V., Friedrich-August-Platz 2, Oldenburg, 26121, Germany. TEL 49-441-81134, FAX 49-441-81165, kindundvater@t-online.de, http://home.t-online.de/home/kindundvater/. Ed. Klaus Anders. adv.: B&W page EUR 615. Circ: 1,800 (controlled).

618 688.72 649 362.7 DEU
KINDER; fuer Eltern, Erzieher und Kinder. Text in German. 1971. 10/yr. EUR 13 domestic (effective 2002); EUR 17 foreign; EUR 1.30 newsstand/cover (effective 2003). adv. 55 p./no. 4 cols./p.; back issues avail. **Document type:** *Magazine, Consumer.*

Published by: Junior-Verlag GmbH und Co. KG, Fehlandtstr 41, Hamburg, 20534, Germany. TEL 49-40-344434, FAX 49-40-352540, info@junior-verlag.de, http://www.junior-verlag.de. Ed. Dagmar von Schweinitz. Pub., R&P Manfred Zedler. Adv. contact Birgit Koenig. B&W page EUR 9,000, color page EUR 16,200; trim 185 x 250. Circ: 280,000 (paid and controlled).

649 DEU
KINDER IN TAGESEINRICHTUNGEN. Text in German. 4/yr. **Document type:** *Journal, Academic/Scholarly.*
Published by: Kallmeyersche Verlagsbuchhandlung GmbH, Im Brande 19, Seelze, 30926, Germany. TEL 49-511-40004175, FAX 49-511-40004176, leserservice@kallmeyer.de, http://www.kallmeyer.de.

KINDER, KINDER; sicher - gesund. see *PUBLIC HEALTH AND SAFETY*

362.7 053.1 DEU
KINDER- UND JUGENDLITERATURFORSCHUNG. Text in German. 1995. a. EUR 39.90 (effective 2002). **Document type:** *Journal, Academic/Scholarly.*
Indexed: IBZ.
Published by: (Arbeitsgemeinschaft Kinder- und Jugendliteraturforschung), J.B. Metzlersche Verlagsbuchhandlung und C.E. Poeschel Verlag GmbH Stuttgart-Weimar, Postfach 103241, Stuttgart, 70028, Germany. TEL 49-711-21940, FAX 49-711-2194249, hexelschneider@metzlerverlag.de, http://www.metzlerverlag.de.

KINDERANALYSE. see *PSYCHOLOGY*

028.5 BEL ISSN 0165-487X
KINDEREN; het maandblad over het zwangerschap, baby's, peuters en kleuters. Text in Dutch. 1979. m. EUR 33.75 (effective 2003). adv. illus. **Document type:** *Magazine, Consumer.* **Description:** Offers advice for pregnant women and mothers of infants, toddlers, and preschoolers.
Published by: Sanoma Magazines Belgium, Telecomlaan 5-7, Diegem, 1831, Belgium. TEL 32-2-7762211, FAX 32-2-776-2317, http://www.sanoma-magazines.be/HomePage.aspx?flash=1&Language=nl.

KINDERGARTEN. see *RELIGIONS AND THEOLOGY—Protestant*

362.7 DEU ISSN 0344-3949
KINDERGARTEN HEUTE; Zeitschrift fuer Erziehung. Text in German. 1970. 10/yr. EUR 37.50; EUR 26.50 to students; EUR 4.50 newsstand/cover (effective 2005). adv. **Document type:** *Journal, Academic/Scholarly.*
Indexed: DIP, IBR, IBZ.
Published by: Verlag Herder GmbH und Co. KG, Hermann-Herder-Str 4, Freiburg Im Breisgau, 79104, Germany. TEL 49-761-27170, FAX 49-761-2717520, kundenservice@herder.de, http://www.herder.de. Adv. contact Bettina Schillinger-Wegmann. B&W page EUR 4,130, color page EUR 7,890. Circ: 51,000.

649 IRL
KINDERGARTEN TIMES. Text in English. q. adv. **Document type:** *Magazine, Consumer.*
Published by: National Children's Nurseries Association, Unit 12c, Bluebell Business Park, Old Naas Rd., Bluebell, Dublin, 12, Ireland. TEL 353-1-4601138, FAX 353-1-4601185, http://www.ncna.net. adv.: page EUR 2,488. Circ: 8,000 (controlled).

267 DEU
KINDERGARTEN UND MISSION; Religionspaedagogischer Arbeitshilfen. Text in German. 1982. s-a. **Document type:** *Academic/Scholarly.*
Published by: Kindermissionswerk, Stephanstr 35, Aachen, 52064, Germany. TEL 49-241-4461-0, FAX 49-241-446140. Ed. Arnold Poll. Circ: 10,000.

649 DEU
KINDERKRAM. Text in German. 1997. 10/yr. adv. **Document type:** *Magazine, Consumer.*
Published by: Raschke und Richter GbR, Zum Forst 62, Kiel-Roenne, 24145, Germany. TEL 49-431-2608898, FAX 49-431-2608897, info@kinderkram-sh.de, http://www.kinderkram-sh.de. adv.: B&W page EUR 707, color page EUR 837. Circ: 12,000 (controlled).

KINDERLEICHT. see *EDUCATION—Teaching Methods And Curriculum*

618.92 362.7 NLD ISSN 0926-0838
KINDEROPVANG. Text in Dutch. 1969. m. (11/yr.). EUR 49.50 (effective 2003). **Document type:** *Trade.* **Description:** Addresses all professionals involved in the care and teaching of children. Reviews toys and books for children and offers practical advice in all areas.
Formerly (until 1990): Kleine Wereld (0166-7106)
—IE, Infotrieve.

Published by: Elsevier Gezondheidszorg bv (Subsidiary of: Reed Business Information bv), Planetenbaan 80-99, Maarssen, 3606 AK, Netherlands. TEL 31-346-577577, FAX 31-346-554287, http://www.elseviergezondheidszorg.nl. **Subscr. to:** Elsevier Den Haag, Postbus 16500, The Hague 2500 BM, Netherlands. TEL 31-70-381-9900, FAX 31-70-333-8399.

305.23 AUT
KINDERSPIEL. Text in German. 4/yr. EUR 15.99; EUR 4.36 newsstand/cover (effective 2005). **Document type:** *Journal, Academic/Scholarly.*
Formerly: Der Helfer
Published by: Kinderfreunde Oesterreich, Rauhensteingasse 5-5, Vienna, W 1010, Austria. TEL 43-1-5121298, FAX 43-1-512129862, elfi.schild@kinderfreunde.at, kind-und-co@kinderfreunde.at, http://www.kinderfreunde.at/index.php?page_new=10555.

KINDERTUIN. see *RELIGIONS AND THEOLOGY—Protestant*

649 NLD
KINDERVERZORGING/JEUGDVERZORGING ✶ . Text in Dutch. 1960. 5/yr.
Published by: K & O-Vereniging voor Jeugdwelzijnswerk, Gr. de Combinatie, Jonker Fransstraat 43, Rotterdam, 3031 AM, Netherlands. Circ: 6,500.

KINDSCHAFTSRECHTLICHE PRAXIS; Zeitschrift fuer die praktische Anwendung und Umsetzung des Kindschaftsrechts. see *LAW—Family And Matrimonial Law*

KIRKUS REVIEWS; adult, young adult and children's book reviews. see *PUBLISHING AND BOOK TRADE*

372.21 DEU ISSN 0943-0237
KITA KINDERTAGESEINRICHTUNGEN AKTUELL. AUSGABE BADEN-WUERTTEMBERG. Text in German. 1992. 11/yr. EUR 82.90; EUR 9 newsstand/cover (effective 2005). **Document type:** *Journal, Academic/Scholarly.*
Published by: Carl Link Verlag (Subsidiary of: Wolters Kluwer Deutschland GmbH), Adolf-Kolping-Str 10, Kronach, 96317, Germany. TEL 49-9261-9694000, FAX 49-9261-9694111, info@wolters-kluwer.de, http://www.carllink.de.

372.21 DEU ISSN 0936-5982
KITA KINDERTAGESEINRICHTUNGEN AKTUELL. AUSGABE BAYERN. Text in German. 1989. 11/yr. EUR 82.90; EUR 9 newsstand/cover (effective 2005). **Document type:** *Journal, Academic/Scholarly.*
Published by: Carl Link Verlag (Subsidiary of: Wolters Kluwer Deutschland GmbH), Adolf-Kolping-Str 10, Kronach, 96317, Germany. TEL 49-9261-9694000, FAX 49-9261-9694111, info@wolters-kluwer.de, http://www.carllink.de.

372.21 DEU ISSN 0941-4347
KITA KINDERTAGESEINRICHTUNGEN AKTUELL. AUSGABE BRANDENBURG, MECKLENBURG-VORPOMMERN, SACHSEN, SACHSEN-ANHALT, THUERINGEN UND BERLIN. Text in German. 1992. 11/yr. EUR 82.90; EUR 9 newsstand/cover (effective 2005). **Document type:** *Journal, Academic/Scholarly.*
Published by: Carl Link Verlag (Subsidiary of: Wolters Kluwer Deutschland GmbH), Adolf-Kolping-Str 10, Kronach, 96317, Germany. TEL 49-9261-9694000, FAX 49-9261-9694111, info@wolters-kluwer.de, http://www.carllink.de.

372.21 DEU ISSN 1437-1790
KITA KINDERTAGESEINRICHTUNGEN AKTUELL. AUSGABE HESSEN, RHEINLAND-PFALZ, SAARLAND. Text in German. 1993. 11/yr. EUR 82.90; EUR 9 newsstand/cover (effective 2005). **Document type:** *Journal, Academic/Scholarly.*
Formerly (until 1996): KiTa KinderTageseinrichtungen Aktuell. Ausgabe Hessen und Rheinland-Pfalz (0944-1379)
Published by: Carl Link Verlag (Subsidiary of: Wolters Kluwer Deutschland GmbH), Adolf-Kolping-Str 10, Kronach, 96317, Germany. TEL 49-9261-9694000, FAX 49-9261-9694111, info@wolters-kluwer.de, http://www.carllink.de.

372.21 DEU ISSN 0944-4173
KITA KINDERTAGESEINRICHTUNGEN AKTUELL. AUSGABE NIEDERSACHSEN, SCHLESWIG-HOLSTEIN, HAMBURG, BREMEN. Text in German. 199?. 11/yr. EUR 82.90; EUR 9 newsstand/cover (effective 2005). **Document type:** *Journal, Academic/Scholarly.*
Published by: Carl Link Verlag (Subsidiary of: Wolters Kluwer Deutschland GmbH), Adolf-Kolping-Str 10, Kronach, 96317, Germany. TEL 49-9261-9694000, FAX 49-9261-9694111, info@wolters-kluwer.de, http://www.carllink.de.

372.21 DEU ISSN 0942-2463
KITA KINDERTAGESEINRICHTUNGEN AKTUELL. AUSGABE NORDRHEIN-WESTFALEN. Text in German. 1992. 11/yr. EUR 82.90; EUR 9 newsstand/cover (effective 2005). **Document type:** *Journal, Academic/Scholarly.*
Published by: Carl Link Verlag (Subsidiary of: Wolters Kluwer Deutschland GmbH), Adolf-Kolping-Str 10, Kronach, 96317, Germany. TEL 49-9261-9694000, FAX 49-9261-9694111, info@wolters-kluwer.de, http://www.carllink.de.

372.21 DEU ISSN 1612-0809
KITA RECHT. Text in German. 2/yr. EUR 22; EUR 15 newsstand/cover (effective 2005). **Document type:** *Journal, Academic/Scholarly.*
Published by: Carl Link Verlag (Subsidiary of: Wolters Kluwer Deutschland GmbH), Adolf-Kolping-Str 10, Kronach, 96317, Germany. TEL 49-9261-9694000, FAX 49-9261-9694111, info@wolters-kluwer.de, http://www.carllink.de.

372.21 DEU ISSN 1437-4013
KITA SPEZIAL. Text in German. 1999. 4/yr. EUR 29.40; EUR 15 newsstand/cover (effective 2005). **Document type:** *Journal, Academic/Scholarly.*
Published by: Carl Link Verlag (Subsidiary of: Wolters Kluwer Deutschland GmbH), Adolf-Kolping-Str 10, Kronach, 96317, Germany. TEL 49-9261-9694000, FAX 49-9261-9694111, info@wolters-kluwer.de, http://www.carllink.de.

KLINGE. see *SOCIAL SERVICES AND WELFARE*

KLOEVERBLADET. see *CHILDREN AND YOUTH—For*

KNIPPIE IDEE. see *CLOTHING TRADE—Fashions*

KNIPPIE BABY. see *CLOTHING TRADE—Fashions*

THE KOBRIN LETTER; concerning children's books about real people, places and things. see *LITERATURE*

KONTRAPUNKTE. see *CHILDREN AND YOUTH—For*

369.4 PRK ISSN 0454-420X
HQ799.K6
KOREAN YOUTH AND STUDENTS. Text in English. bi-m.
Related titles: French ed.
Indexed: RASB.
Address: Pyongyang, Korea, N.

C

KUTTIKALUDE DEEPIKA; children's fortnightly. see *CHILDREN AND YOUTH—For*

KVINNER I BEVEGELSE. see *WOMEN'S INTERESTS*

649 USA
L A FAMILY MAGAZINE. Text in English. m. adv.
Published by: Siwol Media Group, 11835 W Olympic Blvd, 425, Los Angeles, CA 90064. TEL 310-477-2526, FAX 310-477-2512, david@lafamily.com.

155.4 649 USA ISSN 0740-3437
L A PARENT; magazine for Southern California families. Text in English. 1981. m. free newsstand/cover. adv. **Document type:** *Magazine, Consumer.* **Description:** City magazine for informed L.A. parents.
Incorporates (19??-198?): Pony Ride (0745-2314)
Published by: United Parenting Publications (Subsidiary of: Trader Publishing Co.), 443 E Irving Dr, Ste A, Burbank, CA 91504. TEL 818-846-0400, FAX 818-841-4380, http://losangeles.parenthood.com. Ed., R&P Marilyn Martinez. Pub. Maddie Calabrese. Circ: 120,000 (controlled).

LANDSCHAFTSVERBAND WESTFALEN-LIPPE. MITTEILUNGEN DES LANDESJUGENDAMTES; Beitraege zur Jugendhilfe. see *SOCIAL SERVICES AND WELFARE*

LAPSEN MAAILMA/CHILD'S WORLD. see *SOCIAL SERVICES AND WELFARE*

649 USA
LAS VEGAS KIDZ MAGAZINE. Text in English. 1989. m. free. adv. bk.rev. **Document type:** *Bulletin.* **Description:** Monthly calendar of low or no cost Las Vegas event for kids.
Address: 9208 Siena Vista Dr, Las Vegas, NV 89117-7031. TEL 702-233-8388, FAX 702-233-8399. Ed. Mya Collins. Adv. contact Ana Basa. Circ: 40,000.

649 DEU
LEA - KIND & KEGEL; das Magazin fuer die junge Familie. Text in German. a. EUR 1.95 newsstand/cover (effective 2003). adv. **Document type:** *Magazine, Consumer.*
Published by: Klambt Verlag GmbH, Im Neudeck 1, Speyer, 67346, Germany. TEL 49-6232-3100, FAX 49-6232-310226, anzeigen@klambt.de, http://www.klambt.de. Adv. contact Anita Weiss. B&W page EUR 3,420, color page EUR 4,114. Circ: 56,728 (paid and controlled).

369.4 USA
LEADER; for adults in girl scouting. Text in English. 1923. q. illus. cum.index 1982-1993; 1994-2001. reprints avail. **Document type:** *Magazine, Consumer.* **Description:** Contains news and features concerning the national Girl Scout movement for all adults in girl scouting.
Formerly (until 1999): Girl Scout Leader (0017-0577)
Published by: Girl Scouts of the U.S.A., 420 Fifth Ave, New York, NY 10018-2798. TEL 212-852-8000, 800-478-7248, FAX 212-852-6511, leadermagazine@girlscouts.org, misc@girlscouts.org, http://www.girlscouts.org/for_adults/leader_magazine/. Ed. Janet Lombardi. Circ: 800,000 (controlled).

369.4 CAN ISSN 0711-5377
THE LEADER. Text in English. 1923. 10/yr. CND 8.56 domestic; CND 18 foreign; CND 2.95 newsstand/cover (effective 2004). adv. bk.rev. illus.; tr.lit. index. **Document type:** *Magazine, Trade.*
Former titles (until 1976): Canadian Leader (0036-9462); (until 1970): Scout Leader (0319-3500)
Published by: (Scouts Canada), Canyouth Publications Ltd., 1345 Baseline Rd, Ottawa, ON K2C 0A7, Canada. FAX 613-224-5982, leader@scouts.ca, http://www.scouts.ca/inside.asp?cmPageID=108, http://www.scouts.ca/leader.htm. Ed., R&P Andy McLaughlin TEL 613-224-5131. Adv. contact Laureen Duquette. Circ: 44,000.

362.7 USA
LEADER MAGAZINE; the magazine of video-based parent, loss and self-esteem education and teacher training. Text in English. 1985. q. free. adv. bk.rev.
Formerly: Active Parenting Leader
Indexed: RRTA, WAE&RSA.
Published by: Active Parenting Publishers, 1955 Vaughn Rd NW, Ste. 108, Kennesaw, GA 30144-7808. TEL 770-429-0565, FAX 770-429-0334, cservice@activeparenting.com, http://www.activeparenting.com, http://www.activeparenting.com. Ed., Adv. contact Virginia Murray. R&P Terry Gibney. Circ: 55,000 (controlled).

LEARNING DISABILITIES RESEARCH AND PRACTICE. see *EDUCATION—Special Education And Rehabilitation*

THE LEARNING EDGE; home based education program news. see *EDUCATION—Teaching Methods And Curriculum*

649 USA ISSN 8750-2011
LEAVEN (SCHAUMBURG). Text in English. 1965. bi-m. free to League leaders. adv. bk.rev. 24 p./no.; back issues avail. **Document type:** *Magazine, Consumer.* **Description:** Features in-depth articles on breastfeeding issues, as well as research-based information for La Leche League Leader.
Related titles: Online - full text ed.: (from EBSCO Publishing, ProQuest Information & Learning, SoftLine Information).
Indexed: GendWatch.
Published by: La Leche League International, Inc., 1400 N Meacham Rd, Schaumburg, IL 60168-60173. TEL 847-519-7730, FAX 847-519-0035, lllhq@llli.org, http://www.lalecheleague.org. adv.: color page USD 1,105; trim 11 x 8. Circ: 7,500; 7,000 (paid).

C

649 DEU ISSN 0047-4274
LEBEN UND ERZIEHEN; die praktische Eltern-Zeitschrift. Text in German. 1952. m. EUR 23.88; EUR 1.99 newsstand/cover (effective 2003). adv. bk.rev. illus. **Document type:** *Magazine, Consumer.*
Published by: Weltbild Verlag GmbH, Steinerne Furt, Augsburg, 86128, Germany. TEL 49-821-70048309, FAX 49-821-70048133, redfuf@weltbild.de, http://www.leben-und-erziehen.de, http://www.weltbild.de. Ed. Marilis Kurz-Lunkenbein. Adv. contact Thomas Wingenfeld. color page EUR 6,300; trim 175 x 242. Circ: 136,396 (paid).

LEDARTIPS; Oe M Us tidskrift foer foeraeldrar, barn- och ungdomsledare. see *SOCIAL SERVICES AND WELFARE*

369.4 NOR
LEDERFORUM. Text in Norwegian. 5/yr. adv.
Published by: Norges K F U M-Speidere, Postboks 6810, St Olavs Plass, Oslo, 0130, Norway. TEL 47-22-11-50-32, FAX 47-22-20-37-65, forbundskontoret@kfum-speider.no, http://www.kfum-speider.no. Circ: 2,600.

LEESGOED; wat en hoe kinderen (leren) lezen. see *EDUCATION*

LIBERIA. MINISTRY OF LABOUR, YOUTH & SPORTS. ANNUAL REPORT. see *SOCIAL SERVICES AND WELFARE*

LICHT DES LEBENS. see *RELIGIONS AND THEOLOGY*

155 USA
LINDNER EARLY CHILDHOOD TRAINING INSTITUTE NEWSLETTER. Text in English. m.
Published by: North Shore Child & Family Guidance Center, Lindner Early Childhood Training Institute, 480 Old Westbury Rd, Roslyn, NY 11577-2215. TEL 516-626-1971, 800-595-9365, FAX 516-626-8043.

THE LION & THE UNICORN; a critical journal of children's literature. see *LITERATURE*

649 DEU
LISA FAMILY. Text in German. 4/yr. EUR 2.20 newsstand/cover (effective 2003). adv. **Document type:** *Magazine, Consumer.*
Published by: Medien Innovation GmbH (Subsidiary of: Hubert Burda Media Holding GmbH & Co. KG), Am Kestendamm 1, Offenburg, 77652, Germany. TEL 49-89-92500, FAX 49-89-92502745, info@hubert-burda-media.com, http://www.hubert-burda-media.com. adv.: color page EUR 6,000. Circ: 200,000 (paid and controlled).

305.23 SCG
LISA MOJE DETE. Variant title: Moje Dete. Text in Serbian. m. adv. **Document type:** *Magazine, Consumer.*
Published by: Isdavacka Kuca Burda Beograd, Takovska 45, Beograd, 11000. sandi@burda.co.yu. adv.: page USD 700. Circ: 40,000 (paid and controlled).

305.23 HRV
LISA MOJE DIJETE. Text in Croatian. m. HRK 7.90 newsstand/cover (effective 2003). adv. **Document type:** *Magazine, Consumer.*
Published by: Burda Nacional d.o.o., Vlaska 40, Zagreb, 10000, Croatia. TEL 385-1-4896663, FAX 385-1-4814394, danijela.potocnjak@nacional.hr. adv.: page HRK 9,000. Circ: 35,000 (paid and controlled).

LITERACY TIME YEARS 3/4. see *EDUCATION—Teaching Methods And Curriculum*

LITERACY TIME YEARS 5/6. see *EDUCATION—Teaching Methods And Curriculum*

LITERATUUR ZONDER LEEFTIJD; vaktijdschrift over jeugdliteratuur. see *LITERATURE*

649 USA
LITTLE ROCK FAMILY. Text in English. m. USD 15 (effective 2005). **Document type:** *Newspaper, Consumer.*
Published by: Arkansas Business Publishing Group, Little Rock Office, PO Box 3686, Little Rock, AR 72203. TEL 501-372-1443, info@abpg.com, http://www.abpg.com. Ed. Susan VanDusen. Pub. Brigette Williams. Circ: 5,000 (free).

649.05 NZL ISSN 0113-8642
LITTLE TREASURES. Text in English. 1986. bi-m. adv. **Document type:** *Magazine, Consumer.*
Published by: A C P New Zealand, 17B Hargreaves St, College Hill, Pasonby, Auckland, 1036, New Zealand. TEL 64-9-3735408, FAX 64-9-3089498.

▼ **LIVING IN THE SPECTRUM: AUTISM & ASPERGER'S.** see *PSYCHOLOGY*

LIVING WITH TEENAGERS. see *RELIGIONS AND THEOLOGY—Protestant*

305.23 UKR
LIZA. MOI REBENOK. Text in Ukrainian. m. UAK 28.90 for 6 mos. domestic (effective 2004). adv. **Document type:** *Magazine, Consumer.* **Description:** Guides and informs young parents about all aspects of child care.
Published by: Burda Ukraina, Zhyljanskaja ul. 29, Kiev, 01033, Ukraine. TEL 38-044-4908363, FAX 38-044-4908364, advert@burdaua.com, http://www.burda.com.ua. Ed. Yuliya Novgorodskaya TEL 380-44-4908367. adv.: page USD 2,700. Circ: 50,000 (paid and controlled).

362.7 RUS ISSN 1606-8734
LIZA. MOI REBENOK. Text in Russian. 2000. m. RUR 660 domestic; RUR 55 newsstand/cover domestic (effective 2004). adv. **Document type:** *Magazine, Consumer.*
Published by: Izdatel'skii Dom Burda, ul Pravdy 8, Moscow, 125040, Russian Federation. TEL 7-095-7979849, FAX 7-095-2571196, my-baby-magazine@pub.burda.ru, vertrieb@burda.ru, http://www.burda.ru. adv.: page USD 5,500. Circ: 150,000 (paid and controlled).

649 618 GBR
THE LOCAL BABY DIRECTORY: BRISTOL & BATH. Text in English. a., latest 2001-2002. GBP 4.99 newsstand/cover (effective 2001). adv. Website rev. 150 p./no.; **Document type:** *Directory, Consumer.* **Description:** Contains a definitive directory of resources throughout Bristol & Bath for parents and carers. Includes everything from acupuncture to zoos, from adventure playgrounds to yoga.
Published by: Baby Directory Ltd., 10 Grove Park Terrace, London, W4 3QG, United Kingdom. TEL 44-20-8742-8724, FAX 44-20-8580-7085, editor@babydirectory.com, http://www.babydirectory.com. Ed. Gail Boulton.

649 618.2 GBR
THE LOCAL BABY DIRECTORY: HERTS & MIDDLESEX; an a-z of everything for pregnant women, babies and children. Text in English. 1999. a. GBP 4.99 newsstand/cover (effective 2001). adv. Website rev. 150 p./no.; **Document type:** *Directory, Consumer.* **Description:** Provides a definitive directory of resources throughout Herts and Middlesex for parents and carers. Contains everything from acupuncture to zoos, from adventure playgrounds to yoga.
Published by: Baby Directory Ltd., 10 Grove Park Terrace, London, W4 3QG, United Kingdom. TEL 44-20-8742-8724, FAX 44-20-8580-7085, editor@babydirectory.com, http://www.babydirectory.com. Ed., Adv. contact Brigid Phillips TEL 44-20-8429-1849. Pub., R&P Dr. Karen Liebreich. B&W page GBP 350, color page GBP 600;. Circ: 3,000 (paid).

649 618 GBR
THE LOCAL BABY DIRECTORY: OXFORDSHIRE, BERKS & BUCKS; an a-z of everything for pregnant women, babies and children. Text in English. a., latest 2001-2002. GBP 4.99 per issue (effective 2001). adv. Website rev. 150 p./no.; **Document type:** *Consumer.* **Description:** Contains a definitive directory of resources throughout Oxfordshire, Berks & Bucks for parents and carers. Includes everything from acupuncture to zoos, from adventure playgrounds to yoga.
Published by: Baby Directory Ltd., 10 Grove Park Terrace, London, W4 3QG, United Kingdom. TEL 44-20-8742-8724, FAX 44-20-8580-7085, editor@babydirectory.com, http://www.babydirectory.com. Ed. Francesca Lee.

649 618 GBR
THE LOCAL BABY DIRECTORY: SOUTH WALES; an a-z of everything for pregnant women, babies and children. Text in English. a., latest 2001-2002. GBP 4.99 newsstand/cover (effective 2001). adv. Website rev. 150 p./no.; **Document type:** *Directory, Consumer.* **Description:** Contains a definitive directory of resources throughout South Wales for parents and carers. Includes everything from acupuncture to zoos, from adventure playgrounds to yoga.
Published by: Baby Directory Ltd., 10 Grove Park Terrace, London, W4 3QG, United Kingdom. TEL 44-20-8742-8724, FAX 44-20-8580-7085, editor@babydirectory.com, http://www.babydirectory.com. Ed. Gail Boulton.

649 618 GBR
THE LOCAL BABY DIRECTORY: SURREY; an a-z everything for pregnant women, babies and children. Text in English. a., latest 2001-2002. GBP 4.99 newsstand/cover (effective 2001). adv. Website rev. 150 p./no.; **Document type:** *Directory, Consumer.* **Description:** Contains a definitive directory of resources throughout Surrey for parents and carers. Includes everything from acupuncture to zoos, from adventure playgrounds to yoga.
Published by: Baby Directory Ltd., 10 Grove Park Terrace, London, W4 3QG, United Kingdom. TEL 44-20-8742-8724, FAX 44-20-8580-7085, editor@babydirectory.com, http://www.babydirectory.com. Ed. Angela Thompson.

649 618 GBR
THE LOCAL BABY DIRECTORY: SUSSEX & HAMPSHIRE; an a-z of everything for pregnant women, babies and children. Text in English. a., latest 2001-2002. GBP 4.99 newsstand/cover (effective 2001). Website rev. 150 p./no.; **Document type:** *Directory, Consumer.* **Description:** Contains a definitive directory of resources throughout Sussex & Hampshire for parents and carers. Includes everything from acupuncture to zoos, from adventure playgrounds to yoga.
Published by: Baby Directory Ltd., 10 Grove Park Terrace, London, W4 3QG, United Kingdom. TEL 44-20-8742-8724, FAX 44-20-8580-7085, editor@babydirectory.com, http://www.babydirectory.com.

371.2 SWE ISSN 1100-3197
➤ **LOCUS**; tidskrift foer barn- och ungdomsvetenskap. Text in Swedish. 1989. q. SEK 200 domestic; SEK 210 elsewhere (effective 2005). back issues avail. **Document type:** *Journal, Academic/Scholarly.*
Incorporates (1986-1992): Kunskap om Barn (0283-8516); Which was formerly (1982-1984): Kunskap om Barn i Barnomsorg och Skola (0281-1782)
Published by: Laerarhoegskolan i Stockholm, Institutionen foer Individ, Omvaerld och Laerande/Stockholm Institute of Education, PO Box 47308, Stockholm, 10074, Sweden. TEL 46-8-7375585, FAX 46-8-7379630, locus@lhs.se, iol@lhs.se, http://www.lhs.se/iol/locus/index.html. Ed. Tilda Maria Forselius. **Dist. by:** Swedish Science Press.

649 618.2 GBR ISSN 1369-9539
THE LONDON BABY DIRECTORY; an a-z of everything for pregnant women, babies and children. Text in English. 1997. a. GBP 6.99 newsstand/cover (effective 2001). adv. Website rev. index. **Document type:** *Directory, Consumer.* **Description:** Contains a definitive directory of resources throughout London for parents and carers. Includes everything from acupuncture to zoos, from adventure playgrounds to yoga.
Published by: Baby Directory Ltd., 10 Grove Park Terrace, London, W4 3QG, United Kingdom. TEL 44-20-8742-8724, FAX 44-20-8580-7085, editor@babydirectory.com, http://www.babydirectory.com. Ed., Pub., R&P, Adv. contact Dr. Karen Liebreich. B&W page GBP 610, color page GBP 999;. Circ: 7,500 (paid).

649 USA
LONG ISLAND PARENTING NEWS. Text in English. m. USD 30 subscr - mailed (effective 2004); free newsstand/cover domestic. **Document type:** *Newspaper, Consumer.* **Description:** Provides local news, features and a calendar of family events.
Published by: United Advertising Publications, Inc., 585 Stuart Ave, Ste LL30, Garden City, NY 11530. TEL 516-227-0270, FAX 516-227-2127, http://longisland.parenthood.com/. Ed. Heather Hart. Circ: 57,000 (paid).

649 USA
LONG ISLAND PARENTS & CHILDREN. Text in English. 1999. 8/yr. USD 15 per issue (effective 2001). adv. **Description:** Offers advice to parents with newborn children to 12 year olds. Includes fun activities for children, a calendar of events and notable attractions, a wellness section for parents, and more.
Published by: Island Publications, 235 Pinelawn Rd, Melville, NY 11747. TEL 631-843-2362, FAX 631-843-3320, distinction@prodigy.net, http://www.liparent.com/. Circ: 60,000.

LOOK AND LISTEN. see *RELIGIONS AND THEOLOGY—Protestant*

649 USA
LOUISVILLE PARENT; Kentuckian's parenting publication. Text in English. m. adv. **Description:** Covers a variety of parenting topics, focusing on the Louisville area.
Published by: Midwest Parenting Publications, 9509 US Highway 42, 205, Prospect, KY 40059. TEL 502-228-5895, FAX 502-228-9415, louisvilleparent@louivilleparent.com, http://www.louisvilleparent.com. Pub. Tom Wynne.

053.1 DEU
LUFTBALLON; die unabhaengige Elternzeitung der Region Stuttgart. Text in German. 1998. 10/yr. adv. **Document type:** *Magazine, Consumer.*
Published by: Verlag Luftballon Michael Rees und Thomas Muenz GbR mbH, Nadlerstr 12, Stuttgart, 70173, Germany. TEL 49-711-2348795, FAX 49-711-2348796, mail@elternzeitung-luftballon.de, http://www.elternzeitung-luftballon.de. adv.: B&W page EUR 1,475.59, color page EUR 2,252.21; trim 213 x 285. Circ: 32,000 (controlled).

M A K. (Mladosc, Aktivnosc, Kreativnocs) see *CHILDREN AND YOUTH—For*

649 GBR ISSN 1461-8990
M MAGAZINE; the essential magazine for today's parents. Text in English. 1998. bi-m. GBP 2.40 newsstand/cover. adv. **Document type:** *Magazine, Consumer.* **Description:** Information, advice and reassurance for modern parents as they negotiate the needs and wants of family.
—CCC.
Published by: National Magazine Company Ltd., National Magazine House, 72 Broadwick St, London, W1F 9EP, United Kingdom. TEL 44-20-74395000, FAX 44-20-74376886, m.baby@natmags.co.uk, http://www.natmags.co.uk. Ed. Rachel Shattock. Pub. Vivien Cotterill. Adv. contact Holly Galligan. **Dist. by:** Comag, Tavistock Works, Tavistock Rd, W Drayton, Middx UB7 7QX, United Kingdom. TEL 44-1895-444055, FAX 44-1895-433602.

THE MAGAZINE. see *EDUCATION*

028.5 800 AUS ISSN 0817-0088
MAGPIES; talking about books for children. Text in English. 1986. 5/yr. AUD 38.50 domestic; AUD 44 in New Zealand; AUD 55 elsewhere (effective 2004). adv. bk.rev. back issues avail. **Document type:** *Journal, Academic/Scholarly.* **Description:** Articles and reviews on children's literature for teachers, librarians and parents.
Related titles: Online - full text ed.: (from R M I T Publishing).
Indexed: BRI, CBRI, ChLitAb, WBA, WMB.
—BLDSC (5340.215700), IE, ingenta.
Published by: Magpies Magazine Pty. Ltd., PO Box 98, Grange, QLD 4051, Australia. TEL 61-7-33564503, FAX 61-7-33564649, james@magpies.net.au, http://www.magpies.net.au. Ed. Rayma Turton. R&P, Adv. contact James Turton. Circ: 4,500.

649.1 USA
MAIN STREET MOM. Text in English. w. bk.rev. back issues avail. **Document type:** *Consumer.* **Description:** Designed for stay-at-home moms. Includes tips on parenting.
Media: Online - full text.
Published by: Word Results, Co., PO Box 851, Scott Depot, WV 25560. subscribeme@mainstreetmom.com, http://www.mainstreetmom.com/. Ed. Mia Cronan.

362.7 155.4 ITA ISSN 1591-4267
MALTRATTAMENTO E ABUSO ALL'INFANZIA. Text in Italian. 1999. 3/yr. EUR 39 domestic; EUR 68 foreign (effective 2003). **Document type:** *Journal, Academic/Scholarly.*
Published by: (Universita Cattolica del Sacro Cuore, Dipartimento di Psicologia), Franco Angeli Edizioni, Viale Monza 106, Milan, 20127, Italy. TEL 39-02-2837141, FAX 39-02-26144793, redazioni@francoangeli.it, http://www.francoangeli.it.

649.1 DNK ISSN 1603-9726
MAMA. Text in Danish. 1991. m. DKK 399; DKK 42.50 per issue (effective 2004). **Document type:** *Magazine, Consumer.* **Description:** Contains articles and features on child development, psychology, upbringing, and education as well as pregnancy, birth and parenthood.
Formerly (until 2004): Foraeldre & Boern (0907-1644)
Related titles: Online - full text ed.
Published by: Aller International A-S, Marielundsvej 46 E, Herlev, 2730, Denmark. TEL 45-44-85-88-88, 45-44-858888, FAX 45-44-858887, mening@mama.dk, reception@aller.dk, http://www.mama.dk, http://www.aller.dk. Ed. Ann Qvist TEL 45-44-858825. Adv. contact Erling Duelund.

649 360 USA
MAMA LIANYIHUI JIANXUN. Text in Chinese. s-a. **Document type:** *Newsletter.*
Related titles: Online - full content ed.
Published by: Mama Lianyihui/United Moms Charity Association (U M C A), 6 Hardley Dr, Cranbury, NJ 08512. njumca@hotmail.com, http://www.twnet.com/umca/UMCA-chn.html, http://www.twnet.com/umca/UMCA-eng.html.

613.95 POL ISSN 1233-7366
MAMO TO JA. Text in Polish. 1995. m. PLZ 52.80 domestic; PLZ 150 foreign (effective 2005). adv. **Document type:** *Magazine, Consumer.*
Related titles: Supplement(s): Encyklopedia Mamo to Ja. ISSN 1429-6829. 1998.
Published by: Edipresse Polska S A, Ul Wiejska 19, Warsaw, 00-480, Poland. TEL 48-22-5842516, FAX 48-22-5842500, info@mamotoja.pl, uroda.redakcja@edipresse.pl, http://www.mamotoja.pl, http://www.uroda.com.pl. Ed. Anna Zaleska. adv.: page PLZ 32,000; 210 x 280. Circ: 73,806 (paid).

362.7 155.4 NLD ISSN 1382-4406
MANAGEMENT KINDEROPVANG. Text in Dutch. 1995. 10/yr. EUR 82 (effective 2003). **Document type:** *Trade.* **Description:** Discusses all issues in managing daycare centers and nursery schools for directors as well as teacher, caregivers, assistants, and support personnel.
Published by: Elsevier Gezondheidszorg bv (Subsidiary of: Reed Business Information bv), Planetenbaan 80-99, Maarssen, 3606 AK, Netherlands. TEL 31-346-577577, FAX 31-346-554287, http://www.elseviergezondheidszorg.nl. **Subscr. to:** Elsevier Den Haag, Postbus 16500, The Hague 2500 BM, Netherlands. TEL 31-70-381-9900, FAX 31-70-333-8399.

371.95 CAN ISSN 0844-0441
MANITOBA COUNCIL FOR EXCEPTIONAL CHILDREN. Text in English. 1977. s-a.
Former titles (until 1986): Council for Exceptional Children. Manitoba Federation d 338. Magazine (0838-956X); (until 1978): Council for Exceptional Children. Manitoba Branch d 367. Magazine (0706-8913)
—CCC.
Published by: Council for Exceptional Children, Manitoba Federation, 825 Sherbrook St, 2nd Fl, Winnipeg, MB R3M 37, Canada. TEL 204-772-6979, FAX 204-786-0860.

649 LVA ISSN 1407-1614
MANS MAZAIS. Text in Latvian. 1994. m. **Document type:** *Magazine, Consumer.*
Published by: Zurnals Santa, Balasta Dambis 3, PO Box 32, Riga, LV-1081, Latvia. TEL 371-762-8275, FAX 371-746-5450, santa@santa.lv.

649 USA
MARTHA STEWART BABY. Text in English. 2000. s-a. (Title will be published in March & Sept. and alternate in frequency with, Martha Stewart Kids.). USD 4.75 newsstand/cover; USD 5.75 newsstand/cover in Canada (effective 2001). **Document type:** *Magazine, Consumer.* **Description:** Provides information and ideas on infant care. Topics include baby fashion, foods, health, and related issues.
Related titles: ♦ Special ed. of: Martha Stewart Living. ISSN 1057-5251.
Published by: Martha Stewart Living Omnimedia LLC, 20 W 43rd St, 25th Fl, New York, NY 10036. TEL 212-827-8000, FAX 212-827-8188, mstewart@marthastewart.com, http://www.marthastewart.com. Eds. Ayesha Patel, Jodi Levine.

649 USA ISSN 1546-4709
MARTHA STEWART KIDS. Text in English. 2001 (June). q. USD 12; USD 16 in Canada; USD 4.75 newsstand/cover (effective 2004). adv. **Document type:** *Magazine, Consumer.* **Description:** Dedicated to the essentials of caring for a child from three to ten years of age. Offers creative and educational focus, providing an array of ideas, activities and projects that children can create on their own or with parents.
Published by: Martha Stewart Living Omnimedia LLC, 20 W 43rd St, 25th Fl, New York, NY 10036. TEL 212-827-8000, FAX 212-827-8188, mstewart@marthastewart.com, http://www.marthastewart.com. Eds. Ayesha Patel, Jodi Levine.

MASSACHUSETTS PRACTICE SERIES. JUVENILE LAW. see *LAW*

▼ **MATERNAL AND CHILD NUTRITION.** see *NUTRITION AND DIETETICS*

MATHS & STORY TIME. see *EDUCATION—Teaching Methods And Curriculum*

303.32 GBR ISSN 1745-3518
▼ ➤ **THE MATRON**; for matrons and their colleagues. Text in English. 2004. m. GBP 40; GBP 3.80 newsstand/cover (effective 2005). adv. **Document type:** *Journal, Trade.* **Description:** Aimed at those with a pastoral responsibility towards children, including matrons, nannies, teaching assistants, and those working in children homes.
Published by: Douglas Clifford Ltd., 33 Union St, Ryde, Isle of Wight, PO33 2LE, United Kingdom. TEL 44-1983-617888, FAX 44-1983-617889, editor@thematron.com, http://www.thematron.com. Ed., R&P Matthew O'Crowley. Pub. Douglas Clifford. Adv. contact Anna Ward-Pritchard. page GBP 1,000. Circ: 24,000 (paid and controlled).

➤ **MEDIA UPDATE.** see *MUSIC*

305.23 FIN
▼ **MEIDAN PERHE.** Text in Finnish. 2004 (Mar.). m. adv. **Document type:** *Magazine, Consumer.* **Description:** Supports parents in their efforts to raise and educate their children.
Published by: Sanoma Magazines Finland Corporation, Hoylaamotie 1 D, P.O. Box 100, Helsinki, 00040, Finland. TEL 358-9-1201, FAX 358-9-1205171, info@sanomamagazines.fi, http://www.sanomamagazines.fi. Ed. Kristiina Dragon.

649 AUS ISSN 1320-6176
MELBOURNE'S CHILD. Text in English. 1993. m. AUD 30 (effective 2000). adv. **Document type:** *Magazine, Consumer.* **Description:** Contains the very latest information on a wide range of parenting topics.
Related titles: ♦ Online - full text ed.: Melbourne's Child Online.
Published by: Copeland Publishing Pty. Ltd., PO Box 171, Beecroft, NSW 2119, Australia. TEL 61-2-94845334, FAX 61-2-94845540, sydchild@ozemail.com.au, http://www.melbourneschild.com.au. adv.: B&W page AUD 3,341, color page AUD 4,336.

649 AUS
MELBOURNE'S CHILD ONLINE. Text in English. m. adv. **Document type:** *Consumer.*
Media: Online - full text. **Related titles:** ♦ Print ed.: Melbourne's Child. ISSN 1320-6176.
Published by: Copeland Publishing Pty. Ltd., PO Box 171, Beecroft, NSW 2119, Australia. TEL 61-2-94845334, FAX 61-2-94845540, sydchild@ozemail.com.au, http://www.melbourneschild.com.au.

MERRILL - PALMER QUARTERLY; journal of developmental psychology. see *PSYCHOLOGY*

362.7 618.92 FRA ISSN 1258-780X
METIERS DE LA PETITE ENFANCE. Text in French. 1994. 10/yr. EUR 64.64 in France to individuals; EUR 85 in Europe to individuals; JPY 11,300 in Japan to individuals; USD 105 to individuals except Europe and Japan; EUR 64.64 in France to institutions; EUR 86 in Europe to institutions; JPY 8,600 in Japan to institutions; USD 100 to institutions except Europe and Japan (effective 2006). **Description:** Includes articles and research, professional news coverage, medical issues and practical mementos.
Published by: Elsevier France, Editions Scientifiques et Medicales (Subsidiary of: Elsevier Science & Technology), 23 Rue Linois, Paris, 75724, France. TEL 33-1-71724600, FAX 33-1-71724650, academic@elsevier-fr.com, http://www.elsevier.com/locate/mpenf, http://www.elsevier.fr. Circ: 10,000.

362.7 USA
METRO PARENT (SOUTHFIELD). Text in English. 1985. m. USD 30 (effective 2003). adv. music rev.; software rev.; video rev. charts; illus. back issues avail.
Formerly: All Kids Considered
Related titles: Online - full text ed.: 1985.
Published by: Metro Parent Publishing Group, 24567 Northwestern Highway, Ste 150, Southfield, MI 48075-2412. TEL 248-352-0990, FAX 248-352-5066, metparent@aol.com, metroparent@metroparent.com, http://www.metroparent.com/, http://www.metparent.com. Ed., R&P Susan DeMaggio. Pub. Alyssa Martina. Adv. contact Linda Holland. Circ: 80,000.

649 USA
METRO PARENT (WAUWATOSA); greater Milwaukee's family resource. Text in English. 1986. 12/yr. free. adv. bk.rev. **Document type:** *Consumer.*
Published by: Thomson Newspapers, PO Box 13323, Wauwatosa, WI 53213-0323. TEL 414-259-1884, http://www.metroparentmagazine.com. Ed. Kathy Mangold. Pub. Todd Koharek. Adv. contact Kathryn Jensen. Circ: 45,000.

028.5 USA ISSN 1094-8503
METROKIDS. Text in English. 1989. m. USD 18. adv. bk.rev.; video rev. **Document type:** *Consumer.* **Description:** Serves as a resource publication for families who live in the greater metropolitan Philadelphia area.
Published by: KidStuff Publication, Inc., 4623 S. Broad St., Philadelphia, PA 19112-1202. TEL 215-291-5560, 888-890-4668, FAX 215-291-5563, editor@metrokids.com, info@metrokids.com, http://www.metrokids.com. Ed. Michelle Cassin. Pub., R&P Nancy Lisagor. adv.: B&W page USD 1,950. Circ: 125,000 (controlled).

649 ESP ISSN 1135-450X
MI BEBE Y YO. Text in Spanish. 1992. m. **Document type:** *Magazine, Consumer.* **Description:** For pregnant women and new mothers.

C

Published by: Sfera Editores S.L., Pol. Mas Blau Ed. Muntadas, planta baja Esc. B, SOLSONES, 2, El Prat De Llobregat, Barcelona 08820, Spain. TEL 34-93-370-8585, FAX 34-93-370-5060, sfera@intercom.es. Ed. Juan Turu. Circ: 162,074 (controlled).

649   USA
MID SOUTH FAMILY. Text in English. 2001. m. adv. **Document type:** Consumer.
Address: 7566 Nohapa Cove, Germantown, TN 38138. TEL 901-624-0803. Pub. Pamela Turner.

649   USA   ISSN 1075-8305
MINNESOTA PARENT. Text in English. 1987. m. USD 9 (effective 2005). adv. bk.rev.; film rev.; video rev. **Document type:** Consumer. **Description:** Covers health, education, sports and recreation, travel, the home, shopping and older children for parents.
Published by: Minnesota Premier Publications, 1115 Hennepin Ave. S, Minneapolis, MN 55403. TEL 612-825-9205, FAX 612-825-0929, http://www.mnparent.com. Ed. Sharon Secor. Pubs. Janis Hall, Terry Gahan. Circ: 65,000.

MINORI GIUSTIZIA. see CRIMINOLOGY AND LAW ENFORCEMENT

649   ITA   ISSN 0026-5756
IL MIO BEBE. Text in Italian. 1966. s-a. adv. **Document type:** Magazine, Consumer.
Published by: Edizioni Moderne Internazionali, Via Gallarate 230, Milan, MI, Italy. TEL 39-02-36569654, FAX 39-02-66981482, emimil@tin.it. Ed. Luigi Emilio Lodigiani. Circ: 64,000.

028.5   RUS
MISHA DLYA RODITELEI. Text in Russian. q. USD 75 in United States.
Address: Ul Pravdy 24, Moscow, 125805, Russian Federation. TEL 7-095-2573315, FAX 7-095-2573106. **US dist. addr.:** East View Information Services, 3020 Harbor Ln. N., Minneapolis, MN 55447. TEL 612-550-0961.

362.7 051   USA
MISS MOM - MISTER MOM∗. Text in English. 1986. bi-m. USD 15. adv. **Description:** For single parents.
Address: P O Box 1468, Moab, UT 84532-1468. TEL 801-259-5090. Ed. Tina L Lopez. Circ: 7,000.

MISSIONS MOSAIC. see RELIGIONS AND THEOLOGY— Protestant

MITTENDRIN (DETMOLD). see TRAVEL AND TOURISM

369.4   SVK   ISSN 0862-1853
MLADE ROZLETY. Text in Slovak. 1987. w. bk.rev.
Published by: Smena Publishing House, Prazska 11, Bratislava, 81284, Slovakia. Ed. Lubomir Stancel. Circ: 117,000. **Subscr. to:** PNS, Gottwaldovo nam 6, Bratislava 81384, Slovakia.

MOBIEL; tijdschrift voor pleegzorg. see SOCIAL SERVICES AND WELFARE

649   RUS   ISSN 1560-2648
MOI KROKHA I YA; zhurnal prakticheskikh sovetov roditelyam. Text in Russian. 1996. m. **Document type:** Magazine, Consumer.
Published by: Redaktsiya Zhurnala Moi Krokha i Ya, ul Krasnokazarmennaya 12, a/ya 14, Moscow, 111250, Russian Federation. TEL 7-095-3619358, FAX 7-095-9181449, kroha@interovapress.ru. **Dist. by:** M K - Periodica, ul Gilyarovskogo 39, Moscow 129110, Russian Federation. TEL 7-095-2845008, FAX 7-095-2813798, info@periodicals.ru, http://www.mkniga.ru.

649   CAN   ISSN 0384-0816
MON BEBE. Text in English. 1951. s-a. adv. illus. **Document type:** Consumer.
Published by: Family Communications, Inc., 65 The East Mall, Etobicoke, ON M8Z 5W3, Canada. Ed. Manon Leymone. Circ: 51,000.

MONTESSORI INTERNATIONAL; the international Montessori journal. see EDUCATION—Teaching Methods And Curriculum

MONTESSORI LIFE. see EDUCATION—Teaching Methods And Curriculum

MOTDRAG; Accent. see DRUG ABUSE AND ALCOHOLISM

649   GBR   ISSN 0047-8172
MOTHER & BABY. Text in English. 1956. m. GBP 21.60; GBP 1.80 newsstand/cover (effective 1999). adv. bk.rev. **Document type:** Consumer. **Description:** Takes readers through the first two years of life with a new baby. Includes advice to mothers on how to care for their babies.

Published by: Emap Elan Ltd. (Subsidiary of: Emap Consumer Media), Endeavour House, 189 Shaftesbury Ave, London, WC2H 8JG, United Kingdom. TEL 44-207-437-9011, FAX 44-207-208-3709, http://www.emap.com. Circ: 110,000. **Subscr. to:** Tower Publishing Services Ltd., Tower House, Sovereign Park, Market Harborough, Leics LE16 9EF, United Kingdom. TEL 44-1858-435339, FAX 44-1858-432164. **Dist. by:** Frontline Ltd., Unit 6, Stockwell Centre, Stephenson Way, Crawley, W Sussex RH10 1TN, United Kingdom. TEL 44-1733-555161, FAX 44-1293-415009.

MOTHER & BABY. see HOME ECONOMICS

MOTHER AND CHILD. see WOMEN'S INTERESTS

306.874   USA
MOTHER-TO-MOTHER∗ . Text in English. 1980. bi-m. USD 25 to individuals; USD 35 to institutions. **Document type:** Newsletter, Consumer. **Description:** Discusses issues affecting non-custodial mothers.
Published by: Mothers Without Custody; 609 North Ave, Crystal Lake, IL 60014-4981. TEL 800-457-6962. Ed. Jennifer Isham.

MOTHERING; the magazine of natural family living. see WOMEN'S HEALTH

MOUNTAIN SPIRIT. see SOCIAL SERVICES AND WELFARE

MUCHACHA. see CHILDREN AND YOUTH—For

MY FRIEND; a Catholic magazine for kids. see RELIGIONS AND THEOLOGY—Roman Catholic

362.7 364.6   GBR
N A C R O YOUTH CRIME SECTION. Text in English. q. GBP 10 to non-members; GBP 5 to members. **Document type:** Bulletin. **Description:** Essential information for practitioners and others interested in youth crime and young offenders.
Published by: National Association for the Care and Resettlement of Offenders, 169 Clapham Rd, London, SW9 0PU, United Kingdom. TEL 44-20-7582-6500, FAX 44-20-7735-4666.

N A J C A NEWS. see CRIMINOLOGY AND LAW ENFORCEMENT

N A Y S I RESOURCE LIST. see SPORTS AND GAMES

301   GBR
N C O P F ANNUAL REPORT. Text in English. 1979. a. GBP 5 (effective 1999). stat. **Document type:** Corporate. **Description:** Covers news of council's activities and campaigns.
Published by: National Council for One Parent Families, One Parent Families, 255 Kentish Town Rd, London, NW5 2LX, United Kingdom. TEL 44-20-74285400, FAX 44-20-74824851, info@oneparentfamilies.org.uk, http://www.oneparentfamilies.org.uk/.

028.5   IND
NANDAN. Text in Hindi. 1964. m. INR 65; INR 375 foreign. adv. bk.rev.
Published by: Hindustan Times Ltd., 18-20 Kasturba Gandhi Marg, New Delhi, 110 001, India. TELEX TIMES IN 66310, salil@hindustantimes.com, feedback@hindustantimes.com. Ed. Jai Prakash Bharti. Circ: 220,000.

649   USA
NANNY NEWS (ONLINE EDITION); a national newsletter for nannies and their employers. Text in English. 1994. bi-m. looseleaf. adv. bk.rev.; Website rev. charts; illus. back issues avail. **Document type:** Newsletter, Consumer. **Description:** Covers issues relating to providing and managing child care in the home. Includes product reviews.
Formerly: Nanny News (Print Edition) (1082-7951)
Media: Online - full text.
Published by: Nanny News, Inc., PO Box 186, Seligman, AZ 86337-0186. TEL 928-422-4171, 800-634-6266, FAX 928-422-4188, nannynews@nanny.com, http://www.nanny.com. Ed., Pub., R&P, Adv. contact Mary Clurman. B&W page USD 140; trim 11 x 8.5. Circ: 600 (paid); 400 (controlled).

618.92 649 370   RUS
NASH MALYSH. Text in Russian. 1995. m. USD 118 in North America (effective 2004). **Document type:** Magazine, Consumer.
Published by: Izdatel'stvo Zhurnala Nash Malysh, Profsoyuznaya 23, 19-i etazh, Moscow, 117997, Russian Federation. TEL 7-095-1280715, FAX 7-095-1204191, inph@col.ru. Circ: 50,000. **Dist. by:** East View Information Services, 3020 Harbor Ln. N., Minneapolis, MN 55447. TEL 763-550-0961, FAX 763-550-2931, eastview@eastview.com, http://www.eastview.com.

NATIONAL ADOPTION REPORTS. see SOCIAL SERVICES AND WELFARE

NATIONAL ADVOCATE. see SOCIAL SERVICES AND WELFARE

NATIONAL CENTER FOR JUVENILE JUSTICE. ANNUAL REPORT. see CRIMINOLOGY AND LAW ENFORCEMENT

NATIONAL CHILD BENEFIT PROGRESS REPORT. see SOCIAL SERVICES AND WELFARE

362   GBR   ISSN 0302-1998
NATIONAL CHILDREN'S BUREAU. ANNUAL REVIEW. Text in English. a. back issues avail. **Document type:** Corporate. **Description:** Informs members of the Bureau's work during the previous year. Outlines the year's expenditure and income.
Published by: National Children's Bureau, 8 Wakley St, London, EC1V 7QE, United Kingdom. TEL 44-20-78436000, FAX 44-20-72789512, http://www.ncb.org.uk. Ed. Alison Love.

NATIONAL DEAF CHILDREN'S SOCIETY. ANNUAL REPORT. see HANDICAPPED—Hearing Impaired

362.7   USA   ISSN 1072-902X
HV741
NATIONAL DIRECTORY OF CHILDREN, YOUTH & FAMILIES SERVICES. Text in English. 1979. biennial. USD 49. adv. back issues avail.
Formerly (until 1991): National Directory of Children & Youth Services (0190-7476)
Published by: (American Association for Protecting Children), Bookmakers Guild, Inc., 1430 Florida Ave, Ste 202, Longmont, CO 80501. TEL 303-442-5774. Circ: 10,000. **Co-sponsor:** American Humane Association.

NATIONAL INSTITUTE OF CHILD HEALTH AND HUMAN DEVELOPMENT. CENTER FOR POPULATION RESEARCH. PROGRESS REPORT. see MEDICAL SCIENCES

649   AUS
NATIONAL YOUTH AFFAIRS RESEARCH SCHEME REPORTS. Abbreviated title: N Y A R S Reports. Text in English. irreg., latest 2002. price varies. back issues avail. **Document type:** Monographic series, Government. **Description:** Covers the research into current social, political and economic factors affecting young people.
Related titles: Online - full content ed.
Published by: Australian Clearinghouse for Youth Studies, Private Bag 64, Hobart, TAS 7001, Australia. TEL 61-3-6226-2591, FAX 61-3-6226-2578, acys@educ.utas.edu.au, http://www.acys.utas.edu.au/ncys/nyars/index.html.

649   GBR
NATURAL PARENT. Text in English. 1998. bi-m. GBP 2.50 newsstand/cover (effective 2000). adv. **Document type:** Magazine, Consumer. **Description:** Contains information and advice on raising and nurturing a family using alternative and holistic methods.
Indexed: GendWatch.
Published by: Mothers Know Best Ltd., 77 Grosvenor Ave, London, N5 2NN, United Kingdom. TEL 44-20-7354-4592, FAX 44-20-7354-8907.

NEDSLAG I BOERNELITTERATURFORSKNINGEN. see LITERATURE

369.4   AUS   ISSN 0158-9539
NETWORK NEWS. Text in English. 1975. q. AUD 66 (effective 2001). adv. bk.rev. index. **Document type:** Newsletter.
Related titles: Online - full text ed.: (from LexisNexis); (from Northern Light Technology, Inc.).
Published by: Network of Community Activities, Sydney, 66 Albion St, Surry Hills, NSW 2010, Australia. TEL 61-2-9212-3244, FAX 61-2-9281-9645, network@netoosh.org.au, http://www.netoosh.org.au. Ed. Judy Finlason. R&P J Finlason. Adv. contact June Lunsmann. Circ: 1,000.

NEUROPSYCHOLOGY, DEVELOPMENT, AND COGNITION. SECTION C: CHILD NEUROPSYCHOLOGY; a journal on normal and abnormal development in childhood and adolescence. see PSYCHOLOGY

THE NEW ADVOCATE. see LITERATURE

392.1 649   USA   ISSN 8756-9981
NEW BEGINNINGS (SCHAUMBURG); every baby is a new beginning. Text in English. 1958. bi-m. USD 20 domestic; USD 24 foreign (effective 2002). adv. bk.rev. illus. index. 40 p./no.; **Description:** Provides educational information, support and encouragement to women who want to breastfeed their babies. Features regular columns on nutrition, breastfeeding, parenting and practical tips.
Formerly (until 1985): La Leche League News
Related titles: Microfilm ed.: (from PQC); Online - full text ed.: (from EBSCO Publishing, ProQuest Information & Learning).
Indexed: GendWatch.
Published by: La Leche League International, Inc., 1400 N Meacham Rd, Schaumburg, IL 60168-60173. TEL 847-519-7730, FAX 847-519-0035, lllhq@lli.org, http://www.lalecheleague.org. Ed. Judy Torgus. Adv. contact Maureen Schumar TEL 708-366-3153. page USD 1,938; trim 10.75 x 8. Circ: 27,000 (paid).

649 USA ISSN 1533-8916
RA790.A1 CODEN: NMHSEG
NEW DIRECTIONS FOR YOUTH DEVELOPMENT; theory, practice and research. Text in English. 1979. q. USD 180 domestic; USD 220 in Canada & Mexico; USD 254 elsewhere; USD 198 combined subscription domestic print & online eds.; USD 238 combined subscription in Canada & Mexico print & online eds.; USD 272 combined subscription elsewhere print & online eds. (effective 2006). back issues avail.; reprints avail. **Document type:** *Journal, Academic/Scholarly.* **Description:** Dedicated to bringing together everyone concerned with helping young people, including scholars, practitioners, and people from different disciplines and professions. Presents thoughtful, multi-faceted approaches to helping our youth develop into responsible, stable, well-rounded citizens.
Formerly (until 2001): New Directions for Mental Health Services (0193-9416)
Related titles: Microfiche ed.: (from PQC); Online - full text ed.: ISSN 1537-5781. USD 180 (effective 2006) (from EBSCO Publishing, O C L C Online Computer Library Center, Inc., Swets Information Services, Wiley InterScience).
Indexed: CPE, ERA, INI, IndMed, MEDLINE, PSI, PsycholAb, e-psyche.
—BLDSC (6083.477000), GNLM, IE, ingenta. **CCC.**
Published by: Jossey-Bass Inc., Publishers (Subsidiary of: John Wiley & Sons, Inc.), 989 Market St, San Francisco, CA 94103-1741. TEL 415-433-1740, FAX 415-433-0499, jbsubs@jbp.com, http://www.josseybass.com/WileyCDA/WileyTitle/productCd-MHS.html. Ed. Gil Noam. Pub. Sue Lewis. Circ: 400 (paid).

NEW JERSEY FAMILY; a news magazine for parents and kids. see *CHILDREN AND YOUTH—For*

649.1 USA
NEW JERSEY SUBURBAN PARENT MAGAZINE. Text in English. 1973. m. USD 12 (effective 2003). adv. bk.rev.; music rev.; play rev.; video rev. charts; illus.; maps. back issues avail. **Document type:** *Consumer.*
Published by: Middlesex Publications, Inc., 850 Route 1, North Brunswick, NJ 08902. TEL 732-435-0005, FAX 732-435-0677. Ed. Melodie S Drondt. Pub. Mark Chelton. Adv. contact Ellen Parker Keller. color page USD 100; trim 10 x 10.875. Circ: 70,000.

618 649 CAN ISSN 1193-9397
NEW MOTHER. Text in English. 1979. s-a. free. adv. **Description:** Provides articles on parenting the newborn, feeding, development and daily care issues.
Formerly (until 1992): Chatelaine's New Mother (0708-5303)
Related titles: French ed.: Mere Nouvelle. ISSN 1193-9389.
Indexed: CBCARef.
Published by: (Today's Parent Group), Professional Publishing Associates, 269 Richmond St W, Toronto, ON M5V 1X1, Canada. TEL 416-596-8680, FAX 416-596-1991. Ed. Holly Bennett. Circ: 160,000 (controlled).

649 USA
NEW PARENT. Text in English. 2000. s-a. USD 2.95 newsstand/cover (effective 2001). adv. **Document type:** *Consumer.*
Published by: Impact Media Communications, 10 New King Street, White Plains, NY 10604-1205. TEL 914-949-4726, FAX 914-949-8635, http://www.newparent.com. Ed. Anne Studabaker. Pub. Steven Kantor.

NEW YORK (STATE). ASSEMBLY. STANDING COMMITTEE ON CHILDREN AND FAMILIES. ANNUAL REPORT. see *SOCIAL SERVICES AND WELFARE*

790.019 USA ISSN 0896-7199
NEW YORK FAMILY; the magazine just for the NY parent. Text in English. 1986. 11/yr. free newsstand/cover. adv. bk.rev. back issues avail. **Document type:** *Magazine, Consumer.*
Published by: United Parenting Publications (Subsidiary of: Trader Publishing Co.), 141 Halstead Ave, Ste 302, Mamaroneck, NY 10543. TEL 914-381-7474, FAX 914-381-7672, edit2@familygroup.com, mamaroneckreception@unitedad.com, http://newyork.parenthood.com/aboutus.html, http://www.parenthood.com. Ed. Carolyn Rogalsky. Pub. Felice Shapiro. Circ: 65,000 (controlled and free).

NEW ZEALAND CHILDCARE ASSOCIATION. REPORT TO ANNUAL CONFERENCE. see *EDUCATION*

NEWBERRY (YEAR) MEDAL BOOKS. see *BIBLIOGRAPHIES*

369.4 USA ISSN 0199-4530
NEWS & VIEWS (PENDLETON). Text in English. 1947. q. adv. bk.rev. back issues avail. **Document type:** *Newsletter, Consumer.*
Published by: National Association of Extension 4 H Agents, c/o Affinity Plus, 1235-E East Blvd #213, Charlotte, NC 28203. TEL 704-333-3234, http://www.nae4ha.org/n&vindex.htm. Ed. Kimberly Gressley. Circ: 1,800 (paid).

NEWS FROM I C C V O S. (Unesco International Cearinghouse on Children and Violence on the Screen) see *SOCIOLOGY*

NO. see *WOMEN'S INTERESTS*

369.4 IRL ISSN 1393-9742
NO LIMITS. Text in English. 1961. m. adv. bk.rev. **Document type:** *Newsletter.*
Supersedes in part (in 2000): Scouting Ireland (0791-8674); Which was formed by the merger of (1991-1995): Leader (1393-9750); (1991-1995): Irish Scouting (1393-1865); Which was formerly (until 1993): Scouting SAI News (0791-4806)
Related titles: Microfilm ed.; Online - full text ed.
Published by: Scouting Ireland CSI, National Office, Larch Hill, Dublin, 16, Ireland. TEL 353-1-4956300, FAX 353-1-4956301, nolimits@scoutingirelandcsi.com, http://homepage.eircom.net/~cbsi/nolimits/nolimits/nolims2/nolimits2.html, http://www.scoutingireland.com/~cbsi/. Ed., R&P Colm Kavanagh. Adv. contact Pat Hollingsworth. Circ: 6,500.

910.202 USA ISSN 1537-615X
NO LIMITS; life after high school in Wisconsin. Text in English. a. USD 4.95 per issue (effective 2003). adv. **Document type:** *Consumer.* **Description:** Aimed at high school students and contains information about everything from college to military and credit cards to cool movies.
Published by: Trails Media Group, Inc., 1131 Mills St., PO Box 317, Black Earth, WI 53515. TEL 608-767-8000, 800-236-8088, FAX 608-767-5444, info@wistrails.com, http://www.nolimitswisconsin.com/, http://www.trailsmediagroup.com.

371.8 SCG
NON✶; list mladih srbije. Text in Serbo-Croatian. 1973. w. YUN 12,000, USD 30. bk.rev.; film rev.; play rev. abstr.; illus.
Formerly (until 1984): Omladinske Novine
Published by: Savez Socijalisticke Omladine Srbije, Republicka Konferencija, Bulv Umetnosti 27, Novi Beograd, 11070. TEL 011 135804. Ed. Zoran Miljatovic. Circ: 25,000.

305.234 362.7 USA
NORTHEASTERN WISCONSIN KIDS. Variant title: N.E.W. Kids. Text in English. 1994. m. free. adv. bk.rev. back issues avail. **Document type:** *Newspaper, Consumer.*
Formerly: Brown County Kids
Published by: Erickson Publishing LLC, PO Box 45050, Madison, WI 53744-5050. TEL 608-831-2131, FAX 608-831-2141, writeus@ericksonpublishing.com, http://www.newisconsinkids.com/, http://www.ericksonpublishing.com/. Ed. Jennifer Howard. Pub. Kristin Erickson. Adv. contact Marilyn Kous. page USD 870; trim 12.25 x 10. Circ: 24,000.

649 USA
NORTHERN CALIFORNIA PARENT MAGAZINE. Text in English. m.
Published by: United Parenting Publications (Subsidiary of: Trader Publishing Co.), 4983 Sonoma Hwy, L, Santa Rosa, CA 95409. TEL 707-538-7504, FAX 707-538-7578, http://www.parenthood.com.

649.12309416 GBR ISSN 1464-6153
NORTHERN IRELAND BABY MAGAZINE. Text in English. 1996. q. adv. **Document type:** *Magazine, Consumer.*
Published by: Main Stream Publications, 140 Thomas St, Portadown, Craigavon, Co Armagh BT62 3BE, United Kingdom. TEL 44-2838-334272, FAX 44-2838-351046, mainstream@btinternet.com.

649 USA
NORTHWEST FAMILY MAGAZINE✶. Text in English. 1995. m. USD 15 (effective 2003). adv. bk.rev.; film rev.; music rev.; software rev.; tel.rev.; video rev. back issues avail. **Document type:** *Consumer.* **Description:** Parenting resource for families living between Seattle and Vancouver, Canada. Covers local family events and activities, health, education, and entertainment.
Published by: MMB Publications inc, 2275 Lake Whatcom Blvd Ste B1, Bellingham, WA 98226-2777. TEL 360-734-3025, 800-494-3025, FAX 360-734-1550, nwfamily@family.com, nwfamily@earthlink.net, http://www.nwfamily.com. Ed., Pub., R&P, Adv. contact Lisa Laskey. page USD 1,930; trim 10 x 13. Circ: 50,000 (controlled).

649 USA
NORTHWEST PARENT. Text in English. m. adv. **Description:** Resource for parents targets parents of newborns to parents of teens.
Published by: United Parenting Publications (Subsidiary of: Trader Publishing Co.), 123 N W 36th St, Ste 215, Seattle, WA 98107. TEL 206-441-0191, FAX 206-441-4919, http://www.parenthood.com.

369.4 LAO
NOUM LAO/LAO YOUTH. Text in Laotian. 1979. fortn.
Published by: Lao People's Revolutionary Youth Union, Vientiane, Laos. Ed. Douangdy Inthavong. Circ: 6,000.

649 ESP ISSN 1139-7578
NUESTROS HIJOS; revista mensual sobre la familia y la educacion. Text in Spanish. 1999. m. adv. **Document type:** *Consumer.*
Published by: NUHISA, Agastia 80, Madrid, 28043, Spain. TEL 34-91-744-4550, FAX 34-91-744-4891, nhijos@editorial.com. Ed. Paz Hernandez.

NUMERACY TIME YEARS 3/4. see *EDUCATION—Teaching Methods And Curriculum*

NURSERY EDUCATION. see *EDUCATION—Teaching Methods And Curriculum*

NURSERY INDUSTRY. see *INTERIOR DESIGN AND DECORATION—Furniture And House Furnishings*

649 362.7 GBR
NURSERY TODAY. Text in English. 1997. bi-m. GBP 25; GBP 45 foreign. adv. illus.; tr.lit. back issues avail. **Document type:** *Trade.* **Description:** Covers news, new products exhibitions and everything of interest to all retailers of nursery baby products.
Published by: Lema Publishing Co., Unit 1, Queen Mary's Ave, Watford, Herts WD1 7JR, United Kingdom. TEL 44-1923-250909, FAX 44-1923-250995. Ed. Cathy Bryan. Pub. Malcolm Naish. Adv. contact Christine Contreras. B&W page GBP 645, color page GBP 945; trim 210 x 297. Circ: 3,026 (controlled).

649 GBR ISSN 0029-6422
NURSERY WORLD; devoted to professional, child care and pre-school education. Text in English. 1925. w. GBP 55 to individuals; GBP 39 to students; GBP 82 in Europe Europe and Eire; GBP 75 rest of world Surface mail; GBP 106 rest of world Air mail (effective 2001). adv. bk.rev. **Document type:** *Consumer.*
—BLDSC (6187.029500), IE, ingenta.
Published by: T S L Education, Admiral House, 66-68 E Smithfield, London, E1 9XV, United Kingdom. TEL 20-7782-3000, FAX 20-7782-3131, liz.roberts@nursery-world.com, www.nursery-world .com, http://www.nursery-world.com. Ed. Liz Roberts. Adv. contacts Helen Cox TEL 020-7782-3130, John Ladbrook. Circ: 25,061. **Dist. by:** Comag Magazine Marketing, Tavistock Rd, W Drayton, Mddx UB7 7QE, United Kingdom.

362.7 USA
NURTURING THE CHILD AS ARTIST OCCASIONAL PAPERS. Text in English. irreg., latest vol.27, 1994. USD 2.50 to non-members. **Document type:** *Monographic series.*
Published by: Vermont Academy of Arts and Sciences, 2 Buxton Ave, Middletown Springs, VT 05757. TEL 802-235-2302.

613.39 USA ISSN 1094-8309
➤ **NUTRITION FOCUS.** Text in English. 19??. bi-m. USD 36 domestic; USD 45 foreign (effective 2004). **Document type:** *Newsletter, Academic/Scholarly.* **Description:** Focuses on nutrition issues of children with special health care needs and their families.
Published by: University of Washington, Center on Human Development and Disability, PO Box 357920, Seattle, WA 98195-7920. TEL 206-543-7701, FAX 206-543-5771, chdd@u.washington.edu, http://depts.washington.edu/chdd/ucedd/CO/co_NutriFocus.html, http://depts.washington.edu/chdd/contact.html. Ed. Sharon Feucht.

649 RUS
NYANYA. Text in Russian. 1996. m.
Related titles: Online - full content ed.
Published by: Redaktsiya Zhurnala Nyanya, Armianskii Per, dom 11/2a, Moscow, 101963, Russian Federation. TEL 7-095-9258577, office@nanya.ru, http://www.nanya.ru. Ed. Dmitrii Likhanov.

301 GBR ISSN 0143-0211
O P T: ONE PARENT TIMES. Text in English. 1979. irreg. GBP 0.80 per issue (effective 1999). bk.rev. illus. **Document type:** *Newsletter.* **Description:** News of Council activities and campaigns.
Formerly: One Parent Families
Published by: National Council for One Parent Families, One Parent Families, 255 Kentish Town Rd, London, NW5 2LX, United Kingdom. TEL 44-20-74285400, FAX 44-20-74824851, info@oneparentfamilies.org.uk, http://www.oneparentfamilies.org.uk/. Circ: 2,500.

649 GBR
OFFSPRING. Text in English. m. adv. **Document type:** *Magazine, Consumer.*
Published by: Offspring Publications, 22-26 Upper Mulgrave Rd, Cheam, Surrey, SM2 7AZ, United Kingdom. TEL 44-181-330-3474, FAX 44-181408-7122.

370 CYP ISSN 0253-0910
OIKOGENEIA KAI SKOLEIO/FAMILY AND SCHOOL; dimenaio pedagogiko periodiko. Text in Greek. 1970. bi-m. CYP 15 domestic; USD 12 foreign (effective 1999). adv. bk.rev. **Description:** Discusses the theoretical and practical aspects of child development, parent-child relationships, and other relevant problems for parents and teachers.
Published by: Pancyprian School for Parents, 18 Archbishop Makarios III Ave, Flat 8, 5th Fl, Nicosia, Cyprus. TEL 357-2-454466. Ed. A D Christodoulides. Circ: 7,000.

OMVAARDAREN. see *SOCIAL SERVICES AND WELFARE*

ONCE UPON A TIME. see *PUBLISHING AND BOOK TRADE*

C

▼ new title ➤ refereed ✶ unverified ♦ full entry avail.

306.874 362.7 USA ISSN 1078-0831
OPEN ADOPTION BIRTHPARENT. Text in English. 1994. q. USD 16 (effective 1996). bk.rev. back issues avail. **Document type:** *Newsletter.* **Description:** Helps birthparents make the most of their open adoption relationship.
Published by: R-Squared Press, 2113 Arborview Blvd, Ann Arbor, MI 48103. TEL 248-930-6564, brenr@oeonline.com. Ed., R&P Brenda Romanchik. Pub. Daniel M Romanchik. Circ: 500 (paid). **Subscr. to:** 721 Hawthorne St, Royal Oak, MI 48067.

649 GBR
OPEN HOUSE. Text in English. 1894. 3/yr. free. bk.rev. **Document type:** *Newsletter.*
Formerly (until 1984, vol.24, no.10): Within Our Gates (0043-6992)
Published by: Spurgeon's Child Care, 74 Wellingborough Rd, Rushden, Northants NN10 9TY, United Kingdom. TEL 44-1933-412412, FAX 44-1933-412010. Ed. Marilyn Willis. Circ: 17,000.

028.5 SWE ISSN 0283-653X
OPSIS KALOPSIS; om barn- och ungdomskultur. Text in Swedish. 1986. q. SEK 300 in Sweden; SEK 345 other Nordic and Baltic countries; SEK 355 elsewhere. adv. bk.rev.
Indexed: ChLitAb.
Published by: Opsis Kalopsis AB, St Paulsgatan 13, Stockholm, 11846, Sweden. TEL 46-8-640-01-22, FAX 46-8-641-16-68, opsis@nostra.pp.se. Ed. Birgitta Fransson. **Subscr. to:** Datarutin, kundtjaenst, Fack 30044, Stockholm 10425, Sweden. TEL 46-8-6193538, FAX 46-8-6193535.

028.5 RUS
OSTROV SOKROVISHCH. Text in Russian. 1991. w. **Document type:** *Newspaper, Consumer.* **Description:** Newspaper written by teenage correspondents.
Address: Ul Nevel'skogo 31, Yuzhno-Sakhalinsk, Russian Federation. osy@bk.ru, http://osy.by.ru.

649 BEL ISSN 0165-6414
OUDERS VAN NU. Text in Dutch. 1967. m. EUR 33.75 (effective 2003). adv. bk.rev. illus. **Document type:** *Magazine, Consumer.* **Description:** Offers parents useful tips on child rearing.
Published by: Sanoma Magazines Belgium, Telecomlaan 5-7, Diegem, 1831, Belgium. TEL 32-2-7762211, FAX 32-2-776-2317, http://www.oudersvannu.nl, http://www.sanoma-magazines.be/HomePage.aspx?flash=1&Language=nl. Circ: 145,295 (paid).

371.192 649 USA ISSN 1083-3080
LC231
OUR CHILDREN. Text in English. 1906. 5/yr. USD 15 to members; USD 25 domestic to non-members; USD 30 in Canada & Mexico to non-members; USD 45 elsewhere to non-members (effective 2005). bk.rev. index. reprint service avail. from PQC. **Document type:** *Magazine, Consumer.* **Description:** Practical information on parenting.
Incorporates: What's Happening in Washington (0732-8362); Formerly (until vol.21, no.1, Sep. 1995): P T A Today (0195-2781); Which superseded (in 1975): P T A Magazine (0030-8331)
Related titles: Microform ed.: (from PQC); Online - full text ed.
Indexed: CIJE, FamI, HRA, SFSA.
—BLDSC (6314.304800), IE.
Published by: National Parent - Teacher Association, 541 N Fairbanks Ct, Ste 1300, Chicago, IL 60611-3396. TEL 312-670-6782, 800-307-4782, FAX 312-670-6783, info@pta.org, http://www.pta.org. Ed. Marilyn Anderson. Circ: 31,000 (paid).

790.019 370.15 USA ISSN 1055-1336
LC3991
OUR GIFTED CHILDREN. Text in English. 1991. m. USD 30; USD 40 foreign. adv. bk.rev. bibl.; charts; illus.; tr.lit. back issues avail. **Document type:** *Trade.* **Description:** Directed to those concerned with gifted children and covers psychology, schooling, work force, and leadership.
Indexed: e-psyche.
Published by: Royal Fireworks Press, PO Box 399, Unionville, NY 10988. TEL 914-726-4444, FAX 914-726-3824, rfpress@frontier.net. Ed. Michael Clay Thompson. Pub. T M Kemnitz. R&P Myrna Kaye.

649 USA
OUR KIDS ATLANTA. Text in English. 1992. m. USD 12. adv. **Document type:** *Consumer.* **Description:** Covers educational and childhood health issues for parents in the metro Atlanta area.
Published by: United Parenting Publications (Subsidiary of: Trader Publishing Co.), 4840 Roswell Rd, C-300, Atlanta, GA 30342. TEL 404-256-4477, FAX 404-256-6499, ourkids@family.com, http://www.parenthood.com. Ed. Rebekah Hall. Pub. Martha Young. adv.: B&W page USD 1,260; trim 10 x 8.25. Circ: 80,000.

649 USA
OUR KIDS AUSTIN. Text in English. m. adv. **Description:** Includes a wide variety of information for parents of newborns to teens.
Published by: United Parenting Publications (Subsidiary of: Trader Publishing Co.), 500 San Marcos, 200D, Austin, TX 78702. TEL 512-236-8417, FAX 512-236-8197, http://www.parenthood.com.

649 USA
OUR KIDS HOUSTON. Text in English. 1988. m. adv. **Description:** Lists activities and resources for children and their parents.
Published by: Branford Publishing, 8400 Blanco Rd, Ste 201, San Antonio, TX 78216-3055. TEL 713-781-7535, FAX 713-781-0405. Ed. Gail B Goodwin. Pub. Robert Stanley. R&P Nancy Diehl. Adv. contact Mary Chatoney. Circ: 75,000.

649 USA
OUR KIDS SAN ANTONIO. Text in English. 1985. m. adv. **Description:** Lists activities and resources for children and their parents.
Published by: United Parenting Publications (Subsidiary of: Trader Publishing Co.), 8400 Blanco, 201, San Antonio, TX 78216. Ed. Nancy Diehl. Pub. Robert Stanley. Adv. contact Pat Ranotowski. B&W page USD 1,430, color page USD 2,030. Circ: 42,000.

OUR WAY. see *RELIGIONS AND THEOLOGY—Judaic*

362.7 DEU ISSN 1613-1460
P F A D; Fachzeitschrift fuer das Pflege- und Adoptivkinderwesen. Text in German. 1979. q. EUR 17.50; EUR 4.70 newsstand/cover (effective 2005). adv. bk.rev. back issues avail. **Document type:** *Journal, Academic/Scholarly.*
Former titles (until 2001): Kindeswohl (0936-4463); (until 1989): Bundesverband der Pflege- und Adoptiveltern. Info (0721-8648); (until 1981): Bundesverband der Pflege- und Adoptiveltern. Informationen (0721-863X)
Indexed: DIP, IBR, IBZ.
Published by: (Bundesverband der Pflege- und Adoptiveltern e.V.), Schulz - Kirchner Verlag GmbH, Mollweg 2, Idstein, 65510, Germany. TEL 49-6126-93200, FAX 49-6126-932050, info@schulz-kirchner.de, http://www.schulz-kirchner.de/pflegefamilie/zeitschrift.htm. adv.: page EUR 805; trim 180 x 260. Circ: 5,200 (paid).

371.192 USA
P T A COMMUNICATOR. Text in English. 1922. 9/yr. USD 8. bk.rev. **Document type:** *Newsletter.* **Description:** Contains organization news, advocates for children, and informs parents.
Former titles: Texas P T A Communicator; Texas P T A; Texas Parent-Teacher (0040-4578)
Published by: Texas Congress of Parents and Teachers, 408 W 11th St, Austin, TX 78701-2199. TEL 512-476-6769, FAX 512-476-8152, txpta@txpta.org, http://www.txpta.org. Ed., R&P Joann Thurman. Pub. Zane C Chalfant. Circ: 5,000.

P T O TODAY. (Parent Teacher Organization) see *EDUCATION—School Organization And Administration*

P WIE PAPI; das Vaeter-Magazin. see *MEN'S INTERESTS*

PADRES. see *HOME ECONOMICS*

LOS PADRES AUN HACEN LA DIFERENCIA! (ESCUELA SECUNDARIA). see *EDUCATION*

649 USA
PADRES DE SESAME STREET. Text in Spanish. q. adv.
Published by: Sesame Workshop, 1 Lincoln Plaza, New York, NY 10023. TEL 212-875-6466, FAX 212-875-6113, http://www.sesameworkshop.org/. Ed. Susan Lapinski.

649 MEX ISSN 0188-0667
PADRES E HIJOS. Text in Spanish. 1980. m. adv. illus. reprints avail.
Related titles: Online - full text ed.
Published by: Editorial Televisa, Vasco de Quiroga 2000, Edif E 4o Piso, Col Santa Fe, Mexico City, DF 01210, Mexico. TEL 52-5-281-5888, FAX 52-5-281-5896, padres.e.hijos@editorial.televisa.com.mx, http://www.televisa.com.mx. Ed. Alejandra Pastrana Lopez. Circ: 105,000.

LOS PADRES HACEN LA DIFERENCIA! (ELEMENTARY EDITION). see *EDUCATION*

PAEDIATRIC AND PERINATAL DRUG THERAPY. see *PHARMACY AND PHARMACOLOGY*

649 USA ISSN 0737-5158
PAEDONOSON* ; an international journal of chronic illness and disability in childhood. Text in English. 1984. q. adv. bk.rev. abstr.; charts; illus. index.
Published by: Eterna International, Inc., PO Box 5731, Hauppauge, NY 11788-0154. Ed. Stephen B Parrish.

649 USA ISSN 1091-3181
PAGINAS PARA LOS PADRES Y MADRES. Text in Spanish. m.
Related titles: ♦ English ed.: Parent Pages. ISSN 1091-3173.
Published by: Pages Inc., 2 Navajo Ave, Manitou Springs, CO 80829-2059.

306.874 GRC ISSN 1108-622X
TO PAIDI MOU KAI EGO. Text in Greek. 1994. m. adv. **Document type:** *Magazine, Consumer.* **Description:** Contains articles and features for parents of all ages whose children are under six years of age.
Published by: Lambrakis Press SA, Panepistimiou 18, Athens, 106 72, Greece. TEL 30-1-3686-452, FAX 30-1-3686-445, dolinfo@dol.gr, http://www.dol.gr. Circ: 39,344 (paid).

649 PRT
PAIS & FILHOS. Text in Portuguese. 1991. m. EUR 2.75 newsstand/cover (effective 2005). adv. **Document type:** *Magazine, Consumer.*
Related titles: Online - full text ed.
Published by: Motorpress Lisboa, SA, Rua Policarpio Anjos No. 4, Cruz Quebrada, Dafundo 1495-742, Portugal. TEL 351-21-4154500, FAX 351-21-4154501, paisefilhos@motorpress.pt, buzine@motorpress.pt, http://www.autohoje.com/quiosque.aspx?pub=eef938bc, http://www.mpl.pt/. Ed. Joe Ferreira. Circ: 30,767 (paid).

649 618.2 BRA ISSN 0030-9567
PAIS E FILHOS; revista mensal da familia moderna. Text in Portuguese. 1968. m. USD 42. adv. bk.rev.; film rev. charts; illus. **Document type:** *Consumer.* **Description:** Contains information about pregnancy and children from birth to 12 years.
Published by: Bloch Editores S.A., Edificio Manchete, Rua do Russel, 766-804, Gloria, Rio De Janeiro, RJ 22210010, Brazil. TEL 021-5554000, FAX 021-2059998. Ed. Silvia Leal. Circ: 120,000.

369.4 PAK ISSN 0030-9605
THE PAK-SCOUT. Text in English. 1948. m. PKR 35, USD 3. adv. bk.rev. charts; illus. **Document type:** *Bulletin.*
Related titles: Urdu ed.
Published by: Pakistan Boy Scouts Association, Sumabl Park Aabpara, Muree Link Rd., Islambad, Pakistan. Ed. Mohammad Rafiq Aslam. Circ: 1,000.

PAPS; die Welt der Vaeter. see *MEN'S INTERESTS*

649 372.21 USA ISSN 1070-0552
PARENT & CHILD; the learning link between home & school. Text in English. 1993. 6/yr. (during school year). USD 9.97 (effective 2005). adv. **Document type:** *Magazine, Consumer.* **Description:** Covers learning and development from birth to six. Connects parents to their child's day in early education setting.
Related titles: Online - full text ed.: (from EBSCO Publishing, ProQuest Information & Learning).
Published by: Scholastic Inc., 557 Broadway, New York, NY 10012-0399. TEL 212-343-6100, 800-544-2917, FAX 212-343-4808, parentandchild@scholastic.com, http://www.scholastic.com/earlylearner/parentandchild/index.asp. Ed. Judsen Culbreth. Pub. Ellen Christian. adv.: B&W page USD 49,970. Circ: 1,200,000 (paid). **Subscr. to:** 2931 E McCarthy St, PO Box 3710, Jefferson City, MO 65102-9957. TEL 800-724-6527, classmags@scholastic.com.

155 USA ISSN 0887-0365
PARENT AND PRESCHOOLER NEWSLETTER; a monthly exploration of early childhood topics. Text in English, Spanish. 1986. 10/yr. USD 32 domestic; USD 52 foreign Eng/Span version (effective 2005). bk.rev. illus. index. back issues avail.; reprints avail. **Document type:** *Newsletter, Corporate.* **Description:** Explores child development, birth to 6, and family life issues for librarians, educators, and other professionals. Includes theory, practical activities, and children's health information. Lists resources for children and adults. Tpoics covered include discipline, helping children learn, and parenting skills.
Published by: North Shore Child & Family Guidance Center, Lindner Early Childhood Training Institute, 480 Old Westbury Rd, Roslyn, NY 11577-2215. TEL 516-626-1971, FAX 516-626-8043. Ed. Neala Schwartzberg. R&P Sandra Wolkoff. Adv. contact Jane E Yazdpour. Circ: 3,000 (controlled and free).

649 USA
PARENT GUIDE. Text in English. 1999. w. (Mon.). USD 36 (effective 2005). **Document type:** *Newspaper, Consumer.*
Published by: E W A Publications, 2446 E. 65th St., Brooklyn, NY 11234. TEL 718-763-7034, FAX 718-763-7035. Ed. Kevin Browne. Pub. Kenneth Browne. Adv. contact Adrienne Knoll. Circ: 242,000 (paid).

305.23 USA ISSN 1093-0442
HQ755.8
PARENT NEWS (CHAMPAIGN). Text in English. 1995. bi-m. **Document type:** *Magazine.* **Description:** Contains news, information, and resources for parents and those who work with parents.
Media: Online - full content.
Published by: (National Parent Information Network), E C A P Collaborative (Subsidiary of: University of Illinois at Urbana-Champaign, Children's Research Center), 51 Gerty Dr, Champaign, IL 61820-7469. TEL 217-333-1386, 877-275-3227, FAX 217-333-3767, ecap@uiuc.edu, http://ecap.crc.uiuc.edu/. Ed. Anne Robertson.

C

649 USA ISSN 1091-3173
PARENT PAGES. Text in English. 1990. m. USD 88 (effective 2003). bk.rev. **Document type:** *Newsletter.* **Description:** Newsletter for parents of young children. Includes latest information on positive child rearing practices; parents are involved with children through art, cooking and reading. Safety and Health Concerns are also covered.
Related titles: ♦ Spanish ed.: Paginas para los Padres y Madres. ISSN 1091-3181.
Published by: Pages Inc., 2 Navajo Ave, Manitou Springs, CO 80829-2059. TEL 719-632-0916, FAX 719-632-9576, ednaw@parentpagesnews.com, http://www.parentpagesnews.com. R&P Edna Wallace. Circ: 35,000 (paid).

649 USA
PARENT PAPER. Text in English. m. adv. **Description:** News, ideas, and events for families in Northern New Jersey and Rockland County.
Published by: Record, 150 River St, Hackensack, NJ 07601. TEL 973-569-7720, FAX 973-569-7725, info@parentpaper.com, http://www.parentpaper.com. Ed. Mary Vallo. Adv. contact Natalie Jay.

649 GBR
PARENT TALK. Text in English. 1997. m. adv. **Document type:** *Magazine, Consumer.* **Description:** Covers all items of interest involved in raising and participating within a family.
Address: Cricket St Thomas, Chard, Somerset, TA20 4EN, United Kingdom. TEL 44-1460-30500, FAX 44-1460-30681.

649 USA
PARENT.TEEN; the magazine for bay area families with teens. Text in English. 1997. m.
Published by: Parents' Press, 1454 Sixth St, Berkeley, CA 94710-1431. TEL 510-524-1602, FAX 510-524-0912, parentsprs@aol.com, http://members.aol.com/parentsprs/index.html. Ed. Dixie M Jordan. Circ: 80,000.

649 USA ISSN 0896-1468
PARENTGUIDE NEWS. Text in English. 1984. m. USD 11.90. adv. **Document type:** *Newspaper.* **Description:** Parenting newspaper for New York and New Jersey parents of children under 12 years of age.
Published by: Parents Guide Network, Corp., 419 Park Ave S, 13th Fl, New York, NY 10016. TEL 212-213-8840. Ed. Leslie Elgort. Pub. Steve Elgort. Circ: 200,000.

649 USA ISSN 0890-247X
PARENTING. Text in English. 1987. 11/yr. USD 12 domestic; USD 22 in Canada; USD 3.99 per issue (effective 2005). adv. bk.rev.; film rev. illus. index. back issues avail.; reprint service avail. from PSC. **Document type:** *Magazine, Consumer.* **Description:** Covers all issues of raising children, from newborns to adolescence. Reports on day-to-day topics such as diet, discipline, health, and education and on family activities, food, travel, beauty, and self-esteem in girls.
Related titles: Braille ed.; Online - full text ed.: (from EBSCO Publishing, Gale Group, H.W. Wilson, LexisNexis, O C L C Online Computer Library Center, Inc., ProQuest Information & Learning); ♦ Supplement(s): Sesame Street. ISSN 0049-0253; Sesame Street Parent's Guide.
Indexed: MagInd, RGAb, RGPR.
—CCC.
Published by: Time Publishing Ventures (Subsidiary of: Time - Warner Inc.), 1325 Ave of the Americas, 27th Fl, New York, NY 10019. TEL 212-522-8989, FAX 212-522-8699, http://www.parenting.com/parenting. Ed. Janet Chan. adv.: B&W page USD 68,860, color page USD 86,070; trim 10 x 7.38. Circ: 1,300,000 (paid and controlled). **Subscr. to:** PO Box 56861, Boulder, CO 80323.

649.4 IND
PARENTING. Text in English. 1992. m. INR 35 newsstand/cover. **Document type:** *Consumer.*
Published by: First City Publications P. Ltd., A 602 Som Vihar, New Delhi, 110 022, India. TEL 91-11-6169111, FAX 91-11-6103740. Ed., Pub. Bharat Kapur. adv.: B&W page INR 35,000, color page INR 45,000; trim 242 x 178.

PARENTING (MAHWAH); science and practice. see *SOCIOLOGY*

155.4 649 USA
PARENTING (ORANGE COUNTY). Text in English. 1986. m. free at selected locations. adv. **Document type:** *Consumer.* **Description:** Aims to be a "city magazine" for informed Orange County parents.
Published by: United Parenting Publications (Subsidiary of: Trader Publishing Co.), 1920 E Katella Ave K, Orange, CA 92867. TEL 714-771-7454, FAX 714-771-5852, http://orangecounty.parenthood.com/aboutus.html?IDENTIFIER=CA%20-%20Orange%20County&segid=129, http://www.parenthood.com. Ed., R&P Marilyn Martinez. Pub. Kay Mount. Circ: 80,000.

649 GBR
THE PARENTING EDUCATION & SUPPORT FORUM NEWS BULLETIN. Text in English. 1995. bi-m. GBP 15 membership (effective 2001). bk.rev. 8 p./no. 2 cols./p.; back issues avail. **Document type:** *Newsletter.* **Description:** Provides a focal point for information, debate and collaboration in the field of parenting education and support. Aims to heighten awareness and create a professional network to promote parenting.
Formerly (until 1999): The Parenting Forum Newsletter (1361-1569)
Published by: Parenting Education & Support Forum, Unit 431, Highgate Studios, 53-79 Highgate Road, London, NW5 1TL, United Kingdom. info.pest@dial.pipex.com. Pub. Rose Grey. Circ: 1,000.

649.155 USA
PARENTING FOR HIGH POTENTIAL. Text in English. 1996. q. USD 25 membership (effective 2003). adv. **Document type:** *Consumer.* **Description:** For parents and teachers who want to help develop the gifts and talents that will enable all children to reach their full potential.
Indexed: e-psyche.
Published by: National Association for Gifted Children, 1707 L St, N W, Ste 550, Washington, DC 20036-4201. TEL 202-785-4268, FAX 202-785-4248, nagc@nagc.org, http://www.nagc.org/Publications/Parenting/. Ed. Donald Treffinger. Adv. contact Cora Powers. page USD 1,500; 7.1875 x 10.

PARENTING THE 90S; from toddlers to teens. see *HOME ECONOMICS*

PARENTING TRAVEL. see *TRAVEL AND TOURISM*

649 USA
PARENTING YOUR NEW BABY. Text in English. 1999. irreg. **Document type:** *Consumer.*
Published by: Time Publishing Ventures (Subsidiary of: Time - Warner Inc.), 1325 Ave of the Americas, 27th Fl, New York, NY 10019. TEL 212-522-8989, FAX 212-522-8750, http://www.pathfinder.com/parenttime/parenting.

PARENTING'S HEALTHY PREGNANCY. see *MEDICAL SCIENCES—Obstetrics And Gynecology*

PARENTLIFE; a Christian parenting magazine. see *RELIGIONS AND THEOLOGY—Protestant*

649 FRA ISSN 0553-2159
HQ768
PARENTS. Text in French. 1969. m. EUR 15 (effective 2005). **Document type:** *Magazine, Consumer.*
Related titles: ♦ Russian ed.: Parents. ISSN 1560-3202.
Indexed: CLFP, PdeR, RGAb.
Published by: Hachette Filipacchi Medias S.A. (Subsidiary of: Lagardere Media), 149 rue Anatole France, Levallois-Perret, Cedex 92300, France. TEL 33-1-41347330, FAX 33-1-41347123. Circ: 450,000 (paid).

649 USA ISSN 1083-6373
HQ768
PARENTS; on rearing children from crib to college. Text in English. 1926. m. USD 15.98; USD 4 newsstand/cover (effective 2004). adv. bk.rev. illus. index. reprints avail. **Document type:** *Magazine, Consumer.* **Description:** Emphasizes family formation and growth. Focuses on the needs and concerns of today's expectant mother.
Former titles (until 1993): Parents' Magazine (1047-8574); (until 1985): Parents (0195-0967); (until 1978): Parents' Magazine (0161-4193); (until 1977): Parents' Magazine and Better Homemaking; Parents' Magazine and Better Family Living (0031-191X); Incorporates (1976-1981): Parents Home (0278-1409); Which was formerly (until 19??): Handy Andy Magazine (0162-6663)
Related titles: CD-ROM ed.: (from ProQuest Information & Learning); Online - full text ed.: (from H.W. Wilson, O C L C Online Computer Library Center, Inc., ProQuest Information & Learning).
Indexed: ARG, Acal, BRI, CBRI, CHNI, CINAHL, Consl, HlthInd, IHTDI, MagInd, PMR, PdeR, RGAb, RGPR, TOM, WBA.
Published by: Gruner + Jahr U.S.A. Publishing (Subsidiary of: Gruner und Jahr AG & Co.), 375 Lexington Ave, New York, NY 10017. TEL 212-499-2000, 800-727-3682, FAX 212-499-2097, http://www.parents.com. Ed. Sally Lee. Pub. Jan Studin. Adv. contact Jill Herrmann. Circ: 2,200,000 (paid and controlled). **Subscr. to:** PO Box 3042, Harlan, IA 51537-0207. TEL 515-244-1832, 800-727-3682, FAX 515-246-1020, pmmcustserv@cdsfulfillment.com.

649 GBR ISSN 0260-7514
PARENTS; your pregnancy, baby, toddler and child. Text in English. 1976. m. GBP 21; GBP 1.80 newsstand/cover (effective 1999). adv. **Document type:** *Magazine, Consumer.* **Description:** Includes advice and information from pregnancy, through the baby stage and on to the toddler years. Helps you get the most from the first years of parenthood.
Indexed: RGAb.
—CCC.
Published by: Emap Elan Ltd. (Subsidiary of: Emap Consumer Media), Endeavour House, 189 Shaftesbury Ave, London, WC2H 8JG, United Kingdom. TEL 44-207-437-9011, FAX 44-207-208-3709, http://www.emap.com. Ed. Ruth Beattie. Pub. Barbara Patterson. Adv. contact Julie Hughes. **Subscr. to:** Tower Publishing Services Ltd., Tower House, Sovereign Park, Market Harborough, Leics LE16 9EF, United Kingdom. TEL 44-1858-435339, FAX 44-1858-432164. **Dist. by:** Frontline Ltd., Unit 6, Stockwell Centre, Stephenson Way, Crawley, W Sussex RH10 1TN, United Kingdom. TEL 44-1293-415000, FAX 44-1293-415009.

649 RUS ISSN 1560-3202
PARENTS. Text in Russian. 1998. m. **Document type:** *Magazine, Consumer.*
Related titles: ♦ French ed.: Parents. ISSN 0553-2159.
Published by: Hachette Filipacchi, ul Myasnitskaya, d 35, ofis 743, Moscow, 101959, Russian Federation. TEL 7-095-9332256.

PARENTS AND CHILDREN TOGETHER ONLINE. see *CHILDREN AND YOUTH—For*

649 USA
PARENTS BABY. (Avail. in 7 age-specific editions.) Text in English. 1986. 2/yr. USD 4.99 newsstand/cover (effective 2005). adv. illus. **Document type:** *Magazine, Consumer.* **Description:** Offers mothers and fathers of infants advice on caring for their new baby.
Formerly: Parents Baby Care
Published by: Gruner + Jahr U.S.A. Publishing (Subsidiary of: Gruner und Jahr AG & Co.), 375 Lexington Ave, New York, NY 10017. TEL 212-499-2000, 800-727-3682, FAX 212-499-2038, corpcomm@gjusa.com, http://gjusa.com/magazines/expecting_and_baby.html, http://www.gjusa.com. Eds. Jane Traulsen, Sally Lee, Sally Lee. Pub., Adv. contact Jan Studin. color page USD 28,800, B&W page USD 21,600. Circ: 325,000 (controlled).

649 USA
PARENTS' CHOICE (WABAN)✶ ; a review of children's media. Text in English. 1978. bi-m. USD 15 to members. bk.rev.; film rev.; software rev.; video rev. **Document type:** *Consumer.* **Description:** Provides parents with information to help their children learn in and out of school, including reviews of children's books, videos, toys, games, computer products, TV and more.
Formerly (until 1979): It's the Parents' Choice (0161-8164)
Media: Online - full text. **Related titles:** Print ed.: suspended 1997.
Indexed: BRI.
Published by: Parents' Choice Foundation, 201 W. Padonia Rd., Ste. 303, Luthvle Timon, MD 21093-2112. TEL 617-965-5913, FAX 617-965-4516, pchoice@erols.com, dianahg@erols.com, http://www.ctw.org. Ed. Diana Huss Green. R&P Ann Wade.

790.019 CHN ISSN 1003-2983
PARENTS' DIGEST/FUMU WENZHAI. Text in Chinese. 1985. bi-m. CNY 15, USD 48. adv. bk.rev. **Document type:** *Abstract/Index.*
Formerly (until Jan. 1994): Chinese Child Development - Zhongguo Ertong Fazhan
Published by: Zhongguo Ertong Fazhan Zhongxin/Chinese Child Development Center, Guanyuan, Beijing, 100035, China. TEL 603-1897, FAX 602-4579. Ed. Li Shushen.

649 USA
THE PARENTS' JOURNAL. Text in English. m. illus. **Document type:** *Consumer.* **Description:** Aims to inform parents about their children and how to help them in their educational and emotional development.
Related titles: Audio cassette/tape ed.; Online - full text ed.
Published by: Parents' Journal, PO Box 20306, Charleston, SC 29413. TEL 843-881-2142, 800-684-9817, FAX 843-881-1099, editor@parentsjournal.com, http://www.parentsjournal.org. Pub. Tara Stewart.

PARENTS MAKE THE DIFFERENCE!; practical ideas for parents to help their children. see *EDUCATION*

649.124 371.1 USA ISSN 1089-3075
PARENTS MAKE THE DIFFERENCE! (SCHOOL READINESS EDITION); practical ideas for parents to help their children. Text in English. 1996. m. (Sep.-May). looseleaf. USD 97 (effective 2003). 4 p./no. 3 cols./p.; back issues avail. **Document type:** *Newsletter.* **Description:** Ideas for parents of preschool aged children to help their children do better in school.
Published by: Parent Institute, PO Box 7474, Fairfax, VA 22039-7474. TEL 703-323-9170, 800-756-5525, FAX 703-323-9173, http://www.parent-institute.com. Ed. Pat Hodgdon. Pub. John H Wherry.

649 USA
PARENTS' MONTHLY. Text in English. 1982. m. free newsstand/cover (effective 2001). adv. bk.rev.; software rev.; video rev. back issues avail. **Document type:** *Newspaper.* **Description:** For parents with young children.
Published by: United Parenting Publications (Subsidiary of: Trader Publishing Co.), 2020 Hurley Way, Sacramento, CA 95825. TEL 916-921-4370, FAX 916-921-4374. adv.: page USD 1,780; trim 12.25 x 9.75. Circ: 55,000.

▼ new title ➤ refereed ✶ unverified ♦ full entry avail.

362.7 GBR ISSN 1362-5551
PARENTS NEWS. Text in English. 1993. 11/yr. GBP 14 domestic; GBP 21 foreign (effective 2000). adv. bk.rev. **Document type:** *Consumer.*
Address: 10 The Manor Dr, Worcester Park, Surrey KT4 7LG, United Kingdom. TEL 44-20-8337-6337, FAX 44-20-8715-2842, info@parents-news.co.uk, http://www.parents-news.co.uk. Ed. Penny McCarthy. Adv. contact Fergus McCarthy. page GBP 1,514; trim 370 x 270. Circ: 157,000 (controlled).

PARENTS PREGNANCY. see *MEDICAL SCIENCES—Obstetrics And Gynecology*

649 USA ISSN 0889-8863
PARENTS' PRESS. Text in English. 1980. m. USD 15. adv. **Document type:** *Consumer.* **Description:** Covers health, education, child development & other parenting issues for families with children ages 0-18 in the San Francisco Bay area.
Address: 1454 Sixth St, Berkeley, CA 94710-1431. TEL 510-524-1602, FAX 510-524-0912, parentsprs@aol.com, http://www.parentspress.com. Ed., Pub., R&P Dixie M Jordan. Adv. contact Dolores Brewster. Circ: 75,000 (controlled).

PARENTS STILL MAKE THE DIFFERENCE! (HIGH SCHOOL EDITION); practical ideas for parents to help their children. see *EDUCATION*

649.124 371.1 USA ISSN 1071-5118
PARENTS STILL MAKE THE DIFFERENCE! (MIDDLE SCHOOL EDITION); practical ideas for parents to help their children. Text in English. 1993. m. (Sep.-May). looseleaf. USD 97 (effective 2003). 4 p./no. 3 cols./p.; back issues avail. **Document type:** *Newsletter.* **Description:** Ideas for parents of children in grades 6 through 9 to help their children do better in school.
Related titles: Online - full text ed.: ISSN 1523-1283.
Published by: Parent Institute, PO Box 7474, Fairfax, VA 22039-7474. TEL 703-323-9170, 800-756-5525, FAX 703-323-9173, http://www.parent-institute.com/nl/login.htm. Ed. Pat Hodgdon. Pub. John H Wherry.

C

028.5 USA
PARTICIPATING IN EDUCATION. Text in English. 1991. 8/yr. adv. **Description:** Written mainly by and for students in grades 1-8 in the Minneapolis/St.Paul area of Minnesota.
Published by: Blue Sun Inc., PO Box 263, Mound, MN 55364. TEL 612-446-9086, FAX 612-446-1458. Ed. Tami Crea.

369.4 FIN ISSN 0085-4794
PARTIOJOHTAJA/SCOUTLEDAREN. Text in Finnish. 1927. 6/yr. EUR 24 (effective 2005). adv. **Document type:** *Magazine, Consumer.*
Incorporates (1943-1972): Johtajapolku; Which was formed by the merger of (1936-1943): Partiopolku; (1934-1943): S P T L: n Johtajalehti
Published by: Suomen Partiolaiset/Guides and Scouts of Finland, Kylaenvanhimmantie 29, Helsinki, 00640, Finland. TEL 358-9-25331100, FAX 358-9-25331160, info@sp.partio.fi, http://www.partio.fi. Ed. Suvi Erjanti. Circ: 76,929.

362.7 613.9 USA
PASSAGES (WASHINGTON, D.C.) (ONLINE EDITION). Text in English, French, Spanish. 1978-2000; N.S. 2000 (Sep.). 3/yr. bk.rev.; film rev. charts; illus.; stat. back issues avail. **Document type:** *Newsletter.* **Description:** Includes summaries of projects on adolescent reproductive health.
Formerly: Passages (Washington, D.C.) (Print Edition) (1071-3158)
Media: Online - full content.
Published by: Advocates for Youth, 2000 M St NW, Ste 750, Washington, DC 20036. TEL 202-419-3420, FAX 202-419-1448, questions@advocatesforyouth.org, http://www.advocatesforyouth.org/publications/passages/passages.htm.

155.5 NLD ISSN 1382-3272
PEDAGOGIEK IN PRAKTIJK. Text in Dutch. 1995. q. EUR 28 to individuals; EUR 39 to institutions; EUR 23.50 to students (effective 2005). adv. bk.rev. index. back issues avail. **Document type:** *Academic/Scholarly.* **Description:** Gives information relating to the care of young adults.
Incorporates (1995-2001): J (1566-5666); Which was formerly (until 2000): T I A Z (1381-3307)
—KNAW.
Published by: Uitgeverij S W P, Postbus 257, Amsterdam, 1000 AG, Netherlands. TEL 31-20-3307200, FAX 31-20-3308040, swp@swpbook.com, http://pipm.swphost.com/, http://www.swpbook.com. Ed. Bas Levering. Pub. Paul Roosenstein. Circ: 800 (paid).

028.5 RUS
PEDAGOGIKA DETSTVA. Text in Russian. m. **Description:** Focuses on activities for pre-school children.
Published by: Izdatel'skii Dom Karapuz, Izmailovskoe shosse 48a, Moscow, 105318, Russian Federation. TEL 7-095-9182810, http://www.karapuz.com.

PEDIATRICS FOR PARENTS; the newsletter for anyone who cares for a child. see *MEDICAL SCIENCES—Pediatrics*

370 649 USA
PEER HEALTH NEWS. Text in English. 2000. q. free. back issues avail. **Document type:** *Newsletter, Academic/Scholarly.* **Description:** Keeps peer educators and program coordinators in touch with the latest in innovative peer education programming.
Media: E-mail. **Related titles:** Online - full content ed.
Published by: Advocates for Youth, 2000 M St NW, Ste 750, Washington, DC 20036. TEL 202-419-3420, FAX 202-419-1448, empower@advocatesforyouth.org, questions@advocatesforyouth.org, http://www.advocatesforyouth.org/publications/freepubs_type.htm#phn.

PHILOSOPHY FOR CHILDREN NEWSLETTER. see *PHILOSOPHY*

PIED PIPER. see *LAW—Family And Matrimonial Law*

155.649 USA ISSN 1065-2671
PIERCE COUNTY PARENT✶ ; a monthly guide for parents. Text in English. 1985. m. USD 15. adv. bk.rev.; film rev. **Document type:** *Consumer.* **Description:** For parents, educators, and child-care providers. Provides information on what to do and where to go with children.
Formerly: Parent Connection
Published by: Northwest Parent Publishing, Inc. (Portland), 123 NW 36th St., Ste. 215, Seattle, WA 98107-4959. Ed. Susan Garrett. Adv. contact Alayne Sulkin. Circ: 15,000.

362.7 USA
PITTSBURGH PARENT; Pittsburgh's preference for parenting news. Text in English. 1988. m. USD 25 (effective 2003). adv. bk.rev.; video rev. **Document type:** *Magazine, Consumer.* **Description:** Covers health, education, the arts and activities pertaining to parents and children.
Formerly: Pittsburgh's Child
Published by: Honey Hill Publishing, Inc., PO Box 374, Bakerstown, PA 15007. TEL 724-443-1891, FAX 724-443-1877, pgparent@nauticom.net, http://www.pittsburghparent.com/index.asp. Ed., R&P Patricia Poshard. Pub. Marilyn Honeywill. Adv. contact Debbie Iszauk. B&W page USD 1,600; trim 12.38 x 10. Circ: 48,000.

362.7 BRA
PIXOTE; revista sobre meninos e meninas. Text in Portuguese. 1993. BRL 100 per issue.
Published by: Centro de Articulacao de Populacoes Marginalizadas, Nucleo de Comunicacao, Rua da Lapa 200-809, Centro, Rio De Janeiro, RJ 20021, Brazil. TEL 55-21-2246771, FAX 55-21-2326249. Circ: 3,000.

790.019 USA ISSN 1062-6956
PLAY. Text in English. 1992. bi-m. USD 12; USD 3.95 newsstand/cover. adv. **Document type:** *Consumer.* **Description:** Brings together a vast array of information and entertainment for today's parent; bridges the gap of learning and playing.
Published by: Milor Entertainment Group, 2650 North Military Trail, Fountain Sq II Bldg., Ste 140, Boca Raton, FL 33431. TEL 561-893-6868, FAX 561-893-6867, comments@milor.com, http://www.milor.com. Ed. Roy Parkhurst. Adv. contact Lori B Fagien. B&W page USD 3,500, color page USD 4,500; trim 8.375 x 11.125. Circ: 100,000.

PLAY AND FOLKLORE. see *FOLKLORE*

649 362.7 CAN ISSN 0835-4014
PLAY AND PARENTING CONNECTIONS✶ . Text in English. 1978. q. USD 25. adv. bk.rev. back issues avail. **Description:** For and about family resource programs and toy libraries across Canada.
Published by: Canada Association of Toy Libraries and Parent Resource Centres, c/o Canadian Association of Family Resourse Programs, 30 Rosemont Ave., Ste. 101, Ottawa, ON K1Y 1P4, Canada. TEL 613-728-3307, FAX 613-729-5421. Circ: 500.

649 790 AUS
PLAYGROUPER MAGAZINE. Text in English. 1974. q. AUD 25. adv. bk.rev. back issues avail. **Document type:** *Consumer.* **Description:** Covers playgroup news, parenting, play ideas. community group interests, health and safety issues.
Published by: Victorian Playgroup Association Inc., 346 Albert St, Brunswick, VIC 3056, Australia. TEL 61-3-93973499, FAX 61-3-93973047. Ed., R&P, Adv. contact Helen Schwab. B&W page AUD 495; 205 x 290. Circ: 27,000.

649 790 AUS
PLAYGROUPER NEWSLETTER. Text in English. 1989. q. adv. **Document type:** *Newsletter.* **Description:** Covers playgroup news, parenting, play ideas, community group interests, health and safety issues. Alternates with Playgrouper Magazine.
Published by: Victorian Playgroup Association Inc., 346 Albert St, Brunswick, VIC 3056, Australia. TEL 61-3-93973499, FAX 61-3-93973047. Adv. contact Helen Schwab.

790.019 AUS ISSN 1038-2852
PLAYTIMES. Text in English. 1992. q. adv. bk.rev.; music rev.; software rev. illus. 16 p./no.; back issues avail. **Document type:** *Newspaper.* **Description:** Aimed at young families with children under 5 yrs. Specifically about and for our playgroup members.
Formerly (until Apr. 1992): Playgroup (0312-3898)
Published by: Playgroup Association of Queensland, 396 Milton Rd, Auchenflower, QLD 4066, Australia. TEL 61-7-3368-2622, FAX 61-7-3367-2522, info@playgroupqld.com.au. Ed., Adv. contact Robyn Devine. Pub., R&P Mark Brook. B&W page AUD 924, color page AUD 1,155; trim 374 x 260. Circ: 20,000 (controlled).

649 250 USA ISSN 1525-3864
PLUGGED IN (COLORADO SPRINGS). Text in English. 1990. m. USD 20 suggested donation (effective 2005). illus. **Document type:** *Newsletter, Consumer.* **Description:** Informs adults of popular culture, specifically as it relates to media messages being consumed by children and teens.
Formerly (until 1996): Focus on the Family Parental Guidance
Published by: Focus on the Family, Inc., 8605 Explorer Dr, Colorado Springs, CO 80920-1051. TEL 719-531-3400, 800-232-6459, FAX 719-531-3424, pluggedin@family.org, http://www.pluggedinonline.com/, http://www.family.org. Ed. Bob Smithouser. Pub. Dr. James C Dobson. R&P Christine McDonald. Circ: 44,000.

790.019 POL ISSN 1426-4609
PO LEKCJACH; kwartalnik poswiecony problemom czasu wolnego dzieci i mlodziezy. Text in Polish. 1993. q.
Published by: Centrum Mlodziezy im. Dr. Henryka Jordana, Ul Krowoderska 8, Krakow, 31142, Poland. TEL 48-12-4300025 ext 42, sekr_cm@bci.krakow.pl. Ed. Jolanta Szczucka-Bus.

POD WIATR; spoleczno-kulturalne czasopismo mlodziezowe. see *CHILDREN AND YOUTH—For*

028.5 RUS
POKOLENIE. Text in Russian. 1922. 4/yr. **Document type:** *Newspaper, Consumer.*
Address: Ul Brestskaya 6, Dom Pechati 4-i, Orel, 302000, Russian Federation. TEL 7-8622-63483, 7-8622-64683, pokolen@orel1.icn.gov.ru. Ed. A A Mironenko. Circ: 12,000.

PONY BASEBALL - SOFTBALL EXPRESS. see *SPORTS AND GAMES—Ball Games*

649 USA ISSN 1065-2663
PORTLAND PARENT. Text in English. 1991. m. adv. bk.rev. **Document type:** *Newspaper.* **Description:** Provides a reliable source of information about activities of interest to parents in the Portland area.
Published by: United Parenting Publications (Subsidiary of: Trader Publishing Co.), 119 SE Main St. Suite 204B, Portland, OR 97214. TEL 971-244-0735, FAX 971-244-0736, http://www.portland.parenthood.com, http://www.parenthood.com. Ed. Karen Matthee. Adv. contact Gary Marschke. B&W page USD 1,530. Circ: 40,000.

362.7 CAN ISSN 1206-7989
POST-ADOPTION HELPER; support for parents, after the adoption. Text in English. 1997. q. CND 28; USD 28 in United States; USD 42 elsewhere (effective 2000). adv. bk.rev. bibl.; illus. back issues avail. **Document type:** *Consumer.* **Description:** Presents medical issues, behaviour management, family and society, culture and heritage, search and reunion and provides resources.
Published by: Helper Publishing, 185 Panoramic Dr, Sault Ste Marie, ON P6B 6E3, Canada. FAX 705-945-1170, helper@helping.com, http://www.helping.com/family/pa/pa.html. Ed. Jennifer Smart. Pub. Mr. Robin Hilborn. Circ: 500 (paid).

649 GBR ISSN 0954-9846
PRACTICAL PARENTING. Text in English. 1987. m. GBP 27.90 domestic; USD 80.80 in United States (effective 2004). adv. **Document type:** *Magazine, Consumer.* **Description:** Provides interactive practical information, value for money, reader appeal, and in-depth coverage of all parenting issues.
Incorporates (1994-2001): Practical Parenting's Complete Guide to Pregnancy
—BLDSC (6595.315000).
Published by: I P C SouthBank (Subsidiary of: I P C Media Ltd.), Kings Reach Tower, Stamford St, London, SE1 9LS, United Kingdom. TEL 44-161-8722144, http://www.ipcmedia.com/. Ed. Jayne Marsden TEL 44-20-72615058. Pub. Tracey Engel TEL 44-20-72615888. adv.: color page GBP 4,500. Circ: 76,554 (paid). **Subscr. to:** I P C Media Ltd., Perrymount Rd, Haywards Heath RH16 3DA, United Kingdom. TEL 44-1444-475675, FAX 44-1444-445599, ipcsubs@qss-uk.com. **Dist. by:** MarketForce UK Ltd, 247 Tottenham Court Rd, London, Middx W1T 7AU, United Kingdom. TEL 44-207-2615199, FAX 44-207-2617341.

649 AUS ISSN 1442-5459
PRACTICAL PARENTING AUSTRALIA. Text in English. 1995. m. AUD 50 domestic; AUD 65 in New Zealand; AUD 125.95 elsewhere; AUD 5.60 newsstand/cover (effective 2004). adv. **Document type:** *Magazine, Consumer.* **Description:** Contains advice and easy-to-digest information on everything from conception to birth, baby and beyond.
Formerly (until 1998): Practical Parenting (1323-5702)

Published by: A C P Publishing Pty. Ltd., 54-58 Park St, Sydney, NSW 1028, Australia. TEL 61-2-9282-8000, FAX 61-2-9267-4361, info@acp.com.au, http://www.acp.com.au. Ed. Amanda Finch. Adv. contact Lynette Rochford. Circ: 23,543 (paid and controlled).

PRACTITIONERS' CHILD LAW BULLETIN. see *LAW—Family And Matrimonial Law*

PRAXIS DER PSYCHOMOTORIK; Zeitschrift fuer Bewegungserziehung. see *PHYSICAL FITNESS AND HYGIENE*

PRAXIS SPIEL UND GRUPPE. see *EDUCATION*

PREGNANCY & BIRTH. see *MEDICAL SCIENCES—Obstetrics And Gynecology*

THE PREGNANCY BOOK. see *MEDICAL SCIENCES—Obstetrics And Gynecology*

PRESCHOOLERS AT CHURCH AND HOME. see *RELIGIONS AND THEOLOGY—Protestant*

THE PREVENTION RESEARCHER. see *SOCIAL SERVICES AND WELFARE*

649 USA
PREVENTION UPDATE; a publication devoted to preventing the exploitation of children. Text in English. 1985. q.
Published by: Committee For Children, 568 First Ave. South, Ste 600, Seattle, WA 98104-2804. TEL 206-343-1223, 800-634-4449, FAX 206-438-6765, http://www.cfchildren.org/PUs.html. Ed. Lisa Walls. Circ: 17,000.

649 GBR ISSN 1362-8607
PRIMA BABY. Text in English. 1996. m. GBP 14.99; GBP 2.50 newsstand/cover (effective 2004). adv. **Document type:** *Magazine, Consumer.* **Description:** Covers all aspects of life for the baby and mother during the first few years.
—CCC.
Published by: National Magazine Company Ltd., National Magazine House, 72 Broadwick St, London, W1F 9EP, United Kingdom. TEL 44-20-74395000, FAX 44-20-74376886, katie.williamson@natmags.co.uk, http://www.primababy.co.uk, http://www.natmags.co.uk. Ed. Julia Goodwin. Pub. Jessica Burley. adv.: page GBP 6,000. Circ: 48,137 (paid and controlled).

649.1 USA
PRIMEROS 12 MESES. Text in Spanish. s-a. Dist. with The American Baby Basket for New Parents through participating hospitals only. adv. **Document type:** *Magazine, Consumer.*
Published by: Meredith Corp., 1716 Locust St, Des Moines, IA 50309-3023. TEL 515-284-3000, FAX 515-284-3657, http://www.americanbaby.com, http://www.meredith.com.

649 USA
PRIORITY PARENTING✶. Text in English. 1987. m. USD 14. adv. bk.rev. **Document type:** *Newsletter.* **Description:** Encourages parents to raise their children by following basic human nature and instinct.
Published by: Priority Parenting Plus, 830 S Union St, Warsaw, IN 46580-4701. TEL 219-268-1415. Ed. Tamra Orr. Circ: 200 (paid).

790.019 LKA
PRIYAVI. Text in Singhalese. 1976. w. **Description:** Covers teenage pop scene.
Address: 5 Gunasena Mawatha, Colombo, 12, Sri Lanka. TEL 1-23882. Ed. W Waturegama. Circ: 37,000.

PROFESSIONALISM IN PRACTICE: THE P A T JOURNAL. see *EDUCATION*

305.23 CAN ISSN 1208-9109
HQ792.C3
THE PROGRESS OF CANADA'S CHILDREN. Variant title: Canada's Children. Text in English. 1996. a. CND 20 (effective 2004).
Related titles: French ed.: Progres des Enfants au Canada. ISSN 1208-9117.
Published by: Canadian Council on Social Development, 309 Cooper St, 5th Fl, Ottawa, ON K2P 0G5, Canada. TEL 613-236-8977, FAX 613-236-2750, council@ccsd.ca, http://www.ccsd.ca. **Dist. by:** Renouf Books, 1-5369 Canotek Rd, Ottawa, ON K1J 9J3, Canada. TEL 613-745-2665, 888-551-7470, FAX 613-745-7660, order.dept@renoufbooks.com.

THE PROGRESS OF NATIONS; the nations of the world ranked according to their achievements in health, nutrition, education, family planning, and progress for women. see *SOCIAL SERVICES AND WELFARE*

PROTECTING CHILDREN. see *SOCIAL SERVICES AND WELFARE*

PROUD PARENTING. see *SOCIOLOGY*

PSYCHOLOGIE IN ERZIEHUNG UND UNTERRICHT; Organ der Deutschen Gesellschaft fuer Psychologie. see *EDUCATION*

PUERICULTURA MARKET; revista profesional de los productos para bebes y la infancia. see *INTERIOR DESIGN AND DECORATION—Furniture And House Furnishings*

649 USA
PUGET SOUND PARENT. Text in English. m.
Published by: United Parenting Publications (Subsidiary of: Trader Publishing Co.), 123 N W 36th St, Ste 215, Seattle, WA 98107. TEL 206-441-0191, FAX 206-441-4919, http://www.parenthood.com.

028.5 RUS
PYAT' S PLYUSOM; internet-zhurnal aktivnogo pokoleniya. Text in Russian. 2000. w. **Document type:** *Journal, Consumer.*
Media: Online - full content.
Address: info@5plus.ru, http://www.5plus.ru.

369.4 CHN ISSN 1004-3780
QINGNIAN TANSUO/YOUTH STUDIES. Text in Chinese. 1983. bi-m. CNY 3.50 newsstand/cover. **Description:** Covers youth culture, youth studies, youth counselling, youth and society, university students and more.
Related titles: Online - full text ed.: (from East View Information Services).
Published by: Guangzhou Shi Gongqingtuan Tuanxiao, Shibei Gangding, Guangzhou, Guangdong 510360, China. TEL 86-20-8551-6234, FAX 86-20-8551-6817. Ed. Ang Liu. Circ: 5,000.

649 CHN ISSN 1009-7449
QINGSHAONIAN DAOKAN/GUIDE TO JUVENILE. Text in Chinese. 1978. bi-m. CNY 60 (effective 2004). 64 p./no.; **Document type:** *Journal, Academic/Scholarly.*
Former titles (until 2000): Qingshaonian Yanjiu; (until 1999): Zhongguo Qingshaonian Yanjiu; (until 1997): Zhongguo Gongchanzhuyi Qingniantuan (1001-3199)
Indexed: RASB.
Published by: Zhongguo Renmin Daxue, Shubao Zilio Zhongxin/Renmin University of China, Information Center for Social Server, Dongcheng-qu, 3, Zhangzizhong Lu, Beijing, 100007, China. TEL 86-10-64039458, FAX 86-10-64015080, kyes@163.net, http://www.confucius.cn.net/bkdetail.asp?fzt=D421. **Dist. in US by:** China Publications Service, PO Box 49614, Chicago, IL 60649. TEL 312-288-3291, FAX 312-288-8570; **Dist. by:** China International Book Trading Corp, 35 Chegongzhuang Xilu, Haidian District, PO Box 399, Beijing 100044, China. TEL 86-10-68412045, FAX 86-10-68412023, cibtc@mail.cibtc.com.cn, http://www.cibtc.com.cn.

QINGSHAONIAN FANZUI WENTI/ISSUES ON JUVENILE CRIMES AND DELINQUENCY. see *LAW*

649 AUS ISSN 1320-1867
QUALITY TIME; the free magazine for parents. Text in English. 1993. bi-m. AUD 12 (effective 1995). adv. bk.rev. 24 p./no. 6 cols./p.; **Document type:** *Newspaper, Consumer.*
Description: Provides information for parents of young children. Includes articles by experts on child health and development, child safety, play and parenting.
Published by: Telling Words Co. Pty. Ltd., 161 Barkly Ave, Richmond, VIC 3121, Australia. TEL 61-3-94270455, FAX 61-3-94284263. Ed., R&P Margaret Riddle. Adv. contact Cathy Riddle. page AUD 1,890; trim 300 x 240. Circ: 50,121 (controlled).

RAINER FOUNDATION. ANNUAL REPORT. see *CRIMINOLOGY AND LAW ENFORCEMENT*

THE RALLY LEADER. see *CHILDREN AND YOUTH—For*

649 DEU
RATGEBER FUER BABYS ERSTES JAHR. Text in German. 1991. q. free. adv. **Document type:** *Magazine, Consumer.*
Published by: Bonus Marketing GmbH, Liebfrauenstr. 1-3, Frankfurt Am Main, 60313, Germany. TEL 49-69-2097373-0, info@bonus-marketing.de, http://www.baby-bonus.de, http://www.bonus-marketing.de. adv.: page EUR 32,000. Circ: 695,000 (controlled).

READING TIME. see *LITERATURE*

649 362.7 DEU ISSN 0034-1312
K18
➤ **RECHT DER JUGEND UND DES BILDUNGSWESENS**; Zeitschrift fuer Schule, Berufsbildung und Jugenderziehung. Text in German. 1953. q. EUR 98; EUR 25 newsstand/cover (effective 2004). adv. bk.rev. abstr.; bibl. index. reprints avail. **Document type:** *Journal, Academic/Scholarly.*
Formerly (until 1958): Recht der Jugend (0481-9306)
Indexed: AC&P, DIP, IBR, IBZ.
—CCC.
Published by: B W V - Berliner Wissenschafts Verlag GmbH, Axel-Springer-Str 54b, Berlin, 10117, Germany. TEL 49-30-8417700, FAX 49-30-84177021, bwv@bwv-verlag.de, http://www.bwv-verlag.de/files/katalog/zeitschr/rdjb/rdjb.htm. Eds. Hans-Peter Fuessel, Ingo Richter. adv.: page EUR 360; trim 140 x 215. Circ: 1,200.

649 ESP ISSN 0211-1799
RECIEN NACIDO; guta de los papas. Text in Spanish. 1970. s-m. free. adv.
Address: Av. del Jordan s-n, Edificio B-2, Barcelona, Spain. Ed. Joaquin Motger. Circ: 240,000.

RECLAIMING CHILDREN AND YOUTH; the journal of strengh-based interventions. see *PSYCHOLOGY*

649 CAN
RELATIONAL CHILD & YOUTH CARE PRACTICE. Text in English. 1982. q. CND 59 domestic to individuals; USD 59 foreign to individuals; CND 85 domestic to institutions; USD 85 foreign to institutions (effective 2003). adv. Supplement avail.; back issues avail. **Document type:** *Trade.*
Description: Covers all areas of child and youth care with emphasis on the field of social services and welfare.
Former titles (until 2003): Journal of Child and Youth Care (0840-982X); until 1989): Journal of Child Care (0715-5883)
Indexed: CEI, PsycInfo, PsycholAb, SFSA, SWR&A, e-psyche.
—BLDSC (7352.06235), GNLM, IE, ingenta. **CCC.**
Published by: Malaspina University College, Relational Child & Youth Care Practice, ASTEC Bldg, Rm 568, 900 Fifth St, Nanaimo, BC V9R 5S5, Canada. TEL 250-740-6241, FAX 250-740-6466, RCYCP@mala.bc.ca, http://www.cyc-net.org/journals/rcycp.html. adv.: page CND 100. Circ: 450.

REPORT ON EMOTIONAL & BEHAVIORAL DISORDERS IN YOUTH. see *PSYCHOLOGY*

REPRESENTING CHILDREN; a quarterly journal for all professionals concerned with the rights and welfare of children. see *SOCIAL SERVICES AND WELFARE*

647 610 JPN ISSN 0386-8435
HQ767.8
➤ **RESEARCH AND CLINICAL CENTER FOR CHILD DEVELOPMENT. ANNUAL REPORT.** Text and summaries in English. 1978. a. free. cum.index. back issues avail. **Document type:** *Academic/Scholarly.*
Indexed: PsycholAb.
—BLDSC (1289.661000), IE, ingenta.
Published by: Hokkaido University, Research and Clinical Center for Child Development, Nishi 7-chome, Kita 11-jo, Kita-ku, Sapporo-shi, 060-0081, Japan. TEL 81-11-706-2607, FAX 81-11-706-4946, schen@edu.hokudai.ac.jp. Ed. Shing Jen Chen. Pub. Takashi Morotomi. R&P Shing-Jen Chen. Circ: 500 (controlled).

➤ **RESEARCH DEVELOPMENT AND STATISTICS DIRECTORATE. OCCASIONAL PAPERS.** see *SOCIOLOGY*

362.7 USA ISSN 0886-571X
HV59 CODEN: RTCYEY
➤ **RESIDENTIAL TREATMENT FOR CHILDREN & YOUTH.** Abbreviated title: R T C Y. Text in English. 1979. q. USD 465 combined subscription domestic to institutions print & online eds.; USD 627.75 combined subscription in Canada to institutions print & online eds.; USD 674.25 combined subscription elsewhere to institutions print & online eds. (effective academic year 2005 - 2006). adv. bk.rev. 120 p./no.; back issues avail.; reprint service avail. from HAW. **Document type:** *Journal, Academic/Scholarly.* **Description:** Provides a forum for persons engaged in the interdisciplinary task of the residential group care of children and youth. Provides a national exchange of scientific views, innovative practices and perspectives on current issues and developments in the field.
Former titles (until 1986): Residential Group Care and Treatment (0731-7123); (until 1981): Residential and Community Child Care Administration (0162-1408)
Related titles: Microfiche ed.: (from PQC); Microform ed.; Online - full text ed.: ISSN 1541-0358. free to institutions (effective 2003); free with print subs. (from EBSCO Publishing, O C L C Online Computer Library Center, Inc., Swets Information Services).
Indexed: AC&P, AMHA, ASSIA, BehAb, BiolAb, CDA, CJA, CJPI, CPLI, DIP, ECER, ERA, ESPM, ExcerpMed, FamI, HRA, IBR, IBZ, IMFL, PC&CA, PsycInfo, PsycholAb, RehabLit, RiskAb, SEA, SENA, SFSA, SOPODA, SSA, SWR&A, SociolAb, V&AA, e-psyche.
—BLDSC (7777.247000), GNLM, Haworth, IE, Infotrieve, ingenta. **CCC.**
Published by: (American Association of Children's Residential Centers), Haworth Press, Inc., 10 Alice St, Binghamton, NY 13904-1580. TEL 607-722-5857, 800-429-6784, FAX 607-722-1424, 800-895-0582, getinfo@haworthpress.com, http://www.haworthpress.com/web/RTCY. Eds. D Patrick Zimmerman, E C Teather. Pub. William Cohen. R&P Ruth Ann Heath TEL 607-722-5857 ext 316. Adv. contact Rebecca Miller-Baum TEL 607-722-5857 ext 337. B&W page USD 315, color page USD 550; trim 4.375 x 7.125. Circ: 534 (paid).

➤ **RESIDENTIAL TREATMENT NEWS.** see *PSYCHOLOGY*

➤ **RESOURCE.** see *EDUCATION*

649 371.1 USA ISSN 1086-7155
RETHINKING CHILDHOOD. Text in English. 1997. irreg., latest 2003. price varies. back issues avail. **Document type:** *Monographic series.*

C

▼ new title ➤ refereed ✶ unverified ◆ full entry avail.

Published by: Peter Lang Publishing, Inc., 275 Seventh Ave, 28th Fl, New York, NY 10001. TEL 212-647-7700, 800-770-5264, FAX 212-647-7707, customerservice@plang.com, http://www.peterlangusa.com. Eds. Jan Jipson, Joe L Kincheloe.

649 BRA ISSN 1519-3829
REVISTA BRASILEIRA DE SAUDE MATERNO INFANTIL/BRAZILIAN JOURNAL OF MOTHER AND CHILD HEALTH. Text in Portuguese. q. USD 50 to individuals; USD 100 to institutions (effective 2004). **Document type:** *Journal, Academic/Scholarly.*
Related titles: Online - full text ed.: free (effective 2005).
Indexed: AbHyg, DSA, HelmAb, ProtozoAb, RM&VM, RRTA, SIA, SSA, SociolAb, TDB, WAE&RSA.
Published by: Instituto Materno Infantil de Pernanmbuco, Rua dos Coelhos 300, Bia Vista, Recife, PE 50070-550, Brazil. TEL 55-81-21224100, FAX 55-81-21224703, imip@imip.org.br, http://www.imip.org.br.

649 DEU
RHEIN-NECKAR-KIND; die regionale Elternzeitung. Text in German. 2000. 11/yr. free newsstand/cover. adv. **Document type:** *Magazine, Consumer.*
Published by: Verlag Karl Goerner, Hildebrandstr. 23, Karlsruhe, 76227, Germany. TEL 49-721-43536, FAX 49-721-491995, info@karl-goerner.de, http://www.rhein-neckar-kind.de, http://www.karl-goerner.de. adv.: B&W page EUR 1,517, color page EUR 2,655; trim 223 x 315. Circ: 27,500 (controlled).

649 USA
RHODE ISLAND PARENTS' PAPER. Text in English. 1989. m. free at select locations. adv. bk.rev.; video rev.; music rev.; software rev.; play rev. **Document type:** *Newspaper.*
Description: Provides practical parenting information.
Published by: United Parenting Publications (Subsidiary of: Trader Publishing Co.), 670 Centre St, Jamaica Plain, MA 02130. TEL 617-522-1515, FAX 617-522-1694, rhodeisland@unitedad.com, http://rhodeisland.parenthood.com/aboutus.html, http://www.parenthood.com. Ed. Jim McGaw. Circ: 32,000.

C

RIGHT START; your complete guide to parenting. see *CHILDREN AND YOUTH—For*

649 NZL
RIGHT START. Text in English. 1993. bi-m. NZD 12 (effective 2001). adv. bk.rev. **Document type:** *Consumer.* **Description:** Covers parenting, education, early literacy, numeracy, food, teaching ideas and activities for teachers.
Published by: Auckland Kindergarten Association, Myers Park, Queen St, Auckland, New Zealand. TEL 9-529-1121, FAX 9-307-1248. Ed. Victoria Carter. Circ: 30,000.

369.4 DEU
RING JUNGER BUENDE. MITTEILUNGEN. Text in German. 1964. q. free. bk.rev. **Document type:** *Magazine, Consumer.*
Published by: Ring Junger Buende, An der Neckarspitze 6, Heidelberg, 69115, Germany. TEL 49-6221-20263, FAX 49-6221-20263. Ed. Waldemar Wagner. Circ: 2,200.

362.7 USA
THE ROAD HOME. Text in English. s-a. free. **Document type:** *Newsletter.* **Description:** Contains news and views from the VCA, which promotes education and information on child abduction, missing and found children.
Formerly: Vanished Children's Alliance Newsletter
Published by: Vanished Children's Alliance, 991 W. Hedding St., Ste. 101, San Jose, CA 95126-1248. TEL 408-296-1113, FAX 408-296-1117, vca001@aol.com, http://www.vca.org. Ed. Georgia K Hilgeman. Circ: 17,000.

305.23 POL ISSN 1425-8641
RODZIC PO LUDZKU. Text in Polish. 1994. irreg.
Related titles: ♦ Supplement to: Gazeta Wyborcza. ISSN 0860-908X.
Published by: Agora S.A., ul Czerska 8/10, Warsaw, 00732, Poland. TEL 48-22-6994301, FAX 48-22-6994603, http://www.gazeta.pl.

THE ROUNDTABLE (SOUTHFIELD). see *SOCIAL SERVICES AND WELFARE*

649 618.92 DEU
RUND UMS BABY. Text in German. m. adv. **Document type:** *Consumer.* **Description:** Provides information and content on all aspects of pregnancy, birth and baby care for parents.
Media: Online - full text.
Published by: Ulrich Schneider Multimedia, Franziskanerstr 16, Olpe-Biggesee, 57462, Germany. redaktion@rund-ums-baby.de, http://www.rund-ums-baby.de.

S C B W I BULLETIN. see *PUBLISHING AND BOOK TRADE*

S M Y A L NEWS. see *HOMOSEXUALITY*

S O S KINDERDORF INTERNATIONAL. see *SOCIAL SERVICES AND WELFARE*

S O S KINDERDORFBOTE. see *SOCIAL SERVICES AND WELFARE*

S O S S I JOURNAL. see *PHILATELY*

155.4 305.23 370.15 USA
S R C D NEWSLETTER. Text in English. 1958. quadrennial. free. **Document type:** *Newsletter, Academic/Scholarly.*
Description: Reports on news and events of interest to members of the Society for Research in Child Development, including publications, meetings and symposia, memoirs, and reports on Federal legislation.
Media: Online - full content.
Published by: Society for Research in Child Development, University of Michigan, 3131 S State St, Ste 302, Ann Arbor, MI 48108-1623. TEL 734-998-6578, FAX 734-998-6569, pamreid@umich.edu, srcd@umich.edu, http://www.srcd.org/news/default.shtml. Ed. Pam Trotman Reid.

SAMSPRAAK. see *LINGUISTICS*

649 USA
SAN DIEGO FAMILY MAGAZINE. Text in English. 1982. m. USD 18 (effective 2003). adv. **Document type:** *Consumer.*
Description: Provides a country-wide calendar of family events and classes for both parents and children. Includes educational and informative tips for parents, and many San Diego resources.
Formerly: San Diego Family Press
Address: PO Box 23960, San Diego, CA 92193. TEL 619-685-6970, FAX 619-685-6978, family@sandiegofamily.com, publisher@sandiegofamily.com, http://www.sandiegofamily.com. Pub., R&P Sharon Bay. Circ: 120,000.

155.4 649 USA
SAN DIEGO PARENT. Text in English. 1986. m. free at select locations in San Diego. adv. **Document type:** *Consumer.*
Description: Serves as "city magazine" for informed San Diego parents.
Published by: United Advertising Publications, Inc., 443 E Irving Dr, Burbank, CA 91504. TEL 619-624-2770, FAX 619-624-2777. Ed., R&P Christina Elston. Pub. Kay Mount. Adv. contact Kelly Powers. Circ: 80,000.

155.6 USA
SAN FRANCISCO PENINSULA PARENT. Text in English. 1984. m. USD 15. adv. bk.rev. **Document type:** *Newspaper.*
Description: Provides a resource guide for local events and information geared to parents.
Published by: United Advertising Publications, Inc., 1480 Rollins Rd, Burlingame, CA 94010-2307. TEL 650-342-9203, FAX 415-342-9276, sfparent@aol.com, http://www.sfparent.com, http://www.unitedadvertising.com/. Ed. Mary Martin. Pub. Lynn Berardo. R&P Maya Stein. Adv. contact Cathy Lynch. Circ: 56,000 (controlled).

649 USA
SAN JOAQUIN PARENTS PAPER. Text in English. m.
Address: 5346 Oakview Lane, Stockton, CA 95212. TEL 209-608-6274, sjparentspaper@cs.com. Pub. James P King.

028.5 305.896 USA ISSN 1544-0885
PL8009.5
SANKOFA; a journal of African children's and young adult literature. Text in English. 2002. a. USD 20 newsstand/cover in US & Canada to individuals; USD 25 newsstand/cover elsewhere to individuals; USD 30 newsstand/cover in US & Canada to institutions; USD 35 newsstand/cover elsewhere to institutions (effective 2003).
Published by: Sankofa, Inc., 202-E Holmes Hall Morgan State University, 1700 E. Cold Spring Ln., Baltimore, MD 21251. TEL 443-885-3165, FAX 443-885-8225, english@morgan.edu, http://jewel.morgan.edu/~english/english.htm. Ed. Meena G. Khorana.

305.23 USA
▼ **SAVANNAH COASTAL PARENT.** Text in English. 2003. m. free newsstand/cover. adv. **Document type:** *Magazine, Consumer.* **Description:** Contains features related to parenting, youth health and fitness, family lifestyles and community events of an interest to parents with children.
Published by: Morris Communications Company LLC, 725 Broad St, Augusta, GA 30901. TEL 800-622-6358, sabrinamanganella@yahoo.com, http://www.coastal-parent.com, http://morris.com. Ed. Tim Rutherford. Adv. contact Candis Crowder TEL 912-652-0238. Circ: 19,000 (controlled and free).

SAVE THE CHILDREN. ANNUAL REPORT. see *SOCIAL SERVICES AND WELFARE*

362.7 GBR ISSN 0966-6982
SAVE THE CHILDREN DEVELOPMENT MANUALS. Text in English. 1991. irreg. **Document type:** *Monographic series.*
Description: Short practical guides for field staff in particular areas of field work.
Published by: Save the Children Fund, Mary Datchelor House, Grove Ln, London, SE5 8RD, United Kingdom. TEL 44-207-703-5400, FAX 44-207-703-2278, http://www.oneworld.org/scf/.

362.7 GBR ISSN 0966-6931
SAVE THE CHILDREN OVERSEAS DEPARTMENT WORKING PAPER. Text in English. 1992. irreg., latest vol.17, 1997. GBP 2.95. **Document type:** *Monographic series.* **Description:** Disseminates research and project experience to a wider audience, particularly targeting development practitioners, researchers and policy makers throughout the world.
—BLDSC (8077.245000).
Published by: Save the Children Fund, Mary Datchelor House, Grove Ln, London, SE5 8RD, United Kingdom. TEL 44-207-703-5400, FAX 44-207-703-2278, http://www.oneworld.org/scf/.

649 USA
SAVVY FAMILY. Text in English. 12/yr. free (effective 2005). **Document type:** *Magazine, Consumer.*
Published by: Suburban Journals, 14522 S. Outer 40., Chesterfield, MO 63017-5737. mwagner@yourjournal.com, http://www.yourjournal.comel. Pub. Mary Ann Wagner. Adv. contact Mike Giger. Circ: 20,000 (free).

369.4 ITA
SCAUTISMO VENETO. Text in Italian. 1985. bi-m. **Document type:** *Magazine, Consumer.* **Description:** For leaders of scout and guide units.
Related titles: Online - full text ed.
Published by: Cooperativa Veneta Scout, Via Romolo Fowst, 9, Padua, PD 35135, Italy. TEL 39-49-8644003, FAX 39-49-8643605, http://www.scautismoveneto.it. Circ: 4,000.

SCHNELLER-MAGAZIN. see *RELIGIONS AND THEOLOGY—Protestant*

375 USA ISSN 0278-3126
SCHOOL AGE NOTES; the newsletter for school-age care professionals. Text in English. 1980. m. USD 28.95 domestic; USD 38.95 in Canada; USD 33.95 elsewhere (effective 2003). bk.rev. cum.index: 1980-1985. **Document type:** *Newsletter.*
Description: Covers administrative and curriculum issues in after-school programs.
Published by: (School-Age Notes, Inc.), School Age Notes, 476, New Albany, OH 43054-0476. TEL 615-279-0700, 800-410-8780, FAX 615-242-0800, sanotes@aol.com, http://www.schoolagenotes.com. R&P Richard Scofield. Circ: 6,000 (paid).

649 028.5 JPN
SCHOOL CHILDREN LIFE. Text in Multiple languages. irreg. price varies. **Document type:** *Consumer.*
Published by: International Society for Educational Information/Kokusai Kyoiku Joho Senta, Shinko Ofisomu 5th Fl, 20-3 Sanei-cho, Shinjuku-ku, Tokyo, 160-0008, Japan. TEL 81-3-3358-1138, FAX 81-3-3359-7188, kaya@isei.or.jp, http://www.isei.or.jp/.

362.7 USA ISSN 0894-5152
SCHOOL INTERVENTION REPORT. Abbreviated title: S I R. Text in English. 1987. q. USD 22 domestic to non-members; USD 30 foreign to non-members. bk.rev. cum.index 1987-1990. back issues avail. **Document type:** *Newsletter.* **Description:** Covers students at risk from drugs, alcohol, dropping out, physical violence, and adolescent pregnancy.
Published by: Safe Schools Coalition, Inc., 1338, Holmes Beach, FL 34218-1338. TEL 941-778-9140, 800-537-4903, FAX 941-778-6818. Ed. Alan W McEvoy. Pub., R&P Edsel L Erickson. Circ: 3,000. **Subscr. to:** 5400 34th St W., Apt. 15C, Bradenton, FL 34210-3415.

SCHOOL SOCIAL WORK JOURNAL. see *SOCIAL SERVICES AND WELFARE*

028.5 DEU
SCHWARTE. Text in German. 1978. s-a. back issues avail.
Published by: Willibald-Gluck-Gymnasium, Dr Grundler Str 7, Neumarkt, 92318, Germany.

369.4 GBR
SCOTTISH SCOUT NEWS. Text in English. 1977. 5/yr. GBP 5 (effective 2000). adv. back issues avail. **Document type:** *Newsletter.*
Published by: Scottish Council of The Scout Association, Fordell Firs, The Scottish Council, Hillend, Dunfermline, Fife KY11 5HQ, United Kingdom. TEL 44-1383-419073, FAX 44-1383-414892. Ed., Adv. contact James Allan. Circ: 8,000.

649 GBR ISSN 1469-0780
SCOTTISH YOUTH ISSUES JOURNAL. Text in English. 2000. s-a. GBP 15, GBP 25 to individuals (effective 2002). **Document type:** *Journal, Academic/Scholarly.* **Description:** Provides a forum for reflection on policy and practice and for the dissemination of research on all issues affecting young people - from education, health, housing and culture, to unemployment, criminal justice and politics.
—BLDSC (8211.358000).
Published by: Community Learning Scotland, Rosebury House, 9 Haymarket Ter, Edinburgh, EH12 5EZ, United Kingdom. TEL 44-131-313-2488, FAX 44-131-313-6800, info@cls.dircon.co.uk, http://www.communitylearning.org/syijc.asp.

369.4 AUS ISSN 0815-4627
SCOUT MAGAZINE. Text in English. 1912. 11/yr. AUD 17.50. adv. **Document type:** *Bulletin.* **Description:** Discusses program ideas, reports, training and inspirational information.
Formerly: Victorian Scout (0159-897X)
Published by: Scout Association of Australia, Victoria Branch, PO Box 190, Carlton, VIC 3053, Australia. Ed. Andrew Taylor. Circ: 22,000.

369.4 USA ISSN 0036-9500
HS3313.B7
SCOUTING; a family magazine. Text in English. 1913. 6/yr. (Jan-Feb, Mar-Apr, May-June, Sep, Oct, Nov-Dec). USD 15 domestic to non-members; USD 20 foreign to non-members (effective 2005). adv. bk.rev.; film rev. illus. index. reprint service avail. from PQC. **Document type:** *Magazine, Consumer.*
Related titles: Microform ed.: (from PQC); Online - full text ed.: (from Gale Group).
Indexed: MagInd.
Published by: Boy Scouts of America, PO Box 152079, Irving, TX 75015-2079. TEL 972-580-2000, http://www.scoutingmagazine.org. Ed. J D Owen. Pub. J Warren Young. Adv. contact Lisa Hott TEL 972-580-2351. B&W page USD 12,330, color page USD 18,500. Circ: 900,000 (paid).

369.4 CAN
SCOUTING FOR FAMILIES* . Text in English. q. CND 12 to members. adv. **Document type:** *Newsletter.*
Formerly: Scouting News (0318-3521)
Published by: Scouts - Canada, New Brunswick Provincial Office, 201 Union St, St John, NB E2L 1A9, Canada. TEL 506-646-9120. Ed. Tom Heath. Circ: 1,500.

369.4 SWE ISSN 1403-2740
SCOUTING SPIRIT. Text in Swedish. 1998. 6/yr. adv. illus. **Document type:** *Magazine, Consumer.*
Formed by the merger of (1943-1998): Scoutledaren (0036-9519); (1981-1998): Nying (0280-6436)
Related titles: ◆ Supplement to: Redo foer Scouting. ISSN 1650-1594.
Published by: Nykterhetsroerelsens Scoutfoerbund (NSF)/Temperance Guide and Scout Association (NSF), PO Box 12825, Stockholm, 11297, Sweden. TEL 46-8-6726080, FAX 46-8-6726084, info@nsf.scout.se, http://www.nsf.scout.se.

155.649 USA
SEATTLE'S CHILD. Text in English. 1979. m. adv. bk.rev. **Document type:** *Consumer.* **Description:** Guide for parents, educators and child-care providers. Features include a calendar of events, plays, movies, and ideas for outings and restaurants.
Published by: United Parenting Publications (Subsidiary of: Trader Publishing Co.), 123 N W 36th St, Ste 215, Seattle, WA 98107. TEL 206-441-0191, FAX 206-441-4919. Ed. Ann Bergman. Adv. contact Alayne Sulkin. Circ: 30,000.

SEKTOR ERZIEHUNG. see *EDUCATION—School Organization And Administration*

SER PADRES/BEING PARENTS. see *WOMEN'S INTERESTS*

056.1 ESP
SER PADRES BEBE. Text in Spanish. m. free; with Ser Padres Hoy. adv. **Document type:** *Magazine, Consumer.*
Related titles: ◆ Supplement to: Ser Padres Hoy.
Published by: G y J Espana Ediciones S.L., Albasanz, 15 Edificio A, Madrid, 28037, Spain. TEL 34-91-4369800, FAX 34-91-5751280, http://www.gyj.es. adv.: page EUR 8,715; bleed 213 x 277. Circ: 162,625 (paid and controlled).

649 ESP
SER PADRES HOY. Text in Spanish. 1974. m. EUR 23.05 domestic; EUR 57.90 in Europe; EUR 75.95 elsewhere (effective 2004). adv. **Document type:** *Magazine, Consumer.*
Related titles: ◆ Supplement(s): Ser Padres Bebe.
Published by: G y J Espana Ediciones S.L., Albasanz, 15 Edificio A, Madrid, 28037, Spain. TEL 34-91-4369800, FAX 34-91-5751280, serpadres@gyj.es, http://www.gyj.es. Ed. Javier Garcia. Adv. contact Elena Sanchez Fabres. Circ: 105,000.

SERVICES FOR CHILDREN. see *SOCIAL SERVICES AND WELFARE*

SEX EDUCATION; sexuality, society and learning. see *EDUCATION*

613.0432 USA
SHAKEN BABY ALLIANCE; dedicated to prevention, support and justice. Text in English, French, German, Italian, Spanish. 1998. q. **Description:** Includes articles on shaken baby syndrome and child abuse.
Address: PO Box 150734, Ft. Worth, TX 76108. TEL 817-444-9357, jackson4@gte.net, http://www.shakenbaby.com.

369.4 CHN
SHANDONG QINGNIAN/SHANDONG YOUTH. Text in Chinese. m.
Published by: Shandong Gongqingtuan Shengwei, No 4 Yingxiongshan Lu, Jinan, Shandong, 250002, China. TEL 25829. Ed. Zhou Jianqing.

155.5 CHN ISSN 1002-9915
SHAONIAN ERTONG YANJIU/ADOLESCENT STUDIES. Text in Chinese. bi-m. **Document type:** *Academic/Scholarly.*
Related titles: Online - full text ed.: (from East View Information Services).
Published by: Zhongguo Qingnian Zhengzhi Xueyuan, Qingshaonian Yanjiusuo, 25 Xisanhuan Beilu, Beijing, 100081, China. TEL 8021144.

028.5 CHN
SHIJIE ERTONG/WORLD CHILDREN. Text in Chinese, English. q.
Published by: Sichuan Waiyu Xueyuan, Shijie Ertong Bianjibu, Chongqing, Sichuan 630031, China. TEL 661737. Ed. Zheng Huizhong.

362.41 USA
SIBLING INFORMATION NETWORK NEWSLETTER. Text in English. 1981. q. USD 8.50 to individuals; USD 15 to institutions. bk.rev. back issues avail. **Document type:** *Newsletter.*
Published by: A.J. Pappanikou Center, 249 Glenbrook Rd., Storrs, CT 06269-2064. TEL 860-486-4985, http://www.uconnced.org/pubs.htm. Ed., R&P Lisa Glidden. Circ: 1,500.

SIGNAL (STREAMWOOD). see *RELIGIONS AND THEOLOGY—Protestant*

SINGLE MOTHER; a support group in your hands. see *WOMEN'S INTERESTS*

649 USA ISSN 1077-4092
SINGLE - PARENT FAMILY. Text in English. 1994. m. adv. illus. 8 p./no.; reprints avail. **Document type:** *Magazine, Consumer.* **Description:** Encourages and equips single parents to do the best job they can at creating stable, religious homes for themselves and their children.
Indexed: ChrPI.
Published by: Focus on the Family, Inc., 8605 Explorer Dr, Colorado Springs, CO 80920-1051. TEL 719-531-3400, 800-232-6459, FAX 719-531-3424, singleparent@family.org, http://www.family.org/spfmag/. Ed. Lynda Hunter. R&P Christine McDonald. Circ: 29,000 (paid).

SMART DADS. see *SOCIOLOGY*

SOCIAL SERVICES RESEARCH. see *SOCIAL SERVICES AND WELFARE*

362.7 300 USA ISSN 1537-4661
➤ **SOCIOLOGICAL STUDIES OF CHILDREN AND YOUTH.** Text in English. 1986. irreg., latest vol.10, 2005. price varies. back issues avail. **Document type:** *Monographic series, Academic/Scholarly.* **Description:** Provides an outlet for social scientists whose reports on their work with children or youth may not 'fit' in traditional academic journals due to the length of their pieces or for other reasons.
Former titles (until 2001, vol.8?): Sociological Studies of Children (1080-0778); (until 1993): Sociological Studies of Child Development (1058-8930)
Related titles: Online - full text ed.: (from ScienceDirect).
Indexed: CJA, FamI, SOPODA, SSA, SociolAb.
—BLDSC (8319.649270), IE, ingenta. **CCC.**
Published by: J A I Press Inc. (Subsidiary of: Elsevier Science & Technology), 360 Park Ave S, New York, NY 10010-1710. TEL 212-989-5800, FAX 212-633-3990, usinfo-f@elsevier.com, http://www.elsevier.com/wps/find/bookseriesdescription.cws_home/BS_SSOC/description. Ed. D A Kinney.

362.7 CUB ISSN 0864-0564
SOMOS JOVENES. Text in Spanish. 1977. m. USD 34 in South America; USD 36 in North America; USD 42 elsewhere.
Related titles: Online - full text ed.: ISSN 1607-6400. 2000.
Published by: (Editorial Abril), Ediciones Cubanas, Obispo No. 527, Apdo. 605, Havana, Cuba. TEL 7-32-4571, http://www.somosjovenes.cu/. Ed. Guillermo Cabrera. Circ: 200,000.

790.019 646 USA
SOUTH FLORIDA PARENTING. Text in English. 1990. m. adv. bk.rev. illus. **Description:** Focuses on concerns of parents, includes feature articles and activities listings.
Published by: South Florida Parenting Inc, 5555 Nob Hill Rd., Ft. Lauderdale, FL 33351-4707. TEL 954-747-3057, vmccash@tribune.com. Adv. contact L Goodlin. Circ: 165,000.

649.1 USA
SOUTH SHORE BABY JOURNAL. Text in English. 1991. 11/yr. USD 9 (effective 1998). adv. bk.rev. **Document type:** *Newspaper.* **Description:** Provides parents in a local area with information about the health, development, education and entertainment of children pre-birth to age 12.
Published by: Riverside Publishing, 425 Spring Lake Dr, Itasca, IL 60143-2076. TEL 630-467-7000, 800-323-9540, FAX 630-467-7192, http://www.riversidepublishing.com. Ed., Pub., Adv. contact Barbara Chandler. Circ: 26,500.

SPANISH LANGUAGE BOOKS FOR CHILDREN & YOUNG ADULTS. see *PUBLISHING AND BOOK TRADE—Abstracting, Bibliographies, Statistics*

SPECIAL CHILDREN. see *EDUCATION—Special Education And Rehabilitation*

028.5 371.9 USA
SPECIALKIDS. Text in English. 1996. a. USD 18. adv. **Document type:** *Magazine, Consumer.*
Published by: KidStuff Publication, Inc., 4623 S. Broad St., Philadelphia, PA 19112-1202. TEL 215-291-5560, FAX 215-291-5563. Ed., Pub., R&P Nancy Lisagor. Adv. contact Karen Pearlstein. Circ: 40,000.

028.5 USA
SPECTRUM NEWSLETTER (ALBANY). Text in English. 1979. q. free to members. **Document type:** *Newsletter, Trade.*
Published by: Parsons Child and Family Center, 60 Academy Rd, Albany, NY 11208. TEL 518-426-2600, FAX 518-447-5234, development@parsonscenter.org, http://www.parsonscenter.org. Ed. K E Mantas. Circ: 15,000 (paid and controlled).

SPIELEN UND LERNEN. see *EDUCATION*

649 FRA ISSN 1278-4699
SPIRALE (RAMONVILLE SAINT-AGNE); la grande aventure de Monsieur Bebe. Text in French. 1996. q. EUR 30 domestic; EUR 33.50 foreign (effective 2003). **Document type:** *Magazine, Consumer.*
Published by: Editions Eres, 11 rue des Alouettes, Ramonville Saint-Agne, 31520, France. TEL 33-5-61751576, FAX 33-5-61735289, eres@edition-eres.com. Ed. Patrick Ben Soussan. Circ: 1,800.

C

398 028.5 USA
SPOOFING. Text in English. 1983. 5/yr. USD 60 (effective 1999). adv. illus. back issues avail. **Document type:** *Consumer.* **Description:** Devotes to each issue an individual theme, such as space, traditions, nature, elements, humor, and love.
Formerly: Are You Spoofing
Published by: Creative With Words Publications, PO Box 223226, Carmel, CA 93922. FAX 408-655-8627, geltrich@usa.net, http://members.tripod.com/~creativewithwords/. Ed., Pub., R&P, Adv. contact Brigitta Geltrich.

SPORT SCENE; focus on youth programs. see *SPORTS AND GAMES*

SPOTLIGHT ON YOUTH SPORTS. see *SPORTS AND GAMES*

STADT UND RAUM. see *HOUSING AND URBAN PLANNING*

STANDING TOGETHER. see *SOCIAL SERVICES AND WELFARE*

START (BIRMINGHAM). see *RELIGIONS AND THEOLOGY—Protestant*

STARTING LINE. see *SPORTS AND GAMES*

STATE OF AMERICA'S CHILDREN YEARBOOK (YEAR); an analysis of our nation's investment in children. see *SOCIAL SERVICES AND WELFARE*

STATE OF THE WORLD'S CHILDREN. see *SOCIAL SERVICES AND WELFARE*

361 USA ISSN 1090-218X
STEP-UP; America's first independent newsletter about remarriage for stepparents and professionals. Text in English. 1980. bi-m. USD 29.95 (effective 1999). bk.rev. back issues avail. **Document type:** *Newspaper.* **Description:** Articles, announcements, and forum for families of remarriages, with a special children's page.
Former titles (until 1996): Stepfamilies and Beyond; (until 1985): Stepparent News (0271-3225)
Published by: Listening Inc., 8716 Pine Ave, Gary, IN 46403. TEL 219-938-6962, FAX 219-938-7435. Ed. Patricia Work Bennett. Pub. Richard C Bennett.

649 DEU ISSN 0938-0914
STEPPKE; Zeitschrift von und fuer Eltern. Text in German. 1990. m. EUR 10 domestic; EUR 40 foreign (effective 2005). bk.rev.; music rev.; film rev.; play rev.; software rev.; tel.rev.; video rev. 36 p./no.; **Document type:** *Magazine, Consumer.* **Description:** Provides information for and about young parents.
Published by: Hewo Akquisition und Vertrieb, Essener Str 28a, Hattingen, 45529, Germany. TEL 49-2324-947090, FAX 49-2324-947092, info@steppke.net, info@hewo.de, http://www.steppke.net, http://www.hewo.de. Ed. Petra Schmischke. Adv. contact Claus van den Berg. Circ: 10,000.

STUDENT ASSISTANCE JOURNAL. see *DRUG ABUSE AND ALCOHOLISM*

306.85 DEU ISSN 1435-6791
STUDIEN ZUR KINDHEITS- UND JUGENDFORSCHUNG. Text in German. 1992. irreg., latest vol.38, 2005. price varies. **Document type:** *Monographic series, Academic/Scholarly.*
Published by: Verlag Dr. Kovac, Arnoldstr 49, Hamburg, 22763, Germany. TEL 49-40-3988800, FAX 49-40-39888055, info@verlagdrkovac.de, http://www.verlagdrkovac.de/11-5.htm.

649 USA
SU BEBE✶. Text in English. s-a.
Published by: Multicultural Communications, 909 N Aviation Blvd Ste 9, Manhattan Beach, CA 90266-6241. TEL 310-791-0193, FAX 310-791-8492. Pub. Laura L Lentz.

649 USA
SU FAMILIA; la guia de la salud y el bienestar familiar. Text in Spanish. q. adv. **Description:** Covers parenting issues for Hispanics in California.
Published by: Multicultural Communications, 909 N Aviation Blvd Ste 9, Manhattan Beach, CA 90266-6241. TEL 310-791-0193, FAX 310-791-8492. Pub. Laura L Lentz.

649 USA
SUCCESSFUL STUDENT. Text in English. s-a.
Published by: Imagination Publishing, 2222 N. Elston Ave., 2nd Fl., Chicago, IL 60614. TEL 312-627-1020, FAX 312-627-1105, http://www.imaginepub.com. Ed. Lisa Terry. Circ: 550,000.

028.5 808.68 SWE ISSN 0347-5387
SVENSKA BARNBOKSINSTITUTET. SKRIFTER/SWEDISH INSTITUTE FOR CHILDREN'S BOOKS. STUDIES. Text in Swedish. 1971. irreg., latest vol.64, 1998. **Document type:** *Monographic series.*
Published by: Svenska Barnboksinstitutet/Swedish Institute for Children's Books, Odengatan 61, Stockholm, 11322, Sweden. TEL 46-8-332323, FAX 46-8-332423. Ed. Sonja Svensson.

C

028.5 RUS
SVOBODNOE SLOVO. Text in Russian. 2000. m. **Document type:** *Newspaper, Consumer.*
Address: http://slovo.sakh.com. Eds. Andrei Zonov, Oleg Baishev.

649 AUS ISSN 1034-6384
SYDNEY'S CHILD. Text in English. 1989. m. (11/yr.). AUD 41; AUD 68 to schools (effective 2005). adv. bk.rev.; film rev.; music rev.; play rev.; software rev.; tel.rev.; video rev. illus. back issues avail. **Document type:** *Magazine, Consumer.* **Description:** Includes articles, reviews and a calendar of events. For parents, teachers, and childcare workers.
Related titles: Online - full text ed.
Published by: Copeland Publishing Pty. Ltd., PO Box 171, Beecroft, NSW 2119, Australia. TEL 61-2-88764800, FAX 61-2-88764848, info@sydneyschild.com.au, http://www.sydneyschild.com.au. adv.: B&W page AUD 3,672, color page AUD 5,053; trim 277 x 395. Circ: 84,000.

362.7 DEU ISSN 1433-9439
HQ799.2.M35
T V DISKURS; Verantwortung in audiovisuellen Medien. Text in German. 1997. q. EUR 49; EUR 15 newsstand/cover (effective 2004). **Document type:** *Magazine, Academic/Scholarly.* **Description:** Information about developments in the fields of youth protection in audio-visual media, media science, and media pedagogy.
Indexed: IBSS.
Published by: (Freiwillige Selbstkontrolle Fernsehen), Nomos Verlagsgesellschaft mbH und Co. KG, Waldseestr 3-5, Baden-Baden, 76530, Germany. TEL 49-7221-20140, FAX 49-7221-210427, nomos@nomos.de, marketing@nomos.de, http://www.nomos.de. Ed. Joachim von Gottberg.

369.4 SVN ISSN 0492-1127
TABOR. Text in Slovenian. 1951. m. USD 20 domestic; USD 58 foreign (effective 2000). adv. bk.rev. cum.index. back issues avail. **Description:** Covers scouting, mountaineering, bicycling, ecology.
Published by: Zveza Tabornikov Slovenije, Parmova 33, Ljubljana, 1000, Slovenia. TEL 386-61-313180, FAX 386-61-1321107, mateja.susterisic@guest.arnes.si, http://www.2.arnes.si/~ljzts1/index.html. Ed. Matija Tonejc TEL 386-61-3000822. R&P Ivo Stajdohar TEL 386-61-3000821. Adv. contact Frane Merela TEL 386-61-3000823. B&W page MRK 400, color page MRK 500. Circ: 4,000.

TAIWAN TOYS & CHILDREN'S ARTICLES BUYERS' GUIDE. see *GIFTWARE AND TOYS*

TALKING SENSE. see *SOCIAL SERVICES AND WELFARE*

649 USA
TALLAHASSEE'S FAMILY FORUM. Text in English. bi-m. adv.
Formerly: Family Forum
Published by: Roberts Lori Danello, 516 Moss View Way, Tallahassee, FL 32312. TEL 850-894-4447, FAX 850-894-2474.

649 USA
TAMPA BAY FAMILY JOURNAL. Text in English. 1985. m. free.
Published by: Family Journal Publications, Inc., PO Box 1100, Orlando, FL 32802-1100. TEL 813-289-4060, FAX 813-289-4585. Ed. Patrick McGuffin. adv.: B&W page USD 1,350, color page USD 1,750; trim 16 x 14. Circ: 25,000 (controlled).

649 USA
TAMPA BAY FAMILY MAGAZINE.NET. Text in English. bi-m. **Description:** Parenting topics covered include education, growth, health, and family fun.
Published by: Lighthouse Publishing Inc, 1840 Glengary St, Sarasota, FL 34231. TEL 941-922-5437, FAX 941-923-6613, http://www.familymagazines.net. Ed. Donna Hartman. Pub. Paul Winkle.

TANDLAEGERNES NYE TIDSSKRIFT. see *MEDICAL SCIENCES—Dentistry*

TE TARI PUNA ORA O AOTEAROA. ITIREAREA/NEW ZEALAND CHILDCARE ASSOCIATION. NEWSLETTER. see *EDUCATION*

TEENSMAG; Trends, Glaube, Action, Tiefgang. see *RELIGIONS AND THEOLOGY—Protestant*

028.5 BEL ISSN 1568-0924
TELETUBBIES TIJDSCHRIFT. Variant title: Teletubbies. Text in Dutch. 1998. m. EUR 15.90 (effective 2003). illus. **Document type:** *Magazine, Consumer.* **Description:** Offers very young children stories and activities based on the popular BBC Teletubbies series.
Formerly (until 2000): Teletubbies Maandblad (1388-8935)
Published by: Sanoma Magazines Belgium, Telecomlaan 5-7, Diegem, 1831, Belgium. TEL 32-2-7762211, FAX 32-2-776-2317, http://www.sanoma-magazines.be/HomePage.aspx?flash=1&Language=nl.

TENNESSEE COMPILATION OF SELECTED LAWS ON CHILDREN, YOUTH AND FAMILIES. see *LAW—Family And Matrimonial Law*

649 USA ISSN 1049-9466
HQ768
➤ **TEXAS CHILD CARE**; the quarterly journal for caregivers everywhere. Text in English. 1977. q. USD 25; free to qualified personnel (effective 2005); subscr. includes newsletter. bk.rev. 48 p./no.; back issues avail.; reprints avail. **Document type:** *Journal, Government.* **Description:** Features child development theory and professional development, as well as child-building articles that provide hands-on activities for children. Includes product reviews, child-care news events, and regulatory information.
Formerly: Texas Child Care Quarterly (0192-6756)
Indexed: CIJE.
—BLDSC (8798.682500), IE.
Published by: Texas Workforce Commission, PO Box 162881, Austin, TX 78716-2881. TEL 512-441-6633, FAX 512-441-6522, Customers@twc.state.tx.us, http://www.childcarequarterly.com. Ed., R&P Louise Parks. Circ: 30,000.

649 USA ISSN 1059-1710
THE/BOSTON PARENTS' PAPER. Text in English. 1984. m. free (effective 2005); at select locations in Boston. adv. bk.rev.; video rev. **Document type:** *Newspaper.* **Description:** Provides practical parenting information.
Published by: United Parenting Publications (Subsidiary of: Trader Publishing Co.), 670 Centre St, Jamaica Plain, MA 02130. TEL 617-522-1515, FAX 617-522-1694, http://boston.parenthood.com/, http://www.parenthood.com. Ed., R&P Deirdre Wilson. Pub. Mary Norton-Rothman. Adv. contact Lisa Braun. Circ: 63,000.

THEIR WORLD. see *EDUCATION—Special Education And Rehabilitation*

649 268 DEU ISSN 0342-7145
THEORIE UND PRAXIS DER SOZIALPAEDAGOGIK. Text in German. 1949. 10/yr. EUR 40; EUR 7.50 newsstand/cover (effective 2004). adv. bk.rev. **Document type:** *Journal, Academic/Scholarly.*
Formerly: Evangelische Kinderpflege fuer Kindergarten, Hort, Heim und Familie (0014-3421)
Indexed: DIP, IBR, IBZ.
Published by: (Evangelische Bundesarbeitsgemeinschaft fuer Sozialpaedagogik im Kindersalter e.V. (EBASKA)), Kallmeyersche Verlagsbuchhandlung GmbH, Im Brande 19, Seelze, 30926, Germany. TEL 49-511-40004175, FAX 49-511-40004176, leserservice@kallmeyer.de, http://www.kallmeyer.de. Ed. Inge Pape. adv.: B&W page EUR 803, color page EUR 1,207. Circ: 8,000 (controlled).

649 268 DEU
THEORIE UND PRAXIS DER SOZIALPAEDAGOGIK. EXTRA. Abbreviated title: T P S Extra. Text in German. 4/yr. **Document type:** *Journal, Academic/Scholarly.*
Published by: Kallmeyersche Verlagsbuchhandlung GmbH, Im Brande 19, Seelze, 30926, Germany. TEL 49-511-40004175, FAX 49-511-40004176.

649 USA ISSN 1081-2334
TIDEWATER PARENT. Text in English. 1990. m. USD 28.85 (effective 2004). adv. bk.rev. illus. 36 p./no. 4 cols./p.; back issues avail. **Document type:** *Newspaper.* **Description:** Advises parents of children of all ages on issues in health, education, travel and recreation, and development.
Published by: Virginian-Pilot, 1300 Diamond Springs Rd, Virginia Beach, VA 23455. TEL 757-222-3100, FAX 757-363-1767, tidewatr@family.wm. Ed. Jennifer O'Donnell. Pub. Lee Azar. R&P Ann Barry Burrows. Adv. contact Christie Berry. B&W page USD 1,199; trim 13.5 x 11.25. Circ: 40,000 (controlled).

369.4 DNK ISSN 0907-6581
TIDSSKRIFT FOR BOERNE- OG UNGDOMSKULTUR. Text in Danish. 1983. 3/yr., latest vol.47, 2004. DKK 180 to individuals; DKK 320 per week to institutions; DKK 112 per issue (effective 2006). illus. back issues avail. **Document type:** *Journal, Academic/Scholarly.*
Formerly (until 1991): B U K S (0108-8963)
Indexed: RILM.
Published by: Syddansk Universitetsforlag/University Press of Southern Denmark, Campusvej 55, Odense M, 5230, Denmark. TEL 45-66-157999, FAX 45-66-158126, press@forlag.sdu.dk, http://www.universitypress.dk.

649 NOR ISSN 1502-7759
TIDSSKRIFT FOR UNGDOMSFORSKNING. Text in Norwegian. 2001. s-a. NOK 240, USD 58 to individuals; NOK 350 to institutions; NOK 190 to students (effective 2003).
Published by: (Norsk Institutt for Forskning om Opvekst, Velferd og Aldring (NOVA)/Norwegian Social Research), Fagbokforlaget, Kanalveien 51, PO Box 6050, Postterminalen, Bergen, 5892, Norway. TEL 47-22-55388800, FAX 47-22-55388801, redaksjon@ungdomsforskning.no, http://www.ungdomsforskning.no. Ed. Anders Bakken TEL 47-22-541200. Circ: 500.

649 305.89607 USA ISSN 1524-5896
TODAY'S CHILD. Text in English. q. USD 12. **Document type:** *Consumer.*
Published by: Today's Child Communications, 225 W. 34th St., Ste.1011, New York, NY 10122. TEL 212-868-1041, FAX 212-290-9526. Ed. Karen Hopkins. Pub. Michelle Drayton-Martin.

649 USA
TODAY'S FAMILY. Text in English. bi-m. USD 15 (effective 2001).
Published by: Reminder Publications, 280 North Main St, East Longmeadow, MA 01028. TEL 413-525-6661, FAX 413-525-5882, childsplay@family.com. Ed. Carla Valentine. Pub. Christopher Buendo.

TODAY'S FATHER. see *MEN'S INTERESTS*

305.23 IRL
TODAY'S PARENT. Text in English. m. adv. **Document type:** *Magazine, Consumer.*
Published by: Select Media, 11 Clare St., Dublin, 2, Ireland. TEL 353-1-6624887, FAX 353-1-6624886, info@selectmedialtd.com. adv.: B&W page EUR 1,898, color page EUR 2,095; trim 210 x 297. Circ: 50,000 (paid and controlled).

649 CAN ISSN 0823-9258
TODAY'S PARENT. Text in English. 1984. 11/yr. CND 17.95 domestic; CND 22.95 foreign (effective 2005). adv. bk.rev. back issues avail. **Document type:** *Magazine, Consumer.* **Description:** Key topics such as health, education, cooking, social, emotional and physical development are covered through regular departments.
Related titles: Online - full text ed.: (from Micromedia ProQuest, ProQuest Information & Learning); ♦ Special ed(s).: Your Baby. ISSN 1188-2360; ♦ Supplement(s): Today's Parent, Pregnancy & Birth. ISSN 1702-8590.
Indexed: CBCARef, CBPI, CPerl.
—CCC.
Published by: (Today's Parent Group), Rogers Media Publishing Ltd, One Mount Pleasant Rd, 11th Fl, Toronto, ON M4Y 2Y5, Canada. TEL 416-764-2000, FAX 416-764-3941, http://www.todaysparent.com, http://www.rogers.com. Circ: 115,000 (paid); 60,000 (controlled).

028.5 796 USA
TODAY'S PLAYGROUND. Text in English. m. USD 30 (effective 2003). **Description:** Contains extensive information on planning, purchasing and maintaining commercial playgrounds.
Published by: Harris Publishing, Inc. (Idaho Falls), 360 B St, Idaho Falls, ID 83402-3547. TEL 208-524-7000, FAX 208-522-5241, http://www.todaysplayground.com/, http://www.harrispublishing.com. Ed. Steve Smede. Pub. Jason Harris. Adv. contact Richard Holley. Circ: 30,000.

649 USA
TOLEDO AREA PARENT NEWS. Text in English. 1992. m. USD 20 (effective 2003). adv. 60 p./no.; **Document type:** *Newspaper.* **Description:** Contains articles on education, early childhood development, and health and safety tips for parents in northwestern Ohio, and alerts them to product recalls and other safety issues.

Address: 1120 Adams St, Toledo, OH 43624-1509. TEL 419-244-9859, FAX 419-244-9871, editor@toledoparent.com, http://www.toledoparent.com/. Ed. Erin Kramer. Pub. Collette Jacobs. R&P Barbar Manley TEL 419-244-9859. Adv. contact Karen Patrick Meyer. B&W page USD 1,350; trim 13 x 10. Circ: 50,000 (controlled).

TOPICS IN EARLY CHILDHOOD SPECIAL EDUCATION. see *EDUCATION—Special Education And Rehabilitation*

649 640.73 USA
TOWN TRENDS. Text in English. 1975. m. free. adv. bk.rev.; music rev.; play rev.; software rev.; video rev. charts; illus.; maps. back issues avail. **Document type:** *Consumer.*
Published by: Middlesex Publications, Inc., 850 Route 1, North Brunswick, NJ 08902. TEL 732-435-0005, FAX 732-435-0677, mpi@injersey.com. Ed. Melodie S Dhondt. Pub. Mark Chelton. R&P Melanie S Dhondt. Adv. contact Ellen Parker Keller. Circ: 120,000 (paid).

649 USA
TRADITIONAL PARENT. Text in English. q. USD 26.95 (effective 2003). 24 p./no.; back issues avail. **Document type:** *Magazine, Consumer.* **Description:** Contains focused material which helps parents to be better caretakers.
Formerly (until 2001): Affirmative Parenting
Published by: Affirmative Parenting, 1020 E 86th St Ste 26B, Indianapolis, IN 46240. TEL 800-525-2778, FAX 317-575-1083, mwc@iquest.net, http://www.rosemond.com. Ed., Pub. John Rosemond.

362.7 USA ISSN 1097-1254
TRANSITIONS (WASHINGTON, D.C.). Text in English. 1980. q. bk.rev. back issues avail. **Document type:** *Newsletter, Academic/Scholarly.*
Formerly: Options (1073-7022); Incorporates: Issues - Action; Population Options
Related titles: Online - full content ed.
Published by: Advocates for Youth, 2000 M St NW, Ste 750, Washington, DC 20036. TEL 202-419-3420, FAX 202-419-1448, questions@advocatesforyouth.org, http://www.advocatesforyouth.org/. Ed., R&P Sue Alford. Circ: 5,000 (controlled).

649 028.5 CAN ISSN 1485-0729
TREE HOUSE CANADIAN FAMILY. Text in English. 1996. 6/yr. CND 24; USD 20 foreign. adv. **Document type:** *Magazine, Consumer.* **Description:** Contains short, informative articles, family entertainment reviews, news and reader advice.
Former titles (until 1997): Canadian Family (1208-512X); (until 1996): Tree house family (1200-8427)
Indexed: CBCARef, CPerI.
Published by: Multi-Vision Publishing, Inc., 655 Bay St, Ste 1100, Toronto, ON M5G 2K4, Canada. TEL 800-387-4378, FAX 416-971-5294. Ed. Kristin Jenkins. Pub. Greg McNeil. Adv. contact Bill Wolch.

369.4 DNK ISSN 0109-0003
TREKLANGEN; hjem, hjemstavn, faedreland. Variant title: Treklang. Text in Danish. 1951. m. DKK 40. adv. bk.rev. illus.
Published by: Dansk Ungdomssekretariat, Moltkesgade 20 A, Flensborg, 2390, Denmark. Ed. Ingolf Julius. Circ: 6,500.

369.4 CAN
THE TRUMPET. Text in English. 1962. 3/yr. CND 14 (effective 1998). **Document type:** *Newsletter.* **Description:** Covers training and program ideas, camp applications, activities of the Guides for adult members.
Published by: Girl Guides of Canada, Quebec Council/Guides du Canada, 1939 De Maisonneuve Blvd W, Montreal, PQ H3H 1K3, Canada. TEL 514-933-5839, FAX 514-933-7591. Circ: 1,300.

TUCSON TEEN. see *CHILDREN AND YOUTH—For*

649 USA ISSN 0895-0784
TWIN SERVICES REPORTER. Text in English. 1983. biennial. looseleaf. adv. bk.rev. index. back issues avail. **Document type:** *Newsletter.* **Description:** Provides information about multiple births.
Formerly: Twinline Reporter
Address: PO Box 10066, Berkeley, CA 94709. TEL 510-524-0863, FAX 510-524-0863, twinservices@juno.com, http://www.twinservices.org. Ed. Patricia Malmstrom. Circ: 850.

649 USA ISSN 0890-3077
TWINS; the magazine for parents of multiples. Text in English. 1984. bi-m. USD 25.95 domestic; USD 31.95 in Canada; USD 35.95 elsewhere; USD 5.50 newsstand/cover (effective 2005). bk.rev.; software rev. bibl.; illus. 48 p./no. 3 cols./p.; back issues avail.; reprints avail. **Document type:** *Magazine, Consumer.* **Description:** For parents of twins, triplets or more. Covers subjects from birth through the age of six.
Related titles: Online - full text ed.: 2001. USD 30 (effective 2001).
—CCC.
Published by: Business Word, Inc., 11211 E Arapahoe Rd, Ste 101, Centennial, CO 80112-3851. TEL 303-290-8500, 888-558-9467, FAX 303-290-9025, twins.editors@businessword.com, http://www.twinsmagazine.com. Ed. Susan J. Alt. Pub. Donald Johnson. R&P Sharon Withers TEL 303-967-0111. Adv. contact Lyle Sondergard TEL 303-967-0139. Circ: 45,000 (paid and controlled).

TWOJE DZIECKO. see *WOMEN'S INTERESTS*

345.08 USA
U C DAVIS JOURNAL OF JUVENILE LAW & POLICY. (University of California) Text in English. s-a. USD 40; USD 20 to students (effective 2004). **Document type:** *Journal.* **Description:** Addresses the concerns of children in the American legal system by practical information regarding current juvenile, family, and educational law issues.
Indexed: FamI.
Published by: University of California at Davis, School of Law, Martin Luther King, Jr Hall, 400 Mrak Hall Drive, Davis, CA 95616-5201. jjlp@ucdavis.edu, http://www.law.ucdavis.edu/jjlp/. Ed. Kira L. Klatchko.

369.4 GBR
U K YOUTH; the network for quality work with young people. Text in English. 1911. bi-m. GBP 10 to individuals; GBP 20 to institutions. adv. bk.rev. **Document type:** *Consumer.*
Former titles (until 1997): Youth Clubs (0309-7315); (until 1977): N A Y C News
Indexed: ASSIA.
—BLDSC (9082.669600).
Published by: (Youth Clubs UK), Hobsons PLC, Bateman St, Cambridge, Cambs CB2 1LZ, United Kingdom. TEL 44-1223-460366, FAX 44-1223-301506. Ed. Alan Rogers. Adv. contact Carola Adams. Circ: 7,500.

305.230 DNK ISSN 0906-1592
UNDER PARAPLYEN. Text in Danish. 1941. 4/yr. DKK 50, USD 6. adv. bk.rev.; film rev.
Formerly: Du-Bladet (0109-8608)
Published by: Dansk Ungdoms Faellesraad/Danish Youth Council, Scherfigsvej 5, Copenhagen O, 2100, Denmark. TEL 45-39-29-88-88, FAX 45-39-29-83-82. Ed. Erling Boettcher. Circ: 10,000.

362.7 GBR ISSN 1476-6884
UNDERSTANDING CHILDREN'S SOCIAL CARE. Text in English. 2001. irreg., latest 2003, Feb. GBP 7.95 per vol. (effective 2003). **Document type:** *Monographic series, Academic/Scholarly.* **Description:** Reporting on research into children's services.
Published by: (Great Britain. Department of Health), University of London, Institute of Education, 20 Bedford Way, London, WC1H OAL, United Kingdom. TEL 44-20-76126000, FAX 44-20-76126126, mailto:info@ioe.ac.uk, http://www.ioe.ac.uk.

649 USA
UNION COUNTY FAMILY. Text in English. 1991. 8/yr. free. adv. 44 p./no. 4 cols./p.; **Document type:** *Magazine, Consumer.* **Description:** Provides New Jersey parents in Union County with tips on child rearing, health, education, child care, and other issues of importance.
Related titles: Online - full content ed.
Published by: Kids Monthly Publications, Inc., 1122 Rte. 22 W., Mountainside, NJ 07092. editor@njcountyfamily.com, ucfamily@aol.com, http://www.njcountyfamily.com/editorial/13-05/toc_1305.htm. Ed., R&P Farn Dupre. Pub. Cindy Mironovich. Adv. contact Andy Abramowitz. Circ: 250,000 (paid and free).

UNITED NATIONS CHILDREN'S FUND. ANNUAL REPORT. see *SOCIAL SERVICES AND WELFARE*

UNITED NATIONS CHILDREN'S FUND. PROGRAMME DIVISION. STAFF WORKING PAPERS SERIES. see *SOCIAL SERVICES AND WELFARE*

UNITED STATES YOUTH SOCCER. see *SPORTS AND GAMES—Ball Games*

UNSCHOOLERS NETWORK. see *EDUCATION—Teaching Methods And Curriculum*

790.019 DEU
UNSER ARBEITSBRIEF; Materialien fuer Jugendgruppenleiter. Text in German. 1965. m. **Document type:** *Journal, Trade.*
Published by: D J O - Deutsche Jugend in Europa Land Baden-Wuerttemberg e.V., Schlossstr 92, Stuttgart, 70176, Germany. TEL 49-711-625138, FAX 49-711-625168, zentrale@djobw.de, http://www.djobw.de.

649 DEU
UNSER BABY. Text in German. 1991. 4/yr. EUR 2.05 newsstand/cover (effective 2002). adv. **Document type:** *Magazine, Consumer.*
Published by: Klambt Verlag GmbH, Im Neudeck 1, Speyer, 67346, Germany. TEL 49-6232-3100, FAX 49-6232-310226, anzeigen@klambt.de, http://www.klambt.de. Adv. contact Anita Weiss. B&W page EUR 3,320, color page EUR 4,114. Circ: 65,273 (paid).

155.4 DEU ISSN 0342-5258
UNSERE JUGEND. Text in German. 1954. m. EUR 49.50; EUR 39.90 to students; EUR 9.90 newsstand/cover (effective 2005). adv. bk.rev. **Document type:** *Journal, Academic/Scholarly.*
Indexed: DIP, IBR, IBZ.
—CCC.
Published by: Ernst Reinhardt Verlag, Kemnatenstr 46, Munich, 80639, Germany. TEL 49-89-1780160, FAX 49-89-17801630, webmaster@reinhardt-verlag.de, http://www.reinhardt-verlag.de/deutsch/zeitschriften/fi_komplett.htm. Ed. Andreas Mehringer. adv.: page EUR 550. Circ: 1,800 (paid and controlled).

UP BEAT; leaders guide. see *RELIGIONS AND THEOLOGY*

UTAH. JUVENILE COURT. ANNUAL REPORT. see *LAW—Judicial Systems*

791.45 USA ISSN 1096-441X
VARIETY JUNIOR. Text in English. 1997. 5/yr. adv. illus. **Document type:** *Trade, Consumer.* **Description:** Covers entertainment for global children's market, from film and television to music, and technology.
Related titles: ♦ Supplement to: Variety. ISSN 0042-2738.
Published by: Reed Business Information (Subsidiary of: Reed Business), 5700 Wilshire Blvd, Ste 120, Los Angeles, CA 90036. TEL 323-857-6600, 323-965-4475, gbyrne@cahners.com, http://www.variety.com, http://www.reedbusiness.com. Circ: 20,000.

649 DEU
VATER - MUTTER - KIND. Text in German. 1928. 2/yr. free (effective 2005). adv. illus. **Document type:** *Magazine, Consumer.*
Formerly: Mutter und Kind (0047-8482)
—GNLM. CCC.
Published by: Buettner Medien GmbH, Sigmund-Freud-Str 77a, Frankfurt Am Main, 60435, Germany. TEL 49-69-7561900, FAX 49-69-75619041, sbuettner@buemed.de, http://www.buemed.de. adv.: B&W page EUR 12,971, color page EUR 20,672; trim 180 x 264. Circ: 320,000 (controlled).

649 FIN ISSN 0789-9238
VAUVA. Text in Finnish. 1992. 11/yr. EUR 59 (effective 2004). adv. **Document type:** *Magazine, Consumer.* **Description:** Provides professional information to parents of babies and small children on pregnancy, delivery, nursing and children's growth and development.
Published by: Sanoma Magazines Finland Corporation, Hoylaamotie 1 D, P.O. Box 100, Helsinki, 00040, Finland. TEL 358-9-1201, FAX 358-9-1205171, info@sanomamagazines.fi, http://www.vauva-lehti.fi, http://www.sanomamagazines.fi. Ed. Minna McGill. adv.: B&W page EUR 2,820, color page EUR 3,895; 194 x 248. Circ: 35,966 (paid).

649 RUS
VESELYE KARTINKI: IZDANIE DLYA VZROSLYKH. Text in Russian. bi-m. USD 72 in United States.
Published by: Redaktsiya Zhurnala Veselye Kartinki, Novodmitrovskaya ul 5-a, Moscow, 125015, Russian Federation. TEL 7-095-2851920, FAX 7-095-2857274. Ed. T A Varshamov. **US dist. addr.:** East View Information Services, 3020 Harbor Ln. N., Minneapolis, MN 55447. TEL 612-550-0961.

649 SWE ISSN 0346-4245
VI FOERAELDRAR. Text in Swedish. 1968. m. SEK 438; SEK 39.50 newsstand/cover (effective 2001). adv. **Document type:** *Magazine, Consumer.* **Description:** About children ages 0-3.
Published by: Bonnier Tidsskrifter AB, Sveavaegen 53, Stockholm, 10544, Sweden. TEL 46-8-736-53-00, FAX 46-8-34-00-43, vfo@bf.bonnier.se, bsf@bsf.bonnier.se. Ed. Helena Roennberg. Adv. contact Elsbrit Forsstroem. color page SEK 46,900; trim 190 x 265. Circ: 54,300.

649 372.21 DNK ISSN 1600-2482
VI FORAELDRE. Text in Danish. 1999. m. DKK 408 (effective 2005). adv. **Document type:** *Magazine, Consumer.* **Description:** For parents of children age 0 to 6 years.
Published by: Egmont Magasiner A/S, Hellerupvej 51, Hellerup, 2900, Denmark. TEL 45-39-457500, http://www.egmontmagasiner.dk. Ed. Christina Boelling. Adv. contact Pia Kensoe larsen TEL 45-39-457505. page DKK 35,800; 185 x 252. Circ: 12,403.

362.41108 AUS
VICTORIA. DEPARTMENT OF HUMAN SERVICES. COMMUNITY CARE DIVISION. ANNUAL REPORT OF INQUIRIES INTO CHILD DEATHS: PROTECTION AND CARE (YEAR). Text in English. a. back issues avail. **Document type:** *Government.*
Related titles: Online - full content ed.
Published by: Victoria. Department Of Human Services, Community Care Division (Subsidiary of: Victoria. Department of Human Services), Level 13, 555 Collin St, Melbourne, VIC 3000, Australia. TEL 61-3-9616-7121.

VILLAGE NEWS. see *SOCIAL SERVICES AND WELFARE*

VISABILITY. see *EDUCATION—Special Education And Rehabilitation*

C

▼ new title ➤ refereed ✶ unverified ♦ full entry avail.

053.931 028.5 NLD ISSN 0165-4462
VIVA. Text in Dutch. 1925. w. adv. bk.rev.; film rev.; play rev. illus.; tr.lit. index. **Document type:** *Magazine, Consumer.*
Formerly (until 1972): Eva (0014-3294)
Published by: V N U Tijdschriften B.V., Postbus 1900, Hoofddorp, 2130 JH, Netherlands. TEL 31-23-556-6770, FAX 31-23-556-6771, viva@tijdschriften.vnu.com, ServiceTeam@tijdschriften.vnu.com, http://www.vnu.nl/vnu/organisatie/t400.html. Ed. Tienekke Verhoeven. Circ: 126,108.

VOGUE BAMBINI. see *CLOTHING TRADE—Fashions*

362.7 USA ISSN 0160-4201
VOICE OF YOUTH ADVOCATES; the library magazine serving those who serve young adults. Variant title: V O Y A. Text in English. 1978. bi-m., latest vol.25. USD 45 domestic; USD 50 in Canada; USD 52 elsewhere (effective 2004). bk.rev.; film rev.; software rev.; video rev. bibl.; charts; illus. index. back issues avail.; reprints avail. **Document type:** *Journal, Academic/Scholarly.* **Description:** Contains articles, bibliographies, and media reviews of materials for or about adolescents.
Related titles: Microform ed.: (from PQC); Online - full text ed.: (from H.W. Wilson, O C L C Online Computer Library Center, Inc.).
Indexed: BRD, BRI, CBRI, CIJE, ChLitAb, LHTB, LibLit.
—BLDSC (9258.701500), IE, ingenta.
Published by: Scarecrow Press, Inc. (Subsidiary of: Rowman & Littlefield Publishers, Inc.), 4501 Forbes Blvd., Suite 200, Lanham, MD 20706. TEL 301-459-3366, 800-462-6420, FAX 301-429-5748, 800-338-4550, voya@voya.com, custserv@rowman.com, http://www.voya.com/, http://www.scarecrowpress.com. Ed. Cathi Dunn MacRae. Pub. Shirley Lambert. Circ: 6,000. **Orders to:** Scarecrow Subscriptions Dept., 15200 NBN Way, Blue Ridge Summit, PA 17214. TEL 717-794-3800, 800-462-6420, FAX 717-794-3803, 800-338-4550.

267 DEU
VON B BIS Y; Materialhefte fuer Gemeindejugendarbeit. Text in German. 1977. q. bk.rev. **Document type:** *Bulletin.* **Description:** Details Bible study, teacher training, lesson plans for group meetings, biographies, games, retreats and book discussions.
Published by: Oncken Verlag GmbH, Muendener Str 13, Kassel, 34123, Germany. zeitschriften@oncken.de. Ed. Volker Bohle. Circ: 1,500.

649 FRA
VOS ENFANTS. Text in French. 1971. bi-m. adv. illus.
Address: 1 ter rue Chotard, Ales, 30100, France. Ed. J C Manzano.

362.7 GBR ISSN 1745-0128
▼ ➤ **VULNERABLE CHILDREN AND YOUTH STUDIES**; an international interdisciplinary journal for research, policy and care. Text in English. forthcoming 2006. 3/yr. GBP 40, USD 72 to individuals; GBP 130, USD 234 to institutions (effective 2006). **Document type:** *Journal, Academic/Scholarly.* **Description:** Provides an interdisciplinary focus on vulnerable youth and youth at risk, specifically in relation to health and welfare issues, such as mental health, illness (including HIV/AIDS), disability, abuse, neglect, institutionalization, poverty, orphanhood, exploitation, war, famine, and disaster.
Related titles: Online - full text ed.: ISSN 1745-0136. forthcoming 2006.
Published by: Routledge (Subsidiary of: Taylor & Francis Group), 4 Park Sq, Milton Park, Abingdon, Oxon OX14 4RN, United Kingdom. TEL 44-1235-828600, FAX 44-1235-829000, info@routledge.co.uk, http://www.tandf.co.uk/journals/titles/17450128.asp, http://www.routledge.co.uk. Eds. Geoff Foster, Lorraine Sherr.

➤ **WACKENBERGER ECHO**; Stadtzeitung fuer den Saarbruecker Wackenberg. see *HOUSING AND URBAN PLANNING*

649 JPN
WATASHI NO AKACHAN/MY BABY. Text in Japanese. 1973. m. JPY 7,560 domestic; JPY 13,680 foreign (effective 2001). **Document type:** *Consumer.* **Description:** Covers baby nutrition, health, medicine, play, discipline and fasion for parents of babies and infants up to two years of age.
Published by: Shufunotomo Co. Ltd., 2-9 Kanda-Surugadai, Chiyoda-ku, Tokyo, 101-8911, Japan. TEL 81-3-5280-7521, FAX 81-3-5280-7421, information@shufunotomo.co.jp, http://www.shufunotomo.co.jp. Ed. Kazuhiko Mizuno. Circ: 90,000.

649 CHN ISSN 1000-4319
WEILE HAIZI/FOR THE CHILDREN. Text in Chinese. 1982. m. USD 26.
Published by: (Shanghai Funu Lianhehui/Shanghai Women's Association), Weile Haizi Zazhishe, 7 101 Lane, Songshan Lu, Shanghai, 200021, China. TEL 3264961. **Dist. in US by:** China Books & Periodicals Inc, 360 Swift Ave., Ste. 48, S San Fran, CA 94080-6220. TEL 415-282-2994.

WELT DES KINDES; Zeitschrift fuer Kleinkindpaedagogik und ausserschulische Erziehung. see *RELIGIONS AND THEOLOGY—Roman Catholic*

WENXUE SHAONIAN/ADOLESCENT LITERATURE. see *LITERATURE*

WEST SIDE STORY. see *EDUCATION*

649 USA ISSN 1043-6774
WESTCHESTER FAMILY; the magazine just for the Westchester County parent. Text in English. 1989. 11/yr. USD 22 (effective 2005). **Document type:** *Magazine, Consumer.* **Description:** Resource guide for parents includes a calendar of events.
Published by: United Parenting Publications (Subsidiary of: Trader Publishing Co.), 141 Halstead Ave, Ste 302, Mamaroneck, NY 10543. TEL 914-381-7474, 914-381-7474, FAX 914-381-7672, http://www.parenthood.com. Ed. Heather Hart. Pub. Felice Shapiro. Circ: 70,000 (controlled).

649 USA
WESTERN NEW YORK FAMILY. Text in English. 1984. m. **Description:** Regional parenting information.
Address: 287 Parkside Ave, Box 265, Buffalo, NY 14215-0265. TEL 716-836-3486, FAX 716-836-3680, wnyfamily@aol.com, http://www.wnyfamilymagazine.com, http://www.westernnewyork.com. Ed., Pub. Michele Miller. Circ: 22,500.

649 DEU
WILLKOMMEN BABY. Text in German. 1990. 2/yr. adv. **Document type:** *Magazine, Consumer.*
Published by: Junior-Verlag GmbH und Co. KG, Fehlandtstr 41, Hamburg, 20534, Germany. TEL 49-40-344434, FAX 49-40-352540, info@junior-verlag.de, http://www.junior-verlag.de/media/willkbaby.php3. Adv. contact Sabine Raum. color page EUR 15,000; trim 103 x 150. Circ: 220,000 (controlled).

WILSON ON CHILDREN AND THE LAW. see *POLITICAL SCIENCE—Civil Rights*

WISCONSIN JUVENILE COURT PRACTICE AND PROCEDURE. see *LAW—Judicial Systems*

649 USA
▼ **WONDERTIME.** Text in English. forthcoming 2006. q. **Document type:** *Magazine, Consumer.* **Description:** Covers issues on school, nutrition, and other topics affecting parents of pre-schoolers.
Published by: Family and Children's Magazine Group (Subsidiary of: Walt Disney Co.), 244 Main St, Northampton, MA 01060. Ed. Alexandra Kennedy.

649 AUS
WOOLWORTHS AUSTRALIAN PARENTS. Text in English. 1981. bi-m. AUD 19.95 domestic; AUD 37 in New Zealand; AUD 65 elsewhere; AUD 4.95 newsstand/cover (effective 2004). adv. bk.rev. charts; illus. Index. back issues avail. **Document type:** *Magazine, Consumer.* **Description:** Contains all-Australian parenting information to parents of newborns, toddlers and school-aged children, including advice from health experts, features on pregnancy and babies, development, early learning, health and nutrition, and relationships.
Former titles: Australia's Parents (1036-0921); (until 1991): Parents and Children Magazine (0725-8186); Australian Parents and Children Magazine; Australian Parents Magazine (0726-5026)
Related titles: Online - full text ed.: (from EBSCO Publishing).
Indexed: WBA, WMB.
Published by: The Federal Publishing Company, PO Box 199, Alexandria, NSW 1435, Australia. TEL 61-2-93530916, 300-656-933, contactus@fpc.com.au, http://www.parents.com.au/, http://www.fpc.com.au. Ed. Anne Lawton. adv.: page AUD 4,900. Circ: 73,000.

649 USA
WORKING MOMS AND DADS. Text in English. 1988. m. free. adv. bk.rev.; rec.rev.; software rev.; Website rev. illus. **Document type:** *Magazine, Consumer.* **Description:** Directed to working professionals interested in education, health care, child care, changing employment market and camp activities.
Published by: Corporate Marketing and Publishing Inc, 6506 E Calle Bellatrix, Ste 100, Tucson, AZ 85710-5329. TEL 520-790-4044. Ed., R&P Roberta R McGuire. Adv. contact Patrick McGuire TEL 520-790-4044. B&W page USD 1,360, color page USD 1,855; trim 13 x 14. Circ: 10,000 (controlled).

362.7 360 GBR
WORKING TOGETHER FOR CHILDREN IN NEED. CONFERENCE REPORT. Text in English. irreg., latest vol.11, 1996. **Document type:** *Monographic series.* **Description:** Aims to foster innovation and development in the care of abused and neglected children.
Formerly: Working Together for Children's Welfare. Conference Report (1343-5833)
Published by: Michael Sieff Foundation, 74 Cadogan Pl, London, SW1X 9RP, United Kingdom. TEL 44-171-565-0163, FAX 44-171-565-0163. Ed. Jonathan Cooley.

WORLD ALLIANCE OF Y M C A'S DIRECTORY. see *CLUBS*

▼ **WORLD PULSE (PORTLAND).** see *WOMEN'S STUDIES*

369.43 CHE
WORLD SCOUT ORGANIZATION REPORT. Text in English. 1922. triennial. CHF 15.
Former titles: World Scout Bureau Report; Boy Scouts World Bureau
Published by: (World Organization of the Scout Movement/Organisation Mondiale du Mouvement Scout), World Scout Bureau, Case Postale 241, Geneva 4, 1211, Switzerland. TEL 022-204233, FAX 022-7812053, http://www.best.be/OnlineNews/Scout/default.html.

369.4 CHE
WORLD SCOUTING NEWS/BULLETIN DU SCOUTISME MONDIAL. Text in English, French. 1969. m. looseleaf. CHF 42, USD 32. bk.rev.
Formerly: World Scouting Newsletter (0043-9002)
Published by: (World Organization of the Scout Movement/Organisation Mondiale du Mouvement Scout), World Scout Bureau, Case Postale 241, Geneva 4, 1211, Switzerland. TEL 022-204233, FAX 022-7812053, TELEX 428139-WSB-CH. Ed. Mark Clayton. Circ: 300.

WORLD VISION TODAY. see *RELIGIONS AND THEOLOGY—Protestant*

362.7 GBR ISSN 0043-9290
WORLD'S CHILDREN. Text in English. 1920. q. donation. illus. **Document type:** *Magazine, Consumer.* **Description:** International journal of Save the Children's development and relief work overseas.
Published by: Save the Children Fund, Mary Datchelor House, Grove Ln, London, SE5 8RD, United Kingdom. TEL 44-207-703-5400, FAX 44-207-703-2278, enquiries@scf.org.uk, http://www.savethechildren.org. Ed. Lotte Hughes. Circ: 150,000 (controlled).

XIANDAI JIATING/MODERN FAMILY. see *HOME ECONOMICS*

369.4 CHN
XIAO XUESHENG/ELEMENTARY SCHOOL PUPILS. Text in Chinese. m.
Published by: Shanxi Qingshaonian Baokan She, 43, Xinnan 4 Tiao, Qingnian Lu, Taiyuan, Shanxi 030001, China. TEL 222501. Ed. Duan Zhanxiang.

XIAOYISHUJIA/LITTLE ARTIST. see *ART*

369.4 CHN
XIN QINGNIAN/NEW YOUTH. Text in Chinese. 1978. m. CNY 2.50 per issue. adv. **Document type:** *Consumer.*
Published by: Gongqingtuan Heilongjiang Shengwei, 11, Ashihe Jie, Nangang-qu, Harbin, Heilongjiang 150001, China. TEL 0451-3642171. Ed. Yuan Qingguo. Adv. contact Wu Shengshan. **Dist. overseas by:** China International Book Trading Corp, 35 Chegongzhuang Xilu, Haidian District, PO Box 399, Beijing 100044, China.

790.019 CHN ISSN 1003-2975
XUE YU WAN/STUDY AND PLAY. Text in Chinese. 1983. m. CNY 18, USD 60 (effective 1994). adv. **Description:** Contains writings and drawings for teenagers.
Published by: Zhongguo Ertong Shaonian Huodong Zhongxin/Chinese Children Recreational Activities Center, Guanyuan, Beijing, 100035, China. TEL 6024589. Ed. Ma Guangfu. Adv. contact Han Jianxin. page CNY 9,000.

Y C - YOUNG CHILDREN. see *EDUCATION—Teaching Methods And Curriculum*

060 363 367 CHE
Y M C A WORLD. (Young Men's Christian Association) Text in English, Spanish. 1947. q. CHF 27 (effective 2001). adv. **Document type:** *Magazine, Consumer.*
Former titles (until 1992): World Communique; Y M C A World Communique; (until 1979): World Alliance of Young Men's Christian Associations. World Communique
Indexed: HRIR, RefugAb.
Published by: World Alliance of Young Men's Christian Associations, 12 Clos Belmont, Geneva, 1208, Switzerland. TEL 41-22-8495100, FAX 41-22-8495110, office@ymca.int, http://www.ymca.int. Ed. Helga Serrano. R&P Ranjan Solomon. Adv. contact Monika Rudiger. Circ: 3,300.

YES. see *WOMEN'S INTERESTS*

YINGER HUABAO/INFANT PICTORIAL. see *CHILDREN AND YOUTH—For*

362.41 GBR
YOU AND YOUR CHILD. Text in English. m. GBP 24 (effective 2000). **Description:** Offers blind and visually impaired parents and parents-to-be advice on all aspects of raising a child.
Media: Braille. **Related titles:** Diskette ed.
Published by: Royal National Institute for the Blind, Education, Training and Employment Division, 7 Poplar St, Fisher Gate, Nottingham, NG1 1GP, United Kingdom. cservices@rnib.org.uk, webmaster@rnib.org.uk, http://www.rnib.org.uk. **Subscr. to:** RNIB, PO Box 173, Peterborough, Cambs PE2 6WS, United Kingdom. TEL 44-1733-370777, FAX 44-1733-371555.

YOU'ER ZHILI SHIJIE/INFANTS' INTELLIGENCE WORLD. see *PSYCHOLOGY*

305.235 GBR ISSN 1103-3088
HQ796
➤ **YOUNG**; Nordic journal of youth research. Text in Norwegian. 1993. q. GBP 250, USD 437 to institutions; GBP 260, USD 455 combined subscription to institutions print & online eds. (effective 2006). adv. bk.rev. **Document type:** *Journal, Academic/Scholarly.* **Description:** Interdisciplinary journal of youth research, aimed at researchers, students and all who are interested in youth research.
Related titles: Online - full text ed.: ISSN 1552-8480. GBP 247, USD 433 to institutions (effective 2006) (from EBSCO Publishing, O C L C Online Computer Library Center, Inc., Sage Publications, Inc., Swets Information Services).
Indexed: BrEdI, CPE, ERA, FamI, IBSS, SociolAb.
—BLDSC (9421.384550), IE, ingenta. **CCC.**
Published by: Sage Publications Ltd. (Subsidiary of: Sage Publications, Inc.), 1 Oliver's Yard, 55 City Rd, London, EC1 1SP, United Kingdom. TEL 44-20-73248500, FAX 44-20-73248600, info@sagepub.co.uk, http://www.sagepub.co.uk/journal.aspx?pid=105812. Eds. Gestur Gudmundsson, Goran Bolin, Leena Suurpaa. Circ: 350. **Subscr. in the Americas to:** Sage Publications, Inc., 2455 Teller Rd, Thousand Oaks, CA 91320. TEL 805-499-0721, FAX 805-499-0871, journals@sagepub.com.

362.7 028.5 USA ISSN 1075-6523
YOUNG AMERICAN PRESS. Text in English. bi-m.
Published by: Young American Press, Inc., 2650 E 26th St, Brooklyn, NY 11235. TEL 718-332-7062. Ed. Jay Kwasnicki.

YOUNG EXCEPTIONAL CHILDREN. see *EDUCATION—Special Education And Rehabilitation*

790.019 USA
YOUNG IDEAS. Text in English. 1966. s-a. free (effective 2000). adv. bk.rev. illus. index. **Document type:** *Consumer.* **Description:** Reviews children's books, video tapes, cassette tapes and computer software.
Formerly: Vanguard (San Francisco) (0042-255X)
Media: Duplicated (not offset).
Indexed: BHA.
Published by: Vanguard Productions, 160 Aptos Ave, San Francisco, CA 94127-2521. TEL 415-337-1617. Ed. Keith St. Clare. Pub. Keith St Clare. Adv. contact Keith Oliver. Circ: 12,800.

YOUNG OFFENDERS SERVICE. see *LAW*

649 SGP
YOUNG PARENTS. Text in English. 1986. m. SGD 126 (effective 2000). adv. illus. 120 p./no. 3 cols./p.; **Document type:** *Consumer.* **Description:** For parents with growing children. Covers pregnancy, babyhood, the toddler years, and also children up to 13 years.
Published by: Times Periodicals Pte. Ltd., 422 Thomson Rd, Singapore, 298131, Singapore. TEL 65-255-0011, FAX 65-256-8016. Ed. Juleen Shaw. Adv. contact Leong Tscheng Yee. B&W page SGD 1,600, color page SGD 2,200; 205 x 275. Circ: 10,725.

362.41 GBR
YOUNG R N I B. Text in English. 3/yr. **Description:** Offers parents of visually impaired children advice on helping their youngsters with career matters.
Published by: Royal National Institute for the Blind, Education, Training and Employment Division, 7 Poplar St, Fisher Gate, Nottingham, NG1 1GP, United Kingdom. TEL 44-20-73881266, FAX 44-171-383-4921, http://www.rnib.org.uk. **Subscr. to:** RNIB, PO Box 173, Peterborough, Cambs PE2 6WS, United Kingdom. TEL 44-1733-370777, FAX 44-1733-317555.

369.4 UAE
YOUNG TIMES. Text in English. w. (every Tuesday). AED 95, BHD 10.40, QAR 104, OMR 11, KWD 9.50 (effective 2000). **Document type:** *Magazine, Consumer.*
Related titles: ♦ Supplement to: Khaleej Times.
Address: Subscription Agency, P O Box 11243, Dubai, United Arab Emirates. TEL 971-4-3382400, 971-4-3384545, FAX 971-4-3383345, 971-4-3383356, ktimes@emirates.net.ae. Ed. Mr. Surendra. Circ: 72,013.

YOUNGMINDS MAGAZINE. see *MEDICAL SCIENCES—Psychiatry And Neurology*

649.1 CAN ISSN 1188-2360
YOUR BABY. Text in French. 1991. 3/yr. adv. **Document type:** *Consumer.* **Description:** Published for parents of babies and toddlers from birth to 24 months.
Related titles: Online - full text ed.: (from Micromedia ProQuest, ProQuest Information & Learning); French ed.: Mon Enfant. ISSN 1188-2379; ♦ Special ed. of: Today's Parent. ISSN 0823-9258.
Published by: (Today's Parent Group), Professional Publishing Associates, 269 Richmond St W, Toronto, ON M5V 1X1, Canada. TEL 416-596-8680, FAX 416-596-1991. Ed. Holly Bennett. Pub. Kathy Bergen. Adv. contact Lauren McFarlane. Circ: 190,000 (controlled).

649.1 IRL ISSN 1393-1849
YOUR NEW BABY. Text in English. 1995. 3/yr. adv. **Document type:** *Magazine, Consumer.*
Published by: Smurfit Communications, 2 Clanwilliam Ct., Lower Mount St., Dublin, 2, Ireland. TEL 353-1-2405300, FAX 353-1-6619757, info@smurfit-comms.ie, http://www.smurfit.ie/comms. Adv. contact Bob McMahon. B&W page EUR 2,600, color page EUR 3,460; trim 210 x 297. Circ: 50,000 (paid and controlled).

YOUR PROM. see *CHILDREN AND YOUTH—For*

YOUTH ALIYAH REVIEW. see *ETHNIC INTERESTS*

362.7 GBR ISSN 0262-9798
CODEN: YOPOFA
YOUTH AND POLICY; the journal of critical analysis. Text in English. 1982. q. GBP 28; GBP 9 per issue (effective 2005). adv. bk.rev. back issues avail. **Document type:** *Journal, Academic/Scholarly.* **Description:** Devoted to the critical study of youth affairs and youth policy in Britain and in an international context. It maintains a balance between contributions and debates focused upon policy, practice and the issues confronting young people in society.
Indexed: ASSIA, IBSS, PSA, SEA, SOPODA, SSA, SociolAb, TEA.
—BLDSC (9421.509000), IE, ingenta.
Published by: National Youth Agency, Eastgate House, 19-23 Humberstone Rd, Leicester, LE5 3GJ, United Kingdom. TEL 44-116-2427350, FAX 44-116-2427444, andyh@nya.org.uk, nya@nya.org.uk, http://www.nya.org.uk/. Eds. Jean Spence, Ruth Gilchrist, Tony Jeffs. Circ: 1,500.

305.242 USA ISSN 0044-118X
HQ793
➤ **YOUTH & SOCIETY.** Text in English. 1969. q. USD 538, GBP 347 to institutions; USD 560, GBP 362 combined subscription to institutions print & online eds. (effective 2006). adv. bk.rev. illus. index. back issues avail.; reprints avail. **Document type:** *Journal, Academic/Scholarly.* **Description:** Covers the broad social and political implications of youth culture and development, focusing on middle adolescents to young adults.
Related titles: Microfilm ed.: (from PQC); Online - full text ed.: ISSN 1552-8499. USD 532, GBP 344 to institutions (effective 2006) (from C S A, Chadwyck-Healey Inc., EBSCO Publishing, Florida Center for Library Automation, Gale Group, O C L C Online Computer Library Center, Inc., Sage Publications, Inc., Swets Information Services).
Indexed: ABS&EES, AC&P, AMHA, ASCA, ASSIA, Agr, AmH&L, CDA, CIJE, CJA, CPE, ChPerI, CommAb, CurCont, EAA, ERA, ESPM, ETA, FamI, H&SSA, HEA, HECAB, HistAb, IPSA, MEA, MEA&I, PCI, PSA, PsycInfo, PsycholAb, RASB, RHEA, RILM, RiskAb, SEA, SENA, SFSA, SOMA, SOPODA, SRRA, SSA, SSCI, SSI, SUSA, SWA, SWR&A, SociolAb, TEA, V&AA, e-psyche.
—BLDSC (9421.510000), IDS, IE, Infotrieve, ingenta. **CCC.**
Published by: Sage Publications, Inc., 2455 Teller Rd, Thousand Oaks, CA 91320. TEL 805-499-0721, 800-818-7243, FAX 805-499-8096, 800-583-2665, info@sagepub.com, http://www.sagepub.com/journal.aspx?pid=69. Ed. Kathryn G Herr. Pub. Sara Miller McCune. R&P Tanya Udin TEL 805-499-0721 ext 7716. Adv. contact Kirsten Beaulieu TEL 805-499-0721 ext 7160. page USD 350. Circ: 700 (paid). **Overseas subscr. to:** Sage Publications India Pvt. Ltd., M-32 Market, Greater Kailash-I, PO Box 4215, New Delhi 110 048, India. FAX 91-11-647-2426, journalsubs@indiasage.com; **Subscr. to:** Sage Publications Ltd., 1 Oliver's Yard, 55 City Rd, London EC1 1SP, United Kingdom. TEL 44-20-73740645, FAX 44-20-73748741, subscription@sagepub.co.uk.

362.7 AUS ISSN 1440-8651
YOUTH FIELD XPRESS. Text in English. 1995. m. free. Website rev. back issues avail. **Document type:** *Newsletter, Academic/Scholarly.*
Formerly (until 1997): Youth Monitor (1325-2461)
Related titles: Online - full content ed.
Published by: Australian Clearinghouse for Youth Studies, Private Bag 64, Hobart, TAS 7001, Australia. TEL 61-3-6226-2591, FAX 61-3-6226-2578, http://www.acys.utas.edu.au/ncys/yfx/. Ed. Anne Hugo. Circ: 1,500.

362.7 AUS ISSN 0817-5586
YOUTH ISSUES FORUM✶. Text in English. s-a. abstr.; charts; illus. back issues avail. **Document type:** *Academic/Scholarly.* **Description:** Issues about and for workers with young people, including latest research, resources, policy and issues of debate facing the youth sector.
Published by: Youth Affairs Council of Victoria, Level 6, 1 Elizabeth St, Melbourne, VIC 3000, Australia. TEL 61-3-9612-8999, FAX 61-3-9620-4802. Ed. Merryl Key.

YOUTH JUSTICE. see *CRIMINOLOGY AND LAW ENFORCEMENT*

YOUTH LAW NEWS. see *LAW*

649 CAN ISSN 1482-7069
YOUTH LINK. Text in English. 1998. a. **Document type:** *Government.* **Description:** Provides information and resources for 15 to 30 year olds as well as career counselors, parents, educators, employers and community groups.
Related titles: Online - full content ed.: ISSN 1495-9925.
Published by: Human Resources Development Canada, Public Enquiries Centre, 140 Promenade du Portage, Hull, PQ K1A 0J9, Canada. FAX 819-953-7260, http://www.youth.gc.ca/.

305.235 USA ISSN 8756-0909
YOUTH POLICY. Text in English. 1978. irreg. (approx. 12/yr.). USD 127; includes Youth Record. bk.rev. index. back issues avail. **Description:** Policy forum for a broad, comprehensive discussion of issues and presentation of proposed solutions and their status.
Incorporates (1977-199?): American Family (Washington) (0161-1178)
Indexed: Agr, ERA, PAIS.
Published by: Youth Policy Institute, 1320 Fenwick Ln., Ste. 506, Silver Spring, MD 20910-3560. TEL 202-638-2144, FAX 202-638-2325, corpsnet@mnsinc.com. Ed. David Hackett. Circ: 4,500.

353.5 USA ISSN 1047-7144
HV1431
YOUTH RECORD; the semi-monthly report on federal youth-related policy. Text in English. s-m. USD 97 domestic; USD 237 foreign; includes Youth Policy. **Description:** Covers current news of federal legislative and executive actions, and the private sector. Presents viewpoints, solution options and outlook on youth-related policy in areas of housing, health, social services and more.
Published by: Youth Policy Institute, 1320 Fenwick Ln., Ste. 506, Silver Spring, MD 20910-3560. TEL 202-638-2144, FAX 202-638-2325, corpsnet@mnsinc.com. Ed. David Hackett.

YOUTH RESEARCH NEWS. see *CHILDREN AND YOUTH—For*

362.7 AUS ISSN 1038-2569
➤ **YOUTH STUDIES AUSTRALIA.** Text in English. 1987. q. AUD 55 in Australia & New Zealand; AUD 90, USD 60 foreign (effective 2004). adv. bk.rev. abstr.; bibl. cum.index. 64 p./no.; back issues avail. **Document type:** *Journal, Academic/Scholarly.* **Description:** Focuses on issues affecting Australians from early adolescence to young adulthood; for researchers, youth workers, policy makers, health and community practitioners. Includes feature articles, research date, media monitoring and information sources.
Former titles (until 1991): Youth Studies (1035-0888); (until 1989): Youth Studies and Abstracts (0818-7886); Which was formed by the merger of (1981-1987): Youth Studies Abstracts (0813-6211); Which was formerly (until 1984): National Clearinghouse on Transition from School. Abstracts (0729-6606); (1981-1987): Youth Studies (0817-4733); Which was formerly (until 1986): Youth Studies Bulletin (0813-6203); (until 1984): National Clearinghouse on Transition from School. Newsletter (0729-7858); (until 1981): National Clearinghouse on Transition from School. Review Paper (0729-6649)
Related titles: Online - full text ed.: (from EBSCO Publishing, Gale Group).
Indexed: AEI, AbHyg, AusPAIS, RRTA, S&F, WAE&RSA, WBA, WMB.
—BLDSC (9421.581300), IE, ingenta.
Published by: Australian Clearinghouse for Youth Studies, Private Bag 64, Hobart, TAS 7001, Australia. TEL 61-3-6226-2591, FAX 61-3-6226-2578, acys@educ.utas.edu.au, http://www.acys.utas.edu.au/ysa/. Ed., Pub., R&P Sheila Allison. Adv. contact Kathleen Robinson. page AUD 300; trim 210 x 260. Circ: 1,400 (paid).

305 USA ISSN 1089-6724
HQ796
YOUTH TODAY. Text in English. 1992. 10/yr. USD 24.50 (effective 2005); free to qualified personnel (effective 2003). **Document type:** *Newspaper.* **Description:** Addresses youth and youth serving groups, and public policy interest to the youth service field.
Related titles: Online - full text ed.: (from bigchalk, ProQuest Information & Learning, SoftLine Information).
Indexed: AltPI.
Published by: American Youth Work Center, 1200 17th St., NW, 4th Fl, Washington, DC 20036. TEL 202-785-0764, 800-599-2455, FAX 202-728-0657, info@youthtoday.org, http://www.youthtoday.org/youthtoday. Circ: 59,000.

▼ **YOUTH VIOLENCE AND JUVENILE JUSTICE.** see *CRIMINOLOGY AND LAW ENFORCEMENT*

▼ **YOUTH VIOLENCE, CRIME, AND GANGS**; children at risk. see *CRIMINOLOGY AND LAW ENFORCEMENT*

Z - DIE ZEITUNG FUER EVANGELISCHE JUGENDARBEIT. see *RELIGIONS AND THEOLOGY—Protestant*

649 DEU ISSN 1439-586X
ZEITSCHRIFT FUER TAGESMUETTER UND -VAETER. Abbreviated title: Ze T. Text in German. 1978. bi-m. EUR 24; EUR 6 newsstand/cover (effective 2004). adv. **Document type:** *Journal, Consumer.*
Former titles (until 1999): Tagesmuetter (1434-4300); (until 1995): Tagesmuetter, Pflegeeltern (0947-6679); (until 1991): Tagesmuetter (0172-7524)
Indexed: DIP, IBR, IBZ.

C

Published by: Kallmeyersche Verlagsbuchhandlung GmbH, Im Brande 19, Seelze, 30926, Germany. TEL 49-511-40004175, FAX 49-511-40004176, leserservice@kallmeyer.de, http://www.kallmeyer.de. Circ: 1,500 (paid); 4,000 (controlled).

155.4 362.7 USA ISSN 0736-8038 CODEN: JWMOEL
ZERO TO THREE. Text in English. 1980. 6/yr. USD 72 domestic; USD 87 foreign (effective 2005). bk.rev. **Document type:** *Bulletin.* **Description:** A multidisciplinary resource on infants, toddlers, and families, intended to strengthen the critical roles of professionals, policymakers, and parents in giving young children the best possible start in life.
Related titles: Microfiche ed.
Indexed: ABIn, CIJE, CINAHL, EduInd, FamI, PsycholAb. —BLDSC (9512.114970), GNLM, IE, ingenta. **CCC.**
Published by: Zero to Three - National Center for Infants, Toddlers and Families, 2000 M St NW, Ste. 200, Washington, DC 20036-3380. TEL 800-899-4301, FAX 202-638-0851, efenichel@zerotothree.org, http://www.zerotothree.org/ztt_journal.html. Ed. Emily Fenichel. R&Ps Betty Johnson, Nancy Guadagno. Circ: 7,500.

ZHONGGUO ERTONG/CHINESE CHILDREN. see *CHILDREN AND YOUTH—For*

028.5 649 CHN
ZHONGGUO ERTONG BAO/CHINA CHILDREN'S NEWS. Text in Chinese. 1946. w. CNY 40.80 (effective 2004). **Document type:** *Newspaper, Academic/Scholarly.*
Published by: Zhongguo Shaonan Ertong Xinwen Chubanzongshe/China Children's Press & Publication Group, Zhaoyang-qu, 5, Zuojiazhuang Beili, Beijing, 100028, China. TEL 86-10(UNKNOWN CHARACTER)84541086, webmaster@ccppg.com.cn, http://www.ccppg.com.cn/a/etb/index.htm. **Dist. by:** China International Book Trading Corp, 35 Chegongzhuang Xilu, Haidian District, PO Box 399, Beijing 100044, China. TEL 86-10-68412045, FAX 86-10-68412023, cibtc@mail.cibtc.com.cn, http://www.cibtc.com.cn.

028.5 649 CHN
ZHONGGUO ERTONG HUABAO/CHINESE CHILDREN'S PICTORIAL. Text in Chinese. 1994. w. CNY 36 (effective 2004). **Document type:** *Newspaper, Academic/Scholarly.*
Published by: Zhongguo Shaonan Ertong Xinwen Chubanzongshe/China Children's Press & Publication Group, Zhaoyang-qu, 5, Zuojiazhuang Beili, Beijing, 100028, China. TEL 86-10(UNKNOWN CHARACTER)84541086, webmaster@ccppg.com.cn, http://www.ccppg.com.cn/z/ethb/index.htm. **Dist. by:** China International Book Trading Corp, 35 Chegongzhuang Xilu, Haidian District, PO Box 399, Beijing 100044, China. TEL 86-10-68412045, FAX 86-10-68412023, cibtc@mail.cibtc.com.cn, http://www.cibtc.com.cn.

369.4 CHN ISSN 1002-9931
HQ799.C5
ZHONGGUO QINGNIAN YANJIU/CHINA YOUTH STUDY. Text in Chinese. bi-m. USD 18. **Document type:** *Academic/Scholarly.*
Related titles: Online - full text ed.: (from East View Information Services).
Published by: Zhongguo Qingnian Yanjiu Zazhishe, No 25 Xisanhuan Beilu, Beijing, 100081, China. TEL 86-10-8421144, FAX 86-10-8426270. Ed. Huang Zhijian. Circ: 10,000.

028.5 649 CHN
ZHONGGUO ZHONGXUESHENG BAO/CHINESE MIDDLE SCHOOL STUDENTS GAZETTE. Text in Chinese. 1989. s-w. CNY 69 (effective 2004). **Document type:** *Newspaper, Academic/Scholarly.*
Published by: Zhongguo Shaonan Ertong Xinwen Chubanzongshe/China Children's Press & Publication Group, Zhaoyang-qu, 5, Zuojiazhuang Beili, Beijing, 100028, China. TEL 86-10(UNKNOWN CHARACTER)84541086, webmaster@ccppg.com.cn, http://www.ccppg.com.cn/a/zxs/index.htm. **Dist. by:** China International Book Trading Corp, 35 Chegongzhuang Xilu, Haidian District, PO Box 399, Beijing 100044, China. TEL 86-10-68412045, FAX 86-10-68412023, cibtc@mail.cibtc.com.cn, http://www.cibtc.com.cn.

369.4 CHN
ZHONGWAI SHAONIAN. Text in Chinese. bi-m.
Published by: Guangxi Renmin Chubanshe, Qikan Bu/Guangxi People's Publishing House, 14 Heti Lu, Nanning, Guangxi 530021, China. TEL 24571. Ed. Li Yuanjun.

155.5 ARG
ZONA ROJA. Text in Spanish. 1991. bi-m. ARS 20,000 per issue.
Published by: Comite Nacional de la Juventud Radical, Alsino 1786, 4o piso, Capital Federal, Buenos Aires, Argentina. TEL 54-114-3186828. Ed. Sergio Pardo.

649 DEU ISSN 0940-8843
ZWILLINGE; Zeitschrift fuer Mehrlingseltern. Text in German. 1988. m. EUR 3.60 newsstand/cover (effective 2002). adv. bk.rev. illus.; tr.lit. **Document type:** *Magazine, Consumer.*
Published by: Verlag Lutz von Gratkowski, Postfach 1717, Landsberg, 86887, Germany. TEL 49-8191-966739, FAX 49-8191-966740, redaktion@zeitschrift-zwillinge.de. Ed., R&P, Adv. contact Marion von Gratkowski. B&W page EUR 500, color page EUR 1,300. Circ: 5,800 (paid).

0 - 25. see *EDUCATION*

649 371.9 USA ISSN 1546-0762
▼ **2E: TWICE-EXCEPTIONAL NEWSLETTER.** Text in English. 2003. bi-m. USD 45 (effective 2004). illus. **Document type:** *Newsletter, Consumer.*
Related titles: Online - full text ed.
Published by: Glen Ellyn Media, 985 Clifton, P O Box 582, Glen Ellyn, IL 60137. TEL 630-790-2252, FAX 630-790-2267, http://www.2enewsletter.com, info@glenellynmedia.com. Ed. Linda C Neumann.

649 BEL
12 MAANDEN. Text in Dutch. 1987. a. free. adv. back issues avail. **Document type:** *Consumer.* **Description:** Covers the first year of a baby's life for young mothers.
Formerly (until 1995): Eerste 12 Maanden (0778-1881)
Related titles: French ed.: 12 Mois.
Published by: C & B s.a., Chemin des Deux Maisons 61-5, Brussels, 1200, Belgium. TEL 32-2-7624139, FAX 32-2-7706429. Ed. Philippe Derecque. Circ: 62,400.

649 USA
THE 21ST CENTURY: WRITTEN ENTIRELY BY TEENS FOR TEENS. Text in English. 1989. m. USD 25 (effective 2000). **Document type:** *Magazine, Consumer.* **Description:** Contains stories, poems, art reviews and artwork produced by teens from across the nation.
Published by: Young Authors Foundation, PO Box 30, Newton, MA 02461. TEL 617-964-6800.

100 BEST BOOKS. see *PUBLISHING AND BOOK TRADE*

CHILDREN AND YOUTH—Abstracting, Bibliographies, Statistics

A L A'S GUIDE TO BEST READING. see *LIBRARY AND INFORMATION SCIENCES—Abstracting, Bibliographies, Statistics*

AUSTRALIA. BUREAU OF STATISTICS. AUSTRALIAN CAPITAL TERRITORY'S YOUNG PEOPLE. see *REAL ESTATE—Abstracting, Bibliographies, Statistics*

362.7021 AUS ISSN 1037-7921
AUSTRALIA. BUREAU OF STATISTICS. CHILD CARE, AUSTRALIA. Text in English. 1969. triennial. AUD 23 (effective 2003). **Document type:** *Government.* **Description:** Focuses on the family unit with children ages 0-11 years classified by type and hours of childcare, multiplicity of care, day-frequency of care, number and age of children, weekly cost of care and other areas.
Former titles: Child Care Arrangements, Australia (0728-6368); (until 1980): Child Care (Canberra) (0728-6376)
Published by: Australian Bureau of Statistics, PO Box 10, Belconnen, ACT 2616, Australia. TEL 61-2-6252-5249, FAX 61-2-6252-6778, http://www.abs.gov.au. Circ: 234.

333.33021 AUS
AUSTRALIA. BUREAU OF STATISTICS. CHILDREN, AUSTRALIA: A SOCIAL REPORT. Text in English. 1989. irreg., latest 1999. AUD 30 (effective 2003). **Document type:** *Government.* **Description:** Focuses on family life, physical environment, economic environment, health, education and community participation.
Formerly: Australia. Bureau of Statistics. Children in Australia: A Social Report
Published by: Australian Bureau of Statistics, PO Box 10, Belconnen, ACT 2616, Australia. TEL 61-2-6252-5249, FAX 61-2-6252-6778, http://www.abs.gov.au.

AUSTRALIA. BUREAU OF STATISTICS. NEW SOUTH WALES OFFICE. NEW SOUTH WALES' YOUNG PEOPLE. see *REAL ESTATE—Abstracting, Bibliographies, Statistics*

AUSTRALIA. BUREAU OF STATISTICS. NORTHERN TERRITORY OFFICE. NORTHERN TERRITORY'S YOUNG PEOPLE. see *REAL ESTATE—Abstracting, Bibliographies, Statistics*

AUSTRALIA. BUREAU OF STATISTICS. QUEENSLAND OFFICE. QUEENSLAND'S YOUNG PEOPLE. see *REAL ESTATE—Abstracting, Bibliographies, Statistics*

AUSTRALIA. BUREAU OF STATISTICS. SOUTH AUSTRALIAN OFFICE. SOUTH AUSTRALIA'S YOUNG PEOPLE. see *REAL ESTATE—Abstracting, Bibliographies, Statistics*

AUSTRALIA. BUREAU OF STATISTICS. TASMANIAN OFFICE. TASMANIA'S YOUNG PEOPLE. see *REAL ESTATE—Abstracting, Bibliographies, Statistics*

AUSTRALIA. BUREAU OF STATISTICS. VICTORIAN OFFICE. VICTORIA'S YOUNG PEOPLE. see *REAL ESTATE—Abstracting, Bibliographies, Statistics*

AUSTRALIA. BUREAU OF STATISTICS. WESTERN AUSTRALIAN OFFICE. WESTERN AUSTRALIA'S YOUNG PEOPLE. see *REAL ESTATE—Abstracting, Bibliographies, Statistics*

333.33021 AUS
AUSTRALIA. BUREAU OF STATISTICS. YOUTH, AUSTRALIA: A SOCIAL REPORT. Text in English. 1984. irreg., latest 1997. AUD 27 (effective 2001). **Document type:** *Government.* **Description:** Includes population, living arrangements and housing, education and training, employment, health, crime and justice, and social participation.
Published by: Australian Bureau of Statistics, PO Box 10, Belconnen, ACT 2616, Australia. TEL 61-2-6252-5249, FAX 61-2-6252-6778, http://www.abs.gov.au.

028.16 AUS
AUSTRALIAN BUREAU OF STATISTICS. DIRECTORY OF CHILD & FAMILY STATISTICS. Text in English. 1989. a. **Document type:** *Directory.*
Published by: Australian Bureau of Statistics, Family & Community Statistics Section, Canberra, ACT, Australia. TEL 61-2-62527030, FAX 61-2-62528007.

028 016 DEU ISSN 0943-2795
BEITRAEGE JUGENDLITERATUR UND MEDIEN. Text in German. 1893; N.S. 1949. q. EUR 37.20 domestic; EUR 43.50 foreign (effective 2003). adv. bk.rev. bibl. **Document type:** *Abstract/Index.*
Former titles (until 1993): Informationen Jugendliteratur und Medien (0937-6755); (until 1989): Information Jugendliteratur und Medien - Jugendschriften - Warte (0340-7756)
Indexed: DIP, IBR, IBZ.
—CCC.
Published by: (Gewerkschaft Erziehung und Wissenschaft, Arbeitsgemeinschaft Jugendliteratur und Medien), Juventa Verlag GmbH, Ehretstr 3, Weinheim, 69469, Germany. TEL 49-6201-90200, FAX 49-6201-902013, juventa@juventa.de, http://www.juventa.de. Eds. Gudrun Stenzel, Petra Josting, Steffen Peltsch. Adv. contact Annette Hopp. page EUR 250; trim 113 x 193. Circ: 1,300 (paid and controlled).

BERLIN. SENATSVERWALTUNG FUER FRAUEN, JUGEND UND FAMILIE. STATISTISCHER DIENST. see *SOCIAL SERVICES AND WELFARE—Abstracting, Bibliographies, Statistics*

016.0285 USA
BEST BOOKS FOR CHILDREN; preschool through grade 6. Text in English. irreg., latest 2001. USD 65 (effective 2003). **Document type:** *Bibliography.* **Description:** Provides an evaluative listing of more than 18,000 titles that have been recommended by at least two review sources.
Published by: Greenwood Publishing Group Inc. (Subsidiary of: Harcourt International), 88 Post Rd W, PO Box 5007, Westport, CT 06881. TEL 203-226-3571, FAX 203-226-1502, http://www.greenwood.com.

028.5 010 USA ISSN 0067-9070
BLACK EXPERIENCE IN CHILDREN'S BOOKS. Text in English. 1946. quinquennial. USD 6 (effective 2000). index.
Formerly: Books About Negro Life for Children
Published by: New York Public Library, Office of Branch Libraries, 455 Fifth Ave, New York, NY 10016. TEL 212-340-0892, FAX 212-689-3193.

BREASTFEEDING ABSTRACTS. see *MEDICAL SCIENCES—Abstracting, Bibliographies, Statistics*

CANDLELIGHTERS CHILDHOOD CANCER FOUNDATION BIBLIOGRAPHY AND RESOURCE GUIDE. see *MEDICAL SCIENCES—Abstracting, Bibliographies, Statistics*

016.66276 USA
HV713
CHILD ABUSE, CHILD WELFARE & ADOPTION. Text in English. 1993. s-a. free to qualified personnel; Free to institutions and libraries. adv. **Document type:** *Abstract/Index.* **Description:** Provides access to information on child abuse: documents, legal statutes, public awareness materials, audiovisual resources and local, state, federal and international programs.
Formerly: Child Abuse & Neglect (1078-6651)
Media: CD-ROM. **Related titles:** Online - full text ed.: (from National Information Services Corp. (N I S C)).
Published by: (National Clearinghouse on Child Abuse & Neglect Information), National Information Services Corp. (N I S C), Ste 6, Wyman Towers, 3100 St Paul St, Baltimore, MD 21218. TEL 410-243-0797, FAX 410-243-0982, sales@nisc.com, http://www.nisc.com. Ed., Pub. Fred Durr. Adv. contact Debbie Durr. **Subscr. to:** National Clearinghouse on Child Abuse & Neglect Information, PO Box 1182, Washington, DC 20013-1182. TEL 703-385-7565, 800-394-3366, FAX 703-385-3206, NCCANCH@calib.com.

362.7 GBR ISSN 0958-5028
CHILD PROTECTION REGISTER: STATISTICS FOR WALES. Text in English. a. GBP 5 (effective 2000). **Document type:** *Government.* **Description:** Statistics on the number of children recorded on the Child Protection Registers by age, sex and category of abuse.
Published by: National Assembly of Wales, Statistical Directorate, Cathays Park, Cardiff, CF10 3NQ, United Kingdom. TEL 44-2920-825054, FAX 44-2920-825350, stats.pubs@wales.gsi.gov.uk.

028.1 USA ISSN 0147-5681
Z1037.A1
CHILDREN'S BOOK REVIEW INDEX. Text in English. 1976. a., latest 2003. USD 185 (effective 2005). illus. Index. back issues avail.; reprints avail. **Document type:** *Abstract/Index.*
Description: Indexes book reviews of children's books.
Related titles: Online - full text ed.
Published by: Gale Group (Subsidiary of: Thomson Corporation), 27500 Drake Rd, Farmington Hills, MI 48331-3535. TEL 248-699-4253, FAX 248-699-8035, galeord@gale.com, http://www.gale.com.

028.5 USA
CHILDREN'S BOOKWATCH. Text in English. 1980. m. USD 12 (effective 2000). back issues avail. **Document type:** *Newsletter, Trade.* **Description:** Capsule reviews of children's literature for librarians and teachers.
Indexed: BRI, CBRI.
Published by: Midwest Book Review, 278 Orchard Dr, Oregon, WI 53575. TEL 608-835-7937. Eds. Diane C Donovan, James A Cox. Circ: 5,000 (paid).

016 USA
CHILDREN'S CATALOG. Text in English. 1909. quinquennial (plus 4 supplements) (in 1 vol.), latest 18th Ed. USD 185 in US & Canada 5-year service (effective 2006). bk.rev. Supplement avail. **Document type:** *Catalog, Bibliography.*
Description: Classified list of books recommended for children from pre-school through sixth grade, with separate sections for fiction, story collections, and easy books. Includes author, title, subject, and analytical index.
Related titles: Online - full text ed.: USD 170 in US & Canada (effective 2006).
Published by: H.W. Wilson Co., 950 University Ave, Bronx, NY 10452-4224. TEL 718-588-8400, 800-367-6770, FAX 718-590-1617, 800-590-1617, custserv@hwwilson.com, http://www.hwwilson.com/print/childcat.htm. Ed. Juliette Yaakov.

011.0285 USA
CHILDREN'S CHOICES. Text in English. a. USD 1. **Document type:** *Bibliography.* **Description:** Offers teachers and parents a list of new books and perennial classics that children from across the US have selected as their favorites. Annotations and bibliographic data accompany each title.
Published by: (IRA - CBC Joint Committee), International Reading Association, Inc., 800 Barksdale Rd, Newark, DE 19714-8139. TEL 302-731-1600, 800-336-7323, FAX 302-368-2449, journals@reading.org, http://www.reading.org.
Co-sponsor: Children's Book Council.

028.5 011 USA ISSN 0743-9873
AI3
CHILDREN'S MAGAZINE GUIDE; subject index to children's magazines and web sites. Text in English. 1948. 9/yr. (includes a. cumulation (Aug.)). USD 69.95 domestic; USD 75 foreign; USD 10 newsstand/cover (effective 2006). illus. reprints avail. **Document type:** *Magazine, Abstract/Index.*
Description: Indexes more than 60 children's magazines widely used in schools, libraries, and at home. Points elementary and middle school students to a wide range of recent articles and Web Sites they need for school assignments, science projects, or just for fun, including information about science, sports, current events, popular culture, art and more. Every citation includes the name of the article, author, magazine, issue date, and number of pages. Many citations also feature a brief annotation.
Formerly (until 1981): Subject Index to Children's Magazines (0039-4351)
Published by: Greenwood Publishing Group Inc. (Subsidiary of: Harcourt International), 88 Post Rd W, PO Box 5007, Westport, CT 06881. TEL 203-226-3571, 800-225-5800, FAX 603-431-2214, lynn.wright@greenwood.com, http://www.childrensmag.com, http://www.greenwood.com. Circ: 3,000.

649 ZAF
CHILDREN'S STATISTICAL NEWSLETTER. Text in English. irreg. Free. **Document type:** *Newsletter, Government.*
Published by: Statistics South Africa/Statistieke Suid-Afrika, Private Bag X44, Pretoria, 0001, South Africa. TEL 27-12-310-8911, FAX 27-12-310-8500, info@statssa.pwv.gov.za, http://www.statssa.gov.za.

016.1554 USA ISSN 0147-1082
CONTEMPORARY PROBLEMS OF CHILDHOOD; a bibliographic series. Text in English. 1977. irreg. price varies. **Document type:** *Bibliography.*
Published by: Greenwood Publishing Group Inc. (Subsidiary of: Harcourt International), 88 Post Rd W, PO Box 5007, Westport, CT 06881. TEL 203-226-3571, FAX 203-226-1502, bookinfo@greenwood.com, http://www.greenwood.com. Ed. Carol Ann Winchell.

FOR YOUNGER READERS, BRAILLE AND TALKING BOOKS. see *HANDICAPPED—Abstracting, Bibliographies, Statistics*

GERMANY. STATISTISCHES BUNDESAMT. FACHSERIE 13, SOZIALLEISTUNGEN, REIHE 6: JUGENDHILFE. see *SOCIAL SERVICES AND WELFARE—Abstracting, Bibliographies, Statistics*

028.5 DEU
GRUENBUCH DER KINDER- UND JUGENDMEDIEN. Text in German. a. **Document type:** *Bibliography.*
Published by: Eulenhof Verlag, Sartoriusstr 22, Hamburg, 20257, Germany. TEL 49-40-490005-0, FAX 49-40-49000515, verlag@eulenhof.de, http://www.eulenhof.de. Circ: 4,000 (paid).

KINDEX; an index to legal periodical literature concerning children. see *LAW—Abstracting, Bibliographies, Statistics*

362.7 PRY ISSN 1017-2807
MENORES. Text in Spanish. 1989. q. USD 10.
Published by: Centro de Estudios Humanitarios, AZARA, 3267, Asuncion, Paraguay. Ed. Esther Prieto. Circ: 500.

NETHERLANDS. CENTRAAL BUREAU VOOR DE STATISTIEK. JEUGD: FEITEN EN CIJFERS. see *POPULATION STUDIES—Abstracting, Bibliographies, Statistics*

NOTABLE SOCIAL STUDIES TRADE BOOKS FOR YOUNG PEOPLE. see *SOCIAL SCIENCES: COMPREHENSIVE WORKS—Abstracting, Bibliographies, Statistics*

OHIO. DEPARTMENT OF HUMAN SERVICES. CHILD WELFARE STATISTICS. see *SOCIAL SERVICES AND WELFARE—Abstracting, Bibliographies, Statistics*

800 011 500 USA
OUTSTANDING SCIENCE TRADE BOOKS FOR CHILDREN. Text in English. 1971. a. USD 2 (effective 2004). **Document type:** *Bibliography.* **Description:** Annotated, committee-selected bibliography of the year's most outstanding science trade books for children, kindergarten to eighth grade.
Published by: (National Science Teachers Association, Joint Committee Project), Children's Book Council, Inc., 12 W. 37th St., Flr. 2, New York, NY 10018-7391. Staff@CBCBooks.org, staff@cbcbooks.org, http://www.CBCBooks.org., http://www.cbcbooks.org. Ed. Gitta Raffelsbauer.

PARAPARA SELECCION DE LIBROS PARA NINOS Y JOVENES. see *PUBLISHING AND BOOK TRADE*

016.0285 USA
PICTURE BOOKS FOR CHILDREN. Text in English. irreg., latest vol.4, 1997. USD 40 to non-members; USD 36 to members.
Description: Reviews recent children's picture books.
Published by: (Association for Library Collections and Technical Services), American Library Association, 50 E Huron St, Chicago, IL 60611-2795. TEL 800-545-2433, http://www.ala.org. Ed. Patricia J Cianciolo. **Subscr. to:** PO Box 932501, Atlanta, GA 31193-2501. TEL 866-746-7252, FAX 770-442-9742, ala-orders@pbd.com.

016.285 USA
S I R S DISCOVERER. (Social Issues Resources Series) Text in English. 1994. s-a. USD 630 (effective 2003). charts; illus.; maps. **Document type:** *Abstract/Index.* **Description:** General reference database for young researchers grades 1 to 9 which develops research, reading, writing, language and computer skills. Full-text articles and graphics are from more than 1,200 domestic and international publications.
Formerly: S I R S Discoverer Deluxe Edition
Media: CD-ROM. **Related titles:** Online - full text ed.
Published by: S I R S Publishing, Inc., PO Box 272348, Boca Raton, FL 33427-2348. TEL 561-994-0079, 800-232-7477, FAX 561-994-4704, custserve@sirs.com, http://www.sirs.com/products/dow.htm. Ed. Lori Weisman. Pub. Eleanor Goldstein. R&P Cynthia Klivecka. Adv. contact Linda Manis.

016.285 USA
S I R S DISCOVERER ELEMENTARY EDITION. (Social Issues Resources Series) Text in English. 1994. s-a. USD 430 (effective 2002). charts; illus.; maps. **Document type:** *Abstract/Index.* **Description:** General reference database for young researchers grades 1 to 6 which develops research, reading, writing, language and computer skills. Full-text articles and graphics are from more than 700 domestic and international publications.
Supersedes in part (in 1998): S I R S Discoverer
Media: CD-ROM.
Published by: S I R S Publishing, Inc., PO Box 272348, Boca Raton, FL 33427-2348. TEL 561-994-0079, 800-232-7477, FAX 561-994-4704, custserve@sirs.com, http://www.sirs.com. Ed. Lori Weisman. Pub. Eleanor Goldstein. R&P Cynthia Klivecka. Adv. contact Linda Manis.

016.285 USA
➤ **S I R S DISCOVERER MIDDLE EDITION.** (Social Issues Resources Series) Text in English. 1994. s-a. USD 530 (effective 2002). charts; illus.; maps. **Document type:** *Abstract/Index.* **Description:** General reference database for young researchers grades 5 to 9 develops research, reading, writing, language and computer skills. Full-text articles and graphics are from more than 1,000 domestic and international publications.
Supersedes in part (in 1998): S I R S Discoverer
Media: CD-ROM.
Published by: S I R S Publishing, Inc., PO Box 272348, Boca Raton, FL 33427-2348. TEL 561-994-0079, 800-232-7477, FAX 561-994-4704, custserve@sirs.com, http://www.sirs.com. Ed. Lori Weisman. Pub. Eleanor Goldstein. R&P Cynthia Klivecka. Adv. contact Linda Manis.

➤ **SPANISH LANGUAGE BOOKS FOR CHILDREN & YOUNG ADULTS.** see *PUBLISHING AND BOOK TRADE—Abstracting, Bibliographies, Statistics*

016.028 USA
SPECIAL COLLECTIONS IN CHILDREN'S LITERATURE; an international directory. Text in English. irreg., latest vol.3, 1995. USD 40 to non-members; USD 35 to members. **Document type:** *Directory, Bibliography.* **Description:** Compiles some 300 US institutions, listed by collection and subject.
Published by: (American Library Association, Association for Library Service to Children), American Library Association, 50 E Huron St, Chicago, IL 60611-2795. TEL 800-545-2433, http://www.ala.org. **Subscr. to:** PO Box 932501, Atlanta, GA 31193-2501. TEL 866-746-7252, FAX 770-442-9742, ala-orders@pbd.com.

028.5 USA
STORIES: A LIST OF STORIES TO TELL AND TO READ ALOUD. Text in English. irreg., latest vol.8, 1990. USD 6 (effective 2000). **Document type:** *Bibliography.*
Published by: New York Public Library, Office of Branch Libraries, 455 Fifth Ave, New York, NY 10016. TEL 212-340-0892, FAX 212-689-3193. Ed. Marilyn Berg Iarusso.

011.0285 011.37133 USA
TEACHERS' CHOICES. Text in English. a. USD 1. **Document type:** *Bibliography.* **Description:** Identifies and describes those new trade books for children and young adults that teachers surveyed have found to be exceptionally useful in their curricula.
Published by: (Teachers' Choices Committee), International Reading Association, Inc., 800 Barksdale Rd, Newark, DE 19714-8139. TEL 301-731-1600, 800-336-7323, FAX 302-368-2449, journals@reading.org, http://www.reading.org.

028.5 DEU ISSN 1435-5167
UNICUM ABI; das bundesweite Schuelermagazin. Text in German. 1990. m. adv. bk.rev.; film rev.; music rev.; Website rev. 32 p./no. 4 cols./p.; back issues avail. **Document type:** *Magazine, Consumer.* **Description:** Nationwide magazine for high school students.
Formerly: Chance (0945-2133)
Published by: Unicum Verlag GmbH, Willy-Brandt-Platz 5-7, Bochum, 44787, Germany. TEL 49-234-96151-0, FAX 49-234-9615111, redaktion@unicum.de, unicum@unicum.de, http://www.unicum.de. Ed. Jennifer Litters. Pubs. Hermann Josef Billstein, Manfred Baldschus. Adv. contact Joachim Senk. B&W page EUR 8,950, color page EUR 14,260; trim 210 x 295. Circ: 330,000 (controlled).

011.0285 USA
YOUNG ADULTS' CHOICES. Text in English. a. USD 1. **Document type:** *Bibliography.* **Description:** Offers an annotated list of books, both new and classic, that young adults surveyed in middle and high schools across the US have found to be the most enjoyable and informative.
Published by: (Literature for Adolescents Committee), International Reading Association, Inc., 800 Barksdale Rd, Newark, DE 19714-8139. TEL 302-731-1600, 800-336-7323, FAX 302-368-2449, journals@reading.org, http://www.reading.org.

369.4 790.1 ZMB
ZAMBIA. MINISTRY OF YOUTH AND SPORT. DEPARTMENT OF YOUTH DEVELOPMENT. ANNUAL REPORT. Text in English. 1982. a. **Document type:** *Government.* **Description:** Annual report of affairs in Zambia's Ministry of Youth and Sport and the Department of Youth Development.
Published by: (Zambia. Ministry of Youth and Sport, Zambia. Department of Youth Development), Government Printing Department, PO Box 30136, Lusaka, Zambia. Circ: 810.

ZENTRALBLATT FUER JUGENDRECHT; Kindheit - Jugend - Familie. see *LAW—Abstracting, Bibliographies, Statistics*

016.30523 AUT ISSN 1608-6589
1000 UND 1 BUCH. Text in German. 1985. q. EUR 20.35 domestic; EUR 29.07 foreign; EUR 5 newsstand/cover (effective 2004). adv. **Document type:** *Magazine, Trade.*
Related titles: Online - full text ed.
Published by: Institut fuer Jugendliteratur, Mayerhofgasse 6, Vienna, 1040, Austria. TEL 43-1-505035913, FAX 43-1-505035917, redaktion@1001buch.at, office@1001buch.at, http://www.1001buch.at. Ed. Franz Lettner. adv.: page EUR 650. Circ: 2,600 (paid and controlled).

CHILDREN AND YOUTH—For

028.5 500 CZE
A B C. Text in Czech. 1956. bi-w. CZK 572; CZK 24 newsstand/cover (effective 2002). adv. 44 p./no.; **Document type:** *Magazine, Consumer.*

C

Formerly: A B C Mladych Prirodovedcu (0322-9580)
Related titles: Online - full text ed.: ISSN 1213-9009. 1999.
Published by: Ringier CR, U pruhonu 13, Prague 7, 17000, Czech Republic. TEL 420-2-67097720, FAX 420-2-67097718, abc@ringier.cz, info@ringier.cz, http://www.iabc.cz, http://www.ringier.cz. Ed. Miroslava Volfova. Pub. Aleka Cerna. Adv. contact Tomas Filla TEL 420-2-67097427. page USD 80,500; 210 x 285. Circ: 63,000 (paid).

A B C PINPIN DUDU HUABAO/A B C SPELLING AND READING PICTORIAL. see *EDUCATION*

028.5 RUS
A B V G D - SKAZKI, IGRY I UROKI/A B C D - FAIRY TALES, GAMES AND LESSONS; detskaia roman-gazeta. Text in Russian. 1994. m. **Description:** Presents new cheerful fairy tales, stories, verses, script of holidays, performances. Designed for the teachers, librarians, tutors of children's gardens and boarding schools.
Published by: Izdatelstvo A B V G D, P.O. Box 97, Moscow, 123060, Russian Federation. TEL 7-095-1940387, FAX 7-095-1948555. Ed. Sergey Levitskii.

A D MAGAZIN; magazine pro mlade. see *RELIGIONS AND THEOLOGY—Roman Catholic*

595.7 GBR
A E S BUG CLUB NEWS. Text in English. 1997. bi-m. GBP 7; GBP 15 foreign. **Description:** Contains information on invertebrates specifically aimed at under 12's and school teachers. Includes information on special discounts on a wide range of products available to members.
Published by: Amateur Entomologists' Society, Amateur Entomologists Society, PO Box 8774, London, SW7 5ZG, United Kingdom. wayj@nhm.ac.uk, http://www.theaes.org. Ed. Kieren Pitts. Circ: 600.

C

028.5 RUS
A I F. DETSKAYA ENTSIKLOPEDIYA; poznavatel'nyi zhurnal dlya devochek i mal'chikov. (Argumenty i Fakty) Text in Russian. m. USD 56 foreign (effective 2003). illus. **Document type:** *Magazine, Consumer.* **Description:** Articles on a wide range of knowledge, natural and humanitarian sciences, history, culture, and art.
Related titles: Online - full content ed.; ◆ Supplement to: Argumenty i Fakty. ISSN 0204-0476.
Published by: Redaktsiya Argumenty i Fakty, Myasnitskaya ul 42, Moscow, 101000, Russian Federation. TEL 7-095-9286862, info@aif.ru, http://www.aif.ru/online/kids. **US dist. addr.:** East View Information Services, 3020 Harbor Ln. N., Minneapolis, MN 55447. TEL 763-550-0961, FAX 763-559-2931, eastview@eastview.com, http://www.eastview.com.

028.5 RUS
A I F. IKS-PILOT DLYA DEVOCHEK. (Argumenty i Fakty) Text in Russian. m. USD 192 in United States (effective 2003). **Document type:** *Magazine, Consumer.*
Related titles: ◆ Supplement to: Argumenty i Fakty. ISSN 0204-0476.
Published by: Redaktsiya Argumenty i Fakty, Myasnitskaya ul 42, Moscow, 101000, Russian Federation. TEL 7-095-9286862, info@aif.ru, http://www.aif.ru. **US dist. addr.:** East View Information Services, 3020 Harbor Ln. N., Minneapolis, MN 55447. TEL 763-550-0961, FAX 763-559-2931, eastview@eastview.com, http://www.eastview.com.

028.5 RUS
A I F. IKS-PILOT DLYA MAL'CHIKOV. (Argumenty i Fakty) Text in Russian. m. USD 192 in United States (effective 2003). **Document type:** *Magazine, Consumer.*
Related titles: ◆ Supplement to: Argumenty i Fakty. ISSN 0204-0476.
Published by: Redaktsiya Argumenty i Fakty, Myasnitskaya ul 42, Moscow, 101000, Russian Federation. TEL 7-095-9286862, info@aif.ru, http://www.aif.ru. **US dist. addr.:** East View Information Services, 3020 Harbor Ln. N., Minneapolis, MN 55447. TEL 763-550-0961, FAX 763-559-2931, eastview@eastview.com, http://www.eastview.com.

028.5 RUS
A I F K A. (Argumenty i Fakty) Text in Russian. s-m. USD 45 foreign (effective 2003). **Document type:** *Magazine, Consumer.* **Description:** Designed for schoolchildren it contains crosswords, competitions with prizes, puzzles, folk sayings and proverbs.
Published by: Redaktsiya Argumenty i Fakty, Myasnitskaya ul 42, Moscow, 101000, Russian Federation. TEL 7-095-9286862, info@aif.ru, http://www.aif.ru.

028.5 RUS ISSN 1727-2076
A I F. TVOI KURS. (Argumenty i Fakty) Text in Russian. 1992. w. USD 42 foreign (effective 2003). **Document type:** *Magazine, Consumer.* **Description:** Everything to do with youth, music, sex, show business and informal living. Tests, horoscopes, anecdotes and pals.
Formerly (until 2003): A i F. Ya Molodoi (1562-7497)
Related titles: Online - full content ed.; ◆ Supplement to: Argumenty i Fakty. ISSN 0204-0476.
Published by: Redaktsiya Argumenty i Fakty, Myasnitskaya ul 42, Moscow, 101000, Russian Federation. TEL 7-095-9286862, info@aif.ru, http://www.tvoikurs.ru, http://www.aif.ru. **US dist. addr.:** East View Information Services, 3020 Harbor Ln. N., Minneapolis, MN 55447. TEL 763-550-0961, FAX 763-559-2931, eastview@eastview.com, http://www.eastview.com.

028.5 RUS
A I F. YA KHOCHU VSE UZNAT'!. (Argumenty i Fakty) Text in Russian. m. USD 60 foreign (effective 2003). **Document type:** *Newspaper, Consumer.*
Related titles: Online - full content ed.
Published by: Redaktsiya Argumenty i Fakty, Myasnitskaya ul 42, Moscow, 101000, Russian Federation. TEL 7-095-9286862, info@aif.ru, http://www.aif.ru/online/uznat.

028.5 RUS ISSN 0868-7137
A POCHEMU?/BUT WHY?; prilozhenie k zhurnalu yunyi tekhnik. Text in Russian. 1991. m. USD 24 (effective 2002). adv. **Description:** Covers science, travelling, history, literature, answers for many of child's questions, puzzles, riddles, etc.
Published by: Yunyi Tekhnik, Novodmitrovskaya ul 5-a, Moscow, 125015, Russian Federation. TEL 7-095-2854480, FAX 7-095-2851809, yt@got.mmtel.ru. Ed. Boris I Cheremisinov. Adv. contact Alexandr Abmorshev. color page USD 700; 173 x 212. Circ: 10,000. **Dist. by:** East View Information Services, 3020 Harbor Ln. N., Minneapolis, MN 55447. TEL 763-550-0961, FAX 763-559-2931.

A T & F ATHLETES ONLY. see *SPORTS AND GAMES—Outdoor Life*

ABLE-EZINE. see *HANDICAPPED*

028.5 USA ISSN 1542-9776
ABOVE AND BEYOND; for grades 5-8. Text in English. 2002 (Sept./Oct.). 5/yr. USD 24.95 domestic; USD 36.95 foreign (effective 2003). **Document type:** *Journal, Academic/Scholarly.* **Description:** Includes regular features such as a forum, history, motivational topics, imagination and creative thinking.
Published by: Menagerie Publishing, Inc., PO Box 408, Ft Madison, IA 52627. TEL 800-527-3679, FAX 319-376-5734, info@menageriepublishing.com, http://www5.outfitters.com/cgi-bin/menagerie/index.html?id=yqyhClGj.

028.5 FRA ISSN 0994-2653
ABRICOT. Text in French. m. FRF 296 domestic; FRF 407.60 foreign (effective 2000). illus. **Description:** Presents stories to be read to children 2 years to 5 years old.
Published by: Fleurus Presse, 129 bd. Malesherbes, Paris, 75017, France. TEL 33-1-56793636. Ed. Pascal Teulade.

ABSOLUTELY BOYS. see *HANDICAPPED—Visually Impaired*

ABSOLUTELY GIRLS. see *HANDICAPPED—Visually Impaired*

ACADEMIA. see *EDUCATION*

052 GBR
ACE!; just for boys!. Text in English. 1999. m. BRL 1.50 newsstand/cover. **Document type:** *Consumer.* **Description:** Discusses computer games, gadgets, dinosaurs, star interviews, and football (soccer). Contains quizzes and posters.
Published by: L C D Publishing, 2nd Floor, Elm House, 54 Mary Arches St, Exeter, EX4 3BA, United Kingdom. TEL 44-1392-253076. **Dist. by:** Comag, Tavistock Works, Tavistock Rd, W Drayton, Middx UB7 7QX, United Kingdom. TEL 44-1895-444055, FAX 44-1895-433602.

028.5 USA
ACENTO LATINO. Text in English. bi-w. (Tue.). free (effective 2005). adv. **Document type:** *Newspaper, Consumer.*
Published by: Fayetteville Publishing Co., 458 Whitfield St., Fayetteville, NC 28306. TEL 910-323-4848, 910-486-2760, parkerl@acentolatino.com, http://www.thenews-journal.com. Ed. Liliana Parker. Pub. Charles Broodwell. adv.: col. inch USD 19. Circ: 4,700 (free).

ACORN EARLY YEARS STORYTELLER. see *EDUCATION—Teaching Methods And Curriculum*

LES ACTES DE LECTURE. see *LITERATURE*

052 GBR
ACTION HERO. Text in English. m. GBP 1.50 newsstand/cover (effective 2003). adv. **Document type:** *Magazine, Consumer.* **Description:** Contains stories, games, posters, news and reviews of the best toys available for boys ages 4 to 7.
Published by: B B C Worldwide Ltd., 80 Wood Ln, London, W12 0TT, United Kingdom. TEL 44-20-84331070, FAX 44-20-84332231, bbcworldwide@bbc.co.uk, http://www.bbcmagazines.com/actionhero/index.html.

028.5 GBR ISSN 1364-0755
ACTION MAN; the world's greatest hero. Text in English. 1996. m. GBP 26.25 (effective 2005). illus. **Document type:** *Magazine, Consumer.*
Published by: Panini UK Ltd., Panini House Coach and Horses Passage, Tunbridge Wells, Kent TN2 5UJ, United Kingdom. TEL 44-1892-500100, info@panini.co.uk, http://www.paninicomics.co.uk. **Dist. by:** MarketForce UK Ltd, 247 Tottenham Court Rd, London, Middx W1T 7AU, United Kingdom. TEL 44-20-72615555, FAX 44-207-2617341.

ADULESCENS. see *LINGUISTICS*

286.132 USA ISSN 0001-8783
ADVENTURE (NASHVILLE). Text in English. m. (plus regular w. nos.). USD 20.04. **Document type:** *Bulletin.* **Description:** Serves as a devotional magazine for children grades 3-4.
Published by: LifeWay Christian Resources, 1 Lifeway Plaza, Nashville, TN 37234. TEL 615-251-2000, 800-458-2772, FAX 615-251-5933, customerservice@lifeway.com, http://www.lifeway.com.

028.5 FRA ISSN 1366-9001
ADVENTURE BOX. Text in English. 1995. 10/yr. EUR 55.36 domestic; EUR 63.50 foreign (effective 2005). **Document type:** *Magazine, Consumer.*
Published by: Bayard Presse, 3 Rue Bayard, Paris, 75393 Cedex 08, France. TEL 33-1-44356060, FAX 33-1-44356161, redactions@bayard-presse.com, http://www.bayardpresse.com.

028.5 JPN
ADVENTURE KING/BOKEN-O. Text in Japanese. 1949. m. JPY 4,560.
Published by: Akita Shoten Publishing Co. Ltd., 10-8 Iida-Bashi 2-chome, Chiyoda-ku, Tokyo, 102-0072, Japan. Ed. Kiyomi Narita.

028.5 ISL ISSN 1021-7258
AESKAN. Text in Icelandic. 1897. 10/yr. ISK 4,500 (effective 2000). adv. **Document type:** *Magazine, Consumer.*
Published by: Aeskan ehf., Stangarhyl 4, Reykjavik, 110, Iceland. TEL 354-530-5400, FAX 354-530-5401, aeskan@aeskan.is. Ed., R&P Arni Arnason. Pub. Olafur Loftsson. Circ: 6,100.

AFTER HOURS. see *HANDICAPPED—Visually Impaired*

028.5 JPN
AFTERNOON. Text in Japanese. m. **Document type:** *Magazine, Consumer.*
Published by: Kodansha Ltd., 2-12-21 Otowa, Bunkyo-ku, Tokyo, 112-8001, Japan. TEL 81-3-3946-6201, FAX 81-3-3944-9915, http://www.kodansha.co.jp.

028.5 JPN
AFTERNOON SEASON ZOKAN. Text in Japanese. q. **Document type:** *Magazine, Consumer.*
Published by: Kodansha Ltd., 2-12-21 Otowa, Bunkyo-ku, Tokyo, 112-8001, Japan. TEL 81-3-3946-6201, FAX 81-3-3944-9915, http://www.kodansha.co.jp.

AG YOUTH MAGAZINE. see *AGRICULTURE*

028.5 741.5 SWE ISSN 0345-0473
AGENT X9. Text in Swedish. 1969. 13/yr. SEK 290; SEK 24 newsstand/cover (effective 1998). adv. **Document type:** *Consumer.*
Published by: Egmont Serie Foerlaget, Fack 70272, Stockholm, 10722, Sweden. TEL 46-8-736-39-00, FAX 46-8-791-70-95. Ed. Janne Eriksson. Pub. Ulf Granberg. Adv. contact Peter Ask. color page SEK 13,000; trim 220 x 150. Circ: 34,400.

613 DEU
AHA!. Text in German. q. free. **Document type:** *Magazine, Consumer.*
Published by: Deutsche Angestellten Krankenkasse, Nagelsweg 27-35, Hamburg, 20097, Germany. service@dak.de, http://www.dak.de.

629.133 GBR
AIR CADET; the journal for air minded youth. Text in English. 1970. bi-m. GBP 5 (effective 2001). bk.rev. illus. **Document type:** *Magazine, Internal.* **Description:** Publishes articles of interest to cadets in the Air Training Corps of Great Britain.
Former titles: Air Cadet Review (0964-0207); (until Dec. 1991): Air Cadet (0964-6302); (until Feb. 1983): Air Cadet News (0002-2209)
Published by: Headquarters Air Cadets, RAF Cranwell, Sleaford, Lincs NG34 8HB, United Kingdom. TEL 44-1400-261201, FAX 44-1400-261201. Ed., R&P Denise Housby. Circ: 43,500 (controlled).

AKCENTY. see *RELIGIONS AND THEOLOGY—Protestant*

AKILA. see *SPORTS AND GAMES—Outdoor Life*

028.5 FIN ISSN 0355-2101
AKU ANKKA. Text in Finnish. 1951. w. EUR 81 (effective 2004). adv. **Document type:** *Magazine, Consumer.*
Published by: Sanoma Magazines Finland Corporation, Hoylaamotie 1 D, P.O. Box 100, Helsinki, 00040, Finland. TEL 358-9-1201, FAX 358-9-1205171, info@sanomamagazines.fi, http://www.akuankka.fi, http://www.sanomamagazines.fi. Ed. Markku Kivekas. adv.: color page EUR 9,650. Circ: 288,721.

741.5 FIN ISSN 1456-7830
AKU ANKKA KUUKAUDEN SARJISEKSTRA. Variant title: Kuukauden Sarjisekstra. Text in Finnish. 1999. m. EUR 28 (effective 2004). **Document type:** *Magazine, Consumer.*
Published by: Sanoma Magazines Finland Corporation, Hoylaamotie 1 D, P.O. Box 100, Helsinki, 00040, Finland. TEL 358-9-1201, FAX 358-9-1205171, info@sanomamagazines.fi, http://www.sanomamagazines.fi.

AL-HUDA. see *RELIGIONS AND THEOLOGY—Islamic*

028.5 616.861 USA ISSN 1054-1411
ALATEEN TALK. Text in English. 1964. q. looseleaf. USD 2.50 (effective 2005). illus. **Document type:** *Newsletter, Consumer.* **Description:** Alateen members, young people whose lives have been affected by someone else's drinking, share their experiences. Targets young people and professionals working with adolescents.
Published by: (Al-Anon Family Group Headquarters, Inc.), A F G, Inc., 1600 Corporate Landing Pkwy, Virginia Beach, VA 23454-5617. wso@al-anon.org, http://www.al-anon.alateen.org. Ed. Barbara O. Circ: 5,500 (paid and controlled).

028.5 USA ISSN 1090-3712
ALL ABOUT YOU. Text in English. 1984. q. USD 2.95 newsstand/cover. adv. bk.rev.; film rev.; music rev.; tel.rev. illus.; stat. back issues avail.; reprints avail. **Document type:** *Magazine, Consumer.* **Description:** General interest magazine for teenage girls.
Related titles: Online - full text ed.: (from Gale Group).
Published by: Primedia Consumer Media & Magazine Group, 9036 Brittanyway, Tampa, FL 33619. TEL 813-679-3500, FAX 813-679-3999, allaboutyou@petersenpub.com, http://www.primedia.com. Ed. Jane Fort. Pub. Beth Press. Adv. contact Rochelle Carrington. Circ: 325,000 (paid).

028.5 GBR ISSN 1460-6410
ALL NEW TOM & JERRY. Variant title: Tom & Jerry. Text in English. 1998. m. GBP 23.88; GBP 1.99 newsstand/cover (effective 1999). adv. illus. **Document type:** *Consumer.* **Description:** Contains various types of fun and games for children involving the cartoon characters Tom and Jerry.
Published by: Burghley Publishing Ltd., 14 Barn Hill, Stamford, Lincs PE9 2AE, United Kingdom. TEL 44-1780-763366, FAX 44-1780-763365. **Dist. by:** Seymour Distribution Ltd, 86 Newman St, London W1T 3EX, United Kingdom. FAX 44-207-396-8002, enquiries@seymour.co.uk.

028.5 USA
ALL ROUND. Text in English. 2000. s-a. USD 11.50; USD 6 newsstand/cover (effective 2001). **Document type:** *Magazine, Consumer.*
Published by: Parkhurst Publishing Ltd., Box 1783, Sedona, AZ 86339. TEL 888-938-3832, http://www.allroundmagazine.com/. Ed., Pub. David Elkins.

ALLTID SCOUT. see *CHILDREN AND YOUTH—About*

028.5 GRC ISSN 1106-1391
ALMANAKO. Text in Greek. 1990. m. USD 43. adv. illus. **Document type:** *Consumer.* **Description:** Contains adventure stories and comics. Reviews video games.
Published by: Terzopoulos Publishing Ltd., 7 Fragoklisias St, Maroussi, Athens 151 25, Greece. TEL 30-1-689-6366, FAX 30-1-680-6631, gea@compulink.gr. Ed. Stelios Nicolaou. Adv. contact Angela Daramara. Circ: 22,000.

028.5 BRA ISSN 0104-3390
ALMANAQUE DISNEY. Text in Portuguese. 1970. m. **Document type:** *Magazine, Consumer.*
Published by: Editora Abril, S.A., Av. das Nacoes Unidas, 7221, 11 andar Pinheiros, Sao Paulo, SP 05425-902, Brazil. TEL 55-11-50872112, FAX 55-11-50872100, disney.abril@atleitor.com.br, http://www.disney.com.br/, http://www.abril.com.br/. Circ: 4,900 (paid and free).

059.927 LBY
AL-AMAL. Text in Arabic. w.
Indexed: RASB.
Published by: Press Service, P O Box 4845, Tripoli, Libya.

028.5 IND
AMBULI AMMAVAN. Text in Malayalam. 1970. m.
Address: 188 N.S.K .Salai, Chandamama Bldgs., Vadapalani, Chennai, Tamil Nadu 600 026, India. Ed. Nagi Reddi. Circ: 15,000.

028.5 USA ISSN 1062-7812
AMERICAN GIRL; celebrating girls, yesterday and today . Text in English. 1992. bi-m. USD 22.95 domestic; USD 29 foreign (effective 2005). illus. back issues avail.; reprints avail. **Document type:** *Magazine, Consumer.* **Description:** Features articles on American girls, past and present, stories by noted children's authors, paper dolls and cut-out clothes, games and entertainment. For girls ages 8-12.
Indexed: ICM, MASUSE, RGYP.
Published by: Pleasant Company Publications, 8400 Fairway Pl, Middleton, WI 53562. TEL 608-836-4848, FAX 608-831-7089, readermail@ab.pleasantco.com, http://www.americangirl.com/agmg/index.html. Ed. Michelle Watkins. Pub. Diane Morgenthaler. Circ: 740,000 (paid).

028.5 IND
ANANDAMELA. Text in Bengali. 1975. m. INR 10 newsstand/cover. adv.
Published by: Anand Bazar Patrika Ltd., 6 Prafulla Sarkar St, Kolkata, West Bengal 700 001, India. TEL 33-376000, TELEX 215468. Ed. Debashish Bandhopadhayay. Adv. contact S N Roychoudhury. B&W page INR 15,000, color page INR 30,000; trim 23.5 x 16. Circ: 54,000.

028.5 DNK ISSN 0900-0097
ANDERS AND EKSTRA. Text in Danish. 1970. m. DKK 16.95 newsstand/cover (effective 2000). adv. **Description:** Donald Duck and Co.
Formerly (until 1977): Ekstra Haefte (0900-0089)
Published by: Serieforlaget AS, Vognmagergade 9, Copenhagen K, 1148, Denmark. Eds. Jesper Christiansen TEL 45-33-30-50-00, Jesper Christiansen TEL 45-33-30-50-00. Adv. contact Kenneth Diget. color page DKK 16,000; 156 x 225. Circ: 100,000.

808.836 DNK ISSN 0900-4556
ANDERS AND & CO. Key Title: Walt Disney's Anders And & Co. Text in Danish. 1949. w. DKK 17.95 newsstand/cover (effective 2001). adv. **Description:** Mostly Donald Duck cartoons.
Published by: Serieforlaget AS, Vognmagergade 9, Copenhagen K, 1148, Denmark. TEL 45-33-30-50-00, FAX 45-33-30-55-10. Ed. Tommy Melle. Pub. Jesper Christiansen TEL 45-33-30-50-00. Adv. contact Kenneth Diget. color page DKK 38,000; 156 x 225. Circ: 163,553.

028.5 RUS
ANGLIISKII YAZYK DLYA DETEI. Text in English. 26/yr. USD 172 in United States.
Published by: (Stolichnaya Shkola Inostrannykh Yazykov Lingua Viva), Firma Pervoe Sentyabrya, Vorob'evyi gory, MGU 2 Gumanit korp 925, Moscow, 117234, Russian Federation. TEL 7-095-9392926. **US dist. addr.:** East View Information Services, 3020 Harbor Ln. N., Minneapolis, MN 55447. TEL 612-550-0961.

028.5 GBR
ANIMALS AND YOU; for girls who love animals. Text in English. fortn. GBP 28.60; GBP 1.10 newsstand/cover (effective 1999). adv. **Document type:** *Consumer.* **Description:** Offers girls ages 7-10 pictures, stories, and articles on pets and other animals.
Published by: D.C. Thomson & Co. Ltd., 80 Kingsway East, Dundee, Angus, Scotland DD4 8SL, United Kingdom. FAX 44-1382-462097, comment@dcthomson.co.uk, http://www.dcthomson.co.uk. Adv. contact Sharon Mudie. B&W page GBP 1,250, color page GBP 1,500.

028.5 NGA ISSN 0331-6289
APOLLO; magazine for young Nigerians. Text in English. 1973. q. NGN 1.20. back issues avail.
Indexed: AIAP.
Published by: Modern Publications Co. Ltd., Marina, PO Box 2583, Lagos, Nigeria. Ed. Toun Onabanto. Circ: 35,000.

028.5 179 300 USA ISSN 1099-7725
AP201
APPLESEEDS. Text in English. 1998. m. USD 29.95 domestic; USD 41.95 foreign; USD 4.95 per issue domestic (effective 2005). bk.rev. illus.; maps. Index. back issues avail.; reprints avail. **Document type:** *Magazine, Consumer.* **Description:** Social studies based magazine for grades 3 - 5, offering reading in the content areas, activities and games.
Related titles: Online - full text ed.: (from bigchalk, EBSCO Publishing, Gale Group, ProQuest Information & Learning).
Indexed: RGYP.
Published by: Carus Publishing Company, 315 Fifth St, Peru, IL 61354. TEL 603-924-7209, 800-821-0115, FAX 815-224-2256, custsvc@cobblestone.mv.com, http://www.cricketmag.com. Ed. Susan Buckley. R&P Patricia Silvestro. Circ: 5,000 (paid).

052 GBR ISSN 0965-4003
AQUILA. Text in English. 1993. m. GBP 31.50 domestic; GBP 37.80 in Europe; GBP 49.80 in Asia; GBP 46.50 elsewhere (effective 2002). adv. bk.rev.; software rev. 32 p./no.; back issues avail. **Document type:** *Magazine, Consumer.* **Description:** Contains a wide variety of puzzles, information, competitions, special features, jokes and stories for 8-13 year olds who enjoy challenges.
Address: 22 Eversfield Rd., Eastbourne, E Sussex BN21 2AS, United Kingdom. TEL 44-1323-431313, FAX 44-1323-731136, orders@aquila.co.uk, http://www.aquila.co.uk/. Ed., R&P Jackie Berry TEL 44-1323-411659. Adv. contact Mairi Baker. page GBP 825; 210 x 297. Circ: 8,000 (paid).

ARCHIE. see *LITERATURE—Science Fiction, Fantasy, Horror*

028.5 500 ZAF ISSN 0003-8385
ARCHIMEDES; natural science magazine for the whole family. Text in English. 1959. q. adv. abstr.; charts; illus. cum.index.
Related titles: Afrikaans ed.; English ed.
Indexed: ISAP, SFA.
Published by: (Foundation for Education, Science and Technology), South African Bureau for Scientific Publications, PO Box 11663, Pretoria, Hatfield 0028, South Africa. TEL 27-12-322-6404, FAX 27-12-320-7803, bspman@icon.co.za, http://www.safest.org.za/bsp. Ed. Z Raper. Circ: 10,000.

028.5 FRA ISSN 1256-7809
ARKEO JUNIOR. Text in French. 1994. m. (11/yr.).
Published by: Editions Faton S.A., 25 rue Berbisey, Dijon, 21000, France. TEL 33-3-80404120, FAX 33-3-80404129. Ed. Pierrette Fabre-Faton. Pub. Pierrette Fabre Faton. Circ: 30,000.

ARMONIA DI VOCI. see *MUSIC*

028.5 GBR ISSN 1364-0763
ART ATTACK. Text in English. 199?. 17/yr. GBP 29.85 (effective 2005). illus. **Document type:** *Magazine, Consumer.* **Description:** Presents great ideas and fantastic things to make and do in each issue.
Published by: Panini UK Ltd., Panini House Coach and Horses Passage, Tunbridge Wells, Kent TN2 5UJ, United Kingdom. TEL 44-1892-500100, info@panini.co.uk, http://www.hitentertainment.com/artattack/menu_artattacks.html, http://www.paninicomics.co.uk. **Dist. by:** MarketForce UK Ltd, 247 Tottenham Court Rd, London, Middx W1T 7AU, United Kingdom. TEL 44-207-2615199, FAX 44-207-2617341.

028.5 DEU
ART ATTACK. Text in German. m. EUR 2.80 newsstand/cover (effective 2005). adv. **Document type:** *Magazine, Consumer.*
Published by: Egmont Ehapa Verlag GmbH, Wallstr 59, Berlin, 10179, Germany. TEL 49-30-240080, FAX 49-30-24008599, leserservice@ehapa.de, http://www.ehapa.de/ehapa/e14/e40/e175/index_ger.html. adv.: page EUR 3,900. Circ: 119,360 (paid and controlled).

ART DOLL QUARTERLY. see *ARTS AND HANDICRAFTS*

028.5 700 GBR ISSN 1369-6394
ART MAGIC. Text in English. 1997. w. GBP 1.60 newsstand/cover. **Document type:** *Consumer.* **Description:** Teaches young children the hows and whys of painting.
Published by: Fabbri Publishing Ltd., Elme House, 133 Long Acre, London, WC2E 9AW, United Kingdom. TEL 44-171-836-0519. **Dist. by:** Comag, Tavistock Works, Tavistock Rd, W Drayton, Middx UB7 7QX, United Kingdom. TEL 44-1895-444055, FAX 44-1895-433602.

C

ARTICLE 13; law & policy journal of the National Children's and Youth Law Centre. see *LAW*

028.5 840 CHE ISSN 1421-0908
AS TU LU?. Text in French. 1983. 3/yr. **Document type:** *Newsletter, Consumer.*
Related titles: ♦ Supplement to: Parole. ISSN 1421-0851.
Published by: Association Romande de Litterature pour l'Enfance et la Jeunesse, Case Postale, Lausanne 4, 1000, Switzerland. TEL 41-21-3202328.

808.068 USA ISSN 1535-4105
ASK; arts and sciences for kids. Text in English. 2002 (Jan.). 9/yr. USD 32.97 domestic; USD 44.97 foreign (effective 2005). 36 p./no.; **Document type:** *Magazine, Consumer.* **Description:** Contains articles for curious children ages 7-10 with features on science, history, technology, and the arts.
Related titles: Online - full text ed.: (from bigchalk, ProQuest Information & Learning).
Published by: Carus Publishing Company, 315 Fifth St, Peru, IL 61354. TEL 603-924-7209, 800-821-0115, FAX 815-224-2256, custsvc@cobblestone.mv.com, http://www.cricketmag.com. Ed. Marianne Carus.

808.8 GBR ISSN 1360-5178
ASTONISHING SPIDERMAN. Text in English. 1995. m. GBP 28.80 (effective 2005). **Document type:** *Magazine, Consumer.* **Description:** Contains the ongoing adventures of Spiderman as he battles the forces of evil.
Published by: Panini UK Ltd., Panini House Coach and Horses Passage, Tunbridge Wells, Kent TN2 5UJ, United Kingdom. TEL 44-1892-500100, info@panini.co.uk, http://www.paninicomics.co.uk. **Dist. by:** MarketForce UK Ltd, 247 Tottenham Court Rd, London, Middx W1T 7AU, United Kingdom. TEL 44-20-72615199, FAX 44-20-72617341.

028.5 FRA ISSN 0220-1186
ASTRAPI. Text in French. 1978. bi-m. EUR 89.80 domestic; EUR 124.80 foreign (effective 2005). **Document type:** *Magazine, Consumer.* **Description:** Helps children 7 and over to develop autonomy, creativity and curiosity.
Published by: Bayard Presse, 3 Rue Bayard, Paris, 75393 Cedex 08, France. TEL 33-1-44356060, FAX 33-1-44356161, redactions@bayard-presse.com, http://www.bayardpresse.com. Ed. Florence Dutruc-Rosset. Circ: 70,834.

ASTRO-NEWS. see *AERONAUTICS AND SPACE FLIGHT*

028.5 570 CAN ISSN 0843-7777
ATELIERS. Text in English. 1989. irreg. (1-4/yr.). CND 1.50 per issue. illus. **Description:** Suggests games and activities on natural sciences for young people.
Published by: Cercles des Jeunes Naturalistes, 4101 rue Sherbrooke Est, Ste 124, Montreal, PQ H1X 2B2, Canada. TEL 514-252-3023.

087.5 BRA ISSN 0104-205X
ATIVIDADES DISNEY. Text in Portuguese. 1990. m. **Document type:** *Magazine, Consumer.*
Published by: Editora Abril, S.A., Av. das Nacoes Unidas, 7221, 11 andar Pinheiros, Sao Paulo, SP 05425-902, Brazil. TEL 55-11-50872112, FAX 55-11-50872100, http://www.disney.com.br/, http://www.abril.com.br/. Circ: 4,900.

028.5 CMR
AU LARGE✶ **/GO AHEAD**; magazine of young Cameroonian students. Text in French. 1974 (vol.15). m. adv. bk.rev. illus.
Address: BP 504, Yaounde, Cameroon. Ed. Mam Dieudonne.

028.5 AUS ISSN 1446-5507
AUSTRALIAN GIRLZ KLUB MAGAZINE. Text in English. 2001. q. **Document type:** *Journal, Academic/Scholarly.*
Formerly (until 2001): Girlz Klub (1444-2531)
Published by: Australian Girlz Klub and Boyz Klub Magazine Pty. Ltd., PO Box 7078, Leura, NSW 2780, Australia. TEL 61-2-47842466, FAX 61-2-47842477, http://www.girlzklub.com.au/.

808.87 AUS ISSN 0726-1810
AUSTRALIAN MAD MAGAZINE. Text in English. 1979. 8/yr. AUD 29.50 domestic; AUD 40 foreign; AUD 4.95 newsstand/cover (effective 2004). adv. film rev.; tel.rev. illus. cum.indexes. **Document type:** *Magazine, Consumer.* **Description:** Covers adolescent humor aimed at 10-17 year olds.
Published by: Horwitz Publications Pty. Ltd., 55 Chandos St, St Leonards, NSW 2065, Australia. TEL 61-2-9901-6100, FAX 61-2-9901-6198, davidw@horwitz.com.au, dip@horwitz.com.au. Ed., R&P David Williams. Pub. Susan Horwitz. Adv. contact David Gleeson TEL 61-2-99016131. page AUD 3,000. Circ: 60,000.

C

AUSTRALIA'S ECONOMIC STATISTICS; a student guide to recent Australian experience. see *BUSINESS AND ECONOMICS—Abstracting, Bibliographies, Statistics*

028.5 USA ISSN 1040-5682
PS490
AUTHORS & ARTISTS FOR YOUNG ADULTS. Text in English. s-a. USD 115 per vol. (effective 2004). illus. back issues avail. **Description:** Provides source material about international writers, artists, film directors, and graphic novelists.
Published by: Gale Group (Subsidiary of: Thomson Corporation), 27500 Drake Rd, Farmington Hills, MI 48331-3535. TEL 248-699-8061, FAX 248-699-4253, galeord@gale.com, http://www.gale.com. Eds. Agnes Garrett, Helga P McCue.

AUTUMN SCHOOL OF STUDIES ON ALCOHOL & DRUGS. PROCEEDINGS OF SEMINARS. see *DRUG ABUSE AND ALCOHOLISM*

741.5 GBR ISSN 1474-1571
AVENGERS UNITED. Text in English. 2001. m. GBP 28.80 (effective 2005). **Document type:** *Magazine, Consumer.*
Published by: Panini UK Ltd., Panini House Coach and Horses Passage, Tunbridge Wells, Kent TN2 5UJ, United Kingdom. TEL 44-1892-500100, info@panini.co.uk, http://www.paninicomics.co.uk.

028.5 RUS
AVOS'-KA; molodezhnaya gazeta. Text in Russian. 1992. m. **Document type:** *Newspaper, Consumer.*
Published by: (Rossiiskaya Federatsiya. Glazov. Otdel Po Delam Molodezhi Administratsii), Krasnoe Znamya, Ul Kirova 6, Glazov, Udmurtiya, Russian Federation. TEL 7-34141-74742, 7-34141-40406, redflag@udmnet.ru, http://www.glazov.udm.net/~asy/redflag/newpage. Ed. Andrei Vyacheslavovich Patrushev.

AVTO-YUNIOR. see *TRANSPORTATION—Automobiles*

AWARD-WINNING BOOKS FOR CHILDREN AND YOUNG ADULTS. see *BIBLIOGRAPHIES*

AZZURRO; il mensile per il tuo italiano. see *LINGUISTICS*

028.5 GBR ISSN 1364-7393
B B C LEARNING IS FUN. Text in English. 1996. m. GBP 21.99; GBP 1.99 newsstand/cover (effective 2003). adv. **Document type:** *Magazine, Consumer.* **Description:** Aims to teach children school subjects in an exciting, fun and stimulating way.
Published by: B B C Worldwide Ltd., 80 Wood Ln, London, W12 0TT, United Kingdom. TEL 44-20-84331070, FAX 44-20-84332231, bbcworldwide@bbc.co.uk, http://www.bbcmagazines.com/learnfun/index.html.

028.5 GBR
B B C SMART. Variant title: SMart. Text in English. m. GBP 1.50 newsstand/cover. adv. **Document type:** *Consumer.* **Description:** Contains interesting projects to make, and easy art tips for children.
Published by: (British Broadcasting Corp.), B B C Worldwide Ltd., 80 Wood Ln, London, W12 0TT, United Kingdom. TEL 44-208-576-2000, FAX 44-181-576-2931, bbcproducts@bbc.co.uk, http://www.bbc.co.uk. Ed. Becky Leggett. **Dist. by:** Frontline, Park House, 117 Park Rd, Peterborough, Cambs PE1 2TS, United Kingdom. TEL 44-1733-555161, FAX 44-1733-562788.

428 GBR ISSN 1471-8979
B B C THE MAGIC KEY. Text in English. 2000. m. GBP 21; GBP 1.80 newsstand/cover (effective 2003). adv. **Document type:** *Magazine, Consumer.* **Description:** Contains stories and activities designed to support the reading and writing skills of 5-7 year olds.
Published by: B B C Worldwide Ltd., 80 Wood Ln, London, W12 0TT, United Kingdom. TEL 44-20-84331070, FAX 44-20-84332231, bbcworldwide@bbc.co.uk, http://www.bbcmagazines.com/magickey/index.html.

028.5 IRL ISSN 1464-4231
B B M✶. (Baseline and Blank Magazine) Text in English. 1998. m. **Document type:** *Magazine, Consumer.* **Description:** Covers Ireland's clubs & youth culture, including music, events, personalities, and other features.
Formed by the merger of (1995-1998): Bassline (1361-2573); (1997-1998): Blank (1460-1036)
Related titles: Online - full content ed.
Address: 2b Gregg St, Lisburn, BT27 5AN, Ireland. TEL 353-28-92667000, FAX 353-28-92668000, 353-28-92668005, judith@bbmag.co.uk, http://www.bbmag.co.uk/. Circ: 16,000 (paid and controlled).

B D K J JOURNAL. see *RELIGIONS AND THEOLOGY—Roman Catholic*

B U M. (Boerne og Ungdoms-Litteratur Magasinet) see *LITERATURE*

028.5 ISR
BAAMLEH. Text in Hebrew. 1926. m. **Document type:** *Newspaper.*
Address: Rehov Kibbutz Galuot 120, Tel Aviv, Israel. TEL 972-3-834248. Ed. Oded Bar Meir.

305.8924 USA
BABAGANEWZ; jewish kids exploring the world. Text in English. m. USD 19.95 per academic year (effective 2004). **Document type:** *Magazine, Consumer.* **Description:** Analyzes major news stories, religious holidays, cultural events and youth trends that play important parts in the lives of Jewish children.
Related titles: Online - full text ed.
Address: 11141 Georgia Ave, Ste 406, Wheaton, MD 20902. TEL 301-962-9636, FAX 301-962-9635, http://www.babaganewz.com.

028.5 FRA ISSN 1163-6262
BABAR; un journal de roi pour tous les enfants. Text in French. 1991. 8/yr. (plus 4 extras). EUR 39.80 domestic; EUR 54.80 in the European Union; EUR 64.80 elsewhere (effective 2005). **Document type:** *Magazine, Consumer.* **Description:** Follows the adventures of Babar the elephant king, for children 3 and older.
Published by: Bayard Presse, 3 Rue Bayard, Paris, 75393 Cedex 08, France. TEL 33-1-44356060, FAX 33-1-44356161, redactions@bayard-presse.com, http://www.bayardpresse.com. Ed. Nathalie Becht. Circ: 59,970.

305.23 DEU
▼ **BABY BORN.** Text in German. 2004. 4/yr. EUR 2.70 newsstand/cover (effective 2005). adv. **Document type:** *Magazine, Consumer.*
Published by: Panini Verlags GmbH, Ravensstr 48, Nettetal, 41334, Germany. TEL 49-2157-81750, FAX 49-2157-81484528, info@panini-dino.de, http://www.panini-media.de. adv.: page EUR 2,000; trim 210 x 280. Circ: 46,320 (paid and controlled).

808.89 USA ISSN 1077-1131
AP201
BABYBUG. Text in English. 1994. 10/yr. USD 35.97 domestic; USD 47.97 foreign (effective 2005). illus. 22 p./no.; back issues avail. **Document type:** *Magazine, Consumer.* **Description:** Features simple stories, rhymes, and word introductions for infants and toddlers 6 months to 2 years old.
Related titles: Microfilm ed.
Published by: Carus Publishing Company, 315 Fifth St, Peru, IL 61354. TEL 603-924-7209, 800-821-0115, FAX 815-224-2256, custsvc@cobblestone.mv.com, http://www.cricketmag.com. Eds. Paula Morrow, Marianne Carus. Pub. John Olbrych. R&P Mary Ann Hocking. Circ: 47,000 (paid).

BAFF. see *SOCIAL SERVICES AND WELFARE*

028.5 IND ISSN 0005-4194
BAL BHARATI. Text in Hindi. 1948. m. INR 7, USD 2.70. adv. bk.rev. illus. **Document type:** *Government.* **Description:** Contains stories and informative articles for children aged 8-14.
Published by: Ministry of Information & Broadcasting, Publications Division, Patiala House, Tilak Marg, New Delhi, 110 001, India. Ed. Shiv Kumar. Adv. contact Baij Nath Rajbhar. Circ: 30,000. **Subscr. in U.S. to:** InterCulture Associates, Thompson, CT 06277.

028.5 IND
BALARAMA; children's weekly. Text in Malayalam. 1972. w. INR 260; INR 5 newsstand/cover (effective 2000). adv. bk.rev. **Description:** Stories, poems, cartoons, and essays for children up to the age of fifteen.
Published by: M.M. Publications Limited, Erayilkadavu, P O Box 226, Kottayam, Kerala 686 001, India. TEL 91-481-563721, FAX 91-481-564393, TELEX 0888-201 MNR IN, vanbal@satyam.net.in. Ed. N M Mohanan. Pub. K I George. R&P, Adv. contact V Sajeev George. B&W page INR 7,000, color page INR 14,000; trim 178 x 125. Circ: 255,249.

028.5 IND
BALARAMA AMAR CHITHRAKATHA; children's fortnightly. Text in Malayalam. 1990. fortn. INR 72; INR 3 newsstand/cover (effective 2000). adv.
Published by: M.M. Publications Limited, Erayilkadavu, P O Box 226, Kottayam, Kerala 686 001, India. TEL 91-481-563721, FAX 91-481-564393, vanbal@satyam.net.in. Ed. N M Mohanan. Pub. K I George. R&P, Adv. contact V Sajeev George. B&W page INR 4,500, color page INR 8,500. Circ: 30,000.

028.5 IND
BALHANS. Text in Hindi. 1986. fortn. INR 10 newsstand/cover (effective 2003). adv.
Published by: Rajasthan Patrika Private Ltd., J.L.N. Marg, Kesargarh, Jaipur, Rajasthan 302 004, India. TEL 91-141-561582, FAX 91-141-566011, info@rajasthanpatrika.com, http://www.rajasthanpatrika.com. Ed. Gulab Kothari. Pub. J S Kothari. adv.: B&W page INR 6,000, color page INR 10,000; trim 170 x 240. Circ: 26,714 (paid).

028.5 IND ISSN 0005-4291
BALJIVAN. Text in Gujarati. 1920. m. INR 5, USD 1.
Published by: L.M. Patel, Ed. & Pub., Wadi, Vayada Pole, Baroda, Gujarat 1, India.

028.5 ISR
BAMA'ALEH. Text in Hebrew. 1926. m. **Document type:** *Newspaper.*
Published by: Tenuat Hanoar Haoved Vehalomed, 120 Kibbutz Galuyot St, Tel Aviv, 66877, Israel. TEL 972-3-814488, FAX 972-3-816852. Ed. Oded Bar Meir.

028.5 FRA ISSN 0996-5777
BAMBI. Text in French. m. **Document type:** *Consumer.* **Description:** Stories about Bambi and his friends, for children 1 to 3 years old.
Published by: Disney Hachette Presse, 10 rue Thierry le Luron, Levallois Perret, Cedex 92592, France. TEL 33-1-41348500, FAX 33-1-41348989. Ed. Gilles Heylen. Circ: 55,700.

028.5 THA
BANGKOK POST STUDENT WEEKLY. Text in English, Thai. 1969. w. THB 360; THB 7 newsstand/cover. adv. film rev.; music rev.; play rev.; software rev. charts; illus. back issues avail. **Document type:** *Newspaper.* **Description:** News magazine for teenagers.
Formerly: Student Weekly
Related titles: Online - full text ed.
Published by: World Press Co. Ltd., Bangkok Post Bldg, Off Sunthorn, Klong Toey, 136 Na Ranong Rd, Bangkok, 10110, Thailand. TEL 66-2-240-3700, FAX 66-2-240-3792, student-weekly@bangkokpost.net. Ed. Anussorn Thavisin. Adv. contact Vuttiporn Palasab. page THB 38,000; trim 10.88 x 13.38. Circ: 110,000 (paid).

028.5 DEU
BARBIE; lies, spiel, rate und traeume mit. Text in German. 1995. m. EUR 27.60; EUR 2.30 newsstand/cover (effective 2005). adv. **Document type:** *Magazine, Consumer.* **Description:** Contains stories, puzzles, games and other activities involving Barbie.
Published by: Egmont Ehapa Verlag GmbH, Wallstr 59, Berlin, 10179, Germany. TEL 49-30-240080, FAX 49-30-24008599, leserservice@ehapa.de, http://www.ehapa.de. Adv. contact Olaf Hansen. page EUR 4,400. Circ: 90,809 (paid).

028.5 AUS ISSN 1326-267X
BARBIE. Text in English. 1996. m. USD 40 (effective 2004). adv.
Published by: Emap Australia Pty. Ltd. (Subsidiary of: Emap International), 187 Thomas St., Level 6, Haymarket, NSW 2000, Australia. TEL 61-2-95819400, FAX 61-2-95819570, http://www.emap.com.au. Ed. Martine Allars. Circ: 54,382.

028.5 USA ISSN 0743-4898
BARBIE; the magazine for girls. Text in English. 1983. 6/yr. USD 10.30. **Document type:** *Consumer.* **Description:** Fashion and beauty tips for young girls and owners of Barbie dolls.
Published by: Marvel Entertainment Group, 387 Park Ave S Fl 9, New York, NY 10016-8810. TEL 212-687-0680, FAX 212-986-5849.

052 GBR ISSN 0963-8911
BARBIE. Text in English. 1991. m. GBP 1.35 newsstand/cover. adv. back issues avail. **Document type:** *Consumer.* **Description:** Creative stories, crafts, ideas, and activities for Barbie and all of her admirers.
Published by: Egmont Fleetway Ltd., Egmont House, Pl, Flat 25, 31 Tavistock Rd, London, W11 1AS, United Kingdom. TEL 44-20-7344-6400, FAX 44-207-388-4152. Ed. Claire Mewett. Adv. contact Steven Goldsmith. Circ: 133,572 (paid). **Dist. by:** Seymour Distribution Ltd, 86 Newman St, London W1T 3EX, United Kingdom. FAX 44-207-396-8002, enquiries@seymour.co.uk.

087.5 ROM ISSN 1454-6264
BARBIE. Text in Romanian. 1999. m. ROL 290,000; ROL 29,000 newsstand/cover (effective 2002). **Document type:** *Magazine, Consumer.*
Published by: Egmont Romania, Piata Presei Libere nr. 1, corp B2, etaj 4, Bucharest, Romania. TEL 40-21-2246055, FAX 40-21-2246057, cc@ero.egmont.com, http://www.egmont.ro.

808.068 MEX
BARBIE. Text in Spanish. 1985. m. adv. **Document type:** *Consumer.*
Published by: Editorial Armonia S.A., Magdalena 135, Magdalena 135, Mexico City, DF 03100, Mexico. TEL 525-687-2666, FAX 525-543-2073, TELEX 1764640 KENAME. Ed. Liliana Moreno G. Circ: 92,371.

870.55 PRT ISSN 0874-0569
BARBIE. Text in Portuguese. 1996. 3/yr. EUR 17.16 (effective 2002). adv. **Document type:** *Magazine, Consumer.*
Published by: Edimpresa Editora Lda., Rua Calvet de Magalhaes 242, Laveiras, Paco de Arcos, 2770-022, Portugal. TEL 351-21-4698000, FAX 351-21-4698501, edimpresa@edimpresa.pt, http://www.edimpresa.pt. adv.: page EUR 1,371.69; trim 200 x 275.

052 GBR ISSN 1462-7337
BARBIE SPECIAL. Text in English. 1998. 5/yr. GBP 1.99 newsstand/cover. **Document type:** *Consumer.* **Description:** Contains fun activities and games involving Barbie and all her friends.
Published by: Egmont Fleetway Ltd., Egmont House, Pl, Flat 25, 31 Tavistock Rd, London, W11 1AS, United Kingdom. TEL 44-20-7344-6400, FAX 44-207-388-4152. **Dist. by:** Seymour Distribution Ltd, 86 Newman St, London W1T 3EX, United Kingdom. FAX 44-20-73968002, 44-20-73968002.

BARNARDO NEWS. see *SOCIAL SERVICES AND WELFARE*

011.62 NOR ISSN 1503-2337
➤ **BARNE- OG UNGDOMSLITTERATUR (YEAR)**; veiledende liste. Text in Norwegian. 1967. a. free. bk.rev. abstr.; bibl. 240 p./no.; back issues avail. **Document type:** *Catalog, Abstract/Index.* **Description:** Presents an annotated booklist of recommended literature for children and young adults.
Former titles (until 2001): Veiledende Liste (0807-5557); (until 1995): Veiledende Liste for Barne- og Ungdomslitteratur (0802-1147); (until 1985): Barne- og Ungdomslitteratur (0800-5923); (until 1983): Utvalg for Skolebiblioteker av Boeker Utkommet i (Year) (0302-8968); (until 1973): Boeker for Skoleboksamlinger (0332-7922)
Related titles: Online - full content ed.
Published by: A B M - Utvikling/Norwegian Archive, Library and Museum Authority, Kronprinsens Gate 9, Postboks 8145, Dep, Oslo, 0033, Norway. TEL 47-21-02-17-00, FAX 47-21-02-17-01, sb@bibtils.no, http://www.bibsent.no/html/veiledende2.htm. Ed. Elin Thomsen TEL 47-21-02-17-25. Circ: 7,000 (controlled).

028.5 DEU
BART SIMPSON; Naturbursche. Text in German. 2001. q. EUR 2 newsstand/cover (effective 2002). **Document type:** *Magazine, Consumer.*
Published by: Panini Verlags GmbH, Ravensstr 48, Nettetal, 41334, Germany. TEL 49-711-947680, FAX 49-711-94768830, info@panini-dino.de, http://www.panini-media.de.

028.5 GBR ISSN 1319-0849
BASEM. Text in Arabic. 1987. w. GBP 70 (effective 1997). illus. back issues avail. **Document type:** *Consumer.* **Description:** A magazine for children ages 6 to 15, including educational matters, competitions and informative pieces.
Related titles: Microfilm ed.
Published by: Saudi Research and Marketing, Arab Press House, 184 High Holborn, London, WC1V 7AP, United Kingdom. TEL 44-20-7831-8181, FAX 44-20-7831-2310. Ed. Jamal Inayat. adv.: B&W page USD 1,333, color page USD 2,333; trim 285 x 220. Circ: 40,809 (paid). **Subscr. in U.S. to:** Attache International, 3050 Broadway, Ste 300, Boulder, CO 80304-3154. TEL 303-442-8900.

059.927 SAU
BASIM. Text in Arabic. w. adv. **Document type:** *Magazine, Consumer.* **Description:** Contains numerous comic strips, short stories, games and educational articles for 8-15 year olds.
Published by: Saudi Research & Publishing Co., PO Box 4556, Jeddah, 21412, Saudi Arabia. TEL 966-2-669-1888, FAX 966-2-667-1650, http://www.alkhaleejiahadv.com.sa/srpc/. adv.: page SAR 8,500. Circ: 35,129 (paid).

028.5 DNK ISSN 1397-4696
BASSERNE. Text in Danish. 1972. 26/yr. DKK 675 (effective 2002). adv. **Document type:** *Magazine, Consumer.*
Former titles (until 198?): Basserne med Garfield; (until 1984): Basserne
Published by: Egmont Serieforlaget A/S, Mosedalvej 14, Valby, 2500, Denmark. TEL 45-70-20-50-35, FAX 45-36-18-58-90. Circ: 70,000.

087.5 BRA ISSN 0104-7639
BATMAN. Text in Portuguese. 1995. m. **Document type:** *Magazine, Consumer.*
Published by: Editora Abril, S.A., Av. das Nacoes Unidas, 7221, 11 andar Pinheiros, Sao Paulo, SP 05425-902, Brazil. TEL 55-11-50872112, FAX 55-11-50872100, http://www.abril.com.br/.

028.5 GBR ISSN 1351-2625
BATMAN - JUDGE DREDD. Text in English. 1993. m. GBP 1.25 newsstand/cover. adv. **Document type:** *Consumer.*
Published by: Egmont Fleetway Ltd., Egmont House, Pl, Flat 25, 31 Tavistock Rd, London, W11 1AS, United Kingdom. TEL 44-20-7344-6400, FAX 44-207-388-4152. **Dist. by:** Seymour Distribution Ltd, 86 Newman St, London W1T 3EX, United Kingdom. FAX 44-207-396-8002, enquiries@seymour.co.uk.

028.5 DEU ISSN 0005-6790
BAUSTEIN; evangelische Jugendzeitschrift. Text in German. 1946. m. bk.rev.; film rev. illus. **Document type:** *Magazine, Consumer.* **Description:** Helps adolescents aged 14 to 18 live their daily lives as Christians.
Incorporates (1985-1987): Komma (0930-1291)
Published by: C V J M Gesamtverband in Deutschland e.V., C V J M- Westbund, Bundeshoehe 6, Wuppertal, 42285, Germany. TEL 49-202-57420, FAX 49-202-574242, info@cvjm-westbund.de, http://www.cvjm-westbund.de. Ed. Friedhelm Ringelband. Circ: 17,000.

369.463 USA
BAY WINDOW (NEWARK, DE). Text in English. s-a. (spring & fall). free (effective 2005). **Document type:** *Newsletter, Consumer.*
Published by: Chesapeake Bay Girl Scout Council, 501 S College Ave, Newark, DE 19713. TEL 302-456-7150, 800-341-4007, FAX 302-456-7188, cbgscweb@cbgsc.org, http://www.cbgsc.org/. Ed. Ann Marie van den Hurk. Circ: 22,000 (controlled and free).

374 DEU
BAYREUTHER PAUKE; Schuelerzeitung des Gymnasiums, Bayreutherstr. Text in German. 1956. q. USD 3. adv. bk.rev.; play rev. abstr.; bibl.; illus. back issues avail.
Published by: Staedtisches Gymnasium Wuppertal, Bayreuther Str 35, Wuppertal, 42115, Germany. Ed. Joerg Gerald Jagdberg. Circ: 600.

BE TRUE MAGAZINE; the "online" arts magazine for kids. see *ART*

028.5 AUT
BEAMER; Kulturzeitschrift junger Menschen. Text in German. 1947. irreg. bk.rev.; film rev.; play rev. illus. index. **Document type:** *Magazine, Consumer.*
Formerly (until 2002): Neue Wege (0028-3444)
Media: Online - full content.
Published by: Theater der Jugend, Neubaugasse 38, Vienna, W 1070, Austria. TEL 43-1-52110255, FAX 43-1-52110500, dramaturgie@tdj.at, office@tdj.at, http://www.tdj.at/beamer/. Ed. Herman Mayer. Circ: 7,000.

028.5 GBR ISSN 0262-2467
THE BEANO. Text in English. 1950. w. GBP 33.80 domestic; GBP 38.22 foreign; GBP 0.50 newsstand/cover. adv. **Document type:** *Consumer.* **Description:** Classic fun and colorful comics for children ages 7-13.
Published by: D.C. Thomson & Co. Ltd., 80 Kingsway East, Dundee, Angus, Scotland DD4 8SL, United Kingdom. FAX 44-1382-462097, comment@dcthomson.co.uk, http://www.dcthomson.co.uk, http://www.beano.co.uk. Adv. contact Sharon Mudie. B&W page GBP 1,885, color page GBP 3,300.

028.5 GBR ISSN 0964-8194
BEANO SUPERSTARS. Text in English. 1992. m. GBP 1.20 newsstand/cover. **Document type:** *Consumer.*
Published by: D.C. Thomson & Co. Ltd., 80 Kingsway East, Dundee, Angus, Scotland DD4 8SL, United Kingdom. FAX 44-1382-462097, comment@dcthomson.co.uk, http://www.dcthomson.co.uk.

028.5 USA
BEAR ESSENTIAL NEWS FOR KIDS. Text in English. 1979. m. adv. **Document type:** *Newsletter, Consumer.* **Description:** Aims to enrich, educate and entertain children and their families and designed to promote reading and writing skills as well as creativity.
Related titles: ♦ Issued with: Essential News for Kids.
Published by: Kids' View Communications Corp, 10 N Norton, 110, Tucson, AZ 85719. TEL 520-792-9930, FAX 520-792-2580, http://www.azstarnet.com/bearessential/.

028.5 USA
THE BEAT WITHIN; a weekly newsletter of writing and art from the inside. Text in English, Spanish. 1996. w. (w/monthly eds.). $ 100.00 annual donation. **Document type:** *Newsletter.* **Description:** Features writing done by young people who take part in writing workshops.
Media: Online - full text. **Related titles:** Print ed.
Published by: Pacific News Service, 275 9th St, San Francisco, CA 94103. TEL 415-438-4755, FAX 415-438-4935, yo@pacificnews.org, http://www.pacificnews.org/yo/beat/. Ed. Nell Bernstein. Circ: 1,500.

028.5 USA ISSN 1544-9386
▼ **BEAUTIFUL GIRL**; inside and out. Text in English. 2003 (Dec.). q. USD 12 (effective 2004). adv. **Document type:** *Magazine, Consumer.* **Description:** Contains articles and features aimed at hip and trendy Christian teenage girls.
Address: 10920 Baymeadows Rd, Ste 27-226, Jacksonville, FL 32256. TEL 904-993-7001, scarlett@beautifulgirlmagazine.com, http://www.beautifulgirlmagazine.com. Adv. contact Heather Riccio. Circ: 20,000 (controlled).

▼ **BECKETT GOT SPORTS FOR KIDS.** see *SPORTS AND GAMES*

BEENBREEK; Natuur 2000. see *CONSERVATION*

BEGEGNUNG UND AUSTAUSCH MIT FRANZOSEN. see *POLITICAL SCIENCE—International Relations*

028.5 CHN
BEIJING QINGNIAN BAO/BEIJING YOUTH NEWS. Text in Chinese. 1949. d. CNY 24 per month (effective 2004). adv. **Document type:** *Newspaper, Consumer.*
Published by: Beijing Qingnian Bao Wangji Chuanbo Jizhu Youxian Gongsi, Beijing Qingnian Bao Dasha, Chaoyang-qu, 23, Baijia Zhuan Dongli, Beijing, 100026, China. webmaster@ynet.com, http://www.bjyouth.com/, http://www.ynet.com/. **Dist. by:** China International Book Trading Corp, 35 Chegongzhuang Xilu, Haidian District, PO Box 399, Beijing 100044, China. TEL 86-10-68412045, FAX 86-10-68412023, cibtc@mail.cibtc.com.cn, http://www.cibtc.com.cn.

028.5 CHN
BEIJING QINGNIAN ZHOUKAN/BEIJING YOUTH WEEKLY. Text in Chinese. w. **Document type:** *Consumer.*
Related titles: Online - full content ed.
Published by: Beijing Qingnian Bao Wangji Chuanbo Jizhu Youxian Gongsi, Beijing Qingnian Bao Dasha, Chaoyang-qu, 23, Baijia Zhuan Dongli, Beijing, 100026, China. webmaster@ynet.com, http://bjqn.ynet.com/, http://www.ynet.com/.

028.5 CHN
BEIJING SHAONIANBAO/BEIJING CHILDREN'S WEEKLY. Text in Chinese. w. **Document type:** *Consumer.*
Related titles: Online - full content ed.
Published by: Beijing Qingnian Bao Wangji Chuanbo Jizhu Youxian Gongsi, Beijing Qingnian Bao Dasha, Chaoyang-qu, 23, Baijia Zhuan Dongli, Beijing, 100026, China. bjsnb.ynet.com, webmaster@ynet.com, http://bjsn.ynet.com/, http://www.ynet.com/.

028.5 FRA ISSN 0991-8787
LES BELLES HISTOIRES. Variant title: Les Belles Histoires de Pomme d'Api. Text in French. 1972. m. EUR 59.80 domestic; EUR 74.80 in the European Union; EUR 79.80 elsewhere (effective 2005). **Document type:** *Magazine, Consumer.* **Description:** Promotes the development of the senses, the imagination and sense of humor in children 3 to 7 years old through stories and pictures.
Published by: Bayard Presse, 3 Rue Bayard, Paris, 75393 Cedex 08, France. TEL 33-1-44356060, FAX 33-1-44356161, redactions@bayard-presse.com, http://www.bayardpresse.com. Ed. Marie Agnes Gaudrat. Circ: 71,415.

028.1 200 DEU ISSN 0863-2863
BENJAMIN; evangelische Monatszeitschrift fuer Maedchen und Jungen. Text in German. m. EUR 32.40 (effective 2005). adv. **Document type:** *Bulletin.*
Published by: Gemeinschaftswerk der Evangelischen Publizistik e.V., Emil-von-Behring-Str 3, Frankfut Am Main, 60439, Germany. TEL 49-69-580980, FAX 49-69-58098272, info@gep.de, http://www.hallo-benjamin.de, http://www.gep.de. Ed. Kathrin Kommerell. Circ: 8,000.

028.5 DEU
BENJAMIN BLUEMCHEN; lesen - lachen - begreifen. Text in German. fortn. EUR 59.80; EUR 2.30 newsstand/cover (effective 2005). adv. **Document type:** *Magazine, Consumer.*
Published by: Egmont Ehapa Verlag GmbH, Wallstr 59, Berlin, 10179, Germany. TEL 49-30-240080, FAX 49-30-24008599, leserservice@ehapa.de, http://www.ehapa.de/magazine/bb.html. Adv. contact Olaf Hansen. page EUR 4,900; 250 x 290. Circ: 96,759 (paid).

C

305.23 ITA ISSN 1127-3372
BENKYO; tutto su manga e animazione giapponese. Text in Italian. 1998. m. EUR 6.70 newsstand/cover (effective 2003). adv. **Document type:** *Magazine, Consumer.* **Description:** Devoted to Japanese animation. Contains reviews on new video releases and relevant news regarding the importation of videos into Italy.
Published by: Play Press Publishing s.r.l., Via Vitorchiano 123, Rome, RM 00189, Italy. TEL 39-06-3701592, FAX 39-06-3701502, abbonamenti@playpress.com, http://www.playpress.com. Ed. Carlo Chericoni. Pub. Alessandro Ferri. Adv. contact Lorenza Borroni TEL 39-02-45472867. Circ: 35,000 (paid and controlled).

028.5 DEU ISSN 0948-325X
BENNI UND TEDDY; das bunte Magazin fuer Kinder. Text in German. 1984. m. EUR 25.20; EUR 2.10 newsstand/cover (effective 2003). adv. **Document type:** *Magazine, Consumer.*
Formerly (until 1994): Benni (0177-2589)
Published by: Johann Michael Sailer Verlag GmbH & Co. KG, Aeusserer Laufer Platz 17, Nuernberg, 90403, Germany. TEL 49-911-53960, FAX 49-911-5396912, sailer@sailer-verlag.de, http://www.sailer-verlag.de. Ed. Bobby Kastenhuber. adv.: page EUR 2,640. Circ: 45,937.

028.5 JPN
BESSATSU FRIEND. Text in Japanese. m. **Document type:** *Magazine, Consumer.*
Published by: Kodansha Ltd., 2-12-21 Otowa, Bunkyo-ku, Tokyo, 112-8001, Japan. TEL 81-3-3946-6201, FAX 81-3-3944-9915, http://www.kodansha.co.jp.

028.5 USA ISSN 1523-6471
Z1037.A1
THE BEST CHILDREN'S BOOKS OF THE YEAR. Text in English. 1916. a. USD 5.04 (effective 2004). bk.rev. back issues avail. **Document type:** *Bibliography.* **Description:** Includes approximately 600 titles selected from over 4500 new books published each year for children from preschool to 14 years. Annotated and arranged according to age and interest. Includes tips for parents.
Formerly: Children's Books of the Year
Published by: Bank Street College, 610 W 112th St, New York, NY 10025. TEL 212-875-4400, collegepubs@bankstreet.edu, http://www.bankstreet.edu. Eds. Margery Fisher, Nancy M Berner. R&P Alice Belgray. Circ: 3,000.

028.5 GBR ISSN 0956-1951
THE BEST OF 2000 AD MONTHLY. Text in English. 1985. m. GBP 1.25 newsstand/cover. adv. illus. back issues avail. **Document type:** *Consumer.* **Description:** Provides science-fiction stories geared toward teenage males.
Published by: Egmont Fleetway Ltd., Egmont House, Pl, Flat 25, 31 Tavistock Rd, London, W11 1AS, United Kingdom. TEL 44-20-7344-6400, FAX 44-20-7388-4020. Ed. Tharg The Mighty. Circ: 30,000 (paid). **Subscr. to:** Aim, Pallion Industrial Estate, PO Box 10, Sunderland, Tyne and Wear SR4 6SN, United Kingdom. TEL 0191-510-0201. **Dist. by:** Seymour Distribution Ltd, 86 Newman St, London W1T 3EX, United Kingdom. enquiries@seymour.co.uk.

028.5 GBR ISSN 1460-5430
BEST OF POSTMAN PAT. Text in English. bi-m. GBP 9.75; GBP 1.95 newsstand/cover (effective 2001). illus. **Document type:** *Consumer.* **Description:** Offers young readers ages 3 to 7 educational and enjoyable stories, activities, and puzzles based on the Postman Pat character.
Published by: The Redan Company Ltd., Ramillies Building, 1-9 Hills Pl, London, W1R 1AG, United Kingdom. TEL 44-20-7434-1612, FAX 44-20-7734-1929, sam@edan.co.uk. Adv. contact Sarah Warden. **Dist. by:** Comag, Tavistock Works, Tavistock Rd, W Drayton, Middx UB7 7QX, United Kingdom. TEL 44-1895-433600.

028.5 JPN
BEST ONE. Text in Japanese. 1979. m. JPY 4,560.
Published by: Gakken Co. Ltd., 40-5 Kami-Ikedai 4-chome, Ota-ku, Tokyo, 145-0064, Japan. Ed. Hojun Kigidera.

BETREFF; Magazin fuer junge Leute im oeffentlichen Dienst. see *PUBLIC ADMINISTRATION*

028.5 JPN
BETSUCOMI; love story comics for girls. Text in Japanese. m. JPY 340 newsstand/cover (effective 2002). **Document type:** *Magazine, Consumer.*
Published by: Shogakukan Inc., 3-1 Hitotsubashi 2-chome, Chiyoda-ku, Tokyo, 101-8001, Japan. TEL 81-3-3230-5211, FAX 81-3-3264-8471, http://www.shogakukan.co.jp.

028.5 DEU
BIBI BLOCKSBERG; Spass und Spannung mit der lustigen Hexe. Text in German. m. EUR 30; EUR 2.50 newsstand/cover (effective 2005). adv. **Document type:** *Magazine, Consumer.*
Published by: Egmont Ehapa Verlag GmbH, Wallstr 59, Berlin, 10179, Germany. TEL 49-30-240080, FAX 49-30-24008599, leserservice@ehapa.de, http://www.ehapa.de. Adv. contact Olaf Hansen. page EUR 4,200; 215 x 290. Circ: 84,803 (paid).

053.1 DEU
BIBI UND TINA; eine Freundschaft zum Pferdestehlen. Text in German. 2002. m. EUR 2.50 newsstand/cover (effective 2005). adv. **Document type:** *Magazine, Consumer.*
Published by: Egmont Ehapa Verlag GmbH, Wallstr 59, Berlin, 10179, Germany. TEL 49-30-240080, FAX 49-30-24008599, leserservice@ehapa.de, http://www.bibiundtina.de/portal/, http://www.ehapa.de. adv.: page EUR 3,500. Circ: 69,619 (paid and controlled).

BIBLE DISCOVERERS. see *RELIGIONS AND THEOLOGY—Protestant*

BIBLE EXPRESS. see *RELIGIONS AND THEOLOGY—Protestant*

028.5 USA ISSN 0039-5250
BIBLE-IN-LIFE PIX. Text in English. 1948. q. USD 12 (effective 2002). illus.
Formerly: Sunday Pix
Published by: David C. Cook Publishing Co., 4050 Lee Vance View, Colorado Springs, CO 80918. TEL 719-536-0100. Ed. Iva S Hoth.

BIBLE LEARNERS. see *RELIGIONS AND THEOLOGY—Protestant*

028.5 FRA ISSN 0005-335X
BIBLIOTHEQUE DE TRAVAIL. Short title: B T. Text in French. 10/yr. adv. illus.
Published by: Publications de l'Ecole Moderne Francaise, Mouans-Sartoux, Cedex 06376, France. TEL 33-4-92921757, FAX 33-4-92921804. Pub. Pierre Guerin.

028.5 ARG ISSN 0006-2553
BILLIKEN. Text in Spanish. 1919. w. adv. illus. **Document type:** *Magazine, Consumer.*
Published by: Editorial Atlantida S.A., Azopardo 579, 3 piso, Capital Federal, Buenos Aires 1307, Argentina. TEL 54-11-4331-3865, FAX 54-11-4343-1362, info@atlantidadigital.com.ar, http://www.billiken.com.ar, http://www.atlantida.com.ar. Ed. Carlos Silveyra. Circ: 240,000.

BIMBO; der kleine Tierfreund. see *CONSERVATION*

BIOGRAPHY FOR BEGINNERS; sketches for early readers. see *BIOGRAPHY*

BIOGRAPHY TODAY (ANNUAL); profiles of people of interest to young readers. see *BIOGRAPHY*

BIOGRAPHY TODAY (GENERAL SERIES); profiles of people of interest to young readers. see *BIOGRAPHY*

BIOGRAPHY TODAY AUTHOR SERIES. see *BIOGRAPHY*

305.23 DEU
BIONICLE. Text in German. bi-m. EUR 2.70 newsstand/cover (effective 2005). adv. **Document type:** *Magazine, Consumer.*
Published by: Panini Verlags GmbH, Ravensstr 48, Nettetal, 41334, Germany. TEL 49-2157-81750, FAX 49-2157-81484528, info@panini-dino.de, http://www.panini-media.de. adv.: page EUR 2,500; trim 210 x 280. Circ: 51,200 (paid).

BLACKGIRL MAGAZINE. see *ETHNIC INTERESTS*

BLAST!. see *MUSIC*

BLAST OFF. see *HANDICAPPED—Visually Impaired*

028.5 BEL ISSN 1374-920X
BLIKOPENER. Text in Dutch. 1999. 7/yr. illus. **Document type:** *Magazine.* **Description:** Offers teen readers, ages 14 through 16 a variety of articles, stories, and activities.
Published by: Uitgeverij Averbode NV, Abdijstraat 1, Postbus 54, Averbode, 3271, Belgium. TEL 32-13-780111, FAX 32-13-780183, http://www.averbode.be.

305.23 DEU
BLUE'S CLUES. Text in German. 1999. 4/yr. EUR 2.70 newsstand/cover (effective 2005). adv. **Document type:** *Magazine, Consumer.*
Published by: Panini Verlags GmbH, Ravensstr 48, Nettetal, 41334, Germany. TEL 49-2157-81750, FAX 49-2157-81484528, info@panini-dino.de, http://www.panini-media.de. adv.: page EUR 2,500. Circ: 80,000 (paid).

052 GBR
BLUSH!. Text in English. 2002 (Aug.). fortn. GBP 1.60 newsstand/cover (effective 2003). adv. **Document type:** *Magazine, Consumer.* **Description:** Contains articles on the latest celebrities from movies, music and TV as well as features on fashion and beauty for girls ages 10-14.
Published by: H. Bauer Publishing Ltd. (Subsidiary of: Heinrich Bauer Verlag), Academic House, 24-28 Oval Rd, London, NW1 7DT, United Kingdom. TEL 44-20-72418000, FAX 44-20-72418056, simon.priston@bauer.co.uk. Ed. Lesley Jones. Pub. Liz Watkinson. Adv. contact Matt Hayes. page GBP 5,300; trim 205 x 265.

028.5 649.7 PRT
BOA SEMENTE. Text in Portuguese. m.
Published by: Casa Publicadora da Convencao das Assembleias de Deus em Portugal, Avenida Almirante Gago Coutinho, 158, Lisbon, 1700, Portugal. TEL 351-21-8429190, FAX 351-21-840936, capu@capu.pt, http://www.capu.pt. Ed. Fernando Martinez da Silva. Circ: 4,200.

028.5 DEU
BOB DER BAUMEISTER. Text in German. 1999. m. EUR 2.60 newsstand/cover (effective 2003). adv. **Document type:** *Magazine, Consumer.*
Published by: Panini Verlags GmbH, Ravensstr 48, Nettetal, 41334, Germany. TEL 49-711-947680, FAX 49-711-94768830, info@panini-dino.de, http://www.panini-media.de. adv.: page EUR 3,900. Circ: 84,892 (paid and controlled).

052 GBR ISSN 1466-1012
BOB THE BUILDER. Text in English. 1999. m. GBP 18.20; GBP 1.45 newsstand/cover (effective 2003). **Document type:** *Magazine, Consumer.* **Description:** Presents things to make and do as well as stories and puzzles involving Bob the Builder and friends.
Published by: B B C Worldwide Ltd., 80 Wood Ln, London, W12 0TT, United Kingdom. TEL 44-20-84331070, FAX 44-20-84332231, bbcworldwide@bbc.co.uk, http://www.bbcmagazines.com/bobbuilder/.

028.5 NLD ISSN 0165-1196
BOBO. Text in Dutch. 1968. s-w. illus. **Document type:** *Magazine, Consumer.* **Description:** Offers young readers entertaining articles and activities.
Published by: V N U Tijdschriften B.V., Postbus 1900, Hoofddorp, 2130 JH, Netherlands. TEL 31-23-556-6770, FAX 31-23-556-6771, ServiceTeam@tijdschriften.vnu.com, http://www.vnu.nl.

028.5 IDN
BOBO. Text in Indonesian. 1973. w.
Address: P T Gramedia, Jalan Kebahagiaan 4-14, Jakarta, 11140, Indonesia. TEL 021-6297809, FAX 021-6390080, TELEX 41216. Ed. Tineke Latumeten. Circ: 240,000.

087.5 ROM ISSN 1583-6495
BOBO. Text in Romanian. 2002. m. adv. **Document type:** *Magazine, Consumer.*
Published by: Sanoma - Hearst Romania srl, Str. C.A. Rosetti nr. 5, sector 1, Bucharest, Romania. TEL 40-21-3138620, FAX 40-21-3138622, office@sanomahearst.ro.

028.5 SWE ISSN 1100-780X
BOECKER, BILDER OCH SAANT; tidskrift foer barnens kultur. Text in Swedish. 1988. q. SEK 275 (effective 1997).
Published by: Boecker Bilder & Saant, Fack 19, Bromma, 16126, Sweden. TEL 46-8-29-70-09, FAX 46-8-26-27-36.

028.5 NLD ISSN 0926-3985
BOEKIE BOEKIE. Text in Dutch. 1992. 4/yr. EUR 27.50 (effective 2005). adv. bk.rev. back issues avail. **Description:** Contains art, literature and science for children, including book previews, short stories, poems, activities and science experiments.
Published by: Biblion Uitgeverij, Postbus 437, Leidschendam, 2260 AK, Netherlands. post@boekie-boekie.nl, info@nbdbiblion.nl, http://www.boekie-boekie.nl, http://www.nbdbiblion.nl/. Ed. Jet Manrho. Pub. Andre Henderickx. **Co-publisher:** Stichting Autoped.

BOERN & UNGE. see *EDUCATION*

▼ **BOERNE- OG JUNIORBLADET KONRAD.** see *RELIGIONS AND THEOLOGY—Protestant*

028.5 JPN
BOMB. Text in Japanese. 1981. m. JPY 3,600.
Published by: Gakken Co. Ltd., 40-5 Kami-Ikedai 4-chome, Ota-ku, Tokyo, 145-0064, Japan. Ed. Kazuo Kinoshita.

028.5 BEL ISSN 0773-0306
BONJOUR!. Text in French. 1960. w. EUR 46.50 (effective 2005). **Document type:** *Magazine.* **Description:** Aims to develop the full range of early language and mathematics skills, with activities suited for 6- to 8-year-old children (1st grade).
Published by: Editions Averbode SA, Abdijstraat 1, BP 54, Averbode, 3271, Belgium. TEL 32-13-780111, FAX 32-13-780149. Ed. Philippe Brasseur.

070.5083 CAN ISSN 0006-7377
PN1009.A1
➤ **BOOKBIRD**; a journal of international children's literature. Text in English. 1963. q. CND 64 domestic to individuals; USD 40 in United States to individuals; USD 45 in Mexico to individuals; USD 48 elsewhere to individuals; CND 120 domestic to institutions; USD 75 in United States to institutions; USD 80 in Mexico to institutions; USD 85 elsewhere to institutions; USD 11.50 newsstand/cover (effective 2005). adv. bk.rev. bibl.; illus. reprint service avail. from PQC. **Document type:** *Journal, Academic/Scholarly.* **Description:** Special topics in international children's books, plus news, events, prizes worldwide.

C

Related titles: Microform ed.: (from PQC); Online - full text ed.: (from bigchalk, H.W. Wilson, Northern Light Technology, Inc., O C L C Online Computer Library Center, Inc., ProQuest Information & Learning).
Indexed: BRI, BrHumI, CBRI, ChLitAb, LISA, LibLit. —IE, Infotrieve.
Published by: (International Board on Books for Young People USA), University of Toronto Press, Journals Division, 5201 Dufferin St, Toronto, ON M3H 5T8, Canada. TEL 416-667-7810, FAX 416-667-7881, journals@utpress.utoronto.ca, http://www.utpjournals.com/jour.ihtml?lp=bookbird/bookbird.html. Ed. Barbara A. Lehman. Adv. contact Audrey Greenwood. Circ: 1,700.

028.5 USA
BOOKS FOR GROWING MINDS. Text in English. a. **Document type:** *Catalog.* **Description:** Annual listing of children's book titles.
Published by: Baker & Taylor, PO Box 6885, Bridgewater, NJ 08807-0885. TEL 800-775-1800, FAX 704-329-8989.

028.5 USA ISSN 1052-1682
BOOMERANG!; the children's audiomagazine about big ideas. Text in English. 1990. m. USD 43.95. adv. bk.rev. **Document type:** *Magazine, Consumer.* **Description:** Children's audiomagazine featuring stories on current events, economics, history, geography, mysteries and jokes. Geared toward children 6-12 years old.
Media: Audio cassette/tape.
Published by: (Listen and Learn Home Education), Boomerang! Media Inc., PO Box 261, La Honda, CA 94020-0261. TEL 800-333-7858, FAX 415-747-0754, boomkids@aol.com. Eds. Annie Breed, David Strohm. Adv. contact Tony Cacciotti. Circ: 34,000.

028.5 GBR ISSN 0006-7709
BORE DA. Text in English. 1965. m. (Sept.-June). GBP 8 (effective 2000). illus. **Document type:** *Academic/Scholarly.* **Description:** For children up to age 11 learning Welsh as a second language. Follows key stages 1 and 2 of the national curriculum.
Published by: Urdd Gobaith Cymru, Adran Cylchgronau, Swyddfa'r Urdd, Ffordd Llanbadarn, Aberystwyth, Ceredigion, Wales SY23 1EY, United Kingdom. TEL 44-1970-613118, FAX 44-1970-626120, boreda@urdd.org, Cylchgronau@urdd.org, http://www.urdd.org/Cylchgronau/Darllenwyr/Bore%20Da/TudalenDarllenwyrBoreDa.html. Ed. Magi Dodd. Circ: 3,300.

028.5 070.5 USA ISSN 0000-1813
▼ **THE BOWKER BUYER'S GUIDE TO CHILDREN'S BOOKS**; forthcoming juvenile titles. Text in English. 2005 (Winter). s-a. free (effective 2005).
Published by: R.R. Bowker LLC (Subsidiary of: Cambridge Information Group), 630 Central Ave., New Providence, NJ 07974. TEL 908-286-1090, 888-269-5372, 800-526-9537, FAX 908-219-0098, http://www.bowker.com. Ed. Mervaine Ricks. **Subscr. to:** Order Dept., PO Box 32, New Providence, NJ 07974-9903. TEL 800-521-8110, FAX 908-219-0098.

051 USA ISSN 1541-8421
BOY CRAZY!. Text in English. 2001. bi-m. USD 27.95 domestic; USD 42.95 in Canada; USD 51.95 elsewhere; USD 5.95 newsstand/cover; USD 7.95 newsstand/cover in Canada (effective 2002). adv. **Document type:** *Magazine, Consumer.* **Description:** Contains articles and features for girls about romance and relationships written by real boys.
Related titles: Online - full text ed.
Published by: Decipher, Inc., 253 Granby St., Norfolk, VA 23510-1831. TEL 877-787-8626, http://www.boycrazy.com. Ed. Gabrielle Lasting. Pub. Cindy Thornburg.

301.58 GBR ISSN 0068-0605
BOYS' BRIGADE. ANNUAL REPORT. Text in English. 1883. a. GBP 9.50 (effective 1999). **Document type:** *Newsletter.*
Published by: Boys' Brigade Inc., Felden Lodge, Felden, Hemel Hempstead, Herts HP3 0BL, United Kingdom. TEL 44-1442-231681, FAX 44-1442-235391, felden@boys-brigade.org.uk, http://www.boys.brigade.org.uk. Ed. Sydney Jones. Circ: 10,000.

369.4 GBR ISSN 0006-8578
BOYS BRIGADE GAZETTE. Text in English. 1886. bi-m. GBP 9.50 (effective 1999). adv. **Document type:** *Newsletter.* **Description:** Promotes Christian behavior among boys by helping them practice obedience, reverence, discipline, and self-respect.
Published by: Boys' Brigade Inc., Felden Lodge, Felden, Hemel Hempstead, Herts HP3 0BL, United Kingdom. TEL 44-1442-231681, FAX 44-1442-235391, felden@boys-brigade.org.uk, http://www.boys-brigade.org.uk, http://www.boys.brigade.org.uk. Ed. Sydney Jones. Circ: 7,000.

369.4 USA ISSN 0006-8608
BOYS' LIFE; the magazine for all boys. Text in English. 1911. m. USD 21.60 domestic; USD 3.60 newsstand/cover (effective 2005). adv. bk.rev.; film rev.; rec.rev. illus.; tr.lit. index. 75 p./no.; back issues avail.; reprints avail. **Document type:** *Magazine, Consumer.* **Description:** Covers Scouting, sports, science, hobbies, careers, health, history, video games and more.
Related titles: Braille ed.; CD-ROM ed.; Microfiche ed.: (from NBI, PQC); Online - full text ed.: (from bigchalk, EBSCO Publishing, Gale Group, O C L C Online Computer Library Center, Inc., ProQuest Information & Learning).
Indexed: ASIP, CPerI, HlthInd, ICM, IHTDI, JHMA, MASUSE, MagInd, PMR, RGYP, TOM.
Published by: Boy Scouts of America, PO Box 152079, Irving, TX 75015-2079. TEL 972-580-2000, FAX 972-580-2079, bbutterw@netbsa.org, http://www.boyslife.org. Ed. J D Owen. Pub. J Warren Young. R&P B L Peters. Adv. contact Lisa Hott TEL 972-580-2351. B&W page USD 24,840, color page USD 32,400; trim 7 x 10. Circ: 1,300,000 (paid).

028.5 USA ISSN 1078-9006
BOYS' QUEST. Text in English. 1995. bi-m. USD 22.95 domestic; USD 28.95 foreign; USD 3.95 newsstand/cover (effective 2005). bk.rev. illus. back issues avail.; reprints avail. **Document type:** *Magazine, Consumer.* **Description:** Aims to inspire reading among young boys. Offers wholesome, innocent childhood interests.
Related titles: Online - full text ed.: (from EBSCO Publishing, Gale Group).
Indexed: ICM, RGYP.
Published by: Bluffton News Printing and Publishing Co., PO Box 227, Bluffton, OH 45817-0227. TEL 419-358-4610, 800-358-4732, FAX 419-358-5027, http://www.boysquest.com. Ed., R&P Marilyn Edwards. Pub. Tom Edwards. Circ: 12,000 (paid).

BRAILLE AT BEDTIME. see *HANDICAPPED—Visually Impaired*

057.85 POL ISSN 1230-8692
BRAVO. Text in Polish. 1991. fortn. PLZ 1.95 newsstand/cover (effective 2003). adv. **Document type:** *Magazine, Consumer.*
Related titles: Online - full text ed.
Published by: Wydawnictwo Bauer Sp. z o.o. (Subsidiary of: Heinrich Bauer Verlag), ul. Motorowa 1, Warsaw, 04-035, Poland. TEL 48-22-5170500, FAX 48-22-5170125, bravo@bauer.pl, kontakt@bauer.pl, http://www.bravo.pl, http://www.bauer.pl. Ed. Robert Sankowski. Adv. contact Katarzyna Jablonska. page PLZ 33,600.

057.86 CZE ISSN 1211-4294
BRAVO. Text in Czech. 1991. fortn. CZK 18.90 newsstand/cover (effective 2003). adv. **Document type:** *Magazine, Consumer.* **Description:** Contains articles and interviews concerned with music, films and sport for kids ages 11 to 16.
Published by: Europress, komanditni spolecnost (Subsidiary of: Heinrich Bauer Verlag), Viktora Huga 6, Prague 5, 150 00, Czech Republic. TEL 420-225-008111, FAX 420-257-327103, inzerce@europress.cz, http://www.europress.cz. Ed. Sandra Bursakova. Adv. contact Ivo Jerak. color page CZK 240,000; trim 210 x 280.

059.94511 HUN ISSN 1216-0776
BRAVO. Text in Hungarian. 1992. bi-w. adv. film rev.; music rev.; tel.rev.; video rev. **Document type:** *Magazine, Consumer.* **Description:** Contains articles and stories for young people featuring pop music, interviews with stars, movie reviews, and lifestyle issues.
Published by: Euromedia Lapkiado bt, Bokor Utca 15-19, Budapest, 1037, Hungary. TEL 36-1-4371100, FAX 36-1-4371180, aselmeczi@er.hu, http://www.vnubp.hu. adv.: page HUF 890,000; trim 210 x 280. Circ: 59,983 (paid).

028.5 CZE ISSN 1211-4308
BRAVO GIRL!. Text in Czech. 1996. fortn. CZK 22 newsstand/cover (effective 2003). adv. **Document type:** *Magazine, Consumer.* **Description:** Contains articles offering the latest trends in fashion, cosmetics and hairstyles, beauty tips, advice on boys, and how to gain self-confidence for girls ages 12-17.
Published by: Europress, komanditni spolecnost (Subsidiary of: Heinrich Bauer Verlag), Viktora Huga 6, Prague 5, 150 00, Czech Republic. TEL 420-225-008111, FAX 420-257-327103, inzerce@europress.cz, http://www.europress.cz. Ed. Ivana Sochurkova. Adv. contact Ivo Jerak. page CZK 150,000; trim 210 x 280.

028.5 DEU ISSN 0939-8511
BRAVO GIRL!. Text in German. 1988. fortn. EUR 44.20; EUR 1.70 newsstand/cover (effective 2005). adv. **Document type:** *Magazine, Consumer.* **Description:** Magazine for young girls covering lifestyles, entertainment and music.
Published by: Heinrich Bauer Smaragd KG (Subsidiary of: Heinrich Bauer Verlag), Charles-de-Gaulle-Str 8, Munich, 81737, Germany. TEL 49-89-67860, FAX 49-89-6702033, kommunikation@hbv.de, http://www.bravo.de/online/render.php?render=000571, http://www.hbv.de. Ed. Susanne Fett. Adv. contact Anja Visscher. page EUR 17,700; trim 194 x 262. Circ: 235,871 (paid). **Dist. in UK by:** Seymour Distribution Ltd, 86 Newman St, London W1T 3EX, United Kingdom. FAX 44-207-396-8002, enquiries@seymour.co.uk; **Dist. in US by:** GLP International.

057.85 POL ISSN 1231-2150
BRAVO GIRL!. Text in Polish. 1994. fortn. PLZ 1.85 newsstand/cover (effective 2003). adv. **Document type:** *Magazine, Consumer.*
Published by: Wydawnictwo Bauer Sp. z o.o. (Subsidiary of: Heinrich Bauer Verlag), ul. Motorowa 1, Warsaw, 04-035, Poland. TEL 48-22-5170500, FAX 48-22-5170125, bgirl@bauer.pl, kontakt@bauer.pl, http://www.bauer.pl. Ed. Anna Damiecka. Adv. contact Katarzyna Jablonska. page PLZ 20,000.

059.94511 HUN ISSN 1417-510X
BRAVO GIRL!. Text in Hungarian. 1997. m. adv. film rev.; music rev.; tel.rev.; video rev. **Document type:** *Magazine, Consumer.* **Description:** Filled with articles and features on pop music, movies, television shows, celebrities, and other items of interest to young girls.
Published by: Euromedia Lapkiado bt, Bokor Utca 15-19, Budapest, 1037, Hungary. TEL 36-1-4371100, FAX 36-1-4371180, aselmeczi@er.hu, http://www.vnubp.hu. adv.: page HUF 680,000; trim 210 x 280. Circ: 49,026 (paid).

087.5 ESP ISSN 1136-1239
BRAVO POR TI. Text in Spanish. 1995. fortn. EUR 1.75 newsstand/cover. adv. **Document type:** *Magazine, Consumer.*
Published by: H. Bauer Ediciones S.L. (Subsidiary of: Heinrich Bauer Verlag), Jacometrezo 15, Madrid, 28013, Spain. TEL 34-91-5476800, FAX 34-91-5413523, http://www.bravoporti.com.

BRAVO SPORT. see *SPORTS AND GAMES*

▼ **BREAK**; the magazine for STA travel. see *TRAVEL AND TOURISM*

028.5 BEL ISSN 1387-1412
BREAK OUT!. Text in Dutch. 1996. 10/yr. EUR 74.10 (effective 2003). adv. film rev.; music rev.; tel.rev.; video rev. illus. **Document type:** *Magazine, Consumer.* **Description:** Keeps teens and other young readers apprised of what is happening in the worlds of music, film, and other areas of entertainments. Discusses other topics of interest to young readers.
Published by: Sanoma Magazines Belgium, Telecomlaan 5-7, Diegem, 1831, Belgium. TEL 32-2-7762211, FAX 32-2-776-2317, http://www.breakout.nl, http://www.sanoma-magazines.be/HomePage.aspx?flash=1&Language=nl.

028.5 USA ISSN 1048-2881
BREAKAWAY. Text in English. 1990. m. USD 18 donation (effective 2004). adv. **Document type:** *Consumer.* **Description:** For teen boys, ages 12-16. Designed to creatively teach, entertain, inspire, and challenge the emerging teenager, following the teachings of Jesus Christ.
Published by: Focus on the Family, Inc., 8605 Explorer Dr, Colorado Springs, CO 80920-1051. TEL 719-531-3400, 800-232-6459, FAX 719-531-3424, http://www.family.org/teenguys/breakmag/. Ed. Michael Ross. R&P Christine McDonald. Circ: 105,000 (paid).

649 AUT
BRENNPUNKT FAMILIE. Text in German. 1978. irreg., latest vol.86, 2004. price varies. adv. back issues avail. **Document type:** *Monographic series, Consumer.*
Related titles: Online - full text ed.
Published by: Katholischer Familienverband Oesterreichs, Spiegelgasse 3/3/9, Vienna, 1010, Austria. TEL 43-1-515523201, FAX 43-1-515523699, info@familie.at, http://www.familie.at. Circ: 1,000 (paid).

369.463 USA
THE BRIDGE (MINNEAPOLIS). Text in English. q. free to members. **Document type:** *Newsletter, Consumer.*
Formerly: Girl Scout News
Related titles: Online - full content ed.
Published by: Girl Scout Council of Greater Minneapolis, 5601 Brooklyn Blvd, Brooklyn Center, MN 55429-3074. TEL 763-535-4602, FAX 763-535-7524, mpeterson@girlscoutsmpls.org, http://www.girlscoutsmpls.org. Ed. Mike Peterson. Circ: 1,800 (free).

028.5 DEU ISSN 0946-168X
BRIGITTE YOUNG MISS. Variant title: Young Miss. Text in German. 1990. 12/yr. EUR 2.20 newsstand/cover (effective 2003). adv. **Document type:** *Magazine, Consumer.* **Description:** Filled with exciting articles and features covering all the interests of girls and young women.
Published by: Gruner und Jahr AG & Co., Am Baumwall 11, Hamburg, 20459, Germany. TEL 49-40-3703-0, FAX 49-40-37035631, 49-40-37035617, youngmiss.mailbox@guj.de, guj-redaktion@guj.de, http://www.youngmiss.de, http://www.guj.de. Ed. Ulrike Fischer. Adv. contact Rolf Ruediger Nausch. page EUR 12,500. Circ: 317,034 (paid).

028.162 USA ISSN 0884-3635
BRILLIANT STAR. Text in English. 1969. bi-m. USD 18 domestic; USD 28 foreign (effective 2004). bk.rev. index. back issues avail.
Formerly (until Mar. 1983): Child's Way
Published by: National Spiritual Assembly of the Baha'is of the United States, 536 Sheridan Rd, Wilmette, IL 60091. TEL 847-869-9039, FAX 847-869-0247, http://www.us.bahai.org/. Ed. Amethel Parel Sewell. R&P Dale Spenner TEL 847-251-1854. Circ: 1,500. **Subscr. to:** Brilliontstar Subscriber Service, 4703 Fulton Industrial Blvd, Atlanta, GA 30336-2017.

C

087.5 BRA ISSN 0104-7353
BRINQUE COMIGO. Text in Portuguese. 1995. m. **Document type:** *Magazine, Consumer.*
Published by: Editora Abril, S.A., Av. das Nacoes Unidas, 7221, 11 andar Pinheiros, Sao Paulo, SP 05425-902, Brazil. TEL 55-11-50872112, FAX 55-11-50872100, http://www.abril.com.br/.

028.5 250 USA ISSN 1048-2873
BRIO. Text in English. 1990. m. USD 18 (effective 2002). illus. **Document type:** *Magazine, Consumer.* **Description:** For teen girls, ages 12-16. Designed to teach creatively, to entertain, and to challenge girls toward healthy self-concepts and a closer relationship with Jesus Christ.
Published by: Focus on the Family, Inc., 8605 Explorer Dr, Colorado Springs, CO 80920-1051. TEL 719-531-3400, 800-232-6459, FAX 719-531-3424, brio@macmail.fotf.org, http://www.briomag.com, http://www.family.org. Ed. Susie Shellenberger. R&P Christine McDonald. Circ: 210,000 (paid).

028.5 USA
BRIO & BEYOND. Text in English. m. USD 18 (effective 2004). **Document type:** *Magazine, Consumer.* **Description:** Contains articles and features designed for Christian teen girls ages 16 to 19.
Published by: Focus on the Family, Inc., 8605 Explorer Dr, Colorado Springs, CO 80920-1051. TEL 719-531-3400, 800-232-6459, FAX 719-531-3424, http://www.family.org.

BRITISH ORIGAMI. see *ARTS AND HANDICRAFTS*

369.4 DNK ISSN 1602-0502
BROEN. Text in Danish. 1972. 10/yr. adv. **Description:** For scout leaders and adults.
Former titles (until 2002): Spejd, Broen (0905-054X); (until 1988): Broen (0108-7959); (until 1973): DDS-DDP Senior/Lederblad
Published by: Danske Spejderkorps, Arsenalgade 10, Copenhagen K, 1436, Denmark. TEL 45-32-64-00-50, http://www.dds.dk/medier. Ed. Morten Lykkeborg TEL 45-32-64-00-62. Adv. contact Peter Henrichsen TEL 45-32-64-00-61.

C

028.5 ARG
BRONCA. Text in Spanish. 1981. m.
Address: Sarmiento, 2210 1ro A, Capital Federal, Buenos Aires 1044, Argentina. Ed. Mauricio Clansig.

B'TNUA. see *POLITICAL SCIENCE*

059.94511 HUN ISSN 0866-2452
BUCI MACI. Variant title: Rolf Kauka's Buci Maci. Text in Hungarian. 1990. m. adv. **Document type:** *Magazine, Consumer.* **Description:** Filled with stories, games, puzzles and other fun activities for children.
Published by: Euromedia Lapkiado bt, Bokor Utca 15-19, Budapest, 1037, Hungary. TEL 36-1-4371100, FAX 36-1-4371180, aselmeczi@er.hu, http://www.vnubp.hu. adv.: page HUF 390,000; trim 210 x 280. Circ: 23,028 (paid).

028.5 RUS
BUMERANG. Text in Russian. m.
Address: Novodmitrovskaya ul 5-a, Moscow, 125015, Russian Federation. TEL 7-095-1292909, FAX 7-095-2853929. Ed. S V Tupichenkov. **US dist. addr.:** East View Information Services, 3020 Harbor Ln. N., Minneapolis, MN 55447. TEL 612-550-0961.

028.5 DEU ISSN 0323-8954
BUMMI; Das kleine Paradies fuer Kinder. Text in German. 1957. m. EUR 29.40; EUR 2.30 newsstand/cover (effective 2003). adv. **Document type:** *Magazine, Consumer.*
Published by: Pabel-Moewig Verlag KG (Subsidiary of: Heinrich Bauer Verlag), Karlsruherstr 31, Rastatt, 76437, Germany. TEL 49-7222-130, FAX 49-7222-13218, redaktion@bummi.de, empfang@vpm.de, http://www.bummi.de, http://www.vpm-online.de. Ed. Sabine Drachsel. Adv. contact Rainer Gross. color page EUR 4,295; trim 210 x 280. Circ: 84,900.

369.4 DEU
BUNDESINFO - IMPULSE. Text in German. 1977. q. adv. **Document type:** *Newsletter.*
Formerly: Impulse
Published by: Pfadfinderinnenschaft St. Georg, Unstrutstr 10, Leverkusen, 51371, Germany. info@psg-bundesverband.de. Ed. Beate Ebbing. Circ: 1,300.

028.5 DEU ISSN 0721-183X
DER BUNTE HUND; Magazin fuer Kinder in den besten Jahren. Text in German. 1981. 3/yr. EUR 15; EUR 6.40 newsstand/cover (effective 2003). bk.rev. **Document type:** *Magazine, Consumer.* **Description:** Full color children's magazine with stories, pictures, puzzles, comics by a wide range of artists.
Published by: Julius Beltz GmbH & Co. KG, Werderstr 10, Weinheim, 69469, Germany. TEL 49-6201-60070, FAX 49-6201-6007338, info@beltz.de, http://www.beltz.de. Ed., R&P Barbara Gelberg. Circ: 15,000.

028.5 GBR ISSN 0262-2475
BUNTY. Text in English. 1958. w. GBP 36.40; GBP 0.70 newsstand/cover (effective 1999). adv. **Document type:** *Consumer.* **Description:** Colorful weekly for girls in the 7-10 age range which encourages reader participation with competitions, giveaways, letters, and pen pal sections.
Published by: D.C. Thomson & Co. Ltd., 80 Kingsway East, Dundee, Angus, Scotland DD4 8SL, United Kingdom. FAX 44-1382-462097, comment@dcthomson.co.uk, http://www.dcthomson.co.uk. Adv. contact Sharon Mudie. B&W page GBP 510, color page GBP 760. **Subscr. to:** World Wide Subscription Service Ltd., Unit 4, Gibbs Reed Farm, Ticehurst, E Sussex TN5 7HE, United Kingdom. TEL 44-1580-200657, FAX 44-1580-200616.

BURBUJAS. see *HANDICAPPED—Visually Impaired*

028.5 DEU
BURGGEIST; Cochemer Realschulblaetter. Text in German. 1970. s-a. adv. bk.rev.
Published by: Realschule Cochem, Cochem, 56812, Germany. TEL 02671-3051. Circ: 2,500.

BUSINESSDATE. see *BUSINESS AND ECONOMICS—Management*

028.5 GBR
BUSTER. Text in English. fortn. GBP 28; GBP 41 in Europe; GBP 49 elsewhere; GBP 1.10 newsstand/cover (effective 1999). adv. **Document type:** *Consumer.* **Description:** Comics and cartoons for children of all ages.
Incorporates (1981-1992): Whizzer and Chips (0262-3919)
Published by: Egmont Fleetway Ltd., Egmont House, Pl, Flat 25, 31 Tavistock Rd, London, W11 1AS, United Kingdom. TEL 44-20-7344-6400, FAX 44-207-388-4152. Circ: 127,282. **Subscr. to:** PO Box 406, Woking, Surrey GU21 1LB, United Kingdom. **Dist. by:** Seymour Distribution Ltd, 86 Newman St, London W1T 3EX, United Kingdom. FAX 44-207-396-8002, enquiries@seymour.co.uk.

028.5 GBR ISSN 0262-5326
BUTTONS✶. Text in English. 1981. w.
Published by: London Editions Magazine Ltd., Egmont House, Great Ducic St, PO Box 111, Manchester, 3BL, United Kingdom. Circ: 80,000.

028.5 BLR ISSN 0007-7429
BYAROZKA. Text in Belorussian. 1924. m. USD 3.60; BYB 0.30 newsstand/cover (effective 1999 & 2000). bk.rev. illus. index.
Published by: Belaruski Dom Druku, Pr F Skaryny 77, Minsk, 220013, Belarus. TEL 375-172-329466. Ed. U Yagoudzick.

796.1 NOR ISSN 0333-1997
BYGDEUNGDOMMEN. Text in Norwegian. bi-m. NOK 25. adv. bk.rev.
Formerly (until 1981): N B U Nytt (0333-2047)
Published by: Norges Bygdeungdomslag, Schweigaards Gate 34, Postboks 3737, Gamlebyen, Oslo 1, Norway. FAX 02-173668. Circ: 16,000.

C B H S NEWSLETTER. see *PUBLISHING AND BOOK TRADE*

C C L/LITTERATURE CANADIENNE POUR LA JEUNESSE. (Canadian Children's Literature) see *PUBLISHING AND BOOK TRADE*

028.5 BEL ISSN 1373-1432
C J P MAGAZINE. Text in Dutch. 1974. 8/yr. adv. bk.rev. **Document type:** *Consumer.* **Description:** News of culture and youth activities.
Former titles (until 1995): Snippers (0774-8124); Former titles (until 1986): Rimboe (0773-3739); (until 1984): C J P Magazine (0773-3720)
Published by: Cultureel Jeugd Paspoort - C J P v.z.w, P/a Lunatheater, Sainctelettesquare 19, Brussels, 1000, Belgium. TEL 32-2-2030200, FAX 32-2-2010929, http://www.cjp.be/artikeloverzicht.php?ARTType=M, http://www.csp.be. Ed. Peter Ploegaerts. Adv. contact Veerle Moens. Circ: 20,000.

C L I J. (Cuadernos de Literatura Infantil y Juvenil) see *PUBLISHING AND BOOK TRADE*

C M MAGAZINE; Canadian review of materials . see *PUBLISHING AND BOOK TRADE*

028.5 USA
C Y D JOURNAL. (Community Youth Development) Text in English. q. USD 29 (effective 2000). **Description:** Promotes youth and adults working together in partnership to create just safe, and healthy communities by building leadership and influencing public policy.
Published by: National Network for Youth, c/o Bev Baker, The Institute for Just Communities, 40 Old Lancaster Rd, Sudbury, MA 01776. TEL 978-443-8426, FAX 978-443-1017, bfbaker@cydjournal.org, http://www.cydjournal.org.

305.23 791.4 FRA ISSN 1280-8008
CA SE PASSE COMME CA; le magazine de votre restaurant McDonald's. Text in French. 1994. m. free. video rev. illus. **Document type:** *Magazine, Consumer.* **Description:** Covers various aspects of teen-age interests, including videos, computer games, hobbies, music and culture.
Published by: Fun Book, 85 rue de Maubeuge, Paris, 75010, France. TEL 33-1-42814019, FAX 33-1-42814012, delano@cybercable.fr. Ed. Jean Michel Graulier. Adv. contact Christophe Duron. Circ: 400,000 (controlled).

CADET QUEST MAGAZINE. see *RELIGIONS AND THEOLOGY—Protestant*

CAL-SOUTH YOUTH SOCCER NEWS. see *SPORTS AND GAMES—Ball Games*

028.5 USA ISSN 0197-7547
CALIFORNIA WEEKLY EXPLORER. Text in English. 1979. w. (from Sep. to June). USD 10 (effective 2003). bk.rev. charts; illus.; maps. index. **Document type:** *Newsletter, Academic/Scholarly.* **Description:** Contains California geography & history for elementary school children.
Related titles: CD-ROM ed.
Published by: California Weekly Explorer, Inc., 285 E Main St, Ste 3, Tustin, CA 92780. TEL 714-730-5991, FAX 714-730-3548, eurekaCWE@aol.com, http://www.californiaweekly.com. Ed. Rice Don Oliver. Pub., R&P Rice Oliver. Circ: 30,000.

CALLIOPE (PERU); exploring world history. see *HISTORY*

CAMERA CANADA. see *PHOTOGRAPHY*

378.198 USA ISSN 0008-2538
BV3750
CAMPUS LIFE. Text in English. 1942. 9/yr. USD 19.95 (effective 2005). adv. bk.rev.; music rev. illus. reprint service avail. from PQC. **Document type:** *Magazine, Consumer.* **Description:** Communicates to high school students the value and impact of a Christian-centered faith.
Related titles: Microform ed.: (from PQC); Online - full text ed.: ISSN 1551-1820 (from EBSCO Publishing, Gale Group); Supplement(s): College Guide.
Indexed: CCR, ChrPI, MASUSE.
—CCC.
Published by: Christianity Today International, 465 Gundersen Dr, Carol Stream, IL 60188. TEL 630-260-6200, FAX 630-260-0114, clmag@campuslife.com, http://www.campuslife.net, http://www.christianitytoday.com. Ed. Chris Lutes. Pub. Paul Robbins. R&P Marilyn Roe. Adv. contacts Frank Chihowski, Brian Ondracek TEL 630-260-6202. B&W page USD 5,066, color page USD 6,456. Circ: 100,000 (controlled). **Subscr. to:** CDS, PO Box 37060, Boone, IA 50037-0060. TEL 800-523-7964.

028.5 FRA ISSN 1267-7876
CAMPUS MAG; le magazine des annees etudiantes. Text in French. 1995. m. free. adv. bk.rev.
Formed by the merger of (1993-1995): Campus le Mensuel (1248-914X); (1990-1995): Campus Annonces (1155-2077)
Published by: Rayonnement 5, 4 rue Rene Barthelemy, Montrouge, 92120, France. TEL 33-1-42539089, FAX 33-1-42537875. Ed. Patrick Bancarel. Pub., R&P, Adv. contact Serge Zagdanski. Circ: 200,000 (controlled).

CANADIAN BUSINESS. see *BUSINESS AND ECONOMICS*

028.5 BRA ISSN 0104-1584
CARICIA. Text in Portuguese. 1975. fortn. BRL 75.70; BRL 3 newsstand/cover. adv. bk.rev.; music rev. charts; illus. **Document type:** *Consumer.* **Description:** For young girls.
Related titles: ♦ Supplement(s): Caricia Uau. ISSN 0104-2270.
Published by: Editora Abril, S.A., Av. das Nacoes Unidas, 7221, 11 andar Pinheiros, Sao Paulo, SP 05425-902, Brazil. caricia.atleitor@abril.com.br, http://www.abril.com.br/. adv.: color page USD 6,940; 190 x 134. Circ: 73,000 (paid).

028.5 BRA ISSN 0104-2270
CARICIA UAU. Text in Portuguese. 1991. m.
Related titles: ♦ Supplement to: Caricia. ISSN 0104-1584.
Published by: Editora Abril, S.A., Av. das Nacoes Unidas, 7221, 11 andar Pinheiros, Sao Paulo, SP 05425-902, Brazil. http://www.abril.com.br/.

028.5 051 GBR ISSN 1368-6364
CAROUSEL; the guide to children's books. Text in English. 1995. 3/yr. GBP 9 in United Kingdom; GBP 12 newsstand/cover in Europe; GBP 15 newsstand/cover elsewhere (effective 2000); GBP 3 newsstand/cover. adv. bk.rev.; software rev.; video rev. illus. back issues avail. **Document type:** *Bulletin, Consumer.* **Description:** Varied and in-depth articles that inform, educate and stimulate, and prove that the world of children's books can be fun and rewarding.
Address: 7 Carrs Ln, Birmingham, Warks B4 7TG, United Kingdom. TEL 44-121-643-6411, FAX 44-121-643-3152, carouselguide@virgin.net. Ed., Pub. Jenny Blanch. R&P, Adv. contact David Blanch. color page GBP 740. Circ: 10,000.

028.5 GBR ISSN 1462-1231
CARTOON NETWORK COMIC SPECIAL. Text in English. 1998. m. GBP 1.75 newsstand/cover. **Document type:** *Consumer.* **Description:** Contains fun and games with cartoon characters.
Published by: Burghley Publishing Ltd., 14 Barn Hill, Stamford, Lincs PE9 2AE, United Kingdom. TEL 44-1780-763366, FAX 44-1780-763365. **Dist. by:** Seymour Distribution Ltd, 86 Newman St, London W1T 3EX, United Kingdom. FAX 44-207-396-8002, enquiries@seymour.co.uk.

781.64 GBR
CD:UK. Text in English. 2001. m. GBP 1.80 newsstand/cover (effective 2001). adv. **Document type:** *Magazine, Consumer.* **Description:** Aimed at teenagers aged 11-16 who are heavily into pop music and the latest gossip and trends.
Published by: Attic Futura Ltd. (Subsidiary of: Hachette Filipacchi Medias S.A.), c/o Hachette Filipacchi UK, 64 North Row, London, 64 North Row, United Kingdom. TEL 44-20-71507000, FAX 44-20-71507001, http://www.hachettefilipacchiuk.co.uk/. Ed. Jo Upcroft. Pub. Mary McGovern. Adv. contact Matt Slade. Circ: 180,000 (paid and controlled).

CELEBRATE CHORAL MUSIC. see *MUSIC*

028.5 USA
CEMETERY PLOT. Text in English. 1993. q. USD 12 (effective 2003). illus. back issues avail. **Document type:** *Newsletter, Consumer.*
Related titles: Audio cassette/tape ed.; Diskette ed.; Microform ed.
Published by: Tellstar Productions, 2660 Petersbourg, Herndon, VA 20171. Ed. Shannon Bridget Murphy. Circ: 15,000.

CENTRE DE RECHERCHE ET D'INFORMATION SUR LA LITTERATURE POUR LA JEUNESSE. see *LITERATURE*

C'EST FACILE!; le mensuel pour ton francais. see *LINGUISTICS*

CHALLENGE (ALPHARETTA); missions magazines for the high school Baptist young men. see *RELIGIONS AND THEOLOGY—Protestant*

028.5 GBR ISSN 0009-1006
CHALLENGE (LONDON, 1960). Text in English. 1960. q. GBP 6. adv. bk.rev.; play rev. illus. **Description:** Aimed at young people.
Indexed: Acal, CERDIC.
Published by: National Association of Boys' Clubs, 369 Kennington Ln, London, SE11 5QY, United Kingdom. FAX 01-820-9815. Ed. Annette Carson. Circ: 6,000.

028.5 IND ISSN 0009-1332
CHAMPAK. Key Title: Campaka (New Delhi). Text in Hindi. 1968. fortn. INR 168, USD 20 (effective 2003). adv. **Document type:** *Consumer.* **Description:** Contains educative and informative material for children from five to ten years old.
Related titles: Kannada ed.; Marathi ed.; Gujarati ed.; English ed.: ISSN 0971-1651.
Published by: Delhi Press Patra Prakashan Ltd., Delhi Press Bldg., Jhandewala Estate, New Delhi, 110 055, India. TEL 91-11-3529557-62, FAX 91-11-7525020. Ed. Paresh Nath. adv.: B&W page INR 15,000, color page INR 25,000; trim 175 x 105. Circ: 142,000.

028.5 IND
CHANDAMAMA. Text in Hindi. 1947. m. INR 72 domestic; INR 276 foreign; INR 4 newsstand/cover (effective 2005). adv. **Document type:** *Magazine, Consumer.*
Related titles: Assamese ed.; Bengali ed.; English ed.; Gujarati ed.; Kannada ed.; Telugu ed.
Published by: Chandamama Publications, 188 N.S.K. Salai, Chandamama Bldgs., Vadapalani, Chennai, Tamil Nadu 600 026, India. TEL 91-44-4838787, FAX 91-44-4838333. Ed. Nagi Reddi. adv.: B&W page INR 3,250, color page INR 6,500; trim 12.8 x 17.8. Circ: 420,000.

CHANTE ET RIS. see *MUSIC*

028.5 URY
CHARONA. Text in Spanish. 1968. fortn.
Address: Esc. 201, Hector Gutierrez Ruiz, 1276, Montevideo, 11112, Uruguay. TEL 2-986665. Ed. Sergio Boffano. Circ: 25,000.

028.5 GRC ISSN 1106-1405
CHAROUMENES ISTORIES. Key Title: Charoumenes Istories Ntisney. Text in Greek. 1989. m. USD 53. adv. illus. **Document type:** *Consumer.* **Description:** Contains selected Disney stories for young readers and preschool children.
Published by: Terzopoulos Publishing Ltd., 7 Fragoklisias St, Maroussi, Athens 151 25, Greece. TEL 30-1-689-6366, FAX 30-1-680-6631, tpc@terz.hol.gr. Ed. Stelios Nicolaou. Adv. contact Angela Daramara. Circ: 17,000.

CHECK IT OUT!. see *LIBRARY AND INFORMATION SCIENCES*

CHEERING WORDS. see *RELIGIONS AND THEOLOGY—Protestant*

CHEMMATTERS. see *CHEMISTRY*

053.1 DEU
▼ **CHICA.** Text in German. 2003 (Jul.). irreg. EUR 1.90 newsstand/cover (effective 2003). adv. **Document type:** *Magazine, Consumer.*
Published by: cultfish entertainment GmbH, Wallstr 59, Berlin, 10179, Germany. TEL 49-30-24008471, FAX 49-30-24008475, info@cultfish.de, http://cultfish.de/chica.html. Adv. contact Angelika Rossini. page EUR 5,800.

028.5 CAN ISSN 0707-4611
CHICKADEE. Text in English. 1979. 10/yr. CND 29.95 domestic; CND 32.19 in Maritimes & Quebec; USD 22 in United States; CND 59.95 elsewhere (effective 2004). adv. bk.rev. illus. Index. reprints avail. **Document type:** *Magazine, Consumer.* **Description:** An award-wiining magazine for children over 6 years old. A "hands-on" magazine for children to learn about the world around them, featuring animals, experiments, puzzles, crafts and a read-to-me section.
Indexed: CBCARef, CBPI, CPerl, ICM.
Published by: Bayard Canada, The Owl Group, 49 Front St E, 2nd Fl, Toronto, ON M5E 1B3, Canada. TEL 416-340-2700, 800-551-6957, FAX 416-340-9769, chikadeenet@owl.on.ca, bayard@owl.on.ca, http://www.owlkids.com/chickadee. Ed. Hilary Bain. Circ: 100,000.

CHICOS; tu revista en espanol. see *LINGUISTICS*

CHILD AND FAMILY MAGAZINE. see *CONSUMER EDUCATION AND PROTECTION*

028.5 USA ISSN 0009-3971
AP201
CHILD LIFE; the children's own magazine. Text in English. 1921 (Dec.). bi-m. USD 15.95 domestic; USD 19.95 foreign (effective 2005). adv. bk.rev.; software rev. illus. index. back issues avail.; reprints avail. **Document type:** *Magazine, Consumer.* **Description:** Contains stories, articles, and activities for children ages 9-11.
Incorporates: Young World (0162-3664); Which was formerly: Golden Magazine (0017-159X)
Related titles: Microform ed.: (from PQC); Online - full text ed.: (from bigchalk, EBSCO Publishing, Florida Center for Library Automation, Gale Group, Northern Light Technology, Inc., ProQuest Information & Learning).
Indexed: ICM, MASUSE, MagInd.
Published by: (Benjamin Franklin Literary and Medical Society, Inc.), Children's Better Health Institute, 1100 Waterway Blvd, PO Box 567, Indianapolis, IN 46206. TEL 317-634-1100, FAX 317-684-8094, g.joray@cbhi.org, http://www.childlifemag.org, http://www.cbhi.org. Ed. Jack Gramling. Pubs. Cory Servaas, Greg Joray. R&P Daniel Lee. Adv. contact Greg Joray. page USD 1,071; trim 10.13 x 7.63. Circ: 25,622 (paid); 54 (free). **Subscr. to:** PO Box 420235, Palm Coast, FL 32142. TEL 800-829-5579.

CHILDART. see *ART*

305.23 USA
CHILDFUN UPDATE. Text in English. w. adv. **Document type:** *Newsletter.*
Media: Online - full text.
Published by: ChildFun Early Chilhood Education Center, PO Box 1173, Mankato, MN 56002-1173. TEL 507-625-1124, webmaster@childfun.com, http://www.childfun.com.

CHILDREN AND FAMILIES. see *EDUCATION*

CHILDREN'S BOOK INSIDER; your monthly guide to children's writing success. see *PUBLISHING AND BOOK TRADE*

CHILDREN'S BOOK NEWS. see *PUBLISHING AND BOOK TRADE*

CHILDREN'S BOOK NEWS MAGAZINE; for all those interested in children and what they read. see *PUBLISHING AND BOOK TRADE*

CHILDREN'S BOOKS IN PRINT; an author, title, and illustrator index to books for children and young adults. see *LITERATURE—Abstracting, Bibliographies, Statistics*

THE CHILDREN'S CHOIR. see *MUSIC*

028.5 973 USA ISSN 1075-2463
CHILDREN'S CHRONICLE; a Civil War newsletter. Text in English. 1994. q. USD 3.50 (effective 2000). bk.rev.; video rev. bibl.; illus.; maps. back issues avail. **Document type:** *Newsletter.* **Description:** Chronicles aspects of the American Civil War for a younger audience.
Address: 3428 Hess St, Philadelphia, PA 19136. TEL 215-333-0605. Ed., Pub., R&P George McNamara. Circ: 120 (paid); 50 (controlled). **Subscr. to:** PO Box 6293, Philadelphia, PA 19136.

028.5 USA ISSN 0272-7145
CHILDREN'S DIGEST. Text in English. 1950. bi-m. USD 17.95 domestic; USD 1.25 per issue (effective 2005). adv. bk.rev.; software rev.; video rev. illus. index. reprints avail. **Document type:** *Magazine, Consumer.* **Description:** Offers preteen children articles, stories, puzzles, and recipes reflecting a healthy lifestyle.
Former titles (Mar.-Nov. 1980): Children's Digest and Children's Playcraft (0273-7582); (Until 1980): Children's Digest (1950) (0009-4099)
Related titles: Braille ed.; Microform ed.: (from PQC); Online - full text ed.: (from bigchalk, EBSCO Publishing, Gale Group, Northern Light Technology, Inc., ProQuest Information & Learning).
Indexed: ICM, MASUSE, MagInd, RGYP.
Published by: (Benjamin Franklin Literary and Medical Society, Inc.), Children's Better Health Institute, 1100 Waterway Blvd, PO Box 567, Indianapolis, IN 46206. TEL 317-634-1100, FAX 317-684-8094, g.joray@cbhi.org, http://www.childrensdigestmag.org, http://www.cbhi.org. Ed., R&P Daniel Lee. Pub., Adv. contact Greg Joray. page USD 2,550. Circ: 80,000 (paid). **Subscr. to:** PO Box 420235, Palm Coast, FL 32142. TEL 800-829-5579.

CHILDREN'S FRIEND. see *RELIGIONS AND THEOLOGY*

CHILDREN'S LITERATURE REVIEW. see *LITERATURE*

CHILDREN'S LITERATURE SERIES. see *LITERATURE*

070.5 USA ISSN 0734-8169
Z479
CHILDREN'S MEDIA MARKET PLACE. Text in English. 1978. irreg., latest vol.4, 1995. USD 59.95. **Document type:** *Directory.* **Description:** Lists publishers, software and audio-visual producers and other media and services, primarily for grades K-8.
Published by: Neal-Schuman Publishers, Inc., 100 William St, Ste 2004, New York, NY 10038. TEL 212-925-8650, FAX 212-219-8916. Ed. Barbara Stein.

C

CHILDREN'S MUSIC GAZETTE. see *MUSIC*

028.5 JAM ISSN 0009-4153
CHILDREN'S OWN. Text in English. 1951. w. (during school term). JMD 1.50 per issue (effective 1998). adv. illus. **Document type:** *Newspaper.*
Published by: Gleaner Company Ltd., 7 North St., P.O. Box 40, Kingston, Jamaica. TEL 809-922-3400, FAX 809-922-6223, TELEX 2319 GLEANER JA. Ed. Wyvolyn Gager. R&P Jenues Anderson. Adv. contact Yvonne Senior. Circ: 118,000.

028.5 USA ISSN 0009-4161
AP201
CHILDREN'S PLAYMATE. Text in English. 1929. bi-m. USD 15.95 domestic; USD 19.95 foreign (effective 2005). adv. bk.rev. illus. Index. back issues avail.; reprints avail. **Document type:** *Magazine, Consumer.* **Description:** Contains stories, articles, activities, recipes, and crafts for children ages 6-8 with an emphasis on health and safety.
Related titles: Microfilm ed.: (from PQC); Online - full text ed.: (from EBSCO Publishing, Gale Group, Northern Light Technology, Inc., ProQuest Information & Learning).
Indexed: ICM, MagInd, RGYP.
Published by: (Benjamin Franklin Literary and Medical Society, Inc.), Children's Better Health Institute, 1100 Waterway Blvd, PO Box 567, Indianapolis, IN 46206. TEL 317-634-1100, FAX 317-684-8094, satevepst@aol.com, g.joray@cbhi.org, http://www.childrensplaymatemag.org, http://www.cbhi.org. Ed. Terry Harshman. Circ: 115,000 (paid). **Subscr. to:** PO Box 420235, Palm Coast, FL 32142. TEL 800-829-5579.

CHILDREN'S VIDEO REPORT. see *COMMUNICATIONS—Video*

333.9 USA
CHILDREN'S WHALEWATCH. Text in English. q. USD 17 to members. adv. back issues avail. **Document type:** *Newsletter.* **Description:** Designed to educate children about whales and the marine environment.
Published by: International Wildlife Coalition, 70 E Falmouth Hwy, East Falmouth, MA 02536. TEL 508-548-8328. Ed., Adv. contact James Kinney. Circ: 200,000.

028.5 IND ISSN 0009-420X
CHILDREN'S WORLD. Short title: C W. Text in English. 1968. m. USD 12 (effective 2001). adv. bk.rev. 56 p./no. 3 cols./p.; **Document type:** *Magazine, Consumer.*
Published by: Children's Book Trust, Nehru House, 4, Bahadur Shah Zafar Marg, New Delhi, 110 002, India. TEL 91-11-3316970, FAX 91-11-3721090, cbtnd@yahoo.com. Ed., R&P Navin Menon. Pub. Ravi Shankar. Adv. contact C P Ravindran. B&W page INR 1,500, color page INR 3,000; trim 150 x 205. Circ: 25,000.

CHILDREN'S WRITER'S AND ILLUSTRATOR'S MARKET; 800 editors and art directors who buy your writing and illustrations. see *PUBLISHING AND BOOK TRADE*

CHILDREN'S WRITING UPDATE. see *LITERATURE*

028.5 CAN ISSN 1206-4580
CHIRP. Text in English. 1992. 10/yr. CND 29.95 domestic; CND 32.19 in Maritimes & Quebec; USD 22 in United States; CND 59.95 elsewhere (effective 2004). **Document type:** *Magazine, Consumer.* **Description:** A discovery magazine for pre-schoolers. Each issue will entertain and teach pre-schoolers about animals, nature, and letters.
Formerly: Tree House
Indexed: CBPI.
Published by: Bayard Canada, The Owl Group, 49 Front St E, 2nd Fl, Toronto, ON M5E 1B3, Canada. TEL 416-340-2700, 800-551-6957, FAX 416-340-9769, chirp@owl.on.ca, bayard@owl.on.ca, http://www.owlkids.com/chirp/index.htm. Ed. Hilary Bain. Circ: 50,000.

028.5 USA ISSN 0735-6358
Z1039.S5
CHOICES: A CORE COLLECTION FOR YOUNG RELUCTANT READERS. Text in English. 1983. triennial, latest vol.5, 2001. USD 45 per vol. (effective 2003). **Document type:** *Magazine, Consumer.* **Description:** Provides reading recommendations for second - sixth graders and is designed for use by teachers, librarians, reading specialists and parents.
Related titles: CD-ROM ed.
Published by: John Gordon Burke Publisher, Inc., PO Box 1492, Evanston, IL 60204-1492. TEL 847-866-8625, FAX 847-866-6639, info@jgburkepub.com, http://www.jgburkepub.com/choices.html, http://jgburkepub.com.

THE CHORISTER. see *MUSIC*

028.5 362.4 DEU
CHRIS; Kinderzeitschrift der Christoffel-Blindenmission. Text in German. 1997. q. free. **Document type:** *Bulletin, Consumer.* **Description:** Concerns medical and rehabilitation projects in developing nations.
Published by: Christoffel-Blindenmission e.V., Nibelungenstr 124, Bensheim, 64625, Germany. TEL 49-6251-131-0, FAX 49-6251-131-122, communications@cbm-i.org, http://www.christoffel-blindenmission.de. Circ: 90,000.

C

028.5 220 USA
THE CHRISTIAN PATHWAY. Text in English. 1964. w. USD 7.55 domestic; USD 8.70 foreign (effective 2000). back issues avail. **Document type:** *Consumer.* **Description:** Publishes stories promoting Biblical values for children.
Published by: Rod and Staff Publishers, Inc., PO Box 3, Crockett, KY 41413-0003. TEL 606-522-4348, FAX 800-643-1244. Eds. Kenneth Mast, Robert Zimmerman. R&P James L Boll. Circ: 5,100 (paid).

CHUTTI VIKATAN. see *GENERAL INTEREST PERIODICALS—India*

CHUZHONGSHENG SHUXUE XUEXI (CHUER BAN). see *MATHEMATICS*

028.5 780 ITA
CIAO 2001★. Text in Italian. 1969. fortn. illus. **Document type:** *Consumer.* **Description:** Covers various topics in music.
Published by: (Europa 2001 Coop), Editoriale Tuttogiovanni, Athena 2001, Viale Mazzini 145, Rome, 00195, Italy. Ed. Giuseppe de Grassi. Circ: 72,000.

CIAO ITALIA; il mensile per il tuo italiano. see *LINGUISTICS*

028.59 USA ISSN 1097-4008
PS536.3
CICADA (PERU). Text in English. 1998. bi-m. USD 35.97 domestic; USD 47.97 foreign; USD 7.95 per issue (effective 2005). bk.rev. illus. 128 p./no.; back issues avail. **Document type:** *Magazine, Consumer.* **Description:** Aimed at teenagers and young adults, ages 14 and up. Offers a wealth of fiction and poetry that focuses on the issues and attitudes teens encounter as they become adults.
Related titles: Online - full text ed.: (from EBSCO Publishing).
Indexed: MASUSE.
Published by: Carus Publishing Company, 315 Fifth St, Peru, IL 61354. TEL 603-924-7209, 800-821-0115, FAX 815-224-2256, custsvc@cobblestone.mv.com, http://www.cricketmag.com. Ed. Marianne Carus. R&P Diane Sikora. Circ: 14,000 (paid).

CINEMA; Europas groesste Filmzeitschrift. see *MOTION PICTURES*

028.5 GBR ISSN 1350-8547
➤ **CIP.** Text in Welsh. 1963. m. (Sep.-Jun.). GBP 9; GBP 0.90 newsstand/cover (effective 2002). adv. illus. 20 p./no.; **Document type:** *Magazine, Academic/Scholarly.* **Description:** For children ages 7-11.
Incorporates: Cymru'r Plant; Formerly (until 1987): Deryn (0011-9148)
Published by: Urdd Gobaith Cymru, Adran Cylchgronau, Swyddfa'r Urdd, Ffordd Llanbadarn, Aberystwyth, Ceredigion, Wales SY23 1EY, United Kingdom. TEL 44-1970-613118, FAX 44-1970-626120, cip@urdd.org, Cylchgronau@urdd.org, http://www.urdd.org/Cylchgronau/Darllenwyr/Cip/TudalenDarllenwyrCip.html. Ed. Sian Eleri Davies. adv.: page GBP 200;. Circ: 3,000.

➤ **CITROUILLE**; des livres pour vos enfants. see *LITERATURE*

028.5 POL ISSN 1231-1677
CIUCHCIA; miesiecznik nie tylko dla grzecznych dzieci. Text in Polish. 1994. m. PLZ 26.40 domestic; USD 10 in United States; PLZ 2.20 newsstand/cover. adv. bk.rev.; film rev. illus. **Description:** Aims to educate and entertain children 5-10 years of age. Includes adventures of the main characters from the popular TV series for children.
Published by: Telewizja Polska S.A., Biuro Handlu i Promocji, Ul Jana Pawla Woronicza 17, Warsaw, 00999, Poland. TEL 48-22-6476907, FAX 48-22-6476907. Ed. Andrzej Grabowski. adv.: page PLZ 4,000, page USD 1,500. Circ: 200,000. **Dist. by:** RUCH S.A., ul Jana Kazimierza 31/33, Warsaw 00958, Poland. TEL 48-22-5328731.

268 PRT ISSN 0874-4963
O CLARIM. Variant title: Jornal Mensal da Cruzada Eucaristica e Das Criancas de Portugal. Text in Portuguese. 1946. m. EUR 7.50 domestic; EUR 15 foreign (effective 2005). **Document type:** *Magazine, Consumer.*
Published by: Editorial/AO, Lago das Teresinhas, 5, Braga, 4714-509, Portugal. TEL 351-253-201220, FAX 351-253-201221, http://www.ppcj.pt/AO/AO.html. Ed. Fernando Leite. Circ: 23,500.

GBR ISSN 1362-5667
CLASSICS FROM THE COMICS. Text in English. 1996. m. GBP 14.40; GBP 1.20 newsstand/cover (effective 1999). **Document type:** *Consumer.*
Published by: D.C. Thomson & Co. Ltd., 80 Kingsway East, Dundee, Angus, Scotland DD4 8SL, United Kingdom. FAX 44-1382-462097, comment@dcthomson.co.uk, http://www.dcthomson.co.uk.

028.5 FRA ISSN 1167-9883
LES CLES DE L'ACTUALITE. Text in French. w. EUR 62 (effective 2005). **Description:** Covers current events throughout the world for children ages 13 and up.
Published by: Milan Presse, 300 rue Leon Joulin, Toulouse, Cedex 1 31101, France. TEL 33-5-61766464, FAX 33-5-61766400. Ed. Yann Bouffin. Pub. Patrice Amen. Circ: 100,352.

028.5 FRA ISSN 1261-3347
LES CLES DE L'ACTUALITE JUNIOR. Text in French. w. (46/yr). EUR 89 (effective 2005).
Published by: Milan Presse, 300 rue Leon Joulin, Toulouse, Cedex 1 31101, France. TEL 33-5-61766464, FAX 33-5-61766400. Ed. Florence Thinard. Pub. Patrice Amen.

808.89 USA ISSN 1094-4273
Q163
CLICK; opening windows for young minds. Text in English. 1998. 9/yr. USD 32.97 domestic; USD 44.97 foreign; USD 4.95 per issue domestic (effective 2005). bk.rev. illus. reprints avail. **Document type:** *Magazine, Consumer.* **Description:** Unlock the universe for children ages 7-10 by introducing them to science, art,nature, and the environment. CLICK's focus is the hows and whys of children's worlds.
Related titles: Online - full text ed.: (from bigchalk, EBSCO Publishing, ProQuest Information & Learning).
Published by: Carus Publishing Company, 315 Fifth St, Peru, IL 61354. TEL 603-924-7209, 800-821-0115, FAX 815-224-2256, custsvc@cobblestone.mv.com, http://www.cricketmag.com.

028.5 USA
CLIFFORD THE BIG RED DOG. Text in English. 2002. 16/yr. (during school year). USD 4.95 (effective 2003 - 2004); with 10 or more student subscr.. **Document type:** *Magazine, Consumer.* **Description:** Focuses on teaching social development and pre-academic skills to preschoolers. Also covers friendship, sharing, and letter and number recognition.
Published by: Scholastic Inc., 557 Broadway, New York, NY 10012-0399. TEL 212-343-6100, http://www.scholastic.com. Ed. David Goddy. **Subscr. to:** 2931 E McCarthy St, PO Box 3710, Jefferson City, MO 65102-9957. TEL 800-724-6527, classmags@scholastic.com.

053.1 DEU
CLUB TIGERENTE. Text in German. 1995. bi-m. EUR 9.20 (effective 2003). adv. **Document type:** *Magazine, Consumer.*
Published by: Tigerenten Club, Stuttgart, 70150, Germany. FAX 49-711-9294330, tigerentenclub@swr.de, http://www.kindernetz.de/tigerentenclub. adv.: color page EUR 6,200. Circ: 157,852 (paid and controlled).

028.5 USA ISSN 1084-9343
CLUB Z!; it's the place to be. Text in English. 1995. bi-m. USD 13.96 (effective 2000). illus. back issues avail. **Document type:** *Consumer.* **Description:** Offers activities, jokes and educational articles for elementary school children.
Published by: Club Z!, Inc, 15310 Amberly Dr., Ste. 185, Tampa, FL 33647-1641. zfun@club-z.com. Ed. Aimee Sottilaro. Pub. Mark Lucas. R&P James Murphy.

028.5 USA ISSN 1071-4073
CLUBHOUSE. Text in English. 1951. 12/yr. USD 5 (effective 2005). **Document type:** *Magazine, Consumer.* **Description:** For children 9-15 years old. Adventure, true and historical stories, puzzles, crafts, and jokes. Contains religious overtones.
Published by: Your Story Hour, Inc., 464 W Ferry, PO Box 15, Berrien Springs, MI 49103. TEL 269-471-3701, 800-987-7879, FAX 269-471-4661, orders@yourstoryhour.org, comments@yourstoryhour.org, http://www.yourstoryhour.org. Ed. Elaine Trumbo. Circ: 500 (paid).

028.5 973 USA ISSN 0199-5197
E169.1
COBBLESTONE; discover American history. Text in English. 1980. m. USD 29.95 domestic; USD 41.95 foreign; USD 4.95 per issue domestic (effective 2005). bk.rev.; film rev. charts; illus.; maps. cum.index: 1980-1998; a.index. back issues avail.; reprints avail. **Document type:** *Magazine, Consumer.* **Description:** Explores themes in American history through lively articles, puzzles, games, and recipes. For children ages 8-14. Each issue is devoted to a single theme.
Related titles: Online - full text ed.: (from bigchalk, EBSCO Publishing, Gale Group, ProQuest Information & Learning).
Indexed: ICM, JHMA, MASUSE, RGYP.
Published by: Carus Publishing Company, 315 Fifth St, Peru, IL 61354. TEL 603-924-7209, 800-821-0115, FAX 815-224-2256, custsvc@cobblestone.mv.com, http://www.cricketmag.com. Ed. Meg Chorlian. R&P Patricia Silvestro. Circ: 31,000.

COCKPIT; das junge Bordmagazin von Austrian Airlines. see *TRAVEL AND TOURISM—Airline Inflight And Hotel Inroom*

028.5 DEU ISSN 0942-4997
COCKTAIL (FRANKFURT). Text in German. 1988. q. adv. bk.rev.
Published by: Deutsche Jungsozialisten (JUSOS), Fischerfeldstr 7-11, Frankfurt Am Main, 60311, Germany. TEL 069-291096.

028.5 FRA ISSN 1269-8733
COLLECTION AUTREMENT JEUNESSE. Text in French. 1996. irreg. **Document type:** *Monographic series.*
Published by: Editions Autrement, 77, rue du Faubourg St Antoine, Paris, 75011, France. TEL 33-1-44738000, FAX 33-1-44730012, contact@autrement.com, http://www.autrement.com.

028.5 JPN
COMIC BON BON. Text in Japanese. m. **Document type:** *Magazine, Consumer.* **Description:** Features characters from boys' favorite computer games, TV shows, and toys or original characters that will eventually evolve into games, animations, and toys.
Published by: Kodansha Ltd., 2-12-21 Otowa, Bunkyo-ku, Tokyo, 112-8001, Japan. TEL 81-3-3946-6201, FAX 81-3-3944-9915, http://www.kodansha.co.jp.

028.5 USA
COMIC SCENE (YEAR). Text in English. 2000. bi-m. USD 6.99 newsstand/cover (effective 2001). adv. **Document type:** *Consumer.*
Published by: Starlog Group, Inc., 475 Park Ave S, 7th Fl, New York, NY 10016. communications@starloggroup.com. Ed. David McDonnell. Pub. Norman Jacobs.

028.5 267 ITA ISSN 0393-7984
COMUNITA SPORTIVA; settimanale di informazione e orientamento delle attivita CSI. Text in Italian. 1975. w.
Published by: Centro Sportivo Italiano, Via della Conciliazione 1, Rome, 00193, Italy. TEL 39-06-68404550, FAX 39-06-68802940, csi@csi-net.it, http://www.csi-net.it. Circ: 3,000.

087.5 BRA ISSN 0104-2157
CONAN. Text in Portuguese. 1992. m. **Document type:** *Magazine, Consumer.*
Published by: Editora Abril, S.A., Av. das Nacoes Unidas, 7221, 11 andar Pinheiros, Sao Paulo, SP 05425-902, Brazil. TEL 55-011-30372000, FAX 55-011-30375638, relacoes.corporativas@abril.com.br, http://www.abril.com.br/.

THE CONCORD REVIEW. see *HISTORY*

741.5 ARG ISSN 0328-8331
CONDORITO. Text in Spanish. fortn. adv. **Document type:** *Magazine, Consumer.*
Published by: Editorial Televisa Argentina, Av Paseo Colon 275, Piso 10, Buenos Aires, Buenos Aires 1063, Argentina. TEL 54-11-4343-2225, FAX 54-11-4345-0955, http://www.televisa.com.ar.

CONNECT; supporting student participation. see *EDUCATION*

THE CONQUEROR. see *RELIGIONS AND THEOLOGY*

640.73 USA
TX336 CODEN: ZILLEH
CONSUMER REPORTS FOR KIDS ONLINE. Text in English. 1978. irreg. illus. reprints avail. **Document type:** *Magazine, Consumer.* **Description:** Offers product-rating and consumer advice for young people ages 8 and up.
Former titles: Zillions (Online Edition); (until 2000): Zillions (Print Edition) (1050-8163); (until 1990): Penny Power (0190-1966)
Media: Online - full content. **Related titles:** Microfiche ed.: (from NBI, PQC).
Indexed: CPerl, ConsI, ICM, JHMA, RGYP.

Published by: Consumers Union of the United States, Inc., 101 Truman Ave, Yonkers, NY 10703-1057. TEL 914-378-2000, FAX 914-378-2900, http://www.zillions.org/. Ed. Charlotte Baecher. Circ: 200,000.

CONTEMPORARY HEROES AND HEROINES; a biographical guide to heroic figures of the twentieth century. see *BIOGRAPHY*

CONTEMPORARY PRAISE. see *MUSIC*

280.4 DEU
CONTRAPUNKT (ONLINE EDITION); christliche Themenzeitschfrift fuer junge Leute. Text in German. 1925. 10/yr. bk.rev.; music rev. illus. back issues avail. **Document type:** *Magazine, Consumer.* **Description:** Publishes articles on personalities, Christian themes and efforts, with music news, cinema and concert schedules and leisure ideas.
Formerly (until 2003): Contrapunkt (Print Edition) (0343-3935)
Media: Online - full content. **Related titles:** Audio cassette/tape ed.
Published by: M B K Verlag und CVJM-Westbund, Hermann-Loens-Str 9-14, Bad Salzuflen, 32105, Germany. TEL 49-5222-18050, FAX 49-5222-180527, redaktion@contrapunkt.info, info@mbk-web.de, http://www.contrapunkt.info, http://www.mbk-web.de. Ed., R&P Birgit Sowade. Circ: 18,000.

305.23 UKR
COOL. Text in Russian. w. UAK 56.94 for 6 mos. domestic (effective 2004). **Document type:** *Magazine, Consumer.*
Published by: Burda Ukraina, Zhyljanskaja ul. 29, Kiev, 01033, Ukraine. TEL 38-044-4908363, FAX 38-044-4908364, advert@burdaua.com, http://www.burda.com.ua.

305.23 RUS ISSN 1560-5485
COOL. Text in Russian. 1997. w. adv. **Document type:** *Magazine, Consumer.* **Description:** Contains articles on entertainment and serious advice for teenagers aged 12 to 16.
Published by: Izdatel'skii Dom Burda, ul Pravdy 8, Moscow, 125040, Russian Federation. TEL 7-095-7979849, FAX 7-095-2571196, cool-magazine@pub.burda.ru, vertrieb@burda.ru, http://www.burda.ru. adv.: page USD 6,500. Circ: 500,000 (paid and controlled).

028.5 420 DEU
COOL ENGLISH - DAS KINDERWEB. Text in English, German. m. **Document type:** *Consumer.* **Description:** Helps children ages 8-11 learn English interactively through the Internet.
Media: Online - full text.
Published by: Kidoclic - Hortus Soft, Walter-Kolb-Str 9-11, Frankfurt Am Main, 60594, Germany. TEL 49-1805-705605, info@kidoclic.de, http://www.daskinderweb.de/ce.htm.

COOL GIRL. see *WOMEN'S INTERESTS*

305.23 RUS ISSN 1560-5493
COOL GIRL. Text in Russian. 1997. w. adv. **Document type:** *Magazine, Consumer.* **Description:** Contains articles and features for girls between 15 and 20 years of age.
Published by: Izdatel'skii Dom Burda, ul Pravdy 8, Moscow, 125040, Russian Federation. TEL 7-095-7979849, FAX 7-095-2571196, vertrieb@burda.ru, http://www.burda.ru. adv.: page USD 5,500. Circ: 500,000 (paid and controlled).

305.23 RUS ISSN 1606-8742
COOL POSTER. Text in Russian. 1999. q. adv. **Document type:** *Magazine, Consumer.*
Published by: Izdatel'skii Dom Burda, ul Pravdy 8, Moscow, 125040, Russian Federation. TEL 7-095-7979849, FAX 7-095-2571196, vertrieb@burda.ru, http://www.burda.ru. adv.: page USD 3,000. Circ: 100,000 (paid and controlled).

790.133 TWN ISSN 1562-5338
COOL TOYS/WANJU KUBAO. Text in Chinese. 1999. bi-m. TWD 188 newsstand/cover (effective 2001). **Document type:** *Magazine, Consumer.* **Description:** Provides news and information on the latest and hottest toys.
Published by: Jianduan Chuban Qufen Youxian Gongsi/Sharp Point Publishing Ltd., Inc., 231 Xindiansi, Fuyu-Lu 43-Hao 8-Lou, Taipei, Taiwan. TEL 886-2-2218-1582, FAX 886-2-2218-1583, janey@spp.com.tw, http://www.spp.com.tw/asp/mag/cooltoys/index.asp.

028.5 790.1 USA
COPSNKIDS CHRONICLES. Text in English. q. free. **Document type:** *Newspaper.*
Formerly: National P A L League
Published by: National Police Athletic League, 618 U S Hwy 1, Ste 201, North Palm Beach, FL 33408. TEL 561-844-1823, FAX 561-863-6120. Ed. Shirley A McCoy. Circ: 171,311.

028.5 ITA
CORRIERE DEI PICCOLI (ONLINE EDITION). Text in Italian. 1908. w. adv. charts; illus.
Formerly: Corriere dei Piccoli (Print Edition) (0010-9185)
Media: Online - full text.
Published by: R C S Periodici (Subsidiary of: R C S Mediagroup), Via Angelo Rizzoli, 2, Milan, MI 20132, Italy. TEL 39-2-25845413, FAX 39-2-25845444, info@periodici.rcs.it, http://www.corriere.it/Piccoli/home.shtml, http://www.rcsmediagroup.it/siti/periodici.php.

741.5 793.73 GBR ISSN 1369-0892
COSMIC. Text in English. 1997. fortn. GBP 1.25 newsstand/cover. **Document type:** *Consumer.* **Description:** An educational and fun comic book with puzzles and games.
Published by: H. Bauer Publishing Ltd. (Subsidiary of: Heinrich Bauer Verlag), Academic House, 24-28 Oval Rd, London, NW1 7DT, United Kingdom. TEL 44-20-72418000, FAX 44-20-72418056, simon.priston@bauer.co.uk. Pub. Spike Figgett. adv.: color page GBP 2,650; trim 210 x 280. Circ: 140,000. **Subscr. to:** Galleon, PO Box 326, Sittingbourne, Kent ME9 8FA, United Kingdom. TEL 44-1795-414500, FAX 44-1795-414555.

028.5 305.4 CHN
COSMOGIRL!. Text in Chinese. 2001. m. adv. **Document type:** *Magazine, Consumer.*
Published by: Trends Communication Co. Ltd., Rm 616, Tower A, COFCO Plaza, 8 Jianguomennei Ave, Beijing, 100005, China. TEL 86-10-652288002501, FAX 86-10-652288002599, cosmogirl@trendsmag.com, network@trendsmag.com, http://www.trendsmag.com/trendsmag/client/magazine/cosmogirl.jsp.

028.5 305.4 USA ISSN 1528-4824
COSMOGIRL!. Text in English. 1999. 10/yr. USD 8 domestic; USD 23 foreign; USD 2.99 newsstand/cover (effective 2005). adv. illus. **Document type:** *Magazine, Consumer.* **Description:** Cosmopolitan magazine's version for teenage girls. Includes beauty, fashion, money, parents, school and more.
Related titles: Online - full text ed.: (from EBSCO Publishing, Gale Group, ProQuest Information & Learning).
Indexed: MASUSE.
Published by: Hearst Communications, Inc., Cosmopolitan, 224 W 57th St, 3rd Fl, New York, NY 10019. TEL 212-649-3858, FAX 212-582-7067, atoosa@cosmogirl.com, http://www.cosmogirl.com. Ed. Susan Schulz. **Subscr. to:** PO Box 7791, Red Oak, IA 51591. TEL 515-282-1607, 800-827-3221.

057.86 CZE ISSN 1212-9577
COSMOGIRL!. Text in Czech. 2000. m. CZK 539 (effective 2003). adv. **Document type:** *Magazine, Consumer.* **Description:** Contains articles, photos and features on celebrities, pop stars, fashion, health, beauty and other items of interest to young girls.
Published by: Stratosfera s.r.o., Drtinova 8, Prague 5, 150 00, Czech Republic. TEL 420-2-234109542, FAX 420-2-234109264, cosmogirl@stratosfera.cz, online@stratosfera.cz, http://www.stratosfera.cz/cosmogirl. Ed. Michaela Kovarova. Adv. contact Blazena Hlinkova. page CZK 139,000; trim 170 x 230. Circ: 100,000 (paid). **Subscr. to:** SEND Predplatne s.r.o., PO Box 141, Prague 4 140 21, Czech Republic. TEL 42-2-267211301, FAX 42-2-267211305, send@send.cz.

059.9435 TUR
COSMOGIRL!. Text in Turkish. 2000 (May). m. **Document type:** *Magazine, Consumer.*
Published by: 1 Numara Hearst Yayincilik, Sabah Tesisleri, Tesvikiye Caddesi 123, Tesvikiye, Istanbul, 80200, Turkey. TEL 90-212-3158000, FAX 90-212-3159272, http://www.birnumara.com.tr.

268 USA ISSN 0885-0283
COUNSELOR (WHEATON). Text in English. 1941. q. USD 3.29 newsstand/cover (effective 2005). illus. **Document type:** *Newspaper.* **Description:** Sunday school take-home paper, for ages 8-11.
Formerly (until 198?): My Counselor (0011-0019)
Published by: Scripture Press Publications, Inc., 4050 Lee Vance View, Colorado Springs, CO 80918-7102. TEL 719-536-0100, 800-708-5550, FAX 719-535-2928, 800-430-0726, http://www.cookministries.com.

028.5 FRA ISSN 1267-1053
COUSTEAU JUNIOR. Text in French. 1995. m.
Published by: Publications des Generations Futures, 10 rue Thierry-le-Luron, Levallois-Perret, Cedex 92592, France. TEL 33-1-41347758, FAX 33-1-41347716. Ed. Christian Robin. Pub. Bruno Lesouef. Circ: 100,000. **Subscr. to:** TSA 70211, Nanterre Cedex 9 92892, France.

028.5 USA ISSN 1538-6007
CRAFTY KIDS. Text in English. bi-m. USD 5.95 newsstand/cover in United States; USD 8.95 newsstand/cover in Canada (effective 2001). adv. **Document type:** *Magazine, Consumer.* **Description:** Filled with hours of crafting fun, gluing and designing projects that will let kids use their creativity and imagination.
Former titles (until 2002): Mary Beth's Crafty Kids; (until 2001): Looney Tunes Crafty Kids (1532-9259); (until 2000): Mary Beth's Crafty Kids (1528-8846)
Published by: Kappa Publishing Group, Inc., 6198 Butler Pike., Ste. 200, Blue Bell, PA 19422-2606. Adv. contact Marty Kuta. Circ: 180,000.

541 USA ISSN 0892-9599
CREATIVE KIDS; the national voice for kids. Text in English. 1980. q. USD 19.95 domestic; USD 29.95 foreign (effective 2005). 35 p./no.; back issues avail. **Document type:** *Magazine, Consumer.* **Description:** Stories, poems, art, music, and more, all submitted by children for all children to enjoy. Motivates and encourages creative production.
Formerly: Chart Your Course (0744-3420)
Related titles: Online - full text ed.: (from EBSCO Publishing, Gale Group).
Indexed: MASUSE.
Published by: Prufrock Press Inc., PO Box 8813, Waco, TX 76714-8813. TEL 800-998-2208, FAX 800-240-0333, ck@prufrock.com, http://www.prufrock.com/prufrock_jm_createkids.cfm. Eds. Libby Goolsby, Libby Lindsey, Jim Kendrick. Pub. Joel McIntosh. Circ: 35,000 (paid).

808.89 USA ISSN 0090-6034
AP201
CRICKET; the magazine for children . Text in English. 1973. m. USD 35.97 domestic; USD 47.97 foreign (effective 2005). bk.rev. illus. 64 p./no.; back issues avail.; reprint service avail. from PQC. **Document type:** *Magazine, Consumer.* **Description:** Publishes fiction, nonfiction, poetry, and folklore for children ages 9 to 14.
Related titles: Audio cassette/tape ed.; Online - full text ed.: (from EBSCO Publishing).
Indexed: AIPP, CPerI, ICM, JHMA, RGYP.
Published by: Carus Publishing Company, 315 Fifth St, Peru, IL 61354. TEL 603-924-7209, 800-821-0115, FAX 815-224-2256, custsvc@cobblestone.mv.com, http://www.cricketmag.com. Eds. Julia Messina, Paula Morrow, Tracy Schoenle, Marianne Carus. Pub. John Olbrych. Circ: 80,000 (paid).

028.5 USA ISSN 1522-5631
LB1029.G3
➤ **CRINKLES**; because learning makes crinkles in your brain. Text in English. 1998. bi-m. USD 30 domestic; USD 45 foreign; USD 5 newsstand/cover (effective 2006). adv. 50 p./no.; back issues avail. **Document type:** *Journal, Academic/Scholarly.* **Description:** Designed to stimulate a child's curiosity about people, places, things and events - both real and imaginary.
Published by: Libraries Unlimited, Inc. (Subsidiary of: Greenwood Publishing Group Inc.), 88 Post Road W, Westport, CT 06881. TEL 800-225-5800, FAX 203-222-1502, info@crinkles.com, lu-books@lu.com, http://www.crinkles.com, http://www.lu.com/. Ed. Deborah Levitov. Circ: 6,500 (paid).

➤ **CROIRE AUJOURD'HUI JEUNES CHRETIENS.** see *RELIGIONS AND THEOLOGY—Roman Catholic*

➤ **CRUSADER (ALPHARETTA).** see *RELIGIONS AND THEOLOGY—Protestant*

268 PRT ISSN 0011-2194
CRUZADA EUCARISTICA. Text in Portuguese. 1930. m. EUR 7.50 domestic; EUR 15 foreign (effective 2005). **Document type:** *Magazine.*
Published by: Editorial/AO, Lago das Teresinhas, 5, Braga, 4714-509, Portugal. TEL 351-253-201220, FAX 351-253-201221, http://www.ppcj.pt/AO/AO.html. Ed. Fernando Leite. Circ: 125,000.

028.5 IND
CUB MAGAZINE. Text in English. 1984. bi-m. INR 7 newsstand/cover. adv.
Published by: Advertising Concessionaires Pvt. Ltd., 602 Maker Chamber V, Nariman Point, Mumbai, Maharashtra 400 021, India. TEL 2830061. Ed. Bittu Sahgal. Pub., Adv. contact Shashi Kumar. B&W page INR 3,000, color page INR 5,500; trim 168 x 232.

808.068 CRI
CUENTA QUETE CUENTO; revista latinoamericana de literatura infantil. Text in Spanish. 1992. q. CRC 1,300; USD 16 in the Americas; USD 18 in Europe. **Document type:** *Consumer.*
Published by: Fundacion Educativa San Judas Tadeo, Apdo1248, Centro Colon, San Jose 1007, Costa Rica. TEL 506-2215948, FAX 506-2333973. Ed. Helia Betancourt de Sanchez. Circ: 900.

028.5 370 USA ISSN 0011-3492
CURRENT EVENTS. Text in English. 1902. 25/yr. (w. during school year). USD 34.50 per academic year (effective 2004 - 2005). illus. Index. reprint service avail. from PQC. **Document type:** *Magazine, Consumer.* **Description:** Connects students to the world with the latest news each week with a style that makes current events easy to understand for middle- and high-school students.
Related titles: Online - full text ed.: (from bigchalk, EBSCO Publishing, Gale Group, Northern Light Technology, Inc., O C L C Online Computer Library Center, Inc., ProQuest Information & Learning).
Indexed: ICM, JHMA, MASUSE, MagInd, RGYP, TOM.

C

Published by: Weekly Reader Corp. (Subsidiary of: W R C Media Inc.), 200 First Stamford Pl, PO Box 120023, Stamford, CT 06912-0023. TEL 203-705-3500, 800-446-3355, FAX 203-705-1662, science@weeklyreader.com, http://www.weeklyreader.com. Ed. C Colbert. Pub. Peter Esposito. R&P Cathy Pekai TEL 203-705-3426. Circ: 205,153 (paid).

371.911 USA
CURRENT EVENTS (LARGE PRINT EDITION). Text in English. 25/yr. (during school yr.). USD 8.95 (effective 2005).
Media: Large Type (16 pt.). **Related titles:** Braille ed.
Published by: American Printing House for the Blind, Inc., 1839 Frankfort Ave, Louisville, KY 40206. TEL 502-895-2405, 800-223-1839, FAX 502-899-2274, info@aph.org, http://www.aph.org.

CURRENT ISSUES SOURCEFILE. see *SOCIAL SCIENCES: COMPREHENSIVE WORKS*

370 028.5 500 USA ISSN 0011-3905
CURRENT SCIENCE. Text in English. 1927. 16/yr. (during school yr.). USD 34.50 per academic year; USD 10.53 per academic year 10 or more subscriptions (effective 2004 - 2005). illus. Index. reprint service avail. from PQC. **Document type:** *Magazine, Consumer.* **Description:** Uses today's news to demonstrate science concepts to make them interesting and relevant to middle- and high-school students. Includes a separate teacher's guide.
Related titles: Online - full text ed.: (from bigchalk, EBSCO Publishing, Gale Group, H.W. Wilson, Northern Light Technology, Inc., O C L C Online Computer Library Center, Inc., ProQuest Information & Learning).
Indexed: AnalAb, BioDAb, CCI, CLL, CTE, Cadscan, ChemAb, CurCont, FS&TA, ICM, IndVet, JHMA, LeadAb, MASUSE, MSB, NutrAb, ProtozoAb, RGPR, RGYP, RevApplEntom, RiceAb, SCI, SIA, SSCI, VetBull, WBA, WMB, Zincscan. —IE, Infotrieve.
Published by: Weekly Reader Corp. (Subsidiary of: W R C Media Inc.), 200 First Stamford Pl, PO Box 120023, Stamford, CT 06912-0023. TEL 203-705-3500, 800-446-3355, FAX 203-705-1662, science@weeklyreader.com, http://www.weeklyreader.com. Circ: 400,000 (paid).

371.911 028.5 USA
CURRENT SCIENCE (LARGE PRINT EDITION). Text in English. 16/yr. (during school year). USD 9.95 per academic year (effective 2004 - 2005). **Document type:** *Magazine, Consumer.*
Media: Large Type (16 pt.). **Related titles:** Braille ed.
Published by: American Printing House for the Blind, Inc., 1839 Frankfort Ave, Louisville, KY 40206. TEL 502-895-2405, 800-223-1839, FAX 502-899-2274, info@aph.org, http://www.aph.org.

028.5 POL ISSN 1640-307X
CYBER MYCHA. Text in Polish. 2000. m. **Document type:** *Magazine, Consumer.*
Related titles: Supplement(s): Cyber Mycha Extra. ISSN 1643-112X. 2001.
Published by: Egmont Polska, ul Dzielna 60, Warszawa, 01029, Poland. TEL 48-22-8384100, FAX 48-22-8384200, poczta@egmont.pl, http://www.egmont.pl. Circ: 50,000.

028.5 USA
CYBERKIDS. Text in English. 1995. q.
Media: Online - full content.
Published by: Mountain Lake Software, 298 Fourth Ave., San Francisco, CA 94118. http://www.cyberkids.com.

028.5 USA
CYBERTEENS. Text in English. 1996. m. adv.
Media: Online - full text.
Published by: Able Minds, 1750-1 30th St, Ste 170, Boulder, CO 80301. TEL 303-413-0914, FAX 303-413-0915, info@ableminds.com, editor@cyberteens.com, http://www.cyberteens.com/.

028.5 POL ISSN 1643-1278
CZARODZIEJKI W.I.T.C.H. Text in Polish. 2002. m. **Document type:** *Magazine, Consumer.*
Published by: Egmont Polska, ul Dzielna 60, Warszawa, 01029, Poland. TEL 48-22-8384100, FAX 48-22-8384200, poczta@egmont.pl, http://www.disney.pl/Publishing/Witchmagazine, http://www.egmont.pl.

028.5 POL
CZESC!. Text in Polish. m. **Document type:** *Magazine, Consumer.*
Published by: Egmont Polska, ul Dzielna 60, Warszawa, 01029, Poland. TEL 48-22-8384100, FAX 48-22-8384200, poczta@egmont.pl, http://www.egmont.pl.

087.5 BRA ISSN 0104-2947
D C 2000. Text in Portuguese. 1990. m. **Document type:** *Magazine, Consumer.*
Published by: Editora Abril, S.A., Av. das Nacoes Unidas, 7221, 11 andar Pinheiros, Sao Paulo, SP 05425-902, Brazil. TEL 55-011-30372000, FAX 55-011-30375638, relacoes.corporativas@abril.com.br, http://www.abril.com.br/.

028.5 FRA ISSN 1629-9744
D LIRE. Text in French. 2001. m. EUR 59.80 domestic; EUR 79.80 foreign (effective 2005). **Document type:** *Magazine, Consumer.*
Published by: Bayard Presse, 3 Rue Bayard, Paris, 75393 Cedex 08, France. TEL 33-1-44356060, FAX 33-1-44356161, redactions@bayard-presse.com, http://www.bayardpresse.com.

028.5 CHN
DA HUILANG HUABAO. Text in Chinese. bi-m.
Published by: 21 Shiji Chubanshe/21st Century Publishing, No5, Xinwei Lu, Nanchang, Jiangxi 330002, China. TEL 333749. Ed. Zheng Yuanjie.

028.5 CHN
DABAIKE. Text in Chinese. 1999. m. **Document type:** *Consumer.* **Description:** Provides articles, pictures, and other items of interest to children and students.
Contact Dist.: China International Book Trading Corp/Zhongguo Guoji Tushu Maoyi Zonggongsi, 35 Chegongzhuang Xilu, Haidian District, PO Box 399, Beijing, 100044, China. TEL 86-10-68412045, FAX 86-10-68412023, cibtc@mail.cibtc.com.cn, http://www.cibtc.com.cn.

DAILY POWER; daily Bible reading notes for young people for the whole year. see *RELIGIONS AND THEOLOGY*

028.5 GBR ISSN 0262-2807
DANDY. Text in English. 1950. w. GBP 33.80 domestic; GBP 38.22 foreign; GBP 0.50 newsstand/cover. adv. **Document type:** *Consumer.* **Description:** Continues the fast-paced adventures which started in 1937.
Published by: D.C. Thomson & Co. Ltd., 80 Kingsway East, Dundee, Angus, Scotland DD4 8SL, United Kingdom. FAX 44-1382-225511, comment@dcthomson.co.uk, http://www.dcthomson.co.uk. Adv. contact Sharon Mudie. B&W page GBP 1,885, color page GBP 3,300. **Subscr. to:** World Wide Subscription Service Ltd., Unit 4, Gibbs Reed Farm, Ticehurst, E Sussex TN5 7HE, United Kingdom. TEL 44-1580-200657, FAX 44-1580-200616.

DANISH CHILDREN'S LITERATURE. see *LITERATURE*

028.5 GBR
DARE. Text in English. fortn. GBP 1.60 newsstand/cover (effective 2003). adv. **Document type:** *Magazine, Consumer.* **Description:** Contains features on the hottest celebrities, relationship worries and up-to-the-minute fashions for girls ages 10-14.
Published by: B B C Worldwide Ltd., 80 Wood Ln, London, W12 0TT, United Kingdom. TEL 44-20-84331070, FAX 44-20-84332231, bbcworldwide@bbc.co.uk, http://www.bbcmagazines.com/dare/index.html.

028.5 BEL ISSN 0773-0292
DAUPHIN. Text in French. 1978. w. EUR 46.50 (effective 2005). **Document type:** *Magazine.* **Description:** Helps children ages 8 to 10 (grades 3 and 4) discover the world in time and space, to look at things from a different angle and have fun with reading.
Related titles: ◆ Dutch ed.: Zonnestraal. ISSN 0772-9898; Supplement(s): Bonjour Vacances. ISSN 0773-1078. 1987; Bonjour Noel. ISSN 0773-0322. 1983.
Published by: Editions Averbode SA, Abdijstraat 1, BP 54, Averbode, 3271, Belgium. TEL 32-13-780111, FAX 32-13-780186, http://www.averbode.be/fr/revues/publicatie_archief.php?zoek=1&ID=25&pubID=41&menu=l&selectedsubnav=lageronderwijs. Ed. Jan Lembrechts.

DAVAI. see *LINGUISTICS*

059.927 UAE
DAWHAT AL-MUTANABBI'. Text in Arabic. 1987. a. per issue exchange basis. **Description:** Student publication covering literary, cultural and social activities in the school community.
Published by: Al- Mutanabbi' Secondary School, PO Box 46071, Abu Dhabi, United Arab Emirates. TEL 478374. Ed. Ghazi Salim. Circ: 300.

DAYBREAK STAR INDIAN READER. see *ETHNIC INTERESTS*

028.5 CAN ISSN 1187-8681
LES DEBROUILLARDS. Text in French. 1982. m. (10/yr.). CND 27.95 (effective 2004). adv. bk.rev. index. **Document type:** *Magazine, Consumer.* **Description:** Scientific magazine for children ages 9-14. Includes short story of technology, colorfully illustrated dossier, games, comic strips, contests, and collectible cards.
Formerly: Je Me Petit Debrouille (0714-4067)
Related titles: CD-ROM ed.
Indexed: PdeR.
Published by: Bayard Canada, The Owl Group, 49 Front St E, 2nd Fl, Toronto, ON M5E 1B3, Canada. TEL 416-340-2700, 800-551-6957, FAX 416-340-9769, bayard@owl.on.ca, http://www.owlkids.com/. adv.: B&W page CND 1,600, color page CND 2,400; trim 9.75 x 7.25. Circ: 32,000.

028.5 BRA
DEMAIS!. Text in Portuguese. 1992. m. USD 33. **Document type:** *Consumer.* **Description:** Presents a forum for teenagers.
Published by: Bloch Editores S.A., Edificio Manchete, Rua do Russel, 766-804, Gloria, Rio De Janeiro, RJ 22210010, Brazil. TEL 021-5554000, FAX 021-2059998. Ed. Janir Hollanda. Circ: 80,000.

028.5 FIN ISSN 1456-1433
DEMI. Text in Finnish. 1998. m. EUR 72.10 domestic; EUR 74.50 in Europe; EUR 85.30 elsewhere (effective 2005). adv. **Document type:** *Consumer.* **Description:** Covers beauty and healthcare, celebrities, TV and film stars for teenagers.
Published by: A-Lehdet Oy, Risto Rytin tie 33, Helsinki, 00081, Finland. TEL 358-9-75961, FAX 358-9-7598600, a-tilaus@a-lehdet.fi, http://www.a-lehdet.fi/lehdet/lehti/demi/. Ed. Oona Tuomi. Adv. contact Matti Sahravuo TEL 358-9-7596385. color page EUR 3.15; 187 x 241. Circ: 53,346 (controlled).

DETSKOE CHTENIE DLYA SERDTSA I RAZUMA. see *LITERATURE*

028.5 RUS
DETSKOE TVORCHESTVO. Text in Russian. bi-m.
Address: Ul Kedrova 8, korp 2, kom 47-48, Moscow, 117804, Russian Federation. TEL 7-095-1292790, FAX 7-095-1255673. Ed. T N Eregina. **US dist. addr.:** East View Information Services, 3020 Harbor Ln. N., Minneapolis, MN 55447. TEL 612-550-0961.

DEVO'ZINE; just for teens. see *RELIGIONS AND THEOLOGY—Protestant*

028.5 MYS ISSN 0417-3910
DEWAN PELAJAR. Text in Malay. 1967. m.
Published by: Dewan Bahasa dan Pustaka/National Language and Literary Agency, PO Box 10803, Kuala Lumpur, 50926, Malaysia. TEL 03-2481011. Ed. Zaleha Hashim. Circ: 71,000.

028.5 MYS
DEWAN PERINTIS. Text in English, Malay; Summaries in English. 1960. m. MYR 7.20. adv. bk.rev. illus. **Description:** Aimed at children aged 9-12.
Former titles (until Jan. 1978): Dewan Pemadah; Perintis; Pelita Pelajar; Dolphin (0012-5253)
Indexed: AgrForAb.
Published by: Dewan Bahasa dan Pustaka, Cawangan Sarawak/National Language and Literary Agency, PO Box 169, Kuching, Sarawak, Malaysia. Eds. Hamzah Hamdoni, Yeop Johari Yaakob. Circ: 6,000.

DIALOGUE (SALEM); a world of ideas for the visually impaired of all ages. see *HANDICAPPED—Visually Impaired*

028.5 DEU
DIDDL; das Magazin. Text in German. 2001. m. EUR 2.30 newsstand/cover (effective 2003). adv. **Document type:** *Magazine, Consumer.* **Description:** Contains stories, games, puzzles and comics featuring Diddl the Mouse.
Published by: Egmont Ehapa Verlag GmbH, Wallstr 59, Berlin, 10179, Germany. TEL 49-30-24008-0, FAX 49-30-24008599, leserservice@ehapa.de, http://www.ehapa.de. adv.: page EUR 6,100. Circ: 193,226 (paid and controlled).

028.5 DEU
DIGIMON. Text in German. 1999. fortn. EUR 2.50 newsstand/cover (effective 2003). adv. **Document type:** *Magazine, Consumer.*
Published by: Panini Verlags GmbH, Ravensstr 48, Nettetal, 41334, Germany. TEL 49-711-947680, FAX 49-711-94768830, info@panini-dino.de, http://www.panini-media.de. Ed. Anne Berling. Pub. Max Mueller. Adv. contact Petra Sonnenfroh-Kost. page EUR 3,900; trim 170 x 257. Circ: 47,673 (paid).

028.5 ITA ISSN 1591-4941
DIGIMON MAGAZINE. Text in Italian. 2000. m.
Published by: Panini SpA, Viale Emilio Po 380, Modena, 41100, Italy. TEL 39-059-382111, FAX 39-059-827431, info@paninigroup.com, http://www.paninigroup.com.

028.5 ITA ISSN 0391-5468
DIMENSIONI NUOVE. Text in Italian. 1962. m. (10/yr.). **Document type:** *Magazine, Consumer.* **Description:** Review of current events and culture for young students.
Published by: (Centro Catechistico Salesiano), Editrice ELLEDICI, Corso Francia 214, Leumann, TO 10096, Italy. TEL 39-11-9552164, FAX 39-11-9574048, mail@elledici.org, http://www.elledici.org. Ed. Giuseppe Pelizza. Circ: 19,000.

567.9 USA
DINO TIMES✶. Text in English. 1992. m. USD 19.95 membership. **Document type:** *Newspaper.* **Description:** News about dinosaurs and how they lived, recent excavations, and other news of interest to children.
Published by: Dinosaur Society, 1900 Denjamin Franklin Pkwy, Philadelphia, PA 19103-1101. TEL 516-277-7855, FAX 516-277-1479, dsociety@aol.com, http://www.dinosociety.org.

028.5 USA
DINOSAURS!✶. Text in English. bi-w. USD 3.50 newsstand/cover. **Document type:** *Consumer.*

C

Published by: Atlas Editions, 4343 Equity Dr, Columbus, OH 43228-3842. TEL 203-349-1014, FAX 203-349-8896.

DINOSAURS!; discover the giants of the prehistoric world. see *PALEONTOLOGY*

DINOSAURS! POSTER COLLECTION. see *PALEONTOLOGY*

DIRECT. see *RELIGIONS AND THEOLOGY—Roman Catholic*

(YEAR) DIRECTORY OF AMERICAN YOUTH ORGANIZATIONS; a resource guide to 500 clubs, groups, troops, teams, societies, lodges, and more for young people. see *CLUBS*

DIRECTORY OF FAMILY CHILD CARE ASSOCIATIONS, SUPPORT GROUPS, & SUPPORT AGENCIES. see *CHILDREN AND YOUTH—About*

028.5 USA
DISCOVERING TOGETHER. Text in English. 1973. w. USD 14.69 per quarter for 5 copies (effective 2003). back issues avail. **Document type:** *Consumer.*
Published by: Standard Publishing, 8121 Hamilton Ave, Cincinnati, OH 45231. TEL 513-931-4050, FAX 513-931-0950, http://www.standardpub.com. Pub., R&P Mark A Taylor. Circ: 105,000.

028.5 500 GBR
DISCOVERY. Text in English. 1999. m. GBP 1.75 newsstand/cover. adv. **Document type:** *Magazine, Consumer.* **Description:** Presents developments in science and technology in an entertaining and educational style.
Published by: Europa Magazines Ltd., Bradnich Ct, Castle St, Exeter, Devon EX4 5PT, United Kingdom. TEL 44-1392-211113, FAX 44-1392-211533, europa@dial.pipex.com. **Dist. by:** MarketForce UK Ltd, 247 Tottenham Court Rd, London, Middx W1T 7AU, United Kingdom. TEL 44-207-2615199, FAX 44-207-2617341.

028.5 FRA ISSN 1366-9028
DISCOVERY BOX. Text in English. 1995. 10/yr. EUR 55.36 domestic; EUR 63.50 foreign (effective 2005). **Document type:** *Magazine, Academic/Scholarly.*
Published by: Bayard Presse, 3 Rue Bayard, Paris, 75393 Cedex 08, France. TEL 33-1-44356060, FAX 33-1-44356161, redactions@bayard-presse.com, http://www.bayardpresse.com.

028.5 USA
DISCOVERY CREW SCIENCE CLUB NEWS. Text in English. 1987. m. USD 29 to members. **Description:** For children approximately 6-11 years old.
Published by: Discovery Crew, c/o Knickerbocker Publishing, Box 113, Fiskdale, MA 01518. Ed. Michael Glaser.

028 USA ISSN 1535-3230
DISCOVERY GIRLS. Text in English. 2000. bi-m. USD 19.95 domestic; USD 24 in Canada (effective 2003). illus. **Document type:** *Magazine, Consumer.*
Related titles: Online - full text ed.: free.
Address: PO Box 110760, Campbell, CA 95011. TEL 408-379-4199, devon@discoverygirls.com, mary@discoverygirls.com, http://www.discoverygirls.com. Ed. Catherine Lee.

DISCOVERY TRAILS. see *RELIGIONS AND THEOLOGY—Other Denominations And Sects*

028.5 AUS ISSN 1322-0594
DISNEY ADVENTURES. Text in English. 1993. m. AUD 3.90 newsstand/cover (effective 2004). adv. **Document type:** *Magazine, Consumer.* **Description:** Contains stories, comics, puzzles, games, and quizzes as well as the latest news and reviews on books, videos and music for children, including non-Disney related items.
Published by: A C P Publishing Pty. Ltd., 54-58 Park St, Sydney, NSW 1028, Australia. TEL 61-2-9282-8000, FAX 61-2-9267-4361, info@acp.com.au, http://www.acp.com.au. Ed. Wendy Moore. Adv. contact Grant Crossley. Circ: 72,897 (paid and controlled).

028.5 USA ISSN 1050-2491
DISNEY ADVENTURES. Text in English. 1990. 10/yr. USD 15 domestic; USD 23 in Canada; USD 25 elsewhere; USD 3.50 newsstand/cover (effective 2005). adv. bk.rev. illus. **Document type:** *Magazine, Consumer.* **Description:** Covers entertainment, science and technology, travel, the environment, and sports for ages 7-14. Contains comics featuring Disney characters.
Published by: Disney Publishing Worldwide, 114 Fifth Ave, 16th Fl, New York, NY 10011-5690. TEL 212-633-4400, FAX 212-633-4809, http://www.disney.com/disneyadventures. Pub. Kathy Gordon. adv.: B&W page USD 35,905, color page USD 47,875. Circ: 1,200,000 (paid).

028.5 GBR ISSN 0961-477X
DISNEY AND ME. Text in English. 1991. fortn. GBP 32.50 domestic; GBP 48 in Europe; GBP 58 elsewhere; GBP 1.30 newsstand/cover. **Document type:** *Consumer.* **Description:** Stories, puzzles, games and other fun time activities for children.
Published by: Egmont Fleetway Ltd., Egmont House, Pl, Flat 25, 31 Tavistock Rd, London, W11 1AS, United Kingdom. TEL 44-20-7344-6400, FAX 44-207-388-4152. Ed. Claire Mewett. Circ: 77,115 (paid). **Dist. by:** Seymour Distribution Ltd, 86 Newman St, London W1T 3EX, United Kingdom. enquiries@seymour.co.uk.

087.5 PRT ISSN 0874-0593
DISNEY ESPECIAL. Text in Portuguese. 1985. 3/yr. EUR 11.49 (effective 2004). adv. **Document type:** *Magazine, Consumer.*
Published by: Edimpresa Editora Lda., Rua Calvet de Magalhaes 242, Laveiras, Paco de Arcos, 2770-022, Portugal. TEL 351-21-4698000, FAX 351-21-4698501, edimpresa@edimpresa.pt, http://www.edimpresa.pt. adv.: page EUR 1,122.30; trim 134 x 190.

028.5 DEU
▼ **DISNEY FAMILY.** Text in German. 2004. q. EUR 3.50 newsstand/cover (effective 2005). adv. **Document type:** *Magazine, Consumer.*
Published by: Egmont Ehapa Verlag GmbH, Wallstr 59, Berlin, 10179, Germany. TEL 49-30-240080, FAX 49-30-24008599, leserservice@ehapa.de, http://www.ehapa.de. adv.: page EUR 2,400. Circ: 140,000 (controlled).

028.5 POL
DISNEY I JA. Text in Polish. m. **Document type:** *Magazine, Consumer.*
Published by: Egmont Polska, ul Dzielna 60, Warszawa, 01029, Poland. TEL 48-22-8384100, FAX 48-22-8384200, poczta@egmont.pl, http://www.egmont.pl. Circ: 70,000.

028.5 DEU
▼ **DISNEY KLEINE KOECHE.** Text in German. 2004. bi-m. EUR 3.50 newsstand/cover (effective 2005). adv. **Document type:** *Magazine, Consumer.* **Description:** Provides kids with fun and easy to make recipes and stories about cooking.
Published by: Egmont Ehapa Verlag GmbH, Wallstr 59, Berlin, 10179, Germany. TEL 49-30-240080, FAX 49-30-24008599, leserservice@ehapa.de, http://www.ehapa.de/ehapa/e14/e40/e1559/index_ger.html.

028.5 JPN
DISNEYLAND. Text in Japanese. 1964. m. **Document type:** *Magazine, Consumer.* **Description:** For young children between two and four years of age. Features Disney characters.
Published by: Kodansha Ltd., 2-12-21 Otowa, Bunkyo-ku, Tokyo, 112-8001, Japan. TEL 81-3-3946-6201, FAX 81-3-3944-9915, http://www.kodansha.co.jp, http://www.toppan.co.jp/kodansha.

028.5 BEL
DISNEYLAND. Text in Dutch. m. EUR 19.80 (effective 2003). film rev. illus. **Document type:** *Magazine, Consumer.* **Description:** Offers very young readers articles, puzzles, and activities, mostly featuring Disney characters.
Published by: Sanoma Magazines Belgium, Telecomlaan 5-7, Diegem, 1831, Belgium. TEL 32-2-7762211, FAX 32-2-776-2317, http://www.sanoma-magazines.be/HomePage.aspx?flash=1&Language=nl.

DISNEY'S ANIMAL KINGDOM. see *BIOLOGY—Zoology*

028.5 GBR ISSN 1362-8690
DISNEY'S BIG TIME. Text in English. 1996. fortn. GBP 1.30 newsstand/cover. adv. illus. back issues avail. **Document type:** *Consumer.* **Description:** Offers young readers fun items, including films, popstars, fun time activities, and competitions.
Published by: Egmont Fleetway Ltd., Egmont House, Pl, Flat 25, 31 Tavistock Rd, London, W11 1AS, United Kingdom. TEL 44-20-7344-6400, FAX 44-207-388-4152. Ed. Sam Hickman. Pub. Rob McMenemy. Adv. contact Steven Goldsmith. Circ: 126,082 (paid). **Dist. by:** Seymour Distribution Ltd, 86 Newman St, London W1T 3EX, United Kingdom. FAX 44-207-396-8002, enquiries@seymour.co.uk.

053.1 DEU
▼ **DISNEY'S EINFACH TIERISCH.** Variant title: Einfach Tierisch. Text in German. 2003. m. EUR 27.60; EUR 2.30 newsstand/cover (effective 2005). adv. **Document type:** *Magazine, Consumer.*
Published by: Egmont Ehapa Verlag GmbH, Wallstr 59, Berlin, 10179, Germany. TEL 49-30-240080, FAX 49-30-24008599, leserservice@ehapa.de, http://www.ehapa.de. adv.: page EUR 3,600. Circ: 75,718 (paid and controlled).

028.5 GBR ISSN 1462-7345
DISNEY'S PRINCESS. Text in English. 1998. m. GBP 15.60 domestic; GBP 23 in Europe; GBP 28 elsewhere; GBP 1.30 newsstand/cover. **Document type:** *Magazine, Consumer.*
Published by: Egmont Fleetway Ltd., Egmont House, Pl, Flat 25, 31 Tavistock Rd, London, W11 1AS, United Kingdom. TEL 44-20-7344-6400, FAX 44-20-7388-4020. Ed. Liz Wakefield. **Dist. by:** Seymour Distribution Ltd, 86 Newman St, London W1T 3EX, United Kingdom. FAX 44-207-396-8002, enquiries@seymour.co.uk.

028.5 DEU
DISNEY'S PRINZESSIN; maerchenhafte Welten fuer kleine Prinzessinen. Text in German. 1999. m. EUR 2.95 newsstand/cover (effective 2005). adv. **Document type:** *Magazine, Consumer.*
Published by: Egmont Ehapa Verlag GmbH, Wallstr 59, Berlin, 10179, Germany. TEL 49-30-240080, FAX 49-30-24008599, leserservice@ehapa.de, http://www.ehapa.de/ehapa/e14/e40/e176/index_ger.html. adv.: page EUR 4,900. Circ: 93,950 (paid and controlled).

028.5 DEU
DISNEY'S PRINZESSIN SPEZIAL. Text in German. 3/yr. EUR 5.90 newsstand/cover (effective 2002). **Document type:** *Magazine, Consumer.*
Published by: Egmont Ehapa Verlag GmbH, Wallstr 59, Berlin, 10179, Germany. TEL 49-30-24008-0, FAX 49-30-24008599, leserservice@ehapa.de, http://ehapa.funonline.de.

057.86 CZE ISSN 1211-8265
DIVKA. Text in Czech. 1991. m. CZK 39 newsstand/cover (effective 2003). adv. **Document type:** *Magazine, Consumer.* **Description:** Provides advice and tips on fashion trends, cosmetics, relationships, sex, the Internet, music, films and videos for girls ages 14-18.
Formerly (until 1995): Divka - Phoenix Intermedia (1210-6674)
Published by: Europress, komanditni spolecnost (Subsidiary of: Heinrich Bauer Verlag), Viktora Huga 6, Prague 5, 150 00, Czech Republic. TEL 420-225-008111, FAX 420-257-327103, inzerce@europress.cz, http://www.europress.cz. Ed. Petra Slusnakova. Adv. contact Ivo Jerak. color page CZK 140,000; trim 204 x 267.

087.5 HRV ISSN 1330-1349
DJECJI KLUB. Text in Croatian. 1992. m. **Document type:** *Magazine, Consumer.*
Published by: Arena d.d., Slavonska Avenija 4, Zagreb, 10000, Croatia. TEL 385-1-6162062, FAX 385-1-6162062, dj.klub@eph.hr. Ed. Gordana Vukelic.

DJOVENES DEL SIGLO XXI. see *EDUCATION*

028.5 AUS ISSN 1443-1580
DMAG. Text in English. 2001. m. AUD 39.95 in Australia & New Zealand; AUD 59.95 elsewhere (effective 2004). **Document type:** *Magazine, Consumer.*
Published by: Smartypantz Communications Pty Ltd., PO Box 321, Terrey Hills, NSW 2084, Australia. TEL 612-9473-6704, FAX 612-9473-6701, enquiries@dmag.com.au, http://www.dmag.com.au/. **Co-publisher:** Australian Geographic Pty. Ltd.

▼ **DOGS FOR KIDS.** see *PETS*

301 AUS ISSN 0811-7179
DOLLY. Text in English. 1970. m. AUD 50; AUD 4.60 newsstand/cover (effective 2004). adv. **Document type:** *Magazine, Consumer.* **Description:** Contains up-to-date entertainment news, the hottest looks in beauty and fashion, loads of advice, quizzes and real-life stories for girls.
Related titles: Online - full text ed.: (from EBSCO Publishing).
Published by: A C P Publishing Pty. Ltd., 54-58 Park St, Sydney, NSW 1028, Australia. TEL 61-2-9282-8437, FAX 61-2-9267-4911, http://dolly.ninemsn.com.au/dolly/. Ed. Elisa O'Hare. Pub. Chris Gibson. Adv. contact Peter Zavecz. Circ: 196,290.

333.72 USA ISSN 8756-6362
DOLPHIN LOG. Text in English. 1977. bi-m. USD 15 domestic; USD 25 overseas. illus. reprints avail. **Description:** For children ages 7-13 years; covers marine animals, the oceans, science, natural history, and the arts as they relate to the global water system.
Indexed: ICM, RGYP, SFA.
Published by: Cousteau Society, Inc., 870 Greenbrier Cir, Ste 402, Chesapeake, VA 23320. TEL 757-523-9335, FAX 757-523-2747, cousteau@infi.net, cousteau@cousteausociety.org, http://www.cousteau.org. Ed. Lisa Rao. Circ: 60,000.

028.5 SVK ISSN 1210-2245
DOMINO. Text in Slovak. 1970. 12/yr. USD 124 (effective 1998).
Formerly (until 1990): Pionier (1210-227X)
Published by: Smena Publishing House, Prazska 11, Bratislava, 81284, Slovakia.

028.5 NOR
DONALD DUCK & CO. Text in Norwegian. 1948. w. NOK 1,040; NOK 20 newsstand/cover (effective 2000). adv. **Document type:** *Magazine, Consumer.*
Published by: A-S Hjemmet, Kristian Iv S Gate 13, Oslo, 0164, Norway. TEL 47-22-47-13-00, FAX 47-22-47-13-73, donald@egmont.no, http://www.egmont.no. Ed. Svein Erik Soeland. adv.: color page NOK 78,000; trim 170 x 250. Circ: 170,000.

028.5 NLD
DONALD DUCK EXTRA. Text in Dutch. m. illus. **Document type:** *Magazine, Consumer.* **Description:** Offers very young readers a variety of entertaining articles and activities.

Published by: V N U Tijdschriften B.V., Postbus 1900, Hoofddorp, 2130 JH, Netherlands. TEL 31-23-556-6770, FAX 31-23-556-6771, ServiceTeam@tijdschriften.vnu.com, http://www.vnu.nl/vnu.html.

028.5 DEU
DONALD DUCK SONDERHEFT; die tollsten Geschichten. Text in German. 1965. m. EUR 32.40; EUR 2.70 newsstand/cover (effective 2005). adv. **Document type:** *Magazine, Consumer.* **Description:** Publishes materials for children and youth.
Published by: Egmont Ehapa Verlag GmbH, Wallstr 59, Berlin, 10179, Germany. TEL 49-30-240080, FAX 49-30-24008599, leserservice@ehapa.de, http://www.ehapa.de. Adv. contact Olaf Hansen. B&W page EUR 4,200, color page EUR 4,200; trim 175 x 260. Circ: 34,132 (paid and controlled).

028.5 BEL ISSN 0778-0273
DOPIDO (DUTCH EDITION). Text in Dutch. 1991. m. EUR 4 per issue (effective 2005). illus. **Document type:** *Magazine.* **Description:** Offers young preschool children, ages 2 and 3, activities they can make and do.
Related titles: ◆ French ed.: Dopido (French Edition). ISSN 0778-0265; Supplement(s): Dopido Kerst. ISSN 0778-6425.
Published by: Uitgeverij Averbode NV, Abdijstraat 1, Postbus 54, Averbode, 3271, Belgium. TEL 32-13-780111, FAX 32-13-780183, http://www.averbode.be. Ed. Philippe Brasseur.

028.5 BEL ISSN 0778-0265
DOPIDO (FRENCH EDITION). Text in French. 1991. m. EUR 30.50 (effective 2005). **Document type:** *Consumer.* **Description:** Offers young preschool children, ages 2 to 4, activities to make and do.
Related titles: ◆ Dutch ed.: Dopido (Dutch Edition). ISSN 0778-0273; Supplement(s): Dopido Noel. ISSN 0778-6433.
Published by: Editions Averbode SA, Abdijstraat 1, BP 54, Averbode, 3271, Belgium. TEL 32-13-780111, FAX 32-13-776837, http://www.averbode.be/fr/revues/detail.php?ID=7&menu=t&selectedsubnavigation=educatieve. Ed. Philippe Brasseur.

028.5 NLD ISSN 0928-6799
DOPIDO (KAMPEN). Text in Dutch. 1991. 10/yr. illus. **Document type:** *Consumer.* **Description:** For children ages 2-4.
Published by: Kok Tijdschriften, Postbus 5018, Kampen, 8260 GA, Netherlands.

028.5 AUT
DOPPELKLICK; die neue Edition Buchklub. Text in German. 1987. a. membership. **Document type:** *Bulletin.*
Formerly (until 1995): Edition Buchklub
Published by: Oesterreichischer Buchklub der Jugend, Mayerhofgasse 6, Vienna, W 1041, Austria. TEL 43-1-5051754-0, FAX 43-1-505175450.

028.5 USA
DORA THE EXPLORER. Text in English. 10/yr. USD 19.90; USD 4.95 newsstand/cover domestic; USD 5.95 newsstand/cover in Canada (effective 2003).
Published by: Nick Junior Magazines, P O Box 3234, Harlan, IA 51593. doramag@nick.com. Ed. Maria Rosado.

028.5 NLD ISSN 0165-5019
DOREMI. Text in Dutch. 1977. 10/yr. illus. **Document type:** *Consumer.* **Description:** For children ages 4-6.
Published by: Kok Tijdschriften, Postbus 5018, Kampen, 8260 GA, Netherlands.

649 BEL ISSN 0773-0179
DOREMI (FRENCH EDITION). Text in French. 1965. m. EUR 33 (effective 2005). illus. **Document type:** *Magazine.* **Description:** Offers older preschool children, ages 4 and 5, a variety of things to make and do.
Formerly (until 1967): Doremi (French and English Edition) (0773-025X)
Related titles: Dutch ed.: Doremi (Dutch Edition). 1965. BEF 1,000 domestic; BEF 1,450 in the European Union; BEF 1,650 in Europe; BEF 2,460 elsewhere (effective 2000).
Published by: Editions Averbode SA, Abdijstraat 1, BP 54, Averbode, 3271, Belgium. TEL 32-13-780111, FAX 32-13-780149, http://www.averbode.be/fr/revues/detail.php?ID=4&menu=l&selectedsubnavigation=kleuteronderwijs. Ed. Philippe Brasseur.

DOSHKIL'NE VIKHOVANNYA; naukhovo-metodychnyi zhurnal. see *EDUCATION*

028.5 IND
DOST AUR DOSTI. Text in English. 1988. m. INR 55, USD 35.
Published by: Shama Distributors Private Ltd., 13-14 Asaf Ali Rd., New Delhi, 110 002, India. TEL 91-11-732666, TELEX 3161601 SHMA IN. Circ: 50,000.

DRAGONFLY (ARLINGTON). see *SCIENCES: COMPREHENSIVE WORKS*

028.5 DEU ISSN 0946-5081
DRAN. Text in German. 1978. 9/yr. EUR 24.75; EUR 3.30 newsstand/cover (effective 2003). adv. back issues avail. **Document type:** *Magazine, Consumer.*
Former titles (until 1993): Punkt (0721-7145); (until 1978): Pflueger (0342-8605)
Published by: Bundes Verlag GmbH, Bodenborn 43, Witten, 58452, Germany. TEL 49-2302-93093-0, FAX 49-2302-9309310, info@bundes-verlag.de, http://www.dran.ch/, http://www.bundes-verlag.de. Ed. Martin Gundlach. adv.: B&W page EUR 967, color page EUR 1,227; trim 188 x 258. Circ: 20,000 (paid).

DRINK SMART. see *DRUG ABUSE AND ALCOHOLISM*

028.5 USA
DROPOUT. Text in English. 1995. irreg. USD 5 per 6 issues (effective 2000).
Address: 1114 21st St, Sacramento, CA 95814. Ed. Pam Davis.

028.5 MKD ISSN 0012-6632
DRUGARCE. Text in Macedonian. 1950. fortn. USD 2.50. illus.
Indexed: RASB.
Published by: Nova Makedonija, Mito Hadzivasilev Jasmin bb, Skopje, 91000, Macedonia. Ed. Gligor Popovski. Circ: 25,000.

028.5 RUS ISSN 0320-1031
PG3227
DRUZHBA. Text in Russian. 1977. bi-m. USD 30. adv. bk.rev. illus.
Indexed: RASB.
Published by: Izdatel'stvo Molodaya Gvardiya, Sushchevskaya ul 21, Moscow, 103030, Russian Federation. TEL 285-1935. Ed. V I Firosov. Circ: 80,000.

087.5 HRV ISSN 1331-2022
DRVO ZNANJA. Text in Croatian. 1997. m. **Document type:** *Magazine, Consumer.*
Published by: SysPrint, Vurovcice 38, Zagreb, 10000, Croatia. TEL 385-1-6558740, FAX 385-1-6558741, syssprint@zg.tel.hr. Ed. Davor Uskokovic.

028.5 ISR
DUBBON. Text in Hebrew. 1970. fortn. USD 100 (effective 2000).
Published by: Etzb'oni Publishing House, P O Box 28110, Tel Aviv, 61280, Israel. FAX 972-3-5373906. Ed. Michael Shir. Circ: 27,000.

305.23 DEU
▼ **DUEL MASTERS MAGAZIN.** Text in German. 2004. 4/yr. EUR 2.50 newsstand/cover (effective 2005). adv. **Document type:** *Magazine, Consumer.*
Published by: Panini Verlags GmbH, Ravensstr 48, Nettetal, 41334, Germany. TEL 49-2157-81750, FAX 49-2157-81484528, info@panini-dino.de, http://www.panini-media.de. adv.: page EUR 3,900; trim 210 x 280. Circ: 110,000 (controlled).

028.5 ROM ISSN 1224-3957
DUELUL MINTII. Text in Romanian. 1996. m. ROL 1,000 newsstand/cover. **Document type:** *Consumer.* **Description:** Contains puzzles, brainteasers and features for children and teens.
Published by: Trustul de Presa Agenda, Str. Sf. Ioan nr. 2, Hotel Timisoara, et. 5, Timisoara, Timis 1900, Romania. TEL 40-56-195195, FAX 40-56-196196. Ed. Zoltan Kovacs. Circ: 7,000.

028.5 DEU
DUERER!. Text in German. 1995. bi-m. adv. **Document type:** *Newspaper, Consumer.*
Published by: Albrecht-Duerer-Oberschule, Emser Str 137, Berlin, 12051, Germany. TEL 49-30-68092421, ADOMail@freenet.de, http://www.albrecht-duerer-gymnasium.de. Ed. Christian Doganer. Circ: 250.

028.5 330 RUS
DVENADTSAT' S POLOVINOI. Variant title: 12 s 1/2. Text in Russian. 2000. m. RUR 92.40 for 6 mos. (effective 2004). **Document type:** *Magazine, Consumer.* **Description:** Geared towards teenagers who are interested in learning about how to become successful businessmen.
Published by: Izdatel'skii Dom Delovaya Pressa, Staromonetnyi per 10, Moscow, 109180, Russian Federation. TEL 7-095-9508360, sales@delpressa.ru, http://www.delpressa.ru.

DYNAMIC. see *POLITICAL SCIENCE*

808.068 CAN ISSN 0843-1639
DYNAMITE WRITE CHILDREN'S NEWSPAPER. Text in English. 1986. q.
Published by: Canadian Trade and Business Opportunities Inc., 2185 Victoria Park Ave, Scarborough, ON M1R 1V5, Canada. TEL 416-449-1931. Ed. Israelin Shockness. Circ: 20,000.

DZHMIL'; dityam: zhivopis, muzika i literatura. see *EDUCATION*

028.5 POL ISSN 1230-8153
DZIEWCZYNA. Text in Polish. 2000. m. **Document type:** *Magazine, Consumer.*
Published by: Axel Springer Polska, Al Jerozolimskie 181, Warsaw, 02222, Poland. TEL 48-22-6084100, FAX 48-22-6084106, asp@axelspringer.com.pl, http://www.axelspringer.com.pl. Circ: 182,000 (paid).

E C. (Essential Connection) see *RELIGIONS AND THEOLOGY—Protestant*

053.1 DEU
E-FACT. Text in German. 1999. q. adv. **Document type:** *Magazine, Consumer.*
Published by: e-fact Jugendmagazin, Uhlandstr 2, Freiburg, 79102, Germany. TEL 49-761-79197990, FAX 49-761-79197919. adv.: B&W page EUR 685, color page EUR 951. Circ: 10,000 (controlled).

028.5 ZAF
EASYSCIENCE. Text in English. bi-m. illus. **Description:** Introduces young minds to the fun and fascination of science, explaining with colorful examples and illustrations elementary experiments and principles underlying everyday technology.
Published by: South African Bureau for Scientific Publications, PO Box 11663, Pretoria, Hatfield 0028, South Africa. TEL 27-12-322-6404, FAX 27-12-320-7803, bspman@icon.co.za, http://www.safest.org.za/bsp. Ed. I Roos.

ECODATE. see *BUSINESS AND ECONOMICS*

THE EDGE. see *CHILDREN AND YOUTH—About*

028.5 808.8 USA ISSN 1093-2453
NC1426
EDITORIAL CARTOONS BY KIDS. Text in English. 1989. a. USD 10.95. illus. back issues avail. **Description:** Provides a forum whereby children can share their thoughts and feelings on current events and issues through the medium of the editorial cartoon. Publishes those cartoons selected from the NewsCurrents Student Editorial Cartoon Contest.
Published by: Zino Press Children's Books (Subsidiary of: Knowledge Unlimited), PO Box 52, Madison, WI 53791-9438. TEL 608-836-6660, 800-356-2303, FAX 608-831-1570, ku-mail@knowledgeunlimited.com, http://www.zinopress.com, http://www.ku.com/carcon2.html. Pub. Dave Schreiner.

028.5 ISR ISSN 0793-1891
AP221
EINAYIM. Text in Hebrew. 1994. bi-m. ILS 282 domestic; USD 87 foreign (effective 2005). adv. illus. **Document type:** *Consumer.* **Description:** Publishes feature articles on art, history science, nature and other topics of interest to children, along with stories, activities and cartoons.
Published by: Einayim Publishers, P O Box 6334, Jerusalem, 91060, Israel. TEL 972-2-6233933, einayim@netvision.net.il, http://www.einayim.com. Ed., R&P Tamir Rauner. Adv. contact Yoav Ganor.

362.7 DEU
EINE FUER ALLE. Text in German. 1996. q. bk.rev.; play rev. bibl.; illus. **Document type:** *Newsletter, Consumer.*
Formed by the merger of (19??-1996): Unterwegs (Leverkusen); Which was formerly: Doch; Dienen und Fuehren (0012-2564); (1967-1996): Fragezeichen; Which was formerly: Fragechen; Fragezeider; Unser Kleeblatt
Published by: Pfadfinderinnenschaft St. Georg, Unstrutstr 10, Leverkusen, 51371, Germany. TEL 49-214-403920, FAX 49-214-4039222, info@psg-bundesverband.de, http://www.psg-bundesverband.de. Ed. Barbara Runkel. Circ: 6,500.

028.5 JPN
EKUBO. Text in Japanese. 1962. m. **Document type:** *Consumer.*
Formerly (until 1989): Shukan Shojo Friend
Published by: Kodansha Ltd., 2-12-21 Otowa, Bunkyo-ku, Tokyo, 112-8001, Japan. TEL 81-3-3946-6201, FAX 81-3-3944-9915, http://www.kodansha.co.jp, http://www.toppan.co.jp/kodansha. Ed. Yuzuru Utagawa. Circ: 200,000.

305.235 USA
ELASTIC DOG TOY. Text in English. irreg. bk.rev. **Document type:** *Newsletter, Consumer.* **Description:** Covers news, horoscopes, and opinions for teenagers.
Media: Online - full text.
Address: EDTzine@aol.com, http://welcome.to/edt. Ed. Ross Phillips. Pub. Morgan Geppetti.

808 372 USA ISSN 1081-5201
ELEMENTARY SCHOOL WRITER. Text in English. 1995. m. (Sep.-May). USD 59.95 for 25 copies (effective 2003). **Document type:** *Journal, Academic/Scholarly.*
Published by: Writer Publications, PO Box 718, Grand Rapids, MN 55744. TEL 218-326-8025, 888-974-8371, http://www.writerpublications.com/. Ed. Barbara Eiesland. Pub., R&P Teresa Ivanca. Circ: 18,000 (paid).

372.35 USA
ELEMENTARY SCIENCE THIS MONTH. Text in English. 1994. m. **Description:** For elementary school-aged children and the adults who teach them.
Media: Online - full text.
Published by: Mankato State University, College of Education, PO Box 8400, Mankato, MN 56002-8400. drlit@vax1.mankato.msus.edu, http://www.lme.mankato.msus.edu/ci/elem.sci.html. Ed. Karl A Matz.

C

028.5 420 495.6 JPN ISSN 1342-7016
FOREIGN CORRESPONDENT. Text in Japanese. 1995. 3/yr. USD 20 (effective 1999). music rev. illus. back issues avail.
Description: Offers a resource for learners of Japanese or English, teachers and people looking for new friends in Japan.
Related titles: Online - full text ed.
Published by: James Zivney Kaori Zivney Eds.& Pubs., 4-17-27 Midori, Kawachi-gun, Minamikawachi-machi, Tochigi-ken 329-0433, Japan. TEL 81-285-44-2928, FAX 81-285-44-2928, editors@fcjapan.com, http://www.fcjapan.com. Ed. James Zirney. adv.: B&W page USD 100.

THE FOUNTAIN; popular, educational and scientific magazine. see *SCIENCES: COMPREHENSIVE WORKS*

028.5 305.896073 USA
FRESH!. Text in English. 1984. every 3 wks. USD 30 (effective 2004). **Document type:** *Consumer.*
Published by: Ashley Communications, Inc., 19431 Business Center Dr, Northridge, CA 91324. TEL 310-456-3065. Eds. Debi Fee, Ralph Benner. Circ: 100,000.

028.5 GBR
FRESH!; the pop, gossip and fashion magazine for smarter girls. Text in English. 1999. m. GBP 1.70 newsstand/cover. adv. **Document type:** *Consumer.* **Description:** Presents stories and articles on issues and personalities of interest to young girls.
Published by: Europa Magazines Ltd., Bradnich Ct, Castle St, Exeter, Devon EX4 5PT, United Kingdom. TEL 44-1392-211113, FAX 44-1392-211533, europa@dial.pipex.com. **Dist. by:** MarketForce UK Ltd, 247 Tottenham Court Rd, London, Middx W1T 7AU, United Kingdom. TEL 44-207-2615199, FAX 44-207-2617341.

028.5 USA
FRESHANGLES. Text in English. irreg. **Document type:** *Magazine, Consumer.* **Description:** Covers all aspects of teen issues from the perspective of the young, including topics such as current events, music, movies, literary works and more.
Media: Online - full content.
Address: http://www.freshangles.com/. Ed. Kristen Boswell.

FREUNDE; Jugendmagazin in deutscher Sprache. see *LINGUISTICS*

028.5 790.1 SGP
FRIDAY WEEKLY. Text in Chinese. 1991. w. SGD 26; SGD 0.50 newsstand/cover (effective 2003). adv. bk.rev.; film rev.; music rev.; play rev. 20 p./no. 4 cols./p.; back issues avail. **Document type:** *Newspaper, Consumer.* **Description:** Focuses on education, arts, sports & recreational activities for children.
Related titles: Microfilm ed.; Supplement(s): Ad-hoc.
Published by: Singapore Press Holdings Ltd., 1000 Tea Payoh North, News Centre, Singapore, 318994, Singapore. TEL 65-63196319, 65-63198115, FAX 65-63198282, fwltu@sph.com.sg, http://youth.zaobao.com/fw.html, http://www.sph.com.sg/. Ed. Lim Soon Lan. Adv. contact Lawrence Loh. Circ: 36,301 (paid).

FRIEND. see *RELIGIONS AND THEOLOGY—Other Denominations And Sects*

FRIENDLY COMPANION. see *RELIGIONS AND THEOLOGY—Protestant*

028.5 CAN ISSN 1700-0955
FUEL. Text in English. 1992. fortn. CND 15 (effective 2003). adv. bk.rev.; music rev.; software rev. **Document type:** *Magazine, Consumer.* **Description:** Covers music, style and other youth oriented topics.
Former titles (until 2000): Watch (1199-6455); (until 1993): Watch Magazine
Published by: Youth Culture Group, 401 Richmond St W, Ste 245, Toronto, ON M5V 1X3, Canada. TEL 416-595-1313, FAX 416-595-1312, info@youthculture.com, http://www.fuelpowered.com/, http://www.youthculture.com/. Ed. Sara Graham. adv.: B&W page CND 4,495, color page CND 5,295; trim 11 x 10.5. Circ: 125,000 (controlled).

028.5 CHN
FUJIAN QINGNIAN/FUJIAN YOUTH. Text in Chinese. m. CNY 11.40. **Description:** Aimed at college students and young people.
Published by: Fujian Qingnian Zazhishe, No 5, Jinjishan, Fuzhou, Fujian 350001, China. TEL 551944. Ed. Lin Yunqing. **Dist. overseas by:** Jiangsu Publications Import & Export Corp., 56 Gao Yun Ling, Nanjing, Jiangsu, China.

028.5 GBR ISSN 1369-4758
FUN SIZE BEANO. Text in English. m. GBP 0.65 newsstand/cover. **Document type:** *Consumer.*
Formerly (until 1997): Beano Comic Library (0957-9796)
Published by: D.C. Thomson & Co. Ltd., 80 Kingsway East, Dundee, Angus, Scotland DD4 8SL, United Kingdom. FAX 44-1382-462097, comment@dcthomson.co.uk, http://www.dcthomson.co.uk.

028.5 GBR ISSN 1369-4766
FUN SIZE DANDY. Text in English. m. GBP 0.65 newsstand/cover. **Document type:** *Consumer.*
Formerly (until 1997): Dandy Comic Library (0957-9788)
Published by: D.C. Thomson & Co. Ltd., 80 Kingsway East, Dundee, Angus, Scotland DD4 8SL, United Kingdom. FAX 44-1382-462097, comment@dcthomson.co.uk, http://www.dcthomson.co.uk.

028.5 GBR ISSN 1367-7268
FUN TO LEARN - BANANAS IN PYJAMAS. Text in English. 1997. every 3 wks. GBP 21.25; GBP 1.25 newsstand/cover (effective 2001). illus. **Document type:** *Consumer.* **Description:** Offers young readers 3-7 entertaining and educational stories, puzzles, and activities based on the popular Bananas in Pyjamas TV show.
Published by: The Redan Company Ltd., Ramillies Building, 1-9 Hills Pl, London, W1R 1AG, United Kingdom. TEL 44-20-7434-1612, FAX 44-20-7734-1929, sam@edan.co.uk. **Dist. by:** Comag, Tavistock Works, Tavistock Rd, W Drayton, Middx UB7 7QX, United Kingdom. TEL 44-1895-433600, FAX 44-1895-433605.

028.5 GBR ISSN 1362-928X
FUN TO LEARN - BARNEY. Text in English. 1996. fortn. GBP 31.25; GBP 1.30 newsstand/cover (effective 2001). illus. **Document type:** *Consumer.* **Description:** Offers young readers ages 3 to 7 entertaining and educational stories, puzzles, games and activities based on the popular Barney children's TV show.
Published by: The Redan Company Ltd., Ramillies Building, 1-9 Hills Pl, London, W1R 1AG, United Kingdom. TEL 44-20-7434-1612, FAX 44-20-7734-1929, sam@edan.co.uk. **Dist. by:** Comag, Tavistock Works, Tavistock Rd, W Drayton, Middx UB7 7QX, United Kingdom. TEL 44-1895-433600, FAX 44-1895-433605.

028.5 GBR ISSN 1461-6300
FUN TO LEARN - FAVOURITES. Text in English. m. GBP 0.99 newsstand/cover (effective 2001). illus. **Document type:** *Consumer.* **Description:** Offers young readers educational and entertaining stories and activities.
Published by: The Redan Company Ltd., Ramillies Building, 1-9 Hills Pl, London, W1R 1AG, United Kingdom. TEL 44-20-7434-1612, FAX 44-20-7734-1929, sam@edan.co.uk. **Dist. by:** Comag, Tavistock Works, Tavistock Rd, W Drayton, Middx UB7 7QX, United Kingdom. TEL 44-1895-433600, FAX 44-1895-433605.

028.5 GBR ISSN 1357-6046
FUN TO LEARN - FIREMAN SAM. Text in English. 1995. every 3 wks. GBP 21.25; GBP 1.30 newsstand/cover (effective 2001). illus. **Document type:** *Consumer.* **Description:** Offers young readers, children ages 3 to 7, educational and enjoyable stories, puzzles, and exercises based on the popular Fireman Sam character.
Published by: The Redan Company Ltd., Ramillies Building, 1-9 Hills Pl, London, W1R 1AG, United Kingdom. TEL 44-20-7434-1612, FAX 44-20-7734-1929, sam@edan.co.uk. **Dist. by:** Comag, Tavistock Works, Tavistock Rd, W Drayton, Middx UB7 7QX, United Kingdom. TEL 44-1895-433600, FAX 44-1895-433605.

028.5 GBR ISSN 1461-4847
FUN TO LEARN - LETTERLAND. Text in English. 1998. m. GBP 1.30 newsstand/cover (effective 2001). illus. **Document type:** *Consumer.* **Description:** Offers young readers, children ages 3 to 7, educational and fun stories, puzzles, and exercises based on Letterland.
Published by: The Redan Company Ltd., Ramillies Building, 1-9 Hills Pl, London, W1R 1AG, United Kingdom. TEL 44-20-7434-1612, FAX 44-20-7734-1929, sam@edan.co.uk. **Dist. by:** Comag, Tavistock Works, Tavistock Rd, W Drayton, Middx UB7 7QX, United Kingdom. TEL 44-1895-433600, FAX 44-1895-433605.

028.5 GBR ISSN 1357-3705
FUN TO LEARN - POSTMAN PAT. Text in English. 1995. every 3 wks. GBP 31.25; GBP 1.30 newsstand/cover (effective 2001). illus. **Document type:** *Consumer.* **Description:** Offers young readers, children ages 3 to 7, educational and entertaining stories, puzzles, and exercises, all based on the popular storybook character Postman Pat.
Published by: The Redan Company Ltd., Ramillies Building, 1-9 Hills Pl, London, W1R 1AG, United Kingdom. TEL 44-20-7434-1612, FAX 44-20-7734-1929, sam@edan.co.uk. **Dist. by:** Comag, Tavistock Works, Tavistock Rd, W Drayton, Middx UB7 7QX, United Kingdom. TEL 44-1895-433600, FAX 44-1895-433605.

FUNDACAO NACIONAL DO LIVRO INFANTIL E JUVENIL. NOTICIAS. see *PUBLISHING AND BOOK TRADE*

028.5 GBR
FUNDAN GO 4 IT. Text in English. 1998. w. free. **Document type:** *Consumer.* **Description:** Offers young readers who enjoy fun and enjoyable games, stories, articles, and contests.
Media: E-mail.
Published by: Fundano (UK) Ltd, Thurston House, 80 Lincoln Rd, Peterborough, PE1 2SN, United Kingdom. TEL 44-1733-763461, FAX 44-1733-769577, postmaster@fundango.net, http://www.fundango.com. Ed. Jon Cousins.

028.5 AUS ISSN 1447-9850
FUNTIME WITH FRIENDS. Text in English. 2000. m. AUD 4.95 (effective 2004). **Document type:** *Magazine, Consumer.*
Formerly (until 2002): Play Time (1442-5475)
Published by: Australian Broadcasting Corp., PO Box 9994, Sydney, NSW 2001, Australia. TEL 61-1300-360111, FAX 61-1300-360150, http://shop.abc.net.au. **Co-publisher:** B B C Worldwide Ltd.

028.5 DEU
FUTURAMA. Text in German. 2001. bi-m. EUR 2.30 newsstand/cover (effective 2003). adv. **Document type:** *Magazine, Consumer.*
Published by: Panini Verlags GmbH, Ravensstr 48, Nettetal, 41334, Germany. TEL 49-711-947680, FAX 49-711-94768830, info@panini-dino.de, http://www.panini-media.de. adv.: page EUR 3,900; trim 170 x 257. Circ: 51,341 (paid).

FUTURE REFLECTIONS. see *HANDICAPPED—Visually Impaired*

G A WORLD. (Girls in Action) see *RELIGIONS AND THEOLOGY—Protestant*

028.5 282 ITA ISSN 1591-4844
G BABY. Text in Italian. 2000. m. EUR 19 (effective 2004). **Document type:** *Magazine, Consumer.*
Published by: Edizioni San Paolo, Piazza Soncino 5, Cinisello Balsamo, CN 20092, Italy. TEL 39-02-660751, FAX 39-02-66075211, sanpaoloedizioni@stpauls.it, http://www.edizionisanpaolo.it.

GALAXY. see *ASTRONOMY*

C

GAY YOUTH COMMUNITY NEWS. see *HOMOSEXUALITY*

028.5 POL ISSN 1233-2615
GAZETA DZIECI. Text in Polish. 1994. bi-m. PLZ 20 domestic; PLZ 60 foreign; PLZ 2 newsstand/cover. adv. bk.rev. cum.index. **Document type:** *Newspaper.* **Description:** Aims to educate children. Covers arts, literature, music, film, science.
Published by: (Narodowy Fundusz Ochrony Srodowiska), Izba Wydawnicza Swiatowit, Ul Legnicka 84-4, Wroclaw, 54206, Poland. TEL 48-71-517334, FAX 48-71-517334. Ed., R&P Stanislaw Srokowski. Adv. contact Lukasz Srokowski. page PLZ 1,500. Circ: 8,000.

305.23 POL ISSN 1232-1753
GAZETA KALENDARZ MATURZYSTY. Text in Polish. 1993. m. **Document type:** *Consumer.*
Related titles: ♦ Supplement to: Gazeta Wyborcza. ISSN 0860-908X.
Published by: Agora S.A., ul Czerska 8/10, Warsaw, 00732, Poland. TEL 48-22-6994301, FAX 48-22-6994603, http://www.gazeta.pl.

GEAR. see *SPORTS AND GAMES*

028.5 JPN
GEKKAN SHONEN MAGAZINE. Text in Japanese. m. **Document type:** *Magazine, Consumer.*
Published by: Kodansha Ltd., 2-12-21 Otowa, Bunkyo-ku, Tokyo, 112-8001, Japan. TEL 81-3-3946-6201, FAX 81-3-3944-9915, http://www.kodansha.co.jp.

028.5 DEU ISSN 0936-1111
GEMEINSCHAFTS- UND SOZIALKUNDE; Kurzausgabe der Arbeitsmappe Sozial- und Wirtschaftskunde. Text in German. 1969. q. looseleaf. EUR 68 (effective 2004). charts. index. back issues avail. **Document type:** *Journal, Academic/Scholarly.*
Published by: Erich Schmidt Verlag GmbH & Co. (Berlin), Genthiner Str 30G, Berlin, 10785, Germany. TEL 49-30-50085-0, FAX 49-30-25008521, vertrieb@esvmedien.de, http://www.erich-schmidt-verlag.de. Ed. Gerhard Huck.

028.5 JPN
GENKI. Text in Japanese. m. **Document type:** *Magazine, Consumer.*
Published by: Kodansha Ltd., 2-12-21 Otowa, Bunkyo-ku, Tokyo, 112-8001, Japan. TEL 81-3-3946-6201, FAX 81-3-3944-9915, http://www.kodansha.co.jp.

028.5 LTU ISSN 0132-649X
GENYS. Text in Lithuanian. 1940. m. LTL 96, USD 24. adv.
Published by: Lietuvos Rytas, Gedimino 12-a, Vilnius, 2000, Lithuania. TEL 370-2-616334, FAX 370-2-227656. Ed. Gintare Adomaityte. Circ: 11,000.

028.5 DEU
GEO LINO; das Erlebnis-Heft. Text in German. 1996. m. EUR 30.60; EUR 3 newsstand/cover (effective 2003). adv. **Document type:** *Magazine, Consumer.* **Description:** Provides informative and entertaining games and stories for children.

Published by: Gruner und Jahr AG & Co., Am Baumwall 11, Hamburg, 20459, Germany. TEL 49-40-3703-0, FAX 49-40-37035617, guj-redaktion@guj.de, http://www.geo.de/ GEOlino, http://www.guj.de. adv: B&W page EUR 10,700, color page EUR 13,900. Circ: 225,611 (paid and controlled).

GEODATE. see GEOGRAPHY

GEOGRAPHIE HEUTE. see GEOGRAPHY

028.50   USA   ISSN 1554-5008
F281
GEORGIA VOYAGER MAGAZINE. Text in English. q. USD 14 (effective 2005).
Address: 6063 Peachtree Parkway, 101A, Norcross, GA 30092-3302. TEL 800-243-6991, gavoymag@aol.com, http://www.gavoyager.com/.

GET SMART ABOUT DRUGS (GRADE LEVELS 2-3). see DRUG ABUSE AND ALCOHOLISM

GET SMART ABOUT DRUGS (GRADE LEVELS 4-6). see DRUG ABUSE AND ALCOHOLISM

GET SMART ABOUT DRUGS (GRADE LEVELS 7-9). see DRUG ABUSE AND ALCOHOLISM

GHOSTMASTERS: POKEMON, DIGIMON, DRAGON BALL Z. see SPORTS AND GAMES

028.5   GBR   ISSN 1461-1775
GINA'S WORLD. Text in English. 1998. m. GBP 2.99 newsstand/cover. Document type: Consumer.
Published by: Burghley Publishing Ltd., 14 Barn Hill, Stamford, Lincs PE9 2AE, United Kingdom. TEL 44-1780-763366, FAX 44-1780-763365. Dist. by: Seymour Distribution Ltd, 86 Newman St, London W1T 3EX, United Kingdom. FAX 44-207-396-8002, enquiries@seymour.co.uk.

028.5   ITA   ISSN 1123-0541
IL GIORNALINO; settimanale dei ragazzi. Text in Italian. 1924. w. EUR 81.60 (effective 2004). bk.rev. illus. Document type: Magazine, Consumer.
Published by: Edizioni San Paolo, Piazza Soncino 5, Cinisello Balsamo, CN 20092, Italy. TEL 39-02-660751, FAX 39-02-66075211, giornalino@stpauls.it, sanpaoloedizioni@stpauls.it, http://www.sanpaolo.org/gio, http://www.edizionisanpaolo.it. Circ: 180,000.

028.5   ITA   ISSN 1120-2564
GIOVANI AMICI. Text in Italian. 1966. m. USD 19. Document type: Consumer.
Published by: Universita Cattolica del Sacro Cuore, Largo Gemelli 1, Milan, MI 20123, Italy. TEL 39-02-72341, iststoan@mi.unicatt.it, http://www.unicatt.it/. Ed. Roberta Maria Rosa Grazzani. Circ: 45,000.

054.1   FRA   ISSN 1286-577X
GIRL!. Text in French. 1992. m. adv. Document type: Magazine, Consumer.
Formerly (until 1998): Bravo Girl! (1167-783X)
Related titles: Supplement(s): Girl! Hors-Serie. ISSN 1627-3052. 2001.
Published by: Editions Bauer France (Subsidiary of: Heinrich Bauer Verlag), 30-32 Rue de Chabrol, Paris, 75010, France. TEL 33-1-40227640, FAX 33-1-40220272.

305.23   SCG
GIRL. Text in Serbian. fortn. YUN 29 newsstand/cover (effective 2003). adv. Document type: Magazine, Consumer. Description: Contains reports on current topics, comprehensive advice and loads of fashion and styling tips specifically for young women and teenage girls.
Published by: Isdavacka Kuca Burda Beograd, Takovska 45, Beograd, 11000. sandi@burda.co.yu. adv: page EUR 690. Circ: 80,000 (paid and controlled).

028.5   USA
GIRL STUFF. Text in English. w. Document type: Magazine, Consumer. Description: Covers many topics concerning preteen girls such as health, girl-power, celebrities, clothes, fitness, music, books, poetry and more.
Media: Online - full text.
Address: Box 1935, Montrose, CO 81402. girl-stuff-mag@gurlmail.com, http://www.gurlpages.com/zines/girl-stuff-mag. Ed. Allison Masters.

028.5   GBR   ISSN 1357-5538
GIRL TALK. Text in English. 1995. fortn. GBP 28.60 domestic; GBP 71.77 in Europe; GBP 97.77 elsewhere; GBP 1.10 newsstand/cover (effective 2003). adv. Document type: Magazine, Consumer.
Published by: B B C Worldwide Ltd., 80 Wood Ln, London, W12 0TT, United Kingdom. TEL 44-20-84331070, FAX 44-20-84332231, girltalk.magazine@bbc.co.uk, bbcworldwide@bbc.co.uk, http://www.bbcmagazines.com/girltalk/index.html. Circ: 101,173 (paid and controlled). Subscr. to: Galleon Ltd., PO Box 279, Sittingbourne, Kent ME9 8DF, United Kingdom. TEL 44-1795-414746. Dist. by: Frontline, Park House, 117 Park Rd, Peterborough, Cambs PE1 2TS, United Kingdom. TEL 44-1733-555161, FAX 44-1733-562788.

028.5   USA
GIRL TECH. Text in English. 1996. m.
Media: Online - full content.
Published by: Radica Games, Ltd. http://www.girltech.com.

028.5   AUS   ISSN 1033-7288
GIRLFRIEND. Text in English. 1988. m. AUD 45 domestic; AUD 57 in New Zealand; AUD 87 elsewhere; AUD 4.80 newsstand/cover domestic (effective 2004). adv. Document type: Magazine, Consumer. Description: Covers fashion, beauty and celebrities for teen girls.
Related titles: Online - full text ed.
Published by: Pacific Publications, 35-51 Mitchell St, McMahons Point, NSW 2060, Australia. TEL 61-2-94643300, FAX 61-2-94643375, girlfriend@pacpubs.com.au, subscriptions@pacpubs.com.au, http://www.girlfriend.com.au, http://www.pacificpubs.com.au. Ed. Katrina O'Brien. Pub. Mary Giugni.

053.1   DEU
▼ GIRLFRIENDS; Nur fuer Maedchen. Text in German. 2004. m. EUR 2.40 newsstand/cover (effective 2005). adv. Document type: Magazine, Consumer.
Published by: Attic Futura Verlag GmbH, Landsberger Str 76, Munich, 80339, Germany. TEL 49-89-51446100, FAX 49-89-51449199, michaela.moses@atticfutura.de, info@atticfutura.de, http://www.girlfriends-mag.de, http://www.atticfutura.de. adv: color page EUR 5,000.

028.5   DEU
GIRL'S CLUB; das magazin fuer echte Maedchen. Text in German. 2000-2000; N.S. 2002. m. EUR 2.20 newsstand/cover (effective 2002). adv. Document type: Magazine, Consumer. Description: Presents articles and items of interest to young girls.
Published by: Panini Verlags GmbH, Ravensstr 48, Nettetal, 41334, Germany. TEL 49-711-947680, FAX 49-711-94768830, info@panini-dino.de, http://www.panini-media.de. Adv. contact Petra Sonnenfroh-Kost. page EUR 3,500; trim 210 x 297. Circ: 160,000 (paid and controlled).

053.1   DEU
GIRLS CLUB. Text in German. 2000. m. EUR 2.40 newsstand/cover (effective 2003). adv. Document type: Magazine, Consumer.
Published by: Pabel-Moewig Verlag KG (Subsidiary of: Heinrich Bauer Verlag), Karlsruherstr 31, Rastatt, 76437, Germany. TEL 49-7222-130, FAX 49-7222-13218, empfang@vpm.de, http://www.vpm-online.de. adv: page EUR 3,500. Circ: 150,000 (paid and controlled).

028.5   USA   ISSN 1078-3326
HQ798
GIRLS' LIFE. Text in English. 1994. bi-m. USD 14.95 domestic; USD 19.95 in Canada; USD 45 elsewhere; USD 3.50 newsstand/cover domestic; USD 4.50 newsstand/cover in Canada (effective 2003). adv. bk.rev. illus. reprints avail. Document type: Consumer. Description: Includes fashion news, celebrity features, craft activities, discussions about family, school, boys.
Related titles: Online - full text ed.: (from bigchalk, EBSCO Publishing, Gale Group, O C L C Online Computer Library Center, Inc.).
Indexed: CPerl, ICM, RGYP.
Published by: Monarch Avalon, Inc., 4517 Harford Rd., Baltimore, MD 21214-3122. TEL 410-426-9600, 888-999-3222, FAX 410-254-0991, publisher@girlslife.com, http://www.girlslife.com. Ed., Pub. Karen Bokram. Adv. contact Jennifer Brown.

369.463   USA
GIRLS ONLY. Text in English. 1996. m. Document type: Consumer.
Formerly: Just for Girls
Media: Online - full text.
Published by: Girl Scouts of the U.S.A., 420 Fifth Ave, New York, NY 10018-2798. TEL 212-852-8000, 800-478-7248, FAX 212-852-6511, jfg@girlscouts.org, misc@girlscouts.org, http://jfg.girlscouts.org, http://www.girlscouts.org.

028.5   USA
A GIRL'S WORLD. Text in English. 1996. m.
Media: Online - full content.
Published by: A Girl's World Productions, Inc., 825 College Blvd. PMB 322-442, Oceanside, CA 92057. http://www.agirlsworld.com.

070.489   NLD   ISSN 1570-5285
GIRLZ!. Text in Dutch. 1986. m. EUR 27.50 (effective 2003). adv. Document type: Magazine, Consumer. Description: Provides information for young girls on fashion and shopping, body care, relationships, human interest stories and celebrities.
Formerly (until 2002): Top 10 (1381-8171)
Published by: Audax Publishing B.V., Joan Muyskenweg 6-6a, Amsterdam, 1096 CJ, Netherlands. TEL 31-20-5979695, FAX 31-20-5979685, info@publishing.audax.nl, http://213.206.93.53, http://www.audax.nl.

028.5   NLD
GITTA. Text in Dutch. m. adv.
Published by: Holco Publications B.V., Postbus 267, Alkmaar, 1800 AE, Netherlands.

GIV DET STOERSTE TIL DE MINDSTE; evangeliet til boernene. see RELIGIONS AND THEOLOGY—Protestant

028.5   SCG   ISSN 0017-0798
GLAS OMLADINE; list mladih. Text in Serbo-Croatian. 1966 (vol.14). bi-w. YUN 0.50.
Indexed: BAS.
Published by: Narodne Novine, Nis, Balkanska 2, Nis. Ed. Ljubisa Igic.

808.068 915.4   IND
GLORY; a Baha'i youth deepening magazine. Text in English. 1973. q. USD 15 for 6 nos.. bk.rev.
Address: Lucky Bldg., Main Rd., Panchgani, 412 805, India. Ed. Marzia S Rowhani. Circ: 1,000.

GO FUER GOTT. see RELIGIONS AND THEOLOGY—Protestant

028.5   IND
GOKULAM. Text in English. m. INR 100 domestic; USD 25 foreign (effective 2005). Description: Magazine for children offers both information and entertainment in abundance. It covers serial story, short stories, articles, discussions, picture stories, puzzles, activities, jokes.
Related titles: Tamil ed.
Published by: Bharathan Publications Pvt. Ltd., Kalki Buildings, 47NP, Jawaharlal Nehru Rd, Ekkaduthangal, Chennai, Tamil Nadu 600 097, India. TEL 91-44-22345622, FAX 91-44-22345621, http://www.kalkiweekly.com/thisweekissue/gead.asp.

028.5   ZAF
GOOD COMPANY. Text in English. 1982. q. ZAR 20 (effective 1999 - 2000). back issues avail. Document type: Academic/Scholarly. Description: For girl guides ages 10-14. Covers camping, conservation, cooking, and ideas for individual and group activities.
Published by: Girl Guide Association of South Africa, c/o Mrs. P Kirkland, PO Box 3343, Honeydew, 2040, South Africa. TEL 27-11-795-3741, FAX 27-11-7941091, ggasa@sn.apc.org, http://www.hardline.co.za/guides/. Ed. Miranda Lewis. Circ: 3,000.

GOOD-NEWS-LETTER (WASHINGTON, 1990). see NUTRITION AND DIETETICS

GOSPEL STANDARD. see RELIGIONS AND THEOLOGY—Protestant

GRAIN DE SOLEIL; les autres, Dieu et moi. see RELIGIONS AND THEOLOGY—Roman Catholic

028.5   ISR
GRASHUEPFER. Text in German. 1979. m.
Published by: Etzb'oni Publishing House, P O Box 28110, Tel Aviv, 61280, Israel. FAX 972-3-5373906. Ed. Michael Shir. Circ: 78,000.

GRIFFON. see LITERATURE

028.5   NLD   ISSN 1387-3873
GRIP. Text in Dutch. 1952. 8/yr. EUR 32.35; EUR 5.20 newsstand/cover (effective 2005). bk.rev.; film rev.; play rev. illus.
Former titles (until 1998): M.3 (0166-3917); (until 1963): Materiaal, Metodiek, Mededelingen (0025-5254)
Published by: Protestantse Kerk in Nederland, Team Jeugdwerk, Postbus 8504, Utrecht, 3503 RM, Netherlands. TEL 31-30-8801503, FAX 31-30-8801767, jeugdwerk@pkn.nl, http://www.jeugdwerk.pkn.nl. Circ: 2,000.

373.95   USA   ISSN 1099-6230
GRIP MAGAZINE (CARLSBAD). Text in English. 1991. 7/yr. USD 19.95; free on high school campuses (effective 2000). adv. Document type: Magazine, Consumer. Description: Written by and for high school students from campuses nationwide. Offers fresh insights on social issues, arts, entertainment, fashion and athletics.
Related titles: Online - full text ed.
Published by: Grip Publications, Inc., PO Box 1030, Carlsbad, CA 92018. TEL 760-752-8292, FAX 760-730-3819, feedback@gripvision.com, gripmag@mysurf.com, http://www.gripvision.com. Ed. Tim Francis. R&P, Adv. contact Matt Morrison. B&W page USD 4,350. Circ: 250,000.

GROWING (NASHVILLE). see RELIGIONS AND THEOLOGY—Protestant

GRRR!; kids bite back. see ANIMAL WELFARE

GUIDE (HAGERSTOWN); true stories pointing to Jesus. see RELIGIONS AND THEOLOGY—Protestant

369.5 028.5   FRA   ISSN 0750-4152
GUIDE DE FRANCE. Text in French. 1927. q. Description: Directed to girls 12-14.
Published by: Guides de France, 65 rue de la Glaciere, Paris, 75013, France. TEL 33-1-47078559, FAX 33-1-43377769. Ed. Marie Therese Chotard.

028.5   FRA
LE GUIDE PHOSPHORE. Text in French. 6/yr. EUR 49.80 domestic; EUR 58.80 elsewhere (effective 2005). **Document type:** *Consumer.*
Published by: Bayard Presse, 3 Rue Bayard, Paris, 75393 Cedex 08, France. TEL 33-1-44356060, FAX 33-1-44356161, redactions@bayard-presse.com, http://www.phosphore.com, http://www.bayardpresse.com. Ed. Beatrice Toulon.

GUIDE TO TRAINING AND BENEFITS TO YOUNG PEOPLE. see *SOCIAL SERVICES AND WELFARE*

028.5 202.15   USA   ISSN 1551-904X
GUIDEPOSTS SWEET 16. Text in English. 1998. bi-m. USD 19.95 domestic; USD 26.95 in Canada; USD 30.95 elsewhere (effective 2005). 58 p./no. 2 cols./p.; back issues avail.; reprints avail. **Document type:** *Magazine, Consumer.* **Description:** Contains true stories about real people and religious faith as told by teens in their own words.
Formerly (until Aug/Sept 2004): Guideposts for Teens (1522-3663)
Published by: Guideposts Associates, Inc., 39 Seminary Hill Rd, Carmel, NY 10512. TEL 845-225-3681, FAX 845-228-2143, writers@guidepostssweet16mag.com, http://www.guidepostssweet16mag.com, http://www.guideposts.org. Ed. Mary Lou Carney. Circ: 200,000 (paid).

028.5   POL
GULIWER; czasopismo o ksiazce dla dziecka. Text in Polish. 1991. q. PLZ 40 (effective 2003). **Document type:** *Magazine, Consumer.*
Published by: Wydawnictwo Slask Sp. z o.o., Al W Korfantego 51, Katowice, 40161, Poland. TEL 48-32-2585870, FAX 48-32-2583229, guliwer@free.ngo.pl, handel@slaskwn.com.pl, http://free.ngo.pl/guliwer. Ed. Joanna Papuzinska. Circ: 1,200.

GUOYU QINGSHAONAN/MARDARIN TEENAGER MONTHLY. see *LINGUISTICS*

GUOYU YOUER/MANDARIN CHILDREN MONTHLY. see *LINGUISTICS*

GURL. see *WOMEN'S INTERESTS*

GUSHI DAWANG/KING OF STORY TELLERS. see *LITERATURE*

028.5   CHN
GUSHI DAWANG HUABAO/ACE STORY - TELLER PICTORIAL. Text in Chinese. m. USD 36. illus.
Formerly: Wanhuatong Lianhuan Huabao - Kaleidoscope
Published by: Shaonian Ertong Chubanshe/Juvenile & Children Publishing House, 1538 Yan an Xilu, Shanghai, 200052, China. TEL 86-21-6282-3025, FAX 86-21-6282-1726. Ed. Han Shuo.

200   DEU
GUTER START. Text in German. q. EUR 7.18; EUR 2.15 newsstand/cover (effective 2003). **Document type:** *Magazine, Consumer.*
Published by: Bibellesebund e.V., Industriestr 2, Marienheide, 51709, Germany. TEL 49-2264-404340, FAX 49-2264-4043439, r.frey@bibellesebund.de, http://www.bibellesebund.de/hilfen/start.htm.

025.4   DEU
▼ **HAEFFT TIMER.** Text in German. 2003. a. EUR 6.90 newsstand/cover (effective 2003). adv. **Document type:** *Magazine, Academic/Scholarly.*
Published by: Verlag Reiter & Klingberg GbR, Barer Str. 70, Munich, 80799, Germany. TEL 49-89-2782690, FAX 49-89-27826999, info@haefft.de, http://www.haefft.de. adv.: color page EUR 7,500.

028.5   IDN
HAI. Text in Indonesian. 1973. w. **Document type:** *Magazine, Consumer.*
Published by: P T Gramedia, Jalan Palmerah Selatan 22-26, Jakarta, 10270, Indonesia. TEL 62-21-5483008, FAX 62-21-5494035, hai_magazine@gramedia-majalah.com, ulj@gramedia-majalah.com, http://www.hai-online.com, http://www.gramedia.com.

028.5   ITA
HALLO!∗ . Text in Italian. m. adv. illus. **Document type:** *Consumer.*
Published by: (Coop Athena 2001 a.r.l.), Editoriale Tuttogiovanni, Athena 2001, Viale Mazzini 145, Rome, 00195, Italy. Circ: 47,000.

028.5 332   AUT
HALLO SPAREFROH; Freund der Sparjugend. Text in German. 1955. 7/yr. free. illus. **Document type:** *Bulletin.*
Formerly: Sparefroh (0038-6510)
Published by: (Hauptverband der Oesterreichischen Sparkassen), Sparkassenverlag GmbH, Grimmelshausengasse 1, Vienna, W 1030, Austria. TEL 43-1-71170-0, FAX 43-1-71170237. Ed. Franz Josef Barta. Circ: 150,000.

028.5   CHN
HAO ERTONG/GOOD CHILDREN. Text in Chinese. m. USD 21.50.

Published by: (Shanghai Shi Jiaoyu-ju/Shanghai Municipal Bureau of Education), Hao Ertong Bianjibu, 500 Shaanxi Beilu, Shanghai, 200041, China. TEL 2532973. Ed. Zhang Qiusheng. **Dist. in US by:** China Books & Periodicals Inc, 360 Swift Ave., Ste. 48, S San Fran, CA 94080-6220. TEL 415-282-2994.

HARLEMLIVE; Harlem's youth internet publication. see *CHILDREN AND YOUTH—About*

051   USA
HARVEY∗ ; the magazine for kids. Text in English. 1998. m. USD 17.70; USD 2.95 newsstand/cover (effective 1999). **Document type:** *Consumer.* **Description:** Combines comics with great illustrated children's stories, innovative new games, puzzles, jokes, and other special features.
Published by: Harvey Entertainment Company, 11835 W Olympic Blvd Ste 550, Los Angeles, CA 90064-5001. TEL 877-234-8140, http://www.harvey.com. **Dist. by:** Wagner Publishing Services, 1271 Ave of the Americas, New York, NY 10020. TEL 212-522-8900, FAX 212-522-7162.

HEALTHLINES SAY; support for the asthmatic youth. see *MEDICAL SCIENCES—Allergology And Immunology*

HEARTS AFLAME; Catholic youth magazine. see *RELIGIONS AND THEOLOGY—Roman Catholic*

268   FRA
HEBDO DES JUNIORS. Text in French. 1993. w. FRF 372 domestic; FRF 703.70 foreign (effective 2000). **Document type:** *Consumer.* **Description:** Contains news, cultural and TV topics for children 9 to 14 yrs of age.
Formerly: Infos Junior (1240-4454); Which was formed by the 1993 merger of: Fripounet (0016-1446); Which was formerly (until 1969): Fripounet et Marisette (0992-7891); (1945-194?): Message aux Coeurs Vaillants (0992-7883); And: Triolo (0292-2614); Which was formed by the 1981 merger of: Djin (0335-1866); Which was formerly (until 1974): J 2 Magazine (0994-8392); (1937-1963): Ames Vaillantes (0994-8384); And: Formule 1 (0994-8422); Which was formerly (until 1970): J 2 Jeunes (0994-8414); (1928-1963): Coeurs Vaillants (0994-8406)
Published by: Fleurus Presse, 129 bd. Malesherbes, Paris, 75017, France. TEL 33-1-61812009, 33-1-56793636. Ed. Armelle Breton. Circ: 250,000. **Subscr. to:** BP 72, Perthes Cedex 77932, France.

HELIX. see *SCIENCES: COMPREHENSIVE WORKS*

028.5   DEU   ISSN 0018-1099
HESSISCHE JUGEND. Text in German. 1949. 4/yr. bk.rev. **Document type:** *Consumer.*
Published by: Hessischer Jugendring e.V., Bismarckring 23, Wiesbaden, 65183, Germany. TEL 49-611-990830, FAX 49-611-9908360. Ed. Benno Hafenegger.

305.23   DEU
▼ **HEY!.** Text in German. 2004. m. EUR 1 newsstand/cover (effective 2005). adv. **Document type:** *Magazine, Consumer.*
Published by: Panini Verlags GmbH, Ravensstr 48, Nettetal, 41334, Germany. TEL 49-2157-81750, FAX 49-2157-81484528, info@panini-dino.de, http://www.panini-media.de. adv.: page EUR 7,500; trim 210 x 280. Circ: 150,000 (paid).

059.9435   TUR   ISSN 1300-5588
HEY GIRL. Text in Turkish. 1988. m. **Document type:** *Magazine, Consumer.*
Published by: D B R - Dogan Burda Rizzoli Dergi Yayyncylyk ve Pazarlama A.S., Hurriyet Medya Towers, Gunesli - Istanbul, 34212, Turkey. TEL 90-212-4103111, FAX 90-212-4103112, abone@dbr.com.tr, http://www.heygirl.com.tr, http://www.dbr.com.tr.

059.927   USA   ISSN 1550-7475
E169.1
▼ **HI.** Text in Arabic. 2003. m. **Document type:** *Magazine, Consumer.* **Description:** Contains articles and features in Arabic for youg people about families, friends, careers, beliefs, sports, music, technology, education, and relationships.
Related titles: Online - full text ed.: ISSN 1555-0729.
Published by: The Magazine Group, 1707 L St N W, Ste 350, Washington, DC 20036-4201. TEL 202-331-7700, FAX 202-331-7311, editorial@themagazinegroup.com, http://www.himag.com, http://www.themagazinegroup.com. Circ: 50,000 (controlled).

051   USA
▼ **HI INTERNATIONAL.** Text in English. 2004. m. **Document type:** *Magazine, Consumer.* **Description:** Provides a forum for new trends and ideas of interest to young people.
Media: Online - full content.
Published by: The Magazine Group, 1707 L St N W, Ste 350, Washington, DC 20036-4201. TEL 202-331-7700, FAX 202-331-7311, editors.e@hiinternational.com, editorial@themagazinegroup.com, http://www.hiinternational.com, http://www.themagazinegroup.com.

HIGH ADVENTURE (SPRINGFIELD); a Royal Rangers magazine for boys. see *RELIGIONS AND THEOLOGY—Other Denominations And Sects*

808   USA   ISSN 1048-3373
HIGH SCHOOL WRITER (SENIOR HIGH EDITION). (In 2 editions: Senior High, Junior High) Text in English. 1985. 9/yr. USD 75.37 (effective 2003). illus. reprints avail. **Document type:** *Academic/Scholarly.*
Former titles (until 198?): High School Writer of the Midwest (1040-760X); (until 1988): High School Writer of Minnesota (0894-5608)
Published by: Writer Publications, PO Box 718, Grand Rapids, MN 55744. TEL 218-326-8025. Ed. Barbara Eiesland. Pub., R&P Teresa Ivanca. Circ: 38,000 (paid).

028.5   USA   ISSN 0018-165X
AP201
HIGHLIGHTS FOR CHILDREN; fun with a purpose. Text in English. 1946. m. USD 29.64 domestic; USD 3.95 newsstand/cover (effective 2005). bk.rev. illus. Index. back issues avail.; reprints avail. **Document type:** *Magazine, Consumer.* **Description:** Contains fiction, articles, crafts, science, history, and biography, activities, puzzles, and children's submissions.
Incorporates: Children's Activities
Related titles: Microform ed.: (from PQC); Online - full text ed.: (from bigchalk, EBSCO Publishing, Gale Group, Northern Light Technology, Inc., ProQuest Information & Learning).
Indexed by: ICM, JHMA, RGYP, WBA, WMB.
Published by: Highlights for Children, Inc., PO Box 269, Columbus, OH 43216-0269. TEL 614-486-0631, eds@highlights-corp.com, http://www.highlights.com. Eds. Christine French Clark, Kim T. Griswell, Kent L. Brown Jr. Circ: 2,500,000 (paid).

HIGHWIRED SPORTS; America's high school sports magazine & almanac. see *SPORTS AND GAMES*

087.5   PRT
HIPER DISNEY. Text in Portuguese. 6/yr. EUR 32.28 (effective 2004). adv. **Document type:** *Magazine, Consumer.*
Published by: Edimpresa Editora Lda., Rua Calvet de Magalhaes 242, Laveiras, Paco de Arcos, 2770-022, Portugal. TEL 351-21-4698000, FAX 351-21-4698501, edimpresa@edimpresa.pt, http://www.edimpresa.pt.

028.5   DEU
HIRO; action, fun & anime. Text in German. 2002 (Aug.). m. EUR 2.50 newsstand/cover (effective 2003). adv. **Document type:** *Magazine, Consumer.*
Published by: Panini Verlags GmbH, Ravensstr 48, Nettetal, 41334, Germany. TEL 49-711-947680, FAX 49-711-94768830, info@panini-dino.de, http://www.panini-media.de. adv.: page EUR 3,200. Circ: 130,000 (paid and controlled).

HISTORIAS BIBLICAS PARA PREESCOLARES. ALUMNOS. see *RELIGIONS AND THEOLOGY—Protestant*

HISTORIAS BIBLICAS PARA PREESCOLARES. MAESTROS. see *RELIGIONS AND THEOLOGY—Protestant*

HIT SENSATIONS PRESENTS: DIGIMON. see *SPORTS AND GAMES*

HIT SENSATIONS PRESENTS: DIGIMON VS. POKEMON. see *SPORTS AND GAMES*

HIT SENSATIONS PRESENTS: POKEMANIA (YEAR). see *SPORTS AND GAMES*

HIT SENSATIONS PRESENTS: POKEMON BONANZA. see *SPORTS AND GAMES*

HIT SENSATIONS PRESENTS: THE ULTIMATE BATTLE NEO POKEMON VS. DRAGONBALL Z. see *SPORTS AND GAMES*

028.5 793   USA
HIT SENSATION'S TV SERIES: DINOSAURS. Text in English. 2000. m. USD 5.95 newsstand/cover. **Document type:** *Consumer.*
Published by: Fanzine International, Inc., 1250 Broadway 17th Fl, New York, NY 10001.

HMOOBTEEN; the place where hmong teens can speak and be heared. see *ETHNIC INTERESTS*

028.5   AUS
HOA NIEN. Text in Vietnamese. bi-m. AUD 15 domestic; USD 15 foreign (effective 2004). **Document type:** *Magazine, Consumer.*
Published by: Vietnamese Youth Association, PO Box 46, Robinson, VIC 3019, Australia. http://home.vicnet.net.au/~hoanien/magazine.html.

028.5   RWA
HOBE. Text in Kinyarwanda. 1955. m.
Address: BP 761, Kigali, Rwanda. Ed. Andre Sibomana. Circ: 95,000.

▼ *new title*   ➤ *refereed*   ∗ *unverified*   ◆ *full entry avail.*

C

028.5 027.4 COL ISSN 0121-3563
HOJAS DE LECTURA. Text in Spanish. 1989. bi-m.
Formerly (until 1990): Hojas de Asociacion Colombiana para el Libro Infantil y Juvenil (0121-2699)
Published by: Fundacion para el Fomento de la Lectura, Avenida 40 No 16-46, Bogota, Colombia. TEL 57-1-3201511, FAX 57-1-2877071, contactenos@fundalectura.org.co, http://www.fundalectura.org.

028.5 780 RUS
HOLIDAYS AT THE KINDERGARTEN. Text in Russian. 4/yr.
Published by: Izdatel'stvo Muzyka, Petrovka 26, Moscow, 127051, Russian Federation. TEL 7-095-9215170, FAX 7-095-9283304, muz-sekretar@yandex.ru, jvolk@mail.ru.

028.5 DEU
HOLMES; secret agent. Text in German. 2001. m. adv. **Document type:** *Magazine, Consumer.*
Published by: Panini Verlags GmbH, Ravensstr 48, Nettetal, 41334, Germany. TEL 49-711-947680, FAX 49-711-94768830, info@panini-dino.de, http://www.panini-media.de. Adv. contact Petra Sonnenfroh-Kost.

028.5 DEU ISSN 0938-8923
HOPPLA. Text in German. 1990. m. EUR 2.90 newsstand/cover (effective 2003). adv. **Document type:** *Magazine, Consumer.*
Published by: Weltbild Verlag GmbH, Steinerne Furt, Augsburg, 86128, Germany. TEL 49-821-70048350, FAX 49-821-70048349, http://www.weltbild.de. adv.: color page EUR 2,200. Circ: 26,782 (paid).

028.5 USA ISSN 1044-0488
HOPSCOTCH (BLUFFTON); for girls. Text in English. 1989. bi-m. USD 22.95 domestic; USD 28.95 foreign; USD 4.95 newsstand/cover domestic; USD 5.95 newsstand/cover foreign (effective 2005). bk.rev. illus. back issues avail.; reprints avail. **Document type:** *Magazine, Consumer.* **Description:** Contains activities and stories for girls 6 to 12. Promotes reading, creativity, and self-esteem.
Related titles: CD-ROM ed.; Online - full text ed.: (from EBSCO Publishing, Gale Group).
Indexed: ICM, MagInd, RGYP.
Published by: Bluffton News Printing & Publishing Co., P.O. Box 164, Bluffton, OH 45817-0164. TEL 419-358-4610, FAX 419-358-5027, http://www.hopscotchmagazine.com. Ed. Marilyn Edwards. Pub. Tom Edwards. Circ: 14,000 (paid).

HORSEWYSE. see *SPORTS AND GAMES—Horses And Horsemanship*

HOSTELLING INTERNATIONAL GUIDE. see *TRAVEL AND TOURISM*

HOT!. see *COMMUNICATIONS—Television And Cable*

028.5 DEU
HOT WHEELS. Text in German. m. EUR 2.80 newsstand/cover (effective 2005). adv. **Document type:** *Magazine, Consumer.*
Published by: Egmont Ehapa Verlag GmbH, Wallstr 59, Berlin, 10179, Germany. TEL 49-30-240080, FAX 49-30-24008599, leserservice@ehapa.de, http://www.ehapa.de/ehapa/e14/e40/e172/index_ger.html.

028.5 USA ISSN 1550-0918
HOW STUFF WORKS EXPRESS. Variant title: Marshall Brain's How Stuff Works Express. Text in English. 2000. bi-m. **Document type:** *Magazine, Consumer.* **Description:** Aims to make science and technology entertaining and understandable, resulting in greater student interest and enhanced performance.
Related titles: Online - full text ed.
Published by: How Stuff Works, 5625 Dillard Dr, Ste 217, Cary, NC 27511. TEL 919-882-5000, FAX 919-854-9952, publisher@express.howstuffworks.com, http://express.howstuffworks.com. Ed. Mark Mine.

HOY DIA. see *EDUCATION—Teaching Methods And Curriculum*

HUAXI; qingnian wenxue yuekan. see *LITERATURE*

028.5 070.5083 USA
HULLABALLOO; the children's magazine that's going places. Text in English. 2002. 6/yr. USD 23 domestic; USD 33 foreign (effective 2003).
Published by: Hullaballoo, Inc., P O Box 25068, Los Angeles, CA 90025. editor@hullabaloomagazine.com, http://www.hullabaloomagazine.com. Ed. Deirdre Cutter.

028.5 FRA ISSN 0337-2154
LA HULOTTE. Text in French. 1972. 2/yr. **Description:** For children ages 10 and up who want to explore ecological problems.
Published by: Conservatoire du Patrimoine Naturel de Champagne, Boult-aux-Bois, Buzancy, 08240, France. TEL 33-3-24300130. Ed. Pierre Deom. Pub. Christian Deom. Circ: 150,000.

028.5 USA ISSN 0273-7590
AP201
HUMPTY DUMPTY'S MAGAZINE. Text in English. 1952. bi-m. USD 15.95 domestic; USD 19.95 foreign (effective 2005). adv. bk.rev.; software rev. illus. index. reprint service avail. from PQC. **Document type:** *Magazine, Consumer.* **Description:** Contains simple puzzles, crafts, and stories to teach children ages 4 to 6 good health habits.
Formerly (until 1979): Humpty Dumpty's Magazine for Little Children (0018-7666)
Related titles: Microfilm ed.: (from PQC); Online - full text ed.: (from bigchalk, EBSCO Publishing, Gale Group, Northern Light Technology, Inc., ProQuest Information & Learning).
Indexed: ICM, MagInd.
Published by: (Benjamin Franklin Literary and Medical Society, Inc.), Children's Better Health Institute, 1100 Waterway Blvd, PO Box 567, Indianapolis, IN 46206. TEL 317-634-1100, FAX 317-684-8094, g.joray@cbhi.org, http://www.humptydumptymag.org, http://www.cbhi.org. Ed. Phyllis Lybarger. Pub. Greg Joray. R&P Daniel Lee. Adv. contacts Barny Barnhart, Greg Joray. Circ: 200,000. **Subscr. to:** PO Box 420235, Palm Coast, FL 32142. TEL 800-829-5579.

HYOGO KENRITSU KODOMO BYOIN NENPO/HYOGO PREFECTURAL KOBE CHILDREN'S HOSPITAL. ANNUAL REPORT. see *HEALTH FACILITIES AND ADMINISTRATION*

I B B Y CONGRESS PROCEEDINGS. see *PUBLISHING AND BOOK TRADE*

028.5 BEL ISSN 1370-6500
I D (NEDERLANDSE EDITION). (Informatie Documentatie) Text in Dutch. 1995. 14/yr. illus. **Document type:** *Magazine.* **Description:** Offers young readers ages 12 through 14 a variety of articles, stories, and activities.
Related titles: French ed.: I D. ISSN 1370-6519. 1995.
—Infotrieve.
Published by: Editions Averbode SA, Abdijstraat 1, BP 54, Averbode, 3271, Belgium. TEL 32-13-780111, FAX 32-13-776837, http://www.averbode.be/fr/revues/detail.php?ID=32&menu=I&selectedsubnavigation=secundaironderwijs.

I J B - REPORT. see *LITERATURE*

028.5 420 375.4 FRA ISSN 1765-4750
I LOVE ENGLISH. Text in English. 1987. m. (10/yr.). EUR 49.80 domestic; EUR 74.80 foreign (effective 2005). **Document type:** *Magazine, Consumer.* **Description:** Helps children 10 to 15 years old to learn English.
Former titles (until 2000): The World in English (1292-2749); (until 1999): I Love English (0769-1378)
Related titles: CD-ROM ed.; Supplement(s): I Love English Junior.
Published by: Bayard Presse, 3 Rue Bayard, Paris, 75393 Cedex 08, France. TEL 33-1-44356060, FAX 33-1-44356161, redactions@bayard-presse.com, http://www.bayardpresse.com. Ed. Barbara Oudiz. Circ: 47,200.

028.5 USA
IAMERICANSPIRIT; nonpartisan news reports with no political, religious, or ideological affiliation of any kind. Text in English. 1984. irreg. (2-3/yr). free in US & Canada (effective 2005). adv. **Document type:** *Magazine, Consumer.* **Description:** Provides news and accompanying homework assignments for high-school students.
Formerly (until 2002): Fast Times
Published by: Executive Carity, 521 Avenida Verde, San Marcos, CA 92069-1379. TEL 760-598-8739, FAX 760-591-9105, info@iAmericanSpirit.com, http://www.iAmericanSpirit.com, http://www.fast-times.com. Pub. Steve Posner. adv.: B&W page USD 23,500, color page USD 27,500; trim 10.88 x 8.5. Circ: 240,000.

028.5 GBR ISSN 1359-7396
IAW. Text in English. 1965. m. (Sep.-Jun.). GBP 10 (effective 2000). illus. **Document type:** *Academic/Scholarly.* **Description:** For children from age 11 up to the GCSE examination stage. Follows key stages 3 and 4 of the national curriculum.
Formerly (until 1995): Mynd (0026-4431)
Published by: Urdd Gobaith Cymru, Adran Cylchgronau, Swyddfa'r Urdd, Ffordd Llanbadarn, Aberystwyth, Ceredigion, Wales SY23 1EY, United Kingdom. TEL 44-1970-613118, FAX 44-1970-626120, iaw@urdd.org, Cylchgronau@urdd.org, http://www.urdd.org/Cylchgronau/Darllenwyr/Iaw!/Tudalen%20Darllenwyrlaw!.html. Ed. Sian Eleri Davies. Circ: 3,000.

028.5 CHL
ICARITO. Text in Spanish. irreg.
Published by: Consorcio Periodistico de Chile S.A., Vicuna Mackenna 1870, Santiago, Chile. TEL 56-2-550-7000, FAX 56-2-550-7999, icarito@copesa.cl, http://www.icarito.cl, http://www.copesa.cl.

IDEENREICH. see *RELIGIONS AND THEOLOGY—Roman Catholic*

808 891 SCG ISSN 0350-6339
IDEJE; jugoslovenski studentski casopis. Text in Serbo-Croatian. 1970. bi-m. YUN 50, USD 10.
Indexed: RASB.
Published by: Mladost, Marsala Tita 2, Belgrade. Ed. Milutin Stanisavac.

IGNITE. see *MUSIC*

IGRA I DETI; zhurnal dlya roditelei i pedagogov. see *CHILDREN AND YOUTH—About*

ILLINOIS HISTORY (ONLINE EDITION); a magazine for young people. see *HISTORY—History Of North And South America*

028.5 DEU
IM WEBLAND. Text in German. m. **Document type:** *Consumer.* **Description:** Teaches children ages 3-6 how to use e-mail and the Internet in fun and constructive ways.
Media: Online - full text.
Published by: Kidoclic - Hortus Soft, Walter-Kolb-Str 9-11, Frankfurt Am Main, 60594, Germany. TEL 49-1805-705605, info@kidoclic.de, http://www.imwebland.de/index.htm.

028.5 FRA
IMAGES DOC. Text in French. 1989. m. EUR 59.80 domestic; EUR 79.80 foreign (effective 2005). **Document type:** *Magazine, Consumer.* **Description:** Stimulates the desire for knowledge in 8 to 12 year olds through the use of photos.
Published by: Bayard Presse, 3 Rue Bayard, Paris, 75393 Cedex 08, France. TEL 33-1-44356060, FAX 33-1-44356161, redactions@bayard-presse.com, http://www.bayardpresse.com. Ed. Francoise Recamier. Circ: 91,868.

028.5 USA ISSN 1533-3191
"IN" POWER. Text in English. 1999. irreg. USD 4.99 newsstand/cover. **Document type:** *Consumer.* **Description:** Covers what is hot, the new products, and the popular toys, video games and collectables.
Published by: Wizard Entertainment, 151 Wells Ave, Congers, NY 10920. TEL 914-268-3594, FAX 914-268-0053.

028.5 800 USA
IN SEARCH OF A SONG. Text in English. 1981. s-a. illus. back issues avail. **Description:** Comprises a series of miniature chapbooks including fiction, poetry, and drawings by New York City public school children and at risk young adults.
Published by: Ten Penny Players, Inc., 393 St Pauls Ave, Staten Island, NY 10304-2127. TEL 718-442-7429, FAX 718-442-4978, water@tenpennyplayers.org, http://tenpennyplayers.org/x3c.html. Ed. Richard Spiegel. Pub., R&P Barbara Fisher. Circ: 200.

INDIAN COUNCIL FOR CHILD WELFARE. ANNUAL REPORT. see *SOCIAL SERVICES AND WELFARE*

INFOPOST. see *MILITARY*

028.5 SVN ISSN 1318-3877
INFORMACIJE Z P M S. (Zveze prijateljev Mladine Slovenije) Text in Slovenian. 1959. bi-m.
Formerly (until 1990): Glasilo D P M (1318-3885)
Published by: Zveza Prijateljev Mladine Slovenije, Miklosiceva 16-II, Ljubljana, 61000, Slovenia. TEL 061-316 760. Circ: 2,600.

028.5 AUT
INITIATIVE. Text in German. 1966. irreg. (4-6/yr.). membership. adv. illus.
Formerly (until 1972): Magazin Vier und Zwanzig (0024-9785)
Indexed: PAIS.
Published by: (Jugendklub Innere Stadt), Junge Generation in der Volkspartei, Wollzeile 24, Vienna, W 1010, Austria. Ed. Guenter Zillich. Circ: 1,000.

028.5 ESP ISSN 1130-4618
INJUVE. Text in Spanish. 1990. bi-m. free to institutions. bk.rev.; film rev. **Document type:** *Government.* **Description:** Provides information to young people to promote communication between them and participation in society.
Published by: Instituto de la Juventud, Jose Ortega y Gasset, 71, Madrid, 28006, Spain. TEL 347-76-90, FAX 402-21-94. Circ: 15,000.

INNERCITY MAGAZINE. see *MUSIC*

028.5 IND ISSN 0046-9599
INQUISITOR; a student's magazine. Text in English. 1971. m. INR 5. adv. bk.rev.; film rev. reprint service avail. from PQC.
Related titles: Microfilm ed.: (from PQC).
Published by: Sudhir Sharma, Ed. & Pub., 2165 Sector 21-C, Chandigarh, Haryana, India.

028.5 USA ISSN 1541-5872
▼ **THE INSIDE SCOOP.** Text in English. 2003. bi-m. USD 6 newsstand/cover (effective 2003).
Published by: LeapFrog Enterprises, Inc., 6401 Hollis St, Ste 150, Emeryville, CA 94608-1071. TEL 510-420-5000, FAX 510-420-5001, http://www.leapfrog.com.

INSIGHT (HAGERSTOWN); a magazine of Christian understanding for young Adventists. see *RELIGIONS AND THEOLOGY—Protestant*

C

INSIGHTS (FAIRFAX); N R A news for young shooters. see *SPORTS AND GAMES*

INTEEN. see *RELIGIONS AND THEOLOGY—Protestant*

INTERNATIONAL DIRECTORY OF SPORTING GOODS AND TOYS IMPORTERS. see *BUSINESS AND ECONOMICS—Trade And Industrial Directories*

641 GBR
INTERPLAY. Text in English. s-a. GBP 24 (effective 2004).
Description: Designed for anyone concerned with the development of young children, from policy-makers to student nursery nurses and parents.
Published by: Questions Publishing Company Ltd., 1st Fl, Leonard House, 321 Bradford St, Digbeth, Birmingham, Warks B1 3ET, United Kingdom. TEL 44-121-6667878, FAX 44-121-6667879, ssmith@questpub.co.uk, http://www.education-quest.com/. Ed. Sue Smith.

INTO VIEW. see *RELIGIONS AND THEOLOGY—Protestant*

INTRODUCING... see *RELIGIONS AND THEOLOGY—Roman Catholic*

268 ISR ISSN 0334-7397
INYAN HADASH. Text in Hebrew. 1984. w. USD 200 (effective 2000). **Description:** For children ages 8-12.
Published by: Etzb'oni Publishing House, P O Box 28110, Tel Aviv, 61280, Israel. FAX 972-3-5373906. Ed. Talila Rosenboim. Circ: 35,000.

059.927 UAE
IQRA'/READ. Text in Arabic. 1984. a. per issue exchange basis.
Description: Student publication covering literary and cultural activities in the school community.
Published by: Mintaqat Dubai al-Ta'limiyyah/Dubai Educational Region, PO Box 8353, Dubai, United Arab Emirates. TEL 691405. Ed. Hamad Ahmed Al Shaibani. Circ: 3,000.

305.23 DEU
▼ **IRGENDWIE ANDERS.** Text in German. 2005. 3/yr. EUR 2 newsstand/cover (effective 2005). adv. **Document type:** *Magazine, Consumer.*
Published by: Panini Verlags GmbH, Ravensstr 48, Nettetal, 41334, Germany. TEL 49-2157-81750, FAX 49-2157-81484528, info@panini-dino.de, http://www.panini-media.de. adv.: page EUR 2,500; trim 210 x 280. Circ: 80,000 (controlled).

028.5 808 RUS ISSN 0130-6634
PN6071.S33
ISKATEL'. Text in Russian. 1961. bi-m. USD 86 in United States. adv.
—East View.
Published by: Izdatel'stvo Iskatel', Novodmitrovskaya ul 5-a, kom 1606, Moscow, 125015, Russian Federation. TEL 7-095-2858058, FAX 7-095-2850930. Ed. A A Poleshchuk. **Dist. by:** M K - Periodica, ul Gilyarovskogo 39, Moscow 129110, Russian Federation. TEL 7-095-2845008, FAX 7-095-2813798, info@periodicals.ru, http://www.mkniga.ru; **US dist. addr.:** East View Information Services, 3020 Harbor Ln. N., Minneapolis, MN 55447. TEL 612-550-0961.

ISLAND PARENT MAGAZINE. see *CONSUMER EDUCATION AND PROTECTION*

266.2 ITA ISSN 0021-2806
ITALIA MISSIONARIA. Cover title: I M. Text in Italian. 1919. m. bk.rev. bibl.; illus. **Description:** Discusses mission work in third world countries.
Published by: Pontificio Istituto Missioni Estere, Via F D Guerrazzi, Rome, 00152, Italy. TEL 39-06-5839151, FAX 39-06-5894228, http://www.pime.org/. Ed. Marco Pagani. Circ: 13,000.

028.5 GBR ISSN 1476-5225
IT'S HOT!. Text in English. 1993. m. GBP 18.36 domestic; GBP 35.28 in Europe; GBP 47.28 elsewhere; GBP 1.80 newsstand/cover (effective 2003). adv. **Document type:** *Magazine, Consumer.* **Description:** Has the latest news and gossip from the world of TV, film and pop music for girls 9-13 years of age.
Formerly (until 2002): Live and Kicking (1351-3397)
Published by: B B C Worldwide Ltd., 80 Wood Ln, London, W12 0TT, United Kingdom. TEL 44-20-84331070, FAX 44-20-84332231, itshot@bbc.co.uk, bbcworldwide@bbc.co.uk, http://www.bbcmagazines.com/hot/index.html. **Dist. by:** Frontline, Park House, 117 Park Rd, Peterborough, Cambs PE1 2TS, United Kingdom. TEL 44-1733-555161, FAX 44-1733-562788.

IT'S OUR WORLD; mission news from the Holy Childhood Association. see *RELIGIONS AND THEOLOGY—Roman Catholic*

IUVENIS. see *LINGUISTICS*

028.5 USA ISSN 1522-1989
J-14; just for teens!. Text in English. 10/yr. USD 16.95 (effective 2004). adv. **Document type:** *Magazine, Consumer.*
Description: Presents the inside scoop on celebrities and entertainment for teens.
Published by: Bauer Publishing Company, L.P., 270 Sylvan Ave, Englewood Cliffs, NJ 07632. TEL 201-569-6699, FAX 201-569-5303, j14mag@aol.com, http://www.j-14.com. **Subscr. to:** PO Box 1990, Marion, OH 43306-2090. TEL 800-215-7275.

028.5 GBR ISSN 1464-9985
J-17. Text in English. 1983. w. GBP 2 newsstand/cover (effective 2001). adv. **Document type:** *Magazine, Consumer.*
Description: Contains articles for girls ages 12-18.
Formerly (until 1997): Just Seventeen (0266-8173)
Related titles: Audio cassette/tape ed.; Braille ed.
—CCC.
Published by: Emap Elan Ltd. (Subsidiary of: Emap Consumer Media), Endeavour House, 189 Shaftesbury Ave, London, WC2H 8JG, United Kingdom. TEL 44-207-437-9011, FAX 44-207-208-3709, http://www.emap.com. Ed. Sarah Bailey. Pub. Louise Matthews. Adv. contact Sarah Williamson.
Subscr. to: Tower Publishing Services Ltd., Tower House, Sovereign Park, Market Harborough, Leics LE16 9EF, United Kingdom. TEL 44-1858-435339, FAX 44-1858-434958.

028.5 DEU
J P I - JUGEND PRESSE INFORMATIONEN. Text in German. 1978. 8/yr. free. adv. bk.rev. back issues avail. **Document type:** *Bulletin.* **Description:** Provides information and ideas concerning various current topics to editors of school magazines.
Published by: Communications Consulting Network GmbH, Kottenforststr 20, Meckenheim, 53340, Germany. TEL 49-2225-992160, FAX 49-2225-992190. Circ: 6,000.

028.5 USA ISSN 0021-3829
AP201
JACK AND JILL (INKPRINT EDITION). Text in English. 1938. bi-m. USD 15.95 domestic; USD 19.95 foreign (effective 2005). adv. bk.rev.; software rev. charts; illus.; maps. reprint service avail. from PQC. **Document type:** *Magazine, Consumer.* **Description:** Offers children ages 7-10 articles, stories, puzzles, and recipes promoting health and safety.
Related titles: Braille ed.; Microform ed.: (from PQC); Online - full text ed.: (from EBSCO Publishing, Gale Group, ProQuest Information & Learning).
Indexed: ICM, MagInd, RGYP.
Published by: (Benjamin Franklin Literary and Medical Society, Inc.), Children's Better Health Institute, 1100 Waterway Blvd, PO Box 567, Indianapolis, IN 46206. TEL 317-634-1100, FAX 317-684-8094, g.joray@cbhi.org, http://www.jackandjillmag.org, http://www.cbhi.org. Ed., R&P Daniel Lee. Pub. Greg Joray. adv.: page USD 5,000. Circ: 215,000. **Subscr. to:** PO Box 420235, Palm Coast, FL 32142. TEL 800-829-5579.

028.5 IND
JAHANAMAMU. Text in Oriya. 1972. m. INR 4 newsstand/cover.
Published by: Chandamama Publications, 188 N.S.K. Salai, Chandamama Bldgs., Vadapalani, Chennai, Tamil Nadu 600 026, India. Ed. B Nagi Reddi. adv.: B&W page INR 4,250, color page INR 8,500; trim 160 x 198.

028.5 IND
JAHNAMAMU (ORIYA). Text in Oriya. 1972. m.
Address: 188 N S K Salai, Chandamama Bldgs., Vadapalani, Chennai, Tamil Nadu 600 026, India. Ed. Nagi Reddi. Circ: 110,000.

028.5 CAN ISSN 0835-7714
J'AIME LIRE. Text in French. 1987. 10/yr. CND 32.95, USD 39.95 (effective 2004). adv. bk.rev. back issues avail. **Document type:** *Magazine, Consumer.* **Description:** Contains a complete short-story, games around a theme and a comic strip. Intended for early readers.
Published by: Bayard Canada, The Owl Group, 49 Front St E, 2nd Fl, Toronto, ON M5E 1B3, Canada. TEL 416-340-2700, 800-551-6957, FAX 416-340-9769, bayard@owl.on.ca. adv.: color page CND 1,500; trim 7.5 x 6.13. Circ: 23,970 (paid).

028.5 FRA ISSN 0399-4600
J'AIME LIRE. Text in French. 1977. m. EUR 54.80 domestic; EUR 69.80 in Europe; EUR 74.80 elsewhere (effective 2005).
Document type: *Magazine, Consumer.* **Description:** Promotes the love of reading in children 7-years-old and older.
Published by: Bayard Presse, 3 Rue Bayard, Paris, 75393 Cedex 08, France. TEL 33-1-44356060, FAX 33-1-44356161, redactions@bayard-presse.com, http://www.bayardpresse.com. Eds. Beatrice Valentin, Martin Berthommier. Circ: 199,664.

059.915 IRN
JAVANAN EMROOZ. Text in Persian, Modern. 1966. w. GBP 148 in Iran; GBP 148 in Pakistan; GBP 192 in Europe; GBP 192 in Japan; GBP 256 in North America; GBP 256 in Australia (effective 1999). illus. **Document type:** *Consumer.*
Formerly (until 1983): Javanan
Published by: Ettela'at Publications, Mirdamad Blvd., Naft-e Jonubi St., Ettala'at Bldg., Tehran, 1549951199, Iran. TEL 98-21-323401, FAX 98-21-3111223. Ed. Mohammad Javad Rafi.

028.5 373 GBR
JAZZYBOOKS - SECONDARY SCHOOLS. Text in English. 1997. 3/yr. free. adv. **Document type:** *Magazine, Consumer.*
Description: Contains exercises and other materials for students.
Published by: Jazzy Media, 112-114 Great Portland St, London, W1N 5PF, United Kingdom. TEL 44-207-323-3223, FAX 44-207-323-3356, trickit@jazzybooks.co.uk, http://www.jazzybooks.co.uk. adv.: page GBP 37,000; trim 173 x 229. Circ: 2,700,000 (controlled).

028.5 FRA ISSN 0756-564X
JE BOUQUINE. Text in French. 1984. m. EUR 64.80 domestic; EUR 79.80 in the European Union; EUR 84.80 elsewhere (effective 2005). **Document type:** *Magazine, Consumer.*
Description: Inspires the desire to read in children 10 and older.
Published by: Bayard Presse, 3 Rue Bayard, Paris, 75393 Cedex 08, France. TEL 33-1-44356060, FAX 33-1-44356161, redactions@bayard-presse.com, http://www.bayardpresse.com. Ed. Marie Lallouet. Circ: 59,949.

028.5 FRA ISSN 0995-5038
JE LIS DEJA. Text in French. 1989. m. (11/yr.). FRF 296 domestic; FRF 398.60 foreign (effective 2000). illus.
Description: Helps children to read on their own, with emphasis on vocabulary retention and comprehension of difficult vocabulary through illustrations.
Published by: Fleurus Presse, 129 bd. Malesherbes, Paris, 75017, France. TEL 33-1-64812009, 33-1-56793636. Ed. Beatrice Guthart.

028.5 FRA ISSN 1168-7509
JE LIS DES HISTOIRES VRAIES. Text in French. 1993. m. FRF 296 (effective 2000). bibl.
Published by: Fleurus Presse, 129 bd. Malesherbes, Paris, 75017, France. TEL 33-1-61812009, FAX 33-1-40026363. Circ: 33,759. **Subscr. to:** Fleurus Presse Abonnements, BP 72, Perthes Cedex 77932, France. TEL 33-1-64812009, FAX 33-1-56793636.

658.048 FRA ISSN 0750-3806
JEANNETTE. Text in French. 1946. 5/yr. **Description:** Of interest to girls 8-11.
Published by: Guides de France, 65 rue de la Glaciere, Paris, 75013, France. TEL 33-1-47078559, FAX 33-1-43377769. Ed. Marie Therese Chotard.

798.2 DEU
JESSY. Text in German. m. EUR 1.99 newsstand/cover (effective 2005). adv. **Document type:** *Magazine, Consumer.*
Description: Contains comics, stories and features about horses and riding for girls between the ages of 9 and 13.
Published by: Panini Verlags GmbH, Ravensstr 48, Nettetal, 41334, Germany. TEL 49-2157-81750, FAX 49-2157-81484528, info@panini-dino.de, http://www.panini-media.de. adv.: page EUR 3,500; trim 210 x 280. Circ: 86,725 (paid).

268 ESP
JESUS MAESTRO. Text in Spanish. 1872. m. USD 17. bk.rev. cum.index every 5 yrs.
Published by: Compania de Santa Teresa de Jesus, Ganduxer, 85, Barcelona, 08021, Spain. Ed. Maria Victoria Molins. Circ: 14,000.

052 GBR
▼ **THE JETIX MAGAZINE.** Text in English. 2004 (Sep.). m. GBP 2.99 newsstand/cover (effective 2004). adv. **Document type:** *Magazine, Consumer.* **Description:** Contains posters, puzzles, competitions, comic strips and fun features based on the Jetix TV channel shows, including Power Rangers, Teenage Mutant Ninja Turtles, Sonic X and Spider-Man, and Martin Mystery.
Published by: Future Publishing Ltd., Beauford Court, 30 Monmouth St, Bath, Avon BA1 2BW, United Kingdom. TEL 44-1225-442244, FAX 44-1225-446019, customerservice@futurenet.co.uk, http://www.thefuturenetwork.plc.uk. Ed. Cavan Scott.

028.5 AUS
JETSETTER (JUNIOR). Text in English. bi-m. **Document type:** *Magazine, Consumer.*
Published by: Jetsetters of Australia Pty Ltd., 465 Balcombe Rd, Beaumaris, VIC 3193, Australia.

025.8 FRA ISSN 0984-760X
JEUNE ET JOLIE. Text in French. 1987. m. **Document type:** *Consumer.*
Published by: Hachette Filipacchi Medias S.A. (Subsidiary of: Lagardere Media), 149 rue Anatole France, Levallois-Perret, Cedex 92300, France. TEL 33-1-41346155, FAX 33-1-41347959. **Subscr. in N. America to:** Express Magazine, 4011 Blvd Robert, Montreal, PQ H1Z 4H6, Canada. expsmag@expressmag.com.

JEUNES; le mensuel pour ton francais. see *LINGUISTICS*

LES JEUNES. see *SPORTS AND GAMES*

028.5 FRA ISSN 0021-6143
JEUNES ANNEES. Text in French. 1952. q. illus.

C

Related titles: Special ed(s).: Jeunes Annees (Age 3-8 Edition). **Published by:** Federation des Francs et Franches Camarades, 10-14 rue Tolain, Paris, 75020, France. TEL 33-1-44642150, FAX 33-1-44642155. Ed. Catherine Forne. Pub. Francis Vernhes. Circ: 20,000.

JEUNES EN MOUVEMENT. see *RELIGIONS AND THEOLOGY—Roman Catholic*

028.5 338.91 323   FRA   ISSN 0396-7360
JEUNESSE DU QUART MONDE/FOURTH WORLD YOUTH JOURNAL. Text in French. 1974. bi-m. back issues avail. **Document type:** *Newspaper.* **Description:** Provides information on the activities of the young people taking part in the organisation in order to overcome extreme poverty.
Published by: Alternatives 114 - Jeunesse Quart Monde, 29 rue du Stade, Champeaux, 77720, France. TEL 33-1-60669128, FAX 33-1-60699717, youth-centre@atd-fourthworld.org, centre-jeuness@atd-quartmonda.org, http://www.fwym.cie.fr. Circ: 8,000.

790   FIN   ISSN 1455-6189
JIIPEE; paper for boys and girls. Text in Finnish. 1932. 10/yr. (10/yr.). EUR 37 (effective 2005). adv. bk.rev. **Document type:** *Magazine, Consumer.*
Former titles (until 1997): J P (0781-7177); (until 1984): J P Joka Poika (0355-4201); (until 1972): Joka Poika (0047-2050); Incorporates (1900-1987): Totto (1235-0745); Which incorporated (1893-1982): Koitto (0355-659X); Which was formerly (until 1978): Uusi Totto (0355-7138); (until 1976): Totto (1962) (1235-0737); (until 1962): Tuike; (until 1954): Lasten Lahetyslehti
Published by: Suomen Poikien ja Tyttoejen Keskus-PTK ry/Christian Association for Boys and Girls of Finland, Partaharjuntie 361, Partaharju, 76280, Finland. TEL 358-15-7820200, FAX 358-15-7820201, jiipee@ptk.fi, ptk@ptk.fi, http://www.ptk.fi. Ed. Timo Sainio. adv.: B&W page EUR 908, color page EUR 1,555. Circ: 11,000.

028.5   BEL   ISSN 1370-2114
JOEPIE T V - PLUS. Text in Dutch. 1992 (vol.20). w. adv. illus. **Document type:** *Consumer.* **Description:** Covers music, popular culture and other items of interest to young people.
Formerly (until 1994): Joepie (1370-2106)
Published by: N.V. Sparta, Brandekensweg 2, Schelle, 2627, Belgium. TEL 32-3-8446261, FAX 32-3-8446152. Eds. Peter Van Dyck, Serge Vanhellemont.

051   USA   ISSN 1529-6180
JOEY. Text in English. 2000. q. USD 15.95; USD 4.95 newsstand/cover (effective 2000). adv. **Document type:** *Magazine, Consumer.* **Description:** Covers fashion and lifestyle items and issues for gay and bisexual teenage guys.
Related titles: ♦ Online - full content ed.: Joey Online.
Published by: Joey Magazine, LLC, 11901 Santa Monica Blvd, Ste 598, Los Angeles, CA 90025. TEL 888-550-5639, FAX 310-388-1139, jerry@joeymag.com, http://www.joeymag.com. Ed., Pub., R&P, Adv. contact Jerry C Dunn. color page USD 2,000. Circ: 20,000 (paid).

051   USA
JOEY ONLINE. Text in English. 2000. 4/yr. adv. **Document type:** *Consumer.*
Media: Online - full content. **Related titles:** ♦ Print ed.: Joey. ISSN 1529-6180.
Published by: Joey Magazine, LLC, 11901 Santa Monica Blvd, Ste 598, Los Angeles, CA 90025. TEL 888-550-5639, FAX 310-388-1139, feedback@joeymag.com, http://www.joeymag.com. Ed., Pub., R&P, Adv. contact Jerry C Dunn.

613   DEU
JOJO. Text in German. bi-m. free. adv. **Document type:** *Magazine, Consumer.*
Published by: (AOK-Bundesverband), W D V Gesellschaft fuer Medien & Kommunikation mbH & Co. oHG, Siemensstr 6, Bad Homburg, 61352, Germany. TEL 49-6172-6700, FAX 49-6172-670144, info@wdv.de, http://www.jolinchen.de/infos/index.html, http://www.wdv.de. adv.: page EUR 7,200; trim 134 x 178. Circ: 600,000 (controlled).

JONGE KERK. see *RELIGIONS AND THEOLOGY*

028.5   FRA   ISSN 0767-8088
JOURNAL DE MICKEY. Text in French. 1934. w. **Document type:** *Magazine, Consumer.* **Description:** Features comics of various Disney characters as well as spotlights on celebrities, and news.
Published by: Disney Hachette Presse, 10 rue Thierry le Luron, Levallois Perret, Cedex 92592, France. TEL 33-1-41348500, FAX 33-1-41348989, nwaintraub@hfp.fr. Ed. Jacques Lelievre. Circ: 260,000 (paid).

028.5   FRA   ISSN 0986-9050
LE JOURNAL DES ENFANTS. Text in French. 1984. w. **Description:** Covers current events around the world for children ages 8 to 13.
Published by: Societe Alsacienne de Publications, 25 Av du President Kennedy, BP 1160, Mulhouse, Cedex 68053, France. TEL 33-3-89327000. Ed. Beatrice D'Irube. Pub. Remy Pflimlin. Circ: 150,000. **Subscr. to:** BP 1489, Mulhouse Cedex 68072, France.

▼ THE JOURNAL OF CHILDREN'S LITERATURE STUDIES. see *LITERATURE*

JOVENES AGRICULTORES. see *AGRICULTURE*

028.5   MEX
JOVENES SONORENSES. Text in Spanish. 1994. m.
Published by: E R A Comunicacion, S.A. de C.V., Heriberto Aja 155, Hermosillo, SONORA, Mexico. Ed. Ramon Martinez Esquer. Circ: 1,000.

028.5   GBR   ISSN 0960-1813
Comic Book 01025
JUDGE DREDD - THE MEGAZINE. Text in English. 1990. m. GBP 30 domestic; GBP 39 in Europe; GBP 46 elsewhere; GBP 2.50 newsstand/cover. back issues avail. **Document type:** *Consumer.*
Published by: Egmont Fleetway Ltd., Egmont House, Pl, Flat 25, 31 Tavistock Rd, London, W11 1AS, United Kingdom. TEL 44-20-7344-6400, FAX 44-20-7388-4020. **Subscr. to:** PO Box 406, Woking, Surrey GU21 1LB, United Kingdom. **Dist. by:** Seymour Distribution Ltd, 86 Newman St, London W1T 3EX, United Kingdom. FAX 44-207-396-8002, enquiries@seymour.co.uk.

JUGEND FUER CHRISTUS MAGAZIN. see *RELIGIONS AND THEOLOGY*

028.5   AUT
JUGEND IN WIEN. Text in German. 1983. 10/yr. free. adv. **Document type:** *Newsletter.* **Description:** Listing of leisure activities for young people.
Published by: Verein Wiener Jugendkreis, Friedrich Schmidt Platz 5, Vienna, W 1082, Austria. FAX 0222-487000. Ed. Ali Foeger.

028.5 943   DEU
JUGENDBUECHER ZUM THEMA; Drittes Reich. Text in German. 1986. s-a. **Document type:** *Bibliography.*
Published by: Stiftung Lesen, Fischtorplatz 23, Mainz, 55116, Germany. TEL 06131-288900, FAX 06131-230333.

028.5   DEU
JUGENDROTKREUZ. Text in German. 1986. m. EUR 18.30 (effective 2005). **Document type:** *Magazine, Trade.* **Description:** Health information from the Red Cross, geared toward young children.
Formerly: Bernie
Published by: Deutsches Rotes Kreuz, Jugendrotkreuz, Carstennstr 58, Berlin, 12205, Germany. TEL 49-30-85404390, FAX 49-30-85404484, jrk@drk.de, http://www.drk.de/jrk/magazin/index.html.

JUICED. see *LITERARY AND POLITICAL REVIEWS*

249   DNK   ISSN 0905-9466
JUL I FAMILIEN. Text in Danish. 1982. a. illus. **Description:** Contains Christmas readings and Christmas time activities for families.
Former titles (until 1990): Alle Boerns Jul (0109-050X); Boernebladets Jul (0105-709X)
Published by: (Kirkelig Forening for den Indre Mission), Lohses Forlag, Korskaervej 25, Fredericia, 7000, Denmark. FAX 0045-75926146.

028.5   SWE
JULIA; ny tidning foer tjejeri. Text in Swedish. 10/yr. SEK 270 (effective 2001). adv. **Document type:** *Magazine, Consumer.*
Published by: Egmont Seriefoerlaget AB, Oestra Foerstadsgatan 34, Malmo, 20508, Sweden. TEL 46-40-6939400, FAX 46-40-6939476, julia@egmont.se, http://www.julia.egmont.se, http://www.egmont.se. Ed., Pub. Cecilia Sandbring. Adv. contact Denny Grimberg. page SEK 17,500; trim 210 x 297.

028.5   FRA
JULIE; vive les filles de 8 a 12 ans. Text in French. 1998. m. EUR 49 (effective 2005). illus. **Document type:** *Consumer.* **Description:** Covers current events, science, culture, fixing things around the house, and cooking for 8 to 12 year-old girls.
Published by: Milan Presse, 300 rue Leon Joulin, Toulouse, Cedex 1 31101, France. TEL 33-5-61766464, FAX 33-5-61766400, webmaster@milanpresse.com, http://www.milanpresse.com. Pub. Patrice Amen.

JULIET. see *LITERATURE—Adventure And Romance*

JUNGE GEMEINDE; das Magazin fuer evangelische Kinder- und Jugendarbeit. see *RELIGIONS AND THEOLOGY—Protestant*

JUNGE SAMMLER; Zeitschrift fuer junge Briefmarkenfreunde. see *PHILATELY*

280.4   DEU
JUNGSCHAR; Zeitschrift fuer Maedchen und Jungen. Text in German. m. EUR 13.50; EUR 0.65 newsstand/cover (effective 2003). **Document type:** *Magazine, Consumer.*

Published by: C V J M Gesamtverband in Deutschland e.V., C V J M- Westbund, Bundeshoehe 6, Wuppertal, 42285, Germany. TEL 49-202-57420, FAX 49-202-574242, mail@ju4you.de, info@cvjm-westbund.de, http://ju4you.de, http://www.cvjm-westbund.de.

JUNGSCHARHELFER; Mitarbeiterhilfe fuer Jungen- und Maedchenarbeit. see *RELIGIONS AND THEOLOGY*

028.5   CHE   ISSN 0022-6475
JUNIOR. Text in German. 1950. m. free newsstand/cover (effective 2005). adv. illus. **Document type:** *Magazine, Consumer.*
Published by: Hug-Verlag AG, Hohenrainweg 1, Kilchberg - Zurich, 8802, Switzerland. TEL 41-44-7154928, FAX 41-44-7154192, info@junior.ch, http://www.hallojunior.ch. Pub. Piero Hug. adv.: color page EUR 15,100; trim 114 x 155. Circ: 1,163,733.

028.5   CAN
JUNIOR. Text in French. 1991. q. CND 38.17 (effective 1998). adv. **Document type:** *Magazine, Consumer.*
Published by: Editions Multi Concept Inc., 1600 Henri Bourissa West Ste 425, Montreal, PQ H3M 3E2, Canada. TEL 514-331-0661. Ed., Pub. Ronald Lapierre. adv.: B&W page CND 3,465, color page CND 3,850; trim 10.88 x 8.13. Circ: 48,500.

JUNIOR BASEBALL; America's youth baseball magazine. see *SPORTS AND GAMES—Ball Games*

JUNIOR CLUBHOUSE. see *RELIGIONS AND THEOLOGY—Protestant*

028.5   GBR   ISSN 0954-9501
JUNIOR HOLIDAY FUN; puzzles for children of all ages. Text in English. irreg. GBP 1.70 newsstand/cover. illus. **Document type:** *Consumer.* **Description:** Contains puzzles and assorted activities for children of all ages.
Published by: P W A Services, City Gate House, 399-425 Eastern Ave, Gants Hill, Ilford, Essex 1G2 6LR, United Kingdom. Ed. David Norris. **Dist. by:** M M C Ltd., Octagon House, White Hart Meadows, Ripley, Woking, Surrey GU23 6HR, United Kingdom. TEL 44-1483-211222, FAX 44-1483-224541.

028.5   JPN
JUNIOR LAND. Text in Japanese. 1978. m. JPY 3,000. **Description:** Aimed at pre-schoolers.
Published by: Sekai Bunka Publishing Inc., 2-29 Kudan-Kita 4-chome, Chiyoda-ku, Tokyo, 102-0073, Japan.

028.5   GBR   ISSN 0957-2007
JUNIOR MINI FUN. Text in English. 1989. bi-m. illus. **Document type:** *Consumer.* **Description:** Provides youngsters with enjoyable puzzles and activities.
Published by: P W A Services, City Gate House, 399-425 Eastern Ave, Gants Hill, Ilford, Essex 1G2 6LR, United Kingdom. Ed. David Norris. **Dist. by:** M M C Ltd., Octagon House, White Hart Meadows, Ripley, Woking, Surrey GU23 6HR, United Kingdom. TEL 44-1483-211222, FAX 44-1483-224541.

JUNIOR SCHOLASTIC. see *EDUCATION—Teaching Methods And Curriculum*

028.5 500   JPN
JUNIOR SCIENCE∗ /KODOMO NO KAGAKU. Text in Japanese. 1924. m. JPY 12,900.
Published by: Seibundo Shinkosha Inc., 3-3-11 Hongo, Bunkyoku, Tokyo, 164-0013, Japan. Ed. Yoshiaki Kato. Circ: 78,000.

028.5   USA
JUNIOR STATEMENT. Text in English. 1934. 4/yr. membership. bk.rev. illus. **Description:** Directed to high-school students interested in politics and government.
Former titles: Junior State Report; Junior Statesman (0022-6696); Youth News Report
Published by: Junior Statesmen of America, 400 S. El Camino Real., Ste. 300, San Mateo, CA 94402-1728. TEL 650-347-1600, FAX 650-347-7200. Ed., Pub. Richard Prosser. Circ: 20,000 (controlled).

JUPRECU. see *RELIGIONS AND THEOLOGY—Protestant*

JUREN/GIANT. see *LITERATURE*

028.5   DEU
JUROPE∗ ; Magazin fuer junge Leute. Text in German. 1963. q. **Document type:** *Magazine, Consumer.*
Published by: Verlag Ruprecht Kertscher, Am Schlag 1, Eichenau, 82223, Germany. Circ: 10,000.

796.334   DEU
▼ JUST KICK-IT!. Text in German. 2004. m. EUR 2.50 newsstand/cover (effective 2005). adv. **Document type:** *Magazine, Consumer.*

Published by: Panini Verlags GmbH, Ravensstr 48, Nettetal, 41334, Germany. TEL 49-2157-81750, FAX 49-2157-81484528, info@panini-dino.de, http://www.panini-media.de. adv.: page EUR 5,500. Circ: 150,000 (controlled).

028.5.235   USA   ISSN 1548-8241
▼ JUSTINE MAGAZINE. Text in English. 2004. q. USD 9.99 (effective 2004). Document type: Magazine, Consumer. Description: Contains features for teenage girls on fashion, beauty tips, advice on family dilemmas, boosting self-confidence, eating healthier, and more.
Published by: Pinpoint Publishing, 6263 Poplar Ave Ste 430, Memphis, TN 38119. TEL 901-684-4155, FAX 901-684-4156, http://justinemagazine.com. Pub. Jana Pettey.

028.5   USA
JVIBE. Text in English. USD 18 (effective 2005). Description: National website for Jewish teens age 13 and up.
Related titles: Online - full text ed.
Address: info@jvibe.com, http://www.jvibe.com. Ed. Michelle Cove. Pub. Yosef I Abramowitz.

053.1   DEU
K-CLUB. Text in German. m. EUR 25.50; EUR 2.50 newsstand/cover (effective 2005). adv. Document type: Magazine, Consumer.
Published by: Attic Futura Verlag GmbH, Landsberger Str 76, Munich, 80339, Germany. TEL 49-89-51446100, FAX 49-89-51449199, info@atticfutura.de, http://www.k-club-mag.de, http://www.atticfutura.de. adv.: color page EUR 5,900. Circ: 75,391 (paid and controlled).

K I D S REPORT. (Kids Identifying and Discovering Sites) see COMPUTERS—Internet

K I N D NEWS JR. EDITION. (Kids in Nature's Defense) see ANIMAL WELFARE

K I N D NEWS PRIMARY. (Kids in Nature's Defense) see ANIMAL WELFARE

K I N D NEWS SR. EDITION. (Kids in Nature's Defense) see ANIMAL WELFARE

052   AUS
K-ZONE; the magazine for kids. Text in English. m. AUD 39 domestic; AUD 47.40 in New Zealand; AUD 59.40 elsewhere; AUD 3.90 newsstand/cover (effective 2004). adv. Document type: Magazine, Consumer. Description: Contains the latest gossip on new music, movies, TV shows and games aimed at 6 to 13 year olds.
Published by: Pacific Publications, 35-51 Mitchell St, McMahons Point, NSW 2060, Australia. TEL 61-2-94643300, FAX 61-2-94643375, tracy.britton@pacpubs.com.au, http://www.kzone.com.au, http://www.pacificpubs.com.au. Adv. contact Tracy Britton. color page AUD 5,700; trim 145 x 210. Circ: 130,000 (paid).

028.5   POL   ISSN 1231-451X
KACZOR DONALD. Text in Polish. 1994. w. Document type: Magazine, Consumer.
Related titles: Supplement(s): Kaczor Donald. Wydanie Specjalne. ISSN 1640-3800. 2000.
Published by: Egmont Polska, ul Dzielna 60, Warszawa, 01029, Poland. TEL 48-22-8384100, FAX 48-22-8384200, poczta@egmont.pl, http://www.egmont.pl.

028.5   DEU
KAEPT'N BLAUBAER; das fantastische Luegenmagazin. Text in German. 2002 (Jul.). q. EUR 2.50 newsstand/cover (effective 2003). adv. Document type: Magazine, Consumer.
Published by: Panini Verlags GmbH, Ravensstr 48, Nettetal, 41334, Germany. TEL 49-711-947680, FAX 49-711-94768830, info@panini-dino.de, http://www.panini-media.de. adv.: page EUR 3,500. Circ: 130,000 (paid and controlled).

028.5   JPN
KAGAKU LAND. Text in Japanese. 1975. m. JPY 3,000. Description: Aimed at pre-schoolers.
Formerly: Science Land - Kagaku Land
Related titles: Microform ed.: (from PQC).
Published by: Sekai Bunka Publishing Inc., 2-29 Kudan-Kita 4-chome, Chiyoda-ku, Tokyo, 102-0073, Japan. Ed. Zenki Egawa.

028.5   IND
KALIKKUDUKKA. Text in Malayalam. 1994. w. INR 260; INR 5 newsstand/cover (effective 2000).
Published by: M.M. Publications Limited, Erayilkadavu, P O Box 226, Kottayam, Kerala 686 001, India. TEL 91-481-563721, FAX 91-481-564393, vanbal@satyam.net.in. Ed. Manarcad Mathew. Pub. K I George. R&P, Adv. contact V Sajeev George. B&W page INR 9,500, color page INR 19,000. Circ: 112,101.

028.5 741.5   SWE   ISSN 0345-6048
KALLE ANKA & CO. Variant title: Walt Disney's Kalle Anka & Co. Text in Swedish. 1948. w. SEK 845 domestic; SEK 995 elsewhere (effective 2005). adv. Document type: Magazine, Consumer.

Published by: Egmont Kaernan AB (Subsidiary of: Egmont AB), Oestra Foerstadsgatan 34, Malmoe, 20508, Sweden. TEL 46-40-6939400, FAX 46-40-6939498, http://www.disney.se/kalleanka/index2.html, http://www.egmont-karnan.se/. adv.: page SEK 53,900; trim 155 x 210. Circ: 175,000.

028.5   SVK
KAMARAT. Text in Slovak. 1950. 52/yr.
Published by: Vydavatel'stvo King, PO Box 73, Bratislava, 82014, Slovakia. Ed. Vladimir Topercer. Circ: 60,000.

770   SWE   ISSN 0022-8273
KAMRATPOSTEN. Abbreviated title: K P. Text in Swedish. 1892. 17/yr. SEK 385 (effective 2002). bk.rev.; film rev.; play rev. Description: Presents news and current affairs articles for children ages 8-15.
Formerly (until 1950): Folkskolans Barntidning
Published by: Bonnier Tidsskrifter AB, Sveavaegen 53, Stockholm, 10544, Sweden. TEL 46-8-7365200, FAX 46-8-7363842, pren.kp@bp.bonnier.se, http://www.kamratposten.nu. Ed. Anna Kaagstroem. Circ: 67,000.

KANSAS 4-H JOURNAL. see AGRICULTURE

028.5   CHN   ISSN 1006-1614
KANTU SHUOHUA/PICTURE TALK. Text in Chinese. m. CNY 250 foreign. illus. Description: For preschool children.
Published by: Shanghai Jiaoyu Chubanshe/Shanghai Educational Publishing House, 123 Yongfu Rd, Shanghai, 200031, China. TEL 4377165. Ed. Dai Keqi. Circ: 200,000. Dist. in US by: China Books & Periodicals Inc, 360 Swift Ave., Ste. 48, S San Fran, CA 94080-6220. TEL 415-282-2994.

028.5   RUS
KATAVASIYA; detskaya zagadochnaya gazeta. Text in Russian. 1997. m. USD 70 in North America (effective 2000).
Published by: Izdatel'skii Dom Russkaya Sem'ya, 1-ya Tverskaya-Yamskaya 2, str 1, Moscow, 103006, Russian Federation. TEL 7-095-2504797, FAX 7-095-2503000. Dist. by: East View Information Services, 3020 Harbor Ln. N., Minneapolis, MN 55447. TEL 763-550-0961, FAX 763-559-2931.

028.5   IRN   ISSN 1023-182X
KAYHAN-E BACHEHA/CHILDREN'S WORLD. Text in Persian. Modern. 1956. w. USD 164 in North America; USD 101 in Europe. adv. Document type: Consumer.
Published by: Kayhan Publications, Ferdowsi Ave., P O Box 11365-9631, Tehran, Iran. TEL 98-21-3110251, FAX 98-21-3111120, TELEX 212467. Ed. Amir Hossan Fardi. Circ: 150,000.

KICK!. see SPORTS AND GAMES—Ball Games

KID; your English monthly. see LINGUISTICS

305.23   USA
KID KLICKS. Text in English. 1999. d. Document type: Newsletter, Consumer. Description: Features reviews, articles for kids, and jokes.
Media: Online - full text.
Published by: Soda Mail, LLC, PO Box 750246, Petaluma, CA 94975. TEL 707-794-1289, leslie@sodamail.com, http://www.sodamail.com/site/kk.shtml. Ed. Leslie Griswold.

028.5   USA   ISSN 1535-6930
KID PLANET. Text in English. 2001. m. USD 50.58 (effective 2004). Document type: Consumer.
Published by: Celebrity Worldwide, 20 E Sunrise Hwy, Ste 202, Valley Stream, NY 11581. TEL 516-823-1212, kidplanetmag@yahoo.com.

028.5   USA   ISSN 1533-8827
KID POWER!. Text in English. 2001. m. adv.
Published by: Celebrity Worldwide, 20 E Sunrise Hwy, Ste 202, Valley Stream, NY 11581. TEL 516-823-1212, FAX 516-823-1561. Adv. contact Allison Cooper.

790.133   CAN
KID PULSE. Text in English. irreg. free. adv. back issues avail. Document type: Trade. Description: A source for keeping up-to-date on trends and fads in kids culture.
Media: Online - full text.
Published by: Kids Marketing, 580 Eyer Dr, Unit 24, Pickering, ON L1W 3B7, Canada. TEL 905-839-0020, judithj@kidsmarketing.com, http://kidsmarketing.com. Ed., Adv. contact Judith A Jewer.

028.5   USA   ISSN 1547-2019
KID ZONE. Text in English. 2000. bi-m. USD 19.95 domestic; USD 27.95 foreign (effective 2005). Document type: Magazine, Consumer.
Published by: Scott Publications, 30595 Eight Mile, Livonia, MI 48152-1798. TEL 248-477-6650, 800-458-8237, FAX 248-477-6795, contactus@scottpublications.com, http://www.scottpublications.com.

028.5 362.5   USA
KID'N AROUND. Text in English. 1996. m. Description: Educational publication for children ages 6 to 12.
Related titles: Online - full text ed.

Address: 17205 Vashon Hwy S W, Vashon, WA 98070. bluesnow@halcyon.com, http://www.kidnaround.com. Ed. Kaj Berry.

028.5 791.43 730.028   USA   ISSN 1549-814X
▼ KIDS' ACTING FOR BRAIN SURGEONS; the insiders guide for kids in the industry. Text in English. 2003 (Feb.). a. USD 27.50 newsstand/cover in United States to individuals (effective 2003 - 2004). Document type: Journal, Consumer.
Published by: Hollywood Operating System LLC, 400 S Beverly Dr, Ste 307, Beverly Hills, CA 90212-4405. TEL 310-289-9400, HollywoodOS@aol.com, http://www.extracastingguild.com. Ed. Mr. Mike Wood. Pubs. Angela Bertolino, Carla Lewis.

KIDS ALIVE. see RELIGIONS AND THEOLOGY—Protestant

028.5   USA
KIDS CENTRAL STATION. Text in English. 1999. w. back issues avail. Document type: Newsletter.
Media: E-mail. Related titles: Online - full content ed.
Published by: Kids Central Station, Inc, 9858 Glades Rd 2000, Boca Raton, FL 33434. TEL 800-543-7022, FAX 561-470-8250, info@kidscentralstation.com, http://www.kidscentralstation.com/newsletter/newsletter.htm. Ed. Patricia Conte.

028.5   USA   ISSN 1063-9659
KIDS COPY. Text in English. 1992. m. Document type: Newspaper.
Published by: Kids Copy, Inc., PO Box 42, Wyncote, PA 19095. Pub. Kim Landry.

028.5   USA   ISSN 1054-2868
KIDS DISCOVER. Text in English. 1991. 12/yr. USD 19.95 domestic; USD 35.95 foreign (effective 2005). illus. 20 p./no.; reprints avail. Document type: Magazine, Consumer. Description: Provides information and entertainment for children ages 5-12; each issue explores an individual topic.
Related titles: Online - full text ed.: (from Gale Group).
Indexed: ICM, MASUSE, RGYP.
Address: 149 5th Ave, 12th Fl, New York, NY 10010. TEL 212-677-4457, FAX 212-353-8030, info@kidsdiscover.com, https://www.kidsdiscover.com/. Ed. Stella Sands. Circ: 500,000 (paid and controlled). Subscr. to: PO Box 54205, Boulder, CO 80322-4205.

KIDS' GUIDE. see TRAVEL AND TOURISM

305.23   USA   ISSN 1539-5472
THE KIDS HALL OF FAME NEWS; the first magazine to spotlight extraordinary positive achievements of kids by age. Text in English. 1998. 4/yr. USD 12.95 (effective 2002).
Published by: The Kids Hall of Fame, 3 Ibsen Ct., Dix Hills, NY 11746. TEL 631-242-9105, FAX 631-242-8101, http://thekidshalloffame.com. Pub. Victoria C. Nesnick.

KID'S HEALTH. see MEDICAL SCIENCES—Pediatrics

362.4   DEU
KIDS-JOURNAL. Text in German. q. EUR 15 domestic; EUR 20 foreign (effective 2003). Document type: Magazine, Consumer.
Published by: Humanis Verlag fuer Gesundheit GmbH, Im Altenschemel 21, Neustadt, 67435, Germany. TEL 49-6327-974323, FAX 49-6327-974332, info@humanis-verlag.de, http://www.humanis-verlag.de.

790.192   GBR   ISSN 1356-8272
KIDS OUT; the essential magazine for London parents. Variant title: Monthly Guide to Childrens Activity in London. Text in English. 1994. m. GBP 16.95 domestic; GBP 27.95 in Europe; GBP 2 newsstand/cover (effective 2001). 128 p./no. 4 cols./p.
Document type: Consumer. Description: Features special events, travel, and entertainment news for children.
Published by: Time Out Group Ltd., Universal House, 251 Tottenham Court Rd, London, WIT 7AB, United Kingdom. TEL 44-20-7813-6018, FAX 44-20-7813-6153. Ed. Melanie Dakin. Pub. Tony Elliott. Adv. contact Irene Campbell TEL 44 20 7813 3000. Subscr. to: Kids Out Subscriptions, Freepost (SWB 711), Patchway, Bristol BS32 0ZZ, United Kingdom.

028.5   USA   ISSN 0738-7431
KIDS RHYME NEWSLETTER; stories, games and more. Text in English. 1991. a. looseleaf. USD 6 (effective 2005). illus. Document type: Newsletter. Description: Provides parents with educational stories in rhyming verse to read to their children.
Published by: Story Time Stories That Rhyme, PO Box 416, Denver, CO 80201-0416. TEL 303-575-5676, FAX 303-575-1187, starsuccess@excite.com, story@curriculumresourceonline.com, http://www.contentprovidermedia.com, http://www.storytimestoriesthatrhyme.com/. Ed. A Doyle TEL 303-575-5676. R&P A. Doyle TEL 305-575-5676. Circ: 10,000 (paid and controlled).

KIDS TODAY. see CHILDREN AND YOUTH—About

C

053.1 DEU
KIDS UND CO. Text in German. 4/yr. EUR 1.95 newsstand/cover (effective 2003). adv. **Document type:** *Magazine, Consumer.*
Published by: Axel Springer Verlag AG, Axel-Springer-Platz 1, Hamburg, 20350, Germany. TEL 49-40-34722884, FAX 49-40-34725540, http://www.asv.de. Adv. contact Martina Wisser. color page EUR 5,000.

KIDS WEAR. see *CLOTHING TRADE—Fashions*

028.5 USA
KID'S WORLD; the magazine that's all kids. Text in English. 1993. 4/yr. USD 5. **Document type:** *Consumer.*
Published by: Stone Lightning Press, 1300 Kicker Rd, Tuscaloosa, AL 35404-3954. TEL 205-553-2284. Ed. Morgan Kopaska-Merkel. Pub. David Kopaska Merkel. R&P Morgan Kopaska Merkel. Circ: 100.

053.1 794.8 DEU ISSN 1615-5491
KIDS ZONE. Text in German. 1999. fortn. EUR 52 domestic; EUR 58 in Austria; EUR 80.60 elsewhere; EUR 1.99 newsstand/cover (effective 2003). adv. **Document type:** *Magazine, Consumer.* **Description:** Covers all forms of entertainment that appeal to kids.
Published by: Computec Media AG, Dr-Mack-Str 77, Fuerth, 90762, Germany. TEL 49-911-2872100, FAX 49-911-2872200, kidszone@computec.de, info@computec.de, http://www.computec.de. Ed. Hans Ippisch. Adv. contact Thorsten Szameitat. B&W page EUR 4,550, color page EUR 6,500; trim 210 x 297. Circ: 72,952 (paid and controlled).

025.04 USA
KIDSPOTS. Text in English. 1999. w. free. **Document type:** *Newsletter.* **Description:** Published for kids to explore the Internet safely.
Media: Online - full text.
Published by: Nutshell Sports, 3512 CR 1104B, Cleburne, TX 76031. TEL 817-373-2538, stairway@hpnc.com, http://www.yourlinx.com/fokids.htm. Ed. Ray Waits.

C

028.5 DEU ISSN 1438-2210
KIDSPOWER. Text in German. 1997. 4/yr. EUR 10 (effective 2003). **Document type:** *Magazine, Consumer.*
Published by: Naturfreundejugend Deutschlands, Haus Humboldtstein, Remagen, 53424, Germany. TEL 49-2228-94150, FAX 49-2228-941522, nfjd@naturfreundejugend.de, http://www.naturfreundejugend.de.

028.5 CAN ISSN 1490-6341
KIDSWORLD. Text in English. 1993. bi-m. USD 16.99 (effective 2004). adv. **Document type:** *Magazine, Consumer.* **Description:** Educational magazine distributed to elementary schools across Canada.
Formerly: Kids World Magazine (1194-9562)
Related titles: Online - full text ed.: (from Gale Group).
Indexed: CPerI.
Published by: M I R Communications, Inc., 177 Danforth Ave, Ste 301, Toronto, ON M4K 1N2, Canada. kidsworld@kidsworld-online.com, http://www.kidsworld-online.com. Ed. Stuart Slayen. Pub., R&P Nancy Moore. Adv. contact Michael Sheasgreen. Circ: 225,000 (controlled).

028.5 USA
KIDZ CHAT. Cover title: Kidz Ch@t. Text in English. 1886. w. USD 14.69 per quarter for 5 copies (effective 2003). illus. **Document type:** *Consumer.* **Description:** For children 8-10 years old.
Former titles: Radar (0162-5217); Jet Cadet (0022-6645); Junior Life
Published by: Standard Publishing, 8121 Hamilton Ave, Cincinnati, OH 45231. TEL 513-931-4050, FAX 513-931-0950, http://www.standardpub.com. Ed. Carrie Girton. R&P Mark A Taylor. Circ: 112,000.

KINDER; Judgendmagazin in deutscher Sprache. see *LINGUISTICS*

745.5 DEU
KINDER BASTELSPASS. Text in German. 1998. bi-m. EUR 1.60 newsstand/cover (effective 2003). adv. **Document type:** *Magazine, Consumer.*
Published by: OZ Verlag GmbH, Roemerstr 90, Rheinfelden, 79618, Germany. TEL 49-7623-964-0, FAX 49-7623-96464200, vollmar@oz-bpv.de, http://www.oz-verlag.com. adv.: B&W page EUR 2,150, color page EUR 2,800; trim 183 x 244. Circ: 60,000 (paid and controlled).

028.5 DEU ISSN 0721-8486
KINDER JUGEND FILM KORRESPONDENZ. Text in German. 1980. q. adv. bk.rev.; film rev. illus. **Document type:** *Bulletin, Consumer.*
Indexed: FLI.
Published by: Kinderkino Muenchen e.V., Werner-Friedmann-Bogen 18, Munich, 80993, Germany. TEL 49-89-1491453, FAX 49-89-1494836. Ed. Hans Strobel. Adv. contact Christel Strobel. Circ: 1,000.

KINDER-RAETSEL. see *HOBBIES*

028.5 DEU
KINDER- UND JUGENDBUECHER. Text in German. a. **Document type:** *Bibliography.*
Published by: K.F. Koehler Verlag GmbH, Am Wallgraben 110, Stuttgart, 70563, Germany. FAX 49-711-7892-132.

KINDEREN VOORRANG!. see *TRANSPORTATION*

028.5 SVK
KIS EPITO. Text in Slovak. 24/yr.
Published by: Smena Publishing House, Prazska 11, Bratislava, 81284, Slovakia.

KITTY LOVE. see *PETS*

280.4 DEU ISSN 0947-7713
KIZ FUER KIDS. Text in German. 1973. m. EUR 12.40; EUR 1 newsstand/cover (effective 2003). **Document type:** *Magazine, Consumer.*
Formerly (until 1994): Kinderzeitung (0342-3441); Which was formed by the merger of (1949-1973): Samenkorner (0342-3506); (18??-1973): Morgenstern (0342-3492); (185?-1973): Kinderfreund (0342-4812)
—CCC.
Published by: Bundes Verlag GmbH, Bodenborn 43, Witten, 58452, Germany. TEL 49-2302-93093-0, FAX 49-2302-9309310, info@bundes-verlag.de, http://www.bundes-verlag.de.

KIZITO; a children's magazine. see *RELIGIONS AND THEOLOGY—Roman Catholic*

028.5 DEU
KLAEX. Text in German. 1996. q. EUR 11.40; EUR 3.20 newsstand/cover (effective 2003). adv. back issues avail. **Document type:** *Magazine, Consumer.*
Published by: Bundes Verlag GmbH, Bodenborn 43, Witten, 58452, Germany. TEL 49-2302-93093-0, FAX 49-2302-9309310, info@bundes-verlag.de, http://www.klaex.ch/, http://www.bundes-verlag.de. Ed. Martin Gundlach. adv.: page EUR 1,100; trim 188 x 258. Circ: 12,174 (paid).

280.4 DEU
KLARTEXT. Text in German. q. EUR 9; EUR 2.45 newsstand/cover (effective 2003). **Document type:** *Magazine, Consumer.*
Published by: Bibellesebund e.V., Industriestr 2, Marienheide, 51709, Germany. TEL 49-2264-404340, FAX 49-2264-4043439, r.frey@bibellesebund.de, http://www.bibellesebund.de/hilfen/klartext.htm.

028.5 RUS ISSN 1562-3335
KLASSNYI ZHURNAL. Text in Russian. 1999. w. RUR 572 domestic; RUR 11 per issue domestic (effective 2004). **Document type:** *Magazine, Consumer.*
Published by: Izdatel'stvo Otkrytye Sistemy/Open Systems Publications, ul Rustaveli, dom 12A, komn 117, Moscow, 127254, Russian Federation. TEL 7-095-9563306, FAX 7-095-2539204, info@osp.ru, http://www.osp.ru/class.

053.1 DEU
KLEINE PLANETEN. Text in German. 1999. bi-m. EUR 2.70 newsstand/cover (effective 2003). adv. **Document type:** *Magazine, Consumer.*
Published by: Panini Verlags GmbH, Ravensstr 48, Nettetal, 41334, Germany. TEL 49-711-947680, FAX 49-711-94768830, info@panini-dino.de, http://www.panini.de/kleineplaneten.asp, http://www.panini-media.de. adv.: page EUR 2,000.

028.5 RUS ISSN 0869-5814
KLEPA. Text in Russian. bi-m. USD 109.95 in United States. —East View.
Published by: Assotsiatsiya Imazhinariya, Per Bryusova 6, ofis 19, Moscow, 103001, Russian Federation. TEL 7-095-2340604, FAX 7-095-2340604. Ed. N Yu Dubinina. **US dist. addr.:** East View Information Services, 3020 Harbor Ln. N., Minneapolis, MN 55447. TEL 612-550-0961.

028.5 DEU ISSN 0938-3026
KLICK; Zeitschrift fuer Durchblick. Text in German. 1985. s-m. USD 15. **Description:** For young people ages 9 - 14.
Published by: Verl. Die Tollkirsche, Friesenstr 90, Bremen, 28203, Germany. TEL 0421-72993, FAX 0421-700555. Ed. Erwin Bienewald.

369.4 630 SWE ISSN 0281-1278
KLOEVERBLADET. Text in Swedish. 1921. q. SEK 50, USD 10. adv. bk.rev. illus. **Document type:** *Bulletin.*
Former titles (until 1983): 4H - Journalen; (until 1963): Jord och Ungdom; (until 1949): J.U.F. Bladet; (until 1923): Jordbrukareungdomens Foereningsblad (0016-335X)
Published by: Riksfoerbundet Sveriges 4H/Swedish Association of 4H Clubs, Fack 2012, Katrineholm, 64102, Sweden. TEL 0150-50380, FAX 0150-53599. Ed. Pernilla Hjelm. Circ: 27,500.

028.5 230 IND ISSN 0254-6205
KNANAYAMITHRAM; The Magazine for Christian Homes. Text in Malayalam. 1982. m. INR 50, USD 20 (effective 2001). bk.rev.; film rev.; tel.rev.; video rev. 28 p./no. 2 cols./p.; back issues avail. **Document type:** *Magazine, Consumer.*
Published by: Jaffe Publishing Management Service, Kunnuparambil Bldgs., Kurichy, Kottayam, Kerala 686 549, India. TEL 91-481-434141. Ed. K K Kuruvilla. Pub. C Markose. Circ: 5,000.

028.5 741.5 SWE ISSN 0345-620X
KNASEN. Text in Swedish. 1970. 26/yr. SEK 595; SEK 25 newsstand/cover (effective 1998). adv. **Document type:** *Consumer.*
Published by: Egmont Serie Foerlaget, Fack 70272, Stockholm, 10722, Sweden. TEL 46-8-736-39-00, FAX 46-8-791-70-95. Ed., Pub. Alf Thorsjoe. Adv. contact Peter Ask. color page SEK 11,400; trim 220 x 150. Circ: 22,100.

028.5 370 USA ISSN 0163-4844
KNOW YOUR WORLD EXTRA. Text in English. 1967. 12/yr. (Sep.-May). USD 34.50 per academic year; USD 10.50 per academic year 10 or more subscriptions (effective 2004 - 2005). illus. reprint service avail. from PQC. **Document type:** *Magazine, Consumer.* **Description:** Builds reading success and boosts self-esteem for teens struggling to read, by providing high-interest, age-appropriate topics written at the 2nd to 3rd grade reading levels. Includes a separate teacher's guide and a bound set of reproducible skills extenders.
Formerly (until 1977): Know Your World (0023-2483)
Related titles: Online - full text ed.: (from bigchalk, EBSCO Publishing, Gale Group, Northern Light Technology, Inc., ProQuest Information & Learning).
Indexed: ICM.
Published by: Weekly Reader Corp. (Subsidiary of: W R C Media Inc.), 200 First Stamford Pl, PO Box 120023, Stamford, CT 06912-0023. TEL 203-705-3500, 800-446-3355, FAX 203-705-1662, http://www.weeklyreader.com. Ed. M Letourneau. Pub. Peter Esposito. R&P Cathy Pekai TEL 203-705-3426. Circ: 129,353 (paid).

371.911 028.5 USA
KNOW YOUR WORLD EXTRA (LARGE PRINT EDITION). Text in English. 12/yr. (during school yr.). USD 10.50 per academic year (effective 2004 - 2005). **Document type:** *Magazine, Consumer.*
Media: Large Type (16 pt.). **Related titles:** Braille ed.
Published by: American Printing House for the Blind, Inc., 1839 Frankfort Ave, Louisville, KY 40206. TEL 502-895-2405, 800-223-1839, FAX 502-899-2274, info@aph.org, http://www.aph.org.

305.23 DEU
▼ **KOALA BRUEDER.** Text in German. 2005. 4/yr. EUR 2 newsstand/cover (effective 2005). adv. **Document type:** *Magazine, Consumer.*
Published by: Panini Verlags GmbH, Ravensstr 48, Nettetal, 41334, Germany. TEL 49-2157-81750, FAX 49-2157-81484528, info@panini-dino.de, http://www.panini-media.de. adv.: page EUR 2,500; trim 210 x 280. Circ: 80,000 (paid).

028.5 AFG ISSN 0023-2572
KOCHNIANO ANEES✶ /ANEES FOR CHILDREN. Text in Pushto. 1970. w. USD 13. adv. abstr.; charts; illus.; stat.
Published by: Anees Publishing Co., Ansari Ave., Kabul, Afghanistan. Ed. Mohammed Taher Paknihad. Circ: 30,000.

KOL HATNUAH. see *ETHNIC INTERESTS*

282 028.5 SVN ISSN 1408-5593
KOLEDARCEK. Text in Slovenian. a. SIT 300 (effective 2000). **Description:** Calendar includes ministry groups, liturgy and other events.
Published by: Salve D.O.O., Rakovniska 6, pp 2404, Ljubljana, 1001, Slovenia. TEL 386-61-1277310, FAX 386-61-1273040, info@salve.si. Ed. Branko Balazic. Circ: 8,000.

028.5 AUT
KOLPING OESTERREICH. Text in German. 1933. q. free (effective 2005). bk.rev. **Document type:** *Magazine, Consumer.* **Description:** Focuses on social issues from a Catholic perspective.
Formerly: Oesterreichisches Kolpingblatt (0029-9928)
Address: Paulanergasse 11, Vienna, W 1040, Austria. TEL 43-1-58735420, FAX 43-1-5879900, office@kolping.at, http://www.kolping.at/index.php?set_language=de&cccpage=zeitschriften_intro. Ed. Ludwig Zack. Circ: 16,000.

028.5 NLD ISSN 0166-3119
KOMBY; aktiviteiten voor jeugd en jongeren. Text in Dutch. 1979; N.S. 1984. 6/yr. EUR 19.25 (effective 2005). illus. **Document type:** *Bulletin.*
Published by: Y M C A Nederland, Soestdijkerweg 10b, Den Dolder, 3734 MH, Netherlands. TEL 31-35-6668700, FAX 31-35-6668688, info@ymca.nl, http://www.ymca.nl.

028.5 GRC ISSN 1105-1469
KOMIX. Text in Greek. 1988. m. USD 60 (effective 1997). adv. illus. **Document type:** *Consumer.* **Description:** Contains Walt Disney stories and comics for children and adult collectors.

Published by: Terzopoulos Publishing Ltd., 7 Fragoklisias St, Maroussi, Athens 151 25, Greece. TEL 30-1-689-6366, FAX 30-1-680-6631. Ed. Stelios Nicolaou. Adv. contact Angela Daramara. Circ: 18,000.

KOMMI; Magazin fuer junge Christ. see *RELIGIONS AND THEOLOGY—Protestant*

028.5 DEU
KOMPOST. Text in German. 1980. m. USD 7.
Published by: J Z Alte Post, Denkmalplatz 1, Langenzenn, 90579, Germany. Circ: 5,000.

028.5 POL ISSN 1643-8256
▼ **KOMPUTEROWA GRATKA.** Text in Polish. 2003. m. PLZ 99 domestic; PLZ 9.95 per issue domestic (effective 2004). **Document type:** *Magazine, Consumer.*
Published by: Egmont Polska, ul Dzielna 60, Warszawa, 01029, Poland. TEL 48-22-8384100, FAX 48-22-8384200, poczta@egmont.pl, http://www.kgratka.pl, http://www.egmont.pl.

028.5 DEU ISSN 0942-1343
KONFETTI. Text in German. 1964. q. **Document type:** *Magazine, Consumer.*
Formerly (until 1992): Der Goldene Pfennig (0017-1646)
Published by: (Deutscher Raiffeisenverband e.V.), Deutscher Genossenschafts-Verlag eG, Leipziger Str 35, Wiesbaden, 65191, Germany. TEL 49-611-50660, FAX 49-611-50661500, direct@dgverlag.de, http://www.dgverlag.de. Ed. K Vollath.

268 AUT
KONTAKT. Text in German. 1968. m. looseleaf. bk.rev. **Document type:** *Magazine, Consumer.*
Former titles: Kontakt und Reflexionen (0034-3013); Studpress auf Reflexionen
Related titles: Cards ed.
Published by: Katholische Jugend, Erzdioezese Wien, Stephansplatz 6-6-66, Vienna, W 1010, Austria. TEL 43-1-515523391, FAX 43-1-515522743, office@katholische-jugend.at, http://katholische-jugend.at.

028.5 NLD ISSN 0023-3692
KONTAKTO. Text in Esperanto. 1963. bi-m. EUR 19 (effective 2003). adv. bk.rev.; film rev.; music rev.; play rev. illus. back issues avail. **Document type:** *Magazine.*
Published by: (Tutmonda Esperantista Junulara Organizo), Universala Esperanto-Asocio, Nieuwe Binnenweg 176, Rotterdam, 3015 BJ, Netherlands. TEL 31-10-4361044, FAX 31-10-4361751, uea@inter.nl.net, libroservo@uea.org, http://www.uea.org. Ed. Yevgeniya Zvereva. Adv. contact Trevor Steele. B&W page EUR 400. Circ: 2,200.

028.5 DEU
KONTRAPUNKTE. Text in German. 1953. s-a. free. adv. bk.rev.; film rev.; play rev. illus. back issues avail.
Indexed: RASB.
Published by: Kontrapunkte Schuelerzeitung, Zinzendorfgymnasium, Moenchweilerstr 7, Koenigsfeld Im Schwarzwald, 78126, Germany. Ed. Peter Vogt. Circ: 600.

028.5 DEU
KORRESPONDENZ. Text in German. 1978. 3/yr. free. **Document type:** *Academic/Scholarly.*
Published by: Landesjugendring Niedersachsen e.V., Maschstr 24, Hannover, 30169, Germany. TEL 0511-805055, FAX 0511-805057. Eds. Beate Frey, Hans Schwab. Circ: 7,000.

028.5 RUS ISSN 0130-2574
KOSTER. Text in Russian. 1936. m. USD 54 foreign (effective 2000). **Description:** Includes fiction, poetry, sports, reports and popular science for children ages 10-14.
—East View.
Address: Mitninskaya ul 1-20, St Petersburg, 193024, Russian Federation. TEL 7-812-2741572, FAX 7-812-2744626, rot@kostyor.spb.org, root@kostyor.spb.org, http://www.zskostyor.newmail.ru. Ed. N B Kharlampiev. Circ: 7,500.

KOULULAINEN. see *EDUCATION*

028.5 GRC ISSN 0023-4664
KRIKOS TON VATHMOFORON. Text in Greek. 1948. m. included with subscription to Proscopos.
Published by: Boy Scouts of Greece/Soma Hellinon Proscopon, 1 Ptolemeon St, Athens, 516, Greece. Ed. Demetrius Marinopoulos. Circ: 7,500.

028.5 BGR ISSN 1311-1108
PG1020.3.Y68
KRUG/CIRCLE. Text in Bulgarian. 1998. q. BGL 8; BGL 1 newsstand/cover (effective 2002).
Published by: Litavra Publishing House, 163A Rakovski St., 5th Fl., Sofia, 1000, Bulgaria. TEL 359-2-9883136, FAX 359-2-9812357, krug40@hotmail.com, http://www.sca.bg/cultural-periodicals/catalog/krag.htm, http://www.freespeech.org/krug_literary. Ed. Radost Nikolaeva.

028.5 UKR
KRUTO. Text in Russian. m. **Document type:** *Magazine, Consumer.*
Published by: Burda Ukraina, Zhyljanskaja ul. 29, Kiev, 01033, Ukraine. TEL 38-044-4908363, FAX 38-044-4908364, advert@burdaua.com, http://www.burda.com.ua.

028.5 POL ISSN 1509-7935
KSIEZNICZKA. Text in Polish. 2000. m. **Document type:** *Magazine, Consumer.*
Related titles: Supplement(s): Ksiezniczka. Wydanie Specjalne. ISSN 1643-3289. 2002.
Published by: Egmont Polska, ul Dzielna 60, Warszawa, 01029, Poland. TEL 48-22-8384100, FAX 48-22-8384200, poczta@egmont.pl, http://www.egmont.pl. Ed. Jolanta Tomala. Circ: 80,000.

028.5 POL ISSN 1429-6462
KUBUS PUCHATEK. Text in Polish. 1998. m. **Document type:** *Magazine, Consumer.*
Related titles: Supplement(s): Kubus Puchatek. Wydanie Specjalne. ISSN 1640-2286. 2000.
Published by: Egmont Polska, ul Dzielna 60, Warszawa, 01029, Poland. TEL 48-22-8384100, FAX 48-22-8384200, poczta@egmont.pl, http://www.egmont.pl. Ed. Ewa Gucewicz-Mooney. Circ: 150,000.

028.5 ISR ISSN 0334-648X
KULANU. Text in Hebrew. 1985. fortn. ILS 156. adv. bk.rev. **Description:** For children ages 8-14.
Formed by the merger of (1936-1985): Davar (0333-5860); (1945-1985): Mishmar (0333-5364)
Indexed: IJP.
Published by: Z.Z. Printing & Productions, Derech Ben-Zvi 84, Tel Aviv, 68104, Israel. TEL 972-3-5180820, FAX 972-3-820401. Ed. Oren Zivlin. Circ: 40,000.

028.5 ISR ISSN 0792-8149
KULANU - PILON; semi-monthly magazine for children. Text in Hebrew. 1976. 26/yr. ILS 156. adv. bk.rev. **Description:** For children ages 6-8.
Formerly (until 1992): Pilon (0333-5410)
Published by: Z.Z. Printing & Productions, Derech Ben-Zvi 84, Tel Aviv, 68104, Israel. TEL 972-3-5180820, FAX 973-3-820401. Ed. Nurit Yuval. Circ: 12,000.

KUMAR. see *ART*

028.5 MYS ISSN 1511-0117
KUNTUM. Text in Malay. 1980. m. MYR 1.50 newsstand/cover (effective 2002). adv. **Document type:** *Magazine, Consumer.*
Published by: Star Publications (M) Bhd., 13 Jalan 13-6, Petaling Jaya, Selangor, Selangor 46200, Malaysia. TEL 60-3-7955-4039, FAX 60-3-7955-1280, editor@thestar.com.my, http://thestar.com.my.

028.5 155.4 IND
KUTTIKALUDE DEEPIKA; children's fortnightly. Text in Malayalam. s-m. INR 190 for 2 yrs.; INR 5 newsstand/cover. adv.
Published by: Rashtra Deepika Ltd., Deepika Bldg., C.M.S. College Rd., P O Box 7, Kottayam, Kerala 686 001, India. TEL 91-481-566706, FAX 91-481-567947. adv.: page INR 5,000; 110 x 160. Circ: 50,000.

KVANT. see *SCIENCES: COMPREHENSIVE WORKS*

028.5 USA
L A Y A!; eLetter for American Young Adults. Text in English. m. free. **Document type:** *Newsletter.*
Media: Online - full text. **Related titles:** E-mail ed.
Address: chris@laya.com, http://www.laya.com.

028.5 USA
L.A. YOUTH; the newspaper by and about Los Angeles teens. Text in English, Spanish. 1987. bi-m. USD 15 to individuals (effective 2003). film rev.; music rev. illus. back issues avail. **Document type:** *Newspaper.* **Description:** Addresses topics of concern to teens, such as racism, dysfunctional relationships, abuse, school dress codes, and earthquake preparedness.
Published by: Youth News Service, L.A. Bureau, 5967 W Third St, Ste 301, Los Angeles, CA 90036. TEL 323-938-9194, FAX 323-938-0940, layouth@worldsite.net, http://www.layouth.com/. Ed., Pub. Elizabeth Hartigan. R&P Donna C Myrow TEL 323-938-9194. Adv. contact Prisco Serrano. B&W page USD 1,500, color page USD 4,000. Circ: 100,000.

L G ARGOMENTI. (Letteratura Giovanile) see *LITERARY AND POLITICAL REVIEWS*

LAD. see *RELIGIONS AND THEOLOGY—Protestant*

808.89 USA ISSN 1051-4961
AP201
LADYBUG; the magazine for young children. Text in English. 1990. m. USD 35.97 domestic; USD 47.97 foreign; USD 4.95 newsstand/cover domestic; USD 7.50 newsstand/cover in Canada (effective 2005). illus. 34 p./no.; back issues avail.; reprints avail. **Document type:** *Magazine, Consumer.* **Description:** For children ages 2-6. Includes picture stories, songs, poems, rhymes, and read-aloud stories.
Related titles: Online - full text ed.: (from EBSCO Publishing).
Indexed: ICM.
Published by: Carus Publishing Company, 315 Fifth St, Peru, IL 61354. TEL 603-924-7209, 800-821-0115, FAX 815-224-2256, custsvc@cobblestone.mv.com, http://www.cricketmag.com. Eds. Paula Morrow, Marianne Carus. Pub. John Olbrych. Circ: 127,000 (paid).

LANDING ZONE. see *TRAVEL AND TOURISM—Airline Inflight And Hotel Inroom*

028.5 AUT ISSN 0023-7957
LANDJUGEND; Magazin fuer junge Leute. Text in German. 1956. m. adv. bk.rev. **Document type:** *Magazine, Government.*
Published by: Landjugend Oesterreich, Schauflergasse 6, Vienna, 1014, Austria. TEL 43-1-534418560, FAX 43-1-534418569, oelj@landjugend.at. Circ: 40,000.

655 FIN ISSN 1458-4891
LASTEN OMA KIRJAKERHO. Text in Finnish. 1975. 14/yr. adv. **Document type:** *Magazine, Consumer.*
Former titles (until 2001): Kikero (0780-2943); (until 1983): Lasten Oma Kirjakerho (0780-2951)
Published by: Sanoma Magazines Finland Corporation, Hoylaamotie 1 D, P.O. Box 100, Helsinki, 00040, Finland. TEL 358-9-1201, FAX 358-9-1205171, info@sanomamagazines.fi, http://www.lastenomakirjakerho.fi, http://www.sanomamagazines.fi. adv.: color page EUR 2,600.

L'CHAIM; the weekly publication for every Jewish person. see *RELIGIONS AND THEOLOGY—Judaic*

028.5 USA ISSN 1540-3521
LEAP'S POND. Text in English. 2001. 10/yr. USD 49.99 to members (effective 2003). **Document type:** *Magazine, Academic/Scholarly.* **Description:** Interactive learning magazine used with LeapPad or LeapPad Pro and Mind Station or LeapLink connector. Content features more than 40 activities in curriculum areas including language arts, math, music, science, social studies, foreign languages, and also includes parents' guide. Audio portion of each magazine is downloaded from the internet with membership to Leap's Pond Never-Ending Learning Club.
Media: Talking Book.
Published by: LeapFrog Enterprises, Inc., 6401 Hollis St, Ste 150, Emeryville, CA 94608-1071. TEL 510-420-5000, FAX 510-420-5001, http://www.leapfrog.com.

C

THE LEARNING EDGE; home based education program news. see *EDUCATION—Teaching Methods And Curriculum*

▼ **LEARNING THROUGH HISTORY.** see *HISTORY*

373.95692 USA ISSN 1075-8852
LEBANON LIGHT. Text in English. 1919. 8/yr. (Aug.-June). USD 37.95 (effective 2003). adv. bk.rev. illus. 16 p./no.; **Document type:** *Newspaper.* **Description:** Reports on school activities and news of the city of Lebanon, OH.
Published by: Lebanon High School, Journalism Class, 1916 Drake Rd., Lebanon, OH 45036-8624. TEL 513-933-2150, FAX 513-933-2150, leblight@your-net.com. Ed. Jeff Weisenborn. R&P Wayne Dunn. Adv. contact Zach Dilgard. B&W page USD 120. Circ: 1,500.

LES LECTURES DE LA MESSE. see *RELIGIONS AND THEOLOGY—Roman Catholic*

LEGALDATE. see *LAW*

028.5 FIN ISSN 0784-2546
LEPPIS. Text in Finnish. 1987. m. EUR 45 (effective 2005). adv. illus. **Document type:** *Magazine, Consumer.* **Description:** A magazine which children can call their own and which parents enjoy reading with their children. Contains a separate activity sheet and an up-to-date insert for parents.
Formerly (until 1987): Leppakerttu (0359-7482)
Published by: Yhtyneet Kuvalehdet Oy/United Magazines Ltd., Maistraatinportti 1, Helsinki, 00015, Finland. TEL 358-9-15661, FAX 358-9-145650, http://www.kuvalehdet.fi/. Ed. Sirkku Kuusava. adv.: page EUR 1,220; 230 x 260. Circ: 19,280.

LET'S FIND OUT (SPANISH EDITION). see *EDUCATION—Teaching Methods And Curriculum*

808.068 ITA
LETTERATURA PER RAGAZZI IN ITALIA. Text in Italian. a.
Published by: Edizioni Piemme SpA, Via del Carmine, 5, Casale Monferrato, AL 15033, Italy. TEL 39-142-3361, FAX 39-142-74223.

028.5 FRA ISSN 0760-9191
LA LETTRE DE TAPORI. Text in Dutch, English, French, German, Spanish. 1969. m. EUR 12.20 (effective 2002). back issues avail. **Document type:** *Newsletter, Consumer.* **Description:** Connects groups of children in France and around the world who react against injustice and poverty.
Formerly (until 1984): Tapori (0754-362X)
Published by: (Mouvement International A T D Quart Monde/International Movement A T D Fourth World), Editions Quart Monde, 15 rue Maitre Albert, Paris, 75005, France. TEL 33-01-46334977, FAX 33-01-43296448, editions@atd-quartmonde.org, http://www.atd-quartmonde.org. Ed. Noldi Christen.

▼ new title ➤ refereed ✶ unverified ♦ full entry avail.

028.5   RUS
LEVSHA/LEFT HANDED. Text in Russian. 1972. m. USD 24 (effective 2002). adv. **Document type:** *Magazine, Consumer.*
Published by: Yunyi Tekhnik, Novodmitrovskaya ul 5-a, Moscow, 125015, Russian Federation. TEL 7-095-2854480, FAX 7-095-2851809. Ed. Boris I Cheremisinov. Adv. contact Alexandr Abmorshev. color page USD 750; 190 x 252. Circ: 5,000. **US dist. addr.:** East View Information Services, 3020 Harbor Ln. N., Minneapolis, MN 55447. TEL 612-550-0961.

028.5   CHN   ISSN 1002-1922
LIAONING QINGNIAN/LIAONING YOUTH. Text in Chinese. 1972. s-m.
Published by: Gongqingtuan Liaoning Shengwei, 21, Wujing Jie, Heping-qu, Shenyang, Liaoning 110003, China. TEL 23684. Ed. Li Yingmin.

LIBRI PER BAMBINI E RAGAZZI. see *PUBLISHING AND BOOK TRADE*

028.5 242.62   USA   ISSN 1540-1081
LIGHTNING BUG; christian magazine for children. Text in English. 2002. m. free; $5.82 shipping & handling x year.
Published by: Silicon Hills Publishing House, P. O. Box 691539, Tulsa, OK 74169-1539. TEL 918-740-4632, http://www.lightningbugmagazine.com, http://www.siliconhillspublishing.com. Ed. Alex Yar.

028.5   SGP
LIME. Text in English. m. **Document type:** *Magazine, Consumer.*
Published by: MediaCorp Publishing, Caldecott Broadcast Centre, Andrew Road, Singapore, 299939, Singapore. TEL 65-64837118, FAX 65-64812098, subhelp@mediacorppub.com.sg, http://corporate.mediacorpsingapore.com/index.htm.

THE LINCOLNATOR; Abraham Lincoln at home. see *HISTORY—History Of North And South America*

THE LINK. see *RELIGIONS AND THEOLOGY—Other Denominations And Sects*

LIRE POUR COMPRENDRE. see *LITERATURE*

LISSY; ein Herz fuer Pferde. see *SPORTS AND GAMES—Horses And Horsemanship*

LISTEN MAGAZINE; celebrating positive choices. see *RELIGIONS AND THEOLOGY*

LITERARY CAVALCADE. see *EDUCATION—Teaching Methods And Curriculum*

LITERATURE AND LITERACY FOR YOUNG PEOPLE. see *LINGUISTICS*

028.5 820   AUS   ISSN 1034-6244
THE LITERATURE BASE. Text in English. 1990. q. AUD 35 domestic; AUD 55 foreign (effective 2004). adv. back issues avail. **Document type:** *Journal, Academic/Scholarly.*
Description: Contains practical ideas for using literature with children in schools.
Indexed: ChLitAb.
Published by: Magpies Magazine Pty. Ltd., PO Box 98, Grange, QLD 4051, Australia. TEL 61-7-33564503, FAX 61-7-33564649, james@magpies.net.au, http://www.magpies.net.au. Ed. Rayma Turton. R&P, Adv. contact James Turton. Circ: 3,300.

028.162   RUS   ISSN 0203-5847
PG3227
LITERATURNAYA UCHEBA. Text in Russian. 1930. bi-m. USD 48 foreign (effective 2003). adv. bk.rev. illus.
Related titles: Online - full text ed.- (from East View Information Services).
Indexed: RASB.
—East View.
Published by: Molodaya Gvardiya, Novodmitrovskaya ul 5-a, Moscow, 125015, Russian Federation. TEL 7-095-2858903, FAX 7-095-2856298. Ed. V A Malytin. **Dist. by:** M K - Periodica, ul Gilyarovskogo 39, Moscow 129110, Russian Federation. TEL 7-095-2845008, FAX 7-095-2813798, info@periodicals.ru, http://www.mkniga.ru; **US dist. addr.:** East View Information Services, 3020 Harbor Ln. N., Minneapolis, MN 55447. TEL 612-550-0961.

028.5   CHN
LITTLE FROG. Text in Chinese. 1985. bi-w. USD 21.60. **Document type:** *Newspaper.* **Description:** Carries Chinese and foreign fairy tales, poems, children songs, proses and dramas.
Formerly: You'er Wenxue Bao - Literature for Preschool Children
Published by: Shaonian Ertong Chubanshe/Juvenile & Children Publishing House, 1538 Yan an Xilu, Shanghai, 200052, China. TEL 86-21-6282-3025, FAX 86-21-6282-1726. Ed. Shunpei Zhou.

028.5 025.04   USA   ISSN 1547-6065
▼ **THE LITTLE NIPPER'S INTERNET CLUBHOUSE.** Text in English. 2003. a. USD 20 per issue (effective 2003).
Media: Online - full content.

Published by: Harley Hahn, 2022 Cliff Dr., Santa Barbara, CA 93109. TEL 805-564-5000, http://hhe.harley.com/ic/homepage.html, http://www.harley.com. Pub. Hahn Harley.

028.5   BGR   ISSN 1310-8972
LIUBOPITKO/CURIOUS KID. Text in Bulgarian. 1997. q. BGL 0.10 newsstand/cover (effective 2002). **Document type:** *Newspaper.*
Published by: Ritsari Na Poznanieto/Knights of Knowledge, ZhK Slatina, P.O. Box 74, Sofia, 1574, Bulgaria. TEL 359-2-9803052, knightsOK@yahoo.com, http://www.sca.bg/cultural-periodicals/catalog/lyubopit.htm. Ed. Ani Hadjieva.

028.5 230   USA
LIVE WIRE. Text in English. 1997. w. USD 14.69 per quarter for 5 copies (effective 2003). **Document type:** *Consumer.*
Published by: Standard Publishing, 8121 Hamilton Ave, Cincinnati, OH 45231. TEL 513-931-4050, FAX 513-931-0950, http://www.standardpub.com. Pub., R&P Mark A Taylor.

LIVRES JEUNES AUJOURD'HUI. see *LITERATURE*

500 028.5   DEU
LOEWENZAHN; Peter Lustig's Geschichten aus Natur, Umwelt und Technik. Text in German. 2000. m. EUR 27.60; EUR 2.30 newsstand/cover (effective 2005). adv. **Document type:** *Magazine, Consumer.*
Published by: Egmont Ehapa Verlag GmbH, Wallstr 59, Berlin, 10179, Germany. TEL 49-30-240080, FAX 49-30-24008599, leserservice@ehapa.de, http://www.ehapa.de/ehapa/e14/e40/e169/index_ger.html, http://ehapa.funonline.de. adv.: page EUR 4,400. Circ: 64,835 (paid and controlled).

LOOK IN TELEVISION ANNUAL; for children. see *COMMUNICATIONS—Television And Cable*

051   USA
▼ **LOOK-LOOK;** the magazine by young photographers, writers and artists. Text in English. 2004. q. USD 19.97; USD 5.95 newsstand/cover (effective 2005). **Document type:** *Magazine, Consumer.* **Description:** Contains art, writing, photography and other forms of expression created by young people for young people.
Published by: Look-Look, Inc., 6685 Hollywood Blvd, Hollywood, CA 90028. TEL 323-856-5555, FAX 323-856-8511, sharon@look-look.com, ed@look-lookmagazine.com, http://www.look-lookmagazine.com.

028.5   GBR   ISSN 1461-1821
LOONEY TUNES PRESENTS. Text in English. 1998. irreg. GBP 1.99 newsstand/cover. adv. **Document type:** *Consumer.*
Published by: Burghley Publishing Ltd., 14 Barn Hill, Stamford, Lincs PE9 2AE, United Kingdom. TEL 44-1780-763366, FAX 44-1780-763365. Pub. Susan Voss. Adv. contact Joan Wright. **Dist. by:** Seymour Distribution Ltd, 86 Newman St, London W1T 3EX, United Kingdom. FAX 44-207-396-8002, enquiries@seymour.co.uk.

028.5   GBR   ISSN 1460-6399
LOONEY TUNES TRAVEL TIME. Text in English. 1998. bi-m. GBP 15.92; GBP 1.99 newsstand/cover (effective 1999). adv. **Document type:** *Consumer.*
Published by: Burghley Publishing Ltd., 14 Barn Hill, Stamford, Lincs PE9 2AE, United Kingdom. TEL 44-1780-763366, FAX 44-1780-763365. Pub. Susan Voss. Adv. contact Joan Wright. **Dist. by:** Seymour Distribution Ltd, 86 Newman St, London W1T 3EX, United Kingdom. TEL 44-20-73968000, FAX 44-20-73968002.

THE LORD OF THE RINGS; fan club official movie magazine. see *LITERATURE—Science Fiction, Fantasy, Horror*

028.5   GBR   ISSN 1462-2645
LOTS TO DO! FOR CHILDREN. Text in English. 1998. bi-m. GBP 15 domestic; GBP 20 foreign; GBP 2.99 newsstand/cover. adv. back issues avail. **Document type:** *Consumer.*
Published by: Practical Publications Ltd. (Subsidiary of: Highbury House Communications PLC), Columbus House, 28 Charles Sq, London, N1 6HT, United Kingdom. TEL 44-20-76086464, http://www.hhc.co.uk/. Ed. Carina Norris. Adv. contact Beverly Hylton.

028.5   USA
▼ **LOUD;** news of the next generation. Text in English. 2005 (Fall). q. adv. **Document type:** *Magazine, Consumer.* **Description:** Covers entertainment and other information geared toward teens, including issues such as teen rights, higher educations, technology, business, and more.
Published by: LOUD, Inc., 625 Emerson St, Ste 300, Palo Alto, CA 94301. TEL 650-322-7004, FAX 650-322-7009, mail@loudmagazine.com, http://www.loudmagazine.com/. Ed. Anne Schukat. Pub. Don Menn. adv.: B&W page USD 400, color page USD 500; trim 7.25 x 9.5. Circ: 10,000.

369.4   FRA   ISSN 0751-5685
LOUVETEAU. Text in French. 1924. bi-m. adv. **Description:** For scouts ages 8-12.
Formerly: Scouts Louveteau
Published by: Editions Scouts de France, 54 av. Jean Jaures, Paris, 75019, France. TEL 33-1-44523737, FAX 33-1-42380987. Ed. Philippe Da Costa.

028.5   AUS   ISSN 0158-099X
LOWDOWN; youth performing arts in Australia. Text in English. 1978. bi-m. AUD 39.95 domestic; AUD 60 foreign (effective 2000). adv. bk.rev.; play rev. abstr. back issues avail. **Document type:** *Directory, Trade.*
Indexed: ChLitAb.
Published by: Carclew Youth Performing Arts Centre Inc., 11 Jeffcott St, North Adelaide, SA 5006, Australia. TEL 61-8-82675111, FAX 61-8-82390689. Ed. Tony Mack. Adv. contact Leigh Mangin. Circ: 1,000.

028.5   ESP
LUNA DE MADRID. Text in Spanish. 1983. m.
Published by: Ediciones el Jueves S.A., Pintor Moreno Carbonero, 18, Madrid, 28028, Spain. TEL 91-2550505. Ed. Jorge Gines. Circ: 150,000.

028.5 369.4   SCG   ISSN 0350-8080
M A K. (Mladosc, Aktivnosc, Kreativnocs) Text in Serbo-Croatian. 1972. m. YUN 3,000, USD 21. bk.rev.; film rev.; play rev. illus.; tr.lit. back issues avail.
Published by: N I U "Ruske Slovo", Bul 23 Oktobra 31, Novi Sad, Vojvodina 21000. TEL 621-433.

053.1   CHE
M E X - MUSENALP EXPRESS. Text in German. 10/yr. CHF 30 (effective 2000). adv. **Document type:** *Magazine, Consumer.* **Description:** Contains the latest news and information on entertainment and lifestyle issues of interest to kids.
Published by: Ringier AG, Dufourstr 47, Zuerich, 8008, Switzerland. TEL 41-1-2596483, FAX 41-1-2596996, redaktion@musenalp.ch, info@ringier.ch, http://www.musenalp.ch, http://www.ringier.ch. Ed. Sonja Leissing. Circ: 143,413 (paid).

028.5   USA   ISSN 1533-9149
M MAGAZINE; music, movies and more!. Text in English. 2001. 10/yr. USD 14.97 domestic; USD 24.97 foreign; USD 2.99 newsstand/cover domestic; USD 3.99 newsstand/cover in Canada (effective 2003). adv. film rev.; music rev. back issues avail. **Document type:** *Magazine, Consumer.* **Description:** Contains the latest information on favorite music and movie stars for teens.
Published by: Bauer Publishing Company, L.P., 270 Sylvan Ave, Englewood Cliffs, NJ 07632. TEL 201-569-6699, FAX 201-569-5303, mail@mmm-mag.com, http://www.mmm-mag.com. Ed. Molly MacDermot. Pub., Adv. contact Jeanne Sachs TEL 212-764-3344. color page USD 7,350. Circ: 200,000 (paid and controlled).

M P Z PROGRAMM; Schule und Museum. see *MUSEUMS AND ART GALLERIES*

087.5   FRA   ISSN 1253-5532
M6 KID. Text in French. 1997. bi-m. **Document type:** *Magazine, Consumer.*
Published by: M6 Interactions, 89 av Charles-de-Gaulle, Neuilly-sur-Seine Cedex, 92575, France. TEL 33-1-41926936, http://www.m6net.fr.

MA'AGALE KERI'A. see *LITERATURE*

028.5   DEU
MACH MIT. Text in German. m. EUR 27.60; EUR 2.90 newsstand/cover (effective 2002). adv. **Document type:** *Magazine, Consumer.*
Published by: Velber im OZ Verlag GmbH, Guenterstalstr. 57, Freiburg, 79102, Germany. TEL 49-761-705780, FAX 49-761-7057839, butsch@oz-bpv.de, http://www.oz-verlag.com.

MAD; das intelligenteste Magazin der Welt. see *LITERARY AND POLITICAL REVIEWS*

MAD. see *LITERARY AND POLITICAL REVIEWS*

MAD COLOR CLASSICS. see *LITERARY AND POLITICAL REVIEWS*

MAD XL. see *LITERARY AND POLITICAL REVIEWS*

028.5   DEU   ISSN 1420-2239
MAEDCHEN. Text in German. 1976. fortn. EUR 44.20; EUR 1.70 newsstand/cover (effective 2005). adv. **Document type:** *Magazine, Consumer.* **Description:** Contains articles and features on beauty, fashion, boys and other items of interest to young girls.
Related titles: Online - full text ed.- 2002.
Published by: Axel Springer Young Mediahouse, Werinherstr 71, Munich, 81541, Germany. TEL 49-89-697490, FAX 49-89-69749312, redaktion@maedchen.de, http://www.maedchen.de, http://www.asv.de. Ed. Nina Maurischat. Adv. contact Petra Kalb TEL 49-89-69749100. color page EUR 13,300; trim 205 x 285. Circ: 188,079 (paid). **Subscr. to:** DSB, Neckarsulm 74172, Germany. TEL 49-7132-959214, FAX 49-7132-959216, asvabo@dsb.net.

058.82   NOR   ISSN 1501-0058
MAG. Text in Norwegian. 1998. m. adv. **Document type:** *Magazine, Consumer.* **Description:** Aimed at girls between 15-20 years old who like to read about girl stuff, including new trends, fashion, beauty tips, boys, and travel.

C

Published by: Se og Hoer Forlaget A-S, Stenersgaten 2, Postboks 1164, Sentrum, Oslo, 0107, Norway. TEL 47-22-91-22-22, FAX 47-22-91-21-20. Circ: 34,723 (paid).

363.7   DEU   ISSN 1430-9467
MAGAZIN JUNGER MEDIENMACHER. Text in German. 1982. 5/yr. USD 10. bk.rev. Document type: Newsletter. Former titles: Jugendpressedienst des V N J; Krake Published by: Verband der Niedersaechsischen Jugendredakteure e.V., Otto-Brenner-Str 17A, Hannover, 30159, Germany. TEL 49-511-1388-0, FAX 49-511-138833, vnj@jugendpresse.de, http://www.jugendpresse.de/vnj. Ed. Diru Biernoth. Circ: 10,000.

028.5   CAN   ISSN 1189-9069
➤ MAGAZINE JEUNESSE. Text in French. 1990. q. USD 25 (effective 1999). adv. Document type: Academic/Scholarly. Description: Contains kids' views on different subjects and health questions. Also covers music, cinema, arts, and societal issues such as child empoyement and life. Formerly (until 1992): Magazine (1189-9050) Published by: Productions Tel-Art, 7383 rue de la Roche, Montreal, PQ H2R 2T4, Canada. TEL 514-274-6124, FAX 514-272-5939, groupe.jeunesse@comjeune.com, grpjeune@total.net, http://www.groupejeunesse.com, http://www.espace-jelinesse.com. Ed. R&P Charles Gelinas. Adv. contact Patrice Slavinski. B&W page CND 3,000, color page CND 4,300; trim 10.88 x 8.25. Circ: 60,000 (paid).

028.5   JPN
MAGAZINE SPECIAL. Text in Japanese. m. Document type: Magazine, Consumer. Published by: Kodansha Ltd., 2-12-21 Otowa, Bunkyo-ku, Tokyo, 112-8001, Japan. TEL 81-3-3946-6201, FAX 81-3-3944-9915, http://www.kodansha.co.jp.

028.5   JPN
MAGAZINE Z. Text in Japanese. m. Document type: Magazine, Consumer. Description: Features manga that are based on the characters for computer games or TV animation series. Published by: Kodansha Ltd., 2-12-21 Otowa, Bunkyo-ku, Tokyo, 112-8001, Japan. TEL 81-3-3946-6201, FAX 81-3-3944-9915, http://www.kodansha.co.jp.

▼ MAGE (NEW YORK, NY). see LITERATURE—Science Fiction, Fantasy, Horror

MAGYAR CSERKESZ/HUNGARIAN SCOUT MAGAZINE. see CLUBS

059.927   UAE
MAJID. Text in Arabic. 1979. w. AED 300 domestic; AED 420 in Europe; AED 350 elsewhere. adv. Document type: Consumer. Description: For children 4-16 years old. Published by: Al- Ittihad Press Publishing and Distribution Corp., Majallat Majid (Subsidiary of: Emirates Media Inc.), PO Box 3558, Abu Dhabi, United Arab Emirates. TEL 971-2-451804, FAX 971-2-451455, TELEX 22984 ITPRESS EM. Ed. Ahmed Omar. Circ: 170,000.

MAJOR AUTHORS AND ILLUSTRATORS FOR CHILDREN AND YOUNG ADULTS. see LITERATURE

028.5 500   GBR   ISSN 1355-8560
MAKING SENSE OF SCIENCE. Text in English. 1995. irreg., latest 2002, Aug. price varies. Document type: Published by: Portland Press Ltd. (Subsidiary of: Biochemical Society), 3rd Fl, Eagle House, 16 Procter St, London, WC1V 6NX, United Kingdom. TEL 44-20-72804110, FAX 44-20-72804169, sales@portland-services.com, http://www.portlandpress.com, http://www.portlandpress.com/books/. Ed. F Balkwill. R&P Adam Marshall. Subscr. to: Commerce Way, Colchester CO2 8HP, United Kingdom. TEL 44-1206-796351, FAX 44-1206-799331.

MAKULATURA; autorskie pismo mlodych. see LITERARY AND POLITICAL REVIEWS

028.5   CHE
MAKY/RATAPLAN. Text in French. 1949. m. CHF 21. bk.rev. Document type: Consumer. Formerly: Tim (0040-7704) Related titles: German ed. Published by: Editions Maky - Rataplan, 18 rue Camille Martin, Geneva, 1203, Switzerland. TEL 022-7962552, FAX 022-7961583. adv.: B&W page CHF 2,540, color page CHF 3,350; trim 190 x 132. Circ: 82,949.

MALADOSTS'. see LITERARY AND POLITICAL REVIEWS

745.5   DEU
MALSPASS KINDERLEICHT. Text in German. bi-m. EUR 2.60 newsstand/cover (effective 2003). adv. Document type: Magazine, Consumer. Published by: OZ Verlag GmbH, Roemerstr 90, Rheinfelden, 79618, Germany. TEL 49-7623-964-0, FAX 49-7623-96464200, vollmar@oz-bpv.de, http://www.oz-verlag.com.

028.5   UKR   ISSN 0025-1453
MALYATKO. Text in Ukrainian. 1960. m. USD 112 foreign (effective 2005). adv. illus. index. Document type: Magazine, Consumer. Published by: Zhurnal "Malyatko", vul Degtyarivska 38-44, Kyiv, 04119, Ukraine. Ed. Anatoliy Grigoruk. adv.: page USD 1,000. Circ: 33,630. Dist. by: East View Information Services, 3020 Harbor Ln. N., Minneapolis, MN 55447. TEL 763-550-0961, FAX 763-559-2931, eastview@eastview.com, http://www.eastview.com.

028.5 004.678   USA   ISSN 1090-5529
MAMAMEDIA. Text in English. 1996. q. free. Media: Online - full text. Published by: MaMaMedia, Inc., The SoHo Bldg, 110 Greene St, New York, NY 10012. TEL 212-334-3277, FAX 212-334-3276, info@mamamedia.com, http://www.mamamedia.com.

028.5   DEU   ISSN 0945-2400
MAMAMIA. Text in German. 1980. 6/yr. adv. Document type: Newsletter, Consumer. Address: Randersackererstr 81, Nuernberg, 97074, Germany. TEL 49-931-15729, FAX 49-931-3552512. Ed. Barbara Pohl Hildemann. adv.: page EUR 440. Circ: 10,000 (controlled).

059.927   UAE
AL-MANHAL/FOUNTAIN. Text in Arabic, English. 1982. 2/yr. Description: Student publication covering school activities. Published by: Abu Dhabi Secondary School for Boys, PO Box 2616, Abu Dhabi, United Arab Emirates. TEL 662874. Ed. Gumaa Eid M Al Muhairi. Circ: 300.

028.5   CHN   ISSN 1003-7128
MANHUA YUEKAN/CARTOON. Text in Chinese. 1985. m. CNY 47.76 (effective 2004). Document type: Magazine, Consumer. Published by: Henan Ribao Baoye Jituan, 28, Nongye Lu Dong, Zhengzhou, 450008, China. FAX 86-371-5795870, hnby.bgs@800e.net. Dist. by: China International Book Trading Corp, 35 Chegongzhuang Xilu, Haidian District, PO Box 399, Beijing 100044, China. TEL 86-10-68412045, FAX 86-10-68412023, cibtc@mail.cibtc.com.cn, http://www.cibtc.com.cn.

MARTHA'S KIDLIT NEWSLETTER. see LITERATURE

087.5   BRA   ISSN 1415-1359
MARVEL. Text in Portuguese. 1998. m. Document type: Magazine, Consumer. Published by: Editora Abril, S.A., Av. das Nacoes Unidas, 7221, 11 andar Pinheiros, Sao Paulo, SP 05425-902, Brazil. TEL 55-011-30372000, FAX 55-011-30375638, relacoes.corporativas@abril.com.br, http://www.abril.com.br/.

028.5   GBR   ISSN 1368-8111
MARVEL HEROES REBORN. Text in English. 1997. m. GBP 2.25 newsstand/cover. Document type: Consumer. Published by: Marvel Comics Ltd. (Subsidiary of: Panini UK Ltd.), Panini House, Coach & Horses Passage, The Pantiles, Tunbridge Wells, Kent TM2 5UJ, United Kingdom. TEL 44-1892-500100, FAX 44-1892-545666. Ed. Scott Gray. Dist. by: MarketForce UK Ltd, 247 Tottenham Court Rd, London, Middx W1T 7AU, United Kingdom. TEL 44-20-72616996, FAX 44-207-2616951.

059.927   QAT
AL-MASHA'IL. Text in Arabic. 1987. m. Published by: Qatar Establishment for Journalism Printing and Publication, P O Box 1838, Doha, Qatar. TEL 448282, FAX 446723. Ed. Ahmed Abdul Rahman Al Syid. Circ: 22,000.

028.5   RUS
MASTERILKA. Text in Russian. m. RUR 140 (effective 2002). Description: Covers activities for children 5-12 years of age. Published by: Izdatel'skii Dom Karapuz, Izmailovskoe shosse 48a, Moscow, 105318, Russian Federation. TEL 7-095-9182810, http://www.karapuz.com.

028.5   CZE   ISSN 0025-5440
MATERIDOUSKA; literarni mesicnik pro nejmensi ctenare. Text in Czech. 1945. m. CZK 18, USD 10.60. illus. Indexed: RASB. Published by: Mlada Fronta, Radlicka 61, Prague, 15002, Czech Republic. Ed. Josef Brukner. Dist. by: Artia, Ve Smeckach 30, Prague 1 111 27, Czech Republic.

028.5   CYP   ISSN 0025-5904
MATHITIKI ESTIA. Text in English, French, Greek. 1950. a. free. bk.rev.; film rev.; play rev. bibl.; charts; illus. Document type: Academic/Scholarly. Description: Contains essays, poems, articles, interviews, and other materials written by students. Media: Duplicated (not offset). Published by: Ministry of Education and Culture, Pagkyprion Gymnasion, PO Box 1034, Nicosia, 1500, Cyprus. TEL 357-2-430670, FAX 357-2-430915, pankypri@spidernet.com.cy. Ed. Stylianos Papantoniou. Circ: 1,000 (controlled).

MAURIZIO. see PHILATELY

028.5   DEU
DIE MAUS (BERLIN). Text in German. 1997. m. EUR 30; EUR 2.50 newsstand/cover (effective 2005). adv. Document type: Magazine, Consumer. Published by: Egmont Ehapa Verlag GmbH, Wallstr 59, Berlin, 10179, Germany. TEL 49-30-240080, FAX 49-30-24008599, leserservice@ehapa.de, http://www.ehapa.de/ehapa/e14/e40/e174/index_ger.html. adv.: page EUR 4,600. Circ: 74,533 (paid and controlled).

028.5   DEU
DIE MAUS - DAS STICKERMAGAZIN. Text in German. 2001. q. EUR 9.45 newsstand/cover (effective 2002). adv. Document type: Magazine, Consumer. Published by: Panini Verlags GmbH, Ravensstr 48, Nettetal, 41334, Germany. TEL 49-711-947680, FAX 49-711-94768830, info@panini-dino.de, http://www.panini-media.de. adv.: page EUR 3,900. Circ: 150,000 (paid and controlled).

053.1   DEU
MAUSKLICK. Text in German. 1998. m. EUR 2.20 newsstand/cover (effective 2003). adv. Document type: Magazine, Consumer. Published by: Pro Verlag Gesellschaft fuer Publikationen mbH, Berner Str 38, Frankfurt Am Main, 60437, Germany. TEL 49-69-5008050, FAX 49-69-5008051, office@proverlag.com, http://www.proverlag.com. adv.: page EUR 3,400; trim 210 x 280. Circ: 40,200 (paid and controlled).

MAVRICA/RAINBOW. see RELIGIONS AND THEOLOGY—Roman Catholic

059.956   JPN
MCSISTER. Text in Japanese. 1966. m. JPY 420 newsstand/cover (effective 2002). adv. Document type: Magazine, Consumer. Description: Contains fashion, beauty, and culture information for senior high school girls. Published by: Hachette Fujingaho Co. Ltd. (Subsidiary of: Hachette Filipacchi Medias S.A.), 2-9-1 Nishi Shinbashi, Minato-ku, Tokyo, 105-0003, Japan. TEL 81-3-3506-6601, FAX 81-3-3506-6606, http://www.hfm.co.jp. Circ: 139,000 (paid).

MEDIEN & ERZIEHUNG. see COMMUNICATIONS—Television And Cable

028.5 613.7   DEU
MEDIZINI. Text in German. m. adv. Document type: Magazine, Consumer. Published by: Wort und Bild Verlag Konradshoehe GmbH, Konradshoehe, Baierbrunn, 82065, Germany. TEL 49-89-74433-0, FAX 49-89-74433150, http://www.wortundbild.de. Adv. contact Wolfgang Smeilus. page EUR 34,360; trim 210 x 296. Circ: 2,043,308 (controlled).

305.23   DEU
MEGA HIRO. Text in German. 2002. fortn. EUR 2.50 newsstand/cover (effective 2005). adv. Document type: Magazine, Consumer. Published by: Panini Verlags GmbH, Ravensstr 48, Nettetal, 41334, Germany. TEL 49-2157-81750, FAX 49-2157-81484528, info@panini-dino.de, http://www.panini-media.de. adv.: page EUR 4,900; trim 210 x 280. Circ: 113,431 (paid and controlled).

305.23   DEU
MEGA HIRO CARD MASTER. Text in German. m. EUR 2.99 newsstand/cover (effective 2005). adv. Document type: Magazine, Consumer. Published by: Panini Verlags GmbH, Ravensstr 48, Nettetal, 41334, Germany. TEL 49-2157-81750, FAX 49-2157-81484528, info@panini-dino.de, http://www.panini-media.de. adv.: page EUR 4,900; trim 210 x 280. Circ: 168,860 (paid).

794.9   DEU
▼ MEGA HIRO GAME MASTER. Text in German. 2004. 4/yr. EUR 2.99 newsstand/cover (effective 2005). adv. Document type: Magazine, Consumer. Published by: Panini Verlags GmbH, Ravensstr 48, Nettetal, 41334, Germany. TEL 49-2157-81750, FAX 49-2157-81484528, info@panini-dino.de, http://www.panini-media.de. adv.: page EUR 4,900; trim 210 x 280. Circ: 85,014 (paid and controlled).

305.23   DEU
MEGA HIRO RAETSELMASTER. Text in German. bi-m. EUR 1.99 newsstand/cover (effective 2005). adv. Document type: Magazine, Consumer. Published by: Panini Verlags GmbH, Ravensstr 48, Nettetal, 41334, Germany. TEL 49-2157-81750, FAX 49-2157-81484528, info@panini-dino.de, http://www.panini-media.de. adv.: page EUR 3,900; trim 210 x 280. Circ: 77,840 (paid and controlled).

028.5   DEU
MEGAPHON. Text in English, German. 1984. bi-m. USD 15. adv. bk.rev.; play rev. charts. Published by: Schuelerzeitung Megaphon, Philipp-Reis-Schule, Hoher Weg 29, Friedrichsdorf, 61381, Germany. Circ: 2,000.

028.5 DEU
MEIN KLEINES PONY. Text in German. m. adv. **Document type:** *Magazine, Consumer.*
Published by: Ehapa Verlag GmbH, Wallstr. 59, Berlin, 10179, Germany. TEL 49-30-24008-0, FAX 49-30-24008599, http://ehapa.funonline.de. Ed. Elvira Braendle. Adv. contact Olaf Hansen. Circ: 80,000.

369.4 NZL
MEMBERS MAG E.B.R. E.G.R. (Every Boy's Rally Every Girl's Rally) Variant title: New Zealand Rally Council. Members Magazine. Text in English. q. NZD 5.25 (effective 2000). **Document type:** *Bulletin.* **Description:** Contains articles, news, poetry and puzzles for children.
Published by: Every Boy's and Every Girl's Rally Council N.Z. Inc., P.O. Box 1903, Palmerston North, New Zealand. TEL 64-6-3593735. Ed. Gill Lafferty. Circ: 3,100 (paid).

028.5 CAN ISSN 1497-2662
MEMBRES DE COMMUNICATION-JEUNESSE. BULLETIN. Text in French. 1978. irreg.
Former titles (until 1999): Communication Jeunesse (1483-6424); Which incorporated (1993-1998): Grimoire (1196-3263); (1991-1998): Fou Lire (1199-7192); (until 199?): Information de Communication-Jeunesse. Bulletin (1483-6416); Which superseded in part (in 198?): Lurelu (0705-6567)
Indexed: CPerl.
Published by: Communication-Jeunesse, 4388, rue Saint-Denis, bureau 305, Montreal, PQ H2J 2L1, Canada. TEL 514-286-6020, FAX 514-286-6093, info@communication-jeunesse.qc.ca, http://www.communication-jeunesse.qc.ca.

028.5 PAK ISSN 0025-9144
MEMON ALAM. Text in English, Gujarati. 1958. m. PKR 5, USD 1. adv. bk.rev.
Published by: Memon Youths Organisation, O.T. 9-145, Kagazi Bazar, P O Box 5097, Karachi 2, Pakistan. Ed. Umer A Rehman. Circ: 5,000.

655.41 FIN ISSN 1238-5980
MERKURIUS-KIRJAKERHO. Text in Finnish. 1995. 15/yr. adv. **Document type:** *Magazine, Consumer.*
Published by: Sanoma Magazines Finland Corporation, Hoylaamotie 1 D, P.O. Box 100, Helsinki, 00040, Finland. TEL 358-9-1201, FAX 358-9-1205171, info@sanomamagazines.fi, http://www.merkurius.net, http://www.sanomamagazines.fi. adv.: color page EUR 1,730. Circ: 16,000 (controlled).

028.5 FRA ISSN 1297-8671
MES PREMIERS J'AIME LIRE. Text in French. 1993. m. EUR 64.80 domestic; EUR 84.80 foreign (effective 2005). **Document type:** *Magazine, Consumer.*
Published by: Bayard Presse, 3 Rue Bayard, Paris, 75393 Cedex 08, France. TEL 33-1-44356060, FAX 33-1-44356161, redactions@bayard-presse.com, http://www.bayardpresse.com. Ed. Beatrice Valentin.

028.5 ITA ISSN 0026-0304
MESSAGGERO DEI RAGAZZI. Text in Italian. 1922. s-m. EUR 20 domestic (effective 2005). illus. **Document type:** *Magazine, Consumer.*
Published by: Messaggero Sant' Antonio Editrice, Via Orto Botanico 11, Padua, PD 35123, Italy. TEL 39-049-8225000, FAX 39-049-8225650, info@santantonio.org, http://www.santantonio.org. Ed. Giacomo Pantechini. Circ: 60,000.

METAL EDGE; hard rock's #1 magazine. see *MUSIC*

METAL MANIACS. see *MUSIC*

028.5 HRV ISSN 0026-1939
➤ **MI MLADI.** Text in Croatian. 1956. s-a. HRK 10 domestic; USD 20 foreign (effective 2003). dance rev.; music rev.; play rev.; software rev.; tel.rev. illus. **Document type:** *Academic/Scholarly.* **Description:** Covers anything within the interest of high school students connected with the life and work of their school.
Published by: Treca Gimnazija, 52 Kuslanova ul, Zagreb, 10000, Croatia. TEL 385-1-2305454, FAX 385-1-2339628, 3.gimnazija@skole.hinet.hr. Ed. Josip Pilic. Pub. Martin Orsolic. Circ: 1,000.

028.5 BRA ISSN 0104-2114
MICKEY. Text in Portuguese. 1952. m. adv. back issues avail. **Document type:** *Magazine, Consumer.*
Published by: Editora Abril, S.A., Av. das Nacoes Unidas, 7221, 11 andar Pinheiros, Sao Paulo, SP 05425-902, Brazil. TEL 55-11-50872112, FAX 55-11-50872100, http://www.diseny.com.br/, http://www.abril.com.br/. Circ: 4,900.

087.5 ROM ISSN 1221-6038
MICKEY MOUSE. Text in Romanian. 1993. m. ROL 460,000; ROL 23,000 newsstand/cover (effective 2002). **Document type:** *Magazine, Consumer.*
Published by: Egmont Romania, Piata Presei Libere nr. 1, corp B2, etaj 4, Bucharest, Romania. TEL 40-21-2246055, FAX 40-21-2246057, cc@ero.egmont.com, http://www.egmont.ro.

028.5 FRA ISSN 0242-9217
MICKEY PARADE. Text in French. m. **Document type:** *Consumer.*
Published by: Disney Hachette Presse, 10 rue Thierry le Luron, Levallois Perret, Cedex 92592, France. TEL 33-1-41348500, FAX 33-1-41348989. Ed. Gilles Heylen. Circ: 178,000.

028.5 USA
MIDLINK MAGAZINE. Text in English. 1994. q.
Media: Online - full content.
Published by: Ligon Middle School, 706 E Lenoir St, Raleigh, NC 27601. http://longwood.cs.ucf.edu/~MidLink/. Ed. Caroline McCullen.

741.5 GBR ISSN 1479-8050
▼ **THE MIGHTY WORLD OF MARVEL.** Text in English. 2003. m. GBP 28.80 (effective 2005). **Document type:** *Magazine, Consumer.*
Published by: Panini UK Ltd., Panini House Coach and Horses Passage, Tunbridge Wells, Kent TN2 5UJ, United Kingdom. TEL 44-1892-500100, info@panini.co.uk, http://www.paninicomics.co.uk.

028.5 LKA
MIHIRA. Text in Singhalese. 1964. w. LKR 4.50 newsstand/cover (effective 2000).
Published by: The Associated Newspapers of Ceylon Ltd., Lake House, D.R. Wijewardena Mawatha, Colombo, 10, Sri Lanka. TEL 94-1-421181, FAX 94-1-449069. Ed. Dayanate Lankapura. Circ: 145,000.

028.5 EGY ISSN 1110-1024
MIKI/MICKEY. Text in Arabic. 1959. w. USD 65 in Africa in Africa, Asia & Europe; USD 70 in North America in N. American & India; USD 85 in Australia in Australia, Japan & S. America (effective 2001).
Published by: Dar Al-Hilal, 12 Sharia Muhammad Ezz al-Arab, Cairo, Egypt. TEL 02-362-5450, FAX 02-362-5469, darhilal@idsc.gov.eg. Ed. Mrs. Effat Nasser.

028.5 FRA
MILLE ET UNE HISTOIRES. Text in French. 1999. m. FRF 296 domestic; FRF 455.50 foreign (effective 2000). **Description:** Features fairy tales for children 3 to 7 years of age.
Published by: Fleurus Presse, 129 bd. Malesherbes, Paris, 75017, France. TEL 33-1-56793636. Ed. Pascal Teulade.

028.5 CHN
MIMI HUABAO/MIMI PICTORIAL. Text in Chinese. bi-m. CNY 3.90. **Description:** For children 3-7 years of age.
Published by: Fujian Shaonian Ertong Chubanshe, 27 Degui Xiang, Fuzhou, Fujian 350001, China. TEL 537301. Ed. Xu Daojing. **Dist. overseas by:** Jiangsu Publications Import & Export Corp., 56 Gao Yun Ling, Nanjing, Jiangsu, China.

028.5 053.1 DEU
MINI; mit viel Raetsel-Spass. Variant title: Mini Fuer Alle. Text in German. w. EUR 0.80 newsstand/cover (effective 2003). adv. **Document type:** *Magazine, Consumer.* **Description:** Filled with stories and activities for young children's leisure time.
Published by: Pabel-Moewig Verlag KG (Subsidiary of: Heinrich Bauer Verlag), Karlsruherstr 31, Rastatt, 76437, Germany. TEL 49-7222-130, FAX 49-7222-13218, empfang@vpm.de, http://www.vpm-online.de. adv.: B&W page EUR 3,010, color page EUR 4,060. Circ: 279,507 (paid).

028.5 DEU
MINI EXTRA. Text in German. 4/yr. EUR 1.60 newsstand/cover (effective 2003). adv. **Document type:** *Magazine, Consumer.*
Published by: Pabel-Moewig Verlag KG (Subsidiary of: Heinrich Bauer Verlag), Karlsruherstr 31, Rastatt, 76437, Germany. TEL 49-7222-130, FAX 49-7222-13218, empfang@vpm.de, http://www.vpm-online.de. adv.: page EUR 4,550. Circ: 130,000 (paid).

028.1 ZAF ISSN 1022-3053
MINIMAG; the magazine for kids. Text in English. 1994. m. ZAR 60 (effective 2000). adv. bk.rev.; film rev.; music rev. **Description:** Aimed at the young beginner and independent reader.
Published by: Elken Publishing, PO Box 72738, Lynnwood Ridge, Pretoria 0040, South Africa. TEL 27-12-8044044, FAX 27-12-8044044, minimag@global.co.za. Ed., R&P Elva Seymore. Adv. contact Caryl Demeillon. Circ: 20,000 (paid).

MINISTRANT. see *RELIGIONS AND THEOLOGY—Roman Catholic*

028.5 RUS ISSN 0208-1563
MISHA/TEDDY BEAR. Text in Russian. 1983. m. USD 99.95 in United States. illus. **Document type:** *Magazine, Consumer.* —East View.
Address: Ul Pravdy 24, Moscow, 125805, Russian Federation. TEL 7-095-9784788, FAX 7-095-2573106. Ed. N A Gavrilova. **US dist. addr.:** East View Information Services, 3020 Harbor Ln. N., Minneapolis, MN 55447. TEL 612-550-0961.

028.5 ISR
MISHBETZET. Text in Hebrew. 1958. m. USD 50 (effective 2000).
Published by: Etzb'oni Publishing House, P O Box 28110, Tel Aviv, 61280, Israel. FAX 972-3-5373906. Ed. Michael Shir. Circ: 20,000.

MISHKAFAYIM. see *ART*

028.5 HUN
MISS BEAUTY. Text in Hungarian. 3/yr. adv. **Document type:** *Magazine, Consumer.*
Published by: Axel Springer - Budapest Kft., Varosmajor u 11, Budapest, 1122, Hungary. TEL 36-1-4885700, FAX 36-1-2025332, bayerj@axels.hu. Circ: 23,000 (paid).

MISSIONARIES OF THE SACRED HEART. ANNALS AUSTRALIA; journal of Catholic culture. see *RELIGIONS AND THEOLOGY—Roman Catholic*

059.94541 FIN
MIX. Text in Finnish. m. adv. **Document type:** *Magazine, Consumer.* **Description:** Contains articles and features on popular music and celebrities for teenagers.
Published by: Aller Julkaisut OY, Pursimiehenkatu 29-31A, Helsinki, 00150, Finland. TEL 358-9-7777777, FAX 358-9-77777177, http://www.mixworld.net. Circ: 30,697 (paid).

028.5 SCG ISSN 0026-7031
MLADOST. Text in Serbo-Croatian. 1955. w. YUN 80.
Published by: (Savez Socijalisticke Omladine Jugoslavije YUG), Mladost, Marsala Tita 2, Belgrade. Ed. Aleksandar Dukanovic.

621.381 028.5 POL ISSN 0462-9760
MLODY TECHNIK. Text in Polish. 1932. m. PLZ 90 domestic; EUR 46 in Europe; EUR 57 elsewhere (effective 2005). **Document type:** *Magazine, Consumer.*
Published by: A V T- Korporacja Sp. z o. o., ul Burleska 9, Warsaw, 01939, Poland. TEL 48-22-5689941, FAX 48-22-5689944, redakcja@ep.com.pl, http://www.mt.com.pl, http://www.avt.pl. Ed. Adam Debowski.

028.5 FRA
MOBICLIC; le magazine multimedia des 7 a 12 ans. Text in French. 10/yr. USD 95 in US & Canada.
Published by: Milan Presse, 300 rue Leon Joulin, Toulouse, Cedex 1 31101, France. TEL 33-5-61766464, FAX 33-5-61766400, webmaster@milanpresse.com, http://www.milanpresse.com. Pub. Patrice Amen.

028.5 DEU ISSN 0942-7147
MOBILE; Zeitschrift fuer junge Eltern. Text in German. 1992. 9/yr. EUR 7.20; EUR 1.60 newsstand/cover (effective 2005). adv. back issues avail. **Document type:** *Journal, Consumer.*
Published by: Verlag Herder GmbH und Co. KG, Hermann-Herder-Str 4, Freiburg Im Breisgau, 79104, Germany. TEL 49-761-27170, FAX 49-761-2717520, kundenservice@herder.de, http://www.herder.de. Ed. Renate Ferrari. Adv. contact Bettina Schillinger-Wegmann. B&W page EUR 10,960, color page EUR 17,500. Circ: 330,000 (controlled).

028.5 RUS ISSN 0131-2243
MODELIST - KONSTRUKTOR. Text in Russian. 1962. m. USD 152 foreign (effective 2005). bk.rev. illus. Supplement avail. **Document type:** *Magazine, Consumer.* —East View.
Published by: Redaktsiya Zhurnala Modelist - Konstruktor, Novodmitrovskaya ul 5-a, Moscow, 127015, Russian Federation. TEL 7-095-7873552, http://modelist-konstruktor.ru. Ed. A S Raguzin. Circ: 15,000. **Dist. by:** East View Information Services, 3020 Harbor Ln. N., Minneapolis, MN 55447. TEL 763-550-0961, FAX 763-559-2931, eastview@eastview.com, http://www.eastview.com.

028.5 FRA ISSN 1258-5033
MOI, JE LIS DIABOLO. Text in French. 1987. m. EUR 55 (effective 2005).
Formerly (until 1995): Diabolo (0987-1209)
Published by: Milan Presse, 300 rue Leon Joulin, Toulouse, Cedex 1 31101, France. TEL 33-5-61766464, FAX 33-5-61766400. Ed. Alain Oriol. Pub. Patrice Amen. Circ: 55,150.

MOLDE FACIL. see *NEEDLEWORK*

028.5 EST
MOLODEZH' ESTONII. Text in Russian. 260/yr. USD 790 in United States.
Related titles: Microfilm ed.: (from EVP).
Address: Parnu mnt 67-a, Tallin, Estonia. TEL 370-6286140, FAX 370-6461623. Ed. Sergei Sergeev. **US dist. addr.:** East View Information Services, 3020 Harbor Ln. N., Minneapolis, MN 55447. TEL 612-550-0961.

028.5 MDA
MOLODEZH' MOLDOVY. Text in Russian. w. USD 249 in United States.
Address: Ul Pushkin 22, Chisinau, Moldova. TEL 373-2-233731, FAX 373-2-233708. Ed. Nikolai Roshka. **US dist. addr.:** East View Information Services, 3020 Harbor Ln. N., Minneapolis, MN 55447. TEL 612-550-0961.

028.5 UZB
MOLODEZH' UZBEKISTANA. Text in Russian. w. USD 260 in United States.
Address: Matbuotcilar 32, Tashkent, 700000, Uzbekistan. TEL 998-371-21338948, FAX 998-371-21365698. Ed. V Ivanov. **US dist. addr.:** East View Information Services, 3020 Harbor Ln. N., Minneapolis, MN 55447. TEL 512-550-0961.

028.5 780.42 RUS ISSN 0132-8816
PG3201
MOLODEZHNAYA ESTRADA. Text in Russian. 1943. q. USD 74 foreign (effective 2003). adv. bk.rev. **Description:** Presents a collection of popular and modern songs and plays.
Published by: Izdatel'stvo Molodaya Gvardiya, Sushchevskaya ul 21, Moscow, 103030, Russian Federation. TEL 7-095-9720546, FAX 7-095-9720582, TELEX 411261 FAKEL. Ed. N Schantarenkov. Circ: 185,000. **Dist. by:** M K - Periodica, ul Gilyarovskogo 39, Moscow 129110, Russian Federation. TEL 7-095-2845008, FAX 7-095-2813798, info@periodicals.ru, http://www.mkniga.ru; **US dist. addr.:** East View Information Services, 3020 Harbor Ln. N., Minneapolis, MN 55447. TEL 612-550-0961.

MOME; le mensuel pour ton francais. see *LINGUISTICS*

028.5 FRA ISSN 1258-6447
MON QUOTIDIEN. Text in French. 240/yr. **Description:** Covers current events throughout the world for children ages 10 to 14.
Published by: Play Bac Presse, 33 rue du Petit-Musc, Paris, 75004, France. TEL 33-1-42740909, FAX 33-1-42744490. Ed. F Dufour. Pub. J Saltet. **Subscr. to:** BP 460, Sainte Genevieve Cedex 60732, France.

028.5 ITA ISSN 0391-5484
MONDO ERRE. Text in Italian. 1975. m. (10/yr.). EUR 29.95 in Europe; EUR 37.70 in Africa; EUR 47.51 in Australasia; EUR 31.50 Mediterranean basin; EUR 38.22 The Americas & Asia (effective 2002). adv. **Description:** Review of current events for boys and girls.
Published by: (Centro Catechistico Salesiano), Editrice ELLEDICI, Corso Francia 214, Leumann, TO 10096, Italy. TEL 39-11-9552111, FAX 39-11-9574048, mail@elledici.org, abbonamenti@elledici.org, http://www.elledici.org. Ed. Valerio Bocci. Circ: 30,000.

MONKEYSHINES AND EWE EXPLORE THE 7 CONTINENTS. see *GEOGRAPHY*

028.5 USA
MONKEYSHINES ON AMERICA. Text in English. 1986. 5/yr. (during school yr.). USD 38.95 (effective 2004). back issues avail. **Description:** Covers American history and geography for elementary, middle and high school students and their teachers.
Published by: (North Carolina Learning Institute for Fitness and Education), Monkeyshines Publications, PO Box 10245, Greensboro, NC 27404. TEL 336-292-6999, mkshines@nr.infi.net, mkshines@infionline.net, http://www.monkeyshinespublishers.com. Ed., R&P Phyllis Goldman.

MONKEYSHINES ON ANCIENT CULTURES. see *HISTORY*

MONKEYSHINES ON ART AND GREAT ARTISTS. see *ART*

028.5 USA
MONKEYSHINES ON HEALTH AND SCIENCE. Text in English. 1987. 2/yr. USD 28.95 (effective 2001). back issues avail. **Description:** For elementary, middle and high school students and their teachers.
Published by: (North Carolina Learning Institute for Fitness and Education), Monkeyshines Publications, PO Box 10245, Greensboro, NC 27404. TEL 336-292-6999, FAX 775-871-2861, mkshines@nr.infi.net, mkshines@infionline.net, http://www.Monkeyshinespublishers.com. Ed., R&P Phyllis Goldman.

028.5 JPN
MONTHLY BOY'S CHAMPION/GEKKAN SHONEN-CHAMPION. Text in Japanese. 1970. m. JPY 30,000.
Published by: Akita Shoten Publishing Co. Ltd., 10-8 Iida-Bashi 2-chome, Chiyoda-ku, Tokyo, 102-0072, Japan. Ed. Taizo Kabemura.

MORE (NASHVILLE). see *RELIGIONS AND THEOLOGY—Protestant*

028.5 DEU ISSN 0323-8857
MOSAIK (BERLIN); die unglaubliche Reise der Abrafaxe. Text in German. 1955. m. EUR 1.85 newsstand/cover (effective 2003). adv. bk.rev. 54 p./no.; **Document type:** *Magazine, Consumer.*
Published by: Mosaik Steinchen fuer Steinchen Verlag GmbH, Lindenallee 5, Berlin, 14050, Germany. TEL 49-30-306927-0, FAX 49-30-30692729, mosaik@abrafaxe.de, http://www.abrafaxe.com. Ed. Joerg Reuter. Pubs. Anne Hauser Thiele, Klaus Schleiter. Adv. contact Reinhard Fischer. B&W page EUR 3,380, color page EUR 5,930; trim 165 x 235. Circ: 95,428 (paid).

MOSHIACH TIMES. see *RELIGIONS AND THEOLOGY—Judaic*

MOTO KIDS. see *SPORTS AND GAMES—Bicycles And Motorcycles*

MOVE. see *SPORTS AND GAMES*

310.412 CUB ISSN 0864-0327
HQ1104
MUCHACHA. Text in Spanish. 1980. m. CUP 19.20 domestic; USD 21 in North America; USD 27 in South America; USD 30 in Europe; USD 42 elsewhere.
Published by: Federacion de Mujeres Cubanas, Editora de la Mujer, Galiano 264 esq. Neptuno, Apdo. 2545, Havana, 2, Cuba. TEL 7-61-5919. Ed. Silvia Martinez. Circ: 120,000. **Dist. by:** Ediciones Cubanas, Obispo No. 527, Apdo. 605, Havana, Cuba.

MUCHACHOS. see *LINGUISTICS*

028.5 DEU ISSN 0930-7818
MUECKE; die Zeitschrift fuer Kids mit Grips. Text in German. 1960. m. adv. **Document type:** *Magazine, Consumer.* **Description:** Magazine for children in the higher grades. Aims to be educational and informative through the use of stories, pictures, puzzles, games and crafts.
Published by: Universum Verlagsanstalt GmbH KG, Taunusstr 54, Wiesbaden, 65183, Germany. TEL 49-611-9030-0, FAX 49-611-9030382, uv@universum.de, http://www.universum.de/univ/kiju/index_muecke.html. Ed. Jutta Filzek. Adv. contact Jochen Hillesheim.

028.5 IND
MULTICULTURAL CHILDREN'S LITERATURE. Text in English. 1979. 4/yr. INR 495, USD 102 (effective 2000). adv. abstr.; bibl. index.
Indexed: ChLitAb.
Published by: K.K. Roy (Private) Ltd., 55 Gariahat Rd., P O Box 10210, Kolkata, West Bengal 700 019, India. R&P M Misra TEL 91-33-475-4872. Circ: 1,900.

305.232 ESP ISSN 1132-7731
MUNDO DE TU BEBE. Variant title: Tu Bebe. Text in Spanish. 1993. m. EUR 25.24 domestic; EUR 60.84 in Europe; EUR 157.56 elsewhere; EUR 2.10 newsstand/cover (effective 2002). adv. back issues avail. **Document type:** *Magazine, Consumer.*
Published by: H Y M S A, Grupo Editorial Edipresse, Muntaner, 40-42, Barcelona, 08011, Spain. TEL 34-93-508-7000, FAX 34-93-454-1321, tubebe@hymsa.com, hymsa@hymsa.com, http://www.hymsa.com. Ed. Daniel Elies. Pub. Pedro Riano.

028.5 RUS
MURAVEINIK. Text in Russian. m. USD 109.95 in United States.
Published by: Proizvodstvenno-Tekhnicheskoe Predpriyatie Era, Ul Gagarina 11, Reutov, Moscow, 143952, Russian Federation. TEL 7-095-9150886, FAX 7-095-2511589. Ed. N N Starchenko. **US dist. addr.:** East View Information Services, 3020 Harbor Ln. N., Minneapolis, MN 55447. TEL 612-550-0961.

028.162 RUS ISSN 0132-1943
AP215.R9
MURZILKA. Text in Russian. 1924. m. USD 126 foreign (effective 2005). adv. bk.rev. illus. **Document type:** *Magazine, Consumer.*
—East View.
Published by: Redaktsiya Zhurnala Murzilka, Novodmitrovskaya ul 5-a, Moscow, 125015, Russian Federation. http://www.murzilka.km.ru. Ed. Tat'yana Androsenko. Circ: 150,000. **Dist. by:** East View Information Services, 3020 Harbor Ln. N., Minneapolis, MN 55447. TEL 763-550-0961, FAX 763-559-2931, eastview@eastview.com, http://www.eastview.com.

028.5 909 USA ISSN 1090-0381
AP201
MUSE (CHICAGO). Text in English. 1996. 10/yr. USD 32.97 domestic; USD 44.97 foreign; USD 4.95 newsstand/cover domestic (effective 2005). adv. illus. reprints avail. **Document type:** *Magazine, Consumer.* **Description:** This exploration and discovery magazine for curious, intelligent kids ages 10 and up features fascinating articles explaining how and why the natural world works and includes cartoons, contests, and magnificent photos.
Related titles: Online - full text ed.: (from ProQuest Information & Learning).
Indexed: ICM, RGYP.
Published by: (Smithsonian Institution), Carus Publishing Company, 315 Fifth St, Peru, IL 61354. TEL 603-924-7209, 800-821-0115, FAX 815-224-2256, custsvc@cobblestone.mv.com, http://www.cricketmag.com.

MUSIC AT THE KINDERGARTEN. see *MUSIC*

MUSIC CITY MOTORSPORTS. see *SPORTS AND GAMES—Bicycles And Motorcycles*

THE MUSIC LEADER. see *RELIGIONS AND THEOLOGY—Protestant*

MUSIC MAKERS (NASHVILLE). see *MUSIC*

028.5 297 USA ISSN 1542-5371
▼ **MUSLIM KID'S JOURNAL.** Text in English. 2003. m. USD 30 (effective 2003).
Published by: MK Journal, P. O. Box 10226, New Brunswick, NJ 08906. TEL 732-393-1476, editor@mkjournal.com, http://www.mkjournal.com.

087.2 FRA ISSN 1629-6966
MUTEEN; il y a une avant vingt ans...evidemment!. Text in French. 2001. 10/yr. EUR 17 (effective 2002). adv. **Document type:** *Magazine, Consumer.*
Related titles: Online - full text ed.
Published by: Les Editions Jalou, 10 rue du Platre, Paris, 75004, France. TEL 33-1-53011030, FAX 33-1-53019200, info@officielnews.com, http://www.muteen.com, http://www.officielnews.com. Ed. Catherine Nerson.

028.5 COD
MWANA SHABA JUNIOR; magazine des jeunes de la Gecamines. Text in French. 1964. m.
Published by: (Generale des Carrieres et des Mines, Division des Relations Publiques COG), Generale des Carrieres et des Mines, BP 450, Lubumbashi, Congo, Dem. Republic.

MY DEVOTIONS. see *RELIGIONS AND THEOLOGY—Protestant*

MY DEVOTIONS (LARGE PRINT EDITION). see *RELIGIONS AND THEOLOGY—Protestant*

028.5 GBR ISSN 1460-6372
MY FIRST A B C & 1 2 3. Text in English. 1998. m. GBP 18; GBP 1.50 newsstand/cover (effective 1999). **Document type:** *Consumer.* **Description:** Creates a creative and fun environment in which children can acquire literacy and numeracy.
Published by: Burghley Publishing Ltd., 14 Barn Hill, Stamford, Lincs PE9 2AE, United Kingdom. TEL 44-1780-763366, FAX 44-1780-763365. **Dist. by:** Seymour Distribution Ltd, 86 Newman St, London W1T 3EX, United Kingdom. FAX 44-207-396-8002, enquiries@seymour.co.uk.

C

MY FRIEND; a Catholic magazine for kids. see *RELIGIONS AND THEOLOGY—Roman Catholic*

028.5 JPN
N H K - NO OKASANTO ISSHO. Text in Japanese. m. **Document type:** *Magazine, Consumer.*
Published by: Kodansha Ltd., 2-12-21 Otowa, Bunkyo-ku, Tokyo, 112-8001, Japan. TEL 81-3-3946-6201, FAX 81-3-3944-9915, http://www.kodansha.co.jp.

028.5 DEU
N O W SCHUELERZEITUNG DER STAATLICHEN REALSCHULE SPEYER. Text in German. 1970. a.
Published by: Realschule im Georg-Friedrich-Kolb-Schulzentrum, Speyer, 67346, Germany. Circ: 400.

N S T A REPORTS. see *EDUCATION*

028.5 JPN
NAKAYOSI. Variant title: Nakayoshi. Text in Japanese. 1954. m. illus. **Document type:** *Magazine, Consumer.* **Description:** Combines comics with TV tie-ins and special feature articles. For girls in the fifth or sixth grades of elementary school.
Published by: Kodansha Ltd., 2-12-21 Otowa, Bunkyo-ku, Tokyo, 112-8001, Japan. TEL 81-3-3946-6201, FAX 81-3-3944-9915, http://www.toppan.co.jp/kodansha/, http://www.kodansha.co.jp.

808.836 FIN ISSN 0359-1174
NALLE PUH. Text in Finnish. 1981. m. EUR 35 (effective 2004). adv. **Document type:** *Magazine, Consumer.*
Published by: Sanoma Magazines Finland Corporation, Hoylaamotie 1 D, P.O. Box 100, Helsinki, 00040, Finland. TEL 358-9-1201, FAX 358-9-1205171, info@sanomamagazines.fi, http://www.sanomamagazines.fi. Ed. Johani Senqvist. adv.: color page EUR 2,600. Circ: 43,452.

305.23 420 375.4 THA ISSN 1513-2110
NATION JUNIOR. Text in English. 1999. s-m. adv. **Document type:** *Magazine.* **Description:** Covers entertainment and general news for young readers interested in learning English.
Related titles: Online - full content ed.
Published by: Nation Multimedia Group Public Co. Ltd., 44 Moo 10 Bang Na-Trat KM 4.5, Bang Na district, Bangkok, 10260, Thailand. TEL 66-2-3255555, FAX 66-2-3172099, nj@nationjunior.net, info@nationgroup.com, http://www.nationjunior.net, http://www.nationgroup.com/. Ed. Andrew Biggs.

371.83 USA
NATIONAL BETA CLUB JOURNAL. Text in English. 1934. 6/yr. membership. illus. **Document type:** *Newsletter.* **Description:** For honor student members of the club.
Published by: National Beta Club, 151 W Lee St, Spartanburg, SC 29306-3012. TEL 864-583-4553. Ed. Shala Hainer. Circ: 350,000.

NATIONAL CENTRE FOR RESEARCH IN CHILDREN'S LITERATURE. PAPERS. see *LITERATURE*

NATIONAL GEOGRAPHIC EXPLORER. see *GEOGRAPHY*

NATIONAL GEOGRAPHIC KIDS. see *GEOGRAPHY*

NATIONAL PEDICULOSIS ASSOCIATION. PROGRESS. see *PUBLIC HEALTH AND SAFETY*

028.5 025.04 DEU
NATUR - DAS KINDERWEB. Text in German. m. **Document type:** *Consumer.* **Description:** Shows children ages 7-10 how to use the Internet to satisfy their interest in nature and animals.
Media: Online - full text.
Published by: Kidoclic - Hortus Soft, Walter-Kolb-Str 9-11, Frankfurt Am Main, 60594, Germany. TEL 49-1805-705605, info@kidoclic.de, http://www.daskinderweb.de/MV.htm.

NATUR UND TIERSCHUTZ KALENDER DES DEUTSCHEN TIERSCHUTZBUNDES. see *BIOLOGY—Zoology*

028.5 USA
NATURE FRIEND. Text in English. 1983. m. **Description:** Includes stories, puzzles, and science experiments.
Published by: Carlisle Press, 2727 TR 421, Sugarcreek, OH 44681. TEL 330-852-1900, FAX 330-852-3285. Circ: 9,000.

359 028.5 GBR
NAVY NEWS. SEA CADET EDITION. Text in English. 1954. m. GBP 17; GBP 20.50 foreign; GBP 1 newsstand/cover (effective 2002). bk.rev. charts; illus. **Document type:** *Newspaper.* **Description:** Contains information aimed at youths aged 12-18.
Formerly: Sea Cadet (0036-9985)
Related titles: Audio cassette/tape ed.; E-mail ed.; Fax ed.; Microfilm ed.; Online - full content ed.
Published by: (Sea Cadet Association), Navy News, H M S Nelson, Queen St, Portsmouth, Hants PO1 3HH, United Kingdom. TEL 44-2392-826040, FAX 44-2392-830149, enquiries@navynews.co.uk, http://www.navynews.co.uk. Ed. Jim Allaway. R&Ps Anne Driver, Glenys Gould TEL 44-2392-291525. Circ: 80,000.

028.5 792 ALB
NE SKENEN E FEMIJEVE★. Text in Albanian. m.
Published by: Ministry of Culture Youth and Sport, Tirana, Albania.

028.5 RUS
NEDOROSL'; Zhurnal Tvorchestva Detei i Yunoshestva. Text in Russian. bi-m. USD 95 in United States.
Published by: Yunpress, Novaya pl 6, k 21, Moscow, 103012, Russian Federation. TEL 7-095-2060625, FAX 7-095-2068486. Ed. I Koroleva. **US dist. addr.:** East View Information Services, 3020 Harbor Ln. N., Minneapolis, MN 55447. TEL 612-550-0961.

▼ **NEOPETS;** the official magazine. see *SPORTS AND GAMES*

NEUE MUSIKZEITUNG. see *MUSIC*

028.5 USA
NEW EXPRESSION. Text in English. 1977. 8/yr. USD 25. adv. bk.rev.
Published by: Youth Communication - Chicago Center, 104 S Michigan Ave, 1500, Chicago, IL 60605-1901. TEL 312-641-6397, FAX 312-263-5388. Ed. Dennis Sylees. Adv. contact Greg McClain. Circ: 72,000.

028.5 649 USA
NEW JERSEY FAMILY; a news magazine for parents and kids. Text in English. 1993. m. USD 15. adv. bk.rev.; film rev. illus. **Document type:** *Consumer.* **Description:** Advises parents on how to best provide for their children through articles on health, education, and well-being; reviews new products and lists a calendar of local events.
Address: 104 LaBarre Ave, Trenton, NJ 08618. TEL 609-695-5646, http://family.com. Ed., Pub., R&P Barbara M Gaeta. Adv. contact Rebecca Schaeffer. Circ: 30,000 (controlled).

028.5 USA ISSN 1069-238X
HQ1101
NEW MOON; the magazine for girls and their dreams. Text in English. 1993. bi-m. USD 29 domestic; USD 39 in Canada; USD 44 elsewhere; USD 6.75 per issue (effective 2005). bk.rev. illus. Index. back issues avail.; reprints avail. **Document type:** *Magazine, Consumer.* **Description:** By and for girls ages 8-14. Focuses on personal history, inventing, creativity, relationships, and mothers and daughters, with the goal of helping girls ease into adolescence and womanhood with self-confidence.
Related titles: Online - full text ed.: (from bigchalk, EBSCO Publishing, Gale Group, ProQuest Information & Learning, SoftLine Information).
Indexed: AltPI, CWI, DYW, GendWatch, ICM, MASUSE, RGYP. **—CCC.**
Published by: New Moon Publishing, 34 E Superior St, Ste 200, Duluth, MN 55802. TEL 218-728-5507, 800-381-4743, FAX 218-728-0314, newmoon@newmoon.org, http://www.newmoon.org. Ed. Dawn Gorman. Pub. Nancy Gruver. R&P Linda Estel. Circ: 22,000 (paid).

THE NEW REVIEW OF CHILDREN'S LITERATURE AND LIBRARIANSHIP. see *LITERATURE*

NEW VOICES (MINNEAPOLIS); news and arts from a Native youth perspective. see *NATIVE AMERICAN STUDIES*

NEW YORK (CITY). DEPARTMENT OF JUVENILE JUSTICE. ANNUAL REPORT. see *LAW—Family And Matrimonial Law*

371.3 USA ISSN 1525-1292
➤ **THE NEW YORK TIMES UPFRONT;** the news magazine for teens. Text in English. 1983. 14/yr. (during school year). USD 15.95 domestic to individuals; USD 35.95 foreign to individuals; USD 2.25 newsstand/cover (effective 2005). adv. bk.rev.; film rev. charts; illus. index. back issues avail.; reprint service avail. from PQC. **Document type:** *Magazine, Academic/Scholarly.* **Description:** Features topics on current news events, science and technology, social issues of interest to teens, pop culture, and the world of business.
Supersedes (in Sep. 1999): Scholastic Update (0745-7065); Which was formed by the merger of (1972-1983): Scholastic Search (0163-3597); (1920-1983): Senior Scholastic (0037-2242); Which incorporated: American Observer (0003-0201); World Week (0043-9231)
Related titles: Microfiche ed.: (from PQC); Microfilm ed.: (from PQC); Online - full text ed.: (from bigchalk, EBSCO Publishing, Gale Group, H.W. Wilson, O C L C Online Computer Library Center, Inc., ProQuest Information & Learning, The Dialog Corporation).
Indexed: ARG, ICM, JHMA, LRI, MASUSE, MagInd, PMR, PSI, RGAb, RGPR, RGYP, TOM.
Published by: Scholastic Inc., 557 Broadway, New York, NY 10012-0399. TEL 212-343-6100, 866-512-1104, upfront@scholastic.com, http://teacher.scholastic.com/upfront/, http://www.scholastic.com. Ed. Peter S Young. Pub. David Goddy. adv.: B&W page USD 12,160, color page USD 15,200. Circ: 297,029 (paid and free). **Subscr. to:** 2931 E McCarthy St, PO Box 3710, Jefferson City, MO 65102-9957. classmags@scholastic.com. **Co-publishers:** Scholastic-TAB Publications Ltd.; New York Times Company.

051 USA ISSN 0737-285X
NEW YOUTH CONNECTIONS; the magazine written by and for New York youth. Abbreviated title: N Y C. Text in English. 1980. 7/yr. USD 18 (effective 2004). adv. bk.rev. index. **Document type:** *Magazine, Consumer.* **Description:** Covers a wide range of topics targeting urban teens, encouraging teens to get involved in a variety of activities.
Published by: Youth Communication - New York Center, Inc., 224 W 29th St, New York, NY 10001. TEL 212-279-0708, FAX 212-279-8856, info@youthcomm.org, http://www.youthcomm.org/Publications/NYC.htm. Ed. Rachel Blvstain. Pub., R&P Keith Hefner. Circ: 76,000.

372 NZL ISSN 0111-6355
NEW ZEALAND SCHOOL JOURNAL. (In four graded parts) Text in English. 1907. q. NZD 97 (effective 2000). adv. **Document type:** *Government.* **Description:** Aimed at children ages 7-13. **—CCC.**
Published by: Learning Media, PO Box 3293, Wellington, New Zealand. TEL 64-4-4725522, FAX 64-4-4726444. Eds. D Noonan, P Glensor. R&P Vanessa O'Neil. Adv. contact Jenny Burdan. Circ: 70,000.

NEWSCURRENTS. see *EDUCATION—Teaching Methods And Curriculum*

NEWSMATTERS. see *EDUCATION—Teaching Methods And Curriculum*

028.5 500 TWN ISSN 1018-5445
NEWTON. Text in Chinese. 1983. m. TWD 3,360 (effective 2005). **Document type:** *Magazine, Consumer.*
Published by: Newton Publishing Group, Section 2, Alley 107, no. 25-1 Heping East Road, Tapei, Taiwan. TEL 886-2-27060336, FAX 886-2-27060773, service@mail.newton.com.tw, http://www.newton.com.tw/.

051 USA
NICK JR. Text in English. 1999. 8/yr. USD 12.97; USD 2.95 newsstand/cover (effective 2000). adv. **Document type:** *Magazine, Consumer.* **Description:** Provides opportunities for pre-schoolers and their parents to share fun and educational activities and games involving their favorite Nick Jr. television characters.
Published by: Nickelodeon Magazine, Inc. (Subsidiary of: Viacom), 1515 Broadway, New York, NY 10036. TEL 212-258-7500, 800-832-6100, nickjr@nickmail.com, http://www.nickjr.com. Circ: 600,000 (paid and controlled).

051 USA ISSN 1073-7510
NICKELODEON MAGAZINE. Text in English. 1993. 10/yr. USD 22.97 domestic; USD 28.97 in Canada; USD 29.97 elsewhere; USD 3.50 newsstand/cover (effective 2004). adv. illus. reprints avail. **Document type:** *Magazine, Consumer.* **Description:** Provides young readers with stories, games, and puzzles, many featuring characters found in programs aired on Nickolodeon TV.
Published by: Nickelodeon Magazine, Inc. (Subsidiary of: Viacom), 1515 Broadway, New York, NY 10036. TEL 212-258-7500, 212-258-4430, 800-832-6100, NickEditor@aol.com, http://www.nick.com/.

NICKI - JESUS LIEBT KINDER. see *RELIGIONS AND THEOLOGY—Protestant*

NIKI. see *TRAVEL AND TOURISM—Airline Inflight And Hotel Inroom*

NOAH'S ARK; a newspaper for Jewish children. see *RELIGIONS AND THEOLOGY—Judaic*

028.5 GBR
NODDY. Text in English. 1992. m. GBP 1.75 newsstand/cover (effective 2003). adv. illus. **Document type:** *Magazine, Consumer.* **Description:** Offers young readers multiple educational stories, activities, and puzzles featuring Noddy and his friends.
Related titles: ◆ Supplement(s): Noddy Storytime Special. ISSN 1355-9060.
Published by: B B C Worldwide Ltd., 80 Wood Ln, London, W12 0TT, United Kingdom. TEL 44-20-84331070, FAX 44-20-84332231, bbcproducts@bbc.co.uk, http://www.bbc.co.uk, http://www.bbcmagazines.com. Ed. Laura Hill. Pub. Nicky Smith. Adv. contact David Gibson. **Dist. by:** Frontline, Park House, 117 Park Rd, Peterborough, Cambs PE1 2TS, United Kingdom. TEL 44-1733-555161, FAX 44-1733-562788.

028.5 GBR ISSN 1355-9060
NODDY STORYTIME SPECIAL. Text in English. 1994. m. GBP 1.50 newsstand/cover. illus. **Document type:** *Consumer.* **Description:** Designed to interest children in reading, writing and telling stories. Offers a different skill development activity in each issue.
Related titles: ◆ Supplement to: Noddy.
Published by: B B C Worldwide Ltd., 80 Wood Ln, London, W12 0TT, United Kingdom. FAX 44-181-576-2931, bbcproducts@bbc.co.uk, http://www.bbc.co.uk. Ed. Laura Hill. **Dist. by:** Frontline, Park House, 117 Park Rd, Peterborough, Cambs PE1 2TS, United Kingdom. TEL 44-1733-555161, FAX 44-1733-562788.

NORTHWEST INDIANA CATHOLIC. see *RELIGIONS AND THEOLOGY—Roman Catholic*

NOTABLE SOCIAL STUDIES TRADE BOOKS FOR YOUNG PEOPLE. see *SOCIAL SCIENCES: COMPREHENSIVE WORKS—Abstracting, Bibliographies, Statistics*

NOTES FROM THE WINDOWSILL. see *PUBLISHING AND BOOK TRADE*

NOUS VOULONS LIRE. see *LITERATURE*

NOVELS FOR STUDENTS. see *LITERATURE*

028.5 KAZ
NOVOE POKOLENIE. Text in Russian. w. USD 299 in United States.
Indexed: RASB.
Published by: Izdatel'stvo Novoe Pokolenie, PO Box 705, Glavpochtamt, Almaty, 480091, Kazakstan. TEL 7-327-263-5317. Ed. Oleg Chervinskii. **US dist. addr.:** East View Information Services, 3020 Harbor Ln. N., Minneapolis, MN 55447. TEL 612-550-0961.

NU PA VEJ; en bibelnoegle for juniorer. see *RELIGIONS AND THEOLOGY*

NUTRIDATE. see *NUTRITION AND DIETETICS*

267.6 200 NOR ISSN 0804-1997
NY DAG. Text in Norwegian. 1880. s-m. NOK 150. adv.
Formerly (until 1946): Unges Ven (0804-2195)
Indexed: RASB.
Published by: Norges K F U K - K F U M/Norwegian Christian Youth Organization, Postboks 6814, St Olavs Plass, Oslo, 0130, Norway. Eds. Gunnar Mathiesen, Oernolf Elseth. Circ: 15,000.

028.5 NZL
NZGIRL. Text in English. irreg.
Media: Online - full content.
Published by: nzgirl ltd, P.O. Box 65290, Mairangi Bay, Auckland, New Zealand. TEL 64-9-478-5995, FAX 64-9-479-3800, info@nzgirl.co.nz, http://www.nzgirl.co.nz. Ed. Bonnie Frankland. Pub. Jenene Crossan.

O C FAMILY; the news magazine for parents. see *CONSUMER EDUCATION AND PROTECTION*

028.5 DEU
O! KAY!. Text in English, German. m. EUR 35.88 for 6 mos.; EUR 5.37 newsstand/cover (effective 2005). adv. **Document type:** *Magazine, Consumer.* **Description:** Contains stories and games in English and German for children beginning to learn the English language.
Published by: Domino Verlag, Menziger Str 13, Munich, 80638, Germany. TEL 49-89-179130, FAX 49-89-1783788, vertrieb@domino-verlag.de, http://www.o-kay.de, http://www.domino-verlag.de.

C

028.5 UKR
ODNOKLASSNIK. Text in Ukrainian. m. USD 110 in United States.
Address: Ul Degtyarevskaya 38-44, Kiev, Ukraine. TEL 380-44-211-0233. **US dist. addr.:** East View Information Services, 3020 Harbor Ln. N., Minneapolis, MN 55447. TEL 612-550-0961.

520 550 USA ISSN 0163-0946
QB46
ODYSSEY (PERU); adventures in science. Text in English. 1979. 9/yr. USD 29.95 domestic; USD 41.95 foreign; USD 4.95 newsstand/cover domestic. bk.rev. charts; illus. a.index. 52 p./no.; back issues avail.; reprints avail. **Document type:** *Magazine, Consumer.* **Description:** Explores the hottest trends in science, bringing readers ages 10 - 15 up-to-date news about our world. Monthly star charts, mind-boggling puzzles, great graphics, and more.
Related titles: Online - full text ed.: (from bigchalk, EBSCO Publishing, Gale Group, ProQuest Information & Learning).
Indexed: ICM, JHMA, RGYP.
Published by: Carus Publishing Company, 315 Fifth St, Peru, IL 61354. TEL 603-924-7209, 800-821-0115, FAX 815-224-2256, custsvc@cobblestone.mv.com, http://www.odysseymagazine.com, http://www.cricketmag.com. Ed. Elizabeth Lindstrom. Pub. John Olbrych. R&P Patricia Silvestro. Circ: 24,000 (paid).

028.5 NLD
OEK!. Text in Dutch. 1946. 5/yr. EUR 11.95; EUR 2.65 newsstand/cover (effective 2005). illus. **Document type:** *Consumer.*
Formerly: Onze Eigen Krant (0165-8905)
Published by: Kok Tijdschriften, Postbus 5018, Kampen, 8260 GA, Netherlands. TEL 31-38-3392555, http://www.kok.nl.

028.5 AUT ISSN 0029-9243
DER OESTERREICHISCHE JUNGARBEITER. Text in German. 1956. bi-m. adv. bk.rev. illus. **Document type:** *Journal, Trade.*
Published by: Oesterreichische Jungarbeiterbewegung, Mittelgasse 16, Vienna, W 1160, Austria. http://www.oejab.at. Ed. Hubert Schober.

OESTERREICHISCHES JUGENDROTKREUZ. ARBEITSBLAETTER. see *SOCIAL SERVICES AND WELFARE*

052 GBR
▼ **OFFICIAL DUEL MASTERS MAGAZINE.** Text in English. 2004 (Sep.). m. GBP 3.99 newsstand/cover (effective 2004). adv. **Document type:** *Magazine, Consumer.* **Description:** Contains information on all aspects of the Duel Masters toy and entertainment line, including trading card tips and advice, TV episode guides, comic strips, videogame and DVD reviews, and toy news.
Published by: Future Publishing Ltd., Beauford Court, 30 Monmouth St, Bath, Avon BA1 2BW, United Kingdom. TEL 44-1225-442244, FAX 44-1225-446019, customerservice@futurenet.co.uk, http://www.thefuturenetwork.plc.uk.

OFFSPRING - BOING. see *MUSEUMS AND ART GALLERIES*

OGGITALIA; panorama della stampa italiana. see *LINGUISTICS*

028.5 CZE ISSN 0030-1272
AP215.C9
OHNICEK; zabava do kapsy. Text in Czech. 1950. fortn. CZK 12, USD 15.80.
Published by: Mlada Fronta, Radlicka 61, Prague, 15002, Czech Republic. TEL 42-2-544941. Ed. Eva Vondraskova. Circ: 100,000. **Subscr. to:** Artia, Ve Smeckach 30, Prague 1 111 27, Czech Republic.

028.5 SVK ISSN 0139-8911
OHNIK. Text in Slovak. 1948. fortn.
Published by: Smena Publishing House, Prazska 11, Bratislava, 81284, Slovakia. Ed. Magdalena Gocnikova. Circ: 130,000.

087.5 HRV ISSN 1330-7983
OK!. Text in Croatian. 1995. m. **Document type:** *Magazine, Consumer.*
Published by: Arena d.d., Slavonska Avenija 4, Zagreb, 10000, Croatia. TEL 385-1-342127, FAX 385-1-342118, ok@eph.hr. Ed. Neven Kepin.

028.5 FRA ISSN 0751-6002
OKAPI. Text in French. 1971. fortn. EUR 89.80 domestic; EUR 124.80 foreign (effective 2005). adv. bk.rev.; film rev.; play rev. illus. **Document type:** *Magazine, Consumer.* **Description:** Offers a way to learn about and understand the world today to the 10 to 15-year-old age group.
Published by: Bayard Presse, 3 Rue Bayard, Paris, 75393 Cedex 08, France. TEL 33-1-44356060, FAX 33-1-44356161, redactions@bayard-presse.com, http://www.bayardpresse.com. Ed. Jean Jacques Fresko. Circ: 70,666.

OKAY; Schuelerkalender und taegliche Bibellese. see *RELIGIONS AND THEOLOGY—Protestant*

791.43 SWE ISSN 0349-9995
OKEJ. Text in Swedish. 1980. m. SEK 298; SEK 29.50 newsstand/cover (effective 2000). adv. **Document type:** *Magazine, Consumer.* **Description:** Contains articles and features for teenagers on their favorite music, film and television stars.
Published by: Broederna Lindstroems Foerlags AB, Industrigatan 2A, Stockholm, 11285, Sweden. TEL 46-8-692-01-20, FAX 46-8-650-86-25, info@okej.se, http://www.okej.se. Ed. Anders Tengner. R&P Ulla Carle TEL 46-8-6920114. Adv. contact Susane Hellberg. B&W page SEK 20,600, color page SEK 24,780; trim 189 x 269. Circ: 50,000 (paid).

028.5 NLD ISSN 0030-1612
OKKI. Text in Dutch. 1920. fortn. **Document type:** *Consumer.* **Description:** Educational publication for children aged 6-8 years.
Published by: L.C.G. Malmberg B.V., Leeghwaterlaan 16, 's Hertogenbosch, 5223 BA, Netherlands. FAX 31-73-6216154. Ed. M Heemelaar. Circ: 115,000.

OLAM KATAN; a miscellany of studies, teaching and research in children's literature. see *LITERATURE*

087.5 DEU ISSN 0948-4949
OLLI UND MOLLI; die Zeitschrift zum Lernen und Spielen. Text in German. 1995. m. EUR 22.80 (effective 2003). **Document type:** *Magazine, Consumer.*
Published by: Johann Michael Sailer Verlag GmbH & Co. KG, Aeusserer Laufer Platz 17, Nuernberg, 90403, Germany. TEL 49-911-53960, FAX 49-911-5396912, sailer@sailer-verlag.de, http://www.sailer-verlag.de. Ed. Bobby Kastenhuber. Circ: 85,000 (paid).

OLOMEINU/OUR WORLD. see *RELIGIONS AND THEOLOGY—Judaic*

OMNIGRAPHICS' TEEN HEALTH SERIES. see *MEDICAL SCIENCES*

268 USA ISSN 0043-7999
ON THE LINE (SCOTTDALE). Text in English. 1971. m. USD 25.15 (effective 2000). illus. **Document type:** *Consumer.* **Description:** Aimed at adolescents aged 9-14.
Formerly: Words of Cheer
Published by: Herald Press, 616 Walnut Ave, Scottdale, PA 15683-1999. TEL 724-887-8500, FAX 724-887-3111, otl@mph.org. Ed. Mary Clemens Meyer. Circ: 6,000. **Co-publisher:** Faith & Life Press.

028.5 304.5 BEL ISSN 1566-046X
ONE. Text in Dutch. 1999. m. EUR 24.75 (effective 2003). adv. illus. **Document type:** *Magazine, Consumer.* **Description:** Publishes articles on topics of interest to young women.
Published by: Sanoma Magazines Belgium, Telecomlaan 5-7, Diegem, 1831, Belgium. TEL 32-2-7762211, FAX 32-2-776-2317, http://www.sanoma-magazines.be/HomePage.aspx?flash=1&Language=nl.

028.5 ITA
OP LA. Text in Italian. m. USD 54. **Document type:** *Consumer.* **Description:** For children ages 3-7.
Published by: Logos Group, Via Curtatona 5/2, Modena, MO 41100, Italy. TEL 39-059-412603, FAX 39-059-412567, it.market@logos.net, http://www.logos.net.

OPSIS KALOPSIS; om barn- och ungdomskultur. see *CHILDREN AND YOUTH—About*

268 PRT ISSN 0874-498X
ORACAO E VIDA. Text in Portuguese. 1980. q. EUR 7.50 domestic; EUR 11.95 in Europe; EUR 13.45 elsewhere (effective 2005). **Document type:** *Magazine, Consumer.*
Published by: Editorial/AO, Lago das Teresinhas, 5, Braga, 4714-509, Portugal. TEL 351-253-201220, FAX 351-253-201221, http://www.ppcj.pt/AO/AO.html. Ed. Fernando Leite. Circ: 250,000.

ORANA; journal for school and children's librarians. see *LIBRARY AND INFORMATION SCIENCES*

028.5 ZMB
ORBIT "EDUCATION FOR ALL" MAGAZINE. Text in English. 1971. 4/yr. adv. bk.rev. charts; illus. **Document type:** *Consumer.* **Description:** For schools and literacy classes. Includes articles on agriculture, health, sports, music, profiles of women, the environment and more.
Formerly (until 1991): Orbit
Published by: Ministry of Education, Curriculum Development Centre, PO Box 50092, Lusaka, Zambia. FAX 254848. Ed. Mrs. Elidah Banda Chisha. Circ: 65,000. **Subscr. to:** Private Bag RW18X, Lusaka, Zambia.

598.2 CHE ISSN 1424-3423
ORNIS JUNIOR. Text in German. 1985. q. CHF 16 (effective 2001). **Document type:** *Magazine, Consumer.*
Supersedes in part (in 1999): Chumm mit! (1424-280X)
Published by: Schweizer Vogelschutz SVS - BirdLife Schweiz, Wiedingstr 78, Zurich, 8036, Switzerland. TEL 41-1-4637271, FAX 41-1-4614778, svs@birdlife.ch, http://www.birdlife.ch.

028.5 ESP
EL OSO BUSSI. Text in Spanish. 1990. m. EUR 2.10 newsstand/cover. adv. **Document type:** *Magazine, Consumer.*
Published by: H. Bauer Ediciones S.L. (Subsidiary of: Heinrich Bauer Verlag), Jacometrezo 15, Madrid, 28013, Spain. TEL 34-91-5476800, FAX 34-91-5413523.

OSTROV SOKROVISHCH. see *CHILDREN AND YOUTH—About*

028.5 JPN
OTOMODACHI. Text in Japanese. m. **Document type:** *Magazine, Consumer.*
Published by: Kodansha Ltd., 2-12-21 Otowa, Bunkyo-ku, Tokyo, 112-8001, Japan. TEL 81-3-3946-6201, FAX 81-3-3944-9915, http://www.kodansha.co.jp.

OUTYOUTH; for and by lesbian, bisexual, gay and transgender young people. see *HOMOSEXUALITY*

028.162 DEU
OVERBACHER BRUECKE. Text in German. 1980. s-a. back issues avail.
Published by: Gymnasium Haus Overbach in Juelich, Haus Overbach, Juelich, 52428, Germany. TEL 02461-4016.

500.9 CAN ISSN 0382-6627
OWL; the discovery magazine for kids . Text in English. 1976. 10/yr. CND 29.95 domestic; CND 32.19 in Maritimes & Quebec; USD 22 in United States; CND 59.95 elsewhere (effective 2004). bk.rev. illus. Index. reprints avail. **Document type:** *Magazine, Consumer.* **Description:** An award-winning magazine for kids over 9. A fun and funky way to discover art, science, nature and the environment through interactive activities, puzzles and experiments.
Related titles: Online - full text ed.
Indexed: CBCARef, CBPI, CPerl, ICM, RGYP.
Published by: Bayard Canada, The Owl Group, 49 Front St E, 2nd Fl, Toronto, ON M5E 1B3, Canada. TEL 416-340-2700, 800-551-6957, FAX 416-340-9769, bayard@owl.on.ca, http://www.owlkids.com/owl/. Ed. Hilary Bain. Circ: 100,000.

C

028.5 FRA ISSN 1281-2072
OXEBO!. Text in French. 1997. 6/yr. **Description:** Offers activities to create, cook, make gifts and organize little parties.
Published by: Milan Presse, 300 rue Leon Joulin, Toulouse, Cedex 1 31101, France. TEL 33-5-61766464, FAX 33-5-61766400. Ed. Josiane Laguna. Pub. Patrice Amen.

P C ACE. see *COMPUTERS—Personal Computers*

PACIFIC HOSTELLER. see *TRAVEL AND TOURISM*

028.5 CYP ISSN 1022-9582
PAEDIKI HARA. Text in Greek. 8/yr. CYP 3 domestic; CYP 6 in Greece; CYP 10 elsewhere. back issues avail. **Document type:** *Consumer.* **Description:** Teaches children 7-12 about their nation's history. Also chronicles school life in Cyprus and describes myths, books, school curricula, and hobbies.
Published by: Cyprus Greek Teachers Organization, Makarios III Ave, 18, Nicosia, Cyprus. TEL 357-2-442638, FAX 257-2-360410. Circ: 13,000.

PAGINE GIOVANI. see *PUBLISHING AND BOOK TRADE*

PALITRA PEDAGOGA. see *EDUCATION*

PAPERKUTS SCRAPBOOK MAGAZINE. see *ARTS AND HANDICRAFTS*

PAPERS: EXPLORATIONS INTO CHILDREN'S LITERATURE. see *LITERATURE*

028.5 FRA ISSN 1266-7528
PAPOUM. Text in French. 1995. bi-m. FRF 196 domestic; FRF 312.50 foreign (effective 2000). **Description:** Presents stories to be read to children 6 to 18 months.
Published by: Fleurus Presse, 129 bd. Malesherbes, Paris, 75017, France. TEL 33-1-56793636. Ed. Pascal Teulade.

028.5 IND ISSN 0031-1642
PARAG. Text in Hindi. 1958. m. USD 12. bk.rev.; film rev.; play rev. illus.
Address: 10 Daryaganj, New Delhi, 110 002, India. TEL 11-277360. Ed. Hari Krishna Devsare. Circ: 60,000. **U.S. subscr. to:** M-s. Kalpana, 42 75 Main St, Flushing, NY 11355.

PARAPARA BOLETIN INFORMATIVO. see *PUBLISHING AND BOOK TRADE*

PARAPARA SELECCION DE LIBROS PARA NINOS Y JOVENES. see *PUBLISHING AND BOOK TRADE*

028.5 649 USA
PARENTS AND CHILDREN TOGETHER ONLINE. Text in English. 1990. s-a. **Description:** Features original stories, poems and articles for children, and articles on parenting topics for adults.
Media: Online - full text.

Published by: (Distance Education), Edinfo Press, 2805 E 10th St, Ste 150, Bloomington, IN 47408. TEL 812-855-5847, 800-759-4723, disted@indiana.edu, http://www.indiana.edu/~eric_rec/fl/pcto/menu.html. Ed. Christopher Essex.

PARENTS EXPRESS; the newspaper for Philadelphia area parents. see *EDUCATION—Teaching Methods And Curriculum*

028.5 840 CHE ISSN 1421-0851
PAROLE. Text in French. 1985. 3/yr. CHF 35; CHF 45 foreign (effective 2000). bk.rev. back issues avail. **Document type:** *Newsletter, Consumer.*
Related titles: ♦ Supplement(s): As Tu Lu?. ISSN 1421-0908.
Published by: Association Romande de Litterature pour l'Enfance et la Jeunesse, Case Postale, Lausanne 4, 1000, Switzerland. TEL 41-21-3202328. Ed. Sylvie Neeman. Circ: 750.

PARTICIPATING IN EDUCATION. see *CHILDREN AND YOUTH—About*

028.5 FIN ISSN 0556-3488
PARTIO. Text in Finnish. 1937. 6/yr. EUR 27 (effective 2005). adv. **Document type:** *Magazine, Consumer.* **Description:** Covers scouting.
Published by: Suomen Partiolaiset/Guides and Scouts of Finland, Kylaenvanhimmantie 29, Helsinki, 00640, Finland. TEL 358-9-25331100, FAX 358-9-25331160, info@sp.partio.fi, http://www.partio.fi. Ed. Aino Justen. Circ: 57,702.

333.72 ISR ISSN 0334-3022
PASHOSH. Text in Hebrew. m. USD 39.50. **Description:** Articles on nature intended for small children.
Published by: Society for the Protection of Nature in Israel, 4 Hashefela St, Tel Aviv, 66183, Israel. TEL 972-3-375063. Ed. A Bar.

C

PASS IT ON!. see *MUSIC*

028.5 BRA ISSN 0104-2092
PATO DONALD. Text in Portuguese. 1950. fortn. adv. back issues avail. **Document type:** *Magazine, Consumer.*
Published by: Editora Abril, S.A., Av. das Nacoes Unidas, 7221, 11 andar Pinheiros, Sao Paulo, SP 05425-902, Brazil. TEL 55-11-50872112, FAX 55-11-50872100, http://www.disney.com.br/, http://www.abril.com.br/. Circ: 4,900.

087.5 PRT ISSN 0874-0623
PATO DONALD. Text in Portuguese. 1981. 3/yr. EUR 18.36 (effective 2004). **Document type:** *Magazine, Consumer.*
Published by: Edimpresa Editora Lda., Rua Calvet de Magalhaes 242, Laveiras, Paco de Arcos, 2770-022, Portugal. TEL 351-21-4698000, FAX 351-21-4698501, edimpresa@edimpresa.pt, http://www.edimpresa.pt.

PATTI. see *HOBBIES*

028.5 USA
PEN PAL POST; friendship through understanding. Text in English. 1950. a. USD 3 (effective 2001). Website rev. **Document type:** *Newspaper.* **Description:** Helps children 10-20 explore other cultures through letter writing. Promotes international friendship and cultural understanding.
Former titles: Write in There; Silver Lining
Published by: World Pen Pals, PO Box 337, Saugerties, NY 12477-0337. TEL 845-246-7828, FAX 845-246-7828, http://www.world-pen-pals.com. Ed. Robert Carroll. Circ: 16,000.

028.5 AUT
PERPLEX; das Magazin fuer Jugendliche. Text in German. 1978. bi-m. **Document type:** *Magazine, Consumer.*
Published by: Perplex Verlag, Hans-Sachs-Gasse 14-III, Postfach 752, Graz, St 8010, Austria. TEL 43-316-837203, FAX 43-316-829596, perplex-magazin@gmx.at, http://www.perplex.at. Ed. Franz Kirnbauer. Circ: 3,500.

028.5 035.89155 USA
PERSIAN PRINCESS. Text in English, Persian, Modern. 2001 (Mar). bi-m. **Document type:** *Magazine, Consumer.* **Description:** Contains articles and features of interest to young Iranian-American girls.
Published by: Iran Today Publishing, 1177 Branham Ln, Ste 388, San Jose, CA 95123. TEL 408-323-3169, FAX 408-323-3168. Ed. Dokie Riahi. Pub. Susan Akbarpour.

028.5 JPN
PETIT COMIC. Text in Japanese. m. **Document type:** *Magazine, Consumer.*
Published by: Shogakukan Inc., 3-1 Hitotsubashi 2-chome, Chiyoda-ku, Tokyo, 101-8001, Japan. TEL 81-3-3230-5211, FAX 81-3-3264-8471, http://www.shogakukan.co.jp.

028.5 JPN
PETIT FLOWER. Text in Japanese. bi-m. **Document type:** *Magazine, Consumer.*
Published by: Shogakukan Inc., 3-1 Hitotsubashi 2-chome, Chiyoda-ku, Tokyo, 101-8001, Japan. TEL 81-3-3230-5211, FAX 81-3-3264-8471, http://www.shogakukan.co.jp.

028.5 FRA ISSN 1280-9063
LE PETIT LEONARD. Text in French. 1997. m. (11/yr). **Description:** Art magazine for children ages 7 and up.
Published by: Editions Faton S.A., 25 rue Berbisey, Dijon, 21000, France. TEL 33-1-80404120, FAX 33-3-80404129. Ed. Jeanne Faton-Boyance. Pub. Jeanne Faton Boyance.

028.5 JPN
PETIT SEVEN. Text in Japanese. bi-m. **Document type:** *Magazine, Consumer.*
Published by: Shogakukan Inc., 3-1 Hitotsubashi 2-chome, Chiyoda-ku, Tokyo, 101-8001, Japan. TEL 81-3-3230-5211, FAX 81-3-3264-8471, http://www.shogakukan.co.jp.

028.5 FRA
PETITES MAINS. Text in French. bi-m. EUR 26 (effective 2005). **Description:** Includes activities for children ages 3 and up.
Published by: Milan Presse, 300 rue Leon Joulin, Toulouse, Cedex 1 31101, France. TEL 33-5-61766464, FAX 33-5-61766400, webmaster@milanpresse.com, http://www.milanpresse.com. Pub. Patrice Amen.

053.1 DEU
PETTERSSON UND FINDUS. Text in German. 1999. m. EUR 2.30 newsstand/cover (effective 2003). adv. **Document type:** *Magazine, Consumer.*
Published by: Panini Verlags GmbH, Ravensstr 48, Nettetal, 41334, Germany. TEL 49-711-947680, FAX 49-711-94768830, info@panini-dino.de, http://www.panini-media.de. Ed. Axel Nowak. Adv. contact Petra Sonnenfroh-Kost. page EUR 3,900; trim 210 x 280. Circ: 160,000 (paid and controlled).

PEZZI 2-12; boeken en CD-ROMs voor kinderen van 2 tot 12. see *LITERARY AND POLITICAL REVIEWS*

798.2 DEU
PFERDE - FREUNDE FUERS LEBEN. Text in German. 1999. q. EUR 1.99 newsstand/cover (effective 2003). adv. **Document type:** *Magazine, Consumer.* **Description:** Contains articles and pictures about horses and equestrian sports for girls ages 9-13.
Published by: Panini Verlags GmbH, Ravensstr 48, Nettetal, 41334, Germany. TEL 49-711-947680, FAX 49-711-94768830, info@panini-dino.de, http://www.panini-media.de. Adv. contact Petra Sonnenfroh-Kost. page EUR 2,500; trim 210 x 280. Circ: 107,700 (paid and controlled).

028.5 053.5 CHE
PFIFF. Text in German. m. CHF 28; CHF 36 foreign. **Document type:** *Consumer.*
Published by: Buery Verlag AG, Hugostr 2, Postfach 8392, Zuerich, 8050, Switzerland. TEL 01-3126475, FAX 01-3126511. Adv. contact Ariane Demieville. Circ: 12,500.

053.1 DEU
PHILIPP. Text in German. 1997. bi-m. EUR 25; EUR 3 newsstand/cover (effective 2005). adv. **Document type:** *Magazine, Consumer.*
Published by: Verlag Herder GmbH und Co. KG, Hermann-Herder-Str 4, Freiburg Im Breisgau, 79104, Germany. TEL 49-761-27170, FAX 49-761-2717520, kundenservice@herder.de, http://www.philipp-maus.de, http://www.herder.de. adv.: B&W page EUR 2,900, color page EUR 3,800. Circ: 68,500 (paid and controlled).

028.5 AUT
PHILIPP LESEHEFTE. Text in German. 1949. 6/yr. membership. **Document type:** *Bulletin.*
Formerly (until 1990): Oesterreichischer Buchklub der Jugend. Jahrbuch (0078-3560)
Published by: Oesterreichischer Buchklub der Jugend, Mayerhofgasse 6, Vienna, W 1041, Austria. TEL 43-1-5051754-0, FAX 43-1-505175450.

028.5 059.914 PAK
PHOOL. Text in Urdu. 1990. m. USD 30 in United States. adv. bk.rev. illus. back issues avail. **Document type:** *Consumer.* **Description:** News and information of broad appeal.
Published by: Nawa-i-Waqt, Lahore, NIPCO House, 4 Sharae Fatima Jinnah, Lahore, Pakistan. TEL 92-42-6367551, FAX 92-42-6367005. Ed., Pub. Majid Nizami. Adv. contact M A Latif. Circ: 47,000 (paid).

028.5 FRA ISSN 0249-8138
PHOSPHORE. Text in French. 1981. m. EUR 64.80 domestic; EUR 84.80 foreign (effective 2005). adv. bk.rev.; film rev. illus. **Document type:** *Magazine, Consumer.* **Description:** The magazine for 15 to 25-year-olds.
Formerly: Record - Dossier (0151-2404)
Published by: Bayard Presse, 3 Rue Bayard, Paris, 75393 Cedex 08, France. TEL 33-1-44356060, FAX 33-1-44356161, redactions@bayard-presse.com, http://www.phospore.com, http://www.bayardpresse.com. Ed. Beatrice Toulon. Circ: 81,874.

028.5 530 ISR ISSN 0333-6948
PI HA'ATOM; popular physics magazine. Text in Hebrew. 1981. 3/yr. ILS 95. adv. bk.rev.
Indexed: IHP.
Published by: Weizmann Institute of Science, Youth Activities Section, P O Box 26, Rehovot, 76100, Israel. TEL 972-8-9343959, FAX 972-8-9344130, hamish@weizmann.weizmann.ac.il, http://www.weizman.ac.il/youthact/publications.html. Ed. H Shmueli. Circ: 1,000.
Co-sponsor: Faculty of Physics.

028.5 GBR
PICK OF THE YEAR; a selection of 50 recommended books, chosen for families, tried and tested by children, and voted the best of (year). Text in English. a. adv. illus. **Document type:** *Catalog.*
Former titles: About Books for Children (0144-574X); Federation for Children's Book Groups. Yearbook (0307-6091)
Published by: Federation of Children's Book Groups, The Old Malt House, Marlborough Rd, Aldbourne, Marlborough, Wilts SN8 2DD, United Kingdom. Ed., R&P, Adv. contact Marianne Adey TEL 44-1672-540629. Circ: 50,000.

PICO; illustrierte Kinderzeitschrift ab 7 Jahre. see *RELIGIONS AND THEOLOGY*

028.5 FRA ISSN 1150-8019
PICOTI. Text in French. m. EUR 49 (effective 2005).
Published by: Milan Presse, 300 rue Leon Joulin, Toulouse, Cedex 1 31101, France. TEL 33-5-61766464, FAX 33-5-61766400. Ed. Mireille Fronty. Pub. Patrice Amen. Circ: 57,708.

028.5 FRA ISSN 0767-807X
PICSOU. Text in French. 1972. m. **Document type:** *Magazine, Consumer.* **Description:** Leisure magazine for teenagers.
Published by: Disney Hachette Presse, 10 rue Thierry le Luron, Levallois Perret, Cedex 92592, France. TEL 33-1-41348500, FAX 33-1-41348861, picsou@mail.com. Ed. Pascal Pierrey. Circ: 290,000 (paid). **Subscr. to:** 90 rue de Flandre, Paris Cedex 19 75947, France.

808.899282 PHL ISSN 0118-6493
PIK PAK BOOM KIDDIE MAGZINE. Text in English, Tagalog. 1996. m. (except in June, March, April, May). PHP 120 (effective 1999). adv. **Description:** Aims to introduced students to Gospel stories in the form of cyber adventures. Contains 36 pages of informative stories, trivia, games, among others.
Published by: Society of St. Paul, Inc., Makati, MCPO Box 1722, Manila, 1203, Philippines. TEL 632-895-9701, FAX 632-890-7130, spprov@skyinet.net. Adv. contact Hansel B Mapayo.

028.5 GBR ISSN 1351-0304
PINGU. Text in English. 1993. m. GBP 15 domestic; GBP 25 in Europe; GBP 30 elsewhere; GBP 1.25 newsstand/cover. adv. **Document type:** *Consumer.* **Description:** Discusses education and various social and moral issues with children in a fun and entertaining way.
Published by: B B C Worldwide Ltd., 80 Wood Ln, London, W12 0TT, United Kingdom. TEL 44-208-576-2000, FAX 44-208-433-3986, bbcproducts@bbc.co.uk, http://www.bbc.co.uk. Ed. Coralie Noakes. Adv. contact David Gibson. Circ: 30,025 (paid). **Dist. by:** Frontline, Park House, 117 Park Rd, Peterborough, Cambs PE1 2TS, United Kingdom. TEL 44-1733-555161, FAX 44-1733-562788.

028.5 GBR ISSN 1353-3355
PINGU STICKER FUN. Text in English. 1994. m. GBP 15; GBP 1.35 newsstand/cover (effective 1999). adv. **Document type:** *Consumer.*
Published by: B B C Magazines, Woodlands, 80 Wood Ln, London, W12 0TT, United Kingdom. TEL 44-1815-762000. Ed. Helen Mitchell. Pub. Gillian Laskier. Adv. contact David Gibson.

PINNACLE - TEEN BUSINESS!. see *BUSINESS AND ECONOMICS—Small Business*

087.5 BRA ISSN 0104-2408
PINTE LEGAL. Text in Portuguese. 1992. m. **Document type:** *Magazine, Consumer.*
Published by: Editora Abril, S.A., Av. das Nacoes Unidas, 7221, 11 andar Pinheiros, Sao Paulo, SP 05425-902, Brazil. TEL 55-011-30372000, FAX 55-011-30375638, relacoes.corporativas@abril.com.br, http://www.abril.com.br/.

028.5 RUS ISSN 0032-0048
PIONERSKAYA PRAVDA; gazeta dlya detei i podrostkov. Text in Russian. 1925. w. USD 184 foreign (effective 2005). adv. bk.rev. illus. **Document type:** *Newspaper, Consumer.*
Related titles: Microform ed.: (from PQC); Supplement to: Yunaya Moskva.
Indexed: CDSP.
Published by: Redaktsiya Gazety Pionerskaya Pravda, Sushchevskaya ul 21, Moscow, 101502, Russian Federation. TEL 7-095-9722238, FAX 7-095-9721028, pionerka@hotmail.ru. Ed. Olga I Grekova. Circ: 60,000. **Dist. by:** East View Information Services, 3020 Harbor Ln. N., Minneapolis, MN 55447. TEL 763-550-0961, FAX 763-559-2931, eastview@eastview.com, http://www.eastview.com.

369.4 FRA ISSN 0751-5723
PIONNIER. Text in French. 1924. q. adv. charts; illus.
Description: For scouts ages 15-18.
Formerly: Scout Pionnier (0036-9470)
Published by: Editions Scouts de France, 54 av. Jean Jaures, Paris, 75019, France. TEL 33-1-44523737, FAX 33-1-42380987. Ed. Philippe Da Costa.

028.5 362.7 FRA ISSN 1254-874X
PLANETE JEUNES. Text in French. 1993. bi-m. **Document type:** *Magazine, Consumer.* **Description:** For young people, 12 to 18, who are open-minded about the rest of the world and interested in speaking or learning French.
Published by: Bayard Presse, 3 Rue Bayard, Paris, 75393 Cedex 08, France. TEL 33-1-44356060, FAX 33-1-44356161, redactions@bayard-presse.com, http://www.bayardpresse.com. Ed. Simon P Njami.

PLATTFORM. see *RELIGIONS AND THEOLOGY—Protestant*

028.5 GBR ISSN 0960-0272
PLAYDAYS. Text in English. 1990. m. GBP 15 domestic; GBP 25 in Europe; GBP 35 elsewhere; GBP 1.25 newsstand/cover. **Document type:** *Consumer.* **Description:** Presents educational material compatible with the national curriculum and covers reading, writing, numerical skills, nature studies, language and science in an entertaining and interactive format.
Related titles: ♦ Supplement(s): Playdays Magazine Animal Special. ISSN 1352-5425.
Published by: B B C Worldwide Ltd., 80 Wood Ln, London, W12 0TT, United Kingdom. TEL 44-208-576-2000, FAX 44-208-433-3986, bbcproducts@bbc.co.uk, http://www.bbc.co.uk. Ed. Alison Boyle. Circ: 58,381.

028.5 GBR ISSN 1352-5425
PLAYDAYS MAGAZINE ANIMAL SPECIAL. Text in English. 1994.
Related titles: ♦ Supplement to: Playdays. ISSN 0960-0272.
Published by: B B C Worldwide Ltd., 80 Wood Ln, London, W12 0TT, United Kingdom. TEL 44-208-576-2000, FAX 44-181-576-3931, http://www.bbc.co.uk.

PLAYS; the drama magazine for young people. see *THEATER*

790.192 GBR
PLAYTIME. Text in English. m. GBP 1.50 newsstand/cover. **Document type:** *Magazine, Consumer.* **Description:** Contains stories, games and prizes for young children.
Published by: L C D Publishing, 2nd Floor, Elm House, 54 Mary Arches St, Exeter, EX4 3BA, United Kingdom. TEL 44-1392-253076.

028.5 DEU ISSN 0032-1605
PLOMJO. Text in Wendic. 1952. m. EUR 4.40; EUR 0.50 per issue (effective 2003). illus. **Document type:** *Journal, Consumer.*
Related titles: Wendic ed.: Plomje. ISSN 0138-2594.
Published by: Domowina Verlag GmbH, Tuchmacherstr 27, Bautzen, 02625, Germany. TEL 49-3591-5770, FAX 49-3591-577207, domowinaverlag@t-online.de, http://www.domowinaverlag.de.

028.5 GBR
PLUS. Text in English. 1967. m. GBP 5.60 (effective 2000). bk.rev. **Document type:** *Consumer.*
Published by: CPO, Garcia Estate, Canterbury Rd, Worthing, W Sussex BN13 1BW, United Kingdom. TEL 44-1903-824174, FAX 44-1903-824376. Ed. Donald Banks. Circ: 7,008.

POCKETS. see *RELIGIONS AND THEOLOGY—Protestant*

305.23 POL ISSN 1231-0875
POD WIATR; spoleczno-kulturalne czasopismo mlodziezowe. Text in Polish. 1993. m. PLZ 25 domestic; USD 27 foreign; PLZ 1.60 per issue (effective 2005). adv. bk.rev.; film rev.; play rev.; music rev. illus. back issues avail. **Document type:** *Magazine, Consumer.* **Description:** Aims to allow young people to talk about their own problems, to promote individuals who have a talent for journalism, literature, photography and art, and to support youngsters in their aspirations to realize their intellectual potential.
Published by: Agencja Wydawniczo-Reklamowa M T, PO Box 4049, Bydgoszcz 23, 85099, Poland. TEL 48-52-3429310, wiatr@byd.top.pl. Ed., Pub., R&P, Adv. contact Miroslaw Twarog. Circ: 400 (paid).

POETRY FOR STUDENTS. see *LITERATURE—Poetry*

028.5 RUS
POIGRAEM V SKAZKI. Text in Russian. m. RUR 160 (effective 2002).
Published by: Izdatel'skii Dom Karapuz, Izmailovskoe shosse 48a, Moscow, 105318, Russian Federation. TEL 7-095-9182810, http://www.karapuz.com.

028.5 793 USA
POKEMON PLAYER POCKET GUIDE. Text in English. 2000. q. USD 4.95 newsstand/cover (effective 2001). **Document type:** *Magazine, Consumer.*
Published by: Pokemon Player, 701 Shipmaster, Hilton Head Island, SC 29928. TEL 843-341-3200, FAX 843-341-3118, http://www.pokemonplayer.com. Ed. Mike Clark. Pub. David Mouser.

028.5 GBR ISSN 1471-6100
POKEMON WORLD. Text in English. 2000. m. GBP 2.50 newsstand/cover (effective 2001). 52 p./no.; back issues avail. **Document type:** *Magazine, Consumer.* **Description:** Contains the latest news, previews and reviews of Pokemon games, including a guide to the world of Pokemon, UK pricings and latest news on trading cards and a section cataloguing available Pokemon merchandise.
Published by: Paragon Publishing Ltd., Paragon House, 10 St Peters Rd, Bournemouth, Dorset BH1 2JS, United Kingdom. TEL 44-1202-299900, FAX 44-1202-299955, 44-1202-200217, subs@paragon.co.uk, http://www.totalgames.net/pokemonworld, http://www.paragon.co.uk. Ed. Russell Murray. Adv. contact Felicity Mead TEL 44-1202-200224.

028.5 ITA ISSN 1591-2507
POKEMON WORLD. Text in Italian. 2000. m. EUR 3.50 newsstand/cover (effective 2003). adv. **Document type:** *Magazine, Consumer.*
Published by: Play Press Publishing s.r.l., Via Vitorchiano 123, Rome, RM 00189, Italy. TEL 39-06-33221250, FAX 39-06-33221235, abbonamenti@playpress.com, http://www.playpress.com. Ed. Carlo Chericoni. Pub. Alessandro Ferri. Adv. contact Lorenza Borroni TEL 39-02-45472867. Circ: 85,000 (paid and controlled).

028.5 CAN ISSN 1204-4571
POMME D'API. Text in French. 1991. m. (10/yr.). CND 29.95 domestic; USD 37.95 elsewhere (effective 2004). adv. bk.rev. back issues avail. **Document type:** *Magazine, Consumer.* **Description:** For children aged 3 to 7. Includes games, comics, educational tips, and stories to read.
Formerly (until 1994): Pomme d'Api Quebec (1188-1585)
Published by: Bayard Canada, The Owl Group, 49 Front St E, 2nd Fl, Toronto, ON M5E 1B3, Canada. TEL 416-340-2700, 800-551-6957, FAX 416-340-9769, bayard@owl.on.ca, http://www.owlkids.com/. adv.: color page CND 800; trim 8.44 x 6.5. Circ: 18,000 (paid).

028.5 282 FRA ISSN 1267-351X
POMME D'API SOLEIL. Text in French. 1989. bi-m. (Plus one extra issue). EUR 39.80 domestic; EUR 54.80 in the European Union; EUR 64.80 elsewhere (effective 2005).
Published by: Bayard Presse, 3 Rue Bayard, Paris, 75393 Cedex 08, France. TEL 33-1-44356060, FAX 33-1-44356161, redactions@bayard-presse.com, http://www.bayardpresse.com. Ed. Marie Aubinais.

POP GIRL. see *MUSIC*

028.5 780 791.43 DEU ISSN 1420-2263
POPCORN; das Teen People Magazin. Text in German. 1978. m. EUR 2.10 newsstand/cover (effective 2005). adv. **Document type:** *Magazine, Consumer.* **Description:** Covers stars and celebrities from the worlds of music, movies and TV.
Formerly (until 1977): Pop-Club (1421-2250); Incorporates (1980-1998): Pop Rocky (1420-2247); Which was formed by the merger of (1966-1980): Pop (1421-2013); (1979-1980): Rocky (1615-9888)
Published by: Axel Springer Young Mediahouse, Werinherstr 71, Munich, 81541, Germany. TEL 49-89-697490, FAX 49-89-69749312, franca.giorno@popcorn-mag.de, http://www.asv.de. Ed. Norbert Lalla. Adv. contact Petra Kalb TEL 49-89-69749100. page EUR 12,500; trim 205 x 285. Circ: 267,443 (paid). **Subscr. to:** dsb Abo-Betreuung GmbH, Konrad-Zuse-Str 16, Neckarsulm 74172, Germany. TEL 49-7132-959214, FAX 49-7132-959216, asvabo@dsb.net. **Dist. by:** ASV Vertriebs GmbH, Suederstr 77, Hamburg 20097, Germany. TEL 49-40-34725945, FAX 49-40-34723549.

028.5 HUN ISSN 0238-5759
POPCORN. Text in Hungarian. 1988. m. HUF 2,820 (effective 2001). adv. music rev.; film rev. **Document type:** *Magazine, Consumer.*
Published by: Axel Springer - Budapest Kft., Varosmajor u 11, Budapest, 1122, Hungary. TEL 36-1-4885700, FAX 36-1-2025332, bayerj@axels.hu. Circ: 66,000 (paid).

028.5 ROM ISSN 1453-861X
POPCORN. Text in Romanian. 1997. m. ROL 340,000 domestic; EUR 40 foreign (effective 2003). adv. **Document type:** *Magazine, Consumer.* **Description:** Contains stories and features on music and celebrities for teenagers.
Published by: Romanian Publishing Group srl, 77 Emanoil Porumbaru str, Sector 1, Bucharest, Romania. TEL 40-21-2600711, FAX 40-21-2600710, popcorn@rpg.ro, office@rpg.ro, http://www.rpg.ro/en_popcorn/. Circ: 35,000 (paid).

028.5 POL ISSN 1230-8137
POPCORN. Text in Polish. 2000. m. **Document type:** *Magazine, Consumer.* **Description:** Covers events and celebrities from the worlds of music, movies and entertainment for teenagers.
Published by: Axel Springer Polska, Al Jerozolimskie 181, Warsaw, 02222, Poland. TEL 48-22-6084100, FAX 48-22-6084106, asp@axelspringer.com.pl, http://www.axelspringer.com.pl. Circ: 154,000 (paid).

028.5 CZE ISSN 1211-4898
POPCORN. Text in Czech. 1994. m. CZK 39 newsstand/cover (effective 2003). adv. **Document type:** *Magazine, Consumer.*
Published by: Axel Springer Praha a.s., Strelnicna 1680/8, Prague 8, 182 21, Czech Republic. TEL 420-2-66193111, FAX 420-2-66193331, popcorn@axelspringer.cz, http://www.axelspringer.cz. Ed. Ivana Nadvornikova. Pub. Jiri Holna. Adv. contact Marketa Prochazkova. page CZK 80,000; trim 205 x 285. Circ: 21,000 (paid).

059.9193 LVA
▼ **POPCORN.** Text in Latvian. 2004 (Feb.). w. LVL 0.56 newsstand/cover (effective 2004). adv. **Document type:** *Magazine, Consumer.*
Published by: Saunags SIA, Ganu 6-21, Riga, 1010, Latvia. TEL 371-7333292. Ed. Kristaps Smildzins.

028.5 FRA ISSN 0299-3147
POPI. Text in French. 1986. m. EUR 49.80 domestic; EUR 64.80 in the European Union; EUR 74.80 elsewhere (effective 2005). **Description:** Responds to the curiosity of babies 15 months and older through pictures and games.
Published by: Bayard Presse, 3 Rue Bayard, Paris, 75393 Cedex 08, France. TEL 33-1-44356060, FAX 33-1-44356161, redactions@bayard-presse.com, http://www.bayardpresse.com. Ed. Marie Agnes Gaudrat. Circ: 79,825.

028.5 FRA
POPIDOUDOU. Text in French. 9/yr. EUR 49.80 domestic; EUR 64.80 in the European Union; EUR 74.80 elsewhere (effective 2005).
Published by: Bayard Presse, 3 Rue Bayard, Paris, 75393 Cedex 08, France. TEL 33-1-44356060, FAX 33-1-44356161, redactions@bayard-presse.com, http://www.bayardpresse.com.

POPSTAR!. see *MUSIC*

POSTER MOTOMAGAZYN. see *TRANSPORTATION—Automobiles*

028.5 GBR ISSN 0955-0321
POSTMAN PAT PICTURE PAPER✶. Text in English. 1986. w.
Published by: London Editions Magazine Ltd., Egmont House, Great Ducic St, PO Box 111, Manchester, 3BL, United Kingdom. TEL 01-482-3202. Circ: 95,000.

PRESSE - PAPIERS; extraits de la presse francais. see *LINGUISTICS*

028.5 GBR ISSN 1460-0854
PRETTY PONY CLUB. Text in English. 1997. m. GBP 30; GBP 2.50 newsstand/cover (effective 1999). adv. **Document type:** *Consumer.* **Description:** Filled with stories, puzzles and games for young children.
Published by: Burghley Publishing Ltd., 14 Barn Hill, Stamford, Lincs PE9 2AE, United Kingdom. TEL 44-1780-763366, FAX 44-1780-763365. Ed. Peter Nicholls. Adv. contact Joan Wright. **Dist. by:** Seymour Distribution Ltd, 86 Newman St, London W1T 3EX, United Kingdom. FAX 44-207-396-8002, enquiries@seymour.co.uk.

087.5 FIN ISSN 1456-8829
PRINSESSA. Text in Finnish. 1999. m. EUR 46 (effective 2004). adv. **Document type:** *Magazine, Consumer.* **Description:** Filled with Disney princess-themed activity pages, puzzles, games and posters for girls.
Published by: Sanoma Magazines Finland Corporation, Hoylaamotie 1 D, P.O. Box 100, Helsinki, 00040, Finland. TEL 358-9-1201, FAX 358-9-1205171, info@sanomamagazines.fi, http://www.sanomamagazines.fi. adv.: color page EUR 1,730. Circ: 29,218 (paid).

028.5 GRC ISSN 0033-1465
PROSCOPOS. Text in Greek. 1946. m. USD 4; includes Krikos Ton Vathmoforon. illus.
Published by: Boy Scouts of Greece/Soma Hellinon Proscopon, 1 Ptolemeon St, Athens, 516, Greece. Ed. Demetrius Marinopoulos. Circ: 10,000.

028.5 FRA ISSN 0997-3745
P'TIT LOUP. Text in French. m. **Document type:** *Consumer.* **Description:** Fifty questions and answers on subjects of interest to kids between 7 and 10 years old.
Published by: Disney Hachette Presse, 10 rue Thierry le Luron, Levallois Perret, Cedex 92592, France. TEL 33-1-41348500, FAX 33-1-41378989. Ed. Gilles Heylen. Circ: 77,000.

028.5 FRA
LES P'TITES SORCIERES. Text in French. 1999. m. FRF 296 domestic; FRF 570.20 foreign (effective 2000). **Description:** For girls 8 to 12 years old who like reading.
Published by: Fleurus Presse, 129 bd. Malesherbes, Paris, 75017, France. TEL 33-1-56793636. Ed. Beatrice Guthart.

333.72 USA ISSN 1073-8320
PUDDLER. Text in English. bi-m. **Document type:** *Magazine, Consumer.*
Published by: Ducks Unlimited, Inc., 1 Waterfowl Way, Memphis, TN 38120-2351. TEL 901-758-3825, FAX 901-758-3850, http://www.ducks.org/. Ed., R&P Lee Salber. Pub. D A Young Jr.

028.5 746.92 NZL
PULP. Text in English. bi-m. NZD 22.50, USD 35 (effective 1999). adv. bk.rev.; dance rev.; music rev.; play rev.; software rev.; tel.rev. back issues avail. **Document type:** *Consumer.*
Description: Offers news, trends, fashion and information for young consumers.
Published by: Pulp Publishing Ltd., Wellesley St, P.O. Box 7014, Auckland, New Zealand. TEL 64-9-3789996, FAX 64-9-3600708, pulp@ihug.co.nz. Ed., R&P Daya Willis TEL 64-9-3789997. Adv. contact Fiona Morgan. B&W page NZD 1,500, color page NZD 2,585; trim 290 x 230. Circ: 10,000.

028.5 IND ISSN 0033-4227
PULSE OF YOUTH. Text in English. 1968. q. INR 3. adv.
Address: c/o Kamlendra Kanwar, 86 Hindu College Hostel, New Delhi, India.

028.5 DEU
PUMUCKL. Text in German. m. EUR 2.33 newsstand/cover (effective 2003). adv. **Document type:** *Magazine, Consumer.*
Description: Contains stories, games and comics featuring Pumuckl.
Published by: Panini Verlags GmbH, Ravensstr 48, Nettetal, 41334, Germany. TEL 49-711-947680, FAX 49-711-94768830, info@panini-dino.de, http://www.pumuckl.de, http://www.panini-media.de. Ed. Eva Blank. Pub. Roland Brandstaett. Adv. contact Petra Sonnenfroh-Kost. page EUR 3,900; trim 205 x 300. Circ: 76,952 (paid).

028.5 364.4 ITA
PUNGOLO; periodico dei giovani. Text in English, Italian. 1982. m. USD 25 (effective 1998). adv. bk.rev.; software rev.; tel.rev. abstr.; bibl.; illus.; maps; stat. index. **Document type:** *Newspaper, Consumer.* **Description:** Informs young people in Italy who are against the Mafia's power and all forms of corruption.
Related titles: CD-ROM ed.; Diskette ed.; Online - full text ed.
Published by: European Information Service, Via Col Romej, 7, Trapani, TP 91100, Italy. TEL 39-923-546700, FAX 39-923-872055, eisnews@tin.it, http://web.tin.it/eisnews. Ed. Pietro Vento. Adv. contact Sabrina Titone. page USD 3,000. Circ: 12,000. **Co-sponsor:** Centro Internazionale di Studi per i Giovani.

028.5 GBR ISSN 1463-9688
PUPPY IN MY POCKET AND FRIENDS. Text in English. 1998. m. GBP 25.20; GBP 1.75 newsstand/cover (effective 1999). **Document type:** *Consumer.* **Description:** Contains fun activities and games for young children.
Published by: Burghley Publishing Ltd., 14 Barn Hill, Stamford, Lincs PE9 2AE, United Kingdom. TEL 44-1780-763366, FAX 44-1780-763365. **Dist. by:** Seymour Distribution Ltd, 86 Newman St, London W1T 3EX, United Kingdom. FAX 44-207-396-8002, enquiries@seymour.co.uk.

PUPPY LOVE. see *PETS*

028.5 CHN
QINGCHUN SUIYUE/YOUTHFUL YEARS. Text in Chinese. 1982. m. CNY 1.85 per issue. adv. bk.rev.
Published by: Gong Qing Tuan Hebei Sheng Weiyuanhui, 244 Nanma Lu, Shijiazhuang, Hebei 050051, China. TEL 86-311-7027226. Ed. Zhang Hongde. Adv. contact Li Wushen. Circ: 120,000 (paid).

QINGCHUN YIZU. see *WOMEN'S INTERESTS*

028.5 CHN
QINGNIAN BOLAN. Text in Chinese. m. CNY 12. **Description:** Publishes selected articles from other publications, featuring local and international events of general interest.
Indexed: RASB.
Published by: Fujian Qingnian Zazhishe, No 5, Jinjishan, Fuzhou, Fujian 350001, China. TEL 551944. Ed. Lin Yunqing. **Dist. overseas by:** Jiangsu Publications Import & Export Corp., 56 Gao Yun Ling, Nanjing, Jiangsu, China.

028.5 CHN ISSN 1002-2759
QINGNIAN JIZHE/YOUNG JOURNALIST. Text in Chinese. 1941. m. CNY 96 (effective 2004). **Document type:** *Magazine, Consumer.*
Related titles: Online - full content ed.
Published by: Dazhongbao Yejituan/Dazhong News Group, 6, Leyuan Dajie, Jinan, Shangdong 250014, China. TEL 86-531-2968989, http://www.dzwww.com/qingnianjizhe/.

028.5 CHN ISSN 1003-0565
AP95.C4
QINGNIAN WENZHAI. Text in Chinese. m.
Indexed: RASB.
Published by: Zhongguo Qingnian Chubanshe, Qikan Bu/China Youth Press, 21 Dongsi 12 Tiao, Beijing, 100708, China. TEL 442125. Ed. Hu Shouwen.

059.951 CHN ISSN 1000-4807
HQ799.C55
QINGNIAN YIDAI/YOUNG GENERATION. Text in Chinese. m. CNY 26.40. adv. **Document type:** *Consumer.*
Published by: Shanghai Renmin Chubanshe, Qikan Bu/Shanghai People's Publishing House, 54 Shaoxing Rd, Shanghai, 200020, China. Ed. Zhang Baoni. **Dist. outside China by:** China International Book Trading Corp, 35 Chegongzhuang Xilu, Haidian District, PO Box 399, Beijing 100044, China.

028.5 CHN
QINGNIAN YUEKAN/YOUTH MONTHLY. Text in Chinese. m.
Published by: Gongqingtuan Jilin Shengwei, 49 Stalin St, Changchun, Jilin 130051, China. TEL 823744. Ed. Yang Dejun.

QINGNIAN ZUOJIA/YOUNG WRITERS; wenxue shuang yuekan. see *LITERATURE*

028.5 CHN ISSN 1004-1079
QINGSHAONIAN RIJI/YOUTHS DIARY. Text in Chinese. 1984. m. CNY 0.66 per issue. **Description:** Discusses how to keep a diary.
Published by: Shanxi Ribao She/Shanxi Daily Publishing Company, 24 Shuangtasi Jie, Taiyuan, Shanxi 030012, China. TEL 446561. Ed. Guo Huarong.

QUANGUO ZHONGXUE YOUXIU ZUOWEN XUAN (GAOZONG BAN)/SELECTED EXCELLENT COMPOSITIONS FROM NATIONWIDE MIDDLE SCHOOLS (HIGH SCHOOL EDITION). see *LINGUISTICS*

305.42 BRA ISSN 0104-334X
QUERIDA. Text in Portuguese. 1989. bi-w. adv. illus. **Document type:** *Consumer.* **Description:** For young girls. Deals with dating, friendship, sex, family, health, beauty, travel and astrology.
Related titles: ◆ Supplement(s): Querida Super Stars. ISSN 0104-6616.
Published by: Editora Globo S.A., Rua Domingos Sergio dos Anjos, 277, Pirituba, Jd S Elias, Sao Paulo, SP 05136-170, Brazil. TEL 55-11-836-5000, atendimento@edglobo.com.br, http://editoraglobo.globo.com/. Pub. Jose Francisco Queiroz. adv.: color page USD 6,900; trim 274 x 208. Circ: 120,000 (paid).

305.4 BRA ISSN 1413-3075
QUERIDA ESPECIAL. Text in Portuguese. 199?. m. illus. **Document type:** *Consumer.*
Published by: Editora Globo S.A., Rua Domingos Sergio dos Anjos, 277, Pirituba, Jd S Elias, Sao Paulo, SP 05136-170, Brazil. TEL 55-11-836-5000, atendimento@edglobo.com.br, http://www.editoraglobo.com.br, http://editoraglobo.globo.com/. Pub. Jose Francisco Queiroz. adv.: B&W page USD 1,120, color page USD 1,400; trim 190 x 134. Circ: 45,000 (paid).

028.5 BRA ISSN 0104-6616
QUERIDA SUPER STARS. Text in Portuguese. bi-m. adv. illus. **Document type:** *Consumer.* **Description:** Presents profiles of stars from cinema, TV, and popular music. Includes posters and song lyrics.
Related titles: ◆ Supplement to: Querida. ISSN 0104-334X.
Published by: Editora Globo S.A., Rua Domingos Sergio dos Anjos, 277, Pirituba, Jd S Elias, Sao Paulo, SP 05136-170, Brazil. http://editoraglobo.globo.com/. Pub. Jose Francisco Queiroz. Circ: 52,000 (paid).

028.5 ITA
QUIGIOVANI★ . Text in Italian. d.
Published by: Editrice Pentapolis s.r.l., Via Aurelia, 641, Rome, RM 00165, Italy. TEL 6-68-08-809, FAX 6-6808-044. Ed. Salvatore Puzzo.

028.5 GBR ISSN 0956-2117
QUIZKIDS. Text in English. 1989. 10/yr. GBP 15; GBP 1.50 newsstand/cover (effective 2001). adv. bk.rev. **Document type:** *Magazine, Consumer.*
—CCC.
Published by: British European Associated Publishers Ltd., Stonecroft, 69 Station Rd, Redhill, Surrey RH1 1DL, United Kingdom. TEL 44-1737-378700, FAX 44-1737-781800, mail@beap.co.uk, http://www.puzzler.co.uk. Pub. David Sergeant. Circ: 60,000. **Dist. by:** Seymour Distribution Ltd, 86 Newman St, London W1T 3EX, United Kingdom. TEL 44-20-73968000, FAX 44-20-73968002.

794.8 USA
R - ZONE. Text in English. 2002. q. free (effective 2003); Avail. at R-Zone locations within Toys "R" Us stores nationwide.. adv. **Document type:** *Magazine, Consumer.* **Description:** Video-gaming and lifestyle magazine aimed at 12- to 24-year-olds, with a core focus on teens who are not only passionate about video games, but are also into music, movies, fashion and sports.
Published by: P S P Sports, 355 Lexington Ave, New York, NY 10017. TEL 212-697-1460, FAX 212-286-8154, http://www.pspsports.com. adv.: color page USD 28,500; trim 8.125 x 11.125.

RAADGIVEREN; boerne og juniorlederen. see *RELIGIONS AND THEOLOGY—Protestant*

RAEDDA DJUREN!. see *ANIMAL WELFARE*

028.5 ESP ISSN 1133-1917
RAGAZZA. Key Title: Ragazza a la Ultima. Text in Spanish. 1989. m. EUR 20.16 domestic; EUR 49.20 in Europe; EUR 50.76 elsewhere; EUR 2.10 newsstand/cover (effective 2005). adv. **Document type:** *Magazine, Consumer.*
Related titles: Online - full text ed.; ◆ Portuguese ed.: Ragazza (Lisbon). ISSN 0872-6515.
Published by: Hachette Filipacchi SA, Avda Cardenal Herrera Oria 3, Madrid, 28034, Spain. TEL 34-91-7287000, FAX 34-91-3585473, ragazza@hachette.es, comunicacion@hachette.es, http://www.ragazza.es, http://www.hachette.es. Ed. Mentxue Vicente. adv.: color page EUR 8,900; 228 x 297. Circ: 106,755.

028.5 PRT ISSN 0872-6515
RAGAZZA (LISBON). Text in Portuguese. 1993. m. **Document type:** *Magazine, Consumer.*
Related titles: ◆ Spanish ed.: Ragazza. ISSN 1133-1917.
Published by: Hachette Filipacchi Publicacoes (Subsidiary of: Hachette Filipacchi Medias S.A.), Rua Filipe Folque 40-4o, Lisbon, 1069-124, Portugal. TEL 351-21-3164200, FAX 351-21-3164202, http://www.hachette.pt.

RAGAZZI; il mensile per il tuo italiano. see *LINGUISTICS*

028.5 GBR ISSN 1364-0798
RAGDOLL & FRIENDS. Text in English. 1996. m. GBP 1.25 newsstand/cover. **Document type:** *Consumer.* **Description:** Contains stories and other activities for young children.
Published by: Marvel Comics Ltd. (Subsidiary of: Panini UK Ltd.), Panini House, Coach & Horses Passage, The Pantiles, Tunbridge Wells, Kent TM2 5UJ, United Kingdom. TEL 44-1892-500100, FAX 44-1892-545666. **Dist. by:** MarketForce UK Ltd, 247 Tottenham Court Rd, London, Middx W1T 7AU, United Kingdom. TEL 44-207-2615199, FAX 44-207-2617341.

RAINBOW (LONDON). see *RELIGIONS AND THEOLOGY—Protestant*

028.5 CZE
RAINBOW & RAINDROPS. Short title: R & R. Text in English. 1949. 10/yr. CZK 80. adv. **Description:** Aimed at children aged 9-13.
Formerly (until 1989): Ogoniok (0030-073X)
Published by: Publishing House R & R, Preslickova 2886, Prague, 10600, Czech Republic. Ed. Vlasta Herinkova. Circ: 50,000.

369.4 790.019 NZL
THE RALLY LEADER. Text in English. q. NZD 10.50 (effective 2000). **Document type:** *Bulletin.* **Description:** Brings ideas, information, games, hobbies and encouragement to rally leaders.
Former titles: Leader; Rally Leaders Bulletin
Published by: Every Boy's and Every Girl's Rally Council N.Z. Inc., P.O. Box 1903, Palmerston North, New Zealand. TEL 64-6-3593735. Ed. D McClunie. Circ: 700 (paid).

RAN; das junge Magazin der Gewerkschaften. see *POLITICAL SCIENCE*

333.72 USA ISSN 0738-6656
QH48
RANGER RICK. Text in English. 1967. m. USD 17 domestic; USD 29 foreign (effective 2005). bk.rev. illus. index. reprint service avail. from PQC. **Document type:** *Magazine, Consumer.*
Description: Contains articles for children 8 and up with full-color photos about wildlife and children in the outdoors. Advocates the sustainable use of natural resources.
Formerly (until 1983): Ranger Rick's Nature Magazine (0033-9229)
Related titles: Microfiche ed.: (from NBI, PQC); Online - full text ed.: (from bigchalk, EBSCO Publishing, Gale Group, Micromedia ProQuest, Northern Light Technology, Inc., ProQuest Information & Learning).
Indexed: CBCARef, CBPI, CPerI, ICM, JHMA, MASUSE, MagInd, RGYP.
Published by: National Wildlife Federation, 11100 Wildlife Center Dr., Reston, VA 20190-5362. TEL 703-438-6284, 800-822-9919, FAX 703-438-6349, rick@nwf.org, http://www.nwf.org/gowild/kzPage.cfm?siteId=3&CFID=1503634&CFTOKEN=61111810. Ed. Gerry Bishop. Circ: 600,000 (paid). **Subscr. to:** PO Box 2038, Harlan, IA 51593-0017. TEL 800-611-1599.

028.5 IND
RASHTRA DEEPIKA CHILDREN'S DIGEST. Text in English. m. INR 100; INR 10 newsstand/cover. adv.
Published by: Rashtra Deepika Ltd., Deepika Bldg., C.M.S. College Rd., P O Box 7, Kottayam, Kerala 686 001, India. TEL 91-481-566706, FAX 91-481-567947. Ed., Pub. James K Joseph. adv.: B&W page INR 5,000, color page INR 10,000; 110 x 160. Circ: 25,000.

028.5 RUS
RASKRASKI, KOTORYE UCHAT. Text in Russian. s-a. RUR 240 (effective 2002). **Description:** Helps children 5-10 years of age use art and drawing to learn on their own.
Published by: Izdatel'skii Dom Karapuz, Izmailovskoe shosse 48a, Moscow, 105318, Russian Federation. TEL 7-095-9182810, http://www.karapuz.com. Ed. L S Kozlov.

C

051 USA
REACT; the news magazine that raises voices. Text in English. w. **Document type:** *Magazine, Consumer.* **Description:** Covers items of interest to all teenagers.
Media: Online - full content.
Published by: J P Kids, Inc., 989 Market St, 2nd fl, San Francisco, CA 94103. TEL 415-371-8600, http://www.react.com/.

READ MAGAZINE. see *EDUCATION—Teaching Methods And Curriculum*

READING AND WRITING QUARTERLY; overcoming learning difficulties. see *EDUCATION—Special Education And Rehabilitation*

READY FOR ENGLISH. see *LINGUISTICS*

028.5 USA ISSN 1090-4034
REAL (KANSAS CITY); the magazine for growing minds. Text in English. 1995. bi-m. adv.
Published by: Elbert Allan Publishing Co., Inc., 3811 E 75th Ter, Kansas City, MO 64132. TEL 816-363-8336, FAX 816-361-4161, aengage@aol.com. Ed. Susan Campbell. Pub. Alan Harris.

028.5 371.42 USA
REAL LIFE. Text in English. 1996. 16/yr. USD 495 (effective 1998). **Document type:** *Monographic series.* **Description:** Addresses workplace ethics and employment skills through an evolving story about 5 teenage friends who are employed part time. Each story ends in a dilemma students are asked to solve.
Published by: Career Solutions Training Group, 13 E Central Ave, Paoli, PA 19301. TEL 610-993-8292, FAX 610-993-8249, cstg@bellatlantic.net. Ed., Pub. Doris Humphrey. R&P Friede Borst. Circ: 200 (paid).

028.5 BEL ISSN 1373-2404
RECITS EXPRESS. Text in French. 1999. m. EUR 25 (effective 2005). illus. **Document type:** *Magazine.* **Description:** Offers young readers 14 and older a variety of relevant interesting stories, articles, and activities.
Related titles: ♦ Dutch ed.: Vlaamse Filmpjes. ISSN 0773-1027.
Published by: Editions Averbode SA, Abdijstraat 1, BP 54, Averbode, 3271, Belgium. TEL 32-13-780111, FAX 32-13-776837, http://www.averbode.be/fr/revues/detail.php?ID=16&menu=t&selectedsubnavigation=boekenabonnement.

THE RECREATION AND SPORTS MINISTRY NEWSLETTER. see *RELIGIONS AND THEOLOGY—Protestant*

028.5 BRA
RECREIO. Text in Portuguese. w. BRL 465.40 (effective 2005). adv. back issues avail. **Document type:** *Magazine, Consumer.*
Related titles: Online - full text ed.
Published by: Editora Abril, S.A., Av. das Nacoes Unidas, 7221, 11 andar Pinheiros, Sao Paulo, SP 05425-902, Brazil. TEL 55-11-50872112, FAX 55-11-50872100, recreio.abril@atleitor.com.br, http://recreionline.abril.com.br/, http://www.abril.com.br/. adv.: page BRL 17,100. Circ: 199,349.

363.7282 USA
RECYCLING STORIES THAT RHYME. Text in English. 1991. a. looseleaf. USD 5 per issue (effective 2001). **Document type:** *Newsletter.* **Description:** Publishes stories that give children ideas on recycling.
Published by: Prosperity & Profits Unlimited Distribution Services, PO Box 416, Denver, CO 80201-0416. TEL 303-575-5676, mail@coursesmith.com, http://www.storytimestoriesthatrhyme.com. Ed., R&P A Doyle. Circ: 1,500 (paid).

369.4 SWE ISSN 1650-1594
REDO FOER SCOUTING. Text in Swedish. 2000. 6/yr. SEK 100 (effective 2004). adv.
Supersedes in part (in 2000): Scout (0346-0827)
Related titles: Online - full text ed.; ♦ Supplement(s): Scouting Spirit. ISSN 1403-2740.
Published by: Svenska Scoutraadet, PO Box 801, Solna, 16928, Sweden. TEL 46-8-56843290, FAX 46-8-56843299, redo@scout.se, info@scout.se, http://www.redo.scout.se/, http://www.scout.se. Ed. Hanna Modigh Glansholm. Adv. contact Elisabeth All. Circ: 59,000.

REFLECTIONS (DUNCAN FALLS); the national student poetry magazine for grades K-12. see *LITERATURE—Poetry*

▼ **REFLECTIONS (LAKEMBA).** see *RELIGIONS AND THEOLOGY—Islamic*

028.5 BEL ISSN 1374-9218
REFLECTOR. Text in Dutch. 1999. 7/yr. illus. **Document type:** *Magazine.* **Description:** Offers teen readers ages 16 through 18 a variety of topical articles and stories.
Published by: Uitgeverij Averbode NV, Abdijstraat 1, Postbus 54, Averbode, 3271, Belgium. TEL 32-13-780111, FAX 32-13-780183, http://www.averbode.be.

REGENBOGEN; katholische Kinderzeitschrift fuer Maedchen und Buben. see *RELIGIONS AND THEOLOGY*

REPORTS TO THE NATION ON OUR CHANGING PLANET. see *ENVIRONMENTAL STUDIES*

028.5 CAN ISSN 1201-7647
RESOURCE LINKS; connecting classrooms, libraries & Canadians learning resources. Text in English. 1995. 5/yr. CND 39.95 to non-members; CND 29.95 to members (effective 2005). adv. **Document type:** *Journal.* **Description:** Strives to focus greater attention on young adult and children's materials set in Canada and written by Canadian authors.
Related titles: Online - full text ed.: (from bigchalk, Florida Center for Library Automation, Gale Group, Micromedia ProQuest, Northern Light Technology, Inc., ProQuest Information & Learning).
Indexed: BRI, CBCARef, CBRI, CEI, CPerl.
Published by: (Council for Canadian Learning Resources), Resource Links, PO Box 9, Pouch Cove, NF A0A 3L0, Canada. TEL 709-335-2394, FAX 709-335-2978, resourcelinks@nfld.com, http://www.resourcelinks.ca. Ed., R&P, Adv. contact Victoria Pennell.

REV. see *RELIGIONS AND THEOLOGY*

028.5 027.4 COL ISSN 0122-3496
REVISTA LATINOAMERICANA DE LITERATURA INFANTIL Y JUVENIL. Text in Spanish. 1995. s-a.
Published by: Fundacion para el Fomento de la Lectura, Avenida 40 No 16-46, Bogota, Colombia. TEL 57-1-3201511, FAX 57-1-2877071, contactenos@fundalectura.org.co, http://www.fundalectura.org.

REVUE DES LIVRES POUR ENFANTS. see *PUBLISHING AND BOOK TRADE*

028.5 CAN
THE REZ. Text in English. q. CND 16; CND 25 foreign.
Published by: All Right Production Ltd., 443 W Third St, Vancouver, BC V7M 1G9, Canada.

RIGHT ON!. see *ETHNIC INTERESTS*

028.5 GBR ISSN 0957-3704
RIGHT START; your complete guide to parenting. Text in English. 1989. 6/yr. GBP 20.60 domestic; GBP 38 in Europe; GBP 66 elsewhere (effective 1999); GBP 1.80 newsstand/cover. adv. bk.rev. **Document type:** *Consumer.* **Description:** For parents of 1-6 year olds with a special interest in education, health and development.
Published by: Needmarsh Publishing Ltd., 71 Newcomen St, London, SE1 1YT, United Kingdom. TEL 44-171-403-0840, FAX 44-171-378-6883. Ed. Lynette Lowthian. R&P Anita Bevan. Adv. contact Sarah Warden. color page GBP 2,650. **Subscr. to:** Right Start Subscriptions, MDS, Unit 1, Limes Ave, London SE20 8QP, United Kingdom. TEL 44-1816-769989. **Dist. by:** Comag, Tavistock Works, Tavistock Rd, W Drayton, Middx UB7 7QX, United Kingdom. TEL 44-1895-433600, FAX 44-189-543-3606.

808.068 MUS
➤ **RIMJHIM.** Text in Hindi. 1994. every 2 mos. INR 50 (effective 2003). bk.rev. 28 p./no.; back issues avail.; reprints avail. **Document type:** *Magazine, Academic/Scholarly.* **Description:** Children's magazine in Hindi with poems, short stories, articles, exercises, quiz and language skills.
Published by: Mahatma Gandhi Institute, Moka, Mauritius. TEL 230-4331277, FAX 230-4332235. Ed. Dr. B Jugasing. Circ: 500.

028.5 USA
▼ **RIOT MAGAZINE.** Text in English. 2005. irreg. **Document type:** *Magazine, Consumer.*
Published by: Riot Media, LLC., 230 West 41, New York, NY 10036 . publishinginfo@riot101.com, http://www.riot101.com/.

AL-RIYADAH WAL-SHABAB. see *SPORTS AND GAMES*

028.5 BEL ISSN 0771-8128
ROBBEDOES. Text in Dutch. 1938. w. back issues avail.
Related titles: ♦ French ed.: Spirou. ISSN 0771-8071.
Published by: Editions Dupuis S.A., Rue Jules Destree 52, Marcinelle, 6001, Belgium. TEL 32-71-600500, FAX 32-71-600599. Circ: 32,000.

THE ROCK (ELGIN). see *RELIGIONS AND THEOLOGY*

028.5 BGR ISSN 0204-5117
RODNA RECH/NATIVE LANGUAGE. Text in Bulgarian. 1957. 10/yr. USD 60 foreign (effective 2002).
Published by: Ministerstvo na Obrazovanieto i Naukata na Republika Bulgaria/Ministry of Education and Sciences of the Republic of Bulgaria, 125 Tzarigradsko Shosse Blvd., Bl. 5, PO Box 336, Sofia, 1113, Bulgaria. TEL 359-2-705298, http://www.sca.bg/cultural-periodicals/catalog/rodrech.htm, http://www.minedu.government.bg. Ed. Atanas Atanassov-Zvezdinov. **Dist. by:** Sofia Books, ul Silivria 16, Sofia 1404, Bulgaria. TEL 359-2-9586257, info@sofiabooks-bg.com, http://www.sofiabooks-bg.com. **Co-publisher:** Children's Book House.

ROLF KAUKAS BUSSI BAER; fuer Ihr Kind: lesen - malen - lachen - basteln - lernen. see *EDUCATION*

028.5 FIN ISSN 0357-8755
ROOPE-SETA. Text in Finnish. 1978. m. EUR 35 (effective 2004). adv. **Document type:** *Magazine, Consumer.*
Published by: Sanoma Magazines Finland Corporation, Hoylaamotie 1 D, P.O. Box 100, Helsinki, 00040, Finland. TEL 358-9-1201, FAX 358-9-1205171, info@sanomamagazines.fi, http://www.sanomamagazines.fi. Ed. Markku Kivekas. adv.: color page EUR 3,290. Circ: 53,537.

028.5 330 KGZ
ROSSIYA. Text in Russian. 1996. **Description:** Acquaints children with the market economy, market relations, banking, and legal issues.
Published by: Ekho Osha, Kurmanjan Datka 224, 5 et, Osh, 714004, Kyrgyzstan. TEL 996-3332-75016.

028.5 RUS ISSN 0131-5994
ROVESNIK. Text in Russian. 1962. m. USD 173 foreign (effective 2005). adv. bk.rev. illus. **Document type:** *Magazine, Consumer.*
Indexed: RASB.
—East View.
Published by: Redaktsiya Zhurnala Rovesnik, Novodmitrovskaya ul 5-a, 17th Fl, Moscow, 125015, Russian Federation. TEL 7-095-7876307, FAX 7-095-7876308, info@rovesnik.ru, http://www.rovesnik.ru/dom/rovesnik.asp. Ed. I A Chernyshkov. adv.: color page USD 2,200. Circ: 100,000. **Dist. by:** East View Information Services, 3020 Harbor Ln. N., Minneapolis, MN 55447. TEL 763-550-0961, FAX 763-559-2931, eastview@eastview.com, http://www.eastview.com.

ROYAL AMBASSADOR LEADERSHIP. see *RELIGIONS AND THEOLOGY—Protestant*

S A Y MAGAZINE. (Spirit of Aborginal Youth) see *ETHNIC INTERESTS*

S C L NEWS. (Section of Children's Libraries) see *LIBRARY AND INFORMATION SCIENCES*

S I R S DISCOVERER. (Social Issues Resources Series) see *CHILDREN AND YOUTH—Abstracting, Bibliographies, Statistics*

S I R S DISCOVERER ELEMENTARY EDITION. (Social Issues Resources Series) see *CHILDREN AND YOUTH—Abstracting, Bibliographies, Statistics*

S I R S DISCOVERER MIDDLE EDITION. (Social Issues Resources Series) see *CHILDREN AND YOUTH—Abstracting, Bibliographies, Statistics*

S Y T A'S STUDENT & YOUTH TRAVELER. see *TRAVEL AND TOURISM*

741.5 USA ISSN 1094-4869
SABRINA THE TEENAGE WITCH. Text in English. 1997. 8/yr. USD 21; USD 1.75 newsstand/cover; GBP 1.25 newsstand/cover in United Kingdom (effective 1999). illus. **Document type:** *Consumer.* **Description:** Features the comic strip Sabrina, which is based on a popular television series.
Published by: Archie Comic Publications, Inc., 325 Fayette Ave, Mamaroneck, NY 10543-2318. http://www.archiecomics.com. Pubs. Michael Silberkleit, Richard Goldwater. **Dist. in UK by:** Comag, Tavistock Works, Tavistock Rd, W Drayton, Middx UB7 7QX, United Kingdom. TEL 44-1895-444055, FAX 44-1895-433602.

028.5 GBR ISSN 1471-8634
SABRINA'S SECRETS. Text in English. 2000. bi-w. USD 27 for 6 mos.; USD 2.50 newsstand/cover (effective 2001). **Document type:** *Magazine, Consumer.* **Description:** Features articles on beauty for young girls, also include stories, activities, and other related topics.
Published by: G E Fabbri Ltd., Elme House, 133 Long Acre, London, WC2E 9AW, United Kingdom. TEL 44-20-7836-0519, 44-20-7468-5600, FAX 44-20-7836-0280, mail@gefabbri.co.uk, http://www.gefabbri.co.uk/Sabrina%27sSecrets/.

028.5 388 USA ISSN 1523-8261
SAFE RIDE NEWS✶. Text in English. 1985. bi-m. USD 65 (effective 2004). video rev. illus.; stat. Index. back issues avail. **Document type:** *Newsletter.* **Description:** Provides information mainly on passenger safety, but includes coverage of bicycles, pedestrians, and school bus safety for advocates and professionals on child traffic safety.
Indexed: CLT&T, HRIS.

C

▼ *new title* ➤ *refereed* ✶ *unverified* ♦ *full entry avail.*

Published by: Safe Ride News Publications, 14604 9th Ave NE, Shoreline, WA 98155-7039. TEL 206-364-5696, FAX 206-364-5992, info@saferidenews.com, http://www.saferidenews.com. Ed. Deborah Stewart. R&P Lisa Cowan. Circ: 2,200 (paid).

375   CAN
SAFETY NET NEWSLETTER. Text in English. m. **Document type:** *Newsletter.* **Description:** Includes more than 50 sites categorized as curriculum, kids, parents and teachers, and reference.
Media: Online - full text.
Address: Canada. matink@eagle.ca, http://www.eagle.ca/~matink. Ed. Carolyn Bierworth.

028.5   USA   ISSN 0896-8276
ST. PAUL'S FAMILY MAGAZINE. Text in English. 1984. q. USD 25. adv. bk.rev. illus. back issues avail. **Description:** Includes classic children's literature, poetry, art, and music as well as cooking, crafts, and puzzle projects.
Published by: St. Paul's Publishing Co., Inc., 14780 W 159th St, Olathe, KS 66062. TEL 913-780-0405. Ed. James R Leek. Circ: 600.

028.5 613.7   CRI
SALUD PARA TODOS. Text in Spanish. 1977. a. free. illus.; charts.
Published by: Asociacion Demografica Costarricense, Apartado Postal 10203, San Jose, 1000, Costa Rica. TEL 31-4211. Ed. Lia Barth. Circ: 125,000. **Co-sponsor:** Ministerio de Salud.

028.5   FRA   ISSN 0397-7854
SALUT. Text in French. 1962. bi-w. adv. bk.rev. bibl.; illus.; stat.
Formerly (until 1978): Salut les Copains (0036-3650)
Address: 13 rue de la Cerisaie, Paris, 75004, France. Circ: 26,000.

028.5   RUS
LA SAM! LA SAMA!. Text in Russian. 10/yr. USD 149.95 in United States.
Published by: La Sam! La Sama!, Ul Kedrova 8, korp 2, kom 47-48, Moscow, 117804, Russian Federation. TEL 7-095-1292790, FAX 7-095-1255673. Ed. G B Menshikova. **US dist. addr.:** East View Information Services, 3020 Harbor Ln. N., Minneapolis, MN 55447. TEL 612-550-0961.

SAPPORO-SHI SEISHONEN KAGAKUKAN KIYO. see *SCIENCES: COMPREHENSIVE WORKS*

SAUGFINGER. see *CHEMISTRY*

053.1   DEU
SCHLAUKOPF; der Pfiffikus aus deiner Apotheke. Text in German. m. **Document type:** *Magazine, Consumer.*
Published by: Gebr. Storck GmbH & Co. Verlags-oHG, Bebelstr 102, Oberhausen, 46049, Germany. TEL 49-208-8480211, FAX 49-208-8480238, kalender@storckverlag.de, http://www.storckverlag.de.

053.1   DEU
SCHLOSS EINSTEIN MAGAZIN. Text in German. 2000. m. EUR 2.30 newsstand/cover (effective 2002). adv. **Document type:** *Magazine, Consumer.* **Description:** Contains stories, photos and articles related to the television series "Schloss Einstein" for children.
Published by: cultfish entertainment GmbH, Wallstr 59, Berlin, 10179, Germany. TEL 49-30-24008471, FAX 49-30-24008475, http://cultfish.de. adv.: page EUR 3,100. Circ: 150,000 (paid and controlled).

SCHOLAR'S MATE. see *SPORTS AND GAMES*

SCHOLASTIC ACTION. see *EDUCATION—Teaching Methods And Curriculum*

SCHOLASTIC ART. see *EDUCATION—Teaching Methods And Curriculum*

SCHOLASTIC CHOICES; personal development & living skills. see *EDUCATION—Teaching Methods And Curriculum*

SCHOLASTIC DYNAMATH. see *EDUCATION—Teaching Methods And Curriculum*

SCHOLASTIC LET'S FIND OUT. see *EDUCATION—Teaching Methods And Curriculum*

SCHOLASTIC MATH. see *EDUCATION—Teaching Methods And Curriculum*

SCHOLASTIC NEWS EN ESPANOL. EDICION 1. see *EDUCATION—Teaching Methods And Curriculum*

SCHOLASTIC NEWS EN ESPANOL. EDICION 2. see *EDUCATION—Teaching Methods And Curriculum*

SCHOLASTIC NEWS EN ESPANOL. EDICION 3. see *EDUCATION—Teaching Methods And Curriculum*

SCHOLASTIC NEWS. GRADE 1 EDITION. see *EDUCATION—Teaching Methods And Curriculum*

SCHOLASTIC NEWS. GRADE 2 EDITION. see *EDUCATION—Teaching Methods And Curriculum*

SCHOLASTIC NEWS. GRADE 3 EDITION. see *EDUCATION—Teaching Methods And Curriculum*

SCHOLASTIC NEWS. GRADE 4 EDITION. see *EDUCATION—Teaching Methods And Curriculum*

028.5   USA
SCHOLASTIC NEWS. GRADE 5 / 6 EDITION. Text in English. 1998. 24/yr. (during school year). USD 3.95 (effective 2005); with 10 or more student subscr.. illus. Index. reprint service avail. from PQC. **Document type:** *Magazine, Academic/Scholarly.* **Description:** Invites fifth- and sixth-grade students to explore, ponder, and discuss events in the news and other noteworthy issues.
Formed by the merger of (1952-1998): Scholastic News (Edition 6) (1070-1206); Which was formerly (until 1993): Scholastic Newstime (1058-1537); (until 1989): Scholastic News (Newstime Edition) (0736-0622); (until 1982): Scholastic Newstime (0028-9590); (1941-1998): Scholastic News (Citizen Edition) (0736-0614); Which was formerly (until 1982): Scholastic News Citizen (0091-2484); (until 1973): Young Citizen (0044-0744)
Related titles: Microform ed.: (from PQC); Online - full text ed.: Scholastic News Online: Grades 5-6 (from EBSCO Publishing).
Indexed: ICM.
Published by: Scholastic Inc., 557 Broadway, New York, NY 10012-0399. TEL 212-343-6100, FAX 212-343-4808, http://teacher.scholastic.com/scholasticnews/magazines/senior/current/index.asp, http://www.scholastic.com. Ed. Lucille Renwick TEL 212-343-7429. **Subscr. to:** 2931 E McCarthy St, PO Box 3710, Jefferson City, MO 65102-9957. TEL 800-724-6527, classmags@scholastic.com.

SCHOLASTIC SCOPE. see *EDUCATION—Teaching Methods And Curriculum*

SCHOOL CHILDREN LIFE. see *CHILDREN AND YOUTH—About*

028.5   AUS   ISSN 1440-4885
SCHOOL MAGAZINE. BLAST OFF!. Variant title: Blast Off. School Magazine. Text in English. 1916. m. (except Jan. & Dec.). AUD 24 (effective 2004). bk.rev. illus. index. back issues avail. **Document type:** *Magazine, Government.* **Description:** Literary magazine for elementary-school children.
Supersedes in part (in 1998): School Magazine (0155-1108)
Published by: New South Wales Department of Education and Training, PO Box 1928, Macquarie Centre, NSW 2113, Australia. TEL 61-2-9889-0044, FAX 61-2-9889-0040, school.magazine@det.nsw.edu.au, http://www.hotkey.net.au/~schmag. Ed., R&P Jonathan Shaw.

028.5   AUS   ISSN 1440-4907
SCHOOL MAGAZINE. COUNTDOWN. Variant title: Countdown. Text in English. 1916. m. (except Jan. & Dec.). AUD 24 (effective 2004). bk.rev. illus. index. 36 p./no.; back issues avail. **Document type:** *Magazine, Government.* **Description:** Literary magazine for elementary-school children.
Supersedes in part (in 1998): School Magazine (0155-1108)
Published by: New South Wales Department of Education and Training, PO Box 1928, Macquarie Centre, NSW 2113, Australia. TEL 61-2-9889-0044, FAX 61-2-9889-0040, school.magazine@det.nsw.edu.au, http://www.hotkey.net.au/~schmag. Ed., R&P Jonathan Shaw.

028.5   AUS   ISSN 1440-4893
SCHOOL MAGAZINE. ORBIT. Variant title: Orbit. Text in English. 1916. m. (except Jan. & Dec.). AUD 24 (effective 2004). bk.rev. illus. index. 36 p./no.; back issues avail. **Document type:** *Magazine, Government.* **Description:** Literary magazine for elementary-school children.
Supersedes in part (in 1998): School Magazine (0155-1108)
Published by: New South Wales Department of Education and Training, PO Box 1928, Macquarie Centre, NSW 2113, Australia. TEL 61-2-9889-0044, FAX 61-2-9889-0040, school.magazine@det.nsw.edu.au, http://www.hotkey.net.au/~schmag. Ed., R&P Jonathan Shaw.

028.5   AUS   ISSN 1440-4877
SCHOOL MAGAZINE. TOUCHDOWN. Variant title: Touchdown. Text in English. 1916. m. (except Jan. & Dec.). AUD 24 (effective 2004). bk.rev. illus. index. 36 p./no.; back issues avail. **Document type:** *Government.* **Description:** Literary magazine for elementary-school children.
Supersedes in part (in 1998): School Magazine (0155-1108)
Published by: New South Wales Department of Education and Training, PO Box 1928, Macquarie Centre, NSW 2113, Australia. TEL 61-2-9889-0044, FAX 61-2-9889-0040, school.magazine@det.nsw.edu.au, http://www.hotkey.net.au/~schmag. Ed., R&P Jonathan Shaw.

028.5   USA   ISSN 1527-2303
SCHOOL SUPERINTENDENT'S INSIDER. Text in English. m. USD 257 domestic; USD 360 combined subscription domestic print & online eds. (effective 2005). **Document type:** *Newsletter.*
Published by: Brownstone Publishers, Inc., 149 Fifth Ave, 16th Fl, New York, NY 10010-6801. TEL 212-473-8200, FAX 212-473-8786, custserv@brownstone.com, http://www.brownstone.com. Ed. Marion Walsh.

028.5   GBR   ISSN 0036-6862
SCHOOL YARN MAGAZINE∗**.** Text in English. 1946. bi-m.
Published by: School Yarn Publications Ltd., 93 Brownspring Dr, London, SE9 3JZ, United Kingdom.

028.5   GBR   ISSN 0036-6897
SCHOOLGIRL STORY MAGAZINE∗**.** Text in English. 1947. fortn.
Published by: School Yarn Publications Ltd., 93 Brownspring Dr, London, SE9 3JZ, United Kingdom.

371.3   DEU
DAS SCHUELER HAUSAUFGABENHEFT. Text in German. 1990. a. EUR 2.50 newsstand/cover (effective 2002). adv.
Document type: *Magazine, Consumer.*
Published by: Verlag Reiter & Klingberg GbR, Barer Str. 70, Munich, 80799, Germany. TEL 49-89-2782690, FAX 49-89-27826999, info@haefft.de, http://www.haefft.de. adv.: page EUR 25,000. Circ: 379,000 (paid and controlled).

DER SCHWAMM. see *EDUCATION*

SCHWARTE. see *CHILDREN AND YOUTH—About*

028.5   CHE
SCHWEIZERISCHER BUND FUER JUGENDLITERATUR. JAHRESBERICHT/LIGUE SUISSE DE LITTERATURE POUR LA JEUNESSE. RAPPORT ANNUEL. Text in German. 1954. a. CHF 30 to members. **Document type:** *Bulletin.* **Description:** Details the financial situation, activities and important news of the youth union during the last year.
Published by: Schweizerischer Bund fuer Jugendliteratur, Gewerbestr 8, Cham, 6330, Switzerland.

028.5 808.838   USA
SCI-FI TEEN. Text in English. 1998. bi-m. USD 16.97; USD 22.97 foreign (effective 1999). adv. tel.rev. back issues avail. **Document type:** *Consumer.* **Description:** Features sci-fi news for teens.
Published by: Starlog Group, Inc., 475 Park Ave S, 7th Fl, New York, NY 10016. TEL 212-689-2830, http://www.starlog.com. Ed. Tony Timpone. R&P, Adv. contact Rita Eisenstein. B&W page USD 1,840, color page USD 2,295.

SCI-JOURNAL. see *SCIENCES: COMPREHENSIVE WORKS*

SCIENCE AT HOME; connecting science to your home and community. see *SCIENCES: COMPREHENSIVE WORKS*

372.35   FRA   ISSN 1291-1690
SCIENCE & VIE DECOUVERTES. Text in French. 1998. m. EUR 4.40 newsstand/cover (effective 2004). **Description:** Aims to guide children in learning and understand the world around them through science. For children between the ages of 8 and 12.
Published by: Emap France (Subsidiary of: Emap Media Ltd.), 150-152 Rue Gallieni, Boulogne, 92644, France. TEL 33-1-41334961, FAX 33-1-41335010, info@emapfrance.com, http://www.emapmedia.com. Circ: 42,864 (paid).

SCIENCE & VIE JUNIOR. see *SCIENCES: COMPREHENSIVE WORKS*

028.5 500   USA
SCIENCE WEEKLY. Text in English. 1984. 16/yr. (during school yr.). USD 4.95 classroom rate; USD 19.95 to individuals (effective 2003). illus. 4 p./no.; back issues avail.; reprints avail. **Document type:** *Newsletter.* **Description:** Classroom publication for students K-8 designed to stimulate their interest in science, mathematics, and technology. Each issue is developed at 7 reading levels and emphasizes "hands-on" labs and challenging activities.
Related titles: Online - full content ed.; ◆ Series: Science Weekly. Level F. ISSN 1043-0997; ◆ Science Weekly. Level E. ISSN 8756-1794; ◆ Science Weekly. Level D. ISSN 8756-1786; ◆ Science Weekly. Level C. ISSN 8756-1778; ◆ Science Weekly. Level B. ISSN 8756-176X; ◆ Science Weekly. Level A. ISSN 0748-8904; ◆ Science Weekly. Level Pre-A. ISSN 0890-0388.
Published by: Science Weekly, Inc., P.O. Box 70638, Chevy Chase, MD 20813-0638. TEL 301-680-8804, FAX 301-680-9240, scienceweekly@erols.com, http://www.scienceweekly.com. Ed. Deborah Lazar. Pub. Claude Mayberry.

500   USA   ISSN 0748-8904
SCIENCE WEEKLY. LEVEL A. Text in English. 1984. bi-w.
Related titles: ◆ Series of: Science Weekly.
Published by: Science Weekly, Inc., P.O. Box 70638, Chevy Chase, MD 20813-0638. TEL 301-680-8804, FAX 301-680-9240, scienceweekly@erols.com.

500 USA ISSN 8756-176X
SCIENCE WEEKLY. LEVEL B. Text in English. 1984. bi-w.
Related titles: ♦ Series of: Science Weekly.
Published by: Science Weekly, Inc., P.O. Box 70638, Chevy Chase, MD 20813-0638. TEL 301-680-8804, FAX 301-680-9240, scienceweekly@erols.com.

500 USA ISSN 8756-1778
SCIENCE WEEKLY. LEVEL C. Text in English. 1984. bi-w.
Related titles: ♦ Series of: Science Weekly.
Published by: Science Weekly, Inc., P.O. Box 70638, Chevy Chase, MD 20813-0638. TEL 301-680-8804, FAX 301-680-9240, scienceweekly@erols.com.

500 USA ISSN 8756-1786
SCIENCE WEEKLY. LEVEL D. Text in English. 1984. bi-w.
Related titles: ♦ Series of: Science Weekly.
Published by: Science Weekly, Inc., P.O. Box 70638, Chevy Chase, MD 20813-0638. TEL 301-680-8804, FAX 301-680-9240, scienceweekly@erols.com.

500 USA ISSN 8756-1794
SCIENCE WEEKLY. LEVEL E. Text in English. 1984. bi-w.
Related titles: Online - full text ed.: (from Gale Group); ♦ Series of: Science Weekly.
Indexed: MagInd.
Published by: Science Weekly, Inc., P.O. Box 70638, Chevy Chase, MD 20813-0638. TEL 301-680-8804, FAX 301-680-9240, scienceweekly@erols.com.

500 USA ISSN 1043-0997
SCIENCE WEEKLY. LEVEL F. Text in English. 198?. bi-w.
Formerly (until 198?): Science Bi-weekly. Level F (0898-6266)
Related titles: ♦ Series of: Science Weekly.
Published by: Science Weekly, Inc., P.O. Box 70638, Chevy Chase, MD 20813-0638. TEL 301-680-8804, FAX 301-680-9240, scienceweekly@erols.com.

500 USA ISSN 0890-0388
SCIENCE WEEKLY. LEVEL PRE-A. Text in English. 1986. bi-w.
Related titles: Online - full text ed.: (from Gale Group); ♦ Series of: Science Weekly.
Indexed: MagInd.
Published by: Science Weekly, Inc., P.O. Box 70638, Chevy Chase, MD 20813-0638. TEL 301-680-8804, FAX 301-680-9240, scienceweekly@erols.com.

SCIENCE WORLD. see *EDUCATION—Teaching Methods And Curriculum*

SCIENCEMAX. see *SCIENCES: COMPREHENSIVE WORKS*

028.5 ITA
SCOPERTE/DISCOVER. Text in Italian. m. (10/yr.). USD 50. **Document type:** *Consumer.* **Description:** For children ages 8-13.
Published by: Logos Group, Via Curtatona 5/2, Modena, MO 41100, Italy. TEL 39-059-412603, FAX 39-059-412567, it.market@logos.net, http://www.logos.net.

SCOTTISH YOUTH HOSTELS ASSOCIATION HANDBOOK. see *HOTELS AND RESTAURANTS*

028.5 ITA ISSN 1127-0667
SCOUT D'EUROPA. Text in Italian. 1977. m. back issues avail. **Document type:** *Corporate.*
Published by: Associazione Italiana Guide e Scouts d'Europa Cattolici, Via Anicia, 10, Rome, RM 00153, Italy. TEL 39-6-5884430, FAX 39-6-5885229, fse@fse.it, http://www.fse.it. Ed. Giovanni Farella.

SCOUT MEMORABILIA. see *HOBBIES*

028.5 USA
SCOUTER.COM. Text in English. irreg. **Document type:** *Bulletin.* **Description:** Independent publication by Scout leaders for Scout leaders.
Formerly (until 1995): Scouter Magazine (Print Edition)
Media: Online - full content.
Published by: Scouter Magazine, PO Box 5840, Kansas City, MO 64171. TEL 800-726-8837, FAX 816-931-4113, http://www.scouter.com.

369.4 GBR ISSN 0036-9489
SCOUTING; the national magazine of the Scout Association. Text in English. 1909. m. GBP 18; GBP 1.50 newsstand/cover; GBP 30 foreign (effective 1999). adv. bk.rev. illus. index. **Document type:** *Consumer.* **Description:** News, resources, and vital information for all levels of the scouting family.
Related titles: Online - full text ed.: (from The Dialog Corporation).
Indexed: MagInd, RehabLit.
Published by: Scout Association, Baden-Powell House, Queens Gate, London, SW7 5JS, United Kingdom. TEL 44-171-584-7030, FAX 44-171-590-5124, scoutingmag@enterprise.net, http://www.enterprise.net/scoutingmagazine/. Ed. David Easton. Circ: 30,000. **Dist. by:** M M C Ltd., Octagon House, White Hart Meadows, Ripley, Woking, Surrey GU23 6HR, United Kingdom. TEL 44-1483-211222, FAX 44-1483-224541.

028.5 FIN
SCOUTPOSTEN. Text in Swedish. 1918. 7/yr. adv. **Document type:** *Magazine, Consumer.*
Published by: Finlands Svenska Scouter, Byaeldstevaegen 29, Helsinki, 00640, Finland. TEL 358-9-25331100, FAX 358-9-25331160, info@fissc.fi, http://www.fissc.scout.fi/scoutposten, http://www.fissc.scoutfi. Ed. Peter Niemi. Circ: 5,700.

369.4 FRA ISSN 0751-5731
SCOUTS. Text in French. 1924. q. illus. **Description:** For scouts ages 11-15.
Formerly: Ranger (0033-9237)
Indexed: TriticAb.
Published by: Editions Scouts de France, 54 av. Jean Jaures, Paris, 75019, France. TEL 33-1-44523737, FAX 33-1-42380987. Ed. Philippe Da Costa.

369.4 FRA ISSN 0249-2644
SCOUTS - AVENIR. Text in French. 1924. q. illus. **Description:** For scouts ages 17-21.
Published by: Editions Scouts de France, 54 av. Jean Jaures, Paris, 75019, France. TEL 33-1-44523737, FAX 33-1-42380987. Ed. Philippe Da Costa.

SE VUOI. see *RELIGIONS AND THEOLOGY*

SECOND CHOICE. see *MUSIC*

028.5 RUS ISSN 0203-3569
HQ799.R9
SEL'SKAYA MOLODEZH. Text in Russian. 1925. m. USD 129.95. adv. bk.rev. bibl.; illus.
Formerly: Sputnik Sel'skoi Molodezhi
Indexed: RASB.
—East View.
Address: Sushchevskii Val ul 21, Moscow, 101503, Russian Federation. TEL 7-095-2850741, FAX 7-095-2858004. Ed. A D Shevelev. Circ: 26,000. **Dist. by:** M K - Periodica, ul Gilyarovskogo 39, Moscow 129110, Russian Federation. TEL 7-095-2845008, FAX 7-095-2813798, info@periodicals.ru, http://www.mkniga.ru; **US dist. addr.:** East View Information Services, 3020 Harbor Ln. N., Minneapolis, MN 55447. TEL 612-550-0961.

016.80883 DNK ISSN 1601-135X
SERIEKATALOG, SKOENLITTERATUR. Text in Danish. 1967. a. DKK 647.20 (effective 2004). Supplement avail.
Incorporates (1975-2001): Seriekatalog, Faglitteratur (1601-1341); Former titles (until 2000): Boernebogsserier Tegneserier (0106-8199); (until 1975): Boernebogsserier (0901-8492)
Related titles: Online - full text ed.
Published by: Dansk BiblioteksCenter AS, Tempovej 7-11, Ballerup, 2750, Denmark. TEL 45-44-867777, FAX 45-44-867892, dbc@dbc.dk, http://www.dbc.dk.

028.5 741.5 SWE
SERIEPARADEN. Text in Swedish. 1987. 10/yr. SEK 225; SEK 25 newsstand/cover (effective 1998). adv. **Document type:** *Consumer.*
Published by: Egmont Serie Foerlaget, Fack 70272, Stockholm, 10722, Sweden. TEL 46-8-736-39-00, FAX 46-8-791-70-95. Ed. Mikael Burman. Pub. Alf Thorsjoe. Adv. contact Peter Ask. color page SEK 14,500.

369.4 ITA ISSN 0037-2765
➤ **SERVIRE;** rivista scout per educatori. Text in Italian. 1947. bi-m. EUR 20 domestic; EUR 25 foreign (effective 2003). bk.rev. illus. 40 p./no.; **Document type:** *Consumer.*
Media: Duplicated (not offset).
Published by: Cooperativa Servire s.r.l., Via Olona, 25, Milan, MI 20123, Italy. TEL 39-2-8394301. Ed. Giancarlo Lombardi. Circ: 1,500.

028.5 USA ISSN 0049-0253
AP201
SESAME STREET. Text in English, Spanish. 1971. 10/yr. USD 14.97 (effective 2005). adv. illus. 32 p./no.; reprints avail. **Document type:** *Magazine, Consumer.* **Description:** Uses Sesame Street TV Muppets to help teach young children. Includes a 36-page child's book and a separate 36-page Parents' Guide.
Related titles: Online - full text ed.; ♦ Supplement to: Parenting. ISSN 0890-247X.
Indexed: ICM.
Published by: Sesame Workshop, 1 Lincoln Plaza, New York, NY 10023. TEL 212-595-3456, FAX 212-875-6105, privacy@sesameonline.org, http://www.sesameworkshop.org, http://www.sesameworkshop.org/. adv.: B&W page USD 53,200, color page USD 65,400. Circ: 800,000.

028.5 NLD ISSN 1380-3042
SESAMSTRAAT. Text in Dutch. 1993. m. illus. **Document type:** *Magazine, Consumer.* **Description:** Offers very young readers articles, stories, and activities based on the Sesame Street characters.
Published by: V N U Tijdschriften B.V., Postbus 1900, Hoofddorp, 2130 JH, Netherlands. TEL 31-23-556-6770, FAX 31-23-556-6771, ServiceTeam@tijdschriften.vnu.com, http://www.vnu.nl/vnu/organisatie.

028.5 DEU
SESAMSTRASSE. Text in German. 1973-199?; N.S. 1999. m. EUR 2.60 newsstand/cover (effective 2005). adv. illus. **Document type:** *Magazine, Consumer.*
Published by: Panini Verlags GmbH, Ravensstr 48, Nettetal, 41334, Germany. TEL 49-2157-81750, FAX 49-2157-81484528, info@panini-dino.de, http://www.panini-media.de. adv.: page EUR 2,500; trim 220 x 285. Circ: 49,723 (paid and controlled).

379.8 RUS ISSN 1682-2404
SEVENTEEN. Text in Russian. 2001. bi-m. **Document type:** *Magazine, Consumer.*
Published by: S K Press, Marksistkaya 34, str 10, Moscow, 109147, Russian Federation. deliver@skpress.ru, http://www.skpress.ru.

028.5 305.4 MYS
SEVENTEEN (MALAYSIA EDITION). Text in English. m. **Document type:** *Magazine, Consumer.*
Related titles: ♦ Regional ed(s).: Seventeen. ISSN 0037-301X.
Published by: Blu Inc Media Sdn Bhd, 14 Jalan 225, Petaling Jaya, Selangor 46100, Malaysia. TEL 603-79572626, FAX 603-79575446.

028.5 305.4 SGP
SEVENTEEN (SINGAPORE EDITION). Text in English. m. **Document type:** *Magazine, Consumer.*
Related titles: ♦ Regional ed(s).: Seventeen. ISSN 0037-301X.
Published by: Blu Inc Media Pte Ltd., 20 Martin Rd, #08-01, Singapore, 239070, Singapore. TEL 65-68794088, FAX 65-67347727, http://www.bluincmedia.com/.

613.9 GBR ISSN 1353-1689
SEX EDUCATION MATTERS. Text in English. 1994. 3/yr. bk.rev. **Document type:** *Academic/Scholarly.* **Description:** Provides updates on recent developments in sex education. Contains summaries of relevant research and information on new resources.
Indexed: e-psyche.
—CCC.
Published by: National Children's Bureau, 8 Wakley St, London, EC1V 7QE, United Kingdom. TEL 44-20-78436000, FAX 44-20-72789512, http://www.ncb.org.uk. Circ: 1,500.

SFOGLIALIBRO; la biblioteca dei ragazzi. see *PUBLISHING AND BOOK TRADE*

SHALOM INFANTIL. see *ETHNIC INTERESTS*

▼ **SHAMELESS.** see *WOMEN'S INTERESTS*

028.5 CHN ISSN 1001-5590
SHAO NU/YOUNG GIRL. Text in Chinese. m. CNY 18.
Published by: Shanghai Renmin Chubanshe, Qikan Bu/Shanghai People's Publishing House, 54 Shaoxing Rd, Shanghai, 200020, China. TEL 4315882. Ed. Zhang Baoni.

028.5 CHN
SHAONIAN BAO/JUVENILE PRESS. Text in Chinese. 1967. w. CNY 43.20 (effective 1997). adv. tr.lit. **Document type:** *Newspaper.*
Related titles: Microfiche ed.
Published by: (Shanghai Education Bureau), Shaonian Bao She/Juvenile Press Agency, 61 Zhejiang Beilu, Shanghai, 200085, China. TEL 86-21-6306-6161, FAX 86-21-6306-9036. Ed., R&P Renxiao Li. Adv. contact Peisheng Li. Circ: 500,000.

500 CHN
SHAONIAN KEXUE/JUVENILE SCIENCE. Text in Chinese. 1976. m. USD 26.40. **Description:** Introduces new developments in science and technology for young readers.
Published by: Shaonian Ertong Chubanshe/Juvenile & Children Publishing House, 1538 Yan an Xilu, Shanghai, 200052, China. TEL 86-21-6282-3025, FAX 86-21-6282-1726. **Dist. in US by:** China Books & Periodicals Inc, 360 Swift Ave., Ste. 48, S San Fran, CA 94080-6220. TEL 415-282-2994.

500 CHN ISSN 1000-7776
SHAONIAN KEXUE HUABAO/JUVENILE SCIENTIFIC PICTORIAL. Text in Chinese. 1979. m. USD 32.30. illus.
Published by: Beijing Chubanshe/Beijing Publishing House, 6 Beisanhuan Zhonglu, Beijing, 100011, China. TEL 2016699. Ed. Zhao Meng. **Dist. in US by:** China Books & Periodicals Inc, 360 Swift Ave., Ste. 48, S San Fran, CA 94080-6220. TEL 415-282-2994.

808.068 CHN ISSN 1002-0365
SHAONIAN WENYI (NANJING). Text in Chinese. 1976. m. CNY 38.40; CNY 3.40 newsstand/cover (effective 2004). **Document type:** *Magazine, Consumer.* **Description:** Contains stories, poetry, essays geared toward young adults; also covers student life, cities and rural scenes, technology and more.
Published by: Jiangsu Shaonian Ertong Chubanshe/Jiangsu Junveniles and Children's Publishing House, 14F Phoenix Palace Hotel, 47 Hunan Rd, Nanjing, Jiangsu 210009, China. TEL 86-25-3241333, snwy@jlonline.com, sushao@public1.ptt.js.cn, http://www.sushao.com/snwy, http://www.sushao.com/index.php3.

C

808.068 700 CHN ISSN 0559-7412
SHAONIAN WENYI (SHANGHAI)/JUVENILE LITERATURE. Text in Chinese. 1953. m. USD 36. **Document type:** *Consumer.* **Description:** Contains fictions, poems, prose, fairy tales, and translated foreign stories for teenagers.
Indexed: RASB.
Published by: Shaonian Ertong Chubanshe/Juvenile & Children Publishing House, 1538 Yan an Xilu, Shanghai, 200052, China. TEL 86-21-6282-3025, FAX 86-21-6282-1726. Ed. Zhou Jiting. **Dist. in US by:** China Books & Periodicals Inc, 360 Swift Ave., Ste. 48, S San Fran, CA 94080-6220. TEL 415-282-2994; **Dist. by:** China International Book Trading Corp, 35 Chegongzhuang Xilu, Haidian District, PO Box 399, Beijing 100044, China. TEL 86-10-68412045, FAX 86-10-68412023, cibtc@mail.cibtc.com.cn, http://www.cibtc.com.cn.

028.5 BGD
SHISHU. Text in Bengali. 1977. m.
Published by: Bangladesh Shishu Academy, Old High Court Compound, Dhaka, 1000, Bangladesh. TEL 2-238871. Ed. Golam Kibria. Circ: 9,000.

SHKOL'NYI VESTNIK; zhurnal dlya slepykh detei. see *HANDICAPPED—Visually Impaired*

SHORT STORIES FOR STUDENTS. see *LITERATURE*

028.5 GBR ISSN 0968-8382
SHOUT (DUNDEE). Text in English. 1993. fortn. GBP 31.20; GBP 1.20 newsstand/cover (effective 2000). adv. **Document type:** *Magazine, Consumer.* **Description:** Provides celebrity interviews, soap gossip, fashion and beauty tips, music and film reviews, and other entertainment features for girls aged 10-14.
Published by: D.C. Thomson & Co. Ltd., 2 Albert Sq, Dundee, Angus DD1 9QJ, United Kingdom. FAX 44-1382-225511, shout@dcthomson.co.uk, http://www.dcthomson.co.uk. Ed. Jackie Brown. adv.: B&W page GBP 3,960, color page GBP 7,005; trim 225 x 305. Circ: 116,629 (paid).

028.5 JPN
SHUKAN SHONEN MAGAZINE. Text in Japanese. 1959. w. **Document type:** *Magazine, Consumer.* **Description:** Comic magazine aimed at boys in junior and senior high school.
Published by: Kodansha Ltd., 2-12-21 Otowa, Bunkyo-ku, Tokyo, 112-8001, Japan. TEL 81-3-3946-6201, FAX 81-3-3944-9915, http://www.kodansha.co.jp.

028.5 JPN
SHUKAN SHONEN SUNDAY. Text in Japanese. w. JPY 220 newsstand/cover (effective 2002). adv. **Document type:** *Magazine, Consumer.*
Published by: Shogakukan Inc., 3-1 Hitotsubashi 2-chome, Chiyoda-ku, Tokyo, 101-8001, Japan. TEL 81-3-3230-5211, FAX 81-3-3264-8471, http://www.shogakukan.co.jp.

028.5 MMR
SHWE THWE. Text in Burmese, English. w.
Published by: Sarpay Beikman Management Board, 529 Merchant St., Botahtaung PO, Yangon, Myanmar. Circ: 100,000.

028.5 LAO
SIANG KHONG GNAOVASON SONG THANVA/VOICE OF THE 2ND DECEMBER YOUTHS. Text in Laotian. m.
Address: Vientiane, Laos.

028.5 ISR ISSN 0334-276X
SIFRUT YELADIM VANOAR; journal for children's and youth literature. Text in Hebrew. 1974. q. ILS 16, USD 8. bk.rev. index. **Description:** Presents literature for children and teenagers. Includes study, research and personalities sections.
Indexed: IHP.
Published by: Ministry of Education, 8 King David Street, Jerusalem, Israel. Ed. Devora Hanevia. Circ: 1,500.

SIGLO XXI CIENCIA AND TECNOLOGIA. see *SCIENCES: COMPREHENSIVE WORKS*

028.5 USA
SIKIDS.COM. Text in English. d. **Document type:** *Consumer.*
Formerly (until Apr. 2001): siforkids.com
Media: Online - full content. **Related titles:** Online - full text ed.: (from bigchalk, EBSCO Publishing, Gale Group, ProQuest Information & Learning); ♦ Print ed.: Sports Illustrated for Kids. ISSN 1042-394X.
Published by: Time Inc., Sports Illustrated Group (Subsidiary of: Time Warner, Inc.), Sports Illustrated Bldg, 135 W 50th St, 4th Fl., New York, NY 10020-1393. TEL 212-522-1212, sikids_inbox@sikids.com, http://www.sikids.com.

028.5 GBR ISSN 1365-8298
SIMPSONS COMICS. Text in English. 1997. m. GBP 26.40; GBP 2.20 newsstand/cover. adv. **Document type:** *Magazine, Consumer.*
Published by: Titan Magazines (Subsidiary of: Titan Books Ltd.), Titan House, 144 Southwark St, London, SE1 0UP, United Kingdom. TEL 44-20-7620-0200, FAX 44-20-7803-1803. Ed. David Bailet. Pub. Matt Groening. Adv. contact Miles Dunbar. **Dist. by:** Comag, Tavistock Works, Tavistock Rd, W Drayton, Middx UB7 7QX, United Kingdom. TEL 44-1895-433600, FAX 44-189-543-3606.

028.5 DEU
SIMPSONS COMICS. Text in German. 1996. m. EUR 2 newsstand/cover (effective 2002). adv. **Document type:** *Magazine, Consumer.*
Published by: Panini Verlags GmbH, Ravensstr 48, Nettetal, 41334, Germany. TEL 49-711-947680, FAX 49-711-94768830, info@panini-dino.de, http://www.panini-media.de. Ed. Anne Berling. Pub. Max Mueller. Adv. contact Petra Sonnenfroh-Kost. page EUR 6,500; trim 170 x 257. Circ: 159,967 (paid and controlled).

028.5 DEU
SIMPSONS SONDERHEFTE. Text in German. q. EUR 2 newsstand/cover (effective 2002). adv. **Document type:** *Magazine, Consumer.*
Published by: Panini Verlags GmbH, Ravensstr 48, Nettetal, 41334, Germany. TEL 49-711-947680, FAX 49-711-94768830, info@panini-dino.de, http://www.panini-media.de. adv.: page EUR 2,900; trim 170 x 257. Circ: 181,130 (paid and controlled).

028.5 ISR
SINDBAD. Text in Arabic. 1969. 7/yr. USD 10.
Published by: (Histadrut), Arabic Publishing House, P O Box 28049, Tel Aviv, 61280, Israel. TEL 972-3-371438. Ed. Walid Hussein. Circ: 8,500.

SINT MARTEN POST. see *EDUCATION—International Education Programs*

305.23 DEU
▼ **SISSI.** Text in German. 2004. 13/yr. EUR 2.80 newsstand/cover (effective 2005). adv. **Document type:** *Magazine, Consumer.*
Published by: Panini Verlags GmbH, Ravensstr 48, Nettetal, 41334, Germany. TEL 49-2157-81750, FAX 49-2157-81484528, info@panini-dino.de, http://www.panini-media.de. adv.: page EUR 3,500; trim 210 x 280. Circ: 66,750 (paid and controlled).

087.5 FIN ISSN 1458-3372
SISTERS. Text in Finnish. 2000. m. **Document type:** *Magazine, Consumer.*
Formerly (until 2001): Sisters Club (1457-5337)
Published by: Sanoma Magazines Finland Corporation, Hoylaamotie 1 D, P.O. Box 100, Helsinki, 00040, Finland. TEL 358-9-1201, FAX 358-9-1205171, info@sanomamagazines.fi, http://www.sanomamagazines.fi.

SKI CANADA. see *SPORTS AND GAMES—Outdoor Life*

028.5 USA ISSN 0899-529X
SKIPPING STONES; a multicultural magazine. Text in English. 1988. 5/yr. USD 25 to individuals; USD 35 to institutions (effective 2005). bk.rev. illus. back issues avail.; reprints avail. **Document type:** *Magazine, Consumer.* **Description:** Provides an international, multicultural forum for communication among children from various lands and backgrounds. Publishes stories, nonfiction, pictures, games, photos, and poems written by children and adults for youth around the world.
Related titles: Online - full text ed.: (from bigchalk, EBSCO Publishing, Gale Group, Northern Light Technology, Inc., ProQuest Information & Learning).
Indexed: MagInd.
Address: PO Box 3939, Eugene, OR 97403-0939. TEL 541-342-4956, editor@skippingstones.org, http://www.skippingstones.org. Ed., Pub. Arun N Toke. Circ: 2,500.

SKOTAVILLE AFRICAN CLASSICS SERIES. see *LITERATURE*

SKOTAVILLE CHILDREN'S BOOK SERIES. see *LITERATURE*

SLAP; i got the answer for your question. see *SPORTS AND GAMES*

SLINGERVEL. see *RELIGIONS AND THEOLOGY—Protestant*

SLUGS AND SNAILS. see *HANDICAPPED—Visually Impaired*

028.5 CZE ISSN 0231-7222
SLUNICKO; mesicnik pro nejmensi. Text in Czech. 1967. m. CZK 24, USD 7.90.
Published by: Mlada Fronta, Radlicka 61, Prague, 15002, Czech Republic. TEL 42-2-544941. Ed. Jan Kruta. **Dist. by:** Artia, Ve Smeckach 30, Prague 1 111 27, Czech Republic.

SMACKDOWN! MAGAZINE. see *SPORTS AND GAMES*

028.5 RUS ISSN 0131-6656
SMENA. Text in Russian. 1924. m. USD 99 foreign (effective 2005). adv. bk.rev.; film rev. abstr.; bibl.; illus. Index. reprints avail. **Document type:** *Magazine, Consumer.*
Related titles: Microfilm ed.: (from EVP).
Indexed: RASB, RILM.
—East View.
Address: Bumazhnyi pr 14, Moscow, 101457, Russian Federation. TEL 7-095-2121507, FAX 7-095-2505928. Ed. Mikhail Kizilov. adv.: B&W page USD 550, color page USD 720. Circ: 50,000. **Dist. by:** M K - Periodica, ul Gilyarovskogo 39, Moscow 129110, Russian Federation. TEL 7-095-2845008, FAX 7-095-2813798, info@periodicals.ru, http://www.mkniga.ru.

SMILE. see *LEISURE AND RECREATION*

028.5 USA
SMILE MAKERS. Text in English. a. **Document type:** *Magazine, Consumer.* **Description:** Covers stickers, balloons, buttons, costume jewelry, fancy shaped erasers, colored pencils and other items suitable for children's prizes at fairs or as incentives.
Address: PO Box 2543, Spartanburg, SC 29304. FAX 803-585-3958, http://www.smilemakers.com.

SNAPSHOTS; Bible reading for children. see *RELIGIONS AND THEOLOGY*

SOCCER JR.; the soccer magazine for kids. see *SPORTS AND GAMES—Ball Games*

SOMETHING ABOUT THE AUTHOR. see *LITERATURE*

028.5 KOR
SONYON DONG-A. Text in Korean. 1964. d.
Published by: Dong-A Ilbo, 139 Sejongno, Chongno-gu, Seoul, Korea, S. TEL 02-721-7114. Ed. Kwon O Kie. Circ: 381,150.

028.5 GBR ISSN 1362-2862
SOOTY. Text in English. 1996. m. GBP 1.25 newsstand/cover. illus. **Document type:** *Consumer.* **Description:** Teaches and educates young children, using fun and entertaining games and stories.
Published by: Egmont Fleetway Ltd., Egmont House, Pl, Flat 25, 31 Tavistock Rd, London, W11 1AS, United Kingdom. TEL 44-20-7344-6400, FAX 44-207-388-4152. **Dist. by:** MarketForce UK Ltd, 247 Tottenham Court Rd, London, Middx W1T 7AU, United Kingdom. TEL 44-207-2615199, FAX 44-207-2617341.

SOUTH CAROLINA Y F AND F F A. see *AGRICULTURE*

053.1 DEU
SOWIESO. Text in German. w. **Document type:** *Consumer.* **Description:** Contains articles, stories and games for children.
Media: Online - full text.
Published by: sowieso Pressebuero GbR, Taunusstr 23, Berlin, 12161, Germany. TEL 49-30-82704101, FAX 49-30-82704103, sowieso@bln.de, http://www.sowieso.de. Eds. Annette Baessler, Kristine Kretschmer.

028.5 KEN
SPARKLE MAGAZINE; a magazine for young children. Text in English. 1983. m. KES 880 domestic; USD 55.50 in Africa; USD 63.50 in the Middle East; USD 71.50 in Australasia (effective 2000). adv. **Document type:** *Magazine, Consumer.* **Description:** Written for primary school children with educational and entertaining material.
Formerly (until Feb. 1990): Watoto Magazine
Published by: Space Sellers Ltd., Chepkerio Rd., PO Box 47186, Nairobi, Kenya. TEL 254-2-555811, FAX 254-2-557815. Ed. Anna Ndila. Pub., R&P Sylvia King TEL 254-2-530598. Adv. contact Carole Argwins-Kodhek. Circ: 12,000.

590 DEU
▼ **SPARKY.** Text in German. 2004. bi-m. EUR 2 newsstand/cover (effective 2005). adv. **Document type:** *Magazine, Consumer.*
Published by: Panini Verlags GmbH, Ravensstr 48, Nettetal, 41334, Germany. TEL 49-2157-81750, FAX 49-2157-81484528, info@panini-dino.de, http://www.panini-media.de. adv.: page EUR 3,500; trim 210 x 280. Circ: 73,370 (controlled).

028.5 DEU
SPATZ. Text in German. 1969. m. **Document type:** *Magazine, Consumer.* **Description:** Contains puzzles, stories, games and other activities to stimulate children.
Published by: Klens Verlag GmbH, Prinz-Georg-Str 44, Duesseldorf, 40477, Germany. TEL 49-211-4499250, FAX 49-211-4499277.

087.5 BRA ISSN 1413-3350
SPAWN. Text in Portuguese. 1996. m. BRL 5.95 newsstand/cover (effective 2005). adv. **Document type:** *Magazine, Consumer.*
Published by: Editora Abril, S.A., Av. das Nacoes Unidas, 7221, 11 andar Pinheiros, Sao Paulo, SP 05425-902, Brazil. TEL 55-11-50872112, FAX 55-11-50872100, http://jovem.abril.com.br/, http://www.abril.com.br/. adv.: page BRL 4,100.

741.5 GBR ISSN 1360-5208
SPECTACULAR SPIDER-MAN. Text in English. 1995. 17/yr. GBP 26.25 (effective 2005). **Document type:** *Magazine, Consumer.*

Published by: Panini UK Ltd., Panini House Coach and Horses Passage, Tunbridge Wells, Kent TN2 5UJ, United Kingdom. TEL 44-1892-500100, info@panini.co.uk, http://www.paninicomics.co.uk.

028.5 USA
SPEEDMETER. Text in English. 1996. irreg. **Description:** Covers youth culture, pop culture, independent or underground culture.
Media: Online - full text.
Address: 1810 Ashland Ave., Apt 1, St. Paul, MN 55104-6040. speedmeter@frodo.com, http://www.pressenter.com/~emo123/speedmeter/. Ed. Erik Moe.

028.5 369.4 NOR ISSN 0800-0646
SPEIDEREN. Text in Norwegian. 1978. q. NOK 150. adv. bk.rev. **—CCC.**
Published by: Norges Speiderforbund, Oevre Vollgate 9, Oslo, 0158, Norway. TEL 47-22-42-26-60, FAX 47-22-42-07-04. Eds. Jens Doevik, Karen Johanne Stroemstad. Circ: 40,000 (controlled).

369.4 267 NOR
SPEIDING. Text in Norwegian. 4/yr. adv.
Published by: Norges K F U M-Speidere, Postboks 6810, St Olavs Plass, Oslo, 0130, Norway. TEL 47-22-11-50-32, FAX 47-22-20-34-65, forbundskontoret@kfum-speider.no, http://www.kfum-speider.no. Circ: 9,000.

369.4 DNK ISSN 1602-0529
SPEJDERSNUS. Text in Danish. 1970. 6/yr. adv. **Description:** For scouts ages 6-12.
Supersedes in part (in 2001): Spejd (0108-7967); Which was formed by the merger of (1918-1970): Pigespejderne; (1961-1970): Spejderbladet: Medlemsblad for KFUK-Spejderne i Danmark; (1960-1970): Spejdernes Magazin
Published by: Danske Spejderkorps, Arsenalgade 10, Copenhagen K, 1436, Denmark. TEL 45-32-64-00-50, http://www.dds.dk/medier. Ed. Morten Lykkeborg TEL 45-32-64-00-62. Adv. contact Peter Henrichsen TEL 45-32-64-00-61.

SPES NOSTRA - OUR HOPE; a Marian missionary magazine for youth and families. see *RELIGIONS AND THEOLOGY—Roman Catholic*

028.162 DEU
SPHINX✶ . Text in German. 1975. q. adv. **Document type:** *Newsletter, Consumer.*
Published by: Sphinx Schuelerzeitung, Helmholtz Gymnasium, Rosastr 83, Essen, 45130, Germany. TEL 49-201-86067330, FAX 49-201-86067331, info@hg-essen.de. Ed. Joerg Bolender. Circ: 1,000.

SPHINX; the student magazine for Liverpool. see *LITERARY AND POLITICAL REVIEWS*

028.5 781.68 GBR ISSN 1368-8200
SPICE. Text in English. 1996. q. GBP 10; GBP 2.95 newsstand/cover (effective 1999). **Document type:** *Consumer.* **Description:** Contains official news, articles and features on all aspects of the Spice Girls and their adventures.
Published by: John Brown Citrus Publishing, The New Boathouse, 136-142, Bramley Rd, London, W10 6SR, United Kingdom. TEL 44-20-7565-3000, FAX 44-20-7565-3055. **Dist. by:** Seymour Distribution Ltd, 86 Newman St, London W1T 3EX, United Kingdom. FAX 44-207-396-8002, enquiries@seymour.co.uk.

SPICE. see *ETHNIC INTERESTS*

808.89 USA ISSN 1070-2911
SPIDER; the magazine for children. Text in English. 1993. m. USD 35.97 domestic; USD 47.97 foreign (effective 2005). bk.rev. illus. 32 p./no.; reprints avail. **Document type:** *Magazine, Consumer.* **Description:** Fun for independent young readers ages 6-9. Every issue is filled with lively stories and poems, fascinating articles, and challenging puzzles, games, and projects.
Related titles: Online - full text ed.: (from EBSCO Publishing).
Indexed: ICM.
Published by: Carus Publishing Company, 315 Fifth St, Peru, IL 61354. TEL 603-924-7209, 800-821-0115, FAX 815-224-2256, custsvc@cobblestone.mv.com, http://www.cricketmag.com. Circ: 77,000 (paid).

028.5 DEU ISSN 1420-0244
SPIEL MIT. Text in German. 1981. m. **Document type:** *Magazine, Consumer.*
Published by: Velber im OZ Verlag GmbH, Guenterstalstr. 57, Freiburg, 79102, Germany. TEL 49-761-7057780, FAX 49-761-7057839, butsch@oz-bpv.de, http://www.oz-verlag.com.

SPIRIT; lectionary-based weekly for Catholic teens. see *RELIGIONS AND THEOLOGY*

028.5 808.836 BEL ISSN 0771-8071
SPIROU. Text in French. 1938. w. USD 44. adv. back issues avail.
Related titles: ♦ Dutch ed.: Robbedoes. ISSN 0771-8128.
Published by: Editions Dupuis S.A., Rue Jules Destree 52, Marcinelle, 6001, Belgium. TEL 32-71-600500, FAX 32-71-600599. Ed. Jean Denemostier. R&P Cecile Hisette. Circ: 120,000. **Subscr. in Belgium to:** Spirou-Service Abonnements, BP 41, Brussels 1050, Belgium; **Subscr. in other countries to:** Spirou-Service Abonnements, bis 250, Sainte Genevieve Cedex 60732, France.

051 USA ISSN 0892-5089
SPLICE✶ ; for teens. Text in English. 1986. bi-m. USD 11.70.
Published by: Jannis Communications, PO Box 267, Brookfield, CT 06804. TEL 203-740-2606, FAX 203-740-2602. Ed. Bob W Woods. Circ: 200,000.

028.5 DEU
▼ **SPONGEBOB SCHWAMMKOPF.** Text in German. 2003. m. EUR 2.30 newsstand/cover (effective 2005). adv. **Document type:** *Magazine, Consumer.*
Published by: Egmont Ehapa Verlag GmbH, Wallstr 59, Berlin, 10179, Germany. TEL 49-30-240080, FAX 49-30-24008599, leserservice@ehapa.de, http://www.ehapa.de/ehapa/e14/e40/e170/index_ger.html. Adv. contact Andrea Kappel. page EUR 3,600. Circ: 130,548 (paid and controlled).

SPORT AUTO. see *SPORTS AND GAMES*

028.5 USA
SPORTINGKID. Text in English. 2001 (Aug.). bi-m. USD 9.97 (effective 2002). adv. **Document type:** *Magazine, Consumer.* **Description:** Covers youth sports leagues and individual sporting activities.
Related titles: Online - full content ed.
Published by: SportingKid, Inc., 808 Forest Path Ln, Ste 100, Alpharetta, GA 30022. TEL 678-297-3903, http://www.sportingkid.com/. Ed. Michael J Pallerino. Pub. Tina D'Aversa-Williams. Circ: 100,000.

028.5 790.1 USA ISSN 1042-394X
GV705.4
SPORTS ILLUSTRATED FOR KIDS. Abbreviated title: S I for Kids. Text in English. 1989. m. USD 29.99 domestic; USD 39.95 in Canada; USD 49 elsewhere; USD 3.50 newsstand/cover domestic (effective 2005). adv. illus. reprints avail. **Document type:** *Magazine, Consumer.* **Description:** Presents sports aficionados ages 8 to 14 with articles, news, stories, and interviews.
Related titles: ♦ Online - full content ed.: SIKids.com; Online - full text ed.: (from bigchalk, EBSCO Publishing, Gale Group, ProQuest Information & Learning).
Indexed: CPerl, ICM, MASUSE, MagInd, PEI, RGYP, TOM, WBA, WMB.
—CCC.
Published by: Sports Illustrated For Kids (Subsidiary of: Time Warner Inc.), 135 W 50th St, New York, NY 10020-1393. TEL 212-522-1212, FAX 212-522-0120, sikidsinbox@sikids.com, http://www.sikids.com. Adv. contact Sheila Buckley TEL 212-522-4009. page USD 53,000. Circ: 934,000 (paid).

SPORTSTALK; the Women's Sports Foundation newsletter for young female athletes. see *SPORTS AND GAMES*

028.5 GBR ISSN 1354-9308
SPOT. Text in English. 1994. m. GBP 15; GBP 1.25 newsstand/cover. **Document type:** *Consumer.*
Published by: B B C Worldwide Ltd., 80 Wood Ln, London, W12 0TT, United Kingdom. TEL 44-208-576-2000, FAX 44-208-433-3986, bbcproducts@bbc.co.uk, http://www.bbc.co.uk. **Dist. by:** Frontline, Park House, 117 Park Rd, Peterborough, Cambs PE1 2TS, United Kingdom. TEL 44-1733-555161, FAX 44-1733-562788.

SQUIRES NEWSLETTER. see *CLUBS*

028.5 DEU ISSN 0174-5832
STAFETTE; das starke Jugendmagazin. Text in German. 1946. m. EUR 25.20; EUR 2.10 newsstand/cover (effective 2003). adv. bk.rev.; film rev. illus. **Document type:** *Magazine, Consumer.* **Description:** Information and entertainment for children ages 8-15.
Formerly: Neue Stafette
Published by: Johann Michael Sailer Verlag GmbH & Co. KG, Aeusserer Laufer Platz 17, Nuernberg, 90403, Germany. TEL 49-911-53960, FAX 49-911-5396912, sailer@sailer-verlag.de, http://www.sailer-verlag.de. Ed. Ronald Rothenburger. adv.: page EUR 4,460. Circ: 101,462 (paid).

028.5 USA
STAGEBILL FAMILY. Text in English. 3/yr. adv. **Description:** Helps improve the performing arts experience for children with puzzles, games, and art.
Published by: Stagebill, Inc., 520 Madison Ave., New York, NY 10022-4213. TEL 212-476-0640, FAX 212-983-5976. Adv. contact Melissa Smith.

305.234 GBR ISSN 1367-2940
STAR GIRL. Text in English. 1997. m. GBP 19 (effective 1999). adv. **Document type:** *Consumer.* **Description:** Contains articles which 8-10 year old girls like to read about: fashion, hobbies, pets, horoscopes, stories and competitions.
Published by: Maskell Wiles Ltd., Royal Victoria House, The Pantiles, Tunbridge Wells, Kent TN2 5TE, United Kingdom. TEL 44-1892-523767, FAX 44-1892-523801. Ed. Lucy Dawson. **Dist. by:** M M C Ltd., Octagon House, White Hart Meadows, Ripley, Woking, Surrey GU23 6HR, United Kingdom. TEL 44-1483-211222, FAX 44-1483-224541.

028.5 DEU
STARFLASH. Text in German. 2002 (Sep.). m. EUR 2.40 newsstand/cover (effective 2002). adv. **Document type:** *Magazine, Consumer.* **Description:** Features articles and photos of celebrities and stars aimed at teenagers.
Published by: Axel Springer Young Mediahouse, Werinherstr 71, Munich, 81541, Germany. TEL 49-89-697490, FAX 49-89-69749312, http://www.asv.de. Ed. Norbert Lalla. Adv. contact Petra Kalb TEL 49-89-69749100. color page EUR 4,500; trim 210 x 280. Circ: 420,000.

STATION TO STATION. see *GENERAL INTEREST PERIODICALS—Germany*

028.5 500.9 CHE ISSN 1424-3490
STEINI. Text in German. 1985. q. **Document type:** *Magazine, Consumer.* **Description:** Explains the wonders of nature and the necessities of conservation to children.
Supersedes in part (in 1999): Chumm mit! (1424-280X)
Published by: Pro Natura - Schweizerischer Bund fuer Naturschutz, Wartenbergstr 22, Basel, 4020, Switzerland. TEL 41-61-3179191, FAX 41-61-3179266, mailbox@pronatura.ch, http://www.pronatura.ch.

DIE STERNSINGER; diaspora. see *RELIGIONS AND THEOLOGY—Roman Catholic*

028.5 796 CZE ISSN 0862-6553
STEZKA; mesicnik pro sport, turistiku, brannost. Text in Czech. 1970. m. CZK 48, USD 18.50.
Formerly (until 1990): Pionyrska Stezka (0231-5521)
Published by: Mlada Fronta, Radlicka 61, Prague, 15002, Czech Republic. Ed. J Prchal. Circ: 105,000. **Dist. by:** Artia, Ve Smeckach 30, Prague 1 111 27, Czech Republic.

C

028.5 011 DEU
STIFTUNG LESEN. LESE-EMPFEHLUNGEN. Text in German. 1978. bi-m. bk.rev. back issues avail. **Document type:** *Bibliography.*
Former titles: Stiftung Lesen. Buchempfehlungen; Deutsche Lesegesellschaft. Buchempfehlungen
Published by: Stiftung Lesen, Fischtorplatz 23, Mainz, 55116, Germany. TEL 06131-288900, FAX 06131-230333. Circ: 55,000.

028.5 DEU
STIPENDIEN FUER SPRACHKURSE. Text in German. 1974. a. **Document type:** *Bulletin, Academic/Scholarly.*
Published by: Deutsch-Franzoesisches Jugendwerk, Rhoendorferstr 23, Bad Honnef, 53604, Germany. TEL 49-2224-1808-0, FAX 49-2224-1808-52, viale@dfjw.org, http://www.dfjw.org. R&P Annie Viale. Circ: 5,000.

028.5 USA ISSN 0094-579X
PS508.C5
STONE SOUP; the magazine by young writers and artists. Text in English. 1973 (May). bi-m. USD 34 in United States; USD 40 in Canada & Mexico; USD 46 elsewhere (effective 2004). adv. bk.rev. illus. 48 p./no. 2 cols./p.; reprints avail. **Document type:** *Consumer.* **Description:** Publishes fiction and poetry by children ages 8 through 13. Emphasizes topics relevant to children's lives.
Related titles: Braille ed.; Online - full text ed.: (from EBSCO Publishing, Gale Group).
Indexed: CPerl, MagInd.
Published by: Children's Art Foundation, PO Box 83, Santa Cruz, CA 95063. TEL 831-426-5557, 800-447-4569, FAX 831-426-1161, editor@stonesoup.com, http://www.stonesoup.com. Eds., Pubs. Gerry Mandel TEL 831-426-5557, William Rubel. R&P, Adv. contact Gerry Mandel TEL 831-426-5557. Circ: 20,000 (paid).

305.23 808.899 GBR ISSN 1462-2637
STORIES FOR CHILDREN. Text in English. 1998. q. GBP 2.50 newsstand/cover (effective 2003). **Document type:** *Consumer.* **Description:** Contains illustrated, interesting, and educational stories to be read to or to be read by young children, making reading fun.
Published by: Practical Publications Ltd. (Subsidiary of: Highbury House Communications PLC), Columbus House, 28 Charles Sq, London, N1 6HT, United Kingdom. TEL 44-20-76086464, http://www.hhc.co.uk/pages/show/entry_Level/5/entry_code/HCOMUSPREPUB/single_record_flag/171.

028.5 FRA ISSN 1366-901X
STORY BOX. Text in English. 1995. 10/yr. EUR 55.36 domestic; EUR 63.50 foreign (effective 2005). **Document type:** *Consumer.* **Description:** Contains stories for childrens' leisure time.
Published by: Bayard Presse, 3 Rue Bayard, Paris, 75393 Cedex 08, France. TEL 33-1-44356060, FAX 33-1-44356161, redactions@bayard-presse.com, http://www.bayardpresse.com.

STORY FRIENDS. see *RELIGIONS AND THEOLOGY*

028.5   USA   ISSN 1087-755X
STORY RHYME NEWSLETTER FOR SCHOOLS. Text in English. 1992. irreg. USD 7 domestic; USD 11 in Canada (effective 2005). illus. **Document type:** *Newsletter*. **Description:** Contains stories that rhyme for children ages 9-16.
Published by: Story Time Stories That Rhyme, PO Box 416, Denver, CO 80201-0416. TEL 303-575-5676, FAX 303-575-1187, starsuccess@excite.com, mail@contentprovidermedia.com, http://www.storytimestoriesthatrhyme.com/. Ed. A Doyle TEL 303-575-5676. R&P A. Doyle TEL 305-575-5676. Circ: 5,000 (paid and controlled).

028.5   USA
STORY SAMPHLET OF FIVE STORIES. Text in English. 1997. a. USD 9.95 (effective 2005). **Document type:** *Magazine, Consumer*. **Description:** Contains stories that educate, entertain, inform and rhyme.
Published by: Story Time Stories That Rhyme, PO Box 416, Denver, CO 80201-0416. TEL 303-575-5676, FAX 303-575-1187, customerservice@breadpudding.net, http://www.storytimestoriesthatrhyme.com. Ed. A Doyle TEL 303-575-5676. R&P A. Doyle TEL 305-575-5676.

028.5   USA   ISSN 1045-5515
STORY TIME STORIES THAT RHYME NEWSLETTER. Text in English. 1990. q. looseleaf. USD 20 (effective 2005). back issues avail. **Document type:** *Newsletter*. **Description:** Stories that educate, inform, entertain and rhyme.
Published by: Story Time Stories That Rhyme, PO Box 416, Denver, CO 80201-0416. TEL 303-575-5676, FAX 303-575-1187, starsuccess@excite.com, mail@contentprovidermedia.com, http://www.storytimestoriesthatrhyme.com. Ed., R&P A Doyle TEL 303-575-5676.

STORYWORKS. see *EDUCATION—Teaching Methods And Curriculum*

051 614   USA   ISSN 1062-0095
STRAIGHT TALK (PLEASANTVILLE); a magazine for youth. Text in English. 1991. irreg. USD 12.70 set of 4 issues (effective 2005). illus. **Document type:** *Magazine*. **Description:** Deals with health and behavior topics of concern to adolescents.
Formerly (until 1992): Rodale's Straight Talk
Related titles: Supplement(s): Discussion Leader's Magazine. 1991; Talking Straight With Your Teenager. 1998.
Published by: The Learning Partnership, Inc., 394 Bedford Rd., Pleasantville, NY 10570. TEL 914-769-0055, FAX 914-767-5676, stteenmag@aol.com. Ed. Rita V Fisher. Pub., R&P John H Fisher. Circ: 1,000,000 (paid).

STREAMS. see *LITERATURE*

028.5 340 360   AUS
STREETWIZE COMMUNICATIONS; youth rights comics. Text in English. 1984. irreg. free membership. **Document type:** *Consumer*. **Description:** Provides health, legal and survival information, passed on to young disadvantaged people in an entertaining format.
Formerly: Streetwize Comics (0815-0486)
Published by: Streetwize Comics Ltd., Ste 7, 24 S Chalmer St, Redfern, NSW 2016, Australia. TEL 61-2-9319-0220, FAX 61-2-9319-5553, stwize@streetwize.com.au, http://www.streetwize.com. Ed. Liz Stelton. Circ: 10,000.

028.5   RUS   ISSN 0321-3803
STUDENCHESKII MERIDIAN/STUDENT MERIDIAN. Abbreviated title: St M. Text in Russian. 1924. m. USD 193 foreign (effective 2005). bk.rev. illus. **Document type:** *Magazine, Consumer*. **Description:** Aimed at high school and college students, as well as young professionals. Covers current affairs, the arts, popular culture, education, history, and more.
Indexed: RASB, RILM.
—East View.
Published by: Redaktsiya Zhurnala Studencheskii Meridian/Student Meridian, Novodmitrovskaya ul 5-a, Moscow, 125015, Russian Federation. TEL 7-095-2858071, FAX 7-095-9720582. Ed. Y A Rostovtsev. Circ: 1,110,000. Dist. by: East View Information Services, 3020 Harbor Ln. N., Minneapolis, MN 55447. TEL 763-550-0961, FAX 763-559-2931, eastview@eastview.com, http://www.eastview.com.

STUDENT'S MESSAGE/RISALAT AL-TALIB. see *EDUCATION*

028.5   DEU
STUFE; Jugendzeitschrift der Albvereinsjugend. Text in German. 1972. q. bk.rev. **Document type:** *Newsletter*.
Published by: Schwaebischer Albverein e.V., Hospitalstr 21B, Stuttgart, 70174, Germany. TEL 49-711-2258574. Ed. Christian Bendig.

059.95911   THA
SUDSUPDA. Text in Thai. bi-m. THB 70 newsstand/cover (effective 2002). adv. **Document type:** *Magazine, Consumer*. **Description:** Features interviews, lifestyles, in-depth documentaries, as well as columns on books, films, music and foreign features.

Published by: Amarin Printing & Publishing Public Co. Ltd., 7/9-18 Arun Amarin Rd., Bangkoknoi, Bangkok, 10700, Thailand. TEL 66-2-434-0286, FAX 66-2-434-8699, info@amarin.co.th, http://www.amarin.co.th.

052   GBR   ISSN 1355-9672
SUGAR. Text in English. 1995. m. GBP 24 domestic; GBP 30.90 in Europe; GBP 53.40 elsewhere (effective 2004). adv. illus. **Document type:** *Magazine, Consumer*. **Description:** Lifestyle magazine for girls featuring celebrity interviews, real life stories, advice, and make up and fashion tips.
Published by: Hachette Filipacchi (UK) Ltd. (Subsidiary of: Hachette Filipacchi Medias S.A.), 64 North Row, London, W1K 7LL, United Kingdom. TEL 44-20-71507000, FAX 44-20-71507001, http://www.sugarmagazine.co.uk/, http://www.hachettefilipacchiuk.co.uk. adv.: B&W page GBP 10,440, color page GBP 10,440; trim 210 x 275. Circ: 415,973 (paid).

053.1   DEU
SUGAR. Text in German. 1998. m. EUR 2.40 newsstand/cover (effective 2005). adv. **Document type:** *Magazine, Consumer*. **Description:** Contains fashion advice, beauty tips, real life stories, celebrity news, hunky boys, and gossip for teenage girls.
Published by: Attic Futura Verlag GmbH, Landsberger Str 76, Munich, 80339, Germany. TEL 49-89-51446100, FAX 49-89-51449199, info@atticfutura.de, http://www.atticfutura.de. Adv. contact Nina Schwarz TEL 49-89-54589261. color page EUR 16,000; trim 210 x 275. Circ: 261,454 (paid).

SUGAR AND SPICE. see *HANDICAPPED—Visually Impaired*

028.5   IND
SUKTARA. Text in Bengali. 1948. m.
Address: 11 Jhamapooker Ln., Kolkata, West Bengal 700 009, India. TEL 33-355294. Ed. M Majumdar. Circ: 61,300.

028.5   IND   ISSN 0971-149X
SUMAN SAURABH. Text in Hindi. 1983. m. INR 120, USD 20; INR 10 newsstand/cover (effective 2003). **Document type:** *Consumer*. **Description:** Includes fiction, informative articles and regular columns of interest to children from 11-18 years old.
Published by: Delhi Press Patra Prakashan Ltd., Delhi Press Bldg., Jhandewala Estate, New Delhi, 110 055, India. TEL 91-11-3529557-62, FAX 91-11-7525020. Ed. Paresh Nath. adv.: B&W page INR 21,000, color page INR 35,000; 240 x 175. Circ: 52,000.

028.5   FIN   ISSN 0355-4260
SUOSIKKI. Text in Finnish. 1953. m. EUR 45 (effective 2005). adv. **Document type:** *Magazine, Consumer*. **Description:** Covers popular media and music for a youth audience (ages 12-20).
Formerly (until 1961): Musiikkiviesti
Published by: Yhtyneet Kuvalehdet Oy/United Magazines Ltd., Maistraatinportti 1, Helsinki, 00015, Finland. TEL 358-9-15661, FAX 358-9-145650, suosikki@kuvalehdet.fi, http://www.suosikki.fi/, http://www.kuvalehdet.fi/. Ed. Katja Staahl. adv.: color page EUR 4,140; trim 280 x 217. Circ: 74,146.

SUPER 7. see *HOBBIES*

028.5 305.8   USA   ISSN 1548-9302
SUPER ONDA; the magazine for young adults with purpose. Abbreviated title: S O. Text in English. 1999 (Jan./Feb.). 10/yr. USD 12 domestic; USD 32 in Mexico; USD 42 elsewhere (effective 2001). USD 2.25 newsstand/cover. adv. back issues avail. **Document type:** *Consumer*. **Description:** Speaks to students on their own level and in their own language. Explores various definitions of success and introduces readers to other students who are making their own mark on the world. Geared to 16-22 year olds.
Published by: Hispanic Business Inc., 425 Pine Ave, Santa Barbara, CA 93117-3700. TEL 805-964-4554, FAX 805-964-5539, editorial@superonda.com, http://www.superonda.com. Ed. Vaughn Hagerty. Pub. Jesus Chavarria. adv.: B&W page USD 3,900, color page USD 4,500; trim 10.5 x 7.25. Circ: 100,000.

028.5   ESP
SUPER POP. Text in Spanish. 1976. fortn. adv. **Description:** Covers music and cinema for young people (14-19 years old).
Published by: Publicaciones Ekdosis S.A., Gran Via de Carles III, 124, Barcelona, 08034, Spain. TEL 34-3-2061540, FAX 34-3-2800837. Ed. Carmen Grasa. Adv. contact Rosa Martinez. Circ: 390,183.

SUPERSCIENCE. see *EDUCATION—Teaching Methods And Curriculum*

SUPERSTARS. see *MUSIC*

SURE!; the English monthly magazine for you. see *LINGUISTICS*

087.5   HRV   ISSN 1330-9455
SVE O TEBI!. Text in Croatian. 1995. q. **Document type:** *Magazine, Consumer*.

Published by: Revije d.d., Slavonska avenija 4, Zagreb, 10000, Croatia. TEL 385-1-6161035, FAX 385-1-6161028, revije@revije.hr, http://www.revije.hr.

SVIT DYTYACHYKH BIBLIOTEK; shchokvartal'nyi naukovo-metodychnyi zhurnal. see *LIBRARY AND INFORMATION SCIENCES*

028.5   AUS   ISSN 0727-4327
SYDNEY FOR KIDS. Text in English. 1982. biennial. AUD 6.95. —CCC.
Published by: Universal Magazines Pty. Ltd., Unite 5, 6-8 Byfield St, North Ryde, NSW 2113, Australia. TEL 61-2-98870399, FAX 61-2-98050714, info@universalmagazines.com.au, http://www.universalmagazines.com.au/.

499.992   NLD
T E J O - TUTMONDE. Text in Esperanto. 1983. q. EUR 10 (effective 2003). bk.rev. **Document type:** *Newsletter, Internal*.
Published by: (Tutmonda Esperantista Junulara Organizo), Universala Esperanto-Asocio, Nieuwe Binnenweg 176, Rotterdam, 3015 BJ, Netherlands. TEL 31-10-4361044, FAX 31-10-4361751, uea@inter.nl.net, libroservo@uea.org, http://www.uea.org. Ed. Ricardo Newsum. Circ: 1,000.

028.5   CAN   ISSN 0843-4557
T G - VOICES OF TODAY'S GENERATION. Text in English, French. 1940. 6/yr. CND 12, USD 20 (effective 1994). adv. bk.rev. index. back issues avail. **Description:** Covers music, fashion, careers, emotional growth issues, advice and empowerment.
Former titles: Teen Generation; (until Dec.-Jan. 1977): Today's Generation (0384-1405); Canadian High News (0008-3747)
Related titles: Microfiche ed.: (from MML); Microform ed.: (from MML).
Indexed: CBPI, CPerl.
Published by: Teen Generation Inc., 202 Cleveland St, Toronto, ON M4S 2W6, Canada. TEL 416-487-3204. Ed. Donna Douglas. Circ: 165,000.

028.5   SVN   ISSN 0040-7712
T I M; revija za tehnicno in znanstveno dejavnost mladine. Text in Slovenian. 1963. m. SIT 36.
Published by: Tehniska Zalozba Slovenije, Lepi pot 6, Ljubljana, 1000, Slovenia. TEL 386-61-1790220, FAX 386-61-1790230, joze.cuden@tehniska-zalozba.si, http://www.tehniska-zalozba.si. Ed. Bozidar Grabnar.

028.5   FRA   ISSN 1763-8321
T L CATHO. (Tous en Ligne) Text in French. 1955. 11/yr. back issues avail. **Description:** For children ages 11-15. Contains news about different countries and people.
Former titles (until 2004): T L Notre Hebdo (1622-163X); (until 2000): Terres Lointaines (0492-7958)
Published by: Terres Lointaines, 15-27 rue Moussorgati, Paris, Cedex 18 75895, France. TEL 33-1-53263500, FAX 33-1-53263515. Ed. Aline Seeuws. Pub. Vincent Montagne. Circ: 37,391.

371.3   USA
T O W S. (The Online Write Stuff) Text in English. 3/yr. **Document type:** *Newsletter*.
Media: Online - full text.
Address: jpost@santacruz.k12.ca.us, http://www.santacruz.k12.ca.us/~jpost/projects/tows/tows.html. Ed. Jory Post.

052   AUS   ISSN 1032-2973
T V HITS. Text in English. 1988. m. AUD 45 domestic; AUD 92.40 foreign; AUD 4.80 newsstand/cover (effective 2004). adv. **Document type:** *Magazine, Consumer*. **Description:** Contains articles of interest to teens featuring stars, pictures, prizes, gossip and more.
Published by: Pacific Publications, 35-51 Mitchell St, McMahons Point, NSW 2060, Australia. TEL 61-2-94643300, FAX 61-2-94643375, tvhitsonline@pacpubs.com.au, subscriptions@pacpubs.com.au, http://www.tvhits.com.au, http://www.pacificpubs.com.au. Adv. contact Charlie Durrant. B&W page AUD 4,410, color page AUD 6,300; trim 210 x 297. Circ: 103,500 (paid).

T V HITS. see *COMMUNICATIONS—Television And Cable*

T V M S TIGER BEAT. see *MOTION PICTURES*

T V MAGAZINE. see *COMMUNICATIONS—Television And Cable*

028.5   SVK
TABORTUZ. Text in Hungarian. 24/yr.
Published by: Smena Publishing House, Prazska 11, Bratislava, 81284, Slovakia.

053.1   DEU   ISSN 0947-5656
TAKE!; magazine for young people. Text in German. 1992. bi-m. free. adv. dance rev.; music rev.; play rev.; software rev.; video rev. **Document type:** *Magazine, Consumer*.
Related titles: Online - full text ed.

Published by: Schaab Verlag, Kaiserstr 16, Siegburg, 53721, Germany. TEL 49-2241-66115, FAX 49-2241-67862, info@take-online.de, http://www.take-online.de. Ed. Patrick Schaab. adv.: B&W page EUR 824, color page EUR 1,165. Circ: 18,200 (controlled).

028.5 PAK ISSN 0039-9175
TALIM-O-TARBIAT. Text in Urdu. 1941. m. PKR 515 in Asia; PKR 830 in Europe; PKR 950 in US & Canada (effective 2002). bk.rev. bibl. 68 p./no. 2 cols./p.; **Document type:** *Magazine, Consumer.*
Media: Large Type.
Published by: Ferozsons Ltd., 60-Shara-e-Quaid-e-Azam, Lahore, E. Pakistan, Pakistan. TEL 92-42-111626262, FAX 92-42-6369204, support@ferozsons.com.pk. Ed. A Salam. Pub. Zaheer Salam. Adv. contact Muqeet Salam. Circ: 45,000.

TALKS AND TALES. see *RELIGIONS AND THEOLOGY—Judaic*

028.5 JPN
TANOSHII YOCHIEN. Text in Japanese. 1947. m. illus. **Document type:** *Magazine, Consumer.*
Published by: Kodansha Ltd., 2-12-21 Otowa, Bunkyo-ku, Tokyo, 112-8001, Japan. TEL 81-3-3946-6201, FAX 81-3-3944-9915, http://www.kodansha.co.jp. Ed. Yukio Shindo. Circ: 400,000.

028.5 USA ISSN 0882-5424
TAPORI. Text in English. 1974. bi-m. USD 10 (effective 2003). illus. **Document type:** *Newsletter, Academic/Scholarly.*
Description: Brings together children from different backgrounds and allows them to show their concern for and solidarity with children who live in poverty.
Published by: Fourth World Movement, 7600 Willow Hill Dr., Landover, MD 20785-4658. TEL 301-336-9489, FAX 301-336-0092, fourthworld@erols.com, http://www.tapori.org. Ed. Susan M Devins. Circ: 2,000.

028.5 NLD ISSN 0039-9604
TAPTOE. Text in Dutch. 1920. fortn. illus. **Document type:** *Consumer.* **Description:** Educational publicationfor children ages 8-12.
Published by: L.C.G. Malmberg B.V., Leeghwaterlaan 16, 's Hertogenbosch, 5223 BA, Netherlands. FAX 31-73-6126154. Ed. A Bon. Circ: 120,000.

TAR HEEL JUNIOR HISTORIAN; North Carolina history for students. see *HISTORY—History Of North And South America*

028.5 IND
TARGET. Text in English. 1979. fortn. INR 12 newsstand/cover.
Published by: Living Media India Pvt. Ltd., F-14-15, Connaught Place, New Delhi, India. TEL 91-11-23315801, FAX 91-11-23712998, wecare@intoday.com, http://www.indiatoday.com. Ed. Ameena Jayal. adv.: B&W page INR 16,000, color page INR 32,000; trim 273 x 191. **Subscr. to:** We Care, 1-A Hamilton House, New Delhi 110 001, India. TEL 91-11-23352870, FAX 91-11-23352874.

028.5 AUS
TAS TOTS✶. Text in English. 1988. 3/yr. AUD 3. adv. bk.rev. back issues avail. **Description:** Covers child care, playgroups, and activities for children.
Published by: Playgroup Association of Tasmania, St Johns Ave, New Town, TAS 7009, Australia. TEL 61-3-62280925. Circ: 1,100.

TE TARI PUNA ORA O AOTEAROA. ITIREAREA/NEW ZEALAND CHILDCARE ASSOCIATION. NEWSLETTER. see *EDUCATION*

TEAM OF ADVOCATES FOR SPECIAL KIDS NEWSLETTER. see *HANDICAPPED*

028.5 NZL ISSN 0113-3403
TEARAWAY MAGAZINE; the voice of N Z youth. Text in English. 1986. m. NZD 29 (effective 1999). adv. bk.rev.; film rev.; music rev.; video rev. back issues avail. **Document type:** *Consumer.*
Published by: Tearaway Press Ltd., P.O. Box 473, Wanganui, New Zealand. TEL 64-6-3478899, FAX 64-6-3458881, editor@tearaway.co.nz, http://www.tearaway.co.nz. Ed. Sue Pepperell. Pub. John Francis. Adv. contact Lara Churton Hughes. color page NZD 5,367; trim 275 x 385. Circ: 80,000.

TECHNOLOGY AND CHILDREN. see *EDUCATION—Teaching Methods And Curriculum*

607.1 USA ISSN 1066-3428
TECHNOSCENE✶. Text in English. 1992. s-a. **Document type:** *Newsletter.* **Description:** Covers technology for elementary school readers (grades K-2 and 3-5) in activity-based articles for use in the classroom.
Published by: Technology Student Association, 1914 Association Dr, Reston, VA 22091. TEL 703-860-9000, FAX 703-620-4483.

028.5 USA ISSN 0040-2001
TEEN. Text in English. 1957. q. USD 3.99 newsstand/cover (effective 2005); no subscription. adv. bk.rev. illus. reprints avail. **Document type:** *Magazine, Consumer.* **Description:** Offers young women, ages 12 to 15, advice on their physical, intellectual, and social development through the crucial teen years.
Related titles: Microform ed.: suspended (from PQC); Online - full text ed.: suspended (from Gale Group, H.W. Wilson, The Dialog Corporation); ♦ Spanish ed.: Teen en Espanol. ISSN 1523-7273.
Indexed: ASIP, JHMA, MASUSE, MagInd, PMR, PSI, RGAb, RGPR, RGYP, TOM.
—CCC.
Published by: Hearst Magazines (Subsidiary of: Hearst Corporation), 3000 Ocean Park Blvd, Ste 3048, Santa Monica, CA 90405. TEL 310-664-2950, FAX 310-664-2959, http://www.teenmag.com.

087.5 HRV ISSN 1330-8254
TEEN. Text in Croatian. 1994. m. adv. **Document type:** *Magazine, Consumer.*
Formerly (until 1995): Super Teen (1330-8246)
Published by: Revije d.d., Slavonska avenija 4, Zagreb, 10000, Croatia. TEL 385-1-6161035, FAX 385-1-6161028, teen@revije.hr, revije@revije.hr, http://teen.revije.hr, http://www.revije.hr.

TEEN; your English monthly. see *LINGUISTICS*

052 NGA ISSN 0331-4502
TEEN AND TWENTY; Africa's youth magazine. Text in English. 1968. m. NGN 2. adv. charts; illus. **Document type:** *Consumer.*
Published by: Teen Topics Publications, PO Box 14, Ikeja, Lagos, Nigeria. Ed. Adeyola David.

028.5 USA ISSN 0884-1675
TEEN IDOL MANIA. Text in English. 1985. 8/yr. USD 1.95 per issue. **Document type:** *Consumer.*
Published by: Marvel Entertainment Group, 387 Park Ave S Fl 9, New York, NY 10016-8810.

028.5 USA
TEEN INK; written by teens. Variant title: TeenInk. Text in English. m. USD 25 (effective 2003). adv. **Document type:** *Magazine, Consumer.* **Description:** Offers teenagers the opportunity to publish their opinions and creative work on the issues that affect their lives - everything from love and family to teen smoking and community service.
Related titles: Online - full text ed.
Published by: Young Authors Foundation, PO Box 30, Newton, MA 02461. TEL 617-964-6800, editor@teenink.com, http://teenink.com.

TEEN LIFE. see *RELIGIONS AND THEOLOGY—Other Denominations And Sects*

TEEN MOVIELINE. see *MOTION PICTURES*

TEEN MOVIELINE ONLINE. see *MOTION PICTURES*

051 USA ISSN 1527-6775
TEEN NEWSWEEK. Text in English. 1999. 26/yr. USD 8.25 per academic year for 15 or more subscriptions; USD 9.85 per academic year for 10-14 subscriptions (effective 2004 - 2005). adv. **Document type:** *Magazine, Consumer.* **Description:** Delivers international and national current issues and events for students in grades 6-9.
Published by: Weekly Reader Corp. (Subsidiary of: W R C Media Inc.), 200 First Stamford Pl, PO Box 120023, Stamford, CT 06912-0023. TEL 203-705-3500, 800-446-3355, FAX 203-705-1662, ed@teennewsweek.com, http://www.teennewsweek.com, http://www.weeklyreader.com. Ed. Deborah Dolan Nevins. Pub. Peter Esposito. R&P Cathy Pekai TEL 203-705-3426. Circ: 150,000 (paid and controlled).
Co-publisher: Newsweek, Inc.

TEEN PEOPLE. see *GENERAL INTEREST PERIODICALS—United States*

TEEN PEOPLE YEAR-END. see *GENERAL INTEREST PERIODICALS—United States*

028.5 USA
TEEN PROM. Text in English. a. USD 3.50 newsstand/cover; USD 4.50 newsstand/cover in Canada (effective 2001). adv. **Document type:** *Magazine, Consumer.*
Published by: Primedia Consumer Media & Magazine Group, 9036 Brittanyway, Tampa, FL 33619. TEL 813-679-3500, FAX 813-679-3999.

TEEN STYLE. see *LIFESTYLE*

284.1 USA
TEEN TIME (LARGE PRINT EDITION). Text in English. 8/yr. (Oct.-May). free (effective 2005). **Document type:** *Consumer.* **Description:** Inspirational articles and pen pal letters for young adults.
Media: Large Type (22 pt.). **Related titles:** Audio cassette/tape ed.; Braille ed.
Published by: (Lutheran Church - Missouri Synod), Lutheran Library for the Blind, 1333 S Kirkwood Rd, St. Louis, MO 63122-7295. TEL 888-215-2455, FAX 314-965-0959, blind.library@lcms.org, http://www.careministries.org/llb.html. Ed. Lynne Borchelt.

640 USA ISSN 0735-6986
CODEN: HEPBAF
TEEN TIMES. Text in English. 1945. q. free to members (effective 2005). adv. illus. reprints avail. **Document type:** *Magazine.* **Description:** Helps prepare students with skills they can use in everyday life. Articles cover issues such as peer pressure, nutrition and fitness, parenting, family relationships and career options.
Published by: Family Career and Community Leaders of America, 1910 Association Dr, Reston, VA 20191. TEL 703-476-4900, FAX 703-860-2713, commcoor@fhahero.org, http://www.fhahero.org, http://www.fcclainc.org. Ed., R&P, Adv. contact Beth Carpenter. B&W page USD 3,095, color page USD 4,195. Circ: 230,000.

028.5 CAN ISSN 1480-6681
TEEN TRIBUTE. Text in English. 1998. bi-m. CND 15 domestic; CND 35 foreign (effective 2002).
Related titles: Online - full text ed.: (from EBSCO Publishing).
Indexed: MASUSE.
Published by: Tribute Publishing, Inc., 71 Barber Green Rd, Don Mills, ON M3C 282, Canada. TEL 416-445-0544, FAX 416-445-2894, http://www.tribute.ca. Ed., Pub. Sandra I Stewart. Circ: 300,000 (controlled).

TEEN VOGUE. see *CLOTHING TRADE—Fashions*

TEEN VOICES. see *WOMEN'S INTERESTS*

051 USA ISSN 1049-0183
TEENAGE MUTANT NINJA TURTLES MAGAZINE✶. Text in English. 1990. q. USD 7.80. **Description:** A forum for the superheros to defend and protect against the evil Shredder and his clan.
Published by: Mirage Publishers, PO Box 486, Northhampton, MA 01061-0486. Ed. Adam Philips. Circ: 100,000.

028.5 330 305.896 USA
TEENPRENEUR. Text in English. 2002 (Oct.). m. free to subscr. of Black Enterprise. **Document type:** *Magazine, Consumer.*
Published by: Earl G. Graves Publishing Co., Inc., 130 Fifth Ave, New York, NY 10011. TEL 212-242-8000, FAX 212-886-9610, http://www.blackenterprise.com.

028.5 811 USA ISSN 1084-5720
TEENS IN MOTION NEWS. Text in English. 1995. m. USD 10 domestic; USD 15 in Canada; USD 0.75 newsstand/cover. adv. bk.rev.; film rev.; music rev. illus. back issues avail. **Document type:** *Magazine, Consumer.* **Description:** Features work by teen poets, artists, and writers.
Related titles: Online - full text ed.
Published by: Costa Publishing, PO Box 1264, Santa Clara, CA 95052-1264. TEL 408-244-3718, FAX 408-557-8086, pkc@ix.netcom.com, pilc@ix.netcom.com, http://www.hypermart.net/penweb/index.htm. Ed., Pub., Adv. contact Pamela K Costa. Circ: 6,500.

028.5 USA
TEENS TODAY (KANSAS CITY, 1988)✶. Text in English. 1988. 10/yr. adv. **Description:** For, by and about teens. Covers education, health, sports, fashion, art, environment and psychology.
Published by: Elbert Allan Publishing Co., Inc., 3811 E 75th Ter, Kansas City, MO 64132. TEL 816-363-8336, FAX 816-361-4161. Ed. Elbert Harris. Circ: 20,000.

TEKHNIKA MOLODEZHI. see *TECHNOLOGY: COMPREHENSIVE WORKS*

305.233 GBR ISSN 1369-3387
TELETUBBIES. Text in English. 1997. 13/yr. GBP 16.80; GBP 1.40 newsstand/cover (effective 2003). adv. **Document type:** *Magazine, Consumer.* **Description:** A mix of stories, coloring, and activities for very young children.
Published by: B B C Worldwide Ltd., 80 Wood Ln, London, W12 0TT, United Kingdom. TEL 44-20-84331070, FAX 44-20-84332231, bbcproducts@bbc.co.uk, http://www.bbcmagazines.com/teletubbies/index.html. Ed. Ruth Paley. **Dist. by:** Frontline, Park House, 117 Park Rd, Peterborough, Cambs PE1 2TS, United Kingdom. TEL 44-1733-555161, FAX 44-1733-562788.

305.233 GBR
TELETUBBIES SPECIAL. Text in English. m. **Document type:** *Consumer.*
Published by: B B C Worldwide Ltd., 80 Wood Ln, London, W12 0TT, United Kingdom. TEL 44-208-576-2000, FAX 44-208-433-3824, bbcproducts@bbc.co.uk, http://www.bbcworldwide.com. **Dist. by:** Frontline, Park House, 117 Park Rd, Peterborough, Cambs PE1 2TS, United Kingdom. TEL 44-1733-555161, FAX 44-1733-562788.

028.5 FRA
TETE BECHE. Text in French. 10/yr. **Description:** Features themes that correspond to the school programs of children from ages 7 to 9. Includes animals, daily life, world travel, and environment.
Published by: Publications de l'Ecole Moderne Francaise, Mouans-Sartoux, Cedex 06376, France. TEL 33-4-92921757, FAX 33-4-92921804, pemf@wanadoo.fr, http://www.pemf.fr.

C

▼ new title ➤ refereed ✶ unverified ♦ full entry avail.

TEXAS F F A MAGAZINE. see *AGRICULTURE*

028.5   MMR
TEZA. Text in Burmese, English. 1965. m. **Description:** Pictorial publication for children.
Published by: Myawaddy Press, 181-3 Sule Pagoda Rd., Yangon, Myanmar. Circ: 29,500.

028.5   VNM
THIEU NIEN TIEN PHONG/YOUNG PIONEERS. Text in Vietnamese. w.
Address: 15 Ho Xuan Huong, Hanoi, Viet Nam. TEL 64031. Ed. Le Tran. Circ: 80,000.

028.5   USA
THINK AND DISCOVER; for grades 1-4. Text in English. 5/yr. USD 24.95 domestic; USD 36.95 foreign (effective 2003). 64 p./no.; **Document type:** *Journal, Academic/Scholarly.*
Description: Contains regular features in science, reading, creative thinking, motivations and teachers.
Published by: Menagerie Publishing, Inc., PO Box 408, Ft Madison, IA 52627. TEL 800-527-3679, FAX 319-376-5734, info@menageriepublishing.com, http://www5.outfitters.com/cgi-bin/menagerie/index.html?id=yqyhClGj.

028.5   GBR   ISSN 1467-7288
THOMAS & FRIENDS. Text in English. 1988. fortn. GBP 30; GBP 1.25 newsstand/cover (effective 1999). **Document type:** *Consumer.*
Formerly (until 1999): Thomas the Tank Engine and Friends (0954-9390)
Published by: Marvel Comics Ltd. (Subsidiary of: Panini UK Ltd.), Panini House, Coach & Horses Passage, The Pantiles, Tunbridge Wells, Kent TM2 5UJ, United Kingdom. TEL 44-1892-500100, FAX 44-1892-545666. Ed. Alan O'Keefe. **Dist. by:** MarketForce UK Ltd, 247 Tottenham Court Rd, London, Middx W1T 7AU, United Kingdom. TEL 44-20-72615199, FAX 44-20-72617341.

028.5   GBR   ISSN 0964-3850
THOMAS THE TANK ENGINE AND FRIENDS COLLECTED. Text in English. m. GBP 2.10 newsstand/cover. **Document type:** *Consumer.* **Description:** Fun and games with Thomas and all his friends.
Published by: Marvel Comics Ltd. (Subsidiary of: Panini UK Ltd.), Panini House, Coach & Horses Passage, The Pantiles, Tunbridge Wells, Kent TM2 5UJ, United Kingdom. TEL 44-1892-500100, FAX 44-1892-545666. Ed. Alan O'Keefe. **Dist. by:** MarketForce UK Ltd, 247 Tottenham Court Rd, London, Middx W1T 7AU, United Kingdom. TEL 44-207-2615199, FAX 44-207-2617341.

028.5   DEU
THOMAS UND SEINE FREUNDE. Text in German. 1999. bi-m. EUR 2.70 newsstand/cover (effective 2003). adv. **Document type:** *Magazine, Consumer.*
Published by: Panini Verlags GmbH, Ravensstr 48, Nettetal, 41334, Germany. TEL 49-711-947680, FAX 49-711-94768830, info@panini-dino.de, http://www.panini-media.de. adv.: page EUR 2,000. Circ: 38,090 (paid).

THRASHER. see *SPORTS AND GAMES*

028.5   CHN
TIANJIN QINGNIAN BAO. Text in Chinese. 1949. d. (6/week). CNY 156 (effective 2004). **Document type:** *Consumer.*
Published by: Tianjin Ribaoshe, 28F, Tianjinribao Dasha, 873, Dagu Nanlu, Tianjin, 300211, China. TEL 86-22-28201211.

TIEN PHONG/VANGUARD. see *POLITICAL SCIENCE*

028.5   VNM
TIEN PHONG CHU NHAT/SUNDAY VANGUARD. Text in Vietnamese. 1988. w.
Published by: Ho Chi Minh Communist Youth Union, 15 Ho Xuan Huong, Hanoi, Viet Nam. TEL 64031. Ed. Duong Xuan Nam.

028.5   VNM
TIEN PHONG CUOI THANG/MONTHLY VANGUARD. Text in Vietnamese. 1991. m.
Published by: Ho Chi Minh Communist Youth Union, 15 Ho Xuan Huong, Hanoi, Viet Nam. TEL 64031. Ed. Duong Xuan Nam.

TIERFREUND; Natur erleben, verstehen, schuetzen. see *CONSERVATION*

780   USA   ISSN 0040-7380
TIGER BEAT. Text in English. 1965. q. USD 14.95 (effective 2005). adv. bk.rev. illus. **Document type:** *Magazine, Consumer.* **Description:** Covers topics of interest to a young audience. Covers the latest news from Backstreet Boys, Christina Aguilera, Brittney, Ricky Martin and NSYNC.
Formerly: T V & Movie Screen
—CCC.

Published by: Primedia Youth Entertainment Group (Subsidiary of: Primedia Consumer Media & Magazine Group), 6430 Sunset Blvd Ste 700, Hollywood, CA 90028. TEL 323-782-2000, FAX 323-782-2660, editor@tigerbeatmag.com, http://www.tigerbeatmag.com/. Eds. Louise Barile, Louise A. Barile. Pub. Mark Peterson. R&P Steve Spitzer. Adv. contact Alisa Harad. B&W page USD 8,400; trim 8 x 10.5. Circ: 151,185 (paid).

028.5   DEU
TIGERMAEDCHEN; Geschichten und Gedichte von Maedchen. Text in English, German, Turkish. 1984. q. adv. bk.rev.
Document type: *Magazine, Consumer.*
Published by: Bund Demokratische Pfadfinderinnen, Lasiuszeile 2, Berlin, 13585, Germany. TEL 030-3358393. Ed. Anje Tuckermann. Circ: 600.

028.5   USA
TIME FOR KIDS BIG PICTURE (GRADES K-1). Text in English. 22/yr. USD 22.62 (effective 2003).
Related titles: Online - full content ed.
Published by: Time, Inc (Subsidiary of: Time Warner, Inc.), Time & Life Bldg., Rockefeller Center, 29th Fl, 1271 Ave of the Americas, New York, NY 10020-1393. TEL 212-522-1212, FAX 212-522-0003, http://www.timeforkids.com/TFK/magazines/index.html, http://www.timeinc.com.

028.5   USA
AP2
TIME FOR KIDS NEWS SCOOP (GRADE 2-3). Text in English. 1995. w. USD 22.62 (effective 2003). illus. reprints avail.
Document type: *Consumer.*
Supersedes in part (in 1997): Time for Kids (1084-0168)
Related titles: Online - full text ed.: ISSN 1547-3805 (from bigchalk, EBSCO Publishing, Factiva, Gale Group, ProQuest Information & Learning).
Indexed: ICM, RGYP.
Published by: Time, Inc (Subsidiary of: Time Warner, Inc.), Time & Life Bldg., Rockefeller Center, 29th Fl, 1271 Ave of the Americas, New York, NY 10020-1393. TEL 212-522-1212, FAX 212-522-0003, tfk@time.com, http://www.pathfinder.com/TFK/index.html. Ed. Claudia Wallis. R&P Mary Ann Kornelly TEL 212-522-4800.

028.5   USA
AP2
TIME FOR KIDS WORLD REPORT (GRADE 4-6). Text in English. 1995. w. USD 22.62 (effective 2003). illus. reprints avail. **Document type:** *Consumer.*
Supersedes in part (in 1997): Time for Kids (1084-0168)
Related titles: Online - full text ed.: ISSN 1547-3813 (from bigchalk, EBSCO Publishing, Factiva, Gale Group, ProQuest Information & Learning).
Indexed: ICM, RGYP.
Published by: Time, Inc (Subsidiary of: Time Warner, Inc.), Time & Life Bldg., Rockefeller Center, 29th Fl, 1271 Ave of the Americas, New York, NY 10020-1393. TEL 212-522-1212, FAX 212-522-0003, tfk@time.com, http://www.pathfinder.com/TFK/worldreport/index.htm. Ed. Claudia Wallis. R&P Mary Ann Kornelly TEL 212-522-4800. Adv. contact Amy Dunkin.
Subscr. to: PO Box 30603, Tampa, FL 33630-0603.

▼ **TIME OUT NEW YORK KIDS.** see *TRAVEL AND TOURISM*

028.5   BEL   ISSN 0165-1498
TINA. Text in Dutch. 1967. w. EUR 54.60 (effective 2003). adv. illus. **Document type:** *Magazine, Consumer.* **Description:** Talks about rock music and stars, boys and romance, fashion and cosmetics, and other topics of interest to girls.
Published by: Sanoma Magazines Belgium, Telecomlaan 5-7, Diegem, 1831, Belgium. TEL 32-2-7762211, FAX 32-2-776-2317, www.tina.nl, http://www.sanoma-magazines.be/HomePage.aspx?flash=1&Language=nl.

808.836   IND
TINKLE. Text in English. 1980. fortn. INR 725. adv. **Document type:** *Consumer.* **Description:** Entertains and educates using the comics medium.
Related titles: Microfilm ed.; Assamese ed.
Published by: India Book House Ltd., Fleet Bldg. 1st Fl., M V Rd., Marol Naa Andheri (E), Mumbai, Maharashtra 400 059, India. TEL 91-22-2610216, FAX 91-22-8500645, TELEX 011-86297 DANI IN. Ed. Anant Pai. Adv. contact Richardo Furtado. B&W page INR 14,000, color page INR 17,000. Circ: 82,500.

087.5   PRT   ISSN 0874-0607
TIO PATINHAS. Text in Portuguese. 1985. 3/yr. EUR 18.36 (effective 2004). **Document type:** *Magazine, Consumer.*
Published by: Edimpresa Editora Lda., Rua Calvet de Magalhaes 242, Laveiras, Paco de Arcos, 2770-022, Portugal. TEL 351-21-4698000, FAX 351-21-4698501, edimpresa@edimpresa.pt, http://www.edimpresa.pt.

087.5   BRA   ISSN 0104-2076
TIO PATINHAS. Text in Portuguese. 1970. m. **Document type:** *Magazine, Consumer.*
Published by: Editora Abril, S.A., Av. das Nacoes Unidas, 7221, 11 andar Pinheiros, Sao Paulo, SP 05425-902, Brazil. TEL 55-11-50872112, FAX 55-11-50872100, http://www.disney.com.br/, http://www.abril.com.br/. Circ: 4,900.

053.1   DEU
TIPPS FUER KIDS. Text in German. 2000. 2/yr. adv. **Document type:** *Magazine, Consumer.*
Published by: Verlag Joerg Stoeckicht, Friedrichstr 8, Neumuenster, 24534, Germany. TEL 49-4321-16266, FAX 49-4321-12350. adv.: B&W page EUR 655, color page EUR 1,115. Circ: 15,000 (controlled).

028.5 053.5   CHE
TOASTER; junge monatszeitung. Text in German. 1971. m. CHF 30 (effective 1999). adv. bk.rev.; music rev.; play rev.; software rev. back issues avail. **Document type:** *Magazine, Consumer.*
Address: Wasserwertstr 17, PO Box, Zuerich, 8035, Switzerland. TEL 43-1-3665020, FAX 43-1-3665015, toaster@music.ch, http://www.toaster.ch. Eds. Didi Mueller, Esther Banz. Pub. Dietegen Mueller. Adv. contact Dietejen Thieller. B&W page CHF 4,300, color page CHF 5,650. Circ: 11,000.

028.5   FRA   ISSN 0248-2339
TOBOGGAN. Text in French. 1980. m. EUR 52 (effective 2005).
Published by: Milan Presse, 300 rue Leon Joulin, Toulouse, Cedex 1 31101, France. TEL 33-5-61766411, FAX 33-5-61766567. Ed. Claire Kowalski. Pub. Patrice Amen. Circ: 90,200.

028.5   GBR   ISSN 0040-8360
TODAY (KENT)✳ . Text in English. 1966. q. bk.rev. abstr.; bibl.; illus.
Formerly: Today's Topic
Published by: Pollyhaugh Press Ltd., Nealhampton House, Speldhurst, Tunbridge Wells, Kent, United Kingdom. Ed. Jonathan Michael Barker. Circ: 15,000.

TODAY (LAWSON); family magazine. see *RELIGIONS AND THEOLOGY—Protestant*

028.5 420 375.4   FRA   ISSN 1154-5992
TODAY IN ENGLISH. Text in French. 1991. m. (11/yr.). EUR 64.80 domestic; EUR 84.80 foreign (effective 2005); includes 6 CDs. **Description:** Helps students 15 and older to improve their English.
Published by: Bayard Presse, 3 Rue Bayard, Paris, 75393 Cedex 08, France. TEL 33-1-44356060, FAX 33-1-44356161, redactions@bayard-presse.com, http://www.bayardpresse.com. Ed. Stephen Clarke. Circ: 46,546.

TODAY'S CHRISTIAN TEEN; college prep guide. see *RELIGIONS AND THEOLOGY*

028.5   DEU
TOGGOLINO; das Fun-Magazin. Text in German. 2001. 4/yr. EUR 2.70 newsstand/cover (effective 2005). adv. **Document type:** *Magazine, Consumer.*
Related titles: Online - full text ed.
Published by: Panini Verlags GmbH, Ravensstr 48, Nettetal, 41334, Germany. TEL 49-711-947680, FAX 49-711-94768830, info@panini-dino.de, http://www.toggolino.de, http://www.panini-media.de. Adv. contact Petra Sonnenfroh-Kost. page EUR 2,500; trim 170 x 257. Circ: 80,000 (paid and controlled).

808.836   FIN   ISSN 0357-6493
TOM & JERRY. Variant title: Tom ja Jerry. Text in Finnish. 1980. m. EUR 21 (effective 2005). adv. **Document type:** *Magazine, Consumer.*
Published by: Yhtyneet Kuvalehdet Oy/United Magazines Ltd., Maistraatinportti 1, Helsinki, 00015, Finland. TEL 358-9-15661, FAX 358-9-145650, http://www.kuvalehdet.fi/. Ed. Hannele Willberg. adv.: page EUR 950; trim 260 x 170. Circ: 8,559.

087.5   ROM   ISSN 1224-8797
TOM SI JERRY. Variant title: Sa Radem cu Tom si Jerry. Text in Romanian. 1996. m. ROL 250,000; ROL 25,000 newsstand/cover (effective 2002). **Document type:** *Magazine, Consumer.*
Published by: Egmont Romania, Piata Presei Libere nr. 1, corp B2, etaj 4, Bucharest, Romania. TEL 40-21-2246055, FAX 40-21-2246057, cc@ero.egmont.com, http://www.egmont.ro.

268   ISR   ISSN 0040-912X
TOM THUMB; a magazine for the young Jewish child. Text in English. 1960. m. USD 60 (effective 2000). adv. bk.rev. illus.
Published by: Etzb'oni Publishing House, P O Box 28110, Tel Aviv, 61280, Israel. FAX 972-3-5373906. Ed. Michael Shir. Circ: 35,000.

375   USA   ISSN 1068-865X
TOMORROW'S MORNING✳ ; news stories for kids. Text in English. 1992. w. bk.rev.; film rev.; play rev.; video rev.; music rev. illus. back issues avail. **Document type:** *Newspaper.*
Description: Contains news stories written for childrent ages 6 to 12. Includes articles about the arts, science, society, and sports as well as national and international news.
Related titles: Online - full text ed.: 1992 (from CompuServe Inc.); ♦ Supplement(s): Tomorrow's Morning Classroom Edition. ISSN 1085-0821.
Published by: Tomorrow's Morning, Inc., 269 S Beverly Dr, 985, Beverly Hills, CA 90212-3807. TEL 310-440-2778, 800-607-4410, FAX 310-476-6406, tomorrow@morning.com, http://morning.com. Ed., Pub. Adam Linter.

371.3   USA   ISSN 1085-0821
TOMORROW'S MORNING CLASSROOM EDITION✱ ; born to read. Text in English. 1996. bi-w. (Oct.-Apr.), m., (Sept.-May). USD 16.17. bk.rev.; film rev.; play rev.; video rev.; music rev. illus. back issues avail. **Document type:** *Newspaper.* **Description:** Contains news and stories written for elementary school students. Aims to educate children and help teachers put current events into the curriculum.
Related titles: Online - full text ed.: 1996 (from CompuServe Inc.); ♦ Supplement to: Tomorrow's Morning. ISSN 1068-865X.
Published by: Tomorrow's Morning, Inc., 269 S Beverly Dr, 985, Beverly Hills, CA 90212-3807. TEL 310-440-2778, 800-607-4410, FAX 610-476-6406, tomorrow@morning.com, http://morning.com. Ed., Pub. Adam Linter. Circ: 10,000 (paid).
Subscr. to: PO Box 388, Vandalia, OH 45377.

028.5   CHN
TONGHUA YU CHUANSHUO/FAIRY TALES AND LEGENDS. Text in Chinese. bi-m. CNY 2 per issue.
Published by: Zhongguo Minjian Wenyijia Xiehui, Shanxi Fenhui/China Folk Artists' Association, Shanxi Chapter, 62 Yingze Dajie, Taiyuan, Shanxi 030001, China. TEL 4048712. Ed. Li Weijia.

TOO COOL FOR GROWNUPS; bringing the power of the Internet into the classroom. see *EDUCATION*

028.5 790.13   DEU
TOP (BENNINGEN). Text in German. 1980. q. free. back issues avail.
Formerly: Schooltime
Published by: Publikum Verlag GmbH, Otto Hahn Str 10, Benningen Am Neckar, 71726, Germany. TEL 07144-18002. Circ: 5,000.

028.5   CZE   ISSN 1211-4901
TOP DIVKY. Text in Czech. 1994. m. adv. **Document type:** *Magazine, Consumer.*
Published by: Axel Springer Praha a.s., Strelnicna 1680/8, Prague 8, 182 21, Czech Republic. TEL 420-2-66193111, FAX 420-2-66193331, http://www.topdivka.cz, http:// www.axelspringer.cz. Ed. Marie Pisecka. Adv. contact Olga Torsova. page CZK 72,000; 205 x 285. Circ: 31,000 (paid).

TOP GEAR; discipleship studies for youth. see *RELIGIONS AND THEOLOGY—Protestant*

051 028.5   ITA   ISSN 1126-4373
TOP GIRL. Text in Italian. 1998. m. EUR 15.96 (effective 2004). adv. back issues avail. **Document type:** *Magazine, Consumer.* **Description:** Contains editorials about fashion, beauty, music, movies, sports and other things of interest to teenaged girls.
Published by: Gruner und Jahr - Mondadori SpA (Subsidiary of: Arnoldo Mondadori Editore SpA), Corso Monforte, 54, Milan, MI 20122, Italy. TEL 39-02-762101, FAX 39-02-76013439, info@gujm.it. Circ: 243,269.

028.5 371.33   USA
TOPICS✱ ; for today's students in touch with their world. Text in English. 1999. m. (during school year). **Document type:** *Magazine, Consumer.* **Description:** Offers middle- and high-school students a voice in and a connection to the world around them through articles written for and by teenagers. Contains curriculum-standards based material for English, language arts, and social studies classrooms.
Related titles: Supplement(s): Topics Online.
Published by: Topics Education Group, 809 West Hill St, Ste C, Charlotte, NC 28208. TEL 704-358-3198, 888-854-0132, FAX 704-358-3199, infoCS3@topics.mag.com, info@topicseducation.com, http://www.topicseducation.com. Ed. Bruce Nofsinger.

808.836   ITA   ISSN 1120-611X
TOPOLINO. Text in Italian. 1949. w. EUR 69.50 (effective 2005). illus. **Document type:** *Magazine, Consumer.*
Published by: Walt Disney Company Italia SpA (Subsidiary of: Arnoldo Mondadori Editore SpA), Via Sandro Sandri 1, Milan, MI 20121, Italy. TEL 39-02-29085150, FAX 39-02-29085162, redazione@topolino.it, http://www.topolino.it. Ed. Paolo Cavaglione. Pub. Mauro Lepore. R&P Silvia Figini. Adv. contact Paola Gonella.

058.82   NOR   ISSN 1502-2897
TOPP. Text in Norwegian. 1984. m. adv. **Document type:** *Magazine, Consumer.* **Description:** Contains a wide variety of articles and photos on pop music, movies, videos and celebrities.
Published by: Se og Hoer Forlaget A-S, Stenersgaten 2, Postboks 1164, Sentrum, Oslo, 0107, Norway. TEL 47-22-91-22-22, FAX 47-22-91-21-20. Circ: 43,860 (paid).

028.5   PRY   ISSN 1606-0830
TOPTEEN. Text in Spanish. m.
Media: Online - full text.
Published by: TeVeO, S.R. L., Ave. Espana, 560, Asuncion, Paraguay. TEL 595-21-221851, FAX 595-21-222199, topteen@teveo.com.py, martina@teveo.com.py, http://www.topteen.com.py/Topteen.html. Ed. Veronica Busto.

TORTOISE; the conservation magazine. see *ENVIRONMENTAL STUDIES*

A TOT OF ENGLISH; your English monthly. see *LINGUISTICS*

028.5   AUS
TOTAL GIRL. Text in English. m. AUD 39 domestic; AUD 45 in New Zealand; AUD 85 elsewhere; AUD 4.20 newsstand/cover (effective 2004). **Document type:** *Magazine, Consumer.*
Published by: Pacific Publications, 35-51 Mitchell St, McMahons Point, NSW 2060, Australia. TEL 61-2-94643300, FAX 61-2-94643375, subscriptions@pacpubs.com.au, http://www.totalgirl.com.au, http://www.pacificpubs.com.au. Circ: 84,492.

TOUCH. see *RELIGIONS AND THEOLOGY—Protestant*

028.5   FRA   ISSN 0296-8274
TOUPIE. Text in French. 1985. m. EUR 52 (effective 2005).
Published by: Milan Presse, 300 rue Leon Joulin, Toulouse, Cedex 1 31101, France. TEL 33-5-61766464, FAX 33-5-61766400. Ed. Mireille Fronty. Pub. Patrice Amen. Circ: 77,754.

028.5 910.09   ITA
TOURING GIOVANI. Text in Italian. 7/yr. membership. adv.
Published by: (Touring Club Italiano), Touring Editore s.r.l., Corso Italia, 10, Milan, MI 20122, Italy. TEL 02-852673, FAX 02-58300315, TELEX 312476 TCIADM. Ed. Giuseppe Bozzini. Circ: 55,000.

028.5   GBR   ISSN 0968-6940
TOYBOX. Text in English. 1993. m. GBP 15.50; GBP 0.99 newsstand/cover (effective 2003). adv. **Document type:** *Magazine, Consumer.* **Description:** Features children's favorite TV characters in a variety of stories and activities that make learning fun.
Published by: B B C Worldwide Ltd., 80 Wood Ln, London, W12 0TT, United Kingdom. TEL 44-20-84331070, FAX 44-20-84332231, bbcproducts@bbc.co.uk, http://www.bbcmagazines.com/toybox/index.html. Ed. Coralie Noakes. Adv. contact David Gibson. color page GBP 2,100; trim 226 x 300. Circ: 218,000 (paid). **Dist. by:** Frontline, Park House, 117 Park Rd, Peterborough, Cambs PE1 2TS, United Kingdom. TEL 44-1733-555161, FAX 44-1733-562788.

028.5   GBR
TOYBOX TEACH ME. Text in English. m. GBP 18; GBP 1.50 newsstand/cover (effective 2003). adv. **Document type:** *Magazine, Consumer.* **Description:** Contains educational activities and puzzles featuring popular BBC characters such as Bob the Builder, Tweenies and Postman Pat.
Published by: B B C Worldwide Ltd., 80 Wood Ln, London, W12 0TT, United Kingdom. TEL 44-20-84331070, FAX 44-20-84332231, bbcworldwide@bbc.co.uk, http://www.bbcmagazines.com/teachme/index.html.

369.4   DNK   ISSN 1602-0510
TRACK; Vilde Udfordringer. Text in Danish. 1970. 6/yr. adv. **Document type:** *Magazine, Consumer.* **Description:** For scouts ages 12-19.
Supersedes in part (in 2001): Spejd (0108-7967); Which was formed by the merger of (1918-1970): Pigespejderne; (1961-1970): Spejderbladet: Medlemsblad for KFUK-Spejderne i Danmark; (1960-1970): Spejdernes Magazin
Published by: Danske Spejderkorps, Arsenalgade 10, Copenhagen K, 1436, Denmark. TEL 45-32-64-00-50, http://www.dds.dk/medier. Ed. Morten Lykkeborg TEL 45-32-64-00-62. Adv. contact Peter Henrichsen TEL 45-32-64-00-61.

028.5   FRA   ISSN 1254-8626
TRANSFAC✱ ; l'evenement etudiant. Text in French. m. (10/yr.). **Description:** Covers today's fashion, movies, culture, travel, careers, training, multimedia.
Address: 42 bis, rue Sarette, Paris, 75014, France. Ed. Guy Ros. Pub. Philippe Cattelat.

TREE HOUSE CANADIAN FAMILY. see *CHILDREN AND YOUTH—About*

028.5   DEU   ISSN 0177-4719
TREFF; das spannende Schuelermagazin. Text in German. 1974. m. EUR 27.60; EUR 2.90 newsstand/cover (effective 2002). adv. **Document type:** *Magazine, Consumer.*
Published by: Velber im OZ Verlag GmbH, Guenterstalstr. 57, Freiburg, 79102, Germany. TEL 49-761-705780, FAX 49-761-7057839, butsch@oz-bpv.de, http:// www.treffmagazin.de, http://www.oz-verlag.com. Ed. Dietmar Beyer. Adv. contact Bernd Sandvoss. B&W page EUR 1,790, color page EUR 3,220. Circ: 62,742.

TREFFPUNKT JUGENDPRESSE. see *JOURNALISM*

028.5   CHE
TREFLE/KIM. Text in French, German. 1920. 9/yr. CHF 28, USD 20. adv. bk.rev. charts; illus. index.
Former titles (until 1986): Kim; Kim - Trefle (0023-141X)
Published by: Pfadibewegung Schweiz/Mouvement Scout de Suisse, PO Box, Bern 7, 3000, Switzerland. TEL 031-3110545, FAX 031-3119828. Circ: 6,000.

649   BEL   ISSN 0041-2279
TREMPLIN. Text in French. 1960. w. EUR 46.50 (effective 2005). illus. **Document type:** *Magazine.* **Description:** Offers youngsters ages 10-12 (grades 5 and 6) a variety of activities and articles.
Published by: Editions Averbode SA, Abdijstraat 1, BP 54, Averbode, 3271, Belgium. TEL 32-13-780111, FAX 32-13-776837. Ed. Jan Lembrechts.

TREND DISCOTEC. see *MUSIC*

028.5   ESP   ISSN 1134-3427
TRETZEVENTS; l'infantil. Text in Catalan. 1951. m. EUR 38.30 domestic; EUR 55.12 in Europe; USD 88 elsewhere (effective 2004). illus. **Document type:** *Magazine, Consumer.*
Former titles (until 1981): L' Infantil Tretzevents (1134-3419); (until 1972): L' Infantil (1134-3400)
Published by: Publicacions de l' Abadia de Montserrat, Ausias Marc 92-98, Barcelona, 08013, Spain. TEL 34-932-450303, FAX 34-932-473594, tretzevents@pamsa.com, pamsa@pamsa.com, http://www.pamsa.com. Ed. Montse Ginesta. Circ: 6,000.

TRIANGLE. see *TRAVEL AND TOURISM*

028.162   VEN   ISSN 0041-2902
TRICOLOR✱ ; revista Venezolana para los ninos. Text in Spanish. 1950. 9/yr. free. illus. index.
Published by: Ministerio de Educacion, c/o Ministerio de Relaciones Exteriores, Direccion de Relaciones Culturales, Caracas, Venezuela. Ed. Jose Quiaragua. Circ: 150,000.

TROTZDEM; das sozialistische Jugendmagazin. see *POLITICAL SCIENCE*

028.5 790.1 780   USA   ISSN 1044-954X
TUCSON TEEN. Variant title: Teen On-Line. Text in English. 1977. fortn. adv. bk.rev.; film rev.; music rev.; software rev.; tel.rev.; video rev. illus.; mkt. index. back issues avail. **Document type:** *Newspaper.* **Description:** Provides information, listings of events and internet connections for teenagers.
Media: Online - full text.
Published by: Southwest Alternatives Institute, Inc., PO Box 3355, Tucson, AZ 85722. TEL 520-623-3733, teens@emol.org, http://www.emol.org/emol/tucsonteen/. Pub. Robert E Zucker. Adv. contact Robert Laver. page USD 399. Circ: 5,000.

028.5   USA   ISSN 0191-3654
TURTLE MAGAZINE FOR PRESCHOOL KIDS. Variant title: Turtle. Text in English. 1979. bi-m. USD 15.95 domestic; USD 19.95 foreign (effective 2005). adv. bk.rev.; video rev. illus. back issues avail.; reprints avail. **Document type:** *Magazine, Consumer.* **Description:** Provides a publication filled with a colorful assortment of entertaining stories and poems for read-aloud times. Dot-to-dots, hidden pictures, mazes, and other puzzle pages aid in sequencing skills and eye-hand coordination.
Related titles: Online - full text ed.: (from EBSCO Publishing, ProQuest Information & Learning).
Published by: (Benjamin Franklin Literary and Medical Society, Inc.), Children's Better Health Institute, 1100 Waterway Blvd, PO Box 567, Indianapolis, IN 46206. customercare@cbhi.org, g.joray@cbhi.org, http://www.turtlemag.org, http://www.cbhi.org. Ed. Terry Harshman. Pub. Greg Joray. R&P Daniel Lee. adv.: color page USD 7,000; trim 7.63 x 10.13. Circ: 370,000.
Subscr. to: PO Box 420235, Palm Coast, FL 32142. TEL 800-829-5579.

028.5   MEX
TUS ROLLOS. Text in Spanish. 1993. m. MXP 6 per issue. adv. bk.rev. **Document type:** *Consumer.* **Description:** Covers music, video games, health and beauty, food, toys and crafts, current events and social issues, and celebrities.
Published by: Editorial Jakan S.A. de C.V., PATRICIO SANZ 1445, Col Del Valle, Mexico City, DF 03100, Mexico. TEL 575-90-09. Ed. Jorge Planella Gil. **Co-publisher:** Magno Central de Publicaciones, S.A. de C.V.

TUTTI INSIEME; il mensile per il tuo italiano. see *LINGUISTICS*

TUTTO DISCOTECA DANCE. see *MUSIC*

790.192205   GBR   ISSN 1467-7423
TWEENIES MAGAZINE. Text in English. 1999. m. GBP 18.20; GBP 1.45 newsstand/cover (effective 2003). **Document type:** *Magazine, Consumer.* **Description:** Includes songs to sing, things to make, stories to read, and other activities involving the Tweenies.
Published by: B B C Worldwide Ltd., 80 Wood Ln, London, W12 0TT, United Kingdom. TEL 44-20-84331070, FAX 44-20-84332231, bbcproducts@bbc.co.uk, http://www.bbcmagazines.com/tweenies/index.html.

028.5   GBR   ISSN 0262-3021
TWINKLE. Text in English. 1968. w. GBP 31.20; GBP 0.60 newsstand/cover (effective 1999). illus. **Document type:** *Consumer.* **Description:** Offers young readers enjoyable puzzles and challenging stories.

C

▼ *new title*   ➤ *refereed*   ✱ *unverified*   ♦ *full entry avail.*

Published by: D.C. Thomson & Co. Ltd., 80 Kingsway East, Dundee, Angus, Scotland DD4 8SL, United Kingdom. FAX 44-1382-462097, comment@dcthomson.co.uk, http://www.dcthomson.co.uk. **Subscr. to:** World Wide Subscription Service Ltd., Unit 4, Gibbs Reed Farm, Ticehurst, E Sussex TN5 7HE, United Kingdom. TEL 44-1580-200657, FAX 44-1580-200616.

028.5 USA ISSN 1094-4257
TWIST. Text in English. 1997. m. (except Nov.-Dec. & Jan.-Feb. combined). USD 14.97 domestic; CND 24.97 foreign (effective 2003). illus. **Document type:** *Magazine, Consumer.* **Description:** Lifestyle magazine aimed at the teen market.
Published by: Heinrich Bauer Publishing Company, L.P., 270 Sylvan Ave, Englewood, NJ 07632. TEL 201-569-6699, 800-457-4443, FAX 201-569-3584, http://www.twistmagazine.com/. Ed. Lisa Lombardi.

028.5 POL ISSN 1509-3298
TWIST. Text in Polish. 2000. m. PLZ 4 newsstand/cover (effective 2003). adv. **Document type:** *Magazine, Consumer.*
Published by: Wydawnictwo Bauer Sp. z o.o. (Subsidiary of: Heinrich Bauer Verlag), ul. Motorowa 1, Warsaw, 04-035, Poland. TEL 48-22-5170500, FAX 48-22-5170125, twist@bauer.pl, kontakt@bauer.pl, http://www.bauer.pl. Ed. Monika Maciag. Adv. contact Katarzyna Jablonska. page PLZ 18,600; trim 215 x 286.

028.5 USA
TZINE. Text in English. 2000. 6/yr. adv. **Description:** Articles cover a wide variety of topics for teens.
Published by: Campus Ad-Network, 800 S Pacific Coast Hwy, 8-295, Redondo Beach, CA 90277. TEL 310-792-0630, FAX 310-540-0621, inquiry@campusadnetwork.com, http://www.tzine.com/, http://www.capusadnetwork.com. Pub. Milt Lane.

TZIVOS HASHEM CHILDREN'S NEWSLETTER. see *ETHNIC INTERESTS*

028.5 USA ISSN 0895-9471
U S KIDS. Text in English. 1987. 8/yr. USD 15.95; USD 2.95 newsstand/cover (effective 2005). adv. back issues avail. **Document type:** *Magazine, Consumer.* **Description:** Publishes true-life stories and articles promoting sports, health and safety for children ages 5-10.
Related titles: Online - full text ed.: (from bigchalk, EBSCO Publishing, Gale Group, ProQuest Information & Learning).
Indexed: ICM, MagInd, RGYP.
Published by: (Benjamin Franklin Literary and Medical Society, Inc.), Children's Better Health Institute, 1100 Waterway Blvd, PO Box 567, Indianapolis, IN 46206. customercare@cbhi.org, g.joray@cbhi.org, http://www.uskidsmag.org, http://www.cbhi.org. Eds. Daniel Lee, Dr. Cory Servaas. Pub. Dr. Cory Servaas. R&P Daniel Lee. adv.: color page USD 5,950; trim 10.88 x 8. Circ: 225,000. **Subscr. to:** PO Box 420235, Palm Coast, FL 32142. TEL 800-829-5579.

U S Y S A NATIONAL DIRECTORY. see *SPORTS AND GAMES—Ball Games*

248.845 USA ISSN 1093-2615
U U & ME!; a Unitarian Universalist magazine for kids. (Unitarian Universalist) Text in English. 1997. q. USD 17.95 domestic; USD 19.95 in Canada; USD 21.95 elsewhere (effective 2003). **Document type:** *Magazine, Consumer.* **Description:** Includes fiction and non-fiction pieces dealing with religious, social, and ethical issues.
Published by: Unitarian Universalist, Church of the Larger Fellowship, 25 Beacon St, Boston, MA 02108. TEL 617-742-2100, FAX 617-523-4123, clf@uua.org, http://www.uua.org/uume/, http://www.uua.org/clf. Ed. Betsy Hill Williams. Circ: 1,500.

UCITELJ/TEACHER. see *EDUCATION—Computer Applications*

028.5 SVK
UJ IFJUSAG. Text in Hungarian. w.
Published by: Smena Publishing House, Prazska 11, Bratislava, 81284, Slovakia.

028.5 USA
ULTIMATE MARVEL. Text in English. 2001. m. USD 3.99 newsstand/cover (effective 2001). **Document type:** *Consumer.*
Published by: Marvel Comics Group, 387 Park Ave S, New York, NY 10016. Ed. Joe Quesada.

331.702 DNK ISSN 0107-7783
UNGDOMSKALENDER; ideer til aaret skolen. Text in Danish. 1983. a. DKK 175 (effective 1998). adv. bk.rev. illus.
Published by: Ole Camaae Ed. & Pub., Lerbjergstien 18, Birkeroed, 3460, Denmark. TEL 45-48-17-62-82, FAX 45-48-17-78-80. Circ: 2,300.

UNITED STATES BOARD ON BOOKS FOR YOUNG PEOPLE. NEWSLETTER; building bridges of understanding through children's and young adult books. see *PUBLISHING AND BOOK TRADE*

UNITED STATES YOUTH SOCCER. see *SPORTS AND GAMES—Ball Games*

028.5 ZAF ISSN 0257-8697
UPBEAT★; the youth magazine for all. Text in English. 1981. 11/yr. ZAR 22 domestic; ZAR 65 foreign. adv. illus. back issues avail. **Document type:** *Consumer.* **Description:** Educational magazine for youth and teachers in South Africa. Main purpose is to upgrade English skills and encourage reading.
Indexed: ISAP.
Published by: S A C H E D, Allied Bldg, 236 Bree St, Johannesburg, 2001, South Africa. TEL 011-333-9746, FAX 011-333-2297. Ed. Harriet Perlman. Adv. contact Barbara Shaffer. Circ: 63,000. **Subscr. to:** PO Box 11350, Johannesburg 2000, South Africa.

VAMOS; tu revista en espanol. see *LINGUISTICS*

028.5 DEU ISSN 0934-8786
VANESSAS ZEITGEIST. Text in German. 1987. q. USD 5. adv. bk.rev. back issues avail.
Address: Oldenburger Str 13A, Oberhausen, 46149, Germany. TEL 0208-669872. Ed. Marc Mulia. Circ: 5,000.

028.5 SVK
VCIELKA. Text in Slovak. 24/yr.
Related titles: Microform ed.: (from EVP).
Published by: Smena Publishing House, Prazska 11, Bratislava, 81284, Slovakia.

028.5 SWE ISSN 0346-4105
VECKO-REVYN. Variant title: Nya Veckorevyn. Text in Swedish. 1935. 26/yr. SEK 699 (effective 2001). adv. bk.rev.; dance rev.; film rev.; music rev.; rec.rev.; tel.rev.; video rev.; Website rev. illus. **Document type:** *Magazine, Consumer.* **Description:** Publication for teen-age girls.
Formerly (until vol. 32, 1937): Vecko-Revyn med Damernas Vaerld
Related titles: Supplement(s): Svepet.
Published by: Bonnier Tidsskrifter AB, Sveavaegen 53, Stockholm, 10544, Sweden. TEL 46-8-736-52-00, http://www.veckorevyn.net. Ed. Niklas Sessler. Adv. contact Elsbrit Forsstroem. color page SEK 39,500; trim 190 x 265. Circ: 86,700.

028.5 CZE ISSN 1210-0897
VEDA, TECHNIKA A MY/SCIENCE, TECHNOLOGY AND WE. Text in Czech. 1946. 12/yr. CZK 156. adv. bk.rev. **Description:** Tells its readers about the latest trends of development in science and technology, popularizes leading experts in these spheres, inspires creative thinking, deepens young people's self-education and helps them to choose their field of study and profession.
Former titles (until 1990): Veda a Tachnika Mlodezi (0322-9017); (until 1954): Mlady Technik
Published by: Mlada Fronta, Radlicka 61, Prague, 15002, Czech Republic. TEL 54-49-41, FAX 54-51-82, TELEX 123302. Ed. Z Bares. Circ: 35,700. **Dist. by:** PNS, Kafkova 19, Prague 6 160 00, Czech Republic.

028.5 BRA ISSN 1415-5311
AP211
VEJA KID MAIS. Text in Portuguese. 1998. m. BRL 45.60; BRL 3.80 newsstand/cover (effective 1999). adv. **Document type:** *Magazine, Consumer.* **Description:** Contains articles that cover local attractions, events and activities of interest to children. Also covers education, vacations and school news.
Related titles: E-mail ed.; Online - full text ed.
Published by: Editora Abril, S.A., Av. das Nacoes Unidas, 7221, 11 andar Pinheiros, Sao Paulo, SP 05425-902, Brazil. TEL 55-011-30374130, FAX 55-011-30374427, relacoes.corporativas@abril.com.br, http://www.uol.com.br/abriljovem. Ed. Andrea Fornes. Adv. contact Juliana Demoura. Circ: 22,000.

051.13 028.5 CAN ISSN 1700-1005
VERVE (TORONTO). Text in English. 1998. bi-m. CND 15 (effective 2003). **Document type:** *Magazine, Consumer.*
Formerly (until 2000): Bang (1487-3842)
Published by: Youth Culture Group, 401 Richmond St W, Ste 245, Toronto, ON M5V 1X3, Canada. TEL 416-595-1313, FAX 416-595-1312, info@youthculture.com, http://www.vervegirl.com/, http://www.youthculture.com/. Ed. Charmaine Noronha.

028.5 RUS ISSN 0320-8044
VESELYE KARTINKI; detskii yumoristicheskii zhurnal. Text in Russian. 1956. m. USD 49 foreign (effective 2005). adv. bk.rev. illus. **Document type:** *Magazine, Consumer.* —East View.
Published by: Redaktsiya Zhurnala Veselye Kartinki, Novodmitrovskaya ul 5-a, Moscow, 125015, Russian Federation. TEL 7-095-2858894, FAX 7-095-2857274. Ed. R A Varshamov. Circ: 500,000. **Dist. by:** M K - Periodica, ul Gilyarovskogo 39, Moscow 129110, Russian Federation. TEL 7-095-2845008, FAX 7-095-2813798, info@periodicals.ru, http://www.mkniga.ru.

028.5 RUS
VESELYE KARTINKI O PRIRODE. Text in Russian. m. USD 99 in United States. illus.
Published by: Redaktsiya Zhurnala Veselye Kartinki, Novodmitrovskaya ul 5-a, Moscow, 125015, Russian Federation. TEL 7-095-2851920, FAX 7-095-2857274. Ed. T A Varhamov. **US dist. addr.:** East View Information Services, 3020 Harbor Ln. N., Minneapolis, MN 55447. TEL 612-550-0961.

028.5 RUS
VESELYE MEDVEZHATA. Text in Russian. m. USD 125 in United States.
Published by: Izdatel'skii Dom Kedr, Izmailovskoe shosse 71, korp d, Moscow, 105613, Russian Federation. TEL 7-095-1665114, FAX 7-095-1665114. Ed. S A Panfilov.

VEZETOK LAPJA/BULLETIN OF HUNGARIAN SCOUT LEADERS AND PARENTS. see *CLUBS*

028.5 780.92 DNK ISSN 0042-496X
VI UNGE. Text in Danish. 1958. 12/yr. DKK 384; DKK 32 per issue (effective 2004). illus. **Document type:** *Magazine, Consumer.* **Description:** Fashion trends, hitlists, hottest stars, and reports of interest for young girls.
Incorporates (1986-2000): Mix (0902-8137)
Published by: Aller International A-S, Marielundsvej 46 E, Herlev, 2730, Denmark. TEL 45-44-858888, FAX 45-44-858887, redaktionen@viunge.dk, reception@aller.dk, http://www.viunge.dk, http://www.aller.dk. Ed. Katrine Memborg. Circ: 52,066.

028.5 BRA
VIDA INFANTIL. Text in Portuguese. m.
Published by: Carlos Goncalves Fidalgo, Ed. & Pub., Rua Riachuelo 414, Rio De Janeiro, GB, Brazil.

028.5 BRA
VIDA JUVENIL. Text in Portuguese. m.
Published by: Carlos Goncalves Fidalgo, Ed. & Pub., Rua Riachuelo 414, Rio De Janeiro, GB, Brazil.

028.5 059.959 VNM ISSN 0049-6375
VIETNAM YOUTH. Text in English. irreg. illus.
Indexed: BAS.
Published by: (Vietnam Youth Federation), Vietnam National Union of Students, 64 Ba Trieu St, Hanoi, Viet Nam.

371.3 IND
VIJAYAVEEDHI. Text in Malayalam. 1994. w. INR 3 newsstand/cover.
Published by: Malayala Manorama Co. Ltd., P O Box 26, Kottayam, Kerala 686 001, India. FAX 91-481-562479, editor@malayalamanorama.com, customersupport@mm.co.in, http://www.malayalamanorama.com. Ed. K M Mathew. Pub. Jacob Mathew. adv.: B&W page INR 6,000. Circ: 63,000.

▼ **VINSKI.** see *LITERATURE*

VITA DELL'INFANZIA. see *EDUCATION*

VITA E SALUTE JUNIOR; rivista mensile per ragazzi che vogliono crescere e capire. see *PHYSICAL FITNESS AND HYGIENE*

028.5 BEL ISSN 0773-1027
VLAAMSE FILMPJES. Text in Dutch. 1930. 39/yr. EUR 37 (effective 2005). film rev. illus. **Document type:** *Magazine, Consumer.* **Description:** Discusses topics of interest to young readers 11 and older.
Former titles (until 19??): Vlaamse Filmkens (0773-1035); (until 1946): Vlaamsche Filmkens (0773-1043)
Related titles: ♦ French ed.: Recits Express. ISSN 1373-2404.
Published by: Uitgeverij Averbode NV, Abdijstraat 1, Postbus 54, Averbode, 3271, Belgium. TEL 32-13-780111, FAX 32-13-780183, http://www.averbode.be. Ed. Theo Lenaerts.

028.5 USA ISSN 0042-8256
E184.S65
VOICE OF YOUTH. Text in English, Slovenian. 1922. m. membership. bk.rev. bibl.
Published by: Slovene National Benefit Society, 247 W Allegheny Rd, Imperial, PA 15126-9774. TEL 724-695-1100, 800-843-7675, FAX 724-695-1555. Ed., R&P Jay Sedmak. Circ: 4,000.

VOILA LE FRANCAIS. see *LINGUISTICS*

VOLLTREFFER. see *RELIGIONS AND THEOLOGY—Protestant*

028.5 DEU ISSN 0936-9686
VORHANG AUF (SIPPLINGEN); Zeitschrift fuer Kinder und Eltern. Text in German. 1989. q. EUR 31 domestic; EUR 34 foreign; EUR 6.60 newsstand/cover (effective 2005). back issues avail. **Document type:** *Magazine, Consumer.*
Published by: Waldow Verlag, Im Breitenweingarten 2a, Sipplingen, 78354, Germany. TEL 49-7551-308790, FAX 49-7551-308791, http://www.waldowverlag.de. Ed., Pub., Adv. contact Eckehard Waldow.

028.5 RUS
VOROBYSHEK. Text in Russian. s-a. RUR 160 (effective 2002). 16 p./no.; **Description:** Focuses on the importance of play in toddler (ages 3-5) development. Includes problems to develop speech, social development, reading and writing, and numerical agility.
Published by: Izdatel'skii Dom Karapuz, Izmailovskoe shosse 48a, Moscow, 105318, Russian Federation. TEL 7-095-9182810, http://www.karapuz.com.

053.1 DEU ISSN 1618-6729
VOYEUR. Text in German. 1997. 8/yr. EUR 6 newsstand/cover (effective 2003). adv. **Document type:** *Magazine, Consumer.*
Related titles: Online - full text ed.
Published by: youngkombi GmbH, Hildesheimer Str 307, Hannover, 30519, Germany. TEL 49-511-2707080, FAX 49-511-27070888, redaktion@voyeur.de, http://www.voyeur.de, http://www.youngkombi.de. adv.: color page EUR 25,255. Circ: 651,500 (paid and controlled).

VRIEND. see *HANDICAPPED—Hearing Impaired*

028.5 FRA ISSN 1626-5394
W A D. (We'ar Different) Text in French. 1999. q. **Document type:** *Magazine, Consumer.*
Related titles: ♦ Supplement(s): W A D. Hors-Serie. ISSN 1630-3903.
Address: 31 rue Chapon, Paris, 75 003, France. TEL 33-1-4478-0807, FAX 33-1-4478-0702, info@wadmag.com, http://www.wadmag.com/, http://www. wadmag.com. Ed. Bruno Collin.

028.5 FRA ISSN 1630-3903
W A D. HORS-SERIE. (We'ar Different) Text in Multiple languages. 2001. irreg. **Document type:** *Consumer.*
Related titles: ♦ Supplement to: W A D. ISSN 1626-5394.
Published by: W A D, 31 rue Chapon, Paris, 75 003, France. TEL 33-1-4478-0807, FAX 33-1-4478-0702, info@wadmag.com, http://www. wadmag.com. Ed. Bruno Collin.

305.235 HUN ISSN 0049-8076
W F D Y NEWS. Text in English. 1972. bi-m. USD 4. adv.
Related titles: Spanish ed.
Published by: World Federation of Democratic Youth, Frangepan utca 16, PO Box 147, Budapest, 1389, Hungary. TEL 36-1-3443830. Ed. Mun Chol. Adv. contact Halim Awad. Circ: 2,000.

028.5 DEU
W.I.T.C.H.; das magische Maedchenmagazin. (Will, Irma, Taranee, Cornelia, Hay-Lin) Text in German. 2001. m. EUR 27.60; EUR 2.30 newsstand/cover (effective 2005). adv. **Document type:** *Magazine, Consumer.* **Description:** Contains stories, comics, puzzles and games featuring a group of cartoon character girls who are into magic and witchcraft.
Published by: Egmont Ehapa Verlag GmbH, Wallstr 59, Berlin, 10179, Germany. TEL 49-30-240080, FAX 49-30-24008599, leserservice@ehapa.de, http://www.ehapa.de. Adv. contact Andrea Kappel. color page EUR 3,500. Circ: 97,990 (paid and controlled).

741.5 FIN ISSN 1458-9036
W.I.T.C.H. (Will, Irma, Taranee, Cornelia, Hay Lin) Text in Finnish. 2002. m. EUR 3.90 newsstand/cover (effective 2004). **Document type:** *Magazine, Consumer.*
Published by: Sanoma Magazines Finland Corporation, Hoylaamotie 1 D, P.O. Box 100, Helsinki, 00040, Finland. TEL 358-9-1201, FAX 358-9-1205171, info@sanomamagazines.fi, http://www.sistersclub.net/witch/, http://www.sanomamagazines.fi.

W O W; the juniors' magazine of the Baptist Missionary Society. see *RELIGIONS AND THEOLOGY—Protestant*

059.927 028.5 UAE
AL-WA'I. Text in Arabic. 1983. m. per issue exchange basis. **Description:** Covers cultural and Islamic topics of interest to young people in the U.A.E.
Published by: Daba Sports Club, Cultural Group/Nadi Daba al-Riyadi, Al-Lajnah al-Thiqafiyyah, P.O. Box 12002, Fujairah, United Arab Emirates. TEL 44216. Ed. Abdullah Said Rashid. Circ: 500.

333.72 FRA ISSN 0998-2221
WAKOU; pour les petits curieux de nature. Text in French. 1988. m. EUR 52 (effective 2005). **Description:** For children 3 to 7 years old who are interested in nature.
Published by: Milan Presse, 300 rue Leon Joulin, Toulouse, Cedex 1 31101, France. TEL 33-5-61766411, FAX 33-5-61766567, http://www.milanpresse.com. Pub. Patrice Amen. **Subscr. to:** BP 82, Fenouillet 31150, France.

028.5 BEL ISSN 0165-1293
WALT DISNEY'S DONALD DUCK. Variant title: Donald Duck. Text in Dutch. 1952. w. EUR 53.82 (effective 2003). illus. **Document type:** *Magazine, Consumer.* **Description:** Offers very young readers entertaining stories and activities.
Published by: Sanoma Magazines Belgium, Telecomlaan 5-7, Diegem, 1831, Belgium. TEL 32-2-7762211, FAX 32-2-776-2317, http://www.sanoma-magazines.be/HomePage.aspx?flash=1&Language=nl.

028.5 DEU
WALT DISNEY'S LUSTIGES TASCHENBUCH. Variant title: Lustiges Taschenbuch. Text in German. 1967. m. EUR 43.80; EUR 3.95 newsstand/cover (effective 2005). adv. illus. back issues avail. **Document type:** *Magazine, Consumer.*
Published by: Egmont Ehapa Verlag GmbH, Wallstr 59, Berlin, 10179, Germany. TEL 49-30-240080, FAX 49-30-24008599, leserservice@ehapa.de, http://www.lustiges-taschenbuch.de, http://www.ehapa.de. Ed. Harald Saalbach. Adv. contact Andrea Scheiterle. color page EUR 9,800; trim 108 x 165. Circ: 273,365 (paid and controlled).

028.5 DEU ISSN 1437-2185
WALT DISNEY'S MICKY MAUS. Variant title: Micky Maus. Text in German. 1951. w. (Thu.). EUR 96.20; EUR 1.90 newsstand/cover (effective 2005). adv. film rev.; tel.rev. illus. back issues avail. **Document type:** *Magazine, Consumer.*
Related titles: Online - full text ed.
Published by: Egmont Ehapa Verlag GmbH, Wallstr 59, Berlin, 10179, Germany. TEL 49-30-240080, FAX 49-30-24008599, leserservice@ehapa.de, http://www.micky-maus.de, http://www.ehapa.de. Ed. Susanne Pohlmann. Adv. contact Olaf Hansen. color page EUR 15,800; trim 154 x 224. Circ: 429,498 (paid). **Subscr. to:** Vertriebsservice Egmont Ehapa Verlag, Postfach 810640, Stuttgart 70523, Germany. TEL 49-711-7252225, FAX 49-7252392.

028.5 CHN ISSN 1003-4013
WANPI WAWA/NAUGHTY BABY. Text in Chinese. 1989. m. CNY 1.50 per issue.
Published by: Sichuan Shaonian Ertong Chubanshe, 3, Yandao Jie, Chengdu, Sichuan 610016, China. TEL 660232, FAX 028-660320, TELEX 600324 SJCPH CN. Ed. Wang Jitong.

333.72 FRA ISSN 0984-2314
WAPITI; les sciences de la nature. Text in French. 1987. m. EUR 52 (effective 2005). **Description:** For children 7 to 13 years old who are interested in nature.
Published by: Milan Presse, 300 rue Leon Joulin, Toulouse, Cedex 1 31101, France. TEL 33-5-61766464, FAX 33-5-61766400, webmaster@milanpresse.com, http://www.milanpresse.com. Ed. Claudine Masson. Pub. Patrice Amen. Circ: 105,380.

WATERWAYS; poetry in the mainstream. see *LITERATURE—Poetry*

028.5 CHN
WAWA HUABAO/ILLUSTRATED PERIODICAL FOR KINDERGARTENERS. Text in Chinese. 1981. m. USD 24. illus. **Document type:** *Consumer.* **Description:** Contains stories, fairy tales, and poems for children under five years old.
Published by: Shaonian Ertong Chubanshe/Juvenile & Children Publishing House, 1538 Yan an Xilu, Shanghai, 200052, China. TEL 86-21-6282-3025, FAX 86-21-6282-1726. Ed. Hong Zunian. **Dist. in US by:** China Books & Periodicals Inc, 360 Swift Ave., Ste. 48, S San Fran, CA 94080-6220. TEL 415-282-2994.

028.5 DEU
WE ARE ONE WORLD. Abbreviated title: W A O W. Text in German. 1991. a. free. **Document type:** *Academic/Scholarly.* **Description:** Facts and stories about African culture.
Published by: Kindernothilfe e.V., Duesseldorfer Landstr 180, Duisburg, 47249, Germany. TEL 49-203-7789-0, FAX 49-203-7789118, info@kindernothilfe.de, http://www.kindernothilfe.de. Ed. Gunhild Aiyub. Circ: 14,000 (controlled).

WEEKLY BIBLE READER. see *RELIGIONS AND THEOLOGY*

WEEKLY READER. GRADE 1 EDITION. see *EDUCATION—Teaching Methods And Curriculum*

WEEKLY READER. GRADE 2 EDITION. see *EDUCATION—Teaching Methods And Curriculum*

371.911 028.5 USA
WEEKLY READER. GRADE 2 EDITION (LARGE PRINT EDITION). Text in English. 25/yr. (during school yr.). USD 3.55 per academic year (effective 2004 - 2005). **Document type:** *Newspaper, Consumer.*
Media: Large Type (16 pt.). **Related titles:** Braille ed.
Published by: American Printing House for the Blind, Inc., 1839 Frankfort Ave, Louisville, KY 40206. TEL 502-895-2405, 800-223-1839, FAX 502-899-2274, info@aph.org, http://www.aph.org.

WEEKLY READER. GRADE 3 EDITION. see *EDUCATION—Teaching Methods And Curriculum*

371.911 028.5 USA
WEEKLY READER. GRADE 3 EDITION (LARGE PRINT EDITION). Text in English. 25/yr. (during school yr.). USD 3.75 per academic year (effective 2004 - 2005). **Document type:** *Newspaper, Consumer.*
Media: Large Type (16 pt.). **Related titles:** Braille ed.
Published by: American Printing House for the Blind, Inc., 1839 Frankfort Ave, Louisville, KY 40206. TEL 502-895-2405, 800-223-1839, FAX 502-899-2274, info@aph.org, http://www.aph.org.

WEEKLY READER. GRADE 4 EDITION. see *EDUCATION—Teaching Methods And Curriculum*

371.911 028.5 USA
WEEKLY READER. GRADE 4 EDITION (LARGE PRINT EDITION). Text in English. 25/yr. (during school yr.). USD 3.85 per academic year (effective 2004 - 2005). **Document type:** *Newspaper, Consumer.*
Media: Large Type (16 pt.). **Related titles:** Braille ed.
Published by: American Printing House for the Blind, Inc., 1839 Frankfort Ave, Louisville, KY 40206. TEL 502-895-2405, 800-223-1839, FAX 502-899-2274, info@aph.org, http://www.aph.org.

WEEKLY READER. K EDITION. see *EDUCATION—Teaching Methods And Curriculum*

372.4 USA
WEEKLY READER. PRE-K EDITION. Text in English. 1980. 28/yr. (w., during school yr.). USD 24.95 per academic year; USD 4.95 per academic year 5 or more subscriptions (effective 2004 - 2005). **Document type:** *Newspaper, Consumer.* **Description:** Supports nursery school and pre-kindergarten language arts curricula.
Former titles (until 1999): Weekly Reader, Pre-K Edition (0890-3174); Weekly Reader Funday (0271-1443)
Related titles: Online - full text ed.: (from EBSCO Publishing, Gale Group).
Published by: Weekly Reader Corp. (Subsidiary of: W R C Media Inc.), 200 First Stamford Pl, PO Box 120023, Stamford, CT 06912-0023. TEL 203-705-3500, 800-446-3355, FAX 203-705-1662, science@weeklyreader.com, http://www.weeklyreader.com. Ed. Charles Piddock. Pub. Peter Esposito. R&P Cathy Pekai TEL 203-705-3426. Circ: 430,000 (paid).

C

WEEKLY READER. SENIOR EDITION. see *EDUCATION—Teaching Methods And Curriculum*

371.911 028.5 USA
WEEKLY READER. SENIOR EDITION (LARGE PRINT EDITION). Text in English. 25/yr. (during school yr.). USD 3.95 per academic year (effective 2004 - 2005). **Document type:** *Newspaper, Consumer.*
Media: Large Type (16 pt.). **Related titles:** Braille ed.
Published by: American Printing House for the Blind, Inc., 1839 Frankfort Ave, Louisville, KY 40206. TEL 502-895-2405, 800-223-1839, FAX 502-899-2274, info@aph.org, http://www.aph.org.

WEITE WELT; illustrierte Kinderzeitschrift ab 10 Jahre. see *RELIGIONS AND THEOLOGY*

WELLSPRINGS/MA'AYANOT; a quarterly journal exploring the inner dimensions of Torah and Jewish life. see *RELIGIONS AND THEOLOGY—Judaic*

028.5 DEU
WENDY. Text in German. 1986. w. EUR 1.90 newsstand/cover (effective 2005). adv. **Document type:** *Magazine, Consumer.* **Description:** For girls with an interest in horses.
Published by: Egmont Ehapa Verlag GmbH, Wallstr 59, Berlin, 10179, Germany. TEL 49-30-240080, FAX 49-30-24008599, leserservice@ehapa.de, http://www.wendy.de, http://www.ehapa.de. Adv. contact Olaf Hansen. page EUR 6,900; 210 x 280. Circ: 165,320 (paid).

028.5 USA
WE'RE NEXT✶; for us, by us. Text in English. 1992. 10/yr. **Description:** To stimulate teenagers' reading, writing and creativity.
Address: Charles Walter, Jr, 7090 S Union Park Ave, Ste 500, Midvale, UT 84047. TEL 505-395-2053. Ed. John Cox. Circ: 200,000 (controlled).

DE WERELD VAN HET JONGE KIND. see *EDUCATION*

WHAT DO CHILDREN & YOUNG ADULTS READ NEXT?. see *LITERATURE*

028.5 639.9 CAN ISSN 1492-014X
WILD; canada's wildlife magazine for kids. Text in English. 1984. 8/yr. back issues avail. **Document type:** *Magazine, Consumer.*
Formerly (until 1995): Ranger Rick (0828-8739)
Related titles: Online - full text ed.: (from EBSCO Publishing).
Indexed: CBCARef, CPerl, MASUSE.
Published by: Canadian Wildlife Federation, 350 Michael Cowpland Dr, Kanata, ON K2M 2W1, Canada. TEL 613-599-9594, 800-563-9453, FAX 613-599-4428, info@cwf-fcf.org, http://www.cwf-fcf.org. Circ: 30,000 (paid).

WILD ANIMAL BABY. see *CONSERVATION*

▼ new title ➤ refereed ✶ unverified ♦ full entry avail.

333.95416 USA ISSN 1092-0331
WILD OUTDOOR WORLD. Short title: W.O.W. Text in English. 1993. 5/yr. USD 16.95 domestic; USD 27.95 in Canada & Mexico; USD 46.95 elsewhere (effective 2004). bk.rev.; Website rev. index. **Document type:** *Magazine, Consumer.* **Description:** Covers North American wildlife, wildlife habitat conservation, outdoor recreation for 8-12 year olds.
Former titles: Falcon for Kids (1085-5572); (until 1996): Falcon Magazine for Kids (1085-4126)
Published by: Joy Publications, LLC, 2291 W Broadway, PO Box 8249, Missoula, MT 59807-8249. TEL 406-523-4500, 800-225-5355, FAX 406-523-4550, ssamson@quest.net, http://www.wowmag.com, http://www.elkfoundation.org. Ed. Kay Morton Ellerhoff. R&P Carolyn Underwood. Circ: 300,000 (paid).

028.5 FRA ISSN 0296-8576
WINNIE. Text in French. m. **Document type:** *Consumer.* **Description:** Educational magazine for children 3 to 7 years old.
Published by: Disney Hachette Presse, 10 rue Thierry le Luron, Levallois Perret, Cedex 92592, France. TEL 33-1-41378500, FAX 33-1-41348989. Ed. Gilles Heylen. Circ: 95,000.

028.5 DEU
WINNIE PUUH. Text in German. 1997. m. EUR 30; EUR 2.50 newsstand/cover (effective 2005). adv. **Document type:** *Magazine, Consumer.*
Published by: Egmont Ehapa Verlag GmbH, Wallstr 59, Berlin, 10179, Germany. TEL 49-30-240080, FAX 49-30-24008599, leserservice@ehapa.de, http://www.ehapa.de. Adv. contact Olaf Hansen. page EUR 5,400; 280 x 210. Circ: 149,274 (paid).

028.5 GBR ISSN 1357-6194
WINNIE THE POOH. Text in English. 1995. fortn. GBP 1.30 newsstand/cover. adv. **Document type:** *Consumer.* **Description:** Contains fun stories and activities involving Winnie the Pooh and all his friends.
Published by: Egmont Fleetway Ltd., Egmont House, Pl, Flat 25, 31 Tavistock Rd, London, W11 1AS, United Kingdom. TEL 44-20-7344-6400, FAX 44-207-388-4152. **Dist. by:** Seymour Distribution Ltd, 86 Newman St, London W1T 3EX, United Kingdom. FAX 44-207-396-8002, enquiries@seymour.co.uk.

C

028.5 AUS
WINNIE THE POOH & FRIENDS. Text in English. m. AUD 39; AUD 3.50 newsstand/cover (effective 2002). adv. **Document type:** *Magazine, Consumer.* **Description:** Filled with stories, puzzles, guessing games, crafts and coloring pages for children.
Published by: A C P Publishing Pty. Ltd., 54-58 Park St, Sydney, NSW 1028, Australia. TEL 61-2-9282-8000, FAX 61-2-9267-4361, info@acp.com.au, http://www.acp.com.au. Ed. Wendy Moore. Adv. contact Sandra Macnoughton. Circ: 19,903 (paid and controlled).

028.162 DEU
WIR (MINDEN). Text in German. 1959. 3/yr. looseleaf. bk.rev. back issues avail. **Document type:** *Newsletter, Consumer.*
Published by: Wir am Besselgymnasium, Hahler Str 134, Minden, 32427, Germany. TEL 49-571-22869. Ed. Nadine Meier. Circ: 700.

500 CHN ISSN 0510-7148
WOMEN AI KEXUE/WE LOVE SCIENCE. Text in Chinese. m. USD 31.40.
Published by: Zhongguo Shaonian Ertong Chubanshe, 21 Dongsi 12 Tiao, Beijing, 100708, China. TEL 86-10-6403-2266. Ed. Mao Hongqiang. **Dist. in US by:** China Books & Periodicals Inc, 360 Swift Ave., Ste. 48, S San Fran, CA 94080-6220. TEL 415-282-2994.

WONDER TIME. see *RELIGIONS AND THEOLOGY—Protestant*

028.5 USA ISSN 1071-6602
WORD DANCE. Text in English. 1991. q. USD 18 domestic; USD 23 in Canada & Mexico; USD 28 elsewhere (effective 2003). illus. back issues avail. **Document type:** *Consumer.* **Description:** For and by school children, grades K-8.
Published by: Playful Productions, Inc., PO Box 10804, Wilmington, DE 19850. TEL 302-894-1950, FAX 302-894-1957, playful@worddance.com, http://www.worddance.com. Ed., Pub. Stuart Ungar.

WORD UP! (PARAMUS). see *MUSIC*

028.5 USA ISSN 1087-1764
THE WORLD ALMANAC FOR KIDS. Text in English. a., latest 2001. USD 11.95 (effective 2004). **Document type:** *Directory, Consumer.*
Formerly (until 1996): Kid's World Almanac of Records and Facts
Published by: World Almanac Books (Subsidiary of: W R C Media Inc.), 512 7th Avenue, 22nd Floor, New York, NY 10018. TEL 201-529-6900, FAX 201-529-6901, waforkids@waegroup.com, http://www.worldalmanacforkids.com. Adv. contact James R Keenley TEL 646-312-6822. **Dist. by:** St. Martin's Press, 175 Fifth Ave, New York, NY 10010. TEL 212-674-5151.

WORLD ISSUES. see *SOCIAL SERVICES AND WELFARE*

028.5 USA ISSN 1549-8441
WORLD KID MAGAZINE. Text in English. 1999. bi-m. USD 12.05 (effective 2003). **Description:** Covers news and events of interest to children.
Related titles: Online - full content ed.: USD 9.95 (effective 2002).
Address: 3435 SW First Ave, Miami, FL 33145. TEL 305-860-6487, editor@worldkidmag.com, http://www.worldkidmag.com/. Ed. Luis F. Rodriguez.

305.235 HUN ISSN 0043-9274
WORLD YOUTH/JEUNESSE DU MONDE/JUVENTUD DEL MUNDO; international youth magazine. Text in English. 1952. s-a. USD 10. adv. illus.; tr.lit. index.
Related titles: French ed.; Spanish ed.
Published by: World Federation of Democratic Youth, Frangepan utca 16, PO Box 147, Budapest, 1389, Hungary. TEL 36-1-3443830. Ed. Mun Chol. Adv. contact Halim Awad. Circ: 5,000. **Subscr. to:** Kultura, PO Box 149, Budapest 1389, Hungary.

028.5 DEU
WURZEL; regionale Kinderzeitung fuer den Stadt- und Landkreis Karlsruhe. Text in German. 1987. 8/yr.
Published by: Paedagogischer Hochschule Karlsruhe, Didaktische Werkstatt, Bismarckstr 10, Karlsruhe, 76133, Germany. TEL 0721-23991, FAX 0721-28150. Ed. Rolf Siller.

028.5 DEU
X-MAG. Text in German. m. EUR 1.95 newsstand/cover (effective 2002). adv. **Document type:** *Magazine, Consumer.*
Formerly: Junge Zeit (0170-5857)
Published by: Weltbild Verlag GmbH, Steinerne Furt, Augsburg, 86128, Germany. TEL 49-821-70048379, FAX 49-821-70048349. Ed. Andre Lorenz. Adv. contact Kurt Telschig. page EUR 2,600. Circ: 46,800.

028.5 CHN
XIAO HUOJU/LITTLE TORCHES. Text in Chinese. m. CNY 5.04. **Description:** Aims to make science and other knowledge interesting to children.
Published by: (Fujian Sheng Shaoxiandui Gongzuo Weiyuanhui), Fujian Shaonian Ertong Chubanshe, 27 Degui Xiang, Fuzhou, Fujian 350001, China. TEL 537301. Ed. Lu Dasheng. **Dist. overseas by:** Jiangsu Publications Import & Export Corp., 56 Gao Yun Ling, Nanjing, Jiangsu, China.

028.5 CHN ISSN 1005-9881
XIAO MIHOU/LITTLE MACAQUE; intelligence pictorial. Text in Chinese. 1980. bi-m. CNY 24.
Published by: Jiangxi Fine Arts Publishing House, 17 Xinweilu, Nanchang, Jiangxi, Jiangxi 330002, China. TEL 86-791-850-2724, FAX 86-791-851-2107.

028.5 CHN
XIAO PENGYOU/LITTLE FRIENDS. Text in Chinese. 1922. m. USD 16.80; USD 1.40 newsstand/cover (effective 2001). **Document type:** *Consumer.* **Description:** Contains fairy tales, poems, science stories, games, and exercises in composition.
Published by: Shaonian Ertong Chubanshe/Juvenile & Children Publishing House, 1538 Yan an Xilu, Shanghai, 200052, China. TEL 86-21-6282-3025, FAX 86-21-6262-1726. Ed. Hong Zunian. **Dist. in US by:** China Books & Periodicals Inc, 360 Swift Ave., Ste. 48, S San Fran, CA 94080-6220. TEL 415-282-2994; **Dist. by:** China International Book Trading Corp, 35 Chegongzhuang Xilu, Haidian District, PO Box 399, Beijing 100044, China. TEL 86-10-68412045, FAX 86-10-68412023, cibtc@mail.cibtc.com.cn, http://www.cibtc.com.cn.

028.5 CHN
XIAO XINGXING/LITTLE STAR. Text in Chinese. m.
Published by: 21 Shiji Chubanshe/21st Century Publishing, No5, Xinwei Lu, Nanchang, Jiangxi 330002, China. TEL 333749. Ed. Wan Wangming.

028.5 CHN
XIAO XUEHUA. Text in Chinese. 1992. m.?. CNY 1 per issue. adv. **Document type:** *Consumer.*
Published by: Gongqingtuan Heilongjiang Shengwei, 11, Ashihe Jie, Nangang-qu, Harbin, Heilongjiang 150001, China. TEL 0451-3642171. Ed. Yuan Qingguo. Adv. contact Wu Shengshan. page CNY 5,000. Circ: 350,000.

028.5 CHN
XIAOJIZHE/LITTLE REPORTER. Cover title: Junior. Text in Chinese. bi-m. **Document type:** *Magazine, Consumer.*
Published by: Dazhongbao Yejituan/Dazhong News Group, 6, Leyuan Dajie, Jinan, Shangdong 250014, China. TEL 86-531-2968989, http://www.dzwww.com/xiaojizhe/.

XIAOXUE KEJI/ELEMENTARY SCHOOL SCIENCE AND TECHNOLOGY. see *SCIENCES: COMPREHENSIVE WORKS*

028.5 CHN
XIAOXUE SHIDAI/ELEMENTARY SCHOOL YEARS. Text in Chinese. m.
Published by: Beifang Funu Ertong Chubanshe/North Women and Children's Publishers, 102 Stalin St, Changchun, Jilin 130021, China. TEL 884811. Ed. Wu Fei.

XIAOXUESHENG YUWEN XUEXI/CHINESE STUDIES FOR PUPILS. see *LINGUISTICS*

XIAOYISHUJIA/LITTLE ARTIST. see *ART*

XPRESS. see *SPORTS AND GAMES—Ball Games*

028.5 CHN ISSN 1671-1955
XUESHENG GUANGJIAO. Variant title: Manhua Party. Text in Chinese. m. CNY 50.40 (effective 2004). **Document type:** *Magazine, Consumer.*
Published by: Yunnan Jiaoyu Chubanshe/Yunnan Education Publishing House, 4th Floor, Yunnan Press & Publication Building, 609 West Huancheng Road, Kunming, Yunnan Province 650034, China. TEL 86-871-4136301, FAX 86-871-4120359, xueshenggj@21cn.com, yneph@public.km.yn.cn, http://www.yneph.com/skgc/xueshenggj.htm.

028.5 USA
Y E S MAGAZINE✶. (Youth Excited about Success) Text in English. 1992. m. (Sep.-May). USD 15. adv. film rev.; music rev.; software rev.; video rev. back issues avail. **Document type:** *Consumer.* **Description:** Provides valuable resource information on scholarships, resume writing, and study tips for students age 12 to 18. Helps students develop positive self-esteem. Special focus on urban teens.
Published by: Y E S Communications Inc., PO Box 191, Plainfield, NJ 07061-0191. TEL 908-754-4466, FAX 908-753-1036. Ed. Jan M Edgenton Johnson. Pub. Henry C Johnson. R&P Jill Johnson. Adv. contact Jill L Johnson. Circ: 100,000.

028.5 USA ISSN 1526-243X
Y O! YOUTH OUTLOOK. Text in English. 1991. m. USD 15 to individuals; USD 12 to students (effective 2003). adv. bk.rev.; film rev.; music rev.; play rev.; rec.rev.; software rev.; tel.rev.; video rev.; Website rev. illus. back issues avail. **Document type:** *Magazine, Consumer.* **Description:** Offers the voice of today's youth by today's youth on timely national topics, as well as coverage of the world of entertainment.
Published by: Pacific News Service, 275 9th St, San Francisco, CA 94103. TEL 415-503-4170, FAX 415-503-0970, yo@pacificnews.org, http://www.youthoutlook.org, http://www.pacificnews.org. Ed. Kevin Weston. Pub. Sandy Close. Circ: 25,000.

053.1 781.64 DEU
YAM!. Text in German. 2000. w. EUR 67.60 domestic; EUR 1.30 newsstand/cover (effective 2002). adv. **Document type:** *Magazine, Consumer.* **Description:** Contains all the latest news and gossip on music celebrities.
Related titles: Online - full text ed.
Published by: Axel Springer Young Mediahouse, Werinherstr 71, Munich, 81541, Germany. TEL 49-89-697490, FAX 49-89-69749312, team@yam.de, http://www.yam.de, http://www.asv.de. Ed. Simon Peter. Adv. contact Petra Kalb TEL 49-89-69749100. page EUR 12,280; trim 205 x 285. Circ: 370,967 (paid). **Subscr. to:** dsb Abo-Betreuung GmbH, Konrad-Zuse-Str 16, Neckarsulm 74172, Germany. TEL 49-7132-959214, FAX 49-7132-959216, asvabo@dsb.net. **Dist. by:** ASV Vertriebs GmbH, Suederstr 77, Hamburg 20097, Germany. TEL 49-40-34725945, FAX 49-40-34723549.

028.5 808.8 USA
YELLOW TURTLE. Text in English. irreg. (2-4/yr.). **Description:** Publishes children's literature.
Published by: Spring Rain Press, PO Box 277, Port Townsend, WA 98368. Ed., Pub. Karen Gates.

305.23 RUS
YES!. Text in Russian. 1998. m. USD 24.25 domestic; USD 99 foreign (effective 2005). adv. **Document type:** *Magazine, Consumer.*
Published by: Independent Media (Moscow), ul Vyborgskaya dom 16, str 1, Moscow, 125212, Russian Federation. TEL 7-095-2323200, FAX 7-095-2329265, yes@imedia.ru, podpiska@imedia.ru, http://www.yes.ru/, http://www.independent-media.ru. Ed. Irina Il'ina. Circ: 130,000.

770 CHN
YINGER HUABAO/INFANT PICTORIAL. Text in Chinese. m. USD 25.10. illus.
Published by: Zhongguo Shaonian Ertong Chubanshe, 21 Dongsi 12 Tiao, Beijing, 100708, China. TEL 86-10-6403-2266. Ed. Wu Daisheng. **Dist. in US by:** China Books & Periodicals Inc, 360 Swift Ave., Ste. 48, S San Fran, CA 94080-6220. TEL 415-282-2994.

028.5 ALB
YLLKAT/ETOILES. Text in Albanian. m.
Published by: Institutit te Studimeve Pedagogjike/Pedagogical Research Institute, Rr Naim Frasheri 37, Tirana, Albania. TEL 355-42-23860, FAX 355-42-23860.

YO! MAGAZINE. see *MUSIC*

028.5 USA ISSN 0897-7704
YO-YO TIMES; a world of fun on a string for children of all ages. Text in English. 1988. 4/yr. free. adv. **Document type:** *Newsletter, Consumer.*

Media: Online - full content.
Published by: Creative Communications Inc. (Herndon), 1566 Kingstream Cir., Herndon, VA 20170-2752. TEL 703-715-6187. Ed., Pub. Stuart F Crump Jr.

028.5   CHN   ISSN 1006-3579
YOU'ER GUSHING DAWAN/SUPERB STORYTELLER FOR INFANTS. Text in Chinese. 1994. m. CNY 31.20; CNY 2.60 newsstand/cover (effective 2001). adv. back issues avail.
Media: Large Type (12 pt.).
Published by: Zhejiang Shaonian Ertong Chubanshe/Zhejiang Juvenile and Children's Publishing House, Zhejiang Distribution Bureau, Rm 909 & 910, No.347 Tiyuchang Rd, Hangzhou, Zhejiang Province, China. zjsrs@mail.hz.zj.cn, http://www.ses.zjcb.com. Eds. Jian Wan, Jiqing Feng, Liqing Chen. Pub. Chunyue Chen. R&P Ying Wu TEL 86-571-5102968. Adv. contact Jiqing Feng.

028.5   CHN   ISSN 1003-0220
YOU'ER HUABAO/TODDLERS' PICTORIAL. Text in Chinese. m. USD 24.20. illus.
Published by: Zhongguo Shaonian Ertong Chubanshe, 21 Dongsi 12 Tiao, Beijing, 100708, China. TEL 86-10-6403-2266. Ed. Wu Yinni.

YOUNG AMERICAN PRESS. see CHILDREN AND YOUTH—About

YOUNG & ALIVE (LARGE PRINT EDITION). see RELIGIONS AND THEOLOGY

808.068   USA   ISSN 0741-7594
YOUNG AUTHORS MAGAZINE. Abbreviated title: Y A M. Text in English. 1984. a. USD 12 per issue (effective 2005). bk.rev.
Description: Covers creative writing by children and youths.
Published by: Regulus Communications, Inc., 3015 Woodsdale Blvd, Lincoln, NE 68502-5053. TEL 402-730-4926, FAX 402-421-9682, research@regulus.com, http:// www.regulus.com/. Ed. Jane A Austin. Circ: 33,144.

▼ **YOUNG DANCER.** see DANCE

028.5   SGP   ISSN 0129-6639
YOUNG GENERATION. Text in Chinese, English. 1974. m. SGD 30. adv. **Description:** For primary to lower secondary students. Includes riddles, stories, cartoons, contests, and poems. Focuses on science, geography, history, wildlife, and famous people and stories for kids.
Formerly (until 1981): Young Singaporean
Published by: S N P Publishers Pte Ltd, 162 Bukit Merah Central, No 04-3545, Singapore, 150162, Singapore. TEL 65-741-2500, FAX 65-744-3770, http://www.snp.com.sg. R&P Lee Oi Leng TEL 65-374-0177. Adv. contact Jeannette Cheong. Circ: 80,000.

YOUNG JUDAEAN. see RELIGIONS AND THEOLOGY—Judaic

028.5   JPN
YOUNG MAGAZINE. Text in Japanese. w. **Document type:** Magazine, Consumer.
Published by: Kodansha Ltd., 2-12-21 Otowa, Bunkyo-ku, Tokyo, 112-8001, Japan. TEL 81-3-3946-6201, FAX 81-3-3944-9915, http://www.kodansha.co.jp.

YOUNG MONEY. see BUSINESS AND ECONOMICS— Investments

YOUNG MUSICIANS. see MUSIC

028.5   CAN
YOUNG PEOPLE'S PRESS ONLINE. Text in English. 1998. irreg. **Document type:** Bulletin. **Description:** Contains articles written by youth for youth on every topic imaginable.
Media: Online - full text.
Published by: Young People's Press, 110 Eglinton Ave W, Ste 200, Toronto, ON M4R 1A3, Canada. TEL 416-484-4570, FAX 416-484-8173, yppto@planeteer.com, http://www.ypp.net/.

YOUNG RIDER; the magazine for horse and pony lovers. see SPORTS AND GAMES—Horses And Horsemanship

YOUNG SOLDIER. see RELIGIONS AND THEOLOGY— Protestant

052 800   GBR   ISSN 1359-9380
YOUNG WRITER. Text in English. 3/yr. GBP 7.50 domestic; GBP 9.50 in Europe; GBP 11.50 elsewhere; GBP 2.75 newsstand/cover domestic; GBP 3.50 newsstand/cover in Europe; GBP 4 newsstand/cover elsewhere (effective 2001).
Document type: Consumer. **Description:** Lively literary magazine written by and for young writers. Offers creative ideas, technical tips, competitions.
Related titles: Online - full content ed.: Young Writer Online.
Published by: Just Write!, Glebe House, Church Rd, Weobley, Herefords HR4 8SD, United Kingdom. editor@youngwriter.org, http://www.youngwriter.org. Ed. Kate Jones. **Dist. by:** Diamond Magazine Distribution Ltd., Unit 7, Rother Ironworks, Fishmarket Rd, Rye, E Sussex TN31 7LR, United Kingdom. TEL 44-1797-225229, FAX 44-1797-225657.

330   USA
YOUNGBIZ. Text in English. 1996. bi-m. USD 18 (effective 2000). adv. **Document type:** Magazine, Consumer. **Description:** Contains articles and analyses that feature teen entrepreneurs and investors.
Formerly (until 2000): Young Entrepreneur (1090-9478)
Address: 6669 Peachtree Industrial Blvd., Ste. E, Norcross, GA 30092-3699. TEL 888-543-7929, ybmag@youngbiz.com, http://youngbiz.com. Ed., Adv. contact Chad Polazzo.

028.5 362.7   PHL   ISSN 0116-1091
THE YOUNGSTER; the magazine for the young minister of the word. Text in English, Tagalog. 1956. m. (Jun.-Mar.). PHP 250 domestic; PHP 750 foreign (effective 2002). 44 p./no.;
Document type: Magazine, Trade. **Description:** Dedicated to the youth. Contains sections on teen problems and topics aimed at deepening Christian values.
Published by: Society of St. Paul, Inc., PO Box 1722, Makati City Post Office, Makati City Mm, 1203, Philippines. TEL 632-895-9701, youngster@stpauls.ph, http://www.stpauls.ph/ theyoungster/. Ed. Dennis L Figuerres. R&P Dominador G Guzman Jr. Adv. contact Joven Lagdamen TEL 632-895-7328. Circ: 90,000.

028.5   FRA   ISSN 0989-733X
YOUPI; le petit curieux. Text in French. 1988. m. EUR 54.80 domestic; EUR 64.80 in the European Union; EUR 74.80 elsewhere (effective 2005). **Document type:** Magazine, Consumer. **Description:** Introduces 5 to 8-year-olds to the wonders of the world and encourages their literary autonomy.
Formerly: Youpi Decouvertes
Published by: Bayard Presse, 3 Rue Bayard, Paris, 75393 Cedex 08, France. TEL 33-1-44356060, FAX 33-1-44356161, redactions@bayard-presse.com, http://www.bayardpresse.com. Ed. Marie Agnes Gaudrat. Circ: 56,620.

YOUR BIG BACKYARD. see ENVIRONMENTAL STUDIES

028.5   USA   ISSN 1067-005X
YOUR PROM. Text in English. 1990. a. adv. illus. reprints avail.
Document type: Magazine, Consumer. **Description:** Targeted to teenagers. Provides "how-to" advice on preparing for the prom. Includes fashion, beauty, health and relationship coverage.
—CCC.
Published by: Primedia Consumer Media & Magazine Group, 9036 Brittanyway, Tampa, FL 33619. information@primedia.com, http://www.yourprom.com/, http://www.primedia.com. adv.: color page USD 24,500. Circ: 800,000.

028.5   ZMB
YOUTH. Text in English. 1976 (vol.2). fortn. adv. bk.rev. illus.
Published by: United National Independence Party, Youth League, PO Box 302, Lusaka, Zambia. Ed. P J Njeleka. Circ: 15,000.

028.5   GBR
YOUTH AGENDA; participation. Text in English. 6/yr. GBP 45.
Description: Briefing papers on new developments in youth policy and practice.
—BLDSC (9421.508450).
Published by: British Youth Council, British Youth Council, 65-69 White Lion St, London, N1 9PP, United Kingdom. TEL 44-171-278-0582, FAX 44-171278-0583, youthindex@byc.org.uk.

THE YOUTH DISCIPLE. see RELIGIONS AND THEOLOGY—Protestant

YOUTH DISCIPLE LEADER'S PACKET. see RELIGIONS AND THEOLOGY—Protestant

YOUTH EXPLORE THE BIBLE SERIES. STUDENT. see RELIGIONS AND THEOLOGY—Protestant

YOUTH IN ACTION. see RELIGIONS AND THEOLOGY— Protestant

YOUTH IN DISCOVERY. see RELIGIONS AND THEOLOGY—Protestant

028.5   IND
YOUTH LIFE. Text in English. 1973. fortn. adv. illus.
Published by: All India Youth Federation, 4-7 Asaf Ali Rd., New Delhi, 110 001, India. Ed. K C Chandrappan.

YOUTH LINK. see CHILDREN AND YOUTH—About

YOUTH MINISTRY UPDATE. see RELIGIONS AND THEOLOGY—Protestant

028.5   AUS
YOUTH RESEARCH NEWS. Text in English. 1991. irreg. (approx. q.). AUD 40 to individuals; AUD 60 to institutions; AUD 15 to students (effective 2000). back issues avail. **Document type:** Newsletter. **Description:** Provides information about projects, publications and seminars.
Related titles: Online - full text ed.

Published by: Youth Research Centre, Faculty of Education, University of Melbourne, Parkville, VIC 3052, Australia. TEL 61-3-93449633, FAX 61-3-93449632, yrc@edfac.unimelb.edu.au, http://yarn.edfac.unimelb.edu.au/ yarn/yrc-home.html. Ed. Jasmina Raduloric. Circ: 500.

YOUTH THEATRE JOURNAL. see THEATER

YOUTH UPDATE. see RELIGIONS AND THEOLOGY—Roman Catholic

028.5   NCL   ISSN 0294-7579
YOUTHLINK. Text in English. 1979. irreg. **Document type:** Newsletter.
Related titles: French ed.: Interjeunes. ISSN 1021-0024.
Published by: Secretariat of the Pacific Community, PO Box D5, Noumea, Cedex 98848, New Caledonia. TEL 687-262000, FAX 687-263818, spc@spc.int, http://www.spc.int.

YOUTHWALK. see RELIGIONS AND THEOLOGY

YOUTHWORK; ideas, resources & guidance for youth ministry. see RELIGIONS AND THEOLOGY—Protestant

028.5   LKA
YOVUN JANATHA. Text in Singhalese. 1964. w. LKR 4.50 newsstand/cover (effective 2000). adv. **Document type:** Newspaper.
Published by: The Associated Newspapers of Ceylon Ltd., Lake House, D.R. Wijewardena Mawatha, Colombo, 10, Sri Lanka. TEL 94-1-421181, FAX 94-1-449069. Ed. Dayanate Lankapura. Circ: 115,000.

027.5   DEU
▼ **YUKIKO.** Text in German. 2004. m. EUR 2.50 newsstand/cover (effective 2005). adv. **Document type:** Magazine, Consumer.
Published by: Panini Verlags GmbH, Ravensstr 48, Nettetal, 41334, Germany. TEL 49-2157-81750, FAX 49-2157-81484528, info@panini-dino.de, http://www.panini-media.de. adv.: page EUR 3,500. Circ: 155,485 (paid and controlled).

028.5   CAN   ISSN 0044-1384
YUNAK/YOUTH. Text in Ukrainian. 1963. bi-m. CND 30. adv. illus.
Document type: Newsletter. **Description:** For ages 12-17.
Published by: Plast-Ukrainian Youth Organization, 2199 Bloor St W, Toronto, ON M6S 1N2, Canada. TEL 416-763-2186, FAX 416-763-0185. Ed. O Zakydalsky. Adv. contact G Senkiw. Circ: 1,000.

028.5 700   RUS   ISSN 0205-5791
YUNYI KHUDOZHNIK. Text in Russian. 1936. m. USD 108 foreign (effective 2004). adv. bk.rev. illus.
—East View.
Published by: Izdatel'stvo Molodaya Gvardiya, Novodmitrovskaya ul 5-a, Moscow, 125015, Russian Federation. TEL 7-095-2858901, FAX 7-095-9430060. Dist. by: M K - Periodica, ul Gilyarovskogo 39, Moscow 129110, Russian Federation. TEL 7-095-2845008, FAX 7-095-2813798, info@periodicals.ru, http://www.mkniga.ru.

028.5 570   RUS   ISSN 0205-5767
YUNYI NATURALIST. Text in Russian. 1928. m. USD 177 foreign (effective 2005). adv. bk.rev. illus. index. **Document type:** Magazine, Consumer. **Description:** For children in 4th - 10th grades who are interested in biology.
—East View.
Published by: Izdatel'stvo Molodaya Gvardiya, Novodmitrovskaya ul 5-a, Moscow, 125015, Russian Federation. TEL 7-095-2858805, unnat@dateline.ru. Ed. Ludmila Samsonova. Circ: 16,500. **Dist. by:** East View Information Services, 3020 Harbor Ln. N., Minneapolis, MN 55447. TEL 763-550-0961, FAX 763-559-2931, eastview@eastview.com, http://www.eastview.com.

028.5   RUS
YUNYI NAVIGATOR. Text in Russian. m. 16 p./no.
Published by: Izdatel'skii Dom Karapuz, Izmailovskoe shosse 48a, Moscow, 105318, Russian Federation. TEL 7-095-9182810, http://www.karapuz.com. Ed. L S Kozlov.

028.5 600   RUS   ISSN 0131-1417
T4
YUNYI TEKHNIK. Text in Russian. 1956. m. USD 67 foreign (effective 2005). adv. bk.rev. bibl.; illus. **Document type:** Magazine, Consumer. **Description:** Presents technology and science for teenagers, new discoveries, technical skills and crafts, best examples of science fiction by Russian and foreign authors.
—East View.
Address: Novodmitrovskaya ul 5-a, Moscow, 125015, Russian Federation. TEL 7-095-2854480, FAX 7-095-2851809, yt@got.mmtel.ru. Ed. Boris I Cheremisinov. Adv. contact Alexandr Abmorshev. color page USD 600; 104 x 167. Circ: 12,000. **Dist. by:** M K - Periodica, ul Gilyarovskogo 39, Moscow 129110, Russian Federation. TEL 7-095-2845008, FAX 7-095-2813798, info@periodicals.ru, http:// www.mkniga.ru.

C

028.5 820 IND ISSN 0302-6981
YUVA BHARATI; voice of youth. Text in English. 1973. q. USD 25. adv. bk.rev. **Description:** Examines Indian culture for youth.
Published by: Vivekananda Kendra Prakashan, 3 Singarachari St., Triplicane, Chennai, Tamil Nadu 600 005, India. Ed. P Parameswaram. Pub. N Viswanath. **Co-sponsor:** Swami Vivekananda Centenary Celebration.

028.5 NPL
YUWAMANCH. Text in Nepali. bi-m.
Related titles: Online - full content ed.: ISSN 1606-1756. 2000.
Published by: Mercantile Communications Pvt. Ltd., Durbar Marg, P.O. Box 876, Kathmandu, Nepal. TEL 977-1-220773, 977-1-243566, FAX 977-1-225407, http://www.nepalnews.com.np/yuwamanch.htm, http://www.cybermatha.net.

028.5 RUS
Z O O - B U M. Text in Russian. 1995. m. USD 130 in United States (effective 2000).
Published by: Bumerang, Novodmitrovskaya ul 5-a, Moscow, 125015, Russian Federation. TEL 7-095-1292909. **Dist. by:** East View Information Services, 3020 Harbor Ln. N., Minneapolis, MN 55447. TEL 763-550-0961, FAX 763-559-2931.

028.5 POL ISSN 1506-2546
ZABAWY I MARZENIA Z BARBIE. Text in Polish. 1998. m. **Document type:** *Magazine, Consumer.*
Published by: Egmont Polska, ul Dzielna 60, Warszawa, 01029, Poland. TEL 48-22-8384100, FAX 48-22-8384200, poczta@egmont.pl, http://www.egmont.pl. Circ: 90,000.

028.5 LUX ISSN 1016-2399
ZACK; Letzebuerger Kannerzeitung. Text in French, German. 1946. s-m. adv. **Document type:** *Newspaper.* **Description:** Covers daily life, sports, tourism and geography, politics, stories, comic strips, guessing games, coloring and posters.
Published by: Imprimerie Saint Paul S.A., 2 rue Christophe Plantin, Luxembourg, L-2988, Luxembourg. TEL 352-4993-258, FAX 352-4858-386. Ed., R&P, Adv. contact Josiane Heinen.

741.5 DEU ISSN 1438-2792
ZACK. Text in German. 1972. m. EUR 51.60 domestic; EUR 70.80 foreign; EUR 4.55 newsstand/cover (effective 2002). adv. **Document type:** *Magazine, Consumer.*
Published by: Mosaik Steinchen fuer Steinchen Verlag GmbH, Lindenallee 5, Berlin, 14050, Germany. TEL 49-30-306927-0, FAX 49-30-30692729, mosaik@abrafaxe.de, http://www.abrafaxe.com/zack4.htm. adv.: B&W page EUR 510, color page EUR 770. Circ: 10,000 (paid and controlled).

028.5 IND
ZAGMAG. Text in Gujarati. 1952. w.
Address: Samachar Bhavan, Khanpur, Ahmedabad, Gujarat 380 001, India. TEL 272-22821, TELEX 1216642. Ed. Bahubali S Shah. Circ: 38,000.

ZAMZAM; for young people. see *RELIGIONS AND THEOLOGY—Islamic*

ZANY ZINE. see *COMPUTERS—Internet*

028.5 BEL ISSN 0778-2322
ZAP. Text in Dutch. 1983. q. adv. bk.rev. back issues avail. **Document type:** *Consumer.* **Description:** For young people age 14-18.
Formerly (until 1991): Inforclub (0775-8340)
Related titles: Diskette ed.
Published by: Mutualistische Jongeren Aktie - M J A, Sint Jansstraat 32, Brussels, 1000, Belgium. TEL 32-2-5150251, FAX 32-2-5150207. Circ: 10,000.

268 ISR ISSN 0792-9307
ZAV-ZAV. Text in Hebrew. 1989. m. USD 35. **Description:** For children ages 3-6.
Published by: Select Publishing House, P O Box 28110, Tel Aviv, 61280, Israel. FAX 972-3-5373906. Ed. Rami Shir. Circ: 15,000.

028.5 BRA ISSN 0104-3404
ZE CARIOCA. Text in Portuguese. 1961. fortn. adv. **Document type:** *Magazine, Consumer.*
Published by: Editora Abril, S.A., Av. das Nacoes Unidas, 7221, 11 andar Pinheiros, Sao Paulo, SP 05425-902, Brazil. TEL 55-11-50872112, FAX 55-11-50872100, http://www.disney.com.br/, http://www.abril.com.br/. Circ: 4,900.

028.5 ISR
ZERA'IM. Text in Hebrew. bi-m. free.
Published by: Bnei Akiva, P O Box 40027, Tel Aviv, 61400, Israel. TEL 972-3-6917145. Ed. Uri Orbach.

ZHONG GUO KA TONG/CARTOON OF CHINA. see *ART*

028.5 CHN ISSN 0412-4154
PZ10.831
ZHONGGUO ERTONG/CHINESE CHILDREN. Text in Chinese. m. USD 25.10. **Description:** Contains illustrations for elementary school pupils.
Published by: Zhongguo Shaonian Ertong Chubanshe, 21 Dongsi 12 Tiao, Beijing, 100708, China. TEL 86-10-6403-2266, TELEX 4357. Ed. Sun Shiqing. **Dist. in US by:** China Books & Periodicals Inc, 360 Swift Ave., Ste. 48, S San Fran, CA 94080-6220. TEL 415-282-2994.

ZHONGGUO ERTONG BAO/CHINA CHILDREN'S NEWS. see *CHILDREN AND YOUTH—About*

ZHONGGUO ERTONG HUABAO/CHINESE CHILDREN'S PICTORIAL. see *CHILDREN AND YOUTH—About*

059.951 890 CHN ISSN 1002-9532
HX9.C5
ZHONGGUO QINGNIAN/CHINA YOUTH. Text in Chinese. 1923. m. CNY 120, USD 57.60; CNY 5, USD 2.40 newsstand/cover (effective 2005). 64 p./no.; **Document type:** *Magazine, Consumer.*
Published by: Zhongguo Qingnian Zazhishe, 22, Guanyuan Yuqiang Hutong, Xicheng-qu, Beijing, 100034, China. TEL 86-10-66162403, FAX 86-10-66162405, chinayouth@spark.com.cn, http://zgqn.periodicals.net.cn/. Circ: 1,000,000. **Dist. overseas by:** China International Book Trading Corp, 35 Chegongzhuang Xilu, Haidian District, PO Box 399, Beijing 100044, China. TEL 86-10-68412045, FAX 86-10-68412023, cibtc@mail.cibtc.com.cn, http://www.cibtc.com.cn.

895.1 CHN
ZHONGGUO QINGNIAN BAO/CHINESE YOUTH DAILY. Text in Chinese. 1951. d. CNY 270, USD 98.40 (effective 2005). adv. bk.rev. reprints avail. **Document type:** *Newspaper, Consumer.*
Address: Haiyuncang 2#, Dongzhimen, DongCheng District, Beijing, 100702, China. TEL 86-10-64098088, FAX 86-10-64098077, cyd@cyd.net.cn, http://www.cyol.net/. Circ: 1,000,000. **Dist. by:** China International Book Trading Corp, 35 Chegongzhuang Xilu, Haidian District, PO Box 399, Beijing 100044, China. TEL 86-10-68412045, FAX 86-10-68412023, cibtc@mail.cibtc.com.cn, http://www.cibtc.com.cn.

028.5 CHN
ZHONGGUO SHAONIAN BAO/CHINA YOUNGSTER NEWS. Text in Chinese. 1951. w. CNY 39 (effective 2004). **Document type:** *Newspaper, Consumer.*
Published by: Zhongguo Shaonan Ertong Xinwen Chubanzongshe/China Children's Press & Publication Group, Zhaoyang-qu, 5, Zuojiazhuang Beili, Beijing, 100028, China. TEL 86-10(UNKNOWN CHARACTER)84541086, webmaster@ccppg.com.cn, http://www.ccppg.com.cn/a/snb/index.htm. **Dist. by:** China International Book Trading Corp, 35 Chegongzhuang Xilu, Haidian District, PO Box 399, Beijing 100044, China. TEL 86-10-68412045, FAX 86-10-68412023, cibtc@mail.cibtc.com.cn, http://www.cibtc.com.cn; China Books & Periodicals Inc, 360 Swift Ave., Ste. 48, S San Fran, CA 94080-6220. TEL 415-282-2994, FAX 415-282-0994.

ZHONGGUO ZHONGXUESHENG BAO/CHINESE MIDDLE SCHOOL STUDENTS GAZETTE. see *CHILDREN AND YOUTH—About*

028.5 CHN
ZHONGWAI TONGHUA HUAKAN/CHINESE AND FOREIGN FAIRY TALES PICTORIAL. Text in Chinese. m.
Published by: Nei Menggu Zizhiqu Funu Lianhehui/Inner Mongolian Autonomous Region Women's Association, 9 Zhongshan Donglu, Huhhot, Nei Menggu 010020, China. TEL 662584. Ed. Xi Xingfang.

028.5 CHN
ZHONGXUE SHISHI BAO/MIDDLE SCHOOL TIMES. Text in Chinese. w. **Document type:** *Magazine, Consumer.*
Related titles: Online - full content ed.
Published by: Beijing Qingnian Bao Wangji Chuanbo Jizhu Youxian Gongsi, Beijing Qingnian Bao Dasha, Chaoyang-qu, 23, Baijia Zhuan Dongli, Beijing, 100026, China. webmaster@ynet.com, http://zxss.ynet.com/, http://www.ynet.com/.

ZHONGXUESHENG SHUXUE/MATHEMATICS FOR MIDDLE SCHOOL STUDENTS. see *MATHEMATICS*

028.5 CAN ISSN 0832-8242
ZIP: LE MAGAZINE DES JEUNES. Text in English. 1986. m. USD 20 to individuals; USD 18 to institutions.
Published by: Publications Audiovisuelles, 415 80 rue ouest, Charlesbourg, PQ G1H 4M9, Canada. TEL 418-622-3491. Ed. Pierre Coulombe. Circ: 87,000.

028.5 BEL ISSN 1381-5946
ZO ZIT DAT. Text in English. 1994. m. EUR 22.50 (effective 2003). **Document type:** *Magazine, Consumer.*
Published by: Sanoma Magazines Belgium, Telecomlaan 5-7, Diegem, 1831, Belgium. TEL 32-2-7762211, FAX 32-2-776-2317, http://www.zozitdat.nl, http://www.sanoma-magazines.be/HomePage.aspx?flash=1&Language=nl.

028.5 BEL ISSN 0772-7402
ZONNEKIND. Text in Dutch. 1958. w. EUR 14.95 (effective 2005). illus. **Document type:** *Magazine.* **Description:** Aims to develop early language and mathematics skills for children, ages 6-8. Includes relevant activities.
Published by: Uitgeverij Averbode NV, Abdijstraat 1, Postbus 54, Averbode, 3271, Belgium. TEL 32-13-780111, FAX 32-13-780183, http://www.averbode.be. Ed. Philippe Brasseur.

028.5 BEL ISSN 0049-8750
ZONNELAND. Text in Dutch. 1920. w. EUR 69 (effective 2005). adv. illus. **Document type:** *Magazine.* **Description:** Offers children ages 10-12 (grades 5 and 6) a host of activities.
Published by: Uitgeverij Averbode NV, Abdijstraat 1, Postbus 54, Averbode, 3271, Belgium. TEL 32-13-780111, FAX 32-13-780183, http://www.averbode.be. Ed. Jan Lembrechts.

028.5 BEL ISSN 0772-9898
ZONNESTRAAL. Text in Dutch. 1966. w. EUR 4 per issue (effective 2005). illus. **Document type:** *Journal.* **Description:** Helps children ages 8-10 discover the world in time and space, showing them new ways of looking at things from various angles. Presents reading as fun.
Related titles: ♦ French ed.: Dauphin. ISSN 0773-0292.
Published by: Uitgeverij Averbode NV, Abdijstraat 1, Postbus 54, Averbode, 3271, Belgium. TEL 32-13-780111, FAX 32-13-780183, http://www.averbode.be. Ed. Jan Lembrechts.

ZOOBOOKS. see *BIOLOGY—Zoology*

028.5 SVK ISSN 0139-8962
ZORNICKA. Text in Slovak. 1948. 24/yr. USD 12 (effective 2000).
Published by: Smena Publishing House, Prazska 11, Bratislava, 81284, Slovakia.

028.5 CUB
ZUN ZUN; revista infantil. Text in Spanish. m. USD 34 in South America; USD 36 in North America; USD 42 elsewhere.
Published by: (Editorial Abril), Ediciones Cubanas, Obispo No. 527, Apdo. 605, Havana, Cuba.

305.235 305.4 305.89607305 USA ISSN 1540-2088
ZURI; beautiful young woman. Text in English. 2002. bi-m. USD 14.95; USD 4 newsstand/cover (effective 2004). adv. **Description:** Fashion magazine for African American women from 12 to 19.
Published by: Zuri Communications, LLC, P. O. Box 150427, Alexandria, VA 22315. TEL 703-339-0202, FAX 703-339-8898, zurimag@zurimag.com, http://www.zurimag.com. Ed. Donna D. King.

028.5 DEU ISSN 0721-4626
ZUSAMMEN. Text in German. 10/yr. EUR 6.80 newsstand/cover (effective 2003). adv. illus. **Document type:** *Journal, Consumer.*
Indexed: DIP, IBR, IBZ.
Published by: Erhard Friedrich Verlag GmbH, Im Brande 17, Seelze, 30926, Germany. TEL 49-511-40004-0, FAX 49-511-40004119, info@friedrich-verlag.de, http://www.friedrich-verlag.de. adv.: page EUR 1,181. Circ: 19,029 (paid and controlled).

ZUSAMMEN; Jugendmagazin in deutscher Sprache. see *LINGUISTICS*

369.4 NOR ISSN 0800-6032
4 H - KLUBBEN. Text in Norwegian. 1949. m. NOK 150 (effective 2001). adv. **Description:** Contact and information organ of the 4H club in Norway.
Formerly (until 1956): Klubben Vaar (0800-6725)
—CCC.
Published by: Norske 4H, Postboks 113, Skjetten, 2013, Norway. TEL 47-64-83-21-00, FAX 47-64-83-21-19, norske4h@4h.no, http://www.n4h.no. Ed. Ann-Helen Bakkelund. Adv. contact Dagfried Hammersvik. color page NOK 12,800, B&W page NOK 9,100; 185 x 260. Circ: 22,900.

028.5 USA
4'S & 5'S FAMILY FUN. Text in English. 1918. w. USD 14.69 per quarter for 5 copies (effective 2003). illus. **Document type:** *Consumer.*
Formerly: Four and Five (0015-9077)
Published by: Standard Publishing, 8121 Hamilton Ave, Cincinnati, OH 45231. TEL 513-931-4050, FAX 513-931-0950. Ed. Laura Bridenhager. Pub., R&P Mark A Taylor. Circ: 134,000.

028.5 POL ISSN 1640-8993
13; magazyn szczesliwej nastolatki. Variant title: Trzynastka. Text in Polish. 2001. m. **Document type:** *Magazine, Consumer.*
Related titles: Supplement(s): 13. Wydanie Specjalne. ISSN 1730-2854. 2003.
Published by: Egmont Polska, ul Dzielna 60, Warszawa, 01029, Poland. TEL 48-22-8384100, FAX 48-22-8384200, poczta@egmont.pl, http://www.egmont.pl. Circ: 100,000.

028.5 USA ISSN 1075-3109
16. Text in English. 1957. irreg. (m. until 2000; freq. reduced to special eds. only). USD 21.95 domestic; USD 27.95 in Canada; USD 29.95 elsewhere (effective 2000). bk.rev. illus. **Document type:** *Consumer.*

C

Formerly: 16 Magazine (0270-899X)
Published by: Primedia Youth Entertainment Group (Subsidiary of: Primedia Consumer Media & Magazine Group), 470 Park Ave S, 8th Fl, New York, NY 10016. TEL 212-545-3600, FAX 212-532-1980, http://www.primediainc.com. Ed. Ellen Jurcsak. Pub. Mark Peterson. Adv. contact Alisa Harad. Circ: 174,365.
Dist. in UK by: Comag, Tavistock Works, Tavistock Rd, W Drayton, Middx UB7 7QX, United Kingdom. TEL 44-1895-444055, FAX 44-1895-433602.

028.5   GBR   ISSN 0262-1126
19. Text in English. 1968-1975; resumed 19??. m. GBP 31 domestic; USD 69.50 in United States; EUR 61.50 in Europe; GBP 47.50 elsewhere (effective 2004). adv. illus. **Document type:** *Magazine, Consumer.* **Description:** Fashion and beauty, real-life stories, serious issues and celebrities all packed into a bright glossy monthly.
Incorporates (1960-1986): Honey (0018-4551); Vanity Fair (0042-2584)
Indexed: DAAI.
—CCC.
Published by: I P C SouthBank (Subsidiary of: I P C Media Ltd.), Kings Reach Tower, Stamford St, London, SE1 9LS, United Kingdom. TEL 44-161-8722144, http://www.ipc.co.uk. Eds. April Joyce, Samantha Warwick TEL 44-20-72616410. Pub. Kirstin Lee TEL 44-20-72617443. Adv. contact Emma Baldock. color page GBP 6,160. Circ: 173,244. **Subscr. to:** I P C Media Ltd., Perrymount Rd, Haywards Heath RH16 3DA, United Kingdom. TEL 44-1444-475675, FAX 44-1444-445599, ipcsubs@qss-uk.com. **Dist. by:** MarketForce UK Ltd, 247 Tottenham Court Rd, London, Middx W1T 7AU, United Kingdom. TEL 44-20-72611599, FAX 44-20-72617341.

028.5   GBR   ISSN 1357-1028
95 PER CENT. Text in English. 1993. q. GBP 8; GBP 2 newsstand/cover. back issues avail. **Document type:** *Consumer.*
Published by: (Youth Clubs UK), B C Publications, 16C Market Pl, Diss, Norfolk IP22 3AB, United Kingdom. FAX 44-1379-650480. Ed. Richard Ings. Adv. contact Alison Mann. page GBP 320; trim 190 x 297. Circ: 1,500.

305.235   PRT   ISSN 0873-4801
100 POR CENTO JOVEM; para elas. Text in Portuguese. 1996. s-m. EUR 22.80 domestic; EUR 40.32 in Europe; EUR 55.20 rest of world (effective 2005).
Published by: Impala Sociedade Editorial S.A., Remessa Livre No. 154, Sintral, 2714-914, Portugal. TEL 351-219-238218, FAX 351-219-238463, assinaturas@impala.pt, http://www.impala.pt/. Ed. Dr. Luis Peniche. **Dist. by:** Electroliber, Rua Vascoi da Gama 4-A, Queluz 332745, Portugal. TEL 351-9425394.

301   USA
    CODEN: PRFSET
360; the accessible lifestyle. Text in English. 1993. q. adv. bk.rev.; film rev.; music rev.; software rev.; tel.rev.; video rev. back issues avail. **Description:** Interactive ezine that challenges the traditional views of people in wheelchairs.
Formerly: 360 Degrees: The Magazine with Every Angle (Print Edition) (1077-3878)
Media: Online - full text.
Published by: 360 Magazine, PO Box 922, Clifton, NJ 07014. TEL 973-472-4241, FAX 973-472-1307, mag360@aol.com, http://www.360mag.com. Pub. Parker Stanzione. Circ: 40,000.

028.5   GBR   ISSN 0262-284X
Comic Book 01026
2000 A D; featuring Judge Dredd. Text in English. 1977. w. GBP 62 domestic; GBP 90 in Europe; GBP 108 elsewhere; GBP 1.20 newsstand/cover (effective 1999). adv. film rev.; software rev.; music rev. illus. back issues avail. **Document type:** *Consumer.* **Description:** Provides illustrated science fiction stories for teenage males.
Published by: Fleetway Editions, Egmont House, Pl, Flat 25, 31 Tavistock Rd, London, W11 1AS, United Kingdom. TEL 0171-344-6400, FAX 0171-388-4020. Ed. Tharg The Mighty. Circ: 75,000 (paid). **Subscr. to:** Aim, Pallion Industrial Estate, PO Box 10, Sunderland, Tyne and Wear SR4 6SN, United Kingdom. TEL 0191-510-0201. **Dist. by:** Comag, Tavistock Works, Tavistock Rd, W Drayton, Middx UB7 7QX, United Kingdom. TEL 0191-510-0201.

CHIROPRACTIC, HOMEOPATHY, OSTEOPATHY

see MEDICAL SCIENCES—Chiropractic, Homeopathy, Osteopathy

CIRCUITS

see COMPUTERS—Circuits

CIVIL DEFENSE

see also MILITARY

363.34   NLD   ISSN 0920-3168
UA929.N2
ALERT; maandblad voor rampenbestrijding en crisisbeheersing. Text in Dutch. 1984. 11/yr. EUR 95; EUR 48 to students; EUR 16 newsstand/cover (effective 2003). adv. bk.rev. abstr.; illus.; tr.lit. **Document type:** *Trade.* **Description:** Covers all aspects of disaster planning and relief, crisis management and related public safety topics.
Incorporates (1954-1984): Paladijn (0031-0166); (1957-1984): Netherlands. Ministerie van Binnenlandse Zaken. Inspectie voor het Brandweerwezen. Maandelijkse Mededelingen (0020-2045); (in 1984): Noodzaak (0165-1471); Which was formerly (1952-1973): Civiele Verdediging (0009-7802)
Indexed: CISA, ExcerpMed.
—IE, Infotrieve, KNAW.
Published by: Reed Business Information bv (Subsidiary of: Reed Business), Van Bylandthuis, Benoordenhoutseweg 46, Den Haag, 2596 BC, Netherlands. TEL 31-70-441-5166, FAX 31-70-441-5916, info@reedbusiness.nl, http://www.tijdschriftalert.nl, http://www.reedbusiness.nl. Circ: 2,334.

363.32   USA   ISSN 1096-4274
HV6431
▶ **ANNUAL EDITIONS: VIOLENCE AND TERRORISM.** Text in English. 1990. a., latest 2003, 7th ed. USD 20.31 per vol. (effective 2004). illus. **Document type:** *Academic/Scholarly.*
Published by: McGraw-Hill - Dushkin (Subsidiary of: McGraw-Hill Higher Education), 2460 Kerper Blvd, Dubuque, IA 52001. TEL 800-243-6532, customer.service@mcgraw-hill.com, http://www.dushkin.com/text-data/catalog/0073012599.mhtml. Ed. Thomas J. Badey. Pub. Ian Nielsen. R&P Cheryl Greenleaf.

363.34   AUS   ISSN 1324-1540
▶ **THE AUSTRALIAN JOURNAL OF EMERGENCY MANAGEMENT.** Text in English. 1986. q. free. 64 p./no.; back issues avail. **Document type:** *Journal, Academic/Scholarly.* **Description:** Provides access to information and knowledge for an active emergency management research community and practitioners of emergency management.
Formerly (until 1995): Macedon Digest (0817-4024)
Indexed: CivEngAb, ESPM, H&SSA, RiskAb.
Published by: Emergency Management Australia, Mt Macedon Rd, Mt Macedon, VIC 3441, Australia. TEL 61-3-5421-5100, FAX 61-3-5421-5272, ajem@ema.gov.au, ema@ema.gov.au, http://www.ema.gov.au/. Ed., Pub. Anita Cleaver. Circ: 5,500 (controlled).

353.95   ITA   ISSN 1125-7229
AZIONE NONVIOLENTA. Text in Italian. 1964. m. (10/yr.). EUR 29 (effective 2005). adv. bk.rev. back issues avail. **Document type:** *Newsletter, Consumer.* **Description:** Covers peace and war, nonviolence, conscious objection, disarmament, human rights, and democracy.
Published by: Movimento Nonviolento, Via Spagna, 8, Verona, VR 37123, Italy. TEL 39-045-8009803, FAX 39-045-8009212, azionenonviolenta@sis.it, http://www.nonviolenti.org. Ed. Massimo Valpiana. R&P, Adv. contact Stefano Guffanti. Circ: 5,000.

363.3509489   DNK   ISSN 0908-9594
UA926.A1
BEREDSKAB. Text in Danish. 1950. bi-m. DKK 120. adv.
Former titles (until 1994): Civilforsvar (0107-0665); (until 1979): Civilforsvarsbladet (0009-8116)
Published by: Beredskabs-Forbundet, Noerre Brogade 66 D, 3 sal, Copenhagen N, 2200, Denmark. Circ: 18,787.

363.35   DEU   ISSN 0940-7154
UA926.A1
BEVOELKERUNGSSCHUTZ-MAGAZIN; Zeitschrift fuer Zivilschutz, Katastrophenschutz und Selbstschutz. Text in German. 1971. q. EUR 7.50; EUR 1.90 newsstand/cover (effective 2005). bk.rev. back issues avail. **Document type:** *Magazine, Trade.*
Former titles (until 1989): Zivilschutz-Magazin (0173-7872); (until 1980): Z S Magazin (0173-7864); Which was formed by the merger of (1959-1971): Ziviler Bevoelkerungsschutz (0044-4820); (1963-1971): Helferbrief (Ausg. Baden Wuettemberg) (0173-8542); (1963-1971): Helferbrief (Ausg. Bayern) (0173-8534); (1963-1971): Helferbrief (Ausg. Hessen) (0173-8526); (1963-1971): Helferbrief (Ausg. Niedersachse, Bremen) (0173-8518); (1963-1971): Helferbrief (Ausg. Nordrhein-Westfalen) (0173-850X); (1963-1971): Helferbrief (Ausg. Rheinland-Pfalz und Saarland) (0173-8496); (1963-1971): Helferbrief (Ausg. Schleswig-Holstein, Hamburg) (0173-8488)
Indexed: RefZh.
—CCC.
Published by: Bundesamt fuer Bevoelkerungsschutz und Katastrophenhilfe, Deutschherrenstr 93-95, Bonn, 53177, Germany. TEL 49-228-55540, FAX 49-228-5554580, internet-redaktion@bbk.bund.de, http://www.zivilschutz-online.de. Ed. Hans Walter Roth. Circ: 30,000 (paid).

THE BIODEFENCE FUNDING REPORT. see *BIOLOGY— Biotechnology*

363.35   SWE   ISSN 1102-0180
UA929.S5
CIVIL; civila foersvarstidningen; foer foersvar av maenniskovaerde och en humanistisk samhaellssyn. Text in Swedish. 1937. 8/yr.

Incorporates (in 1991): Civila Foersvarsbulletinen (0281-0115); Former titles (until 1991): Civila Foersvarstidningen (0284-4575); (until 1983): Civilt Foersvar (0346-9026); (until 1963): Tidskrift foer Sveriges Civilfoersvar; (until vol.11, 1945): Flyglarm
Published by: Sveriges Civilfoersvarsfoerbund, Fack 2034, Solna, 17102, Sweden.

363.35   USA   ISSN 0009-7810
CIVIL AIR PATROL NEWS. Text in English. 1968. m. USD 5 (effective 2005). adv. bk.rev. **Document type:** *Newspaper, Trade.*
Published by: Civil Air Patrol Corp., 105 S Hansell St, Bldg 714, Maxwell AFB, AL 36112-6334. TEL 334-953-5700, FAX 334-953-4245, capnews@cap.gov, http://www.cap.gov/mediacenter/capnews/capnews.html. Ed. James F Tynan. Circ: 54,000.

363.34   GBR   ISSN 0961-2564
CIVIL PROTECTION. Text in English. 1986. q. back issues avail. **Document type:** *Government.*
Indexed: LHB.
—BLDSC (3273.823500), ingenta. CCC.
Published by: Home Office, 50 Queen Anne's Gate, London, SW1 9AT, United Kingdom. TEL 071-273-3378. Ed. Benard Snyth. Circ: 50,000.

363.35   GBR
COMMUNITY SAFETY JOURNAL. Text in English. 2002 (June). q. GBP 40 domestic to individuals; GBP 45 in Europe to individuals; GBP 55 elsewhere to individuals; GBP 125 domestic to institutions; GBP 135 in Europe to institutions; GBP 145 elsewhere to institutions (effective 2003). adv. **Document type:** *Journal, Academic/Scholarly.* **Description:** Aimed at community safety professionals who are concerned with making community safety work, on the ground.
Published by: Pavilion Publishing Ltd., The Ironworks, Cheapside, Brighton, E Sussex BN1 4GD, United Kingdom. TEL 44-1273-623222, FAX 44-1273-625526, info@pavpub.com, http://www.pavpub.com. Ed. Alan Marlowe. Adv. contact Vicki Smith. B&W page GBP 350.

363.3   ITA
CORPO NAZIONALE SOCCORSO ALPINO E SPELEOLOGICO. NOTIZIE. Text in English, French, Italian. q. membership. bk.rev. illus.; maps; stat. **Document type:** *Bulletin, Consumer.* **Description:** Covers national and international meetings on rescue issues as well as laws regarding alpine and speleological rescues.
Formerly (until 1990): Speleo Soccorso
Published by: Corpo Nazionale Soccorso Alpino e Speleologico, Via E Petrella 19, Milan, MI 20124, Italy. TEL 39-02-29530433, FAX 39-02-29530364, http://www.cnsas.it. Ed., R&P, Adv. contact Alessio Fabbricatore TEL 39-481-531514. Circ: 8,000.

363.32 327.117   USA
COUNTER TERRORISM CHRONICLE. Text in English. 1995. bi-m. free. **Document type:** *Newspaper.* **Description:** Tracks terrorism and encourages constructive dialogue to deal with the issue.
Indexed: PerIslam.
Published by: Muslim Public Affairs Council, 3010 Wilshire Blvd, Ste 217, Los Angeles, CA 90010. TEL 213-383-3443, FAX 213-383-9674. Ed. Salam Al Marayati. Circ: 3,000.

363.34   USA   ISSN 0164-1875
D R C BOOK & MONOGRAPH SERIES. (Disaster Research Center) Text in English. 1968. irreg., latest vol.32, 2001. price varies. **Document type:** *Monographic series, Academic/Scholarly.*
Formerly: Ohio State University. Disaster Research Center. D R C - T R (0078-4109)
Indexed: SOPODA.
Published by: Disaster Research Center, University of Delaware, College of Arts & Science, Newark, DE 19716-2581. TEL 302-831-6618, FAX 302-831-2091, drc-mail@udel.edu, http://www.udel.edu/DRC/books.html.

DEFENCE RESEARCH & ANALYSIS. BRIEFS. see *MILITARY*

353.95   AUS   ISSN 0811-6407
DEFENDER; information and comment on defence matters. Text in English. 1979. q. AUD 50 domestic to libraries; AUD 65 foreign (effective 2005); subscr. incld. with membership. bk.rev. **Document type:** *Journal, Academic/Scholarly.* **Description:** Covers the Australian public debate on national security issues.
Formerly: A.D.A. Journal (0157-4310)
Published by: Australia Defence Association, PO Box 320, Erindale Centre, ACT 2903, Australia. TEL 61-2-6231-4444, defender@ada.asn.au, enquiries@ada.asn.au, http://www.ada.asn.au/defender.htm. Ed. Malcolm Kennedy. Circ: 1,100.

DENMARK. FORSVARSMINISTERIET. AARLIGE REDEGOERELSE. see *MILITARY*

363.34   USA
DISASTER PLANNING SOURCEBOOK. Text in English. 1997. a. USD 269; USD 229 foreign (effective 1999). **Document type:** *Trade.*

Published by: Thomson American Health Consultants, Inc. (Subsidiary of: Thomson Corporation, Healthcare Information Group), 3525 Piedmont Rd, N E, Bldg 6, Ste 400, Atlanta, GA 30305. TEL 404-262-5511, FAX 404-262-7837, customerservice@ahcpub.com, http://www.ahcpub.com.

363.35 USA
DISASTER RESEARCH CENTER. Text in English. a. **Document type:** *Academic/Scholarly.*
Address: University of Delaware, College of Arts & Science, Newark, DE 19716-2581. TEL 302-831-6618, FAX 302-831-2091, drc-mail@udel.edu, http://www.udel.edu/DRC/.

DOCTORS FOR DISASTER PREPAREDNESS NEWSLETTER. see *MEDICAL SCIENCES*

363.35 GBR
EASINGWOLD PAPERS. Text in English. 1990. irreg., latest vol.8, 1994. price varies. **Document type:** *Monographic series, Government.* **Description:** Discusses topics of current importance in emergency planning. Fosters a practical method of understanding developments in emergency planning in both the public and private sectors.
Published by: Home Office Emergency Planning College, Easingwold, Yorks YO6 3EG, United Kingdom. TEL 44-1347-822877, FAX 44-1347-822575.

363.34 CAN ISSN 0837-5771
CODEN: EPDIEO
EMERGENCY PREPAREDNESS DIGEST/REVUE PROTECTION CIVILE. Text in English. 1974. q. CND 20; CND 26 foreign. adv. bk.rev. stat. index. reprint service avail. from PQC. **Document type:** *Government.* **Description:** Provides current information and reference material on a broad range of subjects involving emergency preparedness.
Formerly (until 1986): Emergency Planning Digest (0317-3518); Supersedes: E M O National Digest (0012-7787)
Related titles: Microform ed.: (from PQC).
Indexed: AJEE, CBCARef, CBPI, EEA, MEA&I, MEDLINE, Repind, SOPODA.
Published by: (Canada. Emergency Preparedness Canada), Government of Canada Publications, Publishing and Depository Services, Public Works and Government Services Canada, Ottawa, ON K1A 0S9, Canada. TEL 819-956-5365, FAX 819-956-5134. Ed. Anne Marie Demers. Adv. contact Neil Patterson. B&W page CND 550, color page CND 1,650; 9.5 x 7. Circ: 2,700.

363.34 USA ISSN 0275-3782
EMERGENCY PREPAREDNESS NEWS; contingency planning - crisis management - disaster relief. Text in English. 1977. bi-w. looseleaf. USD 387 in US & Mexico; USD 405 elsewhere; USD 437 combined subscription print & email eds. (effective 2005). 8 p./no. 2 cols./p.; back issues avail. **Document type:** *Newsletter, Trade.* **Description:** For public officials, business executives and nonprofit-sector managers charged with the task of preparing for natural and man-made disasters, protecting the public when they occur, and relieving the suffering that inevitably follows.
Incorporates (in 2003): Port & Rail Security International (1541-3985)
Related titles: E-mail ed.: ISSN 1545-4894. USD 337 (effective 2005); Online - full text ed.: (from Gale Group).
—CCC.
Published by: Business Publishers, Inc., 8737 Colesville Rd., Flr. 10, Silver Spring, MD 20910-3976. TEL 800-274-6737, bpinews@bpinews.com, custserv@bpinews.com, http://www.bpinews.com/hs/pages/epn.cfm. Ed. Deborah Elby.

363.34 AUS ISSN 1329-8755
EMERGENCY SUPPORT. Text in English. 1995. 3/yr. AUD 10 foreign (effective 2002). **Document type:** *Newsletter.*
Formerly (until 1997): Emergency Support Newsletter (1325-8168)
Published by: Emergency Support Network Pty Ltd, PO Box 106, Palmyra, W.A. 6957, Australia. TEL 61-8-9430-4377, FAX 61-8-9430-5017, office@emergencysupport.com.au, http://www.emergencysupport.com.au. Ed. Michael Tunnecliffe. Circ: 5,000.

363.35 NOR ISSN 1503-4682
FARLIG GODS-INFO. Text in Norwegian. 1992. bi-m. **Document type:** *Newsletter, Government.*
Formerly (until 2001): D B E Informerer om Farlig Gods (0807-1292)
Published by: Justis- og Politidepartementet, Direktoratet for Samfunnssikkerhet og Beredskap (DSB)/Norwegian Directorate for Civil Protection and Emergency Planning, Ramsbergveien 9, Toensberg, 3115, Norway. TEL 47-33-412500, FAX 47-33-310660, postmottak@dsb.no, http://www.dsb.no.

363.35 CHE ISSN 0015-0428
FEUILLE OFFICIELLE DE LA PROTECTION CIVILE/FOGLIO D'INFORMAZIONE DELLA PROTEZIONE CIVILE/MITTEILUNGSBLATT DES ZIVILSCHUTZES. Text in French, German, Italian. 1964. s-a. CHF 10. adv. charts; illus.
Published by: Bundesamt fuer Zivilluftfahrt/Federal Office for Civil Aviation (Office Federal de l'Aviation Civile), Case Postale 3003, Bern, 1233, Switzerland. Circ: 19,000.

FOLK OCH FOERSVAR. see *MILITARY*

363.35 SWE ISSN 0349-9715
➤ **FRITT MILITAERT FORUM;** Tidskrift foer Foersvarsfraemjaudet. Text in Swedish. 1939. q. SEK 200; USD 40 foreign (effective 2003). adv. bk.rev. reprints avail. **Document type:** *Magazine, Academic/Scholarly.* **Description:** Publishes information on military and civil defense.
Former titles (until 1981): Fritt Militaert Forum, Folkfoersvaret (0345-0287); (until 1972): Foklfoersvaret (0015-5853)
Related titles: Online - full text ed.
Published by: Foersvarsfraemjandet, Teatergatan 3, Stockholm, 11148, Sweden. info@forsvarsframjandet.org, http://www.forsvarsframjandet.org/fmf.htm. Ed. Stig Wallin.

363.34 JPN
GAKEKUZURE SAIGAI NO JITTAI/RESEARCH DATA OF LANDSLIDE DISASTERS. Text in Japanese. irreg.
Published by: Doboku Kenkyujo/Public Works Research Institute, 1-6, Minamihara, Tsukuba, Ibaraki 305-8516, Japan. TEL 81-29-8796700, mail@pwrc.or.jp, http://www.pwri.go.jp/.

363.34 USA
HAZARD TECHNOLOGY. Text in English. 1980. q. free. adv. **Document type:** *Newspaper.* **Description:** Covers the use of technology in the field of emergency and environmental management.
Formerly: Hazard Monthly (0742-6410); Incorporates: Corporate Emergency Management
Related titles: Online - full text ed.
Published by: Emergency Information System, International, 1401 Rockville Pike, Ste 500, Rockville, MD 20852. TEL 301-738-6900, 800-999-5009, FAX 301-738-1026, info@eisint.com, http://www.eisintl.com. Ed. K C Chartrand. Pub. James W Morentz. Circ: 55,000.

353.95 IND ISSN 0970-0161
UA11
INSTITUTE FOR DEFENCE STUDIES AND ANALYSES. STRATEGIC ANALYSIS. Text in English. 1977. m. INR 350 domestic; USD 150 foreign; INR 30 newsstand/cover domestic; USD 15 newsstand/cover foreign (effective 1999). **Document type:** *Academic/Scholarly.*
Indexed: IPSA, LID&ISL, PAA&I.
Published by: Institute for Defence Studies and Analyses, Block No.3, Old JNU Campus, New Delhi, 110 067, India. TEL 91-11-2617-0856, FAX 91-11-2618-9023, idsa@vsnl.com, http://www.idsa-india.org. Ed. Jasjit Singh. Circ: 2,000.

363.35 IND ISSN 0970-017X
UA840
INSTITUTE FOR DEFENCE STUDIES AND ANALYSES. STRATEGIC DIGEST. Text in English. 1971. m. INR 550, USD 200; INR 50, USD 20 newsstand/cover (effective 1999). **Document type:** *Academic/Scholarly.*
Incorporates: Defence and Disarmament Review
Indexed: IPSA, PAA&I.
Published by: Institute for Defence Studies and Analyses, Block No.3, Old JNU Campus, New Delhi, 110 067, India. TEL 91-11-6187511. Ed. Jasjit Singh. Circ: 2,000.

363.35 CHE ISSN 1022-3908
INTERNATIONAL CIVIL DEFENCE JOURNAL/REVISTA INTERNACIONAL DE PROTECCION CIVIL/REVUE INTERNATIONALE DE PROTECTION CIVILE. Text in Arabic, English, French, Russian, Spanish. 1952. q. CHF 60 in Europe; CHF 80 elsewhere (effective 2000). adv. bk.rev. stat. **Document type:** *Bulletin.* **Description:** Includes information on civil defense, disaster prevention, as well as related laws and directives from an international perspective.
Formerly: International Civil Defence (0020-6369)
Indexed: ASFA, ESPM, H&SSA, RASB, RefZh, RiskAb.
Published by: International Civil Defence Organization/ Organisation Internationale de Protection Civile, Information Service, 10-12 Chemin de Surville, Petit-Lancy - Geneva, 1213, Switzerland. TEL 41-22-7934433, FAX 41-22-7934428. Ed. Pascal Gondrand. Circ: 3,000.

363.35 CHE
INTERNATIONAL DIRECTORY/REPERTOIRE INTERNATIONAL; civil protection, defence and safety emergency management. Text in English, French. 1999. a. **Document type:** *Bulletin, Government.* **Description:** Contains a compilation of national and international structures responsible for risk prevention and the protection of individuals and their property.
Published by: International Civil Defence Organization/ Organisation Internationale de Protection Civile, Information Service, 10-12 Chemin de Surville, Petit-Lancy - Geneva, 1213, Switzerland. TEL 41-22-7934433, FAX 41-22-7934428, icdo@icdo.org, http://www.icdo.org.

INTERNATIONAL JOURNAL OF EMERGENCY MANAGEMENT. see *BUSINESS AND ECONOMICS—Management*

363.35 ITA
ITALIA NOSTRA. SEZIONE DI TRENTO. BOLLETTINO. Text in Italian. 1972. s-a. back issues avail. **Document type:** *Bulletin, Consumer.*
Published by: Italia Nostra, Sezione di Trento, Via Oss Mazzurana 54, Trento, TN 38100, Italy. TEL 39-0461-237336, FAX 39-0461-266490, info@italianostra-tn.it, http://www.italianostra-tn.it. Pub. Luisa Romera. R&P Giorgio Rigo. Circ: 2,100.

363.34 JPN ISSN 0288-8408
JISHIN YOCHI RENRAKUKAI KAIHO/COORDINATING COMMITTEE FOR EARTHQUAKE PREDICTION. REPORT. Text in Japanese. 1969. s-a.
Published by: Kokudo Chiriin/Geographical Survey Institute, Ministry of Construction, 1 Kita-Sato, Tsukuba-shi, Ibaraki-ken 305-0811, Japan.

363.35 USA ISSN 0740-5537
UA926.A1
JOURNAL OF CIVIL DEFENSE. Text in English. 1968. q. USD 18. adv. bk.rev. charts; illus. index. reprint service avail. from PQC. **Document type:** *Academic/Scholarly.* **Description:** Covers subjects in the fields of civil and strategic defense strategies.
Formerly (until Jan. 1976): Survive (0039-6354)
Related titles: Microform ed.
Indexed: AMB, DM&T, Inspec, PROMT, RASB.
Published by: The American Civil Defense Association, PO Box 1057, Starke, FL 32091. TEL 904-964-5397, FAX 904-964-9641. Ed. Walter Murphey. Adv. contact Kathy Eiland. Circ: 1,000.

613.66 621.932 USA
KNIFE DEFENSE. Text in English. 1994. irreg., latest 1994. USD 17.95 (effective 2000). **Description:** Sections include: Use of Force, Readiness and Skill, Seven Basic Lines of a Knife Attack Narrative, Empty Hand Control and Zoning, Ink Pen Defense Common Side, Ink Pen Defense Opposite Side, Zoning Techiques, Knife Grips and Stances, Baton versus Knife, and Confrontational Dynamics, plus Supplemental Material and Text Terms.
Published by: Gould Publications, Inc. (Subsidiary of: LexisNexis), 1333 North US Hwy 17-92, Longwood, FL 32750-3724. TEL 800-717-7917, FAX 407-695-2906, info@gouldlaw.com, http://www.gouldlaw.com. Ed. R A Flesch.

353.95 FRA ISSN 0290-9464
LIEN DES FOURNISSEURS DE LA DEFENSE NATIONALE. Text in French. 1981. 4/yr.
Address: Gepo 19, Villa Croix-Nivert, Paris, 75015, France. Ed. Jacques Vuvan.

363.34 USA ISSN 0197-6672
MISSOURI. EMERGENCY MANAGEMENT AGENCY. NEWSLETTER. Text in English. 1975 (vol.22). q. free. bk.rev. charts; illus. **Document type:** *Newsletter, Government.* **Description:** News and announcements of emergency-preparedness activities for natural and man-made disasters at the local level in Missouri, LEPC information and floodplace management, and the National Flood Insurance Program..
Former titles: Missouri. Disaster Operations Office. Newsletter (0364-0337); Missouri Disaster Planning and Operations Newsletter (0026-6531)
Related titles: Online - full text ed.
Published by: State Emergency Management Agency, PO Box 116, Jefferson City, MO 65102. TEL 573-526-9136, FAX 573-634-7966, sstonner@sema.state.mo.us, http://www.sema.state.mo.us. Ed. Carolyn Stonner. Circ: 1,850.

MIZU SHIGEN KENKYU SENTA KENKYU HOKOKU/WATER RESOURCES CENTER. RESEARCH REPORT. see *WATER RESOURCES*

353.95 USA
N E M A NEWS. (National Emergency Management Association) Text in English. q. USD 20 (effective 2001). **Document type:** *Newsletter, Government.* **Description:** Contains articles on mitigation, preparedness, response and recovery for natural and technological disasters.
Published by: (National Emergency Management Association), Council of State Governments, 2760 Research Park Dr, Box 11910, Lexington, KY 40578-1910. TEL 859-244-8000, FAX 859-244-8001, info@csg.org, http://www.csg.org/.

363.34 JPN ISSN 0919-4304
NAMI TO NAGISA* /JOURNAL OF DISASTER PREVENTION OF HARBOURS. Text in Japanese. q.
Formerly (until 1992): Minato no Bosai (0285-7502)
Published by: Nihon Kowan Kyokai/Japan Port and Harbour Association, 3-3-5, Akasaka, Minato-ku, Tokyo, 105-0001, Japan. TEL 81-3-55499575, http://www.phaj.or.jp/.

NATURAL HAZARDS CENTER. TOPICAL BIBLIOGRAPHIES. see *CIVIL DEFENSE—Abstracting, Bibliographies, Statistics*

363.47 USA
NEW JERSEY DISASTER RECOVERY; people helping people. Text in English. 1999. irreg. free. illus. 8 p./no. 3 cols./p.; **Document type:** *Newsletter, Government.* **Description:** Discusses ways in which people can minimize the chances of being affected by natural disasters and what to do when disaster strikes.
Published by: Federal Emergency Management Agency, 500 C St, SW, Washington, DC 20472. TEL 202-646-4600, 800-525-0321, eipa@fema.gov, http://www.state.nj.us/lps/njsp/outfit-p.html, http://www.fema.gov. Ed. Aileen Cooper.
Co-sponsor: New Jersey Office of Emergency Management.

363.35 DEU ISSN 0948-7913
UA926.A1
NOTFALLVORSORGE; Zeitschrift fuer Katastrophenvorbeugung und Gefahrenabwehr. Text in German. 1970. q. adv. bk.rev. abstr.; charts; illus.; pat.; tr.lit. **Document type:** *Journal, Consumer.*
Former titles: Notfallvorsorge und Zivile Verteidigung (0938-7390); Zivilverteidigung (0044-4839)
Indexed: CISA, RASB.
Published by: Walhalla Fachverlag, Uhlandstr 44, Duesseldorf, 40237, Germany. TEL 49-211-6804214, FAX 49-211-6802082, wollmer@walhalla.de, http://www.osang.de. Ed. Guenther Wollmer. Circ: 6,000.

363.35 RUS
OBORONA I BEZOPASNOST'. Text in Russian. 156/yr. USD 1,500 in United States.
Address: A-ya 90, Moscow, 113191, Russian Federation. TEL 7-095-9552950, FAX 7-095-9552927. **US dist. addr.:** East View Information Services, 3020 Harbor Ln. N., Minneapolis, MN 55447. TEL 612-550-0961.

363.35 SCG ISSN 0029-8344
ODBRANA I ZASTITA. Text in Albanian, Macedonian, Serbo-Croatian, Slovenian. 1965. bi-m. YUN 180. adv. bibl.; illus. index.
Published by: Savezni Sekretarijat za Narodnu Odbranu, Vojska, Novinsko-izdavacka ustanova, Bircaninova 5, Beograd, 11000. Ed. Radko Kovacic.

353.95 ITA
PROTEZIONE CIVILE ITALIANA. Text in Italian. 4/yr.
Published by: Edizioni Nazionali s.r.l., Viale Faenza, 26-5, Milan, MI 20142, Italy. TEL 2-81-36-669, FAX 2-81-34-925. Ed. Luigi Rigo. Circ: 15,000.

363.1 ESP ISSN 0214-8102
UA929.S4
REVISTA DE PROTECCION CIVIL. Text in Spanish. 1984. bi-m.
Formerly (until 1988): Cuadernos de Proteccion Civil (0214-8099)
Published by: Direccion General de Proteccion Civil, Quintiliano, 21, Madrid, 28002, Spain. TEL 34-1-5373125.

363.35 NOR ISSN 1503-7843
UA929.N7
▼ **SAMFUNNSSIKKERHET.** Text in Norwegian. 2003. q. free. bk.rev. charts; illus. back issues avail. **Document type:** *Magazine, Consumer.*
Formed by the merger of (2000-2003): D B E - Aktuelt (1503-2175); Which was formerly (until 2002): Brennaktuelt (0809-0823); (1963-2003): Beredskapsnytt (1503-2566); Which was formerly (until 2002): Sivilt Beredskap (0332-902X); (until 1989): SB; (until 1970): Sivilforvarsblad (0800-2665)
Related titles: Online - full content ed.: ISSN 1503-7878.
Published by: Justis- og Politidepartementet, Direktoratet for Samfunnssikkerhet og Beredskap (DSB)/Norwegian Directorate for Civil Protection and Emergency Planning, Ramsbergveien 9, Toensberg, 3115, Norway. TEL 47-33-412500, FAX 47-33-310660, postmottak@dsb.no, http://www.dsb.no/Article.asp?ArticleID=1382. Eds. Arvid Christensen, Oeyen Janette. Circ: 25,000.

363.35 FRA ISSN 0222-559X
SECURITE CIVILE ET INDUSTRIELLE. Text in French. 1953. q. FRF 440 domestic to individuals; FRF 580 foreign to individuals (effective 2000). adv. bk.rev. bibl.; charts; illus. cum.index. **Document type:** *Trade.* **Description:** Offers information on civil defense and fire prevention.
Formerly: Protection Civile et Securite Industrielle (0033-1724)
Indexed: CISA, INIS AtomInd.
Published by: France-Selection, 9-13 rue de la Nouvelle France, BP 118, Aubervilliers, Cedex 93303, France. TEL 33-1-48331818, FAX 33-1-48332160. Adv. contact Frederique Fardeau. Circ: 8,000.

STRATEGIC AND DEFENCE STUDIES CENTRE. WORKING PAPERS. see *MILITARY*

STUDIES IN CONFLICT AND TERRORISM. see *POLITICAL SCIENCE—International Relations*

363.348 344.05348 SWE ISSN 1400-3120
HV555. A42
➤ **STUDIES ON EMERGENCIES AND DISASTER RELIEF.** Text in English. 1992. irreg., latest vol.10, 2003. SEK 80 per issue (effective 2003). back issues avail.; reprints avail. **Document type:** *Monographic series, Academic/Scholarly.*
Formerly (until 1994): Sida Studies on Emergencies and Disaster Relief (1103-4858)
Related titles: Online - full text ed.
—BLDSC (8490.480200).
Published by: (Styrelsen foer Internationel Utvecklingssamarbete/ Swedish International Development Cooperation Agency (SIDA)), Nordiska Afrikainstitutet/Nordic Africa Institute, PO Box 1703, Uppsala, 75147, Sweden. TEL 46-18-562200, FAX 46-18-562290, nai@nai.uu.se, http://www.nai.uu.se.
Co-sponsors: Sida; University of Oxford, Refugee Studies Programme.

353.95 USA ISSN 0740-0179
T A C D A ALERT. (The American Civil Defense Association) Text in English. 1978. 8/yr. looseleaf. USD 50. back issues avail.; reprint service avail. from PQC. **Document type:** *Newsletter.* **Description:** Covers current events pertaining to the strategic defense initiative and civil defense.
Formerly: T A C D A Update
Published by: The American Civil Defense Association, PO Box 1057, Starke, FL 32091. TEL 904-964-5397, FAX 904-964-9641. Ed. Walter Murphey. R&P Katy Eiland. Circ: 1,000.

363.32 USA ISSN 1062-4007
TERRORISM: DOCUMENTS OF INTERNATIONAL AND LOCAL CONTROL. Text in English. 1979. irreg., latest vol.19, 2000. price varies. back issues avail. **Document type:** *Academic/Scholarly.* **Description:** Compilation of documents focusing on the US role in the terrorist dilemma, including legal responses to international terrorism.
Published by: Oceana Publications, Inc., 75 Main St, Dobbs Ferry, NY 10522. TEL 914-693-8100, FAX 914-693-0402, orders@oceanalaw.com, http://www.oceanalaw.com. Eds. Donald Musch, Yonah Alexander, Joann Mitchell. R&P Susan Demaio. Circ: 250.

363.32 327.117 USA ISSN 1064-9352
➤ **TERRORISM: DOCUMENTS OF INTERNATIONAL AND LOCAL CONTROL. SECOND SERIES.** Text in English. 1992. irreg., latest vol.50, 2004. USD 4,950 for complete set (effective 2005); price varies per vol.. adv. back issues avail. **Document type:** *Monographic series, Academic/Scholarly.* **Description:** Provides commentary, documents, reports and other information pertaining to world terrorism.
Published by: Oceana Publications, Inc., 75 Main St, Dobbs Ferry, NY 10522. TEL 914-693-8100, FAX 914-693-0402, orders@oceanalaw.com, http://www.oceanalaw.com/ main_product_details.asp?ID=152. Eds. Donald Musch, Yonah Alexander, Joann Mitchell. R&P Susan Demaio. Circ: 250 (paid).

363.32 USA
TERRORISM UPDATE. Text in English. m. **Document type:** *Newsletter, Academic/Scholarly.*
Related titles: Online - full content ed.
Published by: Anti-Defamation League, 823 United Nations Plaza, New York, NY 10017. TEL 212-490-2525, 212-490-2525, http://www.adl.org.

TSUNAMI KOGAKU KENKYU HOKOKU/TSUNAMI ENGINEERING TECHNICAL REPORT. see *ENGINEERING—Civil Engineering*

363.34 USA
UNIVERSITY OF DELAWARE. DISASTER RESEARCH CENTER. DISSERTATIONS. Text in English. 1965. irreg., latest vol.36, 2000. USD 25 per issue (effective 2003). **Document type:** *Monographic series, Academic/Scholarly.*
Published by: Disaster Research Center, University of Delaware, College of Arts & Science, Newark, DE 19716-2581. TEL 302-831-6618, FAX 302-831-2091, drc-mail@udel.edu, http://www.udel.edu/DRC/dissertations.html.

363.34 USA
UNIVERSITY OF DELAWARE. DISASTER RESEARCH CENTER. FINAL PROJECT REPORTS. Text in English. 1967 (no.6). irreg., latest vol.48, 2001. USD 15 per issue (effective 2003). **Document type:** *Monographic series, Academic/Scholarly.*
Published by: Disaster Research Center, University of Delaware, College of Arts & Science, Newark, DE 19716-2581. TEL 302-831-6618, FAX 302-831-2091, drc-mail@udel.edu, http://www.udel.edu/DRC/projectreports.html.

363.34 USA
UNIVERSITY OF DELAWARE. DISASTER RESEARCH CENTER. MISCELLANEOUS REPORTS. Text in English. 1978 (no.20). irreg., latest vol.48, 1994. price varies. **Document type:** *Monographic series, Academic/Scholarly.*
Formerly: Ohio State University, Columbus. Disaster Research Center. Miscellaneous Reports
Published by: Disaster Research Center, University of Delaware, College of Arts & Science, Newark, DE 19716-2581. TEL 302-831-6618, FAX 302-831-2091, drc-mail@udel.edu, http://www.udel.edu/DRC/miscreports.html.

363.34 USA
UNIVERSITY OF DELAWARE. DISASTER RESEARCH CENTER. PRELIMINARY PAPERS. Text in English. 1973 (no.5). irreg., latest vol.320, 2001. price varies. **Document type:** *Monographic series, Academic/Scholarly.*
Indexed: SOPODA.
Published by: Disaster Research Center, University of Delaware, College of Arts & Science, Newark, DE 19716-2581. TEL 302-831-6618, FAX 302-831-2091, drc-mail@udel.edu, http://www.udel.edu/DRC/prepapers.html.

363.34 USA
➤ **UNIVERSITY OF DELAWARE. DISASTER RESEARCH CENTER. REPORT SERIES.** Text in English. 1968. irreg., latest vol.19, 1989. price varies. **Document type:** *Monographic series, Academic/Scholarly.*
Formerly: Ohio State University. Disaster Research Center. Report Series (0078-4133)
Published by: Disaster Research Center, University of Delaware, College of Arts & Science, Newark, DE 19716-2581. TEL 302-831-6618, FAX 302-831-2091, drc-mail@udel.edu, http://www.udel.edu/DRC/reports.html.

➤ **URBAN TRANSPORT NEWS**; management - funding - terrorism - ridership - technology. see *TRANSPORTATION*

363.35 DNK ISSN 0109-0100
VAERNSKONTAKT. Text in Danish. 1983. q. free. illus.
Published by: Forsvarskommandoen, Presse- og Informationstjeneste, PO Box 202, Vedbaek, 2950, Denmark.

363.3 RUS
VOPROSY BEZOPASNOSTI. Text in Russian. 24/yr. USD 1,885 in United States.
Related titles: Online - full text ed.
Published by: Tsentr Politicheskikh Issledovanii v Rossii, A-ya 17, Moscow, 117454, Russian Federation. TEL 7-095-3351955, FAX 7-095-2349558. **US dist. addr.:** East View Information Services, 3020 Harbor Ln. N., Minneapolis, MN 55447. TEL 612-550-0961.

363.3 RUS ISSN 0201-7776
ZA BEZOPASNOST' DVIZHENIYA. Text in Russian. bi-m. —East View.
Address: B Dorogomilovskaya 11, Moscow, 121151, Russian Federation. TEL 7-095-2433560. Ed. V V Lipnitskii. **US dist. addr.:** East View Information Services, 3020 Harbor Ln. N., Minneapolis, MN 55447. TEL 612-550-0961.

904 CHN ISSN 1000-811X
ZAIHAIXUE/JOURNAL OF CATASTROPHOLOGY. Text in Chinese. q. CNY 3 per issue domestic (effective 2000). back issues avail. **Document type:** *Academic/Scholarly.*
Related titles: Online - full content ed.: (from WanFang Data Corp.); Online - full text ed.: (from East View Information Services).
Published by: Shaanxi-sheng Dizhen Ju, Bianjia-cun, Shuiwenxiang 4 Hao, Xi'an, 710068, China. Ed. Bo Li.
Co-sponsor: Shaanxi-sheng Jianzai Xiehui.

363.3 RUS
ZASHCHITA INFORMATSII-KONFIDENT. Text in Russian. s-a.
Indexed: RefZh.
Published by: Confident Data Security Association, Pl Proletarskoi Diktatury 2, St Petersburg, 193060, Russian Federation. TEL 812-3251037, FAX 812-3251037. Ed. A P Kuznetsov. **US dist. addr.:** East View Information Services, 3020 Harbor Ln. N., Minneapolis, MN 55447. TEL 612-550-0961.

363.35 CHE
ZIVILSCHUTZ. Text in German. 1954. 9/yr. CHF 49; CHF 60 foreign. adv. **Document type:** *Bulletin.*
Published by: (Schweizerischer Zivilschutzverband), Vogt-Schild AG, Zuchwilerstr 21, Solothurn 1, 4501, Switzerland. TEL 41-32-6247474, FAX 065-247235. Ed. Hans Juerg Muenger. Adv. contact Hansruedi Spiri. B&W page CHF 2,350, color page CHF 3,450; trim 270 x 185. Circ: 21,066.

353.95 AUT
ZIVILSCHUTZ AKTUELL. Text in German. 1987. q. EUR 22.40 domestic; EUR 33.30 foreign (effective 2004). adv. **Document type:** *Magazine, Trade.*
Published by: (Oesterreichischer Zivilschutzverband), Bohmann Druck und Verlag GmbH & Co. KG, Leberstr 122, Vienna, W 1110, Austria. TEL 43-1-740950, FAX 43-1-74095183, zivilschutz.zv@bohmann.co.at, office.gl@bohmann.at, http://www.bohmann.at. Ed. Christian Poettler. Adv. contact Christoph Jenschke TEL 43-1-74095476. B&W page EUR 2,660, color page EUR 3,570; trim 185 x 270. Circ: 41,000.

CIVIL DEFENSE—Abstracting, Bibliographies, Statistics

016.363347 USA
NATURAL HAZARDS CENTER. TOPICAL BIBLIOGRAPHIES. Text in English. 1976. irreg., latest vol.19, 1996. **Document type:** *Proceedings, Academic/Scholarly.* **Description:** Consists of bibliographies on specific subjects compiled by the Center as the need arises, often in response to a request for assistance from an organization or agency. Topics relate to the Center's function as an international clearinghouse for information on natural hazards and human adjustments to hazards and disasters.
Related titles: Online - full text ed.
Published by: University of Colorado, Institute of Behavioral Science, Program on Environment and Behavior, 1201 17th St, IBS #5, Campus Box 482, Boulder, CO 80309. TEL 303-492-6819, FAX 303-492-2151, hazctr@colorado.edu, ibs@colorado.edu, http://www.colorado.edu/hazards, http://www.colorado.edu/ibs.

016.3631 RUS ISSN 0869-4176
OBZORNAYA INFORMATSIYA. PROBLEMY BEZOPASNOSTI PRI CHREZVYCHAINYKH SITUATSIYAKH. Text in Russian. 1990. m. USD 114 foreign (effective 2006). **Document type:** *Journal, Abstract/Index.*

Indexed: RASB.
Published by: Vserossiiskii Institut Nauchnoi i Tekhnicheskoi Informatsii (VINITI), Ul Usievicha 20, Moscow, 125190, Russian Federation. TEL 7-095-1526441, FAX 7-095-9430060, dir@viniti.ru, http://www.viniti.ru. Ed. N A Makhutov. Dist. by: Informnauka Ltd., Ul Usievicha 20, Moscow 125190, Russian Federation. alfimov@viniti.ru.

CIVIL ENGINEERING

see ENGINEERING—Civil Engineering

CIVIL LAW

see LAW—Civil Law

CIVIL RIGHTS

see POLITICAL SCIENCE—Civil Rights

CLASSICAL STUDIES

see also ARCHAEOLOGY ; HISTORY ; LINGUISTICS ; LITERATURE ; MUSEUMS AND ART GALLERIES

880 830   USA   ISSN 1058-238X
A M S ANCIENT AND CLASSICAL STUDIES. Text in English. 1993. irreg. **Document type:** Monographic series, Academic/Scholarly.
Published by: (Abrahams Magazine Service), A M S Press, Inc., 63 Flushing Ave., # 417, Brooklyn, NY 11205-1005. TEL 212-777-4700, FAX 212-995-5413.

930   DNK   ISSN 1399-2686
AARHUS STUDIES IN MEDITERRANEAN ANTIQUITY. Text in English. 1998. irreg., latest vol.6, 2004. price varies. **Document type:** Monographic series, Academic/Scholarly.
Published by: Aarhus Universitetsforlag/Aarhus University Press, Langelandsgade 177, Aarhus N, 8200, Denmark. TEL 45-89425370, FAX 45-89425380, unipress@au.dk, http://www.unipress.dk.

ACCORDIA SPECIALIST STUDIES ON ITALY. see ARCHAEOLOGY

ACTA AD ARCHAEOLOGIAM ET ARTIUM HISTORIAM PERTINENTIA (MISCELLANEOUS). see ARCHAEOLOGY

870 470   HUN   ISSN 0044-5975
CC1   CODEN: AAASAM
ACTA ANTIQUA ACADEMIAE SCIENTIARUM HUNGARICAE. Text in English, French, German, Latin, Russian, Italian. 1951. q. USD 288 (effective 2006). adv. bk.rev. **Document type:** Academic/Scholarly. **Description:** Publishes original articles on classical philology. Covers history, literature, philology and material culture of the Ancient East, the Classical Antiquity and Byzantium.
Related titles: Online - full text ed.: ISSN 1588-2543 (from EBSCO Publishing, Swets Information Services).
Indexed: ArtHuCI, BHA, BibLing, CurCont, DIP, IBR, IBZ, IndIslam, MLA, MLA-IB, NTA, NumL, PCI, RASB, RILM.
—Infotrieve. **CCC.**
Published by: (Magyar Tudomanyos Akademia/Hungarian Academy of Sciences), Akademiai Kiado Rt. (Subsidiary of: Wolters Kluwer N.V.), Prielle Kornelia U. 19, Budapest, 1117, Hungary. TEL 36-1-4648282, FAX 36-1-4648221, journals@akkrt.hu, http://www.akkrt.hu. Ed. Zsigmond Ritook.

800   ZAF   ISSN 0065-1141
PA25
➤ **ACTA CLASSICA.** Text mainly in English; Text occasionally in Afrikaans, French, German. 1958. a. ZAR 50 domestic; USD 40 foreign; free to members (effective 2005). bk.rev. **Document type:** Proceedings, Academic/Scholarly.
Indexed: BibLing, IBR, ISAP, PCI, RASB.
—**CCC.**
Published by: Classical Association of South Africa, PO Box 392, Pretoria, 0001, South Africa. TEL 27-12-429-6501, FAX 27-12-429-3221, http://www.casa-kvsa.org.za/ acta_classica.htm. Ed. U R D Vogel Weidemann. Circ: 500.

➤ **ACTA HYPERBOREA;** Danish studies in classical archaeology. see ARCHAEOLOGY

930 913   HUN   ISSN 0567-7246
CC1
ACTA UNIVERSITATIS SZEGEDIENSIS. ACTA ANTIQUA ET ARCHAEOLOGICA. Text in German, Greek, Latin; Notes in French, German; Section in Hungarian. 1958. irreg., latest vol.27, 1998. exchange basis. **Document type:** Monographic series, Academic/Scholarly. **Description:** Journal of classical studies and archaeology.
Indexed: NumL, RASB.

Published by: (Szegedi Tudomanyegyetem, Bolcseszettudomanyi Kar/University of Szeged, Faculty of Arts), Szegedi Tudomanyegyetem/University of Szeged, c/o E Szabo, Exchange Librarian, Dugonics ter 13, PO Box 393, Szeged, 6701, Hungary. TEL 36-62-544009, FAX 36-62-420895, Eneh.Szabo@bibl.u-szeged.hu, http://www.u-szeged.hu. Ed. Ibolya Tar. Circ: 500.

937 745.1   POL   ISSN 0524-4463
D51
ACTA UNIVERSITATIS WRATISLAVIENSIS. ANTIQUITAS. Text in Polish; Summaries in English, French. 1963. irreg. price varies. **Document type:** Academic/Scholarly.
Indexed: RASB.
Published by: (Uniwersytet Wroclawski), Wydawnictwo Uniwersytetu Wroclawskiego Spolka z o.o., Pl Uniwersytecki 9-13, Wroclaw, 50-137, Poland. TEL 48-71-441006, FAX 48-71-402735. Ed. Tadeusz Kotula. Circ: 300.

937   POL   ISSN 0578-4387
PA9
ACTA UNIVERSITATIS WRATISLAVIENSIS. CLASSICA WRATISLAVIENSIA. Text in German, Polish; Summaries in English, French, German. 1961. irreg. price varies. **Document type:** Academic/Scholarly.
Published by: (Uniwersytet Wroclawski), Wydawnictwo Uniwersytetu Wroclawskiego Spolka z o.o., Pl Uniwersytecki 9-13, Wroclaw, 50-137, Poland. TEL 48-71-441006, FAX 48-71-402735. Ed. Alicja Szastynska Siemion. Circ: 300.

ADULESCENS. see LINGUISTICS

937   ITA   ISSN 1121-8932
PA9
AEVUM ANTIQUUM; Istituto di Filologia Classica e di Papirologia. Text in Italian. 1988. a. EUR 24 domestic; EUR 40 foreign (effective 2003). **Document type:** Academic/Scholarly. **Description:** Features a critical article on a cultural aspect, literary genre or an author of the classical era. Includes analyses of historical-philological or archaeological-antiquarian character.
Indexed: RASB.
Published by: (Universita Cattolica del Sacro Cuore), Vita e Pensiero, Largo Gemelli 1, Milan, 20123, Italy. TEL 39-02-72342335, FAX 39-02-72342260, redazione.vp@mi.unicatt.it. Ed. Mario Cantilena. Circ: 500.

AKADEMIE AKTUELL. see ENCYCLOPEDIAS AND GENERAL ALMANACS

800   ZAF   ISSN 0303-1896
➤ **AKROTERION;** journal for the classics in South Africa. Text in Afrikaans, English. 1956. a., latest 2001. ZAR 30 domestic; USD 8, GBP 5 foreign (effective 2004). adv. bk.rev. abstr. back issues avail. **Document type:** Journal, Academic/Scholarly. **Description:** Deals with Classical Studies.
Formerly: Klassieke Nuusbrief (0023-2033)
Media: Duplicated (not offset). **Related titles:** Online - full text ed.: (from International Network for the Availability of Scientific Publications, African Journals Online).
Indexed: ISAP.
Published by: (Classical Association of South Africa), Universiteit Stellenbosch, Department of Ancient Studies/Stellenbosch University, Private Bag X1, Matieland, 7602, South Africa. TEL 27-21-808-3136, FAX 27-21-808-3480, jcz@sun.ac.za, http://www.sun.ac.za/AS/journals/akro/. Ed. J C Zietsman. Circ: 330.

➤ **ALPHA-OMEGA. REIHE A, LEXIKA, INDIZES, KONKORDANZEN ZUR KLASSISCHEN PHILOLOGIE.** see LINGUISTICS

400   DEU   ISSN 0179-387X
DIE ALTEN SPRACHEN IM UNTERRICHT. Text in German. 1953. q. EUR 15; EUR 5 newsstand/cover (effective 2005). adv. bk.rev. **Document type:** Magazine, Trade.
Published by: (Landesverbaende Bayern und Thueringen im Deutschen Altphilologenverband), C.C. Buchners Verlag GmbH & Co. KG, Laubanger 8, Bamberg, 96052, Germany. TEL 49-951-965010, FAX 49-951-61774, service@ccbuchner.de, http://www.ccbuchner.de. Circ: 1,900.

938   DEU   ISSN 1438-0552
ALTERTUMSWISSENSCHAFTLICHES KOLLOQUIUM. Text in German. 1999. irreg., latest vol.8, 2003. price varies. **Document type:** Monographic series, Academic/Scholarly.
Published by: Franz Steiner Verlag Stuttgart GmbH, Birkenwaldstr 44, Stuttgart, 70191, Germany. TEL 49-711-25820, FAX 49-711-2582390, service@steiner-verlag.de, http://www.steiner-verlag.de. R&P Sabine Koerner.

700   ITA   ISSN 0065-681X
AMERICAN ACADEMY IN ROME. PAPERS AND MONOGRAPHS. Text in Italian. 1919. irreg. price varies. **Document type:** Monographic series.
Indexed: RASB.
Published by: American Academy in Rome, Via Angelo Masina 5, Rome, 00153, Italy. TEL 39-0658461, FAX 39-06-5810788, hgttp://www.aarome.org.

880   USA   ISSN 0196-2086
PA74
AMERICAN CLASSICAL LEAGUE. NEWSLETTER. Text in English. 1978. 3/yr.
Published by: American Classical League, Miami University, Oxford, OH 45056. TEL 513-529-7741, FAX 513-529-7742.

480 880   USA   ISSN 0044-7633
Z7016
AMERICAN CLASSICAL REVIEW. Text in English. 1971. bi-m. USD 5 to individuals; USD 7.50 to institutions. bk.rev. bibl. index. back issues avail.
Published by: City University of New York, Queens College, American Classical Review, 65-30 Casino Blvd, Flushing, NY 11367. TEL 718-997-5000, Eds. Ethyle R Wolfe, Ursula Schoenheim. Circ: 1,400.

AMERICAN JOURNAL OF PHILOLOGY. see LINGUISTICS

AMERICAN PHILOLOGICAL ASSOCIATION. NEWSLETTER. see LITERATURE

AMERICAN PHILOLOGICAL ASSOCIATION. SPECIAL PUBLICATIONS. see LINGUISTICS

667   USA   ISSN 0360-5949
P11   CODEN: TAPAEI
➤ **AMERICAN PHILOLOGICAL ASSOCIATION. TRANSACTIONS.** Text in English. 1870. s-a. USD 90 to institutions; USD 126 combined subscription to institutions print & online eds. (effective 2006). adv. illus. cum.index: 1869-1969. back issues avail.; reprints avail. **Document type:** Proceedings, Academic/Scholarly. **Description:** Academic papers on Greek and Roman literature and civilizations.
Supersedes in part (until 1972): American Philological Association. Transactions and Proceedings (0065-9711); Which was formerly (until 1986): American Philological Association. Transactions (0271-4442)
Related titles: Microfilm ed.: (from PMC); Online - full text ed.: ISSN 1533-0699. 1974. USD 90 (effective 2006) (from EBSCO Publishing, JSTOR (Web-based Journal Archive), O C L C Online Computer Library Center, Inc., Project MUSE, ProQuest Information & Learning, Swets Information Services).
Indexed: ASCA, ArtHuCI, BibLing, CurCont, DIP, IBR, IBZ, L&LBA, NTA, PCI, SOPODA.
—**IE**, Infotrieve. **CCC.**
Published by: (American Philological Association), The Johns Hopkins University Press, Journals Publishing Division, 2715 N Charles St, Baltimore, MD 21218-4363. TEL 410-516-6984, 410-516-6987, 800-548-1784, FAX 410-516-6968, http://www.press.jhu.edu/press/journals/apa/index.html, http://muse.jhu.edu. Ed. Cynthia Damon. Adv. contact Tamara Barnes TEL 410-516-6984. page USD 300; 4.75 x 7.5. Circ: 2,576 (paid). **Subscr. to:** PO Box 19966, Baltimore, MD 21211. jlorder@jhunix.hcf.jhu.edu.

➤ **AMERICAN SCHOOL OF CLASSICAL STUDIES AT ATHENS. ANNUAL REPORT.** see ARCHAEOLOGY

➤ **AMERICAN SCHOOL OF CLASSICAL STUDIES AT ATHENS. NEWSLETTER.** see ARCHAEOLOGY

800   USA   ISSN 0741-9309
AMERICAN UNIVERSITY STUDIES. SERIES 17. CLASSICAL LANGUAGE AND LITERATURE. Text in English. 1986. irreg., latest 1994. price varies. **Document type:** Monographic series, Academic/Scholarly. **Description:** Takes an in-depth look at the literature of classical Greece and Rome.
Indexed: BibLing.
Published by: Peter Lang Publishing, Inc., 275 Seventh Ave, 28th Fl, New York, NY 10001. TEL 212-647-7700, 212-647-7706, 800-770-5264, FAX 212-647-7707, customerservice@plang.com, http://www.peterlang.com. Ed. David Bergeron. Pub. Christopher Myers. R&P Stephanie Archer. Adv. contact Patricia Mulrane.

AMPHORA. see EDUCATION—Teaching Methods And Curriculum

870 937   NLD   ISSN 0928-2130
AMSTERDAM CLASSICAL MONOGRAPHS. Text in English. 1992. irreg., latest 1995. price varies. **Document type:** Monographic series, Academic/Scholarly.
Published by: J.C. Gieben, Entrepotdok 72b, Amsterdam, 1018 AD, Netherlands. TEL 31-20-6234709, FAX 31-20-6275170, http://www.teachtext.net/gieben/. Dist. in N. America by: John Benjamins Publishing Co., PO Box 27519, Philadelphia, PA 19118-0519. TEL 215-836-1200.

ANCIENT CIVILIZATIONS FROM SCYTHIA TO SIBERIA; an international journal of comparative studies in history and archaeology. see HISTORY—History Of Asia

ANCIENT HISTORY BULLETIN/REVISTA DE HISTORIA ANTIGUA/REVUE D'HISTOIRE ANCIENNE/RIVISTA DI STORIA ANTICA/ZEITSCHRIFT FUR ALTE GESCHICHTE. see HISTORY

C

930 BEL ISSN 0066-1619
D51
ANCIENT SOCIETY; journal of ancient history of the Greek, Hellenistic and Roman world. Text in Dutch, English, French, German, Italian. 1970. a., latest vol.34, 2204. EUR 55 (effective 2005). bibl.; illus.; maps. index. **Document type:** *Journal, Academic/Scholarly.* **Description:** Promotes the study of the society of the Greek, Hellenistic, and Roman world in all its aspects, including the relations with peripheral peoples and cultures.
Related titles: Online - full text ed.: (from EBSCO Publishing, Swets Information Services).
Indexed: BrArAb, IBR, IBZ, NumL, PCI, RASB.
—BLDSC (0900.326000).
Published by: (Katholieke Universiteit Leuven), Peeters Publishers, Bondgenotenlaan 153, Leuven, 3000, Belgium. TEL 32-16-235170, FAX 32-16-228500, http://poj.peeters-leuven.be/content.php?url=journal&journal_code=AS, http://www.peeters-leuven.be. Eds. H Verdin, P Van Dessel. Circ: 500.

938 956 NLD ISSN 1570-1921
DE1
ANCIENT WEST & EAST. Text in English. 2002. s-a. EUR 198 domestic; USD 248 foreign (effective 2005). **Description:** Presents the history and archaeology of the periphery of the Graeco-Roman world, with an emphasis on local societies and cultures and their interaction with the Graeco-Roman, Near Eastern and early Byzantine worlds.
—IE.
Published by: Brill Academic Publishers, PO Box 9000, Leiden, 2300 PA, Netherlands. TEL 31-71-53-53500, FAX 31-71-53-17532, cs@brill.nl, http://www.brill.nl/product_id10660.htm. **Subscr. in N. America to:** PO Box 605, Herndon, VA 20172. TEL 703-661-1585, 800-337-9255, FAX 703-661-1501, cs@brillusa.com. **Distr. outside N. America by:** c/o Turpin Distribution, Stratton Business Park, Pegasus Drive, Biggleswade, BEDFORDSHIRE SG 18 8TQ, United Kingdom. TEL 44-1767-604-954, FAX 44-1767-601-640, brill@turpin-distribution.com.

ANCIENT WORLD; a scholarly journal for the study of antiquity. see *HISTORY*

870 470 FRA ISSN 0066-2348
L'ANNEE EPIGRAPHIQUE; revue des publications epigraphiques relatives a l'antiquite romaine. Text in French. 1888. a. EUR 56 domestic (effective 2005). reprints avail. **Document type:** *Journal, Academic/Scholarly.*
Indexed: BrArAb, IBR, RASB, SOPODA.
—CCC.
Published by: Presses Universitaires de France, 6 Avenue Reille, Paris, 75685 Cedex 14, France. TEL 33-1-58103100, FAX 33-1-58103182, revues@puf.com, http://www.puf.com.

880 AUS ISSN 0066-4774
PA1
➤ **ANTICHTHON.** Text in English. 1967. a. AUD 35 to individuals; AUD 40 to institutions (effective 2003). adv. back issues avail. **Document type:** *Journal, Academic/Scholarly.*
Indexed: AusPAIS, BibLing, DIP, IBR, IBZ, NumL, RASB.
—BLDSC (1547.320000), IE, Infotrieve, ingenta.
Published by: Australian Society for Classical Studies, c/o Dr. I. Plant, Ancient History, Macquarie University, NSW 2109, Australia. TEL 61-2-9850-8880, FAX 61-2-9850-8892, ian.plant@mq.edu.au, http://www.arts.uwa.edu.au/classics/ascs/antichthon.html. Eds. H Lindsay, H Tarrant. Circ: 550 (paid).

930 571 HUN ISSN 0003-567X
ANTIK TANULMANYOK/STUDIES IN ANTIQUITY. Text in Hungarian; Summaries in English. 1954. s-a. USD 68 (effective 2006). adv. bk.rev. illus.; abstr.; bibl. index. 160 p./no.; back issues avail.; reprints avail. **Document type:** *Journal, Academic/Scholarly.* **Description:** Original studies on the literature, language, history and material culture of Ancient Greece and Rome as well as articles concerning the Ancient East, mediaeval Latin languages and literature, the history and culture of Byzantium and the reception of Graeco-Roman culture in Hungary.
Related titles: Online - full text ed.: ISSN 1588-2748.
Indexed: BHA, RASB, RILM.
Published by: (Magyar Tudomanyos Akademia/Hungarian Academy of Sciences), Akademiai Kiado Rt. (Subsidiary of: Wolters Kluwer N.V.), Prielle Kornelia U. 19, Budapest, 1117, Hungary. TEL 36-1-4648282, FAX 36-1-4648221, journals@akkrt.hu, http://www.akkrt.hu. Ed. Istvan Borzsak.

930 DEU ISSN 0003-5696
PA3
ANTIKE UND ABENDLAND; Beitraege zum Verstaendnis der Griechen und Roemer und ihres Nachlebens. Text in German. 1945. a. EUR 154; EUR 166 combined subscription for print & online eds. (effective 2006). adv. bk.rev. illus. **Document type:** *Journal, Academic/Scholarly.*
Related titles: Online - full text ed.: (from ProQuest Information & Learning, Swets Information Services).
Indexed: ASCA, ArtHuCI, BHA, CRCL, CurCont, DIP, IBR, IBZ, NTA, PCI, RASB, RILM.
—IDS, IE, Infotrieve. **CCC.**
Published by: Walter de Gruyter GmbH & Co. KG, Genthiner Str. 13, Berlin, 10785, Germany. TEL 49-30-260050, FAX 49-30-26005251, wdg-info@degruyter.de, http://www.degruyter.com/rs/265_440_ENU_h.htm, http://www.degruyter.de. **US subscr. addr.:** 500 Executive Blvd., Ste. 306, Ossining, NY 10562-2563. TEL 914-747-0110.

938 BEL ISSN 0770-2817
DE1
➤ **L'ANTIQUITE CLASSIQUE**; revue interuniversitaire. Text mainly in French, Dutch; Text occasionally in English, Italian, Spanish. 1932. a., latest vol.71, 2002. EUR 81.20 domestic; EUR 89 in Europe; EUR 96.50 elsewhere (effective 2005). bk.rev. illus.; maps. 680 p./no.; back issues avail. **Document type:** *Journal, Academic/Scholarly.* **Description:** Publishes scholarly research on the history, archaeology, and literature of classical Greece and Rome.
Related titles: E-mail ed.; Fax ed.
Indexed: BHA, BibLing, DIP, IBR, IBZ, IPB, MLA-IB, NumL, RASB.
—BLDSC (1550.550000).
Published by: Association Belge L'Antiquite Classique, Place Blaise Pascal 1, Louvain-la-Neuve, 1348, Belgium. TEL 32-2-10474882, FAX 32-2-3455403, moucharte@arke.ucl.ac.be, http://zeus.fltr.ucl.ac.be/recherche/publications/pub_anticlas.htm. R&P Ghislaine Moucharte.

930 800 AUT ISSN 0003-6293
CC5
ANZEIGER FUER DIE ALTERTUMSWISSENSCHAFT. Text in German. 1948. s-a. bk.rev. abstr.; bibl. index. back issues avail.; reprints avail. **Document type:** *Journal, Academic/Scholarly.*
Indexed: AmH&L, BHA, BibInd, BibLing, DIP, HistAb, IBR, IBZ, PCI, RASB.
—IE, Infotrieve.
Published by: Universitaetsverlag Wagner, Andreas Hofer Str 13, Innsbruck, T 6020, Austria. TEL 43-512-587721, FAX 43-512-582209, mail@uvw.at. Ed. Sebastian Posch. Pub., R&P Gottfried Grasl.

APEIRON (KELOWNA); a journal of ancient philosophy and science. see *PHILOSOPHY*

ARBEITEN ZUR GESCHICHTE DES ANTIKEN JUDENTUMS UND DES URCHRISTENTUMS. see *RELIGIONS AND THEOLOGY—Judaic*

ARBEITEN ZUR LITERATUR UND GESCHICHTE DES HELLENISTISCHEN JUDENTUMS. see *RELIGIONS AND THEOLOGY—Judaic*

870 GBR ISSN 0309-5541
PA23
➤ **ARCA**; classical and medieval texts, papers and monographs. Text in English. 1976. irreg., latest vol.43, 2003. price varies. back issues avail. **Document type:** *Monographic series, Academic/Scholarly.*
—BLDSC (1594.460000), IE. **CCC.**
Published by: Francis Cairns (Publications) Ltd., PO Box 296, Cambridge, CB4 3GE, United Kingdom. franciscairns@netscapeonline.co.uk. Ed., Pub., R&P, Adv. contact Sandra Cairns.

➤ **ARCHAEOLOGICAL NEWS.** see *ARCHAEOLOGY*

➤ **ARCHAEOLOGICAL REPORTS (LONDON).** see *ARCHAEOLOGY*

➤ **ARCHAIA HELLAS**; monographs on ancient Greek History and archaeology. see *ARCHAEOLOGY*

➤ **ARCHAIOLOGIA KAI TECHNES.** see *ARCHAEOLOGY*

949.5 938 GRC ISSN 1010-3724
DF901.E8
➤ **ARCHEION EUVOIKON MELETON/ARCHIVES OF EUBOEAN STUDIES**; Braveio Akademias Athenon. Text in Greek. 1935. biennial, latest vol.33, 2000. EUR 50 (effective 2004). adv. bk.rev. bibl.; illus.; maps. cum.index: vols.1-27 in 1988 and 21-30 in 1997. **Document type:** *Bulletin, Academic/Scholarly.* **Description:** Chronicles research on Euboean archaeological sites and artifacts.
Indexed: HistAb, MLA, MLA-IB.
Published by: Hetaireia Euvoikon Spoudon, 60 Charilaou Trikoupi St, Athens, 106 80, Greece. Ed., R&P Charalombos Farantos. Adv. contact Roula Bobola. Circ: 1,100.

➤ **ARCHEOLOGIA CLASSICA.** see *ARCHAEOLOGY*

800 930 POL ISSN 0066-6866
ARCHIWUM FILOLOGICZNE. Text in French, German, Latin, Polish; Summaries in French. 1958. irreg., latest vol.55, 2000. price varies. **Document type:** *Monographic series, Academic/Scholarly.* **Description:** Dissertations and monographical papers on literature, history, archaeology and culture in ancient world.
Published by: Polska Akademia Nauk, Komitet Nauk o Kulturze Antycznej, Palac Kultury i Nauki, Warsaw, 00901, Poland. TEL 48-22-6202161. Ed. Josef Wolski. Circ: 750.

489 FIN ISSN 0570-734X
➤ **ARCTOS; ACTA PHILOLOGICA FENNICA.** Text in English, French, German, Italian. 1954. a., latest vol.36. EUR 45 (effective 2003). adv. bk.rev.; software rev. illus. 300 p./no. 1 cols./p.; back issues avail. **Document type:** *Yearbook, Academic/Scholarly.*
Related titles: ♦ Supplement(s): Arctos; Acta Philologica Fennica. Supplementum. ISSN 0066-6998.
Indexed: BHA, BibLing, IBR, IBZ, RASB.
Published by: Klassillis - Filologinen Yhdistys, University of Helsinki, Vuorikatu 3 A, PL 4, Helsinki, 00014, Finland. TEL 358-9-19122681, FAX 358-9-19122161, http://www.pro.tsv.fi/kfy/arctos. Ed. Heikki Solin. Adv. contact Kalle Korhonen. Circ: 500. **Dist. by:** Bookstore Tiedekirja, Kirkkokatu 14, Helsinki 00170, Finland.

489 FIN ISSN 0066-6998
ARCTOS; ACTA PHILOLOGICA FENNICA. SUPPLEMENTUM. Text in Finnish. 1968. irreg. adv. **Document type:** *Academic/Scholarly.*
Related titles: ♦ Supplement to: Arctos; Acta Philologica Fennica. ISSN 0570-734X.
Indexed: PCI.
Published by: Klassillis - Filologinen Yhdistys, University of Helsinki, Vuorikatu 3 A, PL 4, Helsinki, 00014, Finland. TEL 358-9-19122681, FAX 358-9-19122161. Ed. Jaakko Froesen. Adv. contact Raija Sarasti Wilenius. **Dist. by:** Bookstore Tiedekirja, Kirkkokatu 14, Helsinki 00170, Finland.

930.1 USA ISSN 0004-0975
PA1 CODEN: AETHEE
➤ **ARETHUSA.** Text in English. 1968. 3/yr. USD 33 to individuals; USD 90 to institutions; USD 126 combined subscription to institutions print & online eds.; USD 13 per issue to individuals; USD 36 per issue to institutions (effective 2006). adv. bk.rev. illus. 136 p./no.; reprint service avail. from PQC,PSC. **Document type:** *Journal, Academic/Scholarly.* **Description:** Publishes literary and cultural studies that combine contemporary and traditional theoretical approaches to the study of the classics.
Related titles: Microform ed.: (from PQC); Online - full text ed.: ISSN 1080-6504. USD 85 to institutions (effective 2004) (from Chadwyck-Healey Inc., EBSCO Publishing, O C L C Online Computer Library Center, Inc., Project MUSE, ProQuest Information & Learning, Swets Information Services).
Indexed: ASCA, AmHI, ArtHuCI, BibInd, CurCont, DIP, HumInd, IBR, IBZ, L&LBA, MLA-IB, PCI.
—IDS, IE, Infotrieve. **CCC.**
Published by: The Johns Hopkins University Press, Journals Publishing Division, 2715 N Charles St, Baltimore, MD 21218-4363. TEL 410-516-6984, 800-548-1784, FAX 410-516-6968, jlorder@jhupress.jhu.edu, http://www.press.jhu.edu/press/journals/arethusa/index.html, http://muse.jhu.edu. Ed. Martha Malamud. Adv. contact Monica Queen TEL 410-516-6984. page USD 230; trim 4.75 x 7.5. Circ: 526 (paid). **Subscr. to:** PO Box 19966, Baltimore, MD 21211. jlorder@jhunix.hcf.jhu.edu.

800 ARG ISSN 0325-4194
PA9
ARGOS. Text in Spanish. 1977. a. USD 20 (effective 1993). adv. bk.rev.
Published by: Asociacion Argentina de Estudios Clasicos, Beruti, 3199, Capital Federal, Buenos Aires 1425, Argentina. Ed. R Buzon. Circ: 300.

870 USA ISSN 0095-5809
PA1
ARION; a journal of humanities and the classics. Text in English. 1962-1972; N.S. 1974-1976; N.S. 1990. 3/yr. USD 19 to individuals; USD 22 foreign to individuals; USD 35 to institutions; USD 38 foreign to institutions; USD 12 to students; USD 15 foreign to students (effective 2005). adv. bk.rev. illus. index. reprint service avail. from PSC. **Document type:** *Academic/Scholarly.* **Description:** Takes an interdisciplinary approach to the classics.
Related titles: Microform ed.: (from PQC); Online - full text ed.
Indexed: ASCA, AmHI, ArtHuCI, CurCont, IAPV, MLA-IB, PCI, PhilInd, RILM.
—BLDSC (1668.423000), IE, Infotrieve, ingenta.
Published by: Boston University, 10 Lenox St, Brookline, MA 02146. TEL 617-353-6480, FAX 617-353-5905, arion@acs.bu.edu, http://web.bu.edu/arion/. Ed. Herbert Golder. R&P David Banchs. Adv. contact Julie Seeger. Circ: 800 (controlled). **Subscr. to:** Boston University, Scholarly Publications, 985 Commonwealth Ave, Boston, MA 02215.

ART AND ARCHAEOLOGY NEWSLETTER. see *ARCHAEOLOGY*

ASSOCIATION OF ANCIENT HISTORIANS. PUBLICATIONS. see *HISTORY—History Of Europe*

930 800 400 ITA ISSN 0004-6493
ATENE E ROMA. Text in Italian. 1898. q. EUR 17.50 domestic; EUR 30.60 foreign (effective 2003). bk.rev. reprints avail. **Document type:** *Journal, Academic/Scholarly.* **Description:** Studies the classics, with an emphasis on Greek and Roman history.
Indexed: ASCA, ArtHuCI, BibInd, BibLing, CurCont, DIP, IBR, IBZ, PCI, RASB, SSCI.
—IDS, IE, Infotrieve.

C

Published by: (Associazione Italiana di Cultura Classica), Casa Editrice Edumond Le Monnier, Via Antonio Meucci 2, Grassina, FI 50015, Italy. TEL 39-055-64910, FAX 39-055-643983, lemonnier@lemonnier.it, http://www.lemonnier.it.

470 410 GRC ISSN 1011-1557
AS202
ATHENA. Text in English, French, Greek. 1889. a. bk.rev. bibl. **Document type:** *Journal, Academic/Scholarly.*
Indexed: AmH&L, BibLing, HistAb.
Published by: Athenais Epistemonike Hetaireia/Scientific Society of Athens, 74 Eressou St, Athens, 106 83, Greece. TEL 30-1-3834-069. **Dist. by:** Institute of Books, M. Kardamitsa, 8 Hippokratous St, Athens 106 80, Greece.

800 930 ITA ISSN 0004-6574
PA1.A1
ATHENAEUM; studi periodici di letteratura e storia dell'antichita. Text in English, French, German, Italian. 1913. s-a. USD 80 (effective 2000). adv. bk.rev. index. **Document type:** *Journal, Academic/Scholarly.*
Related titles: Online - full text ed.
Indexed: ASCA, ArtHuCI, BibInd, BibLing, CurCont, DIP, IBR, IBZ, MLA, MLA-IB, NumL, RASB.
—BLDSC (1765.868700), IE, Infotrieve, ingenta.
Published by: Universita degli Studi di Pavia, Facolta di Lettere, Pavia, PV 27100, Italy. Ed. Prof Emilio Gabba. Adv. contact Emilio Gabba. Circ: 600.

B S A NEWSLETTER. see *ARCHAEOLOGY*

BERLINER BYZANTINISTISCHE ARBEITEN. see *HISTORY—History Of Europe*

BERN UNIVERSITAET. SEMINAR FUER KLASSISCHE ARCHAEOLOGIE. HEFTE. see *ARCHAEOLOGY*

BERN UNIVERSITAET. SEMINAR FUER KLASSISCHE ARCHEOLOGIE. BEIHEFT. see *ARCHAEOLOGY*

800 ESP
BIBLIOTECA CLASICA GREDOS. Text in Spanish. 1976. irreg., latest vol.254, 1998. price varies. **Document type:** *Monographic series, Academic/Scholarly.*
Published by: Editorial Gredos S.A., Sanchez Pacheco 85, Madrid, 28002, Spain. TEL 34-91-7444920, FAX 34-91-5192033, http://www.editorialgredos.com.

800 950 ITA
BIBLIOTECA DEGLI STUDI CLASSICI E ORIENTALI. Text in Italian. 1974. irreg., latest vol.12, 1978. price varies. **Document type:** *Monographic series, Academic/Scholarly.*
Published by: Giardini Editori e Stampatori (Subsidiary of: Libra Web), Via Giosue Carducci 60, Ghezzano - La Fontina, Pisa 56123, Italy. TEL 39-050-878066, FAX 39-050-878732, giardinieditori@giardinieditori.it, http://www.libraweb.net.

800 870 ITA
BIBLIOTECA DI STUDI ANTICHI. Text in Greek, Italian, Latin. 1974. q. price varies. back issues avail. **Document type:** *Monographic series, Academic/Scholarly.*
Published by: Giardini Editori e Stampatori (Subsidiary of: Libra Web), Via Giosue Carducci 60, Ghezzano - La Fontina, Pisa 56123, Italy. TEL 39-050-878066, FAX 39-050-878732, giardinieditori@giardinieditori.it, http://www.libraweb.net. Eds. Emilio Gabba, Graziano Arrighetti.

800 CHE ISSN 0067-7965
BIBLIOTHECA HELVETICA ROMANA. Text in French. 1954. irreg., latest vol.26, 1994. **Document type:** *Monographic series, Academic/Scholarly.* **Description:** Ancient, classical and medieval studies.
—CCC.
Published by: (Institut Suisse de Rome ITA), Librairie Droz S.A., 11 rue Massot, Geneva 12, 1211, Switzerland. TEL 41-22-3466666, FAX 41-22-3472391, droz@droz.org, http://www.droz.org.

400 MEX
BIBLIOTHECA HUMANISTICA MEXICANA. Text in Spanish. 1987. irreg., latest vol.6, 1991.
Published by: Universidad Nacional Autonoma de Mexico, Centro de Estudios Clasicos, Ciudad Universitaria, Mexico City, DF 04510, Mexico. TEL 525-6227488, FAX 525-6657874.

938 POL ISSN 0067-8031
BIBLIOTHECA LATINA MEDII ET RECENTIORIS AEVI. Text in Latin. 1960. irreg., latest vol.25, 1994. price varies. **Document type:** *Monographic series, Academic/Scholarly.*
Published by: Polska Akademia Nauk, Komitet Nauk o Kulturze Antycznej, Palac Kultury i Nauki, Warsaw, 00901, Poland. TEL 48-22-6202161. Ed. Jerzy Axer.

937 938 MEX
BIBLIOTHECA SCRIPTORUM GRAECORUM ET ROMANORUM MEXICANA. Text in Spanish. 1944. irreg., latest vol.92, 1989.
Published by: Universidad Nacional Autonoma de Mexico, Centro de Estudios Clasicos, Ciudad Universitaria, Mexico City, DF 04510, Mexico. TEL 525-6227488, FAX 525-6657874.

880 DEU ISSN 0340-7853
➤ **BIBLIOTHEK DER GRIECHISCHEN LITERATUR.** Abbreviated title: B G L. Text in German. 1971. irreg., latest vol.59, 2002. price varies. **Document type:** *Monographic series, Academic/Scholarly.*
Published by: Anton Hiersemann Verlag, Haldenstr 30, Stuttgart, 70376, Germany. TEL 49-711-549971-0, FAX 49-711-54997121, info@hiersemann.de, http://www.hiersemann.de. Eds. P Wirth, W Gessel.

➤ **BIBLIOTHEQUE DE L'ECOLE DES HAUTES ETUDES. QUATRIEME SECTION, SCIENCES HISTORIQUES ET PHILOLOGIQUES.** see *HISTORY*

800 ITA ISSN 0391-8270
PA9
BOLLETTINO DEI CLASSICI. Text in English, French, German, Greek, Italian, Latin, Spanish. 1940. a. EUR 30.99 (effective 2003). reprints avail.
Indexed: BibLing.
Published by: Accademia Nazionale dei Lincei, Via della Lungara 10, Rome, 00165, Italy. TEL 39-06-68801207, FAX 39-06-68801207, redazione@lincei.it, http://www.lincei.it. Ed. Cesare Franco Golisano.

870 ITA ISSN 0006-6583
PA2004
BOLLETTINO DI STUDI LATINI; rassegna semestrale di informazione bibliografica. Text in Italian. 1971. s-a. adv. bk.rev. index. reprint service avail. from SCH. **Document type:** *Bulletin, Academic/Scholarly.*
Indexed: BibInd, BibLing, DIP, IBR, IBZ, PCI.
—IE, Infotrieve.
Published by: Loffredo Editore SpA, Via Consalvo 99 H, Parco S Luigi, Isolato D, Naples, NA 80126, Italy. TEL 39-081-2399318, FAX 39-081-6101714, http://www.loffredo.it. Ed. Fabio Cupaiuolo. Circ: 500.

940 GBR ISSN 0068-113X
DA145
➤ **BRITANNIA**; a journal of Romano-British and kindred studies. Text in English. 1970. a., latest vol.33, 2002. GBP 36, USD 72 per vol. to individuals; GBP 45, USD 90 per vol. to institutions (effective 2005). adv. bk.rev. illus. cum.index. back issues avail. **Document type:** *Journal, Academic/Scholarly.* **Description:** Publishes articles on all aspects of Romano-British studies; includes survey of Romano-British excavations.
Related titles: CD-ROM ed.: 2002. GBP 20, USD 40 per issue to individuals; GBP 60, USD 120 per issue to institutions (effective 2003); Online - full text ed.: (from JSTOR (Web-based Journal Archive)).
Indexed: BHA, BibLing, NumL, PCI, ZooRec.
—BLDSC (2286.300000), IE, Infotrieve, ingenta. **CCC.**
Published by: Society for the Promotion of Roman Studies, The Roman Society, Senate House, Malet St, London, WC1E 7HU, United Kingdom. TEL 44-20-78628727, FAX 44-20-78628728, romansoc@sas.ac.uk, http://www.sas.ac.uk/icls/roman/frame.htm, http://www.romansociety.org/. Ed. L J F Keppie. Adv. contact Helen Cockle. page GBP 165, page USD 330; 139 x 197. Circ: 1,600.

930.1 GBR ISSN 0953-542X
➤ **BRITANNIA MONOGRAPH SERIES.** Text in English. 1981. irreg., latest no.20, 2004, Jan. price varies. illus.; maps. back issues avail. **Document type:** *Monographic series, Academic/Scholarly.* **Description:** Publishes archeological studies of Romano-British sites and general studies related to Roman Britain.
Indexed: BrArAb.
—BLDSC (2286.360000). **CCC.**
Published by: Society for the Promotion of Roman Studies, The Roman Society, Senate House, Malet St, London, WC1E 7HU, United Kingdom. TEL 44-20-78628727, FAX 44-20-78628728, romansoc@sas.ac.uk, http://www.sas.ac.uk/icls/roman/frame.htm, http://www.romansociety.org/. Ed. J P Wild.

➤ **BRITISH SCHOOL AT ATHENS. ANNUAL.** see *ARCHAEOLOGY*

➤ **BRITISH SCHOOL AT ATHENS. STUDIES SERIES.** see *ARCHAEOLOGY*

➤ **BRITISH SCHOOL AT ATHENS. SUPPLEMENTARY VOLUME.** see *ARCHAEOLOGY*

930 USA ISSN 1055-7660
PA1
➤ **BRYN MAWR CLASSICAL REVIEW.** Text in English. 1990. irreg. bk.rev. **Document type:** *Journal, Academic/Scholarly.*
Related titles: Online - full text ed.: Bryn Mawr Classical Review Online. ISSN 1063-2948. 1990. free (effective 2005).
Published by: Bryn Mawr Commentaries, Inc, Bryn Mawr College, Thomas Library, Bryn Mawr, PA 19010. TEL 610-526-7989, FAX 610-526-7475, bmr@ccat.sas.upenn.edu, http://ccat.sas.upenn.edu/bmcr/, http://www.ccat.sas.upenn.edu/bmcr. Ed. Richard Hamilton. Circ: 3,500.

➤ **BULLETIN ANTIEKE BESCHAVING**; annual papers on Mediterranean archaeology. see *ARCHAEOLOGY*

880 FRA ISSN 0007-4217
BULLETIN DE CORRESPONDANCE HELLENIQUE. Text in French. 1877. a. (in 2 vols.). price varies. charts; illus. reprints avail. **Document type:** *Bulletin, Academic/Scholarly.*
Related titles: Microfiche ed.: (from IDC); Microform ed.: (from BHP).
Indexed: ASCA, ArtHuCI, BHA, BibLing, CurCont, DIP, IBR, IBZ, MLA, MLA-IB, NumL, PCI, RASB.
—IDS, IE, ingenta. **CCC.**
Published by: (Ecole Francaise d'Athenes GRC), De Boccard Edition - Diffusion, 11 rue de Medicis, Paris, 75006, France. TEL 33-1-43260037, FAX 33-1-43548583, http://www.deboccard.com.

870 FRA ISSN 0994-8090
BULLETIN DU CANGE. Cover title: Archivum Latinitatis Medii Aevi. Text in French. 1924. q., latest vol.53, 1995. **Document type:** *Bulletin, Academic/Scholarly.* **Description:** Studies in Medieval Latin from the sixth century to the Renaissance.
Indexed: BibLing, MLA-IB.
—BLDSC (2837.980000).
Published by: (Institut de France, Comite du Cange, Union Academique Internationale/International Union of Academies BEL), Editions Honore Champion, 7 quai Malaquais, Paris, 75006, France. TEL 33-1-46340729, FAX 33-1-46346406, champion@easynet.fr, http://www.honorechampion.com.

BYZANTINISCHE FORSCHUNGEN. see *HISTORY—History Of Europe*

BYZANTINOSLAVICA; revue internationale des etudes byzantines. see *ASIAN STUDIES*

C N I PUBLICATIONS. see *HISTORY—History Of The Near East*

CALLIOPE (PERU); exploring world history. see *HISTORY*

870 GBR
CAMBRIDGE CLASSICAL STUDIES. Text in English. irreg. price varies. **Document type:** *Monographic series.*
Published by: Cambridge University Press, The Edinburgh Bldg, Shaftesbury Rd, Cambridge, CB2 2RU, United Kingdom. TEL 44-1223-312393, FAX 44-1223-315052, information@cambridge.org, http://www.cup.cam.ac.uk/. R&P Linda Nicol TEL 44-1223-325757.

880 870 GBR ISSN 0068-6638
CAMBRIDGE CLASSICAL TEXTS AND COMMENTARIES. Text in English. 1965. irreg. price varies. index. **Document type:** *Monographic series.* **Description:** Provides critical editions of Greek and Latin authors for scholars and advanced students.
—BLDSC (3015.942500).
Published by: Cambridge University Press, The Edinburgh Bldg, Shaftesbury Rd, Cambridge, CB2 2RU, United Kingdom. TEL 44-1223-312393, FAX 44-1223-315052, information@cambridge.org, http://publishing.cambridge.org/hss/classical/ cambridge_classica/, http://publishing.cambridge.org/series. R&P Linda Nicol TEL 44-1223-325757.

400 GBR ISSN 0068-6735
P11
CAMBRIDGE PHILOLOGICAL SOCIETY. PROCEEDINGS. Text in English. 1882; N.S. 1950. a. GBP 14 domestic to members; USD 22 in United States to members; GBP 20 domestic to libraries; USD 48 in United States to libraries; GBP 9 to students (effective 2005). Supplement avail.; back issues avail. **Document type:** *Proceedings, Academic/Scholarly.* **Description:** Covers a wide variety of issues pertaining to the history, culture, literature, and archaeology of the ancient Greek and Roman worlds.
Related titles: Microfiche ed.: N.S. (from IDC); Microform ed.: N.S. (from PQC).
Indexed: ASCA, ArtHuCI, BibLing, CurCont, NumL, SSCI.
—BLDSC (6671.900000), IDS, IE. **CCC.**
Published by: Cambridge Philological Society, c/o Prof. C. Austin, Trinity Hall, Cambridge, CB2 1TJ, United Kingdom. Eds. C Kelly, J Warren. R&P C Austin. Circ: 700.

400 GBR ISSN 0068-6743
CAMBRIDGE PHILOLOGICAL SOCIETY. PROCEEDINGS. SUPPLEMENT. Text in English. 1965. irreg., latest vol.24, 1999. GBP 30 per issue in United Kingdom to members (effective 2005). back issues avail. **Document type:** *Proceedings.* **Description:** Covers a variety of topics pertaining to the history, archaeology, literature, and culture of ancient Greece and Rome.
—BLDSC (6671.910000).
Published by: Cambridge Philological Society, c/o Prof. C. Austin, Trinity Hall, Cambridge, CB2 1TJ, United Kingdom. Ed. C Kelly. R&P C Austin.

937 938 ITA ISSN 1123-8968
D51
CASSIODORUS; rivista di studi sulla tarda antichita. Text in French, German, Italian. 1995. a. EUR 51.65 domestic; EUR 97.50 foreign (effective 2003). bk.rev. back issues avail. **Document type:** *Academic/Scholarly.* **Description:** Focuses on the Mediterranean world from 300 A.D. to 850 A.D.

Published by: Rubbettino Editore, Viale Rosario Rubbettino 10, Soveria Mannelli, CZ 88049, Italy. TEL 39-0968-662034, FAX 39-0968-662055, segreteria@rubettino.it, http://www.rubbettino.it. Circ: 400. Dist. by: Brepols Publishers. info.brepols@brepols.net, http://www.brepols.net.

400 MEX
CENTRO DE ESTUDIOS CLASICOS. SERIE DIDACTICA. Text in Spanish. 1977. irreg., latest vol.15, 1990.
Published by: Universidad Nacional Autonoma de Mexico, Centro de Estudios Clasicos, Ciudad Universitaria, Mexico City, DF 04510, Mexico.

930 ITA
CENTRO RICERCHE E DOCUMENTAZIONE SULL'ANTICHITA CLASSICA. MONOGRAFIE. Text in Italian. irreg., latest vol.19, 1998. price varies. **Document type:** *Monographic series, Academic/Scholarly.*
Published by: (Centro Ricerche e Documentazione sull'Antichita Classica), L'Erma di Bretschneider, Via Cassiodoro, 19, PO Box 6192, Rome, RM 00193, Italy. TEL 39-06-6874127, FAX 39-06-6874129, edizioni@lerma.it, http://www.lerma.it.

800 NLD ISSN 0169-7692
➤ **CINCINNATI CLASSICAL STUDIES. NEW SERIES.** Text in Dutch. 1977. irreg., latest vol.8. back issues avail. **Document type:** *Monographic series, Academic/Scholarly.*
Published by: Brill Academic Publishers, PO Box 9000, Leiden, 2300 PA, Netherlands. TEL 31-71-53-53-500, FAX 31-71-53-17-532, cs@brill.nl, http://www.brill.nl. R&P Elizabeth Venekamp. **Subscr. in N. America to:** PO Box 605, Herndon, VA 20172. TEL 703-661-1585, 800-337-9255, FAX 703-661-1501, cs@brillusa.com. **Distr. outside N. America by:** c/o Turpin Distribution, Stratton Business Park, Pegasus Drive, Biggleswade, BEDFORDSHIRE SG 18 8TQ, United Kingdom. TEL 44-1767-604-954, FAX 44-1767-601-640, brill@turpin-distribution.com.

880 ESP
CLASICOS MEDIEVALES. Text in Spanish. irreg., latest vol.28, 2003. price varies. **Document type:** *Monographic series, Academic/Scholarly.*
Indexed: MLA-IB.
Published by: Editorial Gredos S.A., Sanchez Pacheco 85, Madrid, 28002, Spain. TEL 34-91-7444920, FAX 34-91-5192033, http://www.editorialgredos.com. Ed. Carlos Alvar.

800 PRT ISSN 0870-0141
PA2009
CLASSICA; boletim de pedagogia e cultura. Text in Portuguese. 1977. irreg. price varies. bk.rev. **Document type:** *Academic/Scholarly.*
Published by: Universidade de Lisboa, Centro de Estudos Classicos, Faculdade de Letras, Lisbon, 1600-214, Portugal. TEL 351-1-7965162, FAX 351-1-7960063, jabouille@mail.telepc.pt. Ed. Victor Jabouille. Circ: 1,000.

905 DNK ISSN 0106-5815
PA9
➤ **CLASSICA ET MEDIAEVALIA;** revue Danoise de philologie et d'histoire. Text mainly in English; Text occasionally in French, German. 1949. a. DKK 395 newsstand/cover domestic to individuals; GBP 37, USD 65 newsstand/cover elsewhere to individuals (effective 2005). reprints avail. **Document type:** *Journal, Academic/Scholarly.* **Description:** Devoted to philology, history, philosophy Graeco-Roman antiquity and the Middle Ages.
Related titles: CD-ROM ed.; Supplement(s): Classica et Mediaevalia Dissertationes. ISSN 0906-2912.
Indexed: BEL&L, BibLing, DIP, IBR, IBZ, IPB, MLA-IB, PCI, RASB, RILM.
—IE. **CCC.**
Published by: Museum Tusculanum Press, c/o University of Copenhagen, Njalsgade 94, Copenhagen S, 2300, Denmark. TEL 45-35-329109, FAX 45-35-329113, mtp@mtp.dk, http://www.mtp.dk/periodicals/classica. Ed. Ole Thomsen TEL 45-89-422063. **Dist. in U.S. and Canada by:** International Specialized Book Services Inc., 5804 N E Hassalo St, Portland, OR 97213-3644. TEL 503-287-3093, FAX 503-280-8832, orders@isbs.com.

880 930.1 ESP ISSN 1381-2955
CLASSICAL AND BYZANTINE MONOGRAPHS. Text in Multiple languages. 1973. irreg., latest vol.48, 2001. CHF 120 (effective 2001). **Document type:** *Monographic series.*
Published by: A.M. Hakkert, POB 2025, Las Palmas De Gran Canaria, Canary Islands 35080, Spain. TEL 34-928-766089, FAX 34-928-761619, willem@dial.eunet.es, http://www.eunet.es/InterStand/hakkert.

480 880 USA ISSN 0278-6656
DE1
➤ **CLASSICAL ANTIQUITY.** Text in English. 1968. s-a. USD 42 to individuals; USD 140 to institutions (effective 2005 & 2006). adv. illus. Index. 200 p./no.; back issues avail.; reprints avail. **Document type:** *Journal, Academic/Scholarly.* **Description:** Features interdisciplinary research and discussion of major issues in the field of classics.
Formerly (until 1982): California Studies in Classical Antiquity (0068-5895)
Related titles: Microform ed.: (from PQC); Online - full text ed.: ISSN 1067-8344. USD 220 to institutions (effective 2005 & 2006) (from Chadwyck-Healey Inc., EBSCO Publishing, Florida Center for Library Automation, O C L C Online Computer Library Center, Inc., ProQuest Information & Learning, Swets Information Services).
Indexed: ASCA, Acal, AmHI, ArtHuCI, BibLing, CurCont, HumInd, IBR, IBZ, NTA, PCI, RASB, SSCI.
—BLDSC (3274.534500), IDS, IE, Infotrieve, ingenta. **CCC.**
Published by: (University of California at Berkeley, Department of Classics), University of California Press, Journals Division, 2000 Center St, Ste 303, Berkeley, CA 94704-1223. TEL 510-643-7154, FAX 510-642-9917, journals@ucpress.edu, http://www.ucpress.edu/journals/ca. adv.: page USD 325; 5.5 x 8. Circ: 592 (paid).

800 USA
CLASSICAL ASSOCIATION OF NEW ENGLAND. ANNUAL BULLETIN. Text in English. 1906. a. membership only. bibl.; illus. **Document type:** *Bulletin.* **Description:** Presents the minutes of executive committee's meetings. Includes meetings, reports of officers, abstracts of papers delivered at the annual meeting, and a membership list.
Published by: Classical Association of New England (Exeter), Phillips Exeter Academy, Exeter, NH 03833. TEL 603-772-4311 ext. 3258, FAX 603-778-9563, a_wooley@exeter.edu. Ed. Allan Wooley. Circ: 900.

150 USA
CLASSICAL ASSOCIATION OF THE PACIFIC NORTHWEST. BULLETIN. Text in English. 1971. s-a. USD 9 (effective 2000). adv. bibl. **Document type:** *Bulletin.*
Published by: Classical Association of the Pacific Northwest, Univ of Washington, Dept of Classics, Box 353110, Seattle, WA 98195. TEL 206-543-2266, FAX 206-543-2267. Ed., R&P Alain M Gowing. Circ: 150.

800 USA ISSN 0009-8337
PA1
➤ **CLASSICAL BULLETIN.** Text in English. 1925. s-a. USD 25 domestic to individuals; USD 35 foreign to individuals; USD 50 to institutions; USD 20 newsstand/cover (effective 2003). adv. bk.rev. illus. index. back issues avail.; reprint service avail. from PQC. **Document type:** *Journal, Academic/Scholarly.* **Description:** Specializes in publishing scholarship in classical studies from abroad, the history of scholarship in the field, special topics and pedagogy in the field.
Related titles: Microform ed.: (from PQC); Online - full text ed.: (from bigchalk, Chadwyck-Healey Inc., EBSCO Publishing, Northern Light Technology, Inc., ProQuest Information & Learning).
Indexed: ABS&EES, ASCA, ArtHuCI, BEL&L, CurCont, NTA, PCI, SSCI.
Published by: Bolchazy - Carducci Publishers, Inc, 1000 Brown St, Unit 101, Wauconda, IL 60084. TEL 847-526-4344, FAX 847-526-2867, cb@bolchazy.com., info@bolchazy.com, http://www.bolchazy.com/cbindex.html. Ed., Pub. Ladislaus J Bolchazy. R&P, Adv. contact Laurie Haight Keenan. Circ: 700.

938 USA ISSN 0009-8353
PA1
➤ **CLASSICAL JOURNAL.** Text in English. 1905. bi-m. USD 45 in US & Canada; USD 50 elsewhere; USD 17.50 per issue (effective 2005). adv. bk.rev. abstr.; bibl.; charts; illus. index, cum.index every 25 yrs.: vols.26-50 (1931-1955). Supplement avail.; reprints avail. **Document type:** *Journal, Academic/Scholarly.*
Related titles: Microform ed.: (from PMC, PQC); Online - full text ed.: (from H.W. Wilson, O C L C Online Computer Library Center, Inc.).
Indexed: ABIn, AmHI, ArtHuCI, BHA, BRI, BibLing, CBRI, CurCont, EduInd, HumInd, IBRH, IIMP, MLA, MLA-IB, NTA, NumL, PCI, PhilInd, RASB.
—BLDSC (3274.550000), IDS, IE, Infotrieve, ingenta. **CCC.**
Published by: Classical Association of the Middle West and South, Inc., c/o Anne H. Groton, St. Olaf College, Dept. of Classics, 1520 St. Olaf Ave, Northfield, MN 55057-1574. TEL 507-646-3387, FAX 507-646-3732, Classical.Journal@colorado.edu, http://www.camws.org/CJ/. Ed. S Douglas Olson. Circ: 2,900 (paid).

880 USA ISSN 0009-8361
PA2001
CLASSICAL OUTLOOK. Text in English, Greek, Latin. 1923. q. USD 45 domestic membership; USD 47 in Canada membership; USD 50 elsewhere membership (effective 2005). adv. bk.rev. illus. index. reprints avail. **Document type:** *Academic/Scholarly.* **Description:** Specifically for teachers. Offers articles, reports, instructional materials, and reviews of immediate interest and use to active classroom teachers of Latin, Greek, and classical humanities in elementary, middle, secondary schools, and in the colleges and universities.
Related titles: Microform ed.
Indexed: BRI, BibLing, CBRI, CIJE.
—BLDSC (3274.560000), IE, Infotrieve, ingenta.
Published by: American Classical League, Miami University, Oxford, OH 45056. TEL 513-529-7741, FAX 513-529-7742. Ed. Richard La Fleur. Circ: 4,000.

930 800 400 USA ISSN 0009-837X
PA1
➤ **CLASSICAL PHILOLOGY.** Text in English. 1906. q. USD 55 combined subscription to individuals print & online eds.; USD 206 combined subscription to institutions print & online eds.; USD 18 per issue to individuals; USD 60 per issue to institutions (effective 2006). adv. bk.rev. bibl.; illus. Index. 96 p./no.; reprint service avail. from PQC,ISI,PSC. **Document type:** *Journal, Academic/Scholarly.* **Description:** Studies the life and thought of classical antiquity; presents papers on Greek and Roman languages and literatures, history, philosophy, religion, art and society.
Related titles: Microfiche ed.: (from IDC); Online - full text ed.: ISSN 1546-072X. USD 185 (effective 2006) (from EBSCO Publishing, Florida Center for Library Automation, Gale Group, JSTOR (Web-based Journal Archive), O C L C Online Computer Library Center, Inc., ProQuest Information & Learning).
Indexed: ASCA, AmHI, ArtHuCI, BibLing, CurCont, DIP, HumInd, IBR, IBRH, IBZ, IPB, L&LBA, LRI, NTA, NumL, PCI, RASB, SOPODA, SSCI.
—IDS, IE, Infotrieve. **CCC.**
Published by: University of Chicago Press, Journals Division, Journals Division, PO Box 37005, Chicago, IL 60637. TEL 773-753-3347, FAX 773-753-0811, subscriptions@journals.uchicago.edu, http://www.journals.uchicago.edu/CP. Ed. David Wray. Adv. contact Cheryl Jones. B&W page USD 475; trim 6 x 9. Circ: 1,100 (paid).

800 400 GBR ISSN 0009-8388
PA1
➤ **THE CLASSICAL QUARTERLY.** Text in English. 1906; N.S. 1951. s-a. GBP 81 combined subscription to institutions print & online eds.; USD 146 combined subscription in North America to institutions print & online eds. (effective 2006). adv. illus. Index. 320 p./no.; back issues avail.; reprint service avail. from PSC. **Document type:** *Journal, Academic/Scholarly.* **Description:** Covers Greco-Roman antiquity in the English-speaking world. Includes research papers and short notes in the fields of language, literature, history and philosophy.
Related titles: Microform ed.: N.S. (from PQC); Online - full text ed.: ISSN 1471-6844. N.S. GBP 76 to institutions; USD 138 in North America to institutions (effective 2006) (from EBSCO Publishing, Florida Center for Library Automation, Gale Group, HighWire Press, IngentaConnect, JSTOR (Web-based Journal Archive), Northern Light Technology, Inc., O C L C Online Computer Library Center, Inc., ProQuest Information & Learning, Swets Information Services).
Indexed: ASCA, ArtHuCI, BibLing, BrArAb, BrHumI, CurCont, DIP, HumInd, IBR, IBZ, IGCS, IPB, LRI, MLA, MLA-IB, MathSciNet, NTA, NumL, PCI, PhilInd, RASB, RI-1, RI-2, RILM, SSCI, WBA, WMB.
—BLDSC (3274.580000), IDS, IE, Infotrieve, ingenta. **CCC.**
Published by: Cambridge University Press, The Edinburgh Bldg, Shaftesbury Rd, Cambridge, CB2 2RU, United Kingdom. TEL 44-1223-326070, FAX 44-1223-325150, journals@cambridge.org, http://uk.cambridge.org/journals. Eds. Judith Mossman, Miriam Griffin. adv.: B&W page GBP 305, B&W page USD 480; 110 x 195. Circ: 1,600.

930 800 GBR ISSN 0009-840X
PA1
➤ **THE CLASSICAL REVIEW.** Text in English. 1886. s-a. GBP 88 combined subscription to institutions print & online eds.; USD 156 combined subscription in North America to institutions print & online eds. (effective 2006). adv. bk.rev. illus. index. 400 p./no.; back issues avail.; reprint service avail. from PSC. **Document type:** *Journal, Academic/Scholarly.* **Description:** Critical reviews in the field of Graeco-Roman antiquity from all countries.
Related titles: Microform ed.: (from PMC, PQC); Online - full text ed.: ISSN 1464-3561. GBP 83 to institutions; USD 148 in North America to institutions (effective 2006) (from EBSCO Publishing, Gale Group, HighWire Press, IngentaConnect, JSTOR (Web-based Journal Archive), O C L C Online Computer Library Center, Inc., Swets Information Services).
Indexed: ASCA, ArtHuCI, BRD, BRI, BibLing, BrHumI, CBRI, CurCont, DIP, HumInd, IBR, IBRH, IBZ, IGCS, IPB, MEA&I, MLA, MLA-IB, NumL, PhilInd, RASB, RI-1, RI-2, SSCI.
—IDS, IE, Infotrieve. **CCC.**
Published by: (Classical Association), Cambridge University Press, The Edinburgh Bldg, Shaftesbury Rd, Cambridge, CB2 2RU, United Kingdom. Eds. Neil Hopkinson, Roy Gibson. adv.: B&W page GBP 335, B&W page USD 555; 195 x 110. Circ: 1,600.

930 USA ISSN 0009-8418
➤ **CLASSICAL WORLD.** Text in English. 1907. q. USD 35 in North America to individuals; USD 40 elsewhere to individuals; USD 50 to institutions (effective 2005). adv. bk.rev. abstr.; bibl.; illus. Index. reprints avail. **Document type:** *Journal, Academic/Scholarly.* **Description:** Covers all aspects of Greek and Roman literature, history and society, or classical tradition.
Formerly (until 1957): Classical Weekly
Related titles: Microform ed.: (from MIM, PQC); Online - full text ed.: (from Chadwyck-Healey Inc., H.W. Wilson, O C L C Online Computer Library Center, Inc.).
Indexed: ASCA, ArtHuCI, BRD, BRI, CBRI, CurCont, DIP, IBR, IBRH, IBZ, IPB, MEA&I, NTA, NumL, PCI, PhilInd, RILM, SSCI.

C

—BLDSC (3274.590000), IE, Infotrieve, ingenta.
Published by: Classical Association of the Atlantic States, University of the Sciences, 600 S 43rd St, Philadelphia, PA 19104-4495. TEL 215-596-8504, classics@usip.edu, http://www.caas-cw.org/. Ed. Matthew S Santirocco. Adv. contact Lawrence E Gaichas. Circ: 3,000. **Subscr. to:** Philosophy Documentation Center, PO Box 7147, Charlottesville, VA 22906-7147. TEL 800-444-2419, 434-220-3300, FAX 419-372-6987, order@pdcnet.org, http://www.pdcnet.org.

➤ **THE CLASSICIST.** see *ARCHITECTURE*

800 410   AUS   ISSN 0155-0659
➤ **CLASSICUM.** Text in English. 1975. s-a. AUD 22 domestic to non-members; AUD 30 foreign to non-members (effective 2003). adv. bk.rev. 32 p./no.; back issues avail. **Document type:** *Journal, Academic/Scholarly.*
Published by: Classical Association of New South Wales, c/o Dr IM Plant, Ancient History, Macqurie University, Sydney, NSW 2109, Australia. FAX 61-2-9484-5915, ian.plant@mq.edu.au, clhast@cc.newcastle.edu.au. Circ: 300 (controlled).
Co-sponsor: Classical Languages Teachers Association Inc.

➤ **CODICES MANUSCRIPTI**; Zeitschrift fuer Handschriftenkunde. see *LIBRARY AND INFORMATION SCIENCES*

870   GBR   ISSN 0951-7405
COLLECTED CLASSICAL PAPERS. Text in English. 1987. irreg., latest vol.2, 1991. price varies. illus. **Document type:** *Monographic series.*
Published by: Francis Cairns (Publications) Ltd., PO Box 296, Cambridge, CB4 3GE, United Kingdom. franciscairns@netscapeonline.co.uk. Ed., Pub., R&P, Adv. contact Sandra Cairns.

938   FRA   ISSN 0184-7155
COLLECTION DES UNIVERSITES DE FRANCE. Text in French, Latin, Greek, Classical. 1920. irreg.
Related titles: Series: Serie Grecque. ISSN 1275-4234. 1991; Serie Latine. ISSN 1275-4226. 1991.
—CCC.
Published by: Editions Les Belles Lettres, 95 bd. Raspail, Paris, 75006, France. FAX 33-1-4544-9288, http:// www.lesbelleslettres.com.

938   BEL   ISSN 1378-4013
COLLECTION D'ETUDES CLASSIQUES. Text in French. 1986. irreg., latest vol.17, 2003. price varies. **Document type:** *Monographic series, Academic/Scholarly.*
Indexed: MLA-IB.
Published by: (Societe des Etudes Classiques A S B L), Peeters Publishers, Bondgenotenlaan 153, Leuven, 3000, Belgium. TEL 32-16-235170, FAX 32-16-228500, peeters@peeters-leuven.be, http://www.peeters-leuven.be.

800   NLD   ISSN 0166-1302
➤ **COLUMBIA STUDIES IN THE CLASSICAL TRADITION.** Text in Dutch. 1976. irreg., latest vol.24, 2001. price varies. back issues avail. **Document type:** *Monographic series, Academic/Scholarly.* **Description:** Publishes scholarly discussions of literary, historical and cultural issues from European classical antiquity and studies of classical ideas in medieval and Renaissance Europe.
—BLDSC (3323.270000), IE, ingenta.
Published by: Brill Academic Publishers, PO Box 9000, Leiden, 2300 PA, Netherlands. TEL 31-71-53-53-500, FAX 31-71-53-17-532, cs@brill.nl, http://www.brill.nl. R&P Elizabeth Venekamp. **Subscr. in N. America to:** PO Box 605, Herndon, VA 20172. TEL 703-661-1585, 800-337-9255, FAX 703-661-1501, cs@brillusa.com. **Distr. outside N. America by:** c/o Turpin Distribution, Stratton Business Park, Pegasus Drive, Biggleswade, BEDFORDSHIRE SG 18 8TQ, United Kingdom. TEL 44-1767-604-954, FAX 44-1767-601-640, brill@turpin-distribution.com.

880   DEU
COMMENTARIA IN ARISTOTELEM GRAECA; versiones latinaetemporis resuscitatarum litterarum. Abbreviated title: C A G L. Text in Latin. 1990. irreg., latest vol.8, 2001. price varies. **Document type:** *Monographic series, Academic/Scholarly.*
Related titles: Microfilm ed.: (from BHP).
Published by: Friedrich Frommann Verlag Guenther Holzboog, Koenig-Karl-Str 27, Stuttgart, 70372, Germany. TEL 49-711-9559690, FAX 49-711-9559691, vertrieb@frommann-holzboog.de, http://www.frommann-holzboog.de. Ed. Charles Lohr.

COMMISSIONE ARCHEOLOGICA COMUNALE DI ROMA. BULLETTINO/ARCHAEOLOGICAL COMMISSION OF ROME. BULLETIN. see *ARCHAEOLOGY*

870 880   ITA   ISSN 1122-0872
CORPUS DEI PAPIRI FILOSOFICI GRECI E LATINI. STUDI E TESTI. Text in Italian. 1985. irreg., latest vol.10, 2000. price varies. **Document type:** *Monographic series, Academic/Scholarly.*
Published by: (Accademia Toscana di Scienze e Lettere La Colombaria), Casa Editrice Leo S. Olschki, Viuzzo del Pozzetto 8, Florence, 50126, Italy. TEL 39-055-6530684, FAX 39-055-6530214, celso@olschki.it, http://www.olschki.it.

745 091   DEU
CORPUS DER BYZANTINISCHEN MINIATURENHANDSCHRIFTEN (C B M). Text in German. 1977. irreg., latest vol.5, 1997. price varies. **Document type:** *Monographic series, Academic/Scholarly.*
Published by: (Oesterreichische Akademie der Wissenschaften AUT, Kommission fuer Byzantinistik AUT), Anton Hiersemann Verlag, Haldenstr 30, Stuttgart, 70376, Germany. TEL 49-711-549971-0, FAX 49-711-54997121, info@hiersemann.de, http://www.hiersemann.de. Ed. Irmgard Hutter.

069.4   ITA   ISSN 0070-0479
CORPUS VASORUM ANTIQUORUM. ITALIA. Text in Italian. 1927. irreg., latest vol.70, 1998. price varies. illus. back issues avail. **Document type:** *Monographic series, Academic/Scholarly.* **Description:** Researches ceramic vases and other earthenware from classical antiquity currently housed in museum and private collections.
Published by: (Museo Nazionale di Villa Giulia), L'Erma di Bretschneider, Via Cassiodoro, 19, PO Box 6192, Rome, RM 00193, Italy. TEL 39-06-6874127, FAX 39-06-6874129, edizioni@lerma.it, http://www.lerma.it. Ed. Mr. Barbieri.

938   ESP
CRETAN STUDIES. Text in Spanish. 1988. irreg., latest vol.6. CHF 82 (effective 2001). back issues avail. **Document type:** *Academic/Scholarly.*
Indexed: BibLing.
—BLDSC (3487.324000).
Published by: A.M. Hakkert, POB 2025, Las Palmas De Gran Canaria, Canary Islands 35080, Spain. TEL 34-928-766089, FAX 34-928-761619, willem@dial.eunet.es, http://www.eunet.es/InterStand/hakkert.

CUADERNOS DE FILOLOGIA CLASICA. ESTUDIOS GRIEGOS E INDOEUROPEOS. see *LINGUISTICS*

CUADERNOS DE FILOLOGIA CLASICA. ESTUDIOS LATINOS. see *LINGUISTICS*

CYPRUS. DEPARTMENT OF ANTIQUITIES. ANNUAL REPORT. see *ARCHAEOLOGY*

CYPRUS. DEPARTMENT OF ANTIQUITIES. REPORT. see *ARCHAEOLOGY*

DANISH HUMANIST TEXTS AND STUDIES. see *LITERATURE*

489   BEL   ISSN 0070-4792
DIDACTICA CLASSICA GANDENSIA. Text in Dutch. 1962. a.
Indexed: RASB.
Published by: Rijksuniversiteit te Gent, Blandijnberg 2, Gent, 9000, Belgium. http://www.flwi.ugent.be/latijnengrieks/DCG. Ed. Christiane De Pauw. **Subscr. to:** Mrs. Verbeken-De Pauw, Baertsoenkaai 3, Ghent 9000, Belgium.

480 792   GBR   ISSN 1321-4853
PN2131
DIDASKALIA; ancient theater today. Text in English. 1994. irreg., latest vol.6, no.2, 2005. free (effective 2005). bk.rev. illus. back issues avail.; reprints avail. **Document type:** *Journal, Academic/Scholarly.* **Description:** Source for the latest developments in Greek and Roman drama, dance, and music as they are performed today.
Media: Online - full text.
Address: c/o Hugh Denard, Ed, School of Theatre Studies, University of Warwick, Coventry, CV4 AL, United Kingdom. didaskalia@csv.warwick.ac.uk, http://didaskalia.open.ac.uk/index.shtml, http://www.warwick.ac.uk/didaskalia/. Eds C W Marshall, Hugh Denard.

DIOTIMA; epitheoresis philosophikes erevnes - revue de recherche philosophique - review of philosophical research. see *PHILOSOPHY*

DUTCH MONOGRAPHS ON ANCIENT HISTORY AND ARCHAEOLOGY. see *ARCHAEOLOGY*

930   AUS   ISSN 0085-0187
➤ **EDUBBA**; studies ancient history. Text in English. 1967. a. AUD 15 per vol. (effective 1999 & 2000). bk.rev. bibl.; illus.; maps. back issues avail. **Document type:** *Academic/Scholarly.* **Description:** Discusses and explores a wide variety of topics of interest to students of Classical Studies, including the archaeology, history, and literature of ancient Greece and Rome and the Near East.
Published by: University of Sydney, Department of Ancient History, Ancient History A17, Sydney, NSW 2006, Australia. TEL 61-2-9351-2156, FAX 61-2-9351-7760, http://www.arts.usyd.edu.au/Arts/departs/anchistory/edubba.html. R&P Kathryn Welch TEL 61-2-9351-4779. Circ: 500. **Co-sponsor:** Ancient History Society.

880   USA
EIDOS: STUDIES IN CLASSICAL KINDS. Text in English. 1982. irreg., latest vol.3, 1991. price varies. back issues avail. **Document type:** *Monographic series.* **Description:** Discusses the history and literature of ancient Greece and Rome.

Published by: University of California Press, Book Series, 2120 Berkeley Way, Berkeley, CA 94720. TEL 510-642-4247, FAX 510-643-7127, askucp@ucpress.edu, http://www.ucpress.edu/books/EIDOS.ser.html, http://www.ucpress.edu/books/series.html. **Orders to:** California - Princeton Fulfillment Services, 1445 Lower Ferry Rd, Ewing, NJ 08618. TEL 800-777-4726, FAX 800-999-1958.

938   DEU
➤ **EIKON**; Beitraege zur antiken Bildersprache. Text in English, German. 1992. irreg., latest vol.7, 2002. price varies. **Document type:** *Monographic series, Academic/Scholarly.* **Description:** Covers Greek and Roman art and archaeology.
Published by: Ugarit-Verlag, Ricarda-Huch-Str 6, Muenster, 48161, Germany. TEL 49-2534-1590, FAX 49-2534-539983, verlag@ugarit-verlag.de, http://www.ugarit-verlag.de. Ed. K. Staehle.

480 930.1   CZE   ISSN 0046-1628
➤ **EIRENE**; studia Graeca et Latina. Text in English, French, German, Latin, Spanish. 1960-1979; resumed 1980-1991; resumed 1992. a. EUR 67 foreign (effective 2005). bk.rev. charts; illus.; maps; abstr. back issues avail. **Document type:** *Journal, Academic/Scholarly.* **Description:** Covers classical studies published in Central European countries, classical traditions in Europe, essays on the humanities and classical heritage that surpass divisions of subjects.
Indexed: BibLing, PCI.
Published by: Akademie Ved Ceske Republiky, Filozoficky Ustav - Kabinet pro klasika studia/Academy of Sciences of Czech Republic, Institute for Classical Studies, Na Florenci 3, Prague 1, 110 00, Czech Republic. TEL 42-2-22828303, FAX 42-2-22828305, eirene@ics.cas.cz, http://www.lib.cas.cz/knav/journals/cz/Eirene.htm. **Dist. by:** Koniasch Latin Press (KLP), Na Hubalce 7, Prague 6 169 00, Czech Republic. TEL 42-2-20511681, 42-603-256617, jkk@ics.cas.cz. **Co-publisher:** Koniasch Latin Press (KLP).

880   USA   ISSN 1320-3606
PA1
➤ **ELECTRONIC ANTIQUITY**; communicating the classics. Text in English. 1993. irreg. free. bk.rev. illus. reprints avail. **Document type:** *Newsletter, Academic/Scholarly.*
Media: Online - full text.
Published by: Digital Library and Archives at Virginia Polytechnic Institute and State University, Department of Classics, 331 Major Williams Hall, Blacksburg, VA 24061-0225. TEL 540-231-8319, FAX 540-231-4812, electronic.antiquity@vt.edu, http://scholar.lib.vt.edu/ejournals/ElAnt/. Ed. Terry Papillon.

880 930   GRC   ISSN 0013-6336
PA1005   CODEN: HELLFU
➤ **ELLINIKA**; philological, historical and folkloric review. Text in English, French, German, Greek, Italian; Summaries in English, Greek. 1928. s-a. EUR 8, USD 22.01 (effective 2003). adv. bk.rev. bibl. 250 p./no.; back issues avail. **Document type:** *Journal, Academic/Scholarly.* **Description:** Contains articles that promote research in archaeology, classical studies, folklore, history, linguistics, and Greek literature (ancient, Byzantine, and modern).
Indexed: AmH&L, HistAb, L&LBA, MLA-IB.
Published by: Society for Macedonian Studies, Ethnikis Amymis 4, Thessaloniki, 546 21, Greece. TEL 30-2310-268710, FAX 30-2310-271501, ems@hyper.gr, http://www.hyper.gr/ems/. Eds. Nicolaos Konomis, G M Parasoglou. R&P, Adv. contact Vasiliki Papastathi. Circ: 1,000.

➤ **EMERITA**; revista de linguistica y filologia clasica. see *LINGUISTICS*

800   CHE   ISSN 0071-0822
ENTRETIENS SUR L'ANTIQUITE CLASSIQUE. Text in French. 1958 (no.3). a., latest vol.46, 2000. price varies. **Document type:** *Monographic series, Academic/Scholarly.* **Description:** Focuses on ancient classical studies.
Indexed: RI-2.
—CCC.
Published by: (Fondation Hardt pour l'Etude de l'Antiquite Classique), Librairie Droz S.A., 11 rue Massot, Geneva 12, 1211, Switzerland. TEL 41-22-3466666, FAX 41-22-3472391, droz@droz.org, http://www.droz.org. Ed. O Reverdin.

ERANOS; acta philologica Suecana. see *LINGUISTICS*

930   ESP   ISSN 0014-1453
PA9
ESTUDIOS CLASICOS✻. Text in Spanish. 1950. 3/yr. USD 7.75. bk.rev. bibl. index.
Related titles: ◆ Supplement(s): Suplemento de Estudios Clasicos. Serie Textos. ISSN 0423-4820; ◆ Suplemento de Estudios Clasicos. Serie de Traducciones. ISSN 0425-3477.
Indexed: ASCA, ArtHuCI, BibLing, CurCont, MLA-IB, RILM, SSCI.
—CINDOC, IDS.
Published by: (Consejo Superior de Investigaciones Cientificas, Instituto "Antonio de Nebrija"), Consejo Superior de Investigaciones Cientificas, Departamento de Publicaciones, Vitruvio 8, Madrid, 28006, Spain. TEL 34-91-561-2833, FAX 34-91-562-9634, publ@orgc.csic.es, http://www.csic.es/publica. Circ: 1,400. **Co-sponsor:** Sociedad Espanola de Estudios Clasicos.

C

930 870 BEL ISSN 0014-200X
AS241
➤ **LES ETUDES CLASSIQUES.** Text in French. 1932. q. EUR 38 in the European Union; EUR 45 elsewhere; EUR 24 to students (effective 2002 - 2003). adv. bk.rev. abstr.; charts; illus.; maps. index, cum.index every 10 yrs. Supplement avail.; back issues avail. **Document type:** *Journal, Academic/Scholarly.* **Description:** Publishes contributions on Classical culture and its connections with the various modern European literatures.
Indexed: ASCA, ArtHuCI, BHA, BibLing, CurCont, DIP, IBR, IBZ, MLA, MLA-IB, NTA, NumL, RILM, SSCI.
—BLDSC (3817.050000), IE, Infotrieve, ingenta.
Published by: Societe des Etudes Classiques A S B L, Rue de Bruxelles 61, Namur, 5000, Belgium. TEL 32-81-724189, FAX 32-81-724203, etudes.classiques@fundp.ac.be, http://www.fundp.ac.be/~philo-ec/lec.htm. Ed. A Allard. R&P, Adv. contact Paul Pietquin. Circ: 1,000 (paid and controlled).

937 CHE ISSN 0721-3433
EUROPEAN UNIVERSITY STUDIES. SERIES 15: CLASSICS. Text in English. irreg., latest vol.71, 1997. **Document type:** *Monographic series, Academic/Scholarly.*
Published by: Verlag Peter Lang AG, Hochfeldstr. 32, Postfach 746, Bern 9, 3000, Switzerland. TEL 41-31-3061717, FAX 41-31-3061727, langwerbung@datacomm.ch, info@peterlang.com, http://www.peterlang.ch, http://www.peterlang.com. **Dist. in US by:** Peter Lang Publishing, Inc., 275 Seventh Ave, 28th Fl, New York, NY 10001. TEL 800-770-5264.

800 PRT ISSN 0870-0133
EVPHROSYNE. Text in English, French, German, Italian, Portuguese, Spanish. 1957. a. USD 20. bk.rev.
Indexed: PCI.
Published by: Universidade de Lisboa, Centro de Estudos Classicos, Faculdade de Letras, Lisbon, 1600-214, Portugal. TEL 351-21-7920000, FAX 351-21-7920080, centro.classicos@fl.ul.pt, http://cec.catus.net/euphrosyne.htm. Circ: 800.

EXCAVATIONS AT THE ATHENIAN AGORA. PICTURE BOOK. see *ARCHAEOLOGY*

930 GBR
EXCERITUS; bulletin for practical research into the Roman army. Text in English. 1980. s-a. GBP 7, USD 20. bk.rev. **Document type:** *Bulletin.*
Published by: Ermine Street Guard, Oaklands Farm, Dog Ln., Crickley Hill, Witcombe, Glos GL3 4UG, United Kingdom. TEL 045-286-2235. Eds. Bill Mayes, Chris Hayes. Circ: 300.

100 ESP ISSN 1132-7723
EXCERPTA PHILOLOGICA; filologia griega y latina de la univerdad. Text in Spanish. 1991. a. back issues avail.
—CINDOC.
Published by: Universidad de Cadiz, Servicio de Publicaciones, Rectorado Ancha 16, Cadiz, 11001, Spain. TEL 34-956-0150000, http://minerva.uca.es/publicaciones/seccion.asp?secc=R-EP, http://www.uca.es/.

937 USA
EXPLORING THE ROMAN WORLD. Text in English. 1987. irreg., latest vol.4, 1993. price varies. back issues avail. **Document type:** *Monographic series.* **Description:** Covers the history and archaeology of the Roman provinces.
Published by: University of California Press, Book Series, 2120 Berkeley Way, Berkeley, CA 94720. TEL 510-642-4247, FAX 510-643-7127, askucp@ucpress.edu, http://www.ucpress.edu/books/ERW.ser.html, http://www.ucpress.edu/books/series.html. **Orders to:** California - Princeton Fulfillment Services, 1445 Lower Ferry Rd, Ewing, NJ 08618. TEL 800-777-4726, FAX 800-999-1958, orders@cpfs.pupress.princeton.edu.

880 100 GRC ISSN 1107-5392
FILOLOGOS/SCHOLAR. Text in Greek. 1964. q. USD 50. adv. bk.rev. bibl. **Document type:** *Journal, Academic/Scholarly.*
Published by: Syllogos Apophoiton tes Philosophikes Scholes tou Panepistemiou Thessalonikes/Graduate Society of the School of Philosophy for the University of Thessaloniki, PO Box 10836, Thessaloniki, 541 10, Greece. TEL 30-31-226603, FAX 30-31-226603. Ed. Christos L Tsolakis. Circ: 2,500.

938 ESP ISSN 1131-8848
DE1 CODEN: FLILF8
FLORENTIA ILIBERRITANA; revista de estudios de antiguedad clasica. Text in Spanish. 1990. a. price varies. **Document type:** *Monographic series, Academic/Scholarly.*
Indexed: BHA, L&LBA, RILM, SOPODA.
—CINDOC.
Published by: Editorial Universidad de Granada, Antiguo Colegio Maximo, Campus de Cartuja, Granada, 18071, Spain. TEL 34-958-246220, FAX 34-958-243931, comunicacion@editorialugr.com, http://www.editorialugr.com. Ed. Cristobal Gonzalez Roman.

FONDATION DE RECHERCHE ET D'EDITIONS DE PHILOSOPHIE NEOHELLENIQUE. SERIE RECHERCHES; Corpus Philosophorum Graecorum Recentiorum. see *PHILOSOPHY*

400 DEU ISSN 1432-7511
FORUM CLASSICUM; Zeitschrift fuer die Faecher Latein und Griechisch an Schulen und Universitaeten. Text in German. 1958. q. EUR 16.50; EUR 5.20 newsstand/cover (effective 2005). adv. bk.rev. **Document type:** *Magazine, Trade.*
Formerly (until 1997): Deutscher Altphilologen-Verband. Mitteilungsblatt (0011-9830)
Indexed: DIP, IBR, IBZ.
Published by: (Deutscher Altphilologen-Verband), C.C. Buchners Verlag GmbH & Co. KG, Laubanger 8, Bamberg, 96052, Germany. TEL 49-951-965010, FAX 49-951-61774, service@ccbuchner.de, http://www.ccbuchner.de. Ed. Andreas Fritsch. Circ: 7,200.

938 DEU ISSN 1432-542X
FRANKFURTER ALTHISTORISCHE BEITRAEGE. Text in German. 1997. irreg., latest vol.2, 1998. price varies. **Document type:** *Monographic series, Academic/Scholarly.*
Published by: Franz Steiner Verlag Stuttgart GmbH, Birkenwaldstr 44, Stuttgart, 70191, Germany. TEL 49-711-25820, FAX 49-711-2582390, franz.steiner.verlag@t-online.de, http://www.steiner-verlag.de. Eds. Klaus Bringmann, Manfred Clauss. R&P Sabine Koerner.

938 900 DEU ISSN 1381-0472
GEOGRAPHICA HISTORICA. Text in German. 1976. irreg., latest vol.17, 2002. price varies. **Document type:** *Monographic series, Academic/Scholarly.*
Published by: Franz Steiner Verlag Stuttgart GmbH, Birkenwaldstr 44, Stuttgart, 70191, Germany. TEL 49-711-25820, FAX 49-711-2582390, franz.steiner.verlag@t-online.de, http://www.steiner-verlag.de. Ed. Eckart Olshausen.

400 DEU ISSN 0017-1298
PA3
➤ **GLOTTA**; Zeitschrift fuer griechische und lateinische Sprache. Text occasionally in English, French, Italian. 1909. 2/yr. EUR 54; EUR 29.90 newsstand/cover (effective 2005). adv. illus. index. reprint service avail. from SCH. **Document type:** *Journal, Academic/Scholarly.*
Indexed: ASCA, ArtHuCI, BibLing, CurCont, DIP, IBR, IBZ, IndIslam, MLA, MLA-IB, PCI, RASB, RILM.
—BLDSC (4195.850000), IDS, IE. **CCC.**
Published by: Vandenhoeck und Ruprecht, Robert-Bosch-Breite 6, Goettingen, 37079, Germany. TEL 49-551-508440, FAX 49-551-5084422, info@v-r.de, http://www.vandenhoeck-ruprecht.de. adv.: page EUR 400; trim 117 x 190. Circ: 500 (paid and controlled).

800 DEU ISSN 0017-1417
PA3
GNOMON; kritische Zeitschrift fuer die gesamte klassische Altertumswissenschaft. Text in Multiple languages. 1924. 8/yr. EUR 154 (effective 2005). adv. bk.rev. illus. Index. back issues avail.; reprints avail. **Document type:** *Journal, Academic/Scholarly.*
Related titles: CD-ROM ed.: Gnomon Bibliographische Datenbank. ISSN 0945-9790. 1994. EUR 320 base vol(s). per vol.; EUR 160 updates per issue (effective 2005).
Indexed: ASCA, ArtHuCI, BHA, BibInd, BibLing, CurCont, DIP, IBR, IBZ, IPB, MLA, MLA-IB, NTA, NumL, PCI, RASB, RI-1, RI-2, RILM.
—IDS, IE, Infotrieve. **CCC.**
Published by: Verlag C.H. Beck oHG, Wilhelmstr 9, Munich, 80801, Germany. TEL 49-89-381890, FAX 49-89-38189398, abo.service@beck.de, http://www.beck.de. Eds. Ernst Vogt, H W Noerenberg. adv.: page EUR 900; trim 120 x 200. Circ: 1,400 (paid and controlled).

880 ITA ISSN 1108-4707
GRAECOLATINITAS NOSTRA - FONTI. Text in Italian. 1999. irreg., latest vol.1, 1999. price varies. **Document type:** *Monographic series.*
Published by: Istituto Ellenico di Studi Bizantini e Post-Bizantini, Castello 3412, Venice, VE 30122, Italy. FAX 39-41-5238248, hellenic.inst@gold.ghnet.it. Adv. contact Chryssa Maltezou.

GRAEZER BEITRAEGE; Zeitschrift fuer klassische Altertumswissenschaft. see *ARCHAEOLOGY*

930 GBR ISSN 0017-3835
DE1
➤ **GREECE AND ROME.** Text in English. 1931. s-a. GBP 69, USD 129 combined subscription to institutions print & online eds. (effective 2006). adv. bk.rev. abstr.; bibl.; illus. index. back issues avail.; reprint service avail. from PSC. **Document type:** *Journal, Academic/Scholarly.* **Description:** Literary evaluation of the major Greek and Roman authors, and articles on ancient history, art, archaeology, the classical tradition, and the teaching of the classics at the tertiary level.
Related titles: Microform ed.: (from PQC); Online - full text ed.: ISSN 1477-4550. GBP 65 to institutions; USD 121 in North America to institutions (effective 2006) (from bigchalk, EBSCO Publishing, Florida Center for Library Automation, Gale Group, HighWire Press, IngentaConnect, JSTOR (Web-based Journal Archive), O C L C Online Computer Library Center, Inc., ProQuest Information & Learning, Swets Information Services); ♦ Supplement(s): New Surveys in the Classics. ISSN 0533-2451.
Indexed: ASCA, ArtHuCI, BrArAb, BrHumI, CurCont, DIP, HumInd, IBR, IBZ, IGCS, IPB, NTA, PCI, RASB, RILM, WBA, WMB.
—BLDSC (4214.830000), IDS, IE, Infotrieve, ingenta. **CCC.**
Published by: (Classical Association), Cambridge University Press, The Edinburgh Bldg, Shaftesbury Rd, Cambridge, CB2 2RU, United Kingdom. TEL 44-1223-326070, FAX 44-1223-325150, journals@cambridge.org, http://uk.cambridge.org/journals. Eds. Christopher Burnand, John Taylor, Katherine Clarke. adv.: B&W page GBP 335, B&W page USD 555; 110 x 195. Circ: 1,600.

930 940 USA ISSN 0072-7474
➤ **GREEK, ROMAN AND BYZANTINE MONOGRAPHS.** Text in English. 1959. irreg., latest vol.11, 1994. price varies. **Document type:** *Monographic series, Academic/Scholarly.*
Indexed: NTA, NumL.
—BLDSC (4214.909000).
Published by: Duke University, Department of Classical Studies, PO Box 90199, Durham, NC 27708-0199. TEL 919-684-6456. Ed. Kent J Rigsby.

930 USA ISSN 0017-3916
DE1
➤ **GREEK, ROMAN AND BYZANTINE STUDIES.** Text in English. 1958. q. USD 30 domestic; USD 36 foreign (effective 2005). charts; illus. index. 100 p./no.; back issues avail.; reprint service avail. from PSC. **Document type:** *Journal, Academic/Scholarly.* **Description:** Research articles on all aspects of the Greek world, from the prehistoric through the Hellenic, Hellenistic, Roman and Byzantine periods.
Formerly (until 1959): Greek and Byzantine Studies (0884-7304)
Related titles: Microform ed.: (from PQC); Online - full text ed.: (from Chadwyck-Healey Inc., O C L C Online Computer Library Center, Inc., ProQuest Information & Learning); ♦ Supplement(s): Greek, Roman, and Byzantine Studies. Scholarly Aids. ISSN 0072-7482.
Indexed: ASCA, ArtHuCI, BHA, BibLing, CurCont, DIP, HumInd, IBR, IBZ, NTA, NumL, PCI, RASB, RI-1, RI-2, RILM.
—IE.
Published by: Duke University, Department of Classical Studies, PO Box 90199, Durham, NC 27708-0199. TEL 919-684-6456, FAX 919-681-4262, http://www.duke.edu/web/classics/grbs/. Ed., R&P Kent J Rigsby. Circ: 850.

930 940 USA ISSN 0072-7482
➤ **GREEK, ROMAN, AND BYZANTINE STUDIES. SCHOLARLY AIDS.** Text in English. 1961. irreg. price varies. back issues avail. **Document type:** *Monographic series, Academic/Scholarly.*
Related titles: ♦ Supplement to: Greek, Roman and Byzantine Studies. ISSN 0017-3916.
Indexed: CurCont.
—**CCC.**
Published by: Duke University, Department of Classical Studies, PO Box 90199, Durham, NC 27708-0199. TEL 919-684-6456, http://www.duke.edu/web/classics/grbs/index.html. Ed., R&P Kent J Rigsby.

930 NLD ISSN 0169-8206
GRIEKSE EN LATIJNSE SCHRIJVERS. Text in Dutch. irreg. price varies. **Document type:** *Monographic series.*
Published by: Brill Academic Publishers, PO Box 9000, Leiden, 2300 PA, Netherlands. TEL 44-1767-604954, FAX 44-1767-601640, 31-71-5317531, cs@brill.nl, http://www.brill.nl/. R&P Elizabeth Venekamp. **Subscr. in N. America to:** PO Box 605, Herndon, VA 20172. TEL 703-661-1585, 800-337-9255, FAX 703-661-1501, cs@brillusa.com. **Distr. outside N. America by:** c/o Turpin Distribution, Stratton Business Park, Pegasus Drive, Biggleswade, Bedfordshire SG 18 8TQ, United Kingdom. TEL 44-1767-604-954, FAX 44-1767-601-640, brill@turpin-distribution.com.

930 800 DEU ISSN 0342-5231
GYMNASIUM; Zeitschrift fuer Kultur der Antike und Humanistische Bildung. Text in German. 1931. 6/yr. EUR 82; EUR 62 to students; EUR 18 newsstand/cover (effective 2005). adv. bk.rev. index. reprint service avail. from SCH. **Document type:** *Journal, Academic/Scholarly.*
Indexed: ASCA, ArtHuCI, BHA, BibLing, CurCont, DIP, IBR, IBZ, IPB, MLA, MLA-IB, PhilInd, RASB.
—IDS. **CCC.**
Published by: Universitaetsverlag C. Winter Heidelberg GmbH, Dossenheimer Landstr 13, Postfach 10 61 40, Heidelberg, 69051, Germany. TEL 49-6221-770260, FAX 49-6221-770269, info@winter-verlag-hd.de, http://www.winter-verlag-hd.de/programm/Zeitschriften/Zs-GRM/zs-grm.html. Eds. Hermann Steinthal, Richard Klein. adv.: page EUR 558; trim 113 x 190. Circ: 1,200 (paid and controlled).

400 USA ISSN 0073-0688
PA25
➤ **HARVARD STUDIES IN CLASSICAL PHILOLOGY.** Text in English. 1890. irreg., latest vol.101, 2003. price varies. illus. reprints avail. **Document type:** *Journal, Academic/Scholarly.*
Related titles: Online - full text ed.: (from JSTOR (Web-based Journal Archive)).
Indexed: ASCA, ArtHuCI, BibLing, IBR, LIFT, NTA, PCI, PhilInd, RASB, RI-1, RI-2.
—BLDSC (4270.200000), IE, Infotrieve, ingenta.

C

▼ new title ➤ refereed ✶ unverified ♦ full entry avail.

Published by: Harvard University, Department of the Classics, Boylston 320, Cambridge, MA 02138. TEL 617-495-4027, FAX 617-496-6720, rthomas@fas.harvard.edu, http://www.fas.harvard.edu/~classics/hscp.html. Ed. Charles Segal. R&P Brian Breed.

930 410 CHE ISSN 0073-0939
HAUTES ETUDES DU MONDE GRECO-ROMAIN. Text in French. 1964. irreg., latest vol.29, 2000. price varies. **Document type:** *Monographic series, Academic/Scholarly.*
—CCC.
Published by: (Ecole Pratique des Hautes Etudes FRA, Centre de Recherches d'Histoire et de Philologie FRA), Librairie Droz S.A., 11 rue Massot, Geneva 12, 1211, Switzerland. TEL 41-22-3466666, FAX 41-22-3472391, droz@droz.org, http://www.droz.org. Circ: 600.

880 USA ISSN 1073-6050
HAWAII CLASSICAL STUDIES. Text in English. 1994. irreg., latest 1998. price varies. **Document type:** *Monographic series.* **Description:** Focuses on Classics as it pertains to today's world, stresses the influence of ancient Greece and Rome on present-day languages, literatures, and civilization.
Published by: Peter Lang Publishing, Inc., 275 Seventh Ave, 28th Fl, New York, NY 10001. TEL 212-647-7700, 800-770-5264, FAX 212-647-7707, customerservice@plang.com, http://www.peterlangusa.com. Eds. J D Ellsworth, Robert J Ball.

938 DEU ISSN 0930-1208
HEIDELBERGER ALTHISTORISCHE BEITRAEGE UND EPIGRAPHISCHE STUDIEN. Text in German. 1986. irreg., latest 2002. price varies. **Document type:** *Monographic series, Academic/Scholarly.*
Published by: Franz Steiner Verlag Stuttgart GmbH, Birkenwaldstr 44, Stuttgart, 70191, Germany. TEL 49-711-25820, FAX 49-711-2582390, franz.steiner.verlag@t-online.de, http://www.steiner-verlag.de. Ed. Geza Alfoeldy. R&P Sabine Koerner.

480 ITA ISSN 0017-9981
HELIKON; rivista di tradizione e cultura classica. Text in Italian. 1961. a., latest vol.38, 1998. back issues avail. **Document type:** *Academic/Scholarly.* **Description:** Contains studies on classical tradition and culture.
Indexed: DIP, IBR, IBZ, PCI.
Published by: (Universita degli Studi di Messina), Herder Editrice e Libreria s.r.l., Piazza di Montecitorio 117-120, Rome, 00186, Italy. TEL 39-06-6794628, FAX 39-06-6784751, bookcenter@herder.it, http://www.herder.it. Eds. Antonio Mazzarino, Johannes Irmscher. Circ: 450.

949.5 938 480 SWE ISSN 0348-0100
➤ **HELLENIKA.** Text in Swedish. 1977. q. SEK 100; SEK 50 to students (effective 2003). adv. back issues avail. **Document type:** *Journal, Academic/Scholarly.*
Indexed: MLA-IB.
Published by: Foereningen Svenska Atheninstitutets Vaenner, Fack 14124, Stockholm, 10122, Sweden. TEL 46-8-6676455, FAX 46-8-259591, http://www.athenvannerna.org/hellenika.htm. Eds. Per Eric Mattsson, Ingegerd Ekstam. Circ: 2,200.

938 USA ISSN 1054-0857
➤ **HELLENISTIC CULTURE & SOCIETY.** Text in English. 1987. irreg., latest vol.21, 1996. price varies. back issues avail. **Document type:** *Monographic series, Academic/Scholarly.* **Description:** Discusses the cultural legacy of the ancient Greeks from the reign of Alexander the Great to the Roman conquest.
—BLDSC (4285.490000), IE, ingenta. **CCC.**
Published by: University of California Press, Book Series, 2120 Berkeley Way, Berkeley, CA 94720. TEL 510-642-4247, FAX 510-643-7127, askucp@ucpress.edu, http://www.ucpress.edu/books/HCS.ser.html, http://www.ucpress.edu/books/series.html. **Orders to:** California - Princeton Fulfillment Services, 1445 Lower Ferry Rd, Ewing, NJ 08618. TEL 800-777-4726, FAX 800-999-1958, orders@cpfs.pupress.princeton.edu.

938 DEU ISSN 0018-0777
PA3
➤ **HERMES;** Zeitschrift fuer klassische Philologie. Text in English, French, German, Italian. 1866. q. EUR 196; EUR 56 newsstand/cover (effective 2006). adv. index. back issues avail.; reprints avail. **Document type:** *Journal, Academic/Scholarly.*
Related titles: Microfiche ed.: (from IDC); ♦ Supplement(s): Hermes - Einzelschriften. ISSN 0341-0064.
Indexed: ArtHuCI, BibLing, CurCont, DIP, IBR, IBSS, IBZ, IPB, IPSA, MLA, MLA-IB, NTA, PCI, PhilInd, RASB, SSCI.
—IDS, IE, Infotrieve. **CCC.**
Published by: Franz Steiner Verlag Stuttgart GmbH, Birkenwaldstr 44, Stuttgart, 70191, Germany. TEL 49-711-25820, FAX 49-711-2582290, service@steiner-verlag.de, http://www.steiner-verlag.de. Ed. Siegmar Dopp. R&P Sabine Koerner. Adv. contact Susanne Szoradi. Circ: 900.

870 USA ISSN 0741-1286
➤ **HERMES AMERICANUS.** Text in Latin. 1983. irreg. USD 25 to individuals; USD 40 to libraries. adv. bk.rev. back issues avail. **Document type:** *Academic/Scholarly.*
Published by: Academia Latina Danburiensis, 45 Dodgingtown Rd, Bethel, CT 06801-1612. TEL 203-778-1778. Ed. Alvin P Dobsevage. Circ: 500 (paid).

938 DEU ISSN 0341-0064
PA3
HERMES - EINZELSCHRIFTEN. Text in English, German. irreg., latest vol.82, 2000. price varies. **Document type:** *Monographic series, Academic/Scholarly.*
Related titles: ♦ Supplement to: Hermes. ISSN 0018-0777.
Indexed: RASB.
Published by: Franz Steiner Verlag Stuttgart GmbH, Birkenwaldstr 44, Stuttgart, 70191, Germany. TEL 49-711-25820, FAX 49-711-2582390, franz.steiner.verlag@t-online.de, http://www.steiner-verlag.de. R&P Sabine Koerner.

930 ITA
HESPERIA; studi sulla grecita di occidente. Text in Italian. 1990. irreg., latest vol.9, 1997. price varies. **Document type:** *Monographic series, Academic/Scholarly.*
Indexed: ArtInd, CurCont.
Published by: (Universita degli Studi di Venezia, Dipartimento di Antichita e Tradizione Classica), L'Erma di Bretschneider, Via Cassiodoro, 19, PO Box 6192, Rome, RM 00193, Italy. edizioni@lerma.it, http://www.lerma.it. Ed. Lorenzo Braccesi.

HESPERIA. see *ARCHAEOLOGY*

HETHITICA. see *ASIAN STUDIES*

938 DEU ISSN 0018-2311
D51
➤ **HISTORIA;** Zeitschrift fuer Alte Geschichte/revue d'histoire ancienne/journal of ancient history/rivista di storia antica. Text in English, German. 1952. q. EUR 196; EUR 56 newsstand/cover (effective 2006). adv. index. back issues avail. **Document type:** *Journal, Academic/Scholarly.*
Related titles: ♦ Supplement(s): Historia. Einzelschriften. ISSN 0341-0056.
Indexed: ArtHuCI, BibLing, CurCont, DIP, IBR, IBSS, IBZ, NTA, NumL, PCI, RASB, RI-1, RI-2.
—IDS, IE, Infotrieve. **CCC.**
Published by: Franz Steiner Verlag Stuttgart GmbH, Birkenwaldstr 44, Stuttgart, 70191, Germany. TEL 49-711-25820, FAX 49-711-2582290, service@steiner-verlag.de, http://www.steiner-verlag.de. Ed. Mortimer Chambers. R&P Sabine Koerner. Adv. contact Susanne Szoradi. Circ: 1,200.

938 DEU ISSN 0341-0056
HISTORIA. EINZELSCHRIFTEN. Text in English, French, German. irreg., latest vol.176, 2004. price varies. **Document type:** *Monographic series, Academic/Scholarly.*
Related titles: ♦ Supplement to: Historia. ISSN 0018-2311.
Published by: Franz Steiner Verlag Stuttgart GmbH, Birkenwaldstr 44, Stuttgart, 70191, Germany. TEL 49-711-25820, FAX 49-711-2582390, franz.steiner.verlag@t-online.de, http://www.steiner-verlag.de. R&P Sabine Koerner.

HISTORY OF POLITICAL THOUGHT. see *POLITICAL SCIENCE*

938 907.2 GBR
➤ **HISTOS;** the new journal of ancient historiography. Text in English. 1997. a. illus. back issues avail. **Document type:** *Academic/Scholarly.* **Description:** Includes the historiographical texts of Greece and Rome, the influence of historiography and biography on other literary genres, and precursors of historiography and biography.
Media: Online - full text.
Published by: University of Durham, Department of Classics, 38 N Bailey, Durham, Co Durham DH1 3EU, United Kingdom. TEL 44-191-374-7338, histos.journal@durham.ac.uk, http://www.dur.ac.uk/Classics/histos/index.html. Ed. J L Moles.

930 BEL ISSN 0774-2908
HUMANISTICA LOVANIENSIA; journal of Neo-Latin studies. Text in English, French, Italian, Spanish, German, Latin. 1928. a., latest vol.53, 2004. EUR 80 (effective 2005). bk.rev. Supplement avail.; back issues avail.; reprints avail. **Document type:** *Academic/Scholarly.*
Related titles: ♦ Supplement(s): Humanistica Lovaniensia. Supplementa.
Indexed: BibInd, BibLing, IBR, MLA, MLA-IB, RASB.
—KNAW.
Published by: (Katholieke Universiteit Leuven, Seminarium Philologiae Humanisticae), Leuven University Press, Blijde Inkomststraat 5, Leuven, 3000, Belgium. TEL 32-16-325345, FAX 32-16-325352, university.press@upers.kuleuven.ac.be, http://www.kuleuven.ac.be/upers. Circ: 750.

930 BEL
HUMANISTICA LOVANIENSIA. SUPPLEMENTA. Text in English. 1978. irreg., latest vol.16, 2000. price varies. back issues avail. **Document type:** *Academic/Scholarly.*
Related titles: ♦ Supplement to: Humanistica Lovaniensia. ISSN 0774-2908.
Published by: Leuven University Press, Blijde Inkomststraat 5, Leuven, 3000, Belgium. TEL 32-16-325345, FAX 32-16-325352, university.press@upers.kuleuven.ac.be, http://www.kuleuven.ac.be/upers.

937 DEU ISSN 0949-2615
PA1.A1
HYPERBOREUS; studia classica. Text in German. 1994. s-a. EUR 34.90; EUR 19.50 newsstand/cover (effective 2005). **Document type:** *Journal, Academic/Scholarly.*
Indexed: RASB.
Published by: (Bibliotheka Classica Petropolitana RUS), Verlag C.H. Beck oHG, Wilhelmstr 9, Munich, 80801, Germany. TEL 49-89-38189338, FAX 49-89-38189398, abo.service@beck.de, http://www.beck.de. Ed. Dmitri Panchenko.

480 880 DEU ISSN 0085-1671
➤ **HYPOMNEMATA;** Untersuchungen zur Antike und zu ihrem Nachleben. Text in German. 1962. irreg., latest vol.134, 2002. price varies. **Document type:** *Monographic series, Academic/Scholarly.*
Published by: Vandenhoeck und Ruprecht, Robert-Bosch-Breite 6, Goettingen, 37079, Germany. TEL 49-551-508440, FAX 49-551-5084422, info@v-r.de, http://www.vandenhoeck-ruprecht.de.

946 ESP ISSN 1575-0221
DP44
IBERIA; revista de la antiguedad. Text in Spanish, German. 1998. a. EUR 15.02 domestic; EUR 18.03 foreign (effective 2003). back issues avail. **Description:** Covers prehistory and ancient history in the Iberian peninsula as well as in the Mediterranean region.
—CINDOC.
Published by: Universidad de la Rioja, Servicio de Publicaciones, C/ Piscinas s/n, Logrono, La Rioja 26004, Spain. TEL 34-941-299187, FAX 34-941-299193, publicaciones@adm.unirioja.es, http://publicaciones.unirioja.es/revistas/iberia.html, http://www.publicaciones.unirioja.es.

800 USA ISSN 0363-1923
PA1
ILLINOIS CLASSICAL STUDIES. Text in English. 1976. a. illus. back issues avail.; reprints avail. **Document type:** *Academic/Scholarly.* **Description:** Publishes academic papers on classical literature and ancient civilizations.
Indexed: BibLing, NTA, RASB.
—BLDSC (4365.113000), IE. **CCC.**
Published by: University of Illinois at Urbana-Champaign, Department of the Classics, 4080 Foreign Languages Bldg, 707 S Mathews Ave, Urbana, IL 61801-3676. TEL 217-333-1008, FAX 217-244-8430, classics@uiuc.edu, http://www.classics.uiuc.edu/index.html. Circ: 250.

480 880 ITA ISSN 0073-5752
INCUNABULA GRAECA. Text in Italian. 1961. irreg. price varies. **Document type:** *Academic/Scholarly.*
Indexed: RASB.
Published by: Gruppo Editoriale Internazionale (Subsidiary of: Libra Web), Via Giosue' Carducci, 60, Ghezzano La Fontina, PI 56010, Italy. TEL 39-50-878066, FAX 39-50-878732, iepi@sirius.pisa.it, gruppoeditoriale@gruppoeditoriale.it. Circ: 1,500.

870 270 BEL ISSN 0771-5463
INSTRUMENTA LEXICOLOGIA LATINA. Key Title: Corpus Christianorum. Instrumenta Lexicologia Latina. (In 2 Series: A - Formae; B - Lemmata) Text in Latin. 1982. irreg. (approx. 10/yr.). back issues avail. **Document type:** *Monographic series.* **Description:** Provides lexicographical materials relating to the writing of the Latin Fathers of the Christian Church, and works of the Middle Ages.
Published by: (Cetedoc), Brepols Publishers, Begijnhof 67, Turnhout, 2300, Belgium. FAX 32-14-42-89-19, publishers@brepols.com, periodicals@brepols.net.

INTERNATIONAL ASSOCIATION FOR CLASSICAL ARCHAEOLOGY. PROCEEDINGS OF CONGRESS. see *ARCHAEOLOGY*

930 880 USA ISSN 1073-0508
PN883
➤ **INTERNATIONAL JOURNAL OF THE CLASSICAL TRADITION.** Text in English, French, German, Italian, Spanish; Abstracts in English. 1994. q. USD 96 to individuals print or online; USD 240 to institutions print or online; USD 106 combined subscription to individuals print & online; USD 264 combined subscription to institutions print & online (effective 2004). adv. bk.rev. abstr.; bibl.; illus. reprint service avail. from PSC. **Document type:** *Journal, Academic/Scholarly.* **Description:** Publishes scholarly studies on the influence of Greek and Roman antiquity on other cultures, from the ancient world up to the present. Focuses on the reception and use and transformation of the Graeco-Roman heritage in other regions and periods in literature, the arts, philosophy, sciences and the law.
Related titles: Online - full text ed.: (from EBSCO Publishing, O C L C Online Computer Library Center, Inc., Swets Information Services); Supplement(s): Analytical Bibliography of the Classical Tradtion.
Indexed: DIP, IBR, IBZ, RILM.
—BLDSC (4542.167500), IE, ingenta. **CCC.**

C

Published by: (International Society for the Classical Tradition NLD), Transaction Publishers, 390 Campus Dr, Somerset, NJ 07830. TEL 888-999-6778, FAX 732-748-9801, trans@transactionpub.com, http://www.transactionpub.com. Eds. Meyer Reinhold, Wolfgang Haase. Pub. Mary Curtis. R&P Marlena Davidian TEL 732-445-2280 ext 100. Adv. contact Alicja Garbie. page USD 300; 5.25 x 8.25. Circ: 800. **Dist. in Europe by:** Swets Publishing Service, Heereweg 347, Lisse 2161 CA, Netherlands. TEL 31-2521-15888, 31-2521-35111.

➤ **INTERPRETING THE PAST.** see *ARCHAEOLOGY*

870 880 AUS ISSN 1448-1421
➤ **IRIS**; journal of the classical association of Victoria. Text in English. 1973. a. AUD 30 in Australia; AUD 10 in Australia to students (effective 2004 - 2005). bk.rev. **Document type:** *Journal, Academic/Scholarly.*
Formerly: Iris and Res Novissimae (0310-9186)
Related titles: Online - full text ed.
Published by: Classical Association of Victoria, c/o School of A H C C A, Elisabeth Murdoch Building, University of Melbourne, Melbourne, VIC 3010, Australia. TEL 03-8344-4161, http://www.cca.unimelb.edu.au/CAV/iris.html. Ed. John Penwill. Adv. contact K O Chong-Gossard TEL 03-8344-4078. Circ: 200.

➤ **ISTHMIA.** see *ARCHAEOLOGY*

937 ITA
ISTITUTO UNIVERSITARIO ORIENTALE DI NAPOLI. DIPARTIMENTO DI STUDI DEL MONDO CLASSICO E DEL MEDITERRANEO ANTICO. SEZIONE FILOLOGICO - LETTERARIA. Text in Italian. 1979. a., latest vol.21, 1999. back issues avail.
Published by: Universita degli Studi di Napoli, L'Orientale/Dipartimento di Studi del Mondo Classico e del Mediterraneo Antico, Piazza San Domenico Maggiore 12, Palazzo Corigliano, Naples, NA 80134, Italy. Ed. Albio Cesare Cassio. **Dist. by:** Herder Editrice e Libreria s.r.l., Piazza di Montecitorio 117-120, Rome 00186, Italy. TEL 39-6-6794628, FAX 39-6-6784751, http://www.herder.it.

950 ITA ISSN 1125-0240
ISTITUTO UNIVERSITARIO ORIENTALE DI NAPOLI. DIPARTIMENTO DI STUDI DEL MONDO CLASSICO E DEL MEDITERRANEO ANTICO. SEZIONE LINGUISTICA. ANNALI. Text in Italian. 1978. a., latest vol.20, 1998. back issues avail. **Document type:** *Academic/Scholarly.*
Supersedes: Istituto Universitario Orientale di Napoli. Seminario di Studi del Mondo Classico. Annali. Sezione Linguistica (0392-6869)
Indexed: BibLing, DIP, IBZ, LingAb, MLA-IB.
Published by: Universita degli Studi di Napoli, L'Orientale/Dipartimento di Studi del Mondo Classico e del Mediterraneo Antico, Piazza San Domenico Maggiore 12, Palazzo Corigliano, Naples, NA 80134, Italy. **Dist. by:** Herder Editrice e Libreria s.r.l.

938 ITA ISSN 1122-553X
ITALOHELLENIKA; rivista di cultura greco-moderna. Text in Italian. 1988. a. **Document type:** *Academic/Scholarly.*
Published by: Universita degli Studi di Napoli, L'Orientale/Dipartimento di Studi dell'Europa Orientale, Palazzo Giusso, Largo San Giovanni Maggiore, 30, Naples, NA 80134, Italy.

IUVENIS. see *LINGUISTICS*

800 370 GBR ISSN 0268-0181
J A C T REVIEW. Text in English. 1963. 2/yr. USD 30 to members (effective 2001). adv. bk.rev. back issues avail. **Document type:** *Journal, Academic/Scholarly.* **Description:** Articles and book reviews covering all aspects of the classical world.
Incorporates (1913-1987): Latin Teaching (0023-8821); Former titles (until 1984): Hesperiam (0141-7517); (until 1978): Didaskalos (0419-1188)
Indexed: AIAP, CPE.
Published by: Joint Association of Classical Teachers, Senate House, Malet St, London, WC1E 7HU, United Kingdom. TEL 44-20-7862-8706, FAX 44-20-7862-8729, jact@sas.ac.uk, http://www.jact.org. Adv. contact Miss Clare Roberts. page GBP 200. Circ: 2,000. **Subscr. in US to:** Rick LaFleur, Department of Classics, Park Hall, University of Georgia, Athens, GA 30602.

J R A - THE SUPPLEMENTARY SERIES. (Journal of Roman Archaeology) see *ARCHAEOLOGY*

807.1 GBR ISSN 0267-8349
JOINT ASSOCIATION OF CLASSICAL TEACHERS. BULLETIN. Text in English. 1963. 3/yr. USD 30 to members (effective 2001). bibl. back issues avail. **Document type:** *Newsletter.* **Description:** News and information broadsheet for classics teachers in secondary and tertiary levels.
Published by: Joint Association of Classical Teachers, Senate House, Malet St, London, WC1E 7HU, United Kingdom. TEL 44-20-7862-8706, FAX 44-20-7862-8729, jact@sas.ac.uk, http://www.jact.org. Ed. Mrs. F Shaw. Adv. contact Miss Clare Roberts. Circ: 2,000. **Subscr. in US to:** Rick LaFleur, Department of Classics, Park Hall, University of Georgia, Athens, GA 30602.

JOURNAL FOR THE STUDY OF JUDAISM IN THE PERSIAN, HELLENISTIC AND ROMAN PERIOD. see *RELIGIONS AND THEOLOGY—Judaic*

938 ITA ISSN 1121-5275
CC9
JOURNAL OF ANCIENT TOPOGRAPHY/RIVISTA DI TOPOGRAFIA ANTICA. Text in Italian. 1991. irreg., latest 1992. illus.; maps. back issues avail. **Document type:** *Academic/Scholarly.*
Published by: L'Erma di Bretschneider, Via Cassiodoro, 19, PO Box 6192, Rome, RM 00193, Italy. TEL 39-06-6874127, FAX 39-06-6874129, edizioni@lerma.it, http://www.lerma.it. Ed. Giovanni Uggeri.

880 GBR ISSN 0075-4269
DF10
➤ **JOURNAL OF HELLENIC STUDIES.** Text in English. 1880. a. GBP 55, EUR 110, USD 110 per issue to institutions & libraries (effective 2005); current issue is not avaliable online.. adv. bk.rev. illus. index. back issues avail.; reprint service avail. from PQC,PSC. **Document type:** *Journal, Academic/Scholarly.* **Description:** Covers Greek language, literature, history and art in the ancient and Byzantine periods.
Related titles: Microfilm ed.: (from PQC); Online - full text ed.: (from JSTOR (Web-based Journal Archive)); ♦ Supplement(s): Archaeological Reports (London). ISSN 0570-6084.
Indexed: AIAP, AICP, ASCA, ArtHuCI, ArtInd, BHA, BibLing, BrHumI, CurCont, DIP, HumInd, IBR, IBRH, IBZ, IPB, IndIslam, LRI, MLA, MLA-IB, NTA, NumL, PCI, PhilInd, RASB, RI-1, RI-2, SSCI.
—BLDSC (4996.950000), IE. **CCC.**
Published by: Society for the Promotion of Hellenic Studies, Senate House, Malet St, London, WC1E 7HU, United Kingdom. TEL 44-20-78628730, FAX 44-20-78628731, office@hellenicsociety.org.uk, http://www.hellenicsociety.org.uk. Ed. Robert Fowler. Circ: 3,000.

➤ **JOURNAL OF PREHISTORIC RELIGION.** see *ARCHAEOLOGY*

➤ **JOURNAL OF ROMAN ARCHAEOLOGY.** see *ARCHAEOLOGY*

938 666.3 GBR ISSN 0958-3491
NK3850
JOURNAL OF ROMAN POTTERY STUDIES. Abbreviated title: J R P S. Text in English. 1986. a., latest vol.9. price varies. illus. **Document type:** *Academic/Scholarly.*
Indexed: BrArAb, NumL.
—BLDSC (5052.119000).
Published by: (Study Group for Romano-British Pottery), Oxbow Books, Park End Pl, Oxford, OX1 1HN, United Kingdom. TEL 44-1865-241249, FAX 44-1865-794449, oxbow@oxbowbooks.com, http://www.oxbowbooks.com.

870 GBR ISSN 0075-4358
DG11
➤ **JOURNAL OF ROMAN STUDIES.** Text in English, French, German, Greek, Latin. 1911. a. GBP 36, USD 72 per vol. to individuals; GBP 45, USD 90 per vol. to institutions (effective 2005). adv. bk.rev. illus. cum.index: vols.21-60. back issues avail.; reprint service avail. from PSC. **Document type:** *Journal, Academic/Scholarly.* **Description:** Contains articles by leading scholars dealing with the history, archeology, literature and art of Rome, Italy and the Roman Empire to 700 A.D.
Related titles: CD-ROM ed.: 2002. GBP 20, USD 40 per issue to individuals; GBP 60, USD 120 per issue to institutions (effective 2003); Online - full text ed.: (from JSTOR (Web-based Journal Archive)).
Indexed: ASCA, ArtHuCI, BHA, BibLing, BrArAb, BrHumI, CurCont, DIP, HumInd, IBR, IBRH, IBZ, MEA&I, NTA, NumL, PCI, RASB, SSCI.
—BLDSC (5052.120000), IE, Infotrieve, ingenta. **CCC.**
Published by: Society for the Promotion of Roman Studies, The Roman Society, Senate House, Malet St, London, WC1E 7HU, United Kingdom. TEL 44-20-78628727, FAX 44-20-78628728, romansoc@sas.ac.uk, http://www.romansociety.org/. Ed. M D Goodman. Adv. contact Helen Cockle. page GBP 265, page USD 530; 143 x 227. Circ: 3,200.

870 GBR ISSN 0951-6549
➤ **JOURNAL OF ROMAN STUDIES MONOGRAPH SERIES.** Text in English. 1982. irreg., latest vol.9, 2000. price varies. illus.; maps. back issues avail. **Document type:** *Monographic series, Academic/Scholarly.* **Description:** Studies on the history, archaeology, literature and art of Rome, Italy and the Roman empire to 700 A.D.
—BLDSC (5052.120100). **CCC.**
Published by: Society for the Promotion of Roman Studies, The Roman Society, Senate House, Malet St, London, WC1E 7HU, United Kingdom. TEL 44-20-78628727, FAX 44-20-78628728, office@romansociety.org, http://www.romansociety.org/jrsmono.htm. Ed. T P Wiseman.

938 481.7 DEU ISSN 0022-7498
CN1
➤ **KADMOS**; Zeitschrift fuer vor- und fruehgriechische Epigraphik. Text in English, French, German, Spanish, Italian. 1962. a. EUR 142; EUR 154 combined subscription print & online eds. (effective 2006). adv. bk.rev. reprint service avail. from SCH. **Document type:** *Journal, Academic/Scholarly.*
Related titles: Online - full text ed.: ISSN 1613-0723. EUR 142 (effective 2006) (from EBSCO Publishing, Swets Information Services); ♦ Supplement(s): Kadmos. Supplement. ISSN 0453-0586.
Indexed: BibLing, MLA, MLA-IB, NumL, PCI, RASB.
—BLDSC (5079.600000), IE, Infotrieve, ingenta. **CCC.**
Published by: Walter de Gruyter GmbH & Co. KG, Genthiner Str. 13, Berlin, 10785, Germany. TEL 49-30-260050, FAX 49-30-26005251, wdg-info@degruyter.de, http://www.degruyter.de/rs/384_423_DEU_h.htm. Ed. Wolfgang Blumel. Adv. contact Dietlind Makswitat TEL 49-30-260050. page EUR 550; trim 108 x 176. Circ: 450 (paid and controlled).

938 292 BEL ISSN 0776-3824
KERNOS; revue internationale et pluridisciplinaire de religion grecque antique. Text in Multiple languages. 1988. a. EUR 40 to individuals; EUR 48 to institutions (effective 2004). **Document type:** *Journal, Academic/Scholarly.*
Related titles: Online - full content ed.
Published by: Editions de l'Universite de Liege, CEFAL asbl, 31, Boulevard Frere-Orban, Liege, 4000, Belgium. TEL 32-4-2542520, FAX 32-4-2542440, v.pirenne@ulg.ac.be, cefal.celes@skynet.be, http://www.ulg.ac.be/histreli/kernos.htm.

880 SWE ISSN 1104-3180
KLASSIKER. Text in Swedish. 1991. irreg., latest vol.17, 2001. price varies. back issues avail. **Document type:** *Monographic series, Academic/Scholarly.* **Description:** Publishes classical Greek and Roman literature in Swedish translation.
Published by: Paul Aastroems Foerlag, William Gibsons Vaeg 11, Jonsered, 43376, Sweden. TEL 46-31-7956600, FAX 46-31-7956710, paul.astrom@swipnet.se, info@astromeditions.com, http://www.astromeditions.com. Pub. Paul Aastroem. Circ: 1,000.

938 ITA
KLEOS. Text in English, German, Italian. 1995. irreg. price varies. bk.rev.; film rev.; play rev. bibl. back issues avail. **Description:** Explores the influence of classic literature and art.
Published by: Levante Editori, Via Napoli, 35, Bari, BA 70123, Italy. TEL 39-80-5213778, FAX 39-80-5213778, levante@tin.it. Ed. Francesco De Martino.

930 DEU ISSN 0075-6334
D51
➤ **KLIO**; Beitraege zur Alten Geschichte. Text in English, French, German. 1897. 2/yr. EUR 216 domestic; EUR 234 foreign; EUR 53 domestic to students; EUR 59 foreign to students (effective 2005). reprint service avail. from SCH. **Document type:** *Journal, Academic/Scholarly.* **Description:** Contains contributions on the history of ancient Greece and Rome.
Related titles: Microfiche ed.: (from IDC); Online - full text ed.: (from Chadwyck-Healey Inc.).
Indexed: BHA, BibLing, BrArAb, DIP, IBR, IBZ, NumL, PCI, RASB.
—IE, Infotrieve. **CCC.**
Published by: Akademie Verlag GmbH (Subsidiary of: Oldenbourg Wissenschaftsverlag GmbH), Palisadenstr 40, Berlin, 10243, Germany. TEL 49-30-4220060, FAX 49-30-42200657, info@akademie-verlag.de, http://klio.akademie-verlag.de, http://www.akademie-verlag.de. Eds. Hans-Joachim Gehrke, Manfred Clauss.

➤ **KTEMA**; civilisations de l'Orient, de la Grece et de Rome Antiques. see *HISTORY—History Of The Near East*

➤ **LALIES.** see *LINGUISTICS*

800 USA ISSN 0891-4087
LANG CLASSICAL STUDIES. Text in English. 1988. irreg., latest 2004. price varies. back issues avail. **Document type:** *Monographic series, Academic/Scholarly.* **Description:** Monograph series on the history and literature of the Greek and Roman world, embracing all subjects relevant to Classical humanities.
Published by: Peter Lang Publishing, Inc., 275 Seventh Ave, 28th Fl, New York, NY 10001. TEL 212-647-7700, 212-647-7706, 800-770-5264, FAX 212-647-7707, customerservice@plang.com, http://www.peterlang.com. Ed. Daniel Garrison. Pub. Christopher Myers. R&P Stephanie Archer. Adv. contact Patricia Mulrane.

488 DEU ISSN 0945-2257
LATEIN UND GRIECHISCH IN BERLIN UND BRANDENBURG. Text in German. 1954. q. **Document type:** *Magazine, Academic/Scholarly.*
Formerly (until 1993): Latein und Griechisch in Berlin (0723-6050)

C

▼ new title ➤ refereed ✶ unverified ♦ full entry avail.

Published by: (Deutschen Altphilologenverband (DAV), Landesverband Berlin und Brandenburg), C.C. Buchners Verlag GmbH & Co. KG, Laubanger 8, Bamberg, 96052, Germany. service@ccbuchner.de, http://www.ccbuchner.de. Ed. Dr. Eckart Mensching. Circ: 500.

870 GBR ISSN 0951-7391
LATIN AND GREEK TEXTS; classical and medieval. Text in English. 1980. irreg., latest vol.8, 1998. price varies. back issues avail. **Document type:** *Academic/Scholarly.*
Formerly: Liverpool Latin Texts (0144-9451)
—BLDSC (5160.223500).
Published by: Francis Cairns (Publications) Ltd., PO Box 296, Cambridge, CB4 3GE, United Kingdom. franciscairns@netscapeonline.co.uk. Ed., Pub., R&P, Adv. contact Sandra Cairns.

LATINITAS; commentarii linguae latinae excolendae. see *LINGUISTICS*

470 BEL ISSN 0023-8856
PA2002
➤ **LATOMUS**; revue d'etudes latines. Text in English, French, German, Italian, Latin, Spanish. 1937. q. EUR 90 domestic; EUR 105 foreign (effective 2005). adv. bk.rev. bibl.; illus. index, cum.index. reprint service avail. from SCH. **Document type:** *Journal, Academic/Scholarly.* **Description:** Publishes papers researching Latin literature, philology history and archaeology.
Indexed: ASCA, ArtHuCI, BHA, BibLing, BrArAb, CurCont, DIP, IBR, IBZ, IPB, MLA, MLA-IB, NTA, NumL, PCI, RASB, SSCI.
—IE, Infotrieve.
Published by: Societe d'Etudes Latines de Bruxelles, Rue du Palais St Jacques 6, Tournai, 7500, Belgium. latomus@belgacom.net, http://users.belgacom.net/latomus/revue.html. Ed. Carl Deroux. R&P, Adv. contact Jacqueline Dumortier Bibauw. Circ: 1,000.

C

800 DEU ISSN 0938-5835
LAVERNA. Text in German. 1990. a. **Document type:** *Journal, Academic/Scholarly.*
Indexed: DIP, IBR, IBZ.
Published by: Scripta Mercaturae Verlag, Am Roten Berg 5-9, St. Katharinen, 55595, Germany. info@scripta-mercaturae.de, http://www.scripta-mercaturae.de. Eds. H J Drexhage, J Suenskes Thompson.

938 GBR ISSN 1477-3643
LEEDS INTERNATIONAL CLASSICAL STUDIES. Text in English. 2002. irreg. free (effective 2005). **Document type:** *Academic/Scholarly.* **Description:** Publishes articles and interim discussion papers on all aspects of Greek and Roman antiquity, and of the history of the classical tradition.
Media: Online - full content.
Published by: University of Leeds, School of Classics, Leeds, LS2 9JT, United Kingdom. TEL 44-113-343-3537, FAX 44-113-343-3554, classics@leeds.ac.uk, http://www.leeds.ac.uk/classics/lics. Eds. Malcolm Heath, Roger Brock.

480 880 ZAF ISSN 1021-2981
LEWENDE WOORDE. Text in Afrikaans. 1993. q. **Document type:** *Academic/Scholarly.*
Published by: Rand Afrikaans University, PO Box 524, Auckland Park, Johannesburg 2006, South Africa.

937 DEU
LIMESMUSEUM AALEN. SCHRIFTEN. Variant title: Schriften des Limesmuseums Aalen. Text in German. 1997. irreg., latest vol.7, 2003. EUR 14.90 per vol. (effective 2003). **Document type:** *Monographic series, Academic/Scholarly.*
Published by: (Limesmuseum Aalen), Konrad Theiss Verlag GmbH, Moenchhaldenstr 28, Stuttgart, 70191, Germany. TEL 49-711-255270, FAX 49-711-2552717, service@theiss.de, http://www.theiss.de.

938 CZE ISSN 0024-4457
PA9
➤ **LISTY FILOLOGICKE/FOLIA PHILOLOGICA/JOURNAL OF PHILOLOGY**; folia philologica. Text and summaries in Czech, English, French, German, Latin, Slovak, Italian. 1874. s-a. EUR 74 (effective 2005). bk.rev. abstr.; bibl.; charts; illus. index. back issues avail. **Document type:** *Journal, Academic/Scholarly.* **Description:** Focuses on classical studies and classical traditions in medieval and early modern Central Europe, including lingustics, literature, cultural history, and philosophy. Also examines the history of the Czech language and Czech literature.
Related titles: Microfilm ed.: (from PMC); Online - full content ed.
Indexed: AmH&L, BHA, BibLing, DIP, HistAb, IBR, IBZ, LingAb, MLA, MLA-IB, NumL, RASB, RILM, SOPODA.
Published by: Akademie Ved Ceske Republiky, Filozoficky Ustav - Kabinet pro klasika studia/Academy of Sciences of Czech Republic, Institute for Classical Studies, Na Florenci 3, Prague 1, 110 00, Czech Republic. TEL 42-2-22828303, FAX 42-2-22828305, lf@ics.cas.cz, eirene@ics.cas.cz, http://www.lib.cas.cz/casopisy/cz/Listy_filologicke.htm. Ed. Dr. Martin Svatos. Circ: 350. **Dist. by:** Koniasch Latin Press (KLP), Na Hubalce 7, Prague 6 169 00, Czech Republic. TEL 42-2-20511681, 42-603-256617, jkk@ics.cas.cz.
Co-publisher: Koniasch Latin Press (KLP).

800 GBR ISSN 0309-3700
LIVERPOOL CLASSICAL MONTHLY. Text in English. 1976; N.S. 1996. m. (except Aug. & Sep.). looseleaf. GBP 19.50, USD 40 (effective 1998). bk.rev. illus. back issues avail. **Document type:** *Journal, Consumer.*
Indexed: BibLing.
—BLDSC (5281.130500), Infotrieve.
Address: School of Archaeology, Classics and Oriental Studies, 12 Abercromby Sq, Att: Helena H Pinsent, University Of Liverpool, Liverpool, L69 3BX, United Kingdom. TEL 44-151-794-2438, FAX 44-151-794-2442, jennings@liv.ac.uk. Ed. Helena V Hurt Pinsent. Circ: 450.

480 880 DEU ISSN 0024-7421
➤ **LUSTRUM**; Internationale Forschungsberichte aus dem Bereich des Klassischen Altertums. Text in German. 1956. irreg., latest vol.45, 2003. price varies. adv. illus. Index. reprints avail. **Document type:** *Monographic series, Academic/Scholarly.*
Indexed: BibLing, DIP, IBR, IBZ, PCI, RASB.
—BLDSC (5307.600000). **CCC.**
Published by: Vandenhoeck und Ruprecht, Robert-Bosch-Breite 6, Goettingen, 37079, Germany. TEL 49-551-508440, FAX 49-551-5084422, info@v-r.de, http://www.vandenhoeck-ruprecht.de. Eds. Hans Gaertner, Hubert Petersmann. adv.: page EUR 400; trim 117 x 190. Circ: 750 (paid and controlled).

➤ **LYKIA.** see *ARCHAEOLOGY*

938 ITA ISSN 1724-6385
MAECENAS; studi sul mondo classico. Text in Italian. 2001. 3/yr., latest vol.1, 2001. back issues avail. **Document type:** *Monographic series, Academic/Scholarly.*
Published by: Universita degli Studi di Siena, Istituto di Storia Antica, Corso Italia 177, Arezzo, 52100, Italy. Ed. Fabrizio Fabbrini. **Dist. by:** Herder Editrice e Libreria s.r.l.. TEL 39-6-6794628, FAX 39-6-6784751, bookcenter@herder.it, http://www.herder.it.

937 ITA
MAGISTERIVM; rivista di varia cultura. Text in Italian. 1997. a. price varies. **Document type:** *Monographic series, Academic/Scholarly.* **Description:** Contains studies on various disciplines; literature, educational theory, philosophy, philology, jusisprudence and medicine.
Published by: (Universita degli Studi di Messina), Herder Editrice e Libreria s.r.l., Piazza di Montecitorio 117-120, Rome, 00186, Italy. TEL 39-06-6794628, FAX 39-06-6784751, bookcenter@herder.it, http://www.herder.it. Ed. Antonio Mazzarino.

800 ITA ISSN 0025-0538
PA9
MAIA; rivista di letterature classiche. Text in Italian. 1948. 3/yr. EUR 40 domestic; EUR 85 foreign (effective 2003). adv. bk.rev. index. **Document type:** *Academic/Scholarly.*
Indexed: ASCA, ArtHuCI, BibLing, CurCont, DIP, IBR, IBZ, MLA-IB, NTA, PCI, RASB.
—IDS, IE, Infotrieve.
Published by: Cappelli Editore, Via Farini 14, Bologna, 40124, Italy. TEL 39-051-239060, FAX 39-051-239286. Circ: 2,000.

870 880 USA ISSN 0076-471X
PA25
➤ **MARTIN CLASSICAL LECTURES.** Text in English. 1931. irreg., latest 2002. price varies. illus. back issues avail. **Document type:** *Monographic series, Academic/Scholarly.* **Description:** Studies various topics in ancient Greek and Roman (classical) history, literature, philosophy, art, and archaeology.
Published by: (Oberlin College), Princeton University Press, 41 William St, Princeton, NJ 08540-5237. TEL 609-258-4900, 800-777-4726, FAX 609-258-6305, http://pup.princeton.edu/catalogs/series/mcl.html. **Subscr. to:** California - Princeton Fulfillment Services, 1445 Lower Ferry Rd, Ewing, NJ 08618. TEL 800-777-4726, FAX 800-999-1958, orders@cpfs.pupress.princeton.edu. **Dist. in Canada, Australia & New Zealand, and Latin America by:** University Press Group, 164 Hillsdale Ave E, Toronto, ON M4S 1T5, Canada.; **Dist. in Europe & Africa by:** John Wiley & Sons Ltd., The Atrium, Southern Gate, Chichester, West Sussex PO19 8SQ, United Kingdom.

480 CZE ISSN 1211-6335
PA1.A1
MASARYKOVA UNIVERZITA. FILOZOFICKA FAKULTA. SBORNIK PRACI. N: RADA KLASICKA. Text in Multiple languages. 1996. a. price varies. bk.rev. **Document type:** *Academic/Scholarly.* **Description:** Presents articles in classical philology, including Mycenaean philology, ancient history, and Latin medieval culture.
Supersedes in part (in 1996): Masarykova Univerzita. Filozoficka Fakulta. Sbornik Praci. E: Rada Archeologicko - Klasicka; Which was formerly: Univerzita J.E. Purkyne. Filozoficka Fakulta. Sbornik Praci. E: Rada Archeologicko - Klasicka (0231-7915)
Published by: Masarykova Univerzita, Filozoficka Fakulta, A Novaka 1, Brno, 66088, Czech Republic. TEL 420-5-41121102, FAX 420-5-41121406, exchange@phil.muni.cz. R&P Milos Stedron TEL 420-5-41121337.

800 ITA ISSN 0392-6338
PA3001
MATERIALI E DISCUSSIONI PER L'ANALISI DEI TESTI CLASSICI. Text in Italian. 1978. s-a. EUR 50 domestic to individuals; USD 95 foreign to individuals; USD 95 domestic to institutions print & online eds.; USD 155 foreign to institutions print & online eds. (effective 2004). **Description:** Comments on current criticism of Classical literature.
Related titles: Online - full text ed.
Indexed: BibLing, PCI.
Published by: Istituti Editoriali e Poligrafici Internazionali (Subsidiary of: Libra Web), Via Giosue' Carducci, 60, Ghezzano - La Fontina, PI 56010, Italy. TEL 39-050-878066, FAX 39-050-878732, iepi@iepi.it, http://www.iepi.it. Ed. Gian Biagio Conte.

MAVORS. ROMAN ARMY RESEARCHES. see *HISTORY*

MCGILL UNIVERSITY MONOGRAPHS IN CLASSICAL ARCHAEOLOGY AND HISTORY. see *ARCHAEOLOGY*

800 POL ISSN 0025-6285
DE71
MEANDER; dwumiesiecznik poswiecony kulturze swiata starozytnego. Text in Polish; Summaries in Latin. 1946. bi-m. EUR 47 foreign (effective 2005). bibl.; illus. index. **Document type:** *Journal, Academic/Scholarly.* **Description:** Deals with issues of literature, history, history of art, philosophy and religion, as well as the archaeology of the Mediterranean (with special emphasis given to Ancient Greece, the Hellenistic world and Rome).
Indexed: BibLing, MLA, MLA-IB, RASB.
Published by: (Polska Akademia Nauk, Komitet Nauk o Kulturze Antycznej), Wydawnictwo Naukowe P W N SA/Polish Scientific Publishers P W N, ul Miodowa 10, Warsaw, 00251, Poland. TEL 48-22-6954181, FAX 48-22-6954288, ksiegarnia@pwn.pl, http://en.pwn.pl. Ed. Anna Komornicka. Circ: 1,100.

938 FRA ISSN 0995-3310
METIS. Text in Multiple languages. 1986. s-a.
Indexed: PCI.
Published by: Centre Louis Gernet de Recherches Comparees sur les Societes Anciennes, 10, rue Monsieur le Prince, Paris, 75006, France. TEL 33-1-44414650, FAX 33-1-44414661, http://www.ehess.fr/centres/gernet/METISindex.html.
Co-sponsor: Ecole des Hautes Etudes en Sciences Sociales.

MINERVA: REVISTA DE FILOLOGIA CLASICA. see *LINGUISTICS*

800 930 NLD ISSN 0026-7074
PA9
➤ **MNEMOSYNE**; a journal of classical studies. Text in English, French, German, Latin. 1852. q. USD 133 in the Americas to individuals; EUR 106 elsewhere to individuals; USD 399 combined subscription in the Americas to institutions print & online eds.; EUR 319 combined subscription elsewhere to institutions print & online eds. (effective 2006). bk.rev. bibl.; illus. Index. back issues avail.; reprint service avail. from PSC. **Document type:** *Journal, Academic/Scholarly.* **Description:** Focuses on the ancient world, including inscriptions, papyri, language, religion and philosophy.
Related titles: Microform ed.: (from SWZ); Online - full text ed.: ISSN 1568-525X. USD 359 in the Americas to institutions; EUR 287 elsewhere to institutions (effective 2006) (from Chadwyck-Healey Inc., EBSCO Publishing, Gale Group, IngentaConnect, Kluwer Online, O C L C Online Computer Library Center, Inc., Springer LINK, Swets Information Services); ◆ Supplement(s): Mnemosyne. Supplements. ISSN 0169-8958.
Indexed: ArtHuCI, BibLing, CurCont, DIP, HumInd, IBR, IBRH, IBZ, IPB, MLA-IB, NTA, PCI, RASB.
—IDS, IE, Infotrieve. **CCC.**
Published by: Brill Academic Publishers, PO Box 9000, Leiden, 2300 PA, Netherlands. TEL 31-71-53-53500, FAX 31-71-53-17532, cs@brill.nl, http://www.brill.nl/m_catalogue_sub6_id7366.htm. Eds. H Pinkster, S.R. Slings. R&P Elizabeth Venekamp. **Subscr. in N. America to:** PO Box 605, Herndon, VA 20172. TEL 703-661-1585, 800-337-9255, FAX 703-661-1501, cs@brillusa.com. **Distr. outside N. America by:** c/o Turpin Distribution, Stratton Business Park, Pegasus Drive, Biggleswade, BEDFORDSHIRE SG 18 8TQ, United Kingdom. TEL 44-1767-604-954, FAX 44-1767-601-640, brill@turpin-distribution.com.

800 NLD ISSN 0169-8958
➤ **MNEMOSYNE. SUPPLEMENTS**; bibliotheca classica batava. Text in Dutch. 1938. irreg., latest vol.241. price varies. illus. back issues avail. **Document type:** *Monographic series, Academic/Scholarly.* **Description:** Scholarly monographs and bibliographic works on historical, literary, linguistic, cultural, political and economic aspects of classical Greek and Roman civilizations.
Related titles: ◆ Supplement to: Mnemosyne. ISSN 0026-7074.
Indexed: MathR, PCI.
—BLDSC (5879.821000), IE, ingenta.

Published by: Brill Academic Publishers, PO Box 9000, Leiden, 2300 PA, Netherlands. TEL 31-71-53-53-500, FAX 31-71-53-17-532, cs@brill.nl, http://www.brill.nl. R&P Elizabeth Venekamp. Subscr. in N. America to: PO Box 605, Herndon, VA 20172. TEL 703-661-1585, 800-337-9255, FAX 703-661-1501, cs@brillusa.com. Distr. outside N. America by: c/o Turpin Distribution, Stratton Business Park, Pegasus Drive, Biggleswade, BEDFORDSHIRE SG 18 8TQ, United Kingdom. TEL 44-1767-604-954, FAX 44-1767-601-640, brill@turpin-distribution.com.

➤ **MONUMENTA GRAECA ET ROMANA.** see *ARCHITECTURE*

930 930.1   CAN   ISSN 1496-9343
PA1
➤ **MOUSEION/REVUE DE LA SOCIETE CANADIENNE DES ETUDES CLASSIQUES**; journal of the Classical Association of Canada. Text in English, French. 1956. 3/yr. CND 25 domestic to individuals; USD 25 foreign to individuals; CND 40 domestic to institutions; USD 40 foreign to institutions (effective 2004). adv. bk.rev. 150 p./no.; back issues avail. **Document type:** *Journal, Academic/Scholarly.* **Description:** Reports on the activities of Canadian classical archaeologists. Includes articles on various archaeological subjects, as well as classical history and literature.
Formerly (until 2000): Classical Views/Echos du Monde Classique (0012-9356)
Indexed: BHA, CBCARef, DIP, IBR, IBSS, IBZ, NTA. —BLDSC (5980.182000), IE, ingenta. **CCC.**
Published by: (Classical Association of Canada), University of Calgary Press, University of Calgary, Faculty of Education ETD 722, 2500 University Dr N W, Calgary, AB T2N 1N4, Canada. TEL 403-220-7736, FAX 403-282-0085, whildebr@ucalgary.ca, http://www.mun.ca/classics/mouseion/index.html, http://www.uofcpress.com. Eds. James Butrica, Mark Joyal. R&P Mark Joyal. Circ: 750.

930   DEU   ISSN 0722-4532
CODEN: QUTODG
MUENSTERSCHE BEITRAEGE ZUR ANTIKEN HANDELSGESCHICHTE. Text in German. 1982. s-a. **Document type:** *Journal, Academic/Scholarly.*
Indexed: DIP, IBR, IBZ.
Published by: Scripta Mercaturae Verlag, Am Roten Berg 5-9, St. Katharinen, 55595, Germany. info@scripta-mercaturae.de, http://www.scripta-mercaturae.de. Ed. H J Drexhage.

MUSEI COMUNALI DI ROMA. BOLLETTINO. see *MUSEUMS AND ART GALLERIES*

MUSEION 2000; glaube, wissen, kunst in geschichte und gegenwart. see *HISTORY—History Of Europe*

930   CHE   ISSN 0027-4054
PA3
MUSEUM HELVETICUM; Schweizerische Zeitschrift fuer klassische Altertumswissenschaft. Text in English, French, German, Italian. 1944. q. CHF 96; CHF 25 newsstand/cover (effective 2003). adv. bk.rev. charts; illus. index. back issues avail.; reprints avail. **Document type:** *Journal, Academic/Scholarly.* **Description:** Examines classical archeology from an international perspective.
Related titles: Microform ed.: (from SWZ).
Indexed: BHA, BibLing, DIP, IBR, IBZ, IPB, MLA, MLA-IB, PCI, RASB, RI-1, RI-2. —IE, Infotrieve. **CCC.**
Published by: (Schweizerische Vereinigung fuer Altertumswissenschaft), Schwabe und Co. AG, Steinentorstr 13, Basel, 4010, Switzerland. TEL 41-61-2789565, FAX 41-61-2789566, verlag@schwabe.ch, http://www.schwabe.ch. Circ: 1,000.

930   AUT
MYKENISCHE STUDIEN. Text in German. 1972. irreg. price varies. 42 p./no.; back issues avail. **Document type:** *Monographic series, Academic/Scholarly.*
Related titles: ◆ Series of: Oesterreichische Akademie der Wissenschaften. Philosophisch-Historische Klasse. Sitzungsberichte. ISSN 0029-8832.
Published by: (Oesterreichische Akademie der Wissenschaften, Kommission fuer Mykenische Forschung), Verlag der Oesterreichischen Akademie der Wissenschaften, Postgasse 7/4, Vienna, W 1011, Austria. TEL 43-1-515813402, FAX 43-1-515813400, verlag@oeaw.ac.at, http://www.verlag.oeaw.ac.at. Ed. Claus Reinholdt.

MYRTIA: REVISTA DE FILOLOGIA CLASICA. see *LINGUISTICS*

938   KAZ
NATSIONALNAYA AKADEMIYA NAUK RESPUBLIKI KAZAKHSTAN. IZVESTIYA. SERIYA FILOLOGICHESKAYA. Text in Kazakh, Russian. bi-m. USD 245 in North America (effective 2000).
Published by: Academy of Sciences of Kazakhstan, Ul Kabanbai Batyra 69-a, Almaty, 480100, Kazakstan. TEL 7-3732-615608, FAX 7-3272-615314, adm@geol.academ.alma-ata.su. **Dist. by:** East View Information Services, 3020 Harbor Ln. N., Minneapolis, MN 55447. TEL 763-550-0961, FAX 763-559-2931.

470   DEU   ISSN 1438-213X
NEULATEINISCHES JAHRBUCH. Text in German. 1999. a. EUR 42.80 (effective 2002). **Document type:** *Journal, Academic/Scholarly.* **Description:** Contains research on neo-Latin language and literature spanning the period from Petrarch's age to the present.
Published by: Georg Olms Verlag, Hagentorwall 7, Hildesheim, 31134, Germany. TEL 49-5121-1501-0, FAX 49-5121-150150, info@olms.de, http://www.olms.de. Eds. Karl August Neuhausen, Marc Laureys. R&P Christiane Busch. Circ: 300.

800   USA
➤ **NEW ENGLAND CLASSICAL JOURNAL.** Text in English. 1972. q. USD 15 (effective 2002). bk.rev.; software rev. bibl. **Document type:** *Newsletter, Academic/Scholarly.* **Description:** Articles and news of interest to Latin and Greek teachers and classics professors.
Former titles: New England Classical Newsletter and Journal; New England Classical Newsletter (0739-1188); Bay State Classical Newsletter
Published by: Classical Association of New England, Department of Classics, Brown University, Providence, RI 02912. TEL 401-863-2123, FAX 401-863-7484, necj@brown.edu, http://www.wellesley.edu/greekandlatin/Cane/cane.html. Ed. William F Wyatt. Adv. contact Ruth Breindel. Circ: 850 (paid).

800   USA
NEW JERSEY CLASSICAL ASSOCIATION. BULLETIN✶. Text in English. 1930. s-a. bk.rev. bibl.
Media: Duplicated (not offset).
Published by: New Jersey Classical Association, c/o N. McKee, 19 Donna Lynn Ln., Lawrenceville, NJ 08648-2823. Circ: 500.

800   GBR   ISSN 0533-2451
NEW SURVEYS IN THE CLASSICS. Text in English. 1966. a., latest 2003, Apr. price varies. bibl. reprint service avail. from PSC. **Document type:** *Academic/Scholarly.*
Related titles: ◆ Supplement to: Greece and Rome. ISSN 0017-3835.
—BLDSC (6088.784000). **CCC.**
Published by: (Classical Association), Oxford University Press, Great Clarendon St, Oxford, OX2 6DP, United Kingdom. TEL 44-1865-556767, FAX 44-1865-556646, enquiry@oup.co.uk, http://www.oup.co.uk/isbn/0-19-852865-5. Pub. Nina Curtis. R&P Fiona Bennett.

930   GRC   ISSN 1500-0834
NORWEGIAN INSTITUTE AT ATHENS. MONOGRAPHS. Text in English. 1997. irreg., latest vol.2, 1998. price varies. back issues avail. **Document type:** *Monographic series, Academic/Scholarly.* **Description:** Covers Greek, classical and prehistorical archaeology and classical philology.
Published by: Norwegian Institute at Athens, Tsami Karatason, Athens, 11742, Greece. TEL 30-210-9231351, FAX 30-210-9215993, info@norwinst.gr, http://www.norwinst.gr. Circ: 1,000 (controlled). **Dist. by:** Paul Aastroems Foerlag, William Gibsons Vaeg 11, Jonsered 43376, Sweden. TEL 46-31-7956600, FAX 46-31-7956710, paul.astrom@swipnet.se, http://www.astromeditions.com.

001.2 880   GRC   ISSN 1105-4204
NORWEGIAN INSTITUTE AT ATHENS. PAPERS. Text in English. 1991. irreg., latest vol.5, 2002. price varies. back issues avail. **Document type:** *Monographic series, Academic/Scholarly.*
Published by: Norwegian Institute at Athens, Tsami Karatason, Athens, 11742, Greece. TEL 30-210-9231351, FAX 30-210-9215993, info@norwinst.gr, http://www.norwinst.gr. **Dist. by:** Paul Aastroems Foerlag, William Gibsons Vaeg 11, Jonsered 43376, Sweden. TEL 46-31-7956600, FAX 46-31-7956710, paul.astrom@swipnet.se, http://www.astromeditions.com.

NOVA TELLUS. see *HUMANITIES; COMPREHENSIVE WORKS*

938   POL   ISSN 1428-6327
DE1
NOWY FILOMATA; czasopismo poswiecone kulturze antycznej. Text in Polish. 1929. q. PLZ 16 domestic; PLZ 5 newsstand/cover domestic (effective 2000). bk.rev. illus. index. **Document type:** *Journal, Academic/Scholarly.* **Description:** Aims to popularize the knowledge of classical antiquity in all basic aspects, such as Greek and Latin language and literature, ancient history, archaeology. Addresses both educators and students at the secondary and academic level.
Formerly (until 1997): Filomata (0015-1815)
Published by: (Uniwersytet Jagiellonski, Instytut Filologii Klasycznej), Wydawnictwo Uniwersytetu Jagiellonskiego/Jagiellonian University Press, ul Grodzka 26, Krakow, 31044, Poland. TEL 48-12-4312364, FAX 48-12-4301995, wydaw@if.uj.edu.pl, http://www.wuj.pl. Ed., R&P Stanislaw Stabryla. Circ: 600. **Subscr. to:** Enigma Press, ul Borsucza 3-58, Krakow 30408, Poland. TEL 48-12-2674124, FAX 48-12-4226793.

937 938   DNK   ISSN 0107-1378
ODENSE UNIVERSITY CLASSICAL STUDIES. Text in Multiple languages. 1971. irreg., latest vol.21, 2000. price varies. back issues avail. **Document type:** *Monographic series, Academic/Scholarly.*

Published by: Syddansk Universitetsforlag/University Press of Southern Denmark, Campusvej 55, Odense M, 5230, Denmark. TEL 45-66-157999, FAX 45-66-158126, press@forlag.sdu.dk, http://www.universitypress.dk.

938   USA
OKLAHOMA SERIES IN CLASSICAL CULTURE. Text in English. 1989. irreg. price varies. **Document type:** *Monographic series, Academic/Scholarly.*
Published by: University of Oklahoma Press, 4100 28th Ave, N W, Norman, OK 73069. TEL 405-325-2000, FAX 405-364-5798.

OLYMPISCHE FORSCHUNGEN. see *ARCHAEOLOGY*

870   GBR   ISSN 0261-507X
OMNIBUS (LONDON). Text in English. 1981. 2/yr. USD 10 (effective 2001). back issues avail. **Document type:** *Journal, Academic/Scholarly.*
Published by: Joint Association of Classical Teachers, Senate House, Malet St, London, WC1E 7HU, United Kingdom. TEL 44-20-7862-8706, FAX 44-20-7862-8729, jact@sas.ac.uk, http://www.jact.org. Ed. K Clarke. Adv. contact Miss Clare Roberts. Circ: 8,000. **Subscr. in US to:** Rick LaFleur, Department of Classics, Park Hall, University of Georgia, Athens, GA 30602.

938   GRC   ISSN 0078-5520
DE3
OPUSCULA ATHENIENSIA. Text in English, French, German. 1953. a., latest vol.27, 2002. price varies. bk.rev. **Document type:** *Yearbook, Academic/Scholarly.*
Related titles: ◆ Series of: Svenska Institutet i Athen. Skrifter. Serie 4. ISSN 0586-0539.
Indexed: NumL.
Published by: Svenska Institutet i Athen/Swedish Institute at Athens, Mitseon 9, Athens, 11742, Greece. TEL 30-210-9232102, FAX 30-210-9220925, swedinst@sia.gr, http://www.sia.gr/acta.asp. Ed. B Alroth. Circ: 500. **Dist. by:** Paul Aastroems Foerlag, William Gibsons Vaeg 11, Jonsered 43376, Sweden. TEL 46-31-7956600, FAX 46-31-7956710, 46-31-7956710, paul.astrom@swipnet.se, http://www.astromeditions.com.

930   DEU   ISSN 0078-5555
ORBIS ANTIQUUS. Text in German. 1950. irreg. price varies. **Document type:** *Monographic series, Academic/Scholarly.*
Published by: Aschendorffsche Verlagsbuchhandlung, Soester Str 13, Muenster, 48135, Germany. TEL 49-251-690-0, FAX 49-251-690143, buchverlag@aschendorff.de, http://www.aschendorff.de/buch. Ed. Max Wegner. R&P Dirk F Passmann. Adv. contact Petra Landsknecht.

220   CHE   ISSN 1015-1850
ORBIS BIBLICUS ET ORIENTALIS. Text in French, German. 1973. irreg., latest vol.195. price varies. **Document type:** *Monographic series, Academic/Scholarly.*
Published by: Academic Press Fribourg, Perolles 42, Fribourg, 1705, Switzerland. TEL 41-26-4264311, FAX 41-26-4264300, info@paulusedition.ch, http://www.paulusedition.ch/academic_press/.

937   ITA
ORIENS GRAECOLATINUS. Text in Italian. 1994. irreg., latest vol.6, 1999. price varies. **Document type:** *Monographic series.*
Published by: Istituto Ellenico di Studi Bizantini e Post-Bizantini, Castello 3412, Venice, VE 30122, Italy. FAX 39-41-5238248.

ORPHEUS; rivista di umanita classica e cristiana. see *LITERATURE*

937   ITA   ISSN 1122-259X
DG11
OSTRAKA; rivista semestrale di antichita. Text in Italian. 1992. s-a. **Document type:** *Journal, Academic/Scholarly.*
Indexed: BibInd.
Published by: Loffredo Editore SpA, Via Consalvo 99 H, Parco S Luigi, Isolato D, Naples, NA 80126, Italy. TEL 39-081-2399318, FAX 39-081-6101714, http://www.loffredo.it. Ed. Mario Torelli.

OXFORD MONOGRAPHS ON CLASSICAL ARCHAEOLOGY. see *ARCHAEOLOGY*

OXFORD STUDIES IN ANCIENT PHILOSOPHY. see *PHILOSOPHY*

THE OXFORDIAN. see *LITERATURE—Poetry*

PALAESTINA ANTIQUA. see *ARCHAEOLOGY*

800   DEU   ISSN 0552-9638
PALINGENESIA; Monographien und Texte zur klassischen Altertumswissenschaft. Text in English, German. 1964. irreg., latest vol.75, 2001. price varies. **Document type:** *Monographic series, Academic/Scholarly.*

Published by: Franz Steiner Verlag Stuttgart GmbH, Birkenwaldstr 44, Stuttgart, 70191, Germany. TEL 49-711-25820, FAX 49-711-2582390, franz.steiner.verlag@t-online.de, http://www.steiner-verlag.de. Eds. O Lendle, P Steinmetz. R&P Sabine Koerner.

937 480 FRA ISSN 0031-0387
PA2
➤ **PALLAS**; revue d'etudes antiques. Text in French. 1953. s-a. illus. back issues avail. **Document type:** *Academic/Scholarly.* **Description:** Publishes articles on the literature, linguistics, history and archeology of the Greek and Roman periods.
Indexed: BibLing.
Published by: (Universite de Toulouse II (Le Mirail)), Presses Universitaires du Mirail, Universite de Toulouse II (Le Mirail), 5, Allee Antonio Machado, Toulouse, 31058, France. TEL 33-5-61503808, FAX 33-05-61503800. Ed. Helene Guiraud.

800 ITA ISSN 0031-2355
PA9
LA PAROLA DEL PASSATO; rivista di studi antichi. Text in English, French, German, Greek, Italian, Latin, Spanish. 1946. bi-m. adv. bk.rev. charts; illus. index; cum.index every 10 years.
Indexed: BibLing, DIP, IBR, IBZ, NumL, PCI, RASB.
—IE.
Published by: Gaetano Macchiaroli Editore, Via Michetti 11, Naples, NA 80127, Italy. macchiaroli.editore@virgilio.it. Circ: 2,000.

PATRISTIC STUDIES. see *RELIGIONS AND THEOLOGY*

PHILOLOGICAL MONOGRAPHS. see *LINGUISTICS*

PHILOLOGICAL QUARTERLY; devoted to scholarly investigation of the classical and modern languages and literatures. see *LINGUISTICS*

C

938 RUS
PHILOLOGIYA. Text in English, Russian. irreg.
Published by: Izdatel'stvo I.T.S. Garant, Ul Stromynka 3, Moscow, 103009, Russian Federation. TEL 7-095-2902917. **US dist. addr.:** East View Information Services, 3020 Harbor Ln. N., Minneapolis, MN 55447. TEL 612-550-0961.

400 DEU ISSN 0031-7985
PA3
➤ **PHILOLOGUS**; Zeitschrift fuer antike Literatur und ihre Rezeption. Text in English, French, German. 1846. 2/yr. EUR 205 domestic; EUR 210 foreign; EUR 53 domestic to students; EUR 59 foreign to students (effective 2005). charts; illus. index. reprint service avail. from SCH. **Document type:** *Journal, Academic/Scholarly.* **Description:** Contributes to reconstructing and understanding ancient intellectual culture and its lasting influence on European civilization.
Related titles: Microfiche ed.: (from BHP, IDC).
Indexed: ASCA, ArtHuCI, BHA, BibLing, CurCont, DIP, IBR, IBZ, IPB, MLA, MLA-IB, MathSciNet, NTA, PCI, RASB.
—IDS, IE, Infotrieve. **CCC.**
Published by: Akademie Verlag GmbH (Subsidiary of: Oldenbourg Wissenschaftsverlag GmbH), Palisadenstr 40, Berlin, 10243, Germany. TEL 49-30-4220060, FAX 49-30-42200657, info@akademie-verlag.de, http://ph.akademie-verlag.de, http://www.akademie-verlag.de. Eds. Bernd Seidensticker, W W Ehlers.

➤ **PHILOSOPHIA ANTIQUA.** see *PHILOSOPHY*

➤ **PHILOSOPHICAL INQUIRY**; international quarterly. see *PHILOSOPHY*

➤ **PHILOSOPHIE DER ANTIKE.** see *PHILOSOPHY*

800 CAN ISSN 0031-8299
PA1
➤ **PHOENIX (TORONTO, 1946).** Text in English, French. 1946. q. CND 70 to individuals; CND 100 to institutions (effective 2005). adv. bk.rev. charts; illus.; maps. index. back issues avail.; reprints avail. **Document type:** *Academic/Scholarly.* **Description:** Publishes papers on literature, language, history, philosophy, religion, mythology, science, archaeology, art, architecture and culture of the Greek and Roman worlds from earliest times to about A.D. 600.
Related titles: Online - full text ed.: (from JSTOR (Web-based Journal Archive)).
Indexed: ArtHuCI, CurCont, DIP, IBR, IBRH, IBZ, IPB, IndIslam, L&LBA, MLA-IB, NumL, PCI, PhilInd, RASB.
—BLDSC (6465.120000), IE, ingenta. **CCC.**
Published by: Classical Association of Canada, Trinity College, University of Toronto, 6 Hoskin Ave, Toronto, ON M5S 1H8, Canada. TEL 416-978-3037, FAX 416-978-4949, phoenix@chass.utoronto.ca, http://www.chass.utoronto.ca/~phoenix. Ed. A M Keith. R&P, Adv. contact Judith Schutz. page CND 295. Circ: 1,250 (paid and controlled).

800 CAN ISSN 0079-1784
PHOENIX. SUPPLEMENTARY VOLUME. Text in English. 1952. irreg. price varies. **Document type:** *Academic/Scholarly.*
—BLDSC (6465.120020). **CCC.**

Published by: (Classical Association of Canada), University of Toronto Press, Editorial Department, 10 St Mary St, Ste 700, Toronto, ON M4Y 2W8, Canada. TEL 416-978-2239, FAX 416-978-4738, utpbooks@utpress.utoronto.ca. Ed. Catherine Rubincan.

880 410.5 GRC ISSN 1105-073X
PA19
➤ **PLATON.** Text in English, French, German, Greek, Italian. 1949. a. bk.rev. bibl. 400 p./no. 1 cols./p.; back issues avail. **Document type:** *Journal, Academic/Scholarly.*
Published by: Hetaireia Hellenon Philologon, Platon, PO Box 3373, Athens, 102 10, Greece. TEL 30-1-321-3363. Ed., Pub. G Xanthakis-Karamanos TEL 30-1-6812052. Circ: 2,000. **Subscr. to:** Demetrios N. Papadimas, 8 Hippokratous St, Athens 106 79, Greece. TEL 30-1-362-7318, FAX 30-1-361-0271.

800 USA ISSN 0258-655X
PA4382
PLOUTARKHOS. Text mainly in English. 1984. s-a. USD 10 domestic to individuals; USD 15 foreign to individuals; USD 20 to institutions; USD 5 to students. adv. bk.rev. back issues avail. **Document type:** *Academic/Scholarly.*
Published by: International Plutarch Society, c/o Frances B Titchener, Ed, Dept of History, Utah State Univ, Logan, UT 84322-0710. TEL 435-797-1298, FAX 435-797-3899. Ed., R&P, Adv. contact Frances B Titchener. Circ: 650.

POSITIONS FOR CLASSICISTS & ARCHAEOLOGISTS. see *OCCUPATIONS AND CAREERS*

938 DEU ISSN 1437-6032
POTSDAMER ALTERTUMSWISSENSCHAFTLICHE BEITRAEGE. Text in German. 1999. irreg., latest vol.6, 2002. price varies. **Document type:** *Monographic series, Academic/Scholarly.*
Published by: Franz Steiner Verlag Stuttgart GmbH, Birkenwaldstr 44, Stuttgart, 70191, Germany. TEL 49-711-25820, franz.steiner.verlag@t-online.de, http://www.steiner-verlag.de. R&P Sabine Koerner.

937 ITA ISSN 0079-5682
PROBLEMI E RICERCHE DI STORIA ANTICA. Text in Italian. 1951. irreg., latest vol.19, 1997. price varies. **Document type:** *Monographic series, Academic/Scholarly.*
Published by: L'Erma di Bretschneider, Via Cassiodoro, 19, PO Box 6192, Rome, RM 00193, Italy. TEL 39-06-6874127, FAX 39-06-6874129, edizioni@lerma.it, http://www.lerma.it.

880 ITA ISSN 0391-2698
PROMETHEUS (FLORENCE). Text in Italian. 1975. 3/yr. USD 20. bk.rev.
—IE.
Published by: Associazione Culturale Filologi, Amici di Prometheus, Universita degli Studi di Firenze, Cattedra di Letteratura Greca, Via Alfani 31, Florence, FI 50121, Italy. Ed. Adelmo Barigazzi. **Subscr. to:** Prometheus, Via Carlo Pisacane, 11-4, Florence, FI 50134, Italy.

QUADERNI DI ARCHEOLOGIA DELLA LIBIA. see *ARCHAEOLOGY*

480 ITA ISSN 0391-6936
D1
QUADERNI DI STORIA. Text in Italian. 1975. s-a. EUR 22 domestic; EUR 33 foreign (effective 2003). adv. bk.rev. reprints avail. **Document type:** *Journal, Academic/Scholarly.* **Description:** Joins historians from different areas and experiences. Links ancient times and the modern world.
Indexed: DIP, IBR, IBZ, PCI.
—CISTI, IE, Infotrieve.
Published by: Edizioni Dedalo, Casella Postale BA-19, Bari, BA 70123, Italy. TEL 39-080-5311413, FAX 39-080-5311414, info@edizionidedalo.it, http://www.ediziondedalo.it. Ed., Pub., R&P, Adv. contact Claudia Coga. Circ: 4,000.

480 470 ITA ISSN 0033-4987
PA15
QUADERNI URBINATI DI CULTURA CLASSICA; atti di convegni. Text in Italian. 1966. 3/yr. EUR 145 domestic to individuals; EUR 350 foreign to individuals; EUR 220 domestic to institutions; EUR 440 foreign to institutions (effective 2004). bk.rev. bibl.; charts. **Document type:** *Proceedings, Academic/Scholarly.*
Indexed: ArtHuCI, BibLing, CurCont, IBR, PCI.
—IE, Infotrieve.
Published by: Istituti Editoriali e Poligrafici Internazionali (Subsidiary of: Libra Web), Via Giosue' Carducci, 60, Ghezzano - La Fontina, PI 56010, Italy. TEL 39-050-878066, FAX 39-050-878732, iepi@iepi.it, http://www.iepi.it. Ed. Bruno Gentili.

870 DEU ISSN 0721-6203
QUELLEN UND UNTERSUCHUNGEN ZUR LATEINISCHEN PHILOLOGIE DES MITTELALTERS. Text in German. 1981. irreg., latest vol.13, 2000. price varies. **Document type:** *Monographic series, Academic/Scholarly.*
Published by: Anton Hiersemann Verlag, Haldenstr 30, Stuttgart, 70376, Germany. TEL 49-711-549971-0, FAX 49-711-54997121, info@hiersemann.de, http://www.hiersemann.de. Ed. W Berschin.

870 880 AUS ISSN 0048-671X
PA1
➤ **RAMUS**; critical studies in Greek and Roman literature. Text in English. 1972. s-a. AUD 32.50 domestic to individuals; USD 30 foreign to individuals; AUD 46.50 domestic to institutions; USD 41.20 foreign to institutions (effective 2005). adv. bk.rev. bibl.; abstr.; illus. cum.index every 10 vols. back issues avail.; reprint service avail. from ISI. **Document type:** *Journal, Academic/Scholarly.* **Description:** Features articles on the literature of classical Greece and Rome.
Related titles: Online - full text ed.: (from R M I T Publishing).
Indexed: ASCA, ArtHuCI, AusPAIS, CurCont, DIP, IBR, IBZ, PCI.
—BLDSC (7254.250000), IDS, IE, ingenta. **CCC.**
Published by: Aureal Publications, PO Box 49, Bendigo North, VIC 3550, Australia. FAX 61-3-54447970, http://www.latrobe.edu.au/arts/ramus/index.html, http://www.latrobe.edu.au/arts/ramus/aureal.html. Ed. Anthony James Boyle. Pub., R&P John Leonard Penwill. Circ: 300 (paid).

800 ESP ISSN 0210-7694
DE1
REVISTA HABIS. Text in English, French, German, Spanish. 1970. a. EUR 30 per issue (effective 2005). charts; illus. **Document type:** *Monographic series, Academic/Scholarly.*
Indexed: DIP, IBR, IBZ, PCI.
—CINDOC.
Published by: (Universidad de Sevilla, Departamentos de Arqueologia, Filologia Clasica, Historia Antigua), Universidad de Sevilla, Secretariado de Publicaciones, Porvenir 27, Sevilla, 41013, Spain. TEL 34-95-4487444, FAX 34-95-4487443, secpub10@us.es, http://www.us.es/publius/inicio.html.

400 ITA ISSN 1592-419X
REVUE CRITIQUE DE PHILOLOGIE ROMANE. Text in Multiple languages. 1999. a. EUR 31 (effective 2004). **Document type:** *Journal, Academic/Scholarly.*
Published by: Edizioni dell' Orso, Via Rattazzi 47, Alessandria, 15100, Italy. TEL 39-0131-252349, FAX 39-0131-257567, direzione.editoriale@ediorso.it, http://www.ediorso.it.

930 400 800 FRA ISSN 0035-1652
PA2
REVUE DE PHILOLOGIE, DE LITTERATURE ET D'HISTOIRE ANCIENNES. Text in French. 1845. s-a. price varies. bk.rev. bibl. index. **Document type:** *Monographic series, Academic/Scholarly.*
Related titles: Microfiche ed.: 1845 (from IDC); Microfilm ed.: 1845 (from PQC); Microform ed.: 1845 (from PQC); Online - full text ed.: (from Chadwyck-Healey Inc., ProQuest Information & Learning).
Indexed: ASCA, ArtHuCI, BibLing, CurCont, DIP, IBR, IBZ, IPB, MLA, MLA-IB, PCI, RASB, SSCI.
—IE.
Published by: Klincksieck, 6 Rue de la Sorbonne, Paris, 75005, France. TEL 33-1-43544757, FAX 33-1-40517385, http://www.klincksieck.com. Circ: 1,000.

800 FRA ISSN 0035-2004
PA12
REVUE DES ETUDES ANCIENNES. Text in French. 1899. 2/yr. adv. bk.rev. abstr.; bibl.; charts; illus. index. back issues avail.; reprints avail. **Document type:** *Academic/Scholarly.*
Indexed: BHA, BibLing, BrArAb, DIP, IBR, IBZ, IPB, MLA, MLA-IB, NTA, NumL, PCI, RASB.
—IE, Infotrieve.
Published by: Universite de Bordeaux III (Michel de Montaigne), Esplanade des Antilles, Talence, Cedex 33405, France. TEL 33-5-56845171, FAX 33-5-56845167, debord@montaigne.u-bordeaux.fr. Ed. Pierre BeBord. Adv. contact Annie Salomon.

880 480 FRA ISSN 0035-2039
DF10
REVUE DES ETUDES GRECQUES. Text in French. 1888. a. price varies. bk.rev. abstr.; bibl.; illus. index. reprint service avail. from SCH. **Document type:** *Monographic series, Academic/Scholarly.*
Related titles: Microfilm ed.: (from BHP).
Indexed: BHA, BibInd, BibLing, DIP, IBR, IBZ, IPB, MLA, MLA-IB, NTA, NumL, PCI, RASB.
—IE, Infotrieve. **CCC.**
Published by: (Societe des Etudes Grecques), Les Belles Lettres, 95 bd. Raspail, Paris, 75006, France. TEL 33-1-44398421, FAX 33-1-45449288, courrier@lesbelleslettres.com, http://www.lesbelleslettres.com. Circ: 2,000.

930 400 FRA ISSN 0373-5737
PA2002
REVUE DES ETUDES LATINES. Text in French. 1923. a. price varies. bk.rev. bibl. cum.index every 5 yrs. reprints avail. **Document type:** *Journal, Academic/Scholarly.*
Indexed: ASCA, ArtHuCI, BHA, BibLing, BrArAb, CurCont, DIP, IBR, IBZ, IPB, MLA, MLA-IB, PCI, RASB, RI-1, RI-2, SSCI.
—IDS, IE. **CCC.**
Published by: (Societe des Etudes Latines), Les Belles Lettres, 95 bd. Raspail, Paris, 75006, France. TEL 33-1-44398421, FAX 33-1-45449288, courrier@lesbelleslettres.com, http://www.lesbelleslettres.com. Ed. P Grimal. Circ: 2,000.

REVUE DES LANGUES ROMANES. see *LINGUISTICS*

RHEINISCHES MUSEUM FUER PHILOLOGIE. see *LINGUISTICS*

930 ITA ISSN 0035-6085
PA9
RIVISTA DI CULTURA CLASSICA E MEDIOEVALE. Text in English, French, German, Italian, Latin. 1959. s-a. EUR 145 domestic to individuals; EUR 350 foreign to individuals; EUR 220 domestic to institutions print & online eds.; EUR 440 foreign to institutions print & online eds. (effective 2004). adv. bk.rev. bibl. index. **Document type:** *Journal, Academic/Scholarly.* **Description:** Gives preference to philological and linguistic research on Classic and Medieval literature.
Indexed: BHA, BibLing, IndIslam, MLA, MLA-IB, RASB.
Published by: Istituti Editoriali e Poligrafici Internazionali (Subsidiary of: Libra Web), Via Giosue' Carducci, 60, Ghezzano - La Fontina, PI 56010, Italy. TEL 39-050-878066, FAX 39-050-878732, iepi@iepi.it, http://www.iepi.it. Ed. Ettore Paratore.

RIVISTA DI FILOLOGIA E DI ISTRUZIONE CLASSICA. see *LINGUISTICS*

RIVISTA DI STUDI POMPEIANI. see *ARCHAEOLOGY*

ROEMISCHE HISTORISCHE MITTEILUNGEN. see *HISTORY—History Of Europe*

870 930 ITA ISSN 0391-285X
DG504
ROMANOBARBARICA; contributi allo studio dei rapporti culturali tra mondo latino e mondo barbarico. Text in Italian. 1976. a., latest vol.16, 2000. back issues avail. **Document type:** *Academic/Scholarly.*
Indexed: BHA, DIP, IBR, IBZ, NumL, PCI, RASB.
Published by: (Universita degli Studi di Roma "La Sapienza"), Herder Editrice e Libreria s.r.l., Piazza di Montecitorio 117-120, Rome, 00186, Italy. TEL 39-06-6794628, FAX 39-06-6784751, bookcenter@herder.it, http://www.herder.it. Ed. Bruno Luiselli.

930 USA ISSN 0732-9814
RUTGERS UNIVERSITY STUDIES IN CLASSICAL HUMANITIES. Text in English. 1982. s-a., latest vol.12, 2003. USD 69.95 (effective 2003). **Document type:** *Monographic series, Academic/Scholarly.* **Description:** Publishes research and analysis in the classics. Each volume has a particular focus (e.g., Arius Didymus, Theophrastus, Cicero).
—CCC.
Published by: Transaction Publishers, 390 Campus Dr, Somerset, NJ 07830. TEL 888-999-6778, FAX 732-748-9801, trans@transactionpub.com, http://www.transactionpub.com. Ed. William W Fortenbaugh. Pub. Mary Curtis. R&P Marlena Davidian TEL 732-445-2280 ext 100. Adv. contact Alicja Garbie. **Subscr. to:** Transaction Distribution Center, 390 Campus Dr., Somerset, NJ 08873. TEL 732-445-1245, 888-999-6778, FAX 732-748-9801, orders@transactionpub.com.

800 400 ITA ISSN 0392-5099
SANDALION; quaderni di cultura classica, cristiana e medievale. Text in Italian. 1978. a., latest vol.18, 1995. back issues avail. **Document type:** *Academic/Scholarly.*
Indexed: BibLing, DIP, IBR, IBZ, PCI.
Published by: Universita degli Studi di Sassari, Via Universita, 40, Sassari, SS 07100, Italy. TEL 390-6-6795304, FAX 390-6-3225348, TELEX 621427 NATEL. Eds. A M Battegazzore, F Bertini, P Meloni. **Dist. by:** Herder Editrice e Libreria s.r.l., Piazza di Montecitorio 117-120, Rome 00186, Italy. TEL 39-06-6794628, FAX 390-6-3225348, 39-6-6784751, http://www.herder.it.

800 USA ISSN 0080-6684
➤ **SATHER CLASSICAL LECTURES.** Text in English. 1924. irreg., latest vol.59, 1995. price varies. back issues avail. **Document type:** *Monographic series, Academic/Scholarly.* **Description:** Discusses ancient Greek and Roman art, literature, religion, philosophy, economics, and politics.
—BLDSC (8076.575000), ingenta.
Published by: University of California Press, Book Series, 2120 Berkeley Way, Berkeley, CA 94720. TEL 510-642-4247, FAX 510-643-7127, askucp@ucpress.edu, http://www.ucpress.edu/books/SCL.ser.html, http://www.ucpress.edu/books/series.html.

930 880 NZL ISSN 1018-9017
PA1
➤ **SCHOLIA;** studies in classical antiquity. Text mainly in English; Text occasionally in Italian, French, Spanish, German, Afrikaans. 1987; N.S. 1992. a. NZD 80, USD 25 per issue in North America to individuals Europe & Asia; NZD 40 per issue in Australasia to individuals & South America; NZD 20 per issue in Africa to individuals; NZD 80, USD 40 per issue in North America to institutions Europe & Asia; NZD 80 per issue in Australasia to institutions & South America; NZD 30 per issue in Africa to institutions (effective 2004). adv. bk.rev. abstr.; illus. Index. 200 p./no.; back issues avail. **Document type:** *Journal, Academic/Scholarly.* **Description:** Features critical and pedagogical articles on a diverse range of subjects dealing with classical antiquity, including late antique, medieval, Renaissance and early modern studies related to the classical tradition. It also includes review articles, reviews and other sections dealing with classics.
Related titles: Online - full text ed.
Indexed: ISAP.
—BLDSC (8092.543480).
Published by: University of Otago, Department of Classics, PO Box 56, Dunedin, 9015, New Zealand. TEL 64-3-4798710, FAX 64-3-4799029, william.dominik@stonebow.otago.ac.nz, http://www.otago.ac.nz/classics/scholia. Ed., Pub., R&P, Adv. contact William J. Dominik. Circ: 300.

870 ITA ISSN 0080-8393
SCRIPTORES LATINI; collana di scrittori latini ad uso accademico. Text in Italian. 1965. irreg., latest vol.19, 1984. price varies. **Document type:** *Monographic series, Academic/Scholarly.*
Published by: Istituti Editoriali e Poligrafici Internazionali (Subsidiary of: Libra Web), Via Giosue' Carducci, 60, Ghezzano - La Fontina, PI 56010, Italy. TEL 39-050-878066, FAX 39-050-878732, iepi@iepi.it, http://www.iepi.it. Ed. Antonio Traglia. Circ: 1,000.

870 ITA
SCRIPTORUM ROMANORUM QUAE EXTANT OMNIA. Text in Italian. bi-m. price varies. **Document type:** *Monographic series, Academic/Scholarly.*
Published by: Giardini Editori e Stampatori (Subsidiary of: Libra Web), Via Giosue Carducci 60, Ghezzano - La Fontina, Pisa 56123, Italy. TEL 39-050-878066, FAX 39-050-878732, giardinieditori@giardinieditori.it, http://www.libraweb.net. Ed. Francesco Semi.

SCUOLA ARCHEOLOGICA DI ATENE E DELLE MISSIONI ITALIANE IN ORIENTE. ANNUARIO. see *ARCHAEOLOGY*

▼ **SEGNO E TESTO;** international journal of manuscripts and text transmission. see *PUBLISHING AND BOOK TRADE*

930 880 JPN ISSN 0582-4524
SEIYO KOTENGAKU KENKYU/JOURNAL OF CLASSICAL STUDIES. Text in Japanese; Summaries in English. 1928. a. illus.; maps. **Document type:** *Academic/Scholarly.*
Published by: (Classical Society of Japan), Iwanami Shoten, Publishers, 2-5-5 Hitotsubashi, Chiyoda-ku, Tokyo, 101-0003, Japan. FAX 81-3-239-9618. **Dist. overseas by:** Japan Publications Trading Co., Ltd., Book Export II Dept, PO Box 5030, Tokyo International, Tokyo 101-3191, Japan. TEL 81-3-32923753, FAX 81-3-32920410, infoserials@jptco.co.jp, http://www.jptco.co.jp.

938 ITA ISSN 1129-5953
PA9
SEMINARI ROMANI DI CULTURA GRECA. Text in Italian. 1998. 6/yr. EUR 46 in the European Union; EUR 57 elsewhere (effective 2005). **Document type:** *Academic/Scholarly.* **Description:** Publishes papers presented at Greek Seminars held by Luigi E. Rossi, Maria Grazia Bonanno and Roberto Pretagostini at the University of Rome.
Published by: Edizioni Quasar, Via Ajaccio 43, Rome, RM 00198, Italy. TEL 39-6-84241993, FAX 39-6-85833591, qn@edizioniquasar.it, http://www.edizioniquasar.it. Ed. Luigi Enrico Rossi.

937 ITA ISSN 1123-6477
DE1
SIMBOLOS; scritti di storia antica. Text in Italian. 1995. irreg. **Document type:** *Academic/Scholarly.*
Published by: (Universita degli Studi di Bologna), Casa Editrice C L U E B, Via Marsala 31, Bologna, BO 40126, Italy. TEL 39-051-220736, FAX 39-051-237758, clueb@clueb.com, http://www.clueb.com.

SOURCES CLASSIQUES. see *LITERATURE*

937 410 DEU ISSN 0584-9705
SPUDASMATA; Studien zur Klassischen Philologie und ihren Grenzgebieten. Text in German, English, French. irreg., latest vol.83, 2001. **Document type:** *Monographic series, Academic/Scholarly.*
Indexed: CCMJ.
Published by: Georg Olms Verlag, Hagentorwall 7, Hildesheim, 31134, Germany. TEL 49-5121-1501-0, FAX 49-5121-150150, info@olms.de, http://www.olms.de. Eds. Gottfried Kiefner, Ulrich Koepf. R&P Christiane Busch.

938 SWE ISSN 0562-1062
STOCKHOLM STUDIES IN CLASSICAL ARCHAEOLOGY. Text in Multiple languages. 1963. irreg., latest vol.12, 2001. price varies. back issues avail. **Document type:** *Monographic series, Academic/Scholarly.*
Formerly: Studies in Classical Archaeology
Related titles: ♦ Series of: Acta Universitatis Stockholmiensis. ISSN 0346-6418.
Published by: (Stockholms Universitet, Institionen foer Antikens Kultur och Samhaellsliv/University of Stockholm. Department of Classical Archaeology and Ancient History), Stockholms Universitet, Acta Universitatis Stockholmiensis, c/o Stockholms Universitetsbibliotek, Universitetsvaegen 10, Stockholm, 10691, Sweden. FAX 46-8-157776, http://www.antiken.su.se/forskning/acta.html. **Dist. by:** Almqvist & Wiksell International, P O Box 7634, Stockholm 10394, Sweden. TEL 46-8-6136100, FAX 46-8-242543, info@akademibokhandeln.se, http://www.akademibokhandeln.se.

930 950 ITA ISSN 0081-6124
STUDI CLASSICI E ORIENTALI; rivista dei Dipartimenti di Filologia Classica, Linguistica, Scienze Archeologiche, Scienze Storiche del Mondo Antico dell'Universita degli Studi di Pisa. Text in Italian. 1951. a. EUR 61.97 domestic; EUR 165 foreign (effective 2003). **Document type:** *Journal, Academic/Scholarly.*
Indexed: BibLing, PCI, RASB.
—BLDSC (8481.538000).
Published by: (Universita degli Studi di Pisa, Istituto per le Scienze dell'Antichita), Istituti Editoriali e Poligrafici Internazionali (Subsidiary of: Libra Web), Via Giosue' Carducci, 60, Ghezzano - La Fontina, PI 56010, Italy. TEL 39-050-878066, FAX 39-050-878732, iepi@iepi.it, http://www.iepi.it.

880 ITA
STUDI DI METRICA CLASSICA. Text in Italian. 1962. irreg., latest vol.7, 1983. price varies. **Document type:** *Monographic series, Academic/Scholarly.*
Published by: Istituti Editoriali e Poligrafici Internazionali (Subsidiary of: Libra Web), Via Giosue' Carducci, 60, Ghezzano - La Fontina, PI 56010, Italy. TEL 39-050-878066, FAX 39-050-878732, iepi@iepi.it, http://www.iepi.it. Ed. Bruno Gentili. Circ: 1,500.

STUDI ITALIANI DI FILOLOGIA CLASSICA. see *LINGUISTICS*

938 POL
STUDIA CLASSICA ET NEOLATINA. Text in Polish. 1994. irreg.
Published by: (Uniwersytet Gdanski, Wydzial Filologiczno-Historyczny), Wydawnictwo Uniwersytetu Gdanskiego, Ul Armii Krajowej 119-121, Sopot, 81824, Poland. TEL 48-58-5510381, FAX 48-58-5510381. Ed. Zofia Glombiowska. **Dist. by:** Ars Polona, Krakowskie Przedmiescie 7, Warsaw, Poland.

938 880 BEL
STUDIA DEMOTICA. Text in English, French. 1993 (vol 2). irreg., latest vol.5, 2000. price varies. illus. back issues avail. **Document type:** *Monographic series, Academic/Scholarly.* **Description:** Studies demotic and Greek texts in various archaeological contexts.
Published by: Peeters Publishers, Bondgenotenlaan 153, Leuven, 3000, Belgium. TEL 32-16-235170, FAX 32-16-228500, http://www.peeters-leuven.be.

480 470 SWE ISSN 0081-6450
RC952.A1 CODEN: FRGEFJ
STUDIA GRAECA ET LATINA GOTHOBURGENSIA. Text in Multiple languages. 1955. irreg., latest vol.66, 2003. price varies. **Document type:** *Monographic series, Academic/Scholarly.*
Related titles: ♦ Series of: Acta Universitatis Gothoburgensis. ISSN 0346-7740.
Published by: Acta Universitatis Gothoburgensis, Renstroemsgatan 4, P O Box 222, Goeteborg, 40530, Sweden. TEL 46-31-773-17-33, FAX 46-31-163-797. Ed. Staffan Fogelmark.

880 SWE ISSN 1100-7931
STUDIA GRAECA ET LATINA LUNDENSIA. Text in English. 1989. irreg. price varies. **Document type:** *Academic/Scholarly.*
Published by: Lunds Universitet, Department of Classical Studies/Lund University, Soelvegatan 2, Lund, 22362, Sweden. TEL 46-46-2228375, FAX 46-46-2224227, klass@klass.lu.se, http://www.lu.se/klass.

938 SWE ISSN 0562-2743
STUDIA GRAECA UPSALIENSIA. Text in Multiple languages. 1962. irreg., latest vol.20, 1999. price varies. back issues avail. **Document type:** *Monographic series, Academic/Scholarly.*
Related titles: ♦ Series of: Acta Universitatis Upsaliensis. ISSN 0346-5462.
Published by: (Uppsala Universitet), Uppsala Universitet, Acta Universitatis Upsaliensis/University Publications from Uppsala, PO Box 256, Uppsala, 75105, Sweden. TEL 46-18-4713922, http://www.ub.uu.se/upu/auu. Ed. Bengt Landgren. **Dist. by:** Almqvist & Wiksell International.

880 938 BEL ISSN 0779-3448
➤ **STUDIA HELLENISTICA.** Text in English, French, German. 1942. irreg., latest vol.35, 1999. price varies. back issues avail. **Document type:** *Monographic series, Academic/Scholarly.* **Description:** Publishes studies on the history and literature of Egypt and the eastern Mediterranean during the Hellenistic period.
—KNAW.
Published by: (Universite Catholique de Louvain, Departement d'Etudes Greques, Latines et Orientales), Peeters Publishers, Bondgenotenlaan 153, Leuven, 3000, Belgium. TEL 32-16-235170, FAX 32-16-228500, http://www.peeters-leuven.be.

➤ **STUDIA PATRISTICA.** see *RELIGIONS AND THEOLOGY*

932 DEU ISSN 0340-2215
DT61
➤ **STUDIEN ZUR ALTAEGYPTISCHEN KULTUR.** Text in German. 1974. irreg., latest vol.32, 2004. price varies. **Document type:** *Monographic series, Academic/Scholarly.*
Indexed: BibLing, DIP, IBR, IBZ, RASB.

▼ new title ➤ refereed ✶ unverified ♦ full entry avail.

—CCC.
Published by: Helmut Buske Verlag GmbH, Richardstr. 47, Hamburg, 22081, Germany. TEL 49-40-2999580, FAX 49-40-2993614, info@buske.de, http://www.buske.de. Ed. Hartwig Altenmueller.

962 DEU ISSN 0934-7879
STUDIEN ZUR ALTAEGYPTISCHEN KULTUR. BEIHEFTE. Text in German. 1988. irreg., latest vol.6. **Document type:** *Monographic series, Academic/Scholarly.*
Published by: Helmut Buske Verlag GmbH, Richardstr. 47, Hamburg, 22081, Germany. TEL 49-40-2999580, FAX 49-40-2993614, info@buske.de, http://www.buske.de. Ed. H Altenmueller.

STUDIEN ZUR ANTIKEN PHILOSOPHIE. see *PHILOSOPHY*

938 930.1 DEU ISSN 1432-7228
STUDIEN ZUR GESCHICHTE NORDWEST-GRIECHENLANDS. Text in German. 1996. irreg., latest vol.2, 1997. **Document type:** *Monographic series, Academic/Scholarly.*
Published by: (Oberhummer Gesellschaft e.V.), Ergon Verlag, Grombuehlstr 7, Wuerzburg, 97080, Germany. TEL 49-931-280084, FAX 49-931-282872, ergon-verlag@t-online.de, service@ergon-verlag.de.

930 DNK ISSN 0107-9212
➤ **STUDIER FRA SPROG- OG OLDTIDSFORSKNING.** Text in Danish. 1891. s-a., latest vol.38, 2002. DKK 185 newsstand/cover per vol. domestic to individuals; USD 31 newsstand/cover per vol. elsewhere to individuals (effective 2005); price varies. **Document type:** *Monographic series, Academic/Scholarly.* **Description:** Treats subjects from the fields of literature, philosophy, history and philology with an emphasis on ancient Greek and Latin topics.
Indexed: MLA-IB, PCI.
Published by: (Filologisk-Historisk Samfund), Museum Tusculanum Press, c/o University of Copenhagen, Njalsgade 94, Copenhagen S, 2300, Denmark. TEL 45-35-329109, FAX 45-35-329113, mtp@mtp.dk, http://www.mtp.dk. Ed. Minna Skafte Jensen. **Dist. in U.S. and Canada by:** International Specialized Book Services Inc., 5804 N E Hassalo St, Portland, OR 97213-3644. TEL 503-287-3093, FAX 503-280-8832, orders@isbs.com.

C

938 USA
STUDIES IN CLASSICS. Text in English. 1991. irreg., latest vol.25, 2003. price varies. **Document type:** *Monographic series, Academic/Scholarly.*
Published by: Edwin Mellen Press, 415 Ridge St, P.O. Box 450, Lewiston, NY 14092. TEL 716-754-2266, FAX 716-754-4056, cservice@mellenpress.com, http://www.mellenpress.com/.

STUDIES IN MEDITERRANEAN ARCHAEOLOGY AND LITERATURE. POCKET-BOOK SERIES. see *ARCHAEOLOGY*

STUDIES IN MEDITERRANEAN ARCHAEOLOGY. MONOGRAPH SERIES. see *ARCHAEOLOGY*

STUDIES IN THE HISTORY AND CULTURE OF THE ANCIENT NEAR EAST. see *HISTORY—History Of The Near East*

489 890 ROM ISSN 0081-8844
STUDII CLASICE. Text in English, French, German, Italian, Romanian, Russian. 1959. a. bk.rev.
Related titles: Online - full text ed.
Indexed: BibLing, NumL, RASB.
—KNAW.
Published by: (Societatea de Studii Clasice din Romania), Editura Academiei Romane/Publishing House of the Romanian Academy, Calea 13 Septembrie 13, Sector 5, Bucharest, 76117, Romania. TEL 40-21-4119008, FAX 40-21-4103983, edacad@ear.ro, http://www.ear.ro. Eds. I Fischer, Zoe Petre. Circ: 900. **Subscr. to:** Rodipet S.A., Piata Presei Libere 1, sector 1, PO Box 33-57, Bucharest 3, Romania. TEL 40-21-2224126, 40-21-2226407, rodipet@rodipet.ro.

930 ESP ISSN 0425-3477
SUPLEMENTO DE ESTUDIOS CLASICOS. SERIE DE TRADUCCIONES. Text in Spanish. 1950. 3/yr.
Related titles: ♦ Supplement to: Estudios Clasicos. ISSN 0014-1453.
Published by: Consejo Superior de Investigaciones Cientificas, Departamento de Publicaciones, Vitruvio 8, Madrid, 28006, Spain. TEL 34-91-561-2833, FAX 34-91-562-9634, publ@orgc.csic.es, http://www.csic.es/publica.

930 ESP ISSN 0423-4820
SUPLEMENTO DE ESTUDIOS CLASICOS. SERIE TEXTOS. Text in Spanish. 1951. irreg.
Related titles: ♦ Supplement to: Estudios Clasicos. ISSN 0014-1453.
Published by: Consejo Superior de Investigaciones Cientificas, Departamento de Publicaciones, Vitruvio 8, Madrid, 28006, Spain. TEL 34-91-561-2833, FAX 34-91-562-9634, publ@orgc.csic.es, http://www.csic.es/publica.

930 DEU ISSN 0933-5080
➤ **SUPPLEMENTA BYZANTINA.** Text in German. 1968. irreg., latest vol.6, 2002. price varies. **Document type:** *Monographic series, Academic/Scholarly.*
Published by: Walter de Gruyter GmbH & Co. KG, Genthiner Str. 13, Berlin, 10785, Germany. TEL 49-30-260050, FAX 49-30-26005251, wdg-info@degruyter.de, http://www.degruyter.de. Ed. Athanasios Kambylis.

880 938 NLD ISSN 0920-8399
SUPPLEMENTUM EPIGRAPHICUM GRAECUM. Text in Dutch. 1923. a., latest vol.41, 1994, for the year 1991. price varies. cum.index: vols.11-20, 26-35. back issues avail. **Document type:** *Academic/Scholarly.* **Description:** Reviews the progress of research on Greek inscriptions, presents commentary on new research on previously published documents; publishes the complete text of recently discovered inscriptions with full bibliographic citations.
Indexed: RASB.
Published by: J.C. Gieben, Entrepotdok 72b, Amsterdam, 1018 AD, Netherlands. TEL 31-20-6234709, FAX 31-20-6275170, http://www.teachtext.net/gieben/. Eds. H W Pleket, R S Stroud. **Dist. in N. America by:** John Benjamins Publishing Co., PO Box 27519, Philadelphia, PA 19118-0519. TEL 215-836-1200.

938 GRC ISSN 0586-0539
SVENSKA INSTITUTET I ATHEN. SKRIFTER. SERIE 4. Variant title: Acta Instituti Atheniensis Regni Sueciae, 4. Text in Multiple languages. 1951. irreg., latest 2002. price varies. **Document type:** *Monographic series, Academic/Scholarly.*
Related titles: ♦ Series: Opuscula Atheniensia. ISSN 0078-5520.
Indexed: AIAP.
Published by: Svenska Institutet i Athen/Swedish Institute at Athens, Mitseon 9, Athens, 11742, Greece. TEL 30-210-9232102, FAX 30-210-9220925, swedinst@sia.gr, http://www.sia.gr/acta.asp. Ed. B Alroth. **Dist. by:** Paul Aastroems Foerlag, William Gibsons Vaeg 11, Jonsered 43376, Sweden. TEL 46-31-7956600, FAX 46-31-7956710, 46-31-7956710, paul.astrom@swipnet.se, http://www.astromeditions.com.

SVENSKA INSTITUTET I ATHEN. SKRIFTER. SERIE 8/ACTA INSTITUTI ATHENIENSIS REGNI SUECIAE. see *ARCHAEOLOGY*

SVENSKA INSTITUTET I ROM. SKRIFTER. ACTA SERIES PRIMA. 4:O. see *ARCHAEOLOGY*

480 GBR ISSN 0039-7679
PA19
SYMBOLAE OSLOENSES; Norwegian journal of Greek and Latin studies. Text mainly in English; Text occasionally in French, German, Italian. 1922. a. GBP 58, USD 96 combined subscription to institutions print & online eds. (effective 2006). illus. cum.index: vols.1-35. back issues avail.; reprint service avail. from PSC. **Document type:** *Academic/Scholarly.* **Description:** Covers all branches of classical research.
Formerly (until 1926): Symbolae Arctoae
Related titles: Online - full text ed.: ISSN 1502-7805. GBP 55, USD 91 to institutions (effective 2006) (from EBSCO Publishing, Gale Group, IngentaConnect, O C L C Online Computer Library Center, Inc., Swets Information Services).
Indexed: BibLing, DIP, IBR, IBZ, IPB, MLA, MLA-IB, NTA, PCI, RASB.
—BLDSC (8582.050000), IE, Infotrieve. **CCC.**
Published by: Routledge (Subsidiary of: Taylor & Francis Group), 4 Park Sq, Milton Park, Abingdon, Oxon OX14 4RN, United Kingdom. TEL 44-1235-828600, FAX 44-1235-829000, info@routledge.co.uk, http://www.tandf.co.uk/journals/titles/00397679.asp, http://www.routledge.co.uk. Eds. Lars Boje Mortensen, Tomas Hagg. Circ: 350. **Subscr. to:** Taylor & Francis Ltd, Journals Customer Service, Rankine Rd, Basingstoke, Hants RG24 8PR, United Kingdom. TEL 44-1256-813000, FAX 44-1256-330245, enquiry@tandf.co.uk.

480 880 POL ISSN 0302-7384
PA25
SYMBOLAE PHILOLOGORUM POSNANIENSIUM. Text in English, Latin, Polish; Summaries in Latin. 1973. irreg., latest vol.11, 1997. price varies. **Document type:** *Monographic series, Academic/Scholarly.* **Description:** Papers devoted to the history of Latin studies; Latin literatures, linguistics and methods of teaching.
Indexed: BibLing.
Published by: (Uniwersytet im. Adama Mickiewicza w Poznaniu/Adam Mickiewicz University), Wydawnictwo Naukowe Uniwersytetu im. Adama Mickiewicza/Adam Mickiewicz University Press, Nowowiejskiego 55, Poznan, 61-734, Poland. TEL 48-61-527380, FAX 48-61-527701. Ed. Georgius Danielewicz. Pub. Maria Jankowska. R&P Malgorzata Bis.

870 880 USA
T C A'S JOURNAL. (Texas Classical Association) Text in English. s-a.
Published by: Texas Classical Association, 2535 Turkey Oak, San Antonio, TX 78232. http://www.txclassics.org.

880 CAN ISSN 0381-9361
TEIRESIAS; a review and continuing bibliography of Boiotian studies. Text in English. 1971. a. bibl.; illus. **Document type:** *Bibliography.*
Related titles: Online - full text ed.
Indexed: CPerI.
Published by: McGill University, Department of History, 855 Sherbrooke St W, Montreal, PQ H3A 2T7, Canada. TEL 514-398-1797, czas@musica.mcgill.ca. Ed. A Schachter. Circ: 300.

TEKMERIA; Beitraege zur Geschichte der griechischen und roemischen Welt. see *ARCHAEOLOGY*

470 DNK ISSN 0107-2676
THEMATA. Text in Danish. 1980. irreg. free. bk.rev.
Published by: Aarhus Universitet, Institut for Klassisk Arkaeologi/Department of Classical Archaeology, Nordre Ringgade, Bygning 414, Aarhus C, 8000, Denmark. TEL 45-89-42-11-11, FAX 45-89-42-22-87. Circ: 1,000.

THORIKOS; preliminary reports of the excavations at Thorikos. see *ARCHAEOLOGY*

TIRYNS. see *ARCHAEOLOGY*

930 ITA
TITULI. Text in Italian. irreg., latest vol.7, 1996. price varies. **Document type:** *Monographic series, Academic/Scholarly.* **Description:** Contains academic studies on ancient inscriptions.
Published by: (Istituto di Epigrafia e Antichita Greche e Romane, Universita degli Studi di Roma "La Sapienza"), Edizioni di Storia e Letteratura, Via Lancellotti 18, Rome, 00186, Italy. TEL 39-06-68806556, FAX 39-06-68806640, edi.storialett@tiscalinet.it, http://www.weeb.it/edistorialett. Ed. Silvio Panciera.

470 870 USA ISSN 0493-5284
TORCH: U.S. Text in English. 1951. 4/yr. membership. stat. **Document type:** *Newsletter, Academic/Scholarly.*
Media: Duplicated (not offset).
Published by: National Junior Classical League, American Classical League, Miami University, Oxford, OH 45056. TEL 513-529-7741. Circ: 1,400.

930 USA ISSN 1549-0440
➤ **TRANSFORMATION OF THE CLASSICAL HERITAGE.** Text in English. 1981. irreg., latest vol.25, 1996. price varies. back issues avail. **Document type:** *Monographic series, Academic/Scholarly.* **Description:** Explores the cultural, religious, and philosophical traditions of classical Greece and Rome, late antiquity, and the Byzantine Empire.
—BLDSC (9020.595800).
Published by: University of California Press, Book Series, 2120 Berkeley Way, Berkeley, CA 94720. TEL 510-642-4247, FAX 510-643-7127, askucp@ucpress.edu, http://www.ucpress.edu/books/TCH.ser.html, http://www.ucpress.edu/books/series.html. **Orders to:** California - Princeton Fulfillment Services, 1445 Lower Ferry Rd, Ewing, NJ 08618. TEL 800-777-4726, FAX 800-999-1958, orders@cpfs.pupress.princeton.edu.

930 MEX
UNIVERSIDAD NACIONAL AUTONOMA DE MEXICO. CENTRO DE ESTUDIOS CLASICOS. CUADERNOS. Text in Spanish. 1975. irreg., latest vol.32, 1991. price varies. bk.rev.
Published by: Universidad Nacional Autonoma de Mexico, Centro de Estudios Clasicos, Ciudad Universitaria, Mexico City, DF 04510, Mexico. FAX 6657874.

UNIVERSITA DEGLI STUDI DI GENOVA. DIPARTIMENTO DI ARCHEOLOGIA E FILOLOGIA CLASSICA "F. DELLA CORTE". PUBBLICAZIONI. see *LINGUISTICS*

UNIVERSITA DEGLI STUDI DI MACERATA. FACOLTA DI LETTERE E FILOSOFIA. ANNALI. see *ARCHAEOLOGY*

938 ITA ISSN 0557-3122
UNIVERSITA DEGLI STUDI DI ROMA. SEMINARIO DI ARCHEOLOGIA E STORIA DELL'ARTE GRECA E ROMANA. STUDI MISCELLANEI. Text in Italian. 1961. irreg., latest vol.32, 1997. price varies. back issues avail. **Document type:** *Monographic series, Academic/Scholarly.* **Description:** Publishes studies on various aspects of the archaeology, art, and history of ancient Greece and Rome.
Indexed: BHA.
Published by: (Universita degli Studi di Roma, Seminario di Archeologia e Storia dell'Arte Greca e Romana), L'Erma di Bretschneider, Via Cassiodoro, 19, PO Box 6192, Rome, RM 00193, Italy. TEL 39-06-6874127, FAX 39-06-6874129, edizioni@lerma.it, http://www.lerma.it.

800 400 HUN ISSN 0418-453X
PA1.A1
UNIVERSITATIS SCIENTIARUM DEBRECENIENSIS. ACTA CLASSICA. Text in Multiple languages. 1965. a., latest vol.36, 2000. adv. bibl. back issues avail. **Document type:** *Proceedings, Academic/Scholarly.*
Indexed: BibLing, DIP, IBR, IBZ, RASB.
Published by: (Klasszika Filologiai Tanszek), Kossuth Lajos Tudomanyegyetem, PF 51, Debrecen, 4010, Hungary. Ed. Laszlo Havas. Adv. contact Erzsebet Burai.

880 FRA ISSN 0065-4981
UNIVERSITE D'AIX-MARSEILLE I. CENTRE D'ETUDES ET DE RECHERCHES HELLENIQUES. PUBLICATIONS. Text in French. 1958. irreg. illus.; charts. **Document type:** *Monographic series, Academic/Scholarly.*
Published by: (Universite d'Aix-Marseille I (Universite de Provence), Centre d'Etudes et de Recherches Helleniques), Universite d'Aix-Marseille I (Universite de Provence), Centre d'Etudes des Societes Mediterraneennes, Service des Publications, Aix-en-Provence, 13621, France.

489 GBR ISSN 0076-0730
PA25
UNIVERSITY OF LONDON. INSTITUTE OF CLASSICAL STUDIES. BULLETIN. Text in English. 1954. a. GBP 50 per issue (effective Aug. 2005). illus. Supplement avail.; reprints avail. **Document type:** *Bulletin.*
Indexed: ArtHuCI, BibLing, CurCont, NumL, PCI.
—BLDSC (2580.250000).
Published by: University of London, Institute of Classical Studies, School of Advanced Study, Senate House, Malet St, London, WC1E 7HU, United Kingdom. TEL 44-20-78628700, FAX 44-20-78628722, icls.publications@sas.ac.uk, http://www.sas.ac.uk/icls/institute/bics-47-etoc.htm.

489 GBR ISSN 0076-0749
UNIVERSITY OF LONDON. INSTITUTE OF CLASSICAL STUDIES. BULLETIN SUPPLEMENT. Text in English. 1955. irreg., latest vol.84, 2005. price varies. **Document type:** *Monographic series, Academic/Scholarly.*
Indexed: PCI.
—BLDSC (2580.251000).
Published by: University of London, Institute of Classical Studies, School of Advanced Study, Senate House, Malet St, London, WC1E 7HU, United Kingdom. TEL 44-20-78628700, FAX 44-20-78628722, icls.publications@sas.ac.uk, http://www.sas.ac.uk/icls/institute/publicat.htm.

930 913 480 880 SVK ISSN 0083-4114
UNIVERZITA KOMENSKEHO. FILOZOFICKA FAKULTA. ZBORNIK: GRAECOLATINA ET ORIENTALIA. Text in English, French, German; Summaries in Slovak. 1968. irreg. free domestic (effective 2005). **Document type:** *Academic/Scholarly.*
Indexed: RASB.
Published by: Univerzita Komenskeho, Filozoficka Fakulta, Ustredna Kniznica, Gondova 2, Bratislava, 81801, Slovakia. Circ: 500.

UNIWERSYTET IM. ADAMA MICKIEWICZA. FILOLOGIA KLASYCZNA. see *LINGUISTICS*

VERBA SENIORUM; collana di testi e studi patristici. see *RELIGIONS AND THEOLOGY*

809 016 USA ISSN 0506-7294
PA6825.A2
➤ **VERGILIUS.** Text in English. 1938-1940; resumed 1956. a. USD 20 to individuals; USD 100 to institutions (effective 2005). adv. bk.rev. illus. reprint service avail. from PSC. **Document type:** *Academic/Scholarly.* **Description:** Discusses the life and work of the Roman poet Publius Vergilius Maro (70-19 B.C.). Includes the poetry, characters, myths, topography, archaeology, art, religion, philosophy, history, earlier and later authors connected to Vergil, manuscripts, modern translations.
Former titles (until 1959): Vergilian Digest (0272-3026); (until 1940): Vergilius (0276-9832)
—BLDSC (9156.025000).
Published by: Vergilian Society, 22 Bluetop Rd., Setauket, NY 11733. TEL 516-751-3483, FAX 516-751-3483, VergSoc@aol.com, http://www.vergil.clarku.edu. Ed. Patricia A Johnston. R&P Thomas M Hayes. Circ: 1,400.

➤ **VESTNIK DREVNEI ISTORII/JOURNAL OF ANCIENT HISTORY.** see *HISTORY*

➤ **VETERA CHRISTIANORUM.** see *ARCHAEOLOGY*

880 GBR ISSN 0083-629X
VIRGIL SOCIETY. PROCEEDINGS. Text in English. 1961. irreg., latest vol.23, 1998. GBP 12 (effective 2001). bk.rev. **Document type:** *Proceedings, Academic/Scholarly.*
Published by: Virgil Society, c/o M M Willcock, Dept. of Latin, University College, Gower St, London, WC1E, United Kingdom. TEL 44-20-8761-5615. Ed. J C B Foster. Circ: 200.

WIENER STUDIEN; Zeitschrift fuer Klassische Philologie, Patristikund Lateinische Tradition. see *LINGUISTICS*

938 ITA ISSN 1121-9688
DE1
XENIA ANTIQUA. Text in Italian. 1992. irreg., latest 1997. price varies. **Document type:** *Monographic series, Academic/Scholarly.* **Description:** Covers research of the classical world.
Indexed: BHA.
Published by: L'Erma di Bretschneider, Via Cassiodoro, 19, PO Box 6192, Rome, RM 00193, Italy. TEL 39-06-6874127, FAX 39-06-6874129, edizioni@lerma.it, http://www.lerma.it. Ed. Antonio Giuliano.

800 GBR ISSN 0084-330X
PA25
YALE CLASSICAL STUDIES. Text in English. 1928. irreg., latest vol.32, 2004. price varies. back issues avail. **Document type:** *Monographic series, Academic/Scholarly.*
Indexed: IBR, LIFT, PCI, PhilInd.
—BLDSC (9369.920000). **CCC.**
Published by: (Yale University, Department of Classics USA), Cambridge University Press, The Edinburgh Bldg, Shaftesbury Rd, Cambridge, CB2 2RU, United Kingdom. TEL 44-1223-312393, FAX 44-1223-315052, information@cambridge.org, http://uk.cambridge.org/series/sSeries.asp?code=YCS, http://www.cup.cam.ac.uk/. R&P Linda Nicol TEL 44-1223-325757.

CLASSICAL STUDIES—Abstracting, Bibliographies, Statistics

880 016 FRA ISSN 0184-6949
Z7016
L'ANNEE PHILOLOGIQUE; bibliographie critique et analytique de l'antiquite greco-latine. Summaries in English, French, German. 1924; N.S. 1928. a. bk.rev. illus. reprints avail. **Document type:** *Bibliography.*
Related titles: Microfilm ed.: N.S. (from BHP); Online - full text ed.
Indexed: BrArAb, RASB, SSCI.
—CINDOC.
Published by: Societe International de Bibliographie Classique/Internationale Society of Classical Bibliography, c/o Pierre-Paul Corsetti Ed., Tour Chephren, 7 square Dunois, Paris, Cedex 13 75646, France. http://www.annee-philologique.com/aph/. Circ: 2,000. **Dist. by:** Les Belles Lettres, 95 bd. Raspail, Paris 75006, France. TEL 33-1-44398421, FAX 33-1-45449288, courrier@lesbelleslettres.com, http://www.lesbelleslettres.com.

930 NLD ISSN 1386-8063
➤ **BRILL'S ANNOTATED BIBLIOGRAPHIES.** Text in Dutch. 1997. irreg., latest vol.1, 1997. price varies. **Document type:** *Monographic series, Academic/Scholarly.* **Description:** A set of bibliographical tools in the classics.
Published by: Brill Academic Publishers, PO Box 9000, Leiden, 2300 PA, Netherlands. TEL 31-71-53-53-500, FAX 31-71-53-17-532, cs@brill.nl, http://www.brill.nl. **Subscr. in N. America to:** PO Box 605, Herndon, VA 20172. TEL 703-661-1585, 800-337-9255, FAX 703-661-1501, cs@brillusa.com. **Distr. outside N. America by:** c/o Turpin Distribution, Stratton Business Park, Pegasus Drive, Biggleswade, Bedfordshire SG 18 8TQ, United Kingdom. TEL 44-1767-604-954, FAX 44-1767-601-640, brill@turpin-distribution.com.

➤ **NESTOR.** see *ARCHAEOLOGY—Abstracting, Bibliographies, Statistics*

016.938 CAN
T O C S - I N. (Tables of Contents of Interest to Classicists) Text in English, French. 1992. irreg. free. **Description:** Provides the tables of contents of a selection of Classics, Near Eastern Studies, and Religion journals, both in text format and through a Web search program.
Media: Online - full text.
Address: amphoras@chass.utoronto.ca, http://www.chass.utoronto.ca/amphoras/tocs.html, http://www.chass.utoronto.ca.amphoras/tocs/html. Eds., Pubs. Jacques Poucet, Philippa M W Matheson.

CLEANING AND DYEING

see also TEXTILE INDUSTRIES AND FABRICS

A A T C C REVIEW. see *TEXTILE INDUSTRIES AND FABRICS*

A A T C C TECHNICAL MANUAL. see *TEXTILE INDUSTRIES AND FABRICS*

667.1 658.9 USA ISSN 0092-2811
HD9999.L38
AMERICAN COIN-OP; the magazine for coin-operated laundry and drycleaning businessmen. Text in English. 1959. m. free (effective 2005). adv. charts; illus.; tr.lit. reprint service avail. from PQC. **Document type:** *Magazine, Trade.* **Description:** Provides management-related features, columns and news about the industry trends and to stay ahead of the competition.
Formerly: Coin-Op (0010-0404)
Related titles: Microform ed.: (from PQC); Online - full text ed.: (from EBSCO Publishing, Florida Center for Library Automation, Gale Group).
Published by: Crain Communications, Inc., 1155 Gratiot Ave, Detroit, MI 48207-2997. TEL 313-446-6000, FAX 313-446-1687, acomag@aol.com, http://www.americancoin-op.com/, http://www.crain.com. Ed. Paul Partyka. Pub. Charles Thompson. adv.: B&W page USD 3,055, color page USD 4,505; trim 10.88 x 8.13. Circ: 16,800.

667.12 USA ISSN 0002-8258
AMERICAN DRYCLEANER. Text in English. 1934. m. free (effective 2005). adv. bk.rev. illus.; tr.lit. 132 p./no. 2 cols./p.; back issues avail.; reprint service avail. from PQC. **Document type:** *Magazine, Trade.* **Description:** Focuses on providing the industry news to make sound business decisions. Everything from product news and marketing advice to industry observations.
Related titles: Microform ed.: (from PQC); Online - full text ed.: (from EBSCO Publishing, Florida Center for Library Automation, Gale Group).
Indexed: A&ATA, ChemAb, TTI.
—Linda Hall. **CCC.**
Published by: Crain Communications, Inc., 500 N Dearborn St, 10th Fl, Ste 1000, Chicago, IL 60610-4464. TEL 312-337-7700, FAX 312-337-8654, drycleaner@crain.com, http://www.the-drycleaner.com, http://www.crain.com. Ed. Ian P Murphy. Pub. Charles Thompson. adv.: B&W page USD 2,760, color page USD 4,935; trim 5.25 x 7.5. Circ: 16,000.

667.13 USA ISSN 1091-9201
AMERICAN LAUNDRY NEWS. Text in English. 1974. m. free to qualified personnel (effective 2005). adv. **Document type:** *Magazine, Trade.* **Description:** Focuses on coverage of issues facing the industry: productivity, technology, labor, workplace safety, the environment and more.
Formerly (until 1996): Laundry News (0164-5765)
Related titles: Online - full text ed.: (from EBSCO Publishing).
Indexed: MEDLINE, TTI.
Published by: Crain Communications, Inc., 500 N Dearborn St, 10th Fl, Ste 1000, Chicago, IL 60610-4464. TEL 312-337-7700, FAX 312-337-8654, laundrynews@crain.com, http://www.crain.com. Ed. Bruce Beggs. Pub. Charles Thompson. adv.: B&W page USD 3,270, color page USD 4,040; trim 14.5 x 10.75. Circ: 15,539 (controlled).

667.12 AUS
AUSTRALIAN NATIONAL DRYCLEANER & LAUNDERER. Text in English. 1950. m. AUD 86 domestic; AUD 115 foreign (effective 2000). adv. bk.rev.
Formerly: Australian National Drycleaner (0045-074X)
Published by: National Drycleaner & Launderer Pty. Ltd., PO Box 12177, Taren Point, NSW 2229, Australia. TEL 61-2-9525-2277, FAX 61-2-9525-8532. Ed., R&P, Adv. contact Shirley Naylor. Circ: 1,100.

BARWNIKI, SRODKI POMOCNICZE. see *TEXTILE INDUSTRIES AND FABRICS*

667.1 FRA ISSN 1257-3833
BLANCHISSERIE, LOCATION, TEXTILES PROFESSIONALS. Variant title: Blanchisserie. Text in French. 1960. 11/yr. adv.
Formerly (until 1994): Hebdo-Tex. Blanchisserie (1251-3865); Supersedes in part (in 1993): Hebdo-Tex (0989-4985); Which was formed by the merger of: Hebdo de la Blanchisserie - Teinturerie (0046-7154); Tex (0247-8447)
Published by: Editions Henri Belouze, 121, rue Henri Barbusse, Clichy, 92110, France. TEL 01-55-21-08-08, FAX 01-55-21-08-09.

667 GBR ISSN 1470-336X
BUSINESS RATIO. CONTRACT CLEANERS. Text in English. 1981. a. GBP 275 (effective 2001). charts; stat. **Document type:** *Trade.*
Former titles (until 2000): Business Ratio Plus: Contract Cleaners (1358-5185); (until 1995): Business Ratio Report: Contract Cleaners (0261-7765)
Published by: The Prospect Shop Ltd., Field House, 72 Oldfield Rd, Hampton, Middx TW12 2HQ, United Kingdom. TEL 44-20-8461-8730, 44-20-8481-8720, FAX 44-20-8783-1940, info@theprospectshop.co.uk.

338.476672 GBR ISSN 1467-4440
BUSINESS RATIO. DYERS & FINISHERS. Text in English. 1975. a. GBP 275 (effective 2001). charts; stat. **Document type:** *Trade.*
former titles (until 1999): Business Ratio Plus: Dyers & Finishers (1355-6673); (until 1994): Business Ratio Report. Dyers and Finishers (0261-7846)
Published by: The Prospect Shop Ltd., Field House, 72 Oldfield Rd, Hampton, Middx TW12 2HQ, United Kingdom. TEL 44-20-8461-8730, 44-20-8481-8720, FAX 44-20-8783-1940, info@theprospectshop.co.uk.

338.476673 GBR ISSN 1473-4095
BUSINESS RATIO REPORT. TEXTILE RENTAL, LAUNDERERS & DRY CLEANERS (YEAR). Text in English. 1986. a. GBP 275 (effective 2001). charts; stat. **Document type:** *Trade.*
Former titles (until 2000): Business Ratio. Textile Rental, Launderers & Dry Cleaners (1469-2600); (until 1999): Business Ratio Plus: Textile Rental, Launderers and Dry Cleaners (1358-8087); (until 1995): Business Ratio Report: Textile Rental, Launderers and Dry Cleaners (1353-1484); (until 1990): Business Ratio Report: Launderers and Dry Cleaners (0269-087X)
Published by: The Prospect Shop Ltd., Field House, 72 Oldfield Rd, Hampton, Middx TW12 2HQ, United Kingdom. TEL 44-20-8461-8730, 44-20-8481-8720, FAX 44-20-8783-1940, info@theprospectshop.co.uk.

▼ new title ➤ refereed ✶ unverified ♦ full entry avail.

667 330 USA ISSN 1042-6442
CLEANFAX MAGAZINE. Text in English. 1986. 9/yr. USD 19 domestic; USD 29 in Canada; USD 38 elsewhere (effective 2000). **Document type:** *Trade.* **Description:** Contains information on business management, marketing, technical skills and new products and services for professional carpet, upholstery and house cleaning firms.
—CCC.
Published by: N T P Media, 13 Century Hill Dr, Latham, NY 12110-2197. TEL 518-783-1281, FAX 518-783-1386, http://www.ntpinc.com. Ed. Robert Lindsay. Pub., R&P Alice Savino. Adv. contact Michael Paglia. Circ: 22,000.

667.1 677 USA ISSN 0886-9901
HD9999.C48
CLEANING & RESTORATION. Text in English. 1963. m. USD 69 domestic to non-members; USD 79 in Canada to non-members; USD 49 in US & Canada to members; USD 99 to members (effective 2005). adv. bk.rev. charts; illus. index. back issues avail. **Document type:** *Magazine, Trade.* **Description:** Covers cleaning and restoration of textile interior furnishings (carpets, draperies, rugs and upholstery) and restoration of fire, water, smoke and otherwise damaged contents and structures.
Former titles (until 1985): Voice (Falls Church); National Institute of Rug Cleaning Voice (0042-806X)
Related titles: Online - full text ed.
Indexed: A&ATA.
—CISTI.
Published by: (Association of Specialists in Cleaning and Restoration), A S C R International, 8229 Cloverleaf Dr, 460, Millersville, MD 21108-1538. TEL 410-729-9900, 800-272-7012, FAX 410-729-3603, info@ascr.org, http://www.ascr.org/about/magazine.shtml. Ed. Patricia Harmon. Pub., R&P Larry Jacobson TEL 410-729-9900. Adv. contacts Anthony Greenfield, Kerrie Brooks. Circ: 2,600 (paid); 1,000 (controlled).

667 USA
CLEANING BUSINESS DIRECTORY. Text in English. biennial. USD 29.95 (effective 2000). **Document type:** *Directory, Trade.* **Description:** Contains information on cleaning products, services, marketing possibilities, listings and more.
Published by: Frieda Carrol Communications, PO Box 416, Denver, CO 80201-0416. TEL 303-575-5676, FAX 970-292-2136, mail@contentprovidermedia.com.

667 USA ISSN 1535-7074
CLEANTECH. Text in English. 1997. bi-m. free to qualified personnel (effective 2005). **Document type:** *Magazine, Trade.* **Description:** Reports on cleaning issues important to high-technology and industrial applications. Covers technology, as well as the regulatory, environmental, economic and industry forces that impact daily operations.
Formerly (until 2001): Parts Cleaning (1092-6704)
Indexed: BrCerAb, C&ISA, CerAb, CorrAb, E&CAJ, EMA, IAA, M&TEA, MBF, METADEX, WAA.
—Linda Hall.
Published by: Witter Publishing Co., Inc., 20 Commerce St., Flemington, NJ 08822-7700. CleanTechMagazine@WitterPublishing.com, info@witterpublishing.com, http://www.cleantechcentral.com, http://www.witterpublishing.com. Ed. Charlie Simpson. Pub. Kip Kelly.

667.2 GBR ISSN 1472-3581
TP890 CODEN: CTOEAZ
➤ **COLORATION TECHNOLOGY.** Text in English. 1884. 6/yr. free to members (effective 2005). adv. bk.rev. abstr.; bibl.; charts; illus.; stat. index. **Document type:** *Journal, Academic/Scholarly.* **Description:** Research and practical papers on coloration.
Formerly (until 2001): Society of Dyers and Colourists. Journal (0037-9859)
Related titles: Microform ed.: (from PQC); Online - full text ed.: ISSN 1478-4408 (from EBSCO Publishing, Gale Group, IngentaConnect).
Indexed: A&ATA, ASCA, AnalAb, BrTechI, CCI, CEA, CEABA, CIN, CLL, CSNB, ChemAb, ChemTitl, CurCont, EngInd, ExcerpMed, ISR, LHB, PhotoAb, RCI, RefZh, SCI, TTI, WSCA, WTA.
—BLDSC (3322.103000), CASDDS, CISTI, Ei, IE, Infotrieve, ingenta, Linda Hall. **CCC.**
Published by: Society of Dyers and Colourists, Perkin House, Grattan Rd, Box 244, Bradford, Yorks BD1 2LU, United Kingdom. TEL 44-1274-725138, FAX 44-1274-392888, editorial@sdc.org.uk, http://www.sdc.org.uk/publications/coltechnol.htm. Ed. Carmel McNamara. Adv. contact Chris Kendall. Circ: 3,500.

➤ **COLOUR INDEX.** see *TEXTILE INDUSTRIES AND FABRICS*

667.3 IND ISSN 0010-1826
TP890 CODEN: COLOBG
COLOURAGE. Text in English. 1955. m. INR 350, USD 100. adv. bk.rev. abstr.; bibl.; charts; illus. index, cum.index.
Related titles: Supplement(s): Fibres & Polymers. ISSN 0367-1852. 1970.
Indexed: A&ATA, CIN, ChemAb, ChemTitl, CurCont, EngInd, FLUIDEX, PROMT, TTI, WTA.
—BLDSC (3322.400000), CASDDS, Ei, IE, ingenta.
Published by: Colour Publications Pvt. Ltd., Dhuruwadi 126-A, A.V. Nagveka Marg, Prabhadevi, Mumbai, Maharashtra 400 025, India. TEL 91-22-430-9319. Ed. R V Raghavan. Circ: 7,400.

667.3 IND ISSN 0588-5108
TP890 CODEN: COLAB8
COLOURAGE ANNUAL. Text in English. 1955. a.
—BLDSC (3322.410000).
Published by: Colour Publications Pvt. Ltd., Dhuruwadi 126-A, A.V. Nagveka Marg, Prabhadevi, Mumbai, Maharashtra 400 025, India. TEL 91-22-430-9319, FAX 91-22-400601.

667 ZAF
COMING CLEAN. Text in English. 1993. irreg. illus. **Document type:** *Newsletter.*
Indexed: ISAP.
Published by: Carpet and Upholstery Cleaners Association of South Africa, PO Box 19139, Fishers Hill, 1408, South Africa. TEL 27-11-4556243, FAX 27-11-4556800, http://www.mrsteam.co.za/cucasa/.

COMPANY CLOTHING. see *CLOTHING TRADE*

667 ITA ISSN 1120-6942
DETERGO; rivista italiana di lavanderia, pulitura a secco, tintoria. Text in Italian. 1952. m. (11/yr.). EUR 42 domestic; EUR 77.47 foreign (effective 2005). charts; illus. back issues avail. **Document type:** *Magazine, Trade.* **Description:** Focuses on challenges confronting the sector, explores subjects of general interest, encourages examination and debate of issues affecting sector entrepreneurs, assumes the role of spokesman for the category as a whole for sector operators and the industry.
Former titles: Detergo L P T; L P T Lavanderia; Tintoria, Lavanderia e Pulitura a Secco
Published by: (Unione Italiana Manutenzione dei Tessili e Affini), Deterservice s.r.l., Via Angelo Masina 9, Milan, MI 20158, Italy. TEL 39-02-39314120, FAX 39-02-39315160, http://www.detergorivista.com. Ed., Adv. contact Emilia Pecorara. Circ: 15,000.

667.12 USA ISSN 0012-6802
DRYCLEANERS NEWS. Text in English. 1950. m. USD 36; free to qualified personnel in the NE states (effective 2005). adv. 56 p./no. 4 cols./p.; back issues avail.; reprints avail. **Document type:** *Magazine, Trade.* **Description:** Aimed at owners and managers of drycleaning plants in the Northeastern US.
Published by: Zackin Publications, PO Box 2180, Waterbury, CT 06722-2180. info@dcn-online.com, http://www.dcn-online.com/dcn/, http://www.zackin.com. Ed. Michael Griffin. Pub. Paul Zackin. Adv. contact Linda Zackin. Circ: 10,500 (controlled).

DYES IN HISTORY AND ARCHAEOLOGY. see *ARCHAEOLOGY*

667 ESP
E & L. (Empresa & Limpieza) Text in Spanish. q.
Published by: A S C E L, Biscia 441-443, Barcelona, 08027, Spain. TEL 34-3-349-0813, FAX 34-3-349-2004, ascel@sefes.es.

338.476671 ESP
EMPRESA & LIMPIEZA. Text in Spanish; Text occasionally in Catalan. q. free. **Document type:** *Trade.*
Published by: Asociacion Catalana de Empresarios de Limpieza, Biscaia, 441-443, entlo., Barcelona, 08027, Spain. TEL 34-3-3490813, FAX 34-3-3492004, ascel@sefes.es.

667.13 USA ISSN 1084-6778
FABRICARE. Text in English. 1972. 11/yr. free to members. adv. illus.; stat. index. **Document type:** *Magazine, Trade.* **Description:** Provides news and information, including feature stories, that apply to the dry cleaning industry.
Former titles: Fabricare News (0161-8040); Monthly Mailer (0027-0466)
Related titles: ◆ Supplement(s): Textile Analysis Bulletin Service. ISSN 0894-8267.
Indexed: TTI.
Published by: International Fabricare Institute, 14700 Sweitzer Ln, Laurel, MD 20707. TEL 301-622-1900, 800-638-2627, FAX 240-295-0685, communications@ifi.org, http://www.ifi.org. Pub. William E Fisher. R&P Ruby Burns. Adv. contact Paula Spencer. Circ: 6,000 (paid).

667.12 FRA
FEDERATION DES ENTREPRENEURS DE NETTOYAGE DE FRANCE. ANNUAIRE OFFICIEL. Text in French. a. adv.
Published by: (Federation des Entrepreneurs de Nettoyage de France), Heral, 44 rue Jules Ferry, Vitry Sur Seine, 94400, France.

FINANCIAL SURVEY. TEXTILE RENTAL, LAUNDERERS AND DRY CLEANERS. see *BUSINESS AND ECONOMICS—Trade And Industrial Directories*

338.476672 KOR ISSN 1229-0033
HAN'GUG YEOMSAEG GA'GONG HAGHOEJI/JOURNAL OF THE KOREAN SOCIETY OF DYERS AND FINISHERS. Text in Korean. 1989. bi-m. **Document type:** *Journal, Academic/Scholarly.*
—BLDSC (4262.076493).
Published by: Han'gug Yeomsaeg Ga'gong Haghoe/Korean Society of Dyers And Finishers, 404-7, Pyeongri 6, Seoku, Daegu, 307-834, Korea, S. TEL 82-53-3503766, FAX 82-53-3503777, ksdf@ksdf.or.kr, http://www.ksdf.or.kr/.

338.476671 USA
HOUSEKEEPING SOLUTIONS. Text in English. bi-m. free domestic to qualified personnel (effective 2005). adv. **Document type:** *Magazine, Trade.*
Published by: Trade Press Publishing Corp., 2100 W Florist Ave, Milwaukee, WI 53209. TEL 414-228-7701, FAX 414-228-1134, http://www.cleanlink.com/NR/NR1hks.html, http://www.tradepress.com. Eds. Kelly Petterson, D Yake. Pub. R Geissler. adv.: B&W page USD 6,470, color page USD 8,240; trim 10.625 x 14.375. Circ: 41,500 (paid).

I C S CLEANING SPECIALIST. (Installation and Cleaning Specialist) see *INTERIOR DESIGN AND DECORATION—Furniture And House Furnishings*

667 AUS
INCLEAN; Australasia's cleaning industry magazine. Text in English. 1987. bi-m. AUD 60 domestic; AUD 90 foreign (effective 2001). adv. 56 p./no.; back issues avail. **Document type:** *Trade.* **Description:** Provides information on new products technology, industry issues and distribution of products.
Published by: Hardcastle Media, PO Box 180, Thirroul, NSW 2515, Australia. TEL 61-2-42673566, FAX 61-2-42681469, hardcastle@access1.com.au, http://www.incleanmag.com.au/. Ed., R&P, Adv. contact Alan Hardcastle. color page AUD 2,295; trim 210 x 297. Circ: 6,000.

667.13 USA ISSN 0046-9211
INDUSTRIAL LAUNDERER. Text in English. 1950. m. USD 100 to non-members; USD 30 to members (effective 2005). adv. bk.rev. index. **Document type:** *Magazine, Trade.* **Description:** Provides management information for commercial and retail laundering.
Indexed: TTI.
—BLDSC (4457.532000), IE, ingenta.
Published by: Uniform & Textile Service Association, 1300 North 17th St, Ste 750, Arlington, VA 22209. TEL 703-247-2600, FAX 703-841-4750, koepper@utsa.com, info@utsa.com, http://www.ilmagonline.com/, http://www.utsa.com. Ed. Joan Leotta. Pub. Ken Koepper. Adv. contacts John Marrapese, Ken Koepper. Circ: 4,500 (paid).

INTERNATIONAL DYER. see *TEXTILE INDUSTRIES AND FABRICS*

JOURNAL FOR WEAVERS, SPINNERS & DYERS. see *TEXTILE INDUSTRIES AND FABRICS*

667 USA ISSN 1062-8088
JOURNAL OF THE COIN LAUNDRY AND DRYCLEANING INDUSTRY. Text in English. 1990. m. USD 24 (effective 1999). adv. charts; illus.; stat. back issues avail. **Document type:** *Trade.* **Description:** Includes industry news, educational material, legislative alerts, managing tips and guidelines for the coin laundry and dry cleaning industry.
Incorporates (1972-1990): C L A News
Published by: Coin Laundry Association, 1315 Butterfield Rd, Ste 212, Downers Grove, IL 60515. TEL 630-963-5547, FAX 630-963-5864. Ed. Kathy Yolles. R&P John Vassiliades. Adv. contact Laurie Moore. Circ: 26,000.

667 338 GBR
KEY NOTE MARKET REPORT: CONTRACT CLEANING. Variant title: Contract Cleaning Market Report. Text in English. 198?. irreg., latest 2002, May. GBP 340 per issue (effective 2002). **Document type:** *Trade.* **Description:** Provides an overview of the UK contract cleaning market, including industry structure, market size and trends, developments, prospects, and major company profiles.
Formerly (until 1995): Key Note Report: Contract Cleaning (0956-201X)
Related titles: CD-ROM ed.; Online - full text ed.
Published by: Key Note Ltd., Field House, 72 Oldfield Rd, Hampton, Mddx TW12 2HQ, United Kingdom. TEL 44-20-8481-8750, FAX 44-20-8783-0049, info@keynote.co.uk, http://www.keynote.co.uk. Ed. Jenny Baxter.

667.1 338 GBR ISSN 1463-659X
KEY NOTE MARKET REPORT: DRY CLEANING & LAUNDRY SERVICES. Variant title: Dry Cleaning & Laundry Services Market Report. Text in English. 1998. irreg., latest 2002, Feb. GBP 340 per issue (effective 2002). **Document type:** *Trade.* **Description:** Provides an overview of the UK dry cleaning and laundry services markets, including industry structure, market size and trends, developments, prospects, and major company profiles.
Published by: Key Note Ltd., Field House, 72 Oldfield Rd, Hampton, Mddx TW12 2HQ, United Kingdom. TEL 44-20-8481-8750, FAX 44-20-8783-0049, info@keynote.co.uk, http://www.keynote.co.uk. Ed. Emily Pattullo.

667 338.476671 GBR ISSN 1365-0939
KEY NOTE MARKET REPORT: HEAVY INDUSTRIAL CLEANING. Variant title: Heavy Industrial Cleaning. Text in English. 1996. irreg., latest 1996, June. GBP 340 per issue (effective 2002). **Document type:** *Trade.* **Description:** Provides and overview of a specific UK market segment and includes executive summary, market definition, market size, industry background, competitor analysis, current issues, forecasts, company profiles, and more.
Published by: Key Note Ltd., Field House, 72 Oldfield Rd, Hampton, Mddx TW12 2HQ, United Kingdom. TEL 44-20-8481-8750, FAX 44-20-8783-0049, info@keynote.co.uk, http://www.keynote.co.uk. Ed. Kim Potts.

668.12 668.14 658 GBR
KEY NOTE MARKET REPORT: HOUSEHOLD SOAPS & DETERGENTS. Text in English. irreg., latest 2001, July. GBP 340 per issue (effective 2002). **Description:** Provides an overview of a specific UK market segment and includes executive summary, market definition, market size, industry background, competitor analysis, current issues, forecasts, company profiles, and more.
Former titles (until 2001): Key Note Plus Market Report. Household Soaps & Detergents (1460-2040); (until 1997): Key Note Report. Household Soaps & Detergents; Key Note Report. Soaps & Detergents
Published by: Key Note Ltd., Field House, 72 Oldfield Rd, Hampton, Mddx TW12 2HQ, United Kingdom. TEL 44-20-8481-8750, FAX 44-20-8783-0049, info@keynote.co.uk, http://www.keynote.co.uk. Ed. Jacob Howard.

667 677 NLD ISSN 0023-4958
KRUL'S MAANDBLAD VOOR STOOM- EN CHEMISCHE WASSERIJEN, VERVERIJEN EN WASSALONS. Text in Dutch. 1899. m. USD 39.50 foreign. adv. charts; illus. **Document type:** *Journal, Trade.*
Address: PO Box 1332, Rotterdam, Netherlands. TEL 31-10-473-6111, FAX 31-10-473-0393. Ed., Adv. contact W Graveland. Pub., R&P A Schuddebeurs. Circ: 600 (paid).

667.1 GBR
L C N TEXTILE CARE YEARBOOK. (Laundry and Cleaning News) Text in English. a. GBP 43; USD 76 in North America. **Document type:** *Trade.*
Published by: Wilmington Publishing Ltd. (Subsidiary of: Wilmington Group Plc), Maidstone Rd, Footscray, Sidcup, Kent DA14 5HZ, United Kingdom. TEL 44-1322-277788, FAX 44-1322-276474, wbp@wilmington.co.uk.

667.1 ESP
L & E. Text in Spanish. 4/yr.
Published by: L y E, Mora D'Ebre, 55, Barcelona, 08023, Spain. TEL 3-213-41-96, FAX 3-210-28-66.

667.1 GBR ISSN 0142-9442
LAUNDRY AND CLEANING NEWS. Text in English. 1885. m. GBP 47; GBP 65 in Europe; USD 110 in US & Canada; GBP 81 elsewhere (effective 1999). adv. bk.rev. charts; illus.; mkt.; tr.lit. back issues avail. **Document type:** *Trade.* **Description:** Covers professional laundries, dry cleaning, textile rental and launderette operations.
Formerly: Laundry and Cleaning (0023-8961)
Indexed: TTI, WTA.
—BLDSC (5160.569000).
Published by: Wilmington Publishing Ltd. (Subsidiary of: Wilmington Group Plc), Maidstone Rd, Footscray, Sidcup, Kent DA14 5HZ, United Kingdom. TEL 44-1322-277788, FAX 44-1322-276474, wbp@wilmington.co.uk. Ed. Nicholas Marshall. Adv. contact Christopher Shepherd. Circ: 4,894.

667.1 GBR ISSN 0261-4421
LAUNDRY & CLEANING NEWS INTERNATIONAL; the world-wide publication for the fabric care industry. Text in English. 1885. m. USD 47; GBP 65 in Europe; USD 110 in North America; GBP 81 elsewhere (effective 1999). adv. bk.rev. charts; illus. back issues avail. **Document type:** *Trade.*
Formerly: Laundry and Cleaning International (0023-897X)
Published by: Wilmington Publishing Ltd. (Subsidiary of: Wilmington Group Plc), Maidstone Rd, Footscray, Sidcup, Kent DA14 5HZ, United Kingdom. TEL 44-1322-277788, FAX 44-1322-276474, wbp@wilmington.co.uk. Ed. Nicholas Marshall. Adv. contact Christopher Shepherd. Circ: 9,316.

667 ITA ISSN 0393-4365
CODEN: LAINF3
LAVAGGIO INDUSTRIALE. Variant title: L I - Lavaggio, Pulitura e Vibrofinitura Industriale. Text in Italian. 1981. bi-m. EUR 45 domestic; EUR 90 foreign (effective 2005). adv. bk.rev. abstr.; tr.lit. index. **Document type:** *Magazine, Trade.*
Indexed: WSCA.
—CASDDS.
Published by: Rivista del Colore SpA, Palazzo Larice Edificio M, Via Torri Bianche 3, Vimercate, MI 20059, Italy. TEL 39-039-629041, FAX 39-039-62904208, info@larivistadelcolore.com, http://www.larivistadelcolore.com. Ed., R&P Danilo O Malavolti. Adv. contact Francesco Stucchi. Circ: 4,100.

667 ESP ISSN 1135-0733
LIMPIEZA INFORM; revista tecnica limpieras generales. Text in Spanish. 1972. m. EUR 49.55 Print & online eds. (effective 2004). adv. bk.rev. abstr.; illus.; pat.; stat.; tr.lit.
Formerly: Revitec 2
Related titles: Online - full text ed.
Published by: Ediciones Revitec, Instituto Tecnico Espanol de Limpieza, C/ Cadi, 3 Pol, Ind. Riu d'Or, St. Fruitos de Bages, Barcelona 08272, Spain. TEL 34-93-8774101, FAX 34-93-8774078, itel@itelspain.com, http://www.itelspain.com. Ed. Valenti Casas. Circ: 20,500.

667.13 USA
M L A NEWS (RALEIGH). Text in English. 1981. bi-m. membership. adv. charts. **Document type:** *Newsletter.* **Description:** Contains information on professional laundry services for multi-family housing units.
Published by: Multi-Housing Laundry Association, 1500 Sunday Dr., Ste. 102, Raleigh, NC 27607-5151. TEL 919-787-5181, FAX 919-787-4916. Ed. Banner Huggins. Adv. contact Elizabeth Stark. Circ: 300.

667 ESP
MUNDO T & L; tintoreria, lavanderia, limpieza. Text in Spanish. 1989. bi-m. back issues avail. **Document type:** *Trade.* **Description:** For professionals in the cleaning and laundering industry and services and user of these services.
Published by: Planet Press S.L., C. Aragon 63, entlo. 2a, Barcelona, 08015, Spain. TEL 34-3-2265033, FAX 34-3-2265034. Ed. Gonzalo Amoros. Pub. Eduardo Jordan. R&P, Adv. contact Eliana Solsona. Circ: 5,000.

667.13 USA ISSN 0027-5875
N A I L M NEWS. Variant title: Nailm News. Text in English. 1937. m. USD 18 to non-members.
Published by: National Association of Institutional Linen Management, 2130 Lexington Rd, Ste H, Richmond, KY 40475. Ed. Adrienne Grizzell. Circ: 2,400.

667 USA ISSN 0744-6306
NATIONAL CLOTHESLINE. Text in English. 1961. m. free. adv. illus. **Document type:** *Newspaper, Trade.*
Former titles: Clothesline-Laundryline; Clothesline (0009-9473)
Published by: B P S Communications, PO Box 340, Willow Grove, PA 19090-0340. TEL 215-830-8467, FAX 215-830-8490, ncled@aol.com, http://www.natclo.com, http://users.aol.com/ncled. Ed., R&P Hal Horning. Pub. Carol Memberg. Adv. contact Leslie Schaeffer. Circ: 30,000 (controlled).

667.1 USA ISSN 1068-7076
NEW ERA MAGAZINE. Text in English. 1959. m. USD 30 domestic; USD 75 foreign; USD 5 newsstand/cover (effective 2002). adv. bk.rev. **Document type:** *Magazine, Trade.* **Description:** Independent magazine for the laundry and drycleaning trade.
Formerly: New Era Laundry and Cleaning Lines (0028-5056)
Address: 22152 Jonesport Ln, Huntington Beach, CA 92646-8425. TEL 714-962-1351, 888-565-8236, FAX 714-962-1354, 4newera@gte.net. Ed., Pub., R&P Judith E Frye. Adv. contact David Bucknam. Circ: 19,615 (controlled).

667.1 FRA ISSN 1253-8736
PRESSING, LAVERIE, LIBRE-SERVICE. Text in French. 1960. 11/yr.
Formerly (until 1994): Hebdo-Tex. Pressing, Laverie, Libre-Service (1251-3873); Supersedes in part (in 1993): Hebdo-Tex (0989-4985); Which was formed by the merger of: Hebdo de la Blanchisserie - Teinturerie (0046-7154); Tex (0247-8447)
Published by: Editions Henri Belouze, 121, rue Henri Barbusse, Clichy, 92110, France. TEL 46-38-20-00, FAX 46-38-87-74.

667.1 USA ISSN 1087-3260
PROFESSIONAL CARWASHING & DETAILING. Text in English. m. free to qualified personnel (effective 2003). back issues avail. **Document type:** *Magazine, Trade.*
Formerly (until 1976): Professional Carwashing (0191-6823)
Related titles: Online - full content ed.
—CCC.
Published by: N T P Media, 13 Century Hill Dr, Latham, NY 12110-2197. TEL 518-783-1281, FAX 518-783-1386, http://www.carwash.com, http://www.ntpinc.com. Ed. Stephanie Russo.

667 DEU ISSN 1611-468X
TP932
R & W - TEXTILSERVICE. (Reiniger und Waescher) Text in German. 1947. m. EUR 76 domestic; EUR 87 foreign; EUR 7.50 newsstand/cover (effective 2003). adv. bk.rev. pat.; stat.; tr.lit. index. **Document type:** *Magazine, Trade.*
Former titles (until 2003): R & W - Reiniger und Waescher (0942-9263); (until 1992): Reiniger und Waescher (0034-3625); Which was formed by the merger of: Waescherei-Technik und -Chemie; Reiniger - Revue; Faerber-Zeitung
Indexed: A&ATA, CISA, ExcerpMed, TTI.
—CCC.
Published by: Hans Holzmann Verlag GmbH, Gewerbestr 2, Bad Woerishofen, 86825, Germany. TEL 49-8247-35401, FAX 49-8247-354170, info@holzmannverlag.de, http://www.reiniger-und-waescher.de, http://www.holzmannverlag.de. Eds. Annett Sachs, Heinz-Peter Senftleben. Adv. contact Claudia Baur. B&W page EUR 2,225, color page EUR 3,890. Circ: 4,785.

667 CHN ISSN 1006-6632
RANLIAO GONGYE/DYESTUFF INDUSTRY. Text in Chinese. bi-m. **Document type:** *Journal, Trade.*
—BLDSC, IE, ingenta.
Published by: Shenyang Huagong Yanjiuyuan/Shenyang Research Institute of Chemical Industry, No.8, Shenliaodong Road, Shenyang, 110021, China. http://www.syrici.com.cn/.

667.1 DNK ISSN 1397-2782
RENS OG VASK. Text in Danish. 1965. 8/yr. adv. illus. **Document type:** *Magazine, Trade.* **Description:** Directed to individuals in the cleaning and laundry industry, as well as institutes and organizations such as hospitals and sanatoriums.
Former titles (until 1995): Nordisk Tidsskrift for Rensning og Vask (0105-6611); (until 1972): Nordisk Tidsskrift for Rensning, Farvning, Vask (0029-1536); Incorporates (1974-1980): Vask, Rens, Rengoering (0108-9676); Which was formed by the merger of (1944-1965): Renseriejeren; (1958-1965): Dansk Farveri- og Renseri Tidende
Related titles: Online - full text ed.
Published by: TechMedia A/S, Naverland 35, Glostrup, 2600, Denmark. TEL 45-43-242628, FAX 45-43-242626, info@techmedia.dk, http://www.techmedia.dk. Ed. Benno Arndt. Adv. contact John Elmeskov. B&W page DKK 10,700, color page DKK 15,200; 176 x 265. Circ: 3,600 (controlled).

667 SWE ISSN 0282-1168
RENT/CLEAN; Scandinavian laundry and dry cleaning journal. Text in Danish, Norwegian, Swedish. 1956. 6/yr. SEK 551 domestic; SEK 816 elsewhere (effective 2003). adv. illus. **Document type:** *Magazine, Trade.*
Formed by the merger of (1969-1982): Staednytt (0346-198X); (1972-1982): Tvaettnytt (0049-4887); Which was formed by the merger of (1960-1971): Tvaettbranschen (0282-1664); (1961-1971): Tvaettindustrin (0041-4557)
Indexed: ChemAb.
Published by: (Sveriges Tvaetterifoerbund), Mentor Online AB, Tryffelslingan 10, PO Box 72001, Lidingoe, 18172, Sweden. TEL 46-8-6704100, FAX 46-8-6616455, http://www.cleannet.se/rent. Ed. Christina Jedefeldt TEL 46-8-6704135. Adv. contact Susanne Persson TEL 46-8-6704129. B&W page SEK 16,800, color page SEK 23,200. Circ: 2,800.

C

667 ESP ISSN 0214-7394
REVITEC; revista tecnica tintoreria y lavanderia. Text in Spanish. 1963. m. EUR 49.55 Print & online eds. (effective 2004). adv. bk.rev. abstr.; illus.; pat.; stat.; tr.lit.
Formerly (until 1967): Tintoreria y Lavanderia (0214-7408)
Related titles: Online - full text ed.
Published by: Ediciones Revitec, Instituto Tecnico Espanol de Limpieza, C/ Cadi, 3 Pol, Ind. Riu d'Or, St. Fruitos de Bages, Barcelona 08272, Spain. TEL 34-93-8774101, FAX 34-93-8774078, itel@itelspain.com, http://www.itelspain.com/. Ed. Valenti Casas. Circ: 20,500.

668.14 668.55 CHN ISSN 1001-1803
RIYONG HUAXUE GONGYE/CHINA SURFACTANT, DETERGENT & COSMETICS. Text in Chinese; Contents page in English. 1979. bi-m. CNY 36 (effective 2004). **Document type:** *Journal, Academic/Scholarly.*
Related titles: Online - full content ed.; Online - full text ed.: (from East View Information Services).
Indexed: BrCerAb, C&ISA, CerAb, CorrAb, E&CAJ, EMA, IAA, M&TEA, MBF, METADEX, MSB, RefZh, WAA.
—BLDSC (3180.234650), IE, ingenta, Linda Hall.
Published by: (China Information Centre of Light Industry), Zhongguo Riyong Huaxue Gongye Yanjiuyuan/China Research Institute of Daily Chemical Industry, 34 Wenyuan Street, Taiyuan, Shanxi 030001, China. TEL 86-351-4044836, FAX 86-351-4040802, ridci@public.ty.sx.cn, http://www.surfactantchina.com/magazine/magazine.php3. **Dist. by:** China International Book Trading Corp, 35 Chegongzhuang Xilu, Haidian District, PO Box 399, Beijing 100044, China. TEL 86-10-68412045, FAX 86-10-68412023, cibtc@mail.cibtc.com.cn, http://www.cibtc.com.cn.

S OE F W JOURNAL. see *BEAUTY CULTURE—Perfumes And Cosmetics*

667.12 FRA ISSN 0398-8716
SERVICE 2000. Text in French. 1972. q. adv.
Indexed: CISA.
Published by: Heral, 44 rue Jules Ferry, Vitry Sur Seine, 94400, France. TEL 42-66-15-26, FAX 47-42-44-66. Circ: 8,560.

SHUTTLE, SPINDLE & DYEPOT. see *TEXTILE INDUSTRIES AND FABRICS*

667.1 AUT
T W F*. (Oesterreichische Textilreiniger-, Waescher- und Faerberzeitschrift) Text in German. 1948. m. charts. **Document type:** *Journal, Trade.*
Formerly: C W F (0029-9367)
Indexed: TTI.
Published by: Bundesinnung der Textilreiniger, Waescher und Faerber, Wiedner Hauptstr 63, Vienna, 1045, Austria. TEL 43-1-5909003264, FAX 43-1-590900249, big@bi.wko.at. Circ: 2,100.

667.1 ITA
TECNO CLEAN. Text in Italian. 11/yr.

▼ new title ➤ refereed * unverified ♦ full entry avail.

Published by: C I D A Editrice Stampa Periodica, Viale Certosa, 238, Milan, MI 20149, Italy. TEL 2-30-85-141, FAX 2-30-88-503. Ed. Franco Pigozzi.

667 NLD ISSN 0929-2012
➤ **TEXTIEL BEHEER.** Text in Dutch. 1964. bi-m. adv. bk.rev. illus.; mkt.; pat.; tr.mk. **Document type:** *Journal, Academic/Scholarly.*
Former titles (until 1990): Textielverzorging (0169-5584); (until 1984): Vakblad voor Textielreiniging (0042-224X)
Indexed: ExcerpMed, KES.
Published by: Stichting Vakblad Textielreiniging, Postbus 10, Ophemert, 4060 GA, Netherlands. FAX 31-34-465-1525, menp@pi.net. Ed. P N M Wennekes. Circ: 1,000 (controlled).

667.1 BEL ISSN 1780-1052
TEXTIELVERZORGING. Text in Dutch. 1946. bi-m. BEF 1,200. adv. **Document type:** *Journal, Trade.*
Former titles (until 2003): Textielreiniging (1780-1044); (until 1980): Belgische Textielreiniging (0005-8475); (until 1964): Het Wasbedrijf (0770-2469)
Published by: Nationale Confederatie van de Belgische Textielreiniging, Jezusstraat 16, Antwerp, 2000, Belgium. Circ: 1,200.

TEXTILE ANALYSIS BULLETIN SERVICE. see *TEXTILE INDUSTRIES AND FABRICS*

TEXTILE RENTAL. see *CLOTHING TRADE*

667 CHE ISSN 1422-3430
TEXTILPFLEGE SCHWEIZ; les soins aux textiles. Text in German, French. 1996. m. adv. bk.rev. illus.; mkt.; tr.lit. back issues avail. **Document type:** *Bulletin, Trade.*
Formed by the merger of (1967-1996): Nachrichtenblatt V T S (1422-349X); Which was formerly (until 1989): V S T C U Nachrichtenblatt (1422-3457); (until 1972): Nachrichtenblatt des Faerbers (1422-3465); (1906-1996): Fachschrift Textilpflege (1421-0223); (until 1987): Fachschrift fuer Textilreinigung (1421-2307); (until 1974): Schweizerische Waescherei-Zeitung (1421-2293); (until 1965): Schweizerische Waescherei- und Faerberei-Zeitung (1421-2285)
Published by: Verband Textilpflege Schweiz, Sandrainstr 3, Postfach 5853, Bern, 3001, Switzerland. TEL 41-31-3102030, FAX 41-31-3102035, office@textilpflege.ch, http://www.textilpflege.ch. Ed., Pub. Juerg Depierraz. R&P Werner Hulliger TEL 41-31-3821180. adv.: B&W page CHF 1,020, color page CHF 2,220; trim 171 x 248. Circ: 800.

C

TINCTORIA. see *TEXTILE INDUSTRIES AND FABRICS*

667.3 GBR
UNIVERSITY OF LEEDS. DEPARTMENT OF COLOUR CHEMISTRY AND DYEING. REPORT. Text in English. irreg. **Document type:** *Bulletin.*
Formerly (until 1994): University of Leeds. Committee on the Departments of Textile Industries and Colour Chemistry and Dyeing. Report
Published by: University of Leeds, Department of Colour Chemistry and Dyeing, Leeds, W Yorks LS2 9JT, United Kingdom. TEL 44-113-243-1751, FAX 44-113-233-2947.

667.1 DEU ISSN 0938-9067
CODEN: WREID2
W R P - WAESCHEREI- UND REINIGUNGSPRAXIS. Text in German. 1952. m. EUR 8 newsstand/cover (effective 2004). adv. charts; illus. **Document type:** *Magazine, Trade.* **Description:** Trade journal for the whole range of cleaning and dyeing.
Former titles (until 1990): Waescherei- und Reinigungs-Praxis (0042-9937); (until 1960): Waescherei-Praxis (0341-6372)
—CCC.
Published by: (Gesamtverband Neuzeitliche Textilpflege-Betriebe Deutschlands e.V.), S N Verlag Michael Steinert, An der Alster 21, Hamburg, 20099, Germany. TEL 49-40-2484540, FAX 49-40-2803788, bth@snfachpresse.de, http://www.sn-verlag.de. adv.: B&W page EUR 2,515, color page EUR 4,400. Circ: 5,983 (paid and controlled).

WER UND WAS - KOERPERPFLEGE-, WASCH- UND REINIGUNGSMITTEL-INDUSTRIE. see *BEAUTY CULTURE—Perfumes And Cosmetics*

667 USA ISSN 0049-741X
WESTERN CLEANER AND LAUNDERER. Text in English. 1960. m. free to qualified personnel. adv. bk.rev. tr.lit. 52 p./no. 4 cols./p.; back issues avail.; reprints avail. **Document type:** *Magazine, Trade.*
Published by: Wakefield Publishing Co., 3236 Estado St, Pasadena, CA 91107-2916. TEL 626-793-2911, FAX 626-793-5540, rwente@earthlink.net, rwente@earlink.net, http://www.wcl-online.com. Ed. Randy Wente. Pub., R&P Albane Wente TEL 800-793-2911. Adv. contacts Albane Wente TEL 800-793-2911, Randy Wente. B&W page USD 995; trim 10 x 13.5. Circ: 17,000 (controlled).

667 USA ISSN 1073-1709
HD9999.C483
WOLGAN SET'AKIN✶. Text in English. 1993. m.
Published by: Korean Cleaners Monthly Co., P O Box 318, Fort Lee, NJ 07024-0318.

338.476671 GBR
THE WORLD MARKET FOR HOUSEHOLD CARE. Text in English. 1999. irreg. GBP 5,050, EUR 7,900, USD 7,900 (effective 2003). **Description:** Features global investigation into the worldwide cleaning products industry. Includes in-depth sales, share and distribution analysis.
Formerly: The World Market for Household Cleaning Products
Published by: Euromonitor, 60-61 Britton St, London, EC1 5UX, United Kingdom. TEL 44-20-7251-8024, FAX 44-20-7608-3149, info@euromonitor.com, http://www.euromonitor.com.

CLEANING AND DYEING—Abstracting, Bibliographies, Statistics

016.6672 USA ISSN 0734-8789
CODEN: CASDEP
C A SELECTS. COLORANTS AND DYES. Text in English. s-w. USD 315 to non-members; USD 95 to members (effective 2005). **Document type:** *Abstract/Index.* **Description:** Covers the isolation, identification, processing, use of natural dyes and pigments; and the synthesis, manufacture, properties, use of synthetic dyes and pigments.
Published by: Chemical Abstracts Service (C A S) (Subsidiary of: American Chemical Society), 2540 Olentangy River Rd., Columbus, OH 43210-0012. TEL 614-447-3600, FAX 614-447-3713, help@cas.com, http://www.cas.org, http://caselects.cas.org. **Subscr. to:** PO Box 3012, Columbus, OH 43210. TEL 800-753-4227, FAX 614-447-3751.

667.1021 ZAF
SOUTH AFRICA. STATISTICS SOUTH AFRICA. CENSUS OF SOCIAL, RECREATIONAL AND PERSONAL SERVICES - LAUNDRY, CLEANING AND DYEING SERVICES. Text in English. irreg., latest 1988. ZAR 4.40 domestic; ZAR 4.80 foreign (effective 2000). **Document type:** *Government.*
Formerly (until Aug.1998): South Africa. Central Statistical Service. Census of Social, Recreational and Personal Services - Laundry, Cleaning and Dyeing Services
Published by: Statistics South Africa/Statistieke Suid-Afrika, Private Bag X44, Pretoria, 0001, South Africa. TEL 27-12-310-8911, FAX 27-12-310-8500, info@statssa.pwv.gov.za, http://www.statssa.gov.za.

CLOTHING TRADE

see also CLOTHING TRADE—Fashions ; LEATHER AND FUR INDUSTRIES ; SHOES AND BOOTS ; TEXTILE INDUSTRIES AND FABRICS

687 USA
A A M A COMMITTEE MANUAL. Text in English. a. free. **Document type:** *Trade.* **Description:** Covers A A M A's 26 Committees, Divisions and Councils.
Published by: American Apparel Manufacturers Association, 1601 N. Kent St., Ste. 1200, Arlington, VA 22209-2105. TEL 703-524-1864, FAX 703-522-6741.

381.45687 USA
A A P N NEWS. Text in English. m. membership only. adv. **Document type:** *Newsletter.*
Former titles (until 1997): American Apparel Contractors Association News; Ragtime
Published by: American Apparel Producers' Network, 140 Maryeanna Dr, Atlanta, GA 30342. TEL 404-843-3171, FAX 404-256-5380. Ed. Sue C Strickland. Circ: 3,000.

687.1 USA
A N S O M. (Army - Navy Store & Outdoor Merchandiser) Text in English. 1949. m. USD 66; free to qualified personnel (effective 2005). adv. bk.rev. **Document type:** *Magazine, Trade.* **Description:** Reaches retailers of military surplus, sporting goods, camping and closeout items; soft goods such as apparel, not hard goods.
Former titles: Army - Navy Store & Outdoor Merchandiser (0744-0707); Army - Navy Store
Related titles: Online - full text ed.: (from Gale Group, ProQuest Information & Learning).
—CCC.
Published by: Cygnus Business Media, Inc., 3 Huntington Quadrangle, Ste 301N, Melville, NY 11747-3601. TEL 631-856-2700, FAX 631-845-2723, info@ansommag.com, http://www.ansommag.com. Ed. Mark Hawver. Pub. Howard Wasserman. Circ: 10,000 (controlled).

687.19 USA ISSN 8750-2453
ACCESSORIES. Text in English. 1908. 11/yr. USD 35 domestic; USD 62 in Canada; USD 80 elsewhere (effective 2005). adv. bk.rev. charts; illus.; mkt.; stat. **Document type:** *Magazine, Trade.*
Former titles (until 1984): Fashion Accessories (East Norwalk) (0193-0915); (until 1976): Handbags and Accessories (0017-7172)
Indexed: B&I.
Published by: Business Journals, 185 Madison Ave, 5 Fl, New York, NY 10016. TEL 212-686-4412, FAX 212-686-6821, http://www.accessoriesmagazine.com, http://www.busjour.com/. Ed. Irenka Jakuhiak. Pub. Lorrie L Frost TEL LorrieF@busjour.com. adv.: B&W page USD 5,995, color page USD 7,085. Circ: 20,000.

687.19 USA
ACCESSORIES RESOURCES DIRECTORY. Text in English. a. USD 30 (effective 1999). adv. **Document type:** *Directory.*
Formerly: Accessories Directory
Published by: Business Journals, 50 Day St, Norwalk, CT 06856. TEL 203-853-6015. Circ: 11,645.

687 CHE
ANNABELLE CREATION. Text in German. 1955. m. adv. **Document type:** *Magazine, Consumer.*
Former titles (until 1998): Orella (0030-4867); (until 1962): Frauen-Fleiss Masche (1421-282X)
Published by: T A Media AG, Werdstr 21, Zuerich, 8004, Switzerland. TEL 41-1-4046333, FAX 41-1-4046218, redaktion@an-creation.ch, http://www.annabelle.ch/creation. Ed. Christa Loepfe-Feldmann. Adv. contact Daniel Schnueriger. Circ: 107,969.

687 USA ISSN 1543-2009
TT490 CODEN: BOBBFM
APPAREL. Text in English. 1958. m. USD 69 domestic; USD 85 in Canada; USD 190 elsewhere; USD 10 newsstand/cover; free domestic to qualified personnel (effective 2005). adv. bk.rev. charts; illus. index. back issues avail. **Document type:** *Magazine, Trade.* **Description:** For management in the sewn products industry; covers problem solving, technology, legislation and trade, new products and manufacturing.
Former titles (until 2003): Bobbin (0896-3991); Which incorporated (1989-1991): Apparel Manufacturer (1051-4996); (until 1987): Bobbin Magazine (0894-8259); (until 1985): Bobbin (0006-5412)
Related titles: Online - full text ed.: (from EBSCO Publishing, Gale Group, Northern Light Technology, Inc., O C L C Online Computer Library Center, Inc., ProQuest Information & Learning).
Indexed: A&ATA, ABIn, BPI, TTI, WTA.
—BLDSC (1569.931000), IE. **CCC.**
Published by: Edgell Communications, Inc., 4 Middlebury Blvd, Randolph, NJ 07869-4214. sblack@apparelmag.com, edgell@edgellmail.com, http://www.apparelmag.com, http://www.edgellcommunications.com. adv.: B&W page USD 4,935, color page USD 8,020; trim 8 x 10.75. Circ: 19,650 (controlled).

687.19 TWN
APPAREL ACCESSORIES. Text in English. a. USD 30 for 2 yrs.. **Document type:** *Directory.* **Description:** Trade directory focusing on garment accessories, yarns, machines for garment accessories.
Published by: Taiwan Trade Pages Corp., P.O. Box 72-50, Taipei, Taiwan. TEL 02-3050759, FAX 886-2-3071000.

687 USA ISSN 1041-5181
HD9940.U3 CODEN: AIDIFY
APPAREL IMPORT DIGEST. Text in English. a. free. **Document type:** *Trade.* **Description:** Covers statistical information on apparel imports for the previous year.
Indexed: TTI.
Published by: American Apparel Manufacturers Association, 1601 N. Kent St., Ste. 1200, Arlington, VA 22209-2105. TEL 703-524-1864, FAX 703-522-6741.

338.47687 USA
APPAREL INDUSTRY TRENDS. Text in English. bi-m. free. **Document type:** *Trade.* **Description:** Economic reports on apparel industry covering current domestic apparel production, employment, imports and retail sales.
Published by: American Apparel Manufacturers Association, 1601 N. Kent St., Ste. 1200, Arlington, VA 22209-2105. TEL 703-524-1864, FAX 703-522-6741. Circ: 900.

687.0688 GBR ISSN 0263-1008
APPAREL INTERNATIONAL✶. Text in English. 1952. m. membership. adv. bk.rev. charts; illus.; tr.lit. **Document type:** *Trade.*
Formerly: Clothing and Footwear Journal (0142-0534); Which was formed by the merger of: Clothing Institute Journal (0578-5294); British Boot and Shoe Institution. Journal (0007-0351)
Indexed: TTI, WTA.
Published by: (C F I International - Institute for Apparel and Fashion Worldwide), Cowise International Publishing Group, 60 High St, Potters Bar, Herts EN6 5AB, United Kingdom. Circ: 4,500.

338.47687
APPAREL: LATIN AMERICAN INDUSTRIAL REPORT✶. (Avail. for each of 22 Latin American countries) Text in English. 1985. a. USD 435; per country report.
Published by: Aquino Productions, P O Box 15760, Stamford, CT 06901-0760. Ed. Andres C Aquino.

687 USA ISSN 0003-6692
APPAREL MANUFACTURER. Text in English. 1923. m.
Indexed: TTI.
—CCC.
Published by: International Association of Clothing Designers, 34 Thorton Ferry Rd, No 1, Amherst, NH 03031. TEL 603-672-4065, FAX 603-672-4064, dmschmida@aol.com, http://www.iacde.com.

687 USA ISSN 0746-889X
HD9940.U3
APPAREL MERCHANDISING. Text in English. 1982. 8/yr. adv. illus.; tr.lit. **Document type:** *Newsletter, Trade.*
Related titles: Microfiche ed.: (from CIS); ♦ Supplement to: D S N Retailing Today. ISSN 1530-6259.
Indexed: BPI, SRI.
—CCC.
Published by: Lebhar-Friedman, Inc., 425 Park Ave, New York, NY 10022. TEL 212-756-5269. Ed. Jeffrey Arlen. Pub., R&P Paula Lashinsky. Adv. contact Gary Esposito. Circ: 31,000.

APPAREL PLANT WAGES SURVEY. see *TEXTILE INDUSTRIES AND FABRICS*

687 JPN ISSN 0914-7594
APPAREL PRODUCTION NEWS. Text in English. 1953. m. JPY 9,600. adv. **Document type:** *Trade.*
Formerly (until 1987): New Japan Sewing Machine News (0545-1914)
Indexed: TTI.
Published by: New Japan Sewing Machine News Ltd., 2nd Kosumo Bldg, 8-5 Sugamo 1-chome, Toshima-ku, Tokyo, 170-0002, Japan. TEL 81-3-3942-2574, FAX 81-3-3942-1827. Ed., Pub. Makoto Nakajima. Adv. contact Tammie Imai. Circ: 9,000.

687 USA
APPAREL RESEARCH NOTES. Text in English. irreg. free. **Document type:** *Trade.* **Description:** Covers apparel technology and current manufacturing systems.
Published by: American Apparel Manufacturers Association, 1601 N. Kent St., Ste. 1200, Arlington, VA 22209-2105. TEL 703-524-1864, FAX 703-522-6741. Circ: 4,500.

687.0688 USA ISSN 0731-3802
HF5439.7
APPAREL SALES - MARKETING COMPENSATION SURVEY✶. Text in English. a. USD 60 to non-members; USD 25 to members. charts; stat. **Description:** Covers sales structure of apparel manufacturers, compensation programs, benefits and marketing.
Formerly: A A M A Apparel Sales Compensation Survey (0270-2681)
Published by: (American Apparel Manufacturers Association), Systems Publications, PO Box 351, Dunkirk, MD 20754-0351. TEL 301-773-1616, FAX 703-522-6741. Ed. Joan McNeal. Circ: 700.

687 USA ISSN 1085-6781
APPAREL STRATEGIST. Text in English. 198?. m. USD 425 domestic print or email ed.; USD 450 foreign print or email ed.; USD 495 combined subscription domestic print & email eds.; USD 595 combined subscription foreign print & email eds. (effective 2005). **Document type:** *Newsletter, Trade.* **Description:** Covers current news, trends and vital statistics of the apparel and textile industries.
Related titles: E-mail ed.
Published by: Apparel Information Resources, PO Box 406, Fleetwood, PA 19522. TEL 610-944-5995, FAX 610-944-5149, editor@apparelstrategist.com, http://www.apparelstrategist.com/.

687.143 DEU ISSN 0005-3554
BABY & JUNIOR; international trade magazine for children's and youth fashions and supplies. Text in German. 1959. 10/yr. EUR 73 domestic; EUR 77 in Europe; EUR 138 elsewhere (effective 2004). adv. illus.; stat. index. **Document type:** *Magazine, Trade.*
Published by: (Verband der Korbwaren-, Korbmoebel- und Kinderwagen-Industrie), Meisenbach GmbH, Franz-Ludwig-Str 7a, Bamberg, 96047, Germany. TEL 49-951-861126, FAX 49-951-861187, baby.u.junior@meisenbach.de, http://www.meisenbach.de/Baby&Junior/hauptteil_bj.htm. Ed. Hedda Mikuta. Adv. contact Maria Radovanovic. B&W page EUR 2,206, color page EUR 3,540; trim 192 x 263. Circ: 5,473. **Subscr. to:** CSJ, Postfach 140220, Munich 80452, Germany. **Co-sponsors:** Modekreis Kind und Jugend; Bundesverband Spielwaren im Hauptverband des Deutschen Einzelhandels.

687 DEU
DIE BEKLEIDUNGS- UND WAESCHE-INDUSTRIE UND IHRE HELFER/CLOTHING AND LINGERIE INDUSTRIES AND THEIR SUPPLIERS. Text in German. 1952. a. USD 51 (effective 2000). **Document type:** *Directory, Trade.*
Related titles: CD-ROM ed.; Online - full text ed.
Published by: Industrieschau-Verlagsgesellschaft mbH, Postfach 100262, Darmstadt, 64202, Germany. TEL 49-6151-3892-0, FAX 49-6151-33164. Ed., R&P Margit Selka. Circ: 3,000. **U.S. subscr. to:** Western Hemisphere Publishing Corp.. TEL 503-640-3736, FAX 503-640-2748.

687.19 USA
BELT LINE✶. Text in English. m.
Published by: Belt Association, 145 W 45th St, Ste 800, New York, NY 10036-4008. TEL 212-564-2500.

687.1 GBR ISSN 1464-9667
BODYWEAR DIRECTIONS. Text in English, French, German, Italian, Spanish. 1984. s-a. GBP 30, EUR 45 in Europe (effective 2000). **Document type:** *Trade.* **Description:** Covers the professional needs of swim and beachwear buyers and producers worldwide.
Former titles (until 1998): Beachwear and Skinwear (1367-2649); (until 1996): Beachwear Forecast International (0266-5794)
Published by: Benjamin Dent & Co. Ltd. (Subsidiary of: I T B D Publications), 23 Bloomsbury Sq, London, WC1A 2PJ, United Kingdom. TEL 44-20-7637-2211, FAX 44-20-7637-2248, itbd@itbdhquk.demon.co.uk. Ed. J Pierre Adeline.

338.47687 GBR ISSN 0141-1470
THE BRITISH CLOTHING INDUSTRY YEARBOOK. Text in English. 1974. a. GBP 75 (effective 2001). adv. bk.rev. **Document type:** *Trade.*
Formerly (until 1978): Clothing Export Council of Great Britain. Directory for the Clothing Industry
Published by: (British Knitting and Clothing Export Council), Kemps Publishing Ltd., 11 Swan Courtyard, Charles Edward Rd, Birmingham, W Mids B26 1BU, United Kingdom. TEL 44-121-765-4144, FAX 44-121-706-6210.

687 GBR ISSN 0963-9438
BRITISH STYLE. Text in English. 1988. 2/yr. GBP 14 domestic; GBP 20 overseas (effective 2000). adv. bk.rev. illus.; tr.lit. cum. index, vols.1-10 (1988-1997). back issues avail. **Document type:** *Trade.* **Description:** Covers British merchandise, services, and culture especially regarding clothing, giftware, jewelry, and food and drink.
Published by: Scott Taylor Ltd., 2 Beacon Hill, Islington, London, N7 9LY, United Kingdom. TEL 44-20-7700-4368, scotay12@aol.com.uk. Ed. John Taylor. Pub., R&P Marie Scott. Adv. contact Evelyn Bainsfair. B&W page GBP 1,300, color page GBP 1,845; trim 210 x 297. Circ: 8,000 (paid and controlled).

BURDA MODEN (ARABIC EDITION). see *BEAUTY CULTURE*

687.0688 USA
BUREAU NEWS. Text in English. 1980. m. USD 10. adv. bk.rev. charts; illus. **Document type:** *Newsletter.*
Former titles: Bureau News (0747-4598); Bureau of Wholesale Sales Representatives News (0745-5704); Which was formed by the 1980 merger of: N A W C A S Guild News (National Association of Women & Children's Apparel Salesmen); N A M B A C News (National Association Men's & Boys' Apparel Clubs)
Published by: Bureau of Wholesale Sales Representatives, 1100 Spring St, N W, Ste 700, Atlanta, GA 30309-2829. TEL 404-351-7355, FAX 404-352-5298. Ed. Mike Blackman. Circ: 16,250.

687.0688 GBR ISSN 1467-887X
BUSINESS RATIO. CLOTHING MANUFACTURERS. Text in English. 1974. a. GBP 275 (effective 2001). charts; stat. **Document type:** *Trade.*
Formerly (until 1999): Business Ratio Plus: Clothing Manufacturers (1356-5273); Which was formed by the 1994 merger of: Business Ratio Report. Clothing Manufacturers. Intermediate (0950-2297); Business Ratio Report. Clothing Manufacturers. Major (0950-2300); Which both supersedes in part (in 1986): Business Ratio Report. Clothing Manufacturers (0261-7595)
Published by: The Prospect Shop Ltd., Field House, 72 Oldfield Rd, Hampton, Middx TW12 2HQ, United Kingdom. TEL 44-20-8461-8730, 44-20-8481-8720, FAX 44-20-8783-1940, info@theprospectshop.co.uk.

687.0688 GBR ISSN 1467-8888
BUSINESS RATIO. CLOTHING RETAILERS. Text in English. 1979. a. GBP 275 (effective 2001). charts; stat. **Document type:** *Trade.*
Former titles (until 1999): Business Ratio Plus: Clothing Retailers (1355-6274); (until 1994): Business Ratio Report. Clothing Retailers (0261-7617)
Published by: The Prospect Shop Ltd., Field House, 72 Oldfield Rd, Hampton, Middx TW12 2HQ, United Kingdom. TEL 44-20-8461-8730, 44-20-8481-8720, FAX 44-20-8783-1940, info@theprospectshop.co.uk.

687.3 GBR ISSN 1469-6444
BUSINESS RATIO. THE HOSIERY & KNITWEAR INDUSTRY. Text in English. 1975. a. GBP 275 (effective 2001). charts; stat. **Document type:** *Trade.*
Former titles (until 1999): Business Ratio Plus. The Hosiery & Knitwear Industry (1362-3907); (until 1995): Business Ratio Plus. Hosiery and Knitwear Manufacturers (1357-6844); (until 1994): Business Ratio Report: Hosiery and Knitwear Industry (1368-678X); (until 1992): Business Ratio Report: Hosiery and Knitwear (0261-8419)
Published by: The Prospect Shop Ltd., Field House, 72 Oldfield Rd, Hampton, Middx TW12 2HQ, United Kingdom. TEL 44-20-8461-8730, 44-20-8481-8720, FAX 44-20-8783-1940, info@theprospectshop.co.uk.

687 DEU ISSN 0341-521X
BUTONIA. Variant title: Butonia - Modisches Dekor. Text in English, French, German, Italian. 1891. bi-m. adv. **Document type:** *Magazine, Trade.* **Description:** Covers all aspects of the button trade and industry.
Incorporates (1958-1980): Modisches Dekor (0342-9970)
Published by: Butonia Verlag, Bahnhofstr 5 a, Bad Ems, 56130, Germany. TEL 49-2603-2675, FAX 49-2603-2625. Ed. Kurt Schmidt. adv.: B&W page EUR 575. Circ: 1,200.

687 USA
C A U S COLOR FORECASTS. Text in English. 1917. 2/yr. **Description:** Forecasts women's, men's, children's clothing colors; interiors and environmental colors.
Related titles: Supplement(s): Forecast for Fashion; Forecasts for Interiors.
Published by: Color Association of the United States, 409 W 44th St, New York, NY 10036-4402. TEL 212-947-7774, FAX 212-594-6987. Ed. Margaret Walch.

687 USA
C A U S NEWS; color, design, fashion, marketing. Text in English. 1980. bi-m. USD 60 domestic to non-members; free domestic to members (effective 2005). bk.rev. back issues avail. **Document type:** *Newsletter.* **Description:** News and articles on developments in the fashion and decorating industries, with announcements pertaining to the association's activities.
Formerly: C A U S Newsletter
Related titles: Microform ed.
Published by: Color Association of the United States, 315 West 39th St., Studio 507, New York, NY 10018-3005. TEL 212-947-7774, FAX 212-594-6987, caus@colorassiation.com, http://www.colorassociation.com. Eds. Christine Chow, Margaret Walch. Circ: 6,000 (paid and controlled).

338.47687 GBR
C F I INTERNATIONAL DIRECTORY. Text in English. 1956. a. GBP 30. adv. **Document type:** *Directory.*
Former titles (until 1993): Clothing and Footwear Institute. Year Book and Membership Register (0261-2690); (until 1980): Clothing Institute. Year Book and Membership Register (0307-8515); (until 1973): Clothing Institute. Year Book
Indexed: ASCA.
Published by: (C F I International - Institute for Apparel and Fashion Worldwide), McMillan Group PLC, Charles Roe House, Chestergate, Macclesfield, Ches SK11 6DZ, United Kingdom. TEL 01625-6130006, FAX 01625-511446. Circ: 3,000.

381.45687 ITA
C T M NEWS. (Commercio Tessuti Moda) Text in Italian. 1987. bi-m. adv. **Document type:** *Catalog, Trade.*
Published by: Editrice La Martesana s.r.l., Via Breseia, 22, Cernusco Sul Naviglio, MI 20063, Italy. TEL 39-02-92109171, FAX 39-02-92108124. Ed. Saverio Collio. Adv. contact Dario Collio. Circ: 23,000.

687.2 ESP
C Y L MODA INTIMA. (Corseteria y Lenceria) Text in Spanish. 1965. q. USD 80; USD 100 in Europe; USD 130 in the Americas; USD 165 elsewhere. adv. **Document type:** *Trade.*
Published by: Indice S.L., Casp, 118 5o, Barcelona, 08013, Spain. TEL 265-04-41, FAX 34-3-2321361, http://www.networkdessous.it. Ed. Eugenio Rodriguez Fernandez. Adv. contact Esther Masset. Circ: 5,000.

687 USA ISSN 0008-0896
CALIFORNIA APPAREL NEWS. Text in English. 1945. w. USD 78 domestic; USD 165 in Canada; USD 195 elsewhere (effective 2005). adv. charts; illus.; stat.; tr.lit. back issues avail. **Document type:** *Magazine, Trade.* **Description:** For apparel retailers and manufacturers in the U.S. and the Pacific Rim.
Published by: MnM Publishing Corp., 110 E Ninth St, Ste A-777, Los Angeles, CA 90079-1777. TEL 213-627-3737, FAX 213-623-5707, webmaster@apparelnews.net, receptionist@apparelnews.net, http://www.apparelnews.com, http://www.apparelnews.net. Pubs. Carl Wernicke, Teri Fellman. adv.: B&W page USD 4,550, color page USD 5,400. Circ: 40,747 (paid and controlled). **Subscr. to:** 5615 W. Cermak Rd., Cicero, IL 60650.

687 CAN ISSN 1484-3684
CODEN: CAAPF6
CANADIAN APPAREL. Text in English, French. 1977. bi-m. CND 25 domestic; USD 25 in United States; USD 35 elsewhere (effective 2003 - 2004). adv. bk.rev. **Document type:** *Trade.*
Former titles (until 1997): Canadian Apparel Manufacturer Magazine (1484-3676); (until 1994): Apparel (1196-2283); (until 1989): Canadian Apparel Manufacture (0705-3010)
Indexed: A&ATA, CBCARef, CBPI, TTI, WTA.
—CISTI. CCC.
Published by: Canadian Apparel Federation, 504-124 O'Connor St, Ottawa, ON K1P 5M9, Canada. TEL 613-231-3220, 800-661-1187, FAX 613-231-2305, http://www.apparel.ca/magazine. Circ: 4,200.

CATALOG CONNECTION. see *GIFTWARE AND TOYS*

381.45687 ITA
CHARME MODA. Text in Italian. 1986. 6/yr. adv. **Document type:** *Trade.* **Description:** Covers the clothing trade: underwear, nightwear, seawear and hosiery for children, women and men.
Published by: I G O s.r.l., Via Cappuccini, 14-16, Milan, MI 20122, Italy. TEL 39-2-781368, FAX 39-2-76020487. Ed. Andrea Gobbo. R&P, Adv. contact Claudia Manini TEL 39-2-781381. Circ: 25,000.

C

▼ new title ➤ refereed ✶ unverified ♦ full entry avail.

687.143 GBR ISSN 0261-6025
CHILDREN'S CLOTHING INTERNATIONAL. Text in English. 1981. q. GBP 15. adv. illus.; charts. **Document type:** *Trade.*
Published by: Children's Clothing International Magazine Ltd., 83 High St, Waltham Cross, Herts EN8 7AF, United Kingdom. TEL 44-1992-715600, FAX 44-1992-715200. Ed. Sally Bain. Pub., Adv. contact Gillian Walker. R&P Bryan Green. B&W page GBP 1,125, color page GBP 1,545; trim 235 x 290. Circ: 4,500.

687 USA
THE CHILDREN'S PATTERN CATALOG*. Text in English. s-a. USD 10 (effective 2001). **Document type:** *Catalog, Consumer.*
Published by: Simplicity Pattern Co., Inc., 58 E 11th St Fl 8, New York, NY 10003-6020. TEL 212-576-2222, 1-888-588-2700, FAX 212-679-5541, info@simplicity.com, http://www.simplicity.com/.

CHINA TEXTILE & APPAREL. see *TEXTILE INDUSTRIES AND FABRICS*

CLEO EN LA MODA. see *LEATHER AND FUR INDUSTRIES*

687 USA ISSN 0887-302X
TS1760 CODEN: CTRJEZ
➤ **CLOTHING & TEXTILES RESEARCH JOURNAL.** Abbreviated title: C T R J. Text in English. 1982. q. USD 140 domestic; USD 160 foreign (effective 2004). back issues avail. **Document type:** *Magazine, Academic/Scholarly.* **Description:** Presents latest research on all areas of clothing and textiles.
Indexed: ABM, AmH&L, ArtInd, EngInd, FamI, HistAb, PsycInfo, PsycholAb, RefZh, SOPODA, TTI, WTA, e-psyche.
—BLDSC (3286.820000), Ei, IE, Infotrieve, ingenta.
Published by: International Textile and Apparel Association, PO Box 1360, Monument, CO 80132. TEL 719-488-3716, itaaoffice@cs.com, http://www.itaaonline.org. Ed. Kim K.P. Johnson. R&P Sandra Hutton. Circ: 13,000.

C

➤ **CLOTHING MACHINERY TIMES.** see *MACHINERY*

687 USA
CLOTHING MANUFACTURERS ASSOCIATION OF THE U S A. MEMBERS NEWS BULLETIN. Text in English. m. membership. **Document type:** *Bulletin.*
Published by: Clothing Manufacturers Association of the U S A, 730 Broadway, Fl 10, New York, NY 10003-9511. TEL 212-529-0823. Ed., Pub., R&P Robert A Kaplan.

338.47687 GBR ISSN 0967-2311
COMPANY CLOTHING. Text in English. 1992. 10/yr. GBP 65 in United Kingdom; GBP 80 rest of Europe; GBP 90 in United States (effective 2000). adv. **Document type:** *Trade.* **Description:** Encompasses every aspect of corporate clothing including design, trends, fabrics, suppliers, logistics, accessories, etc.
Formerly (until 1991): Corporate Clothing and Textile Care
Indexed: B&I.
Published by: Company Clothing Information Services Ltd., Parkgate House, 356 W. Barnes Ln, Motspur Park, New Malden, Surrey KT3 6NB, United Kingdom. TEL 44-20-8942-7800, FAX 44-20-8949-7033, ccis@company-clothing.co.uk, http://www.company-clothing.co.uk. Ed. Leonie Barrie. Pub. Malcolm Gill. Adv. contact Don Pepper. Circ: 8,500 (controlled).

687 ESP ISSN 0211-3708
CONFECCION INDUSTRIAL. Text in Spanish. 1963. q. EUR 29.56 domestic; EUR 69.87 in Europe; EUR 107.10 elsewhere (effective 2004). adv. abstr.; bibl.; charts; illus.; stat. index. **Document type:** *Magazine, Trade.*
Indexed: WTA.
Published by: Prensa Tecnica S.A., Casp 118-120, 6o, Barcelona, 08013, Spain. FAX 34-93-2322773, 34-93-2322733, http://www.prensa-tecnica.com. Ed. F Canet Tomas.

687 ITA ISSN 0393-4888
CONFEZIONE. Text in Italian. 1985. m. EUR 48 domestic (effective 2004). adv. **Description:** Presents fashion trends, work optimization methods, design automation, market trends, new technology, and cost evaluation and calculation.
Published by: Tecniche Nuove SpA, Via Eritrea 21, Milan, MI 201, Italy. TEL 39-02-390901, FAX 39-02-7570364, confezione@tecnichenuove.com, info@tecnichenuove.com, http://www.tecnichenuove.com. Circ: 6,522.

687.2 USA ISSN 1047-8701
CONTOURS; the US intimate apparel, body fashion, hosiery and swimwear magazine. Text in English. 1988. 5/yr. USD 45 domestic; USD 75 foreign (effective 2000). adv. bk.rev. back issues avail. **Document type:** *Trade.* **Description:** Reports on fashion and styling trends in the intimate apparel, hosiery, body fashion and swimwear industries. For buyers and executives.
Published by: Contour Magazines Inc., 350 Third Ave, Ste 348, New York, NY 10010. TEL 212-802-4646, FAX 212-448-1889. Ed. Kim Rawlings. Pub. Ben Yedder. Adv. contact Pat Shilling. B&W page USD 3,620, color page USD 5,120; trim 9.5 x 12.25. Circ: 8,500 (controlled).

687 USA
THE COSTUME - HALLOWEEN CATALOG*. Text in English. s-a. USD 9 (effective 2000). **Document type:** *Catalog, Consumer.*
Published by: Simplicity Pattern Co., Inc., 58 E 11th St Fl 8, New York, NY 10003-6020. TEL 212-576-2222, 1-888-588-2700, FAX 212-679-5541, info@simplicity.com, http://www.simplicity.com/.

687.2 GBR
COUNTOURS U K; the UK intimate apparel, body fashion, hosiery and swimwear magazine. Text in English. 1988. 5/yr. USD 45 (effective 2000). adv. **Document type:** *Trade.* **Description:** Covers the intimate apparel, body fashion, hosiery and swimwear industries.
Published by: Communications Conferences and Exhibitions Ltd., 392 Richmond Rd, Twickenham, Mddx TW1 2DY, United Kingdom. TEL 44-20-8892-5599, FAX 44-20-8892-4290. Ed. Kim Rawlings. Pub., R&P Ben Yedder. Adv. contact Patricia Shillingford. B&W page GBP 890, color page GBP 1,565; trim 245 x 320. Circ: 8,000. **Subscr. to:** 197 N Main St, Boonton, NJ 07005.

687.1 USA
COWGIRLS & INDIANS. Text in English. 2000. bi-m. USD 27; USD 5 newsstand/cover (effective 2001). adv. **Document type:** *Consumer.*
Published by: C & I, 8214 Westchester Drive, Ste. 800, Dallas, TX 75225. TEL 214-750-8222, FAX 214-750-4522, mail@cowboysindians.com, http://www.cowboysindians.com. Ed., Pub. Reid Slaughter.

687.141 USA ISSN 0011-412X
CUSTOM TAILOR. Text in English. 1912. 3/yr. USD 50 (effective 1999). adv. charts; illus. **Document type:** *Trade.*
Published by: Custom Tailors and Designers Association of America, Inc., 19 Mantua Rd., Mount Royal, NJ 08061-1006. TEL 202-387-7220. Ed., Pub., R&P, Adv. contact Suzanne Kilgore. Circ: 1,000 (controlled).

CUSTOM TAILORS AND DESIGNERS ASSOCIATION OF AMERICA. MAGAZINE. see *CLOTHING TRADE—Fashions*

381.45687 338.47687 USA ISSN 1079-641X
D S N RETAIL FAX. (Discount Store News) Text in English. 1994. w. USD 189 (effective 2004). **Document type:** *Trade.*
Published by: Lebhar-Friedman, Inc., 425 Park Ave, New York, NY 10022. TEL 212-756-5000, FAX 212-756-5395, info@lf.com, http://www.lf.com. Ed. Antoinette Alexander.

687.2 FRA ISSN 0981-1842
DESSOUS MODE INTERNATIONAL. Text in French. 1945. s-a. adv. illus. **Description:** Focuses on foundation garments.
Formerly: Corset de France (0010-9436); Incorporates (in 1978): Votre Ligne les Dessous Elegants; Dessous Elegants (0011-9539)
Published by: Mereau, 175 bd. Anatole France, BP 189, Saint-Denis, Cedex 93208, France. TEL 48-13-38-58, FAX 48-13-09-08. Circ: 38,000.

DIRECTORY OF APPAREL SPECIALITY STORES (YEAR); includes: family wear, sporting goods, and activewear retailers. see *BUSINESS AND ECONOMICS—Trade And Industrial Directories*

687 PHL
DIRECTORY OF PHILIPPINE GARMENT & TEXTILE EXPORTERS. Text in English. 1984. biennial. PHP 300 (effective 2000). adv. stat. **Document type:** *Directory, Trade.* **Description:** Lists over 1,000 garment exporting companies as well as associations.
Published by: Garments and Textile Export Board, Market Development Division, New Solid Bldg, 357 Gil J. Puyat Ave Ext., P.O. Box 1771, Makati Central Post Office, Makati Mm, Philippines. TEL 632-8904651, FAX 632-8904653, http://www.dti.gov.ph/gteb. Ed., R&P Fidelita L de Guzman. Circ: 3,000.

697 GBR ISSN 1479-1617
DRAPERS (LONDON); the fashion business weekly. Text in English. 2002. w. GBP 160 (effective 2005). **Document type:** *Magazine, Consumer.* **Description:** Covers the latest news, views and trends from the womenswear, footwear, lingerie and textiles markets.
Formed by the merger of (1887-2002): Drapers Record (0967-3776); Which was formerly (until 1992): D R (London) (0955-2499); (until 1988): Drapers Record (0012-6020); (1902-2002): Men's Wear (0025-9519); Which incorporates: Tailor & Cutter (0039-9035); Outfitter; Cloth and Clothes
—BLDSC (3623.198460).
Published by: Emap Fashion Ltd. (Subsidiary of: Emap Business Communications Ltd.), Greater London House, Hampstead Rd, London, EC1V 7QP, United Kingdom. TEL 44-20-78740200, drapers@emap.co.uk, http://www.drapersonline.com, http://www.emap.com. Ed. Josephine Collins TEL 44-20-78123765. Adv. contact Lucy Walsh TEL 44-20-78123786.

687 USA
E M B MAGAZINE. (Embroidery Monogram Business) Text in English. m. free domestic to qualified personnel; USD 69 domestic; USD 79 in Canada & Mexico; USD 190 elsewhere (effective 2004). **Document type:** *Magazine.*
Published by: (E M B Magazine), V N U Business Media, 770 Broadway, New York, NY 10003 . TEL 646-654-5000, FAX 646-654-7212, lgonz@mfi.com, http://www.embmag.com. Ed. Richard Lebovitz. Pub. Chris Casey. Circ: 26,000 (paid).

687.143 USA
TT635
EARNSHAW'S REVIEW. Text in English. 1917. m. USD 24 (effective 2005). adv. bk.rev. illus.; mkt. **Document type:** *Magazine.*
Former titles: Earnshaw's Infants, Girls and Boys Wear Review (0161-2786); Earnshaw's Infants' and Children's Review (0012-8198); Infants' and Children's Review
Published by: Earnshaw Publications, Inc., 112 W 34th St, New York, NY 10120. TEL 212-563-2742, FAX 212-629-3249, http://www.fashionmall.com. Eds. Thomas W Hudson Jr., Michelle Silver. Pub. Thomas W Hudson Jr. Adv. contact Patricia Schumann. Circ: 11,500.

ECHO. see *HOME ECONOMICS*

687.0688 GBR
THE EUROPEAN CLOTHING RETAIL HANDBOOK. Text in English. a. **Description:** Provides a picture of the clothing sector across Europe.
Published by: Corporate Intelligence on Retailing, 48 Bedford Sq, London, WC1 B3DP, United Kingdom. TEL 44-20-7696-9006, FAX 44-20-7696-9004, sales@cior.com, http://www.cior.com. **Subscr. in US to:** Lebhar-Friedman, Inc., 425 Park Ave, New York, NY 10022. TEL 212-756-5159, FAX 212-756-5038.

687 GBR ISSN 1473-0391
FASHION BUSINESS INTERNATIONAL. Text in English. 2001. q. GBP 115 domestic; GBP 140 in Europe; GBP 160 elsewhere (effective 2005). **Document type:** *Magazine, Trade.* **Description:** Designed for business and technical decision-makers in apparel retail and manufacturing.
Formerly (until 2004): World Clothing Manufacturer (1350-6773)
Indexed: WTA.
Published by: World Textile Publications Ltd., Perkin House, 1 Longlands St, Bradford, W Yorks BD1 2TP, United Kingdom. TEL 44-1274-378800, FAX 44-1274-378811, info@world-textile.net, http://www.world-textile.net/contact.html. Ed. John Scrimshaw.

687.3 USA
FASHION COLOR FORECAST*. Text in English. s-a. **Description:** Directed to wool growers as well as top makers, designers, spinners, dyers, knitters, and dealers in knitted wool apparel and accessories for women, men, and children.
Published by: Woolknit Associates, Inc., c/o Kairalla Agency, 43 Ancient County Way Ext, Manchester, MA 01944.

687 GBR ISSN 0952-701X
FASHION FORECAST INTERNATIONAL. Text in English, French, German. 1946. s-a. GBP 30, EUR 45 in Europe (effective 2000). adv. **Document type:** *Trade.* **Description:** Predicts the serious style directions to watch for in a wide range of apparel.
Formerly (until 1988): Fashion Forecast for International Buyers (0014-8679); Which incorporates: Fashion Buyers Diary (0264-357X)
—CCC.
Published by: Benjamin Dent & Co. Ltd. (Subsidiary of: I T B D Publications), 23 Bloomsbury Sq, London, WC1A 2PJ, United Kingdom. TEL 44-20-7637-2211, FAX 44-20-7637-2248, itbd@itbdhquk.demon.co.uk. Ed., R&P Stephen Higginson. Pub. Ken Manel. Adv. contact Andrew Sharp. Circ: 11,000.

FASHION MARKET MAGAZINE. see *BUSINESS AND ECONOMICS—Trade And Industrial Directories*

687.142 USA ISSN 0014-9918
HD9940.A1
FEMME-LINES. Text in English. 1957. bi-m. USD 8. adv. bk.rev. illus.; stat.
Indexed: TTI.
Published by: Earl Barron Publications, Inc., 225 E 36th St, New York, NY 10016. TEL 212-683-6593. Ed. Earl Barron. Circ: 11,000.

FINANCIAL SURVEY. TEXTILE RENTAL, LAUNDERERS AND DRY CLEANERS. see *BUSINESS AND ECONOMICS—Trade And Industrial Directories*

338.47687 USA ISSN 0749-8357
HD9940.U3
FOCUS: AN ECONOMIC PROFILE OF THE APPAREL INDUSTRY. Text in English. a. USD 75 to non-members; USD 25 to members. **Document type:** *Trade.* **Description:** Traces economic trends of the American apparel industry and discusses its place in American commerce.
Indexed: SRI.
Published by: American Apparel Manufacturers Association, 1601 N. Kent St., Ste. 1200, Arlington, VA 22209-2105. TEL 703-524-1864, FAX 703-522-6741.

338.47687 TTO
FOCUS ON THE GARMENT INDUSTRY. Text in English. 1983. bi-m. free.
Published by: Management Development Centre, Library, Salvatori Bldg, PO Box 1301, Port-of-Spain, Trinidad, Trinidad & Tobago. Ed. Sheila John. Circ: 1,000.

687 USA
FOR LARGE SIZES ONLY CATALOG✶ . Text in English. a. USD 3 (effective 2001). **Document type:** *Catalog, Consumer.*
Published by: Simplicity Pattern Co., Inc., 58 E 11th St Fl 8, New York, NY 10003-6020. TEL 212-576-2222, 1-888-588-2700, FAX 212-679-5541, info@simplicity.com, http://www.simplicity.com/.

687 CHN
FUZHUANG SHIBAO/FASHION TIMES. Text in English. 1994. w. CNY 96 (effective 2004). **Document type:** *Trade.*
Published by: Jingji Ribao Baoye Jituan/Economic Daily Newspaper Group, 70, Xizhimen Xiaojie, Beijing, 100035, China. TEL 86-10-83086319, http://bkdy.ce.cn/fenlei/t20031119_213107.shtml. **Dist. by:** China International Book Trading Corp, 35 Chegongzhuang Xilu, Haidian District, PO Box 399, Beijing 100044, China. TEL 86-10-68412045, FAX 86-10-68412023, cibtc@mail.cibtc.com.cn, http://www.cibtc.com.cn.

687 USA ISSN 1065-1330
GARMENT MANUFACTURER'S INDEX. Text in English. 1938. a. USD 105 per vol. domestic (effective 2004). adv. tr.lit. 263 p./no.; **Document type:** *Directory, Abstract/Index.* **Description:** Provides sources to purchase any materials such as fabric, trimmings, supplies, and equipment used in the manufacturing of men's, women's, children's apparel. Also includes an international list of sewing contractors.
Published by: Klevens Publications, Ltd., 411 S Main St, Ste 209, Los Angeles, CA 90013-1321. TEL 213-625-9000, FAX 213-625-5002, editor@klevenspub.com, http://www.garmentindex.com, http://www.klevenspub.com. Ed. H B Schwartz. Pub. Gilbert George Klevens. Adv. contact Edward Yale Klevens TEL 213-625-9000. Circ: 18,684.

GARMENT WORKER. see *LABOR UNIONS*

381.45687 CAN
GARMENTS IMPORTS AMERICA DIRECTORY. Text in English. 1994. a. USD 110. bk.rev. charts; illus.; stat. **Document type:** *Directory.*
Published by: Global Traders Association, P O BOX 797, Sta A, Scarborough, ON M1K 5C8, Canada. TEL 416-650-9309, FAX 416-650-9280. Ed. K Bhattacharyya.

687 ITA ISSN 0394-2481
GUIDA ALL'ABBIGLIAMENTO ITALIANO. Text in Italian. 1978. a. price varies. adv. **Document type:** *Directory, Trade.* **Description:** Directory of Italian clothing industry and its suppliers.
Published by: (Associazione Italiana Industriali Abbigliamento), Gesto Editore Srl, Via Mercato 28, Milan, MI 20121., Italy. TEL 39-02-8051511, FAX 39-02-89013553, gesto@gestoeditore.it, http://www.http://www.modainitaly.it. Circ: 15,000.

338.47687 USA
GUIDE TO SOURCING AMERICAN MADE APPAREL. Text in English. a. USD 97.50 to non-members (effective 2000). **Document type:** *Directory.*
Published by: American Apparel Producers' Network, 140 Maryeanna Dr, Atlanta, GA 30342. TEL 404-843-3171, FAX 404-256-5380. Ed. Sue C Strickland.

H K P C TEXTILE AND CLOTHING BULLETIN. see *TEXTILE INDUSTRIES AND FABRICS*

687 SWE ISSN 0283-572X
HABIT BUTIK. Text in Swedish. 1985. q. SEK 250; SEK 79 newsstand/cover (effective 1999). 4 cols./p.; **Document type:** *Consumer.*
Published by: Mentor Online AB, Tryffelslingan 10, PO Box 72001, Lidingoe, 18172, Sweden. TEL 46-8-670-41-28, FAX 46-8-661-64-55. Ed. Nils Ellstroem. adv.: B&W page SEK 18,200, color page SEK 23,600; trim 280 x 205. Circ: 7,900.

687.4 USA ISSN 1066-4122
HD9948.U6
HAT LIFE DIRECTORY✶ ; directory of men's and ladies' hat and cap industry. Text in English. 1872. a. USD 22; USD 31 foreign (effective 2000). adv. **Document type:** *Directory, Trade.* **Description:** Contains information regarding where and how to find supplies and headwear. Also contains a selling manual and sales ideas.
Former titles: Hat Life Yearbook and Directory; American Hatter (0073-0904)
Address: 115 River Rd c/o REFAC, Edgewater, NJ 07020-1009. TEL 201-434-8322, FAX 201-434-8277, cfuller@dmcreative.com, http://www.hatlife.com. Ed. Diane Feen. Pub., R&P, Adv. contact Peter Annunziata. Circ: 7,000.

687.141 GBR ISSN 0961-1266
HE LINES. Text in English. 1991. q. GBP 25; GBP 50 foreign. adv. back issues avail. **Document type:** *Trade.*
Published by: Streamline Fashion Publishing Ltd., 6-8 Vestry St, 2nd Fl, London, N1 7RE, United Kingdom. TEL 0171-490-0745, FAX 0171-490-0709. Ed. Pamela Scott. Pub. Andrew Sharp. Adv. contact Sue Hall. B&W page GBP 1,350, color page GBP 2,350. Circ: 10,000 (controlled).

687.4 USA
HEADPIECE✶ . Text in English. s-a.
Published by: Bridal Marketing Association of America, 2956 S W 30th Ave, Hallandale, FL 33009-5105. TEL 305-463-1773, FAX 305-463-8732. Ed. Phil Youtie. Circ: 10,000.

687.4 USA
HEADWEAR INSTITUTE OF AMERICA. NEWSLETTER. Text in English. irreg. **Document type:** *Newsletter.*
Published by: Headwear Institute of America, One W 64th St, Ste 3G, New York, NY 10023. TEL 212-724-0888.

HENNE. see *CLOTHING TRADE—Fashions*

381.45687 HKG ISSN 1021-8939
HONG KONG APPAREL. Text in English. 1969. s-a. HKD 240 for 2 yrs. in Hong Kong; USD 54 for 2 yrs. in Asia except Japan; USD 72 for 2 yrs. elsewhere (effective 2000). adv. **Document type:** *Trade.* **Description:** Provides information for buyers, wholesalers, importers and exporters, traders of Hong Kong garments and ready-to-wear fashion.
Formerly: Apparel
Related titles: Online - full content ed.
Indexed: HongKongiana, TTI.
Published by: Hong Kong Trade Development Council, 38th Fl Office Tower, Convention Plaza, 1 Harbour Rd, Wanchai, Hong Kong. TEL 852-2584-4333, publications@tdc.org.hk, hktdc@tdc.org.hk, http://www.tdc.org.hk/prodmag/apparel/apparel.htm. Ed. Patrick Lam. Adv. contact Wengi Yuen. color page HKD 13,500; 254 x 318. Circ: 30,000.

HONG KONG ENTERPRISE. see *GIFTWARE AND TOYS*

687.3 IND ISSN 0018-5388
HOSIERY AND TEXTILE JOURNAL; monthly review for manufacturers and merchants. Text in English. 1932. bi-m. (in 70 vols.). INR 500 (effective 2001). adv. 64 p./no. 3 cols./p.; **Document type:** *Journal, Trade.*
Indexed: TTI, WTA.
Published by: Journal's Publication, Near Shingaar Cinema, Samrala Rd., Ludhiana, Punjab 141 008, India. TEL 91-161-600296, FAX 91-161-600296, journal@jla.vsnl.net.in. Ed., Pub. Narinder Mahan. Adv. contacts Mohan S Chawla, Rajeev Sareen. B&W page INR 9,500, color page INR 16,500; trim 19.5 x 26. Circ: 18,000.

687.3 USA ISSN 0742-8065
HD9969.H6
HOSIERY NEWS✶ . Text in English. 1924. m. membership; Membership. adv. mkt.; stat.; tr.lit. 32 p./no.; **Document type:** *Magazine, Trade.* **Description:** Provides information on the hosiery industry, including production, foreign trade, retail sales, marketing, financial and personnel news, legislative issues, and Association activities.
Formerly: Hosiery Newsletter (0018-540X)
Indexed: TTI, WTA.
—BLDSC (4331.925000).
Published by: Hosiery Association, 3623 Latrobe Dr, Ste 130, Charlotte, NC 28211-2117. TEL 704-365-0913, FAX 704-362-2056. Circ: 2,700.

687.688 USA
HOSPITALITY APPAREL. Text in English. 1999. s-a. **Document type:** *Magazine, Trade.* **Description:** Provides a resource for those end users looking to maximize corporate identity through workwear.
Published by: Halper Publishing Company, 830 Moseley Rd., Highland Park, IL 60035-4636. TEL 847-433-1114, FAX 847-433-6602, info@halper.com, http://www.halper.com. Ed. Brian Ness. Pub., Adv. contact Rick Levine. Circ: 20,561.

687 USA
I T A A MONOGRAPHS. Text in English. irreg. **Document type:** *Monographic series.*
Former titles: I T A A Special Publications; A C P T C Special Publications
Published by: International Textile and Apparel Association, PO Box 1360, Monument, CO 80132. TEL 719-488-3716. Ed. Kim K.P. Johnson.

677 USA
I T A A NEWSLETTER. Text in English. 1975. 6/yr. free to qualified personnel. adv. bk.rev. bibl. back issues avail. **Document type:** *Newsletter, Trade.* **Description:** Geared toward scholars of textile and apparel.
Formerly: A C P T C Newsletter
Published by: International Textile and Apparel Association, PO Box 1360, Monument, CO 80132. TEL 719-488-3716, itaaoffice@cs.com, http://www.itaaonline.org. Ed. Sandra S Hutton. Circ: 1,200.

687 USA ISSN 1066-7083
IMPRINTING BUSINESS. Text in English. 1979. m. USD 30 (effective 2000). adv. **Document type:** *Trade.* **Description:** Contains information for the imprinted garment industry.
Formerly (until 1992): T-Shirt Retailer and Screen Printer
Published by: W F C, Inc., 3000 Hadley Rd, South Plainfield, NJ 07080. TEL 908-769-1160, FAX 908-769-1171. Ed. Alan Richman. Pub., R&P Howard V Wainer. Adv. contact Heather Wainer. Circ: 24,000.

687.142 USA
INDEPENDENT WOMEN'S SPECIALTY STORES & BOUTIQUES. Text in English. a. USD 199 (effective 2000). **Description:** Lists about 8,500 independent women's specialty stores and boutiques throughout the United States.
Related titles: CD-ROM ed.; Diskette ed.; Magnetic Tape ed.
Published by: Douglas Publications, Inc., Salesman's Guide, 2807 N Parham Rd, Ste 210, Richmond, VA 23294. TEL 804-762-4455, FAX 804-935-0271, http://www.douglaspublications.com. Ed. Travis Parrish.

687.2 IND
INDIAN HOSIERY DIRECTORY. Text in English. 1950. a. INR 20. **Document type:** *Directory.*
Published by: Journal's Publication, Near Shingaar Cinema, Samrala Rd., Ludhiana, Punjab 141 008, India. Adv. contact Rajeev Sareen.

687 ITA
INFORMATORE TESSILE. Short title: I T. Text in Italian. 1978. 9/yr. free to qualified personnel. adv. **Document type:** *Directory, Trade.*
Published by: Beta Editoriale s.a.s., Via Duomo 305, Naples, NA 80133, Italy. TEL 39-081-207166, FAX 39-081-268943. Ed. Mimmo Tartaglia. Circ: 30,000.

646.32 USA
INSIDE OUTDOOR. Text in English. 2002. bi-m. USD 39 (effective 2004). adv. **Document type:** *Magazine, Trade.*
Published by: Dagda Mor Media, 21001 N Tatum Blvd, Ste 1630-449, Phoenix, AZ 85050. TEL 480-203-2513, FAX 480-203-2514, bob@dagdamore.com, http://www.dagdamor.com. Pubs. Berge Kaprelian, Bob Titsch. adv.: color page USD 3,560, B&W page USD 2,760; trim 8.125 x 10.875. Circ: 10,590 (controlled).

C

INTERNATIONAL DIRECTORY OF APPAREL AND CLOTHING IMPORTERS. see *BUSINESS AND ECONOMICS—Trade And Industrial Directories*

687 GBR ISSN 0955-6222
TS1300 CODEN: ICSTEH
INTERNATIONAL JOURNAL OF CLOTHING SCIENCE AND TECHNOLOGY. Text in English. 1989. bi-m. EUR 9,318.79 in Europe; USD 9,629 in North America; AUD 11,259 in Australasia; GBP 6,523.91 in UK & elsewhere (effective 2006). reprint service avail. from PSC. **Document type:** *Journal, Academic/Scholarly.* **Description:** Aimed at all academics working in the field of clothing science and technology as well as industrialists involved in either research or production in the clothing and allied industries.
Related titles: Online - full text ed.: (from EBSCO Publishing, Emerald Group Publishing Limited, Gale Group, IngentaConnect, O C L C Online Computer Library Center, Inc., ProQuest Information & Learning, Swets Information Services).
Indexed: ABIn, EmerIntel, EngInd, Inspec, TTI, WTA.
—BLDSC (4542.172170), CISTI, Ei, IE, Infotrieve, ingenta. CCC.
Published by: Emerald Group Publishing Limited, 60-62 Toller Ln, Bradford, W Yorks BD8 9BY, United Kingdom. TEL 44-1274-777700, FAX 44-1274-785200, infomation@emeraldinsight.com, http://www.emeraldinsight.com/ijcst.htm. Ed. George Stylios. Pub. Vicky Williams.

687.2 ITA
INTIMA FRANCE. Text in Italian. 1990. 4/yr.
Formerly: Linea Intima France (1120-5644)
Published by: Publitype S.A.S., Via Guintellino 26, Milan, MI 20143, Italy. TEL 39-02-89127117, TELEX 353437 PBT I. Ed. Marco Pisani. Circ: 10,000.

687 DEU ISSN 1616-3737
JAHRBUCH FUER DIE BEKLEIDUNGSWIRTSCHAFT. Text in German. 1970. a. adv. charts; illus.; stat. **Document type:** *Directory, Trade.*
Former titles (until 1999): Jahrbuch fuer die Bekleidungs-Industrie (0722-8929); (until 1983): Taschenbuch fuer die Bekleidungs-Industrie (0341-9703)
Published by: Fachverlag Schiele und Schoen GmbH, Markgrafenstr 11, Berlin, 10969, Germany. TEL 49-30-2537520, FAX 49-30-2517248, service@schiele-schoen.de, http://www.schiele-schoen.de. Ed. W Schierbaum. Circ: 3,000.

JEANSFLASH. see *TEXTILE INDUSTRIES AND FABRICS*

687 ESP
JOBWEAR. Text in Spanish, English. 1991. s-a. EUR 22.17 domestic; EUR 52.41 in Europe; EUR 80.34 elsewhere (effective 2004). **Document type:** *Magazine, Trade.* **Description:** Presents career and work clothing.
Published by: Prensa Tecnica S.A., Casp 118-120, 6o, Barcelona, 08013, Spain. FAX 34-93-2322773, 34-93-2322733, http://www.prensa-tecnica.com.

JOURNAL DU TEXTILE. see *TEXTILE INDUSTRIES AND FABRICS*

687.142 GBR
KEY NOTE MARKET ASSESSMENT. BRIDALWEAR. Text in English. 1997. irreg. (2nd Edition), latest 1999, Nov. GBP 730 per issue (effective 2002). **Document type:** *Trade.* **Description:** Provides an overview of a specific UK market segment and includes executive summary, market definition, market size, industry background, competitor analysis, current issues, forecasts, company profiles, and more.
Formerly (until 2002): Key Note Market Report: Bridalwear (1367-5370)
Published by: Key Note Ltd., Field House, 72 Oldfield Rd, Hampton, Mddx TW12 2HQ, United Kingdom. TEL 44-20-8481-8750, FAX 44-20-8783-0049, info@keynote.co.uk, http://www.keynote.co.uk. Ed. Emma Clarke.

687.143 338 GBR
KEY NOTE MARKET REPORT: CHILDRENSWEAR. Variant title: Childrenswear Market Report. Text in English. 1994. irreg., latest 2000, Nov. GBP 340 per issue (effective 2002). **Document type:** *Bulletin.* **Description:** Provides an overview of a specific UK market segment and includes executive summary, market definition, market size, industry background, competitor analysis, current issues, forecasts, company profiles, and more.
Formerly: Key Note Report: Childrenswear
Related titles: CD-ROM ed.; Online - full text ed.
Published by: Key Note Ltd., Field House, 72 Oldfield Rd, Hampton, Mddx TW12 2HQ, United Kingdom. TEL 44-20-8481-8750, FAX 44-20-8783-0049, info@keynote.co.uk, http://www.keynote.co.uk. Ed. Jacob Howard.

C

687 338 GBR ISSN 1366-1930
KEY NOTE MARKET REPORT: CLOTHING MANUFACTURING. Variant title: Clothing Manufacturers. Text in English. 19??. irreg., latest 2000, May. GBP 340 (effective 2002). **Document type:** *Trade.* **Description:** Provides an overview for the UK clothing manufacturing sector, including industry structure, market size and trends, developments, prospects, and major company profiles.
Formerly (until 1996): Key Note Report: Clothing Manufacturers (0954-4534)
Related titles: CD-ROM ed.; Online - full text ed.
Published by: Key Note Ltd., Field House, 72 Oldfield Rd, Hampton, Mddx TW12 2HQ, United Kingdom. TEL 44-20-8481-8750, FAX 44-20-8783-0049, info@keynote.co.uk, http://www.keynote.co.uk/showReport.asp?report=ClothingMa396. Ed. Nick Bardsley.

687.0688 338 GBR ISSN 1461-5169
KEY NOTE MARKET REPORT: CLOTHING RETAILING. Variant title: Clothing Retailing Marketing Report. Text in English. 1994. irreg., latest 2000, Dec. GBP 340 per issue (effective 2002). **Document type:** *Trade.* **Description:** Provides an overview for the UK clothing retailing sector, including industry structure, market size and trends, developments, prospects, and major company profiles.
Formerly (until 1997): Key Note Report: Clothing Retailing (1354-2133)
Related titles: CD-ROM ed.; Online - full text ed.
Published by: Key Note Ltd., Field House, 72 Oldfield Rd, Hampton, Mddx TW12 2HQ, United Kingdom. TEL 44-20-8481-8750, FAX 44-20-8783-0049, info@keynote.co.uk, http://www.keynote.co.uk. Ed. Lyndsey Barker.

391.42 658 GBR ISSN 1461-6815
KEY NOTE MARKET REPORT: LINGERIE. Text in English. 1989. irreg., latest 2000, Feb. GBP 340 per issue (effective 2002). **Document type:** *Trade.* **Description:** Provides and overview of a specific UK market segment and includes executive summary, market definition, market size, industry background, competitor analysis, current issues, forecasts, company profiles, and more.
Formerly (until 1997): Key Note Report: Lingerie (0959-552X)
Related titles: CD-ROM ed.; Online - full text ed.
Published by: Key Note Ltd., Field House, 72 Oldfield Rd, Hampton, Mddx TW12 2HQ, United Kingdom. TEL 44-20-8481-8750, FAX 44-20-8783-0049, info@keynote.co.uk, http://www.keynote.co.uk.

363.19 614.85 621.992 GBR ISSN 1460-7565
KEY NOTE MARKET REPORT: PROTECTIVE CLOTHING & EQUIPMENT. Text in English. 1997. irreg., latest 2000, July. GBP 340 per issue (effective 2002). **Description:** Provides an overview of a specific UK market segment and includes executive summary, market definition, market size, industry background, competitor analysis, current issues, forecasts, company profiles, and more.
Published by: Key Note Ltd., Field House, 72 Oldfield Rd, Hampton, Mddx TW12 2HQ, United Kingdom. TEL 44-20-8481-8750, FAX 44-20-8783-0049, info@keynote.co.uk, http://www.keynote.co.uk. Ed. Jenny Baxter.

687 GBR ISSN 1368-5996
KEY NOTE MARKET REPORT: SPORTS CLOTHING AND FOOTWEAR. Variant title: Sports Clothing and Footwear. Text in English. 1995. irreg., latest 2000, June. GBP 340 per issue (effective 2002). **Document type:** *Trade.* **Description:** Provides an overview of a specific UK market segment and includes executive summary, market definition, market size, industry background, competitor analysis, current issues, forecasts, company profiles, and more.
Formerly: Key Note Report: Sports Clothing and Footwear
Related titles: CD-ROM ed.; Online - full text ed.
Published by: Key Note Ltd., Field House, 72 Oldfield Rd, Hampton, Mddx TW12 2HQ, United Kingdom. TEL 44-20-8481-8750, FAX 44-20-8783-0049, info@keynote.co.uk, http://www.keynote.co.uk. Ed. Emma Clarke.

687 338 GBR ISSN 1356-6121
KEY NOTE MARKET REVIEW: U K CLOTHING & FOOTWEAR. Text in English. 1990. irreg., latest 2001, April. GBP 565 per issue (effective 2002). **Document type:** *Trade.* **Description:** Provides an overview for the UK clothing and footwear markets, including industry structure, market size and trends, developments, prospects, and major company profiles.
Former titles (until 1994): Key Note Market Review. U K Clothing & Footwear Market (1362-7422); (until 1992): Market Review. U.K. Clothing & Footwear Market (0961-1711)
Related titles: CD-ROM ed.; Online - full text ed.
Published by: Key Note Ltd., Field House, 72 Oldfield Rd, Hampton, Mddx TW12 2HQ, United Kingdom. TEL 44-20-8481-8750, FAX 44-20-8783-0049, info@keynote.co.uk, http://www.keynote.co.uk/showReport.asp?report=Clothingan556. Ed. Emma Wiggin.

687.143 CAN ISSN 1202-7588
KIDS CREATIONS. Text in English, French. 1959. q. CND 37.45, USD 50 (effective 1999). adv. **Document type:** *Trade.*
Former titles: Kids Parade (1183-4501); (until 1991): C A M A Parade (1182-3429); (until 1989): C A M A Parade of Children's Fashion (0847-0847); (until 1988): Children's Apparel Merchandising Aids
Published by: Children's Apparel Manufacturers' Association, 6900 Decarie Blvd, Ste 3110, Montreal, PQ H3X 2T8, Canada. TEL 514-731-7774, FAX 514-731-7459. Ed. Lisa Peters. R&P Murray W Schwartz. Adv. contact Della Druick. Circ: 5,500.

KIDS MARKET. see *BUSINESS AND ECONOMICS—Trade And Industrial Directories*

KOMPASS PROFESSIONNEL. TEXTILE, HABILLEMENT, CUIRS ET PEAUX. see *BUSINESS AND ECONOMICS—Trade And Industrial Directories*

687 TUR ISSN 1300-9974
KONFEKSIYON & TEKNIK. Text in Turkish; Section in English. 1994. m. USD 100 (effective 2001). adv. illus. **Document type:** *Trade.* **Description:** Serves as a link between apparel importers and Turkish designers, manufacturers and exporters.
Published by: Ihlas Magazine Group, Ihlas Holding Mrk. Binasi, 29 Ekim Cad. 23, Yenibosna - Istanbul, 34530, Turkey. TEL 90-212-4542530, FAX 90-212-4542555, bsensoz@img.com.tr, imga@img.com.tr, http://www.img.com.tr. Ed. Ahmet Kizil. Pub. Ferruh Isik. R&P Muhsin Yilmaz. Adv. contact Ms. Bahar Sensoz. page USD 2,000; 21.8 x 30. Circ: 23,270.

687.2 ITA ISSN 0394-8048
LINEA INTIMA. Text in English, Italian. 1958. bi-m. USD 90 in Europe; USD 210 elsewhere. back issues avail.
Formerly (until 1959): Boutique Intima (0394-8056)
Published by: Publitype S.A.S., Via Guintellino 26, Milan, MI 20143, Italy. TEL 39-02-8915-9373, FAX 39-02-8915-9349, publitype.srl@galactica.it. Ed. Marco Pisani. Circ: 18,000. **U.S. subscr. to:** Charles W. Baw, 811 N Longfellow Ave, Tucson, AZ 85711.

687.2 GBR
LINGERIE BUYER. Text in English. 7/yr. GBP 20 domestic; GBP 25 in United States; GBP 2.50 newsstand/cover. adv. bk.rev. tr.lit. back issues avail. **Document type:** *Trade.* **Description:** Contains news and trends reports on lingerie, hosiery and swimwear.
Published by: R A S Publishing Ltd., The Old Town Hall, Lewisham Rd, Slaithwaite, Huddersfield HD7 5AL, United Kingdom. TEL 01484-846069, FAX 01-484-846232. Ed. Anita Saunders. Pub. Colette Mahon. Adv. contact Anne Jones.

687 646.72 910.2 GBR
LUXURY BRIEFING. Text in English. 1996. m. GBP 325.
Published by: Atlantic Publishing Ltd., Coates House, Upper Largo, Fife, KY8 6JF, United Kingdom. TEL 01333-360606, FAX 01333-360607. Ed. Kate Patrick.

687.0688 USA ISSN 1049-6726
M R (NORWALK). (Menswear Retailing) Text in English. 1990. 10/yr. USD 34 domestic; USD 63 in Canada (effective 2005). adv. **Document type:** *Magazine, Trade.* **Description:** Directed to retailers of men's furnishings, accessories and sportswear featuring individual product categories and interviews and what affects the menswear business.
Published by: Business Journals, 50 Day St, Norwalk, CT 06856. TEL 203-853-6015, FAX 203-852-8175, http://www.busjour.com/. Eds. William Kissell, Karen Alberg Grossman. Pub. Stuart Nifoussi. adv.: B&W page USD 6,475, color page USD 7,525. Circ: 30,000 (controlled).

MACHINE KNIT TODAY (UK EDITION). see *BUSINESS AND ECONOMICS—Small Business*

MACHINE KNITTING NEWS. see *NEEDLEWORK*

687 ITA ISSN 1123-8313
MADE IN BIELLA. Text in Italian. 1980. 2/yr. **Document type:** *Trade.*
Address: Via Italia, 50, Biella, VC 13051, Italy. TEL 39-15-31665, FAX 39-15-31726. Ed. Ezio Greggio. Pub. David B Dondena. Adv. contact Gianfranco Ferrari. Circ: 15,000.

687 USA
MADE TO MEASURE. Text in English. 1930. s-a. adv. **Document type:** *Magazine, Trade.* **Description:** Designed to assist the uniform dealer and manufacturer in broadening their business.
Published by: Halper Publishing Company, 830 Moseley Rd., Highland Park, IL 60035-4636. TEL 847-433-1114, FAX 847-433-6602, info@halper.com, http://www.halper.com. Ed. Brian Ness. Pub., Adv. contact Rick Levine. Circ: 24,227.

687.3 ITA ISSN 1127-0470
MAGLIERIA ITALIANA. Text in English, Italian. 1969. q. EUR 40 (effective 2005). adv. **Document type:** *Magazine, Trade.*
Indexed: DAAI.
Published by: Editoriale Moda Srl, Via Giardini 476, Modena, MO 41100, Italy. TEL 39-059-342001, FAX 39-059-351290. Ed. Ettore Zanfi. Circ: 18,000.

687.3 FRA ISSN 1146-5735
MAILLE ET TECHNIQUE. Text in French. 1990. 6/yr. back issues avail. **Document type:** *Newspaper.* **Description:** A magazine for the knitting industries. Includes reports about exhibitions, economics, and industry.
Indexed: WTA.
Published by: Editions Vauclair, 41 bd. General Martial Valin, Paris, 75015, France. TEL 33-1-45576060, FAX 33-1-45576061, ed.vauclair@wanadoo.fr. Ed., R&P, Adv. contact Alain Raye. Pub. Jean Philippe Vauclair. Circ: 4,500 (paid).

687 PHL ISSN 0117-5823
MEGA; the Philippines' best fashion magazine. Text in English. 1992. m. PHP 1,200, USD 142; PHP 120 newsstand/cover. adv. bk.rev.; film rev.; music rev.; software rev.; video rev. mkt. back issues avail. **Document type:** *Consumer.* **Description:** Covers national and Asian fashion industry, as well as lifestyle and cultural topics.
Related titles: Online - full text ed.
Indexed: IPP.
Published by: Mega Magazines & Publications, Inc., Strata 100, 18th Fl., Emerald Ave, Ortigas Center, Pasig Mm, 1605, Philippines. TEL 632-637-2859, FAX 632-631-2862, megamag@info.com.ph. Ed., R&P Sari Yap. Pub. Gigi Calero. Adv. contact Margie Defensor. page PHP 45,000; trim 10.75 x 8.5. Circ: 40,000.

687.141 IRL
MENSWEAR IN IRELAND. Text in English. 2/yr. adv. **Document type:** *Magazine, Trade.*
Published by: Futura Communications Ltd., 5 Main St., Blackrock, Co. Dublin, Ireland. TEL 353-1-2836782, FAX 353-1-2836784. adv.: B&W page EUR 1,263, color page EUR 1,759; trim 210 x 297. Circ: 4,000 (controlled).

687.141 ESP
MERCERIA ACTUALIDAD. Text in Spanish, English. 1990. q. EUR 32.48 domestic; EUR 72.42 in Europe; EUR 109.64 elsewhere (effective 2004). **Document type:** *Magazine, Trade.* **Description:** Covers haberdashery.
Published by: Prensa Tecnica S.A., Casp 118-120, 6o, Barcelona, 08013, Spain. FAX 34-93-2322773, 34-93-2322733, http://www.prensa-tecnica.com.

687.143 ITA ISSN 1127-8943
MODA BIMBI E BEBE. Text in Italian. 1963. q. EUR 20 (effective 2005). adv. **Document type:** *Magazine, Consumer.*
Formerly (until 1996): Moda Bimbi. Cherie Moda (0026-7252)
Published by: Edizioni Moderne Internazionali, Via Gallarate 230, Milan, MI, Italy. TEL 39-02-36569654, FAX 39-02-66981482, emimil@tin.it. Ed. A Maria Pietraccini. Circ: 90,000.

687.0688 JPN
MODE ET MODE. Text in Japanese. 4/yr. USD 118.
Published by: Intercontinental Marketing Corp., I.P.O. Box 5056, Tokyo, 100-3191, Japan. TEL 81-3-3661-7458, tc9w-ball@asahi-net.or.jp.

391 USA ISSN 1548-3258
▼ **MODERN UNIFORMS.** Text in English. 2004 (Feb.). bi-m. USD 35; free to qualified personnel (effective 2004). adv. **Document type:** *Magazine, Trade.* **Description:** Provides dealers and distributors of uniforms and corporate apparel with informative articles and critical sourcing information.

Related titles: Online - full text ed.: (from EBSCO Publishing, Gale Group, H.W. Wilson).
Published by: Primedia Business Magazines & Media, Inc. (Subsidiary of: Primedia, Inc.), 9800 Metcalf Ave, Overland Park, KS 66212-2216. TEL 913-341-1300, FAX 913-967-1898, inquiries@primediabusiness.com, http://www.modernuniformsmag.com, http://www.primediabusiness.com. Ed. Jeff Rundles. Pub. Michael Rand Goldner. Adv. contact Gigi Korosec. color page USD 3,485; trim 7.875 x 10.75. Circ: 17,000 (controlled).

687   FRA   ISSN 0248-0034
MODES ET TECHNIQUES. Text in French. 1957. m. illus.; tr.lit. back issues avail. **Description:** Includes previews, reports about machinery and manufacturing, exhibits, interviews, and information on the economics of the clothing industry.
Former titles (until 1980): L' Homme (0339-543X); (until 1975): L' Homme et le Maitre Tailleur (0339-5448)
Published by: Editions Vauclair, 41 bd. General Martial Valin, Paris, 75015, France. TEL 33-1-45576060, FAX 33-1-45576061, ed.vauclair@wanadoo.fr. Pub. Jean Philippe Vauclair. R&P Jean-Philippe Vauclair. Adv. contact Alain Raye. Circ: 3,000.

687   ESP
MUESTRAS Y MOTIVOS. Text in Spanish. 2/yr.
Published by: Ediciones M Y M, C/ Hermanos Garcia Noblejas 39, Madrid, 28037, Spain. TEL 34-91-4066990, FAX 34-91-3772050, mym@muestras-y-motivos.es, http://www.muestras-y-motivos.es. Ed. Manuel Arroyo.

687   USA
N A M D T NEWSLETTER. Text in English. m. **Document type:** Newsletter.
Published by: National Association of Milliners, Dressmakers and Tailors, c/o Harlem Institute of Fashion, 157 W 126th St, New York, NY 10027. TEL 212-666-1320.

687.141   USA
N A M S B NEWS. Text in English. 1955. m. membership. illus.; tr.lit. back issues avail. **Document type:** Newsletter.
Related titles: Fax ed.
Published by: National Association of Men's Sportswear Buyers, Inc., 60 E 42nd St, Rm 2430, New York, NY 10165-2430. TEL 212-856-9644, FAX 212-856-0825, info@namsb-show.com. Ed. Jack Herschlag. Circ: 1,500.

687   USA
N A U M D NEWS. Text in English. 3/yr.
Published by: National Association of Uniform Manufacturers and Distributors, 1156 Ave of the Americas, New York, NY 10036. TEL 212-869-0670, FAX 212-575-2847, nyoffice@naumd.com, http://www.naumd.com. Ed. Melanie Kangis. Circ: 650.

687   USA
N A U M D OFFICE REPORTS. Text in English. bi-m.
Published by: National Association of Uniform Manufacturers and Distributors, 1156 Ave of the Americas, New York, NY 10036. TEL 212-869-0670.

687   USA
N A U M D POSTAL UPDATE. Text in English. m.
Published by: National Association of Uniform Manufacturers and Distributors, 1156 Ave of the Americas, New York, NY 10036. TEL 212-869-0670.

687.19   USA
N F A A BULLETIN. Text in English. s-w. **Document type:** Bulletin.
Published by: National Fashion Accessories Association, 350 Fifth Ave, Ste 2030, New York, NY 10118. TEL 212-947-3424.

687.19   USA
N F A A NEWSLETTER. Text in English. m. **Document type:** Newsletter.
Published by: National Fashion Accessories Association, 350 Fifth Ave, Ste 2030, New York, NY 10118. TEL 212-947-3424.

687.141   USA
N O S A FASHION BULLETIN. Text in English. irreg.
Description: For manufacturers of men's and boys' sportswear and outerwear.
Published by: National Outerwear and Sportswear Association, c/o A A M A, 2500 Wilson Blvd, Arlington, VA 22201.

687.141   USA
N O S A NEWS. Text in English. irreg. **Document type:** Newsletter. **Description:** For manufacturers of men's and boys' sportswear and outerwear.
Published by: National Outerwear and Sportswear Association, c/o A A M A, 2500 Wilson Blvd, Arlington, VA 22201.

687.141   USA
N O S A. PRODUCTION BULLETIN. Text in English. m.
Description: For manufacturers of men's and boys' outerwear and sportswear.
Published by: National Outerwear and Sportswear Association, c/o A A M A, 2500 Wilson Blvd, Arlington, VA 22201.

338.47687   USA   ISSN 0077-5983
NATIONWIDE DIRECTORY OF MEN'S AND BOYS' WEAR BUYERS. Text in English. 1965. a. USD 229 (effective 2000). index. **Document type:** Directory, Trade. **Description:** Lists 11,300 buyers and executives for 6,500 retail stores carrying men's and boys' wear.
Media: Magnetic Tape. **Related titles:** Diskette ed.
Published by: Douglas Publications, Inc., Salesman's Guide, 2807 N Parham Rd, Ste 210, Richmond, VA 23294. TEL 804-762-4455, FAX 804-935-0271, http://www.douglaspublications.com. Ed. Chasity Roberts.

338.47687   USA   ISSN 0077-5991
NATIONWIDE DIRECTORY OF WOMEN'S AND CHILDREN'S WEAR BUYERS. Text in English. 1963. a. USD 229 (effective 2000). **Document type:** Directory, Trade. **Description:** Lists 17,000 buyers and executives of women's and children's apparel for 8,500 retailers.
Published by: Douglas Publications, Inc., Salesman's Guide, 2807 N Parham Rd, Ste 210, Richmond, VA 23294. TEL 804-762-4455, FAX 804-935-0271, http://www.douglaspublications.com. Ed. Chasity Roberts.

687.0688   USA   ISSN 0077-6009
NATIONWIDE MAJOR MASS MARKET MERCHANDISERS. Text in English. 1964. a. USD 189 (effective 2000). index. reprint service avail. from PQC. **Document type:** Directory, Trade. **Description:** Lists 5,000 buyers of men's, women's, and children's apparel for more than 2,800 discount and chain store operators.
Published by: Douglas Publications, Inc., Salesman's Guide, 2807 N Parham Rd, Ste 210, Richmond, VA 23294. TEL 804-762-4455, FAX 804-935-0271, http://www.douglaspublications.com. Ed. Travis Parrish. Circ: 1,500.

687.19   USA
NECKWEAR INDUSTRY DIRECTORY. Text in English. biennial. USD 20. **Document type:** Directory.
Published by: Neckwear Association of America, 151 Lexington Ave, New York, NY 10016. TEL 212-683-8454. Ed. Gerald Andersen. Circ: 25,000.

687   USA   ISSN 8750-7366
TJ1501
➤ **NEEDLE'S EYE WORLDWIDE.** Text in English. 1930. q. free. adv. charts; illus.; tr.lit. **Document type:** Trade. **Description:** Provides news and information on developments in the needle trades, including new products, technical articles, and profiles of garment and other sewn product manufacturers.
Formerly (until 1998): Needle's Eye (0028-2359)
Indexed: TTI, WTA.
—Linda Hall.
Published by: Union Special Corp., 1 Union Special Plaza, Huntley, IL 60142. TEL 847-669-4334, FAX 847-669-3534, dkiesa@unionspecial.com. Ed., R&P David Kiesa. Adv. contact Daniel Kennedy. Circ: 26,300 (controlled).

➤ **NEW BODIES.** see CLOTHING TRADE—Fashions

687   USA
THE NEW LOOK PATTERN CATALOG✱ . Text in English. q. USD 40; USD 13 newsstand/cover (effective 2001).
Document type: Catalog, Consumer.
Published by: Simplicity Pattern Co., Inc., 58 E 11th St Fl 8, New York, NY 10003-6020. TEL 212-576-2222, 1-888-588-2700, FAX 212-679-5541, info@simplicity.com, http://www.simplicity.com/.

687.142   USA
NEW YORK SKIRT AND SPORTSWEAR ASSOCIATION. BULLETIN. Text in English. irreg. **Document type:** Bulletin.
Published by: New York Skirt and Sportswear Association, 225 W 34th St, Rm 1416, New York, NY 10122. TEL 212-564-0040.

NEWS BULLETIN. see SPORTS AND GAMES

687   POL   ISSN 0471-0320
ODZIEZ. Text in Polish. 1950. bi-m. PLZ 84 domestic; EUR 45 foreign (effective 2005). adv. 32 p./no.; **Document type:** Magazine, Trade.
Indexed: TTI, WTA.
Published by: (Stowarzyszenie Wlokiennikow Polskich), Wydawnictwo SIGMA - N O T Sp. z o.o., ul Ratuszowa 11, PO Box 1004, Warsaw, 00950, Poland. TEL 48-22-8180918, FAX 48-22-6192187, informacja@sigma-not.pl, http://www.sigma-not.pl. Ed. Ireneusz Krawczyk. adv.: B&W page PLZ 900, color page PLZ 1,950. Circ: 700. Dist. by: Ars Polona, Krakowskie Przedmiescie 7, Warsaw, Poland. TEL 48-22-9263914, FAX 48-22-9265334, arspolona@arspolona.com.pl, http://www.arspolona.com.pl.

687.1   USA   ISSN 1066-3991
OUTERWEAR. Text in English. 1984. m. USD 80 (effective 2004). adv. **Document type:** Magazine, Trade. **Description:** Focuses on information of interest to retailers in winter wear sales. Includes retailer, designer and manufacturer profiles and emphasis on new technology.
Published by: Creative Marketing Plus, Inc., 19 W 21st St, Ste 403, New York, NY 10010. TEL 212-727-1210, FAX 212-727-1218, tsullivan@cmponline.com. Ed. Tom Sullivan. Pub. Richard S Harrow TEL 212-727-1210 ext 206. R&P, Adv. contact Fran Harrow. Circ: 15,000 (paid and free).

687 677   GBR   ISSN 1477-6456
PERFORMANCE APPAREL MARKETS; business and market analysis for the world's fibre, textile and apparel industries. Text in English. 2002. q. **Document type:** Magazine, Trade. **Description:** Provides readers with business and market analysis of worldwide trends in high performance activewear and corporate apparel.
—CCC.
Published by: Textiles Intelligence Ltd, 10 Beach Ln, Wilmslow, SK9 5ER, United Kingdom. TEL 44-1625-539067, FAX 44-1625-536137, info@textilesintelligence.com, http://www.textilesintelligence.com/.

687   DEU
PFAFF INFORMATION; fuer die Naehende Industrie. Text in German. 1953. 3/yr. **Document type:** Trade.
Related titles: English ed.; French ed.; Italian ed.; Spanish ed.
Indexed: TTI.
Published by: Pfaff AG, Koenigstr 154, Kaiserslautern, 67655, Germany. TEL 49-631-2000, FAX 49-631-17202. Ed. Karin Geib. Circ: 30,000.

687   USA
PLEATERS, STITCHERS AND EMBROIDERERS ASSOCIATION. NEWSLETTER✱ . Text in English. irreg.
Published by: Pleaters, Stitchers and Embroiderers Association, 145 W 45th St, Ste 800, New York, NY 10036-4008. TEL 212-564-2500.

687   USA
PRIDE (NEW YORK). Text in English. s-a.
Published by: National Association of Milliners, Dressmakers and Tailors, c/o Harlem Institute of Fashion, 157 W 126th St, New York, NY 10027. TEL 212-666-1320.

764.8   USA   ISSN 0898-3313
TT852
PRINTWEAR MAGAZINE. Text in English. 1987. m. USD 36 domestic; USD 75 in Canada; USD 95 in Mexico; USD 125 elsewhere (effective 2005). illus. back issues avail.; reprints avail. **Document type:** Magazine, Trade. **Description:** Covers aspects of the apparel decorating business, including sales techniques, technology, style trends, and marketing.
Indexed: ABIPC, EngInd.
Published by: National Business Media, Inc., PO Box 1416, Broomfield, CO 80038. TEL 303-469-0424, FAX 303-469-5730, alexis.ciesla@nbm.com, http://www.nbm.com/printwear. Pub. Alexis Ciesla. Adv. contact Sandy Maes. Circ: 20,000 (controlled).

687   USA   ISSN 1550-8552
PROFITABLE EMBROIDERER. Abbreviated title: P E. Text in English. 2000. bi-m. USD 32 domestic; USD 37 foreign (effective 2004). adv. **Document type:** Magazine, Trade.
Description: Provides information and advice to market embroidered products, competitive pricing, and marketplaces.
Related titles: Online - full content ed.; Online - full text ed.: (from bigchalk, Gale Group, H.W. Wilson, O C L C Online Computer Library Center, Inc.); ♦ Supplement to: Stitches. ISSN 0899-5893.
Indexed: BPI.
—CCC.
Published by: Primedia Business Magazines & Media, Inc. (Subsidiary of: Primedia, Inc.), 5680 Greenwood Plaza Blvd, Ste 100, Greenwood Village, CO 80111. TEL 303-741-2901, FAX 720-489-3101, inquiries@primediabusiness.com, http://www.profitableembroiderer.com/, http://www.primediabusiness.com. Ed. Ken Parsons.

PROGRESS IN TEXTILES: SCIENCE & TECHNOLOGY. see TEXTILE INDUSTRIES AND FABRICS

764.8   USA   ISSN 1538-5620
PROMOWEAR; for the business of promotional products. Text in English. m. USD 24 in US & Canada; USD 48 elsewhere (effective 2001). adv. **Document type:** Magazine, Trade.
Description: Covers all aspects of the promotional products industry.
Published by: National Business Media, Inc., PO Box 1416, Broomfield, CO 80038. TEL 303-469-0424, FAX 303-469-5730, http://www.nbm.com/promowear. Ed. Mark Buchanan. Pub. Alexis Ciesla. Adv. contact Ann Sparks. Circ: 14,000 (controlled).

687   AUS   ISSN 0728-0904
RAGTRADER; Australia's clothing fashion. Text in English. 1972. fortn. AUD 130 domestic; AUD 165 in New Zealand; AUD 195 in Asia; AUD 260 elsewhere (effective 2005). adv. **Document type:** Magazine, Trade. **Description:** Keeps readers informed of the future directions of womenswear, menswear and childrenswear, what is and isn't working at retail, color trends, the season's fabrics and trimmings, and new labels.
Incorporates: Menswear; Which superseded (1954-19??): Tailor and Men's Wear (0039-9043)
Related titles: Online - full text ed.; ♦ Supplement(s): Ragtrader Label Directory. ISSN 0819-1786.
Indexed: ABIX.
Published by: Yaffa Publishing Group Pty Ltd., 17-21 Bellevue St, Surry Hills, NSW 2010, Australia. TEL 61-2-92812333, FAX 61-2-92812750, yaffa@yaffa.com.au, http://www.yaffa.com.au. Circ: 7,500.

▼ new title   ➤ refereed   ✱ unverified   ♦ full entry avail.

RAGTRADER FASHION DIRECTORY. see *BUSINESS AND ECONOMICS—Trade And Industrial Directories*

687 AUS ISSN 0819-1786
RAGTRADER LABEL DIRECTORY. Text in English. 1987. a.
Document type: *Directory.*
Related titles: ♦ Supplement to: Ragtrader. ISSN 0728-0904.
Published by: Reed Business Information Pty Ltd (Subsidiary of: Reed Business Information International), Locked Bag 2999, Chatswood, NSW 2067, Australia.

687 DEU ISSN 0935-6452
READYWEAR. Text in English. 1972. 2/yr. adv. **Document type:** *Magazine, Trade.*
Indexed: TTI.
Published by: S N Verlag Michael Steinert, An der Alster 21, Hamburg, 20099, Germany. TEL 49-40-2484540, FAX 49-40-2803788, bth@snfachpresse.de, http://www.sn-verlag.de. adv.: B&W page EUR 1,840, color page EUR 2,760. Circ: 5,500 (controlled).

REVISTA TECNICA TEXTIL-VESTIDO. see *TEXTILE INDUSTRIES AND FABRICS*

687 DEU ISSN 0948-8448
RUNDSCHAU - FACHZEITSCHRIFT FUER INTERNATIONALE HERRENMODE UND SCHNITT-TECHNIK. Text in German. 1981. m. adv. bk.rev. index. **Document type:** *Magazine, Consumer.*
Former titles (until 1994): Rundschau fuer Internationale Herrenmode (0944-1786); (until 1991): Rundschau fuer Internationale Herrenmode mit D O B- und Haka-Praxis (0722-2866); Which was formed by the merger of (1970-1981): Rundschau fuer Internationale Herrenmode (0342-8850); (1970-1981): D O B- und Haka-Praxis (0342-1627)
Published by: Rundschau-Verlag Otto G. Koeniger GmbH und Co., Karlstr 41, Ulm, 89073, Germany. TEL 49-731-1520180, FAX 49-731-1520185. Circ: 3,000.

C

687.0688 USA ISSN 1045-6996
THE S & B REPORT. (Sales and Bargains) Text in English. m. USD 59 (effective 2000). **Document type:** *Newsletter.*
Description: Lists between 50 to 250 different New York City designer showroom sales, including addresses, sale dates and a description of merchandise.
Published by: Lazar Media Group, Inc., 56 1/2 Queen St, Charleston, SC 29401-2806. email@lazarshopping.com. Ed. Elysa Lazar.

SCHOOL UNIFORMS. see *BUSINESS AND ECONOMICS—Trade And Industrial Directories*

687.19 ESP
SELECCIONES DE FORNITURAS; y complementos para la confeccion y merceria. Text in Spanish. 1974. q. **Document type:** *Consumer.*
Published by: Ser-Graf, Vilamari, 81, Barcelona, 08015, Spain. TEL 34-3-2260424, FAX 34-3-2263298. Ed. A Palazon Serrano. Pub. Pep Blanes. Adv. contact Javier Palazon Barriuso. Circ: 5,000.

687.0688 USA
SEW UP THE HOLIDAYS. Text in English. a. USD 5.99 newsstand/cover domestic; USD 6.99 newsstand/cover in Canada (effective 2004).
Published by: Primedia Consumer Media & Magazine Group, P O Box 420235, Palm Coast, FL 32142. TEL 800-448-0865, information@primedia.com, http://www.sewnews.com, http://www.primedia.com. Ed. Linda Turner Griepentrog.

SEWING & EMBROIDERY PROFESSIONAL. see *NEEDLEWORK*

687 746.9 GBR
SHOE & FASHION FOOTWEAR NEWS. Text in English. 1998. m. GBP 29 in United Kingdom to individuals; GBP 45 newsstand/cover in Europe; GBP 59 newsstand/cover elsewhere (effective 2000); GBP 3.50 newsstand/cover. adv. back issues avail. **Document type:** *Trade.*
Published by: Reflex Publishing Ltd., 177a High St, Tonbridge, Kent TN9 1BX, United Kingdom. TEL 44-1732-362445, FAX 44-1732-362447, fabuss@mwfree.net. Ed. John Crittenden. Pub. Adrian Watkins. Adv. contact Sharon Saunders.

687 GBR
SHUTTLE PLUS. Text in English. 1979. q. GBP 21; GBP 24 foreign. adv. **Document type:** *Trade.* **Description:** Represents industrial and domestic sewing and clothing machine dealers and distributors, and those selling haberdashery products.
Published by: Sewing Machine Trade Association, 24 Fairlawn Grove, London, W4 5EH, United Kingdom. TEL 44-181-995-0411, FAX 44-181-742-2396. Ed. Arthur Spencer Bolland. adv.: B&W page GBP 470, color page GBP 550. Circ: 3,200 (controlled).

687 RUS ISSN 0132-0955
SHVEINAYA PROMYSHLENNOST'. Text in Russian. 1959. bi-m. USD 120. index. **Description:** Covers the garment industry.
Indexed: CISA, RASB, RefZh, TTI, WTA.
—BLDSC (0397.360000), East View.
Published by: Izdatel'stvo Arina, B Kommunisticheskaya 6-a, Moscow, 109004, Russian Federation. TEL 7-095-9119469, FAX 7-095-9112776. Ed. T A Volchkova. **Dist. by:** M K - Periodica, ul Gilyarovskogo 39, Moscow 129110, Russian Federation. TEL 7-095-2845008, FAX 7-095-2813798, info@periodicals.ru, http://www.mkniga.ru; **US dist. addr.:** East View Information Services, 3020 Harbor Ln. N., Minneapolis, MN 55447. TEL 612-550-0961.

687 SWE ISSN 0346-1386
SKRAEDDERI★; Skraeddarmaestaren - Svensk Skraedderitidning. Text in Swedish. 1938. bi-m. SEK 205. adv.
Formerly (until 1970): Skraeddarmaestaren (0037-6590)
Published by: Sveriges Skraedderiidkarefoerbund, Fack 1011, Stockholm, 10055, Sweden. Ed. Ragnar Bjoerkman. Circ: 1,400.

687.2 ITA
SOLOINTIMO INTERNATIONAL. Text in English, Italian. 1987. 5/yr., latest vol.42, 2001. **Document type:** *Magazine, Trade.*
Formerly: Modasport Intimo
Published by: Editrice Acalifa s.r.l., Via San Rocco 17, Milan, 20135, Italy. TEL 39-02-58315800, FAX 39-02-58316313. Ed., Adv. contact Eva Sabatini. Circ: 31,000.

SPORTS GOODS BUYER'S GUIDE. see *SPORTS AND GAMES*

687 ITA ISSN 1021-0989
SPORTSWEAR INTERNATIONAL (EUROPEAN EDITION). Text in English. 1974. 8/yr. EUR 88.78 in Europe; USD 80 in United States; USD 106 in Canada & Mexico; EUR 106 elsewhere; EUR 12 newsstand/cover (effective 2003). adv. illus. back issues avail. **Document type:** *Magazine, Trade.*
Description: Shows the fashion collections of the coming seasons - for retailers.
Related titles: German ed.; ♦ Supplement(s): Sportswear International News. ISSN 1021-0970.
Indexed: WTA.
Published by: Sportswear International Srl. (Subsidiary of: Deutscher Fachverlag GmbH), Via Forcella 3 - Palazzo c, Milan, 20144, Italy. TEL 39-02-581691, FAX 39-02-89401674, editor@sportswearnet.com, http://www.sportswearnet.com. Pub. Klaus Hang. Adv. contact Christine Zeine. B&W page EUR 9,000, color page EUR 12,500; trim 265 x 330. Circ: 21,050 (paid). **Subscr. to:** Mainzer Landstr 251, Frankfurt am Main 60326, Germany. TEL 49-69-75951987, FAX 49-69-75951980.

687 USA ISSN 0743-1155
TT649
SPORTSWEAR INTERNATIONAL (USA EDITION); fashion, retail, culture. Text in English. 1982. 7/yr. USD 80 (effective 2004). adv. tr.lit. reprints avail. **Document type:** *Magazine, Trade.*
Formerly: Sportswear Jeans International
Address: 580 Broadway., Rm. 1200, New York, NY 10012-3223. TEL 212-768-8450, FAX 212-768-8472, http://www.sportswearnet.com. Ed., Pub. Michael Belluomo. Circ: 18,664. **Subscr. to:** 29 W. 38th St., New York, NY 10018-5583.

687 ITA ISSN 1021-0970
SPORTSWEAR INTERNATIONAL NEWS. Text in English. 1980. 8/yr. EUR 12 newsstand/cover (effective 2003). adv. **Document type:** *Journal, Trade.*
Related titles: ♦ Supplement to: Sportswear International (European Edition). ISSN 1021-0989.
Published by: Sportswear International Srl. (Subsidiary of: Deutscher Fachverlag GmbH), Via Forcella 3 - Palazzo c, Milan, 20144, Italy. TEL 39-02-581691, FAX 39-02-89401674, editor@sportswearnet.com. Pub. Klaus Hang. Adv. contact Christine Zeine. B&W page EUR 3,000, color page EUR 5,000; trim 190 x 270. Circ: 12,500. **Subscr. to:** Mainzer Landstr 251, Frankfurt am Main 60326, Germany. TEL 49-69-75951987, FAX 49-69-75951980.

687.0688 USA ISSN 0899-5893
TS1783
STITCHES. Text in English. 1987. m. free domestic to qualified personnel; USD 41 in Canada; USD 55 foreign (effective 2004). adv. bk.rev. **Document type:** *Magazine, Trade.*
Description: Aimed at the North American commercial monogramming and embroidery industry, both retail and wholesale.
Related titles: Online - full text ed.: (from Gale Group, H.W. Wilson, O C L C Online Computer Library Center, Inc., ProQuest Information & Learning); ♦ Supplement(s): Profitable Embroiderer. ISSN 1550-8552.
Indexed: ABIn, BPI, WTA.
—CCC.
Published by: Primedia Business Magazines & Media, Inc. (Subsidiary of: Primedia, Inc.), 5680 Greenwood Plaza Blvd, Ste 100, Greenwood Village, CO 80111. TEL 303-741-2901, FAX 720-489-3101, inquiries@primediabusiness.com, http://stitches.com, http://www.primediabusiness.com. Ed. Ken Parsons. Circ: 18,284.

STYLE FORECAST. see *CLOTHING TRADE—Fashions*

687.19 USA
SUNGLASS ASSOCIATION OF AMERICA. NEWSLETTER. Text in English. m. membership only. **Document type:** *Newsletter.*
Description: Association and industry news with updates on new members and address corrections.
Published by: Sunglass Association of America, 390 N. Bridge St., Labelle, FL 33935-5091. TEL 203-845-9015, FAX 203-847-1304, http://www.sunglassassociation.com. Ed. Swea Nightingale.

SWIMWEAR U S A. see *CLOTHING TRADE—Fashions*

687 CYP ISSN 1015-3004
SYNTHESIS/COMPOSITION. Text in English. 1988. bi-m. CYP 10. **Document type:** *Consumer.* **Description:** Features Greek-Cypriot interior design.
Address: 5 V Michaelides St, PO Box 3539, Limassol, Cyprus. TEL 357-5-344154, FAX 357-5-357122. Ed. Yiannis Kouzarides. Circ: 5,500.

687.3 ESP ISSN 0211-7932
TECNICA DEL PUNTO. Variant title: T P Tecnica del Punto. Text in Spanish, English. 1956. q. EUR 29.56 domestic; EUR 69.87 in Europe; EUR 107.10 elsewhere (effective 2004). adv. charts; illus.; stat.; tr.lit. **Document type:** *Magazine, Trade.*
Indexed: WTA.
Published by: Prensa Tecnica S.A., Casp 118-120, 6o, Barcelona, 08013, Spain. FAX 34-93-2322773, 34-93-2322733, http://www.prensa-tecnica.com. Ed. F Canet Tomas.

338.47687 TUR ISSN 1300-6436
➤ **TEKSTIL MARATON.** Text in Turkish. 1991. bi-m. TRL 60,000,000 domestic; USD 120 foreign (effective 2003). adv. back issues avail. **Document type:** *Magazine, Academic/Scholarly.* **Description:** Provides information about newest developments in textile industry. Audience: Industrial Managers, Academicians, Engineers and Textile students.
Formerly: Magazine for Textile and Ready to Wear Technology
Published by: Tumateks Textile Consulting - Publishing, Ziyapasa Bulvari Nr.23, Refah Apt.B Blok Kat:7 Da:32, Adana, 01130, Turkey. TEL 90-322-4579397, FAX 90322-4541442, tmtumateksamail@koc.net. Ed. Tugrul Madran. Circ: 3,000.

677 FRA ISSN 1623-6955
TEXNEWS BY FRANCE TEXTILE; l'essentiel de la filiere textile-habillement. Text in French. 1986. 6/yr. **Description:** Features the French textile and clothing industry news. Contains information on the companies, the new products, machines and fabrics.
Former titles (until 2000): France Textile (0993-3042); (until 1989): Info Service (0981-0080)
Published by: S E M A C, 54 rue Saint-Alban, Roanne, Cedex 42301, France. TEL 33-4-77726666, FAX 33-4-77711557, ftextile@accueil.com. Ed. Raphael Bitter. Adv. contact Mexer Bitter. Circ: 12,000.

687 MEX
TEXTIL VESTIDO. Text in Spanish. 1952. m. MXP 200. adv.
Address: Melchor Ocampo 156, Mexico City 4, DF, Mexico. Ed. Ramon Marinello. Circ: 5,000.

677 CZE ISSN 1210-4078
TEXTIL ZURNAL. Text in Czech. 1992. 11/yr. CZK 588 (effective 2003). adv. **Document type:** *Magazine, Trade.* **Description:** Reports on the latest in fashion and on the fashion markets.
Published by: Ceske a Slovenske Odborne Nakladatelstvi (Subsidiary of: Deutscher Fachverlag GmbH), Drtinova 10, Prague 5, 150 00, Czech Republic. TEL 420-2-27018400, FAX 420-2-27018401, textilzurnal@con-praha.cz, prodej@con-praha.cz, http://www.con-praha.cz. Ed. Michal Korol. Adv. contact Jaroslava Chuda. B&W page CZK 31,800, color page CZK 43,200; trim 210 x 297. Circ: 7,000.

667 USA ISSN 0195-0118
TEXTILE RENTAL. Text in English. 1917. m. USD 240 (effective 2004). adv. bk.rev. illus. Index. **Document type:** *Magazine, Trade.* **Description:** Contains management information for uniform and linen rental executives.
Formerly: Linen Supply News (0024-3825)
Related titles: Online - full text ed.
Indexed: MEDLINE, PROMT, TTI, WTA.
—BLDSC (8808.700000), IE, Infotrieve, ingenta.
Published by: Textile Rental Services Association of America, 1800 Diagonal Rd., Ste. 200, Alexandria, VA 22314. TEL 703-519-0029, FAX 703-519-0026, SRBiller@aol.com, dschmitt@trsa.org, http://www.trsa.org. Adv. contact Steven Feldman. B&W page USD 1,675, color page USD 2,670. Circ: 6,000 (paid).

687.0688 DEU
TEXTILWIRTSCHAFT SEASON. Text in German. q. EUR 13.60; EUR 4.30 newsstand/cover (effective 2003). adv. illus. **Document type:** *Magazine, Trade.*
Former titles: Season - Mode im Verkauf; Mode im Verkauf (0342-3689)
Published by: Deutscher Fachverlag GmbH, Mainzer Landstr 251, Frankfurt Am Main, 60326, Germany. TEL 49-69-759501, FAX 49-69-75952999, info@TWnetwork.de, info@dfv.de, http://www.twnetwork.de, http://www.dfv.de. adv.: page EUR 7,465; trim 208 x 294. Circ: 45,000.

687.19 USA
TIE LINES. Text in English. irreg.
Published by: Neckwear Association of America, 151 Lexington Ave, New York, NY 10016. TEL 212-683-8454.

338.47687 USA
TRADE WINDS. Text in English. irreg. membership. **Document type:** *Newsletter.* **Description:** Provides a forum for exchange in industry relations, and exchange of well-being of members.
Formerly: Apparel Guild. Journal
Indexed: TTI.
Published by: Apparel Guild, 2655 Park Cir, East Meadow, NY 11554-3525. TEL 516-735-1595. Ed. Leon Newman.

687 USA
UNIFORM MANUFACTURERS EXCHANGE. NEWSLETTER. Text in English. irreg. **Document type:** *Newsletter.*
Published by: Uniform Manufacturers Exchange, 1156 Ave of the Americas, New York, NY 10036. TEL 212-869-0670.

UNITE HERE!. see *LABOR UNIONS*

687.3 USA
UNITED KNITWEAR MANUFACTURERS LEAGUE. BULLETIN. Text in English. irreg. **Document type:** *Bulletin.*
Published by: United Knitwear Manufacturers League, 500 Seventh Ave, New York, NY 10018. TEL 212-819-1011.

687 FIN ISSN 0356-8083
VAATTURI. Text in Finnish. 1898. q. adv. bk.rev. bibl.; charts; illus.; stat. **Document type:** *Magazine.*
Published by: Suomen Vaatturiliitto r.y., Kaisaniemenkatu 13 A, Helsinki, 00101, Finland. TEL 358-9-229221, FAX 358-9-22922999. Ed. Jukka Sundstedt. Circ: 500.

687 PRT
VESTIR. Text in Portuguese. 4/yr.
Address: Rua da Palma, 219 2o, Lisbon, 1100, Portugal.

687.0688 USA ISSN 0149-5380
HD9940.U3
W W D; the retailer's daily newspaper. (Women's Wear Daily) Text in English. 1892. d. (Mon.-Fri.). USD 99 domestic to retailers; USD 135 domestic to manufacturers; USD 295 in Canada & Mexico; USD 595 elsewhere (effective 2005). adv. play rev. illus.; mkt. back issues avail.; reprints avail. **Document type:** *Newspaper, Trade.* **Description:** Covers news of the fashion industry, trends, designers, and events in the social world.
Formerly (until 197?): Women's Wear Daily (0043-7581)
Related titles: Microfilm ed.: (from FCM, PQC); Online - full text ed.: (from EBSCO Publishing, Factiva, Florida Center for Library Automation, Gale Group, O C L C Online Computer Library Center, Inc., ProQuest Information & Learning, The Dialog Corporation).
Indexed: B&I, BusI, LRI, T&II, TTI.
—CCC.
Published by: Fairchild Publications, Inc., 7 W 34th St, New York, NY 10001-8191. TEL 212-630-4000, 800-289-0273, wwd@espcamp.com, customerservice@fairchildpub.com, http://www.wwd.com, http://www.fairchildpub.com. Ed. Edward Nardoza. Pub. Ralph Erardy. adv.: B&W page USD 26,010. Circ: 161,386. **Subscr. to:** PO Box 15008, North Hollywood, CA 91615. TEL 818-487-4526.

687 USA ISSN 1067-6236
W W D APPAREL & ACCESSORIES BUYER'S GUIDE; women's apparel & accessories manufacturers. (Women's Wear Daily) Text in English. a. USD 159 (effective 2004).
Published by: Chain Store Guide, 3922 Coconut Palm Dr., Tampa, FL 33619. TEL 800-365-6890, FAX 813-627-6882, info@csgis.com, http://www.csgis.com. Pub. William Larned. Adv. contact Tiffany Kreinbrink.

687.0688 USA ISSN 1096-3766
WEARABLES BUSINESS. Text in English. 1997. m. USD 35 domestic; USD 37 in Canada; USD 59 foreign; free domestic to qualified personnel (effective 2004). **Document type:** *Magazine, Trade.* **Description:** Source of information for the wearables segment of the promotional products industry.
Related titles: Online - full text ed.: (from bigchalk, EBSCO Publishing, Florida Center for Library Automation, Gale Group, H.W. Wilson, O C L C Online Computer Library Center, Inc., ProQuest Information & Learning).
Indexed: ABIn, BPI.
—CCC.
Published by: Primedia Business Magazines & Media, Inc. (Subsidiary of: Primedia, Inc.), 5680 Greenwood Plaza Blvd, Ste 100, Greenwood Village, CO 80111. TEL 303-741-2901, FAX 720-489-3101, inquiries@primediabusiness.com, http://wearablesbusiness.com, http://www.primediabusiness.com. Ed. Jeff Rundles.

687.141 USA
WESTERN - ENGLISH INDUSTRY REPORT. Text in English. a. USD 29 (effective 1999). **Document type:** *Newsletter.*
Formerly: W E R A Brochure
Published by: Western English Retailers Association, PO Box 2348, Weatherford, TX 76086-7348. TEL 303-298-7882, FAX 303-292-3468, wera@frii.com, http://www.wera.org. Ed., R&P Susan Leach. Circ: 1,000 (controlled).

677 GBR ISSN 1356-644X
CODEN: WSACF7
WORLD SPORTS ACTIVEWEAR; the international magazine for sports textiles and apparel. Text in English. 1995. q. GBP 45, USD 75 (effective 1998). adv. bk.rev. **Document type:** *Trade.* **Description:** Covers all levels of the activewear and outdoor industry, from design and manufacture to distribution and retail.
Indexed: TTI, WTA.
—BLDSC (9360.041030).
Published by: World Trades Publishing, PO Box 6, Liverpool, Merseyside L22 0QN, United Kingdom. TEL 44-151-928-9288, FAX 44-151-928-4190, wsa@worldtrades.co.uk. Ed. David Buirski. Pub. Raymond Wilson. R&P, Adv. contact Vanessa Knowles. B&W page GBP 3,372, color page GBP 4,452; trim 210 x 297.

687 CHN
ZHONGGUO FUSHIBAO/CHINESE DRESS AND ADORNMENT WEEKLY. Text in Chinese. 1994. w. CNY 96 (effective 2004). **Document type:** *Trade.*
Published by: Jingji Ribao Baoye Jituan/Economic Daily Newspaper Group, Fengtai-qu, Lianhuachi Xili, Beijing, 100073, China. TEL 86-10-65597798, 86-10-63970950, http://bkdy.ce.cn/fenlei/t20031120_213243.shtml. **Dist. by:** China International Book Trading Corp, 35 Chegongzhuang Xilu, Haidian District, PO Box 399, Beijing 100044, China. TEL 86-10-68412045, FAX 86-10-68412023, cibtc@mail.cibtc.com.cn, http://www.cibtc.com.cn.

CLOTHING TRADE—Abstracting, Bibliographies, Statistics

687.141021 USA
ANNUAL STATISTICAL REPORT ON PROFIT, SALES & PRODUCTION TRENDS FOR THE MEN'S & BOY'S TAILORED CLOTHING INDUSTRY (YEAR). Text in English. 1982. a., latest 2001, Jan. USD 30 domestic; USD 33.40 in Canada (effective 2004). bk.rev. stat. back issues avail. **Document type:** *Bulletin.* **Description:** Provides statistics on clothing production with breakdowns by fabrics and dollar volume including imports and exports and profit ratios.
Former titles: Annual Statistical Report on Profit, Sales and Marketing Trends for the Men's and Boy's Tailored Clothing Industry; Special Report on Financial and Economic Data for the Men's and Boy's Clothing Industry
Published by: Clothing Manufacturers Association of the U S A, 730 Broadway, Fl 10, New York, NY 10003-9511. TEL 212-529-0823. Ed., Pub., R&P Robert A Kaplan. Circ: 350.

687.021 CAN ISSN 0835-006X
CANADA. STATISTICS CANADA. CLOTHING INDUSTRIES/CANADA. STATISTIQUE CANADA. INDUSTRIES DE L'HABILLEMENT. Text in English, French. 1918. a. CND 40 domestic; USD 40 foreign (effective 1999). **Document type:** *Government.*
Incorporates: Women's and Children's Clothing Industries (0384-4498); Canada. Statistics Canada. Men's Clothing Industries (0527-5679); Miscellaneous Clothing Industries
Related titles: Microform ed.: (from MML); Online - full text ed.
Indexed: PAIS.
Published by: Statistics Canada, Operations and Integration Division, Circulation Management, Jean Talon Bldg, 2 C12, Tunney's Pasture, Ottawa, ON K1A 0T6, Canada. TEL 613-951-7277, 800-267-6677, FAX 613-951-1584, http://www.statcan.ca.

016.687 USA ISSN 0887-2937
TT507
CLOTHING AND TEXTILE ARTS INDEX. Text in English. 1970. a. USD 75. bk.rev. back issues avail. **Document type:** *Abstract/Index.* **Description:** Covers social, historic and behavioral aspects of clothing, costumes and textile art.
Related titles: CD-ROM ed.
Address: PO Box 1300, Monument, CO 80132. TEL 719-488-3716. Ed. Sandra S Hutton. Circ: 200.

016.74692 USA
COSTUME SOCIETY OF AMERICA BIBLIOGRAPHY. Text in English. irreg. (approx. quadrennial). membership. bibl. back issues avail. **Document type:** *Bibliography.* **Description:** Lists recent reprints and publications relating to fashion and costume.
Published by: Costume Society of America, 55 Edgewater Dr, PO Box 73, Earleville, MD 21919. TEL 410-275-2329, 800-CSA-9447, FAX 410-275-8936, national.office@costumesocietyamerica.com, http://www.costumesocietyamerica.com. Ed. Polly Willman.

016.687 USA
COSTUME SOCIETY OF AMERICA. SYMPOSIA ABSTRACTS. Text in English. a. membership. back issues avail. **Document type:** *Academic/Scholarly.*
Published by: Costume Society of America, 55 Edgewater Dr, PO Box 73, Earleville, MD 21919. TEL 410-275-2329, 800-CSA-9447, FAX 410-275-8936, national.office@costumesocietyamerica.com, http://www.costumesocietyamerica.com. R&P Kaye Boyer TEL 410-275-1619.

687.021 USA
EXPANDED JANUARY (YEAR) STATISTICAL REPORT ON PROFIT, SALES, AND PRODUCTION TRENDS IN MEN'S & BOYS' TAILORED CLOTHING. Text in English. a. USD 30 per issue (effective 2004). **Document type:** *Trade.*
Published by: Clothing Manufacturers Association of the U S A, 730 Broadway, Fl 10, New York, NY 10003-9511. TEL 212-529-0823.

687.021 FRA
FRANCE. SERVICE D'ETUDE DES STRATEGIES ET DES STATISTIQUES INDUSTRIELLES. RESULTATS TRIMESTRIELS DES ENQUETES DE BRANCHE. INDUSTRIE DE L'HABILLEMENT. Text in French. q. stat. **Description:** Provides detailed industry-wide performance statistics for comparative evaluations.
Published by: Service d'Etude des Strategies et des Statistiques Industrielles (SESSI), 85 bd. du Montparnasse, Paris, Cedex 6 75270, France. TEL 45-56-42-34, FAX 45-56-40-71.

687.3021 USA
HOSIERY STATISTICS✱ . Text in English. 1934. a. USD 50 (effective 2001). charts; stat. back issues avail. **Document type:** *Yearbook, Trade.* **Description:** Provides data on annual production, shipments and stocks of various hosiery categories, per capita consumption and imports and exports.
Indexed: TTI.
Published by: Hosiery Association, 3623 Latrobe Dr, Ste 130, Charlotte, NC 28211-2117. TEL 704-365-0913, FAX 704-362-2056. Ed. Mary Ann Blansett. Circ: 1,000 (controlled).

016.687 USA
TS1300
I T A A PROCEEDINGS (ONLINE). Text in English. 1944. a. USD 22 domestic; USD 25 foreign (effective 2003). abstr. **Document type:** *Proceedings, Trade.* **Description:** Presents abstracts of papers introduced at the meeting.
Former titles: I T A A Proceedings (Print) (1067-2850); A C P T C Proceedings (1051-1466)
Media: Online - full content.
—BLDSC (4587.840000).
Published by: International Textile and Apparel Association, PO Box 1360, Monument, CO 80132. TEL 719-488-3716, itaaoffice@cs.com, http://www.itaaonline.org. Ed. Sandra S Hutton. Circ: 1,100.

687.021 USA ISSN 1073-0818
HD9948.5.U6
N S G A TEAM LICENSED & SPORTS CLOTHING DIARY. Text in English. 1991. a. USD 250 to non-members (effective 2000). **Document type:** *Trade.* **Description:** Analyzes sport and nonsport apparel purchases, with demographic data of purchasers for several product categories.
Former titles: N S G A Sports Clothing Diary; N S G A Sports Apparel Diary
Published by: National Sporting Goods Association, 1601 Feehanville Dr, Ste 300, Mt. Prospect, IL 60056-6305. TEL 847-296-6742, 800-815-5422, FAX 847-391-9827, nsga1699@aol.com, http://www.nsga.org. Ed. Thomas B Doyle.

CLOTHING TRADE—Fashions

687.19 ITA ISSN 1120-1991
ACCESSORI COLLEZIONI. Text in English, Italian. s-a. EUR 37.18 domestic; EUR 104 foreign (effective 2001). illus. back issues avail. **Document type:** *Magazine, Trade.* **Description:** Covers all accessories for women's fashion: costume jewelry, jewels, hats, scarves, belts, shoes, gloves.
Published by: Liber S.R.L., Via Curtatona, 5/m, Modena, 41100, Italy. TEL 39-059-412643, FAX 39-059-412567, mcagnoni@liber.it. Ed. Antonio Vergara.

ACCESSORIES. see *CLOTHING TRADE*

AD! DICT. see *ART*

AGENDA PARA LA NOVIA. see *MATRIMONY*

ALLOYGIRL. see *WOMEN'S INTERESTS*

ALLURE. see *WOMEN'S INTERESTS*

AMICA. see *WOMEN'S INTERESTS*

659.152 JPN
AN-AN. Text in Japanese. 1970. w. JPY 400 newsstand/cover (effective 2005). **Document type:** *Magazine, Consumer.* **Description:** Covers topics such as fashion, hair, dieting, love, sex, money, travel and more.
Published by: Magazine House, Ltd., 3-13-10 Ginza, Chuo-ku, Tokyo, 104-8003, Japan. http://anan.magazine.co.jp/index.jsp, http//:www.magazine.co.jp. Circ: 650,000.

746.9 CAN ISSN 1710-4793
ANOKHI VIBE; fusion, fashion & lifestyle. Text in English. 2002. q. **Document type:** *Magazine, Consumer.*

▼ new title ➤ refereed ✱ unverified ♦ full entry avail.

C

Published by: Anokhi Media Corporation, Attn: Raj Girn, 25 Kingsbridge Garden Circle., Ste 2715, Mississauga, ON L5R 4B1, Canada. TEL 905-501-9907, FAX 905-501-9908, publisher@anokhivibe.com, http://www.anokhivibe.com. Ed. Pamela Arora.

746.92   GBR
ANOTHER. Text in English. 2001 (Sep.). s-a. USD 14.99 newsstand/cover (effective 2001). Document type: Magazine, Consumer. Description: Contains articles and features on fashion and lifestyle.
Published by: Waddell Ltd., 112-116 Old St, London, EC1V 9BG, United Kingdom. TEL 44-20-7549-6808, FAX 44-20-7336-0966, contact@confused.co.uk, http://www.confused.co.uk.

ANYBODY. see LIFESTYLE

746.92   USA   ISSN 1089-4322
APPAREL INDUSTRY INTERNACIONAL; la revista avanzada de la industria de la confession Iberoamericana. Text in Spanish. 1991. bi-m. USD 48 in United States; USD 60 in Canada & Mexico; USD 70 elsewhere. adv. illus. Document type: Trade. Description: Covers factory management for apparel companies in Latin America, including technology, personnel, and quality issues.
Published by: Bill Communications, Inc. (Subsidiary of: V N U Tijdschriften B.V.), 770 Broadway, New York, NY 10003-9595. TEL 646-654-5000. Circ: 15,000.

AREA MAGAZINE. see ART

ARIADNE AT HOME. see INTERIOR DESIGN AND DECORATION

ARPEL FUR; Italian & international fur, leather garments fashion magazine. see LEATHER AND FUR INDUSTRIES

ARS SUTORIA; Italian & International Footwear Fashion Magazine. see SHOES AND BOOTS

659.152   SGP
ASIAN SOURCES FASHION ACCESSORIES. Text in English. 1978. m. USD 75 (effective 2005). adv. Document type: Magazine, Trade. Description: Covers the clothing trade, fashions, and fashion accessories.
Incorporates in part (in 2005): Asian Sources Timepieces (0254-1173); Formerly: Asian Sources Fashion Accessories & Supplies; Which was formed by the merger of (1995-1997): Asian Sources Manufacturing Supplies and Fabrics; Asian Sources Fashion Accessories (0255-7290); Which superseded (in 1984): Asian Sources Garments and Accessories (0254-1130)
Indexed: HongKongiana.
Published by: Global Sources, c/o Media Data Systems Pte Ltd, PO Box 0203, Raffles City, 911707, Singapore. TEL 65-65472800, FAX 65-65472888, service@globalsources.com, http://www.globalsources.com/MAGAZINE/BUYERS/HWBR.HTM?pi_proj=GSOLHP. Circ: 20,900.

AUSTIN HOMES & LIVING. see INTERIOR DESIGN AND DECORATION

AUSTRALASIAN TEXTILES & FASHION. see TEXTILE INDUSTRIES AND FABRICS

746.9 910.202 305.4   USA   ISSN 1546-0606
▼ B; a fashion and lifestyle magazine from Bloomingdale's. (Bloomingdale's) Variant title: Bloomingdale's Magazine. Text in English. 2003 (Hol.). q. USD 15.80; USD 3.95 newsstand/cover (effective 2004); free to customers in the loyalty program. adv. 130 p./no.; Document type: Magazine, Consumer. Description: Covers fashion, beauty, travel, interiors, entertainment and celebrities.
Published by: (Bloomingdale's, Inc.), John Brown Publishing Inc., 15 E 32nd St, 8th Fl, New York, NY 10016. TEL 212-931-9800, FAX 212-213-4526, http://www.johnbrownpublishing.com. Ed. George Epaminondas. Pub., R&P Duncan Milne. Adv. contact Jamie Forrest TEL 212-931-9803. page USD 16,200. Circ: 270,000 (controlled).

746   USA   ISSN 0192-5938
B B W; real women - real beauty. (Big Beautiful Woman) Text in English. 1979-1998; N.S. 1999. bi-m. USD 14.95 domestic; USD 22.95 in Canada & Mexico; USD 46.95 elsewhere; USD 4.95 newsstand/cover (effective 2003). adv. bk.rev. illus. reprints avail. Document type: Magazine, Consumer. Description: Contains information and resources in the areas of fashion and beauty, health and well-being, entertainment and romance, and work and leisure for women size 16+.
—CCC.
Published by: Aeon Publishing Group, Inc., 88 Sunnyside Blvd, Ste 203, Plainview, NY 11803. TEL 916-684-7904, FAX 916-684-7628, sesmith@bbwmagazine.com, http://www.bbwmagazine.com. Ed., R&P Sally Smith. Pub. Lisa Krebs. Adv. contact Paula Levine. page USD 5,370; trim 8 x 10.875. Circ: 100,000.

B INTERNATIONAL. see GENERAL INTEREST PERIODICALS—Hong Kong, Special Administrative Region Of P R C

687.13   ITA   ISSN 1120-1983
BAMBINI COLLEZIONI. Text in English, Italian. s-a. EUR 92.96 domestic includes:0 - 3 Baby Collezioni (effective 2001). adv. back issues avail. Document type: Magazine, Trade. Description: Covers children's fashion from age 4 to 14.
Published by: Liber S.R.L., Via Curtatona, 5/m, Modena, 41100, Italy. TEL 39-059-412643, FAX 39-059-412567, mcagnoni@liber.it. Ed. Antonio Vergara.

BEACHSTYLE; your guide to sun fashion and travel. see TRAVEL AND TOURISM

BEACHSTYLE PRESENTS SWIM IN STYLE. see TRAVEL AND TOURISM

746.9   ITA   ISSN 1121-175X
BENISSIMO. Text in Italian. 1982. m. EUR 3.05 newsstand/cover (effective 2005). adv. back issues avail. Document type: Magazine, Consumer.
Published by: Fabbri Editori (Subsidiary of: R C S Libri), Via Mecenate 87-6, Milan, MI 20138, Italy. TEL 39-02-580801, FAX 39-02-5062865. Ed. Mara Santini.

746.92 646.7   FRA   ISSN 0221-7996
BIBA. Text in French. 1980. m. EUR 19.80 (effective 2005). back issues avail. Document type: Magazine, Consumer.
Published by: Emap France (Subsidiary of: Emap Media Ltd.), 150-152 Rue Gallieni, Boulogne, 92644, France. TEL 33-1-41334961, FAX 33-1-41335010, info@emapfrance.com, http://www.bibamagazine.fr/, http://www.emapmedia.com. Circ: 251,100 (paid).

BIBI. see MATRIMONY

BIGTIME; the magazine of urban art and expression. see MUSIC

BILD DER FRAU. see WOMEN'S INTERESTS

BLACK BOOK; progressive urban culture. see LIFESTYLE

BLI. see BEAUTY CULTURE

BLISS FOR BRIDES. see MATRIMONY

646.3   DEU   ISSN 0937-8456
BLOUSES, SKIRTS, TROUSERS. Text in English. s-a. GBP 4.25 newsstand/cover (effective 2000). adv. Document type: Magazine, Consumer.
Published by: Verlag Aenne Burda GmbH & Co. KG, Am Kestendamm 1, Offenburg, 77652, Germany. TEL 49-781-9402, FAX 49-781-843291. Ed. Veronika Hark. Pub. Aenne Burda. Adv. contact Juergen Brandt. Dist. in UK by: Comag, Tavistock Works, Tavistock Rd, W Drayton, Middx UB7 7QX, United Kingdom. TEL 44-1895-444055, FAX 44-1895-433602.

791.43   CHE   ISSN 1420-3944
BOLERO; mode beaute lifestyle. Text in German. 1990. 11/yr. CHF 74 domestic; CHF 105 in Europe; CHF 140 elsewhere (effective 2001). adv. bk.rev. Document type: Magazine, Consumer.
Published by: Bolero Zeitschriftenverlag AG, Giesshuebelstr 62 i, Zuerich, 8045, Switzerland. TEL 41-1-4548282, FAX 41-1-4548272, service@boleroweb.ch, http://www.boleroweb.ch. Ed. Sithara Atasoy. Pub. Susanne Bruengger. Adv. contact Franciska Meier TEL 41-1-4548223. page CHF 9,270; trim 213 x 275. Circ: 27,084 (paid).

BOYS RUSH. see CHILDREN AND YOUTH—About

746.92   BRA
BRASIL VOGUE. Text in Portuguese. 1975. m. USD 170. adv. bk.rev.
Published by: Carta Editorial Ltda., Avda. Brasil 1456, Jardim America, SP 01430, Brazil. TEL 883-3366, FAX 853-7331, TELEX 1138516 CTED BR. Ed. Luiz Carta. Circ: 30,500.

BRAVO GIRL!. see CHILDREN AND YOUTH—For

659.152 392.5   USA
BRIDAL APPAREL NEWS. Text in English. 1980. s-a. USD 10. adv. charts; illus.; stat.; tr.lit. back issues avail. Description: For bridal and formal wear retailers and manufacturers throughout the world.
Published by: MnM Publishing Corp., 110 E Ninth St, Ste A-777, Los Angeles, CA 90079-1777. http://www.apparelnews.net. Ed. Anne Harnagel. Circ: 10,100. Subscr. to: 5615 W. Cermak Rd., Cicero, IL 60650.

BRIDE TO BE. see MATRIMONY

BRIDE'S. see MATRIMONY

BRIDES OF BERKSHIRE. see MATRIMONY

BRIDES OF BRISTOL, BATH & AVON. see MATRIMONY

BRIDES OF BRITAIN SERIES. see MATRIMONY

BRIDES OF DEVON & CORNWALL. see MATRIMONY

BRIDES OF EAST ANGLIA. see MATRIMONY

BRIDES OF HERTS, BUCKS & BEDS. see MATRIMONY

BRIDES OF NORTH EAST ENGLAND. see MATRIMONY

BRIDES OF SCOTLAND. see MATRIMONY

BRIDES OF SOMERSET. see MATRIMONY

746.96   AUT
BRIGITTE. Text in German. 1971. 26/yr. Document type: Magazine, Consumer.
Published by: Gruner und Jahr Verlagsgesellschaft mbH, Parkring 12, Vienna, W 1010, Austria. TEL 43-1-51256470, FAX 43-1-5125732, luthwig.erwin@guj.de. Circ: 65,000 (paid).

BRILLE UND MODE. see BEAUTY CULTURE

391.2   HUN   ISSN 0865-6681
BURDA. Text in Hungarian. 1988. m. Document type: Magazine, Consumer.
Formerly (until 1989): Burda Moden (0238-8863)
Published by: M-Medien Group, 14-16 Ecseri Str., Budapest, 1033, Hungary. TEL 36-1-2808949, FAX 36-1-2826817, medien@ax.hu.

646.4   TUR   ISSN 1300-8013
BURDA. Text in Turkish. 1991. m. adv. Document type: Magazine, Consumer.
Related titles: Online - full text ed.
Published by: D B R - Dogan Burda Rizzoli Dergi Yayyncylyk ve Pazarlama A.S., Hurriyet Medya Towers, Gunesli - Istanbul, 34212, Turkey. TEL 90-212-4103111, FAX 90-212-4103112, burda@dbr.com.tr, abone@dbr.com.tr, http://www.burda.com.tr, http://www.dbr.com.tr.

659.152 746.92   CHE
BURDA. Text in Arabic. 1985. m. adv. illus. Document type: Trade.
Published by: I P M Press and Marketing S.A., 2 Cours de Rive, Geneva, 1204, Switzerland. Ed. Ingrid Kuederle. Circ: 77,000.

746   RUS   ISSN 1560-537X
BURDA. Text in Russian. 1996. m. RUR 900 domestic; RUR 75 newsstand/cover (effective 2004). adv. Document type: Magazine, Consumer.
Published by: Izdatel'skii Dom Burda, ul Pravdy 8, Moscow, 125040, Russian Federation. TEL 7-095-7979849, FAX 7-095-2571196, burda-magazine@pub.burda.ru, vertrieb@burda.ru, http://www.burda.ru. adv.: page USD 9,100. Circ: 420,000 (paid and controlled).

746.92   ROM   ISSN 1454-9441
BURDA. Text in Romanian. 2000. m. adv. Document type: Magazine, Consumer.
Published by: Burda Romania, Str. Izvor nr. 78, sector 5, Bucharest, Romania. TEL 40-21-4105212, FAX 40-21-4110168, sandi@burda.ro, http://www.burda.ro.

746.92   ZAF   ISSN 1022-2405
BURDA; a world of fashion. Text in English. 1993. m. ZAR 93. adv. illus. Document type: Consumer.
Published by: Burda South Africa, PO Box 642, Irene, 1675, South Africa.

746.96   CZE
BURDA. Text in Czech. m. CZK 948 domestic; CZK 89 newsstand/cover (effective 2004). adv. Document type: Magazine, Consumer. Description: Contains information and details on designs and fashion for a wide variety of tastes.
Published by: Burda Praha spol. s.r.o., Uruguayska 17, Prague 2, 120 00, Czech Republic. TEL 420-2-22520618, FAX 420-2-22522648, klincokova@burda.cz, http://www.burda.cz. Adv. contact Renata Belikova. page CZK 99,000; trim 194 x 253. Circ: 105,000 (paid and controlled).

746.96   POL   ISSN 0867-387X
BURDA. Text in Polish. 1990. m. PLZ 106.80 domestic (effective 2004). adv. Document type: Magazine, Consumer.
Related titles: ♦ Supplement(s): Burda. Wydanie Specjalne. ISSN 1642-9974.
Published by: Wydawnictwo Burda Polska Sp. z.o.o., ul Strzegomska 236a, Wroclaw, 54432, Poland. TEL 48-71-3737280, FAX 48-71-3511788, prenumerata@burda.pl, http://www.burda.pl. adv.: page PLZ 10,500. Circ: 75,000 (paid and controlled).

646.3   DEU   ISSN 0942-4326
BURDA BLUSEN, ROECKE, HOSEN. Text in German. 2/yr. adv. Document type: Magazine, Consumer.
Published by: Verlag Aenne Burda GmbH & Co. KG, Am Kestendamm 1, Offenburg, 77652, Germany. TEL 49-781-846270, FAX 49-781-843242, http://www.burdamode.com. Ed. Jutta Kaletka. Pub. Aenne Burda. Adv. contact Sabine Burda. B&W page EUR 3,000, color page EUR 5,000.

641.3 DEU ISSN 0948-7905
BURDA FASCHING. Text in German. a. adv. **Document type:** *Magazine, Consumer.*
Published by: Verlag Aenne Burda GmbH & Co. KG, Am Kestendamm 1, Offenburg, 77652, Germany. TEL 49-781-846270, FAX 49-781-843242, info@burdamode.com, http://www.burdamode.com. Ed. Jutta Kaletka. Pub. Aenne Burda. Adv. contact Sabine Burda. B&W page EUR 3,000, color page EUR 5,000.

646.2 HUN ISSN 1587-5601
BURDA GYEREKDIVAT. Variant title: Burda Special. Text in Hungarian. 1997. s-a. **Document type:** *Magazine, Consumer.*
Formerly (until 2001): Special Burda. Babak es Aprosagok (1417-7994); Which was formed by the merger of (1992-1997): Special Burda. Bebidivat (1216-0873); (1991-1997): Special Burda. Aprosagok Divatja (1216-0881)
Published by: M-Medien Group, 14-16 Ecseri Str., Budapest, 1033, Hungary. TEL 36-1-2808949, FAX 36-1-2826817, medien@ax.hu.

646.3 DEU
BURDA MODE FUER ZIERLICHE. Text in German. s-a. adv. **Document type:** *Magazine, Consumer.*
Formerly: Burda Babymaschen
Published by: Verlag Aenne Burda GmbH & Co. KG, Am Kestendamm 1, Offenburg, 77652, Germany. TEL 49-781-846270, FAX 49-781-843242, info@burdamode.com, http://www.burdamode.com. Ed. Jutta Kaletka. Pub. Aenne Burda. Adv. contact Juergen Brandt. B&W page EUR 3,000, color page EUR 5,000.

687 DEU ISSN 1617-0091
BURDA MODEMAGAZIN; die ganze Welt der Mode. Text in German. 1950. m. EUR 48; EUR 4 newsstand/cover (effective 2005). adv. charts; illus.; tr.lit. **Document type:** *Magazine, Consumer.* **Description:** Provides a bridge between fashion designers, fashion innovation, and the individual creativity of today's women.
Formerly (until 1998): Burda Mode (German Edition) (0007-6031)
Indexed: RASB.
—CCC.
Published by: Verlag Aenne Burda GmbH & Co. KG, Am Kestendamm 1, Offenburg, 77652, Germany. TEL 49-781-8402, FAX 49-781-843207, burdamoden@vab.burda.com, info@burdamode.com, http://www.burdamode.com. Ed. Susanne Walsleben. Pub. Aenne Burda. Adv. contact Karl-Hermann Heise. B&W page EUR 8,300, color page EUR 12,500; bleed 220 x 280. Circ: 169,293 (paid). **Subscr. to:** Burda Medien Abo-Service, Postfach 1351, Lindau 88103, Germany. TEL 49-8382-963180, FAX 49-8382-963119.

659.152 DEU
BURDA MODEN (GREEK EDITION)✶ ; fashion for everyone. Text in Greek. 1983. m. adv. bk.rev. illus. back issues avail. **Document type:** *Consumer.*
Published by: Hubert Burda Media Holding GmbH & Co. KG, Postfach 1230, Offenburg, 77602, Germany. Circ: 90,000.

646.33 DEU ISSN 0945-6163
BURDA PLUS. Text in German. 1987. a. adv. **Document type:** *Magazine, Consumer.*
Formerly (until 1995): Burda Mode fuer Vollschlanke (0937-8499)
Related titles: English ed.: ISSN 1434-7202.
Published by: Verlag Aenne Burda GmbH & Co. KG, Am Kestendamm 1, Offenburg, 77652, Germany. TEL 49-781-846270, FAX 49-781-843242, info@burdamode.com, http://www.burdamode.com. Ed. Jutta Kaletka. Adv. contact Sabine Burda. B&W page EUR 3,000, color page EUR 5,000.
Dist. in UK by: Comag, Tavistock Works, Tavistock Rd, W Drayton, Middx UB7 7QX, United Kingdom. TEL 44-1895-444055, FAX 44-1895-433602.

746.96 POL ISSN 1509-1503
BURDA SPECIAL. BLUZKI, SPODNIE, SPODNICE. Variant title: Bluzki, Spodnie, Spodnice. Text in Polish. 2000. 2/yr. PLZ 8.90 per issue domestic (effective 2004). **Document type:** *Magazine, Consumer.*
Published by: Wydawnictwo Burda Polska Sp. z.o.o., ul Strzegomska 236a, Wroclaw, 54432, Poland. TEL 48-71-3737280, FAX 48-71-3511788, prenumerata@burda.pl, http://www.burda.pl.

646.2 HUN ISSN 1587-5598
BURDA SPECIAL. BOLDOG KARACSONYT. Text in Hungarian. 1994. a. **Document type:** *Magazine, Consumer.*
Formerly (until 1997): Special Burda. Karacsony (1218-9065)
Published by: M-Medien Group, 14-16 Ecseri Str., Budapest, 1033, Hungary. TEL 36-1-2808949, FAX 36-1-2826817, medien@ax.hu.

746.96 POL ISSN 1640-6966
BURDA SPECIAL. MODA DLA DZIECI. Variant title: Moda dla Dzieci. Text in Polish. 2000. 2/yr. PLZ 8.90 per issue domestic (effective 2004). **Document type:** *Magazine, Consumer.*
Published by: Wydawnictwo Burda Polska Sp. z.o.o., ul Strzegomska 236a, Wroclaw, 54432, Poland. TEL 48-71-3737280, FAX 48-71-3511788, prenumerata@burda.pl, http://www.burda.pl.

746.96 372.54 POL ISSN 1509-6866
BURDA. SZYCIE KROK PO KROKU. Variant title: Szycie Krok po Kroku. Text in Polish. 2000. 2/yr. PLZ 8.90 per issue domestic (effective 2004). **Document type:** *Magazine, Consumer.*
Published by: Wydawnictwo Burda Polska Sp. z.o.o., ul Strzegomska 236a, Wroclaw, 54432, Poland. TEL 48-71-3737280, FAX 48-71-3511788, prenumerata@burda.pl, http://www.burda.pl.

746.96 POL ISSN 1642-9974
BURDA. WYDANIE SPECJALNE. Text in Polish. 2001. a. **Document type:** *Magazine, Consumer.*
Related titles: ♦ Supplement to: Burda. ISSN 0867-387X.
Published by: Wydawnictwo Burda Polska Sp. z.o.o., ul Strzegomska 236a, Wroclaw, 54432, Poland. TEL 48-71-3737280, prenumerata@burda.pl, http://www.burda.pl.

646.4 USA ISSN 0895-6871
BUTTERICK HOME CATALOG. Text in English. 1959. q. USD 9.95 domestic; USD 12.95 in Canada; USD 3.50 domestic; USD 4.50 in Canada (effective 2005). adv. illus. **Document type:** *Catalog.*
—CCC.
Published by: Soho Publishing Company, 161 Ave of the Americas, New York, NY 10013. TEL 212-620-2500, FAX 212-620-2650, http://www.butterick.com. Ed. Kathy Marrone. R&P Joe Anselmo. Adv. contact Doreen Connors TEL 212-620-2539. B&W page USD 4,765, color page USD 5,336; trim 8.25 x 10.75. Circ: 185,000. **Subscr. to:** 615 Mccall Rd., Manhattan, KS 66502-5035.

659.152 USA
C S A NEWS (EARLEVILLE). Text in English. 1975. q. USD 60 to individual members; USD 35 to libraries; USD 95 to institutions; USD 350 to corporations (effective 1999). adv. bk.rev. back issues avail. **Document type:** *Newsletter.* **Description:** Covers membership activities and regional events.
Formerly: Costume Society of America Newsletter
Published by: Costume Society of America, 55 Edgewater Dr, PO Box 73, Earleville, MD 21919. TEL 410-275-2329, 800-CSA-9447, FAX 410-275-8936, national.office@costumesocietyamerica.com, http://www.costumesocietyamerica.com. Ed. Man Ed Cathy Taylor. R&P Kaye Boyer TEL 410-275-1619. Adv. contact Kay Boyer. Circ: 1,500.

746.92 JPN
CANCAM. Text in Japanese. 1981. m. JPY 600 newsstand/cover (effective 2002). adv. **Document type:** *Magazine, Consumer.* **Description:** Offers the latest information on fashion, makeup, bags, accessories, etc.
Published by: Shogakukan Inc., 3-1 Hitotsubashi 2-chome, Chiyoda-ku, Tokyo, 101-8001, Japan. TEL 81-3-3230-5211, FAX 81-3-3264-8471, http://www.shogakukan.co.jp.

CAWAII. see *WOMEN'S INTERESTS*

659.152 GBR
CELEBRITY LOOKS. Text in English. m. GBP 2.30 newsstand/cover (effective 2001). adv. **Document type:** *Magazine, Consumer.* **Description:** Contains detailed information on all aspects of the fashion, hair, health and cosmetic secrets of celebrities.
Published by: Emap Elan Ltd. (Subsidiary of: Emap Consumer Media), Endeavour House, 189 Shaftesbury Ave, London, WC2H 8JG, United Kingdom. TEL 44-207-437-9011, FAX 44-207-208-3709, http://www.emap.com. Adv. contact Elaine Wilkinson.

687 USA
CHEAP DATE. Text in English. 2000. q. USD 12; USD 3 newsstand/cover (effective 2002). adv. **Document type:** *Consumer.*
Address: 96 Spring St, 8th Fl, New York, NY 10012. TEL 212-925-6421, cheapdatenyc@hotmail.com. Eds. Bay Garnett, Kira Jolliffe.

646 ITA ISSN 0009-3203
CHERIE MODA/CHERIE MODE. Text in Italian. 1955. q. adv. **Document type:** *Magazine, Consumer.*
Published by: Edizioni Moderne Internazionali, Via Gallarate 230, Milan, MI, Italy. TEL 39-02-36569654, FAX 39-02-66981482, emimil@tin.it. Circ: 125,000.

746.92 920 ITA
CHI E CHI DEL GIORNALISMO E DELLA MODA. Text in English, Italian. 1998. a. **Document type:** *Directory, Consumer.*
Published by: Crisalide Press, Via Brusuglio 66, Milan, MI 20161, Italy. TEL 39-02-6464663, FAX 39-02-6461622, http://www.crisalidepress.it. Ed. Paola Berti. Circ: 50,000.

746.92 649 USA ISSN 1554-2122
CHILDREN'S BUSINESS. Short title: C B. Text in English. 1985. m. USD 49 domestic; USD 85 in Canada & Mexico; USD 145 elsewhere (effective 2005). adv. reprints avail. **Document type:** *Magazine, Trade.* **Description:** Covers children's clothing, fashion, accessories, footwear, and licensed products.
Former titles: W W D Children's Business (1540-0050); (until 2002): Children's Business (0884-2280)
Related titles: Microfilm ed.: (from FCM); Online - full text ed.: (from EBSCO Publishing, Factiva, Gale Group, Northern Light Technology, Inc., O C L C Online Computer Library Center, Inc., ProQuest Information & Learning).
Indexed: B&I.
—CCC.
Published by: Fairchild Publications, Inc., 7 W 34th St, New York, NY 10001-8191. TEL 212-630-4700, FAX 212-630-4760, mitchelt@fairchildpub.com, customerservice@fairchildpub.com, http://www.childrensbusiness.com, http://www.fairchildpub.com. Ed. Tracy Mitchell. Pubs. Bilha Goodman, Michelle Brown. Circ: 12,000 (paid).

CHRISTIAN BRIDE. see *MATRIMONY*

CITY (NEW YORK); design food fashion. see *LIFESTYLE*

746.9 747 USA ISSN 1534-5661
CLEAR. Text in English. 2001. bi-m. USD 18; USD 4.95 newsstand/cover (effective 2001). adv. illus. **Document type:** *Magazine, Consumer.* **Description:** Covers retro & trend-setter decorating styles & fashion.
Published by: V Publications LLC, 433 N. Washington Ave., Royal Oak, MI 48067-1754. clearmag@hotmail.com, http://www.clearmag.com. Ed. Ivana Kalafatic.

646.3 646.72 CAN
CLIN D'OEIL. Text in French. 1980. m. USD 26.95. adv.
Related titles: ♦ German ed.: Der Weg.
Published by: Publicor Inc., 7 Chemin Bates, Outremont, PQ H2V 1A6, Canada. TEL 514-270-1100, FAX 514-270-6900. Ed. Danielle Paquin. Circ: 67,000.

659.152 USA
CLUB MODELE✶ . Text in English. 1991. bi-m. **Description:** For performers, models, photographers, production companies, agencies and night clubs.
Formerly: Model and Performer
Published by: Aquino Productions, P O Box 15760, Stamford, CT 06901-0760. Ed. Elaine Hallgren. adv.: B&W page USD 1,400, color page USD 2,800. Circ: 114,000.

646 FRA ISSN 0750-1900
COLLECTIONS (PARIS). Text in French, German, Spanish. 1952. q. USD 22. adv. illus.
Formerly: Femme Chic (0010-0773)
Published by: Publications Louchel, 8 rue Halevy, Paris, 75009, France. Circ: 45,000.

COLLECTOR. see *ADVERTISING AND PUBLIC RELATIONS*

746.9 ITA
COLLEZIONI. Text in Italian. q. EUR 111.55 domestic (effective 2001). 416 p./no.; **Document type:** *Magazine.*
Published by: Liber S.R.L., Via Curtatona, 5/m, Modena, 41100, Italy. TEL 39-059-412643, FAX 39-059-412567, mcagnoni@liber.it. Ed. Antonio Vergara.

COLLEZIONI SPOSA. see *MATRIMONY*

COMPLEX MAGAZINE. see *LIFESTYLE*

CONFEZIONE. see *CLOTHING TRADE*

▼ **COOKIE**; a lifestyle magazine for sophisticated parents. see *CHILDREN AND YOUTH—About*

▼ **COSMO BEAUTY.** see *BEAUTY CULTURE*

COSMOGIRL!. see *CHILDREN AND YOUTH—For*

COSMOPOLITAN. see *WOMEN'S INTERESTS*

059.9435 TUR ISSN 1300-8072
COSMOPOLITAN. Text in Turkish. 1992. m. **Document type:** *Magazine, Consumer.*
Published by: 1 Numara Hearst Yayincilik, Sabah Tesisleri, Tesvikiye Caddesi 123, Tesvikiye, Istanbul, 80200, Turkey. TEL 90-212-3158000, FAX 90-212-3159272, http://www.birnumara.com.tr.

640 CHN
COSMOPOLITAN. Text in Chinese. m. adv. **Document type:** *Magazine, Consumer.*
Published by: Trends Communication Co. Ltd., Rm 616, Tower A, COFCO Plaza, 8 Jianguomennei Ave, Beijing, 100005, China. TEL 86-10-652288002501, FAX 86-10-652288002599, cosmo@trendsmag.com, network@trendsmag.com, http://www.trendsmag.com/trendsmag/client/magazine/cosmopolitan.jsp.

746.96 HKG
COSMOPOLITAN. Text in Chinese. 1984. m. adv. **Document type:** *Magazine, Consumer.*
Published by: South China Morning Post Ltd., 16/F Somerset House, Taikoo Pl, 979 King's Rd, PO Box 47, Quarry Bay, Hong Kong, Hong Kong. TEL 852-25652222, FAX 852-28111048, editorial@cosmomag.com.hk, info@scmp.com, http://www.cosmopolitan.com.hk, http://www.scmp.com. Ed. Grace Ng. Circ: 25,000.

C

056.1 ARG ISSN 0328-8242
COSMOPOLITAN ARGENTINA. Text in Spanish. 1996. m. adv.
Document type: *Magazine, Consumer.*
Published by: Editorial Televisa Argentina, Av Paseo Colon 275, Piso 10, Buenos Aires, Buenos Aires 1063, Argentina. TEL 54-11-4343-2225, FAX 54-11-4345-0955, http://www.televisa.com.ar. Circ: 15,000 (paid).

391 ITA ISSN 1593-1498
COSTUME. Text in Italian. 2001. bi-m. EUR 4.95 newsstand/cover (effective 2003). **Document type:** *Magazine, Consumer.*
Related titles: French ed.: ISSN 1593-4845; Spanish ed.: ISSN 1593-4837; German ed.: ISSN 1593-4853.
Published by: Trentini S.r.l., Via Pier Luigi Nervi 1/B, Argenta, 44011, Italy. TEL 39-0532-318149, FAX 39-0532-310084, riviverelastoria@3ntini.com, info@3ntini.com, http://www.3ntini.com/costume.htm.

746.92 391 GBR ISSN 0590-8876
➤ **COSTUME.** Text in English. 1967. a. GBP 18 domestic; GBP 20, USD 30 foreign; GBP 24 domestic to individual members; GBP 26, USD 40 foreign to individual members; GBP 48 domestic to institutional members; GBP 52, USD 75 foreign to institutional members; GBP 12 domestic to students membership; GBP 14, USD 20 foreign to students membership (effective 2004). adv. bk.rev. bibl.; charts; illus. back issues avail. **Document type:** *Journal, Academic/Scholarly.* **Description:** Promotes the study and preservation of historic and contemporary costume.
Indexed: ABM, ArtInd, BHA, BrArAb, BrHumI, DAAI, IndIslam, NumL, RILM, WTA.
—BLDSC (3477.300000), IE, ingenta.
Published by: Costume Society, Hon. Secretary c/o Moore Stephens, St Paul's House, 8 Warwick Ln, London, EC4P 4BN, United Kingdom. http://www.maney.co.uk/search?fwaction=show&fwid=295, http://www.costumesociety.org.uk. Ed., R&P Dr. Ann Saunders. Circ: 1,200 (paid). **Subscr. to:** The Membership Secretary, c/o Pat Poppy, 56 Wareham Rd, Lytchett Matravers, Poole, Dorset BH16 6DS, United Kingdom.

C

746.92 390 CAN
COSTUME JOURNAL. Text in English. 1971. 3/yr. CND 25 membership (effective 2004). bk.rev.
Formerly (until 1990): Costume Society of Ontario. Newsletter (0834-2520)
Published by: Costume Society of Ontario, P O Box 981, Sta F, Toronto, ON M4Y 2N9, Canada. TEL 416-977-4280, smclean2@hotmail.com, info@costumesociety.ca, http://www.costumesociety.ca. Ed., R&P Suzanne McLean. Circ: 200 (paid).

COSTUME SOCIETY OF AMERICA BIBLIOGRAPHY. see *CLOTHING TRADE—Abstracting, Bibliographies, Statistics*

COTTET MAGAZINE. see *MEDICAL SCIENCES—Ophthalmology And Optometry*

659.152 HKG
COUTOURE. Text in Chinese, English. 1987. s-a. HKD 160. adv. illus. **Document type:** *Consumer.* **Description:** Forecasts the Spring-Summer and Autumn-Winter women's collections from around the world.
Published by: Communication Management Ltd., 1811 Hong Kong Plaza, 188 Connaught Rd W, Hong Kong, Hong Kong. FAX 852-2858-2671. Ed. Sharie Ross. Pub., R&P Lina Ross. Adv. contact Vera Siu. color page HKD 34,510; 305 x 228. Circ: 35,000.

746.9 HKG
COUTURE MALAYSIA; ultimate fashion and beauty guide for women. Text in English. 1993. s-a. MYR 52.80 (effective 1999). adv. illus. back issues avail. **Document type:** *Catalog, Consumer.* **Description:** Provides a fashion forecast for women in Asia, fully covering the latest seasonal offerings and featuring 2,000 styles from world's top designers.
Related titles: Online - full text ed.
Published by: Communication Management Ltd., 1811 Hong Kong Plaza, 188 Connaught Rd W, Hong Kong, Hong Kong. TEL 852-2859-4361, FAX 852-2559-1920, cmail@cmlink.com, http://www.cmlink.com/. adv.: page MYR 8,160; trim 228 x 305.

CREAM MAGAZINE. see *MUSIC*

687 USA
CUSTOM TAILORS AND DESIGNERS ASSOCIATION OF AMERICA. MAGAZINE. Text in English. bi-m. USD 50 (effective 1999). **Document type:** *Trade.*
Published by: Custom Tailors and Designers Association of America, Inc., 19 Mantua Rd., Mount Royal, NJ 08061-1006. TEL 202-387-7220. R&P Suzanne Kilgore. Circ: 1,000.

746.92 DEU
D M I COLOUR +MAN. Cover title: Tendenzfarben D I H. Text in German. s-a. **Document type:** *Journal, Trade.*
Former titles: Deutsches Institut fuer Herrenmode. Tendenzfarben; Deutsches Institut fuer Herrenmode. Tendenzfarbenkarte
Published by: (Deutsches Mode-Institut), Deutscher Fachverlag GmbH, Mainzer Landstr 251, Frankfurt Am Main, 60326, Germany. TEL 49-69-759501, FAX 49-69-75952999, info@dfv.de, http://www.dfv.de.

DAMERNAS VAERLD. see *GENERAL INTEREST PERIODICALS—Sweden*

391 646.7 PRI
DE MODA. Text in Spanish. 1995. m. USD 210.60 domestic; USD 417.56 foreign; USD 60.20 newsstand/cover domestic; USD 111.80 newsstand/cover foreign (effective 2000). adv. bk.rev. illus.; tr.lit. back issues avail. **Document type:** *Magazine, Consumer.* **Description:** Covers information on fashion and beauty trends as well as health and home decoration.
Published by: El Nuevo Dia Inc., Lot #15, Amelia Industrial Park, Guaynabo, 00968, Puerto Rico. TEL 787-641-5452, FAX 787-641-3927, pdelatorre@elnuevodia.com. Ed. Patricia de la Torre TEL 787-641-5452 ext 6702. Pub., R&P Maria Luisa Ferre. Adv. contact Aidita Gonzalez. color page USD 7,500; trim 10.25 x 12.63. Circ: 80,000 (paid). **Dist. by:** PO Box 7512, San Juan 00902-7512, Puerto Rico.

DETOUR. see *WOMEN'S INTERESTS*

746.92 DEU
DEUTSCHE MODE-INSTITUT. TENDENZFARBEN. Cover title: Tendenzfarben D M I. Text in German. s-a. **Document type:** *Trade.*
Formerly: Deutsche Mode-Institut. Tendenzfarbenkarte
Published by: (Deutsche Mode-Institut e.V.), Deutscher Fachverlag GmbH, Mainzer Landstr 251, Frankfurt Am Main, 60326, Germany. TEL 49-69-75951984, FAX 49-69-75951980, info@dfv.de, http://www.dfv.de.

668.54 GBR
DIARY. (Includes quarterly directory) Text in English. 1969. m. GBP 315 in United Kingdom; GBP 340 rest of Europe; GBP 375 elsewhere (effective 2001). adv. bk.rev. illus.; tr.lit. back issues avail. **Document type:** *Directory, Trade.*
Address: 19 Cato St, London, W1H 5HR, United Kingdom. TEL 44-20-7724-7770, FAX 44-20-7724-7357, info@diaryd.com. Ed., Pub. Gail Raymonde. Adv. contact Francesca Goulay. B&W page GBP 550, color page GBP 800. Circ: 2,000.

DIVKA. see *CHILDREN AND YOUTH—For*

746.92 790.132 USA
DOLL COSTUMING. Text in English. 2001. q. USD 24.95 domestic; USD 39.95 foreign; USD 5.95 per issue (effective 2004). adv. **Document type:** *Magazine, Consumer.*
Published by: Jones Publishing, Inc., N 7450 Aanstad Rd, PO Box 5000, Iola, WI 54945. TEL 715-445-5000, 800-331-0038, FAX 715-445-4053, jonespub@jonespublishing.com, http://www.jonespublishing.com. Ed. Stacy D Carlson. Pub. Joe Jones.

DOMINA SPOSA. see *MATRIMONY*

959.152 ITA ISSN 0393-795X
DONNA; international fashion magazine. Text in Italian. 1979. m. EUR 17.50 (effective 2004). adv. **Document type:** *Magazine, Consumer.*
Indexed: DAAI.
Published by: Hachette Rusconi SpA (Subsidiary of: Hachette Filipacchi Medias S.A.), Viale Sarca 235, Milan, MI 20126, Italy. TEL 39-02-66192629, FAX 39-02-66192469, http://www.rusconi.it. Circ: 38,725.

391 900 USA ISSN 0361-2112
GT605
➤ **DRESS.** Text in English. 1975. a. USD 60 to individuals; USD 95 to institutions; USD 350 to corporations; USD 35 to libraries (effective 2004). bk.rev. illus. back issues avail. **Document type:** *Academic/Scholarly.* **Description:** Covers all areas of study of dress, with scholarly emphasis on history and preservation.
Related titles: Online - full text ed.: (from H.W. Wilson, O C L C Online Computer Library Center, Inc.).
Indexed: ABM, AmH&L, ArtInd, BHA, DAAI, DIP, HistAb, IBR, IBZ, RILM, TTI.
—BLDSC (3623.435000). **CCC.**
Published by: Costume Society of America, 55 Edgewater Dr, PO Box 73, Earleville, MD 21919. TEL 410-275-1619, national.office@costumesocietyamerica.com, http://www.costumesocietyamerica.com. Ed. Linda Welters. R&P Kaye Boyer TEL 410-275-1619. Circ: 1,800.

➤ **DRESS, BODY, CULTURE.** see *ANTHROPOLOGY*

➤ **DUNIA.** see *WOMEN'S INTERESTS*

746.92 NLD ISSN 1383-7508
DUTCH. Text in English. bi-m. USD 58; USD 9.95 newsstand/cover (effective 2001).
Published by: Art View bv, Postbus 94300, GH Amsterdam, 1090, Netherlands. **Subscr. to:** Express Mag, PO Box 2769, Plattsburgh, NY 12901-0239. TEL 514-374-9684, 800-363-1310.

746.92 JPN
EDGE. Text in Japanese. 1983. q. JPY 3,120.
Published by: Gakken Co. Ltd., 40-5 Kami-Ikedai 4-chome, Ota-ku, Tokyo, 145-0064, Japan. Ed. Jun Usami.

746.9 ITA
EDGE (MODAIN) COLLEZIONI. Text in Italian, English. q. EUR 30.99 domestic (effective 2001). **Document type:** *Magazine.*
Published by: Liber S.R.L., Via Curtatona, 5/m, Modena, 41100, Italy. TEL 39-059-412643, FAX 39-059-412567, mcagnoni@liber.it. Ed. Antonio Vergara.

ELEGANCE. see *WOMEN'S INTERESTS*

659.152 646.7 ITA ISSN 1121-8312
ELEGANTISSIMA. Text in Italian. 1945. q. adv.
Published by: IBI s.r.l., Via Camillo Finocchiaro Aprile, 5, Milan, MI 20124, Italy.

ELLE. see *WOMEN'S INTERESTS*

746.9 USA ISSN 1556-5831
▼ **ELLE ACCESSORIES.** Text in English. 2005. a. USD 4.99 newsstand/cover (effective 2006). **Document type:** *Magazine, Consumer.*
Published by: Hachette Filipacchi Media U.S., Inc. (Subsidiary of: Hachette Filipacchi Medias S.A.), 1633 Broadway, 41st Fl, New York, NY 10019. http://www.hfmus.com.

391 ARG ISSN 1514-7355
ELLE ARGENTINA. Text in Spanish. 1994. m. USD 4.90 newsstand/cover (effective 2002). adv. **Document type:** *Magazine, Consumer.*
Related titles: Online - full text ed.
Published by: Hachette Filipacchi Agea Publicaciones, San Martin 448, Buenos Aires, Buenos Aires 1106, Argentina. TEL 54-11-4327-4224, FAX 54-11-4325-4292, mpizzolo@elle.com.ar, http://www.elle.com.ar.

ELLE CANADA. see *WOMEN'S INTERESTS*

ELLE, CHINA. see *WOMEN'S INTERESTS*

▼ **ELLE GIRL.** see *CHILDREN AND YOUTH—For*

391 ARG ISSN 1514-7363
ELLE NOVIAS. Text in Spanish. 1998. 2/yr. adv. **Document type:** *Magazine, Consumer.*
Published by: Hachette Filipacchi Agea Publicaciones, San Martin 448, Buenos Aires, Buenos Aires 1106, Argentina. TEL 54-11-4327-4224, FAX 54-11-4325-4292.

ELLE QUEBEC. see *WOMEN'S INTERESTS*

ELLEGIRL. see *CHILDREN AND YOUTH—For*

ELLEGIRL. see *CHILDREN AND YOUTH—For*

391 305.41 MEX
ERES NOVIA. Text in Spanish. 1994. m. MXP 200, USD 62; MXP 20 newsstand/cover. adv. charts; illus. back issues avail.
Document type: *Consumer.*
Published by: Editorial Televisa, Vasco de Quiroga 2000, Edif E 4o Piso, Col Santa Fe, Mexico City, DF 01210, Mexico. TEL 52-5-261-2600, FAX 52-5-261-2633, evesnovia@siedi.spin.com.mx, http://www.televisa.com.mx. Ed. Norma Rodriguez. **Dist. by:** Distribuidora Intermex, S.A. de C.V., Mexico, LUCIO BLANCO 435, Azcapotzalco, Mexico City, DF 02070, Mexico. TEL 52-5-352-6444.

646.4 641.5 MEX
ESPECIALES TEENAGER INTERNACIONAL. Text in Spanish. 3/yr. adv. **Document type:** *Consumer.* **Description:** Each issue focuses on a topic in sewing, cooking, clothing, knitting and Christmas decoration.
Published by: Consorcio Sayrols, Mier y Pesado 126, Mexico, Col del Valle, Mexico City, DF 03100, Mexico. TEL 52-5-6874699, FAX 525-523-7045, beatrizc@spin.com.mx, http://www.sayrols.com.mx. Ed. Patricia Olvera. R&P Roberto Davo TEL 52-5-5236714. Adv. contact Beatriz Coria. B&W page USD 3,370, color page USD 4,312; 275 x 210. Circ: 45,000.

EUROWOMAN. see *GENERAL INTEREST PERIODICALS—Denmark*

659.152 SVK ISSN 0139-8717
EVA. Text in Slovak. 1970. m. SKK 480 (effective 2005). adv.
Document type: *Magazine, Consumer.* **Description:** Covers fashion, hair and beauty, health, travel, leisure time.
Published by: Ringier Slovakia a. s., Prievozska 14, PO Box 46, Bratislava 24, 82004, Slovakia. TEL 421-2-58227124, FAX 421-2-58227143, eva@ringier.sk. Ed. Katarina Patvarosova. Adv. contact Jana Sokolova. B&W page SKK 70,000, color page SKK 95,000; trim 175 x 260. Circ: 90,000 (paid).

659.152 HKG
EVE ESSENTIALS. Text in English. 1993. a. SGD 10 (effective 1999). adv. **Document type:** *Directory, Consumer.*
Description: Covers fashion and beauty for Singapore's sophisticated and influential men and women.
Related titles: ♦ Supplement to: Eve.

Published by: Communication Management Ltd., 1811 Hong Kong Plaza, 188 Connaught Rd W, Hong Kong, Hong Kong. TEL 852-2859-4361, FAX 852-2559-1920, cmail@cmlink.com, http://www.cmlink.com/. adv.: color page SGD 3,000; trim 228 x 305.

▼ **F G B G**; for girls by girls. see *CHILDREN AND YOUTH—For*

646.042   DEU
F H M COLLECTIONS. (For Him Magazine) Text in German. 2002. 2/yr. EUR 5.50 newsstand/cover (effective 2005). adv. **Document type:** *Magazine, Consumer.*
Published by: Attic Futura Verlag GmbH, Martin-Greif-Str 1, Munich, 80336, Germany. TEL 49-89-51446244, FAX 49-89-51446222, info@atticfutura.de, http://www.atticfutura.de. Ed. Ronald Becker. Adv. contact Susanne Huebner. page EUR 10,000. Circ: 120,000 (paid and controlled).

646.042   GBR   ISSN 1463-3949
F H M COLLECTIONS. (For Him Magazine) Text in English. 1998. s-a. GBP 3.90 newsstand/cover. adv. **Document type:** *Magazine, Consumer.* **Description:** Provides a comprehensive guide to the latest fashions and trends in menswear.
Indexed: DAAI.
Published by: Emap Metro Ltd. (Subsidiary of: Emap Consumer Media), Mappin House, 4 Winsley St, P O Box 2930, London, W1W 8HF, United Kingdom. TEL 44-20-7436-1515, FAX 44-20-7636-5792, http://www.fhm.co.uk.

646.042   USA
F H M COLLECTIONS. (For Him Magazine) Text in English. 2001. s-a. USD 3.99 newsstand/cover; USD 4.99 newsstand/cover in Canada (effective 2001). adv. **Document type:** *Magazine, Consumer.* **Description:** Presents the latest trends and fashions in menswear.
Published by: Emap USA, 110 Fifth Ave, New York, NY 10011. TEL 212-886-3600, FAX 212-886-2824.

746.9   CAN
▼ **F Q MAGAZINE.** Abbreviated title: Fashion Quaterly. Text in English. 2003. q. free with subscription to Globe & Mail. **Document type:** *Magazine, Consumer.* **Description:** Provides up-to-the-minute, behind-the-scenes access to the hottest, hippest fashion and lifestyle trends, developments and stories from Paris & Milan to Toronto & Montreal.
Published by: Kontent Publishing Inc., 133 King St East, Toronto, ON M5C 1G6, Canada. TEL 416-367-7658, FAX 416-367-7659, mail@fqmagazine.com. Ed. Jeanne Beker. Pub. Shelagh Tarleton.

746.92   USA
FABRIC AND FASHION. Text in English. 1992. m. USD 30. adv. bk.rev. **Document type:** *Newsletter.* **Description:** For designers, manufacturers and retailers.
Address: PO Box 237, Murray Hill Sta, New York, NY 10156-0237. TEL 212-683-7886. Ed. Virginia Stiles. Adv. contact Jeanne Coogan. Circ: 2,400.

THE FADER. see *MUSIC*

746.96   LBN   ISSN 1017-7760
FAIRUZ. Text in Arabic. 1981. m. LBP 75,000 domestic; USD 150 in US & Canada; USD 125 in Europe (effective 2003). adv. 148 p./no.; **Description:** Covers women's interests.
Published by: Dar As-Sayad S.A.L., C/o Said Freiha, Hazmieh, P O Box 1038, Beirut, Lebanon. TEL 961-5-456373, FAX 961-5-452700, contactpr@csi.com, alanwar@alanwar.com, http://www.alanwar.com. Ed. Elham Freiha. Adv. contact Said Freiha. color page USD 6,800; bleed 215 x 285. Circ: 96,000.

659.152   GBR
THE FASHION. Text in English. s-a. GBP 5 newsstand/cover (effective 2001). adv. **Document type:** *Magazine, Consumer.* **Description:** Provides a forum and showplace for inspirational image-makers in the world of fashion, beauty and design.
Published by: Emap Elan Ltd. (Subsidiary of: Emap Consumer Media), Endeavour House, 189 Shaftesbury Ave, London, WC2H 8JG, United Kingdom. TEL 44-207-437-9011, FAX 44-207-208-3709, http://www.emap.com. Ed. Sarah Mower. Adv. contact Jane Stevens.

746.92   CAN
FASHION; Canada's style guide. Text in English. 1977. 9/yr. USD 9.95 (effective 2003). adv. illus. **Document type:** *Magazine, Consumer.* **Description:** Covers fashion, cosmetics, skin care, popular personalities and advise.
Former titles (until Sep. 2000): Toronto Life Fashion (0821-7955); (until 1979): Toronto Life Fashion Magazine (0705-2715)
Related titles: Online - full content ed.
Indexed: CBCARef, CBPI, RASB.
Published by: Toronto Life Publishing Co. Ltd., 59 Front St E, 3rd Fl, Toronto, ON M5E 1B3, Canada. TEL 416-364-3334, FAX 416-594-3374, editorial@fashionmagazine.com, http://www.fashionmagazine.com/. Pub. Giorgina Bigioni. Adv. contact Debra Rother. Circ: 130,437.

746.92   USA   ISSN 1091-031X
FASHION ALMANAC. Text in English. 1997. bi-m. USD 12.95 domestic; USD 30.95 in Canada; USD 42.95 elsewhere; USD 3.50 newsstand/cover domestic; CND 4.95 newsstand/cover in Canada. illus. **Document type:** *Consumer.*

Published by: Fashion Almanac Publishing, 235 Park Ave S, 11th Fl, New York, NY 10003. FAX 212-979-1214. Ed., Pub. Amedeo Angiolillo. Circ: 130,000.

659.152   USA   ISSN 0014-8660
FASHION CALENDAR. Text in English. 1941. bi-m. USD 395.19 (effective 2005). **Document type:** *Newsletter, Trade.* **Description:** Targeted to buyers, designers, manufacturers, retailers, and the media regarding national and international fashion events and collection openings.
Published by: Fashion Calendar International, 153 E 87th St, New York, NY 10128. TEL 212-289-0420, FAX 212-289-5917. Pub. Ruth Finley.

FASHION COLOR FORECAST. see *CLOTHING TRADE*

746.92   FRA   ISSN 1298-7638
FASHION DAILY NEWS. Text in French. 2000. d. EUR 122 (effective 2002). adv. **Document type:** *Newspaper, Trade.*
Published by: Editions Lariviere, Espace Clichy, 12 rue Mozart, Clichy, Cedex 92587, France. TEL 33-1-41403105, FAX 33-1-41403250, abo@editions-lariviere.fr, http://www.editions-lariviere.fr.

746.92   USA
FASHION DISH. Text in English. 1998. w.
Media: Online - full content.
Address: amo@fashiondish.com, http://www.fashiondish.com. Ed. Anne-Marie Otey.

746.92   GBR   ISSN 0264-8555
FASHION EXTRAS. Text in English. 1916. m. GBP 29 in United Kingdom; GBP 45 in Europe; GBP 59 elsewhere (effective 2000). adv. bk.rev. stat.; tr.lit. back issues avail. **Document type:** *Magazine, Trade.*
Incorporates: Leathergoods (0023-9798)
Indexed: KES.
Published by: Reflex Publishing Ltd., 177a High St, Tonbridge, Kent TN9 1BX, United Kingdom. TEL 44-1732-362445, FAX 44-1732-362447, fabuss@mwfree.net. Ed., Pub., Adv. contact Adrian Watkins. Circ: 4,280.

746.92   USA
FASHION INTERNATIONAL. Text in English. 1972. m. USD 100 (effective 2005). **Document type:** *Newsletter, Trade.* **Description:** Provides manufacturers and retailers with trends and forecasting information; evaluations of new creations, price ranges, trends in fabric and color; and special reports on current developments in the industry.
Published by: Fashion Calendar International, 153 E 87th St, New York, NY 10128. TEL 212-289-0420, FAX 212-289-5917, http://www.penrose-press.com. Ed. Deborah Brumfield. Pub. Ruth Finley.

746.92   FRA
FASHION LIVE. Text in English, French. w. illus.
Media: Online - full content.
Published by: World Media Live http://www.worldmedia.fr/fashion. Ed. Clara Young.

746.9   USA
THE FASHION MANUSCRIPT. Text in English. m. USD 49.99; USD 4 per issue (effective 2005). **Document type:** *Magazine, Trade.*
Published by: Mann Publications, 1385 Broadway, Ste 1102, New York, NY 10018. TEL 212-840-1549, FAX 212-840-1954, http://www.mannpublications.com. Pub. Jeff Mann. Circ: 100,000 (paid).

659.152   GBR
FASHION MONITOR∗. Text in English. 1954. m. GBP 498. adv. bk.rev. **Document type:** *Directory, Trade.*
Formerly: Fashion Calendar
Published by: Profile Group (UK) Ltd., 6/7 St Cross St, London, EC1N 8UA, United Kingdom. TEL 44-171-405-4455, FAX 44-171-430-1089. Ed. Sam Allen. Circ: 1,000.

659.152   AUT
FASHION NAVIGATOR. Text in English. 1996. irreg. **Document type:** *Magazine, Consumer.* **Description:** Covers all aspects of the world of fashion.
Media: Online - full text.
Published by: Sawetz Communications, Ravelinstrasse 5 a, Vienna, W 1110, Austria. TEL 43-1-76985101, FAX 43-1-76985102, office@fashion.at, http://www.fashion.at/. Ed. Karin Sawetz.

746.92   USA
FASHION NET. Text in English. 1995. w. illus.
Media: Online - full content.
Published by: Triple International Ltd. http://www.fashionnet.com.

746.92   USA   ISSN 0300-7111
FASHION NEWSLETTER; an international forecast of incoming fashion influences. Text in English. 1963. m. (11/yr.). USD 179; CND 219 in Canada; USD 219 elsewhere (effective 2000). bk.rev. 8 p./no.; **Document type:** *Newsletter, Trade.* **Description:** Contains news about international fashion trends, for designers, manufacturers, and store buyers.
Incorporates (1978-1991): Specialty Store Service Bulletin

Published by: Omniprint Inc., 9700 Philadelphia Ct, Lanham, MD 20706-4405. TEL 301-731-5202, 800-345-2611, FAX 301-731-5203, editor@omniprint.net. Ed. Alice Meyer. Pub., R&P Michael Nagan.

746.92   USA
FASHION PLANET. Text in English. m.
Media: Online - full content.
Address: digifash@interport.net, http://www.fashion-planet.com. Ed. Patricia Doran.

FASHION THEORY; journal of dress, body and culture. see *ART*

746.92   GBR
FASHION U K. Text in English. 1995. d. free. adv. **Description:** Covers the UK street fashion scene and delivers up to the minute information to style fans across the planet.
Media: Online - full text.
Published by: Wide Media Ltd., Portland House, 164 New Cavendish St, London, W1M 7FJ, United Kingdom. TEL 44-171-637-4070, FAX 44-171-637-4073, fuk@sunshyne.demon.co.uk, http://www.widemedia.com/fashionuk/. Ed. Marian Buckley. Adv. contact Griselda Billington.

746.92   USA
FASHION UPDATE. Text in English. 1987. q. USD 70 (effective 1997).
Published by: Fashion Update, Inc., 1274 49th St, 209, Brooklyn, NY 11219. TEL 718-377-8873, FAX 718-258-9091, fashionupdate@juno.com. Ed. Sarah Gardner.

746 659   USA   ISSN 1044-3568
CODEN: STSFEY
FASHION WATCH. Text in English. m. USD 299 (effective 1998). **Document type:** *Trade.*
Published by: Visual Reference Publications, Inc., 302 Fifth Ave, New York, NY 10001. TEL 212-279-7000, 800-251-4545, FAX 212-279-7014.

646.4   GBR   ISSN 0957-6630
FASHION WEEKLY. Text in English. 1910. w. GBP 60. **Document type:** *Newspaper, Trade.*
Formerly: Drapery and Fashion Weekly
Indexed: DAAI.
Published by: Emap Fashion Ltd. (Subsidiary of: Emap Business Communications Ltd.), Greater London House, Hampstead Rd, London, EC1V 7QP, United Kingdom. TEL 44-207-8740200, FAX 44-20-75201501, http://www.emap.com. Ed. Martin Raymond. Pub. Paul Keenan. adv.: B&W page GBP 1,550, color page GBP 2,170; trim 400 x 290. Circ: 8,500.

746.92   USA
FASHION WIRE DAILY. Text in English. d. USD 99 (effective 2002). adv. **Document type:** *Trade.* **Description:** Covers the latest news and trends in fashion and celebrity style.
Media: Online - full content.
Published by: Fashion Wire Daily, Inc. TEL 212-792-8282, help@fashionwiredaily.com, http://www.fashionwiredaily.com. Ed. Brandusa Niro. Adv. contact Barbi Jurman.

746.92   USA
FASHIONCLICK; the online fashion and style magazine. Text in English. 1998. m. illus.
Media: Online - full content.
Address: staff@fashionclick.com, http://www.fashionclick.com. Ed. Freddy Vicioso-Galan.

391   GBR
FASHIONINFORMATION.COM; the online fashion forecasting and trend reporting service. Text in English. 1998. d. USD 1,699 (effective 2005). illus. **Document type:** *Magazine, Trade.* **Description:** Covers the womenswear fashion industry.
Media: Online - full content. **Related titles:** Print ed.
Published by: Fashion Information Ltd., P O Box 20224, London, NW1 8FB, United Kingdom. info@fashioninformation.com, editor@fashioninformation.com, http://www.fashioninformation.com. Ed. Dawn C L Pedersen.

391   USA
FASHIONSTANCE. Text in English. 1976. m. USD 12 by e-mail. **Description:** Written by consumers for consumers all over the world, offering information on beauty and fashion.
Media: Online - full text.
Address: jelaine@fashionstance.com. Ed. J Elaine Spear.

FEMINA. see *WOMEN'S INTERESTS*

FEMINA/FEMINA MONTHLY MAGAZINE. see *WOMEN'S INTERESTS*

FEMINA. see *WOMEN'S INTERESTS*

746.96   MYS
FEMININE. Text in English. 1978. m.
Published by: Voice Publications Sdn. Bhd., 2A Jalan 19-1, Petaling Jaya, Selangor, Malaysia. Ed. Yap Choy Hong.

659.152   ESP
FEMME ELEGANTE∗. Text in Spanish. bi-m.

C

Published by: Publicaciones Mundial, Marbella, 60, Madrid, 28034, Spain. Circ: 18,000.

391 CHN
FENGLIU YIDAI. Text in Chinese. 1999. m. **Document type:** *Consumer.* **Description:** Covers the latest trend and fashion.
Contact Dist.: China International Book Trading Corp/Zhongguo Guoji Tushu Maoyi Zonggongsi, 35 Chegongzhuang Xilu, Haidian District, PO Box 399, Beijing, 100044, China. TEL 86-10-68412045, FAX 86-10-68412023, cibtc@mail.cibtc.com.cn, http://www.cibtc.com.cn.

746.9 USA ISSN 1546-0894
▼ **FIGURE**; the new shape of fashion. Text in English. 2003 (Fall). q. USD 9.50; USD 3.95 newsstand/cover (effective 2004). adv. **Document type:** *Magazine, Consumer.* **Description:** Contains articles and features on fashion and lifestyles for women of all ages and sizes.
Published by: Charming Shoppes, Inc., 450 Winks Ln, Bensalem, PA 19020. TEL 215-245-9100, FAX 215-638-6759, http://www.figuremagazine.com, http://www.charmingshoppes.com. Circ: 450,000 (paid and controlled).

746.92 NOR
FJORDS. Text in English. 2000. q. NOK 240, USD 27; USD 8.95 newsstand/cover (effective 2001).
Published by: Fjords Magazine, Toffesgt. 69D, Oslo, 0552, Norway. http://www.fjordsmagazine.com.

640 CAN ISSN 0708-4927
FLARE (TORONTO); Canada's fashion magazine. Text in English. 1964. m. CND 19.98 domestic; CND 51.52 in United States; CND 54.52 elsewhere; CND 3.50 newsstand/cover (effective 2004). adv. illus. reprints avail. **Document type:** *Magazine, Consumer.* **Description:** Features Canadian and international fashions available in Canada. Regular columns include relationships, health, celebrity and culture.
Formerly: Miss Chatelaine (0026-5918)
Related titles: Microfiche ed.: (from MML); Microform ed.: (from MML); Online - full text ed.: (from EBSCO Publishing, Micromedia ProQuest, ProQuest Information & Learning).
Indexed: CBCARef, CBPI, CPerI.
Published by: Rogers Media Publishing Ltd, One Mount Pleasant Rd, 11th Fl, Toronto, ON M4Y 2Y5, Canada. TEL 416-764-2000, editors@flare.com, http://www.flare.com, http://www.rogers.com. Ed. Suzanne Boyd. Circ: 201,000 (paid).

C

392.509 GBR ISSN 1367-6776
FOR THE BRIDE. Text in English. 1997. q. GBP 2.95 newsstand/cover. illus. **Document type:** *Consumer.*
Published by: Montrose Publishing Ltd., 12 Eton St, Richmond-upon-Thames, Surrey TW9 1EE, United Kingdom. TEL 44-1813-321644, FAX 44-1813-321755. Ed. Amanda Hinton. Pub. Colin Lenthall.

FOR THE BRIDE BY DEMETRIOS. see *MATRIMONY*

659.152 USA
FORMALWORDS. Text in English. 1987. bi-m. free to members. adv. **Document type:** *Magazine, Trade.*
Published by: International Formalwear Association, 401 N Michigan Ave, Chicago, IL 60611. TEL 312-644-6610, FAX 312-321-4098, IFA@sba.com, http://www.formalwear.org. Ed., Adv. contact Karen S Hurley. Circ: 450.

746.92 JPN
FUSION PLANNING. Text in Japanese. 1985. bi-m. JPY 10,800.
Published by: Gakken Co. Ltd., 40-5 Kami-Ikedai 4-chome, Ota-ku, Tokyo, 145-0064, Japan. Ed. Shun'ichiro Aikawa.

685 685.31 IRL ISSN 0016-3252
FUTURA. Text in English. 1965-19??; resumed. m. adv. illus.; tr.lit. index. **Document type:** *Magazine, Trade.*
Incorporates: Leather and Footwear Journal
Published by: Futura Communications Ltd., 5 Main St., Blackrock, Co. Dublin, Ireland. TEL 353-1-2836782, FAX 353-1-2836784, futura@indigo.ie. Ed. Una Brankin. Pub. Patrick Codyre. Adv. contact Avril Smith. B&W page EUR 1,570, color page EUR 1,985; trim 237 x 335. Circ: 4,000.

G Q. (Gentlemen's Quarterly) see *MEN'S INTERESTS*

G Q STYLE. (Gentlemen's Quarterly) see *MEN'S INTERESTS*

746.92 ESP
GALICIA MODA. Text in Spanish. 2/yr.
Address: Avda Gran Via, 181, Vigo, Pontevedra 36210, Spain. TEL 86-42-36-99, FAX 86-41-52-96. Ed. Luis Carballo Taboada.

GEARHEAD MAGAZINE. see *LIFESTYLE*

746.92 IND
GLAD RAGS. Text in English. 1987. bi-m. INR 900. adv. bk.rev. abstr.; charts; illus. **Document type:** *Academic/Scholarly.* **Description:** Covers latest fashion, designs, models and interviews.
Published by: IPFonline Ltd., 33 D'Silva Rd, Mylapore, Chennai, 600 004, India. TEL 91-44-4661698, FAX 91-44-4661617. Ed. Samson D'Silva. Circ: 40,000.

GLAMOUR. see *WOMEN'S INTERESTS*

640 USA ISSN 0017-0747
TT500
GLAMOUR. Text in English. 1939. m. USD 18 domestic; USD 36 in Canada; USD 45 foreign (effective 2005). adv. bk.rev. illus. reprint service avail. from PQC. **Document type:** *Magazine, Consumer.* **Description:** Provides information and how-to tips on beauty, health, fashion, and travel.
Incorporates: Charm
Related titles: Microform ed.: (from PQC); Online - full text ed.; ♦ Spanish ed.: Glamour Latinoamerica. ISSN 1556-2131.
Indexed: ASIP, ChPerI, ConsI, HlthInd, LRI, MRD, MagInd, PMR, RGAb, RGPR, TOM, WSI.
Published by: Conde Nast Publications, Inc., 750 3rd Ave, New York, NY 10017. TEL 212-286-2860, FAX 212-286-4557, letters@glamour.com, magpr@condenast.com, http://www.glamour.com. Ed. Cynthia Leive. Pub. Bill Wackermann. adv.: B&W page USD 76,240, color page USD 107,470; trim 10.88 x 8. Circ: 2,300,000 (paid). **Subscr. to:** PO Box 53716, Boulder, CO 80322. **Dist. in UK by:** Comag, Tavistock Works, Tavistock Rd, W Drayton, Middx UB7 7QX, United Kingdom.

640 GRC ISSN 1109-3501
GLAMOUR. Text in Greek. 2001. m. adv. **Document type:** *Magazine, Consumer.* **Description:** Offers expert advice for young women who have passion for life, fashion, beauty, career, love, relationships and more.
Published by: Liberis Publications S.A./Ekdoseon Lymperi A.E., Ioannou Metaxa 80, Karelas, Koropi 19400, Greece. TEL 30-210-6688000, info@glamourmag.gr, info@liberis.gr, http://www.glamourmag.gr, http://www.liberis.gr.

640 GBR
GLAMOUR. Text in English. 2001 (Mar.). m. GBP 9.99; GBP 1.50 newsstand/cover (effective 2001). adv. **Document type:** *Magazine, Consumer.* **Description:** Contains articles and features on the hottest celebrities, great fashion, and beauty secrets.
Related titles: Online - full text ed.
Published by: Conde Nast Publications Ltd., Vogue House, Hanover Sq, London, W1R 0AD, United Kingdom. TEL 44-20-74999080, FAX 44-20-74931345, feedback@glamour.com, http://www.glamourmagazine.co.uk, http://www.condenast.co.uk. Ed. Jo Elvin. Adv. contact Sallie Berkerey. Circ: 450,213 (paid).

640 DEU
GLAMOUR. Text in German. fortn. EUR 41.60; EUR 1.80 newsstand/cover (effective 2003). adv. **Document type:** *Magazine, Consumer.*
Related titles: Online - full text ed.
Published by: Conde Nast Verlag GmbH, Ainmillerstr 8, Munich, 80801, Germany. TEL 49-89-38104-0, FAX 49-89-38104230, leserservice@glamour.de, feedback@condenet.de, http://www.glamour.de, http://www.condenast.de. Adv. contact Michaela Dietz TEL 49-89-38101144. page EUR 20,650; trim 168 x 223. Circ: 544,417 (paid).

640 ESP
GLAMOUR. Text in Spanish. m. EUR 13.50; EUR 1.50 newsstand/cover (effective 2004). adv. **Document type:** *Magazine, Consumer.*
Published by: Conde Nast Espana, Claudio Coello 52 1a Planta, Madrid, 28001, Spain. TEL 34-91-4363192, FAX 34-91-4363191, contacta@condenet.es, http://www.revistaglamour.com, http://www.condenet.es.

640 RUS
▼ **GLAMOUR.** Text in Russian. 2004. m. RUR 468; RUR 40 newsstand/cover (effective 2004). adv. **Document type:** *Magazine, Consumer.*
Published by: Conde Nast Russia, Bolshaya Dmitrovka, 11, Moscow, 101999, Russian Federation. TEL 7-095-745-5565, FAX 7-095-745-5770, podpiska@glamour.ru, http://www.glamour.ru.

GRAPHIS T - SHIRT DESIGN. see *ART*

GYNAIKA/WOMAN. see *WOMEN'S INTERESTS*

687 SWE ISSN 0017-6362
HABIT; Skandinaviens modebranschtidning. Text in Swedish. 1961. 14/yr. SEK 1,302 domestic; SEK 1,623 in Scandinavia (effective 2004). adv. abstr.; charts; illus.; mkt.; stat. Supplement avail. **Document type:** *Magazine, Trade.* **Description:** Reports on the latest trends and news in the Scandinavian fashion industry.
Incorporates (1969-1991): Textil Magazine (0284-6152); Which was formerly (until 1988): Textil; (until 1987): Textilbranschen (0040-4888); (until 1958): S B M - Tidningen Textilbranschen; (until 1970): Herr- och Dammodebranschen; Which was formed by the merger of (1936-1969): Dammodebranschen (0011-5932); (1969-1969): Herrmodebranschen (0018-0882)
Published by: Mentor Online AB, Tryffelslingan 10, PO Box 72001, Lidingoe, 18172, Sweden. TEL 46-8-6704100, FAX 46-8-6616455, habit@mentoronline.se, info@mentoronline.se, http://www.mentoronline.se. Ed. Goeran Sundberg TEL 46-8-6704139. Adv. contact Gabriella Bergqvist TEL 46-8-6704157. B&W page SEK 26,500, color page SEK 34,800; 220 x 265. Circ: 5,400 (paid and controlled).

HAIRTELL. see *BEAUTY CULTURE*

646.3 535 CAN
HAKIM FASHION EYEWEAR MAGAZINE. Text in English. q. **Description:** Presents eyewear fashions, products, and technology.
Published by: Hakim Optical, 1913 Weston Rd, Toronto, ON M9N 1W7, Canada. Ed. Elizabeth Hakim.

HARPER'S BAZAAR. see *WOMEN'S INTERESTS*

640 CHN
HARPER'S BAZAAR. Text in Chinese. m. **Document type:** *Magazine, Consumer.*
Published by: Trends Communication Co. Ltd., Rm 616, Tower A, COFCO Plaza, 8 Jianguomennei Ave, Beijing, 100005, China. TEL 86-10-652288002501, FAX 86-10-652288002599, bazaar@trendsmag.com, network@trendsmag.com, http://www.trendsmag.com/trendsmag/client/magazine/bazaar.jsp.

640 USA ISSN 0017-7873
TT500
HARPER'S BAZAAR. Text in English. 1867. m. USD 3.50 newsstand/cover; USD 18 domestic; USD 28 in Canada (effective 2005). adv. illus. reprint service avail. from PQC. **Document type:** *Magazine, Consumer.* **Description:** Contains news of fashion; features by well-known authors and beauty advice.
Related titles: Microfiche ed.: (from NBI, PMC, PQC); Online - full text ed.: (from bigchalk, EBSCO Publishing, Gale Group, O C L C Online Computer Library Center, Inc., ProQuest Information & Learning).
Indexed: DAAI, HlthInd, MASUSE, MagInd, PMR, PSI, RASB, RGAb, RGPR, WSI.
Published by: Hearst Corporation, 1700 Broadway, Ste 2801, New York, NY 10019. TEL 212-903-5000, FAX 212-262-7101, 212-903-5368, bazaar@hearst.com, http://www.harpersbazaar.com/, http://www.hearstcorp.com. Ed. Glenda Bailey. Pubs. Cynthia Lewis, Kevin O'Malley. adv.: B&W page USD 57,375, color page USD 77,550; trim 8.3 x 10.88. Circ: 730,665 (paid). **Subscr. to:** PO Box 7178, Red Oak, IA 51591-0162. TEL 800-888-3045. **Dist. in UK by:** Comag, Tavistock Works, Tavistock Rd, W Drayton, Middx UB7 7QX, United Kingdom.

640 CZE ISSN 1211-5371
HARPER'S BAZAAR (PRAGUE). Text in Czech. 1996. m. CZK 1,045 (effective 2003). adv. **Document type:** *Magazine, Consumer.* **Description:** Covers the latest trends and personalities in fashion and beauty.
Published by: Stratosfera s.r.o., Drtinova 8, Prague 5, 150 00, Czech Republic. TEL 420-2-234109542, FAX 420-2-234109264, online@stratosfera.cz, http://www.stratosfera.cz. Ed. Barbara Nesvadbova. Adv. contact Hana Hofmanova. page CZK 169,000; trim 200 x 270. Circ: 50,000 (paid). **Subscr. to:** SEND Predplatne s.r.o., PO Box 141, Prague 4 140 21, Czech Republic. TEL 42-2-267211301, FAX 42-2-267211305, send@send.cz.

746.96 AUS ISSN 0814-8821
HARPER'S BAZAAR AUSTRALIA. Text in English. 1977. 10/yr. AUD 55; AUD 7.50 newsstand/cover (effective 2002). adv. **Document type:** *Magazine, Consumer.* **Description:** Contains the latest and best in fashion, beauty, culture and celebrity news.
Former titles (until 1984): Harper's Bazaar & Mode; Mode Australia (0155-4611)
Published by: A C P Publishing Pty. Ltd., 54-58 Park St, Sydney, NSW 1028, Australia. TEL 61-2-9282-8000, FAX 61-2-9267-4361, info@acp.com.au, http://www.acp.com.au. Ed. Alison Veness-McGourty. Pub. Pat Ingram. Adv. contact Sarah Nash. Circ: 51,927.

746.92 USA ISSN 0890-9598
HARPER'S BAZAAR EN ESPANOL. Text in Spanish. 1949. m. USD 18.90; USD 2.95 newsstand/cover (effective 2001). adv. illus. reprints avail. **Document type:** *Consumer.* **Description:** Discusses fashion, beauty, and lifestyle for the sophisticated and affluent Hispanic woman.
Published by: Editorial Televisa, 6355 N W 36th St, Miami, FL 33166. TEL 305-871-6400, 800-288-6677, FAX 305-871-7146, 305-871-5026, subscriptions@editorialtelevisa.com. Ed. Carols Mendez. Pub. Laura D B De Laviada. Adv. contact Enrique Perez. B&W page USD 3,750, color page USD 10,000; trim 10.81 x 8.25. Circ: 52,000.

659.152 ITA ISSN 1121-7375
HARPER'S BAZAAR ITALIA. Text in Italian. 1970. 8/yr. adv. **Document type:** *Magazine, Consumer.*

Published by: Edizioni S Y D S Italia s.r.l., Viale Stelvio, 57, Milan, MI 20159, Italy. TEL 39-2-6988, FAX 39-2-6988337. Ed. Giuseppe Della Schiava. Circ: 56,000. **Dist. by:** A I E SpA, Via Manzoni 12, Rozzano, MI 20089, Italy. TEL 39-02-5753911, FAX 39-02-57512606, http://www.aie-mag.com.

659.152 ITA ISSN 1121-7251
HARPER'S BAZAAR ITALIA UOMO; bimestrale moda uomo. Text in Italian. 1979. bi-m. adv. **Document type:** *Magazine, Consumer.*
Former titles (until 1992): Uomo Harper's Bazaar (1121-5496); (until 1984): Men's Bazaar Italia (1121-550X)
Published by: Edizioni S Y D S Italia s.r.l., Viale Stelvio, 57, Milan, MI 20159, Italy. TEL 39-2-6988, FAX 39-2-6988337. Ed. Giuseppe Della Schiava. Circ: 75,000.

746.9 ITA
HAUTE COUTURE COLLEZIONI. Text in Italian. s-a. EUR 55.78 domestic (effective 2001). **Document type:** *Magazine.*
Published by: Liber S.R.L., Via Curtatona, 5/m, Modena, 41100, Italy. TEL 39-059-412643, FAX 39-059-412567, mcagnoni@liber.it. Ed. Antonio Vergara.

HEADWEAR INSTITUTE OF AMERICA. NEWSLETTER. see *CLOTHING TRADE*

HEIMAT- UND TRACHTENBOTE. see *HISTORY—History Of Europe*

687 NOR ISSN 0804-7464
HENNE. Text in Norwegian. 1994. m. NOK 495 (effective 2000). adv. **Document type:** *Magazine, Consumer.* **Description:** Provides articles and features on fashion, beauty, health, interior design, travel and food.
Published by: Allers Familie-Journal A-S, Stenersgaten 2, Postboks 1169, Sentrum, Oslo, 0107, Norway. TEL 47-21-30-10-00, FAX 47-21-30-12-05, http://www.henne.no. Ed. Ellen Arnstad. Circ: 55,166 (paid).

746.92 JPN
HIGH FASHION. Text in Japanese. 1960. bi-m. JPY 11,820.
Published by: Bunka Publishing Bureau, 22-1 Yoyogi 3-chome, Shibuya-ku, Tokyo, 1510053, Japan. Ed. Shoko Hisada.

746.92 USA
HINT. Text in English. w. adv. **Document type:** *Magazine, Consumer.* **Description:** Features in-depth articles, fashion show coverage and original fashion spreads.
Media: Online - full content.
Published by: Hint Magazine, 134 Tenth Ave, Suite 2, New York, NY 10011. FAX 212-675-6514, leecarter@hintmag.com, http://www.hintmag.com. Ed. Lee Carter.

HONG KONG APPAREL. see *CLOTHING TRADE*

HYPE MAGAZINE. see *MUSIC*

746.92 GBR ISSN 0262-3579
I-D. Text in English. 1980. 11/yr. GBP 38 domestic; GBP 48 in Europe; GBP 64 rest of world; GBP 3.10 newsstand/cover; USD 9.99 newsstand/cover in United States (effective 2002). adv. bk.rev.; film rev. illus. back issues avail. **Document type:** *Consumer.* **Description:** Covers fashion, youth culture, music and film.
Indexed: DAAI.
—IE.
Published by: i-D Magazine, 124 Tabernacle St, London, EC2A 4SA, United Kingdom. TEL 44-20-7490-9710, FAX 44 -20-7251-2225, editor@i-dmagazine.co.uk, eloise.alemany@i-dmagazine.co.uk, http://www.i-dmagazine.co.uk/. Ed. Tony Elliott. Pubs. Terry Jones, Tony Elliott. Circ: 35,000.

I DO. see *MATRIMONY*

659.152 USA ISSN 1045-0629
I F M T MAGAZINE✶. (International Fashion Model & Talent) Text in English. 1989. m. USD 20. adv. bk.rev. index, cum.index. back issues avail. **Description:** Covers up and coming fashion designers, photographers, fashion models and entertainers.
Related titles: Microfiche ed.
Published by: Aquino Productions, P O Box 15760, Stamford, CT 06901-0760. Ed. Andres Aquino. Circ: 90,000.

746.92 USA ISSN 1043-6839
IMPRESSIONS (DALLAS); the magazine for the imprinted sportswear industry. Text in English. 1977. 15/yr. USD 69 domestic; USD 79 in Canada; USD 190 elsewhere; USD 10 newsstand/cover; free to qualified personnel (effective 2005). adv. back issues avail.; reprints avail. **Document type:** *Magazine, Trade.* **Description:** Contains news, trends, how-to information for those involved in decorating and selling imprinted sportswear.
Related titles: Online - full text ed.: (from Gale Group, ProQuest Information & Learning).
Indexed: ABIn.
—CCC.
Published by: V N U Business Publications (Subsidiary of: V N U Business Media), 1145 Sanctuary Pkwy., Ste. 355, Alpharetta, GA 30004-4772. TEL 800-241-9034, impressions@halldata.com, bmcomm@vnuinc.com, http://www.impressionsmag.com/, http:// www.vnubusinessmedia.com/. Ed. Marcia Derryberry TEL 770-291-5574. Pub., Adv. contact Chris Casey TEL 214-290-9972. B&W page USD 5,570, color page USD 7,365; trim 8.25 x 10.875. Circ: 40,940. **Subscr. to:** PO Box 1265, Skokie, IL 60076. FAX 732-380-2434.

IN UNIFORM - THE MAGAZINE. see *HOMOSEXUALITY*

391 USA
INDUSTRY (ALTAMONTE SPRINGS). Text in English. bi-m. USD 19.95 (effective 2005). **Document type:** *Magazine, Trade.* **Description:** Covers the latest fashion trends, models, and artists.
Related titles: Online - full content ed.
Address: 2500 N. Federal Hwy., Ste. 100, Ft Lauderdale, FL 33305-1618. info@industrymagazine.com, http:// www.industrymagazine.com/.

INSTYLE MAKEOVER. see *WOMEN'S INTERESTS*

746.92 USA
INTERNATIONAL ASSOCIATION OF CLOTHING DESIGNERS. BULLETIN✶. Text in English. q. **Document type:** *Newsletter, Trade.* **Description:** For designers of men's and boys' clothing.
Published by: International Association of Clothing Designers, 34 Thorton Ferry Rd, No 1, Amherst, NH 03031. TEL 603-672-4065, FAX 603-672-4064, dmschmida@aol.com.

746.92 USA
INTERNATIONAL ASSOCIATION OF CLOTHING DESIGNERS. CONVENTION YEARBOOK✶. Text in English. a. **Document type:** *Trade.* **Description:** Directed to designers of men's and boys' clothing.
Published by: International Association of Clothing Designers, 34 Thorton Ferry Rd, No 1, Amherst, NH 03031. dmschmida@aol.com.

746.92 USA
INTERNATIONAL ASSOCIATION OF CLOTHING DESIGNERS. INDUSTRY RESOURCES BOOK✶. Text in English. a. **Document type:** *Trade.* **Description:** For men's and boys' clothing designers.
Published by: International Association of Clothing Designers, 34 Thorton Ferry Rd, No 1, Amherst, NH 03031. dmschmida@aol.com.

746.92 USA
INTERNATIONAL ASSOCIATION OF CLOTHING DESIGNERS. TECHNOLOGY AND PRODUCTIVITY RESOURCES DIRECTORY✶. Text in English. a.
Published by: International Association of Clothing Designers, 34 Thorton Ferry Rd, No 1, Amherst, NH 03031. dmschmida@aol.com.

646 GBR ISSN 0952-0708
INTERNATIONAL COLOUR AUTHORITY. (Consists of: Womenswear, Menswear, and Interior Colours (Interior Textile and Carpets)) Text in English, French, German. a. (s-a). GBP 600, EUR 870 in Europe (effective 2000). charts. **Document type:** *Trade.* **Description:** Forecasts the colors in fashion over the following 21 months; includes palettes.
—CCC.
Published by: Benjamin Dent & Co. Ltd. (Subsidiary of: I T B D Publications), 23 Bloomsbury Sq, London, WC1A 2PJ, United Kingdom. TEL 44-20-7637-2211, FAX 44-20-7637-2248, itbd@itbdhquk.demon.co.uk.

646 747 GBR
INTERNATIONAL COLOUR AUTHORITY. COLOUR FORECAST FOR CARPETS. Text in English. 1994. a. GBP 210, EUR 305 in Europe (effective 2000). **Document type:** *Trade.* **Description:** Forecasts the colors for residential and commercial carpeting and provides color samples for analysis and inspiration.
Published by: Benjamin Dent & Co. Ltd. (Subsidiary of: I T B D Publications), 23 Bloomsbury Sq, London, WC1A 2PJ, United Kingdom. TEL 44-20-7637-2211, FAX 44-20-7637-2248, itbd@itbdhquk.demon.co.uk.

646 747 GBR
INTERNATIONAL COLOUR AUTHORITY. COLOUR FORECAST FOR INTERIOR TEXTILES. Text in English. 1994. a. GBP 210, EUR 205 in Europe (effective 2000). **Document type:** *Trade.* **Description:** Forecasts the colors that will be in fashion for interior textiles. Includes color samples.
Published by: Benjamin Dent & Co. Ltd. (Subsidiary of: I T B D Publications), 23 Bloomsbury Sq, London, WC1A 2PJ, United Kingdom. TEL 44-20-7637-2211, FAX 44-20-7637-2248, itbd@itbdhquk.demon.co.uk.

646 747 GBR
INTERNATIONAL COLOUR AUTHORITY. PAINTS AND DECORATIVE EFFECTS. FORECASTS FOR CONTRACT & RESIDENTIAL COLOURS (YEAR). Text in English. 1994. a. GBP 350, EUR 510 in Europe (effective 2000). **Document type:** *Trade.* **Description:** Forecasts paint colors and patterns for the coming year. Includes color palette.
Published by: Benjamin Dent & Co. Ltd. (Subsidiary of: I T B D Publications), 23 Bloomsbury Sq, London, WC1A 2PJ, United Kingdom. TEL 44-20-7637-2211, FAX 44-20-7637-2248, itbd@itbdhquk.demon.co.uk.

746.92 USA
INTERNATIONAL DESIGNER✶. Text in English. q. **Document type:** *Trade.*
Published by: International Association of Clothing Designers, 34 Thorton Ferry Rd, No 1, Amherst, NH 03031. TEL 603-672-4065, FAX 603-672-4064, dmschmida@aol.com.

746.92071 USA ISSN 1081-6879
INTERNATIONAL DIRECTORY OF MODEL - TALENT AGENCIES AND SCHOOLS (YEAR). Text in English. 1970. a. USD 29.95 (effective 1999). adv. **Document type:** *Directory.* **Description:** Lists agencies and schools around the world. Includes related service companies.
Former titles (until 1986): Directory of Talent and Modeling Agencies and Schools International (0742-5570); (until 1984): Directory of Modeling - Talent Agencies and Schools International (0730-9953); (until 1982): Models Mart Directory of Model Agencies, Talent Agencies and Modeling Schools (0272-8206)
Published by: Peter Glenn Publications, Inc., 824 E. Atlantic Ave., Ste. 7, Delray Beach, FL 33483-5300. TEL 888-332-6700, info@pgdirect.com, http://www.pgdirect.com/. Ed. Lauren Gilmore. Pub. Gregory James. Adv. contact Tricia Mazzilli-Blount. Circ: 15,000.

646.3 USA
INTERNATIONAL FASHION GROUP. ANNUAL REPORT. Text in English. a. for members only. **Description:** Directed to women executives in the fashion industry.
Published by: Fashion Group International, Inc., 597 Fifth Ave, 8th Fl, New York, NY 10017-1020. TEL 212-593-1715, FAX 212-593-1925, http://www.fgi.org.

646.3 USA
INTERNATIONAL FASHION GROUP. BULLETIN. Text in English. q. for members only. **Description:** For women executives in fashion and related industries.
Published by: Fashion Group International, Inc., 597 Fifth Ave, 8th Fl, New York, NY 10017-1020. TEL 212-593-1715, FAX 212-593-1925, http://www.fgi.org.

646.3 USA
INTERNATIONAL FASHION GROUP. NEWSLETTER. Text in English. 10/yr. for members only. **Document type:** *Newsletter.* **Description:** For women executives in fashion and related industries.
Published by: Fashion Group International, Inc., 597 Fifth Ave, 8th Fl, New York, NY 10017-1020. TEL 212-593-1715, FAX 212-593-1925, http://www.fgi.org.

746.92 NLD ISSN 1573-5281
INTERNATIONAL JEANS CULT; street corner bulletin. Text in Dutch. 1990. 8/yr. EUR 45; EUR 5 newsstand/cover (effective 2004). adv. bk.rev. illus. **Document type:** *Trade.* **Description:** News and information for the casual clothing trade in the Netherlands and Belgium.
Published by: Uitgeverij Product Promotion bv, Achterwetering 3C, Schoonhoven, 2871 RK, Netherlands. TEL 31-182-329444, FAX 31-182-329455, info@jeanscult.nl, http://www.jeanscult.nl. Ed. Michelle van Kampen TEL 31-182-329477. Pub., Adv. contact Rien Hartelust TEL 31-182-329466. Circ: 5,000. **Subscr. to:** Postbus 233, Schoonhoven 2870 AE, Netherlands.

INTERNATIONAL TEXTILES; information and inspiration. see *TEXTILE INDUSTRIES AND FABRICS*

687.2 ESP
INTIMA. Text in Spanish. 1969. 3/yr. USD 100. **Document type:** *Trade.* **Description:** Specializes in corsetry, lingerie and swimwear designing.
Formerly: Catalogo Moda Intima Femenina (1136-3622)
Published by: Ediciones Esfer, Consejo de Ciento, 383, 5 1, Barcelona, 08009, Spain. TEL 34-3-4881820, FAX 34-3-2150039, http://www.ed.es/buscapress/modaintima. Ed. Esteban Ferrer. Adv. contact Eduardo Ferrer. Circ: 4,000.

746.92 ITA ISSN 1127-0497
INTIMO PIU MARE. Text in English, Italian. 1983. 5/yr. (plus 4 extra issues). adv. **Document type:** *Magazine, Trade.* **Description:** Covers intimate apparel and swimwear.
Published by: Editoriale Moda Srl, Via Giardini 476, Modena, MO 41100, Italy. TEL 39-059-342001, FAX 39-059-351290. Ed. Ettore Zanfi. Circ: 20,000.

IPROPAGANDA. see *MUSIC*

ISSUE (NEW YORK). see *ART*

C

▼ new title ➤ refereed ✶ unverified ♦ full entry avail.

659.152   FRA   ISSN 1281-0282
JALOUSE. Text in French. 1997. 10/yr. adv. Document type:
Magazine, Consumer.
Published by: Les Editions Jalou, 10 rue du Platre, Paris, 75004,
France. info@officielnews.com, http://www.officielnews.com.
Ed. Alexandra Senes. Pub. Laurent Jalou.

▼ JASMINE. see ETHNIC INTERESTS

659.152   MYS   ISSN 0126-6594
AP95.M24
JELITA. Text in Malay. 1973. m.
Published by: Berita Publishing, No. 16-20 Jalan 4/109E, Desa
Business Park, Taman Desa, Kuala Lumpur, 58100, Malaysia.
TEL 60-3-7620 8111, FAX 60-3-7620 8026. Ed. Rohani
Pa'Wan Chik. Circ: 65,000.

746.92   SAU
AL-JOHRAH FASHION. Text in Arabic. q. USD 12 per issue.
Description: Information on hand embroidered wedding
dresses, hand embroidered party dresses, evening dresses,
maternity dresses and children's dresses.
Published by: Johrah Fashion, P O Box 755, Jeddah, 21421,
Saudi Arabia. TEL 643-9911, FAX 643-1293, TELEX
601-863-KINDI-SJ.

746.92   SAU
JOHRATH AL-ARAIES. Text in Arabic. s-a. USD 15 per issue.
Description: Focuses on hand embroidered wedding dresses.
Published by: Al-Johrah Fashion, P O Box 755, Jeddah, 21421,
Saudi Arabia. TEL 6439911, FAX 643-1293.

746.92   SAU
JOHRATH AL-KHALIG. Text in Arabic. q. USD 10 per issue.
Description: Information on hand embroidered wedding
dresses, hand embroidered party dresses, evening dresses,
maternity dresses and children's dresses.
Published by: Al-Johrah Fashion, P O Box 755, Jeddah, 21421,
Saudi Arabia. TEL 6439911, FAX 643-1293, TELEX 601863
KINDI SJ.

JOURNAL OF FASHION MARKETING AND MANAGEMENT. see
BUSINESS AND ECONOMICS—Marketing And Purchasing

646.4   AUT
JUNIORS. Text in German. 2/yr. adv. Document type: Magazine,
Trade.
Published by: Manstein Zeitschriften Verlagsgesellschaft mbH,
Brunner Feldstr 45, Perchtoldsdorf, N 2380, Austria. TEL
43-1-866480, FAX http://www.manstein.at, 43-1-86648100,
office@manstein.at. Ed. Brigitte Medlin. Adv. contact Herta
Hoffmann. B&W page EUR 5,800, color page EUR 7,785; trim
280 x 395. Circ: 10,000 (controlled).

746.9   GBR
KEY NOTE MARKET ASSESSMENT. PLUS-SIZE FASHION. Text
in English. 2001. irreg., latest 2001, Sept. GBP 730 per issue
(effective 2002). Description: Provides an in-depth strategic
analysis across a broad range of industries and contains an
examination on the scope, dynamics and shape of key UK
markets in the consumer, financial, lifestyle and business to
business sectors.
Published by: Key Note Ltd., Field House, 72 Oldfield Rd,
Hampton, Mddx TW12 2HQ, United Kingdom. TEL
44-20-8481-8750, FAX 44-20-8783-0049, info@keynote.co.uk,
http://www.keynote.co.uk. Ed. Simon Taylor.

746.9   GBR
KEY NOTE MARKET REPORT: WOMEN'S FASHIONS. Variant
title: Women's Fashions. Text in English. irreg., latest vol.6,
1991. GBP 265 (effective 1999). Document type: Trade.
Published by: Key Note Ltd., Field House, 72 Oldfield Rd,
Hampton, Mddx TW12 2HQ, United Kingdom. TEL
44-20-8481-8750, FAX 44-20-8783-0049, info@keynote.co.uk,
http://www.keynote.co.uk.

746.9 028.5   DEU   ISSN 1614-0206
KIDS WEAR. Text in English. s-a.
Published by: Kids Wear Verlag, Lichtstrasse 26, Koln, D-50825,
Germany. http://www.kidswear-magazine.com.

659.152   ITA
KING. Text in Italian. m. adv. Document type: Magazine,
Consumer.
Published by: E R I Edizioni R A I (Subsidiary of: R A I -
Radiotelevisione Italiana), Via Verdi 16, Turin, TO 10121, Italy.
http://www.eri.rai.it.

746.92   BEL   ISSN 0926-759X
KNIP MODE. Text in Dutch. 1969. m. EUR 39.15 (effective 2003).
adv. illus. Document type: Magazine, Consumer.
Description: Offers sewing patterns for clothes for the entire
family.
Incorporates (1948-1993): Marion (0025-3383); Formerly (until
1991): Knip (0023-2289)
Published by: Sanoma Magazines Belgium, Telecomlaan 5-7,
Diegem, 1831, Belgium. TEL 32-2-7762211, FAX
32-2-776-2317, http://www.knipmode.nl, http://www.sanoma-
magazines.be/HomePage.aspx?flash=1&Language=nl. Circ:
248,600 (paid).

746.92   BEL   ISSN 1385-6006
KNIPPIE IDEE. Text in Dutch. 1997. q. EUR 15.75 (effective
2003). adv. illus. back issues avail. Document type:
Magazine, Consumer. Description: Fashion patterns and
ideas for children's clothing.
Formed by the merger of (1977-1997): Knippie (0921-2744);
(1993-1997): Kindermode (1383-8296)
Published by: Sanoma Magazines Belgium, Telecomlaan 5-7,
Diegem, 1831, Belgium. TEL 32-2-7762211, FAX
32-2-776-2317, http://www.knippie.nl. http://www.sanoma-
magazines.be/homepage.aspx?. Circ: 111,960 (paid).

746.92   BEL   ISSN 1382-9246
KNIPPIE BABY. Text in Dutch. 1991. s-a. EUR 7.88 (effective
2003). adv. illus. Document type: Magazine, Consumer.
Description: Patterns and ideas for children's fashions, toys
and decorations.
Formerly: Baby en Peuter (0927-1368)
Published by: Sanoma Magazines Belgium, Telecomlaan 5-7,
Diegem, 1831, Belgium. TEL 32-2-7762211, FAX
32-2-776-2317, http://www.knipmode.nl, http://www.sanoma-
magazines.be/homepage.aspx?. Circ: 120,000 (paid).

746.9   CAN
KNITTY. Text in English. q. Document type: Magazine, Trade.
Media: Online - full text.
Published by: Knitty Magazine, 2255b Queen St East, P O Box
527, Toronto, ON M4E 1G3, Canada. http://www.knitty.com,
Ed., Pub. Amy R Singer.

THE KNOT WEDDING PAGES CENTRAL FLORIDA. see
MATRIMONY

THE KNOT WEDDING PAGES COLORADO. see MATRIMONY

THE KNOT WEDDING PAGES CONNECTICUT. see
MATRIMONY

THE KNOT WEDDING PAGES DALLAS FORT WORTH. see
MATRIMONY

THE KNOT WEDDING PAGES GEORGIA. see MATRIMONY

THE KNOT WEDDING PAGES KANSAS CITY. see MATRIMONY

THE KNOT WEDDING PAGES NEW JERSEY. see MATRIMONY

THE KNOT WEDDING PAGES PHILADELPHIA. see
MATRIMONY

THE KNOT WEDDING PAGES SOUTH FLORIDA. see
MATRIMONY

THE KNOT WEDDING PAGES WEST COAST FLORIDA. see
MATRIMONY

THE KNOT WEDDINGS MAGAZINE. see MATRIMONY

▼ LAB MAGAZINE. see ART

391 646   BGR
LADA. Text in Bulgarian. 1959. m. BGL 12, USD 12. illus.
Related titles: German ed.; Russian ed.
Published by: Ministerstvo na Vutreshnita Turgoviia i Uslugite,
Sofia, Bulgaria. Ed. N Gancheva. Circ: 31,000. Dist. by:
Hemus, 6 Rouski Blvd., Sofia 1000, Bulgaria.

LEDERWAREN-REPORT. see LEATHER AND FUR INDUSTRIES

687.12   DEU   ISSN 0344-5224
DIE LINIE (COLOGNE). Text in German. 1950. q. adv. bk.rev.
Document type: Trade.
Published by: Rudolf Heber Verlag GmbH, Stadtwaldguertel 46,
Cologne, 50931, Germany. TEL 49-221-940533-0, FAX
49-221-94053316, TELEX 8882249. Ed. Robert Loy. Adv.
contact Marlis Seger. Circ: 5,000.

THE LITTLE BLACK BOOK. see BUSINESS AND
ECONOMICS—Trade And Industrial Directories

LOADED FASHION. see LEISURE AND RECREATION

646.3   ARG   ISSN 0328-428X
LOOK. Text in Spanish. 1991. m. adv. Document type:
Magazine, Consumer.
Published by: Editorial Perfil S.A., Chacabuco 271, Buenos Aires,
Buenos Aires 1069, Argentina. TEL 54-11-4341-9000, FAX
54-11-4341-9090, look@primavera.com.ar,
correo@perfil.com.ar, http://www.perfil.com.ar. Ed. Teresa
Napolillo. Circ: 31,000 (paid).

746.9 646.72   CAN
THE LOOK. Text in English. 2002. s-a. Document type:
Magazine, Consumer.
Published by: Multi-Vision Publishing, Inc., 655 Bay St, Ste 1100,
Toronto, ON M5G 2K4, Canada. Ed. David Livingstone. Circ:
300,000.

746.92   USA
THE LOOK ONLINE. Text in English. irreg. USD 108 (effective
1999). bk.rev.
Media: Online - full text.
Published by: Look Online, Inc., 529 E 85th St, New York, NY
10028. TEL 212-734-9747, look@lookonline.com,
http://www.lookonline.com/.

746.92 646.7   GBR
LUMIERE. Text in English. 1995. d. free. Description:
International online fashion and style magazine.
Media: Online - full text.
Published by: Triple International, 72 New Bond St, London,
W1Y 9DD, United Kingdom. TEL 800-889-7665,
info@lumiere.com, http://www.lumiere.com. Pub. Stig Harder.

MAANEDSMAGASINET IN. see WOMEN'S INTERESTS

MADAME. see WOMEN'S INTERESTS

MADAME FIGARO. see WOMEN'S INTERESTS

MAG. see CHILDREN AND YOUTH—For

746.92   POL   ISSN 0947-4609
MALE KOBIETKI. Text in Polish. 1995. s-a. PLZ 8.90 per issue
(effective 2004). Document type: Magazine, Consumer.
Published by: Wydawnictwo Burda Polska Sp. z.o.o., ul
Strzegomska 236a, Wroclaw, 54432, Poland. TEL
48-71-3737280, FAX 48-71-3511788, prenumerata@burda.pl,
http://www.burda.pl.

646 746 641.5   BRA   ISSN 0025-2077
MANEQUIM. Text in Portuguese. 1959. m. BRL 94.80 domestic;
USD 84.93 foreign (effective 2005). adv. charts; illus. back
issues avail. Document type: Magazine, Consumer.
Description: Covers fashion, including new styles from major
designers, styles for everyday and evening wear, beauty,
cooking, crocheting, crafts and sewing.
Related titles: Online - full text ed.; Supplement(s): Moldes
Manequim; Atelie Manequim.
Published by: Editora Abril, S.A., Av. das Nacoes Unidas, 7221,
11 andar Pinheiros, Sao Paulo, SP 05425-902, Brazil. TEL
55-11-50872112, FAX 55-11-50872100,
manequim.abril@atelitor.com.br, http://manequim.abril.com.br/,
http://www.abril.com.br/. Ed. Anna Maria Lughetti. adv.: page
BRL 39,000. Circ: 298,600. Subscr. to: Rua do Curtume, Rua
do Curtume, 769, Sao Paulo, SP 0506-900, Brazil. TEL
55-11-823-9100.

646   BRA   ISSN 1415-8582
MANEQUIM. FACA E VENDA. Text in Portuguese. 1998. m. USD
135 (effective 2001). adv. Document type: Magazine,
Consumer.
Published by: Editora Abril, S.A., Av. das Nacoes Unidas, 7221,
11 andar Pinheiros, Sao Paulo, SP 05425-902, Brazil. TEL
55-011-30372000, FAX 55-011-30375638,
relacoes.corporativas@abril.com.br, http://www.abril.com.br/.

646   NLD   ISSN 0168-7883
MANNENMODE. Text in Dutch. 1963. 4/yr. EUR 39.95; EUR
11.28 newsstand/cover (effective 2005). adv. bk.rev. illus.; tr.lit.
Document type: Magazine, Trade.
Former titles (until 1984): Spectrum der Herenmode (0038-7096);
Spectrum Mannenmode
Published by: Blauw Media Uitgeverij B.V., Postbus 1043,
Maarssen, 3600 BA, Netherlands. TEL 31-346-574040, FAX
31-346-576056, mannenmode@blauwmedia.demon.nl,
bmu@blauwmedia.demon.nl, http://www.blauwmedia.demon.nl.
Circ: 2,400.

MARIAGES. see MATRIMONY

640 305.4   FRA   ISSN 0025-3049
MARIE CLAIRE. Text in French. 1937. m. EUR 25; EUR 4.94
newsstand/cover (effective 2005). illus. back issues avail.
Document type: Magazine, Consumer.
Indexed: DAAI.
Published by: Groupe Marie Claire, 10 Boulevard des Freres
Voisins, Issy-les-Moulineaux, 92792 Cedex 9, France. TEL
33-1-41468888, FAX 33-1-41468686, http://
www.marieclaire50ans.fr/, http://www.groupemarieclaire.com.
Ed. Tina Kieffer. Pub. Monique Majerowicz. R&P Christine
Lecomte. Adv. contact Veronique Depery Savarit. Circ:
500,000 (paid).

MARIE CLARIE EN ESPANOL. see WOMEN'S INTERESTS

746.92   DEU   ISSN 0938-8737
MAX. Text in German. 1991. m. EUR 24; EUR 2 newsstand/cover
(effective 2003). adv. Document type: Magazine, Consumer.
Published by: Verlagsgruppe Milchstrasse, Mittelweg 177,
Hamburg, 22786, Germany. TEL 49-40-41311310, FAX
49-40-41312015, service@max.de, abo@milchstrasse.de,
http://www.max.de, http://www.milchstrasse.de. Ed. Uwe
Killing. Pub. Dirk Manthey. Adv. contact Alexandra Garz TEL
49-40-41311222. page EUR 14,000. Circ: 257,736 (paid).
Subscr. to: Neue Verlagsgesellschaft mbH, Am Ziegelplatz
15, Schutterwald 77746, Germany. TEL 49-781-846119, FAX
49-781-846916.

MAXIM. see *MEN'S INTERESTS*

746.92 305.31 USA
MAXIM FASHION. Text in English. 2001. s-a. adv. **Document type:** *Magazine, Consumer.*
Published by: Dennis Publishing, Inc., 1040 Ave of the Americas, 23rd Fl, New York, NY 10018. TEL 212-302-2626, FAX 212-302-2635, http://www.maximonline.com. Ed. Greg Williams. adv.: B&W page USD 14,000, color page USD 20,000.

746.92 DEU
▼ **MAXIM FASHION.** Text in German. 2003 (Mar.). irreg. EUR 5 newsstand/cover (effective 2003). adv. **Document type:** *Magazine, Consumer.* **Description:** Provides a style guide for men interested in fashion, shopping, and other lifestyle trends.
Published by: Axel Springer Verlag AG, Axel-Springer-Platz 1, Hamburg, 20350, Germany. TEL 49-40-34700, FAX 49-40-34725540, http://www.asv.de. Adv. contact Michael Linke. color page EUR 7,000; trim 230 x 275. Circ: 100,000 (paid and controlled).

746.92 GBR ISSN 1474-5755
MAXIM FASHION. Text in English. 2001. 2/yr. adv. **Document type:** *Magazine, Consumer.*
Published by: Dennis Publishing Ltd., 30 Cleveland St, London, W1P 5FF, United Kingdom. TEL 44-20-79076000, FAX 44-20-79076020, http://www.dennis.co.uk/.

MCSISTER. see *CHILDREN AND YOUTH—For*

659.152 HKG
MENMODE. Text in Chinese, English. 1991. s-a. HKD 160. adv. illus. **Document type:** *Consumer.* **Description:** Presents the international men's fashion collections: Spring-Summer and Autumn-Winter.
Published by: Communication Management Ltd., 1811 Hong Kong Plaza, 188 Connaught Rd W, Hong Kong, Hong Kong. FAX 852-2858-2671. Ed. Sharie Ross. Pub., R&P Lina Ross. Adv. contact Winnie Cheng. color page HKD 34,510; 273 x 200. Circ: 35,000.

746.92 790.13 JPN
MEN'S CLUB. Text in Japanese. 1954. m. JPY 630 newsstand/cover (effective 2002). adv. **Document type:** *Magazine, Consumer.* **Description:** Focuses on lifestyle and fashion trends for young men.
Published by: Hachette Fujingaho Co. Ltd. (Subsidiary of: Hachette Filipacchi Medias S.A.), 2-9-1 Nishi Shinbashi, Minato-ku, Tokyo, 105-0003, Japan. TEL 81-3-3506-6601, FAX 81-3-3506-6606, http://www.hfm.co.jp. Circ: 142,000 (paid).

MEN'S CLUB DORSO. see *MEN'S INTERESTS*

746.92 DEU ISSN 1439-7080
MEN'S FASHION INTERNATIONAL. Text in English, German. 1983. 2/yr. EUR 14.50 newsstand/cover (effective 2003). adv. **Document type:** *Magazine, Trade.*
Former titles (until 1999): Men's Fashion (0936-1863); (until 1988): German Men's Fashion (0178-2673)
Published by: Deutscher Fachverlag GmbH, Mainzer Landstr 251, Frankfurt Am Main, 60326, Germany. TEL 49-69-759501, FAX 49-69-75952999, mensfashion.pap@dfv.de, info@dfv.de, http://www.TWnetwork.de, http://www.dfv.de. Ed., Adv. contact Peter Alex Pohl. B&W page EUR 4,300, color page EUR 6,400; trim 208 x 300. Circ: 10,000.

746.9 DEU
MEN'S HEALTH BEST FASHION. Text in German. 2000. 2/yr. EUR 4.50 newsstand/cover (effective 2004). adv. **Document type:** *Magazine, Consumer.*
Related titles: ♦ Supplement to: Men's Health. ISSN 1432-3818.
Published by: Rodale Motor Presse GmbH und Co. KG, Leuschnerstr 1, Stuttgart, 70174, Germany. TEL 49-711-18201, FAX 49-711-1822550, abo@menshealth.de, http://www.menshealth.de/bestfashion. adv.: page EUR 7,600. Circ: 47,113 (paid).

▼ MEN'S VOGUE. see *MEN'S INTERESTS*

MENSTYLE. see *MEN'S INTERESTS*

746.92 MEX
MEXICO VOGUE. Text in Spanish. m.
Published by: Carta Editorial de Mexico, Av. Morelos 16, Planta Baja, Mexico City 1, DF, Mexico.

646 CHE ISSN 0026-1866
MEYERS MODEBLATT. Text in German. 1924. w. CHF 105.80. adv. bk.rev.; film rev. illus. **Document type:** *Magazine, Consumer.*
Published by: Verlag Meyer & Co., Klausstr 33, Zuerich, 8008, Switzerland. TEL 41-1-3868686, FAX 41-1-3868777, http://www.modeblatt.ch. Circ: 209,358.

646.4 ITA ISSN 1121-1741
MIA BOUTIQUE; idee da cucire. Text in Italian. 1986. m. adv. back issues avail. **Document type:** *Magazine, Consumer.*
Published by: Fabbri Editori (Subsidiary of: R C S Libri), Via Mecenate 87-6, Milan, MI 20138, Italy. TEL 39-02-580801, FAX 39-02-5062865. Ed. Bice Invernizzi. Circ: 111,097.

746.92025 USA
MIAMI MODEL AGENCY DIRECTORY. Text in English. 1998. a. USD 11.95 (effective 2003). adv. **Document type:** *Directory.* **Description:** Presents a breakdown of the Miami Model Agencies with names, addresses, telephone numbers, physical requirements,interview policies, type of modelling done and speciality types looked for. Designed for aspiring models.
Published by: Peter Glenn Publications, Inc., 824 E. Atlantic Ave., Ste. 7, Delray Beach, FL 33483-5300. TEL 888-332-6700, info@pgdirect.com, http://www.pgdirect.com/. Pub. Gregory James. Adv. contact Tricia Mazzilli-Blount. B&W page USD 900; trim 9 x 4. Circ: 3,000.

MILE-HIGH WEDDINGS. see *MATRIMONY*

746.92 GBR
MINED. Text in English. 2001 (Aug.). s-a. USD 45 newsstand/cover (effective 2001). **Document type:** *Magazine, Consumer.*
Published by: Tank Publications Ltd., 58 Frith St, London, W1V 5TA, United Kingdom.

MINI. see *WOMEN'S INTERESTS*

746.96 RUS ISSN 1684-3916
MINI. Text in Russian. 2002. m. RUR 660 domestic; RUR 55 newsstand/cover domestic (effective 2004). adv. **Document type:** *Magazine, Consumer.*
Published by: Izdatel'skii Dom Burda, ul Pravdy 8, Moscow, 125040, Russian Federation. TEL 7-095-7979849, FAX 7-095-2571196, mini-magazine@burda.ru, vertrieb@burda.ru, http://www.burda.ru. adv.: page USD 6,500. Circ: 250,000 (paid and controlled).

MIXART NEWS. see *BEAUTY CULTURE*

659.152 ITA
MODA. Text in Italian. m.
Published by: E R I Edizioni R A I (Subsidiary of: R A I - Radiotelevisione Italiana), Via Verdi 16, Turin, TO 10121, Italy. http://www.eri.rai.it.

659.152 PRT
MODA E MODA. Text in Portuguese. 5/yr.
Address: Rua Braamcamp, 12, r-c Dto., Lisbon, 1200, Portugal. TEL 01-562426. Ed. Marionela Gusmao. Circ: 20,000.

746.92 ESP ISSN 1133-6463
MODA EN LAS CALLES. Text in Spanish. 2/yr.
Published by: M E P S A, Abtao, 11 2o C, Madrid, 28007, Spain. TEL 1-551-91-97, FAX 1-552-73-43. Ed. A Ferrer Rosello.

MODA MOLDES. see *NEEDLEWORK*

746.9 646.7 POL ISSN 1230-042X
MODA TOP. Text in Polish. 1992. q. PLZ 28 (effective 1999). adv. **Document type:** *Consumer.* **Description:** Contains a presentation of the newest ideas from top fashion designers, advice on creating a personal style, interviews with top models, beauty secrets, focusing on the art of makeup and personal care, descriptions of the newest interior designs.
Published by: Warsaw Voice S.A., Ksiecia Janusza 65, Warsaw, 01452, Poland. TEL 48-22-366377, FAX 48-22-371995, voice@warsawvoice.com.pl, http://www.warsawvoice.com.pl. Ed. Jadwiga Komorowska. Adv. contact Joanna Staniszewska. page PLZ 9,900.

746.92 ITA
MODAMARKETING. Text in Italian. 1977. m. (10/yr.). EUR 50 (effective 2005). adv. **Document type:** *Newsletter, Trade.* **Description:** Four international issues are mainly photographic, the other 6 supply economic and marketing news and information.
Formerly (until 1994): Panorama Moda Abbigliamento
Published by: (Federazione Nazionale Dettaglianti T.A.), Life Edizioni, Via Stazione 2, Baveno, VB 28831, Italy. TEL 39-0323-924644, FAX 39-0323-925197, http://www.lifed.it. Circ: 20,000.

687.19 ITA ISSN 1126-2680
MODAPELLE BAG & LEATHER GARMENTS. Text in Italian, English. 1985. 2/yr., latest vol.16, 2001. USD 113 foreign; USD 63 per issue (effective 2001). adv. illus.; tr.lit. back issues avail. **Document type:** *Magazine.* **Description:** Exclusively intended for leather goods, luggage and leather garment shops, boutiques and international department stores at the highest level.
Supersedes in part (in 1993): Modapelle
Published by: Muggiani Giampiero Editore srl, Via IV Novembre, 54, Settimo Milanese, MI 20019, Italy. TEL 39-02-335531, FAX 39-02-33501391, info@modapelle.com, http://www.modapelle.com. adv.: color page USD 2,350; bleed 215 x 285.

687.19 ITA ISSN 1126-2699
MODAPELLE SHOES. Text in Italian, English. 1985. q. USD 232; USD 63 per issue (effective 2001). adv. illus.; tr.lit. back issues avail. **Document type:** *Magazine, Trade.* **Description:** Moda Pelle Magazine intends to be a careful and opportune beacon for all purchasers. Each season it presents the best shoe collections.
Supersedes in part (in 1993): Modapelle
Published by: Muggiani Giampiero Editore srl, Via IV Novembre, 54, Settimo Milanese, MI 20019, Italy. TEL 39-02-335531, FAX 39-02-33501391, info@modapelle.com, http://www.modapelle.com. Ed. Silvana Gallo. adv.: color page USD 2,350; bleed 215 x 285. Circ: 60,000.

687 ITA
MODAPELLE STYLING. Text in Italian, English. 1985. 2/yr. USD 160; USD 87 per issue (effective 2001). adv. illus.; tr.lit. back issues avail. **Document type:** *Magazine.* **Description:** Latest trends in the clothing fashion, which is a base of reference for shoe manufacturers. News of meetings and points of view of the opinion leaders in the footwear industry as related to styling and production.
Supersedes in part (in 1993): Modapelle
Published by: Muggiani Giampiero Editore srl, Via IV Novembre, 54, Settimo Milanese, MI 20019, Italy. TEL 39-02-335531, FAX 39-02-33501391, info@modapelle.com, http://www.modapelle.com. adv.: color page USD 2,350; bleed 215 x 285.

MODE CUIR. see *LEATHER AND FUR INDUSTRIES*

MODEL CALL. see *OCCUPATIONS AND CAREERS*

659.152 RUS ISSN 0132-0793
MODELI SEZONA. Text in Russian. 1957. q. RUR 20. **Document type:** *Catalog.* **Description:** Covers modern fashion styles for different ages and sizes, fashion trends; provides knitting instructions and patterns.
Related titles: ♦ Supplement to: Zhurnal Mod. ISSN 0321-1576. —East View.
Published by: Joint-stock Company Fashion Journal, ul Nizhniaia Krasnosel'skaia, 40/12, build 7, Moscow, 105066, Russian Federation. TEL 7-095-9217393, FAX 7-095-9287793. Ed. N A Kasatkina. Circ: 50,000. **US dist. addr.:** East View Information Services, 3020 Harbor Ln. N., Minneapolis, MN 55447. TEL 612-550-0961.

C

659.152 ITA ISSN 1121-8290
MODELLINA. Text in Italian. 1946. q. adv.
Published by: IBI s.r.l., Via Camillo Finocchiaro Aprile, 5, Milan, MI 20124, Italy. Ed. Silvana Mattei.

640 FRA ISSN 0026-8739
MODES ET TRAVAUX. Text in French. 1919. m. EUR 2 per issue (effective 2005). illus. **Document type:** *Magazine, Consumer.*
Published by: Emap France (Subsidiary of: Emap Media Ltd.), 150-152 Rue Gallieni, Boulogne, 92644, France. TEL 33-1-41334961, FAX 33-1-41335010, info@emapfrance.com, http://www.emapmedia.com. Circ: 489,239 (paid).

MODIN. see *TEXTILE INDUSTRIES AND FABRICS*

391 SVN ISSN 1318-4636
MODNA JANA. Text in Slovenian. 1994. 2/yr. SIT 7,920 (effective 2002). adv. **Document type:** *Magazine, Consumer.*
Published by: Delo Revije d.o.o., Dunajska 5, Ljubljana, 1509, Slovenia. TEL 386-1-4737000, FAX 386-1-4737352, narocnine@delo-revije.si, http://www.delo-revije.si/slo/modna_jana/index.htm.

MODUS. see *HOME ECONOMICS*

746.9 RUS
MOLODAYA I PRIVLEKATEL'NAYA. Text in Russian. m. USD 139.95 in United States.
Published by: Post-Shop, Olimpiiskii pr-t 22, Moscow, 129090, Russian Federation. TEL 7-095-3627002, FAX 7-095-9590987. Ed. N A Buduleva. **US dist. addr.:** East View Information Services, 3020 Harbor Ln. N., Minneapolis, MN 55447. TEL 612-550-0961.

746.92 CAN
N MAGAZINE; where fashion meets technology. Text in English. 1998. 3/yr. CND 8.62; CND 3.50 newsstand/cover (effective 1998). adv. **Document type:** *Consumer.* **Description:** Focuses on both the real and virtual worlds of fashion and all that they encompass.
Related titles: French ed.
Published by: Nygard International, 980 St Antoine W, Ste 700, Montreal, PQ H3C 1A8, Canada. TEL 514-866-5000, FAX 514-875-0800, n.mag@nygard.com. Eds. James Parry, Mireille Lemelin. Adv. contact Lise Giroux.

746.92 GBR
N-TOUCH. Text in English. 1996. irreg.
Media: Online - full content.
Published by: London College of Fashion, 20 John Princes St, London, W1M 0BJ, United Kingdom. http://www.dircon.co.uk/ntouch.html.

▼ new title ➤ refereed ✶ unverified ♦ full entry avail.

DAS NEUE; Mit Raetsel- & Reise-Journal. see *GENERAL INTEREST PERIODICALS—Germany*

659.152 USA
NEW BODIES. Text in English. m. USD 2.95 newsstand/cover.
Published by: G C R Publishing Group, Inc., 1700 Broadway, 34th Fl, New York, NY 10019. TEL 212-541-7100, FAX 212-245-1241. Pub. Jason Goodman.

746.9202 USA
NEW YORK CITY MODEL AGENCY DIRECTORY. Text in English. 1987. a. USD 13.95 (effective 2003). adv. **Document type:** *Directory.* **Description:** Presents a breakdown of the New York model agencies with names, addresses, telephone numbers, physical requirements, interview policies, types of modeling done and specialty types looked for. Designed for aspiring models.
Published by: Peter Glenn Publications, Inc., 824 E. Atlantic Ave., Ste. 7, Delray Beach, FL 33483-5300. TEL 888-332-6700, info@pgdirect.com, http://www.pgdirect.com/. Ed. Lauren Gillmore. Pub. Gregory James. Adv. contact Tricia Mazzilli-Blount. B&W page USD 900; trim 9 x 4. Circ: 5,000.

746.92 NZL ISSN 1172-4102
NEW ZEALAND FASHION QUARTERLY. Text in English. 1988. q. NZD 8.75 newsstand/cover (effective 2002). adv. bk.rev. back issues avail. **Document type:** *Magazine, Consumer.*
Formerly (until 1992): Fashion Quarterly (1170-2990)
Related titles: Online - full text ed.
Published by: A C P New Zealand, 17B Hargreaves St, College Hill, Pasonby, Auckland, 1036, New Zealand. TEL 64-9-3735408, FAX 64-9-3089498, fq@acpnz.co.nz, http://www.fashionz.com. adv.: color page USD 5,510. Circ: 270,000.

NEWS BULLETIN. see *SPORTS AND GAMES*

746.92 ESP ISSN 1136-3630
NINSMODA; revista de moda infantil. Text in Spanish. 1971. 4/yr. USD 150. **Document type:** *Trade.* **Description:** Specializes in the designing of infants', children's and youth's apparel.
Formerly (until 1991): Nins (1136-3681)
Published by: Ediciones Esfer, Consejo de Ciento, 383, 5 1, Barcelona, 08009, Spain. TEL 34-3-4881820, FAX 34-3-2150039, http://www.ed.es/buscapress.ninsmoda. Ed. Esteban Ferrer. Adv. contact Eduardo Ferrer. Circ: 4,000.

746 JPN
NON-NO. Text in Japanese. 1971. s-m. JPY 10,120 (effective 2005). **Document type:** *Magazine, Consumer.* **Description:** Covers clothing trade, fashions for young women.
Published by: Shueisha Inc., 1-5-14 Sarugaku-cho, Chiyoda-ku, Tokyo, 101-0064, Japan. TEL 81-3-32306379, http://www.shueisha.co.jp/CGI/magazine/rack.cgi/magazine/nonno.html?key=detail&zashimei=nonno&janru=wom, http://www.shueisha.co.jp/index_f.html. Ed. Hiroshi Otsuka. Circ: 1,500,000.

746.92 CUB
NUEVA LINEA. Text in Spanish. s-a. USD 20 in South America; USD 22 in North America; USD 24 elsewhere.
Published by: Ediciones Cubanas, Obispo No. 527, Apdo. 605, Havana, Cuba.

NUYOU. see *WOMEN'S INTERESTS*

746.9 CAN
NYGARD.COM; the fashion web magazine. Text in English. 2000. s-a. USD 5.75; USD 3.50 newsstand/cover (effective 2001). adv. **Document type:** *Magazine, Consumer.*
Media: Online - full content.
Published by: Nygard.com, Inc., 980 St Antoine West, Ste 700, Montreal, PQ H3C 1A8, Canada. TEL 514-866-8322, FAX 514-875-0800, lise.giroux@nygard.com, http://www.nygard.com. Ed. Peter Nygard.

NYTT LIF; fashion magazine. see *WOMEN'S INTERESTS*

659.152 ITA
OBIETTIVO MODA. Text in Italian. 1978. s-a. adv. **Document type:** *Magazine, Trade.*
Address: Via Baldassare Franceschini 5, Florence, FI 50142, Italy. TEL 39-055-7398932, FAX 39-055-7398935, obiemaoda@iol.it. Ed. Forconi Fulvio. Circ: 15,000.

746.92 TUR
L'OFFICIEL. Text in Turkish. 2000 (Nov.). m. adv. **Document type:** *Magazine, Consumer.*
Published by: Dogus Grubu Iletisim Yayincilik ve Tic. A.S., Eski Buyukdere Cad., Uso Center, Maslak, Istanbul, 80660, Turkey. TEL 90-212-3354820, FAX 90-212-3354899, info@dogusiletisim.com, http://www.dogusiletisim.com.

687 646 FRA ISSN 0030-0403
OFFICIEL DE LA COUTURE ET DE LA MODE DE PARIS. Text in French, English, German, Spanish. 1921. 8/yr. adv. bk.rev. illus. **Document type:** *Magazine, Consumer.*
Indexed: DAAI, RASB.
—IE, Infotrieve.
Published by: Les Editions Jalou, 10 rue du Platre, Paris, 75004, France. info@officielnews.com, http://www.officielnews.com. Ed. Marie-Jose Susskind. Pub. Laurent Jalou. Circ: 70,000.

659.152 FRA ISSN 1295-6473
L'OPTIMUM. Text in French. 1996. bi-m. adv. **Document type:** *Magazine, Consumer.*
Former titles (until 1999): Magazine de l'Optimum (1283-9140); (until 1998): L' Officiel Homme (1284-2079)
Published by: Les Editions Jalou, 10 rue du Platre, Paris, 75004, France. info@officielnews.com, http://www.officielnews.com. Ed. Emmanuel Rubin. Pub. Laurent Jalou.

391 HKG ISSN 1023-7593
ORIENT BEAUTY/FURONG YAJIE. Text in Chinese, English. 1994. bi-m. HKD 33 newsstand/cover. adv. back issues avail. **Document type:** *Consumer.*
Published by: Hachette Filipacchi Hong Kong Ltd., 15-F, East Wing, Warwick House, Taikoo Place, 979 King s Rd, Quarry Bay, Hong Kong, Hong Kong. TEL 852-2567-8707, FAX 852-2568-4650. Ed. Suzanne Ching. Pub. Sandy Kwong. Adv. contact Rosana Wong. page HKD 28,750; trim 275 x 214. Circ: 30,000.

746.92 646.7 USA ISSN 1075-3133
PAGEANTRY; the magazine for the pageant, talent, and fashion industries. Text in English. 1980. q. USD 18 domestic; USD 69 foreign; USD 4.95 newsstand/cover (effective 2005). adv. bk.rev.; dance rev. illus.; tr.lit. back issues avail. **Document type:** *Magazine, Trade.* **Description:** News, interviews and information on the people of the pageant, fashion, talent, and modeling industries.
Published by: (World Pageant Association), Pageantry, Talent & Entertainment Services, Inc., 1855 W State Rd 434, Ste 254, Longwood, FL 32750. TEL 407-260-2262, FAX 407-260-5131, http://www.pageantrymagazine.com. Ed. Fred Abel. Pub., R&P, Adv. contact Charles Dunn. B&W page USD 1,518, color page USD 2,418; trim 10.88 x 8.38. Circ: 100,000.

PAGINAS. see *WOMEN'S INTERESTS*

PANACHE. see *WOMEN'S INTERESTS*

791.43 USA ISSN 1092-6305
PAPER (NEW YORK). Text in English. 1984. m. USD 9.97 domestic; USD 35 in Canada; USD 50 elsewhere (effective 2003). adv. **Document type:** *Magazine, Consumer.* **Description:** Contains articles and reviews covering New York fashion, life style, musics, clubbing scene, and more.
Former titles (until 1996): Paper Magazine (1073-9122); (until 1993): Paper (0892-3809)
Related titles: Online - full text ed.
Published by: Paper Magazine, 365 Broadway, 6th Fl, New York, NY 10013-3906. TEL 212-226-4405, FAX 212-226-0062, edit@papermag.com, http://www.papermag.com. Eds., Pubs. David Hershkovits, Kim Hastreiter. Adv. contact Sharon Phair. B&W page USD 6,275, color page USD 9,850; trim 8.25 x 10.75. Circ: 70,572 (paid); 5,500 (controlled). **Subscr. to:** PO Box 47, Canal St Sta, New York, NY 10013.

746.92 ESP ISSN 1136-0607
PASARELAS INTERNACIONALES. Text in Spanish; Summaries in English. 1995. s-a. back issues avail. **Document type:** *Consumer.*
Published by: Ediciones A.D.G., De Casanova, 209, Barcelona, 08021, Spain. TEL 34-93-201-1216, FAX 34-93-414-0238, edinovias@redes.tb.es. Ed. Silvia Benach. Adv. contact Susanna Conesa. Circ: 50,000.

687.029 USA ISSN 1072-2564
PHELON'S WOMEN'S APPAREL AND ACCESSORY SHOPS. Text in English. 1910. biennial. USD 175 (effective 2001). adv. 300 p./no.; **Document type:** *Directory.* **Description:** Lists executives, owners and buyers in women's apparel and accessory shops.
Formerly: Phelon's Women's Apparel Shops (0737-3430)
Published by: Phelon Sheldon & Marsar, Inc., 1364 Georgetowne Circle, Sarasota, FL 34232-2048. TEL 941-342-7990, 800-234-8804, FAX 941-342-7994. Ed. Joseph Marsar Jr. Pub., R&P, Adv. contact Joseph R Marsar Jr. page USD 500; 7 x 9. Circ: 1,000 (paid).

PICTURE PERFECT. see *PHOTOGRAPHY*

PINKER MODA. see *TEXTILE INDUSTRIES AND FABRICS*

▼ **PISTIL MAGAZINE.** see *WOMEN'S INTERESTS*

051 USA ISSN 1538-9871
PLATINUM MAGAZINE. Text in English. 1999. 10/yr. USD 26; USD 3.50 newsstand/cover; USD 4.95 newsstand/cover in Canada (effective 2001). adv. illus. **Document type:** *Magazine, Consumer.* **Description:** Features extensive coverage of the latest trends in fashion, beauty, lifestyle and entertainment.
Published by: Platinum Magazine, Inc., 129 Kingston St, Fl 5, Boston, MA 02474. TEL 617-521-0004, FAX 617-521-0027, letters@platinummagazine.com, http://www.platinummagazine.com. Ed. Nash Yacoub.

PLAYBOY FASHION. see *MEN'S INTERESTS*

PLAYBOY'S BOOK OF LINGERIE. see *MEN'S INTERESTS*

746.92 CAN ISSN 1198-5666
POINT OF VIEW★. Text in English. 1987. 3/yr. CND 14.98 domestic; CND 25 in United States; CND 30 elsewhere; CND 5 newsstand/cover (effective 2000). adv. **Document type:** *Catalog.*
Related titles: Online - full text ed.: (from Gale Group); French ed.: Point du Vue.
Indexed: CBCARef, CPerl.
—CCC.
Published by: Holt Renfrew & Co., Limited, 50 Bloor St., W, Toronto, ON M4W 1A1, Canada. TEL 416-920-9989, FAX 416-968-9092, POV@total.net. Adv. contact John Duncan. color page CND 13,000; trim 10.88 x 9. Circ: 150,000 (controlled).

659.152 GBR
POP. Text in English. s-a. GBP 5 newsstand/cover (effective 2001). adv. **Document type:** *Magazine, Consumer.* **Description:** Contains articles and features that attempt to fuse the fashion and art markets.
Published by: Emap Metro Ltd, Mappin Ho, 4 Winsley St, London, W1W 8HF, United Kingdom. TEL 44-20-74361515, FAX 44-20-73230276. Ed. Ashley Heath. Adv. contact Catherine Russell.

POPEYE. see *MEN'S INTERESTS*

746.9 JPN
PRETTY STYLE. Text in Japanese. m. adv. **Document type:** *Magazine, Consumer.*
Published by: Shogakukan Inc., 3-1 Hitotsubashi 2-chome, Chiyoda-ku, Tokyo, 101-8001, Japan. TEL 81-3-3230-5211, FAX 81-3-3264-8471, ps41@shogakukan.co.jp, http://www.pretty-style.com, http://www.shogakukan.co.jp.

PREVISIONS GLISSANTES DETAILLEES EN PERSPECTIVES SECTORIELLES (VOL.3): TEXTILE - HABILLEMENT - CUIR. see *BUSINESS AND ECONOMICS—Economic Situation And Conditions*

746.96 FRA ISSN 0293-2407
PRIMA. Text in French. 1982. m. EUR 20 (effective 2005). adv. bk.rev. **Document type:** *Magazine, Consumer.* **Description:** Covers fashion, beauty, crafts, home decoration, cooking, health, the law and education.
Related titles: Online - full text ed.
Indexed: RASB.
Published by: Prisma Presse, 6 rue Daru, Paris, 75379, France. TEL 33-1-44966700, FAX 33-1-44966721, prisma@presse-info.fr, http://www.prima.fr, http://www.prisma-presse.com. Ed. Fabienne Azire. Circ: 657,904 (paid). **Subscr. to:** Service Abonnements, B 140, Sainte Genevieve Cedex 60732, France. TEL 33-3-44625202.

687 ITA
PROGETTI MODA SHOES. Text in Italian, English. 1990. 2/yr. USD 160; USD 87 per issue (effective 2001). illus.; tr.lit. back issues avail. **Document type:** *Magazine.* **Description:** Illustrates collections of women's, men's and children's exclusive models designed by famous Italian designers-stylists from the Veneto region.
Published by: Muggiani Giampiero Editore srl, Via IV Novembre, 54, Settimo Milanese, MI 20019, Italy. TEL 39-02-335531, FAX 39-02-33501391, info@modapelle.com, http://www.modapelle.com.

PULP. see *CHILDREN AND YOUTH—For*

746.92 ZAF
PURSUIT; the journal for the apparel industry. Text in English. 1989. bi-m. ZAR 230; ZAR 460 foreign; includes Index. adv. illus. **Document type:** *Trade.*
Published by: Pursuit Holdings, PO Box 15793, Vlaeberg, Cape Town, South Africa. TEL 27-21-4242154, FAX 27-21-4242212, pursuit@iafrica.co.za, http://www.pursuit.co.za. Ed., Pub., R&P Joanna Broughton. Adv. contact Yasmeen Braaf. B&W page ZAR 6,360, color page ZAR 6,955. Circ: 6,000.

746.92 ZAF
PURSUIT: THE FASHION INDEX. Text in English. 1989. a. ZAR 230; ZAR 460 foreign (effective 1998). adv. illus. **Document type:** *Trade.* **Description:** Covers the fashion textile industry in South Africa.
Published by: Pursuit Holdings, PO Box 15793, Vlaeberg, Cape Town, South Africa. TEL 27-21-4242154, FAX 27-21-4242212, pursuit@iafrica.co.za, http://www.pursuit.co.za. Ed., Pub., R&P Joanna Broughton. Circ: 6,000.

746.92 GBR
RANK. Text in English. q. GBP 25 domestic; GBP 35 in Europe; USD 60 in United States; GBP 40 elsewhere (effective 2001). **Document type:** *Magazine, Consumer.* **Description:** Contains articles and features on experimental fashion photography and art.
Published by: Waddell Ltd., 112-116 Old St, London, EC1V 9BG, United Kingdom. TEL 44-20-7549-6808, FAX 44-20-7336-0966, contact@confused.co.uk, http://www.rankin.co.uk, http://www.confused.co.uk.

C

746.92 CHE
ROBES COUTURE. Text in English, French, German. s-a. CHF 46; CHF 50 foreign; (combined subscr. with Robes Manteaux 84 SFr.(foreign 93 SFr.)). **Document type:** *Trade.*
Published by: Editions C. Weder Ltd., Rennweg 64, Basel, 4052, Switzerland. TEL 41-61-3126263, FAX 41-61-3126266, TELEX 965920-WEDER-CH. Ed. Walter Beyeler.

746.92 CHE
ROBES MANTEAUX. Text in English, French, German. s-a. CHF 46; CHF 50 foreign; (combined subscr. with Robes Couture 84 SFr.(foreign 93 SFr.)). **Document type:** *Trade.*
Published by: Editions C. Weder Ltd., Rennweg 64, Basel, 4052, Switzerland. TEL 41-61-3126263, FAX 41-61-3126266. Ed. Walter Beyeler.

687 DEU ISSN 0948-7980
RUNDSCHAU - FACHZEITSCHRIFT FUER INTERNATIONALE DAMENMODE UND SCHNITT-TECHNIK. Text in German. 1981. m. adv. charts; illus. **Document type:** *Magazine, Consumer.*
Former titles (until 1995): Rundschau fuer Internationale Damenmode; (until 1991): Rundschau fuer Internationale Damenmode mit D O B- und Haka-Praxis (0722-2858); Which was formed by the merger of (1970-1981): Rundschau fuer Internationale Damenmode (0035-9912); (1970-1981): D O B- und Haka-Praxis (0342-1627)
Published by: Rundschau-Verlag Otto G. Koeniger GmbH und Co., Karlstr 41, Ulm, 89073, Germany. TEL 49-731-1520180, FAX 49-731-1520185, redaktion@rundschauverlag.de. Circ: 8,296 (paid); 9,617 (controlled).

687 790.1 DEU ISSN 1437-3114
S A Z SPORTSFASHION MAGAZIN. (Sport Artikel Zeitung) Text in German. 1981. 6/yr. adv. **Document type:** *Magazine, Trade.* **Description:** Contains news, sales trends, and discussion forums on the sports fashion industry.
Formerly (until 1996): S A Z Magazin (0933-3606)
Published by: S A Z Verlag GmbH, Rumfordstr 42, Munich, 80469, Germany. TEL 49-89-2121100, FAX 49-89-21211039. Ed. Florian Bergener. Pub. Horst Frankl. Adv. contact Ulrich Onnasch. color page EUR 4,990; trim 223 x 315. Circ: 15,000 (controlled).

SAMARBETE. see *BUSINESS AND ECONOMICS—Cooperatives*

SAN FRANCISCO BRIDE. see *MATRIMONY*

746.92 JPN
SAN SUN. Text in Japanese. 1983. m. JPY 4,800.
Published by: Gakken Co. Ltd., 40-5 Kami-Ikedai 4-chome, Ota-ku, Tokyo, 145-0064, Japan. Ed. Hiroshi Tsunematsu.

746.9 SAU
SAYIDATY FASHION. Text in Arabic. 2/yr. adv. **Document type:** *Magazine, Consumer.* **Description:** Covers all items of shopping interest to the Arab woman including fashion, beauty accessories, and health items.
Published by: Saudi Research & Publishing Co., PO Box 4556, Jeddah, 21412, Saudi Arabia. TEL 966-2-669-1888, FAX 966-2-667-1650, http://www.alkhaleejiahadv.com.sa/srpc/. adv.: page SAR 25,600.

SEW BEAUTIFUL. see *NEEDLEWORK*

746 646.4 USA ISSN 0273-8120
SEW NEWS; the fashion how-to magazine. Text in English. 1980. m. USD 21.98 domestic; USD 33.98 foreign; USD 5.99 newsstand/cover (effective 2005). adv. bk.rev. illus. **Document type:** *Magazine, Consumer.* **Description:** Editorial content on sewing techniques, projects, new products, fabric and machine information, and seasonal fashion trends.
—CCC.
Published by: Primedia Enthusiast Media (Subsidiary of: Primedia Consumer Media & Magazine Group), 741 Corporate Circle, Ste A, Golden, CO 80401. TEL 303-278-1010, FAX 303-277-0370, sewnews@sewnews.com, information@primedia.com, http://www.sewnews.com, http://www.primedia.com. Ed. Linda Griepentrog. Pub. Tina Battock. Adv. contact Sandy Griggs. B&W page USD 4,995, color page USD 7,600; trim 8 x 10.75. Circ: 185,000 (paid).

746 646.4 USA ISSN 1040-2985
TT705
SEWING UPDATE. Text in English. 1986. bi-m. **Document type:** *Newsletter.* **Description:** Offers the latest information on sewing techniques, equipment and patterns.
Published by: Primedia Enthusiast Media (Subsidiary of: Primedia Consumer Media & Magazine Group), 741 Corporate Circle, Ste A, Golden, CO 80401. TEL 303-278-1010, FAX 303-277-0370, updatespjs@aol.com, http://www.primedia.com.

391 GBR ISSN 0950-3625
SEWING WITH BUTTERICK. Text in English. 1866. q. GBP 11.40 in United Kingdom; GBP 13.40 in Europe; GBP 18.40 elsewhere; GBP 2.85 newsstand/cover (effective 2001). **Document type:** *Magazine, Consumer.* **Description:** Provides patterns and descriptions of all the latest fashions and trends for both the professional and amateur clothesmaker.
Published by: Butterick Company Ltd., New Ln, Havant, Hants PO9 2ND, United Kingdom. TEL 44-2392-486221, 44-870-777-9955, FAX 44-2392-492769, gail@butterick-vogue.co.uk, http://www.butterick.com/. Ed., R&P Gail Goldie TEL 44-2392-489773. Pub. Keith Jones. Adv. contact Marnie Hugo TEL 44-2392-489787. **Dist. by:** Lakeside Publishing Services, Unit 1D. Tideway Industrial Estate, 87 Kirtling St, London SW8 5BP, United Kingdom. TEL 44-20-77206680, FAX 44-20-74989616.

646.4 746.9 GBR ISSN 1467-3339
SEWING WITH BUTTERICK - VOGUE PATTERNS - WEDDINGS. Text in English. 1986. a. GBP 2.25 newsstand/cover (effective 2001). adv. bk.rev. **Document type:** *Magazine, Consumer.* **Description:** Covers sewing for brides and the wedding party. Includes designer outfits which can be sewn. For traditional, avant garde, and "second time around" weddings.
Former titles (until 1998): Vogue Patterns. Weddings & Special Occasions (1352-9358); (until 1993): Weddings & Special Occasions (0959-0870)
Published by: Butterick Company Ltd., New Ln, Havant, Hants PO9 2ND, United Kingdom. TEL 44-2392-486221, 44-870-777-9955, FAX 44-2392-492769, gail@butterick-vogue.co.uk, http://www.butterick.com/. Ed., R&P Gail Goldie TEL 44-2392-489773. Pub. Keith Jones. Adv. contact Marnie Hugo TEL 44-2392-489787. page GBP 1,488; trim 210 x 274. Circ: 40,000 (controlled). **Dist. by:** Lakeside Publishing Services, Unit 1D. Tideway Industrial Estate, 87 Kirtling St, London SW8 5BP, United Kingdom. TEL 44-20-77206680, FAX 44-20-74989616.

746.92 CHN ISSN 1000-8888
SHANGHAI FUSHI. Text in Chinese. q.
Published by: Shanghai Kexue Jishu Chubanshe/Shanghai Scientific and Technical Publishers, 450 Ruijin Er Rd, Shanghai, 200020, China. TEL 86-21-6473-6055. Ed. Gong Gang.

746.9 CHN
SHANGHAI SHIZHUANG BAO/SHANGHAI FASHION TIMES. Text in Chinese. 1988. w. CNY 63.36 (effective 2004). **Document type:** *Newspaper, Consumer.*
Published by: Shanghai Shizhuang Baoshe, Huangpu-qu, 740, Nanjin Lu, Shanghai, 200336, China. TEL 86-21-62748598. **Dist. by:** China International Book Trading Corp, 35 Chegongzhuang Xilu, Haidian District, PO Box 399, Beijing 100044, China. TEL 86-10-68412045, FAX 86-10-68412023, cibtc@mail.cibtc.com.cn, http://www.cibtc.com.cn.

746.92 CHN ISSN 1002-4158
SHIZHUANG/FASHIONABLE CLOTHES. Text in Chinese. 1980. bi-m. USD 23.70.
Published by: China Silk Import and Export General Corporation - Zhongguo Sichou Jinchukou Zonggongsi, 82 Dong anmen Dajie, Beijing, 100744, China. TEL 86-10-6512-038, FAX 86-10-6512-0378. Ed. Rui Wang. **Dist. in US by:** China Books & Periodicals Inc, 360 Swift Ave., Ste. 48, S San Fran, CA 94080-6220. TEL 415-282-2994.

SHOE & FASHION FOOTWEAR NEWS. see *CLOTHING TRADE*

746.9 USA
THE SIMPLICITY FASHION CATALOG✶. Text in English. s-a. USD 12 (effective 2001). **Document type:** *Catalog, Consumer.*
Published by: Simplicity Pattern Co., Inc., 58 E 11th St Fl 8, New York, NY 10003-6020. TEL 212-576-2222, 1-888-588-2700, FAX 212-679-5541, info@simplicity.com, http://www.simplicity.com/.

687 HKG
SINGAPORE EVE MODE. Text in English. 1989. s-a. SGD 28.80 (effective 1999). adv. **Document type:** *Consumer.* **Description:** Covers fashion and beauty for Singapore's sophisticated and influential women.
Formerly (until 1990): Singapore Eve
Published by: Communication Management Ltd., 1811 Hong Kong Plaza, 188 Connaught Rd W, Hong Kong, Hong Kong. TEL 852-2859-4361, FAX 852-2559-1920, cmpl@cmlink.com, cmail@cmlink.com, http://www.cmlink.com/. adv.: color page SGD 3,000; trim 228 x 305. Circ: 17,000.

659.152 HKG
SINGAPORE MENMODE. Text in English. 1993. s-a. SGD 28.80; SGD 18 newsstand/cover (effective 1999). **Document type:** *Consumer.* **Description:** Covers men's fashion for Singapore's sophisticated and influential men.
Published by: Communication Management Ltd., 1811 Hong Kong Plaza, 188 Connaught Rd W, Hong Kong, Hong Kong. TEL 852-2859-4361, FAX 852-2559-1920, cmpl@cmlink.com, cmail@cmlink.com, http://www.cmlink.com/. adv.: color page SGD 3,000; trim 228 x 305. Circ: 27,950.

746.92 640 JPN
SO-EN. Text in Japanese. 1936. m. JPY 14,220.
Formerly: Fashion Garden
Published by: Bunka Publishing Bureau, 22-1 Yoyogi 3-chome, Shibuya-ku, Tokyo, 1510053, Japan. TEL 03-3370-3111, TELEX 32475. Ed. Tamae Ejima.

746.9 ITA ISSN 1124-2949
SPORT & STREET COLLEZIONI. Text in English, Italian. q. EUR 92.96 domestic (effective 2001). **Document type:** *Magazine.* **Description:** Presents sportswear, jeanswear, casualwear, and activewear.
Published by: Liber S.R.L., Via Curtatona, 5/m, Modena, 41100, Italy. TEL 39-059-412643, FAX 39-059-412567, mcagnoni@liber.it. Ed. Antonio Vergara. **Dist. by:** Mode Information GmbH, Pilgerstr 20, Overath 51491, Germany. TEL 49-2206-60070, FAX 49-2206-600717.

391 USA
SPORTS ILLUSTRATED (SWIMSUIT EDITION). Text in English. a. USD 5.99 newsstand/cover (effective 2001); free to subscr. of Sports Illustrated. **Document type:** *Magazine, Consumer.* **Description:** Contains photographs of super-models in exotic locations wearing the latest in swimwear fashion from around the world.
Related titles: CD-ROM ed.; Online - full content ed.; Video ed.; ♦ Regional ed(s).: Sports Illustrated Swimsuit France; ♦ Sports Illustrated Swimsuit Germany; ♦ Sports Illustrated Swimsuit Italy; ♦ Sports Illustrated Swimsuit Issue. ISSN 1461-7773; ♦ Special ed. of: Sports Illustrated. ISSN 0038-822X.
Published by: Time Inc., Sports Illustrated Group (Subsidiary of: Time Warner, Inc.), Sports Illustrated Bldg, 135 W 50th St, 4th Fl., New York, NY 10020-1393. http://www.cnnsi.com.

746.9 GBR
SPORTS ILLUSTRATED SWIMSUIT FRANCE. Text in English. a. GBP 5.95 newsstand/cover (effective 2003). adv. **Document type:** *Magazine, Consumer.*
Related titles: ♦ Regional ed(s).: Sports Illustrated (Swimsuit Edition); ♦ Sports Illustrated Swimsuit Germany; ♦ Sports Illustrated Swimsuit Italy; ♦ Sports Illustrated Swimsuit Issue. ISSN 1461-7773.
Published by: Highbury Customer Publications, The Publishing House, 1-3 Highbury Station Rd, London, N1 1SE, United Kingdom. TEL 44-20-226-2222, FAX 44-20-77040758, customerpublishing@hhc.co.uk, http://www.hhc.co.uk/. Ed. Dan Hayes. Adv. contact Tim Henderson. page EUR 10,595. Circ: 75,000.

746.9 GBR
SPORTS ILLUSTRATED SWIMSUIT GERMANY. Text in German. a. GBP 5 newsstand/cover (effective 2003). adv. **Document type:** *Magazine, Consumer.*
Related titles: ♦ Regional ed(s).: Sports Illustrated (Swimsuit Edition); ♦ Sports Illustrated Swimsuit France; ♦ Sports Illustrated Swimsuit Italy; ♦ Sports Illustrated Swimsuit Issue. ISSN 1461-7773.
Published by: Highbury Customer Publications, The Publishing House, 1-3 Highbury Station Rd, London, N1 1SE, United Kingdom. TEL 44-20-226-2222, FAX 44-20-77040758, customerpublishing@hhc.co.uk, http://www.hhc.co.uk/pages/show/entry_Level/2/entry_code/HCU/single_record_flag/98. Ed. Dan Hayes. Adv. contact Tim Henderson. page EUR 12,714; 210 x 297. Circ: 120,000.

746.9 GBR ISSN 1461-7773
SPORTS ILLUSTRATED SWIMSUIT ISSUE. Text in English. a. GBP 3.25 newsstand/cover (effective 2003). adv. **Document type:** *Magazine, Consumer.*
Related titles: ♦ Regional ed(s).: Sports Illustrated (Swimsuit Edition); ♦ Sports Illustrated Swimsuit France; ♦ Sports Illustrated Swimsuit Germany; ♦ Sports Illustrated Swimsuit Italy.
Published by: Highbury Customer Publications, The Publishing House, 1-3 Highbury Station Rd, London, N1 1SE, United Kingdom. TEL 44-20-226-2222, FAX 44-20-77040758, customerpublishing@hhc.co.uk, http://www.hhc.co.uk/pages/show/entry_Level/2/entry_code/HCU/single_record_flag/101. adv.: page GBP 7,800; 210 x 297. Circ: 100,000.

746.9 GBR
SPORTS ILLUSTRATED SWIMSUIT ITALY. Text in English. a. GBP 3.90 newsstand/cover (effective 2003). adv. **Document type:** *Magazine, Consumer.*
Related titles: ♦ Regional ed(s).: Sports Illustrated (Swimsuit Edition); ♦ Sports Illustrated Swimsuit France; ♦ Sports Illustrated Swimsuit Germany; ♦ Sports Illustrated Swimsuit Issue. ISSN 1461-7773.
Published by: Highbury Customer Publications, The Publishing House, 1-3 Highbury Station Rd, London, N1 1SE, United Kingdom. TEL 44-20-226-2222, FAX 44-20-77040758, customerpublishing@hhc.co.uk, http://www.hhc.co.uk/pages/show/entry_Level/2/entry_code/HCU/single_record_flag/99. Ed. Dan Hayes. Adv. contact Tim Henderson. page GBP 11,328; 210 x 297. Circ: 62,500.

LA SPOSA. see *MATRIMONY*

SPOSABELLA. see *MATRIMONY*

SPOSABELLA IDEE. see *MATRIMONY*

391 ESP
SPOSABELLA NOVIAS. Text in Spanish. 1988. 2/yr. illus. **Document type:** *Trade.* **Description:** Consists of articles on fashion design for wedding clothes.
Address: c/o Madrazo 33-37, Barcelona, Spain. TEL 34-93-218-7666, FAX 34-93-218-7319. Circ: 60,000.

C

746.92 GBR
SPRUCE. Text in English. 2001. s-a. USD 10 newsstand/cover; USD 11 newsstand/cover in Canada (effective 2001). **Document type:** *Magazine, Consumer.* **Description:** Presents an inside look at fashion and the fashion industry for the global consumer.
Published by: Time Inc., Brettenham House, Lancaster Pl, London, WC2E 7TL, United Kingdom. TEL 44-20-7322-1177, FAX 44-20-7322-1171. Ed. Tyler Brule.

STAR & STYLE. see *MOTION PICTURES*

687.1 EST ISSN 1406-2178
STIIL. Text in Estonian. 1991. m. adv. **Document type:** *Magazine, Consumer.*
Published by: Ajakirjade Kirjastus, Maakri 23A, Tallinn, 10145, Estonia. TEL 372-666-2600, FAX 372-666-2557, kirjastus@kirjastus.ee, http://www.stiil.ee, http://www.kirjastus.ee.

646.3 AUS ISSN 0816-939X
STUDIO BAMBINI. Text in English. s-a. AUD 32 (effective 1999). adv. **Document type:** *Consumer.*
Published by: Studio Magazines Pty. Ltd., Level 3, 101-111 William St., Sydney, NSW 2011, Australia. TEL 61-2-9360-1422, FAX 61-2-9360-9550. Ed. Karen Jane Eyre. Pub. Marcello Grand. Adv. contact Louise Canelli.

STUDIO FOR BRIDES. see *MATRIMONY*

STYLE. see *WOMEN'S INTERESTS*

687 LIE
STYLE. Text in German. 1964. 4/yr. adv. **Document type:** *Magazine, Consumer.*
Published by: A V A - Allgemeine Verlagsanstalt, In der Fina 18, Schaan, 9494, Liechtenstein. TEL 423-2334383, FAX 423-2334383. adv.: B&W page EUR 10,400, color page EUR 14,250. Circ: 83,940 (controlled).

C

687 CAN ISSN 0039-4246
STYLE; Canada's fashion news. Text in English. 1888. 12/yr. CND 42 domestic; CND 55 in United States; CND 68 foreign (effective 1999). adv. illus.; stat. index. reprint service avail. from PQC. **Document type:** *Trade.*
Related titles: Microform ed.: (from PQC); Online - full text ed.: (from bigchalk, Northern Light Technology, Inc.); Supplement(s): Style Buyers' Guide. ISSN 0227-4272. 1979.
Indexed: AES, ArtHuCI, CurCont, IBRH, MLA.
—IDS.
Published by: Style Communications Inc., 1448 Lawrence Ave E, Ste 302, Toronto, ON M4A 2V6, Canada. TEL 416-755-5199, FAX 416-755-9123, style@style.ca, http://www.style.ca. Ed. Doris Montanera. Pub. Pat MacLean. Adv. contact Sharon Payne. B&W page CND 4,070, color page CND 4,820; trim 14.63 x 10.88. Circ: 11,800.

746.9 SGP
STYLE. Text in English. 2002. m. **Document type:** *Magazine, Consumer.*
Published by: MediaCorp Publishing, Caldecott Broadcast Centre, Andrew Road, Singapore, 299939, Singapore. TEL 65-64837118, FAX 65-64812098, subhelp@mediacorppub.com.sg, http://corporate.mediacorpsingapore.com/index.htm.

STYLE (BALTIMORE); smart living in Baltimore. see *WOMEN'S INTERESTS*

746.92 USA
STYLE 24-7. Text in English. 2001 (Sep.). w. USD 2.95 newsstand/cover; USD 3.95 newsstand/cover in Canada (effective 2001). adv. **Document type:** *Magazine, Consumer.* **Description:** Contains the latest news, in-depth celebrity gossip, the hottest trends in fashion, and tips on personal style.
Media: Online - full content.
Published by: Fashion Wire Daily, Inc. TEL 212-792-8282, help@fashionwiredaily.com, http://www.fashionwiredaily.com/. Ed. Brandusa Niro. Circ: 200,000 (paid and controlled).

687 USA
STYLE.COM. Text in English. 2000. d. free. **Document type:** *Magazine, Consumer.*
Media: Online - full text. **Related titles:** ♦ Print ed.: Vogue. ISSN 0042-8000; ♦ W. ISSN 0162-9115.
Published by: Condenet Inc. (Subsidiary of: Conde Nast Publications, Inc.), 4 Times Sq., 17th Fl., New York, NY 10036. TEL 212-286-3700, FAX 212-286-5960, http://www.style.com/, http://www.condenet.com/.

687 USA
STYLE FORECAST✶. Text in English. s-a.
Published by: International Association of Clothing Designers, 34 Thorton Ferry Rd, No 1, Amherst, NH 03031. dmschmida@aol.com.

746.9 305.896 USA ISSN 1551-1707
▼ **SUEDE.** Text in English. 2004. 9/yr. USD 14.97; USD 24.97 in Canada; USD 3.50 newsstand/cover (effective 2005). adv. **Document type:** *Magazine, Consumer.*
Published by: Essence Communications Inc., 1500 Broadway, 6th Fl., New York, NY 10036-4015. TEL 212-642-0600, FAX 212-921-5173, sboyd@suedemag.com, http://www.essence.com/essence/suede/home.html. adv.: page USD 25,000; trim 9 x 10.875. Circ: 250,000 (paid and controlled).

687 ITA
SUGGESTIONS SHOE MODELS FOR CHILD. Text in English, Italian. 1990. 2/yr. USD 160 foreign; USD 87 per issue (effective 2001). adv. illus.; tr.lit. back issues avail. **Document type:** *Magazine.* **Description:** Exclusive illustrations of children's models by famous Italian designers and stylists. Emerging trends for the coming season are outlined a year in advance.
Published by: Muggiani Giampiero Editore srl, Via IV Novembre, 54, Settimo Milanese, MI 20019, Italy. TEL 39-02-335531, FAX 39-02-33501391, info@modapelle.com, http://www.modapelle.com. adv.: color page USD 2,350; bleed 215 x 285.

687 ITA
SUGGESTIONS SHOE MODELS FOR MAN. Text in Italian, English. 1990. 2/yr. USD 160; USD 87 per issue (effective 2001). adv. tr.lit.; illus. back issues avail. **Document type:** *Magazine.* **Description:** Exclusive illustrations of men's models designed by famous Italian designers and stylists. Emerging trends are outlined a year in advance of the coming season.
Published by: Muggiani Giampiero Editore srl, Via IV Novembre, 54, Settimo Milanese, MI 20019, Italy. TEL 39-02-335531, FAX 39-02-33501391, info@modapelle.com, http://www.modapelle.com. adv.: color page USD 2,350; bleed 215 x 285.

687 ITA
SUGGESTIONS SHOE MODELS FOR WOMAN. Text in Italian, English. 1990. 2/yr. USD 160; USD 87 per issue (effective 2001). adv. illus.; tr.lit. back issues avail. **Document type:** *Magazine.* **Description:** Exclusive illustrations of women's models designed by famous Italian designers and stylists. Emerging trends are outlined a year in advance of the coming season.
Published by: Muggiani Giampiero Editore srl, Via IV Novembre, 54, Settimo Milanese, MI 20019, Italy. TEL 39-02-335531, FAX 39-02-33501391, info@modapelle.com, http://www.modapelle.com. adv.: color page USD 2,350; bleed 215 x 285.

SUHAAG. see *MATRIMONY*

797.21 USA
SWIM JOURNAL. Text in English. 5/yr. adv. **Document type:** *Magazine, Trade.*
Published by: G P Publishing, 609 E Oregon Ave, 100, Phoenix, AZ 85012. TEL 602-265-7778.

687.2 USA ISSN 0894-4075
SWIMWEAR U S A. Text in English. 198?. m. USD 2.95 newsstand/cover. **Document type:** *Trade.*
Published by: G C R Publishing Group, Inc., 1700 Broadway, 34th Fl, New York, NY 10019. TEL 212-541-7100, FAX 212-245-1241. Pub. Jason Goodman.

746.92 USA
TEAR SHEET. Text in English. 2001. bi-m. USD 25; USD 5 newsstand/cover (effective 2001). adv. **Document type:** *Magazine, Consumer.*
Published by: Tear Sheet Publications, Inc., 134 W. 26th St., #720, New York, NY 10001. TEL 212-206-7193, FAX 212-206-7195, tearsheet@tearsheet.com, http://www.tearsheet.com. Ed. Jill Johnson.

640 USA ISSN 1540-2215
HQ1229
TEEN VOGUE. Text in English. 2000. 6/yr. USD 10; USD 1.50 newsstand/cover (effective 2003). adv. **Document type:** *Magazine, Consumer.* **Description:** Presents articles and photographs on the latest in teen fashions and celebrities.
Incorporates (in 2005): Y M (0888-5842)
Related titles: Online - full text ed.: (from Gale Group, LexisNexis).
Published by: Conde Nast Publications, Inc., 750 3rd Ave, New York, NY 10017. TEL 212-286-2860, 800-444-4653, FAX 212-286-6921, teenvogue@mail.com, magpr@condenast.com, http://www.teenvogue.com, http://www.condenast.com. Ed. Amy Astley. adv.: color page USD 32,400. **Dist. by:** Comag Marketing Group, LLC, 250 W 55th St, New York, NY 10019. TEL 212-649-4468, FAX 212-262-1239.

646.4 MEX
TEENAGER INTERNACIONAL. Text in Spanish. q. adv. **Document type:** *Consumer.* **Description:** Includes sewing patterns and instructions for young women.
Published by: Consorcio Sayrols, Mier y Pesado 126, Mexico, Col del Valle, Mexico City, DF 03100, Mexico. TEL 52-5-6874699, FAX 525-523-7045, beatrizc@spin.com.mx, http://www.sayrols.com.mx. Ed. Patricia Olvera. Pub. Patricia Olivera. R&P Roberto Davo TEL 52-5-5236714. Adv. contact Beatriz Coria. B&W page USD 3,370, color page USD 4,312; 275 x 210. Circ: 100,000.

TEKSTILFORUM; mote, miljoe, velvaere. see *TEXTILE INDUSTRIES AND FABRICS*

659.152 ESP ISSN 0212-2375
TELVA. Text in Spanish. 1963. m. adv. bk.rev. illus.
Related titles: Online - full content ed.: estarGuapa.com. 2000.
Published by: Recoletos Compania Editorial S.A (Subsidiary of: Pearson Publishing Group), Paseo Recoletos, 1 5o, Madrid, 28001, Spain. TEL 34-91-3373220, FAX 34-91-3373266, expansion@recoletos.es, http://www.recoletos.es/general/areas/mujer/telva.html. Circ: 122,707.

759.152 ITA
TEMI - TENDENZE MODA ITALIA. Text in Italian. 1984. bi-m. adv. **Document type:** *Magazine, Trade.*
Published by: Temi, Via Alfonso Lamarmora, 22, Milan, MI 20122, Italy. TEL 39-2-55192002, FAX 39-2-55015325. Ed. Simonetti Edoardo.

TEXBEL INTERNATIONAL. see *TEXTILE INDUSTRIES AND FABRICS*

TEXTIL-REVUE. see *TEXTILE INDUSTRIES AND FABRICS*

796.907 DEU ISSN 0342-7358
TEXTILARBEIT UND UNTERRICHT. Text in German. q. **Document type:** *Academic/Scholarly.*
Indexed: DIP, IBR, IBZ.
—CCC.
Published by: Schneider Verlag Hohengehren GmbH, Wilhelmstr 13, Baltmannsweiler, 73666, Germany. FAX 49-7153-48761, schneider-verlag-hohengehren@t-online.de.

TEXTILWIRTSCHAFT SEASON. see *CLOTHING TRADE*

THOI TRANG TRE/NEW FASHION. see *WOMEN'S INTERESTS*

746.9 USA
▼ **TIME STYLE AND DESIGN.** Text in English. 2003 (Spr.). s-a. **Document type:** *Magazine, Consumer.* **Description:** Provides an insight into the business and culture of fashion, style and design.
Published by: Time, Inc (Subsidiary of: Time Warner, Inc.), Time & Life Bldg., Rockefeller Center, 29th Fl, 1271 Ave of the Americas, New York, NY 10020-1393.

381.45687 DNK ISSN 0107-0290
TOEJ; fashion & business. Text in Danish. 1979. 11/yr. DKK 925 (effective 2004). adv. bk.rev. **Document type:** *Trade.* **Description:** Provides a running commentary on all relevant Dansih and international trade fairs.
Published by: Pej Gruppen - Scandinavian Trend Institute, Bitsovvej 2, Herning, 7400, Denmark. TEL 45-97-118900, FAX 45-97-118511, redaktionen@pejgruppen.dk, info@pejgruppen.dk, http://www.pejgruppen.dk. Ed. Helle Mathiesen. adv.: page DKK 17,000.

TRACE (LONDON). see *MUSIC*

TRACE (NEW YORK, 1998); transcultural styles & ideas. see *LIFESTYLE*

TREND-BOUTIQUE; vakblad voor de eigentijdse ondernemer in lederwaren, bijoux en modeaccessories. see *BUSINESS AND ECONOMICS—Marketing And Purchasing*

TRENDI. see *WOMEN'S INTERESTS*

TRENDZ. see *JEWELRY, CLOCKS AND WATCHES*

TRICOT PRESTIGE. see *NEEDLEWORK*

TRICOTS CHICS; de Paris. see *NEEDLEWORK*

659.152 SGP
TUNE MONTHLY MAGAZINE. Text in Chinese. 1988. m.
Address: Block 203A Henderson Industrial Park, Henderson Rd 0604, Singapore, 0315, Singapore. TEL 2733000, FAX 2749538. Ed. Chan Eng. Circ: 25,000.

646.72 POL ISSN 0867-1826
TWOJ STYL. Text in Polish. 1990. m. PLZ 5 newsstand/cover. adv. illus. **Document type:** *Magazine, Consumer.*
Related titles: Online - full text ed.
Published by: Wydawnictwo Bauer Sp. z o.o. (Subsidiary of: Heinrich Bauer Verlag), ul. Motorowa 1, Warsaw, 04-035, Poland. TEL 48-22-5170500, FAX 48-22-5170125, redakcja@twojstyl.com.pl, kontakt@bauer.pl, http://www.twojstyl.pl, http://www.bauer.pl. Ed. Anna Achmatowicz-Schwendimann. Adv. contact Katarzyna Jablonska. **Dist. in U.S. & Canada by:** Andrew Artistic Distribution Inc., c/o Janusz Czuj, 417 Manhattan Ave, Brooklyn, NY 11222. TEL 718-384-6050, 718-387-0484.

646 MEX ISSN 0041-6223
ULTIMA MODA. Text in Spanish. 1966. fortn. MXP 110, USD 10. adv. charts; illus.
Published by: Publicaciones Herrerias, S.A., Balderas 87, 2o, Mexico City, DF 06040, Mexico. TEL 5-518-5481. Ed. Jose Pichel. Circ: 230,000.

687.11 ITA
UOMO COLLEZIONI. Text in English, Italian. q. EUR 92.96 domestic (effective 2001). illus. back issues avail. **Document type:** *Magazine, Trade.* **Description:** Covers the best of men's fashion shows throughout the world: pret-a-porter, knitwear, accessories, casualwear and more.
Published by: Liber S.R.L., Via Curtatona, 5/m, Modena, 41100, Italy. TEL 39-059-412643, FAX 39-059-412567, mcagnoni@liber.it. Ed. Antonio Vergara.

646 ITA ISSN 1120-7760
TT570
UOMO VOGUE. Text in Italian. 1967. m. (10/yr.). EUR 27 (effective 2005). adv. **Document type:** *Magazine, Consumer.*
Related titles: ♦ Supplement(s): Uomo Sport.
Indexed: DAAI.
—IE, Infotrieve.
Published by: Edizioni Conde Nast SpA (Subsidiary of: Arnoldo Mondadori Editore SpA), Piazza Castello 27, Milan, MI 20122, Italy. info@condenet.it, http://www.condenast.it. Ed. A Premoli. Circ: 40,000.

URODA. see *BEAUTY CULTURE*

746.92 JPN
UTSUKUSHII KIMONO/BEAUTIFUL KIMONO. Text in Japanese. 1953. q. JPY 1,850 newsstand/cover (effective 2002). adv. **Document type:** *Magazine, Consumer.* **Description:** Provides practical information and features on topics of interest to the kimono-wearer, including beauty, travel, and traditional Japanese culture and lifestyle.
Published by: Hachette Fujingaho Co. Ltd. (Subsidiary of: Hachette Filipacchi Medias S.A.), 2-9-1 Nishi Shinbashi, Minato-ku, Tokyo, 105-0003, Japan. TEL 81-3-3506-6601, FAX 81-3-3506-6606, http://www.hfm.co.jp. Circ: 153,000 (paid).

V MAGAZINE. see *ART*

VERENA. see *NEEDLEWORK*

659.152 USA
VIDEOFASHION!; news, men, specials. Text in English. w. USD 595; USD 995 foreign (effective 2000). **Document type:** *Trade.* **Description:** Devoted to men's and women's wear and the fashion industry.
Media: Video.
Published by: Videofashion, Inc., 100 6th Ave, 12th Fl, New York, NY 10013. TEL 212-869-4666, FAX 212-869-8208, info@ideofashion.com, info@videofashion.com. Ed., R&P Anne V Adami. Pub. Nicolas H Charney.

VINGTAINE. see *WOMEN'S INTERESTS*

746.92 391 USA ISSN 1071-5266
N6480
VISIONAIRE. Text in English. 1991. q. USD 675 domestic; USD 800 Europe, Canada & South America; USD 900 Asia, Australia & New Zealand (effective 2004). **Document type:** *Magazine, Consumer.*
Published by: Visionaire Publishing, 11 Mercer St, New York, NY 10013. TEL 212-274-8959, FAX 212-343-2595, http://www.visionaireworld.com. Ed. Stephen Gan.

640 GRC ISSN 1108-6653
VOGUE. Text in Greek. 2000. m. adv. **Document type:** *Magazine, Consumer.* **Description:** Contains the latest news on fashion, accessories, cosmetics, celebrities, travel and interior decoration.
Related titles: Online - full text ed.
Published by: Liberis Publications S.A./Ekdoseon Lymperi A.E., Ioannou Metaxa 80, Karelas, Koropi 19400, Greece. TEL 30-1-6198000, FAX 30-1-6198608, info@voguehellas.gr, info@liberis.gr, http://www.voguehellas.gr, http://www.liberis.gr. Circ: 33,279 (paid and controlled).

640 USA ISSN 0042-8000
CODEN: IBISAL
VOGUE. Text in English. 1892. m. USD 18 domestic; USD 50 in Canada; USD 60 elsewhere (effective 2005). adv. bk.rev. illus. Index. back issues avail.; reprint service avail. from PQC. **Document type:** *Magazine, Consumer.* **Description:** Features trends in haute couture, along with advance information on the international fashion scene.
Related titles: Microfilm ed.: (from PQC); Microform ed.: (from PQC); ♦ Online - full text ed.: Style.com; (from Gale Group, LexisNexis); ♦ Spanish ed.: Vogue Latinoamerica. ISSN 1556-2123; ♦ Regional ed(s).: Vogue Australia. ISSN 0042-8019; ♦ Vogue Italia. ISSN 0042-8027; ♦ Vogue (France). ISSN 0750-3628; ♦ Vogue (British Edition). ISSN 0262-2130; ♦ Vogue (German Edition). ISSN 0176-6104; ♦ Vogue Rossiya. ISSN 1560-2524; Vogue Brasil. ISSN 0104-5121.
Indexed: Acal, BHA, DAAI, MRD, MagInd, PMR, PSI, RASB, RGAb, RGPR, RI-1, RI-2, TOM.
—BLDSC (9251.415000), IE, Infotrieve.
Published by: Conde Nast Publications, Inc., 750 3rd Ave, New York, NY 10017. TEL 212-630-3740, 800-227-5741, FAX 212-630-5899, http://www.style.com, http://www.condenast.com. Eds. Anna Wintour, Thomas J Wallace. Pubs. Thomas Florio, Thomas Florio. Adv. contact Tim O'Connor. B&W page USD 55,265, color page USD 64,985; trim 8 x 10.88. Circ: 1,260,026 (paid). **Subscr. to:** PO Box 55980, Boulder, CO 80322. **Dist. in UK by:** Comag, Tavistock Works, Tavistock Rd, W Drayton, Middx UB7 7QX, United Kingdom. TEL 44-1895-444055, 44-1895-433800.

640 GBR ISSN 0262-2130
VOGUE (BRITISH EDITION). Text in English. 1916. m. GBP 27.50 domestic; GBP 70 in Europe & the US; GBP 96 elsewhere (effective 2004). adv. bk.rev. illus. **Document type:** *Consumer.* **Description:** Presents the up-and-coming and down-and-out, do's and don'ts, and hot and cold styles and personalities involved in the beauty and fashion worlds.
Related titles: Online - full text ed.; ♦ Regional ed(s).: Vogue. ISSN 0042-8000.
Indexed: DAAI, GdIns.
—IE.
Published by: Conde Nast Publications Ltd., Vogue House, Hanover Sq, London, W1R 0AD, United Kingdom. TEL 44-171-499-9080, FAX 44-171-493-1345, pluard@condenast.co.uk, http://www.vogue.co.uk. Ed. Alexandra Shulman. Pub. Stephen Quinn. Circ: 188,669. **Subscr. to:** Tower House, Tower House, Sovereign Park, Market Harborough, Leics LE16 9EF, United Kingdom. TEL 44-1858-438815, FAX 44-1858-434958. **Dist. by:** Comag, Tavistock Works, Tavistock Rd, W Drayton, Middx UB7 7QX, United Kingdom. TEL 44-1895-444055, FAX 44-1895-433602.

640 FRA ISSN 0750-3628
AP20
VOGUE (FRANCE). Text in French. 1921. 10/yr. EUR 29.95 domestic; EUR 154 in Australia & New Zealand; EUR 115.10 in US & Canada; EUR 62.50 newsstand/cover in Europe (effective 2004). adv. bk.rev. **Document type:** *Consumer.* **Description:** French fashion with sections on beauty, health, travel, cinema, and lifestyles.
Related titles: ♦ Regional ed(s).: Vogue. ISSN 0042-8000.
Indexed: DAAI, RASB, RGAb.
—IE, Infotrieve.
Published by: Publications Conde Nast S.A., 56 A rue du Faubourg Saint-Honore, Paris, 75008, France. TEL 33-1-41494149, FAX 33-1-40890430, sante-mag@sante-mag.com, http://www.vogueparis.com/, http://www.sante.mag.tm.fr. Ed. Joan Juliet Buck. Pub. Gardner Bellanger. Adv. contact Helene Mengus. Circ: 102,297 (paid). **Subscr. in US to:** International Subscriptions Inc., 30 Montgomery St., 7th Fl., Jersey City, NJ 07302. TEL 201-451-9420. **Dist. in UK by:** Comag, Tavistock Works, Tavistock Rd, W Drayton, Middx UB7 7QX, United Kingdom. TEL 44-1895-444055, FAX 44-1895-433602.

746.96 DEU ISSN 0176-6104
VOGUE (GERMAN EDITION). Text in German. 1979. m. EUR 51.60; EUR 5 newsstand/cover (effective 2002). adv. **Document type:** *Magazine, Consumer.* **Description:** Beauty, fashion and lifestyle in Germany.
Related titles: ♦ Regional ed(s).: Vogue. ISSN 0042-8000.
Indexed: DAAI.
Published by: Conde Nast Verlag GmbH, Ainmillerstr 8, Munich, 80801, Germany. TEL 49-89-38104-0, FAX 49-89-38104230, hdr@vogue.de, feedback@condenet.de, http://www.vogue.de, http://www.condenast.de. Ed. Angelica Blechschmidt. Pub. Wolf Hoffmann. Adv. contact Dagmar Huber. page EUR 21,700. Circ: 126,644 (paid).

640 AUS ISSN 0042-8019
VOGUE AUSTRALIA. Text in English. 1959. m. AUD 69 domestic; AUD 110 in New Zealand; AUD 160 elsewhere; AUD 6.95 newsstand/cover (effective 2004). adv. bk.rev. **Document type:** *Magazine, Consumer.* **Description:** Covers all aspects of fashion, celebrities, beauty, health, and entertainment.
Related titles: ♦ Regional ed(s).: Vogue. ISSN 0042-8000.
Indexed: GdIns.
Published by: The Federal Publishing Company, 180 Bourke Rd, Alexandria, NSW 2015, Australia. TEL 61-2-93536666, FAX 61-2-93530101, contactus@fpc.com.au, http://www.vogue.com.au, http://www.fpc.com.au. Ed. Kirstie Clements. adv.: page AUD 9,500. Circ: 345,000.

646 ITA ISSN 1120-7787
TT635
VOGUE BAMBINI. Text in Italian. bi-m. EUR 15.60 (effective 2005). adv. **Document type:** *Magazine, Consumer.*
Indexed: DAAI.
Published by: Edizioni Conde Nast SpA (Subsidiary of: Arnoldo Mondadori Editore SpA), Piazza Castello 27, Milan, MI 20122, Italy. info@condenet.it, http://www.condenast.it. Ed. G Parabiago. Circ: 45,000.

640 ITA ISSN 0042-8027
TT500
VOGUE ITALIA. Text in Italian. 1950. m. EUR 30 domestic; EUR 79.20 in Europe; EUR 156.70 elsewhere (effective 2005). adv. illus. **Document type:** *Magazine, Consumer.*
Related titles: ♦ Regional ed(s).: Vogue. ISSN 0042-8000.
Indexed: DAAI.
—IE, Infotrieve.
Published by: Edizioni Conde Nast SpA (Subsidiary of: Arnoldo Mondadori Editore SpA), Piazza Castello 27, Milan, MI 20122, Italy. info@condenet.it, http://www.condenast.it. Ed. Franca Sozzani. Circ: 73,773.

640 USA ISSN 1556-2123
TT500
VOGUE LATINOAMERICA. Text in Spanish. 1999 (Oct.). m. USD 18 domestic; USD 30 in Canada; USD 36 elsewhere (effective 2001). adv. **Document type:** *Magazine, Consumer.*
Formerly (until June 2005): Vogue en Espanol (1527-0424)
Related titles: ♦ English ed.: Vogue. ISSN 0042-8000.
Published by: Conde Nast Americas, 1101 Brickell Ave 15th Fl, Miami, FL 33131. TEL 305-371-9393, 800-792-5999, FAX 305-371-9392, vogue@ideaspublishinggroup.com, http://www.ideaspublishinggroup.com/magazines/vogue.html. adv.: page USD 40,500; trim 8 x 10.875. Circ: 195,000 (paid and controlled).

640 JPN ISSN 1345-0972
VOGUE NIPPON. Text in Japanese. 1999. m. adv. **Document type:** *Magazine, Consumer.*
Published by: Nikkei Business Publications Inc. (Subsidiary of: Nihon Keizai Shimbun, Inc.), 1-9-5 Otemachi Chiyoda-ku, Tokyo, 100 8066, Japan. TEL 81-3-52552312, FAX 81-3-5255-2631, http://www.nikkeipb.com.

646.4 USA ISSN 0095-2788
TT500
VOGUE PATTERNS. Text in English. 1915. bi-m. USD 12.95 (effective 2005). adv. illus. **Document type:** *Magazine, Consumer.*
Formerly (until 1972): Vogue Pattern Book International (0042-8043)
Related titles: ♦ Regional ed(s).: Vogue Patterns. British Edition. ISSN 0142-338X.
—CCC.
Published by: Soho Publishing Company, 161 Ave of the Americas, New York, NY 10013. TEL 212-620-2500, http://www.voguepatterns.com. Eds. Deborah Osis, Kathy Marrone. R&P Joe Anselmo. Adv. contact Doreen Connors TEL 212-620-2539. B&W page USD 5,410, color page USD 7,245; trim 8.25 x 10.75. Circ: 225,000.

646.4 GBR ISSN 0142-338X
VOGUE PATTERNS. BRITISH EDITION. Text in English. 1939. bi-m. **Document type:** *Magazine, Consumer.* **Description:** Provides patterns and descriptions of all the latest fashions and trends for both the professional and amateur clothesmakers.
Related titles: ♦ Regional ed(s).: Vogue Patterns. ISSN 0095-2788.
—CCC.
Published by: Butterick Company Ltd., New Ln, Havant, Hants PO9 2ND, United Kingdom. TEL 44-2392-486221, 44-870-777-9955, FAX 44-2392-492769, gail@butterick-vogue.co.uk, http://www.butterick.com/. Ed., R&P Gail Goldie TEL 44-2392-489773. Pub. Keith Jones. Adv. contact Marnie Hugo TEL 44-2392-489787. Circ: 30,000 (controlled). **Dist. by:** Lakeside Publishing Services, Unit 1D, Tideway Industrial Estate, 87 Kirtling St, London SW8 5BP, United Kingdom. TEL 44-20-77206680, FAX 44-20-74989616.

746.92 685.2 ITA ISSN 1120-7795
VOGUE PELLE. Text in Italian. q. EUR 12.40 (effective 2005). adv. **Document type:** *Magazine, Consumer.*
Published by: Edizioni Conde Nast SpA (Subsidiary of: Arnoldo Mondadori Editore SpA), Piazza Castello 27, Milan, MI 20122, Italy. info@condenet.it, http://www.condenast.it. Ed. A Premoli. Circ: 13,000.

640 RUS ISSN 1560-2524
VOGUE ROSSIYA. Text in Russian. 1998. m. adv. **Document type:** *Magazine, Consumer.*
Related titles: ♦ Regional ed(s).: Vogue. ISSN 0042-8000.
Published by: Conde Nast Russia, Bolshaya Dmitrovka, 11, Moscow, 101999, Russian Federation. TEL 7-095-745-5565, FAX 7-095-745-5770. Ed. Alena Doletskaya. Circ: 150,000 (paid).

VOGUE SPOSA. see *MATRIMONY*

W. see *WOMEN'S INTERESTS*

W A D. (We'ar Different) see *CHILDREN AND YOUTH—For*

W A D. HORS-SERIE. (We'ar Different) see *CHILDREN AND YOUTH—For*

W. EUROPE. see *WOMEN'S INTERESTS*

746.9 305.4 USA ISSN 1545-7400
TT500
W W D THE MAGAZINE. (Women's Wear Daily) Text in English. 2000. s-a.
Published by: Fairchild Publications, Inc., 7 W 34th St, New York, NY 10001-8191. customerservice@fairchildpub.com, http://www.fairchildpub.com.

C

746.92   MYS   ISSN 0126-544X
Orien So. Asia 0313
WANITA. Text in Malay. m. MYR 2.50. adv. charts; illus.
Published by: Utusan Melayu (Malaysia) Berhad, 46 M Jalan
Chan Sow Lin, Kuala Lumpur, Malaysia.

391 306.81   GBR   ISSN 0961-3005
WEDDING DRESSES MAGAZINE. Text in English. 1991. q. GBP
15.60; GBP 2.90 newsstand/cover (effective 1999). **Document
type:** *Consumer.* **Description:** Features articles of interest for
the bride to be. Includes fashion and beauty care.
Published by: Nicaro UK Branch, Standbrook House, 2-5 Old
Bond St, London, W1X 3TB, United Kingdom. TEL
44-171-4998918, FAX 44-171-4991339. Ed. Isabelle Bedouk.
Dist. by: Seymour Distribution Ltd, 86 Newman St, London
W1T 3EX, United Kingdom. FAX 44-207-396-8002;
enquiries@seymour.co.uk.

WEDDINGS MAGAZINE. see *MATRIMONY*

WEDDINGS OF DISTINCTION SOUTHERN CALIFORNIA. see
MATRIMONY

746.96   AUT
WELT DER FRAU; die oesterreichische Frauenzeitschrift. Text in
German. 1946. m. EUR 24 domestic; EUR 36 foreign
(effective 2005). adv. 48 p./no.; **Document type:** *Magazine,
Consumer.*
Published by: Welt der Frau Verlags GmbH, Lustenauerstr 21,
Linz, O 4020, Austria. TEL 43-732-7700010, FAX
43-732-77000124, info@welt-der-frau.at, http://www.welt-der-
frau.at. Ed. Christine Haiden. Pub. Romana Gammer. Adv.
contact Martin Bauer. Circ: 67,073 (paid and controlled).

051   USA
WINK. Text in English. 2000. 2/yr. **Document type:** *Magazine,
Consumer.* **Description:** Contains articles and features on
cross-cultural beauty and fashions inspired by the changing
face of the American woman.
Related titles: Online - full content ed.: 2000.
Address: 601 W 26th St, 14th Fl, New York, NY 10001.
http://www.winkmag.com. Ed., Pub. Ralph Clermount.

659.152   KOR
WOLGAN MOT. Text in Korean. 1984. m.
Published by: Dong-A Ilbo, 139 Sejongno, Chongno-gu, Seoul,
Korea, S. TEL 02-721-7114. Ed. Kwon O Kie. Circ: 120,000.

646.4   JPN
WOMAN BOUTIQUE. Text in Japanese. 1979. bi-m. **Document
type:** *Consumer.* **Description:** Fashion and sewing magazine
for women.
Published by: Kodansha Ltd., 2-12-21 Otowa, Bunkyo-ku, Tokyo,
112-8001, Japan. TEL 81-3-3946-6201, FAX 81-3-3944-9915,
http://www.kodansha.co.jp, http://www.toppan.co.jp/kodansha.
Ed. Takashi Sasagawa. Circ: 150,000.

746.92   USA
WORTHSTYLE. Text in English. q. **Document type:** *Newsletter,
Consumer.* **Description:** Forecasts trends, provides fashion
tips, and shares insider information concerning the upscale
Worth women's fashion company.
Published by: The Publishing Agency, 360 Lexington Ave., 19th
Fl., New York, NY 10017. TEL 212-481-3452, FAX
212-213-1287, lsinger@thepubagency.com,
http://www.thepublishingagency.com.

XPRESS. see *ART*

677 687   ISR   ISSN 0372-7777
CODEN: YLTUAM
YALKUT; Israel textile and fashion magazine. Text in Hebrew;
Summaries in English. 1952. q. USD 80 (effective 1999). adv.
bk.rev. abstr. **Document type:** *Trade.* **Description:** Covers
developments in clothing, fashion and the textile industry in
Israel and the world, including economic issues and new
technology.
Indexed: ChemAb, WTA.
—CASDDS.
Published by: Israel Textile and Fashion Association, 12 Anna
Frank St, P O Box 243, Ramat Gon, 52526, Israel. TEL
972-3-7521133, FAX 972-3-7521141. Adv. contact Isaac
Schechter. color page USD 2,000; trim 210 x 270. Circ: 2,000.

677.028245   CHN
ZHONGGUO BIANZHI. Text in Chinese. 1999. **Document type:**
Consumer. **Description:** Provides information on knitting,
techniques, knitted fashion and more.
Contact Dist.: China International Book Trading Corp/Zhongguo
Guoji Tushu Maoyi Zonggongsi, 35 Chegongzhuang Xilu,
Haidian District, PO Box 399, Beijing, 100044, China. TEL
86-10-68412045, FAX 86-10-68412023,
cibtc@mail.cibtc.com.cn, http://www.cibtc.com.cn.

746.92   CHN   ISSN 1003-1030
ZHONGGUO FUZHUANG/CHINA GARMENTS. Text in Chinese.
1985. m. CNY 120 (effective 2004). **Document type:** *Journal,
Trade.*

Published by: Zhongguo Fuzhuang Jituan Gongsi/China
Garments Company, Jianguomenwei Dajie, Zhongfu Dasha,
Beijing, 100020, China. TEL 86-10-65813501, FAX
86-10-65813502. **Dist. in US by:** China Books & Periodicals
Inc, 360 Swift Ave., Ste. 48, S San Fran, CA 94080-6220.
TEL 415-282-2994; **Dist. by:** China International Book Trading
Corp, 35 Chegongzhuang Xilu, Haidian District, PO Box 399,
Beijing 100044, China. TEL 86-10-68412045, FAX
86-10-68412023, cibtc@mail.cibtc.com.cn,
http://www.cibtc.com.cn.

746.92   CHN
ZHONGGUO SHIZHUANG/FASHION IN CHINA. Text in Chinese.
bi-m.
Published by: Zhongguo Shizhuang Zazhishe, 82 Dong anmen
Dajie, Beijing, 100747, China. TEL 5125588. Ed. Ma Jun.

746.92   CHN
ZHONGWAI FUZHUANG/CHINESE & FOREIGN GARMENTS.
Text in Chinese. q. USD 19.50.
Published by: Dalian Fuzhuang Yanjiusuo/Dalian Garment Design
Institute, 889 Changjiand Lu, Dalian, Liaoning 116021, China.
TEL 443638. **Dist. in US by:** China Books & Periodicals Inc,
360 Swift Ave., Ste. 48, S San Fran, CA 94080-6220. TEL
415-282-2994.

646   RUS   ISSN 0321-1576
ZHURNAL MOD. Text in Russian. 1945. 4/yr. USD 111 foreign
(effective 2005). adv. illus.; pat. index. **Document type:**
Magazine, Consumer. **Description:** Covers modern fashion
styles for different ages and sizes. Provides knitting
instructions and patterns.
Related titles: ♦ Supplement(s): Modeli Sezona. ISSN
0132-0793.
—East View.
Published by: Joint-stock Company Fashion Journal, ul Nizhniaia
Krasnosel'skaia, 40/12, build 7, Moscow, 105066, Russian
Federation. Ed. N A Kasatkina. adv.: color page USD 1,300.
Circ: 100,000. **US dist. addr.:** East View Information Services,
3020 Harbor Ln. N., Minneapolis, MN 55447. TEL
800-477-1005, FAX 800-800-3839, eastview@eastview.com,
http://www.eastview.com.

746.92   USA   ISSN 1546-4717
ZINK; the essential element of style. Text in English. 11/yr. USD
28; USD 3.95 newsstand/cover domestic; USD 4.95
newsstand/cover in Canada (effective 2003). adv. **Document
type:** *Magazine, Consumer.*
Published by: Jormic Media Group, Inc., 535 34th St., Ste. 602,
New York, NY 10001. TEL 646-792-2333,
maria@zinkmag.com, http://www.zinkmag.com. Ed., Pub.
Sheriff J. Ishak. Adv. contact Luz Mejia TEL 646-792-2334.

687.13   ITA   ISSN 1124-299X
0 - 3 BABY COLLEZIONI. Text in Italian. s-a. EUR 92.96
domestic includes:Bambini Collezioni (effective 2001). back
issues avail. **Document type:** *Magazine.* **Description:**
Presents fashions for babies up to 3 years old.
Published by: Liber S.R.L., Via Curtatona, 5/m, Modena, 41100,
Italy. TEL 39-059-412643, FAX 39-059-412567,
mcagnoni@liber.it. Ed. Antonio Vergara.

032C; fashion, art & conflict. see *ART*

746.92   GBR
10. Text in English. 2001. q. GBP 45 domestic; GBP 55 in
Europe; GBP 70 elsewhere; GBP 10, USD 19.99
newsstand/cover (effective 2004).
Published by: Zac Publishing, Ltd., Unit 10, Archer St Studios,
10-11 Archer St, London, W1D 7AZ, United Kingdom.
editorial@10magazine.com, http://www.10magazine.com. Ed.
Sophia Neophitou-Apostolou.

20 ANS. see *WOMEN'S INTERESTS*

CLUBS

see also COLLEGE AND ALUMNI

327   ISR
A B C MAGAZINE INTERNATIONAL. Text in English. 1971. m.
USD 12. adv. bk.rev.
Published by: International Free-Lancers' Organization, c/o Uri
Paz, Ed., 45 Palmach St., Rishon-le-zion, Israel. Circ: 35,000.
Subscr. to: P O Box 26424, Tel Aviv, Israel.

A H E P A N. see *ETHNIC INTERESTS*

A L A WORLDWIDE DIRECTORY AND FACT BOOK. see
MILITARY

367   USA
A M B U C S. (American Business Clubs) Text in English. 1923.
q. USD 12 (effective 2003). adv. **Document type:** *Magazine,
Internal.* **Description:** News and information for officers and
members. Dedicated to creating independence and
opportunities for people with disabilities.

Published by: A M B U C S, PO Box 5127, High Point, NC
27262. TEL 336-869-2166, FAX 336-887-8451,
ambucs@ambucs.com, http://www.ambucs.com. Ed. J Joseph
Copeland. adv.: B&W page USD 600. Circ: 7,000.

A V A CHECKPOINT. see *PHYSICAL FITNESS AND HYGIENE*

367   VEN   ISSN 1316-5232
➤ **ACENTOS.** Text in Spanish. 1987. q. free. adv. bk.rev.
Document type: *Academic/Scholarly.* **Description:** Covers
general social, cultural issues.
Formerly (until Dec. 1997): Encuentros
—CINDOC.
Published by: Asociacion Cultural Humboldt, Goethe-Institut
Caracas, Av. Jorge Washington, c-Av. J. German, Roscio, San
Bernardino, Caracas, Venezuela. TEL 58-2-5526445, FAX
58-2-525621, asohum@internet.ve. Ed. Henning Schroedter
Albers. R&P Virginia Miriaya. Circ: 2,500.

367   USA
ACRON. Text in English. a.
Published by: Lambda Kappa Mu, c/o Mrs Marie Leatheman,
503 Trowbridge, Detroit, MI 48202-1341.

ADCLUBBER. see *ADVERTISING AND PUBLIC RELATIONS*

AGRADOOT. see *CHILDREN AND YOUTH—About*

790.1   UAE
AL-AHLY. Text in Arabic. 1972. m. membership. **Description:**
Covers sports and club activities.
Published by: Al-Ahly Club, P O Box 1551, Dubai, United Arab
Emirates. TEL 660528. Ed. Abdullah Al Ewais. Circ: 500.

371.83   USA
ALBRICIAS. Text in English. 1957. q. free.
Published by: Sociedad Honoraria Hispanica, c/o Frederick N
Raile, William Workman High School, 16303 E Temple Ave,
City Of Industry, CA 91744. TEL 818-867-1166. Circ: 700.
Orders to: Dr. Frank M. Figueroa, Collegium of Comparative
Cultures, Eckerd College, St. Petersburg, FL 33733.

366.16   USA
ALEPPO TEMPLE SHRINERS NEWS. Text in English. 1969.
bi-m. USD 10. adv. 32 p./no. 6 cols./p.; **Document type:**
Newspaper. **Description:** Provides news of Shrine Temple
activities, members, and hospitals.
Published by: Aleppo Shriners, 99 Fordham Rd, Wilmington, MA
01887. TEL 781-665-6466. Ed. Vaughn J McKertich. Pub.
Harvey J Waugh. Adv. contact Rosemary Small. Circ: 9,000
(controlled).

367 790.1   GRC
ALLELOGRAPHIA WORLDWIDE; publication for international
correspondence-hobby exchange personal acquaintance. Text
in English; Text occasionally in French, Greek. 1967. q. USD
6. adv.
Address: PO Box 80 200, Piraeus, 185 10, Greece. Ed. Stavros
Varonakis. Circ: 5,000.

ALPHA CONTROL. see *LITERATURE—Science Fiction, Fantasy,
Horror*

658.048   USA
ALTERNATIVE AMERICA. Text in English. 1974. s-a. USD 29.95.
bk.rev. reprints avail.
Formerly: Resources (Cambridge)
Address: PO Box 1067, St Harvard Sq Sta, Cambridge, MA
02238-1067. TEL 617-623-3795, FAX 617-876-8186. Ed.
Richard Gardner. Circ: 1,500.

**AMERICAN FANCY RAT AND MOUSE ASSOCIATION
DIRECTORY.** see *PETS*

355.1   USA   ISSN 0886-1234
THE AMERICAN LEGION. Text in English. 1937. m. USD 15
domestic to non-members; USD 21 foreign to non-members
(effective 2005). adv. charts; illus. back issues avail.; reprint
service avail. from PQC. **Document type:** *Magazine,
Consumer.*
Formerly (until 1981): American Legion Magazine (0002-9734)
Related titles: Online - full text ed.: (from O C L C Online
Computer Library Center, Inc.)
Indexed: HRIS, LRI, MagInd, PAIS, PSI.
Published by: American Legion Magazine, PO Box 1055,
Indianapolis, IN 46206. TEL 317-630-1200, FAX
317-630-1280, magazine@legion.org, http://www.legion.org/
pubs/publica.htm, http://www.legion.org. R&P Pat Marschand
TEL 317-630-1298. Adv. contact Diane Andretti. B&W page
USD 30,890, color page USD 49,235. Circ: 2,700,000 (paid).

369.1   USA   ISSN 1062-4244
AMERICAN LEGION AUXILIARY. NATIONAL NEWS. Text in
English. 1921. bi-m. USD 7 (effective 2005). adv. **Document
type:** *Trade.*
Related titles: Online - full text ed.

Published by: American Legion Auxiliary, 777 N Meridian St, 3rd Fl, Indianapolis, IN 46204-1189. TEL 317-955-3845, FAX 317-955-3884, nnpr@legion-aux.org, http://www.legion-aux.org/pr/docs/magazine/2004_05/magazine.html. Ed., R&P Tony Miller. Adv. contact Thomas Bowman. B&W page USD 10,676, color page USD 14,097; trim 10.88 x 8.13. Circ: 800,000 (paid).

AMERICAN LEGION PRESS ASSOCIATION NEWS-LETTER. see *JOURNALISM*

THE AMERICAN WANDERER. see *PHYSICAL FITNESS AND HYGIENE*

371.85   USA
ANCHORA. Text in English. 1884. q. membership.
Published by: Delta Gamma Fraternity, 3250 Riverside Dr, Columbus, OH 43221. TEL 614-481-8169, FAX 614-481-0133. Ed., R&P Barbara Fuller. Circ: 106,000.

ANNEE SPORTIVE U.S.M.T. see *SPORTS AND GAMES*

367   USA
ARCHON. Text in English. 1945. s-a. USD 6. **Description:** Serves as the official magazine of Zeta Phi Beta Sorority Inc.
Published by: Zeta Phi Beta, 1734 New Hampshire Ave N W, Washington, DC 20009-1595. TEL 202-387-3103. Ed. Sharon Hardin. Circ: 10,000.

367 917.306   USA
ARKANSAS LEGIONNAIRE. Text in English. 1921. q. USD 0.80 (effective 2000). adv. **Document type:** *Newspaper.*
Address: 702 Victory St, Box 3280, Little Rock, AR 72203. TEL 501-375-1104, FAX 501-375-4236. Ed. R A Stewart. Circ: 30,000.

366.1   GBR   ISSN 0066-7900
ARS QUATUOR CORONATORUM; transaction of the Quatuor Coronati Lodge of Research. Text in English. 1888. a., latest vol.114. USD 30 to members (effective 2003). bk.rev. index. 280 p./no.; **Document type:** *Academic/Scholarly.*
Published by: Q.C. Correspondence Circle Ltd., 60 Great Queen St, London, WC2B 5BA, United Kingdom. TEL 44-20-74057340, FAX 44-20-74048131. Ed. R A Gilbert. R&P P E Holland. Circ: 15,000.

369.43 369.463   PHL
ASIA-PACIFIC SCOUTING∗ . Text in English. 1974. m. PHP 250 domestic; USD 12 foreign (effective 2005). **Document type:** *Newsletter, Consumer.*
Supersedes: Far East Scouting Bulletin (0430-0610); Far East Scouting Newsletter; Asia-Pacific Scouting Newsletter
Published by: World Scout Bureau, Asia-Pacific Region, PO Box 4050, Makati City, MCPO 1280, Philippines. Ed. J Fried. Circ: 600.

AURORA. see *GEOGRAPHY*

369.5   AUS
AUSTRALIAN JUNIOR CHAMBER∗ . Text in English. 1973 (vol.3). 4/yr. AUD 4. adv. **Document type:** *Newsletter.*
Description: Lists events and membership information.
Former titles: Australian Jaycee (0725-3133); Enterprise (Deakin)
Address: 15 Collins St, PO Box 181, East Melbourne, VIC 8003, Australia. FAX 61-3-96960711, 61-3-96960911. Ed. Judith Eadon. Circ: 3,000 (controlled).

658   AUS
AUSTRALIAN JUNIOR CHAMBER NATIONAL DIRECTORY∗ . Text in English. 1970. a. AUD 2. **Document type:** *Directory.*
Formerly: Australian Jaycees National Directory
Published by: Australian Junior Chamber, 15 Collins St, PO Box 181, East Melbourne, VIC 8003, Australia. FAX 61-3-96960711, 61-3-96960911.

AUSTRALIAN MULTIPLES MAGAZINE. see *CHILDREN AND YOUTH—About*

AUTO UND VERKEHR. see *TRANSPORTATION—Automobiles*

367   USA
AUTUMN LEAVES∗ . Text in English. q. USD 5. **Document type:** *Newsletter.*
Published by: National Federation of Grandmother Clubs of America, 27 E Monroe St, Ste 519, Chicago, IL 60603-5600.

367   DEU
B D I C JOURNAL. (Bund Deutscher Ingenieur Corporationen) Text in German. q. EUR 10; EUR 3 newsstand/cover (effective 2003). adv. **Document type:** *Magazine, Trade.*
Published by: B D I C - Korporationsverband an Deutschen Hochschulen, Stolpmuender Str 6, Hamburg, 22147, Germany. TEL 49-40-6476681, FAX 49-40-6476681, geschaeftsstelle@bdic.de, http://www.bdic.de. Ed. Volker Alisch. adv.: B&W page EUR 800, color page EUR 1,250. Circ: 5,500 (controlled).

369.4   ZAF
B P SPIRIT. Text in English. 1993. q. adv. bk.rev. **Document type:** *Newsletter.* **Description:** Contains news items on international scouting, national scouting within South Africa, and practical ideas for Scout and Cub leaders.
Formerly (until 2001): Scouting About (1021-3562)
Published by: South African Scout Association, PO Box 2434, Clareinch, 7740, South Africa. TEL 27-21-6833910, FAX 27-21-6833716, sahq@scouting.org.za, http://www.scouting.org.za/scouts. Ed. Jay Heale. Adv. contact John Hunneyball. Circ: 800.

791.43   USA
BARBARA EDEN'S OFFICIAL FAN CLUB NEWSLETTER. Text in English. 1977. irreg. looseleaf. USD 15 (effective 1999). **Document type:** *Newsletter.* **Description:** Follows career of actress Barbara Eden through her film, television and theater reviews.
Formerly: Barbara Eden International Fan Club Newsletter
Published by: (Barbara Eden Official Fan Club), Bartels Company, PO Box 57593, Sherman Oaks, CA 91403. TEL 818-505-9084, FAX 818-761-0267, bartelsco@aol.com. Circ: 320.

BILLIE JO WILLIAMS INTERNATIONAL FAN CLUB. see *MUSIC*

BLAETTER - REVUE - RIVISTA. see *EDUCATION—Teaching Methods And Curriculum*

BOGVENNEN/BOOKLOVER. see *PUBLISHING AND BOOK TRADE*

BORUSSEN-ECHO; Monatsblatt mit freier Meinungsaeusserung. see *COLLEGE AND ALUMNI*

367   USA   ISSN 0006-8306
BOUMI TEMPLE NEWS. Text in English. 1936. m. USD 5 (effective 1999). **Document type:** *Newsletter.*
Published by: Boumi Temple A.A.O.N.M.S., Oasis of Baltimore, 5050 King Ave, White Marsh, MD 21237. TEL 410-771-0404, FAX 410-771-1999. Ed. William F Wells. Circ: 6,000.

BOYS' LIFE; the magazine for all boys. see *CHILDREN AND YOUTH—For*

369.5   BRA
BRASIL ROTARIO. Text in Portuguese. bi-m.
Address: Ave Rio Branco 125-18 andar, PT 20040-006, Rio de Janeiro, Brazil. TEL 55-21-25098142, FAX 55-21-25098130, brdiretoria@openlink.com.br, http://www.brasil-rotario.com.br/. Ed. Roberto Petis Fernandis.

BRIEFLY SPEAKING. see *LAW*

367   ESP
BROTS DE COLLCEROLA. Text in Catalan. 1970. irreg., latest vol.62, 1994. play rev. abstr.; illus.; pat.
Published by: C.E.A. Aliga de Vallvidrera, Mont D'Orsa, 17, Barcelona, 08017, Spain. Ed. Josep Morero. Circ: 150 (controlled).

BUFFALO. see *CHILDREN AND YOUTH—About*

366   FRA
BULLETIN DES ANYSETIERS. Text in French. bi-m.
Published by: Ordre International des Anysetiers, 76-78 Champs Elysees, Paris, 75008, France. TEL 1-42-25-30-68, FAX 1-45-62-11-51.

366   DEU
C C BLAETTER. Text in German. 4/yr. EUR 1 newsstand/cover (effective 2003). adv. **Document type:** *Newsletter, Academic/Scholarly.*
Published by: Coburger Convent, Triftstr 1, Munich, 80538, Germany. TEL 49-89-223708, FAX 49-89-223122, cc-blaetter@coburger-convent.de, info@coburger-convent.de, http://www.coburger-convent.de/ccblaetter/index.html. Ed. Detlef Frische. adv.: B&W page EUR 1,900, color page EUR 2,450. Circ: 15,000 (paid and controlled).

366   USA
CALIFORNIA ODD FELLOW AND REBEKAH. Text in English. 1949. bi-m. USD 4 in US & Canada; USD 6 elsewhere (effective 1999). back issues avail. **Document type:** *Newsletter, Consumer.* **Description:** Publishes for the societies of Odd Fellows and Rebekahs in California.
Published by: (Independent Order of Odd Fellows, California Lodge), Linden Publications, PO Box 129, Linden, CA 95236. TEL 800-235-8358, dons@inreach.com, http:www.ioof.org. Ed. Don R Smith. Circ: 8,972 (paid).

CALLIGRAPHER. see *HOBBIES*

CASINO CHIP AND TOKEN NEWS. see *HOBBIES*

267.242   USA   ISSN 0007-8530
CATHOLIC KNIGHTS OF AMERICA JOURNAL. Short title: C K of A Journal. Text in English. 1897. m. USD 4.20 (effective 1999). **Document type:** *Bulletin.*
Related titles: Online - full text ed.

Published by: Catholic Knights of America, 1850 Dalton Ave, Cincinnati, OH 45214. TEL 513-721-0781, FAX 513-721-0783. Ed., Pub. Richard J Berning. Circ: 7,500 (controlled).

369.5   ITA
CENTOOTTO A. Text in Italian. bi-m. free to members. adv.
Published by: (Lions International, Distretto 108A), Gruppo Editoriale Faenza Editrice SpA, Via Pier de Crescenzi 44, Faenza, RA 48018, Italy. TEL 39-0546-670411, FAX 39-0546-660440, info@faenza.com, http://www.faenza.com. Circ: 4,000 (controlled).

658.048   USA
CHERRY DIAMOND. Text in English. 1907. m. USD 25. adv.
Published by: Missouri Athletic Club, 405, Washington, MO 63102. TEL 314-231-7220, FAX 314-231-2327. Ed. James M Wilson. Circ: 4,800.

367   USA   ISSN 1075-0185
CHIME. Text in English. 19??. m. **Document type:** *Newsletter, Consumer.*
Published by: Chicago Area Mensa membership@chicago.us.mensa.org, http://www.chicago.us.mensa.org.

CHORMAGAZIN. see *MUSIC*

CHRISTIAN COURIER. see *RELIGIONS AND THEOLOGY—Protestant*

366   FRA
CHRONIQUE DES ANYSETIERS. Text in French. 1981 (no.63). m. membership. illus.
Formerly: Ordre International des Anysetiers. Chronique
Published by: Ordre International des Anysetiers, 76-78 Champs Elysees, Paris, 75008, France. TEL 1-42-25-30-68, FAX 1-45-62-11-51.

366.1   FRA   ISSN 0240-7418
CHRONIQUES D'HISTOIRE MACONNIQUE. Text in French. 1980. a. bk.rev. **Document type:** *Academic/Scholarly.*
Related titles: ♦ Supplement to: Humanisme. ISSN 0018-7364.
Published by: (Francs-Macons du Grand Orient, Institut des Etudes et de Recherches Maconniques), Editions Maconniques de France, 16 rue Cadet, Paris, 75009, France. TEL 47-70-27-15. Ed. Yves Le Bonniec. Circ: 1,500.

371.85   USA
CIRCUMFERENCE. Text in English. 1937. q. looseleaf. free. adv. back issues avail. **Document type:** *Newsletter.* **Description:** Describes activities of chapters and includes messages from the National Office and chairman.
Published by: Phi Epsilon Phi Sorority, PO Box 4096, Burlingame, CA 94011-4096. TEL 650-347-1765, FAX 650-347-1765. Ed. Barbara Latham. Circ: 500.

367   USA   ISSN 0194-5785
CIVITAN MAGAZINE. Text in English. 1920. 5/yr. USD 6 domestic; USD 8 foreign (effective 2000). adv. bk.rev. illus.
Published by: Civitan International, PO Box 130744, Birmingham, AL 35213-0744. TEL 205-591-8910, FAX 205-592-6307, civitan@civitan.org. Ed., R&P Dorothy Wellborn. adv.: B&W page USD 1,000, color page USD 1,700; trim 8.125 x 10.875. Circ: 24,000 (paid).

367   GBR   ISSN 0009-9538
CLUB COMMITTEE & NORTHERN FREE TRADE NEWS∗ . Text in English. 1967. m. adv. abstr.; illus.
Formerly: Northern Club Trade News
Published by: Provincial Trade Press Ltd., 320 Higher Ln, Lymm, Ches WA13 0TP, United Kingdom.

367   USA   ISSN 1050-8600
CLUB DIRECTOR. Text in English. 1962. bi-m. USD 18 (effective 2005). adv. bk.rev. **Document type:** *Magazine, Trade.* **Description:** Covers strategic planning, policies and procedures, taxation and capital improvements, industry trends, and financial and personnel management for officers, directors and managers of private clubs.
Indexed: H&TI.
Published by: National Club Association, One Lafayette Center, 1120 20th St, N W, Ste 725, Washington, DC 20036. TEL 202-822-9822, FAX 202-822-9808, http://www.natlclub.org. Ed. Mary Barnes Embody. Adv. contact Kevin Scullen. Circ: 9,000 (controlled).

658.048   DEU
CLUB-ILLUSTRIERTE. Text in German. 1949. a. membership. **Document type:** *Newsletter, Consumer.*
Published by: Tennisclub Weissenhof e.V., Parlerstr 102-110, Stuttgart, 70192, Germany. TEL 49-711-1654321, FAX 49-711-2572933, info@tennis-weissenhof.de, http://www.tennis-weissenhof.de. Ed. Walter Schweiker. Adv. contact Rudolf Christ. Circ: 3,000.

367   GBR   ISSN 0268-0378
CLUB JOURNAL. Text in English. 1873. m. GBP 6.60; GBP 0.60 newsstand/cover (effective 2003). stat.; tr.lit. 24 p./no.; back issues avail. **Document type:** *Newspaper, Trade.* **Description:** Provides details of club services and news of non-profit members clubs.

Formerly (until 1981): Club and Institute Journal (0009-952X)
Related titles: Online - full text ed.
Published by: Working Men's Club and Institute Union Ltd., Club Union House, 253-254 Upper St, London, N1 1RY, United Kingdom. TEL 44-20-72260221, FAX 44-20-73541847, information@wmciu.org, http://www.wmciu.org/. Ed., Pub. Kevin Smyth. Circ: 60,000.

367   USA   ISSN 0009-9589
CLUB MANAGEMENT; the resource for successful club operations. Text in English. 1922. bi-m. USD 26.95 (effective 2005). adv. illus.; tr.lit. reprints avail. **Document type:** *Magazine, Trade.* **Description:** Designed to provide information and ideas to the managers of all types of private clubs.
Related titles: Microform ed.: (from PQC); Online - full text ed.: (from bigchalk, Florida Center for Library Automation, Gale Group, Northern Light Technology, Inc., O C L C Online Computer Library Center, Inc., ProQuest Information & Learning).
Indexed: ATI, H&TI, Hospl.
Published by: (Club Managers Association of America), Finan Publishing Company, Inc., 107 W Pacific Ave, St. Louis, MO 63119-2323. TEL 314-961-6644, FAX 314-961-4809, tfinan@finan.com, teri@finan.com, http://www.club-mgmt.com. Pub. Thomas Finan. R&P Teri Finan. Adv. contact Dee Kaplan. Circ: 15,733 (paid and controlled).

CLUB MANAGEMENT IN AUSTRALIA. see *BUSINESS AND ECONOMICS—Management*

367   GBR   ISSN 0045-7213
CLUB MIRROR; the national trade newspaper. Text in English. 1968. m. GBP 32. adv. bk.rev. illus.; stat. **Document type:** *Trade.* **Description:** Advises owners and managers about how to operate clubs.
—CCC.
Published by: Quantam Publishing Ltd., 29 Lower Coombe St, Croydon, Surrey CR0 1AA, United Kingdom. TEL 44-181-681-2099, FAX 44-181-681-2389. Ed. Dominic Roskrow. Pub. Sarah Jones. Adv. contact Lorraine Wood. Circ: 25,855 (controlled).

367   GBR   ISSN 0009-9635
CLUB SECRETARY. Text in English. 1953. m. adv. bk.rev. illus.; tr.lit. index. **Document type:** *Trade.*
Published by: United Trade Press Ltd., UTP House, 33-35 Bowling Green Ln, London, EC1R 0DA, United Kingdom. TEL 44-171-837-1212. Ed. Sharon Gailer. Circ: 8,400.

367   USA
CO-ETTE MAGAZINE. Text in English. 1955. a. USD 10. adv. **Description:** Reports on the annual program of the organization and highlights the accomplishments of people associated with the club.
Published by: Co-Ette Club, Inc., 2020 W Chicago Blvd, Detroit, MI 48206. TEL 313-867-0880. Ed. Mary Agnes Mill Davis. Circ: 500.

369.5   COL
COLOMBIA ROTARIA. Text in Spanish. 1970. q. **Document type:** *Magazine.*
Address: Calle 5, no. 62-C-53, Cali, Colombia. TEL 57-2-551-5380, FAX 57-2-551-1704.

367   USA   ISSN 1059-132X
COLUMBIAN (INDIANAPOLIS). Text in English. 1906. 10/yr. USD 36 (effective 1999). adv.
Published by: Columbia Club, 121 Monument Circle, Indianapolis, IN 46204. TEL 317-767-1361, FAX 317-261-1375, http://columbia-club.org. Ed. Beverly Chalfant. Circ: 3,000.

367 615   USA   ISSN 0746-3979
LJ105.P615
COMMUNICATOR (ATHENS). Text in English. 1889. q. USD 10 (effective 1999). adv. back issues avail. **Document type:** *Trade.*
Published by: Phi Delta Chi Pharmacy Fraternity, PO Box 1883, Athens, GA 30603-1883. TEL 706-613-0300, FAX 706-613-0200, phidexnatl@aol.com, http://www.umich.edu/~jbonasso/pdcnew/home.htm. Ed. Thomas Ellington. R&P, Adv. contact Anthony D Chaffee. Circ: 4,500.

CORRESPONDENT (APPLETON). see *INSURANCE*

CROSS & CRESCENT. see *COLLEGE AND ALUMNI*

366   USA   ISSN 0740-0632
CUADERNOS DE A L D E E U. Text in Multiple languages. 1983. s-a.
Indexed: MLA-IB.
Published by: Asociacion de Licenciados y Doctores Espanoles en los Estados Unidos, c/o Reyes Fidalgo, PO Box 6846, Fullerton, CA 92834-6846. rfidalgo@fullerton.edu, http://www.aldeeu-puenteatlantico.net/index1.htm.

CUBE. see *LITERATURE—Science Fiction, Fantasy, Horror*

796   USA   ISSN 0011-4707
D A C NEWS. Text in English. 1916. 10/yr. free membership. adv. **Document type:** *Magazine, Consumer.* **Description:** Features news about social and athletic events, entertainment, membership approvals, membership listing and club activities.
Published by: Detroit Athletic Club, 241 Madison Ave, Detroit, MI 48226. TEL 313-963-9200, FAX 313-963-8891, kenv@thedac.com, http://thedac.com. Ed., Pub. Ken Voyles. Adv. contact Albert C Cochrane. B&W page USD 750, color page USD 1,480. Circ: 4,500 (paid).

367   USA   ISSN 1083-2831
DAEDALUS FLYER. Text in English. 1959. q. membership. **Document type:** *Academic/Scholarly.* **Description:** Contains historical articles, features, and membership news.
Published by: Daedalian Foundation, PO Box 249, Randolph, TX 78148-0249. TEL 210-945-2113. Ed., R&P Clem E Bellion. Circ: 17,000.

367   USA   ISSN 1527-067X
HS125
DAGOBERT'S REVENGE. Text in English. s-a. USD 14 in US & Canada; USD 21.20 elsewhere (effective 2001). **Document type:** *Magazine, Consumer.* **Description:** Covers various topics of Judeo-Christian history, royal blood-lines, modern music, conspiracy theories, the occult, fringe science, Freemasonry, the Holy Grail, the Knights Templar, and various other esoteric subjects.
Address: 10204 SW Conestoga Dr., Apt. 20, Beaverton, OR 97008-4006. http://www.dagobertsrevenge.com/. Pubs. Brian Albert, Tracy R Twyman.

DANISH SISTERHOOD NEWS. see *ETHNIC INTERESTS*

DATA EXTRACT. see *COMMUNICATIONS—Television And Cable*

367   USA   ISSN 0164-8314
DEKE QUARTERLY. Text in English. 1883. q. membership. adv. bk.rev. **Description:** News and feature articles concerning the activities and members of Delta Kappa Epsilon fraternity.
Published by: Delta Kappa Epsilon Fraternity, Inc., 17310, Richmond, VA 23226-7310. TEL 313-886-2400, FAX 313-8862227. Ed. David K Easlick Jr. Circ: 25,000 (controlled).

DER DEUTSCHE SPITZ. see *PETS*

367   USA
DICKIN' AROUND. Text in English. 1986. q. membership. **Document type:** *Newsletter.* **Description:** Contains messages from the founders of this club catering to persons named Richard or any of its variations, as well as special product offerings.
Published by: (Dicks of America), Sunsponges Publishing, PO Box 600782, San Diego, CA 92160. TEL 619-582-5783, FAX 619-582-1750. Ed. Dick Monaco. Circ: 5,500.

367   GBR
DIRECT. Text in English. 1995. q. GBP 5 domestic to members; GBP 7 foreign to members (effective 2000). adv.
Published by: The Directors Guild of Great Britain, Acorn House, 214-320 Gray's Inn Rd, London, WC1X 8DP, United Kingdom. TEL 44-20-7278-4343, FAX 44-20-7278-4742, guild@dggb.co.uk, http://www.dggb.co.uk. adv.: B&W page GBP 600. Circ: 2,500.

369.402573   USA   ISSN 1044-4440
HS3260.U5
(YEAR) DIRECTORY OF AMERICAN YOUTH ORGANIZATIONS; a resource guide to 500 clubs, groups, troops, teams, societies, lodges, and more for young people. Text in English. 1988. biennial. USD 21.95 (effective 1996). adv. **Document type:** *Directory.* **Description:** Lists groups by hobby and special interest, sport, school subject, religion and more.
Published by: National Assembly of Health and Human Service Organizations, 1319 F St, NW, Ste 601, Washington, DC 20004. TEL 202-347-2080, FAX 202-393-4517, nassembly@nassembly.org, http://www.nassembly.org/. Circ: 4,000.

DOMINANT NEWSLETTER. see *PSYCHOLOGY*

796   USA   ISSN 0046-0656
DOWNTOWN ATHLETIC CLUB JOURNAL. Text in English. 1932. m. USD 20. adv. charts; illus.
Published by: Downtown Athletic Club of New York, Inc., 19 West St, New York, NY 10004. TEL 212-425-7000. Ed. Margaret B Koenig. Circ: 3,500.

371.85   USA
TO DRAGMA. Text in English. 1897. q. **Description:** Provides news in the fraternity and Greek world in general.
Published by: Alpha Omicron Pi Fraternity, Inc., 5390 Virginia Way, Brentwood, TN 37027-7529. TEL 615-370-0920. Ed., R&P Mariellen Sasseen. Circ: 70,000.

367   USA
DRY CREEK VALLEY NEWS. Text in English. irreg. (4-6/yr). adv. **Description:** Covers community news and activities.
Published by: Dry Creek Valley Association, PO Box 1221, Healdsburg, CA 95448. TEL 707-433-1120.

366   USA
DUFFLE BAG. Text in English. bi-m. free domestic to qualified personnel; USD 6 domestic (effective 2005). **Document type:** *Magazine, Consumer.*
Published by: St. Louis Area Council, B.S.A., 4568 W Pine Blvd, St. Louis, MO 63108-2179. TEL 314-361-0600, FAX 314-361-5165, jmueller@stlbsa.org, http://www.stlbsa.org. Ed. Joe Mueller.

367   ZAF   ISSN 0012-7221
DURBAN HIGH SCHOOL OLD BOYS' CLUB. BULLETIN. Text in English. 1945. bi-m. adv. abstr.; illus.; stat. **Document type:** *Bulletin.*
Published by: Durban High School Old Boys' Club, 20 Gainsborough Dr, PO Box 20092, Durban North, KwaZulu-Natal 4016, South Africa. Ed. R E Ronaldson. Circ: 2,000.

DYNAMITE INTERNATIONAL. see *MUSIC*

366   USA   ISSN 0194-9047
EAGLE LEADER. Text in English. m. membership only.
Published by: Fraternal Order of Eagles, 1229 S 110th St, West Allis, WI 53214. TEL 614-883-2200, FAX 614-883-2201.

366   USA
EAGLE MAGAZINE. Text in English. 1913. bi-m. USD 1 membership only (effective 2005). **Document type:** *Magazine, Consumer.* **Description:** Covers news, events and activities of the Fraternal Order of Eagles.
Published by: Fraternal Order of Eagles, 1229 S 110th St, West Allis, WI 53214. TEL 614-883-2200, FAX 614-883-2201, http://www.foe.com. Circ: 971,000 (paid).

366   USA   ISSN 0046-1067
ECHO (SKOKIE)∗ . Text in English. 1878. q. membership only. charts; illus.
Published by: United Order True Sisters, Inc., 100 State St, 1020, Albany, NY 12207-1801. Circ: 12,000 (controlled).

ED: ONE CLUB, ONE HORSE, ONE WORLD. see *COMMUNICATIONS—Television And Cable*

EDSELETTER. see *TRANSPORTATION—Automobiles*

306.77   USA
EDUCATIONAL T V CHANNEL NEWSLETTER. Text in English. 1982. bi-m. USD 20 to members. adv. bk.rev. back issues avail. **Document type:** *Newsletter.* **Description:** Membership newsletter of a social and support group of and for transvestites, transsexuals, transgenderists, their spouses and friends.
Published by: (Educational T V Channel), E T V C, PO Box 426486, San Francisco, CA 94142. TEL 510-549-2665. Circ: 650.

EL PASO ARCHAEOLOGY. see *ARCHAEOLOGY*

366.5   USA   ISSN 0013-6263
HS1510.E4
THE ELKS MAGAZINE. Text in English. 1922. 10/yr. USD 12 to non-members (effective 2005). adv. illus. 48 p./no.; back issues avail. **Document type:** *Magazine, Consumer.* **Description:** Contains general-interest feature articles and news of the Elks fraternity. Covers health, business, retirement, and travel.
Related titles: Online - full text ed.
Published by: Benevolent and Protective Order of Elks of the United States of America, 425 W Diversey Pkwy, Chicago, IL 60614-6196. TEL 773-755-4900, FAX 773-755-4792, magad@elks.org, http://www.elks.org/elksmag. Ed. Cheryl Stachura. Adv. contacts Cheryl Stachura, Briseida Hernandez. B&W page USD 9,346, color page USD 13,972; trim 7 x 10. Circ: 1,037,000 (paid and controlled).

367 780   USA
ELVIS NOW FAN CLUB. Text in English. 1973. q. USD 11 domestic; USD 15 foreign (effective 2005). adv. bk.rev. back issues avail. **Document type:** *Newsletter, Trade.*
Published by: International, PO Box 6581, San Jose, CA 95150. TEL 408-745-7077. Ed. Sue McCasland. Adv. contact John McCarthy. Circ: 356 (paid).

ELVIS WORLD. see *MUSIC*

366.1   USA   ISSN 0013-6794
HS351
EMPIRE STATE MASON. Text in English. 1923. q. USD 6 domestic; USD 15 foreign (effective 2000). adv. bk.rev.
Formerly (until 1952): Masonic Outlook
Published by: Grand Lodge Free and Accepted Masons of the State of New York, Committee on Publications, 37 Oliver St, Lockport, NY 14094-4615. TEL 716-434-4946, FAX 716-434-4946, http://www.esmason.com/. Ed. Stewart McCloud. R&P, Adv. contact Ronald Bower. Circ: 120,000 (controlled).

ETCH A SKETCH CLUB. NEWSLETTER. see *CHILDREN AND YOUTH—For*

EUROPHIL NEWS. see *PHILATELY*

367 USA ISSN 1093-7153
EXCHANGE TODAY; an educational publication for Exchange Club members. Text in English. 1921. bi-m. USD 6 to members; USD 10 to non-members (effective 2005). adv. illus. back issues avail. **Document type:** *Magazine, Consumer.* **Description:** Targeted for members of Exchange Club. Topics covered include American citizenship, crime prevention, education, youth, fire prevention,, community service, child abuse prevention, parenting, leadership development, volunteerism, motivation and networking.
Formerly (until 1997): Exchangite (0014-4487)
Published by: National Exchange Club, 3050 Central Ave, Toledo, OH 43606. TEL 419-535-3232, FAX 419-535-1989, magazine@nationalexchangeclub.org, magazine@nationalexchange.com, http://www.nationalexchangeclub.org, http://www.nationalexchangeclub.com. Ed., R&P Peverly Hormann. Pub. David R Nershi. Adv. contact Ellie Williams. B&W page USD 985, color page USD 1,990. Circ: 30,000 (paid).

367 POL
FEDERACJA. Text in Polish. 1929. irreg.
Published by: Federacja Polskich Zwiazkow Obroncow Ojczyzny, Komenda Glowna, Dom im. J. Pilsudskiego - Oleandry, Al 3 Maja 7, PO Box 87, Krakow, 30960, Poland. TEL 48-12-334715, FAX 48-12-322035. Ed. Jan Kucmierczyk.

369.2 POL
FEDERACJA POLSKICH ZWIAZKOW OBRONCOW OJCZYZNY. BIULETYN; narod i wojsko. Text in Polish. 1930. irreg.
Published by: Federacja Polskich Zwiazkow Obroncow Ojczyzny, Komenda Glowna, Dom im. J. Pilsudskiego - Oleandry, Al 3 Maja 7, PO Box 87, Krakow, 30960, Poland. TEL 48-12-334715, FAX 48-12-322035.

070.5 USA
FOOTPRINTS (TEMPE). Text in English. fortn. free to members (effective 2004). **Document type:** *Newsletter.* **Description:** Association newsletter geared to publishing executives.
Published by: Evangelical Christian Publishers Association, 4816 S Ash Ave, Ste 101, Tempe, AZ 85282. TEL 480-966-3998, FAX 480-966-1944, info@ecpa.org, http://www.ecpa.org/ECPA/footprints.html. Ed. Doug Ross. Circ: 700.

366 GBR ISSN 0015-7511
FORESTERS MISCELLANY. Text in English. 1836. 6/yr. GBP 5 (effective 2000). adv. bk.rev. illus.
Published by: Ancient Order of Foresters Friendly Society, College Pl, Southampton, S015 2FE, United Kingdom. Ed. K W Anthony. Circ: 6,000.

FRATERNAL LAW. see *LAW*

658.048 USA
FREE SONS REPORTER. Text in English. 1912. s-a. membership. adv. **Document type:** *Newspaper.* **Description:** Provides news of the fraternal benefit order's national bodies and subordinate lodges, as well as features about members, news on anti-semitism and Jewish interests.
Formerly: Free Son
Published by: Free Sons of Israel, 250 Fifth Ave, 2nd Fl, New York, NY 10001-6405. TEL 212-725-3690, FAX 212-725-5874. Ed. Leo Hoenig. Pub. Arlene Kyler. Adv. contact Ronald Laszlo. Circ: 5,000 (paid).

369.5 USA
FREE STATE WARRIOR. Text in English. 1966. bi-m. USD 1.50. stat.
Published by: American Legion, Department of Maryland, Inc., The War Memorial, 101 N Gay St, Baltimore, MD 21202. TEL 301-752-3104, FAX 301-752-3822. Ed. Paul F Moran. Pub., R&P Tom Davis TEL 410-752-1405. Circ: 90,000.

FRIENDS OF JULIO INTERNATIONAL NEWSLETTER. see *MUSIC*

367 GBR
FRIENDSHIP NEWS. Text in English. 1931. 3/yr. GBP 7 (effective 1999). bk.rev. **Document type:** *Newsletter.* **Description:** Contains news of events in Britain and overseas, along with news of society branches, including information on the I.F.L. Residential Centre, Peace Haven, service work, branch and membership news, and future events.
Former titles: International Friendship League. Newsletter (0020-6806); Friendship News
Published by: International Friendship League (British Section), 3 Creswick Rd, London, W3 9HE, United Kingdom. Ed. M Hewett. adv.: B&W page GBP 100. Circ: 1,100.

366 USA
FRONTIERSMAN. Text in English. 1948. q. membership. back issues avail. **Document type:** *Newsletter.*
Published by: Frontiers International, 6301 Crittenden St, Philadelphia, PA 19188-1081. TEL 215-549-4550. Ed. Chas H Clarke Jr. Circ: 1,200.

367 USA ISSN 0745-2209
HQ1871
G F W C CLUBWOMAN; magazine of the General Federation of Women's Clubs . Text in English. 1897. bi-m. USD 6 domestic; USD 12 foreign (effective 2005). adv. illus. reprints avail. **Document type:** *Magazine, Trade.* **Description:** Contains stories on projects and programs dealing with education, public affairs, conservation, home life, international affairs, and the arts.
Former titles (until 1978): Clubwoman News; (until 1976): General Federation Clubwoman (0016-6537)
Published by: General Federation of Women's Clubs, 1734 N St, NW, Washington, DC 20036. TEL 202-347-3168, FAX 202-835-0246, gfwc@gfwc.org, http://www.gfwc.org/. Ed. Sara Wees. Adv. contact Joshua Moglia. B&W page USD 850, color page USD 1,000. Circ: 15,000.

367 USA
G F W C OF MINNESOTA NEWS. Text in English. 1912. 4/yr. membership. adv. back issues avail. **Document type:** *Newsletter, Consumer.*
Formerly: Minnesota Clubwoman
Published by: General Federation of Women's Clubs of Minnesota, Inc., 5701 Normandale Rd, Ste 345, Minneapolis, MN 55424. TEL 612-920-2057. Ed., R&P Jackie Barrett TEL 507-335-7883. Circ: 3,900 (controlled).

GAY AIRLINE & TRAVEL CLUB NEWSLETTER. see *HOMOSEXUALITY*

369.4 AUT ISSN 0016-9986
GILDENWEG. Text in German. 1950. 4/yr. EUR 7.50 domestic; EUR 11 foreign (effective 2005). adv. **Document type:** *Magazine, Consumer.*
Published by: Pfadfinder-Gilde Oesterreich, Loeschenkohlgasse 25, Vienna, W 1150, Austria. TEL 43-2236-36608, blahahelmuth@gmx.at, http://www.pfadfinder-gilde.org. Ed. Helmuth Blaha. Circ: 1,200.

367 GBR
GLOBE (LONDON). Text in English. 1946. bi-m. looseleaf. GBP 15 in Europe; GBP 18, USD 29 rest of world (effective 2000). adv. bk.rev. back issues avail. **Document type:** *Newsletter.* **Description:** Directed to those who swap travel information; advertising for travel companions for budget travel.
Published by: Globetrotters Club, BCM-Roving, London, WC1N 3XX, United Kingdom. http://www.globetrotters.co.uk. Ed., R&P, Adv. contact Patti Taylor. Circ: 1,500.

GLOS POLEK/POLISH WOMEN'S VOICE. see *ETHNIC INTERESTS*

GOIL TALK. see *MUSIC*

371.85 CAN
THE GOLDEN LINKS. Text in English. 1962. 5/yr., latest vol.40, 2001. CND 7.50. 12 p./no. 3 cols./p.; back issues avail.; reprints avail. **Document type:** *Newsletter.*
Formerly: Golden Links Bulletin
Related titles: E-mail ed.; Fax ed.; Online - full content ed.
Published by: Independent Order of Odd Fellows, Grand Lodge of Manitoba, c/o Lloyd D Shelvey, PSGM, 118-4025 Roblin Blvd, Winnipeg, MB R3R 3V5, Canada. TEL 204-942-8815, FAX 204-956-9397, http://www.ioof.org/manitoba.htm. Ed., R&P Christopher I McPhaden. Circ: 450.

GOOD DAY SUNSHINE; Beatles fan club. see *MUSIC*

658.048 USA
GRAND NEST BULLETIN. Text in English. 1907. s-a. free. adv. back issues avail. **Document type:** *Bulletin.*
Published by: Honorable Order of the Blue Goose International, 12940 Walnut Rd, Elm Grove, WI 53122. TEL 414-782-7608. Ed. T M Maloney. Circ: 10,000.

GRANGE ADVOCATE. see *AGRICULTURE*

658.048 USA ISSN 0279-6694
GYROSCOPE. Text in English. 1917. 4/yr. USD 2. **Description:** Contains news, information, and announcements about the Gyro International Friendship Fraternity (a male-oriented organization promoting friendship through constructive, coherent fellowship based on tolerance, good will, and helpfulness).
Published by: Gyro International, 1096 Mentor Ave, Box 489, Painesville, OH 44077. FAX 216-352-3882. Ed. Leonard D Cary. Circ: 5,400.

366 DEU
HANNOVERSCHE SCHUETZENZEITUNG. Text in German. m. adv. **Document type:** *Magazine, Consumer.*
Published by: (Verband Hannoversche Schuetzenvereine e.V.), Winkler & Stenzel GmbH, Schulze-Delitzsch-Str. 35, Burgwedel, 30938, Germany. TEL 49-5139-89990, FAX 49-5139-899950, info@winkler-stenzel.de, http://www.winkler-stenzel.de. Adv. contact Kerstin Cordes. B&W page EUR 490, color page EUR 1,030; trim 185 x 270. Circ: 1,800 (controlled).

658.048 USA
HELLO AGAIN. Text in English. 1970. bi-m. USD 15 (effective 2001). adv. bk.rev. back issues avail. **Document type:** *Newsletter.*
Published by: Jay Hickerson, Ed.& Pub., PO Box 4321, Hamden, CT 06514-0321. TEL 203-248-2887, FAX 203-281-1322, jayhick@aol.com. Circ: 400.

791.43 USA ISSN 1082-7536
HILL VALLEY TELEGRAPH. Text in English. 1992. q. USD 20 membership; USD 25 foreign membership. adv. bk.rev.; film rev.; software rev.; video rev. illus. back issues avail. **Document type:** *Newsletter.* **Description:** Contains up-to-date news and information on the Back to the Future film series, featuring interviews with the cast and crew, and scientific studies and theories on time travel.
Published by: (Back to the Future... The Fan Club), To Be Continued..., PO Box 880, Athens, AL 35612-0880. TEL 256-757-7979, FAX 256-757-7979, time@traveller.com, http://www.bttf.com/. Ed., Pub., R&P, Adv. contact Stephen M Clark. Circ: 500.

366 HND
HONDURAS ROTARIA. Text in Spanish. 1943. m. USD 10. adv. bk.rev. charts; illus. **Description:** Covers topics of interest to Rotarians, and literary, historic, economic and social themes.
Published by: Club Rotario de Tegucigalpa, Apdo. Postal 2240, Tegucigalpa, DC, Honduras. TEL 32-7505, FAX 33-1812. Ed. Rafael O Castillo. adv.: B&W page USD 200, color page USD 300. Circ: 600.

THE HOOK (SAN DIEGO). see *MILITARY*

HOOSIER LEGIONNAIRE. see *MILITARY*

HOPPY TALK. see *MOTION PICTURES*

HORISONT. see *LITERATURE*

658.048 HUN ISSN 0139-1380
HORIZONT; veszprem megyei kozmuvelodesi tajekoztato. Text in Hungarian. 1973. q. HUF 28, USD 1. bk.rev. index, cum.index. back issues avail. **Description:** Provides information about methods in public culture in Veszprem country. Includes studies on new methods, events, reviews of cultural traditions.
Published by: Veszprem Megyei Tanacs V.B. Muvelodesi Osztaly, Lenin ter 5, Veszprem, 8201, Hungary. TEL 80 12-700. Ed. Toth Dezso. Circ: 600.

366.1 FRA ISSN 0018-7364
HUMANISME. Text in French. 1956. bi-m. adv. bk.rev.; play rev. abstr. **Document type:** *Academic/Scholarly.*
Formerly: Bulletin du Centre de Documentation du Grand Orient de France
Related titles: ♦ Supplement(s): Chroniques d'Histoire Maconnique. ISSN 0240-7418.
Published by: (Francs-Macons du Grand Orient, Institut des Etudes et Recherches Maconniques), Editions Maconniques de France, 16 rue Cadet, Paris, 75009, France. TEL 47-70-27-15. Ed. Edouard Boeglin. Pub. P Kessel. Circ: 33,000.

I F C O CLUB HOUSE. see *MUSIC*

I F C O JOURNAL. see *MUSIC*

367 NLD ISSN 0018-9707
I F L NIEUWS. Text in Dutch. 1936. bi-m. adv. **Document type:** *Newsletter.*
Published by: International Friendship League, Helper Brink 61-142, Groningen, 9722 EK, Netherlands. TEL 050-541-6113. Ed., Pub., R&P Mrs. A Y Schrage. Circ: 200.

367 USA ISSN 0019-3569
I N D A C MAGAZINE. Key Title: Indac. Text in English. 1921. bi-m. USD 20. adv. illus. **Description:** Informs the club's members of events and programs and promotes communication with the community.
Published by: Indianapolis Athletic Club, 111 E. Mccarty St., Indianapolis, IN 46225-3322. TEL 317-634-4331, FAX 317-686-4155. Ed. Aimee Helton. Circ: 3,500 (controlled).

369.5 USA
I O O F NEWS. (Independent Order of Odd Fellows) Text in English. bi-m. USD 5. illus. 30 p./no. 3 cols./p.; back issues avail. **Document type:** *Consumer.*
Published by: Independent Order of Odd Fellows, 422 Trade St. N W, Winston-Salem, NC 27101-2830. TEL 336-725-5955, 800-235-8358, FAX 336-722-7317, ioofsgl@aol.com, http://norm28.hsc.usc.edu/IOOF.shtml. Eds. Arthur A Craig, Harry V. Lohman. Circ: 412,000.

I S D A UNIONE. (Italian Sons and Daughters of America) see *ETHNIC INTERESTS*

780.42 USA
IDOL OF MY HEART ELVIS PRESLEY FAN CLUB NEWSLETTER. Text in English. 1973. m. USD 5. **Document type:** *Newsletter.*

Published by: Idol of My Heart Elvis Presley Fan Club, c/o Genie Rasmussen, Pres, 3307 W Marshall Ave, Phoenix, AZ 85017. TEL 602-841-9219.

366.1   USA   ISSN 0019-6622
INDIANA FREEMASON. Text in English. 1923. m. USD 8. adv.
Published by: Grand Lodge Free and Accepted Masons of Indiana, PO Box 38, Franklin, IN 46131. Ed. Dwight L Smith. Circ: 8,500.

INTERFACE. see EDUCATION—Teaching Methods And Curriculum

366   USA
INTERNATIONAL ODD FELLOW AND REBEKAH. Text in English. 1892. bi-m. USD 4 in US & Canada; USD 6 elsewhere (effective 1999). adv. back issues avail. Document type: Newsletter. Description: Serves a family fraternity which sponsors youth activities, educational scholarships, retirement facilities and nursing homes.
Formerly: International Rebekah News
Published by: (Independent Order of Odd Fellows, The Sovereign Grand Lodge), Linden Publications, 422 N Trade St, Winston Salem, NC 27101. TEL 336-725-5955, FAX 336-722-7317, ioof@aol.com, ioofsgs@aol.com, http://www.ioof.org. Circ: 15,000.

658.048 780   USA
INTERNATIONAL SINATRA SOCIETY NEWSLETTER. Text in English. 1979. bi-m. USD 20; USD 25 foreign (effective 1998). adv. bk.rev.; film rev. back issues avail. Document type: Newsletter. Description: Provides information on Frank Sinatra, including concert dates, records and CD's, reviews and articles.
Published by: International Sinatra Society, PO Box 7176, Lakeland, FL 33807-7176. TEL 813-646-7650. Ed. Dustin Doctor.

500   GBR
INTERNATIONAL SOROPTIMIST. Text in English. 1973. q. GBP 2.50, USD 5 (effective 2001). Document type: Newsletter. Description: Serves the 95,000 members of the Soroptimist Clubs in 121 countries; news of projects and work with the United Nations.
Published by: Soroptimist International, 87 Glisson Rd, Cambridge, CB1 2HG, United Kingdom. TEL 44-1223-311833, FAX 44-1223-467951, sorophq@dial.pipex.com, http://www.sorop.org/. Ed. Pamela Lee. Circ: 38,500.

369   USA
INTERNATIONAL WRITERS AND ARTISTS ASSOCIATION. MONTHLY BULLETIN. Text in English. m. free. Document type: Bulletin, Academic/Scholarly.
Published by: International Writers and Artists Association, PO Box 352048, Toledo, OH 43635-2048. TEL 419-531-8863.

366.1   CHE   ISSN 1562-4226
HS594.A5
INTERNATIONALE FREIMAURER-FORSCHUNG. Variant title: I F - Zeitschrift fuer Internationale Freimaurer-Forschung. Text in German. 1999. 2/yr. CHF 53; EUR 36 in Austria & Germany; EUR 34 in Europe; GBP 24, USD 41 (effective 2006). Document type: Journal, Academic/Scholarly. Description: Covers the historical and social impact of the Freemasons.
Published by: Verlag Peter Lang AG, Hochfeldstr. 32, Postfach 746, Bern 9, 3000, Switzerland. TEL 41-31-3061717, FAX 41-31-3061727, info@peterlang.com, http://www.peterlang.com. Ed. Helmut Reinalter.

INTERSERVICE. see MILITARY

355.15   USA   ISSN 0021-0560
IOWA LEGIONNAIRE. Text in English. 1924. bi-m. USD 2 to non-members. adv.
Published by: American Legion, Department of Iowa, 720 Lyon, Des Moines, IA 50309. TEL 515-282-5068. Ed. James E Demarest. Circ: 82,000.

367   ITA   ISSN 0080-3928
DS834.95
ISTITUTO GIAPPONESE DI CULTURA, ROME. NOTIZIARIO. Text in Italian. 1965. a. free. Document type: Bulletin.
Published by: (Kokusai Koryu Kikin), Istituto Giapponese di Cultura in Roma, Via Antonio Gramsci, 74, Rome, RM 00197, Italy. TEL 06-3224794, FAX 06-3222165. Circ: 2,500.

650   USA
J C I NEWS. (Junior Chamber International) Text in English. 1962. q. free to members (effective 2005). bk.rev. charts; illus. Document type: Newsletter.
Former titles: Leader (Coral Gables); J C I World (0021-3578)
Related titles: Chinese ed.; Finnish ed.; French ed.; German ed.; Icelandic ed.; Japanese ed.; Korean ed.; Spanish ed.
Published by: Jaycees International, Junior Chamber International, 15645 Olive Blvd., Chesterfield, MO 63017-1722. TEL 305-446-7608, FAX 305-442-0041, pfjci@aol.com. Ed. Peggy Fisher. Pub. Benny Ellerbe. Circ: 300,000.

384.55   USA   ISSN 1087-6154
PN2287.B4325
JACK BENNY TIMES. Text in English. 1982. 3/yr. USD 12.39 to members (effective 2004). back issues avail. Document type: Newsletter, Consumer. Description: Contains trivia, photographs, articles, and interviews pertaining to Jack Benny and his associates; providing members with research and information on Benny's life and work.
Related titles: E-mail ed.
Published by: International Jack Benny Fan Club, PO Box 11288, Piedmont, CA 94611. TEL 510-530-1243, jackbenny@aol.com, http://www.jackbenny.org. Ed., Pub., R&P, Adv. contact Ms. Laura Leff. Circ: 150 (paid).

369.5   USA   ISSN 0893-0031
JAYCEES MAGAZINE. Text in English. 1938. q. USD 10 to non-members (effective 2005). adv. bk.rev. illus. index. reprint service avail. from PQC. Document type: Magazine, Trade. Description: Promotes the purposes and objectives of the United States Junior Chambers of Commerce, which is devoted to the development of the individual for the betterment of the community.
Formerly (until Feb. 1987): Future (0016-3260)
Related titles: Microfiche ed.: (from PQC); Microfilm ed.: (from PQC).
Indexed: IAA.
Published by: United States Junior Chamber (Jaycees), 4 W 21st St, Box 7, Tulsa, OK 74102-0007. TEL 918-584-2481, 800-529-2337, FAX 918-584-4422, jayceesmagazine@usjaycees.org, directorinformationservices@usjaycees.org, http://www.usjaycees.org. Ed. Rebecca Currington. Pub., R&P John Shiroma. Adv. contact Beverly Molyneux. B&W page USD 2,400, color page USD 3,000. Circ: 132,000 (paid).

JAZZ INTERACTIONS. see MUSIC

JOCKEY CLUB BIBLIOTECA. BOLETIN. see SPORTS AND GAMES—Horses And Horsemanship

658.048   USA
JONATHAN. Text in English. 1930. m. USD 20 to members. adv. bk.rev. back issues avail. Document type: Newsletter.
Published by: Jonathan Club, 545 S Figueroa St, Los Angeles, CA 90071. TEL 213-624-0881, FAX 213-488-1425. Ed. Wanda White. Circ: 4,000.

366 360   USA   ISSN 0744-3943
JONQUIL. Text in English. 1930. q. USD 9.50. Document type: Newsletter. Description: Provides information and subjects of interest to members, covers fund raising, education, social activities, and leadership.
Published by: Epsilon Sigma Alpha International, 363 W Drake Rd, Drake, CO 80526. TEL 970-223-2824, FAX 970-223-4456, http://www.esaintl.com. Ed. Laurie Scazo. Pub. Michael Burns. Circ: 12,500.

JOURNAL FUER U F O - FORSCHUNG. see AERONAUTICS AND SPACE FLIGHT

367   USA
K J Z T NEWS. (Katolicka Jednota Zen Texaskych) Text occasionally in Czech. 1955. m. membership.
Published by: Catholic Women's Fraternal of Texas, PO Box 1884, Austin, TX 78767. Ed. Benita Pavlu.

KANSAS 4-H JOURNAL. see AGRICULTURE

642.5   DNK   ISSN 0022-8885
KANTINEN. Text in Danish. 1960. m. DKK 200. adv.
Published by: Kantineledernes Landsklub, Kolleruplund 63, Vallensbaek Strand, 2665, Denmark. FAX 45-43-54-34-52. Ed. Benno Arndt. Circ: 4,347 (controlled).

366   USA
KAPPA ALPHA PSI JOURNAL. Text in English. 1914. q. USD 10. adv.
Published by: Kappa Alpha Psi Fraternity, Inc., 2322-24 N Broad St, Philadelphia, PA 19132-4590. TEL 215-228-7184, FAX 215-228-7181, kxreed@aol.com, http://www.kappaalphapsi.com. Ed. Keflyn X Reed. R&P Richard Lee Snow. Adv. contact Melvin Davis. Circ: 23,000 (controlled).

369.43   UAE
KASHSHAFAT AL-IMARAT/EMIRATES BOY SCOUTS. Text in Arabic. 1989. q. Description: News of scouting activities in the U.A.E. and the Arab world.
Published by: Mu'assasat al- Fajr, PO Box 2004, Abu Dhabi, United Arab Emirates. TEL 446562, FAX 448228, TELEX 3516 MABANE EM. Ed. Ubaid Bukhait Al Mazrawi. Circ: 3,000.

366   USA   ISSN 1063-4665
KEY OF KAPPA KAPPA GAMMA. Text in English. 1882. q. Description: Covers career opportunities, member activities, rehabilitation fields served by philanthropy.
Published by: Kappa Kappa Gamma Fraternity, 530 E Town St, Box 2079, Columbus, OH 43215-4820. TEL 614-228-6515. Ed. William Lanford. adv.; B&W page USD 3,000, color page USD 3,950; trim 11 x 8.5. Circ: 109,000.

369.5   USA
KEYNOTER. Text in English. 1950. 7/yr. USD 4 to non-members; USD 1 newsstand/cover to non-members (effective 2001). adv.
Published by: Key Club International, 3636 Woodview Trace, Indianapolis, IN 46268. keynoter@kiwanis.org. Adv. contact Patrick Hatcher. Circ: 180,000. Affiliate: Kiwanis International.

366   CAN   ISSN 0023-1436
KIN. Text in English, French. 1921. 5/yr. CND 3. adv. bk.rev.
Published by: Association of Kinsmen Clubs, P O Box KIN, Cambridge, ON N3H 5C6, Canada. TEL 519-653-1920, FAX 519-650-1091. Ed. J D Booth.

369.5   USA   ISSN 0162-5276
HF5001
KIWANIS MAGAZINE; published for community leaders. Text in English. 1917. 6/yr. USD 12 to non-members; USD 8 to members (effective 2005). adv. illus. back issues avail. Document type: Magazine, Trade.
Related titles: Microform ed.: (from PQC).
Indexed: IFP, RehabLit.
Published by: Kiwanis International, 3636 Woodview Trace, Indianapolis, IN 46268. TEL 317-875-8755, kiwanismail@kiwanis.org, http://www.kiwanis.org. Pub. Eyjolfur Sigurdsson. Adv. contact Glenn Tourville. Circ: 239,452 (paid).

KOLPING BANNER. see RELIGIONS AND THEOLOGY—Roman Catholic

KRIKOS TON VATHMOFORON. see CHILDREN AND YOUTH—For

353.538   USA
LADIES AUXILIARY V F W. (Veterans of Foreign Wars) Text in English. 1939. m. (8/yr.). free to members (effective 2005). adv. bk.rev. Document type: Magazine. Description: Covers the activities of the Auxiliaries, latest information on the national programs, member benefits and more.
Former titles: V F W Auxiliary (0199-865X); Veterans of Foreign Wars. Ladies Auxiliary. National Bulletin
Published by: Ladies Auxiliary to the Veterans of Foreign Wars, 406 W. 34th St., Kansas City, MO 64111. TEL 816-561-8655, FAX 816-931-4753, info@ladiesauxvfw.com, http://www.ladiesauxvfw.com/magazine.html. Eds. Michelle Strausbaugh, Cara Day. Circ: 775,000 (controlled).

367   USA
LAST MONTH'S NEWSLETTER. Text in English. 1968. irreg. membership only. Document type: Newsletter.
Published by: Procrastinators' Club of America, PO Box 712, Bryn Athyn, PA 19009. TEL 215-947-9020, FAX 215-947-7007. Ed., R&P Les Waas. Circ: 16,000.

658.048   USA
LEGEND OF JENNIE LEE. Text in English. 1986. a. USD 10. bibl. back issues avail.
Published by: Exotic World, Exotic Dancers League of North America, 29053 Wild Rd, Helendale, CA 92342. TEL 619-243-5261. Ed. Greg Johnston. Circ: 5,000.

389.1   GBR   ISSN 0144-6533
LEGION. Text in English. 1921. bi-m. adv. bk.rev. Document type: Magazine, Consumer. Description: General lifestyle combining lifestyle issues with modern military developments.
Published by: (Royal British Legion), Centurion Publishing Ltd., 17 Britton St, London, EC1M 5TP, United Kingdom. legionmagazine@centurion-publishing.co.uk, http://www.thepressdesk.com/britishlegion/home.php. Ed. Claire Townley-Jones. Pub. Jason Grant. Adv. contact Sam Cutting TEL 44-20-78806200. B&W page GBP 6,280, color page GBP 8,350; trim 210 x 297. Circ: 541,891 (controlled).

305.851   USA   ISSN 0024-0958
IL LEONE; giornale ufficiale della grande loggia di California dell'Ordine Figli d'Italia in America. Text mainly in English; Text occasionally in Italian. 1929. m. USD 5. adv. illus. Document type: Newspaper.
Published by: Order of the Sons of Italy in America, Grand Lodge of California, 5051 Mission St, San Francisco, CA 94112. TEL 415-285-2933, FAX 415-586-4780. Ed. Lou Cavecche. Circ: 14,250.

367   CAN
LION. Text in English. bi-m. USD 10.
Published by: Lions International, 71 Morton Ave, Sharon, ON L0G 1V0, Canada. TEL 416-491-9905. Ed. Ellerby Farr. Circ: 23,500.

369.1   ITA
THE LION. Text in Italian. 1953. m. (10/yr.). free to members. Document type: Magazine, Consumer.
Published by: Lions International, Distretto Multiplo 108, Via Gramsci 5, Rezzato, BS 25086, Italy. TEL 39-030-2592125, FAX 39-030-2592291. Circ: 42,500.

369.5   ISL
LION. Text in Icelandic. bi-m. membership.
Published by: Lionsumdaemid a Islandi, Sigtuni 9, Reykjavik, 105, Iceland. TEL 354-561-3122, FAX 354-561-5122. Circ: 3,300.

369.5 USA ISSN 0024-4163
HS2705.L5
THE LION (OAK BROOK); an international magazine for service-minded individuals. Text in English. 1918. m. USD 1 newsstand/cover to non-members; USD 6 in North America to non-members; USD 12 elsewhere to non-members (effective 2005). adv. illus. back issues avail. **Document type:** *Magazine, Consumer.*
Published by: International Association of Lions Clubs, 300 W. 22nd St., Oak Brook, IL 60523-8842. TEL 630-571-5466, FAX 630-571-1685, thelionmagazine@lionsclubs.org, http://www.lionsclubs.org, http://www.lionsclubs.org/. Ed. Gary LaPetina. Adv. contact Mary Kay Rietz. B&W page USD 6,660, color page USD 8,175; trim 8 x 10.5. Circ: 479,996 (controlled).

366 USA ISSN 0024-4171
THE LION EN ESPANOL. Text in Spanish. 1944. bi-m. USD 5.50 domestic; USD 10 foreign (effective 2000).
Published by: International Association of Lions Clubs, 300 W. 22nd St., Oak Brook, IL 60523-8842. TEL 708-222-1776, FAX 708-795-1776. Ed. Fernando Fernandez. Pub. Winthrop W Hamilton. Circ: 86,000.

371.85 USA ISSN 1041-6935
LION OF ALPHA EPSILON PI. Text in English. 1920. q. USD 7.50 (effective 1999). adv. bk.rev. illus.
Published by: Alpha Epsilon Pi Fraternity, 8815 Wesleyan Rd, Indianapolis, IN 46268-1171. TEL 317-876-1913, aepihq@indy.net, http://www.aepihq.org. Ed. Sidney N Dunn. Adv. contact Elizabeth Long. Circ: 24,485.

369.5 ITA
LIONISMO. Text in Italian. 1974. bi-m. free to members. **Document type:** *Magazine, Consumer.*
Published by: Lions International, Distretto 108L, Via Ten Lutzu 10, Tempio Pausania, SS 07029, Italy. TEL 39-079-630520, FAX 39-079-678236, http://www.lions108L.it. Ed. D G Dario Pinti.

THE LORD OF THE RINGS; fan club official movie magazine. see *LITERATURE—Science Fiction, Fantasy, Horror*

271.83 SWE ISSN 0345-7338
LUNDAGAARD. Text in Swedish. 1920. 10/yr. SEK 170; SEK 20 newsstand/cover. adv. 32 p./no. 5 cols./p.
Published by: Lunds Studentkaar, Sandgatan 2, Lund, 22350, Sweden. TEL 46-46-14-40-20, FAX 46-211-46-56, lundagard@af.lu.se. Ed. Yens Wahlgren. Pub. Doc Stig Tejning. Adv. contact Ivar Berge. Circ: 28,000.

791.43 USA
M 3. Text in English. 1985. bi-m. USD 12 (effective 2000). back issues avail. **Document type:** *Newsletter.* **Description:** Notifies fans of Michele Lee's acting career and her personal life.
Formerly: Michele's Magic Moments
Published by: Michele Lee Fan Club, 114 Magnolia Dr, Levittown, PA 19054-2004. MLFClub@aol.com, http://www.members.aol.com/mlfclub. Circ: 100.

367 CAN ISSN 0820-4217
M C C MENSA CANADA COMMUNICATIONS. Text in English, French. 1967. 10/yr. CND 25; CND 30 in United States; CND 40 elsewhere. adv. **Document type:** *Bulletin.*
Former titles (until 1981): Mensa Canada Communications (0229-5342); (until 1978): M C 2 (0380-5344)
Published by: Mensa Canada, 329 March Rd, Ste 232, P O Box 11, Kanata, ON K2K 2E1, Canada. TEL 416-497-7070, FAX 416-497-6134. Adv. contact Ian Buyers. B&W page CND 255; trim 10.88 x 8.38. Circ: 2,945.

305.8911 USA ISSN 0024-9009
MACEDONIAN TRIBUNE. Text in English. 1927. m. (Thu.). USD 35 domestic; USD 50 foreign (effective 2005). adv. bk.rev. charts; illus. back issues avail.; reprints avail. **Document type:** *Newspaper, Consumer.*
Related titles: Microfilm ed.
Published by: Macedonian Patriotic Organization of the U S and Canada, 124 W Wayne, Fort Wayne, IN 46802-2505. TEL 260-422-5900, FAX 260-422-1348, mtfw@macedonian.org, http://www.macedonian.org. Ed. Paul Simoff. R&P, Adv. contact Virginia Surso. col. inch USD 10. Circ: 11,000 (paid).

658.048 028.5 USA ISSN 0865-1167
MAGYAR CSERKESZ/HUNGARIAN SCOUT MAGAZINE. Text in English. s-a. USD 5. back issues avail. **Description:** Contains articles of Hungarian ethnic, cultural, and religious interest for members of Hungarian Scout Troops.
Published by: Hungarian Scout Association, PO Box 68, Garfield, NJ 07026. TEL 201-772-8810, FAX 201-772-5145. Ed. Julius Pap. Circ: 1,500.

367 780 DEU
MANNHEIMER LIEDERTAFEL. MITTEILUNGEN. Text in German. 1920. bi-m. membership. adv. **Document type:** *Newsletter.* **Description:** Reports about the club's events and concerts.
Published by: Mannheimer Liedertafel e.V., Nibelungenstr 2, Bruehl, 68782, Germany. TEL 49-6202-77997, http://webrum.uni-mannheim.de/bib/krose/www/default.htm. Ed., R&P Karin Rose. Adv. contact Karin Heinzelmann. Circ: 350.

367 NLD ISSN 1383-1992
MEDEDELINGENBLAD. Variant title: Mededelingenblad / Club van Ankervrienden. Text in Multiple languages. 1979. q. EUR 40.85 domestic membership; EUR 43.15 in Europe membership; EUR 49.95 in US & Canada membership; EUR 56.75 elsewhere membership (effective 2003). **Document type:** *Newsletter, Academic/Scholarly.*
Published by: Club van Anker-vrienden/Club of Anchor Friends, c/o Hans Cornelissen, Rembrandtstraat 64, Nijmegen, NL-6521 MG, Netherlands. TEL 31-24-3235115, Ankerclub@planet.nl, http://www.ankerstein.org. Ed. Jan van der Werff. Circ: 250. **Subscr. in the US to:** 1670 Hawkwood Ct., Charlottesville, VA 22901.

367 USA ISSN 0025-9543
AS36.A4868
MENSA BULLETIN. Text in English. 1962. 10/yr. free to members (effective 2003). adv. bk.rev. illus. **Document type:** *Bulletin.* **Description:** Serves as a forum for the exchange of ideas among Mensa members, including provocative views which may challenge the perceptions, opinions, values and taste of the members.
Formerly: Interim; Incorporates: Mensa Journal; Intelligence
Related titles: Online - full content ed.: 2000 (Dec.).
Published by: American Mensa Ltd., 1229 Corporate Dr W, Arlington, TX 76006-6103. TEL 817-607-0060, FAX 817-649-5332, bulletin@onramp.net, http://www.us.mensa.org. Ed., R&P Julie Olson. Adv. contact Mark Witter. B&W page USD 2,500; trim 8 x 10.875. Circ: 45,000 (controlled).

367 GBR ISSN 0958-0638
MENSA MAGAZINE. Text in English. 1972. m. free membership (effective 2002). adv. **Description:** Contains news, features, ideas, innovations and competitions as well as full details of local group meetings planned for the coming month.
Former titles: Mensa (0958-062X); British Mensa; British Mensa Newsletter (0306-5065)
Published by: British Mensa Ltd., St. John's House, St Johns Square, Wolverhampton, Staffs WV2 4AH, United Kingdom. TEL 44-1902-772771, FAX 44-1902-392500, enquiries@mensa.org.uk, http://www.mensa.org.uk/mensa/magazine.html. Ed. Brian Page. Adv. contact Bobby Raikhy TEL 44-1902-772771. B&W page GBP 600, color page GBP 750; trim 210 x 297. Circ: 33,000.

367 USA ISSN 0025-9969
MERCURY (LOS ANGELES). Text in English. 1911. m. USD 12 (effective 2000). adv. bk.rev. **Document type:** *Newsletter.*
Published by: (Los Angeles Athletic Club), L A A C O, Ltd., 431 W Seventh St, Los Angeles, CA 90014. TEL 213-625-2211, FAX 213-689-1194, vmattera@earthlink.net. Ed., Adv. contact Vince Mattera. R&P Gary McGinley TEL 213-630-5200. Circ: 6,000.

MESEMB STUDY BULLETIN. see *BIOLOGY—Botany*

367 306.109 GBR ISSN 1460-4566
MINISTRY. Text in English. 1997. m. GBP 21; GBP 3.50 newsstand/cover (effective 1999). **Document type:** *Consumer.* **Description:** All about the wild and wonderful world of clubbing and those who participate.
Published by: The Ministry of Sound, 103 Gaunt St, London, SE1 6DP, United Kingdom. TEL 44-20-7378-6528, FAX 44-20-7408-5348. Ed. Scott Manson. **Dist. by:** Comag, Tavistock Works, Tavistock Rd, W Drayton, Middx UB7 7QX, United Kingdom. TEL 44-1895-433600, FAX 44-189-543-3606.

355.1 USA ISSN 0026-6299
MISSISSIPPI LEGION-AIRE. Text in English. 1970 (vol.43). m. USD 7 (effective 2000). **Document type:** *Newspaper.*
Published by: (American Legion, Department of Mississippi), Rankin County News, PO Box 107, Brandon, MS 39043. TEL 601-825-8333, FAX 601-825-8334. Pub. Marcus Bowers. Circ: 16,000.

367 USA ISSN 0279-8670
HS1510.W7
MODERN WOODMEN; a family and financial resource for Modern Woodmen members. Text in English. q. free (effective 2005). illus. reprints avail. **Document type:** *Trade.*
Published by: Modern Woodmen of America, 1701 First Ave, Rock Island, IL 61204-2005. TEL 309-786-6481, http://www.modern-woodmen.org/. Ed. Glough Bergh. R&P Jill L Weaver. Circ: 400,000 (controlled).

781.542 USA ISSN 1092-1125
MONKEES, BOYCE & HART PHOTO FAN CLUB; the photo club. Text in English. 1969. bi-m. looseleaf. USD 10 in US & Canada; USD 15 elsewhere (effective 2005). adv. bk.rev. back issues avail. **Document type:** *Newsletter, Consumer.* **Description:** Presents current news and information on the Monkees, Boyce and Hart.
Address: 1027 Eighth St., NW, Watertown, SD 57201-1023. TEL 605-886-3017, FAX 605-886-5514, tpcinfo@bdt.westhost.com, http://www.westhost.com. Eds. Barbara D Tarcza, Jodi Hammrich. Adv. contact Debra Hubert. Circ: 11,000 (paid).

355.31 USA ISSN 0026-9999
MONTANA LEGIONNAIRE. Text in English. 1919. m. USD 5. adv. **Document type:** *Newsletter.*
Published by: American Legion, Department of Montana, PO Box 6075, Helena, MT 59604. TEL 406-442-5260. Ed. Odelta Thomsen. Circ: 20,000.

366 USA ISSN 0027-0954
MOOSE MAGAZINE. Text in English. 1910. q. USD 2.50 to members (effective 2005). illus. **Document type:** *Magazine, Consumer.*
Published by: Moose International, Inc., Supreme Lodge Bldg, 86 A St, Mooseheart, IL 60539-1174. TEL 630-859-2000, FAX 630-859-6620, Kwehrmeister@mooseintl.org, http://www.mooseintl.org/public/moose_Magazine.aspx. Pub. Donald Ross. Circ: 1,500,000.

366 USA ISSN 0889-4760
MRS. EAGLE. Text in English. 1948. q. membership only. **Document type:** *Newsletter.* **Description:** Reports on Mrs. Eagle programs and activities at local and national levels.
Published by: Fraternal Order of Eagles, 1229 S 110th St, West Allis, WI 53214. TEL 614-883-2200, FAX 614-883-2201. Ed. Peter Ehrman. Circ: 350,000 (controlled).

366 USA
N S C A R MAGAZINE. Text in English. q. **Document type:** *Newsletter.*
Published by: National Society of the Children of the American Revolution, 1776 D St, N W, Washington, DC 20006-5392. TEL 202-638-3153. Ed. Vanra G Decker. Circ: 4,000.

790.1 UAE
NADI ABU DHABI AL-SIYAHI/ABU DHABI TOURIST CLUB. Text in Arabic, English. 1978. m. membership. **Description:** Covers club news and activities.
Formerly (until 1985): Al-Faridah
Address: PO Box 28, Abu Dhabi, United Arab Emirates. TEL 724954. Circ: 1,000 (controlled).

369 790.1 UAE
NADI AL-WASL. Text in Arabic. 1970. m. membership. **Description:** News of sporting and cultural activities.
Formerly (until 1974): Al-Zamalek
Address: PO Box 3888, Dubai, United Arab Emirates. TEL 374487. Circ: 500 (controlled).

NAROD POLSKI/POLISH NATION. see *ETHNIC INTERESTS*

369 790.1 UAE
AL-NASR. Text in Arabic. 1978. m. free. **Description:** Covers club sporting and social activities.
Published by: Nadi al-Nasr, Al-Lajnah al-Thiqafiyyah/Al-Nadi Club, Cultural Committee, PO Box 2226, Dubai, United Arab Emirates. TEL 472220. Ed. Abdullah Ibrahim. Circ: 500.

NATIONAL AMVET. see *MILITARY*

NATIONAL BETA CLUB JOURNAL. see *CHILDREN AND YOUTH—For*

NATIONAL PRESS CLUB RECORD. see *JOURNALISM*

366 USA
NATIONAL SON. Text in English. m. **Document type:** *Newspaper.*
Published by: Sons of Spanish American War Veterans, 646 Scott St, Redwood City, CA 94063-2937.

NAVY NEWS. SEA CADET EDITION. see *CHILDREN AND YOUTH—For*

355.15 USA ISSN 0028-1875
NEBRASKA LEGIONNAIRE. Text in English. 1922. m. (except Jul./Aug.). USD 4 (effective 2001). **Document type:** *Newspaper.* **Description:** Covers national, state and local American Legion activities and veterans issues.
Published by: American Legion, Department of Nebraska, PO Box 5205, Lincoln, NE 68505. TEL 402-464-6338, FAX 402-464-6330. Pub. Robert Craig. Circ: 55,000.

658.048 CHE ISSN 0257-3830
NEUE HELVETISCHE GESELLSCHAFT. MITTEILUNGEN. Text in German. 1913. 4/yr. membership. **Document type:** *Bulletin.* **—CCC.**
Published by: (Neue Helvetische Gesellschaft), Sauerlaender AG, Laurenzenvorstadt 89, Aarau, 5001, Switzerland. FAX 41-62-8245780, TELEX 981196-SAG-CH. adv.: B&W page CHF 431; trim 175 x 117.

366 USA ISSN 0028-5021
NEW ERA (ELY)/NOVA DOBA. Text in English, Slovenian. 1973 (vol.68). m. USD 1.50.
Published by: American Fraternal Union, 111 S 4th Ave E, Ely, MN 55731. TEL 218-365-3143. Ed. Julia F Pirc.

366 DEU
DER NORDDEUTSCHE SCHUETZE. Text in German. 1968. m. adv. **Document type:** *Magazine, Consumer.*

Published by: Winkler & Stenzel GmbH, Schulze-Delitzsch-Str. 35, Burgwedel, 30938, Germany. TEL 49-5139-89990, FAX 49-5139-899950, info@winkler-stenzel.de, http://www.winkler-stenzel.de. Adv. contact Kerstin Cordes. B&W page EUR 1,080, color page EUR 1,620; trim 185 x 270. Circ: 5,650 (controlled).

355.31   USA
NORTH CAROLINA AMERICAN LEGION NEWS. Text in English. 1950. bi-m. **Document type:** *Newspaper.* **Description:** Covers programs sponsored and conducted by the American Legion and news of legion events.
Published by: North Carolina Department of American Legion, PO Box 26657, Raleigh, NC 27611. TEL 919-832-7506. Ed. William Patterson. Circ: 45,000.

366.1   USA   ISSN 1088-4416
NORTHERN LIGHT. Text in English. 1970. q. free to members (effective 2005). bk.rev. cum.index every 5 yrs. **Document type:** *Magazine, Consumer.* **Description:** Contains articles on Freemasonry.
Related titles: Online - full text ed.: (from LexisNexis).
Published by: Supreme Council Ancient Accepted Scottish Rite, Northern Masonic Jurisdiction, U.S.A., PO Box 519, Lexington, MA 02420-0519. TEL 781-862-4410, FAX 781-863-1833, editor@supremecouncil.org, http://supremecouncil.org. Ed. Richard H Curtis. Circ: 320,000.

369.5   VEN
NUEVA REVISTA ROTARIA. Text in Spanish. 1992. q. **Document type:** *Magazine.*
Published by: Revista Rotaria Foundation, Calle Principal de Barrances Porte Baja, Galpon No. 8-36, Apdo Postal, Estado Tachira, Venezuela. TEL 58-76-438265, FAX 58-76-431106. Ed. Fouad Souki.

366   GBR   ISSN 0048-1408
ODD FELLOW. Text in English. 1830. m. GBP 5.30. adv. bk.rev. **Media:** Duplicated (not offset).
Published by: Independent Order of Odd Fellows, Unity Friendly Society, 40 Fountain St, Manchester, Lancs M2 2AB, United Kingdom. TEL 061-832-9361, FAX 061-832-3750. Ed. R J Bell. Circ: 7,000.

367   AUS
ODDFELLOW. Text in English. 1953. q. AUD 0.05 per issue. adv.
Published by: Grand United Order of Oddfellows, PO Box 1507 G P O, Sydney, NSW 2001, Australia. Circ: 20,000.

THE OFFICIAL MCCALLUM OBSERVER PRINT JOURNAL. see *BIOGRAPHY*

355.31   USA
OKLAHOMA LEGIONNAIRE. Text in English. q. USD 5. adv. **Document type:** *Newspaper.* **Description:** Presents national and state American Legion news, with emphasis on local post news.
Published by: American Legion of Oklahoma, PO Box 53037, Oklahoma City, OK 73152. TEL 405-525-3511, FAX 405-521-0178. Ed., R&P Jerry Askins. Circ: 41,300.

366.1   USA   ISSN 0030-1779
OKLAHOMA MASON. Text in English. 1934. m. USD 2. adv. bk.rev. **Description:** Contains news, information, photographs, and announcements on the members and activities of the Grand Lodge of Ancient, Free, and Accepted Masons in the state.
Published by: Grand Lodge of Ancient, Free and Accepted Masons of the State of Oklahoma, PO Box 1019, Guthrie, OK 73044. TEL 405-282-3212. Ed. Thomas K Wright. Circ: 49,000.

366   USA   ISSN 0030-1809
OKLAHOMA ODD FELLOW. Text in English. 1893. 6/yr. USD 3.
Published by: Independent Order of Odd Fellows, Sovereign Grand Lodge, 1610 N W Columbia, Lawton, OK 73507. Ed. Esther Stringer. Circ: 4,000.

366   USA   ISSN 1085-5017
HS2501
THE OPTIMIST (ST. LOUIS). Text in English. 1919. q. USD 4.50 to members; USD 5 to non-members (effective 2005). adv. illus. reprints avail. **Document type:** *Magazine, Consumer.* **Description:** Promotes optimism, volunteerism, and serving children and communities.
Formerly: Optimist Magazine (0744-4672)
Published by: Optimist International, 4494 Lindell Blvd., St. Louis, MO 63108-2404. TEL 314-371-6000, 800-OPT-8389, FAX 314-371-6006, magazine@optimist.org, http://optimist.org. Ed. Krista Grueninger. adv.: page USD 1,900. Circ: 105,000 (paid).

ORDER OF ONTARIO/ORDRE DE L'ONTARIO. see *GENEALOGY AND HERALDRY*

810 366   USA
OZIANA. Text in English. 1971. a. USD 3 (effective 2000). **Description:** Contains stories, artwork and quizzes about the Land of Oz.

Published by: International Wizard of Oz Club, Inc., 1407 A St., Ste. D, Antioch, CA 94509-2357. Ed. Robin Olderman. Circ: 800.

367   USA
P F A TODAY. Text in English. bi-m.
Published by: Professional Fraternity Association, PO Box 90264, Indianapolis, IN 46290. TEL 317-257-5235, FAX 317-253-5067.

P M C C MEMBERSHIP ROSTER. see *PHILATELY*

366   USA
PACIFIC ECHO. Text in English. 1907. q. USD 12 to non-members.
Published by: Neighbors of Woodcraft, PO Box 769, Oregon City, OR 97045-0769. TEL 503-656-8118, FAX 503-656-7656, http://www.nowfbs.com. Ed. Jim Collier. Circ: 10,000 (controlled).

THE PAK-SCOUT. see *CHILDREN AND YOUTH—About*

366   CAN   ISSN 0820-2605
PAPYRUS. Text in English. 1976. bi-m. free. adv. **Document type:** *Newsletter.*
Published by: Rameses Temple A.A.O.N.M.S., 3100 Keele St, Downsview, ON M3M 2H4, Canada. TEL 416-633-6317, FAX 416-633-6345. Ed., R&P, Adv. contact Otto Yoworski. Pub. Rameses Shriners. Circ: 7,300.

PARADE OF ROYALTY (YEAR). see *PETS*

366   USA
PENNSYLVANIA CLUBWOMAN*. Text in English. 1912. q. USD 1.
Published by: Penn Harris Inn, 1150 Camp Hill Bypass, Camp Hill, PA 17011-3734. Circ: 20,000.

369.5   ESP
PERSPECTIVA ROTARIA. Text in Spanish. q.
Published by: Asociacion Editorial Rotaria, PDG Vicente Carmenati Francia, Ed., Urb. los Girasoles 2, Girona, 17248, Spain. TEL 34-972-817554, FAX 34-972-825080. Ed. Vicente Carmenita Francia.

PERSPECTIVES (BLOOMINGTON). see *BUSINESS AND ECONOMICS—Management*

366   USA   ISSN 0149-8754
KF289
PHI ALPHA DELTA REPORTER*. Text in English. q. membership. adv. **Document type:** *Newspaper.* **Description:** Covers association activities.
Published by: Phi Alpha Delta, 345 N Charles St, Baltimore, MD 21201-4307. TEL 818-360-1941, FAX 818-363-5851, PADOffice@aol.com. Ed. Maree Wiggins Blackston. Circ: 95,000 (controlled).

366   CAN
PHILALETHES. Text in English. 1946. bi-m. USD 35. **Document type:** *Academic/Scholarly.* **Description:** Publishes articles of Masonic interest.
Published by: Philalethes Society, 2 Knockbolt Crescent, Agincourt, ON M1S 2P6, Canada. TEL 416-293-8071, nking@freemasonry.org. Ed., R&P Nelson King. Circ: 5,400 (controlled).

PHILATELIC EXHIBITOR. see *PHILATELY*

THE PHILATELIC FREEMASON. see *PHILATELY*

366   PHL
PHILIPPINE ROTARY. Text in English. m. PHP 180; USD 30 foreign. **Description:** Aims to advance high standards, understanding and good will in business and professions.
Address: 87 Visayas Ave, Quezon City, Philippines. TEL 632-920-3141, FAX 632-926-9807, http://www.pworld.net.ph/user/phrotmag/. Ed. Mariano Un Ocampo.

PHOTO STAR. see *AGRICULTURE*

367   USA   ISSN 1045-179X
THE PILOT LOG. Text in English. 1922. 6/yr. USD 10 domestic to non-members; USD 15 foreign to non-members; free to members (effective 2005). **Document type:** *Magazine, Trade.* **Description:** Provides articles of interest for members of an international classified service club for executives and professionals.
Formerly: Pilot International
Published by: Pilot International, PO Box 4844, Macon, GA 31208-4844. TEL 478-743-7403, FAX 478-743-2173, donna@pilothq.org, http://www.pilotinternational.org/html/news/pilotlog.shtml. Eds. Donna Ham, Jan Brown. Circ: 17,500 (controlled).

PIONNIER. see *CHILDREN AND YOUTH—For*

366   USA   ISSN 0032-163X
PLUMB LINE. Text in English. 1970. m. USD 1. illus.

Published by: (M. W. Prince Hall, Grand Lodge Free & Accepted Masons of Louisiana), Fraternal Press, PO Box 2974, Baton Rouge, LA 70821. Ed. Samuel P Jenkins. Circ: 2,800.

PODIUM. see *COMMUNICATIONS*

PORTSEA BOOMER. see *SPORTS AND GAMES*

369.5   PRT
PORTUGAL ROTARIO. Text in Portuguese. q.
Address: Apdo 1367, Porto, 4106, Portugal. TEL 351-2-3721794. Ed. Artur Lopes Cardoso.

POWER STROKE. see *SPORTS AND GAMES—Boats And Boating*

367   USA   ISSN 0887-8420
PRIVATE CLUBS; the magazine for members of city, country, athletic clubs, and resorts. Text in English. 1986. bi-m. USD 15 domestic; USD 24 in Canada; USD 45 elsewhere (effective 2005). adv. **Document type:** *Magazine, Consumer.* **Description:** Informs and entertains club members with articles on travel, health and fitness, business and finance, food and wine, and golf and tennis.
Published by: ClubCorp Publications, Inc., 3030 LBJ Freeway, Ste 350, Dallas, TX 75234-7703. TEL 972-888-7502, FAX 972-888-7338, privateclubs@clubcorp.com, http://www.privateclubs.net. Ed. Patricia Baldwin. Adv. contact Dana Fay. B&W page USD 13,105, color page USD 17,377; trim 8 x 10.875. Circ: 200,000 (paid).

THE PROBLEMIST. see *SPORTS AND GAMES*

369.5   CAN
PROGRESSION. Text in English. 1971. q. **Document type:** *Newsletter.*
Published by: Canadian Progress Club, 2395 Bayview Ave, North York, ON M2L 1A2, Canada. TEL 416-446-1830. Ed. Roy Urbach. Circ: 1,300.

367   USA
PROMETHEUS (NEW YORK). Text in English. 1973. q. USD 35 to non-members; USD 45 foreign to non-members (effective 2001). adv. bk.rev. back issues avail. **Document type:** *Newsletter.* **Description:** Caters to dominance and submissive interests. Lists events, stories, how-to, personal ads, and society news.
Published by: TES Association, PO Box 2783, Grand Central Sta, New York, NY 10163. TEL 212-388-7022, http://www.tes.org/publications/prometheus.html. Ed. M Tod.

PROSCOPOS. see *CHILDREN AND YOUTH—For*

366   USA   ISSN 0199-0144
HS1201
PYTHIAN INTERNATIONAL. Text in English. 1958. q. USD 5 (effective 2005). adv. **Document type:** *Newsletter, Trade.* **Description:** Features subordinate lodge and temple activity, officers' editorials, promotions.
Published by: Knights of Pythias, 59 Coddington St, Ste 202, Quincy, MA 02169-4150. TEL 617-472-8800, PI@pythias.org, http://www.pythias.org/pi/. Ed. Mary Wilson. Circ: 12,500.

366   CAN
PYTHIAN RECORD. Text in English. 1946. 3/yr. membership. **Document type:** *Newsletter.*
Published by: Grand Lodge Knights of Pythias of British Columbia, B 7 7155 ETC Highway, Kamloops, BC V2C 4T1, Canada. TEL 250-492-6520, FAX 250-492-6520. Ed. Edward J Eagles. R&P Marv Wilson. Circ: 2,000.

320   ITA   ISSN 1123-9700
Q C R. (Quaderni del Circolo Rosselli) Text in Italian. 1981. q. price varies. **Document type:** *Monographic series, Consumer.*
Formerly (until 1995): Circolo Rosselli. Quaderni (0392-6656)
Indexed: PAIS, RASB.
Published by: (Fondazione Circolo Rosselli), Alinea Editrice s.r.l., Via Pier Lugi da Palestrina 17-19, Rosso, Florence, FI 50144, Italy. TEL 39-055-333428, FAX 39-055-331013, http://www.alinea.it

QUEENSLAND DOG WORLD. see *PETS*

367 790.1   ZAF   ISSN 0033-6661
QUONDAM MAGAZINE. Text in English. 1944. s-a. membership. adv. bk.rev. illus. **Description:** Covers sports and related activities of the club.
Published by: Jeppe High Schools' Quondam Club, c/o MD Sparke, PO Box 24, Bedfordview, Transvaal 2008, South Africa. TEL 011-53-8720. Ed. Dave Herald. Circ: 1,800.

367   USA   ISSN 0747-2072
QUOTARIAN. Text in English. 1919. q. USD 5. **Description:** Covers quota service related information and news of club activities.
Published by: Quota International, 1420 21st St, N W, Washington, DC 20036. TEL 202-331-9694. Ed. Kathleen Thomas. Circ: 14,000 (controlled).

366 USA
RED MEN MAGAZINE. Text in English. 1970. s-a. membership. adv.
Published by: Improved Order of Red Men, PO Box 683, Waco, TX 76703. TEL 254-756-1221, FAX 254-756-4828, redman@texasinternet.com. Ed. Robert E Davis. Circ: 23,000 (controlled).

367 610.73 USA ISSN 1527-6538
REFLECTIONS ON NURSING LEADERSHIP. Text in English. 1975. q. USD 23 domestic; USD 30 foreign (effective 2005). adv. back issues avail. **Document type:** *Magazine.*
Description: Highlights the meetings, conferences, seminars, and national and international events of the organization.
Formerly (until 2000): Reflections (Indianapolis) (0885-8144)
Indexed: CINAHL, INI, MEDLINE.
—BLDSC (7332.331370). **CCC.**
Published by: Sigma Theta Tau International Honor Society of Nursing, 550 W North St, Indianapolis, IN 46202. TEL 317-634-8171, 888-634-7575, FAX 317-634-8188, melody@stti.iupui.edu, http://www.nursingsociety.org. Eds. Jim Mattson, Jeff Burnham. Adv. contacts Rachael McLaughlin, Rachael McLaughlin. B&W page USD 3,800. Circ: 125,000 (paid).

790 USA
ROBIN RIGHT FAN CLUB. NEWSLETTER. Text in English. 1980. m. free. **Document type:** *Newsletter, Consumer.* **Description:** Provides news and information about Robin Right, The Robin Right Show, Robin's Tribute to Tammy for fan club members, friends and the entertainment industry.
Media: E-mail.
Published by: Robin Right Fan Club, PO Box 676, Concord, MA 01742-0676. TEL 978-456-3457, robinright@usa.net. Ed. Donna Sheppard. Pub. Robin Right. Circ: 1,000.

ROLLING STONE. see *MUSIC*

ROMANSK FILMKLUB. see *MOTION PICTURES*

369.5 USA ISSN 0035-838X
THE ROTARIAN. Text in English. 1911. m. USD 12 (effective 2005). adv. bk.rev. illus. index. reprint service avail. from PQC. **Document type:** *Magazine, Trade.* **Description:** International service organization membership magazine.
Related titles: Microfilm ed.: (from PQC).
Indexed: AgeL, IFP, MagInd.
Published by: Rotary International, 1560 Sherman Ave, Evanston, IL 60201. TEL 847-866-3000, FAX 847-866-9732, http://www.rotary.org. Ed. Vince Aversano. Pub. R R Donnelly. R&P Cynthia Edbrooke TEL 847-866-3206. Adv. contacts Edward A Schimmelpfennig, Edward A. Schimmelpfennig. color page USD 11,150. Circ: 515,000 (paid).

369.5 NLD
DE ROTARIAN KRANT. Text in Dutch. q.
Published by: De Rotarian Krant, Stichting Rotary Administratie Nederland, Amstel 266, Amsterdam, 1017, Netherlands. TEL 31-20-4284734, FAX 31-20-6227642. Ed. Marcel Harlaar.

369.5 TWN
ROTARIAN MONTHLY. Text in Chinese. m.
Published by: Rotarian Monthly (China), 3rd fl, 18-1 Lane 14, Chi Lin Rd, Taipei, Taiwan. TEL 886-2-25418580, FAX 886-2-5418608.

369.5 FRA
LE ROTARIEN. Text in French. q.
Published by: Le Rotarien, 34 rue Pierre-Dupont, Lyon, 69001, France. TEL 33-4-78396905, FAX 33-4-78294941, http://www.le-rotarien.asso.fr.

369.5 DEU ISSN 0344-2306
DER ROTARIER. Text in German. 1951. m. EUR 3 newsstand/cover (effective 2002). adv. **Document type:** *Magazine, Consumer.*
Published by: Der Rotarier Verlags GmbH, Dammtorstr. 30, Hamburg, 20354, Germany. TEL 49-40-3499970, FAX 49-40-34999717, redaktion@rotarier.de, http://www.rotarier.de. Ed. Matthias Schutt. adv.: B&W page EUR 1,950, color page EUR 3,600. Circ: 44,400 (paid and controlled).

369.5 CHL
EL ROTARIO DE CHILE. Text in Spanish.
Published by: El Rotario de Chile, Vega de Sald'as 695, Of. 102, Edificio Lex-Casilla 846, Chillan-Nuble, Chile. TEL 56-42-231030. Ed. Herbert Domte Meindl.

369.5 PER
EL ROTARIO PERUANO. Text in Spanish. 1933. **Document type:** *Magazine.*
Published by: El/Rotario Peruano, PDG Cesar Murrilo Villacorta, Pasaje Las Musas 199, Dept 103, Torre Cesar Vallejo, San Borja, Lima, Peru.

369.5 MEX
ROTARISMO EN MEXICO. Text in Spanish. 1974. q. **Document type:** *Magazine.*
Address: PDG C.P. Jorge Villanueva R., Lopez 24-202, Mexico, 06070, Mexico. rotarismoenmex@prodigy.net.mx, http://www.rotarismoenmexico.org. Ed. Jorge Villanueva R.

369.5 ITA
ROTARY. Text in Italian. 1924. m. free (effective 2005). adv.
Published by: Rotary International, Istituto Culturale Rotariano, Piazzale Brescia 6, Milan, 20149, Italy. TEL 39-02-4818683, FAX 39-02-4819130, http://www.rotary.it/rotary.html. Ed. Gennaro Maria Cardinale. Circ: 42,000.

369.5 BEL
ROTARY CONTACT. Text in Dutch, French, German. bi-m. **Document type:** *Magazine.*
Address: Wereldtentoonstellingslaan 72, Brussels, 1080, Belgium. TEL 32-2-4203500, FAX 32-2-4201110. Ed. Johan Verhaeghe.

369.5 TUR
ROTARY DERGISI. Text in Turkish. 1983. q. **Document type:** *Magazine.*
Address: 1571 Sokak 16, Cinarli-Izmir, 35 110, Turkey. TEL 90-232-4619642, FAX 90-232-4619646, ticinfo@unimedya.net.tr. Ed. Ahmet Tukel.

366 AUS ISSN 0048-8631
ROTARY DOWN UNDER. Text in English. 1965. m. AUD 3.30, NZD 3.40 newsstand/cover (effective 2005). adv. bk.rev. **Document type:** *Magazine, Consumer.* **Description:** Provides information for Rotarians and their families in Australia, New Zealand and South Pacific.
Related titles: Online - full content ed.
Indexed: SPPI.
Published by: Rotary Down Under Inc., PO Box 779, Parramatta, NSW 2124, Australia. TEL 61-2-96334888, FAX 61-2-98915984, editorial@rotarydownunder.com.au, enquiries@rotarydownunder.com.au, http://www.rotarnet.com.au/magazine/Maggen.html. adv.: B&W page AUD 2,310, col. inch AUD 3,520; trim 205 x 276. Circ: 50,752 (paid).

369.5 ZAF
ROTARY IN AFRICA. Text in Afrikaans, English. 1926. m. ZAR 4. adv. charts; illus.
Published by: Rotary Africa, c/o Derrick S. Couper, 11 Prische House, 14 Church Road, Westville, KwaZulu-Natal 3630, South Africa. TEL 27-31-2664157, FAX 27-31-2671849, rotafrica@mweb.co.za, http://www.rotaryafrica.za.org. Ed. Peter Wrinch Schulz. Circ: 7,000.

369.5 KOR
ROTARY KOREA. Text in Korean. q.
Address: Royal Bldg 930, 5 Dangjudong, Chongno-Ku, Seoul, 110071, Korea, S. TEL 82-2-7302515, rotaryko@chollian.net, http://www.rotarykorea.org. Ed. Dong Joon Shin.

369.5 GBR
ROTARY MAGAZINE. Text in English. 1915. bi-m. GBP 6, USD 20 (effective 2000). adv. bk.rev. illus. index. **Document type:** *Bulletin.* **Description:** Information about the organization and its activities, particularly in Great Britain and Ireland.
Former titles: Rotary (0035-8401); Rotary Service
Published by: Rotary International in Great Britain and Ireland, Kinwarton Rd, Alcester, Warks B49 6BP, United Kingdom. TEL 44-1789-765411, FAX 44-1789-765570, http://www.rotary.ribi.org, http://www.rotary.org. Ed. Michael Herd. Adv. contact Esther McKeown. B&W page GBP 469, color page GBP 708; trim 185 x 272. Circ: 63,960.

369.5 EGY
ROTARY MAGAZINE (CAIRO). Text in Arabic, English, French. q.
Address: 4 Ahmed El-Rasheedy, Ard El Golf-Misr Al-Gadida, Cairo, Egypt. TEL 20-2-2914958, FAX 20-1-2915845, praxis@intouch.com, http://www.rotary2450.org.

369.5 JPN
ROTARY-NO-TOMO. Text in Japanese. q.
Related titles: English ed.
Address: 8th floor, abc Kaikan 6-3, Shibakoen 2-chome, Minato-ku, Tokyo, 1050011, Japan. TEL 81-3-34365956, 81-3-34365956. Ed. Isamu Asami.

369.5 IND
ROTARY SMACHAR. Text in Hindi. q.
Related titles: English ed.: Rotary News.
Published by: Rotary News Trust, 8 Vidwan Sundaram St, Chennai, Nungumbakkam, 60034, India. TEL 91-44-8260478, FAX 91-44-4970478. Ed. Krishnan V Chari.

369.5 CHE
ROTARY SUISSE-LIECHTENSTEIN. Text in French. q.
Published by: Schaffner Kommunikation, Aathalstr. 34, Uster, 8613, Switzerland. TEL 41-1-9941666, FAX 41-1-9941665, schaffner@blaurot.ch, http://www.rotary.ch. Ed. Roger Simon-Vermont.

366.1 USA ISSN 0035-8649
ROYAL ARCH MASON. Text in English. 1943. q. USD 1.75. bk.rev. illus. index every 3 yrs.
Published by: (Royal Arch Masons, General Grand Chapter), York Rite Publishing Co., 305 W 12th St, PO Box 529, Trenton, MO 64683. TEL 816-359-6008. Ed. William R Denslow. Circ: 115,000.

367 USA ISSN 0035-905X
HS1510.R895
ROYAL NEIGHBOR. Text in English. 1900. q. free to members (effective 2005). back issues avail. **Document type:** *Magazine, Consumer.*
Published by: Royal Neighbors of America, 230 16th St, Rock Island, IL 61201. TEL 309-788-4561, FAX 309-788-9234, contact@royalneighbors.org, http://www.royalneighbors.org. Ed. Kathy Michel. Circ: 175,000 (paid and controlled).

ROYAL SCOTTISH AUTOMOBILE CLUB OFFICIAL HANDBOOK. see *SPORTS AND GAMES*

367 USA ISSN 0036-0147
RURITAN. Text in English. 1932. q. USD 8. adv. bk.rev. illus.
Description: Promotes fellowship, goodwill and community service, and provides news of membership activities.
Formerly: Ruritan National
Published by: Ruritan National, Inc., PO Box 487, Dublin, VA 24084. TEL 540-674-5431, FAX 540-674-2304, ruritan@swva.net. Ed. Richard N Ely. R&P, Adv. contact Michael Chrisley. Circ: 36,000 (paid).

366 MLT
RUSSIAN GRAND PRIORY OF MALTA. BULLETIN. Text in English. 1964. q. donation. bk.rev. **Document type:** *Bulletin.*
Former titles: Order of St. John. Bulletin; Knights of Malta. Bulletin
Indexed: HistAb.
Published by: Russian Grand Priory of Malta, 223 St. Paul St., Valletta, Malta. Circ: 1,300.

367 SWE ISSN 0036-3790
SAMLARNYTT. Text in Swedish. 1947. 10/yr. SEK 90 to members. adv. bk.rev. illus. cum.index: 1946-1966.
Supersedes: Kaepphaesten
Published by: Samlarfoerbundet Nordstjaernan, Tideliusgatan 59, Stockholm, 11869, Sweden. Ed. Rolf Rundstroem. Circ: 6,000.

658.85 USA ISSN 0036-3898
HF5441
SAMPLE CASE. Text in English. 1891. q. free to members (effective 2005). adv. **Document type:** *Magazine, Trade.*
Description: Focuses on seniors, travel, finances, retirement planning, health, etc.
Published by: Order of United Commercial Travelers of America, 632 N Park St, Columbus, OH 43215. TEL 614-228-3276, FAX 614-228-1898. Ed. Linda Fisher. Circ: 90,000 (paid).

SAMSOM SPORTSECRETARIS. see *SPORTS AND GAMES*

THE SAND PAPER. see *HOBBIES*

SCAUTISMO VENETO. see *CHILDREN AND YOUTH—About*

367 DEU
DER SCHUETZENBRUDER; Zeitschrift fuer die Schuetzenfamilie. Text in German. 1928. m. EUR 2 newsstand/cover (effective 2002). adv. **Document type:** *Magazine, Consumer.*
Published by: Bund der Historischen Deutschen Schuetzenbruderschaften e.V., Am Kreispark 22, Leverkusen, 51379, Germany. TEL 49-2171-72150, FAX 49-2171-2080, bhds@compuserve.com, http://www.bund-bruderschaften.de. Ed. Friedhelm Ruf. Pub. Hubertus Prinz Zu Sayn Wittgenstein. Adv. contact Ralf Heinrichs. B&W page EUR 440. Circ: 10,000 (paid).

366.1 USA ISSN 1076-8572
THE SCOTTISH RITE JOURNAL. Text in English. 1904. m. USD 4 domestic; USD 17 foreign; USD 0.35 per issue (effective 2005). adv. bk.rev. index. back issues avail. **Document type:** *Journal, Internal.*
Formerly (until 1989): New Age (Washington)
Related titles: Online - full text ed.
Published by: The Supreme Council, 33 Degrees, Ancient & Accepted Rite of Freemasonry, Southern Jurisdiction, 1733 16th St, N W, Washington, DC 20009-3103. TEL 202-232-3579, FAX 202-464-0487, http://www.srmason-sj.org/web/journal-files/journal-main.htm, http://www.srmason-sj.org/web/index.htm. Ed., Pub. John W Boettjer. R&P Joan Boettjer TEL 202-232-3579. Circ: 365,000.

SCOUT MEMORABILIA. see *HOBBIES*

SCOUTING; a family magazine. see *CHILDREN AND YOUTH—About*

SCOUTS. see *CHILDREN AND YOUTH—For*

366 CAN ISSN 1711-3989
THE SENTINEL. Text in English. 1875. 6/yr. CND 15 domestic; USD 20 foreign (effective 2005). adv. bk.rev. **Document type:** *Newsletter.*
Former titles (until 2004): New Sentinel (1707-133X); (until 2002): Sentinel (0049-0202)
Related titles: Microfilm ed.
Published by: (Loyal Orange Association), Grand Orange Lodge of Canada, 94 Sheppard Ave West, Willowdale, ON M2N 1M5, Canada. TEL 800-565-6248, FAX 416-223-1324, info@orange.ca, http://www.orange.ca. Ed., R&P, Adv. contact Norman R Ritchie. page CND 150. Circ: 2,000 (paid).

C

▼ new title ➤ refereed ✶ unverified ♦ full entry avail.

366 973   USA
SEVENTEENTH CENTURY REVIEW. Text in English. 1976. 3/yr. free to members. adv. **Description:** Features the history, education, especially the heraldry and genealogy pertaining to the 17th century.
Published by: National Society Colonial Dames XVII Century, 1300 New Hampshire Ave NW, Washington, DC 20036-1595. TEL 202-293-1700. Ed. William Briggs. Circ: 13,000.

296   USA   ISSN 0745-9327
SHOFAR (WASHINGTON); the high school Jewish newspaper. Text in English. 1925. 4/yr. membership.
Indexed: IJP, R&TA.
Published by: B'nai B'rith Youth Organization, 1640 Rhode Island Ave, N W, Washington, DC 20036. TEL 202-857-1099. Ed. Lisa A Witkin. Circ: 30,000.

367 630   USA   ISSN 8750-6866
SICKLE & SHEAF. Text in English. 1910. q. bk.rev. **Description:** Publishes fraternal activities and agricultural articles.
Published by: Alpha Gamma Rho Fraternity, 1001 N Executive Hills Blvd, Kansas City, MO 64153. TEL 816-891-9200, FAX 816-891-9401, agrho@aol.com, http//www.agrs.org. Ed. Ken Root. R&P Katie Thomas. Circ: 40,000.

367 153   USA
SINISTRALIAN. Text in English. 1977. q. USD 5.75. bk.rev. back issues avail. **Description:** Provides information on the recent developments in left-handedness studies for Mensans.
Indexed: e-psyche.
Published by: Sinistral SIG, 200 Emmett Ave, Derby, CT 06418. TEL 203-735-1759. Ed. Sharlene McEvoy. Circ: 100.

367   USA
SKULL. Text in English. s-a.
Published by: Psi Sigma Alpha, 703 W Washington Dr, San Angelo, TX 76903-6717.

THE SMILE. see *MOTION PICTURES*

SOKOL POLSKI/POLISH FALCON. see *ETHNIC INTERESTS*

366   USA   ISSN 0745-0095
SOKOL TIMES. Text in English. 1905. m. USD 7. bk.rev. **Document type:** *Newspaper.* **Description:** Promotes this fraternal organization and their interest in physical activities and Slovak heritage.
Published by: Sokol U S A, 276 Prospect St, East Orange, NJ 07019. TEL 201-676-0280, FAX 973-676-3348. Ed. Ellen Kovac. Circ: 3,000.

367   USA   ISSN 0038-1446
SONS OF ITALY NEWS. Text in English. 1931. m. free. adv. bk.rev.
Formerly: Sons of Italy Magazine
Published by: Order of the Sons of Italy in America, Grand Lodge of Massachusetts, 93 Concord Ave, Belmont, MA 02178-4042. Ed. Dorothy Berlandi. Circ: 17,500 (controlled).

SONS OF ITALY TIMES. see *ETHNIC INTERESTS*

367   USA
SOUTH CAROLINA CLUBWOMAN. Text in English. 1945. q. USD 5. adv. **Document type:** *Newsletter.* **Description:** Covers club activities, and news of interest to women's organizations.
Published by: General Federation of Women's Clubs of South Carolina, 1511 Laurel St, Columbia, SC 29201. TEL 803-781-4442, FAX 803-366-9666. Ed., R&P Marian St Clair. Pub. June Troyan. Circ: 2,400.

369.1   USA   ISSN 0745-5801
SOUTH DAKOTA LEGION NEWS. Text in English. 1932. q. membership. adv. **Document type:** *Newspaper.*
Published by: American Legion, Department of South Dakota, PO Box 67, Watertown, SD 57201. TEL 605-886-3604, FAX 605-886-2870, sdlegion@dailypost.com. Ed., Adv. contact Ron Boyd. Pub. Arlin W Anderson. Circ: 27,040.

367 790.1   NLD   ISSN 1389-3963
SPORTIEF. Text in Dutch. 1999. bi-m. **Document type:** *Bulletin.* **Description:** Practical information for those who manage sports clubs and organizations.
Published by: Nederlandse Christelijke Sport Unie, Korte Bergstraat 15, Amersfoort, .3811 ML, Netherlands. TEL 31-33-4618548, FAX 31-33-4615595, sportief@ncsu.nl, http://www.ncsu.nl. Ed. Hidde van der Ploeg. Circ: 2,500 (paid).

366.1   GBR
THE SQUARE. Text in English. 1975. q. GBP 10, USD 25 (effective 2000). adv. bk.rev. back issues avail. **Document type:** *Newspaper.* **Description:** Presents a general forum for freemasons.
Formerly (until 1997): Masonic Square (0306-6088)
Published by: Ian Allen Regalia, Riverdene Business Park, Molesey Rd, Hersham, Surrey KT12 4RG, United Kingdom. TEL 44-1932-820552, FAX 44-1932-821258, mediafeats@aol.com. Ed. Leo Zanelli. R&P David Allan. Adv. contact Ena Langmead. Circ: 9,000.

366   USA
SQUIRES NEWSLETTER. Text in English. 1929. m. USD 1. bk.rev. illus. **Document type:** *Newsletter.* **Description:** For teenage boys.
Formerly: Squires (0010-2032)
Published by: Knights of Columbus, 1 Columbus Plaza, New Haven, CT 06510-3326. TEL 203-752-4303, FAX 203-752-4109, info@kofc.org, http://www.kofc.org. Ed. William O'Brien. Circ: 25,000.

658.048   USA
STATE OF THE UNION. Text in English. 1925. bi-m. membership. bk.rev.
Formerly: Men and Events
Published by: Union League Club of Chicago, 65 W Jackson Blvd, Chicago, IL 60604. TEL 312-427-7800. Ed. Betsy Buckley. Circ: 4,800 (controlled).

367 336.2   DEU   ISSN 0948-4248
STEUER-BRIEF FUER PERSONENGESELLSCHAFTEN. Text in German. m. EUR 5.80 per issue. **Document type:** *Journal, Trade.*
Published by: Deubner Verlag GmbH & Co. KG, Oststr 11, Cologne, 50996, Germany. TEL 49-221-9370180, FAX 49-221-93701890, kundenservice@deubner-verlag.de, http://www.vrp.de.

367 336.2   DEU   ISSN 0947-5303
STEUER-BRIEF FUER VEREINE. Text in German. m. EUR 5.80 per issue (effective 2005). **Document type:** *Journal, Trade.*
Published by: Deubner Verlag GmbH & Co. KG, Oststr 11, Cologne, 50996, Germany. TEL 49-221-9370180, FAX 49-221-93701890, kundenservice@deubner-verlag.de, http://www.vrp.de.

367   DEU
SUEDDEUTSCHE GEMEINSCHAFTSVERBAND. NACHRICHTEN. Text in German. 1914. m. **Document type:** *Newsletter.*
Published by: Sueddeutsche Gemeinschaftsverband, Kreuznacher Str 43C, Stuttgart, 70372, Germany. TEL 0711-560068, FAX 0711-569264.

367   USA   ISSN 0728-909X
SUNSHINE BULLETIN. Text in English. 1896. q. USD 1 (effective 2000). back issues avail. **Document type:** *Bulletin.*
Published by: International Sunshine Society, Inc., 2144 Canterbury Ct, Troy, OH 45373-9518. TEL 937-335-9244, FAX 937-332-1493. Ed. Mildred L Witham. Circ: 1,000 (paid).

SUZI DEVERAUX INTERNATIONAL FAN CLUB. see *MUSIC*

367   CHE
T C S REVUE ZUERICH. Text in German. 10/yr. **Document type:** *Newsletter.*
Published by: (Touring Club Schweiz), Kretz AG, Postfach, Feldmeilen, 8706, Switzerland. TEL 41-1-9237656, FAX 41-1-9237657, kretz_ag@bluewin.ch. Circ: 203,117 (controlled).

T U S VEREINSNACHRICHTEN. see *SPORTS AND GAMES*

367   USA
TALENT MAGAZINE. Text in English. 1831. q. membership. adv. **Document type:** *Newsletter.*
Published by: International Platform Association, PO Box 250, Winnetka, IL 60093. TEL 847-446-4321. Circ: 16,000.

366.1   TUR   ISSN 1301-2754
➤ **TESVIYE.** Text in Turkish. 1991. bi-m. TRL 200,000, USD 3 per issue. bk.rev. back issues avail. **Document type:** *Proceedings, Academic/Scholarly.* **Description:** Research studies on Masonic subjects.
Published by: Hur ve Kabul Edilmis Masonlar Locasi, Nuru Ziya Sokak 21, Beyoglu, Istanbul, 80050, Turkey. TEL 90-212-2512650, FAX 90-212-2494753, mason@yore.com.tr. Ed. Celil Layiktez. Circ: 5,000.

369.1   USA
TEXAS LEGION TIMES∗. Text in English. 1923. m. USD 2; to non-members; members $0.80. adv. bk.rev.
Formerly: Texas Legion News
Published by: (American Legion, Department of Texas), Adcraft Agency, PO Box 337, Jacksboro, TX 76458-0337. TEL 817-567-6622, FAX 817-567-6372. Ed. Missy Costello Matthews. Circ: 100,500 (controlled).

367   USA
TEXAS MASON. Text in English. 1989. q. USD 6. **Description:** Devoted to matters of interest to Texas Masons.
Formerly: Texas Free Mason
Published by: Grand Lodge of Texas, A F & A M, 715 Columbus, Box 607, Waco, TX 76703. TEL 817-753-7395. Ed. John Rasco. Circ: 185,000.

369.5   THA
THAI ROTERIA. Text in Thai. 1983. q. **Document type:** *Magazine.*

Published by: Thai Rotarian, c/o Amex Team Advertising Ltd, 276 A1, Raintree Office Garden, Rama 9 Road, Huay Kwang, Bangkok, 10320, Thailand. TEL 66-2-7196444 ext 180, FAX 66-2-7196432, kittiiss@ksc.th.com, http://www.thairotarian.org.

367   USA
THREE DOG NIGHT NEWS. Text in English. q. USD 15 domestic; USD 20 foreign (effective 2001). **Document type:** *Consumer.* **Description:** Three Dog Night Fan Club Newsletter.
Published by: Three Dog Night Fan Club, P. O. Box 1975, Rowlett, TX 75030. mad4tdn@aol.com, http:// www.threedognight.com/. Ed. Madonna Nuckolls.

THUNDER FROM HEAVEN. see *MILITARY*

367   USA   ISSN 0040-9448
THE TORCH (NORFOLK). Text in English. 1928. 3/yr. USD 20 domestic to non-members; USD 25 foreign to non-members; USD 7.50 to libraries (effective 2001). bk.rev. illus. index. reprints avail. **Document type:** *Academic/Scholarly.*
Published by: International Association of Torch Clubs, c/o R Patrrick Deans, Ed, Strickland & Jones PC, 749 Boush St, Norfolk, VA 23510-1517. TEL 757-627-7672, FAX 757-623-9740, http://www.torch.org. Ed. Patrick Deans. R&P R Patrick Deans TEL 757-464-2997. Circ: 2,850 (controlled).

369.5   ITA
TOSCANA LIONS. Text in Italian. 1972. m. **Document type:** *Bulletin.*
Published by: Lions International, Distretto 108, Via Valdelsa, 23, Castellina In Chianti, SI 53011, Italy. TEL 39-577-740374. Circ: 3,500 (controlled).

THE TRUTH (PHILADELPHIA). see *INSURANCE*

TUCKER TOPICS. see *TRANSPORTATION—Automobiles*

366 973   USA   ISSN 1070-9487
UNITED DAUGHTERS OF THE CONFEDERACY MAGAZINE∗. Text in English. 1933. 11/yr. USD 12 (effective 2000). adv. index. back issues avail. **Document type:** *Magazine.* **Description:** Focuses on Civil War and related topics.
Published by: United Daughters of the Confederacy, UDC General Headquarters, 328 North Boulevard, Richmond, VA 23220-4057. TEL 804-355-1636, FAX 804-353-1396, hqudc@aol.com, http://www.hqudc.org. Ed. William Wills. R&P, Adv. contact Rebecka Tol. page USD 1,100. Circ: 9,000 (paid).

UP MAGAZINE. see *MUSIC*

367   DEU
VERBAND DER DEUTSCHER-AMERIKANISCHEN CLUBS E.V. GAZETTE. Text in German. 1954. q.
Published by: Verband der Deutsch-Amerikanischen Clubs e.V., Taubenweg 1, Braunfels, 35619, Germany. TEL 06442-8590. Ed. Hans Kubatz. Circ: 8,700.

367   DEU   ISSN 0934-9022
VERBANDS-HANDBUCH. Text in German. 1988. irreg. looseleaf. price varies. **Document type:** *Monographic series, Trade.*
Published by: Erich Schmidt Verlag GmbH & Co. (Berlin), Genthiner Str 30G, Berlin, 10785, Germany. TEL 49-30-250085-0, FAX 49-30-25008521, vertrieb@esvmedien.de, http://www.erich-schmidt-verlag.de.

367 658   DEU   ISSN 0937-4574
DER VEREIN. Text in German. 1989. bi-m. looseleaf. **Document type:** *Bulletin.*
Published by: W R S Verlag GmbH & Co. KG (Subsidiary of: Rudolf Haufe Verlag GmbH & Co. KG), Fraunhoferstr 5, Planegg, 82152, Germany. info@wrs.de, http://www.wrs.de.

VEREIN UND MANAGEMENT. see *BUSINESS AND ECONOMICS—Management*

353.538   USA
VETERANS' BULLETIN. Text in English. 1954. q. **Document type:** *Bulletin.* **Description:** Contains all matters pertaining to veterans' affairs.
Published by: Georgia Department of Veterans Service, Floyd Veterans Bldg, 970 East, Atlanta, GA 30334. TEL 404-656-5933, FAX 404-656-5934. Ed. Charles Willey. Circ: 2,400 (controlled).

658.048 028.5   USA   ISSN 0865-3623
VEZETOK LAPJA/BULLETIN OF HUNGARIAN SCOUT LEADERS AND PARENTS. Text in English. 1952. s-a. USD 5. back issues avail. **Document type:** *Bulletin.* **Description:** Articles of Hungarian ethnic cultural and religious interest and on techniques of passing on such values through scouting and through the family.
Published by: Hungarian Scout Association, PO Box 68, Garfield, NJ 07026. TEL 201-772-8810, FAX 201-772-5145. Ed. Rev. John Adam. Circ: 1,500.

369.5   ARG
VIDA ROTARIA. Text in Spanish. 1955. q. **Document type:** *Magazine.*

Address: Calle Cordoba 954 of J.Y.K., Casilla de Correo 914, Correo Central, Rosario, 2000, Argentina. vrotaria@vidarotaria.com.ar, http://www.vidarotaria.com.ar. Ed. Jose Maria Ferrer.

VIOLA D'AMORE SOCIETY OF AMERICA. NEWSLETTER. see *MUSIC*

369.2 USA
VIRGINIA LEGIONNAIRE. Text in English. 1975 (vol.49). bi-m. USD 1.50 (effective 2001). bk.rev. 8 p./no. 4 cols./p.; **Document type:** *Newspaper.*
Published by: American Legion, Department of Virginia, 1708 Commonwealth Ave., Richmond, VA 23230-3537. TEL 804-353-6606, FAX 804-358-1940. Ed. Dale D Chapman. Circ: 55,000.

369.5 ITA
VITA LIONS. Text in Italian. bi-m. (7/yr.). free to members. **Document type:** *Newsletter, Consumer.*
Published by: Lions International della Lombardia, Via Don Sturzo 7, Monza, MI 20052, Italy. Circ: 10,000.

367 CAN ISSN 1201-6179
VOYAGEUR (WOODBRIDGE). Text in English. 1990. m. CND 30 to members (effective 2000). adv. bk.rev. **Document type:** *Newsletter.* **Description:** Covers Star Trek and other science fiction, as well as media news, puzzles, creative articles.
Published by: (U.S.S. Hudson Bay), Infinite Diversity International Corporation, c/o Lynda Ciaschini, 7050 Weston Rd, Ste 301, Woodbridge, ON L4L 8G7, Canada. TEL 905-850-6080, FAX 905-850-6082, llc@col.com, http://www.clo.com/~bru2/idie/idie2.htm. Ed., Adv. contact Karen Bennett. R&P Lynda L Ciaschini. page CND 25. Circ: 200 (paid and controlled).

366 USA ISSN 0042-9384
HS2008.L49
VYTIS✶ /KNIGHT. Text in English, Lithuanian. 1915. 10/yr. USD 8. adv. bk.rev.
Related titles: Microfilm ed.: 1915.
Published by: Knights of Lithuania, 6591 McEwen Rd., Centerville, OH 45459. TEL 513-433-2702. Ed. Aldona Ryan. Circ: 3,000.

AL-WA'I. see *CHILDREN AND YOUTH—For*

367 USA
WESTCHESTER COUNTRY CLUB NEWS. Text in English. 1933. 7/yr. USD 20. adv.
Published by: Westchester Country Club, 99 Biltmore Ave, Rye, NY 10580. TEL 914-967-6000. Ed. Cathy McCabe.

658 808.838 USA
WESTWIND (SEATTLE). Text in English. 1977. m. USD 15; USD 18 foreign. adv. bk.rev.; film rev. back issues avail. **Description:** Publishes fiction, non-fiction, artwork, editorials, reviews and event listings.
Formerly: Northwest Science Fiction Society. Newsletter.
Published by: Northwest Science Fiction Society, PO Box 24207, Seattle, WA 98124-0207. TEL 206-248-2010. Circ: 300.

WHOOP 'N' HOLLER. see *SPORTS AND GAMES—Outdoor Life*

367 USA ISSN 0043-5864
WINGED HEAD. Text in English. 1911. m. USD 18. adv.
Published by: Pittsburgh Athletic Association, 4215 Fifth Ave, Pittsburgh, PA 15213. TEL 412-621-2400, FAX 412-321-4541. Ed. Kevin J Gordon. Circ: 3,500 (controlled).

367 641.347 USA
WODDIS NEWS. Text in English. 1977. s-a. looseleaf. USD 25 domestic; USD 35 foreign (effective 2000). adv. illus.; stat. **Document type:** *Newsletter.* **Description:** Provides news, tips and positive information on bananas and activities sponsored by the International Banana Club, as well as suggestions on how to keep your spirits up in a world going bananas.
Published by: International Banana Club, 14012 Siesta Rd., Apple Valley, CA 92307-5968. TEL 626-798-2272, FAX 626-446-0220, bananas@aol.com. Ed., R&P L. Ken Bannister. Pub. L Ken Bannister. Circ: 9,000.

WOMAN'S LIFE. see *WOMEN'S INTERESTS*

WOMEN'S CLUBS MAGAZINE. see *WOMEN'S INTERESTS*

658.048 USA
WORKING CLASS HERO. Text in English. 1968. 3/yr. looseleaf. USD 10 domestic; USD 15 foreign (effective 2004). adv. bk.rev.; music rev.; video rev. **Document type:** *Newsletter.* **Description:** Covers news, pictures, and contributions of the Beatles.
Formerly: Beatle Peace Followers; Live Peace in Pepperland
Published by: Working Class Hero Club, 3311 Niagara St, Pittsburgh, PA 15213-4223. Ed. Barb Whatmough. Pub. Maxwell Cameron. R&P Charles Koelmel. Adv. contact Sue Link. Circ: 500.

369.4 CHE ISSN 0513-6032
WORLD ALLIANCE OF Y M C A'S DIRECTORY. Text in English. 1920. quadrennial. CHF 15 (effective 2001). adv. **Document type:** *Directory, Trade.*
Published by: World Alliance of Young Men's Christian Associations, 12 Clos Belmont, Geneva, 1208, Switzerland. TEL 41-22-8495100, FAX 41-22-8495110, office@ymca.int, http://www.ymca.int. Ed. Ruth Rohrbasser. Adv. contact Monika Rudiger. Circ: 5,000.

367 USA
Y W C A INTERCHANGE✶. Text in English. 1974. 2/yr. bk.rev. illus. **Document type:** *Newsletter.*
Published by: Young Women's Christian Association of the United States of America, 350 Fifth Ave, Ste 301, New York, NY 10118-0399. TEL 212-614-2700, FAX 212-677-9716, http://www.ywca.org. Ed. Cindy Sutliff. Circ: 35,000.

369.5 USA
YOUNG WOMEN'S CHRISTIAN ASSOCIATION OF THE UNITED STATES OF AMERICA. NATIONAL BOARD. ANNUAL REPORT✶. Text in English. a. **Document type:** *Corporate.*
Published by: Young Women's Christian Association of the United States of America, 350 Fifth Ave, Ste 301, New York, NY 10118-0399. TEL 212-614-2700, FAX 212-677-9716, http://www.ywca.org. Ed. Cindy Sutliff.

369.2 POL
ZWIAZEK LEGIONISTOW POLSKICH. KOMENDA NACZELNA. BIULETYN. Text in Polish. 1918. irreg.
Published by: Zwiazek Legionistow Polskich, Komenda Naczelna, Dom im. J. Pilsudskiego - Oleandry, Al 3 Maja 7, PO Box 87, Krakow, 30960, Poland. TEL 48-12-334715, FAX 48-12-322035. Ed. Krystian A Waksmundzki. Circ: 3,000.

369.2 POL
ZWIAZEK LEGIONISTOW POLSKICH. KOMENDA OKREGU KRAKOWSKIEGO. BIULETYN. Text in Polish. 1918. irreg. **Document type:** *Bulletin.*
Published by: Zwiazek Legionistow Polskich, Komenda Okregu Krakowskiego, Dom im. J. Pilsudskiego - Oleandry, Al 3 Maja 7, PO Box 87, Krakow, 30960, Poland. TEL 48-12-334715, FAX 48-12-322035. Ed. Stanislaw Chmurzynski. Circ: 1,000.

369.2 POL
ZWIAZEK LEKONISTOW POLSKICH. KOMUNIKATY. Text in Polish. 1918. irreg.
Published by: Zwiazek Legionistow Polskich, Komenda Naczelna, Dom im. J. Pilsudskiego - Oleandry, Al 3 Maja 7, PO Box 87, Krakow, 30960, Poland. TEL 48-12-334715, FAX 48-12-322035. Ed. Stanislaw Chmurzynski. Circ: 3,000.

4 H PILKE. see *AGRICULTURE*

367 USA
THE 170 NEWS. Text in English. 1969. q. USD 35 (effective 1999). adv. back issues avail.
Published by: International Cessna 170 Association Inc., PO Box 1667, Lebanon, MO 65536-1667. TEL 417-532-4847, FAX 417-532-4847, c170hq@mail.llion.org, http://www.cessna170.org. Ed. Velvet Fackeldey. Circ: 1,550 (controlled).

COLLEGE AND ALUMNI

see also CLUBS ; EDUCATION—Higher Education ; LITERARY AND POLITICAL REVIEWS ; LITERATURE

378 910.03 USA
A & T REGISTER. (Agricultural & Technical) Text in English. 1892. w. USD 12. adv. **Document type:** *Newspaper.* **Description:** Oriented toward the collegiate black-American.
Indexed: RefZh.
Published by: North Carolina Agricultural and Technical University, PO Box E25, Greensboro, NC 27411. TEL 919-334-7700. Ed. Esther Woods.

378 USA
A C CURRENT. Text in English. s-a. **Document type:** *Consumer.*
Published by: Amarillo College, PO Box 447, Amarillo, TX 79178. TEL 806-371-5290. Ed. Victor Newton. R&P, Adv. contact Donna Salter.

378 500 AUS ISSN 0727-386X
A N U REPORTER. Text in English. 1970. s-m. AUD 30 to non-members. adv. bk.rev. **Document type:** *Academic/Scholarly.* **Description:** Covers research and science discoveries at ANU. Publishes new academic papers on theories involving ANU.
Related titles: ♦ Online - full text ed.: A N U Reporter Online. ISSN 1326-2254.
Published by: Australian National University, I Block, Canberra, ACT 0200, Australia. TEL 61-6-2494171, FAX 61-6-2495568, editor.anu.reporter@anu.edu.au, http://online.anu.edu.au/pad/theanureporter.html. Ed. Liz Tynan. Adv. contact Christine Callen. Circ: 10,000.

378 AUS ISSN 1326-2254
A N U REPORTER ONLINE. Text in English. 1994. bi-w.
Media: Online - full text. **Related titles:** ♦ Print ed.: A N U Reporter. ISSN 0727-386X.
Published by: Australian National University, I Block, Canberra, ACT 0200, Australia. TEL 61-6-2494171, FAX 61-6-2495568, http://www.anu.edu.au/pad/reporter.

378.198 USA ISSN 0895-5433
A P U LIFE. Text in English. q. back issues avail. **Document type:** *Academic/Scholarly.* **Description:** News of the university for parents, donors, alumni and friends.
Published by: Azusa Pacific University, 901 E Alosta Ave, Box 7000, Azusa, CA 91702-7000. TEL 626-815-5339, FAX 626-815-5346. Ed. Maureen Riegert Foley. Circ: 50,000.

371.83 USA
A T O PALM✶. Text in English. 1880. 2/yr. USD 25 (effective 1998). **Description:** News of interest to Fraternity members - alumni in particular.
Published by: Alpha Tau Omega Fraternity, Inc., 1 N Pennsylvania St, Indianapolis, IN 46204-3101. TEL 317-684-1865, FAX 317-684-1860, http://www.ato.org/library01.htm. Ed. Wynn Smiley. Circ: 100,000.

371.8 DEU
▼ **ABISCENE.** Text in German. 2003. m. free newsstand/cover. adv. **Document type:** *Magazine, Consumer.*
Published by: Hey & Hoffmann Verlagsgesellschaft bR, Colonnaden 104, Hamburg, 20354, Germany. TEL 49-40-99993970, FAX 49-40-330735. adv.: B&W page EUR 1,450, color page EUR 2,100. Circ: 30,000 (controlled).

371.8 DEU
DER ABITURIENT. Text in German. 1994. q. free. adv. **Document type:** *Magazine, Consumer.*
Related titles: Online - full text ed.
Published by: Der Abiturient Verlag, Wittemannstr 3, St Ingbert, 66386, Germany. TEL 49-6894-8950071, FAX 49-6894-8950072, marko@derabiturient.de, jochenwaigel@derabiturient.de, http://www.derabiturient.de. Ed. Marko Voelke. Pub. Sven Burgwedel. Adv. contact Sabine Sauerwein. page EUR 1,680. Circ: 28,500 (controlled).

378.1 CAN ISSN 0044-5843
ACADIA BULLETIN. Text in English. 1912. 3/yr. free. adv. bk.rev. **Document type:** *Bulletin.*
Published by: Acadia University, Associated Alumni, P O Box 520, Wolfville, NS B0P 1X0, Canada. TEL 902-585-1626, FAX 902-585-1058, alumni.office@acadiau.ca, http://acadiau.ca/alumni/alumni.html. Ed. Linda Cann. Pub. Steven Pound. Circ: 20,000.

C

371.8 DEU ISSN 1619-6473
AD REM. Text in German. 1989. w. free newsstand/cover. adv. **Document type:** *Newspaper, Consumer.*
Published by: Dresdner Magazin Verlag GmbH, Ostra-Allee 18, Dresden, 01067, Germany. TEL 49-351-48642593, FAX 49-351-48642592, redaktion@ad-rem.de, http://www.ad-rem.com. Ed. Andreas Herrmann. Adv. contact Joerg Korczynsky. B&W page EUR 3,008.40, color page EUR 3,662.40. Circ: 18,000 (controlled).

378.1 NLD ISSN 0001-8139
ADELAAR. Text in Dutch. 1948. irreg. (3-4/yr.). free. bk.rev.; film rev.; play rev.; rec.rev. illus.
Published by: Sint Janscollege, c/o Editor, Colijnplein 9, The Hague, 2555 HA, Netherlands. Ed. B W Dijkmans. Circ: 850.

378 USA
ADVANCE - TITAN. Text in English. 1894. w. (Wed.). USD 5 (effective 2005). bk.rev.; film rev.; play rev. illus. **Document type:** *Newspaper.*
Formerly: Oshkosh Advance - Titan (0300-676X)
Published by: Advance-Titan, 800 Algoma Blvd., Oshkosh, WI 54901. TEL 920-424-3048, atitan@uwosh.edu, http://www.uwosh.edu/organizations/at/. Circ: 9,000 (paid and free). Wire service: AP.

378.1 USA
ADVOCATE (JOHNSTOWN). Text in English. 1929. 24/yr. USD 6. adv. bk.rev.; film rev. bibl.
Formerly (until vol.46, 1973): Panther (0031-1006)
Related titles: Microform ed.
Published by: University of Pittsburgh at Johnstown, 450 School House Rd, Johnstown, PA 15904. TEL 814-269-7470. Circ: 2,800.

378.198 USA
ADVOCATE (KANSAS CITY). Text in English. 1969. 15/yr. USD 5. adv. bk.rev. back issues avail.
Published by: Kansas City Community College, 7250 State Ave, Kansas City, KS 66112. TEL 913-334-1100, FAX 913-596-9606. Circ: 3,000.

378 USA
THE ADVOCATE (SAN PABLO). Text in English. 1950. w. free. **Document type:** *Newspaper.* **Description:** Covers news and issues about Contra Costa College.
Related titles: Microfilm ed.: (from LIB).
Published by: Contra Costa College, 2600 Mission Bell Dr, San Pablo, CA 94806. TEL 510-235-7800, FAX 510-236-6768. Ed. Nicholas Dunn. R&P Paul Debolt. Adv. contact Teresa Christensen. Circ: 2,500.

352.14 USA
AGENDA (NEW BRUNSWICK). Text in English. q. USD 25 donation. illus. **Document type:** *Newsletter.*

Published by: Rutgers University, Edward J. Bloustein School of Planning and Public Policy, Civic Square Building, 33 Livingston Ave, Ste 300, New Brunswick, NJ 08901-1981. Ed. Henry F de Mena.

378 USA ISSN 1070-1745
AGGIE PANORAMA; for alumni and friends of NMSU. Text in English. 1951. q. free. back issues avail. **Document type:** *Newsletter.* **Description:** Includes alumni and university news.
Related titles: Online - full text ed.
Published by: New Mexico State University, MSC 3E, Box 30001, Las Cruces, NM 88003-0001. TEL 505-646-3221, FAX 505-646-2099, http://www.nmsu.edu/~ncomm/Panorama/Panoramatoc.html. Ed. Rita A Popp. Circ: 60,000.

378 USA
AGNES SCOTT ALUMNAE MAGAZINE. Text in English. 1923. 2/yr. free to qualified personnel. bk.rev. **Document type:** *Academic/Scholarly.*
Published by: Agnes Scott College, 141 E College Ave, Decatur, GA 30030. TEL 404-471-6301, FAX 404-471-6298, http://www.agnesscott.edu. Circ: 12,500 (controlled).

378 DEU ISSN 0177-9265
AGORA. Text in German. 1984. q. adv. illus. **Document type:** *Bulletin.*
Indexed: DIP, IBR, IBZ.
Published by: Katholische Universitaet Eichstaett, Ostenstr 26, Eichstaett, 85072, Germany. TEL 08421-20246. Ed. Thomas Pleil. Circ: 5,000.

378.18 CAN ISSN 0828-5225
AGORA. Text in English. 1968. m. adv. bk.rev. back issues avail. **Document type:** *Newsletter.*
Former titles (until 1985): Alias L U Week 2 (0828-5217); (until 1984): L U Week 2 (0828-5209); (until 1974): L U Week (0827-9616)
Published by: Lakehead University, Student Union, Thunder Bay, ON P7B 5E1, Canada. TEL 807-343-8193, FAX 807-343-8192, TELEX 073-4594. Ed. Frances Harding. Circ: 2,000 (controlled).

C

AGRI-NATURALIST. see *AGRICULTURE*

378.198 USA
AKRON; the magazine of the University of Akron. Text in English. 1986. 4/yr. free. adv. back issues avail. **Description:** Contains news and features about the university for employees, friends and alumni.
Former titles: From the Hilltop; Akron Magazine
Published by: University of Akron, Office of the Alumni Association, 302 Buchtel Mall, Akron, OH 44325. TEL 330-972-7270, FAX 330-384-2608, editor@uakron.edu. Ed., Adv. contact Jennifer Lavy. B&W page USD 2,000, color page USD 2,750; trim 10.88 x 8.38. Circ: 85,000 (controlled).

378 USA
ALABAMA ALUMNI MAGAZINE. Text in English. bi-m. membership. adv. illus. **Description:** Features news of alumni and of events on campus.
Supersedes: Alabama Alumni Bulletin; Incorporates: Alabama Alumni News
Published by: University of Alabama National Alumni Association, PO Box 861928, Tuscaloosa, AL 35486-0017. TEL 205-348-5963, FAX 205-348-5958, alumni@alumni.us.edu. Ed. Pamela T Burt. Pub. Pat Whetstone. Adv. contact Linda Southern. Circ: 33,000.

378 USA
THE ALABAMIAN✶. Text in English. 1922. fortn. USD 7. adv. bk.rev. **Document type:** *Newspaper.*
Related titles: Microfilm ed.: 1922.
Published by: University of Montevallo, Sta. 6230, Montevallo, AL 35115. TEL 205-665-6000. Circ: 2,500.

378 USA
ALBANY; the University at Albany magazine. Text in English. 1991. 3/yr. free. bk.rev. **Document type:** *Consumer.*
Formerly (until 1991): Researcher (Albany)
Published by: State University Of New York at Albany, University Relations LCB31 (Subsidiary of: State University of New York at Albany), 1400 Washington Ave, Albany, NY 12222. TEL 518-442-3070, cmcknight@uamail.albany.edu, http://www.albany.edu. Ed. Christine McKnight. Pub. Mary Fiess. Circ: 115,000 (controlled).

378.198 USA
ALBRIGHTIAN. Text in English. s-m. USD 25. adv. film rev.; play rev. illus.; tr.lit. back issues avail.
Published by: Albright College, Albrightian, PO Box 15234, Reading, PA 19612-5234. Ed. Rebecca Ann York. Circ: 1,600 (controlled).

378.1 USA
THE ALCALDE. Text in English. 1913. bi-m. free to members (effective 2005). adv. bk.rev. charts; illus. back issues avail. **Document type:** *Magazine, Consumer.* **Description:** Contains informational and feature articles about the programs, research, events, faculty, and students at the University of Texas at Austin.
Former titles: Texas Alcalde (1061-561X); (until 1992): Alcalde (0002-497X)
Published by: Ex-Students' Association of the University of Texas, University of Texas at Austin, PO Box 7278, Austin, TX 78713-7278. TEL 512-471-8084, FAX 512-471-8088, alumni@alumni.utexas.edu, http://www.texasexes.org/alcalde/. Ed. Avrel Seale. adv.: B&W page USD 1,540, color page USD 2,600. Circ: 70,000 (paid).

378 USA
ALESTLE. Text in English. 1957. s-w. (Tue. & Thu.). free on campus; USD 50 subscr - mailed (effective 2005). **Document type:** *Newspaper.*
Published by: Southern Illinois University at Edwardsville, SIUE, Campus Box 1167, Edwardsville, IL 62026-1167. TEL 618-650-3528, 618-650-3528, FAX 618-650-3514, 618-650-3514, alestle.editor@hotmail.com, http://www.siue.edu. Circ: 7,000 (free).

378 CAN
ALGONQUIN TIMES. Text in English. 1986. bi-m. adv. film rev. **Document type:** *Newspaper.*
Formerly: Impact (Nepean)
Published by: Algonquin College, 1385 Woodroffe Ave, Nepean, ON K2G 1V8, Canada. FAX 613-727-7684. Ed., R&P Steve Forster TEL 613-727-4723. Circ: 5,000.

378 USA
ALL STATE. Text in English. w. (Sep.-May). USD 12.
Published by: Austin Peay State University, PO Box 8334, Clarksville, TN 37044-8334. TEL 615-648-7376.

378 USA
ALLIANCE (CHARLESTON). Text in English. 1985. a. USD 15 to members (effective 1997). **Document type:** *Newsletter.* **Description:** News, information, and announcements for the alumni of the Medical University of South Carolina, College of Health-Related Professions.
Published by: Medical University of South Carolina, College of Health Related Professions, Alumni Association, 171 Ashley Ave, Charleston, SC 29425. Ed. Wanda Hancock. Circ: 3,200.

378 CHE ISSN 1422-5980
ALMA. Text in German. 1935. q. adv. **Document type:** *Magazine, Consumer.*
Formerly (until 1998): St. Galler Hochschulnachrichten (0581-5800)
Related titles: Online - full text ed.
Indexed: RefZh.
Published by: (Hochschulverein Sankt Gallen), Reinhard Frei & Partner AG, Schlossstr. 211, Balgach, 9436, Switzerland. TEL 41-71-7261040, FAX 41-71-7261050, alma@freiundpartner.ch. Ed. Roger Tinner. Pub. Johannes Kiess. adv.: page CHF 4,500. Circ: 16,000 (controlled).

ALPHA DIGEST. see *GENERAL INTEREST PERIODICALS—India*

378 USA
ALPHA KAPPA PSI. DIARY✶. Text in English. 1908. q. USD 10. adv. **Description:** Provides articles on achieving executive success in business, college education for business, news of chapters and prominent members.
Published by: Alpha Kappa Psi National Business Fraternity, 9595 Angola Ct, Indianapolis, IN 46268. TEL 317-872-1553. Ed. Frank J Brye. Circ: 25,000.

ALPHA PSI OMEGA: PLAYBILL. see *THEATER*

378 USA
ALUMNI & FRIENDS. Text in English. q. free alumni & friends. **Document type:** *Newsletter, Consumer.*
Published by: Jamestown College, 6093 College Ln., Jamestown, ND 58405. TEL 701-252-3467, FAX 701-253-4318, sbates@jc.edu, http://www.jc.edu. Ed. Sandi Bates. Circ: 13,000 (controlled).

378.198 USA
ALUMNI COLUMNS. Text in English. 1975. 4/yr.
Published by: Augusta College, 2500 Walton Way, Augusta, GA 30910. TEL 404-737-1759.

378.198 USA
ALUMNI RELATIONS NEWS - CARSON-NEWMAN COLLEGE. Text in English. 3/yr.
Published by: Carson - Newman College, Office of Alumni Relations, S Russell Ave, Jefferson City, TN 37760.

378 USA
ALUMNI REPORT. Text in English. 1977. a. free (effective 2004). **Document type:** *Magazine, Consumer.*
Formerly: News & Alumni Report
Published by: Los Angeles College of Chiropractic, 16200 E Amber Valley Dr, Box 1166, Whittier, CA 90609-1166. TEL 562-902-3346, FAX 562-902-3349, http://www.scuhs.edu. Ed. Michael Nash. Circ: 6,000 (paid and controlled).

378 USA
ALUMNI TODAY. Text in English. 3/yr. bibl. back issues avail. **Document type:** *Newsletter.* **Description:** Produced and distributed to alumni and friends of the university. Contains information about university initiatives and alumni achievements.
Published by: University of Wisconsin at Platteville, One University Plaza, Platteville, WI 53818-3099. TEL 608-342-1234. Ed. Barbara Davis. Circ: 28,000 (controlled).

378 USA
ALUMNI UPDATE. Text in English. 1990. 3/yr. free to alumni (effective 2004). **Document type:** *Magazine, Consumer.*
Published by: Philadelphia College of Textiles & Science, Paul J Gutman Library, 3243 School House Ln & Henry Ave, Philadelphia, PA 19144-5497. TEL 215-951-2700, FAX 215-951-2569, alumni@laurel.texsci.edu. Circ: 11,000 (free).

378.1 USA
THE ALUMNUS. Text in English. 1926. q. free. adv. bk.rev. charts; illus.
Formerly: Moorehouse College Bulletin (0027-1047)
Published by: Morehouse College, Public Relations and Alumni Affairs Office, 830 Westview Dr, S W, Atlanta, GA 30314. TEL 404-688-3554, FAX 404-681-2800. Ed. Catherine Gianaro. Circ: 6,500.

ALUMNUS (NEW YORK). see *MEDICAL SCIENCES—Orthopedics And Traumatology*

378.1 USA ISSN 1056-6295
ALUMNUS - THE CITY COLLEGE OF NEW YORK. Text in English. 1904. 4/yr. USD 4 to members (effective 1999). bk.rev. illus. back issues avail. **Description:** Presents articles profiling interesting alumni and their endeavors Covers student programs and accomplishments and provides updates on the college and its histroy.
Former titles (until 1993): City College Alumnus (0045-6993); (until 1926): City College Quarterly
Indexed: BAS.
Published by: City College of New York, Alumni Association, PO Box 177, New York, NY 10027. TEL 212-234-3000, FAX 212-368-6576. Ed., R&P Esther Tolkoff. Pub. Donald Jordan. Circ: 20,000.

378 USA
ALVERNO TODAY. Text in English. 1968. 3/yr. free. **Document type:** *Newsletter.* **Description:** Carries news of Alverno alumnae, students, and faculty.
Published by: Alverno College, 3401 S 39th St, Box 343922, Milwaukee, WI 53234-3922. TEL 414-382-6166, FAX 414-382-6167. Ed., R&P Kathleen A Mulvey. Circ: 17,000.

378 USA ISSN 0279-7232
AMERICAN. Text in English. 1977. q. free. **Description:** News and updates about The American University sent to alumni and other constituents of the university community.
Supersedes: American University Report (0300-7421)
Published by: American University, Office of University Publications, 4400 Massachusetts Ave., N W, Washington, DC 20016-8143. TEL 202-885-5970, FAX 202-885-5949. Ed. Mary Jo Binker. Circ: 65,000 (controlled).

378 USA
AMERICAN SCENE (WASHINGTON). Text in English. 1984 (vol.2). bi-w. illus.
Published by: American University, Office of University Relations, University Publications and Printing Office, 4400 Mass Ave N W, Washington, DC 20016. Ed. Marion Martin. Circ: 7,100.

378.1 USA
AMHERST. Text in English. 1949. q. free to alumni. bk.rev. **Document type:** *Bulletin.*
Formerly: Amherst Alumni News (0003-1690)
Published by: Amherst College, Alumni Council, Public Affairs Office, Box 2202, Amherst, MA 01002. TEL 413-542-2313, FAX 413-542-2042. Ed. Douglas C Wilson. Circ: 21,000.

378 USA
THE AMHERST STUDENT. Text in English. 1868. w. (Wed. during academic yr.). free domestic to students; USD 60 (effective 2005). **Document type:** *Newspaper, Consumer.*
Related titles: Online - full text ed.
Contact: Amherst Student, Inc., PO Box 1912, Amherst, MA 01002-5000. TEL 413-542-2304, FAX 413-542-2305, astudent@amherst.edu, http://www.amherst.edu/~astudent. Ed. Sarah Rothbard. Pub. Jessica Rothschild. Circ: 2,500 (paid and free).

ANBA AL-JAMI'AH/JORDAN UNIVERSITY NEWS. see *EDUCATION—Higher Education*

378 FRA ISSN 0180-1430
ANIMA. Text in French. 1973. 6/yr.
Formerly (until 1977): Flash d'Information (0180-1988)
Published by: Universite de Bordeaux II (Victor Segalen), 146 Rue Leo-Saignat, Bordeaux, 33076, France. TEL 33-5-57571010, FAX 33-5-56990380, http://www.u.bordeax2.fr.

378.1 NLD ISSN 0003-3669
ANIMO. Text in Dutch. 1928. bi-m. membership. adv. charts; illus.
Published by: Baarnsch Lyceum, Torenlaan 77, Baarn, Netherlands. Circ: 900.

378.18 USA
ANNANDALE CAMPUS PEASHOOTER. Text in English. 1984. s-m. USD 12 to non-members. adv. bk.rev.; film rev.; play rev. back issues avail.
Formerly: Parthian Shot
Published by: North Virginia Community College, Student Activities, 8333 Little River Tpk, Annandale, VA 22003. TEL 703-323-3147, FAX 703-323-3437. Circ: 5,000.

ANTHEON. see *LITERATURE*

378 USA
THE APPALACHIAN. Text in English. 1934. s-w. (Tue. & Thu.). free on campus (effective 2005). adv. **Document type:** *Newspaper.*
Published by: Appalachian State University, W.H. Plemmons Student Union, Boone, NC 28608. TEL 828-262-3104, FAX 828-262-6502, theapp@appstate.edu. adv.: col. inch USD 4.75. Circ: 7,000 (free).

378 CAN
➤ **AQUINIAN.** Text in English. 1935. bi-w. (during school year). CND 26. adv. bk.rev. **Document type:** *Academic/Scholarly.* **Description:** Student-run publication covering topics of interest at the University.
Published by: Saint Thomas University, Student Union Bldg., Rm. 23, Fredericton, NB E3B 5G3, Canada. TEL 506-460-0300, FAX 506-452-6007, aquinian@stthomasu.ca. Ed., R&P Andy MacDonald. Circ: 3,000 (controlled).

378 USA
THE ARBITER. Text in English. 1955. w. free (effective 2005). adv. bk.rev.; film rev.; music rev.; tel.rev.; play rev. **Document type:** *Newspaper.*
Related titles: Online - full content ed.
Published by: Boise State University, 1910 University Dr, Boise, ID 83725. TEL 208-345-8204, FAX 208-426-3198, editor@arbitermail.com, http://www.arbiteronline.com. Ed. Mary Dawson. Circ: 15,000.

378 CAN ISSN 1493-5716
ARCH. Text in English. 1995. 3/yr. free. **Description:** Features articles on issues related to higher education, as well as information on university research and alumni and academic initiatives.
Formerly (until 1999): University of Calgary. Alumni (1202-970X)
Published by: University of Calgary, Alumni Relations, Craigie Hall D, 2500 University Ave N W, Calgary, AB T2N 1N4, Canada. TEL 403-220-7109, FAX 403-282-7688, aaeditor@ucalgary.ca, http://www.ucalgary.ca/alumni/magazine.html.

378 USA
THE ARCHWAY (SMITHFIELD); Bryant College student newspaper. Text in English. 1905. w. USD 25. adv. **Document type:** *Newspaper.*
Formerly (until 1946): Bryant & Stratton News
Related titles: Online - full text ed.
Published by: Bryant College, 1150 Douglas Pike, PO Box 7, Smithfield, RI 02917-1284. TEL 401-232-6028, FAX 401-232-6319. Ed. Julia M Arovchon. Circ: 3,500.

378 ZAF
ARENA. Text in English. 1994. a. ZAR 7.50 per issue. adv. illus.
Published by: University of the Witwatersrand, Office of Alumni Affairs, PO Box 98034, Sloane Park, Johannesburg 2152, South Africa.

378 USA ISSN 0896-1409
ARGONAUT (MOSCOW). Variant title: University of Idaho Argonaut. Text in English. 1899. 2/w. (Tue. & Fri.). USD 40 per academic year; free newsstand/cover (effective 2005). bk.rev. **Document type:** *Newspaper, Consumer.*
Formerly: Idaho Argonaut
Related titles: Online - full content ed.: ArgOnline.
Published by: University of Idaho, Student Media, 301 Student Union, Moscow, ID 83843. TEL 208-885-8983, argonaut@uidaho.edu, http://www.argonaut.uidaho.edu/. Ed. Abbey Lostrom. Circ: 6,000 (paid and free).

378.1 CAN ISSN 0044-8818
ARGOSY WEEKLY. Text in English. 1875. w. CND 25; CND 18 to students. adv. bk.rev. **Document type:** *Newspaper, Consumer.* **Description:** Independent journal of news, opinion and the arts, written, edited and published by students of Mount Allison University.
Published by: (Mount Allison University), Argosy Publications Inc., Rm 302, University Centre, Sackville, NB E0A 3C0, Canada. TEL 506-364-2235, FAX 506-536-4230. Ed., R&P Dean Lisk. Adv. contact Helyn Tesar. Circ: 2,200.

378.1 USA ISSN 0004-1181
ARGUS (BLOOMINGTON). Text in English. 1894. w. USD 30 (effective 1998). adv. bk.rev.; play rev.; film rev. illus. **Document type:** *Newspaper.*
Related titles: Microfiche ed.: (from PQC); Online - full text ed.
Published by: Illinois Wesleyan University, PO Box 2900, Bloomington, IL 61702. TEL 309-556-3036, FAX 309-556-3977, theargus@sun.iwu.edu, http://www.iwu.edu/~theargus. Ed., R&P Karin McDowell TEL 309-556-3117. Adv. contact Paul Vranas. page USD 295. Circ: 3,000.

371.85 CAN ISSN 0004-1165
THE ARGUS (THUNDER BAY); the student newspaper of Lakehead University. Text in English. 1966. w. CND 6; CND 10 foreign (effective 1999). adv. bk.rev.; film rev.; play rev. **Document type:** *Newspaper, Consumer.*
Indexed: LibLit, PdeR.
Published by: Lakehead University, Student Union, 955 Oliver Rd, Thunder Bay, ON P7B 5E1, Canada. TEL 807-344-6911, FAX 807-343-8598, argus@sky.lakeheadu.ca. Ed., R&P Kevin Taylor. Adv. contact Carrie Aiken. Circ: 5,000.

378.1 USA ISSN 0004-1394
CODEN: EMRREW
ARIZONA ALUMNUS. Text in English. 1923. s-a. free. adv. bk.rev. illus.
Published by: University of Arizona, Alumni Association, 1111 N Cherry Ave, Tucson, AZ 85721. TEL 602-621-3791, FAX 602-621-9030, rochlin@al.arizona.edu. Ed. Jay Rochlin. Circ: 150,000.

378 USA
ARIZONA DAILY WILDCAT. Text in English. 1915. d. (Mon.-Fri.). USD 99 (effective 2005). adv. 20 p./no. 6 cols./p.; **Document type:** *Newspaper.*
Published by: University of Arizona, Board of Publications, 615 Park Ave, Ste 101, Tucson, AZ 85721-0087. TEL 520-621-3195, FAX 520-621-3094, wildcat@wildcat.arizona.edu, http://wildcat.arizona.edu/. Pub. Mark Woodhaus. adv.: col. inch USD 12.55. Circ: 17,000 morning (paid and free). Wire service: AP.

378.1 USA ISSN 0004-1882
ARKA-TECH. Text in English. 1925. w. USD 5. adv. bk.rev.
Published by: Arkansas Tech University, Russellville, AR 72801. TEL 501-968-0284. Circ: 2,500.

378 USA
ARKANSAS TRAVELER. Text in English. 1905. 4/w. (Mon., Wed., Thu., Fri.). free on campus; USD 40 (effective 2005). **Document type:** *Newspaper.*
Published by: University of Arkansas, Media Board, 119 Kimpel Hall, Univ. of Arkansas, Fayetteville, AR 72701. TEL 501-575-3406, 479-575-3408, FAX 501-575-3306, 479-575-3306, traveler@uark.edu, http://www.uark.edu. Circ: 8,000 (paid and free).

378 051 USA
AROUND & ABOUT K S U. Text in English. 1983. bi-w. **Document type:** *Newsletter.* **Description:** Acts as a faculty newsletter.
Published by: Kentucky State University, Office of Publicity Relations, Hume Hall, Frankfort, KY 40601. TEL 502-227-6688. Circ: 450 (controlled).

378.1 CAN ISSN 0044-9091
ARTHUR. Text in English. 1966. w. CND 24. adv. bk.rev.
Formerly: Sword
Published by: Trent University, 1600 West Bank Dr, Peterborough, ON K9J 7B8, Canada. TEL 705-748-1786. Eds. Naomi Petersen, Sharon Charke. Circ: 3,000.

378 USA
ASSOCIATION OF COLLEGE HONOR SOCIETIES. HANDBOOK. Short title: A C H S Handbook. Text in English. 1945. triennial. free. **Document type:** *Directory.*
Formerly: Association of College Honor Societies. Booklet of Information
Published by: Association of College Honor Societies, c/o Dorothy I Mitstifer, Sec -Treas, 4990 Northwind Dr, Ste 140, East Lansing, MI 48823-5031. TEL 517-351-8335, FAX 517-351-8336, dmitstifer@achsnatl.org, http://www.achsnatl.org. R&P Dorothy Mitstifer. Circ: 15,000.

ASSOCIATION OF M B AS ADDRESS BOOK. see *BUSINESS AND ECONOMICS—Management*

378.1 USA ISSN 0004-6434
AT COOPER UNION. Text in English. 1964. irreg. (3-4/yr.). free. **Document type:** *Newspaper.* **Description:** News, articles, announcements, book market, and alumni notes of interest to the students, faculty, and administrators of this science and art institution.
Published by: Cooper Union for the Advancement of Science and Art, 41 Cooper Sq, New York, NY 10003. TEL 212-353-4155, FAX 212-353-4327. Ed. Todd Brewster. R&P Susan Evens. Circ: 15,500.

378 CAN ISSN 0004-6566
ATHENAEUM. Text in English. 1874. w. free. adv. bk.rev. **Document type:** *Newspaper.*
Related titles: Online - full text ed.
Published by: (Acadia University, Students' Union), Athenaeum Publications, P O Box 698, Wolfville, NS B0P 1X0, Canada. TEL 902-585-2147, FAX 902-542-3901, ath@admin.acadiau.ca. Ed. Cherri Greeno. R&P Craig Kennedy. Adv. contact Sujata Dey. Circ: 3,000.

378.1 CAN
ATKINSONIAN. Text mainly in English; Text occasionally in French. 1968. 15/yr. free. adv. bk.rev.
Former titles: Atkinson Balloon; Balloon (0045-1355)
Published by: Atkinson College Students' Association, Atkinson College, 4700 Keel St, Rm 105, Downsview, ON M3J 1P3, Canada. TEL 416-736-2100. Ed., Adv. contact Bruce Sudds. Circ: 6,000.

378 USA
ATLANTA UNIVERSITY BULLETIN. Text in English. 1934. s-a. **Document type:** *Bulletin.*
Published by: Atlanta University, 111 James P. Brawley Dr., SW, Atlanta, GA 30314. TEL 404-653-8400. Ed. Gwen Calleway. Circ: 8,500.

378 USA ISSN 1077-8640
AUBURN MAGAZINE. Text in English. 1946. q. USD 30 to members (effective 2000). adv. bk.rev. back issues avail. **Document type:** *Consumer.*
Formerly (until Jan. 1994): Auburn Alumnews
Published by: Auburn University Alumni Association, 317 S College St, Auburn, AL 36849-5150. TEL 334-844-1149, FAX 334-844-3716, aubmag@alumni.auburn.edu. Ed. Michael Jernigan. Adv. contact Mary Ellen Hendrix. Circ: 45,000.

378 USA ISSN 1071-1279
AUBURN PLAINSMAN. Text in English. 1893. w. USD 15. adv.
Related titles: Microform ed.; Online - full text ed.: (from LexisNexis).
Published by: Auburn University, Board of Student Communications, B 100 Foy Union Bldg, Auburn, AL 36849-3501. TEL 205-844-4130. Ed. Greg Klein. Circ: 18,000.

378 DEU ISSN 1439-233X
AUD!MAX; die Hochschulzeitschrift. Text in German. 1988. m. adv. bk.rev.; music rev.; play rev.; software rev.; film rev.; Website rev. illus. back issues avail. **Document type:** *Magazine, Consumer.* **Description:** Carries articles on many areas of interest to students including career, university life, tips for successful studying.
Related titles: Online - full text ed.
Published by: Audimax Verlag GmbH, Postfach 120240, Nuernberg, 90109, Germany. TEL 49-911-23779-0, FAX 49-911-204939, info@audimax.de, http://www.audimax.de. Ed. Barbara Martin. R&P, Adv. contact Marc Huebner TEL 49-211-353984. B&W page EUR 11,469, color page EUR 16,896; trim 210 x 297. Circ: 415,000 (controlled).

378 USA ISSN 0300-6964
AUGSBURG COLLEGE NOW. Text in English. 1973 (vol.36). 4/yr. free. illus. **Document type:** *Academic/Scholarly.* **Description:** Publications for Augsburg College alumni, parents and friends.
Published by: Augsburg College, 2211 Riverside Ave, Minneapolis, MN 55454. TEL 612-330-1181, now@augsburg.edu, http://www.augsburg.edu/now. Ed. Betsey Norgard. Circ: 18,000.

378.1 USA ISSN 0004-7945
AUGSBURG ECHO. Text in English. 1891. 22/yr. USD 35 (effective 2000). adv. bk.rev.; play rev. **Document type:** *Newspaper.*
Related titles: Online - full text ed.
Published by: Augsburg College, 2211 Riverside Ave, Minneapolis, MN 55454. TEL 612-330-1102, echo@augsburg.edu, http://www.augsburg.edu/now. Circ: 3,000.

378 USA ISSN 0746-1704
AUGUSTANA COLLEGE MAGAZINE. Text in English. 1935. 2/yr.
Published by: Augustana College, 639 38th St, Rock Island, IL 61201-2296. TEL 309-794-7721. Ed. Debbie Blaylock. Circ: 26,000.

378 USA
AUSTIN COLLEGE MAGAZINE. Text in English. 1962. 3/yr. free (effective 2003). illus. 48 p./no.; **Document type:** *Magazine, Academic/Scholarly.*
Formerly: Acknowledge
Related titles: Online - full content ed.
Published by: Austin College, 900 N Grand Ave, Ste 6H, Sherman, TX 75090-4440. TEL 903-813-2414, FAX 903-813-2415, editor@austincollege.edu, http://www.austincollege.edu/development/publications.htm. Ed., R&P Vickie S Kirby. Circ: 14,000 (controlled).

378 GBR ISSN 0950-7167
AVENUE; the magazine for graduates and friends of the University of Glasgow. Text in English. 1987. s-a. free. adv. back issues avail. **Document type:** *Academic/Scholarly.* **Description:** Feature articles on people, research and events in the University of Glasgow.
Published by: University of Glasgow, Publicity Services, Glasgow, Lanarkshire G12 8QQ, United Kingdom. TEL 44-141-339-8855, FAX 44-141-330-5643, http://www.gla.ac.uk. Ed. Mike Brown. Circ: 80,000.

378 USA
AZTEC PRESS. Text in English. 1973. w. free. adv.
Published by: Pima County Community College, 2202 W Anklam Rd, Tucson, AZ 85709. TEL 520-884-6800, FAX 520-884-6215, http://west.pima.edu/~aztec/aztec1.html. Circ: 7,000.

▼ *new title* ➤ *refereed* ✶ *unverified* ♦ *full entry avail.*

810 USA
B C C EVENING REPORTER. (Bronx Community College) Text in English. 1975 (vol.17). q. free to B.C.C. students. illus.
Published by: Bronx Community College, Evening Student Association, University Ave & W 181st St, Bronx, NY 10458. TEL 212-220-6487. Ed. Joe Sanders.

378.198 USA
B G NEWS. (Bowling Green) Text in English. 1920. d. (Mon.-Fri.). free to students; USD 35 subscr - mailed for 6 mos. (effective 2004). **Document type:** *Newspaper, Consumer.*
Related titles: Microfiche ed.
Published by: Bowling Green State University, University Board of Student Publications, 204 West Hall, Bowling Green, OH 43403. TEL 419-372-6966, FAX 419-372-6967, thenews@bgnews.com, http://www.bgnews.com. Ed. Carrie Whitaker. Circ: 9,500 morning (free). Wire service: AP.

378.1 ISR
B G U NOW. (Ben-Gurion University) Text in English. 1975; N.S. 1995. s-a. free. **Document type:** *Bulletin, Academic/Scholarly.*
Supersedes: Negev (0334-374X); Formerly: Ben Gurion University. Bulletin (0334-3790)
Published by: Ben-Gurion University of the Negev, Department of Public Affairs, P O Box 653, Beer-Sheva, 84105, Israel. TEL 972-8-6239943, 972-8-6461753, FAX 972-8-6472937, prpub@bgumail.bgu.ac.il, http://www.bgu.ac.il. Eds. Angie Zamir, Faye Bittker. Circ: 11,000.

053.1 DEU
B U S. (Berlins Universelles Studentenmagazin) Text in German. 1995. 4/yr. adv. **Document type:** *Magazine, Consumer.*
Published by: S D Media Services, Gehlberger Str. 19, Berlin, 13581, Germany. TEL 49-30-36286430, FAX 49-30-36286437, bus@unievent.de, office@sd-media.de, http://www.sd-media.de/indexue.htm. Adv. contact Kai Langner. B&W page EUR 1,350, color page EUR 1,688. Circ: 33,000 (paid and controlled).

C

371.8 USA ISSN 1542-1643
LC2781
B V Q; black voices, the black college quarterly. (Black Voices Quarterly) Text in English. 2000. q. USD 14.95; USD 4.95 newsstand/cover (effective 2001). adv. **Document type:** *Magazine, Consumer.*
Published by: BlackVoices.com, 435 N Michigan Ave, Chicago, IL 60611. TEL 312-222-4326, http://www.blackvoices.com. Pub. Bretland B Moore.

378.1 USA
BABSON BULLETIN. Text in English. 1933. 4/yr. free. illus. **Document type:** *Bulletin, Academic/Scholarly.*
Formerly: Babson Alumni Bulletin (0005-3538)
Published by: Babson College, 231 Forest St, Babson Park, MA 02457-0310. TEL 781-239-5256, FAX 781-239-5989, alumnews@babson.edu, http://www.babson.edu/bulletin. Ed., R&P Melinda Lamb Theodore. Circ: 31,000 (controlled).

378 GBR
BACUS. Text in English. 1972. 8/yr. adv. bk.rev. **Document type:** *Bulletin.*
Published by: University of the West of England, Students' Union, Frenchay Campus, Coldharbour Ln, Bristol, Glos BS16 1QY, United Kingdom. TEL 0117-965-6261, FAX 0117-976-3909. Ed., Adv. contact Mike Lock. page GBP 320. Circ: 8,000.

378.1 USA ISSN 0045-1304
BADGER HERALD. Text in English. 1969. d. USD 160 (effective 1999). adv. bk.rev.; film rev.; play rev.; music rev. illus. **Document type:** *Newspaper, Newspaper-distributed.*
Related titles: Online - full text ed.: (from LexisNexis).
Published by: Badger Herald, Inc., 326 W Gorham St, Madison, WI 53703-2017. TEL 608-257-4712, FAX 608-257-6899, publisher@badgerherald.com, http://www.badgerherald.com. Ed. Alex Conant. Pub. Liz Dego TEL 608-257-4712 ext 111. Adv. contact Jay Scharf TEL 608-257-4712 ext 120. Circ: 16,000.

371.8 PHL
BALINGHAD; an institutional publication of the Notre Dame University. Text in English. 1996. 2/yr. **Description:** Covers university news and activities.
Published by: Notre Dame University, Cotabato City, Maguindanao 9600, Philippines. TEL 63-64-21-4312, FAX 63-64-21-4312.

378 USA
BALL STATE DAILY NEWS. Text in English. 1922. d. (Mon.-Fri.). USD 30; USD 0.10 newsstand/cover (effective 2005). adv. **Document type:** *Newspaper.*
Related titles: Online - full content ed.
Published by: Ball State University, AJ 276, Muncie, IN 47306. TEL 765-285-8255, FAX 765-285-8248, vff.lak@bsu.edu, http://www.bsudailynews.com. Ed. Cole McGrath. adv.: col. inch USD 9.95. Circ: 14,000 morning (free). Wire service: AP.

378 CAN
BANDERSNATCH. Text in English. 1971. bi-w. free. adv. bk.rev.; film rev. **Document type:** *Newspaper.* **Description:** Review of campus news and the entertainment scene.
Published by: John Abbott College, Student Activities Committee, P O Box 2000, St. Anne De Bellvue, PQ H9X 3L9, Canada. TEL 514-457-6610, FAX 514-457-4730. Adv. contact Tara Morrison. B&W page CND 220. Circ: 2,200.

378.198 USA
THE BANNER (ASHEVILLE). Text in English. w. USD 12 (effective 1999). adv. bk.rev.; music rev.; play rev. back issues avail. **Description:** College newspaper with college and local news, college sports, relevant features.
Former titles (until 1998): Blue Banner; Kaleidoscope (Asheville)
Related titles: Online - full text ed.
Published by: University of North Carolina at Asheville, One University Heights, Asheville, NC 28804. TEL 828-251-6591, FAX 828-251-6820, banner@unca.edu, http://www.unca.edu/banner. Ed. Erin King. R&P, Adv. contact Susan Johnson. B&W page USD 56,244; trim 21.5 x 12.75. Circ: 2,200.

378 USA
BARD OBSERVER. Text in English. 1961. w. USD 30. bk.rev.; film rev.; play rev. illus. **Document type:** *Newspaper.*
Published by: Observer Press, Inc., Bard College, Annandale On Hudson, NY 12504. TEL 914-758-0772. Ed. Joshua Ledwell. adv.: B&W page USD 475. Circ: 1,800.

378 USA ISSN 1071-6513
LH1.B23
BARNARD. Text in English. 1912. q. free. bk.rev. back issues avail. **Document type:** *Magazine, Consumer.* **Description:** Includes articles about Barnard College and about issues of interest to educated women of all ages.
Formerly (until 199?): Barnard Alumnae (0749-1263)
Published by: Barnard College, 111 Milbank, 3009 Broadway, New York, NY 10027. http://www.barnard.edu.alum/magazine. Ed. Amy Debra Feldman. Circ: 23,000.

378.1 USA ISSN 0005-6014
BARNARD BULLETIN. Text in English. 1901. w. USD 12. adv. bk.rev.; film rev.; play rev. **Document type:** *Bulletin.* **Description:** Articles on campus news and features on the arts and entertainment.
Related titles: Microform ed.
Published by: Barnard College, 3009 Broadway, New York, NY 10027-6598. TEL 212-854-2005, FAX 212-749-6531. Eds. Ali Stone, Gretchen Crary. Circ: 5,000.

378.1 CAN ISSN 0845-2660
BARON. Text in English. 1966. bi-w. free. adv. bk.rev.; film rev. **Document type:** *Newspaper.*
Former titles (until 1988): Tucker Park Press (0845-2652); (until 1984): Saint John Viewpoint (0046-2381); Equinox
Indexed: CPerI.
Published by: (University of New Brunswick, Students' Representative Council), Tucker Park Press, P O Box 5050, Saint John, NB E2L 4L5, Canada. TEL 506-648-5676, FAX 506-648-5541. Ed., R&P Lindy MacNeill. Circ: 1,500.

378 USA
BARTON SCOPE. Text in English. 1956. 2/yr. free. **Document type:** *Newsletter.* **Description:** Provides alumni and campus news for alumni and friends of Barton College.
Published by: Barton College, PO Box 5000, College Sta, Wilson, NC 27893. TEL 252-399-6529, FAX 252-399-6574, wdaughet@barton.edu, http://www.barton.edu. Ed., R&P Kathy Daughety. Pub. James B Hemby Jr. Circ: 17,500 (controlled).

378.198 USA
BARUCH TODAY. Text in English. 1953. a. free to qualified personnel. stat. **Description:** For the faculty, staff and alumni of Baruch College.
Published by: City University of New York, Baruch College, 17 Lexington Ave, New York, NY 10010. TEL 212-387-1130. Circ: 41,000.

378.198 USA
BATES; the alumni magazine. Text in English. 1921. 3/yr. free to qualified personnel. bk.rev.
Published by: Bates College, 141 Nichols St, Lewiston, ME 04240. TEL 207-786-6330, FAX 207-786-8241, http://www.bates.edu/pubs/mag/. Ed. Betsy Kimball. Circ: 19,000.

378.198 USA
THE BATES STUDENT. Text in English. 1873. w. USD 18. adv. bk.rev. back issues avail. **Document type:** *Newspaper.* **Description:** Informs students and alumni of campus events.
Published by: Trustees of Bates College, 309 Bates College, Lewiston, ME 04240. TEL 207-795-7494. Ed. Laura Mytels. Circ: 2,500.

378.1 USA ISSN 1055-4726
THE BATTALION. Variant title: Texas A & M Battalion. Text in English. 1893. d. (Mon.-Fri.). USD 60 (effective 2005). adv. **Document type:** *Newspaper, Consumer.*
Related titles: Microfilm ed.; Online - full text ed.: (from LexisNexis).
Published by: Texas A & M University, Student Publications, Department of Journalism, 015 Reed McDonald Bldg, College Station, TX 77843-1111. TEL 979-845-2678, FAX 979-845-2647, batt@unix.tamu.edu, http://battalion.tamu.edu. Pub. Robert Wegener. Adv. contact Patricia Heck. col. inch USD 14. Circ: 22,000. Wire service: AP.

378 USA
BATTLER COLUMNS. Text in English. m. adv.
Published by: Alderson-Broaddus College, College Hill Rd, Philippi, WV 26416. TEL 304-457-1700, FAX 304-457-1700. Circ: 1,200 (controlled).

378 USA
BAYLOR LARIAT. Text in English. 1900. 4/w. (Tue.-Fri.). free domestic on campus; USD 45 (effective 2005). adv. **Document type:** *Newspaper, Consumer.*
Formerly: The Lariat
Published by: Baylor University, One Bear Pl #97330, Waco, TX 76798-7330. TEL 254-710-1711, FAX 254-710-1714, lariat@baylor.edu, http://www.baylor.edu/lariat. adv.: col. inch USD 11. Circ: 7,000 (controlled and free); 500 (paid). Wire service: AP, RN.

378.198 USA
BAYOU BENGAL. Text in English. 1967. m. free on campus. adv. **Document type:** *Newspaper.* **Description:** College student newspaper.
Published by: Louisiana State University at Eunice, PO Box 1129, Eunice, LA 70535. TEL 318-457-7311, FAX 318-546-6620. Ed. Sherryl Guillory. Adv. contact David Simpson. Circ: 1,000 (controlled).

378.1 GBR ISSN 0005-7525
BEAVER. Text in English. 1959. w. free. adv. bk.rev.; film rev. illus. **Document type:** *Newspaper.*
Indexed: CBCARef, HistAb, ICM.
Published by: London School of Economics and Political Science, Students' Union, CO23, St Clements Bldg, Houghton St, London, WC2A 2AE, United Kingdom. TEL 0171-955-6705, FAX 0171-955-7717, beaver@lse.ac.uk, http://www.thebeaver.org. Ed., Adv. contact Daniel Lewis. B&W page GBP 250; trim 393 x 256. Circ: 2,500.

378 USA ISSN 1071-9288
THE BEHREND BEACON. Text in English. 1970. w. (Fri.). free on campus (effective 2005). **Document type:** *Newspaper.*
Former titles: The Collegian; Behrend Collegian
Published by: Pennsylvania State University, 5091 Station Rd., Erie, PA 16563. TEL 814-898-6000, FAX 814-898-6019, behrcoll@aol.com, http://www.pserie.psu.edu, http://www.psu.edu. Circ: 3,000 (paid and controlled).

378.198 USA
BELMONT VISION. Text in English. 1951. bi-m. USD 10. adv. bk.rev.; film rev. back issues avail. **Document type:** *Newspaper.*
Related titles: Microfilm ed.
Published by: Belmont University, Belmont Blvd, Box B 16, Nashville, TN 37212. TEL 615-385-6433, FAX 615-386-4532. Ed. Cree Lawson. Circ: 3,000.

378.198 USA
BELOIT COLLEGE MAGAZINE. Text in English. 1909. 3/yr. free to alumni. illus. back issues avail. **Document type:** *Magazine, Academic/Scholarly.* **Description:** Reports news of the college and its alumni and alumnae.
Formerly: Beloit Magazine
Published by: Beloit College, 700 College St, Beloit, WI 53511. TEL 608-363-2828, FAX 608-363-2870, http://www.beloit.edu. Ed. Iris Poliski. Circ: 20,000 (controlled).

378 USA
BENEDICT TIGER NEWSPAPER. Text in English. 1924. m. USD 8 (effective 1999). bk.rev. 12 p./no. 5 cols./p.; **Document type:** *Newspaper.* **Description:** Covers the Benedict College campus: students, faculty and staff, alumni, and organizations.
Published by: Benedict College, 1600 Harden St, Columbia, SC 29204. TEL 803-253-5297. Circ: 2,500.

378 USA
BENEDICTINE VOICES; the news from Benedictine University. Text in English. 1971. s-a. free (effective 2003). illus. 32 p./no. 2 cols./p.; back issues avail. **Document type:** *Magazine, Academic/Scholarly.*
Formerly: Illinois Benedictine Magazine (0744-5806)
Published by: Benedictine University, 5700 College Rd, Lisle, IL 60532. TEL 630-829-6090, http://www.ben.edu/. Ed. Linda Hale. R&P Mercy Robb. Circ: 20,000.

378 USA
THE BENGAL. Text in English. 1910. w. USD 15 (effective 2005). adv. bk.rev.; film rev.; tel.rev.; music rev.; play rev. tr.lit. **Document type:** *Newspaper.*
Published by: Idaho State University, PO Box 8009, Pocatello, ID 83209. TEL 208-236-3990, FAX 208-236-4600, bgchief@isu.edu, http://www.isubengal.com. Ed. Janet Howard. Adv. contact Maureen Vanhorn. Circ: 5,000.

378.198 USA
BENTLEY OBSERVER. Text in English. q. free (effective 2000). **Document type:** *Academic/Scholarly.* **Description:** News and feature stories about Bentley College people, programs, and events.
Published by: Bentley College, Communications & Publications Department, 175 Forest St, Waltham, MA 02452-4705. TEL 781-891-2241, FAX 781-891-3165, http://www.bentley.edu. Ed., R&P Susan Simpson. Circ: 43,000 (controlled).

378.1 USA ISSN 0005-8874
LH1.B35
BEREA ALUMNUS. Text in English. 1931. bi-m. free. adv. bk.rev. illus. back issues avail. **Document type:** *Magazine.* **Description:** Informs alumni of Berea college of developments at their alma mater; profiles present and past students of the college.
Published by: Berea College Alumni Association, CPO 2203, Berea, KY 40404. TEL 606-986-9341, FAX 606-986-4506, jackie_ballinger@berea.edu, http://www.berea.onlinecommunity.com. Ed. Jackie Collier Ballinger. Circ: 45,000.

BERKLEE TODAY; a forum for contemporary music and musicians. see *MUSIC*

378 917.306 USA
BETA THETA PI. Text in English. 1872. q. adv. **Description:** Supplies news about activities of the 142 chapters of the organization and its members, and feature articles on outstanding alumni in all fields.
Published by: Beta Theta Pi Fraternity, PO Box 6277, Oxford, OH 45056-6277. TEL 513-523-7591, FAX 513-523-2381. Ed., Adv. contact Erv Johnson. Circ: 93,000 (controlled).

378 USA
BETHANY MAGAZINE. Text in English. 1907. q. adv. **Document type:** *Academic/Scholarly.*
Published by: Bethany College, 421 N First, Lindsborg, KS 67456-1897. TEL 785-227-3311. Ed., R&P, Adv. contact Harold L Rothgeb. Circ: 7,500 (controlled).

378.198 USA
BETHEL FOCUS. Text in English. 1948. q. free. **Document type:** *Academic/Scholarly.* **Description:** For alumni of Bethel College; reports on college life and campus news.
Published by: Bethel College (St. Paul), 3900, Bethel, MN 55112. TEL 612-638-6083, FAX 612-638-6003. Ed. Phyllis Alsdurf. Circ: 35,000 (controlled).

378 DEU ISSN 0939-4648
BIELEFELDER UNIVERSITAETSZEITUNG. Text in German. 1970. q. adv. bk.rev.; music rev.; play rev. 64 p./no. 3 cols./p.; **Document type:** *Magazine, Consumer.*
Related titles: Online - full text ed.
Published by: Universitaet Bielefeld, Informations- und Pressestelle, Postfach 100131, Bielefeld, 33501, Germany. TEL 49-521-10600, FAX 49-521-1065844, gerhard.trott@uni-bielefeld.de, http://www.uni-bielefeld.de/presse/buz/buzindex.htm. Ed. Gerhard Trott. Adv. contact Marlies Laege-Knuth. Circ: 7,000.

378.1 USA
BILLBOARD (CHAMBERSBURG). Text in English. 1929. m. USD 8. adv. bk.rev. illus. **Document type:** *Newspaper.*
Formerly: Wilson Billboard
Published by: (Wilson College Government Association), Wilson College, 1015 Philadelphia Ave, Chambersburg, PA 17201. TEL 717-264-4141. Ed. Samantha Ainuddin. Circ: 1,000.

378.1 NLD ISSN 0006-2812
BINDEN EN BOUWEN. Text in Dutch. 1933. bi-m. USD 1.50. adv. bk.rev. illus.
Published by: Sint-Bernardinuscollege, Akerstraat 95, Heerlen, Netherlands. Ed. Marcel Gussenhouen. Circ: 2,000 (controlled).

378 GBR
BIRMINGHAM SUN. Text in English. 1948. fortn. adv. film rev.; music rev.; play rev. 16 p./no. 6 cols./p.; **Document type:** *Newspaper.* **Description:** Informs and entertains Aston University students, covering a wide variety of subjects and interests.
Published by: Aston Students' Guild, Aston University, The Triangle, Birmingham, W Mids B4 7ES, United Kingdom. TEL 0121-359-6531, FAX 0121-333-4218. Ed. Simon Hindle. Circ: 3,500.

378.198 USA
BLACK AND MAGENTA. Text in English. 1885. w. USD 27.50 (effective 2000). adv. play rev. illus. **Document type:** *Newspaper.*
Published by: Muskingum College, New Concord, OH 43762. TEL 614-826-8296. Ed. Stephanie Mann. R&P D Edsall. Adv. contact Douglas Prosperi. Circ: 1,500.

THE BLACK COLLEGIAN. see *OCCUPATIONS AND CAREERS*

BLACK COLLEGIAN ONLINE; the career site for students of color. see *OCCUPATIONS AND CAREERS*

378 USA
BLACK HILLS STATE UNIVERSITY TODAY. Text in English. 1902. w. USD 10. bk.rev.; film rev.; play rev. illus. **Document type:** *Newspaper.*
Former titles: Black Hills State College Today; Black Hills Anemone (0006-4173)
Published by: Black Hills State University, 1200 University Ave, USB 9003, Spearfish, SD 57799-9003. TEL 605-642-6389, FAX 605-642-6762. adv.: page USD 33,750. Circ: 2,500.

378.198 USA
BLOOMSBURG LITERARY JOURNAL. Text in English. a. play rev. **Document type:** *Journal, Academic/Scholarly.*
Formerly (until 1989): Bloom Magazine
Indexed: RASB.
Published by: Community Government Association, 400 E Second St, Bloomsburg, PA 17815. TEL 570-389-4461, FAX 570-389-2095. R&P Terrance Riley. Circ: 1,500.

378 USA
BLUEFIELDIAN. Text in English. 1921. s-a. adv. back issues avail. **Document type:** *Newspaper.* **Description:** Includes editorials, feature pages, school news, Greek news, organizational news, entertainment news.
Published by: Bluefield State College, 219 Rock St, Bluefield, WV 24701. TEL 304-327-4159, FAX 304-325-7747. Adv. contact Jack Yates. Circ: 1,000.

378 USA
THE BONA VENTURE. Text in English. 1926. w. free to qualified personnel (effective 2005). adv. bk.rev. index. back issues avail. **Document type:** *Newspaper, Consumer.* **Description:** Student newspaper.
Related titles: Microform ed.
Published by: St. Bonaventure University, Drawer X, St. Bonaventure, NY 14778. TEL 716-375-2128, FAX 716-375-2252, bonavent@sbu.edu. Ed., R&P Rachael Astrachan. Pub. Robert Wickenheiser. Adv. contact Corrie Spike. Circ: 3,200.

378 USA
BONHOMIE. Text in English. 1901. a. free. **Description:** Pictorial review of year's events and personnel directory.
Published by: (Board of Student Communications), Furman University, 3300 Poinsett Hwy, Greenville, SC 29613-0666. TEL 864-294-2096, FAX 864-294-3001. Eds. Christine Hinton, John McArthur. Circ: 2,200.

378.1 AUT ISSN 0006-7865
BORUSSEN-ECHO; Monatsblatt mit freier Meinungsaeusserung. Text in German. 1953. m. free. adv. bk.rev. abstr. **Document type:** *Bulletin.*
Media: Duplicated (not offset).
Published by: Katholische Oesterreichische Studentenverbindung Borussia im MKV, Bandgasse 31-8, Vienna, W 1070, Austria. TEL 43-1-5239097, FAX 43-1-5239097. Ed. Albert Roeder. Circ: 550.

378 USA ISSN 0885-2049
BOSTON COLLEGE MAGAZINE. Text in English. 1978. q. free. adv. bk.rev. **Description:** Focuses on the arts, education, culture and religion for graduates and friends of Boston College.
Published by: Trustees of Boston College, Publications & Print Marketing, Lawrence House, 122 College Rd, Chestnut Hill, MA 02167. Ed. Ben Birnbaum. Circ: 117,000.

378.198 USA ISSN 0895-2604
BOWDOIN. Text in English. 1927. 3/yr. free. adv. back issues avail. **Document type:** *Academic/Scholarly.* **Description:** Articles cover Bowdoin College or its alumni.
Formerly (until 1987): Bowdoin Alumni Magazine (0746-3332)
Related titles: Online - full text ed.: (from LexisNexis).
Published by: Bowdoin College, 4104 College Station, Brunswick, ME 04011. TEL 207-725-3136, FAX 207-725-3127, abeenie@bowdoin.edu. Ed. Alison M Bennie. R&P Alison M Beenie. Adv. contact Norma McLoughlin. Circ: 21,000.

378.1 USA ISSN 0006-8667
BRACKETY - ACK. Text in English. 1915. w. USD 25 (effective 1999). **Document type:** *Newspaper.*
Indexed: LogistBibl.
Published by: Roanoke College, 221 College Ln, Salem, VA 24153. TEL 540-375-2327, FAX 540-375-2404, bracketyack@roanoke.edu, http://www2.roanoke.edu/stuaff/organizations/brackety-ack. R&P Thomas Carter. Circ: 1,000.

378.1 GBR ISSN 0006-8675
BRADFIELD COLLEGE CHRONICLE. Text in English. 1860. s-a. GBP 3 per issue. adv. bk.rev. illus.
Published by: Bradfield College, Bradfield, Reading, Berks RG7 6AU, United Kingdom. TEL 44-1189-744208, FAX 44-1734-744195. Ed. James Nairne. Circ: 2,500.

378.198 USA
BRANDEIS REVIEW. Text in English. 1980. 4/yr. USD 15. bk.rev. back issues avail. **Document type:** *Academic/Scholarly.*
Formerly: Brandeis Quarterly (0273-7175)
Published by: Brandeis University, 415 South St, Waltham, MA 02254. TEL 617-736-4220, FAX 617-736-4227. Ed. Cliff Hauptman. Circ: 30,000.

378 USA
BREEZE (HARRISONBURG). Text in English. 4/w. USD 30. adv. bk.rev. **Document type:** *Newspaper.* **Description:** Maintains communications within the university community and the spirit of intellectual growth and free inquiry.
Published by: James Madison University, Anthony Seeger Hall, Harrisonburg, VA 22807. TEL 703-568-6127, FAX 703-568-6736. Ed. Nicole Motley. Adv. contact Jonathan Rhudy. Circ: 13,500.

378 USA
THE BREEZE (MATHISTON). Text in English. 5/yr. free. adv. bk.rev.; film rev.; music rev. back issues avail. **Document type:** *Newspaper.*
Published by: Wood Junior College, PO Box 289, Mathiston, MO 39752. Ed., Adv. contact Ronnie W Stanley. Circ: 200 (controlled).

378 CAN
THE BRICKLAYER; the student voice at Red Deer College. Text in English. 1972. bi-w. free. adv. bk.rev.; dance rev.; music rev.; play rev. illus. 24 p./no. 3 cols./p.; **Document type:** *Newspaper, Consumer.* **Description:** Contains campus news, reviews of music, movies, upcoming events information, health issues and on-campus sporting events.
Published by: Bricklayer Publishing Society, Students Association of Red Deer College, P O Box 5005, Red Deer, AB T4N 5H5, Canada. TEL 403-346-2400, FAX 403-347-8510, bricklayer@rdc.ab.ca, http://www.sardc.ab.ca. Ed., Pub., R&P Brenda Cosens. Adv. contact Paul Stuebing. B&W page USD 285, color page USD 342; trim 10.75 x 7.65. Circ: 2,000.

378.198 USA
BRIDGEWATER ALUMNI MAGAZINE. Text in English. 1949. q. free to qualified personnel (effective 2000). back issues avail. **Document type:** *Newsletter.* **Description:** Provides news for alumni and friends.
Formerly: Bridgewater
Published by: Bridgewater College, PO Box 33, Bridgewater, VA 22812. TEL 540-828-5452, FAX 540-828-5480, alumnews@bridgewater.edu, http://www.bridgewater.edu. Ed. Ellen K Layman. Circ: 16,400.

378 GBR
BRIG. Text in English. 1971. m. (during school term). free. adv. bk.rev. **Document type:** *Newspaper.* **Description:** Provides news, features, sports and opinion on the latest campus, national and international issues.
Published by: University of Stirling, Students' Association, Stirling, Stirlingshire FK9 4LA, United Kingdom. TEL 44-1786-467166, FAX 44-1786-467190. Ed., Adv. contact Mark Robertson. B&W page GBP 300; trim 400 x 280. Circ: 3,000.

378 USA
BRIGHAM YOUNG MAGAZINE. Text in English. 1946. 4/yr. free to qualified personnel (effective 2005). adv. back issues avail. **Description:** Includes research activities, news and issues relating to the university.
Formerly: B Y U Today
Published by: Brigham Young University (UPB), 207 UPB, Provo, UT 84602. TEL 801-378-4900, 800-437-4663, http://magazine.byu.edu. Ed. Jeff McClellan. Circ: 170,000.
Subscr. to: Alumni Records, Alumni House, Provo, UT 84602. TEL 801-378-6740.

378.198 USA
BROADSIDE (BEND). Text in English. 1935. bi-w. free. adv. bk.rev.
Published by: Central Oregon Community College, 2600 NW College Way, Bend, OR 97701. TEL 503-382-2743, FAX 503-385-5978. Ed. Todd Pittman. Circ: 2,000.

378 USA
BROADSIDE (FAIRFAX); student newspaper. Text in English. 1963. bi-w. free. adv. bk.rev.; film rev. **Document type:** *Newspaper.* **Description:** Covers campus events, and general educational events.
Published by: George Mason University, Mailstop 2C5, 4400 University, Fairfax, VA 22030. TEL 703-993-2945, FAX 703-993-2948. Circ: 15,000.

BROADSIDE (WASHINGTON). see *POLITICAL SCIENCE*

378 CAN ISSN 1483-4561
THE BROCK PRESS. Text in English. 1963. w. free. adv. bk.rev.; film rev.; play rev. illus. Supplement avail. **Document type:** *Newspaper.*
Related titles: Online - full text ed.
Published by: Brock University Student Union Inc., 500 Glenridge Ave, St Catharines, ON L2S 3A1, Canada. TEL 905-688-5550, FAX 905-641-7581, press@www.brocku.ca, http://www.brocku.ca. Ed. Mike Fisher. R&P Mike Fischer. Adv. contact Paula Woodward. Circ: 5,000.

378 USA
BROOKHAVEN COURIER. Text in English. 1978. bi-w. free. adv. **Document type:** *Newspaper.*
Formerly: Courier
Published by: Brookhaven College, 3939 Valley View Lane, Dallas, TX 75244-4906. TEL 972-860-4787, FAX 972-860-4142, bhc2110@gu.dcccd.edu, mst2210@dcccd.edu. Ed. Leigh Ann Hutchins. Adv. contact Helena Engstrom. page USD 630. Circ: 3,000.

378 USA ISSN 1520-863X
LH1.B8
BROWN ALUMNI MAGAZINE. Text in English. 1900. bi-m. USD 35; free to qualified personnel (effective 2005). adv. bk.rev. illus. 96 p./no.; back issues avail. **Document type:** *Magazine, Consumer.*
Formerly: Brown Alumni Monthly (0007-2478)

C

▼ new title ➤ refereed ✶ unverified ♦ full entry avail.

Related titles: Online - full text ed.
Published by: Brown University, PO Box 1854, Providence, RI 02912. alumni_magazine@brown.edu, http://www.brownalumnimagazane.com. Ed., Pub. Norman Boucher. Adv. contact Juli Mahoney. B&W page USD 2,490, color page USD 3,125. Circ: 85,000 (controlled).

378 USA
THE BROWN DAILY HERALD. Text in English. 1866. d. (5/w.). USD 179; free newsstand/cover (effective 2005). adv. bk.rev. 12 p./no. 5 cols./p.; **Document type:** *Newspaper, Trade.* **Description:** An independant newspaper serving the Brown University Community.
Related titles: Online - full text ed.
Published by: The Brown Daily Herald, Inc., 195 Angell St, PO Box 2538, Providence, RI 02906. TEL 401-351-3260, FAX 401-351-9297, herald@browndailyherald.com, http://www.browndailyherald.com. Circ: 4,000. Wire service: AP.

378.1 CAN ISSN 0007-2699
BRUNSWICKAN. Text in English. 1867. w. CND 26.50. adv. bk.rev. illus.
Related titles: Microfilm ed.; Online - full text ed.
Published by: University of New Brunswick, Student Union, PO Box 4400, Fredericton, NB E3B 5A3, Canada. TEL 506-453-4983, FAX 506-458-4958, bruns@unb.ca. Ed. Mark Morgan. adv.: page CND 375. Circ: 10,000 (controlled).

378 USA
BRYN MAWR ALUMNAE BULLETIN. Text in English. 1921. q. free to qualified personnel. bk.rev.
Published by: Bryn Mawr Alumnae Association, Wyndham, 101 N Merion Ave, Bryn Mawr, PA 19010-2899. TEL 215-526-5224, FAX 215-526-5228. Ed. Jan T Trembley. Circ: 17,000.

C

378 USA
BRYN MAWR - HAVERFORD COLLEGE NEWS. Text in English. 1968. w. USD 27. adv. bk.rev.; film rev.; play rev. illus.
Published by: (Haverford College), Students of Haverford and Bryn Mawr Colleges, 370 Lancaster Ave, Haverford, PA 19041-1392. TEL 215-527-8995. Ed. Ruth Polk. Circ: 3,800.

371.805 USA
THE BUCHTELITE. Text in English. 1889. s-w. (Tue. & Thu.). free (effective 2005). **Document type:** *Newspaper.*
Published by: University of Akron, 303 Corroll St, Student Union, Rm 51, Akron, OH 44325. TEL 330-972-7919, FAX 330-972-7870, buchtel@uakron.edu, http://www.uakron.edu/buchtelite. Ed. Martin Lizmar TEL 330-972-6184. Circ: 15,000 (paid). Wire service: AP.

378 USA ISSN 1044-7563
BUCKNELL WORLD. Text in English. 1914. bi-m. free. bk.rev. illus. **Document type:** *Magazine, Academic/Scholarly.* **Description:** Covers Bucknell alumni and issues in higher education as related to Bucknell.
—CCC.
Published by: Bucknell University, Division of University Relations, Moore Ave, Lewisburg, PA 17837. TEL 570-577-3260, FAX 570-524-3683, bworld@bucknell.edu, http://www.departments.bucknell.edu/pr/BucknellWorld/current/, http://www.bucknell.edu. Ed. Kathleen Mohr. Circ: 42,500.

371.805 USA
THE BUCKNELLIAN. Text in English. 1896. w. (Thu.). USD 45 (effective 2005). adv. **Document type:** *Newspaper, Consumer.*
Published by: Bucknell University, Bucknell Hall, Lewisburg, PA 17837. TEL 570-774-1520, FAX 570-577-1176, bucknellian@bucknell.edu, http://www.orgs.bucknell.edu/bucknellian/. Ed. Elisabeth Salemme. Circ: 5,400 (free).

378 USA
BUENA VISTA TODAY. Text in English. 1895. s-a. free to qualified personnel (effective 2003). **Document type:** *Bulletin.* **Description:** Provides information of interest to alumni, parents of students, and friends.
Formerly: View
Related titles: Online - full content ed.
Published by: Buena Vista University, 610 W Fourth St, Storm Lake, IA 50588. TEL 712-749-2120, FAX 712-749-1459, bvunews@bvu.edu, bvtoday@bvu.edu. Ed. Amy Foster. R&P Tim Seydel. Circ: 18,000.

378.1 USA
BULLDOG WEEKLY. Text in English. 1909. w. (during school yr.). USD 30. adv. bk.rev.; film rev.; music rev. **Description:** Covers material relating to the student body including: sports coverage, relevant political and social news, entertainment, editorials and calendar of events.
Formerly: Redlands Bulldog (0034-2130)
Related titles: Online - full text ed.
Published by: University of Redlands, PO Box 3080, Redlands, CA 92373. TEL 904-335-5137. Ed. Greg Huntoon. Adv. contact Richard Carney. B&W page USD 280; 13 x 10.5. Circ: 2,000.

378 USA
THE BULLET (FREDERICKSBURG); Mary Washington's student newspaper since 1922. Text in English. 1922. w. USD 30 (effective 2001). adv. bk.rev.; dance rev.; music rev.; play rev.; tel.rev.; video rev. bibl.; charts; illus.; stat. 12 p./no. 5 cols./p.; back issues avail. **Document type:** *Newspaper, Consumer.*
Related titles: Fax ed.; Microfilm ed.; Online - full content ed.
Published by: University of Mary Washington, 1301 College Ave, Fredericksburg, VA 22401. TEL 703-899-4393, bullet@mwc.edu, http://www.thebulletonline.com, http://www.mwc.edu. Ed. Ryan Hamm. R&P, Adv. contact Lindsey Riley TEL 540-654-1153. Circ: 3,500.

371.8 USA ISSN 0007-7100
BUSINESS TODAY (PRINCETON). Text in English. 1968. 3/yr. USD 9; USD 3.99 newsstand/cover (effective 2005). adv. bk.rev. charts; illus.; stat. reprint service avail. from PQC. **Document type:** *Magazine.* **Description:** Promotes communication between college students and the business community.
Related titles: Microform ed.: (from MIM, PQC); Online - full text ed.
Published by: Foundation for Student Communication, Inc., 48 University Pl, Princeton, NJ 08544-1011. TEL 609-258-1111, FAX 609-258-1222, http://www.businesstoday.org/, http://www.princeton.edu/~fscint. Ed. Meaghan Muntean. Pub. Jennifer Ragus. Circ: 200,000 (controlled).

378 USA
BUTLER COLLEGIAN. Text in English. 1886. w. USD 40 (effective 1998). adv. bk.rev.; film rev.; play rev. back issues avail. **Document type:** *Newspaper.* **Description:** Informs students and faculty of school and national news.
Published by: (Journalism Department), Butler University, 4600 Sunset Ave, Indianapolis, IN 46208. TEL 317-283-9358, FAX 317-283-9930. Ed. Carolyn Parkhill. Adv. contact Kelli Rutherford. Circ: 3,000 (controlled).

378.198 USA
BUTLER MAGAZINE. Text in English. 1989. q. **Document type:** *Academic/Scholarly.* **Description:** Covers issues in higher education, alumni profiles, campus news, class notes, and faculty information.
Formerly: Butler Alumni Quarterly
Published by: Butler University, 4600 Sunset Ave, Indianapolis, IN 46208. TEL 317-283-9966, http://www.butler.edu. Ed., R&P Nancy L Alexander. Circ: 34,000 (controlled).

378.1 USA ISSN 0045-3919
C C A C REVIEW. (California College of Arts and Crafts) Text in English. 1970. 4/yr. free. illus.; stat.
Published by: California College of Arts and Crafts, Office of Alumni Affairs, 5212 Broadway, Oakland, CA 94618. TEL 415-653-8118. Ed. Sandra Meber. Circ: 8,000.

C C BLAETTER. see *CLUBS*

C C H S NEWS. see *MEDICAL SCIENCES—Respiratory Diseases*

378 CAN
C E G E P PLUS. Text in French. bi-m. adv.
Published by: College d'Enseignement Generale et Professionnel de Valleyfield, 169 rue Champlain, Valleyfield, PQ J6T 1X6, Canada. Circ: 2,000.

378 USA
C M✶. (College Magazine) Text in English. 1995. bi-m. adv. back issues avail. **Description:** Covers college lifestyles and topics of interest to college students.
Related titles: Online - full text ed.: 1995.
Published by: Sara Fiedelholtz, Ed. & Pub., 1630 Chicago Ave Apt 1703, Evanston, IL 60201-6023. TEL 212-529-1519, FAX 212-979-8772. Adv. contact Nancy Rosenberg. B&W page USD 10,450, color page USD 12,320.

378.1 USA
C M A NEWSLETTER. Text in English. 1955. bi-m. USD 60 (effective 2003). bk.rev.; film rev. abstr.; bibl.; stat.; tr.lit. **Document type:** *Newsletter, Academic/Scholarly.*
Formerly: N C C P A Newsletter (0027-6251)
Media: Duplicated (not offset).
Published by: College Media Advisers, c/o Department of Journalism, University of Memphis, Memphis, TN 38152. TEL 901-678-2403, rsplbrgr@cc.memphis.edu, http://www.spub.ksu.edu/ncma, http://www.collegemedia.org. Ed. Pat Parish. Circ: 625.

378.198 USA
C U A MAGAZINE. (Catholic University of America) Text in English. 1973. 3/yr. USD 15 (effective 1999). bk.rev. back issues avail. **Description:** General interest magazine circulated to alumni and friends of the university.
Formerly (until 1989): Envoy (Washington) (0896-288X)
Indexed: CPL.
Published by: Catholic University of America, Office of Public Affairs, 620 Michigan Ave, N E, McMahon Hall, Rm 311, Washington, DC 20064. TEL 202-319-6977, FAX 202-635-4440. Ed., R&P Anne Smith. Circ: 46,000.

378.198 USA
THE CABLE. Text in English. 1932. w. USD 15. adv. film rev.; music rev.; play rev.
Published by: College of St. Scholastica, 1200 Kenwood Ave., Duluth, MN 55811. TEL 218-723-6187, FAX 218-723-6290. Ed. Jessica McDonald. Adv. contact Dana Burkovich. B&W page USD 270, color page USD 370; trim 15 x 9.5. Circ: 1,500.

378 CAN ISSN 0226-3467
CADUCEE. Text in French. 1920. 3/yr. adv. bk.rev. **Document type:** *Consumer.*
Published by: Association des Diplomes de l'Ecole des Hautes Etudes Commercials de Montreal, 3000 Ch de la Cote St Catherine, RJ 210, Montreal, PQ H3T 2A7, Canada. TEL 514-340-6025, FAX 514-340-6508. Ed. Michael Lemay. Pub. Francis Blier. Adv. contact Sophia Benabdellah. B&W page CND 1,800, color page CND 2,250; trim 10.88 x 8.13. Circ: 34,500.

371.805 USA
THE CALIFORNIA AGGIE. Text in English. 1915. d. (Mon.-Fri.). USD 100 per academic year; free newsstand/cover (effective 2005). adv. **Document type:** *Newspaper.*
Related titles: Microfilm ed.: (from LIB); Supplement(s): Arena.
Published by: University of California at Davis, 25 Lower Freeborn Hall, Davis, CA 95616. TEL 530-752-0208, FAX 530-752-0355, info@californiaaggie.com, http://www.californiaaggie.com. Ed. Daniel Stone. adv.: col. inch USD .80. Circ: 30,000 morning (paid and free). Wire service: NYT.

378.1 USA ISSN 0008-1302
CALIFORNIA MONTHLY. Text in English. 1909. 6/yr. USD 50 to individuals; USD 35 to senior citizens (effective 2005). adv. bk.rev.
Related titles: Microfilm ed.: (from LIB).
Indexed: BHA, ChPerI.
Published by: California Alumni Association, Alumni House, Berkeley, CA 94720. TEL 510-642-5781, FAX 510-642-6252, calmonthly@cal.alumni.berkeley.edu, http://www.alumni.berkeley.edu/Alumni/Cal_Monthly/main.asp. Ed. Russell Schoch. Adv. contact Lora Dinga. B&W page USD 3,100, color page USD 4,680; 7.5 x 10. Circ: 99,048.

378.1 USA ISSN 0008-1582
CALIFORNIA TECH. Text in English. 1913. w. USD 11. adv. bk.rev.; film rev.; play rev. illus. **Document type:** *Newspaper.*
Published by: (Associated Students of the California Institute of Technology), A S C I T, Inc., 40 58 SAC, California Institute of Technology, 1201 E California Blvd, Pasadena, CA 91125. TEL 818-395-6153. Circ: 3,500.

371.805 USA
THE CAMPUS. Text in English. 1876. w. (Thu.). free (effective 2005). **Document type:** *Newspaper.*
Published by: Allegheny College, PO Box 12, Meadville, PA 16335. TEL 814-332-3100, campus@alleg.edu, nbrenot@allegheny.edu, http://www.alleg.edu. Wire service: AP, LAT-WAT.

378.198 USA
CAMPUS ACTIVITIES. Text in English. 1992. 8/yr. USD 18 domestic; USD 24 in Canada; USD 36 elsewhere (effective 2000). adv. bk.rev. **Document type:** *Trade.* **Description:** Provides information on entertainment, films, music and special events for student activities directors.
Formerly (until 1997): Campus Activities Today
Published by: Cameo Publishing Group, PO Box 509, Prosperity, SC 29127. TEL 800-728-2950, FAX 803-321-2049, cameopub@aol.com, http://www.cameopub.com. Ed. Laura S Moore. Pub. W. C. Kirby. R&P W C Kirby TEL 803-321-2046. Adv. contact Jack Whitesides. B&W page USD 1,150, color page USD 1,800; trim 10.88 x 8.38. Circ: 5,162 (paid and controlled).

378 USA
CAMPUS CAMERA; the student newspaper of Eastern Nazarene College. Text in English. 1936. s-m. USD 20. adv. bk.rev.; play rev. bibl. back issues avail. **Document type:** *Newspaper.* **Description:** Covers world, local and campus news and events.
Published by: Eastern Nazarene College, 23 E. Elm St., Wollaston, MA 02170. TEL 617-745-3577. Ed., R&P Catherine Walchle. Adv. contact Vlad Samarin. page USD 260; 10 x 16.

378 CAN ISSN 0829-3309
CAMPUS CANADA. Text in English. 1983. q. CND 12. adv. **Document type:** *Consumer.* **Description:** University related topics: entertainment, careers, health, travel, money, sports, campus issues.
Related titles: Microfiche ed.: (from MML); Microform ed.: (from MML).
Indexed: CBCARef, CBPI, CEI.
Published by: Canadian Controlled Media Communications, 287 MacPherson Ave, Toronto, ON M4V 1A4, Canada. TEL 416-928-2909, FAX 416-966-1181. Ed. Sarah Moore. Adv. contact Harvey Wolfe. Circ: 125,000.

378.18 USA
CAMPUS CARRIER. Text in English. 1913. w. USD 20. adv. film rev.; music rev.; play rev. **Document type:** *Newspaper.*

Published by: Berry College, PO Box 520, Mt. Berry, GA 30149-0520. TEL 706-236-2294, FAX 706-236-2248. Ed. Richard Quartarone. Pub. Kevin Kleine. Adv. contact Julie Yamamoto. Circ: 2,000.

378 USA ISSN 1547-0989
CAMPUS EVENTS PROFESSIONAL. Text in English. m. USD 159 domestic; USD 163 in Canada; USD 169 elsewhere (effective 2005). **Document type:** *Newsletter.* **Description:** Presents new ideas for inaugurations, groundbreakings, alumni events, student activities, centennials, presidential dinners, as well as office, budget, and volunteer management.
Formerly: Events (Logan) (1079-5650)
Related titles: Online - full content ed.: USD 159 (effective 2005).
Published by: Magna Publications, Inc., 2718 Dryden Dr, Madison, WI 53704. TEL 608-246-3590, 800-433-0499, FAX 608-246-3597, editor@magnapubs.com, http://www.magnapubs.com/pub/magnapubs_ev.

CAMPUS LEADER. see *EDUCATION*

378 USA
CAMPUS TIMES (LA VERNE). Text in English. 1919. w. free. adv. bk.rev.; dance rev.; film rev.; music rev.; play rev.; rec.rev.; software rev.; tel.rev.; video rev.; Website rev. 12 p./no. 5 cols./p.; back issues avail. **Document type:** *Newspaper, Newspaper-distributed.* **Description:** Reports campus news for the University of La Verne, located in southern California.
Related titles: Online - full text ed.: 1997.
Published by: University of La Verne, Communications Department, 1950 Third St, La Verne, CA 91750. TEL 909-392-2712, FAX 909-392-2706, ctimes@ulv.edu, http://www.ulv.edu/campustimes, http://www.ulv.edu/communications. Ed. Jaclyn Ruco. R&P Elizabeth Zwerling TEL 909-593-3511 ext 4293. Adv. contact Jason Walker. B&W page USD 350; trim 17 x 11. Circ: 2,200.

378 USA
CAMPUS TIMES (ROCHESTER). Text in English. 1873. w. (Thu.). USD 20; free to students (effective 2005). **Document type:** *Newspaper.*
Published by: University of Rochester, Students Association, Wilson Commons 102, CPU 277086, Rochester, NY 14627-7086. TEL 716-275-5943, FAX 716-256-3664, cteditor@mail.rochester.edu, http://www.campustimes.org/, http://www.ctrochester.edu. Ed. Jackie Borchardt. Circ: 5,000 (free).

378 ITA ISSN 1594-672X
CAMPUS WEB; il primo mensile degli studenti. Text in Italian. 1988. m. (10/yr.). adv. **Document type:** *Magazine, Consumer.* **Description:** Gives information on universities, post-graduate courses, professions, and the academic world.
Formerly (until 2001): Campus (1594-6789)
Related titles: Online - full text ed.
Published by: Campus Editori Srl, Via Marco Burigozzo 5, Milan, MI 20122, Italy. TEL 39-02-58219735, FAX 39-02-58219709, campus@class.it, http://www.campus.it/servlet/campus?template=_index. Ed. Alessandro Giuoli. Pub. Paolo Panerai. Circ: 70,000.

378.198 USA
CAMPUS WEEKLY. Text in English. 1986 (vol.7). w. free. **Document type:** *Newsletter.*
Formerly: Campus News (Manchester)
Published by: New Hampshire College, 2500 N River Rd, Manchester, NH 03106. TEL 603-645-9635. Ed. Robin Richards. Circ: 1,500.

378 BEL ISSN 0779-0821
CAMPUSKRANT; tijdschrift van de K.U.Leuven. Text in Dutch. 1990. s-m. (except July-Aug.). adv. bk.rev. illus. Supplement avail.; back issues avail. **Document type:** *Newspaper.* **Description:** Contains news of university policy, science, cultural activities and sports for staff, faculty, students and alumni.
Supersedes: Academische Tijdingen
Related titles: Online - full text ed.; Special ed(s).: Campuskrant (Alumni Edition).
Indexed: RASB.
Published by: Katholieke Universiteit Leuven, Dienst Communicatie, Oude Markt 13, Leuven, 3000, Belgium. TEL 32-16-324013, FAX 32-16-324014, mirella.kimpen@dcom.kuleuven.ac.be, http://www.kuleuven.ac.be/ck. Ed., R&P, Adv. contact Mirella Kimpen. Pub. Githa Roelans. Circ: (controlled).

378 USA
CANDOR; a Benedictine University student newspaper. Text in English. w. free (effective 2003). adv. bk.rev.; film rev.; play rev. charts; illus. index. back issues avail. **Document type:** *Newspaper.* **Description:** Aimed at traditional college students. Includes campus activities and issues, world issues and entertainment venues.
Published by: Benedictine University, 5700 College Rd, Lisle, IL 60532. TEL 630-829-6090, http://www.ben.edu/. adv.: B&W page USD 400. Circ: 1,750.

378 CAN
CAPER TIMES. Text in English. 1984 (vol.4). bi-w. CND 23. adv. bk.rev.; film rev. **Document type:** *Newspaper.*
Published by: University College of Cape Breton, Student's Union, P O Box 5300, Sydney, NS B1P 6L2, Canada, TEL 902-562-8857, capertimes@hotmail.com, http://www.uccbsu.com. Ed., Adv. contact Tammy Bernasky. Circ: 2,000.

378 CAN
CAPILANO COURIER. Text in English. 1968. bi-w. CND 10. adv. bk.rev.; film rev. **Document type:** *Newspaper.* **Description:** Includes student news, opinion and letters.
Published by: (Capilano College, Courier Publishing Society), Capilano Press Society, 2055 Purcell Way, North Vancouver, BC V7J 3H5, Canada. TEL 604-984-1712, FAX 604-990-7837, tcr@capcollege.bc.ca. Ed. Keirr Wills. Pub. Dennis Ledoc. Adv. contact Jason Fischer. Circ: 3,500.

371.8975 USA ISSN 1062-6778
THE CAPSTONE (WASHINGTON, DC). Text in English. m. illus. **Document type:** *Newsletter, Academic/Scholarly.* **Description:** Discusses topics of interest to the Howard University community.
Published by: Howard University, Office of University Communications, 2225 Georgia Ave, NW, Washington, DC 20059. TEL 202-238-2334, d_lindsay@howard.edu, http://www.founders.howard.edu/communications/Capstone.htm, http://www.howard.edu/communications. Ed. David Lindsay.

378.1 CAN ISSN 0008-6576
CARILLON (REGINA). Text in English. 1962. w. CND 40. adv. bk.rev.; film rev.; play rev. abstr.; illus. **Document type:** *Newspaper.* **Description:** Covers news, sports, arts. Also accepts editorials, opinions, letters and analysis pieces.
Indexed: CMPI.
Published by: University of Regina, Students' Union, Students Union Bldg, Rm 113, Regina, SK S4S 0A2, Canada. TEL 306-586-8867, FAX 306-586-8812, carillon@ursu.cc.uregina.ca, http://ursu.uregina.ca/~carillon. Ed. Alexis Roman. R&P Craig Saunders. Adv. contact Wade McKim. Circ: 4,000.

371.8 USA ISSN 1534-7583
CARLETON COLLEGE VOICE. Text in English. 1975. bi-m.
Formerly: Carleton Voice (1081-3608)
Published by: Carleton College, 1 North College St, Northfield, MN 55057. TEL 507-646-4000, FAX 507-646-4445, tscalzo@acs.carleton.edu, alumni-office@acs.carleton.edu, http://webapps.acs.carleton.edu/voice/, http://www.carleton.edu. Ed. Teresa Scalzo.

371.805 USA
THE CARLETONIAN. Text in English. 1877. w. USD 38. adv. bk.rev.; dance rev.; film rev.; music rev.; play rev. charts; illus. 12 p./no. 6 cols./p.; back issues avail. **Document type:** *Newspaper.* **Description:** Includes news, viewpoint, features, movie page, calendar, and humor sections.
Published by: Carleton College, 1 North College St, Northfield, MN 55057. TEL 507-646-4158, FAX 507-646-4146, carletonian@carleton.edu, http://www.carletonian.carleton.edu, http://www.carleton.edu. Circ: 3,100.

378 USA ISSN 0747-0835
CAROLINA ALUMNI REVIEW. Text in English. 1912. bi-m. USD 35; USD 6 newsstand/cover (effective 2005). adv. back issues avail. **Document type:** *Magazine, Consumer.* **Description:** Provides alumni and University news, photography & editorial features on subjects of interest to University of N. Carolina and members of the General Alumni Association.
Incorporates (as of Jan. 1995): University Alumni Report; Which was formerly (until 1989): University Report
Related titles: Online - full text ed.
Published by: University of North Carolina, General Alumni Association, PO Box 660, Chapel Hill, NC 27514-0660. TEL 919-962-1208, FAX 919-962-0010, caradvertising@unc.edu, http://www.alumni.unc.edu. Ed. Regina W Oliver. Pub. Doug S Dibbert. Adv. contact Cameron Sweeney. B&W page USD 1,350, color page USD 2,935. Circ: 65,000 (paid).

378.1 GBR ISSN 0008-7033
CARTHUSIAN. Text in English. 1873. 3/yr. GBP 2. adv. bk.rev.; film rev.; play rev. illus.
Published by: Charterhouse School, Godalming, Surrey, United Kingdom. Circ: 1,000.

378.198 USA
CASE ALUMNUS. Text in English. 1921. q. free. back issues avail. **Document type:** *Academic/Scholarly.* **Description:** Articles by, for and about alumni of Case School of Engineering.
Published by: (Case Alumni Association), Case Western Reserve University, 10900 Euclid Ave, Cleveland, OH 44106. TEL 216-231-4567, FAX 216-368-4714, casealum@po.cwra.edu. Ed. Madelyn Lefkowitz. Circ: 16,000 (controlled).

378 USA ISSN 1547-5360
CASE MAGAZINE. Text in English. 1979. q. free (effective 2005). adv. **Document type:** *Academic/Scholarly.* **Description:** Contains news pertaining to Case Western Reserve University.
Former titles (until vol. 16, no. 1, 2003): C W R U Magazine (1523-2344); C W R U: The Magazine of Case Western Reserve University (1042-9220); (until vol.3, no.4, 1988): C W R U Today; Case Reserve Today; (until 1984): Insight (Cleveland); (until 1983): Campus News; Images
Indexed: AgeL.
Published by: Case Western Reserve University, 10900 Euclid Ave, Cleveland, OH 44106. TEL 216-368-6265, FAX 216-368-4835, http://www.case.edu/pubs/casemagazine. Ed., R&P Ken Kesegich. Circ: 90,000 (controlled).

378 AUS
CATALYST (MELBOURNE). Text in English. 1945. every 3 wks. free. adv. bk.rev.; film rev.; play rev. charts; illus. **Description:** Includes arts section, cinema section, music section, poetry, short stories, politics, philosophy, environmental issues, garden design, industrial designs.
Related titles: Online - full text ed.
Indexed: El.
Published by: Royal Melbourne Institute of Technology, Student Union, A'Beckett St., PO Box 12387, Melbourne, VIC 8006, Australia. TEL 61-3-9925-2884, FAX 61-3-9925-3705, catalyst@rmit.edu.au, http://www.su.rmit.edu.au/media/catalyst.html. Circ: 5,000 (controlled).

378 USA
THE CAULDRON. Text in English. 1929. w. (Mon.). free domestic to students (effective 2005). adv. **Document type:** *Newspaper, Consumer.*
Published by: Cleveland State University, 2121 Eastwood Ave, University Center, Cleveland, OH 44115. TEL 216-687-2270, FAX 216-687-5155, cauldroneditors@hotmail.com, http://www.csucauldron.com. Ed. Amanda Richards. adv.: B&W page USD 420. Circ: 3,500 (free).

378 USA
CAULDRON. Text in English. 1947. bi-w. (during academic year). free. adv. bk.rev. **Document type:** *Newspaper.* **Description:** News, features, sports, and opinions for college students, faculty and alumni.
Published by: University of St. Thomas (Houston), 3812 Montrose Blvd, Houston, TX 77006. TEL 713-522-7911, FAX 713-522-9920. Ed. Gia L Gustilo. R&P Gia Gustilo TEL 713-525-3579. Adv. contact Charles Wray. Circ: 2,100.

378.1 USA ISSN 0008-8609
THE CAVALIER DAILY. Text in English. 1890. d. (Mon.-Fri.). USD 44.95 (effective 2005). bk.rev. **Document type:** *Newspaper.*
Related titles: Online - full text ed.: (from LexisNexis).
Published by: (University of Virginia), Cavalier Daily, Inc., PO Box 400703, Charlottesville, VA 22904-4703. TEL 804-924-1086, 804-924-1086, FAX 804-924-7290, 804-924-7290, cavdaily@cavalierdaily.com, http://www.virginia.edu/~cavdaily. Ed. Patrick Harvey. Adv. contact Rachel Dippold. Circ: 10,000. Wire service: AP.

378.198 USA
CAVEAT. Text in English. m. free. film rev.; play rev. abstr.; charts; illus.; stat. **Document type:** *Newspaper, Academic/Scholarly.*
Published by: Golden Gate University, School of Law, 536 Mission St, San Francisco, CA 94105-2968. http://www.ggu.edu/school_of_law. Ed. Tod Manning. Circ: 1,000.

378 USA
CEDAR DIGEST. Text in English. s-a. adv. **Description:** Covers fraternal information and public relations.
Published by: Tall Cedars of Lebanon of North American, 2609 N Front St, Harrisburg, PA 17110. TEL 703-549-3622. Ed. James Wood. Circ: 32,000.

378.1 USA ISSN 0008-9001
CENTENARY COLLEGE CONGLOMERATE. Text in English. 1922. bi-w. USD 10. adv. bk.rev.; play rev.
Published by: Centenary College of Louisiana, Student Government Association, 2911 Centenary Blvd, PO Box 41188, Shreveport, LA 71134-0188. TEL 318-869-5269. Ed. Erica Johnson. Circ: 1,000.

378.1 USA ISSN 0008-9141
CENTO. Text in English. 1863. w. adv. bk.rev.; film rev.; play rev. illus. **Document type:** *Newspaper.*
Published by: Centre College, PO Box 745, Danville, KY 40422. TEL 606-238-5533, FAX 606-236-7925. Ed. Robert Alford. Adv. contact Barcley Houston. Circ: 1,500.

371.805 USA
CENTRAL FLORIDA FUTURE★. Text in English. 1968. s-w. USD 50. **Document type:** *Newspaper.* **Description:** Covers the University of Central Florida.
Published by: Campbell Communications, 94 E Mitchell Hammock Rd, Oviedo, FL 32765-9783. TEL 407-823-8054, FAX 407-823-9495, cffuture@gdi.net. Ed. Sean Perry. Pub. Stephen Norris. Circ: 10,000.

378.1 USA ISSN 0008-9451
CENTRAL MICHIGAN LIFE; the official campus newspaper. Text in English. 1919. 3/w. (Mon., Wed. & Fri.; w. Wed summer). free on campus; USD 75 subscr - mailed (effective 2005). adv. bk.rev.; play rev. charts; illus. reprint service avail. from PQC. **Document type:** *Newspaper.*
Related titles: Microform ed.: (from PQC).

C

Published by: Central Michigan University, 8 Anspach, Mt. Pleasant, MI 48859. TEL 989-774-4000, cmlife@cmuvm.csv.cmich.edu. Circ: 13,500. Wire service: AP.

378.198 USA
CENTRALIGHT✶. Text in English. s-a. **Document type:** *Newspaper.* **Description:** News and features about alumni and the university.
Published by: Central Michigan University, Alumni Relations Office, Carlin Alumni House, Central Michigan University, Mount Pleasant, MI 48859. TEL 517-774-3312, 800-358-6903, FAX 517-774-7159, alumni@cmich.edu, http://www.cmich.edu/centlgt.html. adv.: B&W page USD 1,200. Circ: 40,000.

378.599 PHL
CENTRALITE. Text in English. 1921. irreg. USD 4.50. illus.
Published by: Central Philippine University, PO Box 231, Iloilo City, Iloilo Province 5000, Philippines. FAX 63-33-73470.

378.198 USA
CENTREPIECE. Text in English. 1959. 4/yr. free to qualified personnel. bk.rev.
Indexed: LID&ISL.
Published by: Centre College, Alumni House, Danville, KY 40422. TEL 606-238-5500, FAX 606-238-5507. Ed. Diane Fisher Johnson. Circ: 13,000.

378 USA
CHAMINADE QUARTERLY. Text in English. 1955. q. free. back issues avail. **Document type:** *Magazine, Academic/Scholarly.*
Former titles: Chaminade Newsletter; Chaminade University Newsletter; Chaminade College Newsletter (0009-1286); Kaminaka
Published by: Chaminade University, 3140 Walalae Ave, Honolulu, HI 96816. TEL 808-735-4772, FAX 808-735-4870, alumni@chaminade.edu, http://www.chaminade.edu. Circ: 14,000.

378 CAN
CHAMPLAIN BUGLE. Text in English. 1973. bi-m. adv. bk.rev.; film rev.
Published by: Editions Portes Ouvertes, Rm F 144, 900 Riverside Dr, St Lambert, PQ J4P 3P2, Canada. Circ: 2,500.

378.1 USA ISSN 0009-1561
THE CHANTICLEER. Text in English. 1934. w. USD 10 (effective 1997). adv. bk.rev. **Document type:** *Newspaper.*
Former titles (until 1967): Collegian; Teacola
Published by: Jacksonville State University, Communications Board, 700 Pelham Rd, Jacksonville, AL 36265. TEL 205-782-5701, FAX 205-782-5445. Ed. Mai Martinez. Adv. contact Emily Wester. Circ: 7,000 (controlled).

378.1 CAN ISSN 0315-1859
THE CHARLATAN. Text in English. 1945. w. CND 45 to individuals; CND 55 to institutions. adv. bk.rev.; film rev.; play rev. illus. back issues avail. **Document type:** *Newspaper, Consumer.* **Description:** Covers national news, sports, multicultural issues.
Formerly: Carleton (0008-6630)
Published by: Charlatan Publications Inc., Rm. 531 Unicentre, Ottawa, ON K1S 5B6, Canada. TEL 613-520-6680, FAX 613-520-4051, charlatan@carleton.ca, http://www.charlatan.carleton.ca. Ed. Dave Ebner. Adv. contact Steven Peckett. Circ: 12,000 (controlled).

378 GBR
CHELTENHAM LADIES COLLEGE MAGAZINE. Text in English. 1880. a. GBP 7.50 (effective 1998). bk.rev.
Published by: Cheltenham Ladies' College, Bayshill Rd, Cheltenham, Glos GL50 3EP, United Kingdom. TEL 44-1242-520691, FAX 44-1242-227882. Circ: 2,000.

378 GBR ISSN 0308-731X
CHERWELL; the Oxford University newspaper. Text in English. 1920. 24/yr. GBP 0.20. adv. bk.rev.; film rev.; play rev. illus. **Document type:** *Newspaper.*
Related titles: Online - full text ed.
Published by: Oxford Student Publications Ltd., 7 St Aldates, Oxford, Oxon OX1 1BS, United Kingdom. TEL 44-1865-246461, FAX 44-1865-200341, http://www.cherwell.ospl.co.uk. Ed. Rachel Williams. Pub. Jeremy Sugden. R&P Alex Vontunzelmann. Adv. contact Alex von Tunzelmann. Circ: 17,000.

CHICAGO CHRONICLE. see *EDUCATION—Higher Education*

378.1 USA ISSN 0009-3610
CHICAGO MAROON. Text in English. 1892. s-w. (Tue. & Fri.). USD 80 domestic; USD 150 foreign (effective 2005). adv. bk.rev.; film rev.; play rev. charts; illus. **Document type:** *Newspaper, Consumer.*
Related titles: Microform ed.; Online - full text ed.: (from LexisNexis).
Published by: University of Chicago, Chicago Maroon, 1212 E 59th St, Ste 305, Chicago, IL 60637. TEL 773-702-1403, FAX 773-702-3032, maroon@chicagomaroon.com, http://www.chicagomaroon.com. Ed. George Anesi. Adv. contact Trevor Croxson. B&W page USD 375. Circ: 11,500.

378.198 USA
CHIEFTAIN. Variant title: Black Hawk College Chieftain. Text in English. 1970. bi-m. (during academic year). free. adv. film rev.; play rev. back issues avail. **Document type:** *Newspaper.*
Published by: Black Hawk College, Quad Cities Campus, 6600 34th Ave, Moline, IL 61265. FAX 309-792-5976, http://www.bhc.edu. Ed. Mark Ridolfi. Circ: 3,000 (controlled).

378 USA
THE CHIMES (LA MIRADA)✶. Text in English. 1938. w. USD 20. adv. bk.rev.; film rev. **Document type:** *Newspaper.* **Description:** Student newspaper serving over 2,000 students, faculty and staff at Biola University.
Related titles: Microfilm ed.: 1938 (from LIB).
Published by: Biola University, 1205 100th Pl N E, Bellevue, WA 98004-3511. TEL 310-903-4879. Ed. Jennifer Bunch. Circ: 2,000 (controlled).

CHIMES (NOTRE DAME). see *LITERATURE*

378 USA
THE CHINOOK. Text in English. 1945. s-w. USD 8. adv. **Document type:** *Newspaper.*
Published by: Casper College, 125 College Dr, Casper, WY 82601. TEL 307-268-2236, FAX 307-268-2682. Circ: 2,000.

378 USA
CHIPS-O-WOOD. Text in English. 3/yr. free. adv. play rev. back issues avail. **Document type:** *Newsletter.* **Description:** Includes alumni and development news.
Published by: Wood College, Alumni Development, PO Box 289, Mathiston, MS 39752. TEL 601-263-5352. Ed., R&P, Adv. contact Lou Ann Staggs. Circ: 7,000 (controlled).

CHRISTIAN MEDICAL COLLEGE VELLORE ALUMNI JOURNAL. see *MEDICAL SCIENCES*

378 USA
CHRONICLE (DURHAM). Text in English. 1905. d. (Mon.-Fri.). free (effective 2005). bk.rev. **Document type:** *Newspaper, Consumer.*
Related titles: Supplement(s): Recess; Sportswrap; Blueprint (Durham).
Published by: Duke Student Publishing Company, Inc., 301 Flowers Bldg, Box 90858, Durham, NC 27708. TEL 919-684-2663, FAX 919-684-4696, editor@chronicle.duke.edu, http://www.chronicle.duke.edu. Ed. Seyward Darby. Circ: 15,000. Wire service: APP, NYT.

378.198 USA
CHRONICLE (GRAYSLAKE). Text in English. 1969. bi-w. free to students. adv. bk.rev. **Document type:** *Newspaper.* **Description:** Approaches and defines issues of importance to the students. Covers campus news, sports, arts and entertainment.
Published by: College of Lake County, 19351 W Washington, Grayslake, IL 60030. TEL 847-223-3634, FAX 847-223-9371. Ed. Charles Jurgaitis. Adv. contact Diane Summers. B&W page USD 350. Circ: 3,750 (controlled).

378.18 USA
CHRONICLE (HAMDEN). Text in English. 1967. w. USD 12. adv. bk.rev. back issues avail. **Document type:** *Newspaper.*
Published by: Quinnipiac College, PO Box 10, Hamden, CT 06518-0569. TEL 203-288-5251, FAX 203-288-8098. Circ: 1,500.

378.1 USA
CHRONICLE (HEMPSTEAD). Text in English. 1935. w. (Sep.-May). USD 25 for 6 mos.. adv. bk.rev.; film rev.; play rev. back issues avail.
Formerly: Hofstra Chronicle (0018-3172)
Related titles: Microfiche ed.
Published by: Hofstra University, 107 Hofstra University, Hempstead, NY 11549-1070. TEL 516-463-6965. Circ: 11,000 (controlled).

THE CHRONICLE OF HIGHER EDUCATION. see *EDUCATION—Higher Education*

378.1 HKG ISSN 0009-6261
CHUNG CHI BULLETIN. Text in Chinese, English. 1951. a. bibl.; charts; illus. **Document type:** *Bulletin.*
Formerly: Chung Chi College Bulletin
Published by: Chinese University of Hong Kong, Chung Chi College, Sha Tin, New Territories, Hong Kong. TEL 852-2609-6450. Ed. Angeline Kwok. Circ: 3,800.

378.1 USA ISSN 0745-1962
CIRCLE K; a magazine for student leaders. Text in English. 1956. 5/yr. USD 6 (effective 1999). reprints avail. **Document type:** *Trade.* **Description:** Contains information on the latest trends affecting college students worldwide and activities of the international collegiate service organization, committed to community service and leadership development.
Formerly: Circle K Magazine (0578-3097)
Published by: Circle K International, 3636 Woodview Trace, Indianapolis, IN 46268-3196. TEL 317-875-8755, 800-549-2647, FAX 317-879-0204, cki@kiwanis.org. Ed. Casey Keller. Adv. contact Patrick Hatcher. Circ: 15,000.

378 CAN
CITYSIDE. Text in English. 1980. m. USD 10. adv. bk.rev. **Document type:** *Newspaper.*
Published by: University of Regina, School of Journalism and Communications, 3737 Wascana Parkway, Regina, SK S4S 0A2, Canada. TEL 306-584-5051, FAX 306-585-4867, bryan.olney@uregina.ca. Ed., Adv. contact Bryan Olney. Circ: 1,000 (controlled).

378 CAN
CLAN MACDONALD ANNUAL. Text in English. a. adv.
Published by: McGill University, Macdonald College, P O Box 284, Ste Anne De Bellevue, PQ H9X 1C0, Canada. TEL 514-392-4311. Ed. Elizabeth Koessler.

378.198 USA
CLARION ALUMNI NEWS. Text in English. 1867. q. back issues avail. **Document type:** *Newsletter.* **Description:** Provides articles on Clarion University, faculty, and alumni.
Former titles: Clarion Magazine; Clarion University Alumni Magazine
Published by: Clarion University, 974 E Wood St, Clarion, PA 16214. TEL 814-226-2334. Ed. Ron Wilshire. R&P R Wilshire. Circ: 30,000 (controlled).

CLARION SCIENCE FICTION AND FANTASY WRITERS' WORKSHOP NEWSLETTER. see *LITERATURE—Science Fiction, Fantasy, Horror*

378 USA
CLARKE COLLEGE COURIER. Text in English. 1930. w. **Document type:** *Newspaper.*
Published by: Clarke College, 1550 Clarke Dr, Dubuque, IA 52001. TEL 319-588-6306, FAX 319-588-6789. Circ: 1,000.

378 USA
CLARKNEWS. Text in English. 1978. 4/yr. free to qualified personnel. **Document type:** *Magazine, Consumer.* **Description:** University alumni magazine featuring news of campus events, faculty research, alumni news and profiles of students, faculty and alumni.
Formerly: Clark University News
Related titles: Online - full text ed.
Published by: Clark University, 950 Main St, Worcester, MA 01610. TEL 508-793-7441, FAX 508-793-7311, clarknews@clarku.edu, http://www.clarku.edu/newsite/alumni/clarknews/index.shtml. Ed., R&P Judy Jaeger TEL 508-793-7681. Circ: 25,000 (controlled).

378 USA
CLEMSON WORLD. Text in English. 1956. q. free. adv. bk.rev. **Document type:** *Academic/Scholarly.*
Published by: Clemson University, Office of Publication & Marketing Services, 103 Fike, Clemson, SC 29634-5608. TEL 864-656-2467, FAX 864-656-5004, http://pubnet.clemson.edu/cwonline/cwmag.html. Ed. Liz Newall. R&P Dave Dryden. Adv. contact Sallie Leigh. Circ: 75,000 (controlled).

378 USA
CLIFF NEWS. Text in English. 1946. 15/yr. USD 6.
Published by: Briar Cliff University, 3303 Rebecca St, Sioux City, IA 51104. Ed. Neal Recker. Circ: 1,000.

378.1 USA ISSN 0009-9430
CLOCKTOWER. Text in English. 1927. w. USD 12. adv. bk.rev.; play rev.
—Infotrieve.
Published by: Union College (Lincoln), Associated Student Body, 3800 S 48th St, Lincoln, NE 68506. TEL 402-488-2331. Ed. Leland Krum. Circ: 1,500.

378 USA
CLOSEUP. Text in English. 1990 (vol.22). s-a. free. reprints avail. **Document type:** *Newspaper.* **Description:** Provides news of the college and its alumni, for alumni and supporters.
Related titles: Microfilm ed.: (from PQC).
Published by: Queens College, 1900 Selwyn Ave, Charlotte, NC 28274. TEL 704-337-2252, FAX 704-337-2503. Ed. Anthony T Hoppa. Circ: 15,000.

378.198 USA
COLBY MAGAZINE. Text in English. 1911. 4/yr. **Description:** Covers alumni issues.
Formerly: Colby Alumnus
Related titles: Online - full content ed.
Published by: Colby College, 4000 Mayflower Hill Dr, Waterville, ME 04901. TEL 207-872-3226, FAX 207-872-3555, mag@colby.edu, http://www.colby.edu/mag. Ed., R&P Gerry Boyle TEL 207-872-3226. Circ: 26,000.

378.1 GBR ISSN 0010-0676
COLFEIAN. Text in English. 1900. a. GBP 1. adv. illus.
Published by: Old Colfeians Association, Horn Park, Eltham Rd, London, S.E. 12, United Kingdom. Circ: 1,750.

378.1 USA
COLGATE SCENE. Text in English. 1972. 6/yr. free. bk.rev. illus. **Description:** News of Colgate University, its alumni, faculty and students.
Formed by the merger of: What's New at Colgate (0043-454X); Colgate (0010-0684)

C

Published by: Colgate University, Communications Office, Administration Bldg, Hamilton, NY 13346. TEL 315-228-1000, FAX 315-228-7798, jleach@mail.colgate.edu, http://www.colgate.edu/scene. Ed. James Leach. Circ: 40,000.

278 USA
COLLAGE. Text in English. 1966. 21/yr. USD 40; USD 80 foreign. adv. **Document type:** *Newspaper.*
Published by: Claremont Colleges, 175 E 8th St, Claremont, CA 91711. TEL 909-624-1887. Ed. Kacey Crtig. Pub. John Duke. R&P, Adv. contact Tappan Zee. Circ: 6,000 (controlled).

378 CAN
COLLECTIF (MONTREAL)* . Text in English. s-m. free.
Published by; Publi-Peq, 3575 bd St Laurent, Ste 232, Montreal, PQ H2X 2T7, Canada. TEL 514-845-8628. Circ: 4,000.

378.1 CAN ISSN 0228-734X
LE COLLECTIF (SHERBROOKE). Text in French. 1955. w. CND 15. adv. bk.rev. **Document type:** *Academic/Scholarly.*
Formerly (until 1976): Campus Estrien (0008-2511)
Published by: Journal le Collectif Inc., Local 107, Universite de Sherbrooke, Centre Social, Cite Universitaire, Sherbrooke, PQ J1K 2R1, Canada. TEL 819-821-7641, FAX 819-562-2324. Ed. Martine Cote. Adv. contact Benoit Charpentier. page CND 600. Circ: 5,000.

355 USA ISSN 1046-7602
LH1
COLLEGE ALUMNI AND MILITARY PUBLICATIONS. Text in English. 1980. a. USD 75 (effective 1999).
Formerly: College Alumni Publications
Published by: C A P Communications Associates, Ltd., 35-20 Broadway, Astoria, NY 11106. TEL 718-315-8250. Ed. Bob Madison.

378 USA
THE COLLEGE CONNECTION. Text in English. irreg. free. **Document type:** *Newspaper.*
Published by: Montgomery Community College, PO Box 787, Troy, NC 27371-0787. TEL 910-576-6222, FAX 910-576-2176, harrisk@mcc.montgomerycc.nc.us, http://www.montgomery.ccnc.us. Ed. Kathy Harris. Circ: 530 morning (free).

378 USA
COLLEGE HEIGHTS HERALD. Text in English. 1925. s-w. (Tue. & Thu.). USD 30 subscr - mailed; free domestic on campus (effective 2005). adv. 12 p./no. 6 cols./p.; back issues avail. **Document type:** *Newspaper.*
Related titles: Online - full text ed.
Published by: Western Kentucky University, 122 Garrett Center, Bowling Green, KY 42101. TEL 270-745-2653, FAX 270-745-2697, herald@wku.edu, http://www.wkuherald.com. Adv. contact JoAnn Thompson. col. inch USD 6.35. Circ: 10,000 morning (free).

COLLEGE MEDIA REVIEW. see *JOURNALISM*

378 GBR ISSN 1367-126X
COLLEGE OF ESTATE MANAGEMENT. RESEARCH REPORT. Text in English. 1995. irreg.
—BLDSC (3311.065200).
Published by: College of Estate Management, Whiteknights, Reading, Berkshire RG6 2AW, United Kingdom. TEL 44-0118-9861101, FAX 44-0118-9755344, info@cem.ac.uk, http://www.cem.ac.uk.

378.198 USA
COLLEGE OF ST. SCHOLASTICA TIMES MAGAZINE. Text in English. 1971. q. free.
Published by: College of St. Scholastica, Office of Public Relations, 1200 Kenwood Ave, Duluth, MN 55811. TEL 218-723-6074, FAX 218-723-6290. Circ: 15,000.

378 USA
COLLEGE REPORTER. Text in English. 1881. w. (Mon.). USD 37; free to students (effective 2005). **Document type:** *Newspaper, Consumer.*
Formerly: Franklin & Marshall College Reporter
Published by: Franklin and Marshall College, 1 Fieldstead Ct., Apt. A, Owings Mills, MD 21117-5210. reporter@acad.fandm.edu, http://www.fandm.edu. Circ: 2,500 (free).

378 USA ISSN 0888-210X
LB2341
➤ **COLLEGE STUDENT AFFAIRS JOURNAL (ONLINE EDITION).** Text in English. 1978. s-a. USD 25 membership for students; USD 40 membership for institutions (effective 2005). bk.rev. charts. back issues avail.; reprints avail. **Document type:** *Journal, Academic/Scholarly.* **Description:** Focuses on concepts, practices, and research that have implications and applicability for practitioners involved in college student affairs work.
Former titles: College Student Affairs Journal (Print Edition); (until 1982): Southern College Personnel Association Journal
Media: Online - full content. **Related titles:** Online - full text ed.: (from bigchalk, ProQuest Information & Learning).
Indexed: CIJE, HEA.
—BLDSC (3311.288000).
Published by: Southern Association for College Student Affairs, c/o Dr Joe Buck, Armstrong Atlantic State University, 11935 Abercorn St, Savannah, GA 31419-1997. info@sacsa.org, http://www.sacsa.org. Circ: 1,200.

378.415 IRL ISSN 1649-0495
THE COLLEGE TIMES. Text in English. 2000. m. adv. **Document type:** *Magazine, Consumer.*
Published by: Lacethorn Ltd., 11 Clare St, Dublin, 2, Ireland. TEL 353-1-6624887, FAX 353-1-6624886. Adv. contact Ciaran Vines. B&W page EUR 1,047, color page EUR 1,238; 213 x 301. Circ: 31,000 (paid and controlled).

378.1 USA
COLLEGE VOICE (STATEN ISLAND). Text in English. 1973 (vol.21). every 3 wks. USD 4. adv. bk.rev. illus. **Document type:** *Newspaper.*
Formed by the 1980 merger of: Student Voice; College Times; Which was formed by the June 1975 merger of: Richmond Times; S I C C Dolphin (0046-0516)
Related titles: Microfilm ed.
Published by: City University of New York, College of Staten Island, Student Government, 2800 Victoria Blvd, Staten Island, NY 10314. TEL 718-982-3091. Ed. William Wharton. Circ: 5,000.

371.8 USA
COLLEGEFRESHMAN. Text in English. d. film rev.; music rev. **Description:** Covers college life and lifestyles for college and high school students. Includes a financial aid guide, virtual campus tours, sports, and career and vacation ideas.
Media: Online - full text.
Published by: Strategic Marketing Communications, Inc., 550 N Maple Ave, Ridgewood, NJ 07450. trnds@aol.com, http://www.collegefreshman.com. Ed. Joshua Well.

378 USA
THE COLLEGIAN. Text in English. 1922. 3/w. (Mon., Wed., Fri.). USD 30; USD 17.50 semester; free on campus (effective 2005). **Document type:** *Newspaper.*
Formerly: Daily Collegian
Published by: California State University, College Union 306, Fresno, CA 93740. TEL 559-294-2656, collegian@csufresno.edu, http://collegian.csufresno.edu. Ed. Maurice O Ndole. Circ: 30,000 morning (controlled and free); 18,750 (controlled and free). Wire service: UPI.

378 GBR ISSN 0305-1064
THE COLLEGIAN. Text in English. 1974. a. GBP 4.86. illus. back issues avail. **Document type:** *Academic/Scholarly.* **Description:** Covers various college affairs, as well as art and literature.
Published by: Daniel Stewart's and Melville College, Queensferry Rd, Edinburgh, EH4 2BN, United Kingdom. TEL 0131-332-7925. Ed. Eileen Elder. Circ: 2,400.

378.1 USA
COLLEGIAN (BROOKINGS). Text in English. 1894. w. USD 12. film rev.; play rev. charts; illus. **Document type:** *Newspaper.*
Published by: South Dakota State University, Student Publications, USU 069, Box 2815, Brookings, SD 57007. TEL 605-688-6164, FAX 605-688-4974. Ed. Michael Ridgeway. Circ: 6,900.

378.1 USA ISSN 0010-1206
COLLEGIAN (ELYRIA). Text in English. 1965. 4/yr. free. adv. bk.rev. **Document type:** *Newspaper, Academic/Scholarly.*
Published by: Lorain County Community College, Student Activities Office, 1005 N Abbe Rd, Elyria, OH 44035. TEL 216-365-5122. Ed. Karen Huerner. Adv. contact Deanna White. B&W page USD 210. Circ: (controlled).

378 USA
THE COLLEGIAN (FAYETTE). Text in English. 1883. w. free. **Document type:** *Newspaper.*
Published by: Upper Iowa University, PO Box 1857, Fayette, IA 52142. TEL 319-425-5273, FAX 319-425-5271. Circ: 500.

378.1 USA
COLLEGIAN (RICHMOND). Text in English.
Published by: University of Richmond, Dept. of English, Richmond, VA 23173.

378 USA
COLLEGIAN (TOLEDO). Text in English. 1919. d. (Mon.-Thu.). USD 80. adv. bk.rev. illus. **Document type:** *Newspaper.* **Description:** Publishes news and commentary of interest to students at the University of Toledo.
Published by: University of Toledo, 3504 Student Union, 2801 W Bancroft, Toledo, OH 43606. TEL 419-537-4203, FAX 419-537-2108, Collegian@pop3.utoledo.edu. Ed. Keith Terjanyi. Circ: 11,500.

378.198 USA
COLLEGIAN (TULSA). Text in English. 1912. w. USD 8. adv.
Published by: University of Tulsa, 600 S College Ave, Tulsa, OK 74104-3189. TEL 918-631-3817. Circ: 4,000.

371.805 USA
COLLEGIATE TIMES. Text in English. 1903. d. ((Tues.-Fri of the academic year, except during exams and vacations)). USD 80; USD 60 per semester (effective 2003). **Document type:** *Newspaper, Consumer.*
Related titles: Online - full content ed.
Published by: Virginia Polytechnic Institute and State University, Educational Media Company, 121 Squires Student Center, Blackberg, VA 24061. http://www.collegiatetimes.com/. Ed. Jeremy Doehnert TEL 540-231-9867.

378.1 USA ISSN 0010-1249
COLLEGIO. Text in English. 1910. w. USD 20 (effective 2000). adv. play rev. **Document type:** *Newspaper.*
Related titles: Online - full text ed.: (from LexisNexis).
Published by: Pittsburg State University, 1701 S Broadway, Pittsburg, KS 66762. TEL 316-235-4901, FAX 316-275-4817, psucollegio@hotmail.com, http://www.pittstate.edu/collegio. Ed. Jack Dimand. Adv. contact Bryan Vandiviere. Circ: 6,000.

378 USA
COLONNADE. Text in English. 1924. w. free. bk.rev.; dance rev.; film rev.; music rev.; play rev.; software rev.; video rev. 12 p./no. 6 cols./p.; **Document type:** *Newspaper.* **Description:** Covers news and life on campus, arts and entertainment, previews, local entertainment, and sports.
Related titles: Online - full text ed.
Indexed: AIAP.
Published by: Georgia College & State University, PO Box 2442, Milledgeville, GA 31061. TEL 912-453-4511, FAX 912-454-1472, colonnade@mail.gac.peachnet.edu, http://acs5.gac.peachnet.edu/~colonnade. Pub. Mary Jean Land. adv.: page USD 425. Circ: 2,500.

378.198 USA
COLORADO COLLEGE BULLETIN. Text in English. 1955. q. **Document type:** *Bulletin.* **Description:** For college alumni, staff and parents of current students.
Indexed: AmH&L, HistAb.
Published by: Colorado College, 14 E Cache La Poudre St, Colorado Springs, CO 80903-3294. communications@coloradocollege.edu, http://www.coloradocollege.edu. Ed. Karrie Williams. Circ: 25,000.

378 USA
COLORADO DAILY. Text in English. 1892. d. (Mon.-Fri.). free. **Document type:** *Newspaper, Consumer.*
Address: 2610 Pearl St., Boulder, CO 80302. TEL 303-443-6272, http://www.coloradodaily.com. Pub. Randy Miller. Circ: 20,000 morning (free). Wire service: UPI, KR.

378 USA ISSN 0162-3893
LD1237.5
COLUMBIA (NEW YORK). Text in English. q. **Document type:** *Magazine, Consumer.*
Formerly (until 1978): Columbia Today (0146-423X)
Indexed: IAPV, RehabLit.
Published by: Columbia University, Trustees of Columbia University, 310 Uris Hall, New York, NY 10027. TEL 212-854-3431. Circ: 50,000.

378 USA ISSN 0572-7820
COLUMBIA COLLEGE TODAY. Text in English. 1954. 6/yr. USD 50 for 2 yrs.; free to qualified personnel (effective 2005). adv. bk.rev. illus. back issues avail.; reprints avail. **Document type:** *Magazine, Consumer.* **Description:** Feature articles and news about the college and its alumni.
Related titles: Online - full text ed.
Published by: Columbia College, Office of Alumni Affairs and Development, 475 Riverside Dr, Rm 917, New York, NY 10115. TEL 212-870-2752, FAX 212-870-2747, cct@columbia.edu, http://www.college.columbia.edu/cct/index.html. Ed., Pub. Alex Sachare. R&P Timothy P Cross. adv.: page USD 1,245. Circ: 48,000 (controlled).

378.1 USA ISSN 0010-1893
COLUMBIA DAILY SPECTATOR. Text in English. 1877. 5/w. (Sep.-May). USD 120; USD 65 semester; free on campus (effective 2005). adv. bk.rev.; film rev.; play rev. 16 p./no. 5 cols./p.; reprint service avail. from PQC. **Document type:** *Newspaper.*
Related titles: Microfilm ed.: 1877; Online - full text ed.
Published by: Spectator Publishing Co., Columbia University, 2875 Broadway, 3rd Fl., New York, NY 10025-7846. TEL 212-854-9500, FAX 212-854-9611, spectator@columbia.edu, http://www.columbiaspectator.com. Pub. Lauren Appelbaum. adv.: col. inch USD 14. Circ: 10,000.

378 340
COLUMBIA LAW SCHOOL NEWS. Text in English. 1901. 8/yr.
Published by: Columbia Law School, News Association, 435 W 116th St, Box A 27, New York, NY 10027. TEL 212-854-2640.

378.198 USA ISSN 0747-4504
COLUMBIA UNIVERSITY RECORD. Text in English. 1975. s-m. USD 25 (effective 1999). bk.rev. **Document type:** *Newspaper.*
Published by: Columbia University, Office of Public Affairs, 304 Low Library, 535 W 116th St, MC 4321, New York, NY 10027. TEL 212-854-3282, FAX 212-678-4817, calendar@columbia.edu. Ed., R&P Amy Callahan. Circ: 17,000.

C

378.1 USA ISSN 0010-2091
THE COLUMNS (FAIRMONT). Text in English. 1923. w. USD 15 in state; USD 20 out of state; free to qualified personnel. adv. film rev.; play rev. illus. **Document type:** *Newspaper, Consumer.* **Description:** Includes campus events, sports, movie and music reviews, opinion, schedules for exams.
Published by: Fairmont State College, Office of Publications, 121 Library Bldg, Locust Ave, Fairmont, WV 26554. TEL 304-367-4864, bes@fscvax.wvnet.edu. Ed. Dustin Benge. R&P Beth Slusser. Adv. contact Patricia Whiting. Circ: 2,000.

378.198 USA ISSN 1047-8604
COLUMNS (SEATTLE); the University of Washington alumni magazine. Text in English. 1908. q. USD 35 membership (effective 2001). adv. bk.rev. **Document type:** *Consumer.* **Description:** Contains news of the University of Washington.
Formerly (until Dec. 1989): Washington Alumnus
Published by: University of Washington Alumni Association, 1415 N E 45th St, Seattle, WA 98105. TEL 206-543-0540, FAX 206-685-0611, columns@u.washington.edu, griffin@u.washington.edu, http://www.washington.edu/alumni/columns. Ed. Tom Griffin. Pub. David Fagerlie. Adv. contact Kirk Tourtillotte TEL 206-367-2420 ext 1205. B&W page USD 3,920, color page USD 4,870; bleed 8.625 x 11.25. Circ: 230,000.

378.1 296 USA ISSN 0010-2652
COMMENTATOR. Text in English. 1935. bi-w. (Sep.-Jun.). adv. bk.rev.; film rev.; play rev. illus. back issues avail. **Document type:** *Newspaper.*
Related titles: Microfilm ed.: (from AJP).
Published by: Yeshiva College Student Council, Student Information Center, 500 W 185th St, New York, NY 10033. TEL 212-740-2155. Ed. Joshua Feldman. Circ: 5,000.

378 USA
COMMONWEALTH TIMES. Text in English. 1969. s-w. (Mon. & Thu. academic yr.). free (effective 2005). **Document type:** *Newspaper.*
Published by: Virginia Commonwealth University, 901 W. Main St., Richmond, VA 23284. TEL 804-828-1058, FAX 804-828-9201, CTeditor03@yahoo.com, http://www.commonwealthtimes.com. Circ: 6,000 (free).

378 610 USA
COMMUNIQUE (ITHACA). Text in English. 1978. s-a. free. **Document type:** *Newsletter, Academic/Scholarly.* **Description:** Published as a leadership report to alumni and friends of Cornell University.
Published by: Cornell University, Office of University Development, 55 Brown Rd, Ithaca, NY 14850-1266. TEL 607-254-7111, FAX 607-254-7167, gpl5@cornell.edu. Ed. George Lowery. Circ: 30,000 (controlled).

378 USA
THE COMMUNIQUE (PITTSBURGH, 1984). Text in English. 1984. s-m. USD 12. adv. back issues avail. **Document type:** *Newspaper.*
Formerly: First Edition
Published by: Chatham College, Woodland Rd, Box 596, Pittsburgh, PA 15232. TEL 412-365-1561. Ed. Julie Saunders. Adv. contact Amy Huseman. B&W page USD 125. Circ: 800.

371.8974 USA ISSN 1061-446X
COMMUNITY NEWS (WASHINGTON, DC). Text in English. 1982. w. **Document type:** *Newspaper, Academic/Scholarly.* **Description:** Provides Howard University students and faculty with an alternative coverage of news and issues in their community.
Published by: Howard University, School of Communications, 2400 Sixth St, NW, Washington, DC 20059. TEL 202-806-6100, http://www.soc.howard.edu/CommunityNews.htm.

378.198 USA
COMMUTER. Text in English. 1979. fortn. free to qualified personnel. adv. 12 p./no. 4 cols./p.; **Document type:** *Newspaper.*
Formerly: Macon Junior College Commuter
Published by: Macon State College, 100 College Station Dr, Macon, GA 31206-5144. TEL 912-757-3605, FAX 912-471-2813, commuter@mcmail.maconstate.edu. Ed. Whitney V McMath. Circ: 3,600.

378.198 GBR ISSN 0140-315X
CONCETTO; newspaper of Chelsea College students. Text in English. 1960. fortn. free. adv. bk.rev.; film rev.; play rev. **Document type:** *Newspaper.*
Published by: Chelsea College, Students Union, Manresa Rd, London, SW3 6LX, United Kingdom. Ed. Pete Sawyer. Circ: 1,000.

378 GBR ISSN 1466-2280
CONCORD. Text in English. 1989. q.
—BLDSC (3399.471500).
Published by: University of Wales Institute, Western Ave, Cardiff, S Glam CF5 2YB, United Kingdom. TEL 44-29-20416277, FAX 44-29-20416286, http://www.uwic.ac.uk.

378 USA
CONCORDIA. Text in English. 1961. 3/yr. free to alumni (effective 2005). back issues avail. **Document type:** *Newsletter.* **Description:** Covers news and features for alumni and friends of the college.
Formerly: Concordia Alumni News
Published by: Concordia College, 901 S Eighth St, Moorhead, MN 56562. TEL 218-299-4000, FAX 218-299-3646. Ed. Roger Degerman. Circ: 34,000 (controlled).

378 GBR
CONCOURSE. Text in English. N.S. 1978. 3/yr. (during school term). adv. bk.rev.
Published by: University of Keele, Keele University Students' Union, Keele University, Keele, Newcastle, Staffs ST5 5BJ, United Kingdom. TEL 0782-711411, FAX 0782-712671. Eds. Clare Alverson, Rick Crownshaw. Circ: 1,000.

CONFRONTATION; a literary journal of Long Island University. see *LITERATURE*

378 CAN ISSN 0829-044X
CONRAD GREBEL REVIEW. Text in English. 1983. 3/yr. CND 32 to individuals; CND 38 to institutions (effective 2005). **Document type:** *Journal, Academic/Scholarly.*
Indexed: NTA, RI-1.
—BLDSC (3417.852000), ingenta. **CCC.**
Published by: Conrad Grebel University College (Subsidiary of: University of Waterloo), 200 University Av W, Waterloo, ON N2L 3G6, Canada. TEL 519-885-0220, FAX 519-885-0014, congreb@uwaterloo.ca, http://grebel.uwaterloo.ca/academic/cgreview.

378.1 USA
CONTEXT. Text in English. 1914. 3/yr. free (effective 2003). bk.rev. **Document type:** *Magazine, Academic/Scholarly.* **Description:** Features Bethel College events, news and alumni.
Formerly (until Jun.2002): Bethel College Bulletin (0005-982X)
Published by: Bethel College, 300 E 27th St, North Newton, KS 67117-0531. TEL 316-283-2500, http://www.bethelks.edu. Ed., R&P Carla Reimer TEL 316-284-5287. Circ: 13,000.

378.198 USA ISSN 0888-7586
CONTRABAND (LAKE CHARLES). Text in English. 1939. w. USD 30 (effective 1999). adv. film rev.; play rev. illus. **Document type:** *Newspaper.*
Published by: McNeese State University, PO Box 91375, Lake Charles, LA 70609-1375. TEL 318-437-5645. Ed., R&P Todd McCardle TEL 318-475-5647. Adv. contact Chris Ererritt. Circ: 4,500.

378 CAN
THE CORD. Text in English. 1926. w. CND 40 (effective 1998). adv. bk.rev.; film rev. **Document type:** *Newspaper.*
Formerly: Cord Weekly
Published by: Wilfrid Laurier University, Student Publications, 75 University Ave W, Waterloo, ON N2L 3C5, Canada. TEL 519-884-0710, FAX 519-884-7723, 22cord@mach1.wlv.ca, http://www.wlu.ca/~wwwcord/. Ed. Katherine M Harding. R&P Kevin MacDonald. Adv. contact Lars Parstrik. Circ: 5,000.

378 USA ISSN 1548-8810
LH1.C8
CORNELL ALUMNI MAGAZINE. Text in English. 1899. bi-m. USD 29 domestic; USD 44 foreign (effective 2004). adv. bk.rev. **Document type:** *Magazine, Consumer.*
Former titles (until 2001): Cornell Magazine (1070-2733); (until 1993): Cornell Alumni News (1058-3467)
Related titles: Online - full text ed.
Published by: Cornell Alumni Federation, 55 Brown Rd, Ithaca, NY 14850-1247. TEL 607-272-8530, FAX 607-272-8532, cornell_magazine@cornell.edu, http://cornell-magazine.cornell.edu. Ed., Pub. Jim Roberts. Adv. contact Alanna Downey. Circ: 28,500 (paid).

378 USA ISSN 1095-8169
CORNELL DAILY SUN. Text in English. 1880. d. (Mon.-Fri.). USD 21.50, USD 45 for semester in town; USD 0.25 newsstand/cover (effective 2005). bk.rev.; film rev.; play rev. illus. back issues avail. **Document type:** *Newspaper.*
Related titles: Microfiche ed.
Published by: Cornell Daily Sun, Inc., 139 W State St, Ithaca, NY 14850. TEL 607-273-3606, FAX 607-273-0746, business@cornelldailysun.com, http://www.cornellsun.com. Ed. Erica Temel. Circ: 3,100 morning (paid). Wire service: AP, UPI.

CORNELL MEDICINE. see *MEDICAL SCIENCES*

635 USA ISSN 0010-8863
CORNELL PLANTATIONS MAGAZINE. Text in English. 1944. s-a. USD 35; includes membership. bk.rev. illus. **Document type:** *Academic/Scholarly.* **Description:** Presents articles about Cornell Plantations and on topics related to horticulture, ecology, conservation, gardening tips, landscape design, and plant and natural sciences.
Related titles: Microform ed.: (from PQC).
Indexed: BiolAb, FPA, ForAb, SCI.
Published by: Cornell University, Cornell Plantations, One Plantations Rd, Ithaca, NY 14850. TEL 607-255-3020, FAX 607-255-2404, ew28@cornell.edu, http://www.plantations.cornell.edu. Ed., R&P Elissa Wolfson TEL 607-255-8721. Circ: 3,600.

371.85 DEU ISSN 1615-8180
CORPS; Nachrichten fuer Weinheimer Corpsstudenten. Text in German. 1993. q. adv. bk.rev. **Document type:** *Magazine, Consumer.*
Formerly (until 2000): Der Corpsstudent (0947-3297); Which was formed by the merger of (1953-1993): Wachenburg (0935-0659); (1914-1993): Deutsche Corpszeitung (0931-0215)
Published by: Weinheimer Verband Alter Corpsstudenten, Karlstr 6, Karlsruhe, 76133, Germany. TEL 49-721-2036729, FAX 49-721-2036730, vorort.wsc@die-corps.de, http://www.die-corps.de/CORPS_Magazin.200.0.html. Eds. Michael Schur, Peter Philipp Schmitt. Circ: 10,000.

378 GBR
THE COURIER. Text in English. 1947. w. (during school term). adv. bk.rev. **Document type:** *Newspaper.*
Related titles: Online - full text ed.
Indexed: M&MA, PAIS.
Published by: University of Newcastle upon Tyne, Union Society, University Of Newcastle Upon Tyne, Kings Walk, Newcastle upon Tyne, Northd NE1 8QB, United Kingdom. TEL 44-191-232-4050, FAX 44-191-222-1876, http://www.ncl.ac.uk/~ncourier/. Ed., R&P James Jordan. Adv. contact Jonathan Munro. page GBP 550; trim 283 x 401. Circ: 3,000 (controlled).

378 USA
COURIER (MEQUON). Text in English. q. free.
Published by: Concordia University Wisconsin, 12800 N Lake Shore Dr, Mequon, WI 53097. TEL 414-243-5700, FAX 414-243-4351. Ed. Jeffrey Bandurski. Circ: 80,000.

378 USA
COURIER (SOUTH HOLLAND). Text in English. 1927. m. free. adv. bk.rev.; film rev.; play rev. charts; illus. **Document type:** *Newspaper.* **Description:** Discusses all matters of concern to college students.
Published by: South Suburban College, 15800 S State St, South Holland, IL 60473. TEL 708-596-2000, FAX 708-210-5758. Ed. Susan Sebok.

378 USA
THE COWL. Text in English. w. USD 8.
Published by: Providence College, PO BOX 2981, FRAIAR STA, Providence, RI 02918. TEL 401-865-2214.

378 USA
COYOTE. Text in English. 1909. 6/yr. free to students. **Document type:** *Newspaper.*
Published by: Albertson College, Associated Students, 2112 Cleveland Blvd, Caldwell, ID 83605. TEL 208-459-5508, FAX 208-454-2077. Circ: 1,000.

CRAB ORCHARD REVIEW. see *LITERATURE*

378 GBR ISSN 0308-048X
CRANFIELD SCHOOL OF MANAGEMENT ADDRESS BOOK. Text in English. 1975. a. **Document type:** *Directory.* **Description:** Lists all graduates of Cranfield School of Management in alphabetical, chronological, geographical, and professional order.
Related titles: Diskette ed.
Published by: A P Information Services, Marlborough House, 298 Regents Park Rd, London, N3 2UU, United Kingdom. TEL 44-20-8349-9988, FAX 44-20-8349-9797. adv.: page GBP 600; 150 x 210. Circ: 4,800.

378 USA
CRESCENT. Text in English. 1915. q. USD 15. **Document type:** *Newsletter.* **Description:** Contains information for and about the members of the fraternity.
Published by: Phi Beta Sigma Fraternity, Inc., 145 Kennedy St, N W, Washington, DC 20011. TEL 202-726-5434, FAX 202-881-1681.

378.198 USA
CREST. Text in English. 1939. w. USD 10. adv. bk.rev. back issues avail. **Document type:** *Newspaper.*
Published by: Teikyo Maycrest University, 1607 W 12th St, Davenport, IA 52804. TEL 319-327-9610, FAX 319-325-9250. Ed. Jennifer Holbo. Adv. contact Tina Burgmeier. Circ: 1,200.

378 USA
CRIMSON - WHITE. Text in English. 1894. 4/w. USD 125. adv. **Document type:** *Newspaper.*
Formerly: Crimson News
Published by: University of Alabama, Media Planning Board, 923 University Blvd, Box 2389, Tuscaloosa, AL 35403. TEL 205-348-7845, FAX 205-348-8036, cw@sa.ua.edu, http://www.cw.ua.edu. Ed. Melissa Wyllie. R&P Joel Mask TEL 205-348-7839. Adv. contact Tony Meggs. Circ: 15,000.

C

378 USA
THE CRIMSON WHITE. Text in English. 1894. 3/yr. (Wed. (summer only)). USD 125 (effective 2005). adv. **Document type:** *Newspaper.*
Published by: University of Alabama, Office of Student Media, 923 University Blvd., Tuscaloosa, AL 35403. TEL 205-348-7845, FAX 205-348-8036, cwletters@sa.ua.edu, http://www.cw.ua.edu. Adv. contact Elizabeth de Shazo. col. inch USD 10.25. Circ: 13,000 morning (paid and free). Wire service: AP.

378 CAN
LA CRISE*. Text in English. m. free.
Published by: Publi-Peq, 3575 bd St Laurent, Ste 232, Montreal, PQ H2X 2T7, Canada. TEL 514-845-8628. Circ: 2,000.

070 378 USA
CRITERION (RIVERSIDE)*. Text in English. 1939. bi-m. USD 15. adv. bk.rev.
Indexed: CERDIC, R&TA, RI-1, RI-2.
Published by: (Associated Students of Loma Linda University), Riverside County Publishing Co., 7190 Jurupa Ave, Riverside, CA 92504-1016. Ed. Peter Thornburgh. Circ: 2,000 (controlled).

371.85 USA
CROSS & CRESCENT. Text in English. 1914. q. USD 3. adv. illus. back issues avail. **Document type:** *Newsletter, Consumer.* **Description:** Includes articles on successful alumni and higher education.
Related titles: Online - full text ed.
Published by: Lambda Chi Alpha Fraternity, Inc., 8741 Founders Rd, Indianapolis, IN 46268-1389. TEL 317-872-8000, FAX 317-875-3828, bbly@lambdachi.org, information@lambdachi.org, http://www.lambdachi.org. Ed., Pub., R&P, Adv. contact Jason A Pearce. Circ: 127,500.

378 GBR ISSN 0956-1013
CROSS-NATIONAL RESEARCH PAPERS. Text in English. 1985. a. **Document type:** *Monographic series.*
—BLDSC (3488.860000), IE, ingenta.
Published by: Aston University, Aston Modern Languages Club, Department of Modern Languages, Aston Triangle, Birmingham, W Mids B4 7ET, United Kingdom. TEL 44-121-3593611, FAX 44-121-3596350, http://www.aston.ac.uk.

378 280.4 USA
THE CRUSADER. Text in English. 1942. w. (Tue.). free on campus; USD 24 subscr - mailed (effective 2005). **Document type:** *Newspaper, Consumer.*
Published by: Associated Students of Northwest Nazarene University, 623 Holly St, Nampa, ID 83686. TEL 208-467-8011, FAX 208-467-8645, crusader@student.nnc.edu, http://www.nnu.edu. Circ: 1,100 (paid and free). Wire service: RN.

378.198 USA
THE CRUSADER (LANCASTER). Text in English. 1936. w. free. adv. bk.rev.
Formerly: Marauder Times
Published by: Antelope Valley College, 3041 W Ave K, Lancaster, CA 93536. TEL 805-943-3241, FAX 805-943-5573. Ed. Catherine Dodson. Adv. contact Sandy Rowley. Circ: 1,850.

378 USA ISSN 1082-0523
CRUSADER (SELINSGROVE). Text in English. 1956. w. (Sep.-Apr.). USD 21.25 (effective 2001). adv. bk.rev.; film rev.; play rev. **Document type:** *Newspaper, Consumer.* **Description:** Covers campus events, student life, college sports, and national issues of interest to students, faculty, staff, and parents.
Related titles: Online - full text ed.: (from LexisNexis).
Published by: Susquehanna University, Campus Activities, PO Box 22, Selinsgrove, PA 17870. TEL 717-372-4298, FAX 717-372-2757, crusader@susqu.edu, http://www.susqu.edu/crusader. Ed. Brett Marcy. R&P Catherine Hastings TEL 717-372-9359. Adv. contact Christy Walter. Circ: 1,800.

378.1 GBR
CRY WOLF. Text in English. 1985. m. free. **Document type:** *Newspaper.*
Former titles (until 1999): Sheeps Clothing; (until 1998): Cry Wolf; (until 1995): Wolverhampton Polytechnic Students' Union Handbook
Published by: University of Wolverhampton, Students Union, Wulfruna St, Wolverhampton, W Mids WV1 1LY, United Kingdom. TEL 44-1902-322021, FAX 44-1902-322020, uwsu@wlv.ac.uk, http://www.wlv.ac.uk/su/John/crywolf/cwo.htm. Ed. Mark Wilson. Circ: 4,500.

378 GBR
CUB T N G. (The Next Generation) Text in English. 1947. m. free. adv. bk.rev. **Document type:** *Newspaper.*
Formerly: Cub (0964-8070)
Published by: Queen Mary & Westfield College, Students' Union, 432 Bancroft Rd, London, E1 4DH, United Kingdom. TEL 0171-975-5390, FAX 0181-981-0802. Ed. Samuel Welbeck. Circ: 3,000.

378 GBR
CULFORDIAN. Text in English. 1895. a. GBP 3, USD 6 (effective 1999). adv. bk.rev. back issues avail. **Document type:** *Newsletter.*
Published by: Culford School, Culford School, Culford, Bury St Edmunds, Suffolk IP28 6TX, United Kingdom. TEL 44-1284-728615, FAX 44-1284-728631, culford_edu@msn.com. Ed. Adam Pernak. Circ: 2,250.

378 USA
CUMBERLAND LAWYER. Text in English. a. USD 10. **Document type:** *Corporate.* **Description:** Published for alumni and friends of Cumberland School of Law, Samford University. Includes scholarly activities, school and international program news, and alumni updates.
Published by: Samford University, Cumberland School of Law, 800 Lakeshore Dr, ROBBH 315, Birmingham, AL 35229. TEL 205-726-2757, FAX 205-870-2673, http://cumberland.samford.edu. Ed. Elaine D Chambless. Circ: 7,000.

378 AUS ISSN 1440-866X
CURIO. Text in English. 1970. fortn. free. adv. bk.rev. **Document type:** *Newspaper.*
Former titles (until 1989): Ccaesarian (0311-1229); Yarruga
Related titles: Online - full text ed.: CUrio Online. 1997.
Published by: University of Canberra Students' Association, PO Box 1, Belconnen, ACT 2616, Australia. TEL 61-6-2012063, FAX 61-6-2514248, curio@student.canberra.edu.au, http://sa.canberra.edu.au/curio/. R&P Darren Langlands. Adv. contact Carol Battle. Circ: 2,000.

371.83 USA
CURRENT (KENOSHA); student voice of Carthage College. Text in English. 1892. w. free. adv. bk.rev.; film rev.; play rev. illus. **Document type:** *Newspaper.* **Description:** News, features, sports and opinions pertaining to student activities at the college.
Former titles: Arrow (0001-3056); Crimson Arrow
Published by: Carthage College, 2001 Alford Park Dr, Kenosha, WI 53140-1994. TEL 414-551-6150, FAX 414-551-6629, current%student%carthage@cns.carthage.edu, http://www.carthage.edu/current. Ed., R&P Lisa Liljegren. Adv. contact Kimberly Robenstein. Circ: 2,000.

378 071 USA
THE CURRENT SAUCE. Text in English. 1914. w. USD 20 (effective 2001). adv. illus. 8 p./no. 6 cols./p.; **Document type:** *Newspaper.*
Published by: Northwestern State University of Louisiana, Student Publications, NSU Box 5306, Natchitoches, LA 71497. TEL 318-357-5213, FAX 318-357-6564. Ed. Rondray Hill. R&P Neil Ralston TEL 318-357-4439. Adv. contact Braden Guy. Circ: 3,500 (controlled).

D U Z; das unabhaengige Hochschulmagazin. (Deutsche Universitaets Zeitung) see *EDUCATION—Higher Education*

378.1 USA ISSN 0011-5371
THE DAILY ATHENAEUM. Text in English. 1887. d. (Mon.-Fri.) (Aug.-May; w. , June-Aug.). USD 20 in state; USD 35 out of state (effective 2005). adv. bk.rev.; film rev.; play rev. **Document type:** *Newspaper.*
Related titles: Online - full text ed.: (from LexisNexis); Seasonal ed(s).: Summer Athenaeum.
Published by: West Virginia University, Committee for Student Publications, 284 Prospect St, Morgantown, WV 26506. TEL 304-293-5092, FAX 304-293-6857, awaters2@wvu.edu, http://www.da.wvu.edu. Circ: 15,000. Wire service: AP.

378 USA
THE DAILY AZTEC. Text in English. 1913. w. (Mon.-Thu.). free (effective 2005). **Document type:** *Newspaper.*
Published by: Independent of the University, San Diego State Univ., BAM-2, San Diego, San Diego, CA 92182-7800. TEL 619-594-4199, FAX 619-594-7277, office@thedailyaztec.com, http://www.thedailyaztec.com. Ed. Raven Tyson. Adv. contact Lindsey Quinby. Circ: 14,000 (free).

378 USA ISSN 1080-5060
DAILY BRUIN. Text in English. 1919. d. (Mon.-Fri.). USD 165; free on campus (effective 2005). 17 p./no. 6 cols./p.; **Document type:** *Newspaper.*
Published by: Associated Students of U C L A, Communications Board, 118 Kerckhoff Hall, 308 Westwood Plz, Los Angeles, CA 90024-1641. TEL 310-825-9898, FAX 310-206-0906, editor@media.ucla.edu, http://www.dailybruin.ucla.edu. Ed. Tyson Evans. Circ: 20,000 morning (free). Wire service: AP.

378.198 USA ISSN 1050-2300
DAILY CALIFORNIAN. Text in English. 1871. d. (Mon.-Fri.). USD 95 (effective 2005). adv. bk.rev.; film rev.; play rev. charts; illus. **Document type:** *Newspaper.* **Description:** Serves the University of California and the city of Berkeley.
Related titles: Microfilm ed.: (from LIB); Online - full text ed.: (from LexisNexis).
Published by: Independent Berkeley Student Publishing Co., Inc., PO Box 1949, Berkeley, CA 94701-1949. TEL 510-548-8300, FAX 510-849-2803, dailycal@dailycal.org., http://www.dailycal.org. Ed. Rich Bunnell. Circ: 23,000. Wire service: LAT-WAT.

378 USA
THE DAILY CAMPUS (DALLAS). Text in English. 1915. 4/w. free on campus (effective 2005). **Document type:** *Newspaper.*
Related titles: Online - full text ed.
Published by: Student Media Co., Inc., PO Box 750456, Dallas, TX 75275-0456. TEL 214-768-4555, FAX 214-768-8787, http://www.smudailycampus.com/. Circ: 5,000 morning (free). Wire service: AP.

378 USA
DAILY CAMPUS (STORRS MANSFIELD). Text in English. 1896. d. free on campus; USD 40 subscr - mailed (effective 2005). adv. bk.rev. **Document type:** *Newspaper.*
Published by: University of Connecticut Board of Trustees, 11 Dog Ln, Storrs Mansfield, CT 06268. TEL 203-486-3407, 860-486-3407, FAX 203-486-4388, 860-486-4388, http://www.dailycampus.com. Circ: 10,000.

051 USA ISSN 0011-5398
DAILY CARDINAL. Text in English. 1892. d. (except w. June-Aug.). USD 120 domestic; USD 240 foreign (effective 2005). adv. bk.rev.; film rev.; play rev. **Document type:** *Newspaper.* **Description:** Covers campus and local events, news and sports.
Formerly: New Daily Cardinal
Related titles: Online - full text ed.: (from LexisNexis).
Published by: Daily Cardinal Media Corporation, 821 University Ave, Madison, WI 53706. TEL 608-262-5857, FAX 608-262-0404, edit@cardinal.wics.edu, http://www.cardinal.wisc.edu. Ed. Alexander Balistreri. adv.: B&W page USD 438, color page USD 479; trim 12.5 x 10.25. Circ: 10,000.

378 USA
DAILY COLLEGIAN (FRESNO). Text in English. 1921. 4/w. (Mon.-Thur., academic year). USD 17.50 for 6 mos.. adv. bk.rev. Supplement avail. **Document type:** *Newspaper.*
Incorporates (1969-1998): Insight (Fresno)
Related titles: Microfilm ed.: (from LIB).
Published by: California State University, Fresno, 5241 N Maple Ave, Fresno, CA 93740-8027. TEL 559-278-4240, webmaster@csufresno.edu, http://www.csufresno.edu. Ed. Chris Branam. Adv. contact Lance Jackson. Circ: 3,500.

378 USA
DAILY COLLEGIAN (UNIVERSITY PARK). Text in English. 1887. d. (Mon.-Fri.). USD 0.50 newsstand/cover; free on campus (effective 2005). **Document type:** *Newspaper.* **Description:** Independent student newspaper serving the University Park campus of Penn State University.
Published by: Daily Collegian, Inc., James Building, 123 S. Burrowes St., University Park, PA 16801-3882. TEL 814-865-2531, FAX 814-863-1126, glh5@psu.edu, http://www.collegian.psu.edu. Circ: 19,500 morning (paid). Wire service: AP.

378 USA
THE DAILY COUGAR. Text in English. 1934. d. (Mon.-Fri.) (academic yr.). USD 70 (effective 2004); free to students. **Document type:** *Newspaper.*
Published by: University of Houston, Student Publications Department, 151L Communication Bldg, Houston, TX 77204-4015. TEL 713-743-5350, FAX 713-743-5384, rcigler@uh.edu, http://www.uh.edu/campus/cougar. Ed. Matt Dulin. Adv. contact Chelsea Bloom. Circ: 13,000 morning (free).

378.1 USA ISSN 0894-1599
DAILY EASTERN NEWS. Text in English. 1915. d. (Mon.-Fri.). USD 68 (effective 2005). adv. bk.rev.; play rev. index. **Document type:** *Newspaper.*
Formerly: The Daily Eastern News (0012-8864)
Related titles: Microfilm ed.; Online - full content ed.
Published by: (Student Publications), Eastern Illinois University, Student Publications, Charleston, IL 61920. TEL 217-581-2812, FAX 217-581-2923, http://www.thedailyeasternnews.com. Ed. Jennifer Chiariello. Pub. John Ryan. Circ: 8,900. Wire service: AP.

378 071 USA
DAILY EVERGREEN. Text in English. 1894. d. (Mon.-Fri.). USD 190 (effective 2005). adv. bk.rev. **Document type:** *Newspaper.*
Published by: Washington State University, Student Publications Board, PO Box 642510, Pullman, WA 99165-2008. TEL 509-335-4573, FAX 509-335-7401, online@dailyevergreen.com, http://www.dailyevergreen.com. Ed. Jake Dorcy. R&P Bob Hilliard TEL 509-335-8920. Circ: 12,000.

378 USA
DAILY FORTY-NINER. Variant title: Daily 49er. Text in English. 1949. 4/w. (Mon.-Thu.). USD 49 (effective 2004); free on campus. adv. **Document type:** *Newspaper.*
Published by: California State University, Long Branch, 1250 Bellflower Blvd, SSPA 010-B, Long Branch, CA 90840. TEL 562-985-5568, FAX 562-985-5833, mulligan@csulb.edu, http://www.csulb.edu/~d49er/. Pub. William A Mulligan. Adv. contact Stacey Nail. col. inch USD 12. Circ: 10,000 morning (free). Wire service: AP.

C

378.198 USA ISSN 1094-7337
DAILY FREE PRESS. Text in English. 1970. d. (Mon.-Fri.). USD 85 (effective 2005). adv. bk.rev.; film rev.; play rev. charts; illus.; stat. back issues avail. **Document type:** *Newspaper.*
Related titles: Online - full text ed.: (from LexisNexis).
Published by: Back Bay Publishing Co., Inc., 842 Commonwealth Ave, Boston, MA 02215. TEL 617-232-6841, FAX 617-232-0592, dfpletters@dailyfreepress.com, http://dailyfreepress.com. Ed. Patrick Gillooly. adv.: col. inch USD 10.90. Circ: 12,000. Wire service: CNS, AP.

378 USA
THE DAILY HELMSMAN. Text in English. d. (Tue.-Fri.). free (effective 2005). **Document type:** *Newspaper.*
Published by: University of Memphis, Department of Journalism, 3711 Veterans Bldg, Memphis, TN 38152-0001. TEL 901-678-2191, FAX 901-678-4792, morgan@dailyhelmsman.com, http://www.dailyhelmsman.com. Adv. contact Bob Willis. Circ: 9,500 morning (free).

378 USA
DAILY ILLINI. Text in English. 1874. d. (Mon.-Fri.). free (effective 2005). **Document type:** *Newspaper.*
Published by: Illini Media Co., 57 E Green St, Champaign, IL 61820. TEL 217-333-3733, editor@dailyillini.com, http://www.dailyillini.com. Pub. Mary Cory. Circ: 20,000 morning (free). Wire service: AP.

378 USA
THE DAILY IOWAN. Text in English. 1868. d. (Mon.-Fri.). USD 50 in city; USD 95 out of city; USD 20 semester (effective 2005). **Document type:** *Newspaper.*
Published by: Student Publications, Inc., 111 Communications Ctr., Iowa City, IA 52242. TEL 319-353-6210, daily-iowan@uiowa.edu, http://www.dailyiowan.com. Ed. Jennifer Sturm. Pub. William Casey. Circ: 20,000 morning (paid). Wire service: AP.

C

378.1 USA ISSN 0011-5444
DAILY KENT STATER. Text in English. 1926. 4/w. (Tue.-Fri.). USD 80; USD 60 per academic year (effective 2005). adv. bk.rev. illus. **Document type:** *Newspaper.*
Related titles: Microform ed.: (from PQC); Online - full text ed.: (from LexisNexis).
Published by: Kent State University, Student Media Policy Committee, Taylor Hall, Rm 101, Kent, OH 44242. TEL 216-672-2586, stater@kent.edu, http://www.stateronline.com, http://www.stater.kent.edu. Ed. Mike Kiesta TEL 330-672-0885. Adv. contact Lori Cantor. col. inch USD 9. Circ: 12,000. Wire service: AP.

378 USA ISSN 1077-8667
DAILY MISSISSIPPIAN. Text in English. 1912. d. (Mon.-Fri.). USD 50 (effective 2006). adv. bk.rev. **Document type:** *Newspaper.*
Address: Farley Hall, University, MS 38677. TEL 601-232-7118, FAX 601-232-5703, smc@olemiss.edu, http://www.thedmonline.com, http://www.lemiss.edu/news/dm. Ed. Emery Carrington. adv.: col. inch USD 7.15. Circ: 11,500. Wire service: AP.

378.198 USA ISSN 1090-4085
DAILY NEBRASKAN. Text in English. 1901. d. (Mon.-Fri.). USD 75 (effective 2005). adv. bk.rev.; film rev.; play rev.; music rev.; rec.rev. charts; illus. 12 p./no. 6 cols./p.; **Document type:** *Newspaper.*
Published by: University of Nebraska at Lincoln, 20 Nebraska Union, 1400 R St, Lincoln, NE 68588-0448. webmaster@dailynebraskan.com, http://www.dailynebraskan.com. Ed. Van Jensen. Adv. contact Nick Partsch TEL 402-472-2589. col. inch USD 13. Circ: 13,600. Wire service: AP.

378 USA ISSN 1523-5033
THE DAILY NORTHWESTERN. Text in English. 1881. d. (Mon.-Fri.). USD 149; free on campus (effective 2005). bk.rev. **Document type:** *Newspaper, Consumer.*
Published by: Northwestern University, Students Publishing Co., 1999 Sheridan Rd, Evanston, IL 60208. TEL 708-491-7206, FAX 708-491-9905, forum@dailynorthwestern.com, http://www.dailynorthwestern.com. Ed. Robert Samuels. Circ: 7,500 morning (free). Wire service: AP, LAT-WAT.

378 USA
THE DAILY O'COLLEGIAN. Text in English. 1895. d. (Mon.-Fri.). USD 174.50; USD 0.25 newsstand/cover (effective 2005). **Document type:** *Newspaper, Consumer.*
Published by: O'Collegian Publishing Co., 106 Paul Miller Journalism Bldg, Stillwater, OK 74078. TEL 405-744-8372, FAX 405-744-7936, http://www.ocolly.com. Adv. contact Kelsey Johnson. Circ: 11,100 morning (paid). Wire service: AP.

378 USA
THE DAILY OF THE UNIVERSITY OF WASHINGTON. Text in English. 1893. d. (Mon.-Fri.). USD 90 subscr - mailed (effective 2005); free to students. **Document type:** *Newspaper, Consumer.*
Published by: University of Washington, 144 Communications Bld DS-20, Seattle, WA 98195. TEL 206-543-7666, 206-543-2700, editor@the daily.washington.edu, http://www.thedaily.washington.edu. Ed. Christina Siderius. Pub. Oren Campbell. Adv. contact Jordan Blasdel. Circ: 50,000 morning (paid).

535 USA
DAILY ORANGE. Text in English. 1903. d. (Mon.-Fri.). USD 160; USD 90 for 6 mos. (effective 2005). adv. **Document type:** *Newspaper.*
Related titles: Microform ed.
Published by: Daily Orange Corp., Syracuse University, 744 Ostrom Ave, Syracuse, NY 13210. TEL 315-443-2314, FAX 315-443-3689, pwaack@dailyorange.com, http://www.dailyorange.com. Ed. Jared Novack. adv.: col. inch USD 9.80. Circ: 9,040 morning (paid and free). Wire service: LAT-WAT.

378 USA
DAILY PENNSYLVANIAN. Text in English. 1885. d. (Mon.-Fri.) ((Sep.-Apr)). USD 225; free to students (effective 2005). adv. 14 p./no. 6 cols./p.; back issues avail. **Document type:** *Newspaper.* **Description:** Daily newspaper covering news, sports and opinion at University of Pennsylvania and surrounding Philadelphia community.
Related titles: CD-ROM ed.; Online - full content ed.; Alternate Frequency ed(s).: Weekly Pennsylvanian. w. USD 42 (effective 2004).
Published by: Daily Pennsylvanian, Inc., 4015 Walnut St., 2nd Fl., Philadelphia, PA 19104-6198. TEL 215-898-6585, FAX 215-898-2050, info@dailypennsylvanian.com, http://www.dailypennsylvanian.com. adv.: col. inch USD 11.90. Circ: 14,000 morning (free). Wire service: AP.

378.1 USA ISSN 0885-7601
LH1.P8
THE DAILY PRINCETONIAN. Text in English. 1876. d. (Mon.-Fri.) (Sep.-May). USD 66 (effective 2000). adv. illus. **Document type:** *Newspaper.*
Related titles: Online - full text ed.: (from LexisNexis).
Published by: Daily Princetonian, Inc., PO Box 469, Princeton, NJ 08542. TEL 609-258-8110, FAX 609-258-8117, newsroom@dailyprincetonian.com, http://www.dailyprincetonian.com. Ed. Richard Just. Adv. contact Alexandra Melby. Circ: 4,000. Wire service: AP.

378 USA
DAILY REVEILLE. Text in English. 1898. d. (Tue.-Fri..). USD 75 (effective 1999). **Document type:** *Newspaper.*
Published by: Louisiana State University, B-26 Hodges Hall, Baton Rouge, LA 70803. TEL 225-388-1697, FAX 225-388-1698. Ed. Mari Serebrov. Circ: 19,000.

378 USA
DAILY SUNDIAL. Text in English. 1957. 4/yr. (Mon.-Thu.). free. **Document type:** *Newspaper, Consumer.*
Published by: California State University, Northridge, 18111 Nordhoff St, Northridge, CA 91325-8258. TEL 818-667-2998, FAX 818-677-3638, ads@sundial.csun.edu, http://sundial.csun.edu. Pub. Manley Witten. Circ: 30,500 morning (free); 8,000 (free). Wire service: AP.

378 USA ISSN 1070-9436
DAILY TAR HEEL. Text in English. 1893. d. (Mon.-Fri.). USD 172 (effective 2005). adv. **Document type:** *Newspaper.*
Related titles: Online - full text ed.
Published by: (University of North Carolina), D T H Publishing Corp., PO Box 3257, Chapel Hill, NC 27515. TEL 919-962-1163, FAX 919-962-1609, dth@unc.edu, http://www.dailytarheel.com. adv.: col. inch USD 11. Circ: 20,000. Wire service: AP.

378 USA
DAILY TARGUM. Text in English. 1869. d. (Mon.-Fri.) (academic yr.). USD 67.50; free (effective 2005). bk.rev. illus. **Document type:** *Newspaper.* **Description:** Offers Rutgers students, faculty, staff, and alumni news and commentary on issues affecting the University and the community.
Related titles: Online - full text ed.: Targum Online: The Daily Targum on the Web.
Published by: Targum Publishing Co., 126 College Ave., Ste. 431, New Brunswick, NJ 08901. TEL 732-932-7051, FAX 732-246-7299, webmaster@dailytargum.com, http://www.dailytargum.com. Ed. Nick Sevilis. Circ: 17,000 morning (free). Wire service: AP.

378 USA ISSN 1090-1108
THE DAILY TEXAN. Text in English. 1900. d. (Mon.-Fri.). USD 75; USD 0.25 newsstand/cover (effective 2005). bk.rev.; film rev.; play rev. illus. **Document type:** *Newspaper.*
Related titles: Microfilm ed.; Online - full text ed.
Published by: Texas Student Publications, PO Box D, Austin, TX 78712. editor@dailytexanonline.com, http://www.dailytexanonline.com. Ed. A. J. Bauer. Circ: 32,000 morning (paid). Wire service: AP.

378 USA
DAILY TITAN. Text in English. 1960. 5/w. (Mon.-Fri.). USD 65; free on campus (effective 2005). adv. 12 p./no. 6 cols./p.; **Document type:** *Newspaper, Consumer.*
Related titles: Microfilm ed.: (from LIB).
Published by: California State University, Fullerton, College Park Bldg, Ste 660, 2600 E Nutwood Ave, Fullerton, CA 92834. TEL 714-278-3373, FAX 714-278-2702, dailytitan@fullerton.edu, http://www.dailytitan.com. Adv. contact Kevin Cook. col. inch USD 7.50. Circ: 6,000 morning (paid and free).

378 USA
THE DAILY TOREADOR. Text in English. 1925. s-w. (Mon.-Fri. academic yr.; Tue. & Fri. summer). USD 90 (effective 2005). **Document type:** *Newspaper, Consumer.*
Formerly: University Daily
Published by: Texas Tech University, Student Media, 211 Student Media Bldg., Lubbock, Lubbock, TX 79409-3081. TEL 806-742-3393, FAX 806-742-2434, dailytoreador@ttu.edu, http://www.dailytoreador.com/. Ed. Nikki Siegrist. Circ: 11,500 morning (paid). Wire service: AP.

378 USA
DAILY TROJAN. Text in English. 1912. d. (Mon.-Fri.) (academic yr.). USD 90 (effective 2005); free on campus. **Document type:** *Newspaper, Consumer.*
Published by: University of Southern California, Student Union 404, University Park, Los Angeles, CA 90089-0895. TEL 213-740-8829, FAX 213-740-5666, dtrojan@usc.edu, http://www.dailytrojan.com. Circ: 10,000 morning (paid and free).

378 USA
THE DAILY UNIVERSE. Text in English. 1902. d. (Mon.-Fri.). USD 232 Fall & Winter semester; USD 88 Fall & Winter semester; USD 88 Spring & Summer semester (effective 2005). **Document type:** *Newspaper.*
Published by: Brigham Young University, 152 Brim Hall Bldg, Provo, UT 84602. TEL 801-422-2957, FAX 801-422-0177, john@du2.byu.edu, http://www.newsnet.byu.edu. Ed. Kaylene Armstrong. Adv. contact Casey Stauffer. Circ: 18,500 morning (paid). Wire service: AP.

378.198 USA
DAILY UNIVERSITY STAR. Text in English. 1911. 4/w. USD 35. adv. bk.rev. **Document type:** *Newspaper.*
Formerly: University Star
Related titles: Microfilm ed.
Published by: Texas State University - San Marcos, Department of Journalism, 102 Old Main, San Marcos, TX 78666-4616. TEL 512-245-3487, FAX 512-245-3708. Circ: 12,000.

378 USA
THE DAILY UTAH CHRONICLE. Text in English. 1890. w. (Mon.-Fri. academic yr.; Wed. summer). free. adv. **Document type:** *Newspaper, Consumer.*
Published by: University of Utah, 200 S Central Campus Dr, Rm 236, Salt Lake City, UT 84112-9106. TEL 801-581-6397, FAX 801-581-3299, letters@chronicle.utah.edu., http://www.dailyutahchronicle.com. Ed. Steve Gehrke. adv.: col. inch USD .75. Circ: 14,000 morning (free). Wire service: AP.

378 USA
DAILY VIDETTE. Text in English. 1888. d. (Mon.-Fri.). USD 150; free on campus (effective 2005). **Document type:** *Newspaper.*
Indexed: ChPerl.
Published by: Illinois State University, Vidette Publications Board, Locus & University, Campus Box 890, Normal, IL 61761. TEL 309-438-7685, FAX 309-438-5211, http://www.dailyvidette.com. Ed. Kari Lee. Circ: 7,500 morning (free). Wire service: AP.

378.1 CAN ISSN 0011-5819
DALHOUSIE GAZETTE; Canada's oldest college newspaper. Text in English. 1867. w. CND 25. adv. bk.rev.; film rev.; play rev.
Published by: Dalhousie Gazette Publications Society, Dalhousie University, Halifax, NS B3H 4J2, Canada. TEL 902-424-2507. Circ: 10,000.

378.198 CAN ISSN 1185-4014
DALHOUSIE MAGAZINE; the alumni magazine. Text in English. 1983. 3/yr. free. back issues avail. **Document type:** *Bulletin.* **Description:** Provides alumni and campus news.
Published by: Dalhousie Alumni Affairs, Dalhousie University, Macdonald Bldg, Halifax, NS B3H 3J5, Canada. TEL 902-494-2071, FAX 902-494-1141, jdavidso@kilcom1.ucis.dal.ca. Ed., R&P June Davidson. Circ: 45,000.

378 USA
DANA REVIEW. Text in English. 1944. q. free (effective 2005). **Document type:** *Newsletter, Consumer.*
Published by: Dana College, 2848 College Dr, Blair, NE 68008. TEL 402-426-7385, FAX 402-426-7386, creed@fs1.dana.edu. R&P Carrie L Reed. Circ: 12,500 (controlled and free).

378 USA ISSN 0199-9931
LH1.D3
THE DARTMOUTH. Text in English. 1799. d. (Mon.-Fri.). USD 60 (effective 2005). adv. bk.rev. **Document type:** *Newspaper, Consumer.*
Related titles: Online - full text ed.: (from LexisNexis).
Published by: Dartmouth, 6175 Robinson Hall, Hanover, NH 03755. TEL 603-646-2600. Circ: 2,500. Wire service: AP.

378 USA
DARTMOUTH ALUMNI MAGAZINE. Text in English. 1908. 6/yr. USD 26; USD 5 per issue (effective 2005). bk.rev. **Document type:** *Magazine, Consumer.*
Published by: Dartmouth College, 7 Allen St, Hanover, NH 03755-1814. TEL 603-646-2256, FAX 603-646-1209, alumni.magazine@dartmouth.edu. Ed. Sean Plottner. Circ: 47,000 (paid).

DARTMOUTH MEDICINE. see *MEDICAL SCIENCES*

378.1   USA   ISSN 1074-083X
DARTMOUTH REVIEW. Text in English. 1980. w. USD 40; USD 50 foreign (effective 2000). adv. bk.rev. **Document type:** *Newspaper.* **Description:** Covers campus news for Dartmouth College, as well as national news.
Published by: Hanover Review, Inc., PO Box 343, Hanover, NH 03755. TEL 603-643-4370, FAX 603-643-3070, http://www.dartreview.com. Ed. Doris Brewer. Adv. contact Mark Kelly. Circ: 12,300.

378   GBR
DARTS. Text in English. 1947. fortn. film rev.; music rev. 20 p./no. 5 cols./p.; **Document type:** *Newspaper.*
Published by: Sheffield University, Students Union, Western Bank, Sheffield, S Yorks S10 2TG, United Kingdom. TEL 44-114-222-8672. R&P Amanda Folkes. adv.: page GBP 500. Circ: 6,000.

378   AUS
DEAKIN UNIVERSITY, OFF-CAMPUS GUIDE. Text in English. 1978. a.
Formerly: Deakin University. Guide to Off-Campus Studies
Published by: Deakin University, Toorak Campus, 336 Glenferrie Rd, Malvern, VIC 3144, Australia. Circ: 30,000.

378   CAN
LE DECLIN. Text in French. 6/yr. adv.
Formerly (until 1987): Bof
Published by: College d'Enseignement Generale et Professionnel de l'Abitibi - Tesmiscaminque, 425 boul. du College, C P 1500, Rouyn, PQ J9X 5E5, Canada. TEL 819-762-1894. Circ: 700.

378.1   USA   ISSN 0011-7501
DEFENDER (DEFIANCE). Text in English. 1970 (vol.10). w. free to students. adv. film rev.; play rev. illus. reprint service avail. from PQC.
Related titles: Microform ed.: (from PQC).
Published by: Defiance College, 701 N Clinton St, Defiance, OH 43512. TEL 419-784-4010. Circ: 800.

378   CAN
DEFI-SCIENCES. Text in French. s-m. free.
Published by: Publi-Peq, 3575 bd St Laurent, Ste 232, Montreal, PQ H2X 2T7, Canada. TEL 514-845-8628. Circ: 3,500.

378.1   CAN
DEFISCIENCE; journal des etudiants en sciences et genie de l'univers-cite laval. Text in French. 1977. 8/yr. CND 14. bk.rev. **Document type:** *Academic/Scholarly.* **Description:** Humoristic student publication addressing science and engineering majors.
Former titles: Eprouvette (0046-2373); Carabin
Published by: Universite Laval, Association des Etudiants en Sciences et Genie, Pavillon Vachon, Ste 0060, Cite Universitaire, Quebec, PQ G1K 7P4, Canada. TEL 418-656-2131, FAX 418-656-3082, vpcom@aesgul.ulaval.ca. Ed. Jean Paul Vermette. adv.: page CND 325. Circ: 3,000.

378.1   GBR
DEGREES NORTH (SUNDERLAND). Text in English. 1959. 12/yr. free. adv. bk.rev.; film rev.; play rev. **Document type:** *Newspaper.*
Former titles (until 1996): Monopoly; (until 1981): Dais (0011-5754)
Published by: University of Sunderland, Students Union, Wearmouth Hall, Sunderland, Chester Rd, Sunderland, SR1 3SD, United Kingdom. TEL 44-191-5145512. Ed. Alex Dippie. R&P Joe Williams. Adv. contact Allen Humes. Circ: 5,000.

378.1   NLD   ISSN 0011-782X
DELFTS BOUWKUNDIG STUDENTEN GEZELSCHAP STYLES. MEDEDELINGEN∗ . Text in Dutch. 1961. w. (Sep.-Jun.). free. charts; stat.
Published by: Delfts Bouwkundig Studenten Gezelschap Stylos, Berlageweg 1, Delft, Netherlands. Circ: 2,500.

378   CAN
LE DELIRE. Text in French. 1984. fortn. adv.
Published by: Publi-Peq, 3575 bd St Laurent, Ste 232, Montreal, PQ H2X 2T7, Canada. TEL 514-845-8628. Circ: 700.

378   USA
DELTA (LEXINGTON). Text in English. 1883. q. USD 15. adv. **Document type:** *Consumer.* **Description:** Provides news from the fraternity's college chapters and alumni and features on Sigma Nu's past and present. Reports on issues affecting the fraternity community and its relationship to higher education.
Published by: Sigma Nu Fraternity, Inc., PO Box 1869, Lexington, VA 24450. TEL 540-463-1869, FAX 540-463-1669, snhqdelta@aol.com, http://www.sigmanu.org. Ed. Jason R Guyton. R&P James A Owens. Circ: 100,000.

378   USA
DELTA CHI QUARTERLY. Text in English. 1903. q. USD 1. adv. **Description:** Devoted exclusively to programs, events and news for undergraduate members.

Published by: Delta Chi Fraternity, PO Box 1817, Iowa City, IA 52244-1817. TEL 319-337-4811, rayg@deltachi.com, http://www.deltachi.com. Ed. Raymond Galbreth. Circ: 36,000.

378   USA
DELTA COLLEGIATE. Text in English. 1961. w. (Thu.). free domestic to students (effective 2005). **Document type:** *Newspaper.*
Published by: Delta College, 1961 Delta Rd., University Cent er, MI 48710. TEL 989-686-9000, kerandol@alpha.delta.edu, http://delta.edu/. Circ: 3,500 (free).

371.85   USA   ISSN 0745-0958
LJ75
DELTA EPSILON SIGMA JOURNAL. Text in English. 1947. 3/yr. membership. index. **Document type:** *Academic/Scholarly.* **Description:** Publishes articles on a wide range of subjects, as well as fiction and poetry.
Formerly: Delta Epsilon Sigma Bulletin (0011-8028)
Indexed: CPL, MLA-IB.
Published by: Delta Epsilon Sigma National Scholastic Honor Society, c/o George Herndl, Ed, 117 Channel Lane, Belmont, NC 28012-3262. TEL 704-825-5026, FAX 305-899-3026, jplee@jeanne.barry.edu, http://dominic.barry.edu/~des/. R&P George Herndl. Circ: 20,000 (controlled).

328.8   USA   ISSN 0416-9336
DELTA PI EPSILON. RESEARCH BULLETIN. Text in English. 1962. irreg. price varies. reprint service avail. from PQC. **Document type:** *Bulletin.*
Indexed: BusEdI.
Published by: Delta Pi Epsilon Graduate Business Education Society, National Office, P O Box 4340, Little Rock, AR 72214. TEL 501-562-1233, FAX 501-562-1293. Circ: 10,000.

378   USA
DELTAN (NEW YORK)∗ . Text in English. 1914. q. free to members. **Description:** Provides reports on the state of the Fraternity, Chapter news, alumni awards and donors.
Published by: Zeta Beta Tau Fraternity, Inc., 3905 Vincennes Rd, Ste 101, Indianapolis, IN 46268-3025. TEL 212-629-0888, FAX 212-643-0717. Ed. Howard A Siegel. Circ: 55,000.

669   RUS
DENNITSA. Text in Russian. 1966. w. **Document type:** *Newspaper.*
Formerly (until Dec. 1990): Za Kadry
Published by: Magnitogorskii Gorno-Metallurgicheskii Institut im. G.I. Nosova, Pr Lenina 38, aud 248, Magnitogorsk, 455000, Russian Federation. TEL 2-85-36. Ed. A Yu Shemetova. Circ: 1,067.

DENTAL IMAGES. see *MEDICAL SCIENCES—Dentistry*

378   USA
DEPAUW. Text in English. 1852. s-w. (Tue. & Fri.). USD 40; free on campus (effective 2005). **Document type:** *Newspaper.* **Description:** Contains local news, commentary, sports and features covering the DePauw University campus.
Published by: DePauw University, Student Publication Board, Center for Contemporary Media, 609 S Locust, Greencastle, IN 46135-0512. TEL 765-6585972, FAX 765-658-5991, business@thedepauw.com, http://www.depauw.edu. Circ: 3,300 (paid).

378   PRI
DIALOGO. Text in Spanish. 198?. m. USD 1 newsstand/cover. **Document type:** *Newspaper, Consumer.* **Description:** Researches and covers issues related to academic life, culture and social issues.
Published by: Universidad de Puerto Rico, Apdo 364984, San Juan, 00936-4984, Puerto Rico. TEL 787-763-1015, FAX 787-250-8729, dialogo@upri.upr.clu.edu. Ed. Luis Fernando Coss Ponton. Circ: 35,000.

378   USA
DIAMOND (SIOUX CENTER). Text in English. 1957. 12/yr. USD 10 (effective 2003). 8 p./no. 5 cols./p.; **Document type:** *Newspaper.* **Description:** Covers news and events of interest to college students.
Published by: Dordt College, 498 Fourth Ave N E, Sioux Center, IA 51250. TEL 712-722-6000, 800-343-6738, http://www.dordt.edu. Ed. Stephen Kloostermann. R&P Lorna Van Gilst. Circ: 1,000.

378   USA
THE DIAMONDBACK. Text in English. 1910. d. (Mon.-Fri.) ((Sep.-May)). USD 150 (effective 2005); free on campus. **Document type:** *Newspaper, Consumer.*
Contact: Maryland Media, Inc., 3150 South Campus Dining Hall, College Park, MD 20742. TEL 301-314-8200, FAX 301-314-8358, diamondb@umail.umd.edu, http://www.umd.edu/diamondback. Ed. Jonathan Cribbs. Circ: 17,000 morning (paid and free). Wire service: AP.

378   RWA
DIAPASON. Text in Kinyarwanda. 1966. q. **Document type:** *Journal, Academic/Scholarly.*
Published by: Universite Nationale du Rwanda, BP 117, Butare, Rwanda. TEL 250-32110, FAX 250-32149. Ed. Pierre Turatsinze. Circ: 300.

378   USA
DIORAMA. Text in English. 1948. a. USD 15. back issues avail. **Description:** Covers events of the previous academic year.
Published by: University of North Alabama, 330 Keller Hall, Florence, AL 35632. TEL 256-765-4426, FAX 256-765-4275. Ed. Kristin J Burt. Circ: 3,000.

378.198   CAN   ISSN 0228-9636
LES DIPLOMES. Text in French. 1973 (vol.14). 2/yr. CND 6, USD 8 (effective 2000). adv. bk.rev. illus. **Document type:** *Academic/Scholarly.* **Description:** Each issues presents a particular topic of interest to university graduates and the general public.
Former titles (until Sep. 1980): Interdit (0300-3965); Inter
Published by: Les Diplomes de l'Universite de Montreal, 3744 rue Jean Brillant, Ste 410, Montreal, PQ H3C 3J7, Canada. TEL 514-343-6230, FAX 514-343-5798, http:// www.umontreal.ca. Ed. Michel Saint Laurent. adv.: B&W page CND 2,000, color page CND 2,700; trim 24 x 19. Circ: 150,000.

378   USA
DIRECTIONS (AUSTIN). Text in English. q. free. **Document type:** *Newsletter, Consumer.* **Description:** Reports on news on the programs and students at the University of Texas at Austin College of Communications.
Media: Online - full text.
Published by: University of Texas at Austin, College of Communications, 1 University Station, A0900, Austin, TX 78712-0109. http://communication.utexas.edu/alumni/ directions/index.html.

378.198   USA
DIRECTIONS (EDGERTON). Text in English. 1981. a. adv. bk.rev.
Published by: Directions Publishing, Inc., 21 N Henry St, Edgerton, WI 53534. TEL 608-884-3367, FAX 608-884-8187. Ed. Diane Everson. Circ: (controlled).

DIRITTO ALLO STUDIO; il mensile universitario di informazione e orientamento al lavoro. see *OCCUPATIONS AND CAREERS*

378   USA
DOLPHIN. Text in English. 1946. w. (during academic yr.). USD 6. adv. **Document type:** *Newspaper.*
Address: Loyola Hall, LeMoyne College, Syracuse, NY 13214-1399. TEL 315-445-4542. Ed. Rob Weston. Circ: 2,500.

378.198   GBR
DOUBLE TAKE. Text in English. 1981. w. free.
Published by: (Students Union), University College of Swansea, Mandela House, Singleton Park, Swansea, Glam SA2 8PP, United Kingdom. Ed. Steven Bird. Circ: 2,250.

378   USA
DOUGLASS ALUMNAE MAGAZINE. Text in English. 1922. q. USD 10.
Formerly: Douglass Alumnae Bulletin
Published by: Douglass College, Associate Alumnae, 80 Clifton Ave, New Brunswick, NJ 08901-1599. TEL 908-247-0700, FAX 908-247-1974. Ed. Beth Demavro. Circ: 13,000.

378.198   USA
DRAKE UPDATE. Text in English. 1987. 3/yr. free to qualified personnel. **Document type:** *Newspaper.* **Description:** Contains alumni and campus news and features.
Published by: Drake University, Office of Marketing and Communications, 316 Old Main, Des Moines, IA 50311. TEL 515-271-3273, FAX 515-271-3798, barbara.boose@drake.edu, http://www.drake.edu/alumni/alumni-publications.html. Ed., R&P Barbara Dietrich Boose. Circ: 44,000.

DROEMMEN OM ELIN. see *BUSINESS AND ECONOMICS*

378.198   USA
DRURY MIRROR∗ . Text in English. 1885. w. USD 20. adv. bk.rev.; film rev.; play rev. charts; illus. back issues avail. **Document type:** *Newspaper.* **Description:** Campus newspaper for students, alumni, and others interested in the college.
Published by: Drury College, 900 N Benton, Springfield, MO 65802. TEL 417-865-8731, FAX 416-865-3138. Circ: 1,000 (controlled).

378   DEU   ISSN 0937-3780
DUESSELDORFER UNI-ZEITUNG. Text in German. 1972. 6/yr. adv. bk.rev. **Document type:** *Corporate.*
Published by: Heinrich-Heine-Universitaet Duesseldorf, Pressestelle, Universitaetsstr 1, Duesseldorf, 40225, Germany. FAX 49-211-8115279, TELEX 8587384-UNI-D. Ed. Rolf Willhardt. Circ: 7,500.

378   USA
DUSTER. Text in English. bi-w.
Published by: Lubbock Christian College, 5601 W 19th, Lubbock, TX 79407-2099. TEL 806-792-3221.

378   USA
E T S U SPECIAL. (East Texas State University) Text in English. irreg. (2-4/yr.). **Document type:** *Newspaper.*

C

Published by: Texas A & M - Commerce, Student Publications Business Office, Journalism & Printing Dept, Box 4104, ET Sta, Commerce, TX 75427. TEL 903-886-5985, FAX 903-886-5230, busm@boisdarc.etsu.edu. Ed. Michael Tribble. R&P Annette Black. adv.: page USD 100; trim 11 x 8.5. Circ: 3,000.

378 USA ISSN 1543-4699
E V M S NOW. (Eastern Virginia Medical School) Text in English. 1994. s-a.
Published by: Eastern Virginia Medical School, P. O. Box 1980, Norfolk, VA 23501-1980. TEL 757-446-5600, http://www.evms.edu.

378
THE EAGLE (PRICE). Text in English. 1937. bi-m. adv. bk.rev.; dance rev.; play rev.; tel.rev.; video rev. charts; illus.; stat. 12 p./no. 5 cols./p.; back issues avail.; reprints avail. **Document type:** *Newspaper.*
Published by: College of Eastern Utah, 451 E 400 North, Price, UT 84501. TEL 435-613-5213, FAX 435-637-4102, spolster@ac.ceu.edu. Ed. Miranda Oldendahl. R&P, Adv. contact Susan Polster. B&W page USD 260, color page USD 400; trim 13 x 10. Circ: 1,500.

378.1 USA ISSN 0012-8082
EAGLE (WASHINGTON). Text in English. 1925. w. USD 50. adv. bk.rev.; film rev.; play rev. charts; illus. **Document type:** *Newspaper.*
Related titles: Microfiche ed.; Online - full text ed.: (from LexisNexis).
Published by: American University, 277 Mary Graydon Center, Massachusetts & Nebraska Aves, N W, Washington, DC 20016-8028. TEL 202-885-1414. Ed. Erik Diehn. Circ: 10,000.

378 USA
EAGLE EYE. Text in English. 1924. w. (Fri.). free; 1st copy free, 2nd copy USD 1. **Document type:** *Newspaper.*
Published by: Lock Haven University, Parsons Union Bldg, Lock Haven, PA 17745. TEL 570-893-2334, FAX 570-893-2436, dcampbel@lhup.edu, http://www.lhueagleeye.com. Circ: 2,500 (free).

378 USA
THE EAST CAROLINIAN. Text in English. 1925. 3/w. (Tue. , Wed., Thu. academic yr.). free; USD 135 (effective 2005). **Document type:** *Newspaper, Consumer.*
Published by: East Carolina University, Student Media Board, East Carolina University, Student Publications Bldg., Greenville, NC 27858-4353. editor@theeastcarolinian.com, http://www.theeastcarolian.com. Ed. Amanda Lingerfelt. Circ: 9,000 (paid and free). Wire service: AP.

378.198 USA
EAST TENNESSEAN. Text in English. 1926. s-w. USD 10.
Address: PO Box 70688, Johnson City, TN 37614. TEL 615-929-4387, etnews@etsu.edu, http://www.easttennessean.com. Ed. Erika King. Circ: 6,000.

378 USA
EAST TEXAN. Text in English. w. USD 10 for 6 mos.. adv. **Document type:** *Newspaper.*
Published by: Texas A & M - Commerce, Student Publications Business Office, Journalism & Printing Dept, Box 4104, ET Sta, Commerce, TX 75427. TEL 903-886-5985, FAX 903-886-5230, busm@boisdarc.etsu.edu. Ed. Michael Tribble. R&P, Adv. contact Annette Black. Circ: 4,500.

378.1 GBR ISSN 0012-8643
EASTBOURNIAN. Text in English. 1870. a. GBP 1.50. adv. illus.
Published by: Eastbourne College, Eastbourne, Sussex, United Kingdom. Ed. N L Wheeler. Circ: 1,200 (controlled).

378 USA
EASTERN ECHO. Text in English. 1881. w. (3/wk. Mon., Wed., Fri. academic yr.; Fri. online). USD 65 subscr - mailed; free domestic on campus (effective 2005). 12 p./no. 6 cols./p.; **Document type:** *Newspaper.*
Published by: Eastern Michigan University, Student Media Board, 18-B Goddard Hall, Ypsilanti, MI 48197. TEL 734-487-1010, FAX 734-487-1241, kevin.devine@emich.edu, http://www.easternecho.com. Circ: 7,000 (free).

THE EASTERN PROGRESS. see *EDUCATION—Higher Education*

378 USA
EASTERN TODAY★ . Text in English. 1987. 3/yr. free. **Document type:** *Newsletter.*
Published by: Eastern Kentucky University, Division of Public Information, 7A Coates Bldg, 521 Lancaster Ave, Richmond, KY 40475-3101. TEL 606-622-2301, FAX 606-622-1595. Ed. Ron Harrell. Circ: 45,000.

378 CAN ISSN 0849-9748
ECLOSION. Text in English. 3/yr.
Formerly (until 1989): Moucheurs du Montreal Metropolitan (0849-973X)
Published by: Acces Media, 1124 Marie Anne Rd, East, Ste 31, Montreal, PQ H2J 2B7, Canada. TEL 514-524-1182, FAX 514-524-7771, accesmedia@horizon.net, http://www.horizon.net/acces/media.html. Circ: 2,000.

378 ZAF
EDGE (FLORIDA). Text in English. 1993. irreg.
Published by: Technikon of Southern Africa, Private Bag X6, Florida, Transvaal 1710, South Africa. TEL 27-11-4713299, mail@tsa.ac.za, http://www.tsa.ac.za. Ed. Juliet Ntonjana Mdluli.

378 USA
EDGEWOOD COLLEGE TODAY. Text in English. 1981. 3/yr.
Published by: Edgewood College, 855 Woodrow St, Madison, WI 53711. TEL 608-663-4861. Ed. David E Smith. Circ: 8,000.

378 GBR
THE EDINBURGH STUDENT. Text in English. 1887. 12/yr. adv. bk.rev. **Document type:** *Newspaper.* **Description:** Provides news, services, advertising, reviews and communication between students and staff in Edinburgh.
Formerly (until 1997): Student
Published by: Student Newspaper Society, 60 Pleasance, Edinburgh, EH8 9TJ, United Kingdom. TEL 44-131-650-2363, FAX 44-131-650-2358, http://www.edstudent.com. R&P, Adv. contact Dan Baring. page GBP 500; 268 x 365. Circ: 5,000.

378 GBR
EDIT. Text in English. 1992. s-a. adv. bk.rev. illus. back issues avail. **Document type:** *Bulletin.*
Published by: University of Edinburgh, Old College, South Bridge, Edinburgh, EH8 9YL, United Kingdom. TEL 44-131-650-2252, FAX 44-131-650-2253, http://www.cpa.ed.ac.uk/edit, http://www.ed.ac.uk. Ed., R&P Anne McKelvie. Circ: 90,000.

378 USA
EDWARDIAN. Text in English. m.
Published by: St. Edward's University, 30010 S Congress, Box 714, Austin, TX 78704. TEL 512-448-8426.

378 DEU ISSN 0930-8253
EINBLICKE; Forschungsmagazin der Carl-von-Ossietzky Universitaet Oldenburg. Text in German; Summaries in English. 1985. 2/yr. illus. **Document type:** *Journal, Academic/Scholarly.*
Published by: Carl von Ossietzky Universitaet Oldenburg, Ammerlaender Heerstr 114-118, Oldenburg, 26111, Germany. TEL 49-441-7985446, FAX 49-441-7985545, presse@uni-oldenburg.de, http://www.uni-oldenburg.de/presse/einblicke/. Circ: 3,000.

378.198 USA ISSN 0897-2303
ELMHURST COLLEGE MAGAZINE. Text in English. 1967. q. **Description:** For alumni, donors, parents and friends.
Published by: Elmhurst College, 190 Prospect Ave, Elmhurst, IL 60126. TEL 630-617-3033, FAX 630-617-3282. Ed., R&P Kristin Whitehurst. Circ: 35,000 (controlled).

378.1 USA ISSN 0013-6727
EMORY MAGAZINE. Text in English. 1924. q. free to qualified personnel. bk.rev. illus.
Published by: Emory University, Office of University Periodicals, 1655 N Decatur Rd, Atlanta, GA 30322. TEL 404-727-7872, FAX 404-727-0169. Ed. Andrew W M Beierle. R&P Andrew W.M. Beierle. Circ: 78,000 (controlled).

378.198 USA
EMORY WHEEL. Text in English. 1918. s-w. (Tue.& Fr.). USD 65. adv. **Document type:** *Newspaper.* **Description:** Student newspaper that covers Atlanta and the university community.
Published by: Emory University, Drawer W, Atlanta, GA 30322. TEL 404-727-6175, FAX 404-727-3613. Ed. Kimberly L Freeman. R&P Richard Daigle. Adv. contact Shyam Reddy. Circ: 7,500.

378 CAN ISSN 0822-8531
EN TETE. Text in English. 1983. w. adv. bk.rev. **Document type:** *Academic/Scholarly.*
Formerly: Trouvez un Nom (0822-8523)
Published by: (Service de l'Information et des Relations Publiques), Universite du Quebec a Trois Rivieres, C P 500, Trois Rivieres, PQ G9A 5H7, Canada. TEL 819-376-5151, FAX 819-376-5209, http://www.uqtr.uquebec.ca/ENTETE/. R&P Denise Lemarier. Adv. contact Sylvie Gervais. Circ: 5,000.

378 USA
ENCORE!. Text in English. q. **Description:** Discusses academic issues and events of interest to alumni.
Media: Online - full content. **Related titles:** ♦ Supplement to: Scene (Tacoma). ISSN 0886-3369.
Published by: Pacific Lutheran University, 12180 Park St., S, Tacoma, WA 98447-0003. TEL 253-531-6900, 253-531-6900, encore@plu.edu, http://www.plu.edu/encore/. Ed. Katherine Hedland Hansen TEL 253-535-8410.

378 AUS
ENCOUNTER. Text in English. s-a. free. back issues avail. **Document type:** *Newsletter.* **Description:** Provides news and articles for the graduates of Flinders University.
Formerly: Convocation News
Published by: Flinders University of South Australia, Public Relations and Information Office, GPO Box 2100, Adelaide, SA 5001, Australia. TEL 61-8-8201-2752, FAX 61-8-8201-3141, sheryl.chandler@flinders.edu.au, http://adminwww.flindersedu.au/alumni. Ed. Nick Carne. Circ: 20,000.

378.198 USA
ENCOUNTER (JOLIET). Text in English. 1976. fortn. free. adv. bk.rev.; film rev. **Document type:** *Newspaper.* **Description:** Informs, entertains, educates and provides a forum for public debate. Also functions as a laboratory newspaper for students majoring in journalism - communications.
Published by: College of St. Francis, Journalism - Communications Department, 500 N Wilcox, Joliet, IL 60435. TEL 815-740-3461, FAX 815-740-4285. Ed. Rita Travis. Circ: 1,200 (controlled).

378 CAN
ENTREMETTEUR★ . Text in English. s-m. free.
Published by: Publi-Peq, 3575 bd St Laurent, Ste 232, Montreal, PQ H2X 2T7, Canada. TEL 514-845-8628. Circ: 3,000.

ENTUSIASMEN. see *EDUCATION—Higher Education*

378.1 USA
ENVOY (SAN DIEGO). Text in English. 1955. 15/yr. (bi-w. during academic yr.). USD 1 per issue. adv. bk.rev.; film rev. **Document type:** *Newspaper.* **Description:** Aimed at students, staff, and friends of the university. Includes news from USIU campuses around the world, athletic team schedules, editorials, and information on financial aid and job opportunities for students. Also contains general information that would interest readers in the campus community.
Former titles (until 1991): U S I U News; (until 1986): U S I U International News; Western Tide (0008-1647)
Published by: United States International University, 10455 Pomerado Rd, San Diego, CA 92131. TEL 858-635-4540, FAX 858-635-4853, envoy@usiu.edu, http://www.usid.edu/student/studpubl.htm. Ed. Paul Bridges. Adv. contact Yasmeen Hosain. page USD 325; 16 x 10.5. Circ: 2,000.

EQUILIBRE. see *SPORTS AND GAMES*

378 SWE ISSN 0345-2875
ERGO. Text in Swedish. 1924. 15/yr. SEK 150. adv. bk.rev.
Published by: Uppsala Studentkaar, Ovre Slottsgatan 7, Uppsala, 75310, Sweden. TEL 46-18-10-90-29, FAX 46-18-12-07-90, red.ergo@us.uu.se. Ed. Gert Helgesson. Circ: 30,000.

051 USA ISSN 1074-2174
ETHOS (AMES). Text in English. 1953. bi-m. Free to Iowa State University students. adv. bk.rev. back issues avail. **Document type:** *Magazine, Consumer.* **Description:** Examines academic issues and trends related to today's college student.
Incorporates (in July 1993): Outlook (Ames)
Related titles: Online - full text ed.
Indexed: MEA&I.
Address: Hamilton Hall Rm 06, Iowa State University, Ames, IA 50011. feedback@ethosmagazine.com, http://www.ethosmagazine.com/. Ed. Dustin Kass. adv.: page USD 410; 8 x 11. Circ: 5,600.

371.8 FRA ISSN 0766-6330
L'ETUDIANT. Text in French. 1972. m. adv. bk.rev.
Formerly (until 1985): Dossiers de l'Etudiant (0181-513X)
Related titles: ♦ Supplement(s): L' Etudiant. Guide Pratique. ISSN 0765-4812; ♦ L' Etudiant Plus. ISSN 0766-6349; ♦ Le Guide des Etudes Superieures. ISSN 0997-1025; ♦ Le Guide des Metiers. ISSN 1166-7419.
Published by: Editions Generation, 27 rue du Chemin Vert, Paris, Cedex 11 75543, France. TEL 33-1-48074141, FAX 33-1-47007980. Ed. Philippe Mandry. Pub. Benoit Prot. Adv. contact Elisabeth Levy. Circ: 100,000.

371.8 FRA ISSN 0765-4812
L'ETUDIANT. GUIDE PRATIQUE. Text in French. 1984. a.
Related titles: ♦ Supplement to: L' Etudiant. ISSN 0766-6330.
Published by: Editions Generation, 27 rue du Chemin Vert, Paris, Cedex 11 75543, France. TEL 33-1-48074141, FAX 33-1-47007980.

371.8 FRA ISSN 0766-6349
L'ETUDIANT PLUS. Text in French. 1985. irreg.
Related titles: ♦ Supplement to: L' Etudiant. ISSN 0766-6330.
Published by: Editions Generation, 27 rue du Chemin Vert, Paris, Cedex 11 75543, France. TEL 33-1-48074141, FAX 33-1-47007980.

378.1 CAN ISSN 0014-3987
EXCALIBUR. Text in English. 1966. w. CND 60 domestic; CND 80 in United States; CND 120 elsewhere (effective 2000). adv. bk.rev.; film rev. illus. **Document type:** *Newspaper.* **Description:** Provides news coverage for the York University community.

Published by: Excalibur Publications Inc., 420 Student Centre, York University, 4700 Keele St, North York, ON M3J 1P3, Canada. TEL 416-736-5239, 416-736-5238, FAX 416-736-5841, excal@excal.on.ca, excalibur@better.net, http://www.excal.on.ca/, http://www.yorku.ca/. Ed. Shawn Jeffords. Adv. contact Kamilah Munroe. page CND 860; 10.25 x 15.25. Circ: 17,000 (controlled).

378 GBR
EXEPOSE; probably the best student newspaper in the world. Text in English. 1988. w. GBP 50. adv. bk.rev.; dance rev.; music rev.; play rev.; software rev.; tel.rev.; film rev. charts; illus. 5 cols./p.; reprints avail. **Document type:** *Newspaper.* **Description:** University students' magazine covers news, arts, film and music, features, local events, sports and travel.
Former titles: Third Degree; Signature
Published by: (University of Exeter, Guild of Students), Exepose, Devonshire House, Stocker Rd, Exeter, EX4 4PZ, United Kingdom. TEL 44-1392-263540, 44-1392-263513, FAX 44-1392-263531, 44-1392-263540, exepose@ex.ac.uk, guild@ex.ac.uk, http://www.exepose.co.uk, http://www.x-net.ex.ac.uk. Eds. Ben Luscombe, Jon Hicks, Jon Treliving, Karl Fitzpatrick. adv.: B&W page GBP 800, color page GBP 950. Circ: 2,500.

373 USA
LD7501.E9
EXETER BULLETIN. Text in English. 1905. q. bk.rev. charts; illus. **Document type:** *Academic/Scholarly.* **Description:** Publishes articles of interest to alumni, class news, events schedules.
Former titles: Exeter (0195-0207); Philips Exeter Bulletin (0031-7942)
Published by: Phillips Exeter Academy, 20 Main St, Exeter, NH 03833-2460. TEL 603-777-3450, FAX 603-777-4397, bulletin@exeter.edu, http://www.exeter.edu. Ed., R&P Stephanie Casale. Circ: 26,500 (controlled).

378.1 USA ISSN 0014-5076
EXPONENT; Montana's premier student newspaper. Variant title: M S U Exponent. Text in English. 1895. s-w. USD 19.95; free distribution on campus. adv. bk.rev. **Document type:** *Newspaper.*
Related titles: Online - full text ed.
Indexed: PROMT.
Published by: Montana State University, Associated Students, Rm 305, Strand Union, Bozeman, MT 59717. TEL 406-994-2611, FAX 406-994-2253. Circ: 7,500.

378.1 CAN ISSN 0014-5513
EYEOPENER. Text in English. 1967. w. (during academic yr.). CND 10. adv. bk.rev.; film rev.; play rev. illus. **Document type:** *Newspaper.* **Description:** Campus and community news, entertainment, sports and features.
Related titles: Microfilm ed.: (from MML).
Indexed: CBPI, CPerI.
Published by: Rye Eye Publishing Inc, 380 Victoria, Rm A 54, Toronto, ON M5B 1W7, Canada. TEL 416-595-1490, FAX 416-595-1374, eyeopenr@acs.ryerson.ca. Ed. Matthew Sherped. Adv. contact Ryad Ali. Circ: 8,000.

F A C C C T S. see *EDUCATION—Higher Education*

378.1 USA
F A U FREE PRESS. Text in English. 1966. w. USD 10. adv. bk.rev.; film rev.; play rev. illus. **Document type:** *Newspaper.*
Formerly: Atlantic Sun (0004-685X)
Published by: Florida Atlantic University, 777 Glades Rd, PO Box 3091, Boca Raton, FL 33431-0991. TEL 407-363-2393. Ed. Ross A Levy. Adv. contact Bryan Bates. Circ: 17,000.

378.1 USA
➤ **F D U MAGAZINE.** Text in English. 1993. s-a. free. illus.; charts. back issues avail. **Document type:** *Academic/Scholarly.* **Description:** Offers news and commentary on a variety of issues that affect or interest students and alumni of Fairleigh Dickinson University.
Published by: (Office of Institutional Advancement), Fairleigh Dickinson University, 1000 River Rd, Teaneck, NJ 07666-1996. TEL 201-692-7025, FAX 201-692-7039, angelo@alpha.fdu.edu, http://www.fdu.edu. R&P Angelo Carfagna. Circ: 80,000.

378 DEU ISSN 0944-0585
F U: NACHRICHTEN. Text in German. m. film rev.; play rev. **Document type:** *Bulletin, Academic/Scholarly.*
Former titles (until 1992): F U Info (0173-4105); (until 1979): F U Berlin. Info (0302-2161)
Published by: Freie Universitaet Berlin, Kaiserswerther Str 16-18, Berlin, 14195, Germany. TEL 49-30-83873180, FAX 49-30-83873187, aretin@zedat.fu-berlin.de, fupresse@zedat.fu-berlin.de, http://www.fu-berlin.de/fun/index.html. Ed. Felicitas von Aretin. Circ: 16,000 (controlled).

378 DEU ISSN 0179-6607
FACHHOCHSCHULE-BOCHUM-JOURNAL. Key Title: FH-Bo-Journal. Text in German. 1982. 2/yr. **Document type:** *Academic/Scholarly.*
Published by: Fachhochschule Bochum, Universitaetsstr 150, Bochum, 44801, Germany. TEL 0231-7007800, FAX 0234-7094312, TELEX 825860-RUB-D. Ed. Detlef Bremkens. Circ: 2,000.

378 GBR ISSN 0141-4704
FALMER. Text in English. 1983. 2/yr. free (effective 2003). adv. bk.rev. back issues avail. **Document type:** *Newsletter.* **Description:** Newsletter for alumni of University of Sussex.
Formerly: Falmer News
Published by: University of Sussex Alumni Society, Alumni Centre, Bramber House, University of Sussex, Falmer, Brighton, BN1 9QU, United Kingdom. TEL 44-1273-678258, FAX 44-1273-877002, alumni@sussex.ac.uk, http://www.sussex.ac.uk/alumni/. Ed., R&P Marina Pedreira. Circ: 50,000.

378.198 AUS ISSN 0159-2920
FARRAGO. Text in English. 1920. every 3 wks. (during school yr.). free in Australia. adv. bk.rev.; film rev.; play rev. illus. back issues avail. **Document type:** *Newspaper.* **Description:** Focuses on music,the arts, politics and "university-inner city coffee culture.".
Published by: Melbourne University, Students Union, 1st Fl., Union Bldg., Parkville, VIC 3052, Australia. TEL 61-3-9344-6957, FAX 61-3-9347-9453, http://www.union.unimelb.edu.au/farrago. Pub. Elizabeth Humphrys. Circ: 11,000.

378 USA
FAST FORWARD. Text in English. m. (during academic year). free. **Document type:** *Newsletter.*
Published by: Davis and Elkins College, 100 Campus Dr, Elkins, WV 26241. TEL 304-636-1900. Ed. Pat Schumann.

051 USA
FEATURE EDITION. Text in English. 2002 (Mar.). m. USD 60 per month to individuals (effective 2005 - 2006). back issues avail. **Document type:** *Journal, Academic/Scholarly.* **Description:** Covers all subjects of interest to students and teachers/professors.
Published by: Franklin Publishing Company, 2723 Steamboat Circle, Arlington, TX 76006. TEL 817-548-1124, FAX 817-299-0930, luotto@comcast.net, http://www.franklinpublishing.net/pages/580546/index.htm. Ed. Mrs. Maxime E Knight. Pub. Dr. Ludwig Otto.

378.198 USA
FEDERALIST PAPER; a student newspaper in the tradition of Columbians Hamilton and Jay. Text in English. 1986. m. free (effective 2001). adv. **Document type:** *Newspaper.*
Related titles: CD-ROM ed.; Microform ed.; Online - full text ed.
Published by: Columbia University, 401 Lerner Hall MC 2601, New York, NY 10027. TEL 212-854-1653, FAX 212-854-3434, federalist@columbia.edu, thefed@columbia.edu, http://www.columbia.edu/cu/federalist. Ed. Meghan Keane. Circ: 6,000 (free).

378 GBR ISSN 0140-0711
FELIX; the student's newspaper at imperial college. Text in English. 1949. w. (every Mon. during college term). adv. bk.rev. **Document type:** *Newspaper.*
Indexed: FLI.
Published by: Imperial College Union Publications Board, Belt Quad, Prince Consort Rd, London, SW7 2BB, United Kingdom. TEL 44-171-594-8072, FAX 44-171-594-8072, felix@ic.ac.uk, http://www.su.ic.ac.uk/Felix. Ed., R&P Ed Sexton. Adv. contact David Roberts. Circ: 4,500.

378 USA
FERRUM MAGAZINE. Text in English. q. free. **Document type:** *Newsletter.* **Description:** Contains alumni news and information about activities at Ferrum.
Formerly: Ferrum Bulletin
Published by: Ferrum College, PO Box 1000, Ferrum, VA 24088. TEL 540-365-4302, FAX 540-365-4203. Ed. Lisa Bowling. R&P Wes Astin. Circ: 14,000 (controlled).

378 AUS
FLINDERS JOURNAL. Text in English. 1988 (no.277). fortn. **Document type:** *Newspaper.*
Formerly (until 1990): Flindersweek
Published by: Flinders University of South Australia, Public Relations and Information Office, GPO Box 2100, Adelaide, SA 5001, Australia. TEL 61-8-82012916, FAX 61-8-82013027. Ed. Charles Gent. Circ: 3,000.

378 USA
FLOR-ALA. Text in English. 1931. w. USD 20 (effective 1998). adv. bk.rev.; film rev.; music rev.; play rev. **Document type:** *Consumer.*
Published by: University of North Alabama, PO Box 5300, Florence, AL 35632-0001. TEL 256-765-4426, FAX 256-765-4275. Ed. Steve Price. Adv. contact Theresa Grosso. page USD 504; 21 x 6. Circ: 4,500.

378 GBR
FLY MAGAZINE; the official student publication of the University of Plymouth. Text in English. 1972. w. free. adv. film rev.; music rev.; play rev.; video rev. charts; illus. back issues avail. **Document type:** *Newspaper.* **Description:** Covers anything remotely connected to student life.
Related titles: Online - full text ed.
Published by: University of Plymouth, Student Union, Drake Circus, Plymouth, Devon OL4 8AA, United Kingdom. TEL 44-1752-663337, FAX 44-1752-251669, fly@plym.ac.uk. Ed., Adv. contact Pete Everett. page GBP 220. Circ: 2,000.

378 USA
FLYER NEWS. Text in English. 1953. s-w. (Tue. & Fri. (Sep.-May)). free to students; USD 35 (effective 2005). adv. **Document type:** *Newspaper, Consumer.*
Published by: University of Dayton, 300 College Park, Dayton, OH 45469. TEL 937-229-3226, FAX 937-229-3893, editor@flyernews.com, http://www.flyernews.com. Ed. William Geoghegan. R&P Larry Lane TEL 937-229-2742. adv.: col. inch USD 7. Circ: 5,000 (free).

378 ZAF
➤ **FOCUS.** Text in English. 1990. q. ZAR 48. adv. bk.rev. illus. back issues avail. **Document type:** *Academic/Scholarly.* **Description:** Offers academic discourse on topical events according to themes such as environment, globalization, teaching and learning information technology and transformation.
Formerly (until 1993): N U Focus (1016-3425)
Related titles: Online - full text ed.
Published by: University of KwaZulu-Natal, Pietermaritzburg, Communication & Publicity Division, Durban, KwaZulu-Natal 4041, South Africa. TEL 27-331-2602027, FAX 27-331-2602813, mabasof@pro.und.ac.za, http://www.nu.ac.za. Ed. George Parker. R&P William Saunderson Meyer. adv.: B&W page ZAR 4,412, color page ZAR 5,945; trim 210 x 285. Circ: 50,000.

378.1 GHA ISSN 0046-4260
FOCUS. Text in English. 1969. 8/yr. USD 16; USD 2 newsstand/cover. adv. bk.rev. illus.; stat. **Document type:** *Newspaper.*
Published by: University of Science and Technology, Students' Representative Council, Editorial Office, Kumasi, Ghana. focus@fkjcc.africaonline.com.gh. Circ: 20,000.

378.1 USA ISSN 1077-9345
FOCUS (BERRIEN SPRINGS). Text in English. q.
Published by: Andrews University, Student Association, Berrien Springs, MI 49104.

378.1 USA ISSN 1056-3199
FOCUS (WASHINGTON, D.C. 1976). Variant title: N Y S D Focus. Text in English. 1976 (vol.25). 3/yr. membership. illus.
Former titles (until 1990): A A U W New Yorker (0744-2173); (until 1977): A A U W New York Division. Newsletter (0001-0286)
Published by: American Association of University Women, New York State Division, c/o Barbara P Carier, Ed, 295, Lakewood, NY 14226. Circ: 9,000.

378 USA ISSN 1520-7641
FOCUS (WESTFIELD). Text in English. 1974. s-a. free (effective 2003). reprints avail. **Document type:** *Magazine.* **Description:** Contains news and features pertaining to the college.
Formerly (until 1992): Westfield State College. Alumni Chronicle
Published by: Westfield State College, Public Affairs Office, Western Ave, Westfield, MA 01085. TEL 413-572-5208, FAX 413-572-5438, jjulian@wisdom.wsc.mass.edu, http://www.wsc.ma.edu. Ed. Jeanne M Julian. Circ: 35,000 (controlled).

051 USA
FOCUS MAGAZINE (OKLAHOMA CITY). Text in English. 3/yr. free. **Document type:** *Magazine, Consumer.*
Published by: Oklahoma City University, University Relations Department, 2501 N Blackwelder, Oklahoma City, OK 73106-1493. TEL 405-521-5818, FAX 405-521-5191, http://www.okcu.edu. Ed. Vicki Patterson. Circ: 23,000 (free).

(YEAR) FOOTBALL MEDIA GUIDE. see *SPORTS AND GAMES—Ball Games*

378 CAN ISSN 0824-6017
FOOTPRINT✶. Key Title: Zhu Ji. Text mainly in Chinese; Section in English. 1982 (vol.2). bi-m. free. adv. bk.rev.
Published by: University of Toronto, c/o John Robbart Library, Serial Dept., 130 St. George St., Toronto, ON M5S 1A5, Canada. TEL 416-978-7694. Ed. Lester Wong. Circ: 5,000.

378 USA
FOOTPRINTS (PLAINVIEW). Text in English. 1953. q. free to alumni. **Document type:** *Consumer.* **Description:** Covers topics of interest to alumni of Wayland Baptist University.
Published by: Wayland Baptist University, 1900 W 7th St, Plainview, TX 79072. TEL 806-296-4844, FAX 806-291-5040, Provencej@wbu1.wbu.edu, provencej@mail.wbu.edu. Ed., R&P Joe L Provence. Circ: 16,000; 15,000 (controlled).

378.198 USA
THE FORESTER. Text in English. 1956. irreg. adv. **Document type:** *Newsletter.* **Description:** Contains university news, features, alumni news, and development news.
Published by: Concordia University, 7400 Augusta St, River Forest, IL 60305-1499. TEL 708-209-3110, FAX 708-209-3176. Ed., R&P, Adv. contact Susan Montgomery. Circ: 45,000.

FORSCHUNG AN DER UNIVERSITAET BIELEFELD; Bielefelder Forschungsmagazin. see *SCIENCES: COMPREHENSIVE WORKS*

C

▼ *new title* ➤ *refereed* ✶ *unverified* ♦ *full entry avail.*

378 USA
THE FORUM (SOUTH ROYALTON). Text in English. 1976. fortn. USD 19.95 (effective 2000). adv. bk.rev. **Document type:** *Newspaper.*
Published by: Vermont Law School, PO Box 96, South Royalton, VT 05068. TEL 802-763-8303. Ed. Nick Goldstein. Adv. contact Robert Weisberg. Circ: 1,000.

371.8974 USA
FORUM (WASHINGTON, 1970). Text in English. 1970. 2/yr. **Document type:** *Newsletter.* **Description:** Alumni magazine circulated to School of Library and Information Science alumni only.
Published by: Catholic University of America, School of Library & Information Science, 620 Michigan Ave, N E, Marist Hall, Rm 228, Washington, DC 20064. TEL 202-319-5085, FAX 202-319-5574. Ed. Elizabeth Aversa. Circ: 2,600.

378 USA
THE FORWARD (ELKINS). Text in English. 2/yr. free.
Published by: Davis and Elkins College, 100 Campus Dr, Elkins, WV 26241. TEL 304-636-1900. Ed. Mary McMahon.

378 USA
FRANKLIN AND MARSHALL. Text in English. q.
Formerly: F and M Today
Published by: Franklin and Marshall College, 1 Fieldstead Ct., Apt. A, Owings Mills, MD 21117-5210. http://www.fandm.edu. Ed. Linda Whipple.

378 DEU ISSN 0947-1251
FREIBURGER UNI-MAGAZIN. Text in German. 1988. 3/school-academic yr. adv. **Document type:** *Magazine, Academic/Scholarly.*
Published by: Albert-Ludwigs-Universitaet Freiburg, Fahnenbergplatz, Freiburg, 79085, Germany. TEL 49-761-203-0, FAX 49-761-2034369, info@pr.uni-freiburg.de, http://www.uni-freiburg.de. adv.: B&W page EUR 1,505, color page EUR 1,956.50. Circ: 15,000 (controlled).

C

378.1 DEU ISSN 0016-0717
FREIBURGER UNIVERSITAETSBLAETTER. Text in German. 1960. q. EUR 26 (effective 2003). adv. bk.rev.; rec.rev. charts; illus.; stat.; tr.lit. **Document type:** *Journal, Academic/Scholarly.* —BLDSC (4033.452400).
Published by: Rombach Druck und Verlagshaus GmbH & Co. KG, Unterwerkstr. 5, Freiburg, 79115, Germany. TEL 49-761-4500-0, FAX 49-761-45002125, info@buchverlag.rombach.de, http://www.rombach.de. Circ: 3,070.

378 DEU ISSN 0941-0155
FREIE UNIVERSITAET BERLIN. ZENTRALEINRICHTUNG STUDIENBERATUNG UND PSYCHOLOGISCHE BERATUNG. STUDIENHANDBUCH. Text in German. 1978. a. adv. **Document type:** *Directory, Academic/Scholarly.*
Related titles: CD-ROM ed.; Online - full text ed.
Published by: Freie Universitaet Berlin, Zentraleinrichtung Studienberatung und Psychologische Beratung, Bruemmerstr 50, Berlin, 14195, Germany. TEL 49-30-83870000, FAX 49-30-83853913, hwr@zedat.fu-berlin.de, http://www.fu-berlin.de/studienberatung/wiesie.html, http://www.fu-berlin.de/studienberatuus. Ed. H.-W. Rueckert.

371.805 USA
FROM THE HILLTOP. Text in English. m. free (effective 2005). **Document type:** *Newspaper, Consumer.*
Formerly: Hilltop News
Published by: Birmingham Southern College Student Government Association, PO Box A-14, Birmingham, AL 35254. TEL 205-226-4729, http://www.bsc.edu/communications/publications.htm. Circ: 1,400 (free). Wire service: AP.

378 CAN
LE FRONT. Text in French. 1984 (vol.21). w.
Published by: Federation des Etudiants de l'Universite de Moncton, Moncton, NB, Canada.

378 GBR
FRONT PAGE. Text in English. 1982. m. free. adv. bk.rev.
Published by: Anglia Polytechnic University, East Rd, Cambridge, CB1 1PT, United Kingdom. TEL 44-1223-363271, FAX 44-1223-352973, http://www.anglia.ac.uk. Circ: 2,000.

378 USA
FRONTLINES. Text in English. 1990. m. free. bk.rev.; film rev.; play rev. **Document type:** *Newspaper.*
Published by: Northern Virginia Community College, 8333 Little River Tpk, Annandale, VA 22003. TEL 703-323-3579, FAX 703-323-3399. Ed. Joseph Wink. adv.: page USD 190; 10.25 x 13.5. Circ: 3,000.

378.1 IND ISSN 0046-5259
FULBRIGHT NEWSLETTER. Text in English. 1953. q. free. **Document type:** *Newsletter.*
Indexed: NumL.
Published by: United States Educational Foundation in India, Fulbright House, 12 Hailey Rd., New Delhi, 110 001, India. Ed. P D Sayal. Circ: 6,500.

378.1 CAN ISSN 0016-2604
THE FULCRUM. Text in English. 1942. w. CND 50; CND 100 foreign (effective 1999). adv. bk.rev.; film rev.; play rev. abstr.; illus. back issues avail. **Document type:** *Newspaper, Consumer.*
Related titles: Microfilm ed.
Published by: University of Ottawa Student Federation, 07-85 University Private, Ottawa, ON K1N 6N5, Canada. TEL 613-562-5260, FAX 613-562-5259, fulcrum@thefulcrum.com, http://www.thefulcrum.com. Ed., R&P Chris Bodnar. Adv. contact Hilary Schaenfield. Circ: 10,000.

378 USA
FURMAN MAGAZINE. Text in English. 1951. a. free. **Description:** Contains articles on Furman-related issues, events and individuals.
Published by: (University Relations), Furman University, 3300 Poinsett Hwy, Greenville, SC 29613-0666. TEL 864-294-2185, FAX 864-294-3023. Ed. Jim Stewart. Circ: 32,000.

378 GBR
FUSION; the magazine for students at De Montfort University. Text in English. 1992. m. GBP 4.50 (effective 1999). adv. bk.rev.; film rev.; play rev. illus. back issues avail. **Document type:** *Newspaper.* **Description:** Informs and entertains De Montfort University students and communicates the actions of the student union executive.
Formerly: Inta-Site; Formed by the merger of (1987-1992): Catch; Catch Monthly; Catchline
Published by: Catch Student Publications, D.S.U., 4 Newarke Close, Leicester, Leics LE2 7BJ, United Kingdom. TEL 44-116-555576, FAX 44-116-470926. Ed. Ron Maylan. R&P Rob Maylan.

378 GBR
G: ECHO. Variant title: Guildhall Echo. Text in English. 1969. w. free. adv. bk.rev.; film rev.; play rev. back issues avail. **Document type:** *Newsletter, Academic/Scholarly.*
Former titles: City Reflections; Graffiti; (until 1984): Pepys
Published by: London Guildhall University, Students' Union, 2 Goulston St, London, E1 7TP, United Kingdom. Ed., R&P, Adv. contact Islam Khan TEL 44-171-247-1441. Circ: 4,000.

G S B CHICAGO. (Graduate School of Business) see *BUSINESS AND ECONOMICS*

378.198 USA
G S M CHRONICLE. Text in English. 1974. q. free. **Document type:** *Newsletter.*
Published by: (Department of Communications), University of Dallas, Graduate School of Management, 1845 E Northgate Dr, Irving, TX 75062-4799. TEL 214-721-5199, FAX 214-721-5017. Circ: 6,500.

056 ESP
G U GACETA UNIVERSITARIA. Text in Spanish. 1991. w. free.
Related titles: Online - full content ed.: tuGUeb.com. 2000.
Published by: Recoletos Compania Editorial S.A (Subsidiary of: Pearson Publishing Group), Paseo Recoletos, 1 5o, Madrid, 28001, Spain. TEL 34-91-3373220, FAX 34-91-3373266, expansion@recoletos.es, http://www.recoletos.es/general/areas/juventud/gaceta_universitaria.html. Circ: 174,115.

378.1 USA
G W HATCHET. Text in English. 1904. s-w. (Sep.-May). USD 50. adv. bk.rev.; film rev.; play rev. illus. **Description:** News, opinions, editorials, arts, music, and sports coverage, announcements, and classifieds pertaining to faculty, students, and activities at the George Washington University, Washington, D.C.
Formerly: Hatchet (0017-8357)
Related titles: Microfilm ed.; Online - full text ed.: (from LexisNexis).
Published by: George Washington University, 800 21 St, N W, Washington, DC 20052. FAX 202-994-1309. Circ: 10,000.

378.1 USA
G W MAGAZINE. (George Washington) Text in English. 1972. 6/yr. free to qualified personnel. adv. bk.rev. illus. **Document type:** *Consumer.* **Description:** Focuses on news and features related to the university and its alumni.
Former titles (until 1990): G W Times (0279-2435); G W: George Washington University Magazine' (0016-366X)
Published by: George Washington University, University Relations, 512 Rice Hall, Washington, DC 20052. TEL 202-994-6460, FAX 202-994-9025, magazine@gwisz.circ.gwu.edu. Ed., R&P Robert Guldin TEL 202-994-6462. Pub. Sandy Holland. Adv. contact Dan Feller. Circ: 120,000.

378 DEU
GAESDONCKER BLAETTER. Text in German. 1949-1993; N.S. 1998. a. EUR 15 (effective 2003). **Document type:** *Yearbook, Academic/Scholarly.*
Published by: Collegium Augustinianum Gaesdonck, Gaesdoncker Str 220, Goch, 47574, Germany. TEL 02823-961-0, FAX 02823-961100. Eds. Alois Kisters, Joseph Boehmer. Circ: 2,000.

378 USA
THE GAMECOCK (RICHLAND). Text in English. 1908. 3/w. (Mon., Wed. & Fri.). free (effective 2004). back issues avail. **Document type:** *Newspaper.*
Published by: The Gamecock, 1400 Greene St, Russell House, Rm 343, Columbia, SC 29208. TEL 803-777-3888, FAX 803-777-6482, gamecockeditor@gwm.sc.edu, sclinden@gwm.sc.edu, http://www.dailygamecock.com. Ed. Steven van Harren. Circ: 14,000 (free).

378 USA
GARNET LETTER. Text in English. 1979. s-a. free.
Published by: Swarthmore College, 500 College Ave., Swarthmore, PA 19081. TEL 610-328-8009, FAX 610-328-7796. Ed. Susan Hodge. Circ: 23,200.

378 USA
THE GATEPOST. Text in English. 1932. w. (Fri.). free (effective 2005). **Document type:** *Newspaper.*
Published by: Framingham State College, 100 State St, Rm 420, Framingham, MA 01701. TEL 508-626-4605, fscgatepost@yahoo.com, http://www.thegatepost.com. Circ: 2,500 (free).

378.1 CAN ISSN 0016-5190
GATEWAY. Text in English. 1910. s-w. CND 40. adv. bk.rev.; film rev.; play rev. illus. **Document type:** *Newspaper.* **Description:** Covers news, opinion, entertainment and sports.
Published by: University of Alberta, Students Union, Students Union Building, Rm 2900, Edmonton, AB T6G 2J7, Canada. TEL 403-492-5168, FAX 403-492-4643, gateway@pybus.su.ualberta.ca, http://www.su.ualberta.ca/gateway. Ed. Rose Yewchuk. Adv. contact Clark Johnson. Circ: 12,500 (controlled).

378.1 SWE ISSN 0016-5247
GAUDEAMUS. Text in Swedish. 1924. 9/yr. SEK 120. adv. bk.rev.; film rev.; play rev. illus. **Document type:** *Magazine, Consumer.*
Published by: Stockholms Universitets Studentkaar, Fack 50006, Stockholm, 10405, Sweden. TEL 46-8-612-03-83, FAX 46-8-612-71-68, gaudeamus@sus.su.se, http://www.sus.su.se/gadden/. Ed. Karin Lindblom. Adv. contact Anders Ingaarda. B&W page SEK 19,900, color page SEK 24,900; trim 220 x 325. Circ: 32,300 (paid and controlled).

378 GBR
GAUDIE. Text in English. 1934. w. free. adv. bk.rev.; film rev.; play rev. back issues avail. **Document type:** *Newspaper.*
Published by: (University of Aberdeen), S.R.C. Publications Department, 50-52 College Bounds, Old Aberdeen, AB2 3DS, United Kingdom. TEL 44-1224-272965, FAX 44-1224-272977, TELEX 73458 UNIABN G. Ed. David Welsh. R&P Alexander Cole Hamilton. Adv. contact Louise Curran. Circ: 4,000.

378 CAN
GAUNTLET. Text in English. 1960. w. CND 35. adv. bk.rev.; film rev.; play rev.
Published by: University of Calgary, Gauntlet Publications Society, Rm 310, MacEwan Hall, 2920 24th Ave, N W, Calgary, AB T2N 1N4, Canada. TEL 403-220-7755, FAX 403-282-3218. Adv. contact Wayne Cropper. B&W page CND 840. Circ: 13,000.

371.83 IRL
THE GAZETTE (CORK). Text in English. 1980. w. free. adv. bk.rev. illus.
Formerly: Sage (Cork)
Published by: University College, Cork, Student's Union, 4 Carrigside, College Rd., Cork, Ireland. TEL 021-276871, FAX 021-272065.

378 CAN
GEM. Text in English. 1984 (vol.2). w. CND 24. adv. bk.rev.; film rev. **Document type:** *Newspaper.*
Former titles (until Mar. 1995): U P E I X-Press (1193-3984); (until 1990): X-Press (1193-3976); (until 1990): Gem (0839-2625); (until 1986): Netted Gem (0839-2617)
Published by: University of Prince Edward Island, Faculty of Education, 550 University Avenue, Charlottetown, PE C1A 4P3, Canada. TEL 902-566-0330, FAX 902-894-2840, eec@upei.ca, http://www.upei.ca/~fac_ed/. Ed., R&P Vianne Timmons TEL 902-566-0330. Adv. contact Finley Martin. Circ: 1,300.

378.198 USA
GENERAL STUDIES NEWSLETTER. Text in English. q. **Document type:** *Newsletter.*
Published by: Columbia University, School of General Studies, 411 Lewisohn Hall, New York, NY 10027.

378.198 USA
GEODE. Text in English. 1925. 2/yr. USD 7. back issues avail.
Published by: University of Wisconsin at Platteville, Engineering Chapter of the Alumni Association, College of Engineering, 100 Ottensman Hall, One University Plaza, Platteville, WI 53818. Circ: 1,500.

378 USA
GEORGE - ANNE. Text in English. 1927. s-w. USD 55 (effective 1999). adv. bk.rev.; film rev.; play rev. charts; illus. back issues avail. **Document type:** *Newspaper.* **Description:** Reports on issues of interest to campus community.
Published by: (Georgia Southern University), George-Anne, Rm 2022, Williams Ctr, Box 8001, Georgia Southern Univ, Statesboro, GA 30460. TEL 912-681-5246, FAX 912-486-7113, stud_pub@gsaix2.gasou.edu, http://www.stp.gasou.edu. Ed. Kelley McGrunell. R&P Bill Neville. Circ: 7,000.

378 USA ISSN 0745-9009
LH1.G5
GEORGETOWN MAGAZINE. Text in English. 4/yr. free. adv. bk.rev. **Document type:** *Academic/Scholarly.*
Published by: Georgetown University, Office of Alumni and University Relations, 37th & O Sts, N W, Washington, DC 20057. TEL 202-687-4317, FAX 202-687-2311. Ed., R&P, Adv. contact Nancy Robertson. Circ: 113,000.

378.1 USA ISSN 0016-8130
LH1.U47
GEORGIA ALUMNI RECORD. Text in English. 1920. 4/yr. USD 25. adv. bk.rev.
Published by: University of Georgia Alumni Society, Alumni House, Athens, GA 30602-4370. TEL 706-542-3354, FAX 706-542-9492. Ed. Kent Hannon. Circ: 25,000 (controlled).

378.198 USA
GEORGIA COLLEGE ALUMNI NEWS QUARTERLY. Text in English. 1920. q. free to qualified personnel. adv.
Indexed: WAE&RSA.
Published by: Georgia College Alumni Association, Campus Box 98, Milledgeville, GA 31061. TEL 912-453-5400, FAX 912-453-6795. Circ: 20,000.

378 USA ISSN 1557-1025
KF292.G414
GEORGIA LAW ADVOCATE. Text in English. 1970. s-a. free to qualified persons. **Document type:** *Newsletter.*
Former titles (until 2002?): Georgia Advocate (0435-5253); Georgia Advocate Advance Sheet
Related titles: Online - full text ed.: ISSN 1557-1033.
Published by: University of Georgia Law School Association, University of Georgia School of Law, Athens, GA 30602. TEL 706-542-5172, FAX 706-542-5556, lawcomm@uga.edu, http://www.law.uga.edu/news/advocate/index.html. Circ: 8,000 (controlled).

378.198 USA ISSN 1061-9747
GEORGIA TECH ALUMNI MAGAZINE. Text in English. 1923. q. USD 10 (effective 2001). adv. illus. 76 p./no. 3 cols./p.; back issues avail. **Document type:** *Magazine, Consumer.* **Description:** Contains articles relating to Georgia Tech and the management of technology.
Supersedes: Georgia Tech Alumnus (0016-8440)
Published by: Georgia Tech Alumni Association, 190 North Ave, Atlanta, GA 30313. TEL 404-894-2391, FAX 404-894-5113, http://www.gtalumni.org. Ed. John Dunn. Pub. Joseph Irwin. Adv. contact Jeff Colburn. B&W page USD 2,000, color page USD 2,750; trim 7 x 10. Circ: 30,000.

278 USA
GILA MONSTER. Text in English. 1921. m. free. illus. back issues avail. **Document type:** *Newspaper, Academic/Scholarly.*
Published by: Eastern Arizona College, Editor, Thatcher, AZ 85552-0769. TEL 520-428-8321, 800-678-3808, FAX 520-428-8462, http://www.eac.cc.az.us. Ed., R&P Paul Phelps. Circ: 1,000.

378.1 GBR ISSN 0017-0917
GLASGOW UNIVERSITY GUARDIAN. Text in English. 1956. fortn. free. adv. bk.rev.; dance rev.; music rev.; play rev.; tel.rev.; video rev. illus. 20 p./no. 6 cols./p.; back issues avail. **Document type:** *Newspaper.*
Related titles: Online - full text ed.
—CCC.
Published by: University of Glasgow, Students' Representative Council, John McIntyre Bldg, Glasgow, G12 8QQ, United Kingdom. TEL 44-141-339-8541, FAX 44-141-337-3557, guardian@src.gla.ac.uk, http://www.src.gla.ac.uk/guardian. Ed., R&P, Adv. contact Yakub Qureshi. B&W page GBP 250. Circ: 13,000.

GLASGOW UNIVERSITY STUDENTS' HANDBOOK. see *EDUCATION—Higher Education*

378 CAN ISSN 0712-337X
GLOBULE ROUGE✶ . Text in English. m. free.
Published by: Publi-Peq, 3575 bd St Laurent, Ste 232, Montreal, PQ H2X 2T7, Canada. TEL 514-845-8628. Circ: 600.

371.8975 DEU
GO UNI. Text in German. 2001. 2/yr. adv. **Document type:** *Magazine, Consumer.*
Published by: Muenchner Stadtmedien GmbH, Arcisstr 68, Munich, 80801, Germany. TEL 49-89-5505660, FAX 49-89-55056612, go@gomuenchen.com, http://www.gomuenchen.com. adv.: B&W page EUR 1,520, color page EUR 2,200. Circ: 36,000 (controlled).

378 USA
GOLD AND BLUE. Text in English. 1961. q. free. **Document type:** *Newsletter.*
Published by: Atlanta Christian College, 2605 Ben Hill Rd, East Point, GA 30344. TEL 404-761-8861. Ed. Charles F Turner. Circ: 12,500.

378.198 USA
GOLD TORCH. Text in English. 1950. s-m. adv. bk.rev. **Document type:** *Newspaper.*
Published by: Central State University, PO Box 1004, Wilberforce, OH 45384. TEL 513-376-6103, FAX 513-376-6530. Circ: 2,400.

371.805 USA
GOLDEN GATE EXPRESS. Text in English. 1931. w. (Thu.). USD 30; free newsstand/cover (effective 2005). adv. 24 p./no. 5 cols./p.; **Document type:** *Newspaper.*
Formerly: Golden Gater
Published by: San Francisco State University, 1600 Holloway Ave., San Francisco, CA 94132-1722. TEL 415-338-3123, FAX 415-338-3111, labaron@sfsu.edu, http://xpress.sfsu.edu/, http://www.journalism.sfsu.edu. adv.: col. inch USD 14. Circ: 10,000 (free).

070 USA
GOLDEN GATER. Text in English. 1931. s-w. USD 30. bk.rev.; film rev.; play rev. **Document type:** *Newspaper, Consumer.* **Description:** Contains news for students and alumni.
Published by: San Francisco State University, 1600 Holloway Ave, San Francisco, CA 94132. TEL 415-338-3123, FAX 415-338-3111. Ed., Pub. Douglas Allen. Circ: 10,000 (controlled).

378 CAN
GOLDEN WORDS. Text in English. 1967. w. CND 28; CND 40 foreign (effective 1997). adv. **Document type:** *Newspaper.*
Published by: Queen's University, Engineering Society, Clark Hall, Kingston, ON K7L 3N6, Canada. TEL 613-545-6000, FAX 613-545-6678. Eds. Jess Aldred, Peter Lynn. Adv. contact Becky Pearce.

378 USA
THE GOOD 5-CENT CIGAR; student newspaper at the University of Rhode Island. Variant title: The Good 5 Cent Cigar. The Good Five Cent Cigar. Text in English. 1971. 4/w. free (effective 2005). adv. bk.rev.; film rev.; play rev. charts; illus. **Document type:** *Newspaper, Consumer.* **Description:** Provides the university community with salient information regarding the on-campus issues and events, as well as providing information about the world around us.
Media: Online - full content. **Related titles:** E-mail ed.: free (effective 2005).
Published by: (Student Senate), University of Rhode Island, University of Rhode Island, Room 125, Memorial Union Bldg, Kingston, RI 02881. http://www.ramcigar.com/. Ed. Robert Hanson TEL 401-874-4325. Circ: 5,000.

378.1 USA ISSN 0017-2308
GOSHEN COLLEGE BULLETIN. Text in English. 1956 (vol.50). 4/yr. free. bk.rev. illus. 32 p./no.; **Document type:** *Bulletin, Academic/Scholarly.* **Description:** News of alumni and college events.
Published by: Goshen College, 1700 S Main St, Goshen, IN 46526. TEL 574-535-7000, FAX 574-535-7670, pr@goshen.edu, http://www.goshen.edu/news/bulletin. Circ: 23,000 (free).

378 USA ISSN 0739-5795
LH1
GOUCHER QUARTERLY. Key Title: Goucher. Text in English. q. USD 3. **Description:** News, notes, articles, features, and announcements on issues affecting the alumni, faculty, students, and educational activities of this coeducational college in Baltimore.
Former titles: Goucher Quarterly (0274-5046); Goucher College Quarterly
Published by: Goucher College, 1021 Dulaney Valley Rd, Baltimore, MD 21204. TEL 410-337-6180. Ed. Susan Gossling. Circ: 15,000.

378.1 GBR ISSN 0017-2693
GOWN. Text in English. 1954. 6/yr. (during academic yr.). free. adv. bk.rev. **Document type:** *Newspaper.*
Published by: Gown Publications, Students' Union, University Rd, Belfast, N Ireland 7 1NN, United Kingdom. TEL 324803, gown@queens-belfast.ac.uk. Ed. Colin Blackstock. Adv. contact Gillian Duffy. Circ: 3,000.

371.85 610 USA
GOZZLE NIPPER. Text in English. 1915. a. **Document type:** *Bulletin.* **Description:** Includes information on the medical professional fraternity.
Published by: (Iota Tau Sigma Fraternity), Journal Publishing Corp., PO Box 792, Kirksville, MO 63501-0792. TEL 816-665-9808, FAX 816-665-0331. Ed. James J Woodruff. Circ: 15,000 (controlled).

378.198 200 USA
GRACE TIDINGS. Text in English. 1943. q. **Description:** Informs alumni and friends of the activities of the college.
Published by: Grace University, 1311 S 9th St, Omaha, NE 68108-3629. TEL 402-449-2800, FAX 402-341-9587, guevents@graceu.edu. Ed. James P Eckman. R&P Scott Dingfield TEL 402-449-2809. Circ: 23,000 (controlled).

378 CAN
GRAFFITI✶ . Text in English. s-m. free.
Indexed: CMPI.
Published by: Publi-Peq, 3575 bd St Laurent, Ste 232, Montreal, PQ H2X 2T7, Canada. TEL 514-845-8628. Circ: 2,500.

378.1 CAN ISSN 0017-3924
GREEN AND WHITE. Text in English. 1939. 2/yr. free to alumni of the U. of S.. adv. bk.rev. **Document type:** *Newspaper.* **Description:** Helps to maintain bonds among the alumni and carries a variety of material presenting the U of S and its alumni.
Related titles: Online - full text ed.
Published by: University of Saskatchewan, Alumni and Development, 232-117 Science Pl, Saskatoon, SK S7N 5C8, Canada. TEL 306-966-5186, FAX 306-966-5571, rossnagel@admin.usask.ca, craig@marketingden.com, http://www.usask.ca/alumni/. Ed. Paul Martin. Pub. Murray Osborn. R&P Laurel Rossnagel. Adv. contact Marsha Martin. Circ: 75,000.

378.1 USA ISSN 0017-3991
GREEN RIVER CURRENT. Text in English. 1965. w. free. adv. film rev.; play rev. illus. **Document type:** *Newspaper.* **Description:** Aims to bring forth and objectively report issues and events for students, faculty and staff at Green River Community College, offers a valuable learning experience and supplies a forum by which the voice of the college may be heard.
Related titles: Online - full text ed.
Published by: Green River Community College, Associated Student Body, 12401 S E 320th St, Auburn, WA 98002. TEL 206-833-9111, FAX 206-288-3457. Ed. Stephanie Jacobson. Adv. contact Amanda Kleinert. B&W page USD 110; trim 10 x 7.5. Circ: 1,500.

378 CAN ISSN 0384-5907
LA GREFFE✶ . Text in English. m. free.
Published by: Publi-Peq, 3575 bd St Laurent, Ste 232, Montreal, PQ H2X 2T7, Canada. TEL 514-845-8628. Circ: 1,500.

378.198 USA ISSN 0276-1947
GRIFFIN. Text in English. 1933. 22/yr. USD 12. **Document type:** *Newspaper.*
Related titles: Online - full text ed.
Indexed: P&BA.
Published by: Canisius College, 2001 Main St, Buffalo, NY 14028-1098. TEL 716-888-2195, FAX 716-888-2525, griffin@gort.canisius.edu, http://www.canisius.edu. adv.: page USD 420; trim 16 x 10. Circ: 3,500.

378.198 USA
GRIZZLY. Text in English. 1978. w. USD 10. adv. film rev.; play rev. stat. back issues avail.
Published by: (Ursinus College), Evening Phoenix, 225 Bridge St, Phoenixville, PA 19460. TEL 610-933-8926. Eds. Jean Marie Kiss, Lora L Hart. Circ: 1,800.

378 AUS ISSN 1326-2815
GROK NEWSMAGAZINE. Text in English. 1998. m.
Media: Online - full text.
Published by: Curtin University of Technology, PO Box V1987, Perth, W.A. 6845, Australia. TEL 61-8-9266-9266, ngrok@cc.curtin.edu.au, http://www.curtin.edu.au/curtin/guild/grok/.

378 USA
GROVE CITY COLLEGE ALUMNI BULLETIN. Text in English. 1912. q. free. **Document type:** *Bulletin.*
Published by: Grove City College, Public Relations Office, Grove City, PA 16127. TEL 724-458-3100, FAX 724-458-3334, http://www.gcc.edu. Ed. Lee Wishing. R&P Janice Inman. Circ: 18,500 (free).

378.198 USA
GROWL. Text in English. 1930. 9/yr. USD 10 (effective 1999). adv. bk.rev. **Document type:** *Newspaper.*
Published by: Holmes Community College, PO Box 367, Goodman, MS 39079. TEL 601-472-2312, FAX 601-472-2566, BulldogPR@aol.com. R&P Jim Williams. Circ: 6,031.

378 USA
THE GUARDIAN (DAYTON). Text in English. 1965. w. (Wed.). free to students. adv. **Document type:** *Newspaper, Consumer.*
Published by: Wright State University, WO16C Student Union, Dayton, OH 45435. TEL 937-775-5537, FAX 937-775-5535, guardianadv@netscape.net, http://www.theguardianonline.com. Ed. Jessica Lander. adv.: col. inch USD 9.50. Circ: 6,000 (free).

378.18 USA
THE GUARDSMAN. Text in English. 1935. bi-w. adv. bk.rev. back issues avail. **Document type:** *Newspaper.* **Description:** Contains campus news and local arts and entertainment news, with a calendar and free classified section for students and faculty.

C

Related titles: Microfilm ed.: (from LIB).
Published by: City College of San Francisco, Journalism Department, 50 Phelan Ave, San Francisco, CA 94112. TEL 415-239-3446, FAX 415-239-3884, http://www.ccsf.cc.ca.us/guardman. Ed. Genn Chryst. Adv. contact Larry Cook. Circ: 10,000 (controlled and free).

378 CAN ISSN 0830-3630
GUELPH ALUMNUS. Text in English. 1968. 3/yr. adv. **Document type:** *Bulletin, Consumer.* **Description:** Contains research and features pertaining to the university campus, profiles of graduates, personal news items, and obits from graduates.
Published by: University of Guelph, Communications and Public Affairs, Guelph, ON N1G 2W1, Canada. TEL 519-824-4120, FAX 519-824-7962, mdickies@exec.admin.uoguelph.ca, http://www.uoguelph.ca. Ed., R&P, Adv. contact Mary Dickieson. color page CND 2,000; trim 10.75 x 8.25. Circ: 70,000.

378.1 GBR
GUILD AND CITY GAZETTE. Text in English. 1936. every 3 wks. free. adv. bk.rev. illus.
Formerly: Guild Gazette (0017-5374)
Published by: University of Liverpool, Guild of Undergraduates, N Liverpool, Merseyside L7 7BD, United Kingdom. TEL 051-709-4147. Ed. Kate Sandilands. Circ: 5,000.

378 USA
GWYNMERCIAN. Text in English. 1948. m. free. adv. bk.rev.; film rev.; play rev. charts; illus. **Document type:** *Newspaper.* **Description:** Covers campus news, world events, and student and faculty profiles.
Published by: Gwynedd Mercy College, Gwynedd, PA 19437. TEL 215-646-7300. Eds. Laura Stimson, Michele Diehl. Circ: 1,000.

378 USA
THE H C C TIMES. Text in English. m. free (effective 2005). **Document type:** *Newspaper, Consumer.*
Published by: Howard Community College, 10901 Patuxent Pkwy, Columbia, MD 21044. TEL 410-772-4023, newspape@ccm.howardcc.edu, http://www.howardcc.edu. Circ: 1,200 (free).

C

378.1 USA ISSN 0017-6249
H S U BRAND★. Text in English. 1915. w. (Sep.-May). adv. **Document type:** *Newspaper.*
Published by: Hardin - Simmons University, PO Box 16175, Abilene, TX 79698-6175. TEL 915-670-1438. Circ: 1,200.

378 ISR
HA-ACADAMAI. Text in Hebrew. bi-m. free.
Published by: Union of Graduates in the Social Sciences and Humanities, 93 Arlozorov St., Tel Aviv, Israel. TEL 972-3-6919239, FAX 972-3-5441285. Ed. Uzi Berlinski. Circ: 30,000.

378.1 USA ISSN 0017-7067
LH1.H12
HAMILTON ALUMNI REVIEW. Text in English. 1935. q. free. illus. **Document type:** *Academic/Scholarly.* **Description:** Provides news about the college, the alumni, faculty and administrators.
Published by: Hamilton College, Trustees of Hamilton College, 198 College Hill Rd, Anderson Connell Alumni Center, Clinton, NY 13323. TEL 315-859-4680, FAX 315-859-4035. Ed., R&P Frank K Lorenz TEL 315-859-4684. Circ: 19,000 (controlled).

378 USA
HAMPTON SCRIPT. Text in English. 1930. bi-w. USD 10 (effective 2005); free on campus. adv. bk.rev.; play rev. **Document type:** *Newspaper, Consumer.*
Published by: Hampton University, Queen & Tyler Sts., Hampton, VA 23668. TEL 757-727-5385, FAX 757-727-5085, http://www.hamptonscript.com. Ed. Talia Buford. adv.: page USD 963; trim 19.5 x 12. Circ: 5,000 morning (paid and free).

378.198 USA ISSN 0749-4882
CODEN: REFIAS
HARBUS NEWS; Hravard Business School student newspaper. Text in English. 1936. w. USD 85 to individuals; USD 100 to institutions (effective 2001). adv. bk.rev. back issues avail. **Document type:** *Newspaper, Academic/Scholarly.* **Description:** Includes news, opinions, humor, sports and entertainment.
Published by: (Harvard Business School), Harbus News Corp., Harvard Business School, Gallatin Hall E, Boston, MA 02163. TEL 617-495-6528, FAX 617-495-8619, harbus@hbs.edu, http://www.harbus.org. Ed. Prashant Agarwap. Pub. Jim Tutigi. R&P Ines Cobee. Circ: 4,000.

378.198 USA
HARTFORD COLLEGE FOR WOMEN. CHRONICLE. Text in English. 1979. s-a. free. adv. bk.rev.
Published by: Hartford College for Women, 1265 Asylum Ave, Hartford, CT 06105. TEL 203-768-5653. Ed. Kathleen P Teso. Circ: 3,000.

378 GBR ISSN 0308-0463
HARVARD BUSINESS SCHOOL CLUB OF LONDON ADDRESS BOOK. Text in English. 1974. a. free to members. adv. **Document type:** *Directory.* **Description:** Lists members of the Harvard Business School in the UK.
Related titles: Diskette ed.
Published by: A P Information Services, Marlborough House, 298 Regents Park Rd, London, N3 2UU, United Kingdom. TEL 44-20-8349-9988, FAX 44-20-8349-9797. Ed. Alan Phillipp. adv.: page GBP 600; 105 x 150. Circ: 13,000.

371.805 USA
HARVARD CRIMSON. Text in English. 1873. d. (Mon.-Fri.). USD 140; USD 0.30 newsstand/cover; free to students (effective 2005). **Document type:** *Newspaper, Consumer.*
Contact Owner: The Harvard Crimson Inc., 14 Plympton St, Cambridge, MA 02138-6606. TEL 617-576-6600, FAX 617-576-7860, news@thecrimson.com, http://www.thecrimson.com. Circ: 3,500 morning (paid and free).

378.1 USA ISSN 0017-8098
LH1.H3
HARVARD LAMPOON. Text in English. 1876. 5/yr. USD 15. adv. bk.rev. illus. reprint service avail. from PQC. **Description:** Humor magazine from Harvard University.
Related titles: Microform ed.: (from PQC).
Published by: Harvard Lampoon, Inc., 44 Bow St, Cambridge, MA 02138. TEL 617-495-7801. Ed. Jon D Beckerman. Circ: 25,000.

378.198 340 USA ISSN 1053-8186
KF292.H34
HARVARD LAW BULLETIN. Text in English. 1948. 3/yr. free to qualified personnel (effective 2005). bk.rev. 64 p./no.; **Document type:** *Magazine.* **Description:** News for Harvard Law School alumni.
Formerly (until 1986): Harvard Law School Bulletin (0017-8128)
Indexed: ABRCLP, ILP.
—BLDSC (4267.490000).
Published by: Harvard University, Law School, 125 Mount Auburn St., Cambridge, MA 02138. TEL 617-495-3118, bulletin@law.harvard.edu, http://www.law.harvard.edu/alumni/bulletin/. Ed. Rob London TEL 617-496-4481. R&P Emily Newburger TEL 617-495-9724. Circ: 32,000.

378 610 USA ISSN 0191-7757
R747
HARVARD MEDICAL ALUMNI BULLETIN. Text in English. 1891. q. free (effective 2005). adv. bk.rev. illus. index. **Document type:** *Bulletin, Academic/Scholarly.*
—BLDSC (4268.230000).
Published by: Harvard Medical School Alumni Association, Landmark Center, 401 Park Dr, 2nd Flr West, Boston, MA 02115. TEL 617-384-8520, FAX 617-384-8539, hmsalum@hms.harvard.edu, http://www.hms.harvard.edu/alumni. Ed. William Ira Bennett. Adv. contact Sarah Jane Nelson. Circ: 15,000.

378 USA ISSN 0364-7692
HARVARD UNIVERSITY GAZETTE. Text in English. 1890. w. (except s-m. Jul.-Aug.; m. Dec., Jun.). USD 25 domestic; USD 32 foreign (effective 2004). **Document type:** *Newspaper, Consumer.*
Published by: Harvard University, Office of News & Public Affairs, 1350 Massachusetts Ave, Cambridge, MA 02138. TEL 617-495-1585, FAX 617-495-0754, http://www.hno.harvard.edu/gazette/, http://www.news.harvard.edu. Ed. Terry Murphy. R&P John Lenger. Circ: 31,000.

HARVARD UNIVERSITY. GRADUATE SCHOOL OF EDUCATION. BULLETIN. see *EDUCATION*

378 USA
HASTINGS COLLEGE COLLEGIAN. Text in English. 1898. w. USD 10 (effective 2000). adv. film rev.; music rev.; tel.rev.; video rev. charts; illus. back issues avail. **Document type:** *Newspaper, Consumer.* **Description:** Covers news of interest to Hastings College community.
Published by: Hastings College, 7th & Turner, Box 269, Hastings, NE 68902-0269. TEL 402-461-7399, FAX 402-461-7442, collegian@hastings.edu, http://www.hastings.edu. Ed. Katherine Gotto. R&P Kathy Stofer. Adv. contact Scott Miller. page USD 425; trim 13.75 x 11.25. Circ: 1,100 (paid).

378 USA
HAWKEYE (LA PLATA). Text in English. 197?. bi-w. free. **Document type:** *Newspaper.*
Related titles: CD-ROM ed.
Published by: Charles County Community College, PO Box 910, Mitchell Rd, La Plata, MD 20646-0910. TEL 301-934-2251, FAX 301-934-7698. Ed. Theresa Chaney. R&P Mike Shields. Circ: 1,000.

378 USA
HEALTH PROFESSIONS NEWS AND NOTES. Text in English. 1986. irreg. USD 24 (effective 1999). adv. bk.rev. **Document type:** *Newsletter.*
Formerly: Mobile Graduate News and Notes (0887-3887)
Published by: (University of Maine, Houlton Center), Consulting Group, Inc., c/o Lloyd R Chase, Ed, Box 323, Houlton, ME 04730-0323. TEL 207-532-4780, FAX 207-532-4780. Ed., Adv. contact Lloyd R Chase. Circ: 350.

378.1 USA ISSN 0017-9175
HEAR THIS; Kings Points monthly newspaper. Text in English. 1946. m. USD 10. bk.rev. **Document type:** *Newspaper.*
Published by: United States Merchant Marine Academy, 300 Steamboat Rd, Kings Point, NY 11024. TEL 516-482-8416. Circ: 3,000.

378 USA ISSN 0017-9590
THE HEIGHTS (CHESTNUT HILL). Text in English. 1919. w. (Tue.). free (effective 2005). adv. bk.rev.; film rev.; play rev. abstr.; illus. 32 p./no. 6 cols./p.; **Document type:** *Newspaper.*
Related titles: Online - full text ed.: (from LexisNexis).
Contact: The Heights Inc., Boston College, McElroy Commons 113, Chestnut Hill, MA 02167. TEL 617-552-2223, FAX 617-552-4823, http://www.bcheights.com. Ed. Ryan Hefferman. adv.: col. inch USD 8.50, page USD 9.50. Circ: 18,500 (free).

300 USA ISSN 0734-4031
HENRY GEORGE NEWSLETTER. Text in English. 1937. m. USD 10. bk.rev. **Description:** Reports on the activities of the school and its affiliates.
Formerly: Henry George News (0018-0424)
Published by: Henry George School of Social Science, 121 E 30th St, New York, NY 10016. TEL 212-889-8020. Ed. Mark A Sullivan. Circ: 1,000.

378.198 USA
THE HIGHLANDER (HIGHLAND). Text in English. 1958. fortn. (during school yr.). USD 5. adv. **Document type:** *Newspaper.*
Published by: Highland Community College, Journalism Department, PO Box 68, Highland, KS 66035. TEL 913-442-3236. Circ: 2,000.

378.198 USA
HILLSDALE MAGAZINE. Text in English. 1988 (vol.63). q. free (effective 2005). back issues avail. **Document type:** *Magazine, Consumer.* **Description:** Coverage of Hillsdale College programs, activities, students, faculty, and on- and off-campus public policy seminars.
Published by: Hillsdale College, 33 E College St, Hillsdale, MI 49242. TEL 517-437-7341, FAX 517-607-2658, monica.vanderweide@hillsdale.edu, http://www.hillsdale.edu. Ed. Monica Van Der Weide. Circ: 20,000 (free).

371.8974 USA ISSN 1068-1566
HILLTOP MAGAZINE. Text in English. 1924. w. adv. bk.rev.; film rev.; play rev. illus. **Document type:** *Newspaper, Academic/Scholarly.* **Description:** Reports on news and events and issues in the Howard University community.
Related titles: Online - full text ed.: (from LexisNexis).
Published by: Howard University, Office of University Communications, 2225 Georgia Ave, NW, Washington, DC 20059. TEL 202-238-2334, http://www.founders.howard.edu/communications/HMagazine.htm, http://www.howard.edu/communications. adv.: page USD 1,150. Circ: 10,000 (controlled).

371.805 USA
HILLTOP VIEWS. Text in English. bi-w. (Sep.-May). free (effective 2005). 6 p./no. 6 cols./p.; **Document type:** *Newspaper.*
Published by: St. Edward's University, 30010 S Congress, Box 714, Austin, TX 78704. TEL 512-448-8400, FAX 512-448-8492, http://www.stedwards.edu/stulife/hilltop/hilltop.htm. Circ: 1,000 (controlled).

HOCHSCHULSPORT. see *SPORTS AND GAMES*

HOLZAUGE. see *LITERARY AND POLITICAL REVIEWS*

378.1 AUS ISSN 1325-6734
HONI SOIT. Text in English. 1929. w. AUD 30; AUD 60 foreign; free to Sydney University campuses. adv. bk.rev.; film rev.; play rev. illus. **Document type:** *Newspaper.* **Description:** Covers social, political and cultural issues, and student issues.
Published by: Students Representative Council, University Of Sydney, NSW 2006, Australia. TEL 61-2-96605222, FAX 61-2-96604260. R&P, Adv. contact Mark West. Circ: 6,000.

378 USA
HOOD TODAY. Text in English. 1986. irreg. (every 2-3 wks.). USD 15. film rev.; play rev. charts. **Document type:** *Newspaper.*
Published by: Hood College, 401 Rosemount Ave, Frederick, MD 21701. TEL 301-696-3641, FAX 301-696-3727. Circ: 1,500.

378.198 USA
HOPKINS NEWS-LETTER. Text in English. 1897. 26/yr. USD 40 (effective 1998). adv. bk.rev.; film rev.; play rev. 26 p./no. 6 cols./p.; **Document type:** *Newspaper.*
Published by: Johns Hopkins University, Shriver 6, 3400 N Charles St, Baltimore, MD 21218. TEL 410-516-6000, FAX 410-516-6565, News.Letter@jhu.edu, http://www.jhu.edu/~newslett. Eds. Douglas Steinke, Gianna Abruzzo. R&P Douglas Steinke. Adv. contact Neal Dalal. B&W page USD 800, color page USD 1,120; trim 12.6667 x 21.5. Circ: 6,000.

378 USA
HORIZON (SALT LAKE CITY). Text in English. 1949. w. USD 15. adv.
Formerly: Points West
Published by: S L C C S A - Salt Lake Community College, 4600 S Redwood Rd, Box 30808, Salt Lake City, UT 84130-0808. TEL 801-967-4019. Circ: 5,000.

371.8 USA
HORIZONS (KINGSTON). Text in English. 3/yr. free to qualified personnel. **Document type:** *Newsletter.* **Description:** For alumni, faculty members, donors, foundations, corporations and friends of the University of Rhode Island.
Published by: U R I Foundation, 21 Davis Hall, 10 Lippitt Rd, Kingston, RI 02881-2011. TEL 401-874-5836, http://www.urifoundation.org/. Ed. Janet Heffernan. Pub., R&P Bob Coleman. Circ: 20,000.

378.1 USA ISSN 0018-5086
HORNET. Text in English. 1923. w. free to qualified personnel. adv. bk.rev.; film rev.; play rev. illus. **Document type:** *Newspaper.*
Published by: Fullerton College, 321 E Chapman Ave, Fullerton, CA 92634. TEL 714-871-8000. Ed. Mark Ngttles. R&P, Adv. contact David Burke TEL 714-992-7725. Circ: 5,000.

378.198 USA
HOUGHTON STAR. Text in English. 1908. w. free. adv. bk.rev. **Document type:** *Newspaper, Academic/Scholarly.*
Related titles: ♦ Regional ed(s).: Washington Star; Hartlepool Star; Peterlee Star; Seaham Star; South Tyne Star; Sunderland Star.
Published by: Houghton College, PO Box 378, Houghton, NY 14744. TEL 716-567-9210. Ed., R&P Dale Schuurman. Adv. contact Scott Taylor. Circ: 1,250.

378 USA ISSN 0888-4013
HOUSTONIAN. Text in English. 1984. s-m. USD 15. adv.
Formerly (until 1986): Houston Style (8750-7013)
Related titles: Online - full text ed.
Published by: Sam Houston State University, PO Box 2178, Huntsville, TX 77341. TEL 409-294-1495. Ed. Jenna Jackson. Adv. contact Kerri Tuma. Circ: 6,000.

378.198 USA ISSN 0742-2075
F127.H8
HUDSON VALLEY REGIONAL REVIEW; a journal of regional studies. Text in English. 1984. s-a. USD 12 domestic; USD 16 foreign (effective 2000). bk.rev. illus. Index. back issues avail.; reprints avail. **Document type:** *Academic/Scholarly.*
Indexed: AmH&L, HistAb.
Published by: Marist College, Hudson River Valley Institute, 3399 N Rd, Poughkeepsie, NY 12601-1387. TEL 845-575-3052, FAX 845-575-3560, hrvi@Marist.edu, http://www.hudsonrivervalley.net. Circ: 375.

378 GBR
HULLFIRE. Text in English. 1974. fortn. (during school term). free. adv. bk.rev. **Document type:** *Newspaper.* **Description:** Student newspaper of Hull University Union.
Published by: Hull University, Students' Union, University House, Cottingham Rd, Hull, N Humberside HU6 7RX, United Kingdom. TEL 44-1482-466269, FAX 44-1482-466280. Ed. Danny Blackburn. Adv. contact Nicola Edgar. Circ: 8,000 (controlled).

HUMAN ECOLOGY (ITHACA). see *SOCIAL SCIENCES: COMPREHENSIVE WORKS*

370 CAN
HUMBER ETC... Text in English. 1967. w. (Sep. to May). CND 50. adv. bk.rev.; dance rev.; film rev.; music rev.; play rev.; software rev.; video rev. back issues avail. **Document type:** *Newspaper.*
Formerly: Coven (1184-3071)
Published by: Humber College of Applied Arts and Technology, Journalism Department, School of Media Studies, 205 Humber College Blvd, Toronto, ON M9W 5L7, Canada. TEL 416-675-3111. Pub. William Hanna. Circ: 4,000.

378 USA
HUMPHREYS COLLEGE QUARTERLY NEWS BULLETIN. Text in English. 1896. q. free. **Document type:** *Newsletter.*
Description: Provides news and editorial regarding events, students, faculty, staff and alumni of Humphreys College.
Published by: Humphreys College, 6650 Inglewood Ave, Stockton, CA 95207. TEL 209-478-0800, FAX 209-478-8721. Ed. Pamela Knapp. Circ: 20,000 (controlled).

378.1 USA
HUNTER MAGAZINE. Text in English. 1981. 2/yr. free. bibl.; charts; illus.
Supersedes: Newshunter (0048-0274)
Published by: City University of New York, Hunter College, 695 Park Ave, New York, NY 10021. TEL 212-772-4070. Ed. Margo Viscusi. Circ: 73,000.

378.198 USA
HURON UNIVERSITY ALPHOMEGA. Text in English. 1883. m. membership. adv. bk.rev.
Formerly: Huron College Alphomega
Published by: Huron University, Student Senate, 220, Eagle Butte, SD 57625-0220. TEL 605-352-8721. Circ: 500.

HUSKERS ILLUSTRATED. see *SPORTS AND GAMES—Ball Games*

▼ **ICARAMBA U.** see *ETHNIC INTERESTS*

378.1 USA
ILLINOIS ALUMNI. Text in English. 1907. 6/yr. USD 30 to members (effective 2000). adv. bk.rev. illus. **Document type:** *Academic/Scholarly.*
Formerly (until 1997): Illinois Quarterly (1047-4536); Which supersedes (in 1989): Illinois Alumni News (0019-1841)
Published by: University of Illinois at Urbana-Champaign, Alumni Association, University of Illinois, 1401 W Green St, Urbana, IL 61801. TEL 217-333-1471, FAX 217-333-7803, illinoisalumni@uiuc.edu, http://www.uiaa.org. Ed., R&P, Adv. contact Vanessa Faurie. Pub. Loren R Taylor. Circ: 87,000 (controlled).

378.1 USA
ILLINOIS STATE ALUMNI MAGAZINE. Text in English. 1966. q. free. **Document type:** *Magazine, Consumer.*
Former titles: Illinois State University Alumni Today; Illinois State University Today; Illinois State University Alumni Today; Illinois State University Alumni News; Alumni Register (0002-7235); American Alumni Newspaper
Published by: Illinois State University, Alumni Office, Campus Box 3100, Normal, IL 61790-3100. TEL 309-438-2586. Ed. Susan Callahan. Pub. Barbara Tipsord Todd. Circ: 113,000.

371.8 DEU
ILMENAUER UNI-NACHRICHTEN. Text in German. 1958. 6/yr. adv. **Document type:** *Journal, Academic/Scholarly.*
Published by: Technische Universitaet Ilmenau, Postfach 100565, Ilmenau, 98684, Germany. TEL 49-3677-692549, FAX 49-3677-691718, bettina.wegner@tu-ilmenau.de, http://www.tu-ilmenau.de/deutsch/iun/. adv.: B&W page EUR 600, color page EUR 1,050. Circ: 2,200 (controlled).

378 CAN
IMPACT (NORTH YORK). Text in English. m. free. adv. bk.rev.; film rev. **Document type:** *Newspaper, Consumer.*
Description: Discusses student business and politics.
Former titles: O B T; Oblique Times
Published by: Seneca College, Student Federation Council, 1750 Finch Ave E, North York, ON M2J 2X5, Canada. TEL 416-491-5050, FAX 416-756-2765, impanews@learn.senecac.on.ca. Ed. Holly V Pagnacco. Adv. contact Christopher York. Circ: 5,000 (controlled).

378 CAN ISSN 0820-5116
IMPACT CAMPUS; le journal des etudiants et des etudiantes de l'Universite Laval. Text in French. 1986. w. free to students (effective 2005). adv. back issues avail. **Document type:** *Newspaper, Consumer.*
—CCC.
Published by: Impact Campus Inc., 1244 pavillon Maurice Pollack, Universite Laval, Sainte Foy, PQ G1K 7P4, Canada. TEL 418-656-5079, FAX 418-656-2398, impact-campus@public.ulaval.ca, http://www.ulaval.ca/impact. Ed. Christian Dubois. Adv. contact Myriam Thiffault. B&W page CND 665, color page CND 1,150; trim 14 x 10. Circ: 15,000.

378 GBR
IMPERIAL COLLEGE ENGINEER. Text in English. 1903. s-a. membership (effective 2003). adv. bk.rev. **Document type:** *Journal, Academic/Scholarly.* **Description:** Covers news relating to Imperial College and City & Guilds Colleges, as well as reports relating to association activities and features.
Formerly: The Central
Published by: City & Guilds College Association, Shefield Bldg, Imperial College, London, SW7 2AZ, United Kingdom. TEL 44-20-75946131, FAX 44-20-75946128, cgca@ic.ac.uk, http://www.cgca.org.uk. Ed. Colleen Richardson. R&P, Adv. contact Adrian Winchester. color page GBP 300; 8.2 x 11.7. Circ: 4,500.

378 CAN ISSN 0706-7380
IMPRINT. Text in English. 1978. w. free (effective 2004). adv. bk.rev.; film rev. **Document type:** *Newspaper, Consumer.*
Description: Official student newspaper of the University of Waterloo.
Related titles: Online - full text ed.
Published by: University of Waterloo, Student Life Centre, Rm 1116, Waterloo, ON N2L 3G1, Canada. TEL 519-888-4048, FAX 519-884-7800, editor@imprint.uwaterloo.ca, http://imprint.uwaterloo.ca. Circ: 10,000 (paid).

783 USA
IMPRINT (WALTHAM). Text in English. 3/yr. USD 25 to members (effective 1999). illus. **Document type:** *Newspaper.*
Description: Contains news and articles about Brandeis University alumnae, along with information about activities to support the library.
Published by: Brandeis University, National Women's Committee, MS132, Box 9110, Waltham, MA 02454-7110. TEL 617-736-4160, bunwc@brandeis.edu. Ed. Mary Pat Prado. Circ: 4,900 (paid).

378 USA ISSN 1076-4224
IN MOTION (DAYTONA BEACH). Text in English. 1991. m. USD 20. adv. bk.rev.; film rev.; play rev. back issues avail.
Description: Covers news, features, entertainment, sports of interest to DBCC community.
Published by: Daytona Beach Community College, 1200 International Spdy Blvd, Daytona Beach, FL 32114. TEL 904-255-8131, FAX 904-254-4458. Ed. Rosanne Garrity. Adv. contact Torrie Mathis. Circ: 5,000 (paid).

378.198 USA
THE INDEPENDENT (DURANGO). Text in English. 1931. w. USD 15. adv. bk.rev.; film rev.; play rev. illus.; stat. **Document type:** *Newspaper.*
Published by: Fort Lewis College, 1000 Rim Dr, Durango, CO 81301-3999. TEL 303-247-7405, http://www.fortlewis.edu/. Ed. Clara Woodmansee. Adv. contact Kitty Wild. Circ: 3,000.

378 USA
THE INDEPENDENT COLLEGIAN. Text in English. 1919. s-w. (Mon. & Thu.). free. adv. 10 p./no. 6 cols./p.; **Document type:** *Newspaper.*
Formerly: The Collegian
Published by: Collegia Media Foundation, 2132 Middlesex Dr, Toledo, OH 43606. TEL 419-534-2438, FAX 419-534-2884, icads@accesstoledo.com, http://www.independentcollegian.com. Ed. Emily Barnes. adv.: col. inch USD 8. Circ: 9,500 (free).

378.1 USA ISSN 0889-2423
THE INDEPENDENT FLORIDA ALLIGATOR. Text in English. 1906. d. (Mon.-Fri.). USD 35 (effective 2005). adv. bk.rev.; film rev.; play rev.; rec.rev. **Document type:** *Newspaper, Consumer.*
Formerly: Florida Alligator (0015-3877)
Related titles: Online - full text ed.: (from LexisNexis).
Published by: Campus Communications, Inc. (Gainesville), PO Box 14257, Gainesville, FL 32604. TEL 904-376-4446, editor@alligator.org, http://www.alligator.org. Circ: 35,000. Wire service: AP.

378.198 970.1 USA ISSN 0364-8028
E97
INDIAN LEADER. Text in English. 1897. fortn. USD 5. adv. **Document type:** *Newspaper.*
Related titles: Microfilm ed.: (from BHP).
Published by: (Indian Leader Association), Haskell Indian Nation University, PO Box 258, Lawrence, KS 66046-4800. TEL 913-749-8477, FAX 913-749-8406. Ed., Adv. contact Darrel Deon James. Circ: 7,000.

C

378.1 USA ISSN 0019-6517
INDIANA ALUMNI MAGAZINE. Text in English. 1938. bi-m. adv. bk.rev. illus. 84 p./no.; back issues avail. **Document type:** *Magazine, Consumer.*
Published by: Indiana University Alumni Association, 1000 E 17th St, Bloomington, IN 47408. TEL 812-855-5785, FAX 812-855-4228, iualumni@indiana.edu, http://www.indiana.edu/~alumni/home.html. Ed., R&P Judith Schroeder. Adv. contact Rita Colorito TEL 812-855-6415. Circ: 96,000 (controlled).

378 USA ISSN 0740-9664
INDIANA DAILY STUDENT. Text in English. 1867. d. (Mon.-Fri.). USD 88 (effective 2005). **Document type:** *Newspaper.*
Related titles: Online - full text ed.: (from LexisNexis).
Published by: Indiana University, 940 E 7th St, Ernie Pyle Hall, Rm 120, Bloomington, IN 47405. TEL 812-335-0763, FAX 812-855-8009, ids@indiana.edu, letters@indiana.edu, http://www.idsnews.com. Ed. Josh Sanburn. Circ: 17,000. Wire service: AP, LAT-WAT.

378.1 USA ISSN 0019-6789
INDIANA STATESMAN. Text in English. 1895. 3/w. (Mon., Wed., Fri.). free to students on campus; USD 47 subscr - mailed (effective 2005). adv. bk.rev.; film rev.; play rev. tr.lit. **Document type:** *Newspaper.*
Related titles: Microform ed.; Online - full text ed.: (from LexisNexis).
Published by: Indiana State University, 200 N Seventh St, Terre Haute, IN 47809. TEL 812-237-3025, 812-237-6311, FAX 812-237-7629, saseditr@scifac.indstate.edu, http://www.indianastatesman.com. Circ: 8,000. Wire service: AP.

378 CAN
L'INDICE PENSABLE. Text in French. m. adv.
Published by: Universite du Quebec a Trois Rivieres, C P 500, Trois Rivieres, PQ G9A 5H7, Canada. Circ: 2,500.

378 CAN ISSN 0229-2068
L'INFOMANE. Text in French. 1973. 10/yr. free. adv. bk.rev.; film rev.; play rev. abstr.; illus. **Document type:** *Newspaper, Academic/Scholarly.* **Description:** Covers society, arts, student life and other topics.
Related titles: E-mail ed.
Published by: College de Bois-de-Boulogne, 10500 Av Bois de Boulogne, Montreal, PQ H4N 1L3, Canada. TEL 514-332-3000, FAX 514-332-9579, infoman@collegebdeb.qc.ca. Ed. Marc Ouimet. R&P, Adv. contact Leonie Marin. page CND 200. Circ: 1,500.

378.1 DNK ISSN 1395-7791
INFORMATION & DEBAT. Text in Danish. 2002. irreg.
Media: Online - full content.
Published by: Studenterraadet ved Koebenhavns Universitet, Fiolstraede 10, Copenhagen K, 1171, Denmark. TEL 45-35-32-38-38, FAX 45-35-32-38-48, id@fsr.dk, http://www.fsr.ku.dk/index.php?/afd=bl.

378 USA
INFORMATION X-III. Text in English. 1990. bi-m. **Document type:** *Newsletter.* **Description:** News and information of interest to students, faculty and alumni of the institute.
Former titles: Information x-III-i; Information x-IV
Published by: National Education Center, Tampa Technical Institute Campus, 2410 E Busch Blvd, Tampa, FL 33612. TEL 813-935-5700, FAX 813-935-7415. Ed. Wiley E Koon Jr. Circ: 2,000.

378 GBR
INKING. Text in English. 1929. 3/yr. adv. bk.rev. **Description:** Arts and general interest for students.
Formerly: Arrows
Published by: Sheffield University, Students Union, Western Bank, Sheffield, S Yorks S10 2TG, United Kingdom. TEL 0742-724076, FAX 0742-752506. Circ: 1,500.

378 CAN
INNIS HERALD; heading into the next millennia with a new voice. Text in English. 1966. m. free. adv. bk.rev.; music rev.; play rev.; software rev.; tel.rev.; video rev. illus.; stat. back issues avail. **Document type:** *Newspaper, Consumer.* **Description:** Aims to be an alternative to the news and politically-oriented newspapers at the University of Toronto. Focuses on student lifestyles at the college, and also includes artistic, humourous and satirical content.
Published by: University of Toronto, Innis College Student Society, 2 Sussex Ave, Toronto, ON M5S 1J5, Canada. TEL 416-978-4748, FAX 416-978-5508, innis.herld@utoronto.ca. Ed. Victoria Loh. Circ: 3,000 (controlled).

052 AUS ISSN 0020-1618
INNOMINATE. Text in English. 1946. irreg. (approx. 7/yr). free. adv. bk.rev. **Document type:** *Newspaper.* **Description:** Includes medical news in local, national and international arenas.
Related titles: Online - full text ed.
Published by: University of Sydney, Medical Society, Blackburn Bldg., D06, University of Sydney, Sydney, NSW 2006, Australia. TEL 61-2-9351-2635, FAX 61-2-9351-6198, innom@medsoc.usyd.edu.au, http://www.blackburn.med.su.ua/medsoc/innom/. Ed., R&P Mitchell Lai. Adv. contact Warwick Jonge. Circ: 800 (controlled).

378 USA ISSN 0046-9572
INNOVATOR (ANN ARBOR). Text in English. 1969. irreg. free to alumni and current donors. **Document type:** *Newsletter.*
Published by: University of Michigan, School of Education, 610 East University Ave, Ann Arbor, MI 48109. TEL 734-763-4880, FAX 313-763-4062, educalum@umich.edu. Ed., R&P Eric Warden. Circ: 49,000 (controlled).

378.198 USA ISSN 0888-8469
INNOVATOR (UNIVERSITY PARK). Text in English. 1969. fortn. free. adv. bk.rev.; film rev.; play rev. illus. **Document type:** *Newspaper.*
Published by: Governors State University, University Pkwy, University Park, IL 60466. TEL 708-534-4517, FAX 708-534-8953. Ed. Sean Carr. R&P Rita Nagy. Adv. contact Lisa Loschetter. Circ: 3,000.

371.8 GBR ISSN 0304-4270
INSEAD ALUMNI ASSOCIATION ADDRESS BOOK. Text in English. 1970. a. GBP 125 to non-members; free to members (effective 2001). adv. **Document type:** *Directory.* **Description:** Lists all alumni of INSEAD (Fountainbleau). Alphabetical, chronological, geographical and professional order.
Related titles: Diskette ed.
Published by: (I N S E A D Alumni Association), A P Information Services, Marlborough House, 298 Regents Park Rd, London, N3 2UU, United Kingdom. TEL 44-20-83499888, FAX 44-20-83499797, info@ap-info.co.uk, info@apinfo.co.uk, http://www.ap-info.co.uk. Ed., Pub. Alan Philipp. adv.: B&W page USD 4,200, color page USD 64; trim 210 x 148. Circ: 12,800.

378.198 USA
INSIDE BARUCH. Text in English. s-a. free to qualified personnel. **Document type:** *Newsletter.* **Description:** College newspaper reporting on students, faculty and administration.
Published by: City University of New York, Baruch College, 17 Lexington Ave, New York, NY 10010. TEL 212-387-1182. Circ: 5,000.

378.1 USA
INSIDE U S U. Text in English. 1970 (vol.10). m. free to qualified personnel. **Document type:** *Newspaper, Consumer.*
Formerly: U S U Staff News (0041-5561)
Published by: Utah State University, Media Relations, 0500 Old Man Hill, Logan, UT 84322-0500. TEL 801-797-1353, FAX 801-797-1250, janek@media.usu.edu, http://www.usu.edu. Ed. Craig Hislop. Circ: 3,500.

378 USA ISSN 1070-6534
INSIDER (SKOKIE); careers, issues and entertainment for the next generation. Text in English. 1984. bi-m. USD 24.95 (effective 2003). adv. bk.rev.; film rev.; music rev.; play rev.; video rev. back issues avail. **Document type:** *Magazine, Consumer.*
Formerly: Collegiate Insider
Published by: College Marketing Bureau, Inc., 11168 Acama St., Ste. 3, North Hollywood, CA 91602. TEL 847-673-3703, FAX 847-329-0358, insideread@aol.com, http://www.incard.com, http://www.incard.com/insider.htm. Eds. Mark Jansen TEL 847-673-3703, Rita Cook TEL 818-753-0480. R&P Rita Cook TEL 818-753-0480. Adv. contact Mark Jansen TEL 847-673-3703. Circ: 1,018,350 (controlled).

378.1 PRI ISSN 8750-5428
INTERAMERICANA. Text in Spanish. 1938. 4/yr. free. bk.rev.; film rev. illus. back issues avail. **Document type:** *Newspaper, Academic/Scholarly.*
Supersedes (in 1979): Polygraph - I A U News; Which was formed by the 1971 merger of: Polygraph (0032-3837); I A U News (0018-8484)
Published by: Inter American University of Puerto Rico, Public Relations Office, PO Box 363255, San Juan, 00936-3255, Puerto Rico. TEL 787-766-1912, FAX 787-758-1696, http://www.inter.edu/. Ed. Maria Socorro Rosario. Circ: 15,000.

INTERNATIONAL UNIVERSITY COLLEGIATE SPORTS REPORT. see *SPORTS AND GAMES*

378.1 USA ISSN 0021-0358
IONIAN. Text in English. 1946. bi-w. free. adv. bk.rev.; film rev.; play rev. illus. **Document type:** *Newspaper.*
Related titles: Online - full text ed.
Published by: (Iona College), Media Trends, 715 North Ave, New Rochelle, NY 10801. TEL 914-633-2370, FAX 914-633-2406. Ed. Michelle Langone. Circ: 4,000.

378 CAN ISSN 0229-7493
IOTA. Text in English. 1978. m.
Formerly (until 1980): Meche (0229-7485)
Published by: College d'Enseignement Generale et Professionnel, 1111 rue Lapierre, La Salle, PQ H8N 2J4, Canada.

378 USA ISSN 1079-0985
IOWA ALUMNI QUARTERLY. Text in English. 1947. q. membership. adv.
Formerly: Iowa Alumni Review
Published by: University of Iowa Alumni Association, Main Campus, Iowa City, IA 52242. FAX 319-335-1079. Ed., R&P Carol Hacker TEL 319-335-3294. Pub. Vicki Nelson. Adv. contact Carrie Sheridan. Circ: 40,000.

378 USA
IOWA STATE DAILY. Text in English. 1890. d. (Mon.-Fri.). USD 62; USD 0.40 newsstand/cover (effective 2005). adv. bk.rev. **Document type:** *Newspaper.*
Contact: Iowa State Daily Publications Board, Inc., Hamilton Hall, Rm 108, Ames, IA 50011. TEL 515-294-4120, FAX 515-294-4119, aforbes@iastate.edu, http://www.iowastatedaily.com. adv.: col. inch USD 9.30. Circ: 14,000 morning (paid). Wire service: AP.

378 USA ISSN 0746-2204
IOWA STATER. Text in English. 1974. 3/yr. membership. **Document type:** *Newspaper.*
Published by: Iowa State University, Ames, IA 50011. TEL 515-294-3129, FAX 515-294-9748, htpp://www.iastate.edu/iastater, http://www.iastate.edu/iastater. Ed., R&P Linda A Charles. Circ: 135,000 (controlled).

378.198 GBR
ISIS; the Oxford University magazine. Text in English. 1892. 6/yr. GBP 1. adv. bk.rev.; film rev.; play rev. illus. reprints avail. **Description:** Covers arts, politics, fashion and society.
Indexed: Acal, GSI, MEA&I.
Published by: Oxford Student Publications Ltd., 7 St Aldates, Oxford, Oxon OX1 1BS, United Kingdom. TEL 44-1865-246464, FAX 44-1865-200341, isis@ospl.co.uk, http://cherwell.ospl.co.uk/. Ed. Barney Jones. Pub. Fatema Ahmed. R&P Alex Vontunzelmann. Adv. contact Alex von Tunzelmann. Circ: 10,000.

378.1 CUB ISSN 0047-1542
ISLAS. Text in Spanish. 1958. q. USD 21 domestic; USD 31 foreign (effective 1999). illus.; maps. back issues avail. **Description:** Covers literature, linguistics, history, philosophy, art, geography and so on.
Related titles: E-mail ed.
Indexed: AmH&L, HAPI, HistAb, IBR, L&LBA, PSA, SOPODA, SSA, SSI, SociolAb.
Published by: Universidad Central de las Villas (UCLV), Faculty of Humanities, Carretra a Camajvani km 5, 5, Santa Clara, Villa Clara 54830, Cuba. editorial@informat.vcl.sld.cu. Eds. Miriam Artiles Castro, Misael Moya. Circ: 500 (paid).

378 615.1 ITA
ISTITUTO DI RICERCHE FARMACOLOGICHE MARIO NEGRI. ALUMNI NEWS. Text in Italian. 1998. m. free. **Document type:** *Bulletin.* **Description:** Presents news about the institute and its activities.
Media: Online - full text.
Published by: Istituto di Ricerche Farmacologiche Mario Negri, Via Eritrea 62, Milan, MI 20157, Italy. TEL 39-02-390141, FAX 39-02-3546277, http://www.irfmn.mnegri.it/perp/aa/.

THE ITALIAN AMERICAN REVIEW. see *ETHNIC INTERESTS*

378.198 USA
ITHACA COLLEGE QUARTERLY. Text in English. 1983. q. free to alumni, parents and friends. **Document type:** *Academic/Scholarly.*
Related titles: Online - full text ed.
Published by: (Office of College Relations), Ithaca College, Alumni Hall, Ithaca, NY 14850. TEL 607-274-3830, FAX 607-274-1490, http://www.ithaca.edu/icq. Ed., R&P Maura Stephens. Circ: 42,000; 42,000 (controlled).

378 USA
IT'S ALLEN NEWSLETTER. Text in English. q. back issues avail. **Document type:** *Newsletter.* **Description:** For faculty-staff, alumni, students, parents and friends of the institution. Covers faculty and staff activities on and off campus.
Published by: Allen University, 1530 Harden St, Columbia, SC 29204. TEL 803-254-4165, FAX 803-376-5709. Eds. Anne Coleman, Rebecca Mbuh.

371.85 USA ISSN 0021-3276
IVY LEAF. Text in English. 1921. q. USD 12. adv. bk.rev.
Published by: Alpha Kappa Alpha Sorority, Inc., 5656 S Stony Island Ave, Chicago, IL 60637. Ed. Vanessa Lovelace. Adv. contact Connie L Cochran. Circ: (controlled).

378 USA
J C S U NEWS. Text in English. 1984. 4/yr. USD 6.
Published by: (Communication Arts Department), Johnson C. Smith University, 100 Beatties Ford Rd, Charlotte, NC 28216. TEL 704-378-1000. Circ: 1,800. **Subscr. to:** Office of Alumni Affairs, Charlotte, NC 28216.

378.379 USA
J U MAGAZINE. (Jacksonville University) Text in English. 1968. s-a. free. **Description:** Informs alumni and parents of the activities and development of the administration, faculty, alumni and students.
Formed by the 1995 merger of: Compass; Lamplighter
Published by: Jacksonville University, Office of Public Affairs, 2800 University Blvd N, Jacksonville, FL 32211-3394. TEL 904-745-7033, FAX 904-775-7020, jdaigle@mail.ju.edu, http://www.ju.edu. Eds. John Daigle Jr., Peter A Casella. Circ: 25,000 (controlled).

378 USA
THE JAMBAR. Text in English. 1930. s-w. (Tue. & Thu.). USD 20 (effective 2005). **Document type:** *Newspaper, Consumer.*
Published by: Youngstown State University, One University Plaza, Youngstown, OH 44555. TEL 330-941-3095, FAX 330-941-2322, jambar@cc.ysu.edu, http://www.thejambar.com. Adv. contact Caroline Perjessy. Circ: 5,500 morning (paid).

378 USA
JAMESTOWN COLLEGE. ALUMNI & FRIENDS. Text in English. q. free. illus. **Document type:** *Newsletter, Consumer.* **Description:** Covers college events, alumni and student news.
Published by: Jamestown College, 6093 College Ln., Jamestown, ND 58405. TEL 701-252-3467, FAX 701-253-4318, lsims@acc.jc.edu. Ed., R&P Lori Sims. Circ: 13,000 (controlled).

378 UAE
JAMI'I. Text in Arabic. 1984. m. free. **Description:** Covers student activities in the U.A.E.
Published by: Emirates National Student Union, Emirates Branch/Al-Ittihad al-Watani li-Talabat al-Imarat, Far' al-Imarat, P.O. Box 15966, Al-ain, United Arab Emirates. TEL 655508. Ed. Abd Al Aziz Harib Al Muhairi. Circ: 5,000.

378 DEU
JOHANN WOLFGANG GOETHE UNIVERSITAET. UNIREPORT. Text in German. 1967. irreg. adv. **Document type:** *Journal, Academic/Scholarly.*
Published by: Johann Wolfgang Goethe Universitaet, Senckenberganlage 31, Frankfurt Am Main, 60054, Germany. TEL 49-69-79822683, FAX 49-69-79823610, Presse@ltg.uni-frankfurt.de, http://www.uni-frankfurt.de/presse/infos/unireport.html. adv.: B&W page EUR 4,303.54, color page EUR 5,837.41. Circ: 15,000 (controlled).

378 USA
JOHN CARROLL. Text in English. 1960. q. free to qualified personnel. **Document type:** *Newsletter.*
Formerly: Carroll Alumni Journal
Published by: John Carroll University, Department of Public Affairs, University Heights, Cleveland, OH 44118. TEL 216-397-1687, FAX 216-397-3028. Ed. Jerome Pockar. Circ: 28,000.

051 USA ISSN 0021-7255
LH1.J7
JOHNS HOPKINS MAGAZINE. Text in English. 1950. 5/yr. USD 20 domestic; USD 24 foreign (effective 2004). adv. bk.rev. illus. back issues avail.; reprint service avail. from PQC. **Document type:** *Magazine, Consumer.* **Description:** General interest magazine for faculty, alumni and friends of Johns Hopkins University.
Related titles: Microform ed.: (from PQC); Online - full text ed.
Indexed: PAIS, RASB, RehabLit.

C

Address: Johns Hopkins University, 901 S Bond St, Ste 540, Baltimore, MD 21231. TEL 443-287-9900, FAX 443-287-9898, jhmagazine@jhu.edu, http://www.jhu.edu/~jhumag/. Ed. Sue De Pasquale. Circ: 93,000.

371.805 USA
JOHNS HOPKINS NEWS-LETTER. Variant title: Johns Hopkins Newsletter. Text in English. 1896. w. (Thu.). USD 35 semester; USD 65 (effective 2005). adv. **Document type:** *Newspaper.* **Description:** Provides comprehensive coverage of the Hopkins community.
Address: 3400 N Charles St, Levering Ste 102, The John Hopkins University, Baltimore, MD 21218. TEL 410-516-6000, FAX 410-516-6565, news.letter@jhu.edu, http://www.jhunewsletter.com/. Circ: 6,200 (controlled and free).

378.1 USA
THE JOHNS HOPKINS PEABODY NEWS. Text in English. 1981. 5/yr. free (effective 2005). adv. illus. **Document type:** *Newsletter, Academic/Scholarly.* **Description:** Contains news of interest to Peabody friends and alumni.
Supersedes: Peabody Notes (0031-3440)
Related titles: Online - full content ed.
Published by: Johns Hopkins University, Peabody Institute, 1 E Mt Vernon Pl, Baltimore, MD 21202-2397. TEL 410-659-8163, FAX 410-783-8576, http://www.peabody.jhv.edu. Ed., R&P Miss Anne Garside. Adv. contact Ms. Carey Scanlon TEL 410-584-1958. Circ: 25,000 (controlled).

378.1 USA
JOHNSON C. SMITH NEWSLETTER. Text in English. 196?. q. free.
Published by: (Alumni Office), Johnson C. Smith University, 100 Beatties Ford Rd, Charlotte, NC 28216. TEL 704-378-1000. Ed. Scott Scheer. Circ: 7,500.

JOURNAL OF COLLEGE AND UNIVERSITY STUDENT HOUSING; A C U H O journal. see *EDUCATION—Higher Education*

378.1 CAN ISSN 0837-3760
JOURNAL - SAINT MARY'S UNIVERSITY. Text in English. 1935. w. free to students (effective 2005). adv. bk.rev.; film rev.; play rev. **Document type:** *Newspaper.* **Description:** Covers University news, arts, entertainment and sports; current affairs of Canadian universities.
Formerly (until 1969): Saint Mary's University Journal (0036-3138)
—CCC.
Published by: Saint Mary's University, Journal Publishing Society, Ste 517, SUB, Halifax, NS B3H 3C3, Canada. TEL 902-496-8200, FAX 902-496-8209. Circ: 7,500.

378.198 USA
JUDSON CAMEO. Text in English. 1974. s-a. free. **Description:** News on campus and features on alumnae of Judson College.
Published by: Judson College, Bibb St, Marion, AL 36756. TEL 205-683-6161. Ed. Barbara Creswell. Circ: 15,000.

378 364 USA
JUSTNOTES. Text in English. s-a. **Document type:** *Newsletter.* **Description:** Contains news of the department and alumni as well as resources and opportunities related to criminal justice.
Published by: Sonoma State University, Department of Criminal Justice Administration, c/o Patrick Jackson, 1801 Cotati Ave, Rohnert Park, CA 94928-3609. TEL 707-664-2934, jackson@sonoma.edu, http://www.sonoma.edu/cja/.

378.1 USA
K E N. (Kent English News) Text in English. 1992. a. free. **Document type:** *Newsletter.*
Published by: Kent State University, Department of English, PO Box 5190, Kent, OH 44242-0001. TEL 216-672-1212. Ed. Kyle Friedow.

535 USA
KA LEO O HAWAII. Text in English. 1922. d. (Mon.-Fri.). USD 54 per academic year; free newsstand/cover on campus (effective 2005). **Document type:** *Newspaper, Consumer.*
Published by: University of Hawaii, Board of Publications, Ka Leo Bldg, 1755 Pope Rd 31 D, Honolulu, HI 96822. TEL 808-956-7043, FAX 808-956-9962, kaleo@kaleo.org, http://www.kaleo.org. Circ: 18,000 morning (paid and free).

378 USA ISSN 8750-5746
➤ **KALAMAZOO COLLEGE QUARTERLY.** Text in English. 1934. q. free. **Document type:** *Academic/Scholarly.* **Description:** For alumni, parents, and friends of the college.
Related titles: Online - full text ed.
Published by: Kalamazoo College, 1200 Academy St, Kalamazoo, MI 49006-3295. TEL 269-377-7304, FAX 269-337-7305, aluminfo@kzoo.edu. Ed. Carol A S Derks. Circ: 15,500 (controlled).

378 USA
KALEIDOSCOPE (BIRMINGHAM). Text in English. 1967. w. USD 25. adv. **Document type:** *Newspaper.*
Published by: University of Alabama at Birmingham, Box 76, University Center, Birmingham, AL 35294-1150. TEL 205-934-3354. Ed. Hunter Ford. Circ: 8,000 (controlled).

378 USA ISSN 0745-3345
KANSAS ALUMNI MAGAZINE. Text in English. 1902. 6/yr. USD 40. bk.rev.
Related titles: Online - full text ed.
Published by: University of Kansas Alumni Association, 1266 Oread Ave, Lawrence, KS 66045-1600. TEL 785-864-4760, FAX 785-864-5397, http://www.kualumni.org/magazine_home.html. Ed. Jennifer Jackson Sanner. Pub. Fred B Williams. Adv. contact Sarah Lober TEL 785-843-5511. Circ: 40,000.

378 USA
KANSAS STATE COLLEGIAN. Text in English. 1893. d. (Mon.-Fri.). USD 95; free to students (effective 2005). **Document type:** *Newspaper, Consumer.*
Published by: Student Publications, Inc., Kedzie Hall, Kansas State University, Manhattan, KS 66506. TEL 785-532-6555, collegn@ksu.edu, http://kstatecollegian.com. Adv. contact Linda Puntney. Circ: 11,500 morning (paid). Wire service: AP.

371.85 USA ISSN 0022-894X
KAPPA DELTA EPSILON CURRENT. Text in English. 1937. 3/yr. USD 5. illus. **Document type:** *Newsletter.* **Description:** Newsletter of the activities of Kappa Delta Epsilon, a co-educational national honorary fraternity which emphasizes and promotes professional education.
Formerly (until 1947): Circle of Kappa Delta Epsilon
Published by: Kappa Delta Epsilon, c/o Toni Gorrell, Ed, 201 Suelynn Dr, Normal, IL 61761. TEL 309-438-2164, FAX 309-438-8659. Circ: 1,500 (controlled).

KAPPA OMICRON NU DIALOGUE. see *HOME ECONOMICS*

KAPPA OMICRON NU FORUM. see *HOME ECONOMICS*

371.8 SVN ISSN 0022-9296
KATEDRA; akademiski casopis. Text in Slovenian. 1961. m. SIT 400, USD 20. adv. bk.rev.
Published by: Akademska Zalozba - Katedra, Tyrseva 23, Maribor, 62000, Slovenia. FAX 38-62-22-742. Eds. Petra Vidali, Saso Dravinec. Circ: 4,000.

378 ISR
KAV P'NIM. Text in Hebrew. 1968. q. bk.rev. charts; illus. back issues avail. **Document type:** *Newsletter.*
Formerly: Dushavon
Published by: Hebrew University of Jerusalem, Jerusalem, 91905, Israel. TEL 972-2-5882844, FAX 972-2-5811264, ryuval@mscc.huji.ac.il, http://www.huji.ac.il. Ed. Rivka Yuval. Circ: 10,000.

378.379 USA
KENT ALUMNI. Text in English. 1990. q. USD 35 to members (effective 1998).
Published by: Kent Alumni Association, PO Box 5190, Kent, OH 44242-0001. TEL 330-672-5368, FAX 330-672-4723, alumni@kent.edu, http://www.saed.kent.edu/alumni. Ed. Kelly Viancourt.

378 USA
KENTUCKY KERNEL. Text in English. 1894. d. (Mon.-Fri.). free domestic on campus (effective 2005). bk.rev. **Document type:** *Newspaper.*
Published by: Kernel Press, Inc., 026 Journalism Bldg, University of Kentucky, Lexington, KY 40506. TEL 859-257-1915, FAX 859-323-1906, kernel@pop.uky.edu, http://www.kykernel.com. Circ: 18,000 morning (free). Wire service: AP.

378.198 USA
KETTERING PERSPECTIVE. Text in English. 1970. q. free. **Document type:** *Academic/Scholarly.* **Description:** Informs alumni of current activities and events.
Formerly: G M I Alumni News
Published by: Kettering University, 1700 W Third Ave, Flint, MI 48504-4898. TEL 810-762-9824, FAX 810-762-7435, lallen@elite.gmi.edu. Ed., R&P Gary Erwin. Circ: 21,000 (controlled).

378 USA
KEUKA CONNECTION. Text in English. 1929. q. free. **Document type:** *Newsletter.* **Description:** Information on the activities of the college.
Published by: Keuka College, Keuka Park, NY 14478. TEL 315-536-4411, FAX 315-536-5216. Ed. James P Kuehl.

371.85 USA ISSN 0023-0804
LJ85.P2
KEY REPORTER. Text in English. 1936. q. USD 5 to non-members; free to members (effective 2005). bk.rev. cum.index: 1940-1950. back issues avail. **Document type:** *Newsletter, Academic/Scholarly.* **Description:** Contains news of the society's activities, feature articles, and scholarly book recommendations.
Related titles: Online - full text ed.
Indexed: ChLitAb.
Published by: Phi Beta Kappa Society, 1606 New Hampshire Ave, NW, Washington, DC 20009. TEL 202-265-3808, FAX 202-968-1601. Ed., R&P Barbara Haddad Ryan. Circ: 470,000 (paid and controlled).

378.198 USA
KNIGHT EXAMINER. Text in English. 1966. s-w. USD 10. adv. bk.rev.; film rev.; play rev. illus. back issues avail. **Document type:** *Newspaper.*
Formerly: Gothic Times
Related titles: Online - full text ed.
Published by: Jersey City State College, 2039 Kennedy Blvd., Jersey City, NJ 07305-1597. TEL 201-200-3575, FAX 201-200-3238. Ed., Adv. contact Larry D Fowler. Circ: 4,000.

378 USA
THE KNIGHT'S PAGE. Text in English. 1897. m. (during school year). USD 6. adv. bk.rev. illus. index. **Document type:** *Academic/Scholarly.*
Formerly (until vol.98, 1995): Black and Red
Published by: Martin Luther College, 1884 College Heights, New Ulm, MN 56073. TEL 507-354-8221, FAX 507-354-8225. Ed. Dave Rau. Circ: 600.

378.1 USA
KNOX ALUMNUS. Text in English. 1917. 3/yr. free. bk.rev. illus. back issues avail. **Document type:** *Consumer.* **Description:** Focuses on Knox College, its alumni, faculty and students.
Former titles: Knox Now and the Knox Alumnus; Knox Alumnus (0047-3499)
Published by: Knox College, Office of Public Relations, PO Box K233, Galesburg, IL 61401. TEL 309-341-7337, FAX 309-341-7718, damor@knox.edu, alumnus@knox.edu, http://www.knox.edu. Ed., R&P William J Spilman TEL 309-341-7337. Circ: 17,500 (controlled).

378 GBR
KRED. Text in English. w. adv. bk.rev. back issues avail. **Document type:** *Newspaper, Consumer.*
Formerly: Kred Student
Published by: University of Kent Students' Union, Mandela Bldg, University of Kent, Canterbury, Kent CT2 7NW, United Kingdom. TEL 01227-765224, FAX 01227-464625. Ed. Alice Lythgoe Goldstein. Adv. contact Andrew Green. Circ: 3,000.

C

378 500 JPN ISSN 0911-8233
KWANSEI GAKUIN DAIGAKU RIGAKUBU TSUSHIN. Text in Japanese. 1970. 2/yr. free. abstr. **Document type:** *Newsletter.* **Description:** Contains news of the school.
Indexed: MLA-IB.
Published by: Kwansei Gakuin University, School of Science/Kwansei Gakuin Daigaku Rigakubu Tsushin, 1-155 Uegahara-Ichiban-cho, Nishinomiya-shi, Hyogo-ken 662-0000, Japan. TEL 81-798-53-6111, FAX 81-798-51-0914. Ed. Kouhei Asano. Circ: 1,200 (controlled).

378.1 GBR ISSN 0023-639X
HB1
L S E MAGAZINE. Text in English. 1951-1990; resumed 199?. 2/yr. free. bk.rev. illus. reprints avail. **Document type:** *Bulletin.*
Indexed: AICP.
—CCC.
Published by: London School of Economics and Political Science, Houghton St., London, WC2A 2AE, United Kingdom. TEL 44-20-7405-7686. Ed. Doug Standring. adv.: B&W page GBP 1,000, color page GBP 1,500; trim 210 x 297. Circ: 50,000.

378.198 620 USA ISSN 0023-6411
L S U ENGINEERING NEWS. Text in English. 1966. 2/yr. free. **Document type:** *Newsletter.* **Description:** Contains news of engineering research carried out at the University, plus profiles of faculty, student activities, and alumni news.
Published by: (Louisiana State University, College of Engineering), Edward McLaughlin, Ed. & Pub., Department of Civil and Environmental Engineering, Baton Rouge, LA 70803. TEL 504-388-6003, FAX 504-388-5990. Ed. Amy Groves. Circ: 14,200.

378.1 USA ISSN 8750-2526
L S U MAGAZINE. (Louisiana State University) Text in English. 1905. q. USD 35 (effective 1998). adv. bk.rev. illus. **Document type:** *Bulletin.* **Description:** Published for members and supporters of Louisiana State University to apprise them of current LSU events.
Formerly (until 1984): L S U Alumni News (0023-6403)
Published by: Louisiana State University, Alumni Association, 3838 W Lakeshore Dr, Baton Rouge, LA 70808. TEL 504-388-3838, FAX 504-388-3816, magazine@lsualumni.org. Ed., R&P, Adv. contact Kelly Lewis. Pub. Charlie Roberts. Circ: 22,000.

371.8 USA
LA SALLE. Text in English. 1956. q. free to alumni. **Document type:** *Magazine, Consumer.*
Contact Owner: La Salle University, 1900 W Olney Ave, Philadelphia, PA 19141. TEL 215-951-1500, FAX 215-951-1086, piche@lasalle.edu, alumni@lasalle.edu, http://www.lasalle.edu/alumni/newsletter.shtml. Circ: 45,000 (free).

378.198 USA ISSN 1046-1329
LAFAYETTE MAGAZINE. Text in English. 1931. 3/yr. USD 2.50. **Description:** Covers higher education issues, news on alumni, and issues of interest to Lafayette College.

Published by: Lafayette College, 17 Watson Hall, Easton, PA 18042. TEL 215-250-5126, FAX 215-250-5127. Ed. Allta Rusman. Circ: 25,000.

378.198 **USA**
THE LAKELAND MIRROR. Text in English. 1934. bi-w. free to students. adv. bk.rev. **Document type:** *Newspaper.*
Formerly: Mirror (Sheboygan)
Published by: Lakeland College, PO Box 359, Sheboygan, WI 53082-0359. TEL 414-565-1316, FAX 414-565-1206. Ed. Nick Reichhoff. Pub. Martha Schott. Adv. contact Nicholas Reichhoff. Circ: 1,600.

378 **CAN**
LAMBDA. Text in English, French. 1961. w. adv. bk.rev.; film rev. **Document type:** *Newspaper.* **Description:** Bilingual student newspaper of the Laurentian University.
Published by: Laurentian University, Ramsey Lake Rd, Sudbury, ON P3E 2C6, Canada. TEL 705-673-6548, FAX 705-675-4849. Ed. Dominic Vidmar. Circ: 3,000.

378.1 **CAN** **ISSN 0023-7493**
LANCE. Text in English. 1927. w. CND 18, USD 20. bk.rev.; film rev.; play rev.
Related titles: Online - full text ed.
Published by: University of Windsor, Student Media Corp, 401 Sunset Ave, Windsor, ON N9B 3P4, Canada. TEL 519-253-4232, FAX 519-971-3624. adv.: B&W page CND 520, color page CND 920. Circ: 10,000 (controlled).

378 **CAN**
L'ASSETU∗ . Text in English. m. free.
Published by: Publi-Peq, 3575 bd St Laurent, Ste 232, Montreal, PQ H2X 2T7, Canada. TEL 514-845-8628. Circ: 2,000.

378 **USA**
THE LASSO. Text in English. 1914. w. (Thu.). free. **Document type:** *Newspaper.*
Formerly: Daily Lasso
Published by: Texas Woman's University, PO Box 525828,TWUSTATION, Denton, TX 76204-5828. TEL 940-898-2185, lass@exchange.twu.edu, http://www.twu.edu/lasso/. Ed. Kristina Walta. Circ: 3,000 (free). Wire service: AP.

371.85 **USA** **ISSN 0023-8996**
THE LAUREL OF PHI KAPPA TAU∗ . Text in English. 1919. 3/yr. USD 15 (effective 1999). illus. back issues avail. **Document type:** *Academic/Scholarly.*
Published by: Phi Kappa Tau Foundation, 5221 Morning Sun Rd, Oxford, OH 45056-8928. TEL 513-523-1778, FAX 513-524-4812, laurel_editor@phikappatau.org, http://www.phikappatau.org. Ed., R&P Terri L Nackid. Circ: 50,000 (controlled).

378.1 **CAN** **ISSN 0700-5105**
LAURIER CAMPUS. Text in English. 1962. 3/yr. free to college and alumni. adv. illus.
Formerly: Waterloo Campus (0043-146X)
Published by: Wilfrid Laurier University, University Advancement, 75 University Ave W, Waterloo, ON N2L 3C5, Canada. TEL 519-884-1970, FAX 519-884-8848, mmartinu@wlu.ca. Ed., R&P, Adv. contact Melodee Martinuk. Circ: 40,000.

378 **USA** **ISSN 0458-8665**
LAW QUADRANGLE NOTES. Text in English. 1957. 3/yr. free (effective 2005). bk.rev. back issues avail. **Document type:** *Academic/Scholarly.* **Description:** Covers news of the law school, faculty and alumni.
Published by: (Law School) University of Michigan, Law School, 625 South State St, Ann Arbor, MI 48109-1215. TEL 734-763-6100, FAX 734-764-8309, trogers@umich.edu, http://www.law.umich.edu. Ed. Kathy A Okwn. Circ: 22,500 (controlled).

378 **USA**
LAWRENCE TECHNOLOGICAL UNIVERSITY MAGAZINE. Text in English. 1977. s-a. free (effective 2005). **Document type:** *Magazine, Academic/Scholarly.* **Description:** Information on the activities of the university, its students, alumni, and faculty.
Published by: Lawrence Technological University, 21000 W Ten Mile Rd, Southfield, MI 48075-1058. TEL 248-204-2200, FAX 248-204-2207, http://www.ltu.edu. Ed., Pub. Bruce Annett. Circ: 35,000 (free).

378.198 **USA**
LAWRENTIAN. Text in English. 1906. q. **Document type:** *Academic/Scholarly.* **Description:** Provides news and information for alumni, parents, and friends of the school.
Formerly: Lawrenceville Bulletin
Published by: Lawrenceville School, PO Box 6125, Lawrenceville, NJ 08648. Ed. David S Ruiter.

378 **URY** **ISSN 1510-1835**
LAZOS. Text in Spanish. 1997.
Published by: Universidad Catolica del Uruguay "Damaso Antonio Larranaga", 8 de Octubre 2738, Montevideo, 11600, Uruguay. TEL 598-2-472717, FAX 598-2-470323, http://www.ucu.edu.uy.

378 **GBR**
LEEDS METROPOLITAN UNIVERSITY. ANNUAL REVIEW. Text in English. a. **Document type:** *Bulletin.*
Formerly: Leeds Metropolitan University. Review —BLDSC (1520.257000).
Published by: Leeds Metropolitan University, Leeds Metropolitan University, Calverley St, Leeds, LS1 3HE, United Kingdom. TEL 44-113-283-2600.

378.1 **GBR** **ISSN 0041-6975**
LEEDS STUDENT. Text in English. 1970. w. adv. bk.rev.; film rev.; play rev. illus. **Document type:** *Newspaper.* **Description:** Constitutes a student newspaper carrying news, current affairs, careers section and sports pages.
Incorporates: Union News
Published by: University of Leeds Union, Leeds University Union, PO Box 157, Leeds, LS1 1UH, United Kingdom. TEL 44-113-243-4727, FAX 44-113-246-7953. Ed. Ben East. Adv. contact Helen Whiteoak. B&W page GBP 799, color page GBP 949. Circ: 40,000.

378 **USA**
LEHIGH ALUMNI BULLETIN. Text in English. 1912. q. free to alumni. adv. **Description:** Articles, essays, and photographs of general interest to educated readers, especially those with ties to the university. Covers Lehigh's intellectual, cultural and social life, and alumni news and announcements.
Published by: Lehigh University, Alumni Association, 436 Broadhead Ave, Bethlehem, PA 18015. TEL 610-758-3170, FAX 610-758-5566, http://www.lehigh.edu/alumweb/. Ed. Ron Ticho. Adv. contact Janet Tucker. Circ: 50,000 (controlled).

378.1 **USA** **ISSN 0047-4452**
LEX. Text in English. 1971 (vol.6). w. (during school term). adv. illus.
Published by: John Jay College of Criminal Justice, Newspaper Society, City University of New York, 445 W 59th St, New York, NY 10019. TEL 212-489-5183.

378.198 **USA**
LEX REVIEW. Text in English. 1966. m. free. adv. **Document type:** *Newspaper.*
Published by: John Jay College, Lex Newspaper Society, 445 W 59th St, New York, NY 10019. TEL 212-237-8308. Ed. Richard Durant.

320.51 **SWE** **ISSN 1100-3693**
LIBERTAS. Text in Swedish. 1988. bi-m. SEK 100 (effective 1998). bk.rev. **Description:** Serves as a forum for social-democratic debate.
Indexed: IPSA.
Published by: Sveriges Socialdemokratiska Studentfoerbund, Fack 11544, Stockholm, 10061, Sweden. TEL 46-8-714-48-40, FAX 46-8-714-95-08. Ed. Magnus Wennerhag. Circ: 2,000.

378 **DEU**
LIMA; liberales magazin. Text in German. 1989. s-a. adv. stat. back issues avail.
Published by: Bundesverband Liberaler Hochschulgruppen, Prinz-Albert-Str 55, Bonn, 53113, Germany. TEL 0228-213744, FAX 0228-218491. Circ: 45,000.

378 **USA**
LINFIELD REVIEW. Text in English. 1895. w. (during school yr.). USD 30. adv. bk.rev. illus. **Document type:** *Newspaper.* **Description:** Student-run newspaper covering news and events for the Linfield College community.
Formerly (until 1967): Linews
Published by: Linfield College, 900 S Baker St, Unit 4009, McMinnville, OR 97128-6894. TEL 503-472-7715, FAX 503-472-7715, review@linfield.edu, www.linfield.edu/review/. R&P Raymond Ochs. Adv. contact Melissa Wolf. B&W page USD 225; 10 x 16. Circ: 1,700.

LINK (BURNABY). see *EDUCATION*

371.8 **USA** **ISSN 1071-5487**
LINK (NEW YORK, 1995); where college students get it. Text in English. 1995. bi-m. USD 10; USD 2.95 newsstand/cover (effective 2000). adv. bk.rev.; film rev.; rec.rev. illus. **Document type:** *Magazine, Consumer.* **Description:** Contains news and articles on lifestyle and cultural items of interest to college students.
Published by: College Television Network, Inc., 32 E 57th St, 11th Fl, New York, NY 10022-2513. TEL 212-980-6600, 800-586-4636, FAX 212-755-5992, editor@linkmag.com, http://www.linkmag.com. Ed. Jana Martin. Pub., Adv. contact Peter Kraft. R&P Jeff Howe. B&W page USD 28,678, color page USD 39,830. Circ: 1,000,000; 1,000,000 (controlled).

658 334 **CAN** **ISSN 0703-9972**
L'INTERET∗ . Text in French. 1955. s-m. free. adv. bk.rev.
Formerly: Lit-Pot-Hec
Published by: (Ecole des Hautes Etudes Commerciales), Publi-Peq, 3575 bd St Laurent, Ste 232, Montreal, PQ H2X 2T7, Canada. TEL 514-644-1000. Ed. Sophie Lemaire. Circ: 5,000.

378.198 **GBR**
LLAIS. Text in English. 1974. m. free to students. adv. bk.rev.
Formerly: C A S A

Published by: South East Wales Students Association, Joint Students Union, Park Pl, Cardiff, United Kingdom. Circ: 8,000.

378 **USA**
LOGOS (MASON CITY). Text in English. 1968. m. reprints avail.
Published by: North Iowa Area Community College, 500 College Dr, Mason City, IA 50401. TEL 515-421-4304. Ed. Melinda Bass. Circ: 2,000.

378 **USA**
LOGOS (SAN ANTONIO). Text in English. 1932. bi-m. USD 5; free to students. adv. bk.rev. reprints avail. **Document type:** *Newspaper.*
Published by: University of the Incarnate Word, 4301 Broadway, San Antonio, TX 78209. TEL 210-829-3964, thelogos@universe.uiwtx.edu. Ed. Jennifer Walsh. Adv. contact Scarlett Flinn. B&W page USD 500; trim 14 x 10. Circ: 3,000.

LONDON COLLEGE OF MUSIC MAGAZINE. see *MUSIC*

378.1 307.1 **GBR**
LONDON SCHOOL OF ECONOMICS AND POLITICAL SCIENCE. REGIONAL AND URBAN PLANNING STUDIES. NEWSLETTER. Text in English. q. **Document type:** *Newsletter.* **Description:** Contains news of LSE's urban planning graduates.
Published by: London School of Economics and Political Science, Regional and Urban Planning Studies, Houghton St, London, WC2A 2AE, United Kingdom. http://www.lse.ac.uk/.

378 **GBR**
LONDON STUDENT. Text in English. 1952. fortn. free. adv. bk.rev.; film rev.; play rev. back issues avail. **Document type:** *Newsletter.*
Published by: University of London Union, Malet St, London, WC1E 7HY, United Kingdom. TEL 0171-580-7369, FAX 0171-436-4604. Ed. Liz Llewellyn. Circ: 12,000.

378.198 **USA** **ISSN 1073-0249**
LONGVIEW CURRENT. Text in English. 1969. every 3 wks. free. adv. bk.rev.; film rev. **Document type:** *Newspaper.* **Description:** Prints news, features, and announcements pertaining to this Kansas City suburban community college.
Published by: Longview Community College, 500 Longview Rd., Lee's Summit, MO 64081. TEL 816-672-2303, FAX 816-672-2078, current@longview.cc.mo.us. Eds. Andrea Jomerson, Leslie Culbertson. Adv. contact Angie Richman. Circ: 2,000.

378.198 **USA**
THE LOOKOUT (LANSING). Text in English. 1959. fortn. free (effective 2000). adv. bk.rev.; film rev.; music rev.; play rev. charts; illus. 16 p./no.; back issues avail. **Document type:** *Newspaper.*
Published by: Lookout (Lansing), Lansing Community College, Student Personnel Bldg, Rm 208, 430 N Capitol Ave, Lansing, MI 48901. TEL 517-483-1290, 517-483-1295, FAX 517-483-1629. Ed. Erin Anter. Pub., R&P Bill Loewenstein TEL 517-483-1291. Adv. contact Christina Bennett. B&W page USD 562. Circ: 5,000.

LOS ANGELES COLLEGE OF CHIROPRACTIC. NEWS & ALUMNI REPORT. see *MEDICAL SCIENCES—Chiropractic, Homeopathy, Osteopathy*

378 **USA** **ISSN 1540-3246**
LOS ANGELES LOYOLAN. Text in English. 1923. w. USD 25. adv. bk.rev.; film rev.; play rev. back issues avail.
Related titles: Online - full text ed.: ISSN 1541-860X.
Published by: Loyola Marymount University, 7101 W 80th St, Los Angeles, CA 90045. TEL 213-338-2879, FAX 213-338-190. Ed. Beverly Butler. Circ: 3,500.

378.1 **GBR**
LOUGHBOROUGH STUDENTS' UNION. NEWSPAPER. Text in English. 1963. 34/yr. bk.rev.; film rev.; play rev. illus. **Document type:** *Newspaper.* **Description:** Reports news of interest to students.
Former titles: Loughborough University. Newspaper; Fast Forward (0950-5059); Loughborough Student; Venture (0042-3548)
Published by: Loughborough Students' Union, Union Bldg, Loughborough Students Union, Ashby Rd, Loughborough, Leics LE11 3TT, United Kingdom. TEL 44-1509-217766, FAX 44-1509-235593, lsu.news@lboro.ac.uk. Ed. Claire Tomlinson. R&P Emily Dubberley. adv.: page GBP 309; 206 x 283. Circ: 3,000.

378.198 **USA** **ISSN 1054-7614**
➤ **LOYOLA.** Text in English. 1971. q. free to alumni. bk.rev. back issues avail. **Document type:** *Journal, Academic/Scholarly.* **Description:** Presents news and features of interest to Loyola University alumni and benefactors.
Formerly: Loyola Today
Published by: Loyola University Chicago, 820 N Michigan Ave, Ste 1514, Chicago, IL 60611. TEL 312-915-7250, FAX 312-915-6185, luc-alum@luc.edu, sfink@luc.edu, http://www.luc.edu/loyolamagazine/index.shtml. Ed. Gail Mansfield. Circ: 110,000 (controlled and free).

378.198 610 USA
LOYOLA MEDICINE. Text in English. 1986. s-a. free. back issues avail. **Document type:** *Academic/Scholarly.*
Formerly: Stritch M.D. (1054-7649)
Published by: Loyola University, Stritch School of Medicine, 2160 S First Ave, Maywood, IL 60153. TEL 708-216-6700, FAX 708-216-8199, http://www.lumc.edu. Circ: 5,500 (controlled).
Co-sponsor: Loyola University Medical Center.

378 USA
LUMBERJACK. Text in English. 1929. w. USD 14 (effective 2000). adv. **Document type:** *Newspaper, Consumer.*
Related titles: Microfilm ed.: (from LIB).
Published by: Humboldt State University, Nelson Hall East 6, Arcata, CA 95521. TEL 707-826-3259, FAX 707-826-5921. Ed. Jessica LeGrue. R&P Jerry Reynolds. Adv. contact Pam Yagotin. Circ: 6,500.

378.1 AUS ISSN 1320-0747
LUMEN. Text in English. 1952. s-a. free. adv. bk.rev. stat. **Document type:** *Academic/Scholarly.*
Former titles: University of Adelaide. Graduates Union. Monthly Newsletter and Gazette (0001-8163); Adelaide University Graduates's Union. Gazette
Published by: University of Adelaide, Media, Marketing & Publications Unit, Rm G07, Mitchell Bldg, Adelaide, SA 5005, Australia. TEL 61-8-8303-5174, FAX 61-8-8303-4838, john.edge@adelaide.edu.au, http://www.adelaide.edu.au/PR/home.html. Ed., R&P John Edge. adv.: B&W page AUD 500, color page AUD 900. Circ: 8,500.

378 CAN
L'UNITE✶. Text in French. 1975. s-m. adv. bk.rev.; film rev.; play rev. back issues avail.
Published by: (Universite du Quebec a Montreal), Publi-Peq, 3575 bd St Laurent, Ste 232, Montreal, PQ H2X 2T7, Canada. Circ: 10,000.

378.198 USA
LUTHER ALUMNI MAGAZINE. Text in English. 1964. 3/yr. free to qualified personnel. **Document type:** *Newsletter.* **Description:** For alumni and friends of the college. Contains college news, alumni news, and feature articles.
Former titles (until 1997): Luther Alumni Quarterly; (until 1991): Luther; Luther Magazine
Published by: Luther College, Office of Publications, 700 College Dr, Decorah, IA 52101-1045. TEL 319-387-1350, FAX 319-387-1075, magazine@luther.edu, http://www.luther.edu. Ed., R&P Greg Vanney. Circ: 31,000.

378.198 USA
THE M C C CONNECTION. Text in English. 1930. q. free. bk.rev. **Document type:** *Newsletter.* **Description:** Informational newsletter for constituents of the Manhattan Christian College.
Formerly: M C C News
Published by: Manhattan Christian College, c/o Jolene Rupe, 1415 Anderson, Manhattan, KS 66502-4081. TEL 785-539-3571, FAX 785-539-0832, http://www.mccks.edu/. Ed. Jolene Rupe. Circ: 10,000 (controlled).

378.198 USA
M C C POST. Text in English. 1928. fortn. adv. bk.rev. back issues avail. **Document type:** *Newspaper.*
Published by: Mott Community College, 1401 E Court St, Flint, MI 48502-2392. TEL 313-239-8224. Adv. contact Ben Kratz. Circ: 4,000.

371.8 USA
M C W ALUMNI NEWS. Text in English. 1980. 3/yr. free to alumni. **Document type:** *Magazine, Consumer.*
Published by: Medical College of Wisconsin, 8701 Watertown Plank Rd, Milwaukee, WI 53226-4801. TEL 414-456-4700, FAX 414-456-6166, alumni@mcw.edu, jpodolsk@mail.mcw.edu, http://www.mcw.edu/alumni. Ed. Jeremy Podolski. Circ: 11,200 (paid and controlled).

378 610 DEU
M H H - INFO. Text in German. 1972. m. bk.rev. **Document type:** *Newsletter.*
Published by: Medizinische Hochschule Hannover, Carl-Neuberg-Str 1, Hannover, 30625, Germany. TEL 49-511-532-6771, FAX 49-511-532-3852, TELEX 0922044-MEDHO-D. Circ: 2,600.

378.198 USA
M S M C HAPPENINGS. Text in English. 1972. q. free. bk.rev. 16 p./no.; **Document type:** *Newsletter.*
Formerly: Alumni Happenings
Published by: Mount Saint Mary College, 330 Powell Ave, Newburgh, NY 12550. TEL 845-561-0800, FAX 845-562-6762, coyne@msmc.edu, http://www.msmc.edu. Ed. Brendan G Coyne. Circ: 10,000.

378.1 USA ISSN 0273-6977
M S U ALUMNI MAGAZINE. (Michigan State University) Text in English. 1896. q. USD 35 (effective 1999). adv. bk.rev. back issues avail. **Document type:** *Academic/Scholarly.*
Formerly: Michigan State University Alumni Magazine (0026-2463)
Related titles: Online - full text ed.
Published by: Michigan State University, Alumni Association, Rm 108, Student Union, E, Lansing, MI 48824-1029. TEL 517-355-8314, FAX 517-355-5265. Ed., R&P Robert Bao TEL 517-432-1889. Adv. contact Sara Stid. B&W page USD 1,200. Circ: 35,000 (controlled).

HA-MAAPIL. see *POLITICAL SCIENCE*

378 USA
MACALESTER TODAY. Text in English. 1971. q. free. bk.rev.
Formerly: Mac Today
Published by: Macalester College, 1600 Grand Ave, St. Paul, MN 55105. TEL 612-696-6203, FAX 612-696-6192. Ed. Nancy A Peterson. Circ: 25,000.

378 CAN ISSN 0823-1672
MACEWAN JOURNALIST. Text in English. 1973. bi-m. free. adv. **Document type:** *Newspaper.*
Formerly: MacEwan Journal (0229-3439)
Published by: Grant MacEwan Community College, City Centre Campus, 10700 104 Ave, Edmonton, AB T5J 4S2, Canada. TEL 780-497-5644, brittainj@admin.gmec.ab.ca. Ed., Adv. contact Margaret Huff. Pub., R&P John Brittain. B&W page CND 600; trim 15.5 x 10.38. Circ: 1,800.

371.600 DEU ISSN 1433-7843
MAGAZIN DER FACHHOCHSCHULE KARLSRUHE HOCHSCHULE FUER TECHNIK. Text in German. 1980. 2/yr. adv. **Document type:** *Magazine, Academic/Scholarly.* **Description:** Provides information and articles of interest on activities and research related to the application of technology to industrial needs.
Published by: Rektor der Fachhochschule Karlsruhe Hochschule fuer Technik, Moltkestr 30, Karlsruhe, 76133, Germany. TEL 49-721-9251001, FAX 49-721-9251005, http://www.fh-karlsruhe.de/fh/magazin. Ed. Ralph Werner. Adv. contact Ute del Amo TEL 49-721-9251056. Circ: 6,000 (controlled and free).

371.85 USA
THE MAGAZINE OF SIGMA CHI. Text in English. 1881. 4/yr. USD 25 to members (effective 2005). **Document type:** *Magazine, Consumer.*
Published by: Sigma Chi International Fraternity, 1714 Hinman Ave, Evanston, IL 60201. TEL 847-869-3655, FAX 847-869-4906, headquarters@sigmachi.org, http://www.sigmachi.org. Adv. contact Sarah Penager. Circ: 55,000 (paid).

371.198 USA
MAINESTREAM. Text in English. 1975. w. adv. bk.rev.; film rev.; play rev. illus. back issues avail. **Document type:** *Newspaper.*
Related titles: Diskette ed.
Published by: University of Maine, 5 South St, Farmington, ME 04938. TEL 207-778-7330. Ed., R&P Dan Ryder. Adv. contact Kerri Butler. Circ: 2,000.

378 USA
THE MANEATER NEWSPAPER. Text in English. 1955. s-w. (Tue. & Fri.). free; USD 60 (effective 2005). adv. **Document type:** *Newspaper.* **Description:** Contains news of the university campus.
Published by: University of Missouri at Columbia, Student Publications Board, 214 Brady Commons, Columbia, MO 65211. TEL 573-882-5500, FAX 573-882-5550, maneater@themaneater.com, http://www.themaneater.com. Ed. Tim Elfrink. adv.: col. inch USD 6. Circ: 12,000 (paid and free). **Dist. by:** The Columbia Tribune, 101 N 4th St, Columbia, MO 65201. TEL 573-815-1500, FAX 573-815-1601.

378 USA
MANHATTAN. Text in English. 1974. q. free to qualified personnel. illus. back issues avail. **Document type:** *Newsletter.* **Description:** Publishes institutional news and alumni features.
Published by: (Office of College Relations), Manhattan College, Manhattan College Parkway, Riverdale, NY 10471. TEL 718-862-7235, FAX 718-862-8012, http://www.manhattan.edu. Ed. Darcy A Lis. Circ: 40,000.

378.1 CAN ISSN 0025-2298
MANITOBAN. Text in English. 1913. w. CND 40 domestic; CND 50 foreign (effective 2002). adv. bk.rev.; film rev.; music rev.; play rev. illus.; stat. 24 p./no.; **Document type:** *Newspaper, Consumer.* **Description:** Includes news, sports, editorial opinions and letters.
Related titles: Microform ed.: (from MML).
Published by: Manitoban Newspaper Publications Corporation, 105 University Centre, University of Manitoba, Winnipeg, MB R3T 2N2, Canada. TEL 204-474-6535, FAX 204-474-7651, toban@cc.umanitoba.ca, http://www.umanitoba.ca/manitoban. Ed. David Leibl. Adv. contact Rob Aoki. Circ: 10,000 (controlled).

378 DEU ISSN 0935-3348
MANNHEIMER UNIVERSITAETS-REDEN. Text in German. 1988. irreg. **Document type:** *Monographic series, Academic/Scholarly.*
Published by: Universitaet Mannheim, Schloss, Mannheim, 68131, Germany. TEL 49-621-1811013, FAX 49-621-1811014, presse@rektorat.uni-mannheim.de, http://www.uni-mannheim.de.

378.1 USA ISSN 0025-2867
MARCOLIAN. Text in English. 1874. w. (during school yr.). USD 30. adv. bk.rev. **Document type:** *Newspaper.*
Related titles: Online - full text ed.: (from LexisNexis).
Published by: Marietta College, PO Box A 20, Marietta, OH 45750-4000. TEL 614-376-4937, FAX 614-376-4810. Ed. Melissa Kenreigh. Adv. contact Jeff Border. B&W page USD 360; trim 21.5 x 13. Circ: 4,000.

378 USA ISSN 0889-2016
MAROON TIGER. Text in English. 1898. every 3 wks. USD 10 (effective 2000). adv. bk.rev.; film rev.; play rev. back issues avail. **Document type:** *Newspaper.*
Related titles: Online - full text ed.
Published by: Morehouse College, 830 Westview Dr., S.W., Atlanta, GA 30314. TEL 404-215-2681. Eds. Obinna Lewis, Jonathan Howard. R&P Steven Baker TEL 404-614-6041. Adv. contacts Brian Carter, Curtis Brown. B&W page USD 338. Circ: 2,500.

378.1 USA ISSN 0025-3995
MARQUETTE TRIBUNE. Text in English. 1917. s-w. (Tue. & Thu.). USD 50 (effective 2005). adv. **Document type:** *Newspaper.*
Related titles: Online - full text ed.: (from LexisNexis).
Published by: Marquette University, Sensenbrenner Hall, 1103 W Wisconsin Ave, Milwaukee, WI 53233. TEL 414-288-7090, FAX 414-288-1979, http://www.marquettetribune.org. Ed. Jen Haberkorn. Circ: 7,500 (controlled). Wire service: AP.

378 CAN
MARTLET. Text in English. 1946. w. (Sep.-Apr.). CND 25, USD 20. adv. bk.rev.; film rev.; play rev. **Document type:** *Newspaper.*
Published by: Martlet Publishing Society, P O Box 3035, Victoria, BC V8W 3P3, Canada. TEL 250-721-8360, FAX 250-472-4556, martlet@uvic.ca, http://kafka.uvic.ca/~martlet. Ed. Keith Woodley. R&P Keith Powell. Adv. contact Todd Orchard. Circ: 10,000 (controlled).

MASSACHUSETTS COLLEGE OF PHARMACY. BULLETIN. see *PHARMACY AND PHARMACOLOGY*

378.1 USA ISSN 0890-0434
THE MASSACHUSETTS DAILY COLLEGIAN. Text in English. 1890. d. (Mon.-Fri.). USD 115; free on campus (effective 2005). adv. **Document type:** *Newspaper, Consumer.*
Formerly: Daily Collegian (0025-4797)
Related titles: Microfilm ed.; Online - full text ed.: (from LexisNexis).
Published by: University of Massachusetts, 113 Campus Ctr, Amherst, MA 01003. TEL 413-545-3500, FAX 413-545-3699, news@dailycollegian.com, http://www.dailycollegian.com. adv.: col. inch USD 9.50. Circ: 15,000 morning (free). Wire service: AP.

378 ITA ISSN 0391-772X
IL MASSIMO. Text in Italian. 1924. bi-m. free.
Published by: Istituto Massimiliano Massimo, Via Massimiliano Massimo, 7, Rome, RM 00144, Italy. TEL 06 592 5656, FAX 06-5914556.

378.1 GBR
MASSIVE (LONDON). Text in English. 1947. 6/yr. free. adv. bk.rev.; film rev.; music rev.; play rev. illus. 32 p./no.; **Document type:** *Magazine, Internal.* **Description:** Publication of the Student Union. Includes relevant political and social issues, social and sporting events, art reviews and more from a student point of view.
Former titles: Cityscape; (until 1988): Beacon (0005-7320)
Published by: City University Union Society, Northampton Sq, London, EC1V 0HB, United Kingdom. TEL 44-20-7505-5600, 44-20-7505-5601, massive@city.ac.uk, president@city.ac.uk, http://www.massiveonline.org, http://cusuonline.org. Ed., R&P, Adv. contact Fearghal Corbett. Circ: 3,000.

378.1 ZAF ISSN 0025-5947
MATIELAND. Text in English. 1957. 3/yr. free. adv. illus.
Published by: Universiteit Stellenbosch/Stellenbosch University, Stellenbosch, 7600, South Africa. Circ: 29,000.

378 CAN ISSN 1192-4608
MCGILL DAILY. Text in English. 1911. 3/w. adv. bk.rev.; film rev. **Document type:** *Newspaper.*
Related titles: French ed.: ISSN 1192-4616.
Published by: Daily Publications Society, 3480 McTavish, Montreal, PQ H3A 1X9, Canada. TEL 514-398-6784, FAX 514-398-8318, daily@ssmu.mcgill.ca, daily@generation.net, http://www.mcgilldaily.ca, http://www.generation.net/~daily/. R&P Marian A Schrier. Adv. contact Boris Shedov. B&W page CND 1,100. Circ: 11,000.

378.1 CAN ISSN 0024-9068
LH3.M2
MCGILL NEWS. Text in English. 1919. q. adv. bk.rev. charts; illus. —CCC.
Published by: McGill Alumni Association, Rabinovitch House, 3640 Mountain St, Montreal, PQ H3G 2A8, Canada. TEL 514-398-3549, FAX 514-398-7338, news.alumni@mcgill.ca, http://www.mcgill.ca/news/masthead. Ed., R&P Diana Grier Ayton. Adv. contact Donna Henchey. B&W page CND 2,000; trim 9.13 x 7. Circ: 70,000.

C

▼ *new title* ➤ *refereed* ✶ *unverified* ♦ *full entry avail.*

378   CAN   ISSN 0848-8436
MCGILL REPORTER. Text in English. 1965. bi-w. USD 25. adv. bk.rev. **Document type:** *Newspaper.*
Former titles (until 1989): Reporter (0834-0773); (until 1984): McGill Reporter (0580-8537); (until 1968): McGill University Reporter (0541-6213)
Related titles: Online - full text ed.: (from LexisNexis).
Published by: McGill University, University Relations Office, Rm 110, Burnside Hall, 805 Sherbrooke St W, Montreal, PQ H3A 2K6, Canada. TEL 514-398-6751, FAX 514-398-7364, http://www.mcgill.ca/Reporter. Ed., R&P Daniel McCabe. Adv. contact Leslie Stojsic. Circ: 11,000.

378   CAN   ISSN 0843-0217
MCGILL UNIVERSITY GRADUATE SCHOOL OF LIBRARY AND INFORMATION STUDIES NEWSLETTER. Text in English. 1981. a. only for Alumni. **Document type:** *Newsletter.* **Description:** Gives up-to-date information about the school and attempts to locate "lost" alumni.
Formerly (until 1985): McGill University Graduate School of Library Science Newsletter (0715-481X)
Published by: McGill University, Graduate School of Library and Information Studies, 3459 McTavish St, Montreal, PQ H3A 1Y1, Canada. TEL 514-398-4204, FAX 514-398-7193. Circ: 1,800 (controlled).

610   USA
MEDICINE ON THE MIDWAY. Variant title: University of Chicago. Biological Sciences Division. Pritzker School of Medicine. Alumni Association. Magazine. Text in English. 1944. 3/yr. free (effective 2003). 44 p./no.; **Document type:** *Magazine, Academic/Scholarly.* **Description:** Covers news of graduates and their achievements, and updates alumni and alumnae of events of interest at the University of Chicago Hospital and University of Chicago Biological Sciences Division.
Formerly: University of Chicago. Pritzker School of Medicine. Alumni Association. Bulletin (0009-3734)
Related titles: Online - full content ed.
Published by: University of Chicago Hospitals, Office of Public Affairs, 5841 S Maryland Ave, Mail Code 6063, Chicago, IL 60637. TEL 773-702-6241, FAX 773-702-3171, momedit@uchospitals.edu, http://www.uchospitals.edu/midway. Ed., R&P Catherine Gianaro. Circ: 17,000 (controlled).

378.198   USA
THE MEDIUM (NEW BRUNSWICK); the weekly entertainment paper. Text in English. 197?. w. USD 5. adv. bk.rev.; film rev.; play rev. **Document type:** *Newspaper.* **Description:** Weekly news, features, announcements, and personals for Rutgers University and the campus of Livingston College.
Published by: Rutgers University, Livingston College, 54 Joyce Kilmer Ave, Piscataway, NJ 08855. TEL 732-932-4721. Circ: 10,000.

378   CAN   ISSN 0841-2731
MEDIUM II∗. Text in English. 1974. w. free. adv. bk.rev.; film rev.
Published by: (Erindale College), Campus Network, 315 Avenue Rd, Ste 8, Toronto, ON M4V 2H2, Canada. TEL 416-924-2502. Ed. Norman B Sanders. Circ: 7,000.

378.1   USA   ISSN 0025-8687
MEGAPHONE (CANTON). Text in English. 1919. fortn. USD 15 (effective 1998). adv. dance rev.; play rev.; film rev.; music rev.; rec.rev.; Website rev. illus. 20 p./no. 4 cols./p.; back issues avail. **Document type:** *Newspaper.*
Published by: Culver-Stockton College, Attn: Steve Wiegenstein, Canton, MO 63435. TEL 217-231-6380, FAX 217-231-6611, megaphone@culver.edu. Ed. Jennifer Tate. R&P Steve Wiegenstein TEL 217-231-6371. Adv. contact Christy Rentfro TEL 217-231-6380. Circ: 1,000 (controlled).

378.1   USA   ISSN 0025-8709
MEGAPHONE (GEORGETOWN). Text in English. 1906. w. adv. illus. **Document type:** *Newspaper.*
Published by: Southwestern University, Student Publications, PO Box 6048, S U Sta, Georgetown, TX 78626. TEL 512-863-1345, FAX 512-863-5788. Circ: 1,300.

178   AUS   ISSN 1442-1348
MELBOURNE UNIVERSITY MAGAZINE. Text in English. 1945. a. (s-a. until 2000), latest 2001. free. adv. bk.rev. illus. 36 p./no.; back issues avail. **Document type:** *Newsletter, Academic/Scholarly.* **Description:** Includes news items and articles on current issues relating to the University of Melbourne and reports on alumni activities and news - nationally and internationally.
Formerly (until 1999): University of Melbourne. Gazette (0085-3275)
Related titles: Online - full content ed.
Published by: University of Melbourne, Development Office, Communcations, Parkville, VIC 3052, Australia. TEL 61-3-9344-7469, FAX 61-3-9344-6895, MUM@development.unimelb.edu.au, gdscholz@unimelb.edu.au, http://www.unimelb.edu.au/alumni/mum/index.html. Ed., R&P Gerlinde Scholz. Circ: 120,000.

378   CAN
MELIORIST. Text in English. 1967. w. CND 12. adv. bk.rev.; film rev.

Published by: Meliorist Publishing Society, University of Lethbridge, Rm SU 166, 4401 University Dr, Lethbridge, AB T1K 3M4, Canada. TEL 403-329-2334, FAX 403-329-2224. Ed. Rose Herbut. Pub. Times Taber. Circ: 3,000.

378.18   CAN   ISSN 0228-8877
MEMORIAL UNIVERSITY OF NEWFOUNDLAND. GAZETTE. Text in English. 1968. fortn. adv. **Document type:** *Newspaper, Consumer.*
Published by: Memorial University of Newfoundland, Division of University Relations, Arts & Administration Bldg, Rm A-1024, St. John's, NF A1C 5S7, Canada. TEL 709-737-8663, FAX 709-737-8699, gazette@mun.ca, gazette@kean.ucs.mun.ca, http://www.mun.ca/univrel/gazette/. Ed. Pamela Frampton. R&P Peter Morris TEL 709-737-8665. Circ: 8,000.

378   DEU
MENSA SPEZIAL. Text in German. 1986. 12/yr. adv. **Document type:** *Bulletin, Academic/Scholarly.*
Former titles: Mensa Spezial - Sozial Info; Sozial Info
Published by: Studentenwerk Goettingen, Platz der Goettinger Sieben 4, Goettingen, 37073, Germany. TEL 49-551-390, FAX 49-551-395186, geschaeftsfuehrung@studentenwerk-goettingen.de, http://www.studentenwerk-goettingen.de. Ed. Christa Mirwald. Circ: 10,000.

378.1   USA   ISSN 0025-9853
MERCER CLUSTER. Text in English. 1920. w. free. adv. bk.rev.; film rev.; play rev. illus. **Document type:** *Newspaper.*
Published by: Judd Publishing, 1400 Coleman Ave, Box 72728, Macon, GA 31207. TEL 912-745-6811. Eds. Jaime Helmer, Jonathan Linneman. Adv. contact Brett Greenberg. Circ: 2,000.

378.002   GBR
MERCHISTONIAN. Text in English. 1866. a. adv. play rev. back issues avail. **Description:** School magazine available to pupils, former pupils and others associated with the school.
Indexed: NutrAb.
Published by: Merchiston Castle School, Merchiston Castle School, Colinton Rd, Edinburgh, EH13 0PU, United Kingdom. TEL 44-131-3122200, FAX 44-131-4416060, http://www.mcsch.org.uk. Ed. D Turner. Circ: 4,000.

378   USA
MERCURY (GLENVILLE). Text in English. 1929. w. USD 10. adv. bk.rev. **Document type:** *Newspaper.*
Published by: Glenville State College, 200 High St, Box 207, Glenville, WV 26351. TEL 304-462-7361, FAX 304-462-4407. Ed. Annie McCourt. Adv. contact Roger Carpenter. Circ: 2,000.

378   USA
MESA LEGEND. Text in English. 1964. bi-w. free to qualified personnel. adv. **Document type:** *Newspaper.* **Description:** Informs and entertains students and staff.
Published by: Mesa Community College, 1833 W Southern Ave, Mesa, AZ 85202. TEL 602-461-7334, FAX 602-461-7804. Ed. Dale Sutton. R&P Lynn Milner TEL 602-461-7329. Adv. contact John Kearns. Circ: 15,000.

378.198   USA
THE METER. Text in English. 1950. bi-w. USD 20. adv. back issues avail. **Document type:** *Newspaper, Newspaper-distributed.* **Description:** Covers campus and community news and events.
Published by: Tennessee State University, PO Box 1246, 304 Kean Hall, Nashville, TN 37209-1500. TEL 615-963-5652, FAX 615-963-5051. Ed., R&P Mia D McNeil TEL 615-963-5560. Adv. contact Dorian Wynn. page USD 375; trim 12.5 x 10. Circ: 5,000.

378.198   USA
METHODIST COLLEGE TODAY. Text in English. 1960. q. back issues avail. **Document type:** *Bulletin.* **Description:** Contains news and features about the college and its alumni.
Published by: Methodist College, 5400 Ramsey St, Fayetteville, NC 28311. TEL 910-630-7043, FAX 910-630-7253. Ed., R&P William Billings. Circ: 16,000 (controlled).

378.198   USA
METROPOLITAN. Text in English. 1979. w. USD 66 (effective 2001). adv. bk.rev.; film rev. back issues avail.
Published by: Metropolitan State College, Student Publications, Campus Box 57, PO Box 173362, Denver, CO 80217-3362. TEL 303-556-8361, FAX 303-556-2596, http://www.mscd.edu. Ed. Shawn Weaver. Circ: 10,000.

378.1   USA   ISSN 1064-6442
MIAMI HURRICANE. Text in English. 1927. s-w. (Tue. & Fri.). free on campus; USD 30 subscr - mailed (effective 2005). adv. bk.rev. illus. **Document type:** *Newspaper.*
Published by: (University of Miami, Coral Gables Campus), Miami Hurricane, PO Box 248132, Miami, FL 33124. http://www.miami.edu. Circ: 388,913 (paid).

378   USA
THE MIAMI STUDENT. Text in English. 1826. 2/w. (Tue. & Fri.). free (effective 2005). **Document type:** *Newspaper, Consumer.*

Published by: Miami University, 17 MacMillan Hall, Oxford, OH 45056. TEL 513-529-2210, FAX 513-529-1893, themiamistudent@hotmail.com, http://www.mustudent.muohio.edu. Ed. Lean Rupp. Circ: 10,000 (free). Wire service: AP.

378   USA
MIAMIAN. Text in English. 1982. 3/yr. free.
Published by: Miami University Alumni Association, Murstein Alumni Center, 725 E Chestnut St, Oxford, OH 45056. TEL 513-529-5957, FAX 513-529-1466, Alumni@muohio.edu, http://www.miami.muohio.edu/University_Advancement/MUAA/miamian.cfm, http://www.miamialum.org/. Ed. Donna J Boen. Circ: 112,000.

378.1   USA   ISSN 0745-967X
THE MICHIGAN DAILY. Text in English. 1890. d. (Mon-Fri. academic year; w.: Mon. summer). USD 190 (effective 2005). bk.rev. **Document type:** *Newspaper.*
Related titles: Online - full text ed.: (from LexisNexis).
Published by: University of Michigan, Board for Student Publications, 420 Maynard St, Ann Arbor, MI 48109. TEL 734-764-0552, FAX 734-763-2459, business@michigandaily.com, http://michigandaily.com. Ed. Jason Z Pesick. Circ: 16,500. Wire service: AP, UPI.

371.8975   USA
THE MICHIGAN INDEPENDENT. Text in English. irreg. free to students. back issues avail. **Document type:** *Academic/Scholarly.* **Description:** Covers issues and news items relevent to the University of Michigan at Ann Arbor Community.
Published by: University of Michigan, Michigan Independent, 3909 Michigan Union, Ann Arbor, MI 48109. michind@umich.edu, http://www.umich.edu/~michind. Eds. Dorothy McGivney, Matt Schultz.

378   USA
MICHIGAN REVIEW; the campus affairs journal of the University of Michigan. Text in English. 1982. bi-w. USD 20. adv. bk.rev.; music rev. back issues avail. **Description:** Campus and local news coverage, editorials and opinion essays, sports coverage, interviews and informal opinion polls.
Published by: Michigan Review, Inc., 911 N University Ave, Ste 1, Ann Arbor, MI 48109-1265. TEL 313-662-1909, FAX 313-936-2505. Circ: 10,000.

378   USA
MICHIGAN TECH ALUMNUS. Text in English. q. USD 25. back issues avail. **Description:** General interest publication for alumni, students, faculty and friends of the university, heavily oriented towards engineering and science.
Published by: Michigan Technological University, Alumni Association, 1400 Townsend Dr, Houghton, MI 49931. TEL 906-487-3327, FAX 906-487-3056. Ed. Dean Woodbeck. Circ: 13,000.

378.198   USA
MICHIGAN TIMES. Text in English. 1971. bi-w. free to students. adv. film rev.; play rev. charts; illus. back issues avail. **Document type:** *Newspaper.*
Published by: University of Michigan-Flint, 381 U C E N, Flint, MI 48503-2186. TEL 313-762-3475, FAX 313-762-3687. Ed. David Neil. Adv. contact Keith Bearup. Circ: 3,500.

378.1   USA   ISSN 0041-9850
➤ **MICHIGAN TODAY.** Text in English. 1968. 3/yr. free. adv. bk.rev. illus. **Document type:** *Newsletter, Academic/Scholarly.*
Supersedes: Vital Margin.
Related titles: Online - full text ed.
—CCC.
Published by: University of Michigan, Office of University Relations, News and Information Services, 412 Maynard St, Ann Arbor, MI 48109-1399. TEL 734-764-0105, FAX 734-764-7084, johnwood@umich.edu, http://www.umich.edu/news/MT/04/Sum04/index.html?indexx, Office of University Relations, News and Information Services. Ed. John Woodford. Adv. contact Barbara Wilson. Circ: 388,000.

378   USA
MIDDLEBURY CAMPUS. Text in English. w. USD 45; USD 55 foreign.
Published by: Middlebury College, Drawer 30, Middlebury, VT 05753. Ed. Chris Morgan. Circ: 3,200.

378.1   USA   ISSN 0745-2454
MIDDLEBURY COLLEGE MAGAZINE. Text in English. 1926. q. free. bk.rev. illus.
Formerly: Middlebury College News Letter
Published by: Middlebury College, Wilson House, Middlebury, VT 05753. TEL 802-388-3711, FAX 802-388-6436. Ed. Tim Etchells. Circ: 33,000.

378   CAN
THE MIKE. Text in English. 1947. bi-w. CND 25. adv. bk.rev.; film rev. **Document type:** *Newspaper.*
Published by: Mike Publications Inc., 81 St Mary St, Toronto, ON M5S 1J4, Canada. TEL 416-926-7272, FAX 416-926-7276. Ed. Mark Slade. Adv. contact Grace McSorley. Circ: 5,000.

378.1 USA
MILLS WEEKLY. Text in English. 191?. w. USD 20. adv. bk.rev. illus.
Formerly: Mills Stream (0026-430X)
Published by: Mills College, Associated Students, 5000 MacArthur Blvd, P O Box 9974, Oakland, CA 94613. TEL 510-430-2246, FAX 510-430-3314. Ed. Colleen Almeida. Circ: 1,200.

378 USA
THE MINARET (TAMPA). Text in English. 1963. w. (Fri.). free on campus. **Document type:** *Newspaper.*
Published by: University of Tampa, PO Box 11F, Tampa, FL 33606. minaret@hotmail.com, http://www.utampa.edu. Circ: 2,000 (free).

378.1 USA ISSN 0164-9450
LD3342
MINNESOTA. Text in English. 1901. bi-m. USD 30 to members (effective 2000). adv. bk.rev. illus. **Document type:** *Consumer.*
Former titles (until 1978): Minnesota Alumni News (0162-5209); (until 1977): University of Minnesota Alumni News (0041-9869); Minnesota Alumni Weekly
Published by: University of Minnesota Alumni Association, 200 McNamora Alumni Center, 200 Oak St SE, Minneapolis, MN 55455-2040. TEL 612-624-2323, FAX 612-626-8167, umalumni@maroon.tc.umn.edu, http://www.wmumaa.umn.edu. Ed. Tom Garrison. R&P Shelly Fling. Adv. contact Michael Armel. Circ: 40,000 (paid).

378.1 USA
THE MINNESOTA DAILY. Text in English. 1900. d. (Mon.-Fri.). free on campus; USD 100 (effective 2005). **Document type:** *Newspaper, Consumer.*
Published by: Minnesota Daily Board of Directors, 2301 University Ave, S E, Minneapolis, MN 55414. TEL 612-627-4080, FAX 612-627-4159, letters@mndaily.com, http://www.mndaily.com. Ed. Britt Johnsen. Pub. Justin Scott. Circ: 40,000 morning (free). Wire service: AP.

378.1 USA
MINNESOTA STATE UNIVERSITY, MANKATO REPORTER. Text in English. 1888. s-w. USD 35; free to students (effective 2005). adv. bk.rev.; film rev.; play rev. illus.; stat. **Document type:** *Newspaper, Consumer.*
Former titles: Mankato State Reporter; Mankato State Independent; Mankato State Reporter; Minnesota State Daily Reporter (0025-231X)
Related titles: Online - full text ed.
Published by: Minnesota State University, 293 CSU, Mankato, MN 56001. TEL 507-389-1776, FAX 507-389-5812, reporternews@mnsu.edu, http://www.msureporter.com/, http://www.mnsu.edu/. Ed. Tanner Kent TEL 507-389-5454. Adv. contacts Cassie Tastad TEL 507-389-5451, Shelly Witthus TEL 507-389-5097. Circ: 7,500. Wire service: AP, UPI.

MINORITY TODAY. see *ETHNIC INTERESTS*

378.18 USA
MIRROR (SOMERSET). Text in English. 1966. s-m. membership. film rev.; rec.rev.
Published by: Somerset Community College, Communications Department, 808 Monticello Rd, Somerset, KY 42501. TEL 606-679-8501. Ed. Linda Stephens. Circ: 1,000.

378.1 USA
MIRROR NEWS. Text in English. 1967. bi-w. free. adv. bk.rev.; film rev.; play rev. charts; illus. **Document type:** *Newspaper.* **Description:** College news, local events, human interest, comics, puzzles, and college sports.
Formerly: Ford Estate (0015-6981)
Published by: Henry Ford Community College, Student Center, Rm C 4K, 5101 Evergreen, Dearborn, MI 48128. TEL 313-845-9639, FAX 313-845-9876, layout@mail.henrford.cc.mi.us. Ed., R&P, Adv. contact Maria Reyes. Circ: 3,000.

378.198 USA
MISCELLANY MAGAZINE. Text in English. 1983. s-a. adv.
Formerly: Black Swamp Magazine
Published by: Bowling Green State University, University Board of Student Publications, 204 West Hall, Bowling Green, OH 43403. TEL 419-372-2601, FAX 419-372-0202. Adv. contact Todd Wise. Circ: 5,000.

378 USA
LH1.M63
MIZZOU MAGAZINE. Text in English. 1912. q. free to members; USD 5 per issue to non-members (effective 2005). adv. **Document type:** *Magazine, Consumer.* **Description:** Covers happenings at the university. Includes articles on student life, teaching, research and educational issues.
Formerly (until 1995): Missouri Alumnus (0745-0583)
Published by: M U Alumni Association, 407 Donald W Reynolds Alumni and Visitor Center, Columbia, MO 65211. TEL 573-882-7357, FAX 573-882-7290, MIZZOU@missouri.edu, http://www.mizzou.com/magazine.htm. Ed., R&P Karen Worley. Adv. contact Scott Reeter. B&W page USD 3,050, color page USD 3,600. Circ: 170,000 (controlled).

378 USA
MODERATOR. Text in English. fortn. free. adv. **Document type:** *Newspaper.*
Published by: Mt. Marty College, 1105 W 8th St, Yankton, SD 57078. TEL 605-668-1543. Circ: 1,000 (controlled).

378.198 USA
MONARCH MESSENGER. Text in English. s-m. adv. bk.rev. **Document type:** *Newspaper.*
Former titles: Pride (Fayetteville); Small Talk
Published by: Methodist College, 5400 Ramsey St, Fayetteville, NC 28311. TEL 910-630-7292, FAX 910-630-7253. Eds. Chuck Heaton, Cindy Bridges. R&P, Adv. contact Jami Sheppard. Circ: 1,800.

371.805 USA ISSN 1088-2839
LB3621.65
MONITOR (ST. PAUL). Text in English. 1985. m. (11/yr.). free. adv. bk.rev. charts; illus. 12 p./no. 5 cols./p.; back issues avail. **Document type:** *Newspaper.*
Published by: Minnesota State University Student Association, Inc., 106 Como Ave., Saint Paul, MN 55103-1820. TEL 651-224-1518, FAX 651-224-9753, monitor@msusa.net, msusa@msusa.net, http://www.msusa.net/monitor. Ed., R&P Shannah B Moore. Adv. contact Nicole Farber. B&W page USD 796. Circ: 22,000.

378 USA
MONMOUTH MAGAZINE. Text in English. 1985. 3/yr. free. bk.rev. **Document type:** *Bulletin.*
Formerly: Scots Newse
Published by: Monmouth College, Office of College Relations, 700 E Broadway, Monmouth, IL 61462. TEL 309-457-2311, FAX 309-457-2310, alumni@monm.edu, http://www.monm.edu. Ed. Jeffrey D Rankin. Circ: 12,000.

371.8 362.1 USA
THE MONTAGE. Text in English. 1968. m. free. 28 p./no. 4 cols./p.
Published by: Essex Community College, Office of College Life, 7201 Rossville Blvd, Baltimore, MD 21237. TEL 410-780-6576, FAX 410-686-9503. Ed. Gwyneth B Howard. adv.: B&W page USD 280; trim 13 x 11. Circ: 3,500.

378 USA
MONTANA KAIMIN. Text in English. 1898. d. (Tue.-Fri.). free to students (effective 2005). **Document type:** *Newspaper, Consumer.*
Published by: University of Montana, Journalism Bldg, Rm 206, Missoula, MT 59812. TEL 406-243-6541, FAX 406-243-4303, editor@kaimin.org, http://www.kaimin.org. Circ: 6,000 morning (free). Wire service: AP.

378.1 USA
➤ **MONTANAN.** Text in English. 1969. 3/yr. free; USD 15 voluntary (effective 2003). adv. bk.rev. charts; illus. **Document type:** *Magazine, Academic/Scholarly.* **Description:** Aims to provide UM alumni, faculty, and students with educational and entertaining stories about UM faculty, alumni, students and events.
Former titles: University; Profiles; U M Profiles (0041-5200)
Indexed: CA&I.
Published by: University of Montana, University Relations, Missoula, MT 59812. TEL 406-243-2522, FAX 406-243-4520, joan.melcher@mso.umt.edu, http://www.umt.edu/comm/. Ed., R&P Joan Melcher TEL 406-243-4842. Pub. Rita Munzenrider. Adv. contact Lowell Hanson TEL 406-728-3951. B&W page USD 1,150, color page USD 1,450; bleed 7.5 x 10. Circ: 62,000.

378 USA
MONTPELIER; James Madison University magazine. Text in English. q. **Document type:** *Magazine, Academic/Scholarly.* **Description:** Contains articles and features for JMU faculty and staff members, alumni, parents of JMU students, donors, and friends of the university.
Published by: James Madison University, Division of University Relations and External Programs, 26 Medical Arts W., MSC 5718, Harrisonburg, VA 22807. TEL 540-568-3191, FAX 540-568-7520, montpelier@jmu.edu, http://www.jmu.edu/montpelier.

378 CAN ISSN 0838-9985
MONTREAL CAMPUS. Text in French. 1980. s-m. CND 24. adv. bk.rev. **Document type:** *Newspaper.*
Published by: Editions Montreal Camping Inc., Succ Centre Ville, C P 8888, Montreal, PQ H3C 3P8, Canada. TEL 514-987-7018, FAX 514-987-0391, mtl.campus@uqam.ca, http://www.unites.uqam.ca/~campus. Ed. Philippe Giroux. R&P, Adv. contact Remi Plourde. B&W page CND 1,200; trim 14 x 10. Circ: 18,000.

371.805 USA
THE MOORING MAST. Text in English. 1972. w. (11 each semester). free on campus; USD 25 subscr - mailed per academic year on campus (effective 2005). **Document type:** *Newspaper.*
Formerly: The Mast
Published by: Pacific Lutheran University, 122nd St S, Tacoma, WA 98447. TEL 253-535-7494, FAX 253-536-5076, mast@plu.edu, http://www.plu.edu/~mast. Ed. Laine Walters. Circ: 2,500 (paid and controlled).

378 USA ISSN 0886-8409
MORAVIAN (BETHLEHEM, 1912). Key Title: Moravian Alumni Quarterly. Text in English. 1912. 3/yr. free to qualified personnel. charts; illus. **Description:** Moravian College Alumni Magazine.
Published by: Moravian College, Alumni Association, 1200 Main St, Bethlehem, PA 18018. TEL 215-861-1366. Ed. Susan Overath Woolley. Circ: 17,500.

378.198 USA ISSN 0888-7780
MOSAIC (CLEVELAND). Text in English. w. free. adv. bk.rev. back issues avail.
Published by: Cuyahoga Community College (Western Campus), 2900 Community College Ave, Cleveland, OH 44115. TEL 216-987-4231. Ed. Erick Sanders. Circ: 3,500.

378 CAN
MOTADIT. Text in French. fortn. adv.
Published by: College d'Enseignement Generale et Professionnel (d'Ahuntsic), 9155 rue St Hubert, Montreal, PQ H2M 1Y8, Canada. Circ: 3,000.

378.1 CAN ISSN 0027-2485
MOUNT ALLISON RECORD. Text in English. 1916. 3/yr. CND 20; CND 7.50 newsstand/cover (effective 2000). adv. bk.rev. **Document type:** *Consumer.* **Description:** Publishes general interest stories about the Mount Allison commmunity and its constituents, including alumni.
Published by: Mount Allison University, Federated Alumni, 82 York Street, Sackville, NB E4L 1G2, Canada. TEL 506-364-2345, FAX 506-364-2262, cbourque@mta.ca, http://www.mta.ca. Ed., R&P, Adv. contact Carla Bourque. B&W page CND 1,000, color page CND 1,400; trim 10.75 x 8.5. Circ: 18,000.

378.1 305.4 USA ISSN 0027-2493
LH1
MOUNT HOLYOKE ALUMNAE QUARTERLY. Text in English. 1917. q. free to members. **Document type:** *Bulletin.* **Description:** To keep alumnae informed of each other, the college and issues of mutual concern.
Published by: Alumnae Association of Mount Holyoke College, Inc., 50 College St, South Hadley, MA 01075-1486. TEL 413-538-2251, FAX 413-538-2254, scray@mtholyoke.edu, http://www.alumnae.mtholyoke.edu. Ed., R&P Sabine H Cray. Circ: 30,100.

C

378.198 USA
MOUNT MAGAZINE; alumni magazine of the college of Mount St. Joseph. Text in English. 1939. 3/yr. free. **Document type:** *Magazine, Internal.* **Description:** Provides a college magazine for alumni, parents and friends of the institution.
Formerly (until 1985): Mountings
Published by: College of Mount St. Joseph, Office of Public Information, 5701 Delh Pike, Cincinnati, OH 45233. TEL 513-244-4723, FAX 513-244-4654, linda_liebau@mail.msj.edu, http://www.msj.edu. Ed., R&P Linda B Liebau. Circ: 11,000.

378 CAN ISSN 0826-2748
MOUTON NOIR✶. Text in French. 1978. m. free.
Published by: Publi-Peq, 3575 bd St Laurent, Ste 232, Montreal, PQ H2X 2T7, Canada. Circ: 1,400. **Co-sponsor:** College de Drummondville.

378 DEU ISSN 0940-0141
MUENCHNER UNI MAGAZIN; Zeitschrift der Ludwig-Maximilians-Universitaet Muenchen. Text in German. 1989. 5/yr. adv. **Document type:** *Magazine, Academic/Scholarly.*
Published by: Universitaet Muenchen, Geschwister-Scholl-Platz 1, Munich, 80539, Germany. TEL 49-89-21803664, FAX 49-89-338297, mum@verwaltung.uni-muenchen.de. Ed. Franziska Mueller-Haerlin. Adv. contact Gisela Zeeb. page EUR 1,500; trim 245 x 260. Circ: 11,000.

378 USA
MUHLENBERG MAGAZINE. Text in English. 1991. q. free to alumni. adv. illus. **Document type:** *Magazine, Academic/Scholarly.* **Description:** Covers college life, alumni news, and feature stories.
Formerly: Muhlenberg Door to Door
Published by: (Public Relations Office), Muhlenberg College, 2400 Chew St, Allentown, PA 18104-5586. TEL 484-664-3230, FAX 484-664-3230, bruckner@muhlenberg.edu, bergalum@muhlenberg.edu, http://www.muhlenberg.edu. Ed. Carla Kologie. R&P, Adv. contact Mike Bruckner. Circ: 25,000.

378 USA
MULESKINNER. Text in English. 1878. w. (Thu.). USD 20 (effective 2005). **Document type:** *Newspaper.*
Published by: Central Missouri State University, PO Box 800, Warrensburg, MO 64093. TEL 660-543-4050, FAX 660-543-8663, http://www.themuleskinner.com/. Circ: 6,000 (free). Wire service: AP.

378 COL ISSN 0120-3460
MUNDO UNIVERSITARIO. Text in Spanish. 1972. q.
Published by: Asociacion Colombiana de Universidades, Calle 93, No16-43, Bogota, Colombia. TEL 57-1-6231580, FAX 57-1-2185059, informa@ascun.org.co, http://www.ascun.org.co.

▼ new title ➤ refereed ✶ unverified ♦ full entry avail.

378 CAN ISSN 0820-5299
MUSE (ST. JOHN'S). Text in English. 1950. w. adv. bk.rev.; film rev. **Document type:** *Newspaper.* **Description:** Contains student related news, sports event, features and opinion.
Published by: Muse Board of Directors, Council of the Students' Union, Memorial University of Newfoundland, P O Box A-118, St. John's, NF A1C 5S7, Canada. TEL 709-737-8919, FAX 709-737-4743, muse@morgan.ucs.mun.ca, http://www.mun.ca/muse/muse.html. Ed., R&P Kelly Batstone. Adv. contact Sam Whiffen. Circ: 10,000.

378 USA
MUSTANG DAILY. Text in English. 1927. d. (Mon.-Fri.) (academic yr.). free domestic on campus; USD 50 subscr - mailed (effective 2005). **Document type:** *Newspaper.*
Related titles: Microfilm ed.: (from LIB).
Published by: California Polytechnic State University, 1 Grand Ave, San Luis Obispo, CA 93407. TEL 805-756-2508, FAX 805-756-6784, bizmanager@mustangdaily.net, http://www.mustangdaily.net. Circ: 6,000 morning (free). Wire service: AP.

378 USA
N I C SENTINEL. Text in English. 1940. bi-m. free. **Document type:** *Newspaper, Consumer.*
Published by: North Idaho College, 1000 W Garden, Coeur D Alene, ID 83814. TEL 208-769-3388, FAX 208-769-3431, sentinel@nic.edu, http://www.nic.edu/sentinel. Circ: 2,300 (free).

371.85 USA
N I F NOTES. Text in English. 1950. m. (Sep.-May). USD 8 (effective 2005). bk.rev. **Document type:** *Bulletin, Trade.* **Description:** Provides articles on national Greek-letter fraternities and sororities, professional fraternities, campus and student trends; calendar of related events.
Former titles (until 2005): Interfraternity Bulletin; Interfraternity Research and Advisory Council. Bulletin
Published by: North American Interfraternal Foundation, 10023 Cedar Point Dr, Carmel, IN 46032. TEL 317-848-7829, FAX 317-571-9686, headquarters@nif-inc.net, http://www.nif-inc.net. Ed. Terri L Nackid. Circ: 3,000.

378 USA ISSN 0277-9749
N Y U PHYSICIAN. Text in English. 1969 (vol.24). s-a. free. **Document type:** *Consumer.* **Description:** Alumni magazine focusing on education, patient care and research at the NYU School of Medicine.
Formerly (until 1980): New York University Medical Quarterly (0028-7903)
Published by: New York University School of Medicine, 550 First Ave, New York, NY 10016. FAX 212-263-8425. Ed. Peter L Ferrara. R&P Gail Buckley TEL 212-263-5488. Circ: 18,000 (controlled).

378.1 USA
N Y U TODAY. (New York University) Text in English. 1974. fortn. (Sep.-June). USD 12.
Former titles: New York University Report; Internal (0020-5737)
Published by: New York University, Public Affairs Department, 25 W Fourth St, New York, NY 10012. FAX 212-995-4021. Ed. Craig Smith. Circ: 15,000.

378.198 USA ISSN 1075-5004
NASSAU WEEKLY. Text in English. 1978. w. USD 30. **Document type:** *Newspaper.* **Description:** Student-produced news, opinion, humor and cultural analysis.
Published by: Nassau Inc., 317 Aaron Burr Hall, Princeton University, Princeton, NJ 08544. TEL 609-258-1899. Ed. Renee Kaplan. Pub. Steve Mercel. adv.: B&W page USD 200; trim 10 x 15. Circ: 8,000.

378 USA ISSN 0300-6646
NATIONAL ON-CAMPUS REPORT. Text in English. 1972. s-m. USD 169 domestic; USD 173 in Canada; USD 179 elsewhere (effective 2005). adv. bk.rev. **Document type:** *Newsletter.* **Description:** Articles and news about college students for student service professionals.
Related titles: Online - full text ed.: USD 169 (effective 2005) (from EBSCO Publishing, H.W. Wilson, O C L C Online Computer Library Center, Inc.).
Indexed: ABIn, EduInd.
—CCC.
Published by: Magna Publications, Inc., 2718 Dryden Dr, Madison, WI 53704. TEL 608-246-3590, FAX 608-246-3597, editor@magnapubs.com, http://www.magnapubs.com/pub/magnapubs_nocr. Ed. Terese Kattner. Pub. David Burns. Circ: 1,700.

378.1 USA
NEBRASKA. Text in English. 1913. q. USD 35. illus.
Formerly (until Jan. 1994): Nebraska Alumnus (0028-1794)
Related titles: Microfilm ed.
Published by: University of Nebraska at Lincoln, Alumni Association, 1520 R St, Lincoln, NE 68588-0216. TEL 402-472-2841, FAX 402-472-4635, acranfor@unlinfo.unl.edu, http://www.unl.edu/alumni. Ed. Andrea W Cranford. Circ: 23,000 (paid).

NEGRI NEWS. see *PHARMACY AND PHARMACOLOGY*

052 GBR
NERVE. Text in English. 1991. m. free. adv. bk.rev.; film rev.; play rev. illus.; stat. back issues avail. **Description:** Publishes news, features, student-related comedy, and music reviews of interest to students at Bournemouth University. Editorials are apolitical.
Published by: Bournemouth University, Students Union, Talbot Campus, Fern Barrow, Poole, Dorset BH1 5BB, United Kingdom. TEL 44-1202-5237555, FAX 44-1202-535990. Ed., Adv. contact Mike Gregory. page GBP 290. Circ: 3,000.

378.1 AUS ISSN 1036-4587
NEUCLEUS; U.N.E. student newspaper. Text in English. 1936. 8/yr. free. adv. bk.rev.; film rev.; play rev. abstr. index. **Document type:** *Newspaper.*
Related titles: ◆ Supplement(s): Kangaroo. ISSN 1036-3262.
Published by: University of New England, Armidale Students' Association, Armidale, NSW 2351, Australia. TEL 61-67-732851, FAX 61-67-727633. R&P Nigel Spence. Adv. contact Michael Epworth. Circ: 2,500.

378.1 USA ISSN 0028-6001
LH1
NEW JOURNAL. Text in English. 1967. 5/yr. (Sep.-Apr.). USD 18 (effective 2005). adv. bk.rev. illus. **Description:** Provides insight into the trends and changes in the Yale and New Haven communities.
Published by: New Journal at Yale, Inc., PO Box 203432, New Haven, CT 06520. TEL 203-432-1957, FAX 203-432-0519, tnj@yale.edu, http://www.yale.edu/tnj/aboutuscontent.htm. Circ: 10,000.

378 USA
NEW MEXICO DAILY LOBO. Text in English. 1895. d. (Mon.-Fri.). USD 35 (effective 2005). bk.rev.; film rev. **Document type:** *Newspaper.* **Description:** Daily newspaper for the University of New Mexico.
Related titles: Online - full text ed.
Published by: University of New Mexico, Student Publications Board, Marron Hall, Rm 131, Albuquerque, NM 87131-7061. TEL 505-277-5656, FAX 505-277-7530, lobonews@unm.edu, http://www.dailylobo.com. Ed. Arthur Simoni. Adv. contact Daven Quelle. Circ: 12,500 (controlled and free). Wire service: AP.

301 USA ISSN 0883-6248
NEW SCHOOL OBSERVER. Text in English. 1981. w. USD 20 to individuals; USD 45 to institutions; USD 12 to students (effective 2004). **Document type:** *Newsletter.* **Description:** Provides news and current information for the students, faculty, alumni and friends of the New School for Social Research, with campuses in New York and Paris.
Published by: New School University, 65 Fifth Ave, Rm 344, New York, NY 10003. TEL 212-229-5776, FAX 212-229-5476, observer@newschool.edu, http://www.newschool.edu/observer.

378.1 USA
NEW TECH TIMES. Text in English. m. free. adv. bk.rev.; film rev. **Document type:** *Newspaper.*
Formerly (until 1975): Arts and Sciences (0004-394X)
Indexed: MLA-IB.
Published by: New York City Technical College, 300 Jay St, Rm A310, Brooklyn, NY 11201. TEL 718-260-5453, FAX 718-260-5455. Ed. Fred Sahakian. Adv. contact Pat Gay. Circ: 8,000 (controlled).

378.1 CAN ISSN 0028-6907
NEW TRAIL. Text in English. 1942. 4/yr. CND 15 (effective 2000). adv. bk.rev. charts; illus. **Document type:** *Magazine.*
Published by: University of Alberta Alumni Association, University of Alberta, 6th Fl General Services Bldg, Edmonton, AB T6G 2H1, Canada. TEL 780-492-3224, FAX 780-492-1568. Ed., R&P Rick Pilger TEL 780-492-9534. Adv. contact Katherine Irwin. Circ: 101,500.

378 USA
NEW UNIVERSITY. Text in English. 1967. w. (Mon.). USD 38.75; free on campus (effective 2005). **Document type:** *Newspaper, Consumer.*
Related titles: Microfilm ed.: (from LIB); Online - full content ed.
Published by: University of California, Irvine, 3100 Gateway Commons, Irvine, CA 92697-4250. TEL 949-824-4286, FAX 949-824-4287, editor@newuniversity.org, http://www.newu.uci.edu/. Ed. Sona Patel. Adv. contact Carol Potter. Circ: 10,000 (free).

378.198 USA
NEW YORK LAW SCHOOL REPORTER. Text in English. 1969. m. adv. **Document type:** *Academic/Scholarly.*
Published by: New York Law School, 57 Worth St, New York, NY 10013-2960. ilj@nyls.edu. Circ: 27,000.

378.198 USA
NEWS FROM HOPE COLLEGE. Text in English. 1969. 6/yr. free. cum.index: 1969-2001. 16 p./no.; back issues avail. **Document type:** *Newspaper, Internal.* **Description:** News of interest to alumni and friends of Hope College.
Published by: Hope College, 141 E 12th St, Holland, MI 49423. TEL 616-395-7860, FAX 616-395-7991, newsfromhope@hope.edu. Ed. Thomas L Renner. R&P Tom Renner. Circ: 40,000 (controlled).

378 USA ISSN 0028-923X
NEWS, NOTES, AND QUOTES. Text in English. 1956. q. membership only. illus. **Document type:** *Newsletter, Internal.*
Related titles: Online - full content ed.
Published by: Phi Delta Kappa International, 408 N Union St, Bloomington, IN 47402-0789. TEL 812-339-1156, FAX 812-339-0018, http://www.pdkintl.org./whatis/newscurr.htm. Ed. Donovan Walling. R&P Terri Hampton TEL 812-339-1156. Circ: 85,000.

378 USA ISSN 0891-6063
NEWSBREAK (SAN FRANCISCO). Text in English. 1986. fortn. (exc. Jun.-Aug., Dec., m.). free. bk.rev. **Document type:** *Newsletter.*
Formerly: Today and Tomorrow
Published by: University of California at San Francisco, Department of Public Affairs, 3333 California St, Ste 103, San Francisco, CA 94143. TEL 415-476-3256, FAX 415-476-3541. Ed. Lisa Cisneros. Circ: 25,000 (paid).

378 620 790.1 USA ISSN 1093-0051
NEWSPEAK. Text in English. 1909. w. USD 20. adv. bk.rev.; film rev.; play rev. charts; illus.; stat. back issues avail. **Document type:** *Newspaper.*
Related titles: Online - full text ed.
Published by: (Worcester Polytechnic Institute), W P I Newspeak Association, c/o W P I Student Activities, 100 Institute Rd, Worcester, MA 01609. TEL 508-831-5464, FAX 508-831-5721, newspeak@wpi.edu, http://www.wpi.edu/~newspeak. Ed. Edward J Cameron Jr. Adv. contact Brandon Ngo. B&W page USD 304; 16 x 10.25. Circ: 2,000.

378 CAN
NEXUS (VICTORIA). Text in English. 1990. 16/yr. CND 18. adv. bk.rev.; film rev. **Document type:** *Newspaper.* **Description:** covers events and issues relevant to students at the college.
Published by: Nexus Publishing Society, Camosun College, 3100 Foul Bay Rd, Victoria, BC V8P 5J2, Canada. TEL 250-370-3591, FAX 250-370-3580. Ed. Barbara Risto. Circ: 4,000.

051 USA
THE NICHOLLS WORTH. Text in English. 1955. w. USD 12 (effective 2000). adv. bk.rev. 18 p./no. 5 cols./p.; **Document type:** *Newspaper.*
Published by: Nicholls State University, PO Box 2010, Thibodaux, LA 70310. TEL 504-448-4258, FAX 504-448-4267, nw@mail.nich.edu, nw@nich-nsunet.nich.edu, http://nich.edu. Ed. Jennifer Boquet. R&P Lesley Marcello. Adv. contact Jewel Bush. page USD 227.50.

378 USA
NICHOLS NEWS; newsletter for alumni, parents, and friends. Text in English. 1932. 4/yr. free. **Document type:** *Newsletter.* **Description:** Includes general news of activities and events at the College including alumni events and class notes.
Formerly: Nichols Alumnus (0300-6778)
Published by: Nichols College, PO Box 5000, Dudley, MA 01571. TEL 508-943-1560. Ed., R&P Brian Rossetti. Circ: 10,000 (controlled).

378 CAN ISSN 0845-8278
NOMAD. Text in English. 1967. fortn. (Sep.-Apr.). free to current students. adv. bk.rev.; film rev.; music rev. 16 p./no.; **Document type:** *Academic/Scholarly.* **Description:** Contains campus news, events, sports, area news and events of interest to students, and Web surfing info.
Published by: Student Association, St Lawrence College, Kingston, ON K7L 5A6, Canada. TEL 613-544-5532, FAX 613-544-1763. Ed. Chris Price. Circ: 1,000.

378 GBR ISSN 0964-4652
NONESUCH. Text in English. 1991. s-a. adv. bk.rev. back issues avail. **Document type:** *Bulletin, Academic/Scholarly.*
Published by: (Information Office), University of Bristol, Senate House, Tyndall Ave, Bristol, Avon BS8 1TH, United Kingdom. TEL 44-117-928-7777, FAX 44-117-929-2396, info.office@bristol.ac.uk. Ed. Sarah Whittingham. Adv. contact Joan Fryer. B&W page GBP 1,800, color page GBP 2,700. Circ: 57,000 (controlled).

378 DEU ISSN 0944-8446
NORDRHEIN-WESTFAELISCHE AKADEMIE DER WISSENSCHAFTEN. JAHRBUCH. Text in German. 1977. a. **Document type:** *Bulletin, Academic/Scholarly.*
Formerly (until 1994): Rheinisch-Westfaelische Akademie der Wissenschaften. Jahrbuch (0944-6834)
Published by: (Nordrhein-Westfaelische Akademie der Wissenschaften), V S - Verlag fuer Sozialwissenschaften (Subsidiary of: Springer Science+Business Media), Abraham-Lincoln-Str 46, Wiesbaden, 65189, Germany. TEL 49-611-78780, FAX 49-611-7878400, info@vs-verlag.de, http://www.vs-verlag.de.

378 GBR
NORTH CIRCULAR. Text in English. 1973. w. (during school yr.). free. adv. bk.rev. back issues avail. **Document type:** *Newspaper.*
Published by: Middlesex University, Bramley Rd, London, N14 4YZ, United Kingdom. FAX 44-181-362-6231. Ed. Michael Brown. Adv. contact Frank Jeffs. Circ: 5,000.

378 USA
NORTH TEXAS DAILY. Text in English. 1852. s-w. (Tue.-Fri. academic yr.; Tue. & Thu. summer). free. **Document type:** *Newspaper.*
Published by: University of North Texas, 117 GAB, Ave. B Mulberry, Denton, Denton, TX 76203. TEL 940-565-3575, FAX 940-565-4659, dailymail@ntdaily.com, http://www.ntdaily.com. Ed. Jeff Andrews. Circ: 11,700 morning (free). Wire service: AP.

378.1 USA
NORTH WIND. Text in English. 1899. w. USD 21; free on campus. bk.rev.; film rev.; play rev. **Document type:** *Newspaper.*
Formerly (until 1971): Northern News (0029-3202)
Related titles: Online - full text ed.: (from LexisNexis).
Indexed: MLA.
Published by: Northern Michigan University, 1401 Presque Isle Ave, Marquette, MI 49855. TEL 906-227-2545, FAX 906-227-2449. Circ: 6,000 (controlled).

378.1 USA ISSN 0029-3032
NORTHEASTERN NEWS. Text in English. 1921. w. USD 21. adv. bk.rev. illus.
Related titles: Online - full text ed.: (from LexisNexis).
Published by: Northeastern University, 360 Huntington Ave., 598 CP, Boston, MA 02115. TEL 617-437-2648, FAX 609-437-2649. Circ: 10,000.

378 USA ISSN 1069-3521
NORTHEASTERN UNIVERSITY MAGAZINE. Text in English. 1975. 5/yr. USD 25 (effective 2005). adv. bk.rev. **Document type:** *Magazine, Consumer.* **Description:** News and features of interest to alumni.
Formerly: Northeastern Alumni Magazine
Published by: (Office of University Relations), Northeastern University, 360 Huntington Ave., 598 CP, Boston, MA 02115. TEL 617-373-5444, 617-373-5724, FAX 617-373-5430, 617-373-2000, spiland@neu.edu, http://www.numag.neu.edu. Adv. contact Rickey Ezrin. B&W page USD 3,500, color page USD 5,250. Circ: 140,000 (controlled).

378 USA
NORTHERN IOWA TODAY. (Spring & Fall eds. in Tabloid formate; Summer & Winter eds. in magazine formate.) Text in English. 1915. s-a. free. **Description:** Covers issues and trends in higher education.
Formerly: Nonpareil
Published by: University of Northern Iowa, LO11 Mauker Union, Cedar Falls, IA 50614-0166. TEL 319-273-2311. Circ: 7,600.

378 USA
NORTHERN IOWAN. Text in English. 1874. s-w. (Tue. & Fri.). free on campus (effective 2005). adv. 20 p./no. 5 cols./p.; **Document type:** *Newspaper.*
Published by: University of Northern Iowa, LO11 Mauker Union, Cedar Falls, IA 50614-0166. TEL 319-273-2157, FAX 319-273-5931, northern-iowan@uni.edu, http://www.uni.edu/ni. adv.: col. inch USD 6.55. Circ: 9,000 (paid and free).

378 USA
NORTHERN NOW. Text in English. 1900. q. free. charts; illus.; stat. back issues avail. **Description:** Covers University news, faculty research, and higher education issues for alumni, parents, and friends.
Formerly: Alumni News
Published by: Northern Illinois University, Office of Public Affairs, Dekalb, IL 60115. TEL 815-753-1681, FAX 815-753-3299, nnow@niu.edu. Ed., R&P Elizabeth Elving Bass. Circ: 150,000.

378 USA
NORTHERN STAR (DEKALB). Text in English. 1899. d. (Mon.-Fri.). USD 92.50 1st semester; USD 180 2nd semester (effective 2005 - 2006). **Document type:** *Newspaper.*
Published by: Northern Illinois University, College of Business, Dekalb, IL 60115. TEL 815-753-0101, FAX 815-753-0708, editor@northernstar.info, http://www.northernstar.info. Ed. Derek Wright. Circ: 16,000 morning (paid and free). Wire service: KR, AP.

378 USA
NORTHWEST PHOENIX. Text in English. 1959. fortn. adv. bk.rev.; film rev.; software rev. back issues avail. **Document type:** *Newspaper.* **Description:** Deals with both campus and community issues.
Related titles: Online - full text ed.
Published by: Indiana University Northwest, 3400 Broadway, Moraine 110, Gary, IN 46408. TEL 219-980-6795, FAX 219-981-4233, phoenix@iunlabl.iun.indiana.edu. Ed., R&P Margaret Holland. Adv. contact Shelia Turner. Circ: 3,500.

378 USA
NORTHWESTERN MAGAZINE; for alumni and friends of Northwestern University. Text in English. 1988. q. free to alumni (effective 2005). adv. bk.rev. **Document type:** *Magazine, Consumer.* **Description:** Focuses on faculty research student life, university news and alumni who are outstanding in their field.
Formerly (until 1999): Northwestern Perspective (0897-7488)
Published by: Northwestern University, Department of University Relations, 1800 Sheridan Rd, Evanston, IL 60208-1800. TEL 847-491-5000, FAX 847-491-3040, letters@northwestern.edu, http://www.northwestern.edu/magazine. Ed., R&P Stephanie Russell TEL 847-491-4891. Pub. Alan Cubbage. Adv. contact Nancy Isaacson. B&W page USD 3,000, color page USD 4,000; trim 10.88 x 9. Circ: 169,000 (controlled).

378 USA
NORWICH GUIDON. Text in English. 1921. s-m. free. adv.
Formerly: Guidon
Published by: Norwich University, Communications Bldg, Northfield, VT 05663. TEL 802-485-2438, FAX 802-485-2580.

378.1 USA ISSN 0161-987X
NOTRE DAME MAGAZINE. Text in English. 1923. q. USD 20 to non-alumni (effective 2004). bk.rev.; music rev. illus. 96 p./no.; reprints avail. **Document type:** *Magazine, Consumer.* **Description:** In addition to campus news, each issue contains a dozen stories that reflect the university's Catholic intellectual tradition. Stories deal with current affairs, societal trends, and moral and ethical concerns.
Supersedes (in 1971): Notre Dame Alumnus (0029-4497)
Related titles: Online - full text ed.
Indexed: RI-1, RI-2.
Published by: University of Notre Dame, 538 Grace Hall, Notre Dame, IN 46556. TEL 574-631-5000, ndmag@nd.edu, http://www.nd.edu/~ndmag. Eds. Carol Schaal, Kerry Temple. Circ: 150,000 (controlled).

378 USA
NOTRE DAME REPORT. Text in English. 1971. s-m. free to faculty and staff. index. **Document type:** *Newsletter.*
Incorporating: Office of the Provost at Notre Dame (0034-5148)
Published by: University of Notre Dame, Office of the Provost, 300 Main Building, Notre Dame, IN 46556. TEL 219-631-5337. Ed. Melissa Pluta. Circ: 1,600; 1,600 (controlled).

378 CAN ISSN 1185-717X
NOUVEAU QUARTIER LIBRE✶. Text in French. 1973. s-m. free.
Published by: Publi-Peq, 3575 bd St Laurent, Ste 232, Montreal, PQ H2X 2T7, Canada. TEL 514-526-0235. Circ: 2,500.
Co-sponsor: College de Rosemont.

378.1 USA ISSN 0029-4985
NOVA (EL PASO). Text in English. 1965. q. free. bk.rev. charts; illus. **Document type:** *Academic/Scholarly.*
Published by: University of Texas at El Paso, 500 W University Ave, El Paso, TX 79968-0522. TEL 915-747-5526, FAX 915-747-5969. Ed. Kathleen Rogers. Circ: 37,000.

NOVA NEWS NET. see *JOURNALISM*

378 USA ISSN 1066-3347
NOW (LONGVIEW). Text in English. 1936. q. free. back issues avail. **Document type:** *Magazine.* **Description:** For alumni and friends of LeTourneau University.
Published by: LeTourneau University, PO Box 7001, Longview, TX 75607. TEL 903-233-3000, FAX 903-233-3618, alumni@james.letu.edu. Ed. William Gibbs. Pub. Alvin O Austin.

371.83 GBR ISSN 0307-9244
LE NURB. Text in English. 1973. 9/yr. free. adv. bk.rev. **Document type:** *Consumer.*
Former titles: Isam; Needle
Published by: Brunel University, Union of Brunel Students, Cleveland Rd, Uxbridge, Mddx UB8 3PH, United Kingdom. TEL 44-1895-462232, FAX 44-1895-810477. Ed. Jel McGill. Adv. contact Matt Osborne. Circ: 7,000 (controlled).

NURSING PROGRESS. see *MEDICAL SCIENCES—Nurses And Nursing*

378.1 ZAF ISSN 0029-6716
NUX. Text in English. 1948. m. free. adv. bk.rev.; play rev. illus.
Published by: University of KwaZulu-Natal, Students Representative Council, PO Box 375, Pietermaritzburg, KwaZulu-Natal, South Africa. Circ: 2,500 (controlled).

378.1 GBR ISSN 0029-7380
OAKHAMIAN. Text in English. 1883. 3/yr. GBP 8. adv. **Document type:** *Newsletter.*
Published by: Oakham School, Chapel Close, Market Pl, Oakham, Leics, United Kingdom. Ed. D N Gilvary. Circ: 1,600.

378 USA ISSN 1054-6480
OAKLAND UNIVERSITY MAGAZINE. Text in English. 1982. q. USD 10 (effective 2000); free to qualified personnel. illus. back issues avail. **Description:** Covers campus activities, research projects, academic issues, and personalities of Oakland University.
Published by: Oakland University, Communications & Marketing Department, 119 N Foundation Hall, Rochester, MI 48309-4401. TEL 248-370-3184, FAX 248-370-3182, coutilis@oakland.edu. Circ: 50,000 (controlled).

378.1 USA ISSN 0029-7518
OBERLIN ALUMNI MAGAZINE. Text in English. 1904. q. USD 15; alumni free. adv. bk.rev. illus. **Document type:** *Academic/Scholarly.* **Description:** Covers news and issues affecting Oberlin College and its students and alumni.
Published by: Oberlin College, 145 W Lorain St, Oberlin, OH 44074-1089. TEL 440-775-8182, FAX 440-775-6575, alum.mag@oberlin.edu, http://www.oberlin.edu. Ed. Kelly Viancourt. Adv. contact Mavis Clark. Circ: 30,500.

378.1 USA ISSN 0029-7526
OBERLIN REVIEW. Text in English. 1874. w. USD 35; free to Oberlin residents (effective 2000). adv. bk.rev.; film rev.; play rev. illus. **Document type:** *Newspaper.* **Description:** Features college news, student life, local plays and music, and college sports.
Published by: Oberlin News Tribune, Wilder Box 90, Oberlin, OH 44074. TEL 216-775-8123, FAX 216-775-6733, oreview@oberlin.edu, http://www.oberlin.edu/~ocreview/. Ed. Lauren Viera. R&P Jan Cooper. Adv. contact Matt Franks. Circ: 3,500.

378 USA
THE OBSERVER. Text in English. 1966. d. (Mon.-Fri.). USD 85; free to students (effective 2005). adv. **Document type:** *Newspaper, Consumer.*
Published by: Students of Notre Dame-St. Mary's College, PO Box Q, Notre Dame, IN 46556. TEL 219-631-7471, observer@nd.edu, http://www.nd.edu/~observer. Ed. Claire Heininger. adv.: col. inch USD 5.50. Circ: 13,000 morning (paid and free). Wire service: AP.

378.1 USA
OBSERVER (ELLENSBURG). Text in English. 1927. w. USD 20. adv. bk.rev.; film rev.; play rev. **Document type:** *Newspaper.*
Formerly: Campus Crier (0008-2503)
Published by: Central Washington University, 400 E 8th Ave, Ellensburg, WA 98926. TEL 509-963-1026. R&P, Adv. contact Christine Page. Circ: 6,000.

C

378 USA
OBSERVER (FT. LAUDERDALE). Text in English. 1986. bi-w. USD 15. adv. bk.rev. **Document type:** *Newspaper.* **Description:** Covers events, activities and other stories related to the BCC audience.
Published by: Broward Community College Board of Trustees, 225 E. Las Olas Blvd., Ft. Lauderdale, FL 33301. TEL 305-973-2237, FAX 305-968-2448. Eds. Gary Band, Greta Penenori. Adv. contact Ann Chisholm. Circ: 10,000 (controlled). **Subscr. to:** 1000 Coconut Creek Blvd, Pompano Beach, FL 33066.

378 USA
THE OBSERVER (NEW YORK, 1981). Text in English. 1981. bi-w. adv. bk.rev.; dance rev.; film rev.; music rev.; play rev.; tel.rev. charts; illus.; stat. back issues avail. **Document type:** *Newspaper.* **Description:** Covers topics relevant to the college student, as a student and as a member of the NYC community.
Related titles: Microform ed.: (from PQC).
Published by: Fordham College at Lincoln Center, 113 W 60th St, Rm 408, New York, NY 10023-7484. TEL 212-636-6015, FAX 212-636-7819. Ed. Adam C Wolvek. Adv. contact Ben Billingsley. Circ: 10,000.

378 USA
OBSERVER (NOTRE DAME). Text in English. 1966. 5/w. USD 85 (effective 2003). adv. bk.rev. **Document type:** *Newspaper, Consumer.* **Description:** Covers campus news, features, entertainment, sports & opinions.
Related titles: Supplement(s): Irish Football.
Published by: University of Notre Dame, 024 South Dining Hall, PO Box Q, Notre Dame, IN 46556. http://www.ndsmcobserver.com/. Circ: 13,000.

378 USA ISSN 1063-1631
OBSERVER (ROCK ISLAND). Text in English. 1902. w. USD 12. **Description:** For students, contains campus news.
Published by: Augustana College, 639 38th St, Rock Island, IL 61201-2296. TEL 309-794-7280.

378.1 USA ISSN 1072-3234
LD4249
OHIO STATE ALUMNI MAGAZINE. Text in English. 1909. 9/yr. USD 35 to members (effective 1999). adv.
Former titles: Ohio State (0889-4116); O S U (0744-8899); O S U Monthly (0744-0758); (until 1980): Ohio State University Monthly (0030-1167)
—Linda Hall.
Published by: Ohio State University Alumni Association, Inc., 2400 Olentangy River Rd, Columbus, OH 43210-1061. TEL 614-292-3811, FAX 614-292-7697. Ed. Lynne M Bonenberger. Pub. Dan L Heinlen. R&P Judy R Foust. Adv. contact Deborah S Sawyer. B&W page USD 1,240, color page USD 2,365. Circ: 121,200.

378.1 USA ISSN 0030-1116
OHIO STATE LANTERN. Text in English. 1881. d. (Mon.-Fri.) (during sessions; s-w.: summer). USD 62 (effective 2005). adv. bk.rev.; film rev.; play rev. charts; illus. 16 p./no. 6 cols./p.; **Document type:** *Newspaper.*

▼ new title ➤ refereed ✶ unverified ♦ full entry avail.

Related titles: Microfilm ed.; Online - full text ed.: (from LexisNexis).
Published by: Ohio State University, School of Communication, 242 W 18th Ave, Columbus, OH 43210. TEL 614-292-2031, FAX 614-292-3722, lantern@osu.edu, http://www.thelantern.com. R&P Ray Catalino TEL 614-292-6749. Adv. contact Dominic Stellutto. col. inch USD 13. Circ: 200 (paid); 28,000 (controlled). Wire service: AP.

378.1 USA ISSN 0030-1221
OHIO WESLEYAN MAGAZINE. Text in English. 1923. q. free. bk.rev.
Published by: Ohio Wesleyan University, Delaware, OH 43015. TEL 614-369-4431. Ed. Pamela Besel. Circ: 26,000.

378.1 USA ISSN 0030-171X
OKLAHOMA DAILY; a student newspaper serving the University of Oklahoma. Text in English. 1916. d. (Mon.-Fri.; w. summer). USD 165 (effective 2005). adv. bk.rev. **Document type:** *Newspaper.*
Related titles: Microfilm ed.; Online - full text ed.: (from LexisNexis).
Published by: University of Oklahoma, Board of Regents, 860 Van Vleet, Norman, OK 73019. TEL 405-325-2521, FAX 405-325-7517, Susan@ou.edu, http://www.daily.ou.edu. Ed. Aesha Rasheed. Pub. Susan E Sasso. R&P Susan Sasso. Adv. contact Wila Smith. col. inch USD 14. Circ: 12,000 (controlled). Wire service: KR.

378.1 GBR
OLD BRADFIELDIAN. Text in English. 1994. s-a. **Document type:** *Consumer.* **Description:** Covers matters of interest to alumni of Bradfield College.
Published by: Bradfield College, Old Bradfieldian Society, Bradfield, Berks RG7 6AY, United Kingdom. TEL 01734-744356, FAX 01734-744330. Ed. John Coldstream.

C

378.83 USA
OLE MISS ALUMNI REVIEW. Text in English. 1951. q. USD 30 (effective 2001). adv. **Description:** Publishes for alumni and friends of the university. Covers campus events, alumni, activities, faculty research and activities and sports.
Published by: University of Mississippi, Alumni Association, 172 Triplett Alumni Center, University, MS 38677. TEL 662-915-7375. Ed., Adv. contact Bill Dabney. Pub. Herb Dewees. color page USD 1,450. Circ: 14,500; 60,000 Summer.

378 AUS ISSN 0310-8864
ON CAMPUS. Text in English. 1992. fortn. **Document type:** *Newspaper.*
Published by: Flinders University of South Australia, Public Relations and Information Office, GPO Box 2100, Adelaide, SA 5001, Australia. TEL 61-8-82012965, FAX 61-8-82013027. Ed. Charles Gent. Circ: 1,600.

378.83 USA ISSN 1087-3163
TX945
ON-CAMPUS HOSPITALITY. Text in English. 1979. 9/yr. USD 30 domestic; USD 40 foreign (effective 2004). adv. **Document type:** *Magazine, Trade.*
Former titles (until 1992): College Union and On-Campus Hospitality (0887-431X); (until 1986): College Union (0192-3307)
Published by: Executive Business Media, Inc., 825 Old Country Rd, PO Box 1500, Westbury, NY 11590. TEL 516-334-3030, FAX 516-334-8958, ebm-mail@ebmpubs.com, http://www.ebmpubs.com/och_web.html. Eds. Carl Laron, Cory Harris. Pub. Murry Greenwald. R&P Fred Schaen. Adv. contacts Marty McCallen, Nancy Wildermuth. Circ: 9,229 (controlled).

378.1 AUS ISSN 0030-2333
ON DIT. Text in French. 1932. w. AUD 8 (effective 1999). adv. bk.rev.; film rev.; play rev. illus.; stat.; tr.lit. **Document type:** *Newspaper.*
Published by: University of Adelaide, Students Association, Adelaide, Australia. Eds. Anthony Paxton, Penny Fredericks. Adv. contact Bonnie Claire Yates. Circ: 6,000.

378.18 USA
ON THE EDGE (MADISON). Text in English. 1983. s-m. USD 5. adv. bk.rev.; film rev.; play rev. **Document type:** *Newspaper.*
Formerly (until vol.7, 1989): Screed
Published by: Edgewood College, 855 Woodrow St, Madison, WI 53711. TEL 608-257-4861. Circ: 650.

378 USA
ON THE GREEN. Text in English. 1952. q. free. adv. **Document type:** *Consumer.*
Formerly: Bloomfield College. Bulletin
Published by: Bloomfield College, Office of College Relations, 229 Liberty St, Bloomfield, NJ 07003. TEL 973-748-9000 ext 561, FAX 973-743-2040, http://www.bloomfield.edu. Ed. Veronica Clinton. Circ: 10,000.

378 USA
ON WISCONSIN MAGAZINE. Text in English. 1899. q. USD 39 membership (effective 2003). adv. bk.rev. illus.; stat.; tr.lit. back issues avail. **Document type:** *Consumer.* **Description:** Directed to University of Wisconsin at Madison alumni, faculty and friends. Includes articles and news items regarding research and activities at the university.
Former titles: Wisconsin Alumni Magazine; Wisconsin Alumnus
Published by: Wisconsin Alumni Association, 650 N Lake St, Madison, WI 53706. TEL 608-262-2551, FAX 608-262-3332, WAA@uwalumni.com, http://www.uwalumni.com/onwisconsin/. Ed. Michael Penn. adv.: B&W page USD 6,534, color page USD 9,504; 10.88 x 8.38. Circ: 250,000.

378 CAN
ONCAMPUS. Text in English. 1967. w. (during acad. year). CND 30. adv. bk.rev. charts; illus.; stat. **Document type:** *Newspaper, Consumer.*
Former titles (until 2003): University of Calgary Gazette (0300-4333); (until 1969): University Gazette (0575-2043)
Related titles: Online - full text ed.
Published by: University of Calgary, Communications Office, Administration Bldg, Rm 113, 2500 University Dr NW, Calgary, AB T2N 1N4, Canada. TEL 403-220-2920, FAX 403-282-8413, bfrank@ucalgary.ca, http://www.ucalgary.ca/oncampus/weekly/. Adv. contact Ken Bendiktson TEL 403-220-3502. Circ: 6,600 (controlled).

378 CAN ISSN 0834-7603
ONTARION. Text in English. 1951. w. CND 20; CND 65 foreign. adv. bk.rev.; film rev.; play rev.; rec.rev. **Document type:** *Newspaper.*
Published by: Ontarion, Inc., University of Guelph, University Centre, Rm 264, Guelph, ON N1G 2W1, Canada. TEL 519-824-4120, FAX 519-824-7838, ontarion@uoguelph.ca, http://www.uoguelph.ca/~ontarion/. Ed. Marshal McLernon. Adv. contact Brigit Atkinson. Circ: 12,000 (controlled).

378.1 USA ISSN 0030-4069
OPTIMIST (ABILENE). Text in English. 1912. s-w. USD 20 (effective 1998). adv. bk.rev. **Document type:** *Newspaper.*
Indexed: CWPI.
Published by: Abilene Christian University, Journalism & Mass Communication Department, PO Box 27618, ACU Sta, Abilene, TX 79699-7618. TEL 915-674-2000. Ed. Jessica Gray. Pub., R&P Merlin Mann TEL 915-674-2297. Adv. contact Kent Barnett. Circ: 4,500.

371.8 USA
ORANGE & BLUE. Text in English. 1982. s-a. free domestic to students (effective 2005). **Document type:** *Magazine, Consumer.*
Contact: University of Florida, College of Journalism, 2070 Weimer Hall, Gainesville, FL 32611. TEL 352-392-0500, FAX 352-846-2673, o&b@jou.ufl.edu, http://www.jou.ufl.edu. Circ: 10,000 (free).

378.1 USA ISSN 0030-4662
OREGON DAILY EMERALD. Text in English. 1898. d. (Mon.-Fri., Sep.-May). USD 100 (effective 2005). adv. film rev.; play rev. **Document type:** *Newspaper.*
Related titles: Microfilm ed.
Published by: Oregon Daily Emerald Publishing Co., Inc., University of Oregon, 300 Erb Memorial Union, Box 3159, Eugene, OR 97403. TEL 541-346-5511, FAX 541-346-5821, ode@oregon.uoregon.edu, http://www.dailyemerald.com. Ed. Parker Howell. R&P Judy Riedl. adv.: col. inch USD 9.75. Circ: 10,000. Wire service: KR.

378 USA
OREGON QUARTERLY; the Northwest perspective from the University of Oregon. Text in English. 1919. q. USD 25 domestic; USD 35 foreign; USD 5 per issue; free to alumni (effective 2005). adv. **Document type:** *Magazine, Consumer.* **Description:** Covers the issues, problems, and accomplishments of higher education in the Pacific Northwest, with a special emphasis on the friends and alumni of the university.
Formerly (until 1993): Old Oregon
Published by: University of Oregon, 130 Chapman Hall, 5228 University of Oregon, Eugene, OR 97403-5228. FAX 503-346-2220, gmaynard@oregon.uoregon.edu, http://www.uoregon.edu/~oq/. Ed., R&P Guy Maynard TEL 541-346-5048. Adv. contact Susan Thelen. B&W page USD 2,750, color page USD 3,250; trim 7.875 x 10.375. Circ: 100,000 (paid and controlled).

378 USA ISSN 0885-3258
S537
THE OREGON STATER. Text in English. 1916. bi-m. USD 35. bk.rev. **Document type:** *Newspaper.*
Published by: Oregon State University, Alumni Association, Administration Bldg 416, Oregon State University, Corvallis, OR 97331. TEL 503-737-0780, FAX 503-737-2130. Ed. George P Edmonston. Circ: 18,000 (paid).

378 USA
ORION (CHICO). Text in English. 1975. w. USD 25. adv. bk.rev. **Document type:** *Newsletter.*
Related titles: Online - full text ed.
Indexed: RGAb.
Published by: California State University, Chico, College of Communication, Department of Journalism, Chico, CA 95929-0600. TEL 916-898-5625, FAX 916-898-4839, http://www.orion.csuchico.edu. Ed. Elisa Bongiovanni. Pub., R&P Dave Waddell TEL 530-898-4782. Adv. contact Matt Mueller. page USD 750. Circ: 10,000 (controlled).

378.198 USA
THE OSWEGONIAN. Text in English. 1935. w. free. adv. **Document type:** *Newspaper.* **Description:** Directed to students and faculty of the college and the surrounding community.
Published by: State University of New York, Oswego, 15B Hewitt Union, Oswego, NY 13126. TEL 315-341-3600, FAX 315-341-3542, gonian@oswego.oswego.edu. Ed. Jennifer L Fregoe. R&P Jennifer L Fegow. Adv. contact Faith Chaffee. page USD 390. Circ: 6,000 (controlled).

378 CAN
OTHER PRESS. Text in English. 1976. m. free. adv. bk.rev. **Document type:** *Newspaper.*
Published by: Other Publications Society, Douglas College, 700 Royal Ave, P O Box 2503, New Westminster, BC V3L 5B2, Canada. TEL 604-525-3542, FAX 604-527-5095. Circ: 5,000.

378.18 CAN
OTTAWA CAMPUS. Text in English. 1891. irreg. USD 7.50. adv.
Published by: University of Ottawa, 550 Cumberland, Ottawa, ON K1N 6N5, Canada. TEL 613-562-5700, http://www.uottawa.ca. Circ: 1,000.

378 USA
OUR BUSINESS. Text in English. 1974. s-a. USD 25 to members. **Document type:** *Newsletter.* **Description:** Discusses topics of interest to alumni both within the college and outside.
Formerly (until Apr. 1990): Dialog (Norman)
Published by: University of Oklahoma, College of Business Administration, 307 W Brooks Hall, Rm 208, Norman, OK 73019. TEL 405-253-5833, FAX 405-325-2096, rgibson@uoknor.edu. Ed. Randy Gibson. Circ: 22,000.

378 USA
OUR LADY OF HOLY CROSS COLLEGE. JOURNAL. Text in English. s-m.
Published by: Our Lady of Holy Cross College, 4123 Woodland Dr, New Orleans, LA 70114. Circ: 400.

378 GBR ISSN 0954-1306
OXFORD TODAY. Text in English. 1988. 3/yr. EUR 17 in Europe to individuals; GBP 11 in Europe; USD 23 in the Americas; GBP 16 elsewhere (effective 2006). adv. **Document type:** *Bulletin.* **Description:** Covers news and developments, alumni news, sports, finance, restaurants, museums and galleries.
Related titles: Online - full text ed.: (from EBSCO Publishing).
Indexed: ABM, ChLitAb.
—CCC.
Published by: (University of Oxford), Blackwell Publishing Ltd., 9600 Garsington Rd, Oxford, OX4 2ZG, United Kingdom. TEL 44-1865-776868, FAX 44-1865-714591, customerservices@oxon.blackwellpublishing.com, http://www.blackwellpublishing.com/journals/OXTO. Ed. Christina Hardyment TEL 44-1865-278111. Circ: 110,977.

P A S S; the first choice for Rart Qualified Accountants. (Professional Accountancy Student Service) see *BUSINESS AND ECONOMICS—Accounting*

378 USA
P C C ALUMNI NEWS. Text in English. 1961. q. free to alumni. **Document type:** *Newsletter.* **Description:** For college alumni and chiropractic professionals.
Related titles: Online - full content ed.
Published by: Palmer College of Chiropractic, 741 Brady St, Davenport, IA 52803. TEL 563-884-5150, FAX 563-884-5227, research@palmer.edu, http://www.palmer.edu. Ed. Keith Poehlman. Circ: 15,000.

378 USA
PACE MAGAZINE. Text in English. s-a. free (effective 2005). **Document type:** *Magazine, Academic/Scholarly.*
Published by: Pace University Alumni Association, One Pace Plz., New York, NY 10038. TEL 212-346-1200, FAX 212-346-1643, http://www.utoday.com/pace/. Ed. Lee Vaccaro. Circ: 80,000 (paid and controlled).

378.198 USA
PACE PRESS. Text in English. 1948. w. free. **Description:** Covers students, faculty, and administrative activities at the university and the downtown NYC campus.
Published by: Pace University, Student Life Office, 41 Park Row, 8th Fl, New York, NY 10038. TEL 212-346-1553, FAX 212-346-1563. Ed. Ian B Fernander.

378 USA
PACER. Text in English. w. (academic yr. only). free. adv. bk.rev. **Document type:** *Newspaper.* **Description:** Serves as the student newspaper, covering news, features, opinions, and sports.

Published by: University of Tennessee at Martin, 305 Gooch Hall, Martin, TN 38238. TEL 901-587-7780, pacer@mars.utm.edu, http://mars.utm.edu/~pacer/. Ed. J K Devine. R&P Tomi McCutchen TEL 901-587-7558. Adv. contact Jackie Taylor. Circ: 5,000.

378 USA
PACER TIMES. Text in English. w.
Published by: University of South Carolina, 171 University Pkwy, Aiken, SC 29801.

371.8 USA ISSN 0164-9426
PACIFIC REVIEW (STOCKTON). Text in English. q.
Published by: (University of the Pacific, Office of Alumni Relations), University of the Pacific, 3601 Pacific Ave, Stockton, CA 95211. TEL 209-946-2344, http://www.pacificalumni.org/pacificreview.htm. Circ: 40,000.

378 USA ISSN 0030-8994
PACIFICAN. Text in English. 1908. w. (Thu.). USD 30 (effective 1998). adv. bk.rev. **Document type:** *Newspaper.*
Related titles: Online - full text ed.: (from LexisNexis).
Published by: Pacifican Publication Board, 3601 Pacific Ave, Stockton, CA 95211. TEL 209-946-2115, FAX 209-946-2195, pacifican@uop.edu. Ed. Trent Allen. R&P Morris Brown TEL 209-946-3049. Adv. contact Elena Ramano. Circ: 4,500.

378 DEU
PADERBORNER UNIVERSITAETS ZEITSCHRIFT. Text in German. q. adv. **Document type:** *Magazine, Consumer.*
Published by: Universitaet Paderborn, Warburger Str 100, Paderborn, 33098, Germany. TEL 49-5251-602559, FAX 49-5251-603236, http://www.uni-paderborn.de. Ed. Dr. Wolfgang Weber. Adv. contact Martin Heynen. Circ: 5,000.

738 DEU
PAEDAGOGISCHE HOCHSCHULE WEINGARTEN. PERSONEN- UND VORLESUNGSVERZEICHNIS. Text in German. 1962. s-a. adv. **Document type:** *Directory, Academic/Scholarly.*
Published by: Paedagogische Hochschule Weingarten, Kirchplatz 2, Weingarten, 88250, Germany. TEL 49-751-501240, FAX 49-751-501200, info@ph-weingarten.de, http://www.ph-weingarten.de. Ed. Dr. R Meissner. R&P, Adv. contact Rolf Ehe. Circ: 2,500 (controlled).

378 USA
PALADIN. Text in English. w. (Sep.-May). USD 16.95 (effective 2000). adv. **Document type:** *Newspaper.* **Description:** Student paper of campus events, issues and news.
Published by: (Board of Student Communications), Furman University, PO Box 28584, Greenville, SC 29613. TEL 864-294-2077, FAX 864-294-3001. Ed. Stacy Schorr. Circ: 3,000.

PALATINATE. see *LITERATURE*

378 USA
THE PAN - AMERICAN. Text in English. 1927. s-w. (Tue. & Thu.). adv. bk.rev. **Document type:** *Newspaper.*
Published by: University of Texas - Pan American, Student Publications, CAS 170, Austin, TX 78712. TEL 210-381-2541, FAX 210-316-7122. R&P, Adv. contact Juanita Sanchez. Circ: 5,000.

378.198 USA ISSN 0031-062X
PS501
PANACHE✶. Text in English. 1987. q.
Published by: Nervous, Inc., 363 7th Ave, 16th Fl, New York, NY 10001-3904. Circ: 35,000.

378 USA
PANORAMA (EDINBURG). Text in English. a. **Description:** Contains news and features about the University and chronicle events on campus.
Formerly: Rio (Edinburg)
Published by: University of Texas - Pan American, Student Publications, CAS 170, Austin, TX 78712. TEL 210-381-2541, FAX 210-316-7122.

280.044 USA ISSN 8755-0954
PANORAMA (PITTSBURGH, 1960). Text in English. 1960. 5/yr. **Document type:** *Newsletter.* **Description:** Provides news of the seminary, faculty and alumni activities, fundraising efforts and similar items of interest.
Published by: Pittsburgh Theological Seminary, 616 N Highland Ave, Pittsburgh, PA 15206. TEL 412-362-5610, FAX 412-363-3260. Ed. Lisa Dormire Foster.

378 CAN
THE PAPER CUT. Text in English. 1981. fortn. adv. bk.rev.; film rev. **Document type:** *Newspaper.* **Description:** Covers a wide range of topics, mostly related to college life, including sports, arts and entertainment, news and commentary sections.
Formerly (until 1995): Paper
Published by: Marianopolis College, Student Union, 3880 rue Cote des Neiges, Rm G7, Montreal, PQ H3H 1W1, Canada. TEL 514-931-8792, FAX 514-931-6786. Eds. Danistan Saverimuthu, Marc Miresco. Adv. contact Michael Tricot. B&W page USD 180, color page USD 320; trim 15 x 10. Circ: 1,000.

600 378 PNG ISSN 1019-5343
PAPUA NEW GUINEA UNIVERSITY OF TECHNOLOGY. REPORTER. Text in English. 1979 (no.34). w. adv. charts; illus. **Document type:** *Newsletter, Academic/Scholarly.*
Related titles: Microform ed.
Published by: Papua New Guinea University of Technology, Prviate Mail Bag, Lae, Papua New Guinea. TEL 675-473-4449, FAX 675-475-7667, TELEX TLX 42428. Ed., Adv. contact Corney Lahies. Circ: 1,500.

378 DEU
PAR T U; Alumni Magazin des Technischen Universitaet Berlin. Text in German. 1999. 2/yr. free. adv. **Document type:** *Magazine, Consumer.*
Published by: Technische Universitaet Berlin, Presse- und Informationsreferat, Str des 17 Juni 135, Berlin, 10623, Germany. TEL 49-30-31423922, FAX 49-30-314-23909, pressestelle@tu-berlin.de, http://www.tu-berlin.de/presse/. Ed. Kristina Zerges. adv.: B&W page EUR 2,100, color page EUR 2,600. Circ: 12,000 (controlled).

378 USA ISSN 1099-4351
THE PARTHENON. Text in English. d. USD 100 (effective 2005); free. back issues avail. **Document type:** *Newspaper.*
Related titles: Microform ed.: (from PQC); Online - full text ed.
Published by: Marshall University, 400 Hal Greer Blvd, Smith Hall, Rm 311, Huntington, WV 25755. TEL 304-696-6696, FAX 304-696-2519, parthenon@marshall.edu, http://www.marshallparthenon.com/. Circ: 18,000 morning (paid). Wire service: AP.

378.1 USA ISSN 0031-2657
PASQUINO. Text in English. 1921. irreg. (10-11/yr.). USD 10. adv.
Related titles: Microform ed.: (from PQC).
Published by: Potomac State College, Journalism Dept, Keyser, WV 26726. TEL 304-788-6966. Ed. Fred Jacoby. Circ: 2,000.

378.18 CAN ISSN 1194-8302
PASSPORT. Text in English. 1940. q. free. bibl.; charts; illus.; stat. **Document type:** *Newsletter.* **Description:** Reports on news, events, alumni, academic, programs of Briercrest Family of Schools.
Former titles (until 1993): Briercrest Echo (0821-5839); (until 1982): Echo (0824-9288)
Published by: Briercrest Family of Schools, 510 College Dr, Caronport, SK S0H 0S0, Canada. TEL 306-756-3200, FAX 306-756-3366, info@briercrest.ca. Ed. Dwight Friesen. Pub., R&P Larry Hamm. Circ: 27,000 (controlled).

378 USA
THE PATHFINDER (LEWISTON). Text in English. bi-w. free on campus (effective 2005). adv. **Document type:** *Newspaper.*
Published by: Lewis & Clark State College, 500 Eighth Ave., Lewiston, ID 83501. TEL 208-799-2307, 208-799-5272, FAX 208-792-2831, triver@lcsc.edu. Ed. Jeff Grygny.

378.1 USA ISSN 0031-3459
LH1.G28
PEABODY REFLECTOR. Text in English. 1927. s-a. free (effective 2005). illus. index. **Document type:** *Magazine, Academic/Scholarly.* **Description:** Covers campus events, faculty-student research, development news and alumni news and profiles.
Published by: George Peabody College of Vanderbilt University, Office of Alumni and Development, 230 Appleton Pl., PO Box 161, Nashville, TN 37203. TEL 615-322-2601, FAX 615-343-8547, phillip.b.tucker@vanderbilt.edu, http://www.vanderbilt.edu. Ed., R&P Phillip B Tucker. Circ: 8,000 (controlled).

378.1 CAN ISSN 0031-3629
PEAK. Text in English. 1965. 39/yr. CND 36. adv. bk.rev. **Document type:** *Newspaper.*
Published by: Peak Publications Society, Simon Fraser Univ, Burnaby, BC V5A 1S6, Canada. TEL 604-291-3598, FAX 604-291-3786. Circ: 10,000.

378 USA
PENDULUM. Text in English. 1974. w. adv. **Document type:** *Newspaper.* **Description:** Covers news of Elon University and the local community.
Published by: Elon University, Campus Box 2800, Elon College, NC 27244. TEL 910-584-2331, FAX 910-584-2467. adv.: B&W page USD 210. Circ: 3,000.

378 USA
THE PENN. Text in English. 1927. 3/w. (Mon., Wed., Fri.). free. **Document type:** *Newspaper, Consumer.*
Published by: Student Cooperative Association, 319 Pratt Dr, Indiana, PA 15701. TEL 724-357-1306, FAX 724-357-5555, the-penn@iup.edu, http://www.thepenn.org. Ed. Cynthia J Anzulewicz. Adv. contact Ashley Suhr. Circ: 11,000 (paid and free). Wire service: AP.

378.198 USA
THE PENN STATER. Text in English. 1913. bi-m. USD 35; USD 15 to students (effective 2005). adv. **Document type:** *Magazine, Consumer.*
Published by: Penn State Alumni Association, Hintz Family Alumni Ctr., University Park, PA 16802-1439. TEL 814-865-2709, FAX 814-863-5690, pennstater@psu.edu, http://www.alumni.psu.edu/membership/benefits/publications.htm#pennstater, http://www.alumni.alu.psu.edu. Ed. Tina Hay TEL 814-863-4546. adv.: B&W page USD 2,650, color page USD 3,550. Circ: 127,000 (paid).

378 USA ISSN 1520-4650
PENNSYLVANIA GAZETTE. Text in English. 1902. bi-m. USD 28. adv. bk.rev. **Document type:** *Magazine, Consumer.* **Description:** Contains articles for the alumni of the University of Pennsylvania.
Published by: University of Pennsylvania, 3910 Chestnut St., 3rd Fl., Philadelphia, PA 19104. TEL 215-898-5555, FAX 215-573-4812, gazette@ben.dev.upenn.edu, http://www.upenn.edu/gazette. Eds. John Prendergast, John Prendergast, Molly Selzer. Pub. Robert Alig TEL 215-898-7811. Adv. contact Burt Ploner. Circ: 140,000.

378 ARG ISSN 0327-9901
CODEN: JOHTEN
PENSAMIENTO UNIVERSITARIO. Text in Spanish. 1993. 3/yr. ARS 10 per issue; USD 75 foreign.
Address: Casilla de Correo 333, Suc. 12-B, Capital Federal, Buenos Aires 1412, Argentina. TEL 54-114-8058429, FAX 54-114-8037001. Ed. Pedro Krotsch.

378 USA
THE PERSPECTIVE (WAUKESHA). Text in English. 1874. fortn. USD 18. adv. bk.rev. **Document type:** *Newspaper.*
Formerly: New Perspective
Published by: Carroll College, 100 E College Ave, Waukesha, WI 53186. TEL 414-524-7351, FAX 414-524-7139. Ed. Rene Schweitzer. Circ: 1,200.

371.85 USA
PERSPECTIVES (INDIANAPOLIS). Text in English. 1974. **Document type:** *Newsletter.* **Description:** Publishes articles pertaining to campus advisement of fraternities and sororities.
Formerly: A F A Newsletter
Published by: Association of Fraternity Advisors, Inc., 3901 W 86th St, Ste 390, Indianapolis, IN 46268-1702. TEL 317-876-4691, FAX 317-872-1134, http://fraternityadvisors.org. R&P Gayle Webb. Circ: 1,000 (controlled).

378 CAN
LE PETIT MENSUEL. Text in English. 1983. m. adv.
Published by: (CEGEP St. Jean sur Richelieu), College d'Enseignement Generale et Professionnel, 1581 Dufresne, Montreal, PQ H2K 3J6, Canada. TEL 514-526-0235. Circ: 2,500.

378 CAN ISSN 0712-2705
PETITE CAISSE✶. Text in French. 1980. s-m. free.
Formerly: Alternatif
Published by: Publi-Peq, 3575 bd St Laurent, Ste 232, Montreal, PQ H2X 2T7, Canada. TEL 514-845-8628. Circ: 6,000.
Co-sponsor: Universite du Quebec a Chicoutimi.

371.85 USA
PHI ETA SIGMA. FORUM. Text in English. a.
Published by: Auburn University at Montgomery, PO Box 244023, Montgomery, AL 36194-4023. TEL 205-826-5856. Circ: 20,000.

378 USA
PHI GAMMA DELTA. Text in English. 1879. q. USD 1 per issue. **Description:** Publishes college and fraternity news.
Published by: Phi Gamma Delta Fraternity, PO Box 4599, Lexington, KY 40544-4599. TEL 606-255-1848. Ed. William Martin. Circ: 79,000.

378 USA ISSN 1538-5914
LJ85.P45
PHI KAPPA PHI FORUM. Text in English. 1913. q. USD 25 domestic to non-members (effective 2005). adv. bk.rev.; film rev. illus. 48 p./no.; back issues avail.; reprint service avail. from PQC. **Document type:** *Journal, Academic/Scholarly.* **Description:** Forum for analysis of issues of general social and scientific concerns such as education, public policy, medicine, and technology. A single theme treated in each issue.
Former titles (until 2002): National Forum (Auburn) (0162-1831); Phi Kappa Phi Journal (0031-7225)
Related titles: Microform ed.: (from PQC).
Indexed: AgeL, AmH&L, BPIA, BRI, CBRI, CIJE, EIA, EduInd, EnvAb, EnvInd, FamI, HEA, HistAb, LRI, MASUSE, MagInd, ManagCont, PAIS, PhilInd, SOPODA, T&II.
—BLDSC (6449.430000), CIS, IDS, IE, ingenta. **CCC.**
Published by: Honor Society of Phi Kappa Phi (Auburn), Louisiana State University, PO Box 16000, Baton Rouge, LA 70893. TEL 334-844-5200, FAX 334-844-5994, kaetzjp@mail.auburn.edu, http://www.auburn.edu/natforum. Ed., R&P James Kaetz. adv.: B&W page USD 1,000; 7.5 x 9.5. Circ: 105,000 (controlled).

371.852 USA ISSN 0093-5328
PHI KAPPA PHI NEWSLETTER. Text in English. 1969. q. looseleaf. membership. 12 p./no. 3 cols./p.; back issues avail.
Document type: *Newsletter, Academic/Scholarly.*
Description: Contains articles on outstanding Phi Kappa Phi members and national and regional organization activities.
Related titles: Diskette ed.; E-mail ed.; Fax ed.; Online - full text ed.
—CCC.
Published by: Honor Society of Phi Kappa Phi (Baton Rouge), Louisiana State University, PO Box 16000, Baton Rouge, LA 70893-1600. TEL 225-388-4917, 800-804-9880, FAX 225-388-4900, info@phikappaphi.org, http://www.phikappaphi.org. Ed., R&P Trang Nguyen TEL 225-388-4917. Circ: 125,000.

371.85 USA ISSN 0022-3581
R745
PHI RHO SIGMA. JOURNAL. Key Title: Journal of Phi Rho Sigma. Text in English. 1900. q. membership only. bk.rev. bibl.; illus.
Published by: Phi Rho Sigma Medical Society, PO Box 90264, Indianapolis, IN 46290-0264. TEL 317-255-4379, FAX 317-253-5067. Ed. Dr. James Jackson. Circ: 16,000 (controlled).

378.1 USA
PHILADELPHIA COLLEGE OF TEXTILES & SCIENCE. PORTFOLIO. Text in English. 1988. s-a. free to alumni.
Document type: *Newsletter.* **Description:** Current news and events of the college, including features on faculty, alumni, students and staff.
Published by: Philadelphia College of Textiles & Science, Paul J Gutman Library, 3243 School House Ln & Henry Ave, Philadelphia, PA 19144-5497. TEL 215-951-2851, FAX 215-951-2569. Ed. Regina De Angelo. Circ: 15,000.

C

378.1 PHL ISSN 0031-7853
PHILIPPINE WOMEN'S UNIVERSITY ADMINISTRATIVE NEWS. Text in English. q. illus.
Published by: Philippine Women's University, Taft Ave, Manila, 2801, Philippines. Eds. Alegria A Albano, Edgardo Ray Pedroche. Circ: 500.

378.1 PHL ISSN 0031-8272
PHILWOMENIAN. Text in English, Tagalog. m. free. illus.
Published by: Philippine Women's University, Taft Ave, Manila, 2801, Philippines. Ed. Delia T Arjona.

378 USA
THE PHOENIX. Text in English. 1881. w. (Thu.). free; USD 50 subscr - mailed (effective 2005). 20 p./no. 5 cols./p.;
Document type: *Newspaper.*
Published by: Swarthmore College, 500 College Ave., Swarthmore, PA 19081-1397. TEL 610-328-8000, FAX 610-328-8674, phoenix@swarthmore.edu, http://phoenix.swarthmore.edu. Ed. Benjamin Kabak. Circ: 2,000 (paid and free).

371.805 USA
THE PHOENIX (WESTMINSTER). Text in English. 1981. bi-w. USD 15. adv. dance rev.; film rev.; music rev.; play rev. charts; illus. back issues avail. **Document type:** *Newspaper.*
Description: Student newspaper covering the school and student activities.
Published by: Western Maryland College, Attn: Phoenix, 2 College Hill, Westminster, MD 21157. TEL 410-751-8600, FAX 410-857-2729. Ed., R&P Kate Hampson. Adv. contact Laura Kelley. page USD 47,250; trim 10 x 15. Circ: 2,000.

378 USA
PHRENO - COSMIAN. Text in English. 8/yr. USD 10. adv. bk.rev.
Document type: *Newspaper.*
Published by: Dakota Wesleyan University, 1200 W University Ave, Mitchell, SD 57301. TEL 605-995-2814. Ed. Chad Larson. Circ: 1,000.

378 GBR ISSN 0263-2128
PI; University College London students news. Text in English. 1946. fortn. adv. bk.rev.; film rev.; play rev. illus.
Published by: University College London Student Union, U C L Students Union, 25 Gordon St, London, WC1H 0AH, United Kingdom. TEL 071-387-3611, FAX 071-383-3937. Ed. Luke Hoyland. Circ: 3,500.

378 USA
PINE LOG. Text in English. 1923. s-w. (Mon. & Thu.). USD 25 (effective 1999). adv. bk.rev.; music rev.; play rev.; Website rev. **Document type:** *Newspaper.*
Related titles: Microfiche ed.
Published by: Stephen F. Austin State University, 13049 S F A Sta, Nacogdoches, TX 75962. TEL 936-468-4703, FAX 936-468-1016. Ed. Chris Anderson. R&P Pat Spence. Adv. contact Kaylea Howell TEL 936-468-1346. Circ: 7,000.

378 USA
PIPE DREAM. Text in English. 1970. s-w. (Tue. & Fri.). free to students (effective 2005). **Document type:** *Newspaper.*
Related titles: Microfiche ed.
Published by: State University of New York at Binghamton, University Union, 168, Binghamton, NY 13902. TEL 607-777-2515, FAX 607-777-2600, editor@pipedream.com, http://www.pipedreamonline.com. Ed. Dave Friedman. Circ: 9,000 (free). Wire service: AP, LAT-WAT.

PITT MAGAZINE. see *EDUCATION—Higher Education*

378 USA
PITT NEWS. Text in English. 1906. d. (Mon.-Fri.) (academic yr.). free. **Document type:** *Newspaper.*
Address: 434 William Pitt Union, University of Pittsburgh, Pittsburgh, PA 15260. TEL 412-648-7980, FAX 412-648-8491, pittnews@pitt.edu, http://www.pittnews.com. Ed. Jessica Heller Lear. Circ: 14,000 morning (free). Wire service: AP.

378 CAN
THE PLANT (WESTMOUNT). Text in English. 1971. w. free (effective 2004). adv. bk.rev.; film rev. **Document type:** *Newspaper.*
Indexed: CBCABus, CBPI.
Published by: Dawson College, 3040 Sherbrooke St West, Ste 2C.10, Westmount, PQ H3Z 1A4, Canada. TEL 514-931-8731 ext 1115, FAX 514-931-1864, theplant@graffiti.net, http://www.theplant.ca. Ed. Kavita Saini. Circ: 5,000.

081 USA ISSN 0092-4318
AS36.K36 CODEN: PVREE7
PLATTE VALLEY REVIEW. Text in English. 1973. s-a. USD 5 (effective 2000). illus. **Document type:** *Academic/Scholarly.*
Indexed: MLA, MLA-IB.
Published by: University of Nebraska at Kearney, 905 W 25th St, Kearney, NE 68849. TEL 308-865-8295, Plambeck@platte.UNK.edu, http://www.unk.edu/acad/english/faculty/bloomfields/plattevalley/home.html. Ed. Vern Plambeck. Circ: 1,000.

378 CAN
PLUMBERS POT. Text in English. 1904. 8/yr. CND 4. adv.
Published by: McGill University, Engineering Undergraduate Society, McConnell Engineering Bldg, 3480 University, Montreal, PQ H3A 2A7, Canada. TEL 514-392-4311. Ed. Jeff Sprenger. Circ: 7,000.

378 CAN
LE POINGT✶. Text in French. s-m. free.
Published by: Publi-Peq, 3575 bd St Laurent, Ste 232, Montreal, PQ H2X 2T7, Canada. TEL 514-845-8628. Circ: 800.
Co-sponsor: College de Shawinigan.

378.198 USA
POINTER (WEST POINT). Text in English. 1922. 6/yr. USD 20. adv. bk.rev. back issues avail.
Published by: United States Military Academy, Directorate of Cadet Activities, West Point, NY 10996. TEL 914-938-2780. Circ: 4,500.

371.805 USA
POLY POST. Text in English. w. (Tue. academic yr.). free (effective 2005). adv. **Document type:** *Newspaper, Consumer.*
Contact Owner: California State Polytechnic University, 3801 W Temple Ave, Pomona, CA 91768. TEL 909-869-3530, FAX 909-869-3845, polypost@csupomona.edu, http://www.thepolypost.com. adv.: col. inch USD 7.50. Circ: 6,500 (free). Wire service: AP.

378 CAN
LE POLYSCOPE. Text in French. 1967. w. (Sep.-Apr.). free. adv.
Document type: *Academic/Scholarly.*
Published by: (Association des Etudiants de Polytechnique Inc.), Acces Media, 1124 Marie Anne Rd, East, Ste 31, Montreal, PQ H2J 2B7, Canada. TEL 514-340-4645. Circ: 5,000.
Subscr. to: C P 6079, Succ A, Montreal, PQ H3C 3A7, Canada.

378.198 USA
POLYTECHNICABLE. Text in English. 1970. q.
Formerly (until Jul. 1987): Polytechnic Cable
Published by: Polytechnic University, 333 Jay St, Brooklyn, NY 11201. TEL 718-260-3400. Circ: 35,000.

378.1 USA
POMONA COLLEGE MAGAZINE. Text in English. 1963. 3/yr. free. bk.rev. illus.
Former titles (until 1994): Pomona College Today (1042-0827); (until 1988): Pomona Today (0032-4183)
Published by: Pomona College, Alexander Hall 247, 550 N College Ave, Claremont, CA 91711. FAX 909-621-8203. Ed., R&P Mark Wood. Circ: 26,000.

378 USA
POOP SHEET SPORTS JOURNAL. Text in English. 1977. fortn. USD 35. **Document type:** *Newspaper.*
Published by: Sports Letter, Inc., PO Box 4323, Chapel Hill, NC 27515. TEL 919-967-7789. Circ: 25,000.

378.1 USA
THE POST. Text in English. 1871. d. (Mon.-Fri.) (academic yr.). free to students; USD 65 subscr - mailed (effective 2005).
Document type: *Newspaper, Consumer.*
Formerly: Ohio University Post (0030-1205)
Related titles: Microform ed.
Published by: (Ohio University), The Post, Inc., Ohio University, 20 E Union St, Athens, OH 45701. TEL 740-593-4010, FAX 740-593-0561, post@ohiou.edu, http://www.thepost.baker.ohiou.edu. Circ: 14,000 morning (free). Wire service: AP, UPI.

378 USA
POST SCRIPT (COLUMBIA). Text in English. 1947. fortn. USD 7.50. adv. bk.rev. **Document type:** *Newspaper.*
Published by: Columbia College, 312 Epworth, Columbia, SC 29203. TEL 803-786-3449, FAX 803-786-3674. Ed. Trish Willingham. Adv. contact Cindy Jamison. Circ: 1,200.

378 USA
THE PRAIRIE. Text in English. w. adv. **Document type:** *Newspaper.*
Published by: West Texas A&M University, PO BOX 747, W T STA, Canyon, TX 79016. TEL 806-656-2416. Ed. Jennifer Sicking. Adv. contact Kevin D Handley. B&W page USD 236.

378 CAN ISSN 0383-7653
PRAIRIE HARVESTER. Text in English. 1954. 4/yr. free. bk.rev. illus. **Document type:** *Newsletter.* **Description:** News and information about Prairie Bible Institute for alumni and family.
Published by: (Prairie Alumni Fellowship), Prairie Bible Institute, Three Hills, AB T0M 2A0, Canada. TEL 403-443-5511, FAX 403-443-5540. Ed. Phil Callaway. Circ: 13,000 (controlled).

378 USA
PRATTFOLIO. Text in English. 1983. 2/yr. free. back issues avail.
Document type: *Newsletter.* **Description:** Articles and features about architecture, art & design, liberal arts & sciences, library and information science that would be of interest to Pratt Institute Alumni.
Published by: Pratt Institute, Office of Public Relations, 200 Willoughby Ave, Brooklyn, NY 11205. TEL 718-636-3473, FAX 718-636-3455, prattfol@pratt.edu, http://www.pratt.edu. Ed., R&P Bob Howe. Pub. Thomas F Schutte. Circ: 30,000 (controlled).

378 USA ISSN 1071-4928
PRESBYTERIAN COLLEGE MAGAZINE. Text in English. 1946. q. free. **Document type:** *Academic/Scholarly.* **Description:** Contains news of faculty, students, alumni, programs and achievements.
Formerly (until 1993): Presbyterian College Report (0886-8352)
Published by: Presbyterian College, Office of Public Relations, PO Box 975, Clinton, SC 29325. TEL 864-833-2820, FAX 864-833-8481, gvosburg@admin.presby.edu, http://www.presby.edu. Ed. Grant Vosburgh TEL 864-833-8380. Circ: 14,500 (controlled).

378 USA ISSN 0149-9270
LH1.P8
PRINCETON ALUMNI WEEKLY. Text in English. 1900. 15/yr. USD 22 domestic; USD 26 foreign; free to qualified personnel (effective 2005). adv. bk.rev. illus. back issues avail.
Document type: *Magazine, Consumer.* **Description:** Records news of the alumni and reviews without partiality the achievements and problems of the administration, the faculty, and the student body of Princeton University.
Supersedes: Alumni Princetonian
Published by: Princeton Alumni Publications, 194 Nassau St, Princeton, NJ 08542. TEL 609-258-4885, FAX 609-258-2247, paw@princeton.edu, http://www.princeton.edu/~paw. Ed. Marilyn Marks. Pub. Nancy S. MacMillan. Adv. contact Beth Perrino. Circ: 58,000 (controlled).

378 USA
PRINCETON PARENTS NEWS. Text in English. 1978. 3/yr. free to qualified personnel.
Formerly: Princeton Parents
Published by: Princeton University, Office of Communications, Stanhope Hall, Princeton, NJ 08544. TEL 609-258-5725. Ed. Caroline Moseley. Circ: 13,000.

378.198 USA
PRINCETON WEEKLY BULLETIN. Text in English. 1975. 30/yr. USD 24 to individuals (effective 1999); USD 12 to senior citizens; free to qualified personnel. **Document type:** *Newspaper.*
Published by: Princeton University, Office of Communications, Stanhope Hall, Princeton, NJ 08544. TEL 609-452-3600. Ed. Sally Freedman. Circ: 14,200.

378 CHE
PRISMA; Studentenzeitschrift der Universitaet St. Gallen. Text in German. 1959. 7/yr. free. adv. back issues avail. **Document type:** *Bulletin.*
Published by: Universitaet St. Gallen, Hoehenweg 2, St. Gallen, 9000, Switzerland. TEL 41-71-2231727, FAX 41-71-2237470, prisma@student.unisg.ch, http://www.students.unisg.ch/~prisma/index.html. Ed., R&P Patrick Mueller. Adv. contact Roger Bischof. page CHF 720.

378 USA ISSN 0276-4830
AS30
PRO REGE. Text in English. 1972. q. free (effective 2005).
Document type: *Academic/Scholarly.* **Description:** Explores academic topics relevant to reformed Christian higher education.

Indexed: GSS&RPL.
Published by: Dordt College, 498 Fourth Ave N E, Sioux Center, IA 51250. TEL 712-722-6000, 800-343-6738, prorege@dordt.edu, http://www.dordt.edu/publications/pro_rege/. Ed. Mary Dengler. Circ: 3,000.

378.1 CAN ISSN 0032-9134
PRO TEM. Text in English, French. 1961. w. (Sep.-Apr.). CND 20. adv. bk.rev.; film rev.; play rev. illus. **Document type:** *Bulletin.*
Published by: Glendon College, Student Union, 2275 Bayview Ave, Toronto, ON M4N 3M6, Canada. TEL 416-487-6736. Circ: 4,000.

378 DEU
PROFIL (BAD HARZBURG). Text in German. 1964. q. adv. back issues avail. **Document type:** *Bulletin.*
Published by: Werner-von-Siemens Gymnasium, Herzog Wilhelm Str 25, Bad Harzburg, 38667, Germany. TEL 05322-4354. Ed. Eike Bruns.

378 USA
THE PROFILE (CONWAY). Text in English. 1913. bi-m. USD 25 (effective 1999). adv. bk.rev.; film rev.; music rev. back issues avail. **Document type:** *Newspaper.* **Description:** Aims to cover campus news, issues and opinions. Serves as a medium for information, entertainment and debate.
Published by: Hendrix Student Association, Hendrix College, 1600 Washington Ave, Box 3238, Conway, AR 72032. TEL 501-450-1269, FAX 501-950-1200, profile@mercury.hendrix.edu 275 (effective 1999). Ed., R&P David Scott Cunningham. Adv. contact Jennifer Carman. Circ: 1,200.

378 USA
PROMETHEAN (LOUDONVILLE). Text in English. 1938. fortn. USD 4. **Document type:** *Newspaper.*
Formerly: Indian (Loudonville)
Published by: Siena College, Loudonville, NY 12211. TEL 518-783-2560. Circ: 2,400.

378 USA
PROMETHEAN (SUPERIOR). Text in English. 1920. w. USD 12. adv. bk.rev. **Document type:** *Newspaper.*
Published by: University of Wisconsin at Superior, Holden Fine Arts Bldg, Superior, WI 54880. TEL 715-394-8387, FAX 715-394-8404. R&P John Marder. Adv. contact Katie Gurgel. Circ: 2,500.

378.1 NLD ISSN 0033-1414
PROPRIA CURES. Abbreviated title: P C. Text in Dutch. 1890. w. EUR 50; EUR 30 to students (effective 2005). adv. bk.rev.; film rev.; play rev. abstr.; illus.
Published by: Stichting Propria Cures/Propria Cures Foundation, Vendelstraat 2, Amsterdam, 1012 XX, Netherlands. redactie@propriacures.nl, http://www.propriacures.nl. Circ: 3,300.

378.198 USA
PROSPECTOR. Text in English. 1914. s-w. USD 12.
Published by: University of Texas at El Paso, Student Publications, 105 E Union UT, El Paso, TX 79968. TEL 915-747-5161. Circ: 11,000.

378.198 GBR
THE PULSE. Text in English. 1961. 3/yr. free. adv. bk.rev.; film rev.; play rev. illus. **Document type:** *Consumer.*
Former titles: Sussed; Unionews
Published by: University of Sussex, Students Union, University Of Sussex, Falmer, Brighton, Sussex BN1 9QF, United Kingdom. TEL 44-1273-678555, FAX 44-1273-678875. Ed., R&P Jemima Kingsley. Adv. contact Nicola Stait. Circ: 7,500.

378 USA ISSN 0883-6590
PULTENEY ST. SURVEY. Text in English. 1973. q. free. 52 p./no.; back issues avail. **Document type:** *Magazine, Consumer.*
Published by: Hobart & William Smith Colleges, 295 Pulteney St, Geneva, NY 14456. TEL 315-781-3540, FAX 315-781-3400, cawilliam@hws.edu, http://www.hws.edu/new/pss. Ed. Catherine Williams. Circ: 24,000.

378.1 USA ISSN 0033-4502
LH1.P9
PURDUE ALUMNUS. Text in English. 1912. 6/yr. membership. adv.
Indexed: CADCAM.
Published by: Purdue Alumni Association, Memorial Union Bldg 160, W, Lafayette, IN 47906-6212. TEL 317-494-5175, FAX 317-494-9179. Ed. Tim Newton. Adv. contact Sharon Martin. Circ: 65,000.

378 USA
PURDUE EXPONENT. Text in English. 1884. d. (Mon.-Fri.) (academic yr.; 3/wk. Mon., Wed., Fri. summer). free on campus; USD 50 per academic semester (effective 2005). **Document type:** *Newspaper.*
Published by: Purdue Student Publishing Foundation, 460 N Western Ave, West Lafayette, IN 47906. TEL 765-743-1111, FAX 765-743-6087, help@purdueexponent.org, http://www.purdueexponent.org. Ed. Yuri Victor. Adv. contact Christy Harrison. Circ: 20,000 morning (controlled and free). Wire service: AP.

378 CAN ISSN 0706-8808
QUAD. Text in English. 1953. a. CND 12. adv. **Document type:** *Newsletter.*
Published by: Bishop's University, Student's Representative Council, P O Box 2133, Lennoxville, PQ J1M 1Z7, Canada. TEL 819-569-9551. Ed. Eryn Whitehead. Circ: 1,050.

378.1 USA ISSN 0033-5045
QUAKER CAMPUS. Text in English. 1914. w. USD 20; suggested donation. adv. bk.rev.; film rev.; play rev. illus.
Published by: Whittier College, Quaker Campus, PO Box 8613, Whittier, CA 90608. TEL 310-907-4354, FAX 310-945-5301. Circ: 2,000 (controlled).

378 CAN ISSN 0843-8048
QUEEN'S ALUMNI REVIEW. Text in English. 1927. bi-m. CND 15 (effective 1999). adv. bk.rev. back issues avail. **Document type:** *Consumer.* **Description:** Keeps Q.U. graduates up to date on new developments in all Faculties of the University, contains news of fellow graduates, and provides opinions and comments on news of current interest to grads.
Related titles: Online - full text ed.
Published by: Queen's University Alumni Association, Summerhill, 99 University Ave, Kingston, ON K7L 3N6, Canada. TEL 613-533-2060, 800-267-7837, FAX 613-533-6828, review@post.queensu.ca, http://advancement.queensu.ca/alumni_review. Ed. Ken Cuthbertson. Adv. contact Daphne Tao. B&W page USD 1,750, color page USD 2,485; trim 10.88 x 8.5. Circ: 91,000.

378 CAN
QUEEN'S JOURNAL. Text in English. 1873. s-w. (Sep.-Apr.; w. May-Aug.). CND 12. adv. bk.rev.; film rev.
Related titles: Microfiche ed.
Published by: Queen's University, Alma Mater Society Inc., 99 University Ave, Kingston, ON K7L 3N6, Canada. TEL 613-547-5511. Ed. Chris Armstrong. Circ: 9,500.

378 CAN
THE QUILL. Text in English. 1910. w. CND 20; CND 30 foreign. adv. bk.rev.; film rev. **Document type:** *Newspaper.*
Published by: Brandon University, 270 18th Ave, Brandon, MB R7A 6A9, Canada. TEL 204-727-9660, FAX 204-726-3498. Ed. Trevor Rinn. Circ: 2,000.

378.1 USA
QUINCY UNIVERSITY BULLETIN. Text in English. 1944. 4/yr. free. illus. **Document type:** *Bulletin.*
Formerly (until 1993): Quincy College Bulletin (0033-6556)
Media: Duplicated (not offset).
Published by: Quincy University, Office of Public Relations, 1800 College Ave, Quincy, IL 62301. TEL 217-222-8020, FAX 217-228-5473. Ed., R&P Pam Sherman TEL 217-228-5275. Circ: 12,000.

R A U - RAPPORT. see *EDUCATION—Higher Education*

745.4071 USA
R I S D VIEWS. Text in English. 1989. 3/yr. free. back issues avail. **Description:** For the alumni, students, parents, faculty and staff of the college and museum of art.
Published by: Rhode Island School of Design, Two College Street, Providence, RI 02903-2784. TEL 401-454-6349, FAX 401-454-6351, lsilander@risd.edu. Ed. Liisa Silander. Circ: 21,000.

378 USA
R U MAGAZINE. (Radford University) Text in English. 1979. 3/yr. free. adv. bk.rev.
Formerly (until July 1993): Radford
Published by: Radford University, Office of Public Information, PO Box 6916, Radford, VA 24142. TEL 703-831-5182, FAX 703-831-5036. Ed. Rob Tucker. Circ: 48,000.

378.1 AUS
RABELAIS. Text in English. 1968. fortn. (during school term). AUD 12. adv. bk.rev.; film rev.; play rev. illus.
Published by: La Trobe University, Students Representative Council, Bundoora, VIC 3083, Australia. Circ: 15,000.

378.1 USA ISSN 0033-930X
RACQUET (LA CROSSE). Text in English. 1909. w. (during school yr.). free. adv. **Document type:** *Newspaper.*
Indexed: SPI, SportS.
Published by: University of Wisconsin at La Crosse, 1725 State St, La Crosse, WI 54601. TEL 608-785-8378. Circ: 5,000.

378.1 USA ISSN 0033-7447
RACQUETTE. Text in English. 1926. w. free. adv. bk.rev.; film rev.; play rev. charts; illus.
Published by: State University of New York, College at Potsdam, 119 Borrington Student Union, Potsdam, NY 13676. TEL 315-267-8451, FAX 315-267-2170. Ed. Jude Kiah. Circ: 3,500 (controlled).

378.198 USA ISSN 1042-3052
RADCLIFFE NEWS. Text in English. 1980. q. free. illus. **Document type:** *Newsletter.* **Description:** For alumnae and students. Covers events at the college.
Formerly: Second Century Radcliffe News
Published by: (Office of Communications), Radcliffe College, 10 Garden St, Cambridge, MA 02138. TEL 617-495-8608, FAX 617-496-4640. Ed. Liz Brown Lavoie. Circ: 50,000 (controlled).

378.1 USA ISSN 0033-7528
LH1.R2
RADCLIFFE QUARTERLY. Text in English. 1916. s-a. USD 25 domestic; USD 35 foreign (effective 2005); free to alumni. bk.rev. charts; illus. 32 p./no. 2 cols./p.; **Document type:** *Magazine, Academic/Scholarly.* **Description:** For students and alumnae. Covers issues of interest to educated women.
Published by: Radcliffe Institute for Advanced Study at Harvard University, President and Fellows of Harvard College, 10 Garden St., Cambridge, MA 02138. TEL 617-495-8608, FAX 617-496-0255, quarterly@radcliffe.edu, http://www.radcliffe.edu/about/news/quarterly/index/php. Ed. Patricia Harrison. Circ: 35,000 (controlled).

378 USA
THE RAM. Text in English. 1918. w. (Thu.). free; USD 20 subscr - mailed. **Document type:** *Newspaper.*
Published by: Fordham University, 441 E. Fordham Rd., Bronx, NY 10458. TEL 718-817-1000, FAX 718-817-4319, http://www.edu/student_services/ram. Circ: 12,000 (paid and free).

378 USA
THE RAM PAGE. Text in English. 1936. w. adv. bk.rev. **Document type:** *Newspaper.*
Published by: Angelo State University, Department of Communication, Drama and Journalism, 2601 W Ave N, San Angelo, TX 76909. TEL 325-942-2322, FAX 325-942-2078, ram.page@mailserv.angelo.edu, http://www.angelo.edu/aorg.rampage. Ed. Jerry Becker Jr. Adv. contact Cindee Sharp. Circ: 4,500 (controlled).

C

378.1 USA
RANDOLPH-MACON COLLEGE. BULLETIN. Text in English. 1930. 3/yr. free. **Document type:** *Bulletin.*
Formerly: Randolph-Macon Alumni Bulletin (0033-9180)
Published by: Randolph-Macon College, PO Box 5005, Ashland, VA 23005. TEL 804-752-4721, FAX 804-752-3712, levans@rmc.edu. Ed., R&P Linda N Evans. Circ: 12,100.

378 USA
RANGER (AMARILLO). Text in English. 1929. w. free. adv. bk.rev. **Document type:** *Newspaper.*
Published by: Amarillo College, PO Box 447, Amarillo, TX 79178. TEL 806-371-5290, FAX 806-371-5398. Ed. Glenda Taylor. R&P, Adv. contact Donna Salter. Circ: 2,500.

371.83 GBR ISSN 0048-6809
RATCLIFFIAN. Text in English. 1870. a. GBP 7 (effective 1998). adv. illus. index. **Document type:** *Bulletin.*
Published by: Ratcliffe College, Syston, Leics, United Kingdom. TEL 44-1509-817000, FAX 44-1509-817004. Ed. Terence Stanford. Circ: 1,000.

378 USA
THE RATTLE. Text in English. 1912. s-a. adv. bk.rev. **Document type:** *Trade.* **Description:** Provides leadership and education information in support of fundraising programs.
Formerly: Rattle of Theta Chi
Published by: Theta Chi Funds for Leadership and Education, Inc., 3330 Founders Rd, Indianapolis, IN 46268. TEL 317-824-1881, FAX 317-824-1908, IHQ@thetachi.org, http://www.thetachi.org. Ed., R&P, Adv. contact El Ahlwardt. Circ: 35,000 (controlled).

378.198 USA ISSN 1081-8375
RAVEN REVIEW. Text in English. 1987. s-a. looseleaf. free. back issues avail. **Document type:** *Newsletter.* **Description:** Contains alumni news, faculty updates, campus and community information.
Published by: Coffeyville Community College, 400 W 11th St, Coffeyville, KS 67337. TEL 316-251-7700, FAX 316-252-7098, tonij@raven.ccc.cc.ks.us, http://www.ccc.cc.ks. Ed. Toni R Jabben. Circ: 10,000.

378 USA
THE RECORD (BUFFALO). Text in English. 1913. s-w. (Tue. & Fri.). USD 15; free domestic to students (effective 2005). **Document type:** *Newspaper, Consumer.* **Description:** For the students and faculty of Buffalo State College.
Published by: Buffalo State College, 1300 Elmwood Ave., Buffalo, NY 14222. TEL 716-878-4000. Ed. Carl Burke. Circ: 10,000 (free).

378 USA ISSN 0745-1679
THE RECORD OF SIGMA ALPHA EPSILON. Text in English. 1880. q. free to qualified personnel. adv. **Document type:** *Academic/Scholarly.* **Description:** Covers chapter news, alumni news, directory and major fraternity activities.
Published by: Sigma Alpha Epsilon National Fraternity, PO Box 1856, Evanston, IL 60204. TEL 847-475-1856, FAX 847-475-2250, cmundy@saefraternity.org, http://www.saefraternity.org. Ed., R&P, Adv. contact Christopher Mundy. Circ: 150,000 (controlled).

▼ new title ➤ refereed ✶ unverified ♦ full entry avail.

C

378 USA
THE RED & BLACK (ATHENS). Text in English. 1893. d. (Mon.-Fri.). USD 195; free on campus (effective 2005). adv. **Document type:** *Newspaper.*
Related titles: Supplement(s): Between the Hedges.
Published by: The Red & Black Publishing Co., Inc., 540 Baxter St., Athens, GA 30605. TEL 706-443-3000, FAX 706-433-3033, advertising@randb.com, http://www.redandblack.com. Pub. Harry Montevideo. adv.: col. inch USD 18.90. Circ: 17,000 morning (paid). Wire service: AP.

378.198 USA
RED AND BLACK (BALTIMORE). Text in English. 1958. s-m. adv. **Description:** Covers campus news and sports, student organizations and clubs.
Published by: Catonsville Community College, 800 S Rolling Rd, Baltimore, MD 21228. TEL 301-455-4485. Ed. Kitty Williams. Circ: 4,000.

378.1 USA ISSN 0034-1940
RED AND BLACK (WASHINGTON). Text in English. 1909. s-m. free to students and faculty. adv. film rev.
Published by: Washington & Jefferson College, 60 S Lincoln St, Washington, PA 15301. TEL 412-222-4400. Circ: 1,500 (controlled).

378.1 USA ISSN 0034-1959
RED AND GREEN. Text in English. 1923. w. adv. bk.rev.; play rev. illus. **Document type:** *Newspaper.*
Published by: Minot State University, Publications Board, 500 University Ave W, Minot, ND 58707. TEL 701-858-3354, FAX 701-858-3353, http://www.misu.nodak.edu/redgreen/. Adv. contact Karen Holmen. Circ: 3,000.

378 GBR
REDBRICK; the University of Birmingham student newspaper. Text in English. 1950. bi-w. free. **Document type:** *Newspaper.*
Published by: University of Birmingham, Guild of Students, Edgbaston Park Rd, Edgbaston, Birmingham B12 9PD, United Kingdom. TEL 0121-472-1841, FAX 0121-472-2099. Ed. Roland Buerk. Circ: 3,500.

378 CAN
THE REFLECTOR. Text in English. 1965. fortn. CND 15 domestic; CND 25 foreign (effective 2004). adv. bk.rev.; dance rev.; music rev.; play rev.; software rev.; video rev. illus. **Document type:** *Newspaper.*
Published by: Reflector Publications Society, 4825 Richard Rd, S W, Calgary, AB T3E 6K6, Canada. TEL 403-440-6268, FAX 403-440-6762, TheReflector@TheReflectorOnline.com, http://www.TheReflectorOnline.com. Ed., R&P, Adv. contact Ivar Bergs. B&W page CND 800, color page CND 1,250; trim 17 x 11. Circ: 10,000.

387 USA
REGIS COLLEGE. Text in English. 1936. 3/yr. free to qualified personnel. bk.rev. **Document type:** *Academic/Scholarly.* **Description:** Articles about and of interest to alumnae, students, parents, faculty and administration of the College.
Formerly: Regis Today
Published by: Regis College, Publications Office, 235 Wellesley St, Weston, MA 02193. TEL 617-768-7000, http://www.regiscollege.edu. Ed. Anne Souza. Circ: 12,000.

378.1 USA
RENSSELAER POLYTECHNIC. Text in English. 1869. w. free. adv. bk.rev.; film rev.; play rev. illus. **Document type:** *Newspaper.*
Formerly: Polytechnic (0032-4051)
Published by: Rensselaer Union, Rensselaer Union, PO Box 35, Troy, NY 12180-3590. TEL 518-276-6770, FAX 518-276-8728, http://poly.union.rpi.edu/. Ed. Erika Zamek. R&P, Adv. contact Theresa Kaseta-Nguyen. color page USD 325. Circ: 8,000.

378 CAN
LA REPLIQUE✶ . Text in French. m. free.
Published by: Publi-Peq, 3575 bd St Laurent, Ste 232, Montreal, PQ H2X 2T7, Canada. TEL 514-845-8628. Circ: 500.
Co-sponsor: College de Victoriaville.

378 USA
REPORTER (RIVER FOREST). Text in English. 1923. bi-w. free. adv. **Document type:** *Newspaper.*
Related titles: Microfilm ed.
Published by: Rosary College, 7900 W Division, River Forest, IL 60305. TEL 708-524-6035, FAX 708-366-5360.

378 USA ISSN 1084-6093
RESPONSE (SEATTLE). Text in English. 1975. bi-m. free.
Published by: Seattle Pacific University, Office of University Relations, Third Ave W & W Nickerson, Seattle, WA 98119. Ed. Jennifer Johnson Gilnett. Circ: 30,000.

378 USA
THE REVEILLE. Text in English. 1898. s-w. (Mon.-Fri.). free domestic on campus; USD 75 subscr - mailed (effective 2005). **Document type:** *Newspaper.*
Formerly: Daily Reveille
Published by: Louisiana State University, B-26 Hodges Hall, Baton Rouge, LA 70803. TEL 225-578-1697, FAX 225-578-1698, editor@lsureveille.com, http://www.lsureveille.com. Ed. Dorothy Pan. Circ: 19,000 morning (free). Wire service: AP.

378 GBR
THE REVIEW (LEEDS). Text in English. 1992. s-a. back issues avail. **Document type:** *Newsletter.* **Description:** Keeps alumni of the University of Leeds in touch, informed and involved with their university and each other.
Formerly (until 1997): Degrees North
Published by: University of Leeds, Alumni Office, Leeds, W Yorks LS2 9JT, United Kingdom. TEL 44-113-233-6109, FAX 44-113-233-4029, review@leeds.ac.uk, http://www.leeds.ac.uk/. Ed., R&P, Adv. contact Jayne Glennon. Circ: 70,000 (controlled).

378 USA
THE REVIEW (NEWARK). Text in English. 1882. s-w. (Tue. & Fri.). free on campus; USD 40 (effective 2005). **Document type:** *Newspaper, Consumer.*
Published by: University of Delaware, Office of Public Relations, 150 S College Ave, Newark, DE 19716. TEL 302-831-2771. Circ: 10,000 (paid).

378 600 COL ISSN 0120-1557
REVISTA DE EGRESADOS. Text in Spanish. 1976. q. free.
Published by: Universidad Tecnologica de Pereira, Asociacion de Egresados, Apartado Aereo 97, Pereira, RIS, Colombia. Circ: 3,000.

378 COL ISSN 0121-6279
K5
REVISTA EXTERNADISTA. Key Title: Externadista. Text in Spanish. 1992. s-a. COP 10,000 per issue (effective 1997). **Document type:** *Academic/Scholarly.*
Published by: Universidad Externado de Colombia, Departamento de Publicaciones, Calle 12, No 0-38 Este, Apartado Aereo 034141, Santafe de Bogota, Colombia. publicaciones@uexternado.edu.co, http://www.uexternado.edu.co. Ed. Camilo Calderon.

378.1 ESP
REVISTA U D. (Universidad de Deusto) Text in Spanish, Basque. 1984. q. EUR 6.01 domestic; USD 10 foreign (effective 2002).
Former titles: Boletin de Informacion Universitaria (1578-813X); (until 1994): Universidad de Deusto. Noticias (1130-9040)
Published by: Universidad de Deusto, Apdo 1/E, Bilbao, 48080, Spain. TEL 34-94-4139162, FAX 34-94-4456817, publicaciones@deusto.es.

378 CAN
REVUE MATRICULE✶ . Text in French. s-m.
Published by: Publi-Peq, 3575 bd St Laurent, Ste 232, Montreal, PQ H2X 2T7, Canada. TEL 514-526-0235. Circ: 17,000.

378 USA
RHODE ISLAND COLLEGE ALUMNI MAGAZINE. Text in English. 1952. s-a. free to qualified personnel. adv. **Document type:** *Newsletter, Academic/Scholarly.*
Former titles: Perspectives (Providence); (until 1986): Rhode Island College Alumni Association. Alumni Review; Rhode Island College Alumni Association. Review (0035-4589)
Published by: Rhode Island College, Alumni Association, 600 Mt Pleasant Ave, Providence, RI 02908. TEL 401-456-8086, FAX 401-456-8851. Ed. Ellie O'Neill. Circ: 28,000 (paid).

378.1 ZAF
RHODES ALUMNI NEWSLETTER. Text in English. 1951. a. free. adv. bk.rev. **Document type:** *Newsletter.*
Formerly: Rhodes Newsletter; Which superseded in part (in 1993): Rhodes Review; Which was formerly: Rhodes Newsletter (0035-4678)
Published by: Rhodes University, PO Box 94, Grahamstown, East Cape 6140, South Africa. FAX 27-46-6361902, l.griffiaen@ru.ac.za, http://www.ru.ac.za. Ed. Lisl Griffioen. R&P Lisl Griffioen Paterson. Circ: 28,000.

378 ZAF
RHODES UNIVERSITY. ANNUAL REPORT. Text in English. 1975. a. free. **Document type:** *Corporate.*
Supersedes in part (in 1996): Rhodes Review and Annual Report; Which supersedes in part (in 1993): Rhodes Review; Which was formerly: Rhodes Newsletter (0035-4678)
Published by: (Office of the Vice Chancellor), Rhodes University, PO Box 94, Grahamstown, East Cape 6140, South Africa. TEL 27-46-603-8457, FAX 27-46-6361902, http://www.ru.ac.za. Ed., R&P Linda Haschick. Circ: 31,000.

378.198 USA
RICE THRESHER. Text in English. 1916. w. USD 40 domestic; USD 105 foreign (effective 2001). adv. bk.rev.; film rev.; play rev. **Document type:** *Newspaper.*
Related titles: Online - full text ed.
Published by: Rice University, Student Publications, 6100 Main St, Houston, TX 77005. TEL 713-527-4801, FAX 713-285-5238, thresher@rice.edu, http://www.rice.edu/thresher. Ed. Robert Reichle. Adv. contact Robert Lee TEL 713-348-3967. Circ: 6,000.

378.198 USA ISSN 1076-6677
RIDER UNIVERSITY MAGAZINE. Text in English. 1991. q. free to alumni and friends. **Document type:** *Academic/Scholarly.*
Formerly (until 1994): Rider College Magazine (1060-4316); Which supersedes (1971-1991): Directions (0279-408X)
Published by: Rider University, 2083 Lawrenceville Rd., Lawrenceville, NJ 08648-3099. TEL 609-896-5165, FAX 609-895-5440, magazine@rider.edu, http://www.rider.edu. Ed., R&P Cathy Carter-Romero TEL 609-896-5119. Circ: 32,500 (controlled).

378 USA ISSN 1058-1855
RIPON MAGAZINE. Text in English. 1968. 4/yr. free. bk.rev. illus. **Document type:** *Bulletin.*
Formerly: Ripon College Magazine (0300-7928)
Published by: Ripon College, PO Box 248, Ripon, WI 54971. TEL 920-748-8364, FAX 920-748-9262. Ed., R&P Loren J Boone TEL 920-748-8365. Circ: 14,000 (controlled).

378.1 USA ISSN 0035-7510
ROCKHURST HAWK. Text in English. 1917. fortn. USD 4. adv. bk.rev. illus. reprint service avail. from PQC,ISI. **Document type:** *Newspaper.*
Published by: Rockhurst College, 1100 Rockhurst Rd, Kansas City, MO 64110-2561. TEL 816-926-4051, hawk@vax1.rockhurst.edu. Ed. Mark E Costaldi. Adv. contact Robert J Remack. Circ: 1,500.

378.1 USA ISSN 0035-7936
ROLLINS SANDSPUR. Text in English. 1894. w. free. adv. bk.rev.; dance rev.; music rev.; play rev. 16 p./no. 5 cols./p.; **Document type:** *Newspaper, Newspaper-distributed.*
Related titles: Microfilm ed.
Published by: Rollins College Student Association, Rollins College, Box 2742, Winter Park, FL 32789. http://www.rollins.edu. Eds. Elyssa Rokicki, J Anthony Guadalupe. Adv. contacts Eva Kotylak, Jennifer Williams. Circ: 1,500.

378 CAN
LA ROTONDE. Text in French. 1932. w. CND 25. adv. bk.rev.; film rev. 5 cols./p.; **Document type:** *Academic/Scholarly.*
Published by: Federation Etudiante de l'Universite d'Ottawa, 85 University, Ottawa, ON K1N 6N5, Canada. TEL 613-562-5264, FAX 613-562-5265, rotonde@uottawa.ca, http://www.uottawa.ca/~rotonde/. Ed. Charles-Antoine Allain. R&P Charles Antoine Allain. Adv. contact Edgar Donelle. Circ: 8,000.

378 USA ISSN 1071-9369
ROTUNDA. Text in English. 1921. w. USD 30. adv. bk.rev.
Indexed: RILM.
Published by: Longwood College, PO Box 1133, Farmville, VA 23901. TEL 804-395-2120, FAX 804-395-2237. Circ: 3,000.

378 USA
ROUGH WRITER. Text in English. m. free. adv. bk.rev. back issues avail. **Document type:** *Newspaper.* **Description:** Student newspaper covering education, sports, and campus activities.
Formerly: Y C News
Published by: Yavapai Community College, 1100 E Sheldon St, Prescott, AZ 86301. TEL 928-776-2221. Circ: 6,500.

378 USA ISSN 1053-5020
THE ROUND TABLE (BELOIT). Text in English. 1853. w. (during academic yr). USD 15 domestic; USD 30 foreign (effective 2000). adv. **Document type:** *Newspaper.* **Description:** Reports campus and local news and events.
Published by: Beloit College, Student Government, PO Box 109, Beloit, WI 53511. TEL 608-363-2475, rndtable@beloit.edu, http://www.beloit.edu/~rndtable. Ed., R&P Lisa J Ampleman. Circ: 2,000.

378 USA ISSN 0744-5555
THE ROUND UP. Text in English. 1907. s-w. (Mon. & Thu.). USD 52 subscr - mailed (effective 2005); free. **Document type:** *Newspaper, Consumer.*
Related titles: Online - full text ed.: (from LexisNexis).
Published by: New Mexico State University, PO Box 30004, Las Cruces, NM 88003. TEL 505-646-6397, FAX 505-646-7905, roundup@nmsu.edu, http://www.roundupnews.com/. Ed. Megan Ewald. Circ: 10,000 (free). Wire service: KR, AP.

378 USA
ROYAL PURPLE. Text in English. 1901. w. USD 15. adv.
Published by: University of Wisconsin at Whitewater, 268 E University Center, Whitewater, WI 53190. TEL 414-472-5100. Ed. Aaron Hanson. Circ: 7,000.

371.8975 DEU ISSN 0942-6639
RUBIN. Text in German. 1962. 2/yr. EUR 5; EUR 2.50 newsstand/cover (effective 2002). adv. **Document type:** *Magazine, Academic/Scholarly.*
Former titles (until 1991): Ruhr-Universitaet Bochum. Jahrbuch (0557-8981); (until 1968): Die Ruhr-Universitaet (0485-5949)
Published by: Ruhr-Universitaet Bochum, Pressestelle, Bochum, 44780, Germany. TEL 49-234-3222830, FAX 49-234-3214136, rubin@presse.ruhr-uni-bochum.de, http://www.ruhr-uni-bochum.de/rubin/. Ed. Barbara Kruse. adv.: B&W page EUR 1,750, color page EUR 3,100. Circ: 4,000 (paid and controlled).

378.1 DEU ISSN 0035-998X
LH5.H4
RUPERTO-CAROLA. Text in German. 1948. 4/yr. EUR 30; EUR 5 newsstand/cover (effective 2005). adv. bk.rev. abstr.; bibl.; charts; illus.; stat. index, cum.index. **Document type:** *Magazine, Academic/Scholarly.*
Indexed: AmH&L, HistAb, MLA-IB.
—CCC.
Published by: (Rektor der Universitaet Heidelberg), Universitaetsverlag C. Winter Heidelberg GmbH, Dossenheimer Landstr 13, Postfach 10 61 40, Heidelberg, 69051, Germany. TEL 49-6221-770260, FAX 49-6221-770269, info@winter-verlag-hd.de, http://www.winter-verlag-hd.de. Ed. Michael Schwarz. Adv. contact Edeltraud Conen. Circ: 2,200.

378 DEU ISSN 0944-4181
RUPRECHT KARLS UNIVERSITAET HEIDELBERG. PERSONALVERZEICHNIS. Text in German. a. adv. **Document type:** *Journal, Academic/Scholarly.*
Formerly (until 1993): Ruprecht Karls Universitaet Heidelberg. Personal- und Informationsverzeichnis (0178-5338)
Published by: Universitaetsverlag C. Winter Heidelberg GmbH, Dossenheimer Landstr 13, Postfach 10 61 40, Heidelberg, 69051, Germany. TEL 49-6221-770260, FAX 49-6221-770269, info@winter-verlag-hd.de, http://www.winter-verlag-hd.de.

378 DNK
RUST; Odenses studentermagasin. Text in Danish. 2001. 8/yr. free. adv.
Related titles: Online - full text ed.
Published by: Odense Studenterforlag, c/o Syddansk Universitet, Campusvej 55, Odense M, 5230, Denmark. TEL 45-65-50-27-22, rust@rust-online.dk, http://www.rust-online.dk. Ed. Pernille Redder. Circ: 4,500.

367 USA
RUTGERS MAGAZINE; for alumni & friends of New Jersey's state university. Text in English. 1914. q. USD 12; USD 3 newsstand/cover. adv. bk.rev. illus. back issues avail. **Document type:** *Academic/Scholarly.* **Description:** Features articles of interesting and noteworthy activities and projects in which Rutgers students and alumni are actively involved. Includes news of the university itself.
Former titles: Rutgers Alumni Magazine (0036-0457); Rutgers Alumni Monthly; Rutger University. Alumni Quarterly; Incorporates: Matrix; Rutgers Today
Published by: Rutgers University, Department of University Communications, Alexander Johnston Hall, College Ave & Somerset St, New Brunswick, NJ 08903. TEL 732-932-7315, FAX 732-932-8412. Ed. Lori Chambers. Pub. Christine M Haska. Adv. contact Diana Baroni. Circ: 110,000 (controlled). **Co-sponsor:** Rutgers University, Department of Alumni Relations.

378 CAN
RYERSON MAGAZINE. Text in English. 1962. 2/yr. free. adv. **Description:** Focuses on university news and developments.
Formerly: Ryerson Rambler (0705-9191)
Published by: Ryerson Polytechnic University, Office of University Advancement, 350 Victoria St, Toronto, ON M5B 2K3, Canada. TEL 416-979-5304, FAX 416-979-5166. Ed., Adv. contact Jean Burrows. B&W page CND 1,680; trim 11 x 8.5. Circ: 65,000 (controlled).

S A I S REVIEW; a journal of international affairs. see *POLITICAL SCIENCE—International Relations*

371.8 CAN ISSN 1200-815X
S A S C A NEWSLETTER. Text in English. 1986. irreg., latest 1999. CND 15 membership (effective 2000). **Document type:** *Newsletter, Trade.*
Former titles (until 1995): S A S C A Journal (1180-9698); (until 1988): Sashatchewan Association of Students Council Advisors. Newsletter (0836-2785); (until 1987): Sashatchewan Association of Students Council Advisors. Journal (0834-5163)
Published by: (Saskatchewan Association of Student Council Advisors), Saskatchewan Teachers' Federation, 2317 Arlington Ave., Saskatoon, SK S7J 2H8, Canada. TEL 306-373-1660, 800-667-7762, FAX 306-374-1122, http://www.stf.sk.ca.

378 USA
S D S U ALUMNUS. (South Dakota State University) Text in English. 1910. 4/yr. free. adv. **Document type:** *Newsletter.* **Description:** Publishes campus news, university sports news, and alumni news.
Published by: South Dakota State University, Alumni Association, Tompkins Alumni Center, Box 515, Brookings, SD 57007. TEL 605-697-5198, FAX 605-697-5487, Cathy@foundation.SDstate.edu. Ed. Cathy Nelson. Circ: 40,000.

378 USA
S D S U MAGAZINE; for alumni and friends of San Diego State University. (San Diego State University) Text in English. 1994. q. adv. **Description:** Contains features and news about the university.
Published by: San Diego State University, University Communications, 5500 Campanile Dr, San Diego, CA 92182-0763. TEL 619-594-5204, FAX 619-594-5956, sdsumag@mail.sdsu.edu. Ed., Adv. contact Rick Moore. page USD 3,500; trim 10.75 x 8.5. Circ: 15,000 (controlled).

378 CAN
S R C BULLETIN. Text in English. w. **Document type:** *Newsletter.*
Published by: Bishop's University, Student's Representative Council, P O Box 2133, Lennoxville, PQ J1M 1Z7, Canada. TEL 819-822-9697.

378 DEU
S V ZEITUNG. Text in German. 1884. q.
Published by: (Sondenhaeuser Verband), Georgi GmbH, Theaterstr 77, Aachen, 52062, Germany. Ed. Johannes Zuehlsdorff. Circ: 5,000.

378 USA
SAGA OF SIGMA TAU GAMMA. Text in English. 1927. q. USD 20 to libraries (effective 2000). adv. **Document type:** *Newsletter.* **Description:** Covers activities of the 86 chapters and 50,000 alumni members of the fraternity.
Published by: Sigma Tau Gamma Fraternity, PO Box 54, Warrensburg, MO 64093. TEL 660-747-2222, FAX 660-747-9599. Ed., R&P, Adv. contact Janille Martens. Pub. William P Bernier. Circ: 28,000 (controlled).

378 USA
SAGAMORE. Text in English. 1969. w.
Published by: Indiana University, 425 Agnes St, Indianapolis, IN 46202. TEL 317-274-2976. Circ: 12,000.

378 USA
SAGEBRUSH. Text in English. 1893. s-w. (Tue. & Fri.). free to students on campus; USD 25 subscr - mailed (effective 2005). **Document type:** *Newspaper, Consumer.*
Published by: Associated Students of the University of Nevada, The Donald W. Reynolds School of Journalism, Mail Stop 310, Reno, NV 89557. TEL 775-784-6531, FAX 775-784-1955, editor@nevadasagebrush.com. Circ: 6,200 (paid and free).

378 GBR
THE SAINT. Text in English. 1984. fortn. GBP 0.50 per issue (effective Sep. 2001). adv. bk.rev.; dance rev.; film rev.; music rev.; play rev.; rec.rev.; software rev.; tel.rev.; video rev.; Website rev. 32 p./no. 6 cols./p.; back issues avail. **Document type:** *Newspaper.* **Description:** Independent student newspaper featuring sports, arts, music and book reviews and interviews.
Former titles (until 1997): Chronicle (St. Andrews); Aein
Related titles: Online - full content ed.
Indexed: RiceAb.
Published by: The Saint, Students' Union, Students Association Building, St Mary's Pl, St Andrews, Fife KY16 9U2, United Kingdom. TEL 44-1334-477355, FAX 44-1334-462716, thesaint@st-andrews.ac.uk, contact@saintonline.co.uk, http://www.saintonline.co.uk. Ed. John Bowker. Adv. contact Eleanor Hirsch TEL 44-7773-769934. Circ: 1,500.

378.198 USA ISSN 0747-1025
ST. CLOUD STATE CHRONICLE. Text in English. 1892. s-w. USD 20. adv. **Document type:** *Newspaper.*
Published by: St. Cloud State University, 13, Stewart, MN 56301. TEL 320-255-4086. Ed. Eric Hedlund. Adv. contact David Tjornhom. Circ: 7,000.

378 GBR
ST. EDWARDS SCHOOL CHRONICLE. Text in English. 1863. s-a. back issues avail. **Document type:** *Bulletin.*
Published by: St. Edwards School, Woodstock Rd, Oxford, Oxon OX2 7NN, United Kingdom. TEL 44-1865-319231, FAX 44-1865-319206, NRQ@stedward.oxon.sch.uk, http://www.stedward.oxon.sch.uk. Ed. N R Quartley. Circ: 6,500.

378.1 CAN
ST. FRANCIS XAVIER UNIVERSITY ALUMNI NEWS. Text in English. 1963. 3/yr. CND 21. adv. bk.rev. illus. **Document type:** *Bulletin.*
Formerly: St. Francis Xavier University Contemporary and Alumni News (0036-2824)
Published by: St. Francis Xavier University, PO Box 5000, Antigonish, NS B2G 2W5, Canada. TEL 902-867-2286. Eds. Kimberly Dickson, Verna MacDonald. Circ: 21,500.

SAINT JOHN'S. see *EDUCATION—Higher Education*

ST. JOHN'S REPORTER. see *EDUCATION—Higher Education*

ST. JOHN'S REVIEW. see *EDUCATION—Higher Education*

378 USA
SAINT MARY-OF-THE-WOODS COLLEGE. ALUMNAE NEWS MAGAZINE. Variant title: Alumnae News Magazine. Text in English. q. **Document type:** *Academic/Scholarly.*
Published by: Saint Mary-of-the-Woods College, Public Relations Office, Saint Mary Of The Woods, IN 47876. TEL 812-535-5212, FAX 812-535-5241, pr-smwc@woods.smwc.edu. Ed. Ann Marie Foste. Circ: 9,000 (controlled). **Dist. by:** PO Box 2336, Terre Haute, IN 47802.

378.198 USA
SAINT MICHAEL'S COLLEGE MAGAZINE. Text in English. 1979. q. free. bk.rev. 48 p./no.; back issues avail. **Document type:** *Magazine.* **Description:** For alumni, parents and friends of the College.
Formerly (until 2001): Founders Hall (0279-3016)
Related titles: Online - full text ed.
Published by: St. Michael's College, One Winooski Park, Colchester, VT 05439. TEL 802-654-2000, FAX 802-654-2592, smcmagazine@smcvt.edu, http://www.smcvt.edu/Admin2.asp?SiteAreaID=562&Level=1. Ed. Caroline Crawford. R&P Buff Lindan. Circ: 200,000 (controlled).

378.198 USA
SAINT PETER'S; the college magazine. Text in English. 1970. 3/yr. membership only. **Document type:** *Consumer.* **Description:** News of the college and its alumni.
Published by: Saint Peter's College, Office of Public Affairs, Hilsdorf Hall, 5 Glenwood Ave, Jersey City, NJ 07306. TEL 201-915-9160. Ed. Fred Cranwell.

378 USA
SALEM STATE LOG. Text in English. 1927. bi-w. free. **Document type:** *Newspaper.* **Description:** College literary magazine.
Published by: Salem State College, Department of English, 352 Lafayette St, Salem, MA 01970-4589. TEL 508-741-7920, FAX 508-740-7204. Ed. Jon Zahlaway. R&P Ellen Golub. Circ: 4,000.

378 IDN
SALEMBA✶; suratkabar kampus Universitas Indonesia. Text in Indonesian. 1976. fortn. IDR 50 per issue.
Published by: University of Indonesia, Jalan Salemba Raya 4, Jakarta, 10430, Indonesia.

378 USA
SAMFORD CRIMSON. Text in English. w. (Wed.). USD 10 in county; USD 12 out of county (effective 2005). **Document type:** *Newspaper, Consumer.*
Published by: Samford University, 800 Lake Shore Dr., Birmingham, AL 35209. TEL 205-726-2998, crimson@samford.edu. Circ: 4,000 (paid).

378 ITA ISSN 1593-5442
SANT'ANNA NEWS; newsletter dell'Associazione Ex Allievi Scuola Superiore Sant'Anna, Pisa. Text in Italian. 1993. s-a. **Document type:** *Newsletter, Consumer.*
Published by: (Associazione Ex Allievi Scuola Superiore Sant'Anna), Edizioni E T S, Piazza Carrara 16-19, Pisa, Italy. TEL 39-050-29544, FAX 39-050-20158, info@edizioniets.it, http://www.edizioniets.it.

371.85 378 USA
SCALPEL. Text in English. 1931. s-a. USD 3.50. adv. bk.rev. illus. **Document type:** *Academic/Scholarly.*
Indexed: CISA.
Published by: Alpha Epsilon Delta, Jones Junior College, Ellisville, MS 39437. TEL 601-426-6019. Ed. Hugh E Bateman. Circ: 8,500.

371.8 IRL
AN SCEAL ON ARAS. Text in English. m. adv. **Document type:** *Magazine, Consumer.* **Description:** Contains features on entertainment, crossword puzzles, film reviews, band reviews, and information on upcoming events.
Published by: University College Cork Student Media, Aras na Mac Leinn, Cork, Ireland. TEL 353-21-4903052, FAX 353-21-4903108, studentmedia@ucc.ie, http://www.ucc.ie/anml. adv.: B&W page EUR 445.

378 USA ISSN 0886-3369
SCENE (TACOMA). Variant title: Pacific Lutheran University Scene. Text in English. 1970. q. free (effective 2005). adv. bk.rev. illus. 20 p./no. 4 cols./p.; **Document type:** *Magazine, Consumer.* **Description:** Discusses academic issues and events of interest to alumni.
Related titles: ♦ Supplement(s): Encore!.
Published by: Pacific Lutheran University, 12180 Park St., S, Tacoma, WA 98447-0003. TEL 253-531-6900, FAX 253-535-8331, scene@plu.edu, http://www.plu.edu. Circ: 45,000 (free).

378.198 USA
SCEPTER. Text in English. 1968. m. free. adv. bk.rev. back issues avail.
Published by: City University of New York, Kingsborough Community College, 2001 Oriental Blvd, Brooklyn, NY 11235. TEL 718-934-5603. Ed. Thomas Vellios. Circ: 10,000.

378 DEU ISSN 0448-1348
LH5.B7
SCHLESISCHE FRIEDRICH-WILHELMS-UNIVERSITAET. JAHRBUCH. Text in German. 1955. a. bk.rev. **Document type:** *Yearbook, Academic/Scholarly.*
Indexed: DIP, IBR, IBZ, MLA-IB.
Published by: (Stiftung Kulturwerk Schlesien, Schlesische Friedrich-Wilhelms-Universitaet), Jan Thorbecke Verlag GmbH und Co., Senefelder Str 12, Ostfildern, 73760, Germany. TEL 49-711-4406-0, FAX 49-711-4406199, auslieferung@thorbecke.de, http://www.thorbecke.de.

C

378 USA
SCHOLASTIC MAGAZINE. Text in English. 1867. w. USD 30. adv. bk.rev.; film rev.; play rev. back issues avail. **Description:** Campus magazine highlighting the entertainment, student life, and sports concerning the University of Notre Dame.
Published by: University of Notre Dame, La Fortune Center, 315 LaFortune Student Center, Notre Dame, IN 46556-5635. TEL 219-239-7569, FAX 219-63-9648, scholastic.scholast.1@nd.edu. Ed., R&P Steve Myers TEL 219-631-5029. Adv. contact Jenny Stachowiak. Circ: 8,070.
Subscr. to: Business Manager, Scholastic, 303 La Fortune, Notre Dame, IN 46556.

378 USA
SCHOOL OF ART INSTITUTE OF CHICAGO. ALUMNI NEWS. Text in English. 1982. s-a. free to alumni. bk.rev. **Document type:** *Newsletter.*
Formerly: Visions (St. Louis)
Published by: School of the Art Institute of Chicago, 37 S Wabash, Chicago, IL 60603. FAX 312-263-0141, kpapaicd@artic.edu. Ed., R&P Rita Price. Circ: 12,000 (controlled).

SCHOOL OF BUSINESS UPDATE. see *BUSINESS AND ECONOMICS*

371.8975 ISR ISSN 0334-7591
LG341.J438
SCOPUS. Text in English. 1969. a. free. adv. illus. **Description:** Feature magazine on the university's research, researchers, and topics related to the university.
—BLDSC (8205.940000).
Published by: The Hebrew University of Jerusalem, Department of Media Relations and Publications, Mount Scopus, Jerusalem, 91905, Israel. TEL 972-2-5882811. Ed., R&P, Adv. contact Lisa Clayton. Circ: 25,000.

C

378.1 GBR
SCRAPIE. Text in English. 1967. bi-m. free. adv. bk.rev.; play rev. illus. **Document type:** *Consumer.*
Former titles: Fleece; Javelin (0047-1941)
Published by: University of Bradford, Students' Union, Richmond Rd, Bradford, W Yorks BD7 1DP, United Kingdom. TEL 44-1274-383254, FAX 44-1274-308340. Ed. Helen Dalley. Adv. contact Elizabeth Tatlaw. page GBP 250. Circ: 2,800.

378 USA ISSN 1083-6934
CODEN: JVADAJ
THE SCRIBE (BRIDGEPORT); student newspaper of the University of Bridgeport. Text in English. 1929. bi-w. free to qualified personnel (effective 2005). adv. bk.rev.; film rev.; play rev. **Document type:** *Newspaper, Consumer.* **Description:** Informs undergraduate and graduate students, faculty, and staff of news and events at the university and the community.
Related titles: Online - full text ed.
Published by: University of Bridgeport, Student Center, 244 University Ave, Bridgeport, CT 06601. TEL 203-576-4382, FAX 203-576-4485, scribe@cse.bridgeport.edu, http://www.bridgeport.edu/scribe/. Ed. Sharon Loh. R&P, Adv. contact Aurora Lee. page USD 25,280. Circ: 2,500 (controlled).

371.8975 810 770 USA ISSN 1543-091X
PS508.C6
SCRIBENDI. Text in English. 1995. a. free. **Description:** Publishes the writing, photography and art of undergraduate students of Western Regional Honors Council (WRHC) schools.
Published by: University of New Mexico, University Honors Program, University College, Rm 21, Albuquerque, NM 87131. TEL 505-277-7407, scribend@unm.edu, honors@unm.edu, http://www.unm.edu/%7Escribend/, http://www.unm.edu/%7Ehonors. Ed. Sandy Askew. **Co-sponsor:** Western Regional Honors Council.

378 USA
SCROLL. Text in English. 1888. w. (Tue.). USD 30 for 6 mos.; USD 60; free newsstand/cover (effective 2005). 24 p./no. 6 cols./p.; **Document type:** *Newspaper, Consumer.*
Published by: Brigham Young University - Idaho, 525 S Center, Rexburg, ID 83460. TEL 208-496-2900, FAX 208-496-2911, scrolleditor@byui.edu, http://www.byui.edu/scroll/. R&P Lee Warnick. Circ: 8,000 (paid and free).

371.85 USA ISSN 0036-9799
SCROLL OF PHI DELTA THETA. Text in English. 1874. q. membership. adv. bk.rev.
Media: Duplicated (not offset). **Related titles:** Online - full text ed.
Published by: Phi Delta Theta Fraternity, 2 So Campus, Oxford, OH 45056. TEL 513-523-6345, FAX 513-523-9200, htttp://www.phidelt-ghq.com. Ed., R&P Rob Pasquinucci. Adv. contact Bob Biggs. Circ: (controlled).

378 CRI
SEMANARIO UNIVERSIDAD. Text in Spanish. 1970. w. USD 40 in Central America; USD 50 in the Americas; USD 60 elsewhere (effective 2001). adv. bk.rev. back issues avail. **Document type:** *Newspaper.* **Description:** Contains sections covering the nation, culture, opinion, sports, foreign affairs, and letters to the editor.
Related titles: E-mail ed.; Supplement(s): Forja.
Published by: Universidad de Costa Rica, Apdo. 21-2060, 2050 San Pedro de Montes de Oca, San Jose, Costa Rica. TEL 506-207-5355, FAX 506-207-4774, TELEX 2544 UNICORI, carlosmc@cariari.ucr.ac.cr, http://cariari.ucr.ac.cr/~semana/univ.html. Ed. Carlos Morales Castro. Pub., Adv. contact Carlos Campos Vargas TEL 506-207-5460. B&W page CRC 90,000, color page CRC 110,000. Circ: 15,000.

378.1 BRA ISSN 0101-3742
SEMINA (LONDRINA). Text in Portuguese. 1978. irreg.
Indexed: AgBio, AnBrAb, BioCN&I, CPA, DSA, FCA, FS&TA, ForAb, HelmAb, HerbAb, HortAb, IndVet, MEDLINE, MaizeAb, NemAb, NutrAb, PBA, PGrRegA, PHN&I, PN&I, PoultAb, ProtozoAb, RDA, RM&VM, RPP, S&F, SIA, SeedAb, SoyAb, TDB, VetBull, WAE&RSA, WeedAb.
—CISTI, Infotrieve.
Published by: Universidade Estadual de Londrina, Caixa Postal 6001, Londrina, PR 86051-990, Brazil. TEL 55-43-33714000, FAX 55-43-33284440, http://www.uel.br.

378 USA
THE SENATOR. Text in English. 1921. a. USD 12. adv. **Document type:** *Newspaper.*
Published by: Davis and Elkins College, 100 Campus Dr, Elkins, WV 26241. TEL 304-636-1900. Circ: 1,000.

378 GBR ISSN 0267-033X
SESAME; the newspaper of the Open University. Text in English. 1972. 6/yr. GBP 5. adv. bk.rev. illus. **Document type:** *Newspaper.* **Description:** Links students and staff of the Open University.
Indexed: HECAB.
—BLDSC (8253.096500).
Published by: Open University, The Open University, Walton Hall, Milton Keynes, Bucks MK7 6AA, United Kingdom. TEL 44-1908-653761, FAX 44-1908-652247, http://www.open.ac.uk. Ed. Margaret Salter. Adv. contact Sheila Forman. page GBP 3,000; trim 265 x 370. Circ: 140,000.

378.1 USA
SEWANEE. Text in English. 1934. q. free. adv. illus. **Document type:** *Consumer.* **Description:** Contains news and features of interest to alumni and friends.
Formerly: Sewanee News (0037-3044)
Indexed: ArtHuCI.
Published by: The University of the South, 735 University Ave, Sewanee, TN 37383-1000. TEL 931-598-1424. Ed., R&P, Adv. contact Sarah Metzgar. Circ: 35,000.

378 USA
THE SEWANEE PURPLE. Text in English. bi-w. adv. **Document type:** *Newspaper.*
Published by: The University of the South, 735 University Ave, Sewanee, TN 37383-1000. TEL 615-598-1204. Ed. Kelly M Smith. Adv. contact Ashley Saunders.

079.62 059.927 EGY
AP95.A6S395
AL-SHABAB AL-ARABI; jaridat al-mab'uthin wal-mughtaribin wal-tullab al-'arab. Text in Arabic. 1960. w. illus. **Document type:** *Newspaper.*
Published by: Majlis al-A'la lil-Shabab wal-Riyadiyyah, P O Box 1466, Cairo, 61511, Egypt. TEL 20-2-3452426.

SHANGHAI JIAOTONG DAXUE XUEBAO. see *TECHNOLOGY: COMPREHENSIVE WORKS*

378 CAN
SHEAF. Text in English. 1912. w. CND 25 (effective 2002). adv. bk.rev.; film rev.; music rev. **Document type:** *Newspaper.*
Published by: Sheaf Publishing Society, University of Saskatchewan, 93 Campus Dr, Saskatoon, SK S7N 5B2, Canada. TEL 306-966-8688, FAX 306-966-8699, ss_sheaf@duke.usask.ca, http://www.usask.ca/~ss_sheaf. Eds. Bree Hagan, Mark Ferguson. Adv. contact Don Charabin. Circ: 10,000.

378 USA
THE SHEPHERD COLLEGE PICKET. Text in English. 1896. m. free to students and college personnel. adv. bk.rev. **Document type:** *Newspaper.*
Related titles: Microfilm ed.
Published by: Shepherd College, PO Box 3210, Shepherdstown, WV 25443. TEL 304-876-2511, FAX 304-876-3262. Eds. Barbara Walker, Trish Reid. R&P Jim Lewin. Adv. contact Pascha Adamo. Circ: 4,000 (controlled).

371.85 USA ISSN 8750-7536
SHIELD & DIAMOND. Text in English. 1891. q. adv. **Description:** Provides news of general interest to members regarding chapter and alumni activities, fraternity's administration. Includes profiles and interviews of social alumni.
Published by: Pi Kappa Alpha Fraternity, 8347 W Range Cove, Memphis, TN 38125. TEL 901-748-1868. Ed. Timothy J McNary. Circ: 92,000.

359 USA ISSN 0488-6720
VA49
SHIPMATE. Text in English. 1938. 10/yr. USD 50 membership (effective 2005). adv. bk.rev. back issues avail. **Document type:** *Magazine, Consumer.* **Description:** All material is oriented to the Naval Academy, the Sea Services, and Naval Academy alumni. Articles are historical, of current developments, philosophical or anecdotal.
Related titles: Online - full text ed.
Published by: U S Naval Academy Alumni Association, Inc., 247 King George St., Annapolis, MD 21402-5068. TEL 410-295-4000, FAX 410-295-4004, mike.collins@usna.com, http://www.usna.com. Circ: 30,000.

THE SHORTHORN. see *EDUCATION—Higher Education*

378 USA
SIDELINES. Text in English. 1912. 2/w. USD 17.50 (effective 2000). adv. bk.rev.
Published by: Middle Tennessee State University, PO Box 42, Murfreesboro, TN 37132. TEL 615-898-2815. Circ: 8,000.

378.1 USA ISSN 0097-6563
LJ75.S82
SIGMA PHI EPSILON JOURNAL. Text in English. 1902. 3/yr. membership. adv. back issues avail. **Document type:** *Newsletter.*
Related titles: Microfilm ed.
Published by: Sigma Phi Epsilon Fraternity, Inc., PO Box 1901, Richmond, VA 23215. TEL 804-353-1901, FAX 804-359-8160, journal@sigephg.org, http://www.sigep.org. Ed., Adv. contact Nathan Gamble. Circ: 140,000.

378.1 USA
SIGNATURES. Text in English. 1918. 4/yr. free.
Formerly (until 1986): Anderson College News (0003-293X)
Published by: Anderson University, 1100 E 5th St, Anderson, IN 46012-3495. TEL 317-649-9071. Ed. Jack W Williams. Circ: 32,000.

378 USA
THE SIGNPOST. Text in English. 1940. 3/w. (Mon., Wed., Fri.). free; USD 9 subscr - mailed for 3 mos. (effective 2005). **Document type:** *Newspaper.*
Published by: Weber State University, 3750 Harrison Blvd., P.O. Box 2110, Ogden, UT 84408-2110. TEL 801-626-7121, FAX 801-626-7401, ahess@weber.edu, http://www.wsusignpost.com/. Ed. Natalie Clemens. Circ: 5,000 evening (free).

SILHOUETTE. see *LITERARY AND POLITICAL REVIEWS*

378 USA ISSN 1054-3031
SILVER & BLUE. Text in English. 1980. bi-m. USD 15. bk.rev. back issues avail. **Document type:** *Academic/Scholarly.*
Published by: University of Nevada at Reno, Office of Communications, Jones Visitor Center 165, Reno, NV 89557-0129. TEL 702-784-1447, FAX 702-784-1422, silverblue@unr.edu. Ed. C J Hadley. Pub. Sandra Rogers. adv.: B&W page USD 1,700; trim 10.88 x 8.38. Circ: 33,000 (controlled). **Subscr. to:** University of Nevada Foundation, MS 162, Reno, NV 89557. TEL 702-784-1587.

SIMMONS LIBRARIAN. see *LIBRARY AND INFORMATION SCIENCES*

378.1 USA ISSN 0049-0512
LH1.S45
SIMMONS REVIEW. Text in English. 1921. 3/yr. free. bk.rev. illus. **Document type:** *Academic/Scholarly.*
Published by: Simmons College, 300 The Fenway, Boston, MA 02115. TEL 617-521-2363, FAX 617-521-3193, pwalsh@simmons.edu, http://www.simmons.edu/new-notable/new-review.html. Ed., R&P Patricia Walsh. Circ: 23,000 (controlled).

371.85 USA ISSN 8750-5347
ML27.U5
THE SINFONIAN. Variant title: Sinfonian Magazine. Text in English. 195?-1988; resumed 19??. s-a. USD 15. adv. bk.rev. illus. **Description:** Covers activities of members and alumni of Phi Mu Alpha.
Formerly: Sinfonian Newsletter (0037-5594)
Published by: Phi Mu Alpha Sinfonia Fraternity of America, Inc., 10600 Old State Rd, Evansville, IN 47711. TEL 812-867-2433, 800-473-2649, FAX 812-867-0633, lyrecrest@sinfonia.org, http://www.sinfonia.org. Eds. James Morris, Lori Richardson. Circ: 17,500 (controlled).

378.1 SGP ISSN 0049-0547
SINGAPORE UNDERGRAD✶. Text in English. 1972 (vol.6). 3/yr. SGD 10. adv. illus.
Published by: National University of Singapore, Students' Union, 10 Kent Ridge Crescent, Singapore, Singapore.

378 USA
THE SISKIYOU. Text in English. 1938. w. USD 25. bk.rev.; film rev.; play rev. charts; illus. 5 cols./p.; back issues avail. **Document type:** *Newspaper.*

Published by: Southern Oregon State College, 1250 Siskiyou Blvd, Ashland, OR 97520. TEL 503-552-6307, FAX 503-552-6440, siskiyou@tao.sosc.osshe.edu. Ed. Jessica Smith. adv.: page USD 511. Circ: 3,000.

378 SWE ISSN 0566-3091
AS284
SKRIFTER ROERANDE UPPSALA UNIVERSITET. B, INBJUDNINGAR. Text in Swedish. 1961. irreg., latest vol.131, 2001. price varies. back issues avail. **Document type:** *Monographic series, Academic/Scholarly.*
Related titles: ♦ Series of: Acta Universitatis Upsaliensis. ISSN 0346-5462.
Published by: Uppsala Universitet, Acta Universitatis Upsaliensis/University Publications from Uppsala, PO Box 256, Uppsala, 75105, Sweden. TEL 46-18-4713922, http://www.ub.uu.se/upu/auu. Ed. Bengt Landgren. **Dist. by:** Almqvist & Wiksell International.

378 USA
SLANT (MADISON). Text in English. 1971. m. USD 10. adv.
Published by: Madison Area Technical College, 3550 Anderson St, Madison, WI 53704. TEL 608-246-6809, FAX 608-246-6880. Circ: 4,000.

378.198 USA
SMITH ALUMNAE QUARTERLY. Text in English. 1909. q. USD 35 to members. bk.rev. **Document type:** *Consumer.*
Published by: Smith College, Alumnae Association, Alumnae House, Northampton, MA 01063. FAX 413-585-2073. Ed. Judith Gingerich. Circ: 20,000.

378 CAN ISSN 0838-4401
SOMMETS. Text in French. 1988. q. free. adv. bk.rev. **Document type:** *Academic/Scholarly.* **Description:** Articles of interest to graduates and friends of the University.
Published by: Universite de Sherbrooke, Pavillon J S Bourque, 2500 bd de l Universite, Sherbrooke, PQ J1K 2R1, Canada. TEL 819-821-7388, FAX 819-821-7900, bruno.levesque@courrier.usherb.ca, http://www.usherb.ca/scsi/sommets/s-index.html. Ed. Bruno Levesque. Adv. contact France Champagne. B&W page CND 1,500, color page CND 2,100. Circ: 55,000 (controlled).

378 USA
SOUTH DAKOTAN. Text in English. 1905. 3/yr. free. adv. **Document type:** *Newsletter.*
Published by: University of South Dakota, Alumni Association, 414 E Clark St, Vermillion, SD 57069. TEL 605-677-6714, FAX 605-677-6717, http://www.usd.edu/foundation/alumni.html, http://www.usd.edu/foundation/alumni.html. Ed. Nancy H McCahren. Circ: 35,000 (controlled).

051 USA ISSN 0038-3430
THE SOUTH END. Text in English. 1969. d. (Mon.-Fri.). USD 75 (effective 2005). adv. bk.rev. charts; illus.; tr.lit. **Document type:** *Newspaper, Consumer.*
Related titles: Microfiche ed.; Online - full text ed.: (from LexisNexis).
Published by: Wayne State University, 5425 Woodward Ave., Detroit, MI 48202. TEL 313-577-7878, FAX 313-993-8108, editor@southend.wayne.edu, http://www.southend.wayne.edu. Ed. Joseph Wilson. adv.: col. inch USD 10. Circ: 8,000. Wire service: AP.

378 USA
SOUTH SUBURBAN COLLEGE COURIER. Text in English. 1927. m. free. bk.rev.; film rev.; play rev. charts; illus. **Document type:** *Newspaper.*
Published by: South Suburban College, 15800 S State St, South Holland, IL 60473. TEL 708-596-2000, FAX 708-210-5758. adv.: page USD 400. Circ: 10,000.

SOUTHEASTERNER. see *JOURNALISM*

378 USA
SOUTHERN ALUMNI. Text in English. 1939. q. USD 40 membership (effective 2005). adv. bk.rev. back issues avail. **Document type:** *Magazine, Consumer.*
Formerly: Alumnus (Carbondale) (8750-3360)
Published by: S I U Alumni Association, Colyer Hall, Southern Illinois University, Carbondale, IL 62901-6809. alumni@siualumni.com, http://www.siualumni.com, http://www.siualumni.com/. Eds. Gene Green, Gene Green. Circ: 100,000 (paid and controlled).

378.198 USA ISSN 1540-7276
SOUTHERN DIGEST. Text in English. 1928. bi-w. (Tue. & Fri.). USD 30 (effective 2005). adv. bk.rev. 16 p./no. 5 cols./p.; **Document type:** *Newspaper.*
Published by: Southern University, PO Box 10180, Southern Branch P O, Baton Rouge, LA 70813. TEL 504-771-2230, FAX 504-771-3253, digest@subr.edu, http://www.southerndigest.com. Adv. contact Stephanie Cain. Circ: 8,000. Wire service: AP, LAT-WAT.

SOUTHERN GAMEPLAN. see *SPORTS AND GAMES*

378.1 USA ISSN 0038-4380
SOUTHERN NEWS AND VIEWS. Text in English. 1961. q. illus. **Description:** Update on University of Southern Mississippi news, alumni meetings and alumni news.
Published by: University of Southern Mississippi, Alumni Association, PO Box 5013, Hattiesburg, MS 39406. TEL 601-266-5013. Ed. J Claire Gerald. Circ: 48,500.

378.198 USA
SOUTHWEST BAPTIST UNIVERSITY OMNIBUS. Text in English. w. USD 38 (effective 2000). adv. **Document type:** *Newspaper.*
Published by: Southwest Baptist University, 1600 University Ave, Bolivar, MO 65613. TEL 417-326-1833, FAX 417-326-0935, omnibus@sbuniv.edu. Ed. Jill Detwiler. R&P Ronda Middleton TEL 417-328-1826. Adv. contact Kelli Fulton. Circ: 2,000 (controlled).

378 USA ISSN 0038-4852
SOUTHWESTERN (GEORGETOWN). Text in English. 1970. q. illus. **Document type:** *Newspaper.*
Published by: Southwestern University, Student Publications, PO Box 6048, S U Sta, Georgetown, TX 78626. TEL 512-863-1345, FAX 512-863-1347. Circ: 1,000.

378 GBR
SPAGEHETTI JUNCTION; the monthly voice of the biggest university in Birmingham. Text in English. 1992. m. free (effective 2005). adv. bk.rev. back issues avail. **Document type:** *Magazine, Consumer.* **Description:** Serves as a platform for students views and interests and features articles on awide range of subjects of interest to both students and staff.
Formerly (until 2001): deUCE
Published by: University of Central England, Union of Students, The Union Building, Franchise St, Birmingham, B42 2SZ, United Kingdom. TEL 44-121-3316801, FAX 44-121-3316802, donna.powell@uce.ac.uk, union.comms@uce.ac.uk, http://www.unionofstudents.com/. Ed. Michelle Singer. Adv. contact Donna Powell. page GBP 525; 210 x 297. Circ: 4,000 (controlled).

378 USA
SPARTAN DAILY. Text in English. 1934. d. (Mon.-Fri.). USD 25 (effective 2005). adv. 6 p./no. 6 cols./p.; **Document type:** *Newspaper.*
Related titles: Microfilm ed.: (from LIB).
Published by: San Jose State University, Washington Sq., San Jose, CA 95192. TEL 408-924-3275, FAX 408-924-3282, spartandailyads@casa.sjsu.edu, http://www.thespartandaily.com. adv.: col. inch USD 9.05. Circ: 6,500 morning (paid). Wire service: AP.

SPEAKER AND GAVEL (ONLINE EDITION). see *EDUCATION*

378 USA
THE SPECTATOR (SEATTLE). Text in English. 1933. w. (Thu.). free to students (effective 2005). bk.rev.; film rev.; play rev. **Document type:** *Newspaper.*
Published by: Seattle University, 900 Broadway, Seattle University, Seattle, WA 98122-4460. TEL 206-296-6000, FAX 206-296-7163, spectator@seattleu.edu, http://www.spectator-online.com. Circ: 5,500 (free).

378 USA
THE SPECTRUM. Text in English. 1950. 3/w. (Mon., Wed., Fri.). free to students on campus; USD 35 subscr - mailed semester; USD 70 subscr - mailed (effective 2005). **Document type:** *Newspaper.*
Contact Owner: Spectrum Student Periodical, Inc., SUNY-Buffalo, 132 Student Union, Amherst, NY 14260. TEL 716-645-2468, FAX 716-645-2766, wings.buffaloedu/publications/spectrum. Circ: 10,000 (paid). Wire service: AP.

378.198 USA
SPECTRUM (FAIRFIELD). Text in English. 1983. w. USD 20. adv. bk.rev.; film rev.; play rev. **Document type:** *Newspaper.*
Formerly: Obelisk
Published by: Sacred Heart University, 5151 Park Ave, Fairfield, CT 06432. TEL 203-371-7963. Circ: 2,500.

SPHINX; the student magazine for Liverpool. see *LITERARY AND POLITICAL REVIEWS*

378 GBR
SPIKE. Text in English. 1968. every 3 wks. free. adv. bk.rev.; play rev. **Document type:** *Academic/Scholarly.* **Description:** News and reviews of general interest.
Published by: (Students Union), University of Bath, Claverton Down, Bath, Avon BA2 7AY, United Kingdom. TEL 0225-826151, FAX 0225-462508. Ed. Ellie Barker. Circ: 3,000.

378.1 USA
SPOTLIGHT (EMPORIA). Text in English. 192?. 5/yr. (4 newspaper, 1 magazine format). membership. illus. **Document type:** *Newsletter.*
Formerly: Kansas State Teachers College Alumni Association. Alumni News (0022-8818)
Indexed: RehabLit.
Published by: (Emporia State University, Alumni Association), Emporia State University Press, 1200 Commercial, Emporia, KS 66801-5087. TEL 316-341-5454, FAX 316-341-5589. Ed. Cora Shown. Circ: 6,800.

378.1 USA
SPRING ARBOR COLLEGE JOURNAL. Text in English. 1970 (vol.50). q. free to alumni. illus.
Former titles: Spring Arbor College Update; Spring Arbor College Bulletin (0038-8564)
Published by: Spring Arbor College, 106 E. Main, Spring Arbor, MI 49283. TEL 517-750-1200, FAX 517-750-6604. Ed. Shannon Scholten. Circ: 12,000.

378 USA
SPRINGHILLIAN. Text in English. 1923. w. USD 25 (effective 1999). adv. bk.rev. **Document type:** *Newspaper.*
Published by: Spring Hill College, 4000 Dauphin St, Mobile, AL 36608. TEL 334-380-3850, FAX 334-460-2185, pmcgraw@shc.edu. Ed. Kristine Thompson. Adv. contact Pat McGraw. Circ: 2,100 (controlled).

378.198 USA ISSN 0888-7411
STALL. Text in English. 1969. 16/yr. (every 3 wks.). adv. bk.rev.; film rev.; play rev. charts; illus. back issues avail. **Document type:** *Newspaper.* **Description:** Contains reviews, sports items, entertainment, letters, comics, public opinions and classifieds.
Related titles: Microfilm ed.
Published by: Brookdale Community College, 765 Newman Springs Rd, Lincroft, NJ 07738. TEL 201-842-1900. Ed. Joan Raymond. Adv. contact Meredith Monroe. Circ: 5,000.

378.198 USA ISSN 1063-2778
STANFORD. Text in English. 1973. bi-m. adv. bk.rev.
Formerly: Stanford Magazine (0745-3981)
Related titles: Online - full text ed.
Published by: (Stanford Alumni Association), Stanford Magazine, Frances C. Arrillaga Alumni Center, Stanford, CA 94305-6105. TEL 650-723-2021, FAX 650-725-8676, http://www.stanfordmag.org, http://www.stanford.mag.org. Ed. Walter W Forsiak. Circ: 125,000 (controlled).

650 USA ISSN 1094-5423
HF1134
STANFORD BUSINESS. Text in English. 1931. q. USD 10; USD 12 foreign. bk.rev. **Document type:** *Bulletin.* **Description:** Articles focus on the people, programs, events and ideas of the Business School.
Former titles (until 1997): Stanford Business School Magazine (0883-265X); (until 1984): Stanford G S B (0164-6605); (until 1979): Stanford Business School Alumni Bulletin (0361-3615); Stanford University. Graduate School of Business. Bulletin (0038-9803)
Published by: Stanford University, Graduate School of Business, 518 Memorial Way, Stanford, CA 94305-5015. FAX 415-725-6750, gsb_newsline@gsb.stanford.edu, http://gsb-www.stanford.edu/gsbhome.html. Ed. Cathy Castillo. Circ: 20,000.

378.1 USA ISSN 0038-9757
STANFORD CHAPARRAL. Text in English. 1899. bi-m. USD 15; USD 25 foreign (effective 1999). adv. bk.rev.; rec.rev.; film rev. illus. **Description:** Student humor magazine.
Address: PO Box 18916, Stanford, CA 94309. TEL 650-723-1468, oldboy@chappie.stanford.edu, http://chappie.stanford.edu. Ed. Old Boy. adv.: page USD 450. Circ: 14,000.

371.805 USA
STANFORD DAILY. Text in English. 1892. d. (Mon.-Fri.). USD 216.50 in state; USD 200 out of state; free domestic on campus (effective 2005); Shorter term rates for any one academic quarter are also available.. **Document type:** *Newspaper, Consumer.*
Related titles: Alternate Frequency ed(s).: Stanford Weekly. w. (Summer).
Published by: Stanford Daily Publishing Corp., Storke Student Publication Bldg, Ste 101, (corner of Santa Teresa St and Lomita Dr), Stanford, CA 94305-2240. TEL 650-725-2100, FAX 650-725-1329, eic@daily.stanford.edu, http://www.stanforddaily.com. Ed. Cynthia H Cho. Adv. contact Lilla Toal. Circ: 10,000 morning (paid and free). Wire service: AP, RN.

378 USA
THE STATE HORNET. Text in English. 1947. w. (Wed.). free domestic to students (effective 2005). **Document type:** *Newspaper.*
Published by: California State University - Sacramento, University Union Bldg. 2nd Fl, Sacramento, CA 95819-6102. TEL 916-278-6583, FAX 916-278-5578, statehornet@yahoo.com, http://www.statehornet.com/. Circ: 12,000 (paid and free). Wire service: AP.

378 USA
THE STATE NEWS. Text in English. 1906. d. (Mon.-Fri.). free on campus; USD 50, USD 90 subscr - mailed; USD 30 per semester (effective 2005). **Document type:** *Newspaper, Consumer.*
Contact: State News, Inc., 345 Student Services Bldg, East Lansing, MI 48824-1113. TEL 517-355-3447, FAX 517-353-6355, editorchief@statenews.com, http://www.statenews.com/. Ed. Amy Bartner. Circ: 31,500 morning (paid and free). Wire service: AP.

C

▼ new title ➤ refereed ✶ unverified ♦ full entry avail.

C

378   USA
STATE PRESS. Text in English. 1912. d. (Mon.-Fri.) (Fall-Spring; w. Tue. Summer). USD 125 subscr - mailed per academic year & Spring semester (effective 2005); free on campus. **Document type:** Newspaper, Consumer.
Published by: Arizona State University, Student Publications, Matthews Center, Rm. 2, Tempe, AZ 85287-1502. TEL 480-965-7572, FAX 480-965-8484, state.press@asu.edu, http://www.statepress.com. Ed. Cameron Eickmeyer. Wire service: AP.

378   USA
STATE UNIVERSITY OF NEW YORK AT ALBANY. UPDATE. Text in English. 1977. bi-w. (Sep.-May). free. 8 p./no.; back issues avail. **Document type:** Newsletter. **Description:** Reports on university activities and achievements.
Related titles: Online - full content ed.
Published by: State University of New York at Albany, Media & Marketing Office, UAB 212, University at Albany, State University of New York, Albany, NY 12222. TEL 518-437-4980. Ed. Greta Petry. Circ: 3,500.

378.1   USA
STATEMENT (FREDONIA). Text in English. 1971. 4/yr. free. illus. back issues avail. **Document type:** Newspaper, Internal. **Description:** Covers alumni news.
Formerly: Fredonia Statement (0046-4988)
Published by: State University of New York, College at Fredonia, Office of Public Information, Fredonia, NY 14063. TEL 716-673-3323, FAX 716-673-3156, http://www.fredonia.edu. Ed. Christine Davis Mantai. Circ: 36,000.

378   USA
STATESMAN (WANTAGH). Text in English. 1957. s-w. (Mon. & Thu.). free (effective 2005). adv. **Document type:** Newspaper.
Published by: Statesman Association, PO Box 1530, Stony Brook, NY 11790. TEL 631-632-6480, advertising@sbstatesman.org, http://www.sbstatesman.org. Adv. contact Patricia Gallo. page USD 395; bleed 9.75 x 14. Circ: 6,000. Wire service: AP.

378   USA
STEPHENS LIFE. Text in English. 1929. w. USD 20. **Document type:** Newspaper. **Description:** Informs students, faculty, and staff of Stephens College of community events and issues of interest.
Published by: Stephens College, PO Box 2014, Columbia, MO 65215. TEL 573-876-7112. Circ: 2,000.

STERN BUSINESS REPORT. see BUSINESS AND ECONOMICS

620   USA   ISSN 0039-1328
STEVENS INDICATOR. Text in English. 1884. q. free to alumni, students, and other qualified personnel. adv. bk.rev. **Document type:** Consumer.
—Linda Hall.
Published by: Stevens Alumni Association, Castle Point, Hoboken, NJ 07030. TEL 201-216-5161, FAX 201-216-5374, alumni-log@stevens-tech.edu. Ed., R&P Ellen Usher Durkin. Adv. contact Harry W Bodemann. Circ: 21,000 (controlled).

378   CAN   ISSN 0710-4537
THE STRAND. Text in English. 1958. fortn. adv. bk.rev.; film rev.
Published by: Victoria University, 150 Charles St West, Toronto, ON M5S 1K9, Canada.

378.1   GBR   ISSN 0039-2243
STRATHCLYDE TELEGRAPH. Text in English. 1960. fortn. free. adv. bk.rev.; film rev.; play rev.
Published by: University of Strathclyde, Students' Association, 90 John St, Glasgow, G1 1JH, United Kingdom. FAX 041-552-0775. Circ: 6,000.

053   NLD   ISSN 0165-6759
STUDENT. Text in Dutch. 1963. 10/yr. adv. bk.rev. **Document type:** Academic/Scholarly.
Formerly: Forum Academiale
Published by: De Studenten Uitgeverij, Smidtstraat 12, Schraard, 8746 NG, Netherlands. TEL 31-517-531583, FAX 31-517-532042, studenten.uitgeverij@wxs.nl. Circ: 65,000.

059.9277   MLT
THE STUDENT/L-ISTUDENT. Text in Maltese. 1977. 3/yr.
Published by: University of Malta, University Students' Council, Msida, Malta.

378.198   IND
STUDENT ACTION. Text in English. 1982. m. film rev.
Published by: (All Indian Students Federation), Atul Kumar Anjan, 4-7 Asaf Ali Rd., New Delhi, 110 002, India.

378   USA
STUDENT AFFAIRS JOURNAL ONLINE✳. Text in English. 1996. irreg. **Description:** For professionals, practitioners and scholars in the field of college student affairs.
Media: Online - full text.
Indexed: HEA.
Address: PO Box 1682, Glendora, CA 91740. connect@sajo.org, http://www.digiserve.com/connect/sajo/. Ed. Steve Eubanks.

378   GBR
STUDENT DIRECT. Text in English. 1932. w. free. adv. bk.rev.; film rev.; play rev. back issues avail. **Document type:** Newspaper.
Formerly: Mancunion
Published by: University of Manchester, Student Union, University Of Manchester, Oxford Rd, Manchester, Lancs M13 9PR, United Kingdom. TEL 44-161-275-2943, FAX 44-161-275-2936, umunews@umu.man.ac.uk. Ed. Andrew Ward. Adv. contact Jacqui Soo. Circ: 25,000.

378   USA
STUDENT ECHO. Text in English. w.
Published by: University of Tennessee at Chattanooga, 641 Vine St, Chattanooga, TN 37402. TEL 615-755-4298.

378   GBR
STUDENT HACK. Text in English. 1991. fortn. free. **Document type:** Newsletter.
Formerly: Lister
Published by: University of Bradford, Students' Union, Richmond Rd, Bradford, W Yorks BD7 1DP, United Kingdom. TEL 44-1274-383254, FAX 44-1274-305340. Ed. Justin Coe. Circ: 2,500.

368   USA   ISSN 1070-9657
STUDENT LEADER. Text in English. 1993. 3/yr. adv. illus. **Document type:** Consumer. **Description:** Covers issues of interest to student leaders and members of student governments throughout the U.S.
Related titles: Online - full text ed.: (from SoftLine Information).
Indexed: DYW.
Published by: Oxendine Publishing, Inc., PO Box 14081, Gainesville, FL 32604-2081. TEL 352-373-6907, FAX 352-373-8120, info@studentleader.com, http://www.studentleader.com. Ed. W H Oxendine Jr. Pub., Adv. contact W.H. Oxendine Jr. page USD 17,135. Circ: 115,000.

378.1   USA   ISSN 0039-2758
STUDENT LIFE (ST. LOUIS). Text in English. 1878. s-w. USD 65. adv.
Published by: (Washington University), Student Life Publishers Board, PO Box 1039, St. Louis, MO 63130. TEL 314-935-5995. Ed. Benjamin Cannon. R&P, Adv. contact Andrew O'Dell. Circ: 8,000.

378.198   USA
STUDENT MOVEMENT. Text in English. 1915. w. USD 18. adv. bk.rev.
Published by: Andrews University, Student Association, Berrien Springs, MI 49104. Ed. Patricia Nash. Circ: 3,000.

378   USA
STUDENT PRINTZ. Text in English. 1910. s-w. (Tue. & Thu.). free (effective 2005). **Document type:** Newspaper. **Description:** Informs students of events on campus.
Related titles: Online - full content ed.
Published by: University of Southern Mississippi, Student Printz, 118 College Dr. #5088, Hattiesburg, MS 39406-0001. TEL 601-266-4266, FAX 601-266-4268, printz@usm.edu, http://www.printz.usm.edu. Circ: 7,000 (free).

371.8 796.3   SWE
STUDENT PULSEN. Text in Swedish. 1983. q. membership. 24 p./no. 5 cols./p.
Published by: (Studentpulsen), S S I F - Stockholms Studenters I F, Fack 50093, Stockholm, 10405, Sweden. TEL 46-8-15-10-75, FAX 46-8-15-76-28. Ed. Eva Wiklund. adv.: B&W page SEK 18,000, color page SEK 21,000; trim 375 x 250. Circ: 52,500.

378   GBR
THE STUDENT TIMES; the Dundee students newspaper. Text in English. 1967. irreg. (3/term). adv. **Document type:** Newspaper.
Formerly (until 1995): Annasach
Published by: University of Dundee, Students Association, Airlie Pl, Dundee, Angus DD1 4HP, United Kingdom. studenttimes@dundee.ac.uk, president@dusa.co.uk, http://www.dusa.dundee.ac.uk. Circ: 6,000.

378.1   PAK   ISSN 0039-2790
STUDENT TIMES INTERNATIONAL. Text in English. 1953. q. PKR 4, USD 1.
Published by: Student Times Publications, 22D Block D, N. Nizamabad, Karachi, Pakistan. Ed. Qaseemuddim Pasha. Circ: 16,000.

STUDENT TRAVELLER. see TRAVEL AND TOURISM

378.1   USA   ISSN 0039-2804
STUDENT VOICE. Text in English. 1916. w. USD 10. bk.rev.; film rev. illus. **Document type:** Newspaper.
Related titles: Microform ed.
Published by: University of Wisconsin at River Falls, 410 S Third St, River Falls, WI 54022. TEL 715-425-3118, FAX 715-425-4486, student.voice@urwf, http://www.urs.edu.com. Circ: 4,000.

371.8   GHA
STUDENTS WORLD. Text in English. 1974. m. adv.

Address: PO Box M 18, Accra, Ghana. TEL 233-21-774248, TELEX 2171. Ed. Emmanuel Manful. Pub., R&P Eric Ofei. Adv. contact Anthony M Eiwuley. Circ: 10,000.

378   DEU
STUDIEREN IN GOETTINGEN. Text in German. 1965. a. free. adv. **Document type:** Bulletin, Academic/Scholarly. **Description:** Contains general information for students studying in Goettingen.
Published by: Studentenwerk Goettingen, Platz der Goettinger Sieben 4, Goettingen, 37073, Germany. TEL 49-551-390, FAX 49-551-395186, http://www.studentenwerk-goettingen.de. Ed. Christa Mirwald. Circ: 10,000 (controlled).

378   USA
THE STUTE. Text in English. 1904. w. USD 20. adv. **Document type:** Newspaper.
Related titles: Online - full text ed.
Published by: Stevens Institute of Technology, CastlePoint on the Hudson, Hoboken, NJ 07030. TEL 201-659-3404, the_stute@stevens-tech.edu, http://stute.jacobus.stevens-tech.edu/. Ed. Michael Andreano. Adv. contact John Beek. Circ: 2,500.

378   DEU
STUTTGARTER UNIKURIER. Text in German. 1980. 5/yr. adv. **Document type:** Newsletter.
Published by: Universitaet Stuttgart, Referat fuer Presse- und Oeffentlichkeitsarbeit, Keplerstr 7, Stuttgart, 70174, Germany. TEL 49-711-1212297, FAX 49-711-1212188, presse@uni-stuttgart.de. Ed. Ursula Zitzler.

378.1   USA   ISSN 0039-4289
THE STYLUS. Text in English. 1931. 24/yr. (12 issues per semester). USD 10 for 6 mos.. adv. bk.rev.; film rev.; play rev.; dance rev.; music rev. illus.; stat. 42 p./no. 5 cols./p.; **Document type:** Newspaper, Academic/Scholarly.
Published by: (State University of New York at Brockport), Downtowner Publishing, 209 Student Union, Brockport, NY 14420. TEL 716-395-2230, FAX 716-395-2246, stylus@brockport.edu. Ed. Andrew L Simpson. Circ: 5,000.

378   CAN
SUITES; le magazine des diplomes de l'U Q A M. Text in English. 1991. 3/yr. adv.
Published by: (Bureau des Diplomes de l'Universite du Quebec a Montreal), Editions Montreal Camping Inc., Succ Centre Ville, C P 8888, Montreal, PQ H3C 3P8, Canada. TEL 514-987-7018, FAX 514-987-8210, magazine.suites@uqam.ca. Ed. Linda Mongeau. Adv. contact Rene Plourde. B&W page CND 1,570; trim 9.69 x 7.13. Circ: 75,000.

378   USA
SUMMIT. Text in English. 1963. w. adv. **Document type:** Newspaper.
Formerly: G
Published by: Grossmont College, 8800 Grossmont College Dr, El Cajon, CA 92020. TEL 619-465-1700. Circ: 3,600.

SUMMONS. see LAW

378   USA
THE SUNDIAL. Text in English. w. looseleaf. film rev.; play rev. abstr. back issues avail.
Published by: Randolph - Macon Women's College, 2500 Rivermont Ave, Box 396, Lynchburg, VA 24503. Ed. Lou Ann Graham. Circ: 1,000.

378   USA
THE SUNFLOWER (WICHITA). Text in English. 1895. 3/w. (Mon., Wed., Fri.). USD 43.60 (effective 2005); free. **Document type:** Newspaper.
Published by: Wichita State University, 1845 N. Fairmount, Wichita, KS 67240-0134. TEL 316-689-3640, FAX 316-978-3778, editor@wichita.edu, http://www.sunflower.wichita.edu/. Ed. Daxton Spencer. Adv. contacts Anne Weierich, Dominique Gomez. Circ: 8,000 (paid and controlled). Wire service: AP.

378   USA
SUSQUEHANNA TODAY. Text in English. 1931. q. free to qualified personnel.
Formerly: Susquehanna Alumnus
Published by: Susquehanna University, Susquehanna University, Selinsgrove, PA 17870. TEL 570-372-4119, FAX 570-372-4048, wells@susqu.edu. Ed. Gwenn E Wells. Circ: 18,000.

378   USA   ISSN 0888-2126
SWARTHMORE COLLEGE BULLETIN. Text in English. 1938. q. free. **Document type:** Bulletin.
Indexed: BHA, RILM.
Published by: Swarthmore College, 500 College Ave., Swarthmore, PA 19081. TEL 610-328-8401. Ed. Jeffrey Lott. Circ: 23,200.

378   USA
SWARTHMORE COLLEGE PHOENIX. Text in English. 1881. w. USD 26. **Document type:** Newspaper.

Published by: Swarthmore College, 500 College Ave., Swarthmore, PA 19081. TEL 610-328-8173, FAX 610-328-8674. Circ: 2,700 (controlled).

378.379 USA
SWEET BRIAR ALUMNAE MAGAZINE. Text in English. 1931. 3/yr. free. bk.rev. illus. **Document type:** *Bulletin.* **Description:** Provides alumnae and friends of Sweet Briar College with news about the association, individual alumnae and the college.
Formerly: Sweet Briar College. Alumnae Magazine (0039-7342)
Published by: Sweet Briar Alumnae Association, Sweet Briar College, Sweet Briar, VA 24595. TEL 804-381-6131, FAX 804-381-6132, sbcmagazine@sbc.edu. Ed. Nancy Godwin Baldwin. R&P Nancy G Baldwin TEL 804-381-6321. Circ: 11,500.

051 USA ISSN 0740-2619
SYNAPSE (SAN FRANCISCO). Text in English. 1955. w. USD 30 domestic; USD 40 foreign. adv. bk.rev. illus. **Document type:** *Newspaper.*
Published by: University of California at San Francisco, Synapse Publication Board, Millberry Union 123W, 500 Parnassus Ave., San Francisco, CA 94143-0376. TEL 415-476-2211, FAX 415-502-4537, Synapse@itsa.ucsf.edu, http://student.ucsf.edu/synapse, http://saawww.ucsf.edu. Circ: 5,000.

378 USA
T C U MAGAZINE. Text in English. 1956. q. **Document type:** *Newsletter.* **Description:** Provides information about TCU and topics of general interest to alumni.
Published by: Texas Christian University, PO Box 298940, Ft. Worth, TX 76129. TEL 817-921-7807, FAX 817-921-7110. Ed. John Ohendalski. Circ: 51,000 (controlled). **Subscr. to:** PO Box 297044, Ft. Worth, TX 76129.

378 DEU
T U INTERN. (Technische Universitaet) Text in German. 1985. m. free. adv. **Document type:** *Newsletter, Academic/Scholarly.*
Published by: Technische Universitaet Berlin, Presse- und Informationsreferat, Str des 17 Juni 135, Berlin, 10623, Germany. TEL 49-30-31423922, FAX 49-30-314-23909, pressestelle@tu-berlin.de, http://www.tu-berlin.de/presse/. Ed. Kristina Zerges. Circ: 13,000.

378 CAN ISSN 1187-8622
TABARET. Text in English, French. 1949. 3/yr. CND 10 (effective 2001). adv. bk.rev. **Document type:** *Academic/Scholarly.*
Formerly: University of Ottawa. Alumni and Development. Alumni News. (0832-7424)
Published by: University of Ottawa, Alumni and Development/Universite d'Ottawa, 178 Laurier ave, Ottawa, ON K1N 6N5, Canada. TEL 613-562-5857, 800-465-1888, FAX 613-562-5113, aluminfo@uottawa.ca, http://www.alum-develop.uottawa.ca, http://www.ca/alum-develops. Ed. Linda Scales. adv.: B&W page CND 1,100, color page CND 1,800; trim 10.75 x 8. Circ: 86,300.

378.198 USA
TALLADEGA STUDENT STAR. Text in English. 1921. m. USD 5. adv. bk.rev.
Formerly: Talladega Student
Published by: Talladega College, Communications Department, W Battle St, Talladega, AL 35160. TEL 205-362-0206. Circ: 1,000.

378 USA
TALLADEGAN. Text in English. 1975 (vol.93). s-a. free. illus. **Document type:** *Academic/Scholarly.*
Published by: Talladega College, 627 W Battle St, Talladega, AL 35160. TEL 256-761-6113, FAX 256-761-6197. Ed. Angela Tuck. Circ: 5,000.

378 USA
THE TALON. (University of Southern Mississippi) Text in English. 1947. q. membership. adv. illus. 48 p./no.; **Document type:** *Magazine.* **Description:** Features and news for and about former students of the University of Southern Mississippi.
Formerly (until 2000): U S M Alumni News
Published by: University of Southern Mississippi, Alumni Association, PO Box 5013, Hattiesburg, MS 39406. alumni@usm.edu. Ed. Bonnie J Gibbs. Adv. contact Mark Boyles TEL 601-266-5013. Circ: 14,750.

378 IND
TAMIL CEITHI MALAR. Text in Tamil. 1982. m. INR 5, USD 4.
Published by: Tamil University, Thanjavur, Tamil Nadu 613 001, India.

378 IND
TAMIL UNIVERSITY. NEWS BULLETIN. Text in English. 1982. m. INR 5, USD 4. **Document type:** *Bulletin.*
Published by: Tamil University, Thanjavur, Tamil Nadu 613 001, India.

TAYLOR; a magazine for Taylor University alumni and friends. see *EDUCATION—Higher Education*

TE DEUM; alumni newsletter. see *RELIGIONS AND THEOLOGY—Protestant*

TE DEUM TODAY. see *RELIGIONS AND THEOLOGY—Protestant*

378.198 USA ISSN 0148-9607
T171
THE TECH. Text in English. 1881. s-w. (Tue. & Fri.). USD 45 (effective 2005). adv. bk.rev. 20 p./no. 5 cols./p.; Supplement avail. **Document type:** *Newspaper.*
Related titles: Microfiche ed.; Online - full text ed.: (from LexisNexis).
Published by: Massachusetts Institute of Technology, 77 Massachusetts Ave, Room E60-100, Cambridge, MA 02139-4307. TEL 617-253-1541, 617-253-1541, FAX 617-258-8226, 617-258-8226, general@the-tech.mit.edu, http://tech.mit.edu. Ed. Kathy Lin. adv.: col. inch USD 15. Circ: 8,000. Wire service: LAT-WAT.

378 USA
TECH COLLEGIAN. Text in English. 1920. w. (Aug.-Apr.). free. adv. **Document type:** *Newspaper.*
Published by: West Virginia Institute of Technology, Student Service Center, Box 81 Old Main, Montgomery, WV 25136. TEL 304-442-3371, FAX 304-442-3239, dibran@wvit.wvnet.edu. Ed., Adv. contact Debra L Brannon. B&W page USD 125, color page USD 180; 12.5 x 10.25. Circ: 2,500.

378.1 USA ISSN 1062-077X
TECH TOPICS. Text in English. 1971. 4/yr. free to qualified personnel. adv. bk.rev. **Document type:** *Newspaper, Consumer.*
Published by: Georgia Tech Alumni Association, 190 North Ave, Atlanta, GA 30313. TEL 404-894-2391, FAX 404-894-5113, http://www.gtalumni.org. Ed. John Dunn. Pub. Joseph Irwin. Adv. contact Jeff Colburn. B&W page USD 2,000, color page USD 2,750; trim 9.5 x 13. Circ: 100,000.

378 USA ISSN 1072-1916
TECHNICIAN; North Carolina State University's newspaper since 1920. Text in English. 1920. d. (Mon.-Fri.). USD 75 domestic; USD 150 foreign (effective 2005). adv. bk.rev.; dance rev.; music rev.; play rev. charts; illus.; stat. 10 p./no. 4 cols./p.; back issues avail. **Document type:** *Newspaper.* **Description:** Covers music, entertainment, college issues, sports and opinion colums.
Related titles: Online - full text ed.: (from LexisNexis).
Published by: North Carolina State University, Student Media Authority, 323 Witherspoon Study Center, PO Box 8608 NCSU, Raleigh, NC 27695-8608. TEL 919-515-2411, FAX 919-515-5133, editor@technicianonline.com, http://www.technicianonline.com, http://www.ncstate.net/sma. Pub., R&P Fran Russ TEL 919-515-1515. Adv. contact Alan Hart. B&W page USD 1,200, color page USD 2,000; trim 21 x 13. Circ: 15,000. Wire service: LAT-WAT, UPI.

378 USA
TECHNIQUE (ATLANTA); the South's liveliest college newspaper. Text in English. 1914. w. USD 15. adv. bk.rev.; film rev.; play rev. illus. **Document type:** *Newspaper.*
Indexed: SPI.
Published by: Georgia Tech University, Research Institute, 353 1st Dr, O Keefe Bldg, Rm 035, Atlanta, GA 30332-0290. TEL 404-894-2830, editor@technique.gatech.edu. Ed. Greg Scherrer. Circ: 1,300.

378 USA
TELLURIDE NEWSLETTER. Text in English. 1912. 2/yr. looseleaf. membership. bk.rev. **Document type:** *Newsletter.*
Published by: Telluride Association, 217 West Ave, Ithaca, NY 14850. TEL 607-273-5011. Ed. Andrew R Walkling. Circ: 3,000.

378 USA
TEMPLE NEWS. Text in English. 1920. w. (Thu.). free (effective 2005). **Document type:** *Newspaper.*
Address: Temple University, 315 Student Activities Ctr., 1755 N. 13th St., Philadelphia, PA 19122. TEL 215-204-7416, FAX 215-204-1119, templenews@gmail.com. Ed. Brian White. Circ: 10,000 evening (free).

378.1 USA ISSN 0040-3156
TENNESSEE ALUMNUS. Text in English. 1917. q. donation. adv. bk.rev.
Published by: University of Tennessee at Knoxville, National Alumni Association, 107 Communications Bldg, Knoxville, TN 37996. TEL 865-974-2225, FAX 865-974-6435, http://ur.utenn.edu/alumnus. Ed. Diane Ballard. Adv. contact Tom Looney. Circ: 53,000.

378 DEU ISSN 0720-1303
TEX; die Zeitschrift der Fachhochschule fuer Technik und Wirtschaft. Text in German. 1966. a. free. back issues avail. **Document type:** *Journal, Academic/Scholarly.*
Published by: Fachhochschule Reutlingen, Hochschule fuer Technik und Wirtschaft, Alteburgstr 150, Reutlingen, 72762, Germany. TEL 49-7121-2710, FAX 49-7121-271224, studieninfo@fh-reutlingen.de, http://www.fh-reutlingen.de. Circ: 2,500. **Co-sponsor:** Betriebsverein des Technikums fuer Textilindustrie e.V., Vereinigung Reutlinger Ingenieure e.V.

378 USA ISSN 0747-1661
TEXAS AGGIE. Text in English. 1921. bi-m. USD 50 membership (effective 2005). adv. **Document type:** *Magazine, Consumer.*
Published by: Texas A & M University, Association of Former Students, 505 George Bush Dr, College Station, TX 77840-2918. TEL 979-845-7514, FAX 979-845-9263, JCooper63@AggieNetwork.com, http://aggienet.tamu.edu/programs/Texas_Aggie/Texas_Aggie.html. Ed., R&P Rebekah Carter. Adv. contact Alejandra Merheb. B&W page USD 1,400, color page USD 2,400. Circ: 65,000 (controlled and free).

378 USA
T171
TEXAS TECHSAN MAGAZINE. Text in English. 1950. bi-m. USD 25. adv. bk.rev. 56 p./no.; **Document type:** *Magazine, Consumer.*
Formerly: Texas Techsan (0040-4721)
Published by: Texas Tech University, Ex-Students Association, 17th and University, Box 45001, Lubbock, TX 79409. TEL 806-742-3641, FAX 806-742-0283, http://www.techsan.org. Ed., R&P, Adv. contact Jean Ann Cantore. Pub. Bill Dean. color page USD 1,195; trim 10.88 x 8.38. Circ: 56,000 (paid).

378 027.7 USA
TEXAS WOMAN'S UNIVERSITY. SCHOOL OF LIBRARY AND INFORMATION STUDIES. ALUMNAE NEWSLETTER. Text in English. 1978. a. **Document type:** *Newsletter.*
Formerly: Texas Woman's University. School of Library Science. Alumnae Newsletter
Published by: Texas Woman's University, School of Library and Information Studies, PO Box 425438, Denton, TX 76204-5438. FAX 817-898-2611, a_swigger@twu.edu. Ed. Keith Swigger. Circ: 3,000.

378 AUS
THARUNKA. Text in English. 1954. fortn. AUD 3. **Description:** Covers New South Wales Students Union events.
Published by: University of New South Wales, Sydney, NSW 2052, Australia. TEL 61-2-385-2840, FAX 61-2-662-2163.

C

371.85 USA
THEMIS. Text in English. 1903. q. USD 2 to non-members (effective 2000). bk.rev. illus. **Document type:** *Magazine, Consumer.* **Description:** Presents news of collegiate and alumnae chapters, their local and national philanthropic efforts, and general news of interest to women.
Indexed: FLP.
Published by: Zeta Tau Alpha, International Office, 3450 Founders Rd, Indianapolis, IN 46268. TEL 317-872-0540, FAX 317-876-3948, jill_ciminillo@zetataualpha.org, http://www.zetataualpha.org. Ed., R&P, Adv. contact Jill Anne Ciminillo. Circ: 85,000 (controlled).

378.198 CAN ISSN 0843-7092
THIRD DEGREE. Text in English. 1975 (vol.2). 2/yr. CND 50 in US & Canada; CND 75 elsewhere. adv. back issues avail. **Document type:** *Academic/Scholarly.*
Formerly (until 1989): Insight (Regina) (0706-0262)
Published by: University of Regina, Communications Office, 3737 Wascana Parkway, Regina, SK S4S 0A2, Canada. TEL 306-585-4402, FAX 306-585-4997. Ed., R&P Therese Stecyk. Circ: 30,000 (controlled).

378 USA ISSN 0160-9823
THUNDERBIRD. Text in English. 1976. 3/yr. free to alumni. adv. **Document type:** *Magazine, Consumer.* **Description:** Keeps the Thunderbird community connected with in-depth features, intriguing profiles, alumni updates, faculty research and institutional news.
Published by: Thunderbird - The Garvin School of International Management, Alumni Relations Office, 15249 N 59th Ave, Glendale, AZ 85306. TEL 602-978-7358, FAX 602-978-6814, amtb@t-bird.edu, http://www.thunderbird.edu/about_us/publications/tbird_mag/index.htm. Circ: 35,000 (controlled).

378.198 USA
THE TICKER (NEW YORK). Text in English. fortn. adv. bk.rev.; film rev.; play rev. **Document type:** *Newspaper.* **Description:** Student newspaper of Baruch College.
Published by: City University of New York, Baruch College, 17 Lexington Ave, New York, NY 10010. TEL 212-387-1182. Circ: 10,000.

378 USA
THE TIGER. Text in English. 1907. w. USD 30. adv. bk.rev. **Document type:** *Newspaper.*
Related titles: Microfilm ed.
Published by: Clemson University, PO Box 2097, Clemson, SC 29632. TEL 803-656-2150, FAX 803-656-4772. Ed. Greg Schmidt. Adv. contact Joel Moss. Circ: 12,000.

378.1 USA ISSN 0040-7879
TIMES AND CHALLENGE. Text in English. 1923. m. USD 12. adv. bk.rev.; film rev.; play rev. illus. **Document type:** *Journal, Consumer.*
Formerly: Times and Chimes
Published by: Wesleyan College, 4760 Forsyth Rd, Macon, GA 31201-4462. TEL 478-477-1110, FAX 478-757-4030, http://www.wesleyan-college.edu. Ed. Jaquis Dravis. Circ: 800.

▼ new title ➤ refereed ✶ unverified ♦ full entry avail.

378.1 ISR
TOAR; The Hebrew. Text in Hebrew. 1996. s-a. adv. **Description:** Includes information on the university, its researchers, and graduates.
Published by: Hebrew University of Jerusalem, Alumni Department Divison for Public Relations, Mount Scopus, Jerusalem, 91905, Israel. alumni@pob.huji.ac.il. Ed. Lea Tzivoni. Circ: 70,000 (controlled).

TODAY (KENT). see *CHILDREN AND YOUTH—For*

378 USA
TORCH (SEGUIN); the magazine of Texas Lutheran University. Text in English. q. free. 36 p./no.; back issues avail. **Document type:** *Magazine, Academic/Scholarly.*
Published by: Texas Lutheran University, 1000 W Court St, Seguin, TX 78155. TEL 830-372-8028, 830-372-8000, FAX 830-372-8036, 830-372-8096, torch@tlu.edu, http://www.tlu.edu. Ed., R&P Jennifer Roolf Laster TEL 830-372-8020. Pub. Stephen Anderson. Circ: 21,000.

378 USA
THE TORCH (VALPARAISO). Text in English. 1915. w. USD 40 (effective 1998). adv. bk.rev.; film rev.; play rev. charts; illus.; stat. **Document type:** *Newspaper, Consumer.* **Description:** Provides news, opinion pieces, sports stories, arts and entertainment features, and reviews to the students, faculty, and staff of Valparaiso University.
Published by: Valparaiso University, 816 Union St, Valparaiso, IN 46383. TEL 219-464-5426, torch@exodus.valpo.edu. Ed. Missy Cwik. R&P Erin Carey. Adv. contact Kim Giles. B&W page USD 400. Circ: 4,000.

378 CAN ISSN 1191-7032
TORCH (VICTORIA). Text in English. 1981. 2/yr. adv. **Document type:** *Academic/Scholarly.* **Description:** News and information about the University of Victoria, the campus, faculty and researchers.
Former titles (until 1991): U Vic Torch (University of Victoria) (1182-3836); (until 1986): Torch (Victoria, 1981) (0712-9351)
Published by: University of Victoria Communications, PO Box 1700 Stn CSC, Victoria, BC V8W 2Y2, Canada. TEL 250-721-7642, FAX 250-721-8955, mmcneney@uvic.ca, http://www.uvic.ca/torch. Ed. Mike McNeney. adv.: B&W page CND 1,300; trim 10.5 x 8. Circ: 5,200.

378 USA
TORCH & TREFOIL. Text in English. 1925. q. **Document type:** *Newsletter.* **Description:** Contains information about college service fraternity activities.
Published by: Alpha Phi Omega, 14901 E 42nd St, Independence, MO 64108. TEL 816-471-8667. Ed. Patrick W Burke. Circ: 24,000 (controlled).

378.198 USA
TOWER. Text in English. 1946. w. USD 25 (effective 1998). adv. stat.; tr.lit. back issues avail. **Document type:** *Newspaper.*
Published by: Bethany College (Bethany), c/o Gael L Cooper, Pub, Bethany, WV 26032. TEL 304-829-7951. Pub., R&P Gael L Cooper. Circ: 1,200.

378 ITA
TRA NOI; alunni ed ex-alunni del Sociale. Text in Italian. 1925. bi-m. free.
Published by: Istituto Sociale, Corso Siracusa, 10, Turin, TO 10136, Italy. TEL 39-011-357835, FAX 39-011-327487. Circ: 1,300.

378 USA ISSN 1081-3098
TRADITIONS. Text in English. 1995. q. **Document type:** *Newspaper.* **Description:** Publishes features and news about the University of Connecticut for alumni, friends and supporters.
Published by: University of Connecticut, 1266 Storrs Rd., U-144, Storrs, CT 06269-4144. TEL 860-486-2237, FAX 860-486-2063, gefrank@univrelpr.uconn.edu, http://www.uconn.edu. Ed., R&P Gary E Frank. Circ: 120,000 (controlled).

378 CAN
TRAIT-D'UNION ∗ . Text in French. 1938. s-m. free.
Published by: Publi-Peq, 3575 bd St Laurent, Ste 232, Montreal, PQ H2X 2T7, Canada. TEL 514-845-8628. Circ: 2,500.
Co-sponsor: College Maisonneuve.

371.85 USA ISSN 0041-1167
LJ121.C47
TRANSIT OF CHI EPSILON. Text in English. 1928. s-a. USD 4. illus.
—Linda Hall.
Published by: Chi Epsilon, c/o Neil J. Rowan, Ed., Civil Engineering Dept., Texas A & M University, College Sta., TX 77843. TEL 409-845-9883. Circ: 10,000.

378.198 USA
TRANSITIONS (NEW YORK). Text in English. 1989. q.
Published by: Columbia University, School of General Studies, PO Box 405 S Lewisohn Hall, New York, NY 10027. Ed. Anthony Rainone.

378.1 CAN ISSN 1498-2250
TREK MAGAZINE; the magazine of the University of British Columbia. Text in English. 1941. 3/yr. CND 15, USD 25 (effective 2001). adv. bk.rev. illus. back issues avail.
Document type: *Academic/Scholarly.*
Former titles (until 2000): University of British Columbia. Alumni Association. Chronicle (0824-1279); (until 1981): U B C Alumni Chronicle (0041-4999); (until 1948): Graduate Chronicle (0227-7786)
Indexed: CEI, CPerl.
Published by: University of British Columbia, Alumni Association, Cecil Green Park, 6251 Cecil Green Park Rd, Vancouver, BC V6T 1Z1, Canada. TEL 604-882-3313, FAX 604-822-8928, cpetty@alumni.ubc.ca, alumni@alumni.ubc.ca, http://www.alumi.ubc.ca. Ed. Chris Petty. R&P Oiyce Kwan. Adv. contact Mangot Dear. B&W page USD 1,600, color page USD 2,100; 9.75 x 7.5. Circ: 130,000 (controlled).

378 USA
TREVECCAN. Text in English. q. free. adv. **Document type:** *Consumer.* **Description:** Provides news about Treveccan University and the alumni.
Published by: Trevecca Nazarene University, 333 Murfreesboro Rd, Nashville, TN 37210. TEL 615-248-7782, FAX 615-248-1414, jmgreathous@trevecca.edu, http://www.trevecca.edu. Ed., R&P Janice M Greathouse. Circ: 17,000.

378.198 USA
TRIANGLE (DAYTON). Text in English. 1978. bi-w. USD 18. adv. bk.rev.; film rev.; play rev. charts. **Document type:** *Newspaper.*
Published by: Bryan College, PO Box 7646, Dayton, TN 37321. TEL 615-775-2041, FAX 615-775-7330, triangle@bryan.edu. Ed. David Ritterbush. R&P, Adv. contact John Carpenter. Circ: 500.

378 USA
TRIANGLE (MARION). Text in English. 1924. 5/yr.
Published by: Judson College, Bibb St, Marion, AL 36756. TEL 205-683-6161. Circ: 700.

378 USA
TRIDENT OF DELTA DELTA DELTA. Text in English. 1891. q. **Document type:** *Consumer.*
Address: PO Box 5987, Arlington, TX 76005-5987. TEL 817-633-8001, FAX 817-652-0212. Ed. Karen Jenkins. Circ: 125,000.

378 USA
TRINITONIAN. Text in English. 1942. w. USD 20. adv. bk.rev. **Document type:** *Newspaper.*
Published by: Trinity University, 715 Stadium Dr, Box 62, San Antonio, TX 78284. TEL 210-736-8556, FAX 210-736-0998. Circ: 3,000.

378.1 IRL ISSN 0041-3062
TRINITY NEWS. Text in English. 1953. w. (during school yr.). adv. bk.rev.; film rev.; play rev. charts; illus. **Document type:** *Newspaper.*
Published by: Trinity College, College Green, Dublin, 2, Ireland. TEL 01-7022535, FAX 01-6778996. Ed., Adv. contact Barbara Collins. Circ: 8,000.

378.198 USA
TRINITY TODAY!. Text in English. 1969. q. free. bk.rev. **Document type:** *Newsletter, Academic/Scholarly.* **Description:** Provides general college news to alumni and friends of the college, as well as prospective students.
Formerly (until 1997): Trinity Report; Incorporates (1991-1995): Sermon of the Month; Formerly: Trinity Tidings
Published by: Trinity Bible College, 50 S Sixth Ave, Ellendale, ND 58436. TEL 701-349-3621, FAX 701-349-5443, tbc2day@juno.com. Ed. Denis D Niles. Circ: 5,000.

378 USA
TRINITY TRIPOD. Text in English. 1863. w. USD 15. adv. bk.rev. illus. back issues avail.
Related titles: Microfilm ed.
Published by: Trinity College, 300 Summit St, Box 1310, Hartford, CT 06106. Circ: 3,000.

371.8 USA
➤ **TRUMAN REVIEW.** Text in English. 1946. s-a. free. illus. **Document type:** *Magazine, Academic/Scholarly.* **Description:** Includes current features on alumni, faculty, staff, students and current topics.
Former titles: Northeast Review; Nemoscope
Related titles: Online - full text ed.
Published by: Truman State University, Office of Advancement, McClain Hall, 100 E Normal St, Kirksville, MO 63501. TEL 660-785-4192, drood@truman.edu, http://alumni.truman.edu/review. Ed., R&P Deanna Rood. Circ: 53,000 (controlled).

378 DEU ISSN 0930-3642
DD901.T91
TUEBINGER BLAETTER. Text in German. 1898. a. EUR 8.90 (effective 2005). bk.rev. **Document type:** *Magazine, Consumer.*

Published by: Buerger- und Verkehrsverein Tuebingen e.V., An der Neckarbruecke 1, Tuebingen, 72072, Germany. TEL 49-7071-91360, FAX 49-7071-35070, mail@tuebingen-info.de, http://www.tuebingen-info.de. Ed. Albrecht Locher. Adv. contact Wolfgang Schuetz. Circ: 4,500.

378 USA
THE TUFTS DAILY. Text in English. 1980. w. (Mon.-Fri.). free to students; USD 50 per academic year; USD 25 per quarter Spring semester (effective 2005). 18 p./no.; **Document type:** *Newspaper, Consumer.*
Published by: Tufts University, School of Nutrition, Medford, MA 02155. TEL 617-627-3090, FAX 617-627-3910, editor@tuftsdaily.com; daily@tuftsdaily.com, http://www.tuftsdaily.com. Circ: 5,000 morning (controlled). Wire service: LAT-WAT.

TULANE MEDICINE. see *MEDICAL SCIENCES*

378.1 USA ISSN 0041-4026
TULANIAN. Text in English. 1927. q. free. bk.rev. 56 p./no.
Published by: Tulane University Publications, 3439 Prytania St, 400, New Orleans, LA 70115. TEL 504-865-5714, FAX 504-865-5621, tulanian@tulane.edu. Adv. contact Suzanne Johnson. Circ: 75,000 (controlled).

378 USA
TYLER JUNIOR COLLEGE NEWS. Text in English. 1928. fortn. free. adv. bk.rev.; film rev.; music rev.; play rev.; tel.rev. **Document type:** *Newspaper.* **Description:** Covers community college student interests.
Published by: Tyler Junior College, PO Box 9020, Tyler, TX 75711. TEL 903-510-2335, FAX 903-510-2708, izei@tjc.tyler.cc.tx.us. R&P Linda Zeigler.

378 USA
U A F ALUMNUS; information for University of Alaska Fairbanks graduates and former students. (University of Alaska at Fairbanks) Text in English. q. USD 35 to members. adv. **Document type:** *Newsletter.* **Description:** Contains information about the university and the alumni association; reports on new jobs, spouses, and residents of alumni.
Published by: University of Alaska at Fairbanks, Alumni Association, PO Box 750126, Fairbanks, AK 99775-0126. TEL 907-474-7081, FAX 907-474-6712. Ed., Adv. contact Brenda Wilcox. Pub. Brenda Wilcom. R&P Brenda Wilco.

378 DEU ISSN 0161-9810
HD6350.A8
U - A S T A - INFO. Text in German. 1974. w. adv. illus.
Published by: Allgemeiner Studentenausschuss der Albert-Ludwigs-Universitaet, Bertoldstr 26, Freiburg Im Breisgau, 79098, Germany. TEL 0761-203-3872. Circ: 2,000.

378 DEU
U - A S T A - INFO FUER ERSTSEMESTER. Text in German. s-a. adv. illus.
Published by: Allgemeiner Studentenausschuss der Albert-Ludwigs-Universitaet, Bertoldstr 26, Freiburg Im Breisgau, 79098, Germany. TEL 0761-2033782. Circ: 3,500.

378.4183 IRL ISSN 1393-4457
U C D CONNECTIONS. (University College Dublin) Text in English. 1993. s-a. **Document type:** *Magazine, Consumer.* **Description:** Features stories and articles for graduates of University College Dublin worldwide.
Formerly (until 1997): U C D Alma Mater (0791-8747)
Published by: (University College Dublin, Alumni Development Office), Mac Communications, Taney Hall, Eglinton Terrace, Dundrum, Dublin, Dublin 14, Ireland. TEL 353-1-2960000, FAX 353-1-2960383, info@maccommunications.ie. Ed. Sarah McQuaid. Circ: 40,000 (controlled).

U C DAVIS MAGAZINE. (University of California) see *EDUCATION—Higher Education*

378 USA
U C S B DAILY NEXUS. (University of California at Santa Barbara) Text in English. 1919. d. (Mon.-Fri.). free on campus (effective 2005). **Document type:** *Newspaper, Consumer.*
Published by: University of California at Santa Barbara, Press Council, Santa Barbara, CA 93107. TEL 805-961-2691, FAX 805-893-3905, http://www.dailynexus.com/. Ed. Stephanie Bautista. Circ: 15,000 morning (free). Wire service: AP.

378 USA ISSN 1064-6205
U C S D GUARDIAN. Text in English. 1967. s-w. USD 75. adv. **Document type:** *Newspaper.*
Published by: University of California at San Diego, Mail Code 0316 UCSD, La Jolla, CA 92093-0316. TEL 619-534-3466, FAX 619-534-7691, http://www.ucsdguardian.org. Eds. Julia Kulla Mader, Marc Comer. R&P Ann Barefield. Adv. contact Brock Halter. col. inch USD 9. Circ: 11,000.

U E NEWS. see *EDUCATION—Higher Education*

U E TODAY. see *EDUCATION*

378.1 USA ISSN 1067-4969
U I C ALUMNI MAGAZINE. (University of Illinois at Chicago) Text in English. 1996. bi-m. adv. **Description:** Covers events related to the university and its alumni, including alumni working for the public good.
Published by: University of Illinois at Chicago, Alumni Association, 322 S Green St, Ste 204, Chicago, IL 60607. TEL 312-413-2390, 800-556-2586, FAX 312-413-2327, uicaamag@uic.edu, http://www.uic.edu:80/orgs/alumni/. Ed. Patricia Weismantel. Pub. Loren Taylor. Adv. contact Debra Kozlowski.

378 DEU
U-MAIL; Regensburger Universitaetszeitung. Text in German. 1976. 6/yr. EUR 5; EUR 1 newsstand/cover (effective 2005). bk.rev. back issues avail. **Document type:** *Newspaper, Consumer.* **Description:** Provides review of research activities and academic affairs at the university.
Formerly: Regensburger Universitaetszeitung (0557-6377)
Published by: Universitaet Regensburg, Pressestelle, Universitaetsstr 31, Regensburg, 93040, Germany. TEL 49-941-943-2302, FAX 49-941-943-4929, rudolf.dietze@verwaltung.uni-regensburg.de, https://www.uni-r.de/Universitaet/RUZ/, http://www.uni-regensburg.de. Ed., R&P Rudolf Dietze. Circ: 6,000.

U N E CONVOCATION BULLETIN & ALUMNI NEWS. see *EDUCATION—Higher Education*

378.198 USA
U N L V MAGAZINE. (University of Nevada Las Vegas) Text in English. s-a. back issues avail.
Related titles: Online - full text ed.
Published by: University of Nevada, 4505 Maryland Parkway, Las Vegas, NV 89154-1012. TEL 702-895-3101, http://www.nscee.edu/unlv/News_Bureau/UNLV_Magazine/. Ed. Suzan DiBella.

378 USA
U OF L; the magazine of the University of Louisville. (University of Louisville) Text in English. 1982. q. free (effective 2005). **Document type:** *Magazine.*
Published by: University of Louisville, Communications and Marketing, 19 Development and University Relations Bldg, University of Louisville, Louisville, KY 40292. TEL 502-852-6171, FAX 502-852-7658, http://www.louisville.edu/ur/ucomm/mags/. Ed. Kevin Hyde. R&P Loren Reni Beard. Adv. contact John Chamberlain TEL 502-852-6430. Circ: 100,000 (controlled).

378.1 ZAF ISSN 0041-5405
U P E N. (University of Port Elizabeth Newspaper) Text in Afrikaans, English. 1966. irreg. free. adv. bk.rev.; film rev.; play rev. illus. **Document type:** *Newspaper.*
Published by: University of Port Elizabeth, PO Box 1600, Port Elizabeth, 6000, South Africa. TEL 27-41=5042173, FAX 27-41-5042574, piaddp@upe.ac.za. Circ: 3,000 (controlled).

378 PHL ISSN 0117-245X
U P NEWSLETTER; the community newspaper of the University of the Philippines. Text in English, Tagalog. 1972. s-m. adv. bk.rev. **Document type:** *Newspaper.*
Related titles: Online - full text ed.
Published by: University of the Philippines, Diliman, Quezon City, 1128, Philippines. TEL 63-2-9205301, http://www.upd.edu.ph. Circ: 5,000.

378 CAN
U Q A M JOURNAL. Text in English. bi-m.
Formerly: U Q A M Hebdo
Published by: (University of Quebec at Montreal), Acces Media, 1124 Marie Anne Rd, East, Ste 31, Montreal, PQ H2J 2B7, Canada. TEL 514-524-1182, FAX 514-524-7771, accesmedia@horizon.net, http://www.horizon.net/acces/media.html. Circ: 10,000.

378.1 USA ISSN 8750-7927
U S C TROJAN FAMILY. (University of Southern California) Text in English. 1970. q. free (effective 2005). illus. **Document type:** *Magazine, Academic/Scholarly.*
Former titles: Trojan Family (0042-0085); University of Southern California Alumni Review
Published by: University of Southern California, U S C Magazines, University Park KAP 248, Los Angeles, CA 90089-2538. TEL 213-740-2684, FAX 213-821-1100, magazines@usc.edu, http://www.usc.edu/dept/pubrel/trojan_family. Ed. Susan Heitman. Adv. contact Vicki Kebler TEL 213-740-3162. Circ: 195,000.

378 USA
U S F ORACLE. Text in English. 1965. d. (Mon.-Fri.). USD 20 per semester; USD 10 per Summer (effective 2005). **Document type:** *Newspaper.*
Formerly: Oracle
Published by: University of South Florida, 4202 E Fowler, SVC 0002, Tampa, FL 33620. TEL 813-974-2617, FAX 813-974-4887, http://www.usforacle.com. Ed. Tom Pedicini. Adv. contact Carolyn Stanley. Circ: 15,000 (free). Wire service: AP.

278 USA
U S NAVAL ACADEMY ALUMNI ASSOCIATION. REGISTER OF ALUMNI. Text in English. 1938. a. USD 35. adv. index. **Document type:** *Directory.*
Media: Duplicated (not offset).
Published by: U S Naval Academy Alumni Association, Inc., Alumni House, Annapolis, MD 21402. TEL 301-263-4448. Ed. Yvonne Parker. Adv. contact Bobbie Collins. Circ: 2,000.

378 USA
U T DAILY BEACON. Text in English. 1906. d. (Mon.-Fri.). USD 188 (effective 2005); free to students. **Document type:** *Newspaper.*
Published by: University of Tennessee at Knoxville, 5 Communications Bldg, Knoxville, TN 37996. TEL 865-974-3226, FAX 865-974-5569, beacon@utk.edu, http://dailybeacon.utk.edu/. Ed. Jason Johnson. Circ: 16,000 morning (free). Wire service: AP.

378 USA ISSN 1524-0517
U W M POST. (University of Wisconsin Milwaukee) Text in English. 1956. w. (Wed.). USD 80 (effective 2005). **Document type:** *Newspaper.*
Related titles: Online - full text ed.
Published by: U W M Post, Inc., PO Box 413/Union Box 88, Milwaukee, WI 53201. TEL 414-229-4578, FAX 414-229-4579, post@uwm.edu, http://www.uwmpost.com. Ed. Mackenzie Renner. Adv. contact Dan Schuze. Circ: 7,000 (paid and free).

378 CAN ISSN 1186-4745
➤ **UBYSSEY.** Text in English. 1918. s-w. CND 40. adv. bk.rev.; film rev. **Document type:** *Newspaper, Academic/Scholarly.*
Former titles (until 1949): Daily Ubyssey (1186-4737); (until 1948): Ubyssey (1186-4729)
Address: University of British Columbia, Rm 245 K, S U B, Vancouver, BC V6T 1Z1, Canada. TEL 604-822-6681, FAX 604-822-1658. R&P, Adv. contact Fernie Pereira. Circ: 12,000.

378 USA
THE UMASS LOWELL CONNECTOR. (University of Massachusetts) Text in English. 1921. w. (Tue.). free on campus (effective 2005). 12 p./no. 6 cols./p.; **Document type:** *Newspaper.* **Description:** Contains on-campus news and news from other colleges and universities. Includes art, entertainment and sports news.
Published by: University of Massachusetts Lawell Connector, One University Ave., Lowell, MA 01854. TEL 978-934-4000, connector@uml.edu, http://www.uml.edu/student-services. Circ: 100 (controlled); 4,500 (free).

378 DEU
UNI-FORUM. Text in German. 1985. m. free. adv. **Document type:** *Bulletin.*
Published by: Justus-Liebig-Universitaet, Ludwigstr 23, Giessen, 35390, Germany. TEL 49-641-9912040, FAX 49-641-9912049, christel.lauterbach@admin.uni-giessen.de, http://www.uni-giessen.de. Ed. Christel Lauterbach. Circ: 8,000.

371.805 DEU ISSN 0943-4399
UNI-INFO. Text in German. 1973. 9/yr. free. adv. **Document type:** *Newspaper, Academic/Scholarly.* **Description:** University of Oldenburg politics, news, science and culture.
Published by: Carl von Ossietzky Universitaet Oldenburg, Ammerlaender Heerstr 114-118, Oldenburg, 26111, Germany. TEL 49-441-7985446, FAX 49-441-7985545, presse@admin.uni-oldenburg.de, presse@uni-oldenburg.de, http://www.admin.uni-oldenburg.de/presse/uni-info. Ed. Gerhard Harms. Circ: 4,500 (controlled).

378 DEU
UNI-PLAERRER. Text in German. 2/yr. adv. **Document type:** *Magazine, Consumer.* **Description:** Covers student and university life in the city of Nuernberg.
Published by: plaerrer Verlags GmbH, Singerstr 26, Nuernberg, 90443, Germany. TEL 49-911-42478-0, FAX 49-911-4247899, info@plaerrer.de, http://www.plaerrer.de. Ed. Jochen Schmoldt. Adv. contact Silvia Schmausser. B&W page EUR 782, color page EUR 1,166; trim 224 x 300. Circ: 20,000 (controlled).

378 DEU
UNI-REPORT (MANNHEIM). Variant title: Universitaet Mannheim. Uni-Report. Text in German. 4/yr. adv. **Document type:** *Newspaper, Consumer.*
Published by: (Universitaet Mannheim), Grunert Medien & Kommunikation GmbH, Am Paradeplatz 5-6, Mannheim, 68161, Germany. TEL 49-621-400404-0, FAX 49-621-40040488, info@grunert-medien.de, http://www.grunert-medien.de. adv.: B&W page EUR 1,496. Circ: 8,000 (controlled).

378 DEU ISSN 0176-036X
UNI ULM INTERN; das Ulmer Universitaetsmagazin. Text in German. 1971. 8/yr. EUR 3.75 newsstand/cover (effective 2002). adv. bk.rev. **Document type:** *Newsletter, Academic/Scholarly.* **Description:** Publication for university personnel, students, scientists, engineers, and freelance professionals. Features include education, current issues, research, student news, and calendar of events.
Indexed: SCI.
Published by: Universitaet Ulm, Pressestelle, Albert-Einstein-Allee 5, Ulm, 89081, Germany. TEL 49-731-5022020, FAX 49-731-5022016, peter.pietschmann@rektoramt.uni-ulm.de, http://blitz.chemie.uni-ulm.de/ulm/uui.htm. Ed. Peter Pietschmann. Adv. contact Sabine Kindermann. B&W page EUR 1,800, color page EUR 2,850. Circ: 8,700.

378 DEU
UNICOMPACT. Text in German. 1995. bi-m. adv. **Document type:** *Magazine, Consumer.*
Published by: Evoluzione Media AG, Plinganserstr 150, Munich, 81369, Germany. TEL 49-89-7690030, FAX 49-89-76900340, redaktion@unicompact.de, http://www.unicompact.de. adv.: B&W page EUR 9,462, color page EUR 15,261. Circ: 410,000 (controlled).

378 USA
UNICORN (PHILADELPHIA). Text in English. q. **Document type:** *Newsletter.*
Formerly: Today (Philadelphia)
Published by: Peirce College, 1420 Pine St, Philadelphia, PA 19102-4699. TEL 215-545-6400, FAX 215-546-5996. Ed. Len McLean.

378 DEU ISSN 0939-4826
UNICUM; das Hochschulmagazin. Text in German. 1983. m. adv. bk.rev.; film rev.; music rev.; Website rev. illus. back issues avail. **Document type:** *Magazine, Consumer.* **Description:** Provides news and features on campus life nationwide for university students.
Published by: Unicum Verlag GmbH, Willy-Brandt-Platz 5-7, Bochum, 44787, Germany. TEL 49-234-96151-0, FAX 49-234-9615111, unicum@unicum.de, http://www.unicum.de. Ed. Wolfgang Koschny. Pubs. Hermann Josef Billstein, Manfred Baldschus. Adv. contact Joachim Senk. B&W page EUR 11,490, color page EUR 17,970; trim 210 x 295. Circ: 450,000 (controlled).

C

378 DEU ISSN 1437-8809
UNICUM BERUF; das Magazin fuer Einstieg und Aufstieg. Text in German. 1998. bi-m. adv. bk.rev.; film rev.; music rev.; software rev.; Website rev. charts; illus.; stat. back issues avail. **Document type:** *Magazine, Consumer.* **Description:** Includes articles about career, business, health and lifestyle.
Related titles: Online - full text ed.
Published by: Unicum Verlag GmbH, Willy-Brandt-Platz 5-7, Bochum, 44787, Germany. TEL 49-234-96151-0, FAX 49-234-9615111, unicum@unicum.de, http://www.unicum.de. Ed. Uwe Heinrich. Pubs. Hermann Josef Billstein, Manfred Baldschus. Adv. contact Joachim Senk. B&W page EUR 7,230, color page EUR 10,300; trim 210 x 297. Circ: 200,000.

378 DEU
UNICUM NEXT. Text in German. bi-m. bk.rev.; software rev.; Website rev. **Document type:** *Magazine, Consumer.*
Formerly: Unicum Extra
Published by: Unicum Verlag GmbH, Willy-Brandt-Platz 5-7, Bochum, 44787, Germany. TEL 49-234-961510, FAX 49-234-9615111, unicum@unicum.de, http://www.unicum.de. Pubs. Hermann Josef Billstein, Manfred Baldschus. Adv. contact Joachim Senk. Circ: 1,000,000 (controlled).

378 DEU
UNICUM SCHECKHEFT FUER STUDIENANFAENGER. Text in German. 2/yr. **Document type:** *Catalog, Consumer.*
Published by: Unicum Verlag GmbH, Willy-Brandt-Platz 5-7, Bochum, 44787, Germany. TEL 49-234-96151-0, FAX 49-234-9615111, unicum@unicum.de, http://www.unicum.de. Circ: 180,000 (controlled).

378 DEU
UNIJOURNAL; Zeitschrift der Universitaet Trier. Text in German. 1971. 5/yr. adv. bk.rev. illus. **Document type:** *Journal, Academic/Scholarly.*
Published by: Universitaet Trier, Pressestelle, Universitaetsring 8, Trier, 54286, Germany. TEL 49-651-2014239, FAX 49-651-2014247, presse@uni-trier.de, http://www.uni-trier.de. Ed., R&P, Adv. contact Heidi Neyses.

378.1 AUS ISSN 0041-7017
UNION RECORDER. Text in English. 1921. 13/yr. AUD 30. adv. bk.rev.; film rev.; play rev. illus.; stat. **Document type:** *Newsletter, Academic/Scholarly.*
Published by: University of Sydney, Level 6 Main Quadrangle A14, Sydney, NSW 2006, Australia. TEL 61-2-93513167, FAX 61-2-93513289, union@usyd.edu.au. Circ: 9,000.

378 DEU
UNISCENE; das Hamburger Hochschulmagazin. Text in German. 2000. m. adv. **Document type:** *Magazine, Consumer.* **Description:** Covers all aspects of university life including academics, health, entertainment, jobs and more.
Published by: Hey & Hoffmann Verlagsgesellschaft bR, Colonnaden 104, Hamburg, 20354, Germany. TEL 49-40-99993970, FAX 49-40-330735, http://www.uniscene.de. Ed. Kai Hoffmann. adv.: B&W page EUR 1,685, color page EUR 2,450. Circ: 29,800 (controlled).

378 DEU
UNISCENE HANNOVER. Text in German. 1989. 3/yr. adv. **Document type:** *Magazine, Consumer.*

▼ new title ➤ refereed ✶ unverified ♦ full entry avail.

Published by: Stroetmann Verlag & Agentur GmbH, Lange Laube 22, Hannover, 30159, Germany. TEL 49-511-15551, FAX 49-511-1316169. adv.: B&W page EUR 1,260, color page EUR 2,100. Circ: 15,000 (controlled).

378 CAN ISSN 1181-8409
UNISCOPE. Text in English. 1981. 20/yr.
Formerly (until 1990): Nouvel Introspec (0711-0162)
Published by: (Service de l'Information et des Relations Publiques), Universite du Quebec a Hull, C P 1250, succ B, Hull, PQ J8X 3X7, Canada. TEL 819-595-3960, FAX 819-595-3924. Ed. Roger Labelle. Circ: 600.

UNISPIEGEL (HEIDELBERG). see *EDUCATION—Higher Education*

UNIVERSAL POST. see *EDUCATION—Higher Education*

378 CRI
UNIVERSIDAD. Text in Spanish. 1970. w. CRC 2,000, USD 40. adv. bk.rev. **Document type:** *Newspaper.*
Published by: Universidad de Costa Rica, Revista Universidad, Apdo 21, San Jose, 2060, Costa Rica. TEL 25-58-57, FAX 342382-340452. Ed. Carlos Morales. Adv. contact Carlos Campos. Circ: 15,000.

378 CRI ISSN 1017-7507
UNIVERSIDAD AUTONOMA DE CENTRO AMERICA. ACTA ACADEMICA✶ . Text in Spanish. 1987. biennial.
Published by: Universidad Autonoma de Centro America, Apdo 7637, San Jose, 1000, Costa Rica.

378 BRA ISSN 0102-731X
UNIVERSIDADE FEDERAL DE PELOTAS. DEPARTAMENTO DE PESQUISA E POS-GRADUACAO. TRABALHOS PUBLICADOS: RESUMOS. Text in Portuguese. 1981. a.
Indexed: ESPM.
Published by: Universidade Federal de Pelotas, Departamento de Pesquisa e Pos-Graduacao, Caixa Postal 354, Pelotas, RS 96010-900, Brazil. http://www.ufpel.tche.br.

C

378 DEU ISSN 0938-2569
UNIVERSITAET AUGSBURG. PERSONEN- UND STUDIENVERZEICHNIS. Text in German. 1970. s-a. adv. back issues avail. **Document type:** *Academic/Scholarly.*
Published by: Presse Druck- und Verlagsgesellschaft mbH, Curt-Frenzel-Str 2, Augsburg, 86167, Germany. TEL 49-821-777-0, FAX 49-821-7772383. Ed. Alois Zimmerman. Adv. contact Wolfgang Hoffmann. Circ: 7,500.

378 DEU ISSN 0931-0746
UNIVERSITAET ERLANGEN - NUERNBERG. VORLESUNGSVERZEICHNIS. Text in German. 1920. s-a. adv. **Document type:** *Directory, Academic/Scholarly.*
Published by: Universitaet Erlangen - Nuernberg, Schlossplatz 4, Erlangen, 91054, Germany. TEL 49-9131-854036, TELEX 629830-UNIER-D, pressestelle@zuv.uni-erlangen.de, http://www.uni-erlangen.de. adv.: page EUR 400.

378 DEU ISSN 0947-1049
UNIVERSITAET LEIPZIG. Text in German. 8/yr. adv. **Document type:** *Academic/Scholarly.*
Indexed: RASB.
Published by: (Universitaet Leipzig, Pressestelle), Leipziger Universitaetsverlag GmbH, Augustusplatz 10, Leipzig, 04109, Germany. FAX 49-341-9730099, middell@rz.uni-leipzig.de. Ed. Volker Schulte. Circ: 9,000 (controlled).

378 DEU ISSN 0179-1109
UNIVERSITAET PASSAU. VORLESUNGSVERZEICHNIS. Text in German. s-a. **Document type:** *Directory.*
Published by: (Universitaet Passau), L I S Verlag GmbH, Theresienstr 9, Passau, 94032, Germany. TEL 49-851-93200-0, FAX 49-851-9320049.

378.1 NLD ISSN 0920-7368
UNIVERSITEITSKRANT GRONINGEN. Short title: U K. Text in Dutch. 1971. w. adv. bk.rev. illus. **Document type:** *Newspaper.*
Former titles: Rijksuniversiteit te Groningen. Universiteitskrant; Rijksuniversiteit te Groningen. Mededelingenblad (0035-5348)
Published by: Stichting Universiteitsblad, Postbus 80, Groningen, 9700 AB, Netherlands. TEL 31-50-363-6700, FAX 31-50-363-6698, uk@bureau.rug.nl, http://docserver.ub.rug.nl/edoc/uk/inhoud.html. Circ: 27,000.

378.1 PHL ISSN 0042-0360
UNIVERSITY. Text in English. q. charts; illus.
Related titles: Online - full text ed.
Published by: Philippine Women's University, Taft Ave, Manila, 2801, Philippines. Ed. Edgardo Ray Pedroche. Circ: 1,000.

UNIVERSITY AVIATION ASSOCIATION. NEWSLETTER. see *TRANSPORTATION—Air Transport*

378 USA
THE UNIVERSITY CHRONICLE. Text in English. 1924. s-w. (Mon. & Thu. school yr., wkly in summer). free on campus; USD 12 subscr - mailed per quarter (effective 2005). **Document type:** *Newspaper.*
Formerly: St. Cloud State University Chronicle
Published by: St. Cloud State University Student Organization, 200 Administrative Services, St. Cloud, MN 56301. TEL 320-255-2122, http://www.universitychronicle.com. Circ: 5,500 morning (free).

UNIVERSITY COLLEGE LONDON. EASTMAN ACADEMY. NEWSLETTER. see *MEDICAL SCIENCES—Dentistry*

378 USA ISSN 0746-4967
UNIVERSITY DAILY KANSAN. Text in English. 1889. d. (Mon.-Fri.). USD 120 (effective 2005). adv. 14 p./no. 6 cols./p.; **Document type:** *Newspaper, Newspaper-distributed.* **Description:** Covers topics of interest to the university community.
Formerly: Daily Kansan
Related titles: Online - full text ed.
Published by: University of Kansas, 111 Stauffer-Flint Hall, Lawrence, KS 66045. TEL 785-864-4810, FAX 785-864-0391, editor@kansan.com, http://www.kansan.com. Ed. Andrew Vaupel. Circ: 11,500. Wire service: AP.

371.8 IRL
THE UNIVERSITY EXAMINER. Text in English. 1997. w. adv. **Document type:** *Newspaper, Consumer.* **Description:** Covers items of interest to students such as news, sports, entertainment, information technology, education, and travel.
Published by: University College Cork Student Media, Aras na Mac Leinn, Cork, Ireland. TEL 353-21-4903052, FAX 353-21-4903108, studentmedia@ucc.ie, http://www.ucc.ie/anml. adv.: B&W page EUR 480, color page EUR 575; 266 x 334. Circ: 4,000 (controlled).

378 USA
UNIVERSITY GAZETTE. Text in English. s-m. (Sep.-May; m. June-Aug. & Dec.). free domestic faculty & staff (effective 2005). **Document type:** *Newspaper.*
Published by: University of North Carolina-Chapel Hill, 210 Pittsboro St., Chapel Hill, NC 27516. TEL 919-962-7124, gazette@email.unc.edu, http://gazette.unc.edu. Ed. Lee Kennedy. Circ: 9,500 (paid and controlled).

371.8975 USA
THE UNIVERSITY MAGAZINE. Variant title: R I T The University Magazine(Rochester Institute of Technology). Text in English. 1999 (May). q. free to qualified persons. illus. 32 p./no.; back issues avail. **Document type:** *Magazine, Academic/Scholarly.* **Description:** Informs alumni and donors of the Rochester Institute of Technology of noteworthy campus news and events. Highlights news and accomplishments of RIT alumni and alumnae.
Published by: Rochester Institute of Technology, University News Services, 132 Lomb Memorial Dr, Rochester, NY 14623-5608. TEL 716-475-5064, 716-475-5414, FAX 716-475-5097, umagwww@rit.edu, http://www.rit.edu/~930www. Ed. Kathy Quinn Thomas. Circ: 95,000 (controlled and free).
Co-sponsor: Rochester Institute of Technology, Office of Alumni Relations.

378.198 USA
THE UNIVERSITY NEWS. Text in English. 1976. w. USD 32. adv. bk.rev.; film rev. reprints avail. **Document type:** *Newspaper, Consumer.*
Published by: University of Dallas, University News, 1845 E Northgate Dr, Box 732, Irving, TX 75062. TEL 972-721-5089, FAX 972-721-5048, http://www.acad.udanas.edu. Ed. Aaron Deacon. R&P Brian Bourque. Adv. contact Susannah West. page USD 400. Circ: 2,000.

378.1 NZL
UNIVERSITY OF AUCKLAND NEWS. Text in English. 1971. m. (11/yr). NZD 20 domestic; NZD 30 foreign (effective 2000). adv. bk.rev.
Supersedes: University of Auckland Gazette (0041-9397)
Published by: University of Auckland, Auckland, New Zealand. TEL 64-9-3737599, FAX 64-9-3737047, ma.thomson@auckland.ac.nz. Ed., Adv. contact Margie Thomson. Circ: 6,000.

378 GBR ISSN 0143-1951
UNIVERSITY OF BRISTOL. NEWSLETTER. Text in English. 1969. fortn. GBP 17.50 (effective 1999). adv. bk.rev.; film rev.; play rev. illus.; stat. back issues avail. **Document type:** *Newsletter.* **Description:** Covers activities of the University of Bristol, and items of interest to members and friends of the university.
Published by: (Information Office), University of Bristol, Senate House, Tyndall Ave, Bristol, Avon BS8 1TH, United Kingdom. TEL 44-117-928-7777, FAX 44-117-929-2396, info.office@bristol.ac.uk. Ed. Sarah Whittingham. Adv. contact Joanne Fryer. page GBP 400; trim 205 x 256. Circ: 7,000.

378.1 USA ISSN 0041-9508
LD908
UNIVERSITY OF CHICAGO MAGAZINE. Text in English. 1907. bi-m. free to alumni. adv. bk.rev. index. **Document type:** *Magazine, Consumer.* **Description:** Covers a variety of topics pertaining to the history of the university and its alumni.
Indexed: RI-1, RI-2.
Published by: University of Chicago, 5801 S. Ellis Ave, Chicago, IL 60637. TEL 773-702-2163, FAX 773-702-0495, uchicago-magazine@uchicago.edu, http://www2.uchicago.edu/alumni/alumni.mag/, http://www.uchicago.edu. Ed. Mary Ruth Yoe. adv.: B&W page USD 5,955, color page USD 8,800. Circ: 100,000.

UNIVERSITY OF CHICAGO RECORD. see *EDUCATION—Higher Education*

378 USA
UNIVERSITY OF DELAWARE MESSENGER. Text in English. 1991. q. USD 5 (effective 2000). adv. **Document type:** *Academic/Scholarly.* **Description:** Reports on noteworthy alumni and college and university events.
Published by: University of Delaware, Office of Public Relations, 150 S College Ave, Newark, DE 19716. TEL 302-831-2791, FAX 302-831-1440, themessenger@mvs.udel.edu, http://www.udel.edu/PR/Messenger/. Ed., R&P Cornelia Weil TEL 302-831-1421. Adv. contact Rich Ruggerio. Circ: 74,000 (paid).

378 USA
UNIVERSITY OF DELAWARE. STUDENT CENTER. REVIEW. Text in English. 1882. 104/yr. adv. bk.rev. **Document type:** *Newspaper.*
Published by: University of Delaware, Student Center, B 1 Student Ctr, Newark, DE 19716. TEL 302-451-2771, FAX 032-451-1396. Circ: 15,000 (controlled).

378 USA
UNIVERSITY OF DENVER CLARION. Text in English. 1895. w. (Mon.). free (effective 2005). **Document type:** *Newspaper.*
Published by: University of Denver, Student Media Board, 2055 E. Evans Ave., Denver, CO 80208-3131. TEL 303-871-3131, FAX 303-871-2568, clarion_news@hotmail.com, http://www.duclarion.com. Ed. Charmaine Robledo. Circ: 2,500 (free).

378.1 USA
UNIVERSITY OF DENVER JOURNAL. Text in English. 1961. q. free to alumni. bk.rev. charts; illus. **Document type:** *Newspaper.*
Former titles: University of Denver News (0891-6020); University of Denver Alumni News (0041-9532)
Published by: University of Denver, Office of Communications, 2199 S. University Blvd, Denver, CO 80208. TEL 303-871-2711, FAX 303-871-3827. Ed. Rebecca Brant. Circ: 70,000 (controlled).

378 GBR
UNIVERSITY OF EDINBURGH BULLETIN. Text in English. bi-m. adv. bk.rev. **Document type:** *Bulletin.*
Published by: University of Edinburgh, Old College, South Bridge, Edinburgh, EH8 9YL, United Kingdom. TEL 44-131-650-2252, FAX 44-131-650-2253, http://www.cpa.ed.ac.uk/bulletin, http://www.ed.ac.uk. Ed. Ray Footman. Circ: 6,500.

378 GBR ISSN 0041-9567
LH5.E4
UNIVERSITY OF EDINBURGH JOURNAL. Text in English. 1925. s-a. GBP 7.50 per issue to non-members (effective 2005). adv. bk.rev. index. **Document type:** *Journal, Academic/Scholarly.*
Indexed: MLA-IB.
Published by: University of Edinburgh, Graduates' Association, 5 Buccleuch Pl, Edinburgh, EH8 9JN, United Kingdom. TEL 44-131-650-4292, FAX 44-131-650-4293, gradassoc@ed.uk, http://www.dev.ed.ac.uk/gradassoc/journal.htm. Ed. Valerie R Robertson. Adv. contact Rena Tough. Circ: 3,000 (paid).

378 USA ISSN 0747-3028
UNIVERSITY OF HARTFORD OBSERVER. Text in English. 1974. q. free to qualified personnel. **Document type:** *Newspaper.* **Description:** Contains news, information, and feature articles pertaining to the university, its faculty, staff, alumni, and students.
Published by: University of Hartford, Office of University Affairs, 200 Bloomfield Ave, West, Hartford, CT 06117-1599. TEL 860-768-4348, FAX 860-768-4378, observer@mail.hartford.edu, http://www.hartford.edu. Ed., R&P Diana Simonds. Circ: 70,000.

378 617.6 USA ISSN 1088-9108
UNIVERSITY OF ILLINOIS AT CHICAGO. COLLEGE OF DENTISTRY. ALUMNI REPORT. Text in English. 1985. s-a. USD 6 (effective 2000). bk.rev. **Document type:** *Bulletin.*
Published by: University of Illinois at Chicago, College of Dentistry, 801 S Paulina St, Chicago, IL 60612-7211. TEL 312-413-2927, FAX 312-413-2927, billbike@uic.edu. Ed., R&P William Bike TEL 312-996-8495. Pub. Irwin Robinson. Circ: 5,500 (controlled).

378.1 CAN ISSN 0706-9847
UNIVERSITY OF MANITOBA. ALUMNI JOURNAL. Text in English. 1936. 3/yr. CND 35 to non-members. adv. bk.rev. illus. **Document type:** *Academic/Scholarly.*
Published by: University of Manitoba, Alumni Association, 180 Dafoe Rd, Winnipeg, MB R3T 2N2, Canada. TEL 204-474-9946, FAX 204-474-7531. Ed. Russ Medvedev. Adv. contact Jo-Anne Thompson. Circ: 120,000.

378 USA ISSN 1048-9606
UNIVERSITY OF MARYLAND. MEDICAL ALUMNI ASSOCIATION. BULLETIN. Text in English. 1988 (vol.72). q. USD 15. adv. back issues avail. **Document type:** *Bulletin.*
Formerly (until 1978): University of Maryland. School of Medicine. Bulletin (1048-9614)
—GNLM.
Published by: University of Maryland, Medical Alumni Association, 522 W Lombard St, Baltimore, MD 21201. TEL 410-706-7454, FAX 410-706-3658. Ed. Carole Miller. Circ: 8,000.

378 USA
UNIVERSITY OF MASSACHUSETTS MAGAZINE. Cover title: U Mass Magazine. Text in English. 1975. q. free. bk.rev. **Document type:** *Consumer.* **Description:** Contains news and items of interest to alumni and friends of the University of Massachusetts at Amherst.
Former titles: Massachusetts Magazine; (until vol.14, no.4, 1989): Contact (Amherst)
Related titles: Microform ed.: (from PQC).
Published by: University of Massachusetts at Amherst, 103 Munson Hall, Amherst, MA 01003. TEL 413-545-2991, FAX 413-545-3824, umassmag@admin.umass.edu, http://www.umassmag.com/. Ed., R&P Elizabeth Pols. Adv. contact Thorr Bjorn TEL 413-577-0232. Circ: 140,000.

378.1 USA
➤ **UNIVERSITY OF NEW HAMPSHIRE MAGAZINE.** Text in English. 1924. 3/yr. USD 12 domestic; USD 15 foreign (effective 2002). adv. bk.rev. 64 p./no.; **Document type:** *Magazine, Academic/Scholarly.* **Description:** Articles of general interest for alumni(ae), donors and other friends of the University.
Former titles (until 1998): Alumni Companion; (until 1991): New Hampshire Alumnus (0028-5196); (until 1984): New Hampshire State Alumnus
Published by: University of New Hampshire, Alumni Association, Elliott Alumni Center, 9 Edgewood Rd, Durham, NH 03824. TEL 603-862-2040, FAX 603-862-4126, alumni@unh.edu, http://www.unhmagazine.unh.edu, http://www.alumni.unh.edu/. Ed., R&P Maggie Paine. Adv. contact Lucie Asselin. Circ: 100,000 (controlled).

378.1 USA ISSN 0895-5409
UNIVERSITY OF NORTH DAKOTA. ALUMNI REVIEW. Text in English. 1940. bi-m. free to alumni. adv. bk.rev. **Document type:** *Newsletter.*
Published by: University of North Dakota, Alumni Association and Foundation, PO Box 8157, Grand Forks, ND 58201. TEL 701-777-4849, FAX 701-777-4859. Ed. Heidi L Amundson. R&P, Adv. contact Heidi Amundson. Circ: 76,000.

378.1 ZAF ISSN 0259-1871
UNIVERSITY OF PRETORIA. ANNUAL REPORT/UNIVERSITEIT VAN PRETORIA. JAARVERSLAG. Text in Afrikaans, English. 1954. a. free. adv. bibl. **Document type:** *Corporate.* **Description:** Reports on the activities, exchanges, students and faculties of the university.
Published by: University of Pretoria/Universiteit van Pretoria, Marketing and Communication, Pretoria, 0002, South Africa. TEL 27-12-420-2263, FAX 27-12-420-2262, jcroos@ccnet.up.ac.za. Ed. J C Roosrgh. Circ: 3,500.

378 200 USA
UNIVERSITY OF ST. THOMAS MAGAZINE✶. Text in English. 1985. q. free. illus. back issues avail. **Document type:** *Magazine, Consumer.* **Description:** Keeps alumni informed about campus life.
Formerly (until 1990): College of St. Thomas. Magazine; Incorporates (1969-1990): Memorandum (St. Paul)
Published by: University of St. Thomas (Houston), 3812 Montrose Blvd, Houston, TX 77006. TEL 713-525-3120, FAX 713-942-3410, marion@basil.stthom.edu, http://www.stthom.edu. Ed. Marionette Mitchell. Circ: 39,000.

378 USA
UNIVERSITY OF SAN FRANCISCO MAGAZINE. Text in English. 1975. q. free.
Formerly: University of San Francisco. Alumni Association. Alumnus; Which supersedes: U S F View; Which was formerly: View from the University of San Francisco
Published by: University of San Francisco, Office of Public Affairs, 416 Corvell Hall, 2130 Fulton St, San Francisco, CA 94117. Ed. Mel Taylor. Circ: 70,000.

378.1 GBR
UNIVERSITY OF SHEFFIELD. DIARY OF EVENTS. Text in English. 1961. 13/yr. membership. **Document type:** *Newsletter.*
Supersedes in part: University of Sheffield. Newsletter Diary (0309-0191); University of Sheffield. Diary of Events (0042-0034); University of Sheffield Reporter
Published by: University of Sheffield, Sheffield, S Yorks S10 2TN, United Kingdom. TEL 44-114-222-1030, FAX 44-114-279-8603. Ed., R&P Roger Allum. Circ: 5,250.

378.1 GBR
UNIVERSITY OF SHEFFIELD. NEWSLETTER. Text in English. 1976. 14/yr. **Document type:** *Newsletter.*
Supersedes in part: University of Sheffield. Newsletter Diary (0309-0191)
Published by: University of Sheffield, Sheffield, S Yorks S10 2TN, United Kingdom. TEL 44-114-222-1030, FAX 44-114-279-8603. Ed. Roger Allum. Circ: 5,250.

378.1 AUS ISSN 0042-0107
UNIVERSITY OF SYDNEY. GAZETTE. Text in English. 1950. s-a. free. adv. bk.rev. **Document type:** *Newsletter.* **Description:** Contains news of graduates, academic research, personality profiles etc.
Indexed: ChLitAb.
Published by: University of Sydney, Level 6 Main Quadrangle A14, Sydney, NSW 2006, Australia. TEL 61-2-9351-3168, FAX 61-2-9351-6868, m.theobald@publications.usyd.edu.au, http://www.alumni.usyd.edu.au. Ed. Marian Theobald. adv.: color page AUD 2,500; trim 270 x 205. Circ: 110,000 (free).

UNIVERSITY OF TEXAS AT AUSTIN. GRADUATE SCHOOL OF LIBRARY AND INFORMATION SCIENCE. ALUMNI NEWS. see *LIBRARY AND INFORMATION SCIENCES*

378.1 CAN ISSN 1483-6181
UNIVERSITY OF TORONTO. Text in English. 1967. q. CND 25 (effective 2000). adv. bk.rev. illus. back issues avail. **Document type:** *Consumer.* **Description:** Contains information about activities for alumni.
Former titles: University of Toronto Magazine (0840-562X); University of Toronto Alumni Magazine (0833-4536); University of Toronto Graduate; University of Toronto News (0042-0212)
Related titles: Online - full content ed.
Published by: University of Toronto, Department of Public Affairs, 21 King's College Circle, Toronto, ON M5S 3J3, Canada. TEL 416-946-3192, FAX 416-978-7430, karen.hanley@utoronto.ca. Eds. Karen Hanley, Karina Dahlin. R&P Margaret MacAulay. Adv. contact Nancy Bush. Circ: 240,000.

378 CAN
UNIVERSITY OF TORONTO BULLETIN. Text in English. 21/yr. CND 35 (effective 2000). adv. bk.rev. **Document type:** *Newspaper.* **Description:** News for faculty and staff about University events, announcements.
Related titles: Online - full text ed.
Published by: University of Toronto, Department of Public Affairs, 21 King's College Circle, Toronto, ON M5S 3J3, Canada. TEL 416-978-7016, FAX 416-978-7430, suzanne.soto@utoronto.ca. R&P Suzanne Soto. Adv. contact Nancy Bush. Circ: 14,500.

378 USA
UNIVERSITY OF VIRGINIA. DECLARATION. Text in English. w.
Published by: University of Virginia, PO Box 418, Newcomb Hall, Charlottesville, VA 22901. TEL 804-924-7068.

378 USA
UNIVERSITY OF WASHINGTON DAILY. Text in English. 1909. d. (Mon.-Fri.). USD 95 (effective 2005); free. adv. **Document type:** *Newspaper.*
Published by: University of Washington, Board of Student Publications, 144 Communications, PO Box 353720, Seattle, WA 98195. TEL 206-543-2700, FAX 206-543-2345, editor@thedaily.washington.edu, http://www.thedaily.washington.edu. Ed. Christina Sidenus. Pub. Oren Campbell. adv.: col. inch USD 8.20. Circ: 15,000 morning (free). Wire service: LAT-WAT.

378.198 CAN ISSN 0227-2199
UNIVERSITY OF WATERLOO COURIER. Text in English. 1980. q. free.
Published by: University of Waterloo, Student Life Centre, Rm 1116, Waterloo, ON N2L 3G1, Canada. TEL 519-888-4048, FAX 519-884-7800, editor@imprint.uwaterloo.ca, http://imprint.uwaterloo.ca. Circ: 50,000 (controlled).

371.805 USA
UNIVERSITY OF WISCONSIN. DEPARTMENT OF FRENCH & ITALIAN. NEWSLETTER. Text in English. a. free. illus. **Description:** Covers activities of professors, students and alumni of the department for the previous year.
Published by: University of Wisconsin at Madison, Department of French & Italian, 618 Van Hise Hall, 1220 Linden Dr, University of Wisconsin, Madison, WI 53706-1558. TEL 608-262-3941, FAX 608-265-3892, http://polyglot.lss.wisc.edu/frit/. Ed. Robert Rodini.

378 AUS ISSN 0313-6906
UNIVERSITY OF WOLLONGONG. ANNUAL REPORT. Text in English. a. free. **Document type:** *Corporate.* **Description:** Reports on academic and research activities of the University.
Published by: University of Wollongong, Northfields Ave, Wollongong, NSW 2522, Australia. TEL 61-42-213555, FAX 61-42-213477.

378 AUS ISSN 1036-7985
UNIVERSITY OF WOLLONGONG. POSTGRADUATE CALENDAR. Text in English. a. AUD 8. **Description:** Provides description of postgraduate courses available at the university.
Former titles: University of Wollongong. Postgraduate Handbook; University of Wollongong. Faculties Sector Postgraduate Handbook (0726-1586); Which supersedes in part: University of Wollongong. Calendar (0312-0007)
Published by: University of Wollongong, Northfields Ave, Wollongong, NSW 2522, Australia. TEL 61-42-213555, FAX 61-42-213477.

378 AUS ISSN 1032-0741
UNIVERSITY OF WOLLONGONG. RESEARCH REPORT. Text in English. a. free. **Description:** Reports on research activities of the university.
Published by: University of Wollongong, Northfields Ave, Wollongong, NSW 2522, Australia. TEL 61-42-213386, FAX 61-42-214338.

378 AUS ISSN 1036-2371
UNIVERSITY OF WOLLONGONG. UNDERGRADUATE CALENDAR. Text in English. a. AUD 12. **Description:** Provides descriptions of undergraduate courses available at the university.
Former titles: University of Wollongong. Undergraduate Handbook (0726-0717); University of Wollongong. Institute Sector Handbook (0810-5294); Which supersedes in part: University of Wollongong. Calendar (0312-0007)
Published by: University of Wollongong, Northfields Ave, Wollongong, NSW 2522, Australia. TEL 61-42-213555, FAX 61-42-213477.

378 USA
THE UNIVERSITY PACER. Text in English. 1984. m. free. illus. **Document type:** *Newspaper.* **Description:** Discusses events taking place at the University of Rhode Island.
Published by: University of Rhode Island, Division of University Advancement, 22 Davis Hall, Kingston, RI 02881. TEL 401-874-2116, FAX 401-789-3435, jredlich@dowis.uri.edu, http://www.davis.uri.edu. Ed. Jhodi R Redlich. R&P Jhodi Redlich. Circ: 24,000.

371.8 IRL
THE UNIVERSITY RECORD. Text in English. fortn. adv. **Document type:** *Newspaper, Consumer.*
Published by: Trinity College, Students' Union, House 6, Dublin, 2, Ireland. TEL 353-1-6776545, FAX 353-1-6777957, deputypres@tcdsu.org, http://www.tcdsu.org. adv.: B&W page EUR 698, color page EUR 1,016.

378 USA
UNIVERSITY SCOPE. Text in English. 1933. q. free. adv.
Published by: Loma Linda University, Nichol Hall Rm 1521, Loma Linda, CA 92350. TEL 909-824-4526, rweismeyer@llu.edu, lquijano@univ.llu.edu, http://www.llu.edu/news/scope/. Eds. Richard W Weismeyer, W Augustus Cheatham. Circ: 35,000.

378 USA
UNIVERSITY TIMES (CHARLOTTE). Text in English. 1965. s-w. USD 30. adv. **Document type:** *Newspaper.* **Description:** Covers university news.
Formerly: Forty-Niner Times
Published by: University of North Carolina at Charlotte, Cone Center, 9201 Univ City Blvd, Charlotte, NC 28223-0001. TEL 704-547-2663. Ed. Mike Twist. R&P Wayne Maikranz. Adv. contact Dixie Tew. Circ: 20,000.

378 USA
UNIVERSITY TIMES (LOS ANGELES). Text in English. 1946. s-w. (Mon. & Thu.). free (effective 2005). adv. **Document type:** *Newspaper.*
Published by: California State University, Los Angeles, 5151 State University Dr, Los Angeles, CA 90032. TEL 323-343-4215, FAX 323-343-5337. adv.: col. inch USD 364.32. Circ: 14,000 morning (free).

378 CAN
L'UQUOI. Text in French. m. adv.
Published by: Universite du Quebec a Hull, C P 1250, succ B, Hull, PQ J8X 3X7, Canada. Circ: 2,000.

371.8 DEU ISSN 0936-8299
URSPRING NACHRICHTEN. Text in English, French, German. 1964. a. **Document type:** *Academic/Scholarly.* **Description:** Information on student life for alumni.
Published by: Stiftung Urspringschule, Postfach 60, Schelklingen, 89598, Germany. TEL 07394-2460. Ed. Uli Teuscher. Circ: 2,250.

378.18 USA ISSN 1082-1201
UTAH STATE UNIVERSITY MAGAZINE. Text in English. 1969. q. USD 10 (effective 2000). adv. **Document type:** *Consumer.* **Description:** For alumni, staff, and friends. Publishes articles about university issues, events, and people.
Formerly (until 1994): Outlook (Logan) (1073-0281)
Published by: Utah State University, Media Relations, 0500 Old Main Hill, Logan, UT 84322-0500. TEL 435-797-1353, FAX 435-797-1250, janek@media.usu.edu, http://www.usu.edu/~alumi/alumagazine. Ed., R&P, Adv. contact Jane Koerner. Circ: 70,000 (controlled).

378 USA
THE UTAH STATESMAN; Utah State University student newspaper. Text in English. 1902. 3/w. (Mon., Wed., Fri). USD 45 (effective 2005); free. 16 p./no. 6 cols./p.; **Document type:** *Newspaper.*
Published by: Associated Students of Utah State University, PO Box 1249, Logan, UT 84322-0165. TEL 435-797-NEWS, FAX 435-797-1760, statesman@cc.usu.edu, http://www.utahstatesman.com. Ed. Jay Wamsley. Circ: 7,000 (paid and free). Wire service: AP.

▼ new title ➤ refereed ✶ unverified ♦ full entry avail.

378 USA
V U U INFORMER. Text in English. 1900. m. free. adv. bk.rev. back issues avail. **Document type:** *Newspaper.* **Description:** Presents local, state, national, and international events as they relate to the university.
Formerly: Campus Informer
Published by: Virginia Union University, 1500 N Lombardy St, Richmond, VA 23220-1790. TEL 804-257-5655, FAX 804-257-5818. Ed. A H Benson. Adv. contact A.H. Benson. Circ: 2,000.

378.18 USA
VALENCIA SOURCE; Valencia student press. Text in English. 1978. fortn. USD 5 (effective 2000). adv. bk.rev.; film rev.; play rev. **Document type:** *Newspaper.*
Formerly: Paper
Published by: Valencia Community College, PO Box 3028, Orlando, FL 32802. TEL 407-299-5000, FAX 407-293-8839, http://www.ValenciaSource.com. Ed. Chris Vaughn. Pub., R&P, Adv. contact Joe Gisondi. page USD 350. Circ: 6,000.

378.198 USA ISSN 0889-0935
THE VALLEY FORGE. Text in English. 1965. bi-w. looseleaf. USD 15. adv. bk.rev.; film rev.; music rev.; play rev. illus. **Document type:** *Newspaper.*
Published by: Rock Valley Community College, 3301 N Mulford, Rockford, IL 61114. TEL 815-654-4458, FAX 815-654-5245. Ed. Susan La Salla. Circ: 3,200.

378.1 USA ISSN 0042-2517
VANDERBILT HUSTLER. Text in English. 1888. s-w. (Tue. & Fri.). USD 200 (effective 2005). adv. bk.rev.; film rev.; play rev. illus. **Document type:** *Newspaper.* **Description:** Provides students with university news; includes a weekly arts and entertainment supplement.
Related titles: Online - full text ed.: (from LexisNexis).
Published by: Vanderbilt Student Communications, Inc., 2301 Vanderbilt Place, PO Box 1504 B, Nashville, TN 37235. TEL 615-322-3757, editor@vanderbilthustler.com, http://www.vanderbilthustler.com. adv.: page USD 375. Circ: 10,000. Wire service: AP.

378 USA
VANDERBILT MAGAZINE. Text in English. 1915. q. free to qualified personnel. bk.rev.
Published by: Vanderbilt University, PO BOX 7703, STA B, Nashville, TN 37235. TEL 615-322-2601, FAX 615-343-8547. Ed. Mary Tom Bass. Circ: 32,000.

378 USA
THE VANGUARD (MOBILE). Text in English. 1964. w. USD 30 (effective 2000). adv. bk.rev.; music rev.; play rev.; software rev.; video rev. charts; illus. back issues avail. **Document type:** *Newspaper.* **Description:** The audience is the university community including students, faculty and staff.
Related titles: Microfilm ed.; Online - full text ed.
Published by: University of South Alabama, c/o Student Media Manager, PO Drawer U-25100, Mobile, AL 36688. TEL 334-460-6442, FAX 334-414-8293, vanguard@jaguar1.usouthal.edu, http://www.usavanguard.com Ed. Jamie Sims. Adv. contacts Rob Holbert TEL 334-460-6897, Sylvia Ash. B&W page USD 693; trim 21 x 13. Circ: 8,000 weekly.

378 USA
VANGUARD (PORTLAND). Text in English. 4/w. (Tue.-Fri.). USD 85 (effective 2005). bk.rev.; dance rev.; film rev.; music rev.; play rev.; video rev. **Document type:** *Newspaper.*
Formerly: Daily Vanguard
Related titles: Seasonal ed(s).: Summer Vanguard.
Published by: Portland State University, Student Publications Board, 1825 S.W. Broadway, Portland, Multnomah, OR 97201. TEL 503-725-5691, FAX 503-725-4534, editor@dailyvanguard.com, http://www.dailyvanguard.com. Circ: 5,000 evening (paid and free).

378 USA
EL VAQUERO. Text in English. 1927. fortn. USD 25. adv. bk.rev. **Document type:** *Newspaper.*
Published by: Glendale Community College, 1500 N Verdugo Rd, Glendale, CA 91208-2894. TEL 818-240-1000, FAX 818-549-9436. Ed. R J Dewitt. Adv. contact Don Johnson. Circ: 2,500 (controlled).

378.1 CAN ISSN 0042-2789
THE VARSITY. Text in English. 1880. s-w. (during academic year). CND 35. adv. bk.rev.; film rev.; play rev. back issues avail.
Related titles: Microfilm ed.
Published by: (University of Toronto), Varsity Publications Inc., 21 Sussex Ave., Toronto, ON M5S 1J6, Canada. TEL 416-946-7600, FAX 416-946-7606, http://www.varsity.utoronto.ca. Circ: 25,000.

378.1 ZAF ISSN 0042-2797
VARSITY. Text in English. 1940. every 3 wks. adv. bk.rev.; film rev.; play rev. illus. **Document type:** *Newspaper.*
Published by: University of Cape Town, Student Affairs Committee, Rondebosch, Cape Town 7700, South Africa. TEL 27-21-6503543, FAX 27-21-6502904, news09@its.uct.ac.za, http://www.uct.ac.za/dept/src. Circ: 7,000 (controlled).

378 KEN
VARSITY FOCUS. Text in English. 1979. bi-m. free. bk.rev. **Document type:** *Newsletter.*
Published by: (University of Nairobi, School of Journalism, Office of the Vice-Chancellor), Nairobi University Press, PO Box 30197, Nairobi, Kenya. TEL 254-2-230588, FAX 254-2-212604, TELEX VARSITY KE 22095. Ed. Josphat K Kirimania. Circ: 2,000.

378 USA
THE VARSITY NEWS. Text in English. 1917. w. free on campus (effective 2005). **Document type:** *Newspaper, Consumer.* **Description:** Publishes entertainment stories on the people and events that affect the University of Detroit Mercy.
Published by: University of Detroit Mercy, 4001 W McNichols Rd, Detroit, MI 48219. TEL 313-993-1000, FAX 313-993-1120, varnews@udmercy.edu, http://www.udmercy.edu. Circ: 5,000 (free). Wire service: LAT-WAT.

378 CAN ISSN 0229-9119
VARSITY STUDENT HANDBOOK. Text in English. 1980. a. free. adv. film rev.; play rev. illus. back issues avail.
Published by: (Varsity Newspaper), Varsity Publications Inc., 21 Sussex Ave., Toronto, ON M5S 1J6, Canada. TEL 416-946-7600. Circ: 25,000.

378.1 USA
LH1.V3
VASSAR; the alumnae/i quarterly. Text in English. 1916. q. USD 10 (effective 2000). bk.rev. charts; illus. **Document type:** *Consumer.*
Former titles: Vassar Quarterly (0042-2851); Vassar Alumnae Magazine
Published by: Vassar College, Alumnae and Alumni, Alumnae House, Poughkeepsie, NY 12603. TEL 914-437-5447, FAX 914-437-7425. Ed. Georgette Weir. Circ: 31,000.

378 USA
VASSAR VIEWS. Text in English. 1971. q. free. illus. **Document type:** *Newsletter.*
Published by: Vassar College, Office of College Relations, 124 Raymond Ave, Poughkeepsie, NY 12604. TEL 914-437-7400. Ed. Susan Dekrey. Circ: 33,000.

378.1 NLD ISSN 1567-6668
VERENIGING VAN VROUWEN MET HOGERE OPLEIDING. NIEUWSBRIEF. Text in Dutch. 1930. bi-m. adv. bk.rev. charts; illus. **Document type:** *Newsletter, Academic/Scholarly.* **Description:** Issues of concern to women with a background in higher education.
Former titles (until 1997): Vereniging van Vrouwen met Academische Opleiding. Nieuwsbrief (1385-3198); (until 1992): Nederlandse Vereniging van Vrouwen met Academische Opleiding. Mededelingen (0028-2332); Incorporates (in 1988): Nederlandse Vereniging van Vrouwen met Academische Opleiding. Nieuwsbrief (1385-318X); Which was formerly (until 1986): Nieuws van het Hoofbestuur (1385-3171)
Published by: Vereniging van Vrouwen met Hogere Opleiding/Association of University Women, Graaf Adolfstraat 30, Utrecht, 3583 VV, Netherlands. TEL 31-30-2109907, FAX 31-30-2109908, kantoor@vvao.nl, http://www.vvao.nl/. Circ: 5,000.

378 USA ISSN 0892-3132
VERMONT CYNIC. Text in English. 1883. w. USD 15. adv. bk.rev.; film rev.; play rev. illus. **Document type:** *Newspaper.* **Description:** University of Vermont student newspaper.
Related titles: Online - full text ed.
Address: University of Vermont, Lower Billings, Burlington, VT 05405-0040. TEL 802-656-4413, FAX 802-656-7719. Ed. Alex Johnson. Circ: 10,000.

378 790.1 USA ISSN 1055-3894
LA VERNE MAGAZINE. Text in English. 1976. s-a. USD 7 (effective 1999). back issues avail. **Description:** Contains articles of interest to University of La Verne students and alumni and the La Verne community.
Related titles: Online - full text ed.
Published by: University of La Verne, 1950 Third St, La Verne, CA 91750. TEL 909-392-2712, FAX 909-392-2706, http://www.ulv.edu/~comms/lvm/lvm.htm. Eds. Erin Grycel, George Keeler. Circ: 2,200.

378 051 SWE ISSN 0346-4164
VERTEX. Text in Swedish. 1960. m. SEK 100 (effective 1999). bk.rev.; music rev. illus. **Document type:** *Newspaper.* **Description:** Concerns many aspects of student life at the University of Umea, from parties to politics, sports to science.
Related titles: Online - full text ed.
Published by: Umea Studentkaer, Fack 7652, Umea, 90713, Sweden. TEL 90-7869020, FAX 90-7869023, vertex.red@us.umu.se. Ed. Bertil Janson. R&P Linda Johnson TEL 90-7869022. adv.: B&W page SEK 10,500, color page SEK 12,000. Circ: 19,000.

378.1 GBR ISSN 0042-5125
VICTORIAN. Text in English. 1871. a. GBP 10. adv. bk.rev. illus. **Document type:** *Consumer.* **Description:** Reports on activities of Victoria College, Jersey and its Old Boy Association. Includes sports reports, reviews of related art and theatre, and features.
Published by: Victoria College, School and Old Victorians' Association, Jersey, Channel Islands, United Kingdom. TEL 44-1534-37591, FAX 44-1534-27448, http://wwww.user.itl.net/~rcco/. Ed. T A Ozturk. Adv. contact Anthony Ozturk. Circ: 2,000.

378.198 USA
THE VIKING PRESS. Text in English. 1981. fortn. free. adv. play rev. back issues avail.
Formerly (until vol.9, no.5, 1990): Barstow College Collegiate
Published by: Barstow Community College District, 2700 Barstow Rd, Barstow, CA 92311. TEL 619-252-2411, FAX 619-252-1875. Ed. Vincent C Lovato Jr. Circ: 8,000.

378.198 USA
LH1.V6
VIRGINIA (CHARLOTTESVILLE). Text in English. 1912. q. USD 30 (effective 1997 & 1998). adv. bk.rev. illus. **Document type:** *Consumer.*
Former titles: University of Virginia Alumni News; (until 1925): University of Virginia Alumni Bulletin (0195-8798)
Published by: University of Virginia, Alumni Association, PO Box 3446, Charlottesville, VA 22903. TEL 804-971-9721, FAX 804-296-4577, alumnews@virginia.edu. Ed. Kathleen D Valenzi. Pub. John B Syer. Adv. contact Bonnie Coggin. Circ: 51,500.

378 USA
VIRGINIA TECH COLLEGIATE TIMES. Text in English. 1903. s-w. USD 22. adv. bk.rev. **Document type:** *Newspaper.*
Related titles: Microfiche ed.
Published by: Virginia Polytechnic Institute and State University, 363 Squires Hall, Student Center, Blacksburg, VA 24061. TEL 703-231-9860, FAX 703-231-5057. Ed. Heather McElrath. Circ: 14,000.

371.8 IRL
THE VOICE. Text in English. m. adv. **Document type:** *Magazine, Consumer.* **Description:** Aims to provide comprehensive news and information for students throughout Ireland.
Published by: Union of Students in Ireland, Grattan St., Dublin, 2, Ireland. TEL 353-1-4353400, FAX 353-1-4353450, thevoice@usi.ie, enquiries@usi.ie, http://www.usi.ie/voice/index.html. adv.: page EUR 1,904; 210 x 297. Circ: 30,000 (controlled).

378.1 CAN ISSN 0822-7896
VOICE. Text in English. 1970 (vol.7). w. (Sep.-Apr.). USD 15. adv. bk.rev.; film rev.; play rev. charts; illus. **Document type:** *Newspaper.*
Former titles: V C C Voice (0821-5871); Savant (0036-5084)
Related titles: Online - full text ed.: (from Northern Light Technology, Inc.).
Indexed: RASB.
Published by: Langara College, Journalism Department, Langara, 100 W 49th Ave, Vancouver, BC V5Y 2Z6, Canada. TEL 604-323-5396, FAX 604-323-5398. R&P Gene Keith TEL 604-323-5415. Circ: 1,000.

378 USA
THE VOICE (BLOOMSBURG). Text in English. 1924. w. (Thu.). free. **Document type:** *Newspaper, Consumer.*
Formerly: Campus Voice
Published by: Bloomsburg University, Campus Voice, 400 E. Second St., Bloomsburg, PA 17815. TEL 570-389-4000, FAX 570-389-2095, editor@voice.bloomu.edu, http://www.buvoice.com. Circ: 5,000 (free).

378 USA ISSN 1522-6840
VOICE (SIOUX CENTER). Text in English. 1956. q. free (effective 2003). 16 p./no. 4 cols./p.; **Document type:** *Newspaper.* **Description:** Covers news and events of interest to alumni and supporters.
Related titles: Online - full text ed.
Published by: Dordt College, 498 Fourth Ave N E, Sioux Center, IA 51250. TEL 712-722-6000, 800-343-6738, http://www.dordt.edu/publications/voice. Ed. Sally Jongsma. Circ: 35,000.

378.18 USA
VOICE - SOUTHEASTERN COMMUNITY COLLEGE - SOUTH. Text in English. 1980. w. free.
Published by: Southeastern Community College, South Campus, 335 Messenger Rd, Keokuk, IA 52632. TEL 319-524-3221. Ed. Thomas P Gardner. Circ: 300.

378.198 USA
VOICES OF THE WILDCATS. Text in English. m.
Published by: Bethune-Cookman College, 640 Second Ave, Daytona Beach, FL 32014. TEL 904-255-1401.

378 USA
VOLANTE. Text in English. 1887. w. USD 14 (effective 2000). adv.
Published by: Student Publications Board, Inc, University of South Dakota, 414 East Clark, Vermillion, SD 57069. TEL 605-677-5494, FAX 605-677-5105, volante@usd.edu, http://www.volante.usd.edu. Ed. Karen Robb. Adv. contact Trent Menning. Circ: 6,500.

378.18 CAN ISSN 0830-5315
VOX ME D A L. Text in English. 1958. s-a. free to members. adv. bk.rev. back issues avail. **Document type:** *Newsletter, Academic/Scholarly.* **Description:** Contains programs and services of the Dalhousie Medical Alumni Association and activities of faculty, students and staff.
Formerly (until 1988): Me D A L (0318-0735)
Related titles: Online - full text ed.
Published by: Dalhousie University, Dalhousie Medical Alumni Association, Dalhousie University, First Floor, Tupper Bldg, Halifax, NS B3H 4H7, Canada. TEL 902-494-8800, FAX 902-494-2033, dilly.macfarlane@dal.ca, http://www.medicine.dal.ca/dmaa. Ed. Dr. D C S Brown. R&P D.E. MacFarlane. Adv. contact D E MacFarlane. color page CND 7,000; trim 11 x 8.5. Circ: 6,700 (controlled).

378.1 USA
VOYAGER (PENSACOLA). Text in English. 1967. w. USD 10. adv. bk.rev. **Document type:** *Newspaper.* **Description:** For the University student body. Provides information on campus events, local events, and national news of interest to the students, faculty and staff of the University.
Published by: University of West Florida, English Department, 11000 University Pkwy, Pensacola, FL 32514-5751. TEL 904-474-2191. Eds. Lloyd Goodman, Nancy Schwartz. Adv. contact Neil Reichmuth. Circ: 4,000.

378 USA
LA VOZ (CUPERTINO). Text in English. 1967. w. USD 7 (effective 2000). adv.
Published by: De Anza College, 21250 Stevens Creek Blvd, Cupertino, CA 95014. TEL 408-996-4785. Circ: 3,000.

378.1 USA ISSN 0042-952X
W & L MAGAZINE. Text in English. 1925. q. free to alumni. bk.rev. **Document type:** *Magazine.*
Published by: Washington and Lee University, 2 Lee Ave, Lexington, VA 24450. TEL 540-463-8957, FAX 540-463-8024, dmarquardt@wlu.edu. Ed., R&P Deborah Marquardt TEL 540-463-8956. Circ: 28,500.

378 USA
WAR WHOOP. Text in English. 1923. bi-m. USD 10. adv. **Document type:** *Newspaper.*
Published by: McMurry University, PO BOX 248, McMURRY STA, Abilene, TX 79697. TEL 325-691-6375, FAX 325-691-6599. Ed. Steven Bristow. R&P Bill Hartley. Adv. contact Stacey Nixon. Circ: 1,000.

378.198 USA
WAREHOUSE JOURNAL. Text in English. 1971. a. free to qualified personnel.
Published by: Northern Virginia Community College, Alexandria Campus, 3001 N Beauregard St, Alexandria, VA 22311. TEL 703-845-6239. Circ: 2,000.

387 USA
WASHINGTON SQUARE. Text in English. q. **Document type:** *Newsletter.* **Description:** Reports news of campus events, faculty research, athletics, fund-raising events, and alumni for alumni and friends of the university.
Formerly (until 1994): San Jose State University Digest
Indexed: IAPV.
Published by: San Jose State University, One Washington Sq, San Jose, CA 95192-0149. TEL 408-924-1166, FAX 408-924-1168. Ed. Sylvia Hutchinson. Circ: 115,000.

378.198 USA ISSN 1549-9383
WASHINGTON SQUARE NEWS. Text in English. 1970. d. (Mon.-Fri.) (during school year). free. adv. **Document type:** *Newspaper, Consumer.*
Related titles: Online - full text ed.: ISSN 1549-9375.
Published by: New York University, 7 E 12th St, Ste 500, New York, NY 10003. TEL 212-998-4300, FAX 212-995-3790, http://www.nyunews.com. Ed. Kaie Meyer. Pub. Angela Kluwin. adv.: col. inch USD 14.71. Circ: 10,000 evening (controlled).

378 USA
LH1
WASHINGTON UNIVERSITY MAGAZINE AND ALUMNI NEWS. Text in English. 1992. q. **Document type:** *Academic/Scholarly.* **Description:** Describes university people and events for alumni, faculty, staff, parents, donors, university presidents, and the national media.
Formed by the 1992 merger of: Washington University Alumni News; (1956-1992): Washington University Magazine (0162-7570)
Indexed: CLI, ILP.
Published by: Washington University, Publications Office, 7509 Forsyth, St Louis, MO 63105-2103. TEL 314-935-5284, FAX 314-935-8533, magazine_editor@aismail.wustl.edu. Eds. Teresa A Nappier, Mary Ellen Benson. Pub. Fred Volkmann. Circ: 118,000 (controlled).

378 GBR
WATT'S ON. Text in English. 1986. bi-w. free. adv. bk.rev. back issues avail. **Document type:** *Newspaper.*
Published by: Heriot-Watt University, Students' Association, The Union, Riccarton, Currie, EH14 4AS, United Kingdom. TEL 0131-451-5333. Ed. Toby Jones. Adv. contact Keith Marshall. Circ: 2,000.

378.1 USA
WAYNE STATE MAGAZINE. Text in English. 1987. q. free to members. adv. illus.
Published by: Wayne State University, Alumni Association, Office of Alumni Relations, Detroit, MI 48202. TEL 313-577-2300, FAX 313-577-2302. Ed., R&P Beauford Cranford TEL 313-577-2164. Circ: 19,500 (controlled).

378.198 USA ISSN 0043-163X
WAYNE STATE UNIVERSITY ALUMNI NEWS. Text in English. 1944. s-a. free to qualified personnel. adv. illus.
Published by: Wayne State University, Alumni Association, Office of Alumni Relations, Detroit, MI 48202. TEL 313-577-2300. Ed. Beauford Cranford TEL 313-577-2164. Circ: 120,000.

378.1 CAN
WEAL. Text in English. 1926. w. CND 15; free to students. adv. bk.rev.; film rev. **Document type:** *Newsletter.*
Formerly: Emery Weal
Related titles: Microfiche ed.
Published by: (Southern Alberta Institute of Technology, Students' Association), S A I T S A Publications, 1301 16th Ave N W, Calgary, AB T2M 0L4, Canada. TEL 403-284-8458, FAX 403-284-8037. Ed. Allan Connery. Pub., Adv. contact Suzanne Trudel. Circ: 2,600.

378.198 USA
WEEKLY COLLEGIAN. Text in English. 1979. w. USD 34 (effective 1999). back issues avail. **Document type:** *Newspaper.* **Description:** College newspaper serving the branch campuses of Penn State, parents, alumni and sports fans.
Published by: Collegian Inc., James Bldg, 123 S Burrowes St, University Park, PA 16801-3882. TEL 814-865-2531, http://www.collegian.psu.edu. Ed. Stacy Confer. Circ: 5,000.

378 CAN
WELCOME BACK STUDENT MAGAZINE. Text in English. 1983. a. adv. **Document type:** *Directory.* **Description:** Provides restaurant, night life and shopping info, and student related editorial to students and faculty at RMC, St. Lawrence College and Queens University.
Formerly: Welcome Back Student Guide (0839-1483)
Published by: Kingston Publications, P O Box 1352, Kingston, ON K7L 5C6, Canada. TEL 613-549-8442. Ed. Mary Laflamme. Adv. contact Ruth Kirkby. Circ: 18,000 (controlled).

378 USA
WELLESLEY MAGAZINE. Text in English. 1892. q. free to alumni and friends. bk.rev. back issues avail. **Document type:** *Academic/Scholarly.* **Description:** Aims to connect the alumnae to the college and to each other.
Published by: Wellesley College Alumnae Association, 106 Central St, Wellesley, MA 02181-8201. TEL 617-283-2341, FAX 1617-283-3638, lkatz@wellesley.edu. Ed. Alice Hummer. R&P Laura Katz. Circ: 33,000.

378 USA ISSN 1062-1636
THE WELLS COLLEGE EXPRESS. Text in English. 1948. q. bk.rev.; dance rev.; music rev.; play rev. back issues avail. **Document type:** *Academic/Scholarly.* **Description:** Produced by Wells, a women's college, primarily for alumnae and parents. Presents college news including articles on faculty research, students, and women's issues.
Published by: Wells College, Pettibone House, Aurora, NY 13026. TEL 315-364-3260, FAX 315-364-3445. Eds. Devillo Sloan, Sue F Jones. Circ: 10,000.

378 DEU
WER - WAS - WO IM STUDENTENWERK. Text in German. 2/yr. **Document type:** *Journal, Academic/Scholarly.*
Published by: Studentenwerk Goettingen, Platz der Goettinger Sieben 4, Goettingen, 37073, Germany. TEL 49-551-390, FAX 49-551-395186, geschaeftsfuehrung@studentenwerk-goettingen.de, http://www.studentenwerk-goettingen.de. Ed. Christa Mirwald. Circ: 1,500 (controlled).

WESLEYAN UNIVERSITY ALUMNI MAGAZINE. see *EDUCATION—Higher Education*

378 USA
WEST VIRGINIA FOURTH ESTATESMAN. Text in English. 1941. q. free. **Document type:** *Newsletter.* **Description:** Covers alumni, student, and faculty news.
Published by: West Virginia University, School of Journalism, 112 Martin Hall, Box 6010, Morgantown, WV 26506-6010. TEL 304-293-3505, FAX 304-293-3027, wslater@wvnvm.wvu.edu, http://www.wvu.edu/~journals. Ed. Ronda Weese. Pub. William T Slater. Circ: 3,500 (controlled).

378 USA
WEST VIRGINIA UNIVERSITY ALUMNI NEWS. Text in English. 1939. m. USD 30. adv. **Document type:** *Newsletter.*
Published by: West Virginia University Alumni Association, Erickson Center, Morgantown, WV 26506. TEL 304-293-4731, FAX 304-293-4733. Ed., R&P Heather Cahill. Pub. Stephen L Douglas. Adv. contact Will Armistead. Circ: 28,000.

378.1 CAN ISSN 1189-6272
WESTERN ALUMNI GAZETTE. Text in English. 1939. 4/yr. free to alumni. adv. bk.rev. illus. **Description:** Aims to educate, inform, entertain and stimulate interest and positive attitudes among graduates toward the university and its goals.
Formerly: University of Western Ontario. Alumni Gazette (0042-0344)
Published by: University of Western Ontario, Department of Communications and Public Affairs, Stevenson Lawson Bldg, London, ON N6A 5B8, Canada. TEL 519-679-2111, FAX 519-661-3921, ambass@julian.uwo.ca. Ed. Alan Bass. Circ: 130,000 (controlled).

378 USA
WESTERN CAROLINIAN. Text in English. 1935. bi-m. (Wed.). USD 22; free to students (effective 2005). **Document type:** *Newspaper, Consumer.*
Related titles: Microfiche ed.
Published by: Western Carolina University, PO Box 66, Cullowhee, NC 28723. TEL 704-227-7234, carolinian@wcu.edu, http://www.westerncarolinian.com. Circ: 6,000 (free).

070 USA
WESTERN CONCEPT. Text in English. bi-w. adv. **Document type:** *Newspaper.*
Published by: Dickinson State University, Campus Dr, Dickinson, ND 58601. TEL 701-227-2846. Ed. Diane Jandt. Circ: 700.

378 USA
WESTERN COURIER. Text in English. 1905. 3/w. USD 36; USD 18 per semester (effective 2005); free. adv. **Document type:** *Newspaper.*
Published by: Western Illinois University, One University Cir, Macomb, IL 61455. TEL 309-298-1876, FAX 309-298-2309, micour@wiu.edu, http://www.westerncourier.com/. Ed. Crystal Lindell. adv.: col. inch USD 7.50. Circ: 6,500 evening (paid and free). Wire service: LAT-WAT.

378 USA
WESTERN HERALD. Text in English. 1916. s-w. (Mon.-Thu. Fall/Spring semester.; Mon. & Wed. summer 1st semester; w. Wed. summer 2nd semester). USD 29 in state; USD 31 out of state (effective 2005); free on campus. **Document type:** *Newspaper, Consumer.*
Published by: Western Michigan University, 1523 Faunce Student Services Bldg, Kalamazoo, MI 49008. TEL 269-387-2092, FAX 269-387-2267, wmu_herald@wmich.edu, http://www.westernherald.com. Ed. Jason Morton. Adv. contact Shawna Kaiser. Circ: 12,500 morning (controlled). Wire service: AP.

378 USA
WESTERN PRESS. Text in English. 1962. w.
Published by: Arizona Western College, PO Box 929, Yuma, AZ 85364. TEL 602-726-1000. Circ: 1,000.

378.198 USA
WESTERN STATE COLLEGE TOP O' THE WORLD. Text in English. 1919. w. USD 8. adv. **Document type:** *Newspaper.*
Related titles: Microfilm ed.
Published by: Western State College, Student Government Association, 600 N Adams, Gunnison, CO 81231. TEL 303-943-3062, FAX 303-943-2702. Ed. Leah Neilson. Circ: 2,000.

378 USA
WESTERN SUN. Text in English. 1966. w. adv.
Published by: Golden West College, 15744 Golden West St, Huntington Beach, CA 92647. TEL 714-895-8786, FAX 714-895-8795. Ed. Vu Nguyen. Pub. Jim Tortolano. Adv. contact Mary Quinn. Circ: 6,000.

378 USA
WESTERN TEXAN. Text in English. forth.
Published by: Western Texas College, Department of Journalism, 6200 College Ave, Synder, TX 79549. TEL 915-573-8511.

378 USA ISSN 0279-3628
THE WESTERNER. Text in English. 1980. a. free. back issues avail. **Document type:** *Magazine, Trade.* **Description:** Presents a forum for the activities and events that relate to the alumni and friends of Western Michigan University.
Published by: Western State Equipment Co., 500 E. Overland Rd., Meridian, ID 83642. TEL 208-888-2287, FAX 208-884-2314, http://www.wseco.com. Ed. Chris Hollibaugh. Circ: 100,000.

378.198 USA ISSN 1062-6700
➤ **WESTMINSTER MAGAZINE.** Text in English. 1981. q. free. **Document type:** *Academic/Scholarly.* **Description:** Includes campus updates, features, and news items about student life and alumni.
Supersedes (1932-1981): Blue and White
Published by: Westminster College, Office of Communication Services, Market St, New Wilmington, PA 16172. TEL 724-946-7226, FAX 724-946-6159, broadwps@westminster.edu, http://www.westminster.edu. Ed., R&P Patrick Broadwater. Circ: 20,225 (controlled).

C

378.1   USA
WESTMONT. Text in English. 1977. q. free. **Document type:** *Newsletter.* **Description:** Provides college news and articles about and by alumni, students, faculty and friends of Westmont. Includes class notes for alumni.
Formerly (until 1996): La Paz
Published by: Westmont College, 955 La Paz Rd, Santa Barbara, CA 93108-1089. TEL 805-565-6055, FAX 805-565-7349, nphinney@westmont.edu, http://www.westmont.edu. Ed. Nancy Lee Phinney. R&P Nancy L Phinney. Circ: 27,000.

378   USA
WHAT'S HAPPENING AT VASSAR. Text in English. 1984. 3/yr. free. illus. **Document type:** *Newsletter.*
Published by: Vassar College, Office of College Relations, 124 Raymond Ave, Poughkeepsie, NY 12604. TEL 914-437-7400. Ed. Susan Dekrey. Circ: 20,000.

378   USA
WHEATON ALUMNI. Text in English. 1929. q. free to qualified personnel. bk.rev.
Published by: Wheaton College, Evangelism and Missions Information Service, 500 College Ave, 3rd Fl, Billy Graham Center, Wheaton, IL 60187. TEL 708-752-5511. Ed. Georgia Douglass. Circ: 27,000.

378   USA
WHIRLWIND. Text in English. 1978. m. free. adv. bk.rev.; film rev.; play rev.
Published by: State University of New York, A & T College at Cobleskill, Cobleskill, NY 12043. Circ: 2,750.

378   USA
WHIT. Text in English. 1938. w. free. adv. **Document type:** *Newspaper.*
Formerly: Glassboro Whit
Published by: (Student Government), Glassboro State College, Student Center, Glassboro, NJ 08028. TEL 609-863-7105. Ed. Carol Katarsky. Adv. contact Ron Hayeck. Circ: 4,000.

378   USA
WHITWORTH TODAY. Text in English. 1973. s-a. free. bk.rev. **Document type:** *Academic/Scholarly.*
Former titles: Today Whitworth College; Today (Spokane)
Published by: Whitworth College, 300 W Hawthorne Rd, Spokane, WA 99251-3102. FAX 509-466-3729. Ed. Pat Sturko. Circ: 19,000.

378.198   USA
THE WHITWORTHIAN. Text in English. 1910. w. USD 20. adv. bk.rev. **Document type:** *Newspaper.*
Published by: Associated Students of Whitworth College, 300 W Hawthorne Rd, Spokane, WA 99251. TEL 509-466-3248, FAX 509-466-3710, whitworthian@whitworth.edu. Ed. Mark Jackson. R&P Gordon Jackson. Adv. contact Carin Sepa. Circ: 2,000.

378   USA
WICHITA STATE UNIVERSITY ALUMNI NEWS MAGAZINE. Text in English. 1990. a. (plus irreg. newsletter, approx. 8/yr.). adv. **Document type:** *Newsletter.* **Description:** Contains association news, university news and alumni profiles.
Formerly (until 1992): Confluence (Wichita)
Published by: Wichita State University, Alumni Association, 1845 N Fairmount, Campus Box 54, Wichita, KS 67260-0054. TEL 316-978-3290, FAX 316-978-3277, white@twsuvm.uc.twsu.edu. Ed. Connie Kachel White. Circ: 53,000.

378   USA
WICHITAN. Text in English. 1922. w. USD 15 (effective 1998). adv. **Document type:** *Newsletter.*
Published by: Midwestern State University, PO Box 14, Wichita Falls, TX 76308-2099. TEL 940-397-4704, FAX 940-397-4511, fsernoej@nexus.mwsv.edu. Eds. Alisha Ferguson, Josh Deskin. R&P Jim Sernoe. Adv. contact Donna Payton. page USD 654. Circ: 2,500.

378.198   USA
THE WICK. Text in English. 3/yr. **Description:** Directed to the alumni and friends of Hartwick College.
Published by: Hartwick College, Sponsor-Alumni Association, Clinton West St, Oneonta, NY 13820. TEL 607-431-4042. Circ: 16,500.

378.1   USA
WILLIAMS ALUMNI REVIEW. Text in English. 1909. q. free. bk.rev. back issues avail. **Document type:** *Consumer.* **Description:** Provides news of the college and its alumni for distribution to all alumni, parents of undergraduates and friends.
Published by: Williams College, Society of Alumni, Hopkings Hall, 880 Main St, Box 676, Williamstown, MA 01267. TEL 413-597-4151, FAX 413-597-4158, alumni.review@williams.edu, http://www.williams.edu:803/AlumRev/review.html. Ed., R&P Thomas W Bleezarde TEL 413-597-4981. Circ: 30,000 (controlled).

378   USA
THE WILLIAMS RECORD. Text in English. 1886. w. (Tue.). USD 60; free on campus (effective 2005). adv. **Document type:** *Newspaper, Consumer.* **Description:** Reports issues concerning Williams College and its students and staff.
Published by: Williams Record, Williams College, Baxter Hall, Williamstown, MA 01267. TEL 413-597-4233, FAX 413-597-2450, record@williamsrecord.com, http://www.williamsrecord.com. Ed. Mike Needham. Adv. contact Ted Unger. col. inch USD 8.75. Circ: 4,650 (paid and free).

378   USA
WINDOW (OMAHA). Text in English. 1984. q. free to qualified personnel. **Document type:** *Academic/Scholarly.*
Published by: Creighton University, Public Relations and Information, 2500 California Plaza, Omaha, NE 68178. TEL 402-280-1784, FAX 402-280-2549. Ed. Steve Kline. Circ: 55,000.

378   USA   ISSN 1093-2844
WINGSPAN (CHEYENNE). Text in English. 1969. m. USD 7 (effective 2001). adv. bk.rev.; film rev.; play rev. 16 p./no.; back issues avail. **Document type:** *Newspaper.* **Description:** Covers student news at the college.
Related titles: Online - full content ed.
Published by: Wyoming Tribune-Eagle, 1400 E College Dr, Cheyenne, WY 82007. TEL 307-634-3361, FAX 307-778-1177, schliske@mail.lcc.whecn.edu, http://www.lccc.cc.wy.us/wingspan. Eds. Chris Wolf, Sarah Hamilton. R&P Rosalind Schliske TEL 307-778-1109. Adv. contact Nina Bartholomew TEL 307-778-1304. B&W page USD 50. Circ: 1,000.

378   USA
WISCONSIN SOUTH ASIAN AREA CENTER NEWS REPORT. Text in English. 1975. 3/yr. **Description:** Covers academic activities related to South Asia.
Published by: Wisconsin South Asian Area Center, University of Wisconsin, 1242 Van Hise Hall, Madison, WI 53706. TEL 608-262-3384. Circ: 2,000.

378   DEU
WIWI-PRESS. Text in German. 1972. bi-m. adv. bk.rev.; play rev. charts; illus.; stat. **Description:** University news of interest to students of economics.
Published by: Johannes-Gutenberg-Universitaet Mainz, Allgemeine Studentausschuss, Saarstr 21, Mainz, 55122, Germany. TEL 06131-39-4801. Circ: 600.

378   USA
WOLF TALES. Text in English. 1968. m. USD 10. adv. **Document type:** *Newspaper.* **Description:** College newspaper.
Published by: Copiah-Lincoln Community College, PO Box 649, Wesson, MS 39191. TEL 601-643-8332, FAX 601-643-2366. Adv. contact Ann H Hawkins. Circ: 2,000.

378.198   USA   ISSN 0894-8798
WOOSTER. Text in English. 1886. 4/yr. free. bk.rev.
Formerly: Wooster Alumni Magazine
Published by: College of Wooster, 1189 Beall Ave, Wooster, OH 44691. TEL 330-263-2243, FAX 330-263-2594, class-notes@acs.wooster.edu. Ed. Jeffery G Hanna. Circ: 26,000.

378.1   CAN   ISSN 0043-9886
XAVERIAN WEEKLY. Text in English. 1895. 22/yr. USD 10. adv. bk.rev.; film rev.; play rev. illus. **Document type:** *Newspaper.*
Published by: St. Francis Xavier University, Students Union, P O Box 970, Antigonish, NS B2G 2W5, Canada. TEL 902-867-2412. Circ: 3,500.

378   USA   ISSN 1075-1017
XAVIER. Text in English. q. **Description:** Covers news and activities of Xavier University for alumni, friends, and faculty.
Formerly (until 1993): Xavier Today
Published by: Xavier University, Office of Public Relations, 3800 Victory Pkwy, Cincinnati, OH 45207. TEL 513-745-3178, FAX 513-745-2083. Ed. Bill Noblitt.

378.1   USA   ISSN 8750-409X
YALE ALUMNI MAGAZINE. Text in English. 1891. 8/yr. USD 25 domestic; USD 34 foreign (effective 2004). adv. bk.rev. index. back issues avail. **Document type:** *Magazine, Consumer.*
Fomer titles (until 1984): Yale Alumni Magazine and Journal (0164-9264); (until 1976): Yale Alumni Magazine (0044-0051)
Related titles: Online - full text ed.
Indexed: AmH&L, HistAb.
Published by: Yale Alumni Publications, Inc., 149 York St., New Haven, CT 06511. TEL 203-432-0645, FAX 203-432-0651, yam@yale.edu, http://www.yalealumnimagazine.com. Eds. Carter Wiseman, Kathrin Day Lassila. Pub., R&P Eugenia T Hayes TEL 203-432-0652. Adv. contact Barbara Durland. B&W page USD 3,875, color page USD 5,805. Circ: 70,000 (paid).

378.198   USA   ISSN 0890-2240
YALE DAILY NEWS. Abbreviated title: O C D(Oldest College Daily). Y D N. Text in English. 1878. d. (Sep.-May). free on campus (effective 2003). adv. bk.rev.; dance rev.; film rev.; music rev.; play rev.; rec.rev. 10 p./no.; **Document type:** *Newspaper, Consumer.*

Related titles: Microfilm ed.; Online - full text ed.: 1997 (from LexisNexis)
Published by: Yale Daily News Publishing, Co., Inc., PO Box 209007, New Haven, CT 06520-9007. TEL 203-432-2424, 203-432-2424, FAX 203-432-7425, 203-432-7425, ydn@yale.edu, http://www.yaledailynews.com. Ed. Rebecca Dana. Adv. contact Susan Zucker. col. inch USD 14. Circ: 75,000. Wire service: AP.

378   USA
THE YALE HERALD. Text in English. 1986. w. (Fri.). free on campus (effective 2005). **Document type:** *Newspaper.*
Published by: Yale University, PO Box 201653, New Haven, CT 06520-1653. herald@yale.edu, http://www.yaleherald.com. Ed. Dan Feder. Pub. Grace Yuen. Circ: 5,500 (free).

378   USA
YELLOW JACKET. Text in English. w.
Published by: Howard Payne University, Jennings Hall, Box 173, Brownville, TX 76801. TEL 915-646-2502.

378   CAN   ISSN 0827-522X
YORK GAZETTE. Text in English. 1971. m. free. bk.rev. back issues avail.
Published by: York University, Communication Department, 280 York Lanes, North York, ON M3J 1P3, Canada. FAX 416-736-5681. Circ: 5,100.

371.8   DEU   ISSN 1611-504X
YOU SEE. Text in German. 2002. q. adv. **Document type:** *Magazine, Consumer.*
Formed by the merger of (1971-2002): Uni H H Forschung (0724-9101); (1970-2002): Uni H H (0948-1583)
Published by: Universitaet Hamburg, Kommunikation und Oeffentlichkeitsarbeit, Edmund-Siemers-Allee 1, Hamburg, 20146, Germany. TEL 49-40-428384520, FAX 49-40-428382449, yousee@uni-hamburg.de, presse@uni-hamburg.de, http://www.uni-hamburg.de/uc/index.htm, http://www.verwaltung.uni-hamburg.de/pr/2/21/index.html. Ed. Christian Hild. Adv. contact Thomas Thiele. B&W page EUR 1,200, color page EUR 1,950; trim 190 x 280. Circ: 17,000 (controlled).

378   USA
YOUNGTOWN EDITION. Text in English. fortn. (during the spring and fall terms). adv. illus. 12 p./no. 4 cols./p.; **Document type:** *Newspaper.* **Description:** Covers campus news and events. Presents news and opinions on local, state, and national issues.
Published by: County College of Morris, News Desk, Mail Sta SCC 140, 214 Center Grove Rd, Randolph, NJ 07869-2086. TEL 201-328-5224.

Z V S - INFO. see *EDUCATION—Higher Education*

378   USA
▼ **02138.** Text in English. 2005. bi-m. USD 66 (effective 2005). **Document type:** *Magazine, Consumer.* **Description:** Covers the issues facing Harvard today.
Address: 41 Winter St., Ste. 53, Boston, MA 02108 . TEL 617-451-8010, info@02138magazine.com, http://www.02138magazine.com/.

378   USA
1766. Text in English. s-a.
Published by: (Rutgers Alumni Association), Targum Publishing Company, 172 College Ave, New Brunswick, NJ 08903. TEL 201-932-7474.

COMMUNICABLE DISEASES

see MEDICAL SCIENCES—Communicable Diseases

COMMUNICATIONS

see also COMMUNICATIONS—Computer Applications ; COMMUNICATIONS—Postal Affairs ; COMMUNICATIONS—Radio ; COMMUNICATIONS—Telephone And Telegraph ; COMMUNICATIONS—Television And Cable ; COMMUNICATIONS—Video ; JOURNALISM

384.54   AUS   ISSN 1039-2750
A B A UPDATE. (Australian Broadcasting Authority Update) Text in English. 1992. m.
Published by: Australian Broadcasting Authority, GPO Box Q500, Queen Victoria, NSW 1230, Australia. TEL 61-2-9334-7799, online@aba.gov.au, http://www.aba.gov.au.

621.38   AUS
A C A ANNUAL REPORT. Text in English. 1996. a.
Published by: Australian Communications Authority, PO Box 13112, Melbourne, VIC 8010, Australia. TEL 61-3-9963-6967, FAX 61-3-9963-6899, candinfo@aca.gov.au, http://www.aca.gov/.

A C M CONFERENCE ON COMPUTER AND COMMUNICATIONS SECURITY. PROCEEDINGS. see *COMPUTERS—Computer Security*

A C M INTERNATIONAL SYMPOSIUM ON MOBILE AD HOC NETWORKING AND COMPUTING. PROCEEDING. see *COMPUTERS*

004.62 USA
A C M INTERNATIONAL WORKSHOP ON WIRELESS MOBILE APPLICATIONS AND SERVICES ON W L A N HOTSPOTS. Text in English. a. USD 18 per issue to non-members; USD 9 per issue to members (effective 2005).
Related titles: Online - full content ed.
Published by: Association for Computing Machinery, Inc., 1515 Broadway, 17th Fl, New York, NY 10036-5701. TEL 212-626-0500, usacm@acm.org, http://www.acm.org.

343.099 340 USA
A C M WORKSHOP ON WIRELESS SECURITY. PROCEEDINGS. Text in English. a. **Document type:** *Proceedings, Academic/Scholarly.*
Published by: Association for Computing Machinery, Inc., 1515 Broadway, 17th Fl, New York, NY 10036-5701. TEL 212-626-0500, usacm@acm.org, http://www.acm.org.

A C U T A JOURNAL OF TELECOMMUNICATIONS IN HIGHER EDUCATION. see *EDUCATION—Higher Education*

384 USA
A C U T A NEWS. Text in English. 1982. m. USD 45 (effective 2000). adv. bk.rev. **Document type:** *Newsletter.* **Description:** Stories of new installations, applications, industry and regulatory updates, problems solved.
Related titles: Online - full text ed.
Published by: Association of College and University Telecommunications Administrators, 152 W Zandale Dr, Ste 200, Lexington, KY 40503-2486. TEL 606-278-3338, FAX 606-278-3268, pscott@acuta.org, kadkins@acuta.org, http://www.acuta.org. Ed., R&P Pat Scott. Pub. Jeri A Semer. Adv. contact Kevin Adkins. Circ: 2,200.

621.382 DEU ISSN 1434-8411
TK7800 CODEN: AEUTAH
➤ **A E UE: INTERNATIONAL JOURNAL OF ELECTRONICS AND COMMUNICATION.** (Archiv fuer Elektronik und Uebertragungstechnik) Text in English. 1947-1995; resumed 1999. 8/yr. EUR 765 domestic to institutions; EUR 775 in Europe to institutions; JPY 103,200 in Japan to institutions; USD 830 elsewhere to institutions (effective 2006). adv. bk.rev. **Document type:** *Journal, Academic/Scholarly.* **Description:** Covers all aspects of theory and design of circuits, systems and devices for electronics, signal processing, and communication.
Former titles (until 1996): A E Ue: Archiv fuer Elektronik und Uebertragungstechnik (0001-1096); (until 1971): Archiv der Elektrischen Ubertragung (0374-2393)
Related titles: Microform ed.: (from PQC); Online - full text ed.: (from EBSCO Publishing, Gale Group, IngentaConnect, O C L C Online Computer Library Center, Inc., ScienceDirect, Swets Information Services).
Indexed: ASCA, C&ISA, CurCont, E&CAJ, EngInd, ExcerpMed, Inspec, RefZh, SCI, SolStAb.
—BLDSC (4542.232100), AskIEEE, CISTI, Ei, IE, Infotrieve, ingenta, Linda Hall. **CCC.**
Published by: (Informationstechnische Gesellschaft im VDE (ITG)), Elsevier GmbH, Urban & Fischer Verlag (Subsidiary of: Elsevier Science & Technology), Loebdergraben 14a, Jena, 07743, Germany. TEL 49-3641-626444, FAX 49-3641-626443, info@urbanfischer.de, http://www.elsevier.com/locate/aeue, http://www.urbanfischer.de. Ed. Dr. Ralf Lehnert TEL 49-351-463-33942. R&P Frances Rothwell. Adv. contact Cora Grotzke. B&W page EUR 400, color page EUR 1,345; 210 x 280. Circ: 430 (paid and controlled). **Non-German speaking countries subscr. to:** Nature Publishing Group, Brunel Rd, Houndmills, Basingstoke, Hamps RG21 6XS, United Kingdom. TEL 44-1256-302629, FAX 44-1256-476117, subscriptions@nature.com.

384 ESP ISSN 0213-1226
HE7820.5
A H C I E T REVISTA DE TELECOMUNICACIONES. Text in Spanish. 1984. q. EUR 30 (effective 2004).
Indexed: IECT.
—CINDOC.
Published by: Asociacion Hispanoamericana de Centros de Investigacion y Estudio de Telecomunicaciones, Ramirez de Arellano, 15, 3a Planta, Madrid, 28043, Spain. TEL 34-91-5104425, FAX 34-91-5195192, http://www.ahciet.net/REVISTA/default.asp?id=10427&idm=10007.

A L C T S COLLECTION AND DEVELOPMENT GUIDES. (Association for Library Collections & Technical Services) see *LIBRARY AND INFORMATION SCIENCES*

A L S I C. (Apprentissage de Langues et Systemes d'Information et de Communication) see *EDUCATION—Teaching Methods And Curriculum*

384 AUT
A P A - JOURNAL. MEDIEN. Text in German. w. EUR 380 combined subscription for print & online eds. (effective 2003). **Document type:** *Journal, Trade.*
Related titles: Online - full text ed.
Published by: Austria Presse Agentur, Gunoldstr 14, Vienna, W 1190, Austria. TEL 43-1-360600, FAX 43-1-360603099, kundenservice@apa.at, http://www.apa.at.

384 AUT
A P A - JOURNAL. TELEKOM. Text in German. w. EUR 380 combined subscription for print & online eds. (effective 2003). **Document type:** *Journal, Trade.*
Related titles: Online - full text ed.
Published by: Austria Presse Agentur, Gunoldstr 14, Vienna, W 1190, Austria. TEL 43-1-360600, FAX 43-1-360603099, kundenservice@apa.at, http://www.apa.at.

621.38 KOR ISSN 1226-8844
A P S C C NEWSLETTER. Text in English. 1995. q. adv. **Description:** Provides technical information and commentary on developments, trends, and current debates in the fields of satellite communications and broadcasting.
Indexed: BrCerAb, C&ISA, CerAb, CorrAb, E&CAJ, EMA, IAA, M&TEA, MBF, METADEX, WAA.
—Linda Hall.
Published by: Asia-Pacific Satellite Communications Council, Suite 401, Kyung-il Bldg., B-dong, 440-30 Sungnae 3-dong, Kangdong-gu, Seoul, 134-847, Korea, S. TEL 82-2-5084883, FAX 82-2-5688593, editor@apscc.or.kr, info@apscc.or.kr, http://www.apscc.or.kr/pub/news.asp. Ed. Sarah Yi. adv.: color page USD 2,000; bleed 216 x 303.

384 USA
A P S CONFERENCE ON ANTENNAS AND PROPAGATION FOR WIRELESS COMMUNICATIONS. PROCEEDINGS. (Antennas and Propagation Society) Text in English. a., latest 2000. price varies. **Document type:** *Proceedings, Trade.*
—BLDSC (4362.805750).
Published by: Institute of Electrical and Electronics Engineers, Inc., 3 Park Ave, 17th Fl, New York, NY 10016-5997. TEL 212-419-7900, 800-678-4333, FAX 212-752-4929, customer.service@ieee.org, http://www.ieee.org. **Co-sponsor:** Antennas and Propagation Society.

621.382 JPN ISSN 0915-2563
A T R JOURNAL. Text in Japanese. 1987. s-a. JPY 700 per issue.
Published by: Advanced Telecommunications Research Institute International/Kokusai Denki Tsushin Kiso Gijutsu Kenkyujo, Inuidani Sanpeidani, Soraku-gun, Seikacho, Kyoto 619-02, Japan.

621.38 BEL ISSN 0778-0303
A V INDUSTRIE. Text in Dutch, French. 1989. bi-m. EUR 25 domestic; EUR 30 foreign; EUR 5 per issue (effective 2005). adv. **Document type:** *Trade.* **Description:** For professionals in the audio-visual sector and related services.
Published by: Making Magazines, Blekersdijk, 14, Gent, 9000, Belgium. TEL 32-9-268-2800, FAX 32-9-268-2817, AVindustrie@MakingMagazines.be, http://www.av.be/avfrframe.html. Ed. Dirk Rasschaert. Circ: 5,000.

378 DEU ISSN 0940-0486
A V INVEST. (Audio Video) Text in German. 1991. 11/yr. EUR 40 domestic; EUR 50 foreign; EUR 5 newsstand/cover (effective 2004). adv. **Document type:** *Magazine, Trade.*
Published by: WEFGO-Verlag GmbH, Mozartstr 24, Germering, 82110, Germany. TEL 49-89-8414866, FAX 49-89-8415632, info@avinvest.de, http://www.avinvest.de. Ed. R. Auer. Adv. contact Monika Auer. B&W page EUR 1,469, color page EUR 2,204; trim 210 x 297. Circ: 2,200 (paid and controlled).

A3 VOLT; Automatisierung, Elektrotechnik, Elektronik, Logistik. see *ELECTRONICS*

384 GBR ISSN 0143-3253
ACTION NEWSLETTER. Text in English. 1969. 10/yr. free membership (effective 2003). bk.rev. **Document type:** *Newsletter.*
Related titles: Online - full text ed.
Published by: World Association for Christian Communication, 357 Kennington Rd, London, SE11 5QY, United Kingdom. TEL 44-20-75829139, FAX 44-20-77350340, sh@wacc.org.uk, http://www.wacc.org.uk/publications/action/250/contents.html. Ed. Sean Hawkey. Circ: 2,200.

▼ **AD HOC NETWORKS.** see *COMPUTERS—Computer Networks*

384 USA
ADAD; working the media substance since 1917. Text in English. w. **Document type:** *Bulletin.* **Description:** Devoted to the investigation of the media substance.
Media: Online - full text.
Address: jhanas@adadmedia.com, http://adadmedia.com. Ed. Jim Hanas.

ADVERTISING & MARKETING REVIEW. see *ADVERTISING AND PUBLIC RELATIONS*

621.382 USA
AFRICA TELECOM MONTHLY. Text in English. m. USD 850 to individuals; USD 3,300 to institutions (effective 2000). **Document type:** *Journal, Trade.* **Description:** Contains a concise synopsis of all major developments in the telecom industry on the African continent.
Published by: Gist, Inc., 2200 Wilson Blvd, Ste 102G, Arlington, VA 22201. TEL 703-527-7459, FAX 703-528-1477, info@gist.net, http://www.gist.net.

AFRICAN COMPUTING & COMMUNICATIONS YEARBOOK; key information for Africa's IT managers. see *COMPUTERS—Computer Industry Directories*

AFRICAN COUNCIL FOR COMMUNICATION EDUCATION. REPORTS ON WORKSHOPS - SEMINARS. see *JOURNALISM*

384 KEN
AFRICOM. Text in English, French. 3/yr. USD 30 in Africa; USD 35 elsewhere. **Document type:** *Newsletter, Academic/Scholarly.* **Description:** Covers communications and media news in Africa.
Published by: African Council for Communication Education/Conseil Africain pour l'Enseignement de la Communication, PO Box 47495, Nairobi, Kenya. TEL 254-2-227043, FAX 254-2-216135, acce@wananchi.com. Ed. Charles Okigbo.

621.382 DEU
ALLENSBACHER COMPUTER- UND TELEKOMMUNIKATIONSANALYSE. Abbreviated title: A C T A. Text in German. 1997. a. **Document type:** *Bulletin, Trade.* **Description:** Features market and media research, as well as information on the computer and telecommunications market and media.
Related titles: Online - full text ed.
Published by: Institut fuer Demoskopie Allensbach, Radolfzellerstr 8, Allensbach, 78476, Germany. TEL 49-7533-8050, FAX 49-7533-3048, info@ifd-allensbach.de, http://www.media.spiegel.de. Circ: 700.

C

384 IND
ALPHA. Text in English. 1977 (vol.15). m. INR 1.25 per issue.
Published by: Rajendra Prasad Institute of Communications, Bharatiya Vidya Bhavan, Mumbai, Maharashtra 400 007, India. Ed. G S Pohekar.

621.380711 IND
ALPHA COMMUNICATIONS MONTHLY. Text in English. 1964. m.
Published by: (Bhavan's College of Mass Communication), Bharatiya Vidya Bhavan, Kulapati K.M. Munshi Marg, Mumbai, Maharashtra 400 007, India. Ed. M K B Nairar.

808.53 USA
AMERICAN FORENSIC ASSOCIATION NEWSLETTER. Text in English. 1979. 3/yr. USD 75 to individual members; USD 70 to institutional members; USD 20 to students (effective 2005); includes Argumentation and Advocacy. adv. back issues avail. **Document type:** *Newsletter, Internal.*
Published by: American Forensic Association, PO Box 256, River Falls, WI 54022-0256. TEL 715-425-3198, 800-228-5424, FAX 715-425-9533, 888-314-9533, amforensicassoc@aol.com, http://www.americanforensics.org. R&P James Pratt TEL 715-425-3198. adv.: page USD 75. Circ: 800.

AMERICAN JOURNALISM. see *JOURNALISM*

384 USA ISSN 0740-5111
AMERICAN UNIVERSITY STUDIES. SERIES 15. COMMUNICATIONS. Text in English. 1984. irreg., latest 1994. USD 34.95 per vol. (effective 2004). **Document type:** *Monographic series, Academic/Scholarly.* **Description:** Delves into the study of various aspects of communications.
Published by: Peter Lang Publishing, Inc., 275 Seventh Ave, 28th Fl, New York, NY 10001. TEL 212-647-7700, 212-647-7706, 800-770-5264, FAX 212-647-7707, customerservice@plang.com, http://www.peterlang.com. Ed. David Bergeron. Pub. Christopher Myers. R&P Stephanie Archer. Adv. contact Patricia Mulrane.

345 USA ISSN 1555-8908
KF2763.A2
ANDREWS LITIGATION REPORTER: TELECOMMUNICATIONS INDUSTRY. Text in English. 1997. bi-w. USD 892 (effective 2005). **Document type:** *Journal, Trade.* **Description:** Covers the latest case law developments, including authority and jurisdiction of federal, state, and local governmental authorities, preemption, regulation of satellite and cable TV, FCC proceedings, construction of cellular towers and zoning disputes.
Formerly (until 200?): Andrews Telecommunications Industry Litigation Reporter (1096-4746)
Related titles: Online - full content ed.: USD 999 (effective 2003).
—**CCC.**
Published by: Andrews Publications (Subsidiary of: Thomson West), 175 Strafford Ave, Ste 140, Wayne, PA 19087. TEL 610-225-0510, 800-345-1101, FAX 610-225-0501, west.customer.service@thomson.com, http://findlaw.west.thomson.com/product/40211182/product.asp, http://www.andrewsonline.com. Ed. Deborah Nathan.

384 DEU
ANGEWANDTE MEDIENFORSCHUNG. Text in German. 1996. irreg., latest vol.28, 2003. price varies. **Document type:** *Monographic series, Academic/Scholarly.*
Published by: (Medien Institut Ludwigshafen), Verlag Reinhard Fischer, Weltistr 34, Munich, 81477, Germany. TEL 49-89-7918892, FAX 49-89-7918310, verlagfischer@compuserve.de, http://www.verlag-reinhard-fischer.de. Ed. Hans Bernd Brosius.

621.382 FRA ISSN 0003-4347
TK2 CODEN: ANTEAU
➤ **ANNALES DES TELECOMMUNICATIONS.** Text in English, French. 1946. bi-m. EUR 255 in the European Union; EUR 300 elsewhere (effective 2003). bk.rev. illus. index. **Document type:** *Academic/Scholarly.* **Description:** Disseminates research results and engineering developments in the field of telecommunications.
Indexed: ASCA, AcoustA, C&ISA, CIS, CMCI, ChemAb, CompC, CurCont, E&CAJ, EngInd, INIS AtomInd, ISMEC, ISR, Inspec, MathR, PROMT, SCI, SolStAb, ZentMath.
—BLDSC (1002.000000), AskIEEE, CASDDS, CISTI, Ei, IDS, IE, Infotrieve, ingenta, Linda Hall. **CCC.**
Published by: Lavoisier, 11 rue Lavoisier, Paris, 75008, France. TEL 33-1-42653995, FAX 33-1-42650246, info@lavoisier.fr, http://www.lavoisier.fr. Circ: 2,500. **Subscr. to:** Lavoisier - Dept Abonnements, 14 rue de Provigny, Cachan 94236, France. TEL 33-1-47406700, FAX 33-1-47406702, abo@lavoisier.fr.

621.382 USA
ANNUAL FORUM REPORTS. Text in English. 1993. a. USD 475 (effective 1998). **Document type:** *Trade.* **Description:** Publishes talks, speeches, lectures and invited papers on specific topics relevant to the information industry.
Related titles: Online - full text ed.
Published by: (International Engineering Consortium), Professional Education International, Inc., 300 W. Adams St., Ste. 1210, Chicago, IL 60606-5114. TEL 312-559-4100, FAX 312-559-4111. Ed. Dan Coran. R&P Mike Janowiak TEL 312-559-3733. Circ: 2,000.

C

621.382 USA ISSN 1073-0885
TK5
ANNUAL REVIEW OF COMMUNICATIONS. Text in English. 1944. a. USD 395 (effective 2005). charts. index. back issues avail. **Document type:** *Proceedings.* **Description:** Broad compilation of the latest technical and business thinking of experts in the telecommunications, computer and electronics fields.
Former titles (until 1992): National Communications Forum. Proceedings (0886-229X); National Electronics Conference National Communications Forum. Proceedings; (until 1979): National Electronics Conference. Proceedings (0077-4413)
Related titles: Online - full text ed.
—BLDSC (1522.251000), CISTI, Linda Hall.
Published by: (International Engineering Consortium), Professional Education International, Inc., 300 W. Adams St., Ste. 1210, Chicago, IL 60606-5114. TEL 312-559-4100, FAX 312-559-4111, info@iec.org, http://www.iec.org, http://www.iec.com. R&P Mike Janowiak TEL 312-559-3733. Circ: 4,000.

ANRITSU TECHNICAL BULLETIN/ANRITSU TEKUNIKARU. see *ENGINEERING—Electrical Engineering*

621.382 ESP
ANTENA DE TELECOMUNICACION. Text in Spanish. 1965. bi-m. free. adv. bk.rev. charts; illus.
Published by: Asociacion Espanola de Ingenieros de Telecomunicacion/Spanish Association of Telecommunications Engineers, General Arrando, 38, Madrid, 28010, Spain. TEL 34-91-3291701, FAX 34-91-7479341. Ed. Carlos Dominquez. Circ: 3,000.

384 USA
ANTENNA MEASUREMENT TECHNIQUES ASSOCIATION. ANNUAL MEETING AND SYMPOSIUM PROCEEDINGS. Text in English. a.
—BLDSC (1087.965830).
Published by: Antenna Measurement Techniques Association, 6065 Roswell Rd, Suite 2252, Atlanta, GA 30328. fliss@erim-int.com, http://www.amta.org/amtainfo. Ed. Jerry Fliss TEL 414-453-7450.

384 USA
ANTENNA MEASUREMENT TECHNIQUES ASSOCIATION. NEWSLETTER. Text in English. s-a.
Related titles: Online - full text ed.
Published by: Antenna Measurement Techniques Association, 6065 Roswell Rd, Suite 2252, Atlanta, GA 30328. fliss@erim-int.com, http://www.amta.org/amtainfo. Ed. Jerry Fliss TEL 414-453-7450.

384 GBR
ANTENNAS SERIES. Text in English. irreg., latest vol.12, 2003. price varies. **Document type:** *Monographic series.*
Related titles: CD-ROM ed.
—BLDSC (1545.210000).
Published by: Research Studies Press Ltd., 16 Coach House Cloisters, 10 Hitchin St, Baldock, Hertfordshire SG7 6AE, United Kingdom. TEL 44-1462-895060, FAX 44-1462-892546, http://www.research-studies-press.co.uk. Ed. J R James. **Dist. by:** America Technical Publishers, 27-29 Knowl Piece Way, Wilbury Way, Hitchin, Herts SG4 0SX, United Kingdom. TEL 44-1462-437933, FAX 44-1462-433678.

384 FRA ISSN 0396-8995
ANTENNES✶. Text in French. 12/yr. **Description:** Provides audio-visual information and new communication techniques.
Published by: Telediffusion de France, 10 rue d'Oradour-sur-Glane, Paris, Cedex 15 75732, France. TEL 49-65-13-20. Ed. Philippe Baudelot.

ANUARIO DE INOVACOES EM COMUNICACOES E ARTES. see *ART*

APPLIED ENVIRONMENTAL EDUCATION AND COMMUNICATION; an international journal. see *ENVIRONMENTAL STUDIES*

ARMY COMMUNICATOR; voice of the Signal Regiment. see *MILITARY*

ART, DESIGN & COMMUNICATION IN HIGHER EDUCATION. see *ART*

THE ART OF COMMUNICATION. see *PUBLIC ADMINISTRATION*

ARTS AND MEDIA SERIES. see *ART*

384 GBR ISSN 1084-0710
HE8341
ASIACOM. Text in English. 1995. fortn. (23/yr.). GBP 895, EUR 1,343, USD 1,700 (effective 2005). back issues avail. **Document type:** *Newsletter, Trade.* **Description:** Covers Asia's fixed line and mobile telecoms, Internet, cable and satellite TV industries.
Incorporates (in 1999): Pan-Asian Telecom
—**CCC.**
Published by: Baskerville (Subsidiary of: T & F Informa plc), Sheepen Place, Colchester, Essex C03 3LP, United Kingdom. TEL 44-20-70175537, FAX 44-20-70174783, telecoms.enquiries@informa.com, http://www.baskerville.telecoms.com/asiacom. Eds. Nicole McCormick, Tony Brown.

384 SGP
ASIAN COMMUNICATIONS. Text in English. m. adv. **Document type:** *Magazine, Trade.* **Description:** Provides news and analysis on market opportunities, management strategies, finance and technology in the telecoms sector.
Published by: Charlton Media Group, 9B Stanley St, Singapore, 068728, Singapore. TEL 65-6223-7660, admin@charltonmedia.com, http://www.charltonmedia.com. Ed. Angela McFeeters. Pub. Timothy Charlton.

384 GBR ISSN 0129-2986
P92.A7
➤ **ASIAN JOURNAL OF COMMUNICATION.** Text in English. 1990. q. GBP 152, USD 250 combined subscription to institutions print & online eds. (effective 2006). biennial index. back issues avail.; reprint service avail. from PSC. **Document type:** *Journal, Academic/Scholarly.* **Description:** Aims to advance understand of the process of communication in the Asia-Pacific region with articles that develop communication theory, report empirical research and describe advances in research methodology.
Related titles: Online - full text ed.: ISSN 1742-0911. GBP 144, USD 238 to institutions (effective 2006) (from EBSCO Publishing, Gale Group, IngentaConnect, O C L C Online Computer Library Center, Inc., Swets Information Services).
Indexed: BAS, CommAb, HRA, IBSS, PSA, SociolAb.
—BLDSC (1742.478000), IE, Infotrieve, ingenta.
Published by: (Nanyang Technological University, School of Communication and Information SGP, Asian Media Information and Communication Centre SGP), Routledge (Subsidiary of: Taylor & Francis Group), 4 Park Sq, Milton Park, Abingdon, Oxon OX14 4RN, United Kingdom. TEL 44-1235-828600, FAX 44-1235-829000, info@routledge.co.uk, http://www.tandf.co.uk/journals/titles/01292986.asp. Ed. Eddie C Y Kuo. R&P, Adv. contact Gordon Hogan.

384 SGP ISSN 1741-7139
ASIAN SOURCES TELECOM PRODUCTS. Text in Chinese, English. m. USD 75 (effective 2005). **Document type:** *Magazine, Trade.* **Description:** Covers telecom, datacom and satellite products.
Formerly (until 1998): Telecom Sources (1021-1276)
Related titles: CD-ROM ed.; Online - full text ed.; Chinese ed.: Tongxin KeJi Shangqing. ISSN 1028-091X.
Published by: Global Sources, c/o Media Data Systems Pte Ltd, PO Box 0203, Raffles City, 911707, Singapore. TEL 65-65472800, FAX 65-65472888, service@globalsources.com, http://www.globalsources.com/MAGAZINE/BUYERS/TSBR.HTM?pi_proj=GSOLHP.

AUDIO VISUELLE MEDIA. see *ADVERTISING AND PUBLIC RELATIONS*

384 RUS
AURAMEDIA. Text in Russian. 6/yr. USD 169.95 in United States.
Related titles: CD-ROM ed.; Online - full text ed.
Address: Okruzhnoi pr 19, Moscow, 105058, Russian Federation. TEL 7-095-3664536, http://www.auramedia.ru. **US dist. addr.:** East View Information Services, 3020 Harbor Ln. N., Minneapolis, MN 55447. TEL 612-550-0961.

621.382 AUS ISSN 1440-8031
AUSTRALASIAN TELECOMMUNICATIONS MANAGEMENT AND MARKETING. Text in English. 1989. m. (11/yr.). USD 425 domestic; USD 455 foreign (effective 2001). index. back issues avail. **Document type:** *Newsletter.* **Description:** Covers national and international management and marketing applications, trends and developments on optical fibres, HDTV, ISDN, optical media, EDI, videotex, pay TV, electronic publishing, mobile communications, teletext and satellite communications.
Former titles (until 1998): Australasian Telecommunications Marketing and Management Newsletter (1440-8023); (until 1996): Australasian Telecommunications Management and Marketing Newsletter (1440-799X); (until 1995): Telecommunications Management and Marketing Newsletter (1034-7496)
Published by: Paul Budde Communication Pty. Ltd., 2643 George Downes Dr, Bucketty, NSW 2250, Australia. TEL 61-2-4998-8144, FAX 61-2-49988144, sally@budde.com.au, pbc@budde.com.au, http://www.budde.com.au. Ed. Paul Budde. Circ: 250.

384 AUS ISSN 0726-3252
AUSTRALIAN COMMUNICATION REVIEW✶. Text in English. 1979. q. AUD 70 to individuals; to individuals; institutions Aus.$90. adv. bk.rev. **Description:** Articles about communication issues of interest to communication scholars, specialists and practitioners.
Published by: Australian Communication Association, c/o Univ. of Western Sydney, Information Officer, PO Box 10, Kingswood, NSW 2747, Australia. TEL 062-573155, FAX 61-2-416-7174. Ed. Ray Archee. Circ: 200. **Subscr. to:** CRIA, GPO Box 655, Canberra, ACT 2601, Australia.

302.2 AUS ISSN 0811-6202
P87 CODEN: AJCOEJ
➤ **AUSTRALIAN JOURNAL OF COMMUNICATION.** Text in English. 1982. 3/yr. subscr. incl. with membership. bk.rev. Index. **Document type:** *Journal, Academic/Scholarly.*
Related titles: Online - full text ed.: (from R M I T Publishing).
Indexed: AusPAIS, CommAb, EAA, HRA, L&LBA, PRA, PSA, RILM, SOPODA, SSA, SociolAb, V&AA.
—BLDSC (1806.500000), IE, ingenta.
Published by: Australia and New Zealand Communication Association, PO Box 371, Mitchell, ACT 2911, Australia. TEL 61-7-38642065, http://www.anzca.net/. Circ: 500.

384 AUS
AUSTRALIAN TELECOM. Text in English. 2000. m. AUD 55 domestic; AUD 110 foreign (effective 2004). **Document type:** *Magazine, Trade.* **Description:** Covers the news, technology, people and forces behind the Australian telecommunications industry, including key events, as well as forecasting and analyzing future trends.
Published by: First Charlton Communications, Level 9, Tenix House, 100 Arthur St, North Sydney, NSW 2060, Australia. TEL 61-2-99556299, FAX 61-2-99571512, pctc@charlton.com.au, http://www.charlton.com.au/. Ed. Randolph Ramsay. Adv. contact Tony May TEL 61-2-99579809.

343.0994 AUS ISSN 1321-4470
AUSTRALIAN TELECOMMUNICATIONS LAW JOURNAL. Text in English. 1994. q. AUD 99. bk.rev. back issues avail. **Document type:** *Journal, Academic/Scholarly.* **Description:** Provides analysis of the law relating to telecommunications for scholars, professionals and consumers.
Published by: Australian Law Publishers Pty. Ltd., 254 Hawken Dr, St Lucia, QLD 4067, Australia. TEL 61-7-38709111, FAX 61-7-38702222, la510737@student.uq.edu.au. Ed. Russell Mathews. Circ: 200.

384 DEU
AUTO HIFI. Text in German. 1990. bi-m. EUR 37.20 domestic; EUR 43.10 in Austria; CHF 72.90 in Switzerland; EUR 5 newsstand/cover (effective 2004). adv. **Document type:** *Magazine, Consumer.*
Related titles: Online - full text ed.
Published by: Vereinigte Motor-Verlage GmbH & Co. KG, Leuschnerstr 1, Stuttgart, 70174, Germany. TEL 49-711-18201, FAX 49-711-1821669, http://www.autohifi-netedition.de, http://www.motorpresse.de. Ed. Klaus-Peter Bredschneider. Pub. F Stein. Adv. contact Michael Roy. B&W page EUR 3,990, color page EUR 6,390; trim 185 x 248. Circ: 33,254 (paid and controlled).

384 GBR ISSN 1475-861X
THE B A P C O JOURNAL. Text in English. 1992. 10/yr. GBP 28 domestic; GBP 35 foreign (effective 2004). adv. **Document type:** *Journal, Trade.* **Description:** Designed to provide a platform for a regular and accurate means of exchanging information relating to all aspects of communications and information technology for the public safety sector.
—**CCC.**

Published by: (British Association of Public Safety Communication Officers), Datateam Publishing Ltd, 15a London Rd, Maidstone, Kent ME16 8LY, United Kingdom. TEL 44-1622-687031, FAX 44-1622-757646, bapco@datateam.co.uk, info@datateam.co.uk, http://www.datateam.co.uk/business_publications/bapco_journal.htm, http://www.datateam.co.uk/home/home.htm. adv.: color page GBP 1,540; trim 210 x 284.

384 GBR ISSN 1473-4575
B B C MONITORING GLOBAL NEWSLINE. MEDIA. Text in English. d.
Media: Online - full content.
Published by: B B C Monitoring, Caversham Park, Peppard Rd, Reading, Berks RG4 8TZ, United Kingdom. TEL 44-118-948-6289, FAX 44-118-946-3823, marketing@monitor.bbc.co.uk, http://www.monitor.bbc.co.uk.

384 DEU ISSN 0939-8317
B L M SCHRIFTENREIHE. Text in German. 1989. irreg., latest vol.73, 2003. price varies. **Document type:** *Monographic series, Academic/Scholarly.*
Published by: (Bayerische Landeszentrale fuer neue Medien), Verlag Reinhard Fischer, Weltistr 34, Munich, 81477, Germany. TEL 49-89-7918892, FAX 49-89-7918310, verlagfischer@compuserve.de, http://www.blm.de, http://www.verlag-reinhard-fischer.de.

B M A MEMBERSHIP DIRECTORY AND RESOURCE GUIDE. see *ADVERTISING AND PUBLIC RELATIONS*

384.5452 310 USA ISSN 1094-4494
B - STATS. (Broadcast) Text in English. 1997. m. USD 925 (effective 2001). **Document type:** *Newsletter.* **Description:** Presents the numbers behind the broadcast companies. Exclusive data, analysis and projections of radio and TV market billings, revenues and cash flows, plus complete data on the buy-sell market. The industry's key reference source.
Related titles: E-mail ed.: USD 925 (effective 2001); Fax ed.: USD 925 (effective 2001).
Published by: Kagan Research, LLC, 1 Lower Ragsdale Dr., Ste. 130, Monterey, CA 93940-5741. TEL 831-624-1536, FAX 831-625-3225, info@kagan.com, http://www.kagan.com. Pub. Paul Kagan.

621.38 USA ISSN 1358-3948
TK5101.A1 CODEN: BTJUEH
➤ **B T TECHNOLOGY JOURNAL.** (British Telecommunications) Text in Dutch. 1983. q. EUR 478, USD 488, GBP 298 combined subscription to institutions print & online eds. (effective 2005). back issues avail.; reprints avail. **Document type:** *Journal, Academic/Scholarly.* **Description:** Contains research and review papers for development engineers, whether in companies, laboratories, or academic institutions involved in telecommunications and related technologies.
Formerly (until 1991): British Telecom Technology Journal (0265-0193)
Related titles: Online - full text ed.: ISSN 1573-1995 (from EBSCO Publishing, Gale Group, IngentaConnect, Kluwer Online, O C L C Online Computer Library Center, Inc., Ovid Technologies, Inc., ProQuest Information & Learning, Springer LINK, Swets Information Services).
Indexed: ABIn, AHCI, AcoustA, BibLing, C&CSA, CurCont, EngInd, ErgAb, ISR, Inspec, RefZh, SCI.
—BLDSC (2354.395000), AskIEEE, CISTI, Ei, IDS, IE, Infotrieve, ingenta, Linda Hall. **CCC.**
Published by: (British Telecommunications plc. GBR), Springer-Verlag New York, Inc. (Subsidiary of: Springer Science+Business Media), 233 Spring St, New York, NY 10013. TEL 212-460-1500, FAX 212-460-1575, service@springer-ny.com, http://springerlink.metapress.com/openurl.asp?genre=journal&issn=1358-3948, http://www.springer-ny.com. Ed. Ian G Dufour. **Subscr. to:** Journal Fulfillment, PO Box 2485, Secaucus, NJ 07096-2485. TEL 201-348-4033, FAX 201-348-4505, journals@springer-ny.com.

➤ **BACKBONE TECHNOLOGIES.** see *BUSINESS AND ECONOMICS—Marketing And Purchasing*

621.38 CHN ISSN 1000-1506
TA1001
BEIFANG JIAOTONG DAXUE XUEBAO/NORTH COMMUNICATIONS UNIVERSITY. JOURNAL. Text in Chinese. q. **Document type:** *Academic/Scholarly.*
Related titles: Online - full text ed.: (from East View Information Services).
Indexed: EngInd.
Published by: Beifang Jiaotong Daxue, Xuebao Bianjibu, Xizhimenwai, Beijing, 100044, China. TEL 8316622. Ed. Hu Shuliang.

384 CHN ISSN 1005-8028
BEIJING DIANXIN KEJI/BEIJING TELECOM SCIENCE AND TECHNOLOGY. Text in Chinese. 1984. q. back issues avail. **Document type:** *Academic/Scholarly.*
Related titles: Online - full content ed.: (from WanFang Data Corp.); Online - full text ed.: (from East View Information Services).
Published by: Beijing Shi Dianxin Kexue Yanjiusuo, 18 Taipinghu dong Li, Xicheng-qu, Beijing, 100031, China. Ed. Feng-E Hu.

621.382 CHN ISSN 1005-8885
TK5101.A1
BEIJING UNIVERSITY OF POSTS AND TELECOMMUNICATIONS. JOURNAL. Text in English. 1994. s-a. CNY 20, USD 10 (effective 2003). **Document type:** *Journal, Academic/Scholarly.*
Related titles: ♦ CD-ROM ed.: Chinese Academic Journals Full-Text Database. Electronic Technology & Information Science. ISSN 1008-6293; Online - full content ed.: (from WanFang Data Corp.); Online - full text ed.: (from East View Information Services); ♦ Chinese ed.: Beijing Youdian Daxue Xuebao. ISSN 1007-5321.
Indexed: C&ISA, E&CAJ, IAA, Inspec, RefZh.
—BLDSC (4729.219330), IE, ingenta.
Published by: Beijing Youdian Daxue/Beijing University of Posts and Telecommunications, BUPT, PO Box 231, Beijing, 100876, China. Wangwn@noya.bupt.deu.cn, wangwn@bupt.edu.cn, http://zgydgxxb-e.periodicals.net.cn/default.html. Ed. Yinghua Lu.

621.382 CHN ISSN 1007-5321
TK5101.A1
BEIJING YOUDIAN DAXUE XUEBAO. Text in Chinese. 1960. q. CNY 56; CNY 14 per issue (effective 2003). illus. 46 p./no.; back issues avail. **Document type:** *Journal, Academic/Scholarly.*
Formerly: Beijing Youdian Xueyuan Xuebao (1000-5145)
Related titles: ♦ CD-ROM ed.: Chinese Academic Journals Full-Text Database. Electronic Technology & Information Science. ISSN 1008-6293; Online - full content ed.: (from WanFang Data Corp.); ♦ English ed.: Beijing University of Posts and Telecommunications. Journal. ISSN 1005-8885.
Indexed: EngInd, Inspec, RefZh.
Published by: Beijing Youdian Daxue/Beijing University of Posts and Telecommunications, Editorial Department of Journal of BUPT, Haidian-qu, 10, Xi Tucheng Lu, Beijing, 100876, China. byxb@bupt.edu.cn, wangwn@bupt.edu.cn, http://www.bupt.edu.cn/quick/link/journal/www/Homepage/chupt.html. Ed. Yi Xian Yang. Circ: 290 (paid); 210 (controlled).

384 GBR ISSN 1472-8168
BEST PRACTICE MEASUREMENT STRATEGIES. Text in English. 1998. 10/yr. GBP 195, USD 295 (effective 2000). **Document type:** *Newsletter.* **Description:** Evaluates the tools and methods for assessing the impact of communication strategy on business performance.
Formerly (until 2001): Total Communication Measurement (1464-1445)
Related titles: Online - full text ed.: (from EBSCO Publishing).
—CCC.
Published by: Melcrum Publishing, 1st Floor, Chelsea Reach, 79-89 Lots Rd, London, SW10 0RN, United Kingdom. TEL 44-171-229-9900, 877-226-2764, FAX 44-171-243-5554, 312-803-1871, info@melcrum.com, http://www.melcrum.com.

384 GBR ISSN 1472-7188
BLUETOOTH WORLD. Text in English. 2000. q. **Document type:** *Magazine, Trade.* **Description:** Covers news, analysis, technology and the market of the Bluetooth industry; contains product previews and group tests.
Related titles: Online - full text ed.: (from Gale Group).
Published by: Informa Telecoms & Media (Subsidiary of: T & F Informa plc), 37-41 Mortimer St, London, W1T 3JH, United Kingdom. TEL 44-20-70175533, FAX 44-20-70174783, http://www.telecoms.com/.

388 CAN ISSN 1488-6286
BOARDS. Text in English. 1999. m. CND 79 domestic; USD 59 in United States; USD 99 elsewhere (effective 2003).
Related titles: Online - full text ed.: (from Micromedia ProQuest).
Published by: Brunico Communications Inc., 366 Adelaide St W, Ste 500, Toronto, ON M5V 1R9, Canada. TEL 416-408-2300, FAX 416-408-0870, circ@brunico.com, http://www.boardsmag.com, http://www.brunico.com.

THE BOOKMAN MEDIA GUIDE. see *BUSINESS AND ECONOMICS—Trade And Industrial Directories*

BOOKS IN THE MEDIA. see *PUBLISHING AND BOOK TRADE*

384 BWA
BOTSWANA MEDIA DIRECTORY. Text in English. 1992. quinquennial. free. adv. **Document type:** *Directory, Government.* **Description:** Lists media organizations, newspapers, radio stations, publishers, printers, bookshops, libraries, etc.
Published by: Botswana, Department of Information and Broadcasting, Private Bag 0060, Gaborone, Botswana. TEL 267-35254, FAX 267-301675. Ed. Tefo Ray Mangope. Adv. contact Thomas Lesego. Circ: 60,000.

384 CAN ISSN 1203-6463
BOTTIN DES COMMUNICATIONS DU QUEBEC. Text in English. a. CND 27.95 (effective 1999). **Document type:** *Directory.* **Description:** Contains listings of professionals in telecommunications, marketing, publicity, and the press in Quebec.
Published by: Quebec dans le Monde, C P 8503, Sainte Foy, PQ G1V 4N5, Canada. TEL 418-659-5540, FAX 418-659-4143.

384 BRA ISSN 0103-9318
P92.B7
BRAZILIAN COMMUNICATION RESEARCH YEARBOOK. Text in English. 1992. a. **Document type:** *Academic/Scholarly.*
Published by: Universidade de Sao Paulo, Escola de Comunicacoes e Artes, Av. Prof. Lucio Martins Rodrigues 443, Butanta, SP 05508-900, Brazil.

621.382 GBR ISSN 1475-8407
BROADBAND ACCESS EUROPE; essential intelligence on Europe's broadband industry. Text in English. 2001. m. GBP 59, USD 90 (effective 2002). **Document type:** *Magazine, Trade.* **Description:** Provides intelligence for members of the broadband community. Includes news, features, personality profiles, and product information.
Related titles: Online - full content ed.
Published by: Institute of Physics Publishing, Dirac House, Temple Back, Bristol, BS1 6BE, United Kingdom. TEL 44-117-9297481, FAX 44-117-9294318, custserv@iop.org, http://broadband.iop.org/, http://www.iop.org/. Ed. Susan Curtis TEL 44-117-930-1035. Adv. contact James Garmston TEL 44-117-930-1093.

384.5452 332 USA ISSN 0889-2644
BROADCAST BANKER/BROKER. Text in English. m. USD 925 domestic; USD 960 foreign (effective 2001). **Document type:** *Newsletter.* **Description:** Your guide to equity deals and debt financing for radio and TV. Station buying and selling analyzed. Where capital comes from, who places it and how much it costs. Also, key details on station trades with critical yardsticks of value.
Formerly (until 1986): Broadcast Banking (0749-677X)
Related titles: E-mail ed.: USD 925 (effective 2001); Fax ed.: USD 925 (effective 2001).
—CCC.
Published by: Kagan Research, LLC, 1 Lower Ragsdale Dr., Ste. 130, Monterey, CA 93940-5741. TEL 831-624-1536, FAX 831-625-3225, info@kagan.com, http://www.kagan.com. Pub. Paul Kagan.

384 JPN ISSN 1345-4099
TK6562.D54
BROADCAST TECHNOLOGY; N H K Science and Technical Research Laboratories bulletin. Text in English. 2000. q. free. **Document type:** *Bulletin, Academic/Scholarly.*
Indexed: RefZh.
—Linda Hall.
Published by: Nippon Hoso Kyokai, Gijutsu Kenkyujo/Japan Broadcasting Corp., Science and Technical Research Laboratories, 10-11 Kinuta 1-chome, Setagaya-ku, Tokyo, 157-0073, Japan. FAX 81-3-5494-2418, okada@strl.nhk.or.jp, http://www.strl.nhk.or.jp/. Ed. Keiichi Kubota. Pub. Osamu Yamada. Circ: 2,000 (controlled).

621.382 JPN
BROADCASTING EQUIPMENT AND TECHNOLOGY. Text in English. a. (Apr.). USD 18 newsstand/cover (effective 2005). **Document type:** *Trade.* **Description:** Covers broadcasting and content production equipment including digital camcorders, extended recording, VTRs, multi-function monitors, anti-vibration/image stabilizing lenses, digital switchers, DTV transmitters, recording media.
Related titles: Print ed.
Published by: Dempa Publications Inc., 1-11-15 Higashi Gotanda, Shinagawa-Ku, Tokyo, 141-8715, Japan. TEL 81-3-34456111, FAX 81-3-34447515, http://www.dempa.net/.

384 BRN
BRUNEI DARUSSALAM NEWSLETTER. Text in English. s-m. **Document type:** *Newsletter, Government.*
Published by: Information Department, Prime Minister's Office, Bandar Seri Begawan, 2041, Brunei Darussalam. TEL 673-2-383400, FAX 673-2-382242. Ed. Mahari H J Ismail. Circ: 12,000.

384 GBR
BTEXACT COMMUNICATIONS TECHNOLOGY. Text in English. 2001. irreg., latest vol.5, 2002. price varies. back issues avail. **Document type:** *Monographic series, Academic/Scholarly.* **Description:** Presents state-of-the-art reviews of evolving technologies in communications and covers the industrial, research and business aspects of a key communications technology.
—BLDSC (2354.451400).
Published by: Institution of Electrical Engineers, Michael Faraday House, Six Hills Way, Stevenage, Herts SG1 2AY, United Kingdom. TEL 44-1438-313311, FAX 44-1438-313465, inspec@iee.org, http://www.iee.org/Publish/Books/Btexact/. Eds. John Turnbull, Simon Garrett.

384.025 HUN ISSN 1419-2063
BUDAPEST BUSINESS JOURNAL'S WHO'S WHO IN HUNGARIAN TELECOM/KI KICSODA A MAGYAR TAVKOZLESBEN. Text in Hungarian. 1998. **Document type:** *Directory.*
Related titles: ♦ Supplement to: Budapest Business Journal. ISSN 1216-7304.
Published by: New World Publishing Inc., Szent Istvan Korut 11, III emelet, Budapest, 1055, Hungary. TEL 36-1-374-3344, FAX 361-374-3345, editor@bbj.hu, http://www.ceebiz.com.

C

▼ new title ➤ refereed ✶ unverified ♦ full entry avail.

384 BGR
BULGARIA. MINISTERSTVO NA INFORMATSIIATA I SUOBSHTENIIATA. SUOBSHTENIIA; nauchno i proizvodstveno-tekhnichesko spisanie. Text in Bulgarian. m. illus.
Published by: Komitet na Informatsiiata i Suobshteniiata, Foreign Trade Co "Hemus", 1-B Raiko Daskalov pl, Sofia, 1000, Bulgaria. TEL 395-2-971686, FAX 359-2-9803319.

BULGARSKI ZHURNALIST/BULGARIAN JOURNALIST. see *JOURNALISM*

621.382 FRA ISSN 0007-5302
BULLETIN SIGNALETIQUE DES TELECOMMUNICATIONS. Text in French. 1958. m. FRF 885; FRF 935 foreign (effective 1999). index.
Media: Online - full text.
—Linda Hall.
Published by: (France. Service de Documentation Interministerielle), France Telecom Recherche et Developpement, 38-40 rue du General Leclerc, Issy-les-Moulineaux, Cedex 92131, France. TEL 33-1-45295464, FAX 33-1-45290106. Circ: 1,500.

384 USA
BURRELLE'S MEDIA DIRECTORY (CD-ROM EDITION). Text in English. 1994. a. (plus 3/yr updates). free with 6-vol print ed. **Document type:** *Directory, Trade.* **Description:** Lists more than 2,200 daily and 10,400 non-daily newspapers, 12,500 Magazines, 10,350 radio stations, 1,700 television stations and cable systems, and related media.
Media: CD-ROM. **Related titles:** ♦ Print ed.: Burrelle's Media Directory. Vol 1, Newspapers & Related Media. ISSN 1074-9446; ♦ Burrelle's Media Directory. Vol 2, Magazines & Newsletters. ISSN 1074-9454; ♦ Burrelle's Media Directory. Vol 3, Broadcast & Related Media. ISSN 1074-9462.
Published by: Burrelle's Media Directories, 75 E Northfield Rd, Livingston, NJ 07039. TEL 973-992-6600, 800-876-3342, FAX 800-898-6677, directory@burrelles.com, info@burrelles.com, http://www.burrelles.com. Ed. Kathleen M. Guindon. Adv. contact Fay Shapiro.

384 USA ISSN 1074-9446
BURRELLE'S MEDIA DIRECTORY. VOL 1, NEWSPAPERS & RELATED MEDIA. Text in English. 1994. a. (in 2 vols, plus s-a. updates). USD 275; USD 350 with Vol 2; USD 600 with complete set (includes free CD-ROM ed) (effective 2001). adv. **Document type:** *Directory, Trade.* **Description:** Lists more than 2,200 daily and 10,400 non-daily newspapers, along with related media.
Related titles: ♦ CD-ROM ed.: Burrelle's Media Directory (CD-ROM Edition); ♦ Print ed.: Burrelle's Media Directory. Vol 2, Magazines & Newsletters. ISSN 1074-9454; ♦ Burrelle's Media Directory. Vol 3, Broadcast & Related Media. ISSN 1074-9462.
Published by: Burrelle's Media Directories, 75 E Northfield Rd, Livingston, NJ 07039. TEL 973-992-6600, 800-876-3342, FAX 800-898-6677, directory@burrelles.com, info@burrelles.com, http://www.burrelles.com. Ed. Kathleen M. Guindon. Adv. contact Fay Shapiro.

384 USA ISSN 1074-9454
P88.8
BURRELLE'S MEDIA DIRECTORY. VOL 2, MAGAZINES & NEWSLETTERS. Text in English. 1994. a. (plus s-a updates). USD 275; USD 350 with Vol 1; USD 600 with Vols 1 & 3 (includes CD-ROM ed) (effective 2001). adv. **Document type:** *Directory, Trade.* **Description:** Lists more than 12,500 magazines and newsletters.
Related titles: ♦ CD-ROM ed.: Burrelle's Media Directory (CD-ROM Edition); ♦ Print ed.: Burrelle's Media Directory. Vol 1, Newspapers & Related Media. ISSN 1074-9446; ♦ Burrelle's Media Directory. Vol 3, Broadcast & Related Media. ISSN 1074-9462.
Published by: Burrelle's Media Directories, 75 E Northfield Rd, Livingston, NJ 07039. TEL 973-992-6600, 800-876-3342, FAX 800-898-6677, directory@burrelles.com, info@burrelles.com, http://www.burrelles.com. Ed. Kathleen M. Guindon. Adv. contact Fay Shapiro.

384 USA ISSN 1074-9462
BURRELLE'S MEDIA DIRECTORY. VOL 3, BROADCAST & RELATED MEDIA. Text in English. 1994. a. (plus s-a. updates) (in 2 vols.). USD 275; USD 600 for complete set (includes CD-ROM ed) (effective 2001). adv. **Document type:** *Directory, Trade.* **Description:** Lists 10,350 radio stations, 1,700 television stations and cable systems, and related media.
Related titles: ♦ CD-ROM ed.: Burrelle's Media Directory (CD-ROM Edition); ♦ Print ed.: Burrelle's Media Directory. Vol 1, Newspapers & Related Media. ISSN 1074-9446; ♦ Burrelle's Media Directory. Vol 2, Magazines & Newsletters. ISSN 1074-9454.
Published by: Burrelle's Media Directories, 75 E Northfield Rd, Livingston, NJ 07039. directory@burrelles.com, http://www.burrelles.com. Ed. Kathleen M. Guindon. Adv. contact Fay Shapiro.

621.382 GBR ISSN 1467-4548
BUSINESS RATIO. THE TELECOMMUNICATIONS INDUSTRY. Text in English. 1980. a. GBP 275 (effective 2001). charts; stat.
Former titles (until 1999): Business Ratio Plus: Telecommunications (1364-0410); (until 1995): Business Ratio Plus: Telecommunications Industry (1355-8862); (until 1993): Business Ratio Report: Telecommunications Industry (0261-9601)
Published by: The Prospect Shop Ltd., Field House, 72 Oldfield Rd, Hampton, Middx TW12 2HQ, United Kingdom. TEL 44-20-8461-8730, 44-20-8481-8720, FAX 44-20-8783-1940, info@theprospectshop.co.uk.

THE BUSINESS - TO - BUSINESS MARKETER. see *ADVERTISING AND PUBLIC RELATIONS*

384 KGZ
C A M E L. (Central Asian Media Electronic Bulletin) Text in English. m.
Media: Online - full content.
Published by: Proekt Podderzhki Regional'nykh S M I Tsentral'noi Azii/Central Asia Media Support Project, Kurmazhan Datka 217, Osh, 71400, Kyrgyzstan. TEL 996-3222-55259, http://www.camsp.osh.kg.

C C NEWS (EMAIL); the business newspaper for call centers and customer care professionals. (Call Center) see *BUSINESS AND ECONOMICS—Marketing And Purchasing*

C E P JOURNAL/JOURNAL S C E P. see *PAPER AND PULP*

621.382 JPN
C I A J ANNUAL REPORT. Text in Japanese. a. free.
Description: Contains outline of recent CIAJ activities and major figures in Japan's telecommunications equipment industry.
Formerly: Outline of Communications Industry
Published by: Communications Industry Association of Japan/Tsushin Kikai Kogyokai, Sankei Bldg Annex, 1-7-2 Ote-Machi, Chiyoda-ku, Tokyo, 100-0004, Japan. TEL 81-03-3231-3156, FAX 81-3231-3110, http://www.ciaj.or.jp. Ed. Eizo Tamura.

C L C WEB; a WWWeb journal. (Comparative Literature and Culture) see *LITERATURE*

384 FRA ISSN 1290-6824
C N R S COMMUNICATION. (Centre Nationale de la Recherche Scientifique) Text in French. 1998. irreg. price varies. **Document type:** *Monographic series, Academic/Scholarly.*
Published by: (France. Centre National de la Recherche Scientifique), C N R S Editions, 15 Rue Malebranche, Paris, 75005, France. TEL 33-1-53102700, FAX 33-1-53102727, http://www.cnrseditions.fr.

621.382 CAN ISSN 1491-6851
C R C BUSINESS PLAN. Text in English. a.
Formerly (until 1999): Communication Research Center. Business Plan (1209-4730)
Published by: Communications Research Centre Canada, 3701 Carling Ave, PO Box 11490, Stn. H, Ottawa, ON K2H 8S2, Canada. TEL 613-991-3313, FAX 613-998-5355, coops@agr.gc.ca.

384 ITA ISSN 0393-2648
TK5101.A1
C S E L T TECHNICAL REPORTS/C S E L T RAPPORTI TECNICI. Text in English, Italian. 1973. bi-m. per issue exchange basis. biennial index. back issues avail. **Document type:** *Corporate.*
Formerly: C S E L T Rapporti Tecnici (0390-1815)
Indexed: B&BAb, C&ISA, E&CAJ, EngInd, IAA, ISMEC, Inspec, RefZh, SolStAb.
—BLDSC (3490.179100), AskIEEE, CISTI, Ei, Linda Hall.
Published by: C S E L T - Centro Studi e Laboratori Telecomunicazioni SpA, Via Guglielmo Reiss Romoli, 274, Turin, TO 10148, Italy. TEL 39-11-2285111, FAX 39-11-2285520, TELEX 220539, http://www.cselt.it. Circ: 1,300.

621.382 HKG ISSN 1024-5847
C T C NEWS. (China Telecommunication Construction) Text in English. 1995. 22/yr., latest vol.7, 2001. USD 469 (effective 2001). **Document type:** *Newsletter.* **Description:** Covers latest developments in telecommunications in China.
Indexed: HongKongiana.
Published by: State Business Development Ltd., Room 401, Charm Centre Kowl, 700 Castle Peak Rd., Hong Kong, Hong Kong. TEL 852-2517-2095, FAX 852-2517-2101, 852-2517-2101, ctccwc@netvigator.com, http://www.chinatelecomnrws.com, http://www.chinatelecomnews.com. Ed. Teresa Leung.

C W A NEWS (WASHINGTON). see *LABOR UNIONS*

621.382 USA ISSN 1051-1938
CODEN: NZFBEC
CABLE OPTICS; covering worldwide developments in the application of fiber optics in cable television systems. Key Title: CableOptics Newsletter. Text in English. 1989. m. USD 695 in US & Canada; USD 745 elsewhere (effective 2001). back issues avail. **Document type:** *Trade.* **Description:** Covers fiber optics technology and applications to the CATV industry, new products, plans, regulations, standards, and business developments.
Related titles: Online - full text ed.: (from ProQuest Information & Learning).
Indexed: ABIn.
—CCC.
Published by: Information Gatekeepers, Inc., 320 Washington St, Ste 302, Brighton, MA 02135. TEL 617-782-5033, 800-323-1088, FAX 617-734-8562, info@igigroup.com, http://www.igigroup.com. Ed. Tony Carmona. Pub. Dr. Paul Polishuk.

384 AUS
CABLING INSTALLATION & MAINTENANCE. Text in English. bi-m. AUD 59.95 domestic; AUD 89 foreign (effective 2001). adv. charts; mkt.; tr.lit.; illus. 84 p./no.; **Document type:** *Trade.* **Description:** Covers what's happening in data and voice communications cabling, installation, fiber optics, broadband technology, and wireless standards, including technology, industry news, market trends, expert opinion, case studies and installation advice.
Published by: Connection Magazines Pty. Ltd., 118 Atkinson St, Oakleigh, VIC 3166, Australia. TEL 61-3-9564-2100, 800-623-214, FAX 61-3-9568-4955, toddtrimble@build.com.au, editor@build.com.au, http://www.build.com.au. Ed. Todd Trimble. Pub. Jeff Patchell. R&P David Beer TEL 61-3-9564-2125. Adv. contact Peter Harris TEL 61-3-9564-2103. Circ: 10,000.

CABLING WORLD. see *BUSINESS AND ECONOMICS—Trade And Industrial Directories*

CADERNOS DE POS-GRADUACAO EM COMUNICACAO E LETRAS. see *LITERATURE*

384 GBR ISSN 1357-4868
CALL CENTRE EUROPE. Text in English. m. GBP 49 domestic; GBP 79.50 foreign. **Document type:** *Trade.*
Indexed: B&I.
Published by: Stanworth Communications, PO Box 220, Walton-on-Thames, Surrey KT12 1YQ, United Kingdom. TEL 44-1932-254400, FAX 44-1932-240294. Ed., Pub. Paul Liptrot. Circ: 16,500.

384.5 DEU
CALL MAGAZIN; das Infosystem fuer Festnetz, Mobilfunk, Internet, WAP. Text in German. d. adv. **Document type:** *Consumer.* **Description:** Covers all aspects of mobile, wireless and Internet communications systems, services and products.
Media: Online - full text.
Published by: i12 AG, Turmstr 5, Wetzlar, 35578, Germany. TEL 49-6441-210220, redaktion@call-magazin.de, kontakt@i12.de, http://www.call-magazin.de, http://www.i12.de. Ed. Oliver Kruse.

CANADIAN JOURNAL OF REMOTE SENSING. see *AERONAUTICS AND SPACE FLIGHT*

354.75 CAN ISSN 1483-7420
CANADIAN RADIO-TELEVISION AND TELECOMMUNICATIONS COMMISSION. PERFORMANCE REPORT. Text in English, French. 1997. a.
Related titles: Online - full text ed.: ISSN 1490-1692.
Published by: (Canadian Radio-Television and Telecommunications Commission), Treasury Board of Canada Secretariat, Corporate Communications, West Tower, Rm P-135, 300 Laurier Ave W, Ottawa, ON K1A 0R5, Canada. TEL 613-995-2855, FAX 613-996-0518, services-publications@tbs-sct.gc.ca, http://www.crtc.gc.ca/eng/publications/reports.htm, http://www.tbs-sct.gc.ca.

005.5 CHE
CATALOGUE OF SOFTWARE FOR RADIO SPECTRUM MANAGEMENT. Text in English. a. free. **Document type:** *Catalog.*
Related titles: French ed.; Spanish ed.
Published by: International Telecommunication Union, Place des Nations, Geneva 20, 1211, Switzerland. TEL 41-22-7306141, FAX 41-22-7305194, sales@itu.ch, http://www.itu.int/publications.

384 ZAF
CELLEXPO AWARDS MAGAZINE. Text in English. a.
Published by: What Media Publishing Pty Ltd., Postnet Ste 367, Private Bag X6, Benmore, Johannesburg 2010, South Africa. TEL 27-11-784-0655, FAX 27-11-784-0657, what@icon.co.za, http://www.whatsa.com. Ed. Beth Porter. adv.: color page ZAR 705; trim 210 x 275.

384 USA
CENSORED ALERT. Text in English. 1996. 3/yr. looseleaf. illus.; stat. back issues avail. **Document type:** *Newsletter.* **Description:** Covers issues of media censorship and news stories not covered in mainstream media.
Related titles: E-mail ed.; Fax ed.
Published by: (Project Censored), Sonoma State University, Sociology Department, 1801 E Lotati Ave, Rohnert Park, CA 94928. TEL 707-664-2588, FAX 707-664-2108, censored@sonoma.edu, http://www.sonoma.edu/~projectcensored. Eds. Peter Phillips, Trish Boreta. Circ: 10,000 (controlled).

384 ECU ISSN 1390-1079
CHASQUI. Text in Spanish. 1983. q.
Indexed: L&LBA.
Published by: Centro Internacional de Estudios Superiores de Comunicacion para America Latina, Avenida Diego de Almagro N32-133 y Andrade Marin, Quito, Ecuador. TEL 593-2-2548011, FAX 593-2-2502487, info@ciespal.net, http://www.ciespal.net.

CHINA ENTERTAINMENT. see *SOCIOLOGY*

CHINA I T AND TELECOM TIMES. (Information Technology) see *COMPUTERS—Data Communications And Data Transmission Systems*

070.5 CHN
CHINA MEDIA NEWSLETTER. Text in English. 1993. 11/yr. USD 260. **Document type:** *Newsletter.* **Description:** Provides up-to-date information on the Chinese media and publishing industries.
Published by: Art Text Pty. Ltd., Youyi Binguan Ste. 40626, Beijing, 100873, China. TEL 86-10-6849-8987. Ed. Bruce Doar.

384 USA ISSN 1078-2214
TK5102.3.C6
CHINA TELECOM NEWSLETTER. Text in English. 1994. m. USD 695 in US & Canada; USD 745 elsewhere (effective 2004). **Document type:** *Newsletter, Trade.* **Description:** Devoted to tracking the latest developments in the China telecommunications market.
Related titles: E-mail ed.; Online - full text ed.: (from Florida Center for Library Automation, Gale Group, ProQuest Information & Learning).
—CCC.
Published by: Information Gatekeepers, Inc., 320 Washington St, Ste 302, Brighton, MA 02135. TEL 617-782-5033, 800-323-1088, FAX 617-782-5735, info@igigroup.com, http://www.igigroup.com/nl/pages/chinatel.html. Ed. Hui Pan. Pub. Dr. Paul Polishuk.

621.382 USA
CHINA TELECOM WEEKLY. Text in English. w. USD 1,200 to individuals (effective 2000). **Document type:** *Journal, Trade.* **Description:** Provides current and comprehensive information on critical developments in the Chinese telecommunications and Internet markets.
Published by: Gist, Inc., 2200 Wilson Blvd, Ste 102G, Arlington, VA 22201. TEL 703-527-7459, FAX 703-528-1477, info@gist.net, http://www.gist.net.

CHURCH PRODUCTION MAGAZINE; an educational magazine for houses of worship covering: audio, video and lighting technologies. see *RELIGIONS AND THEOLOGY*

CHURCHART PRO. see *RELIGIONS AND THEOLOGY—Protestant*

330 JPN
COMLINE: TELECOMMUNICATIONS INDUSTRY OF JAPAN. Text in English. irreg. **Document type:** *Trade.*
Media: Online - full content.
Published by: O D S Corp., Kuyo Bldg, 5-10-5 Minami-Aoyama, Minato-ku, Tokyo, 107, Japan. TEL 81-3-3486-2676, http://www.ods.co.jp/. **Dist. by:** COMLINE International Corp., 10601 South DeAnza Blvd Ste 216, Cupertino, CA 95014. TEL 408-257-9956.

COMMA; magazine voor communicatie in de publieke sector. see *PUBLIC ADMINISTRATION*

384 305.8 USA
COMMERCE AND MASS CULTURE. Text in English. 1999. irreg., latest 2002. price varies. illus. back issues avail. **Document type:** *Monographic series, Academic/Scholarly.* **Description:** Examines the implications of various forms of mass media, including film, television, and print, and how they are shaped and distributed within the framework of the marketplace.
Published by: University of Minnesota Press, 111 Third Ave S, Ste 290, Minneapolis, MN 55401-2520. TEL 612-627-1970, FAX 612-627-1980, http://www.upress.umn.edu/byseries/commerce.html. Ed. Justin Wyatt. **Dist. by:** c/o Chicago Distribution Center, 11030 S Langley Ave, Chicago, IL 60628; Plymbridge Distributors Ltd, Plymbridge House, Estover Rd, Plymouth, Devon PL6 7PY, United Kingdom. TEL 44-1752-202300, FAX 44-1752-202330, enquiries@plymbridge.com, http://www.plymbridge.com.

384 GBR
COMMERCIAL COMMUNICATIONS. Text in English. m. GBP 150, EUR 250 in Europe; GBP 175, EUR 300 elsewhere (effective 2001).
—BLDSC (3336.765000).
Published by: A S I, 111 Whitchurch Rd, Tavistock, PL19 9BQ, United Kingdom. TEL 44-1822-618628, FAX 44-1822-618629, asi@dial.pipex.com. Ed. Mike Sainsbury.

343.099 USA ISSN 1068-5871
K3
COMMLAW CONSPECTUS; journal of communications law and policy. Text in English. 1993. s-a. USD 40 (effective 2005). back issues avail.; reprint service avail. from WSH. **Document type:** *Journal, Academic/Scholarly.* **Description:** Dedicated to the providing the legal community with articles addressing communications law and policy.
Related titles: Microfiche ed.: (from WSH); Microform ed.: (from WSH); Online - full text ed.: (from LexisNexis).
Indexed: CLI, ILP, LRI.
—BLDSC (3337.864000), IE, ingenta.
Published by: Catholic University of America, Columbus School of Law, 3600 John McCormack, N E, Washington, DC 20064. TEL 202-319-5732, http://commlaw.cua.edu/, http://www.law.edu/. **Co-sponsor:** Institute for Communications Law Studies.

384 ZAF ISSN 0259-0069
➤ **COMMUNICARE**; Journal of Communication Sciences. Text and summaries in English. 1981. s-a. ZAR 120 domestic to individuals; ZAR 190 foreign to individuals; ZAR 180 domestic to institutions; ZAR 250 foreign to institutions (effective 2003). adv. bk.rev. abstr.; charts; illus.; stat. 120 p./no. 1 cols./p.; back issues avail. **Document type:** *Journal, Academic/Scholarly.* **Description:** Academic journal of communication studies.
Indexed: CommAb, ISAP.
Published by: Randse Afrikaanse Universiteit, Department of Communication/Southern African Communication Association/Rand Afrikaans University, PO Box 524, Auckland Park, Johannesburg 2006, South Africa. TEL 27-11-4892911, FAX 27-11-4892191, lloc@rau.ac.za. Eds. Liani Lochner, Sonja Verwey. R&P, Adv. contact Annette Gouwg. Circ: 400.

384 BEL ISSN 0771-7342
COMMUNICATIE; tijdschrift voor communicatiewetenschap en mediacultuur. Text in Dutch. 1970. q. adv. bk.rev. bibl. back issues avail. **Document type:** *Academic/Scholarly.* **Description:** Publishes academic articles on communication science and media culture.
Formerly (until 1975): Centrum voor Communicatiewetenschap. Informatie Bulletin (0771-7334)
Indexed: L&LBA, SSA, SociolAb.
—KNAW.
Published by: (Katholieke Universiteit Leuven), Garant Uitgevers n.v., Tiensesteenweg 83, Kessel Lo (Leuven), 3010, Belgium. TEL 23-16-253131, FAX 32-16-251314, E.vanEvenstraat@soc.kuleuven.ac.be. Circ: 500.

384 DEU ISSN 1439-748X
COMMUNICATIO (HAMBURG). Text in German. 2000. irreg., latest vol.6, 2003. price varies. **Document type:** *Monographic series, Academic/Scholarly.*
Published by: Verlag Dr. Kovac, Arnoldstr 49, Hamburg, 22763, Germany. TEL 49-40-3988800, FAX 49-40-39880055, info@verlagdrkovac.de, http://www.verlagdrkovac.de/17-1.htm.

384 001.3 USA ISSN 1479-1420
P87
▼ **COMMUNICATION AND CRITICAL/CULTURAL STUDIES.** Text in English. 2004 (Mar.). q. GBP 132, USD 200 combined subscription to institutions print & online eds. (effective 2006). bk.rev. **Document type:** *Journal, Academic/Scholarly.* **Description:** Publishes for an international readership on communication as a theory, practice, technology, and discipline of power.
Related titles: Online - full text ed.: ISSN 1479-4233. GBP 125, USD 190 to institutions (effective 2006) (from EBSCO Publishing, Gale Group, IngentaConnect, O C L C Online Computer Library Center, Inc., Swets Information Services).
Indexed: CommAb.
—IE. **CCC.**
Published by: (National Communication Association), Routledge (Subsidiary of: Taylor & Francis Ltd), 325 Chestnut St., Suite 800, Philadelphia, PA 19106. TEL 215-625-8900, 800-354-1420, FAX 215-625-8914, journals@routledge.com, http://www.tandf.co.uk/journals/titles/14791420.asp, http://www.routledge.com. Ed. Robert L Ivie.

384 USA
HQ471.L56
COMMUNICATION CONCEPTS. Text in English. irreg., latest vol.5, 1993. adv. **Document type:** *Monographic series.* **Published by:** Sage Publications, Inc., Books, 2455 Teller Rd, Thousand Oaks, CA 91320. TEL 805-499-0721, FAX 805-499-0871, libraries@sagepub.com, journals@sagepub.com, http://www.sagepub.com. Adv. contact Margaret Travers. **Subscr. in UK to:** Sage Publications India Pvt. Ltd., M-32 Market, Greater Kailash-I, PO Box 4215, New Delhi 110 048, India. TEL 91-11-645-3915, FAX 91-11-647-2426; **Subscr. overseas to:** Sage Publications Ltd., 1 Oliver's Yard, 55 City Rd, London EC1 1SP, United Kingdom. TEL 44-20-73740645, FAX 44-20-73748741.

COMMUNICATION EDUCATION. see *EDUCATION—Teaching Methods And Curriculum*

COMMUNICATION, JOURNALISM EDUCATION TODAY. see *EDUCATION*

COMMUNICATION LAW AND POLICY. see *LAW*

COMMUNICATION MONOGRAPHS. see *EDUCATION*

658.45 ZAF
COMMUNICATION NEWS. Text in English. 1992. m. ZAR 14 newsstand/cover. adv. **Document type:** *Newspaper, Trade.* **Description:** Covers the telecommunications industry, including sections on internet, satellite, cellular and fixed network news.
Published by: What Media Publishing Pty Ltd., Postnet Ste 367, Private Bag X6, Benmore, Johannesburg 2010, South Africa. TEL 27-11-784-0655, FAX 27-11-784-0657, what@icon.co.za, http://www.whatsa.com. Ed. Richard Hurst. Adv. contact Eugene Kitney. color page ZAR 650; trim 10.81 x 8.25. Circ: 60,000.

COMMUNICATION REPORTS. see *LINGUISTICS*

384 USA ISSN 1071-4421
P87 CODEN: CURVEA
➤ **THE COMMUNICATION REVIEW.** Text in French. 1975. q. GBP 172, USD 277 combined subscription to institutions print & online eds. (effective 2006). adv. index. back issues avail.; reprint service avail. from PSC. **Document type:** *Journal, Academic/Scholarly.* **Description:** Seeks a synthesis of concerns traditional to the field of communication and humane studies scholarship.
Formerly: Communication (Langhorne) (0305-4233)
Related titles: Microform ed.; Online - full text ed.: ISSN 1547-7487. GBP 163, USD 263 to institutions (effective 2006) (from EBSCO Publishing, Gale Group, IngentaConnect, O C L C Online Computer Library Center, Inc., Swets Information Services).
Indexed: CommAb, FLI, FamI, IBSS, PRA, PSA, PsycholAb, SOPODA, SSA, SociolAb.
—BLDSC (3363.141500), IE, Infotrieve. **CCC.**
Published by: Routledge (Subsidiary of: Taylor & Francis Ltd), 325 Chestnut St., Suite 800, Philadelphia, PA 19106. TEL 215-625-8900, 800-354-1420, FAX 215-625-8914, journals@routledge.com, http://www.tandf.co.uk/journals/titles/10714421.asp, http://www.routledge.com. Eds. Andrea Press, Bruce A Williams. **Subscr. outside N. America to:** Taylor & Francis Ltd, Journals Customer Service, Rankine Rd, Basingstoke, Hants RG24 8PR, United Kingdom. TEL 44-1256-813000, FAX 44-1256-330245, enquiry@tandf.co.uk.

384 DEU ISSN 0341-2059
P87
➤ **COMMUNICATIONS**; the European journal of communication research. Text in English. 1974. q. EUR 208; EUR 225 combined subscription print & online eds.; EUR 52 newsstand/cover (effective 2006). adv. bk.rev. reprint service avail. from ISI,SCH. **Document type:** *Journal, Academic/Scholarly.* **Description:** Provides a forum for scholarship and academic debate in the field of communication science and research.
Formerly (until 1976): International Journal of Communication Research (0340-0158)
Related titles: Online - full text ed.: ISSN 1613-4087. EUR 208 (effective 2006) (from EBSCO Publishing, O C L C Online Computer Library Center, Inc., Swets Information Services).
Indexed: DIP, IBR, IBZ, PCI, PSA, PsycholAb, RASB, RefZh, SOPODA, SSA, SociolAb.
—BLDSC (3343.800000), IE, ingenta. **CCC.**
Published by: (Deutsche Gesellschaft fuer Kommunikationsforschung), Mouton de Gruyter (Subsidiary of: Walter de Gruyter GmbH & Co. KG), Genthiner Str 13, Berlin, 10785, Germany. TEL 49-30-260050, FAX 49-30-26005251, mouton@degruyter.de, http://www.degruyter.com/rs/384_401_ENU_h.htm, http://www.degruyter.de. Eds. Karsten Renckstorf, Keith Roe. Adv. contact Dietlind Makswitat. page EUR 400; trim 115 x 195. **Co-sponsor:** Internationale Vereinigung fuer Kommunikationswissenschaft.

384 USA
COMMUNICATIONS A S P. Text in English. bi-m. free to qualified personnel. adv. **Document type:** *Trade.* **Description:** Serves the needs of communications ASPs, service providers, and resellers building a business delivering communications solutions. It does this by focusing on the technology which drives the services that create opportunities for ASPs, service providers and resellers.
Related titles: Online - full content ed.

C

Published by: Technology Marketing Corporation, One Technology Plaza, Norwalk, CT 06854. TEL 203-852-6800, 800-243-6002, FAX 203-853-2845, tmc@tmcnet.com, http://www.tmcnet.com/casp/. adv.: B&W page USD 5,040, color page USD 6,490; trim 8.125 x 10.875.

621.382 GBR ISSN 0962-3841
HE8461
COMMUNICATIONS AFRICA/COMMUNICATIONS AFRIQUE. Text in English, French. 1987. bi-m. GBP 48, USD 78, EUR 80 (effective Oct. 2002). adv. **Document type:** *Magazine, Trade.* **Description:** Covers all aspects relating to the telecommunications, broadcasting and information technology with regional relevance to both the public telecommunication authorities and private sector.
Indexed: ISAP.
Published by: Alain Charles Publishing Ltd., Alain Charles House, 27 Wilfred St, London, SW1E 6PR, United Kingdom. TEL 44-20-78347676, FAX 44-20-79730076, post@alain.demon.co.uk, http://www.alaincharles.com. Ed. Phil Northam. Adv. contact Cecile Coin. Circ: 9,295.

343.099 USA ISSN 0162-9093
K3 CODEN: COMLDE
COMMUNICATIONS AND THE LAW. Text in English. 1978. q. USD 135 (effective 2004). bk.rev. reprints avail. **Document type:** *Journal, Academic/Scholarly.*
Related titles: Microfiche ed.: (from WSH); Microfilm ed.: (from PMC, WSH); Microform ed.: (from WSH); Online - full text ed.: (from EBSCO Publishing, Florida Center for Library Automation, Gale Group, O C L C Online Computer Library Center, Inc.).
Indexed: ABIn, ABRCLP, CLI, CommAb, FLI, FamI, ILP, Inspec, LRI, LegCont, SPAA, SUSA.
—BLDSC (3359.314000), AskIEEE, IE, Infotrieve, ingenta.
Published by: (Communications & the Law), William S. Hein & Company, Incorporated, 1285 Main St, Buffalo, NY 14209-1987. TEL 716-882-2600, 800-828-7571, FAX 716-883-8100, mail@wshein.com, http://www.wshein.com. Ed. Theodore R Kupferman. Circ: 600 (paid).

384 USA ISSN 1555-3426
▼ **COMMUNICATIONS BUSINESS DAILY.** Text in English. 2005. d. (Mon.-Fri.). USD 2,495; USD 50 per issue (effective 2005).
Published by: Warren Communications News, Inc., 2115 Ward Ct, N W, Washington, DC 20037. TEL 202-872-9200, 800-327-7205, FAX 202-293-3435, info@warren-news.com, http://www.warren-news.com/cbd.htm.

384 GBR ISSN 1352-4399
COMMUNICATIONS COMPANIES ANALYSIS. MANUFACTURERS VOLUME. Text in English. a. (plus m. updates). GBP 795, USD 1,425 (effective 2000). **Document type:** *Trade.* **Description:** Provides detailed profiles on over 60 major telecommunications equipment manufacturers.
Related titles: CD-ROM ed.; Online - full text ed.
Published by: Espicom Business Intelligence, Lincoln House, City Fields Business Park, City Fields Way, Tangmere, Chichester, W Sussex PO20 6FS, United Kingdom. TEL 44-1243-533322, FAX 44-1243-533418, sales_desk@espicom.com, http://www.espicom.com. Ed. Andrew Kitson. Pub. Eric Wigart. R&P Nigel Chivers.

384 GBR ISSN 1352-4380
COMMUNICATIONS COMPANIES ANALYSIS. OPERATORS VOLUME. Text in English. 1991. a. (plus m. updates). looseleaf. GBP 995, USD 1,795 (effective 2000). **Document type:** *Directory.* **Description:** Provides highly detailed profiles on over 75 major operating companies.
Related titles: CD-ROM ed.; Online - full text ed.
Published by: Espicom Business Intelligence, Lincoln House, City Fields Business Park, City Fields Way, Tangmere, Chichester, W Sussex PO20 6FS, United Kingdom. TEL 44-1243-533322, FAX 44-1243-533418, sales_desk@espicom.com, http://www.espicom.com. Ed. Jayne-Ann Lidstone. R&P Nigel Chivers.

384 GBR ISSN 1479-8352
TK6540 CODEN: ECEJE9
➤ **COMMUNICATIONS ENGINEER.** Text in English. 1939. bi-m. USD 270 in the Americas to non-members; GBP 160 elsewhere to non-members; USD 45 per issue in the Americas to non-members; GBP 25 per issue elsewhere to non-members (effective 2003). adv. bk.rev. bibl.; charts; illus. index. back issues avail.; reprints avail. **Document type:** *Journal, Academic/Scholarly.* **Description:** Provides an in-depth coverage of new work at a level which will be informative and accessible to engineers active in areas of communications, including the design, development, operations and application of systems for communication and information networking.
Former titles (until 2003): Electronics & Communication Engineering Journal (0954-0695); (until 1988): Institution of Electronic and Radio Engineers. Journal (0267-1689); (until 1985: Radio and Electronic Engineer (0033-7722); (until 1963): British Institution of Radio Engineers. Journal (0538-0022); Incorporates: Institution of Electronic and Radio Engineers. Proceedings
Related titles: Online - full text ed.: (from EBSCO Publishing).
Indexed: AS&TI, ASCA, BrTechI, C&ISA, ChemAb, CurCont, E&CAJ, EngInd, ExcerpMed, F&EA, IAA, ISMEC, ISR, Inspec, RefZh, SCI, SolStAb, WTA.
—BLDSC (3359.837000), AskIEEE, CISTI, Ei, IDS, IE, Infotrieve, ingenta, Linda Hall. **CCC.**
Published by: Institution of Electrical Engineers, Michael Faraday House, Six Hills Way, Stevenage, Herts SG1 2AY, United Kingdom. TEL 44-1438-313311, FAX 44-1438-313465, inspec@iee.org, http://www.iee.org/Publish/Journals/MagsNews/Mags/Ce.cfm. Ed. John Cooper. R&P Michael McCabe TEL 732-321-5575. Circ: 35,000. **Subscr. to:** INSPEC, I E E, Publication Sales Dept., PO Box 96, Stevenage, Herts SG1 2SD, United Kingdom. TEL 44-1438-313311, FAX 44-1438-742840; **US subscr. addr.:** INSPEC/I E E, 379 Thornall St., Edison, NJ 08837. TEL 732-321-5575, FAX 732-321-5702.

384 FRA ISSN 1157-8637
COMMUNICATIONS ET STRATEGIES. Text in Multiple languages. 1979. q.
Formerly (until 1990): Institut pour le Developpement et l'Amenagement des Telecommunications et de l'Economie. Bulletin (0249-2571)
Indexed: JEL, PSA.
—BLDSC (3359.330000), IE, Infotrieve.
Published by: Institut de l'Audiovisuel et des Telecommunications en Europe, BP 4167, Montpellier, 34092, France. TEL 33-467-144444, FAX 33-467-144400, info@idate.fr, http://www.idate.fr.

384 GBR ISSN 1472-1228
COMMUNICATIONS FINANCE. Text in English. 2000. a. free; Free to subscibers of Telecom Finance, Satellite Finance, Internet & Technology Finance or Media Finance.. **Document type:** *Journal, Trade.* **Description:** Annual review of worldwide debt & equity funding in the communications industry.
Published by: Thompson Stanley Publishers Ltd., Clerkenwell House, 45-47 Clerkenwell Green, London, EC1R 0EB, United Kingdom. TEL 44-20-7553-3919, FAX 44-20-7251-1833, http://www.telecomfinance.com. Ed. Carol Dean. R&P Chris Thompson. Adv. contact Danny Grasso. Circ: 9,750.

384.071025 USA
P91.5.U5
COMMUNICATIONS INSTITUTE COMMUNICATIONS LIBRARY (YEAR); worldwide courses in communications. Variant title: C I N C O M (Year). Text in English. 1983. biennial, latest 2002. adv. bk.rev. **Document type:** *Directory, Abstract/Index.* **Description:** Contains over 1,500 accredited American, Asian, Canadian, European, and Middle Eastern IHEs offering courses and degrees in communications, data telecom, telephony, telecommunications and CATV.
Formerly: C I N C O M - Courses in Communications (0742-3632)
Published by: Communications Institute, Communications Library, Lockbox 472139, Marina Station, San Francisco, CA 94147-2139. TEL 415-626-5050. Ed. T S Connelly. R&P Phillip Greenleaf. Circ: 5,000.

621.382 USA
COMMUNICATIONS: LATIN AMERICAN INDUSTRIAL REPORT✶. (Avail. for each of 22 Latin American countries) Text in English. 1985. a. USD 435; per country report.
Published by: Aquino Productions, P O Box 15760, Stamford, CT 06901-0760. Ed. Andres C Aquino.

343.099 USA ISSN 0898-2457
KF4774
COMMUNICATIONS LAW. Text in English. a. price varies. **Document type:** *Proceedings, Trade.*
Former titles (until 1982): Annual Communications Law Institute (0898-2449); (until 1981): Communications Law (0160-2616)
Published by: Practising Law Institute, 810 Seventh Ave, New York, NY 10019. TEL 212-824-5700, 800-260-4754, FAX 800-321-0093, info@pli.edu, http://www.pli.edu.

COMMUNICATIONS LAW & POLICY IN AUSTRALIA. see *LAW*

COMMUNICATIONS LAWYER. see *LAW*

384 GBR ISSN 1356-3327
COMMUNICATIONS MARKETS ANALYSIS. Text in English. 1995. a. (plus updates 2-4/m.). looseleaf. GBP 995, USD 1,795 (effective 2000). **Document type:** *Directory.* **Description:** Includes over 40 country reports which provide information on the regulatory environment, type approvals, major operators and their networks, markets indicators and the domestic manufacturing industry.
Related titles: CD-ROM ed.; Online - full text ed.
Published by: Espicom Business Intelligence, Lincoln House, City Fields Business Park, City Fields Way, Tangmere, Chichester, W Sussex PO20 6FS, United Kingdom. TEL 44-1243-533322, FAX 44-1243-533418, sales_desk@espicom.com, http://www.espicom.com. Ed. Sacha Kavanagh. R&P Nigel Chivers.

384 GBR
COMMUNICATIONS MARKETS IN EASTERN EUROPE (YEAR). Text in English. a. GBP 195 (effective 1999). **Description:** Provides an overview of all sectors of the telecommunications industry in eastern Europe. Covers basic network services, mobile communications, satellite, cable, multimedia and business networks. Includes country and company profiles, and a directory.
Published by: (Communications and Information Technology Research Ltd.), C I T Publications Ltd., 3 Colleton Crescent, Exeter, Devon EX2 4DG, United Kingdom. TEL 44-1392-315-555, FAX 44-1392-315-556, citpubs@eurobell.co.uk, http://www.telecoms-data.com. Ed. Tania Harvey. R&P Ross Parsons TEL 44-1392-315577.

384 GBR ISSN 0961-7590
COMMUNICATIONS MIDDLE EAST - AFRICA. Text in English. m. GBP 80, USD 155. adv. bk.rev. back issues avail. **Document type:** *Newspaper, Trade.* **Description:** Combines market news and technology features aimed at giving readers a total picture of telecommunications developments.
Formerly (until 1991): Arabian Communications News
Address: Angus House, 13 Tilehouse St, Hitchin, Herts SG5 2DU, United Kingdom. TEL 01462-630000, FAX 01462-630063. Ed. Christine Norton. Pub. Damon Thompson. Adv. contact Terry Good. Circ: 14,073.

384 330 GBR ISSN 0954-0709
COMMUNICATIONS NEWS. Text in English. m. free to qualified personnel. adv. **Document type:** *Trade.* **Description:** Keeps the industry abreast of the latest developments, delivers informed opinion from key players and analyses emerging trends and technologies.
Indexed: ASCA, B&I, Inspec.
Published by: Nexus Media Ltd. (Subsidiary of: Highbury House Communications PLC), Nexus House, Azalea Dr, Swanley, Kent BR8 8HU, United Kingdom. TEL 44-1322-660070, FAX 44-1322-616311, info@nexusmedia.com, http://www.communications-news.com/, http://www.hhc.co.uk/. Ed. Keith Dyer TEL 44-1322-660070 ext 2269. Adv. contact Raif Hassan TEL 44-1322-660070 ext 2446. page GBP 3,915; trim 287 x 380. Circ: 20,462.

621.382 USA ISSN 0010-3632
TK5101.A1
COMMUNICATIONS NEWS. Text in English. 1964. m. USD 105 domestic; USD 172 in Canada; USD 200 elsewhere; free to qualified personnel (effective 2005). adv. bk.rev. charts; illus.; stat. back issues avail.; reprints avail. **Document type:** *Magazine, Trade.* **Description:** New developments in communications equipment, techniques and management for individuals involved in the design, engineering, construction, operation and maintenance of voice, video and data communications systems.
Related titles: Online - full text ed.: (from bigchalk, EBSCO Publishing, Florida Center for Library Automation, Gale Group, H.W. Wilson, O C L C Online Computer Library Center, Inc., ProQuest Information & Learning, The Dialog Corporation).
Indexed: ABIn, BPI, BrCerAb, BusI, C&ISA, CerAb, CompB, CompC, CompD, CorrAb, E&CAJ, EMA, EngInd, IAA, Inspec, M&TEA, MBF, METADEX, MicrocompInd, PROMT, SolStAb, T&II, WAA.
—BLDSC (3361.300000), AskIEEE, Ei, IDS, IE, Infotrieve, ingenta, Linda Hall. **CCC.**
Published by: Nelson Publishing, Inc., 2500 Tamiami Trail N, Nokomis, FL 34275-3482. TEL 941-966-9521, FAX 941-966-2590, kanderberg@comnews.com, http://www.comnews.com, http://www.nelsonpub.com. Ed. Ken Anderberg. Pub. Vern Nelson. Circ: 85,001 (controlled).

384 GBR
COMMUNICATIONS NEWSFILE. Text in English. 1989. fortn. GBP 495 (effective 1999). charts; stat. index. **Document type:** *Trade.* **Description:** Covers the world communications market. Includes news, company profiles, interviews with industry executives, and analysis.
Formerly (until 1997): European Communications Newsfile (0960-5479); Incorporates (1995-1997): Multimedia Networks Newsfile; Value Added Networks Newsfile (1352-8351)
Published by: (Communications and Information Technology Research Ltd.), C I T Publications Ltd., 3 Colleton Crescent, Exeter, Devon EX2 4DG, United Kingdom. TEL 44-1392-315-555, FAX 44-1392-315-556, citpubs@eurobell.co.uk, http://www.telecoms-data.com. Ed. Tania Harvey.

621.38 USA ISSN 1094-4753
COMMUNICATIONS PRODUCTS. Text in English. 1995. bi-m. **Document type:** *Trade.* **Description:** Dedicated to educating design engineers and engineering managers working on all types of communications systems, subsystems and components.
Formerly (until 1997): Microwaves and R F Communications Products (1085-7702)
Published by: Penton Media, Inc. (Hasbrouck Heights) (Subsidiary of: Pittway Company), 611 Rte 46 W, Hasbrouck Heights, NJ 07604. TEL 201-293-6225, FAX 201-393-6043, http://www.penton.com. Circ: 35,000 (controlled).

621.382 GBR
COMMUNICATIONS SYSTEMS, TECHNIQUES & APPLICATIONS. Text in English. 1996. irreg., latest vol.4, 2004. price varies. **Document type:** *Monographic series.* **Description:** Publishes material for researchers in academia and industry as well as graduate students and engineers in industry and commerce.
Related titles: Online - full text ed.

Published by: Research Studies Press Ltd., 16 Coach House Cloisters, 10 Hitchin St, Baldock, Hertfordshire SG7 6AE, United Kingdom. TEL 44-1462-895060, FAX 44-1462-892546, info@research-studies-press.co.uk, http://www.research-studies-press.co.uk. Ed. P Farrell.

COMMUNICATIONS TEACHER. see *EDUCATION*

384 USA ISSN 1092-0587
COMMUNICATIONS TECHNOLOGY'S PIPELINE. Text in English. 1996. bi-w.
Related titles: Online - full text ed.: (from ProQuest Information & Learning).
Indexed: ABIn.
Published by: Phillips Business Information Inc., 7811 Montrose Rd, Potomac, MD 20854. TEL 301-424-3700, FAX 301-309-3847.

343.099 AUS ISSN 0815-1210
COMMUNICATIONS UPDATE; a monthly round-up of media and communications. Text in English. 1985. m. AUD 95 to individuals; AUD 160 to institutions; AUD 180 foreign; AUD 60 to students (effective 1999). bk.rev. bibl.; stat. back issues avail. **Document type:** *Newsletter.* **Description:** Covers policy developments and important initiatives in broadcasting and communications.
Published by: Communications Law Centre, White House, University of New South Wales, Sydney, NSW 2052, Australia. TEL 61-2-9663-0551, FAX 61-2-9662-6839, admin@comslaw.org.au, http://www.comslaw.org.au. Ed., R&P Karen Winton. Circ: 400.

621.382 GBR ISSN 0953-3699 CODEN: CMMUES
COMMUNICATOR. Text in English. 1965. 4/yr. GBP 25; GBP 35 in Europe; GBP 45 elsewhere (effective 2000). adv. bk.rev.; software rev. charts; illus.; abstr.; tr.lit. back issues avail. **Document type:** *Journal.*
Former titles: Communicator of Scientific and Technical Information (0308-6925); Communicator of Technical Information (0045-768X)
Indexed: Inspec.
—Ei.
Published by: Institute of Scientific and Technical Communicators, First Floor, 17 Church Walk, St. Neots, Cambs PE19 1JH, United Kingdom. TEL 44-1480-211550, FAX 44-1480-211560, http://www.istc.org.uk. Ed. Colin Battson. R&P, Adv. contact Carol Battson. B&W page GBP 485, color page GBP 645; trim 194 x 266. Circ: 2,000.

384 364.16 005.8 USA
COMMUNICATOR (PHOENIX, 1986). Text in English. 1986. q. free to members (effective 2004).
Published by: Communications Fraud Control Association, 3030 N. Central Ave. Ste. 707, Phoenix, AZ 85012. TEL 602-265-2322, FAX 602-265-1015, fraud@cfca.org, http://www.cfca.org. Ed. Dana Bruce Berry.

384 ZAF
COMMUNITAS; joernaal vir gemeenskapskommunikasie - journal for community communication. Text in Afrikaans, English. 1994. a. ZAR 15. **Document type:** *Academic/Scholarly.*
Indexed: ISAP.
Published by: (Einheid vir Gemeenskapskommunikasie), Universiteit van die Oranje-Vrystaat, Departement van Kommunikasiekunde/University of the Orange Free State, Department of Communications, Community Communications Unit, Posbus 339, Bloemfontein, 9300, South Africa.

353.52793 USA ISSN 0736-7147
COMMUNITY RELATIONS REPORT. Text in English. 1981. m. USD 160. **Document type:** *Newsletter.* **Description:** Reports on community relations ideas, programs, trends, and issues.
Published by: Joe Williams Communications, Inc., PO Box 924, Bartlesville, OK 74005. TEL 918-336-2267. Ed., Pub. Joe Williams.

COMMWEB. see *COMPUTERS—Computer Networks*

384 ZWE
COMPUTER AND TELECOM NEWS. Text in English. m. ZWD 181.20; ZWD 224.40 in Africa; ZWD 414 elsewhere. adv.
Published by: Thomson Publications Zimbabwe (Pvt) Ltd., Thomson House, PO Box 1683, Harare, Zimbabwe. TEL 263-4-736835, FAX 263-4-752390.

COMPUTER-MEDIATED COMMUNICATION MAGAZINE. see *COMPUTERS*

384 004 GEO ISSN 1512-1232
➤ **COMPUTER SCIENCE AND TELECOMMUNICATIONS.** Text in Georgian, Russian, English. 2002. irreg. free (effective 2005). **Document type:** *Journal, Academic/Scholarly.* **Description:** Covers computational methods, information technology, cryptology, artificial intelligence, computational linguistics.
Media: Online - full text.
Published by: Georgian Internet Academy, 272a, 4th Fl, Block 2, Iv Javakhishvili State University, 3 Chavchavadze Ave, Tbilisi, 01280, Georgia. TEL 995-32-290812, http://gesj.internet-academy.org.ge/en/title_en.php?b_sec=&section_l=comp.

➤ **COMPUTER SPECTRUM;** magazine for automation, computers and telecommunication. see *COMPUTERS*

➤ **COMPUTERS IN AFRICA;** the definitive guide to information technology in Africa. see *COMPUTERS*

384 BRA ISSN 0101-2657
COMUNICACAO E SOCIEDADE. Text in Portuguese; Abstracts in English, Portuguese. 1979. s-a. USD 12. bibl. **Document type:** *Academic/Scholarly.*
Indexed: HAPI, PAIS.
Published by: Instituto Metodista de Ensino Superior, Curso de Pos-Graduacao em Comunicacao Social, Rua do Sacramento, 230, R Ramos, Sao Bernardo Do Campo, SP 09735-460, Brazil. TEL 011-457-3733 ext. 78, FAX 455-3349, TELEX 11-47203 MTOD BR. Ed. Onesimo de Oliveira Cardoso.

621.382 ESP
COMUNICACION DIRECTIVOS. Text in Spanish. 6/yr.
Published by: Instituto Nacional de Industria, Plaza Marques de Salamanca 8, Madrid, 28006, Spain. TEL 34-91-4014004. Ed. Pablo Gonzalez.

384 659.111 ESP ISSN 0214-0039
➤ **COMUNICACION Y SOCIEDAD.** Text in Spanish; Summaries in Spanish, English. 1988. s-a. bk.rev. Index. back issues avail. **Document type:** *Magazine, Academic/Scholarly.* **Description:** Focuses on the study of communication phenomena, at their historical, theoretical, practical and sociological levels. It publishes original academic works on topics related to this area of knowledge, and it is addressed to academics and communication professionals.
Related titles: Online - full text ed.: (from EBSCO Publishing).
Indexed: IBSS, SociolAb.
—CINDOC.
Published by: (Universidad de Navarra, Facultad de Communicacion), Universidad de Navarra, Servicio de Publicaciones, Edificio de Ciencias Sociales, Pamplona, Navarra 31080, Spain. TEL 34-948-425600, FAX 34-948-425664, http://www.unav.es/cys/. Ed. Carlos Enriquez Sotelo. Pub. Maria Jesus Santos. Circ: 300 (paid); 250 (controlled).

621.382 USA ISSN 0748-3104
HE7601
COMUNICACIONES; telecomunicaciones, comunicaciones de datos, computadoras y satelites. Text in Spanish. 1979. q. USD 30. adv. back issues avail. **Document type:** *Trade.* **Description:** Distributed throughout Latin America for the telecommunication and computer technologies.
Published by: Intercom Corp., 9200 S Dadeland Blvd, Ste 309, Miami, FL 33156-2703. TEL 305-670-9444, FAX 305-670-9459. Ed. Thomas Will. Pub. Kenneth Bleakley. Adv. contact John Bull. B&W page USD 4,061, color page USD 4,884. Circ: 12,250.

384 ESP ISSN 1578-1194
COMUNICACIONES HOY; informacion profesional de las comunicaciones. Text in Spanish. 2001. 11/yr. EUR 86.25 domestic; EUR 151.20 in Europe (effective 2004). **Document type:** *Magazine, Trade.*
Published by: Goodman Business Press S.A., Goya 115, 4to. dcha., Madrid, 28009, Spain. TEL 34-91-3096310, FAX 34-91-4018090, info@goodman-bp.com, http://www.goodman-bp.com.

621.382 ESP ISSN 1139-0867
COMUNICACIONES WORLD; Magazine for the professional users of networks and telecommunications. Text in Spanish. 1986. 11/yr. EUR 51 (effective 2003). adv. **Document type:** *Magazine, Trade.* **Description:** Provides coverage of the latest news and trends in the data and telecommunications industry.
Related titles: Online - full content ed.
Indexed: IECT.
—CINDOC.
Published by: I D G Communications, Fortuny, 18 4, Madrid, 28010, Spain. TEL 34-91-3496600, FAX 34-91-3196104, comunicaciones@idg.es, http://www.idg.es/comunicaciones. Ed. Francisco Sanchez. Adv. contact Angeles de la Marca TEL 34-91-3496677. color page USD 4,273; trim 240 x 335. Circ: 8,587 (paid).

302.23 BRA ISSN 0102-0242
P92.B7
COMUNICARTE. Text in Portuguese. 1982. 2/yr., latest vol.15, no.21, 1997. **Document type:** *Magazine, Academic/Scholarly.*
Published by: Pontificia Universidade Catolica de Campinas, Instituto de Artes, Comunicacoes e Turismo, Rod. D. Pedro I, Km 136, CP 317, Campinas, SP 13020-904, Brazil. TEL 55-19-7567164, 55-19-7567176, FAX 55-19-2556376. Ed. Cleonice Furtado de M Van Raij.

621.382 ITA ISSN 1590-864X
➤ **LA COMUNICAZIONE;** Note Recensioni Notizie. Text in Italian. 1952. a. free. bk.rev. back issues avail. **Document type:** *Magazine, Academic/Scholarly.*
Formerly (until 2001): Istituto Superiore delle Poste e delle Telecomunicazioni. Note Recensioni Notizie (0374-3829)
Indexed: Inspec, ZentMath.
—AskIEEE, CISTI, Ei.
Published by: Istituto Superiore delle Comunicazioni e delle Tecnologie dell'Informazione, Viale America, 201, Rome, RM 00144, Italy. TEL 39-06-59584370, FAX 39-06-5410904, TELEX 616250 ISTSUP I, mauro.bergamini@istsupcti.it, http://www.comunicazioni.it. Ed. Carmelo Basso. Circ: 1,500.

384 320 ITA ISSN 1594-6061
COMUNICAZIONE POLITICA. Variant title: ComPol. Text in Multiple languages. 2000. s-a. EUR 26 domestic to individuals; EUR 47 foreign to individuals; EUR 47 domestic to institutions; EUR 62 foreign to institutions (effective 2003). **Document type:** *Journal, Academic/Scholarly.*
Published by: Franco Angeli Edizioni, Viale Monza 106, Milan, 20127, Italy. TEL 39-02-2837141, FAX 39-02-26144793, redazioni@francoangeli.it, http://www.francoangeli.it.

384 CZE ISSN 1211-3085
CONNECT!. Text in Czech. 1996. m. CZK 680 (effective 2003). adv. **Document type:** *Magazine, Consumer.*
Related titles: Online - full text ed.
Published by: Computer Press a.s., Pod Vinici 23, Prague 4, 143 11, Czech Republic. TEL 420-2-225273930, FAX 420-2-225273934, connect_listarna@cpress.cz, webmaster@cpress.cz, http://connect.cpress.cz, http://www.cpress.cz. Ed. Michal Hroch. Adv. contact Miroslava Doubkova. page CZK 83,000; trim 210 x 297.

384 DEU ISSN 0944-6141
CONNECT; Europas groesstes Magazin zu Telekommunikation. Text in German. 1992. fortn. EUR 42.80; EUR 3.80 newsstand/cover (effective 2005). adv. **Document type:** *Magazine, Trade.*
Published by: Vereinigte Motor-Verlage GmbH & Co. KG, Leuschnerstr 1, Stuttgart, 70174, Germany. TEL 49-711-18201, FAX 49-711-1821779, aglaessing@motorpresse.de, http://www.connect.de, http://www.motorpresse.de. Ed. Dirk Waasen. Adv. contact Michael Roy. B&W page EUR 6,450, color page EUR 8,950; trim 185 x 248. Circ: 130,629 (controlled). **Subscr. to:** SCW-Media Vertriebs GmbH & Co. KG, Stuttgart 70162, Germany. TEL 49-711-1821678, FAX 49-711-1822550, aboservice@scw-media.de.

621.39 ROM ISSN 1582-7895
CONNECT. Text in Romanian. 2001 (Dec.). m. ROL 499,000; ROL 44,900 newsstand/cover (effective 2002). adv. **Document type:** *Magazine, Consumer.*
Related titles: Online - full text ed.
Published by: M T R Press, Str. Vasile Alecsandri nr. 19, Oradea, 3700, Romania. TEL 40-59-406101, FAX 40-59-410914, connect@mtr.ro, office@mtr.ro, http://www.connect.com.ro, http://www.mtr.ro. Ed. Harris Wallmen.

681.324 SVN ISSN 1580-450X
CONNECT; revija za digitalno prihodnost. Text in Slovenian. 2000. m. SIT 6,372; SIT 790 newsstand/cover (effective 2003). adv. **Document type:** *Magazine, Trade.* **Description:** Deals with information technology, computer science, telecommunications and the Internet.
Related titles: Online - full text ed.: ISSN 1581-0283. 2002.
Published by: Burda d.o.o., Dunajska 106, Ljubljana, 1000, Slovenia. TEL 386-1-5604350, FAX 386-1-5604351, connect@burda.si, info@burda.si, http://www.burda.si/connect/. adv.: page SIT 280,000. Circ: 6,400 (paid and controlled).

384 004.6 GBR ISSN 1367-2495
CONNECT (LONDON). Text in English. 1995. m. GBP 72; GBP 90 foreign (effective 2002). adv. software rev. mkt.; stat.; tr.lit. back issues avail. **Document type:** *Trade.* **Description:** A call center environment covering all aspects of telecommunications data, voice & video conferencing.
Published by: Callan, Unit 34, Cremer Business Centre, Cremer St., London, E2 8HD, United Kingdom. TEL 44-207-295052, FAX 44-207-295052, information@connectweb.co.uk, http://www.connectweb.co.uk. Ed. Anthony Plewes. Pub., R&P Muiris O'Loingsigh. Adv. contact Katherine House. color page GBP 2,350. Circ: 10,000.

384 RUS ISSN 1563-1958
CONNECT! MIR SVYAZI. Text in Russian. 1996. m. USD 230 in United States (effective 2004). **Document type:** *Journal, Trade.*
Indexed: RefZh.
Published by: Izdatel'skii Dom Connect!, ul Dolgorukovskaya 23A, 4 etazh, Moscow, 127006, Russian Federation. TEL 7-095-1051118, FAX 7-095-9785100, editors@connect.ru, post@connect.ru, http://www.connect.ru/journal.asp?id=10. Ed. A D Povshenko. **US dist. addr.:** East View Information Services, 3020 Harbor Ln. N., Minneapolis, MN 55447. TEL 800-477-1005, FAX 800-800-3839, eastview@eastview.com, http://www.eastview.com.

384 USA
CONNECTIONS NEWSLETTER (MEMPHIS). Text in English. 1980. 3/yr. USD 30; free with subscr. to Southern Communication Journal. adv. back issues avail. **Document type:** *Newsletter.* **Description:** Covers communications research.
Related titles: Online - full text ed.

C

Published by: Southern States Communication Association, Georgia Southern University, PO Box 8091-02, Statesboro, GA 30460. TEL 912-681-5502, http://ssca.net. R&P Richard R Ranta. Adv. contact Jef Dolan. Circ: 2,500.

▼ **CONTEMPORANEA (PISA)**; rivista di studi sulla letteratura e sulla comunicazione. see *LITERATURE*

384 DEU
CORPORATE A V (YEAR). Text in German. 1981. a. EUR 10 (effective 2004). adv. **Document type:** *Newsletter, Trade.*
Formerly: A V - Branche (Year)
Published by: Medienreport Verlags GmbH, Hegnacher Str 30, Waiblingen, 71336, Germany. TEL 49-7151-23331, FAX 49-7151-23338, http://www.medienreport.de. Ed. Rolf G Lehmann. adv.: B&W page EUR 1,980; trim 175 x 244. Circ: 4,300 (paid and controlled).

658.45 659.2 GBR ISSN 1356-3289
HD30.3
➤ **CORPORATE COMMUNICATIONS**; an international journal. Text in English. 1996. q. EUR 2,478.41 in Europe; USD 2,649 in North America; AUD 3,649 in Australasia; GBP 1,738.91 in UK & elsewhere (effective 2006). reprint service avail. from PSC. **Document type:** *Journal, Academic/Scholarly.*
Description: Addresses the theory and best practice of corporate communication and strategic public relations.
Related titles: Online - full text ed.: (from EBSCO Publishing, Emerald Group Publishing Limited, Gale Group, IngentaConnect, O C L C Online Computer Library Center, Inc., ProQuest Information & Learning, Swets Information Services).
Indexed: ABIn, EmerIntel, Emerald, Inspec, LISA, PsycInfo, PsycholAb.
—BLDSC (3472.060695), IE, Infotrieve, ingenta. **CCC.**
Published by: Emerald Group Publishing Limited, 60-62 Toller Ln, Bradford, W Yorks BD8 9BY, United Kingdom. TEL 44-1274-777700, FAX 44-1274-785200, infomation@emeraldinsight.com, http://www.emeraldinsight.com/ccij.htm. Ed. Sandra M Oliver. R&P Mr. John Eggleton.

➤ **CORPORATE I T UPDATE.** see *BUSINESS AND ECONOMICS*

384 USA
CORPORATE WRITER & EDITOR. Text in English. 1984. m. USD 239 (effective 2005). **Document type:** *Newsletter.*
Formerly: Strategic Employee Publications; Editor'S Workshopnewsletter
Published by: Lawrence Ragan Communications, Inc., 316 N. Michigan Ave, Ste 300, Chicago, IL 60601-3300. TEL 312-960-4100, cservice@ragan.com, http://www.ragan.com. Circ: 4,000 (controlled and free).

343.099 384 ITA
IL CORRIERE DELLE TELECOMUNICAZIONI; political and economic weekly magazine of information and communication technology. Text in Italian. w. **Document type:** *Trade.*
Published by: Edicomp Holding SpA, Piazza San Lorenzo in Lucina 26, Rome, 00186, Italy. TEL 39-06-68809644, FAX 39-06-6873645, direzione@edicomp.it, http://www.edicomp.net. Ed. G Carretti.

COURTROOM COMMUNICATION STRATEGIES. see *LAW—Judicial Systems*

CRITICAL CULTURAL COMMUNICATIONS STUDIES. see *SOCIOLOGY*

384 CAN
CRITICAL MASS. Text in English. 1995. m.
Media: Online - full content.
Published by: Simon Fraser University, Department of Communication, Burnaby, BC H3T 3B4, Canada. http://hoshi.cic.sfu.ca/~cm/issue6/contents.html.

384 JPN ISSN 0911-5625
CROSS AND TALK∗; for communications between you and the world. Text in Japanese. a.
Published by: A L C Press Inc., Eifuku 2-chome, Suginami-ku, Tokyo, 168-0064, Japan.

CTRL_Z MAGAZINE. see *ART*

621.38 USA ISSN 1533-3078
HF5415.1265 CODEN: TELMES
CUSTOMER INTER@CTION SOLUTIONS. Text in English. 1982. m. free domestic. adv. back issues avail. **Document type:** *Magazine, Trade.* **Description:** Presents information to help build profits for every type of business, including: proven marketing strategies, business-to-business and business-to-consumers, using approaches for telemarketing.
Incorporates (199?-2002): Communications Solutions (1529-1790); Which was formerly (until 2000): C T I (1093-8176); Former titles (until 2000): C@ll Center C R M Solutions (1529-1782); (until 1999): Call Center Solutions (1521-0774); (until 1998): Telemarketing & Call Center Solutions (1521-0766); (until 1996): Telemarketing (0730-6156)
Related titles: Online - full text ed.: (from Florida Center for Library Automation, Gale Group, O C L C Online Computer Library Center, Inc.).
Indexed: ABIn, BPI, CADCAM, CompC, CompD, PROMT.
—BLDSC (3506.120680), CASDDS, IE, ingenta.
Published by: Technology Marketing Corporation, One Technology Plaza, Norwalk, CT 06854. TEL 203-852-6800, 800-243-6002, FAX 203-853-2845, tmc@tmcnet.com, http://www.tmcnet.com/cis/. Circ: 50,000 (paid and free).

384.5 070 GBR ISSN 1742-9234
▼ ➤ **CYFRWNG**; Media Wales Journal - Cyfnodolyn Cyfrangau Cymru. Text in English, Welsh. 2004. a. GBP 15 per issue (effective 2004). **Document type:** *Journal, Academic/Scholarly.* **Description:** Provides a forum for the presentation of research and scholarly discussion concerning the media in Wales, namely film, television, new media, radio, journalism, theatre and performance studies. Each issue will contain six thought-provoking articles together with reviews of new publications and productions.
Published by: University of Wales Press, 10 Columbus Walk, Brigantine Pl, Cardiff, CF10 4UP, United Kingdom. TEL 44-29-2049-6899, FAX 44-29-2049-6108, s.charles@press.wales.ac.uk, journals@press.wales.ac.uk, http://www.cyfrwng.com, http://www.uwp.co.uk. Eds. Dr. Gwenno Ffrancon Jenkins, Dr. James Thomas.

621.382 USA ISSN 0740-5405
CYRANO'S JOURNAL. Text in English. 1982. q. USD 18 to individuals; USD 24 to libraries. adv. bk.rev.; film rev. abstr.; bibl.; charts; illus. index. back issues avail.
Indexed: AltPI.
Published by: New England Communications Task Force, Inc., PO Box 68, Westport, CT 06881. Ed. D P Greanville. Circ: 15,000.

DATA IN WORLD DATA CENTER C2 FOR IONOSPHERE. CATALOGUE. see *EARTH SCIENCES—Geophysics*

384 GBR
DATAFILE OF ASIA-PACIFIC TELECOMMUNICATIONS. Text in English. base vol. plus m. updates. looseleaf. GBP 585 (effective 2000). stat. **Description:** Covers the telecommunications industry in the Asia-Pacific region. Includes information on regulations, basic telephone services, mobile communications, cable, satellite, and multimedia. Contains country and company profiles, and a directory.
Published by: (Communications and Information Technology Research Ltd.), C I T Publications Ltd., 3 Colleton Crescent, Exeter, Devon EX2 4DG, United Kingdom. TEL 44-1392-315-555, FAX 44-1392-315-556, citpubs@eurobell.co.uk, http://www.telecoms-data.com, http://www.telecomsprofiles.com. Ed. Tania Harvey.

384 GBR
DATAFILE OF EASTERN EUROPEAN COMMUNICATIONS. Text in English. base vol. plus m. updates. looseleaf. GBP 585 (effective 2000). **Description:** Aims to provide a comprehensive overview of the telecommunications market in eastern Europe.
Published by: (Communications and Information Technology Research Ltd.), C I T Publications Ltd., 3 Colleton Crescent, Exeter, Devon EX2 4DG, United Kingdom. TEL 44-1392-315-555, FAX 44-1392-315-556, citpubs@eurobell.co.uk, http://www.telecoms-data.com. Ed. Tania Harvey.

384 GBR
DATAFILE OF EUROPEAN TELECOMMUNICATIONS. Text in English. base vol. plus m. updates. looseleaf. GBP 585 (effective 2000). **Description:** Provides coverage of Europe's telecoms markets. Includes 16 country profiles and over 50 profiles of major operators active in the region.
Published by: (Communications and Information Technology Research Ltd.), C I T Publications Ltd., 3 Colleton Crescent, Exeter, Devon EX2 4DG, United Kingdom. TEL 44-1392-315-555, FAX 44-1392-315-556, citpubs@eurobell.co.uk, http://www.telecoms-data.com. Ed. Tania Harvey.

384 GBR
DATAFILE OF LATIN AMERICAN TELECOMMUNICATIONS. Text in English. base vol. plus m. updates. looseleaf. GBP 585 (effective 2000). stat. **Description:** Provides country and company profiles and a directory for the telecommunications industry in Latin America. Includes coverage of regulations, basic services, mobile communications, satellite, cable, and multimedia.
Published by: C I T Publications Ltd., 3 Colleton Crescent, Exeter, Devon EX2 4DG, United Kingdom. TEL 44-1392-315-555, FAX 44-1392-315-556, citpubs@eurobell.co.uk, http://www.telecoms-data.com. Ed. Tania Harvey.

621.382 JPN ISSN 0911-7601
TK5101.A1
DENKI TSUSHIN/TELECOMMUNICATIONS. Text in Japanese. 1938. m. JPY 7,560.
Related titles: Online - full text ed.
—**CCC.**
Published by: Telecommunications Association/Denki Tsushin Kyokai, POB 2522, Tokyo Opera City Tower, 3-20-2, Nishi-Shinjuku, Shinjuku-ku, Tokyo, 163-1455, Japan. TEL 81-3-53530185, FAX 81-3-53530195, http://www.tta.or.jp/pub/denkiBM.html.

621.382 JPN ISSN 0915-0935
AS552.C48784 CODEN: DTDKED
DENKI TSUSHIN DAIGAKU KIYO/UNIVERSITY OF ELECTRO-COMMUNICATIONS. BULLETIN. Text in English, Japanese; Summaries in English. 1950. s-a. **Document type:** *Bulletin.*
Formerly (until 1988): Denki Tsushin Daigaku Gakuho (0493-4253)
Indexed: CCMJ, ChemAb, Inspec, MathR, MathSciNet, RefZh.
—BLDSC (2786.650000), AskIEEE, CASDDS.
Published by: Denki Tsushin Daigaku/University of Electro-Communications, 1-5-1 chofugaoka, Chofu-shi, Tokyo-to 182-0021, Japan. TEL 81-424-83-2161, FAX 81-424-84-3554, ohashi@pc.uec.ac.jp, http://www.baloo.cc.uec.ac.jp. Ed. Hatsuo Yabe. Circ: 481.

DENSHI JOHO TSUSHIN GAKKAI GIJUTSU KENKYU HOKOKU/INSTITUTE OF ELECTRONICS, INFORMATION AND COMMUNICATION ENGINEERS. TECHNICAL REPORT. see *ENGINEERING—Electrical Engineering*

384 JPN ISSN 1344-4697
TK5101.A1
DENSHI JOHO TSUSHIN GAKKAI ROMBUNSHI. B/INSTITUTE OF ELECTRONICS, INFORMATION AND COMMUNICATION ENGINEERS. TRANSACTIONS. B. Text in Japanese. 1999. m. **Document type:** *Academic/Scholarly.* **Description:** Covers topics such as: communication networks and services switching, signaling systems and protocols, software, theory, source encoding, transmission equipment, optical communication, cable and wave guides, equipment, power supply, measurement and metrology, radio, satellite, antennas and propagation, electronic and radio applications, electromagnetic compatibility.
Formed by the 1999 merger of: Denshi Joho Tsushin Gakkai Rombunshi. B-1 (0915-1877); Denshi Joho Tsushin Gakkai Rombunshi. B-2 (0915-1885); Which both superseded (in 1989): Denshi Joho Tsushin Gakkai Rombunshi. B (0913-5715); Which was formerly (until 1986): Denshi Tsushin Gakkai Rombunshi. B (0373-6105); Which superseded in part (in 1967): Denshi Tsushin Gakkai Zasshi (0914-529X); Former titles (until 1967): Denki Tsushin Gakkai Zasshi (0020-286X); (1917-1936): Denshin Denwa Gakkai Zasshi (0914-5281)
Related titles: ♦ English ed.: I E I C E Transactions on Communications. ISSN 0916-8516.
Indexed: IAOP, Inspec.
—BLDSC (8939.441000), CISTI, Linda Hall. **CCC.**
Published by: Denshi Joho Tsushin Gakkai/Institute of Electronics Information and Communication Engineers, IEICE Publishing Office, Kikai-Shinko-Kaikan Bldg., Annex 3F, 5-22, Shibakoen 3 chome, Minato-ku, Tokyo, 105-0011, Japan. TEL 81-3-3433-6692, FAX 81-3-3433-6616, shuppan@ieice.or.jp, http://www.ieice.or.jp/. Ed. Shigeo Tsujii.

DENSHI JOHO TSUSHIN GAKKAI TAIKAI KOEN RONBUNSHU/INSTITUTE OF ELECTRONICS, INFORMATION AND COMMUNICATION ENGINEERS. NATIONAL CONVENTION RECORD. see *ELECTRONICS*

DENSHI JOHO TSUSHIN GAKKAISHI/INSTITUTE OF ELECTRONICS INFORMATION AND COMMUNICATION ENGINEERS. JOURNAL. see *ELECTRONICS*

621.382 CHN ISSN 1000-0801
DIANXIN KEXUE/TELECOMMUNICATIONS SCIENCE. Text in Chinese. 1956. m. CNY 84; CNY 7 newsstand/cover. adv. Index. **Document type:** *Journal, Trade.*
Related titles: Online - full text ed.: (from East View Information Services).
Indexed: C&ISA, E&CAJ, EngInd, IAA.
Published by: (China Institute of Communications), Renmin Youdian Chubanshe/People's Posts and Telecommunications Publishing House, Dongcheng-qu, Hepingli Binhe Lu, no.1, Hangtian Xinxi Dasha 9-ceng, Beijing, 100013, China. FAX 86-10-68373422, dxkx@ptpress.com.cn, abc@ptpress.com.cn, http://www.telecomsci.com.cn/, http://www.ptpress.com.cn/. Ed. Yi Dongshan. adv.: color page USD 1,000; 285 x 210. Circ: 30,000 (paid). **Dist. overseas by:** China International Book Trading Corp, 35 Chegongzhuang Xilu, Haidian District, PO Box 399, Beijing 100044, China.

384 USA
DIGITAL COMMUNICATION. Text in English. 1985. irreg., latest 2001. price varies. **Document type:** *Monographic series.*
Indexed: MLA-IB.
Published by: M I T Press, 55 Hayward St, Cambridge, MA 02142-1493. TEL 617-253-5646, FAX 617-258-6779, http://mitpress.mit.edu. **Dist. by:** c/o Trilateral, 100 Maple Ridge Dr, Cumberland, RI 02864. TEL 401-658-4226, 800-405-1619, FAX 401-531-2801, 800-406-9145.

C

384 004.678 USA ISSN 1526-3169
▼ **DIGITAL FORMATIONS.** Text in English. 2003. irreg., latest 2004. price varies. **Document type:** *Monographic series, Academic/Scholarly.* **Description:** Examines broad issues in realms such as digital culture, electronic commerce, law, politics and governance, gender, the Internet, race, art, health and medicine, and education.
Published by: Peter Lang Publishing, Inc., 275 Seventh Ave, 28th Fl, New York, NY 10001. TEL 212-647-7700, 800-770-5264, FAX 212-647-7707, customerservice@plang.com, http://www.peterlangusa.com. Ed. Steve Jones.

384 USA
DIGITAL KIDS. Text in English. m. USD 545; USD 645 with online ed.. **Document type:** *Newsletter.* **Description:** Tracks the lucrative traditional kids market - film, cartoons, television, games, education and consumer products.
Related titles: Online - full text ed.
Published by: Jupiter Communications, 627 Broadway, New York, NY 10012. TEL 212-780-6060, FAX 212-780-6075, http://www.jup.com/newsletter/.

384 ZAF
DIRECTORY OF CONTACTS. Text in English. 1994. q. **Document type:** *Directory.*
Published by: (South Africa. Directorate: Research), South African Communication Service, Private Bag X745, Pretoria, 0002, South Africa. TEL 27-12-3142105, FAX 27-12-3233831, emuller@sacs.org.za. R&P E C Muller.

DIREKTMARKETING PRAXIS. see *BUSINESS AND ECONOMICS—Marketing And Purchasing*

384 617.89 BRA ISSN 0102-762X
RJ496.C67
➤ **DISTURBIOS DE COMUNICACAO.** Text in Portuguese; Abstracts in Portuguese, English, Spanish. 1986. 3/yr. BRL 90 domestic; USD 40 foreign (effective 2005). bk.rev. 150 p./no.; **Document type:** *Journal, Academic/Scholarly.*
Published by: Pontificia Universidade Catolica de Sao Paulo, Faculdade de Fonoaudiologia, Rua Monte Alegre, 984, Perdizes, Sao Paulo, SP 05014-001, Brazil. TEL 55-11-3670-8168, FAX 55-11-3873-3359, revidisc@pucsp.br, revisdic@pucsp.br, http://www.pucsp.br/~fonopuc. Eds. Beatriz Mendes TEL 55-11-36708170, Maria Angelina Martinez. R&P Beatriz Mendes TEL 55-11-36708170.

384 FRA ISSN 0767-4775
DOSSIERS DE L'AUDIOVISUEL. Text in French. 6/yr. EUR 59 domestic; EUR 64.50 in the European Union; EUR 63.60 DOM-TOM; EUR 66.70 elsewhere (effective 2003). **Document type:** *Government.*
Related titles: Microfiche ed.
—BLDSC (3619.754000).
Published by: (Institut National de l'Audiovisuel), Documentation Francaise, 29-31 quai Voltaire, Paris, Cedex 7 75344, France. FAX 33-1-40157230.

621.388 CHE ISSN 1019-6587
TK6540 CODEN: ETEREG
E B U TECHNICAL REVIEW. Text in English. 1958. q. CHF 160 (effective 1999). adv. bk.rev. index. back issues avail. **Document type:** *Bulletin, Trade.* **Description:** Covers broadcast engineering, including radio, television and data broadcasting technologies, with reports of international standardization efforts and regulatory activities.
Formerly (until 1992): E B U Review, Technical (1018-7391)
Related titles: Online - full text ed.; French ed.: U E R - Revue Technique. ISSN 1019-6595.
Indexed: EngInd, IIFP, Inspec.
—CISTI, Ei, IE, Linda Hall.
Published by: European Broadcasting Union/Union Europeenne de Radio-Television, Ancienne Route 17 A, Case Postale 67, Grand Saconnex - Geneva, 1218, Switzerland. TEL 41-22-7172111, FAX 41-22-7172200, techreview@ebu.ch, http://www.ebu.ch/trev_home.html, http://www.ebu.ch/. Eds. Eric Piraux, Philip Laven. R&P Mike Meyer TEL 41-22-7172206. Adv. contact Richard McKillop. Circ: 2,500.

E-BUSINESS WORLD. see *BUSINESS AND ECONOMICS*

654.19 215 DEU ISSN 1439-6041
E P D MEDIEN. (Evangelischer Pressedienst) Text in German. 1949. 2/w. EUR 61 per month (effective 2005). **Document type:** *Magazine, Trade.*
Formerly (until 1997): Kirche und Rundfunk (0720-7603)
Published by: Gemeinschaftswerk der Evangelischen Publizistik e.V., Emil-von-Behring-Str 3, Frankfurt Am Main, 60439, Germany. TEL 49-69-580980, FAX 49-69-58098272, info@gep.de, http://www.epd.de/medien/medien_index.html, http://www.gep.de.

E R T DIRECTORY (YEAR). (Electrical & Radio Trading) see *ELECTRONICS*

E T R I JOURNAL. see *ELECTRONICS*

384.55 CAN ISSN 1494-0051
E T R NEWS. Text in English. 1996. bi-m. CND 22.47; USD 42 in United States; USD 60 elsewhere. adv. **Document type:** *Trade.* **Description:** Reports on the broadcasting, cable and telecommunications industries.
Formerly (until 1999): Electronic Times Report (1480-0985)
Published by: Crailer Communications, 360 Dupont St, Toronto, ON M5R 1V9, Canada. TEL 416-966-9944, FAX 416-966-9946, crailer@interlog.com, info@building.ca, http://interlog.com/~crailer/etr, http://www.building.ca. Ed., R&P Sheri Craig. Pub., Adv. contact Jack Ruttle. B&W page CND 2,700; trim 10.75 x 8. Circ: 7,580.

621.382 USA
EASTERN EUROPEAN TELECOM MONTHLY. Text in English. m. USD 850 (effective 2000). **Document type:** *Journal, Trade.* **Description:** Contains current news and information on telecom markets in Eastern Europe.
Published by: Gist, Inc., 2200 Wilson Blvd, Ste 102G, Arlington, VA 22201. TEL 703-527-7459, FAX 703-528-1477, info@gist.net, http://www.gist.net.

EBLUE BOOK; international directory for people who are deaf, hard of hearing, late-deafened, deaf-blind. see *HANDICAPPED—Hearing Impaired*

621.382 FRA ISSN 0012-9283
TK5101.A1
ECHO DES RECHERCHES. Text in French. 1950. 4/yr. bibl.; charts; illus.
Indexed: AcoustA, CybAb, ExcerpMed, Inspec, RefZh.
—AskIEEE, CISTI, IE. **CCC.**
Published by: France Telecom Recherche et Developpement, 38-40 rue du General Leclerc, Issy-les-Moulineaux, Cedex 92131, France. TEL 33-1-45295464, FAX 33-1-45290106. Ed. P M Pignal. **Co-sponsor:** Ecole Nationale Superieure des Telecommunications.

384 FRA ISSN 1165-8045
ECRAN TOTAL. Text in French. w. **Description:** Written for professionals working in television, motion pictures, radio, multimedia.
Address: 18 rue Camille Desmoulins, Levallois-Perret, 92300, France. FAX 33-1-47577271, ecrantot@club-internet.fr. Ed. Serge Siritzky.

384 DNK ISSN 1602-799X
EDANMAK; om kommunikation, innovation og teknik. Text in Danish. 1990. q. free (effective 2005). **Document type:** *Magazine, Government.*
Formerly (until 2002): Teletema (0905-6343)
Related titles: Online - full text ed.: ISSN 1604-7400.
Published by: Ministeriet for Videnskab, Teknologi og Udvikling, IT- og Telestyrelsen, Holsteinsgade 63, Copenhagen OE, 2100, Denmark. TEL 45-35-450000, FAX 45-35-450001, itst@itst.dk, http://www.itst.dk/wimpdoc.asp?page=tema&objno=115891331. Ed. Lisann Troelsen. Circ: 7,000.

384 GBR ISSN 0959-9371
EDINBURGH P I C T WORKING PAPER. (Programme on Information & Communication Technologies) Text in English. 1988. irreg. **Document type:** *Monographic series.*
—BLDSC (3661.018200).
Published by: University of Edinburgh, Old College, South Bridge, Edinburgh, EH8 9YL, United Kingdom. TEL 44-131-650-2252, FAX 44-131-650-2253, http://www.ed.ac.uk.

621.382 JPN ISSN 1342-6907
EIZO JOHO MEDIA GAKKAISHI/INSTITUTE OF IMAGE INFORMATION AND TELEVISION ENGINEERS. Text in Japanese; Summaries in English, Japanese. 1947. m. JPY 1,700 per issue.
Formerly (until 1997): Terebijon Gakkaishi (0386-6831)
Indexed: B&BAb, C&ISA, E&CAJ, EngInd, Inspec, SolStAb.
—BLDSC (4776.260000), AskIEEE, CISTI, Ei, Linda Hall. **CCC.**
Published by: Eizo Joho Media Gakkai/Institute of Image Information and Television Engineers, 5-8 Shibakoen 3-chome, Minato-ku, Tokyo, 105-0011, Japan. TEL 81-3-3432-4677, FAX 44-81-3-3432-4675, ite@ie.or.jp.

621.382 JPN ISSN 1342-6893
EIZOU JOHO MEDIA GAKKAI GIJUTSU HOKOKU/I T E TECHNICAL REPORT. Text in Japanese. 1977. irreg.
Formerly (until 1997): Terebijon Joho Media Gakkai Gijutsu Hokoku (0386-4227)
—BLDSC (3668.410500). **CCC.**
Published by: Eizo Joho Media Gakkai/Institute of Image Information and Television Engineers, 5-8 Shibakoen 3-chome, Minato-ku, Tokyo, 105-0011, Japan. TEL 81-3-3432-4677, FAX 81-3-3432-4675, ite@ite.or.jp.

621.382 JPN ISSN 1343-1846
EIZOU JOHO MEDIA GAKKAI NENJI TAIKAI KOEN YOKOSHU/INSTITUTE OF IMAGE INFORMATION AND TELEVISION ENGINEERS. PROCEEDINGS OF ANNUAL CONVENTION. Text in English, Japanese; Summaries in English. a. JPY 8,000. **Document type:** *Proceedings.*
Formerly (until 1997): Terebijon Gakkai Nenji Taikai Koen Yokoshu (0919-1879); Formerly (until 1990): Terebijon Gakkai Zenkoku Taikai Koen Yokoshu
—BLDSC (6741.845000). **CCC.**
Published by: Eizo Joho Media Gakkai/Institute of Image Information and Television Engineers, 5-8 Shibakoen 3-chome, Minato-ku, Tokyo, 105-0011, Japan. TEL 81-3-3432-4677, FAX 81-3-3432-4675, ite@ite.or.jp.

ELECTRONIC JOURNAL OF COMMUNICATION/LA REVUE ELECTRONIQUE DE COMMUNICATION. see *SOCIAL SCIENCES: COMPREHENSIVE WORKS*

ELECTRONICS AND COMMUNICATIONS IN JAPAN. PART 1: COMMUNICATIONS. see *ELECTRONICS*

ELECTRONICS AND COMMUNICATIONS IN JAPAN. PART 2: ELECTRONICS. see *ELECTRONICS*

621.382 GBR ISSN 0261-2666
ELECTROSONIC WORLD. Text in English. 1980. irreg., latest 1999, Oct. free. illus. **Document type:** *Newspaper, Trade.* **Description:** Directed to A-V professionals; video walls, audio-visual, professional video, emphasizing business communications and leisure-time applications.
Published by: Electrosonic Limited, Hawley Mill, Hawley Rd, Dartford, Kent DA2 7SY, United Kingdom. TEL 44-1322-222211, FAX 44-1322-282282, Robert.Simpson@electrosonic-uk.com, http://www.electrosonic.com. Ed. Robert Simpson. R&P Yvonne Hegarty. Circ: 80,000 (controlled).

ELECTROSUISSE, S E V, VERBAND FUR ELEKTRO-, ENERGIE- UND INFORMATIONSTECHNIK. BULLETIN. see *ENGINEERING—Electrical Engineering*

ELEKTRONIKA TA ZV'YAZOK/ELEKTRONIKA I SVYAZ'. see *ELECTRONICS*

ELEKTRONIKTIDNINGEN. see *ELECTRONICS*

C

ELETTRONICA E TELECOMUNICAZIONI. see *ELECTRONICS*

371.42 USA ISSN 0882-3316
EMERGING PATTERNS OF WORK AND COMMUNICATIONS IN AN INFORMATION AGE. Text in English. 1985. irreg. price varies. **Document type:** *Monographic series, Academic/Scholarly.*
Published by: Greenwood Publishing Group Inc. (Subsidiary of: Harcourt International), 88 Post Rd W, PO Box 5007, Westport, CT 06881. TEL 203-226-3571, FAX 203-226-1502, webmaster@greenwood.com, http://www.greenwood.com.

621.382 BRA
EMPRESA BRASILEIRA DE TELECOMUNICACOES. RELATORIO ANUAL. Text in Portuguese. 1972. a.
Published by: (Empresa Brasileira de Telecomunicacoes S.A., Assessoria de Comunicacao Social), P L V Assessoria e Design, Rua das Marrecas, 36 Sala 401, Centro, Rio De Janeiro, RJ 20031-120, Brazil. Circ: 6,000.

ESTUDIOS DE CONSTRUCCION, TRANSPORTES Y COMUNICACIONES. see *TRANSPORTATION*

ESTUDIOS SOBRE LAS CULTURAS CONTEMPORANEAS; revista de investigacion y analisis de la cultura. see *HUMANITIES: COMPREHENSIVE WORKS*

384.170 301 302.23 GBR ISSN 1742-0105
▼ ➤ **ETHICAL SPACE**; the international journal of communication ethics. Text in English. 2004. q. GBP 115 domestic to libraries; GBP 140 foreign to libraries (effective 2005). **Document type:** *Journal, Academic/Scholarly.*
Related titles: Online - full text ed.
Published by: Troubador Publishing Limited, 9 de Montfort Mews, Leicester, LE1 7FW, United Kingdom. TEL 44-116-2559311, FAX 44-116-2559323, es@troubador.co.uk, http://www.troubador.co.uk/ethicalspace. Ed. Mr. Richard Keeble. Pub. Mr. Jeremy B Thompson.

384 FRA ISSN 1270-6841
➤ **ETUDES DE COMMUNICATIONS.** Text in French. 1980. a. bk.rev. back issues avail. **Document type:** *Monographic series, Academic/Scholarly.* **Description:** Contains university research on communication.
Former titles (until 1992): Universite de Lille III. Centre de Recherche en Techniques d'Expression, Information et Communication. Bulletin (0981-8596); (until 1986): Universite de Lille III. Centre de Recherche en Techniques d'Expression. Bulletin (0767-7030)
Published by: Universite de Lille III (Charles de Gaulle), S E G E S, B P 149, Villeneuve d'Ascq, Cedex 59653 , France. TEL 33-3-20416497, FAX 33-3-20416191, guiot@univ-lille3.fr. Ed. Pierre Delcambre. Circ: 250 (paid).

384.5 FRA ISSN 0999-582X
ETUDES TELECOM. Text in French. 10/yr. bk.rev.
Published by: Attis Communications, 14 rue des Reculettes, Paris, 75013, France. TEL 43-31-47-04, FAX 43-31-48-21. Ed. Leonid Tkatchenko. Circ: 4,000.

▼ new title ➤ refereed ✶ unverified ♦ full entry avail.

384 BEL ISSN 0963-5734
EURO INFOTECH. Text in English. 1990. 23/yr. looseleaf. GBP 695, USD 550 (effective 1999). **Document type:** *Newsletter.*
Description: Covers news and views from European Union organizations and explains how they affect policy, regulation, and research and development programs in computer, telecommunication and consumer electronic sectors.
Related titles: Online - full text ed.
Published by: Europe Information Service SA, Av Adolphe Lacomble 66-68, Brussels, 1030, Belgium. FAX 32-2-7326608, eis@eis.be, http://www.eis.be.

EUROPEAN CONFERENCE ON OPTICAL COMMUNICATION. PROCEEDINGS. see *ENGINEERING*

EUROPEAN INFORMATION TECHNOLOGY OBSERVATORY (YEAR). see *COMPUTERS—Electronic Data Processing*

THE EUROPEAN JOURNAL OF TELEWORKING. see *BUSINESS AND ECONOMICS—Abstracting, Bibliographies, Statistics*

EUROPEAN MEDIA DIRECTORY. see *BUSINESS AND ECONOMICS—Trade And Industrial Directories*

384.04109405 GBR ISSN 1468-4543
EUROPEAN TELECOM'S INTELLIGENCE BULLETIN. Text in English. 1999. m. GBP 545 domestic; GBP 590 foreign (effective 2001). **Document type:** *Bulletin, Trade.*
Description: Analyzes major developments in the European telecoms market.
Published by: SMi Publishing, 1 New Concordia Wharf, Mill St, London, SE1 2BB, United Kingdom. TEL 44-207-827-6000, FAX 44-207-827-6001, etib@smipublishing.co.uk, ordering@smipublishing.co.uk, http://www.smipublishing.co.uk.

C

621.382 ITA ISSN 1124-318X
TK5101.A1 CODEN: ETTTET
EUROPEAN TRANSACTIONS ON TELECOMMUNICATIONS. Text in English. bi-m. EUR 385 in Europe to institutions; USD 400 elsewhere to institutions; EUR 424 combined subscription in Europe to institutions print & online eds.; USD 440 combined subscription elsewhere to institutions print & online eds. (effective 2006). adv. abstr.; bibl.; charts; illus. index, cum.index. **Document type:** *Magazine, Trade.*
Formerly (until 1995): European Transactions on Telecommunications and Related Technologies (1120-3862); Formed by the merger of (1979-1989): N T Z Archiv (0170-172X); (1932-1990): Alta Frequenza (0002-6557)
Related titles: Online - full text ed.: ISSN 1541-8251. EUR 385 in Europe to institutions; USD 400 elsewhere to institutions (effective 2006) (from EBSCO Publishing, Swets Information Services, Wiley InterScience).
Indexed: ASFA, C&ISA, ChemAb, CurCont, E&CAJ, ESPM, EngInd, ExcerpMed, ISMEC, Inspec, RefZh, RiskAb, SolStAb. —BLDSC (3830.315000), AskIEEE, CASDDS, CISTI, Ei, IDS, IE, Infotrieve, ingenta, Linda Hall. **CCC.**
Published by: Associazione Elettrotecnica ed Elettronica Italiana, Piazzale Rodolfo Morandi 2, Milan, MI 20121, Italy. TEL 39-02-777901, FAX 39-02-798817, soci@aei.it, http://www.aei.it. Ed. Ezio Biglieri. Circ: 1,400. **Subscr. to:** John Wiley & Sons Ltd., The Atrium, Southern Gate, Chichester, West Sussex PO19 8SQ, United Kingdom. TEL 44-1243-843335, FAX 44-1243-843232.

384 DEU
EX LIBRIS KOMMUNIKATION. Text in German. irreg., latest vol.9, 2000. price varies. **Document type:** *Monographic series, Academic/Scholarly.*
Published by: Verlag Reinhard Fischer, Weltistr 34, Munich, 81477, Germany. TEL 49-89-7918892, FAX 49-89-7918310, verlagfischer@compuserve.de, http://www.verlag-reinhard-fischer.de. Eds. Detlef Schroeter, Hans Wagner.

384 AUS ISSN 1033-2014
EXCHANGE; the communications news weekly. Text in English. 1989. w. (48/yr.). AUD 1,190, USD 1,100 (effective 2001). 16 p./no.; **Document type:** *Newsletter, Consumer, Corporate, Government, Trade.* **Description:** Provides news and analysis on the latest developments in telecommunications in Australia & New Zealand.
Published by: 3rd Wave Communication Pty. Ltd., PO Box 40, Enmore, NSW 2042, Australia. TEL 61-2-9557-9337, FAX 61-2-9557-9554, info@3rdwave.com.au, http://www.exchange.com.au. Ed., Pub. Stuart Corner.

384 AUS
EXCHANGE ASIA; telecommunications news from India to the Pacific. Text in English. 1993. fortn. (25/yr.). AUD 1,305, USD 1,295 (effective 2001). 12 p./no.; **Document type:** *Newsletter, Consumer, Corporate, Government, Trade.* **Description:** Provides news and analysis on the latest developments in telecommunications markets in Asia.
Formerly (until 2002): Telenews Asia (1320-2669)
Media: E-mail. **Related titles:** Online - full text ed.: (from Gale Group, Northern Light Technology, Inc., O C L C Online Computer Library Center, Inc., ProQuest Information & Learning).
Indexed: ABIn, B&I.
Published by: 3rd Wave Communication Pty. Ltd., PO Box 40, Enmore, NSW 2042, Australia. TEL 61-2-9557-9337, FAX 61-2-9557-9554, info@3rdware.com.au, info@3rdwave.com.au, http://www.telenews.com.au. Ed. Charles Dodgson. Pub., R&P Stuart Corner.

EXPLORATIONS IN MEDIA ECOLOGY. see *SOCIAL SCIENCES: COMPREHENSIVE WORKS*

384 GBR ISSN 1358-8915
EXPRESS; magazine for account holders of D H L International. Text in English. 1992. q. adv. **Document type:** *Consumer.*
Published by: (D H L International), Mediamark Publishing Ltd., 11 Kingsway, London, WC2B 6PH, United Kingdom. TEL 44-171-212-9000, FAX 44-171-212-9001, express@mediamark.co.uk, http://www.mediamark.co.uk. Ed. Karen Taylor. Pub. Peter Moore. R&P Susan Freegrove. Adv. contact Alan Cotton. Circ: 50,000 (controlled).

384 FRA ISSN 0297-2301
EXPRESSION D'ENTREPRISE; le magazine de la communication. Text in French. 1984. 10/yr. adv. **Description:** For corporate spokespeople, marketing and communication directors.
Formerly (until 1985): Expression Audiovisuelle (0762-9974)
Published by: Editions de l'Expression, 22 rue Plumet, Paris, 75015, France. TEL 47-34-02-70, FAX 47-34-00-46. Ed. Patrice Legendre. Adv. contact Francoise Casenave.

354.75 USA ISSN 1057-5766
KF2763.3.A2
F C C RECORD. Text in English. 1986. fortn. USD 535 (effective 2001). back issues avail. **Document type:** *Government.*
Description: Contains compilation of decisions, reports, public notices and other documents of the Federal Communications Commission of the United States.
Related titles: Supplement(s): USD 46 newsstand/cover (effective 2001).
Published by: U.S. Federal Communications Commission, 445 12th St SW Rm TW-B505, Washington, DC 20554. **Subscr. to:** U.S. Government Printing Office, Superintendent of Documents, PO Box 371954, Pittsburgh, PA 15250-7954. TEL 202-512-1800, FAX 202-512-2250, orders@gpo.gov, http://www.access.gpo.gov.

343.0994 USA ISSN 1081-9541
F C C REPORT; an exclusive report on domestic and international telecommunications policy and regulation. (Federal Communications Commission) Text in English. 1981. bi-w. (26/yr.). USD 670 domestic; USD 693 foreign (effective 2005). adv. back issues avail. **Document type:** *Newsletter.*
Formerly: F C C Week (0738-5714)
Related titles: Online - full text ed.: (from bigchalk, Gale Group, The Dialog Corporation).
Published by: Warren Communications News, Inc., 2115 Ward Ct, N W, Washington, DC 20037. TEL 202-872-9200, 800-327-7205, FAX 202-293-3435, info@warren-news.com, http://www.warren-news.com. Eds. Edie Herman, John Spofford.

F I T C E FORUM. see *ENGINEERING—Electrical Engineering*

384 BRA
FACOM; revista de comunicacao. Text in Portuguese. 1994. s-a.
Published by: Fundacao Armando Alvares Penteado, Faculdade de Comunicacao, Rua Alagoas, 903, Predio 5, Higienopolis, Sao Paulo, SP 01242-001, Brazil. TEL 55-11-824-0233, FAX 55-11-8251636.

FEDERAL ACQUISITION REGULATION (WASHINGTON). see *PUBLIC ADMINISTRATION*

384 USA ISSN 0098-3942
KF2763.35
FEDERAL COMMUNICATIONS COMMISSION REPORTS. Variant title: Cumulative Index Digest of Decisions and Reports of the Federal Communications Commission of the United States. Text in English. 1934; N.S. 1965. irreg. price varies. **Document type:** *Government.*
Related titles: Microform ed.: N.S. (from PMC).
Published by: U.S. Federal Communications Commission, 445 12th St SW Rm TW-B505, Washington, DC 20554. TEL 202-418-0450. **Orders to:** U.S. Government Printing Office, Superintendent of Documents, PO Box 371954, Pittsburgh, PA 15250-7954. TEL 202-512-1800, FAX 202-512-2250, orders@gpo.gov, http://www.access.gpo.gov.

FEDERAL COMMUNICATIONS LAW JOURNAL. see *LAW*

FEMINIST MEDIA STUDIES. see *WOMEN'S STUDIES*

621.382 USA ISSN 1082-2119
FIBER IN THE LOOP; covering worldwide developments in bringing fiber to the home. Text in English. 1989. m. USD 695 in US & Canada; USD 745 elsewhere (effective 2004). back issues avail. **Document type:** *Newsletter, Trade.* **Description:** Covers fiber to the home technology, products, trials, and services.
Formerly (until 1995): Fiber to the Home (1051-192X)
Related titles: Online - full text ed.: (from Factiva, Northern Light Technology, Inc., ProQuest Information & Learning).
Published by: Information Gatekeepers, Inc., 320 Washington St, Ste 302, Brighton, MA 02135. TEL 617-782-5033, 800-323-1088, FAX 617-782-5735, info@igigroup.com, http://www.igigroup.com/nl/pages/fiberloop.html. Pub. Dr. Paul Polishuk. **Dist. by:** Publications Resource Group, 121 Union St., Box 792, North Adams, MA 01247. TEL 413-664-6185, FAX 413-664-9343.

621.382 USA ISSN 1075-5268
HD9696.F52
FIBER OPTICS YELLOW PAGES. Text in English. 1978. a. USD 89.95 domestic; USD 104.95 foreign (effective 2000 - 2001). **Document type:** *Directory.* **Description:** Covers equipment and suppliers of fiber optics worldwide, reference materials, standards, sources of information, and review articles.
Formerly (until 1993): Fiber Optics Handbook and Buyers Guide (1075-525X)
Published by: Information Gatekeepers, Inc., 320 Washington St, Ste 302, Brighton, MA 02135. TEL 617-782-5033, 800-323-1088, FAX 617-734-8562, info@igigroup.com, http://www.igigroup.com. Ed. Tony Carmona. Pub. Dr. Paul Polishuk.

FIBEROPTIC PRODUCT NEWS BUYER'S GUIDE. see *BUSINESS AND ECONOMICS—Trade And Industrial Directories*

FIBERSYSTEMS INTERNATIONAL. see *PHYSICS—Optics*

384 600 AUS ISSN 1449-1443
▼ ➤ **FIBRECULTUREJOURNAL**; internet theory criticism research. Text in English. 2003. irreg. free (effective 2005). **Document type:** *Journal, Academic/Scholarly.* **Description:** Covers information and communication technologies and their policy frameworks, network cultures and their informational logic, new media forms and their deployment, and the possibilities of socio-technical invention and sustainability.
Media: Online - full text.
Published by: Fibreculture Publications, School of Media and Communications, Faculty of Arts and Social Sciences, University of New South Wales, Sydney, NSW 2052, Australia. http://journal.fibreculture.org/.

808.5 USA ISSN 1050-3366
PN4071
➤ **FLORIDA COMMUNICATION JOURNAL.** Text in English. 1973. s-a. USD 30. adv. bk.rev. back issues avail. **Document type:** *Journal, Academic/Scholarly.*
Formerly (until 1987): Florida Speech Communication Journal (0093-6138)
Published by: Florida Communication Association, School of Communication, University of Central Florida, Orlando, FL 32816-1344. TEL 407-823-5958, FAX 407-823-6360, http://www.flcom.org/journal.asp, http://www.flcom.org/default.asp. Ed. Wally Schmidt. Circ: 400.

384 ITA
FONDAZIONE UGO BORDONI. ANNUAL REVIEW. Text in Italian. a. **Document type:** *Corporate.*
Published by: Fondazione Ugo Bordoni, Via Baldassarre Castiglione 59, Rome, 00142, Italy. TEL 39-06-54801, FAX 39-06-54804400, http://www.fub.it.

808.53 USA ISSN 0015-735X
PN4177
FORENSIC. Text in English. 1915. q. USD 30 to non-members. adv. bk.rev. illus. **Document type:** *Academic/Scholarly.*
Related titles: Microform ed.: (from PQC).
Published by: Pi Kappa Delta, c/o Robert S Littlefield, Box 5075, Univ Sta, North Dakota State University, Fargo, ND 58105-5075. TEL 701-231-7783, FAX 701-231-7784, rlittlef@badlands.nodak.edu. Ed. Michael Bartanen. Pub., R&P, Adv. contact Robert S Littlefield. Circ: 1,000.

FRANCE MUSIQUE IMAGE ET SON. see *MUSIC*

621.382 FRA
FRANCE TELECOM; revue francaise des telecommunications. Text in French; Summaries in English, Spanish. 1971. q. FRF 100; FRF 150 foreign. adv. bk.rev. bibl.; stat. index.
Description: Covers the services, economics, world industry and history of telecommunications.
Formerly: Revue Francaise des Telecommunications (0183-8636)
Indexed: KES, PROMT, RASB. —CISTI. **CCC.**
Published by: France Telecom, Direction Generale des Telecommunications, 6 place d'Alleray, Paris, Cedex 15 75505, France. TEL 1-44-44-22-22, FAX 1-48-42-51-26. Ed. Bruno Grassin Delyle. Circ: 35,000.

621.382 USA ISSN 1050-9046
FRONTIERS IN COMMUNICATIONS. Text in English. 198?. irreg. **Document type:** *Proceedings, Trade.*
Indexed: Inspec.
Published by: (I E E E Communications Society), Institute of Electrical and Electronics Engineers, Inc., 445 Hoes Ln, Piscataway, NJ 08854-1331. TEL 732-981-0060, FAX 732-981-1721, http://www.ieee.org.

FRONTIERS IN POLITICAL COMMUNICATION. see *POLITICAL SCIENCE*

FRONTRUNNER. see *POLITICAL SCIENCE*

384.5   DEU   ISSN 0947-9953
FUNKY HANDY & MOBILFUNK MAGAZIN. Variant title: Funky Handy. Text in German. 1995. m. EUR 28.05 domestic; EUR 38.50 in Europe; EUR 41.80 elsewhere; EUR 3 newsstand/cover (effective 2003). adv. **Document type:** *Magazine, Consumer.* **Description:** Contains the latest product and service information for wireless phones and devices.
Published by: Funky Verlags GmbH, Am Schoppbuechel 2, Linz, 53545, Germany. TEL 49-2644-808120, FAX 49-2644-808410, info@funky.de, http://www.funky.de. Ed. Rolf Dickopp. Pub. Monika Dickopp. Adv. contact Birthe Fiedler. color page EUR 6,200. Circ: 55,000 (paid and controlled).

621.382   CAN   ISSN 0845-1354
G 5 REPORT. Text in English. bi-m. adv.
Published by: 187084 Ontario Inc.; 26 Gailcrest Circle, Thornhill, ON L4J 5V1, Canada. TEL 416-764-1184, FAX 416-764-7339. Circ: 100,000.

G P S SOLUTIONS. (Global Positioning System) see *GEOGRAPHY*

▼ **G P S USER MAGAZINE.** (Global Positioning System) see *ENGINEERING*

384   ZAF
G S M DIRECT. (Global System for Mobile) Text in English. 1992. m.
Published by: What Media Publishing Pty Ltd., Postnet Ste 367, Private Bag X6, Benmore, Johannesburg 2010, South Africa. TEL 27-11-784-0655, FAX 27-11-784-0657, what@icon.co.za, http://www.whatsa.com. Ed. Robert Pope. adv.: color page ZAR 650; trim 210 x 277. Circ: 130,000.

621.382   GBR   ISSN 1360-6603
G S M QUARTERLY; Variant title: Global System for Mobile Communications Quarterly. (Global System for Mobile) Text in English. 1996. q. **Document type:** *Trade.*
Published by: Mobile Communications International (MCI), I B C Business Publishing Ltd. (Subsidiary of: I B C Group Plc), Gilmoora House, 57-61 Mortimer St, London, W1N 8JK, United Kingdom. TEL 44-20-7637-4383, FAX 44-20-7636-6414.

384   GBR   ISSN 1462-2262
G S M WORLD FOCUS. (Global System for Mobile) Text in English. 1998. a. **Document type:** *Trade.*
Published by: Mobile Communications International (MCI), I B C Business Publishing Ltd. (Subsidiary of: I B C Group Plc), Gilmoora House, 57-61 Mortimer St, London, W1N 8JK, United Kingdom. TEL 44-20-7637-4383, FAX 44-20-7636-6414.

778.53   USA
GADNEY'S GUIDES TO INTERNATIONAL CONTESTS, FESTIVALS & GRANTS IN FILM & VIDEO, PHOTOGRAPHY, TV-RADIO BROADCASTING, WRITING & JOURNALISM. Text in English. 1979. biennial. USD 15.95 (effective 2000). adv. **Document type:** *Directory.*
Former titles: Gadney's Guides to International Contests, Festivals and Grants in Film and Video, Photography, TV-Radio Broadcasting, Writing, Poetry, Playwriting and Journalism; Gadney's Guide to 1800 International Contests, Festivals and Grants in Film and Video, Photography, TV-Radio Broadcasting, Writing, Poetry, Playwriting and Journalism
Published by: Film-Video Publications, 7944 Capistrano Ave., West Hills, CA 91304-4603. TEL 818-340-6620. Ed., Pub. Alan Gadney. Circ: 15,000.

384   GBR   ISSN 0016-5492
PN4699   CODEN: GIJMAZ
➤ **GAZETTE**; international journal for communication studies. Text in English. 1955. bi-m. GBP 51, USD 87 to individuals; GBP 403.20, USD 685.44 to institutions; GBP 420, USD 714 combined subscription to institutions print & online (effective 2005). adv. bk.rev. bibl.; charts; illus. Index. reprints avail. **Document type:** *Journal, Academic/Scholarly.* **Description:** Covers all aspects of communications including the modern mass media, the traditional media, community and alternative media, telecommunications and information and communication technologies.
Related titles: Microform ed.: (from PQC, SWZ); Online - full text ed.: ISSN 1460-3594. GBP 399, USD 678.30 to institutions (effective 2005) (from C S A, EBSCO Publishing, Gale Group, O C L C Online Computer Library Center, Inc., Sage Publications, Inc., Swets Information Services).
Indexed: ARDT, AmH&L, CommAb, DIP, EI, ERA, HistAb, IBR, IBSS, IBZ, IPSA, MLA-IB, PAIS, PRA, PSA, RASB, SPAA, SSA, SociolAb, V&AA.
—BLDSC (4092.700000), IE, Infotrieve, ingenta. **CCC.**

Published by: (Institute of the Science of the Press), Sage Publications Ltd. (Subsidiary of: Sage Publications, Inc.), 1 Oliver's Yard, 55 City Rd, London, EC1 1SP, United Kingdom. TEL 44-20-73248500, FAX 44-20-73248600, info@sagepub.co.uk, http://www.sagepub.co.uk/journal.aspx?pid=105560. Ed. Cees J Hamelink. Adv. contact Jenny Kirby. page GBP 215. **Subscr. in the Americas to:** Sage Publications, Inc., 2455 Teller Rd, Thousand Oaks, CA 91320. TEL 805-499-0721, FAX 805-499-0871, journals@sagepub.com.

➤ **GEBBIE PRESS ALL-IN-ONE DIRECTORY.** see *BUSINESS AND ECONOMICS—Trade And Industrial Directories*

384   USA   ISSN 1067-2931
GEORGIA PRESS BULLETIN. Key Title: G A Press Bulletin. Text in English. 1984. m. USD 20; free to members (effective 2005). **Document type:** *Newsletter, Trade.* **Description:** Publishes material relating to Georgia newspapers.
Formerly: Georgia Press Association. Bulletin (8750-6181)
Published by: Georgia Press Association, 3066 Mercer University Drive, Ste. 200, Atlanta, GA 30341-4137. TEL 770-454-6776, FAX 770-454-6778, mail@gapress.org, http://www.gapress.org. Eds. Jeremy Carter, Sean Ireland. Circ: 1,000 (paid and free).

621.39   ROM   ISSN 1582-5256
GHID G S M. Text in Romanian. 2001. m. adv. **Document type:** *Magazine, Trade.*
Published by: Mobi Press, Bd. N. Balcescu nr. 32-34. et. 7, ap. 28, sector 1, Bucharest, Romania. TEL 40-21-3100655, FAX 40-21-3100655, mobipress@xnet.ro.

621.39   ROM   ISSN 1582-5264
GHID G S M SUPLIMENT. Text in Romanian. 2000. s-m. **Document type:** *Magazine, Trade.*
Published by: Mobi Press, Bd. N. Balcescu nr. 32-34. et. 7, ap. 28, sector 1, Bucharest, Romania. TEL 40-21-3100655, FAX 40-21-3100655, mobipress@xnet.ro.

384   ITA   ISSN 0394-8234
G E C IL GIORNALE DEL CARTOLAIO. Text in Italian. 1988. bi-m. EUR 20 domestic; EUR 43 in Europe; EUR 65 elsewhere (effective 2005). adv. **Document type:** *Magazine, Trade.* **Description:** For wholesalers and retailers selling stationery products to the world of schools, offices, art and graphics.
Published by: Tecniche Nuove SpA, Via Eritrea 21, Milan, MI 201, Italy. TEL 39-02-390901, FAX 39-02-7570364, gec@tecnichenuove.com, info@tecnichenuove.com, http://www.tecnichenuove.com/epages/tecnichenuove.storefront/4309d7a9010431202740c0a80105058c/Product/View/GEC&2D3. Ed. Rossella Radicchi. Circ: 5,000.

384   USA
THE GLOBAL COMMUNICATOR. Text in English. 1997. q. **Document type:** *Bulletin.* **Description:** Information on localization and associated services.
Published by: International Communications, Inc., 492 Old Connecticut Path, Framingham, MA 01701. TEL 508-620-3900, FAX 508-620-3999, info@intl.com, http://www.intl.com. Ed. Ellen Lutvak.

384   GBR   ISSN 1742-7665
▼ ➤ **GLOBAL MEDIA AND COMMUNICATION.** Text in English. 2005 (Apr.). 3/yr. GBP 245, USD 429 to institutions; GBP 255, USD 447 combined subscription to institutions print & online eds. (effective 2006). adv. **Document type:** *Journal, Academic/Scholarly.* **Description:** Forum for articulating critical debates and developments in the continuously changing global media and communications environment.
Related titles: Online - full content ed.: (from HighWire Press); Online - full text ed.: ISSN 1742-7673. GBP 243, USD 424 to institutions (effective 2006) (from EBSCO Publishing, Sage Publications, Inc.).
—CCC.
Published by: Sage Publications Ltd. (Subsidiary of: Sage Publications, Inc.), 1 Oliver's Yard, 55 City Rd, London, EC1 1SP, United Kingdom. TEL 44-20-73248500, FAX 44-20-73248600, info@sagepub.co.uk, http://www.sagepub.co.uk/journal.aspx?pid=106149. Eds. Daya K Thussu, John D H Downing, Terhi Rantanen, Zhao Zhao. **Subscr. in the Americas to:** Sage Publications, Inc., 2455 Teller Rd, Thousand Oaks, CA 91320. TEL 805-499-0721, FAX 805-499-0871, journals@sagepub.com.

621.382   GBR   ISSN 1088-8934
GLOBAL MOBILE. Text in English. fortn. GBP 995 domestic; EUR 1,493 in the European Union; USD 1,890 elsewhere (effective 2005). back issues avail. **Document type:** *Newsletter, Trade.* **Description:** Provides news, analysis and market intelligence from around the world.
Related titles: Online - full content ed.: GBP 2,985 domestic for 1-5 users; EUR 4,478 in the European Union for 1-5 users; USD 5,671 elsewhere for 1-5 users (effective 2005); Online - full text ed.: (from Gale Group).
Indexed: CompD.
—CCC.

Published by: Baskerville (Subsidiary of: T & F Informa plc), Sheepen Place, Colchester, Essex C03 3LP, United Kingdom. TEL 44-20-70175537, FAX 44-20-70174783, telecoms.enquiries@informa.com, http://www.baskerville.telecoms.com/globalmobile. Ed. Gavin Patterson.

384.5   GBR
GLOBAL MOBILE DAILY (ONLINE EDITION). Text in English. d. GBP 2,130, EUR 3,514, USD 3,621 (effective 2003); subscr. incls. E-mail or fax ed.. back issues avail. **Document type:** *Newsletter, Trade.*
Media: Online - full content. **Related titles:** E-mail ed.; Fax ed.: GBP 710, EUR 825, USD 850 for E-mail or fax ed. (effective 2003).
Published by: Baskerville (Subsidiary of: T & F Informa plc), Sheepen Place, Colchester, Essex C03 3LP, United Kingdom. TEL 44-20-70175537, FAX 44-20-70174783, telecoms.enquiries@informa.com, http://www.informatelecoms.com/cod/display1.asp?pid=ITGT0091&category=T&company=ITG&team=&m=1&w=company%3D%27itg%27+AND+type%3D%27nl%27+and+not+hide%3, http://www.baskerville.telecoms.com/. Ed. Gavin Patterson.

343.099   GBR
GLOBAL TELECOMMUNICATIONS LAW AND PRACTICE. Text in English. 2000. base vol. plus updates 3/yr. looseleaf. GBP 335 (effective 2006). **Document type:** *Journal, Trade.* **Description:** Covers regulation of telecommunications law and practice around the world.
Published by: Sweet & Maxwell Ltd., 100 Avenue Road, London, NW3 3PF, United Kingdom. TEL 44-20-74491111, FAX 44-20-74491144, customer.services@sweetandmaxwell.co.uk, http://www.sweetandmaxwell.co.uk. Ed. Colin Long. **Subscr. to:** Cheriton House, North Way, Andover, Hants SP10 5BE, United Kingdom.

384   GBR   ISSN 0969-7500
HE7601
GLOBAL TELECOMS BUSINESS. Text in English. 1993. q. GBP 440 combined subscription domestic print & online eds.; EUR 686 combined subscription in Europe print & online eds.; USD 765 combined subscription elsewhere print & online eds. (effective 2005). **Document type:** *Trade.*
Related titles: Online - full text ed.: (from Gale Group, H.W. Wilson, O C L C Online Computer Library Center, Inc., ProQuest Information & Learning).
Indexed: ABIn, B&I, BPI, CurCont.
—IE. **CCC.**
Published by: Euromoney Institutional Investor Plc., Nestor House, Playhouse Yard, London, EC4V 5EX, United Kingdom. TEL 44-20-7779-8673, FAX 44-20-7779-8541, http://www.globaltelecomsbusiness.com, http://www.euromoneyplc.com. Ed. Alan Burkitt-Gray. Pub. Roger Davies. Adv. contact David Samuel TEL 212-224-3466. **Subscr. to:** Eclipse, The In-house Fulfillment Bureau, PO Box 18083, London EC4V 5JS, United Kingdom. TEL 44-20-7779-8610, FAX 44-20-7779-8602, CustomerService@euromoneyplc.com. **Dist. in US by:** American Educational Systems, PO Box 246, New York, NY 10024-0246. TEL 800-431-1579.

GLOBAL TELECOMS BUSINESS YEARBOOK. see *BUSINESS AND ECONOMICS*

384 600   USA
GLOBAL WIRELESS (ONLINE EDITION); the international newspaper for the wireless communications industry. Text in English. 2002 (Jan.). bi-m. adv. charts. **Document type:** *Magazine, Trade.* **Description:** Provides analyses, data and news on teh international wireless communications industry.
Media: Online - full content (from Northern Light Technology, Inc.). **Related titles:** Online - full text ed.: (from EBSCO Publishing).
Indexed: B&I.
Published by: Crain Communications, Inc., 1746 Cole Blvd, Ste 150, Golden, CO 80401. TEL 303-872-9100, info@crain.com, http://www.globalwirelessnews.com, http://www.crain.com. Ed. Sandra Wendelken. Pub. John Sudmeier. Adv. contact Mary Pemberton. Circ: 14,500.

621.382   USA
GLOBALCONNECT; an update on localization, technology and multilingual issues. Text in English. 1997. m. **Document type:** *Bulletin.* **Description:** Geared toward those individuals looking to keep up-to-date on issues affecting global business strategy.
Media: Online - full text.
Published by: International Communications, Inc., 492 Old Connecticut Path, Framingham, MA 01701. TEL 508-620-3900, FAX 508-620-3999, eyellin@intl.com, http://www.intl.com/globalconnect. Ed. Elana Yellin.

THE GLOBE (ROLLINSVILLE); I C O M's monthly electronic newsletter. see *ADVERTISING AND PUBLIC RELATIONS*

C

▼ *new title*   ➤ *refereed*   * *unverified*   ♦ *full entry avail.*

621.382 USA ISSN 1054-5921
TK5101.A1
GLOBECOM. I E E E GLOBAL TELECOMMUNICATIONS CONFERENCE. CONFERENCE RECORD. Text in English. 1982. a. USD 680 per vol.; USD 340 per vol. to members (effective 2004). **Document type:** *Proceedings, Trade.* **Description:** Discusses communication technology and its impact on the progress of scientific and industrial technical advances and development.
Former titles (until 1988): I E E E - I E I C E Global Telecommunications Conference. Conference Record (1054-593X); (until 1987): I E E E Global Telecommunications Conference. Record (0895-1195); National Telemetering Conference. Record
Related titles: CD-ROM ed.; Microfiche ed.
Indexed: Englnd.
—BLDSC (4195.610000), IE, ingenta. **CCC.**
Published by: Institute of Electrical and Electronics Engineers, Inc., 3 Park Ave, 17th Fl, New York, NY 10016-5997. TEL 212-419-7900, FAX 212-752-4929, customer.service@ieee.org, http://www.ieee.org. **Co-sponsor:** Communications Society.

384 GBR
GLOSSARY OF COMMUNICATION TERMS. Text in English. a. GBP 30, USD 55 Includes supplements (effective 2000).
Published by: Icom Publications Ltd., Chancery House, St Nicholas Way, Sutton, Surrey SM1 1JB, United Kingdom. TEL 44-20-86421117, FAX 44-20-86421941, admin@icompub.com, http://www.icompub.com.

GREY ROOM. see *ARCHITECTURE*

302.23 DEU ISSN 1434-0461
GRUNDLAGEN DER MEDIENKOMMUNIKATION. Text in German. 1997. irreg., latest vol.14, 2002. price varies. **Document type:** *Monographic series, Academic/Scholarly.* **Description:** Looks at the historical roots of mass communication methods, the various specific communicative functions of the individual media, and the effects they have on people's everyday lives and communicative habits.
Published by: Max Niemeyer Verlag GmbH, Postfach 2140, Tuebingen, 72011, Germany. TEL 49-7071-98940, FAX 49-7071-989450, info@niemeyer.de, http://www.niemeyer.de. Ed. Erich Strassner.

621.382 CHN ISSN 1002-5561
➤ **GUANG TONGXIN JISHU/OPTICAL COMMUNICATIONS TECHNOLOGY.** Text in Chinese. 1977. q. CNY 15 (effective 1996). adv. **Document type:** *Academic/Scholarly.* **Description:** Covers optical communications in China.
Formerly (until 1984): Jiguang Tongxin - Laser Communications
Related titles: Online - full text ed.: (from East View Information Services).
—BLDSC (6273.174550).
Published by: Guilin Institute of Optical Communications, P.O. Box 5, Guilin, Guangxi 541004, China. TEL 0773-5813838, FAX 0773-5812724. Ed. Zhou Shaohui. Circ: 5,000.

384 CHN ISSN 1006-6403
GUANGDONG TONGXIN JISHU/GUANGDONG TELECOMMUNICATION TECHNOLOGY. Text in Chinese. 1981. bi-m. CNY 5 per issue domestic (effective 2000). back issues avail. **Document type:** *Academic/Scholarly.*
Related titles: Online - full content ed.: (from WanFang Data Corp.); Online - full text ed.: (from East View Information Services).
Indexed: RefZh.
Address: Tianhe-qu, 109 Zhongshan Dadao 10 Lou, Guangdong, 510630, China. TEL 86-20-38639258, FAX 86-20-38639260, gdtx@gsta.com, http://www.gsta.com. Ed. Yongheng Liu.

621.382 CHN ISSN 1002-4530
➤ **GUOJI GUANGBO DIANSHI JISHU/INTERNATIONAL BROADCASTING TECHNOLOGY**; youxian yu weixing guangbo disnshi. Text in Chinese; Abstracts in Chinese, English. 1987. bi-m. USD 30 (effective 1997). **Document type:** *Academic/Scholarly.* **Description:** Covers the development of new technologies and practical techniques in the field of radio and television.
Published by: Guangbo Yingshi Bu, Keji Xinxi Yanjiusuo/Ministry of Radio, Film and Television, Institute of Science and Technology Information, PO Box 2116, Beijing, 100866, China. TEL 86-10-6092081, FAX 86-10-6092040, crftmi@10.sti.ac.cn. Ed. Xiana Chen. adv.: color page USD 1,400; trim 210 x 285. Circ: 15,000.

▼ ➤ **HEALTH CARE AND INFORMATICS REVIEW ONLINE.** see *HEALTH FACILITIES AND ADMINISTRATION*

➤ **HIGH PERFORMANCE COMPUTING AND COMMUNICATIONS WEEK.** see *COMPUTERS—Personal Computers*

621.382 HUN ISSN 0018-2028
TK501.A1
HIRADASTECHNIKA/JOURNAL ON COMMUNICATIONS, COMPUTERS, CONVERGENCE, CONTENTS, COMPANIES. Text in Hungarian; Summaries in English, French, German. 1949. m. USD 43. adv. bk.rev. charts; illus.
Formerly (until 1961): Magyar Hiradastechnika (0324-5403); Incorporates (1991-1997): Journal on Communications (0866-5583); (1961-1979): Horadastechnikai Ipari Kutato Intezet Kozlemenyei (0521-3916)
Indexed: CybAb, Inspec.
—AskIEEE, CISTI.
Published by: (Scientific Association for Infocommunications), Typotex, Retek u 33-35, Budapest, 1024, Hungary. TEL 36-1-316-3759, info@typotex.hu, http://www.typotex.hu. Circ: 2,750. **Subscr. to:** Kultura, PO Box 149, Budapest 1389, Hungary.

384 ESP ISSN 1137-0734
P92.S7
HISTORIA Y COMUNICACION SOCIAL. Text in Spanish. 1996. a., latest vol.6, 2001. EUR 21 in the European Union; EUR 35 elsewhere (effective 2004). back issues avail. **Document type:** *Journal, Academic/Scholarly.* **Description:** Covers communications from three different points of view; journalism, political science and history.
Indexed: AmH&L, HistAb, PSA.
—CINDOC.
Published by: (Universidad Complutense de Madrid, Facultad de Ciencias de la Informacion), Universidad Complutense de Madrid, Servicio de Publicaciones, C Isaac Peral s/n, Ciudad Universitaria, Madrid, 28040, Spain. TEL 34-91-3946934, FAX 34-91-3946978, dephisin@ccinf.ucm.es, servicio@publicaciones.ucm.es, http://www.ucm.es/publicaciones. Ed. Alejandro Pizarroso.

384 USA ISSN 1531-4847
HOME NETWORKS NEWSLETTER. Text in English. 199?. m. USD 695 in US & Canada; USD 745 elsewhere (effective 2004). bk.rev. tr.lit. **Document type:** *Newsletter, Trade.*
Published by: Information Gatekeepers, Inc., 320 Washington St, Ste 302, Brighton, MA 02135. TEL 617-782-5033, 800-323-1088, FAX 617-782-5735, info@igigroup.com, http://www.igigroup.com/nl/pages/homenetwork.html. Ed. Tony Carmona. Pub. Dr. Paul Polishuk.

384 USA ISSN 1064-6175
P87 CODEN: HJCOES
➤ **HOWARD JOURNAL OF COMMUNICATIONS.** Text in English. 1988. q. GBP 162, USD 268 combined subscription to institutions print & online eds. (effective 2006). adv. illus. Index. reprint service avail. from PSC. **Document type:** *Journal, Academic/Scholarly.* **Description:** Emphasizes the link between communication and culture. Designed to foster exchange among scholars of all communications disciplines on theory, application, policy and pathology, especially from a cultural perspective.
Related titles: Online - full text ed.: ISSN 1096-4649. 1998. GBP 154, USD 255 to institutions (effective 2006) (from EBSCO Publishing, Gale Group, IngentaConnect, O C L C Online Computer Library Center, Inc., Swets Information Services).
Indexed: ABS&EES, BAS, CINAHL, CJA, CPE, CommAb, ERA, ETA, FLI, FamI, HRA, IIBP, IJCS, IPSA, L&LBA, MEA, PRA, PSA, PsycInfo, PsycholAb, RHEA, SEA, SENA, SFSA, SOMA, SOPODA, SPAA, SRRA, SSA, SSI, SWA, SociolAb, TEA, V&AA, e-psyche.
—IE, Infotrieve. **CCC.**
Published by: (Howard University), Taylor & Francis Inc. (Subsidiary of: Taylor & Francis Group), 325 Chestnut St, Ste 800, Philadelphia, PA 19016. TEL 215-625-8900, 800-354-1420, FAX 215-625-2940, info@taylorandfrancis.com, http://www.tandf.co.uk/journals/titles/10646175.asp, http://www.taylorandfrancis.com. Ed. Carolyn A. Stroman. **Subscr. outside N. America to:** Taylor & Francis Ltd, Journals Customer Service, Rankine Rd, Basingstoke, Hants RG24 8PR, United Kingdom. TEL 44-1256-813000, FAX 44-1256-330245, enquiry@tandf.co.uk.

384 FIN ISSN 1795-6889
▼ ➤ **HUMAN TECHNOLOGY**; an interdisciplinary journal on humans in I C T environments. Text in English. 2005. s-a. free (effective 2005). **Document type:** *Journal, Academic/Scholarly.* **Description:** Focuses on everyday and vocational life. Covers social, psychological, educational, cultural, philosophical, cognitive scientific, and communication aspects of human-centered technology. Pays special attention to information and communication technology themes that serve to create a holistic human dimension in the future information society.
Media: Online - full content.
Published by: Jyvaskylan Yliopisto, Agora Center, University of Jyvaskyla, PO Box 35, Jyvaskyla, 40014, Finland. TEL 358-14-2601211, http://www.humantechnology.jyu.fi/. Ed. Pertti Saariluoma.

384 BEL ISSN 1023-425X
HE8090.5 CODEN: XIMAEZ
I & T MAGAZINE. (Industrie et Telecoms) Text in English. 1991. q. adv. bk.rev. illus. **Description:** Covers the activities and programs supported by DGXIII. Supplement provides information on current events, key decisions, new services, conferences, more.
Formerly (until 1993): X I I I Magazine (1017-6950); Which was formed by the merger of: I & T T; (1985-1991): I E S News; (1985-1991): Information Market (0256-5056); Which was formerly (1979-1985): Euronet Diane News (0250-5789)
Related titles: Online - full text ed.; French ed.: ISSN 1022-8713; German ed.: ISSN 1023-4268; Italian ed.: ISSN 1023-4276; Spanish ed.: ISSN 1023-4284.
Indexed: Inspec, RASB.
—AskIEEE.
Published by: European Commission, Directorate General - Information Society, Rue de la Loi 200, Brussels, 1049, Belgium. TEL 32-2-2968800, FAX 32-2-2994170, http://europa.eu.int/information_society/.

I C O M NEWSLETTER. see *ADVERTISING AND PUBLIC RELATIONS*

I D A MEMBERSHIP AND SURVIVAL GUIDE. see *MOTION PICTURES*

384 USA
I E E E ANTENNAS AND PROPAGATION SOCIETY. INTERNATIONAL SYMPOSIUM. Text in English. USD 342 to institutions (effective 2001). **Document type:** *Proceedings.*
Media: CD-ROM.
Indexed: Englnd.
—BLDSC (4362.805650), ingenta.
Published by: Institute of Electrical and Electronics Engineers, Inc., 3 Park Ave, 17th Fl, New York, NY 10016-5997. TEL 800-678-4333, customer.service@ieee.org, http://www.ieee.org.

384 USA ISSN 1536-1225
TK7871.6 CODEN: IAWPA7
I E E E ANTENNAS AND WIRELESS PROPAGATION LETTERS. Text in English. 2001. a. USD 420 combined subscription print & online eds (effective 2006). **Document type:** *Journal, Trade.*
Related titles: Online - full content ed.: USD 345 (effective 2005); Online - full text ed.: (from EBSCO Publishing).
Indexed: Inspec, RefZh.
—BLDSC (4362.805660), CISTI, IE, Linda Hall. **CCC.**
Published by: Institute of Electrical and Electronics Engineers, Inc., 445 Hoes Ln, Piscataway, NJ 08854-1331. TEL 908-981-0060, 800-701-4333, FAX 908-981-9667, subscription-service@ieee.org, http://www.ieee.org. **Subscr. in India to:** Universal Subscription Agency, Pvt. Ltd., 877, Udyog Vihar, V, Gurgoan 122001, India. TEL 91-124-347261, FAX 91-124-342496; **Subscr. in Japan to:** Maruzen Co., Ltd., 3-10 Nihonbashi 2-chome, Chuo-ku, Tokyo 103-0027, Japan. FAX 81-3-3275-0657.

384 USA ISSN 1089-7798
TK5101.A1 CODEN: ICLEF6
I E E E COMMUNICATIONS LETTERS. Text in English. 1997. m. USD 340 (effective 2006). **Document type:** *Journal, Trade.* **Description:** Includes all telecommunications, multiplexing and carrier techniques, communication switching systems, data communications and communication theory.
Related titles: CD-ROM ed.; Microfiche ed.; Online - full text ed.: (from EBSCO Publishing).
Indexed: C&CSA, CurCont, ISR, Inspec, RefZh, SCI.
—BLDSC (4362.812700), CISTI, IDS, IE, Infotrieve, ingenta, Linda Hall. **CCC.**
Published by: Institute of Electrical and Electronics Engineers, Inc., 445 Hoes Ln, Piscataway, NJ 08854-1331. TEL 732-981-0060, 800-701-4333, FAX 732-981-1721, subscription-service@ieee.org, http://www.ieee.org. Ed. Z Bar Ness. R&P Michael Spada TEL 732-981-3430. **Subscr. to:** Maruzen Co., Ltd., 3-10 Nihonbashi 2-chome, Chuo-ku, Tokyo 103-0027, Japan. FAX 81-3-3275-0657; Universal Subscription Agency, Pvt. Ltd., 877, Udyog Vihar, V, Gurgoan 122001, India. TEL 91-124-347261, FAX 91-124-342496. **Co-sponsor:** Communications Society.

384 USA ISSN 1086-5195
I E E E COMMUNICATIONS THEORY MINI-CONFERENCE. PROCEEDINGS. Text in English. 1992. a. **Document type:** *Proceedings, Trade.*
Published by: Institute of Electrical and Electronics Engineers, Inc., 3 Park Ave, 17th Fl, New York, NY 10016-5997. TEL 212-419-7900, 800-678-4333, FAX 212-752-4929, customer.service@ieee.org, http://www.ieee.org.

I E E E INFORMATION THEORY AND COMMUNICATIONS WORKSHOP. see *COMPUTERS—Information Science And Information Theory*

621.382 USA
I E E E INTELLIGENT NETWORKS WORKSHOP. Text in English. a. **Document type:** *Proceedings, Trade.*
Indexed: Englnd.
Published by: Institute of Electrical and Electronics Engineers, Inc., 3 Park Ave, 17th Fl, New York, NY 10016-5997. TEL 212-419-7900, 800-678-4333, FAX 212-752-4929, customer.service@ieee.org, http://www.ieee.org.

621.382 USA ISSN 1044-4556
TK5101.A1
I E E E INTERNATIONAL CONFERENCE ON COMMUNICATIONS. PROCEEDINGS. Text in English. 1965. a. USD 151 membership (effective 2005). bibl.; illus. **Document type:** *Proceedings, Trade.*
Formerly (until 1982): I E E E International Conference on Communications. Conference Record (0536-1486)
Related titles: CD-ROM ed.; Microfiche ed.
Indexed: Englnd.
—BLDSC (4362.945000), Ei, IE, ingenta. **CCC.**

C

Published by: Institute of Electrical and Electronics Engineers, Inc., 3 Park Ave, 17th Fl, New York, NY 10016-5997. TEL 212-419-7900, FAX 212-752-4929, customer.service@ieee.org, http://www.ieee.org. **Co-sponsor:** Communications Society.

384 004.6 USA
I E E E INTERNATIONAL TELECOMMUNICATIONS SYMPOSIUM. Text in English. a. USD 404; USD 202 to members (effective 2004). **Document type:** *Proceedings, Trade.*
Published by: Institute of Electrical and Electronics Engineers, Inc., 3 Park Ave, 17th Fl, New York, NY 10016-5997. TEL 212-419-7900, 800-678-4333, FAX 212-752-4929, customer.service@ieee.org, http://www.ieee.org.

384 USA ISSN 0733-8716
TK5101.A1 CODEN: ISACEM
➤ **I E E E JOURNAL ON SELECTED AREAS IN COMMUNICATIONS.** Text in English. 1983. m. USD 750 (effective 2006). **Document type:** *Journal, Academic/Scholarly.* **Description:** Reports on the newest communications technologies. Covers fiber optics, digital satellite and computer communications, and local area networks.
Related titles: CD-ROM ed.; Microfiche ed.; Online - full text ed.: ISSN 1558-0008 (from EBSCO Publishing, Swets Information Services).
Indexed: AS&TI, ASCA, AcoustA, C&CSA, CADCAM, CMCI, CurCont, ESPM, EngInd, ErgAb, IAA, ISR, Inspec, RefZh, RiskAb, RoboAb, SCI, SSCI, TelAb.
—BLDSC (4362.985000), AskIEEE, CISTI, Ei, IDS, IE, Infotrieve, ingenta, Linda Hall. **CCC.**
Published by: Institute of Electrical and Electronics Engineers, Inc., 445 Hoes Ln, Piscataway, NJ 08854-1331. TEL 732-981-0060, 800-701-4333, FAX 732-981-1721, subscription-service@ieee.org, http://www.ieee.org. Ed. N F Maxemchuk. **Subscr. to:** Maruzen Co., Ltd., 3-10 Nihonbashi 2-chome, Chuo-ku, Tokyo 103-0027, Japan. FAX 81-3-3275-0657; Universal Subscription Agency, Pvt. Ltd., 877, Udyog Vihar, V, Gurgoan 122001, India. TEL 91-124-347261, FAX 91-124-342496. **Co-sponsor:** Communications Society.

➤ **I E E E NATIONAL RADAR CONFERENCE. PROCEEDINGS.** see *ENGINEERING—Electrical Engineering*

384 004.6 USA
I E E E OPEN ARCHITECTURES AND NETWORK PROGRAMMING. Text in English. 1998. a. USD 156; USD 78 to members (effective 2004). **Document type:** *Proceedings, Trade.*
—BLDSC (4363.007850).
Published by: Institute of Electrical and Electronics Engineers, Inc., 3 Park Ave, 17th Fl, New York, NY 10016-5997. TEL 212-419-7900, 800-678-4333, FAX 212-752-4929, customer.service@ieee.org, http://www.ieee.org.

384 USA
TK503.59
▼ **I E E E OPTICAL COMMUNICATIONS.** Text in English. 2003. q. **Document type:** *Journal, Trade.*
Media: Online - full content. **Related titles:** Print ed.: ISSN 1550-381X.
Published by: I E E E Computer Society, 305 E 47th St, New York, NY 10017. TEL 212-705-8900, FAX 212-705-8999, customer.service@ieee.org, http://www.comsoc.org/optical/, http://www.computer.org. Eds. Chunming Qiao, Stamatios Kartalopoulos.

I E E E POSITION LOCATION AND NAVIGATION SYMPOSIUM. RECORD. see *ENGINEERING—Electrical Engineering*

I E E E SIGNAL PROCESSING ON HIGHER ORDER STATISTICS. see *COMPUTERS—Hardware*

384 620 USA
I E E E SOUTH AFRICAN SYMPOSIUM ON COMMUNICATIONS AND SIGNAL PROCESSING. Text in English. a. USD 140. **Document type:** *Proceedings, Trade.*
Indexed: EngInd.
Published by: Institute of Electrical and Electronics Engineers, Inc., 3 Park Ave, 17th Fl, New York, NY 10016-5997. TEL 212-419-7900, 800-678-4333, FAX 212-752-4929, customer.service@ieee.org, http://www.ieee.org.

621.382 USA ISSN 0090-6778
TK5101.A1 CODEN: IECMBT
➤ **I E E E TRANSACTIONS ON COMMUNICATIONS.** Text in English. 1953. m. USD 750 (effective 2006). bk.rev. abstr.; illus. index. **Document type:** *Journal, Academic/Scholarly.* **Description:** State-of-the-art, archival and technical data covering the wide array of topics pertinent to the communications professional.
Former titles (until 1971): I E E E Transactions on Communication Technology (0018-9332); (until 1964): I E E E Transactions on Communications Systems (0096-1965); (until 1962): I R E Transactions on Communications Systems (0096-2244); (until 1955): I R E Professional Group on Communications Systems. Transactions (0277-6243)
Related titles: CD-ROM ed.; Microfiche ed.; Online - full text ed.: ISSN 1558-0857 (from EBSCO Publishing, Swets Information Services).
Indexed: AS&TI, ASCA, AcoustA, ApMecR, C&CSA, CADCAM, CIS, CMCI, ChemAb, CompAb, CompD, CompLI, CurCont, EngInd, IAA, ISR, Inspec, MathR, RefZh, SCI, TelAb, ZentMath.
—BLDSC (4363.170400), AskIEEE, CISTI, Ei, IDS, IE, Infotrieve, ingenta, Linda Hall. **CCC.**
Published by: Institute of Electrical and Electronics Engineers, Inc., 445 Hoes Ln, Piscataway, NJ 08854-1331. TEL 732-981-0060, 800-701-4333, FAX 732-981-1721, subscription-service@ieee.org, http://www.ieee.org. Ed. Ender Ayanoglu. **Subscr. to:** Maruzen Co., Ltd., 3-10 Nihonbashi 2-chome, Chuo-ku, Tokyo 103-0027, Japan. FAX 81-3-3275-0657; Universal Subscription Agency, Pvt. Ltd., 877, Udyog Vihar, V, Gurgoan 122001, India. TEL 91-124-347261, FAX 91-124-342496. **Co-sponsor:** Communications Society.

384 USA ISSN 1536-1276
TK6570.M6 CODEN: IWCEAS
I E E E TRANSACTIONS ON WIRELESS COMMUNICATIONS. Text in English. 2002. m. USD 525; USD 625 combined subscription print & online eds. (effective 2006). **Document type:** *Journal, Trade.*
Related titles: Online - full content ed.: USD 525 (effective 2006).
Indexed: C&CSA, CurCont, Inspec, RefZh.
—BLDSC (4363.231450), CISTI, IE, ingenta, Linda Hall. **CCC.**
Published by: Institute of Electrical and Electronics Engineers, Inc., 445 Hoes Ln, Piscataway, NJ 08854-1331. TEL 908-981-0060, FAX 908-981-9667, subscription-service@ieee.org, http://www.ieee.org. **Subscr. to:** Maruzen Co., Ltd., 3-10 Nihonbashi 2-chome, Chuo-ku, Tokyo 103-0027, Japan. FAX 81-3-3275-0657; Universal Subscription Agency, Pvt. Ltd., 877, Udyog Vihar, V, Gurgoan 122001, India. TEL 91-124-347261, FAX 91-124-342496.

384 USA ISSN 1525-3511
TK5103.2
I E E E WIRELESS COMMUNICATIONS AND NETWORKING CONFERENCE. PROCEEDINGS. (Institute of Electrical and Electronic Engineers) Text in English. a. **Document type:** *Proceedings, Academic/Scholarly.*
Related titles: Online - full text ed.: (from I E E E).
—BLDSC (4363.240102).
Published by: I E E E Communications Society, 3 Park Ave, New York, NY 10016. TEL 212-705-8900, FAX 212-705-8999, publications@comsoc.org, http://www.comsoc.org.

384 USA ISSN 1536-1284
TK5103.2 CODEN: ITWCAX
➤ **I E E E WIRELESS COMMUNICATIONS MAGAZINE.** Text in English. 1994. bi-m. USD 295 (effective 2006). adv. **Document type:** *Journal, Academic/Scholarly.* **Description:** Deals with all technical and policy issues related to personalization, location-independent communications in all media.
Formerly: I E E E Personal Communications (1070-9916)
Related titles: CD-ROM ed.; Microfiche ed.; Online - full text ed.: (from EBSCO Publishing).
Indexed: ASCA, C&CSA, CMCI, CurCont, EngInd, ISR, Inspec, RefZh, SCI.
—BLDSC (4363.240101), AskIEEE, CISTI, Ei, IDS, IE, Infotrieve, Linda Hall. **CCC.**
Published by: Institute of Electrical and Electronics Engineers, Inc., 3 Park Ave, 17th Fl, New York, NY 10016-5997. TEL 212-419-7900, 800-701-4333, FAX 212-752-4929, c.kemelmacher@comsoc.org, customer.service@ieee.org, http://www.ieee.org. Ed. Mahmoud Naghshineh. **Subscr. in India to:** Universal Subscription Agency, Pvt. Ltd., 877, Udyog Vihar, V, Gurgoan 122001, India. TEL 91-124-347261, FAX 91-124-342496; **Subscr. in Japan to:** Maruzen Co., Ltd., 3-10 Nihonbashi 2-chome, Chuo-ku, Tokyo 103-0027, Japan. FAX 81-3-3275-0657.

➤ **I E E E WORKSHOP ON INTERACTIVE VOICE TECHNOLOGY FOR TELECOMMUNICATIONS APPLICATIONS.** see *COMMUNICATIONS—Computer Applications*

➤ **I E E E WORKSHOP ON SPEECH CODING FOR TELECOMMUNICATIONS.** see *COMPUTERS—Artificial Intelligence*

➤ **I E E REVIEW.** (Institution of Electrical Engineers) see *ENGINEERING—Electrical Engineering*

621.382 GBR ISSN 0263-5852
CODEN: ITESDS
I E E TELECOMMUNICATIONS SERIES. (Institution of Electrical Engineers) Text in English. 1976. irreg., latest 2002. price varies. charts; stat. **Document type:** *Monographic series, Academic/Scholarly.*
Indexed: Inspec.
—BLDSC (4362.769500), IE, ingenta.
Published by: Institution of Electrical Engineers, Michael Faraday House, Six Hills Way, Stevenage, Herts SG1 2AY, United Kingdom. TEL 44-1438-313311, FAX 44-1438-313465, inspec@iee.org, http://www.iee.org/Publish/Books/TeleComm/. R&P Michael McCabe TEL 732-321-5575.

▼ **I E I C E ELECTRONICS EXPRESS.** see *COMPUTERS—Information Science And Information Theory*

621.382 GBR ISSN 0916-8516
TK5101.A1 CODEN: ITRCEC
➤ **I E I C E TRANSACTIONS ON COMMUNICATIONS.** Variant title: Institute of Electronics Information and Communication Engineers Transactions on Communications. Text in English. 1976. m. GBP 207, USD 352, EUR 311 to institutions; GBP 119, USD 202, EUR 179 in developing nations to institutions; GBP 218, USD 371, EUR 327 combined subscription to institutions print & online eds. (effective 2006). back issues avail. **Document type:** *Journal, Academic/Scholarly.* **Description:** Covers topics such as: Communication networks and services switching and communication processing, signaling system and communication protocol, communication software, communication theory, source encoding, communication systems and transmission equipment, optical communication, communication cable and wave guides, communication terminal and equipment, power supply, communication device and circuit, measurement and metrology, radio communication, satellite communication, antennas and propagation, electronic and radio applications, and electromagnetic compatibility.
Supersedes in part (in 1991): I E I C E Transactions on Communications Electronics Information and Systems (0917-1673); Former titles (until 1991): Transactions of the Institute of Electronics, Information and Communication Engineers (0913-574X); (until 1987): Transactions of the Institute of Electronics and Communication Engineers of Japan. Section E (0387-236X); (until 1976): Transactions of the Institute of Electronics and Communication Engineers of Japan. Abstracts (0418-6869); (until 1956): Journal of the Institute of Electrical Communication Engineers of Japan. Abstracts (0914-5273)
Related titles: Online - full text ed.: ISSN 1745-1345. GBP 196, USD 333, EUR 294 to institutions (effective 2006) (from HighWire Press); ♦ Japanese ed.: Denshi Joho Tsushin Gakkai Rombunshi. B. ISSN 1344-4697.
Indexed: ASCA, C&ISA, CMCI, CurCont, E&CAJ, EngInd, INIS AtomInd, ISMEC, ISR, Inspec, MSCI, RefZh, SCI, SSCI, SolStAb.
—BLDSC (4363.240666), AskIEEE, CISTI, Ei, IDS, IE, Infotrieve, ingenta, Linda Hall. **CCC.**
Published by: (Denshi Joho Tsushin Gakkai/Institute of Electronics Information and Communication Engineers JPN), Oxford University Press, Great Clarendon St, Oxford, OX2 6DP, United Kingdom. TEL 44-1865-556767, FAX 44-1865-556646, jnl.orders@oup.co.uk, http://ietcom.oxfordjournals.org/, http://www.oxfordjournals.org/. R&P Fiona Bennett.

621.38 IND
➤ **I E T E JOURNAL OF EDUCATION.** Text in English. 1959. q. INR 100 domestic; USD 35 foreign (effective 2004). adv. bk.rev. Index. back issues avail. **Document type:** *Journal, Academic/Scholarly.* **Description:** Contains tutorial type education articles for diploma and undergraduate level.
Formerly (until 1997): Institution of Electronics and Telecommunication Engineers. Students' Journal (0970-1664)
Indexed: ChemAb, CompC, EngInd, Inspec, PhysBer.
—BLDSC (4363.253850), AskIEEE, CISTI, Ei, ingenta.
Published by: Institution of Electronics and Telecommunication Engineers, 2 Institutional Area, Lodi Rd., New Delhi, 110 003, India. TEL 91-011-4631820, FAX 91-011-4649429, ietend@giasdl01.vsnl.net.in, http://www.iete.org. Ed., Adv. contact P D Badoni. R&P K B Jhaldiyal. Circ: 25,000.

621.382 IND
TK5101 CODEN: JIETAU
➤ **I E T E JOURNAL OF RESEARCH.** Text in English. 1955; N.S. 1984. bi-m. INR 400 domestic; USD 100 foreign (effective 2004). bk.rev. back issues avail.; reprints avail. **Document type:** *Journal, Academic/Scholarly.*
Former titles (until 1997): Institution of Electronics and Telecommunication Engineers. Journal (0377-2063); (until 1973): Institution of Telecommunication Engineers. Journal (0020-353X)
Indexed: ASCA, C&ISA, CADCAM, ChemAb, CompC, CompD, E&CAJ, EngInd, INIS AtomInd, Inspec, PhysBer, RefZh, SolStAb, TelAb.
—BLDSC (4363.253900), AskIEEE, CASDDS, CISTI, Ei, IDS, IE, ingenta, Linda Hall.
Published by: Institution of Electronics and Telecommunication Engineers, 2 Institutional Area, Lodi Rd., New Delhi, 110 003, India. TEL 91-011-4631850, FAX 91-011-4631810, ietend@giasdl01.vsnl.net.in, http://www.iete.org. Ed., Adv. contact P D Badoni. R&P K B Jhaldiyal. Circ: 2,000.

621.382 IND ISSN 0256-4602
➤ **I E T E TECHNICAL REVIEW.** Text in English. 1984. bi-m. INR 400 domestic; USD 100 foreign (effective 2004). adv. bk.rev. **Document type:** *Academic/Scholarly.* **Description:** Devoted to current research and developments in the field of electronics and telecommunications.
Indexed: ASCA, C&ISA, CMCI, E&CAJ, EngInd, Inspec, RefZh, SolStAb, TelAb.
—BLDSC (4363.254000), AskIEEE, Ei, IDS, IE, ingenta.
Published by: Institution of Electronics and Telecommunication Engineers, 2 Institutional Area, Lodi Rd., New Delhi, 110 003, India. TEL 91-011-4631850, FAX 91-011-4649429, ietend@giasdl01.vsnl.net.in. Ed. P D Badoni. R&P K B Jhaldiyal. adv.: B&W page INR 7,000, color page INR 8,500; trim 170 x 250. Circ: 7,000.

C

808.5 USA
I G A B NEWSLETTER BUREAU TALK. Text in English. 1986. m. membership. **Document type:** *Newsletter.*
Formerly: I G A B Newsletter
Published by: International Group of Agencies and Bureaus, 6845 Parkdale Pl, Ste A, Indianapolis, IN 46254. TEL 317-297-0872, FAX 317-387-3387, info@igab.org, http://www.igab.org. Ed. Jim D Montoya. R&P James D Montoya. Circ: 150; 150 (controlled).

I M S A JOURNAL. see *TRANSPORTATION—Roads And Traffic*

621.382 USA
I S D N YELLOW PAGES. (Integrated Services Digital Network) Text in English. 1986. a. USD 69.95 domestic; USD 84.95 foreign (effective 2000 - 2001). **Document type:** *Directory.* **Description:** Worldwide directory of ISDN equipment and service suppliers, reference materials, applications, standards, publications, sources of information, and review articles.
Former titles (until 200?): Broadband - I S D N Yellow Pages; (until 1999): International I S D N Yellow Pages (1075-5276); I S D N Handbook and Buyers Guide
—CCC.
Published by: Information Gatekeepers, Inc., 320 Washington St, Ste 302, Brighton, MA 02135. TEL 617-782-5033, 800-323-1088, FAX 617-734-8562, info@igigroup.com, http://www.igigroup.com. Ed. Tony Carmona. Pub. Dr. Paul Polishuk.

384 POL ISSN 1644-9274
I T & TELECOMS MONITOR. Text in English. 2002. bi-w. EUR 350 foreign (effective 2005). 10 p./no.; **Document type:** *Newsletter, Trade.* **Description:** Containis expert analyses of the IT, telecommunications and e-business markets in Central and Eastern Europe.
Media: E-mail.
Published by: Polish Market Review Ltd., ul Supniewskiego 9, Krakow, 31527, Poland. TEL 48-12-4280360, FAX 48-12-4134012, pmr@pmrpublications.com, http://www.pmrpublications.com.

C

384 CHE ISSN 1027-7420
I T U GLOBAL DIRECTORY. Text in English, French, Spanish. irreg., latest vol.12, 1997. CHF 39. **Document type:** *Directory.*
Published by: International Telecommunication Union, Place des Nations, Geneva 20, 1211, Switzerland. TEL 41-22-7306141, FAX 41-22-7305194, sales@itu.ch, http://www.itu.int/publications.

384 CHE ISSN 1020-4148
HE7601 CODEN: ITNEFX
I T U NEWS. Text in English. 1934. 10/yr. adv. bk.rev. bibl.; charts; illus. **Document type:** *Newsletter.*
Former titles (until 1996): I T U Newsletter (1020-1173); (until 1994): Telecommunication Journal (0497-137X); U I T Journal
Related titles: Microfilm ed.: (from PMC).
Indexed: AS&TI, ASCA, C&ISA, CADCAM, CompD, CurCont, E&CAJ, EngInd, ISMEC, Inspec, RASB, SSCI, SolStAb, TelAb.
—AskIEEE, CISTI, Ei, Linda Hall.
Published by: International Telecommunication Union, Place des Nations, Geneva 20, 1211, Switzerland. TEL 41-22-7305239, FAX 41-22-7305321, dominique.bourne@itu.ch, http://www.itu.int/publications.

384 CHE
I T U WEEKLY CIRCULAR AND SPECIAL SECTIONS. Text in English, French, Spanish. w. CHF 4,300. **Document type:** *Bulletin.*
Published by: International Telecommunication Union, Place des Nations, Geneva 20, 1211, Switzerland. TEL 41-22-7306141, FAX 41-22-7305194, sales@itu.ch, http://www.itu.int/publications.

384 ITA
ICOM: ISTITUZIONI E COMUNICAZIONE. Text in Italian. 1988. m.
Published by: Presidenza del Consiglio dei Ministri, Dipartimento per l'Informazione e l'Editoria, Via Po, 14, Rome, RM 00198, Italy. TEL 39-6-85981, FAX 39-6-8553851.

384 ITA
PN1795 CODEN: IRIFDT
IKON; forme e processi del comunicare. Text in Italian; Summaries in English, French. 1982. s-a. EUR 38 domestic; EUR 57 foreign (effective 2003). bk.rev.; film rev. charts; illus. index.
Formed by the merger of (1948-1981): Ikon (0019-1744); Ricerche sulla Comunicazione
Indexed: DIP, FLI, IBR, IBZ, IIFP, IITV, RASB.
—GNLM.
Published by: (Istituto Agostino Gemelli), Franco Angeli Edizioni, Viale Monza 106, Milan, 20127, Italy. TEL 39-02-2837141, FAX 39-02-26144793, redazioni@francoangeli.it, http://www.francoangeli.it. Ed. Giovanni Cesareo. Circ: 1,000.

808.508 USA ISSN 0145-5516
PN4073
➤ **ILLINOIS SPEECH AND THEATRE ASSOCIATION. JOURNAL.** Text in English. a. adv. back issues avail. **Document type:** *Academic/Scholarly.*
Indexed: CIJE.
Published by: Illinois Speech and Theatre Association, Rend Lake College, 468 Ken Gray Pkwy, Ina, IL 62846. TEL 618-437-5321, FAX 613-437-5677, rust@rlc.cc.il.us. Ed. Terry M Perkins. R&P Terry Perkins. Circ: 650.

384 USA ISSN 1083-4672
HE8371
INDIA TELECOM. Text in English. 1995. m. USD 695 in US & Canada; USD 745 elsewhere (effective 2004). **Document type:** *Newsletter, Trade.* **Description:** Covers the telecommunications market in India.
Related titles: Online - full text ed.: (from Florida Center for Library Automation, Gale Group, O C L C Online Computer Library Center, Inc., ProQuest Information & Learning).
Published by: Information Gatekeepers, Inc., 320 Washington St, Ste 302, Brighton, MA 02135. TEL 617-782-5033, 800-323-1088, FAX 617-734-8562, info@igigroup.com, http://www.igigroup.com/nl/pages/indiatel.html. Eds. Hui Pan, Tony Carmona. Pub. Dr. Paul Polishuk.

621.382 USA
INDIA TELECOM MONTHLY. Text in English. m. USD 850 to individuals; USD 3,300 to institutions (effective 2000). **Document type:** *Bulletin, Trade.* **Description:** Provides coverage of current developments in the Indian telecommunications market.
Published by: Gist, Inc., 2200 Wilson Blvd, Ste 102G, Arlington, VA 22201. TEL 703-527-7459, FAX 703-528-1477, info@gist.net, http://www.gist.net.

384 GBR ISSN 1463-6697
HE7601 CODEN: INFCFD
➤ **INFO (CAMBRIDGE)**; the journal of policy, regulation and strategy for telecommunications, information and media. Text in English. 1999. bi-m. EUR 1,303.91 in Europe; USD 1,249 in North America; AUD 2,379 in Australasia; GBP 912.41 in UK & elsewhere (effective 2006). bk.rev. 96 p./no.; back issues avail.; reprint service avail. from PSC. **Document type:** *Journal, Academic/Scholarly.* **Description:** Covers policy, regulation and strategy for telecommunications, information and media.
Related titles: Online - full text ed.: ISSN 1465-9840. GBP 55, USD 95 to individuals; GBP 229, USD 389 to institutions (effective 2001) (from EBSCO Publishing, Emerald Group Publishing Limited, Gale Group, IngentaConnect, O C L C Online Computer Library Center, Inc., ProQuest Information & Learning, Swets Information Services).
Indexed: ABIn, ASFA, ESPM, GEOBASE, Inspec, JEL, PSA, RiskAb.
—BLDSC (4478.864000), IE, Infotrieve, ingenta. **CCC.**
Published by: Emerald Group Publishing Limited, 60-62 Toller Ln, Bradford, W Yorks BD8 9BY, United Kingdom. TEL 44-1274-777700, FAX 44-1274-785200, help@emeraldinsight.com, infomation@emeraldinsight.com, http://www.emeraldinsight.com/info.htm. Ed. Mr. Colin Blackman. **Subscr. addr. in N America:** Emerald Group Publishing Ltd., 44 Brattle St, 4th Fl, Cambridge, MA 02138. TEL 617-497-2175, 888-622-0075, FAX 617-354-6875.

➤ **INFORMACAO & SOCIEDADE**; estudos. see *LIBRARY AND INFORMATION SCIENCES*

384 JPN
INFORMATION & COMMUNICATION IN JAPAN✶. Text in English. 1990. a. JPY 4,500 newsstand/cover (effective 2004). **Document type:** *Trade.* **Description:** Comprehensive data book in English, covering major trends in Information & Communications industry.
Published by: Infocom Research Inc./Joho Tsushin Sogo Kenkyujo, Urban Net Nihonbashi Bldg., 2-14-10, Nihonbashi Ningyo-cho, Chuo-ku, Tokyo, 102-0013, Japan. TEL 81-3-36637500, FAX 81-3-36637570, http://www.icr.co.jp/publications/book/ehand_2004.html.

343.099 GBR ISSN 1360-0834
K12 CODEN: ICTLFX
INFORMATION AND COMMUNICATIONS TECHNOLOGY LAW. Text in English. 1992. 3/yr. GBP 380, USD 645 combined subscription to institutions print & online eds. (effective 2006). back issues avail.; reprint service avail. from PSC. **Document type:** *Journal, Academic/Scholarly.* **Description:** Covers topics such as: the implications of information technology for legal processes and legal decision-making and related ethical and social issues; the liability of programmers and expert system builders; computer misuse and related policing issues; intellectual property rights in algorithms, chips, databases, software etc; IT and competition law; data protection; freedom of information; the nature of privacy, legal controls in the dissemination of pornographic, racist and defamatory material on the Internet; network policing; regulation of the IT industry; problems of computer representation and the computational semantics of law; the role of visual or image-based legal 'mental models'; general public policy and philosophical aspects of law and IT.
Formerly (until 1996, vol.5): Law, Computers and Artificial Intelligence (0962-9580)
Related titles: Online - full text ed.: ISSN 1469-8404. GBP 361, USD 613 to institutions (effective 2006) (from EBSCO Publishing, Gale Group, IngentaConnect, O C L C Online Computer Library Center, Inc., ProQuest Information & Learning, Swets Information Services).
Indexed: ABIn, C&CSA, CLI, CompLI, ELJI, ILP, Inspec, L&LBA, LISA, LJI, LRI, PSA, SOPODA.
—BLDSC (4481.763000), IE, Infotrieve, ingenta. **CCC.**
Published by: Routledge (Subsidiary of: Taylor & Francis Group), 4 Park Sq, Milton Park, Abingdon, Oxon OX14 4RN, United Kingdom. TEL 44-1235-828600, FAX 44-1235-829000, info@routledge.co.uk, http://www.tandf.co.uk/journals/titles/13600834.asp, http://www.routledge.co.uk. Ed. Dr. Indira Mahalingam Carr. **Subscr. to:** Taylor & Francis Ltd, Journals Customer Service, Rankine Rd, Basingstoke, Hants RG24 8PR, United Kingdom. TEL 44-1256-813000, FAX 44-1256-330245.

384 NLD ISSN 0167-6245
➤ **INFORMATION ECONOMICS AND POLICY.** Text in English. 1984. 4/yr. EUR 54 in Europe to individuals; JPY 7,300 in Japan to individuals; USD 59 elsewhere to individuals; EUR 478 in Europe to institutions; JPY 63,600 in Japan to institutions; USD 536 elsewhere to institutions (effective 2006). bk.rev. abstr. back issues avail.; reprints avail. **Document type:** *Journal, Academic/Scholarly.* **Description:** Provides an interdisciplinary and international forum for publications with telecommunications economics and policy as its core, including related issues on information economics and media policy.
Related titles: Microform ed.: (from PQC); Online - full text ed.: (from EBSCO Publishing, Gale Group, IngentaConnect, ScienceDirect, Swets Information Services).
Indexed: ABIn, BAS, CREJ, CommAb, CompC, CurCont, EAA, EngInd, GEOBASE, IBSS, IPSA, Inspec, JEL, PSA, SPAA, SSCI.
—BLDSC (4493.565300), AskIEEE, Ei, IE, Infotrieve, ingenta. **CCC.**
Published by: Elsevier BV, North-Holland (Subsidiary of: Elsevier Science & Technology), Sara Burgerhartstraat 25, Amsterdam, 1055 KV, Netherlands. TEL 31-20-485-3911, FAX 31-20-485-2457, nlinfo-f@elsevier.nl, http://www.elsevier.com/locate/iep, http://www.elsevier.nl. Eds. A. Geuna, Donald M. Lamberton, T. Valletti. **Subscr. to:** Elsevier BV, PO Box 211, Amsterdam 1000 AE, Netherlands. TEL 31-20-485-3757, FAX 31-20-485-3432, http://www.elsevier.nl.

621.382 AUS ISSN 1442-1674
INFORMATION HIGHWAYS AND TELECOMMUNICATIONS IN ASIA. Text in English. a. (in 3 vols.), latest 2001. USD 595 domestic; USD 625 foreign (effective 2001). **Description:** Covers trends and developments in telecommunications, broadcasting and pay TV in 36 Asian countries and company profiles on major Asian companies.
Formerly titles (until 1999): Superhighways and Telecommunications in Asia (1329-2609); (until 1997): Superhighways in Asia (1324-0471)
Published by: Paul Budde Communication Pty. Ltd., 2643 George Downes Dr, Bucketty, NSW 2250, Australia. TEL 61-2-4998-8144, FAX 61-2-4998-8247, pbc@budde.com.au, http://www.budde.com.au. Circ: 100.

384.0285 GBR ISSN 1356-0395
INFORMATION MANAGEMENT & TECHNOLOGY. Text in English. 1967. q. GBP 95 in United Kingdom print & online eds.; GBP 100 in Europe print & online eds.; GBP 115 elsewhere print & online eds. (effective 2003). adv. bk.rev. abstr.; charts; illus. index, cum.index. **Document type:** *Magazine, Trade.* **Description:** Covers major developments in electronic document and records management, BPR, recognition technology, and document mapping.
Former titles (until 1992): Information Media and Technology (0266-6960); (until 1984): Reprographics Quarterly (0306-2880); (until 1973): N R C D Bulletin (0027-6928)
Related titles: Online - full content ed.; Online - full text ed.: (from EBSCO Publishing).
Indexed: ConsI, Emerald, InfoSAb, Inspec, LISA, PhotoAb.
—BLDSC (4493.687070), AskIEEE, CISTI, IE. **CCC.**
Published by: Cimtech Ltd., University of Hertfordshire, 45 Grosvenor Rd, St Albans, Herts AL1 3AW, United Kingdom. TEL 44-1727-813651, FAX 44-1727-813049, c.cimtech@herts.ac.uk, http://www.cimtech.co.uk. Ed., R&P Anne Grimshaw. Adv. contact Cathy Godfrey. Circ: 850 (paid).

▼ **INFORMATION TECHNOLOGIES AND INTERNATIONAL DEVELOPMENT.** see *COMPUTERS—Information Science And Information Theory*

384 USA ISSN 1389-6938
INFORMATION TECHNOLOGY; transmission, processing and storage. Text in English. 1999. irreg., latest 2005. price varies. **Document type:** *Monographic series.* **Description:** Examines and discusses technical and practical issues in telecommunications.
Formerly: Plenum Series in Telecommunications
Published by: Springer-Verlag New York, Inc. (Subsidiary of: Springer Science+Business Media), 233 Spring St, New York, NY 10013. TEL 212-460-1500, FAX 212-460-1575, service@springer-ny.com, http://www.springer-ny.com. Ed. Jack Keil Wolf.

384 USA ISSN 1082-961X
INSIDE N I S T. (National Institute of Standards & Technology) Text in English. 1995. bi-w.
Related titles: Online - full text ed.: (from ProQuest Information & Learning).

Published by: Phillips Business Information Inc., 7811 Montrose Rd, Potomac, MD 20854. TEL 301-424-3700, FAX 301-309-3847.

INSIDE RUSSIA & THE F S U. (Former Soviet Union) see *JOURNALISM*

384 004.6 GBR
INTEGRATED DEALER NEWS. Abbreviated title: I D N. Text in English. 1997. m. GBP 36 (effective 2000). adv. **Document type:** *Magazine, Trade.* **Description:** Provides information for dealers and resellers of IT, high tech,comms, mobile, Internet, computing and office solutions.
Published by: Castle Publications Ltd., 35-37 Mile End Rd, London, E1 4TP, United Kingdom. TEL 44-7000-436835, FAX 44-7000-436329, idn@castle-publications.freeserve.co.uk. Ed. Jack Mills.

384 USA
INTELE-CARDNEWS. Text in English. 1995. m. free. adv. **Document type:** *Magazine, Consumer.* **Description:** Covers all aspects of the prepaid telecommunications business.
Published by: Quality Publishing Inc., 523 N Sam Houston Pkwy, Ste 300, Houston, TX 77060. TEL 281-272-2744, FAX 281-847-5368, editor@intelecard.com, http://www.intelecard.com. Ed. Randy Moser. Pub. Marlene Eastland. Adv. contact Cynthia Leonard.

INTELLIGENCE; the future of computing. see *COMPUTERS*

INTERACTION STUDIES; social behaviour and communication in biological and artificial systems. see *LINGUISTICS*

384 332.6 USA ISSN 1529-3939
INTERACTIVE T V INVESTOR. Text in English. 1996. s-m. USD 895 (effective 2001). **Document type:** *Newsletter.* **Description:** Your guide to the latest developments, perceptive analysis and exclusive projections in this promising field. Reports on cable, broadcast, computer, satellite, telephone and wireless pursuits into the ITV market. All about new technology, consumer rollouts and programming options.
Formerly: Interactive Television (1091-9406)
Related titles: E-mail ed.: USD 895 (effective 2001); Fax ed.: USD 895 (effective 2001).
Published by: Kagan Research, LLC, 1 Lower Ragsdale Dr., Ste. 130, Monterey, CA 93940-5741. TEL 831-624-1536, FAX 831-625-3225, info@kagan.com, http://www.kagan.com. Pub. Paul Kagan.

384 305.4 USA
INTERCOM (SEVERNA PARK). Text in English. 1997. q. free to members. **Document type:** *Magazine, Trade.* **Description:** Communications and business topics.
Formerly: Matrix
Media: Online - full text.
Contact Owner: Association for Women in Communications, 780 Ritchie Hwy., Ste. 28-S, Severna Park, MD 21114. TEL 410-544-7442, FAX 410-544-4640. Circ: 4,000.

384 USA ISSN 0164-6206
INTERCOM (WASHINGTON, DC). Text in English. 1968. 10/yr. free to members (effective 2004). **Document type:** *Magazine, Trade.* **Description:** Publishes articles of professional interest to technical communicators, including writers, editors, illustrators, teachers, managers, consultants, and others involved in preparing technical documents.
Related titles: Online - full text ed.: (from EBSCO Publishing).
—CCC.
Published by: Society for Technical Communication, 901 N Stuart St, Ste 904, Arlington, VA 22203-1822. TEL 703-522-4114, http://www.stc.org/intercomGeneral.asp.

INTERFACE (LONDON); newsletter of the FEI. see *ELECTRONICS*

384 USA
INTERFAX. CHINA I T & TELECOM REPORT. (Information Technology) Text in English. 2001. w. **Document type:** *Trade.* **Description:** Covers the operations of national and foreign corporations, joint ventures, new projects, statistics, tenders, industrial policies and regulations as well as market activity of the People's Republic of China.
Contact Dist.: Interfax America, Inc. (Subsidiary of: Interfax Ltd.), 3025 S Parker Rd, Ste 737, Aurora, CO 80014-2925. TEL 852-2537-2262, FAX 852-2537-2264. **Dist. in Germany, Austria and Switzerland by:** Interfax Deutschland GmbH, IndustriestraBe 6, Kronberg/Tx 61476 , Germany. TEL 49-61-7361369, FAX 49-61-7361206; **Dist. in West Europe by:** Interfax Europe Ltd., 1st Fl, 50 Hans Crescent, Knightsbridge, London SW1X 0N, United Kingdom. TEL 44-20-7581-5550, FAX 44-20-7581-4490.

384 621.381 USA ISSN 1096-3103
INTERFAX. COMMUNICATIONS & ELECTRONICS REPORT. Text in English. w. **Document type:** *Trade.*
Related titles: E-mail ed.; Fax ed.; Online - full content ed.
Contact Dist.: Interfax America, Inc. (Subsidiary of: Interfax Ltd.), 3025 S Parker Rd, Ste 737, Aurora, CO 80014-2925. TEL 852-2537-2262, FAX 852-2537-2264. **Dist. in Germany Austria and Switzerland by:** Interfax Deutschland GmbH, IndustriestraBe 6, Kronberg/Tx 61476 , Germany. TEL 49-61-7361369, FAX 49-61-7361206; **Dist. in Western Europe by:** Interfax Europe Ltd., 1st Fl, 50 Hans Crescent, Knightsbridge, London SW1X 0N, United Kingdom. TEL 44-20-7581-5550, FAX 44-20-7581-4490.

384 070.5 ESP ISSN 1134-0533
INTERMEDIOS DE LA COMUNICACION. Key Title: Inter Medios de la Comunicacion. Text in Spanish. 1994. s-m. (22/yr.). q. index. back issues avail. **Document type:** *Newsletter.* **Description:** Covers the media industry in Spain.
Address: Hortaleza 118, 1o, 5a, Madrid, 28004, Spain. TEL 34-1-3198239, FAX 34-1-3084771, intermedios@intermeco.es, lpalacio@intermeco.es, http://www.intermeco.es. Ed. Luis Palacio. Adv. contact Maria Antenia Castales. Circ: 470 (paid).

384 USA
INTERNATIONAL CONFERENCE ON COMMUNICATIONS TECHNOLOGY. PROCEEDINGS. Text in English. a. USD 388; USD 194 to members (effective 2004). **Document type:** *Proceedings, Trade.*
Published by: Institute of Electrical and Electronics Engineers, Inc., 3 Park Ave, 17th Fl, New York, NY 10016-5997. TEL 212-419-7900, 800-678-4333, FAX 212-752-4929, customer.service@ieee.org, http://www.ieee.org.

INTERNATIONAL CONFERENCE ON COMPUTER COMMUNICATIONS AND NETWORKS. PROCEEDINGS. see *COMPUTERS—Computer Networks*

612.382 USA
INTERNATIONAL CONFERENCE ON SIGNAL PROCESSING. PROCEEDINGS. Text in English. a. USD 350; USD 175 to members (effective 2004). **Document type:** *Proceedings, Trade.*
Indexed: Englnd.
—BLDSC (4538.881110).
Published by: Institute of Electrical and Electronics Engineers, Inc., 3 Park Ave, 17th Fl, New York, NY 10016-5997. TEL 212-419-7900, 800-678-4333, FAX 212-752-4929, customer.service@ieee.org, http://www.ieee.org.

INTERNATIONAL CONFERENCE ON TELECOMMUNICATIONS IN MODERN SATELLITE, CABLE AND BROADCASTING SERVICES. PROCEEDINGS. see *COMPUTERS—Computer Networks*

INTERNATIONAL DIRECTORY OF COMMUNICATIONS EQUIPMENT AND SUPPLIES IMPORTERS. see *BUSINESS AND ECONOMICS—Trade And Industrial Directories*

INTERNATIONAL GEOSCIENCE AND REMOTE SENSING SYMPOSIUM DIGEST. see *GEOGRAPHY*

621.382 GBR ISSN 1462-4613
➤ **INTERNATIONAL JOURNAL OF ADVANCED MEDIA AND COMMUNICATION.** Abbreviated title: I J A M C. Text in English. 2002. q. USD 450 to institutions print or online; USD 545 combined subscription to institutions print & online (effective 2005). adv. back issues avail. **Document type:** *Journal, Academic/Scholarly.* **Description:** Covering multi-media and advanced media, telematics and communication technologies, and their use on different levels in public and private organizations and services. It aims to provide a forum for professionals and academics in the field to exchange ideas and disseminate knowledge.
Related titles: Online - full text ed.: ISSN 1741-8003. USD 430 (effective 2004).
Published by: Inderscience Publishers, IEL Editorial Office, PO Box 735, Olney, Bucks MK46 5WB, United Kingdom. TEL 44-1234-240519, FAX 44-1234-240515, ijamc@inderscience.com, editor@inderscience.com, http://www.inderscience.com/ijamc. Ed. Ming-Hui Huang. R&P Jeanette Brooks. Adv. contact Cheryl Busby. **Subscr. to:** World Trade Centre Bldg, 29 route de Pre-Bois, Case Postale 896, Geneva 15 1215, Switzerland. FAX 41-22-7910885, subs@inderscience.com.

384 IND
➤ **INTERNATIONAL JOURNAL OF COMMUNICATION**; an international review of cognition, culture and communication. Text in English; Summaries in English. 1991. s-a. INR 300 domestic; USD 100 foreign (effective 2001). adv. bk.rev. **Document type:** *Magazine, Academic/Scholarly.* **Description:** Presents new theoretical and applied aspects of communication studies in all its ramifications, with special emphasis on cognition, culture studies, AI, journalism, semiotics, cybernetics, communication and ideology and communication across cultures.
Indexed: MLA-IB.
Published by: Bahri Publications, 1749A/5, Gobindpuri Extension, Kalkaji, P O Box 4453, New Delhi, 110 019, India. TEL 91-11-644-5710, FAX 91-11-6448606, bahrius@ndf.vsnl.net.in, bahrius@del6.vsnl.net.in, bahrius@vsnl.com. Ed., Pub., R&P Ujjal Singh Bahri. Adv. contact Deepinder Singh Bahri. B&W page INR 1,500, B&W page USD 150; trim 4 x 7. Circ: 150 (paid).

▼ ➤ **INTERNATIONAL JOURNAL OF DISTANCE EDUCATION TECHNOLOGIES**; the international source for technological advances in distance education. see *EDUCATION*

▼ ➤ **INTERNATIONAL JOURNAL OF INFORMATION AND COMMUNICATION TECHNOLOGY EDUCATION.** see *EDUCATION*

➤ **INTERNATIONAL JOURNAL OF INFORMATION MANAGEMENT.** see *COMPUTERS—Information Science And Information Theory*

▼ ➤ **INTERNATIONAL JOURNAL OF INFORMATION POLICY AND LAW.** see *LAW—Corporate Law*

➤ **INTERNATIONAL JOURNAL OF LISTENING.** see *HUMANITIES: COMPREHENSIVE WORKS*

306.2 384 GBR ISSN 1740-8296
▼ **INTERNATIONAL JOURNAL OF MEDIA AND CULTURAL POLITICS.** Text in English. 2005. 3/yr. GBP 30 in the European Union to individuals; GBP 38 elsewhere to individuals; GBP 140 in the European Union to institutions; GBP 148 elsewhere to institutions (effective 2005). **Document type:** *Journal, Academic/Scholarly.* **Description:** Addresses cultural politics in their local, international and global dimensions, recognizing equally the importance of issues defined by their specific cultural geography and those which run across cultures and nations.
Published by: Intellect Ltd., PO Box 862, Bristol, BS99 1DE, United Kingdom. TEL 44-117-9589910, FAX 44-117-9589911, journals@intellectbooks.com, info@intellectbooks.com, http://www.intellectbooks.com/journals/mcp/index.htm. Eds. Dr. Katherine Ross, Dr. Neil Blain. R&P, Adv. contact Mr. Robin Beecroft.

621.382 GBR ISSN 1470-949X
➤ **INTERNATIONAL JOURNAL OF MOBILE COMMUNICATIONS.** Abbreviated title: I J M C. Text in English. 2001. 4/yr. USD 450 to institutions; USD 545 combined subscription to institutions print & online eds. (effective 2005). **Document type:** *Journal, Academic/Scholarly.* **Description:** Publishes articles that present current practice and theory of mobile communications, mobile technology, and mobile commerce applications.
Related titles: Online - full text ed.: ISSN 1741-5217. USD 450 to institutions (effective 2005) (from EBSCO Publishing).
Indexed: BrCerAb, C&ISA, CerAb, CorrAb, E&CAJ, EMA, ErgAb, IAA, Inspec, M&TEA, MBF, METADEX, RefZh, WAA.
—BLDSC (4542.364700), CISTI, IE, Linda Hall.
Published by: Inderscience Publishers, IEL Editorial Office, PO Box 735, Olney, Bucks MK46 5WB, United Kingdom. TEL 44-1234-240519, FAX 44-1234-240515, ijmc@inderscience.com, editor@inderscience.com, http://www.inderscience.com/ijmc. Ed. Dr. Binshan Lin. **Subscr. to:** World Trade Centre Bldg, 29 route de Pre-Bois, Case Postale 896, Geneva 15 1215, Switzerland. FAX 41-22-7910885, subs@inderscience.com.

621.39 GBR ISSN 1055-7148
TK5105.5 CODEN: INMTEU
➤ **INTERNATIONAL JOURNAL OF NETWORK MANAGEMENT.** Text in English. 1991. bi-m. USD 1,010 to institutions; USD 1,111 combined subscription to institutions print & online eds. (effective 2006). adv. back issues avail.; reprint service avail. from PSC. **Document type:** *Journal, Academic/Scholarly.* **Description:** Dedicated to the dissemination of practical information that enables readers to better manage, operate and maintain communications networks.
Related titles: Microform ed.: (from PQC); Online - full content ed.: ISSN 1099-1190. 1997. USD 1,010 to institutions (effective 2006); Online - full text ed.: (from Association for Computing Machinery, Inc., EBSCO Publishing, Swets Information Services, Wiley InterScience).
Indexed: CompLI, Englnd, Inspec.
—BLDSC (4542.373300), AskIEEE, CISTI, Ei, IE, Infotrieve, ingenta. **CCC.**
Published by: John Wiley & Sons Ltd. (Subsidiary of: John Wiley & Sons, Inc.), The Atrium, Southern Gate, Chichester, West Sussex PO19 8SQ, United Kingdom. TEL 44-1243-779777, FAX 44-1243-775878, customer@wiley.co.uk, http://www3.interscience.wiley.com/cgi-bin/jhome/5703, http://www.wiley.co.uk. Ed. Gilbert Held. adv.: B&W page GBP 650, color page GBP 1,550; trim 200 x 260. Circ: 500. **Subscr. in the Americas to:** John Wiley & Sons, Inc., 111 River St, Hoboken, NJ 07030-5774. TEL 201-748-6645, 800-225-5945, subinfo@wiley.com.

▼ ➤ **INTERNATIONAL JOURNAL OF PERVASIVE COMPUTING AND COMMUNICATIONS.** see *COMPUTERS*

384.51 GBR ISSN 1742-7568
▼ ➤ **INTERNATIONAL JOURNAL OF SATELLITE COMMUNICATIONS POLICY AND MANAGEMENT.** Text in English. forthcoming 2006. q. EUR 430, USD 450 to institutions print or online ed.; EUR 520, USD 545 combined subscription to institutions print & online eds. (effective 2005). **Document type:** *Journal, Academic/Scholarly.*
Related titles: Online - full text ed.: ISSN 1742-7576. forthcoming 2006.

C

▼ new title ➤ refereed ✶ unverified ♦ full entry avail.

Published by: Inderscience Publishers, IEL Editorial Office, PO Box 735, Olney, Bucks MK46 5WB, United Kingdom. TEL 44-1234-240519, FAX 44-1234-240515, ijscpm@inderscience.com, info@inderscience.com, http://www.inderscience.com/ijscpm. Ed. John B Pasaribu. **Subscr. to:** World Trade Centre Bldg, 29 route de Pre-Bois, Case Postale 896, Geneva 15 1215, Switzerland. FAX 41-22-7910885, subs@inderscience.com.

▼ ➤ **INTERNATIONAL JOURNAL OF STRATEGIC COMMUNICATION.** see *BUSINESS AND ECONOMICS*

384 020   AUS   ISSN 1447-9516
▼ ➤ **INTERNATIONAL JOURNAL OF THE BOOK.** Text in English. 2003. a., latest vol.1, 2003. AUD 300 (effective 2004). Index. back issues avail. **Document type:** *Monographic series, Academic/Scholarly.* **Description:** Covers the history, form and future of books, including such issues as copyright, digitalization, and diversity.
Related titles: CD-ROM ed.; Online - full content ed.
Published by: Common Ground, PO Box 463, Altona, VIC 3018, Australia. kathryn@commongroundpublishing.com, http://commongroundgroup.com/. Eds. Howard Dare, Mary Kalantzis. Pub. Kathryn Otte.

▼ ➤ **INTERNATIONAL JOURNAL OF WEB ENGINEERING AND TECHNOLOGY.** see *COMPUTERS—Information Science And Information Theory*

621.384   USA   ISSN 1068-9605
TK5103.2   CODEN: IJWNEY
➤ **INTERNATIONAL JOURNAL OF WIRELESS INFORMATION NETWORKS.** Text in English. 1993. q. EUR 455, USD 458, GBP 285 combined subscription to institutions print & online eds. (effective 2005). adv. reprint service avail. from PSC. **Document type:** *Journal, Academic/Scholarly.* **Description:** Covers research advances affecting all aspects of wireless communication and information networks, including cellular phone networks.
Formerly (until 1994): International Journal of Wireless Communication
Related titles: Online - full text ed.: ISSN 1572-8129 (from EBSCO Publishing, Gale Group, IngentaConnect, Kluwer Online, O C L C Online Computer Library Center, Inc., Ovid Technologies, Inc., Springer LINK, Swets Information Services).
Indexed: BibLing, CompLI, EngInd, Inspec, LISA, RefZh. —BLDSC (4542.701350), AskIEEE, CISTI, Ei, IE, Infotrieve, ingenta. **CCC.**
Published by: Plenum US (Subsidiary of: Springer Science+Business Media), 233 Spring St, New York, NY 10013. TEL 212-460-1500, FAX 212-460-1575, service@springer-ny.com, http://springerlink.metapress.com/openurl.asp?genre=journal&issn=1068-9605, http://www.springeronline.com. Ed. Kaveh Pahlavan.

384 535   SGP   ISSN 1548-548X
▼ **INTERNATIONAL JOURNAL ON WIRELESS & OPTICAL COMMUNICATIONS.** Text in English. 2003. s-a. SGD 72, USD 42, EUR 40 to individuals; SGD 177, USD 104, EUR 97 combined subscription to institutions print & online eds. (effective 2005). **Document type:** *Journal, Academic/Scholarly.*
Related titles: Online - full text ed.: SGD 168, USD 99, EUR 92 (effective 2005).
Published by: World Scientific Publishing Co. Pte. Ltd., 5 Toh Tuck Link, Singapore, 596224, Singapore. TEL 65-466-5775, FAX 65-467-7667, wspc@wspc.com.sg, http://www.worldscinet.com/ijwoc/ijwoc.shtml, http://www.worldscientific.com. Ed. Tjeng T Tjhung. **Subscr. to:** Farrer Rd, PO Box 128, Singapore 912805, Singapore. TEL 65-382-5663, FAX 65-382-5919. **Dist. in Europe by:** World Scientific Publishing Ltd., 57 Shelton St, London WC2H 9HE, United Kingdom. TEL 44-20-78360888, FAX 44-20-78362020, sales@wspc.co.uk; **Dist. in the US by:** World Scientific Publishing Co., Inc., 1060 Main St, River Edge, NJ 07661. TEL 201-487-9655, FAX 201-487-9656, wspc@wspc.com.

384.5 621.3827   SGP   ISSN 0219-7995
▼ ➤ **INTERNATIONAL JOURNAL ON WIRELESS AND OPTICAL COMMUNICATIONS.** Text in English. 2003. 3/yr. SGD 80, USD 46, EUR 44 to individuals; SGD 196, USD 115, EUR 107 combined subscription to institutions print & online eds. (effective 2006). back issues avail. **Document type:** *Journal, Academic/Scholarly.* **Description:** Covers wireless access to the Internet and the evolution of third generation cellular systems including ITU IMT/UMTS, radio interface design, adaptive antennas and arrays and indoor propagation, measurements and predictions. Also includes home digital devices and the application of Ultra Wide Band, as well as Spectrum efficiency and low power consumption including low cost and secure wireless personal access, Ad Hoc and Sensor networks, Imbedded systems and miniaturization, space exploration.
Related titles: Online - full content ed.; Online - full text ed.: (from EBSCO Publishing, O C L C Online Computer Library Center, Inc., Swets Information Services).
Indexed: C&ISA, E&CAJ, IAA.
—BLDSC (4542.701320), IE.

Published by: World Scientific Publishing Co. Pte. Ltd., 5 Toh Tuck Link, Singapore, 596224, Singapore. TEL 65-466-5775, FAX 65-467-7667, wspc@wspc.com.sg, http://www.worldscinet.com/ijwoc/ijwoc.shtml, http://www.worldscientific.com. Ed. Tjeng T Tjhung. **Dist. by:** World Scientific Publishing Co., Inc., 1060 Main St, River Edge, NJ 07661. TEL 201-487-9655, FAX 201-487-9656, 888-977-2665, wspc@wspc.com; World Scientific Publishing Ltd., 57 Shelton St, London WC2H 9HE, United Kingdom. TEL 44-20-78360888, FAX 44-20-78362020, sales@wspc.co.uk.

➤ **INTERNATIONAL MEDIA LAW**; bulletin on rights, clearances and legal practice. see *LAW—International Law*

621.3692   GBR
INTERNATIONAL OPTICAL COMMUNICATIONS. Text in English. s-a. free to qualified personnel. adv. **Document type:** *Trade.* **Description:** Covers both the scientific and commercial aspects of the optical communications industry, as well as the business and education issues. Also contains analysis and commentary by leading academic and industry figures.
Published by: Nexus Media Ltd. (Subsidiary of: Highbury House Communications PLC), Nexus House, Azalea Dr, Swanley, Kent BR8 8HU, United Kingdom. TEL 44-1322-660070, FAX 44-1322-616311, info@nexusmedia.com, http://www.hhc.co.uk/ioc. Eds. Per Danielsen TEL 45-3-3135618, Robert Riggs TEL 44-1322-660070 ext 2272. Adv. contact David Girecourt TEL 44-1322-660070 ext 2237. B&W page GBP 3,425, B&W page USD 5,480, B&W page EUR 6,000, color page GBP 4,430, color page USD 7,800, color page EUR 7,700; 275 x 210. Circ: 8,900.

621.382   USA
INTERNATIONAL PROFESSIONAL COMMUNICATION CONFERENCE. CONFERENCE RECORD. Short title: I P C C. Text in English. 1981. a. USD 202; USD 101 to members (effective 2004). **Document type:** *Proceedings, Trade.* **Description:** Discusses current issues and developments relevant to the creation, production, transmission and presentation of scientific and technical information.
Formerly (until 1985): I E E E Professional Communication Society Conference. Record
Related titles: CD-ROM ed.; Microfiche ed.
Indexed: EngInd.
Published by: Institute of Electrical and Electronics Engineers, Inc., 3 Park Ave, 17th Fl, New York, NY 10016-5997. TEL 212-419-7900, 800-678-4333, FAX 212-752-4929, customer.service@ieee.org, http://www.ieee.org. **Co-sponsor:** Professional Communications Society.

621.38   USA
INTERNATIONAL RADAR CONFERENCE. RECORD. Variant title: International Conference on Radar (Publication). Text in English. 1973. a. price varies. **Document type:** *Proceedings, Trade.*
Related titles: CD-ROM ed.; Microfiche ed.
—BLDSC (4362.965000).
Published by: Institute of Electrical and Electronics Engineers, Inc., 3 Park Ave, 17th Fl, New York, NY 10016-5997. TEL 212-419-7900, 800-678-4333, FAX 212-752-4929, customer.service@ieee.org, http://www.ieee.org. **Co-sponsor:** Aerospace and Electronic Systems Society.

387.2   GBR
INTERNATIONAL SAFETYNET MANUAL. Text in English. irreg., latest 1994. GBP 8; GBP 10 overseas. illus. **Description:** Discusses the design and use of SafetyNET, an international automatic satellite-based navigation system to relay important navigation and meteorological information among ships.
Published by: International Maritime Organization/Organisation Maritime Internationale, 4 Albert Embankment, London, SE1 7SR, United Kingdom. TEL 44-20-7735-7611, FAX 44-20-7587-3210.

384   USA   ISSN 1041-4541
TL512
INTERNATIONAL SATELLITE DIRECTORY; a complete guide to the satellite communications industry. Text in English. 1982. a. USD 395 (effective 2001); plus postage. adv. Satellites & Companies. 1200 p./no. 3 cols./p.; back issues avail. **Document type:** *Directory, Trade.*
Related titles: CD-ROM ed.: S A T finder. ISSN 1073-9181; Online - full text ed.
Published by: Satnews Publishers, 800 Siesta Way, Sonoma, CA 95476-4413. http://www.satnews.com. Ed. Silvano Payne. Circ: 3,500.

621.382   CHE
INTERNATIONAL TELECOMMUNICATION UNION. BOOKLETS. Text in English. 1969 (no.3). irreg., latest vol.41, 1993. CHF 12.
Related titles: French ed.; Spanish ed.
Published by: International Telecommunication Union, Place des Nations, Geneva 20, 1211, Switzerland. TEL 41-22-7306141, FAX 41-22-7305194, sales@itu.ch, http://www.itu.int/publications.

621.382   CHE
INTERNATIONAL TELECOMMUNICATION UNION. SEMINARS. Text in English. 1974. irreg., latest 1986. price varies.
Related titles: French ed.; Spanish ed.

Published by: International Telecommunication Union, Place des Nations, Geneva 20, 1211, Switzerland. TEL 41-22-7306141, FAX 41-22-7305149, sales@itu.ch, http://www.itu.int/publications.

621.382   USA   ISSN 0275-0473
TK6271   CODEN: IITPDH
INTERNATIONAL TELECOMMUNICATIONS ENERGY CONFERENCE. PROCEEDINGS. Short title: I N T E L E C. (Published by other organizations when held outside of U.S.) Text in English. 1978. a. USD 232; USD 116 to members (effective 2004). **Document type:** *Proceedings, Trade.* **Description:** Details state-of-the-art and future developments in the field of power supply for equipment and services.
Formerly: International Telephone Energy Conference. Proceedings
Related titles: CD-ROM ed.; Microfiche ed.
Indexed: EngInd.
—BLDSC (4531.818700), Ei, IE, ingenta. **CCC.**
Published by: Institute of Electrical and Electronics Engineers, Inc., 3 Park Ave, 17th Fl, New York, NY 10016-5997. TEL 212-419-7900, 800-678-4333, FAX 212-752-4929, customer.service@ieee.org, http://www.ieee.org. **Co-sponsor:** Communications Society.

621.382   GBR   ISSN 0268-9960
INTERNATIONAL TELECOMMUNICATIONS INTELLIGENCE. Text in English. 1984. w. looseleaf. GBP 595, USD 1,065 (effective 2000). adv. back issues avail. **Document type:** *Newsletter, Trade.*
Related titles: CD-ROM ed.
—**CCC.**
Published by: Espicom Business Intelligence, Lincoln House, City Fields Business Park, City Fields Way, Tangmere, Chichester, W Sussex PO20 6FS, United Kingdom. TEL 44-1243-533322, FAX 44-1243-533418, sales_desk@espicom.com, http://www.espicom.com. Ed. Jayne Hardwell. R&P Nigel Chivers. adv.: page GBP 250; trim 170 x 240.

384   GBR   ISSN 1361-603X
INTERNATIONAL TELECOMS REVIEW. Text in English. 1996. a. GBP 75, USD 135. **Description:** Covers developments in the international telecommunications market with contributions from financiers, lawyers, manufacturers and associations active in the market.
—**CCC.**
Published by: Euromoney Publications plc, Nestor House, Playhouse Yard, London, EC4V 5EX, United Kingdom. TEL 44-207-7798673, FAX 44-20-77798541.

621.382   USA   ISSN 0091-7702
INTERNATIONAL WIRE AND CABLE SYMPOSIUM. PROCEEDINGS. Text in English. a.
Published by: International Wire & Cable Conference, 174 Main St, Eatontown, NJ 07724. TEL 732-389-0990, FAX 732-389-0991, admin@iwcs.org, http://www.iwcs.org.

384   USA
INTERNATIONAL WORKSHOP ON DISCRETE ALGORITHMS AND METHODS FOR MOBILE COMPUTING AND COMMUNICATIONS. PROCEEDINGS. Text in English. a. USD 20 per issue to non-members; USD 10 per issue to members (effective 2005). **Document type:** *Proceedings, Academic/Scholarly.*
Published by: Association for Computing Machinery, Inc., 1515 Broadway, 17th Fl, New York, NY 10036-5701. TEL 212-626-0500, usacm@acm.org, http://www.acm.org.

384 004.6   USA
INTERNATIONAL WORKSHOP ON QUALITY OF SERVICE. Text in English. a. USD 156; USD 78 to members (effective 2004). **Document type:** *Proceedings, Trade.*
—BLDSC (4552.198750).
Published by: Institute of Electrical and Electronics Engineers, Inc., 3 Park Ave, 17th Fl, New York, NY 10016-5997. TEL 212-419-7900, 800-678-4333, FAX 212-752-4929, customer.service@ieee.org, http://www.ieee.org.

384   GBR   ISSN 1474-2012
INTERNET & TECHNOLOGY FINANCE. Text in English. 2000. m. GBP 690, USD 1,000 (effective 2001). adv. **Document type:** *Journal, Trade.* **Description:** Worldwide primary source information on debt & equity funding in the internet & technology industry.
Related titles: Online - full content ed.: GBP 375, USD 540 (effective 2001).
Published by: Thompson Stanley Publishers Ltd., Clerkenwell House, 45-47 Clerkenwell Green, London, EC1R 0EB, United Kingdom. TEL 44-20-7553-3919, FAX 44-20-7251-1833, chris.thompson@telecomfinance.com, http://www.internettechfinance.com. Ed. Dominic Lowndes. R&P Chris Thompson. Adv. contact Danny Grasso. Circ: 1,250.

▼ **THE INTERNET JOURNAL OF MEDICAL INFORMATICS.** see *MEDICAL SCIENCES*

INTERSECTIONS IN COMMUNICATIONS AND CULTURE; global approaches and transdisciplinary perspectives. see *SOCIOLOGY*

591 USA
INTERSPECIES NEWSLETTER. Text in English. 1978. q. looseleaf. USD 30 (effective 2000). bk.rev. 8 p./no.; back issues avail. **Document type:** *Newsletter.* **Description:** Relates field projects involving humans and other species seeking a common base for communication exchange. Networks writings on the perceptual bases of ecology.
Published by: Interspecies Communication Inc., 301 Hidden Meadow, Friday Harbor, WA 98250. http://www.interspecies.com. Ed. Jim Nollman. Circ: 1,000.

384 JPN ISSN 0913-8293
J A T E TSUSHIN/J A T E NEWS. Text in Japanese. 1984. bi-m. JPY 1,200 per issue. **Document type:** *Bulletin.*
Published by: Japan Approvals Institute for Telecommunications Equipment/Denki Tsushin Tanmatsu Kiki Shinsa Kyokai, 1-3 Toranomon 1-chome, Minato-ku, Tokyo, 105-0001, Japan. TEL 81-3-3591-4300, FAX 81-3-3591-4355.

338.47 USA ISSN 1424-1277
P87
J M M. (Journal on Media Management) Variant title: International Journal on Media Management. Text in English. 1999. q. USD 355 in US & Canada to institutions; USD 385 elsewhere to institutions; USD 375 combined subscription in US & Canada to institutions; USD 405 combined subscription elsewhere to institutions (effective 2006). back issues avail. **Document type:** *Journal, Academic/Scholarly.* **Description:** Focuses on the rich array of media related issues brought about by rapid technological developments in the media and telecommunications industries.
Related titles: ♦ Online - full text ed.: J M M Online. ISSN 1424-1250.
—BLDSC (4669.448500), IE.
Published by: (Media and Communications Management Institute CHE), Lawrence Erlbaum Associates, Inc., 10 Industrial Ave, Mahwah, NJ 07430-2262. TEL 201-258-2200, 800-926-6579, FAX 201-236-0072, journals@erlbaum.com, http://www.leaonline.com/loi/ijmm, http://www.erlbaum.com. Eds. Alan B Albarran, Beat F Schmid, Bozena I Mierzejewska.

338.47 USA ISSN 1424-1250
J M M ONLINE. (Journal on Media Management) Variant title: International Journal on Media Management. Text in English. 1999. q. USD 340 worldwide (effective 2006). **Document type:** *Journal, Academic/Scholarly.* **Description:** Presents close analysis of new industry structures, organizational forms and critical competencies developing as a result of reconfigurations in the media value chain.
Media: Online - full text (from EBSCO Publishing, Gale Group, O C L C Online Computer Library Center, Inc., Swets Information Services). **Related titles:** ♦ Print ed.: J M M. ISSN 1424-1277.
Indexed: CommAb.
Published by: (Media and Communications Management Institute CHE), Lawrence Erlbaum Associates, Inc., 10 Industrial Ave, Mahwah, NJ 07430-2262. TEL 201-258-2200, 800-926-6579, FAX 201-236-0072, journals@erlbaum.com, http://www.leaonline.com/loi/ijmm. Ed. Doerte Wittig.

J U M - JUGEND UND MEDIEN; Lehrerzeitung des Buchklubs. see *CHILDREN AND YOUTH—About*

621.382 DEU
JAHRBUCH DER TELEKOM PRAXIS. Text in German. 1963. a. EUR 45 (effective 2005). adv. **Document type:** *Directory, Trade.*
Former titles (until 2003): Taschenbuch der Telekom Praxis (0940-0311); (until 1991): Taschenbuch der Fernmelde-Praxis (0082-1764)
Published by: Fachverlag Schiele und Schoen GmbH, Markgrafenstr 11, Berlin, 10969, Germany. TEL 49-30-2537520, FAX 49-30-2517248, service@schiele-schoen.de, http://www.schiele-schoen.de. Ed. B Seiler. Circ: 4,000.

384 DEU ISSN 1438-4485
P87
➤ **JAHRBUCH FUER KOMMUNIKATIONSGESCHICHTE.** Abbreviated title: Jb K G. Text in German. 1999. a. EUR 79 (effective 2006). adv. bibl. **Document type:** *Journal, Academic/Scholarly.*
Indexed: DIP, IBR, IBSS, IBZ.
Published by: Franz Steiner Verlag Stuttgart GmbH, Birkenwaldstr 44, Stuttgart, 70191, Germany. TEL 49-711-25820, FAX 49-711-2582290, service@steiner-verlag.de, http://www.steiner-verlag.de. Eds. Arnulf Kutsch, Holger Boening, Rudolf Stoeber. R&P Sabine Koerner. Adv. contact Susanne Szoradi. Circ: 500.

➤ **JAHRBUCH MEDIENPAEDAGOGIK.** see *EDUCATION—Teaching Methods And Curriculum*

➤ **JANE'S AIR AND SYSTEMS LIBRARY.** see *MILITARY*

➤ **JANE'S ELECTRONIC MISSION AIRCRAFT.** see *AERONAUTICS AND SPACE FLIGHT*

➤ **JANE'S MILITARY COMMUNICATIONS.** see *MILITARY*

➤ **JANE'S RADAR AND ELECTRONIC WARFARE SYSTEMS.** see *MILITARY*

➤ **JANE'S SEA AND SYSTEMS LIBRARY.** see *MILITARY*

➤ **JAPAN (YEAR) MARKETING AND ADVERTISING YEARBOOK.** see *ADVERTISING AND PUBLIC RELATIONS*

384 USA ISSN 1081-9983
JAPAN TELECOM. Text in English. 1995. s-m. USD 695 in US & Canada; USD 745 elsewhere (effective 2004). **Document type:** *Newsletter, Trade.* **Description:** Covers all aspects of the telecommunications market in Japan.
Related titles: Online - full text ed.: (from Florida Center for Library Automation, Gale Group).
Published by: Information Gatekeepers, Inc., 320 Washington St, Ste 302, Brighton, MA 02135. TEL 617-782-5033, 800-323-1088, FAX 617-782-5735, info@igigroup.com, http://www.igigroup.com. Pub. Dr. Paul Polishuk.

384 CHN ISSN 1009-0940
JIANGXI TONGXIN KEJI/JIANGXI COMMUNICATION SCIENCE & TECHNOLOGY. Text in Chinese. 1980. q. **Document type:** *Journal, Academic/Scholarly.*
Related titles: Online - full text ed.: (from East View Information Services, WanFang Data Corp.).
Address: Shengzhengfu Dayuan, 16, Bei-Yi-Lu, Nanchang, 330046, China. TEL 86-791-6218155, jxtx@jxca.gov.cn, http://jxtxkj.periodicals.net.cn/.

384 JPN ISSN 0914-6504
JOHO TSUSHIN JANARU/TELECOM JOURNAL. Text in Japanese. 1984. m. JPY 500 per issue. **Document type:** *Government.*
Formerly (until 1988): Denki Tsushin Jiho (0910-2590)
Published by: (Japan. Yuseisho/Ministry of Posts and Telecommunications, Japan. Tsushin Seisakukyoku/Ministry of Posts and Telecommunications, Communications Policy Bureau), Denki Tsushin Shinkokai/Association for the Promotion of Telecommunications, 3-10 Komagome 2-chome, Toshima-ku, Tokyo, 170-0003, Japan. TEL 81-3-3940-3951, FAX 81-3-3940-4055. Circ: 6,500.

004.62 USA
JOINT WORKSHOP ON FOUNDATIONS OF MOBILE COMPUTING. PROCEEDINGS. Text in English. a. USD 14 per issue to non-members; USD 7 per issue to members (effective 2005). **Document type:** *Proceedings, Academic/Scholarly.*
Formerly: A C M International Workshop on Principles of Mobile Computing. Proceedings
Related titles: Online - full content ed.
Published by: Association for Computing Machinery, Inc., 1515 Broadway, 17th Fl, New York, NY 10036-5701. TEL 212-626-0500, usacm@acm.org, http://www.acm.org.

THE JOKESMITH. see *LITERARY AND POLITICAL REVIEWS*

384 USA ISSN 0090-9882
HM258
➤ **JOURNAL OF APPLIED COMMUNICATION RESEARCH.** Text in English. 1973. q. GBP 170, USD 275 combined subscription to institutions print & online eds. (effective 2006). adv. bk.rev. abstr.; illus. back issues avail.; reprint service avail. from PSC. **Document type:** *Journal, Academic/Scholarly.*
Related titles: Microform ed.: (from PQC); Online - full text ed.: ISSN 1479-5752. GBP 162, USD 261 to institutions (effective 2006) (from EBSCO Publishing, Gale Group, IngentaConnect, Northern Light Technology, Inc., O C L C Online Computer Library Center, Inc., Swets Information Services).
Indexed: ASCA, ASG, AgeL, CIJE, CommAb, CurCont, EAA, Faml, HRA, IJCS, L&LBA, PRA, PsycInfo, PsycholAb, SFSA, SOPODA, SPAA, SRRA, SSA, SSCI, SociolAb, V&AA, e-psyche.
—BLDSC (4942.369000), IDS, IE, Infotrieve, ingenta. **CCC.**
Published by: (National Communication Association), Routledge (Subsidiary of: Taylor & Francis Ltd), 325 Chestnut St., Suite 800, Philadelphia, PA 19106. TEL 215-625-8900, 800-354-1420, FAX 215-625-8914, jkeyton@ku.edu, journals@routledge.com, http://www.tandf.co.uk/journals/titles/00909882.asp, http://www.routledge.com. Ed. Joann Keyton. Circ: 2,000. **Subscr. to:** Routledge, Customer Services Dept, Rankine Rd, Basingstoke, Hants RG24 8PR, United Kingdom. TEL 44-1256-813000, FAX 44-1256-330245, journals@routledge.com.

➤ **JOURNAL OF BUSINESS COMMUNICATION.** see *BUSINESS AND ECONOMICS—Management*

➤ **JOURNAL OF COMMUNICATION MANAGEMENT.** see *BUSINESS AND ECONOMICS—Management*

621.38 RUS ISSN 1064-2269
TK7800 CODEN: JTELEJ
➤ **JOURNAL OF COMMUNICATIONS TECHNOLOGY AND ELECTRONICS.** Text in English. 1956. m. USD 4,012 in North America; USD 4,613 elsewhere (effective 2004). adv. bk.rev. bibl.; charts; illus.; pat. index. **Document type:** *Journal, Academic/Scholarly.* **Description:** Deals with circuit theory, electrodynamics, wave propagation, magnetics, communications theory, antennas and waveguides, signal processing, solid-state theory and devices.
Former titles (until 1992): Soviet Journal of Communications Technology and Electronics (8756-6648); (until 1984): Radio Engineering and Electronic Physics (0033-7889); (until 1961): Radio Engineering and Electronics (0097-2142)
Related titles: Microform ed.: (from PQC); ♦ English ed.: Radiotekhnika i Elektronika. ISSN 0033-8494; ♦ Translation of: Radiotekhnika i Elektronika. ISSN 0033-8494.
Indexed: AcoustA, CurCont, Englnd, ISR, Inspec, SCI, TelAb.
—BLDSC (0414.227000), AskIEEE, CISTI, Ei, IE, Infotrieve, ingenta, Linda Hall. **CCC.**
Published by: (Rossiiskaya Akademiya Nauk/Russian Academy of Sciences), M A I K Nauka - Interperiodica, Profsoyuznaya ul 90, Moscow, 117997, Russian Federation. TEL 7-095-3347420, FAX 7-095-3360666, compmg@maik.ru, http://www.maik.rssi.ru/journals/comtech.htm, http://www.maik.ru. Ed. Yurii V Gulyaev. R&P Vladimir I Vasil'ev. Circ: 500. **Subscr. to:** Interperiodica, PO Box 1831, Birmingham, AL 35201-1831. TEL 205-995-1567, 800-633-4931, FAX 205-995-1588.

384 USA ISSN 1712-4441
HM716
▼ ➤ **JOURNAL OF COMMUNITY INFORMATICS.** Text in Multiple languages. 2004. q. free (effective 2005). **Document type:** *Journal, Academic/Scholarly.* **Description:** Seeks to work with communities towards the effective use of information and Communication Technologies to improve their processes, achieve their objectives, overcome the "digital divides" that exist both within and between communities, and empower communities and citizens in the range of areas of ICT application including health, cultural production, civic management and e-governance.
Media: Online - full text.
Address: Apt 7C, 20 Waterside Plaza, New York, NY 10010. http://ci-journal.net/index.php.

C

▼ ➤ **JOURNAL OF DIGITAL CONTENTS**; an international journal. see *COMPUTERS—Microcomputers*

➤ **JOURNAL OF FAMILY COMMUNICATION.** see *SOCIOLOGY*

➤ **JOURNAL OF HEALTH COMMUNICATION**; international perspectives. see *MEDICAL SCIENCES*

▼ ➤ **JOURNAL OF INFORMATION, COMMUNICATION AND ETHICS IN SOCIETY**; addressing the social and ethical impacts of new media and ICTS. see *SOCIOLOGY*

380 USA ISSN 1547-2450
TE228.3 CODEN: ITSJF5
➤ **JOURNAL OF INTELLIGENT TRANSPORTATION SYSTEMS**; technology, planning, and operations. Short title: I T S Journal. Text in English. 1993. q. GBP 418, USD 559 combined subscription to institutions print & online eds. (effective 2006). reprint service avail. from PSC. **Document type:** *Journal, Academic/Scholarly.* **Description:** Devoted to scholarly research on the development, management, operation and evaluation of intelligent transportation systems.
Former titles (until 2005): Intelligent Transportation Systems Journal (1024-8072); (until 1995): I V H S Journal (1065-5123)
Related titles: CD-ROM ed.; Online - full text ed.: ISSN 1547-2442. GBP 397, USD 531 to institutions (effective 2006) (from EBSCO Publishing, Gale Group, IngentaConnect, O C L C Online Computer Library Center, Inc., Swets Information Services).
Indexed: ASCA, C&ISA, CurCont, E&CAJ, Englnd, ErgAb, HRIS, IAA, ICEA, Inspec.
—BLDSC (5007.538900), AskIEEE, CISTI, IE, Infotrieve, ingenta. **CCC.**
Published by: (Intelligent Transportation Society of America CHE), Taylor & Francis Inc. (Subsidiary of: Taylor & Francis Group), 325 Chestnut St, Ste 800, Philadelphia, PA 19106. TEL 215-625-8900, 800-354-1420, FAX 215-625-8914, info@taylorandfrancis.com, http://www.tandf.co.uk/journals/titles/15472450.asp, http://www.taylorandfrancis.com. Ed. Asad Khattak. **Subscr. to:** Taylor & Francis Ltd, Journals Customer Service, Rankine Rd, Basingstoke, Hants RG24 8PR, United Kingdom. TEL 44-1256-813000, FAX 44-1256-330245.

➤ **JOURNAL OF INTERCULTURAL COMMUNICATION RESEARCH.** see *SOCIAL SCIENCES: COMPREHENSIVE WORKS*

➤ **JOURNAL OF MARKETING COMMUNICATIONS.** see *BUSINESS AND ECONOMICS—Marketing And Purchasing*

▼ new title ➤ refereed ✶ unverified ♦ full entry avail.

384 200 USA ISSN 1534-8423
BL638
JOURNAL OF MEDIA AND RELIGION. Text in English. 2002. q. USD 250 in US & Canada to institutions; USD 280 elsewhere to institutions; USD 265 in US & Canada to institutions print & online eds. (effective 2006); USD 295 elsewhere to institutions print & online eds. (effective 2005). back issues avail.
Document type: *Journal, Academic/Scholarly.* **Description:** Addresses the broad question of how religion as a social and cultural phenomenon broadens understanding of mass communication in society.
Related titles: Online - full text ed.: ISSN 1534-8415. 2002. USD 240 worldwide (effective 2006) (from EBSCO Publishing, Gale Group, O C L C Online Computer Library Center, Inc., Swets Information Services).
Indexed: PsycInfo, PsycholAb.
—BLDSC (5017.044300), IE, ingenta. **CCC.**
Published by: Lawrence Erlbaum Associates, Inc., 10 Industrial Ave, Mahwah, NJ 07430-2262. TEL 201-258-2200, 800-926-6579, FAX 201-236-0072, journals@erlbaum.com, http://www.leaonline.com/loi/jmr. Eds. Daniel Stout TEL 801-378-7551, Judith Buddenbaum.

384 USA ISSN 0899-7764
➤ **JOURNAL OF MEDIA ECONOMICS.** Text in English. 1988. q. USD 360 in US & Canada to institutions; USD 390 elsewhere to institutions; USD 380 combined subscription in US & Canada to institutions print & online eds.; USD 410 combined subscription elsewhere to institutions print & online eds. (effective 2005). adv. bk.rev. back issues avail.; reprint service avail. from PSC. **Document type:** *Journal, Academic/Scholarly.* **Description:** Source for contemporary research and commentary about economic forces and policy affecting media.
Related titles: Online - full text ed.: ISSN 1532-7736. USD 300 worldwide to institutions (effective 2004) (from EBSCO Publishing, Gale Group, O C L C Online Computer Library Center, Inc., Swets Information Services).
Indexed: ABIn, ASCA, CommAb, CurCont, ESPM, HRA, PAIS, RiskAb, SSCI.
—BLDSC (5017.044500), IE, Infotrieve, ingenta. **CCC.**
Published by: (California State University, Fullerton, Department of Communications), Lawrence Erlbaum Associates, Inc., 10 Industrial Ave, Mahwah, NJ 07430-2262. TEL 201-258-2200, 800-926-6579, FAX 201-236-0072, journals@erlbaum.com, http://www.leaonline.com/loi/me. Ed. Alan B Albarran TEL 940-565-2537. adv.: page USD 350; trim 5 x 8.

C

384 GBR ISSN 1468-2753
➤ **JOURNAL OF MEDIA PRACTICE.** Text in English. 2000. 3/yr. GBP 30 in the European Union to individuals; GBP 38 elsewhere to individuals; GBP 140 combined subscription in the European Union to institutions print & online; GBP 140 combined subscription elsewhere to institutions print & online (effective 2005). back issues avail. **Document type:** *Journal, Academic/Scholarly.* **Description:** Contains articles that build a profile of established and innovative practical approaches to teaching and research, providing and interdisciplinary forum where practice in one field stimulates thinking in another. Encourages analysis of practical work on the shifting boundaries between existing and emerging media forms and explores paths that connect education with creative and industry oriented practice.
Related titles: Online - full content ed.; Online - full text ed.: (from EBSCO Publishing, O C L C Online Computer Library Center, Inc., Swets Information Services).
—BLDSC (5017.045700), IE, ingenta.
Published by: (University of Bristol, Dept. of Drama), Intellect Ltd., PO Box 862, Bristol, BS99 1DE, United Kingdom. TEL 44-117-9589910, FAX 44-117-9589911, info@intellectbooks.com, http://www.intellectbooks.com/journals/jmp.htm. Ed. John Adams TEL 44-1179-287838. R&P, Adv. contact Mr. Robin Beecroft.

➤ **JOURNAL OF ONLINE LEARNING.** see *EDUCATION—Computer Applications*

621.3692 USA ISSN 1619-8638
▼ ➤ **JOURNAL OF OPTICAL AND FIBER COMMUNICATIONS.** Text in English. 2005. 6/yr. EUR 898 to institutions (effective 2005). **Document type:** *Journal, Academic/Scholarly.* **Description:** Academic/Scholarly journal.
Media: Online - full content (from EBSCO Publishing, Springer LINK).
—IE. **CCC.**
Published by: Springer-Verlag New York, Inc. (Subsidiary of: Springer Science+Business Media), 233 Spring St, New York, NY 10013. TEL 212-460-1500, FAX 212-473-6272, journals@springer-ny.com, http://www.springer-ny.com.

621.382 DEU ISSN 0173-4911
CODEN: JOCODG
JOURNAL OF OPTICAL COMMUNICATIONS. Text in English. 1980. 6/yr. EUR 486 domestic; EUR 495.50 in Europe; EUR 506.40 elsewhere; EUR 77.50 newsstand/cover (effective 2005). adv. bk.rev. **Document type:** *Magazine, Trade.* **Description:** Covers all fields of optical communications with guided waves serving the scientific community.
Indexed: C&ISA, ChemAb, ChemTitl, CurCont, E&CAJ, EngInd, Inspec, SolStAb.
—BLDSC (5026.355000), AskIEEE, CASDDS, CISTI, Ei, IDS, IE, Infotrieve, ingenta, Linda Hall. **CCC.**
Published by: Fachverlag Schiele und Schoen GmbH, Markgrafenstr 11, Berlin, 10969, Germany. TEL 49-30-2537520, FAX 49-30-2517248, RThKersten@t-online.de, service@schiele-schoen.de, http://www.schiele-schoen.de/telekommunikation/joc.asp. Ed. R Th Kersten. adv.: B&W page EUR 1,076, color page EUR 1,883. Circ: 1,230 (paid and controlled).

JOURNAL OF ORGANIZATIONAL CULTURE, COMMUNICATIONS AND CONFLICT. see *BUSINESS AND ECONOMICS—Management*

JOURNAL OF SCHOOL PUBLIC RELATIONS. see *EDUCATION*

384 500 ITA ISSN 1824-2049
➤ **JOURNAL OF SCIENCE COMMUNICATION.** Abbreviated title: J C O M. Text in English, Italian. 2002. 4/yr. free (effective 2005). **Document type:** *Journal, Academic/Scholarly.* **Description:** Since the world of communications and the scientific community are now undergoing a rapid, crucial and uncertain transition, JCOM is trying to become an interdisciplinary melting-pot capable of providing some theoretical guidelines for science communication.
Formerly (until 2004): Jekyll.comm (1824-2030)
Media: Online - full text.
Published by: Scuola Internazionale Superiore di Studi Avanzati/International School of Advanced Studies, Via Beirut 4, Trieste, 34014, Italy. TEL 39-040-3787463, FAX 39-040-3787528, http://jcom.sissa.it/common/archive.html, http://www.sissa.it.

384 621.399 POL ISSN 1509-4553
➤ **JOURNAL OF TELECOMMUNICATIONS AND INFORMATION TECHNOLOGY.** Text in English. 2000. q. PLZ 160 domestic; USD 80 foreign; PLZ 40 per issue domestic (effective 2005). back issues avail. **Document type:** *Journal, Academic/Scholarly.* **Description:** Contains the results of scientific research, fundamental and experimental, broadening the knowledge in the field of telecommunications and other fields of information technology - in particular informatics and computer science, photonics, electronics, control science, telematics etc.
Related titles: Online - full content ed.; ♦ Polish ed.: Telekomunikacja i Techniki Informacyjne. ISSN 1640-1549.
Published by: Instytut Lacznosci/National Institute of Telecommunications, ul Szachowa 1, Warsaw, 04894, Poland. TEL 48-22-8724388, FAX 48-22-5128400, redakcja@itl.waw.pl, http://fjg.org.pl/publ/jtit, http://www.itl.waw.pl. Ed. Pawel Szczepanski. **Dist. by:** Ars Polona, Krakowskie Przedmiescie 7, Warsaw, Poland. TEL 48-22-9263914, FAX 48-22-9265334, arspolona@arspolona.com.pl, http://www.arspolona.com.pl.

➤ **JOURNAL OF VISUAL LITERACY.** see *EDUCATION—Teaching Methods And Curriculum*

➤ **JOURNAL ON TELECOMMUNICATIONS & HIGH TECHNOLOGY LAW.** see *LAW*

➤ **JOURNALISTEN JAHRBUCH.** see *JOURNALISM*

➤ **K E S.** (Kommunikations- und EDV Sicherheit) see *COMPUTERS—Computer Security*

384 JPN
KAGAKU SHINBUN TSUSHIN JOHO/SCIENCE NEWS. TELECOMMUNICATION EDITION. Text in Japanese. 1946. w. JPY 600 per month. **Document type:** *Newspaper.*
Published by: Kagaku Shinbunsha, 8-1 Hamamatsu-cho 1-chome, Minato-ku, Tokyo, 105-0013, Japan.

KAGAN'S LATIN AMERICAN BROADBAND. see *COMPUTERS—Data Communications And Data Transmission Systems*

338 USA ISSN 1523-7125
KAGAN'S MEDIA MERGERS & ACQUISITIONS. Text in English. 199?. a. USD 1,095 (effective 2005). **Document type:** *Directory, Trade.* **Description:** Contains data, analysis and statistics covering the latest deal activity across the media industry.
Published by: Kagan Research, LLC, One Lower Ragsdale Dr, Bldg One, Ste 130, Monterey, CA 93940. TEL 831-624-1536, FAX 831-625-3225, info@kagan.com, http://www.kagan.com.

384 JPN ISSN 1346-0404
KENKYUU CHOUSA HOUKOKUSHO (CD-ROM EDITION)✶ /TELECOMMUNICATIONS ADVANCEMENT FOUNDATION. RESEARCH REPORT. Text in Japanese. 1986. a. **Document type:** *Bulletin.*
Formerly (until 2000): Denki Tsushin Fukyu Zaidan Kenkyu Chosa Hokokusho (Print Edition) (0918-7332)
Media: CD-ROM. **Related titles:** Online - full content ed.
Published by: Denki Tsushin Fukyu Zaidan/Telecommunications Advancement Foundation, 2-3-9 Nishi-Shinbashi, Minato-ku, Tokyo, 105-0003, Japan. http://www.taf.or.jp/publication.html. Ed. Hiroshi Inaba. Circ: 1,000.

384 USA ISSN 1533-3140
➤ **KENTUCKY JOURNAL OF COMMUNICATION.** Text in English. 1968-19??; resumed 1996. s-a. (Spr. & Fall). USD 20 domestic to members; USD 30 foreign to members; USD 25, USD 35 domestic to institutions; USD 15 domestic to libraries; USD 25 foreign to libraries; USD 15 newsstand/cover (effective 2005). adv. **Document type:** *Journal, Academic/Scholarly.* **Description:** Covers all aspects of communications, including communications in social change activism, entertainment, education and technologies.
Formerly (until 1987): Kentucky Journal of Communication Arts
Published by: Kentucky Communication Association, Jefferson Community College, Department of Communication, 109 E Broadway, Louisville, KY 40202. TEL 502-213-5120, http://comm.uky.edu/KCA/journal.htm, http://www.kycommunication.com/. Ed. Thomas J Sabetta. Adv. contact Vijay Krishna TEL 812-941-2621. B&W page USD 50, color page USD 60. Circ: 250.

➤ **KEP- ES HANGTECHNIKA.** see *PHYSICS—Optics*

354.75 ISR
KESHER ELEKTRONIKA MACHSHEVIM. Text in Hebrew. q.
Published by: Ministry of Defense Publishing House, 25 David Eleazer St., Hakirya, Tel Aviv, Israel. TEL 03-205403. Ed. Avraham Granit. Circ: 7,000.

070.19 GBR
KEY NOTE MARKET ASSESSMENT. BROADCAST MEDIA. Variant title: Broadcast Media Market Assessment. Text in English. 1999 (Jan). irreg., latest 1999, Jan. GBP 730 per issue (effective 2002). **Description:** Provides an in-depth strategic analysis across a broad range of industries and contains an examination on the scope, dynamics and shape of key UK markets in the consumer, financial, lifestyle and business to business sectors.
Published by: Key Note Ltd., Field House, 72 Oldfield Rd, Hampton, Mddx TW12 2HQ, United Kingdom. TEL 44-20-8481-8750, FAX 44-20-8783-0049, info@keynote.co.uk, http://www.keynote.co.uk.

384.043 338 GBR
KEY NOTE MARKET ASSESSMENT. NEW MEDIA MARKETING. Text in English. 1999. irreg., latest 2000, Nov. GBP 340 per issue (effective 2002). **Description:** Provides an in-depth strategic analysis across a broad range of industries and contains an examination on the scope, dynamics and shape of key UK markets in the consumer, financial, lifestyle and business to business sectors.
Formerly (until 2000): Key Note Market Report: New Media Marketing (1468-1927)
Published by: Key Note Ltd., Field House, 72 Oldfield Rd, Hampton, Mddx TW12 2HQ, United Kingdom. TEL 44-20-8481-8750, FAX 44-20-8783-0049, info@keynote.co.uk, http://www.keynote.co.uk. Ed. Nick Bardsley.

KEY NOTE MARKET REPORT: ACCESS CONTROL. see *CRIMINOLOGY AND LAW ENFORCEMENT—Security*

384 004 302.23 658 GBR
KEY NOTE MARKET REPORT: MULTIMEDIA IN U K. Text in English. 1994. irreg., latest 1994, Jul. GBP 340 per issue (effective 2002). **Document type:** *Trade.* **Description:** Provides and overview of a specific UK market segment and includes executive summary, market definition, market size, industry background, competitor analysis, current issues, forecasts, company profiles, and more.
Formerly: Key Note Market Review: Multimedia in U K (1357-1370)
Related titles: CD-ROM ed.; Online - full text ed.
Published by: Key Note Ltd., Field House, 72 Oldfield Rd, Hampton, Mddx TW12 2HQ, United Kingdom. TEL 44-20-8481-8750, FAX 44-20-8783-0049, info@keynote.co.uk, http://www.keynote.co.uk.

384 GBR ISSN 1367-515X
KEY NOTE MARKET REPORT: TELECOMMUNICATIONS. Variant title: Telecommunications. Text in English. a. (16th Edition), latest 2001, Nov. GBP 340 per issue (effective 2002). **Document type:** *Trade.* **Description:** Provides an overview of a specific UK market segment and includes executive summary, market definition, market size, industry background, competitor analysis, current issues, forecasts, company profiles, and more.
Formerly (until 1995): Key Note Report: Telecommunications (0269-3917)
Related titles: CD-ROM ed.; Online - full text ed.
Published by: Key Note Ltd., Field House, 72 Oldfield Rd, Hampton, Mddx TW12 2HQ, United Kingdom. TEL 44-20-8481-8750, FAX 44-20-8783-0049, info@keynote.co.uk, http://www.keynote.co.uk. Ed. Jacob Howard.

384 GBR
KEY NOTE MARKET REVIEW: U K TELECOMMUNICATIONS. Variant title: U K Telecommunications. Text in English. 1992. irreg. GBP 465 (effective 1999). **Document type:** *Trade.*
Related titles: CD-ROM ed.; Online - full text ed.
Published by: Key Note Ltd., Field House, 72 Oldfield Rd, Hampton, Mddx TW12 2HQ, United Kingdom. TEL 44-20-8481-8750, FAX 44-20-8783-0049, info@keynote.co.uk, http://www.keynote.co.uk.

384 CHE
KOMMUNIKATION. Text in German. 1979. 10/yr. CHF 29; CHF 4 newsstand/cover (effective 2001). adv. **Document type:** *Magazine, Trade.*
Published by: B & L Verlags AG, Steinwiesenstr 3, Schlieren, 8952, Switzerland. TEL 41-1-7333999, FAX 41-1-7333989, info@blverlag.ch, http://www.blverlag.ch. Eds. Juerg Buob, Volker Richert. Circ: 15,200 (paid).

384 DEU
KOMMUNIKATION UND GESELLSCHAFT; in Theorie und Praxis. Text in German. 1995. irreg., latest vol.5, 1998. **Document type:** *Monographic series, Academic/Scholarly.*
Published by: Verlag Reinhard Fischer, Weltistr 34, Munich, 81477, Germany. TEL 49-89-7918892, FAX 49-89-7918310, verlagfischer@compuserve.de, http://www.verlag-reinhard-fischer.de.

343.099 DEU ISSN 1434-6354
KOMMUNIKATION UND RECHT; Betriebs-Berater fuer Medien - Kommunikation - Multimedia. Text in German. 1998. m. EUR 267 domestic; EUR 297 foreign; EUR 25 newsstand/cover (effective 2005). adv. **Document type:** *Magazine, Trade.*
Indexed: DIP, IBR, IBZ.
Published by: Verlag Recht und Wirtschaft GmbH, Mainzer Landstr 251, Frankfurt am Main, 60326, Germany. TEL 49-69-759501, FAX 49-69-75952780, k&r@betriebs-berater.de, verlag@ruw.de, http://www.ruw.de/ruw/zeitschriften/kur/index.html, http://www.ruw-ruw.de. Ed. Thomas Wegerich. Adv. contact Iris Biesinger. color page EUR 2,100, B&W page EUR 1,200; trim 180 x 257. Circ: 2,000 (paid).

384 DEU
KOMMUNIKATIONS-WISSENSCHAFTLICHE STUDIEN. Text in German. irreg., latest vol.17, 1996. **Document type:** *Monographic series, Academic/Scholarly.*
Published by: Verlag Reinhard Fischer, Weltistr 34, Munich, 81477, Germany. TEL 49-89-7918892, FAX 49-89-7918310, verlagfischer@compuserve.de, http://www.verlag-reinhard-fischer.de.

KOMPASS PROFESSIONNEL. ELECTRICITE, ELECTRONIQUE, INFORMATIQUE. see *BUSINESS AND ECONOMICS—Trade And Industrial Directories*

384 SVK ISSN 1335-4205
KOMUNIKACIE/COMMUNICATIONS. Text in Slovak, English. 1999. q. **Document type:** *Journal, Academic/Scholarly.*
Published by: (Zilinska Univerzita, Oddelenie pre Vedu a Vyskum), Vydavatelstvo Zilinskej Univerzity Edis, ul J M Hurbana, Zilina, Slovakia. TEL 42-89-5625919.

KONTAKT. see *BUSINESS AND ECONOMICS—Labor And Industrial Relations*

384 DEU ISSN 1618-7202
KRESS REPORT. Text in German. 1966. w. EUR 312 (effective 2004). adv. **Document type:** *Magazine, Trade.* **Description:** Covers the latest developments, news and personalities in print and online media.
Related titles: ♦ Online - full content ed.: Taeglich Kress; Online - full text ed.: (from LexisNexis).
Published by: Kress Verlag GmbH, Haberstr 17, Heidelberg, 69126, Germany. TEL 49-6221-33100, FAX 49-6221-3310333, post@kress.de, http://www.kress.de/kressinside/kressreport. Ed. Jose Redondo-Vega. Adv. contact Thomas Wengenroth. page EUR 2,500; trim 180 x 240. Circ: 2,327 (paid).

LAMY DROIT DES MEDIAS ET DE LA COMMUNICATION. see *LAW*

LANGUAGE, SPEECH, AND COMMUNICATION. see *LINGUISTICS*

384 USA ISSN 1541-1265
HE7821
LATIN AMERICA TELECOM. Text in English. 1995. m. USD 695 in US & Canada; USD 745 elsewhere (effective 2005). software rev. charts; illus.; mkt.; maps; stat. back issues avail. **Document type:** *Newsletter, Trade.* **Description:** Covers all aspects of telecommunications in Mexico including new installations, technology trends, carrier plans, route maps, contract awards, market demand forecasts, publications, market trends, regulations, competitive analysis, cost trends, new studies, market assessments, potential contracts, PTT plans, and policy.
Formerly: Mexico Telecom (1081-9975)
Related titles: Online - full text ed.: ISSN 1541-1273 (from Florida Center for Library Automation, Gale Group, ProQuest Information & Learning).
Published by: Information Gatekeepers, Inc., 320 Washington St, Ste 302, Brighton, MA 02135. TEL 617-782-5033, 800-323-1088, FAX 617-734-8562, info@igigroup.com, http://www.igigroup.com. Pub. Dr. Paul Polishuk.

621.382 USA
LATIN AMERICA TELECOM WEEKLY. Text in English. w. USD 1,200 to individuals; USD 7,500 to institutions (effective 2000). **Document type:** *Trade.* **Description:** Contains reports on the most critical developments in Latin American, Mexican and Central American telecommunications.
Media: E-mail.
Published by: Gist, Inc., 2200 Wilson Blvd, Ste 102G, Arlington, VA 22201. TEL 703-527-7459, FAX 703-528-1477, info@gist.net, http://www.gist.net.

LATIN AMERICAN LAW AND BUSINESS REPORT. see *LAW—Corporate Law*

384.5 GBR
LATINCOM (ONLINE EDITION). Text in English. fortn. (23/yr.). GBP 2,085, EUR 3,440, USD 3,544 for 1-5 users; online or email ed. (effective 2003). back issues avail. **Document type:** *Newsletter, Trade.* **Description:** Covers the Latin American wireless and broadband communications industries.
Media: Online - full content. **Related titles:** E-mail ed.
Published by: Baskerville (Subsidiary of: T & F Informa plc), Sheepen Place, Colchester, Essex C03 3LP, United Kingdom. TEL 44-20-70175537, FAX 44-20-70174783, telecoms.enquiries@informa.com, http://www.baskerville.telecoms.com/LatinCom. Ed. Leslie Hillman.

343.099 FRA ISSN 1244-9288
LEGICOM; revue du droit de la communication. Text in French. 1993. q. back issues avail. **Description:** Discusses legal issues regarding business communication, marketing, and the media.
Published by: Victoires - Editions, 38 rue Croix des Petits Champs, Paris, 75001, France.

343.099 FRA ISSN 0751-9478
LEGIPRESSE; revue mensuelle du droit de la communication. Text in French. m. (10/yr.). **Description:** keeps readers updated on all French, European, and international news which cover communication laws.
Published by: Victoires - Editions, 38 rue Croix des Petits Champs, Paris, 75001, France. TEL 33-1-53458915, FAX 33-1-42962578.

621.382 FRA
LETTRE DE L'AUDIOVISUEL. Text in French. 1977. w. **Document type:** *Newsletter.*
Published by: Societe des Gens de Lettres de France, Hotel de Massa, 38 rue du Fg. Saint-Jacques, Paris, 75014, France. TEL 40-51-33-00, TELEX SCAMSGL 206963F. Ed. Laurent Duvillier. **Co-sponsor:** Societe Civile des Auteurs Multimedia.

THE LIBERATOR (CARTERSVILLE). see *POLITICAL SCIENCE*

621.382 LBR
LIBERIA. MINISTRY OF POSTS AND TELECOMMUNICATIONS. ANNUAL REPORT✶. Text in English. a.
Published by: Ministry of Posts and Telecommunications, Monrovia, Liberia.

621.382 USA ISSN 0741-5834
TA1800 CODEN: LIGHBR
LIGHTWAVE; fiber optics technology and applications worldwide. Text in English. 1984. m. USD 137 domestic; USD 163 in Canada; USD 197 elsewhere; USD 23 per issue; free (effective 2004); includes Buyers Guide. adv. bk.rev. **Document type:** *Magazine, Trade.* **Description:** For producers and users of the technology enabling the transmission of information via light.
Formerly: Cable Installation & Maintenance
Related titles: Online - full text ed.: (from EBSCO Publishing, Florida Center for Library Automation, Gale Group, O C L C Online Computer Library Center, Inc., ProQuest Information & Learning); ♦ Regional ed(s).: Lightwave Europe.
Indexed: BrCerAb, C&ISA, CADCAM, CerAb, CorrAb, E&CAJ, EIA, EMA, EngInd, EnvAb, IAA, Inspec, M&TEA, MBF, METADEX, MicrocompInd, TelAb, WAA.
—CIS, IE, Infotrieve, Linda Hall. **CCC.**
Published by: PennWell Corp., 98 Spit Brook Rd, Nashua, NH 03062-5737. TEL 603-891-0123, 800-331-4463, FAX 603-891-9177, stephenh@pennwell.com, Headquarters@PennWell.com, http://lw.pennnet.com/home.cfm, http://www.pennwell.com. Eds. Stephen M Hardy TEL 603-891-9454, Patrick McLaughlin. Pub. Jay Regan. adv.: B&W page USD 7,590, color page USD 8,890; trim 14.25 x 11. Circ: 30,000 (paid and controlled).

621.382 USA
LIGHTWAVE BUYERS GUIDE. Text in English. a. USD 79 in US & Canada; USD 95 elsewhere (effective 2004). adv. illus. **Document type:** *Directory, Trade.*
Published by: PennWell Corp., 1421 S Sheridan Rd, Tulsa, OK 74112. TEL 918-835-3161, 800-331-4463, FAX 918-831-9804, http://www.pennwell.com. Ed. Greg Reed. Pub. Marsha Robertson. R&P Brian Taylor. Adv. contact Jane Harrod.

621.382 USA
TK5103.592.F52
LIGHTWAVE EUROPE. Text in English. 2002 (Mar.). m. USD 90 in US & Canada; USD 60 in Europe; free to qualified personnel (effective 2004). **Document type:** *Magazine, Trade.* **Description:** Covers the European fiber optics industries.
Related titles: Online - full content ed.: 2002; ♦ Regional ed(s).: Lightwave. ISSN 0741-5834.
Published by: PennWell Corp., 98 Spit Brook Rd, Nashua, NH 03062-5737. TEL 603-891-0123, 800-331-4463, FAX 603-891-9177, Headquarters@PennWell.com, http://lw.pennnet.com/home.cfm, http://www.pennwell.com. Circ: 15,000.

384 CHE
LIST OF COAST STATIONS. Text in English. biennial. CHF 79. **Document type:** *Bulletin.*
Related titles: Supplement(s):.
Indexed: IIS.
Published by: International Telecommunication Union, Place des Nations, Geneva 20, 1211, Switzerland. TEL 41-22-7306141, FAX 41-22-7305194, sales@itu.ch, http://www.itu.int/publications.

384 CHE
LIST OF I T U - R RECOMMENDATIONS. Text in English. a. free. **Document type:** *Bulletin.*
Related titles: CD-ROM ed.; Online - full text ed.
Published by: International Telecommunication Union, Place des Nations, Geneva 20, 1211, Switzerland. TEL 41-22-7306141, FAX 41-22-7305194, sales@itu.ch, http://www.itu.int/publications. **Dist. in N. America by:** Publications Resource Group, 121 Union St., Box 792, North Adams, MA 01247. TEL 413-664-6185, FAX 413-664-9343.

384 USA
LIST OF MATERIALS ACCEPTABLE FOR USE ON TELECOMMUNICATIONS SYSTEMS OF R U S BORROWERS. Text in English. base vol. plus irreg. updates. looseleaf. USD 200 (effective 2001). **Document type:** *Government.* **Description:** Gives names of manufacturers and catalog numbers for materials acceptable for use on telecommunications systems of RUS borrowers.
Related titles: Online - full content ed.
Published by: U.S. Department of Agriculture, Rural Utilities Service, Technical Standards Committee "A" (Electric), Stop 1569, 1400 Independence Ave, SW, Washington, DC 20250-1569. hbowles@rus.usda.gov, http://www.usda.gov/rus/telecom/materials/lstomat.htm. **Subscr. to:** U.S. Government Printing Office, Superintendent of Documents, PO Box 371954, Pittsburgh, PA 15250-7954. TEL 202-512-1800, FAX 202-512-2250, orders@gpo.gov, http://www.access.gpo.gov.

384 CHE
LIST OF SHIP STATIONS. Text in English, French, Spanish. a. (plus q. updates). CHF 98. **Document type:** *Bulletin.*
Indexed: IIS.
Published by: International Telecommunication Union, Place des Nations, Geneva 20, 1211, Switzerland. TEL 41-22-7306141, FAX 41-22-7305194, sales@itu.ch, http://www.itu.int/publications.

THE LISTENING PROFESSIONAL. see *HUMANITIES: COMPREHENSIVE WORKS*

621.38 SWE ISSN 1403-4387
LJUD & BILD; elektronikvaerlden. Text in Swedish. 1929. 10/yr. SEK 370 (effective 2005). adv. bk.rev. back issues avail. **Document type:** *Magazine, Consumer.*
Former titles (until l998): Elektronikvaerlden (0281-1189); (until 1983): Radio och Television (0033-7749); (until l955): Populaer Radio och Television; (until 1954): Populaer Radio
Related titles: Online - full text ed.
Published by: Elektronikvaerlden Foerlag AB, Oe Koepmangatan 1, PO Box 529, Karlskrona, 37123, Sweden. TEL 46-455-308040, FAX 46-455-308049, ev@ev.se, http://www.ev.se/index.29.html. Pub. Anders Albinsson. adv.: page SEK 20,140; trim 192 x 275. Circ: 23,600.

384 USA
▼ **M 2 M.** Text in English. 2003 (Sep.). q. **Document type:** *Magazine, Trade.* **Description:** Covers the various business and technical applications of communications between man, machine, and mobile devices.
Published by: Specialty Publishing Co., 135 E Saint Charles Rd, Carol Stream, IL 60188. TEL 630-933-0844, FAX 630-933-0845, psmedley@m2mmag.com, http://www.m2mmag.com/, http://www.specialtypub.com. Ed. Michael Jarosik. Pub. Peggy Smedley.

384 DEU
M I M - MEDIEN INSIGHT MULTIMEDIA. Text in German. 1997. w. EUR 120 (effective 2004). adv. **Document type:** *Magazine, Trade.*
Published by: Mediatainment Publishing GmbH, Kolbergerstr 11, Sehnde, 31319, Germany. TEL 49-5138-70010, FAX 49-5138-700129, ad@mediatainmentpublishing,de, http://www.mpnow.de. Ed. Marius Hopp. Adv. contact Jeannine Konrad. color page EUR 3,000. Circ: 8,500 (paid and controlled).

384 RUS ISSN 1682-7201
M KMOBIL'. Text in Russian. 2002. w. **Document type:** *Newspaper, Consumer.*
Published by: Moskovskii Komsomolets, ul 1905 goda, dom 7, Moscow, 123995, Russian Federation. TEL 7-095-2532094, podpiska@mk.ru, http://www.mk.ru.

THE MAGAZINE HANDBOOK (YEAR). see *ADVERTISING AND PUBLIC RELATIONS*

MAGAZINE NEWS. see *ADVERTISING AND PUBLIC RELATIONS*

C

▼ new title ➤ refereed ✶ unverified ♦ full entry avail.

MAJOR TELECOMMUNICATIONS COMPANIES OF EUROPE (YEAR). see *BUSINESS AND ECONOMICS—Trade And Industrial Directories*

MAJOR TELECOMMUNICATIONS COMPANIES OF THE FAR EAST & AUSTRALASIA (YEAR). see *BUSINESS AND ECONOMICS—Trade And Industrial Directories*

384 GBR
MAJOR TELECOMMUNICATIONS COMPANIES OF THE WORLD (YEAR). Text in English. 1998. a. (in 2 vols.). GBP 490 (effective 2001). **Document type:** *Directory, Trade.*
Description: Contains extensive information on the largest companies in the telecommunications and internet industries worldwide. Covering over 4,000 companies with over 24,000 named senior executives.
Published by: Graham & Whiteside Ltd (Subsidiary of: Gale Group), Tuition House, 5-6 Francis Grove, London, SW19 4DT, United Kingdom. TEL 44-20-8947-1011, FAX 44-20-8947-1163, sales@graham-whiteside.com, http://www.galegroup.com/graham&whiteside/. Eds. D Butler, J Bradley, V Bentley. **Dist. by:** Current Pacific Ltd., PO Box 36-536, Northcote, Auckland, New Zealand. TEL 64-9-480-1388, FAX 64-9-480-1387, info@cplnz.com, http://www.cplnz.com.

384 ITA
MANAGEMENT & TELECOMUNICAZIONI. Text in Italian. 10/yr. **Document type:** *Trade.*
Published by: Edicomp Holding SpA, Piazza San Lorenzo in Lucina 26, Rome, 00186, Italy. TEL 39-06-68809644, FAX 39-06-6873645, direzione@edicomp.it, http://www.edicomp.net. Ed. G Carretti.

MASSACHUSETTS INSTITUTE OF TECHNOLOGY. RESEARCH LABORATORY OF ELECTRONICS. R L E PROGRESS REPORT. see *ENGINEERING—Electrical Engineering*

C

MEDIA. see *JOURNALISM*

302 USA ISSN 1098-4208
MEDIA AND CULTURE. Text in English. 2000. irreg., latest 2002. price varies. **Document type:** *Monographic series, Academic/Scholarly.* **Description:** Publishes textbooks and monographs in media and cultural studies, based on research embracing a variety of critical perspectives.
Published by: Peter Lang Publishing, Inc., 275 Seventh Ave, 28th Fl, New York, NY 10001. TEL 212-647-7700, 800-770-5264, FAX 212-647-7707, customerservice@plang.com, http://www.peterlang.com. Eds. Justin Lewis, Sut Jhally.

384 302.23 305.3 GBR
MEDIA AND GENDER MONITOR. Text in English. 1997. s-a. free (effective 2003). **Document type:** *Newsletter.* **Description:** Contains gender perspectives on communication.
Related titles: Online - full text ed.
Published by: World Association for Christian Communication, 357 Kennington Rd, London, SE11 5QY, United Kingdom. TEL 44-20-75829139, FAX 44-20-77350340, wacc@wacc.org.uk, http://www.wacc.org.uk/publications/mgm/main_index.html.

MEDIA & MARKETING. see *ADVERTISING AND PUBLIC RELATIONS*

MEDIA ASIA; an Asian mass communication quarterly operations index. see *PUBLISHING AND BOOK TRADE*

MEDIA DATEN: REGIONALE MAERKTE UND MEDIEN. see *ADVERTISING AND PUBLIC RELATIONS*

384 GBR ISSN 0143-5558
MEDIA DEVELOPMENT. Text in English, Spanish. 1970. q. USD 30 worldwide to individuals; USD 60 in North America to institutions; GBP 40 elsewhere to institutions. bk.rev. illus. **Document type:** *Journal, Academic/Scholarly.* **Description:** Offers informed and critical opinions on a broad range of topics related to the main theme, publishes relevant documents, conference reports, a section on cinema, and book reviews. It articulates common concerns in the search for equality, justice and human dignity in mass and alternative communications.
Formerly: World Association for Christian Communication. Journal (0092-7821)
Related titles: Online - full text ed.
Indexed: CERDIC, ChrPI, CommAb, PRA, V&AA.
—BLDSC (5525.257500), IE, Infotrieve, ingenta. **CCC.**
Published by: World Association for Christian Communication, 357 Kennington Rd, London, SE11 5QY, United Kingdom. TEL 44-20-75829139, FAX 44-20-77350340, wacc@wacc.org.uk, http://www.wacc.org.uk/wacc/publications/media_development. Eds. Philip Lee, Pradip Thomas. Circ: 2,000.

384 BWA
MEDIA DIRECTORY BOTSWANA (YEAR). Text in English. 1992. biennial. adv. **Document type:** *Directory, Government.* **Description:** Lists all public and private printers and broadcasters in Botswana.
Published by: Botswana, Department of Information and Broadcasting, Private Bag 0060, Gaborone, Botswana. TEL 267-3653000, FAX 267-301675, ib.publicity@gov.bw. Ed. Tefo Ray Mangope. Adv. contact Thomas Lesego. color page BWP 300. Circ: 20,000.

MEDIA FACTS. see *ADVERTISING AND PUBLIC RELATIONS*

302.23 GBR ISSN 1472-3352
MEDIA FINANCE. Text in English. 2001. fortn. GBP 345, USD 485 (effective 2001). **Document type:** *Journal, Trade.* **Description:** Primary source information on debt & equity funding in the European media industry.
Media: Online - full content.
Published by: Thompson Stanley Publishers Ltd., Clerkenwell House, 45-47 Clerkenwell Green, London, EC1R 0EB, United Kingdom. TEL 44-20-7553-3919, FAX 44-20-7251-1833, http://www.mediafinance.com. Ed. Tom Rebbeck. R&P Chris Thompson. Circ: 1,000.

343.099 USA ISSN 0148-1045
KF2750
MEDIA LAW REPORTER. Text in English. 1977. w. looseleaf. USD 1,856 (effective 2005 - 2006). index. back issues avail. **Document type:** *Trade.* **Description:** Reference service containing the full-text of federal and state court decisions and selected agency rulings affecting newspapers, magazines, radio, television, film and other media.
Related titles: Online - full text ed.: (from The Bureau of National Affairs, Inc.).
Indexed: LRI.
—**CCC.**
Published by: The Bureau of National Affairs, Inc., 1231 25th St., NW, Washington, DC 20037. TEL 202-452-4200, 800-372-1033, 800-452-7773, FAX 202-822-8092, customercare@bna.com, http://www.bna.com/products/ip/med.htm. Ed. Cynthia J Bolbach. Pub. Greg C McCaffery.

384 USA
MEDIA LIFE. Text in English. d. adv. **Document type:** *Magazine, Trade.* **Description:** Covers news, events and personalities of the mass media.
Media: Online - full content.
Address: http://209.61.190.23/. Ed., Pub. E S Ely.

370 658 USA ISSN 1090-0969
MEDIA MANAGEMENT REVIEW. Text in English. 1997. a.
Published by: Lawrence Erlbaum Associates, Inc., 10 Industrial Ave, Mahwah, NJ 07430-2262. TEL 201-258-2200, FAX 201-236-0072, http://www.erlbaum.com. Ed. Charles Warner.

384 USA
(YEAR) MEDIA MANUFACTURING MARKETPLACE. Text in English. a. USD 39.95 domestic; USD 49.95 foreign (effective 2000). **Document type:** *Directory, Trade.*
Published by: Knowledge Industry Publications, Inc. (Subsidiary of: Access Intelligence, LLC), 701 Westchester Ave, White Plains, NY 10604. TEL 914-328-9157, 800-800-5474, FAX 914-328-9093, http://www.kipinet.com.

384 GBR ISSN 0958-6350
MEDIA MONITOR. Text in English. w. GBP 465, USD 800. **Document type:** *Newsletter, Abstract/Index.* **Description:** Briefs readers on important news items and developments in the media and communications industry.
Related titles: Online - full text ed.: (from Data-Star).
Published by: Financial Times Telecoms & Media Publishing (Subsidiary of: Financial Times Group), Maple House, 149 Tottenham Court Rd, London, W1P 9LL, United Kingdom. TEL 0171-896-2234, FAX 0171-896-2256.

384 CAN ISSN 1492-1340
MEDIA NAMES & NUMBERS; the comprehensive directory of Canada's print and broadcast media. Text in English. 2000. a. CND 89.95 per issue (effective 2003). **Document type:** *Directory.*
Published by: Sources Publishing, 489 College St, Ste 305, Toronto M6G 1A5, ON M6G 1A5, Canada. TEL 416-964-7799, FAX 416-964-8763, sources@sources.com, http://www.sources.com.

MEDIA PLAN. see *ADVERTISING AND PUBLIC RELATIONS*

384 GBR ISSN 0967-0076
MEDIA POCKET BOOK. Text in English. a. GBP 26 (effective 2000). **Document type:** *Trade.* **Description:** Comprehensive statistical profile of British commercial media.
—**CCC.**
Published by: (Advertising Association), N T C Publications Ltd. (Subsidiary of: World Advertising Research Center Ltd.), Farm Rd, Henley-on-Thames, Oxon RG9 1EJ, United Kingdom. TEL 44-1491-411000, FAX 44-1491-571188, info@ntc.co.uk.

MEDIA PSYCHOLOGY. see *PSYCHOLOGY*

384 CHE
MEDIA TREND JOURNAL. Text in English. 10/yr. **Document type:** *Trade.*
Published by: Verlag Media-Daten AG, Kanzleistr 80, Zuerich, 8026, Switzerland. TEL 41-1-2417776, FAX 41-1-2417884. Ed. Raymond Ludi. Circ: 1,500.

070 USA ISSN 0885-4610
MEDIAFILE. Text in English. 1980. bi-m. USD 35 to members (effective 1998). adv. bk.rev.; film rev. illus.
Former titles (until 1980): Media Alliance News; (until 1979): Media Alliance Newsletter
Indexed: AltPI.
Published by: Media Alliance, 1904 Franklin St., Ste. 500, Oakland, CA 94612-2926. TEL 415-546-6334. Ed. Andrea Buffa. Circ: 4,200.

343.099 CHE ISSN 1420-3723
MEDIALEX; revue de droit de la communication - Zeitschrift fuer Kommunikationsrecht. Text in French, German. 1995. q. CHF 99.15 domestic; CHF 107 foreign (effective 2003). **Document type:** *Journal, Trade.*
Indexed: DIP, IBR, IBZ.
Published by: Staempfli Verlag AG (Subsidiary of: LexisNexis Europe and Africa), Woelflistr 1, Bern, 3001, Switzerland. TEL 41-31-3006666, FAX 41-31-3006688, verlag@staempfli.com, http://www.medialex.ch, http://www.staempfli.com. Eds. Denis Barrelet, Franz Riklin. Circ: 600 (paid).

343.099 BEL ISSN 0777-7094
MEDIALEX; selectie van bronnen van de media- en infromatiewetgeving. Text in Dutch. 1990. biennial. EUR 132.62 (effective 2003). **Document type:** *Trade.* **Description:** Covers national and international legal issues pertaining to the mass media.
Related titles: French ed.
Published by: Kluwer Uitgevers (Subsidiary of: Wolters Kluwer Belgique), Ragheno Business Park, Motstraat 30, Mechelen, B-2800, Belgium. TEL 32-15-800-94571, info@kluwer.be, http://www.kluwer.be.

384 USA ISSN 1550-5316
HD9696
MEDIALINE; media, manufacturing & storage for the entertainment industry. Text in English. 1996. m. USD 52 domestic; USD 76 in Canada; USD 90 elsewhere; USD 6 newsstand/cover (effective 2005). back issues avail. **Document type:** *Magazine, Trade.* **Description:** Covers the business and technology issues encountered by the replicators and duplicators of the packaged media. Particular emphasis is given to the business impact of emerging technologies as well as the viability of existing media systems, from electronic to optical to tape-based formats.
Former titles (until 2002?): Replication News Medialine (1529-2029); (until 2000): Replication News (1087-531X)
Related titles: Online - full content ed.; Online - full text ed.: (from Gale Group).
—**CCC.**
Published by: C M P Information, Inc., Entertainment Technology Group (Subsidiary of: C M P Information Ltd.), 460 Park Ave South, 9th Fl, New York, NY 10016. TEL 212-378-0400, FAX 212-378-2160, http://www.MedialineNews.com, http://www.uemedia.com. Ed. Larry Jaffee. Pub. Larry Spitzer.

384 NZL ISSN 1173-8863
MEDIAPEOPLE NZ. Text in English. 1989. q. NZD 520 (effective 2001). 300 p./no.; **Document type:** *Directory.*
Published by: David Reade Limited, PO Box 47 085, Ponsonby, Auckland, 1034, New Zealand. TEL 64-9-376-1055, FAX 64-9-378-1911, publisher@mediapeople.co.nz, http://www.mediapeople.co.nz. Ed. Davide Reade. Circ: 400 (paid).

384 CAN ISSN 1206-209X
MEDIAS D'INFORMATION DU QUEBEC. Text in English. a. CND 39.95 (effective 2000). **Document type:** *Directory.*
Description: Contains listings of communications journals, radio and television stations, public relations agencies, and newspapers in Quebec.
Formerly: Media et Communications au Quebec (1192-330X)
Published by: Quebec dans le Monde, C P 8503, Sainte Foy, PQ G1V 4N5, Canada. TEL 418-659-5540, FAX 418-659-4143.

302.23 USA ISSN 1546-6442
HD9696.O67
▼ **MEDIAWARE;** the professional journal of media makers, movers + shakers. Text in English. 2003 (Mar./Apr.). bi-m.
Published by: International Recording Media Association, 182 Nassau St. Ste. 204, Princeton, NJ 08542. TEL 609-279-1700, FAX 609-279-1999, info@recordingmedia.org, http://www.recordingmedia.org. Ed., Pub. Bruce Apar.

MEDIAWEEK DIRECTORY (CD-ROM EDITION). see *BUSINESS AND ECONOMICS—Trade And Industrial Directories*

302.23 DNK ISSN 0900-9671
➤ **MEDIEKULTUR.** Text in Danish. 1981. biennial. DKK 190; DKK 110 to students; DKK 100 newsstand/cover (effective 2004). **Document type:** *Journal, Academic/Scholarly.*
Formerly (until 1985): Massekultur og Medier (0107-3753)
Indexed: RILM.
Published by: Sammenslutningen af Medieforskere i Danmark, Helsingforsgade 14, Aarhus N, 8200, Denmark. TEL 45-89-429200, FAX 45-89-429202, http://www.media.ku.dk/mediekultur/. Ed. Rikke Schubart.

➤ **MEDIEN IN FORSCHUNG UND UNTERRICHT. SERIE A.** see *SOCIOLOGY*

384 DEU ISSN 0939-9712
MEDIEN-SKRIPTEN; Beitraege zur Medien- und Kommunikationswissenschaft. Text in German. 1988. irreg., latest vol.29, 1997. price varies. **Document type:** *Monographic series, Academic/Scholarly.*
Published by: Verlag Reinhard Fischer, Weltistr 34, Munich, 81477, Germany. TEL 49-89-7918892, FAX 49-89-7918310, verlagfischer@compuserve.de, http://www.verlag-reinhard-fischer.de. Ed. Michael Schenk.

302.23 DEU ISSN 1616-007X
MEDIEN UND FIKTIONEN. Text in German. 2001. irreg., latest vol.3, 2002. EUR 40.20 per vol. (effective 2003). **Document type:** *Monographic series, Academic/Scholarly.*
Published by: Peter Lang GmbH Europaeischer Verlag der Wissenschaften, Eschborner Landstr 42-50, Frankfurt Am Main, 60489, Germany. TEL 49-69-7807050, FAX 49-69-78070543, zentrale.frankfurt@peterlang.com, http://www.peterlang.de. Ed. Helmut Schanze.

371.3 DEU ISSN 1611-9347
▼ **MEDIENPAEDAGOGIK UND MEDIENDIDAKTIK.** Text in German. 2003. irreg., latest vol.6, 2005. price varies. **Document type:** *Monographic series, Academic/Scholarly.*
Published by: Verlag Dr. Kovac, Arnoldstr 49, Hamburg, 22763, Germany. TEL 49-40-3988800, FAX 49-40-39888055, info@verlagdrkovac.de, http://www.verlagdrkovac.de/7-18.htm.

384 DEU ISSN 0179-5724
MEDIENSPIEGEL. Text in German. 1975. m. EUR 142.08 (effective 2005). **Document type:** *Bulletin, Trade.*
Formerly (until 1986): Institut der Deutschen Wirtschaft. Medienspiegel (0171-3930)
Published by: (Institut der Deutschen Wirtschaft), Deutscher Instituts Verlag GmbH, Gustav-Heinemann-Ufer 84-88, Cologne, 50968, Germany. TEL 49-221-4981510, FAX 49-221-4981533, div@iwkoeln.de, http://www.iwkoeln.de. Ed. Karl Schawinsky.

384 DEU
MEDIENZUKUNFT HEUTE. Text in German. 1998. irreg., latest vol.6, 2000. **Document type:** *Monographic series, Academic/Scholarly.*
Published by: (Sozialforschungsstelle Dortmund), Lit Verlag, Grevener Str. 179, Muenster, 48159, Germany. TEL 49-251-235091, FAX 49-251-231972, lit@lit-verlag.de, http://www.lit-verlag.de.

384 DEU
MERCVRIVS; Informationsdienst der Motivgruppe Post- und Fernmeldewesen. Text in German. 1960. q. back issues avail. **Document type:** *Newsletter.*
Address: c/o Fritz Baeker, Ed. & Pub., Am Osterberg 19, Hankensbuettel, 29386, Germany. TEL 05832-2422. Circ: 120.

384 USA
METRO VOICE. Variant title: S T C Metro Voice. Text in English. 199?. 5/yr. adv. **Document type:** *Newsletter.* **Description:** Promotes ideas in the multifaceted field of technical communication. Offers career advice and informs STC NY Metro chapter members of forthcoming professional events.
Published by: Society of Technical Communication, N Y Metro Chapter, c/o Beneficial Technology Corp, 500 Beneficial Center, Peapack, NJ 07977. http://www.stc.org/region1/nyc/www/index.html, http://www.stc-va.org. Eds. John Dechiara, Margaret Teegan.

MICHIGAN TELECOMMUNICATIONS & TECHNOLOGY LAW REVIEW. see *LAW*

621.382 SGP
MIDDLE EAST COMMUNICATIONS. Text in English. m. adv. **Document type:** *Magazine, Trade.* **Description:** Covers the public and private communications networks, applications and support services in the Middle East.
Published by: Charlton Media Group, 9B Stanley St, Singapore, 068728, Singapore. TEL 65-6223-7660, admin@charltonmedia.com, http://www.charltonmedia.com. Ed. Angela McFeeters. Pub. Timothy Charlton.

621.382 USA
MIDDLE EAST TELECOM MONTHLY. Text in English. m. USD 850 to individuals; USD 3,300 to institutions (effective 2000). **Document type:** *Bulletin, Trade.* **Description:** Contains vital information for telecom investors, equipment sellers, and operators in the following markets: Saudi Arabia, Pakistan, Turkey, Lebanon, Iran, Jordan, Israel, Syria, Iraq, Kuwait, Bahrain, Qatar, UAE, Oman and Yemen.
Published by: Gist, Inc., 2200 Wilson Blvd, Ste 102G, Arlington, VA 22201. TEL 703-527-7459, FAX 703-528-1477, info@gist.net, http://www.gist.net.

384 CUB
MINISTERIO DE COMUNICACIONES DE CUBA. CENTRO DE INFORMACION DE COMUNICACIONES. COMUNICACIONES. Text in Spanish. s-a. USD 15 in the Americas; USD 16 in Europe.
Published by: (Cuba. Ministerio de Comunicaciones, Cuba. Centro de Informacion de Comunicaciones), Ediciones Cubanas, Obispo No. 527, Apdo. 605, Havana, Cuba. TEL 32-5556-60.

621.395 HRV ISSN 1332-1951
MOBIL. Text in Croatian. 1999. m. adv. **Document type:** *Magazine, Consumer.*
Address: Trg Sportova 11, Zagreb, 10000, Croatia. TEL 385-1-4856575, FAX 385-1-3092200, direktor@mobil.hr. Ed. Dario Hofman.

681.3 CZE ISSN 1211-6343
MOBIL. Text in Czech. 1996. m. CZK 495 (effective 2003). adv. **Document type:** *Magazine, Consumer.*
Related titles: Online - full text ed.: ISSN 1213-6662.
Published by: Trade & Leisure Publications, s.r.o., Pernerova 35a, Prague 8, 186 00, Czech Republic. TEL 420-2-225386561, FAX 420-2-225386555, mobilmag@mobilmag.cz, tlp@tlp.cz, http://mobilmag.cz, http://www.tlp.cz. Ed. Petr Sedlak.

621.382 NLD
MOBILE AND PERSONAL COMMUNICATIONS. Text in Dutch. irreg., latest 1995. price varies. **Document type:** *Proceedings, Academic/Scholarly.*
Formerly: Mobile and Personal Satellite Communications
Published by: Elsevier BV (Subsidiary of: Elsevier Science & Technology), Radarweg 29, Amsterdam, 1043 NX, Netherlands. TEL 31-20-4853911, FAX 31-20-4852457, nlinfo-f@elsevier.nl, http://www.elsevier.nl. Ed. E Del Re.

621.382 GBR ISSN 1462-1959
MOBILE COMMUNICATIONS (LONDON). Text in English. 1988. fortn. GBP 995, EUR 1,642, USD 1,692 (effective 2004). **Document type:** *Newsletter, Trade.* **Description:** Covers commercial aspects of the mobile communications industry, including cellular radio, private mobile radio, paging services, cordless telephones, airborne communications and satellite mobile services.
Formerly (until 1990): FinTech 7 Mobile Communications (0953-539X)
Related titles: Microform ed.: (from PQC); Online - full text ed.: (from Gale Group, O C L C Online Computer Library Center, Inc., ProQuest Information & Learning).
Indexed: B&I, RefZh.
Published by: Baskerville (Subsidiary of: T & F Informa plc), Sheepen Place, Colchester, Essex C03 3LP, United Kingdom. TEL 44-20-70175537, FAX 44-20-70174783, telecoms.enquiries@informa.com, http://www.baskerville.telecoms.com/. Ed. Shani Raja.

621.38 GBR ISSN 1352-9226
MOBILE COMMUNICATIONS INTERNATIONAL. Text in English. 1988. q. GBP 100, USD 180. **Document type:** *Trade.*
Formerly (until 1992): Pan-European Mobile Communications (0958-157X)
Related titles: Online - full text ed.: (from ProQuest Information & Learning); ♦ Supplement(s): Wireless Evolution. ISSN 1472-7226.
Indexed: CurCont.
—BLDSC (5879.953210), IE, Infotrieve, ingenta. **CCC.**
Published by: I B C Business Publishing Ltd., I B C Business Publishing Ltd. (Subsidiary of: I B C Group Plc), 37-41 Mortimer St, London W1N 7RJ, London, W1N 8JK, United Kingdom. TEL 44-20-7637-4383, FAX 44-20-7636-6414, http://www.bankingtech.com.

384 GBR
MOBILE COMMUNICATIONS WEEKLY✶. Text in English. 1992. 50/yr. GBP 499; USD 995 foreign. **Document type:** *Trade.*
Published by: F T Media & Telecom, 149 Tottenham Court Rd, London, W1P 9LL, United Kingdom. Ed. Frazer Nicolson. Circ: 50.

621.382 USA
➤ **MOBILE COMPUTING AND COMMUNICATIONS REVIEW.** Variant title: MC2R. Text in English. q. adv. **Document type:** *Journal, Academic/Scholarly.* **Description:** Covers state-of-the-art research and practice in the field of mobile computing and communications.
Related titles: Online - full text ed.
Indexed: Inspec.
Published by: Association for Computing Machinery, Inc., 1515 Broadway, 17th Fl, New York, NY 10036-5701. TEL 212-626-0500, 212-626-0520, 800-342-6626, FAX 212-869-0481, sigs@acm.org, usacm@acm.org, http://www.acm.org.

621.38 USA ISSN 1523-763X
MOBILE ELECTRONICS. Text in English. 1983. m. (plus Factbook in Nov). USD 35 domestic; USD 42 in Canada; USD 75 elsewhere; USD 5 newsstand/cover; free to qualified personnel (effective 2005). adv. charts; illus.; mkt.; tr.lit. 84 p./no.; back issues avail.; reprints avail. **Document type:** *Journal, Trade.* **Description:** Technical journal covering automotive aftermarket electronics.
Former titles (until 1999): Mobile Electronics Retailer (1522-0656); (until 199?): Installation News (0887-2287)
Related titles: Online - full text ed.; Supplement(s): Security Supplement; Technical Supplement.
Published by: Bobit Business Media, 3520 Challenger St, Torrance, CA 90503. TEL 310-533-2400, FAX 310-533-2500, info@me-mag.com, http://www.me-mag.com, http://www.bobit.com. Pub. Joni Reilly. adv.: B&W page USD 3,380, color page USD 4,310; bleed 8.125 x 11. Circ: 22,520 (controlled).

384 004 NLD ISSN 1574-017X
▼ ➤ **MOBILE INFORMATION SYSTEMS.** Text in English. 2005. q. EUR 312, USD 373 combined subscription print & online eds. (effective 2006). **Document type:** *Journal, Academic/Scholarly.* **Description:** Aims to be a source for mobile information systems research and development and to serve as an outlet for facilitating communication and networking among mobile information systems researchers and practitioners and professionals across academics, government, industry and students.
Media: Online - full text (from Swets Information Services).
—**CCC.**
Published by: I O S Press, Nieuwe Hemweg 6B, Amsterdam, 1013 BG, Netherlands. TEL 31-20-6883355, FAX 31-20-6203419, info@iospress.nl, http://www.iospress.nl/1574017x.php. Ed. David Taniar. R&P Ms. Carry Koolbergen TEL 31-20-6382189. Adv. contact Ms. Jolijn van Eunen.

➤ **MOBILE INTERNET.** see *COMPUTERS—Internet*

621.382 GBR
MOBILE MAGAZINE TECHNOLOGY TO GO. Text in English. m. USD 12 domestic; USD 26 in Canada; USD 39 elsewhere (effective 2005). **Document type:** *Magazine, Consumer.*
Published by: Future Publishing Ltd., Beauford Court, 30 Monmouth St, Bath, Avon BA1 2BW, United Kingdom. TEL 44-1225-442244, FAX 44-1225-446019, http://www.mobilemagazine.com. Ed. Christopher Null. **Subscr. to:** Mobile Magazine, Customer Care, P.O. Box 5515, Harlan, IA 51593-3015. TEL 800-865-7240.

MOBILE MEDIA. see *COMPUTERS—Internet*

MOBILE NETWORKS AND APPLICATIONS. see *COMPUTERS—Computer Networks*

384 AUS
MOBILE'S IN CHINA NEWSLETTER. Text in English. m. **Document type:** *Newsletter.* **Description:** Reports developments in the mobile telecommunications market in China.
Media: Online - full text.
Address: moh1@tig.com.au, http://homepages.tig.com/au/~moh1/index.html. Ed. Mike Haill.

384 FRA ISSN 1253-4560
MOBILES MAGAZINE; the number one in mobile communication. Text in French. 1997. 11/yr. EUR 49 domestic; EUR 68 foreign (effective 2005). illus.; mkt.; maps. back issues avail. **Document type:** *Magazine, Trade.* **Description:** Contains information about wireless technology, including tariffs and consumer guides for mobile phones and PDA.
Published by: Oracom, 53 Rue de Tubigo, Paris, 75003, France. TEL 33-1-48740341, FAX 33-1-48740125, redac@mobilesmagazine.com, http://www.mobilesmagazine.com. Ed. Anne Bleuzen. Pub. Jean Philippe Pecoul. R&P Nathalie Cohen. Adv. contact Anne Rambier. Circ: 60,000.

681.3 CZE ISSN 1212-9879
MOBILITY. Text in Czech. 2000. m. CZK 350 (effective 2003). adv. **Document type:** *Magazine, Consumer.*
Published by: Computer Press a.s., Pod Vinici 23, Prague 4, 143 11, Czech Republic. TEL 420-2-225273930, FAX 420-2-225273934, webmaster@cpress.cz, http://mobility.cpress.cz, http://www.cpress.cz. Ed. Marek Lutonsky. Adv. contact Miroslava Doubkova. page CZK 83,000; trim 210 x 297.

621.38 CZE ISSN 1214-1887
MOBILMANIA.CZ. Text in Czech. 2000. d. adv. **Document type:** *Consumer.*
Media: Online - full content.
Published by: Computer Press a.s., Pod Vinici 23, Prague 4, 143 11, Czech Republic. TEL 420-2-225273930, FAX 420-2-225273934, webmaster@cpress.cz, http://www.mobilmania.cz, http://www.cpress.cz. Ed. Petr Broza. Adv. contact Jan Vobecky. online banner CZK 560.

384 RUS ISSN 1562-4293
MOBIL'NYE TELEKOMMUNIKATSII/MOBILE COMMUNICATIONS INTERNATIONAL. Text in Russian. 1999. 10/yr. **Document type:** *Magazine, Trade.*
Indexed: RefZh.
Published by: Profi-Press, ul Sel's'kokhozyaistvennaya, d 19, korp 2, Moscow, 129226, Russian Federation. TEL 7-095-1814317, FAX 7-095-7428032, info@mobilecomm.ru, http://www.mobilecomm.ru. Ed. Vyacheslav Afanasiev.

MOBISYS: INTERNATIONAL CONFERENCE ON MOBILE SYSTEMS, APPLICATIONS AND SERVICES. see *COMPUTERS*

MODEM & TELECOMUNICAZIONI. see *ELECTRONICS*

621.395 HRV ISSN 1332-3423
MOJ MOBY. Text in Croatian. 2000. m. adv. **Document type:** *Magazine, Consumer.*
Related titles: Online - full text ed.

C

▼ new title ➤ refereed ✶ unverified ♦ full entry avail.

Published by: A1 Video d.o.o., Cvijete Zuzoric 25, Zagreb, 10000, Croatia. TEL 385-1-6117354, FAX 385-1-6154563, moby@mojmoby.com, http://www.mojmoby.com. Ed. Bojan Muscet.

384　　　USA　　　ISSN 1099-7229
MOTIVATIONAL MANAGER. Text in English. 1993. m. USD 119.
Document type: Newsletter. **Description:** Ideas and techniques for those who speak in public.
Formerly: Speaker's Idea File
Related titles: Online - full text ed.: (from EBSCO Publishing).
Published by: Lawrence Ragan Communications, Inc., 316 N Michigan Ave, Ste 300, Chicago, IL 60601. TEL 312-960-4140, 800-878-5331, FAX 312-960-4106, cservice@ragan.com, http://www.ragan.com. Ed. John Cowan.

MULTILINGUAL COMMUNICATIONS & TECHNOLOGY. see *COMPUTERS*

MULTIMIND - N L P AKTUELL. see *PSYCHOLOGY*

MULTINATIONAL TELECOMMUNICATIONS COMPANIES. see *BUSINESS AND ECONOMICS—International Commerce*

N & C - NETWORKS UND COMMUNICATIONS. see *COMPUTERS—Computer Networks*

621.382　　　NLD　　　ISSN 1567-892X
　　　　　　　　　　　　　　CODEN: NERTA9
➤ **N E R G.** Text in Dutch, English. 1920. bi-m. bk.rev. bibl.; charts; illus. index. **Document type:** Journal, Academic/Scholarly. **Description:** Publishes in areas of research and development in information science, electronics and data transmission systems.
Former titles (until 1997): Nederlands Elektronica- en Radiogenootschap. Tijdschrift (0374-3853); (until 1972): Elektronica en Telecommunicatie (0013-5623)
Indexed: Inspec.
—AskIEEE, CISTI, IE, Infotrieve, Linda Hall.
Published by: Nederlands Elektronica- en Radiogenootschap, PO Box 39, Leidschendam, 2260 AA, Netherlands. TEL 31-70-3325112, FAX 31-70-3326477, secretariat@nerg.nl, http://www.nerg.nl. Ed. A A Spanjersberg. Circ: 900 (controlled).

384　　　JPN
N T T DO CO MO TECHNICAL JOURNAL. Text in English. 1999. q. JPY 3,000. **Document type:** Journal, Trade.
Published by: (N T T Mobile Communications Network, Inc. USA), Telecommunications Association/Denki Tsushin Kyokai, New Yurakucho Bldg, 1-11 Yuraku-cho, Chiyoda-ku, Tokyo, 1000006, Japan. http://www.tta.or.jp/.

621.38　　　JPN　　　ISSN 1348-3447
TK5101.A1　　　　　　　　CODEN: NTTREK
N T T TECHNICAL REVIEW. Text in English. 1989. m. JPY 28,920; JPY 2,100 newsstand/cover (effective 2005).
Document type: Journal, Academic/Scholarly.
Formerly (until Mar. 2003): N T T Review (0915-2334); Which was formed by the merger of (1959-1989): Japan Telecommunications Review (0021-4744); (1960-1989): Electrical Communications Laboratories. Review (0029-067X); Which was formerly (1953-1959): Electrical Communication Laboratory. Reports (0418-6338)
Indexed: C&ISA, E&CAJ, Inspec, SolStAb.
—BLDSC (6180.610100), CISTI, IE, ingenta, Linda Hall.
Published by: Telecommunications Association/Denki Tsushin Kyokai, POB 2522, Tokyo Opera City Tower, 3-20-2, Nishi-Shinjuku, Shinjuku-ku, Tokyo, 163-1455, Japan. TEL 81-3-53530185, FAX 81-3-53530195, jrr@tta.or.jp, http://www.tta.or.jp/. **Dist. outside of Japan by:** Maruzen Co., Ltd., Import & Export Dept, PO Box 5050, Tokyo International, Tokyo 100-3191, Japan. TEL 81-3-32733234, FAX 81-3-32716076. **Co-sponsor:** Nippon Telegraph and Telephone Corp.

621.382　　　DEU　　　ISSN 0948-728X
　　　　　　　　　　　　　　CODEN: NAZEAA
N T Z; Informationstechnik und Telekommunikation. (Nachrichtentechnische Zeitschrift) Text in German. 1948. m. EUR 90.90; EUR 9.50 newsstand/cover (effective 2004). adv. bk.rev.; software rev. abstr.; charts; illus.; mkt. index. 66 p./no. 3 cols./p.; **Document type:** Magazine, Trade.
Formerly (until 1995): N T Z - Nachrichtentechnische Zeitschrift (0027-707X)
Indexed: ChemAb, CybAb, EngInd, IBR, Inspec, PROMT, RASB, RefZh.
—BLDSC (6011.300000), AskIEEE, CISTI, IE, Infotrieve, ingenta, Linda Hall. **CCC.**
Published by: V D E Verlag GmbH, Bismarckstr 33, Berlin, 10625, Germany. TEL 49-30-34800148, FAX 49-30-34800188, http://www.vde-verlag.de/ntz.html, zeitschriftenvertrieb@vde-verlag.de, ntz.redaktion@vde-verlag.de, http://www.vde-verlag.de. Ed. Stephan Mayer. Adv. contact Markus Lehnert. B&W page EUR 2,580, color page EUR 3,755; trim 189 x 270. Circ: 8,662 (paid and controlled).

808.53　　　USA　　　ISSN 0749-1042
➤ **NATIONAL FORENSIC JOURNAL.** Text in English. 1983. s-a. USD 15 to non-members. adv. bk.rev. back issues avail.
Document type: Journal, Academic/Scholarly. **Description:** Includes articles and reviews on individual events, speaking, and Lincoln-Douglas debating.
Published by: National Forensic Association, PO Box 256, River Falls, WI 54022-0256. TEL 715-425-3198, 800-228-5424, FAX 715-425-9533, http://cas.bethel.edu/dept/comm/nfa/nfj.html. Ed. Dr. Andrew C Billings TEL 864-656-1477. Circ: 300 (paid).

384　　　ZMB　　　ISSN 1010-8394
NATIONAL MIRROR. Text in English. 1971. w. ZMK 72,800, USD 32.50. adv. bk.rev. **Document type:** Newspaper.
Formerly: With One Voice
Published by: Multimedia Zambia Registered Trustees, PO Box 320199, Lusaka, Zambia. TEL 260-1-261960. Ed. Fanwell Chembo. Circ: 12,000.

387.2　　　GBR
NAVTEX MANUAL. Text in English. 1988. irreg., latest vol.2, 1994. GBP 8, GBP 10. illus. **Description:** Describes the design and use of NAVTEX, an automated information system to relay important navigational and meteorological warnings among ships.
Related titles: French ed.; Spanish ed.
Published by: International Maritime Organization/Organisation Maritime Internationale, 4 Albert Embankment, London, SE1 7SR, United Kingdom. TEL 44-171-735-7611, FAX 44-171-587-3210.

NETIVERK; medlemsblad for el & it forbundet. see *LABOR UNIONS*

384　　　FRA　　　ISSN 1763-7864
▼ **NETSUDS.** Text in French. 2003. irreg. **Document type:** Journal, Academic/Scholarly.
Related titles: Online - full text ed.
Published by: L' Harmattan, 5 rue de l'Ecole Polytechnique, Paris, 75005, France. TEL 33-1-43257651, FAX 33-1-43258203, a.chenau-loquay@sciencespobordeaux.fr, http://www.africanti.org, http://www.editions-harmattan.fr.

NETWORK CONTRACTS REPORT. see *COMPUTERS—Computer Industry, Vocational Guidance*

NETWORK OPERATIONS AND MANAGEMENT SYMPOSIUM. see *COMPUTERS—Computer Systems*

384　　　DEU　　　ISSN 0548-3093
NEUES VON ROHDE UND SCHWARZ. Text in German. 1961. 3/yr. free. abstr.; charts; illus. index. **Document type:** Bulletin.
Related titles: English ed.: News from Rohde & Schwarz. ISSN 0028-9108; French ed.: Actualites de Rohde et Schwarz. ISSN 0174-0660.
Indexed: Inspec.
—CCC.
Published by: Rohde und Schwarz, Muehldorfstr 15, Munich, 81671, Germany. FAX 49-89-4129-3208, TELEX 523703-20. Eds. G Soennichsen, H Wegener. Circ: 100,000.

384　　　GBR
NEW CARRIER. Text in English. m. **Document type:** Trade. **Description:** Helps senior management readers spot that next selling opportunity while offering solid advice on where to buy up-to-spec equipment, software, and services from tuned-in suppliers.
Published by: Emap Media Ltd. (Subsidiary of: Emap Business Communications Ltd.), 33-39 Bowling Green Ln, London, EC1R 0DA, United Kingdom. TEL 44-20-7505-8000, FAX 44-20-7505-8504, http://www.totaltele.com/media/nc. Circ: 20,000 (controlled).

621.382　　　JPN　　　ISSN 0912-0076
NEW ERA OF TELECOMMUNICATIONS IN JAPAN. Text in English. 1985. s-m. USD 700. **Document type:** Newsletter.
Related titles: Japanese ed.: New Era of Telecommunications in Japan (Nihongo-ban). ISSN 0912-0084. 1985.
Published by: Telecommunications Association/Denki Tsushin Kyokai, POB 2522, Tokyo Opera City Tower, 3-20-2, Nishi-Shinjuku, Shinjuku-ku, Tokyo, 163-1455, Japan. TEL 81-3-53530185, FAX 81-3-53530195, http://www.tta.or.jp/. Ed. Kazuki Shibuta. Circ: 500.

NEW JERSEY MEDIA GUIDE. see *BUSINESS AND ECONOMICS—Trade And Industrial Directories*

384　　　GBR　　　ISSN 1364-7776
NEW MEDIA AGE. Text in English. 1996. w. GBP 149 domestic; GBP 175 in Europe; GBP 208 elsewhere (effective 2000). adv. back issues avail. **Document type:** Trade. **Description:** Covers the issues of publishing in the new media - Internet publishing, on-line databases, CD-ROM, video-on-demand - and all other ways there are of representing digital content or material.
Related titles: Online - full text ed.: N M A Online (from EBSCO Publishing, Gale Group, H.W. Wilson, LexisNexis, O C L C Online Computer Library Center, Inc., ProQuest Information & Learning).
Indexed: ABIn, BPI, CompD.
—IE, Infotrieve.

Published by: Centaur Publishing, St Giles House, 50 Poland St, London, W1V 4AX, United Kingdom. TEL 44—20-7970-4000, FAX 44-20-7970-4009, http://www.newmediazero.com/nma/, http://www.nma.co.uk. Ed. Phil Dwyer. R&P Nigel Roby. Adv. contact Davina Lines.

384　　　GBR　　　ISSN 1471-4329
NEW MEDIA CREATIVE. Text in English. 1999. m. adv.
Document type: Magazine, Trade. **Description:** Covers the stylistic and technological aspects of all types of digital media.
Related titles: Online - full text ed.: (from Gale Group, LexisNexis).
Published by: Centaur Publishing, St Giles House, 50 Poland St, London, W1V 4AX, United Kingdom. TEL 44-20-7970-4000, http://www.newmediazero.com/nmc/, http://www.centaur.co.uk.

384　　　JPN　　　ISSN 0289-1115
NEW MEDIA INFORMATION. Text in Japanese. 1983. m. JPY 1,000 per issue.
Published by: Kyoto Nyu Media Kondankai, Kyoto Shinbunsha, Ebisugawa Agaru, Karasuma Dori, Nakagyo-ku, Kyoto-shi, Kyoto 604, Japan.

NEW YORK GENERATOR. see *LABOR UNIONS*

384　　　JPN　　　ISSN 0910-7215
NIKKEI COMMUNICATIONS. Text in Japanese. 1985. s-m. JPY 15,100. adv. **Document type:** Trade. **Description:** Contains technical and business-oriented reviews of the communications industry, including reports on equipment, framework, and regulatory environment.
Published by: Nikkei Business Publications Inc. (Subsidiary of: Nihon Keizai Shimbun, Inc.), 2-1-1 Hirakawa-cho, Chiyoda-ku, Tokyo, 102-8622, Japan. TEL 81-3-5210-8311, FAX 81-3-5210-8530, info@nikkeibpnyc.com, http://www.nikkeibp.com. Ed. Kazuhito Zde. Pub. Takuzou Niwa. Adv. contact Zenta Kishi. B&W page JPY 564,000, color page JPY 846,000; trim 208 x 280. Circ: 40,455. **Dist. in America by:** Nikkei Business Publications America Inc., 575 Fifth Ave, 20th Fl, New York, NY 10017.

NIKKEI INTERNET TECHNOLOGY. see *COMPUTERS—Internet*

384　　　JPN
NIKKEI MOBILE COMPUTING. Text in Japanese. 1998. m. JPY 680 newsstand/cover. adv. **Document type:** Trade.
Description: Reports on how to make efficient use of mobile communications including PHS, portable phones, related software and communications services.
Formerly: Nikkei Mobile
Published by: Nikkei Business Publications Inc. (Subsidiary of: Nihon Keizai Shimbun, Inc.), 2-1-1 Hirakawa-cho, Chiyoda-ku, Tokyo, 102-8622, Japan. TEL 81-3-5210-8311, FAX 81-3-5210-8530, info@nikkeibpnyc.com, webmaster@nikkeibp.com, http://www.nikkeibp.com. Ed. Yoshiki Mashimo. Pub. Tamio Ota. Adv. contact Hiroshi Shirai. B&W page JPY 374,000, color page JPY 530,000; trim 210 x 280. Circ: 110,000. **Dist. in America by:** Nikkei Business Publications America Inc., 575 Fifth Ave, 20th Fl, New York, NY 10017.

384　　　JPN　　　ISSN 0387-0235
NIPPON SHINGO GIHO★ /NIPPON SIGNAL TECHNICAL JOURNAL. Text in Japanese. 1977. q. JPY 500 per issue.
Published by: Nippon Shingo K.K., Gijutsu Kenkyu Senta/Nippon Signal Co., Ltd., Technical Research Center, 3-1-1 Higashi-Ikebukuro, Toshima, Tokyo, 170-6047, Japan. TEL 81-3-59544600, FAX 81-3-59544610, http://www.signal.co.jp/.

621.382　　　NLD　　　ISSN 0923-0068
➤ **NORTH-HOLLAND STUDIES IN TELECOMMUNICATION.** Text in English. 1982. irreg., latest vol.19, 1993. price varies.
Document type: Monographic series, Academic/Scholarly.
Description: Examines trends in various areas of telecommunications.
Supersedes (in 1986): Studies in Telecommunications (0923-005X)
Indexed: Inspec.
—BLDSC (6150.024000), ingenta.
Published by: Elsevier BV, North-Holland (Subsidiary of: Elsevier Science & Technology), Sara Burgerhartstraat 25, Amsterdam, 1055 KV, Netherlands. TEL 31-20-485-3911, FAX 31-20-485-2457, nlinfo-f@elsevier.nl, http://www.elsevier.nl/ homepage/about/us/regional_sites.htt, http://www.elsevier.nl. **Subscr. to:** Elsevier BV, PO Box 211, Amsterdam 1000 AE, Netherlands. TEL 31-20-485-3757, FAX 31-20-485-3432.

➤ **NORTHERN LIGHTS**; film og media studies yearbook. see *MOTION PICTURES*

385　　　JPN
NYU MEDIA HAKUSHO/WHITE PAPER ON NEW MEDIUM. Text in Japanese. 1984. a. JPY 4,800.
Published by: (Nihon Joho Tsushin Shinko Kyokai), Nikkan Kogyo Shimbun, Ltd., 14-1 Nihonbashikoamicho, Chuo-ku, Tokyo, 103-8548, Japan.

659.111   CAN   ISSN 0381-8632

O C S NOUVELLES. Text in French. 1970. q. CND 25; CND 35 foreign. adv. bk.rev.; film rev.; video rev. bibl. **Document type:** *Newsletter.* **Description:** Provides articles on current issues such as media literacy, ethics and media, information on Web sites, world media events and activities for its members. —CCC.
Published by: Office des Communications Sociales, 1340 E boul St Joseph, Montreal, PQ H2J 1M3, Canada. TEL 514-524-8223, FAX 514-524-8522, ocs@cam.org. Ed. Bertrand Ouellet. R&P, Adv. contact Denis Dompierre. Circ: 900.

OCEAN VOICE; maritime information technology and electronics. see *TRANSPORTATION—Ships And Shipping*

O'DWYER'S DIRECTORY OF CORPORATE COMMUNICATIONS. see *BUSINESS AND ECONOMICS—Trade And Industrial Directories*

384   JPN

ON THE LINE. Text in Japanese. 1953. 10/yr. free. **Document type:** *Corporate.*
Published by: K D D, Office of Public Relations, 3-2 Nishi-Shinjuku 2-chome, Shinjuku-ku, Tokyo, 160-0023, Japan. TEL 81-3-3504-6413. Ed. Yoshitada Ishida. Circ: 25,000.

384   USA   ISSN 1542-0639
TK5104

ONLINE JOURNAL OF SPACE COMMUNICATION. Text in English. 2002. q. free (effective 2005). **Document type:** *Journal, Academic/Scholarly.* **Description:** A cross-disciplinary scholarly publication designed to advance space communication as a profession and as an academic discipline.
Media: Online - full text.
Published by: Ohio University, Institute for Telecommunications Studies, Athens, OH 45701. TEL 740-593-4866, FAX 740-593-9184, http://satjournal.tcom.ohiou.edu/.

384   USA   ISSN 1089-8980

OPERATOR; devoted to coverage of issues affecting the operator services and directory industries. Text in English. 1991. m. looseleaf. USD 795; USD 820 foreign (effective 1999). back issues avail. **Document type:** *Newsletter.* **Description:** Focuses on news of technology, regulations, and competition in the telecommunications industry. Topics covered operator services and directories.
Related titles: Online - full text ed.
Published by: Whitaker Associates, 2226 Mohegan Dr., Apt. A1, Falls Church, VA 22043-2534. TEL 703-506-1220, operator@whitaker.com, http://www.whitaker.com. Ed., Pub. Stuart M Whitaker. Circ: 100 (paid).

OPTOELECTRONICS CONFERENCE. TECHNICAL DIGEST. see *ELECTRONICS*

621.382   JPN   ISSN 0386-4987
Q4

OSAKA DENKI TSUSHIN DAIGAKU KENKYU RONSHU. SHIZEN KAGAKU HEN/OSAKA ELECTRO-COMMUNICATION UNIVERSITY. MEMOIRS. NATURAL SCIENCE. Text in Japanese; Summaries in English. 1965. a.
Indexed: JPI.
Published by: Osaka Denki Tsushin Daigaku/Osaka Electro-Communication University, 18-8 Hatsu-cho, Neyagawa-shi, Osaka-fu 572-0000, Japan.

384.5   USA   ISSN 1522-6867

THE P C I A WASHINGTON BULLETIN. Text in English. bi-w. free to members. **Document type:** *Newsletter, Trade.*
Former titles: P C I A Bulletin; Telocator Bulletin
Related titles: Online - full text ed.: (from Florida Center for Library Automation, Gale Group).
Published by: Personal Communication Industry Association, 500 Montgomery St, Ste 700, Alexandria, VA 22314-1561. TEL 703-739-0300, 800-759-0300, FAX 703-836-1608, http://www.pcia.com. Ed. Sam Hupart. Circ: 1,700 (paid).

384   GBR   ISSN 1462-0820

P C S FOCUS. (Personal Communications Service) Text in English. 1995. biennial. GBP 35, USD 60 (effective 1999). **Document type:** *Trade.* **Description:** Provides a comprehensive review of all aspects of PCS.
Published by: Mobile Communications International (MCI), I B C Business Publishing Ltd. (Subsidiary of: I B C Group Plc), Gilmoora House, 57-61 Mortimer St, London, W1N 8JK, United Kingdom. TEL 44-20-7637-4383, FAX 44-20-7636-6414. Ed. Vaughan O'Grady.

384   FRA   ISSN 0475-302X

P T T SYNDICALISTE. Text in French. 10/yr.
Published by: Force Ouvriere, 60 rue Vergniaud, Paris, Cedex 13 75640, France. TEL 40-78-30-57, FAX 40-78-30-58, TELEX 200 644 F. Ed. Bernard Vignaud. Circ: 58,158.

384   FJI   ISSN 1605-6728

PACIFIC ISLANDS COMMUNICATION JOURNAL. Text in English. 1986 (vol.14). irreg., latest vol.16, no.2, 1995. USD 16 (effective 2001). adv. bk.rev. 120 p./no.; back issues avail. **Document type:** *Journal, Academic/Scholarly.* **Description:** Covers information about television, radio, publishing, newspapers, wrtings, any media of communication, freepress and cultural issues.
Published by: University of the South Pacific, Institute of Pacific Studies, c/o IPS, USP, Suva, Fiji. TEL 679-212248, FAX 679-301594, ips@usp.ac.fj. Ed., R&P Linda Crowl. Circ: 500.

PEAK; elektronikk, data og telekommunikasjon. see *ELECTRONICS*

384.043   USA

PERVASIVE WEEKLY. Text in English. 2000. d. adv. **Document type:** *Trade.* **Description:** Covers all aspects of the telecommunications industry.
Media: Online - full text.
Published by: Rising Tide Studios, 307 W 36th St, 10th Fl, New York, NY 10018-6403. TEL 646-473-2222, FAX 646-473-2223, subscribe@pervasiveweekly.com, http://www.pervasiveweekly.com. Ed. Jason McCabe Calacanis. Pub. Karol Martesko-Fenster. Adv. contact Keith Long.

384   BRA   ISSN 0553-8483

PESQUISAS: PUBLICACOES DE COMMUNICATIONS. Key Title: Pesquisas. Communications. (Numbering continues those articles published in Pesquisas) Text in Portuguese. 1957. irreg. **Document type:** *Academic/Scholarly.*
Supersedes in part (in 1960): Instituto Anchietano de Pesquisas. Pesquisas (0480-1873)
—CISTI.
Published by: (Universidade do Vale do Rio dos Sinos, Instituto Anchietano de Pesquisas), Unisinos, Av Unisinos, 950, Sao Leopoldo, RS 93022-000, Brazil. TEL 55-51-5908239, FAX 55-51-5908238.

PHILOSOPHY AND RHETORIC. see *PHILOSOPHY*

384   CAN   ISSN 1206-0801

PHONE-TAP MAGAZINE; tapping into the world of call centres and telemarketing. Text in English. 1996. m. CND 5.95; USD 6.95 foreign. adv.
Formerly: Phone-Taps
Published by: Canadian Telemarketing Corporation, 4 Dearbourne Ave, 1st Fl, Toronto, ON M4K 1M7, Canada. TEL 416-466-6943. Ed. Deborah Aaron. Pub., Adv. contact Brian Wilson. Circ: 5,000.

384   NIC

PIEDRA BOCONA; comunicacion para el desarrollo. Text in Spanish. 1991. m.
Address: Apdo 93, Granada, Nicaragua. TEL 2839. Ed. Ronald Puerto Lazo.

384   USA   ISSN 1064-1068

PLASTIC OPTICAL FIBER. Abbreviated title: P O F. Text in English. 1993. bi-m. USD 395 in US & Canada; USD 425 elsewhere (effective 2004). back issues avail. **Document type:** *Newsletter.* **Description:** Covers industry news, trends and applications.
Published by: Information Gatekeepers, Inc., 320 Washington St, Ste 302, Brighton, MA 02135. TEL 617-782-5033, 800-323-1088, FAX 617-782-5735, info@igigroup.com, http://www.igigroup.com/nl/pages/pof.html. Pub. Dr. Paul Polishuk.

384   USA

PODIUM. Text in English. 2/yr. USD 65 to members. **Document type:** *Newsletter.*
Published by: International Platform Association, PO Box 250, Winnetka, IL 60093. TEL 847-446-4321. Circ: 10,000.

POLICY MATTERS!. see *COMPUTERS*

384   USA   ISSN 1540-5702
P87

▼ **POPULAR COMMUNICATION.** Text in English. 2003. q. USD 260 in US & Canada to institutions; USD 290 elsewhere to institutions; USD 275 combined subscription in US & Canada to institutions print & online eds.; USD 305 combined subscription elsewhere to institutions print & online eds (effective 2006). adv. **Document type:** *Journal, Academic/Scholarly.* **Description:** Provides a forum for the scholarly investigation, analysis, and dialogue on communication symbols, forms, phenomena, and strategic systems of symbols within the context of contemporary popular culture. Publishes articles on all aspects of popular communication texts, artifacts, audiences, events, and practices, including the Internet, youth culture, representation, fandom, film, sports, spectacles, the digital revolution, sexuality, advertising/consumer culture, television, radio, music, magazines, and dance.
Related titles: Online - full text ed.: ISSN 1540-5710. USD 250 worldwide to institutions (effective 2006) (from EBSCO Publishing, Gale Group, O C L C Online Computer Library Center, Inc., Swets Information Services).
Indexed: CommAb, SociolAb.
—BLDSC (6550.310000), IE. **CCC.**

Published by: Lawrence Erlbaum Associates, Inc., 10 Industrial Ave, Mahwah, NJ 07430-2262. TEL 201-258-2200, 800-926-6579, FAX 201-236-0072, journals@erlbaum.com, http://www.leaonline.com/loi/pc, http://www.erlbaum.com. Eds. Norma Pecora TEL 740-593-4864, Sharon R Mazzarella. adv.: page USD 300; trim 5 x 8.

384   USA   ISSN 0733-3315
TK9956

POPULAR COMMUNICATIONS. Text in English. 1982. m. USD 28.95 domestic; USD 35.95 in Canada & Mexico; USD 45.95 elsewhere (effective 2003). adv. bk.rev. illus. reprints avail. **Document type:** *Consumer.* **Description:** Devoted to users and enthusiasts of VHF scanners, short wave receivers, radar detectors, satellite TV and cellular telephones.
Incorporates: Scan Magazine
Related titles: Braille ed.
Indexed: ABS&EES, IHTDI.
—IE, Infotrieve.
Published by: C Q Communications, Inc., 25 Newbridge Rd, Ste 405, Hicksville, NY 11801-2805. TEL 516-681-2922, 800-853-9797, FAX 516-681-2926, cq@cq-amateur-radio.com, www.popular-communications.com, http://www.cq-amateur-radio.com. Ed. Harold Ort. Pub. Richard A Ross. Adv. contact Donald R Allen. Circ: 92,238.

621.38   USA   ISSN 0891-5628
TR897.5

POST (CLEVELAND); the international magazine for post production professionals. Text in English. 1986. m. USD 48 domestic; USD 72 in Canada & Mexico; USD 102 elsewhere; USD 12 newsstand/cover domestic; USD 24 newsstand/cover in Canada & Mexico; USD 36 newsstand/cover elsewhere (effective 2005). adv. bk.rev.; software rev. tr.lit. back issues avail. **Document type:** *Magazine, Trade.* **Description:** Reports news and features about post production audio, animation and graphics, compositing, and video film editing.
Related titles: Online - full text ed.: (from Florida Center for Library Automation, Gale Group).
—CCC.
Published by: Advanstar Communications, Inc., 201 Sandpointe Ave, Ste 600, Santa Ana, CA 92707-8700. TEL 714-513-8400, FAX 714-513-8680, raltman@advanstar.com, info@advanstar.com, http://www.postmagazine.com, http://www.advanstar.com. Eds. Ken McGorry, Randi Altman. Pub. Kathleen A Mackay. Adv. contacts Marty Bond, Anne Morris. page USD 5,195; trim 10 x 12. Circ: 30,000 (paid and controlled).

POST- UND TELEKOMMUNIKATIONSGESCHICHTE. see *COMMUNICATIONS—Postal Affairs*

384   CZE

POSTOVNI VESTNIK. Text in Czech, Slovak. 1965. s-m. USD 54.20.
Former titles (until 1993): Vestnik Spoju (0862-4844); (until 1989): Federalni Ministerstvo Spoju. Vestnik (0139-6927); (until 1970): Ustredni Sprava Spoju. Vestnik (0042-4722)
Published by: Nakladatelstvi Dopravy a Turistiky Nadatur Ltd. Co., Hybernska 5, Prague 1, 110 00, Czech Republic. TEL 420-2-24224749, FAX 420-2-24219547. Ed. Ilona Stepanova.

PREVISIONS GLISSANTES DETAILLEES EN PERSPECTIVES SECTORIELLES (VOL.14): TELECOMMUNICATIONS. see *BUSINESS AND ECONOMICS—Economic Situation And Conditions*

PREVISIONS GLISSANTES DETAILLEES EN PERSPECTIVES SECTORIELLES (VOL.32): INDUSTRIES DE LA COMMUNICATION. see *BUSINESS AND ECONOMICS—Economic Situation And Conditions*

384.5   ITA   ISSN 0390-3311

PRIMA COMUNICAZIONE. Text in Italian. 1973. m. (11/yr.). EUR 80 domestic; EUR 155 foreign (effective 2005). adv. bk.rev. charts; illus. **Document type:** *Magazine, Consumer.* **Description:** Covers news in media, newspapers, television, radio, advertising and communication. It's geared for publishers, editors, journalists, general managers, marketing managers and advertising agencies.
Related titles: Online - full text ed.: Prima Comunicazione Online; Supplement(s): Gli Uomini Comunicazione, Grande Libro della Stampa Italiana.
Published by: Editoriale Genesis, Via Aurelio Saffi 12, Milan, MI 20123, Italy. TEL 39-02-48194401, FAX 39-02-4818658, http://www.primaonline.it. Ed. Umberto Brunetti. Adv. contact Gianfranco Rizzini. Circ: 12,500.

384   USA

PRO AV. Text in English. 1946. m. free domestic; USD 45 foreign (effective 2003). adv. bk.rev. **Document type:** *Trade.* **Description:** Provides information about the communications industry. Includes articles on video, multimedia, interactive technology and presentation, computer, audio-visual and teleconferencing.
Former titles: Presenting Communications (1523-6242); Communications Industries Report (1070-4426); (until 1984): N A V A News (0027-609X)
Related titles: Online - full text ed.
Address: 11600 College Blvd, Overland Park, KS 66210. TEL 913-344-1379, http://www.proavmagazine.com/. Ed. Mark Mayfield. Pub. Donna Sanford. Circ: 15,000 (controlled).

PRODUCER'S MASTERGUIDE; the international production manual for broadcast-television, feature films, television, commercials, cable, digital and videotape industries in the United States, Canada, the United Kingdom, Bermuda, the Caribbean Islands, Mexico, South America, Europe, Israel, the Far East, Australia and New Zealand. see *MOTION PICTURES*

384 CAN ISSN 1480-1930
PROFESSIONAL LIGHTING. Text in English. 1997. bi-m. CND 19 domestic; USD 24 foreign (effective 2002). **Document type:** *Trade.*
Published by: Norris - Whitney Communications Inc., 23 Hannover Dr, 7, St Catharines, ON L2W 1A3, Canada. TEL 905-641-3471, FAX 905-641-1648. Ed. Jeff MacKay. Circ: 12,000.

621.382 GBR ISSN 0810-9028
HC79.T4
➤ **PROMETHEUS.** Text in English. 1983. q. GBP 271, USD 446, AUD 379 combined subscription to institutions print & online eds. (effective 2006). adv. bk.rev. reprint service avail. from PSC. **Document type:** *Journal, Academic/Scholarly.* **Description:** Covers issues in technological change, innovation, information economics, communication and science policy.
Related titles: Online - full text ed.: ISSN 1470-1030. GBP 257, USD 424, AUD 360 to institutions (effective 2006) (from EBSCO Publishing, Gale Group, IngentaConnect, O C L C Online Computer Library Center, Inc., R M I T Publishing, Swets Information Services).
Indexed: AEI, AESIS, AusPAIS, CompLI, DIP, GEOBASE, IBR, IBSS, IBZ, Inspec, PAIS, SOPODA, SSA, SociolAb.
—BLDSC (6925.048000), AskIEEE, IE, Infotrieve, ingenta. **CCC.**
Published by: (Research School of Social Science AUS, Urban Research Program AUS), Routledge (Subsidiary of: Taylor & Francis Group), 4 Park Sq, Milton Park, Abingdon, Oxon OX14 4RN, United Kingdom. TEL 44-1235-828600, FAX 44-1235-829000, info@routledge.co.uk, http://www.tandf.co.uk/journals/titles/08109028.asp, http://www.routledge.co.uk. Ed. Don Lamberton. Circ: 500 (paid). **Subscr. to:** Taylor & Francis Ltd, Journals Customer Service, Rankine Rd, Basingstoke, Hants RG24 8PR, United Kingdom. TEL 44-1256-813000, FAX 44-1256-330245.

▼ ➤ **PSICOTECH.** see *PSYCHOLOGY*

C

➤ **PUBLIC SAFETY COMMUNICATIONS.** see *PUBLIC HEALTH AND SAFETY*

384 DEU ISSN 0033-4006
PN4703
➤ **PUBLIZISTIK**; Vierteljahreshefte fuer Kommunikationsforschung. Text in German; Summaries in English. 1956. q. EUR 73; EUR 54 to students; EUR 21 newsstand/cover (effective 2004). adv. bk.rev. bibl.; charts; illus. index. reprints avail. **Document type:** *Journal, Academic/Scholarly.* **Description:** Covers everything connected with communications and journalism from history to law.
Indexed: DIP, EI, IBR, IBSS, IBZ, IPSA, PCI, RILM, SOPODA.
—IE, Infotrieve. **CCC.**
Published by: V S - Verlag fuer Sozialwissenschaften (Subsidiary of: Springer Science+Business Media), Abraham-Lincoln-Str 46, Wiesbaden, 65189, Germany. TEL 49-611-78780, FAX 49-611-7878400, info@vs-verlag.de, http://www.vs-verlag.de. adv.: B&W page EUR 950, color page EUR 1,850. Circ: 750 (paid).

384 GBR ISSN 1745-9435
QUALITATIVE RESEARCH REPORTS IN COMMUNICATIONS. Text in English. 2000. a. GBP 17, USD 28 per issue to individuals; GBP 120, USD 198 per issue to institutions (effective 2005). **Document type:** *Journal, Academic/Scholarly.*
Related titles: Online - full text ed.: ISSN 1745-9443.
—CCC.
Published by: Routledge (Subsidiary of: Taylor & Francis Group), 4 Park Sq, Milton Park, Abingdon, Oxon OX14 4RN, United Kingdom. TEL 44-1235-828600, FAX 44-1235-829000, info@routledge.co.uk, http://www.tandf.co.uk/journals/titles/17459435.asp, http://www.routledge.co.uk. Ed. Michael J Hostetler.

QUARTERLY JOURNAL OF SPEECH. see *EDUCATION*

QWEST LIGHTSPEED. see *LIFESTYLE*

384.5 USA ISSN 1533-0796
R C R WIRELESS NEWS. Text in English. 1981. w. USD 69 domestic; USD 115 in Canada; USD 132 in Mexico; USD 298 elsewhere (effective 2005). adv. back issues avail. **Document type:** *Newspaper, Trade.* **Description:** Provides breaking news and in-depth analysis into the issues related to wireless telecommunications.
Former titles (until 2000): R C R (1521-5652); (until 199?): Radio Communications Report (0744-0618); Which superseded in part (in 1981): Two - Way Radio Dealer (0191-5436)
Related titles: Online - full content ed.: (from Florida Center for Library Automation); Online - full text ed.: (from EBSCO Publishing, Gale Group, O C L C Online Computer Library Center, Inc.).
—CCC.
Published by: Crain Communications, Inc., 1746 Cole Blvd, Ste 150, Golden, CO 80401. TEL 303-733-2500, FAX 303-733-9941, http://www.rcrnews.com, http://www.crain.com. Eds. David Shaw, Tracy Ford. Pub. John Sudmeier. Adv. contact Mary Pemberton. B&W page USD 5,810; trim 14.5 x 10.875. Circ: 40,041 (paid).

R F I D IN EUROPE NEWSLETTER. (Radio Frequency Identification) see *BUSINESS AND ECONOMICS—Computer Applications*

RADIOCOMMUNICATIONS MARITIMES. see *TRANSPORTATION—Ships And Shipping*

RADIONAVIGATION. see *TRANSPORTATION—Ships And Shipping*

384 USA
RAGAN'S STRATEGIC TRAINING REPORT. Text in English. s-m. USD 199. **Document type:** *Newsletter.* **Description:** Provides details, insights, and information you need to enhance your curriculum, improve your measurement practices, and capitalize on the latest technology.
Published by: Lawrence Ragan Communications, Inc., 316 N Michigan Ave, Ste 300, Chicago, IL 60601. TEL 312-960-4106, 800-878-5331, FAX 312-960-4106, http://www.ragan.com.

384 FRA
RAPPORT MONDIAL SUR LA COMMUNICATION ET L'INFORMATION. Text in French. irreg. EUR 22.87 newsstand/cover (effective 2003).
Formerly (until 1999): Rapport Mondial sur la Communication
Related titles: ◆ English ed.: World Communication Report.
Published by: UNESCO Publishing, 7 place de Fontenoy, Paris, 75352, France.

343.099 DEU ISSN 0940-9122
RECHTSVORSCHRIFTEN DER TELEKOMMUNIKATION. Text in German. 5 base vols. plus updates 8/yr. EUR 128 (effective 2005). **Document type:** *Bulletin, Trade.*
Published by: Deutscher Wirtschaftsdienst (Subsidiary of: Wolters Kluwer Deutschland GmbH), Schoenhauser Str 64, Cologne, 50968, Germany. TEL 49-221-937630, FAX 49-221-9376399, box@dwd-verlag.de, http://www.dwd-verlag.de.

384 BOL
RED DE RECURSOS DE COMUNICACION ALTERNATIVA. Text in Spanish. 1987. bi-m. USD 12 (effective 1993). bk.rev.; film rev. **Document type:** *Bulletin.* **Description:** Contains reviews from Latin America and the Caribbean and news of alternative media related events and competitions.
Published by: Centro de Integracion de Medios de Comunicacion Alternativa, PO Box 11365, La Paz, Bolivia. TEL 591-2-328318. Circ: 400.

384 DEU
REIHE KOMMUNIKATIONSWISSENSCHAFTEN. Text in German. 1986. irreg., latest vol.7, 1995. price varies. **Document type:** *Monographic series, Academic/Scholarly.*
Published by: Herbert Utz Verlag GmbH, Zieblandstr 7, Munich, 80799, Germany. TEL 49-89-27779100, FAX 49-89-27779101, utz@utzverlag.com, http://www.utzverlag.de.

384 CHN
RENMIN YOUDIAN BAO/PEOPLE'S POST AND TELECOMMUNICATIONS NEWS. Text in Chinese. 1950. 4/w. CNY 159.24 (effective 2004). **Document type:** *Newspaper, Academic/Scholarly.*
Published by: Renmin Youdian Chubanshe/People's Posts and Telecommunications Publishing House, 14 A Xizhaosi Street, Chongwen District, Beijing, 100061, China. TEL 86-10-67152042, abc@ptpress.com.cn, http://www.ptpress.com.cn/. **Dist. by:** China International Book Trading Corp, 35 Chegongzhuang Xilu, Haidian District, PO Box 399, Beijing 100044, China. TEL 86-10-68412045, FAX 86-10-68412023, cibtc@mail.cibtc.com.cn, http://www.cibtc.com.cn.

621.382 CAN ISSN 1206-7628
REPORT ON WIRELESS. Text in English. 1998. 24/yr. CND 895 domestic; CND 945 foreign; CND 50 newsstand/cover (effective 2003). **Document type:** *Newsletter, Trade.* **Description:** Reports and analyzes all types of wireless communications in Canada including technology, product development, licensing, manufacturing, distribution, regulation and public policy.
Related titles: E-mail ed.; Fax ed.; Online - full text ed.
Published by: Decima Publishing Inc., 1800-160 Elgin St, Ottawa, ON K2P 2C4, Canada. TEL 613-230-1984, FAX 613-230-9048, cjeffrey@decima.ca, http://www.decima.com/publishing. Ed. Jeff Leiper. Pub. Mario Mota.

381 GBR ISSN 1367-8620
RESEARCH PAPERS IN MEDIA AND CULTURAL STUDIES. Text in English. 1995. irreg. **Document type:** *Monographic series.*
—BLDSC (3491.530000).
Published by: University of Sussex, Graduate Research Centre in Culture and Communication, Sussex House, Falmer, Brighton, BN1 9RH, United Kingdom. TEL 44-1273-678412, FAX 44-1273-678335, http://www.sussex.ac.uk/units/CULCOM.

621.39 FRA ISSN 0751-7971
RESEAUX. Text in French. 1983. bi-m.
Indexed: SociolAb.
Published by: France Telecom Recherche et Developpement, 38-40 rue du General Leclerc, Issy-les-Moulineaux, Cedex 92131, France. TEL 33-1-45295464, FAX 33-1-45290106.

621.382 FRA ISSN 1251-8964
RESEAUX & TELECOMS. Text in French. 1986. 10/yr. EUR 50 domestic (effective 2005). adv. **Document type:** *Magazine, Trade.* **Description:** Contains in-depth articles dedicated to networking experts using a pure technical approach as well as information for non-specialists written in an easy-to-read style.
Former titles: Telecoms Reseaux International (1163-9180); (until 1991): Telecoms International (0987-4119)
Related titles: Online - full text ed.
—IE.
Published by: I D G Communications France, 5 rue Chantecoq, Puteaux, 92808, France. TEL 33-1-4197-6161, FAX 33-1-4197-6160, http://www.reseaux-telecoms.com/, http://www.idg.fr. Ed. Frederic Berge. R&P Pierre Mangin. Adv. contact Valerie Feneon. color page USD 7,253; trim 230 x 300. Circ: 26,039.

384 GBR ISSN 0969-9864
P87 CODEN: RFJCE7
RESEAUX: FRENCH JOURNAL OF COMMUNICATION. Text in English. 1993. s-a. GBP 25 to individuals; GBP 45 to institutions (effective 2000). **Document type:** *Academic/Scholarly.* **Description:** Covers all disciplines and fields of theoretical and empirical research on information and communication.
Indexed: CommAb, IBR, IBZ, IPSA, SOPODA, SociolAb.
—IE.
Published by: University of Luton Press, University of Luton, 75 Castle St, Luton, Beds LU1 3AJ, United Kingdom. TEL 44-1582-743297, FAX 44-1582-743298, ulp@luton.ac.uk. Eds. Patrice Flichy, Paul Beaud.

RETAIL IN$IGHTS. see *BUSINESS AND ECONOMICS—Marketing And Purchasing*

384 USA ISSN 1535-8593
➤ **THE REVIEW OF COMMUNICATION.** Text in English. 2001. q. USD 123, GBP 186 to institutions (effective 2006). bk.rev. **Document type:** *Journal, Academic/Scholarly.*
Media: Online - full text (from EBSCO Publishing, O C L C Online Computer Library Center, Inc.).
—CCC.
Published by: (National Communication Association), Routledge (Subsidiary of: Taylor & Francis Ltd), 325 Chestnut St., Suite 800, Philadelphia, PA 19106. TEL 215-625-8900, 800-354-1420, FAX 215-625-8914, journals@routledge.com, http://www.tandf.co.uk/journals/titles/15358593.asp, http://www.routledge.com. Ed. James Chesebro.

➤ **REVISTA CAILOR FERATE ROMNE.** see *TRANSPORTATION*

384 ESP ISSN 1696-2508
▼ **REVISTA CIENTIFICA DE INFORMACION Y COMUNICACION.** Text in Spanish. 2003. a. EUR 15 per issue (effective 2005). **Document type:** *Journal, Academic/Scholarly.*
Published by: Universidad de Sevilla, Secretariado de Publicaciones, Porvenir 27, Sevilla, 41013, Spain. TEL 34-95-4487444, FAX 34-95-4487443, secpub10@us.es, http://www.us.es/publius/inicio.html.

384 MEX
REVISTA IBEROAMERICANA DE COMUNICACION. Text in Spanish. 2001. s-a. USD 25 evening (effective 2002). 170 p./no.; **Document type:** *Academic/Scholarly.* **Description:** Covers communications in particular and the social sciences in general.
Published by: Universidad Iberoamericana, Prol Paseo de la Reforma 880, Col Lomas de Santa Fe, Mexico City, DF 01210, Mexico. FAX 52-5-2674240. Ed. Luis Octavio Elizondo Martinez. Circ: 1,000.

384 MEX ISSN 0187-8190
REVISTA MEXICANA DE COMUNICACION. Text in English, Spanish. 1988. bi-m. back issues avail.
Related titles: CD-ROM ed.; Online - full text ed.: ISSN 1605-4083 (from EBSCO Publishing).
Published by: Fundacion Manuel Buendia A.C., Guaymas No 8-408, Col Roma, Mexico City, DF 06700, Mexico. TEL 52-5-208426, FAX 52-5-2087756, http://www.cem.itesm.mx/dacs/buendia. Ed. Miguel Angel Sanchez de Armas.

384 BRA
REVISTA NACIONAL DE TELECOMUNICACOES. Text in Portuguese. 1979. m. free to qualified personnel. adv. **Document type:** *Trade.* **Description:** For professionals in the telecommunications sector. Provides a mix of news, features, solutions and technology analysis.
Former titles: Revista Nacional de Telematica (0102-3446); (until 1983): Revista Nacional de Telecomunicacoes (0102-3438)

Published by: Advanstar Editora e Com. Ltda., Rua Gomes de Carvalho, 1329 Andar 9, Vila Olimpia, Sao Paulo - SP, SP 04547-005, Brazil. TEL 55-11-31707000, FAX 55-11-31707010, http://www.advanstar.com.br. Ed. Ethevaldo Siqueira. adv.: B&W page USD 6,136, color page USD 7,670; trim 275 x 208. Circ: 21,272.

REVISTA TRANSPORTURILOR. AUTO, DRUMURI, NAVIGATIE. see *TRANSPORTATION*

384 TUN ISSN 0330-8480
P87
REVUE TUNISIENNE DE COMMUNICATION. Text in Arabic, English, French. 1982. s-a. TND 10, USD 20 (effective 2000). bibl. back issues avail. **Document type:** *Academic/Scholarly.* **Description:** Covers issues affecting journalism and information sciences in the Arab world, Africa, the Third World, and other countries.
Published by: Institut de Presse et des Sciences de l'Information (IPSI), 7 Impasse Mohamed Bachrouch Montfleury, Tunis, 1008, Tunisia. TEL 216-1-600980, 216-1-600981, FAX 216-1-600465, TELEX 15254 IPSI TN. Ed. Mohamed Hamdane. R&P Mustapha Hassen. Circ: 3,000.

384 351 ITA ISSN 1591-7304
RIVISTA ITALIANA DI COMUNICAZIONE PUBBLICA. Text in Italian. 1999. q. EUR 62 domestic; EUR 84 foreign (effective 2003). **Document type:** *Journal, Academic/Scholarly.*
Published by: Franco Angeli Edizioni, Viale Monza 106, Milan, 20127, Italy. TEL 39-02-2837141, FAX 39-02-26144793, redazioni@francoangeli.it, http://www.francoangeli.it.

384 USA ISSN 1542-6394
▼ ➤ **ROCKY MOUNTAIN COMMUNICATION REVIEW.** Text in English. 2003 (Sum.). q. **Document type:** *Journal, Academic/Scholarly.*
Media: Online - full content.
Published by: University of Utah, Department of Communication, 255 S. Central Campus Dr. Rm. 2400, Salt Lake City, UT 84112-0491. TEL 801-581-5862, FAX 801-585-6255, RMCR@utah.edu, http://www.utah.edu/rockymountain, http://www.hum.utah.edu/communication. Ed. James A. Anderson.

621.382 USA
RUSSIA - NIS TELECOM WEEKLY. Text in English. w. USD 1,200 (effective 2000). **Document type:** *Trade.* **Description:** Reports on the most critical developments in Russian and NIS telecommunications.
Media: E-mail.
Published by: Gist, Inc., 2200 Wilson Blvd, Ste 102G, Arlington, VA 22201. TEL 703-527-7459, FAX 703-528-1477, info@gist.net, http://www.gist.net.

621.382 USA
RUSSIAN TELECOMMUNICATIONS INVESTOR'S GUIDE. Text in English. 1996. a. USD 500 (effective 2000). back issues avail. **Document type:** *Directory, Trade.* **Description:** Provides an overview of direct and portfolio investment opportunities in the Russian telecommunications sector, analysis of restructuring and privatization in the industry, surveys of leading public network operators.
Related titles: CD-ROM ed.: USD 500 (effective 2000).
Published by: Gist, Inc., 2200 Wilson Blvd, Ste 102G, Arlington, VA 22201. TEL 703-527-7459, FAX 703-528-1477, dkbain@gist.net, http://www.gist.net. Ed. David Bain TEL 203-527-7459. R&P Michael Peil. Adv. contact Daniel Radack.

S I M I L E. (Studies in Media & Information Literacy Education) see *LIBRARY AND INFORMATION SCIENCES*

621.382 USA ISSN 1094-2785
S O N E T / S D L A / M A N. Text in English. 1990. m. USD 695 in US & Canada; USD 745 elsewhere (effective 2001). **Document type:** *Newsletter.* **Description:** Covers technology, products, applications, services, standards, regulations and business developments.
Formerly (until 1996): Metropolitan Area Networks (1057-5383)
Published by: Information Gatekeepers, Inc., 320 Washington St, Ste 302, Brighton, MA 02135. TEL 617-782-5033, 800-323-1088, FAX 617-734-8562, info@igigroup.com, http://www.igigroup.com. Ed. Sebastian Wargacki. Pub. Dr. Paul Polishuk.

384 USA ISSN 1242-5125
S P A W C : SIGNAL PROCESSING ADVANCES IN WIRELESS COMMUNICATIONS. Text in English. 1992. biennial.
Published by: Institute of Electrical and Electronics Engineers, Inc., 445 Hoes Ln, Piscataway, NJ 08854-1331. TEL 732-981-0060, FAX 732-981-1721, customer.service@ieee.org, http://www.ieee.org.

384 CHN ISSN 1003-109X
SANYUEFENG/SPRING BREEZES. Text in Chinese. 1985. m. CNY 26.40. **Description:** Coordinates interpersonal relations to create a harmonious social environment for the people.
Published by: (Zhongguo Canjiren Lianhehui/China Disabled Persons' Federation), Disability in China Inc., A-8 Huixin Li Anwai, Chaoyang-qu, Beijing, 100101, China. TEL 86-10-6496-8360. Ed. Li Zhiqi. Circ: 50,000. **Dist. in US by:** China Books & Periodicals Inc, 360 Swift Ave., Ste. 48, S San Fran, CA 94080-6220. TEL 415-282-2994.

384 332 GBR ISSN 1460-9754
SATELLITE FINANCE. Text in English. 1998. m. GBP 725, USD 1,050 (effective 2001). adv. back issues avail. **Document type:** *Journal, Trade.* **Description:** Worldwide primary source information on debt & equity funding in the satellite industry.
Related titles: CD-ROM ed.; Fax ed.; Online - full content ed.: GBP 375, USD 540 (effective 2001).
—CCC.
Published by: Thompson Stanley Publishers Ltd., Clerkenwell House, 45-47 Clerkenwell Green, London, EC1R 0EB, United Kingdom. TEL 44-20-7553-3919, FAX 44-20-7251-1833, chris.thompson@telecomfinance.com, http://www.satellitefinance.com. Ed. Tom Rebbeck. R&P Chris Thompson. Adv. contact Jo Nhan. Circ: 2,500.

384.51029 USA
TK5104
SATELLITE INDUSTRY DIRECTORY. Text in English. 1979. a. USD 447 per issue (effective 2004). **Document type:** *Directory, Trade.* **Description:** Provides a comprehensive guide to worldwide satellite communications systems and all related manufacturing and service industries.
Incorporates (1985-1999): Phillips World Satellite Almanac; (1994-1997): Asia - Pacific Satellite Directory (1080-370X); (1994-1997): European Satellite Directory (1080-4242); Former titles (until 18th ed., 1996): World Satellite Directory (1046-0950); (1979-1988): Satellite Directory (0731-0293)
Related titles: Online - full text ed.
Published by: Access Intelligence, LLC (Subsidiary of: Veronis, Suhler & Associates Inc.), 1201 Seven Locks Rd, Ste 300, Potomac, MD 20854. TEL 301-354-2000, FAX 301-424-2058, clientservices@accessintel.com, http://www.pbimedia.com. Ed. Monica L Kenny.

621.382 USA ISSN 1521-1436
SATELLITE TODAY. Text in English. 199?. d. USD 1,885 (effective 2003). adv. **Document type:** *Trade.*
Media: Online - full content. **Related titles:** Online - full text ed.: (from ProQuest Information & Learning).
Indexed: ABIn.
Published by: Access Intelligence, LLC (Subsidiary of: Veronis, Suhler & Associates Inc.), 1201 Seven Locks Rd, Ste 300, Potomac, MD 20854. TEL 301-354-2000, FAX 301-424-2058, pdykewicz@pbimedia.com, clientservices@accessintel.com, http://www.telecomweb.com/satellite/, http://www.pbimedia.com.

343.009 DEU ISSN 0935-4239
SCHRIFTEN ZU KOMMUNIKATIONSFRAGEN. Text in German. 1982. irreg., latest vol.34, 2002. price varies. **Document type:** *Monographic series, Academic/Scholarly.*
Published by: Duncker und Humblot GmbH, Carl-Heinrich-Becker-Weg 9, Berlin, 12165, Germany. TEL 49-30-7900060, FAX 49-30-79000631, info@duncker-humblot.de, http://www.duncker-humblot.de.

340 DEU ISSN 1613-2831
▼ **SCHRIFTEN ZUM MEDIENRECHT.** Text in German. 2004. irreg., latest vol.8, 2005. price varies. **Document type:** *Monographic series, Academic/Scholarly.*
Published by: Verlag Dr. Kovac, Arnoldstr 49, Hamburg, 22763, Germany. TEL 49-40-3988800, FAX 49-40-39888055, info@verlagdrkovac.de, http://www.verlagdrkovac.de/12-19.htm.

340 DEU ISSN 1613-7922
▼ **SCHRIFTENREIHE ZUM KOMMUNIKATIONS- UND MEDIENRECHT.** Text in German. 2004. irreg., latest vol.2, 2004. price varies. **Document type:** *Monographic series, Academic/Scholarly.*
Published by: Verlag Dr. Kovac, Arnoldstr 49, Hamburg, 22763, Germany. TEL 49-40-3988800, FAX 49-40-39888055, info@verlagdrkovac.de, http://www.verlagdrkovac.de/12-24.htm.

384 USA
SCIPHERS (ONLINE). Text in English. 1979. q. **Document type:** *Newsletter, Academic/Scholarly.*
Media: Online - full content.
Published by: Association for Education in Journalism and Mass Communication, Science Communication Interest Group, c/o Donnalyn Pompper, Department of Communication, Florida State University, 339 Diffenbaugh Bldg., Tallahassee, FL 32306-1531. http://comm2.fsu.edu/programs/comm/aejmc/.

384 USA ISSN 0736-1882
SELF PUBLISHING UPDATE. Text in English. 1988. a. looseleaf. USD 11.95 domestic; USD 14.95 in Canada; USD 18.95 elsewhere (effective 2005). abstr. 21 p./no.; **Document type:** *Newsletter.* **Description:** Provides a reference source for self-publishers on publishing and the book trade, advertizing, public relations, business, economics and small business.
Published by: Prosperity and Profits Unlimited, PO Box 416, Denver, CO 80201-0416. TEL 303-575-5676, FAX 303-575-1187, starsuccess@excite.com, http://selfpublishing.bigstep.com, http://www.curriculumresourceonline.com. Ed., R&P A Doyle TEL 303-575-5676. Circ: 10,000.

SEMIOSFERA; revista internacional de humanidades y tecnologias. see *SOCIAL SCIENCES: COMPREHENSIVE WORKS*

621.382 CAN ISSN 1209-5648
HE7811
SENATE OF CANADA. SUBCOMMITTEE ON COMMUNICATIONS. PROCEEDINGS. Text in English. 1996. irreg.
Published by: Senate of Canada, Subcommittee on Transportation Safety, Parliament of Canada, Ottawa, ON K1A 0A9, Canada. TEL 613-992-4793, 866-599-4999.

384 USA ISSN 1047-4692
Z6951
SENIOR MEDIA DIRECTORY✶. Text in English. 1989. a. USD 99. **Document type:** *Directory.*
Related titles: Diskette ed.: USD 375.
Published by: Ascend Media Gaming Group, 1771 E Flamingo Rd, Ste 208A, Las Vegas, NV 89119. Ed. Gene E Malott. Pub. Adele Malott.

384 SGP
SERIES IN REMOTE SENSING. Text in English. 1996. irreg., latest vol.4. price varies. **Document type:** *Monographic series, Academic/Scholarly.*
Published by: World Scientific Publishing Co. Pte. Ltd., 5 Toh Tuck Link, Singapore, 596224, Singapore. TEL 65-466-5775, FAX 65-467-7667, wspc@wspc.com.sg, series@wspc.com.sg, http://www.wspc.com.sg/books/series/srs_series.shtml, http://www.worldscientific.com. Ed. A P Cracknell. **Dist. by:** World Scientific Publishing Co., Inc., 1060 Main St, River Edge, NJ 07661. TEL 201-487-9655, 800-227-7562, FAX 201-487-9656, 888-977-2665; World Scientific Publishing Ltd., 57 Shelton St, London WC2H 9HE, United Kingdom. TEL 44-20-78360888, FAX 44-20-78362020.

621.382 DEU ISSN 1611-2970
▼ **SERIES IN WIRELESS COMMUNICATIONS.** Text in German. 2003. irreg., latest vol.3, 2003. price varies. **Document type:** *Monographic series, Academic/Scholarly.*
Published by: Logos Verlag Berlin, Comeniushof, Gubener Str 47, Berlin, 10243, Germany. TEL 49-30-42851090, FAX 49-30-42851092, redaktion@logos-verlag.de, http://www.logos-verlag.de. Ed. Armin Wittneben.

C

384.3 RUS ISSN 1605-5055
SETI I SISTEMY SVYAZI. Text in Russian. 1995. m. RUR 739.20 domestic (effective 2003). **Document type:** *Journal, Trade.*
Related titles: Online - full content ed.: ISSN 1684-1794. 1997.
Indexed: Inspec, RefZh.
Address: Prospekt Mira, V V Ts, Biznestsentr Technopark, str 3, PO Box 41, Moscow, 129223, Russian Federation. TEL 7-095-2345321, FAX 7-095-9747110, info@ccc.ru, http://www.ccc.ru.

621.382 CHN ISSN 1001-4802
➤ **SHIJIE DIANXIN/WORLD TELECOMMUNICATIONS.** Text in Chinese; Abstracts in Chinese, English. 1988. bi-m. CNY 90; USD 48 foreign. adv. **Document type:** *Academic/Scholarly.*
Related titles: Online - full text ed.: (from East View Information Services).
Published by: Youdian-bu, Keji Qingbao Zhongxin/Ministry of Posts and Telecommunications, Science and Technology Information Center, 40 Xueyuan Rd, Haidian, Beijing, 100083, China. TEL 86-10-6230-1569, FAX 86-10-6230-4077, worldtel@public.bta.net.cn. Ed. Sen Zhang. Adv. contact Zhongcheng Hou. B&W page USD 1,000, color page USD 1,800. Circ: 20,000.

384.5 USA
▼ **SHORT-RANGE WIRELESS.** Text in English. 2004. bi-m. free with subscr. to Remote Site & Equipment Management. adv. back issues avail. **Document type:** *Magazine, Trade.* **Description:** Focuses totally on the technology of wireless data networking and communications within distances of several hundred yards.
Related titles: ♦ Supplement to: Remote Site & Equipment Management. ISSN 1535-0347.
Published by: Webcom Communications Corp., 7355 E Orchard Rd, Ste 100, Greenwood Village, CO 80111. TEL 720-528-3770, 800-803-9488, FAX 720-528-3771, johncg@infowebcom.com, http://www.remotemagazine.com, http://www.infowebcom.com. Ed., Pub. David Webster. adv.: B&W page USD 3,700; trim 10.875 x 14.75. Circ: 10,000.

621.382 CHN ISSN 1004-9037
SHUJU CAIJI YU CHULI/JOURNAL OF DATA ACQUISITION & PROCESSING. Text in Chinese. 1986. q. **Document type:** *Journal, Academic/Scholarly.*
Related titles: Online - full text ed.: (from East View Information Services).
Indexed: BrCerAb, C&ISA, CerAb, CorrAb, E&CAJ, EMA, IAA, Inspec, M&TEA, MBF, METADEX, RefZh, WAA.
—BLDSC (4967.385000), Linda Hall.
Published by: (Nanjing Hangkong Hangtian Daxue, Zhongguo Wuli Xuehui/Chinese Physical Society, Zhongguo Dianzi Xuehui/Chinese Institute of Electronics), Shuju Caiji Yu Chuli, Editorial Dept. of Journal of Data Acquisition & Processing, 29, Yudaojie, 403 Xinxiang, Nanjing, 210016, China. TEL 86-25-4892726, FAX 86-25-4892742, sjcj@nuaa.edu.cn, http://sjcjycl.wanfangdata.com.cn/default.html.

384 363.22 ITA ISSN 1723-5065
▼ **SICUREZZA DIGITALE.** Text in Italian. 2003. bi-m. EUR 30 domestic (effective 2004). **Document type:** *Magazine, Trade.*

▼ new title ➤ refereed ✶ unverified ♦ full entry avail.

Published by: Tecniche Nuove SpA, Via Eritrea 21, Milan, MI 201, Italy. TEL 39-02-390901, FAX 39-02-7570364, sicurezza.digitale@tecnichenuove.com, info@tecnichenuove.com, http://www.tecnichenuove.com.

621.38 USA ISSN 0037-4938 CODEN: SGNAAZ
SIGNAL MAGAZINE (FAIRFAX). Text in English. 1946. m. USD 56 domestic to non-members; USD 76 foreign to non-members (effective 2005). adv. bk.rev. illus.; tr.lit. cum.index: 1989-1998. 100 p./no.; back issues avail.; reprints avail. **Document type:** *Magazine, Trade.* **Description:** Covers communications-electronics with articles on research, innovative technologies and business trends, as well as their ramifications in defense, intelligence and geopolitics.
Related titles: Microform ed.: (from PQC); Online - full text ed.: (from O C L C Online Computer Library Center, Inc., ProQuest Information & Learning).
Indexed: AUNI, Inspec, LID&ISL, TelAb.
—BLDSC (8275.970000), CISTI, IE, Infotrieve, ingenta, Linda Hall. **CCC.**
Published by: Armed Forces Communications and Electronics Association, 4400 Fair Lakes Court, Fairfax, VA 22033-3899. TEL 703-631-6178, FAX 703-631-6188, signalnews@afcea.org, signal@afcea.org, http://www.afcea.org/signal/. Ed. Robert K Ackerman. Pub. Herbert A Browne. R&P Beverly Mowery TEL 703-631-6184. Adv. contact Marsha Carpenter TEL 703-631-6181. page USD 5,860; trim 10.88 x 8.25. Circ: 33,000 (paid).

384 USA ISSN 1050-799X
HC101
SIMMONS STUDY OF MEDIA & MARKETS (YEAR). Text in English. 2/yr. **Document type:** *Trade.*
Related titles: Online - full text ed.
Published by: Simmons Market Research Bureau, Inc., 309 W 49th St, New York, NY 10019. TEL 212-373-8900, FAX 212-373-8918.

384 USA ISSN 1050-8015
HC101
SIMMONS STUDY OF MEDIA AND MARKETS. TECHNICAL GUIDE. Text in English. 2/yr. **Document type:** *Trade.*
Published by: Simmons Market Research Bureau, Inc., 309 W 49th St, New York, NY 10019. TEL 212-373-8900, FAX 212-373-8918.

SISTEMI DI TELECOMUNICAZIONI; audio video networking. see *ELECTRONICS*

621.382 RUS
SISTEMY BEZOPASNOSTI SVYAZI I TELEKOMMUNIKATSII. Text in Russian. bi-m. USD 125 in United States.
Indexed: RefZh.
Published by: Kompaniya Grotesk, Miusskaya pl 7, kom 228, Moscow, 125811, Russian Federation. TEL 7-095-2516845, FAX 7-095-2513389. Ed. S N Reshetnikov. **US dist. addr.:** East View Information Services, 3020 Harbor Ln. N., Minneapolis, MN 55447. TEL 612-550-0961.

621.382 RUS
SISTEMY BEZOPASNOSTI SVYAZI I TELEKOMMUNIKATSII. KATALOG. Text in Russian. s-a. USD 110 in United States.
Published by: Kompaniya Grotesk, Miusskaya pl 7, kom 228, Moscow, 125811, Russian Federation. TEL 7-095-2516845, FAX 7-095-2513389. Ed. S N Reshetnikov. **US dist. addr.:** East View Information Services, 3020 Harbor Ln. N., Minneapolis, MN 55447. TEL 612-550-0961.

621.382 RUS
SISTEMY I SREDSTVA TELEKOMMUNIKATSII. Text in Russian. bi-m. USD 99.95 in United States.
Address: Zyuzinskaya 6, Moscow, 117418, Russian Federation. TEL 7-095-3323552. **US dist. addr.:** East View Information Services, 3020 Harbor Ln. N., Minneapolis, MN 55447. TEL 612-550-0961.

SKATE EXTENSION. see *BUSINESS AND ECONOMICS—Investments*

384 BRA
SOCIEDADE BRASILEIRA DE TELECOMUNICACOES. REVISTA. Text in Portuguese. 1986. m.
Indexed: Inspec.
Published by: Sociedade Brasileira de Telecomunicacoes, Rua Marques de Sao Vicente 225, 255 Ala K, 7o Andar, Rio de Janeiro, RJ 22453-900, Brazil. sbrt@cetuc.puc-rio.br, http://www.sbrt.com.br.

384 USA
SOCIETY FOR TECHNICAL COMMUNICATION. ANNUAL CONFERENCE PROCEEDINGS. Text in English. 1956. a. USD 90 to non-members; USD 60 to members. bibl. back issues avail.; reprints avail. **Document type:** *Proceedings.*
Formerly (until 1992): International Technical Communication Conference Proceedings
Indexed: EnglInd.
—BLDSC (1082.370135), ingenta.
Published by: Society for Technical Communication, 901 N Stuart St, Ste 904, Arlington, VA 22203-1822. TEL 703-522-4114. Ed. William Stolgitis. R&P Anita Dosik. Circ: 2,500.

384 GBR
SOCIETY OF TELECOM EXECUTIVES. REVIEW. Text in English. m. (10/yr.). GBP 10, USD 25. adv. **Document type:** *Newsletter.*
Related titles: Audio cassette/tape ed.
Published by: Society of Telecom Executives, 75 York Rd, London, SE1 7AQ, United Kingdom. TEL 44-171-928-9951, FAX 44-171-928-5440, jane.mc@ge02.poptel.org.uk. Ed. Jane McCarten. Adv. contact T G Scott. page GBP 1,250. Circ: 24,000 (controlled). **Subscr. to:** 1 Park Rd, Teddington, Mddx TW11 0AR, United Kingdom.

384 FIN
SONERASOUND. Text in Finnish. 1987. 4/yr. **Document type:** *Trade.*
Former titles: Telelinkki (0784-6436); (until 1987): Linkki (0783-8891)
Published by: Helsinki Media Company Oy, PL 2, Helsinki, 00040, Finland. TEL 358-9-1201, FAX 358-9-120-5988. Ed. Kaisa Hakala. Circ: 65,000 (controlled).

621.382 FRA ISSN 0768-956X
SONOVISION. Text in French. 1969. 11/yr. EUR 70.40 domestic; EUR 104.80 foreign (effective 2004). adv. bk.rev. **Document type:** *Magazine, Consumer.*
Published by: Groupe Studio Press (Subsidiary of: Roularta Media Group), 11, rue Charles Schmidt, St Ouen, 93400, France. info@sonovision.com, http://www.sonovision.com.

SONOVISION QUI FAIT QUOI?. see *BUSINESS AND ECONOMICS—Trade And Industrial Directories*

SOUND & COMMUNICATIONS. see *SOUND RECORDING AND REPRODUCTION*

621.382 FRA ISSN 1608-1315
SOURCE O E C D. TELECOMMUNICATIONS DATABASE/SOURCE O C D E BASE DE DONNEES DES TELECOMMUNICATIONS DE L'O C D E. Text in English, French. 2000. irreg. EUR 235, USD 270, GBP 156, JPY 31,700 (effective 2005). **Description:** Provides key indicators on the communications sector in twenty-nine OECD member countries.
Media: Online - full content. **Related titles:** Online - full text ed.: (from Gale Group, IngentaConnect).
Published by: Organization for Economic Cooperation and Development, 2 Rue Andre Pascal, Paris, 75775 Cedex 16, France. TEL 33-1-45248200, FAX 33-1-45248500, http://www.oecd.org.

SOURCES. see *BUSINESS AND ECONOMICS—Trade And Industrial Directories*

384 USA ISSN 1089-117X
SOUTH AMERICAN TELECOM. Text in English. 1996. m. USD 695 in US & Canada; USD 745 elsewhere (effective 2001). back issues avail.
Related titles: Online - full text ed.: (from Florida Center for Library Automation).
Published by: Information Gatekeepers, Inc., 320 Washington St, Ste 302, Brighton, MA 02135. TEL 617-782-5033, 800-323-1088, FAX 617-734-8562, info@igigroup.com, http://www.igigroup.com. Ed. Jeremy Awori. Pub. Dr. Paul Polishuk.

621.382 USA
SOUTHEAST ASIA TELECOM MONTHLY. Text in English. m. **Document type:** *Bulletin, Trade.* **Description:** Provides concise and insightful reporting of significant developments in the telecommunications industries in the following countries: Malaysia, Thailand, Indonesia and the Philippines.
Published by: Gist, Inc., 2200 Wilson Blvd, Ste 102G, Arlington, VA 22201. TEL 703-527-7459, FAX 703-528-1477, info@gist.net, http://www.gist.net.

384 USA ISSN 1041-794X
PN4071
➤ **SOUTHERN COMMUNICATION JOURNAL.** Text in English. 1935. q. USD 154, GBP 93 combined subscription to institutions print & online eds. (effective 2006). adv. bk.rev. illus. index. reprints avail. **Document type:** *Journal, Academic/Scholarly.*
Former titles (until 1988): Southern Speech Communication Journal (0361-8269); (until 1971): Southern Speech Journal (0038-4585)
Related titles: Microform ed.: (from PQC); Online - full text ed.: USD 146, GBP 88 to institutions (effective 2006) (from Northern Light Technology, Inc., O C L C Online Computer Library Center, Inc., ProQuest Information & Learning).
Indexed: AES, AmH&L, CIJE, CommAb, HistAb, IBRH, IJCS, L&LBA, MLA-IB, PCI, PRA, RILM, SOPODA, SSA, SociolAb, V&AA.
Published by: (Southern States Communication Association), Taylor & Francis Inc. (Subsidiary of: Taylor & Francis Group), 325 Chestnut St, Ste 800, Philadelphia, PA 19016. TEL 215-625-8900, 800-354-1420, FAX 215-625-2940, info@taylorandfrancis.com, http://ssca.net/SCJ/scj.html, http://www.taylorandfrancis.com. Ed. Craig Smith. Circ: 2,500.

➤ **SPEECHWRITER'S NEWSLETTER.** see *JOURNALISM*

070.5 384 RUS ISSN 1726-5282
P92.R9
SREDA; rossiisko-evropeiskii zhurnal o media. Text in Russian. 1998. 10/yr. RUR 960 domestic; USD 75 foreign (effective 2004). **Document type:** *Magazine, Trade.* **Description:** Provides description of all media dimensions: TV, radio, press, book-publishing, new media, advertising, media research, professional, political, regulatory and economic aspects of media activities, concentration of media property and the media landscape in the Russian regions.
Address: a/ya 36, Moscow, 125047, Russian Federation. TEL 7-095-2512115, sreda.mag@g23.relcom.ru, http://www.sreda-mag.ru. Ed. Aleksei Pankin.

STANDARD TIME & FREQUENCY SERVICE BULLETIN. see *METROLOGY AND STANDARDIZATION*

388 CAN ISSN 1189-2005
STANDING SENATE COMMITTEE ON TRANSPORT AND COMMUNICATIONS. PROCEEDINGS. Text in Multiple languages. 1951. irreg.
Related titles: Online - full text ed.: ISSN 1493-3985. 1999.
Published by: Privacy Commissioner, Senate Standing Committee on Transport and Communications, 112 Kent St, Place de Ville Tower B 3rd Fl, Ottawa, ON K1A 1H3, Canada. TEL 613-995-8210, FAX 613-947-6850, info@privcom.gc.ca, http://www.privcom.gc.ca/.

384 USA ISSN 1538-7534
STATE & LOCAL COMMUNICATIONS REPORT. Text in English. 1982. fortn. USD 645 in North America; USD 795 elsewhere (effective 2000). **Document type:** *Newsletter.* **Description:** Covers state and local telecom regulation and market strategies.
Formerly (until 1995): Telecommunications Week (1040-418X)
Related titles: Online - full text ed.
—**CCC.**
Published by: Telecommunications Reports (Subsidiary of: Aspen Publishers, Inc.), 1333 H St, N W, Ste 100, Washington, DC 20005. TEL 800-822-6338, FAX 202-842-3023, customerservice@tr.com, http://www.tr.com. Ed. Lynn Stanton. R&P Eileen Callahan.

STATIONS RADIOMETEOROLOGIQUES. see *TRANSPORTATION—Ships And Shipping*

384 USA ISSN 0161-5173
HE7761
STATISTICS OF COMMUNICATIONS COMMON CARRIERS. Text in English. 1939. a. USD 31 domestic; USD 43.40 foreign (effective 2005).
Formerly (until 1957): Statistics of the Communications Industry in the United States (0081-5179)
Published by: U.S. Federal Communications Commission, 445 12th St SW Rm TW-B505, Washington, DC 20554. TEL 888-225-5322, FAX 202-418-0232, fccinfo@fcc.gov, http://www.fcc.gov/Bureaus/Common_Carrier/Reports/FCC-State_Link/socc.html. **Subscr. to:** U.S. Government Printing Office, Superintendent of Documents, PO Box 371954, Pittsburgh, PA 15250-7954. TEL 202-512-1800, FAX 202-512-2250, orders@gpo.gov, http://www.access.gpo.gov.

384 DEU ISSN 1435-1048
➤ **STAUFFENBURG MEDIEN.** Text in English, German. 1998. irreg., latest vol.3, 2002. price varies. **Document type:** *Monographic series, Academic/Scholarly.*
Published by: Stauffenburg Verlag, Postfach 2525, Tuebingen, 72015, Germany. TEL 49-7071-97300, FAX 49-7071-973030, info@stauffenburg.de, http://www.stauffenburg.de.

384 USA ISSN 1547-2809
TA1635
▼ **STORAGE & ENTERTAINMENT**; the storage magazine for entertainment and broadcast technologies. Text in English. 2003. m.
Published by: West World Productions, Inc., 420 N Camden Dr, Beverly Hills, CA 90210-4507. TEL 310-276-9500, FAX 310-777-6670, http://www.wwpi.com. Circ: 30,000.

384.3 USA
STRATEGIC NEWS SERVICE. Text in English. 1995. w. USD 495. back issues avail. **Document type:** *Newsletter.* **Description:** Contains predictions of trends of strategic events and issues for the computer and telecom industries.
Media: Online - full text. **Related titles:** E-mail ed.
Published by: Technology Alliance Partners, PO Box 1969, Friday Harbor, WA 98250. TEL 360-378-3431, FAX 360-378-7041, sbs@interisland.net, sns@tapsns.com, http://www.tapsns.com. Ed. Mark R Anderson.

384 SWE ISSN 0280-5634
STUDIES IN COMMUNICATION. Abbreviated title: S I C. Text in Swedish. 1982. irreg. **Document type:** *Monographic series.*
Indexed: BibLing.
Published by: Linkoeping Universitet, Institutionen foer Tema, Linkoeping, 58183, Sweden.

STUDIES IN COMMUNICATION SCIENCES/STUDI DI SCIENZE DELLA COMUNICAZIONE. see *SOCIOLOGY*

384 USA ISSN 0275-7982
P87
STUDIES IN COMMUNICATIONS. Text in English. 1980. irreg., latest vol.6, 2004. price varies. back issues avail. **Document type:** *Monographic series, Academic/Scholarly.* **Description:** Presents contemporary scholarship on the central dynamic of society - communications.
Indexed: SOPODA, SSA, SociolAb.
—CCC.
Published by: J A I Press Inc. (Subsidiary of: Elsevier Science & Technology), 360 Park Ave S, New York, NY 10010-1710. TEL 212-989-5800, FAX 212-633-3990, usinfo-f@elsevier.com, http://www.elsevier.com/wps/find/bookdescription.cws_home/BS_SC/description#description. Ed. D Papademas.

384 RUS
SVYAZ'INFORM. Text in Russian. 1995. 16/yr. USD 299 in United States (effective 2000).
Indexed: RefZh.
Address: Ul Utkina 44, Moscow, 105275, Russian Federation. TEL 7-095-2733060. **Dist. by:** East View Information Services, 3020 Harbor Ln. N., Minneapolis, MN 55447. TEL 763-550-0961, FAX 763-559-2931.

621.382 SWE
SWEDISH TELECOM. ANNUAL REPORT✶. Text in English. a. back issues avail. **Document type:** *Corporate.*
Formerly: Sweden. Televerket. Annual Report (0586-1926)
Published by: Televerket/Swedish Telecommunications Administration, Maarbackagatan 11, Farsta, 12386, Sweden. Circ: 5,000.

SYDNEY INSTITUTE QUARTERLY. see *JOURNALISM*

384 NLD
T I C. (Trends In Communication) Text in English. 1996. 2/yr. **Description:** Publishes thematic issues on subjects of interest in the fields of communication and information.
—BLDSC (8820.645900).
Published by: Uitgeverij Boom, PO Box 400, Meppel, 7940 AK, Netherlands. TEL 31-522-257012, FAX 31-522-253864.

384 GBR
T M A NEWSLINE. (Telecommunications Managers Association) Text in English. m. GBP 75; GBP 6.50 newsstand/cover (effective 1999). adv. mkt. back issues avail. **Document type:** *Magazine.* **Description:** Highly focused editorial on news and current trends in the communications market place. Aimed at TMA members, individual & corporate subscribers in the area of telecommunications.
Related titles: Online - full text ed.
Published by: T M A Ventures Limited, Ranmore House, The Crescent, Leatherhead, Surrey KT22 8DY, United Kingdom. TEL 44-1372-361000, FAX 44-1372-818888, sgrant@tmaventures.co.uk, http://www.tmav.com. Ed. George Wallace. adv.: B&W page GBP 1,500, color page GBP 2,300; trim 210 x 297.

621.382 USA ISSN 1082-9350
T R DAILY. Text in English. 1995. d. USD 2,495 (effective 2004). **Document type:** *Newsletter.*
Media: Online - full text. **Related titles:** ♦ Supplement to: Telecommunications Reports. ISSN 0163-9854.
Published by: Telecommunications Reports International, Inc. (Subsidiary of: Aspen Publishers, Inc.), 1333 H St. NW Ste 100-E, Washington, DC 20005-4707. TEL 202-312-6100, FAX 202-312-6065, customerservice@tr.com, http://www.aspenpublishers.com, http://www.tr.com. Ed. John Curran.

343.099 USA
T R'S LAST-MILE TELECOM REPORT. Text in English. bi-w. USD 779 in North America; USD 939 elsewhere (effective 2004). **Document type:** *Newsletter.* **Description:** Covers the convergence of high-speed data, voice and video services.
Former titles: TeleCompetition Report; Telco Competition Report (1079-9958); Incorporated: Video Competition Report; Which was formerly: Cable - Telco Report (1050-0553)
Related titles: Online - full text ed.
—CCC.
Published by: Telecommunications Reports (Subsidiary of: Aspen Publishers, Inc.), 1333 H St, N W, Ste 100, Washington, DC 20005. TEL 202-312-6060, FAX 202-312-6111, customerservice@tr.com, http://www.tr.com/newsletters/lmtr/info.html.

384 USA ISSN 1542-3328
T R'S STATE NEWSWIRE...WITH T R INSIGHT. (Telecommunications Reports) Text in English. 1998. d. (Mon.-Fri.). USD 629 (effective 2002).
Media: Online - full content.
Published by: Telecommunications Reports International, Inc. (Subsidiary of: Aspen Publishers, Inc.), 1333 H St. NW Ste 100-E, Washington, DC 20005-4707. TEL 202-312-6100, 800-822-6338, FAX 202-312-6065, customerservice@tr.com, http://www.tr.com/tr-insight. Ed. Gayle Kansagor.

T V DISKURS; Verantwortung in audiovisuellen Medien. see *CHILDREN AND YOUTH—About*

384.554 USA
T V Y VIDEO. Text in Spanish, English, Portuguese. m.
Published by: B 2 B Portales, Inc (Subsidiary of: Carvajal International, Inc.), 901 Ponce De Leon Blvd, Ste 601, Coral Gables, FL 33134-3073. TEL 305-448-6875, FAX 305-448-9942, http://www.tvyvideo.com/, http://www.b2bportales.com. Ed. Santiago Algorta. Pub. Carmen Alonso-Lake.

384 DEU
TAEGLICH KRESS. Text in German. 1996. d. adv. **Document type:** *Trade.* **Description:** Provides daily content on the latest media news and events.
Media: Online - full content. **Related titles:** Online - full text ed.: (from LexisNexis); ♦ Print ed.: Kress Report. ISSN 1618-7202.
Published by: Kress Verlag GmbH, Haberstr 17, Heidelberg, 69126, Germany. TEL 49-6221-33100, FAX 49-6221-3310333, post@kress.de, http://www.kress.de/kressinside/kressonline.

384 TWN
TAIWAN TELECOM. Text in Chinese. m. adv. **Description:** Covers news and products from multinational and regional telecommunications manufacturers.
Related titles: Online - full text ed.
Published by: Arco Publications Inc., 4F, No. 5, Sec. 1, Pa-Te Rd, Taipei, Taiwan. http://www.taiwantelecommg.com. adv.: page USD 1,700. Circ: 40,000.

TAIWAN TELECOM DIRECTORY. see *BUSINESS AND ECONOMICS—Trade And Industrial Directories*

621.38 GBR
TALKING BUSINESS. Text in English. q. **Document type:** *Consumer.* **Description:** Provides a unique resource by writing about communications using simple language.
Published by: (British Telecom), Redwood Publishing, 7 St Martin's Pl, London, WC2N 4HA, United Kingdom. TEL 44-20-7747-0700, FAX 44-20-7747-0701, amy.wislocki@redwood-publishing.com, http://www.redwood-publishing.com. Ed. Amy Wislocki.

TALKING MACHINE REVIEW INTERNATIONAL. see *SOUND RECORDING AND REPRODUCTION*

384 DEU
TALKLINE BUSINESS. Text in German. q. **Document type:** *Newsletter, Consumer.*
Published by: (Talkline GmbH & Co. KG), G & J Corporate Media GmbH (Subsidiary of: Gruner und Jahr AG & Co.), Griegstr 75, Hamburg, 22763, Germany. TEL 49-40-88303401, FAX 49-40-88303402, http://www.guj-corporate-media.de. Ed. Thomas van Laak. Circ: 30,000 (controlled).

384 DEU
TALKLINER. Text in German. bi-m. **Document type:** *Magazine, Consumer.*
Published by: (Talkline GmbH & Co. KG), G & J Corporate Media GmbH (Subsidiary of: Gruner und Jahr AG & Co.), Griegstr 75, Hamburg, 22763, Germany. TEL 49-40-88303401, FAX 49-40-88303402, http://www.guj-corporate-media.de. Ed. Thomas van Laak. Circ: 2,000 (controlled).

384 USA ISSN 0049-3155
CODEN: TLCMBT
➤ **TECHNICAL COMMUNICATION.** Text in English. 1953. q. USD 60 to non-members (effective 2005); free to members. adv. bk.rev. bibl.; illus. index. reprint service avail. from PQC. **Document type:** *Journal, Academic/Scholarly.*
Related titles: Microfiche ed.: (from MIM, PMC, PQC); Online - full text ed.: (from EBSCO Publishing, Florida Center for Library Automation, Gale Group, IngentaConnect, Northern Light Technology, Inc., O C L C Online Computer Library Center, Inc., ProQuest Information & Learning).
Indexed: AbAn, BPI, BusI, CIJE, CommAb, CompAb, CompLI, CurCont, ETA, IAA, InfoSAb, LISA, MagInd, SSCI.
—BLDSC (8646.600000), CISTI, IE, Infotrieve, ingenta, Linda Hall. **CCC.**
Published by: Society for Technical Communication, 901 N Stuart St, Ste 904, Arlington, VA 22203-1822. TEL 703-522-4114, FAX 703-522-2075, stc@stc.org, http://www.stc.org/techcommGeneral.asp. Ed. George F Hayhoe. Circ: 21,000 (controlled).

621.382 DEU ISSN 1436-1809
TECHNISCHE KOMMUNIKATION. Text in German. bi-m. **Document type:** *Journal, Trade.*
Formerly (until 1998): Tekom-Nachrichten (0942-9905)
Published by: (Tekom Gesellschaft e.V.), Schmidt-Roemhild Verlag, Mengstr 16, Luebeck, 23552, Germany. TEL 49-451-7031-01, FAX 49-451-7031281, eickershoff@beleke.de, http://www.schmidt-roemhild.de. Circ: 4,500 (paid and controlled).

TECHNO - FILE NEWS. see *COMPUTERS—Internet*

TEK I PRESSA. see *ENERGY*

384 RUS ISSN 1562-7144
TEKHNOLOGII I SREDSTVA SVYAZI. Text in Russian. 1997. bi-m. **Document type:** *Journal, Trade.*
Published by: Groteck, 7 Miusskaya sq, 4th Fl, PO Box 53, Moscow, 103030, Russian Federation. TEL 7-095-2516845, FAX 7-095-2513389, tss@groteck.ru, http://www.groteck.ru/communication_ru.php, http://www.groteck.net.

TEKNIK, KOMMUNIKATION OCH HANDIKAPP/TECHNOLOGY, COMMUNICATION, DISABILITY; forskningsrapport. see *HANDICAPPED*

TEL-COM - BRIEF; Telekommunikation, Datenverarbeitung und Organisation. see *BUSINESS AND ECONOMICS—Office Equipment And Services*

384 FRA ISSN 0180-7234
TELE 7 JEUX. Text in French. 1978. 12/yr. **Document type:** *Consumer.*
Published by: Hachette Filipacchi Medias S.A. (Subsidiary of: Lagardere Media), 149 rue Anatole France, Levallois-Perret, Cedex 92300, France. TEL 33-1-41346155, FAX 33-1-41347959.

384 SGP
TELE.COM (ASIAN EDITION)✶. Text in English. 1990. m. USD 80 in Asia; USD 90 elsewhere (effective 2000). adv. back issues avail. **Document type:** *Trade.* **Description:** Covers business and technology for Asia's next generation.
Formerly (until Mar. 2000): Asia - Pacific Telecommunications (0217-510X)
Related titles: Online - full text ed.
Indexed: B&I.
Published by: C M P Business Media Pte Ltd. (Subsidiary of: United News & Media), 390 Havelock Rd, #05-00 King's Centre, Singapore, 169662, Singapore. TEL 65-735-3366, FAX 65-732-1191, info@cmpasia.com.sg, http://www.cmpasia.com.sg/. Circ: 12,000.

621.382 USA
TELE-COMMUNICATIONS ASSOCIATION. TECHNICAL BULLETIN. Text in English. bi-m. **Document type:** *Bulletin.*
Published by: Tele-Communications Association, 424 S Pima Ave, West Covina, CA 91790.

621.382 DEU ISSN 1619-2036
TELE KOMMUNIKATION AKTUELL. Text in German; Summaries in English, French, German. 1941. m. abstr.; bibl.; charts; illus.; mkt. index, cum.index.
Formerly (until 2001): Der Fernmelde-Ingenieur (0015-010X)
Indexed: Englnd, Inspec.
—BLDSC (8779.461120), AskIEEE, CISTI, IE, ingenta, Linda Hall. **CCC.**
Published by: Verlag fuer Wissenschaft und Leben Georg Heidecker, Rathenaustr 20, Erlangen, 91052, Germany. TEL 09131-32162, FAX 09131-304144.

621.382 ESP
TELECAST & BROADCAST. Text in Spanish. 12/yr.
Address: Ciudad de los Periodistas, Efc. Azorin Torre 2, Avda Cardenal Herrera Oria, 171, Madrid, 28034, Spain. TEL 1-730-71-77.

384 USA ISSN 1522-7634
TELECOM A.M. Text in English. 1995. d. **Document type:** *Newsletter, Trade.* **Description:** Provides daily coverage of regulatory issues, court decisions, state and federal legislative activity, FCC rulings, press briefings and industry announcements.
Media: E-mail.
Published by: Warren Communications News, Inc., 2115 Ward Ct, N W, Washington, DC 20037. TEL 202-872-9200, FAX 202-293-3435, info@warren-news.com, http://www.warren-news.com/tamtrial.htm.

TELECOM & NETWORK SECURITY REVIEW. see *COMPUTERS—Computer Networks*

384 HKG
TELECOM ASIA PACIFIC. Text in Chinese. q. USD 86 in Asia & the Pacific; USD 96 elsewhere (effective 2004). adv. back issues avail. **Description:** Provides the Chinese telecoms market information for purchasing and strategy decisions.
Published by: Advanstar Asia Ltd. (Subsidiary of: Advanstar Communications, Inc.), 2501-2, 25/F, Pacific Plaza, 401 Des Voeux Rd W, Hong Kong, Hong Kong. TEL 852-2559-2772, FAX 852-2559-7002, customer_service@telecomasia.net, http://www.telecomasia.net, http://www.telecomasia.net/telecomasia/. R&P Emily Fu.

621.382 USA ISSN 1057-6002
TELECOM CALENDAR. Text in English. 1980. q. USD 395 in US & Canada; USD 425 elsewhere (effective 2001). **Document type:** *Newsletter.* **Description:** Presents worldwide 10-year calendar of telecommunications, including computer, electronics, applications conferences and trade shows.
Published by: Information Gatekeepers, Inc., 320 Washington St, Ste 302, Brighton, MA 02135. TEL 617-782-5033, 800-323-1088, FAX 617-734-8562, info@igigroup.com, http://www.igigroup.com. Pub. Dr. Paul Polishuk.

C

▼ new title ➤ refereed ✶ unverified ♦ full entry avail.

384 TWN
TELECOM LIFE. Text in Chinese. m. adv. **Description:** Provides information on globally and locally produced telecommunications products and services available in the Taiwan marketplace.
Related titles: Online - full text ed.
Published by: Arco Publications Inc., 4F, No. 5, Sec. 1, Pa-Te Rd, Taipei, Taiwan. http://www.telecomlife.com. adv.: page USD 1,000. Circ: 40,000.

384 BEL
TELECOM PLUS INTERNATIONAL. Abbreviated title: T P N. Text in English. 1997. 8/yr. USD 90 in Europe Africa and Asia; USD 95 in the Americas (effective 2002). adv. illus. **Document type:** *Magazine, Trade.* **Description:** Reports on telecommunications products and services.
Formerly: Telecom Product News
Published by: Reed Business Information - Belgium (Subsidiary of: Reed Business Information International), Rue des Palais 100, Brussels, B-1030, Belgium. TEL 32-2-240-2611, FAX 32-2-242-7111, ebi@ebi.be, http://www.ebi.be. Ed. Kristopher Akana. Pub., R&P Jean-Michel Clement. Adv. contact Philippe Pera. Circ: 35,014 (controlled).

384 USA ISSN 1544-3353
▼ **TELECOM POLICY REPORT**; analysis, insight and forecasts on regulation and legislative affairs. Text in English. 2003. w. USD 1,095 (effective 2005). **Document type:** *Newsletter, Trade.* **Description:** Delivers valuable analysis, insight and forward-thinking intelligence on telecom policy and regulation.
Formerly: Wireless Today (1096-4347); Which Incorporated (1991-1997): Wireless Business and Finance (1077-2235)
Related titles: Online - full content ed.; Online - full text ed.: (from bigchalk, Gale Group, LexisNexis).
Published by: Access Intelligence, LLC (Subsidiary of: Veronis, Suhler & Associates Inc.), 1201 Seven Locks Rd, Ste 300, Potomac, MD 20854. TEL 301-354-2101, FAX 301-309-3847, clientservices@accessintel.com, http://www.telecomweb.com/, http://www.pbimedia.com. Pub. Diane Schwartz.

384 CHN ISSN 1006-4222
TELECOM PRODUCT WORLD. Text in Chinese. 1990. m. adv. **Document type:** *Magazine, Trade.* **Description:** Contains business information, technical articles, new product information and interviews with leading figures in the Chinese telecom industry.
Formerly (until 1994): New Product World (1001-7984)
Related titles: Online - full text ed.: (from East View Information Services).
Published by: I D G China, Rm. 616, Tower A, COFCO Plaza, Jianguomennei Dajie, Beijing, 100005 , China. TEL 86-10-6526-0959, FAX 86-10-6526-0866, dumin@idg.com.cn, http://www.tele.com.cn, http://www.idgchina.com. Ed. Wensheng Xing. adv.: color page CNY 9,500; trim 205 x 270. Circ: 25,000 (paid and controlled).

621.382 USA ISSN 1064-1076
TELECOM STANDARDS NEWSLETTER. Text in English. 1992. m. USD 695 in US & Canada; USD 745 elsewhere (effective 2003). **Document type:** *Newsletter.*
—CCC.
Published by: Information Gatekeepers, Inc., 320 Washington St, Ste 302, Brighton, MA 02135. TEL 617-782-5033, 800-323-1088, FAX 617-734-8562, info@igigroup.com, http://www.igigroup.com/nl/pages/telstan.html. Ed. Sebastian Wargacki. Pub. Dr. Paul Polishuk.

384 USA
TELECOM WEB NEWS DIGEST. Text in English. 1993. d. USD 3,585 (effective 2005). **Document type:** *Magazine, Trade.*
Formerly: Communications Today
Published by: Access Intelligence, LLC (Subsidiary of: Veronis, Suhler & Associates Inc.), 1201 Seven Locks Rd, Ste 300, Potomac, MD 20854. TEL 301-354-2000, FAX 301-340-1451.

621.382 DEU ISSN 1432-9093
TELECOMMUNICATION; Zeitschrift fuer Wirtschaft, Recht und Technik. Text in German. 1997. bi-w. adv. **Document type:** *Newspaper, Trade.*
Published by: T C TeleCommunication Verlag GmbH, Am Buschhof 8, Bonn, 53227, Germany. TEL 49-228-970970, FAX 49-228-444296, tc-redaktion@t-online.de. Ed. Sveu-Olaf Suhl. Pub. R Uwe Proll. R&P Sveu Olaf Suhl. Adv. contact Helga Woll. Circ: 20,000 (paid).

384 GBR ISSN 1025-000X
TELECOMMUNICATION IN AFRICA; charting Africa's telecommunications transformation. Text in English. 1995. 11/yr. GBP 20 (effective 2001). adv. bk.rev.; software rev. stat. 40 p./no.; back issues avail. **Document type:** *Magazine, Trade.* **Description:** Provides advertisers with access to key decision-makers and specifiers in the telecommunications sector throughout Africa.
Related titles: Online - full content ed.
Published by: A I T E C, 15 High St, Graveley, Cambs PE18 6PL, United Kingdom. TEL 44-1480-831300, FAX 44-1480-831131, info@aitec.co.uk, admin@aitecafrica.com, http://www.aitecafrica.com/telecomms2/telecomms.html. Ed. Matthew White. Pub., R&P Sean Moroney. Adv. contact Peter Irvine. page GBP 1,750. Circ: 12,000.

621.382 AUS ISSN 0040-2486
TK5101.A1 CODEN: TCJAAW
➤ **TELECOMMUNICATION JOURNAL OF AUSTRALIA.** Text in English. 1935. q. AUD 80 membership; AUD 320 to institutional members; AUD 30 to students (effective 2003). bk.rev. charts; illus. index, cum.index: 1935-1970, 1971-1980, 1981-1990. back issues avail. **Document type:** *Journal, Academic/Scholarly.*
Related titles: Online - full text ed.: (from R M I T Publishing).
Indexed: CADCAM, CompC, EngInd, IAA, Inspec, TelAb.
—BLDSC (8780.000000), AskIEEE, CISTI, Ei, IE, ingenta, Linda Hall.
Published by: Telecommunication Society of Australia Ltd., PO Box 4050, Melbourne, VIC 3001, Australia. TEL 61-3-96390906, FAX 61-3-96391515, tsa@tsa.org.au, http://www.tsa.org.au/tsa/public/pubs.asp. Ed. P Gerrand. R&P, Adv. contact Tricia Collinson. Circ: 2,000.

621.382 FRA ISSN 0981-6895
TELECOMMUNICATIONS; la lettre des operateurs de services a valeur ajoutee. Text in French. 1987. 22/yr. adv. bk.rev. index. back issues avail.
Formerly: Innovation et Produits Nouveaux (0246-9715)
Published by: A Jour (Subsidiary of: Groupe Tests), 26 Rue d'Oradour-sur-Glane, Paris, 75504, France. TEL 33-1-44253500, redac.ajour@groupe-tests.fr, http://www.01net.com, http://www.ajour.fr. Ed. Jean Claude Streicher. Circ: 1,500.

621.382 USA ISSN 1534-956X
TK5101.A1 CODEN: TLCOAY
TELECOMMUNICATIONS AMERICAS. Text in English. 1981. m. USD 145 domestic; USD 230 foreign; free to qualified personnel (effective 2005). adv. charts. Index. reprints avail. **Document type:** *Journal, Trade.* **Description:** Covers telecommunications systems and research.
Formerly (until 2001): Telecommunications (North American Edition) (0278-4831)
Related titles: Microform ed.: (from PQC); Online - full text ed.: Telecommunications Online (from EBSCO Publishing, Florida Center for Library Automation, Gale Group, O C L C Online Computer Library Center, Inc., ProQuest Information & Learning); ♦ Regional ed(s).: Telecommunications (International Ed.). ISSN 0040-2494.
Indexed: ABIn, BMT, BusI, C&ISA, CompB, CompC, CompD, CurCont, E&CAJ, ESPM, EngInd, Inspec, PROMT, RiskAb, SoftBase, SolStAb, T&II, TelAb.
—BLDSC (8781.012000), CISTI, Ei, IDS, IE, ingenta, Linda Hall. **CCC.**
Published by: Horizon House Publications, 685 Canton St, Norwood, MA 02062. TEL 781-769-9750, FAX 781-762-9230, editorial@telecommagazine.com, http://www.telecommagazine.com/default.asp?journalid=3, http://www.horizonhouse.com. Ed. Sue O'Keefe. Pub. Heidi Copeland. adv.: color page USD 15,880, B&W page USD 13,885. Circ: 80,000. **Subscr. to:** Telecommunications, PO Box 3255, Northbrook, IL 60065-3255. FAX 847-291-4816, 44-20-7596-8749.

621.38 AZE
TELECOMMUNICATIONS AND INFORMATION TECHNOLOGIES. Text in English. 3/w. **Document type:** *Bulletin.*
Related titles: Ed.: Telekommunikatsii i Informatsionnye Tekhnologii.
Published by: Turan Information Agency/Turna Informasiya Agentliyi, Khagani ul 33, Baku, 370000, Azerbaijan. TEL 994-12-984226, 994-12-935967, FAX 994-12-983817, root@turan.baku.az, http://www.turaninfo.com.

621.382 USA ISSN 0040-2508
CODEN: TCREAG
TELECOMMUNICATIONS AND RADIO ENGINEERING. Text in English. 1962. m. USD 3,654 (effective 2004). adv. bk.rev. bibl.; charts; illus. **Document type:** *Journal, Academic/Scholarly.* **Description:** Covers digital and analog wire, radio, video and optical communications, facsimile, micro- and millimeter-wave communications, switching and coding theory, signal processing, voice and pattern recognition, antennae and waveguides.
Formed by the 1963 merger of: Telecommunications and Radio Engineering. Part 1. Telecommunications (0497-1396); Telecommunications and Radio Engineering. Part 2. Radio Engineering (0497-140X)
Related titles: Microform ed.: (from PQC); Online - full text ed.: (from EBSCO Publishing); ♦ Translation of: Elektrosvyaz'. ISSN 0013-5771; ♦ Translation of: Antenny. ISSN 0320-9601; ♦ Translation of: Zarubezhnaya Radioelektronika. Uspekhi Sovremennoi Elektroniki.
Indexed: C&ISA, CIS, CivEngAb, E&CAJ, EngInd, IAA, ISMEC, Inspec, M&TEA, SCI, SSCI, SolStAb, TelAb.
—BLDSC (0426.010000), AskIEEE, CISTI, Ei, IDS, IE, Infotrieve, ingenta, Linda Hall. **CCC.**
Published by: (Russian Society of Electronics and Communications Engineers RUS), Begell House Inc., 145 Madison Ave, New York, NY 10016-6717. TEL 212-725-1999, FAX 212-213-8368, orders@begellhouse.com, http://www.begellhouse.com/tre/tre.html. Eds. B. M. Bulgakov, Dr. William Begell. Circ: 228 (paid).

TELECOMMUNICATIONS DIRECTORY; an international descriptive guide to approximately 4,300 telecommunications organizations, systems, and services. see *BUSINESS AND ECONOMICS—Trade And Industrial Directories*

343.0994 USA ISSN 1534-4398
TELECOMMUNICATIONS MONITOR. Text in English. d. back issues avail. **Document type:** *Newsletter, Trade.* **Description:** Reports on regulatory, legislative, and judicial decisions and developments affecting telecommunications.
Media: Online - full text (from The Bureau of National Affairs, Inc.).
—CCC.
Published by: The Bureau of National Affairs, Inc., 1231 25th St., NW, Washington, DC 20037. TEL 800-372-1033, 800-452-7773, FAX 800-253-0332, customercare@bna.com, http://www.bna.com/products/corplaw/tcdm.htm. **Subscr. to:** 9435 Key West Ave, Rockville, MD 20850.

621.382 GBR ISSN 0308-5961
HE7601 CODEN: TEPODJ
➤ **TELECOMMUNICATIONS POLICY.** Text in English. 1977. 11/yr. EUR 266 in Europe to individuals; JPY 35,500 in Japan to individuals; USD 298 to individuals except Europe and Japan; EUR 1,067 in Europe to institutions; JPY 141,700 in Japan to institutions; USD 1,194 to institutions except Europe and Japan (effective 2006). adv. bk.rev. abstr. back issues avail. **Document type:** *Academic/Scholarly.* **Description:** Takes an international interdisciplinary view of the social, economic, political and regulatory aspects of telecommunications and information systems.
Related titles: Microform ed.: (from PQC); Online - full text ed.: (from EBSCO Publishing, Gale Group, IngentaConnect, ScienceDirect, Swets Information Services).
Indexed: ABIn, ASCA, C&ISA, CADCAM, CommAb, CompC, CurCont, E&CAJ, ESPM, EngInd, FutSurv, IBSS, ILD, ISR, InfoSAb, Inspec, JEL, KES, LISA, M&MA, PAIS, PRA, RiskAb, SCI, SSCI, SUSA, SolStAb, TelAb.
—BLDSC (8781.520000), AskIEEE, CISTI, Ei, IDS, IE, Infotrieve, ingenta, Linda Hall. **CCC.**
Published by: Pergamon (Subsidiary of: Elsevier Science & Technology), The Boulevard, Langford Ln, East Park, Kidlington, Oxford OX5 1GB, United Kingdom. TEL 44-1865-843000, FAX 44-1865-843010, http://www.elsevier.com/locate/telpol. Eds. Colin Blackman, Douglas Pitt, Lihe Liu. **Subscr. to:** Elsevier BV, PO Box 211, Amsterdam 1000 AE, Netherlands. TEL 31-20-485-3757, FAX 31-20-485-3432, nlinfo-f@elsevier.nl, http://www.elsevier.nl.

621.382 USA ISSN 0163-9854
HE7775
TELECOMMUNICATIONS REPORTS. Text in English. 1934. s-m. USD 1,789 in North America to institutions; USD 3,213 combined subscription in North America to institutions print & online eds. (effective 2004). bk.rev. q. cum.index. back issues avail. **Document type:** *Newsletter.* **Description:** Covers federal and state regulatory, legislative, technological, legal, and corporate news, as well as international telecommunications developments.
Related titles: Online - full text ed.: (from EBSCO Publishing, Florida Center for Library Automation, Gale Group); ♦ Supplement(s): T R Daily. ISSN 1082-9350.
Indexed: CompC.
—CCC.
Address: 1333 H St, N W, Ste 100, Washington, DC 20005. TEL 202-312-6060, 800-822-6338, FAX 202-312-6111, http://www.tr.com. Ed. Victoria A Mason. R&P Eileen Callahan.

621.382 USA ISSN 1054-1942
HE7601
TELECOMMUNICATIONS REPORTS INTERNATIONAL. Text in English. 1990. 23/yr. USD 1,789 (effective 2005); USD 1,435 foreign (effective 2000). **Document type:** *Newsletter, Trade.* **Description:** Provides a global perspective on telecommunications. Areas of coverage include trade battles, industry and government actions, liberalization and regulatory issues, satellites, new international telecom tariffs and services, financial development and more.
Related titles: Online - full text ed.
Indexed: CurCont.
—CCC.
Published by: Telecommunications Reports (Subsidiary of: Aspen Publishers, Inc.), 1333 H St, N W, Ste 100, Washington, DC 20005. TEL 800-822-6338, FAX 202-842-3023, customerservice@tr.com, http://www.tr.com. Ed. Fred Donovan. R&P Eileen Callahan.

384.041 USA ISSN 1467-5234
TELECOMS DEAL REPORT. Text in English. 1999. fortn. adv. **Document type:** *Magazine, Trade.*
Related titles: Online - full text ed.: (from Gale Group).
Published by: Access Intelligence, LLC (Subsidiary of: Veronis, Suhler & Associates Inc.), 1201 Seven Locks Rd, Ste 300, Potomac, MD 20854. TEL 301-354-2000, FAX 301-424-2058, clientservices@accessintel.com, http://www.pbimedia.com.

384 GBR ISSN 1368-1559
TELECOMS WORLD. Text in English. 1997. q. **Document type:** *Newsletter, Trade.* **Description:** Delivers news about the opportunities and pitfalls that the rapidly developing telecoms sector provides.

Formerly (until 2000): Financial Times Telecoms World (1469-6991)
Published by: Financial Times Telecoms & Media Publishing (Subsidiary of: Financial Times Group), Maple House, 149 Tottenham Court Rd, London, W1P 9LL, United Kingdom. TEL 44-20-74532213, FAX 44-20-74535947, http://www.informa.com.

621.382 ROM ISSN 1220-8655
TELECOMUNICATII. Text in Romanian; Summaries in English, French, German, Russian. m. bibl.; charts; illus. **Document type:** *Government.*
Supersedes in part (in 1989): Revista Transporturilor si Telecomunicatiilor (0379-2390); Which was formed by the 1974 merger of: Posti si Telecomunicatii (0048-492X); Transporturi Auto, Navale si Ariene (0373-7136); Revista Cailor Ferate Romane (0482-5020)
Indexed: Inspec.
—Linda Hall.
Published by: Ministerul Transporturilor si Telecomunicatiilor, Calea Grivitei 193 b, Bucharest, 78141, Romania. **Co-sponsor:** Institutul de Cercetari si Proiectari Tehnologice in Transporturi.

384 SWE ISSN 1104-9804
TELEKOM IDAG. Variant title: Telecom Idag. Text in Swedish. 1994. 8/yr. SEK 650 (effective 2003). adv.
Published by: A B Nordreportern, PO Box 104, Umeaa, 90103, Sweden. TEL 46-90-700900, FAX 46-90-142330, info@nordreportern.se, http://www.telekomidag.com, http://www.nordreportern.se. Eds. Stefan Eriksson TEL 46-90-700902, Anders Pauser TEL 46-90-700901. Circ: 27,000.

621.382 NLD
TELEKOMMUNIKATIE VISIE. Text in Dutch. q. free.
Published by: Koning en Hartman Elektrotechniek B.V., PO Box 125, Delft, 2600 AC, Netherlands. TEL 015-619194. Circ: 3,200.

343.0994 DEU ISSN 1618-9299
TELEKOMMUNIKATIONS- & MEDIENRECHT. Abbreviated title: T K M R. Text in German. 1949. bi-m. EUR 164 domestic; EUR 173 foreign; EUR 40 newsstand/cover (effective 2003). **Document type:** *Magazine, Trade.*
Former titles (until 2002): RTkom (1438-1621); (until 1999): Archiv fuer Post und Telekommunikation (0943-2337); (until 1992): Archiv fuer das Post- und Fernmeldewesen (0170-8988)
Indexed: DIP.
Published by: C.F. Mueller Verlag Huethig GmbH & Co. KG, Im Weiher 10, Heidelberg, 69121, Germany. TEL 49-6221-4890, FAX 49-6221-489529, Info@HJR-Verlag.de, http://www.huethig-jehle-rehm.de/content/cfmueller.html. Adv. contact Brigitte Quinones.

384 621.399 POL ISSN 1640-1549
TELEKOMUNIKACJA I TECHNIKI INFORMACYJNE. Text in Polish. 2000. q. **Document type:** *Journal, Academic/Scholarly.*
Related titles: ♦ English ed.: Journal of Telecommunications and Information Technology. ISSN 1509-4553.
Published by: Instytut Lacznosci/National Institute of Telecommunications, ul Szachowa 1, Warsaw, 04894, Poland. TEL 48-22-8724388, FAX 48-22-5128400, redakcja@itl.waw.pl, http://www.itl.waw.pl. Pub. Pawel Szczepanski. R&P Maria Lopuszniak.

621.382 NOR ISSN 0085-7130
TK6001 CODEN: TKTKAW
➤ **TELEKTRONIKK.** Text in English. 1904. q. free (effective 2004). index. back issues avail. **Document type:** *Monographic series, Academic/Scholarly.*
Formerly (until 1959): Telegrafstyret. Tekniske Meddelelser (0802-6815)
Indexed: Englnd, Inspec, RefZh.
—BLDSC (8782.900000), AskIEEE, CISTI, Ei, IE, ingenta. **CCC.**
Published by: Telenor AS, Snaroeyveien 30, Fornebu, 1331, Norway. TEL 47-678-90000, telektronikk@telenor.com, http://www.telenor.no/fou/publisering. Ed. Per Hjalmar Lehre. Circ: 5,000.

621.382 USA ISSN 0736-5853
TK5101.A1 CODEN: TEINEG
➤ **TELEMATICS AND INFORMATICS.** Text in English. 1984. 4/yr. EUR 928 in Europe to institutions; JPY 123,200 in Japan to institutions; USD 1,039 to institutions except Europe and Japan (effective 2006). index. back issues avail. **Document type:** *Journal, Academic/Scholarly.* **Description:** Contains information on applied telecommunications and information technology, policy and legislation resource management. Examines the resulting socio-economic implications.
Related titles: Microfilm ed.: (from PQC); Online - full text ed.: (from EBSCO Publishing, Gale Group, IngentaConnect, ScienceDirect, Swets Information Services).
Indexed: AHCI, AIA, B&BAb, BioEngAb, CADCAM, CommAb, CompAb, CompC, CompLI, CurCont, CybAb, ESPM, Englnd, HRA, IBR, InfoSAb, Inspec, LISA, PRA, RiskAb, SPAA, TelAb.
—BLDSC (8782.955000), AskIEEE, CISTI, Ei, IE, Infotrieve, ingenta. **CCC.**

Published by: Elsevier Inc. (Subsidiary of: Elsevier Science & Technology), 360 Park Ave. S, New York, NY 10010-1710. TEL 212-989-5800, 888-437-4636, FAX 212-633-3140, http://www.elsevier.com/locate/tele. Ed. J B Thompson. Circ: 3,000.

➤ **TELEMEDICINE TODAY**; the health news magazine. see *MEDICAL SCIENCES*

384 NLD ISSN 1385-1527
➤ **TELEOMMUNICATIONS POLICY RESEARCH.** Text in English. 1989. irreg., latest vol.7, 1997. price varies. back issues avail. **Document type:** *Monographic series, Academic/Scholarly.* **Description:** Covers changing telecommunications policies in Europe, as well as the impact of worldwide trends to deregulation.
Supersedes (in 1994): European Communication Policy Research Series (0926-9819)
Published by: I O S Press, Nieuwe Hemweg 6B, Amsterdam, 1013 BG, Netherlands. TEL 31-20-6883355, FAX 31-20-6203419, order@iospress.nl, http://www.iospress.nl. **Subscr. to:** I O S Press, Inc, 4502 Rachael Manor Dr., Fairfax, VA 22032-3631. iosbooks@iospress.com.

384 BRA ISSN 0103-6025
TELEPRESS LATINOAMERICA. Text in Spanish. 1991. m. (10/yr.). free to qualified personnel. adv. **Document type:** *Trade.* **Description:** Presents a series of business and technology solutions to telecom executives. Covers a wide range of technology and business analysis.
Published by: Advanstar Editora e Com. Ltda., Rua Gomes de Carvalho, 1329 Andar 9, Vila Olimpia, Sao Paulo - SP, SP 04547-005, Brazil. TEL 55-11-31707000, FAX 55-11-31707010, info@advanstar.com, http://www.advanstar.com.br. adv.: B&W page USD 6,656, color page USD 8,320; trim 275 x 208. Circ: 20,081.

TELESPAN (E-MAIL EDITION); a bulletin on teleconferencing. see *COMPUTERS—Data Communications And Data Transmission Systems*

TELEVIZIA A ROZHLAS; programovy tyzdennik. see *COMMUNICATIONS—Radio*

384 AUS
TELSTRA CORPORATION LIMITED. ANNUAL REPORT. Text in English. 1992. a. free. **Document type:** *Corporate.*
Formerly: Australian and Overseas Telecommunications Corporation. Annual Report; Formed by the 1992 merger of: Overseas Telecommunications Commission. Report (0404-1747); (1975-1992): Telecom Australia. Annual Report
Published by: Telstra Corporation Limited, Corporate Headquarters, 242 Exhibition St, Melbourne, VIC 3000, Australia. TEL 61-3-9632-7711, FAX 61-3-9634-4553. Eds. D Hoare, F Blount. R&P Michael Montalto TEL 31-3-9634-6431. Circ: 40,000.

384 URY ISSN 0797-6488
TEMAS DE COMUNICACION✶. Text in Spanish. 1992. q.?. **Document type:** *Academic/Scholarly.*
Published by: Universidad de la Republica, Licenciatura de Ciencias de la Comunicacion, Avda 18 de Julio 1968, Piso 2, Montevideo, 11200, Uruguay. TEL 5982-417995, FAX 5982-486796. Ed. Sergio Israel.

621.38 JPN
TEREMATIKUSU SHINPOJUMU/TELEMATICS SYMPOSIUM. Text in Japanese. 1988. irreg.
Published by: Gazo Denshi Gakkai, Terematikusu Kenkyu Senmon linkai/Institute of Image Electronics Engineers of Japan, Telematics Committee, Waseda Daigaku Rikogakubu, Denshi Tsushingakka Tominaga Kenkyushitsu, 4-1 Okubo 3-chome, Shinjuku-ku, Tokyo, 169-0072, Japan.

TEST & MEASUREMENT NEWS. see *COMPUTERS—Hardware*

621.382 JPN ISSN 0910-3732
THIS IS N E C (YEAR). Text in Japanese. 1989. a. **Document type:** *Corporate.* **Description:** Provides facts and figures on the communications equipment of this manufacturer. Major product areas are communications systems and equipment, computers and industrial electronic systems, electronic devices, and home electronics products.
Published by: Nippon Electric Company/Nippon Denki K.K., 7-1 Shiba 5-chome, Minato-ku, Tokyo, 108-0014, Japan. TEL 03-4541111, FAX 03-7986529.

621.38 CHN ISSN 1006-7442
TIANJIN TONGXIN JISHU/TIANJIN COMMUNICATIONS TECHNOLOGY. Text in Chinese. 1984. q. **Document type:** *Journal, Academic/Scholarly.*
Related titles: Online - full content ed.: (from WanFang Data Corp.); Online - full text ed.: (from East View Information Services).
Indexed: BrCerAb, C&ISA, CerAb, CorrAb, E&CAJ, EMA, IAA, Inspec, M&TEA, MBF, METADEX, WAA.
—BLDSC (8820.515200), IE, Linda Hall.

Published by: Zhongguo Dianxinjietuan, Tianjinshi Dianxin Gongsi/China TeleCom, Tianjin TeleCom Corp., Heping-qu, 27, Xinxing Lu, Tianjin, 300052, China. TEL 96-22-27880107, FAX 86-22-27880121, tjtxjs@public.tpt.tj.cn, http://tjtxjs.periodicals.net.cn/default.html, http://www.bjx.com.cn/dl/qikan/tjtxjs/default.asp.

384 NLD ISSN 1384-6930
TIJDSCHRIFT VOOR COMMUNICATIEWETENSCHAP. Text in Dutch. 1972. q.
Formerly (until 1995): Massacommunicatie (0921-2620)
—Infotrieve.
Published by: Uitgeverij Boom, PO Box 400, Meppel, 7940 AK, Netherlands. info@uitgeverijboom.nl, http://www.uitgeverijboom.nl.

DER TITELSCHUTZ ANZEIGER. see *PUBLISHING AND BOOK TRADE*

TOHOKU DAIGAKU DENTSU DANWAKAI KIROKU. see *ENGINEERING—Electrical Engineering*

384 JPN
TOHOKU UNIVERSITY. RESEARCH INSTITUTE OF ELECTRICAL COMMUNICATION. TECHNICAL REPORT. Text in English. 1964. irreg. per issue exchange basis.
Indexed: Inspec.
Published by: Tohoku Daigaku, Denki Tsushin Kenkyujo/Tohoku University, Research Institute of Electrical Communication, 1-1 Katahira 2-chome, Aoba-ku, Sendai, Miyagi 980-8577, Japan.

TOKYO DAIGAKU KOGAKUBU. DENKI KOGAKU DENSHI KOGAKU IHO/UNIVERSITY OF TOKYO. ELECTRICAL AND ELECTRONIC ENGINEERING DEPARTMENTS. BULLETIN. see *ENGINEERING—Electrical Engineering*

343.099 GBR ISSN 1361-9918
K24 CODEN: TCLAFD
➤ **TOLLEY'S COMMUNICATIONS LAW.** Text in English. 1984. bi-m. GBP 155 in United Kingdom; GBP 178 overseas (effective 2000). adv. bk.rev. **Document type:** *Journal, Academic/Scholarly.* **Description:** Covers all aspects of communications law and practice.
Former titles (until 1996): Tolley's Computer Law and Practice (1359-5989); (until 1992): Computer Law and Practice (0266-4801)
Related titles: Online - full text ed.
Indexed: CLI, ELJI, Inspec, LISA, LJI, LRI.
—BLDSC (8863.685560), AskIEEE, IE, Infotrieve, ingenta. **CCC.**
Published by: Butterworths Tolley (Subsidiary of: LexisNexis UK (Scottish Office)), 2 Addiscombe Rd, Croydon, Surrey CR9 5AF, United Kingdom. TEL 44-20-8686-9141, FAX 44-20-8686-3155, comms l@tolley.co.uk, http://www.tolley.co.uk. Ed. David Goldberg.

C

621.382 CHN ISSN 1000-436X
TONGXIN XUEBAO/CHINA INSTITUTE OF COMMUNICATIONS. JOURNAL. Text in Chinese. 1980. bi-m. CNY 240 (effective 2004). **Document type:** *Journal, Academic/Scholarly.*
Related titles: Online - full text ed.: (from East View Information Services).
Indexed: C&ISA, E&CAJ, IAA, Inspec.
—BLDSC (4729.218500), AskIEEE, IE, ingenta, Linda Hall.
Published by: (Zhongguo Tongxin Xuehui/Chinese Society of Communications), Renmin Youdian Chubanshe/People's Posts and Telecommunications Publishing House, 14 A Xizhaosi Street, Chongwen District, Beijing, 100061, China. abc@ptpress.com.cn, http://www.ptpress.com.cn/. Ed. Zhou Jiongpan. **Dist. overseas by:** China International Book Trading Corp, 35 Chegongzhuang Xilu, Haidian District, PO Box 399, Beijing 100044, China. TEL 86-10-68412045, FAX 86-10-68412023, cibtc@mail.cibtc.com.cn, http://www.cibtc.com.cn.

659.111 659.14 330.9 GBR ISSN 0968-2155
TOP 50 EUROPEAN MEDIA OWNERS. Text in English. 1991. a. GBP 495 (effective 2001). charts; stat. **Document type:** *Trade.* **Description:** The who's who of European media ownership.
Published by: Zenith Media, Bridge House, 63-65 N. Wharf Rd, London, W2 1LA, United Kingdom. TEL 44-20-7224-8500, FAX 44-20-7706-2650, publications@zenithmedia.co.uk, http://www.zenithmedia.com. Ed., Pub. Adam Smith.

384 GBR ISSN 1740-1267
TK5101.A1
▼ **TOTAL TELECOM.** Text in English. 2003. d. GBP 300 (effective 2003). **Document type:** *Trade.* **Description:** Provides coverage of key business, technology, and market issues, supported by regular analysis and opinion from industry experts.
Related titles: Online - full text ed.: USD 150 (effective 2003) (from EBSCO Publishing).
Published by: Emap Media Ltd. (Subsidiary of: Emap Business Communications Ltd.), 33-39 Bowling Green Ln, London, EC1R 0DA, United Kingdom. TEL 44-20-7505-8000, FAX 44-20-7505-8504, http://www.totaltele.com/, http://www.totaltele.com/media/tt/.

384 332.6 USA ISSN 1524-5160
HE7761
TOWER INVESTOR. Text in English. 1999. m. USD 1,045; USD 1,440 combined subscription print & e-mail eds. (effective 2005). adv. **Document type:** *Newsletter, Trade.* **Description:** Includes private market valuations and detailed analysis of the markets and the players within them and also has a monthly rundown of all the latest deals providing readers with the latest details on recently announced/proposed industry transactions.
Related titles: E-mail ed.: USD 945 (effective 2005); Fax ed.: USD 945 (effective 2001).
Published by: Kagan Research, LLC, One Lower Ragsdale Dr, Bldg One, Ste 130, Monterey, CA 93940. TEL 831-624-1536, FAX 831-625-3225, info@kagan.com, http://research.kagan.com/keo/subscriptionsDetailPage.aspx?SubscriptionID=23, http://www.kagan.com. Pub. Paul Kagan. adv.: color page USD 3,400.

621.382 CAN
TRANSMITTER. Text in English. 1978. 6/yr. free. **Document type:** *Newsletter.*
Published by: Telecommunications Workers Union, 5261 Lane St, Burnaby, BC V5H 4A6, Canada. TEL 604-437-8601, FAX 604-435-7760. Ed., R&P Myron Johnson. Circ: 13,000.

TRANSPORT AND COMMUNICATIONS. see *TRANSPORTATION*

TRANSPORT AND COMMUNICATIONS (SINGAPORE). see *TRANSPORTATION—Abstracting, Bibliographies, Statistics*

TRANSPORT & COMMUNICATIONS BULLETIN FOR ASIA & THE PACIFIC. see *TRANSPORTATION*

384 GBR ISSN 0963-0317
TREND MONITOR REPORTS. COMMUNICATIONS. Text in English. 1991. s-a. **Document type:** *Trade.*
Published by: Trend Monitor International Ltd., 3 Tower St, Portsmouth, Hants PO1 2JR, United Kingdom. TEL 01705-864714, FAX 01705-828009. Ed. Jan Wyllie.

C

384 USA ISSN 1383-8857
P87
TRENDS IN COMMUNICATION. Text in English. 1997. q. USD 135 in US & Canada to institutions; USD 165 elsewhere to institutions; USD 150 combined subscription in US & Canada to institutions online & print eds.; USD 180 combined subscription elsewhere to institutions online & print eds. (effective 2004). back issues avail. **Document type:** *Journal, Academic/Scholarly.* **Description:** Covers subjects of interest in the field of information and communication.
Related titles: Online - full text ed.: ISSN 1542-7439. USD 130 worldwide to institutions (effective 2004) (from EBSCO Publishing, Gale Group, O C L C Online Computer Library Center, Inc., Swets Information Services).
Indexed: CommAb.
—BLDSC (8820.645900), IE, ingenta.
Published by: Lawrence Erlbaum Associates, Inc., 10 Industrial Ave, Mahwah, NJ 07430-2262. TEL 201-258-2200, 800-926-6579, FAX 201-236-0072, journals@erlbaum.com, http://www.erlbaum.com. Ed. David Ward.

057.1 KGZ
TSENTRALNO-AZIATSKII EZHEKVARTNAL'NOE PECHATNOE IZDANIE. Text in Russian. q.
Related titles: Print ed.: Central Asia Quarterly.
Published by: Proekt Podderzhki Regional'nykh S M I Tsentral'noi Azii/Central Asia Media Support Project, Kurmazhan Datka 217, Osh, 71400, Kyrgyzstan. TEL 996-3222-55259.

384 JPN
TSUSHIN HAKUSHO/WHITE PAPER OF COMMUNICATIONS. Text in Japanese. a. JPY 3,200. **Document type:** *Government.*
Published by: (Japan. Yuseisho/Ministry of Posts and Telecommunications), Okurasho Insatsukyoku/Ministry of Finance, Printing Bureau, 2-4 Toranomon 2-chome, Minato-ku, Tokyo, 105-0001, Japan.

621.382 JPN ISSN 0916-5754
TSUSHIN SOGO KENKYUJO NENPO/JAPAN. MINISTRY OF POSTS AND TELECOMMUNICATIONS. COMMUNICATIONS RESEARCH LABORATORY. ANNUAL REPORT. Text in Japanese. a. **Document type:** *Government.*
Published by: Yuseisho, Tsushin Sogo Kenkyujo/Ministry of Posts and Telecommunications, Communications Research Laboratory, 2-1 Nukui-Kita-Machi 4-chome, Koganei-shi, Tokyo-to 184-0015, Japan.

U C L A ENTERTAINMENT LAW REVIEW. (University of California at Los Angeles) see *LAW*

659.111 659.14 330.9 GBR ISSN 0968-2198
U K MEDIA YEARBOOK. Text in English. 1988. a. GBP 275 (effective 2001). charts; stat. **Document type:** *Trade.* **Description:** Facts and figures on the United Kingdom's advertising media.
Published by: Zenith Media, Bridge House, 63-65 N. Wharf Rd, London, W2 1LA, United Kingdom. TEL 44-20-7224-8550, FAX 44-20-7298-6902, publications@zenithmedia.co.uk, http://www.zenithmedia.com. Ed., Pub. Adam Smith. Circ: 500 (paid).

U.S. ADMINISTRATIVE OFFICE OF THE UNITED STATES COURTS. REPORT ON APPLICATIONS FOR ORDERS AUTHORIZING OR APPROVING THE INTERCEPTION OF WIRE OR ORAL COMMUNICATIONS. see *LAW*

384 USA ISSN 0083-0607
U.S. FEDERAL COMMUNICATIONS COMMISSION. I N F BULLETINS. Text in English. 1949. irreg., latest 1988. free. **Document type:** *Bulletin, Government.*
Published by: U.S. Federal Communications Commission, 445 12th St SW Rm TW-B505, Washington, DC 20554. TEL 202-418-0450.

384 UKR
UKRAINS'KII PAUKOVO-DOSLIDNII INSTITUT RADIO I TELEBACHENIYA. TRUDY. Text in English, Russian, Ukrainian; Abstracts in Ukrainian, Russian. 1995. q. bibl.; illus. **Document type:** *Academic/Scholarly.* **Description:** Covers the theory and practice of telecommunications techniques, development and implementation of communication systems, information processing, design and technology, and new technologies.
Published by: Ukrains'kyi Naukovo-Doslidnyi Insyitut Radio i Telebachennya, Bunin vul 31, Odessa, 270026, Ukraine. TEL 380-482-222868, FAX 380-482-224583, bod@uniirt.com.ua, http://www.uniirt.com.ua. Ed., R&P Nick Mykhaylov. Pub. Anatoly Gutsaluk. Circ: 500.

384 ITA
UNIVERSITA DEGLI STUDI DI PARMA. CENTRO STUDI E ARCHIVIO DELLA COMUNICAZIONE. ARCHIVI DEL PROGRETTO - COLLANA. Text in Italian. 1989. a. price varies. **Document type:** *Academic/Scholarly.*
Published by: (Centro Studi e Archivio della Comunicazione), Universita degli Studi di Parma, Piazzale della Pace, 7 A, Parma, PR 43100, Italy. TEL 0521-270847, FAX 0521-207125.

384 ITA
UNIVERSITA DEGLI STUDI DI PARMA. CENTRO STUDI E ARCHIVIO DELLA COMUNICAZIONE. CATALOGHI. Text in Italian. 1976. irreg., latest vol.72, 1989. price varies. **Document type:** *Catalog.*
Published by: (Centro Studi e Archivio della Comunicazione), Universita degli Studi di Parma, Piazzale della Pace, 7 A, Parma, PR 43100, Italy. TEL 0521-270847, FAX 0521-207125.

621.382 URY
URUGUAY. ADMINISTRACION NACIONAL DE TELECOMUNICACIONES. MEMORIA ANUAL. Short title: Memoria A N T E L Uruguay. Text in Spanish. a. **Document type:** *Government.*
Published by: Administracion Nacional de Telecomunicaciones, Fernandez Crespo 1534, Casilla de Correo 989, Montevideo, Uruguay. TELEX 23850 UY.

THE UTILITIES JOURNAL. see *ENERGY*

384 USA
▼ **V D V WORLD.** (Voice Data Video) Text in English. 2003. bi-m. **Document type:** *Magazine, Trade.*
Published by: Cygnus Business Media, Inc., 3 Huntington Quadrangle, Ste 301N, Melville, NY 11747-3601. http://www.vdvworld.com/, http://www.cygnusb2b.com/. Ed., Pub. Arnold Blumenthal.

621.382 RUS ISSN 1563-194X
V K S S CONNECT. (Vedomstvennye Korporativnye Sistemy Seti) Text in Russian. 2000. bi-m. **Document type:** *Journal, Trade.*
Published by: Izdatel'skii Dom Connect!, ul Dolgorukovskaya 23A, 4 etazh, Moscow, 127006, Russian Federation. TEL 7-095-1051118, FAX 7-095-9785100, post@connect.ru, http://www.connect.ru.

VAASAN YLIOPISTON JULKAISUJA. SELVITYKSIA JA RAPORTTEJA/PROCEEDINGS OF THE UNIVERSITY OF VAASA. REPORTS. see *BUSINESS AND ECONOMICS—Economic Systems And Theories, Economic History*

THE VANGUARD (MOBILE). see *COLLEGE AND ALUMNI*

VERONIS, SUHLER & ASSOCIATES COMMUNICATIONS INDUSTRY FORECAST. see *BUSINESS AND ECONOMICS*

VERONIS, SUHLER & ASSOCIATES COMMUNICATIONS INDUSTRY REPORT. see *BUSINESS AND ECONOMICS*

VERSO E REVERSO. see *HUMANITIES: COMPREHENSIVE WORKS*

621.382 RUS ISSN 0320-8141
CODEN: VSVYAQ
VESTNIK SVYAZI. Text in Russian. 1941. m. USD 180 foreign (effective 2004). adv. charts; illus.; tr.lit. index.
Indexed: RASB, RefZh.
—CASDDS, CISTI, East View, Linda Hall.
Published by: Izdatel'stvo IRIAS, Krovokolennyi per 14, str 1, Moscow, 101000, Russian Federation. TEL 7-095-9254257, FAX 7-095-9212797. Ed. E B Konstantinov. Circ: 17,254. **Dist. by:** M K - Periodica, ul Gilyarovskogo 39, Moscow 129110, Russian Federation. TEL 7-095-2845008, FAX 7-095-2813798, info@periodicals.ru, http://www.mkniga.ru.

621.382 USA ISSN 1041-0643
VIA SATELLITE. Text in English. 1986. m. free to qualified personnel (effective 2005). adv. back issues avail. **Document type:** *Magazine, Trade.* **Description:** Looks at commercial communication via satellite and competing technologies. Includes technical information, applications and case studies.
Related titles: Online - full text ed.: (from bigchalk, Gale Group, LexisNexis, ProQuest Information & Learning).
—BLDSC (9231.756000), IE, Infotrieve, ingenta. **CCC.**
Published by: Access Intelligence, LLC (Subsidiary of: Veronis, Suhler & Associates Inc.), 1201 Seven Locks Rd, Ste 300, Potomac, MD 20854. TEL 301-354-2000, 800-777-5006, FAX 301-424-2058, clientservices@accessintel.com, http://www.pbimedia.com/cgi/catalog/info?VIA. Ed. Scott Chase. Circ: (controlled).

621.382 GBR ISSN 0267-3584
VIDEOTEX VIEWPOINT✶. Text in English. q. GBP 15. back issues avail.
Indexed: Inspec.
—AskIEEE.
Published by: Marathon Information Services, 243-253 Lower Mortlake Rd, Richmond, Surrey TW9 2LL, United Kingdom.

VIDURA. see *GENERAL INTEREST PERIODICALS—India*

VISIBLE EVIDENCE SERIES. see *SOCIOLOGY*

384.5 SGP
VISTAS✶. Text in English. 1992. q. free. **Document type:** *Newsletter.*
Published by: Infocomm Development Authority of Singapore, 8 Temasek Blvd, #14-00 Suntec Tower 3, Singapore, 038988, Singapore. TEL 65-211-0888, FAX 65-211-2222, info@ida.gov.sg, http://www.ida.gov.sg/. Circ: 8,000.

VISUAL. see *ART*

302.23 GBR ISSN 1470-3572
P93.5
VISUAL COMMUNICATION. Text in English. 2002 (Feb). 3/yr. GBP 235, USD 410 to institutions; GBP 244, USD 427 combined subscription to institutions print & online (effective 2006). **Document type:** *Journal, Academic/Scholarly.* **Description:** Provides an international forum for the growing body of work in visual communications.
Related titles: Online - full text ed.: ISSN 1741-3214. GBP 232, USD 406 to institutions (effective 2006) (from C S A, EBSCO Publishing, O C L C Online Computer Library Center, Inc., Sage Publications, Inc., Swets Information Services).
Indexed: ABM, CommAb, DIP, IBR, IBSS, IBZ.
—BLDSC (9241.234200), IE. **CCC.**
Published by: Sage Publications Ltd. (Subsidiary of: Sage Publications, Inc.), 1 Oliver's Yard, 55 City Rd, London, EC1 1SP, United Kingdom. TEL 44-20-73248500, FAX 44-20-73248600, info@sagepub.co.uk, http://www.sagepub.co.uk/journal.aspx?pid=105807. Eds. Carey Jewitt, Ron Scollon, Theo van Leeuwen. **Subscr. in the Americas to:** Sage Publications, Inc., 2455 Teller Rd, Thousand Oaks, CA 91320. TEL 805-499-0721, FAX 805-499-0871, journals@sagepub.com.

384 USA ISSN 1555-1393
➤ **VISUAL COMMUNICATION QUARTERLY.** Text in English. 1994. q. USD 200 in US & Canada to institutions; USD 230 elsewhere to institutions; USD 210 combined subscription in US & Canada to institutions print & online eds.; USD 240 combined subscription elsewhere to institutions print & online eds. (effective 2006). adv. bk.rev. back issues avail. **Document type:** *Journal, Academic/Scholarly.* **Description:** Offers useful and timely information about visual communication research to professionals, scholars and educators.
Related titles: Online - full text ed.: ISSN 1555-1407. USD 190 worldwide to institutions (effective 2006).
Published by: (Association for Education in Journalism and Mass Communication, Visual Communication), Lawrence Erlbaum Associates, Inc., 10 Industrial Ave, Mahwah, NJ 07430-2262. TEL 201-258-2200, 800-926-6579, FAX 201-236-0072, journals@erlbaum.com, http://www.leaonline.com/loi/vcq, http://www.erlbaum.com. Ed. Julianne H Newton. adv.: page USD 450; trim 6 x 9.

384 ITA ISSN 1120-5512
P92.I8
VITA ITALIANA. ISTITUZIONI E COMUNICAZIONE. Text in Italian. 1987. q. **Description:** Covers problems in the information sciences and communications field.
Published by: Presidenza del Consiglio dei Ministri, Dipartimento per l'Informazione e l'Editoria, Via Po, 14, Rome, RM 00198, Italy. TEL 39-6-85981, FAX 39-6-8553851.

384.043 DEU
VODAFONE WORLD; das Magazin fuer Vodafone Kunden. Text in German. 1995. q. adv. **Document type:** *Magazine, Consumer.*
Published by: Kuntze & Partner Kommunikationsdesign GmbH, Burgmuellerstr. 28, Duesseldorf, 40235, Germany. TEL 49-211-577241-0, FAX 49-211-57724115, media@kuntzeundpartner.de, http://www.kuntzeundpartner.de. adv.: B&W page EUR 19,000, color page EUR 28,000; trim 210 x 280. Circ: 2,500,000 (controlled).

VODAWORLD; worldwide cellular communication update. see *COMMUNICATIONS—Telephone And Telegraph*

384 IND
VOICE & DATA. Text in English. m. adv. **Document type:** *Trade.*
Published by: Cyber Media India Ltd., Cyber House, B-35 Sector 32-Institutional, Gurgaon, Haryana 122022, India. TEL 91-11-6433999, FAX 91-11-6469018. Ed. Shyam Malhotra. Pub. Pradeep Gupta. R&P Prasanth Kumar Roy. Adv. contact Akhila Doraswamy. B&W page USD 473, color page USD 1,008; trim 276 x 206.

621.382 020 004.6 AUS ISSN 1446-2230
VOICE AND DATA. Text in English. 1997. m. AUD 100 (effective 2003). adv. back issues avail. **Document type:** *Magazine, Trade.* **Description:** Contains features, trends and breaking news, plus a strong new product base, this magazine delivers the latest information on merging communications technologies and how best to apply them.
Formerly (until Mar.2002): What's New in Communications (1327-9815); Formed by the 1997 merger of: What's New in Telecommunications (1038-1511); What's New in Data Communications (1038-152X)
Published by: Westwick-Farrow Pty. Ltd., Locked Bag 1289, Wahroonga, NSW 2076, Australia. TEL 61-2-94872700, FAX 61-2-94891265, admin@westwick-farrow.com.au, http://www.westwick-farrow.com.au. Ed. Pam Carroll. Pub. Geoff Hird. Adv. contact Scott Haines. Circ: 7,500 (controlled).

384.5 AUS ISSN 1444-2450
VOICE & DATA AUSTRALIA. Text in English. 2000. a., latest 2000. USD 550 domestic; USD 580 foreign (effective 2001). **Document type:** *Directory, Trade.* **Description:** Covers Australian telecom and data markets.
Published by: Paul Budde Communication Pty. Ltd., 2643 George Downes Dr, Bucketty, NSW 2250, Australia. TEL 61-2-4998-8144, FAX 61-2-4998-8247, pbc@budde.com.au, http://www.budde.com.au. Circ: 150 (paid).

384.5 DEU
W A P MAGAZIN. (Wireless Application Protocol) Text in German. 1999. w. adv. **Document type:** *Consumer.* **Description:** Covers the latest news, products and developments involving wireless application protocol services and technology.
Media: Online - full text.
Published by: skywire.de, Pelikanstr 7, Hannover, 30177, Germany. TEL 49-511-625063, FAX 49-511-625068, presse@skywire.de, info@skywire.de, http://www.wap-magazin.de. Ed. Ulf Schroeder.

384 GRC ISSN 1109-2742
W S E A S TRANSACTIONS ON COMMUNICATIONS. (World Scientific and Engineering Academy and Society) Text in English. 2002. q. EUR 100 to individuals; EUR 200 to institutions (effective 2005). **Document type:** *Journal, Academic/Scholarly.*
Indexed: BrCerAb, C&ISA, CerAb, CorrAb, E&CAJ, EMA, IAA, M&TEA, MBF, METADEX, WAA.
—BLDSC (9364.918000).
Published by: World Scientific and Engineering Academy and Society, Ag Ioannou Theologou 17-23, Zographou, Athens 15773, Greece. TEL 30-210-7473313, FAX 30-210-7473314, http://www.wseas.org. Ed. N Mastorakis.

384 USA
➤ **WEB JOURNAL OF MASS COMMUNICATION RESEARCH.** Text in English. 1997. q. free (effective 2003). **Document type:** *Journal, Academic/Scholarly.* **Description:** Publishes scholarly investigations in mass communications research. Topics range from a study of integrated marketing communication to the effects of television viewing on college students' use of alcohol.
Media: Online - full content.
Published by: Ohio University, E. W. Scripps School of Journalism, Athens, OH 45701-2979. stewartr@ohio.edu, http://www.scripps.ohiou.edu/wjmcr. Eds. Guido Stempel, Robert Stewart.

384 GBR ISSN 1744-6708
▼ ➤ **WESTMINSTER PAPERS IN COMMUNICATION AND CULTURE.** Text in English. 2004. s-a. **Document type:** *Journal, Academic/Scholarly.* **Description:** Aims to help develop a de-westernized and transcultural sphere that engages both young and established scholars from different parts of the world in a critical debate about the relationship between communication, culture and society in the 21st Century.
Related titles: Online - full text ed.: ISSN 1744-6716. free (effective 2005).
Published by: University of Manchester, Centre for Research and Education in Art and Media, 309 Regent St, London, W1B 2UW, United Kingdom. TEL 44-20-79115000, http://www.wmin.ac.uk/mad/page-880.

➤ **WHAT SA CELLPHONE SATELLITE INTERNET.** see *ELECTRONICS*

384 USA ISSN 0952-7001
WHAT'S NEW IN BUSINESS INFORMATION. Text in English. 1987. 20/yr. GBP 375 combined subscription domestic print & online eds.; EUR 610 combined subscription in Europe print & online eds.; USD 580 combined subscription elsewhere print & online eds. (effective 2003). **Document type:** *Newsletter, Trade.* **Description:** Discusses new products, important reference works, online files, and information technology. Covers news affecting producers, distributors, and users of business information and alerts readers to important articles they may have missed.
Related titles: Online - full text ed.: (from Gale Group).
Published by: C S A Journal Division (Subsidiary of: Cambridge Information Group), 7200 Wisconsin Ave, Ste 715, Bethesda, MD 20814. TEL 301-961-6798, 800-843-7751, FAX 301-961-6799, journals@csa.com, http://www.csa.com.

621.382 USA ISSN 1067-0793
WHAT'S ON SATELLITE. Text in English. 1993. 3/yr. USD 125 (effective 2000). adv. back issues avail. **Document type:** *Directory.*
Related titles: CD-ROM ed.; Online - full text ed.
Published by: Satnews Publishers, 800 Siesta Way, Sonoma, CA 95476-4413. TEL 707-939-9306, design@satnews.com, http://www.satnews.com/. Ed. Silvano Payne. Pub. S Payne. Circ: 1,000 (paid).

384 USA ISSN 1094-6985
P92.5.A1
WHO'S WHO IN THE MEDIA AND COMMUNICATIONS. Text in English. 1997. biennial. USD 259.95 per vol.. **Document type:** *Directory, Trade.* **Description:** Contains biographies of people in the field of media and communications.
Published by: Marquis Who's Who, 562 Central Ave, New Providence, NJ 07964. TEL 908-673-1000, 800-621-9669, FAX 908-673-1179, marquisinfo@renp.com, http://www.marquiswhoswho.com. Ed. Dawn Melley.

355.31 621.382 GBR ISSN 1462-9259
THE WIRE (MARESFIELD). Text in English. 1920. bi-m.
Incorporates (1954-1997): Royal Signals Institution. Journal (0374-3519); Which was formerly (until 1953): Royal Signals Quarterly Journal
Indexed: Inspec.
Published by: Royal Signals Institution, Griffin House, Blandford Garrison, Blandford Forum, Dorset, DT11 8RH, United Kingdom. rhq_rsignals@mail.army.mod.uk, http://www.army.mod.uk/royalsignals/rsi.

621.382 GBR
WIRELESS AMERICA MAGAZINE. Abbreviated title: W A M. Text in English. 1998. m. **Document type:** *Trade.*
Published by: I B C Business Publishing Ltd., 69-77 Paul St, London, EC2A 4LQ, United Kingdom. TEL 44-20-7453-2212, FAX 44-20-7553-1593. Pub. Tim Molloy. Circ: 25,000.

384.5 HKG ISSN 1681-1399
WIRELESS ASIA. Text in English. 1998. 10/yr., latest vol.4. HKD 440 domestic; USD 79 in Asia & the Pacific; USD 88 elsewhere; HKD 50 newsstand/cover (effective 2005). adv. back issues avail. **Document type:** *Magazine, Trade.* **Description:** Industry intelligence about wireless, mobile, and satellite communications services and equipment.
Related titles: Online - full text ed.: (from EBSCO Publishing, Gale Group).
—CCC.
Published by: Advanstar Asia Ltd. (Subsidiary of: Advanstar Communications, Inc.), 2501-2, 25/F, Pacific Plaza, 401 Des Voeux Rd W, Hong Kong, Hong Kong. TEL 852-2559-2772, FAX 852-2559-7002, customer_service@telecomasia.net, http://www.telecomasia.net/telecomasia/. adv.: color page USD 8,515; bleed 203 x 273.

384 USA ISSN 1533-6735
TK5103.2
WIRELESS BUSINESS & TECHNOLOGY; your source for unwired technology. Text in English. 2001. bi-m. USD 29.99 domestic; USD 49.99 in Canada & Mexico; USD 69.99 elsewhere; USD 5.99 newsstand/cover (effective 2005). adv. **Document type:** *Magazine, Trade.* **Description:** Provides industry insight and analysis of fresh voices and seasoned gurus of the unwired world and mobile commerce.
Related titles: Online - full text ed.: USD 19.99 (effective 2005) (from Gale Group).
Indexed: CompD.
Published by: SYS-CON Media, Inc., 135 Chestnut Ridge Rd, Montvale, NJ 07645. TEL 201-802-3040, 888-303-5282, FAX 201-782-9600, info@sys-con.com, http://wireless.sys-con.com, http://www.sys-con.com. Ed. Robert Diamond. Adv. contact Miles Silverman. Circ: 150,000 (paid).

384 NLD ISSN 1383-4231
WIRELESS COMMUNICATION CD-ROM. Text in Dutch. irreg., latest vol.4, 1999. CHF 375 to individuals; CHF 726 to institutions. charts; illus. **Document type:** *Trade.* **Description:** Publishes information about wireless and mobile communication systems in a hypertext format.
Media: CD-ROM.
—CCC.
Published by: Baltzer Science Publishers B.V., Hooftlaan 51, Bussum, 1401 EC, Netherlands. TEL 31-35-695-4250, FAX 31-35-695-4258, publish@baltzer.nl, http://www.baltzer.nl. Ed. Jean Paul M G Linnartz.

384.5 GBR ISSN 1530-8669
TK5103.2 CODEN: WCMCCK
➤ **WIRELESS COMMUNICATIONS AND MOBILE COMPUTING.** Text in English. 8/yr. USD 590 to institutions; USD 649 combined subscription to institutions print & online eds. (effective 2006). **Document type:** *Journal, Academic/Scholarly.*
Related titles: Online - full text ed.: ISSN 1530-8677. USD 590 to institutions (effective 2006) (from EBSCO Publishing, Swets Information Services, Wiley InterScience).
Indexed: CompLI, CurCont, Inspec.
—BLDSC (9323.860000), IE.
Published by: John Wiley & Sons Ltd. (Subsidiary of: John Wiley & Sons, Inc.), The Atrium, Southern Gate, Chichester, West Sussex PO19 8SQ, United Kingdom. TEL 44-1243-779777, FAX 44-1243-775878, customer@wiley.co.uk, http://www3.interscience.wiley.com/cgi-bin/jhome/76507157, http://www.wiley.co.uk. Eds. Michelle Zorzi, Moshen Guizani. **Subscr. in the Americas to:** John Wiley & Sons, Inc., 111 River St, Hoboken, NJ 07030-5774. TEL 201-748-6645, FAX 201-748-6088, subinfo@wiley.com.

384.5 BRA
WIRELESS COMUNICACIONES. Text in Spanish. bi-m. USD 50. adv. **Document type:** *Trade.* **Description:** Provides Latin American service providers with a guide to the technology and business issues driving the growth of wireless services in the region.
Published by: Advanstar Editora e Com. Ltda., Rua Gomes de Carvalho, 1329 Andar 9, Vila Olimpia, Sao Paulo - SP, SP 04547-005, Brazil. TEL 55-11-31707000, FAX 55-11-31707010, info@advanstar.com, http://www.advanstar.com.br. Ed. Luiza Rodrigues. Pub. Ethevaldo Siqueira. adv.: B&W page USD 5,356, color page USD 6,695; trim 275 x 208. Circ: 11,900.

WIRELESS DATA NEWS. see *COMPUTERS—Data Communications And Data Transmission Systems*

WIRELESS EVOLUTION. see *COMPUTERS—Computer Networks*

384.5 HKG
WIRELESS INTERNATIONAL. Text in English. 12/yr. adv. **Description:** Covers the manufacturers and leading trends found within the Asian wireless communications and telecommunications industries.
Related titles: Online - full text ed.
Published by: ACE Media Co., Ltd., c/o ACE Marketing and Publications Ltd., 10F, Ultragrace Commercial Bldg, 5 Jordan Rd, Kowloon, Hong Kong. TEL 886-2-2395-5037, FAX 886-2-2394-1726, services@acemedia.com.tw, http://www.wireless.com.tw. Ed. Lore Levin Devra. Pub. Lai Hiram. adv.: page USD 2,070. Circ: 15,000.

WIRELESS INTERNET MAGAZINE. see *COMPUTERS—Internet*

621.382 USA
WIRELESS L A N. Text in English. 1991. m. USD 695 in US & Canada; USD 745 elsewhere (effective 2004). **Document type:** *Newsletter.* **Description:** Covers wireless applications such as LANs, building and point-of-sale technology, markets, standards, regulatory developments, and business developments.
Formerly (until 2004): Wireless Telecommunications (1057-5391)
Related titles: E-mail ed.: USD 725 (effective 2001).
—CCC.
Published by: Information Gatekeepers, Inc., 320 Washington St, Ste 302, Brighton, MA 02135. TEL 617-782-5033, 800-323-1088, FAX 617-782-5735, info@igigroup.com, http://www.igigroup.com. Ed. Tony Carmona. Pub. Dr. Paul Polishuk.

621.38 USA ISSN 1094-2807
WIRELESS LOCAL LOOP NEWSLETTER. Text in English. 1991. m. USD 695 in US & Canada; USD 745 elsewhere (effective 2001). **Document type:** *Newsletter.* **Description:** Covers radio spectrum management, regulatory developments, technology, applications, standards, worldwide developments, and spectrum auction and sale.
Formerly (until 1997): Wireless - Spectrum Management (1058-6709)
Published by: Information Gatekeepers, Inc., 320 Washington St, Ste 302, Brighton, MA 02135. TEL 617-782-5033, 800-323-1088, FAX 617-734-8562, info@igigroup.com, http://www.igigroup.com. Ed. Tony Carmona. Pub. Dr. Paul Polishuk.

C

384 USA ISSN 1539-1639
▼ **WIRELESS NETWORK NEWS.** Text in English. 2003 (Fall). bi-m. free domestic; USD 60 foreign (effective 2003). adv.
Document type: *Magazine, Trade.*
Published by: Webcom Communications Corp., 7355 E Orchard Rd, Ste 100, Greenwood Village, CO 80111. TEL 720-528-3770, 800-803-9488, FAX 720-528-3771, johncg@infowebcom.com, http://www.wirelessnetworkmagazine.com, http://www.infowebcom.com. Adv. contact Debra Hall TEL 720-528-3770 ext 114.

621.382 USA ISSN 1022-0038
TK5103.2 CODEN: WINEF8
➤ **WIRELESS NETWORKS**; the journal of mobile communication, computation and information. Text in English. 1995. bi-m. USD 64, USD 84 to members; USD 77, USD 97 combined subscription to members print & online eds. (effective 2006). adv. back issues avail.; reprint service avail. from PSC.
Document type: *Journal, Academic/Scholarly.* **Description:** Publishes original articles addressing networks, systems, algorithms, and applications that support the symbiosis of portable computers, wireless networks, mobile communication and computation, and their integration into the global network of the future.
Related titles: Online - full text ed.: ISSN 1572-8196. USD 51 (effective 2006) (from Association for Computing Machinery, Inc., EBSCO Publishing, Gale Group, IngentaConnect, Kluwer Online, O C L C Online Computer Library Center, Inc., Ovid Technologies, Inc., ProQuest Information & Learning, Springer LINK, Swets Information Services).
Indexed: ABIn, AS&TI, BibLing, BrCerAb, C&CSA, C&ISA, CMCI, CerAb, CompLI, CompR, CorrAb, CurCont, E&CAJ, EMA, EngInd, IAA, ISR, Inspec, M&TEA, MBF, METADEX, RefZh, SCI, SolStAb, WAA.
—BLDSC (9324.550000), AskIEEE, CISTI, IDS, IE, Infotrieve, ingenta, Linda Hall. **CCC.**
Published by: (Association for Computing Machinery, Inc.), Springer-Verlag New York, Inc. (Subsidiary of: Springer Science+Business Media), 233 Spring St, New York, NY 10013. TEL 212-460-1500, FAX 212-460-1575, service@springer-ny.com, http://springerlink.metapress.com/openurl.asp?genre=journal&issn=1022-0038, http://www.springer-ny.com. Ed. Imrich Chlamtac. **Subscr. to:** Journal Fulfillment, PO Box 2485, Secaucus, NJ 07096-2485. TEL 201-348-4033, FAX 201-348-4505, journals@springer-ny.com.

C

621.382 USA
WIRELESS SATELLITE AND BROADCASTING TELECOMMUNICATIONS. Text in English. 1991. m. USD 695 in US & Canada; USD 745 elsewhere (effective 2003).
Document type: *Newsletter.* **Description:** Covers wireless applications for broadcasting, satellites, new technology, markets, regulations, products, standards, and business developments.
Former titles: Satellite and Broadcasting Telecommunications; Wireless - Satellite and Broadcasting (1058-6695)
Related titles: Online - full text ed.: (from Gale Group, O C L C Online Computer Library Center, Inc.).
Published by: Information Gatekeepers, Inc., 320 Washington St, Ste 302, Brighton, MA 02135. TEL 617-782-5033, 800-323-1088, FAX 617-734-8562, info@igigroup.com, http://www.igigroup.com/nl/pages/wiresb.html. Ed. Tony Carmona. Pub. Dr. Paul Polishuk.

384 CAN ISSN 1201-8538
WIRELESS TELECOM. Text in English. 1968. q. CND 40, USD 50 to non-members. adv. bk.rev. stat. back issues avail.
Document type: *Journal, Trade.* **Description:** Features articles on technology, market issues, industry news and events, new products, and the activities of government and regulatory agencies. Distributed to licensed radio common carriers in Canada, suppliers to the industry, governments, and regulatory agencies.
Former titles: Radiocomm Magazine (1196-0809); Radiocomm in Canada (0845-4531)
Published by: Canadian Wireless Telecommunication Association, CWTA 500 275 Slater St, Ottawa, ON K1P 5H9, Canada. TEL 613-233-4888, FAX 613-233-2032, mchoma@cwta.ca, http://www.cwta.ca. Ed. Marc Choma. R&P Carrie Moussa. Adv. contact Karen Mohindra. B&W page USD 1,725, color page USD 2,640; trim 10.88 x 8.38. Circ: 12,500.

384 USA ISSN 1085-0473
WIRELESS WEEK. Text in English. 1995. s-m. (plus bonus issue in Mar.). USD 99 domestic; USD 105 in Canada; USD 126 elsewhere; USD 4 per issue domestic (effective 2005).
Document type: *Magazine, Trade.* **Description:** Covers business, technology and regulatory news in cellular, personal communications services, paging, specialized mobile radio, wireless data, satellite, wireless local loop and microwave.
Related titles: Online - full text ed.: (from bigchalk, EBSCO Publishing, Gale Group, H.W. Wilson, LexisNexis, Northern Light Technology, Inc., O C L C Online Computer Library Center, Inc., ProQuest Information & Learning).
Indexed: ABIn, B&I, BPI.
—**CCC.**
Published by: Reed Business Information (Subsidiary of: Reed Business), 8878 S Barrons Blvd, Highlands Ranch, CO 80129-2345. TEL 303-470-4800, FAX 303-470-4892, http://www.wirelessweek.com, http://www.reedbusiness.com. Ed. Monica Alleven TEL 303-470-4818. Pub. Debby Denton TEL 303-470-4867. Circ: 37,111. **Subscr. to:** Reed Business Information, PO Box 9020, Maple Shade, NJ 08052-9020. TEL 303-470-4466, 800-446-6551, FAX 303-470-4691, http://www.pubservice.com/CH.htm.

WOMEN'S STUDIES IN COMMUNICATION. see *WOMEN'S STUDIES*

384 IND ISSN 0043-7948
WORD. Text in English. 1963. a. INR 30. adv. bk.rev.
Indexed: CurCont, LingAb, MEA&I.
Published by: Bharatiya Vidya Bhavan, Kulapati K.M. Munshi Marg, Mumbai, Maharashtra 400 007, India. Ed. G S Pohekar. Circ: 1,000.

384 FRA
WORLD COMMUNICATION REPORT; the media and the challenge of the new technologies. Text in English. 1997. irreg. EUR 38.11 newsstand/cover (effective 2003).
Related titles: ♦ French ed.: Rapport Mondial sur la Communication et l'Information.
Indexed: IIS.
Published by: UNESCO Publishing, 7 place de Fontenoy, Paris, 75352, France. TEL 33-1-45684300, FAX 33-1-45685737, http://www.unesco.org/publications. **Dist. in the US by:** Bernan Associates, Bernan, 4611-F Assembly Dr., Lanham, MD 20706-4391. TEL 800-274-4447, FAX 800-865-3450.

384 USA ISSN 1014-871X
P88.8
WORLD MEDIA HANDBOOK (YEAR). Text in English. 1990. triennial. stat. back issues avail. **Document type:** *Directory.*
Description: Provides a summary of selected media and related data covering countries around the world.
Published by: United Nations, Department of Public Information. Communications Coordination Service, Room S1037B, New York, NY 10017. TEL 212-963-6851, FAX 212-963-8409, http://www.un.org/publications. Ed. Raquel Cohen Orantes. Circ: 6,500. **Dist. by:** United Nations DPI Sales and Marketing Section, Two UN Plaza, DC2 853, New York, NY 10017. TEL 212-963-8302, FAX 212-963-3489.

384.51029 USA ISSN 1052-7842
TK5104
THE WORLD SATELLITE ANNUAL. Text in English. 1980. a.
Document type: *Trade.*
Related titles: ♦ Supplement to: Phillips World Satellite Almanac.
Published by: Access Intelligence, LLC (Subsidiary of: Veronis, Suhler & Associates Inc.), 1201 Seven Locks Rd, Ste 300, Potomac, MD 20854. TEL 301-354-2000, 800-777-5006, FAX 301-424-2058, clientservices@accessintel.com, http://www.telecomweb.com/satellite/, http://www.pbimedia.com. **Dist. by:** Publications Resource Group.

621.382 GBR
WORLD SATELLITE SERVICING (YEAR). Text in English. a.
Document type: *Trade.*
Formerly: Satellite Servicing
Published by: U-View, Unit 3F, Plumtree Farm Industrial Estate, Plumtree Rd, Bircotes, Nr. Doncester, S Yorks DN11 8EW, United Kingdom. TEL 01302-719997, FAX 01302-719995. Ed. Colin Barlow. Pub. Roger Yaxley.

621.382 USA ISSN 1462-4702
K4301.2
WORLD TELECOM LAW REPORT. Text in English. 2001. m.
Document type: *Newsletter.*
Related titles: Online - full text ed.: (from The Bureau of National Affairs, Inc.).
—**CCC.**
Published by: The Bureau of National Affairs, Inc., 1231 25th St., NW, Washington, DC 20037. TEL 800-372-1033, http://www.bna.com. **Subscr. to:** 9435 Key West Ave, Rockville, MD 20850.

384 GBR
▼ **WORLD TELECOMS AGENDA.** Text in English. 2003. a. GBP 29.95 per issue; free to qualified personnel (effective 2003).
Description: Covers areas such as billing & customer care, multimedia applications, mobile & wireless technology, global e-commerce, infrastructure and network solutions, optical networking and outsourcing.
Published by: S P G Media Ltd. (Subsidiary of: Sterling Publishing Group Plc.), Brunel House, 55-57 North Wharf Rd, London, W2 1LA, United Kingdom. TEL 44-20-79159600, FAX 44-20-77242089, info@sterlingpublications.com, http://www.spgmedia.com/. Pub. Sarah Woddis.

WRITE IT RIGHT; quarterly for corrections personnel. see *CRIMINOLOGY AND LAW ENFORCEMENT*

807 USA ISSN 0741-0883
P211
➤ **WRITTEN COMMUNICATION**; an international quarterly of research, theory, and application. Text in English. 1984. q. USD 569, GBP 367 to institutions; USD 592, GBP 382 combined subscription to institutions print & online eds. (effective 2006). adv. back issues avail.; reprints avail.
Document type: *Journal, Academic/Scholarly.* **Description:** Provides a forum for ideas, theoretical viewpoints, and methodological approaches that better define and further develop thought and practice in the study of the written word.
Related titles: Online - full text ed.: ISSN 1552-8472. USD 563, GBP 363 to institutions (effective 2006) (from C S A, EBSCO Publishing, Florida Center for Library Automation, Gale Group, O C L C Online Computer Library Center, Inc., Sage Publications, Inc., Swets Information Services).
Indexed: ASCA, ArtHuCI, BibLing, CIJE, CommAb, CurCont, EAA, HumInd, L&LBA, LT&LA, LingAb, PRA, PsycInfo, PsycholAb, RHEA, SFSA, SOPODA, SSCI.
—BLDSC (9364.797000), IDS, IE, Infotrieve, ingenta. **CCC.**
Published by: Sage Publications, Inc., 2455 Teller Rd, Thousand Oaks, CA 91320. TEL 805-499-0721, 800-818-7243, FAX 805-499-8096, 800-583-2665, info@sagepub.com, http://www.sagepub.com/journal.aspx?pid=24. Ed. Christina Haas. Pub. Sara Miller McCune. R&P Tanya Udin TEL 805-499-0721 ext 7716. Adv. contact Kirsten Beaulieu TEL 805-499-0721 ext 7160. page USD 350. Circ: 1,350. **Subscr. overseas to:** Sage Publications Ltd., 1 Oliver's Yard, 55 City Rd, London EC1 1SP, United Kingdom. TEL 44-20-73740645, FAX 44-20-73748741, subscription@sagepub.co.uk.

621.382 CHN ISSN 1001-2362
XINXI XITONG GONGCHENG/INFORMATION SYSTEM ENGINEERING. Text in Chinese. 1988. q. USD 20. adv.
Related titles: Online - full text ed.: (from East View Information Services).
Published by: Guojia Xinxi Zhongxin/State Information Center, 39 Youyi Lu, Hexi-qu, Tianjin 300201, China. TEL 354273, FAX 344270. Ed. Zhou Hongren. adv.: B&W page USD 3,500.

384 GBR
YEARBOOK OF ASIA-PACIFIC TELECOMMUNICATIONS (YEAR). Text in English. a. GBP 225 (effective 2000). stat.
Document type: *Trade.* **Description:** Provides information about telecommunications services, companies and markets in the Asia-Pacific region. Includes an evaluation of basic network construction and the growth of mobile services across the region.
Published by: (Communications and Information Technology Research Ltd.), C I T Publications Ltd., 3 Colleton Crescent, Exeter, Devon EX2 4DG, United Kingdom. TEL 44-1392-315-555, FAX 44-1392-315-556, citpubs@eurobell.co.uk, http://www.telecoms-data.com. Ed. Tania Harvey.

THE YEARBOOK OF COPYRIGHT AND MEDIA LAW. see *PATENTS, TRADEMARKS AND COPYRIGHTS*

384.029 GBR
YEARBOOK OF EUROPEAN TELECOMMUNICATIONS. Variant title: Y E T: The Yearbook of European Telecommunications. Text in English. a. GBP 250 (effective 2000). charts.
Document type: *Directory.* **Description:** Lists and profiles Western European telecommunications firms and the markets of the countries in which they operate.
Published by: (Communications and Information Technology Research Ltd.), C I T Publications Ltd., 3 Colleton Crescent, Exeter, Devon EX2 4DG, United Kingdom. TEL 44-1392-315-555, FAX 44-1392-315-556, citpubs@eurobell.co.uk, http://www.telecoms-data.com. Ed. Tania Harvey.

384 GBR
YEARBOOK OF LATIN AMERICAN TELECOMMUNICATIONS (YEAR). Text in English. a. GBP 225 (effective 2000). stat.
Document type: *Trade.* **Description:** Provides information on the telecommunications industry in Latin America.
Published by: (Communications and Information Technology Research Ltd.), C I T Publications Ltd., 3 Colleton Crescent, Exeter, Devon EX2 4DG, United Kingdom. TEL 44-1392-315-555, FAX 44-1392-315-556, citpubs@eurobell.co.uk, http://www.telecoms-data.com. Ed. Tania Harvey.

384 JPN ISSN 0289-551X
THE YOKE. Text in English. 1983. bi-m. free. back issues avail.
Document type: *Newsletter.* **Description:** Provides communication information about Japan and the city of Yokohama.
Published by: Yokohama Association for International Communications and Exchanges, Sangyo Boeki Center Bldg, 2 Yamashita-cho, Naka-ku, Yokohama-shi, Kanagawa-ken 231-0023, Japan. FAX 045-671-7187, TELEX 3822844-GREEN-J. Ed. Isao Tonooka. Circ: 2,500.

384 JPN ISSN 0914-7721
YUSEISHO TSUSHIN SOGO KENKYUJO NYUSU/JAPAN. MINISTRY OF POSTS AND TELECOMMUNICATIONS. COMMUNICATIONS RESEARCH LABORATORY. NEWS. Key Title: C R L Nyusu. Text in Japanese. 1976. m.
Document type: *Government.*

Published by: Yuseisho, Tsushin Sogo Kenkyujo/Ministry of Posts and Telecommunications, Communications Research Laboratory, 2-1 Nukui-Kita-Machi 4-chome, Koganei-shi, Tokyo-to 184-0015, Japan.

621.382   CHN   ISSN 1002-8617
ZHONGGUO JIAOTONG NIANJIAN/CHINA COMMUNICATIONS AND TRANSPORTATION YEARBOOK. Text in Chinese. 1986. a. USD 120 (effective 1997). bk.rev. **Document type:** *Directory.* **Description:** Covers the management and development of China's communication and transportation industries, including railroads, roads and traffic, air transportation, automobiles, ships and shipping, postal affairs, telecommunications, pipline transportation, and national defense transportation. Also contains related authoritative transportation statistics.
Published by: Zhongguo Jiaotong Yunshu Xiehui/China Communications and Transportation Association, 23 Shijin Huayuan Hutong, Dongsi, Beijing, 100007, China. TEL 86-10-6401-4601, FAX 86-10-6405-3979, TELEX SPC CN 22552. Ed. J T Liu. adv.: page USD 1,200. Circ: 15,000.

384   JPN
ZUSETSU TSUSHIN HAKUSHO/ILLUSTRATED REPORT OF COMMUNICATIONS. Text in Japanese. a. JPY 850. **Document type:** *Government.*
Published by: (Japan. Yuseisho/Ministry of Posts and Telecommunications, Japan. Daijin Kanbo), Daiichi Hoki Shuppan/Ministry of Posts and Telecommunications, Minister's SecretariatDai-ichi Hoki Publishing Co., Ltd., 11-17 Minami-Aoyama 2-chome, Minato-ku, Tokyo, 107-0062, Japan.

621.382   FRA   ISSN 1252-4786
01 RESEAUX. Variant title: Zero un Reseaux. Text in French. 1987. m. EUR 44 combined subscription with Internet Professionnel (effective 2003). **Document type:** *Magazine, Trade.* **Description:** Information on communication systems and services and research for business users.
Formerly (until 1994): Telecoms Magazine (0982-8524); Which incorporated (1985-1989): Resources Informatiques (0998-2361); Which was formerly (until 1988): Resources, Temps Reel (0766-6055); Which was formed by the merger of (1980-1985): Temps Reel (0247-4751); (1984-1985); Resources Informatiques (0762-8110); Which was formed by the merger of (1977-1984): Bureau Gestion (0181-2297); (1958-1984): Informatique et Gestion (0020-062X); Which was formerly (until 1968): Gestion (1166-8725); (1980-1984): Mediatique Com'7 (0754-1937); Which was formerly (until 1982): Com'7 (0244-8971)
Related titles: Online - full text ed.
Indexed: ABIn, Inspec.
—Infotrieve. **CCC.**
Published by: Groupe Tests, 26 rue d'Oradour-sur-Glane, Paris, Cedex 15 75504, France. TEL 33-1-44253500, http://www.groupetests.fr. Ed. Jean Francois Ruiz. Circ: 32,700.

621.382   USA   ISSN 1540-0719
2.5 G-3 G. Text in English. 1991. m. USD 695 in US & Canada; USD 745 elsewhere (effective 2003). **Document type:** *Newsletter.* **Description:** Covers cellular mobile radio technology, markets, applications, services, standards, regulations, products, business developments.
Former titles (until 2002): Wireless Cellular; Cellular Telecommunications; Wireless Cellular (1058-6717)
Related titles: Online - full text ed.: (from Gale Group).
Indexed: CompD.
Published by: Information Gatekeepers, Inc., 320 Washington St, Ste 302, Brighton, MA 02135. TEL 617-782-5033, 800-323-1088, FAX 617-734-8562, info@igigroup.com, http://www.igigroup.com/nl/pages/253G.html. Ed. Tony Carmona. Pub. Dr. Paul Polishuk.

384.5   GBR   ISSN 1524-9492
HE9713
3 G MOBILE. Text in English. 1999. fortn. GBP 995 domestic; EUR 1,641 in the European Union; USD 1,691 elsewhere (effective 2003). **Document type:** *Newsletter, Trade.* **Description:** Contains news and data and analysis on the next-generation mobile communications market.
Related titles: Online - full content ed.: GBP 2,985 domestic for 1-5 users; EUR 4,925 in the European Union for 1-5 users; USD 5,074 elsewhere for 1-5 users (effective 2003).
Published by: Baskerville (Subsidiary of: T & F Informa plc), Sheepen Place, Colchester, Essex C03 3LP, United Kingdom. TEL 44-20-70175537, FAX 44-20-70174783, telecoms.enquiries@informa.com, http://www.baskerville.telecoms.com/3gmobile. Ed. Gavin Patterson. **Subscr. in Asia Pacific to:** Informa Asia Publishing Ltd., 6/F Hollywood Centre, 233 Hollywood Rd, Hong Kong, Hong Kong. TEL 852-2854-3222, FAX 852-2854-1538, informa.asia@informa.com; **Subscr. in N America to:** Baskerville, PO Box 1017, Westborough, MA 01581-6107.

362.1   USA   ISSN 1040-7316
HV551.3
9-1-1 MAGAZINE. Text in English. 1988. 7/yr. USD 29.95 domestic; USD 46.95 in Canada & Mexico; USD 53.95 elsewhere (effective 2003). adv. bk.rev. 84 p./no. 3 cols./p.; back issues avail.; reprints avail. **Document type:** *Magazine, Trade.* **Description:** Covers managing emergency communications for PSAPs, dispatch and fields communications for EMS, fire, law enforcement and emergency/disaster management.
Published by: Official Publications, Inc., 18201 Weston Pl., Tustin, CA 92780. TEL 714-544-7776, FAX 714-838-9233, info@9-1-1magazine.com, publisher@9-1-1magazine.com, http://www.9-1-1magazine.com. Ed. Randall Larson. Pub., R&P James E Voelkl. Adv. contact Pam Martin. B&W page USD 1,960. Circ: 18,000.

384   PER   ISSN 1609-817X
LOS 13. Text in Spanish. irreg.
Media: Online - full text.
Published by: Pontificia Universidad Catolica del Peru, Facultad de Ciencias y Artes de la Comunicacion, Ave. Universitaria Cdra, 18, San Miguel, Lima, 32, Peru. TEL 51-1-4602870, FAX 51-1-2613175, comunic@pucp.edu.pe, http://www.pucp.edu.pe/fac/comunic/.

384   ARG   ISSN 0328-8323
P92.A6
60 X 60 - NOTICIAS DE MEDIOS Y COMUNICACION. Text in Spanish. 1990. m. USD 25; USD 30 in North America; USD 40 elsewhere. adv. **Document type:** *Newsletter.* **Description:** Contains national and international news about communication, media, advertising, culture and education.
Supersedes (in 1996): Consignas - Medios y Comunicacion (0327-5809); Formerly: Consignas de la Nueva Caledonia
Published by: Consignas - Comunicacion y Producciones Graficas, Dto. 6, Carlos Calvo, 735, Capital Federal, Buenos Aires 1102, Argentina. TEL 54-114-4321618, FAX 54-114-3003976, consigna@satlink.com. Eds. Fernando Gigena, Lorena Sanchez. adv.: B&W page ARS 1,250; 370 x 250. Circ: 20,000.

2600; the quarterly journal of the American hacker. see *COMPUTERS—Computer Security*

COMMUNICATIONS—Abstracting, Bibliographies, Statistics

016.38455   USA   ISSN 0891-8775
PN4888.T4
A B C NEWS INDEX. Text in English. 1986. q. (plus a. cumulation). USD 243.80. back issues avail. **Document type:** *Abstract/Index.* **Description:** Index to transcripts of ABC-TV news programs available in microfiche.
Related titles: Microfiche ed.: (from RPI).
Published by: Primary Source Microfilm (Subsidiary of: Gale Group), 12 Lunar Dr, Woodbridge, CT 06525. TEL 203-397-2600, 800-444-0799, FAX 203-397-3893.

016.384   HKG
A C NIELSEN CHINA MEDIA INDEX. (In 18 city editions: Beijing, Shanghai, Guangzhou, Chengdu, Chongqing, Fuzhou, Hangzhou, Nanjing, Qingdao, Shenyang, Tianjin, Wuhan, Dalian, Harbin, Ji'nan, Shenzhen, Xi'an, Xiamen) Text in Chinese, English. 1986. q. (for Beijing, Shanghai & Guangzhou eds; s-a. for Chengdu, Chongqing, Fuzhou, Hangzhou, Nanjing, Qingdao, Shenyang, Tianjin & Wuhan eds.; a. for other city editions). USD 6,500. back issues avail. **Document type:** *Consumer.* **Description:** Multi-media survey provides a comprehensive picture of the media consumptions in key cities in China.
Formerly: S R G China Media Index
Related titles: Online - full text ed.
Published by: S R G China Ltd., 2-F, Warwick House, 979 King s Rd, Quarry Bay, Hong Kong, Hong Kong. TEL 852-2563-9688, FAX 852-2516-6856, alau@nielsensrg.com. Ed. Alic Lau.

016.38454   USA
AMATEUR RADIO SERVICE MASTER FILE UPDATES. Text in English. m. USD 295 in North America; USD 590 elsewhere (effective 2001). **Description:** Contains only additions and changes to the master file, not the master file itself. Limited to only those requiring a new license to be issued (approximately 95 per cent of the changes).
Media: Magnetic Tape.
Published by: (Federal Communications Commission), U.S. Department of Commerce, National Technical Information Service, 5285 Port Royal Rd, Springfield, VA 22161. TEL 703-605-6000, info@ntis.gov, http://www.ntis.gov.

384.5021   USA   ISSN 0738-8675
HE8698
AMERICAN RADIO. Text in English. 1976. q. USD 350. **Document type:** *Directory.*
Related titles: Microfiche ed.: (from CIS).
Indexed: SRI.
Published by: Duncan's American Radio, 50 E. Rivercenter Blvd., Ste. 1200, Covington, KY 41011-1654. TEL 513-731-1800. Ed. James H Duncan. Circ: 4,000.

384.54021   USA
ANTENNA SURVEY TOWER FILE. Text in English. q. USD 1,144 in North America; USD 2,288 elsewhere (effective 2001). **Document type:** *Government.* **Description:** Contains data on all towers requiring FCC or FAA clearance.
Media: CD-ROM.
Published by: (Federal Communications Commission), U.S. Department of Commerce, National Technical Information Service, 5285 Port Royal Rd, Springfield, VA 22161. TEL 703-605-6000, info@ntis.gov, http://www.ntis.gov.

384.55021   AUS
AUSTRALIA. BUREAU OF STATISTICS. FILM AND VIDEO PRODUCTION AND DISTRIBUTION, AUSTRALIA. Text in English. 1994. irreg., latest 2000. AUD 19.50 (effective 2003). **Document type:** *Government.*
Published by: Australian Bureau of Statistics, PO Box 10, Belconnen, ACT 2616, Australia. TEL 61-2-6252-5249, FAX 61-2-6252-6778, http://www.abs.gov.au.

383.021   AUS
▼ **AUSTRALIA. BUREAU OF STATISTICS. NATIONAL LOCALITIES INDEX, AUSTRALIA (ONLINE EDITION).** Text in English. 2003. a. free. stat. **Document type:** *Government.*
Media: Online - full text.
Published by: Australian Bureau of Statistics, PO Box 10, Belconnen, ACT 2616, Australia. TEL 61-2-6252-5249, FAX 61-2-6252-6778, http://www.abs.gov.au.

383.021   AUS
AUSTRALIA. BUREAU OF STATISTICS. POSTAL AREA TO STATISTICAL LOCAL AREA CONCORDANCE, AUSTRALIA. Text in English. 1991. irreg., latest 1996. price varies. **Document type:** *Government.*
Published by: Australian Bureau of Statistics, PO Box 10, Belconnen, ACT 2616, Australia. TEL 61-2-6252-5249, FAX 61-2-6252-6778, http://www.abs.gov.au.

621.382021   AUS   ISSN 1440-7434
AUSTRALIA. BUREAU OF STATISTICS. TELECOMMUNICATION SERVICES, AUSTRALIA, PRELIMINARY. Text in English. 1997. irreg. AUD 15 (effective 2002). **Document type:** *Government.*
Published by: Australian Bureau of Statistics, PO Box 10, Belconnen, ACT 2616, Australia. TEL 61-2-6252-5249, FAX 61-2-6252-6778, http://www.abs.gov.au.

384.5021   AUS
AUSTRALIA. BUREAU OF STATISTICS. TELEVISION SERVICES, AUSTRALIA. Text in English. 1994. irreg., latest 1996. AUD 17.50 (effective 2003). **Document type:** *Government.*
Formerly: Australia. Bureau of Statistics. Radio and Television Services, Australia
Published by: Australian Bureau of Statistics, PO Box 10, Belconnen, ACT 2616, Australia. TEL 61-2-6252-5249, FAX 61-2-6252-6778, http://www.abs.gov.au.

791.45021   AUS
AUSTRALIA. BUREAU OF STATISTICS. VIDEO HIRE OUTLETS, AUSTRALIA. Text in English. 2001 (May). irreg. AUD 18 (effective 2001). **Document type:** *Government.*
Published by: Australian Bureau of Statistics, PO Box 10, Belconnen, ACT 2616, Australia. TEL 61-2-6252-5249, FAX 61-2-6252-6778, http://www.abs.gov.au.

016.38454   USA
AVIATION MASTER FILE. Text in English. q. USD 20 in North America; USD 40 elsewhere. **Description:** Contains radio license data of aircraft records in FAA number sequence. Cross reference indexes are also included by fleet and name licensees.
Published by: (Federal Communications Commission), U.S. Department of Commerce, National Technical Information Service, 5285 Port Royal Rd, Springfield, VA 22161. TEL 703-605-6000, info@ntis.gov, http://www.ntis.gov.

016.38455   USA   ISSN 0742-4914
BIBLIOGRAPHY ON CABLE TELEVISION. Cover title: B C T V. Text in English. 1975. a. USD 40 (effective 2000). index, cum.index: 1975-1992. back issues avail. **Document type:** *Bibliography.* **Description:** Presents an open-ended, non-cumulative bibliography on access, advertising and marketing, audience and subscribers, programming, finance, law, technology and other issues of cable television.
Published by: Communications Institute, Communications Library, Lockbox 472139, Marina Station, San Francisco, CA 94147-2139. TEL 415-626-5050. Ed. T S Connelly.

384.55021   USA
BROADCAST INVESTOR: DEALS & FINANCE. Text in English. 1984. m. USD 1,045; USD 1,440 combined subscription print & online eds. (effective 2005). adv. **Document type:** *Newsletter.*
Formerly (until 2005): Broadcast Stats (0749-2936)
Related titles: Online - full text ed.: USD 945 (effective 2005).
Published by: Kagan World Media (Subsidiary of: Primedia, Inc.), 1 Lower Ragsdale Dr., Ste. 130, Monterey, CA 93940-5741. TEL 831-624-1536, FAX 831-625-3225, info@kagan.com, http://www.kagan.com/. Pub. Paul Kagan. adv.: page USD 3,670.

C

▼ *new title*   ➤ *refereed*   ✱ *unverified*   ◆ *full entry avail.*

384.021 CAN ISSN 1497-0422
BROADCASTING AND TELECOMMUNICATIONS. Text in English, French. 1971. q. CND 42 domestic; USD 42 foreign (effective 1999). **Document type:** *Government.* **Description:** Summary information on telecommunications, including the telephone industry and other carriers, radio and television broadcasting, cable TV. Includes methodology and data quality.
Formerly (until 2000): Canada. Statistics Canada. Communications (0380-0334)
Related titles: Microform ed.: (from MML); Online - full text ed.: ISSN 1492-4455; ♦ French ed.: Radiodiffusion et Telecommunications. ISSN 1706-8452.
Published by: Statistics Canada, Operations and Integration Division, Circulation Management, Jean Talon Bldg, 2 C12, Tunney's Pasture, Ottawa, ON K1A 0T6, Canada. TEL 613-951-7277, 800-267-6677, FAX 613-951-1584, http://www.statcan.ca.

384.555021 CAN ISSN 0703-7244
CANADA. STATISTICS CANADA. CABLE TELEVISION/ CANADA. STATISTIQUE CANADA. TELEDISTRIBUTION. Text in English, French. 1967. a. CND 42 domestic; USD 42 foreign. **Document type:** *Government.* **Description:** Financial statistics on the Canadian cable television industry by area and revenue group.
Formerly: Canada. Statistics Canada. Community Antenna Television - Services de Television a Antenne Collective (0575-8238)
Related titles: Microform ed.: (from MML); Online - full text ed.
Published by: Statistics Canada, Circulation Management, Jean Talon Bldg, 2 C12, Tunney's Pasture, Ottawa, ON K1A 0T6, Canada. TEL 613-951-7277, 800-267-6677, FAX 613-951-1584, http://www.statcan.ca.

384.5021 CAN ISSN 0575-9560
CANADA. STATISTICS CANADA. RADIO AND TELEVISION BROADCASTING/CANADA. STATISTIQUE CANADA. RADIODIFFUSION ET TELEVISION. Text in English, French. 1961. a. CND 42 domestic; USD 42 foreign (effective 1999). **Document type:** *Government.* **Description:** Presents detailed financial statistics on the Canadian radio and television industry by province and by revenue group, operational data on the privately owned radio and television industry and the C B C.
Formerly: Canada. Statistics Canada. Radio and Television Broadcasting Statistics (0833-6784)
Related titles: Microform ed.: (from MML); Online - full text ed.
Published by: Statistics Canada, Operations and Integration Division, Circulation Management, Jean Talon Bldg, 2 C12, Tunney's Pasture, Ottawa, ON K1A 0T6, Canada. TEL 613-951-7277, 800-267-6677, FAX 613-951-1584, http://www.statcan.ca.

384.6021 CAN ISSN 0707-9753
CANADA. STATISTICS CANADA. TELEPHONE STATISTICS/CANADA. STATISTIQUE CANADA. STATISTIQUE DU TELEPHONE. Text in English, French. 1977. m. CND 70 domestic; USD 70 foreign (effective 1999). **Document type:** *Government.* **Description:** Presents monthly and year-to-date data aggregated from reports of 13 major telephone systems along with comparisons to data from the previous year.
Related titles: Online - full text ed.
Published by: Statistics Canada, Operations and Integration Division, Circulation Management, Jean Talon Bldg, 2 C12, Tunney's Pasture, Ottawa, ON K1A 0T6, Canada. TEL 613-951-7277, 800-267-6677, FAX 613-951-1584, http://www.statcan.ca.

016.384 CHE
CATALOGUE OF I T U PUBLICATIONS. Text in English. s-a. free. **Document type:** *Catalog.*
Related titles: Online - full text ed.; French ed.; Spanish ed.
Published by: International Telecommunication Union, Place des Nations, Geneva 20, 1211, Switzerland. TEL 41-22-7306141, FAX 41-22-7305194, sales@itu.ch, http://www.itu.int/publications.

CHILE. INSTITUTO NACIONAL DE ESTADISTICAS. ANUARIO DE TRANSPORTE Y COMUNICACIONES. see *TRANSPORTATION—Abstracting, Bibliographies, Statistics*

CHILE. INSTITUTO NACIONAL DE ESTADISTICAS. TRANSPORTE, COMUNICACIONES, TURISMO. see *TRANSPORTATION—Abstracting, Bibliographies, Statistics*

016.384 USA ISSN 0162-2811
P87
COMMUNICATION ABSTRACTS; an international information service. Text in English. 1978. bi-m. USD 1,335, GBP 861 to institutions (effective 2006). adv. abstr.; bibl.; illus. index. back issues avail.; reprints avail. **Document type:** *Journal, Abstract/Index.* **Description:** Covers recent literature in all areas of communication studies, both mass and interpersonal. Includes expanded coverage of new communications technologies.
Related titles: Online - full text ed.: Communication Abstracts Online. ISSN 1551-1677 (from O C L C Online Computer Library Center, Inc., Swets Information Services).
Indexed: RASB.
—BLDSC (3359.130000), IE. **CCC.**
Published by: Sage Publications, Inc., 2455 Teller Rd, Thousand Oaks, CA 91320. TEL 805-499-0721, FAX 805-499-8096, info@sagepub.com, http://www.sagepub.com/journal.aspx?pid=168. Ed. Thomas F Gordon. Pub. Sara Miller McCune. R&P Tanya Udin TEL 805-499-0721 ext 7716. Adv. contact Kirsten Beaulieu TEL 805-499-0721 ext 7160. B&W page USD 385. Circ: 550 (paid). **Subscr. overseas to:** Sage Publications Ltd., 1 Oliver's Yard, 55 City Rd, London EC1 1SP, United Kingdom. TEL 44-20-73740645, FAX 44-20-73748741, subscription@sagepub.co.uk.

016.384 USA ISSN 1094-8007
P87
COMMUNICATION BOOKNOTES QUARTERLY. Abbreviated title: C B Q. Text in English. 1969. q. USD 345 in US & Canada to institutions; USD 375 elsewhere to institutions; USD 365 combined subscription in US & Canada to institutions print & online eds.; USD 395 combined subscription elsewhere to institutions print & online eds. (effective 2006). adv. bk.rev. abstr.; bibl.; illus. index. back issues avail.; reprint service avail. from PSC. **Document type:** *Journal, Bibliography.* **Description:** Reviews books, reports, documents and electronic publications on all aspects of mass communication. Audience consists of researchers, academics, and librarians in the telecommunication and information industtries and all related mass communication disciplines.
Former titles (until 1998): Communication Booknotes (0748-657X); Mass Media Booknotes; Mass Media Publications Reporting Service; Which superseded: Broadcasting Bibliophile's Booknotes (0045-3188)
Related titles: Online - full text ed.: ISSN 1532-6896. USD 330 worldwide to institutions (effective 2006) (from EBSCO Publishing, Gale Group, O C L C Online Computer Library Center, Inc., Swets Information Services).
Indexed: IIPA.
—BLDSC (3359.502000), IE, Infotrieve. **CCC.**
Published by: Lawrence Erlbaum Associates, Inc., 10 Industrial Ave, Mahwah, NJ 07430-2262. TEL 201-258-2200, 800-926-6579, FAX 201-236-0072, journals@erlbaum.com, http://www.erlbaum.com/Journals/journals/CBQ/cbq.htm. Ed. Christopher H Sterling TEL 202-994-6210. adv.: page USD 275; trim 5 x 8. Circ: 700.

016.621382 USA ISSN 1041-7893
Z5632
COMMUNICATION SERIALS; an international guide to periodicals in communication, popular culture and the performing arts. Text in English. 1992. biennial. USD 135 (effective 1999). **Document type:** *Bibliography.* **Description:** Contains over 2,700 fully annotated publication titles in 40 areas of communication, popular culture, and the performing arts from 24 nations.
Published by: Blue Ridge Interactive, Inc., 1750 Kraft Dr, 1200, Blacksburg, VA 24060-6376. TEL 434-420-0840, FAX 434-420-3564. Ed. Harry Sova.

621.382021 PRT
CORREIOS E TELECOMUNICACOES DE PORTUGAL. ANUARIO ESTATISTICO. Text in Portuguese. 1975. a. illus.
Published by: Correios e Telecomunicacoes de Portugal, Servico de Impressos e Publicacoes, Rua Visconde de Santarem, 69 1o, Lisbon, 1000, Portugal. TEL 3127100, FAX 1-3127298. Circ: 1,000.

384.558021 USA
D V D STATISTICAL REPORT. (Digital Video Disc Statistical Report) Text in English. 1998. a. USD 327 domestic; USD 387 foreign (effective 2001). software rev.; video rev. charts; stat. 100 p./no.; back issues avail.; reprints avail. **Document type:** *Trade.* **Description:** Surveys and analyzes the market DVD software and hardware.
Related titles: E-mail ed.; Fax ed.; Online - full content ed.
Published by: Corbell Publishing Company, 11500 W Olympic Blvd, Ste 400, Los Angeles, CA 90064. TEL 310-444-3048, FAX 310-312-4551, mhealy@corbell.com, http://www.corbell.com. Pub. Maureen A Healey.

302.23021 GBR ISSN 1469-6622
EASTERN & CENTRAL EUROPEAN MARKET & MEDIAFACT. Key Title: Central and Eastern European Market and Media Fact. Text in English. 1990. a. GBP 60 (effective 2001). stat. **Document type:** *Trade.* **Description:** Contains media statistics for TV & radio audiences, press circulation & readership, cinema screens & admissions, etc.
Supersedes in part (in 2000): European Market and Media Fact (0966-8608)
—BLDSC (3105.917000).
Published by: Zenith Media, Bridge House, 63-65 N. Wharf Rd, London, W2 1LA, United Kingdom. TEL 44-20-7298-4926, FAX 44-20-7298-6902, publications@zenithmedia.co.uk, http://www.zenithmedia.com. Ed. Adam Smith.

016.621382 USA
TK7800 CODEN: ECAJA
ELECTRONICS AND COMMUNICATIONS ABSTRACTS JOURNAL. Text in English. 1966. q. (5 issues). USD 1,865 combined subscription print & online eds. (effective 2006). bk.rev. abstr. a. index on CD-ROM. back issues avail. **Document type:** *Abstract/Index.* **Description:** Covers theoretical and applied research in electronic systems, circuits, and devices; surveys all aspects of communications.
Former titles (until 1993): Electronics and Communications Abstracts; (until 1992): Electronics and Communications Abstracts Journal (0361-3313); (until 1972): Electronics Abstracts Journal (0013-5097)
Related titles: CD-ROM ed.; Online - full text ed.: ISSN 1555-6549. USD 1,395 (effective 2006).
—BLDSC (3703.160000), Linda Hall.
Published by: C S A Journal Division (Subsidiary of: Cambridge Information Group), 7200 Wisconsin Ave, Ste 715, Bethesda, MD 20814. TEL 301-961-6798, 800-843-7751, FAX 301-961-6799, journals@csa.com, http://www.csa.com/factsheets/electronics-set-c.php. Ed. Esther Hovis. Pub. Ted Caris. **Co-publisher:** Elsevier Engineering Information, Inc.

016.384 HUN ISSN 0231-066X
ELEKTRONIKAI ES HIRADASTECHNIKAI SZAKIRODALMI/ ELECTRONICS & COMMUNICATIONS ABSTRACTS. Text in Hungarian. 1974. m. HUF 9,900. abstr. index.
Supersedes (in 1982): Muszaki Lapszemle. Hiradastechnika - Technical Abstracts. Telecommunication (0303-2019)
Published by: Orszagos Muszaki Informacios Kozpont es Konyvtar/National Technical Information Centre and Library, Muzeum utca 17, PO Box 12, Budapest, 1428, Hungary. Ed. Ottmar Klavida. Circ: 320. **Subscr. to:** Kultura, PO Box 149, Budapest 1389, Hungary.

621.382021 PAN ISSN 1012-3547
HE7881
ESTADISTICA PANAMENA. SITUACION ECONOMICA. SECCION 334. COMUNICACIONES. Text in Spanish. 1985. a. PAB 0.75 domestic (effective 2000). **Document type:** *Bulletin, Government.* **Description:** Contains statistics on the mail, telegraph, telephone, radio, and television systems in Panama.
Supersedes in part (in 1985): Estadistica Panamena. Situacion Economica. Seccion 333-334. Transporte y Comunicaciones (0378-7389)
Published by: Direccion de Estadistica y Censo, Contraloria General, Apdo. 5213, Panama City, 5, Panama. FAX 507-210-4801. Circ: 600.

ESTATISTICAS DOS TRANSPORTES E COMUNICACOES. see *TRANSPORTATION—Abstracting, Bibliographies, Statistics*

384.6021 USA ISSN 1079-5359
FACSIMILE FACTS AND FIGURES. Text in English. 1989. a. (plus irreg. updates). looseleaf. USD 1,500. stat. index. back issues avail. **Description:** Includes global installed base figures, OEM study, official import and export figures, manufacturers market share percentages, dealer numbers, public fax transmission numbers.
Related titles: Diskette ed.
Published by: International Facsimile Consultative Council, 4019 Lake View Dr, Lake Havasu City, AZ 86406. TEL 520-453-3850, FAX 520-453-9234. Ed. David Day.

016.77859 USA ISSN 0898-1582
LB1044.Z9
FILM & VIDEO FINDER. Text in English. 1987. irreg., latest 1997. USD 295 (effective 2003). **Document type:** *Directory.* **Description:** Lists 115,000 films and videos by subject heading outline and index. Includes subject section by title and distributor code, producers and distributors.
Formed by the merger of (1967-1987): N I C E M Index to 16mm Educational Films (0734-5488); (1971-1987): N I C E M Index to Educational Video Tapes (0734-6921)
Related titles: CD-ROM ed.: (from SilverPlatter Information, Inc.); Online - full text ed.
Published by: (National Information Center for Educational Media), Plexus Publishing, Inc., 143 Old Marlton Pike, Medford, NJ 08055. TEL 609-654-6500, FAX 609-654-4309, info@plexuspublishing.com, http://www.plexuspublishing.com/FilmandVideo.shtml.

070.5021 FIN ISSN 0784-8765
P94.65.F5
FINLAND. TILASTOKESKUS. KULTTUURI JA VIESTINTA/FINLAND. STATISTICS FINLAND. CULTURE AND THE MEDIA. Text in English, Finnish, Swedish. 1988. a. EUR 35 (effective 2005). **Document type:** *Government.*
Related titles: ♦ Series: Finland. Tilastokeskus. Kulttuuritilasto. ISSN 1456-825X; ♦ Finland. Tilastokeskus. Suomessa Liikkuvat Liikkuvat Kuvat. ISSN 1237-4407; ♦ Finland. Tilastokeskus. Joukkoviestimet. ISSN 1455-9447; Finland. Tilastokeskus. Finnish Mass Media. ISSN 0788-1347. 1990.
Published by: Tilastokeskus/Statistics Finland, Tyopajakatu 13, Statistics Finland, Helsinki, 00022, Finland. TEL 358-9-17341, FAX 358-9-17342750, http://www.stat.fi/.

384.55021 FIN ISSN 1237-4407
FINLAND. TILASTOKESKUS. SUOMESSA LIIKKUVAT LIIKKUVAT KUVAT; tilastoja televisio-, elokuva- ja videotarjonnasta ja televisio-ohjelmien viennista. Text in English, Finnish, Swedish. 1992. biennial. **Document type:** *Government.*
Related titles: ♦ Series of: Finland. Tilastokeskus. Kulttuuri ja Viestinta. ISSN 0784-8765.
Published by: Tilastokeskus/Statistics Finland, Tyopajakatu 13, Statistics Finland, Helsinki, 00022, Finland. TEL 358-9-17341, FAX 358-9-17342750, http://www.stat.fi/.

016.384 USA ISSN 0148-7566
GET READY SHEET. Text in English. 1976. bi-w. looseleaf. USD 45 (effective 1999). adv. **Document type:** *Bibliography.* **Description:** Offers a current listing of books and authors featured on National TV and radio talk shows, and discusses current and upcoming movies and TV specials.
Published by: Mid-York Library System, c/o Diana Norton, Ed, 1600 Lincoln Ave, Utica, NY 13502. TEL 315-735-8328. R&P Malcolm K Hill. Circ: 1,300.

GREECE. NATIONAL STATISTICAL SERVICE. TRANSPORT AND COMMUNICATION STATISTICS. see *TRANSPORTATION—Abstracting, Bibliographies, Statistics*

HONG KONG SPECIAL ADMINISTRATIVE REGION OF CHINA. CENSUS AND STATISTICS DEPARTMENT. REPORT ON ANNUAL SURVEY OF STORAGE, COMMUNICATION, FINANCING, INSURANCE AND BUSINESS SERVICES. see *BUSINESS AND ECONOMICS—Abstracting, Bibliographies, Statistics*

384.021 CHE
I T U STATISTICAL YEARBOOK/ANNUAIRE STATISTIQUE DES L'U I T. Text in English, French, Spanish. a. CHF 68. **Document type:** *Corporate.*
Formerly (until 1995): Yearbook of Common Carrier Telecommunication Statistics (0252-1563); Incorporates: Telecommunication Statistics
Related titles: Diskette ed.; Microfiche ed.: (from CIS).
Indexed: IIS.
Published by: International Telecommunication Union, Place des Nations, Geneva 20, 1211, Switzerland. TEL 41-22-7306141, FAX 41-22-7305194, sales@itu.ch, http://www.itu.int/publications.

016.384 DEU
INFORMATIONSDIENST F I Z TECHNIK. LICHTLEITER UND GLASFASERKABEL. Variant title: Lichtleiter und Glasfaserkabel. Text in German. m. EUR 320 (effective 2003). **Document type:** *Journal, Abstract/Index.*
Published by: Fachinformationszentrum Technik e.V., Ostbahnhofstr 13-15, Frankfurt Am Main, 60314, Germany. TEL 49-69-4308213, kundenberatung@fiz-technik.de, http://www.fiz-technik.de.

016.384 DEU
INFORMATIONSDIENST F I Z TECHNIK. MIKROWELLENTECHNIK. Variant title: Mikrowellentechnik. Text in German. m. EUR 320 (effective 2003). **Document type:** *Journal, Abstract/Index.*
Published by: Fachinformationszentrum Technik e.V., Ostbahnhofstr 13-15, Frankfurt Am Main, 60314, Germany. TEL 49-69-4308213, kundenberatung@fiz-technik.de, http://www.fiz-technik.de.

016.384 DEU
INFORMATIONSDIENST F I Z TECHNIK. MOBILFUNK. Variant title: Mobilfunk. Text in German. m. EUR 310 (effective 2003). **Document type:** *Journal, Abstract/Index.*
Published by: Fachinformationszentrum Technik e.V., Ostbahnhofstr 13-15, Frankfurt Am Main, 60314, Germany. TEL 49-69-4308213, kundenberatung@fiz-technik.de, http://www.fiz-technik.de.

016.384 DEU ISSN 1439-8206
INFORMATIONSDIENST F I Z TECHNIK. NACHRICHTENLEITUNGEN UND ANTENNEN. Variant title: Nachrichtenleitungen und Antennen. Text in German. 1984. m. EUR 220 (effective 2003). **Document type:** *Journal, Abstract/Index.*
Formerly (until 1995): Informationsdienst F I Z Technik. Nachrichtenleitungen, Antennen, Wellenausbreitung (0176-5639)
Published by: Fachinformationszentrum Technik e.V., Ostbahnhofstr 13-15, Frankfurt Am Main, 60314, Germany. TEL 49-69-4308213, kundenberatung@fiz-technik.de, http://www.fiz-technik.de.

016.384 DEU
INFORMATIONSDIENST F I Z TECHNIK. NACHRICHTENUEBERTRAGUNG, VERFAHREN, GERAETE UND SYSTEME. Variant title: Nachrichtenuebertragung, Verfahren, Geraete und Systeme. Text in German. 1984. m. EUR 360 (effective 2003). **Document type:** *Journal, Abstract/Index.*
Formerly: Informationsdienst F I Z Technik. Nachrichtenuebertragung (0176-5817)
Published by: Fachinformationszentrum Technik e.V., Ostbahnhofstr 13-15, Frankfurt Am Main, 60314, Germany. TEL 49-69-4308213, kundenberatung@fiz-technik.de, http://www.fiz-technik.de.

016.384 DEU ISSN 0176-5620
INFORMATIONSDIENST F I Z TECHNIK. NACHRICHTENVERMITTLUNG, NETZE, TEILNEHMEREINRICHTUNGEN. Variant title: Nachrichtenvermittlung, Netze, Teilnehmereinrichtungen. Text in German. 1984. m. EUR 310 (effective 2003). **Document type:** *Journal, Abstract/Index.*
Published by: Fachinformationszentrum Technik e.V., Ostbahnhofstr 13-15, Frankfurt Am Main, 60314, Germany. TEL 49-69-4308213, kundenberatung@fiz-technik.de, http://www.fiz-technik.de.

016.384 DEU
INFORMATIONSDIENST F I Z TECHNIK. VERSTAERKER, OSZILLATOREN UND FILTER. Variant title: Verstaerker, Oszillatoren und Filter. Text in German. 1984. m. EUR 310 (effective 2003). **Document type:** *Journal, Abstract/Index.*
Formerly: Informationsdienst F I Z Technik. Nachrichtentechnische Schaltungen, Verstaerker, Oszillatoren, Netzwerke (0176-5647)
Published by: Fachinformationszentrum Technik e.V., Ostbahnhofstr 13-15, Frankfurt Am Main, 60314, Germany. TEL 49-69-4308213, kundenberatung@fiz-technik.de, http://www.fiz-technik.de.

016.621382 CHE
INTERNATIONAL TELECOMMUNICATION UNION. CENTRAL LIBRARY. LIST OF PERIODICALS/UNION INTERNACIONAL DE TELECOMUNICACIONES. BIBLIOTECA CENTRAL. LISTA DE REVISTAS/UNION INTERNATIONALE DES TELECOMMUNICATIONS. BIBLIOTHEQUE CENTRALE. LISTE DES PERIODIQUES. Text in English, French, Spanish. 1967. a. **Document type:** *Bibliography.*
Published by: (Central Library), International Telecommunication Union, Place des Nations, Geneva 20, 1211, Switzerland. TEL 41-22-7306141, FAX 41-22-7305194, sales@itu.ch, http://www.itu.int/publications. Ed. A G El Zanati. Circ: 1,500.

016.621382 CHE
INTERNATIONAL TELECOMMUNICATION UNION. CENTRAL LIBRARY. LIST OF RECENT ACQUISITIONS/UNION INTERNACIONAL DE TELECOMUNICACIONES. BIBLIOTECA CENTRAL. LISTA DE ADQUISICIONES RECIENTES/UNION INTERNATIONALE DES TELECOMMUNICATIONS. BIBLIOTHEQUE CENTRALE. LISTE DES ACQUISITIONS RECENTES. Text in English, French, Spanish. 1972. q. **Document type:** *Bibliography.*
Published by: International Telecommunication Union, Place des Nations, Geneva 20, 1211, Switzerland. TEL 41-22-7306141, FAX 41-22-7305194, sales@itu.ch, http://www.itu.int/publications. Ed. A G El Zanati. Circ: 600.

016.621382 CHE
INTERNATIONAL TELECOMMUNICATION UNION. LIST OF ANNUALS/UNION INTERNACIONAL DE TELECOMUNICACIONES. LISTA DE PUBLICACIONES ANUALES/UNION INTERNATIONALE DES TELECOMMUNICATIONS. LISTES DES PUBLICATIONS ANNUELLES. Text in English, French, Spanish. 1972. a. **Document type:** *Bibliography.*
Published by: International Telecommunication Union, Place des Nations, Geneva 20, 1211, Switzerland. TEL 41-22-7306141, FAX 41-22-7305194, sales@itu.ch, http://www.itu.int/publications. Ed. A G El Zanati. Circ: 1,500.

384.021 ISR ISSN 0075-1308
ISRAEL. MINISTRY OF COMMUNICATIONS. STATISTICS/ISRAEL. MISRAD HA-TIKSHORET. STATISTIKAH. Text in English. 1955. a. **Document type:** *Government.*
Published by: Ministry of Communications, Jaffa Rd. 23, Jerusalem, Israel. Circ: 300.

KATALOG MEDIOW POLSKICH. see *BIBLIOGRAPHIES*

016.6845 GBR ISSN 0950-4761
KEY ABSTRACTS - ANTENNAS & PROPAGATION. Text in English. 1987. m. GBP 145, USD 250 (effective 2001). index. **Document type:** *Abstract/Index.* **Description:** Covers radio links and equipment, radiowave propagation, antenna theory and antennas, radar, and radio navigation.
Published by: INSPEC, I.E.E., Michael Faraday House, Six Hills Way, Stevenage, Herts SG1 2AY, United Kingdom. TEL 44-1438-313311, FAX 44-1438-742840, inspec@iee.org.uk, http://www.iee.org.uk. R&P Michael McCabe TEL 732-321-5575. **Subscr. to:** INSPEC, I E E, Publication Sales Dept., PO Box 96, Stevenage, Herts SG1 2SD, United Kingdom; **US subscr. addr.:** INSPEC, Inc., 379 Thornall St, Edison, NJ 08837-2225. TEL 732-321-5575, FAX 732-321-5702.

KEY ABSTRACTS - OPTOELECTRONICS. see *PHYSICS—Abstracting, Bibliographies, Statistics*

016.621382 GBR ISSN 0950-4877
TK5101.A1
KEY ABSTRACTS - TELECOMMUNICATIONS. Text in English. 1975. m. GBP 145, USD 250 (effective 2001). index. **Document type:** *Abstract/Index.* **Description:** Covers information theory, modulation, switching theory, applications of telecommunications, stations and equipment, switching centers, transmission line links, and optical communications.
Formerly (until 1987): Key Abstracts - Communications Technology (0306-5588)
Published by: INSPEC, I.E.E., Michael Faraday House, Six Hills Way, Stevenage, Herts SG1 2AY, United Kingdom. TEL 44-1438-313311, FAX 44-1438-742840, inspec@iee.org.uk, http://www.iee.org.uk. **US subscr. addr.:** INSPEC, Inc., 379 Thornall St, Edison, NJ 08837-2225. TEL 732-321-5575, FAX 732-321-5702.

KUWAIT. CENTRAL STATISTICAL OFFICE. ANNUAL STATISTICAL BULLETIN FOR TRANSPORT AND COMMUNICATION/KUWAIT. AL-IDARAH AL-MARKAZIYYAH LIL-IHSA'. AL-NASHRAH AL-IHSA'IYYAH AL-SANAWIYYAH LIL-NAQL WAL-MUWASALAT. see *TRANSPORTATION—Abstracting, Bibliographies, Statistics*

016.384 USA
LICENSEE NAME INDEX TO NON-GOVERNMENT MASTER FREQUENCY DATA BASE. Text in English. q. USD 25 in North America; USD 40 elsewhere. **Description:** Includes frequency of service and call sign for use in finding detailed information about the station in Master Frequency Data Base.
Media: Microfiche.
Published by: (Federal Communications Commission), U.S. Department of Commerce, National Technical Information Service, 5285 Port Royal Rd, Springfield, VA 22161. TEL 703-605-6000, info@ntis.gov, http://www.ntis.gov.

016.38454 USA
M A P S DATA BASE. (Mid-Atlantic Preservation Service) Text in English. 3/yr. USD 25 in North America; USD 40 elsewhere (effective 1999). **Description:** Contains data in call sign sequence and includes name, address, transmitter information, as well as data pertaining to the site and frequency path.
Media: Microfiche.
Published by: (U.S. Federal Communications Commission, Private Radio Bureau), U.S. Department of Commerce, National Technical Information Service, 5285 Port Royal Rd, Springfield, VA 22161. TEL 703-605-6000, info@ntis.gov, http://www.ntis.gov.

016.3845 USA
MARINE DATA BASE. Text in English. q. USD 1,320 in North America (effective 1999); USD 2,640 elsewhere. **Description:** Contains data for applicants and licensees operating under the Marine (Telephone) Radio Service.
Published by: (Federal Communications Commission), U.S. Department of Commerce, National Technical Information Service, 5285 Port Royal Rd, Springfield, VA 22161. TEL 703-605-6000, info@ntis.gov, http://www.ntis.gov.

016.3845 USA
MASTER FREQUENCY DATA BASE (FREQUENCY SEQUENCE). Text in English. q. USD 25 in North America; USD 40 elsewhere (effective 1999). **Description:** Includes the following files: aviation, broadcast, auxiliary land transportation, public safety, experimental, miscellaneous. Also contains geographical information from the Tower File.
Media: Microfiche.
Published by: (Federal Communications Commission), U.S. Department of Commerce, National Technical Information Service, 5285 Port Royal Rd, Springfield, VA 22161. TEL 703-605-6000, info@ntis.gov, http://www.ntis.gov.

016.38454 USA
MASTER FREQUENCY DATA BASE (SERVICE GROUP CODE SEQUENCE). Text in English. q. USD 25 in North America; USD 40 elsewhere (effective 1999). **Description:** Contains the non-government frequency assignments. Includes class, frequency, call sign, power, mobile units as well as other data. Does not include Tower File information.
Media: Microfiche.
Published by: (Federal Communications Commission), U.S. Department of Commerce, National Technical Information Service, 5285 Port Royal Rd, Springfield, VA 22161. TEL 703-605-6000, info@ntis.gov, http://www.ntis.gov.

016.79145 NLD
MEDIA NETWORK BOOKLIST; survey of publications international broadcasting. Text in English. 1980. s-a. free. **Document type:** *Bibliography.* **Description:** Guide to books about international broadcasting.
Published by: Stichting Radio Nederland Wereldomroep, Public Relations Dept, PO Box 222, Hilversum, 1200 JG, Netherlands. TEL 31-35-6724211, FAX 31-35-6724239, letter@rnw.nl. Ed. Jonathan Marks. Circ: 40,000.

016.30223 FRA ISSN 0987-3090
MEMOIRE DE TRAME; le bimensuel des ecrits sur la communication. Text in French. 1986. bi-m. bk.rev. **Description:** Selected bibliography of French and foreign production.
Published by: Librairie Tekhne, 7 rue des Carmes, Paris, 75005, France. TEL 33-1-43547084, FAX 33-1-44070739. Ed. Marie-Laure Raynaud. Pub. Caroline de Peyster.

C

▼ new title ➤ refereed ✶ unverified ♦ full entry avail.

016.621382 USA
N T I S ALERTS: COMMUNICATION. Text in English. 1974. s-m. USD 241.50 in North America; USD 316.25 elsewhere (effective 2005). bibl. index. back issues avail. **Document type:** *Newsletter, Government.* **Description:** Contains summaries of the latest government-sponsored projects and their findings for professionals. Covers common carrier and satellite communication, information theory, graphics, and policy.
Former titles: Abstract Newsletter: Communication; Weekly Abstract Newsletter: Communication; Weekly Government Abstracts. Communication (0364-4944)
Related titles: Microform ed.: (from NTI).
Published by: U.S. Department of Commerce, National Technical Information Service, 5285 Port Royal Rd, Springfield, VA 22161. TEL 703-605-6000, info@ntis.gov, http://www.ntis.gov.

383.021 SWE ISSN 1403-5472
POSTVERKSAMHET/POSTAL SERVIES. Text in English, Swedish. 1998. a.
Related titles: Online - full text ed.; ♦ Series of: S I K A Statistik. ISSN 1404-854X.
Published by: Statens Institut foer Kommunikationsanalys (SIKA)/Swedish Institute for Transport and Communications Analysis, PO Box 17213, Stockholm, 10462, Sweden. TEL 46-8-50620600, FAX 46-8-50620610, sika@sika-institute.se, http://www.sika-institute.se.

016.38455 USA ISSN 0897-9642
Z695.1.T24
PUBLIC TELEVISION TRANSCRIPTS INDEX. Variant title: P B S News Index. Text in English. 1987. q. (plus a. cumulation). USD 195. back issues avail. **Document type:** *Abstract/Index.* **Description:** Index to transcripts of Public Television news programs available in microfiche.
Related titles: Microfiche ed.: (from RPI).
Published by: Primary Source Microfilm (Subsidiary of: Gale Group), 12 Lunar Dr, Woodbridge, CT 06525. TEL 203-397-2600, FAX 203-397-3893.

621.382021 CAN ISSN 1706-8452
RADIODIFFUSION ET TELECOMMUNICATIONS. Text in French. 2001. irreg. stat. **Document type:** *Government.*
Related titles: Online - full content ed.: ISSN 1499-1462; ♦ English ed.: Broadcasting and Telecommunications. ISSN 1497-0422.
Published by: Statistics Canada, Operations and Integration Division, Circulation Management, Jean Talon Bldg, 2 C12, Tunney's Pasture, Ottawa, ON K1A 0T6, Canada. TEL 613-651-7277, 800-267-6677, FAX 603-951-1584, cstsc@statcan.ca, http://www.statcan.ca.

REFERATIVNYI ZHURNAL. AVTOMATIKA, TELEMEKHANIKA I SVIAZ' NA ZHELEZNYKH DOROGAKH. see *TRANSPORTATION—Abstracting, Bibliographies, Statistics*

REFERATIVNYI ZHURNAL. EKONOMIKA TRANSPORTA, SVIAZI I TELEKOMMUNIKATSII. see *BUSINESS AND ECONOMICS—Abstracting, Bibliographies, Statistics*

REFERATIVNYI ZHURNAL. ELEKTROAKUSTIKA. ZAPIS' I VOSPROIZVEDENIE SIGNALOV. see *ELECTRONICS—Abstracting, Bibliographies, Statistics*

REFERATIVNYI ZHURNAL. RADIOLOKATSIYA, RADIONAVIGATSIYA, RADIOUPRAVLENIE, TELEVIZIONNAYA TEKHNIKA. see *ELECTRONICS—Abstracting, Bibliographies, Statistics*

016.62138 RUS ISSN 0235-2087
REFERATIVNYI ZHURNAL. RADIOSVYAZ'. RADIOVESHCHANIE. TELEVIDENIE. Text in Russian. 1967. m. USD 156 foreign (effective 2006). **Document type:** *Abstract/Index.*
Related titles: CD-ROM ed.; Online - full text ed.
Published by: Vserossiiskii Institut Nauchnoi i Tekhnicheskoi Informatsii (VINITI), Ul Usievicha 20, Moscow, 125190, Russian Federation. TEL 7-095-1526441, FAX 7-095-9430060, dir@viniti.ru, http://www.viniti.ru. Ed. Yurii Arskii. **Dist. by:** Informnauka Ltd., Ul Usievicha 20, Moscow 125190, Russian Federation. alfimov@viniti.ru.

016.384 RUS ISSN 0235-2095
REFERATIVNYI ZHURNAL. SETI I SISTEMY SVYAZI. Text in Russian. 1967. m. USD 407 foreign (effective 2006). **Document type:** *Abstract/Index.*
Related titles: CD-ROM ed.; Online - full text ed.
Indexed: Inspec, RefZh.
Published by: Vserossiiskii Institut Nauchnoi i Tekhnicheskoi Informatsii (VINITI), Ul Usievicha 20, Moscow, 125190, Russian Federation. TEL 7-095-1526441, FAX 7-095-9430060, dir@viniti.ru, http://www.viniti.ru. Ed. Yurii Arskii. **Dist. by:** Informnauka Ltd., Ul Usievicha 20, Moscow 125190, Russian Federation. alfimov@viniti.ru.

016.66 RUS ISSN 0235-2079
REFERATIVNYI ZHURNAL. SVYAZ'. Text in Russian. 1967. m. USD 561 foreign (effective 2006). **Document type:** *Abstract/Index.*
Related titles: CD-ROM ed.; Online - full text ed.
—East View.
Published by: Vserossiiskii Institut Nauchnoi i Tekhnicheskoi Informatsii (VINITI), Ul Usievicha 20, Moscow, 125190, Russian Federation. TEL 7-095-1526441, FAX 7-095-9430060, dir@viniti.ru, http://www.viniti.ru. Ed. Yurii Arskii. **Dist. by:** Informnauka Ltd., Ul Usievicha 20, Moscow 125190, Russian Federation. alfimov@viniti.ru.

384.5021 ZAF
S A A R F RADIO AUDIENCE MEASUREMENT SURVEY. Text in Afrikaans, English. 1976. s-a. ZAR 10,350 (effective 2001). charts; stat. **Description:** Contains information on radio listening by South Africans.
Formerly: A M P S Radio Diary; Which superseded: A M P S White - Colored - Asian Radio Diary; A M P S Black Radio and Television Diary; Which superseded in part: A M P S Broadcast Media; Formerly: Listening Index (0047-4762)
Related titles: Online - full text ed.
Indexed: R&TA.
Published by: S A Advertising Research Foundation, PO Box 98874, Sloane Park, Johannesburg 2152, South Africa. TEL 27-11-463-5340, FAX 27-11-463-5010, saarf@saarf.co.za, http://www.saarf.co.za. Ed. Piet Smit.

SAFETY ABSTRACTS. see *PUBLIC HEALTH AND SAFETY—Abstracting, Bibliographies, Statistics*

384.021 SWE ISSN 0082-0334
HE260.A15
SWEDEN. STATISTISKA CENTRALBYRAAN. STATISTISKA MEDDELANDEN. SERIE T, TRANSPORT OCH KOMMUNIKATIONER. Text in Swedish; Summaries in English. 1969. irreg. SEK 1,200.
Formerly (until 1976): Sweden. Statistiska Centralbyraan. Statistiska Meddelanden. T
Published by: Statistiska Centralbyraan/Statistics Sweden, Publishing Unit, Orebro, 70189, Sweden. Circ: 1,000.

016.38455 USA
T V TRANSLATORS ENGINEERING DATA BASE IN ORDER BY STATE, CHANNEL, CALL. Text in English. m. USD 25 in North America; USD 40 elsewhere (effective 1999).
Media: Microfiche.
Published by: (Federal Communications Commission), U.S. Department of Commerce, National Technical Information Service, 5285 Port Royal Rd, Springfield, VA 22161. TEL 703-605-6000.

016.384 USA
T V TRANSLATORS ENGINEERING DATA BASE IN ORDER BY STATE, CITY, CHANNEL. Text in English. m. USD 25 in North America (effective 1999); USD 40 elsewhere.
Media: Microfiche.
Published by: (Federal Communications Commission), U.S. Department of Commerce, National Technical Information Service, 5285 Port Royal Rd, Springfield, VA 22161. TEL 703-605-6000, info@ntis.gov, http://www.ntis.gov.

621.382021 SWE ISSN 1650-3465
TELEVERKSAMHET. Text in English, Swedish. 1997. a.
Formerly (until 2000): Telekommunikation (1404-1642)
Related titles: Online - full text ed.; ♦ Series of: S I K A Statistik. ISSN 1404-854X.
Published by: Statens Institut foer Kommunikationsanalys (SIKA)/Swedish Institute for Transport and Communications Analysis, PO Box 17213, Stockholm, 10462, Sweden. TEL 46-8-50620600, FAX 46-8-50620610, sika@sika-institute.se, http://www.sika-institute.se.

TRANSPORT AND COMMUNICATIONS (SINGAPORE). see *TRANSPORTATION—Abstracting, Bibliographies, Statistics*

310 USA
U.S. BUREAU OF THE CENSUS. (YEAR) ECONOMIC CENSUS. INFORMATION. Text in English. every 5 yrs. stat. **Document type:** *Government.* **Description:** Provides statistical data on the publishing industries, including software publishing, the motion picture and sound recording industries, the broadcasting and telecommunications industries, and the information services and data processing services industries.
Supersedes in part: Census of Transportation, Communications, and Utilities: Final Reports (0082-9404)
Related titles: ♦ CD-ROM ed.: Economic Census CD-ROM Series; Online - full content ed.
Published by: U.S. Bureau of the Census (Subsidiary of: U.S. Department of Commerce), Customer Services, Washington, DC 20233. TEL 310-457-4100, FAX 301-457-4714, http://www.census.gov.

384.6021 USA ISSN 0896-0585
HE8801
UNITED STATES TELEPHONE ASSOCIATION. STATISTICS OF THE LOCAL EXCHANGE CARRIERS. Text in English. 1954. a. USD 550 to non-members; USD 275 to members. index. **Document type:** *Trade.*
Formerly: United States Independent Telephone Association. Annual Statistical Volume (0083-1298)
Indexed: SRI.
—Linda Hall.
Published by: United States Telecom Association, 607 14th St NW, # 400, Washington, DC 20005-2000. TEL 202-326-7300, FAX 202-326-7333. Circ: 1,000.

384.558021 USA
THE VIDEO STATISTICAL REPORT. Text in English. 1989. a. looseleaf. USD 540 domestic; USD 590 foreign (effective 2002). adv. charts; stat.; tr.lit. 100 p./no.; back issues avail. **Document type:** *Journal, Trade.* **Description:** Provides statistics on pre-recorded video, blank tape, video hardware, VCR's, laser discs, 8mm and penetration data.
Formerly: Video Industry Statistical Report
Related titles: Diskette ed.; E-mail ed.; Fax ed.; Online - full content ed.
Published by: Corbell Publishing Company, 11500 W Olympic Blvd, Ste 400, Los Angeles, CA 90064. TEL 310-444-3048, FAX 310-312-4551, mhealy@corbell.com, http://www.corbell.com. Ed. Deborah Rolfe. Pub. Maureen Healy. Adv. contact Peter White. B&W page USD 1,500; trim 8.5 x 11.

302.23021 GBR ISSN 1469-6614
WESTERN EUROPEAN MARKET & MEDIA FACT. Text in English. 1990. a. GBP 60 (effective 2001). stat. **Document type:** *Trade.* **Description:** Contains media statistics for TV and radio audiences, press cirulation and readership, cinema screens and admissions.
Supersedes in part (in 2000): European Market and Media Fact (0966-8608)
—BLDSC (9300.722500).
Published by: Zenith Media, Bridge House, 63-65 N. Wharf Rd, London, W2 1LA, United Kingdom. TEL 44-20-7224-8500, FAX 44-20-7298-6902, publications@zenithmedia.co.uk, http://www.zenithmedia.com. Ed., Pub. Adam Smith.

COMMUNICATIONS—Computer Applications

621.38 AUS ISSN 1440-3846
A C A CONNECTIONS. Text in English. 1998. q. **Description:** Features news about mobile services and telecommunications.
Published by: Australian Communications Authority, PO Box 13112, Melbourne, VIC 8010, Australia. TEL 61-3-9963-6967, FAX 61-3-9963-6899, candinfo@aca.gov.au, http://www.aca.gov/.

384.0285 USA ISSN 1042-0711
TK8315 CODEN: ADIMEZ
ADVANCED IMAGING; solutions for the electronic imaging professional. Text in English. 1988. 11/yr. USD 30; free to qualified personnel (effective 2005). adv. illus.; tr.lit. back issues avail. **Document type:** *Magazine, Trade.* **Description:** Features real world video, photographic, and document electronic image acquisition, processing, display, storage, output transmission and communication for all application areas using imaging technologies.
Incorporates (1967-1993): A V C Presentation for the Visual Communicator (1064-7112); Which was formerly (until 1992): A V C Presentation Development & Delivery (1062-2683); (until 1991): A V C Development & Delivery (1058-6229); (until 1990): Audio Visual Communications (1057-7254); (until 1989): A V C Presentation, Technology & Applications (1045-6910); (until 1989): Audio-Visual Communications (0004-7562); Formerly (until 1988): Tech Photo Pro Imaging Systems (1040-0141); Which was formed by the merger of (1969-1988): Technical Photography (0040-0971); (19??-1988): Functional Photography (0360-7216); Which was formerly (until 1975): Photographic Applications in Science, Technology and Medicine (0098-8227); (until 1968): Photographic Applications in Science and Technology
Related titles: Online - full text ed.: (from Florida Center for Library Automation, Gale Group, Northern Light Technology, Inc., O C L C Online Computer Library Center, Inc., ProQuest Information & Learning).
Indexed: B&I, BPI, BRI, BiolDig, BrCerAb, C&ISA, CerAb, CorrAb, E&CAJ, EMA, EngInd, IAA, Inspec, M&TEA, MBF, METADEX, MicrocompInd, SoftBase, SolStAb, WAA.
—BLDSC (0696.854750), AskIEEE, CISTI, Ei, IE, Infotrieve, ingenta, Linda Hall. **CCC.**
Published by: Cygnus Business Media, Inc., 3 Huntington Quadrangle, Ste 301N, Melville, NY 11747-3601. TEL 631-856-2700, FAX 631-845-2723, comments@advancedimagingpro.com, http://www.advancedimagingpro.com. Ed. Larry Adams. Pub. David Brambert. Circ: 40,509 (controlled).

AKADEMIA GORNICZO-HUTNICZA IM. STANISLAWA STASZICA. TELEKOMUNIKACJA CYFROWA - TECHNOLOGIA I USLUGI. see *COMMUNICATIONS—Telephone And Telegraph*

ALCATEL TELECOM RUNDSCHAU. see *ENGINEERING—Electrical Engineering*

384.0285 USA ISSN 0893-0597
APPLICATIONS OF COMMUNICATIONS THEORY. Text in English. 1980. irreg., latest 1997. price varies. back issues avail. **Document type:** *Monographic series.*
Indexed: Inspec.
Published by: Springer-Verlag New York, Inc. (Subsidiary of: Springer Science+Business Media), 233 Spring St, New York, NY 10013. TEL 212-460-1500, FAX 212-460-1575, service@springer-ny.com, http://www.springer-ny.com. Ed. R W Lucky.

C

AUDIOTEX DIRECTORY & BUYER'S GUIDE. see *COMMUNICATIONS—Telephone And Telegraph*

384.35 USA ISSN 1045-5795
AUDIOTEX UPDATE. Text in English. 1981. m. USD 150 in North America; USD 165 elsewhere (effective 2001). bk.rev.
Document type: *Newsletter, Trade.* **Description:** Covers voice mail, voice recognition and response, automated telemarketing, dial-it-information, and talking yellow pages and gab lines.
Related titles: Online - full text ed.: (from bigchalk, Data-Star, EBSCO Publishing, Factiva, Gale Group, LexisNexis, ProQuest Information & Learning, The Dialog Corporation).
—CCC.
Published by: Worldwide Videotex, PO Box 3273, Boynton Beach, FL 33424-3273. TEL 561-738-2276, markedit@juno.com, http://www.wvpubs.com. Ed., Pub. Mark Wright.

AUSTRALASIAN TELECOMMUNICATIONS MANAGEMENT AND MARKETING. see *COMMUNICATIONS*

B T TODAY. see *COMMUNICATIONS—Telephone And Telegraph*

621.382 AUS ISSN 1443-5632
BROADBAND & HIGHSPEED NETWORK MARKET. Text in English. 1984. a., latest 2001. USD 425 domestic; USD 440 foreign (effective 2001). stat. **Document type:** *Directory.*
Description: Covers technologies of the high-speed Internet, cable modem, DSL, and LMDS.
Former titles (until 1999): Telecommunications Networks Market Australia (1444-0679); (until 1998): Telecommunications Networks Market - Australia and New Zealand (1326-6802); Which superseded in part: Directory of Electronic Services and Communications Networks in Australia and New Zealand
Published by: Paul Budde Communication Pty. Ltd., 2643 George Downes Dr, Bucketty, NSW 2250, Australia. TEL 61-2-4998-8144, FAX 61-2-4998-8247, pbc@budde.com.au, http://www.budde.com.au. Ed. Paul Budde. Circ: 150 (paid).

C I T INFOBITS. see *EDUCATION—Higher Education*

C X O CANADA. see *COMPUTERS—Computer Networks*

CALL CENTER & C R M MARKTFUEHRER. see *BUSINESS AND ECONOMICS—Marketing And Purchasing*

384.0285 DEU
CAMGAROO. Text in German. 2000. 6/yr. EUR 25; EUR 4.90 newsstand/cover (effective 2005). adv. **Document type:** *Magazine, Trade.* **Description:** Provides insights and information on all aspects of digital video production.
Published by: Camgaroo AG, Landsberger Str 478, Munich, 81241, Germany. TEL 49-89-1301790, FAX 49-89-13017919, redaktion@camgaroo.com, info@camgaroo.com, http://www.camgaroo.com. Ed. Gabriele Lechner. Adv. contact Sabine Moll. B&W page EUR 2,200, color page EUR 2,990.

384.0285 USA
CARIBECOM NEWS. Text in English. 1986. a. USD 5. adv.
Document type: *Newsletter.* **Description:** Dedicated to telecommunications and communication technology in the Caribbean.
Published by: Intercom Corp., 9200 S Dadeland Blvd, Ste 309, Miami, FL 33156-2703. TEL 305-670-9444. Ed. Thomas Will. Pub. Kenneth Bleakley. Adv. contact John Butt. Circ: 4,000.

CHANNEL X AUSTRALIA. see *COMPUTERS—Computer Networks*

006.4 USA ISSN 1086-4644
COMMUNICATION SYSTEMS DESIGN. Text in English. m. free to qualified personnel; USD 57 in Canada & Mexico; USD 95 elsewhere (effective 2005). **Description:** Covers the development of OEM communications products or systems for personal, home, enterprise and infrastructure applications using wired, optical and wireless technologies.
Related titles: Online - full text ed.: (from Gale Group, O C L C Online Computer Library Center, Inc., ProQuest Information & Learning).
—BLDSC (3363.436500), IE, ingenta. **CCC.**
Published by: C M P Media LLC (Subsidiary of: United News & Media), 600 Harrison St, 6th Fl., San Francisco, CA 94107. TEL 415-947-6746, FAX 415-947-6041, eoconnell@cmp.com, http://www.csdmag.com/, http://www.cmp.com. Ed. Rob Keenan TEL 716-872-9390. Pub. Paul Miller. Circ: 50,000.

COMMUNICATIONS CONVERGENCE. see *COMMUNICATIONS—Telephone And Telegraph*

384.0285 CHN
COMPUTER & COMMUNICATIONS; electronics international. Text in Chinese. w.
Published by: China Computerworld Publishing & Servicing Co., 74 Lu Gu Rd, PO Box 750, Beijing, 100036, China. TEL 86-10-885-2033, FAX 86-10-885-2055. Ed. Fulai Zhu. adv.: B&W page USD 3,400; trim 395 x 275. Circ: 80,000.

384.0285 GBR
COMPUTER AND COMMUNICATIONS TECHNOLOGY DOCUMENTS SERVICE. Text in English, French. 1982. s-a. adv. **Document type:** *Abstract/Index.*
Former titles (until 199?): Computer and Communications Technology Documents Microfile; Computer and Communications Documents Microfile
Media: CD-ROM.
Published by: Technical Indexes Ltd., c/o Sopie Johnson, Willoughby Rd, Bracknell, Berks RG12 8DW, United Kingdom. TEL 44-1344-426311, FAX 44-1344-424971, systems@techindex.co.uk, http://www.tionestop.com. Adv. contact Mark Winslett.

004.6 DEU ISSN 1436-0993
COMPUTER TELEPHONY. Text in German. 1998. m. EUR 18 domestic; EUR 25 in Europe; EUR 30 elsewhere; EUR 3.50 newsstand/cover (effective 2004). adv. **Document type:** *Magazine, Trade.*
Related titles: Online - full text ed.
Published by: telepublic Verlag GmbH & Co. Medien KG, Podbielskistr. 325, Hannover, 30659, Germany. TEL 49-511-3348400, FAX 49-511-3348499, info@teletalk.de, http://www.computertelephony.de. Ed. Kai-Werner Fajga. adv.: B&W page EUR 2,400, color page EUR 3,545. Circ: 25,708 (paid and controlled).

384.0285 GBR ISSN 1367-5680
COMPUTER VIDEO. Text in English. 1997. bi-m. GBP 17 domestic; GBP 19 in Europe; GBP 35 elsewhere; GBP 3.75 newsstand/cover (effective 2003). **Document type:** *Consumer.*
Description: Covers all aspects of producing and editing video footage using desktop computers, with tests of specialist equipment and software, tutorials, and extensive technical advice.
Published by: Highbury - WV (Subsidiary of: Highbury House Communications PLC), 53-79 Highgate Rd, London, NW5 1TW, United Kingdom. TEL 44-20-73311000, FAX 44-20-73311273, http://www.computervideo.net/, http://www.hhc.co.uk/. Ed. Bob Crabtree.

384.0285 GBR
COMPUTERS, COMMUNICATIONS AND MEDIA NEWSLETTER. Text in English. q. **Document type:** *Newsletter.*
Published by: Lovell White Durrant, 65 Holburn Viaduct, London, EC1A 2DY, United Kingdom. TEL 44-20-7236-0066, FAX 44-20-7248-4212, publications@lovellwhitedurrant.com, http://www.lovellwhitedurrant.com.

384.0285 USA
CONTENT; envisioning digital media. Text in English. 1991. q. USD 29.95 in North America; USD 69.95 elsewhere; USD 2.95 newsstand/cover; CND 3.95 newsstand/cover in Canada. adv. software rev. illus.; tr.lit. **Document type:** *Trade.*
Description: Reviews new products and services covering digital media and electronic content.
Related titles: Online - full text ed.: ISSN 1099-6192.
Published by: ContentWorld Publishing Ventures (Subsidiary of: Syllabus Press Inc.), 345 Northlake Dr, San Jose, CA 95117. TEL 408-261-7200, 800-773-0670, FAX 408-261-7280, info@content.net, http://www.content.net. Ed., Pub. John P Noon. R&P Mary Grasz.

004.6 BEL
DATA NEWS; l'actualite informatique. Text in English. 1979. w. EUR 99; EUR 25 to qualified personnel (effective 2005). adv. bk.rev. bibl. back issues avail.
Related titles: Dutch ed.; French ed.
Published by: V N U Business Publications (Belgium), Jean Monnetlaan z.n., Vilvoorde, 1804, Belgium. TEL 32-2-6781611, FAX 32-2-6603600, http://www.vnunet.be/datanews/. Circ: 23,400 (controlled).

384.0285 GBR ISSN 1366-3216
DATASITE CD-ROM; the key to successful marketing in the IT industry. Text in English. 1996. s-a. GBP 995 (effective 2001).
Document type: *Directory.*
Media: CD-ROM.
Published by: Learned Information Europe Ltd. (Subsidiary of: V N U Business Publications Ltd.), Woodside, Hinksey Hill, Oxford, Oxon OX1 5BE, United Kingdom. TEL 44-1865-388100, FAX 44-1865-388056, customerservice@datasite.co.uk, http://www.datasite.co.uk.

004.6 GBR ISSN 1363-9072
E T H O S NEWSLETTER. (European Telematics Horizontal Observatory Service) Text in English. 1996. q. back issues avail. **Document type:** *Newsletter.* **Description:** Provides strategic technology and market watch services of interest to all projects in telematics and communications.
Media: Online - full text.
Published by: Tagish Ltd., Bolams Mill, 5 Dispensary St, Alnwick, Northd NE66 1LN, United Kingdom. TEL 44-1665-604895, FAX 44-1665-510624, ethos@tagish.co.uk, http://www.tagish.co.uk/ethos/.

384.0285 USA
EDITTECH INTERNATIONAL✶; reporting worldwide on high technology. Text in English. 1987. d. looseleaf. back issues avail. **Description:** Information about computer technology, communication and electronics.
Address: 2647 Hill Pk Dr, San Jose, CA 95124-1735. TEL 408-243-9788, FAX 408-985-5932. Ed. John Sterlicchi.

004.6 001.30285 USA
ELECTRONIC MEDIATIONS SERIES. Text in English. 1999. irreg., latest vol.8, 2002. price varies. back issues avail.
Document type: *Monographic series, Academic/Scholarly.*
Description: Explores the humanistic and social implications of electronic communication.
—BLDSC (3702.599600).
Published by: University of Minnesota Press, 111 Third Ave S, Ste 290, Minneapolis, MN 55401-2520. TEL 612-627-1970, FAX 612-627-1980, http://www.upress.umn.edu/byseries/electronic.html. Eds. Katherine Hayles, Mark Poster, Samuel Weber. **Dist. by:** c/o Chicago Distribution Center, 11030 S Langley Ave, Chicago, IL 60628; Plymbridge Distributors Ltd, Plymbridge House, Estover Rd, Plymouth, Devon PL6 7PY, United Kingdom. TEL 44-1752-202300, FAX 44-1752-202330, enquiries@plymbridge.com, http://www.plymbridge.com.

621.39 USA ISSN 1687-3955
▼ **EURASIP JOURNAL ON EMBEDDED SYSTEMS.** Text in English. 2005. q. EUR 30 to individuals; EUR 100 to institutions (effective 2005). **Document type:** *Journal, Academic/Scholarly.* **Description:** Serves the large community of researchers and professional engineers who deal with the theory and practice of embedded systems, particularly encompassing all practical aspects of theory and methods used in designing homogeneous as well as heterogeneous embedded systems that combine data-driven and control-driven behaviors.
Related titles: Online - full text ed.: ISSN 1687-3963. free.
Published by: Hindawi Publishing Corporation, PO Box 1210, Sylvania, OH 43560. FAX 866-446-3294, orders@hindawi.com, http://www.hindawi.com/journals/es/index.html. Ed. Zoran Salcic.

621.39 USA ISSN 1687-1472
TK5103.2
▼ **EURASIP JOURNAL ON WIRELESS COMMUNICATIONS AND NETWORKING.** Text in English. 2004. 4/yr. EUR 30 to individuals; EUR 100 to institutions (effective 2005).
Document type: *Journal, Academic/Scholarly.* **Description:** Aims to bring science and applications together on wireless communications and networking technologies with emphasis on signal processing techniques and tools.
Related titles: Online - full text ed.: ISSN 1687-1499. free (effective 2005) (from EBSCO Publishing, Swets Information Services).
Indexed: C&ISA, E&CAJ, IAA, Inspec.
—BLDSC (3828.089350), CISTI.
Published by: Hindawi Publishing Corporation, PO Box 1210, Sylvania, OH 43560. FAX 866-446-3294, wcn@wcn.hindawi.com, hindawi@hindawi.com, http://www.hindawi.com/journals/wcn/index.html. Ed. Phillip Regalia.

004.6 GBR ISSN 1472-3638
FIBRESYSTEMS EUROPE. Text in English. 1996. bi-m. free to qualified readers. adv. **Description:** Aimed at readers who are actively using and applying fibre-optic products or systems. Carries a mix of news, features, products, special reports, and analysis with a focus on activity in Western Europe.
Formerly (until 2000): FibreSystems (1368-5627)
Published by: Institute of Physics Publishing, Dirac House, Temple Back, Bristol, BS1 6BE, United Kingdom. TEL 44-117-9297481, FAX 44-117-9294318, custserv@iop.org, http://www.iop.org/Mags/FSE/. Ed. Joe McEntee. Pub. Sarah Chilcott. Adv. contact Rebecca Griffiths.

FIERCE VO I P; the voip business & technology report. (Voice Internet Provider) see *COMPUTERS—Internet*

384.0285 USA
FIERCEDEVELOPER; the weekly wireless developer reporter. Text in English. w. free. adv. **Document type:** *Newsletter, Trade.* **Description:** Contains the latest wireless developer news with technical insights, practical tips, special downloads, and expert commentary.
Published by: FierceMarkets, Inc., 1319 F St, NW, Ste 604, Washington, DC 20004. TEL 202-628-8778, info@fiercemarkets.com, http://www.wirelessdevreport.com, http://www.fiercemarkets.com. Ed. Eli Dickinson. Adv. contact Jason Nelson.

384.3 USA ISSN 1567-2190
▼ ➤ **FOUNDATIONS AND TRENDS IN COMMUNICATIONS AND INFORMATION THEORY.** Text in English. 2004. 4/yr. USD 375 domestic; EUR 375 foreign; USD 420 combined subscription domestic print & online eds.; EUR 420 combined subscription foreign print & online eds. (effective 2006).
Document type: *Journal, Academic/Scholarly.* **Description:** Provides tutorial coverage of subjects, research retrospectives as well as survey papers that offer state-of-the-art reviews involving communications and information theory.
Related titles: Online - full text ed.: ISSN 1567-2328. USD 375 domestic; EUR 375 foreign (effective 2005).
Indexed: Inspec.
Published by: Now Publishers Inc., PO Box 1024, Hanover, MA 02339. TEL 781-871-0245, FAX 781-871-6172, sales@nowpublishers.com, http://www.nowpublishers.com/pages/5/index.htm. Ed. Sergio Verdu. Pub., R&P Mike Casey.

▼ ➤ **FOUNDATIONS AND TRENDS IN TECHNOLOGY, INFORMATION AND OPERATIONS MANAGEMENT.** see *COMPUTERS—Information Science And Information Theory*

004.6 USA ISSN 0742-6151
TK1 CODEN: GAEJDG
G T E NETWORK SYSTEMS WORLD-WIDE COMMUNICATIONS JOURNAL. (General Telephone & Electronics) Contents page in English, French, Italian, Spanish. 1948. 6/yr. illus. reprint service avail. from PQC.
Former titles (until 1983): G T E Automatic Electric World-Wide Communications Journal (0273-141X); (until 1979): G T E Automatic Electrical Journal (0147-3328); (until 1977): G T E Automatic Electric Technical Journal (0099-9490); (until 1971): Automatic Electric Technical Journal (0005-1063)
Related titles: Microform ed.: 1948 (from PQC).
Indexed: ABIn, EngInd, Inspec.
—AskIEEE, CISTI, Linda Hall.
Published by: G T E Communications Systems, 2500 W. Utopia Rd., Phoenix, AZ 85027-4129. Circ: 9,000 (controlled).

004.6 DEU
GO AHEAD. Text in German. m. **Document type:** *Magazine, Trade.* **Description:** Contains the latest trends and developments in information technology.
Published by: C S C Ploenzke AG, Am Hahnwald 1, Kiedrich, 65399, Germany. TEL 49-6123-93-0, FAX 49-6123-933499, goahead@csc.com, info@cscploenzke.de, http://www.cscploenzke.de.

384.3 DEU ISSN 1612-1023
GROUPWARE MAGAZIN. Text in German. 2001. 7/yr. EUR 70; EUR 10 newsstand/cover (effective 2005). adv. **Document type:** *Magazine, Trade.*
Published by: H & T Verlag GmbH & Co. KG (Subsidiary of: Verlagsgruppe Handelsblatt GmbH), Konrad-Zuse-Platz 1, Munich, 81829, Germany. TEL 49-89-4447870, FAX 49-89-44478710, rm@htverlag.de, info@htverlag.de, http://www.groupware-online.de, http://www.htverlag.de. Ed. Rainer Mueller. adv.: page EUR 3,750; trim 210 x 297. Circ: 12,890 (paid).

GUIDE INTERNATIONAL DES BANQUES DE DONNEES SUR LES BREVETS ET LES MARQUES. see *PATENTS, TRADEMARKS AND COPYRIGHTS*

HI-TECH INFORMATION. see *COMPUTERS—Computer Networks*

004.6 DEU ISSN 1618-162X
CODEN: ICOMC8
I-COM; Zeitschrift fuer interaktive und kooperative Medien. Text in German. 2001. 3/yr. EUR 138; EUR 1,580 combined subscription print & online eds.; EUR 54 newsstand/cover (effective 2005). adv. **Document type:** *Magazine, Trade.*
Related titles: Online - full text ed.: EUR 138 (effective 2005) (from EBSCO Publishing, Swets Information Services).
Indexed: Inspec.
Published by: (Gesellschaft fuer Informatik e.V.), Oldenbourg Wissenschaftsverlag GmbH, Rosenheimer Str 145, Munich, 81671, Germany. TEL 49-89-450510, FAX 49-89-45051204, i-com-redaktion@verlag.oldenbourg.de, vertrieb-zs@verlag.oldenbourg.de, http://www.i-com-media.de, http://www.oldenbourg.de. adv.: page EUR 1,979; trim 185 x 270. Circ: 2,850 (paid and controlled).

385.0285 USA ISSN 0743-166X
TK5105.5
I E E E INFOCOM. PROCEEDINGS. Variant title: Joint Conference of the I E E E Computer and Communications Societies. Text in English. 1982. a. price varies. adv. **Document type:** *Proceedings, Academic/Scholarly.* **Description:** Presents recent advances in computer and communication disciplines.
Formerly (until 1982): I N F O C O M Proceedings
Related titles: Online - full text ed.: (from I E E E).
Indexed: EngInd.
—BLDSC (4362.934500), Ei, IE, ingenta. **CCC.**
Published by: (Institute of Electrical and Electronics Engineers, Inc.), I E E E Computer Society, 3 Park Ave, 17th Fl, New York, NY 10017. TEL 714-821-8380, 800-678-4333, FAX 714-821-4641, customer.service@ieee.org, http://www.ieee-infocom.org/, http://www.ieee.org. **Co-sponsor:** Communications Society.

004.6 USA ISSN 1555-5798
TK5101.A1
I E E E PACIFIC RIM CONFERENCE ON COMMUNICATIONS, COMPUTERS AND SIGNAL PROCESSING. CONFERENCE PROCEEDINGS. Text in English. 1987. biennial. USD 270; USD 135 to members (effective 2004). **Document type:** *Proceedings, Trade.* **Description:** Covers communications, computer technology, and signal processing as they relate to the Pacific Rim area.
Former titles (until 1997): I E E E Pacific Rim Conference on Communications, Computers and Signal Processing. Proceedings; (until 1993): I E E E Pacific Rim Conference on Communications, Computers and Signal Processing. Conference Proceedings (0893-4266)
Related titles: CD-ROM ed.; Microfiche ed.
Indexed: EngInd, Inspec.
—BLDSC (4363.012800). **CCC.**
Published by: Institute of Electrical and Electronics Engineers, Inc., 3 Park Ave, 17th Fl, New York, NY 10016-5997. TEL 212-419-7900, 800-678-4333, FAX 212-752-4929, customer.service@ieee.org, http://www.ieee.org. **Co-sponsor:** I E E E Victoria Section.

384.0285 USA ISSN 1063-6676
TK7882.S65 CODEN: IESPEJ
➤ **I E E E TRANSACTIONS ON SPEECH AND AUDIO PROCESSING.** Text in English. 1993. 7/yr. USD 600 (effective 2006). adv. **Document type:** *Journal, Academic/Scholarly.* **Description:** Covers speech analysis, synthesis, coding speech recognition, speaker recognition, language modeling, speech production and perception, and speech enhancement.
Related titles: Microform ed.; Online - full text ed.: (from EBSCO Publishing).
Indexed: AS&TI, AcoustA, B&BAb, CurCont, EngInd, Inspec, RefZh.
—BLDSC (4363.224000), AskIEEE, CISTI, Ei, IDS, IE, Infotrieve, ingenta, Linda Hall. **CCC.**
Published by: Institute of Electrical and Electronics Engineers, Inc., 445 Hoes Ln, Piscataway, NJ 08854-1331. TEL 732-981-0060, 800-701-4333, FAX 732-981-1721, subscription-service@ieee.org, http://www.ieee.org. Ed. B H Juang. **Subscr. to:** Maruzen Co., Ltd., 3-10 Nihonbashi 2-chome, Chuo-ku, Tokyo 103-0027, Japan. FAX 81-3-3275-0657; Universal Subscription Agency, Pvt. Ltd., 877, Udyog Vihar, V, Gurgoan 122001, India. TEL 91-124-347261, FAX 91-124-342496. **Co-sponsor:** Signal Processing Society.

004.6 384 USA
I E E E WORKSHOP ON INTERACTIVE VOICE TECHNOLOGY FOR TELECOMMUNICATIONS APPLICATIONS. Text in English. a. **Document type:** *Proceedings, Trade.*
Indexed: EngInd.
Published by: Institute of Electrical and Electronics Engineers, Inc., 3 Park Ave, 17th Fl, New York, NY 10016-5997. TEL 800-678-4333, customer.service@ieee.org, http://www.ieee.org.

371.33 USA
I I C S NEWSLINE. Text in English. 1986. m. looseleaf. USD 120 to members (effective 2000). adv. bk.rev. **Description:** Information on interactive technologies, including CD-ROM, videodisc and other interactive media.
Former titles: I I C S Quarterly; I I C S Reporter (1047-5346)
Media: Online - full text.
Published by: International Interactive Communications Society, 4840 McKnight Rd, Ste A1, Pittsburgh, PA 15237. TEL 412-734-1928, worldhq@iics.org, http://www.iics.org. Ed., Adv. contact Debra Palm. Circ: 5,000.

384.0285 USA
I S A UPDATE✶. Text in English. 1981. m. looseleaf. membership. bk.rev. back issues avail. **Description:** Examines online telecommunications and interactive services that are used anywhere for transmitting time-sensitive information, paying bills, gaining access to travel information, and much more.
Formerly: V I A Update
Published by: Interactive Services Association, PO Box 65782, Washington, DC 20035-5782. TEL 301-495-4955, FAX 301-495-4959. Circ: 230.

681.3 CZE ISSN 1212-6780
I T - NET. (Information Technology) Text in Czech. 1999. m. adv. **Document type:** *Magazine, Trade.* **Description:** Contains the latest communications and telecommunications information and developments from the Czech market and the world.
Published by: Vogel Burda Communications s.r.o., Sokolovska 73, Prague 8, 18621, Czech Republic. TEL 42-2-21808566, FAX 42-2-21808500, http://www.it-net.cz, http://www.vogel.cz. Ed. Pavel Louda. Pub. Pavel Filipovic. Adv. contact Jaroslava Tajcmanova. color page EUR 1,650; trim 270 x 340. Circ: 4,000 (paid and controlled).

384.0285 DEU
INFO-SYS JOURNAL. Text in German. 1994. bi-m. **Document type:** *Trade.*
Published by: Dekotec GmbH, Gasstr 18, Haus 1, Hamburg, 22761, Germany. TEL 040-891027, FAX 040-896069. Ed. Joern Fandrey. Circ: 10,000.

INFORMATION AND COMMUNICATIONS TECHNOLOGY LAW. see *COMMUNICATIONS*

384.0285 IND
INFORMATION COMMUNICATIONS WORLD. Text in English. 1987. m. INR 25 newsstand/cover. adv.
Published by: Media Transasia India Ltd., K-35 Green Park (Main), New Delhi, 110 016, India. TEL 91-11-6960926, FAX 91-11-686-7641, murlim@giasdl01.vsnl.net.in, mtilit@ndf.vsnl.net.in. Ed. Rajesh Prothi. Pub. Xavier Collaco. Adv. contact M Roopshree. B&W page USD 1,100, color page USD 1,500; trim 26.5 x 20. Circ: 150,000.

INFORMATION MANAGEMENT & TECHNOLOGY. see *COMMUNICATIONS*

INFORMATION TECHNOLOGY MANAGEMENT; non-technical report on IT and its applications. see *BUSINESS AND ECONOMICS—Office Equipment And Services*

384.0285 GBR ISSN 0950-9879
Z699.A1 CODEN: IWRED4
INFORMATION WORLD REVIEW; the newspaper for the information industry. Text in English. 1986. 11/yr. free domestic (effective 2005). bk.rev. back issues avail. **Document type:** *Newspaper, Trade.* **Description:** Reports on the information industry events and trends, software companies, electronic and optical publishing, new products, database, network, telecommunications developments and library automation.
Related titles: CD-ROM ed.: ISSN 1366-3232; Online - full text ed.: (from bigchalk, EBSCO Publishing, Gale Group, LexisNexis, Northern Light Technology, Inc., ProQuest Information & Learning).
Indexed: ABIn, AHCI, B&I, CINAHL, InfoSAb, Inpharma, Inspec, LISA, MicrocompInd, PE&ON, RAPRA, RASB, Reac, SoftBase.
—BLDSC (4496.412500), CASDDS, CINDOC, IE. **CCC.**
Published by: Learned Information Europe Ltd. (Subsidiary of: V N U Business Publications Ltd.), Woodside, Hinksey Hill, Oxford, Oxon OX1 5BE, United Kingdom. FAX 44-1865-388056, http://www.iwr.co.uk/, http://www.learned.co.uk. Ed. Bobby Pickering TEL 44-20-73169611. **Dist. in North America by:** Information Today, Inc., 143 Old Marlton Pike, Medford, NJ 08055-8750.

INFORMATIZATION DEVELOPMENTS AND THE PUBLIC SECTOR. see *PUBLIC ADMINISTRATION—Computer Applications*

384.0285 JPN ISSN 0918-3752
HD9696.C63
INFORMATIZATION WHITE PAPER. Text in English. 1967. a. JPY 6,000. adv. back issues avail. **Document type:** *Magazine, Trade.* **Description:** Reviews and updates the current status of Japan's information processing industry. Includes many graphs and tables to give a clear picture of the industry.
Formerly: Computer White Paper
Published by: Japan Information Processing Development Corporation, Kikai Shinko Kaikan Bldg, 5-8 Shibakoen 3-chome, Minato-ku, Tokyo, 105-0011, Japan. TEL 81-3-3432-9381, FAX 81-3-3432-9389, http://www.jipdec.or.jp. Ed. Hiroshi Ikawa. Adv. contact Junko Fukada TEL 81-3-3432-9384. Circ: 500.

384.53 GBR ISSN 1744-2869
▼ ➤ **INTERNATIONAL JOURNAL OF MOBILE NETWORK DESIGN AND INNOVATION.** Text in English. 2005. 4/yr. USD 450; USD 545 combined subscription print & online eds. (effective 2005). **Document type:** *Journal, Academic/Scholarly.* **Description:** Addresses the state-of-the-art in computerization for the deployment and operation of current and future wireless networks.
Related titles: Online - full text ed.: ISSN 1744-2850. USD 450 (effective 2005).
Published by: Inderscience Publishers, IEL Editorial Office, PO Box 735, Olney, Bucks MK46 5WB, United Kingdom. TEL 44-1234-240519, FAX 44-1234-240515, ijmndi@inderscience.com, info@inderscience.com, http://www.inderscience.com/ijmndi. Ed. Stuart Allen.

004.6 GBR ISSN 1741-1874
▼ ➤ **INTERNATIONAL JOURNAL OF VIRTUAL TECHNOLOGY AND MULTIMEDIA.** Text in English. 2005. q. USD 450 to institutions; USD 545 to institutions print & online eds. (effective 2005). **Document type:** *Journal, Academic/Scholarly.* **Description:** Reports on the latest developments of how information technology is utilized to harness a much wider variety of products and their impact on the scientific world.
Related titles: Online - full text ed.: USD 450 to institutions (effective 2005).
Published by: Inderscience Publishers, IEL Editorial Office, PO Box 735, Olney, Bucks MK46 5WB, United Kingdom. TEL 44-1234-240519, FAX 44-1234-240515, ijvtm@inderscience.com, info@inderscience.com, http://www.inderscience.com/ijvtm. Ed. Madya Hamouda. **Subscr. to:** World Trade Centre Bldg, 29 route de Pre-Bois, Case Postale 896, Geneva 15 1215, Switzerland. FAX 41-22-7910885, subs@inderscience.com.

004.6 GBR ISSN 1741-1084
▼ ➤ **INTERNATIONAL JOURNAL OF WIRELESS AND MOBILE COMPUTING.** Text in English. 2004. q. USD 450 to institutions; USD 545 combined subscription to institutions (effective 2005). **Document type:** *Journal, Academic/Scholarly.* **Description:** Addresses the state-of-the-art of all aspects of wireless communications and mobile computing including devices, hardware, software, architectures, networks, systems, support services, algorithm/protocol design and analysis, mobile environments, wireless communications and networks, applications, implementation issues, and emerging technologies.
Related titles: Online - full text ed.: ISSN 1741-1092. USD 450 to institutions (effective 2005).
Published by: Inderscience Publishers, IEL Editorial Office, PO Box 735, Olney, Bucks MK46 5WB, United Kingdom. TEL 44-1234-240519, FAX 44-1234-240515, ijwmc@inderscience.com, info@inderscience.com, http://www.inderscience.com/ijwmc. Ed. Laurence T Yang. **Subscr. to:** World Trade Centre Bldg, 29 route de Pre-Bois, Case Postale 896, Geneva 15 1215, Switzerland. FAX 41-22-7910885, subs@inderscience.com.

384.0285   NLD
TK6679.I57
➤ **INTERNATIONAL WORKSHOP ON H D T V. PROCEEDINGS.** (High Definition Television) Variant title: Signal Processing of H D T V. Text in English. irreg. price varies. back issues avail. **Document type:** *Proceedings, Academic/Scholarly.* **Description:** Publishes research into the design and applications of high-density television, presented at a workshop on HDTV.
Indexed: EngInd.
Published by: Elsevier BV (Subsidiary of: Elsevier Science & Technology), Radarweg 29, Amsterdam, 1043 NX, Netherlands. TEL 31-20-4853911, FAX 31-20-4852457, nlinfo-f@elsevier.nl, http://www.elsevier.nl. Eds. L Chiariglione, Y Nimomiya.

➤ **INTERNET MAGAZINE**; Thailand's leading Internet magazine. see *COMPUTERS—Internet*

004.6   USA   ISSN 1528-3844
D1
➤ **THE JOURNAL FOR MULTIMEDIA HISTORY.** Abbreviated title: J M M H. Text mainly in English. 1998. irreg. (approx 1/yr), latest vol.2, 1999. free. back issues avail. **Document type:** *Journal, Academic/Scholarly.* **Description:** Publishes articles on the history of multimedia communication and explores how radio, television, CD-ROM and DVD technologies, World Wide Web hypertext documents, Internet radio and video, and other multimedia applications are transforming and expanding the possibilities for researching, documenting, and disseminating scholarship in various history disciplines.
Media: Online - full content.
Indexed: AmH&L, HistAb.
Published by: State University of New York at Albany, Department of History, TenBroeck 105, Albany, NY 12222. TEL 518-442-4488, FAX 518-442-3477, jmmh@csc.albany.edu, http://www.albany.edu/jmmh.

384.0285   ISR   ISSN 1083-6101
TK5105.6
➤ **JOURNAL OF COMPUTER-MEDIATED COMMUNICATION.** Text in English. q. free (effective 2005). illus. Index. reprints avail. **Document type:** *Journal, Academic/Scholarly.* **Description:** Devoted to research and essays on the social, organizational and political aspects of computerized communication.
Related titles: Online - full text ed.: free (effective 2005).
Indexed: CommAb, PsycInfo, PsycholAb.
Published by: Hebrew University of Jerusalem, School of Business Administration, Jerusalem, 91905, Israel. http://jcmc.indiana.edu, http://jcmc.huji.ac.il. Eds. Margaret McLaughlin, Rafaeli Sheizaf, Dr. Susan C Herring.

➤ **JOURNAL OF VISUAL COMMUNICATION AND IMAGE REPRESENTATION.** see *COMPUTERS—Computer Graphics*

384.0285   GBR
KEY NOTE MARKET REPORT: CD-ROM. Variant title: CD-ROM. Text in English. 1992. irreg. GBP 265 (effective 1999). **Document type:** *Trade.*
Formerly: Key Note Report: CD-ROM
Related titles: CD-ROM ed.; Online - full text ed.
Published by: Key Note Ltd., Field House, 72 Oldfield Rd, Hampton, Mddx TW12 2HQ, United Kingdom. TEL 44-20-8481-8750, FAX 44-20-8783-0049, info@keynote.co.uk, http://www.keynote.co.uk.

LOGISTIK HEUTE. see *BUSINESS AND ECONOMICS—Computer Applications*

004.6   DEU
▼ **M X MAGAZIN.** Text in German. 2003. q. EUR 39.60; EUR 9.90 newsstand/cover (effective 2005). adv. **Document type:** *Magazine, Trade.*
Published by: Software & Support Verlag GmbH, Kennedyallee 87, Frankfurt am Main, 60596, Germany. TEL 49-69-6300890, FAX 49-69-63008989, redaktion@mxmagazin.de, info@software-support.biz, http://www.mxmagazin.de, http://www.software-support.biz.

MARKTFUEHRER MOBILE SOLUTIONS. see *BUSINESS AND ECONOMICS—Marketing And Purchasing*

004.6   CHE   ISSN 1420-5661
MEGALINK. Text in German. 12/yr. CHF 85 (effective 2000). adv. **Document type:** *Magazine, Trade.*
Formed by the merger of (1984-1994): E C Woche (0256-4629); (1961-1994): Elektroniker (0374-3020)
Indexed: Inspec.
—BLDSC (5536.235950), AskIEEE, CISTI, IE, ingenta. **CCC.**
Published by: A Z Fachverlage AG, Neumattstr 1, Aarau, 5001, Switzerland. TEL 41-62-8366565, FAX 41-62-8366566. Ed. Ruedi Bolliger. Adv. contact Alfred Markstahler. Circ: 13,500.

MICROCOMPUTER; for general P C user. see *COMPUTERS—Microcomputers*

MICROCOMPUTER USER; for PC buyers and general public. see *COMPUTERS—Microcomputers*

004.6   DEU
▼ **MOBILITY.** Text in German. 2003. q. EUR 20; EUR 7.95 newsstand/cover (effective 2003). adv. **Document type:** *Magazine, Consumer.*
Published by: Vogel IT-Medien GmbH, Gutermannstr 25, Augsburg, 86154, Germany. TEL 49-821-21770, FAX 49-821-2177150, media.mobility@vogel-it.de, marliese_bernhardt@vogel-medien.de, http://www.vogel-it.de. adv.: B&W page EUR 3,990, color page EUR 4,590; trim 185 x 260. Circ: 50,000 (paid and controlled).

681.324   HRV   ISSN 1331-2839
MREZ@. Text in Croatian. 1996. m. HRK 179 (effective 2001). adv. **Document type:** *Magazine, Consumer.*
Related titles: Online - full text ed.: ISSN 1332-6422. 1998.
Published by: Bug d.o.o., Tratinska 36, Zagreb, 10000, Croatia. TEL 385-1-3821555, FAX 385-1-3821669, mreza@bug.hr, http://www.bug.hr/mreza. Ed. Miroslav Rosandic. Adv. contact Aron Paulic.

N V R REPORTS. see *COMMUNICATIONS—Video*

384.0285   USA
NAUTILUS (DUBLIN). Text in English. 1990. m. USD 136. illus. **Description:** Covers computer applications in multimedia environments.
Published by: Metatec, 7001 Discovery Blvd, Dublin, OH 43017. Ed. Mike Espindle.

NETWORK & TELECOM. see *COMPUTERS—Computer Networks*

NETWORK WORLD. see *COMPUTERS—Computer Networks*

004.6   CAN   ISSN 1187-2985
NETWORK WORLD CANADA. Text in English. 1991. 24/yr. CND 55 domestic; CND 75 in United States; CND 95 elsewhere; free to qualified personnel (effective 2003). adv. **Document type:** *Magazine, Trade.* **Description:** Helps networking and telecom professions to skillfully utilize the wide range of available network products and services to improve business operations and provide sensible, long-term solutions.
Incorporates (in 2000): Canadian Telecom (0836-0782)
Related titles: Online - full text ed.
Indexed: CBCABus, CBCARef.
Published by: I T World Canada, Inc., No.302 - 55 Town Centre Court, Scarborough, ON M1P 4X4, Canada. TEL 416-290-0240, FAX 416-290-0233, computerworld_canada@itworldcanada.com, http://www.itworldcanada.com/nw/. Ed. Greg Enright. Pub., R&P John Jones. Adv. contact Stephen Kranabetter. B&W page CND 4,530, color page CND 5,680; trim 10.5 x 13.5. Circ: 15,875.

NETWORK WORLD PORTUGAL. see *COMPUTERS—Computer Networks*

NETWORKWORLD ARGENTINA. see *COMPUTERS—Computer Networks*

NETWORKWORLD ROMANIA. see *COMPUTERS—Computer Networks*

004.6   DEU
NEWS FUER ENTSCHEIDER. Text in German. q. **Document type:** *Magazine, Trade.* **Description:** Contains news on the latest developments in telecommunications and information technology.
Published by: (C S C Ploenzke AG), BurdaYukom Publishing GmbH (Subsidiary of: Hubert Burda Media Holding GmbH & Co. KG), Schleissheimer Str 141, Munich, 80797, Germany. TEL 49-89-306200, FAX 49-89-30620100, info@burdayukom.de, http://www.yukom.de. Circ: 8,000 (controlled).

384.0285   USA   ISSN 1071-8990
QA75.5
O E M MAGAZINE. (Original Equipment Manufacturer) Text in English. 1993. 8/yr. USD 59. illus. **Document type:** *Trade.*
Related titles: Online - full text ed.: (from EBSCO Publishing, Gale Group, O C L C Online Computer Library Center, Inc.).
Indexed: ABIn, SoftBase.
—CCC.
Published by: C M P Media LLC (Subsidiary of: United News & Media), 600 Community Dr, Manhasset, NY 11030. TEL 516-562-5000. Ed. Rick Boyd Merritt. Pub. Steve Weitzner. Circ: 35,000.

384.0285   USA
OPEN CHANNEL. Text in English. 1981. m. **Document type:** *Newsletter.*
Published by: University of Houston, Information Technology Information Services, Information Technology Division, Houston, TX 77204-1961. TEL 713-743-1500, InfoServ@Jetson.UH.edu, http://www.uhiedu/toc. Ed., R&P Rhonda Rubin TEL 713-743-1505. Pub. Jim Bradley.

004.6   USA
P C VIDEOLOG. Text in English. 1988. m. (updates on diskette). USD 240.
Formerly: Videoscan Database for IBM Compatible Computers

Published by: Phonolog Publishing (Subsidiary of: Trade Service Corporation), 10996 Torreyana Rd, Box 85007, San Diego, CA 92138. TEL 619-457-5920.

P T C (YEAR) PROCEEDINGS. see *COMMUNICATIONS—Telephone And Telegraph*

PACIFIC TELECOMMUNICATIONS REVIEW. see *COMMUNICATIONS—Telephone And Telegraph*

384.0285   DEU   ISSN 0944-4033
POINT OF SALE. Short title: P O S. Text in German. m. adv. **Document type:** *Trade.*
Related titles: ♦ Supplement to: iBusiness.
Published by: HighText Verlag, Wilhelm-Riehl-Str 13, Munich, 80687, Germany. TEL 49-89-578387-0, FAX 49-89-57838799, info@hightext.de. Ed. Joachim Graf. R&P Daniel Treplin. Adv. contact Stefan Kratz.

004.6   USA
POINT-TO-POINT. Text in English. m. USD 500 (effective 1999). **Document type:** *Trade.* **Description:** Review of the telecommunications industry.
Published by: Gartner Inc., 56 Top Gallant Rd, Stamford, CT 06904-2212. TEL 203-316-1111, 800-544-7337, FAX 203-316-6300, jwhitney@info-edge.com, http://www.gartner3.gartnerweb.com, http://www.info-edge.com.

004.6   USA   ISSN 1521-3110
PREMISE WIRING. Text in English. 1987. m. USD 695 in US & Canada; USD 725 elsewhere (effective 2001). back issues avail. **Document type:** *Newsletter.* **Description:** Publishes latest news and analysis on markets, technology, and applications of copper and fiber optics for data communications.
Formerly (until 1997): Fiber Datacom (1051-1954)
Related titles: Online - full text ed.: (from Northern Light Technology, Inc.).
—CCC.
Published by: Information Gatekeepers, Inc., 320 Washington St, Ste 302, Brighton, MA 02135. TEL 617-782-5033, 800-323-1088, FAX 617-734-8562, info@igigroup.com, http://www.igigroup.com. Ed. Tony Carmona. Pub. Dr. Paul Polishuk. Circ: 350.

PROFESSIONAL SYSTEM. see *BUSINESS AND ECONOMICS—Computer Applications*

004.6 621.3822   RUS
R M MAGAZINE. (Read Me) Text in Russian. bi-m. **Document type:** *Magazine, Trade.*
Published by: Informatsionnyi Izdatel'skii Tsentr Baltika, ul Bol'shaya Monetnaya, dom 16, ofis 2, St Petersburg, 197101, Russian Federation. editor@readmemag.spb.su, http://www.rmmagazine.ru.

004.6   ESP   ISSN 1695-8144
REDES & TELECOM. Text in Spanish. 1987. m. EUR 35 (effective 2005). adv. **Description:** For MIS and networking professionals.
Former titles (until 1998): Redes Lan (1134-9182); (until 1992): Redes de Telecomunicaciones (1130-2151); (until 1988): Redes (1130-2143); (until 1987): Network (1130-2135)
—CINDOC. **CCC.**
Published by: V N U Business Publications (Spain), San Sotero 8 4a Planta, Madrid, 28037, Spain. TEL 34-91-3137900, FAX 34-91-3273704, http://www.vnubp.es/. Circ: 102,010.

REGULATORY AND COMPETITION AUSTRALIA. see *COMMUNICATIONS—Telephone And Telegraph*

384.0285   USA   ISSN 1077-4653
HE8220.2
RUSSIA ONLINE AND WIRELESS. Text in English. 1994. m. USD 850 (effective 2000). adv. index. back issues avail. **Document type:** *Newsletter, Trade.* **Description:** Provides news of telecommunications and information markets in Russia and the New Independent States, prediction and analysis of investment opportunities and regulatory climate.
Related titles: Online - full text ed.: (from Florida Center for Library Automation, Gale Group).
Published by: Gist, Inc., 2200 Wilson Blvd, Ste 102G, Arlington, VA 22201. TEL 703-527-7459, FAX 703-528-1477, dkbain@gist.net, http://www.gist.net. Ed., Pub. David K Bain. R&P, Adv. contact David Bain TEL 203-527-7459.

S R D S INTERACTIVE ADVERTISING SOURCE. see *ADVERTISING AND PUBLIC RELATIONS*

SETI/NETWORK WORLD. see *COMPUTERS—Computer Networks*

004.6   NLD   ISSN 0927-5444
➤ **STUDIES IN COMPUTER AND COMMUNICATIONS SYSTEMS.** Text in English. 1992. irreg. latest vol.8, 1995. price varies. back issues avail. **Document type:** *Monographic series, Academic/Scholarly.* **Description:** Covers research in ADA programming language.
Indexed: ZentMath.
—BLDSC (8490.281500), CISTI, ingenta. **CCC.**

C

Published by: I O S Press, Nieuwe Hemweg 6B, Amsterdam, 1013 BG, Netherlands. TEL 31-20-6883355, FAX 31-20-6203419, market@iospress.nl, order@iospress.nl, http://www.iospress.nl. **Subscr. to:** I O S Press, Inc, 4502 Rachael Manor Dr., Fairfax, VA 22032-3631. iosbooks@iospress.com.

384.0285   BEL   ISSN 1021-4232
TECH EUROPE. Text in English. m. (11/yr). EUR 625 (effective 2000). bk.rev. **Document type:** *Bulletin.* **Description:** Covers information technology, telecommunications, multimedia, broadcasting, electronics, European policies, markets and production, legislation and standards, corporate activity.
Related titles: CD-ROM ed.: EUR 635; Online - full text ed.: (from Gale Group); French ed.: ISSN 0775-2857.
Indexed: B&I, ELLIS.
Published by: Europe Information Service SA, Av Adolphe Lacomble 66-68, Brussels, 1030, Belgium. TEL 32-2-737-7709, FAX 32-2-732-6757, eis@eis.be, http://www.eis.be. Pub. Eric Damiens. Circ: 500.

TECHSCAN NEWSLETTER; the manager's guide to technology. see *BUSINESS AND ECONOMICS—Computer Applications*

TELCO COMPANY PROFILES AUSTRALIA. see *COMPUTERS—Computer Networks*

621.38   USA
TELCORDIA DIGEST OF TECHNICAL INFORMATION. Text in English. m.
Media: Online - full content.
Published by: Telcordia Technologies, Inc, 445 South St, MCC-10346G, Morristown, NJ 07960-9975. http://www.telcordia.com/resources/genericreq/digest/.

621.38   USA
TELCORDIA DIGEST PLUS. Text in English. q.
Published by: Telcordia Technologies, Inc, 445 South St, MCC-10346G, Morristown, NJ 07960-9975..

621.38   USA
TELCORDIA EXCHANGE. Text in English. 198?. bi-m.
Former titles (until 1999): Bellcore Exchange (1040-2020); (until 1988): Bell Communications Research Exchange (0891-4877)
—BLDSC (8779.425000), IE.
Published by: Telcordia Technologies, Inc, 445 South St, MCC-10346G, Morristown, NJ 07960-9975. TEL 973-829-2181, FAX 973-829-2193. Ed. Barbara Kellam-Scott. Pub. Judith L Shannon.

TELECOMMUNICATIONS INDUSTRY IN AUSTRALIA; packaging of value added telecommunication & broadcasting services & networks. see *COMMUNICATIONS—Telephone And Telegraph*

621.38   AUS
TELECOMMUNICATIONS PERFORMANCE MONITORING BULLETIN. Text in English. 1996. q.
Formerly (until 1997): Quality of Service Bulletin
Media: Online - full text.
Published by: Australian Communications Authority, PO Box 13112, Melbourne, VIC 8010, Australia. TEL 61-3-9963-6967, FAX 61-3-9963-6899, candinfo@aca.gov.au, http://www.aca.gov.au/publications/performance/index.htm, http://www.aca.gov/.

621.38   AUS   ISSN 1441-6670
TELECOMMUNICATIONS PERFORMANCE REPORTS. Text in English. 1998. a.
Media: Online - full text.
Published by: Australian Communications Authority, PO Box 13112, Melbourne, VIC 8010, Australia. TEL 61-3-9963-6967, FAX 61-3-9963-6899, http://www.aca.gov/. Ed. Sue Evans.

621.38   NLD
TELECOMMUNICATIONS TECHNOLOGY & APPLICATIONS SERIES. Text in English. 1994. irreg., latest vol.9, 2001. price varies. back issues avail. **Document type:** *Proceedings, Academic/Scholarly.* **Description:** Discusses research in telecommunications technology, both experimental and applied.
—BLDSC (8781.579000).
Published by: Springer-Verlag Dordrecht (Subsidiary of: Springer Science+Business Media), Van Godewijckstraat 30, Dordrecht, 3311 GX, Netherlands. TEL 31-78-6576050, FAX 31-78-6576474, http://www.springeronline.com.

TELECOMTACTICS: BUSINESS SYSTEMS. see *COMMUNICATIONS—Telephone And Telegraph*

384.0285   IND   ISSN 0970-3934
TK5101.A1   CODEN: TELIEG
TELEMATICS INDIA. Text in English. 1987. m. INR 200, USD 50 (effective 1995). adv. bk.rev. charts; illus.; stat.; tr.lit. index. back issues avail. **Document type:** *Trade.* **Description:** Aims to fill information or technical gaps for professionals, laymen and college students.
Indexed: Inspec.
—BLDSC (8782.956000), AskIEEE, CISTI, Ei, ingenta.

Published by: Vimot Publishers Pvt. Ltd., 3Fl., Grandlay Complex, Community Centre, New Friends Colony, New Delhi, 110 065, India. TEL 91-11-6924496, FAX 91-11-6836375. Ed., R&P Rajendra Prabhu. Pub. B K Singhal. Adv. contact Shashi Dharan. Circ: 21,000.

TELESPAN (E-MAIL EDITION); a bulletin on teleconferencing. see *COMPUTERS—Data Communications And Data Transmission Systems*

TELETALK. see *BUSINESS AND ECONOMICS—Marketing And Purchasing*

TELETRAFFIC MARKTFUEHRER. see *BUSINESS AND ECONOMICS—Marketing And Purchasing*

384.0285   NLD   ISSN 1388-3437
➤ **TELETRAFFIC SCIENCE AND ENGINEERING.** Text in English. 1994. irreg., latest vol.4, 2001. price varies. back issues avail. **Document type:** *Monographic series, Academic/Scholarly.* **Description:** Publishes proceedings of world conferences, special conferences and selected monographs on topics relating to teletraffic theory and its applications to the design, planning and operation of telecommunications systems and networks.
—BLDSC (8786.651000).
Published by: (International Teletraffic Conference), Elsevier BV, North-Holland (Subsidiary of: Elsevier Science & Technology), Sara Burgerhartstraat 25, Amsterdam, 1055 KV, Netherlands. TEL 31-20-485-3911, FAX 31-20-485-2457, nlinfo-f@elsevier.nl, http://www.elsevier.nl. **Subscr. to:** Elsevier BV, PO Box 211, Amsterdam 1000 AE, Netherlands. TEL 31-20-485-3757, FAX 31-20-485-3432, http://www.elsevier.nl.

004.6   ISR
TIKSHORET. Text in Hebrew. s-a.
Published by: Motorola Communication Israel Ltd., Customer Relations Manager, Rehov Karmanski 16, Tel Aviv, 67899, Israel. TEL 03-388257. Ed. Meir Eshkol.

004.6   GBR
U K O L U G NEWSLETTER. Text in English. 1988. bi-m. GBP 50 (effective 2001). adv. bk.rev. abstr. back issues avail. **Document type:** *Newsletter, Consumer.*
Formerly (until 1994): U K Online User Group Newsletter (0957-8544)
Published by: U K Online Users Group, The Old Chapel, Walden, West Burton, Leyburn, N Yorks DL8 4LE, United Kingdom. cabaker@ukolug.org.uk, http://www.ukolug.org.uk. Ed., R&P, Adv. contact Chris Armstrong TEL 44-1974-251302. page GBP 200. Circ: 1,200.

004.6   DEU   ISSN 1615-5289
➤ **UNIVERSAL ACCESS IN THE INFORMATION SOCIETY;** international journal. Abbreviated title: U A I S. Text in English. 2001. q. EUR 260 combined subscription to institutions print & online eds. (effective 2005). adv. back issues avail. **Document type:** *Journal, Academic/Scholarly.* **Description:** Focuses on theoretical, empirical and methodological research on all aspects of information society technologies and accompanying measures that facilitate participation in the information society for virtually everyone.
Related titles: Online - full text ed.: ISSN 1615-5297 (from EBSCO Publishing, ProQuest Information & Learning, Springer LINK, Swets Information Services).
Indexed: ErgAb, Inspec.
—BLDSC (9100.515050), Infotrieve. **CCC.**
Published by: Springer-Verlag (Subsidiary of: Springer Science+Business Media), Tiergartenstr 17, Heidelberg, 69121, Germany. TEL 49-6221-3450, FAX 49-6221-345229, http://link.springer.de/link/service/journals/10209/index.htm. Ed. Constantine Stephanidis. Adv. contact Stephan Kroeck TEL 49-30-827875739. **Subscr. in the Americas to:** Springer-Verlag New York, Inc., Journal Fulfillment, PO Box 2485, Secaucus, NJ 07096-2485. TEL 800-777-4643, 201-348-4033, FAX 201-348-4505, journals@springer-ny.com, http://www.springer-ny.com; **Subscr. to:** Springer GmbH Auslieferungsgesellschaft, Haberstr 7, Heidelberg 69126, Germany. TEL 49-6221-345-0, FAX 49-6221-345-4229, subscriptions@springer.de.

▼ ➤ **V O N MAGAZINE.** (Voice on the Net) see *COMPUTERS—Internet*

004.6   USA
▼ **VO I P MONITOR.** (Voice Over Internet Provider) Text in English. 2004. w. USD 595 (effective 2004). **Document type:** *Magazine, Trade.* **Description:** Provides a guide to business, regulatory and market developments in the fast-paced IP telephony world.
Media: Online - full content.
Published by: Pike & Fischer, Inc. (Subsidiary of: The Bureau of National Affairs, Inc.), 1010 Wayne Ave, Ste 1400, Silver Spring, MD 20910. TEL 301-562-1530, 800-255-8131, FAX 301-562-1521, cbrumfield@pf.com, pike@pf.com, http://www.voip-monitor.com, http://www.pf.com.

384   GBR
WELSH ADVISORY COMMITTEE ON TELECOMMUNICATIONS. REPORT. Text in English. a. **Description:** Promotes the interests of everyone who uses telecommunications services.

Published by: Welsh Advisory Committee on Telecommunications, Caradog House, St Andrews Pl, Cardiff, CF1 3BE, United Kingdom. TEL 44-29-2023-9174, FAX 44-29-2066-8536, wact@acts.org.uk, http://www.acts.org.uk/wact/.

384.0285   USA
WIRELESS P C S - G S M. (Personal Communications System) Text in English. m. USD 695 in US & Canada; USD 745 foreign (effective 2001). reprints avail. **Document type:** *Newsletter.* **Description:** Covers personal communications networks technology, regulatory developments, markets, products, standards, and business developments.
Former titles (until 2001): Wireless P C S Telecommunications (1082-2100); (until 1995): Wireless P C N Telecommunications (1058-6725); (until 1991): Wireless - Personal Communication Networks
Published by: Information Gatekeepers, Inc., 320 Washington St, Ste 302, Brighton, MA 02135. TEL 617-782-5033, 800-323-1088, FAX 617-734-8562, info@igigroup.com, http://www.igigroup.com. Ed. Tony Carmona. Pub. Dr. Paul Polishuk.

THE WORKS OF DANTE. see *COMPUTERS—Internet*

004.6   BRA
WORLD TELECOM. Text in Portuguese. 1998. m. BRL 88 (effective 2002). adv. **Document type:** *Magazine, Trade.* **Description:** Provides complete coverage of three essential areas: corporate networks, intranets, and the newly privatized area of telecommunications.
Formerly: Networkworld Telecom (1415-8787)
Published by: I D G Computerworld do Brasil, Rua Tabapua, 145-3 e 4 andar, Itaim Bibi, Sao Paulo, 04533-010, Brazil. TEL 55-11-3049-2000, FAX 55-11-3071-4022, negocios@idg.com.br, http://www.idg.com.br. adv.: color page USD 7,650; trim 210 x 280.

COMMUNICATIONS—Postal Affairs

A G M. see *PHILATELY*

383   USA
THE ABYSSINIAN PRINCE. Text in English. every 3 wks. back issues avail. **Description:** Features articles on postal issues.
Media: Online - full text.
Published by: Abyssinian Prince, 664 Smith St, Providence, RI 02908-4327. TEL 401-351-0287, FAX 401-277-9904, burgess@world.std.com, http://devel.igo.org/DipPouch/Postal/Zines/TAP/index.html. Pub. Jim Burgess.

383.12409489   DNK   ISSN 1396-4828
ADRESSELOESE FORSENDELSER. Text in Danish. a. free. illus.
Formerly (until 199?): Adresseloese Postforsendelser (0107-4350); Which superseded in part (in 1980): Postomdeling af Reklamer
Published by: Post Danmark, Hovedkontoret, Tietgensgade 37, Copenhagen V, 1566, Denmark. TEL 45-33-754475, FAX 45-33-754450. Circ: 10,000.

383.492   USA   ISSN 0044-7811
THE AMERICAN POSTAL WORKER. Text in English. 1903. m. free membership (effective 2005). adv. charts; illus.; tr.lit.
Document type: *Magazine, Trade.*
Incorporates (in 1971): Union Postal Clerk and Postal Transport Journal (0041-6991)
Published by: American Postal Worker's Union, A F L - C I O, 1300 L St, N W, Washington, DC 20005. TEL 202-842-4212, FAX 202-682-2528, http://www.apwu.org. Ed. William Burrus. Circ: 300,000.

383.12404989   DNK
ANTAL MODTAGERE. Text in Danish. 1985. q. free.
Formerly: Antal Modtagere, Adresseloese Postforsendelser (0900-8829)
Published by: Post Danmark, Hovedkontoret, Tietgensgade 37, Copenhagen V, 1566, Denmark. TEL 45-33-754475, FAX 45-33-754450. Circ: 10,000.

ARTISTAMP NEWS. see *ART*

383   USA
ASSOCIATION OF PRIVATE POSTAL SYSTEMS. DIRECTORY∗
Text in English. 1975. a. **Document type:** *Directory.*
Published by: Association of Private Postal Systems, 5580 Power Inn Rd, No F, Sacramento, CA 95820-6748. TEL 916-929-3300. Ed. Donald F Marford.

383   USA
ASSOCIATION OF PRIVATE POSTAL SYSTEMS. UPDATE∗.
Text in English. 1975. m.
Published by: Association of Private Postal Systems, 5580 Power Inn Rd, No F, Sacramento, CA 95820-6748. TEL 916-929-3300.

383   BEL
BELGIUM. LA POSTE. RAPPORT D'ACTIVITE. Text in French. 1954. a. free. illus. **Document type:** *Corporate.* **Description:** Report on the activities of the Belgian Postal Service.
Supersedes: Belgium. Regie des Postes. Rapport d'Activite (0377-337X)

Published by: La Poste, Direction de la Communication, Centre Monnaie, Brussels, 1000, Belgium. Circ: 6,000.

BERMUDA POST. see *PHILATELY*

383.12209489 DNK ISSN 0908-7796
BREVE INDLAND. Text in Danish. 1980-1983; resumed 1985. a. free. illus.
Former titles (until 1991): Adresserede Brevforsendelser (0901-263X); (until 1985): Adresserede Forsendelser i Stoerre Antal (0107-4369)
Published by: Post Danmark, Hovedkontoret, Tietgensgade 37, Copenhagen V, 1566, Denmark. TEL 45-33-754475, FAX 45-33-754450. Circ: 10,000.

383 USA ISSN 0068-4201
BULLINGER'S POSTAL AND SHIPPERS GUIDE FOR THE UNITED STATES AND CANADA✶. Text in English. 1871. a. USD 360. **Document type:** *Directory.* **Description:** Lists approximately 200,000 place names throughout the United States and Canada.
Published by: Alber - Leland Publishing, 4110 Prairie Rd, Highland, IL 62249-3446. Ed. D L Cundari. Circ: 3,000.

383.4 USA ISSN 0739-3873
CODEN: BMAREG
BUSINESS MAILERS REVIEW. Text in English. 1980. bi-w. USD 287 in North America; USD 302 elsewhere. **Document type:** *Newsletter.* **Description:** Covers US Postal Service policy and activities as well as commercial postal vendors as they relate to the volume business mailer.
Related titles: Online - full text ed.
Published by: Van H. Seagraves, 1813 Shepherd St N W, Washington, DC 20011. Circ: 2,500 (paid).

CALLIGRAPHER. see *HOBBIES*

383 CAN
CANADA POSTAL GUIDE PART 1: POSTAL LAW AND REGULATIONS. Text in English. irreg. looseleaf. CND 31.75.
Published by: Supply and Services Canada, Printing and Publishing, 270 Albert St, Ottawa, ON K1A 0S9, Canada. TEL 613-997-2560.

383 CAN
CANADA POSTAL GUIDE PART 2: INTERNATIONAL MAILS, RATES AND CONDITIONS. Text in English. irreg. looseleaf. CND 28.
Published by: Supply and Services Canada, Printing and Publishing, 270 Albert St, Ottawa, ON K1A 0S9, Canada. TEL 613-997-2560.

383.1455 CAN ISSN 1480-4085
THE CANADIAN POSTAL CODE DIRECTORY. Text in English, French. 1998. a. CND 21.95 (effective 2004). **Document type:** *Directory, Trade.*
Formed by the merger of (1987-1998): Canada's Postal Code Directory. Ontario, Yukon, Northwest Territories (1206-4157); (1987-1998): Canada's Postal Code Directory. Eastern Canada, Atlantic Provinces & Quebec, Yukon, Northwest Territories (1206-4165); (1987-1998): Canada's Postal Code Directory. Western Canada, Yukon, Northwest Territories (1206-4173); All of which superseded in part (in 1996): Canada's Postal Code Directory (0835-4693); Which was formed by the merger of (1973-1987): Directory. Atlantic Provinces. Postal Code (0833-6725); Which was formerly (until 1984): Directory. Atlantic Postal Region. Postal Code (0317-4174); (1973-1987): Directory. Western Provinces. Postal Code (0833-675X); Which was formerly (until 1984): Directory. Western Postal Region. Postal Code (0317-4239); (197?-1987): Repertoire. Province de Quebec. Code Postal (0833-6741); Which was formerly (until 198?): Repertoire. Region Postale de Quebec. Code Postal (0317-5146); (1973-1987): Directory. Ontario Province. Postal Code (0833-6733); Which was formerly (until 198?): Directory. Ontario Postal Region. Postal Code (0317-4271)
—CISTI.
Published by: Canada Post Corporation, 4567 Dixie Rd, Mississauga, ON L4W 1S2, Canada. TEL 800-565-4362, http://www.canadapost.ca/.

CANADIAN POSTMASTER/MAITRE DE POSTE CANADIEN. see *LABOR UNIONS*

383.4 USA ISSN 1079-7661
HE6188.W73
LA CATASTROPHE; quarterly publication of the wreck & crash mail society. Text in English. 1995. q. USD 20; USD 12.50 in United Kingdom. adv. bk.rev. charts; illus.; mkt.; maps; stat. back issues avail. **Document type:** *Newsletter.* **Description:** Contains articles on postal history including various aspects of damaged and delayed mail, especially mail service interruptions involving ships, trains, and airplanes.
Published by: Wreck & Crash Mail Society, 132 Livingston Pl W, Metairie, LA 70005. TEL 504-835-2856, 74137.2275@compuserve.com. Ed., Pub., R&P, Adv. contact Henry J Berthelot. Circ: 105. **Subscr. to:** 10 Lady Jane Park, Bradgate Rd, Newtown Linford, Leics LE6 0HD, United Kingdom.

383 TWN ISSN 0529-2786
HE6009.F6
CHIN JIH YU CHENG/POSTAL SERVICE TODAY. Text in Chinese, English. 1958. m. TWD 510 domestic; HKD 150 in Hong Kong; USD 24 elsewhere (effective 2001). illus.
Published by: Postal Service Today, 55 Chin Shan S. Rd Sec2, Taipei, 106, Taiwan. FAX 02-34193400. Ed. W Y Fang. Circ: 10,000.

CORREIOS E TELECOMUNICACOES DE PORTUGAL. ANUARIO ESTATISTICO. see *COMMUNICATIONS—Abstracting, Bibliographies, Statistics*

383 ESP
CORREO C B. Text in Spanish. 12/yr.
Address: Los Yebenes, 96, Apartado 156193, Madrid, 28047, Spain. TEL 7183058.

383 ESP
CORREO POSTAL Y TELEGRAFICO. Text in Spanish. 12/yr.
Address: Palacio de Comunicaciones, Alcala, 50, Madrid, 28014, Spain. TEL 1-531-50-39, FAX 1-396-21-32. Ed. Manuel Navalles Castro.

383 GBR ISSN 0011-0396
COURIER (LONDON); the post office newspaper. Text in English. 1966. m. free. adv. bk.rev. illus. **Document type:** *Newspaper, Consumer.*
Indexed: SPPI.
Published by: British Post Office, 5th Fl, 130 Old St, London, EC1V 9PQ, United Kingdom. TEL 44-207-320-7353, FAX 44-207-320-7474. Ed. John Schofield. adv.: B&W 1/2 page GBP 3,500, color 1/2 page GBP 4,500; trim 134 x 370. Circ: 280,000.

383.4 DEU ISSN 1438-0633
D P V KOM MAGAZIN. Text in German. 1998. m. adv. **Document type:** *Magazine, Trade.*
Formerly (until 1997): Deutsche Postzeitung
Published by: (Deutsche Post AG), Kommunikationsgewerkschaft D P V, Schaumburg-Lippe-Str 5, Bonn, 53113, Germany. TEL 49-228-911400, FAX 49-228-9114098, bgst-ref2@dpvkom.de, http://www.dpvkom.de. adv.: B&W page EUR 1,750, color page EUR 2,600. Circ: 45,000 (controlled).

383 IND ISSN 0011-5762
DAK TAR. Text in Hindi. 1956. m. INR 12. adv. bk.rev. illus.
Related titles: English ed.
Published by: Department of Posts & Telecommunications, Parliament St., New Delhi, 110 001, India. Ed. V Naraynswamy. Circ: 10,000.

DATA IN WORLD DATA CENTER C2 FOR IONOSPHERE. CATALOGUE. see *EARTH SCIENCES—Geophysics*

383 GBR
DESPATCH MANAGER. Text in English. 1997. bi-m. GBP 15. **Document type:** *Trade.*
Published by: C W Publishing, The Old Smultry, Adwell, Twame OX9 7DQ, United Kingdom. TEL 01844-281122, FAX 01844-281144. Ed. Laurie O'Caddell. Pub. Ian Ward. Circ: 15,000.

383.125 DEU
DEUTSCHER POSTKALENDER. Text in German. 1994. base vol. plus updates 3/yr. EUR 70.56 (effective 2004). adv. **Document type:** *Directory, Trade.*
Published by: Walhalla Fachverlag, Haus an der Eisernen Bruecke, Regensburg, 93042, Germany. TEL 49-941-56840, FAX 49-941-5684111, walhalla@walhalla.de, http://www.walhalla.de. adv.: B&W page EUR 355. Circ: 1,000 (controlled).

383 FRA
ECOLE NATIONALE SUPERIEURE DES POSTES ET TELECOMMUNICATIONS. ASSOCIATION DES ELEVES ET ANCIENS ELEVES. CAHIERS D'ETUDES ET D'INFORMATION. Text in French. 1951-1978; resumed 1979. q. adv. charts. **Document type:** *Academic/Scholarly.*
Formerly (until 1978): Courrier: Cahiers d'Etudes et d'Informations (0011-0469)
Published by: Ecole Nationale Superieure des Postes et Telecommunications, Association des Eleves et Anciens Eleves, 46 rue Barrault, Paris, Cedex 13 75634, France. Ed. R Fort. Circ: 30,525.

383.4 ITA ISSN 1121-2624
IL GABBIANO. Text in Italian. 1991. bi-m. **Document type:** *Magazine, Consumer.*
Published by: Emmeffe Srl, Via della Cavona 2, Casal Morena, RM 00040, Italy. TEL 39-06-79840020, FAX 39-06-79840024. Ed. Enrico Veschi. Adv. contact Riccardo Marini.

383 USA ISSN 1072-3862
HE6031
GUIDE TO WORLDWIDE POSTAL-CODE AND ADDRESS FORMATS. Text in English. 1989. a. USD 119.50 domestic; USD 129.50 foreign (effective 2000). **Document type:** *Directory.* **Description:** Provides practical information for formatting and standardizing international addresses.

Published by: Nelson Intersearch Company, PO Box 20546 Park W, New York, NY 10025. TEL 212-531-0599, FAX 212-531-0578, MarNelson@aol.com. Ed., Pub. Marian Nelson.

383 HRV ISSN 1330-8661
H P T. Text in Croatian. 1991. m. **Document type:** *Magazine, Trade.*
Published by: Hrvatska Posta i Telekomunikacije, Jurisiceva 13, Zagreb, 10000, Croatia. TEL 385-1-4815505, FAX 385-1-4815510. Ed. Milena Supe.

HOLY LAND POSTAL HISTORY. see *PHILATELY*

INTERNATIONAL ART POST. see *ART*

383 USA ISSN 1058-0875
HE6445 CODEN: IMAMEA
INTERNATIONAL MAIL MANUAL. Text in English. s-a. looseleaf. USD 36 (effective 2001). back issues avail. **Document type:** *Government.* **Description:** Includes international postal rates, prohibitions and restrictions, and information on insurance availability, special services, and international mailing.
Formerly (until 1981): Directory of International Mail
Related titles: Online - full content ed.
Published by: U.S. Postal Service, 475 L'Enfant Plaza, S.W., Rm. 5300, Washington, DC 20260-1300. TEL 202-268-2393, http://pe.usps.gov/. **Subscr. to:** U.S. Government Printing Office, Superintendent of Documents, PO Box 371954, Pittsburgh, PA 15250-7954. TEL 202-512-1800, FAX 202-512-2250, orders@gpo.gov, http://www.access.gpo.gov.

383.4 UAE
ITTIHAD AL-BARIDI AL-ARABI/ARAB POSTAL UNION. REVIEW. Text in Arabic. 1955. q. per issue exchange basis. **Description:** Covers news and activities of the Arab Postal Union, with a focus on modernization efforts.
Published by: Arab Postal Union/Al-Ittihad al-Baridi al-Arabi, PO Box 7999, Dubai, United Arab Emirates. TEL 690508, TELEX 46284 BRDIM EM. Ed. Hussein Rashid Al Hamdani. Circ: 3,000.

C

JIAOTONG YUNSHU JINGJI, YOUDIAN JINGJI/ECONOMY IN COMMUNICATIONS AND TRANSPORTATION & IN POST AND TELECOMMUNICATION. see *TRANSPORTATION*

383.4 338 GBR ISSN 1460-0978
KEY NOTE MARKET REPORT: COURIER & EXPRESS SERVICES. Variant title: Courier & Express Services Market Report. Text in English. 198?. a., latest 2001, June. GBP 340 per issue (effective 2002). **Document type:** *Trade.* **Description:** Provides an overview of the UK courier and express services market, including industry structure, market size and trends, developments, prospects, and major company profiles.
Formerly (until 1995): Key Note Report: Courier and Express Services (0957-7351)
Related titles: CD-ROM ed.; Online - full text ed.
Published by: Key Note Ltd., Field House, 72 Oldfield Rd, Hampton, Mddx TW12 2HQ, United Kingdom. TEL 44-20-8481-8750, FAX 44-20-8783-0049, info@keynote.co.uk, http://www.keynote.co.uk. Ed. Dominic Fenn.

383.1 DEU
LABEL & LOGISTIK. Text in German. 3/yr. **Document type:** *Magazine, Trade.*
Published by: (Stielow GmbH & Co. KG), Medienfabrik Guetersloh GmbH, Carl-Bertelsmann-Str 33, Guetersloh, 33311, Germany. TEL 49-5241-2348010, FAX 49-5241-2348022, kontakt@medienfabrik-gt.de, http://www.medienfabrik-gt.de. Circ: 15,500 (controlled).

LONDON POSTAL HISTORY GROUP NOTEBOOK. see *PHILATELY*

383 USA ISSN 1051-824X
HF5761 CODEN: MSTTE8
M A S T; for mailing professionals. (Mailing and Systems Technology) Key Title: Mast. Text in English. 1988. 6/yr. USD 27 domestic; USD 47 foreign. adv. illus.; tr.lit. **Document type:** *Trade.*
Indexed: AnthLit.
Published by: R B Publishing, Inc., 2901 International Ln, Ste 200, Madison, WI 53704-3177. TEL 608-241-8777, FAX 608-241-8666, http://www.rbpub.com, http://www.psdmag.com. Ed. Daniel O'Rourke. Pub., Adv. contact Ron Brent TEL 608-241-8777 ext 204. R&P Linda Marx. B&W page USD 4,955, color page USD 6,355; trim 10.88 x 8. Circ: 4,000 (paid); 36,000 (controlled).

383 USA ISSN 1081-9347
M P C WORLD. (Mail and Parcel Centers) Text in English. 1995. q. USD 25 domestic; USD 35 foreign (effective 2001). adv. bk.rev.; software rev. illus.; tr.lit. 32 p./no. 3 cols./p.; back issues avail. **Document type:** *Magazine, Trade.* **Description:** Provides coverage of trends, marketing, technology, legal issues, legislative activities, human resources management, cost-cutting and conventions for owners and managers of mail and packaging retail stores.

▼ new title ➤ refereed ✶ unverified ♦ full entry avail.

Published by: (Associated Mail & Parcel Centers), B K B Publications Inc, 98 Greenwich Ave, 1st Fl, New York, NY 10011-7743. TEL 212-807-7933, FAX 212-807-1821, bkbpub1@ix.netcom.com. Ed. Charlene Komar Storey. Pub., R&P, Adv. contact Brian K Burkart TEL 212-807-7933. B&W page USD 1,525, color page USD 2,565; trim 10.875 x 8.25. Circ: 9,000 (paid and controlled).

383   USA   ISSN 1053-0703
HE6300   CODEN: MJCDEG
MAIL: THE JOURNAL OF COMMUNICATION DISTRIBUTION.
Text in English. 1989. 9/yr. USD 31; USD 72 foreign (effective 1999). **Document type:** *Trade.*
Published by: Excelsior Publication, One Milstone Rd, Gold Key Box 2425, Milford, PA 18337-9607. TEL 717-686-2111, FAX 717-686-3495. Ed. Francis P Ruggiero.

383   MUS
MAURITIUS. POSTS & TELEGRAPHS. ANNUAL REPORT. Text in English. a. MUR 20. **Document type:** *Government.*
Formerly: Mauritius. Posts and Telegraphs Department. Annual Report
Published by: (Mauritius. Posts and Telegraphs Department), Government Printing Office, La Tour Koenig, Pointe aux Sables, Port Louis, Mauritius. TEL 234-53-20, FAX 234-53-22.

383   USA
MEMO TO MAILERS. Text in English. m. free. charts; illus.; stat. **Document type:** *Trade.* **Description:** Contains news articles and items on the latest issues and developments affecting U.S. Postal Service business and its customers.
Published by: U.S. Postal Service, Corporate Relations, 475 L Enfant Plaza, Rm 10541, Washington, DC 20260-3100. Circ: 100,000. **Subscr. to:** U.S. Postal Service, National Address Information Center, 6060 Primacy Pkwy, Ste 101, Memphis, TN 38188-0001.

MILITARY POSTAL HISTORY SOCIETY BULLETIN. see *PHILATELY*

383.4   USA   ISSN 1078-1625
HE6376.A1
N J P H. Text in English. 1973. 5/yr. USD 15 (effective 1999 & 2000). adv. bk.rev.
Published by: New Jersey Postal History Society Inc., 144 Hamilton Ave, Clifton, NJ 07011. TEL 973-772-1413. Ed., R&P, Adv. contact Robert G Rose. Circ: 150 (paid).

383   CHN   ISSN 1000-1972
NANJING YOUDIAN XUEYUAN XUEBAO. Text in Chinese. q.
Related titles: Online - full text ed.: (from East View Information Services).
Indexed: EngInd.
Published by: Nanjing Youdian Xueyuan, 38 Guangdong Lu, Nanjing, Jiangsu 210003, China. TEL 635561. Ed. Wang Hongsheng.

383   USA   ISSN 0028-0089
HD6350.P77
THE NATIONAL RURAL LETTER CARRIER. Text in English. 1903. m. USD 150 (effective 2005). adv. illus.; stat. **Document type:** *Magazine, Trade.*
Published by: National Rural Letter Carriers Association, 1630 Duke St, 4th Fl, Alexandria, VA 22314-3465. TEL 703-684-5545, FAX 703-548-8735, http://www.nrlca.org. Adv. contact Kathleen O'Connor. col. inch USD 60. Circ: 105,000 (paid).

383   GBR   ISSN 0548-5924
NEW MANAGEMENT. Text in English. 1968. m. GBP 2.50. adv. bk.rev.
Published by: Communication Managers Association, Ltd., Hughes House, Twyford, Reading, Berks RG10 9JD, United Kingdom. Ed. T L Deegan. Circ: 20,000.

383   USA   ISSN 0049-5298
NEW YORK METRO AREA POSTAL UNION. UNION MAIL. Key Title: Union Mail. Text in English. 1957. m. USD 1. charts; illus. **Document type:** *Newspaper, Government.*
Formerly: Manhattan - Bronx Postal Union. Union Mail
Published by: New York Metro Area Postal Union, 350 West 31st St, New York, NY 10001. TEL 212-563-7553. Ed. Robert Knolle. Circ: 31,500.

383   USA
NEWS AND IDEAS∗. Text in English. 1982. m. USD 160. adv. bk.rev. back issues avail. **Document type:** *Newsletter.*
Former titles: A C M R A News; (until 1987): Mail Center News
Published by: Associated Mail & Parcel Centers, 5605 Bosque Vista Dr NE, Albuquerque, NM 87111-8067. TEL 505-294-6425, FAX 505-271-2050. Ed. James W Baer. Circ: 900.

NEWSPAPER AND MAIL DELIVERERS' UNION BULLETIN. see *LABOR UNIONS*

383.4   USA
OPTIMUM DELIVERY; the newsletter for professionals competing with the postal service. Text in English. 1990. bi-m. USD 89. **Document type:** *Trade.* **Description:** Discusses trends in private postal systems.

Published by: Willow Bend Communications, Inc., PO Box 7977485, Dallas, TX 75379-7485. TEL 214-248-0451, FAX 214-733-0995. Ed. Alexander Thompson. Pub. Stephen Thompson. Circ: 950.

383   ITA   ISSN 0030-5634
ORIZZONTI PROFESSIONALI; rivista bimestrale di tecnica, cultura ed informazioni. Text in Italian. 1960. bi-m. illus.
Published by: Istituto Professionale di Stato per l'Industria e l'Artigianato "E. Ascione" Palermo, Via Leonardo Da Vinci, 364, Palermo, PA 90135, Italy. Ed. Giuseppe Maggio.

383 790.13   CAN   ISSN 0714-8305
P H S C JOURNAL. Text in English. 1972. q. free to members. adv. bk.rev. illus. **Document type:** *Academic/Scholarly.* **Description:** Articles and research papers on all facets of postal history of Canada.
Former titles: Postal History Society of Canada Journal (0703-5365); Postal Histo-Mine
Indexed: BiolAb, SJI.
Published by: Postal History Society of Canada, c/o R.F. Narbonne, 216 Mailey Dr, Carleton Pl, ON K7C 3X9, Canada. knierim@bmts.com, lacumo@cogeco.ca, http://postalhistory.tripod.com/. Ed. Gus Knierim. Circ: 600 (paid).

P H S G NEWSLETTER. see *PHILATELY*

383   USA   ISSN 1520-3611
PAR AVION; the international mail & delivery newsletter. Text in English. 1998. bi-w. USD 845 (effective 2000). **Document type:** *Newsletter.* **Description:** Covers worldwide market for mail, periodical and package delivery services. Includes private-sector and government postal affairs.
Published by: Harry L. Baisden, Ed. & Pub., 3523 Slade Run Dr, Falls Church, VA 22042. TEL 703-538-6416, FAX 703-538-6378.

PARCEL SHIPPING & DISTRIBUTION; small shipment logistics management. see *TRANSPORTATION*

383   GBR   ISSN 1368-2865
POST EXPRESS. Text in English. 1997. fortn. GBP 305, USD 470 (effective 2004). adv. **Document type:** *Magazine, Trade.* **Description:** Covers all aspects of the postal industry throughout the world.
—CCC.
Published by: AutoIntermediates Ltd. (Subsidiary of: U K & International Press), Abinger House, Church St, 120 South St, Dorking, Surrey RH4 1DF, United Kingdom. TEL 44-1306-743744, FAX 44-1306-742525, info@ukintpress.com, http://www.ukintpress.com/. Circ: 8,000 (paid).

383.4   ZAF
POST OFFICE XPRESS. Text in English. 1971. m. free. bk.rev. illus. **Document type:** *Newspaper.* **Description:** Covers postal matters for staff members.
Formerly (until July 1991): Postel
Published by: S A Post Office, PO Box 9255, Pretoria, 0001, South Africa. TEL 27-12-4217714, FAX 27-12-4217606. Ed. Sandile Madelo. R&P Martie Gilchrist. Circ: 33,000 (controlled).

383   CHE
POST, TELEFON UND TELEGRAFEN. AMTSBLATT∗. Text in German. 1849. w. CHF 25; CHF 45 foreign (effective 1997). **Document type:** *Government.*
Published by: Swiss Posts Telephones and Telegraphs (PTT), Viktoriastr 21, Bern, 3030, Switzerland. TEL 41-31-626389, FAX 41-31-629059. Circ: 24,000.

384   DEU   ISSN 0947-9945
HE6995
POST- UND TELEKOMMUNIKATIONSGESCHICHTE. Text in German. 1953. q. EUR 18 (effective 2005). bk.rev. illus.; stat. index. back issues avail. **Document type:** *Bulletin, Trade.*
Formerly (until 1995): Archiv fuer Deutsche Postgeschichte (0003-8989)
Indexed: AmH&L, HistAb, IBR, IBZ.
Published by: Deutsche Gesellschaft fuer Post- und Telekommunikationsgeschichte, Schaumainkai 53, Frankfurt Am Main, 60596, Germany. TEL 49-69-94139577, FAX 49-69-6060365, geschaeftsstelle@dgpt.org, http://www.dgpt.org. Ed., R&P Gottfried North. Circ: 28,000.

769.56   USA   ISSN 0885-7385
HE6371
LA POSTA; a journal of American postal history. Text in English. 1969. bi-m. USD 20 domestic; USD 28 in Canada; USD 55 elsewhere (effective 2001). adv. bk.rev. charts; illus.; maps; mkt.; stat. 80 p./no.; back issues avail. **Document type:** *Journal, Academic/Scholarly.* **Description:** Includes articles on postal history research, postmark collecting, town histories, airmail, train and military mail.
Published by: La Posta Publications, 33470 SW Chinook Plz 216, Scappoose, OR 97056-3726. TEL 503-657-5685, helbock@la-posta.com, http://www.la-posta.com. Ed., Pub., R&P Richard W Helbock. Adv. contact Cath Clark. page USD 420.

383   ZAF
POSTAL AND TELKOM HERALD/POS- EN TELKOMHERALD. Text in Afrikaans, English. 1904. m. membership. adv. index.
Document type: *Newspaper, Consumer.*
Formerly: Postal and Telegraph Herald - Pos- en Telegraafherald (0032-5317)
Published by: Postal and Telkom Association of South Africa, PO Box 9186, Johannesburg, 2000, South Africa. TEL 27-11-725-5422, FAX 27-11-725-6540. Ed. F A Gerber. Adv. contact F.A. Gerber. Circ: 10,000.

383   USA   ISSN 0364-863X
HE6311
THE POSTAL BULLETIN. Text in English. 1880. fortn. USD 140 domestic; USD 175 foreign; USD 10 newsstand/cover domestic; USD 12.50 newsstand/cover foreign (effective 2001). charts; illus. back issues avail. **Document type:** *Bulletin, Government.* **Description:** Contains current orders, instructions, and information relating to the U.S. Postal Service and on commemorative-stamp posters.
Related titles: Online - full content ed.
—IDS.
Published by: U.S. Postal Service, 475 L'Enfant Plaza, S.W., Rm. 5300, Washington, DC 20260-1300. TEL 202-268-2393, pbulleti@email.usps.gov, http://www.usps.gov/cpim/ftp/bulletin/pb.htm. Circ: 130,000. **Subscr. to:** U.S. Government Printing Office, Superintendent of Documents, PO Box 371954, Pittsburgh, PA 15250-7954. TEL 202-512-1800, FAX 202-512-2250, orders@gpo.gov, http://www.access.gpo.gov.

383   USA   ISSN 0032-5341
HE6001
POSTAL HISTORY JOURNAL. Text in English. 1957. 3/yr. USD 30; USD 35 in Canada & Mexico; USD 40 elsewhere (effective 2000). adv. bk.rev. charts; illus. cum.index: 1957-1993. reprint service avail. from PQC. **Document type:** *Academic/Scholarly.* **Description:** Includes research articles on all aspects of postal history worldwide, society news, and commentary on philatelic writing and exhibiting.
Related titles: Microform ed.: (from PQC).
Indexed: SJI.
Published by: Postal History Society, Inc., c/o Kalman V. Illyefalvi, Sec.-Treas., 8207 Daren Ct., Pikesville, MD 21208-2211. TEL 410-653-0665. Eds. Diane F DeBlois, Robert Dalton Harris. R&P Kalman V Illyefalvi. Circ: 600 (controlled).

POSTAL RECORD. see *LABOR UNIONS*

383   USA   ISSN 0554-8373
HE6187
POSTAL STATIONERY. Text in English. 1948. bi-m. USD 10 to non-members (effective 1999). adv. bk.rev. 32 p./no. 2 cols./p.; back issues avail. **Document type:** *Magazine.*
Incorporates (1972-1999): Pantograph of Postal Stationery (0893-9055); **Formerly:** Postal Stationery Journal (0278-6362)
Indexed: SJI.
Published by: United Postal Stationery Society, PO Box 1116, Thousand Oaks, CA 91358. TEL 201-933-6026, FAX 209-797-6536, cutsquare@yahoo.com. Ed., Adv. contact Wayne Menuz. Circ: 1,300 (paid).

383.492   USA   ISSN 0032-5384
HE6001
THE POSTAL SUPERVISOR. Text in English. 1911. s-m. USD 18 (effective 2000). illus. **Document type:** *Newsletter, Trade.*
Indexed: WorkRelAb.
Published by: National Association of Postal Supervisors, 1727 King St, Ste 400, Alexandria, VA 22314-2753. TEL 703-836-9660, FAX 703-836-9665, napshq@naps.org, http://www.naps.org. Ed. Ray Martin. R&P Vincent Pallandino. Circ: 35,000 (paid and controlled).

383   GBR   ISSN 1362-5209
POSTAL TECHNOLOGY INTERNATIONAL. Text in English. 1996. q. GBP 65, USD 100 (effective 2004). adv. **Document type:** *Magazine, Trade.* **Description:** Covers a blend of world news, case studies, interviews, strategy updates, technology profiles and expert commissioned articles.
—BLDSC (6561.944000). **CCC.**
Published by: AutoIntermediates Ltd. (Subsidiary of: U K & International Press), Abinger House, Church St, 120 South St, Dorking, Surrey RH4 1DF, United Kingdom. TEL 44-1306-743744, FAX 44-1306-742525, info@ukintpress.com, http://www.ukintpress.com/post.html. Circ: 8,000 (paid).

383   USA
POSTAL WORLD. Text in English. 1974. bi-w. USD 387 (effective 2005). illus. **Document type:** *Trade.* **Description:** Provides information and advice to mail industry professionals; discusses how to trim postage costs, speed delivery, improve mailroom productivity, and plan for rate increases.
Incorporates: E M World (Electronic Mail)
Published by: Argosy Group (Subsidiary of: United Communications Group), 11300 Rockville Pike, Ste 1100, Rockville, MD 20852. TEL 888-287-2223, FAX 301-816-8945, pwcustomer@ucg.com, http://www.mypostalworld.com/pwjsp/index.jsp, http://www.ucg.com/argosy.html.

383 SWE ISSN 1404-4358
POSTBULLETINEN; iagr, idag, i morgon. Text in Swedish. 1962. 7/yr. SEK 50 (effective 2000). adv. charts; illus.; stat.
Document type: *Magazine, Corporate.* **Description:** Contains articles and features for members of the Swedish Postal Union.
Formerly (until 1999): Postmaennens Tidning (0032-5503)
Published by: Foereningen Postkamraterna, Fack 418, Stockholm, 10128, Sweden. Ed., R&P Josef Lundell. Circ: 5,000.

343.0992 DEU ISSN 0944-5633
POSTDIENST. Text in German. 1964. irreg. price varies.
Document type: *Monographic series, Trade.*
Formerly (until 1993): Postordnung und Ergaenzende Vorschriften (0940-0192)
Published by: Erich Schmidt Verlag GmbH & Co. (Berlin), Genthiner Str 30G, Berlin, 10785, Germany. TEL 49-30-250085-0, FAX 49-30-25008511, esv@esvmedien.de, http://www.erich-schmidt-verlag.de.

383 USA ISSN 0032-5511
HE6001
POSTMASTERS ADVOCATE. Text in English. 1894. m. USD 24 domestic; USD 34 foreign (effective 2000). adv. bk.rev. illus.
Document type: *Trade.*
Published by: National League of Postmasters, 1023 N Royal St, Alexandria, VA 22314-1569. TEL 703-548-5922, FAX 703-836-8937. Ed., R&P Allen T Lanier. Adv. contact Rick Weinberg. B&W page USD 700; 11 x 8.5. Circ: 23,000 (controlled).

383.492 USA ISSN 0032-552X
HE6001
POSTMASTERS GAZETTE. Text in English. 1903. m. (combined convention issue). USD 12. adv. illus. **Document type:** *Trade.*
Published by: National Association of Postmasters of the United States, 8 Herbert St, Alexandria, VA 22305-2628. TEL 703-683-9027, FAX 703-683-6820. Ed. Shirlene Roberts. Pub., R&P, Adv. contact Ray Martin. Circ: 42,000.

383 DEU
POSTPLUS. Text in German. bi-m. **Document type:** *Magazine, Consumer.*
Published by: (Deutsche Post AG), Medienfabrik Guetersloh GmbH, Carl-Bertelsmann-Str 33, Guetersloh, 33311, Germany. TEL 49-5241-2348010, FAX 49-5241-2348022, kontakt@medienfabrik-gt.de, http://www.medienfabrik-gt.de. Circ: 400,000 (controlled).

383.125 DEU
POSTSTELLENREPORT. Text in German. q. **Document type:** *Magazine, Trade.*
Published by: (Stielow GmbH & Co. KG), Medienfabrik Guetersloh GmbH, Carl-Bertelsmann-Str 33, Guetersloh, 33311, Germany. TEL 49-5241-2348010, FAX 49-5241-2348022, kontakt@medienfabrik-gt.de, http://www.medienfabrik-gt.de. Circ: 17,000 (controlled).

383.4 GBR ISSN 0269-1396
PRATIQUE; newsletter of the disinfected mail study circle. Text in English. 1974. 3/yr. (Normally one volume per year), latest vol.26. looseleaf. GBP 15 domestic membership; GBP 18 in Europe membership; GBP 23, USD 36 elsewhere membership (effective 2003). adv. bk.rev. charts; maps. 36 p./no.; back issues avail. **Document type:** *Journal, Academic/Scholarly.*
Description: Focuses on accounts of the treatment of mail, worldwide. Also includes related topics such as maritime and other certificates of health, ships' documents, public health proclamations restricting or restoring the freedom to trade with ports or regions suspected of harbouring infections diseases, and vaccination ephemera.
Published by: Disinfected Mail Study Circle, 25 Sinclair Grove, London, NW11 9JH, United Kingdom. TEL 44-20-84559190, vdvpractique@aol.com. Ed., R&P, Adv. contact V. Denis Vandervelde. Pub. V Denis Vandervelde. B&W page GBP 75. Circ: 140 (paid); 20 (controlled).

383 DEU ISSN 1434-8128
REGULIERUNGSBEHOERDE FUER TELEKOMMUNIKATION UND POST. AMTSBLATT. Text in German. 1846. fortn. looseleaf. EUR 39.88 domestic; EUR 79.76 foreign; EUR 5.11 newsstand/cover (effective 2005). illus. index. **Document type:** *Government.*
Former titles (until 1998): Germany. Bundesministerium fuer Port und Telekommunikation. Amtsblatt (0940-4848); Germany. Bundesminister fuer das Post- und Telekommunikation. Amtsblatt; Germany (Federal Republic, 1949-) Bundesministerium fuer das Post- und Fernmeldewesen. Amtsblatt (0003-2263)
Published by: Regulierungsbehoerde fuer Telekommunikation und Post, Tulpenfeld 4, Bonn, 53113, Germany. TEL 49-228-140, FAX 49-228-148975, poststelle@regtp.de, http://www.regtp.de.

383 BEL
REVUE DE LA POSTE/TIJDSCHRIFT VAN DE POST. Text in French. 1937. bi-m. free. adv. bk.rev. **Document type:** *Bulletin.*
Formerly: Revue des Postes Belges - Tijdschrift der Belgische Posterijen (0778-3817)
Published by: La Poste, Direction de la Communication, Centre Monnaie, Brussels, 1000, Belgium. TEL 32-2-2262205, FAX 32-2-2262173, post.com@pophost.eunet.be, http://www.post.be. Ed. Fred Lens. Pub., R&P Monique Van Trappen. Circ: 70,000.

383.4 USA
RHODE ISLAND POSTAL HISTORY JOURNAL. Text in English. 1987. q. USD 16 membership; USD 21 foreign membership. back issues avail. **Document type:** *Academic/Scholarly.*
Published by: Rhode Island Postal History Society, c/o Thomas Greene, Ed, Box 113822, North Providence, RI 02911. TEL 401-353-1161, TGBG@aol.com. Ed. Thomas E Greene.

SCOTTISH POSTMARK GROUP. HANDBOOK. see *PHILATELY*

383 ESP
SPAIN. DIRECCION GENERAL DE CORREOS Y TELECOMUNICACION. BOLETIN OFICIAL DE CORREOS Y TELECOMUNICACION. Text in Spanish. 1975. s-w.
Formerly: Spain. Direccion General de Correos y Telecomunicacion. Boletin Oficial. Telecomunicacion
Published by: Direccion General de Correos y Telecomunicacion, Madrid, Spain.

383 USA
STAR CARRIER. Text in English. 1937. m. free to members. adv. index. **Document type:** *Trade.* **Description:** Provides news of association activities and relevant legislative changes.
Published by: National Star Route Mail Contractors Association, 324 E Capitol St, Washington, DC 20003. TEL 202-543-1661, FAX 202-543-8863. Ed. John V Maraney. Circ: 5,000 (controlled).

383 DEU ISSN 0720-4183
STUDIEN UND QUELLEN ZUR POSTGESCHICHTE. REIHE A: FORSCHUNGEN. Text in German. 1979. irreg., latest vol.4, 1981. price varies. **Document type:** *Monographic series, Academic/Scholarly.*
Supersedes in part (in 1981): Studien und Quellen zur Postgeschichte (0172-5327)
Published by: Verlag Michael Lassleben, Lange Gasse 19, Kallmuenz, 93183, Germany. TEL 49-9473-205, FAX 49-9473-8357, druckerei@oberpfalzverlag-lassleben.de, http://www.oberpfalzverlag-lassleben.de.

383 DEU ISSN 0720-4191
STUDIEN UND QUELLEN ZUR POSTGESCHICHTE. REIHE B: FAKSIMILEDRUCKE. Text in German. 1979. irreg., latest vol.2, 1984. price varies. **Document type:** *Monographic series, Academic/Scholarly.*
Supersedes in part (in 1981): Studien und Quellen zur Postgeschichte (0172-5327)
Published by: Verlag Michael Lassleben, Lange Gasse 19, Kallmuenz, 93183, Germany. TEL 49-9473-205, FAX 49-9473-8357, druckerei@oberpfalzverlag-lassleben.de, http://www.oberpfalzverlag-lassleben.de.

383 GBR ISSN 0039-4335
SUB-POSTMASTER. Text in English. 1897. m. GBP 25. adv. charts; stat. index. **Document type:** *Newspaper.*
Published by: National Federation of Sub-Postmasters, Evelyn House, 22 Windlesham Gardens, Shoreham-by-Sea, Sussex BN43 5AZ, United Kingdom. TEL 44-1273-452324, FAX 44-1273-465403, nfsp@subpostmasters.org.uk, http://www.subpostmasters.org.uk. Ed. Malcolm Roger. Adv. contact Lesley Hogan. B&W page GBP 1,740; trim 274 x 368. Circ: 21,000 (controlled).

383 DEU
TELEFAXBUCH DER DEUTSCHEN TELEKOM AG. Text in German. 1984. a. adv. **Document type:** *Directory.*
Formerly: Amtliches Telefax- und Telebriefverzeichnis der Deutschen Bundespost Telecom
Related titles: CD-ROM ed.; Online - full text ed.
Published by: Deutsche Telekom Medien GmbH, Wiesenhuettenstr 18, Frankfurt Am Main, 60329, Germany. TEL 49-69-26821805, FAX 49-69-26821801. Ed. Christine Pechel. Adv. contact Manfred Skudrzek.

383 CHE ISSN 0041-7009
HE6251.A1
UNION POSTALE. Text and summaries in Arabic, Chinese, English, French, German, Russian, Spanish. 1875. 3/m. CHF 21. adv. film rev. bibl.; illus. index. **Document type:** *Bulletin.*
Published by: Universal Postal Union/Union Postale Universelle, Weltpoststr 4, Bern 15, 3000, Switzerland. TEL 41-31-350-3111, FAX 41-31-350-3110, TELEX 912 761 UPU CH, publications@upu.int, http://www.upu.int. Circ: 4,000.

383 CHE ISSN 0252-3973
UNION POSTALE UNIVERSELLE. ACTES. Text in French. 1874. quinquennial. CHF 220 (effective 1999).
Formerly: Universal Postal Union. Documents du Congres (0083-3878)
Related titles: Spanish ed.: Union Postal Universal. Actas. ISSN 1010-7428; English ed.: Universal Postal Union. Acts. ISSN 0252-3981.
Published by: Universal Postal Union/Union Postale Universelle, Weltpoststr 4, Bern 15, 3000, Switzerland. TEL 41-31-350-3111, FAX 41-31-350-3110, publications@upu.int, http://www.upu.int.

383 CHE ISSN 0252-3752
UNION POSTALE UNIVERSELLE. STATISTIQUE DES SERVICES POSTAUX. Text in English, French. 1966. a. CHF 75.
Related titles: Microfiche ed.: (from CIS).
Indexed: IIS.
Published by: Universal Postal Union/Union Postale Universelle, Weltpoststr 4, Bern 15, 3000, Switzerland. TEL 41-31-350-31111, FAX 41-31-350-3110, publications@upu.int, http://www.upu.int. Circ: 870.

383 CHN ISSN 1000-6559
XIANDAI TONGXIN/COMMUNICATIONS TODAY. Text in Chinese. 1981. m. CNY 12. adv. **Document type:** *Government.*
Related titles: Online - full text ed.: (from East View Information Services).
—Linda Hall.
Published by: Zhongguo Tongxin Xuehui/Chinese Society of Communications, No 8 Lane 232 Bei Suzhou Lu, PO Box 085 253, Shanghai, 200009, China. TEL 86-21-6324-0842, FAX 86-21-6324-8733, sptjph@publicsta.net.ca. Ed. Xunjiong Zhong. Adv. contact Lihua Feng. Circ: 100,000.

383 ZMB
ZAMBIA. POSTS AND TELECOMMUNICATIONS CORPORATION. ANNUAL REPORT. Text in English. 1963. a.
Document type: *Government.*
Formerly (until 1974): Zambia. General Post Office. Annual Report of the Postmaster-General (0084-5019)
Published by: Posts and Telecommunications Corporation, c/o Director-General, PO Box 71630, Ndola, Zambia.

383 CHN ISSN 1002-2287
ZHONGGUO YOUZHENG/CHINA POSTAL AFFAIRS. Text in Chinese. 1990. m. CNY 72 (effective 2004). **Document type:** *Trade.*
Related titles: Online - full text ed.: (from East View Information Services).
Published by: Renmin Youdian Chubanshe/People's Posts and Telecommunications Publishing House, 14 A Xizhaosi Street, Chongwen District, Beijing, 100061, China. chnpost@public.bta.net.cn, abc@ptpress.com.cn, http://www.ptpress.com.cn/. Ed. Bai Jinliang. **Dist. by:** China International Book Trading Corp, 35 Chegongzhuang Xilu, Haidian District, PO Box 399, Beijing 100044, China. TEL 86-10-68412045, FAX 86-10-68412023, cibtc@mail.cibtc.com.cn, http://www.cibtc.com.cn.

C

COMMUNICATIONS—Radio

621.384 384.5 USA
THE A A R L'S F C C RULE BOOK; complete guide to the Federal Communications Commission regulations. Text in English. irreg., latest vol.11. USD 12 (effective 1999).
Document type: *Government.* **Description:** Compiles and organizes all U.S. Federal Communications Commission (FCC) rules governing amateur radio operators.
Published by: American Radio Relay League, Inc., 225 Main St, Newington, CT 06111. TEL 860-594-0200, 888-277-5289, FAX 860-594-0303, http://www.arrl.org. R&P Mark Wilson.

384.5 USA ISSN 0044-7676
A F T R A. Text in English. 1937. 3/yr. free to members (effective 2005). adv. bk.rev. charts; illus. **Document type:** *Magazine, Trade.* **Description:** Union publication with relevant information on contracts, negotiations, etc.
Formerly: American Federation of Television and Radio Artists. A F T R A
Published by: American Federation of Television and Radio Artists, 260 Madison Ave, 7th Fl, New York, NY 10016-2401. TEL 212-532-0800, FAX 212-532-2242, http://www.aftra.org/news/magazine.htm. Ed. Dick Moore. Circ: 85,000 (controlled).

621.384 USA ISSN 1047-3076
A M S A T JOURNAL. Text in English. 1989. bi-m. USD 39 membership; USD 45 in Canada membership; USD 50 elsewhere membership (effective 2005). **Description:** Publishes articles of interest to users of amateur satellites for ham radio broadcasting and reception.
Published by: Radio Amateur Satellite Corporation, 850 Sligo Ave, Ste 600, Silver Spring, MD 20910. TEL 301-589-6062, 888-322-6728, FAX 301-608-3410, callsign@amsat.org, http://www.amsat.org.

621.38 USA
A M S A T SPACE SYMPOSIUM PROCEEDINGS. (Amateur Satellite) Text in English. 198?. a. USD 15 domestic; USD 20 in Canada & Mexico; USD 25 elsewhere. back issues avail.
Document type: *Proceedings.* **Description:** Presents research regarding the use of satellite transmission among amateur-radio broadcasters and listeners.
Published by: American Radio Relay League, Inc., 225 Main St, Newington, CT 06111. TEL 860-594-0200, 888-277-5289, FAX 860-594-0303, http://www.arrl.org. R&P Mark Wilson.

621.384 USA
A N S BULLETIN. Text in English. 1994. w. free. back issues avail. **Document type:** *Bulletin.* **Description:** Offers amateur radio satellite enthusiasts updates on information of interest.
Media: Online - full text. **Related titles:** E-mail ed.

Published by: (AMSAT News Service), Radio Amateur Satellite Corporation, 850 Sligo Ave, Ste 600, Silver Spring, MD 20910. FAX 301-608-3410, callsign@amsat.org, http://www.amsat.org.

384.54 USA
A P R A NEWS. Text in English. m.
Published by: American Private Radio Association, Inc., PO Box 4221, Scottsdale, AZ 85261-4221. TEL 602-947-1100, FAX 602-947-3131. Ed. Mark W Dobronski. Circ: 9,000.

A R A LOG. see *LABOR UNIONS*

384 DEU ISSN 0066-5746
A R D - JAHRBUCH. Text in German. 1969. a. **Document type:** *Yearbook, Trade.*
Published by: (Arbeitsgemeinschaft der Oeffentlich-Rechtlichen Rundfunkanstalten der Bundesrepublik Deutschland), Hans Bredow Institut, Heimhuder Str 21, Hamburg, 20148, Germany. TEL 49-40-45021741, FAX 49-40-45021777, nomos@nomos.de, http://www.nomos.de. Ed. Horst Halefeldt. Circ: 13,000. **Subscr. to:** NOMOS Verlag, Postfach 610, Baden-Baden 76484, Germany. TEL 49-7221-2104-0, FAX 49-7221-210427.

621.38 USA ISSN 1048-1699
TK6565.A6
THE A R R L ANTENNA BOOK. Text in English. 1939. irreg. USD 30 (effective 1999). **Document type:** *Bulletin.* **Description:** Includes information on designing, building and installing all types of attenas, both low- and high-frequency.
Published by: American Radio Relay League, Inc., 225 Main St, Newington, CT 06111. TEL 860-594-0200, 888-277-5289, FAX 860-594-0303, rdstraw.arrl.org, pubsales@arrl.org, http://www.arrl.org. Ed. R Dean Straw. R&P Mark Wilson.

621.38 USA ISSN 1054-9293
TK9956
A R R L - D X X C COUNTRIES LIST. Text in English. irreg. **Document type:** *Directory.*
Published by: American Radio Relay League, Inc., 225 Main St, Newington, CT 06111. TEL 860-594-0200, 888-277-5289, FAX 860-594-0303, rdstraw.arrl.org, pubsales@arrl.org, http://www.arrl.org. R&P Mark Wilson. **Co-sponsor:** D X Century Club.

621.384 USA
A R R L DIGITAL COMMUNICATIONS CONFERENCE. Text in English. a. USD 15. back issues avail. **Document type:** *Proceedings.*
Formerly (until 1993): A R R L Computer Networking Conference (1080-5117)
Published by: American Radio Relay League, Inc., 225 Main St, Newington, CT 06111. TEL 860-594-0200, 888-277-5289, FAX 860-594-0303, rdstraw.arrl.org, pubsales@arrl.org, http://www.arrl.org. R&P Mark Wilson.

621.384 USA ISSN 0890-3565
TK6550
A R R L HANDBOOK FOR RADIO AMATEURS; the standard in applied electronics and communications. Text in English. 1926. a. USD 32 (effective 1999). illus. index. **Document type:** *Bulletin.* **Description:** Discusses all aspects of building, maintaining, and using ham radios.
Formerly (until 1985): Radio Amateur's Handbook (0079-9440)
Related titles: CD-ROM ed.: USD 49.95.
—Linda Hall.
Published by: American Radio Relay League, Inc., 225 Main St, Newington, CT 06111. TEL 860-594-0200, 888-277-5289, FAX 860-584-0303, rdstraw.arrl.org, pubsales@arrl.org, http://www.arrl.org. Ed. Paul Danzer. R&P Mark Wilson. Circ: 30,000.

621.38 USA
A R R L LICENSE MANUAL SERIES. Text in English. a. price varies. **Document type:** *Academic/Scholarly.* **Description:** Offers amateur radio operators advice and study guides to help them get their various class licenses.
Formerly: Radio Amateur's License Manual
Published by: American Radio Relay League, Inc., 225 Main St, Newington, CT 06111. TEL 860-594-0200, 888-277-5289, FAX 860-594-0303, rdstraw.arrl.org, pubsales@arrl.org, http://www.arrl.org. Ed. Larry Wolfgang. R&P Mark Wilson.

621.38 USA
A R R L NATIONAL EDUCATIONAL WORKSHOP PROCEEDINGS. Text in English. 1989. a. USD 12 (effective 1999). back issues avail. **Document type:** *Proceedings.* **Description:** Provides a forum in which enthusiasts of amateur radio can share ideas, thoughts, and experiences, enabling volunteer instructors will gain valuable knowledge for their classes.
Published by: American Radio Relay League, Inc., 225 Main St, Newington, CT 06111. TEL 860-594-0200, FAX 530-594-0303, http://www.arrl.org. R&P Mark Wilson.

621.384 384.5 USA
THE A R R L NET DIRECTORY. Text in English. irreg., latest 1998. USD 4. **Document type:** *Directory.* **Description:** Lists a wealth of amateur radio nets of interest to ham radio operators in North America.
Published by: American Radio Relay League, Inc., 225 Main St, Newington, CT 06111. TEL 860-594-0200, 888-277-5289, FAX 860-594-0303, http://www.arrl.org. R&P Mark Wilson.

621.384 USA
(YEAR) A R R L PERIODICALS CD-ROM; all (year) issues of three ARRL periodicals on one CD-ROM. Text in English. 1996. a. USD 29.95 to non-members; USD 19.95 to members. illus. index. back issues avail. **Document type:** *Consumer.* **Description:** Offers ham-radio enthusiasts the full text of QST, QEX, and the National Contest Journal with searchable keywords.
Media: CD-ROM.
Published by: American Radio Relay League, Inc., 225 Main St, Newington, CT 06111. TEL 860-594-0200, 888-277-5289, FAX 860-594-0303, rdstraw.arrl.org, pubsales@arrl.org, http://www.arrl.org. R&P Mark Wilson.

621.38 USA ISSN 0190-3632
THE A R R L REPEATER DIRECTORY; the authoritative source of VHF-UHF repeater listings. Text in English. a. USD 8 (effective 1999). **Document type:** *Directory.* **Description:** Lists nearly 21,000 FM voice and ATP repeaters located throughout the Americas. Includes updated listings of frequency coordinators.
Published by: American Radio Relay League, Inc., 225 Main St, Newington, CT 06111. TEL 860-594-0200, 888-277-5289, FAX 860-594-0303, rdstraw.arrl.org, pubsales@arrl.org, http://www.arrl.org. Ed. Jay Mabey. R&P Mark Wilson. Circ: 55,000.

A V MAGAZINE. see *COMMUNICATIONS—Television And Cable*

621.384 DEU ISSN 1684-9965
▼ ➤ **ADVANCES IN RADIO SCIENCE - KLEINHEUBACHER BERICHTE.** Text in English. 2003. irreg. **Document type:** *Journal, Academic/Scholarly.*
Related titles: Online - full text ed.: ISSN 1684-9973. free (effective 2005).
Published by: (Landesausschuss in der Bundesrepublik Deutschland e.V.), Copernicus GmbH, Max-Planck Str 13, Katlenburg-Lindau, 37191, Germany. TEL 49-5556-91099, info@copernicus.org, http://www.copernicus.org/URSI/ars/ars.html.

384.5 IND ISSN 0002-3620
AKASHI. Text in Assamese. 1959. fortn. INR 6. adv. bk.rev. charts; illus.
Published by: All India Radio, Akashvani Bhavan, Eden Gardens, Kolkata, West Bengal 700 001, India. Ed. S C Basu. Circ: 175.

384.54 USA
ALL OHIO SCANNER CLUB NEWSLETTER∗. Text in English. 1979. bi-m. USD 18.50 domestic; USD 22 in Canada & Mexico; USD 30 elsewhere. adv. **Document type:** *Newsletter.* **Description:** Covers Ohio plus Illinois, Indiana, Kentucky, Michigan, Pennsylvania, West Virginia and Ontario. Nationwide coverage of federal government, military, land, sea and air transportation.
Published by: All Ohio Scanner Club, 20 Philip Dr, New Carlisle, OH 45544-9108. Ed., Pub., R&P, Adv. contact Dave Marshall. Circ: 200.

384.5 CZE ISSN 0322-9572
AMATERSKE RADIO. Text in Czech. 1952. m. USD 44 (effective 1996).
Indexed: RASB.
Published by: Vydavatelstvi Magnet Press, Vladislavova 26, Prague, 11366, Czech Republic. TEL 42-2-24239435, FAX 42-2-261226. Ed. Miroslav Wagner. Circ: 80,000.

621.384 CZE ISSN 0139-7087
AMATERSKE RADIO PRO KONSTRUKTERY. Text in Czech. 1965. bi-m. USD 23 (effective 1996).
Formerly (until 1976): Radiovy Konstrukter (0033-8516)
Published by: Vydavatelstvi Magnet Press, Vladislavova 26, Prague, 11366, Czech Republic. TEL 42-2-24239435, FAX 42-2-261226. Ed. Miroslav Wagner. Circ: 50,000.

621.384 AUS ISSN 0002-6859
AMATEUR RADIO. Text in English. 1933. m. AUD 60. adv. bk.rev. abstr.; charts; illus. cum.index every 5 yrs. **Description:** A radio communication service for self training, intercommunication and technical investigation carried by amateurs.
Indexed: Pinpoint.
Published by: Wireless Institute of Australia, PO Box 2175, Caulfield Junction, VIC 3161, Australia. TEL 61-3-95285962, FAX 61-3-95238191. Ed. W Rice. Circ: 5,000.

621.384 GBR ISSN 0264-2557
CODEN: AMRDEE
AMATEUR RADIO. Text in English. 1982. m. GBP 10.80. adv.
Indexed: Inspec.
Published by: Goodhead Publications Ltd., 27 Murdock Rd, Bicester, Oxon OX6 7PP, United Kingdom. Ed. Richard Lamont. Circ: 30,000.

AMATEUR RADIO SERVICE MASTER FILE UPDATES. see *COMMUNICATIONS—Abstracting, Bibliographies, Statistics*

384.5 USA
AMATEUR RADIO TRADER. Text in English. 2000. s-m. adv. **Document type:** *Magazine, Trade.*
Published by: T A P Publishing Co., 174 Fourth St, Crossville, TN 38555. TEL 931-484-5137, 800-337-5263, FAX 931-484-2532, 800-423-9030. Ed. Nick Smith.

AMERICAN RADIO. see *COMMUNICATIONS—Abstracting, Bibliographies, Statistics*

384.54 USA
AMERICAN SCANNERGRAM∗. Text in English. bi-m. USD 18.50 to members. **Document type:** *Newsletter.* **Description:** Helps the beginners in the scanning hobby, including topics about antennas and other improved reception techniques, and other subjects that are technical in nature.
Published by: All Ohio Scanner Club, 20 Philip Dr, New Carlisle, OH 45544-9108. Ed. Dave Marshall. Circ: 867.

ANTENA DE PROFESIONALES, DE RADIO Y TELEVISION. see *COMMUNICATIONS—Television And Cable*

ANTENNA SURVEY TOWER FILE. see *COMMUNICATIONS—Abstracting, Bibliographies, Statistics*

384.54 USA ISSN 8750-7471
ANTIQUE RADIO CLASSIFIED. Text in English. 1984. m. USD 39.49 domestic; USD 51 in Canada; USD 58 elsewhere (effective 2000). adv. bk.rev. back issues avail. **Description:** Covers old radios, TVs ham equipment, 40s and 50s radios, telegraph equipment, and books.
Published by: John V. Terrey, Ed.& Pub., PO Box 2, Carlisle, MA 01741. TEL 978-371-0512, FAX 978-371-7129, arc@antiqueradio.com, http://www.antiqueradio.com. Ed., Pub., R&P John V Terrey. Adv. contact Cindie Bryan.

384.5 SGP
ASIA IMAGE. Text in English. 1995. m. USD 100 (effective 2001). adv. illus. **Document type:** *Magazine, Trade.* **Description:** Business magazine for creative professionals in Asia's broadcast, production and post-production industries.
Published by: Cahners Asia Ltd. (Singapore), 58A Smith Street, Singapore, 058962, Singapore. TEL 65-223-8823, FAX 65-220-5015, asiai@asiai.com.sg, http://www.ai-interactive.com, http://www.cahners.com. Ed. France Lee. Pub. Jonathan Hallett. Adv. contact Geraldine Mahalingam. B&W page USD 4,741, B&W page GBP 2,964, color page USD 5,414, color page GBP 3,413; trim 335 x 245. Circ: 5,537 (controlled).

ASIA - PACIFIC BROADCASTING. see *COMMUNICATIONS—Television And Cable*

384.5 RUS
ASSOTSYATSIYA RADIO. VESTNIK. Text in Russian. s-a.
Published by: Assotsiatsiya Radio, B Cherkasskii per 7-8, Moscow, 103012, Russian Federation. TEL 7-095-9232638, FAX 7-095-9214450. **US dist. addr.:** East View Information Services, 3020 Harbor Ln. N., Minneapolis, MN 55447. TEL 612-550-0961.

AUDIO PROGRAMMERS' DATABASE. see *MUSIC*

AUDIOPHILE. see *SOUND RECORDING AND REPRODUCTION*

AUSTRALIA. BUREAU OF STATISTICS. TELEVISION SERVICES, AUSTRALIA. see *COMMUNICATIONS—Abstracting, Bibliographies, Statistics*

791.450711 AUS ISSN 0819-2316
AUSTRALIAN FILM, TELEVISION AND RADIO SCHOOL ANNUAL REPORT. Text in English. 1972. a. free. back issues avail. **Document type:** *Corporate.* **Description:** Reports on the year's activities at the school.
Former titles (until 1986): Australian Film and Television School Annual Report (0728-6619); (until 1976): Film and Television School Annual Report (0819-2286); Australian Film and Television School. Interim Council. Annual Report (0310-8376)
Published by: Australian Film Television and Radio School, PO Box 126, North Ryde, NSW 1670, Australia. TEL 61-2-98056611, FAX 61-2-98871030, meredith.quinn@syd.aftrs.edu.au, meredithq@aftrs.edu.au, http://www.aftrs.edu.au. Pub., R&P Meredith Quinn. Circ: 1,200.

791.450711 AUS ISSN 1035-1019
AUSTRALIAN FILM, TELEVISION AND RADIO SCHOOL HANDBOOK. Text in English. 1978. a. free. back issues avail. **Document type:** *Directory.* **Description:** Description of courses, activities and resources of the school.
Formerly: Australian Film and Television School Handbook (0313-8461)
Published by: Australian Film Television and Radio School, PO Box 126, North Ryde, NSW 1670, Australia. TEL 61-2-98056611, FAX 61-2-98871030, meredith.quinn@syd.aftrs.edu.au, meredithq@aftrs.edu.au, http://www.aftrs.edu.au. Ed. R McHugh. Pub., R&P Meredith Quinn. Circ: 1,000.

AVIATION MASTER FILE. see *COMMUNICATIONS—Abstracting, Bibliographies, Statistics*

C

384.54 GBR
B B C AL-MUSHAHID. Text in Arabic. 1995. w. USD 150. adv. **Document type:** *Consumer.* **Description:** Contains current-affairs and general-interest articles and TV listings of interest to Arabic-speaking persons.
Published by: (British Broadcasting Corp., Arabic Service), Media World Services Ltd., Awdry House, 11 Kingsway, London, WC2B 6YE, United Kingdom. TEL 0171-240-4550, FAX 0171-240-4607. Ed. Nasr Al Majali. Pub. Ken Whittingham.

384.54 GBR ISSN 1365-1978
PN1991
B B C ON AIR. Text in English. 1996. m. GBP 20, USD 32 (effective 2000); GBP 2 newsstand/cover. adv. illus. reprints avail. **Document type:** *Consumer.* **Description:** Serves as the international programme guide for the BBC. Contains comprehensive program schedules for BBC World Service radio, and BBC World and BBC Prime television channels. Includes advice on how best to receive the output as well as previews and background information.
Supersedes (in 1996): B B C Worldwide (0967-5442); Which was formerly (until 1992): London Calling (0024-600X)
Indexed: RASB.
Published by: British Broadcasting Corp., Bush House NW, Rm 310, Strand, London, WC2B 4PH, United Kingdom. TEL 44-20-7557-2875, FAX 44-20-7240-4899, on.air.magazine@bbc.co.uk, http://www.bbc.co.uk/worldservice/onair. Ed. Kirsty Cockburn. Adv. contact Adam Ford.

791.44 USA ISSN 1063-1011
B R E. (Black Radio Exclusive) Text in English. 1976. w. (46/yr.). USD 200 domestic; USD 375 in Canada; USD 400 elsewhere (effective 2004). adv. bk.rev.; dance rev.; film rev.; music rev.; play rev.; tel.rev.; video rev. charts; illus.; mkt.; stat. back issues avail. **Document type:** *Magazine, Consumer.* **Description:** Covers the entire spectrum of the black music industry, with particular emphasis on the importance of black radio.
Former titles (until 1988): Black Radio Exclusive (0745-5992); Sidney Miller's Black Radio Exclusive (0161-1526)
Related titles: Online - full text ed.
Indexed: EngInd.
Published by: Sidney Miller's Black Radio Exclusive Corp., 15030 Ventura Blvd, Ste 864, Sherman Oaks, CA 91403-2444. TEL 818-907-9959, FAX 818-907-9958, bremagazine@aol.com, http://www.bremagazine.com. Ed., Adv. contact Susan Miller. Pub. Sidney Miller. B&W page USD 2,900, color page USD 3,600; trim 11.75 x 8.75.

BACON'S RADIO - T V - CABLE DIRECTORY. see *COMMUNICATIONS—Television And Cable*

384.5 GBR
BERNARDS AND BABANI PRESS RADIO & ELECTRONICS & COMPUTER BOOKS. Text in English. 1942. 20/yr. price varies. **Document type:** *Monographic series.*
Formerly: Bernards and Babani Press Radio and Electronics Books
Published by: Bernard Babani (Publishing) Ltd., The Grampians, Shepherds Bush Rd, London, W6 7NF, United Kingdom. TEL 44-20-7603-2581, FAX 44-20-7603-8203.

384.5 IND ISSN 0005-9773
BETAR JAGAT. Text in Bengali. 1929. fortn. INR 20. adv. bk.rev. charts; illus.
Published by: All India Radio, Akashvani Bhavan, Eden Gardens, Kolkata, West Bengal 700 001, India. Ed. A B Ganguly. Circ: 33,000.

384.5 USA ISSN 0006-0194
BETTER RADIO AND TELEVISION. Text in English. 1960. q. USD 6. bk.rev. illus.
—Linda Hall.
Published by: National Association for Better Broadcasting, PO Box 43640, Los Angeles, CA 90043. Ed. Frank Orme. Circ: 2,500.

BOOKING. see *BUSINESS AND ECONOMICS—Trade And Industrial Directories*

BRAILLE RADIO TIMES. see *HANDICAPPED—Visually Impaired*

621.38 NZL ISSN 0006-9523
BREAK-IN. Text in English. 1928. bi-m. NZD 95 membership (effective 2005). adv. bk.rev.; software rev. charts; illus. Index. 48 p./no.; back issues avail. **Document type:** *Journal, Consumer.* **Description:** Contains technical construction articles, news and general operating information.
—CCC.
Published by: New Zealand Association of Radio Transmitters, Inc., PO Box 1733, Christchurch, New Zealand. TEL 64-3-3489084, FAX 64-3-3489480, break-in@nzart.org.nz, http://www.nzart.org.nz/NZART/Breakin/. Ed. John Walker. Circ: 2,100.

384.5 NLD
BREAKER; kontaktorgaan voor radiocommunicatie. Text in Dutch. 10/yr. bk.rev.
Published by: J.V.D. Berg Ed. & Pub., Brittenburg 2, Gouda, 2804 ZX, Netherlands. Circ: 250.

384.5 USA
BROADCAST ARCHIVE. Text in English. irreg. free.
Media: Online - full text.
Address: 2033 S. Augusta Pl., Tuscon, AZ 85710. barry@broadcast.net, http://www.oldradio.com. Ed. Barry Mishkind.

BROADCAST ENGINEERING; the journal of digital television. see *COMMUNICATIONS—Television And Cable*

384.5 GBR ISSN 0269-493X
BROADCAST HARDWARE INTERNATIONAL. Text in English. 1986. bi-m. GBP 66. adv. back issues avail. **Document type:** *Trade.* **Description:** Offers the international broadcast engineering industry information and news, as well as detailed equipment descriptions and updates.
Related titles: ♦ Supplement(s): Broadcast Hardware's U K Network. ISSN 0953-7627.
Indexed: RefZh.
Published by: Hardware Magazine Co. Ltd., 48 Broadway, Maidenhead, Berks SL6 1PW, United Kingdom. TEL 44-1628-773935, FAX 44-1628-773537. Ed. David Sparks. R&P Cathy Ward. Adv. contact Peter Gorland. Circ: 15,500.

384.5 GBR ISSN 0953-7627
BROADCAST HARDWARE'S U K NETWORK. Text in English. 1988. bi-m. free to subscribers of Broadcast Hardware International. adv. **Document type:** *Trade.* **Description:** Offers news and information on U.K. product launches, recent equipment installations and major hardware sales to engineers, executives, and equipment users in broadcast, video productions, and video-audio postproduction fields in the U.K. and Ireland.
Related titles: ♦ Supplement to: Broadcast Hardware International. ISSN 0269-493X.
Published by: Hardware Magazine Co. Ltd., 48 Broadway, Maidenhead, Berks SL6 1PW, United Kingdom. TEL 44-1628-773935, FAX 44-1628-773537. Ed. David Sparks. R&P Cathy Word. Adv. contact Peter Gorland.

BROADCAST INVESTOR; newsletter on radio-TV station finance. see *BUSINESS AND ECONOMICS—Investments*

BROADCAST REGULATION. see *COMMUNICATIONS—Television And Cable*

BROADCASTER. see *COMMUNICATIONS—Television And Cable*

BROADCASTER DIRECTORY. see *COMMUNICATIONS—Television And Cable*

BROADCASTING & CABLE. see *COMMUNICATIONS—Television And Cable*

BROADCASTING & CABLE INTERNATIONAL. see *COMMUNICATIONS—Television And Cable*

BROADCASTING: TELEVIDENIE I RADIOVESHCHANIE. see *COMMUNICATIONS—Television And Cable*

384.54 USA ISSN 0746-8911
TK6540
BUSINESS RADIO✶. Text in English. 1965. 10/yr. USD 65. adv. bk.rev. illus. **Document type:** *Trade.* **Description:** Offers information of interest to two-way radio dealers, tower and site managers, operators of private carrier paging and specialized mobile radio systems, technicians, wireless systems integrators, system users, manufacturers and suppliers of mobile communications equipment and services.
Former titles: Business Radio - Action (0093-0245); Action (0567-8412)
Published by: Personal Communications Industry Association (P C I A), 500 Montgomery St, Ste 700, Alexandria, VA 22314. TEL 703-739-0300, FAX 703-836-1608. Ed. A E Goetz. Adv. contact Robin E Little. Circ: 3,000.

384.4 DEU ISSN 0938-4022
C B FUNK. Text in German. m. **Document type:** *Magazine, Consumer.*
Published by: Verlag fuer Technik und Handwerk GmbH, Robert-Bosch-Str 4, Baden-Baden, 76532, Germany. TEL 49-7221-50870, FAX 49-7221-508752, verlag@vth.de, http://www.vth.de. Ed. Michael Buege. **Subscr. to:** P M S GmbH & Co. KG, Postfach 104139, Duesseldorf 40032, Germany. TEL 49-211-6907890, FAX 49-211-69078950.

384.4 DEU
C B-KURIER. Text in German. q. EUR 18.50; EUR 4.80 newsstand/cover (effective 2005). adv. **Document type:** *Magazine, Consumer.* **Description:** Provides information and features on various aspects of CB radios.
Published by: CB-Kurier, Postfach 1201, Weissach, 71287, Germany. TEL 49-7044-33441, FAX 49-7044-33441, info@cb-kurier.de, http://www.cb-kurier.de.

384.54 USA
THE C B RADIO STORY. (Citizens Band) Text in English. 1998. m. free. back issues avail. **Document type:** *Consumer.* **Description:** Offers articles for enthusiasts of citizens band radios.
Published by: C B Radio Story, 3416 Columbus Ave 108, Sandusky, OH 44870-5598. dougd@cros.net, http://www.cros.net/dougd/cb.htm.

384.5 USA
C C I R PLENARY ASSEMBLY (PROCEEDINGS). Text in English. quadrennial.
Formerly: C C I R Green Books
Published by: (International Telecommunication Union, International Radio Consultative Service), U.S. Department of Commerce, National Technical Information Service, 5285 Port Royal Rd, Springfield, VA 22161. TEL 703-605-6000, info@ntis.gov, http://www.ntis.gov. **Subscr. outside N. America to:** International Telecommunication Union, Place des Nations, Geneva 20 1211, Switzerland.

621.38 CAN ISSN 0045-3706
C I D X MESSENGER. Text in English. 1962. m. membership. adv. bk.rev.
Media: Duplicated (not offset).
Published by: Canadian International DX Radio Club, 169 Grandview Ave, Winnipeg, MB R2G 0L4, Canada. Ed. R L Jennings. Circ: 1,100.

621.384 USA ISSN 0007-893X
TK6540 CODEN: CQCQAO
C Q; the radio amateurs' journal. Text in English. 1945. m. USD 31.95 domestic; USD 44.95 in Canada & Mexico; USD 56.95 elsewhere (effective 2005). adv. bk.rev. charts; illus. reprints avail. **Document type:** *Magazine, Consumer.* **Description:** For radio amateurs who are actively involved in operating, building and using amateur radio equipment and related devices.
Incorporates: C Q: V H F Ham Radio Above 50 MHZ (1085-0708)
Indexed: IHTDI, Inspec.
—AskIEEE, CISTI, Ei, IE, Infotrieve, Linda Hall.
Published by: C Q Communications, Inc., 25 Newbridge Rd, Ste 405, Hicksville, NY 11801-2805. TEL 516-681-2922, 800-853-9797 (orders only), FAX 516-681-2926, w2vu@cq-amateur-radio.com, http://www.cq-amateur-radio.com. Ed. Richard Moseson. Pub. Richard A Ross. Adv. contacts Arnie Sposato, Donald R Allen. Circ: 90,000 (paid).

621.384 USA ISSN 1085-0716
C Q CONTEST; people - analysis - techniques - reporting - technology. (Communications Quarterly) Text in English. 1996. 10/yr. USD 30 domestic; USD 40 in Canada & Mexico; USD 42.95 elsewhere (effective 2000). **Document type:** *Consumer.*
Published by: C Q Communications, Inc., 25 Newbridge Rd, Ste 405, Hicksville, NY 11801-2805. TEL 516-681-2922, 800-853-9797, FAX 516-681-2926, cq@cq-amateur-radio.com, http://www.cq-amateur-radio.com.

621.384 DEU ISSN 0178-269X
C Q - D L. Text in German. 1928. m. EUR 49.40 to non-members (effective 2003). adv. bk.rev. charts; illus.; tr.lit. index, cum.index: 1951-1954, 1955-1959, 1960-1965, 1966-1970. **Document type:** *Bulletin, Consumer.*
Formerly: D L - Q T C (0011-4995)
—IE.
Published by: Deutscher Amateur-Radio-Club, Lindenallee 6, Baunatal, 34225, Germany. TEL 49-561-9498894, FAX 49-561-9498861, redaktion@darc.de, http://www.darc.de/cqdl, http://www.cqdl.de. Ed. Harry Radke. Adv. contact Claudia Levien. B&W page EUR 1,660, color page EUR 2,581. Circ: 50,945 (controlled).

621.384 JPN ISSN 0007-8964
C Q HAM RADIO. Text in Japanese. 1954. m. JPY 13,680. charts; illus. **Description:** Provides the latest technology, trends and equipments on ham radio.
Published by: C Q Publishing Co., 14-2 Sugamo 1-chome, Toshima-ku, Tokyo, 170-0002, Japan. TEL 81-3-5395-2149, FAX 81-3-5395-2100. Ed. Tadayuki Tominaga. adv.: B&W page USD 1,750, color page USD 5,775; trim 7.19 x 10.13. Circ: 97,331. **Dist. outside Japan by:** Nippon IPS Co. Ltd., 11-6 Iida-Bashi 3-chome, Chiyoda-ku, Tokyo 102-0072, Japan. TEL 81-3-3238-0700, 81-3-3238-7944.

384.5 ESP ISSN 0212-4696
C Q RADIO AMATEUR. Text in Spanish. 1971. m. EUR 43 domestic; EUR 52.79 in Europe; EUR 79.08, USD 95 rest of world (effective 2005). bk.rev. abstr.; charts; illus.; stat. index. back issues avail. **Document type:** *Consumer.* **Description:** Publishes everything related to all amateur communications systems.
Indexed: Inspec.
—CCC.
Published by: Cetisa Editores S.A., Enrique Granados, 7, Barcelona, 08019, Spain. TEL 34-93-2431040, FAX 34-93-3492350, cqra@cetisa.com, info@cetisa.com, http://www.cq-radio.com/, http://www.cetisa.com/. Ed. Miquel Pluvinet. R&P Lluis Lleida. Adv. contact Nuria Bora. Circ: 11,500 (controlled).

C R A F NEWS. (Committee on Radio Astronomy Frequencies) see *ASTRONOMY*

C

CANADA. STATISTICS CANADA. RADIO AND TELEVISION BROADCASTING/CANADA. STATISTIQUE CANADA. RADIODIFFUSION ET TELEVISION. see *COMMUNICATIONS—Abstracting, Bibliographies, Statistics*

621.38 CAN ISSN 0318-0867
THE CANADIAN AMATEUR✶; Canadian amateur radio from coast to coast. Short title: T C A. Text in English. 1973. m. (Jul.& Aug. combined). CND 28. adv. bk.rev.
Incorporates: V E News (0049-576X)
Published by: (Canadian Amateur Radio Federation Inc.), C A R F Publications Ltd., 71 Main St, P O Box 730, Bloomfield, ON K0K 1G0, Canada. TEL 613-545-9100. Ed. George Sansom. Circ: 5,000.

621.38 CAN
CANADIAN AMATEUR ADVANCED STUDY GUIDE✶. Text in English. 1976. a. CND 33.
Published by: Radio Amateurs of Canada, Inc., 720 Belfast Rd, Ste 217, Ottawa, ON K1G 0Z5, Canada. TEL 613-244-4360. Ed. Debbie Norman. Circ: 10,000.

621.38 CAN
CANADIAN AMATEUR STUDY GUIDE FOR THE BASIC QUALIFICATION✶. Text in English. 1976. a. CND 33.
Supersedes: Canadian Amateur Certificate Study Guide
Published by: Radio Amateurs of Canada, Inc., 720 Belfast Rd, Ste 217, Ottawa, ON K1G 0Z5, Canada. TEL 613-244-4367. Ed. Debbie Norman. Circ: 15,000.

CHAMPS DE L'AUDIOVISUELS. see *COMMUNICATIONS—Video*

CHART MAGAZINE; Canada's music magazine. see *MUSIC*

CIRCUIT FERME; journal des employes de Radio-Canada. see *BUSINESS AND ECONOMICS—Personnel Management*

621.384 USA ISSN 1053-9433
TK5101.A1
➤ **COMMUNICATIONS QUARTERLY**; a journal of communications technology. Text in English. 1990. q. USD 33 domestic; USD 39 in Canada & Mexico; USD 46 elsewhere (effective 2005). **Document type:** *Magazine, Academic/Scholarly.* **Description:** Technically oriented amateur radio magazine that offers in-depth coverage of the science of communications.
Supersedes (in 1990): Ham Radio Magazine (0148-5989); Which was formerly (1968-1969): Ham Radio (0017-6842); And incorporated (1977-198?): Ham Radio Horizons (0147-8818)
—CISTI, Linda Hall.
Published by: American Association of Retired Persons, 601 E St, NW, Washington, DC 20049. TEL 202-434-2277, FAX 202-434-6881, cq@cq-amateur-radio.com, http://www.cq-amateur-radio.com, http://www.aarp.org. Circ: 8,100.

621.38 USA ISSN 1075-5721
COMMUNICATIONS STANDARDS SUMMARY. Text in English. 1994. q. USD 325 (effective 2000). back issues avail. **Document type:** *Directory.* **Description:** Directory of all Telecommunications Industry Association active datacom and telecom standards projects.
Published by: Telcordia Standards Knowledgebase (Subsidiary of: Telcordia Technologies, Inc), 664 Kaimalino St., Kailua, HI 96734. TEL 866-875-4636, chalevi@telcordia.com, http://tsk.telcordia.com. Circ: 150 (paid).

384.5 IND
COMMUNICATOR (NEW DELHI). Text in English. 1966. q. INR 80, USD 30 (effective 2000). bk.rev. bibl. index. **Description:** Covers radio and other media in India.
Published by: Indian Institute of Mass Communication, Aruna Asaf Ali Marg, J N U New Campus, New Delhi, 110 067, India. TEL 91-11-6107492. Ed. Subhash Dhuliya.

384.5 USA ISSN 1041-7117
PN4841
COMMUNICATOR (WASHINGTON, 1988). Text in English. 1946. m. USD 75 to non-members; free to members (effective 2005). adv. bk.rev. abstr.; bibl.; illus. back issues avail. **Document type:** *Magazine, Trade.*
Formerly (until 1988): R T N D A Communicator (0033-7153); Which superseded (in 1971): R T N D A Bulletin
Published by: Radio - Television News Directors Association, 1600 K St NW, Ste 700, Washington, DC 20006-2806. TEL 202-659-6510, FAX 202-223-4007, rtnda@rtnda.org, http://www.rtnda.org. Ed. Noreen Welle. Adv. contact Rich Harless. B&W page USD 1,925, color page USD 3,015. Circ: 3,500 (paid).

384.54 USA ISSN 1089-8263
HE8698
COMMUNITY RADIO NEWS. Text in English. 1974. m. USD 75 to non-members. adv. **Document type:** *Newsletter.* **Description:** Covers public radio policy and issues. Includes information on programming, fundraising, management, volunteer coordination, and production.
Former titles: N F C B News; N F C B Newsletter
Published by: National Federation of Community Broadcasters, Ft Mason Center, Bldg D, San Francisco, CA 94123. TEL 415-771-1160. Ed., Pub., R&P Sean Simplicio. Circ: 500.

384.5 CRI
CONTRAPUNTO. Text in Spanish. 1978. fortn.
Published by: (Sistema Nacional de Radio y Television), Uruca, Apdo. 7-1980, San Jose, Costa Rica. TEL 31-3333. Ed. Fabio Munoz Campos. Circ: 10,000.

CONVERGENCE; the journal of research into new media technologies. see *COMMUNICATIONS—Television And Cable*

384.5453 DEU
DAMPF-RADIO. Text in German. w. EUR 130 (effective 2005). adv. **Document type:** *Magazine, Consumer.* **Description:** Contains listings and descriptions of radio programs broadcast throughout Germany.
Published by: Dampf-Radio Marketing, Pfarrer-Reinartz-Str 7, Kall-Heistert, 53925, Germany. TEL 49-2444-911330, FAX 49-2444-911332, radioprogramm@dampf-radio.de, http://www.dampf-radio.de. Adv. contact Christoph Chur.

DENPA GIJUTSU KYOKAIHO/RADIO ENGINEERING AND ELECTRONICS ASSOCIATION. JOURNAL. see *ELECTRONICS*

DENPA KOHO/ELECTRONIC NAVIGATION REVIEW. see *TRANSPORTATION—Ships And Shipping*

621.384 JPN
DENPA TAIMUZU/DENPA TIMES. Text in Japanese. 1950. 3/w. JPY 3,200 per month.
Address: 23-12 Nishi-Shinbashi 3-chome, Minato-ku, Tokyo, 105-0003, Japan.

621.384 CHN ISSN 1005-0388
DIANPO KEXUE XUEBAO/CHINESE JOURNAL OF RADIO SCIENCE. Text in Chinese. 1986. q. CNY 14 newsstand/cover (effective 2005). **Document type:** *Journal, Academic/Scholarly.*
Related titles: Online - full text ed.: (from East View Information Services, WanFang Data Corp.).
—BLDSC (3580.139270).
Published by: (Zhongguo Dianzi Xuehui/Chinese Institute of Electronics), Dianpo Kexue Xuebao, PO Box 138-3, Xinxiang, 453003, China. TEL 86-373-3712409, FAX 86-373-3052232, xuebao@public.xxptt.ha.cn, http://dbkxxb.periodicals.net.cn/.

384.5443 384.5452 CHE ISSN 1021-3465
PN1992.3.E78
DIFFUSION (ENGLISH EDITION). Text in English. 1992. q.
Related titles: Online - full text ed.: ISSN 1609-1159; ♦ French ed.: Diffusion (French Edition). ISSN 1021-3457.
—BLDSC (3584.249000).
Published by: European Broadcasting Union/Union Europeenne de Radio-Television, Ancienne Route 17 A, Case Postale 67, Grand Saconnex - Geneva, 1218, Switzerland. TEL 41-22-7172111, FAX 41-22-7172481, http://www.ebu.ch/.

384.5443 384.5452 CHE ISSN 1021-3457
DIFFUSION (FRENCH EDITION). Text in French. 1992. q.
Related titles: Online - full text ed.: ISSN 1609-1167; ♦ English ed.: Diffusion (English Edition). ISSN 1021-3465.
Published by: European Broadcasting Union/Union Europeenne de Radio-Television, Ancienne Route 17 A, Case Postale 67, Grand Saconnex - Geneva, 1218, Switzerland. TEL 41-22-7172111, FAX 41-22-7172481, http://www.ebu.ch/.

DIRECTORY OF RELIGIOUS MEDIA. see *BUSINESS AND ECONOMICS—Trade And Industrial Directories*

DIRITTO DELLE RADIODIFFUSIONI E DELLE TELECOMUNICAZIONI. see *LAW*

384.5 DNK
DOMESTIC BROADCASTING SURVEY. Text in English. 1999. a., latest vol.5, 2003. DKK 40, USD 5, EUR 5, GBP 3 (effective 2003). 48 p./no.; **Document type:** *Directory.* **Description:** Of interest to listeners to domestic radio stations broadcasting on shortwave between 2200 and 30000 kHz.
Media: E-mail.
Published by: Danish Shortwave Club International, c/o Bent Nielsen, Egekrogen 14, Vaerloese, 3500, Denmark. TEL 45-43-394052, FAX 45-43-394888, anker.petersen@get2net.dk, http://www.dswci.dk. Ed. Anker Petersen.

DUNCAN'S RADIO MARKET GUIDE. see *BUSINESS AND ECONOMICS—Trade And Industrial Directories*

621.38 DEU ISSN 0175-6877
DX MAGAZINE; monthly magazine for international radio-telecommunication. Text mainly in English; Text occasionally in German. 1966. m. EUR 15.60 in Europe membership; EUR 20.40 elsewhere membership (effective 2005). adv. bk.rev. 32 p./no.; back issues avail. **Document type:** *Magazine, Trade.* **Description:** Contains news about national and international radio stations, especially on longwave, mediumwave and shortwave.
Indexed: IHTDI.
Published by: Worldwide DX Club, Postfach 1214, Bad Homburg, 61282, Germany. TEL 49-6172-390918, FAX 49-6102-800999, info@wwdxc.de, http://www.wwdxc.de. Ed., R&P, Adv. contact Michael Bethge. Circ: 500.

384.5 USA ISSN 0899-9732
DX MONITOR✶. Text in English. 1964. 34/yr. USD 25. adv. bk.rev. charts; illus. back issues avail. **Description:** Covers the hobby of listening to distant stations on the AM broadcast band.
Published by: International Radio Club of America, PO Box 1831, Perris, CA 92572-1831. Ed. Ralph Sanserino. Circ: 275.

384.54 CAN ISSN 1183-0344
DX ONTARIO; monitoring the world via radio. Text in English. 1975. m. CND 35, USD 28 (effective 1999). adv. bk.rev. index. **Document type:** *Newsletter.* **Description:** Provides transmission schedules, program information, equipment reviews and station profiles on international shortwave broadcasting and radio communications.
Related titles: Magnetic Tape ed.
Published by: Ontario DX Association, P O Box 161, Sta A, Willowdale, ON M2N 5S8, Canada. odxa@compuserve.com, http://www.durhamradio.com/odxa. Ed., R&P, Adv. contact Harold Sellers. page CND 50. Circ: 1,300.

621.384 GBR ISSN 1740-1615
E R T WEEKLY; the only weekly serving the electrical retailing industry. (Electrical and Radio Trading) Text in English. 1890. 48/yr. GBP 93 domestic; GBP 127, USD 231 foreign; USD 3 newsstand/cover (effective Oct. 2004). adv. bk.rev. illus.; tr.lit. Supplement avail. **Document type:** *Magazine, Trade.* **Description:** Electrical retail magazine covering all aspects of the UK market.
Formerly (until 1995): Electrical and Radio Trading (0013-4228)
Related titles: Online - full content ed.; Online - full text ed.: (from Gale Group).
Indexed: B&I.
Published by: D M G Business Media Ltd. (Subsidiary of: D M G World Media Ltd.), Queensway House, 2 Queensway, Redhill, Surrey RH1 1QS, United Kingdom. TEL 44-1737-768611, FAX 44-1737-855477, info@uk.dmgworldmedia.com, http://www.ertweekly.com/, http://www.dmgworldmedia.com/BusinessMediaPublications.html. Eds. Anthony Clark TEL 44-20-85156885, Sean Hannam TEL 44-1737-855375. adv.: page GBP 3,444; trim 210 x 297. Circ: 8,083.

E-RADIO; the business of audio on the internet. see *COMPUTERS—Internet*

384.5 621.381 500 AUS
▼ **E S R.** Variant title: Electronic - Science - Radio. Text in English. 2003. m. AUD 69 domestic; AUD 80 in New Zealand & SE Asia; AUD 95 elsewhere in New Zealand & SE Asia (effective 2003). **Document type:** *Magazine, Academic/Scholarly.*
Address: PO Box 288, Beerwah, QLD 4519, Australia. TEL 300-736-566, editor@esr-mag.com, http://www.esr-mag.com/.

621.38 USA
EASTERN V H F - U H F CONFERENCE PROCEEDINGS. (Very High Frequency - Ultra High Frequency) Text in English. 197?. a. USD 15 (effective 1999). back issues avail. **Document type:** *Proceedings.* **Description:** Publishes papers on all aspects of amateur radio broadcasting, on both VHF and UHF frequencies.
Published by: American Radio Relay League, Inc., 225 Main St, Newington, CT 06111. TEL 860-594-0200, FAX 860-594-0303, http://www.arrl.com. R&P Mark Wilson. **Co-sponsor:** Eastern VHF-UHF Society, North East Weak Signal Group.

621.384 NLD ISSN 0013-4767
ELECTRON; maandblad voor de Nederlandse radio-amateur. Text in Dutch. 1945. m. EUR 41 to members (effective 2005). adv. bk.rev. charts; illus.; tr.lit. index. **Document type:** *Newsletter, Consumer.* **Description:** For radio amateurs. Covers technology, amateur satellites, antennas, international news, reports of events and contest results. Includes a calendar of events and association library news.
Published by: Vereniging voor Experimenteel Radio Onderzoek in Nederland, Postbus 1166, Arnhem, 6801 BD, Netherlands. TEL 31-26-4426760, FAX 31-26-3685865, redactie@mailelectron.org, info@veron.nl, http://www.veron.nl/electron/. Ed. G J Huijsman. Circ: 13,000.

ELEKTRO JOURNAL. see *COMMUNICATIONS—Television And Cable*

ELEKTRONICA; markt en techniek. see *ELECTRONICS*

ELEKTRONIKKBRANSJEN. see *ELECTRONICS*

621.384 621.388 RUS ISSN 0013-5771
TK5101.A1 CODEN: EKVZAO
ELEKTROSVYAZ'. Text in Russian. 1938. m. USD 257 foreign (effective 2005). adv. bk.rev. charts; illus. index. **Document type:** *Journal, Trade.* **Description:** Devoted to wire communication, radio communication, TV and radio broadcasting.
Related titles: ♦ English Translation: Telecommunications and Radio Engineering. ISSN 0040-2508.

Indexed: BrCerAb, C&ISA, CerAb, ChemAb, CorrAb, E&CAJ, EMA, Englnd, Inspec, M&TEA, MBF, METADEX, RefZh, SolStAb, WAA.
—BLDSC (0399.030000), AskIEEE, CINDOC, CISTI, East View, Linda Hall. **CCC.**
Published by: (Nauchno-Tekhnicheskoe Obshchestvo Radiotekhniki, Elektroniki i Svyazi im. A.S. Popova), Izdatel'stvo Radio i Svyaz', Kuznetskii Most 20/6, Moscow, 103031, Russian Federation. TEL 7-095-9258436, FAX 7-095-9245290, elsv@garnet.ru. Ed. V A Shamshin. Circ: 4,000. **Dist. by:** East View Information Services, 3020 Harbor Ln. N., Minneapolis, MN 55447. TEL 800-477-1005, FAX 800-800-3839, eastview@eastview.com, http://www.eastview.com.

EMC/ESD - PRAKTIJK. (Electromagnetic Compatibility/ Electrostatic Discharge) see *ELECTRONICS*

EMIRATES TV & RADIO/TELFUZOON WA EDHA'AH. see *COMMUNICATIONS—Television And Cable*

791.4 USA ISSN 0014-5971
F M GUIDE✶. (NY Edition) Text in English. 1962. m. USD 10. adv. film rev.; play rev.
Indexed: CMPI.
Published by: Hampton International Communications, 1350 N Kolb Rd, Ste 220, Tucson, AZ 85715-4944. Circ: 72,000.

384.5 FRA
F M MAGAZINE. Text in French. 4/yr.
Address: B.P. 28, Paris, Cedex 8 75362, France. TEL 42-93-39-45. Ed. Chris Simon. Circ: 8,000.

FACE TO FACE WITH TALENT. see *COMMUNICATIONS—Television And Cable*

FAMILY RADIO NEWS. see *RELIGIONS AND THEOLOGY*

FINE MUSIC; 2 M B S Sydney. see *MUSIC*

384.5 USA ISSN 0890-6718
FMEDIA!; the FM radio newsletter. Text in English. 1987. m. USD 75 (effective 2005). illus. 8 p./no.; reprints avail. **Document type:** *Newsletter, Consumer.* **Description:** Contains fact and opinion about FM radio and related technologies.
Published by: F M Atlas Publishing, PO Box 336, Esko, MN 55733-0336. TEL 218-879-7676, FAX 218-879-8333, FmAtlas@aol.com, http://users.aol.com/fmatlas/. Ed., R&P Bruce F Elving. Circ: 300 (paid and controlled).

384.5 USA
FOLIO (NORTH HOLLYWOOD). Text mainly in English; Text occasionally in Spanish. 195?. m. USD 50 to members. adv. back issues avail.
Formerly: Folio - K P F K (0274-4856)
Related titles: Audio cassette/tape ed.
Published by: K P F K - F M (Pacifica Radio), 3729 Cahuenga Blvd West, North Hollywood, CA 91604. TEL 818-985-2711, FAX 818-763-7526, comments@kpfk.org. Ed. Jill Smolin. Circ: 16,000.

384.54 DEU ISSN 0342-1651
FUNK; das internationale Magazin der Funktechnik. Text in German. 1977. m. EUR 43.20 domestic; EUR 49.20 foreign; EUR 4 newsstand/cover (effective 2005). adv. **Document type:** *Magazine, Consumer.*
Incorporates (1981-1994): Beam (0722-0421); (1979-1980): Drahtlos (0720-6291); Which was formerly (until 1979): C B Europa Journal (0720-9908)
Published by: Verlag fuer Technik und Handwerk GmbH, Robert-Bosch-Str 4, Baden-Baden, 76532, Germany. TEL 49-7221-50870, FAX 49-7221-508752, verlag@vth.de, http://www.vth.de/funk. Ed. Michael Buege. Adv. contact Peter Kuepper. B&W page EUR 1,193, color page EUR 1,491. Circ: 20,000 (paid and controlled). **Subscr. to:** P M S GmbH & Co. KG, Postfach 104139, Duesseldorf 40032, Germany. TEL 49-211-6907890, FAX 49-211-69078950.

384.5 DEU ISSN 0016-2833
CODEN: FUAMBU
FUNK AMATEUR; das Magazin fuer Funk - Elektronik - Computer. Text in German. 1952. m. adv. charts; illus. **Document type:** *Magazine, Consumer.* **Description:** Contains articles and features on all aspects of radio, electronics and computers for hobbyists.
Indexed: Inspec, RefZh.
Published by: Theuberger Verlag GmbH, Berliner Str 69, Berlin, 13189, Germany. TEL 49-30-44669460, FAX 49-30-44669469, info@funkamateur.de, http://www.funkamateur.de. Ed. Bernd Petermann. Circ: 40,000 (paid). **Dist. by:** ASV Vertriebs GmbH, Suederstr 77, Hamburg 20097, Germany. TEL 49-40-3472573.

384.5 DEU
FUNK - SPOT; Radioservice des Instituts der deutschen Wirtschaft. Text in German. w. **Document type:** *Bulletin, Trade.*
Published by: (Institut der Deutschen Wirtschaft), Deutscher Instituts Verlag GmbH, Gustav-Heinemann-Ufer 84-88, Cologne, 50968, Germany. TEL 49-221-4981510, FAX 49-221-4981533, div@iwkoeln.de, http://www.iwkoeln.de.

201.6 DEU
FUNKKORRESPONDENZ. Text in German. w. EUR 368.46 to individuals; EUR 474 to institutions; EUR 162 to students (effective 2003). adv. **Document type:** *Newspaper, Consumer.*
Published by: Katholisches Institut fuer Medieninformation GmbH, Am Hof 28, Cologne, 50667, Germany. TEL 49-221-9254630, FAX 49-221-92546337, info@kim-info.de, http://funkkorrespondenz.kim-info.de, http://www.kim-info.de. Ed. Dieter Anschlag. Adv. contact Petra Herrmann. B&W page EUR 600; trim 150 x 263. Circ: 850 (paid).

G B C RADIO AND T V TIMES. see *COMMUNICATIONS—Television And Cable*

621.384 JPN
GEKKAN MUSEN SHUCHI/MONTHLY NEWS ON RADIO. Text in Japanese. 1933. m. JPY 800 per issue. **Document type:** *Bulletin.*
Published by: (Senpaku Tsushinshi Rodo Kumiai/Marine Radio Officer's Union), Musen Tsushinsha/Radio News Agency, 14-8 Shibaura 1-chome, Minato-ku, Tokyo, 105-0023, Japan. TEL 81-3-3451-4729, FAX 81-3-3451-4727. Ed. Koumei Kikuta.

384.5 ESP
GUIA DE LA RADIOAFICION Y C B. Text in Spanish. a. **Document type:** *Directory.*
Published by: Cetisa Editores S.A., Enrique Granados, 7, Barcelona, 08019, Spain. TEL 34-93-2431040, FAX 34-93-3492350, info@cetisa.com, http://www.cetisa.com/.

621.38 GBR ISSN 0269-8269
HAM RADIO TODAY. Text in English. 1983. m. GBP 26.50 domestic; GBP 36.50 in Europe; GBP 38.50 elsewhere (effective 1999); GBP 2.50 newsstand/cover. adv. bk.rev. back issues avail. **Document type:** *Consumer.* **Description:** Contains news, reviews, features and do-it-yourself projects for radio amateurs.
Published by: Radio Society of Great Britain, Lamgda House, Cranbourne Rd, Potters Bar, Herts EN6 3JE, United Kingdom. TEL 44-1707-853300, FAX 44-870-904-7373, hrt@rsgb.org.uk, http://www.rsgb.org. Ed. Steve Telenius Lowe. **Dist. by:** Comag, Tavistock Works, Tavistock Rd, W Drayton, Middx UB7 7QX, United Kingdom. TEL 44-1895-444055, FAX 44-1895-433602.

384 CAN
HANDBOOK ON RADIO FREQUENCY SPECTRUM REQUIREMENTS FOR CIVIL AVIATION. Text in English, French, Russian, Spanish. irreg., latest 2000, 2nd ed. CND 62 (effective 2000). **Document type:** *Academic/Scholarly.*
Published by: International Civil Aviation Organization, c/o Document Sales Unit, 999 University St, Montreal, PQ H3C 5H7, Canada. TEL 514-954-8022, FAX 514-954-6769, TELEX 05-24513, icaohq@icao.int.

384.5 USA
HEARTLAND✶. Text in English. 1990. m. free. adv. **Document type:** *Consumer.*
Published by: W F M S Radio, 6810 N Shadeland Ave, Indianapolis, IN 46220-4236. TEL 317-842-9550, FAX 317-577-3361. Adv. contact Kevin Isaacs. B&W page USD 3,500, color page USD 4,150; trim 16.75 x 11.38. Circ: 108,872 (controlled).

621.384 FIN ISSN 1456-3835
HELSINKI UNIVERSITY OF TECHNOLOGY. RADIO LABORATORY PUBLICATIONS. Text in English. 1989. irreg.
Former titles (until 1998): Helsinki University of Technology. Department of Electrical and Communications Engineering. Radio Laboratory. Report (1239-7350); (until 1996): Helsinki University of Technology. Faculty of Electrical Engineering. Radio Laboratory. Report (1237-4938)
Indexed: RefZh.
Published by: Helsinki University of Technology, Department of Electrical and Communications Engineering, Radio Laboratory, Otakaari 5 A, PO Box 3000, Espoo, 02015, Finland. TEL 358-9-4512251, FAX 358-9-4522152, pertti.vainikainen@hut.fi, http://www.hut.fi/Units/Radio/index-e.html. Ed. Vainikainen Pertti.

384.5 CHE
HIGH FREQUENCY BROADCASTING SCHEDULE. Text in English, French, Spanish. 1986. q. CHF 231.
Published by: International Telecommunication Union, Place des Nations, Geneva 20, 1211, Switzerland. TEL 41-22-7306141, FAX 41-22-7305194, sales@itu.ch, http://www.itu.int/publications.

384.5 NLD ISSN 1382-2160
HILVERSUMMARY. Text in English. 1987. q. looseleaf. free. **Document type:** *Newsletter, Trade.* **Description:** Provides information on developments in Dutch media, especially public service radio and TV of interest to foreign journalists and students of mass communications.
Related titles: Online - full text ed.
Published by: Nederlandse Omroep Stichting, Postbus 26444, Hilversum, 1202 JJ, Netherlands. TEL 31-35-6773197, FAX 31-35-6773586, louis.heinsman@qsd.nos.nl, http://www.omroep.nl/nos/rtv/voorlichting/hsumm. Ed. Louis Heinsman.

HISTORICAL JOURNAL OF FILM, RADIO AND TELEVISION. see *HISTORY*

HITMAKERS - WEEKLY TOP 40 RADIO & MUSIC INDUSTRY MAGAZINE. see *MUSIC*

384.5 USA
HOBBY BROADCASTING. Text in English. q.
Published by: Cabinet Communications, PO Box 642, Mont Alto, PA 17237. ayoder@cvn.net, http://www.frn.net/rfi. Ed. Andrew Yoder.

384.54 DEU ISSN 0179-1869
HOERUEBERSICHT INTERNATIONAL; aktuelle Programmzeitschrift des Deutschsprachigen internationalen Rundfunks. Text in German. 1978. q. USD 9. adv. bk.rev. back issues avail.
Published by: DX Listeners Service, Postfach 1122, Homberg, 34576, Germany. TEL 05684-8215. Circ: 3,000.

HORN SPEAKER; the newspaper for the hobbyist of vintage electronics and sound. see *ANTIQUES*

HUMO. see *COMMUNICATIONS—Television And Cable*

I A A I S NEWSLETTER. (International Association of Audio Information Services) see *HANDICAPPED—Visually Impaired*

384.5 USA
I E E E EMERGING TECHNOLOGIES ON WIRELESS COMMUNICATIONS AND SYSTEMS. Text in English. a. USD 110. **Document type:** *Proceedings, Trade.*
Published by: Institute of Electrical and Electronics Engineers, Inc., 3 Park Ave, 17th Fl, New York, NY 10016-5997. TEL 212-419-7900, 800-678-4333, FAX 212-752-4929, customer.service@ieee.org, http://www.ieee.org.

384.5 USA ISSN 1541-1354
TK5103.2
I E E E INTERNATIONAL CONFERENCE ON PERSONAL WIRELESS COMMUNICATIONS. PROCEEDINGS. Text in English. 1994. a. USD 194 per vol.; USD 97 per vol. to members (effective 2004). **Document type:** *Proceedings, Trade.*
Indexed: Englnd.
—BLDSC (4362.949750).
Published by: Institute of Electrical and Electronics Engineers, Inc., 3 Park Ave, 17th Fl, New York, NY 10016-5997. TEL 212-419-7900, 800-678-4333, FAX 212-752-4929, customer.service@ieee.org, http://www.ieee.org.

384.5 USA
I E E E INTERNATIONAL SYMPOSIUM PERSONAL, INDOOR AND MOBILE RADIO COMMUNICATIONS. Text in English. a. (in 3 vols.). USD 538; USD 269 to members (effective 2004). **Document type:** *Proceedings, Trade.*
Published by: Institute of Electrical and Electronics Engineers, Inc., 3 Park Ave, 17th Fl, New York, NY 10016-5997. TEL 212-419-7900, 800-678-4333, FAX 212-752-4929, customer.service@ieee.org, http://www.ieee.org.

384.5 USA
I E E E INTERNATIONAL SYMPOSIUM SPREAD SPECTRUM TECHNIQUES AND APPLICATIONS. Text in English. a. USD 256; USD 128 to members (effective 2004). **Document type:** *Proceedings, Trade.*
—BLDSC (4362.973100).
Published by: Institute of Electrical and Electronics Engineers, Inc., 3 Park Ave, 17th Fl, New York, NY 10016-5997. TEL 212-419-7900, 800-678-4333, FAX 212-752-4929, customer.service@ieee.org, http://www.ieee.org.

384.5 USA
I E E E - M T T S INTERNATIONAL TOPICAL SYMPOSIUM ON TECHNOLOGIES FOR WIRELESS APPLICATIONS. (Microwave Theory and Techniques Society) Text in English. a. **Document type:** *Proceedings, Trade.*
Indexed: Englnd.
Published by: Institute of Electrical and Electronics Engineers, Inc., 3 Park Ave, 17th Fl, New York, NY 10016-5997. TEL 212-419-7900, 800-678-4333, FAX 212-752-4929, customer.service@ieee.org, http://www.ieee.org.

384.5 USA
I E E E RADIO AND WIRELESS CONFERENCE. PROCEEDINGS. Text in English. a. USD 160; USD 80 to members (effective 2004). **Document type:** *Proceedings, Trade.*
Published by: Institute of Electrical and Electronics Engineers, Inc., 3 Park Ave, 17th Fl, New York, NY 10016-5997. TEL 212-419-7900, 800-678-4333, FAX 212-752-4929, customer.service@ieee.org, http://www.ieee.org.

791.4 IND ISSN 0019-4158
INDIA CALLING✶; overseas programme journal. Text in English. 1954. m. free. illus.
Published by: All India Radio, Akashvani Bhavan, Eden Gardens, Kolkata, West Bengal 700 001, India. Circ: 10,000.

INFORMAZIONE RADIO TV; studi documenti e notizie. see *COMMUNICATIONS—Television And Cable*

C

384.5 USA ISSN 0731-9312
INSIDE RADIO; the latest news, trends and management information. Text in English. 1987 (vol.12); N.S.. d. USD 375 (effective 2005). adv. **Document type:** *Newsletter, Trade.*
Incorporates (in 2002): M Street Daily
Media: E-mail. **Related titles:** Fax ed.
Published by: M Street Corporation, 81 Main St, Ste 2, Littleton, NH 03561. TEL 603-444-5720, FAX 603-444-2872, streaming@insideradio.com, http://www.insideradio.com, http://www.mstreet.net. Ed. Tom Taylor.

384.5 POL ISSN 0032-6259 CODEN: PITRAT
INSTYTUT TELE- I RADIOTECHNICZNY. PRACE. Contents page in English, Russian. 1957. q. PLZ 40. charts; illus. index.
Indexed: Inspec.
—AskIEEE, CISTI.
Published by: Instytut Tele-i Radiotechniczny, Ratuszowa 11, Warsaw, 03450, Poland. Circ: 370.

621.384 USA
INTERNATIONAL CALLBOOK✶. Text in English. 1920. a. USD 29.95; includes update Service Editions. adv.
Former titles: Foreign Callbook; Foreign Radio Amateur Callbook Magazine (0015-7260)
Published by: Radio Amateur Callbook, Inc., 575 Prospect St, Lakewood, NJ 08701-5040.

621.384 GBR ISSN 1745-3216
▼ ➤ **INTERNATIONAL JOURNAL OF RADIO FREQUENCY IDENTIFICATION TECHNOLOGY AND APPLICATIONS.** Text in English. 2005. q. USD 450 to institutions; USD 545 to institutions print & online eds. (effective 2005). **Document type:** *Journal, Academic/Scholarly.*
Related titles: Online - full text ed.: ISSN 1745-3224. USD 450 to institutions (effective 2005).
Published by: Inderscience Publishers, IEL Editorial Office, PO Box 735, Olney, Bucks MK46 5WB, United Kingdom. TEL 44-1234-240519, FAX 44-1234-240515, ijrfita@inderscience.com, info@inderscience.com, http://www.inderscience.com/ijrfita. **Subscr. to:** World Trade Centre Bldg, 29 route de Pre-Bois, Case Postale 896, Geneva 15 1215, Switzerland. FAX 41-22-7910885, subs@inderscience.com.

384.54 DEU ISSN 0178-9287
INTERNATIONAL LISTENING GUIDE; the basic directory of international short wave broadcasting. Text in English. 1978. q. USD 15. adv. back issues avail. **Document type:** *Directory.*
Published by: DX Listeners Service, Postfach 1122, Homberg, 34576, Germany. TEL 05684-8215. Ed. Bernd Friedewald. Circ: 4,500.

384.5 CHE
INTERNATIONAL RADIO CONSULTATIVE COMMITTEE. PLENARY ASSEMBLY. PROCEEDINGS. Text in English, French, Spanish; Text occasionally in Chinese. 1982 (15th). quadrennial. price varies. Supplement avail. **Document type:** *Proceedings.*
Published by: (International Radio Consultative Committee), International Telecommunication Union, Place des Nations, Geneva 20, 1211, Switzerland. TEL 41-22995111, FAX 41-22337256.

621.38 BEL
INTERNATIONAL UNION OF RADIO SCIENCE. RECORDS OF GENERAL ASSEMBLIES. Text in English. 1928. triennial. EUR 40 (effective 2001). **Document type:** *Proceedings.*
Formerly: International Union of Radio Science. Proceedings of General Assemblies (0074-9516)
Published by: International Union of Radio Science - URSI/Union Radio-Scientifique Internationale, Ghent University (INTEC), Sint Pietersnieuwstraat 41, Gent, 9000, Belgium. TEL 32-9-2643320, FAX 32-9-2644288, http://www.intec.rug.ac.be/ursi. Circ: 500.

INTERNATIONALES HANDBUCH FUER HOERFUNK UND FERNSEHEN. see *COMMUNICATIONS—Television And Cable*

AL-IZAA WAL-TELEVISION/RADIO AND TELEVISION. see *COMMUNICATIONS—Television And Cable*

621.384 UKR ISSN 0021-3470
TK6540 CODEN: IVUZB5
➤ **IZVESTIYA VYSSHIKH UCHEBNYKH ZAVEDENII. RADIOELEKTRONIKA.** Text in Ukrainian. 1958. bi-m. USD 184 foreign (effective 2005). charts. index. **Document type:** *Journal, Academic/Scholarly.* **Description:** Covers aspects of radio electronics. Generalizes experience in operation of microwave systems, computer-assisted designing of microwave devices, etc.
Related titles: ♦ English Translation: Radioelectronics and Communications Systems. ISSN 0735-2727.
Indexed: C&ISA, ChemAb, CurCont, Djerelo, E&CAJ, EngInd, INIS AtomInd, Inspec, RefZh, SolStAb.
—BLDSC (0077.780000), AskIEEE, CINDOC, CISTI, East View, IDS, Linda Hall. **CCC.**
Published by: Natsional'nyi Tekhnichnyi Universytet Ukrainy "Kyivs'kyi Politekhnichnyi Instytut", pr-kt Peremohy 37, Kyiv, 03056, Ukraine. TEL 380-44-2367989, post@ntu-kpi.kiev.ua, http://www.ntu-kpi.kiev.ua. **US dist. addr.:** East View Information Services, 3020 Harbor Ln. N., Minneapolis, MN 55447. TEL 763-550-0961, FAX 763-559-2931, eastview@eastview.com, http://www.eastview.com.

➤ **IZVESTIYA VYSSHIKH UCHEBNYKH ZAVEDENII. RADIOFIZIKA.** see *PHYSICS*

384.5 DEU ISSN 0948-3756
JAHRBUCH DER LANDESMEDIENANSTALTEN; privater Rundfunk in Deutschland. Text in German. 1988. a. **Document type:** *Directory, Trade.*
Formerly (until 1995): D L M Jahrbuch (0940-287X)
Published by: Arbeitsgemeinschaft der Landesmedienanstalten, c/o Hessische Landesanstalt fuer privaten Rundfunk, Wilhelmshoeher Allee 262, Kassel, 34131, Germany. TEL 49-561-9358615, FAX 49-561-9358633, dlm@lpr-hessen.de, http://www.alm.de.

384.5 USA ISSN 0010-1133
JOURNAL OF COLLEGE RADIO. Text in English. 1941-1982; resumed 1984-1987; resumed 1989. 4/yr. USD 12 (effective 2001). adv. bk.rev. abstr.; charts; illus.; tr.lit. **Document type:** *Journal, Academic/Scholarly.* **Description:** Contains articles for and about college radio stations.
Formerly: College Radio
Published by: Intercollegiate Broadcasting System, Inc., 367 Windsor Hwy, New Windsor, NY 12553-7900. TEL 845-563-0003, FAX 845-565-7446, ibshq@aol.com, http://www.ibsradio.org/. Ed. Jeffrey N Tellis. Pub., R&P Fritz Kass. Circ: 2,500.

384.5443 USA ISSN 1095-5046
PN1991.3.U6
JOURNAL OF RADIO STUDIES. Text in English. 1992. s-a. USD 75 in US & Canada to institutions; USD 105 elsewhere to institutions (effective 2006); USD 80 combined subscription in US & Canada to institutions print & online eds.; USD 110 combined subscription elsewhere to institutions print & online eds. (effective 2005). adv. bk.rev.; video rev. back issues avail. **Document type:** *Journal, Academic/Scholarly.* **Description:** Publishes studies of contemporary and historical radio broadcasting.
Related titles: Online - full text ed.: ISSN 1550-6843. USD 70 worldwide to institutions (effective 2006) (from EBSCO Publishing, O C L C Online Computer Library Center, Inc.).
Indexed: CommAb, PAIS, PSA.
—BLDSC (5043.870000).
Published by: (Broadcast Education Association), Lawrence Erlbaum Associates, Inc., 10 Industrial Ave, Mahwah, NJ 07430-2262. TEL 201-258-2200, 800-926-6579, FAX 201-236-0072, journals@erlbaum.com, http://www.leaonline.com/loi/jrs, http://www.erlbaum.com. Ed. Douglas A Ferguson. adv.: page USD 400; trim 5 x 8.

K P B S ON AIR. see *COMMUNICATIONS—Television And Cable*

KAGAN'S MEDIA TRENDS. see *COMMUNICATIONS—Television And Cable*

384.5 USA ISSN 1098-0989
KAGAN'S RADIO FINANCIAL DATABOOK. Variant title: Radio Financial Databook. Text in English. 1998. a. USD 1,295 (effective 2005). **Document type:** *Directory, Trade.*
Published by: Kagan Research, LLC, One Lower Ragsdale Dr, Bldg One, Ste 130, Monterey, CA 93940. TEL 831-624-1536, FAX 831-625-3225, info@kagan.com, http://www.kagan.com.

KATALOG MEDIOW POLSKICH. see *BIBLIOGRAPHIES*

KATSO. see *COMMUNICATIONS—Television And Cable*

621.38 629.44 USA
KEPLERIAN ELEMENTS. Text in English. w. free. charts; stat. back issues avail. **Document type:** *Bulletin.* **Description:** Enables enthusiasts of radio communications satellite broadcasting to use standard mathematical models to track a satellite's orbit and, thereby, know how to direct antennas.
Media: Online - full text. **Related titles:** E-mail ed.
Published by: Radio Amateur Satellite Corporation, 850 Sligo Ave, Ste 600, Silver Spring, MD 20910. FAX 301-608-3410, callsign@amsat.org, http://www.amsat.org.

KEY ABSTRACTS - ANTENNAS & PROPAGATION. see *COMMUNICATIONS—Abstracting, Bibliographies, Statistics*

621.388 GBR ISSN 1360-1881
KEY NOTE MARKET REPORT: BROADCASTING IN THE U K. Text in English. 1992. irreg., latest vol.2, 1995. GBP 565 per issue (effective 2002). **Document type:** *Trade.* **Description:** Provides an overview of a specific UK market segment and includes executive summary, market definition, market size, industry background, competitor analysis, current issues, forecasts, company profiles, and more.
Related titles: CD-ROM ed.; Online - full text ed.
—**CCC.**
Published by: Key Note Ltd., Field House, 72 Oldfield Rd, Hampton, Mddx TW12 2HQ, United Kingdom. TEL 44-20-8481-8750, FAX 44-20-8783-0049, info@keynote.co.uk, http://www.keynote.co.uk.

384.5 338 GBR
KEY NOTE MARKET REPORT: COMMERCIAL RADIO. Variant title: Commercial Radio Market Report. Text in English. irreg., latest 2000, Sept. GBP 340 per issue (effective 2002). **Document type:** *Trade.* **Description:** Provides an overview for the UK commerical radio market, including industry structure, market size and trends, developments, prospects, and major company profiles.
Formerly: Key Note Report: Commercial Radio
Related titles: CD-ROM ed.; Online - full text ed.
Published by: Key Note Ltd., Field House, 72 Oldfield Rd, Hampton, Mddx TW12 2HQ, United Kingdom. TEL 44-20-8481-8750, FAX 44-20-8783-0049, info@keynote.co.uk, http://www.keynote.co.uk. Ed. Nick Bardsley.

621.38 DEU
KLINGENFUSS (YEAR) GUIDE TO UTILITY RADIO STATIONS. Text in German. 1983. a. **Document type:** *Directory.*
Formerly (until 1994): Klingenfuss Guide to Utility Stations
Published by: Joerg Klingenfuss Publications, Hagenloher Str 14, Tuebingen, 72070, Germany.

621.38 FIN ISSN 0783-4632
KODINTEKNIIKKA. Text in Finnish. 1952. 8/yr. EUR 60 (effective 2005). adv. bk.rev. illus. **Document type:** *Magazine.*
Formerly (until 1987): Radiokauppias (0355-6735)
Published by: (Radioliikkeiden Liitto r.y./Radio Retailers Association), Kodintekniikkaliitto, Mannerheimintie 76 A, Helsinki, Finland. TEL 358-9-53052301, FAX 358-9-53052304, http://www.kodintekniikkaliitto.info. Ed. Kalevi Aro. adv.: color page EUR 2,455, B&W page EUR 1,360. Circ: 1,800.

384.5 USA
L C D. (Lowest Common Denominator) Text in English. 1983. 3/yr. USD 10; per issue contribution. adv. music rev. illus. **Document type:** *Newsletter.* **Description:** Program guide and articles of interest to listeners of independent, free-form radio station WFMU in the metro New York area.
Published by: W F M U, PO Box 1568, Montclair, NJ 07042. TEL 201-678-8264, wfmu@wfmu.org, http://www.wfmu.org. Ed. Rex Doane.

384.5 DEU
LANDESANSTALT FUER RUNDFUNK NORDRHEIN-WESTFALEN. SCHRIFTENREIHE MEDIENFORSCHUNG. Text in German. irreg., latest vol.47, 2003. price varies. **Document type:** *Monographic series, Academic/Scholarly.*
Published by: (Landesanstalt fuer Rundfunk Nordrhein-Westfalen), V S - Verlag fuer Sozialwissenschaften (Subsidiary of: Springer Science+Business Media), Abraham-Lincoln-Str 46, Wiesbaden, 65189, Germany. TEL 49-611-78780, FAX 49-611-7878400, info@vs-verlag.de, http://www.vs-verlag.de.

384.54 USA
THE LOWDOWN. Text in English. m.
Published by: Longwave Club of America, 45 Wildflower Rd, Levittown, PA 19057. Ed. Ken Stryker.

M A P S DATA BASE. (Mid-Atlantic Preservation Service) see *COMMUNICATIONS—Abstracting, Bibliographies, Statistics*

384.54 USA ISSN 1052-7109
HE8698
THE M STREET JOURNAL; radio's journal of record. Text in English. 1984. w. USD 159 (effective 2005). adv. illus. reprints avail. **Document type:** *Magazine, Trade.* **Description:** Reports on AM and FM stations' format, technical, call letter and ownership changes; major decisions and actions taken by the FCC regarding radio broadcasting each week.
Related titles: Online - full text ed.
Published by: M Street Corporation, 81 Main St, Ste 2, Littleton, NH 03561. TEL 603-444-5720, FAX 603-444-2872, info@mstreetjournal.com, streaming@insideradio.com, http://www.mstreetjournal.com, http://www.mstreet.net. Ed. Tom Taylor. Adv. contacts Pat McCrummen, Beth Dell' Isola. Circ: 1,100 (paid).

384.54 USA ISSN 1052-7117
HE8698
THE M STREET RADIO DIRECTORY. Text in English. a. USD 65. adv. **Document type:** *Directory.* **Description:** Presents a guide to all radio stations in the US and Canada.
Published by: M Street Corporation, 81 Main St, Ste 2, Littleton, NH 03561. TEL 603-444-5720, FAX 603-444-2872, streaming@insideradio.com, http://www.mstreet.net. Ed., Pub. Robert Unmacht. Adv. contact Pat McCrummen.

384.5 USA
MANAGER'S BUSINESS REPORT. Text in English. 1997. m. USD 105 (effective 2000). adv. **Document type:** *Trade.* **Description:** Covers management and operation issues pertaining to the radio.
Address: PO Box 782, Springfield, VA 22150. TEL 703-719-9500, FAX 703-719-7910, radiobiz@aol.com, http://www.rbr.com. Ed. Jack Messmer. Pub. Jim Carnegie. R&P Ken Lee. Adv. contact John Neff. Circ: 5,000.

384.5443 USA
MANUAL OF REGULATIONS & PROCEDURES FOR FEDERAL RADIO FREQUENCY MANAGEMENT. Text in English. base vol. plus irreg. updates. looseleaf. USD 313 (effective 2001). **Document type:** *Government.* **Description:** Covers the regulation of Federal interstate and foreign telecommunications.
Related titles: Online - full content ed.
Published by: National Telecommunications and Information Administration (Subsidiary of: U.S. Department of Commerce), Rm 4898, 1401 Constitution Ave, NW, Washington, DC 20230. TEL 202-482-7002, http://www.ntia.doc.gov/osmhome/redbook/redbook.html. **Subscr. to:** U.S. Government Printing Office, Superintendent of Documents, PO Box 371954, Pittsburgh, PA 15250-7954. TEL 202-512-1800, FAX 202-512-2250, orders@gpo.gov, http://www.access.gpo.gov.

MARINE DATA BASE. see *COMMUNICATIONS—Abstracting, Bibliographies, Statistics*

MASTER FREQUENCY DATA BASE (FREQUENCY SEQUENCE). see *COMMUNICATIONS—Abstracting, Bibliographies, Statistics*

MASTER FREQUENCY DATA BASE (SERVICE GROUP CODE SEQUENCE). see *COMMUNICATIONS—Abstracting, Bibliographies, Statistics*

MEDIA & MEDIA. see *MUSIC*

384.5 DEU ISSN 1610-0840
P92.G4
MEDIA-DATEN: RADIO - T V. Text in German. 1961. 7/yr. EUR 126; EUR 43 newsstand/cover (effective 2003). adv. **Document type:** *Directory, Trade.*
Former titles (until 2002): Media-Daten: Radio - T V - Video (0935-5936); (until 1988): Media-Daten: Radio - T V (0931-3257); Which superseded in part (in 1985): Media-Daten: Zeitungen - Radio - T V - Anzeigenblaetter (0931-3184); Which was formerly (until 1980): Media-Daten: Zeitungen, Radio und T V (0170-4184); Which superseded in part (in 1976): Media-Daten (0543-2405)
Published by: Media-Daten Verlag GmbH (Subsidiary of: Springer Science+Business Media), Postfach 1546, Wiesbaden, 65173, Germany. TEL 49-611-78780, FAX 49-611-7878465, info@media-daten.de, http://www.media-daten.de. adv.: B&W page EUR 2,385, color page EUR 3,615. Circ: 1,154 (paid).

384.5 643 NLD
MEDIA NETWORK RECEIVER SHOPPING LIST; consumer survey of shortwave portable radios for international radio listening. Text in English. 1980. s-a. free. **Document type:** *Catalog.*
Published by: Stichting Radio Nederland Wereldomroep, Public Relations Dept, PO Box 222, Hilversum, 1200 JG, Netherlands. TEL 31-35-6724211, FAX 31-35-6724239, letters@rnw.nl. Ed. Jonathan Marks. Circ: 45,000.

MEDIA PROFESSIONAL. see *JOURNALISM*

MEDIAWEEK. see *JOURNALISM*

384.5 DEU ISSN 1615-634X
HE8690
MEDIEN UND KOMMUNIKATIONSWISSENSCHAFT. Text in German. 1953. q. EUR 73; EUR 45 to students; EUR 22 newsstand/cover (effective 2004). adv. **Document type:** *Journal, Academic/Scholarly.*
Formerly (until 2000): Rundfunk und Fernsehen (0035-9874)
Indexed: DIP, IBR, IBSS, IBZ, IIFP, IITV, RASB, RILM, SociolAb.
—BLDSC (5534.257100), IE, ingenta. **CCC.**
Published by: (Hans Bredow Institut), Nomos Verlagsgesellschaft mbH und Co. KG, Waldseestr 3-5, Baden-Baden, 76530, Germany. TEL 49-7221-20140, FAX 49-7221-210427, nomos@nomos.de, http://www.nomos.de. Ed. Christiane Matzen. Adv. contact Bettina Kohler. page EUR 650; trim 135 x 200. Circ: 1,300 (paid and controlled).

MERCATOR MEDIA FORUM. see *COMMUNICATIONS—Television And Cable*

384.54 USA
MICROWAVE LICENSES ISSUED. Text in English. m. USD 25 in North America; USD 40 elsewhere (effective 1999).
Media: Microfiche. **Related titles:** Supplement(s): Microwave Licenses Issued Report.
Published by: (Federal Communications Commission), U.S. Department of Commerce, National Technical Information Service, 5285 Port Royal Rd, Springfield, VA 22161. TEL 703-605-6000, info@ntis.gov, http://www.ntis.gov.

621.38 USA
MICROWAVE UPDATE. Text in English. a. USD 15 (effective 1999). back issues avail. **Document type:** *Proceedings.* **Description:** Publishes papers presented on amateur-radio broadcasting on microwave frequencies.
Published by: American Radio Relay League, Inc., 225 Main St, Newington, CT 06111. TEL 860-594-0200, 888-277-5289, FAX 860-594-0303, http://www.arrl.org. R&P Mark Wilson.

MILLECANALI; tv, radio, communicazione, spettacolo. see *COMMUNICATIONS—Television And Cable*

384.5 USA ISSN 1544-9556
MISSIONCRITICAL COMMUNICATIONS. Text in English. 1987. 10/yr. free to qualified personnel (effective 2005). adv. 3 cols./p.; back issues avail.; reprints avail. **Document type:** *Magazine, Trade.*
Formerly (until 2003): Radio Resource Magazine (1080-3017)
Published by: Pandata Corporation, 7108 S Alton Way, Bldg H, Centennial, CO 80112. TEL 303-792-2390, FAX 303-792-2391, info@radioresourcemag.com, http://www.radioresourcemag.com/. Ed. Jeffrey Elliott TEL 303-792-2390 ext 20. Pub. Paulla A Nelson-Shira. Adv. contact Mark Shira TEL 303-792-2390 ext 11. B&W page USD 4,525, color page USD 5,400; 8.1875 x 10.875. Circ: 35,000 (controlled).

621.38 JPN
MOBILE HAM; amateur radio magagazine. Text in Japanese. 1974. m. JPY 8,580 domestic; JPY 9,840 foreign; JPY 600 newsstand/cover (effective 1999). adv. **Description:** Discusses amateur radio operating.
Formerly (until 1995): Ham Journal (0388-2306)
Published by: Denpa - Jikkensha, 6-15-4 Shimouma 6-Chrome, Setagaya-ku, Tokyo, 154-0002, Japan. TEL 81-3-3418-4111, FAX 81-3-5431-7456, mh-mag@po.iijnet.or.jp, http://www.iijnet.or.jp/MOBILE-HAM. Ed. Shinzaburo Kawai. Pub. T Masuda. Adv. contact Masaaki Aoyama. Circ: 70,000.
Dist. outside Japan by: Nippon IPS Co. Ltd., 11-6 Iida-Bashi 3-chome, Chiyoda-ku, Tokyo 102-0072, Japan. TEL 81-3-3238-0700.

384.5 USA ISSN 0745-7626
TK6570.M6 CODEN: MRTEFP
MOBILE RADIO TECHNOLOGY; technical information for paging, SMR and private wireless networks. Text in English. 1983. m. free domestic; USD 55 foreign (effective 2005). adv. bk.rev. tr.lit. **Document type:** *Magazine, Trade.* **Description:** Technical coverage of the wireless voice and data communications industry.
Related titles: Microform ed.: (from PQC); Online - full text ed.: (from bigchalk, EBSCO Publishing, Florida Center for Library Automation, Gale Group, H.W. Wilson, LexisNexis, O C L C Online Computer Library Center, Inc.).
Indexed: AS&TI, Inspec.
—BLDSC (5879.953840), AskIEEE, CISTI, IE, ingenta, Linda Hall. **CCC.**
Published by: Primedia Business Magazines & Media, Inc. (Subsidiary of: Primedia, Inc.), 330 N Wabash Ave, Ste 2300, Chicago, IL 60611. TEL 312-595-1080, FAX 312-595-0296, glen.bischoff@intertec.com, inquiries@primediabusiness.com, http://www.mrtmag.com, http://www.primediabusiness.com. Ed. Glenn Bischoff TEL 720-489-3288. Pub. Mark Hickey TEL 720-489-3196. adv.: page USD 4,727. Circ: 31,373 (controlled).

384.5 DEU ISSN 0937-7042
MOBILFUNK NEWS. Text in German. 1989. m. **Document type:** *Trade.*
Published by: Neue Mediengesellschaft Ulm mbH, Konrad-Celtis-Str 77, Munich, 81369, Germany. TEL 49-89-74117190, FAX 49-89-74117195. Circ: 5,000.

621.384 JPN
MOBIRU HAMU/RADIO AMATEUR'S MAGAZINE. Text in Japanese. 1973. m. JPY 520 per issue. adv.
Published by: Denpa Jikkensha, 15-4 Shimo-Uma 6-chome, Setagaya-ku, Tokyo, 154-0002, Japan. TEL 81-3-3418-4111, FAX 81-3-3418-4702. Ed. Shinzaburo Kawai. Adv. contact Takashi Kimura. Circ: 80,000.

MONITOR - RADIO T V. see *COMMUNICATIONS—Television And Cable*

384.5 CHE
MONITORING INFORMATION SUMMARY. Text in English, French, Spanish. q. CHF 122.
Media: Microform.
Published by: International Telecommunication Union, Place des Nations, Geneva 20, 1211, Switzerland. TEL 41-22-7306141, FAX 41-22-7305194, sales@itu.ch, http://www.itu.int/publications.

621.384 USA ISSN 0889-5341
TK6553
MONITORING TIMES. Text in English. 1982. m. USD 28.95; USD 5.95 per issue (effective 2005). adv. bk.rev. illus. index. back issues avail.; reprints avail. **Document type:** *Magazine, Trade.* **Description:** News on radio communications, scanner monitoring with loggings, international radio broadcast schedules, station, program, product, personality, technological profiles, and technical advice.
Related titles: ♦ Online - full content ed.: MT Express.
Indexed: ASIP.
Published by: Grove Enterprises, Inc., PO Box 98, 7540 Hwy 64 W, Brasstown, NC 28902-0098. TEL 828-837-9200, 800-438-8155, FAX 828-837-2216, mteditor@grove-ent.com, http://www.grove-ent.com/hmpgmt.html. Ed. Rachel Baughn. Pub. Bob Grove. Adv. contact Beth Leinbach. Circ: 28,000 (paid).

621.384 USA
MT EXPRESS. Text in English. m. USD 19.95 (effective 2000). **Document type:** *Trade.*
Media: Online - full content. **Related titles:** ♦ Print ed.: Monitoring Times. ISSN 0889-5341.
Published by: Grove Enterprises, Inc., PO Box 98, 7540 Hwy 64 W, Brasstown, NC 28902-0098. TEL 828-837-9200, 800-438-8155, FAX 828-837-2216, mteditor@grove-ent.com, http://www.grove-ent.com/hmpgmt.html.

MUZIEK & WOORD. see *COMMUNICATIONS—Television And Cable*

N R B MAGAZINE. (National Religious Broadcasters) see *COMMUNICATIONS—Television And Cable*

621.384 USA ISSN 0899-0131
NATIONAL CONTEST JOURNAL. Short title: N C J. Text in English. 1973. bi-m. USD 15 in North America; USD 25 elsewhere; USD 3 newsstand/cover. illus.; stat. **Document type:** *Bulletin.* **Description:** Includes articles on all contests of interest to amateur radio enthusiasts.
Related titles: CD-ROM ed.
Published by: American Radio Relay League, Inc., 225 Main St, Newington, CT 06111. TEL 860-594-0200, 888-277-5289, FAX 860-594-0303, rdstraw.arrl.org, pubsales@arrl.org, http://www.arrl.org. Ed. Bruce Draper. R&P Mark Wilson.

384.5453 USA ISSN 0889-2784
HE8664
NATIONAL RADIO PUBLICITY OUTLETS✶. Text in English. 1972. a. USD 99. adv.
Formerly (until 1986): National Radio Publicity Directory
Published by: Morgan-Rand Inc., 1 Sentry Pkwy, 1000, Blue Bell, PA 19422. TEL 215-938-5500, FAX 215-938-5541. Ed. Nancy Sherker.

384.5 EGY ISSN 1110-6972
NATIONAL RADIO SCIENCE CONFERENCE. PROCEEDINGS/AL-MU'TAMAR AL-QAWMI LI-'ILM AL-RADYU. Text in English. 1983. a. USD 200; USD 100 to members (effective 2004). **Document type:** *Proceedings, Trade.*
Related titles: CD-ROM ed.: ISSN 1110-6980. 1999.
Indexed: EngInd.
—BLDSC (6848.105200).
Published by: (Institute of Electrical and Electronics Engineers, Inc. USA), Academy of Scientific Research and Technology, Ain Shams University, Faculty of Engineering, Abbasia, Cairo, Egypt. http://derp.sti.sci.eg/data/0330.htm.

621.384 JPN
NAVIGATIONAL RADIO AIDS. Text in English. 1978. a. JPY 9,000 per issue.
Published by: (Marine Radio Officer's Union/Senpaku Tsushinshi Rodo Kumiai), Radio News Agency/Musen Tsushinsha, 14-8 Shibaura 1-chome, Minato-ku, Tokyo, 105-0023, Japan. TEL 81-3-3451-4729, FAX 81-3-3451-4727. Ed. Koumei Kikuta.

384.5 USA
NEW DIMENSIONS JOURNAL. Text in English. 2001. a. USD 45 per issue membership (effective 2005). **Document type:** *Journal.*
Media: Online - full content.
Published by: New Dimensions Foundation, PO Box 569, Ukiah, CA 95482-0569. TEL 707-468-5215, FAX 707-468-0530, info@newdimensions.org, http://www.newdimensions.org/online-journal/journal-home.html. Ed. Justines Willis Toms.

384.5 NGA ISSN 0331-4774
NIGERIAN RADIO - T V TIMES. Text in English. 1958. m. adv. bk.rev.
Published by: Nigerian Broadcasting Corporation, PO Box 12504, Ikoyi, Lagos State, Nigeria. Circ: 10,000.

621.384 JPN ISSN 0287-1564
CODEN: NMGIDE
NIHON MUSEN GIHO/J R C REVIEW. Text in Japanese; Summaries in English. 1965. a. **Document type:** *Corporate.*
Indexed: Inspec.
—BLDSC (5073.719000), AskIEEE, IE, ingenta.
Published by: Nihon Musen K.K./Japan Radio Co., Ltd., 17-22 Akasaka 2-chome, Minato-ku, Tokyo, 107-0052, Japan. TEL 03-3584-8836, FAX 03-3584-8878, TELEX 2425420 JRCTOK J. Ed. Kouhei Nishino. Pub. Hiroshi Yokomizo.

621.384 JPN
NIHON RAJIO SHINBUN/JAPAN RADIO NEWS. Text in Japanese. 1946. 3/m. JPY 10,000.
Published by: Nihon Rajio Shinbunsha, 14-15 Komagome 2-chome, Toshima-ku, Tokyo, 170-0003, Japan.

384.5 CHE ISSN 0252-1814
NOMENCLATURE DES STATIONS DE RADIOCOMMUNICATIONS SPATIALES ET DES STATIONS DE RADIOASTRONOMIE/LIST OF SPACE RADIOCOMMUNICATION STATIONS AND RADIOASTRONOMY STATION/NOMENCLATOR DE LAS ESTACIONES DE RADIOCOMUNICACION ESPACIAL Y DE LAS ESTACIONES DE RADIOASTRONOMIA. Text in English, French, Spanish. s-a. CHF 736.

▼ new title ➤ refereed ✶ unverified ♦ full entry avail.

Formerly: List of Radiocommunication Stations and Radioastronomy Stations
Media: Microform. **Related titles:** CD-ROM ed.
Published by: (Radiocommunication Bureau), International Telecommunication Union, Place des Nations, Geneva 20, 1211, Switzerland. TEL 41-22-730-5801, FAX 41-22-730-5785, TELEX 421 000 UIT CH.

621.38 USA
NORTH AMERICAN CALLBOOK✶. Text in English. 1920. a. USD 29.95. adv. **Description:** Now includes Canada, US, and Mexico.
Former titles: U S Callbook; Radio Amateur Callbook Magazine: U S Listings (0033-7706)
Published by: Radio Amateur Callbook, Inc., 575 Prospect St, Lakewood, NJ 08701-5040.

621.38 USA
NORTH AMERICAN REPEATER ATLAS. Text in English. a. USD 12. charts; maps. **Document type:** *Directory.* **Description:** Lists repeaters at all frequencies throughout North America.
Published by: American Radio Relay League, Inc., 225 Main St, Newington, CT 06111. TEL 860-594-0200, 888-277-5289, FAX 860-594-0303, http://www.arrl.org. Ed. Bob Martin. R&P Mark Wilson.

781.546 USA
OFF THE AIR✶. Text in English. 1994. q. USD 6. adv. bk.rev.; dance rev.; film rev.; music rev.; play rev.; video rev. stat. back issues avail. **Document type:** *Newsletter, Trade.* **Description:** Covers trends in music, politics and broadcasting, including trends in independent and micro radio. Aims to support independent music labels and artists and increase awareness of community based listener responsive broadcasting.
Published by: Syracuse Community Radio, 320 Greenwood Pl, Syracuse, NY 13210. TEL 315-474-9507, FAX 315-474-9507, syrcomrad@aol.com. Ed., Adv. contact Frederic W Noyes IV. Circ: 2,500.

ON-AIR JOB TIPSHEET. see *OCCUPATIONS AND CAREERS*

384.54 NLD
ON TARGET. Text in English. s-a. free. illus. **Document type:** *Newsletter, Consumer.* **Description:** News and programming schedules for Radio Netherlands external radio service.
Published by: Radio Netherlands, English Department, PO Box 222, Hilversum, 1200 JG, Netherlands. TEL 31-35-672-4222, FAX 31-35-672-4239, letters@rnw.nl, http://www.rnw.nl. Ed. Jonathan Marks.

384.5 USA
ONE TO ONE (FRESNO); the journal of creative broadcasting. Text in English. 1976. 50/yr. USD 200. adv. index. Supplement avail.; back issues avail. **Document type:** *Newsletter.* **Description:** Provides radio talent with guidance in delivery techniques; plus weekly humor, calendar and "Today in History," promotions, and artist biography.
Formerly: Fruitbowl
Related titles: Online - full text ed.: (from CompuServe Inc.).
Published by: CreeYadio Services, PO Box 9787, Fresno, CA 93794. TEL 559-448-0700, FAX 559-448-0761, 121@worldnet.att.net. Ed. Jay Trachman. Circ: 3,000.

384.5443 USA
OPEN LINE. Text in English. 1990. bi-w. adv. bk.rev.; music rev.; software rev. tr.lit. **Document type:** *Newsletter.* **Description:** Includes information about or for talk radio, and golf travel and tournaments.
Related titles: Online - full text ed.
Published by: Nashe Group, 566 Commonwealth Ave, Boston, MA 02215. TEL 617-437-9757, FAX 617-437-0797, nashe@priority1.net, http://www.talkshowhosts.com. Ed., R&P Carol Nashe. Adv. contact Keith Taylor.

384.5 FRA
LES OUVRAGES DE RADIOSIGNAUX. Text in French. irreg., latest vol.99, 1995. price varies. **Document type:** *Government.* **Description:** Offers mariners up-to-date information on radiocommunications.
Related titles: ♦ Series: Repertoire des Radiosignaux. ISSN 0989-5981; ♦ Radionavigation; ♦ Radiocommunications Maritimes; ♦ Stations Radiometeorologiques.
Published by: Service Hydrographique et Oceanographique de la Marine, 3 av. Octave Greard, Armees, 00300, France. TEL 98-03-09-17, FAX 98-47-11-42. **Subscr. to:** EPSHOM, B.P. 426, Brest Cedex 29275, France.

621.38 DNK ISSN 0901-2567
OZ; tidsskrift for amatoer-radio. Text in Danish. 1929. m. adv. bk.rev. charts; illus. index.
Formerly: Tidsskrift for Kortboelge Radio (0040-7100)
Indexed: AIAP.
Published by: Eksperimenterende Danske Radioamatoerer, Klokkestoebervej 11, Odense, 5230, Denmark. TEL 45-66-15-65-11, FAX 45-66-15-65-98. Ed. Flemming Hessel TEL 45-75-83-38-89.

384.54 USA ISSN 0897-0157
TK6555
PASSPORT TO WORLD BAND RADIO. Text in English. 1984. a. USD 22.95 (effective 2005). adv. charts; illus.; stat.; maps. 592 p./no. 2 cols./p.; back issues avail. **Document type:** *Magazine, Consumer.* **Description:** Refers to news, sports and entertainment shortwave broadcasts available from abroad.
Formerly: Radio Database International
Indexed: CurCont.
Published by: International Broadcasting Services, Ltd., 825 Cherry Ln, Penn's Park, PA 18943-0300. TEL 215-598-3298, FAX 215-598-3794, mktg@passband.com, http://www.passband.com. Eds. Tony Jones, Lawrence Magne. Adv. contact Jock Elliott. B&W page USD 1,975, color page USD 2,825. Circ: 42,300 (paid).

THE PERFECT VISION; high performance home theater. see *COMMUNICATIONS—Television And Cable*

PLAYBACK. see *COMMUNICATIONS—Television And Cable*

384.5 USA
POLICE CALL. Text in English. 1963. a. (in 7 vols.). USD 119; USD 19.99 per vol. (effective 2002). **Description:** Lists radio frequencies for police, fire, emergency and certain government services in the U.S.
Related titles: CD-ROM ed.
Published by: U.S. Radio Data, P O Box 263, Lebanon, NJ 08833. TEL 908-236-7110, http://www.policecall.com/.

POPTRONIX EXPERIMENTERS HANDBOOK (YEAR). see *ELECTRONICS*

POWER MEDIA YEARBOOK. see *COMMUNICATIONS—Television And Cable*

343 USA
PRIVATE RADIO REGULATION. Text in English. 2 base vols. plus bi-m. updates. USD 390 combined subscription print & online eds.; USD 365 combined subscription CD-ROM & online eds. (effective 2004). **Document type:** *Journal, Trade.* **Description:** Contains up-to-date information on FCC rules and government regulation relating to the private radio industry.
Related titles: CD-ROM ed.; Online - full text ed.
Published by: Pike & Fischer, Inc. (Subsidiary of: The Bureau of National Affairs, Inc.), 1010 Wayne Ave, Ste 1400, Silver Spring, MD 20910. TEL 301-562-1530, 800-255-8131, FAX 301-562-1521, pike@pf.com, http://privateradioregs.pf.com, http://www.pf.com.

PROGRAMME NEWS. see *COMMUNICATIONS—Television And Cable*

PROMAX INTERNATIONAL. see *COMMUNICATIONS—Television And Cable*

343.09945 USA
PUBLIC RADIO LEGAL HANDBOOK. Text in English. irreg. looseleaf. USD 75 to non-members; USD 50 to members. index. **Document type:** *Trade.* **Description:** Provides a reference checklist and explanation of FCC rules and regulations concerning regular station operation.
Formerly: N F C B Legal Handbook for Non-Commercial Stations
Published by: National Federation of Community Broadcasters, Ft Mason Center, Bldg D, San Francisco, CA 94123. TEL 415-771-1160. R&P Sean Simplicio.

621.384 USA ISSN 0886-8093
TK5103
Q E X; forum for communications experimenters. Text in English. bi-m. USD 37 domestic; USD 40 in Canada; USD 59 elsewhere (effective 2005). **Document type:** *Bulletin, Trade.* **Description:** Offers a means for experimenters in amateur radio to exchange ideas and information.
Related titles: CD-ROM ed.
—CISTI.
Published by: American Radio Relay League, Inc., 225 Main St, Newington, CT 06111. TEL 860-594-0200, 888-277-5289, FAX 860-594-0303, rdstraw.arrl.org, pubsales@arrl.org, http://www.arrl.org/qex. Ed. Doug Smith. R&P Mark Wilson. Circ: 4,000.

384.5 SWE ISSN 0033-4820
Q T C; amatoerradio. Text in Swedish. 1927. 12/yr. SEK 390 domestic; SEK 520 in Scandinavia; SEK 560 in Europe; SEK 650 elsewhere (effective 2001). adv. bk.rev. illus. Accumulative index on website. 56 p./no.; back issues avail. **Document type:** *Magazine, Consumer.* **Description:** Journal of the Swedish Amateur Radio Society.
Related titles: Audio cassette/tape ed.
Published by: Foereningen Sveriges Saendareamatoerer (SSA)/Swedish Amateur Radio Society, Turebergs Alle 2, P O Box 45, Sollentuna, 19121, Sweden. TEL 46-8-585-70273, FAX 46-8-585-70274, hq@ssa.se, http://www.ssa.se/index.php. Ed. Tomas Lysjoe. adv.: color page USD 500. Circ: 6,200.

621.384 USA ISSN 0033-4812
TK1
QST; devoted entirely to amateur radio. Text in English. 1915. m. USD 39 membership (effective 2005). adv. bk.rev. charts; illus. index. reprint service avail. from PQC. **Document type:** *Magazine, Consumer.* **Description:** Offers enthusiasts of amateur radio news and other practical information on their hobby, with product reviews, feature and technical articles, and readers' tips.
Related titles: CD-ROM ed.: QST View; Microform ed.: (from PQC); Online - full text ed.: (from H.W. Wilson, Northern Light Technology, Inc., O C L C Online Computer Library Center, Inc., ProQuest Information & Learning).
Indexed: AS&TI, ConsI, EEA, Inspec, MELSA.
—BLDSC (7164.000000), CISTI, IE, Infotrieve, ingenta, Linda Hall.
Published by: American Radio Relay League, Inc., 225 Main St, Newington, CT 06111. TEL 860-594-0200, 888-277-5289, FAX 860-584-0239, rdstraw.arrl.org, pubsales@arrl.org, http://www.arrl.org/qst. Ed. Steve Ford. Pubs. David Summer, Mark Wilson. Adv. contact Brad Thomas. Circ: 175,000 (paid and controlled).

384.5 ITA
QUI RAI. Text in English. N.S. 1995. q. **Description:** News of Italian international radio and programs. Covers news from Italy for those abroad.
Published by: Rai International, Casella Postale 320, Rome, RM 00100, Italy. TEL 39-6-33171895, FAX 39-6-33171895, http://www.planetitaly.com, http://www.rai.it/international. Ed. Augusto Milana.

384.5 NLD ISSN 0927-9628
R A M; magazine voor zend- en luisteramateurs, 27 MC en DX'ers. (Radio Amateur Magazine) Text in Dutch. 1979. m. adv. index. **Document type:** *Consumer.*
Former titles (until 1985): Radio Amateur Magazine (0927-9644); (until 1982): Break Break (0927-9636)
Related titles: CD-ROM ed.
—IE, Infotrieve.
Published by: Televak Uitgeverij N.V., Postbus 75985, Amsterdam, 1070 AZ, Netherlands. TEL 31-20-6659220, FAX 31-20-6657316. Ed. J Boers. Adv. contact Maarten Ponssen. Circ: 25,000 (paid).

781.546 USA ISSN 1076-6502
R & R. Text in English. 1973. w. (Fri.). USD 325 domestic; USD 330 in Canada & Mexico; USD 495 elsewhere (effective 2005). adv. **Document type:** *Newspaper, Trade.*
Formerly: Radio & Records (0277-4860)
Related titles: Online - full text ed.
Published by: Radio & Records, Inc., 2049 Century Park East, 41st Fl, Los Angeles, CA 90067. TEL 310-788-1625, FAX 310-203-8727, mailroom@radioandrecords.com, http://www.radioandrecords.com/. Ed. Gail Mitchell. Adv. contact Michael Atkinson. B&W page USD 2,820, color page USD 4,250. Circ: 9,000.

R / C EXCELLENCE MAGAZINE. (Radio Control) see *HOBBIES*

384.54 USA
HE8811
R C R CELLULAR DATABASE. (Radio Communications Report) Text in English. 1977. a. USD 250 (effective 1999). adv. index. **Document type:** *Trade.* **Description:** Provides information for the cellular communications industry, with listings of manufacturers, service providers, representatives, distributors, and cellular operators.
Former titles: R C R Cellular Handbook (1060-0868); Which superseded in part (in 1991): Mobile Communications Handbook (1048-0323); Which was formerly (until 1986): Mobile Radio Handbook
Media: Diskette.
Published by: Crain Communications, Inc., 1746 Cole Blvd, Ste 150, Golden, CO 80401. TEL 303-872-9100, info@crain.com, http://www.crain.com. Ed. Melody Spurrier.

R C R - P C S. (Radio Communications Report) see *COMMUNICATIONS—Telephone And Telegraph*

384.534 USA
TK6555
R C R PAGING DATABASE. (Radio Communications Report) Text in English. 1977. a. USD 100 (effective 1999). adv.
Former titles: R C R Paging Handbook (1062-3779); Which superseded in part (in 1991): Mobile Communications Handbook (1048-0323); Which was formerly (until 1986): Mobile Radio Handbook
Media: Diskette.
Published by: Crain Communications, Inc., 1746 Cole Blvd, Ste 150, Golden, CO 80401. TEL 303-872-9100, info@crain.com, http://www.crain.com. Ed. Melody Spurrier.

R F E; Technik und Markt der Medienelektronik. (Radio Fernsehen Elektronik) see *ELECTRONICS*

384.5 USA ISSN 1554-5806
▼ **R F I D PRODUCT NEWS.** (Radio Frequency Identification) Text in English. 2004 (Nov./Dec.). bi-m. free to qualified personnel (effective 2005). **Document type:** *Magazine, Trade.*

Published by: Lyons Media, Inc., 20 Valley Stream Pkwy Ste 265, Malvern, PA 19355. TEL 610-296-3001, http://www.rfidproductnews.com. Ed. Christopher Yeich.

621.38 GBR ISSN 1366-5537
R S G B - ISLANDS ON THE AIR DIRECTORY & YEARBOOK. Short title: R S G B - I O T A Directory & Yearbook. Text in English. 1996. biennial. charts; illus.; maps; stat. **Document type:** *Directory.* **Description:** Lists radio relay information for thousands of islands off every continent, along with award rules, application information and forms, and other pertinent information. Includes articles of interest to island broadcasters and operators of amateur radios receiving island broadcasts. Offers rules and guidelines for persons wishing to find out more about and participate in the RSGB Islands on the Air Programme.
Published by: Radio Society of Great Britain, Lamgda House, Cranbourne Rd, Potters Bar, Herts EN6 3JE, United Kingdom. TEL 44-870-904-7373, FAX 44-870-904-7373, http://www.rsgb.org.uk. Eds. Martin Atherton, Roger Balister. **Dist. in the US by:** American Radio Relay League, Inc., 225 Main St, Newington, CT 06111. TEL 860-594-0200, 860-594-0303.

621.38 GBR ISSN 1460-454X
R S G B YEARBOOK. Text in English. 1951. a. GBP 14.50 to non-members; GBP 6.25 to members (effective 1999). adv. **Document type:** *Directory.* **Description:** Listing of names and addresses of UK radio amateurs and other useful information on UK amateur radio.
Former titles (until 1997): R S G B Amateur Radio Call Book and Information Directory (1368-003X); (until 1992): R S G B Amateur Radio Call Book
Related titles: CD-ROM ed.: CallSeeker.
Published by: Radio Society of Great Britain, Lamgda House, Cranbourne Rd, Potters Bar, Herts EN6 3JE, United Kingdom. TEL 44-870-904-7373, FAX 44-870-904-7373, http://www.rsgb.org. Ed. Mike Dennison. Circ: 3,500.

R T C A DIGEST. see *AERONAUTICS AND SPACE FLIGHT*

791.44 IRL ISSN 0033-7145
R T E GUIDE. Text and summaries in English, Irish. 1961. w. (Wed.). adv. film rev.; play rev. illus. **Document type:** *Consumer.*
Formerly: R T V Guide
Published by: Radio Telefis Eireann, Rm. 8, Annex 5, Donnybrook, Dublin, Dublin 4, Ireland. info@rte.ie, http://www.rte.ie. Adv. contact Ken Nugent. B&W page EUR 5,710; trim 228 x 297. Circ: 106,213.

R T V; illustriertes Programm. see *COMMUNICATIONS—Television And Cable*

384.5 621.38 GBR ISSN 1367-1499
TK6540 CODEN: RADCB7
RADCOM. Text in English. 1924. m. GBP 40.50 to institutions (effective 2001). adv. bk.rev. bibl.; charts. index. back issues avail.; reprint service avail. from PQC. **Document type:** *Bulletin.* **Description:** Offers information of interest to enthusiasts of amateur radio, both broadcasters and amateurs.
Formerly (until 1995): Radio Communication (0033-7803)
Related titles: CD-ROM ed.; Microform ed.: (from PQC).
Indexed: BrTechI, Inspec, M&TEA.
—BLDSC (7226.910000), AskIEEE, CISTI, Ei, IE, Infotrieve, ingenta, Linda Hall. **CCC.**
Published by: Radio Society of Great Britain, Lamgda House, Cranbourne Rd, Potters Bar, Herts EN6 3JE, United Kingdom. TEL 44-870-904-7373, FAX 44-870-904-7373, radcom@rsgb.org.uk, http://www.rsgb.org/radcom, http://www.rsgb.org.uk. Ed. Steve Telenius Lowe. adv.: B&W page GBP 890, color page GBP 1,210; 182 x 270. Circ: 25,000.

621.38 RUS ISSN 0033-765X
RADIO. Text in Russian. 1924. m. USD 184 foreign (effective 2005). adv. bk.rev. charts; illus. **Document type:** *Magazine, Consumer.*
Indexed: RefZh.
—East View, Linda Hall.
Address: Seliverstov per 10, korp 1, Moscow, 107045, Russian Federation. TEL 7-095-2073118, FAX 7-095-2087713, editor@radio.ru, http://www.radio.ru. Ed. Y I Krilov. R&P Y I Krylov. adv.: B&W page USD 1,100, color page USD 1,800. Circ: 51,000. **US dist. addr.:** East View Information Services, 3020 Harbor Ln. N., Minneapolis, MN 55447. TEL 763-550-0961, FAX 763-559-2931, eastview@eastview.com, http://www.eastview.com.

621.384 USA ISSN 1542-0620
RADIO; the radio technology leader. Text in English. 1995. m. USD 50 domestic; USD 65 foreign (effective 2003). **Document type:** *Magazine, Trade.* **Description:** Presents need-to-know technical information in a non-technical format to help readers solve the challenges of technology and the equipment problems they face.
Formerly: B E Radio (1081-3357)
Related titles: Online - full text ed.: (from H.W. Wilson, LexisNexis, O C L C Online Computer Library Center, Inc., ProQuest Information & Learning); ♦ Supplement to: Broadcast Engineering. ISSN 0007-1994.
Indexed: AS&TI.
—**CCC.**
Published by: Primedia Business Magazines & Media, Inc. (Subsidiary of: Primedia, Inc.), 9800 Metcalf Ave, Overland Park, KS 66212-2216. TEL 913-341-1300, FAX 913-967-1898, inquiries@primediabusiness.com, http://www.beradio.com, http://www.primediabusiness.com. Ed. Chriss Scherer TEL 913-967-7201. Pub. Dennis Triola. **Subscr. to:** PO Box 12993, Overland Park, KS 66282-2993. TEL 800-441-0294, FAX 913-967-1331.

621.38 GBR ISSN 1460-7409
RADIO ACTIVE. Text in English. 1980. m. GBP 23 domestic; GBP 25.80 in Europe; USD 48 in United States; GBP 2.25 newsstand/cover. adv. **Document type:** *Trade.* **Description:** Focuses on the world of radio communications and features new technology.
Former titles (until 1997): C B (1366-0705); (until 1996): New C B (1365-9855)
Published by: Radio Active Publications, 189 London Rd, North End, Portsmouth, Hants PO2 9AE, United Kingdom. TEL 44-1705-613800, FAX 44-1705-690626, elaine.richards@binternet.com, http://www.radio-active.co.uk. Ed. Elaine Richards. Pub. Mike Devereux. Adv. contact Marcia Brogan. **Dist. by:** Seymour Distribution Ltd, 86 Newman St, London W1T 3EX, United Kingdom. FAX 44-207-396-8002, enquiries@seymour.co.uk.

659.142 USA
RADIO AD BIZ. Text in English. 1997. m. USD 120 (effective 2000). back issues avail. **Document type:** *Journal, Trade.* **Description:** Reports on the radio business as it relates to ad agencies, advertisers and company brand managers.
Published by: Radio Business Report, 2050 Old Bridge Rd., Ste. B1, Woodbridge, VA 22192-2484. radiobiz@aol.com, http://www.radioadbiz.com. Ed. Jack Messmer. Pub. Jim Carnegie. Circ: 7,000 (controlled).

RADIO ADVERTISING BUREAU. RADIO FACTS. see *ADVERTISING AND PUBLIC RELATIONS—Abstracting, Bibliographies, Statistics*

RADIO ADVERTISING BUREAU. RETAIL MARKETING KIT. see *ADVERTISING AND PUBLIC RELATIONS*

621.384 CAN ISSN 1498-8356
VK397
RADIO AIDS TO MARINE NAVIGATION. ATLANTIC, ST. LAWRENCE, GREAT LAKES, LAKE WINNIPEG AND EASTERN ARCTIC. Text in English. 1956. a. CND 18.95 (effective 2004). charts; maps. **Document type:** *Government.*
Formerly (until 2001): Radio Aids to Marine Navigation. Atlantic and Great Lakes (0410-7535); Which superseded in part (in 1956): Radio Aids to Marine Navigation (0033-7692)
Related titles: Online - full text ed.: ISSN 1702-2770; Ed.: Aides Radio a la Navigation Maritime. Atlantique, St.-Laurent, Grands Lacs, Lac Winnipeg et de l'Arctique-Est. ISSN 1498-8364.
Published by: Canadian Coast Guard, Marine Communications and Traffic Services, 200 Kent St, 5th fl Station 5005, Ottawa, ON K1A 0E6, Canada. FAX 613-991-4593. Ed. A Groves. R&P S Martin TEL 613-990-3031. Circ: 4,000 (paid). **Dist. by:** Canadian Hydrographic Chart Dealers, Fisheries and Oceans, Ottawa, ON K1G 3H6, Canada.

621.384 CAN ISSN 1702-2673
VK560
RADIO AIDS TO MARINE NAVIGATION. PACIFIC AND WESTERN ARCTIC. Text in English. 1956. a. CND 14.95 (effective 2004).
Formerly (until 2001): Radio Aids to Marine Navigation. Pacific (0410-7543); Which superseded in part (in 1956): Radio Aids to Marine Navigation (0033-7692)
Related titles: Online - full text ed.: ISSN 1702-269X.
Published by: Canadian Coast Guard, Marine Communications and Traffic Services, 200 Kent St, 5th fl Station 5005, Ottawa, ON K1A 0E6, Canada. FAX 613-991-4593. **Dist. by:** Canadian Hydrographic Chart Dealers, Fisheries and Oceans, Ottawa, ON K1G 3H6, Canada. TEL 613-998-4931, FAX 613-998-1217, chs_sales@dfo-mpo.gc.ca, http://www.charts.gc.ca.

621.38 SCG ISSN 0033-8168
RADIO-AMATER. Text in Serbo-Croatian. 1947. m. YUN 3,360, USD 30.
Published by: (Savez Radio-Amatera Jugoslavije YUG), Privredni Pregled, Marsala Birjuzova 3-5, Belgrade, 11000. Ed. Zarko Resanovic.

RADIO & T V. see *COMMUNICATIONS—Television And Cable*

RADIO AND TELEVISION CAREER DIRECTORY. see *OCCUPATIONS AND CAREERS*

384.5 USA
RADIO BUSINESS REPORT. Text in English. 1993. w. USD 89. adv. **Description:** Reports late-breaking news pertaining to the radio.
Formerly: Mid-Week News Brief
Address: 2050 Old Bridge Rd., Ste. B1, Woodbridge, VA 22192-2484. FAX 703-719-7910, radiobiz@aol.com, http://www.radioadbiz.com. Ed. Carl Marcucci. Adv. contact John Neff.

384.5 GBR ISSN 0956-974X
RADIO BYGONES. Text in English. bi-m. USD 30 domestic; USD 32 foreign (effective 2002). back issues avail. **Document type:** *Consumer.* **Description:** Contains articles on restoration and repair, history, circuit techniques, personalities, reminiscences and just plain nostalgia.
Related titles: Online - full content ed.: USD 9.99 (effective 2002).
Published by: Wimborne Publishing Ltd. (Subsidiary of: Crosstown Publications), 408 Wimborne Rd E, Ferndown, Doreset BH22 9ND, United Kingdom. TEL 44-1202-873872, FAX 44-1202-874562, radiobygones@wimborne.co.uk, enquiries@wimborne.co.uk, http://www.radiobygones.com, http://www.epemag.com, http://www.radiobygones.co.uk. Ed. Mike Kenward. Adv. contact Peter Mew.

384.5 USA ISSN 1044-9647
PN1991.3.U6
RADIO - CHICAGO✶. Text in English. 1989. q. USD 12. adv. **Description:** Covers radio personalities and events in the Chicago metropolitan market.
Published by: Radio - Chicago, Inc., 233 E Wacker Dr, Apt 1112, Chicago, IL 60601-5107. TEL 312-939-5480, FAX 312-341-0222. Ed. Donna Walters. Circ: 15,000.

621.38 USA ISSN 0033-779X
TK6540 CODEN: PRCAAO
RADIO CLUB OF AMERICA. PROCEEDINGS. Text in English. 1920. s-a. USD 35 to members (effective 2000). adv. bk.rev. illus. index. **Document type:** *Proceedings.*
Indexed: Inspec.
—AskIEEE, CISTI, Linda Hall.
Published by: Radio Club of America, Inc., c/o Gerri Hopkins, 244 Broad St, 2nd Fl, Red Bank, NJ 07701-2003. TEL 732-842-5070, FAX 732-219-1938, info@radio-club-of-america.org. Ed. Cindy Stevens. R&P Ray Trott TEL 972-580-1911. Adv. contact Mercy Contreras. Circ: 1,500 (controlled).

384.5029 USA
RADIO CO-OP SOURCES. Text in English. 1978. a. **Document type:** *Directory.* **Description:** Cooperative advertising fund directory for radio station sales people.
Published by: Radio Advertising Bureau, 261 Madison Ave, 23rd Fl, New York, NY 10016-2303. TEL 800-232-3131, FAX 972-753-6727. Circ: 5,000.

621.384 USA
RADIO FREQUENCY IDENTIFICATION OPERATIONS. Text in English. m. USD 185 (effective 2005). **Document type:** *Magazine, Trade.*
Published by: Argosy Group (Subsidiary of: United Communications Group), 11300 Rockville Pike, Ste 1100, Rockville, MD 20852. TEL 888-287-2223, FAX 301-816-8945, http://www.rfidoperations.com/newsletter.html, http://www.ucg.com/argosy.html.

RADIO FUN. see *HOBBIES*

384.5 025.04 CAN
RADIO H.F. INTERNET NEWSLETTER. Text in English. m. free (effective 2001). back issues avail. **Document type:** *Newsletter, Consumer.* **Description:** Covers websites of interest to radio enthusiasts.
Media: Online - full text. **Related titles:** E-mail ed.
Published by: Radio H.F., P O Box 67063, St. Lambert, PQ J4R 2T8, Canada. hfnewsletter@yahoo.com, http://www.anarc.org/cidx/radiohf/index.html. Ed. Sheldon Harvey.

384.5 DEU
RADIO HOEREN UND SCANNEN; Hobby-Magazin fuer weltweiten Funkempfang. Text in German. m. **Document type:** *Consumer.*
Formerly: Radio Hoeren (0944-0232)
Published by: Verlag fuer Technik und Handwerk GmbH, Robert-Bosch-Str 4, Baden-Baden, 76532, Germany. TEL 49-7221-50870, FAX 49-7221-508752. Ed. Rainer Pinkau. Circ: 15,000. **Subscr. to:** P M S GmbH & Co. KG, Postfach 104139, Duesseldorf 40032, Germany. TEL 49-211-6907890, FAX 49-211-69078950.

384.54 USA ISSN 1064-587X
RADIO INK. Text in English. 1986. fortn. USD 199 domestic; USD 225 foreign (effective 2005). adv. bk.rev. illus. reprints avail. **Document type:** *Magazine, Trade.* **Description:** Provides news, interviews and features to help radio station owners, operators and managers.
Published by: Streamline Publishing, Inc., 224 Datura St, Ste 701, West Palm Beach, FL 33401. TEL 561-655-8778, FAX 561-655-6164, radiolink@aol.com, http://www.radioink.com. Eds. Ed Ryan, Eric Rhoads. Pub. Eric Rhoads. Circ: 9,000.

384 JPN ISSN 0033-7927
RADIO JAPAN NEWS. Text in English. 1956. m. free. illus.
Related titles: Japanese ed.: Rajio Nippon Nyusu. ISSN 0388-0702.

C

▼ new title ➤ refereed ✶ unverified ♦ full entry avail.

Published by: Japan Broadcasting Corp./Nippon Hoso Kyokai, 2-2-1 Jinnan, Shibuya-ku, Tokyo, 150-0041, Japan. TEL 03-3465-1111, FAX 03-3481-1350. Circ: 14,000.

384.5   GBR   ISSN 1476-4504
▶ ➤ **THE RADIO JOURNAL**; international studies in broadcast and audio media. Text in English. 2003. 3/yr. GBP 30 in the European Union to individuals; GBP 38 elsewhere to individuals; GBP 140 combined subscription in the European Union to institutions print & online eds.; GBP 148 combined subscription elsewhere to institutions print & online eds. (effective 2005). bk.rev. back issues avail. **Document type:** *Journal, Academic/Scholarly.* **Description:** Designed for all those interested in research into the production, reception, texts and contexts of radio and audio media. This includes all structures, forms and genres of radio broadcasting and also embraces net distribution and audio streaming of radio services and texts, CD-ROMs, books-on-tape, and sound art.
Related titles: Online - full content ed.; Online - full text ed.: (from EBSCO Publishing, O C L C Online Computer Library Center, Inc., Swets Information Services).
—BLDSC (7232.531070), IE.
Published by: Intellect Ltd., PO Box 862, Bristol, BS99 1DE, United Kingdom. TEL 44-117-9589910, FAX 44-117-9589911, journals@intellectbooks.com, info@intellectbooks.com, http://www.intellectbooks.com/journals/radio.htm. Ed. Dr. Ken Garner. R&P, Adv. contact Mr. Robin Beecroft.

384.384   DEU
RADIO-KURIER - WELTWEIT HOEREN; alle Sender - alle Laender. Text in German. 1967. fortn. EUR 38.35 domestic; EUR 44 in Europe; EUR 58.80 elsewhere (effective 2001). adv. bk.rev. **Document type:** *Journal, Consumer.*
Formerly (until 1999): Kurier (Duesseldorf) (0170-768X)
Published by: A D D X e.V., Postfach 130124, Duesseldorf, 40551, Germany. TEL 49-211-790636, FAX 49-211-793272. Ed. Michael Schmitz. Circ: 4,500.

791.4   NLD
RADIO NETHERLANDS PROGRAMME SCHEDULE. Text in English. 1949. s-a. free.
Formerly: Radio Nederland (0033-7951)
Related titles: Dutch ed.; Indonesian ed.; Spanish ed.
Published by: Stichting Radio Nederland Wereldomroep, Public Relations Dept, PO Box 222, Hilversum, 1200 JG, Netherlands. TEL 31-35-6724211, FAX 31-35-6724239, letters@rnw.nl. Circ: 200,000.

384.5   USA
HE8698
RADIO ONLY MAGAZINE✱ ; the monthly management tool. Text in English. 1978. m. USD 95; USD 150 foreign. tr.lit. back issues avail. **Document type:** *Trade.* **Description:** Management information for radio executives and their sales representatives containing the latest trends and programming techniques.
Former titles: Radio Magazine; Radio Only (0731-8294)
Published by: Inside Radio, Inc. (Subsidiary of: M Street Corporation), PO Box 1436, Mount Laurel, NJ 08054-7436. TEL 609-424-6800, FAX 609-424-2301. Ed. Kyle Ruffin.

RADIO POWER BOOK. see *BUSINESS AND ECONOMICS—Trade And Industrial Directories*

621.388   FRA   ISSN 0033-7994
RADIO R E F; revue officielle de l'Union francaise des radioamateurs. Text in French. 1925. 11/yr. adv. bk.rev. abstr.; charts; illus.; tr.lit. index.
Indexed: RefZh.
Published by: Reseau des Emetteurs Francais, 32 rue de Suede, BP 7429, Tours, Cedex 2 37074, France. TEL 33-2-47418873, FAX 33-2-47418888. Ed. Serge Phalippou. Adv. contact Jean Marie Gaucheron. Circ: 11,000.

384.5   USA   ISSN 1080-3025
TK6570.M6
RADIO RESOURCE INTERNATIONAL. Text in English. 1987. 4/yr. free to qualified personnel (effective 2005). adv. back issues avail.; reprints avail. **Document type:** *Magazine, Trade.* **Description:** Covers the international mobile communications market.
Published by: Pandata Corporation, 7108 S Alton Way, Bldg H, Centennial, CO 80112. TEL 303-792-2390, FAX 303-792-2391, info@radioresourcemag.com, http://www.radioresourcemag.com. Eds. Jeffrey Elliott TEL 303-792-2390 ext 20, Lola Friday. Pub. Paulla A Nelson-Shira. Adv. contact Mark Shira TEL 303-792-2390 ext 11. color page USD 5,400, B&W page USD 4,525; trim 8.1875 x 10.875. Circ: 14,528 (controlled).

621.384   ITA   ISSN 0033-8036
➤ **RADIO RIVISTA.** Text mainly in Italian; Text occasionally in English. 1949. m. USD 60 (effective 1995). adv. bk.rev. bibl.; charts; illus.; pat. index. **Document type:** *Proceedings, Academic/Scholarly.*
Published by: (Associazione Radioamatori Italiani), Ediradio, Via Domenico Scarlatti, 31, Milan, MI 20124, Italy. TEL 2-6692894, FAX 2-66714809. Ed. Sergio Pesce. Circ: 25,000.

384.5   DEU
RADIO-SCANNER; Magazin fuer Funk und Elektronik. Text in German. 4/yr. EUR 20 domestic; EUR 22 foreign; EUR 5.50 newsstand/cover (effective 2002). adv. **Document type:** *Magazine, Consumer.* **Description:** Covers all aspects of amateur radio broadcasting and equipment.
Published by: Redaktions- und Medienbuero Dieter Hurcks, Buergerweg 5, Burgdorf, 31303, Germany. TEL 49-5136-896460, FAX 49-5136-896461, mail@radio-scanner.de, http://www.radio-scanner.de. Ed., Pub. Dieter Hurcks. adv.: B&W page EUR 1,020, color page EUR 1,300; trim 185 x 280. Circ: 16,500 (paid).

621.384   BEL   ISSN 1024-4530
TK6540   CODEN: RABUEK
THE RADIO SCIENCE BULLETIN. Text mainly in English; Text occasionally in French. 1994. q. free to qualified personnel. bk.rev. **Document type:** *Bulletin.*
Formerly (until 1995): Radioscientist and Bulletin (0779-9993); Formed by the merger of (1990-1994): Radioscientist (1170-5833); (1938-1994): U R S I Information Bulletin (0041-543X)
Indexed: BrCerAb, C&ISA, CerAb, CorrAb, E&CAJ, EMA, IAA, Inspec, M&TEA, MBF, METADEX, WAA.
—BLDSC (7232.999600), AskIEEE, CISTI, Linda Hall.
Published by: International Union of Radio Science - URSI/Union Radio-Scientifique Internationale, Ghent University (INTEC), Sint Pietersnieuwstraat 41, Gent, 9000, Belgium. TEL 32-9-264-3320, FAX 32-9-264-4288, ursi@intec.rug.ac.be, rsb@intec.rug.ac.be, http://www.ursi.org/RSB.htm. Ed. Dr. W Ross Stone. Circ: 2,900.

384.5   ALB
RADIO SHQIP. Text in Albanian. fortn. ALL 10, USD 3. adv. **Document type:** *Newspaper.*
Formerly (until 1996): Radio Perhapja
Published by: Albanian Language Radio Union, Rr Ismail Qemali 11 (pranie Radio Tiranes), Tirana, Albania. TEL 355-42-23239, FAX 355-42-23239. R&P Buraj Skendaj. Adv. contact Bujar Skendaj. Circ: 1,000.

384.5   BRA
RADIO T V TECNICO. Text in Portuguese. 1969. m. USD 300. bk.rev. **Description:** Instruction on radio technology for the radio technician.
Published by: Editora Signo Ltda, Centro, Caixa Postal 2483, Rio De Janeiro, RJ 20001-970, Brazil. Ed. Apollon Fanzeres. Circ: 80,000.

RADIO TECHNICAL COMMISSION FOR AERONAUTICS. PROCEEDINGS OF THE ANNUAL TECHNICAL SYMPOSIUM. see *AERONAUTICS AND SPACE FLIGHT*

384   GBR   ISSN 0033-8060
TK6540
RADIO TIMES. Text in English. 1923. w. GBP 58 (effective 2005). adv. illus. **Document type:** *Magazine, Consumer.* **Description:** Contains TV and radio listings plus related feature articles.
Related titles: Microform ed.: (from PQC); (from PQC); (from PQC); Online - full text ed.
Indexed: ChLitAb, IIFP, IITV.
Published by: B B C Worldwide Ltd., 80 Wood Ln, London, W12 0TT, United Kingdom. TEL 44-20-84331070, FAX 44-20-84332231, radio.times@bbc.co.uk, bbcworldwide@bbc.co.uk, http://www.radiotimes.com/, http://www.bbcmagazines.com. Ed. Sue Robinson. Pub. Nicholas Brett. Adv. contact Ashley Munday. color page GBP 21,500; trim 226 x 300. Circ: 1,337,036 (paid). **Dist. by:** Frontline, Park House, 117 Park Rd, Peterborough, Cambs PE1 2TS, United Kingdom. TEL 44-1733-555161, FAX 44-1733-562788.

RADIO TV8. see *COMMUNICATIONS—Television And Cable*

384.5   NGA
RADIO - VISION TIMES. Text in English. m. adv.
Published by: Western Nigeria Radio - Vision Service, Television House, PO Box 1460, Ibadan, Oyo, Nigeria. Ed. Alton A Adedeji. Circ: 20,000.

384.5   USA   ISSN 1054-9048
RADIO WEEK. Text in English. 1933. w. membership only. adv. **Document type:** *Newsletter.* **Description:** Update on association news and broadcast industry news on Capitol Hill and at the FCC.
Incorporates (in 1988): Radioactive (0747-4032); (in 1985): N A B Highlights; Formerly: N A B Today (Radio Edition)
Related titles: Fax ed.; Online - full text ed.
Published by: National Association of Broadcasters, 1771 N St, N W, Washington, DC 20036. TEL 202-429-5350, FAX 202-429-5406, cnicholson@nab.org, http://www.nab.org. Ed. Chris Nicholson. R&P Ben Ivins. Adv. contact David Dziedzic. Circ: (controlled).

384.5453   DEU
RADIO WORKS; die ganze Amplitude des Radios. Text in German. 2001. m. adv. **Document type:** *Magazine, Trade.* **Description:** Covers all aspects of the radio broadcasting and programming industries.

Published by: Radio Works Verlag GmbH, Schaarsteinwegsbruecke 2, Hamburg, 20459, Germany. TEL 49-40-37491422, FAX 49-40-37491428, info@radio-works.de, http://www.radio-works.de.

621.38   USA   ISSN 0274-8541
RADIO WORLD. Text in English, Portuguese, Spanish. 1977. bi-w. free (effective 2005). adv. bk.rev. tr.lit. back issues avail.; reprints avail. **Document type:** *Newspaper, Trade.* **Description:** Offers technology news, applications-oriented engineering and production articles, management features, and user-written reviews and new-product introductions.
Formerly (until 1980): Broadcast Equipment Exchange (0194-2190)
Related titles: Online - full content ed.
Published by: I M A S Publishing Group, 5827 Columbia Pike, Ste 310, Falls Church, VA 22041. TEL 703-998-7600, FAX 703-998-2966, radioworld@imaspub.com, adsales@imaspub.com, http://www.radioworld.com/, http://www.imaspub.com. Ed. Paul McLane. Pub. Carmel King. Adv. contact Simone Mullins. Circ: 15,000 (controlled).
Subscr. to: PO Box 1214, Falls Church, VA 22041-0241.

384.5   USA
RADIO WORLD. EDICION INTERNACIONAL. Text in Spanish, Portuguese. m. USD 79; USD 99 foreign (effective 1999). tr.lit. back issues avail.; reprints avail. **Document type:** *Newspaper, Trade.* **Description:** Regional editions of Radio World are edited for Mexico, Central and South America, and the Spanish-speaking Caribbean.
Published by: I M A S Publishing Group, 5827 Columbia Pike, Ste 310, Falls Church, VA 22041. TEL 703-998-7600, FAX 703-998-2966, adsales@imaspub.com, http://www.imaspub.com.

384.5   USA   ISSN 0279-151X
RADIO WORLD. INTERNATIONAL EDITION. Text in English. 1990. m. USD 79; USD 99 foreign (effective 1999). adv. tr.lit. back issues avail.; reprints avail. **Document type:** *Newspaper, Trade.* **Description:** Covers radio station technology, developments and applications. Geared toward radio station engineers, producers, technical staff and managers.
Published by: I M A S Publishing Group, 5827 Columbia Pike, Ste 310, Falls Church, VA 22041. TEL 703-998-7600, 800-336-3045, FAX 703-998-2966, adsales@imaspub.com, http://www.imaspub.com. Ed. Alan Carter. Pub. Stevan B Dana. Adv. contact Carmel King. Circ: 18,000.

621.38   ZAF   ISSN 0033-815X
RADIO Z S. Text in Afrikaans, English. 1947. m. ZAR 215 to members (effective 2000). adv. bk.rev. charts. index. **Document type:** *Newsletter.* **Description:** Covers various aspects of amateur radio and electronics.
Published by: South African Radio League/Suid-Afrikaanse Radioliga, PO Box 807, Houghton, Johannesburg 2041, South Africa. TEL 27-11-484-2830, FAX 27-11-484-2831. Ed. Tony Ruwawan. R&P Michelle Velweme TEL 27-11-6752393. Circ: 3,000.

384.5   DNK   ISSN 1601-9415
RADIOBRANCHEN HORISONT; magasinet for radio-, tv- og fotobranchen. Text in Danish. 1974. 9/yr. DKK 665 (effective 2003). adv. bk.rev. charts; illus.; pat.; stat. index. **Description:** Audiovisual products and techniques.
Formerly (until 2002): Radiobranchen (0108-6626); Which was formed by the merger of(1946-1974): Dansk Radio Industri (0011-6440); (1940-1974): Rateksa (0033-9970)
Published by: (Radiofaghandlens Brancheorganisation), Horisont Gruppen A/S, Center Boulevard 5, Copenhagen S, 2300, Denmark. TEL 45-32-473230, FAX 45-32-473239, info@horisontgruppen.dk, http://www.horisontgruppen.dk. adv.: B&W page DKK 11,433, color page DKK 17,060; 265 x 185. Circ: 3,500.

621.384   FRA
RADIOCOMMUNICATIONS MAGAZINE. Text in French. 6/yr.
Published by: Societe d'Edition et de Publication Electronique, 87 rue Principale, Viefvillers, 60360, France. TEL 48-20-63-72, FAX 48-20-63-73. Ed. Yves Leclerc Darras. Circ: 8,000.

621.388   ITA   ISSN 0033-8257
RADIOCORRIERE - T V. Text in Italian. 1924. w. adv. **Document type:** *Magazine, Consumer.*
Indexed: RASB.
Published by: E R I Edizioni R A I (Subsidiary of: R A I - Radiotelevisione Italiana), Via Verdi 16, Turin, TO 10121, Italy. http://www.eri.rai.it. Circ: 150,446.

RADIOELECTRONICS AND COMMUNICATIONS SYSTEMS. see *ELECTRONICS*

621.384   CZE   ISSN 1210-2512
RADIOENGINEERING. Text in English. 1992. q. CZK 350 in Czech Republic; SKK 500 in Slovakia; USD 20 in Europe; USD 30 elsewhere (effective 2002). adv. **Description:** Publishes papers on research and development in the field of radio engineering.
Indexed: Inspec.
—BLDSC (7236.275000), IE, ingenta.

Published by: (Czech Technical University, Department of Electromagnetic Field), Brno University of Technology, Faculty of Electrical Engineering and Communication, Department of Radio Electronics, Purkynova 118, Brno, 612 00, Czech Republic. http://www.feec.vutbr.zc/UREL/RADIOENG/. Ed. Ivana Jakubova. adv.: B&W page USD 250. **Subscr. to:** Czech Technical University, Department of Electromagnetic Field, Technicka 2, Prague 166 27, Czech Republic.

621.38   BLR   ISSN 0236-4964
RADIOLYUBITEL'. Text in Russian. 1991. m. USD 36 (effective 1995). adv.
Published by: Infotekh, PO Box 41, Minsk, 220050, Belarus. TEL 375-172-786750, FAX 375-172-783016. Ed. Valentin Benzar'. Circ: 50,000.

384.5   GBR
THE RADIOPHILE. Text in English. q. GBP 20 domestic; GBP 26 foreign (effective 2000). adv. **Document type:** Newsletter. **Description:** Covers all aspects of the vintage radio hobby.
Published by: Radiophile, Dept. NC, Larkhill, Newport Rd,, Woodseaves, Staffs ST20 0NP, United Kingdom. TEL 44-1785-284696, FAX 44-1785-284696. Ed., Pub., R&P, Adv. contact Chas E Miller.

RADIORAMA; practica electronica - t.v. - radio - hi-fi - ciencia. see COMMUNICATIONS—Television And Cable

621.38   RUS   ISSN 0033-8486
TK5700   CODEN: RATEAO
RADIOTEKHNIKA. Text in Russian. 1946. m. USD 683 foreign (effective 2005). adv. bk.rev. charts; illus. index. **Document type:** Journal, Academic/Scholarly.
Indexed: C&ISA, E&CAJ, EngInd, IAA, Inspec, MathR, RefZh, SolStAb.
—AskIEEE, CISTI, East View, Linda Hall. **CCC.**
Published by: (Rossiiskoe Nauchno-Tekhnicheskoe Obshchestvo Raditekhniki), Izdatel'stvo Radiotekhnika, Kuznetskii Most 20/6, Moscow, 103031, Russian Federation. iprzhr@online.ru, http://webcenter.ru/~iprzhr/. Ed. Yu.V Gulyaev. **US dist. addr.:** East View Information Services, 3020 Harbor Ln. N., Minneapolis, MN 55447. TEL 763-550-0961, FAX 763-559-2931, eastview@eastview.com, http://www.eastview.com.

621.38   RUS   ISSN 0033-8494
TK7800   CODEN: RAELA4
RADIOTEKHNIKA I ELEKTRONIKA. Contents page in English. 1956. m. RUR 930 for 6 mos. domestic (effective 2004). adv. bk.rev. charts; illus. index. **Document type:** Journal, Academic/Scholarly. **Description:** Deals with circuit theory, electrodynamics, wave propagation, magnetics, communications theory, antennas and waveguides, signal processing, solid-state theory and devices.
Related titles: Online - full text ed.; ♦ English ed.: Journal of Communications Technology and Electronics. ISSN 1064-2269; ♦ English Translation: Journal of Communications Technology and Electronics. ISSN 1064-2269.
Indexed: ASCA, BrCerAb, C&ISA, CIN, CMCI, CerAb, ChemAb, ChemTitl, CorrAb, CurCont, E&CAJ, EMA, EngInd, IAA, ISR, Inspec, M&TEA, MBF, METADEX, MathR, RefZh, SCI, SolStAb, WAA.
—BLDSC (0139.000000), AskIEEE, CASDDS, CINDOC, CISTI, East View, IDS, Linda Hall. **CCC.**
Published by: (Rossiiskaya Akademiya Nauk/Russian Academy of Sciences), Izdatel'stvo Nauka, Profsoyuznaya ul 90, Moscow, 117864, Russian Federation. TEL 7-095-3347151, FAX 7-095-4202220, secret@naukaran.ru, http://www.maik.rssi.ru/cgi-bin/list.pl?page=radel, http://www.naukaran.ru. Circ: 5,500.

384.5   SWE   ISSN 1400-7053
RATEKO & FOTO. Text in Swedish. 1955. 10/yr. adv.
Former titles (until vol. 10, 1994): Rateko (0033-9962); (until vol. 3, 1983): Rateko med Radiohandlaren; (until vol. 5, 1967): Rateko
Indexed: B&I.
Published by: Elektronikfoerbundet Svenska, Kungsgatan 19, PO Box 1408, Stockholm, 11184, Sweden. TEL 46-08-545-168-80, FAX 46-08-545-168-91, jan@elektronikforbundet.se, http://www.elektronikforbundet.se. Ed. Jan Ljuhs TEL 08-545-168-80. Circ: 5,300.

REFERATIVNYI ZHURNAL. PROEKTIROVANIE, KONSTRUIROVANIE, TEKHNOLOGIYA I OBORUDOVANIE DLYA RADIOTEKHNICHESKOGO PROIZVODSTVA. see ELECTRONICS—Abstracting, Bibliographies, Statistics

REFERATIVNYI ZHURNAL. RADIOPEREDAYUSHCHIE I RADIOPRIEMNYE USTROISTVA. RADIOTEKHNICHESKIE IZMERENIYA. see ELECTRONICS—Abstracting, Bibliographies, Statistics

REFERATIVNYI ZHURNAL. RADIOSVYAZ'. RADIOVESHCHANIE. TELEVIDENIE. see COMMUNICATIONS—Abstracting, Bibliographies, Statistics

REFERATIVNYI ZHURNAL. RADIOTEKHNIKA. see ELECTRONICS—Abstracting, Bibliographies, Statistics

REFERATIVNYI ZHURNAL. TEORETICHESKAYA RADIOTEKHNIKA. ANTENNY. VOLNOVODY. OB'EMNYE REZONATORY. RASPROSTRANENIE RADIOVOLN. see ELECTRONICS—Abstracting, Bibliographies, Statistics

384.5   FRA   ISSN 0989-5981
REPERTOIRE DES RADIOSIGNAUX. Text in French. 1977. a. **Document type:** Government. **Description:** Lists the major radio signals, beacons, and stations giving navigation information.
Related titles: ♦ Series of: Les Ouvrages de Radiosignaux.
Published by: Service Hydrographique et Oceanographique de la Marine, 3 av. Octave Greard, Armees, 00300, France. TEL 98-03-09-17, FAX 98-47-11-42, TELEX HYDRO 940568. **Subscr. to:** EPSHOM, B.P. 426, Brest Cedex 29275, France.

384.5   BRA
REVISTA MONITOR DE RADIO E TELEVISAO∗ . Text in Portuguese. 1947. m. adv.
Published by: Instituto Radio Tecnico Monitor S.A., Rua Timburiba, 263, VI Mariana, Sao Paulo, SP 04119-080, Brazil. Ed. Octavio A de Toledo Assumpacao. Circ: 23,000.

384.5   DEU   ISSN 0323-5998
RUNDFUNK- UND FERNSEHPROGRAMM. Text in German. 1969. w. adv. **Document type:** Consumer.
Published by: Deutscher Supplement Verlag GmbH, Breslauer Str 300, Nuernberg, 90471, Germany. TEL 0911-89201-0, FAX 0911-8920135. Adv. contact Annelore Rupp. Circ: 510,202.

S A A R F RADIO AUDIENCE MEASUREMENT SURVEY. see COMMUNICATIONS—Abstracting, Bibliographies, Statistics

S P E R ANNUAIRE. see ELECTRONICS

S R D S RADIO ADVERTISING SOURCE. see ADVERTISING AND PUBLIC RELATIONS—Abstracting, Bibliographies, Statistics

384.5   CHE
S R G - S S R IDEE SUISSE. GESCHAEFTSBERICHT. Text in German. 1931. a. free. back issues avail. **Document type:** Monographic series, Trade.
Former titles: Schweizerische Radio- und Fernsehgesellschaft. Geschaeftsbericht; (until 1992): Schweizerische Radio- und Fernsehgesellschaft. Jahrbuch
Related titles: French ed.
Published by: S R G - S S R Idee Suisse, PO Box, Bern 15, 3000, Switzerland. TEL 41-31-3509111, FAX 41-31-3509735, christine.stalder@srg-ssr-idee-suisse.ch, http://www.srg-ssr-idee-suisse.ch. Circ: 8,000.

384.5   CHE
S R G - S S R IDEE SUISSE. PORTRAIT. Text in French. 1999. a. free. **Document type:** Monographic series, Trade.
Related titles: Online - full text ed.; English ed.: S R G - S S R Idee Suisse. Profile; German ed.: S R G - S S R Idee Suisse. Portraet; Italian ed.: S R G - S S R Idee Suisse. Primo Piano.
Published by: S R G - S S R Idee Suisse, PO Box, Bern 15, 3000, Switzerland. TEL 41-31-3509111, FAX 41-31-3509735, christine.stalder@srg-ssr-idee-suisse.ch, http://www.srg-ssr-idee-suisse.ch. Circ: 8,000 (controlled).

384.5   DEU
S R INFO. Text in German. 1972. m. **Document type:** Bulletin.
Published by: Saarlaendischer Rundfunk, Funkhaus Halberg, Saarbruecken, 66100, Germany. TEL 0681-6022040, FAX 0681-6022049. Ed. Rolf Dieter Ganz. Circ: 8,000.

SAT - AUDIO - VIDEO; postepy w elektronice powszechnego uzytku. see ELECTRONICS

384.5   USA   ISSN 1099-9612
SCANNING USA MAGAZINE. Text in English. 199?. m. USD 24.95, USD 35.95 (effective 2001). adv. **Document type:** Magazine, Consumer. **Description:** Contains the latest information on all aspects of radio scanning in the U.S. and Canada, including federal, military, trucking, aviation, and other fields.
Published by: Scanning USA, PO Box 9580, Naperville, IL 60567-0111. TEL 800-651-0922, FAX 815-722-0717, scanusa@compuserve.com, http://www.scanningusa.com. Pub. Alex Blaha.

384.5   SWE   ISSN 1104-909X
SE & HOER. Text in Swedish. 1994. w. SEK 790 (effective 2005). adv. bk.rev.; film rev.; play rev. abstr.; illus. **Document type:** Magazine, Consumer. **Description:** Program guide for radio and television in Sweden.
Formed by merger of (1964-1994): Haent i Veckan (0345-4843); (1957-1994): Roester i Radio TV (0035-7839)
Indexed: RILM.
Published by: Allers Foerlag AB, Landskronavaegen 23, Helsingborg, 25185, Sweden. TEL 46-42-173500, FAX 46-42-173682, http://www.soh.se, http://www.allersforlag.se. Ed. Tua Lundstroem. Adv. contact Lilimor Werre TEL 46-8-6794681. page SEK 30,000; trim 190 x 265. Circ: 139,300 (paid).

621.384   USA
SHORTWAVE RADIO TODAY; the DX radio magazine for active SWL'S. Text in English. 1971. m. USD 23. bk.rev. **Document type:** Bulletin. **Description:** Provides up-to-date information on shortwave radio broadcasting, including schedules, rare catches of distant stations, and general radio news.
Formerly: Speedx (0882-8091)
Published by: Donald Thornton Ed. & Pub., 401 Amwell Rd., Bell Mead, NJ 08502. FAX 903-255-9220. Circ: 500. **Subscr. to:** PO Box 196, Du Bois, PA 15801-0196.

SIGNIS MEDIA; cine video radio internet television. see MOTION PICTURES

384.54   FRA
SON - MAGAZINE. Text in French. 1969. m. adv.
Published by: N E M M, 63 av. des Champs Elysees, Paris, 75008, France.

384.5   USA
THE SOURCE GUIDE. Text in English. 1993. a. USD 129 (effective 2000). adv.
Published by: Source Guide, PO Box 782, Springfield, VA 22150. TEL 703-719-9500, FAX 703-719-7910. Ed. Dave Segler. R&P Ken Lee. Adv. contact John Neff.

621.38   USA
SOUTHEASTERN V H F SOCIETY CONFERENCE PROCEEDINGS. (Very High Frequency) Text in English. a. USD 15 (effective 1999). back issues avail. **Document type:** Proceedings. **Description:** Publishes papers presented on broadcasting in the VHF spectrum for amateur-radio enthusiasts.
Published by: American Radio Relay League, Inc., 225 Main St, Newington, CT 06111. TEL 860-594-0200, FAX 860-594-0303, http://www.arrl.org. R&P Mark Wilson. **Co-sponsor:** Southeastern VHF Society.

621.3673 616.07572   AUS
SPECTRUM (COLLINGWOOD). Text in English. 1994. 10/yr. AUD 100 (effective 2000). adv. back issues avail. **Document type:** Newsletter, Academic/Scholarly.
Published by: Australian Institute of Radiography, c/o E.M. Hughes Sec., PO Box 1169, Collingwood, VIC 3066, Australia. TEL 61-3-94193336, FAX 61-3-94160783, air@a-i-r.com/au. R&P E M Hughes. adv.: page AUD 550; trim 210 x 297.

SPOTS PLANUNGSDATEN HOERFUNK - FERNSEHEN. see BUSINESS AND ECONOMICS—Trade And Industrial Directories

STAND BY. see LABOR UNIONS

STREAMING MEDIA. see COMPUTERS—Internet

384.5   DEU
SUEDWESTDEUTSCHER EINZELHANDEL (FREIBURG). Text in German. m.
Published by: Landesgemeinschaft Radio-Elektro im Einzelhandel Baden-Wuerttemberg, Eisenbahnstr 68-70, Freiburg Im Breisgau, 79098, Germany.

384.5   DEU
SUEDWESTFUNK JOURNAL. Text in German. 1971. 10/yr. back issues avail. **Document type:** Newsletter.
Formerly: S W F Journal
Published by: Suedwestfunk Journal Verlag, Hans-Bredow-Str, Baden-Baden, 76530, Germany. TEL 49-7221-92203, FAX 49-7221-922013. Ed. Arthur Landwehr. Circ: 35,000.

SUMMARY OF WORLD BROADCASTS. PART 1: FORMER SOVIET UNION (DAILY). see BUSINESS AND ECONOMICS—Economic Situation And Conditions

SUMMARY OF WORLD BROADCASTS. PART 1: FORMER SOVIET UNION (WEEKLY ECONOMIC REPORT). see BUSINESS AND ECONOMICS—Economic Situation And Conditions

SUMMARY OF WORLD BROADCASTS. PART 2: CENTRAL EUROPE, THE BALKANS (DAILY). see BUSINESS AND ECONOMICS—Economic Situation And Conditions

SUMMARY OF WORLD BROADCASTS. PART 2: CENTRAL EUROPE, THE BALKANS (WEEKLY ECONOMIC REPORT). see BUSINESS AND ECONOMICS—Economic Situation And Conditions

SUMMARY OF WORLD BROADCASTS. PART 3: ASIA - PACIFIC (DAILY). see BUSINESS AND ECONOMICS—Economic Situation And Conditions

SUMMARY OF WORLD BROADCASTS. PART 3: ASIA - PACIFIC (WEEKLY ECONOMIC REPORT). see BUSINESS AND ECONOMICS—Economic Situation And Conditions

SUMMARY OF WORLD BROADCASTS. PART 4: MIDDLE EAST (DAILY). see BUSINESS AND ECONOMICS—Economic Situation And Conditions

▼ new title   ➤ refereed   ✳ unverified   ♦ full entry avail.

SUMMARY OF WORLD BROADCASTS. PART 4: MIDDLE EAST (WEEKLY ECONOMIC REPORT). see *BUSINESS AND ECONOMICS—Economic Situation And Conditions*

SUMMARY OF WORLD BROADCASTS. PART 5: AFRICA, LATIN AMERICA AND THE CARIBBEAN (DAILY). see *BUSINESS AND ECONOMICS—Economic Situation And Conditions*

SUMMARY OF WORLD BROADCASTS. PART 5: AFRICA, LATIN AMERICA AND THE CARIBBEAN (WEEKLY ECONOMIC REPORT). see *BUSINESS AND ECONOMICS—Economic Situation And Conditions*

621.384 POL ISSN 1425-1701
SWIAT RADIO. Text in Polish. 1995. m. PLZ 92.40 domestic; EUR 54 in Europe; EUR 68 elsewhere (effective 2005). **Document type:** *Magazine, Trade.*
Supersedes in part (in 1995): Od Radio do Audio (1233-5894)
Published by: A V T- Korporacja Sp. z o. o., ul Burleska 9, Warsaw, 01939, Poland. TEL 48-22-5689941, FAX 48-22-5689944, sp5aht@swiatradio.com.pl, redakcja@ep.com.pl, http://www.swiatradio.com.pl, http://www.avt.pl.

SYNDICAT DES INDUSTRIES DE MATERIEL PROFESSIONNEL ELECTRONIQUE ET RADIOELECTRIQUE. RAPPORT D'ACTIVITE. see *ELECTRONICS*

384.5 USA
TALK RADIO - TALK TV. Text in English. 1996. 2/yr. **Document type:** *Newsletter.* **Description:** Promotes and publicizes non-fiction book writers as potential interview guests on radio and television talk shows.
Published by: Strategic Marketing, 304 Warren Way, Bldg 2, Chapel Hill, NC 27516. TEL 919-942-8020, 800-277-8960, FAX 919-942-3094. Ed. Stephanie Volpe. Pub. H N Quoyoon. Circ: 3,874 (controlled).

TALK SHOW HOST DIRECTORY AND RESOURCE GUIDE. see *BUSINESS AND ECONOMICS—Trade And Industrial Directories*

384.5 USA
TALK SHOWS & HOSTS ON RADIO★ . Text in English. 1993. a. USD 37.95. **Document type:** *Directory.* **Description:** Lists radio talk shows and formats and contains biographical information on their hosts.
Published by: Whitefoord Press, 23814 Michigan Ave, 314, Dearborn, MI 48124-1829. TEL 800-972-2584, FAX 313-274-9263. Ed., Pub. Annie M Brewer.

384.5443 USA
TALKERS MAGAZINE. Text in English. 1990. 10/yr. USD 75 domestic; USD 100 foreign (effective 2004). adv. **Document type:** *Magazine, Trade.* **Description:** Covers news and issues about the talk radio industry.
Address: 650 Belmont Ave, Springfield, MA 01108. TEL 413-739-8255, FAX 413-746-6786, info@talkers.com, http://www.talkers.com/. Ed., Pub. Michael Harrison.

TELECOMMUNICATIONS AND RADIO ENGINEERING. see *COMMUNICATIONS*

TELEVISION WEEK. see *COMMUNICATIONS—Television And Cable*

384.5 SVK ISSN 0862-8122
TELEVIZIA A ROZHLAS; programovy tyzdennik. Text in Slovak. w. SKK 8.50 newsstand/cover. adv. film rev.; play rev. illus. **Document type:** *Consumer.* **Description:** Lists the week's television programs. Contains recipes and brief reviews.
Published by: Ringier Slovakia a. s., Prievozska 14, PO Box 46, Bratislava 24, 82004, Slovakia. TEL 42-7-363677, FAX 42-7-2104192. Ed. Ladislav Balaj. Adv. contact Monika Tordova. B&W page SKK 23,000, color page SKK 32,000; trim 212 x 270. Circ: 55,000.

TELEVIZIIA I RADIO. see *COMMUNICATIONS—Television And Cable*

621.384 CHN ISSN 1001-540X
TONGXIN JISHU YU FAZHAN/COMMUNICATION - TECHNOLOGY AND DEVELOPMENT. Text in Chinese; Abstracts in English. 1975. bi-m. CNY 54. adv.
Published by: Dianzi Gongye Bu, Wuxian Tongxin Zhuanye Qingbaowang/Ministry of Electronic Industry, Radio Communication Technology Information Exchange Organization, P.O. Box 174-215, Shijiazhuang, Hebei 050002, China. TEL 86-311-3033330. Ed. Zhao Hong. Adv. contact Cao Yutai. Circ: 5,000.

TRANS WORLD RADIO. see *RELIGIONS AND THEOLOGY*

384.5 NLD ISSN 0921-6677
TRANS WORLD RADIO INFO BULLETIN. Text in Dutch. 1966. 10/m. free. adv. illus. 4 p./no. 3 cols./p.; back issues avail. **Document type:** *Bulletin, Consumer.* **Description:** Includes missionary news, letters from listeners, updates of situations, and items for fundraising.
Former titles (until 1987): Toont de Wereld Haar Redder (0921-6707); (until 1974): Trans World Radio (0921-6715)
Published by: Trans World Radio Nederland en Belgie, Noordersingel 90a, Postbus 91, Voorthuizen, 3780 BB, Netherlands. TEL 31-342-478432, FAX 31-342-478343, twr.netherlands@wxs.nl, http://www.transworldradio.nl. Ed., Pub., R&P R Postuma. Circ: 15,000.

TVR-HET. see *COMMUNICATIONS—Television And Cable*

TVR USJAG. see *COMMUNICATIONS—Television And Cable*

791.4 CZE ISSN 1213-2098
TYDENIK ROZHLAS. Text in Czech. 1923. w. CZK 182 (effective 1992).
Formerly: Rozhlas (0231-6811)
Published by: Vydavatelstvi Radioservis a.s., Jeseniova 36, Praha 3, 13000, Czech Republic. TEL 02-21551348, info@radioservis-as.cz, http://www.radioservis-as.cz/. Ed. Stanislav Pscheidt. Circ: 170,000. **Subscr. to:** PNS - Ustredni Expedice a Dovoz Tisku Praha, Heliodora Piky 26, Zavod 1, Prague, Czech Republic.

384.5 GBR
U K SCANNING DIRECTORY. Text in English. irreg., latest vol.6, 1997. GBP 18.50. **Document type:** *Directory.*
—BLDSC (9082.667350).
Published by: Interproducts, 8 Abbot St, Perth, PH2 0EB, United Kingdom. TEL 44-1738-441199. Pub. R. Barnes. R&P R Barnes.

621.38 CAN ISSN 0049-5778
V E 6. Text in English. 1964. m. CND 5. adv.
Formerly (until 1971): Alberta Amateur (0002-4716)
Published by: Amateur Radio League of Alberta, P O Box 447, Thorhild, AB T0A 3J0, Canada. Ed. Vic Prodanink. Circ: 500.

384.5 GBR ISSN 0177-7505
V H F COMMUNICATIONS; a publication for the radio amateur, especially covering VHF, UHF and microwaves. (Very High Frequency) Text in English. 1969. q. GBP 20.75 (effective 2005). adv. index, cum.index: 1970-1989. back issues avail. **Document type:** *Magazine, Trade.* **Description:** Contains articles for radio amateurs, professionals and school personnel. Covers VHF, UHF and microwaves. Includes information about components.
Indexed: Inspec.
—BLDSC (9231.756000), CISTI, Linda Hall. **CCC.**
Published by: K M Publications, 63 Ringwood Rd, Luton, Beds LU2 7BG, United Kingdom. TEL 44-1582-581051, FAX 44-1582-581051, andy@vhfcomm.co.uk, http://www.vhfcomm.co.uk. Ed., R&P, Adv. contact Andy Barter. Circ: 4,500. **Affiliate:** A T V Q.

VERONICA; weekblad voor radio en TV. see *COMMUNICATIONS—Television And Cable*

VINTAGE NEWS; vintage radio and electronics collecting stuff. see *HOBBIES*

384.54 DEU
W W F TRANSPARENT. Text in German. 1988. bi-m.
Published by: Westdeutsche Rundfunkwerbung GmbH, Ludwigstr 11, Cologne, 50667, Germany. TEL 0221-2035208, FAX 0221-2035286. Ed. Thomas Straetling.

621.384 AUS ISSN 1031-6353
WHAT'S NEW IN RADIO COMMUNICATIONS. Text in English. 1982. bi-m. AUD 64 (effective 2003). adv. back issues avail. **Document type:** *Trade.* **Description:** New product information for radio communication engineers.
Published by: Westwick-Farrow Pty. Ltd., Locked Bag 1289, Wahroonga, NSW 2076, Australia. TEL 61-2-94872700, FAX 61-2-94891265, admin@westwick-farrow.com.au, http://www.westwick-farrow.com.au. Ed. Paul Searle. Pub. Adrian Farrow. Adv. contact Sandra Romanin TEL 61-3-93812952. Circ: 6,000 (controlled).

621.384 USA ISSN 0929-6212
TK6570.M6 CODEN: WPCOFW
➤ **WIRELESS PERSONAL COMMUNICATIONS**; an international journal. Text in English. 1994. 16/yr. EUR 1,418, USD 1,448, GBP 788 combined subscription to institutions print & online eds. (effective 2005). adv. reprint service avail. from PSC. **Document type:** *Journal, Academic/Scholarly.* **Description:** Publishes original archival-quality research studies considering theoretical, engineering and experimental aspects of wireless personal communications and radio communication of voice, data, images and multimedia combinations.
Related titles: Online - full text ed.: ISSN 1572-834X (from EBSCO Publishing, Gale Group, IngentaConnect, Kluwer Online, O C L C Online Computer Library Center, Inc., Ovid Technologies, Inc., Springer LINK, Swets Information Services).
Indexed: BibLing, CompLI, CurCont, EngInd, Inspec, RefZh.
—BLDSC (9324.700000), AskIEEE, CISTI, Ei, IE, Infotrieve, ingenta, Linda Hall. **CCC.**
Published by: Springer-Verlag New York, Inc. (Subsidiary of: Springer Science+Business Media), 233 Spring St, New York, NY 10013. TEL 212-460-1500, FAX 212-460-1575, service@springer-ny.com, http://springerlink.metapress.com/openurl.asp?genre=journal&issn=0929-6212, http://www.springer-ny.com. Ed. Ramjee Prasad. **Subscr. to:** Journal Fulfillment, PO Box 2485, Secaucus, NJ 07096-2485. TEL 201-348-4033, FAX 201-348-4505, journals@springer-ny.com.

384.5 GBR ISSN 1362-0983
P87
WORLD MEDIA. BROADCASTING NEWS. Variant title: Broadcasting News. Text in English. 1987. w. GBP 410 domestic; GBP 440 rest of Europe; GBP 456 elsewhere (effective 2000). adv. back issues avail. **Document type:** *Newspaper.*
Formerly (until 1996): Summary of World Broadcasts. Media. World Broadcasting Information (1352-1438); Which superseded in part (in Sep. 1993): World Broadcasting Information: Broadcasting News and Transmission (1350-8237)
Related titles: Online - full text ed.: GBP 425 (effective 2000) (from The Dialog Corporation).
Published by: B B C Monitoring, Caversham Park, Peppard Rd, Reading, Berks RG4 8TZ, United Kingdom. TEL 44-118-948-6289, FAX 44-118-946-3823, marketing@mon.bbc.co.uk, http://www.monitor.bbc.co.uk. Ed. Mike Elliott. R&P Rosy Wolfe. Adv. contact Marian Martin. Circ: 1,000.

384.5 USA ISSN 0144-7750
TK6540
WORLD RADIO T V HANDBOOK. Text in English. 1947. a. USD 19.95 (effective 1999). **Description:** Complete guide to international broadcasting.
—BLDSC (9358.700000).
Published by: V N U Business Publications (Subsidiary of: V N U Business Media), 770 Broadway, New York, NY 10003-9595. TEL 212-764-7300, 800-344-7119, FAX 212-944-1719. Ed. A G Sennitt. Circ: 55,000.

384.54 USA ISSN 1061-9240
WORLD SCANNER REPORT; a journal of VHF-UHF scanner technology & engineering. Text in English. 1991. m. USD 35 (effective 1999). adv. bk.rev. **Document type:** *Newsletter.* **Description:** Features do-it-yourself mods, soup-ups, hints and kinks for serious scanner needs.
Published by: Commtronics Engineering, PO Box 262478 C, San Diego, CA 92196-2478. TEL 619-578-9247, bcheek@cts.com, http://ourworld.compuserve.com/homepages/bcheek. Ed., Pub., R&P Bill Cheek. Adv. contact Cynthia Cheek.

384.5 USA
WORLDRADIO. Text in English. 1971. m. USD 15 domestic; USD 25 foreign (effective 2003). bk.rev. illus. 64 p./no.; back issues avail.; reprints avail. **Document type:** *Magazine, Consumer.* **Description:** Contains articles for the amateur radio hobbyist.
Published by: Worldradio, Inc., 2120 28th St, Sacramento, CA 95818. TEL 916-457-3655, n6wr@msn.com, http://www.wr6wr.com. Ed. Nancy Kott. Pub. Armond Noble. R&P Glen Rudesill. Adv. contact Brenda Evans. Circ: 30,000.

621.384 CHN ISSN 0512-4174
WUXIANDIAN/RADIO. Text in Chinese. 1955. m. CNY 81.60 (effective 2004). **Document type:** *Journal, Academic/Scholarly.*
Published by: Renmin Youdian Chubanshe/People's Posts and Telecommunications Publishing House, 14 A Xizhaosi Street, Chongwen District, Beijing, 100061, China. radio@radio.com.cn, abc@ptpress.com.cn, http://www.radio.com.cn/, http://www.ptpress.com.cn/. Ed. Wang Weimin.

621.384 CHN ISSN 1003-3106
WUXIANDIAN GONGCHENG/RADIO ENGINEERING. Text in Chinese. bi-m.
Related titles: Online - full text ed.: (from East View Information Services).
Published by: Jixie Dianzi Gongye Bu, 54 Suo/Ministry of Engineering and Electronic Industry, Institute No. 54, 11 Zhongshan Xilu, P.O. Box 174-215, Shijiazhuang, Hebei 050002, China. TEL 33330. Ed. Cui Yuchang.

621.384 CHN ISSN 1003-3114
WUXIANDIAN TONGXIN JISHU/RADIO COMMUNICATION TECHNOLOGY. Text in Chinese. bi-m.
Related titles: Online - full text ed.: (from East View Information Services).
Published by: Jixie Dianzi Gongye Bu, 54 Suo/Ministry of Engineering and Electronic Industry, Institute No. 54, 11 Zhongshan Xilu, P.O. Box 174-215, Shijiazhuang, Hebei 050002, China. TEL 33330. Ed. Yang Bangzhen.

WUXIANDIAN YU DIANSHI/RADIO AND TELEVISION. see *COMMUNICATIONS—Television And Cable*

ZIMPEL. TEIL 3: FUNK UND FERNSEHEN. see *COMMUNICATIONS—Television And Cable*

ZVUKOREZHISSIOR; informatsionno-tekhnicheskii zhurnal. see *COMMUNICATIONS—Television And Cable*

384.5443 AUS
2 C B A - F M NEWS. Text in English. 1967. m. AUD 10 (effective 1999). **Document type:** *Newsletter.* **Description:** Covers matters of interest to radio listeners, particularly 2CBA-FM Sydney.
Formerly (until 199?): Australian Radio Times (1035-106X)
Published by: Christian Broadcasting Association Ltd., 420 Lyons Rd, Five Dock, NSW 2046, Australia. TEL 61-2-9712-1111. Ed. Ken Bock. Circ: 10,000.

LES 2 ECRANS. see *COMMUNICATIONS—Television And Cable*

3 F M. see *HANDICAPPED—Visually Impaired*

621.384 USA ISSN 1073-1024
50 MHZ DX BULLETIN. Text in English. 1990. m. USD 24 domestic; USD 27 in Canada & Mexico; USD 30 elsewhere (effective 2005). adv. back issues avail. **Document type:** *Bulletin, Newsletter.* **Description:** Dedicated to the understanding and utilization of long-distance propagation in the 6-meter Amateur band.
Published by: Victor R. Frank, Ed. & Pub., 12450 Skyline Blvd, Woodside, CA 94062-4541. TEL 650-851-7031, frank@horizon.sri.com. R&P, Adv. contact Victor R Frank. Circ: 110.

COMMUNICATIONS—Telephone And Telegraph

A P A - JOURNAL. TELEKOM. see *COMMUNICATIONS*

384.029 GBR ISSN 1353-0356
HE8341
A P T YEARBOOK. (Asia - Pacific Telecommunity) Text in English. 1994. a. GBP 195, USD 315 (effective 2000). adv. **Document type:** *Directory.* **Description:** Lists communications services in Asia.
Published by: Icom Publications Ltd., Chancery House, St Nicholas Way, Sutton, Surrey SM1 1JB, United Kingdom. TEL 44-20-86421117, FAX 44-20-86421941, admin@icompub.com, http://www.icompub.com. Ed. A Narayan. adv.: B&W page USD 4,960, color page USD 6,485.

338.0029 USA
A T & T NATIONAL TOLL-FREE DIRECTORY - BUSINESS BUYER'S GUIDE - BUSINESS EDITION*. Text in English. 1984. s-a. USD 24.99 (effective 1999). adv. **Document type:** *Directory, Consumer.* **Description:** Lists over 120,000 toll-free numbers operating in the US. Listings that are included would be of interest to businesses.
Former titles (until Sep. 1996): A T & T Toll-Free 800 National Directory - Business Edition; A T & T Toll-Free 800 Directory for Business
Published by: A T & T Yellow Page Directories, National Toll Free Directory, P O Box 414991, Kansas City, MO 64141-4991. TEL 980-658-2255, 800-562-2255, http://www.tollfree.att.net. Pub. Patricia G Selden.

384.6 USA ISSN 1096-3537
A T & T NATIONAL TOLL-FREE DIRECTORY - SHOPPER'S GUIDE - CONSUMER EDITION*. Variant title: A T & T Nation Toll-Free Directory; A T & T National Toll-Free Shopper's Guide. Text in English. 1984. a. USD 14.99 (effective 1996). adv. **Document type:** *Directory, Consumer.*
Former titles (until Sep. 1996): A T & T Toll-Free 800 National Directory - Consumer Edition (1075-5950); A T & T Toll-Free 800 Directory - Consumer Edition; A T & T Toll-Free 800 Directory for Consumers (1064-962X)
Published by: A T & T Yellow Page Directories, National Toll Free Directory, P O Box 414991, Kansas City, MO 64141-4991. TEL 908-658-2255, 800-562-2255, http://www.tollfree.att.net.

384.1 USA
ABERDEEN GROUP. NEWSLETTER. Text in English. 2002. w. free.
Media: Online - full text.
Published by: Aberdeen Group, 260 Franklin St, Ste 1700, Boston, MA 02110. TEL 617-723-7890, http://www.aberdeen.com/. Ed. Isaac Roed.

384.53 384.555 USA
▼ **ABOVE GROUND LEVEL.** Text in English. 2005. 6/yr. **Document type:** *Magazine, Trade.* **Description:** Designed for communication professionals involved in the antenna siting, including site owners, site managers, operations/maintanance supervisors, service providers, consultants, investors and telecommunications tenants.
Published by: Biby Publishing, LLC, PO Box 284, Waterford, VA 20197. TEL 540-882-9292, http://www.agl-mag.com. Ed. Don Bishop. Pub. Rich Biby. Circ: 15,000.

384 378 USA
THE ACUTA JOURNAL OF TELECOMMUNICATIONS IN HIGHER EDUCATION. Text in English. 1997. q. **Document type:** *Trade.*
Published by: Acuta, 152 W Zandale Dr, Ste 200, Lexington, KY 40503-2486. TEL 606-278-3338, FAX 606-278-3268, pscott@acuta.org, http://www.acuta.org. Circ: 2,200 (paid).

384.6 USA ISSN 1541-1184
AFRICA & THE MIDDLE EAST TELECOM. Text in English. m. USD 1,240 in US & Canada; USD 1,340 elsewhere (effective 2003). **Document type:** *Newsletter, Trade.*
Related titles: E-mail ed.: USD 1,240 (effective 2003).
Published by: Information Gatekeepers, Inc., 320 Washington St, Ste 302, Brighton, MA 02135. TEL 617-782-5033, 800-323-1088, info@igigroup.com, http://www.igigroup.com/nl/pages/africa.html.

384.6 USA
AFRICA & THE MIDDLE EAST TELECOM NEWSLETTER. Text in English. 1999. m. USD 1,240 in US & Canada; USD 1,340 elsewhere (effective 2003). back issues avail.; reprints avail. **Document type:** *Newsletter, Trade.* **Description:** Keeps you up to date with these new developments, market opportunities, technologies and much more.
Formerly: Africa Telecom Newsletter (1531-4855)
Related titles: E-mail ed.: USD 1,240 (effective 2001); Online - full text ed.: (from Gale Group).
Published by: Information Gatekeepers, Inc., 320 Washington St, Ste 302, Brighton, MA 02135. TEL 617-782-5033, FAX 617-782-5735, editor@igigroup.com, info@igigroup.com, http://www.igigroup.com/nl/pages/africa.html. Ed. Hui Pan.

004.6 POL
➤ **AKADEMIA GORNICZO-HUTNICZA IM. STANISLAWA STASZICA. TELEKOMUNIKACJA CYFROWA - TECHNOLOGIA I USLUGI.** Text and summaries in Polish, English. 1998. s-a. PLZ 5 (effective 2002). abstr.; bibl. 90 p./no. 2 cols./p.; back issues avail. **Document type:** *Journal, Academic/Scholarly.* **Description:** Covers data collection systems, the technoeconomical aspects of telecommunication systems, Wireless Local Loop WLL, security of the information systems, ATM networks, broadband access networks, the management applications within computer and telecommunication networks, satellite communications, intelligent networks, cellular mobile networks, multimedia systems.
Published by: (Akademia Gorniczo-Hutnicza im. Stanislawa Staszica/University of Mining and Metallurgy), Wydawnictwo A G H, al Mickiewicza 30, Krakow, 30059, Poland. TEL 48-12-6364038, FAX 48-12-6364038, wydagh@uci.agh.edu.pl, http://galaxy.uci.agh.edu.pl~wydagh/. Ed. A J Wichur. Circ: 200 (paid). **Dist. by:** Ars Polona, Krakowskie Przedmiescie 7, Warsaw, Poland. arspolona@arspolona.com.pl, http://www.arspolona.com.pl.

621.38 FRA ISSN 1267-7167
TK5101.A1 CODEN: ATREFX
ALCATEL TELECOMMUNICATIONS REVIEW. Text in English. 1922. q. USD 20. charts; illus. index. reprint service avail. from PQC.
Former titles (until 1995): Electrical Communication (Paris) (1242-0565); (until 1993): Electrical Communication (Romford) (0013-4252)
Related titles: Microfilm ed.: (from PQC); ♦ German ed.: Alcatel Telecom Rundschau. ISSN 1266-3840; ♦ Spanish ed.: Revista de Telecomunicaciones de Alcatel. ISSN 1266-9091; ♦ French ed.: Revue des Telecommunications. ISSN 1243-7492.
Indexed: AS&TI, AcoustA, BrCerAb, BrTechI, C&ISA, CADCAM, Cadscan, CerAb, ChemAb, CompC, CompR, CorrAb, CurCont, E&CAJ, EMA, EngInd, IAA, Inspec, LeadAb, M&TEA, MBF, METADEX, RefZh, SSCI, SolStAb, TelAb, WAA, Zincscan.
—BLDSC (0786.707500), AskIEEE, CINDOC, CISTI, Ei, IDS, IE, ingenta, Linda Hall. **CCC.**
Published by: Alcatel, 54 rue la Boetie, Paris, 75008, France. TEL 33-1-69631650, http://www.alcatel.fr/. Ed. Catherine Camus. Circ: 31,000.

AMERICAN TELEMARKETING ASSOCIATION. JOURNAL. see *BUSINESS AND ECONOMICS—Marketing And Purchasing*

384.6 USA ISSN 1075-5292
TK1 CODEN: ANETE4
AMERICA'S NETWORK. Text in English. 1909. 18/yr., latest vol.105. USD 100 domestic; USD 135 in Canada & Mexico; USD 150 elsewhere; USD 10 newsstand/cover domestic; USD 12 newsstand/cover in Canada & Mexico; USD 14 newsstand/cover elsewhere (effective 2005). adv. bk.rev. illus.; tr.lit. back issues avail. **Document type:** *Magazine, Trade.* **Description:** For the telephone operating industry: management, engineering, plant installation, commercial, marketing, traffic and accounting.
Formerly (until 1994): Telephone Engineer and Management (0040-263X)
Related titles: Microform ed.: (from PMC, PQC); Online - full text ed.: (from bigchalk, EBSCO Publishing, Florida Center for Library Automation, Gale Group, H.W. Wilson, Northern Light Technology, Inc., O C L C Online Computer Library Center, Inc., ProQuest Information & Learning, The Dialog Corporation).
Indexed: ABIn, B&I, BPI, BusI, CADCAM, CurCont, Inspec, LRI, Microcompind, PROMT, T&II, TelAb.
—BLDSC (0858.570000), AskIEEE, CISTI, IDS, IE, ingenta, Linda Hall. **CCC.**
Published by: Advanstar Communications, Inc., 100 W Monroe St, Ste 1100, Chicago, IL 60603-1905. TEL 312-553-8900, FAX 312-553-8926, jengebretson@advanstar.com, info@advanstar.com, http://www.americasnetwork.com, http://www.advanstar.com. Ed. Lester Craft. adv.: B&W page USD 6,660, color page USD 8,880. Circ: 62,787 (paid and controlled). **Subscr. to:** Advanstar Marketing Services, Customer Service Department, 131 West, First St, Duluth, MN 55802. TEL 218-723-9477, 888-527-7008, FAX 218-723-9437.

384.6 USA
AMERICA'S PAY-PER-CALL DIRECTORY*; a billion dollar baby. Text in English. 1991. a. USD 19.95. **Document type:** *Directory.* **Description:** Comprehensive listing of 900 and 976 phone numbers and the cost to make these phone calls.
Published by: Infoman Publishing, c/o Barry Winton, Box 3707, Stateline, NV 89449-3707.

ARAB BANKING AND FINANCE. see *BUSINESS AND ECONOMICS—Banking And Finance*

384.6 USA ISSN 1097-8283
ASIA - PACIFIC TELECOM NEWSLETTER. Text in English. 1997. m. USD 695 in US & Canada; USD 745 elsewhere (effective 2005). **Document type:** *Newsletter, Trade.* **Description:** Provides market insights into the effect of developments, products, competition, technology and standards in the Asia-Pacific telecom market.
Related titles: Online - full text ed.: USD 695 (effective 2004) (from Florida Center for Library Automation, Gale Group, O C L C Online Computer Library Center, Inc., ProQuest Information & Learning).
Published by: Information Gatekeepers, Inc., 320 Washington St, Ste 302, Brighton, MA 02135. TEL 617-782-5033, 617-782-5735, 800-323-1088, info@igigroup.com, http://www.igigroup.com/nl/pages/teleasia.html. Ed. Hui Pan. Pub. Dr. Paul Polishuk.

384.5 GBR
ASIA - PACIFIC TELECOMMUNITY JOURNAL. Abbreviated title: A P T. Text in English. 1989. q. GBP 45, USD 75 (effective 1999). adv. **Document type:** *Trade.* **Description:** Publishes research papers on telecommunications developments in Asia.
Published by: (Asia - Pacific Telecommunity), Icom Publications Ltd., Chancery House, St Nicholas Way, Sutton, Surrey SM1 1JB, United Kingdom. TEL 44-20-86421117, FAX 44-20-86421941, admin@icompub.com, http://www.icompub.com. Ed. A Narayan. Pub. Alec Barton. Adv. contact Kevin French. B&W page USD 1,428, color page USD 2,142. Circ: 1,172.

384.6 GBR ISSN 1355-0071
ASIA - PACIFIC TELECOMS ANALYST. Text in English. 1994. fortn. GBP 495, USD 742. charts; stat. **Document type:** *Newsletter.* **Description:** Covers business, legislative, and technical developments in the Asia-Pacific telecommunications market. Provides market analyses and forecasts.
Related titles: Online - full text ed.: (from Gale Group, O C L C Online Computer Library Center, Inc.).
Indexed: B&I.
Published by: Financial Times Telecoms & Media Publishing (Subsidiary of: Financial Times Group), Maple House, 149 Tottenham Court Rd, London, W1P 9LL, United Kingdom. TEL 0171-896-2234, FAX 0171-896-2256. Ed. Jenny Walker.

384 GBR ISSN 0952-7516
HE8410.5.A1
ASIAN COMMUNICATIONS. Text in English; Summaries in Chinese, English. 1987. 11/yr. GBP 115, USD 185 includes supplements (effective 2000). adv. **Document type:** *Trade.* **Description:** Contains news, product information and technical features.
Related titles: Online - full text ed.: (from O C L C Online Computer Library Center, Inc.).
Indexed: ASFA, B&I, ESPM.
Published by: Icom Publications Ltd., Chancery House, St Nicholas Way, Sutton, Surrey SM1 1JB, United Kingdom. TEL 44-20-86421117, FAX 44-20-86421941, admin@icompub.com, http://www.icompub.com. Ed. Michael Schwartz. Pub. Alec Barton. adv.: B&W page USD 5,450, color page USD 7,540; trim 210 x 280. Circ: 20,000.

384.53 SGP
ASIAN MOBILE NEWS. Text in English. m. USD 360 (effective 2005). adv. **Document type:** *Magazine, Trade.* **Description:** Covers all new handsets, applications, technology and people in mobile telecoms in Asia.
Published by: Charlton Media Group, 9B Stanley St, Singapore, 068728, Singapore. TEL 65-6223-7660, admin@charltonmedia.com, http://www.charltonmedia.com. Ed. Angela McFeeters. Pub. Timothy Charlton.

384 USA
AT THE L A T A LEVEL; news digest of telecommunications activities on a state-by-state basis. Text in English. 50/yr. USD 365.
Published by: United Communications Group, 11300 Rockville Pike Ste 1100, Rockville, MD 20852-3030. TEL 301-816-8950.

C

384.646029 USA ISSN 1042-6329
AUDIOTEX DIRECTORY & BUYER'S GUIDE. Text in English. 1988. a. USD 55 domestic; USD 60 in Canada; USD 65 elsewhere. adv. **Document type:** *Directory.* **Description:** Lists products and services in the audiotex, fax, and voice processing marketplace. Helps users locate hardware and software vendors, telephone companies, service bureaus, voiceover producers, consultants, and other support firms from over 1200 company listings.
Published by: A D B G Publishing, PO Box 25929, Los Angeles, CA 90025. TEL 310-479-3533, FAX 310-479-0654. Circ: 10,000.

384.5 658 USA ISSN 1063-1348
AUDIOTEX NEWS✶; the information & entertainment-by-phone newsletter. Text in English. 1989. m. looseleaf. USD 249 (effective 1998). bk.rev. back issues avail.; reprints avail. **Document type:** *Newsletter.* **Description:** Covers the domestic and international pay-per-call industry. Provides insights, analysis, information, news, trends and regulations, and related products.
Formerly: Ideal Dial
Related titles: Diskette ed.: 1989.
Address: PO Box 220214, Great Neck, NY 11022-0214. TEL 516-735-3398, FAX 516-735-3682, carol@audiotexnews.com, http://www.audiotexnews.com. Ed. Carol Morse Ginsburg. R&P Dory Kane TEL 800-735-3398. Circ: 1,000.

384.0285 GBR
B T TODAY. Text in English. 1981. m. free to B T staff and pensioners. adv. bk.rev. illus. back issues avail. **Document type:** *Newspaper.*
Formerly (until Apr. 1991): Telecom Today
Related titles: Online - full text ed.: (from Data-Star, The Dialog Corporation).
Published by: British Telecommunications plc., 81 Newgate St, Rm B6.G, London, EC14 7AJ, United Kingdom. TEL 44-171-356-6543, FAX 44-171-356-5520, TELEX 261127, martin.burr@bt.com. Ed. Ken Runicles. Circ: 190,000.

621.38 USA ISSN 1089-7089
TK5101.A1 CODEN: BLTJFD
➤ **BELL LABS TECHNICAL JOURNAL.** Text in English. 1922. q. USD 270 domestic to institutions; USD 310 in Canada & Mexico to institutions; USD 344 elsewhere to institutions; USD 297 combined subscription domestic to institutions print & online eds.; USD 337 combined subscription in Canada & Mexico to institutions print & online eds.; USD 371 combined subscription elsewhere to institutions print & online eds. (effective 2006). bibl.; charts; illus. Index. **Document type:** *Journal, Academic/Scholarly.* **Description:** Fosters technical excellence and innovation among the technical community of Lucent Technologies and promotes progress in communications fields worldwide.
Former titles (until 1997): A T & T Technical Journal (8756-2324); (until 1985): A T & T Bell Laboratories Technical Journal (0748-612X); (until 1984): Bell System Technical Journal (0005-8580)
Related titles: Microform ed.: (from PMC, PQC); Online - full text ed.: ISSN 1538-7305. USD 270 to institutions (effective 2006) (from EBSCO Publishing, H.W. Wilson, O C L C Online Computer Library Center, Inc., ProQuest Information & Learning, Swets Information Services, Wiley InterScience).
Indexed: AIA, AJEE, AS&TI, ASCA, ApMecR, C&CSA, CADCAM, CIS, ChemAb, CompAb, CompC, CompD, CurCont, EEA, EngInd, ErgAb, IAA, ISR, Inspec, JCLA, MathR, PsycholAb, RefZh, SCI, SSCI, ST&MA, TelAb, ZentMath.
—BLDSC (1889.100000), AskIEEE, CASDDS, CISTI, Ei, IDS, IE, Infotrieve, ingenta, Linda Hall. **CCC.**
Published by: (Lucent Technologies), John Wiley & Sons, Inc., 111 River St, Hoboken, NJ 07030-5774. TEL 201-748-6000, FAX 201-748-5915, http://www.wiley.com/WileyCDA/WileyTitle/productCd-BLTJ.html. Ed. Frances A Grimes. R&P Sally Kempner TEL 908-582-4823. Circ: 28,000.

621.38 USA ISSN 1094-3323
P96.T42
BELL LABS TECHNOLOGY. Text in English. 1997. q.
Indexed: Inspec.
—Linda Hall.
Published by: Lucent Technologies, 600 Mountain Ave., Rm. 3C-412, Box 636, Murray Hill, NJ 07974-0636. TEL 908-582-4834, FAX 908-582-4430, technology@bell-labs.com, http://lucent.netlabs.net/minds/trends. Ed. Patrick S Regan.

BETTER BUSINESS BY TELEPHONE. see *BUSINESS AND ECONOMICS—Management*

384.6 DEU
BILLIGER-TELEFONIEREN. Text in German. 1998. bi-m. adv. **Document type:** *Magazine, Consumer.* **Description:** Provides information on the latest mobile communications hardware and calling plans available.
Published by: Michael E. Brieden Verlag GmbH, Gartroper Str 42, Duisburg, 47138, Germany. TEL 49-203-42920, FAX 49-203-4292149, info@brieden.de, http://www.billiger-telefonieren.de, http://www.brieden.de.

BILLING & CUSTOMER CARE REVIEW. see *BUSINESS AND ECONOMICS—Accounting*

384.6 USA ISSN 1544-7375
BILLING WORLD AND O S S TODAY. (Operational Support Systems) Text in English. 2001. m. USD 95 foreign (effective 2001); Free to qualified subscribers. adv. **Document type:** *Magazine, Trade.* **Description:** Covers billing systems and operational support systems for the telecommunications industry.
Formed by the merger of (1995-2001): Billing World (1081-9401); (19??-2001): TelOSSource
Related titles: Online - full content ed.
Published by: TeleStrategies, Inc., 7918 Jones Branch Drive, Third Fl, McLean, VA 22102. TEL 703-734-7050, FAX 703-893-3197, info@telestrategies.com, http://www.billingworld.com, http://www.telestrategies.com/. Ed. Jill Morgan.

THE BLUE BOOK (YEAR) T D I NATIONAL DIRECTORY & RESOURCE GUIDE; promoting equal access to telecommunications and media for people who are deaf, late-deafened, hard-of-hearing or deaf-blind. see *HANDICAPPED—Hearing Impaired*

384.6 CAN ISSN 1198-0249
BOTTIN INTERNATIONAL DU QUEBEC. Text in French. 1993. a. CND 39.95. **Document type:** *Directory.*
Published by: Quebec dans le Monde, C P 8503, Sainte Foy, PQ G1V 4N5, Canada. TEL 418-659-5540, FAX 418-659-4143. Ed. Denis Turcotte.

BROADBAND WIRELESS DATA REVIEW. see *COMPUTERS—Data Communications And Data Transmission Systems*

384 USA ISSN 0162-3885
HF5717 CODEN: BCORBD
BUSINESS COMMUNICATIONS REVIEW. Text in English. 1971. m. USD 45 in US & Canada; USD 70 elsewhere (effective 2005). adv. bk.rev. illus. index. back issues avail.; reprint service avail. from PQC. **Document type:** *Journal, Trade.* **Description:** Analysis of issues, trends, new products and services affecting communications network.
Related titles: Microform ed.: (from PQC); Online - full text ed.: (from bigchalk, EBSCO Publishing, Florida Center for Library Automation, Gale Group, H.W. Wilson, Northern Light Technology, Inc., O C L C Online Computer Library Center, Inc., ProQuest Information & Learning).
Indexed: ABIn, BPI, CADCAM, CompC, CurCont, Inspec, TelAb.
—BLDSC (2933.360000), AskIEEE, CASDDS, IDS, IE, Infotrieve, ingenta. **CCC.**
Published by: Key3Media Group, Inc., 795 Folsom St., San Francisco, CA 94107-1243. fknight@bcr.com, http://www.bcr.com/bcrmag, http://www.key3media.com/. Circ: 13,759 (paid and free).

384.5 USA
C C M I GUIDE TO NETWORKING SERVICES. VOLUME 1: INTERLATA SWITCHED SERVICES. Text in English. base vol. plus m. updates. looseleaf. USD 629. adv. **Document type:** *Directory.* **Description:** Provides the rates for AT&T, MCI, Sprint, Worldcom, Frontier, Vnet, VPN, SDN, Plat, Rate Plus, 800 services, Clarity, Premier, etc. Includes high-volume WATS and virtual networks. Includes interstate rates and intrastate, interLATA rates for each of the 48 continental states.
Former titles: Planning Guide 3. Value-Added Networks and Data Private Line. Telecommunications Rates Services; V A N and Resale Carrier Guide
Published by: C C M I (Subsidiary of: United Communications Group), 11300 Rockville Pike, Ste 1100, Rockville, MD 20852-3030. TEL 301-287-2257, FAX 301-816-8945, http://www.ucg.com. Ed. Belinda Jarvis. Pub. George David. R&P Michael Peck. Adv. contact Betty Lehnus.

384.5 USA
C C M I GUIDE TO NETWORKING SERVICES. VOLUME 2: INTRALATA SWITCHED SERVICES. Text in English. base vol. plus m. updates. looseleaf. USD 629. **Document type:** *Directory.* **Description:** Gives rates for local calling plans for every Bell operated company for all states.
Published by: C C M I (Subsidiary of: United Communications Group), 11300 Rockville Pike, Ste 1100, Rockville, MD 20852-3030. TEL 301-287-2257, FAX 301-816-8945, http://www.ucg.com. Ed. Belinda Jarvis. Pub. George David. R&P Michael Peck.

384.5 USA
C C M I GUIDE TO NETWORKING SERVICES. VOLUME 3: INTERLATA PRIVATE LINE SERVICES. Text in English. base vol. plus m. updates. looseleaf. USD 629. **Document type:** *Directory.* **Description:** Gives exect current rates for all the dedicated services offered by long-distance carrirs, Accunet, TDS, and Clearline digital services from fractional T-1 to T-45, plus DDS and voicegrade private line, exchange carrier special access and a special section on Frame relay from the IXCs and LECs.
Published by: C C M I (Subsidiary of: United Communications Group), 11300 Rockville Pike, Ste 1100, Rockville, MD 20852-3030. TEL 301-287-2257, FAX 301-816-8945. Ed. Belinda Jarvis. Pub. George David. R&P Michael Peck.

384.5 USA
C C M I GUIDE TO NETWORKING SERVICES. VOLUME 4: INTRALATA PRIVATE LINE SERVICES. Text in English. base vol. plus m. updates. looseleaf. USD 629. **Document type:** *Directory.* **Description:** Describes high-capacity, DDS and voice grade services offered by local exchange carriers. Organized by Bell regional holding company.
Published by: C C M I (Subsidiary of: United Communications Group), 11300 Rockville Pike, Ste 1100, Rockville, MD 20852-3030. TEL 301-287-2257, FAX 301-816-8945. Ed. Belinda Jarvis. Pub. George David. R&P Michael Peck.

384.5 USA
C C M I GUIDE TO NETWORKING SERVICES. VOLUME 5: INTERNATIONAL SERVICES. Text in English. base vol. plus m. updates. looseleaf. USD 629. **Document type:** *Directory.* **Description:** Gives rates for basic international toll and special services such as AT&T International Skynet. Other services covered include international Megacom, international SDN, international DDS, international Clarity from Sprint. A comprehensive Canadian section includes MTS, WATS and 800 services, plus private line services.
Published by: C C M I (Subsidiary of: United Communications Group), 11300 Rockville Pike, Ste 1100, Rockville, MD 20852-3030. TEL 301-287-2257, FAX 301-816-8945. Ed. Belinda Jarvis. Pub. George David. R&P Michael Peck.

384.5 USA
C C M I GUIDE TO NETWORKING SERVICES. VOLUME 6: REFERENCE FACTBOOK. Text in English. base vol. plus updates 4/yr. looseleaf. USD 395. **Document type:** *Directory.* **Description:** Lists all the NPA-NXXs in the country; points of presence, with service available, for the Big Three; area codes organized numerically and alphabetically; a list of LATAs by state and states by LATAs; maps of all 50 states showing the territories of both Bell and independent operating companies.
Published by: C C M I (Subsidiary of: United Communications Group), 11300 Rockville Pike, Ste 1100, Rockville, MD 20852-3030. TEL 301-287-2257, FAX 301-816-8945. Ed. Belinda Jarvis. Pub. George David. R&P Michael Peck.

621.3845 GBR ISSN 1467-1034
C D M A WORLD. (Code Division Multiple Access) Text in English. 1997. a.
Formerly (until 1999): C D M A Spectrum (1368-9460)
Related titles: Online - full text ed.: (from Gale Group).
Published by: Mobile Communications International (MCI), I B C Business Publishing Ltd. (Subsidiary of: I B C Group Plc), Gilmoora House, 57-61 Mortimer St, London, W1N 8JK, United Kingdom. TEL 44-20-7637-4383, FAX 44-20-7636-6414.

621.38 GBR
C E M A TELECOMMUNICATIONS. Text in English. 1987. m. GBP 2,000 (effective 1999). bk.rev. **Document type:** *Newsletter.*
Published by: (Cores European Market Analysis), Portman Communications Ltd., 52 Foundling Ct, London, WC1N 1AN, United Kingdom. TEL 44-171-837-0815, FAX 44-171-278-9917, 100141.676@compuserve. Ed., Pub., R&P Philip Gallagher. Circ: 500.

C S E L T TECHNICAL REPORTS/C S E L T RAPPORTI TECNICI. see *COMMUNICATIONS*

384.6 USA ISSN 1060-3050
TK5101.A1
CABLING BUSINESS MAGAZINE. Text in English. 1991. m. USD 25 in Canada & Mexico; USD 75 elsewhere. adv. **Document type:** *Trade.* **Description:** For users and providers of voice and data wiring and cabling.
Published by: Cabling Publications Inc., 12035 Shiloh Rd, Ste 350, Dallas, TX 75228. TEL 214-328-1717, FAX 214-319-6077, http://www.cablingbusiness.com. Ed. Stephen C Paulov. Pub. Stephen S Paulov. R&P Felicity Reed-Sumner. Adv. contact Teresa McCore. B&W page USD 3,512, color page USD 4,602; trim 10.88 x 8.38. Circ: 35,000.

384.6 CAN ISSN 1711-7666
CABLING NETWORKING SYSTEMS. Abbreviated title: C N S. Text in English. 1998. 8/yr. CND 22.95 domestic; USD 30.95 foreign (effective 2005). **Document type:** *Magazine, Trade.* **Description:** Covers industry-related news, developments, issues, and resources for those involved in all aspects of the cabling arena.
Formerly (until 2004): Cabling Systems (1488-2027)
Published by: Business Information Group, 12 Concorde Pl, Ste 800, Toronto, ON M3C 4J2, Canada. TEL 416-442-5600, 800-668-2374, FAX 416-442-2191, http://www.cablingsystems.com, http://www.businessinformationgroup.ca. Circ: 11,000.

384.6 TWN ISSN 1562-1227
CALL. Text in English. 1999. m. TWD 1,357; TWD 119 newsstand/cover (effective 2001). **Document type:** *Magazine, Consumer.* **Description:** Covers the latest in telephone, wireless technology, and handheld communication devices.

Published by: Jianduan Chuban Qufen Youxian Gongsi/Sharp Point Publishing Ltd., Inc., 231 Xindiansi, Fuyu-Lu 43-Hao 8-Lou, Taipei, Taiwan. TEL 886-2-2218-1582, FAX 886-2-2218-1583, call@spp.com.tw, janey@spp.com.tw, http://www.spp.com.tw/asp/mag/call/index.asp.

384.6 NLD ISSN 1382-4767
CALL CENTER MAGAZINE. Cover title: C C M. Text in Dutch. 1995. 10/yr. EUR 99 (effective 2003).
Superseded (in 1997): Call Center Agent (1386-5978) —IE, Infotrieve.
Published by: F & G Publishing, Posbus 1245, Heerhugowaard, 1700 BE, Netherlands. TEL 31-72-5762888, FAX 31-72-5762889, info@fngpubli.com, http://www.fngpubli.com.

CALL CENTER PROFI; das Magazin fuer Call Center, e-Marketing und CRS. see *BUSINESS AND ECONOMICS—Marketing And Purchasing*

384.6 658 GBR ISSN 1353-5439
CALL CENTRE FOCUS. Text in English. 1994. m. free in Europe to qualified personnel; GBP 49 rest of world to non-qualified personnel (effective 1999). adv. bk.rev.; software rev. back issues avail. **Document type:** *Magazine, Trade.* **Description:** Focuses on management, strategy, workplace and technology issues in the call centre for all call centre professionals.
Related titles: Online - full content ed.
Published by: CALLcraft, The Loft, Dean House Farm, Church Road, Newdigate, Surrey RH5 5DL, United Kingdom. TEL 44-1306-631661, FAX 44-1306-631412, info@callcentre.co.uk, http://www.callcentre.co.uk. Ed., Pub., R&P Janette Menday. Adv. contact Louise Chuter. B&W page GBP 1,495, color page GBP 1,895; trim 210 x 297. Circ: 250 (paid); 9,000 (controlled).

658.812 AUS
CALL CENTRE MAGAZINE; customer service management. Text in English. 1995. w. AUD 595 for print, CD-ROM or online ed.; USD 795 (effective 2001). adv. bk.rev.; software rev.; Website rev. abstr.; charts; mkt.; illus.; stat. back issues avail.; reprints avail. **Document type:** *Magazine, Trade.*
Related titles: CD-ROM ed.; Online - full content ed.
Published by: (Australian Call Centre Association), I I A Publishing Pty. Ltd., PO Box 861, Double Bay, NSW 2028, Australia. TEL 61-2-93440586, 61-2-9386-0065, FAX 61-2-93440718, 61-2-9386-0663, subs@callcentre.com.au, http://www.callcentre.com.au. Ed. Martin Grace. Pub. Frank Garvin. R&P Grace Marvin. Adv. contact Norv Turner. B&W page USD 2,600, color page USD 3,300. Circ: 16,700 (controlled).

CALLCENTER. see *BUSINESS AND ECONOMICS—Marketing And Purchasing*

CANADA. STATISTICS CANADA. TELEPHONE STATISTICS/CANADA. STATISTIQUE CANADA. STATISTIQUE DU TELEPHONE. see *COMMUNICATIONS—Abstracting, Bibliographies, Statistics*

CANADIAN NATIONAL. ANNUAL REPORT. see *TRANSPORTATION*

384.6 658.8 USA ISSN 1086-7716
TK6570.M6
CELLULAR INTEGRATION. Text in English. 1984. m. USD 32 domestic; USD 52 in Canada & Mexico; USD 92 elsewhere. adv. reprint service avail. from PQC. **Document type:** *Magazine, Trade.* **Description:** Serves cellular professionals with features geared towards the marketing and sales aspects of the industry.
Formerly (until 199?): Cellular Marketing (0890-2402)
Related titles: Online - full text ed.: (from Gale Group, Northern Light Technology, Inc.).
—CCC.
Published by: Argus Inc., 6151 Powers Ferry Rd, N W, Atlanta, GA 30339-2941. TEL 404-955-2500, FAX 404-955-0400. Ed. Bob Chapin. Adv. contact Elaine Baugh. Circ: 22,040.

384.6 USA ISSN 0892-2683
CELLULAR SALES & MARKETING; cell the world!. Text in English. 1987. bi-m. USD 347; USD 371 foreign (effective 1999). back issues avail. **Document type:** *Newsletter, Trade.* **Description:** News coverage of sales and marketing strategies in the industry.
Published by: Creative Communications Inc. (Herndon), 1566 Kingstream Cir., Herndon, VA 20170-2752. TEL 703-715-6113. Ed., Pub. Stuart F Crump Jr.

384.1 384.6 GBR ISSN 1460-6186
CELLULAR, WIRELESS & PAGING (YEAR). Text in English. a. GBP 150, USD 250 includes supplements (effective 2000).
Published by: Icom Publications Ltd., Chancery House, St Nicholas Way, Sutton, Surrey SM1 1JB, United Kingdom. TEL 44-20-86421117, FAX 44-20-86421941, admin@icompub.com, http://www.icompub.com. Ed. Giovanni Verlini.

384.5 USA
THE CHANGING TIMES OF TELECOMMUNICATIONS. Text in English. 1991. a. USD 395. **Description:** Examines the telecommunication industry from the deregulation of AT&T in the early 1980's to today's expansion of American telecommunication companies in foreign countries. Also covers cellular technology, satellite communications, microwave communication developments and innovations in fiber optics.
Published by: Dun & Bradstreet Information Services (Murray Hill) (Subsidiary of: Dun & Bradstreet, Inc.), 103 John F Kennedy Pkwy., Short Hills, NJ 07078-2708. TEL 908-665-5224, FAX 908-771-7599. Ed. Lynette Alvarez.

621.38 HKG ISSN 1017-5199
CHINA TELECOMMUNICATIONS CONSTRUCTION/ZHONGGUO DIANXIN JIANSHE. Text in Chinese, English. 1988. 10/yr., latest vol.13, 2001. USD 129 (effective 2000). adv. back issues avail. **Document type:** *Magazine, Trade.* **Description:** Covers the current and future development of telecommunication in China, co-operation project with Western countries, new products and technologies.
Indexed: HongKongiana.
Published by: State Business Development Ltd., 1301 New Victory House, 93-103 Wing Lok St, Hong Kong, Hong Kong. TEL 852-2517-2095, FAX 852-2517-2101, ctccwc@netvigator.com, http://www.chinatelecomnews.com. Pub. S Y Cheung. Adv. contact K M Han. B&W page USD 2,000, color page USD 3,200; trim 275 x 210. Circ: 27,000.

621.38 HKG ISSN 1025-7004
CHINA WIRELESS COMMUNICATIONS. Text in Chinese, English. 10/yr., latest vol.7, 2001. USD 120 (effective 2000). adv. **Document type:** *Magazine, Trade.* **Description:** Covers wireless communications including mobile, satellite and microwave in China, Hong Kong and Taiwan.
Published by: (China. State Radio Regulatory Commission), State Business Development Ltd., 1301 New Victory House, 93-103 Wing Lok St, Hong Kong, Hong Kong. TEL 852-2517-2095, FAX 852-2517-2101, ctccwc@netvigator.com. Ed., Pub. S Y Cheung. R&P Sherwin Chan. Adv. contact K M Han. B&W page USD 2,000, color page USD 3,200. Circ: 25,000.

384.6 USA ISSN 1535-3060
CO-LO DATA CENTERS NEWSLETTER. Text in English. 2001. m. USD 695 in US & Canada; USD 745 elsewhere (effective 2001). **Document type:** *Newsletter, Trade.* **Description:** Covers the global market for co-location, data centers and web hosting.
Published by: Information Gatekeepers, Inc., 320 Washington St, Ste 302, Brighton, MA 02135. TEL 617-782-5033, 800-323-1088, FAX 617-734-8562, info@igigroup.com, http://www.igigroup.com. Ed. Hui Pan.

384.1 CHE
CODES AND ABBREVIATIONS FOR THE USE OF THE INTERNATIONAL TELECOMMUNICATIONS SERVICES. Text in English. irreg., latest vol.4, 1982. CHF 32.
Related titles: French ed.; Spanish ed.
Published by: International Telecommunication Union, Place des Nations, Geneva 20, 1211, Switzerland. TEL 41-22-7306141, FAX 41-22-7305194, sales@itu.ch, http://www.itu.int/publications.

384.6 DEU
COM.UNIQUE; DeTeWe Kundenmagazin. Text in German. q. adv. **Document type:** *Magazine, Consumer.*
Published by: (DeTeWe - Deutsche Telephonwerke Aktiengesellschaft & Co.), corps - Corporate Publishing Services GmbH, Schanzenstr. 56, Duesseldorf, 40549, Germany. TEL 49-211-9541613, FAX 49-211-9541606, info@corps-verlag.de, http://www.corps-verlag.de. adv.: page EUR 3,300. Circ: 18,000 (controlled).

384 GBR ISSN 0264-4509
CODEN: CTUSD8
COMMUNICATE. Text in English. 1980. 10/yr. GBP 67 domestic; GBP 100 foreign; GBP 11 newsstand/cover (effective 1999 - 2000). adv. charts; illus. **Document type:** *Trade.* **Description:** Contains news and informational items, articles, and product reviews about telecommunications and data communications products, systems, and services in the U.K. Lists corporate appointments and contracts, calendar of events, and employment opportunities.
Related titles: Online - full text ed.: (from Florida Center for Library Automation, Gale Group).
Indexed: B&I, Inspec.
—BLDSC (3341.361000), AskIEEE, IE, ingenta.
Published by: D M G World Media Ltd. (Subsidiary of: Daily Mail and General Trust PLC), Queensway House, 2 Queensway, Redhill, Surrey RH1 1QS, United Kingdom. TEL 44-1737-855527, FAX 44-1737-855470, http://www.dmg.co.uk, http://www.dmgworldmedia.com. Ed. Ken Young. Circ: 15,500 (controlled).

384.0285 USA ISSN 1534-2840
TK6397
COMMUNICATIONS CONVERGENCE. Text in English. 1993. m. free in US & Canada to qualified personnel (effective 2005). adv. back issues avail. **Document type:** *Magazine, Trade.* **Description:** Contains lab-based reviews, comprehensive equipment roundups, strategic case studies, timely product news and industry analysis, technical tutorials, and expert market opinion.
Formerly (until June, 2001): Computer Telephony (1072-1711)
Related titles: Online - full text ed.: (from bigchalk, EBSCO Publishing, Factiva, Gale Group, ProQuest Information & Learning).
Indexed: ABIn, CompD, MicrocompInd, SoftBase.
—BLDSC (3394.309000), IE, ingenta, Linda Hall. **CCC.**
Published by: C M P Media LLC (Subsidiary of: United News & Media), 600 Community Dr, Manhasset, NY 11030. TEL 516-562-5000, FAX 516-562-5036, Computertelephony@halldata.com, http://www.cconvergence.com/, http://www.cmp.com. Ed. John Jainschigg.

343.09943 USA
COMMUNICATIONS ENVIRONMENTAL & LAND USE LAW REPORT. Text in English. m. USD 465 combined subscription print & online eds. (effective 2004). **Document type:** *Newsletter, Trade.* **Description:** Provides thorough coverage of the growing, complex overlap of zoning, land use, environmental, and federal communications law.
Related titles: Online - full text ed.
Published by: Pike & Fischer, Inc. (Subsidiary of: The Bureau of National Affairs, Inc.), 1010 Wayne Ave, Ste 1400, Silver Spring, MD 20910. TEL 301-562-1530, 800-255-8131, FAX 301-562-1521, pike@pf.com, http://www.celulr.com, http://www.pf.com.

621.385 GBR ISSN 1477-4739
TK5101.A1 CODEN: BTEND4
THE COMMUNICATIONS NETWORK. JOURNAL. Variant title: The Journal. Text in English. 1908; N.S. 1982. q. GBP 36 to individuals; GBP 41 foreign to individuals; GBP 60 to institutions; GBP 65 foreign to institutions (effective 2002). adv. bk.rev. charts. index. back issues avail. **Document type:** *Journal, Academic/Scholarly.* **Description:** Covers a wide range of aspects of telecommunications and related disciplines.
Former titles (until Apr. 2002): Institution of British Telecommunications Engineers. Journal (1470-5826); (until 1999): British Telecommunications Engineering (0262-401X); (until 1982): Post Office Electrical Engineers' Journal (0032-5287)
Related titles: Supplement(s): Telecommunications Engineer: A Structured Information Programme.
Indexed: ASCA, CADCAM, CISA, CompC, CurCont, EngInd, IAA, Inspec, SSCI, TelAb.
—BLDSC (4731.703000), AskIEEE, CISTI, Ei, IE, ingenta, Linda Hall. **CCC.**
Published by: The Communications Network, Post Point 2D05, The Angel Centre, 403 St John St, London, EC1V 4PL, United Kingdom. TEL 44-20-7843-7622, FAX 44-20-7843-7888, http://www.tcn-uk.org/pubs/ibtepubs_hi.php. Ed., R&P, Adv. contact Paul Nichols TEL 44-171-8437623. Circ: 20,000.

COMMUNICATIONS STANDARDS SUMMARY. see *COMMUNICATIONS—Radio*

384 USA
COMTEL PARTNERS. Text in English. bi-m. **Document type:** *Trade.*
Published by: Trader National Publications, 4108 Amon Caster Blvd, 202, Fort Worth, TX 76155. TEL 817-835-0628, http://www.thewwbn.com/html/tbpmag.html.

384.6 ESP ISSN 1130-4693
COMUNICACIONES DE TELEFONICA I & D. Text in Spanish. 1990. w.
Indexed: IECT.
—CINDOC.
Published by: Telefonica I & D, Emilio Vargas, 6, Madrid, 28043, Spain.

384.5 PRT
CONNECT. Text in Portuguese. 1997. bi-m. EUR 3.50 newsstand/cover (effective 2005). adv. **Document type:** *Magazine, Consumer.*
Published by: Motorpress Lisboa, SA, Rua Policarpio Anjos No. 4, Cruz Quebrada, Dafundo 1495-742, Portugal. TEL 351-21-4154500, FAX 351-21-4154501, connect@motorpress.pt, buzine@motorpress.pt, http://www.autohoje.com/quiosque.aspx?pub=f9317ea0, http://www.mpl.pt/. Ed. Vitor Sousa. Pub. Cristina Pereira. Circ: 9,559 (paid).

384.5 ESP
CONNECT. Text in Spanish. 1998. m. EUR 2.80 per issue (effective 2005). adv. **Document type:** *Magazine, Consumer.*
Related titles: ♦ Supplement(s): Connect Catalogo.
Published by: Motorpress - Iberica, S A, Ancora 40, Madrid, 28045, Spain. TEL 34-91-3470100, FAX 34-91-3470204, connect@mpib.es, http://www.motorpress-iberica.es. Ed. Jose Luis Fdez. Conradi. Pub. Javier Pedroche. Adv. contact Miguel A Zubillaga. color page EUR 2,690. Circ: 16,000 (paid).

▼ new title ➤ refereed ✶ unverified ♦ full entry avail.

384.5 ESP
CONNECT CATALOGO. Text in Spanish. 1996. a. EUR 4.50 per issue (effective 2005). adv. **Document type:** *Catalog, Consumer.*
Related titles: ♦ Supplement to: Connect.
Published by: Motorpress - Iberica, S A, Ancora 40, Madrid, 28045, Spain. TEL 34-91-3470100, FAX 34-91-3470204, http://www.motorpress-iberica.es. Ed. Jose Luis Fdez. Conradi. Pub. Javier Pedroche. Adv. contact Miguel A Zubillaga. color page EUR 2,690. Circ: 10,000 (paid).

384 PRT
CORREIOS E TELECOMUNICACOES DE PORTUGAL. BOLETIM OFICIAL. Text in Portuguese. 1948. m.
Formerly: Portugal. Administracao Geral dos Correios e Telegrafos. Boletim Oficial dos C T T
Related titles: Microform ed.
Published by: Correios e Telecomunicacoes de Portugal, Servico de Impressos e Publicacoes, Rua Visconde de Santarem, 69 1o, Lisbon, 1000, Portugal. TEL 1-3127100, FAX 1-3127298. Circ: 6,000.

CORREO POSTAL Y TELEGRAFICO. see *COMMUNICATIONS—Postal Affairs*

COURIER (LONDON); the post office newspaper. see *COMMUNICATIONS—Postal Affairs*

384.6 SGP
CUSTOMER CONNECT. Text in English. m. adv. **Document type:** *Magazine, Trade.* **Description:** Contains news and information on the regional CRM and call center industries.
Published by: Charlton Media Group, 9B Stanley St, Singapore, 068728, Singapore. TEL 65-6223-7660, admin@charltonmedia.com, http://www.charltonmedia.com. Ed. Angela McFeeters. Pub. Timothy Charlton.

C

DAK TAR. see *COMMUNICATIONS—Postal Affairs*

621.38 JPN
DENDEN KENSETSU NYUSU/TELEPHONE AND TELEGRAPH CONSTRUCTION NEWS. Text in Japanese. 1967. s-m. JPY 8,400.
Published by: Nihon Sogo Tsushinsha, 8-27 Kamata 1-chome, Ota-ku, Tokyo, 144-0052, Japan.

384.1 CHN ISSN 1000-1247
DIANXIN JISHU/TELECOMMUNICATION TECHNOLOGY. Text in Chinese. 1954. m. CNY 96 per issue (effective 2004). **Document type:** *Journal, Trade.*
Related titles: Online - full text ed.: (from East View Information Services).
Published by: Renmin Youdian Chubanshe/People's Posts and Telecommunications Publishing House, 14 A Xizhaosi Street, Chongwen District, Beijing, 100061, China. TEL 86-10-68372930, FAX 86-10-84225350, dj@pptph.com.cn, abc@ptpress.com.cn, http://www.ttm.com.cn/, http://www.ptpress.com.cn/. Ed. Zhang Xiufang.

384.6 USA
DIRECT DIAL. Text in English. 1990. m. (except Jan.). USD 20. **Document type:** *Trade.* **Description:** Guide for buyers of business telecommunications products.
Published by: United Advertising Publications, Inc., 2323 Mcdaniel Dr., Ste. 200, Carrollton, TX 75006-8355. TEL 214-233-5131, FAX 214-788-5367. adv.: B&W page USD 1,085; trim 10.75 x 7.63. Circ: 25,000.

384.6 USA
DISCOUNT LONG DISTANCE DIGEST✶. Text in English. 1993. m. free. **Description:** Covers issues affecting long distance carriers, long distance resellers, long distance agents and consumers.
Media: Online - full text.
Published by: Vantek Communications, 3144 Broadway St Ste 4, Eureka, CA 95501-3838. TEL 707-826-8446, FAX 707-826-8449, vantek@thedigest.com, http://www.thedigest.com/. Ed. William Van Hefner.

384 USA
DOTS AND DASHES✶. Text in English. 1950. q. USD 10 (effective 2000). bk.rev. back issues avail. **Document type:** *Newsletter.*
Published by: Morse Telegraph Club, Inc., 502 S Washington St, Dillon, MT 59725-2564. TEL 406-683-2798, FAX 406-683-2332, dotndash@bmt.net. Ed. John M Lbarrows. Circ: 2,500 (controlled).

621.38 GBR ISSN 1465-0029
EAST EUROPEAN TELECOMS. Abbreviated title: E E N. Text in English. 1991. bi-w. USD 1,162 out of North America; (effective 1997). **Document type:** *Newsletter.* **Description:** For telecoms operators, banks and other funding agencies, equipment manufacturers, regulators, consultants, ministries, and corporate users.
Former titles (until 1998): Eastern Europe Newsletter (1366-5049); (until 1996): Telecomeuropa's Eastern Europe Newsletter (0962-3825)
Published by: FT Media and Telecoms, Maple House, 149 Tottenham Court Rd, London, W1P 9LL, United Kingdom. **Dist. in N. America by:** Publications Resource Group, 121 Union St., Box 792, North Adams, MA 01247. TEL 413-664-6185, FAX 413-664-9343.

EL & ENERGI. see *ENGINEERING—Electrical Engineering*

ELECTRONICS LETTERS. see *ELECTRONICS*

621.38 SWE ISSN 0014-0171 CODEN: ERREAO
ERICSSON REVIEW; the telecommunications technology journal. Text in English. 1924. q. free. charts; illus. index. **Document type:** *Journal, Trade.* **Description:** Reports on the research, development and production achievements made in telecommunications technology at Ericsson.
Formerly (until 1933): L M Ericsson Review
Indexed: ApMecR, C&ISA, CADCAM, CompC, CurCont, E&CAJ, Englnd, ISR, Inspec, RefZh, SCI, SolStAb, TelAb.
—BLDSC (3809.000000), AskIEEE, CINDOC, CISTI, Ei, IDS, IE, ingenta, Linda Hall.
Published by: Telefonaktiebolaget L M Ericsson, Stockholm, 12625, Sweden. TEL 46-8-719-0000, FAX 46-8-681-2710, er@pressdata.se, http://www.ericsson.se/. Ed., R&P Eric Peterson TEL 46-8-719-0337. Pub. Jan Uddenfeldt. Circ: 40,000.

384.5 GBR ISSN 1367-9996
HE8081
EUROPEAN COMMUNICATIONS. Text in English. a. GBP 28; GBP 3.95 newsstand/cover. back issues avail. **Document type:** *Trade.* **Description:** Serves officials of national governments and the European Commission, as well as senior management of major telecommunications firms.
—BLDSC (3829.625000).
Published by: Highbury House Communications PLC, 13 The Publishing House, 1-3 Highbury Station Rd, London, N1 1SE, United Kingdom. TEL 44-20-7226-2222, FAX 44-20-7704-3151, TELEX 263174 HKP G, lynd@dircon.co.uk. Ed. Lynd Morley. Circ: 15,048 (controlled).

384.6 USA
EUROPEAN TELECOM EAST & WEST. Text in English. 1995. m. USD 695 in US & Canada; USD 745 elsewhere (effective 2004). **Document type:** *Newsletter, Trade.* **Description:** Covers all aspects of telecommunications in Europe both on a Pan-European level and country-by-country.
Formerly (until 2002): European Telecom Newsletter (1091-6873)
Related titles: Online - full text ed.: (from Gale Group, O C L C Online Computer Library Center, Inc., ProQuest Information & Learning).
Published by: Information Gatekeepers, Inc., 320 Washington St, Ste 302, Brighton, MA 02135. TEL 617-782-5033, 800-323-1088, FAX 617-734-8562, info@igigroup.com, http://www.igigroup.com/nl/pages/eurotel.html. Ed. Tony Carmona. Pub. Dr. Paul Polishuk.

EUROPEAN TRANSACTIONS ON TELECOMMUNICATIONS. see *COMMUNICATIONS*

EUROWIRED. see *BUSINESS AND ECONOMICS—Management*

621.385 USA
F C C TELEPHONE EQUIPMENT REGISTRATION LIST. Text in English. q. USD 25 in North America; USD 40 elsewhere. **Description:** Sequential file of all applications for approval to the telephone network. Listed in order of equipment type.
Media: Microfiche.
Published by: (Federal Communications Commission), U.S. Department of Commerce, National Technical Information Service, 5285 Port Royal Rd, Springfield, VA 22161. TEL 703-605-6000, info@ntis.gov, http://www.ntis.gov.

FACSIMILE FACTS AND FIGURES. see *COMMUNICATIONS—Abstracting, Bibliographies, Statistics*

621.385 USA
FIBEROPTIC PRODUCT NEWS TECHNOLOGY REFERENCE MANUAL. Text in English. a. (Jul.). free with subscr. to Fiberoptic Product News. **Document type:** *Trade.* **Description:** It is a technical resource for fiberoptic products, systems and services.
Published by: Reed Business Information (Subsidiary of: Reed Business), 100 Enterprise Dr, Ste 600, PO Box 912, Rockaway, NJ 07866-0912. TEL 973-920-7000, 800-222-0289, http://www.fpnmag.com/, http://www.reedbusiness.com.

621.385 USA ISSN 1552-5511
TA1800
FIBEROPTIC TECHNOLOGY. Text in English. 1986. 13/yr. (plus annual directory and 5 European editions). USD 157.30 domestic; USD 167.75 in Canada; USD 157.30 in Mexico; USD 207.90 elsewhere; USD 11 newsstand/cover domestic; USD 16.50 newsstand/cover foreign (effective 2004); Incl. Buyer's Guide. adv. back issues avail. **Document type:** *Newsletter, Trade.* **Description:** Reaches managers and supervisors of operations - manufacturing, engineering - technical, quality assurance, design, corporate and research and development in the fields of data and telecommunications equipment manufacturing, telecom services and end-users, test and measurement equipment, and suppliers of fiber, cable and fiberoptic components and system construction.
Formerly (until 2004): Fiberoptic Product News (0890-653X)
Related titles: Online - full text ed.: (from EBSCO Publishing, Florida Center for Library Automation, Gale Group, O C L C Online Computer Library Center, Inc.).
—CCC.
Published by: Reed Business Information (Subsidiary of: Reed Business), 100 Enterprise Dr, Ste 600, PO Box 912, Rockaway, NJ 07866-0912. TEL 973-920-7000, 800-222-0289, http://www.fpnmag.com/, http://www.reedbusiness.com. Ed. Diane Himes TEL 973-292-5100 ext 330. Pub. Todd Baker TEL 973-292-5100 ext 230. Adv. contact Tim Purpura TEL 207-846-7815. Circ: 35,100. **Subscr. to:** Reed Business Information, PO Box 9020, Maple Shade, NJ 08052-9020. TEL 303-470-4466, FAX 303-470-4691.

384.53 USA
FIERCEWIFI; the wireless broadband business & technology report. Text in English. w. free. **Document type:** *Newsletter, Trade.* **Description:** Covers WiFi, WiMax, and other wireless broadband technologies.
Media: E-mail.
Published by: FierceMarkets, Inc., 1319 F St, NW, Ste 604, Washington, DC 20004. TEL 202-628-8778, info@fiercemarkets.com, http://www.fiercewifi.com, http://www.fiercemarkets.com. Adv. contacts Jason Nelson, Rahul Dubey.

384.53 USA
FIERCEWIRELESS; the wireless industry's daily monitor. Text in English. d. free. **Document type:** *Newsletter, Trade.* **Description:** Contains information on wireless industry developments and their implications.
Media: E-mail.
Published by: FierceMarkets, Inc., 1319 F St, NW, Ste 604, Washington, DC 20004. TEL 202-628-8778, info@fiercemarkets.com, http://www.fiercewireless.com, http://www.fiercemarkets.com. Ed. Stephen Wellman. Adv. contact Jason Nelson.

FRANCE TELECOM; revue francaise des telecommunications. see *COMMUNICATIONS*

384.6 JPN
GLOBAL NEWS. Variant title: N T T International Researcher's Newsletter. Text in English. 1993. irreg. **Document type:** *Newsletter.*
Media: Online - full text.
Published by: Nippon Telegraph and Telephone Corporation, Basic Research Laboratories, 3-1 Morinosato Wakamiya, Atsugi-shi, Kanagawa 243-01, Japan. TEL 81-462-40-4720, http://www.brl.ntt.co.jp/GlobalNews/index.html. Ed. Tadaka Thoshihiro.

384.6 USA
GUIDELINES. Text in English. 1984. q. free to qualified personnel. abstr.; bibl.; stat. **Document type:** *Trade.* **Description:** Contains information on optical fiber for customers, end users, and others interested in the opto-electronics industry.
Published by: Corning Inc., Opto-Electronics Group, MP RO 03, Corning, NY 14831. TEL 607-974-4025, FAX 607-974-7522, fiber@corning.com. Ed. Sarah Creath. Circ: 20,000.

384 GBR ISSN 0964-6485
I P T C SPECTRUM. Text in English. 1965. s-a. free to qualified personnel. adv. **Document type:** *Newsletter.* **Description:** Reviews I.P.T.C. activities.
Former titles: I P T C News; I P T C Newsletter (0579-6903)
Published by: International Press Telecommunications Council/Comite International des Telecommunications de Presse, 10 Sheet St, Windsor, Berks SL4 1BG, United Kingdom. TEL 44-1753-833728, FAX 44-1753-833750, 100321.2156@compuserve.com, www.iptc.org/iptc. Ed. H Johnstone. Pub., Adv. contact David M Allen. Circ: 250.

I S A UPDATE. see *COMMUNICATIONS—Computer Applications*

384.6 USA ISSN 1521-3137
I S P BUSINESS NEWSLETTER. (Internet Service Providers) Text in English. 1996. m. USD 695 in US & Canada; USD 745 elsewhere (effective 2001). **Document type:** *Newsletter, Trade.* **Description:** Covers news of the business aspects of Internet service providers worldwide.
Related titles: Online - full text ed.: (from Florida Center for Library Automation, Gale Group).
Indexed: CompD.

Published by: Information Gatekeepers, Inc., 320 Washington St, Ste 302, Brighton, MA 02135. TEL 617-782-5033, 800-323-1088, FAX 617-734-8562, info@igigroup.com, http://www.igigroup.com/nl/pages/isp.html. Ed. Tony Carmona.

384 USA
IMPACT (ROCKVILLE); analysis of communication common carrier rate changes and competitive offerings. Variant title: C C M I Reports. Text in English. m. USD 325.
Published by: United Communications Group, 11300 Rockville Pike Ste 1100, Rockville, MD 20852-3030. TEL 301-816-8950.

384.1 CHE
INDICATORS FOR THE TELEGRAM RETRANSMISSION SYSTEM (TRS) - TELEX IDENTIFICATION CODES. Text in English, French, Spanish. 1966. triennial. CHF 84. Supplement avail.
Formerly: List of Destination Indicators and Telex Identification Codes (0074-901X)
Published by: International Telecommunication Union, Place des Nations, Geneva 20, 1211, Switzerland. TEL 41-22-7306141, FAX 41-22-7305194, sales@itu.ch, http://www.itu.int/publications.

384.5 USA
INDUSTRY BEAT. Text in English. w. (50/yr.). USD 50 to non-members. **Document type:** *Bulletin.* **Description:** Summarizes the week's industry and association news. Alerts telecommunications industry professionals to meetings and important notices.
Media: Fax. **Related titles:** Fax ed.
Published by: Telecommunications Industry Association, 2500 Wilson Blvd, Ste 300, Arlington, VA 22201-3834. TEL 703-907-7700, FAX 703-907-7727. **Co-sponsor:** Electronic Industries Alliance.

621.38 USA
INDUSTRY PULSE. Text in English. 1979. 10/yr. USD 65 to non-members (effective 2005). charts; illus.; stat.; tr.lit. **Document type:** *Newsletter.* **Description:** Evaluates public policy, regulatory issues and trends affecting the telecommunications industry.
Published by: Telecommunications Industry Association, 2500 Wilson Blvd, Ste 300, Arlington, VA 22201-3834. TEL 703-907-7700, FAX 703-907-7727, tia@tiaonline.org, http://www.tiaonline.org. Ed. Sharon Grace. Circ: 4,500.
Co-sponsor: Electronic Industries Alliance.

INFORMATION TECHNOLOGY & MANAGEMENT. see *BUSINESS AND ECONOMICS—Office Equipment And Services*

INFORMATION TECHNOLOGY LAW REPORTS. see *LAW—Corporate Law*

INFORMATION TECHNOLOGY MANAGEMENT; non-technical report on IT and its applications. see *BUSINESS AND ECONOMICS—Office Equipment And Services*

384.6 USA ISSN 1043-3694
HD9999.A93
INFOTEXT; integrating commerce and communications. Text in English. 1988. bi-m. USD 30 (effective 1999). adv. back issues avail. **Document type:** *Trade.* **Description:** Serves the interactive telephone industry. Includes industry trends, new applications and products, regulatory issues, and technical and marketing advice.
Related titles: Online - full text ed.
Published by: G P G Publishing, Inc. (Subsidiary of: R.J. Gordon & Co.), 9200 Sunset Blvd, Ste 710, Los Angeles, CA 90069. TEL 310-724-6750, FAX 310-786-2448, jmccully@mail.rjgordon.com, http://www.infotext.com. Ed. Marilyn Pitts. Pub., Adv. contact John W McCully. B&W page USD 3,030. Circ: 19,000.

384.6 USA ISSN 1055-9000
HE7761
INSIDE THE INDEPENDENTS; status and trends. Text in English. 1989. irreg., latest 1994. USD 995. **Description:** Reviews status and trends of the independent telephone industry, including competitive forces, acquisition and consolidation, network enhancements and business ventures.
Published by: Telecom Publishing Group, 1011 King St., PO Box 1455, Alexandria, VA 22313-2055. TEL 800-327-7205, FAX 800-645-4104.

INSTITUTION OF ENGINEERS (INDIA). ELECTRONICS AND TELECOMMUNICATION ENGINEERING DIVISION. JOURNAL. see *ELECTRONICS*

INTERACTIVE HOME; consumer technology monthly. see *TECHNOLOGY: COMPREHENSIVE WORKS*

▼ **INTERNATIONAL JOURNAL OF AD HOC AND UBIQUITOUS COMPUTING.** see *COMPUTERS—Computer Networks*

INTERNATIONAL KEMPS FILM, T V AND VIDEO. see *MOTION PICTURES*

384.6 USA ISSN 1047-8744
HE7621
INTERNATIONAL TELECOM DIRECTORY. Text in English. a. USD 85; USD 90 foreign. adv. **Document type:** *Directory.* **Description:** Lists titles of key officials, addresses, phone numbers, telex and telegraph numbers for telecom agencies in over 200 countries. Includes PTTs, satellite operating agencies, frequency allocation offices and standard organizations.
Published by: Capitol Publications Inc., Telecom Publishing Group, 1333 H St NW, Ste. 100E, Washington, DC 20005-4746. TEL 800-327-7205, FAX 703-739-6490, http://www.telecommunications.com. Pub. Chris Vestal. Adv. contact Stuart Lilly.

384.1 CHE ISSN 0074-9044
INTERNATIONAL TELECOMMUNICATION UNION. LIST OF TELEGRAPH OFFICES OPEN FOR INTERNATIONAL SERVICE. Prefatory materials in English, French, Spanish. 1869. quinquennial. CHF 61.
Published by: International Telecommunication Union, Place des Nations, Geneva 20, 1211, Switzerland. TEL 41-22-7306141, FAX 41-22-7305194, sales@itu.ch, http://www.itu.int/publications.

384.1 CHE ISSN 0047-1224
INTERNATIONAL TELECOMMUNICATION UNION. OPERATIONAL BULLETIN. Text in English. 1966. fortn. CHF 385. **Document type:** *Bulletin.*
Related titles: Online - full text ed.
Published by: International Telecommunication Union, Place des Nations, Geneva 20, 1211, Switzerland. TEL 41-22-7306141, FAX 41-22-7305194, sales@itu.ch, http://www.itu.int/publications.

384.1 CHE ISSN 0085-2201
INTERNATIONAL TELECOMMUNICATION UNION. REPORT ON THE ACTIVITIES. Text in English. 1948. a. CHF 5. **Document type:** *Corporate.*
Related titles: Spanish ed.: Union Internacional de Telecomunicaciones. Informe sobre las Actividades. ISSN 0252-1687; French ed.: Union Internationale des Telecommunications. Rapport des Activites. ISSN 0252-1679.
Indexed: IIS.
Published by: International Telecommunication Union, Place des Nations, Geneva 20, 1211, Switzerland. TEL 41-22-7306141, FAX 41-22-7305464, sales@itu.int, http://www.itu.int/publications.

384.1 384.6 CHE
INTERNATIONAL TELEGRAPH AND TELEPHONE CONSULTATIVE COMMITTEE. PLANS. Text in English, French, Spanish. 1971. irreg., latest 1991. price varies.
Published by: (International Telegraph and Telephone Consultative Committee), International Telecommunication Union, Place des Nations, Geneva 20, 1211, Switzerland. TEL 41-22-7305111, FAX 41-22-7305149, sales@itu.ch, http://www.itu.int/publications.

384.1 CHE
INTERNATIONAL TELEGRAPH AND TELEPHONE CONSULTATIVE COMMITTEE. PLENARY ASSEMBLY. PROCEEDINGS. Text in English. 1980. quadrennial. price varies. Supplement avail. **Document type:** *Proceedings.*
Related titles: Arabic ed.; Chinese ed.; French ed.; Russian ed.; Spanish ed.
Published by: (International Telegraph and Telephone Consultative Committee), International Telecommunication Union, Place des Nations, Geneva 20, 1211, Switzerland. TEL 41-22-7305111, FAX 41-22-7305149, sales@itu.ch, http://www.itu.int/publications.

384 AUS ISSN 0310-8031
INTERNATIONAL TELEX DIRECTORY. INTERNATIONAL SERVICE. Text in English. 1972. a.
Published by: Playfair Publishing Group, PO Box 52, Northbridge, NSW 2063, Australia.

384.6 USA ISSN 1541-1249
INTERNET BUSINESS NEWSLETTER. Text in English. 1998. m. USD 695 in US & Canada; USD 745 elsewhere (effective 2004). **Document type:** *Newsletter, Trade.* **Description:** Provides marketing and technology information on opportunities involving voice transmission over the Internet.
Formerly (until 2002): Internet Telephone Newsletter (1521-3129)
Related titles: Online - full text ed.: (from Gale Group).
Published by: Information Gatekeepers, Inc., 320 Washington St, Ste 302, Brighton, MA 02135. TEL 617-782-5033, 800-323-1088, FAX 617-782-5735, info@igigroup.com, http://www.igigroup.com/nl/pages/business.html. Ed. Tony Carmona. Pub. Dr. Paul Polishuk.

384.6 USA ISSN 1098-0008
TK5105.8865
INTERNET TELEPHONY MAGAZINE; the authority on voice, video, fax and data convergence. Text in English. 1998. m. USD 29 domestic; USD 60 foreign (effective 2002); free to qualified personnel. adv. back issues avail.
Related titles: Online - full text ed.
Indexed: MicrocompInd, SoftBase.

Published by: Technology Marketing Corporation, One Technology Plaza, Norwalk, CT 06854. TEL 203-852-6800, 800-243-6002, FAX 203-853-2845, http://www.intertelephony.com/. Ed. Gregorii Galitzine. Pub. Richard Tehani. Adv. contact Rory Beglin.

621.38 CHE
JOURNAL DES FONCTIONNAIRES DES P T T. Text in French. w.
Address: Friedeggstr 4, Burgdorf, 3400, Switzerland. TEL 034-225881. Circ: 5,895.

384.6 FRA ISSN 1628-1241
LE JOURNAL DES TELECOMS. Text in French. 1988. m.
Former titles (until 2001): Le Journal du Telephone (1291-438X); (until 1998): Le Journal du Telephone et des Mobiles (1243-3314); (until 1993): Le Journal du Telephone (0989-6325)
Published by: L B G Presse, 118, rue Legendre, Paris, 75017, France. TEL 33-1-4485-2150, FAX 33-1-4485-2159.

JOURNAL OF HEALTHCARE INFORMATION MANAGEMENT. see *HEALTH FACILITIES AND ADMINISTRATION*

384.53 USA ISSN 1550-4646
▼ ➤ **JOURNAL OF MOBILE MULTIMEDIA.** Text in English. 2005 (Mar.). q. USD 285 in US & Canada to institutions; USD 319 elsewhere to institutions (effective 2005). adv. **Document type:** *Journal, Academic/Scholarly.* **Description:** Aims to provide a forum for the discussion and exchange of ideas and information by researchers, students, and professionals on the issues and challenges brought by the emerging multimedia technologies for mobile multimedia applications and services, and the control and management of such networks to support multimedia applications.
Related titles: Online - full content ed.
Published by: Rinton Press, Inc., 565 Edmund Terrace, Paramus, NJ 07652. TEL 201-261-9408, FAX 201-261-7374, jmm@rintonpress.com, editorial@rintonpress.com, http://www.rintonpress.com/journals/jmm/index.html. Eds. Dr. David Taniar, Dr. Ismail Khalil Ibrahim, Dr. Jianhua Ma, Dr. Kevin H Liu. Pub. Dr. Wei Chen. R&P, Adv. contact Dr. X P Zhang.

384.6 GBR
KEY NOTE MARKET ASSESSMENT. CALL CENTRES. Text in English. 1999. irreg., latest 2001, Feb. GBP 730 per issue (effective 2002). **Document type:** *Trade.* **Description:** Contains the latest market information on the call centre industry in the UK.
Formerly: Call Centres (1469-5537)
Published by: Key Note Ltd., Field House, 72 Oldfield Rd, Hampton, Mddx TW12 2HQ, United Kingdom. TEL 44-20-8481-8750, FAX 44-20-8783-0049, info@keynote.co.uk, http://www.keynote.co.uk.

384.6 338 GBR ISSN 1474-239X
KEY NOTE MARKET ASSESSMENT. DOMESTIC TELECOMMUNICATIONS. Text in English. 1997. a., latest 2001, Jan. GBP 730 per issue (effective 2002). **Description:** Provides an in-depth strategic analysis across a broad range of industries and contains an examination on the scope, dynamics and shape of key UK markets in the consumer, financial, lifestyle and business to business sectors.
Formerly (until 2001): M A P S Strategic Market Report: The U K Domestic Telecommunications Market (1461-9377)
Published by: Key Note Ltd., Field House, 72 Oldfield Rd, Hampton, Mddx TW12 2HQ, United Kingdom. TEL 44-20-8481-8750, FAX 44-20-8783-0049, info@keynote.co.uk, http://www.keynote.co.uk.

384.6 658 GBR
KEY NOTE MARKET REPORT: MOBILE PHONES. Text in English. 1995. irreg., latest 2001, Nov. GBP 340 per issue (effective 2002). **Document type:** *Bulletin.* **Description:** Provides and overview of a specific UK market segment and includes executive summary, market definition, market size, industry background, competitor analysis, current issues, forecasts, company profiles, and more.
Published by: Key Note Ltd., Field House, 72 Oldfield Rd, Hampton, Mddx TW12 2HQ, United Kingdom. TEL 44-20-8481-8750, FAX 44-20-8783-0049, info@keynote.co.uk, http://www.keynote.co.uk. Ed. Jacob Howard.

384 SWE ISSN 0345-6471
KONTAKTEN/CONTACT. Text in English, Swedish. 1939. 21/yr. free. adv. illus. **Document type:** *Newsletter, Internal.* **Description:** Internal magazine of the Ericsson Corporation.
Related titles: Online - full content ed.
Published by: L.M. Ericsson AB, HF-LME, Stockholm, 12625, Sweden. FAX 46-8-681-27-10. Ed. Lars Goeran Hedin. Adv. contact Kjell Marklund TEL 46-90-7145-00. Circ: 90,000.

384.6 USA
L A T A DIRECTORY. Text in English. USD 225 (effective 1998). **Document type:** *Directory.* **Description:** Lists area codes and exchange numbers within each LATA across the U.S.
Published by: C C M I (Subsidiary of: United Communications Group), 11300 Rockville Pike, Ste 1100, Rockville, MD 20852-3030. TEL 301-287-2257, 800-929-4824, FAX 301-816-8945, ccmisale@ucg.com, info@ccmi.com. Ed. Belinda Jarvis. Pub. George David. R&P Michael Peck.

C

384.1 CHE ISSN 0074-9001
LIST OF CABLES FORMING THE WORLD SUBMARINE NETWORK. Text in English, French, Spanish. 1877. irreg., latest vol.19, 1977. CHF 21.
Published by: International Telecommunication Union, Place des Nations, Geneva 20, 1211, Switzerland. TEL 41-22-7306141, FAX 41-22-7305149, sales@itu.ch, http://www.itu.int/publications.

384.1 CHE ISSN 0074-9028
LIST OF INTERNATIONAL TELEPHONE ROUTES. Text in English, French, Spanish. 1961. a. CHF 44. **Document type:** *Bulletin.*
Published by: International Telecommunication Union, Place des Nations, Geneva 20, 1211, Switzerland. TEL 41-22-7306141, FAX 41-22-7305194, sales@itu.ch, http://www.itu.int/publications.

385.6 USA
LOCAL CALLING AREA DIRECTORY. Text in English. USD 225 (effective 1998). **Document type:** *Directory.* **Description:** Lists local calling areas and plans for U.S. cities with populations of more than 100,000.
Published by: C C M I (Subsidiary of: United Communications Group), 11300 Rockville Pike, Ste 1100, Rockville, MD 20852-3030. TEL 301-287-2257, 800-929-4824, FAX 301-816-8945, ccmisale@ucg.com, info@ccmi.com. Ed. Belinda Jarvis. Pub. George David. R&P Michael Peck.

384.6 USA ISSN 1087-8998
LOCAL COMPETITION REPORT. Text in English. 1992. bi-w. (26/yr.). USD 525 domestic; USD 548 foreign (effective 2001). adv. **Document type:** *Newsletter.* **Description:** Reports regulation, technology, and competitive strategies in the local telephone exchange market. Features interviews with top decision makers. Covers CLACs, utilities competition, competitive telecom strategies, cable TV and wireless participation, and new technologies.
Related titles: Online - full text ed.: (from Factiva).
Published by: Warren Communications News, Inc., 2115 Ward Ct, N W, Washington, DC 20037. TEL 202-872-9200, 800-327-7205, FAX 202-293-3435, info@warren-news.com, http://www.warren-news.com. Ed. Marie Gretchen.

384.6 DEU
LOGO4HANDY. Text in German. q. EUR 1.75 newsstand/cover (effective 2003). adv. **Document type:** *Magazine, Consumer.*
Published by: Der Heisse Draht Verlag GmbH und Co., Drostestr 14-16, Hannover, 30161, Germany. TEL 49-511-390910, FAX 49-511-39091252, zentrale@dhd.de, http://www.dhd.de. Adv. contact Kai Burkhardt. B&W page EUR 3,438, color page EUR 3,796. Circ: 100,000 (paid and controlled).

LONG DISTANCE COMPETITION REPORT. see *COMPUTERS—Microcomputers*

384.6 CAN ISSN 0849-6501
M T S ECHO. Text in English. 1921. fortn. free. **Document type:** *Trade.*
Formerly (until 1990): Telephone Echo (0381-4556)
Published by: Manitoba Telephone System, 489 Empress St, Winnipeg, MB R3C 3V6, Canada. TEL 204-941-8256, FAX 204-775-0718. Ed. Mike Daly. Circ: 6,000 (controlled).

384.6 CAN
MARITIME TEL & TEL. BULLETIN. Text in English. 1907. m. free to qualified personnel. **Document type:** *Newsletter.* **Description:** News about the telephone industry in Nova Scotia.
Formerly: Maritime Telegraph and Telephone. Bulletin
Published by: Maritime Tel & Tel, P O BOX 880, STA CENTRAL RPO, Halifax, NS B3J 2W3, Canada. TEL 902-421-4959, FAX 902-425-1274. Ed. Pearleen Mofford. Circ: 5,200.

384.6 USA
MARKET VIEW. Text in English. base vol. plus m. updates. USD 2,675 base vol(s). (effective 2005). Supplement avail. **Document type:** *Trade.* **Description:** Gives summaries of the most popular telecommunications services of the major telcos and carriers.
Former titles (until 2005): Telview Express; Guide to Networking Services
Media: Online - full text.
Published by: C C M I (Subsidiary of: United Communications Group), 11300 Rockville Pike, Ste 1100, Rockville, MD 20852-3030. TEL 301-287-2257, 800-275-2264, FAX 301-287-2689, info@ccmi.com, http://www.ccmi.com/telviewexp.html.

384 USA ISSN 1073-5348
THE MART. Text in English. 1991. m. adv. **Document type:** *Magazine, Trade.*
Published by: Story Communications, 116 N Camp St, Seguin, TX 78155. TEL 830-303-3328, 800-864-1155, FAX 830-372-3011, kaw@storycomm.com, http://www.telecom-mart.com/, http://www.storycomm.com. adv.: page USD 1,380.

384 MUS
MAURITIUS. TELECOMMUNICATIONS DEPARTMENT. ANNUAL REPORT. Text in English. a.
Published by: Government Printing Office, Elizabeth II Ave, Port Louis, Mauritius.

MESSAGE (BRONX). see *LABOR UNIONS*

384 GBR ISSN 0269-9567
MIDDLE EAST COMMUNICATIONS. Text in English; Summaries in Arabic. m. GBP 115, USD 185 includes supplements (effective 2000). adv. **Document type:** *Trade.* **Description:** Covers voice and data communications, broadcasting, information technology and networking.
Published by: Icom Publications Ltd., Chancery House, St Nicholas Way, Sutton, Surrey SM1 1JB, United Kingdom. TEL 44-20-86421117, FAX 44-20-86421941, admin@icompub.com, http://www.icompub.com. Ed. John Fenn. Pub. Alec Barton. adv.: B&W page USD 3,905, color page USD 5,865; trim 297 x 210. Circ: 10,200.

384.6 SWE ISSN 1401-2235
MOBIL (STOCKHOLM). Text in Swedish. 1995. m. SEK 549 (effective 2005). adv. **Document type:** *Magazine, Consumer.*
Related titles: Online - full text ed.
Published by: Modern Kommunikation Foerlag AB, PO Box 1054, Stockholm, 10139, Sweden. TEL 46-8-54512110, FAX 46-8-54512119, redaktion@mobil.nu, http://mobil.mkf.se/, http://www.mkf.se. Adv. contact Jonas Ekstrand TEL 46-8-54512112. page SEK 42,900; 190.5 x 254.

384.5 DEU ISSN 0948-163X
MOBILCOM. Text in German. m. **Document type:** *Magazine, Trade.*
Related titles: ◆ Supplement to: Funkschau. ISSN 0016-2841.
Published by: W E K A Computerzeitschriften-Verlag GmbH, Gruberstr 46a, Poing, 85586, Germany. TEL 49-8121-951001, FAX 49-8121-951657.

621.38 GBR ISSN 1351-6515
MOBILE AND CELLULAR MAGAZINE. Text in English. 1989. m. GBP 38; GBP 52 in Europe; GBP 75 elsewhere. adv. bk.rev. **Document type:** *Trade.*
Indexed: B&I, Inspec.
Published by: Nexus Media Ltd. (Subsidiary of: Highbury House Communications PLC), Nexus House, Azalea Dr, Swanley, Kent BR8 8HU, United Kingdom. TEL 44-1322-660070, FAX 44-1322-661257. Ed. Catherine Haslam. Pub. Christina Wood. Adv. contact Mark Edginton. Circ: 8,809 (controlled).

621.38 GBR ISSN 1355-0039
MOBILE ASIA PACIFIC. Text in English. 1993. 6/yr. GBP 52. adv. **Document type:** *Trade.*
Indexed: B&I.
Published by: Nexus Media Ltd. (Subsidiary of: Highbury House Communications PLC), Nexus House, Azalea Dr, Swanley, Kent BR8 8HU, United Kingdom. TEL 44-1322-660070, FAX 44-1322-616311, info@nexusmedia.com, http://www.hhc.co.uk. Ed. Mike McLeod. Adv. contact Jon Rawling.

621.38 GBR ISSN 0957-4980
MOBILE BUSINESS. Text in English. m.
Address: 134 Petherton Rd, London, N5 2RT, United Kingdom. TEL 071-359-0493, FAX 071-354-2702. Ed. Ian White.

384.6 GBR ISSN 1365-4969
MOBILE CHOICE; mobile phone made easy. Text in English. 1996. m. GBP 2.95 newsstand/cover. **Document type:** *Consumer.* **Description:** Features news and articles about mobile phones, including styles, efficiency, money-saving tips, buying guides, and innovations.
Published by: Noble House Publishing Ltd., Silver House, 31-35 Beak St, London, W1R 3LD, United Kingdom. TEL 44-171-287-5003, FAX 44-171-287-4964, mobilechoice@dial.pipex.com.

MOBILE COMPUTER & KOMMUNIKATION. see *COMPUTERS—Personal Computers*

621.38 GBR ISSN 1350-7362
MOBILE EUROPE. Text in English. m. (11/yr.). free to qualified personnel. adv. **Document type:** *Journal, Trade.* **Description:** Provides information for those involved in the European mobile communications industry.
Indexed: B&I.
—IE, Infotrieve.
Published by: Nexus Media Ltd. (Subsidiary of: Highbury House Communications PLC), Nexus House, Azalea Dr, Swanley, Kent BR8 8HU, United Kingdom. TEL 44-1322-660070, FAX 44-1322-616311, info@nexusmedia.com, http://www.hhc.co.uk/mobileeurope. Ed. Catherine Haslam. Adv. contact David Girecourt TEL 44-1322-660070 ext 2237. B&W page GBP 1,800, color page GBP 2,500; trim 297 x 420. Circ: 10,699.

621.385 AUS ISSN 1036-014X
MOBILES. Text in English. 1990. m. (11/yr.). AUD 544.50 domestic; AUD 595 foreign (effective 2001). charts; stat. 20 p./no.; back issues avail. **Document type:** *Newsletter.* **Description:** Analyses and reports on the Asia-Pacific mobile communication sector. Outlines details of new technologies, products and services and examines their impact on the region.
Related titles: E-mail ed.
Published by: Teleresources Engineering (Aust) Pty. Ltd., PO Box 693, Brookvale, NSW 2100, Australia. TEL 61-2-99752230, FAX 61-2-99752240, teleres@teleres.com.au, http://www.teleres.com.au. Ed. Maurie Dobbin.

MOBILES MAGAZINE; the number one in mobile communication. see *COMMUNICATIONS*

384 GBR ISSN 0953-6426
MORSUM MAGNIFICAT; The Morse Magazine. Variant title: The International Journal of Morse Telegraphy. Text in English. 1986. bi-m. GBP 15; GBP 17 in Europe; GBP 20 elsewhere (effective 2001). 48 p./no. 2 cols./p.; back issues avail. **Document type:** *Newsletter.* **Description:** Devoted to Morse past, present and future.
Published by: Nilski Partnership, The Poplars, Wistanswick, Market Drayton, Shrops TF9 2BA, United Kingdom. TEL 44-1630-638306, FAX 44-1630-638051, zyg@morsemag.com, zyg@morsum.demon.co.uk, http://www.morsemag.com. Ed., R&P, Adv. contact Zyg Nilski.

621.385 620 USA ISSN 0887-5286
T173.8 CODEN: MTDEDP
MOTOROLA TECHNICAL DEVELOPMENTS. Text in English. 1982. irreg.
Indexed: Inspec.
—IE, Linda Hall.
Published by: Motorola Inc., 1313 E Algonquin Rd, Schaumburg, IL 60196. TEL 847-576-5000, FAX 847-576-9159, http://www.motorola.com.

384.6 DEU
MYHANDY. Text in German. bi-m. EUR 15.50 domestic; EUR 33 foreign; EUR 3.50 newsstand/cover (effective 2003). adv. **Document type:** *Magazine, Consumer.*
Published by: Der Heisse Draht Verlag GmbH und Co., Drostestr 14-16, Hannover, 30161, Germany. TEL 49-511-390910, FAX 49-511-39091252, zentrale@dhd.de, http://www.dhd.de. Adv. contact Kai Burkhardt. page EUR 4,122. Circ: 150,000 (paid and controlled).

384.6 USA
N T C A EXCHANGE✶. Text in English. 1982. bi-m. USD 10 (effective 1998). **Document type:** *Newsletter.*
Published by: National Telephone Cooperative Association, 4121 Wilson Blvd, 10th Fl, Arlington, VA 22203-1839. TEL 703-351-2000, FAX 703-351-2088. Ed. Matthew W Green Jr. Circ: 4,200.

621.38 JPN ISSN 0915-2318
TK5101.A1
N T T GIJUTSU JANARU/N T T TECHNICAL JOURNAL. Text in Japanese. 1989. m. JPY 12,540. **Document type:** *Trade.*
Formed by the merger of (1948-1989): Tsuken Geppo/Electrical Communication Laboratory. Monthly Journal (0388-3728); (1985-1989): N T T Shisetsu (0911-520X); Which was formerly (1949-1985): Shisetsu (0285-550X)
—CISTI.
Published by: Telecommunications Association/Denki Tsushin Kyokai, POB 2522, Tokyo Opera City Tower, 3-20-2, Nishi-Shinjuku, Shinjuku-ku, Tokyo, 163-1455, Japan. TEL 81-3-53530185, FAX 81-3-53530195, http://www.tta.or.jp/.
Co-sponsor: Nippon Telegraph and Telephone Corp.

621.38 JPN
N T T KENKYUJO KONO ICHINEN/N T T TELECOMMUNICATIONS LABORATORIES. ANNUAL REPORT. Text in Japanese. 1967. a. **Document type:** *Bulletin.*
Published by: Nippon Denshin Denwa K.K., Kenkyu Kaihatsu Suishinbu/Nippon Telegraph and Telephone Corp., Research and Development Management Department, 19-2, 3-chome, Nishi-Shinjuku, Shinjuku-ku, Tokyo, 163-19, Japan. TEL 81-3-5359-4200, FAX 81-3-5359-1185, rd-annual@ecl-inet.ecl.ntt.co.jp, http://www.nttinfo.ntt.co.jp/dlij/RD_J/. Ed. Toshimitsu Moroki.

621.38 JPN ISSN 0915-2326
TK5101.A1 CODEN: NTTDEC
N T T R & D. (Nippon Telegraph and Telephone Research and Development) Text in Japanese; Summaries in English, Japanese. 1952. m. JPY 27,660 per issue.
Indexed: C&ISA, CIN, ChemAb, ChemTitl, E&CAJ, EngInd, INIS AtomInd, ISMEC, Inspec, SolStAb.
—BLDSC (6180.610070), AskIEEE, CASDDS, CISTI, Ei, Linda Hall.
Published by: Telecommunications Association/Denki Tsushin Kyokai, POB 2522, Tokyo Opera City Tower, 3-20-2, Nishi-Shinjuku, Shinjuku-ku, Tokyo, 163-1455, Japan. TEL 81-3-53530185, FAX 81-3-53530195, http://www.tta.or.jp/.

384.6 USA ISSN 0895-089X
N T T TOPICS✶. Text in English. q. free.
Related titles: Online - full text ed.: (from Factiva, Gale Group).
Published by: (Nippon Telegraph & Telephone Company/Nippon Denshin Denwa Kabushiki Kaisha), Ruder, Finn & Rotman, 301 E 57th St, New York, NY 10022.

384.5 USA
NATIONAL EXCHANGE BULLETIN. Text in English. m. price varies. **Document type:** *Bulletin.*
Published by: C C M I (Subsidiary of: United Communications Group), 11300 Rockville Pike, Ste 1100, Rockville, MD 20852-3030. TEL 301-287-2257, 800-929-4824, FAX 301-816-8945, listverv@usa.net. Ed. Juliana Cole. Pub. George David. R&P Michael Peck.

C

621.38 GBR ISSN 1360-1369
NETWORK BRIEFING. Text in English. 1986. w. GBP 495. **Document type:** *Newsletter, Trade.*
Incorporates (1996-1997): Online Reporter (1364-7113); Former titles (until 1995): Network Week (0965-3031); (until 1991): Telegram (0953-5284)
Related titles: Online - full text ed.: (from Gale Group, Northern Light Technology, Inc.).
Indexed: CompD, Inspec.
Published by: A P T Data Group plc., 4th Fl, 12 Sutton Row, London, W1V 5FH, United Kingdom. TEL 44-171-208-4200, FAX 44-171-439-1105. Ed. Matthew Woollacott. Circ: 2,000 (paid). **US subscr. to:** APT Data Services Inc., 828 Broadway, Ste 800, New York, NY 10010. TEL 212-677-0409, FAX 212-677-0463.

384 CAN ISSN 1497-1518
NETWORKLETTER. Text in English. 1979. 40/yr. CND 895 domestic; CND 945 foreign; CND 50 newsstand/cover (effective 2003). **Document type:** *Newsletter, Trade.* **Description:** Focuses on competitive, regulatory and policy issues in Canadian telecommunications.
Former titles (until 2000): Canadian Communications Network Letter (0825-3021); (until 1984): Communications Week (0227-0382); (until 1981): Tele Communicator (0707-6401)
Related titles: Online - full text ed.: ISSN 1700-5159 (from Northern Light Technology, Inc.).
Indexed: ABIn, CADCAM, TelAb.
—CCC.
Published by: Decima Publishing Inc., 1800-160 Elgin St, Ottawa, ON K2P 2C4, Canada. TEL 613-230-1984, FAX 613-230-9048, cjeffrey@decima.ca, http://www.decima.com/publishing. Eds. Paul Park, Mario Mota.

621.38 USA ISSN 0195-7627
HF5001
NEW JERSEY BELL✶. Text in English. 1927-19??; resumed 1978. q. illus.
Published by: New Jersey Telephone Co., 540 Broad St, Newark, NJ 07012-3178. Circ: 40,000.

384.53 USA
▼ **NEW TELEPHONY.** Text in English. 2005. bi-w. **Document type:** *Magazine.* **Description:** Designed to carry analysis of technology, market strategies, information on regulations and legislation on VoIP services and related data relevant to the VoIP industry.
Media: Online - full text.
Published by: Virgo Publishing, Inc., 3300 N. Central Ave., Ste 300, Phoenix, AZ 85012. TEL 480-990-1101, FAX 480-990-0819, cs@vpico.com, http://www.newtelephony.com, http://www.vpico.com. Ed. Charlotte Wolter. Circ: 6,600 (controlled).

384.6 NER
NIGER. OFFICE DES POSTES ET TELECOMMUNICATIONS. ANNUAIRE OFFICIEL DES TELEPHONES. Text in French. a.
Published by: Office des Postes et Telecommunications, Niamey, Niger.

384.6 621.3 FIN ISSN 1457-4055
NOKIA LINK. Text in English. 1983. q. **Description:** Covers developments within the telecommunications industry.
Formerly (until 1999): Discovery (0780-3931)
Indexed: Inspec.
Published by: Nokia Group, Keilalahdentie 4, Espoo, 02150, Finland. TEL 358-7180-08000, FAX 358-7180-38226, nokia.link@nokia.com, http://www.nokia.com.

384.1 CHE ISSN 0252-1792
NOMENCLATURE DES VOIES DE TELECOMMUNICATION UTILISEES POUR LA TRANSMISSION DES TELEGRAMMES/LIST OF TELECOMMUNICATION CHANNELS USED FOR THE TRANSMISSION OF TELEGRAMS/NOMENCLATOR DE LAS VIAS DE TELECOMUNICACION EMPLEADAS PARA LA TRANSMISION DE TELEGRAMAS. Text in English, French, Spanish. irreg., latest vol.7, 1988. CHF 50.
Published by: International Telecommunication Union, Place des Nations, Geneva 20, 1211, Switzerland. TEL 41-22-7305111, FAX 41-22-7305149, sales@itu.ch, http://www.itu.int/publications.

384.1 ARG
CODEN: RTELB2
➤ **NUEVA TELEGRAFICA - ELECTRONICA.** Text in Spanish. 1912. m. USD 50. adv. bk.rev. abstr.; bibl.; charts; illus. index. back issues avail. **Document type:** *Academic/Scholarly.*
Former titles (until 1993): Revista Telegrafica Electronica (0035-0516); (until 1946): Revista Telegrafica (0325-0199)
Indexed: CIS, Inspec.
—BLDSC (6184.410010), AskIEEE, CISTI, ingenta, Linda Hall.
Published by: Arboeditores S.H., Cuba 2480, 5o, Buenos Aires, 1428 AEN, Argentina. TEL 54-11-4781-1884, FAX 54-11-4780-1884, arboeditores@arnet.com.ar. Ed. Ariel Arbo. Circ: 13,000.

384.6 USA ISSN 1066-1425
Z699.22
O P A C DIRECTORY; a guide to internet-accessible online public access catalogs. Text in English. 1991. a. USD 70 (effective 1999). **Document type:** *Directory.* **Description:** Lists the Internet addresses of more than 1,400 online public-access catalogs; includes logon instructions.
Formerly: Dial In (1047-3424)
Published by: Information Today, Inc., 143 Old Marlton Pike, Medford, NJ 08055-8750. TEL 609-654-6266, FAX 609-654-4309, custserv@infotoday.com, http://www.infotoday.com. Ed. Bonnie R Nelson.

384.6 USA ISSN 1043-6073
HE8801
O P A S T C O ROUNDTABLE; the magazine of ideas for small telephone companies. Text in English. 1988. bi-m. USD 35 (effective 2000). adv. bk.rev. charts; illus.; tr.lit. index. back issues avail. **Document type:** *Trade.* **Description:** Covers business issues, new technology, regulations, and opportunities; for owners and managers of independent telephone companies.
Published by: Organization for the Promotion and Advancement of Small Telecommunications Companies, 21 Dupont Circle, N W, Ste 700, Washington, DC 20036. TEL 202-659-5990, FAX 202-659-4619, roundtable@opastco.org. Ed., R&P Martha K Silver. Adv. contact Sue Partyke. B&W page USD 1,985, color page USD 2,915; trim 11 x 8.25. Circ: 3,200.

384.5 GBR
OFFSHORE INTERNATIONAL. Text in English. 1992. q. GBP 50; GBP 60 foreign. adv. charts; illus.; stat.; maps; tr.lit. back issues avail. **Document type:** *Trade.*
Published by: Highbury House Communications PLC, 13 The Publishing House, 1-3 Highbury Station Rd, London, N1 1SE, United Kingdom. TEL 44-20-7573-5432, FAX 44-20-7222-9836, offshoreinternational@hhc.co.uk. Ed. Bob Morris. adv.: color page GBP 3,250; trim 190 x 278. Circ: 7,500 (paid). **Dist. by:** Warnes Mailing, 577 Kingston Rd, London SW20 8YA, United Kingdom. TEL 44-181-540-0313, FAX 44-181-540-0113.

621.38 SWE ISSN 1404-4595
ON. Text in English. 1993. q.
Formerly (until 1999): Ericsson Connexion (1401-1166)
Published by: Telefonaktiebolaget L M Ericsson, Stockholm, 12625, Sweden. TEL 46-8-719-0000, FAX 46-8-681-2710, http://www.ericsson.se/.

384.6 USA
ON THE LINE (LAKE HAVASU CITY)✶. Text in English. 1985. bi-m. USD 25; USD 30 foreign. adv. bk.rev. back issues avail. **Document type:** *Trade.* **Description:** Covers regulatory and legislative issues, new products, and privately owned pay telephones.
Published by: California Payphone Association, 1866 Clayton Rd, Ste 213, Concord, CA 94520-2505. Ed., Adv. contact Erica Robinson. Pub., R&P Mary Lougheed. B&W page USD 1,000. Circ: 5,300.

004.6 384.6 USA
OPTICAL NETWORKS DAILY. Text in English. d. USD 1,395 (effective 2003). **Document type:** *Newsletter, Trade.* **Description:** Covers new companies and new products in the optical networks industry.
Media: E-mail.
Published by: Information Gatekeepers, Inc., 320 Washington St, Ste 302, Brighton, MA 02135. TEL 617-782-5033, 800-323-1088, FAX 617-734-8562, info@igigroup.com, http://www.igigroup.com/nl/pages/opticaldaily.html.

384.6 USA ISSN 1097-8275
OPTICAL NETWORKS / W D M NEWSLETTER. Text in English. 1998. m. USD 695 in US & Canada; USD 745 elsewhere (effective 2005). **Document type:** *Newsletter, Trade.* **Description:** Provides worldwide coverage of technology, markets and applications of optical networks.
Published by: Information Gatekeepers, Inc., 320 Washington St, Ste 302, Brighton, MA 02135. TEL 617-782-5033, 800-323-1088, FAX 617-782-5735, info@igigroup.com, http://www.igigroup.com/nl/pages/opticalwdm.html. Pub. Dr. Paul Polishuk.

621.385 USA ISSN 0747-8763
CODEN: APMDD9
OUTSIDE PLANT MAGAZINE. Text in English. 1983. m. free domestic; USD 50 in Canada; USD 115 elsewhere (effective 2004). adv. **Document type:** *Magazine, Trade.* **Description:** Focuses on the nation's 1300 local and interexchange telephone companies. Serves the construction, maintenance, outside plant planning and engineering people employed by these telephone companies and related contractors.
Published by: Practical Communications, Inc., 2615 Three Oaks Rd, Cary, IL 60013. TEL 847-639-2200, FAX 847-639-9542. Ed. Sharon Stober. Circ: 20,000.

384.5 USA ISSN 1075-7821
TK6570.M6
P C I A JOURNAL✶. Text in English. 1977. m. USD 80. adv. charts; illus.; tr.lit. **Document type:** *Trade.*
Formerly (until 1994): Telocator (0193-1458); Which superseded (1958?-1977): National Association of Radiotelephone Systems. Communicator
Indexed: HRIS.
Published by: Personal Communications Industry Association (P C I A), 500 Montgomery St, Ste 700, Alexandria, VA 22314. Ed. Lindsay Smith. Circ: 3,500 (controlled).

384.0285 USA
P T C (YEAR) PROCEEDINGS. Text in English. 1979. a., latest vol.20, 1998. USD 50 to members; USD 100 to non-members. adv. **Document type:** *Proceedings.*
Formerly: Pacific Telecommunications Council. Conference Proceedings
Related titles: CD-ROM ed.
Published by: Pacific Telecommunications Council, 2454 S Beretania, Ste 302, Honolulu, HI 96826-1596. TEL 808-941-3789, FAX 808-944-4874, info@ptc.org. Ed. Richard Nickelson. Pub. Richard Barber. Adv. contact Puja Borries.

384.1 CHE
P T T REVUE. Text in French, German, Italian. m. **Document type:** *Newsletter.*
Formerly: P T T Zeitschrift
Published by: Postes Telephones et Telegraphes Suisses, Viktoriastr 21, Bern, 3030, Switzerland. TEL 031-3383137, FAX 031-3386574, TELEX 911919-PTT-CH. Circ: 85,000.

384.1 CHE
P T T UND ZOLLBEAMTE. Text in German. w. **Document type:** *Bulletin.*
Published by: Postes Telephones et Telegraphes Suisses, Monbijoustr 130, Bern, 3007, Switzerland. TEL 031-452886, FAX 031-460592. Ed. Jean Marc Eggenberger. Circ: 12,242.

621.382 USA ISSN 1066-3894
PACIFIC TELECOMMUNICATIONS REVIEW. Abbreviated title: P T R. Text in English. 1980. q. USD 35 in North America; USD 50 elsewhere (effective 1999). adv. bk.rev. back issues avail. **Document type:** *Trade.* **Description:** Covers telecommunication developments and their impact on the Pacific region, specifically Asia, the Americas, and Oceania.
Former titles: Pacific Telecommunications (0899-434X); P T C Quarterly (0894-8143)
—CCC.
Published by: Pacific Telecommunications Council, 2454 S Beretania, Ste 302, Honolulu, HI 96826-1596. TEL 808-941-3789, FAX 808-944-4784, info@ptc.org. Ed. Richard Nickelson. Pub. Richard Barber. Adv. contact Puja Borries. Circ: 2,500.

C

384.6 DEU
PHONE. Text in German. 1999. q. adv. **Document type:** *Magazine, Trade.*
Published by: Vereinigte Verlagsanstalten GmbH, Hoeherweg 278, Duesseldorf, 40231, Germany. TEL 49-211-73570, FAX 49-211-7357123, info@vva.de, http://www.vva.de. adv.: color page EUR 8,800. Circ: 600,000 (controlled).

384.6 MEX
PHONE; la revista de la comunicacion inalambrica. Text in Spanish. 1997. m. MXP 120; MXP 25 newsstand/cover. charts; illus.; mkt. **Document type:** *Trade.* **Description:** Surveys the wireless telecommunications industry and market in Mexico.
Published by: Phone Company de Mexico S.A. de C.V., BETA 97, Col Romero de Terreros, Mexico City, DF 04310, Mexico. TEL 52-5-659-4582, phoneco@df1.telmex.net.mx. Ed. Carlos M Cinta. adv.: B&W page MXP 1,300, color page MXP 1,500; 280 x 215. Circ: 17,000. **Subscr. to:** INDIANA 260-807, Ciudad de los Deportes, Mexico City, DF 03710, Mexico.

384.6 GBR
THE PHONE BOOK. Text in English. a. GBP 3.95 (effective 1998). **Document type:** *Consumer.*
Published by: Highbury - WV (Subsidiary of: Highbury House Communications PLC), 53-79 Highgate Rd, London, NW5 1TW, United Kingdom. TEL 44-20-7331-1000, FAX 44-20-7331-1273.

384.6 USA ISSN 1555-0044
HE7761
PHONE FACTS PLUS; telecom trends. Text in English. a. USD 99 to non-members; USD 75 to members (effective 2005). charts; illus.; stat. **Document type:** *Trade.*
Former titles (until 2003): Phone Facts & Telecom Trends (1555-0176); (until 2001): Phonefacts (0897-0890); (until 1984): Independent Phone Facts
—Linda Hall.
Published by: United States Telecom Association, 607 14th St NW, # 400, Washington, DC 20005-2000. http://www.usta.org. Ed. Cheryl Sullivan.

394.6 USA ISSN 1046-2007
PHONE PLUS. Variant title: Phone+. Text in English. 1987. 15/yr. USD 80 domestic; USD 115 in Canada; USD 155 elsewhere (effective 2005). adv. **Document type:** *Magazine, Trade.* **Description:** Contains information and advice for carriers, resellers and agents of telecommunications services.
Formerly (until 198?): Telecommunications Equipment Retailer (1045-0106)
Indexed: TelAb.

Published by: Virgo Publishing, Inc., 3300 N. Central Ave., Ste 300, Phoenix, AZ 85012. TEL 480-990-1101, FAX 480-990-0819, cs@vpico.com, http://www.phoneplusmag.com, http://www.vpico.com. Ed. Khali Henderson. Adv. contact Marla Ellerman. B&W page USD 5,880, color page USD 7,280; 7 x 10. Circ: 30,000 (controlled).

PLANET P D A. (Personal Digital Assistant) see *COMPUTERS—Personal Computers*

384.6 USA
PLANNING GUIDE 1. INTER-L A T A TELECOMMUNICATIONS RATES AND SERVICES. Text in English. base vol. plus m. updates. USD 595.
Formerly: Executive Telecommunication Planning Guide
Published by: United Communications Group, 11300 Rockville Pike Ste 1100, Rockville, MD 20852-3030. TEL 301-816-8950.

384 USA
PLANNING GUIDE 2. INTRA-L A T A TELECOMMUNICATIONS RATES AND SERVICES. Text in English. base vol. plus m. updates. USD 650.
Formerly: Guide to Intra L A T A Communications Services
Published by: United Communications Group, 11300 Rockville Pike Ste 1100, Rockville, MD 20852-3030. TEL 301-816-8950.

384.6 USA
PLANNING GUIDE X-1. Text in English. base vol. plus m. updates. USD 345.
Formerly: Guide to Communication Services
Published by: United Communications Group, 11300 Rockville Pike Ste 1100, Rockville, MD 20852-3030. TEL 301-816-8950.

384.6 USA
PLASTIC OPTICAL FIBER NEWSLETTER. Abbreviated title: P O F Newsletter. Text in English. 1998. m. USD 395 in US & Canada; USD 425 elsewhere (effective 2001). bk.rev. tr.lit. **Document type:** *Newsletter, Trade.* **Description:** Keeps end users, design engineers, installers, distributors, and systems integrators up-to-date on developments in POF technology, applications, products, standards and other aspects of plastic optical fiber components and systems.
Formerly: 1394 Newsletter (1097-1742)
Related titles: E-mail ed.
Published by: Information Gatekeepers, Inc., 320 Washington St, Ste 302, Brighton, MA 02135. TEL 617-782-5033, 800-323-1088, FAX 617-782-5735, info@igigroup.com, http://www.igigroup.com/nl/pages/pof.html. Pub. Dr. Paul Polishuk.

384.6 USA
HE7621
PLUNKETT'S TELECOMMUNICATIONS INDUSTRY ALMANAC. Text in English. 1999. biennial. USD 249.99 (effective 2005); includes CD-ROM. **Document type:** *Directory, Trade.* **Description:** Contains profiles of leading companies in wireless and cellular, long-distance data networks and long-distance local services. Also includes chapters on technology, trends, careers and contacts.
Related titles: CD-ROM ed.: ISSN 1550-4514.
Published by: Plunkett Research, Ltd, PO Drawer 541737, Houston, TX 77254-1737. TEL 713-932-0000, FAX 713-932-7080, info@plunkettresearch.com, http://www.plunkettresearch.com. Ed., Pub. Jack W Plunkett.

POST- UND TELEKOMMUNIKATIONSGESCHICHTE. see *COMMUNICATIONS—Postal Affairs*

POSTAL AND TELKOM HERALD/POS- EN TELKOMHERALD. see *COMMUNICATIONS—Postal Affairs*

621.38 POL ISSN 1230-3496
TK5101.A1 CODEN: PZTKAP
PRZEGLAD TELEKOMUNIKACYJNY I WIADOMOSCI TELEKOMUNIKACYJNE/TELECOMMUNICATION REVIEW & TELECOMMUNICATION NEWS; tele-radio-elektronika. Text in Polish; Summaries in English, Polish. 1992. m. PLZ 168; PLZ 14 per issue (effective 2004). adv. bk.rev. 68 p./no.; **Document type:** *Trade.*
Formed by the merger of (1929-1992): Przeglad Telekomunikacyjny (0033-2399); (1961-1992): Wiadomosci Telekomunikacyjne (0043-5198); Which was formerly (1956-1959): Tele-Radio (0492-5971); (1939-1956): Wiadomosci Telekomunikacyjne
Indexed: ChemAb, Inspec.
—BLDSC (6944.871000), AskIEEE, CISTI, Linda Hall.
Published by: (Poland. Stowarzyszenie Elektrykow Polskich/Association of Polish Electrical Engineers), Wydawnictwo SIGMA - N O T Sp. z o.o., ul Ratuszowa 11, PO Box 1004, Warsaw, 00950, Poland. TEL 48-22-8180918, FAX 48-22-6192187, informacja@sigma-not.pl, http://www.sigma-not.pl. Ed. Bogdan B Zbierzchowski. adv.: B&W page PLZ 2,000, color page PLZ 3,200. Circ: 4,100 (paid).

621.38 GBR ISSN 0963-5084
PUBLIC NETWORK EUROPE. Text in English. 1990. 10/yr. USD 180; USD 15 per issue (effective 2003). adv. **Document type:** *Magazine, Trade.*
Related titles: Online - full text ed.: PNEwire.
—BLDSC (6967.783000), IE, Infotrieve, ingenta.
Address: Axe and Bottle Ct, 70 Newcomen St, London, SE1 1YT, United Kingdom. TEL 44-1322-614836, FAX 44-1322-666866, pnepost@pnewire.com, http://www.pnewire.com/. Ed. Jim Chalmers. adv.: B&W page USD 7,470, color page USD 8,270; trim 10.875 x 8.25. Circ: 25,111 (paid and controlled).

384.6 FIN ISSN 0048-5977
PUHELIN/TELEPHONE. Text in Finnish, Swedish; Summaries in English, Swedish. 1951. 6/yr. EUR 40 (effective 2005). adv. **Document type:** *Magazine, Trade.*
Indexed: RefZh.
Published by: (Puhelinlaitosten Liitto r.y./Association of Telephone Companies in Finland), Focus Finland, Sinebrychoffinkatu 11, Helsinki, 00120, Finland. TEL 358-9-331538261, http://www.puhelin.fi. Ed. Seppo Toivonen TEL 358-9-31538200. Circ: 12,222.

384.6029 USA
QUICK GUIDE TO THE NEW TELECOM LINGO. Text in English. irreg., latest vol.8. USD 45. **Document type:** *Directory.* **Description:** Includes definitions and explanations of more than 800 telecom words and acronyms regarding voice and data communications.
Published by: Capitol Publications, Inc. (Subsidiary of: Aspen Publishers, Inc.), 1333 H St NW, Ste. 100E, Washington, DC 20005-4746. TEL 800-327-7205, FAX 703-739-6490, http://www.telecommunications.com.

384.5 USA
R B O C UPDATE. (Regional Bell Operating Company) Text in English. m. USD 150 in North America; USD 165 elsewhere (effective 2001). bk.rev. **Document type:** *Newsletter, Trade.* **Description:** Covers all the activities of the regional Bell operating companies, including videotex trials, gateway operations, and their struggle in the courts to provide more services. Also covers marketing strategies.
Related titles: Online - full text ed.
Published by: Worldwide Videotex, PO Box 3273, Boynton Beach, FL 33424-3273. TEL 561-738-2276, markedit@juno.com, http://www.wvpubs.com. Ed., Pub. Mark Wright.

384 USA
R C R - P C S. (Radio Communications Report) Text in English. 1997. a. USD 250 (effective 1999).
Formerly: R C R - P C S Handbook
Media: Diskette.
Published by: Crain Communications, Inc., 1746 Cole Blvd, Ste 150, Golden, CO 80401. TEL 303-872-9100, info@crain.com, http://www.crain.com.

384.6 FRA ISSN 1288-5215
RADIOCOM TELECOM MAG. Text in French. 1987. bi-m.
Formerly (until 1998): Radiocommunications magazine (0986-2900)
—IE, Infotrieve.
Published by: Sircom, 1, rue du Parc, Levallois-Perret Cedex, 92593, France. TEL 33-1-4968-5196, FAX 33-1-4968-5178, http://www.sircom.com.

RADIOTELEGRAFEN. see *COMMUNICATIONS—Television And Cable*

621.388 AUS ISSN 1444-2515
REGULATORY AND COMPETITION AUSTRALIA. Text in English. 1998. a., latest 2001. USD 550 domestic; USD 500 elsewhere (effective 2001). **Description:** Presents statistical data, developments, trends, market research on the fixed, mobile and data markets in Australia, including the Internet.
Formerly (until 2000): Market Strategies and Developments in Australia (1440-9852)
Published by: Paul Budde Communication Pty. Ltd., 2643 George Downes Dr, Bucketty, NSW 2250, Australia. TEL 61-2-4998-8144, FAX 61-2-4998-8247, sally@budde.com.au, http://www.budde.com.au. Circ: 200 (paid).

621.38 ESP ISSN 1266-9091
REVISTA DE TELECOMUNICACIONES DE ALCATEL. Text in Spanish. 1992. q.
Formerly (until 1995): Comunicaciones Electricas (1242-0573)
Related titles: Online - full text ed.; ♦ English ed.: Alcatel Telecommunications Review. ISSN 1267-7167; ♦ German ed.: Alcatel Telecom Rundschau. ISSN 1266-3840; ♦ French ed.: Revue des Telecommunications. ISSN 1243-7492.
—CINDOC.
Published by: Alcatel Espana, Ramirez de Prado, 5, Madrid, 28045, Spain. TEL 34-91-3305041, http://www.alcatel.es/Review/ReviewList.asp. Ed. Gustavo Arroyo.

621.38 FRA ISSN 1243-7492
REVUE DES TELECOMMUNICATIONS. Text in French. 1992. q. free.
Related titles: Online - full text ed.; ♦ English ed.: Alcatel Telecommunications Review. ISSN 1267-7167; ♦ German ed.: Alcatel Telecom Rundschau. ISSN 1266-3840; ♦ Spanish ed.: Revista de Telecomunicaciones de Alcatel. ISSN 1266-9091.
—CCC.
Published by: Alcatel, 54 rue la Boetie, Paris, 75008, France. TEL 33-1-69631650, http://www.alcatel.com/atr/?_requestid=2056840, http://www.alcatel.fr/. Ed. Catherine Camus.

621.38 ITA ISSN 0035-8185
RONZATORE★. Text in Italian. 1953. q. free. bk.rev. illus.; stat.; tr.lit. index.
Published by: Societa Generale di Telefonia ed Elettronica, Via Bernina 12, Milan, MI 20133, Italy. Ed. Gianluigi Rossi. Circ: 4,000.

384.6 USA ISSN 0744-2548
HE8801
RURAL TELECOMMUNICATIONS. Text in English. 1963. bi-m. USD 25 to members; USD 125 to non-members (effective 2005); includes N T C A Exchange. adv. bk.rev. illus. **Document type:** *Magazine, Trade.*
Formerly (until 1982): Phone Call
Related titles: Online - full text ed.: (from EBSCO Publishing, Florida Center for Library Automation, Gale Group, Northern Light Technology, Inc., O C L C Online Computer Library Center, Inc., ProQuest Information & Learning).
Indexed: ABIn.
—BLDSC (8052.640550), IE, ingenta.
Published by: National Telephone Cooperative Association, 4121 Wilson Blvd, 10th Fl, Arlington, VA 22203-1839. TEL 703-351-2000, FAX 703-351-2088, tjenkins@ntca.org, http://www.ntca.org. Ed. Tennille Jenkins. Adv. contact Lisa Freedman. Circ: 5,000 (paid and controlled).

384.53 RUS
RUSSIAN MOBILE. Text in Russian. 1998. m. illus. **Document type:** *Magazine, Consumer.* **Description:** Presents information on the newest devices of mobile communication.
Published by: Izdatel'skii Dom S P N, ul Kedrova, 15, Moscow, 117036, Russian Federation. valle@spn.ru, http://www.spn.ru/publishing/journals/russianmobile. Ed. Sergey Efremenko. Circ: 200,000.

384 CAN ISSN 0080-6633
SASKATCHEWAN TELECOMMUNICATIONS. ANNUAL REPORT. Text in English. 1947. a. free. **Document type:** *Corporate.* **Description:** Provides an overview of the corporation's activities.
—BLDSC (1432.008000).
Published by: Saskatchewan Telecommunications, 2121 Saskatchewan Dr, Regina, SK S4P 3Y2, Canada. TEL 306-777-2005. Ed. Evan Flude. Circ: 10,000.

384.1 CAN ISSN 0036-4851
SASKTEL NEWS. Text in English. 1960. m. free. charts; illus.; stat. **Document type:** *Newsletter.* **Description:** Highlights SaskTel's role in the telecommunications industry.
Formerly: S.G.T.
Published by: Saskatchewan Telecommunications, 2121 Saskatchewan Dr, Regina, SK S4P 3Y2, Canada. TEL 306-777-2006. Ed. Lee Cowie. Circ: 5,100.

621.38 CZE ISSN 0036-9942
SDELOVACI TECHNIKA/TELECOMMUNICATIONS ENGINEERING. Text in Czech, Slovak; Summaries in English, French, German, Russian. 1953. m. USD 58.30. bk.rev. charts; illus.; mkt.; pat. index in English and German.
Indexed: CISA, CybAb, Inspec.
—BLDSC (8213.500000), AskIEEE, CISTI.
Address: V Stihlach 1311-3, Prague 4, 142 00, Czech Republic. Ed. Petr Benes. Circ: 25,000. **Dist. by:** Artia, Ve Smeckach 30, Prague 1 111 27, Czech Republic.

384.1 ITA
SELEZIONANDO S I P; giornale aziendale. Text in Italian. 1950. bi-m. free. bk.rev.
Published by: Societa Italiana per l'Esercizio delle Telecomunicazioni P.A., Via Flaminia, 189, Rome, RM 00196, Italy. TEL 01139-636881. Circ: 95,000.

384.6 BRA ISSN 0037-5764
SINO AZUL★. Text in Portuguese. 1928. s-a. free. adv. illus.
Published by: Telecomunicacoes do Rio de Janeiro S.A., c/o Embratel, Av. Presidente Vargas 1012, C.P. 2586, Rio De Janeiro, RJ 20179-900, Brazil. Ed. Renato F Goncalves. Circ: 10,000.

384.6 USA ISSN 1522-5143
SITE MANAGEMENT & TECHNOLOGY. Text in English. 1998. q. Free to qualified subscribers. adv. **Document type:** *Magazine, Trade.* **Description:** Publishes technical features, product information and news about tower site and cell site construction, management and maintenance.
Related titles: Online - full text ed.: (from EBSCO Publishing, Gale Group, H.W. Wilson, O C L C Online Computer Library Center, Inc.).
Indexed: BPI, CompD.
—CCC.
Published by: Primedia Business Magazines & Media, Inc. (Subsidiary of: Primedia, Inc.), 9800 Metcalf Ave, Overland Park, KS 66212-2216. TEL 913-341-1300, FAX 913-967-1898, inquiries@primediabusiness.com, http://industryclick.com/magazine.asp?magazineid=10&siteid=29, http://www.primediabusiness.com. Ed. Don Bishop. **Subscr. to:** PO Box 12993, Overland Park, KS 66282-2993. TEL 800-441-0294, FAX 913-967-1331.

621.38 SVN ISSN 1408-5763
SKRJANCEK; glasilo telekom Slovenije. Text in Slovenian. 1998. 11/yr. free.

C

Published by: Telekom Slovenije, Cigaletova 15, Ljubljana, Slovenia. TEL 386-61-1382540, FAX 386-61-1330431. Eds. Boris Ziherl, Stanka Ritonja.

384.6 USA ISSN 0038-3856
SOUTHERN BELL VIEWS. Text in English. 1971. bi-m. free to qualified personnel.
Published by: Southern Bell Telephone Co., 2850 Campbellton Rd, Atlanta, GA 30311. TEL 404-529-8611.

SPAIN. DIRECCION GENERAL DE CORREOS Y TELECOMUNICACION. BOLETIN OFICIAL DE CORREOS Y TELECOMUNICACION. see *COMMUNICATIONS—Postal Affairs*

384.1 USA ISSN 0741-8388
STATE TELEPHONE REGULATION REPORT. Text in English. 1983. bi-w. (26/yr.). USD 589 domestic; USD 615 foreign (effective 2005). **Document type:** *Newsletter, Trade.*
Related titles: Online - full text ed.: (from Factiva).
Published by: Warren Communications News, Inc., 2115 Ward Ct, N W, Washington, DC 20037. TEL 202-872-9200, FAX 202-293-3435, info@warren-news.com, http://www.warren-news.com/strtrial.htm. Ed. Herb Kirchhoff. Pub. Albert Warren.

621.369 USA ISSN 1070-096X
SUBMARINE FIBER OPTIC COMMUNICATIONS SYSTEMS. Text in English. 1993. m. USD 695 in US & Canada; USD 745 elsewhere (effective 2003). **Document type:** *Newsletter.*
Published by: Information Gatekeepers, Inc., 320 Washington St, Ste 302, Brighton, MA 02135. TEL 617-782-5033, 800-323-1088, FAX 617-734-8562, info@igigroup.com, http://www.igigroup.com/nl/pages/sfoc.html. Ed. Sebastian Wargacki. Pub. Dr. Paul Polishuk.

▼ **SYMBIAN DEVELOPER'S JOURNAL.** see *COMPUTERS—Software*

T I A - M M T A DIRECTORY AND DESK REFERENCE. see *BUSINESS AND ECONOMICS—Trade And Industrial Directories*

384.1 CHE ISSN 0074-9052
TABLE OF INTERNATIONAL TELEX RELATIONS AND TRAFFIC. Text in English, French, Spanish. 1964. a. price varies.
Related titles: Microfiche ed.: (from CIS).
Indexed: IIS.
Published by: International Telecommunication Union, Place des Nations, Geneva 20, 1211, Switzerland. TEL 41-22-7306141, FAX 41-22-7305149, sales@itu.ch, http://www.itu.int/publications.

384.6 USA ISSN 1073-8134
TELCO BUSINESS REPORT; executive briefings on the Bell operating companies - regional holding companies and independent telcos. Text in English. 1985. bi-w. (26/yr.). USD 759; USD 785 foreign (effective 1998). back issues avail. **Document type:** *Newsletter.*
Former titles (until 1993): Telephone Week (1062-4724); (until 1992): B O C Week (8755-3511); Incorporates (in 1992): Independent Telco News (1051-3124); Formerly: Report on Telco Marketing
Related titles: Online - full text ed.: (from Factiva, Northern Light Technology, Inc., The Dialog Corporation).
Published by: Capitol Publications, Inc. (Subsidiary of: Aspen Publishers, Inc.), 1333 H St NW, Ste. 100E, Washington, DC 20005-4746. TEL 800-327-7205, FAX 703-739-6490, http://www.telecommunications.com. Ed. Jennifer Freer. **Dist. by:** Publications Resource Group, 121 Union St., Box 792, North Adams, MA 01247. TEL 413-664-6185, FAX 413-664-9343.

384.6 USA ISSN 0882-1720
TELE✶; the communications magazine for business. Text in English. 1985. m. USD 24.97. adv.
Indexed: ABIn, CADCAM, TelAb.
Published by: Wayne Greene Enterprises, 70 Route 202 N, Peterborough, NH 03458. TEL 603-924-0058. Ed. Dan Muse. Circ: 50,000.

384.6 USA
TELE-SERVICE NEWS. Text in English. 1990. m. USD 150 in North America; USD 165 elsewhere (effective 2001). bk.rev. back issues avail. **Document type:** *Newsletter, Trade.* **Description:** Provides news and information on the telecommunications and telephone industry, with a focus on products, services, research and development, and business plans of regional Bell operating companies, long-distance carriers, and other industry vendors. Coverage includes cellular service, electronic data interchange, gateways, fiber optics, and effects of government regulations.
Related titles: Online - full text ed.: (from Data-Star, The Dialog Corporation).
Published by: Worldwide Videotex, PO Box 3273, Boynton Beach, FL 33424-3273. TEL 561-738-2276, markedit@juno.com, http://www.wvpubs.com. Ed., Pub. Mark Wright.

621.38 HKG ISSN 1681-181X
TK5101.A1
TELECOM ASIA. Text in Chinese, English. 1990. m. HKD 480 domestic; USD 86 in Asia & the Pacific; USD 96 elsewhere; USD 9 newsstand/cover in Asia & the Pacific (effective 2005). adv. back issues avail. **Document type:** *Magazine, Trade.* **Description:** Provides the latest information on technological, business, and regulatory developments to the Asian telecom professional.
Related titles: Online - full text ed.: (from Gale Group).
—CCC.
Published by: Advanstar Asia Ltd. (Subsidiary of: Advanstar Communications, Inc.), 2501-2, 25/F, Pacific Plaza, 401 Des Voeux Rd W, Hong Kong, Hong Kong. TEL 852-2559-2772, FAX 852-2559-7002, customer_service@telecomasia.net, http://www.telecomasia.net. R&P Emily Fu. adv.: color page USD 10,955; trim 197 x 267. Circ: 12,000.

621.38 HKG
TELECOM CHINA. Text in English. q. **Document type:** *Magazine, Trade.*
Published by: Advanstar Asia Ltd. (Subsidiary of: Advanstar Communications, Inc.), 2501-2, 25/F, Pacific Plaza, 401 Des Voeux Rd W, Hong Kong, Hong Kong. TEL 852-2559-2772, FAX 852-2559-7002, customer_service@telecomasia.net, http://www.telecomasia.net/telecomasia/.

384.6 USA
TELECOM FACTBOOK (WASHINGTON). Text in English. 1985. a. USD 135.
Published by: Warren Communications News, Inc., 2115 Ward Ct, N W, Washington, DC 20037. TEL 202-872-9200, 800-327-7205, FAX 202-293-3435, info@warren-news.com, http://www.warren-news.com.

621.38 USA
TELECOM GEAR. Text in English. 1984. m. USD 31. adv. **Document type:** *Trade.* **Description:** Information on the supply and demand of equipment in the telecommunications industry. Edited for a master list of end-users, interconnects, BOC's, OEM's and dealers.
Published by: United Advertising Publications, Inc., 2323 Mcdaniel Dr., Ste. 200, Carrollton, TX 75006-8355. TEL 214-233-5131, FAX 214-233-5514. Circ: 40,000.

384.6 DEU
TELECOM HANDEL; die Zeitung fuer den Telekommunikations-Fachhandel. Text in German. bi-w. free to qualified personnel; EUR 5.50 newsstand/cover (effective 2003). adv. **Document type:** *Magazine, Trade.* **Description:** Contains industry news and information for telecommunications dealers and resellers.
Related titles: ♦ Online - full content ed.: Telecom Handel Online.
Published by: Neue Mediengesellschaft Ulm mbH, Konrad-Celtis-Str 77, Munich, 81369, Germany. TEL 49-89-74117-0, FAX 49-89-74117787, redaktion@telecom-handel.de, empfang@nmg.de, http://www.telecom-channel.de/th/index.html, http://www.nc-online.de. Ed. Ove Struck. Pub. Guenter Goetz. Adv. contact Bettina Guenther. Circ: 23,542 (controlled).

384.6 DEU
TELECOM HANDEL ONLINE. Text in German. d. adv. **Document type:** *Trade.*
Media: Online - full content. **Related titles:** ♦ Print ed.: Telecom Handel.
Published by: Neue Mediengesellschaft Ulm mbH, Konrad-Celtis-Str 77, Munich, 81369, Germany. TEL 49-89-74117-0, FAX 49-89-74117787, redaktion@telecom-handel.de, empfang@nmg.de, http://www.telecom-channel.de/th/index.html, http://www.nc-online.de.

384.6 DEU
TELECOM INVESTOR. Text in German. m. adv. **Document type:** *Magazine, Trade.* **Description:** Focuses on how modern communication technologies can be integrated within existing business environments in the most effective and economic way.
Related titles: ♦ Online - full content ed.: Telecom Investor Online.
Published by: Neue Mediengesellschaft Ulm mbH, Konrad-Celtis-Str 77, Munich, 81369, Germany. TEL 49-89-74117-0, FAX 49-89-74117787, redaktion@telecom-investor.de, empfang@nmg.de, http://www.telecom-channel.de, http://www.nc-online.de. Ed. Roland Bernhard. Pub. Guenter Goetz. Adv. contact Bettina Guenther. Circ: 50,000 (controlled).

384.6 DEU
TELECOM INVESTOR ONLINE. Text in German. d. adv. **Document type:** *Trade.*
Media: Online - full content. **Related titles:** ♦ Print ed.: Telecom Investor.
Published by: Neue Mediengesellschaft Ulm mbH, Konrad-Celtis-Str 77, Munich, 81369, Germany. TEL 49-89-74117-0, FAX 49-89-74117787, redaktion@telecom-investor.de, empfang@nmg.de, http://www.telecom-channel.de, http://www.nc-online.de.

TELECOM LAW REPORT. see *LAW*

384 USA
TELECOM MANAGER. Text in English. q. adv. **Document type:** *Magazine, Trade.*
Published by: Story Communications, 116 N Camp St, Seguin, TX 78155. TEL 830-303-3328, 800-864-1155, FAX 830-372-3011, kaw@storycomm.com, http://www.telecom-manager.com/, http://www.storycomm.com. adv.: page USD 2,000.

384.6 USA ISSN 1527-3032
THE TELECOM MANAGER'S VOICE REPORT. Text in English. 1995. s-m. USD 293. **Description:** Provides complete coverage of regulatory, wireless, business, local service, and long distance news for the US, Canadian and Mexican telecommunications industry.
Former titles (until 1997): North American Telecom NewsWatch (1090-0179); (until 1996): Telecommunications Alert (0742-5384)
Related titles: Online - full text ed.
—CCC.
Published by: C C M I (Subsidiary of: United Communications Group), 11300 Rockville Pike, Ste 1100, Rockville, MD 20852-3030. TEL 301-287-2257, 800-929-4824, FAX 301-816-8945, cust_svc@evcg.com. **Dist. by:** Publications Resource Group, 121 Union St., Box 792, North Adams, MA 01247. TEL 413-664-6185, FAX 443-664-9343.

TELECOM MARKETS. see *BUSINESS AND ECONOMICS—Production Of Goods And Services*

384.5 USA
TELECOM NEWSFAX TODAY. Text in English. d. (Mon.-Fri.). USD 249. **Description:** An exclusive daily executive briefing on the biggest telecom business news from the US and overseas.
Formerly: Daily Telecom News Bulletin
Published by: C C M I (Subsidiary of: United Communications Group), 11300 Rockville Pike, Ste 1100, Rockville, MD 20852-3030. TEL 301-287-2257, 800-929-4824, FAX 301-816-8945, cust_svc@vcg.com, http://www.ccmi.com. Ed. Fritz McCormick. Pub. George David. Adv. contact Kristina Greggs.

TELECOM REAL ESTATE ADVISER. see *LAW*

384.6 USA ISSN 0898-9087
TELECOM RESOURCES. Text in English. 1985. m. free to qualified personnel. **Document type:** *Bulletin.* **Description:** Covers current news stories and lists information products.
Published by: Capitol Publications, Inc. (Subsidiary of: Aspen Publishers, Inc.), 1333 H St NW, Ste. 100E, Washington, DC 20005-4746. TEL 800-327-7205, FAX 703-739-6490, http://www.telecommunications.com. Ed. Dick Stirba.

384.029 USA
TELECOM SOURCEBOOK. Text in English. 1935. a., latest 2005. USD 150 per issue (effective 2005). adv. charts. 400 p./no.; back issues avail. **Document type:** *Directory.* **Description:** Contains vital operating data statistics, important industry information and over 4,300 listings of both telecommunications companies and suppliers.
Former titles: America's Network Directory & Buyers' Guide; America's Network T I A Directory and Buyers' Guide; (until 1994): Telephone Engineer and Management Directory (0082-2655)
Published by: Advanstar Communications, Inc., 100 W Monroe St, Ste 1100, Chicago, IL 60603-1905. TEL 440-891-2767, 312-553-8900, FAX 312-553-8926, info@advanstar.com, http://www.advanstar.com/marketingservices/telecomsource. Circ: 1,500. **Subscr. to:** Advanstar Marketing Services, Customer Service Department, 131 West, First St, Duluth, MN 55802. TEL 218-723-9180, 800-598-6008, FAX 218-723-9456.

384.1 NLD ISSN 1566-8118
TELECOMBRIEF; telecommunicatie - kabel - Internet. Text in Dutch. 1980. s-m. EUR 269 (effective 2005). adv. bk.rev. back issues avail. **Document type:** *Newsletter, Trade.* **Description:** Publishes information on telecommunications, cable, satellite, the Internet, and new media.
Former titles (until 1997): Telecombrief - Telematica Trends (1382-9998); Which incorporated (1994-1995): Combrief (1383-5009); (until 1993): Telecom-Brief (0921-3651); (until 1987): Media-Info (0921-366X)
—IE, Infotrieve.
Published by: Broadcast Press Hilversum BV, Postbus 576, Hilversum, 1200 AN, Netherlands. TEL 31-35-6252444, FAX 31-35-6214559, info@broadcastpress.nl, http://www.broadcastpress.nl/telecombrief/. Ed. Ed Achterberg. Circ: 1,500 (paid).

TELECOMMAGAZINE; toonaangevend vaktijdschrift over telecommunicatie. see *COMPUTERS—Data Communications And Data Transmission Systems*

621.38 SGP
TELECOMMUNICATION AUTHORITY OF SINGAPORE. SINGAPORE TELECOM ANNUAL REPORT✶. Text in English. 1974. a. price varies. **Document type:** *Government.*
Formerly (until 1992): Telecommunication Authority of Singapore. Telecoms Annual Report (0217-3891); Formed by the 1974 merger of: Telecommunication Authority of Singapore. T A S Annual Report; Singapore Telephone Board Annual Report

Published by: Infocomm Development Authority of Singapore, 8 Temasek Blvd, #14-00 Suntec Tower 3, Singapore, 038988, Singapore. TEL 65-211-0888, FAX 65-211-2222, info@ida.gov.sg, http://www.ida.gov.sg/. Circ: 5,000 (controlled).

621.385 USA ISSN 1018-4864
CODEN: TESYEV

➤ **TELECOMMUNICATION SYSTEMS**; modeling, analysis, dssign and management. Text in English. 1993. 12/yr. (in 4 vols.). EUR 1,228, USD 1,248, GBP 768 combined subscription to institutions print & online eds. (effective 2005). adv. back issues avail.; reprint service avail. from PSC. **Document type:** *Journal, Academic/Scholarly.* **Description:** Publishes original research on the modeling, analysis, design, and management of telecommunications systems.
Related titles: Online - full text ed.: ISSN 1572-9451 (from EBSCO Publishing, Gale Group, IngentaConnect, Kluwer Online, O C L C Online Computer Library Center, Inc., Ovid Technologies, Inc., ProQuest Information & Learning, Springer LINK, Swets Information Services).
Indexed: ABIn, ASCA, BibLing, C&CSA, CMCI, CurCont, Inspec, RefZh.
—BLDSC (8780.680000), AskIEEE, CISTI, IDS, IE, Infotrieve, ingenta. **CCC.**
Published by: Springer-Verlag New York, Inc. (Subsidiary of: Springer Science+Business Media), 233 Spring St, New York, NY 10013. TEL 212-460-1500, FAX 212-460-1575, service@springer-ny.com, http://springerlink.metapress.com/openurl.asp?genre=journal&issn=1018-4864, http://www.springer-ny.com. Ed. Bezalel Gavish. **Subscr. to:** Journal Fulfillment, PO Box 2485, Secaucus, NJ 07096-2485. TEL 201-348-4033, FAX 201-348-4505, journals@springer-ny.com.

384.1 IND ISSN 0497-1388
TELECOMMUNICATIONS. Text in English. 1951. bi-m. INR 15; USD 7 foreign. adv. **Document type:** *Government.* **Description:** Publishes technical journals in the field of telecommunication.
Indexed: Inspec.
—BLDSC (8781.000000), AskIEEE, CISTI, IE, ingenta.
Published by: Department of Telecommunications, c/o Chief General Manager, Technical and Development Circle, Jabalpur, India. TEL 91-761-323440, FAX 91-761-322322. Ed. A K Pandey. Circ: 9,300 (paid).

621.38 USA ISSN 0040-2494
CODEN: TLCOAY
TELECOMMUNICATIONS (INTERNATIONAL ED.). Text in English. 1967. m. USD 145 domestic; USD 230 foreign; USD 10 newsstand/cover domestic; USD 20 newsstand/cover foreign (effective 2004); free to qualified personnel. adv. **Document type:** *Magazine, Trade.* **Description:** Focuses on the public, wide area network represented by operators, carriers and service providers in both a technology and business context.
Related titles: Online - full text ed.: ISSN 1534-9594 (from Factiva, Florida Center for Library Automation, Gale Group, H.W. Wilson, O C L C Online Computer Library Center, Inc., ProQuest Information & Learning); ♦ Regional ed(s).: Telecommunications Americas. ISSN 1534-956X.
Indexed: ABIn, BPI, CompD, Inspec.
—BLDSC (8781.010000), IE, ingenta, Linda Hall. **CCC.**
Published by: (Telecommunications International GBR), Horizon House Publications, 685 Canton St, Norwood, MA 02062. TEL 781-769-9750, http://www.telecommagazine.com, http://www.horizonhouse.com. Pub. Sam Baird. adv.: B&W page GBP 3,740, color page GBP 4,720; trim 208 x 276. Circ: 27,488. **Subscr. to:** Telecommunications, PO Box 3255, Northbrook, IL 60065-3255. TEL 847-291-5216, FAX 847-291-4816, 44-20-7596-8749.

621.38 GBR
TELECOMMUNICATIONS AMERICAS. Text in English. m. **Document type:** *Trade.* **Description:** Provides coverage of communications applied technology and business topics.
Related titles: Online - full text ed.
Indexed: B&I.
Address: Portland House, Stag Pl, London, SW1E 5XT, United Kingdom. TEL 44-171-957-0030, FAX 44-171-957-0031. Ed. Steve McClelland. Circ: 54,050 (controlled).

621.388 AUS ISSN 1441-4716
TELECOMMUNICATIONS AND INFORMATION HIGHWAYS IN NEW ZEALAND. Text in English. 1997. a., latest 2000. USD 425 domestic; USD 440 foreign (effective 2001). **Description:** Covers telecommunications and superhighways development in New Zealand, including major companies and service providers involved and an overview of services and networks with providers.
Former titles: Telecommunications and Information in New Zealand (1329-9042); Telecommunications and Superhighways in New Zealand
Published by: Paul Budde Communication Pty. Ltd., 2643 George Downes Dr, Bucketty, NSW 2250, Australia. TEL 61-2-4998-8144, FAX 61-2-4998-8247, pbc@budde.com.au, http://www.budde.com.au. Circ: 50.

621.388 AUS ISSN 1444-2477
TELECOMMUNICATIONS INDUSTRY IN AUSTRALIA; packaging of value added telecommunication & broadcasting services & networks. Text in English. 1988. a., latest 2001. USD 750 domestic; USD 700 foreign (effective 2001). **Description:** Covers Australian developments and strategies in telecommunication and broadcasting. Includes regulatory developments.
Formerly (until 2000): Telecommunications Strategies in Australia (1441-7952); (until 1998): Telecommunications Strategies Report, Australia, New Zealand and Pacific Islands (1328-2077); (until 1997): Telecommunications Strategies (1322-3518); Strategic V A S - V A N S Report
Published by: Paul Budde Communication Pty. Ltd., 2643 George Downes Dr, Bucketty, NSW 2250, Australia. TEL 61-2-4998-8144, FAX 61-2-4998-8247, pbc@budde.com.au, http://www.budde.com.au. Ed. Paul Budde. Circ: 500.

384.6 USA ISSN 1531-4871
TELECOMMUNICATIONS MERGERS AND ACQUISITIONS NEWSLETTER. Text in English. 1998. m. USD 695 in US & Canada; USD 745 elsewhere (effective 2003). **Document type:** *Newsletter, Trade.* **Description:** Provides dependable and timely information on new opportunities, technology, applications, products, and market trends.
Related titles: Online - full text ed.: (from ProQuest Information & Learning).
—CCC.
Published by: Information Gatekeepers, Inc., 320 Washington St, Ste 302, Brighton, MA 02135. TEL 617-782-5033, 800-323-1088, FAX 617-734-8562, info@igigroup.com, http://www.igigroup.com. Ed. Tony Carmona. Pub. Dr. Paul Polishuk.

621.38 GBR ISSN 0264-4568
TELECOMMUNICATIONS NEWS. Text in English. 1983. 24/yr. **Document type:** *Trade.*
Indexed: B&I.
Address: 5 Riverside, Wooburn Moor, High Wycombe, Bucks HP10 0NU, United Kingdom. TEL 44-1628-523458, FAX 44-1628-523458. Ed. Alan Forberg.

343.09943 USA ISSN 1058-3181
KF2765.Z9
TELECOMMUNICATIONS POLICY AND REGULATION. Text in English. 1990. a.
Published by: Practising Law Institute, 810 Seventh Ave, New York, NY 10019.

343.09943 AUS
TELECOMMUNICATIONS REPORTER. Text in English. 1990. 3 base vols. plus irreg. updates. looseleaf. AUD 746.12 (effective 2004). **Document type:** *Trade.* **Description:** Offers news for persons in the telecommunications industry and lawyers practicing in this field.
Published by: Lawbook Co. (Subsidiary of: Thomson Legal & Regulatory Ltd.), PO Box 3502, Rozelle, NSW 2039, Australia. LRA.Service@thomson.com, http://onlineecom01.thomson.com.au/thomson/Catalog.asp?EES_CMD=SI&EES_ID=100482, http://www.lawbookco.com.au/. Eds. A Hurley, M McDonnell.

621.38 GBR ISSN 0968-0497
TELECOMS INDUSTRY. Text in English. 1989. 6/yr. GBP 28.80 in United Kingdom; GBP 34.50 rest of Europe; GBP 45.90 elsewhere (effective 2000). adv. bk.rev. charts; illus.; stat.; tr.lit. back issues avail. **Document type:** *Trade.* **Description:** Products, services, and marketing and business advice for the U.K. telecoms trade and industry.
Published by: Stanworth Communications, PO Box 220, Walton-on-Thames, Surrey KT12 1YQ, United Kingdom. TEL 44-1932-254400, FAX 44-1932-240294. Ed., Pub., R&P Paul Liptrot. Adv. contact Perry Sanger. B&W page GBP 1,650, color page GBP 2,310; trim 210 x 297. Circ: 12,500.

384.6 TWN ISSN 0258-0284
TK5101.A1
TELECOMS TECHNICAL QUARTERLY✶. Key Title: Dianxin Jishu Jikan. Text in Chinese; Summaries in English. 1957. q. USD 25 in Asia; USD 30 elsewhere. bk.rev. abstr.; illus.
Formerly (until 1980): Taiwan Telecommunications Technical Quarterly
Published by: Ministry of Transportation and Communications, Directorate General of Telecommunications, 31 Aikuo E Rd, Taipei, 10605, Taiwan. TEL 886-2-3443633, FAX 886-2-3519514, TELEX 21733 GENTEL. Circ: 3,000.

384.0285 USA
TELECOMTACTICS: BUSINESS SYSTEMS. Text in English. 1989. m. USD 1,695 (effective 1998). **Description:** Electronic telecommunication product reference. Provides specifications, features, strengths and weaknesses of PBX's, key sets, ACD's, call accounting and voice mail.
Formerly: M I C - Tech-Telecommunications
Related titles: CD-ROM ed.; Online - full text ed.
Published by: Phillips Infotech, 1111 Marlkress Rd, Ste 101, Cherry Hill, NJ 08003. TEL 609-424-1100, FAX 609-424-1999. Ed. Don Stuart.

384.1 USA ISSN 0740-9354
TK6001
TELECONNECT. Text in English. 1983. m. free to qualified personnel. adv. tr.lit. **Document type:** *Trade.* **Description:** Provides information on new telecom products, technologies, techniques and strategies.
Related titles: Online - full text ed.: (from EBSCO Publishing, Gale Group).
Indexed: CADCAM, CompD, CurCont, ResCtrInd, SoftBase, TelAb.
—BLDSC (8781.767000), IDS, IE, Infotrieve. **CCC.**
Published by: C M P Media LLC (Subsidiary of: United News & Media), 11 W 19th St, New York, NY 10011-4280. http://www.teleconnect.com. Ed. Warren Hersch TEL 917-305-3367. Pub. Ruthann Fisher TEL 215-396-4037. Circ: 35,000.

384.53 RUS
TELEFON. Text in Russian. 2001. m. **Document type:** *Magazine, Consumer.* **Description:** Presents information of interest to the owners of mobile phones. Includes catalogue of newest telephones and accessories.
Published by: Izdatel'skii Dom S P N, ul Kedrova, 15, Moscow, 117036, Russian Federation. valle@spn.ru, http://www.spn.ru/publishing/journals/protelefon. Circ: 180,000.

384.6 DEU ISSN 1438-6755
TELEFON MAGAZIN; der Kaufberater fuer Telekommunikation. Text in German. m. adv. **Document type:** *Magazine, Consumer.* **Description:** Contains product and service information for all types of telecommunication.
Published by: Komunik Verlag & Marketing GmbH, Konrad-Celtis-Str 77, Munich, 81369, Germany. TEL 49-89-74117233, FAX 49-89-74117178, redaktion@telefon-magazin.de, coroli@komunik.de, http://www.telecom-channel.de, http://www.komunik.de. Ed. Klaus Albers.

384.6 ITA
TELEFONI CELLULARI MAGAZINE. Text in Italian. 1994. bi-m. EUR 13.65 (effective 2003). adv. **Document type:** *Magazine, Consumer.*
Former titles (until 2001): La Grande Guida Telefoni Cellulari Magazine (1126-4268); (until 1997): Guida ai Telefoni Cellulari (1126-4276)
Published by: Gruppo Editoriale Futura, Via XXV Aprile, 39, Bresso, MI 20091, Italy. TEL 39-02-665261, FAX 39-02-66526222, tcm@futura-ge.com, info@futura-ge.com, http://www.futura-ge.com/prodotti/riviste/tcm.

621.385 ITA ISSN 1122-2735
TELEFONO. Text in Italian. 1991. bi-m.
Published by: Studio Zeta S.r.l., Via S Fruttuoso, 10, Monza, MI 20052, Italy. TEL 039-736451, FAX 039-736500. Ed. Eugenio Zigliotto. Circ: 25,000.

384 DEU
TELEKOMMUNIKATION JAHRBUCH FUER UNTERNEHMENSMANAGEMENT. Text in German. 1970. a. adv. **Document type:** *Magazine, Trade.*
Former titles: Telekommunikation Jahrbuch fuer Unternehmensmanagement in Europe (0948-3608); Verwaltungsjahrbuch fuer die Deutsche Bundespost (0939-4400); Taschenbuch der Post- und Fernmelde-Verwaltung (0082-190X); Taschenbuch fuer Fernmelde-Verwaltung
Published by: Fachverlag Schiele und Schoen GmbH, Markgrafenstr 11, Berlin, 10969, Germany. TEL 49-30-2537520, FAX 49-30-2517248, service@schiele-schoen.de, http://www.schiele-schoen.de. Ed. H Bernd. Circ: 3,000.

621.388 621.385 RUS ISSN 1684-2588
➤ **TELEKOMMUNIKATSII.** Text in Russian. 2000. m. USD 629 foreign (effective 2005). **Document type:** *Journal, Academic/Scholarly.* **Description:** Presents news about the development and production of telephone equipment, development forecasts, information, training and methodological material in the field of telephony, networks, satellite, optic and mobile networks.
Published by: Nauka i Tekhnologii, Stromynskii per, 4/1, Moscow, 107076, Russian Federation. admin@nait.ru, http://www.nait.dacom.ru/journals/index.php?p_journal_id=9, http://www.nait.ru. Ed. I S Zakharov. **Dist. by:** East View Information Services, 3020 Harbor Ln. N., Minneapolis, MN 55447. TEL 800-477-1005, FAX 800-800-3839, eastview@eastview.com, http://www.eastview.com.

384 CZE ISSN 0040-2591
TELEKOMUNIKACE; casopis pro pracovniky provozu, udrzby a vystavby telefonu, telegrafu, rozhlasu po drate a radiokomunikaci. Text in Czech. 1962. m. CZK 12, USD 27. bk.rev. abstr.; charts; illus.; stat.
Published by: (Czech Republic. Federalni Ministerstvo Spoju), S P T Telecom, a.s., Plzenska 166, Prague 5, 150 00, Czech Republic. Ed. Vera Novotna. **Dist. by:** Artia, Ve Smeckach 30, Prague 1 111 27, Czech Republic. **Co-publisher:** S T Bratislava, s.p., Slovakia.

621.38   CAN   ISSN 0840-5476
TELEMANAGEMENT; the Angus report on communications systems, services and strategies. Text in English. 1983. 10/yr. CND 350, USD 295 (effective 1999). bk.rev. index. back issues avail. **Document type:** *Newsletter.* **Description:** Provides practical guidance for managers of business telecommunications systems.
—CISTI. **CCC.**
Published by: Angus Telemanagement Group Inc., 8 Old Kingston Rd, Ajax, ON L1T 2Z7, Canada. TEL 905-686-5050, FAX 905-686-2655, editors@angustel.ca, http://angustel.ca. Eds. Ian Angus, Lis Angus.

621.38   GBR
TELEPHONE ENGINEER AND MANAGEMENT. Text in English. 24/yr.
Address: 302 Whitchurch Ln, Edgware, Mddx HA8 6QX, United Kingdom. TEL 081-952-7991, FAX 081-9511490. Ed. Adrian Morant. Circ: 40,000.

384.6   USA
TELEPHONE I P NEWS. (Information Provider) Text in English. m. USD 150 in North America; USD 165 elsewhere (effective 2001). bk.rev. **Document type:** *Newsletter, Trade.* **Description:** Covers the telephone information provider industry, including new products and marketing strategies. Also reports on public service commission rulings.
Related titles: Online - full text ed.
Published by: Worldwide Videotex, PO Box 3273, Boynton Beach, FL 33424-3273. TEL 561-738-2276, markedit@juno.com, http://www.wvpubs.com. Ed., Pub. Mark Wright.

384.6   USA
TELEPHONE INTERNATIONAL. Text in English. 1985. m. USD 60 for 2 yrs. domestic; USD 70 for 2 yrs. in Canada & Mexico; USD 50 elsewhere (effective 2001). adv. **Document type:** *Trade.* **Description:** Publishes information for buyers and sellers of new and refurbished telecommunications equipment.
Published by: Telephone International, Inc., PO Box 3589, Crossville, TN 38557-3589. TEL 931-484-3685, 800-492-3685, FAX 931-456-2721, info@telephoneinternational.com, http://www.telephoneinternational.com/.

384.6   THA
TELEPHONE ORGANIZATION OF THAILAND. ANNUAL REPORT. Text in English, Thai. 1954. a. **Document type:** *Corporate.*
Published by: Telephone Organization of Thailand, Thanon Phloen Chit, Bangkok Metropolis, 10500, Thailand. TEL 02-257-1000. Ed. Kamphonwut Sukhsong.

TELEPHONE SELLING REPORT. see *BUSINESS AND ECONOMICS—Marketing And Purchasing*

384   USA   ISSN 0040-2656
CODEN: TLPNAS
TELEPHONY; intelligence for the broadband economy. Text in English. 1901. bi-w. USD 114 domestic; USD 133 foreign; free (effective 2005). adv. bk.rev. illus.; stat. s-a. index. reprints avail. **Document type:** *Magazine, Trade.* **Description:** Written for decision makers in the service provider market, including telcos, wireless and PCS carriers, cable companies, Internet service providers, and access providers.
Incorporates (in 2001): Upstart (1527-5248)
Related titles: Microform ed.: (from PQC); Online - full text ed.: InternetTelephony (from bigchalk, EBSCO Publishing, Florida Center for Library Automation, Gale Group, H.W. Wilson, O C L C Online Computer Library Center, Inc., ProQuest Information & Learning).
Indexed: ABIn, B&BAb, BPI, BusI, CADCAM, CompB, CompC, CompD, CurCont, Inspec, LRI, PROMT, SRI, T&II, TelAb.
—BLDSC (8785.000000), AskIEEE, CASDDS, CISTI, Ei, IDS, IE, Infotrieve, ingenta, Linda Hall. **CCC.**
Published by: Primedia Business Magazines & Media, Inc. (Subsidiary of: Primedia, Inc.), 330 N Wabash Ave, Ste 2300, Chicago, IL 60611. TEL 312-595-1080, FAX 312-595-0296, telephony@primediabusiness.com, inquiries@primediabusiness.com, http:// www.telephonyonline.com/, http://www.primediabusiness.com. Ed. Jason Meyers. Pub. Mark Hickey TEL 720-489-3196. adv.: B&W page USD 8,285, color page USD 11,105. Circ: 62,761 (controlled).

621.38   GBR
TELEPHONY. Text in English. w.
Address: 71 Coval Ln, Chelmsford, Essex CM1 1TG, United Kingdom. TEL 44-1245-283984, FAX 44-1245-257630. Ed. John Williamson. Circ: 45,000.

384.1   CAN   ISSN 0040-2710
TK5101.A1   CODEN: TLSSAO
TELESIS (OTTAWA). Text in English. 1967. 3/yr. free to qualified personnel. charts; illus. reprint service avail. from PQC. **Description:** Presents BNR's and Northern Telecom's technical progress to an international audience in telecommunications, office information management systems, industry and government.
Related titles: Online - full text ed.: (from Micromedia ProQuest, O C L C Online Computer Library Center, Inc., ProQuest Information & Learning).

Indexed: ABIn, CADCAM, ChemAb, EIP, EngInd, Inspec, SCI, TelAb.
—AskIEEE, CISTI, Ei, Linda Hall. **CCC.**
Published by: Bell-Northern Research Ltd., 3500 Carling Ave, Ottawa, ON K1Y 4H7, Canada. TEL 613-765-2520, FAX 613-763-2008. Ed. Jo Anne Dyer. Circ: 35,000 (controlled).

384.6   USA   ISSN 1074-5823
TK6401
TELETIMES. Text in English. 1990. bi-m. USD 60 domestic to non-members; USD 85 foreign to non-members; USD 15 to members. **Document type:** *Trade.* **Description:** Addresses the challenges and opportunities that face the rapidly changing telecommunications industry.
Published by: United States Telecom Association, 607 14th St NW, # 400, Washington, DC 20005-2000. TEL 202-326-7300, FAX 202-326-7333, csulliva@usta.org, http://www.usta.org. Ed. Cheryl Sullivan.

TOLL-FREE DIGEST. see *BUSINESS AND ECONOMICS—Trade And Industrial Directories*

384   JPN   ISSN 0041-381X
TSUSHIN KOGYO/C I A J JOURNAL. Text in Japanese. 1953. m. JPY 10,800. adv. bk.rev. stat. **Description:** Contains articles on recent telecommunications developments, including CIAJ activities.
Indexed: JCT, JTA.
Published by: Tsushin Kikai Kogyokai/Communications Industry Association of Japan, Sankei Bldg Annex, 7-2 Ote-Machi 1-chome, Chiyoda-ku, Tokyo, 100-0004, Japan. TEL 81-3-3231-3156, FAX 81-3-3231-3110, http://www.ciaj.or.jp. Ed. Takayoshi Masuzawa. Circ: (controlled).

384.6   GBR
THE U K CALL CENTRE MARKET PERFORMANCE REPORT. Text in English. 1990. a. GBP 795 per issue (effective 2000). **Document type:** *Trade.* **Description:** Targeted at experienced users and vendors who must know and understand how the market is developing.
Published by: Wharton Information Systems, 11 Beaumont Ave, Richmond, Surrey TW9 2HE, United Kingdom. TEL 44-20-8332-1120, n_wharton.compuserve.com. Ed. Andrea Wharton. Pub. Keith Wharton.

384.6   USA   ISSN 0731-8251
TK4018
U.S. RURAL ELECTRIFICATION ADMINISTRATION. ANNUAL STATISTICAL REPORT. RURAL TELEPHONE BORROWERS. Text in English. 1958. a. USD 12. **Document type:** *Government.*
Formerly: U.S. Rural Electrification Administration. Annual Statistical Report. Rural Telephone Program (0083-3185)
Published by: U.S. Rural Electrification Administration, U S Department of Agriculture, Washington, DC 20250. TEL 202-382-8674, FAX 202-382-1915. **Subscr. to:** U.S. Government Printing Office, Superintendent of Documents.

384.6   USA
UNITED STATES TELEPHONE ASSOCIATION. HOLDING COMPANY REPORT. Text in English. 1963. a. USD 125 to non-members; USD 75 to members. stat. **Document type:** *Trade.*
Formerly: United States Independent Telephone Association. Holding Company Report
Indexed: SRI.
Published by: United States Telecom Association, 607 14th St NW, # 400, Washington, DC 20005-2000. TEL 202-326-7300, FAX 202-326-7333. R&P Amy Fabian. Circ: 3,000.

UNITED STATES TELEPHONE ASSOCIATION. STATISTICS OF THE LOCAL EXCHANGE CARRIERS. see *COMMUNICATIONS—Abstracting, Bibliographies, Statistics*

384.6   GBR   ISSN 1358-8923
UP TO DATE; one2one magazine for subscribers to mobile phone network. Text in English. 1994. q. **Document type:** *Consumer.*
Published by: (One2one), Mediamark Publishing International Ltd., Tudor House, 35 Gresse St, Rathbone Pl, London, W1P 1PN, United Kingdom. TEL 44-171-212-9000, FAX 44-171-212-9001, 121@mediamark.co.uk, http:// www.mediamark.co.uk. Pub., R&P Peter Moore. Circ: 650,000 (controlled).

384.6   USA   ISSN 1541-9398
UTILITY & TELECOM FLEETS. Text in English. 1987. 8/yr. USD 60 in Canada; USD 85 elsewhere (effective 2005); free domestic to qualified personnel. adv. **Document type:** *Magazine, Trade.* **Description:** For fleet managers and maintenance supervisors employed by telephone companies, utilities, CATV operators, municipalities, public works, and related contractors.
Former titles (until 2002): Utility Fleets (1535-9719); (until 2001): Utility and Telephone Fleets (1058-9090)
Published by: Practical Communications, Inc., 220 N. Smith St., # 228, Palatine, IL 60067-8500. utfmag@utfmag.com, http://www.utfleets.com/. Ed. Carol Birkland. Pub. J. Chance. Circ: 18,000.

VISTAS. see *COMMUNICATIONS*

384.6   MEX
VOCES DE TELEFONOS DE MEXICO. Text in Spanish. 1953. m. free.
Published by: Telefonos de Mexico, S.A., Via Parque 198, Mexico City 5, DF, Mexico. Circ: 15,000.

384   ZAF   ISSN 1024-0357
VODAWORLD∗ ; worldwide cellular communication update. Text in English. 1994. m. ZAR 5.40 per issue. adv. illus. **Document type:** *Trade.*
Published by: (Vodacom), Interactive Publishing, S-F, Foretrust Bldg, Martin Hammerschlag Way, Cape Town, 8001, South Africa.

384.029   USA   ISSN 8755-2876
HE7771
WASHINGTON TELECOM DIRECTORY. Text in English. a. USD 35; USD 50 foreign. **Document type:** *Directory.* **Description:** Lists telecom contacts in Washington, D.C.: names, phone numbers and addresses for key people at the FCC, Departments of Commerce, Defense, Justice, International Trade Commission, other federal agencies, congressional committees, industry associations, international organizations and public interest groups.
Published by: Capitol Publications, Inc. (Subsidiary of: Aspen Publishers, Inc.), 1333 H St NW, Ste. 100E, Washington, DC 20005-4746. TEL 800-327-7205, FAX 703-739-6490, http://www.telecommunications.com.

621.385   GBR   ISSN 1368-8677
WHAT CELLPHONE; the biggest and best bying guide for mobile communications. Variant title: What Cellular Phone. Text in English. 1993. m. GBP 32.40 domestic; GBP 50.40 in Europe; GBP 72 elsewhere; GBP 3.40 newsstand/cover (effective 2003). adv. **Document type:** *Magazine, Trade.* **Description:** Contains news and reviews of the latest handsets, accessories, tariffs and services, along with essential buying advice.
Published by: Highbury - WV (Subsidiary of: Highbury House Communications PLC), 53-79 Highgate Rd, London, NW5 1TW, United Kingdom. TEL 44-20-73311000, FAX 44-20-73311273, http://www.what-cellphone.com/, http://www.hhc.co.uk/. Ed. Philip Lattimore.

384.6   GBR
WHAT MOBILE AND CELLPHONE MAGAZINE (UK EDITION). Text in English. 1993. m. GBP 39.95 domestic; GBP 55 in Europe; GBP 95 elsewhere; GBP 2.50 newsstand/cover. adv. back issues avail. **Document type:** *Consumer.* **Description:** Offers persons looking to purchase mobile or cellular phone equipment and services practical advice. Includes phone and tariff tables.
Published by: Blah Publishing Ltd., 11 Clerkenwell Green, London, EC1R ODN, United Kingdom. TEL 44-171-251-6688, FAX 44-171-251-6699, simon@blah.com. Ed., Pub. Simon Rockman. Adv. contact Chris Hanage. color page GBP 2,100. Circ: 30,000 (paid).

384.53   USA
WI-FI REVOLUTION. Text in English. m. adv. **Document type:** *Consumer.* **Description:** Contains articles and features aimed at technology developers, equipment vendors, resellers, and systems integrators in the wireless and networking markets.
Published by: Technology Marketing Corporation, One Technology Plaza, Norwalk, CT 06854. TEL 203-852-6950, 800-243-6002, FAX 203-853-2845, tmc@tmcnet.com, http://www.wifirevolution.com, http://www.tmcnet.com. Ed. Laura Guevin. Adv. contact Michelle Tehrani.

384.53   USA
WI-FI TELEPHONY. Text in English. m. adv. **Document type:** *Newsletter, Trade.* **Description:** Provides up-to-date and relevant information on wireless communications and technology.
Media: Online - full content.
Published by: Technology Marketing Corporation, One Technology Plaza, Norwalk, CT 06854. TEL 203-852-6950, 800-243-6002, FAX 203-853-2845, tmc@tmcnet.com, http://www.tmcnet.com/wifi-telephony/about.htm. Adv. contact Michelle Tehrani.

384.55   USA
WIRELESS BROADBAND. Text in English. m. USD 945; USD 1,340 combined subscription print & e-mail eds. (effective 2005). adv. **Document type:** *Newsletter, Trade.* **Description:** Covers all licensed and unlicensed wireless broadband frequencies.
Incorporates (in 2005): Broadband Fixed Wireless
Related titles: E-mail ed.: USD 875 (effective 2005).
Published by: Kagan Research, LLC, One Lower Ragsdale Dr, Bldg One, Ste 130, Monterey, CA 93940. TEL 831-624-1536, FAX 831-625-3225, info@kagan.com, http:// research.kagan.com/keo/subscriptionsDetailPage.aspx? SubscriptionID=29, http://www.kagan.com. adv.: page USD 1,575.

384.5   GBR   ISSN 1471-3888
WIRELESS EUROPE. Text in English. 2000. 8/yr. free to qualified personnel (effective 2003). adv. **Document type:** *Magazine, Trade.* **Description:** Provides a mix of news, in-depth articles, personality profiles and product updates for the wireless industry.

C

▼ *new title*   ➤ *refereed*   ∗ *unverified*   ◆ *full entry avail.*

Published by: Institute of Physics Publishing, Dirac House, Temple Back, Bristol, BS1 6BE, United Kingdom. TEL 44-117-9297481, FAX 44-117-9294318, wireless@iop.org, custserv@iop.org, http://wireless.iop.org/, http://www.iop.org/. Ed. Hamish Johnston TEL 44-117-930-1023. Pub. Jo Nicholas TEL 44-117-930-1029. Adv. contact James Garmston TEL 44-117-930-1093.

384.53 USA
▼ **WIRELESS FIDELITY**; opportunities along the broadband wireless service delivery chain. Text in English. 2003. q. USD 55 domestic; USD 100 in Canada; USD 130 elsewhere; USD 15 per issue (effective 2005). adv. **Document type:** *Magazine, Trade.* **Description:** Covers business opportunities across the broadband wireless value chain.
Published by: Virgo Publishing, Inc., 3300 N. Central Ave., Ste 300, Phoenix, AZ 85012. TEL 480-990-1101, FAX 480-990-0819, cs@vpico.com, http://www.wirelessfidelitymag.com/, http://www.vpico.com. Pub. Marla Ellerman. adv.: B&W page USD 3,630; trim 8.125 x 10.875.

384.6 AUS ISSN 1444-075X
WIRELESS MARKET. Text in English. 1984. a., latest 2001. USD 425 domestic; USD 440 in United States; USD 450 in Europe (effective 2001). 100 p./no.; **Document type:** *Directory, Trade.* **Description:** Covers cellular, paging, satellite, mobile data, MDS and telemetry services and networks. Includes information on developments and trends in Australia.
Former titles (until 1999): Wireless Markets Australia (1444-0741); (until 1997): Wireless Markets - Australia and New Zealand (1326-6829); Which superseded in part: Directory of Electronic Services and Communications Networks in Australia and New Zealand (1322-350X)
Published by: Paul Budde Communication Pty. Ltd., 2643 George Downes Dr, Bucketty, NSW 2250, Australia. TEL 61-49-988144, FAX 61-49-988247, pbc@budde.com.au, http://www.budde.com.au. Ed. Paul Budde.

C

WIRELESS PERSONAL COMMUNICATIONS; an international journal. see *COMMUNICATIONS—Radio*

384.6 USA ISSN 1099-9248
HD9697.T45
WIRELESS REVIEW; intelligence for competitive providers. Text in English. 1998. m. free in North America; USD 80 elsewhere (effective 2005). adv. back issues avail. **Document type:** *Magazine, Trade.* **Description:** Provides the very latest in technology, engineering, operational, maintenance and sales and marketing intelligence for use to promote network innovation, market development and industry evolution.
Former by merger of (1984-1998): Cellular Business (0741-6520); (1994-1998): Wireless World (1075-4385)
Related titles: Online - full text ed.: (from EBSCO Publishing, Florida Center for Library Automation, Gale Group, H.W. Wilson, O C L C Online Computer Library Center, Inc., ProQuest Information & Learning).
Indexed: ABIn, AS&TI, B&I, CADCAM, TelAb.
—BLDSC (9324.780000), IE, Infotrieve, ingenta. **CCC.**
Published by: Primedia Business Magazines & Media, Inc. (Subsidiary of: Primedia, Inc.), One IBM Plaza, Ste 2300, Chicago, IL 60611. TEL 312-595-1080, 800-458-0479, FAX 312-595-0295, inquiries@primediabusiness.com, http://www.wirelessreview.com/, http://www.primediabusiness.com. Ed. Jason Meyers TEL 312-840-8418. Pub. Mark Hickey TEL 720-489-3196. adv.: B&W page USD 6,430, color page USD 7,450; trim 7.875 x 10.75. Circ: 30,000.

384.6 USA ISSN 1075-413X
WIRELESS TELECOM INVESTOR. Text in English. 1988. m. USD 1,095; USD 1,490 combined subscription print & e-mail eds. (effective 2005). adv. **Document type:** *Newsletter, Trade.* **Description:** Analyzes private and public values of cellular telephone companies, PCS, ESMR and paging companies.
Formerly: Cellular Investor (0898-0403)
Related titles: E-mail ed.: USD 995 (effective 2005); Fax ed.: USD 995 (effective 2001).
Published by: Kagan Research, LLC, One Lower Ragsdale Dr, Bldg One, Ste 130, Monterey, CA 93940. TEL 831-624-1536, FAX 831-625-3225, info@kagan.com, http://research.kagan.com/keo/subscriptionsDetailPage.aspx?SubscriptionID=33, http://www.kagan.com. Pub. Paul Kagan. adv.: page USD 3,670.

343.09943 USA
WIRELESS TELECOMMUNICATIONS REGULATION. Text in English. bi-m. USD 465 combined subscription print & online eds. (effective 2005). **Document type:** *Newsletter, Trade.* **Description:** Offers complete and comprehensive coverage of private radio and commercial wireless law and regulation and RF equipment regulation.
Related titles: CD-ROM ed.: USD 395 combined subscription CD-ROM & online eds. (effective 2005); Online - full text ed.: USD 375 (effective 2005).
Published by: Pike & Fischer, Inc. (Subsidiary of: The Bureau of National Affairs, Inc.), 1010 Wayne Ave, Ste 1400, Silver Spring, MD 20910. TEL 301-562-1530, 800-255-8131, FAX 301-562-1521, pike@pf.com, http://wirelessregs.pf.com, http://www.pf.com.

384.5 USA
THE WORLD WIRELESS BEACON. Text in English. 1989. q. USD 15 membership. adv. bk.rev. back issues avail. **Document type:** *Newsletter.* **Description:** Includes experiences and anecdotes from members who are or were radio-telegraph operators in the U.S. Merchant Marine or military services. Also covers history of maritime and military communications.
Related titles: Talking Book ed.
Published by: Society of Wireless Pioneers, 5319 Sierra Vista Rd, Murphys, CA 95247. TEL 614-866-6289, w8tp@jun.com. Ed., Pub., R&P Earl D Wilson. Circ: 3,000. **Subscr. to:** PO Box 86, Geyserville, CA 95441.

384.6 USA
WORLDWIDE TELECOM. Text in English. 1989. m. USD 150 in North America; USD 165 elsewhere (effective 2001). bk.rev. back issues avail. **Document type:** *Newsletter, Trade.* **Description:** Provides the news and information on international telecommunications products, services, and contracts with emphasis on U.S. telecommunications companies doing business in foreign markets and on products with a potential market overseas.
Related titles: Online - full text ed.: (from Data-Star, The Dialog Corporation).
Published by: Worldwide Videotex, PO Box 3273, Boynton Beach, FL 33424-3273. TEL 561-738-2276, markedit@juno.com, http://www.wvpubs.com. Ed., Pub. Mark Wright.

384.6 USA
X-CHANGE. Text in English. 1996. 18/yr. USD 80 domestic; USD 110 in Canada; USD 145 elsewhere (effective 2005). adv. **Document type:** *Magazine, Trade.* **Description:** Designed for industry manufacturers and suppliers who are targeting emerging and new carriers in the local telephone service.
Related titles: Online - full text ed.
Published by: Virgo Publishing, Inc., 3300 N. Central Ave., Ste 300, Phoenix, AZ 85012. TEL 480-990-1101, FAX 480-990-0819, xchngmag@vpico.com, cs@vpico.com, http://www.x-changemag.com, http://www.vpico.com. adv.: B&W page USD 4,440, color page USD 5,590; 8.125 x 10.875. Circ: 34,076.

384.6 USA
X D S L NEWSLETTER. Text in English. 1996. m. USD 695 in US & Canada; USD 745 elsewhere (effective 2004). bk.rev. tr.lit. **Document type:** *Newsletter, Trade.* **Description:** Devoted to worldwide developments in digital subscriber line technologies.
Formerly (until 200?): A D S L Newsletter (1094-2815)
Related titles: Online - full text ed.: (from Gale Group).
Published by: Information Gatekeepers, Inc., 320 Washington St, Ste 302, Brighton, MA 02135. TEL 617-782-5033, 800-323-1088, FAX 617-782-5735, info@igigroup.com, http://www.igigroup.com. Ed. Tony Carmona. Pub. Dr. Paul Polishuk.

384.53 USA
3 G BULLETIN; the on-going report bulletin for the 3 G market. (Third Generation Bulletin) Text in English. m. USD 1,307 in Europe; USD 1,420 elsewhere; USD 1,495 combined subscription in US & Canada print & E-mail; USD 1,607 combined subscription elsewhere print & E-mail (effective 2005). **Document type:** *Newsletter, Trade.* **Description:** Examines the explosive growth of the mobile market both in Europe and worldwide and offers unique insights into the next generation of wireless telecommunications.
Related titles: E-mail ed.
Contact: Global Information Inc., 195 Farmington Ave., Ste. 305, Farmington, CT 06032-1700. TEL 866-353-3335, 860-236-2392, us-info@gii.co.jp, http://www.gii.co.jp/english/kt4493_mn_3g_bulletin.html, http://www.the-infoshop.com/. Pub. John Uhlman.

384 USA ISSN 1092-6038
411 NEWSLETTER; the telecom manager's money-saving guide to services, technologies and equipment. Variant title: Four One One Newsletter. Text in English. 1979. bi-w. USD 379. back issues avail. **Document type:** *Newsletter.* **Description:** Directed to telecom managers who oversee voice communications; it gives advice for trimming expenses, boosting productivity, buying equipment and the pros and cons of new systems.
Formerly: Telephone Angles
Related titles: Online - full text ed.: (from Data-Star, Factiva).
Published by: C C M I (Subsidiary of: United Communications Group), 11300 Rockville Pike, Ste 1100, Rockville, MD 20852-3030. TEL 301-287-2257, FAX 301-816-8945, ccmisale@ucg.com, info@ccmi.com. Ed. Steve Pastorkovich. Pub. George David.

COMMUNICATIONS—Television And Cable

A B C NEWS INDEX. see *COMMUNICATIONS—Abstracting, Bibliographies, Statistics*

791.456 USA ISSN 1525-7800
A B C SOAPS IN DEPTH. Text in English. 1997. m. USD 19.95 domestic; USD 33.97 foreign (effective 2005). adv. **Document type:** *Magazine, Consumer.* **Description:** Contains inside information on the cast and characters of soap operas on the ABC television network.
Superesedes in part (in 1999): Soaps in Depth (1092-518X)
Published by: Bauer Publishing Company, L.P., 270 Sylvan Ave, Englewood Cliffs, NJ 07632. TEL 201-569-6699, FAX 201-569-5303, abcmail@soapsindepth.com, http://abc.soapsindepth.com. Ed. Dawn Mazurko.

384.55 MYS ISSN 0126-6209
TK6630.A1
A B U TECHNICAL REVIEW. Text in English. 1969. bi-m. USD 40 (effective 2000). adv. bk.rev. index. back issues avail. **Document type:** *Trade.* **Description:** Contains news, technical developments and equipment trends in the field of engineering.
Indexed: C&ISA, E&CAJ, EngInd, IAA, Inspec.
—BLDSC (0570.300000), AskIEEE, CISTI, Ei, IE, ingenta.
Published by: Asia - Pacific Broadcasting Union, PO Box 1164, Kuala Lumpur, 59700, Malaysia. TEL 60-3-2823108, FAX 60-3-2825292, TELEX MA-32227-ABU, dtd@abu.org.my, http://www.abu.org.my. Ed., R&P, Adv. contact Om P Khushu. Circ: 1,000 (paid and controlled).

621.388 GBR
A C E INTERNATIONAL. Text in English, French, German, Italian. 1977. 10/yr. USD 50. adv.
Published by: A C E Publishing Ltd., House, Queensway House, 2 Queensway, Redhill, Surrey RH1 1QS, United Kingdom. Ed. Roger Packer. Circ: 25,000.

384.55 AUS
A C T A C NEWSLETTER∗. Text in English. 1974. 5/yr. AUD 20. bk.rev. back issues avail. **Document type:** *Newsletter.*
Published by: Australian Children's Television Action Committee, c/o Australian Children's Television Foundation, 3rd Fl, 145 Smith St, Fitzroy, Melbourne, VIC 3065, Australia. TEL 61-3-9419-8800, FAX 61-3-9419-0660, http://actf.com.au. Ed. Jo James. Circ: 2,000.

A F C NEWS. see *MOTION PICTURES*

A F T R A. see *COMMUNICATIONS—Radio*

A M I A NEWSLETTER. see *LIBRARY AND INFORMATION SCIENCES*

621.388 USA
A-V ADVISOR. (Audio-Visual) Text in English. m.
Address: 66 12th St, Atlanta, GA 30309. TEL 404-876-7841, FAX 404-875-5258. Ed. Bill Weber.

384.55 NLD ISSN 0928-8562
A V JOURNAAL; tweewekelijks nieuwsbulletin voor de audiovisuele branche. Text in Dutch. 1992. fortn. adv. illus.; tr.lit. **Document type:** *Trade.*
Published by: Televak Uitgeverij N.V., Postbus 75985, Amsterdam, 1070 AZ, Netherlands. TEL 31-20-6659220, FAX 31-20-6657316. Ed. J Boers. Adv. contact Maarten Ponssen. Circ: 2,500 (paid).

621.384 384.55 GBR ISSN 1361-3685
TS2301.A7 CODEN: AVMAFA
A V MAGAZINE. Variant title: Audio Visual Magazine. Text in English. 1972. m. GBP 55 (effective 2005). adv. bk.rev.; film rev. illus.; tr.lit. index. reprint service avail. from PQC. **Document type:** *Magazine, Trade.* **Description:** Covers all aspects off the audio-visual industry from management issues, event staging, presentations and training applications.
Formerly (until 1995): Audio Visual (0305-2249); Which superseded: Film User (0015-1459)
Related titles: Microfilm ed.: (from PQC).
Indexed: ADPA, BldManAb, ERA, ETA, FLUIDEX, HECAB, Inspec, MRD, RASB.
—BLDSC (1836.542000), AskIEEE, IE, Infotrieve, ingenta. **CCC.**
Published by: Quantum Business Media Ltd., Quantum House, 19 Scarbrook Rd, Croydon, Surrey CR9 1LX, United Kingdom. TEL 44-20-85654200, FAX 44-20-85654444, enquiries@quantumbusinessmedia.com, http://www.quantumbusinessmedia.com. Ed. Peter Lloyd. Circ: 16,000.

791.45 NLD ISSN 0929-7758
A V R O-BODE. Text in Dutch. 1958. w. EUR 47.45 (effective 2005). adv. film rev.; play rev. illus. **Document type:** *Magazine, Consumer.* **Description:** Provides radio and television listings, as well as news and information on showbiz, movies, stars and related topics.
Published by: (Algemene Vereeniging Radio Omroep), B.V. Programmabladen, Postbus 580, Hilversum, 1200 AN, Netherlands. TEL 31-35-6726726, FAX 31-35-6726704, http://avro.bvpb.nl/. Circ: 679,109 (controlled).

▼ **ABOVE GROUND LEVEL.** see *COMMUNICATIONS—Telephone And Telegraph*

ACADEMY PLAYERS DIRECTORY. see *MOTION PICTURES*

ACTORS CD-ROM. see THEATER

ACTORS SPOTLIGHT CASTING DIRECTORY. see THEATER

ACTRESSES CD-ROM. see THEATER

ACTRESSES SPOTLIGHT CASTING DIRECTORY. see THEATER

AD - TIER NEWSLETTER. see ADVERTISING AND PUBLIC RELATIONS

AGENCIES: WHAT THE ACTOR NEEDS TO KNOW (HOLLYWOOD EDITION). see MOTION PICTURES

AGENTS, MANAGERS & CASTING DIRECTORS 411. see MOTION PICTURES

791.456   GBR   ISSN 1468-4047
ALL ABOUT SOAP. Text in English. 1999. m. GBP 15 domestic; GBP 21 in Europe; GBP 23 elsewhere (effective 2004). adv. Document type: Magazine, Consumer. Description: Reveals the latest gossip and hottest plots involving soap operas on television.
Published by: Hachette Filipacchi (UK) Ltd. (Subsidiary of: Hachette Filipacchi Medias S.A.), 64 North Row, London, W1K 7LL, United Kingdom. TEL 44-20-71507000, FAX 44-20-71507001, http://www.allaboutsoap.co.uk/, http://www.hachettefilipacchiuk.co.uk. Circ: 121,156 (paid).

ALL ACCESS. see MOTION PICTURES

ALPHA CONTROL. see LITERATURE—Science Fiction, Fantasy, Horror

621.388   USA   ISSN 0889-6089
TK9956
AMATEUR SATELLITE REPORT. Text in English. 1981. m. USD 30 domestic; USD 36 in Canada; USD 45 elsewhere (effective 1999). adv. back issues avail. Document type: Academic/Scholarly.
Former titles (until 1989): Satellite Journal (8750-7617); (until 1985): Orbit (8756-2480)
Published by: Radio Amateur Satellite Corporation, 850 Sligo Ave, Ste 600, Silver Spring, MD 20910. FAX 301-608-3410, callsign@amsat.org, http://www.amsat.org. Ed. Russ Tillman. Circ: 7,000.

AMERICAN COMMUNICATION JOURNAL. see SOCIOLOGY

AMERICAN MOVIE CLASSICS MAGAZINE. see MOTION PICTURES

ANNUAIRE DU CINEMA TELEVISION VIDEO. see MOTION PICTURES

ANNUARIO DEGLI ATTORI/EUROPEAN PLAYERS' DIRECTORY. see MOTION PICTURES

384.55   ITA   ISSN 1123-6523
ANNUARIO EUROSAT. Text in Italian. 1993. a. price varies. adv. Document type: Yearbook, Consumer. Description: Describes components of satellite reception equipments, interviews leaders of the field and provides with information on how to install a satellite reception equipment.
Formerly (until 1995): Satellite Eurosat Annuario (1123-1068)
Related titles: ♦ Supplement to: Satellite Eurosat. ISSN 1122-9284.
Published by: Gruppo Editoriale J C E, Via Patecchio 2, Milan, MI 20141, Italy. TEL 39-02-57316011, FAX 39-02-57316291, info@jce.it, http://www.jce.it. Ed. Jacopo Castelfranchi. Circ: 80,000.

384.5   ESP
ANTENA DE PROFESIONALES, DE RADIO Y TELEVISION. Text in Spanish. 12/yr.
Published by: Antena de Profesionales de Radio y Television, Evaristo San Miguel, 8 1o, Madrid, 28008, Spain. TEL 248-98-38. Ed. E G Toledano.

621.388   RUS
ANTENNA. Text in Russian. w. USD 149.95 in United States.
Published by: Ekspress Gazeta, Vadkovskii per 18-a, etazh 15, Moscow, 103055, Russian Federation. TEL 7-095-9733876, FAX 7-095-9733920. Ed. T Filimonova. US dist. addr.: East View Information Services, 3020 Harbor Ln. N., Minneapolis, MN 55447. TEL 612-550-0961.

384.55   BRA   ISSN 0101-9112
ANTENNA - ELETRONICA POPULAR. Text in Portuguese. 1926. m. BRL 27 for 6 mos. domestic; USD 30 for 6 mos. foreign (effective 2000). adv. bk.rev. s-a. index. Document type: Consumer.
Formed by the merger of: Eletronica Popular (0013-6085); Antenna (0003-5378)
—CCC.

Published by: Antenna Edicoes Tecnicas Ltda., Av Marechal Floriano, 143, Centro, Rio De Janeiro, RJ 20080-005, Brazil. TEL 55-21-223-2442, FAX 55-21-263-8840, antenna@unisys.com.br. Adv. contact Sergio Porto. Circ: 19,550.

621.388   RUS   ISSN 0320-9601
TK7871.6
ANTENNY. Text in Russian. 1966. m. USD 285 foreign; RUR 300 per issue domestic (effective 2004). Document type: Journal, Academic/Scholarly.
Related titles: ♦ English Translation: Telecommunications and Radio Engineering. ISSN 0040-2508.
Indexed: RefZh.
—CISTI, Linda Hall.
Published by: (Nauchno-Tekhnicheskoe Obshchestvo Radiotekhniki, Elektroniki i Svyazi im. A.S. Popova), Izdatel'stvo Radiotekhnika, Kuznetskii Most 20/6, Moscow, 103031, Russian Federation. iprzhr@online.ru, http://webcenter.ru/~iprzhr/. Ed. L D Bachrach. Dist. by: East View Information Services, 3020 Harbor Ln. N., Minneapolis, MN 55447. TEL 763-550-0961, FAX 763-559-2931, eastview@eastview.com, http://www.eastview.com.

791.45   USA
APE CULTURE. Text in English. 1998. q. bk.rev.; music rev. Description: Dedicated to popular television, movies, music, magazines and the stripmall life.
Media: Online - full text.
Address: apemail@apeculture.com, http://www.apeculture.com. Eds. Julie Wiskirchen, Mary Ladd.

ARAB FILM AND TELEVISION CENTER NEWS. see MOTION PICTURES

384.55   GBR   ISSN 0004-1335
ARIEL. Text in English. 1970 (vol.15). w. GBP 50 in United Kingdom; GBP 60 in Europe; GBP 68 rest of world (effective 2000). adv. bk.rev. charts; illus. Description: Serves as the BBC's weekly in-house magazine. Contains BBC news and topical features, with columns and contributions from staff from all areas of the Corporation. Includes a comprehensive guide to all the current BBC job vacancies.
Indexed: ArtHuCI, LIFT, MEA&I.
Published by: British Broadcasting Corp., Bush House, Rm 227 NW, Strand, London, WC2B 4PH, United Kingdom. TEL 44-171-257-2875, FAX 44-171-240-4899, http://www.bbc.co.uk/info/bbc/ariel.shtml, http://www.bbc.co.uk/info/andyou/ariel.shtml. Ed. Robin Reynolds. Subscr. to: Ariel Subscriptions, Griffin House, Griffin Ln, PO Box 324, Aylesbury, Bucks HP19 3BP, United Kingdom. TEL 44-1296-489550.

384.51   DEU   ISSN 1288-3263
ARTE T V MAGAZIN. Text in German. 1995. m. EUR 1.40 newsstand/cover (effective 2004). adv. Document type: Magazine, Consumer.
Former titles (until 1998): Arte Monatsheft (1282-2841); (until 1997): Arte (1267-7515)
Published by: Arte G.E.I.E., Postfach 1980, Kehl am Rhein, 77679, Germany. http://www.arte-tv.com/magazin. adv.: B&W page EUR 4,750, color page EUR 7,900. Circ: 94,520 (controlled).

ASIA IMAGE. see COMMUNICATIONS—Radio

621.388   SGP
ASIA - PACIFIC BROADCASTING. Text in English. m. USD 70 in Asia; USD 80 elsewhere. adv. back issues avail. Document type: Trade. Description: Reviews of hardware, software available to radio and TV studios, production houses, and recording studios.
Published by: Editor International Pt. Ltd., Trademart, 60 Martin Rd, Ste 07 33, Singapore, 239065, Singapore. TEL 65-7356885, FAX 65-7356891. Ed. Andrew Yeo. Adv. contact Johnny Kwan.

384.55   GBR   ISSN 1358-0396
ASIA - PACIFIC SATELLITE. Text in English. 1995. 9/yr. free to qualified personnel (effective 2003). adv. Document type: Trade. Description: Contains news, market reports, and technical and business features on the satellite market in the Asia-Pacific region.
Published by: Icom Publications Ltd., Chancery House, St Nicholas Way, Sutton, Surrey SM1 1JB, United Kingdom. TEL 44-20-86421117, FAX 44-20-86421941, admin@icompub.com, http://www.icompub.com. Pub. Alec Barton. adv.: B&W page USD 4,535, color page USD 6,440; trim 210 x 280. Circ: 7,503 (controlled).

384.51   GBR   ISSN 1460-6194
ASIA - PACIFIC SATELLITE YEARBOOK (YEAR). Text in English. a. GBP 150, USD 250 includes supplements (effective 2000).
Published by: Icom Publications Ltd., Chancery House, St Nicholas Way, Sutton, Surrey SM1 1JB, United Kingdom. TEL 44-20-86421117, FAX 44-20-86421941, admin@icompub.com, http://www.icompub.com.

▼ AUDIO VIDEO FOTO BILD. see COMMUNICATIONS—Video

791.45   AUS
AUSTAR MAGAZINE. Text in English. m. free to subscr. of AUSTAR Pay TV. adv. film rev.; music rev.; tel.rev. Document type: Magazine, Consumer. Description: Contains celebrity interviews, games, reviews of CDs, upcoming cinema film and crosswords.
Published by: (AUSTAR Communications), Emap Australia Pty. Ltd. (Subsidiary of: Emap International), 187 Thomas St., Level 6, Haymarket, NSW 2000, Australia. TEL 61-2-95819400, FAX 61-2-95819570, http://www.emap.com.au. Ed. Jason Blake. adv.: color page AUD 6,500; trim 200 x 275. Circ: 353,712.

621.388   AUS   ISSN 1325-197X
AUSTRALASIAN SUPERHIGHWAYS NEWSLETTER. Text in English. 1994. m. (11/yr.). USD 425 domestic; USD 455 foreign (effective 2001). Document type: Newsletter. Description: Covers such topics as superhighways and superskyway; cable, satellite, pay TV and MDS; video-on-demand, video servers and set-top boxes; interactive TV, internet, online and hybrid ramps; multimedia; HDTV; teleconferencing; programming and content; homeshopping and consumer electronics regulatory issues; national and international developments.
Formerly: Australasian Cable and Pay T V Newsletter (1322-3534)
Published by: Paul Budde Communication Pty. Ltd., 2643 George Downes Dr, Bucketty, NSW 2250, Australia. TEL 61-2-4998-8144, FAX 61-2-4998-8247, sally@budde.com.au, pbc@budde.com.au, http://www.budde.com.au. R&P Paul Budde. Circ: 150.

AUSTRALIAN SCREEN EDUCATION. see EDUCATION—Teaching Methods And Curriculum

621.38   GBR   ISSN 1367-5729
B B C RESEARCH AND DEVELOPMENT REPORT. Text in English. 1987. irreg.
Formerly (until 1994): B B C Research Department Report (1367-5710)
—ingenta.
Published by: B B C Worldwide Ltd., 80 Wood Ln, London, W12 0TT, United Kingdom. TEL 44-181-576-2000, FAX 44-181-576-3824, http://www.bbc.co.uk.

B F I FILM AND TELEVISION HANDBOOK (YEAR). see MOTION PICTURES

384.55   USA
B I B CHANNELS; what's new in domestic and international television programming and syndication. Text in English. 1992. q. free to Television Programming Source Books subscribers. Description: Features updates on the latest program availabilities.
Related titles: ♦ Supplement to: (Years) Television Programming Source Books. ISSN 1056-6104; ♦ Supplement to: (Year) World Guide to Television. ISSN 1084-9475.
Published by: North American Publishing Co., 1500 Spring Garden St., Ste 1200, Philadelphia, PA 19130-4094. TEL 215-238-5300, FAX 215-238-5457, http://www.napco.com.

B N. see MOTION PICTURES

BABYLON 5: THE OFFICAL MAGAZINE. see LITERATURE—Science Fiction, Fantasy, Horror

BACK STAGE; the performing arts weekly. see THEATER

384.5029   USA
HE8689.8
BACON'S RADIO - T V - CABLE DIRECTORY. Text in English. a. (in 2 vols.). USD 395 (effective 2005). Document type: Directory, Trade. Description: Directory of all US broadcast media.
Formerly: Bacon's Radio - T V Directory (0891-0103)
Published by: Bacon's Information, Inc., 332 S Michigan Ave, Ste 900, Chicago, IL 60604. TEL 312-922-2400, 800-621-0561, FAX 312-987-9773, directories@bacons.com, http://www.bacons.com. Pub. Ruth McFarland. R&P Ruth Cox McFarland TEL 312-986-2728. Circ: 6,000.

384.5532   DEU
BEST OF THE DOME; das offizielle Magazin zur Mega Party!. Text in German. 2000. 4/yr. EUR 2.50 newsstand/cover (effective 2003). adv. Document type: Magazine, Consumer. Description: Provides companion articles and news on the music variety television series "The Dome".
Published by: cultfish entertainment GmbH, Wallstr 59, Berlin, 10179, Germany. TEL 49-30-24008471, FAX 49-30-24008475, http://cultfish.funonline.de/thedome.html, http://cultfish.de. adv.: page EUR 4,400. Circ: 100,226 (paid and controlled).

BETTER RADIO AND TELEVISION. see COMMUNICATIONS—Radio

621.388   GBR   ISSN 1354-2605
BETTER SATELLITE. Text in English. 1993. q. GBP 9.80 domestic; GBP 17 in Europe; GBP 21 elsewhere (effective 2003). adv. Document type: Magazine, Consumer.

C

Published by: Highbury - WV (Subsidiary of: Highbury House Communications PLC), 53-79 Highgate Rd, London, NW5 1TW, United Kingdom. TEL 44-20-7485-0011, FAX 44-20-7482-6269, http://www.hhc.co.uk/bettersatellite. Ed. Mark Newman. Adv. contact Scott Lewis. **Orders to:** ASM Ltd., Unit 6, Pipewell Rd Industrial Estate, Desborough, Northants NN14 2SW, United Kingdom. TEL 44-1536-762860, FAX 44-1536-760306. **Dist. by:** Comag, Tavistock Works, Tavistock Rd, W Drayton, Middx UB7 7QX, United Kingdom. TEL 44-1895-444055, FAX 44-1895-433602.

BIBLIOGRAPHY ON CABLE TELEVISION. see *COMMUNICATIONS—Abstracting, Bibliographies, Statistics*

384.041 GBR
BILLING PLUS. Text in English. 1998. fortn. GBP 995, EUR 1,493; GBP 2,985, EUR 4,925 combined subscription print & online eds. (effective 2004). **Document type:** *Newsletter, Trade.* **Description:** Covers the billing and customer care elements of the fixed and mobile telecommunications, broadband and Internet delivery markets.
Formerly: Billing International (1461-1252)
Related titles: Online - full text ed.: (from Florida Center for Library Automation).
Published by: Baskerville (Subsidiary of: T & F Informa plc), Sheepen Place, Colchester, Essex C03 3LP, United Kingdom. TEL 44-20-70175537, FAX 44-20-70174783, telecoms.enquiries@informa.com, http://www.baskerville.telecoms.com/.

791.45 USA ISSN 1092-7891
BIOGRAPHY (NEW YORK); every life has a story. Text in English. 1997. q. free to members. adv. bk.rev. illus. back issues avail.; reprints avail. **Document type:** *Magazine, Consumer.* **Description:** Features current and historical stories and articles about the famous and the infamous.
Former titles (until 1997): A and E Monthly (1083-1738); A and E Program Guide
Related titles: Online - full text ed.: (from EBSCO Publishing).
Indexed: BRI, CBRI, MASUSE, RGPR.
—Infotrieve.
Published by: Arts & Entertainment, 235 E 45th St, New York, NY 10017. TEL 212-210-9750, 800-975-5353, 800-975-5353, biographyclub@aetv.com, http://www.biography.com. Ed., R&P Carey McCoy. Pub. Paulette McLeod. Adv. contact Thomas McCluskey. B&W page USD 21,910, color page USD 32,610. Circ: 575,000. **Subscr. to:** PO Box 7418, Red Oak, IA 51591-0418. **Dist. in UK by:** Seymour Distribution Ltd, 86 Newman St, London W1T 3EX, United Kingdom. FAX 44-207-396-8002, enquiries@seymour.co.uk.

C

BLUE BOOK OF BRITISH BROADCASTING. see *BUSINESS AND ECONOMICS—Trade And Industrial Directories*

384.55 USA
BLUE LIGHTS. Text in English. bi-m. **Document type:** *Newsletter.* **Description:** Covers TV and videotapes.
Published by: Spotlight Starman, 16563 Ellen Springs Dr, Lower Lake, CA 95457. Ed. Vicki Werkley.

BOOKING. see *BUSINESS AND ECONOMICS—Trade And Industrial Directories*

621.388 ZAF
BOPHUTHATSWANA BROADCASTING CORPORATION. ANNUAL REPORT. Text in English. a. **Document type:** *Corporate.*
Published by: Bophuthatswana Broadcasting Corporation, Private Bag X2150, Mmabatho, North West Province 8681, South Africa. TEL 27-140-897111, FAX 27-140-897299.

343.099 USA
BOTEIN'S REGULATION OF THE ELECTRONIC MASS MEDIA: LAW AND POLICY FOR RADIO, TELEVISION, CABLE AND NEW VIDEO TECHNOLOGIES. Text in English. latest 1998, 3rd ed., base vol. plus irreg. updates. Price varies. 657 p./no.; **Document type:** *Monographic series, Trade.* **Description:** Covers electronic media regulatory, technology and economics issues, including FCC jurisdiction of broadcast, FCC licensing selection and procedure, regulation of market structure, ownership, and network influence. Also insight into the First Amendment standard and the fairness doctrine, legal and copyright issues, federal preemption of state and local regulation.
Related titles: ♦ Series of: American Casebook Series. ISSN 1555-8053.
Published by: Thomson West (Subsidiary of: Thomson Corporation, The), 610 Opperman Dr, Eagan, MN 55123-1396. TEL 800-328-4880, http://www.westgroup.com/store/product.asp?product%5Fid=18255667&catalog%5Fname=wgstore, http://west.thomson.com. Ed. Michael H Botein.

791.45 CAN ISSN 1182-9893
BOW VALLEY THIS WEEK. Text in English. 1987. w. adv. **Description:** Features television listings and entertainment news.
Address: 223 Bear St, P O Box 129, Banff, AB T0L 0C0, Canada. TEL 403-762-2453, FAX 403-762-5274. Circ: 10,450.

BRAILLE B B C ON AIR. see *HANDICAPPED—Visually Impaired*

BRAILLE TELEVISION TIMES. see *HANDICAPPED—Visually Impaired*

384.55 GBR
BROADBAND ASIA. Text in English. bi-m. GBP 75 domestic; USD 128 foreign (effective 2000).
Formerly: Cable and Satellite Asia (1462-2270)
Indexed: B&I.
Published by: Informa Publishing, 69-77 Paul St, London, EC2A 4IQ, United Kingdom. TEL 44-20-7553-1000, FAX 44-20-7553-1105. Circ: 8,000.

384.555 USA ISSN 1536-8491
HE8700.7.C6
BROADBAND CABLE FINANCIAL DATABOOK. Text in English. 1980. a. USD 995 (effective 2005). adv. charts; stat. back issues avail. **Document type:** *Directory, Trade.*
Former titles (until 2001): Cable T V Financial Databook (0736-8143); (until 1982): Cable T V Databook (0276-895X)
Published by: Kagan Research, LLC, One Lower Ragsdale Dr, Bldg One, Ste 130, Monterey, CA 93940. TEL 831-624-1536, FAX 831-625-3225, info@kagan.com, http://www.kagan.com.

384.555 USA
TK6675
BROADBAND PROPERTIES. Text in English. 1982. m. free domestic; USD 55 in Canada; USD 75 elsewhere (effective 2005). adv. **Document type:** *Magazine, Trade.*
Formerly (until 1999): Private Cable & Wireless Cable (1080-9570); Which incorporated (in June 1999): Wireless Pay - TV International (1095-8959); Which had former titles: Wireless International (1085-7877); (until 1994): Private Cable (0745-8711); Which incorporated: T V R O Technology (0885-7598); Which incorporated: Satellite T V (0744-9739)
Published by: Broadband Properties, LLC, 1909 Avenue G, Rosenberg, TX 77471. TEL 281-342-9655, 877-588-1649, FAX 281-342-1158, http://www.broadbandproperties.com. Eds. Steven Ross, Scott De Garmo. Pub. Nancy McCain. Adv. contact Irene Gonzales. Circ: 13,590.

384.555 USA ISSN 1530-1532
BROADBAND TECHNOLOGY. Text in English. 1981. m. USD 1,045; USD 1,440 combined subscription print & e-mail eds. (effective 2005). adv. charts. index. **Document type:** *Newsletter, Trade.* **Description:** Delivers a host of digital video, audio and high-speed Internet services to a bandwidth-thirsty customer base as well as the latest in IP telephony strategies and trends in the rollout of digital set-top boxes.
Formerly (until 2000): Cable T V Technology (0276-5713)
Related titles: E-mail ed.: USD 945 (effective 2005); Fax ed.: USD 895 (effective 2001).
Published by: Kagan Research, LLC, One Lower Ragsdale Dr, Bldg One, Ste 130, Monterey, CA 93940. TEL 831-624-1536, FAX 831-625-3225, info@kagan.com, http://research.kagan.com/keo/subscriptionsDetailPage.aspx?SubscriptionID=3, http://www.kagan.com. adv.: page USD 3,670.

▼ **BROADBANDNOW!.** see *MOTION PICTURES*

384.5452 GBR ISSN 0040-2788
BROADCAST; the weekly newspaper of the television and radio industry. Text in English. 1960. w. GBP 129 domestic (effective 2005); GBP 140 in Europe; GBP 170 elsewhere (effective Jun. 2005). adv. bk.rev.; tel.rev. charts; illus.; stat. **Document type:** *Newspaper, Trade.* **Description:** Covers the UK TV and radio industry.
Formerly (until 1973): Television Mail; Incorporates (1983-1985): Television Weekly (0264-2905)
Related titles: Online - full text ed.: (from EBSCO Publishing).
Indexed: B&I, IIFP.
—CCC.
Published by: Emap Media Ltd. (Subsidiary of: Emap Business Communications Ltd.), 33-39 Bowling Green Ln, London, EC1R 0DA, United Kingdom. TEL 44-20-75058000, bcasted@media.emap.co.uk, admin@broadcastnow.co.uk, http://www.broadcastnow.co.uk/, http://www.emap.com. Ed. Jon Rogers. Adv. contact Katherine Plunkett TEL 44-20-75058066. Circ: 11,042.

384.5452 004.678 SGP
BROADCAST & BROADBAND ASIA PACIFIC. Text in English. 1986. bi-m. adv. back issues avail. **Document type:** *Magazine, Trade.* **Description:** Reports on regional news and issues for engineers and managers working in the broadcast industry.
Formerly (until Jun. 2000): Broadcast Asia Journal
Published by: Meson Technical Press Pte. Ltd., 531 Upper Cross St, #04-47 Hong Lim Complex, Singapore, 050531, Singapore. TEL 65-5320208, FAX 65-7521068, meson@singnet.com.sg, http://web.singnet.com.sg/~meson/. Ed., Pub. Peter Tham. adv.: B&W page USD 2,620, color page USD 3,950.

384.55 USA
BROADCAST AND PRODUCTION. BRASIL EDITION. Text in Portuguese. bi-m. USD 39.95; USD 55 foreign (effective 1999). tr.lit. back issues avail.; reprints avail. **Document type:** *Trade.*
Published by: I M A S Publishing Group, 5827 Columbia Pike, Ste 310, Falls Church, VA 22041. TEL 703-998-7600, FAX 703-998-2966, adsales@imaspub.com, http://www.imaspub.com.

384.5452 USA ISSN 1024-8390
BROADCAST & PRODUCTION. CHINESE EDITION. Text in English, Chinese. 1995. m. USD 55; USD 39.95 foreign (effective 1999). adv. tr.lit. **Document type:** *Trade.* **Description:** Provides up-to-date broadcasting and production technology and hands-on application experience to professionals and managers in radio, television, CATV, education and other institutions and businesses in China, including Hong Kong and Taiwan.
Published by: I M A S Publishing Group, 5827 Columbia Pike, Ste 310, Falls Church, VA 22041. TEL 703-998-7600, 800-336-3045, FAX 703-998-2966, adsales@imaspub.com, http://www.imaspub.com. Ed., Pub. Wengong Wang. Circ: 16,000.

384.55 USA
BROADCAST AND PRODUCTION. FRENCH EDITION. Text in French. bi-m. USD 65; USD 55 foreign (effective 1999). tr.lit. back issues avail. **Document type:** *Trade.* **Description:** Regional edition of Broadcast and Production emphasizes the broadcast industries of France, Switzerland, and Belgium.
Published by: I M A S Publishing Group, 5827 Columbia Pike, Ste 310, Falls Church, VA 22041. TEL 703-998-7600, FAX 703-998-2966, adsales@imaspub.com, http://www.imaspub.com.

384.55 USA
BROADCAST & PRODUCTION. ITALIAN EDITION. Text in Italian. 1999. 4/yr. **Document type:** *Trade.* **Description:** Provides the latest information as well as advice from industry experts on new events and developments in the Italian broadcasting world.
Published by: I M A S Publishing Group, 5827 Columbia Pike, Ste 310, Falls Church, VA 22041. TEL 703-998-7600, FAX 703-998-2966, adsales@imaspub.com, http://www.imaspub.com.

621.388 USA ISSN 0007-1994
TK6540
BROADCAST ENGINEERING; the journal of digital television. Text in English. 1959. m. (14/yr.). USD 55 in US & Canada; USD 130 elsewhere; free to qualified personnel (effective 2005). adv. bk.rev. charts; illus.; stat.; tr.lit. index. back issues avail.; reprint service avail. from PQC. **Document type:** *Magazine, Trade.* **Description:** Delivers practical, informative articles on digital technology, systems integration, management, how-to installation, and systems and equipment maintenance.
Related titles: Microform ed.: (from PQC); Online - full text ed.: (from bigchalk, EBSCO Publishing, Florida Center for Library Automation, Gale Group, H.W. Wilson, O C L C Online Computer Library Center, Inc., ProQuest Information & Learning); ♦ Supplement(s): Radio. ISSN 1542-0620.
Indexed: ABIn, AS&TI, BrCerAb, C&ISA, CerAb, CorrAb, E&CAJ, EMA, IAA, M&TEA, MBF, METADEX, RefZh, WAA.
—BLDSC (2348.900000), CISTI, IE, Infotrieve, ingenta, Linda Hall. **CCC.**
Published by: Primedia Business Magazines & Media, Inc. (Subsidiary of: Primedia, Inc.), 9800 Metcalf Ave, Overland Park, KS 66212-2216. TEL 913-341-1300, FAX 913-967-7276, dtriola@primediabusiness.com, inquiries@primediabusiness.com, http://www.broadcastengineering.com/, http://www.primediabusiness.com. Ed. Brad Dick. Pub. Dennis Triola. adv.: color page USD 7,100. Circ: 33,000 (controlled). **Subscr. to:** PO Box 12993, Overland Park, KS 66282-2993. TEL 800-441-0294, FAX 913-967-1331.

621.388 USA
BROADCAST ENGINEERING (WORLD EDITION). Text in English. 1978. 10/yr. USD 65 domestic; USD 80 foreign; free to qualified personnel (effective 2003). **Document type:** *Trade.* **Description:** Delivers news and technology about broadcast and related industries from a global perspective.
Former titles: World Broadcast Engineering (1529-5052); (until 1999): World Broadcast News (1050-012X); B M E's World Broadcast News
Related titles: Microform ed.: (from PQC); Online - full text ed.: (from EBSCO Publishing, H.W. Wilson, O C L C Online Computer Library Center, Inc., ProQuest Information & Learning).
Indexed: ABIn, AS&TI, RefZh.
—CCC.
Published by: Primedia Business Magazines & Media, Inc. (Subsidiary of: Primedia, Inc.), 9800 Metcalf Ave, Overland Park, KS 66212-2216. TEL 913-341-1300, FAX 913-967-1898, inquiries@primediabusiness.com, http://www.broadcastengineering.com, http://www.primediabusiness.com. Ed. Brad Dick. Circ: 12,597 (controlled). **Subscr. to:** PO Box 12993, Overland Park, KS 66282-2993. TEL 800-441-0294, FAX 913-967-1331.

621.388 AUS ISSN 0155-3720
BROADCAST ENGINEERING NEWS. Abbreviated title: B N E. Text in English. 1974. m. AUD 85.47 (effective 2001). adv. **Document type:** *Trade.* **Description:** Reflects technological and legislative change in the areas of duplication, transmission and signal duplication, desktop video and multimedia, video production, professional audio and more.
Related titles: Online - full text ed.: (from Gale Group, LexisNexis).
Published by: Reed Business Information Pty Ltd (Subsidiary of: Reed Business Information International), Locked Bag 2999, Chatswood, NSW 2067, Australia. customerservice@reedbusiness.com.au, http://www.reedbusiness.com.au. Ed. Aaron Greenwood. Pub. Barrie Parsons. Adv. contact Anthony Head. Circ: 4,280.

BROADCAST INVESTOR; newsletter on radio-TV station finance. see *BUSINESS AND ECONOMICS—Investments*

621.388 USA ISSN 0736-9069
BROADCAST INVESTOR CHARTS; monthly service showing price movements of broadcast stocks over two-year spans. Text in English. 1983. m. USD 425 (effective 2001). charts. reprints avail. **Description:** Chart service on stock price movements of 41 publicly held broadcast companies for the past two years.
Published by: Kagan World Media (Subsidiary of: Primedia, Inc.), 1 Lower Ragsdale Dr., Ste. 130, Monterey, CA 93940-5741. TEL 831-624-1536, FAX 831-625-3225.

BROADCAST INVESTOR: DEALS & FINANCE. see *COMMUNICATIONS—Abstracting, Bibliographies, Statistics*

384.55 NLD ISSN 1380-9237
BROADCAST MAGAZINE. Text in Dutch. 1989. m. EUR 155 (effective 2005). adv. illus. **Document type:** *Journal, Trade.* **Description:** Covers all the broadcast media, both digital and traditional.
Incorporates (1997-1999): Producer (1387-506X)
Related titles: ♦ Supplement(s): Nederlands Omroep Handboek. ISSN 0925-6261.
Published by: Broadcast Press Hilversum BV, Postbus 576, Hilversum, 1200 AN, Netherlands. TEL 31-35-6252444, FAX 31-35-6214559, info@broadcastmagazine.nl, info@broadcastpress.nl, http://www.broadcastmagazine.nl, http://www.broadcastpress.nl. Ed. Jeroen te Nuijl. Pub. Rob van Beek. Adv. contact Ilja van Zijl. B&W page EUR 1,335, color page EUR 2,210; trim 210 x 285. Circ: 8,000.

384.5452029 GBR ISSN 0967-2095
BROADCAST PRODUCTION GUIDE. Text in English. 1982. a. GBP 45. adv. **Document type:** *Directory.* **Description:** Lists names and addresses of independent production companies and facility houses for the broadcasting industry.
Published by: E M A P Media (Subsidiary of: E M A P Business Communications), 33-39 Bowling Green Ln, London, EC1R 0DA, United Kingdom. TEL 44-171-505-8328, FAX 44-171-505-8336, bcasted@media.emap.co.uk. Pub. Martin Jackson. **Subscr. to:** RSS, Lansdowne Mews, 196 High St, Tonbridge, Kent TN9 1HQ, United Kingdom. TEL 44-1732-770823, FAX 44-1732-361708.

343.09946 USA
BROADCAST REGULATION. Text in English. bi-m. USD 425 combined subscription print & online eds. (effective 2005). **Document type:** *Newsletter, Trade.* **Description:** Offers complete and comprehensive coverage of broadcast law and regulation.
Related titles: CD-ROM ed.: USD 375 combined subscription CD-ROM & online eds. (effective 2005); Online - full text ed.: USD 355 (effective 2005).
Published by: Pike & Fischer, Inc. (Subsidiary of: The Bureau of National Affairs, Inc.), 1010 Wayne Ave, Ste 1400, Silver Spring, MD 20910. TEL 301-562-1530, 800-255-8131, FAX 301-562-1521, pike@pf.com, http://broadcastregs.pf.com, http://www.pf.com.

BROADCAST TIMES. see *HANDICAPPED—Visually Impaired*

384.5452 CAN
BROADCAST WEEK. Text in English. w. adv. **Document type:** *Consumer.*
Related titles: Online - full text ed.
Published by: Globe and Mail Publishing, 444 Front St W, Toronto, ON M5V 2S9, Canada. TEL 416-585-5045. Ed. Trevor Cole. Adv. contact Irene Patterson. Circ: 180,000.

384.5452 GBR
BROADCAST YEARBOOK AND DIARY. Text in English. 1961. a. GBP 25. adv. **Document type:** *Trade.*
Published by: E M A P Media (Subsidiary of: E M A P Business Communications), 33-39 Bowling Green Ln, London, EC1R 0DA, United Kingdom. TEL 44-171-505-8014, FAX 44-171-505-8030, bcasted@media.emap.co.ik. Pub. Jon Baver. Circ: 1,000. **Subscr. to:** RSS, Lansdowne Mews, 196 High St, Tonbridge, Kent TN9 1HQ, United Kingdom. TEL 44-1732-770823, FAX 44-1732-361708.

384.5452 AUS
BROADCASTAWAY. Text in English. s-a. **Description:** Publishes short articles on Australian and international film and television, culture and communications.
Media: Online - full text.
Published by: Techtonic Webzine, Australia. jjc@merlin.com.au, http://www.merlin.com.au/tech/index.html. Ed. Jeffrey Cook.

384.5 CAN ISSN 0008-3038
HE8690
BROADCASTER. Text in English. 1942. m. (s-a. directory nos.). CND 45.95 domestic; USD 45.95 in United States; USD 59.95 elsewhere (effective 2005). adv. bk.rev. **Document type:** *Magazine, Trade.* **Description:** Covers Canada's communications industry.
Formerly: Canadian Broadcaster
Related titles: Microfilm ed.: (from CML); Online - full text ed.: (from Gale Group, Micromedia ProQuest, O C L C Online Computer Library Center, Inc.).
Indexed: B&I, CBCABus, CBCARef, CBPI.
—CCC.
Published by: Business Information Group, 12 Concorde Pl, Ste 800, Toronto, ON M3C 4J2, Canada. TEL 416-442-5600, 800-668-2374, FAX 416-442-2191, http://www.broadcastermagazine.com, http://www.businessinformationgroup.ca. Circ: 7,844.

384.5452 LKA
BROADCASTER. Text in English. 1978. m. LKR 17.
Published by: Sri Lanka Broadcasting Corporation, Publications and Information, P O Box 574, Colombo, Sri Lanka.

384.5 CAN
BROADCASTER DIRECTORY. Text in English. a. CND 47.95 per issue domestic; USD 47.95 per issue foreign (effective 2005). **Document type:** *Directory, Trade.*
Published by: Business Information Group, 12 Concorde Pl, Ste 800, Toronto, ON M3C 4J2, Canada. TEL 416-442-5600, 800-668-2374, 800-268-7742, FAX 416-442-2191, http://www.businessinformationgroup.ca/communications/broadcasterdir.asp.

384.5 USA ISSN 1068-6827
TK6540
BROADCASTING & CABLE. Text in English. 1931. w. (51/yr.). USD 189 combined subscription domestic print & online eds.; USD 249 combined subscription in Canada print & online eds.; USD 360 combined subscription elsewhere print & online eds. (effective 2005). adv. bk.rev. charts; illus.; stat.; tr.lit. cum.index: 1972-1981. 50 p./no.; back issues avail.; reprint service avail. from PQC. **Document type:** *Magazine, Trade.* **Description:** Covers the broadcasting and cable industries in-depth, including news and reports on radio, television, cable and satellite. Features legislative updates, radio and television ownership changes, new stations, facilities changes, band allocations, classified, calendar of events and major meetings, and more.
Former titles (until 1993): Broadcasting (Washington) (0007-2028); (until 1957): Broadcasting Telecasting; (until 1948): Broadcasting - The News Magazine of the Fifth Estate; Incorporated (in 1961): Television; (in 1953): Telecast; (in 1933): Broadcast Reporter; Broadcast Advertising
Related titles: ♦ Fax ed.: Broadcasting & Cable T V Fax; Microfiche ed.: (from CIS); Microfilm ed.: (from PQC); Online - full text ed.: USD 14.95 per month (effective 2003) (from EBSCO Publishing, Factiva, Florida Center for Library Automation, Gale Group, H.W. Wilson, LexisNexis, Northern Light Technology, Inc., O C L C Online Computer Library Center, Inc., ProQuest Information & Learning, The Dialog Corporation).
Indexed: ABIn, Acal, BPI, BusI, CADCAM, ChPerI, IIPA, IPARL, LRI, PAIS, PROMT, RASB, SRI, T&II, TelAb.
—BLDSC (2349.076300), IE, Infotrieve, ingenta, Linda Hall. **CCC.**
Published by: Reed Business Information (Subsidiary of: Reed Business), 360 Park Ave South, New York, NY 10010. TEL 646-746-6544, FAX 646-746-6948, bncletters@reedbusiness.com, http://www.broadcastingcable.com/, http://www.reedbusiness.com. Eds. Mark Robichaux, P J Bednarski, J Max Robins TEL 646-746-7671. Pubs. Chuck Bolkcom, Paul Audino TEL 646-746-7111. adv.: B&W page USD 7,850, color page USD 10,575. Circ: 35,000 (paid and controlled). **Subscr. to:** Reed Business Information, PO Box 15157, North Hollywood, CA 91615-5157. TEL 800-554-5729, 818-487-4552, FAX 818-487-4550.

384.5452 USA
BROADCASTING & CABLE INTERNATIONAL. Text in English. 1983. bi-m. adv. film rev.; tel.rev. charts; illus.; mkt.; tr.lit. back issues avail. **Document type:** *Trade.* **Description:** An international publication dedicated to providing global information on radio, television, cable and satellites.
Formerly (until Sep. 1993): Broadcasting Abroad (1064-6124)
Related titles: Online - full text ed.: (from Gale Group).
—CCC.
Published by: Reed Business Information (Subsidiary of: Reed Business), 360 Park Ave South, New York, NY 10010. TEL 646-746-6400, pconlon@cahners.com, http://www.broadcastingcable.com, http://www.reedbusiness.com. Ed. J Max Robins TEL 646-746-7671. Circ: 13,600 (controlled).

384.5452 USA
BROADCASTING & CABLE T V FAX. Text in English. d. (Monday-Friday). USD 199 domestic (effective 2004). **Document type:** *Newsletter, Trade.* **Description:** Reports late-breaking news in the broadcast and cable television, radio, satellite, and interactive-media industries.
Media: Fax. **Related titles:** Microfiche ed.: (from CIS); Microfilm ed.: (from PQC); Online - full text ed.: USD 14.95 per month (effective 2003) (from EBSCO Publishing, Factiva, Florida Center for Library Automation, Gale Group, H.W. Wilson, LexisNexis, Northern Light Technology, Inc., O C L C Online Computer Library Center, Inc., ProQuest Information & Learning, The Dialog Corporation); ♦ Print ed.: Broadcasting & Cable. ISSN 1068-6827.
Published by: Reed Business Information (Subsidiary of: Reed Business), 360 Park Ave South, New York, NY 10010. TEL 646-746-6400, http://www.broadcastingcable.com, http://www.reedbusiness.com. Ed. Harry A Jessell TEL 212-337-6964. **Subscr. to:** Reed Business Information, PO Box 15157, North Hollywood, CA 91615-5157. TEL 800-554-5729, 818-487-4552, FAX 818-487-4550.

384.5452 USA ISSN 0000-1511
HE8689
BROADCASTING & CABLE YEARBOOK. Text in English. 1980. a. (in 2 vols.). USD 199.95 (effective 2004 & 2005). adv. 2100 p./no.; **Document type:** *Directory, Trade.* **Description:** Provides a comprehensive guide to the broadcasting and cable industries. Contains listings of US and Canadian radio stations and television stations, top cable MSOs and their systems, satellite services, programming services, production services, manufacturing services, advertising and marketing services (including Arbitron and Nielsen market data), industry books, periodicals and videos, communications lawyers, industry trade shows and more. Includes yellow pages for TV, cable and radio stations and contacts.
Former titles (until 1993): Broadcasting and Cable Market Place (0000-1384); (until 1992): Broadcasting Yearbook (1051-1792); (until 1990): Broadcasting Cable Yearbook (1045-9162); (until 1989): Broadcasting, Cablecasting Yearbook (0732-7196); (until 1982): Broadcasting Cable Yearbook (0277-3678); Which was formed by the merger of (1968-1980): Broadcasting Yearbook (0068-2713); (19??-1980): Broadcasting, Cable Sourcebook (0097-8132); Which was formerly: Broadcasting Yearbook - Marketbook Issue (0731-6836); (until 1960): Broadcasting Yearbook Issue (0731-6828); Which was formed by the 1958 merger of: Broadcasting Telecasting, Broadcasting Yearbook - Marketbook Issue (0731-681X); Broadcasting Telecasting, Telecasting Yearbook - Marketbook Issue (0731-6801); Which was formerly (until 1954): Broadcasting Telecasting, Telecasting Yearbook Issue (0731-6569); (until 1953): Broadcasting Telecasting, Telecasting Yearbook (0731-6542); Which superseded in part (1948-1951): Broadcasting Telecasting Yearbook (0731-6534)
Related titles: Microfiche ed.: (from CIS).
Indexed: SRI.
Published by: Reed Business Information (Subsidiary of: Reed Business), 360 Park Ave South, New York, NY 10010. TEL 646-746-6544, FAX 646-746-6948, http://www.reedbusiness.com. Circ: 15,000. **Subscr. to:** Reed Business Information, PO Box 15157, North Hollywood, CA 91615-5157. TEL 818-487-4552, FAX 818-487-4550.

621.388 AUS
BROADCASTING & PAY TV AUSTRALIA. Text in English. 199?. a. USD 425 domestic; USD 445 foreign (effective 2001). **Description:** Reports on Australian cable and pay TV markets: interactive TV, FSN's, ADSL and other interactive broadband developments.
Former titles (until 1999): Information Highways in Australia (1329-9085); (until 1998): Superhighways Strategies Report (1326-6764)
Indexed: CINAHL.
Published by: Paul Budde Communication Pty. Ltd., 2643 George Downes Dr, Bucketty, NSW 2250, Australia. TEL 61-2-4998-8144, FAX 61-2-4998-8247, sally@budde.com.au, pbc@budde.com.au, http://www.budde.com.au. Circ: 100.

384.5452 USA ISSN 0161-5823
KF2801.A3
BROADCASTING AND THE LAW. Text in English. 1970. m. looseleaf. USD 150. index. **Document type:** *Newsletter.* **Description:** Provides current information about regulations and all aspects of station operations to help cut legal costs.
Formerly (until 1985): Perry's Broadcasting and the Law
Related titles: Online - full text ed.
Published by: Broadcasting and the Law, Inc., 1 S E Third Ave, Ste 1450, Miami, FL 33131-1715. TEL 305-530-8322, FAX 305-530-9417. Ed., R&P Edward S Hammerman. Pub. Matthew Leibowitz. Circ: 7,000.

384.5452 USA
HE8689.8
BROADCASTING BOARD OF GOVERNORS. ANNUAL REPORT. Text in English. a. free. **Document type:** *Government.*
Formerly: Board for International Broadcasting. Annual Report (0362-8272)
Published by: Broadcasting Board of Governors, 330 Independence Ave S W, Ste 3360, Washington, DC 20547. TEL 202-401-3736.

C

384.5 384.55 RUS
BROADCASTING: TELEVIDENIE I RADIOVESHCHANIE. Text in Russian. 8/yr. **Document type:** *Journal, Trade.*
Published by: Groteck, 7 Miusskaya sq, 4th Fl, PO Box 53, Moscow, 103030, Russian Federation. TEL 7-095-2516845, FAX 7-095-2513389, groteck@groteck.ru, http://www.groteck.ru/tele_ru.php, http://www.groteck.net. Circ: 15,000.

791.456 GBR ISSN 1467-680X
BUFFY THE VAMPIRE SLAYER (U.K. EDITION). Text in English. 1999. 13/yr. GBP 33; GBP 2.75 newsstand/cover. adv. **Document type:** *Magazine, Consumer.*
Related titles: ♦ Regional ed(s).: Buffy The Vampire Slayer (U.S. Edition).
Published by: Titan Magazines (Subsidiary of: Titan Books Ltd.), Titan House, 144 Southwark St, London, SE1 0UP, United Kingdom. TEL 44-20-7620-0200, FAX 44-20-7803-1803, buffymail@titanemail.com. Ed. Martin Eden. Pub. Nick Landau. Adv. contact Scott Ferguson-Caisley.

791.456 USA
BUFFY THE VAMPIRE SLAYER (U.S. EDITION). Text in English. q. USD 19.99 domestic; USD 31.99 in Canada (effective 2002). **Document type:** *Magazine, Consumer.*
Related titles: ♦ Regional ed(s).: Buffy The Vampire Slayer (U.K. Edition). ISSN 1467-680X.
Published by: Titan Publishing Group, Customer Service, 1550 East Higgins Road #133, Elkgrove Village, IL 60007. TEL 847-330-5549, FAX 847-806-8113.

621.388 USA
THE BULLET (NASHVILLE). Text in English. 1982. 3/yr. looseleaf. USD 14 (effective 2000). bk.rev. illus. back issues avail. **Document type:** *Newsletter.* **Description:** Covers news and products of interest to fans of the Andy Griffith Show.
Published by: Andy Griffith Show Rerun Watchers Club, 9 Music Sq S, Ste 146, Nashville, TN 37203-3286. Ed. Jim Clark. Circ: 15,000.

BURGUNDY BOOK OF EUROPEAN BROADCASTING. see *BUSINESS AND ECONOMICS—Trade And Industrial Directories*

621.388 JPN ISSN 0288-9323
C B C GIJUTSU HOKOKUKAI/C B C TECHNICAL INFORMATION. Text in Japanese. 1953. a.
Published by: Chubu - Nippon Broadcasting Co., 2-8 Shinsakae 1-chome, Naka-ku, Nagoya-shi, Aichi-ken 460-0007, Japan.

791.456 USA ISSN 1533-967X
C B S SOAPS IN DEPTH. Text in English. 1997. m. USD 19.95 domestic; USD 33.97 foreign (effective 2002). adv. **Document type:** *Magazine, Consumer.* **Description:** Contains in depth features, news and previews about soap operas on the CBS television network.
Superesedes in part (in 1999): Soaps in Depth (1092-518X)
Published by: Bauer Publishing Company, L.P., 270 Sylvan Ave, Englewood Cliffs, NJ 07632. cbsmail@soapsindepth.com, http://cbs.soapsindepth.com.

384.55 GBR ISSN 1352-2272
C C T V TODAY. Text in English. 1994. bi-m. GBP 38 (effective 2000). adv. **Document type:** *Magazine, Trade.*
Related titles: Online - full text ed.: (from Gale Group).
Indexed: CompD.
Published by: C M P Information Ltd. (Subsidiary of: United Business Media), 630 Chiswick High Rd, London, W4 5BG, United Kingdom. uprotectit@cmpinformation.com, enquiries@cmpinformation.com, http://www.cctvmags.com/, http://www.cmpinformation.com. Ed. Ron Alaloff. Pub. Rob Lozowski. Adv. contact Simon Press.

621.388 USA ISSN 1044-2871
TK6675
C E D; the premier magazine of broadband communications. (Communications, Engineering & Design) Text in English. 1975. 13/yr. USD 70.90 domestic; USD 95 in Canada & Mexico; USD 107 elsewhere; USD 6 newsstand/cover domestic; USD 10 newsstand/cover foreign (effective 2004). adv. bk.rev. illus.; mkt.; tr.lit. Supplement avail.; back issues avail. **Document type:** *Magazine, Trade.* **Description:** Written and edited for engineering and technical personnel involved in the evolving full-service network of video, voice and data.
Former titles (until 1988): Communications Engineering and Design (0191-5428); (until 1983): Communications - Engineering Digest (1046-574X)
Related titles: Online - full text ed.: (from EBSCO Publishing, Florida Center for Library Automation, Gale Group, O C L C Online Computer Library Center, Inc., ProQuest Information & Learning); ♦ Supplement(s): C E D Annual Buyer's Guide.
Indexed: EngInd, Inspec.
—BLDSC (3096.949000), CISTI, IE, ingenta, Linda Hall. **CCC.**
Published by: Reed Business Information (Subsidiary of: Reed Business), 8878 S Barrons Blvd, Highlands Ranch, CO 80129-2345. TEL 303-470-4000, FAX 303-470-4890, rbrown@reedbusiness.com, http://www.cedmagazine.com, http://www.reedbusiness.com. Ed., Pub. Roger Brown TEL 303-470-4840. adv.: B&W page USD 5,143, color page USD 6,618; trim 10.75 x 8.25. Circ: 23,000 (controlled). **Subscr. to:** Reed Business Information, PO Box 9020, Maple Shade, NJ 08052-9020. TEL 303-470-4466, FAX 303-470-4691.

621.388 USA
C E D ANNUAL BUYER'S GUIDE. (Communications, Engineering and Design) Text in English. a. free with subscr to C E D. **Document type:** *Directory, Trade.* **Description:** Lists persons and businesses in full-service video, voice, and data communications.
Related titles: ♦ Supplement to: C E D. ISSN 1044-2871.
Published by: Reed Business Information (Subsidiary of: Reed Business), 8878 S Barrons Blvd, Highlands Ranch, CO 80129-2345. TEL 303-470-4800, FAX 303-470-4890, http://sourcebook.cahners1.com/ced/, http://www.reedbusiness.com. Ed. Paul Beck. Pub. Robert Stuehrk TEL 303-470-4859.

791.43071 BEL
C I L E C T NEWS. Text in French. 1978. q. free. bk.rev. **Document type:** *Newsletter, Trade.* **Description:** Contains information on film schools.
Former titles: C I L E C T Newsletter (1036-2215); C I L E C T News; Centre International de Liaison des Ecoles de Cinema et de Television. Bulletin d'Informations (0528-4759)
Published by: Centre International de Liaison des Ecoles de Cinema et de Television/International Liaison Centre for Cinema and Television Schools, CILECT Secretariat, Rue Theresienne 8, Brussels, 1000, Belgium. TEL 32-2-511-9839, FAX 32-2-511-9839, hverh.cilect@skynet.be, http://www.cilect.org. Ed., R&P Henry Verhasselt. Circ: 400 (controlled).

C M J NEW MUSIC REPORT. (College Media Journal) see *MUSIC*

384.55 GBR
C N N TRAVELLER. Text in English. 1995-199?; resumed 1998 (Oct.). q. free. adv. **Document type:** *Magazine, Consumer.* **Description:** Provides information and entertainment for business and high-end leisure travelers, including articles on travel, news, and current affairs.
Formerly: Network (1358-8931)
Published by: (C N N USA), Highbury Columbus Travel Publishing, Nexus House, Swanley, Kent BR8 H8U, United Kingdom. TEL 44-1322-616344, FAX 44-1322-616323, http://www.hhc.co.uk/pages/show/entry_Level/2/entry_code/HCU/single_record_flag/73, http://www.columbustravelguides.com/. Ed. Dan Hayes. Adv. contact Mohammed Rami. B&W page GBP 9,050, color page GBP 13,800; 210 x 275. Circ: 120,658.

384.55 DEU
C O M FUER EINSTEIGER. Text in German. 1987. s-a. **Document type:** *Trade.*
Former titles: Btx fuer Einsteiger (0948-521X); Bildschirmtext fuer Einsteiger (0932-1977)
Published by: Neue Mediengesellschaft Ulm mbH, Konrad-Celtis-Str 77, Munich, 81369, Germany. TEL 49-89-74117190, FAX 49-89-74117195. Ed. Guenter Goetz. Circ: 40,000.

384.5452 USA
C P B TODAY. Text in English. 1969. m. free. bk.rev. **Document type:** *Newsletter.*
Former titles (until Sep. 1993): C P B Report; (until Sep. 1974): Corporation for Public Broadcasting. Memo
Published by: Corporation for Public Broadcasting, 901 E St, N W, Washington, DC 20004-2037. TEL 202-879-9600, FAX 202-783-1039. Ed. Cristina Delsesto. Circ: 15,000.

621.388 GBR
CODEN: CTEVB3
C T E; the cable communications quarterly. (Cable Telecommunication Engineering) Text in English. q. GBP 35 in Europe; GBP 45 elsewhere. adv. bk.rev. **Document type:** *Trade.* **Description:** Reports on developments in the industry.
Former titles: Cable Television Engineering (0308-4213); (until 1973): Relay Engineer (0048-718X); (until 1971): Society of Relay Engineers. Proceedings (0374-3985)
Indexed: Inspec.
—BLDSC (3490.495000), AskIEEE, CISTI.
Published by: (Society of Cable Telecommunications Engineers), David Sheppard & Associates, 35 Picadilly, London, W1V 1PB, United Kingdom. TEL 44-171-734-6143, FAX 44-171-734-1737. Ed. Dan Smart. Adv. contact Barbara Sewell. Circ: 1,000 (paid); 1,400 (controlled).

384.555 GBR ISSN 0265-6973
CABLE AND SATELLITE EUROPE. Text in English. 1984. 10/yr. GBP 110, EUR 168, USD 187 (effective 2004). **Description:** Covers market trends in the European cable and satellite industry.
Related titles: Online - full text ed.: (from ProQuest Information & Learning).
Indexed: CurCont, Inspec.
—BLDSC (2943.951000), CISTI, IE, Infotrieve, ingenta.
Published by: Informa Media (Subsidiary of: T & F Informa plc), Mortimer House, 37-41 Mortimer St, London, W1T 3JH, United Kingdom. media.enquiries@informa.com, http://www.informamedia.com/cabsateurope.

384.555 384.51 GBR ISSN 1467-5935
CABLE & SATELLITE INTERNATIONAL. Text in English. 1999. bi-m. GBP 68 domestic; GBP 98 foreign; free to qualified personnel (effective 2005). adv. **Document type:** *Magazine, Trade.* **Description:** Reports on the standards, technology trends and products that shape this market, monitor the activities of network operators, and keep readers informed about the finances and activities of key suppliers.
Published by: Perspective Publishing Ltd., 408 Fruit & Wool Exchange, Brushfield St, London, E1 6EP, United Kingdom. TEL 44-20-74260636, FAX 44-20-74260123, muir@perspectivepublishing.com, http://www.cable-satellite.com/, http://www.perspectivepublishing.com/. Ed. John Moulding TEL 44-20-74260424. Adv. contact Justin Lebbon TEL 44-20-74260101.

384.555 GBR ISSN 0956-6872
CABLE AND SATELLITE YEARBOOK (YEAR). Text in English. 1985. a., latest 2004. GBP 365, EUR 548, USD 621; GBP 639, EUR 959, USD 1,089 combined subscription print & online eds. (effective 2004). adv. back issues avail. **Document type:** *Directory.* **Description:** Covers the cable and satellite broadcast, manufacturing and retailing industries.
Published by: Informa Media (Subsidiary of: T & F Informa plc), Mortimer House, 37-41 Mortimer St, London, W1T 3JH, United Kingdom. media.enquiries@informa.com, http://www.informamedia.com/. Ed. Kevin Scott. Circ: 3,000 (paid).

384.55 USA ISSN 1047-9902
HE8700.7.C6
CABLE AND STATION COVERAGE ATLAS. Text in English. 1966. a. USD 474; USD 584 foreign (effective 1998). index. **Document type:** *Trade.*
Former titles: Cable and Station Coverage Atlas and 35-Mile Zone Maps (0193-3639); C A T V and Station Coverage Atlas and 35-Mile Zone Maps (0068-4694)
Published by: Warren Communications News, Inc., 2115 Ward Ct, N W, Washington, DC 20037. TEL 202-872-9200, 800-327-7205, FAX 202-293-3435, info@warren-news.com, http://www.warren-news.com. Ed., Pub. Albert Warren.

384.555 USA
CABLE CONNECTION MAGAZINE✶. Text in English. fortn. USD 35.40. **Document type:** *Consumer.* **Description:** Lists basic, premium, and pay-per-view programs available to subscribers to Sammons cable television. Contains Features on movies, stars, and shows.
Address: P O Box 304, Fort Worth, TX 76101-0304. TEL 800-950-7999.

384.555 USA ISSN 1547-7223
CODEN: QFLREH
CABLE FAX'S CABLE WORLD. Text in English. 1989. s-m. USD 89 domestic; USD 99 in Canada; USD 129 elsewhere; free to qualified personnel (effective 2003). adv. illus. back issues avail. **Document type:** *Magazine, Trade.* **Description:** Business news magazine for the cable television industry. Includes in-depth reports on trends and issues affecting the cable business.
Formerly (until 2003): Cable World (1042-7228)
Related titles: Online - full text ed.: 1989 (from bigchalk, EBSCO Publishing, Factiva, Gale Group, H.W. Wilson, LexisNexis, Northern Light Technology, Inc., O C L C Online Computer Library Center, Inc., ProQuest Information & Learning).
Indexed: ABIn, B&I, BPI.
—**CCC.**
Published by: Access Intelligence, LLC (Subsidiary of: Veronis, Suhler & Associates Inc.), 4 Choke Cherry Rd, 2nd fl, Rockville, MD 20850. TEL 301-354-2000, 800-777-5006, FAX 301-738-8153, clientservices@accessintel.com, http://www.pbimedia.com/cgi/catalog/info?CW, http://www.broadband-pbimedia.com. adv.: B&W page USD 7,210, color page USD 8,690. Circ: 23,000 (controlled).

384.555 USA ISSN 1539-5324
HE8700.72.U6
CABLE NETWORK START-UP STRATEGIES & BUSINESS MODELS. Text in English. a. USD 1,495 (effective 2005). **Document type:** *Directory, Trade.* **Description:** Contains a comprehensive study of successful cable network business strategies.
Published by: Kagan Research, LLC, One Lower Ragsdale Dr, Bldg One, Ste 130, Monterey, CA 93940. TEL 831-624-1536, FAX 831-625-3225, info@kagan.com, http://research.kagan.com/keo/databooksdetailpage.aspx?DatabookID=7, http://www.kagan.com.

384.555 332 USA ISSN 1097-8895
HE8700.72.U6
CABLE PROGRAM INVESTOR. Text in English. 1997. m. USD 1,045; USD 1,440 combined subscription print & e-mail eds. (effective 2005). adv. **Document type:** *Newsletter, Trade.* **Description:** Covers the economics of basic cable programming networks and keeps you informed of private market values of public cable networks, growth projections for networks and programs, analyses of balance sheet data, rankings of competitors and insights into corporate financings.
Formerly: Cable Network Investor
Related titles: E-mail ed.: USD 945 (effective 2005); Fax ed.: USD 895 (effective 2001).

Published by: Kagan Research, LLC, One Lower Ragsdale Dr, Bldg One, Ste 130, Monterey, CA 93940. TEL 831-624-1536, info@kagan.com, http://research.kagan.com/keo/subscriptionsDetailPage.aspx?SubscriptionID=7, http://www.kagan.com. Pub. Paul Kagan. adv.: B&W page USD 3,670.

CABLE T V AND NEW MEDIA; law & finance. see *LAW*

CABLE T V FACTS. see *ADVERTISING AND PUBLIC RELATIONS*

384.55 USA ISSN 1061-5652
HE8700.72.U6
CABLE T V FINANCE; newsletter on bank, insurance, commercial loans to cable operators. Text in English. 1982. m. USD 845 in United States (effective 2001). charts. index.
Document type: *Newsletter.* **Description:** Covers sources of funding for cable TV. Analysis of bank, insurance and bridge loans. Case studies of financing strategies.
Former titles (until 1992): Cable T V Banker - Broker (0893-2131); Cable T V Finance (0734-6816)
Related titles: E-mail ed.: USD 845 (effective 2001); Fax ed.: USD 845 (effective 2001).
Published by: Kagan World Media (Subsidiary of: Primedia, Inc.), 1 Lower Ragsdale Dr., Ste. 130, Monterey, CA 93940-5741. TEL 831-624-1536, FAX 831-625-3225, info@kagan.com, http://www.kagan.com/. Pub. Paul Kagan.

384.555 USA ISSN 0731-0250
HE8700.72.U6
CABLE T V INVESTOR; newsletter on investments in cable T V systems and publicly held cable T V stocks. Text in English. 1969. m. USD 1,295; USD 1,690 combined subscription print & e-mail eds. (effective 2005). adv. charts. Index. **Document type:** *Newsletter, Trade.* **Description:** Provides readers with the latest details on recently announced/proposed industry transactions backed by a database of deals going back nearly 20 years. Includes private market valuations and detailed analysis of the markets and the cable players within it.
Formerly: Cablecast (0146-0080)
Related titles: E-mail ed.: USD 1,195 (effective 2005); Fax ed.: USD 995 (effective 2001).
Published by: Kagan Research, LLC, One Lower Ragsdale Dr, Bldg One, Ste 130, Monterey, CA 93940. TEL 831-624-1536, FAX 831-625-3225, info@kagan.com, http://research.kagan.com/keo/subscriptionsDetailPage.aspx?SubscriptionID=9, http://www.kagan.com. adv.: color page USD 3,400.

343.09946 USA ISSN 0749-7652
KF2844.A59
CABLE T V LAW REPORTER. Text in English. 1984. m. USD 995; USD 1,390 combined subscription print & e-mail eds. (effective 2005). adv. **Document type:** *Newsletter, Trade.* **Description:** Issues concerning cable TV. Includes anti-trust, first amendment, franchising, taxation, copyright, rate regulation, privacy and international law.
Related titles: E-mail ed.: USD 925 (effective 2005); Fax ed.: USD 845 (effective 2001).
Published by: Kagan Research, LLC, One Lower Ragsdale Dr, Bldg One, Ste 130, Monterey, CA 93940. TEL 831-624-1536, FAX 831-625-3225, info@kagan.com, http://www.kagan.com. adv.: color page USD 3,400.

343.09946 USA
CABLE T V REGULATION. Text in English. bi-m. USD 365 combined subscription print & online eds. (effective 2005). **Document type:** *Newsletter, Trade.* **Description:** Offers complete and comprehensive coverage of cable TV law and regulation.
Related titles: CD-ROM ed.: USD 320 combined subscription CD-ROM & online eds. (effective 2005); Online - full text ed.: USD 295 (effective 2005).
Published by: Pike & Fischer, Inc. (Subsidiary of: The Bureau of National Affairs, Inc.), 1010 Wayne Ave, Ste 1400, Silver Spring, MD 20910. TEL 301-562-1530, 800-255-8131, FAX 301-562-1521, pike@pf.com, http://cableregs.pf.com, http://www.pf.com.

384.555 USA
CABLE TELEVISION & OTHER NON-BROADCAST MEDIA. Text in English. 2 base vols. plus a. updates. looseleaf. USD 261 base vol(s). (effective 2004). **Document type:** *Trade.* **Description:** Covers present law and the emerging regulatory patterns for all areas of nonbroadcast video.
Published by: Thomson West (Subsidiary of: Thomson Corporation, The), 610 Opperman Dr, Eagan, MN 55123-1396. TEL 800-328-4880, FAX 651-687-7302, customer.service@westgroup.com, http://west.thomson.com/product/13512916/product.asp. Eds. Daniel L Brenner, Michael I Meyerson, Monroe E Price.

343.09946 USA
CABLE TELEVISION LAW; a video communications practice guide. Text in English. 1983. irreg. (in 3 vols.). looseleaf. USD 650 (effective 1999).
Related titles: CD-ROM ed.
Published by: Matthew Bender & Co., Inc. (Subsidiary of: LexisNexis North America), 1275 Broadway, Albany, NY 12204. international@bender.com, http://bender.lexisnexis.com.

384.555 USA
CABLE THEFT NEWSLETTER✶. Text in English. m. USD 72.
Published by: Skybridge Publishing Inc., c/o Schreff, 5 Lindsay Dr, Greenwich, CT 06830-3402.

384.555 USA ISSN 0739-8166
HE8700.72.U6
CABLE VIDEO BRIEFS✶. Text in English. m. USD 72.
Published by: Skybridge Publishing Inc., c/o Schreff, 5 Lindsay Dr, Greenwich, CT 06830-3402.

384.555 CAN ISSN 0840-9153
CABLECASTER; Canada's cable magazine. Text in English. 1989. 12/yr. CND 35.95 domestic; USD 41.95 in United States; USD 46.95 elsewhere (effective 2005). adv. bk.rev. charts; illus.; stat.; tr.lit. back issues avail. **Document type:** *Magazine, Trade.* **Description:** Services Canada(UNKNOWN CHARACTER)s converging cable, telephone and satellite communications markets and appeals to both management and technical readers.
Related titles: Online - full text ed.: (from Micromedia ProQuest).
Indexed: CBCABus, CBCARef.
Published by: Business Information Group, 12 Concorde Pl, Ste 800, Toronto, ON M3C 4J2, Canada. TEL 416-442-5600, 800-668-2374, FAX 416-442-2191, http://www.cablecastermagazine.com, http://www.businessinformationgroup.ca. Circ: 6,075.

384.555 CAN
CABLECASTER DIRECTORY. Text in English. a. CND 28.95 per issue domestic; USD 28.95 per issue foreign (effective 2005). **Document type:** *Directory, Trade.* **Description:** Contains comprehensive information and facts on cable companies, telephone companies, satellite providers, specialty channels and networks.
Published by: Business Information Group, 12 Concorde Pl, Ste 800, Toronto, ON M3C 4J2, Canada. TEL 416-442-5600, 800-668-2374, 800-268-7742, FAX 416-442-2191, http://www.businessinformationgroup.ca/communications/cablecasterdir.asp.

384.55 USA ISSN 1069-6644
CABLEFAX. Text in English. 1990. d. (5/w.). USD 895 (effective 2005). adv. **Document type:** *Newsletter, Trade.* **Description:** Covers industry news, legislation, finance, acquisitions, programming, hardware and personnel.
Media: E-mail. **Related titles:** Fax ed.: USD 695 (effective 2004).
Indexed: ABIn.
—CCC.
Published by: Access Intelligence, LLC (Subsidiary of: Veronis, Suhler & Associates Inc.), 1201 Seven Locks Rd, Ste 300, Potomac, MD 20854. TEL 301-354-2000, 800-777-5006, FAX 301-738-8453, clientservices@accessintel.com, http://www.cablefax.com/, http://www.pbimedia.com. Ed. Stephen Donohue. adv.: page USD 4,045. Circ: 6,700 (paid).

621.388 USA ISSN 1073-3108
TK5103
CABLING INSTALLATION AND MAINTENANCE. Text in English. 1993. m. USD 70 domestic; USD 80 in Canada includes annual Buyer Guide; USD 95 elsewhere; USD 15 per issue (effective 2004). adv. bk.rev.; software rev. charts; illus.; mkt.; stat.; tr.lit. **Document type:** *Magazine, Trade.* **Description:** Aims at an audience of cabling vendors and installers. Covers design, installation practice, technology, standards, updates, case studies, product category reviews, industry news, and installer tips. This journal represents a joint effort between Connection Magazines and Pennwell Publishing USA (Cabling Installation Maintenance USA.).
Related titles: Online - full text ed.: (from EBSCO Publishing, Factiva, Florida Center for Library Automation, Gale Group, O C L C Online Computer Library Center, Inc., ProQuest Information & Learning).
—CCC.
Published by: PennWell Corp., 1421 S Sheridan Rd, Tulsa, OK 74112. TEL 918-835-3161, 800-331-4463, FAX 918-831-9804, http://cim.pennnet.com/home.cfm, http://www.pennwell.com. Ed. Greg Reed. Pub. Marsha Robertson. R&P Brian Taylor. Adv. contact Jane Harrod. B&W page USD 7,493, color page USD 9,282; trim 8 x 10.75. Circ: 10,000 (paid); 30,000 (controlled).

CANADA. STATISTICS CANADA. CABLE TELEVISION/CANADA. STATISTIQUE CANADA. TELEDISTRIBUTION. see *COMMUNICATIONS—Abstracting, Bibliographies, Statistics*

CANADA. STATISTICS CANADA. RADIO AND TELEVISION BROADCASTING/CANADA. STATISTIQUE CANADA. RADIODIFFUSION ET TELEVISION. see *COMMUNICATIONS—Abstracting, Bibliographies, Statistics*

384.555 CAN ISSN 1193-5898
CANADIAN CABLE TELEVISION ASSOCIATION. COMMUNIQUE. Text in English. 1975 (vol.5). bi-m. free. adv. illus. **Document type:** *Newsletter, Trade.*
Former titles: C C T A Cable Communique (0710-2240); C C T A Communique; C C T A News
Related titles: French ed.: Communique - Association canadienne de television par cable. ISSN 1192-5035.
Published by: Canadian Cable Television Association, 360 Albert St, Ste 1010, Ottawa, ON K1R 7X7, Canada. TEL 613-232-2631, FAX 613-232-2137. Ed. Patricia Devine. Circ: 2,700.

384.5452 CAN ISSN 0316-3083
CANADIAN COMMUNICATIONS REPORTS. Text in English. 1973-1990; resumed 1993. 24/yr. CND 695 domestic; CND 745 foreign; CND 50 newsstand/cover (effective 2003). **Document type:** *Newsletter, Trade.* **Description:** Details and analyzes developments in the provision of broadcast distribution services in Canada.
Related titles: Online - full text ed.: (from Northern Light Technology, Inc.).
—CCC.
Published by: Decima Publishing Inc., 1800-160 Elgin St, Ottawa, ON K2P 2C4, Canada. TEL 613-230-1984, FAX 613-230-9048, cjeffrey@decima.ca, http://www.decima.com/publishing. Ed. Norma Reveler. Pub. Mario Mota.

CANADIAN JOURNAL OF FILM STUDIES/REVUE CANADIENNE D'ETUDES CINEMATOGRAPHIQUES. see *MOTION PICTURES*

384.55 CAN ISSN 1495-1002
CANADIAN TELEVISION FUND. ACTIVITY REPORT. Text in English. 1999. a.
Related titles: Online - full content ed.: ISSN 1493-678X.
Published by: Canadian Television Fund, 111 Queen St E, 5th Fl, Toronto, ON M5C 1S2, Canada. TEL 877-975-0766, FAX 416-214-4420.

354.55 USA
CAPTION✶. Text in English. 1980. a. free.
Published by: National Captioning Institute, Inc., 1900 Gallows Rd, Ste 3000, Vienna, VA 22182-3865. FAX 703-998-2450. Ed. Morgan Bramlet. Circ: 100,000 (controlled).

384.55 USA
CAPTION CENTER NEWS. Text in English. 1989. s-a. looseleaf. free. back issues avail. **Document type:** *Newsletter.* **Description:** Information about captioning in television programming for corporate advertisers, educators, and professionals.
Related titles: Online - full text ed.
Published by: Caption Center, 125 Western Ave, Boston, MA 02134. TEL 617-492-9225, FAX 617-562-0590, caption@wgbh.org, http://www.wgbh.org/caption. Ed., R&P Mary Watkins. Circ: 30,000.

C

384.55 GBR
CARLTON COMMUNICATIONS PLC. ANNUAL REPORT AND ACCOUNTS. Text in English. a. **Document type:** *Corporate.* **Description:** Discusses trends in broadcast television, home entertainment, video, film processing and creative image processing, and the participation of the company in these fields. Includes information about the company's finances, personnel, and marketing.
Published by: Carlton Communications Plc, 25 Knightsbridge, London, SW1X 7RZ, United Kingdom. TEL 44-171-663-6363, FAX 44-171-663-6300.

384.55 GBR ISSN 0142-6079
CASTINGDEX. Text in English. 1979. a. GBP 18 (effective 2002). **Document type:** *Directory.*
Address: PO Box 11, London, N1 7JZ, United Kingdom. TEL 44-20-7566-8282, FAX 44-20-7566-8284. Ed. Bobbi Dunn.

791.43 BEL ISSN 1569-9587
CELEBRITY. Text in Dutch. 2001. m. EUR 24.34 (effective 2003). **Document type:** *Magazine, Consumer.*
Published by: Sanoma Magazines Belgium, Telecomlaan 5-7, Diegem, 1831, Belgium. TEL 32-2-7762211, FAX 32-2-776-2317, http://www.sanoma-magazines.be/HomePage.aspx?flash=1&Language=nl.

CELEBRITY STYLE: SOAP STARS AT HOME. see *BEAUTY CULTURE*

384.55 USA ISSN 1096-701X
F159.H3
CENTRAL PA. Text in English. 1984. m. free to members; USD 3 newsstand/cover (effective 2005). adv. bk.rev.; music rev. back issues avail. **Document type:** *Magazine, Consumer.* **Description:** Aims to promote public television station WITF/Channel 33 and public radio station WITF-FM 89.5. Includes program listings as well as program-related features in order to make readers aware of programs of interest and importance, and to encourage their support of public broadcasting. Covers regional issues, people, and politics, plus the arts, books, music, homes, gardens, cars, health and fitness, senior and family life, the outdoors, sports, and festivals.
Former titles (until 1997): Central Pennsylvania's Apprise (1086-816X); (until 199?): Apprise (0883-9336)
Published by: W I T F, Inc., 1982 Locust Lane, Harrisburg, PA 17109. TEL 717-221-2800, FAX 717-221-2630, centralpa@centralpa.org, http://www.centralpa.org. Ed., R&P Steve Kennedy TEL 717-221-2854. adv.: page USD 2,295. Circ: 38,030.

▼ new title ➤ refereed ✶ unverified ♦ full entry avail.

CHAMPS DE L'AUDIOVISUELS. see *COMMUNICATIONS—Video*

384.5532 DEU
CHICAGO COUNTY GENERAL WAITING ROOM NEWS. Text in English, German. 1996. q. USD 38 elsewhere. **Document type:** *Consumer.* **Description:** Covers all aspects of the television program ER and the fans who watch it.
Related titles: Online - full text ed.
Published by: International Emergency Room Fan Center, Postfach 521, Goeppingen, 73005, Germany. patricia.herpel@t-online.de, http://www.geocities.com/televisioncity/studio/4847/index.html. Ed. Patricia Herpel.

THE CHRISTIANNET. see *MUSIC*

791.45 BEL ISSN 0778-5526
CINE TELE REVUE. Text in French. 1921. w. EUR 63 domestic; EUR 131.42 in the European Union (effective 2005). **Document type:** *Newspaper.* **Description:** Cinema and TV magazine with programs of 26 different channels. Also includes star interviews, environmental, and practical subjects about everyday life.
Former titles (until 1987): Cine - Revue (0045-6918); (until 1945): Theatre et Cine (0773-1086)
Related titles: Online - full text ed.
Indexed: RASB.
Published by: Editions Cine Revue S.A., Av Reine Marie Henriette 101, Brussels, 1190, Belgium. TEL 32-2-3459968, FAX 32-2-3431272, http://www.cinetelerevue.be.

CINE & TELE INFORME. see *MOTION PICTURES*

CINEGUIA; anuario espanol del espectaculo y audiovisuales. see *MOTION PICTURES*

384.55 ITA ISSN 1129-5066
CINEMA IN CASA; la prima rivista di audio e video ad alta fedelta. Text in Italian. 1993. bi-m. adv. film rev. **Document type:** *Magazine, Consumer.*
Published by: Editore Progest s.r.l., Via Rovereto 6, Rome, RM 00198, Italy. TEL 39-06-8552649, FAX 39-06-8558885, progestsrl@infinito.it. Eds. Gianni Caserta, Giovanni B Rodinis. Circ: 140,000.

CINEMA LOMBARDIA; periodico d'informazione a cura della sezione regionale dell'A.N.E.C. see *MOTION PICTURES*

CINEMA TECHNOLOGY. see *MOTION PICTURES*

CINEMACTION. see *MOTION PICTURES*

CINESCAPE. see *MOTION PICTURES*

621.388 VEN
CIRCUIT - FOTON. Text in Spanish. 1980. m. VEB 200, USD 40. adv.
Formerly: Circuit
Published by: M.G. Ediciones Especializadas, S.A., Av. Maturin, No. 15, Urb. Los Cedros, El Bosque, Caracas, 1050, Venezuela. Circ: 3,500.

384.55 USA
COLUMBO NEWSLETTER. Text in English. 1991. q. USD 12 domestic; USD 16 foreign (effective 2000). back issues avail. **Document type:** *Newsletter, Consumer.* **Description:** Covers the TV program Columbo, that stars Peter Falk as Lt. Columbo.
Address: PO Box 1703, Pittsburgh, PA 15230-1703. Ed., R&P Sheldon P Catz. Circ: 100.

384.55 NLD ISSN 1380-9679
COMEDIA. Text in Dutch. 1989. m. (10/yr.). **Document type:** *Newsletter.* **Description:** News on broadcasting and other media.
Published by: Commissariaat voor de Media, Postbus 1426, Hilversum, 1200 BK, Netherlands. TEL 31-35-672-1721, FAX 31-35-672-1722, cudm@cudm.nl, http://www.cudm.nl. Circ: (controlled).

COMEDY WRITERS ASSOCIATION NEWSLETTER. see *LITERATURE*

COMEDY WRITERS BULLETIN. see *LITERATURE*

621.388 GBR ISSN 1461-5576
HE8689
COMMONWEALTH BROADCASTER. Text in English. 1966. q. USD 20; USD 25 foreign (effective 2000). adv. bk.rev. **Document type:** *Consumer.*
Formerly (until 1997): Combroad (0951-0826)
Related titles: Supplement(s): Commonwealth Broadcaster. Directory. ISSN 1466-0784.
Indexed: CommAb, IIFP, IITV.
—BLDSC (3339.626500).
Published by: Commonwealth Broadcasting Association, 17 Fleet St, London, EC4Y 1AA, United Kingdom. TEL 44-171-583-5550, FAX 44-171-583-5549, cba@cba.org.uk, http://www.oneworld.org/cba/. Ed. Elizabeth Smith. Adv. contact Derek Inall. Circ: 10,000.

384.5452 GBR
COMMONWEALTH BROADCASTER DIRECTORY. Text in English. 1976. a. GBP 25 domestic; GBP 28 foreign (effective 1999). adv. **Document type:** *Trade.*
Former titles: Who's Who in Commonwealth Broadcasting; (until 1995): Commonwealth Broadcasting Association. Handbook
Published by: Commonwealth Broadcasting Association, 17 Fleet St, London, EC4Y 1AA, United Kingdom. TEL 44-171-583-5550, FAX 44-171-583-5549, cba@cba.org.uk, http://www.oneworld.org/cba/. Ed. Elizabeth Smith. Adv. contact Derek Inall.

384.55 NLD
COMMUNICATIE ONLINE; voor communicatie professionals. Text in Dutch. m. **Description:** Reports developments in the communications industry in the Netherlands.
Media: Online - full content. **Related titles:** ◆ Print ed.: Communicatie. ISSN 1381-4974.
Published by: Samsom Bedrijfsinformatie BV (Subsidiary of: Wolters Kluwer N.V.), Postbus 4, Alphen aan den Rijn, 2400 MA, Netherlands. TEL 31-172-466932, FAX 31-172-466373, r.mooy@samsom.nl, http://www.communicatieonline.nl, http://www.samsom.nl. Eds. Sandra Schuiten, Rocco Mooij. Pub. Berend Jan Veldkamp.

621.388 USA ISSN 0277-0679
COMMUNICATIONS DAILY; the authoritative news service of electronic communications. Text in English. 1981. d. (5/w.). looseleaf. USD 4,195 (effective 2005). **Document type:** *Newsletter, Consumer.*
Related titles: Online - full text ed.: (from bigchalk, Data-Star, LexisNexis, The Dialog Corporation).
Indexed: CompD.
Published by: Warren Communications News, Inc., 2115 Ward Ct, N W, Washington, DC 20037. TEL 202-872-9200, 800-327-7205, FAX 202-293-3435, info@warren-news.com, http://www.warren-news.com. **Dist. by:** Publications Resource Group, 121 Union St., Box 792, North Adams, MA 01247. TEL 413-664-6185, FAX 413-664-9343.

384.555 USA ISSN 0884-2272
TK6675
COMMUNICATIONS TECHNOLOGY. Text in English. 1984. m. (13 issues). USD 89 domestic; USD 129 foreign; free to qualified personnel (effective 2005). adv. charts; illus. index. back issues avail. **Document type:** *Magazine, Trade.* **Description:** Covers cable TV engineering and technology.
Incorporates (1990-2000): International Cable (1069-5494)
Related titles: Online - full text ed.
Indexed: MicrocompInd.
—BLDSC (3363.456300). **CCC.**
Published by: (Society of Cable Television Engineers), Access Intelligence, LLC (Subsidiary of: Veronis, Suhler & Associates Inc.), 1201 Seven Locks Rd, Ste 300, Potomac, MD 20854. TEL 301-354-2000, 800-777-5006, FAX 301-738-8453, clientservices@accessintel.com, http://www.omeda.com/ct/, http://www.pbimedia.com. Ed. Laura Hamilton. Adv. contact Tish Ott. Circ: 27,500 (paid and controlled).

COMMUNICATOR (WASHINGTON, 1988). see *COMMUNICATIONS—Radio*

384.55 USA ISSN 1083-0685
COMMUNITY TELEVISION BUSINESS. Text in English. 1994. 18/yr. USD 150 (effective 1999). adv. back issues avail. **Document type:** *Newsletter, Trade.* **Description:** Covers news for low power TV and class TV industry.
Published by: K B Ltd., PO Box 250813, Milwaukee, WI 53225. TEL 262-781-0188, FAX 262-781-5313. Ed., Pub., R&P, Adv. contact Jackie Biel. page USD 2,000; trim 11 x 8.5. Circ: 877 (paid).

621.388 ZAF
CONNECTIVITY. Text in English. q. adv.
Published by: Technews (Pty.) Ltd., PO Box 626, Kloof, 3640, South Africa. TEL 27-31-764-0593, FAX 27-31-764-0386. Adv. contact Jane Fortmann TEL 27-31-764-5316. B&W page ZAR 7,000, color page ZAR 8,500; trim 210 x 297.

▼ **CONSCIOUSNESS, LITERATURE AND THE ARTS.** see *LITERATURE*

CONSOLE-ING PASSIONS; television and cultural power. see *SOCIOLOGY*

CONTACTS; the media pipeline for public relations people. see *ADVERTISING AND PUBLIC RELATIONS*

CONTACTS. see *THEATER*

384.5532 BRA ISSN 0104-1444
CONTIGO. Text in Portuguese. 1963. w. BRL 306.80 domestic; USD 302.43 foreign (effective 2005). adv. film rev. illus. back issues avail. **Document type:** *Magazine, Consumer.* **Description:** Guide to television broadcasts. Includes coverage of personalities.
Former titles (until July 1994): Contigo Superstar; (until May 1983): T V Contigo (0010-7662)
Related titles: Online - full text ed.
Published by: Editora Abril, S.A., Av. das Nacoes Unidas, 7221, 11 andar Pinheiros, Sao Paulo, SP 05425-902, Brazil. TEL 55-11-50872112, FAX 55-11-50872100, contigo.abril@atleitor.com.br, http://contigo.abril.com.br/, http://www.abril.com.br/. Ed. Cynthia de Almeida. R&P Ana Vidotti TEL 55-11-30372125. Adv. contact Ana Serra. page BRL 38,500; trim 202 x 266. Circ: 200,690 (paid).

CONTRAPUNTO. see *COMMUNICATIONS—Radio*

384.55 GBR ISSN 1354-8565
P96.T42
CONVERGENCE; the journal of research into new media technologies. Text in English. 1995. q. USD 72 in North America to individuals; GBP 30 elsewhere to individuals; USD 126 in North America to institutions; GBP 60 elsewhere to institutions; GBP 5.95 per issue (effective 2004). **Document type:** *Journal, Academic/Scholarly.* **Description:** Provides a forum for the creative, social, political and pedagogical issues raised by the advent of new media technologies.
Indexed: CommAb, RRTA.
—BLDSC (3463.544500), IE, ingenta. **CCC.**
Published by: University of Luton Press, University of Luton, 75 Castle St, Luton, Beds LU1 3AJ, United Kingdom. TEL 44-1582-743297, FAX 44-1582-743298, convergence@luton.ac.uk, http://www.luton.ac.uk/convergence, http://www.ulp.org.uk. Eds. Alexis Weedon, Jeanette Steemers, Julia Knight TEL 44-1582-734111.

CORPORATE A V (YEAR). see *COMMUNICATIONS*

791.45 HKG
COSMOS WEEKLY. Text in Chinese. 1987. w. **Description:** Covers entertainment.
Address: B2, 14-F, Fuk Keung Ind. Bldg, 66-68 Tong Mei Rd, Tai Kok Tsu, Kowloon, Hong Kong. TEL 3905461, FAX 7893869. Ed. Vincent Leung. Circ: 60,000.

384.55 GBR
CREWFINDER CYMRU WALES. Text in English. 1992. a. GBP 10. adv. index. back issues avail. **Document type:** *Trade.* **Description:** Provides information on freelance personnel in production, camera, sound art, special effects, costume, make-up, and post-production, as well as a who's who, facts and figures, photos, and diary.
Published by: (Broadcasting, Entertainment, Cinematograph and Theatre Union), Adleader Publications, Marlborough House, 348 Lisburn Rd, Belfast, BT9 6GH, United Kingdom. TEL 44-1232-661666, FAX 44-1232-681888, adleader@dial.pipex.com. Ed. Alan Mairs. R&P Alain Mairs. Adv. contact Sinead Balmer. B&W page GBP 425, color page GBP 595. Circ: 2,000.

CRONACHE; per il personale de Gruppo Philips. see *ENGINEERING—Electrical Engineering*

384.5532 HRV ISSN 1330-769X
CROSAT TELSTAR. Text in Croatian. 1995. m. **Document type:** *Magazine, Consumer.*
Published by: CroSat, Kvarnerska 57, Rijeka, 51000, Croatia. TEL 385-51-227559, FAX 385-51-227852, crosat@ri.tel.hr. Ed. Dean Cvjetkovic.

384.55 GBR ISSN 1360-6530
CULT TIMES. Text in English. 1995. m. GBP 43 domestic; USD 75 in US & Canada; GBP 51 elsewhere (effective 2000); includes Cult Times Special. adv. tel.rev. illus. **Document type:** *Consumer.* **Description:** Offers fans of cult television programs information about their favorite shows and stars.
Related titles: ◆ Supplement(s): Cult Times Special. ISSN 1365-862X.
Published by: Visual Imagination Ltd., 9 Blades Ct, Deodar Rd, London, SW15 2NU, United Kingdom. TEL 44-20-8875-1520, FAX 44-208-875-1588, culttimes@visimag.com, http://www.visimag.com. Ed. Richard Atkinson. Pub., R&P Stephen Payne. Adv. contact Martin Clark. B&W page GBP 1,270, color page GBP 1,940; trim 222 x 300. **Subscr. to:** PO Box 371, London SW14 8J, United Kingdom. **Dist. by:** Comag, Tavistock Works, Tavistock Rd, W Drayton, Middx UB7 7QX, United Kingdom. TEL 44-1895-433600, FAX 44-189-543-3606.

384.55 GBR ISSN 1365-862X
CULT TIMES SPECIAL; the best guide to cult TV. Text in English. 1996. q. GBP 41 domestic; GBP 49 in Europe; GBP 63 elsewhere; GBP 3.50 newsstand/cover domestic; USD 6.99 newsstand/cover in United States; CND 7.95 newsstand/cover in Canada (effective 2000); includes Cult Times. adv. tel.rev. illus. back issues avail. **Document type:** *Consumer.* **Description:** Takes an in-depth look into a featured popular TV show.
Related titles: ◆ Supplement to: Cult Times. ISSN 1360-6530.
Published by: Visual Imagination Ltd., 9 Blades Ct, Deodar Rd, London, SW15 2NU, United Kingdom. TEL 44-20-8875-1520, FAX 44-208-875-1588, culttimes@visimag.com, http://www.visimag.com. Ed. Richard Atkinson. Pub., R&P Stephen Payne. Adv. contact Martin Clark. **Dist. by:** Comag, Tavistock Works, Tavistock Rd, W Drayton, Middx UB7 7QX, United Kingdom. TEL 44-1895-433600, FAX 44-189-543-3606.

384.55 USA ISSN 0739-991X
CURRENT (WASHINGTON, 1980); The Public Telecommunications Newspaper. Text in English. 1980. bi-w. USD 70 domestic; USD 132 in Canada; USD 155 elsewhere (effective 2003). adv. bk.rev.; tel.rev. illus. 28 p./no. 4 cols./p.; reprints avail. **Document type:** *Newspaper, Trade.* **Description:** News, features, and commentary about public television, public radio and noncommercial telecommunications.
Former titles: N A E B Letter; National Association of Educational Broadcasters Newsletter (0027-8610)
Related titles: Microfilm ed.
Indexed: GSS&RPL, PMR, RGAb.
Published by: Current Publishing Committee (Subsidiary of: Educational Broadcasting Corporation), 1612 K St, N W, Ste 704, Washington, DC 20006. TEL 202-463-7055, FAX 202-463-7056, news@current.org, current@ix.netcom.com, http://www.current.org. Ed., Pub., R&P Steve Behrens. Adv. contact Denese Scott. Circ: 6,100 (paid).

621.388 USA ISSN 1557-315X
TK6540
▼ **DIGITAL T V & SOUND**; the ultimate guide to hdtv, plasma, flat-panel, projection, sound. Variant title: Digital Television and Sound. Text in English. 2004 (Spr.). q. USD 12 domestic; USD 22 in Canada; USD 52 elsewhere; USD 5.95 newsstand/cover (effective 2004). adv. **Document type:** *Magazine, Trade.* **Description:** Focuses on HDTV, plasma screens and digital TV technologies.
Formerly (until Spr. 2005): CurtCo's Digital T V (1548-6273)
Published by: CurtCo Media Labs, 29160 Heathercliff Rd, Ste 200, Malibu, CA 90265. TEL 310-589-7700, FAX 310-589-7701, http://www.dtvmag.com, http://www.curtco.com/. Ed. Mike Wood. Pub., Adv. contact Mark Mendelsohn. R&P Brent Butterworth. page USD 9,800. Circ: 80,000 (paid).

CUT; Journalismus, Fiction & Teknik bei elektronische Medien. see *JOURNALISM*

CYRANO'S JOURNAL. see *COMMUNICATIONS*

THE D B S REPORT. (Direct Broadcast Satellite) see *BUSINESS AND ECONOMICS—Banking And Finance*

▼ **D V.** (Digital Video) see *COMMUNICATIONS—Video*

791.45 USA ISSN 1541-0943
TR899
D V. (Digital Video) Text in English. 1993. m. USD 29.97 domestic; USD 44.97 in Canada; USD 42.97 in Mexico; USD 84.97 elsewhere; USD 3.95 newsstand/cover domestic; CND 4.95 newsstand/cover in Canada (effective 2004). adv. software rev. illus. back issues avail.; reprints avail. **Document type:** *Magazine, Consumer.* **Description:** Covers the convergence of computers and video, providing information on digital video hardware and software for major platforms for videographers creating computer-enhanced videos. Includes graphics, animation, video capture and editing, image processing and multimedia.
Former titles (until 1996): Digital Video Magazine (1075-251X); (until Jun. 1994): Desktop Video World (1067-7720)
Related titles: Online - full text ed.: (from Florida Center for Library Automation, Gale Group, H.W. Wilson, O C L C Online Computer Library Center, Inc.).
Indexed: BPI, MicrocompInd, SoftBase.
—IE, Infotrieve. **CCC.**
Published by: C M P Media LLC (Subsidiary of: United News & Media), 600 Harrison St, 6th Fl., San Francisco, CA 94107. TEL 415-947-6746, 888-776-7002, FAX 415-947-6041, gentry@dv.com, http://www.dv.com. Ed. Dominic Milano. Pub. Scott Gentry. adv.: B&W page USD 4,500, color page USD 5,850; trim 10.75 x 8. Circ: 64,382 (paid and controlled).

371.3358 USA
D V S GUIDE (E-MAIL EDITION). Text in English. q. **Document type:** *Consumer.* **Description:** WGBH television station publication. Provides news related to making television accessible to visually impaired audiences; includes program schedule of selected public television series and cable programming.
Media: E-mail.
Published by: (Descriptive Video Service), W G B H Educational Foundation, PO Box 200, Boston, MA 02134. TEL 617-300-5400, 800-333-1203, FAX 617-783-8668, dvs@wgbh.org, http://www.wgbh.org. Circ: 3,100.

384.55 USA ISSN 0011-5509
PN1993
DAILY VARIETY (LOS ANGELES); news of the entertainment industry. Text in English. 1933. d. (Mon.-Fri.). USD 259 domestic; USD 1,099 foreign; USD 3.50 newsstand/cover domestic; USD 12.95 newsstand/cover foreign (effective 2005); Includes 10 issues of VLife. adv. bk.rev.; film rev.; music rev.; play rev.; tel.rev. charts. **Document type:** *Newspaper, Trade.* **Description:** Covers the entire scope of the entertainment business, including film, legitimate theatre, music, cable and home video.
Related titles: Microfilm ed.: (from LIB); Online - full text ed.: (from EBSCO Publishing, Florida Center for Library Automation, Gale Group, LexisNexis, O C L C Online Computer Library Center, Inc.); Regional ed(s).: Daily Variety (Hollywood Edition); Daily Variety (Gotham Edition). ISSN 1554-3862. 1998. USD 299 domestic; USD 1,099 foreign; USD 3.50 newsstand/cover domestic; USD 12.95 newsstand/cover foreign (effective 2004).
Indexed: WBA, WMB.
—**CCC.**
Published by: Reed Business Information (Subsidiary of: Reed Business), 5700 Wilshire Blvd, Ste 120, Los Angeles, CA 90036. TEL 323-857-6600, FAX 323-857-0494, comments@variety.cahners.com, http://www.variety.com, http://www.reedbusiness.com. Ed. Peter Bart TEL 323-965-4434. Pub. Charlie Koones TEL 323-965-4441. adv.: B&W page USD 7,550, color page USD 14,060; trim 270 x 365. Circ: 35,500. Wire service: DJNS, AP. **Subscr. to:** Reed Business Information, PO Box 15878, North Hollywood, CA 91615-5878. FAX 818-487-4550.

DANGDAI XIJU/CONTEMPORARY DRAMA; xiju - dianshi shuangyuekan. see *THEATER*

DARATHAI MAGAZINE. see *MOTION PICTURES*

THE DATA BOOK; New Zealand film, television, video, photographic stills and theatre. see *BUSINESS AND ECONOMICS—Trade And Industrial Directories*

791.45 AUS ISSN 0729-7920
DATA EXTRACT. Text in English. 1980. 8/yr. AUD 12; AUD 2.50 newsstand/cover. bk.rev.; video rev. illus. back issues avail. **Document type:** *Newsletter.* **Description:** Alerts Australian aficionados of the British science fiction series Dr. Who to events of interest, including conventions, screenings of episodes, and appearances by the show's stars.
Published by: Doctor Who Fan Club of Australia, GPO Box 2870, Sydney, NSW 2001, Australia. neelix@eagles.bbs.net.au, http://www.eagles.bbs.net.au/~draco/dwca. Ed. Neil Hogan. adv.: page AUD 60. Circ: 700.

791.45 USA
DAYS OF OUR LIVES NEWSLETTER. Text in English. w. **Document type:** *Newsletter.* **Description:** Features upcoming spoilers, rumors, and news about your favorite soap opera.
Media: Online - full text.
Address: daysofourlives.guide@miningco.com, http://daysofourlives.miningco.com/gi/pages/mmail.htm.

384.55 USA
DAYTIME T V'S GREATEST STORIES. Text in English. bi-m. adv. **Document type:** *Consumer.* **Description:** Provides material of an entertaining and diversionary nature for women. Devoted to T.V. personalities.
Published by: Dorchester Media, 35 Wilbur St, Lynbrook, NY 11563. TEL 516-593-1220, FAX 516-593-0065.

384.55 CHN ISSN 1003-4005
DAZHONG DIANSHI/POPULAR T V. Text in Chinese. 1980. m. CNY 72. **Document type:** *Magazine, Consumer.* **Description:** Covers movie, TV and pop song stars, new TV plays and series, and more.
Published by: (Zhejiang Sheng Guangbo Dianshi-ting/Zhejiang Provincial Broadcasting and Television Bureau), Dazhong Dianshi Bianjibu, No 31, Changsheng Lu, Hangzhou, Zhejiang 310006, China. TEL 86-571-7065558, FAX 86-571-7084024. Ed. Ruolin Ruan. Adv. contact Jian Shen. Circ: 400,000 (paid). **Dist. in US by:** China Books & Periodicals Inc, 360 Swift Ave., Ste. 48, S San Fran, CA 94080-6220. TEL 415-282-2994.

DENSHI JOHO TSUSHIN GAKKAI RONBUNSHI (A)/INSTITUTE OF ELECTRONICS, INFORMATION AND COMMUNICATION ENGINEERS. TRANSACTIONS (SECTION A). see *ENGINEERING*

384.55 USA ISSN 1065-1535
PN1992.3.U5
DESTINATION DISCOVERY. Text in English. 1985. m. USD 19.95. **Document type:** *Consumer.*
Formerly (until Aug. 1992): Disney Channel Magazine (0747-4644)
Published by: (The Discovery Channel), Discovery Publishing, 7700 Wisconsin Ave, 7th Fl, Bethesda, MD 20814. TEL 301-986-0444, FAX 301-986-4628. Circ: 200,000.

DEUTSCHES ENTERTAINMENT MAGAZIN. see *MOTION PICTURES*

384.55 DEU
DEUTSCHLANDFUNK. GESCHAEFTSBERICHT. Text in German. 1962. biennial. **Document type:** *Corporate.*
Formerly: Deutschlandfunk. Jahrbuch (0084-9790)
Published by: Deutschlandfunk, Raderbergguertel 40, Cologne, 50968, Germany. TEL 0221-345-2110.

DIANSHI DIANYING WENXUE/T V AND FILM LITERATURE. see *MOTION PICTURES*

384.55 CHN
DIANSHI YUEKAN/TELEVISION MONTHLY. Text in Chinese. 1982. m. USD 43.10. adv. **Document type:** *Consumer.* **Description:** General interest television entertainment magazine.
Published by: (Hubei Dianshi Tai), Dianshi Yuekan Zazhishe, Te-1, Zijincun, Liangdao Jie, Wuchang-qu, Wuhan, Hubei 430071, China. TEL 86-27-7816964. Ed. Liu Chuncheng. **Dist. in US by:** China Books & Periodicals Inc, 360 Swift Ave., Ste. 48, S San Fran, CA 94080-6220. TEL 415-282-2994; **Dist. overseas by:** China International Book Trading Corp, 35 Chegongzhuang Xilu, Haidian District, PO Box 399, Beijing 100044, China. TEL 86-10-68412045, FAX 86-10-68412023, cibtc@mail.cibtc.com.cn, http://www.cibtc.com.cn.

DIFFUSION (ENGLISH EDITION). see *COMMUNICATIONS—Radio*

DIFFUSION (FRENCH EDITION). see *COMMUNICATIONS—Radio*

384.54 GBR ISSN 1460-1354
DIGITAL BROADCASTER. Text in English. 1997. bi-w. GBP 495 (effective 2000). **Description:** Covers all aspects of digital interactive television industry, including cable, satellite and the Internet.
Published by: PS Publishing, Old Ale House, 129 Bengeo St, Hertford, Herts, SG14 3EX, United Kingdom. TEL 44-1992-410487, FAX 44-1992-410487, pbright@dial.pipex.com. Pub. Peter Bright.

621.388 GBR
DIGITAL T V TESTS. Text in English. a. GBP 3.99 newsstand/cover (effective 2003). **Document type:** *Magazine, Consumer.*
Indexed: ISAP.
Published by: Highbury - WV (Subsidiary of: Highbury House Communications PLC), 53-79 Highgate Rd, London, NW5 1TW, United Kingdom. TEL 44-20-73311000, FAX 44-20-73311273, http://www. wotsat.com, http://www.hhc.co.uk/. Ed. Alex Lane. Circ: 61,847.

330 384 USA ISSN 1096-0740
DIGITAL TELEVISION. Text in English. 1997. m. USD 945; USD 1,340 combined subscription print & e-mail eds. (effective 2005). adv. **Document type:** *Newsletter, Trade.* **Description:** Publishes information on the latest strategies the broadcast, cable, satellite, home video and computer industries have for implementing digital technology. Exclusive projections for consumer electronics on digital platforms.
Related titles: E-mail ed.: USD 875 (effective 2005); Fax ed.: USD 945 (effective 2001).
—**CCC.**
Published by: Kagan Research, LLC, One Lower Ragsdale Dr, Bldg One, Ste 130, Monterey, CA 93940. TEL 831-624-1536, FAX 831-625-3225, info@kagan.com, http://www.kagan.com. adv.: color page USD 3,400.

384.55 ITA
DIGITALE TV SAT. Text in Italian. 1998. m. **Description:** Contains a new program guide.
Published by: Gruppo Editoriale J C E, Via Patecchio 2, Milan, MI 20141, Italy. TEL 39-02-57316011, FAX 39-02-57316291, info@jce.it, http://www.jce.it. Ed. Amedeo Bozzoni. Pub. Jacopo Castelfranchi. Circ: 120,000.

DIRECTORY OF BRITISH FILM-MAKERS. see *MOTION PICTURES*

DIRECTORY OF INTERNATIONAL FILM AND VIDEO FESTIVALS (YEAR). see *MOTION PICTURES*

DIRECTORY OF RELIGIOUS MEDIA. see *BUSINESS AND ECONOMICS—Trade And Industrial Directories*

DIRECTV ON SPORTS. see *SPORTS AND GAMES—Ball Games*

DIRITTO DELLE RADIODIFFUSIONI E DELLE TELECOMUNICAZIONI. see *LAW*

791.45 GBR ISSN 0963-1275
DOCTOR WHO MAGAZINE. Text in English. 1979. 13/yr. GBP 40.80 (effective 2005). adv. bk.rev. back issues avail. **Document type:** *Magazine, Consumer.* **Description:** Covers the BBC Program "Doctor Who," as well as licensed off-shoots such as plays and film, actors involved, history of show, and related books.
Published by: Panini UK Ltd., Panini House Coach and Horses Passage, Tunbridge Wells, Kent TN2 5UJ, United Kingdom. TEL 44-1892-500100, info@panini.co.uk, http://www.paninicomics.co.uk. Circ: 33,000 (paid). **Dist. by:** MarketForce UK Ltd, 247 Tottenham Court Rd, London, Middx W1T 7AU, United Kingdom. TEL 44-207-2615199, FAX 44-207-2617341.

DOCUMENT & IMAGE AUTOMATION. see *LIBRARY AND INFORMATION SCIENCES*

DOCUMENTER. see *MOTION PICTURES*

C

DREAMWATCH. see *LITERATURE—Science Fiction, Fantasy, Horror*

E B U TECHNICAL REVIEW. see *COMMUNICATIONS*

E.P. MAGAZINE; Music, Video, Games...and Other Crimes. (Extended Play) see *MUSIC*

384.55 DEU ISSN 1616-9387
E.PUNKT N R W; aktuelle Nachrichten fuer die elektro- und informationstechnischen Handwerke Nordrhein-Westfalen. Text in German. m. **Document type:** *Bulletin, Corporate.* **Description:** Contains news reports for electrical contractors, electric motor repair, television retail and repair and telecommunications personnel.
Formerly (until 2001): Strom und Welle (0344-4252)
Published by: Fachverband Elektrotechnische Handwerke Nordrhein-Westfalen, Hannoeversche Str 22, Dortmund, 44143, Germany. TEL 49-231-519850, FAX 49-231-5198544, info@feh-nrw.de, http://www.feh-nrw.de. Ed. Simone Merkel. R&P Josef Hillebrand. Adv. contact Magdalene Wessel. Circ: 8,950.

E T R NEWS. see *COMMUNICATIONS*

384.5532 USA ISSN 1525-4399
ECONOMICS OF T V PROGRAMMING & SYNDICATION. Text in English. 1994. a. USD 1,195 (effective 2005). **Document type:** *Directory, Trade.* **Description:** Deals with the financial realities, programming challenges and best practices for developing actionable next steps and workable strategies.
Published by: Kagan Research, LLC, One Lower Ragsdale Dr, Bldg One, Ste 130, Monterey, CA 93940. TEL 831-624-1536, FAX 831-625-3225, info@kagan.com, http://www.kagan.com.

384.55 USA
ED: ONE CLUB, ONE HORSE, ONE WORLD✶. Text in English. q. membership. **Document type:** *Consumer.* **Description:** Geared to fans of the television show Mr. Ed.
Published by: Mister Ed Fan Club, PO Box 720714, Dallas, TX 75372-0714.

EKKO; magasinet om film og medier. see *MOTION PICTURES*

EKRAN; revija za film in televizijo. see *MOTION PICTURES*

621.38 AUT
ELEKTRO JOURNAL. Text in German. 11/yr. EUR 60 domestic; EUR 89 foreign (effective 2005). adv. illus. **Document type:** *Journal, Trade.*
Former titles: Elektro and Radio (0029-9855); Oesterreichisches Elektro- und Radio-Gewerbe
Indexed: CISA.
Published by: (Bundesinnung der Elektro-, Radio- und Fernsehtechniker), Oesterreichischer Wirtschaftsverlag GmbH (Subsidiary of: Sueddeutscher Verlag GmbH), Wiedner Hauptstr 120-124, Vienna, W 1051, Austria. TEL 43-1-546640, FAX 43-1-54664406, office@wirtschaftsverlag.at, http://www.elektrojournal.at, http://www.wirtschaftsverlag.at. Ed. Willy Duschka. adv.: color page EUR 3,675; trim 176 x 252. Circ: 10,391 (paid and controlled).

ELEKTROSVYAZ'. see *COMMUNICATIONS—Radio*

791.45 USA ISSN 0896-2502
ELEVEN; WTTW Chicago member magazine. Text in English. 1987. 10/yr. USD 40 to members. adv. bk.rev. **Document type:** *Consumer.* **Description:** Contains articles relating to programming on WTTW Channel 11 in Chicago (including a complete program listing) as well as articles on cuisine, family and at-home topics, travel, financial matters, education, fiction and communications.
Published by: (Window To The World Communications, Inc.), General Learning Communications, 900 Skokie Blvd, Ste 200, Northbrook, IL 60062. TEL 847-205-3000, http://www.wttw.com, http://www.glcomm.com. Ed. Carol Spielman Lezak. Pub., R&P Julian Berkin. Adv. contact Shaunese Teamer. Circ: 162,000.

384.55 UAE
EMIRATES TV & RADIO/TELFUZOON WA EDHA'AH. Text in Arabic, English. 1992. bi-m. free. adv. **Description:** For Emirates Airline featuring audio & video program listings.
Published by: Motivate Publishing, PO Box 2331, Dubai, United Arab Emirates. TEL 971-4-824060, FAX 971-4-824436, motivate@emirates.net.ae. Ed. Allen Armstrong. R&P Shawki Abd El Malik. Adv. contact Shawki Abd Elmalik. color page USD 3,000; trim 185 x 260. Circ: 268,000.

384.55 USA ISSN 0164-3495
PN1992.3.U5
EMMY. Text in English. 1979. bi-m. USD 28 domestic; USD 42 in Canada; USD 65 elsewhere; USD 4.95 newsstand/cover (effective 2004). adv. bk.rev. illus. **Document type:** *Trade.* **Description:** Covers matters of interest to the television industry, including members of the academy.
Indexed: ASIP, BRI, CCR, IIFP, IIPA, IITV.
Published by: Academy of Television Arts & Sciences, 5220 Lankershim Blvd., N. Hollywood, CA 91601-3109. TEL 818-754-2800, FAX 818-761-8340, emmysmag@emmys.org, madonna@emmys.org, http://www.emmys.org. Ed., R&P Gail Polevoi. Pub. Jim Chabin. Adv. contact John McCarthy. Circ: 14,000.

ENCORE. see *MOTION PICTURES*

ENCORE DIRECTORY. see *MOTION PICTURES*

ENTERTAINMENT LAW & FINANCE. see *LAW*

ENTERTAINMENT LAW REPORTER; movies, television, music, theater, publishing, multimedia, sports. see *LAW*

791.45 USA ISSN 0739-1897
KF4290.A152
ENTERTAINMENT, PUBLISHING AND THE ARTS HANDBOOK. Text in English. a. price varies. **Document type:** *Monographic series, Trade.* **Description:** Covers copyright, right of publicity, privacy libel, music, motion pictures, television, contracts, entertainment and business.
Indexed: ATI.
Published by: Thomson West (Subsidiary of: Thomson Corporation, The), 610 Opperman Dr, Eagan, MN 55123-1396. TEL 651-687-8000, 800-328-4880, FAX 651-687-7302, customer.service@westgroup.com, http://www.westgroup.com/store/product.asp?product%5Fid=14825179&catalog%5Fname=wgstore, http://west.thomson.com. Eds. John David Viera, Robert Thome.

384.55 USA ISSN 1058-109X
EPI-LOG✶; the television magazine of science fiction, fantasy, comedy, drama and adventure. Text in English. 1990. bi-m. USD 30; USD 35 in Canada; USD 40 elsewhere. **Description:** Covers TV shows of science fiction, fantasy and adventure.
Published by: Epi-log Communications, Inc., PO Box 456, Dunlap, TN 37327-0456. Ed. William E Anchors Jr.

384.55 USA
THE ESSENTIAL SUBWOOFER BUYER'S GUIDE. Text in English. 2000. bi-m. USD 40; USD 9.95 newsstand/cover (effective 2001). adv. **Document type:** *Consumer.*
Published by: Widescreen Review, 26864 Mandelieu Dr, Murrieta, CA 92562. TEL 909-677-0335, FAX 909-677-2604, EditorGary@WidescreenReview.com, http://www.WidescreenReview.com. Ed., Pub. Gary Reber.

621.388 SWE ISSN 0014-1658
ETER-AKTUELLT; tidningen foer DX-are och vaerldsradiolyssnare. Text in Swedish. 1958. m. SEK 135, USD 20. adv. bk.rev. abstr.; charts; illus.
Published by: Sveriges DX-Foerbund/Swedish DX Federation, Fack 3108, Stockholm, 10362, Sweden. Ed. Paer Mattisson. Circ: 1,500.

384.55 USA ISSN 1053-8313
EURO CABLE T V PROGRAMMING. Text in English. 1990. m. USD 795 (effective 2001). adv. **Document type:** *Newsletter, Trade.* **Description:** Analyzes programming economics, network values, carriage fees, viewer shares and the financial impact of changes in Europe's cable and DBS/DTH industries.
Published by: Kagan Research, LLC, 1 Lower Ragsdale Dr., Ste. 130, Monterey, CA 93940-5741. TEL 831-624-1536, FAX 831-625-3225, info@kagan.com., http://www.pkbaseline.com, http://www.kagan.com. Pub. Paul Kagan.

384.555 USA ISSN 1537-0011
EUROPEAN BROADBAND. Text in English. 1988. m. USD 845, GBP 495 (effective 2001). adv. **Document type:** *Newsletter.* **Description:** Examines companies pioneering cable growth, consolidation; identifies cable funding sources; tracks pay tv progress; analyzes emerging programming sources.
Former titles (until 2001): European Cable - Pay T V (1050-3579); (until 1990): Euromedia Investor (1041-3014)
Related titles: E-mail ed.: USD 845 (effective 2001); Fax ed.: USD 845 (effective 2001).
—CCC.
Published by: Kagan Research, LLC, 1 Lower Ragsdale Dr., Ste. 130, Monterey, CA 93940-5741. TEL 831-624-1536, FAX 831-625-3225, info@kagan.com, http://www.kagan.com/cgi-bin/pkcat/ecp.html. Pub. Paul Kagan.

621.388 DEU ISSN 1021-5700
EUROPEAN MEDIAFACTS. Text in German, English, French. irreg. **Document type:** *Monographic series, Academic/Scholarly.*
Published by: Europaeisches Medieninstitut e.V., Zollhof 2A, Duesseldorf, 40221, Germany. TEL 49-211-90104-0, FAX 49-211-9010456, orders@eim.org, http://www.eim.org. R&P Jo Groebel.

384.51 USA ISSN 1052-5068
EUROPEAN TELEVISION. Text in English. 1989. m. adv. **Document type:** *Newsletter, Trade.* **Description:** Includes valuation of private and public networks, stations, program producers, distributors, and prices, spot costs, owner and buyer names, and markets' values.
Formerly (until 1989): Euro TV Investor (1043-9420)
Related titles: E-mail ed.: USD 745 (effective 2001); Fax ed.: USD 745 (effective 2001).
—CCC.
Published by: Kagan Research, LLC, 1 Lower Ragsdale Dr., Ste. 130, Monterey, CA 93940-5741. TEL 831-624-1536, FAX 831-625-3225, info@kagan.com, http://www.kagan.com/cgi-bin/pkcat/etv.html. Pub. Paul Kagan.

384.51 ITA
EUROSAT; satellite TV technology. Text in Italian. 1986. m. EUR 42 (effective 2005). **Document type:** *Magazine, Consumer.*
Incorporates (1993-199?): Tutto T V Satellite (1123-6515)
Published by: Gruppo Editoriale J C E, Via Patecchio 2, Milan, MI 20141, Italy. TEL 39-02-57316011, FAX 39-02-57316291, info@jce.it, http://www.jce.it.

384.55 SVK
EUROTELEVIZIA. Text in Slovak. 1965. w. SKK 960 (effective 2005). adv. film rev.; play rev. illus. **Document type:** *Magazine, Consumer.* **Description:** Provides the program information about more than twenty television channels, and interviews with film stars.
Formerly: Televizia (0139-7451)
Published by: Ringier Slovakia a. s., Prievozska 14, PO Box 46, Bratislava 24, 82004, Slovakia. TEL 421-2-58227124, FAX 421-2-58227143, eurotelevizia@eurotelevizia.sk, http://www.eurotelevizia.sk. Ed. Renata Klacanska. Adv. contact Pavol Sakal. B&W page SKK 94,000, color page SKK 120,000; trim 212 x 270. Circ: 190,000 (paid).

F K T; Fachzeitschrift fuer Fernsehen, Film und elektronische Medien. (Fernseh- und Kino-Technik) see *MOTION PICTURES*

791.45 CAN ISSN 0829-4747
FACE TO FACE WITH TALENT. Text in English. 1970. biennial. CND 53.50 (effective 1999). **Document type:** *Directory.* **Description:** Features over 2,300 members of ACTRA and Canadian Actors' Equity Association, a significant proportion of the professional actors, performers and broadcasters in Canada. Includes photographs and contact information.
Related titles: Online - full text ed.
Published by: Alliance of Canadian Cinema, Television and Radio Artists, Performers Guild, 2239 Yonge St, Toronto, ON M4S 2B5, Canada. TEL 416-489-1311, FAX 416-489-8076, ftf@actra.com. Ed., R&P Ferne Downey. Circ: 3,000.

FAMA; el secreto del exito. see *MOTION PICTURES*

791.45 GBR ISSN 1473-3633
FARSCAPE; the official magazine. Text in English. 2001. bi-m. USD 5.99 newsstand/cover in United States; USD 7.99 newsstand/cover in Canada (effective 2001). adv. **Document type:** *Magazine, Consumer.* **Description:** Provides interviews, stories, and behind-the-scenes information on the television series Farscape.
Published by: Titan Magazines (Subsidiary of: Titan Books Ltd.), Titan House, 144 Southwark St, London, SE1 0UP, United Kingdom. TEL 44-20-7620-0200, FAX 44-20-7803-1803, farscapesubs@titanemail.com. **Dist. by:** Comag Marketing Group, LLC, 250 W 55th St, New York, NY 10019. TEL 212-649-4468, FAX 212-262-1239.

384.55 USA ISSN 0147-4871
PN1990.83
FEEDBACK. Text in English. 1977 (vol.19). q. bk.rev. **Document type:** *Trade.* **Description:** Provides a forum for the exchange of ideas among members on subjects relevant to educational programs and the industry.
—BLDSC (3902.124800).
Published by: Broadcast Education Association, 1771 N St, N W, Washington, DC 20036. TEL 202-429-5354, FAX 202-775-2981, jmisiewicz@bsu.edu, mckenzie@esu.edu, http://www.beaweb.org/feedback/info.html. Ed. Joe Misiewicz. Circ: 1,000.

791.45 DEU ISSN 0015-0134
FERNSEH-INFORMATIONEN; unabhaengige Korrespondenz fuer Hoerfunk und Fernsehen. Text in German. 1949. s-m. EUR 12.50 newsstand/cover (effective 2004). bk.rev. **Document type:** *Magazine, Trade.*
Published by: Televisions-Verlag Gauting, Hangstr 44 1/2, Gauting, 82131, Germany. FAX 49-89-8508932, fernsehinformationen@gmx.de, wagenfuehr@t-online.de, http://www.fernsehinformationen.de. Ed. Margarete Keilacker. Circ: 500.

FILM; kino - televiziya - video. see *MOTION PICTURES—Abstracting, Bibliographies, Statistics*

FILM AND T V PRODUCTION REVIEW. see *MOTION PICTURES*

FILM CANADA YEARBOOK. see *MOTION PICTURES*

FILM & TELEVISIE - VIDEO. see *MOTION PICTURES*

FILM MUSIC. see *MUSIC*

FILM TV DAILY YEARBOOK OF MOTION PICTURES AND TELEVISION. see *MOTION PICTURES*

C

FILM UND FERNSEHEN. see *MOTION PICTURES*

FILMAARSBOKEN/FILM YEAR BOOK (YEAR). see *MOTION PICTURES*

791.43 GBR
FILMSCAN. Text in English. 1985. a. GBP 20. adv. index. back issues avail. **Document type:** *Trade.* **Description:** Serves as an information source encompassing all areas of film, TV and video production in Ireland: crews, locations, facilities, associations, technical and local information.
Published by: (Broadcasting, Entertainment, Cinematography and Theatre Union), Adleader Publications, Marlborough House, 348 Lisburn Rd, Belfast, BT9 6GH, United Kingdom. TEL 44-1232-661666, FAX 44-1232-681888, adleader@dial.pipex.com. Ed., R&P Alain Mairs. Adv. contact Sinead Balmer. B&W page GBP 425, color page GBP 525. Circ: 3,000.

658.84 USA
THE FINANCIAL MANAGER. Text in English. 1972. bi-m. USD 69; USD 15 per issue (effective 2004). adv. illus.; stat. index. **Document type:** *Trade.* **Description:** For professional financial and business managers of broadcasting and cable properties.
Formerly: Broadcast Cable Financial Journal
Published by: Broadcast Cable Financial Management Association, 550 W. Frontage Rd., Ste. 3600, Northfield, IL 60093-1243. info@bcfm.com, http://www.bcfm.com. Ed. Stewart Schley. Adv. contact Doreen Colletti-Muhs TEL 847-304-1548. B&W page USD 1,255; trim 8.5 x 11. Circ: 3,582.

791.45 USA
FINE TUNING. Text in English. 1983. m. USD 35 to members (effective 1998). adv.
Published by: Channel 10-36 Friends, Inc., 700 W Eighth St, Milwaukee, WI 53233. TEL 414-297-8000. Ed. Debbie O'Connor-Callahan. Circ: 45,000.

384.5452 FIN
FINNISH BROADCASTING COMPANY. PLANNING AND RESEARCH DEPARTMENT. RESEARCH REPORTS. Text in English. irreg. free.
Formerly: Finnish Broadcasting Company. Section for Long-Range Planning. Research Reports (0084-4225)
Published by: Finnish Broadcasting Company, Kesaekatu 2, Helsinki, 00260, Finland. Ed. Matti Oksanen. Circ: 400.

FOLLOW UP FILE. see *JOURNALISM*

384.5532 AUS ISSN 1324-9762
FOXTEL. Text in English. 1995. m. adv. **Document type:** *Magazine, Consumer.* **Description:** Provides a monthly television listings guide and communications forum for FOXTEL customers.
Published by: A C P Custom Media, Level 7, 50 Park St, Sydney, NSW 2000, Australia. TEL 61-2-9282-8019, FAX 61-2-9267-3625, custominfo@acp.com.au, http://www.custompubs.acp.com.au/docs/foxtel.html. Circ: 790,000 (controlled).

791.45 DEU ISSN 0932-6901
FUNK UHR. Variant title: Funk Uhr (Ausgabe Sud). Text in German. 1952. w. (Fri.). EUR 1 newsstand/cover (effective 2005). adv. **Document type:** *Magazine, Consumer.*
Related titles: Regional ed(s).: Funk Uhr (Ausgabe Ost) (Eastern Edition). ISSN 0949-4790.
Published by: Axel Springer Verlag AG, Axel-Springer-Platz 1, Hamburg, 20350, Germany. TEL 49-40-34700, FAX 49-40-34728460, funkuhr@axelspringer.de, information@axelspringer.de, http://www.asv.de. Ed. Jan von Frenkell. Adv. contact Holger Braack. B&W page EUR 15,320, color page EUR 23,810; trim 206 x 270. Circ: 844,231 (paid). **Subscr. to:** P M S GmbH & Co. KG, Grafenbergerstr 100, Duesseldorf 40237, Germany. TEL 49-211-6907890, FAX 49-211-69078915.

384.5 GHA
G B C RADIO AND T V TIMES★. Text in English. 1960. w. GHC 10.40. adv. illus.
Formerly: Ghana Radio and Television Times (0435-9437)
Published by: Ghana Broadcasting Corporation, PO Box 1633, Accra, Ghana. TEL 233-21-221161, TELEX 2114. Ed. Ernest Asamoah. Circ: 5,000.

791.45 USA
G B H; the members' magazine. Text in English. 1987. m. membership. adv. **Document type:** *Consumer.* **Description:** Program guide and magazine for members of WGBH, Boston's PBS and NPR station. All editorial content is program-related and explores issues, events, personalities associated with station programming, which includes the arts, history, science, adventure, and public affairs.
Published by: W G B H Educational Foundation, PO Box 200, Boston, MA 02134. TEL 617-300-5400, 800-333-1203, FAX 617-783-8668, dvs@wgbh.org, http://www.wgbh.org. Ed. Diane Dion. Circ: 175,000.

384.5532 POL ISSN 1232-1702
GAZETA TELEWIZYJNA. Text in Polish. 1990. w.
Related titles: ◆ Supplement to: Gazeta Wyborcza. ISSN 0860-908X.
Published by: Agora S.A., ul Czerska 8/10, Warsaw, 00732, Poland. TEL 48-22-6994301, FAX 48-22-6994603, http://www.gazeta.pl.

621.388 JPN ISSN 1346-1923
GEKKAN SORYUSHON I T★ /SOLUTION I T. Text in Japanese. 1990. m. JPY 12,234 (effective 2004).
Former titles (until 2000): Nettowaku Konpyutingu/Network Computing (0918-4503); (until 1992): Komyunikeshon Tekunoroji/Communication Technology (0916-4669)
Published by: Rikku Terekomu/R I C Telecom, 3-7-7 Yushima Bunkyo-ku, Rikkubiru, Tokyo, 113-0034, Japan. TEL 81-3-38348380, FAX 81-3-38322990, http://www.ric.co.jp/sol/index.html.

384.55 USA
GENE PERRET'S ROUND TABLE; a gathering place for comedy writers and humorists. Text in English. 1981. m. USD 54.95 domestic; USD 59.95 in Canada; USD 67 elsewhere (effective 2000). bk.rev. back issues avail. **Document type:** *Newsletter.*
Address: PO Box 786, Agoura Hills, CA 91376-0786. TEL 818-865-7833, FAX 818-865-0115, rtcomedy@aol.com. Ed., Pub. Linda Perret. Circ: 200 (paid).

384.5452 USA ISSN 1550-7521
P87
➤ **GLOBAL MEDIA JOURNAL.** Text in English. 2002. s-a. free (effective 2005). **Document type:** *Journal, Academic/Scholarly.* **Description:** Is devoted to the exploration of the fascinating, evolving, and ever-expanding field of communication.
Media: Online - full text.
Published by: Purdue University Calumet, Department of Communication and Creative Arts, 2200 169th St, Hammond, IN 46323-2094. TEL 219-989-2880, FAX 219-989-2008, kamaliyr@calumet.purdue.edu, http://lass.calumet.purdue.edu/cca/gmj/. Ed. Yahya R Kamalipour.

384.5532 USA
▼ **GLUED;** stuck on tv. Text in English. 2004. m. USD 24.95; USD 3.49 newsstand/cover (effective 2005). adv. **Document type:** *Magazine, Consumer.* **Description:** Contains reviews, previews, celebrity profiles, insightful features, behind the scenes tales from popular shows, and more.
Published by: Vogel Communications Inc., 701 5th Ave, 36th Fl, Seattle, WA 98104. TEL 206-262-8183, FAX 206-262-8187, http://www.vogelpublishing.com. Pub. Steven R Vogel. Adv. contact Christina Guzak TEL 206-262-8183 ext 221. color page USD 5,737, B&W page USD 4,875. Circ: 50,000.

384.5452 DEU
GO SEVEN; ProSiebenClub Magazin. Text in German. 6/yr. **Document type:** *Magazine, Consumer.*
Published by: (ProSieben Sat 1 Media AG), Journal International Verlags- und Werbegesellschaft mbH, Hanns-Seidel-Platz 5, Munich, 81737, Germany. TEL 49-89-642797-0, FAX 49-89-64279777, info@journal-international.de, http://www.journal-international.de. Circ: 600,000 (controlled).

791.45 DEU ISSN 0017-1999
GONG; das aktuelle deutsche Fernseh-Magazin. Text in German. 1948. w. (Fri.). EUR 72.80; EUR 1.40 newsstand/cover (effective 2005). adv. bk.rev.; film rev.; play rev. bibl.; illus.; mkt. **Document type:** *Magazine, Consumer.*
Related titles: Supplement(s): Rundfunkhoerer und Fernseher.
Published by: Gong Verlag GmbH & Co. KG, Muenchener Str 101, Ismaning, 85737, Germany. TEL 49-89-272700, FAX 49-89-272707290, kontakt@gongverlag.de, gonginfo@gongverlag.de, http://www.gong.de, http://www.gong-verlag.de. Ed. Carsten Pfefferkorn. Adv. contact Werner Witt. B&W page EUR 20,650, color page EUR 23,900; trim 198 x 260. Circ: 751,654 (paid). **Subscr. to:** P M S GmbH & Co. KG, Grafenberger Allee 100, Duesseldorf 40237, Germany. TEL 49-203-76908-0, FAX 49-203-7690830.

GREATEST HOME CINEMA BOOK EVER. see *ELECTRONICS*

384.55 DEU ISSN 1437-2916
LB1043.2.G4
GRIMME. Text in German. 1978. irreg. adv. bk.rev. **Document type:** *Magazine, Trade.* **Description:** Platform for discussing issues and themes in production, media research and programming in television, radio, telecommunications and changes in media culture.
Former titles (until 1998): Agenda (0941-5491); (until 1992): W and M - Weiterbildung & Medien (0170-866X)
Indexed: DIP, IBZ.
Published by: Adolf Grimme Institut GmbH, Postfach 1148, Marl, 45741, Germany. TEL 49-2365-9189-0, FAX 49-2365-918989, grimme@grimme-institut.de, http://www.grimme-institut.de/scripts/zeitschr/zeitschr.html. Ed. Andreas Schuemchen. Adv. contact Jochen Blum. Circ: 3,000.

384.55 DEU
GRIMME INFOSERVICE. Text in German. 1998. 8/yr. adv. **Document type:** *Newsletter.*
Published by: Adolf Grimme Institut GmbH, Postfach 1148, Marl, 45741, Germany. TEL 49-2365-9189-0, FAX 49-2365-918989, grimme@grimme-institut.de, http://www.grimme-institut.de. Ed. Andreas Schuemchen. Adv. contact Jochen Blum.

791.45 CHN
GUANGDONG DIANSHI/GUANGDONG TELEVISION. Text in Chinese. w.
Published by: Guangdong Dianshi Tai/Guangdong Television Station, No 686, Renmin Beilu, Guangzhou, Guangdong 510012, China. TEL 674356. Ed. Ma Yan.

384.55 BRA
GUIA DE PROGRAMACAO N E T; t v por assinatura. Text in Portuguese. 1994. m. adv. illus. **Document type:** *Consumer.* **Description:** Presents all the programming of Globo System cable television. Includes reports, articles, news on films, personalities and other matters.
Published by: Editora Globo S.A., Rua Domingos Sergio dos Anjos, 277, Pirituba, Jd S Elias, Sao Paulo, SP 05136-170, Brazil. atendimento@edglobo.com.br, http://www.editoraglobo.com.br, http://editoraglobo.globo.com/. Circ: 1,500,000.

GUIA FAMILIAR. see *MOTION PICTURES*

384.5532 DEU
GUTE ZEITEN - SCHLECHTE ZEITEN; das offizielle Magazin. Text in German. 1995. m. EUR 2 newsstand/cover (effective 2003). adv. **Document type:** *Magazine, Consumer.*
Published by: Panini Verlags GmbH, Ravensstr 48, Nettetal, 41334, Germany. TEL 49-711-947680, FAX 49-711-94768830, info@panini-dino.de, http://www.panini-media.de. Ed. Stephanie Walker. Pub. Roland Brandstaett. Adv. contact Petra Sonnenfroh-Kost. page EUR 9,900; trim 205 x 275. Circ: 208,019 (paid).

791.456 DEU
GUTE ZEITEN - SCHLECHTE ZEITEN MY WORLD. Text in German. 1995. 4/yr. EUR 3.60 newsstand/cover (effective 2003). adv. **Document type:** *Magazine, Consumer.*
Published by: Panini Verlags GmbH, Ravensstr 48, Nettetal, 41334, Germany. TEL 49-711-947680, FAX 49-711-94768830, info@panini-dino.de, http://www.panini-media.de. adv.: page EUR 4,500. Circ: 81,150 (paid and controlled).

C

GUTE ZEITEN - SCHLECHTE ZEITEN RAETSELSPASS. see *HOBBIES*

384.55 USA ISSN 1550-7858
TK6679
▼ **H D T V ETC.** (High Definition Television) Text in English. 2003. 6/yr. USD 24.95 domestic; USD 34.95 in Canada; USD 39.95 elsewhere; USD 9.95 newsstand/cover domestic; USD 12.95 newsstand/cover in Canada (effective 2004). adv. **Document type:** *Magazine, Consumer.*
Published by: Avodah Publishing, LLC, 6414 Hwy 93 S, Whitefish, MT 59937. TEL 406-863-9595, FAX 406-863-2940, http://www.hdtvetc.com. Ed. Clint Walker.

621.388 USA
H D T V INSIDER NEWSLETTER. (High Definition Television) Text in English. 1999. m. USD 500 domestic; USD 1,000 foreign (effective 2003). **Document type:** *Newsletter, Consumer.* **Description:** Covers all issues concerning High Definition Television including pricing, previews of upcoming hardware, copy protection issues, new technologies, retailing, programming and broadcasting as well as industry trends and insights.
Media: E-mail.
Published by: Home Theater Perfection LLC TEL 516-933-0246, FAX 516-933-2106, http://www.hdtvinsider.com. Ed., Pub. Gary Merson.

HILVERSUMMARY. see *COMMUNICATIONS—Radio*

HISTORICAL JOURNAL OF FILM, RADIO AND TELEVISION. see *HISTORY*

HIT SENSATION'S TV SERIES: DINOSAURS. see *CHILDREN AND YOUTH—For*

384.555 JPN
HITACHI CABLE NEWS. Text in Japanese. bi-m.
Related titles: Online - full content ed.
Published by: Hitachi Cable Co. Ltd./Hitachi Densen K.K., 1-6-1 Otemachi, Chiyoda-ku, Tokyo, 100-8166, Japan. TEL 81-3-32161611, FAX 81-3-32145779, http://www.hitachi-cable.co.jp/hc-news.stm.

384.55 DEU ISSN 0018-3113
HOERZU. Text in German. 1946. w. (Fri.). EUR 79.56 domestic; EUR 226.72 foreign; EUR 1.40 newsstand/cover (effective 2005). adv. tel.rev. illus.; tr.lit. reprints avail. **Document type:** *Magazine, Consumer.*
Published by: Axel Springer Verlag AG, Axel-Springer-Platz 1, Hamburg, 20350, Germany. TEL 49-40-34700, FAX 49-40-34728460, online@hoerzu.de, http://www.hoerzu.de, http://www.asv.de. Ed. Thomas Garms. Adv. contact Holger Braack. B&W page EUR 32,780, color page EUR 41,660; trim 206 x 270. Circ: 1,673,357 (paid). **Subscr. to:** P M S GmbH & Co. KG, Grafenbergerstr 100, Duesseldorf 40237, Germany. TEL 49-211-6907890, FAX 49-211-69078915.

▼ new title ➤ refereed ★ unverified ◆ full entry avail.

791.45 USA
HOLA - MAGAZINE✱. Text in English. 1977. w. free. adv. back issues avail. **Document type:** *Consumer.* **Description:** Television entertainment guide.
Formerly: Fiesta Guia
Published by: Spanish Publications, Inc., 6601 Tarnef Dr, Houston, TX 77074. TEL 713-774-4652, FAX 713-774-4666. Ed., R&P Hernan Duenas. Pub. Mario Duenas. Adv. contact Raul Alonso. Circ: 60,000.

HOLA PAGES; national directory of Hispanic talent. see *MOTION PICTURES*

HOLLYWOOD ACTING COACHES AND TEACHERS DIRECTORY. see *EDUCATION—Teaching Methods And Curriculum*

HOLLYWOOD REPORTER BLU-BOOK DIRECTORY. see *MOTION PICTURES*

384.55 ITA
HOME CINEMA. Text in Italian. 1993. s-a. adv. **Document type:** *Directory, Consumer.*
Published by: Editore Progest s.r.l., Via Rovereto 6, Rome, RM 00198, Italy. TEL 39-06-8552649, FAX 39-06-8558885, progestsrl@infinito.it. Circ: 130,000.

384.55 384.558 USA ISSN 1096-3065
HOME THEATER. Text in English. 1994. m. USD 4.99 newsstand/cover domestic; USD 6.99 newsstand/cover in Canada; USD 12.97 domestic; USD 25.97 in Canada (effective 2005). adv. **Document type:** *Magazine, Consumer.* **Description:** Dedicated to the home theater market, covering the latest in audio, video surround sound, movies and music.
Former titles: CurtCo's Home Theater (1088-1530); CurtCo's Home Theater Technology (1082-9555)
Related titles: Online - full content ed.
Indexed: FLI.
Published by: Primedia Consumer Media & Magazine Group, 9036 Brittanyway, Tampa, FL 33619. TEL 813-679-3500, FAX 813-679-3999, htletters@primedia.com, http://www.hometheatermag.com, http://www.primedia.com. Ed. Maureen Jenson. Pub. Dave Colford.

C

384.55 ITA
HOME THEATER. Text in Italian. 1993. q. adv. **Document type:** *Newsletter, Trade.*
Published by: Editore Progest s.r.l., Via Rovereto 6, Rome, RM 00198, Italy. TEL 39-06-8552649, FAX 39-06-8558885, progestsrl@infinito.it.

384.55 HKG
HONG KONG. TELEVISION ADVISORY BOARD. ANNUAL REPORT. Text in English. a. HKD 45.
Related titles: Chinese ed.
Published by: (Hong Kong. Television Advisory Board), Government Publications Centre, G.P.O. Bldg, Ground Fl, Connaught Pl, Hong Kong, Hong Kong. **Subscr. to:** Director of Information Services, Information Services Dept., 1 Battery Path G-F, Central, Hong Kong, Hong Kong.

791.45 GBR ISSN 1365-8263
HOT!. Variant title: T V Hits Hot!. Text in English. 1996. m. GBP 2.50 newsstand/cover. adv. illus. **Document type:** *Consumer.* **Description:** Covers the exciting worlds of TV, pop music, films and entertainment for a teenage audience.
Published by: Attic Futura Ltd. (Subsidiary of: Hachette Filipacchi Medias S.A.), c/o Hachette Filipacchi UK, 64 North Row, London, 64 North Row, United Kingdom. TEL 44-20-71507000, FAX 44-20-71507001, http://www.hachettefilipacchiuk.co.uk/. **Dist. by:** Comag, Tavistock Works, Tavistock Rd, W Drayton, Middx UB7 7QX, United Kingdom. TEL 44-1895-433600, FAX 44-189-543-3606.

384.5 BEL ISSN 0771-8179
HUMO. Text in Dutch. 1936. w. EUR 96 (effective 2005). film rev. back issues avail. **Document type:** *Magazine, Consumer.*
Published by: Sanoma Magazines Belgium, Uitbreidingstr 82, Berchem, 2600, Belgium. TEL 32-3-290-1200, FAX 32-3-290-1237, humo@sanoma-magazines.be, http://www.humo.be, http://www.sanoma-magazines.be/homepage.aspx?. Circ: 248,636 (paid).

621.388 USA ISSN 0018-9316
TK6561 CODEN: IETBAC
➤ **I E E E TRANSACTIONS ON BROADCASTING.** Text in English. 1955. q. USD 115 (effective 2006). bk.rev. abstr.; illus. index. **Document type:** *Journal, Academic/Scholarly.* **Description:** Examines broadcast transmission systems engineering, including the design and utilization of equipment.
Related titles: CD-ROM ed.; Microfiche ed.; Online - full text ed.: (from EBSCO Publishing).
Indexed: AS&TI, ASCA, AcoustA, ChemAb, CurCont, EngInd, IAA, ISR, Inspec, MathR, RefZh, SCI.
—BLDSC (4363.161400), AskIEEE, CISTI, Ei, IDS, IE, Infotrieve, ingenta, Linda Hall. **CCC.**
Published by: Institute of Electrical and Electronics Engineers, Inc., 445 Hoes Ln, Piscataway, NJ 08854-1331. TEL 732-981-0060, 800-701-4333, FAX 732-981-1721, subscription-service@ieee.org, http://www.ieee.org. Ed. Thomas L Mann. **Subscr. to:** Maruzen Co., Ltd., 3-10 Nihonbashi 2-chome, Chuo-ku, Tokyo 103-0027, Japan. FAX 81-3-3275-0657; Universal Subscription Agency, Pvt. Ltd., 877, Udyog Vihar, V, Gurgoan 122001, India. TEL 91-124-347261, FAX 91-124-342496. **Co-sponsor:** Broadcast Technology Society.

➤ **I E I C E TRANSACTIONS ON FUNDAMENTALS OF ELECTRONICS, COMMUNICATIONS AND COMPUTER SCIENCES.** see *ELECTRONICS*

384.555 365.34 USA ISSN 1521-916X
I O M A'S SECURITY DIRECTOR'S REPORT. Variant title: Security Director's Report. Text in English. 1998. m. USD 271.95 combined subscription in US & Canada print & online eds.; USD 283 combined subscription elsewhere print & online eds. (effective 2006). **Document type:** *Newsletter, Trade.* **Description:** Provides ratings on the newest digital CCTV equipment, as well as other products and services. Offers tips from the experts on hiring and retaining the best security staff in today's market. Includes current pay standards for security guards and reviews of all the pre-employment screening services.
Related titles: Online - full text ed.: (from EBSCO Publishing, Florida Center for Library Automation, Gale Group, O C L C Online Computer Library Center, Inc.); ♦ Cumulative ed(s).: Security Director's Report Yearbook.
—CCC.
Published by: Institute of Management & Administration, Inc., 3 Park Ave, New York, NY 10016-5902. TEL 212-244-0360, FAX 212-564-0465, subserve@ioma.com, http://www.ioma.com/products/prod_detail.php?prodid=45. Ed. Garett Seivold.

384.5452 GBR
I T C ANNUAL REPORT & ACCOUNTS; licensing and regulating commercial television. Text in English. 1954-1991; resumed 1993. a. free. **Document type:** *Corporate.*
Formerly (until 1991): Independent Broadcasting Authority. Report and Accounts
Published by: Independent Television Commission, 33 Foley St, London, W1P 7LB, United Kingdom. TEL 44-20-7255-3000, FAX 44-20-7306-7800, publicaffairs@itc.org.uk. Ed., R&P Amy Bailey TEL 44-20-7306-7770.

384.55 DEU
I W Z ONLINE. (Illustrierte Wochenzeitung) Text in German. d. adv. **Document type:** *Consumer.*
Media: Online - full text. **Related titles:** ♦ Print ed.: Illustrierte Wochenzeitung.
Published by: Illustrierte Wochenzeitung GmbH & Co., Postfach 102461, Stuttgart, 70020, Germany. TEL 49-711-7205861, FAX 49-711-7205374, http://www.iwz.de. Eds. Andreas Mueller, Dorothea Kallenberg. Adv. contact Werner Baur.

384.55 DEU
ILLUSTRIERTE WOCHENZEITUNG. Abbreviated title: I W Z. Text in German. 1973. w. adv. **Document type:** *Magazine, Consumer.* **Description:** Contains listings and features related to television and cable programs.
Related titles: ♦ Online - full text ed.: I W Z Online.
Published by: Illustrierte Wochenzeitung GmbH & Co., Postfach 102461, Stuttgart, 70020, Germany. TEL 49-711-7205861, FAX 49-711-7205374, http://www.iwz.de. Eds. Andreas Mueller, Dorothea Kallenberg. Adv. contact Werner Baur. B&W page EUR 17,760, color page EUR 25,760; trim 201 x 252. Circ: 1,748,511 (controlled).

IMAGE TECHNOLOGY; technology of motion picture film, sound, television, audio, visual. see *MOTION PICTURES*

384.5532 POL ISSN 1427-2202
IMPERIUM T V. Variant title: Imperium TV. Text in Polish. 1996. w. PLZ 1.45 newsstand/cover (effective 2003). adv. **Document type:** *Magazine, Consumer.*
Published by: Wydawnictwo Bauer Sp. z o.o. (Subsidiary of: Heinrich Bauer Verlag), ul. Motorowa 1, Warsaw, 04-035, Poland. TEL 48-22-5170500, FAX 48-22-5170125, imptv@bauer.pl, kontakt@bauer.pl, http://www.bauer.pl. Ed. Beata Bialy. Adv. contact Katarzyna Jablonska. page PLZ 11,000; trim 215 x 286.

IN FOCUS (LOS ANGELES). see *MOTION PICTURES*

384.55 GBR
IN THE VILLAGE. Text in English. 1977; N.S. 1994. q. GBP 27, USD 45 (effective 2000). bk.rev.; tel.rev.; video rev. back issues avail. **Document type:** *Consumer.* **Description:** Comprehensive interviews, production details and underlying symbolism concerning the 1967 British cult TV series "The Prisoner" starring Patrick McGoohan.
Formerly (until 1994): Number Six
Published by: Six of One - Prisoner Appreciation Society, Six Of One, PO Box 66, Ipswich, IP2 9TZ, United Kingdom. Ed. David Healey. Circ: 3,000. **Co-sponsor:** Carlton International Media Ltd.

INFORMATION TECHNOLOGY & MANAGEMENT. see *BUSINESS AND ECONOMICS—Office Equipment And Services*

INFORMATION TECHNOLOGY MANAGEMENT; non-technical report on IT and its applications. see *BUSINESS AND ECONOMICS—Office Equipment And Services*

384.5 ITA ISSN 0300-3973
INFORMAZIONE RADIO TV; studi documenti e notizie. Text in Italian. 1970. s-a. free. bk.rev. bibl.; illus.; stat. index.
Media: Duplicated (not offset).
Indexed: IIFP, IITV.
Published by: R A I - Radiotelevisione Italiana, Viale Giuseppe Mazzini 14, Rome, 00195, Italy. http://www.rai.it. Circ: 1,000.

621.388 DEU ISSN 0933-6907
INFOSAT; die Multimedia-Illustrierte. Text in German. 1987. m. adv. **Document type:** *Magazine, Trade.* **Description:** Covers all aspects of the use of satellites to deliver communications and media.
Related titles: ♦ Online - full text ed.: Infosat Online. ISSN 1608-0416.
Published by: Infosat GmbH (Subsidiary of: Euro Info Media SA), Postfach 100, Daun, 54541, Germany. TEL 49-6592-929716, FAX 49-6592-929709, service@infosat.de, redaktion@infosat.de, http://www.infosat.de.

621.388 DEU
INFOSAT EUROPE. Text in English. 2000. m. adv. **Document type:** *Magazine, Trade.* **Description:** Covers all aspects of satellite transmission and reception in Europe.
Published by: Infosat GmbH (Subsidiary of: Euro Info Media SA), Postfach 100, Daun, 54541, Germany. TEL 49-6592-929716, FAX 49-6592-929709, redaktion@infosat.de, http://www.infosat.de/iseurope.

621.388 DEU ISSN 1608-0416
INFOSAT ONLINE. Text in German. 199?. m. adv. **Document type:** *Trade.*
Media: Online - full text. **Related titles:** ♦ Print ed.: Infosat. ISSN 0933-6907.
Published by: Infosat GmbH (Subsidiary of: Euro Info Media SA), Postfach 100, Daun, 54541, Germany. TEL 49-6592-929716, FAX 49-6592-929709, service@infosat.de, redaktion@infosat.de, http://www.infosat.de.

384.55 USA ISSN 1464-603X
INSIDE DIGITAL T V. Variant title: Inside Digital Television. Text in English. bi-w. USD 897 (effective 2004). **Document type:** *Newsletter, Trade.* **Description:** Covers the latest developments in the digital broadcasting industry.
Published by: Access Intelligence, LLC (Subsidiary of: Veronis, Suhler & Associates Inc.), 1201 Seven Locks Rd, Ste 300, Potomac, MD 20854. TEL 301-354-2000, FAX 301-424-2058, clientservices@accessintel.com, http://www.pbimedia.com.

791.45 GBR ISSN 0966-8497
INSIDE SOAP. Text in English. 1992. fortn. GBP 39.99 domestic; GBP 102 in Europe; GBP 199.99 elsewhere (effective 2004). adv. illus. **Document type:** *Magazine, Consumer.* **Description:** Covers all aspects of UK soaps and soap stars.
Published by: Hachette Filipacchi (UK) Ltd. (Subsidiary of: Hachette Filipacchi Medias S.A.), 64 North Row, London, W1K 7LL, United Kingdom. TEL 44-20-71507000, FAX 44-20-71507001, http://www.insidesoap.co.uk/, http://www.hachettefilipacchiuk.co.uk. adv.: color page GBP 3,850; trim 205 x 275. Circ: 255,965 (paid).

051 USA
▼ **INSIDE T V.** Text in English. 2005 (Apr.). w. USD 1.99 newsstand/cover (effective 2005). adv. **Document type:** *Magazine, Consumer.* **Description:** Contains information and features on TV celebrities.
Published by: T V Guide Magazine Publishing, 1211 Avenue of Americas, 4th Fl, New York, NY 10036. TEL 212-752-7444, FAX 212-752-7471. Ed. Steve LeGrice. Circ: 400,000 (controlled).

INSIDERS SPORTSLETTER. see *SPORTS AND GAMES*

384.55 GBR ISSN 0969-9872
INSTITUTE OF LOCAL TELEVISION. RESEARCH MONOGRAPH. Text in English. 1993. irreg. **Document type:** *Monographic series.*
Published by: (Institute of Local Television), University of Luton Press, University of Luton, 75 Castle St, Luton, Beds LU1 3AJ, United Kingdom. TEL 44-1582-743297, FAX 44-1582-743298, ilp@luton.ac.uk. Ed. Dave Rushton.

INSTITUTION OF ENGINEERS (INDIA). ELECTRONICS AND TELECOMMUNICATION ENGINEERING DIVISION. JOURNAL. see *ELECTRONICS*

(YEAR) INTERACTIVE SOURCEBOOK. see *COMPUTERS—Computer Networks*

INTERLIT. see *RELIGIONS AND THEOLOGY*

384.5452 GBR ISSN 0309-118X
INTERMEDIA. Text in English. 1973. q. GBP 90 to individual members; GBP 3,500 to institutional members (effective 2004). adv. bk.rev. bibl.; illus. reprint service avail. from PQC. **Document type:** *Magazine, Trade.* **Description:** Focuses on all aspects of international broadcasting, telecommunications, media developments, and communications in general.
Formerly: I B I Newsletter
Related titles: Microform ed.: (from PQC); Online - full text ed.: (from EBSCO Publishing, ProQuest Information & Learning).
Indexed: ABIn, CADCAM, CLOSS, CommAb, CompD, FutSurv, IIFP, IITV, PAIS, RASB, TelAb.
—BLDSC (4534.480000), IE, Infotrieve, ingenta. **CCC.**
Published by: International Institute of Communications (IIC), Regent House, 24-25 Nutford Pl, London, W1H 5YN, United Kingdom. TEL 44-20-73239622, FAX 44-20-73239623, enquiries@iicom.org, http://intermedia.almamedia.fi/, http://www.iicom.org/. adv.: B&W page GBP 600, color page GBP 1,100. Circ: 1,500.

INTERNATIONAL BLUEGRASS. (I B M - International Bluegrass Music Association) see *MUSIC*

621.388 GBR ISSN 0020-6229
INTERNATIONAL BROADCAST ENGINEER. Variant title: I B E(International Broadcast Engineer). Text in English. 1958. 8/yr. free to qualified personnel (effective 2004). adv. bk.rev. abstr.; charts; illus.; pat.; tr.lit.; tr.mk. index. **Document type:** *Magazine, Trade.*
Incorporates: International T V Technical Review
Related titles: Online - full text ed.: (from Florida Center for Library Automation, Gale Group).
Indexed: Inspec.
—BLDSC (4537.600000), AskIEEE, CISTI, IE, Infotrieve, ingenta. **CCC.**
Published by: B P L Business Media Ltd., Queensway House, 2 Queensway, Redhill, Surrey RH1 1QS, United Kingdom. TEL 44-1409-241166, FAX 44-1409-241177, info@ibeweb.com, http://www.ibeweb.com/. Ed. Neil Nixon. Pub. Clare Sturzaker. Adv. contact Julie Bertram TEL 44-1737-855102. B&W page GBP 2,370, color page GBP 3,150; trim 210 x 297. Circ: 9,637.

INTERNATIONAL CONNECTION. see *MOTION PICTURES*

384.55 USA
INTERNATIONAL EMMY ALMANAC. Text in English. 1980. a. adv. stat.; tr.lit. **Document type:** *Trade.*
Published by: International Council - National Academy of Television, 142 W 57th St, 16th Fl, New York, NY 10019-3300. TEL 212-489-6969, FAX 212-489-6557, http://www.iemnys.tv. Ed., Pub. George Dessart. R&P Linda Alexander. Adv. contact Gerry Brahney. B&W page USD 2,800, color page USD 4,200; trim 11 x 8.5.

384.55 CHE ISSN 0252-7235
INTERNATIONAL FREQUENCY LIST/LISTA INTERNACIONAL DE FRECUENCIAS/LISTE INTERNATIONALE DES FREQUENCES. Text in English, French, Spanish. s-a. CHF 400. Supplement avail. **Document type:** *Bulletin.*
Media: Microfiche. **Related titles:** CD-ROM ed.
Published by: International Telecommunication Union, Place des Nations, Geneva 20, 1211, Switzerland. TEL 41-22-7306141, FAX 41-22-7305464, sales@itu.ch, http://www.itu.int/publications.

384.55 CHE ISSN 0252-1725
INTERNATIONAL FREQUENCY LIST. PREFACE. Text in English. 1970. irreg. CHF 68. Supplement avail. **Document type:** *Bulletin.*
Related titles: French ed.; Spanish ed.
Published by: International Telecommunication Union, Place des Nations, Geneva 20, 1211, Switzerland. TEL 41-22-7306141, FAX 41-22-7305464, sales@itu.ch, http://www.itu.int/publications.

384.51 GBR ISSN 1542-0973
TK5104 CODEN: IJSCEF
➤ **INTERNATIONAL JOURNAL OF SATELLITE COMMUNICATIONS AND NETWORKING.** Text in English. 1983. bi-m. USD 2,170 to institutions; USD 2,387 combined subscription to institutions print & online eds. (effective 2006). adv. bk.rev. back issues avail.; reprints avail. **Document type:** *Journal, Academic/Scholarly.* **Description:** Provides rapid communication of new results and trends in the industry of satellite communications.
Formerly (until 2003): International Journal of Satellite Communications (0737-2884)
Related titles: Microform ed.: (from PQC); Online - full text ed.: ISSN 1542-0981. 1997. USD 2,170 to institutions (effective 2006) (from EBSCO Publishing, Swets Information Services, Wiley InterScience).
Indexed: ASCA, BrCerAb, C&ISA, CerAb, CivEngAb, CorrAb, CurCont, E&CAJ, EMA, EngInd, IAA, ISMEC, Inspec, M&TEA, MBF, METADEX, SolStAb, TelAb, WAA.
—BLDSC (4542.542850), AskIEEE, CISTI, Ei, IDS, IE, ingenta, Linda Hall. **CCC.**
Published by: John Wiley & Sons Ltd. (Subsidiary of: John Wiley & Sons, Inc.), The Atrium, Southern Gate, Chichester, West Sussex PO19 8SQ, United Kingdom. TEL 44-1243-779777, FAX 44-1243-775878, customer@wiley.co.uk, http://www.wiley.co.uk. Eds. Anthony Ephremides, B G Evans. adv.: B&W page GBP 750, color page GBP 1,650; trim 200 x 260. Circ: 800. **Subscr. in the Americas to:** John Wiley & Sons, Inc., 111 River St, Hoboken, NJ 07030-5774. TEL 201-748-6645, FAX 201-748-6088, subinfo@wiley.com.

384.55 USA ISSN 0895-2213
HE8700
INTERNATIONAL TELEVISION & VIDEO ALMANAC; reference tool of the television and home video industries. Text in English. 1956. a. USD 150 newsstand/cover per vol. (effective 2005). adv. 900 p./no.; **Document type:** *Trade.* **Description:** Covers the TV and video field with updates on broadcast networrks, TV stations, services, cable networks, biographies, film commissions, and guilds and unions.
Formerly: International Television Almanac (0539-0761)
Related titles: Microfilm ed.: (from BHP).
Published by: Quigley Publishing Co. (Subsidiary of: Q P Media, Inc.), 64 Wintergreen Ln, Groton, MA 01450. TEL 860-228-0247, FAX 860-228-0157, quigleypub@aol.com, http://www.quigleypublishing.com/. Ed. Eileen Quigley. Pub. William Quigley.

INTERNATIONAL WORKSHOP ON H D T V. PROCEEDINGS. (High Definition Television) see *COMMUNICATIONS—Computer Applications*

384.5 DEU ISSN 0946-3348
HE8690
INTERNATIONALES HANDBUCH FUER HOERFUNK UND FERNSEHEN. Text in German. 1957. biennial. adv. 1000 p./no. 2 cols./p.; **Document type:** *Journal, Trade.*
Formerly: Internationales Handbuch fuer Rundfunk und Fernsehen (0535-4358)
—CISTI.
Published by: Hans Bredow Institut, Heimhuder Str 21, Hamburg, 20148, Germany. TEL 49-40-45021741, FAX 49-40-45021777, nomos@nomos.de, http://www.nomos.de. Ed. Christiane Matzen. Circ: 2,500. **Subscr. to:** NOMOS Verlag, Postfach 610, Baden-Baden 76484, Germany. TEL 49-7221-2104-0, FAX 49-7221-210427.

INTERNET BROADCASTER. see *COMPUTERS—Internet*

621.388 IRL
IRISH ELECTRICAL REVIEW. Text in English. 1962. m. adv. illus.; tr.lit. **Document type:** *Journal, Trade.*
Formerly: Irish Electrical Industries Review (0021-1141); Which incorporates: Irish Radio and Electrical Journal
Published by: Sky Publishing Ltd., 5 Main St., Blackrock, Co. Dublin, Ireland. TEL 353-1-2836755, FAX 353-1-2836784, ier@indigo.ie. Ed., Adv. contact Patrick J Codyre. B&W page EUR 1,495, color page EUR 1,965; trim 237 x 335. Circ: 2,000.

621.388 EGY
AL-IZAA WAL-TELEVISION/RADIO AND TELEVISION. Text in Arabic. 1935. w. adv.
Published by: Izaa wal-Television, 13 Sharia Muhammed Ezz El-Arab, Cairo, Egypt. Ed. Sakeena Fouad. Circ: 80,000.

JACK BENNY TIMES. see *CLUBS*

JAHRBUCH DER LANDESMEDIENANSTALTEN; privater Rundfunk in Deutschland. see *COMMUNICATIONS—Radio*

JEE (GUJARATI EDITION). see *MOTION PICTURES*

JEE (HINDI EDITION). see *MOTION PICTURES*

JEE (MARATHI EDITION). see *MOTION PICTURES*

384.55 791.43 GBR ISSN 1743-4521
▼ **JOURNAL OF BRITISH CINEMA AND TELEVISION.** Text in English. 2004 (Fall). s-a. GBP 52.50 in Europe; USD 103 in North America; GBP 57 elsewhere (effective 2005). **Document type:** *Journal, Academic/Scholarly.* **Description:** Indispensable for anyone seriously interested in British cinema and television, and the prime site for those concerned with publishing cutting-edge work in these fields.
—BLDSC (4954.435000).
Published by: Edinburgh University Press, 22 George Sq, Edinburgh, Midlothian EH8 9LF, United Kingdom. TEL 44-131-650-6207, FAX 44-131-662-0053, journals@eup.ed.ac.uk, http://www.eup.ed.ac.uk. Ed. Julian Petley.

384.5452 USA ISSN 0883-8151
PN1991
➤ **JOURNAL OF BROADCASTING AND ELECTRONIC MEDIA.** Text in English. 1956. q. USD 135 in US & Canada to institutions; USD 165 elsewhere to institutions; USD 140 combined subscription in US & Canada to institutions print & online eds.; USD 170 combined subscription elsewhere to institutions print & online eds. (effective 2006). adv. bk.rev. charts. index, cum.index every 25 yrs. back issues avail.; reprint service avail. from PQC,WSH. **Document type:** *Journal, Academic/Scholarly.* **Description:** Scholarly journal of communication and electronic media research, including media uses, effect, regulation, history, organization, advertising, technology, news, and entertainment.
Formerly (until 1985): Journal of Broadcasting (0021-938X)
Related titles: Microfiche ed.: (from WSH); Microfilm ed.: (from WSH); Microform ed.: (from PMC, PQC, WSH); Online - full text ed.: ISSN 1550-6878. USD 125 worldwide to institutions (effective 2006) (from EBSCO Publishing, Florida Center for Library Automation, Gale Group, O C L C Online Computer Library Center, Inc., ProQuest Information & Learning).
Indexed: ASCA, AcaI, AgeL, AmHI, ArtHuCI, BRI, CIJE, CJA, CLI, ChPerI, CommAb, CurCont, ERA, ETA, FamI, HumInd, IIFP, IITV, IJCS, ILP, LRI, MEA&I, PAIS, PerIslam, PsycInfo, PsycholAb, RI-1, RI-2, RILM, SFSA, SOPODA, SPAA, SSCI, SSI, SWA, V&AA, e-psyche.
—BLDSC (4954.552000), IDS, IE, Infotrieve, ingenta.
Published by: (Broadcast Education Association), Lawrence Erlbaum Associates, Inc., 10 Industrial Ave, Mahwah, NJ 07430-2262. TEL 201-258-2200, FAX 201-236-0072, http://www.leaonline.com/loi/jobem, http://www.erlbaum.com. Ed. Donald G Godfrey. adv.: page USD 600; 5 x 8. Circ: 2,200.

➤ **JOURNAL OF FILM AND VIDEO.** see *MOTION PICTURES*

➤ **JOURNAL OF MEDIA PRACTICE.** see *COMMUNICATIONS*

▼ ➤ **JOURNAL OF VIRTUAL REALITY AND BROADCASTING.** see *COMPUTERS—Computer Graphics*

384.55 USA ISSN 1045-5744
K A E T MAGAZINE. Text in English. 1975. m. (exep. July). USD 40 (effective 2001). back issues avail. **Document type:** *Magazine, Consumer.*
Published by: (Arizona State University), K A E T, PO Box 1405, Tempe, AZ 85287-1405. TEL 480-965-3506, FAX 480-965-1000, kaet@asu.edu, http://www.kaet.asu.edu/. Ed. Sondra Mesnik. Adv. contact Jameo Balk. Circ: 50,000.

791.45 USA ISSN 1050-513X
PN1992
K C T S - NINE. Text in English. 1987. m. adv. **Description:** Television program guide distributed to contributors to KCTS-9, with additional articles on arts, travel, and personalities.
Formerly (until 1989): K C T S Magazine
Address: 2505 Second Ave, Ste 602, Seattle, WA 98121-2384. TEL 206-441-8415, FAX 206-441-8325. Ed. Linda Johns. Circ: 150,000.

384.5 USA
K P B S ON AIR. Text in English. 1969. m. USD 45 (effective 1999). adv. **Document type:** *Directory, Consumer.* **Description:** Publishes information about San Diego arts and entertainment and public television and radio programming for KPBS members.
Published by: K P B S - T V and F M Radio, San Diego State University, 5200 Campanile Dr, San Diego, CA 92182-5400. TEL 619-594-3766. Ed. Michael Good. Adv. contact Bruce Bauer. Circ: 62,000 (paid).

384.555 DEU ISSN 0177-9249
KABEL & SATELLIT. Text in German. 1983. w. adv. bk.rev. **Document type:** *Trade.*
Published by: Neue Mediengesellschaft Ulm mbH, Konrad-Celtis-Str 77, Munich, 81369, Germany. TEL 49-89-74117190, FAX 49-89-74117195. Circ: 1,500.

384.55 NLD ISSN 0165-439X
KABELVISIE; vakblad voor kabeltelevisie, omroep en telecommunicatie. Text in Dutch. 1973. m. adv. illus. index. **Document type:** *Trade.*
—IE, Infotrieve.
Published by: Televak Uitgeverij N.V., Postbus 75985, Amsterdam, 1070 AZ, Netherlands. TEL 31-20-6659220, FAX 31-20-6657316. Ed. J Boers. Pub. M de Rooij. Adv. contact Maarten Ponssen. Circ: 2,000 (paid).

384.555 USA ISSN 1089-7585
KAGAN'S ECONOMICS OF BASIC CABLE NETWORKS. Variant title: Economics of Basic Cable Networks. Text in English. 199?. a. USD 1,995 (effective 2005). **Document type:** *Directory, Trade.* **Description:** Contains exclusive revenue, cash flow, programming expenses and operating statistics for virtually every basic cable network.
Published by: Kagan Research, LLC, One Lower Ragsdale Dr, Bldg One, Ste 130, Monterey, CA 93940. TEL 831-624-1536, FAX 831-625-3225, info@kagan.com, http://www.kagan.com.

C

384.555 USA ISSN 1070-6917
KAGAN'S MEDIA TRENDS. Variant title: Media Trends. Text in English. 19??. a. USD 1,695 (effective 2005). **Document type:** *Directory, Trade.* **Description:** Provides actionable metrics, benchmarks and projections for all the major media sectors, featuring sections on broadcast TV and radio, cable MSOs, cable networks, and consumer entertainment.
Published by: Kagan Research, LLC, One Lower Ragsdale Dr, Bldg One, Ste 130, Monterey, CA 93940. TEL 831-624-1536, FAX 831-625-3225, info@kagan.com, http://research.kagan.com/keo/databooksdetailpage.aspx?DatabookID=64, http://www.kagan.com.

KATALOG MEDIOW POLSKICH. see *BIBLIOGRAPHIES*

384.5 FIN ISSN 0355-2969
KATSO. Text in Finnish. 1960. 48/yr. EUR 179 domestic; EUR 187.40 in Europe; EUR 225.80 elsewhere (effective 2005). adv. 4 cols./p.; Supplement avail. **Document type:** *Consumer.* **Description:** Provide a complete weekly program guide, as well as follow-up articles about domestic and foreign TV stars and popular TV series.
Related titles: Supplement(s): Saippuaooppera.
Published by: A-Lehdet Oy, Risto Rytin tie 33, Helsinki, 00081, Finland. TEL 358-9-75961, FAX 358-9-7598600, a-tilaus@a-lehdet.fi, http://www.a-lehdet.fi/lehdet/lehti/katso/. Ed. Markku Veijalainen. Adv. contact Matti Sahravuo TEL 358-9-7596385. color page EUR 3,000; 204 x 276. Circ: 96,443 (controlled).

KEMPS FILM, TV & VIDEO HANDBOOK (UK ED.). see *MOTION PICTURES*

KEY NOTE MARKET ASSESSMENT. NEW MEDIA MARKETING. see *COMMUNICATIONS*

KEY NOTE MARKET REPORT: BROADCASTING IN THE U K. see *COMMUNICATIONS—Radio*

384.555 GBR ISSN 1366-6207
KEY NOTE MARKET REPORT: CABLE & SATELLITE T V. Variant title: Cable & Satellite T V Market Report. Text in English. 1987. irreg., latest 2000, April. GBP 340 per issue (effective 2002). **Document type:** *Trade.* **Description:** Provides an overview of a specific UK market segment and includes executive summary, market definition, market size, industry background, competitor analysis, current issues, forecasts, company profiles, and more.
Former titles (until 1996): Key Note Report: Cable and Satellite T V (1352-5484); Key Note Report: Cable T V - D B S Services
Related titles: CD-ROM ed.; Online - full text ed.
Published by: Key Note Ltd., Field House, 72 Oldfield Rd, Hampton, Mddx TW12 2HQ, United Kingdom. TEL 44-20-8481-8750, FAX 44-20-8783-0049, info@keynote.co.uk, http://www.keynote.co.uk.

384.55 GBR ISSN 1363-2787
KEY NOTE MARKET REPORT: CABLING & WIRING. Variant title: Cabling & Wiring. Text in English. 1996. irreg., latest 1996, Feb. GBP 340 per issue (effective 2002). **Document type:** *Trade.* **Description:** Provides an overview of a specific UK market segment and includes executive summary, market definition, market size, industry background, competitor analysis, current issues, forecasts, company profiles, and more.
Published by: Key Note Ltd., Field House, 72 Oldfield Rd, Hampton, Mddx TW12 2HQ, United Kingdom. TEL 44-20-8481-8750, FAX 44-20-8783-0049, info@keynote.co.uk, http://www.keynote.co.uk. Ed. Kim Potts.

384.556 338 GBR ISSN 1461-3387
KEY NOTE MARKET REPORT: CLOSED CIRCUIT T V. Variant title: Closed Circuit Television Market Report. Text in English. 1997. irreg., latest 2001, Sept. GBP 340 per issue (effective 2002). mkt.; stat. **Document type:** *Trade.* **Description:** Provides an overview for the UK closed circuit TV market, including industry structure, market size and trends, developments, prospects, and major company profiles.
Published by: Key Note Ltd., Field House, 72 Oldfield Rd, Hampton, Mddx TW12 2HQ, United Kingdom. TEL 44-20-8481-8750, FAX 44-20-8783-0049, info@keynote.co.uk, http://www.keynote.co.uk. Ed. Dominic Fenn.

384.55 338 GBR ISSN 1461-6807
KEY NOTE MARKET REPORT: COMMERCIAL T V. Variant title: Commercial T V Market Report. Text in English. irreg., latest 2001, Oct. GBP 340 per issue (effective 2002). **Document type:** *Trade.* **Description:** Provides an overview for the UK commercial TV market, including industry structure, market size and trends, developments, prospects, and major company profiles.
Formerly (until 1997): Key Note Report: Commercial T V (0954-5107)
Related titles: CD-ROM ed.; Online - full text ed.
Published by: Key Note Ltd., Field House, 72 Oldfield Rd, Hampton, Mddx TW12 2HQ, United Kingdom. TEL 44-20-8481-8750, FAX 44-20-8783-0049, info@keynote.co.uk, http://www.keynote.co.uk. Ed. Jenny Baxter.

384.55 658 GBR
KEY NOTE MARKET REPORT: DIGITAL T V. Variant title: Digital T V Market Report. Text in English. 1998. irreg., latest 1998, Dec. GBP 340 per issue (effective 2002). **Description:** Provides an overview of a specific UK market segment and includes executive summary, market definition, market size, industry background, competitor analysis, current issues, forecasts, company profiles, and more.
Published by: Key Note Ltd., Field House, 72 Oldfield Rd, Hampton, Mddx TW12 2HQ, United Kingdom. TEL 44-20-8481-8750, FAX 44-20-8783-0049, info@keynote.co.uk, http://www.keynote.co.uk.

384.55 GBR
KEY NOTE MARKET REPORT: INDEPENDENT T V & FILM PRODUCTION. Variant title: Independent T V & Film Production. Text in English. 1991. irreg. GBP 265 (effective 1999). **Document type:** *Trade.*
Published by: Key Note Ltd., Field House, 72 Oldfield Rd, Hampton, Mddx TW12 2HQ, United Kingdom. TEL 44-20-8481-8750, FAX 44-20-8783-0049, info@keynote.co.uk, http://www.keynote.co.uk.

384.55 GBR ISSN 0966-3371
THE KNOWLEDGE. Text in English. 1986. a. GBP 95; GBP 120 for print & CD-ROM (effective 2001). adv. charts; maps. **Document type:** *Directory, Trade.* **Description:** For companies and individuals working in the TV, film and video production industries in the UK. Includes over 10,000 crew and company contacts.
Related titles: CD-ROM ed.
—BLDSC (5100.429800).
Published by: C M P Information Ltd. (Subsidiary of: United Business Media), Sovereign House, Sovereign Way, Tonbridge, Kent TN9 1RW, United Kingdom. TEL 44-1732-362666, FAX 44-1732-367301, enquiries@cmpinformation.com, http://www.theknowledgeonline.com, http://www.cmpinformation.com. Ed. Gwen Young. R&P Adria Kinloch. Adv. contact Elaine Soni TEL 44-1732-377423. B&W page GBP 1,625, color page GBP 2,025; 201 x 135. Circ: 3,000.

384.5532 DEU
KOCHDUELL. Text in German. 2000. m. adv. **Document type:** *Magazine, Consumer.* **Description:** Contains news, hints and recipes from the popular "kochduell" cooking television series.
Published by: cultfish entertainment GmbH, Wallstr 59, Berlin, 10179, Germany. TEL 49-30-24008471, FAX 49-30-24008475, http://www.vox.de/kochduell.html, http://cultfish.de.

621.388 ITA ISSN 0392-470X
L'ANTENNA; rassegna mensile di tecnica elettronica. Text in Italian. 1928. m. adv. charts; illus. index.
Former titles (until 1979): L'Antenna Nuova (0392-4696); (until 1977): Antenna (0003-5386); Incorporates (1957-1961): Alta Fedelta (0393-0882)
Indexed: Inspec.
—CISTI.
Published by: Editrice Il Rostro, Via B Buozzi 5, Segrate, MI 20090, Italy. TEL 39-02-2135366, FAX 39-02-2132869, info@ilrostro.it, http://www.ilrostro.it. Ed. Alfonso Giovene. Circ: 25,000.

384.555 USA ISSN 1536-7878
CODEN: EBMLCC
LATIN AMERICAN BROADBAND MARKETS. Text in English. m. USD 995 (effective 2001). **Document type:** *Newsletter.* **Description:** Tracks the performance of broadband operators in every market south of Texas, measuring such operating indicators as monthly subscriber growth, average revenue per user and EBITDA performance. Also provides detailed country analysis with ten-year subscriber and revenue forecasts broken down by operator.
Related titles: E-mail ed.: USD 995 (effective 2001); Fax ed.: USD 995 (effective 2001).
Published by: Kagan Research, LLC, 1 Lower Ragsdale Dr., Ste. 130, Monterey, CA 93940-5741. TEL 831-624-1536, FAX 831-625-3225, info@kagan.com, http://www.kagan.com. Pub. Paul Kagan.

LEONARD MALTIN'S MOVIE GUIDE. see *MOTION PICTURES*

384.55 USA
LEWIS LETTER ON CABLE MARKETING*✶*. Text in English. 1977. m. USD 95. back issues avail. **Description:** Marketing, public relations and advertising advice for cable companies.
Published by: Lewis Associates, Inc., PO Box 567, Housatonic, MA 01236-0567. TEL 413-528-9445. Ed. Eiken Willner.

LIFE VIDEO; przeglad sprzetu i kaset. see *ELECTRONICS*

791.45 FRA ISSN 1627-9395
LOFT STORY. Text in French. 2001. bi-m. **Document type:** *Magazine, Consumer.*
Published by: M6 Interactions, 89 av Charles-de-Gaulle, Neuilly-sur-Seine Cedex, 92575, France. TEL 33-1-41926936, http://www.m6net.fr.

791.45 ZWE ISSN 0024-6352
LOOK & LISTEN. Text in English. 1966. fortn. ZWD 330 domestic; ZWD 433 in Africa; ZWD 459.80 in Europe; ZWD 481.80 elsewhere (effective 2000); ZWD 15 newsstand/cover. adv. bk.rev. illus. **Document type:** *Magazine, Consumer.*
Published by: Munn Publishing (Pvt) Ltd, Union Ave, Box UA 589, Harare, Zimbabwe. TEL 263-4-752063, 263-4-752144, 263-4-750339, 263-4-756160, 263-4-752136, FAX 263-4-752062, TELEX 24748 ZW, munn@masasa.samaro.co.zw, munn@samara.co.zw. Ed., R&P Alasdair Munn. Adv. contact Jane Ralston. Circ: 21,700.

384.55 GBR
LOOK IN TELEVISION ANNUAL✶; for children. Text in English. a. GBP 3.95. illus. **Document type:** *Consumer.*
Published by: I P C SouthBank (Subsidiary of: I P C Media Ltd.), Kings Reach Tower, Stamford St, London, SE1 9LS, United Kingdom. TEL 44-161-8722144, http://www.ipcmedia.com/. Ed. Colin Shelbourn.

LOYOLA OF LOS ANGELES ENTERTAINMENT LAW REVIEW. see *LAW*

LURZER'S INTERNATIONAL ARCHIVE; ads, TV and posters world-wide. see *ADVERTISING AND PUBLIC RELATIONS*

M T V S S N. (Music Television's Spankin New) see *MUSIC*

384.55 DEU
MAINZER TAGE DER FERNSEH-KRITIK. Text in German. irreg., latest vol.32, 1999. **Document type:** *Monographic series.*
Published by: Zweites Deutsches Fernsehen, Kommunikation, Mainz, 55100, Germany. TEL 49-6131-702210, FAX 49-6131-705366, TELEX 4187930-ZDF-D, info@zdf.de, http://www.zdf.de.

384.55 USA
MAN FROM U N C L E FAN CLUB NEWSLETTER. Text in English. q. USD 25 membership (effective 2001).
Published by: Man from U N C L E Fan Club, PO Box 251, Davenport, IA 52805. prophet_livingood@hotmail.com.

791.456 DEU
MARIENHOF MAGAZIN. Text in German. bi-m. EUR 2.50 newsstand/cover (effective 2003). adv. **Document type:** *Magazine, Consumer.*
Published by: Schau & Partner Medien GmbH, Gruener Deich 1, Hamburg, 20097, Germany. TEL 49-40-3287270, FAX 49-40-32872722, info@sp-m.de, http://www.sp-m.de. adv.: color page EUR 3,100. Circ: 120,000 (paid and controlled).

MEDIA BIZ; film - tv - radio - video - audio. see *MOTION PICTURES*

MEDIA BIZ BRANCHENFUEHRER; film - tv - radio - video - audio. see *BUSINESS AND ECONOMICS—Trade And Industrial Directories*

MEDIA BUYER'S DAILY. see *MOTION PICTURES*

MEDIA ETHICS. see *JOURNALISM*

343.09946 AUS
MEDIA LAW AND PRACTICE. Text in English. 1987. 5-6 updates/yr.), 2 base vols. plus bi-m. updates. looseleaf. AUD 845 (effective 2004). **Document type:** *Trade.* **Description:** Examines laws relating to broadcasting, radio communications and other media related issues, such as defamation, copyright, advertising and complaints. Includes commentary, legislation, standards, codes and guidelines.
Formerly (until 1995): Broadcasting Law and Practice
Published by: Lawbook Co. (Subsidiary of: Thomson Legal & Regulatory Ltd.), PO Box 3502, Rozelle, NSW 2039, Australia. LRA.Service@thomson.com, http://onlineecom01.thomson.com.au/thomson/Catalog.asp?EES_CMD=SI&EES_ID=100499, http://www.lawbookco.com.au/. Eds. Jaclyn Moriarty, Paul Mallam, Sophie Dawson.

070.4 GBR
MEDIA MAP OF EASTERN EUROPE. Text in English. 1990. a. GBP 195 (effective 1999). **Description:** Provides an overview of the eastern European media market. Covers consumer media in 13 countries with profiles of all of the major players. Includes television and cable as well as print media.
Supersedes in part (in 1997): Media Map (1355-0055)
Published by: (Communications and Information Technology Research Ltd.), C I T Publications Ltd., 3 Colleton Crescent, Exeter, Devon EX2 4DG, United Kingdom. TEL 44-1392-315-555, FAX 44-1392-315-556, citpubs@eurobell.co.uk, http://www.telecoms-data.com. Ed. Tania Harvey.

MEDIA MAP OF WESTERN EUROPE. see *BUSINESS AND ECONOMICS—Marketing And Purchasing*

070.4 GBR
MEDIA MAP YEARBOOK. Text in English. base vol. plus m. updates. looseleaf. GBP 585 (effective 2000). **Description:** Contains profiles of over 150 companies including their latest financial results, contact details and media interests, plus circulation figures, viewing shares and media regulations. Includes a media directory. Covers television and cable as well as print media.
Formerly (until 2003): Media Map Datafile; Supersedes in part: Media Map
—BLDSC (5525.258257).
Published by: (Communications and Information Technology Research Ltd.), C I T Publications Ltd., 3 Colleton Crescent, Exeter, Devon EX2 4DG, United Kingdom. TEL 44-1392-315-555, FAX 44-1392-315-556, citpubs@eurobell.co.uk, http://www.telecoms-data.com. Ed. Tania Harvey.

MEDIA MATTERS. see *ADVERTISING AND PUBLIC RELATIONS*

621.388 DEU ISSN 0267-4467
MEDIA MONOGRAPH. Text in English, German, French. 1984. irreg. **Document type:** *Monographic series, Academic/Scholarly.*
—BLDSC (5525.258300), IE, ingenta.
Published by: Europaeisches Medieninstitut e.V., Zollhof 2A, Duesseldorf, 40221, Germany. TEL 49-211-90104-0, FAX 49-211-9010456, orders@eim.org, http://www.eim.org. R&P Jo Groebel.

384.55 DEU ISSN 0170-1754
P87
MEDIA PERSPEKTIVEN. Text in German. 1970. m. adv. bk.rev. index. back issues avail. **Document type:** *Trade.*
Indexed: DIP, IBR, IBZ, IIFP, IITV.
—BLDSC (5525.258550), IE, Infotrieve.
Published by: Arbeitsgemeinschaft der ARD - Werbegesellschaften, Am Steinernen Stock 1, Frankfurt Am Main, 60320, Germany. FAX 49-69-1552857. Ed. Klaus Berg. Circ: 7,000.

MEDIA PROFESSIONAL. see *JOURNALISM*

MEDIAWEEK. see *JOURNALISM*

621.388 DEU ISSN 0723-2128
MEDIEN BULLETIN; Medienbusiness - Broadcast - New Media. Text in German. 1982. m. EUR 91.50 domestic; EUR 119.10 foreign; EUR 16 newsstand/cover (effective 2002). adv. bk.rev. **Document type:** *Magazine, Trade.*
Published by: Kellerer und Partner GmbH, An der Wachsfabrik 8, Cologne, 50996, Germany. TEL 49-2236-96217105, FAX 49-2236-962175, info@medienbulletin.de, http://www1.medienbulletin.de. Ed. Mathias van Hulst. Adv. contact Katja Mayr. B&W page EUR 3,900, color page EUR 6,900. Circ: 7,339 (paid).

384.55 DEU
MEDIEN DIALOG; Gespraech - Diskussion - Meinung - Information. Text in German. 1987. m. adv. bk.rev. **Document type:** *Journal, Trade.* **Description:** Covers media policy, TV and radio markets.
Published by: Wilfried Ahrens Verlag, Postfach 1360, Bruckmuehl, 83046, Germany. TEL 49-8062-6550, FAX 49-8062-6591. Ed. Wilfried Ahrens. Circ: 3,500.

371.3358 DEU ISSN 0176-4918
P87
MEDIEN & ERZIEHUNG. Text in German. 1957. bi-m. EUR 27; EUR 21.60 to students (effective 2005). adv. bk.rev.; film rev.; software rev.; tel.rev.; video rev.; Website rev. bibl.; illus. index. 68 p./no.; back issues avail. **Document type:** *Journal, Academic/Scholarly.* **Description:** Explores film, television, electronic games and computers as matters and instruments of learning and education..
Former titles (until 1984): M E R Z - Medien und Erziehung (0723-399X); (until 1979): Medien and Erziehung (0341-6860); Jugend Film Fernsehen (0022-5886)
Indexed: DIP, FLI, IBR, IBZ.
—CCC.
Published by: KoPaed Verlag, Pfaelzer-Wald-Str 64, Munich, 81539, Germany. TEL 49-89-68890098, FAX 49-89-6891912, info@kopaed.de, http://www.merz-zeitschrift.de, http://www.kopaed.de. Ed. Hans-Peter Kistner. Circ: 2,200.

MEDIEN UND KOMMUNIKATIONSWISSENSCHAFT. see *COMMUNICATIONS—Radio*

MEDIEN UND RECHT INTERNATIONAL. see *LAW*

MEDIENREPORT. see *ADVERTISING AND PUBLIC RELATIONS*

028.1 DEU ISSN 1431-5262
P87
MEDIENWISSENSCHAFT; Zeitschrift fuer Rezensionen ueber Veroeffentlichungen zu saemtlichen Medien. Text in German. 1984. q. EUR 49.80 domestic; EUR 57.80 foreign (effective 2003). adv. bk.rev. index. **Document type:** *Journal, Academic/Scholarly.* **Description:** Reviews books in all fields of mass media communications, including radio, TV, motion pictures and theater.

Formerly (until 1995): Medienwissenschaft: Rezensionen (0176-4241)
Indexed: DIP, IBR, IBZ, PCI.
—CCC.
Published by: Schuerenverlag GmbH, Universitaetsstr 55, Marburg, 35037, Germany. TEL 49-6421-63084, FAX 49-6421-681190, schueren.verlag@t-online.de, http://www.schueren-verlag.de, http://staff-www.uni-marburg.de/~medrez. R&P Annette Schueren TEL 49-6421-63085. Circ: 800.

384.55 GBR ISSN 1357-7220
P94.5.M552
MERCATOR MEDIA FORUM. Text in English. 1996. a. GBP 10 per vol. (effective 2004). **Document type:** *Academic/Scholarly.* **Description:** Promotes discussion and the flow of information between those in the European Union who work in the field of media.
Related titles: Online - full text ed.: (from Gale Group, IngentaConnect).
Indexed: IBR, IBZ.
—BLDSC (5678.818600). CCC.
Published by: (University of Wales, Mercator Media), University of Wales Press, 10 Columbus Walk, Brigantine Pl, Cardiff, CF10 4UP, United Kingdom. TEL 44-29-2049-6899, FAX 44-29-2049-6108, journals@press.wales.ac.uk, http://www.uwp.co.uk. Ed. George Jones. Circ: 200 (paid).

METRO. see *MOTION PICTURES*

384.55 CAN ISSN 1191-7962
METRO WEEKLY TELECASTER. Text in English. 1974. w.
Former titles (until 1992): Metro Telecaster (0708-2568); (until 1977): Metro Telecaster and Entertainment Guide (0708-255X)
Published by: Fundy Group Publications, 2 Second St, P O Box 128, Yarmouth, NS B5A 4B1, Canada. TEL 902-742-7111, FAX 902-742-2311. Ed. Jeremy Akerman. Circ: 16,000 (paid).

384.55 GBR ISSN 0968-4344
MIDDLE EAST BROADCAST AND SATELLITE. Text in English; Summaries in Arabic. 1993. 9/yr. GBP 65, USD 105 includes supplements (effective 2000). adv. **Document type:** *Trade.* **Description:** Reports industry news and contains features and market data.
Published by: Icom Publications Ltd., Chancery House, St Nicholas Way, Sutton, Surrey SM1 1JB, United Kingdom. TEL 44-20-86421117, FAX 44-20-86421941, admin@icompub.com, http://www.icompub.com. Ed. Farah Jifri. Pub. Alec Barton. adv.: B&W page USD 3,140, color page USD 4,800; trim 297 x 210.

384.5 ITA ISSN 1122-9276
MILLECANALI; tv, radio, comunicazione, spettacolo. Text in Italian. 1974. m. (11/yr.). EUR 50 (effective 2005). adv. **Document type:** *Magazine, Consumer.* **Description:** Presents articles on radio, TV broadcasting, and audiovisual production.
Published by: Gruppo Editoriale J C E, Via Patecchio 2, Milan, MI 20141, Italy. TEL 39-02-57316011, FAX 39-02-57316291, info@jce.it, http://www.jce.it. Ed. Mauro Roffi. Pub. Jacopo Castelfranchi. Circ: 18,000.

MILLIMETER; the magazine of the motion picture and television production industries. see *MOTION PICTURES*

791.45 CAN
MINI-DISH GUIDE. Text in English. m. CND 29.99 (effective 1997). adv.
Published by: T V Publishing Group, 201 4201 25A Ave, Vernon, BC V1T 7G8, Canada. TEL 250-542-0469, 800-663-4424, FAX 250-542-0942. Ed., R&P Deeny Grazier. Pub. Tom Monahan. Adv. contact Norm Metcalf.

791.546 IRL
MODEST PROPOSALS. Text in English. 1997. bi-w. **Description:** Encourages new and deeper thinking on the pressing cultural issues of the day: TV shows, advertisements, music, celebrities and other consumer products.
Media: Online - full text.
Published by: Nua Ltd., Merrion House, Merrion Road, Dublin, 4, Ireland. TEL 353-1-676-8996, FAX 353-1-283-9988, modest@nua.ie, http://www.nua.ie/modestproposals/. Ed. David Moore.

384.55 AUS ISSN 1323-5435
TK6540
MONITOR; the I E Aust magazine for communications and information technology engineers. Text in English. 1937. bi-m. AUD 50; AUD 80 foreign (effective 1999). adv. bk.rev. back issues avail. **Document type:** *Trade.*
Indexed: Inspec.
—CISTI.
Published by: Institution of Radio and Electronics Engineers Society, Level 1, 118 Alfred St, Milsons Point, NSW 2061, Australia. TEL 61-2-99290099, FAX 61-2-99290587, ireesoc@ozemail.com.au, http://www.ozemail.com.au/~ireesoc. Ed., Adv. contact Cherie Morris. B&W page AUD 675, color page AUD 1,080; 222 x 309. Circ: 2,400.

384.55 ITA
MONITOR∗ . Text in Italian. 1978. m. free to qualified personnel. adv.

Published by: Media Edizioni srl., c/o Media Age, Via Jacini 4, Milan, MI 20121, Italy. Ed. Edoardo Fleischner. Circ: 12,500.

384.5 ITA ISSN 0394-0896
MONITOR - RADIO T V. Text in Italian. 1978. m. EUR 75 (effective 2005). adv. bk.rev. **Document type:** *Magazine, Trade.*
Related titles: Online - full content ed.
Published by: Media Age s.r.l., Via Stefano Jacini, 4, Milan, MI 20121, Italy. TEL 39-02-862534, callerio@monitor-radiotv.com, info@monitor-radiotv.com, http://www.monitor-radiotv.com, http://www.mediaage.it. Ed., Pub. Enrico Callerio. R&P Maria Ronchetti TEL 39-02-862534. Adv. contact Alberto Pellizzari. Circ: 15,000.

MOTION PICTURE, T V & THEATRE DIRECTORY; for services & products. see *BUSINESS AND ECONOMICS—Trade And Industrial Directories*

MOVIE - T V MARKETING. see *MOTION PICTURES*

791.45 JPN
MOVIE - T V MARKETING ANNUAL WORLDWIDE TELEVISION SURVEY. Text in English. 1964. a. JPY 10,000. adv. **Document type:** *Trade.*
Formerly: Annual Worldwide T V Survey
Published by: Movie - TV Marketing, CPO Box 30, Tokyo, 100-8691, Japan. TEL 03-3587-2855, FAX 03-3587-2820. Ed. Asia M Ireton. Circ: 100,000.

MOVIE - T V MARKETING GLOBAL MOTION PICTURE YEAR BOOK. see *MOTION PICTURES*

MOVING IMAGE. see *MOTION PICTURES*

MOVING PICTURES TELEVISION. see *MOTION PICTURES*

384.55 USA ISSN 0276-8593
MULTICHANNEL NEWS. Text in English. 1980. w. (Mon.). USD 159 domestic; USD 219 foreign; USD 4 per issue domestic; USD 5 per issue foreign (effective 2005). adv. index. **Document type:** *Newspaper, Trade.* **Description:** Covers all the related fields of cable television industry: programming, pay per view, marketing and promotion, advertising sales, technology, operations, customer service, policy and business.
Incorporates (2000-2001): Broadband Week (1531-4251)
Related titles: Microfilm ed.: (from FCM); Online - full text ed.: (from EBSCO Publishing, Factiva, Florida Center for Library Automation, Gale Group, LexisNexis, Northern Light Technology, Inc., O C L C Online Computer Library Center, Inc., ProQuest Information & Learning).
Indexed: B&I.
—CCC.
Published by: Reed Business Information (Subsidiary of: Reed Business), 360 Park Ave South, New York, NY 10010. TEL 646-746-6544, FAX 646-746-6406, Loliver@reedbusiness.com, http://www.multichannel.com, http://www.reedbusiness.com. Eds. Kent Gibbons TEL 646-746-6590, Marianne Paskowski TEL 646-746-6581. adv.: B&W page USD 9,116, color page USD 10,916. Circ: 22,000. **Subscr. to:** Reed Business Information, PO Box 16118, North Hollywood, CA 91615-6118. TEL 818-487-4556, 888-343-5563.

384.555 384.55 330 USA
MULTICHANNEL NEWSDAY FAX. Text in English. d. USD 199 (effective 2004). **Document type:** *Newspaper, Trade.* **Description:** Provides up-to-the-minute news and information about the cable and telecommunications industries.
Media: Fax.
Published by: Reed Business Information (Subsidiary of: Reed Business), 360 Park Ave South, New York, NY 10010. TEL 646-746-6544, FAX 646-746-6406. Ed. Marianne Paskowski TEL 646-746-6581. **Subscr. to:** Reed Business Information, PO Box 16118, North Hollywood, CA 91615-6118. TEL 818-487-4556, 888-343-5563, FAX 818-487-4550.

384.55 USA
MUNICIPAL CABLE TV & TELECOMMUNICATIONS NEWS. Text in English. 1993. q. USD 25 (effective 2000). bk.rev. **Document type:** *Newsletter.*
Published by: O'Reilly, Rancillo, Nitz, Andrews, Turnbull & Scott, P.C., 12900 Hall Rd, Ste 350, Sterling, MI 48313. TEL 810-726-1000, FAX 810-726-1560, nlehto@ameritech.net, http://www.ameritech.net.users/nlehto/index.html. Ed., R&P Neil Jed Lehto. Circ: 371.

MUSIC VIDEO MAGAZINE. see *MUSIC*

791.45 BEL
MUZIEK & WOORD. Text in Dutch. 1974. m. EUR 30 (effective 2005). adv. bk.rev.; film rev. index. **Document type:** *Consumer.*
Published by: (Belgische Radio en Televisie), Decom M.V., Gosselilaan 30, Groot-Bijgaarden, 1702, Belgium. TEL 32-2-4817859, FAX 32-2-4817882, lieven.delaet@decom.be, http://www.decom.be/Portfolio2.asp?select=1&realisatielijst=2. Ed., R&P Leen Boereboom. Pub. Geert Van Nieuwenborch. Adv. contact Anja Stuerbout.

N A B E T - C W A NEWS. see *LABOR UNIONS*

C

384.55 USA
N A P T E GUIDE TO NORTH AMERICAN MEDIA. Text in English. 1999. 2/yr. USD 100 to members; USD 150 to non-members (effective 2003). adv. **Document type:** *Directory, Trade.* **Description:** Reference to North American TV stations, station representatives, station group owners, cable networks, advertising agencies, and MSO's. Includes listings of key personnel, addresses, phone and fax numbers.
Formerly: Reps, Groups, Distributors, Networks, Ad Agencies, Telco - D B S Guide
Published by: National Association of Television Program Executives, 2425 Olympic Blvd, Ste 550E, Santa Monica, CA 90404-4030. TEL 310-453-4440, FAX 310-453-5258. adv.: B&W page USD 2,500; trim 7 x 9.

384.545 USA
N A T P E MONTHLY. Text in English. 1999. m. USD 75 to non-members; free to members. **Description:** Reports on industry news, Washington updates, international developments, convergence, and trends in the television and cable industries.
Related titles: Supplement(s): Online Connection.
Published by: National Association of Television Program Executives, 2425 Olympic Blvd, Ste 550E, Santa Monica, CA 90404-4030. TEL 310-453-4440, FAX 310-453-5258, http://www.natpe.org.

621.388 DEU
TK7800 CODEN: NETTEN
N E T - ZEITSCHRIFT FUER KOMMUNIKATIONSMANAGEMENT. (Nachrichten - Elektronik - Telematik) Text in German. 1946. 10/yr. EUR 117 domestic; EUR 123 foreign; EUR 10.50 newsstand/cover (effective 2003). adv. bk.rev. bibl.; illus.; pat.; tr.lit. **Document type:** *Magazine, Trade.*
Former titles: N E T - Erfolgreiches Kommunikationsmanagement (0947-4765); (until 1993): N E T - Zeitschrift fuer Angewandte Telekommunikation (0947-4757); (until 1989): N E T: Nachrichten - Elektronik und Telematik (0177-5499); (until 1982): Nachrichten - Elektronik und Telematik (0723-8703); (until 1976): Nachrichten - Elektronik (0341-4035); (until 1963): Internationale Elektronische Rundschau (0020-9236); (until 1955): Elektronische Rundschau (0367-0686); (until 1947): Funk und Ton (0367-3383)
Indexed: B&I, ChemAb, Engind, Inspec.
—AskIEEE, CISTI, IE, Linda Hall. **CCC.**
Published by: N E T Verlagsservice GmbH, Baltzerstr. 30, Waltersdorf, 15569, Germany. TEL 49-3362-75858, FAX 49-3362-75857, vertrieb@net-im-web.de, http://www.net-im-web.de. Ed. Brigitte Kasper. Pub., Adv. contact Frank Backasch. B&W page EUR 2,900, color page EUR 3,890; trim 210 x 297. Circ: 10,230 (paid and controlled).

384.5 CAN ISSN 1198-6107
N F B ON T V. Text in English. 1989. m. free. 4 p./no.; back issues avail. **Document type:** *Newsletter, Government.* **Description:** Lists and describes films broadcast on Canadian television, including U.S. border stations.
Published by: National Film Board of Canada/Office National du Film du Canada, PO Box 6100, Sta Centre-Ville, Montreal, PQ H3C 3H5, Canada. TEL 514-496-4891, 800-267-7710, FAX 514-283-7564, p.l.lewis@nfb.ca, http://www.nfb.ca. Ed. Philip Lewis. Circ: 4,700.

621.388 JPN
N H K HOSO HAKUBUTSUKAN DAYORI/N H K BROADCAST MUSEUM NEWS. (Nippon Hoso Kyokai) Text in Japanese. 1964. a.
Published by: Nippon Hoso Kyokai, Hoso Hakubutsukan/Japan Broadcasting Corp., Broadcast Museum, 1-1 Atago 2-chome, Minato-ku, Tokyo, 105-0002, Japan.

621.388 JPN ISSN 0027-657X
N H K LABORATORIES NOTE. (Nippon Hoso Kyokai) Text in English. 1966. irreg. (10-12/yr.). per issue exchange basis. cum.index. **Document type:** *Monographic series, Academic/Scholarly.*
Media: Duplicated (not offset).
Indexed: Engind, ExcerpMed, Inspec, JCT, JTA, RefZh, SCI.
—BLDSC (6109.495000), AskIEEE, CISTI, Ei, IE, ingenta, Linda Hall.
Published by: Nippon Hoso Kyokai, Gijutsu Kenkyujo/Japan Broadcasting Corp., Science and Technical Research Laboratories, 10-11 Kinuta 1-chome, Setagaya-ku, Tokyo, 157-0073, Japan. FAX 81-3-5494-2418, http://www.strl.nhk.or.jp/publica/labnote/index.html. Ed. Katsumi Nakabayashi. Circ: 1,000.

384.55 USA
N J C T A. Text in English. s-a.?. **Document type:** *Newsletter.* **Description:** Discusses issues affecting cable television in New Jersey.
Published by: New Jersey Cable Television Association, 132 W State St, Trenton, NJ 08608.

791.43 USA
N J N GUIDE. Text in English. 1975. m. USD 40. **Document type:** *Consumer.* **Description:** Includes TV listings and articles for members of New Jersey Network, a public television network.
Published by: New Jersey Network, PO Box 777, Trenton, NJ 08625. TEL 609-777-5000, FAX 609-633-2927, http://www.njn.net. Ed., R&P, Adv. contact Joanne Bergin TEL 609-777-5060.

201.66 USA ISSN 1521-1754
BV655
N R B MAGAZINE. (National Religious Broadcasters) Text in English. 1969. m. USD 24 domestic; USD 48 foreign; free to members; free domestic to qualified personnel (effective 2005). adv. bk.rev. charts; illus. back issues avail.; reprint service avail. from PQC. **Document type:** *Magazine, Trade.* **Description:** Trade publication for Christian communicators in all forms of media.
Formerly (until 1998): Religious Broadcasting (0034-4079)
Related titles: Online - full text ed.
Indexed: ChrPI.
Published by: National Religious Broadcasters, Inc., 9510 Technology Dr., Manassas, VA 20110-4167. TEL 703-330-7000, FAX 703-330-7100, vfraedrich@nrb.org, http://www.nrb.org. Ed., R&P Ms. Valerie Fraedrich. Pub. Dr. Frank Wright. Adv. contact Steve Cross TEL 703-330-7000. B&W page USD 1,680, color page USD 1,980; trim 10.88 x 8.38. Circ: 6,845 (paid and controlled).

NATIONAL FILM AND SOUND ARCHIVE NEWSLETTER. see *SOUND RECORDING AND REPRODUCTION*

384 CAN ISSN 0382-151X
PN1993
NATIONAL FILM BOARD OF CANADA. ANNUAL REPORT. Text in English, French. 1940. a.
Incorporates (1940-1969): Office National du Film du Canada. Rapport Annuel (0382-1528)
—CISTI.
Published by: National Film Board of Canada/Office National du Film du Canada, PO Box 6100, Sta Centre-Ville, Montreal, PQ H3C 3H5, Canada. TEL 514-283-9000, 800-267-7710, FAX 514-283-7564, http://www.nfb.ca/e/publications/annual_reports.html.

621.388 JPN ISSN 1349-3205
QC973 CODEN: JCRLEX
NATIONAL INSTITUTE OF INFORMATION AND COMMUNICATIONS TECHNOLOGY. JOURNAL/TSUSHINSOGO KENKYUJO EIBUN RONBUNSHU. Text in English. 1954. 3/yr. free or on exchange basis. bibl.; charts; illus.; stat. **Document type:** *Academic/Scholarly.*
Former titles (until 2002): Communications Research Laboratory. Journal (0914-9260); (until 1988): Radio Research Laboratory. Journal (0033-8001)
Indexed: B&BAb, BrCerAb, C&ISA, CerAb, CivEngAb, CorrAb, CurCont, E&CAJ, EMA, Engind, IAA, INIS AtomInd, Inspec, JCT, JTA, M&TEA, MBF, METADEX, RefZh, WAA.
—BLDSC (4731.704000), AskIEEE, CINDOC, CISTI, IE, ingenta, Linda Hall.
Published by: (Japan. Technical Support Section), Ministry of Posts and Telecommunications, Communications Research Laboratory/Yuseisho Tsushinsogo Kenkyujo, 2-1 Nukui-Kita-Machi 4-chome, Koganei-shi, Tokyo-to 184-0015, Japan. TEL 81-423-21-1211, FAX 81-423-27-7603, TELEX 2832611-DEMPA-J, pub@crl.go.jp. Circ: 1,000.

384.55 USA
NATIONAL NEWS. Text in English. bi-m. membership only. **Document type:** *Newsletter.*
Published by: Association of Independent Commercial Producers, 3 W, 18th St., 5th Fl, New York, NY 10011-4610. TEL 212-929-3000, FAX 212-929-3359, aicpl@aol.com, mattm@aicp.com, http://www.aicp.com. Ed. Renee Paley. Pub. Matt Miller.

384.55 NLD ISSN 0925-6261
NEDERLANDS OMROEP HANDBOEK. Text in Dutch. 1990. a. EUR 67.50 per vol. (effective 2005). **Document type:** *Trade.* **Description:** Provides a reference source for all broadcast media in the Netherlands.
Related titles: ♦ Supplement to: Broadcast Magazine. ISSN 1380-9237.
Published by: Broadcast Press Hilversum BV, Postbus 576, Hilversum, 1200 AN, Netherlands. TEL 31-35-6252444, FAX 31-35-6214559, info@broadcastmagazine.nl, info@broadcastpress.nl, http://www.broadcastpress.nl/broadcastmagazine/.

384.555 CAN ISSN 1711-4632
NETWORK CABLING. Text in English. 1997. bi-m. CND 40 domestic; USD 60 in United States; USD 75 elsewhere (effective 2005). **Document type:** *Magazine, Trade.* **Description:** Dedicated to serving the informational needs of readers, including service providers and end-users, in telecommunications wiring and products.
Former titles (until 2004): Structured Cabling (1488-5298); (until 1999): Structured Cabling & Connecting Systems (1206-6761)
Published by: C L B Media, Inc. (Subsidiary of: Canada Law Book Inc.), 240 Edward St, Aurora, ON L4G 3S9, Canada. TEL 905-727-0077, FAX 905-727-0017, pyoung@clbmedia.ca, fshoniker@clbmedia.ca, http://www.networkcablingmag.ca, http://www.clbmedia.ca.

791.45 USA
NETWORK FUTURES & PROLOG. Text in English. w. USD 100. **Document type:** *Trade.*
Formed by the merger of: Network Futures; T V Pro-Log (0739-5574)
Published by: Television Index, Inc., 40 29 27th St, Long Island City, NY 11101. TEL 718-937-3990. Ed. Timothy Hunter.

NEW ACTORS AND ACTRESSES. see *THEATER*

621.388 GBR ISSN 0265-4717
NEW MEDIA MARKETS. Text in English. 1983. s-m. GBP 895, EUR 1,343, USD 1,343; GBP 2,685, EUR 4,028, USD 4,028 combined subscription print & online eds. (effective 2005). **Document type:** *Newsletter, Trade.* **Description:** Provides global reporting on the commercial aspects of satellite television, terrestrial television, cable TV, programming and channel development.
Related titles: Microform ed.: (from PQC); Online - full text ed.: (from Gale Group, LexisNexis, Northern Light Technology, Inc., O C L C Online Computer Library Center, Inc.).
Indexed: ABIn, B&I.
—IE, Infotrieve. **CCC.**
Published by: Informa Media (Subsidiary of: T & F Informa plc), Mortimer House, 37-41 Mortimer St, London, W1T 3JH, United Kingdom. TEL 44-20-70175533, FAX 44-20-70174783, media.enquiries@informa.com, http://www.informamedia.com/. Ed. Chris Wynn.

384.55 GBR ISSN 1740-0309
PN1995.9.E9
▼ **THE NEW REVIEW OF FILM AND TELEVISION STUDIES.** Text in English. 2003. 3/yr. GBP 190, USD 333 combined subscription to institutions print & online eds. (effective 2006). back issues avail. **Document type:** *Journal, Academic/Scholarly.* **Description:** Publishes research dedicated to clearly formulated, reliable methods of analysis, well posed questions examining resolvable problems, and focused deliberation on those problems.
Related titles: Online - full text ed.: ISSN 1740-7923. GBP 181, USD 316 to institutions (effective 2006) (from EBSCO Publishing, Gale Group, IngentaConnect, O C L C Online Computer Library Center, Inc., Swets Information Services).
Indexed: CommAb.
Published by: Routledge (Subsidiary of: Taylor & Francis Group), 4 Park Sq, Milton Park, Abingdon, Oxon OX14 4RN, United Kingdom. TEL 44-1235-828600, FAX 44-1235-829000, info@routledge.co.uk, http://www.tandf.co.uk/journals/titles/17400309.asp, http://www.routledge.co.uk. Ed. Warren Buckland. **Subscr. to:** Taylor & Francis Ltd, Journals Customer Service, Rankine Rd, Basingstoke, Hants RG24 8PR, United Kingdom. TEL 44-1256-813000, FAX 44-1256-330245, enquiry@tandf.co.uk.

384.5452 GBR ISSN 1466-3988
NEW T V STRATEGIES. Text in English. 1999. m. GBP 345 domestic; GBP 345 in Europe; GBP 365 elsewhere (effective 2001). adv. **Document type:** *Newsletter, Trade.* **Description:** Provides news and analysis of the commercial developments of digital and interactive TV.
Related titles: Online - full content ed.; Online - full text ed.: (from Gale Group).
Published by: Centaur Publishing, St Giles House, 50 Poland St, London, W1V 4AX, United Kingdom. TEL 44-20-7970-4000, ntvs.info@centaur.co.uk, http://www.newmediazero.com/ntvs/, http://www.centaur.co.uk.

004 USA ISSN 1060-7188
QA76.575
NEWMEDIA; the magazine for creators of the digital future. Variant title: New Media. Text in English. 1991. m. USD 52 domestic; USD 76 foreign; USD 4.95 newsstand/cover; CND 5.95 newsstand/cover in Canada (effective 2000). adv. back issues avail.; reprints avail. **Document type:** *Magazine, Trade.* **Description:** Discusses the social, economic, technical, legal, and philosophical issues concerning new digital media.
Formerly (until 1991): NewMedia Age (1058-0492)
Related titles: Online - full text ed.
Indexed: CompD, CompLI, InfoSAb, MicrocompInd, SoftBase.
—BLDSC (6084.477250).
Published by: HyperMedia Communications, Inc., 710 Oakfield Dr., Ste. 202, Brandon, FL 33511-4954. FAX 650-573-7446, edit@newmedia.com, http://www.newmedia.com. Ed. Becky Waring. Pub. Richard Landry. Adv. contact Dan Hudson. Circ: 40,000 (controlled). **Subscr. to:** PO Box 3039, Northbrook, IL 60065-3039.

384.55 USA
NEWS - BROADCAST NETWORK. Text in English. q.
Address: 9431 Beloit Rd, Milwaukee, WI 53227-4365. TEL 414-321-6210, FAX 414-321-3608. Ed. Thomas Hill. Circ: 2,000.

NEWSBANK REVIEW OF THE ARTS: FILM AND TELEVISION. see *MOTION PICTURES*

NICK JR. see *CHILDREN AND YOUTH—For*

NICKELODEON MAGAZINE. see *CHILDREN AND YOUTH—For*

384.55 USA
NIELSEN REPORT ON TELEVISION. Text in English. 1955. a. USD 25. **Document type:** *Trade.* **Description:** Summary of program audiences for broadcast network local and syndication, trends and related data on cable and VCR usage.
Indexed: SRI.
Published by: Nielsen Media Research, 770 Broadway., New York, NY 10003-9593. TEL 212-708-7500. Ed. J Loftus. Circ: 30,000.

NIGERIAN RADIO - T V TIMES. see *COMMUNICATIONS—Radio*

791.45 CAN
NORTH ISLAND TELEVIEWER. Text in English. 1981. w. USD 41.73 (effective 1999). adv. **Document type:** *Newspaper.* **Description:** Contains satellite TV listings.
Published by: North Island Gazette Ltd., P O Box 458, Port Hardy, BC V0N 2P0, Canada. TEL 250-949-6225. Ed. Rob Giblak. Pub. Bill MacAdam. Circ: 3,683.

791.45 ITA
NOTIZIE MESE. Text in Italian. m.
Published by: Sogeco s.a.s., Via Fiume, 13, Vimercate, MI 20059, Italy. Ed. Silvana Antonioli. Circ: 8,000.

384.55 ESP
NUEVO CLAN. Text in Spanish. 1987. w.
Formerly: Clan T V
Address: Gran Via de Carles III, 124 5o, Barcelona, 08034, Spain. TEL 93-2800088, FAX 93-2805555. Circ: 247,620.

384.5532 DEU
NUR T V. Text in German. 1997. m. EUR 17.50 domestic; EUR 45.50 foreign; EUR 1.20 newsstand/cover (effective 2003). adv. **Document type:** *Magazine, Consumer.*
Published by: Nur T V Verlagsgesellschaft mbH, Am Rupenhorn 9, Berlin, 14055, Germany. TEL 49-30-3012990, FAX 49-30-30129911, info@nurtv.de, http://www.nurtv.de. adv.: page EUR 7,950. Circ: 550,000 (paid).

791.45 GBR ISSN 1352-1519
OFFICIAL MAGAZINE OF CORONATION STREET. Text in English. 1994. m. GBP 27 domestic; GBP 78.09 in Canada; GBP 67.90 in United States; GBP 78 in New Zealand; GBP 84 in Australia; GBP 2.25 newsstand/cover. **Document type:** *Consumer.* **Description:** Coverage of Great Britain's television drama series "Coronation Street.".
Published by: (Granada Television), Newsstand Publishing Services, Office Block 1, Southlink Business Park, Southlink Rd, Oldham, Lancs OL4 1DE, United Kingdom. TEL 44-161-6240414, FAX 44-1616-284655, truenews@passport.ca, http://www.coronationstreet.co.uk. Ed. Brian Clark. Pub. Alan Young. Circ: 60,000 (paid). **Subscr. to:** RPO The Beaches, 2060 Queen St, P O Box 51545, Toronto, ON M4E 3V7, Canada. TEL 800-743-3552, FAX 416-684-7303. **Dist. by:** Comag, Tavistock Works, Tavistock Rd, W Drayton, Middx UB7 7QX, United Kingdom. TEL 44-1895-433600, FAX 44-189-543-3606, 44-1895-433602.

THE OFFICIAL MCCALLUM OBSERVER PRINT JOURNAL. see *BIOGRAPHY*

OKEJ. see *CHILDREN AND YOUTH—For*

621.388 CHE ISSN 0030-2007
OLD MAN. Text in English, French, German, Italian. 1932. m. (11/yr.). CHF 40. adv. bk.rev. index.
Published by: Union of Swiss Short Wave Amateurs, Postfach, Rumisberg, 4539, Switzerland. Eds. Peter Erni, Werner Mueller. Circ: 4,000.

384.55 USA ISSN 1076-0334
HE8700.7
ON DEMAND. Text in English. 1994. m. **Document type:** *Trade.* **—CCC.**
Published by: Cowles Business Media (Subsidiary of: Cowles Media Company), 11 River Bend Dr., S., Box 4949, Stamford, CT 06907-0949. TEL 203-358-9900, FAX 203-358-5811, ondemandms@aol.com. Ed., Pub. Matt Stump.

384.553 GBR
ON DIGITAL; digital television made simple. Text in English. m. adv. **Document type:** *Magazine, Consumer.* **Description:** Provides information on and features about programs available via On Digital channels.
Published by: T P D Ltd, 1-4 Long Island House Block A, Westpoint 33-34, Warple Way, London, W3 0RG, United Kingdom. TEL 44-208-600-9104, FAX 44-208-600-9101, lucy.ryan@tpd.co.uk, http://www.tpd.co.uk/print/ondigital.asp. Ed. Lucy Ryan. adv.: color page GBP 15,400; trim 210 x 292. Circ: 772,000 (controlled).

791.45 ITA ISSN 0393-814X
ONDA TIVU. Text in Italian. 1978. w. adv. **Document type:** *Magazine, Consumer.* **Description:** A light magazine that talks about television and programs in general.
Published by: Superprint Srl (Subsidiary of: Monrif Group), Viale Milanofiori Strada 3, Palazzo B11, Assago, MI 20090, Italy. TEL 39-02-575771, FAX 39-02-57577263, http://www.monrifgroup.net/eng/periodici.html, http://www.monrifgroup.net/ita/periodici.html. Circ: 159,947.

ONDIRECTV. see *SPORTS AND GAMES—Ball Games*

384.55 DEU ISSN 0948-2113
ONLINE AKTUELL. Text in German. 1979. fortn. **Document type:** *Trade.*
Incorporates (1995-1997): Internet Report (0948-2601); (1991-1995): Audiotex News (0941-6900); Which was formerly (until 1995): Btx Aktuell (0935-6991); (until 1988): Bildschirmtext Aktuell (0724-1828)
Published by: Neue Mediengesellschaft Ulm mbH, Konrad-Celtis-Str 77, Munich, 81369, Germany. TEL 49-89-74117190, FAX 49-89-74117195. Ed. Max Bold. Circ: 1,500.

791.45 USA ISSN 0747-4059
ONSAT; America's weekly satellite guide. Text in English. 1984. w. USD 59.95 in North America (effective 2005). adv. **Document type:** *Magazine, Consumer.* **Description:** Includes listings and articles concerning satellite TV programming.
Published by: Triple D Publishing, Inc., 1300 S DeKalb St, PO Box 2347, Shelby, NC 28151-2384. TEL 704-482-9673, 800-234-0021, FAX 704-484-6976, onsat@tripled.com, http://www.tripled.com. Ed. Jim H. Cothran. Pub. Douglas G Brown. Adv. contact Nelli Williams. B&W page USD 8,750, color page USD 10,675; trim 8 x 10.75. Circ: 472,468 (paid).

384.5532 AUS
OPTUS T V GUIDE. Text in English. 2000. m. **Document type:** *Magazine, Consumer.* **Description:** Combines a comprehensive, easy-to-use television listings guide with interesting, quality reading.
Published by: A C P Custom Media, Level 7, 50 Park St, Sydney, NSW 2000, Australia. TEL 61-2-9282-8019, FAX 61-2-9267-3625, custominfo@acp.com.au, http://www.custompubs.acp.com.au/docs/optustv.html. Circ: 250,000 (controlled).

384.55 USA
ORBITER. Text in English. 1984. bi-m. looseleaf. membership. adv. bk.rev. back issues avail. **Document type:** *Newsletter.* **Description:** Contains articles and news on the satellite industry.
Published by: Society of Satellite Professionals International, 1 World Trade Ctr., Ste. 8665, New York, NY 10048-8665. TEL 703-549-8696, FAX 703-549-9728, http://www.sspi.org. Ed. Carol McKibben. Circ: 800 (paid).

791.45 GBR
OXFORD TELEVISION STUDIES. Text in English. 1997. irreg., latest 2001. price varies. illus. back issues avail. **Document type:** *Monographic series, Academic/Scholarly.* **Description:** Explores the literary and cultural dimensions of television as a medium.
Published by: Oxford University Press, Great Clarendon St, Oxford, OX2 6DP, United Kingdom. TEL 44-1865-556767, FAX 44-1865-556646, enquiry@oup.co.uk, http://www.oup-usa.org/catalogs/general/series/Oxford_Television_Studies.html, http://www.oup.co.uk/.

791.45 USA
P B S PREVIEWS. (Pubic Broadcasting Service) Text in English. 1995. w.
Media: Online - full text.
Published by: Public Broadcasting Service, 1320 Braddock Pl, Alexandria, VA 22314. TEL 703-739-5000, http://www.pbs.org/previews/.

P B S TEACHER PREVIEWS. see *EDUCATION—Teaching Methods And Curriculum*

621.388 USA
P W. (Production Weekly) Text in English. w. USD 450 (effective 1999). **Description:** Provides breakdown of projects in pre-production, preparation and development for film, television, music videos, and commercials.
Media: Online - full text. **Related titles:** E-mail ed.; Fax ed.
Address: PO Box 10101, Burbank, CA 91510-0101. TEL 818-951-0298, FAX 818-951-0248, info@productionweekly.com, http://www.productionweekly.com/. Ed. Rich Browski.

384.55 SWE ISSN 1100-3138
PAA T V. Text in Swedish. 1954. w. SEK 598; SEK 17.50 newsstand/cover. adv. 112 p./no.
Published by: Medviks T V - Foerlag AB, Skeppsbron 32, Fack 2155, Stockholm, 10314, Sweden. TEL 46-8-791-19-40, FAX 46-8-20-27-22. Ed. Bert Willborg. Adv. contact Karin Brunnsjoe Lind. B&W page SEK 9,000, color page SEK 12,000; trim 210 x 140. Circ: 63,000.

384.5 USA ISSN 0895-4143
TK7881.3
THE PERFECT VISION; high performance home theater. Text in English. 1986. bi-m. USD 14.95 domestic; USD 29.95 in Canada; USD 34.95 elsewhere; USD 5.95 newsstand/cover (effective 2005). adv. illus. reprints avail. **Document type:** *Magazine, Consumer.*
Related titles: Online - full text ed.
Published by: Absolute Multimedia Inc., 8121 Bee Caves Rd., Ste. 100, Austin, TX 78746-4938. TEL 512-479-4661, 888-475-5991, FAX 512-328-7528, editor@theperfectvision.com, info@avguide.com, http://www.theperfectvision.com. Ed. Robert Harley. Pub. Mark Fisher. Adv. contact Cheryl Smith. Circ: 20,000. **Dist. by:** International Publishers Direct, 27500 Riverview Center Blvd, Bonita Springs, FL 34134. TEL 858-320-4563, FAX 858-677-3220.

PHI PI EPSILON STAGE SCREEN & RADIO. see *LABOR UNIONS*

PHOTONICS COMPONENTS & SUBSYSTEMS. see *PHYSICS—Optics*

384.5 IRL ISSN 0791-2161
PLAYBACK. Text in English. 1989. 10/yr. adv. **Description:** Covers issues in broadcast TV and radio.
Published by: Production Industry Publications Ltd., Prospect House 1 Prospect Rd., Glangevlin, Co. Cavan, Ireland. TEL 303455, FAX 300888. Adv. contact Stephen Roche. B&W page USD 2,529, color page USD 4,427; trim 8.25 x 11.75. Circ: 3,500.

621.388 CAN ISSN 0836-2114
PLAYBACK; Canada's broadcast and production journal. Text in English. 1986. 25/yr. CND 69.50 domestic; USD 99.50 in United States; USD 186 elsewhere. adv. illus.; stat. back issues avail. **Document type:** *Trade.*
Related titles: Online - full text ed.: (from Micromedia ProQuest).
Indexed: CBCARef, CBPI.
Published by: Brunico Communications Inc., 366 Adelaide St W, Ste 500, Toronto, ON M5V 1R9, Canada. TEL 416-408-2300, FAX 416-408-0870, circ@brunico.com, http://www.brunico.com. Ed. Allison Vale. adv.: B&W page CND 2,985, color page CND 3,875; trim 10.88 x 8.13. Circ: 9,800 (controlled).

384.55 CAN
PLAYBACK INTERNATIONAL. Text in English. 1991. 2/yr. **Document type:** *Trade.* **Description:** Covers production facilities, services and locations of the motion picture industry in Canada.
Incorporates: Canada on Location (1194-3068)
Published by: Brunico Communications Inc., 366 Adelaide St W, Ste 500, Toronto, ON M5V 1R9, Canada. TEL 416-408-2300, FAX 416-408-0870, circ@brunico.com. Ed. Allison Vale. adv.: color page CND 2,775; trim 10.88 x 8.13. Circ: 6,700.

791.45029 USA ISSN 1521-6160
P88.8
PLUNKETT'S ENTERTAINMENT AND MEDIA INDUSTRY ALMANAC. Text in English. 1998. a. USD 249.99 (effective 2005); includes CD-ROM. **Document type:** *Directory, Trade.*
Related titles: CD-ROM ed.
Published by: Plunkett Research, Ltd, PO Drawer 541737, Houston, TX 77254-1737. TEL 713-932-0000, FAX 713-932-7080, info@plunkettresearch.com, http://www.plunkettresearch.com. Ed., Pub. Jack W Plunkett.

POLITICS, MEDIA, AND POPULAR CULTURE. see *SOCIOLOGY*

384.5532 DEU
POPSTARS; das Magazin zur TV-Serie. Text in German. 2000. fortn. EUR 2 newsstand/cover (effective 2003). adv. **Document type:** *Magazine, Consumer.* **Description:** Contains inside news and gossip on the stars of the television series "Popstars".
Published by: Axel Springer Young Mediahouse, Werinherstr 71, Munich, 81541, Germany. TEL 49-89-697490, FAX 49-89-69749312, http://cultfish.funonline.de/popstars.htm, http://www.asv.de. Circ: 280,000 (paid and controlled).

384.5 USA
P88.8
POWER MEDIA YEARBOOK. Text in English. 1989. a. USD 166.50 (effective 2000). **Document type:** *Directory.* **Description:** Directory of top contacts in the media, including newsletters, magazines, newspapers, radio and television.
Formerly (until 2002): Power Media Selects (1045-9545)
Related titles: Diskette ed.: USD 260 (effective 2000).
Published by: Broadcast Interview Source, 2233 Wisconsin Ave, N W, Washington, DC 20007. TEL 202-333-4904, FAX 202-342-5411, editor@yearbook.com, http://www.yearbook.com. Ed., Pub., R&P, Adv. contact Mitchell P Davis.

384.55 GBR ISSN 0141-0857
PRACTICAL WIRELESS. Text in English. 1932. m. adv. **Document type:** *Magazine, Consumer.*
Formerly (until 1948): Practical Wireless and Practical Television
Indexed: BrTechI, Inspec, M&TEA.
—BLDSC (6596.995000), AskIEEE, CISTI, IE, Infotrieve, ingenta. **CCC.**
Published by: P W Publishing Ltd., Arrowsmith Ct, Station Approach, Broadstone, Dorset BH18 8PW, United Kingdom. TEL 44-870-2247810, FAX 44-1425-461883, http://www.pwpublishing.ltd.uk/. Ed. Rob Mannion. Adv. contact Roger Hall. B&W page GBP 745. Circ: 20,000.

▼ new title ➤ refereed ✶ unverified ♦ full entry avail.

384.555 DEU
PREMIERE MAGAZIN. Text in German. 1999. m. adv. **Document type:** *Magazine, Consumer.*
Published by: Premiere Fernsehen GmbH & Co. KG, Medienallee 4, Unterfoehring, 85774, Germany. service@premiere.de, http://www.premiere.de. adv.: page EUR 33,000. Circ: 2,430,000 (controlled).

791.45 USA
PREVIEW (RADNOR). Text in English. m. USD 12. adv. **Document type:** *Consumer.*
Related titles: Online - full text ed.
Published by: T V Guide Magazine Group, 4 Radnor Corporate Center, 100 Matsonford Rd, Radnor, PA 19088. tvg.customer.service@tvguide.com, http://www.tvguide.com. Ed. Steven Reddicliffe. adv.: B&W page USD 22,500, color page USD 28,125; trim 10.75 x 7.88. Circ: 220,000.

PREVIEW (RICHARDSON). see *MOTION PICTURES*

791.45 CAN
PRIMETIME. Text in English. 1983. m. CND 19.26 (effective 2000). adv. film rev.; tel.rev. **Document type:** *Magazine, Consumer.* **Description:** Pay-television program source carrying schedules and program descriptions for the Western Canadian movie channels and the major specialty networks.
Published by: PrimeTime Publishing Inc, 6211 Roper Rd, Edmonton, AB T6B 3G6, Canada. TEL 780-466-0087, FAX 780-466-1009, info@primetimepublishing.com. Ed. Helen Baggaley. Pub. Debbie Tansley. Adv. contact Aurea Vasseur. B&W page USD 8,350, color page USD 9,825. Circ: 520,000.

384.55 CAN
PRIMEURS MAGAZINE. Text in French. 1984. m. CND 21 (effective 2000). adv. film rev.; tel.rev. illus. **Document type:** *Consumer.* **Description:** Publishes stories and descriptions of feature films, as well as programming information for Eastern Canadian French pay T.V. subscribers.
Formerly: Super Ecran
Published by: Feature Publishing Ltd., 2100 rue Ste-Catherine Ouest, 10th Fl., Montreal, PQ H3H 2T3, Canada. TEL 514-939-5024, FAX 514-939-1515. Ed. Mireille Duhamel. Pub. Marvin Boisvert. Circ: 325,000.

THE PRIZE. see *FOLKLORE*

388.55 ROM ISSN 1224-9483
PRO T V. Text in Romanian. 1996. w. adv. **Document type:** *Magazine, Consumer.*
Published by: Publimedia International, Str. Luterana nr. 11, bloc CINOR, et. 5, Bucharest, Romania. TEL 40-21-3033907, FAX 40-21-3033958, office@protv.ro, http://www.protv.ro.

PRODUCER'S MASTERGUIDE; the international production manual for broadcast-television, feature films, television, commercials, cable, digital and videotape industries in the United States, Canada, the United Kingdom, Bermuda, the Caribbean Islands, Mexico, South America, Europe, Israel, the Far East, Australia and New Zealand. see *MOTION PICTURES*

621.388 GBR
TK6540 CODEN: IBSODS
PRODUCTION EUROPE; acquisition, post-production, audio, transmission, new media. Text in English. 1978. m. GBP 82, USD 174. adv. **Document type:** *Trade.* **Description:** Comments on technological developments in the radio and television industry.
Incorporates: Sound Engineer and Producer (0957-9508); International Broadcasting (0957-4425); Which was formerly: International Broadcasting Systems and Operation (0141-1748); Broadcasting Systems and Operation
Indexed: B&I, Inspec.
—AskIEEE.
Published by: E M A P Media (Subsidiary of: E M A P Business Communications), 33-39 Bowling Green Ln, London, EC1R 0DA, United Kingdom. TEL 44-171-505-8073, FAX 44-171-833-4519, production@media.emap.co.uk. Ed. Paul Marks. Adv. contact Julie Moore. Circ: 10,000. **Subscr. to:** Readerlink Ltd., Audit House, 260 Field End Rd, Ruislip, Mddx HA4 9LT, United Kingdom. TEL 44-20-8868-4499, FAX 44-20-8429-3117.

384.55 GBR ISSN 1460-5007
PRODUCTION SOLUTIONS. Text in English. 1990. m. GBP 54 domestic; GBP 90 in Europe; GBP 135 elsewhere; GBP 3 newsstand/cover. adv. tr.lit. back issues avail. **Document type:** *Trade.* **Description:** Covers all aspects of broadcast television production and reviews professional broadcasting and production equipment.
Formerly (until 1997): Television Buyer (0959-6917)
—IE. **CCC.**
Published by: Emap Media Ltd. (Subsidiary of: Emap Business Communications Ltd.), 33-39 Bowling Green Ln, London, EC1R 0DA, United Kingdom. TEL 44-20-7505-8000, FAX 44-20-7505-8504, production@media.emap.co.uk, http://www.emap.com. Ed. Hilary Curtis. Pub. Steve Buckley. Adv. contact Julie Moore. page GBP 2,135; 297 x 210. Circ: 7,927 (controlled). **Subscr. to:** Readerlink, Audit House, 260 Field End Ln, Eastcote, Ruislip, Middx HA4 9LT, United Kingdom. TEL 44-181-868-4499, FAX 44-181-429-3117.

384.55 USA ISSN 1099-8632
PRODUKTION UND TECHNOLOGIE. Text in German. 1997. bi-m. USD 79; USD 55 foreign (effective 1999). tr.lit. back issues avail.; reprints avail. **Document type:** *Trade.* **Description:** Regional edition of Broadcast and Production covers the broadcast industries in Germany, Switzerland, Austria, and Luxembourg.
Related titles: Chinese ed.; French ed.; Portuguese ed.
Published by: I M A S Publishing Group, 5827 Columbia Pike, Ste 310, Falls Church, VA 22041. TEL 703-998-7600, FAX 703-998-2966.

791.45 POL ISSN 1231-2142
PROGRAM T V. Text in Polish. 1989. w. PLZ 33.80; PLZ 0.65 newsstand/cover (effective 1998). adv. film rev.; video rev. **Document type:** *Bulletin.* **Description:** TV Guide containing national, local, satellite and cable TV programs.
Published by: Oficyna Wydawnicza Press - Media, Ul Trembeckiego 5, Rzeszow, 35234, Poland. TEL 48-17-8525555, FAX 48-17-8525555, supnowosci@pressmedia.com.pl, http:// www.pressmedia.com.pl. Ed., R&P Roman Oraczewski. Adv. contact Roman Orzczewski. Circ: 350,000 (controlled).

791.45 GBR ISSN 1353-1395
PROGRAMME NEWS*. Text in English. 1993. q. **Document type:** *Consumer.* **Description:** Contains advance television and radio program information.
Published by: Profile Group (UK) Ltd., 6/7 St Cross St, London, EC1N 8UA, United Kingdom. TEL 44-171-405-4455, FAX 44-171-430-1089. Ed. Keith Claxton.

384.55 USA
PROGRAMMER'S GUIDE. Text in English. 1999. a. USD 75 to non-members; USD 50 to members. **Description:** Offers a complete listing of television program distributors and service companies.
Published by: National Association of Television Program Executives, 2425 Olympic Blvd, Ste 550E, Santa Monica, CA 90404-4030. TEL 310-453-4440, FAX 310-453-5258, http://www.natpe.org.

384.5 USA
PROMAX INTERNATIONAL. Text in English. 1985. q. membership. adv. bk.rev. index. **Document type:** *Trade.* **Description:** Directed to radio and TV stations and networks, cable systems, cable networks, radio, program distributors.
Formerly: B P M E Image
Related titles: Online - full text ed.
Published by: Promotion & Marketing Executives in the Electronic Media, 2029 Century Pk E, Ste 555, Los Angeles, CA 90067-2906. TEL 310-788-7600, FAX 310-788-7616, http://www.promax.org. Ed., R&P Dominick Morra. Pub. Jim Chabin. Adv. contact Suzanne Marie Gutierrez. Circ: 2,000 (controlled).

384.55 USA ISSN 0193-3663
PN1990.9.P82
PUBLIC BROADCASTING REPORT; the authoritative news service for public broadcasting and allied fields . Text in English. 1978. bi-w. USD 680 (effective 2005). illus. index. reprints avail. **Document type:** *Newsletter, Trade.*
Incorporates (1967-1997): E T V Newsletter (Educational Television) (0012-8023)
Related titles: Online - full text ed.: (from bigchalk, LexisNexis, Northern Light Technology, Inc.).
Published by: Warren Communications News, Inc., 2115 Ward Ct, N W, Washington, DC 20037. TEL 202-872-9200, 800-327-7205, FAX 202-293-3435, info@warren-news.com, http://www.idpa.org/ndpawarr.html, http://www.warren-news.com. Ed. Michael Feazel. Pub. Albert Warren.

PUBLIC TELEVISION TRANSCRIPTS INDEX. see *COMMUNICATIONS—Abstracting, Bibliographies, Statistics*

621.388 USA
Q C W A JOURNAL. Text in English. 1954. q. membership. adv. bk.rev.
Formerly: Q C W A News
Published by: Quarter Century Wireless Association, Inc., 159 E 16th Ave, Eugene, OR 97401-4017. TEL 503-683-0987, FAX 503-683-4181. Ed. J C Walsh. Circ: 9,500.

QU YI. see *THEATER*

791.45 DEU
QUIZTIME; Fit fuer die TV-Shows. Text in German. 2001. m. adv. **Document type:** *Magazine, Consumer.* **Description:** Provides information and test quizzes on how to play with or participate on TV quiz shows.
Published by: Panini Verlags GmbH, Ravensstr 48, Nettetal, 41334, Germany. TEL 49-711-947680, FAX 49-711-94768830, info@panini-dino.de, http://www.dinoag.de/magazin/quiztime.htm, http://www.panini-media.de. Adv. contact Petra Sonnenfroh-Kost. page EUR 5,000; trim 210 x 280. Circ: 350,000 (paid and controlled).

791.45 DEU
R & R - A F N CABLE & SATELLITE T V. (Rest & Relaxation) Text in German. 1971. m. adv. film rev. **Document type:** *Magazine, Consumer.* **Description:** Entertainment magazine for Americans and Canadians stationed in Germany.
Former titles: R and R Shoppers News; R and R Entertainment Digest; R and R Entertainment Digest - with Guide T V; Guide to T V and Easy Living
Published by: R & R Communications GmbH, Kolpingstr 1, Leimen, 69181, Germany. TEL 49-6224-706-0, FAX 49-6224-70616, info@rrcomm.de, http://www.rrmagazine.com, http://www.rrcomm.de. Ed. Marjorie Hess. R&P, Adv. contact Ailsa Mattaj TEL 49-6224-70630. B&W page EUR 3,450, color page EUR 4,095; trim 210 x 280. Circ: 66,000.

384.55 CAN
R B WEEKENDER. Text in English. w. CND 35.
Published by: Robinson-Blackmore Ltd., 18 O'Leary Ave., P O Box 8660, St. John's, NF A1B 3T7, Canada. TEL 709-722-8500, FAX 709-722-2228. Ed. G French. Circ: 75,450.

R F E; Technik und Markt der Medienelektronik. (Radio Fernsehen Elektronik) see *ELECTRONICS*

621.388 DEU ISSN 0942-7295
R F MAGAZIN FUER UNTERHALTUNGS- UND KOMMUNIKATIONSELEKTRONIK. Text in German. 1957. m.
Former titles (until 1991): R F Magazin fuer Unterhaltungs- und Informationselektronik (0930-3898); (until 1980): Deutsche Rundfunk-Einzelhandel (0012-0634)
Published by: Deutscher Radio- und Fernseh- Fachverband e.V., Sachsenring 89, Cologne, 50677, Germany. TEL 0221-3398115.

791.45 DEU
R T V; illustriertes Programm. Text in German. 1961. w. included in subscription to newspaper. adv. illus. **Document type:** *Magazine, Consumer.*
Formerly: Radio und Television (0033-7757)
Related titles: Online - full text ed.; ♦ Supplement to: Fraenkisches Volksblatt.
Indexed: ISAP.
Published by: Deutscher Supplement Verlag GmbH, Breslauer Str 300, Nuernberg, 90471, Germany. TEL 49-911-8003161, FAX 49-911-8003639, TELEX 622061-DSV-D, info@rtv.de, info@supplement-verlag.de, http://www.rtv.de, http://www.deutscher-supplement-verlag.de. Ed. Dieter Klink. Adv. contact Ulrich Witt. B&W page EUR 59,104, color page EUR 73,400; trim 210 x 260. Circ: 8,284,642 (controlled).

059.94511 HUN ISSN 1418-4796
R T V MUSOR MAGAZIN. (Radio es Televizio) Text in Hungarian. 1998. w. adv. bk.rev.; film rev.; music rev.; tel.rev. **Document type:** *Magazine, Consumer.* **Description:** Contains detailed television program listings and weekly recommendationa as well as articles on celebrities, travel destinations, horoscopes, and other items of general interest.
Published by: Sanoma Budapest Kiadoi Rt. (Subsidiary of: Sanoma Magazines Finland Corporation), Bokor Utca 15-19, Budapest, 1037, Hungary. TEL 36-1-4371100, FAX 36-1-2502303, info@sanomabp.hu, http://www.sanoma.hu. Adv. contact Gabriella Rakosi. page HUF 550,000; trim 240 x 330. Circ: 110,253 (paid).

RAABTA. see *MOTION PICTURES*

384.5 ZAF
RADIO & T V. Text in English. q. illus. **Document type:** *Consumer.*
Formerly: Interkom
Published by: South African Broadcasting Corporation, Private Bag X1, Auckland Park, Johannesburg 2006, South Africa. TEL 27-11-714-3741, FAX 27-11-714-6514.

RADIO AND TELEVISION CAREER DIRECTORY. see *OCCUPATIONS AND CAREERS*

RADIO T V TECNICO. see *COMMUNICATIONS—Radio*

384.5 CHE
RADIO TV8. Text in French. 1923. w. CHF 128; CHF 3 newsstand/cover (effective 1999). adv. **Document type:** *Consumer.* **Description:** Connects viewers to the vast selection of Swiss television programs.
Published by: Ringier AG, Dufourstr 47, Zuerich, 8008, Switzerland. TEL 41-1-2596483, FAX 41-1-2596996, thd@ringier.ch, info@ringier.ch, http://www.ringier.ch. Ed. Corinne Badoux. Adv. contact Daniela Thuring. B&W page CHF 3,296, color page CHF 5,832. Circ: 55,721 (paid).

RADIO - VISION TIMES. see *COMMUNICATIONS—Radio*

RADIOCORRIERE - T V. see *COMMUNICATIONS—Radio*

RADIOLYUBITEL'. see *COMMUNICATIONS—Radio*

621.388 ESP ISSN 0211-3546
RADIORAMA; practica electronica - t.v. - radio - hi-fi - ciencia. Text in Spanish. 1967. 11/yr. USD 170 (effective 1999). adv. charts; illus.; tr.lit.
Published by: (Club de Radiorama), Ediciones Tecnicas Rede, S.A., Ecuador 91, 1o, Barcelona, 08029, Spain. TEL 34-93-4302872, FAX 34-93-4392813, TELEX 50662 SCTBE. Ed. Jose M Prades. Circ: 7,000.

C

621.38 DNK ISSN 0033-8508
RADIOTELEGRAFEN. Contents page in English. 1918. m. free membership. adv. charts; illus.; stat.; tr.lit.
Published by: Radiotelegrafistforeningen af 1917, Havnegade 55, Copenhagen K, 1058, Denmark. TEL 45-33-14-19-17, FAX 45-33-14-19-24.

384.55 AUS
REAL 2 REEL. Text in English. q. free. tel.rev.; video rev. illus. back issues avail. **Document type:** *Newsletter, Corporate.* **Description:** Reports on film and video programs being produced by Film Australia and updates regarding production facilities at Film Australia and corporate news.
Related titles: E-mail ed.; Fax ed.; Online - full content ed.
Published by: Film Australia Pty. Ltd., 101 Eton Rd, Lindfield, NSW 2070, Australia. TEL 61-2-9413-8723, FAX 61-2-9416-9401, ktilgals@filmaust.com.au, http://www.filmaust.com.au. Ed. Kirsten Tilgals. Circ: 1,750.

384.55 USA
REALISA SON. Text in French. 1999. bi-m. **Document type:** *Trade.* **Description:** Offers pro audio news, new product announcements, trade show reviews, and user reports on fixed and mobile audio installations.
Published by: I M A S Publishing Group, 5827 Columbia Pike, Ste 310, Falls Church, VA 22041. TEL 703-998-7600, FAX 703-998-2966, adsales@imaspub.com, http://www.imaspub.com.

384.55 USA
THE RECORD (WILKSBORO). Text in English. 1982. w. adv. **Document type:** *Newspaper.* **Description:** Informs readers of news and events in Wilkes County, NC; includes features and columns.
Formerly: Thursday Magazine
Published by: Thursday Publications, Inc., 316 E St, Box 1061, N, Wilkesboro, NC 28659. TEL 910-667-0134, FAX 910-667-6694. Ed., R&P Jerry Lankford. Pub. Kenneth P Welborn. Adv. contact Linda Bumgarner. Circ: 22,500.

REGISTER OF STUNT CO-ORDINATORS - ARRANGERS & PERFORMERS. see *THEATER*

REGULATORY AND COMPETITION AUSTRALIA. see *COMMUNICATIONS—Telephone And Telegraph*

RESPONSE MAGAZINE; multi-channel direct advertising. see *ADVERTISING AND PUBLIC RELATIONS*

384.5452 USA ISSN 0149-9971
REVIEW OF INTERNATIONAL BROADCASTING✶. Text in English, Spanish. 1977. m. USD 18. adv. bk.rev. charts; illus.
Published by: Glenn Hauser, Ed. & Pub., PO Box 1684, Enid, OK 73702-1684. Circ: 2,000.

REVISTA MONITOR DE RADIO E TELEVISAO. see *COMMUNICATIONS—Radio*

RIGHTS AND LIABILITIES OF PUBLISHERS, BROADCASTERS, AND REPORTERS. see *LAW—Civil Law*

RIVISTA DEL CINEMATOGRAFO; e della communicazione sociale. see *MOTION PICTURES*

ROAD & TRACK ROAD GEAR; in-car audio and video. see *ENGINEERING—Electrical Engineering*

791.45 USA ISSN 1520-7722
PN1992.3.U5
ROSS REPORTS TELEVISION AND FILM; agents & casting directors, television production, films & development. Text in English. 1949. 6/yr. USD 65 domestic; USD 76 in Canada; USD 88 foreign; USD 9.95 newsstand/cover (effective 2005). adv. charts. **Document type:** *Magazine, Trade.* **Description:** Lists industry professionals: actors, production personnel, talent agents, casting directors, aspiring performers, talent unions, guilds and associations.
Formerly: Ross Reports Television (0035-8355)
Related titles: Online - full text ed.: (from Gale Group).
—CCC.
Published by: V N U Business Publications (Subsidiary of: V N U Business Media), 770 Broadway, New York, NY 10003-9595. http://www.rossreports.com, http://www.vnubusinessmedia.com.Ed. Bruce B Morris. Pub., Adv. contact Scott Berg. Circ: 13,545 (paid). **Subscr. to:** PO Box 2054, Marion, OH 43306. TEL 800-745-8922.

RUNDFUNK- UND FERNSEHPROGRAMM. see *COMMUNICATIONS—Radio*

384.55 USA
S E T FREE; the newsletter against television. Text in English. 1982. q. USD 5. adv. bk.rev. **Document type:** *Newsletter.* **Description:** Contains news and updates about television's harmful role in society with summaries of scholarly reports and empirical data.
Formerly: News and Notes From All Over
Published by: Society for the Eradication of Television, PO Box 10491, Oakland, CA 94610-0491. TEL 510-763-8712. Ed. Steve Wagner. Circ: 1,200.

S M P T E MOTION IMAGING JOURNAL. see *MOTION PICTURES*

S R G - S S R IDEE SUISSE. GESCHAEFTSBERICHT. see *COMMUNICATIONS—Radio*

S R G - S S R IDEE SUISSE. PORTRAIT. see *COMMUNICATIONS—Radio*

SABRINA'S SECRETS. see *CHILDREN AND YOUTH—For*

384.5532 DEU
SAT.1 - MEINE WELT. Text in German. 2001. 4/yr. **Document type:** *Magazine, Consumer.* **Description:** Contains information and articles on programming and entertainment broadcast by the SAT1 network.
Address: Postfach 2361, Offenburg, 77613, Germany. TEL 49-180-5131111, FAX 49-180-5278174, info@sat1-meinewelt.de, http://www.sat1.de/meinewelt.

384.51 ITA ISSN 1126-5140
SAT & CO. Text in Italian. 1998. m. **Description:** Contains articles dedicated to satellite television.
Published by: Techno Publishing S.r.l., Via Tacito 5, Corsico, MI 20094, Italy. TEL 39-02-4402360, FAX 39-02-45101659, tcp@tcp.it, http://www.tcp.it.

SAT - AUDIO - VIDEO; postepy w elektronice powszechnego uzytku. see *ELECTRONICS*

384.51 ITA
SAT TV TIME. Text in Italian. m. **Document type:** *Magazine, Consumer.* **Description:** Contains a monthly programming guide for satellite television channels.
Published by: Techno Publishing S.r.l., Via Tacito 5, Corsico, MI 20094, Italy. TEL 39-02-4402360, FAX 39-02-45101659, tcp@tcp.it, http://www.tcp.it. Ed. Guido da Rozze.

384.51 DEU
SAT UND KABEL; Digital T V - Medien - Breitband. Text in German. 1994. m. EUR 39; EUR 3.90 newsstand/cover (effective 2003). adv. **Document type:** *Magazine, Consumer.*
Related titles: Online - full text ed.
Published by: Cybermedia Verlagsgesellschaft mbH, Wallbergstr. 10, Mering, 86415, Germany. TEL 49-8233-74010, FAX 49-8233-740117, redaktion@satundkabel.de, http://www.satundkabel.de, http://www.maniac.de/oldhome/cybermediaverlag.de/index.htm. Ed. Alexander Roesch. Adv. contact Verena Zach. B&W page EUR 4,000, color page EUR 5,500. Circ: 100,000 (paid and controlled).

384.554 DEU
SATELLIT; die unabhaengige Zeitschrift fuer den Fernseh- und Radioempfang via Satellit und Kabel. Text in German. 1999. m. EUR 48 domestic; EUR 54 foreign; EUR 4.20 newsstand/cover (effective 2003). adv. **Document type:** *Magazine, Trade.*
Published by: Verlag fuer Technik und Handwerk GmbH, Robert-Bosch-Str 4, Baden-Baden, 76532, Germany. TEL 49-7221-50870, FAX 49-7221-508752, verlag@vth.de, http://www.vth.de/funk/satellit/satellit.htm. Ed. Michael Buege. Adv. contact Kai-Christian Gaaz. B&W page EUR 1,840, color page EUR 2,300. Circ: 49,500 (paid and controlled). **Subscr. to:** P M S GmbH & Co. KG, Postfach 104139, Duesseldorf 40032, Germany. TEL 49-211-6907890, FAX 49-211-69078950.

621.388 ZAF
SATELLITE. Text in English. 1993. m. adv. illus. **Document type:** *Consumer.*
Published by: (Bop T V - Mmabatho T V), Bophuthatswana Broadcasting Corporation, Private Bag X2150, Mmabatho, North West Province 8681, South Africa. TEL 27-140-897111, FAX 27-140-897299. Pub. Peter Godson. Adv. contact Thorsten Stamer.

384.51 USA ISSN 1547-6707
▼ **SATELLITE BUSINESS SOLUTIONS.** Text in English. 2003. q. USD 89 domestic; USD 99 in Canada; USD 129 elsewhere (effective 2003). adv. **Document type:** *Magazine.*
Published by: Access Intelligence, LLC (Subsidiary of: Veronis, Suhler & Associates Inc.), 1201 Seven Locks Rd, Ste 300, Potomac, MD 20854. TEL 301-354-2000, FAX 301-424-2058, http://www.sbsmagazine.com, http://www.pbimedia.com. Ed. Nick Mitsis. Pub. Joe Rosone. Adv. contact Janis Davis.

384.55 USA ISSN 1075-1823
PN1992.3.U5
SATELLITE CHOICE. Text in English. m. USD 52 (effective 1999). adv. **Document type:** *Consumer.* **Description:** Contains listings and reviews for the 18-inch DSS Satellite System. Includes complete information on on DIRECTV and USSB Satellite programming.
Published by: Fortuna Communications Corporation, PO Box 310, Fortuna, CA 95540-0310. TEL 707-725-6591, FAX 707-725-4311. Ed. James Scott. Pub. Patrick O'Dell. Adv. contact George Bryant. Circ: 125,000.

621.388 USA ISSN 0892-3329
SATELLITE DIRECT; the magazine of direct-broadcast satellite communications. Text in English. 1983. m. USD 34.95 domestic; USD 52 in Canada (effective 2005). adv. illus. s-a. index. reprints avail. **Document type:** *Magazine, Consumer.*
Formerly (until 1987): Satellite Dealer (0739-876X)
Published by: Vogel Communications Inc., 701 5th Ave, 36th Fl, Seattle, WA 98104. TEL 206-262-8183, FAX 206-262-8187, info@directmagazine.com, http://www.directmagazine.com. Ed. Candace Korchinski. Pub. Steven R Vogel. Circ: 300,000.

621.388 CAN
SATELLITE DISH GUIDE. Text in English. w. CND 69.99 (effective 1997). adv.
Published by: T V Publishing Group, 201 4201 25A Ave, Vernon, BC V1T 7G8, Canada. TEL 250-542-0469, 800-663-4424, FAX 250-542-0942. Ed., R&P Deeny Grazier. Pub. Tom Monahan. Adv. contact Norm Metcalf.

791.45 CAN ISSN 0843-8617
SATELLITE ENTERTAINMENT GUIDE. Text in English. m. CND 57 (effective 2001).
Published by: Vogel Satellite TV Publishing, 1109 TD Tower, Edmonton, AB AB T5J 2Z1, Canada. feedback@satguide.com, http://www.satguide.com. Ed. Gene Kosowan.

384.55 ITA ISSN 1122-9284
SATELLITE EUROSAT; tecnologia della televisione via satellite. Text in Italian. 1986. m. EUR 42 (effective 2005). **Document type:** *Magazine, Trade.* **Description:** Provides broad information on satellite TV, exhibitions, products and a program guide.
Related titles: ♦ Supplement(s): Annuario Eurosat. ISSN 1123-6523.
Published by: Gruppo Editoriale J C E, Via Patecchio 2, Milan, MI 20141, Italy. TEL 39-02-57316011, FAX 39-02-57316291, info@jce.it, http://www.jce.it. Ed. Amedeo Bozzoni. Pub. Jacopo Castelfranchi. Circ: 120,000.

C

621.388 GBR
SATELLITE INTERNATIONAL✶. Text in English. 1998. s-m. (23/yr.). USD 885, GBP 558 (effective 2000). back issues avail. **Document type:** *Newsletter.* **Description:** Provides analytical reports on the satellite industry and satellite services, including TV and video, fixed and mobile telecoms, and distribution of broadband multimedia service.
Published by: Baskerville (Subsidiary of: T & F Informa plc), Sheepen Place, Colchester, Essex C03 3LP, United Kingdom. TEL 44-20-70175537, FAX 44-20-70174783, telecoms.enquiries@informa.com, http://www.baskerville.telecoms.com/.

384.51 USA ISSN 0161-3448
SATELLITE NEWS. Text in English. 1978. w. (48/yr.). looseleaf. USD 1,197 domestic (effective 2005). **Document type:** *Newsletter, Trade.*
Incorporates (1983-2003): Interspace (0269-3615); (1991-2001): Global Positioning & Navigation News (1072-3080); (1983-2001): Space Business News (0738-9884); (1989-2000): Mobile Satellite News (1046-5286); (1982-199?): D B S News (0733-9739); (1986-1994): World Satellite Update (1054-920X)
Related titles: Online - full text ed.: (from bigchalk, Gale Group, LexisNexis, Northern Light Technology, Inc., O C L C Online Computer Library Center, Inc., ProQuest Information & Learning).
Indexed: ABIn, PROMT.
—CCC.
Published by: Access Intelligence, LLC (Subsidiary of: Veronis, Suhler & Associates Inc.), 1201 Seven Locks Rd, Ste 300, Potomac, MD 20854. TEL 301-354-2000, 800-777-5006, FAX 301-424-2709, dbross@pbimedia.com, clientservices@accessintel.com, http://www.pbimedia.com/cgi/catalog/info?SN. Ed. Paul Dykewicz. **Dist. by:** Publications Resource Group, 121 Union St., Box 792, North Adams, MA 01247. TEL 413-664-6185, FAX 413-664-9643.

384.51 USA
SATELLITE ONLINE MAGAZINE. Text in English. w. **Document type:** *Newsletter.* **Description:** Dedicated to satellites and satellite communication.
Media: Online - full text.
Address: FAX 707-939-9235, engineer@satnews.com, http://www.satmagazine.com/toc.html.

621.388 USA ISSN 0732-7668
PN1992
SATELLITE ORBIT; complete national TV programming guide. Text in English. 1982. m. USD 45.95 domestic; USD 59.95 in Canada (effective 2005). adv. illus. back issues avail.; reprints avail. **Document type:** *Magazine, Consumer.* **Description:** TV viewing guide for home satellite dish owners.
Supersedes (in 1985): Satguide
Published by: Vogel Communications Inc., 701 5th Ave, 36th Fl, Seattle, WA 98104. TEL 206-262-8183, FAX 206-262-8187, info@orbitmagazine.com, http://www.orbitmagazine.com. Ed. Gene Kosowan TEL 206-262-8183 ext 248. Pub. Steven R Vogel. adv.: B&W page USD 7,325, color page USD 9,300. Circ: 214,953.

384.55 GBR ISSN 0268-8425
SATELLITE T V EUROPE. Text in English. 1986. m. GBP 30 domestic; GBP 49 in Europe; GBP 64 elsewhere; GBP 2.75 newsstand/cover (effective 2003). adv. film rev.; music rev.; tel.rev. illus. back issues avail. **Document type:** *Magazine, Consumer.* **Description:** Contains comprehensive programme information for all the English-language channels available in the UK plus the most popular foreign stations. It also includes a film guide to all the movies on digital satellite television, an A-Z sports diary and many exciting features on the action, drama, soaps, documentaries and music on satellite.
Related titles: Spanish ed.
Published by: Highbury - WV (Subsidiary of: Highbury House Communications PLC), 53-79 Highgate Rd, London, NW5 1TW, United Kingdom. TEL 44-20-73311000, FAX 44-20-73311273, mail@satellitetvtoday.com, http://www.satellitetvtoday.com/, http://www.hhc.co.uk/. Circ: 100,000 (paid).

791.45 GBR ISSN 0955-4602
SATELLITE TIMES. Text in English. 1988. m. GBP 24 domestic; GBP 48 in Europe; GBP 2.20 newsstand/cover. **Document type:** *Consumer.* **Description:** Contains information on satellite television as well as programs and general entertainment features.
Published by: Everpage Ltd., PO Box 50, Leeds, W Yorks LS18 5XQ, United Kingdom. TEL 44-113-258-5008, stimes@cix.co.uk. Ed. Eric Woods. **Dist. by:** Seymour Distribution Ltd, 86 Newman St, London W1T 3EX, United Kingdom. FAX 44-207-396-8002, enquiries@seymour.co.uk.

384.51 USA ISSN 1529-0212
TK5104
SATELLITE TRANSPONDER GUIDE. Text in English. 1998. bi-m. USD 395 (effective 2004). **Document type:** *Directory, Trade.*
Published by: Access Intelligence, LLC (Subsidiary of: Veronis, Suhler & Associates Inc.), 1201 Seven Locks Rd, Ste 300, Potomac, MD 20854. TEL 301-354-2000, 800-777-5006, FAX 301-424-2058, clientservices@accessintel.com, http://www.pbimedia.com.

384.55 USA ISSN 0193-2861
SATELLITE WEEK. Text in English. 1979. w. USD 1,185 (effective 2004). **Document type:** *Magazine, Trade.* **Description:** Reports on all developments in space communications technology and market news.
Related titles: Online - full text ed.: USD 1,135 (effective 2004) (from bigchalk, LexisNexis, Northern Light Technology, Inc.).
Published by: Warren Communications News, Inc., 2115 Ward Ct, N W, Washington, DC 20037. TEL 202-872-9200, 800-327-7205, FAX 202-293-3435, pbi@phillips.com, info@warren-news.com, http://www.prgguide.com/newsletters/cellular/n3-001w.html, http://www.warren-news.com. Ed., Pub. Albert Warren. **Dist. by:** Publications Resource Group, 121 Union St., Box 792, North Adams, MA 01247. TEL 413-664-6185, FAX 413-664-9343.

384.51 USA
SATNEWS ONLINE MAGAZINE. Text in English. 1998. w. free. **Document type:** *Trade.*
Media: Online - full content.
Published by: SatNews Publishers, 800 Siesta Way, Sonoma, CA 95476. TEL 707-939-9306, FAX 707-939-9235, design@satnews.com, http://www.satnews.com/.

384.55 USA
SATVISION MAGAZINE. Text in English. 1987. m. USD 35. adv. back issues avail. **Document type:** *Trade.* **Description:** Provides information for satellite television dealers.
Published by: Satellite Broadcasting & Communications Association, 225 Reinekers Ln, Ste 600, Alexandria, VA 22314-2322. TEL 703-549-6990, FAX 703-549-7640. Circ: 10,000 (controlled).

SCHLOSS EINSTEIN MAGAZIN. see *CHILDREN AND YOUTH—For*

SCHULFERNSEHEN (MUNICH). see *EDUCATION*

791.45 USA ISSN 1527-5779
PN1995.9.S26
SCI-FI; the official magazine of the Sci-Fi Channel. Text in English. 1994. 9/yr. USD 16.95 domestic; USD 18.56 elsewhere; USD 4.99 per issue (effective 2003). adv. film rev. illus. back issues avail.; reprints avail. **Document type:** *Magazine, Consumer.* **Description:** Covers cable programming for the Sci-Fi Channel. Includes news, interviews and profiles of actors, filmmakers and writers, and articles about science fiction and horror films and TV series.
Formerly (until 1999): Sci-Fi Entertainment (1075-8860)
Published by: (Sci-Fi Channel), Sovereign Media, 453 Carlisle Dr, Herndon, VA 20170-4819. TEL 703-964-0361, FAX 703-964-0366, http://www.scifi.com/. Ed. Scott Edelman. Pub., Adv. contact Mark Hintz. Circ: 75,000. **Dist. by:** Curtis Circulation Co., 730 River Road, New Milford, NJ 07646. TEL 201-634-7400; **Dist. in UK by:** Comag, Tavistock Works, Tavistock Rd, W Drayton, Middx UB7 7QX, United Kingdom. TEL 44-1895-444055, FAX 44-1895-433602.

384.55 808.838 USA
SCI-FI TV. Text in English. 1998. bi-m. USD 4.99 newsstand/cover. adv. tel.rev. back issues avail. **Document type:** *Consumer.* **Description:** Covers reviews of sci-fi on television.
Published by: Starlog Group, Inc., 475 Park Ave S, 7th Fl, New York, NY 10016. TEL 212-689-2830, http://www.starlog.com. Ed. David McDonnell. R&P, Adv. contact Rita Eisenstein. B&W page USD 1,840, color page USD 2,295.

384.55 USA ISSN 1070-7573
PN1995.9.P7
SCREEN; trade magazine for Chicago's film industry. Text in English. 1979. bi-m. (plus an annual directory). USD 75 (effective 2003). adv. 64 p./no. 3 cols./p.; back issues avail. **Document type:** *Magazine, Consumer.* **Description:** Covers film, video, and audiovisual production within the Chicagoland area: television commercials, industrial and corporate programs, audiovisuals, theatrical features.
Formerly (until 1993): Ruth L Ratny's Screen (0276-153X)
Related titles: Online - full text ed.
Published by: Screen Enterprises, 222 W Ontario St, Ste 500, Chicago, IL 60610-3655. TEL 312-640-0800, FAX 312-640-1928, screen@screenmag.com, http://www.screenmag.com. Ed., Pub., R&P Ruth L Ratny TEL 312-664-5236. Adv. contact Kenn Peterson. Circ: 15,000.

791.45 USA ISSN 0036-9543
➤ **SCREEN.** Text in English. 1959. q. GBP 107, USD 203, EUR 161 to institutions; GBP 113, USD 215, EUR 170 combined subscription to institutions print & online eds. (effective 2006). adv. bk.rev.; film rev. illus. index. 128 p./no.; back issues avail.; reprint service avail. from PQC,PSC. **Document type:** *Journal, Academic/Scholarly.* **Description:** Forum for the development of film and TV studies and cultural theory.
Related titles: Microform ed.: (from PQC); Online - full text ed.: GBP 102, USD 194, EUR 153 to institutions (effective 2005) (from EBSCO Publishing, HighWire Press).
Indexed: ArtHuCI, ArtInd, BAS, CurCont, DIP, FLI, IBR, IBZ, IIFP, IIPA, IITV, MEA, MLA-IB, MRD, RASB, RILM, SSCI, SWA. —BLDSC (8211.754800), IDS, IE, Infotrieve, ingenta. **CCC.**
Published by: (John Logie Baird Centre GBR), Oxford University Press (Subsidiary of: Oxford University Press), 2001 Evans Rd, Cary, NC 27513. TEL 919-677-0977, 800-852-7323, FAX 919-677-1714, jnorders@oup-usa.org, http://screen.oxfordjournals.org/, http://www.us.oup.com. adv.: B&W page GBP 230, B&W page USD 388. Circ: 1,525.

➤ **SCREEN & STAGE DIRECTORY**; national casting guide. see *THEATER*

384.55 GBR
SCREEN DIGEST. Text in English. 1971. m. GBP 375 domestic; GBP 545 foreign (effective 2001). bk.rev. bibl.; charts; stat. index. back issues avail. **Document type:** *Newsletter.* **Description:** Summaries of world news in film, television, video, satellite, multimedia and consumer electronics with statistical surveys and research data, along with lists of events and publications pertaining to screen media worldwide.
Related titles: Online - full text ed.: (from CompuServe Inc., Data-Star).
Indexed: B&I, IIFP, IITV.
Published by: Screen Digest Ltd., Lyme House Studios, 38 Georgiana St, London, NW1 0EB, United Kingdom. TEL 44-20 7482-5842, FAX 44-20-7580-0060, sales@screendigest.com, http://www.screendigest.com/. Ed. David Fisher. R&P Allan Hardy.

SCREEN INTERNATIONAL; the voice of the international film business. see *MOTION PICTURES*

SCREEN INTERNATIONAL DAILIES. see *MOTION PICTURES*

SCREENTALK; the international voice of screenwriting. see *MOTION PICTURES*

384.55 791.43 GBR
SCREENWRITER✶. Text in English. 1992. q. GBP 30 (effective 1999). adv. bk.rev.; software rev.; tel.rev.; video rev. abstr.; bibl.; illus. back issues avail. **Document type:** *Newsletter, Trade.* **Description:** To inform, educate and entertain on screenwriting and the film industry.
Related titles: E-mail ed.
Published by: Screenwriters' Workshop, Suffolk House, 1-8 Whitfield Pl, London, W1T 5JV, United Kingdom. http://dspace.dial.pipex.com/town/square/gh91/lsw.htm, http://www.lsw.org.uk/. Ed., R&P Paul Gallagher. adv.: B&W page GBP 100, color page GBP 250. Circ: 1,500 (controlled).

SCRIPTWRITERS MARKET. see *LITERATURE*

SE & HOER. see *COMMUNICATIONS—Radio*

SECOM ANNUAL REPORT (YEAR). see *CRIMINOLOGY AND LAW ENFORCEMENT—Security*

384.55 USA
SECURE SIGNALS. Text in English. 1986. q. membership only. stat.; tr.lit. Supplement avail. **Document type:** *Newsletter.* **Description:** Industry-oriented information covering legal and technical aspects of theft of cable television services and means of preventing losses.
Published by: (Office of Cable Signal Theft), National Cable Television Association, 1724 Massachusetts Ave, N W, Washington, DC 20036. TEL 202-775-3684, FAX 202-775-3696, ocst@ncta.com. Ed. Staci M Pittman. Circ: 1,000. **Co-sponsor:** Coalition Opposing Signal Theft.

384.555 365.34 USA
SECURITY DIRECTOR'S REPORT YEARBOOK. Text in English. a. USD 224.95 print & online eds. (effective 2003). **Description:** Provides advice on managing security operations and protecting your organization's people, property, and assets. Also covers crisis management, crime and workplace violence prevention, investigations, and information security.
Related titles: Online - full text ed.: USD 219 (effective 2003); ♦ Cumulative ed. of: I O M A's Security Director's Report. ISSN 1521-916X.
Published by: Institute of Management & Administration, Inc., 3 Park Ave, New York, NY 10016-5902. TEL 212-244-0360, FAX 212-564-0465, subserve@ioma.com, http://www.ioma.com. Ed. Garett Seivold.

384.554 USA
SEE. Text in English. m. USD 47.40; USD 4.95 newsstand/cover (effective 2001). adv. **Description:** Provides programming information for DirectTV subscribers. Includes features on movies, Hollywood stars, and sports.
Published by: T V S M, Inc., 1211 Ave of the Americas, New York, NY 10036. TEL 212-852-7500, FAX 212-852-7323. Pub. Richard Porter. Adv. contact Keith Baldwin.

384.55 621.381 794.8 ITA
SELL OUT. Text in Italian. m. (10/yr.). EUR 20 (effective 2005).
Published by: Editoriale Duesse SpA, Via Donatello 5b, Milan, 20131, Italy. TEL 39-02-277961, FAX 39-02-27796300, e-duesse@e-duesse.it, http://www.e-duesse.it.

384.55 CHN
SHANGHAI DIANSHI/SHANGHAI TELEVISION. Text in Chinese. m. USD 40.40.
Published by: (Shanghai Dianshitai/Shanghai Television Station), Shanghai Dianshi Bianjibu, 651 Nanjing Xilu, Shanghai, 200041, China. TEL 2562213. **Dist. in US by:** China Books & Periodicals Inc, 360 Swift Ave., Ste. 48, S San Fran, CA 94080-6220. TEL 415-282-2994.

SHICHOKAKU KYOIKU/AUDIO-VISUAL EDUCATION. see *EDUCATION*

SHOOT. see *ADVERTISING AND PUBLIC RELATIONS*

384.55 USA
PN1998.A1
SHOOT DIRECTORY FOR COMMERCIAL PRODUCTION AND POSTPRODUCTION. Text in English. 1965. a. USD 95 (effective 2003). adv. bk.rev. **Document type:** *Directory, Trade.*
Former titles: Shoot Commercial Production Directory; Back Stage Shoot Commercial Production Directory; Back Stage T V Film - Tape and Syndication Directory (0098-5481)
Published by: V N U Business Publications (Subsidiary of: V N U Business Media), 770 Broadway, New York, NY 10003-9595. TEL 646-654-5780, FAX 646-654-5813, bmcomm@vnuinc.com, http://www.vnubusinessmedia.com/. Ed. Theresa Pitti. Pub. Roberta Griefer. Adv. contact Patti Fahn. Circ: 5,500.

681.388 GBR ISSN 0037-4261
TK9956
SHORT WAVE MAGAZINE. Text in English. 1937. m. GBP 30; GBP 3.99 newsstand/cover (effective 1999). adv. charts; illus. back issues avail. **Document type:** *Consumer.* **Description:** Articles and features on the joys of shortwave radio.
Indexed: EngInd, Inspec. —BLDSC (8270.000000), AskIEEE, Ei, IE, Infotrieve, ingenta, Linda Hall.
Published by: P W Publishing Ltd., Arrowsmith Ct, Station Approach, Broadstone, Dorset BH18 8PW, United Kingdom. TEL 44-1202-659910, FAX 44-1202-659950, kevin@pwpublishing.ltd.uk, http://www.pwpublishing.ltd.uk/. Ed. Kevin Nice. Adv. contact Chris Steadman. B&W page GBP 400. Circ: 20,000. **Dist. by:** Seymour Distribution Ltd, 86 Newman St, London W1T 3EX, United Kingdom. FAX 44-20-7896-8002, enquiries@seymour.co.uk.

SHOWBIZ MAGAZINE. see *MOTION PICTURES*

SIGNIS MEDIA; cine video radio internet television. see *MOTION PICTURES*

SILVER SCREEN. see *COMPUTERS—Computer Graphics*

SINATRA INTERNATIONAL. see *MUSIC*

C

791.45 ISL ISSN 1017-3617
SJONVARPSVISIR. Text in Icelandic. 1987. m. free to qualified personnel. adv. **Description:** Guide for viewers of TV-Channel 2 in Iceland.
Published by: Islenska Utvarpsfelagid hf. - Stoed 2/Icelandic Broadcasting Corp., Inc. - Channel 2, Lynghalsi 5, PO Box 10110, Reykjavik, 130, Iceland. TEL 354-515-6770, FAX 354-515-6870. Ed. Olafur Jon Jonsson. Pub. Jafet S Olafsson. Adv. contact Halldor Kristjansson. B&W page ISK 82,960, color page ISK 117,840; trim 11.5 x 8.25. Circ: 50,000 (controlled).

SKRIEN. see *MOTION PICTURES*

384.51 GBR
SKY. Text in English. m. **Document type:** *Magazine, Consumer.* **Description:** Provides important information about BSkyB's services and programming as well as entertainment and lifestyle features.
Published by: (BSkyB), John Brown Citrus Publishing, The New Boathouse, 136-142 Bramley Rd, London, W10 6SR, United Kingdom. TEL 44-20-75653000, FAX 44-20-75653060, andrew.hirsch@jbcp.co.uk, http://www.jbcp.co.uk. Circ: 6,000,000 (controlled).

384.5532 IRL
SKY CUSTOMER. Text in English. m. adv. **Document type:** *Magazine, Consumer.*
Published by: B Sky B, 1-2 Baggot Ct., Dublin, 2, Ireland. TEL 353-1-6611400, FAX 353-1-6611402. adv.: color page EUR 6,400; trim 210 x 290. Circ: 226,134 (controlled).

791.45 USA ISSN 1081-7840
SKY GUIDE✶. Text in English. 1983. m. USD 27. adv. **Document type:** *Magazine, Trade.* **Description:** Contains satellite television listings and articles.
Former titles (until 199?): Sky-View (1074-4592); (until 199?): Satellite T V Pre Vue (0896-3673)
Published by: O'Rourke Brothers, 1205 Fourth Ave, Moline, IL 61265. TEL 800-475-9484. Circ: 5,000.

384.553 GBR
SKYVIEW (ANALOGUE). Text in English. 1994. m. adv. **Document type:** *Magazine, Consumer.* **Description:** Delivers accurate information and in-depth articles that cover all aspects of programming on Sky TV.
Formerly: Sky T V Guide (1355-381X)
Published by: (British Sky Broadcasting), Redwood Publishing, 7 St Martin's Pl, London, WC2N 4HA, United Kingdom. TEL 44-20-7747-0700, FAX 44-20-7747-0701, Penny.McDonald@redwood-publishing.com, infohub@redwoodgroup.net, http://www.redwood-publishing.com. Eds. Nick Bradshaw, Penny McDonald. Pub. Jules Rastelli. Adv. contact Amanda Pitt. page GBP 28,050; trim 210 x 290. Circ: 570,000 (controlled).

384.51 GBR
SKYVIEW (DIGITAL). Text in English. 1998. m. adv. **Document type:** *Consumer.* **Description:** Delivers accurate information and in-depth articles on all aspects of SkyDigital programming as well as listings for all major digital channels.
Formerly (until 2000): SkyDigital T V Guide (1463-5739)
Published by: (British Sky Broadcasting), Redwood Publishing, 7 St Martin's Pl, London, WC2N 4HA, United Kingdom. TEL 44-20-7747-0700, FAX 44-20-7747-0701, nigel.ambrose@redwood-publishing.com, infohub@redwoodgroup.net, http://www.redwood-publishing.com. Eds. Nick Bradshaw, Penny McDonald. Adv. contact Amanda Pitt. page GBP 8,500.

SKYWAVES. see *RELIGIONS AND THEOLOGY*

384.55 USA ISSN 1545-0244
TK6630.A1
SMART T V & SOUND; interactive T V & D V D - MP3 - Internet audio & video - satellite tv. Text in English. 1997. 2/yr. USD 14.97 domestic; USD 24.97 in Canada; USD 39.97 elsewhere; USD 2.99 newsstand/cover (effective 2003). adv. illus. back issues avail.; reprints avail. **Document type:** *Magazine, Consumer.* **Description:** Devoted to educating home entertainment product owners primarily with regard to television, home entertainment systems and portable audio products; and all sources of video and audio content including websites, compact discs, video cassettes, satellite and network TV programming.
Formerly (until 2001): Smart T V (1094-6500)
Published by: York Publishing, PO Box 4591, Chico, CA 95927. TEL 530-891-8410, FAX 530-891-8443, editorial@smarttvandsound.com, http://www.smarttvandsound.com. Ed. Stephen Muratore. Pub. Matthew York. Adv. contact David Arnold. B&W page USD 8,000, color page USD 9,440; trim 10.5 x 7.88. Circ: 50,000.

791.456 USA ISSN 0164-3584
SOAP OPERA DIGEST. Text in English. 1975. w. USD 37.44 domestic; USD 2.99 newsstand/cover domestic (effective 2005). adv. illus. reprint service avail. from PQC. **Document type:** *Magazine, Consumer.* **Description:** Covers soap operas aired on network television, focusing on synopses of episodes.
Related titles: Microfiche ed.: (from NBI).
—CCC.
Published by: Primedia Consumer Media & Magazine Group, 260 Madison Ave, New York, NY 10016. TEL 212-726-4300, FAX 212-726-4310, digestweeklyonline@primediamags.com, http://www.soapdigest.com, http://www.primedia.com. Eds. Lynn Leahey, Stephanie Sloane. Pub. Linda Vaughan. adv.: B&W page USD 28,584, color page USD 34,839; trim 7.38 x 5.13. Circ: 1,100,000 (paid).

791.456 USA ISSN 1063-9055
SOAP OPERA ILLUSTRATED. Text in English. 1992. bi-m. **Document type:** *Consumer.*
Published by: K-III Communications Corp., 745 Fifth Ave, New York, NY 10151. TEL 212-745-0100.

791.456 USA ISSN 0199-3003
SOAP OPERA STARS. Text in English. q. USD 9; USD 14 foreign. adv. **Document type:** *Consumer.* **Description:** For the entertainment of female readers. Focuses on soap opera stars.
Published by: Dorchester Media, 35 Wilbur St, Lynbrook, NY 11563. TEL 516-593-1220, FAX 516-593-0065.

791.456 USA ISSN 1047-7128
PN1992.8.S4
SOAP OPERA WEEKLY. Text in English. 1989. w. (Tue.). USD 19.97 for 6 mos. domestic 26 issues; USD 32.97 for 6 mos. in Canada 26 issues; USD 35.97 for 6 mos. foreign 26 issues; USD 4 newsstand/cover foreign (effective 2005). adv. illus. **Document type:** *Magazine, Consumer.* **Description:** Covers the weekly soap opera story lines aired on network television, profiles the stars, lifestyles and more.
Related titles: Microfiche ed.: (from NBI).
—CCC.
Published by: Primedia Consumer Media & Magazine Group, 260 Madison Ave, New York, NY 10016. TEL 212-726-4300, FAX 212-726-4310, soapubop@primediamags.com, http://www.soapoperaweekly.com, http://www.primedia.com. Ed. Carolyn Hinsey. Pub. Linda Vaughan. adv.: B&W page USD 9,566, color page USD 11,813; trim 11.25 x 9.31. Circ: 450,000 (paid).

791.456 GBR
SOAPLIFE. Text in English. 2001. m. GBP 15.60 domestic; USD 78 in United States (effective 2004). **Document type:** *Magazine, Consumer.* **Description:** Covers soap stars, news, interviews, story-lines, pull-out posters, puzzles and more.
Published by: I P C tx (Subsidiary of: I P C Media Ltd.), Kings Reach Tower, Stamford St, London, SE1 9LS, United Kingdom. TEL 44-161-8722155, http://www.ipcmedia.com/. Ed. Helen Gardner. Circ: 114,965. **Subscr. to:** I P C Media Ltd., Perrymount Rd, Haywards Heath RH16 3DA, United Kingdom. TEL 44-1444-475675, FAX 44-1444-445599, ipcsubs@qss-uk.com.

384.55 AUS ISSN 1032-3899
SOUND & IMAGE; Australia's no.1 guide to home theatre. Text in English. 1988. 9/yr. AUD 64.30 domestic; AUD 150 foreign; AUD 7.95 newsstand/cover (effective 2004). adv. bk.rev. **Document type:** *Magazine, Consumer.* **Description:** Covers lifestyle, home electronics, entertainment.
Published by: Horwitz Publications Pty. Ltd., 55 Chandos St, St Leonards, NSW 2065, Australia. TEL 61-2-9901-6100, FAX 61-2-9901-6166, dip@horwitz.com.au. Ed., R&P Anika Hillery. Pub. Jim Preece TEL 61-2-99016150. Adv. contact Samantha Klooger TEL 61-2-99016149.

384.55 USA
▼ **SOUND & VISION H D T V GUIDE.** (High Definition Television) Text in English. 2004. a. USD 4.99 newsstand/cover (effective 2005). adv. **Document type:** *Magazine, Consumer.*
Published by: Hachette Filipacchi Media U.S., Inc. (Subsidiary of: Hachette Filipacchi Medias S.A.), 1633 Broadway, 45th Fl, New York, NY 10019. TEL 212-767-6000, FAX 212-333-2434, http://www.hfmus.com. Ed. Bob Ankosko TEL 212-767-6019. Adv. contact Angela Stolfi TEL 212-767-6032. B&W page USD 8,625, color page USD 12,500; trim 8.25 x 10.875. Circ: 100,000.

384.5452 ZAF
SOUTH AFRICAN BROADCASTING CORPORATION. ANNUAL REPORT. Text in Afrikaans, English. a. charts; illus.; stat. **Document type:** *Corporate.*
Published by: South African Broadcasting Corporation, Private Bag X1, Auckland Park, Johannesburg 2006, South Africa. TEL 27-11-714-3741, FAX 27-11-714-6514. Ed. Des Celliers.

SPACE COMMUNICATIONS; an international journal. see *AERONAUTICS AND SPACE FLIGHT*

SPECTATOR (LOS ANGELES, 1987); journal of film and television criticism. see *MOTION PICTURES*

SPOTLIGHT CHILDREN'S. see *THEATER*

SPOTLIGHT ON PRESENTERS. see *THEATER*

SPOTS PLANUNGSDATEN HOERFUNK - FERNSEHEN. see *BUSINESS AND ECONOMICS—Trade And Industrial Directories*

791.45 GBR
PN2001
THE STAGE. Text in English. 1880. w. GBP 45 domestic; GBP 85.96 foreign; GBP 1 newsstand/cover (effective 2002). adv. bk.rev.; play rev.; tel.rev.; dance rev.; music rev. illus. 48 p./no. 6 cols./p.; back issues avail. **Document type:** *Newspaper, Trade.*
Formerly: Stage and Television Today (0038-9099)
Related titles: Microfilm ed.; Online - full content ed.
—CCC.
Published by: Stage Newspaper Ltd., Stage House, 47 Bermondsey St, London, SE1 3XT, United Kingdom. TEL 44-20-7403-1818, FAX 44-20-7403-1418, admin@thestage.co.uk, editor@thestage.co.uk, http://www.thestage.co.uk. Ed. Brian Attwood. Pub. Catherine Comerford. Adv. contact Marcus Collingbourne. Circ: 41,198 (paid).

STAGE SCREEN & RADIO. see *LABOR UNIONS*

STAND BY. see *LABOR UNIONS*

STANDING NAKED IN THE WINGS; anecdotes from Canadian actors. see *THEATER*

791.43 DEU
STAR TREK. Text in German. 1998. q. EUR 3.90 newsstand/cover (effective 2003). adv. **Document type:** *Magazine, Consumer.*
Published by: OZ Verlag GmbH, Roemerstr 90, Rheinfelden, 79618, Germany. TEL 49-7623-964-0, FAX 49-7623-96464200, vollmar@oz-bpv.de, http://www.oz-verlag.com. adv.: B&W page EUR 2,400, color page EUR 3,100. Circ: 70,000 (paid and controlled).

791.45 GBR ISSN 1357-3888
STAR TREK. Text in English. 1995. m. GBP 42.25; GBP 3.50 newsstand/cover (effective 2000). adv. **Document type:** *Magazine, Consumer.* **Description:** Gives the public access to the official, studio-sanctioned information and tidbits on all the Star Trek series.
Published by: Titan Magazines (Subsidiary of: Titan Books Ltd.), Titan House, 144 Southwark St, London, SE1 0UP, United Kingdom. TEL 44-20-7620-0200, FAX 44-20-7620-0032, startrekmail@titanemail.com. Ed. Darryl Curtis. Adv. contact Miles Dunbar. **Dist. by:** Comag, Tavistock Works, Tavistock Rd, W Drayton, Middx UB7 7QX, United Kingdom. TEL 44-1895-444055, FAX 44-1895-433602.

791.45 DEU
STAR TREK (STUTTGART). Text in German. 2000. bi-m. adv. **Document type:** *Magazine, Consumer.*
Published by: Panini Verlags GmbH, Ravensstr 48, Nettetal, 41334, Germany. TEL 49-711-947680, FAX 49-711-94768830, info@panini-dino.de, http://www.panini-media.de. Adv. contact Petra Sonnenfroh-Kost. page EUR 1,500; trim 170 x 257. Circ: 15,000 (paid and controlled).

791.43 USA ISSN 1080-3793
STAR TREK COMMUNICATOR. Text in English. 1980. bi-m. USD 29.95 domestic membership (effective 2005). adv. bk.rev.; film rev. illus. 100 p./no.; back issues avail. **Document type:** *Magazine, Consumer.* **Description:** Covers anything and everything pertaining to Star Trek: movies, TV and fandom.
Formerly (until 1994): Star Trek 3 (0883-3125)
Published by: Decipher, Inc., 253 Granby St., Norfolk, VA 23510-1831. TEL 757-623-3600, 877-787-8626, FAX 757-623-8368, http://www.startrek.fanhq.com, http://www.decipher.com. Pub. Peter Lobred TEL 757-664-1110. Circ: 110,000 (paid).

791.45 GBR ISSN 1462-7639
STAR TREK FAN CLUB. Text in English. 1993. 4/yr. **Document type:** *Magazine, Consumer.*
Former titles (until 1997): Star Trek: Official Fan Club of the UK (1364-7717); (until 1996): Official Star Trek Fan Club of the UK (1353-5714)
Published by: Titan Magazines (Subsidiary of: Titan Books Ltd.), Titan House, 144 Southwark St, London, SE1 0UP, United Kingdom. TEL 44-20-7620-0200, FAX 44-20-7803-1803, stfanclubmail@titanemail.com.

STAR WARS: THE OFFICIAL MAGAZINE. see *LITERATURE—Science Fiction, Fantasy, Horror*

384.55 USA ISSN 0191-4626
STARLOG; the science fiction universe. Text in English. 1976. m. USD 56.97 domestic; USD 66.97 foreign; USD 7.99 newsstand/cover (effective 2005). adv. bk.rev.; film rev. charts; illus. reprints avail. **Document type:** *Magazine, Consumer.* **Description:** Presents science fiction in TV and movies.
Published by: Starlog Group, Inc., 475 Park Ave S, 7th Fl, New York, NY 10016. TEL 212-689-2830, 800-877-5549, FAX 212-889-7933, http://www.starlog.com. Ed. David McDonnell. Pub. Norman Jacobs. R&P, Adv. contact Rita Eisenstein. B&W page USD 3,210, color page USD 4,495. Circ: 226,855.

C

▼ new title ➤ refereed ✶ unverified ♦ full entry avail.

621.388 USA ISSN 1549-5582
THE STATE OF HIGH DEFINITION TELEVISION. Text in English. biennial. USD 1,295 (effective 2005). **Document type:** *Directory, Trade.* **Description:** Delivers data, accurate analyses, actionable strategies, buildout histories, exclusive revenue estimates and new growth forecasts for high definition televisions and programming.
Formerly (until 2003): Kagan's The State of Digital T V
Published by: Kagan Research, LLC, One Lower Ragsdale Dr, Bldg One, Ste 130, Monterey, CA 93940. TEL 831-624-1536, FAX 831-625-3225, info@kagan.com, http://www.kagan.com.

384.55 USA
STATION LISTING GUIDE. Text in English. 1999. a. USD 50 to non-members; USD 35 to members. **Description:** Offers a listing of key personnel, addresses, phone and fax numbers for over 1400 television stations across the US and Canada.
Address: NATPE HQS, 2425 Olympic Blvd, Ste 600E, Santa Monica, CA 90404. TEL 310-453-4440, FAX 310-453-5258, http://www.natpe.org.

379.8 HRV ISSN 1333-5863
STORY. Text in Croatian. 2002. w. adv. **Document type:** *Magazine, Consumer.*
Published by: Sanoma Magazines Zagreb d.o.o., Vlaska 121, Zagreb, 10000, Croatia. TEL 385-91-4649111, FAX 385-91-6000201.

STUDIO SOUND. see *SOUND RECORDING AND REPRODUCTION*

791.45 CAN
SUNDAY SUN TELEVISION MAGAZINE (CALGARY). Text in English. w. CND 130. adv. **Document type:** *Newspaper.*
Published by: Calgary Sun, 2615 12 St N E, Calgary, AB T2E 7W9, Canada. TEL 403-250-4200, FAX 403-250-4180. Ed. Ray Djuff. Circ: 99,505.

791.45 SWE ISSN 1401-8519
SUPER PLAY. Text in Swedish. 1993. m. SEK 479 (effective 2005). adv. **Document type:** *Magazine, Consumer.*
Formerly (until 1996): Super Power (Solna) (1104-5647)
Related titles: Includes: Super Play Special.
Published by: Hjemmet Mortensen AB (Subsidiary of: Hjemmet-Mortensen AS), Gaevlegatan 22, Stockholm, 11378, Sweden. TEL 46-8-6920100, FAX 46-8-6509705, info@hjemmetmortensen.se, http://www.superplay.net, http://www.hjemmetmortensen.se. Ed. Tommy Rydling. Adv. contact Tony Gustavsson. color page SEK 32,000; trim 210 x 271. Circ: 20,800.

384.55 DEU ISSN 0863-3614
SUPER T V. Text in German. 1990. w. EUR 54.60; EUR 0.90 newsstand/cover (effective 2003). adv. **Document type:** *Magazine, Consumer.*
Published by: Super TV Verlag GmbH & Co. KG, Mollstr 1, Berlin, 10178, Germany. TEL 49-30-23876460, FAX 49-30-23877231, http://www.supertv.de, http://www.super-tv.de. Ed. Jochen Wolff. Adv. contact Heinz Scheiner. B&W page EUR 6,240, color page EUR 8,740. Circ: 332,912 (paid).

384.5532 POL ISSN 1230-9788
SUPER T V. Text in Polish. 1992. w. PLZ 0.80 newsstand/cover (effective 2003). adv. **Document type:** *Magazine, Consumer.*
Published by: Wydawnictwo Bauer Sp. z o.o. (Subsidiary of: Heinrich Bauer Verlag), ul. Motorowa 1, Warsaw, 04-035, Poland. TEL 48-22-5170500, FAX 48-22-5170125, kontakt@bauer.pl, http://www.bauer.pl. Ed. Wlodzimierz Krawczyk. Adv. contact Katarzyna Jablonska. page PLZ 15,000; trim 222 x 305.

384.55 ESP
SUPERTELE. Text in Spanish. 1986. w. EUR 1 newsstand/cover (effective 2005). adv. back issues avail. **Document type:** *Magazine, Consumer.*
Related titles: Online - full text ed.
Published by: Hachette Filipacchi SA, Avda Cardenal Herrera Oria 3, Madrid, 28034, Spain. TEL 34-91-7287000, FAX 34-91-3585473, supertele@hachette.es, comunicacion@hachette.es, http://www.supertele.es/, http://www.hachette.es. Ed. Mentxue Vicente. Circ: 96,793.

SVERIGES DRAMATIKERFOERBUND. JOURNAL. see *THEATER*

791.456 POL ISSN 1640-2294
SWIAT SERIALI. Text in Polish. 2000. fortn. PLZ 1.80 newsstand/cover (effective 2003). adv. **Document type:** *Magazine, Consumer.*
Published by: Wydawnictwo Bauer Sp. z o.o. (Subsidiary of: Heinrich Bauer Verlag), ul. Motorowa 1, Warsaw, 04-035, Poland. TEL 48-22-5170500, FAX 48-22-5170125, sseriali@bauer.pl, kontakt@bauer.pl, http://www.bauer.pl. Ed. Anna Wiejowska. Adv. contact Katarzyna Jablonska. page PLZ 8,000; trim 215 x 286.

388.55 HUN ISSN 1585-5708
SZINES KETHETES TEVEMUSOR. Text in Hungarian. 1999. fortn. HUF 3,848 (effective 2001). adv. **Document type:** *Magazine, Consumer.*
Published by: Axel Springer - Budapest Kft., Varosmajor u 11, Budapest, 1122, Hungary. TEL 36-1-4885700, FAX 36-1-2025332, bayerj@axels.hu. Circ: 43,000 (paid).

059.94511 HUN ISSN 1217-4211
SZINES R T V. (Radio es Televizio) Text in Hungarian. 1993. w. adv. **Document type:** *Magazine, Consumer.* **Description:** Contains extensive television program listings along with articles on celebrities, movies, books and music.
Published by: Sanoma Budapest Kiadoi Rt. (Subsidiary of: Sanoma Magazines Finland Corporation), Bokor Utca 15-19, Budapest, 1037, Hungary. TEL 36-1-4371100, FAX 36-1-2502303, szinesrtv@sanomabp.hu, info@sanomabp.hu, http://www.sanoma.hu. Adv. contact Gabriella Rakosi. page HUF 2,450,000; trim 215 x 285. Circ: 266,019 (paid).

388.55 HUN
SZINES T V UJSAG. Text in Hungarian. 2002 (Dec.). w. **Document type:** *Magazine, Consumer.*
Published by: Axel Springer - Budapest Kft., Varosmajor u 11, Budapest, 1122, Hungary. TEL 36-1-4885700, FAX 36-1-2025332, bayerj@axels.hu. Ed. Andor Kloss. Circ: 100,000 (controlled).

384.5 GBR
▼ **T B I BUYERS' BRIEFING.** (Television Business International) Text in English. 2004. w. free to qualified personnel. **Document type:** *Newsletter, Trade.* **Description:** Contains news and information for all buyers of TV content around the world.
Published by: Informa Publishing, 69-77 Paul St, London, EC2A 4IQ, United Kingdom. TEL 44-20-7553-1000, FAX 44-20-7553-1105, media.enquiries@informa.com, http://www.informamedia.com.

384.55 DEU
T V 14. Text in German. fortn. EUR 26; EUR 1 newsstand/cover (effective 2005). adv. **Document type:** *Magazine, Consumer.* **Description:** Contains articles, listings and information on all aspects of television programming and personalities.
Published by: Heinrich Bauer Programmzeitschriftenverlag KG, Burchardstr 11, Hamburg, 20077, Germany. TEL 49-40-30190, FAX 49-40-30191043, kommunikation@hbv.de, http://www.hbv.de. Ed. Uwe Bokelmann. Adv. contact Karsten Voelker. page EUR 28,000. Circ: 2,271,971 (paid).

791 RUS ISSN 1726-0876
T V 7. Text in Russian. 2002. w. adv. **Document type:** *Magazine, Consumer.* **Description:** Keeps readers up-to-date on TV program listings, celebrities and movie stars.
Published by: Izdatel'skii Dom Burda, ul Pravdy 8, Moscow, 125040, Russian Federation. TEL 7-095-7979849, FAX 7-095-2571196, vertrieb@burda.ru, http://www.burda.ru. adv.: page USD 4,500. Circ: 300,000 (paid and controlled).

384.55 PRT
T V 7 DIAS. Text in Portuguese. 1987. w. EUR 65 domestic; EUR 161.72 in Europe; EUR 213.20 rest of world (effective 2005). adv. **Document type:** *Consumer.*
Published by: Impala Sociedade Editorial S.A., Remessa Livre No. 154, Sintral, 2714-914, Portugal. TEL 351-219-238218, FAX 351-219-238463, assinaturas@impala.pt, http://www.impala.pt/. Ed. Antonio Mateus. **Distr. by:** Electroliber, Rua Vasco da Gama 4-A, Sacavem 2865, Portugal. TEL 942-53-94.

791.45 CAN ISSN 1192-7615
T V 7 JOURS. Text in English. 1989. w. **Document type:** *Consumer.*
Published by: Trustar Ltee., 2020 rue Universite, Ste 2000, Montreal, PQ H3A 2A5, Canada. TEL 514-848-7000, FAX 514-847-0945. Ed. Claude Leclerc. Pub. Jean Louis Podlesak. adv.: color page CND 9,250; trim 8.25 x 5. Circ: 161,130.

384.55 USA ISSN 1054-4259
T V & CABLE PUBLICITY OUTLETS - NATIONWIDE✶. Text in English. 1970. a. USD 99.
Formerly: All T V Publicity Outlets - Nationwide; Formed by the merger of: T V Publicity Outlets - Nationwide (0041-4514); (1982-1985): Cable T V Publicity Outlets - Nationwide
Published by: Morgan-Rand Inc., 1 Sentry Pkwy, 1000, Blue Bell, PA 19422. TEL 215-938-5500, FAX 215-938-5549. Ed. Nancy Shenker. Circ: 1,500.

T V & CABLE SOURCE. see *ADVERTISING AND PUBLIC RELATIONS—Abstracting, Bibliographies, Statistics*

791.45 USA
T V & FILM EXTRAS. Text in English. bi-w. USD 69 (effective 2000).
Published by: The John King Network, 244 Madison Ave, Ste 393, New York, NY 10016. TEL 212-969-8715, 212-969-8715.

384.55 GBR
T V & SATELLITE WEEK. Text in English. 1993. w. GBP 46.65; USD 153 in United States (effective 2004). adv. **Document type:** *Consumer.* **Description:** Comprehensive weekly guide to satellite, cable and terrestrial television.
Related titles: Regional ed(s).: T V & Satellite Week. North West - Anglia. ISSN 0968-851X; T V & Satellite Week. South - Southwest. ISSN 1369-9016; T V & Satellite Week. Midlands - Wales and West. ISSN 0968-8544; T V & Satellite Week. Northwest - Ulster. ISSN 1369-9040; T V & Satellite Week. North West - Border. ISSN 0968-8528; T V & Satellite Week. Yorkshire - Tyne - Tees. ISSN 0968-8560.
Published by: I P C tx (Subsidiary of: I P C Media Ltd.), Kings Reach Tower, Stamford St, London, SE1 9LS, United Kingdom. TEL 44-161-8722155, http://www.ipcmedia.com/. Ed. Johnson Bowman. Pub. Rachel Pearce. adv.: color page GBP 6,000. Circ: 247,507. **Dist. addr.:** I P C Media Ltd., Perrymount Rd, Haywards Heath RH16 3DA, United Kingdom. TEL 44-1444-475675, FAX 44-1444-445599, ipcsubs@qss-uk.com.

384.55 IND
T V & VIDEO WORLD. Text in English. 1983. m.
Published by: Nariman Point Building Services & Trading Pvt. Ltd., 920 Tulsiani Chambers, Nariman Point, Mumbai, Maharashtra 400 021, India. Ed. Maneck Davar. adv.: B&W page INR 10,000, color page INR 20,000; trim 195 x 265.

791.43 DEU
T V ANZEIGER; das regionale Fernsehmagazin. Text in German. 1985. m. adv. film rev. **Description:** Television information and regional news.
Address: Theodor Hanloser Str 7, Singen, 78224, Germany. TEL 07731-41001. Ed. Roswitha Bosch. Circ: 80,000.

384.55 AUS
T V AUDIENCE PROFILES. Text in English. 1989. 4/yr. **Document type:** *Consumer.*
Published by: Roy Morgan Research, PO Box 2282 U, Melbourne, VIC 3001, Australia. TEL 61-3-96296888, FAX 61-3-96291250. Ed. Geoffrey Smith.

384.5532 GBR
T V CHOICE. Text in English. 1999. w. GBP 0.40 newsstand/cover (effective 2003). adv. **Document type:** *Magazine, Consumer.* **Description:** Provides listings and reviews of television programs for the week.
Published by: H. Bauer Publishing Ltd. (Subsidiary of: Heinrich Bauer Verlag), Academic House, 24-28 Oval Rd, London, NW1 7DT, United Kingdom. TEL 44-20-72418000, FAX 44-20-72418056, simon.priston@bauer.co.uk. Ed. Lori Miles. Pub. Julie Lavington. Adv. contact Laura Cohen. page GBP 18,700; trim 210 x 280. Circ: 902,954 (paid).

384.55 DEU
▼ **T V DIGITAL.** Text in German. 2004 (Mar.). fortn. EUR 1.40 newsstand/cover (effective 2004). adv. **Document type:** *Magazine, Consumer.*
Published by: Axel Springer Verlag AG, Axel-Springer-Platz 1, Hamburg, 20350, Germany. TEL 49-40-34700, FAX 49-40-34722049, bams.leser@asv.de, http://www.asv.de. Ed. Christian Hellmann. Adv. contact Martina Knop-Sydow. color page EUR 17,000; trim 230 x 290.

384.55 USA ISSN 0884-1098
HE8700.8
T V DIMENSIONS. Text in English. 1984. a. USD 260; USD 143 to students.
Published by: Media Dynamics, Inc., 570 7th Ave Rm 1906, New York, NY 10018-1619. TEL 212-704-0024, FAX 212-704-0023, info@mediadynamicsinc.com, http://www.mediadynamicsinc.com.

384.55 DEU ISSN 1616-8992
T V DIREKT. Text in German. 1998. fortn. EUR 0.90 newsstand/cover (effective 2002). adv. **Document type:** *Magazine, Consumer.* **Description:** Contains articles, listings and feautres on television programs and personalities.
Published by: Gong Verlag GmbH & Co. KG, Muenchener Str 101, Ismaning, 85737, Germany. TEL 49-911-5325-0, FAX 49-911-5325309, gonginfo@gongverlag.de, http://www.gong-verlag.de. Adv. contact Guenther Granzow. B&W page EUR 11,100, color page EUR 13,000; trim 215 x 275. Circ: 774,860 (paid).

791.45 CZE ISSN 1214-4770
▼ **T V DUEL & FILM.** Text in Czech. 2003. bi-w. CZK 34 newsstand/cover (effective 2005). 132 p./no.; **Document type:** *Magazine, Consumer.*
Published by: Sanoma Magazines Praha s.r.o., Lomnickeho 7, Prague 4, 12079, Czech Republic. TEL 420-2-96162111, FAX 420-2-24922995, vedrova@sanomamag-praha.cz, http://www.tvduel.cz, http://www.sanomamag-praha.cz. Ed. Simona Cernikova. Pub. Jiri Vavra.

791.45 BEL
T V EKSPRES. Text in Dutch. 1970. w. adv. **Document type:** *Consumer.*
Published by: Sanoma Magazines Belgium, Uitbreidingstr 82, Berchem, 2600, Belgium. TEL 32-3-290-1200, FAX 32-3-290-1237, http://www.sanoma-magazines.be/HomePage.aspx?flash=1&Language=nl. Circ: 183,224.

384.55 USA ISSN 0736-2986
HE8700.8
T V EXECUTIVE; a printed marketplace for programming and production. Text in English. 1983. 2/yr. (subscr. includes Annual Directory Who's Who of Promo - Ad Executives). **Document type:** *Trade.* **Description:** Contains news and information about the TV industry with profiles, analysis, and commentary.
Published by: T V Trade Media, Inc., 216 E 75th St, Ste PW, New York, NY 10021. TEL 212-288-1549, FAX 212-734-9033. Ed., Pub. Dom Serafini. R&P Monica Gorghetto.

791.43 CAN
T V FACTS - LONDON✶. Text in English. 1980. w. free. adv. back issues avail.
Published by: 533064 Ontario Ltd., 177 Albert St, London, ON N6A 1L9, Canada. TEL 519-438-5413, FAX 519-438-5418. Ed. Terry Woods. Circ: 25,000.

384.553 791.437 ITA
T V FILM; l'unico settimanale di cinema. Text in Italian. w. **Document type:** *Consumer.* **Description:** Contains news articles and reviews on recent film releases. Includes a weekly television programming schedule.
Published by: Rimonti S.r.l., Corso Venezia, 6, Milan, MI 20121, Italy. TEL 39-02-76022562, FAX 39-02-76003678. Eds. Emanuela Martini, Luca Saverio Griffini.

384.5532 JPN
T V GAIDO/T V GUIDE. Text in Japanese. w. JPY 260 newsstand/cover (effective 2004). **Document type:** *Magazine, Consumer.*
Published by: Tokyo Nyusu Tsushinsha/Tokyo News Service Ltd., Tsukiji Hamarikyu Bldg 10th Fl, 3-3 Tsuki-Ji 5-chome, Chuo-ku, Tokyo, 104-8004, Japan. http://www.tokyonews.co.jp/index.htm.

791.45 PRT ISSN 0871-7362
T V GUIA. Text in Portuguese. 1979. w. EUR 27.68 (effective 2005). illus. **Document type:** *Magazine, Consumer.* **Description:** Contains a program guide and entertainment features.
Published by: Investec Media, Ave Joao Crisostomo, 72, Lisbon, 1069-043, Portugal. TEL 351-213-307741, FAX 351-213-540643, http://www.investec.pt. Circ: 155,000 (paid).

THE T V GUIDE. see *LEISURE AND RECREATION*

384.5532 SAU
T V GUIDE. Text in Arabic. w. adv. **Document type:** *Magazine, Consumer.* **Description:** Provides a comprehensive guide to Arab and satellite television programs, including penetrating analysis of the contents of programs as well as in-depth looks at events relevant to the TV, film and entertainment industries.
Published by: Saudi Research & Publishing Co., PO Box 4556, Jeddah, 21412, Saudi Arabia. TEL 966-2-669-1888, FAX 966-2-667-1650, http://www.alkhaleejiahadv.com.sa/srpc/. adv.: page SAR 13,200. Circ: 129,322 (paid).

791.45 USA ISSN 0039-8543
CODEN: NIMBEU
T V GUIDE. Text in English. 1953. w. USD 46.28; USD 1.99 newsstand/cover (effective 2005). adv. bk.rev. illus. 38 yr. cum.index. reprints avail. **Document type:** *Magazine, Consumer.* **Description:** Personality profiles and articles on television and entertainment of national interest. Published in regional editions with comprehensive listing of local network and cable TV programs.
Related titles: E-mail ed.; Microfilm ed.; Online - full text ed.
Indexed: ASIP, LRI, MagInd, PMR, PROMT, RASB, RGAb, RGPR.
Published by: Gemstar - TV Guide International, 1211 Ave of the Americas, New York, NY 10036. TEL 212-852-7500, 800-866-1400, FAX 21-2852-7363, http://www.tvguide.com. Ed. Ian Birch. Adv. contact Mindy Nathanson. B&W page USD 113,900, color page USD 136,700; 4.5 x 6.875. Circ: 13,000,000 (paid).

791.45 CAN ISSN 1191-5315
T V GUIDE (CANADIAN EDITION). (Published in 15 regional editions) Text in English. 1953. w. CND 39.98 (effective 2005); CND 1.49 newsstand/cover (effective 2003). adv. illus. **Document type:** *Consumer.* **Description:** Provides schedules of television programming for the comming week and reports on television films, mini-series, situation comedies, and news of actors, actresses, and other celebrities.
Indexed: RGAb.
—CCC.
Published by: Transcontinental Media, Inc. (Subsidiary of: Transcontinental, Inc.), 25 Sheppard Ave West, Ste 100, Toronto, ON M2N 6S7, Canada. TEL 416-733-7600, FAX 416-218-3544, info@transcontinental.ca, http://www.tvguide.ca, http://www.transcontinental-gtc.com/en/home.html. Circ: 761,000 (paid).

791.45 CAN ISSN 0039-8551
T V HEBDO. Text in English. 1960. w. adv. illus. **Document type:** *Magazine, Consumer.*
Related titles: Microfilm ed.: (from BNQ).
Published by: Trustar Ltee., 2020 rue Universite, Ste 2000, Montreal, PQ H3A 2A5, Canada. TEL 514-848-7000, FAX 514-843-3529. Ed. Jean Louis Podlesak. adv.: color page CND 9,575; trim 5 x 8.25. Circ: 200,053.

384.55 DEU
T V HIGHLIGHTS. Text in German. 1995. m. EUR 3.95 newsstand/cover (effective 2003). adv. **Document type:** *Magazine, Consumer.* **Description:** Provides detailed commentary and reviews on television listings and programming.
Published by: Medien Publikations- und Werbegesellschaft, Wiehenweg 14, Hille, 32479, Germany. TEL 49-5703-95904, FAX 49-5703-95906, http://www.tvhighlights.de. Ed. Manfred Knorr. adv.: page EUR 4,280. Circ: 42,000 (paid and controlled).

791.45 GBR ISSN 0958-2363
T V HITS. Text in English. 1989. m. GBP 22.80 domestic; GBP 32.40 in Europe; GBP 42.40 elsewhere (effective 2004). adv. illus. back issues avail. **Document type:** *Magazine, Consumer.* **Description:** Features interviews with stars, competitions, and advice for every modern teenager.
Published by: Hachette Filipacchi (UK) Ltd. (Subsidiary of: Hachette Filipacchi Medias S.A.), 64 North Row, London, W1K 7LL, United Kingdom. TEL 44-20-71507000, FAX 44-20-71507001, mattslade@hf-uk.com, http://www.tvhits.co.uk/, http://www.hachettefilipacchiuk.co.uk. adv.: color page GBP 7,815; trim 228 x 300. Circ: 204,805 (paid).

384.55 DEU ISSN 0940-0656
T V HOEREN UND SEHEN. Text in German. 1962. w. (Fri.). EUR 72.80; EUR 1.40 newsstand/cover (effective 2005). adv. **Document type:** *Magazine, Consumer.*
Indexed: RASB.
Published by: Heinrich Bauer Programmzeitschriftenverlag KG, Burchardstr 11, Hamburg, 20077, Germany. TEL 49-40-30190, FAX 49-40-30191043, redaktion@tv-hoeren-und-sehen.de, kommunikation@hbv.de, http://www.tv-hoeren-und-sehen.de, http://www.hbv.de. Ed. Uwe Bokelmann. Pub. Heinz Bauer. Adv. contact Susann Harms. B&W page EUR 25,000, color page EUR 31,650; trim 208 x 278. Circ: 1,187,185 (paid). **Dist. in UK by:** Powers International Ltd., 100 Rochester Row, London SW1P 1JP, United Kingdom. TEL 44-20-7630-9966, FAX 44-20-7630-9922.

384.55 DEU
T V INFO. Variant title: TVinfo. Text in German. d. adv. tel.rev. **Document type:** *Consumer.* **Description:** Provides up-to-date listings and program descriptions for television and cable broadcasts.
Media: Online - full text.
Published by: TVinfo Internet GmbH, Ronsdorfer Str 74, Duesseldorf, 40233, Germany. TEL 49-211-30203325, FAX 49-211-30203328, presse@tvinfo, info@tvinfo.de, http://www.tvinfo.de. Eds. Alex Zehe, Ana-Maria Cuza. Adv. contact Michael Schanz.

384.55 GBR
T V INTERNATIONAL. (Television) Text in English. 1993. fortn. GBP 625, EUR 938, USD 938 (effective 2004). adv. back issues avail. **Document type:** *Newsletter, Trade.* **Description:** Covers worldwide television, cable and satellite markets. Includes news and strategic analysis on international broadcast, cable, satellite, digital, pay and pay-per-view, program ratings, in-depth market and company profiles.
Formerly: Broadcasting and Cable's TV International (1071-9261)
Related titles: Online - full text ed.: GBP 1,875, EUR 2,813, USD 2,813 (effective 2004) (from Florida Center for Library Automation, Gale Group).
—CCC.
Published by: Informa Media (Subsidiary of: T & F Informa plc), Mortimer House, 37-41 Mortimer St, London, W1T 3JH, United Kingdom. media.enquiries@informa.com, http://www.informamedia.com/tvinternational. Ed. Toby Scott. Circ: 1,500 (paid).

384 GBR
T V INTERNATIONAL DAILY (ONLINE EDITION). Text in English. d. GBP 999, EUR 1,559, USD 1,499 (effective 2003). **Document type:** *Newsletter, Trade.*
Media: Online - full content. **Related titles:** E-mail ed.; Fax ed.
Published by: Informa Media (Subsidiary of: T & F Informa plc), Mortimer House, 37-41 Mortimer St, London, W1T 3JH, United Kingdom. media.enquiries@informa.com, http://www.informamedia.com/.

384.55 GBR ISSN 1082-3913
HE8700
T V INTERNATIONAL SOURCEBOOK. Text in English. a. **Document type:** *Directory, Trade.*
Related titles: Online - full text ed.: (from Gale Group).
Published by: Baskerville (Subsidiary of: T & F Informa plc), Sheepen Place, Colchester, Essex C03 3LP, United Kingdom. TEL 44-20-70175537, FAX 44-20-70174783, telecoms.enquiries@informa.com, http://www.baskerville.telecoms.com/.

384.55 ITA
T V KEY; mensile professionale di communicazione televisiva. Text in Italian. 1982. m. (9/yr.). adv. index. **Document type:** *Trade.* **Description:** Covers commercial tv, new technology, production, marketing, programs and advertising.
Published by: Media Key s.r.l., Via Lippi Filippino, 33 C, Milan, MI 20131, Italy. TEL 39-2-236-66-25, FAX 39-2-236-26-62. Ed. Roberto Albano. Adv. contact Silvana Carazzina. Circ: 10,500.

384.55 DEU ISSN 0945-5981
T V KLAR. Variant title: TV Klar. Text in German. 1992. w. (Thu.). EUR 49.40; EUR 0.70 newsstand/cover (effective 2005). adv. **Document type:** *Magazine, Consumer.*
Published by: Heinrich Bauer Programmzeitschriftenverlag KG, Burchardstr 11, Hamburg, 20077, Germany. TEL 49-40-3019-0, FAX 49-40-30194032, tvklar@hbv-red.de. Ed. Andrea Wicherek. Adv. contact Karsten Voelker. page EUR 21,450; trim 208 x 278. Circ: 525,612 (paid). **Dist. in UK by:** Powers International Ltd., 100 Rochester Row, London SW1P 1JP, United Kingdom. TEL 44-20-7630-9966, FAX 44-20-7630-9922.

791.45 NLD ISSN 0927-3204
T V KRANT. Text in Dutch. 1966. w. EUR 31.45; EUR 0.63 newsstand/cover (effective 2005). adv. bk.rev. charts; illus. **Document type:** *Magazine, Consumer.*
Formerly (until 1991): Tros-Kompas (0041-3321)
Address: Lage Naarderweg 45-47, Hilversum, 1217 GN, Netherlands. TEL 31-35-6728630. adv.: B&W page EUR 4,328; trim 233 x 322. Circ: 183,531.

791.45 JPN
T V LIFE. Text in Japanese. 1983. w. JPY 6,760.
Published by: Gakken Co. Ltd., 40-5 Kami-Ikedai 4-chome, Ota-ku, Tokyo, 145-0064, Japan. Ed. Seiji Yokoyama.

791.45 CAN ISSN 0316-2397
T V MAGAZINE. Text in English. 1967. w. CND 50. adv. illus.
Published by: Spartan Printing, 101 Marsh Dr, Quesnel, BC V2J 3K3, Canada. TEL 604-992-2713, FAX 604-992-3902. Ed. J P Hartnett. Circ: 10,000.

791.45 JPN
T V MAGAZINE. Text in Japanese. 1971. m. **Document type:** *Magazine, Consumer.* **Description:** Contains information on childrens' television programming and shows.
Published by: Kodansha Ltd., 2-12-21 Otowa, Bunkyo-ku, Tokyo, 112-8001, Japan. TEL 81-3-5395-3491, FAX 81-3-3492-7705, TELEX J34059 KODANSHA, http://www.kodansha.co.jp. Ed. Tohru Ogawa. Circ: 360,000.

384.55 PRT ISSN 0872-3559
T V MAIS. Text in Portuguese. 1993. w. adv. **Document type:** *Magazine, Consumer.*
Published by: Edimpresa Editora Lda., Rua Calvet de Magalhaes 242, Laveiras, Paco de Arcos, 2770-022, Portugal. TEL 351-21-4698000, FAX 351-21-4698501, tvmais@acj.pt, edimpresa@edimpresa.pt, http://www.edimpresa.pt. adv.: page EUR 2,670; trim 205 x 275. Circ: 88,507 (paid and controlled).

384.55 ROM
T V MANIA. Text in Romanian. 1998. w. ROL 331,000 domestic; ROL 125,000 foreign (effective 2001). adv. film rev.; music rev.; tel.rev. illus.; mkt.; stat.; tr.lit. 52 p./no.; back issues avail. **Document type:** *Magazine, Trade.* **Description:** Covers television and cable programs and personalities.
Published by: Ringier Romania, Str Fabrica de Glucoza 5, Bucharest, Romania. TEL 40-01-2030901, FAX 40-01-2425363, rio@tvmania.ro, office@ringier.ro, http://www.tvmania.ro, http://www.ringier.ro. Ed. Razvan Ionescu. Pub., R&P Claudiu Serban. Adv. contact Lucian Romascanu TEL 40-01-2030601. B&W page USD 3,000; trim 220 x 300. Circ: 90,000 (paid).

384.5532 AUT
T V MEDIA. Text in German. 1996. w. EUR 109.90 (effective 2002). adv. **Document type:** *Magazine, Consumer.*
Related titles: Online - full text ed.: ISSN 1605-1092. 1997.
Published by: Verlagsgruppe News Gesellschaft mbH (Subsidiary of: Gruner und Jahr AG & Co.), Alfred-Feierfeil-Str. 3, Perchtoldsdorf, N 2380, Austria. TEL 43-1-863315340, FAX 43-1-86331590, http://www.news.at/tv-media/. Circ: 291,067 (paid and controlled).

384.55 DEU
T V MOVIE. Text in German. 1991. fortn. EUR 45.50; EUR 1.45 newsstand/cover (effective 2002). adv. **Document type:** *Magazine, Consumer.* **Description:** Lists movies on television as well as features on motion pictures, music, videos, books and PC games.
Published by: Heinrich Bauer Verlag, Burchardstr 11, Hamburg, 20077, Germany. TEL 49-40-30193040, FAX 49-40-30193046, userservice@tvmovie.de, kommunikation@hbv.de, http://www.tvmovie.de. Ed. Michael Hopp. Adv. contact Karl Keller. page EUR 49,200. Circ: 2,233,608 (paid). **Dist. in UK by:** Powers International Ltd., 100 Rochester Row, London SW1P 1JP, United Kingdom. TEL 44-20-7630-9966, FAX 44-20-7630-9922.

C

384.55 DEU ISSN 0949-4502
T V NEU. Text in German. 1992. w. (Thu.). EUR 0.70 newsstand/cover (effective 2005). adv. **Document type:** *Magazine, Consumer.*
Published by: Axel Springer Verlag AG, Axel-Springer-Platz 1, Hamburg, 20350, Germany. TEL 49-40-34700, FAX 49-40-34728460, tvneu@axelspringer.de, information@axelspringer.de, http://www.asv.de. Ed. Jan von Frenkell. Adv. contact Holger Braack. color page EUR 8,000; trim 206 x 270. Circ: 262,766 (paid).

384.55 USA
T V NEWS (NEW YORK). (Geographic editions avail.) Text in English. 1973. w. free. adv. bk.rev.; rec.rev. **Document type:** *Consumer.* **Description:** Contains TV listings, stories about television and TV stars, book and music reviews. Also local dinning and entertainment articles, reviews and listings; plus horoscope and crossword puzzle.
Published by: T V News, 80 Eighth Ave, Ste 315, New York, NY 10011. TEL 212-243-6800, FAX 212-243-7457. Ed., R&P Elizabeth Farkas. Pub., Adv. contact Allan Horwitz. Circ: 526,000 (controlled).

791.457 IRL ISSN 1393-9475
T V NOW. Text in English. 2000. w. adv. **Document type:** *Magazine, Consumer.*
Address: 77 Lower Leeson St., Dublin, 2, Ireland. TEL 353-1-6769832, FAX 353-1-6614629. adv.: page EUR 3,300; 230 x 297. Circ: 34,000 (paid and controlled).

791.45 GBR
T V OBSERVER. Text in English. w. back issues avail. **Description:** English television listings guide including editorial and features.
Published by: Bullivant - Wilde Publishing Ltd., Webb House, 20 Church Green E., Redditch, Worcs B98 8BP, United Kingdom. TEL 0527-585588.

C

384 ZAF
T V PLUS!. Text in English. w. **Description:** Includes features on television programs and personalities.
Published by: National Magazines (Subsidiary of: National Media Ltd.), PO Box 1802, Cape Town, 8000, South Africa. TEL 27-21-406-3678, FAX 27-21-406-3289, http://www.natmags.com.

384.55 CZE ISSN 1212-6500
T V PLUS. Text in Czech. 1999. w. CZK 7 newsstand/cover (effective 2002). adv. 32 p./no.; **Document type:** *Magazine, Consumer.* **Description:** Provides news and information on television and cable programming and celebrities.
Published by: Ringier CR, U pruhonu 13, Prague 7, 17000, Czech Republic. TEL 420-2-67097720, FAX 420-2-67097718, tvplus@ringier.cz, info@ringier.cz, http://www.ringier.cz/tvplus. Adv. contact Tomas Filla TEL 420-2-67097427. page CZK 71,500; 215 x 260. Circ: 93,000 (paid and controlled).

621.388 USA
T V PLUS. Text in English. 1994. w. USD 59 (effective 1999). adv. **Description:** Listings and articles concerning DBS satellite TV programming.
Published by: Triple D Publishing, Inc., 1300 S DeKalb St, PO Box 2347, Shelby, NC 28151-2384. TEL 704-482-9673, FAX 704-484-8558, tvplus@tripled.com, http://www.tripled.com. Ed. Jim H Cothran. Adv. contact Nelli Williams.

381.1 USA ISSN 0885-2340
T V PROGRAM INVESTOR. Text in English. 1985. m. USD 895; USD 1,290 combined subscription print & e-mail eds. (effective 2005). adv. **Document type:** *Newsletter, Trade.* **Description:** Covers trends in TV program syndication, values of TV networks and programs, public stocks and private companies in the TV program business, and analysis of mergers and acquisitions.
Related titles: E-mail ed.: USD 825 (effective 2005); Fax ed.: USD 845 (effective 2001).
Published by: Kagan Research, LLC, One Lower Ragsdale Dr, Bldg One, Ste 130, Monterey, CA 93940. TEL 831-624-1536, FAX 831-625-3225, info@kagan.com, http://research.kagan.com/keo/subscriptionsDetailPage.aspx?SubscriptionID=25, http://www.kagan.com. Pub. Paul Kagan. adv.: B&W page USD 3,670.

384.55 DEU
T V PUR. Text in German. m. EUR 13.80; EUR 0.80 newsstand/cover (effective 2005). adv. **Document type:** *Magazine, Consumer.* **Description:** Contains extensive television program listings and schedules.
Published by: Heinrich Bauer Programmzeitschriftenverlag KG, Burchardstr 11, Hamburg, 20077, Germany. TEL 49-40-30190, FAX 49-40-30191043, kommunikation@hbv.de, http://www.hbv.de. Ed. Stefan Westendorp. Adv. contact Elke Rieck. page EUR 17,069. Circ: 662,553 (paid).

384.55 GBR ISSN 0961-9615
T V QUICK. Text in English. 1991. w. GBP 0.95 newsstand/cover (effective 2005). adv. bk.rev.; tel.rev.; video rev. **Document type:** *Magazine, Consumer.* **Description:** Provides TV listings and features.
—CCC.
Published by: H. Bauer Publishing Ltd. (Subsidiary of: Heinrich Bauer Verlag), Academic House, 24-28 Oval Rd, London, NW1 7DT, United Kingdom. TEL 44-20-72418000, FAX 44-20-72418056, simon.priston@bauer.co.uk, http://www.bauer.co.uk/website/tvquick.cfm. Ed. Jon Peake. Pub. Julie Lavington. Adv. contact Simon Coomes. page GBP 13,250; trim 230 x 290. Circ: 337,149 (paid).

384.55 CZE
T V REVUE. Text in Czech. 1999. w. CZK 10.50 newsstand/cover (effective 2002). adv. 48 p./no.; **Document type:** *Magazine, Consumer.*
Published by: Ringier CR, U pruhonu 13, Prague 7, 17000, Czech Republic. TEL 420-2-67097720, FAX 420-2-67097718, surname@ringier.cz, info@ringier.cz, http://tvrevue.cz, http://www.ringier.cz. Ed. Daniela Kupsova. Pub. Aleka Cerna. Adv. contact Tomas Filla TEL 420-2-67097427. page CZK 130,000; 226 x 290.

384.55 ROM ISSN 1221-6453
T V SATELIT. Text in Romanian. 1992. s-m. adv. **Document type:** *Magazine, Consumer.*
Related titles: Supplement(s): Info Satelit. ISSN 1224-807X. 1997; T V Cablu. ISSN 1221-6445. 1993.
Published by: R.I.P. Impex, Str. Iasilor nr. 20, Cluj-Napoca, Romania. TEL 40-64-433236, FAX 40-64-433528.

791.45 ITA ISSN 0038-156X
T V SORRISI E CANZONI. Key Title: Sorrisi e Canzoni T V. Text in Italian. 1952. w. EUR 54 (effective 2005). illus. **Document type:** *Magazine, Consumer.*
Formerly (until 1972): Sorrisi e Canzoni d'Italia (1121-7502)
Published by: Arnoldo Mondadori Editore SpA, Via Mondadori 1, Segrate, 20090, Italy. TEL 39-02-66814363, FAX 39-030-3198412, http://www.mondadori.com.

384.55 SVN ISSN 1408-0877
T V SPECIAL. Text in Slovenian. 1996. m. adv. **Document type:** *Magazine, Consumer.*
Published by: Delo Revije d.o.o., Dunajska 5, Ljubljana, 1509, Slovenia. TEL 386-1-4737000, FAX 386-1-4737352, narocnine@delo-revije.si, http://www.delo-revije.si. adv.: page SIT 55,000.

384.55 DEU ISSN 0938-8729
T V SPIELFILM. Text in German. 1990. fortn. EUR 46.80; EUR 1.45 newsstand/cover (effective 2005). adv. **Document type:** *Magazine, Consumer.*
Related titles: Online - full text ed.
Published by: Verlagsgruppe Milchstrasse, Mittelweg 177, Hamburg, 22786, Germany. TEL 49-40-41311310, FAX 49-40-41312015, echo@tvspielfilm.de, abo@milchstrasse.de, http://www.tvspielfilm.de, http://www.milchstrasse.de. Ed. Christian Hellmann. Pubs. Dirk Manthey, Joerg Altendorf. Adv. contact Rainer Gierke. B&W page EUR 46,500, color page EUR 47,800. Circ: 1,819,546 (paid). **Subscr. to:** Postfach 302, Offenburg 77649, Germany. TEL 49-781-6396997. **Dist. by:** IPV GmbH, Postfach 103246, Hamburg 20022, Germany. TEL 49-40-23711-0, FAX 49-40-23711215.; **Dist. in UK by:** Seymour Distribution Ltd, 86 Newman St, London W1T 3EX, United Kingdom. FAX 44-207-396-8002, enquiries@seymour.co.uk.

T V SPORTSFILE. see *SPORTS AND GAMES*

791.45 GBR ISSN 0965-6057
T V STARS. Text in English. 199?. m. GBP 1.95 newsstand/cover. music rev. illus. **Document type:** *Consumer.* **Description:** Examines the lives and work of established and rising television stars.
Published by: Europa Publications Ltd., Bradninch Ct, Castle St, Exeter, Devon EX4 3PL, United Kingdom. TEL 44-1392-211113. **Dist. by:** MarketForce UK Ltd, 247 Tottenham Court Rd, London, Middx W1T 7AU, United Kingdom.

384.555 USA ISSN 1542-9164
T V STATION DEALS & FINANCE DATABOOK. Text in English. 200?. biennial. USD 1,995 (effective 2005). **Document type:** *Directory, Trade.*
Published by: Kagan Research, LLC, One Lower Ragsdale Dr, Bldg One, Ste 130, Monterey, CA 93940. TEL 831-624-1536, FAX 831-625-3225, info@kagan.com, http://www.kagan.com.

654.9 ROM ISSN 1583-6533
T V STORY. Text in Romanian. 2002. fortn. adv. **Document type:** *Magazine, Consumer.*
Published by: Sanoma - Hearst Romania srl, Str. C.A. Rosetti nr. 5, sector 1, Bucharest, Romania. TEL 40-21-3138620, FAX 40-21-3138622, office@sanomahearst.ro.

384.55 CHE
T V TAEGLICH. Text in German. w. adv. **Document type:** *Magazine, Consumer.* **Description:** Contains television program listings and schedules as well as features on shows and celebrities.
Published by: Ringier AG, Dufourstr 47, Zuerich, 8008, Switzerland. TEL 41-1-2596483, FAX 41-1-2596996, tvmail@ringier.ch, info@ringier.ch, http://www.ringier.ch. Ed. Klaus Kriesel. adv.: B&W page CHF 17,900, color page CHF 23,940. Circ: 1,360,000 (controlled).

384.55 USA ISSN 0887-1701
T V TECHNOLOGY. Text in English. 1983. bi-w. USD 39 (effective 2005). adv. tr.lit. back issues avail.; reprints avail. **Document type:** *Magazine, Trade.* **Description:** Includes technology news, applications-oriented features, trade show coverage, new-product introductions, and end-user evaluations.
Related titles: International ed.: T V Technology (Asia-Pacific Edition); T V Technology (European Edition); T V Technology (Japanese Edition); T V Technology (Latin American Edition).
—Linda Hall.
Published by: I M A S Publishing Group, 5827 Columbia Pike, Ste 310, Falls Church, VA 22041. TEL 703-998-7600, 800-336-3045, FAX 703-671-7409, adsales@imaspub.com, http://www.imaspub.com/tvtechnology.shtml. Ed. Deborah McAdams. Pub. Stevan B Dana. Adv. contact Carmel King. Circ: 43,000.

621.388 USA
T V TECHNOLOGY AMERICA LATINA. Text in Spanish, Portuguese. 10/yr. USD 35; USD 45 foreign (effective 1999). tr.lit. back issues avail.; reprints avail. **Document type:** *Trade.* **Description:** Regional edition of TV Technology serves Mexico, South and Central America, and the Spanish-speaking Caribbean.
Published by: I M A S Publishing Group, 5827 Columbia Pike, Ste 310, Falls Church, VA 22041. TEL 703-998-7600, FAX 703-998-2966, adsales@imaspub.com, http://www.imaspub.com.

621.388 USA
T V TECHNOLOGY AND PRODUCTION. ASIA-PACIFIC EDITION. Text in English. 10/yr. USD 55; USD 45 foreign (effective 1999). tr.lit. back issues avail.; reprints avail. **Document type:** *Trade.* **Description:** Reaches video professionals at broadcast, cable, production, post-production, corporate and industrial facilities around the world.
Published by: I M A S Publishing Group, 5827 Columbia Pike, Ste 310, Falls Church, VA 22041. TEL 703-998-7600, FAX 703-998-7600, adsales@imaspub.com, http://www.imaspub.com.

621.388 USA
T V TECHNOLOGY AND PRODUCTION. EUROPEAN EDITION. Text in English. 11/yr. USD 75; USD 65 foreign (effective 1999). tr.lit. back issues avail.; reprints avail. **Document type:** *Trade.* **Description:** Covers emerging technologies affecting video professionals at broadcast, cable, production, post-production, corporate and industrial facilities.
Published by: I M A S Publishing Group, 5827 Columbia Pike, Ste 310, Falls Church, VA 22041. TEL 703-998-7600, FAX 703-998-2966, adsales@imaspub.com, http://www.imaspub.com. adv.: B&W page USD 2,050.

384.55 USA
T V TECHNOLOGY NIHONGO BAN. Text in Japanese. m. USD 75; USD 55 foreign (effective 1999). tr.lit. back issues avail.; reprints avail. **Document type:** *Trade.* **Description:** Regional edition of TV Technology focuses on Japan and surrounding broadcast countries.
Published by: I M A S Publishing Group, 5827 Columbia Pike, Ste 310, Falls Church, VA 22041. TEL 703-998-7600, FAX 703-998-2966, adsales@imaspub.com, http://www.imaspub.com.

384.55 CAN
T V TELESCOPE. Text in English. 1979. w. CND 49.99 (effective 1997). adv. back issues avail.
Formerly: Tele-Scope Magazine
Published by: T V Publishing Group, 201 4201 25A Ave, Vernon, BC V1T 7G8, Canada. TEL 250-542-0469, 800-663-4424, FAX 250-542-0942. Ed., R&P Deeny Grazier. Pub. Tom Monahan. Adv. contact Norm Metcalf. Circ: 36,000.

384.5452 GBR ISSN 0962-1660
T V TIMES. Key Title: TV Times. Thames - LWT, C4, BBC1 and BBC2. Variant title: TVTimes. Text in English. 1955. w. GBP 86.50 domestic; EUR 150 in Europe eurozone; GBP 100 in Europe non eurozone; USD 220 in United States; GBP 114.58 in Canada; GBP 153.50 elsewhere (effective 2005). adv. rec.rev. illus. **Document type:** *Magazine, Consumer.* **Description:** Trusted family favorite offering detailed program information.
Published by: I P C tx (Subsidiary of: I P C Media Ltd.), Kings Reach Tower, Stamford St, London, SE1 9LS, United Kingdom. TEL 44-161-8722155, http://www.ipcmedia.com/magazines/tvtimes/. Ed. Mike Hollingsworth TEL 44-20-72617767. Adv. contact Steve Judd TEL 44-20-72617063. color page GBP 14,400. Circ: 824,895. **Dist. by:** I P C Media Ltd., Perrymount Rd, Haywards Heath RH16 3DA, United Kingdom.

384.5452 USA
T V TODAY. Text in English. 1933. w. membership. adv. **Document type:** *Newsletter.* **Description:** Updates on association news and broadcast industry news at Capitol Hill and the FCC.
Incorporates (in 1985): N A B Highlights; Formerly: N A B Today (Television Edition)
Related titles: Fax ed.

Published by: National Association of Broadcasters, 1771 N St, N W, Washington, DC 20036. TEL 202-429-5350, FAX 202-429-5406, cnicholson@nab.org, http://www.nab.org. Ed. Chris Nicholson. R&P Ben Ivins. Adv. contact David Dziedzic. Circ: (controlled).

791.45 DEU ISSN 0948-2717
T V TODAY. Text in German. 1994. fortn. EUR 40.30; EUR 1.40 newsstand/cover (effective 2005). adv. **Document type:** *Magazine, Consumer.*
Published by: Magazin Verlag am Fleetrand GmbH, Griegstr 75, Hamburg, 22763, Germany. TEL 49-40-37037914, FAX 49-40-37037845, plathner@tvtoday.de, gremmelspacher.birgitta@tvtoday.de, http://www.tvtoday.de. Ed. Karsten Flohr. Adv. contact Birgitta Gremmelspacher. page EUR 16,830; trim 224 x 295. Circ: 727,190 (paid).

T V TRANSLATORS ENGINEERING DATA BASE IN ORDER BY STATE, CHANNEL, CALL. see *COMMUNICATIONS—Abstracting, Bibliographies, Statistics*

384.545 USA
T V TRENDS. Text in English. 1999. m. free to members. stat. **Description:** Identifies trends in programming and other statistic analysis on the various areas that affect the television industry.
Address: 2425 Olympic Blvd, Ste 550E, Santa Monica, CA 90404. TEL 310-453-5258, FAX 310-453-5258, http:///www.natpe.org.

384.5532 DEU ISSN 1438-0250
T V UND SERIEN. Text in German. 1999. m. adv. tel.rev. **Document type:** *Magazine, Consumer.* **Description:** Provides information on the latest television programs and series.
Supersedes in part (in 1998): Deutsches Entertainment Magazin (1435-2214)
Media: Online - full content.
Published by: Next Step Mediendienste GmbH, Bahnhofstr 12, Gemuenden, 55460, Germany. TEL 49-6765-960196, FAX 49-6765-960198, http://www.tvundserien.de, http://www.next-step-mediendienste.de. Ed., Pub. Dirk Jasper. Adv. contact Christine Volkert TEL 49-89-38356380.

384.5532 CHE
▼ **T V VIER.** Text in German. 2003 (Mar.). 13/yr. CHF 44 (effective 2004). adv. **Document type:** *Magazine, Consumer.*
Published by: Zollikofer AG, Fuerstenlandstr 122, Postfach 2362, St. Gallen, 9001, Switzerland. TEL 41-71-2727370, FAX 41-71-2727586, info@tv-vier.com, leserservice@zollikofer.ch, http://www.tv-vier.com, http://www.zollikofer.ch.

791.45 AUS ISSN 0810-249X
T V WEEK. Text in English. 1957. w. AUD 166.40; AUD 3.30 newsstand/cover (effective 2005). adv. back issues avail. **Document type:** *Magazine, Consumer.* **Description:** Includes news articles on movies and television.
Published by: A C P Publishing Pty. Ltd., 54-58 Park St, Sydney, NSW 1028, Australia. TEL 61-2-92828000, FAX 61-2-92674361, tvweek@acp.com.au, info@acp.com.au, http://tvweek.ninemsn.com.au/tvweek/, http://www.acp.com.au. Ed. Emma Nolan. Adv. contact Jo Shambler. color page AUD 12,420; trim 198 x 275. Circ: 290,818. **Subscr. to:** Magshop, Reply Paid 4967, Sydney, NSW 2001, Australia.

791.45 HKG
T V WEEK. Text in Chinese. 1967. w.
Published by: T V Week Ltd., 1 Leighton Rd, Hong Kong, Hong Kong. TEL 8366188, FAX 8910421. Circ: 62,000.

791.45 CAN
T V WEEK MAGAZINE. Text in English. 1976. w. CND 37.95. adv. film rev.; play rev. **Document type:** *Consumer.* **Description:** Television magazine with listings and television-related features.
Published by: Canada Wide Magazines & Communications Ltd., 4180 Lougheed Hwy, 4th Fl, Burnaby, BC V5C 6A7, Canada. TEL 604-299-7311, FAX 604-299-9188, cwm@canadawide.com, http://www.canadawide.com. Ed. Brent Furdyk. Pub. Peter Legge. Adv. contact Harry Vanhemmen. Circ: 86,600.

384.55 DEU
T V WORLD. Text in German. fortn. EUR 31.20; EUR 1 newsstand/cover (effective 2005). adv. **Document type:** *Magazine, Consumer.*
Published by: Heinrich Bauer Programmzeitschriftenverlag KG, Burchardstr 11, Hamburg, 20077, Germany. TEL 49-40-30190, FAX 49-40-30191043, leserservice@tvworld.de, kommunikation@hbv.de, http://www.hbv.de. Ed. Stefan Westendorp. Adv. contact Elke Rieck. page EUR 5,000. Circ: 350,000 (paid and controlled).

384.55 GBR ISSN 0142-7466
HE8700
T V WORLD; international business magazine for television. Text in English. 1977. 10/yr. GBP 50; GBP 60 in Europe; GBP 80 elsewhere (effective 1999). adv. back issues avail. **Document type:** *Trade.* **Description:** Reports on television programming developments worldwide.
Indexed: IIFP, IITV, RASB.
Published by: Emap Media Ltd. (Subsidiary of: Emap Business Communications Ltd.), 33-39 Bowling Green Ln, London, EC1R 0DA, United Kingdom. TEL 44-20-7505-8000, FAX 44-20-7505-8504, janem@media.emap.co.uk, http://www.emap.com. Ed. Jane Millichip. Pub. Jon Baker. adv.: B&W page GBP 3,150; trim 204 x 272. **Subscr. to:** Readerlink Ltd., Audit House, 260 Field End Rd, Ruislip, Mddx HA4 9LT, United Kingdom. TEL 44-20-8956-3016, FAX 44-20-8936-3020.

791.45 CAN
T V WORLD. Text in English. w. CND 48.99 (effective 1997). adv.
Published by: T V Publishing Group, 201 4201 25A Ave, Vernon, BC V1T 7G8, Canada. TEL 250-542-0469, 800-663-4424, FAX 250-542-0942. Ed., R&P Deeny Grazier. Pub. Tom Monahan. Adv. contact Norm Metcalf.

791.456 USA ISSN 0188-0683
T V Y NOVELAS. Text in Spanish. 1982. bi-w. USD 29 domestic; USD 79.70 foreign (effective 2005). adv. film rev.; music rev.; tel.rev.; video rev. **Document type:** *Magazine, Consumer.* **Description:** Covers the Spanish-language soap operas and their stars.
Published by: Editorial Televisa, 6355 N W 36th St, Miami, FL 33166. TEL 305-871-6400, 800-288-6677, FAX 305-871-7146, 305-871-5026, subscriptions@editorialtelevisa.com, info@editorialtelevisa.com, http://www.editorialtelevisa.us/. Ed. Gloria Calzada. Adv. contact Roberto Sroka TEL 305-871-6400. B&W page USD 8,625, color page USD 11,500; trim 10.69 x 7.75. Circ: 144,994 (paid).

384.55 GBR ISSN 0957-3844
T V ZONE. Text in English. 1989. m. GBP 46 domestic; USD 82 in US & Canada; GBP 56 elsewhere; GBP 2.99 newsstand/cover (effective 2000). adv. illus. **Document type:** *Consumer.* **Description:** Covers cult television programs such as Star Trek, X-Files and Babylon 5.
Related titles: ♦ Supplement(s): T V Zone Special. ISSN 0960-8230.
Published by: Visual Imagination Ltd., 9 Blades Ct, Deodar Rd, London, SW15 2NU, United Kingdom. TEL 44-20-8875-1520, FAX 44-208-875-1588, tvzone@visimag.com, http://www.visimag.com. Ed. Jan Vincent Rudzki. R&P Stephen Payne. Adv. contact Martin Clark. B&W page GBP 1,270, color page GBP 1,940; trim 298 x 210. **Dist. by:** Comag, Tavistock Works, Tavistock Rd, W Drayton, Middx UB7 7QX, United Kingdom. TEL 44-1895-444055, FAX 44-189-543-3606.

384.55 GBR ISSN 0960-8230
T V ZONE SPECIAL. Text in English. 1990. q. adv. **Document type:** *Consumer.*
Related titles: ♦ Supplement to: T V Zone. ISSN 0957-3844.
Published by: Visual Imagination Ltd., 9 Blades Ct, Deodar Rd, London, SW15 2NU, United Kingdom. TEL 44-20-8875-1520, FAX 44-208-875-1588. Ed. Jan Vincent Rudzki. R&P Stephen Payne. Adv. contact Martin Clark. Circ: 40,000 (paid).

TALK RADIO - TALK TV. see *COMMUNICATIONS—Radio*

384.55 USA
PN1991.8.T35
TALK SHOW YEARBOOK. Text in English. 1989. a. USD 185 (effective 2000). **Document type:** *Directory.* **Description:** Lists the top-rated radio and television news and talk programs in the United States.
Formerly: Talk Show Selects (1045-9553)
Related titles: Diskette ed.: USD 280 (effective 2000).
Published by: Broadcast Interview Source, 2233 Wisconsin Ave, N W, Washington, DC 20007. TEL 202-333-4904, FAX 202-342-5411, editor@yearbook.com, http://www.yearbook.com. Ed., Pub., R&P, Adv. contact Mitchell P Davis.

384.55 USA ISSN 0896-3215
TECHLINE; a publication for the cable engineering community. Text in English. 1979. bi-m. membership only. bibl. **Document type:** *Newspaper.* **Description:** Geared to the U.S. cable television engineering community.
Published by: National Cable Television Association, 1724 Massachusetts Ave, N W, Washington, DC 20036. TEL 202-775-3550. Ed. Katherine Rutkowski. Circ: 2,500.

384.55 AUS ISSN 1326-0014
TECHTONIC. Text in English. 1995. irreg. **Document type:** *Newsletter.* **Description:** Aims to be an opinion space about Australian television, communications and media.
Media: Online - full text.
Published by: Techtonic Webzine, PO Box 849, Bondi Junction, NSW 20222, Australia. TEL 61-2-9281-7955, 61-2-9281-7955, 3v@media.com.au, http://www.culture.com.au/techtonic/. Ed. Jeffrey Cook.

791.45 USA ISSN 1073-7669
CODEN: HCSOEP
TEENAGE GANG DEBS. Text in English. 1989. a. USD 3. bk.rev. **Document type:** *Newsletter.* **Description:** Carries articles, photos, interviews, satire, criticism, reviews, and letters.
Published by: Erin & Don Smith, Eds. & Pubs., PO Box 1754, Bethesda, MD 20827-1754. Circ: 2,000 (paid).

621.388 RUS ISSN 0040-2249
CODEN: TKTEAE
TEKHNIKA KINO I TELEVIDENIYA/MOTION PICTURE AND TELEVISION TECHNOLOGY. Text in Russian; Summaries in English. 1957. m. USD 158 foreign (effective 2005). adv. bk.rev.; film rev.; rec.rev.; tel.rev.; video rev. illus. index. 96 p./no.; **Document type:** *Magazine, Trade.* **Description:** Contains news about Russian and foreign equipment, art, economics, advice to cinema and video amateurs.
Indexed: CIN, ChemAb, ChemTitl, Inspec, PhotoAb, RefZh. —BLDSC (0180.200000), AskIEEE, CASDDS, CINDOC, CISTI, East View, Linda Hall. **CCC.**
Published by: (International Service Production Advertising S.A. CHE), Lerusha Ltd., Leningradskii pr-t 47, ofis 128, Moscow, 125167, Russian Federation. TEL 7-095-1586118, FAX 7-095-1573816, tkt@aha.ru. Ed. Valery V Makartsev. R&P Valery Khleborodov. Adv. contact Sergei Karpachev TEL 7-095-1586625. Circ: 10,000. **US dist. addr.:** East View Information Services, 3020 Harbor Ln. N., Minneapolis, MN 55447. TEL 800-477-1005, FAX 800-800-3839, eastview@eastview.com, http://www.eastview.com.

384.55 CHE ISSN 1420-519X
TELE. Text in German. 1967. w. CHF 149; CHF 3.60 newsstand/cover (effective 2000). adv. **Document type:** *Magazine, Consumer.* **Description:** Contains information on TV, cinema and the world wide web.
Related titles: ♦ Print ed.: Tele Online. ISSN 1422-1268.
Published by: Ringier AG, Dufourstr 47, Zuerich, 8008, Switzerland. TEL 41-1-2596483, FAX 41-1-2596996, redaktion@tele.ch, info@ringier.ch, http://www.tele.ch. Ed. Klaus Kriesel. Adv. contact Daniela Thuring. B&W page CHF 12,398, color page CHF 15,120; trim 189 x 261. Circ: 229,509 (paid).

791.45 FRA ISSN 0153-0747
TELE 7 JOURS. Text in French. 1960. w. EUR 49.40. illus. **Document type:** *Magazine, Consumer.*
Indexed: RASB.
Published by: Hachette Filipacchi Medias S.A. (Subsidiary of: Lagardere Media), 149 rue Anatole France, Levallois-Perret, Cedex 92300, France. TEL 33-1-41346000, FAX 33-1-42081620, redaction@t7j.com, http://www.t7j.com. Ed. Patrick Mahe. Circ: 2,850,000 (paid). **Dist. in UK by:** Seymour Distribution Ltd, 86 Newman St, London W1T 3EX, United Kingdom. FAX 44-207-396-8002, enquiries@seymour.co.uk.

791.45 384.553 ITA ISSN 1123-3516
TELE BOLERO. Text in Italian. 1987. w. **Document type:** *Magazine, Consumer.* **Description:** Contains biographical articles about TV celebrities. Also includes a weekly programming schedule and highlights from various TV series.
Published by: Alberto Peruzzo Editore s.r.l., Via Ercole Marelli 165, Sesto San Giovanni, MI 20099, Italy. TEL 39-02-242021, FAX 39-02-2485736.

388.55 ROM ISSN 1223-9844
TELE CABLU. Text in Romanian. 1995. w. adv. **Document type:** *Magazine, Consumer.*
Published by: R.I.P. Impex, Str. Iasilor nr. 20, Cluj-Napoca, Romania. TEL 40-64-433236, FAX 40-64-433528.

791.45 MEX
TELE GUIA; primera revista de la television mexicana. Text in Spanish. 1952. w. adv. back issues avail. **Document type:** *Magazine, Consumer.*
Published by: Editorial Televisa, Vasco de Quiroga 2000, Edif E 4o Piso, Col Santa Fe, Mexico City, DF 01210, Mexico. TEL 52-55-52612761, FAX 52-55-52612704, http://www.esmas.com/get/. adv.: color page MXP 110,000; trim 190 x 135. Circ: 420,000.

791.45 USA
TELE GUIA DE CHICAGO. Text in Spanish. 1985. w. USD 15; USD 0.30 per issue (effective 2004). adv. **Description:** A TV guide in Spanish.
Published by: Tele Guia Publications, 3116 S Austin Blvd, Cicero, IL 60804-3729. TEL 708-656-6666, FAX 708-222-6822, cmontes@teleguia.us, http://www.teleguia.us, http://www.teleguia.org. Ed. Rose Montes. Pub. Zeke Montes.

791.45 CAN
TELE HORAIRE (MONTREAL). Text in English. w. **Description:** Provides daily coverage of daily television listings of all major Canadian and American networks.
Published by: Journal de Montreal, 4545 Frontenac St, Montreal, PQ H2H 2R7, Canada. TEL 514-521-4545, FAX 514-525-5442, TELEX 05-827591. Ed. Gilles Crevier.

791.45 CAN
TELE HORAIRE (QUEBEC). Text in English. 1982. w. CND 1. adv. **Description:** Guide for readers that includes TV listings and interviews with TV personalities, features on current TV shows, mini-series and films.
Related titles: Microfilm ed.
Published by: Journal de Quebec, 450 Ave Bechart, Vanier, PQ G1M 2E9, Canada. TEL 418-683-1573, FAX 418-683-1027. Ed. Serge Cote. Circ: 108,561.

C

▼ new title ➤ refereed ✶ unverified ♦ full entry avail.

791.45 FRA ISSN 0297-8695
TELE LOISIRS. Text in French. 1986. w. EUR 45 (effective 2005). adv. **Document type:** *Magazine, Consumer.* **Description:** Provides TV listings and covers tourism, cars, fashion, beauty, health and fitness, cuisine, do-it-yourself activities, legal advice, horoscope, and games.
Published by: Prisma Presse, 6 rue Daru, Paris, 75379, France. TEL 33-1-44153000, FAX 33-1-47641042, prisma@presse-info.fr, http://www.teleloisirs.fr, http://www.prisma-presse.com. Ed. Gilles de Prevaux. Circ: 1,521,361 (paid).

791.45 CAN
TELE-MAGAZINE LE SOLEIL. Text in French. w. CND 504.35. adv. **Document type:** *Consumer.* **Description:** Carries articles of special interest to TV viewers. Included are: TV and movie listings, star profiles, films to see, behind the camera, choice of cable, pay-TV, TSN, inter-vision.
Published by: Soleil, 925 chemin St Louis, Terminus, C P 1547, Quebec, PQ G1K 7J6, Canada. TEL 418-686-3233, FAX 418-686-3260. Ed. Magella Soucy.

384.55 CHE ISSN 1422-1268
TELE ONLINE. Text in German. 1995. w.
Related titles: ♦ Print ed.: Tele. ISSN 1420-519X.
Published by: Ringier AG, Dufourstr 47, Zuerich, 8008, Switzerland.

791.45 FRA ISSN 1274-9192
TELE POCHE. Text in French. 1966. w. EUR 0.95 per issue (effective 2005). **Document type:** *Magazine, Consumer.*
Published by: Emap France (Subsidiary of: Emap Media Ltd.), 150-152 Rue Gallieni, Boulogne, 92644, France. TEL 33-1-41334961, FAX 33-1-41335010, info@emapfrance.com, http://www.emapmedia.com. Circ: 805,497 (paid).

384.55 CAN ISSN 0049-3252
TELE PRESSE. Text in English. 1969. w. free. adv.
Related titles: Microfilm ed.
Published by: Presse Ltee., 7 St James St W, Montreal, PQ H2Y 1K9, Canada. TEL 514-285-7272. Circ: 210,000.

621.38 GBR ISSN 1435-7003
TELE-SATELLITE INTERNATIONAL; Europe's satellite magazine. Text in German, English. 1981. bi-m. EUR 50 in Europe; USD 60 elsewhere (effective 2000). adv. **Document type:** *Journal, Trade.* **Description:** Covers global satellite operator news, satellite business news, satellite channel news, and frequency changes.
Former titles (until 1997): Tele-Satellit (0931-4733); (until 1987): Tele-Audiovision (0721-5444)
Address: PO Box 1124, Ascot, Berkshire SL5 0XH, United Kingdom. TEL 44-1344-620799, FAX 44-1344-620354, chris@tele-satellite.com, http://www.tele-satellite.com. Circ: 56,000.

791.45 FRA ISSN 0150-2581
TELE STAR. Text in French. 1976. w. EUR 0.95 newsstand/cover (effective 2004). **Document type:** *Magazine, Consumer.*
Published by: Emap France (Subsidiary of: Emap Media Ltd.), 150-152 Rue Gallieni, Boulogne, 92644, France. TEL 33-1-41334961, FAX 33-1-41335010, info@emapfrance.com, http://www.emapmedia.com.

791.45 FRA ISSN 0757-438X
TELE STAR JEUX. Text in French. 1988. m. EUR 2.45 combined subscription per issue (effective 2004). **Document type:** *Consumer.*
Formerly (until 1982): Tele Star Special Jeux (0757-3944)
Published by: Emap France (Subsidiary of: Emap Media Ltd.), 150-152 Rue Gallieni, Boulogne, 92644, France. TEL 33-1-41334961, FAX 33-1-41335010, info@emapfrance.com, http://www.emapmedia.com.

384.5532 POL ISSN 1234-267X
TELE SWIAT. Text in Polish. 1994. w. PLZ 1.65 newsstand/cover (effective 2003). adv. **Document type:** *Magazine, Consumer.*
Formerly (until 1995): Telekino (1233-4448)
Published by: Wydawnictwo Bauer Sp. z o.o. (Subsidiary of: Heinrich Bauer Verlag), ul. Motorowa 1, Warsaw, 04-035, Poland. TEL 48-22-5170500, FAX 48-22-5170125, telesw@bauer.pl, kontakt@bauer.pl, http://www.bauer.pl. Ed. Malgorzata Mokrzycka. Adv. contact Katarzyna Jablonska. page PLZ 23,000; trim 235 x 296.

791.45 CHE
TELE-TOP-MATIN. Text in French. w. CHF 119 (effective 2000). adv. **Document type:** *Magazine, Consumer.*
Published by: Edipresse Publications SA, 33 av de la Gare, Lausanne, 1001, Switzerland. TEL 41-21-3494949, FAX 41-21-3494939, tele-top-redaction@edicom.ch, http://www.edicom.ch/tele-top/present.html. Ed. Didier Dana. adv.: B&W page CHF 10,840, color page CHF 18,960; trim 200 x 275. Circ: 219,503 (paid).

384.5532 POL ISSN 1230-7912
TELE TYDZIEN. Text in Polish. 1993. w. PLZ 1.80 newsstand/cover (effective 2003). adv. **Document type:** *Magazine, Consumer.*
Published by: Wydawnictwo Bauer Sp. z o.o. (Subsidiary of: Heinrich Bauer Verlag), ul. Motorowa 1, Warsaw, 04-035, Poland. TEL 48-22-5170500, FAX 48-22-5170125, teletydz@bauer.pl, kontakt@bauer.pl, http://www.bauer.pl. Ed. Tomasz Milkowski. Adv. contact Katarzyna Jablonska. page PLZ 92,000; trim 215 x 286.

TELECOMMUNICATIONS AND INFORMATION HIGHWAYS IN NEW ZEALAND. see *COMMUNICATIONS—Telephone And Telegraph*

TELECOMMUNICATIONS INDUSTRY IN AUSTRALIA; packaging of value added telecommunication & broadcasting services & networks. see *COMMUNICATIONS—Telephone And Telegraph*

384.55 LUX
TELECRAN. Text in German. 1978. w. EUR 68 (effective 2005). adv. illus.
Related titles: Online - full content ed.: ISSN 1563-6038.
Published by: Editions Saint Paul, Postfach 1008, Luxembourg, L-1010, Luxembourg. TEL 352-49-93500, FAX 352-49-93590, telecran@telecran.lu. Circ: 43,000.

384.55 USA
TELEGUIA U S A. (In 4 regional eds.: San Fernando Valley, Los Angeles, Orange County, S. Los Angeles) Text in Spanish, English. 1985. w. free (effective 2005). adv. film rev. **Document type:** *Magazine, Consumer.* **Description:** Guide to television broadcasts. Includes coverage of sports, food, entertainment, cars, health and beauty.
Formerly (until 1992): Teleguia
Address: 10153 1/2 Riverside Dr, Ste 114, Toluca, CA 91602. TEL 323-881-6515, FAX 323-881-6524, teleguiausa@aol.com. Ed. Luz O'chod. Adv. contact Liz Di Carlo. B&W page USD 2,000; 9.88 x 7.38. Circ: 100,000 (controlled and free).

384.55 ESP
TELEINDISCRETA. Text in Spanish. 1999. w. EUR 1 newsstand/cover (effective 2005). adv. illus. back issues avail. **Document type:** *Magazine, Consumer.*
Related titles: Online - full text ed.
Published by: Hachette Filipacchi SA, Avda Cardenal Herrera Oria 3, Madrid, 28034, Spain. TEL 34-91-7287000, FAX 34-91-3585473, teleindiscreta@hachette.es, comunicacion@hachette.es, http://www.teleindiscreta.es, http://www.hachette.es. Ed. Arcadio J Velasco. adv.: color page EUR 6,025; 210 x 297. Circ: 50,434.

TELEKOMMUNIKATSII. see *COMMUNICATIONS—Telephone And Telegraph*

384.55 SVK ISSN 1335-9061
TELEMAGAZIN. Text in Slovak. 1995. w. SKK 7.90 newsstand/cover (effective 2002). adv. **Document type:** *Magazine, Consumer.*
Formerly (until 1999): MiniTele (1335-4612)
Published by: Ringier Slovakia a. s., Prievozska 14, PO Box 46, Bratislava 24, 82004, Slovakia. TEL 421-7-325390, FAX 421-7-364995, etv@euroskop.ringier.sk, http://www.euroskop.sk. Ed. Renata Klacanska. Adv. contact Pavol Sakal. page SKK 120,000; trim 200 x 280. Circ: 280,000 (paid).

384.55 FRA ISSN 0040-2443
TELEMAGAZINE. Text in French. 1955. w. adv. tel.rev. charts; illus. index. **Document type:** *Magazine, Consumer.*
Published by: Axel Springer France, 28, rue Jean Jaures, Puteaux, 92800, France. TEL 33-1-47626000, FAX 33-1-47626046, frmorel@mediamag.fr. Circ: 530,000 (paid and controlled).

384.55 BEL ISSN 0772-0963
TELEMOUSTIQUE. Text in French. 1924. w. EUR 81.60 (effective 2005). adv.
Published by: Sanoma Magazines Belgium, Telecomlaan 5-7, Diegem, 1831, Belgium. FAX 32-2-776-2317, http://www.telemoustique.be/FS_index.htm, http://www.sanoma-magazines.be/HomePage.aspx?flash=1&Language=nl. Circ: 189,116.

384.55 ESP
TELENOVELA. Text in Spanish. 1993. w. EUR 0.90 newsstand/cover (effective 2003). adv. **Document type:** *Magazine, Consumer.*
Published by: Hachette Filipacchi SA, Avda Cardenal Herrera Oria 3, Madrid, 28034, Spain. TEL 34-91-7287000, FAX 34-91-3585473, telenovela@hachette.es, comunicacion@hachette.es, Http://www.tele-novela.com, http://www.hachette.es. Adv. contact Luisa Ruiz de Velasco. color page EUR 5,025; 228 x 297.

791.456 PRT
TELENOVELAS. Text in Portuguese. w. adv. **Document type:** *Magazine, Consumer.*
Published by: Edimpresa Editora Lda., Rua Calvet de Magalhaes 242, Laveiras, Paco de Arcos, 2770-022, Portugal. TEL 351-21-4698000, FAX 351-21-4698501, tpais@acj.pt, edimpresa@edimpresa.pt, http://www.edimpresa.pt. adv.: page EUR 1,750; trim 150 x 195. Circ: 160,143.

384.5532 JPN
TELEPAL. Text in Japanese. bi-w. adv. **Document type:** *Magazine, Consumer.*
Published by: Shogakukan Inc., 3-1 Hitotsubashi 2-chome, Chiyoda-ku, Tokyo, 101-8001, Japan. TEL 81-3-3230-5211, FAX 81-3-3264-8471, telepal@net.shogakukan.co.jp, http://net.shogakukan.co.jp/telepal/, http://www.shogakukan.co.jp.

384.55 BEL ISSN 0040-2664
TELEPRO; l'hebdomadaire de la television. Text in French. 1954. w. adv. tel.rev. illus. **Document type:** *Magazine, Consumer.*
Published by: Roularta Media Group, Research Park, Zellik, 1731, Belgium. TEL 32-2-4675611, FAX 32-2-4675757, communication@roularta.be, http://www.roularta.be. Ed. Roger Mackels. Circ: 168,808 (paid).

384.5532 ESP ISSN 0040-2672
TELEPROGRAMA. Text in Spanish. 1966. w. EUR 80 newsstand/cover (effective 2005). adv. film rev.; play rev. illus. back issues avail. **Document type:** *Magazine, Consumer.*
Related titles: Online - full text ed.
Published by: Hachette Filipacchi SA, Avda Cardenal Herrera Oria 3, Madrid, 28034, Spain. TEL 34-91-7287000, FAX 34-91-3585473, tp@hachette.es, comunicacion@hachette.es, http://www.t-p.es, http://www.hachette.es. Ed. Mentxue Vicente. adv.: color page EUR 6,025; 137 x 207. Circ: 152,917 (paid).

791.43 FRA ISSN 0040-2699
TELERAMA. Text in French. 1950. w. bk.rev. **Document type:** *Consumer.*
Indexed: IIFP, IITV.
—CCC.
Published by: Publications de la Vie Catholique, 36 rue de Naples, Paris, 75008, France. TEL 33-1-55305530, FAX 33-1-45220826, osterman.n.p@mail.telerama.fr, http://www.telerama.fr. Ed. Marc Gerabel. Circ: 676,103.

384.55 CAN ISSN 0838-0953
TELEROMAN. Text in English. q.
Published by: Transcontinental Media, Inc. (Subsidiary of: Transcontinental, Inc.), 25 Sheppard Ave West, Ste 100, Toronto, ON M2N 6S7, Canada. TEL 416-733-7600, info@transcontinental.ca, http://www.transcontinental-gtc.com/en/home.html. Circ: 75,000.

384.55 RUS
TELESEM'. Text in Russian. w.
Published by: TeleSem', Vokzal'naya Magistral 15, ofis 524, Novosibirsk, 630099, Russian Federation. http://www.tele7.nsk.su. Ed. Valentina Dobrynina.

791.43 ITA ISSN 1124-1713
TELESETTE. Text in Italian. 1979. w. EUR 0.80 newsstand/cover (effective 2005). charts; illus. **Document type:** *Magazine, Consumer.* **Description:** Outlines daily schedules of TV programs for the week. Discusses TV news.
Related titles: ♦ Supplement to: Corriere della Sera. ISSN 1120-4982.
Published by: Del Duca Edizioni Srl (Subsidiary of: Casa Editrice Universo SpA), Corso di Porta Nuova 3A, Milan, MI 20121, Italy. TEL 39-02-636751.

791.45 GBR
TELETRONIC; the classic television magazine. Text in English. 2000. bi-m. free. tel.rev.
Media: Online - full text.
Published by: Television Heaven, 12 Wynndale Rd, S Woodford, London, E18 1DX, United Kingdom. TEL 44-20-8505-3605, lol.marcus@virgin.net, http://www.teletronic.co.uk, http://www.televisionheaven.co.uk. Ed., R&P, Adv. contact Laurence Marcus.

384.55 IND
TELEVISION. Text in Bengali. 1988. m. INR 10 newsstand/cover.
Published by: AAjkaal Publishers Ltd., 96 Raja Rammohan Sarani, Kolkata, West Bengal 700 009, India. TEL 3509803. Ed. Ashok Dasgupta. Circ: 36,297.

384.55 GBR ISSN 0308-454X
TK6630.A1 CODEN: TELED3
TELEVISION (LONDON, 1927). Text in English. 1927. 10/yr. GBP 82 domestic; GBP 118 foreign; free to members (effective 2005). adv. bk.rev. abstr.; bibl.; charts; illus. index. **Document type:** *Magazine, Trade.* **Description:** Provides news, views and features both technical and non-technical about the latest developments in the television industry.
Former titles: Royal Television Society. Journal (0035-9270); Television Society. Journal.
Related titles: E-mail ed.; Fax ed.; Microfilm ed.: (from PQC).
Indexed: ETA, EngInd, IIFP, IITV, Inspec.
—AskIEEE, CISTI, IE, Infotrieve, Linda Hall.
Published by: Royal Television Society, Holborn Hall, 100 Grays Inn Rd, London, WC1X 8AL, United Kingdom. TEL 44-20-7430-1000, FAX 44-20-7430-0924, publications@rts.org.uk, http://www.rts.org.uk. Ed. Steve Clarke. R&P, Adv. contact Sue Griffith TEL 44-20-76912465. B&W page GBP 700, color page GBP 1,000; trim 190 x 270. Circ: 4,000.

791.45   USA
TK6645
TELEVISION & CABLE ACTION UPDATE (ONLINE EDITION);
the authoritative news service of actions affecting television
stations and cable TV activities. Short title: T V & Cable
Update. Text in English. 1991. w. USD 555 (effective 2005).
stat. Supplement avail.; back issues avail. **Document type:**
Newsletter, Trade. **Description:** Highlights a weekly listing of
new applications including permits, sales franchises, grants
and regulatory changes.
Former titles (until 2004): Television & Cable Action Update (Print
Edition) (1061-5741); Weekly Television and Cable Action
Update
Media: Online - full content.
Published by: Warren Communications News, Inc., 2115 Ward
Ct, N W, Washington, DC 20037. TEL 202-872-9200,
800-327-7205, FAX 202-293-3435, info@warren-news.com,
http://www.warren-news.com. Pub. Albert Warren.

384.55   USA   ISSN 0732-8648
TK6540
TELEVISION AND CABLE FACTBOOK. Text in English. 1945. a.
USD 795 print or online ed.; USD 1,090 print & online eds.
(effective 2004). **Document type:** *Trade.*
Formerly: Television Factbook (0082-268X)
Published by: Warren Communications News, Inc., 2115 Ward
Ct, N W, Washington, DC 20037. TEL 202-872-9200,
800-327-7205, FAX 202-293-3435, info@warren-news.com,
http://www.warren-news.com. Ed. Albert Warren.

384.55   GBR
                              CODEN: TELED3
TELEVISION AND HOME ELECTRONICS. Text in English. 1934.
m. GBP 33 domestic; GBP 38.95 in Ireland; GBP 49 in
Europe; GBP 63.50 elsewhere (effective 2005). adv. charts;
illus. back issues avail. **Document type:** *Magazine, Trade.*
Description: Provides package of news, servicing solutions,
new products, fault finding methods, equipment reviews and
access to the most comprehensive marketplace for
components and services for personnel working with
televisions, videos and satellites.
Former titles (until May 2004): Television and Home Electronics
Repair (1475-7052); (until 2001): Television (London, 1934)
(0032-647X); (until 1969): Practical Television
Indexed: IIFP, Inspec, Pinpoint.
—BLDSC (8788.070500), CASDDS, IE, ingenta. **CCC.**
Published by: Highbury Business Communications (Subsidiary of:
Highbury House Communications PLC), Ann Boleyn House,
9-13 Ewell Rd, Cheam, Surrey SM3 8BZ, United Kingdom.
TEL 44-20-87226000, http://www.hhc.co.uk/
tvandhomeelectronicsrepair. Ed. Martin Eccles. Adv. contact
Pat Bunce TEL 44-20-87226091. Circ: 25,000 (paid).

384.55 302.23   USA   ISSN 1527-4764
PN1992
➤ **TELEVISION & NEW MEDIA.** Text in English. 2000. q. USD
382, GBP 246 to institutions; USD 397, GBP 257 combined
subscription to institutions print & online eds. (effective 2006).
adv. **Document type:** *Journal, Academic/Scholarly.*
Related titles: Online - full text ed.: ISSN 1552-8316. USD 378,
GBP 244 to institutions (effective 2006) (from C S A, EBSCO
Publishing, Gale Group, O C L C Online Computer Library
Center, Inc., Sage Publications, Inc., Swets Information
Services).
Indexed: CJA, CommAb, IBSS, PSA, RRTA, SociolAb.
—BLDSC (8788.077000), IE, Infotrieve, ingenta. **CCC.**
Published by: Sage Publications, Inc., 2455 Teller Rd, Thousand
Oaks, CA 91320. TEL 805-499-0721, 800-818-7243, FAX
805-499-8096, 800-583-2665, info@sagepub.com,
http://www.sagepub.com/journal.aspx?pid=13. Ed. Toby Miller.
Pub. Sara Miller McCune. Adv. contact Kirsten Beaulieu TEL
805-499-0721 ext 7160. page USD 350. Circ: 250 (paid and
free). **Subscr. to:** Sage Publications Ltd., 1 Oliver's Yard, 55
City Rd, London EC1 1SP, United Kingdom. TEL
44-20-73740645, FAX 44-20-73748741,
subscription@sagepub.co.uk.

384.55   SGP
TELEVISION ASIA. Text in English. 1993 (Jul.). 10/yr. USD 100
(effective 2001). adv. **Document type:** *Trade.* **Description:**
Offers in-depth coverage of Asian television broadcasting and
programming.
Indexed: WMB.
Published by: Cahners Asia Ltd. (Singapore), 58A Smith Street,
Singapore, 058962, Singapore. TEL 65-220-8823, FAX
65-220-5015, tvasia@tvasia.com.sg, http://www.tvasia.com.sg,
http://www.cahners.com. Ed. Janine Stein. Pub. Jonathan
Hallett. Adv. contacts Geraldine Mahalingam, Lisa Wagner.
B&W page USD 3,735, color page USD 5,440; trim 335 x
245. Circ: 5,100 (controlled).

384.55   GBR   ISSN 1353-8586
PN1992
THE TELEVISION BOOK (YEAR). Text in English. 199?. a. GBP
9.99 (effective 1999). **Document type:** *Academic/Scholarly.*
Description: Discusses various topics of television history,
culture, and programming.
Published by: Edinburgh International Television Festival, 2nd Fl,
24 Neal St, London, WC2H 9PS, United Kingdom. TEL
44-171-379-4519, FAX 44-171-836-0702. Ed. James Saynor.
Pub. Wendy Hutton.

384.55   USA   ISSN 1556-3588
TK6678
TELEVISION BROADCAST. Text in English. 1978. m. USD 52
domestic; USD 76 in Canada; USD 90 elsewhere; USD 6
newsstand/cover (effective 2005). adv. bk.rev. 52 p./no.; back
issues avail. **Document type:** *Magazine, Trade.* **Description:**
Covers news, products and applications in both the broadcast
and narrowcast industries through a blend of hard news
reporting, survey articles and news analysis columns.
Former titles (until 2005): Digital T V Television Broadcast
(1551-1928); (until Aug. 2002): Videography's Digital T V
(1543-1266); (until Mar. 2002): Television Broadcast's Digital T
V (1534-6064); (until 2001): Television Broadcast (0898-767X);
(until 1985): Television - Broadcast Communications
(0746-5777); (until 1983): Broadcast Communications
(0164-999X)
Related titles: Online - full text ed.: (from Gale Group, Northern
Light Technology, Inc.).
—CCC.
Published by: C M P Information, Inc. (Subsidiary of: C M P
Media LLC), 460 Park Ave South, 9th Fl, New York, NY
10016-7315. TEL 212-378-0400, FAX 212-378-2158,
msilbergleid@cmpinformation.com, http://
www.televisionbroadcast.com. adv.: page USD 6,680. Circ:
26,000 (controlled).

384.55 384.5452   GBR   ISSN 1461-4197
TELEVISION BROADCAST EUROPE. Text in English. 1992. m.
free to qualified personnel (effective 2002). adv. **Document
type:** *Magazine, Trade.*
Related titles: Online - full text ed.: (from EBSCO Publishing,
Gale Group, O C L C Online Computer Library Center, Inc.).
Indexed: WBA.
Published by: C M P Information Ltd. (Subsidiary of: United
Business Media), Ludgate House, 245 Blackfriars Rd.,
London, SE1 9UR, United Kingdom. TEL 44-20-79408500,
FAX 44-20-74077102, tvbeurope@scope.ie,
enquiries@cmpinformation.com, http://www.tvbeurope.com,
http://www.cmpinformation.com. Ed. Fergal Ringrose TEL
353-1-8303-455. Pub. Joe Hosken. Adv. contact Steve Grice
TEL 44-20-7579-4458.

384.55   GBR   ISSN 0953-6841
HE8700
TELEVISION BUSINESS INTERNATIONAL. Text in English.
1988. 10/yr. GBP 99, EUR 168, USD 168 (effective 2005).
Document type: *Magazine, Trade.* **Description:** Covers the
production and distribution of TV programming in the
international market, as well as comprehensive coverage of
major programme markets, industry trends, territory and
company profiles and interviews. TBI aims to update its
readers on new research and developments in interactive TV
and new media sectors.
Related titles: Online - full text ed.: (from Gale Group, O C L C
Online Computer Library Center, Inc., ProQuest Information &
Learning).
Indexed: B&I.
—IE, Infotrieve.
Published by: Informa Publishing, 69-77 Paul St, London, EC2A
4IQ, United Kingdom. TEL 44-20-7553-1000, FAX
44-20-7553-1105. Ed. Dominic Schreiber. Circ: 10,000.
Subscr. to: Informa Publishing Group Ltd, North America
Customer Services, PO Box 1017, Westborough, MA
01581-6017. TEL 800-493-4080, FAX 508-231-0856;
Customer Services Department, Sheepen Pl, Colchester,
Essex CO3 3LP, United Kingdom. TEL 44-1206-772866, FAX
44-1206-772771.

384.55   USA
TELEVISION CONTACTS (YEAR). Text in English. 1976. a. (plus
m. updates). USD 195. **Document type:** *Directory.*
Published by: V N U Business Publications (Subsidiary of: V N U
Business Media), 770 Broadway, New York, NY 10003-9595.
TEL 212-536-5261, FAX 212-536-5294. Ed. Mitch Tebo. Circ:
5,000.

621.388   USA   ISSN 0497-1515
TELEVISION DIGEST WITH CONSUMER ELECTRONICS. Text
in English. 1945. w. USD 944; USD 1,054 foreign (effective
1998). **Document type:** *Trade.*
Formerly: Television Digest (0497-1507)
Related titles: Online - full text ed.: (from LexisNexis).
Indexed: BusI, T&II.
Published by: Warren Communications News, Inc., 2115 Ward
Ct, N W, Washington, DC 20037. TEL 202-872-9200,
800-327-7205, FAX 202-293-3435, info@warren-news.com,
http://www.warren-news.com. Ed. Albert Warren. **Dist. by:**
Publications Resource Group, 121 Union St., Box 792, North
Adams, MA 01247. TEL 413-664-6185, FAX 413-664-9343.

TELEVISION DIRECTORS GUIDE. see *BUSINESS AND
ECONOMICS—Trade And Industrial Directories*

384.55   GBR   ISSN 1280-1224
TELEVISION EUROPE. Text in English. 8/yr. (plus 4 satellite &
cable guides). USD 100 (effective 2001). adv. bk.rev.
Document type: *Trade.* **Description:** Offers in-depth
coverage of the European broadcast, cable, and satellite
television and radio industries.
Indexed: WMB.

Published by: Reed Business Information Ltd. (Subsidiary of:
Reed Business), 6 Bell Yard, London, WC2A 2JR, United
Kingdom. TEL 44-207-5205287, FAX 44-207-5205226,
http://www.television-europe.com/, http://www.reedinfo.co.uk/.
Ed. Debra Johnson TEL 44-207-520-5281. adv.: B&W page
USD 3,235, color page USD 4,735; trim 245 x 335. Circ:
5,512 (controlled).

384.55 659.14 330.9   GBR   ISSN 1358-6815
TELEVISION IN ASIA PACIFIC TO THE YEAR... Text in English.
1995. a. GBP 275 (effective 2001). charts; stat. **Document
type:** *Trade.* **Description:** Forecasts the next five years of
multichannel and pay television growth in the fourteen most
important markets in the region.
Published by: Zenith Media, Bridge House, 63-65 N. Wharf Rd,
London, W2 1LA, United Kingdom. TEL 44-20-7224-8500,
FAX 44-20-7298-6902, publications@zenithmedia.co.uk,
http://www.zenithmedia.com. Ed., Pub. Adam Smith.

384.55 659.14 330.9   GBR   ISSN 0968-218X
TELEVISION IN EUROPE TO THE YEAR... Text in English. 1989.
a. GBP 275 (effective 2001). charts; stat. **Document type:**
Trade. **Description:** Facts and figures on today's audiences,
channels and advertising in 28 markets, with long-range
forecasts of satellite and cable growth for most western
European countries.
Published by: Zenith Media, Bridge House, 63-65 N. Wharf Rd,
London, W2 1LA, United Kingdom. TEL 44-20-7224-8500,
FAX 44-20-7298-6902, publications@zenithmedia.co.uk,
http://www.zenithmedia.com. Ed., Pub. Adam Smith.

384.55   GBR
TELEVISION IN LATIN AMERICA TO 2005. Text in English.
2000. a. GBP 195 (effective 2001). **Document type:** *Trade.*
Description: Covers Latin America and its television markets.
Provides background information about 15 television markets
in the region and examines the current state of free -TV and
pay-TV in each. It also forecasts the development of nine
markets until 2005.
Published by: Zenith Media, Bridge House, 63-65 N. Wharf Rd,
London, W2 1LA, United Kingdom. TEL 44-20-7224-8500,
FAX 44-20-7298-6902, publications@zenithmedia.co.uk,
http://www.zenithmedia.com.

384.55   USA   ISSN 0739-5531
PN1992
TELEVISION INDEX; television network program and production
reporting service. Text in English. 1949. w. USD 250 domestic;
USD 250 foreign; USD 5 newsstand/cover. cum.index.
Document type: *Trade.*
Published by: Television Index, Inc., 40 29 27th St, Long Island
City, NY 11101. TEL 718-937-3990. Ed. Jonathan Miller.

384.55   USA
TELEVISION INTERNATIONAL MAGAZINE. Text in English.
1956. bi-m. USD 42 domestic; USD 52 foreign (effective
2005). adv. bk.rev. bibl.; illus. **Document type:** *Magazine,
Trade.*
Formerly: Telefilm International Magazine
Indexed: IITV.
Published by: T V I Publishing, PO Box 8471, Universal City, CA
91618-8471. TEL 323-462-1099, 702-939-4725,
tvi@smart90.com, http://www.tvimagazine.com,
http://www.lookradio.com. Ed., Pub. Josie Cory. R&P
Catherine Rosen. Adv. contact Ginger Adams. Circ: 16,000
(controlled).

384.55   USA
TELEVISION LATIN AMERICA. Text in English. 6/yr. USD 90
(effective 2001). adv. charts; stat. **Document type:** *Trade.*
Description: Reports on the business of broadcast, cable,
and satellite television and radio in Latin America.
Published by: Reed Business Information (Subsidiary of: Reed
Business), 360 Park Ave South, New York, NY 10010. TEL
646-746-6819, FAX 646-746-6734, http://www.television-
latinamerica.com, http://www.reedbusiness.com. Ed. Olimpia
Del Boccio. adv.: B&W page USD 3,235, color page USD
4,735; trim 13.25 x 8.63. Circ: 5,300 (controlled).

384.55   USA   ISSN 1056-6104
PN1992.8.F5
(YEARS) TELEVISION PROGRAMMING SOURCE BOOKS. Text
in English. 1989. a. USD 895 for 4 vol. set; USD 545 for 3
vol. set. adv. **Document type:** *Directory.* **Description:** Lists
materials available for television programming, including films,
series and miniseries.
Formed by the 1989 merger of: T V Feature Film Source Book
(0739-2400); T V Series, Serials, and Packages (Domestic
Edition) (0895-2337); Which was formerly (until 1987): Series,
Serials, and Packages (Domestic Edition) (0162-9743); T V
Series, Serials, and Packages (Foreign Language Edition)
(0895-2345); Which was formerly (until 1987): Series, Serials,
and Packages (Foreign Language Edition) (0162-9751)
Related titles: CD-ROM ed.: USD 1,195; ◆ Supplement(s): B I B
Channels.
Published by: North American Publishing Co., 1500 Spring
Garden St., Ste 1200, Philadelphia, PA 19130-4094. TEL
215-238-5300, FAX 215-238-5457, http://www.napco.com. Ed.
D Witzleben.

C

384.55 USA ISSN 0040-2796
PN1992 CODEN: MAGJBM
TELEVISION QUARTERLY. Text in English. 1962. q. USD 30 domestic; USD 35 foreign; USD 22 to students; USD 6 newsstand/cover (effective 2004). adv. bk.rev. reprint service avail. from PQC. **Document type:** *Journal, Academic/Scholarly.* **Description:** Presents scholarly and professional views and interpretations of patterns and trends in the television industry, and provides a critique of industry performance.
Related titles: Microform ed.: (from PQC); Online - full text ed.: (from EBSCO Publishing, H.W. Wilson, O C L C Online Computer Library Center, Inc.).
Indexed: ASCA, ArtHuCI, BRI, CBRI, CommAb, CurCont, FLI, IIFP, IIPA, IITV, PAIS, RGAb, RGPR, RILM.
—IE, Infotrieve.
Published by: National Television Academy, 111 West 57th St, Ste 600, New York, NY 10019. TEL 212-586-8424, FAX 212-246-8129, hq@natasonline.com, http://www.tvquarterly.com, http://www.emmys.org. Ed. Frederick Jacobi. Circ: 11,500.

TELEVISION SERVICING. see *ELECTRONICS*

TELEVISION SPONSORS DIRECTORY; product cross-reference directory. see *BUSINESS AND ECONOMICS—Trade And Industrial Directories*

384.5 USA ISSN 1544-0516
PN1990
TELEVISION WEEK. Text in English. 1982; N.S. 2003 (Mar.). w. USD 119 domestic; USD 171 in Canada; USD 309 elsewhere (effective 2005). adv. charts; illus. back issues avail. **Document type:** *Newspaper, Trade.* **Description:** Provides for the management of television and radio stations, broadcast networks, cable systems and the emerging electronic media, as well as advertising agency media executives and producers and syndicators of programming.
Former titles (until Mar. 2003): Electronic Media (0745-0311); (until 1982): Advertising Age. Electronic Media Edition (0744-6675)
Related titles: Online - full text ed.: (from EBSCO Publishing, Gale Group, H.W. Wilson, LexisNexis, Northern Light Technology, Inc., O C L C Online Computer Library Center, Inc.).
Indexed: B&I, BPI, MicrocompInd.
—CCC.
Published by: Crain Communications, Inc., 1155 Gratiot Ave, Detroit, MI 48207-2997. TEL 313-446-6000, FAX 313-446-1687, http://www.tvweek.com, http://www.crain.com. Eds. Alex Ben Block, Rance Crain. Pub. Chuck Ross. adv.: B&W page USD 7,280, color page USD 9,890. Circ: 34,877 (paid and controlled).

TELEVISION WRITERS GUIDE. see *BUSINESS AND ECONOMICS—Trade And Industrial Directories*

384.55 USA
TELEVISIONWEEK. Text in English. 1991. 4/w. USD 119 (effective 2003). adv. **Description:** Provides each day's breaking news, ratings results, and other timely information.
Related titles: Fax ed.
Published by: Crain Communications, Inc., 711 Third Ave, New York, NY 10017-4036. TEL 212-210-0280, info@crain.com, http://www.emonline.com, http://www.crain.com. Ed. Alex Ben Block. Pub. Chuck Ross. Adv. contact Elizabeth Cherry TEL 323-370-2400. Circ: 25,421.

384.5452 384.558 GBR ISSN 0264-9845
TELEVISUAL. Text in English. 1982. m. GBP 35 domestic; GBP 60 foreign (effective 2001). **Document type:** *Magazine, Trade.* **Description:** Publishes news, features and surveys for broadcasters, producers and service providers.
Related titles: Online - full content ed.; Online - full text ed.: (from EBSCO Publishing, Gale Group, H.W. Wilson, O C L C Online Computer Library Center, Inc.).
Indexed: BPI.
—BLDSC (8788.550000).
Published by: Centaur Publishing, St Giles House, 50 Poland St, London, W1V 4AX, United Kingdom. TEL 44-20-7970-4000, mundye@centaur.co.uk, http://www.mad.co.uk/tv/, http://www.centaur.co.uk.

791.45 NLD ISSN 0049-3325
TELEVIZIER. Text in Dutch. 1960. w. EUR 50.10 (effective 2005). adv. **Document type:** *Magazine, Consumer.*
Incorporates (in 1993): TV Film (0929-1628)
Published by: B.V. Programmabladen, Postbus 580, Hilversum, 1200 AN, Netherlands. TEL 31-35-6726726, FAX 31-35-6726704, http://www.televizier.nl. Circ: 262,500.

384.55 BGR ISSN 0205-1281
TELEVIZIIA I RADIO. Text in Bulgarian. 1964. w. USD 78. illus.
Published by: Komitet za Televiziia i Radio/Bulgarian National Television, 29 San Stefano ul, Sofia, 1000, Bulgaria. TEL 359-2-443294. Ed. St Kolev. Circ: 70,300. **Dist. by:** Foreign Trade Co. "Hemus", 1-B Raiko Dashalov Pl, Sofia 1000, Bulgaria. TEL 359-2-871686, FAX 359-2-9803319.

621.388 RUS ISSN 0869-7914
TELEVIZIONNYI INFORMATSIONNO-TEKHNICHESKII ZHURNAL; broadcasting. Text in Russian. 1994. q. free (effective 2004). adv. tel.rev.; video rev. 64 p./no.; **Document type:** *Bulletin, Corporate.* **Description:** Informs organizations of the industry on research and development, advanced technologies, exhibitions, seminars, scientific conferences. Also treats problems of legislation, taxation, tecnnical control, certification and other topical problems of the industry.
—East View.
Published by: Vserossiiskii Nauchno-Issledovatel'skii Institut Televideniya i Radioveshchaniya, 3-ya Khoroshevskaya ul 12, Moscow, 123298, Russian Federation. TEL 7-095-1928196, FAX 7-095-9430006, trvinform@vniitr.ru, vniitr@vniitr.ru, http://www.vniitr.ru. Ed. Alexander Mkrtumov. Adv. contact Irina Gogoleva. color page USD 300. Circ: 1,000 (paid). **US dist. addr.:** East View Information Services, 3020 Harbor Ln. N., Minneapolis, MN 55447. TEL 800-477-1005, FAX 800-800-3839, eastview@eastview.com, http://www.eastview.com.

621.388 USA
TENNESSEE BROADCASTER✶. Text in English. 1978. m.
Published by: Tennessee Association of Broadcasters, PO Box 101015, Nashville, TN 37224-1015.

TEREBI GIJUTSU/TELEVISION TECHNICS & ELECTRONICS. see *ELECTRONICS*

791.45 BEL ISSN 0770-2396
TEVE BLAD. Text in Dutch. 1981. w. EUR 38.40 (effective 2003). **Document type:** *Magazine, Consumer.*
Published by: Sanoma Magazines Belgium, Telecomlaan 5-7, Diegem, 1831, Belgium. TEL 32-2-7762211, FAX 32-2-776-2317, teveblad@sanoma-magazines.be, Http://www.teveblad.be, http://www.sanoma-magazines.be/HomePage.aspx?flash=1&Language=nl. Circ: 215,645 (paid).

384.5452 CHN
TIANJIN GUANGBO DIANSHI BAO/TIANJIN BROADCASTING AND T V WEEKLY. Text in Chinese. 1955. w. **Document type:** *Newspaper, Trade.*
Published by: Tianjin Guangbo Dianshi Baoshe, Heping-qu, 143 Weijing Lu, Tianjin, 300070, China. TEL 86-22-23341114, FAX 86-22-23374263. Ed. Zhang Jian Guo. Circ: 1,340,000.

384.5532 GRC ISSN 1107-8421
TILE KONTROL. Text in Greek. 1993. w. adv. **Document type:** *Magazine, Consumer.* **Description:** Provides detailed schedules of all television channels as well as celebrity news and gossip.
Published by: Liberis Publications S.A./Ekdoseon Lymperi A.E., Ioannou Metaxa 80, Karelas, Koropi 19400, Greece. TEL 30-1-6198000, FAX 30-1-6198608, info@liberis.gr, http://www.liberis.gr. Circ: 24,039 (paid).

791.45 SAU ISSN 1319-1403
TILIVISYON AL-KHALIJ. Key Title: Magalat Tilifizun al-Halig. Text in Arabic. q. **Document type:** *Consumer.*
Formerly (until 1980): Gulfvision Nashrat al-Ma'lumat
Published by: Gulf Vision, P O Box 6802, Riyadh, Saudi Arabia. TEL 4032912.

384.55 ITA
TIVU. Text in Italian. m. (11/yr.). EUR 15 (effective 2005). **Document type:** *Magazine, Consumer.*
Published by: Editoriale Duesse SpA, Via Donatello 5b, Milan, 20131, Italy. TEL 39-02-277961, FAX 39-02-27796300, e-duesse@e-duesse.it, http://www.e-duesse.it.

384.5532 POL ISSN 1230-8331
TO I OWO. Text in Polish. 1989. w. PLZ 1.90 newsstand/cover (effective 2003). adv. **Document type:** *Magazine, Consumer.*
Published by: Wydawnictwo Bauer Sp. z o.o. (Subsidiary of: Heinrich Bauer Verlag), ul. Motorowa 1, Warsaw, 04-035, Poland. TEL 48-22-5170500, FAX 48-22-5170125, tygodnik@to-owo.lodz.pl, kontakt@bauer.pl, http://www.bauer.pl. Ed. Wlodzimierz Krawczyk. Adv. contact Katarzyna Jablonska. page PLZ 21,000; trim 235 x 296.

TONE (AUCKLAND). see *ELECTRONICS*

791.4 778 USA
TOTAL ACCESS. Text in English. 2001. m. USD 3.99 newsstand/cover (effective 2002). adv. **Document type:** *Consumer.*
Published by: Multi-Media International, 1359 Broadway, Ste 1203, New York, NY 10018. Ed. Kelly Bryant. Pub. Robert Maiello.

791.45 USA ISSN 1063-2883
TOTAL T V✶. Text in English. 1990. w. **Document type:** *Consumer.* **Description:** System-specific cable guide.
Formerly (until 1992): T V Times (Horsham) (1054-8858); Incorporates (in 1993): Total
Published by: T V Guide Magazine Publishing, 1211 Avenue of Americas, 4th Fl, New York, NY 10036. TEL 215-443-9300, 800-540-5643, http://www.total.com. Ed. Jay Gissen. Pub. Michael Perlis.

384.5532 CHE
TR7; das schweizer TV-Magazin. Text in German. w. CHF 125 (effective 2000). adv. **Document type:** *Magazine, Consumer.* **Description:** Contains TV program listings along with entertaining and informative articles on current events in the world of entertainment.
Published by: Tevag Basel AG, Foerlibuckstr 10, Zuerich, 8021, Switzerland. TEL 41-1-4488112, FAX 41-1-4488825, fhubrath@tr7.ch, kschwarz@tr7.ch, http://www.tr7.ch. Ed. Frank Hubrath. adv.: B&W page CHF 6,390, color page CHF 10,715. Circ: 169,372 (paid and controlled).

TRADE HOME ENTERTAINMENT. see *COMMUNICATIONS—Video*

621.388 JPN ISSN 0914-9279
QC676 CODEN: TSKKED
TSUSHIN SOGO KENKYUJO KIHO/COMMUNICATIONS RESEARCH LABORATORY. REVIEW. Text in Japanese; Summaries in English. 1954. q. per issue exchange basis. **Document type:** *Academic/Scholarly.*
Formerly (until 1988): Denpa Kenkyujo Kiho - Radio Research Laboratory. Review (0033-801X)
Indexed: IAA, INIS AtomInd, Inspec, JCT, JTA, RefZh.
—BLDSC (7786.031000), AskIEEE, CISTI, Linda Hall.
Published by: Ministry of Posts and Telecommunications, Communications Research Laboratory/Yuseisho Tsushinsogo Kenkyujo, 2-1 Nukui-Kita-Machi 4-chome, Koganei-shi, Tokyo-to 184-0015, Japan. TEL 81-423-21-1211, FAX 81-423-27-7603, pub@crl.go.jp. **Co-sponsor:** Denki Tsushin Shinkokai - Association for the Promotion of Telecommunications.

384.55 HUN ISSN 1585-3586
TV KETHETES. Variant title: Televizio Kethetes. Text in Hungarian. 1999. fortn. HUF 1,776 (effective 2001). adv. **Document type:** *Magazine, Consumer.*
Published by: Axel Springer - Budapest Kft., Varosmajor u 11, Budapest, 1122, Hungary. TEL 36-1-4885700, FAX 36-1-2025332, bayerj@axels.hu. Circ: 113,000 (paid).

384.555 USA
TV Y MAS. Text in English. 1983. w. adv. **Description:** Includes features on Spanish-language television stars, recording artists and movie stars. It also contains weekly comprehensive television listings extends the shelf life of the publications. Editorial information on food, real estate, restaurant and automotive areas, helps the Hispanic consumers make educated buying decisions.
Published by: Telecommunications Reports (Subsidiary of: Aspen Publishers, Inc.), 800 N. 1st Ave, Phoenix, AZ 85002. TEL 602-253-9080, FAX 602-253-9071, dan@ashlandmedia.com. Pub. Alvira Ortiz. adv.: B&W page USD 2,179; trim 8 x 10.5. Circ: 85,497 (controlled).

384.55 CHE
TV8. Text in French. w. adv. **Document type:** *Magazine, Consumer.* **Description:** Contains articles and special features as well as listings on television programs.
Published by: Ringier Romandie, Pont Bessieres 3, Case postale 3733, Lausanne, 1002, Switzerland. TEL 41-21-3317130, FAX 41-21-3317121, rtv8@ringier.ch, info@ringier.ch, http://www.ringier.ch. Ed. Corinne Badoux. adv.: B&W page CHF 3,296, color page CHF 5,715. Circ: 57,083 (paid).

384.55 CHE
TVGUIDE. Text in French. w. adv. **Document type:** *Magazine, Consumer.*
Published by: Edipresse Publications SA, 33 av de la Gare, Lausanne, 1001, Switzerland. TEL 41-21-3494545, FAX 41-21-3494319, tvguide-redaction@edicom.ch, groupe@edipresse.com, http://www.edicom.ch/tvguide/index.html. Ed. Laurent Delaloye. Adv. contact Patrice Matthey. B&W page CHF 7,222, color page CHF 12,644. Circ: 202,140 (controlled).

384.55 HUN ISSN 0864-9251
TVR-HET. Variant title: Televizio-radio-het. Text in Hungarian. 1989. w. HUF 6,192 (effective 2001). adv. **Document type:** *Magazine, Consumer.*
Published by: Axel Springer - Budapest Kft., Varosmajor u 11, Budapest, 1122, Hungary. TEL 36-1-4885700, FAX 36-1-2025332, bayerj@axels.hu. Circ: 493,000 (paid).

384.55 HUN ISSN 1419-0931
TVR USJAG. Variant title: Televizio Radio Ujsag. Text in Hungarian. 1998. w. HUF 690 per quarter (effective 2001). adv. **Document type:** *Magazine, Consumer.*
Published by: Axel Springer - Budapest Kft., Varosmajor u 11, Budapest, 1122, Hungary. TEL 36-1-4885700, FAX 36-1-2025332, bayerj@axels.hu. Circ: 141,000 (paid).

384.55 CZE ISSN 1211-7625
TYDENIK TELEVIZE. Text in Czech. 1993. w. CZK 17 newsstand/cover (effective 2002). adv. 72 p./no. 4 cols./p.; **Document type:** *Magazine, Consumer.* **Description:** Contains televsion, cable and satellite program listings and features.
Supersedes (in 1994): Tydenik Televize a Teletip (1210-728X)

Published by: Ringier CR, U pruhonu 13, Prague 7, 17000, Czech Republic. TEL 420-2-67097720, FAX 420-2-67097718, program@televize.cz, info@ringier.cz, http://www.televize.cz, http://www.ringier.cz. Ed. Daniela Kupsova. Pub. Aleka Cerna. Adv. contact Tomas Filla TEL 420-2-67097427. page CZK 190,600; trim 215 x 300. Circ: 201,000 (paid).

070 USA
THE TYNDALL REPORT (ONLINE). Text in English. 1988. bi-m. looseleaf. free (effective 2005). back issues avail.
Description: Analysis of television news: monitors the nightly newscasts of the three US broadcast networks with statistical data and commentary. Tracks trends in major news stories, social issues, domestic and foreign affairs, and politics.
Formerly: The Tyndall Report (Print)
Published by: A D T Research, 135 Rivington St, New York, NY 10002. TEL 212-674-8913, FAX 212-979-7304, andrew@tyndallreport.com, http://www.tyndallreport.com. Ed. Aleksandra Scepanovic. Pub. Andrew Tyndall. Circ: 500.

621.388 RUS
TYSYACHI PROGRAMMYKH PRODUKTOV. Text in Russian. 1994. bi-m. USD 100 in United States (effective 2000).
Published by: Kompaniya Vest, Pr-d Kolomenskii 1a, Moscow, 115487, Russian Federation. TEL 7-095-1159713. **Dist. by:** East View Information Services, 3020 Harbor Ln. N., Minneapolis, MN 55447. TEL 763-550-0961, FAX 763-559-2931.

384.5452 GBR ISSN 1470-3157
U K BROADCAST MEDIA. Text in English. 1965. **Document type:** *Directory.* **Description:** Covering TV, radio, online media wire services and news agencies.
Supersedes in part (in 2000): P I M S Media Directory (Press Information and Mailing Services) (0261-5169); Which was formerly (until 1981): P R A D S Media List (0144-3933) —BLDSC (6501.340500).
Published by: P I M S (UK) Ltd., PIMS House, Mildmay Ave, London, N1 4RS, United Kingdom. TEL 44-20-7354-7000, FAX 44-20-7354-7053.

THE U K CABLE REPORT (YEAR). see *BUSINESS AND ECONOMICS—Trade And Industrial Directories*

360 659.14 330.9 GBR
U K TELEVISION FORECASTS. Text in English. 2/yr. GBP 420 (effective 2001). **Document type:** *Trade.* **Description:** Includes detailed forecasts to 2005 with backdata to 1987. Forecasts include advertising expenditure , cable and dish proliferation or share of viewing, net advertising revenue and pricing by channel, size of audience, etc.
Published by: Zenith Media, Bridge House, 63-65 N. Wharf Rd, London, W2 1LA, United Kingdom. TEL 44-20-7224-8500, FAX 44-20-7298-6902, publications@zenithmedia.co.uk, http://www.zenithmedia.com. Ed., Pub. Adam Smith.

U.S. DIRECTORY OF ENTERTAINMENT EMPLOYERS. see *BUSINESS AND ECONOMICS—Trade And Industrial Directories*

384.55 USA ISSN 1064-9557
VARIETY AND DAILY VARIETY TELEVISION REVIEWS. Text in English. 1950. biennial.
Formerly (until 1988): Variety Television Reviews (1064-9565)
Published by: Garland Publishing, Inc., 270 Madison Ave., # 3, New York, NY 10016-0601. http://www.garlandpub.com.

VARIETY JUNIOR. see *CHILDREN AND YOUTH—About*

384.5 NLD
VERONICA; weekblad voor radio en TV. Text in Dutch. 1971. w. EUR 42.50; EUR 1.05 newsstand/cover (effective 2005). adv. bk.rev.; film rev. **Document type:** *Magazine, Consumer.* **Description:** Contains features and radio and TV listings.
Published by: Veronica Blad B.V., PO Box 22000, Hilversum, 1202 CA, Netherlands. TEL 31-35-6463406, 31-35-6463333, FAX 31-35-6463400, bladredactie@veronica.nl, http://www.veronica.nl, http://www.veronicauitgeverij.nl. Adv. contact Erik Wijnberg. B&W page EUR 19,265; trim 175 x 250. Circ: 924,987.

384.558 USA ISSN 0278-5013
PN1992
VIDEO AGE INTERNATIONAL; the business journal of film, TV broadcasting, cable, pay TV, PPV, home video, DBS, production. Text in English. 1981. 10/yr. USD 30 in North America; USD 45 elsewhere. adv. bk.rev. **Document type:** *Trade.* **Description:** International trade publication for the video industry, including profiles, information, and analysis.
Related titles: Online - full text ed.: (from Florida Center for Library Automation, Gale Group, Northern Light Technology, Inc.).
Published by: T V Trade Media, Inc., 216 E 75th St, Ste PW, New York, NY 10021. TEL 212-288-3933, FAX 212-734-9033, TELEX 428669 VIDEO. Ed., Pub. Dom Serafini. R&P Monica Gorghetto. Adv. contact Lily Weinzick. Circ: 15,000.

VIDEO & TELEVISION (YEAR). see *COMMUNICATIONS—Video*

384.55 DNK ISSN 0903-5117
VIDEO TRAILEREN. Text in Danish. 1986. m. DKK 350, USD 70 (effective 1997). **Document type:** *Trade.*
Published by: Bladforlaget Nygaard ApS, Naestvedvej 12, PO Box 12, Herlufmagle, 4160, Denmark. TEL 45-53-75-10-11, FAX 45-53-75-10-11. Ed. Jens Nygaard. adv.: B&W page DKK 4,100, color page DKK 8,300; trim 175 x 266. Circ: 5,289.

VISIE. see *RELIGIONS AND THEOLOGY—Protestant*

384.55 FIN ISSN 0780-4199
VISIO. Text in Finnish. 1977. 6/yr. EUR 59 domestic; EUR 77 in Scandinavia and Baltic countries; EUR 83 in Europe; EUR 87 elsewhere (effective 2005). adv. bk.rev. **Document type:** *Magazine, Trade.* **Description:** For A-V, video and new media professionals and users in Finland.
Formerly (until 1983): Kuva ja Aani (0357-2943); Incorporates (1983-1990): Uudet Viestimet (0782-8152); Which was formerly (until 1986): Telset Uutiset (0780-0576)
Published by: Stellanum Oy, Tyoepajankatu 6, Helsinki, 00580, Finland. TEL 358-9-8689700, FAX 358-9-86897070, http://www.stellanum.fi. Ed. Matti Laipio. adv.: B&W page EUR 1,600, color page EUR 2,400; 186 x 270. Circ: 7,000.

791.45 USA ISSN 1088-1824
HE8689.7.P82
THE VISION MAKER. Text in English. 1995. q. free. adv. **Document type:** *Newsletter.* **Description:** Informs, educates, and encourages awareness of tribal cultures, opportunities, histories, languages, and aspirations by employing educational and public telecommunications.
Published by: Native American Public Telecommunications, 1800 N 33rd St, PO Box 83111, Lincoln, NE 68501-3111. TEL 402-472-3522, FAX 402-472-8675, native@unlinfo.unl.edu, http://www.nativetelecom.org. Ed. Frank Blythe. Adv. contact Preston Thomas. Circ: 12,000.

VOICE OF PROPHECY NEWS. see *RELIGIONS AND THEOLOGY—Protestant*

791.45 USA ISSN 1041-2700
PN1992.3.U5
W E T A MAGAZINE. (Washington Educational Telecommunications Association) Text in English. m. adv.
Formerly (until 1988): Dial W E T A (0898-1779)
Published by: W E T A, 2775 S Quincy St, Arlington, VA 22206. TEL 703-998-2441, FAX 703-998-3412, http://www.wera.org. Ed. Laurie Fry. Adv. contact Pat Good. Circ: 125,000.

WESTERNS & SERIALS. see *MOTION PICTURES*

WHAT HOME CINEMA. see *ELECTRONICS*

621.388 GBR
WHAT SATELLITE BOOK OF TESTS. Text in English. a. GBP 3.50 (effective 1998). **Document type:** *Consumer.*
Published by: Highbury - WV (Subsidiary of: Highbury House Communications PLC), 53-79 Highgate Rd, London, NW5 1TW, United Kingdom. TEL 44-20-7485-0011, FAX 44-20-7482-6269. **Orders to:** ASM Ltd., Unit 6, Pipewell Rd Industrial Estate, Desborough, Northants NN14 2SW, United Kingdom. TEL 44-1536-762860, FAX 44-1536-760306.

384.51 GBR ISSN 1470-1960
WHAT SATELLITE T V. Text in English. 198?. m. GBP 34 domestic; GBP 52 in Europe; GBP 80 elsewhere; GBP 3.25 newsstand/cover (effective 2003). **Document type:** *Magazine, Consumer.* **Description:** Contains comprehensive coverage of all aspects of the biggest consumer electronics success story of all time, featuring equipment tests, industry news, technical and buying advice, technical tutorials, program backgrounds, guides to reception equipment, European channels and English language program listings.
Formerly (until 199?): What Satellite (0956-2362)
Published by: Highbury - WV (Subsidiary of: Highbury House Communications PLC), 53-79 Highgate Rd, London, NW5 1TW, United Kingdom. TEL 44-20-73311000, FAX 44-20-73311273, http://www.hhc.co.uk/whatsatellitetv. Ed. Geoff Bains.

791.45 GBR ISSN 0961-8538
WHAT'S ON T V. Text in English. 1991. w. **Document type:** *Consumer.*
Published by: I P C tx (Subsidiary of: I P C Media Ltd.), Kings Reach Tower, Stamford St, London, SE1 9LS, United Kingdom. TEL 44-161-8722155, http://www.ipcmedia.com/. Ed. Colin Tough TEL 44-20-72617535. Pub. Rachel Pearce. Circ: 1,630,850. **Dist. by:** I P C Media Ltd., Perrymount Rd, Haywards Heath RH16 3DA, United Kingdom. TEL 44-1444-475675, FAX 44-1444-445599, ipcsubs@qss-uk.com.

791.45 GBR ISSN 0965-4038
WHAT'S ON T V (ANGLIA EDITION). Text in English. 1992. w. GBP 0.40 newsstand/cover (effective 2005). adv. **Document type:** *Magazine, Consumer.* **Description:** Provides a unique mix of entertaining features, puzzles, competitions, and easy-to-use television listings.
Published by: I P C tx (Subsidiary of: I P C Media Ltd.), Kings Reach Tower, Stamford St, London, SE1 9LS, United Kingdom. TEL 44-161-8722155, http://www.ipcmedia.com/magazines/whatsontv/. Ed. Colin Tough TEL 44-20-72617535. Pub. Amy Culligan TEL 44-20-72615343. Adv. contact Steve Judd TEL 44-20-72617063. page GBP 20,160. Circ: 1,587,578.

384.55 USA
WIDESCREEN REVIEW PRESENTS: THE ULTIMATE WIDESCREEN D V D MOVIE GUIDE. Text in English. 2000. a. USD 9.95 newsstand/cover (effective 2001). adv. **Document type:** *Consumer.*
Published by: W S R Publishing, 27645 Commerce Center Dr., Temecula, CA 92590. TEL 909-676-4914, FAX 909-693-2960, EditorGary@WidescreenReview.com. Ed., Pub. Gary Reber.

384.555 USA
TS270.A1 CODEN: WTINEI
WIRE & CABLE TECHNOLOGY INTERNATIONAL. Text in English. 1973. bi-m. USD 35 in US & Canada; free to qualified personnel (effective 2005). adv. illus. **Document type:** *Magazine, Trade.*
Former titles (until 1997): Wire Technology International (0898-9850); (until 1987): Wire Tech (0745-7510); (until 1983): Wire Technology (0361-4565)
Indexed: BrCerAb, C&ISA, CerAb, CivEngAb, CorrAb, E&CAJ, EMA, IAA, Inspec, M&TEA, MBF, METADEX, SolStAb, WAA. —BLDSC (9320.350000), AskIEEE, CISTI, Linda Hall. **CCC.**
Published by: Initial Publications Inc., 3869 Darrow Rd, Ste 109, Stow, OH 44224. TEL 330-686-9544, FAX 330-686-9563, info@wiretech.com, http://www.wiretech.com/. Ed. Michael J McNulty. Pub. John L Jones. Circ: 10,725.

384.55 USA ISSN 1084-9475
PN1992.1
(YEAR) WORLD GUIDE TO TELEVISION. Text in English. 1990. a. USD 495 (effective 1997). **Document type:** *Directory.* **Description:** Guide to the international television marketplace including program buyers at every station around the world.
Former titles (until 1996): World Guide to Television and Film (1072-6144); (until 1994): World Guide to Television and Programming (1058-1944); (until 1992): T B I's World Guide (1052-7192)
Related titles: CD-ROM ed.; ♦ Supplement(s): B I B Channels.
Published by: North American Publishing Co., 1500 Spring Garden St., Ste 1200, Philadelphia, PA 19130-4094. TEL 215-238-5300, FAX 215-238-5457, http://www.napco.com. Ed. Dana Witzleben.

WORLD RADIO T V HANDBOOK. see *COMMUNICATIONS—Radio*

621.388 CHN ISSN 1000-1417
WUXIANDIAN YU DIANSHI/RADIO AND TELEVISION. Text in Chinese. bi-m.
Published by: Shanghai Kexue Jishu Chubanshe/Shanghai Scientific and Technical Publishers, 450 Ruijin Er Rd, Shanghai, 200020, China. TEL 86-21-6473-6055. Ed. Sun Heming.

791.456 GBR ISSN 1368-700X
X-FILES MAGAZINE. Text in English. 1997. m. GBP 39; GBP 3.25 newsstand/cover (effective 2000). adv. **Document type:** *Magazine, Consumer.*
Published by: Titan Magazines (Subsidiary of: Titan Books Ltd.), Titan House, 144 Southwark St, London, SE1 0UP, United Kingdom. TEL 44-20-7620-0200, FAX 44-20-7803-1803, xfilesmail@titanemail.com. Ed. Martin Eden. Pub. Nick Landau. Adv. contact Scott Ferguson-Caisley.

XIJU SHIJIE/COMEDY WORLD. see *THEATER*

XPOSE. see *MOTION PICTURES*

XPOSE SPECIAL. see *MOTION PICTURES*

384.55 USA ISSN 1051-4058
AS29.5
YEARBOOK OF EXPERTS, AUTHORITIES & SPOKESPERSONS; an encyclopedia of sources. Text in English. 1984. a. USD 39.95 (effective 2000). adv. **Document type:** *Directory.* **Description:** Reviews 1,500 groups and individuals of interest to the media, and provides contact names and phone numbers.
Formerly (until 8th, 1990): Directory of Experts, Authorities and Spokespersons (1045-9537)
Related titles: Online - full text ed.
Published by: Broadcast Interview Source, 2233 Wisconsin Ave, N W, Washington, DC 20007. TEL 202-333-4904, FAX 202-342-5411, editor@yearbooknews.com, editor@yearbook.com, http://www.yearbooknews.com, http://www.yearbook.com. Ed., R&P Mitchell P Davis. Circ: 10,000.

YINGSHI YISHU/FILM AND T V ART. see *MOTION PICTURES*

384.55 IND
YUGSHREE. Text in Hindi. 1985. m. adv. music rev.; tel.rev. illus. 72 p./no. 3 cols./p.; **Description:** Guides people to TV programs, and commercial products.

C

▼ new title ➤ refereed ✶ unverified ♦ full entry avail.

Published by: Ranchi Prakashan Pvt. Ltd., 55 Baralal St., Ranchi, Bihar 834 001, India. TEL 91-651-206320, FAX 91-651-203466. Ed. Vijay Maroo. Adv. contact Rakesh Dosi. B&W page INR 12,000, color page INR 24,000; trim 175 x 240. Circ: 55,000.

384.55 DEU ISSN 0342-5886
Z D F JAHRBUCH. (Zweites Deutsches Fernsehen) Text in German. 1964. a. **Document type:** *Corporate.* **Description:** Contains details and information on programming and production at the ZDF television channel.
Formerly: Zweites Deutsches Fernsehen. Jahrbuch (0514-8391)
Related titles: CD-ROM ed.
Indexed: IIFP, IITV.
Published by: Zweites Deutsches Fernsehen, Presse und Oeffentlichkeitsarbeit, Postfach 4040, Mainz, 55100, Germany. TEL 49-6131-702210, FAX 49-6131-705366, TELEX 4187930-ZDF-D, info@zdf.de, http://www.zdf.de. Ed. Philipp Baum. Pub. Dieter Schwarzenau. Circ: 10,000.

384.55 DEU
Z D F SCHRIFTENREIHE. (Zweites Deutsches Fernsehen) Text in German. irreg., latest vol.57. **Document type:** *Monographic series.*
Published by: Zweites Deutsches Fernsehen, Kommunikation, Mainz, 55100, Germany. TEL 49-6131-702210, FAX 49-6131-705366, TELEX 4187930-ZDF-D, info@zdf.de, http://www.zdf.de.

384.55 DEU
ZAP! FERNSEHEN UND BUECHER. Text in German. 1995. m. **Document type:** *Consumer.*
Published by: Stiftung Lesen, Fischtorplatz 23, Mainz, 55116, Germany. TEL 06131-288900, FAX 06131-230333. Circ: 10,000.

ZEITSCHRIFT FUER URHEBER- UND MEDIENRECHT. see *LAW*

C

621.388 GBR ISSN 0261-1686
ZERB. Text in English. 1973. s-a. GBP 3.75 per issue; GBP 6 per issue foreign. adv. bk.rev. illus. back issues avail. **Document type:** *Trade.* **Description:** Official journal of the guild which aims to act as an authoritative source of advice and informtion on all matters of concern to television cameramen, and provide a forum for comments, ideas and criticism on the operational aspects of cameras, lenses, mountings and other equipment.
Published by: Guild of Television Cameramen, Church Barn, Harberton, Totnes, Decon TQ9 7SQ, United Kingdom. TEL 44-1803-868652, FAX 44-1803-868444, 100701.1712@compuserve.com. Adv. contact Paul Sampson. B&W page GBP 745, color page GBP 1,425; 185 x 270. Circ: 1,750. **Subscr. to:** 43 Mote Park, Saltash, Decon PL12 4JY, United Kingdom.

384.55 CHN
ZHONGGUO DIANSHI BAO/CHINA TV GUIDE. Text in Chinese. w. CNY 41.64 (effective 2004). **Document type:** *Newspaper, Consumer.*
Address: 11, Fuxing Lu Yi, Meidiyabinguang, Gongyu 439 Fangjian, Beijing, 100038, China. TEL 86-10-68574194, FAX 86-10-68516201. **Dist. by:** China International Book Trading Corp, 35 Chegongzhuang Xilu, Haidian District, PO Box 399, Beijing 100044, China. TEL 86-10-68412045, FAX 86-10-68412023, cibtc@mail.cibtc.com.cn, http://www.cibtc.com.cn.

384.55 CHN
ZHONGWAI DIANSHI/CHINESE & WORLD T V. Text in Chinese. m. CNY 31.20 domestic; USD 58 foreign. **Description:** Covers Chinese and foreign movie and TV scripts, stories, and profiles of movie stars and singers.
Indexed: IBZ.
Published by: (Zhongguo Dianshi Yishu Weiyuanhui/China Television Drama Committee), Zhongwai Dianshi Zazhishe, 2 Fuxingmenwai Dajie, Beijing, 100866, China. TEL 867127. Ed. Ruan Ruolin. **Dist. in US by:** China Books & Periodicals Inc, 360 Swift Ave., Ste. 48, S San Fran, CA 94080-6220. TEL 415-282-2994.

384.55 DEU ISSN 0177-0837
ZIMPEL. TEIL 3: FUNK UND FERNSEHEN. Text in German. 1990. base vol. plus bi-m. updates. **Document type:** *Directory.*
Published by: Verlag Dieter Zimpel (Subsidiary of: Springer Science+Business Media), Angererstr 36, Munich, 80796, Germany. TEL 49-89-3073445, FAX 49-89-302409. Ed. Ingrid Finsterwald. **Subscr. to:** Gabler Verlag, Abraham-Lincoln-Str 46, Wiesbaden 65189, Germany. TEL 49-611-7878297, FAX 49-611-7878466.

621.388 621.384 RUS
ZVUKOREZHISSIOR; informatsionno-tekhnicheskii zhurnal. Text in Russian. 10/yr.
Published by: Izdatel'stvo 625, P.O. Box 143, Moscow, 121069, Russian Federation. TEL 7-095-2904968, FAX 7-095-2904968, v625@glas.apc.org, http://www.625-net.ru.

384.55 DEU ISSN 0946-6673
DIE ZWEI. Text in German. w. (Thu.). EUR 0.92 newsstand/cover (effective 2002). adv. **Document type:** *Magazine, Consumer.*
Published by: Gong Verlag GmbH & Co. KG, Muenchener Str 101, Ismaning, 85737, Germany. TEL 49-911-5325-0, FAX 49-911-5325309, gonginfo@gongverlag.de, http://www.gong-verlag.de. Adv. contact Simone Raeck. B&W page EUR 3,530, color page EUR 5,300. Circ: 228,001 (paid). **Subscr. to:** dsb Abo-Betreuung GmbH, Konrad-Zuse-Str 16, Neckarsulm 74172, Germany. TEL 49-1805-959500, FAX 49-1805-959511, gongverlag.abo@dsb.net, http://www.dsb.net.

384.5 DZA
LES 2 ECRANS✶. Text in French. m. (10/yr.). DZD 45.
Published by: Radiodiffusion Television Algerienne (RTA), Immeuble RTA, 21, blvd. des Martyr, Algiers, Algeria. Ed. B Abdou.

621.388 JPN ISSN 1342-2189
3 D EIZO/JOURNAL OF THREE DIMENSIONAL IMAGES. Text in English, Japanese. 1987. q. JPY 1,000 per issue (effective 2004). **Document type:** *Academic/Scholarly.*
—BLDSC (5069.340000).
Published by: Forum for Advancement of Three Dimensional Image Technology and Arts, c/o Hiroaki Yamada, Dept of Electronic Engineering, Shibaura Institue of Technolog, 3-9-14 Shibaura, Minato-ku, Tokyo, Japan. hagura@mmda.net, http://www.ricoh.co.jp/net-messena/ACADEMIA/3D/3Dkaishi.html, http://www.ricoh.co.jp/net-messena/ACADEMIA/3D/3Dhome.html.

384.5532 GRC ISSN 1108-5673
7 MERES T V. Text in Greek. 1990. w. adv. **Document type:** *Magazine, Consumer.* **Description:** Contains schedules of all available television and cable channels along with program reviews and interviews with celebrities and actors.
Published by: Liberis Publications S.A./Ekdoseon Lymperi A.E., Ioannou Metaxa 80, Karelas, Koropi 19400, Greece. TEL 30-1-6198000, FAX 30-1-6198608, info@7merestv.gr, info@liberis.gr, http://www.7merestv.gr, http://www.liberis.gr. Circ: 127,625 (paid).

384.55 HUN
100 X SZEP. Text in Hungarian. m. HUF 2,640 (effective 2001). adv. **Document type:** *Magazine, Consumer.*
Published by: Axel Springer - Budapest Kft., Varosmajor u 11, Budapest, 1122, Hungary. TEL 36-1-4885700, FAX 36-1-2025332, bayerj@axels.hu. Circ: 30,000 (free).

621.388 RUS
625. Text in Russian. 1993. 10/yr. **Description:** Covers aspects of activities in area of broadcasting. Describes modern equipment for broadcasting such as digital video-interfaces, television and radio plants, studio complexes, modern communication facilities, color television systems, developments of modern engineering.
Related titles: Online - full content ed.: 625-net. 1993.
Published by: Izdatel'stvo 625, P.O. Box 143, Moscow, 121069, Russian Federation. TEL 7-095-2904968, FAX 7-095-2904968, v625@glas.apc.org, http://www.625-net.ru. Ed. S. Fedotov.

COMMUNICATIONS—Video

A F C NEWS. see *MOTION PICTURES*

A M I A NEWSLETTER. see *LIBRARY AND INFORMATION SCIENCES*

A V JOURNAAL; tweewekelijks nieuwsbulletin voor de audiovisuele branche. see *COMMUNICATIONS—Television And Cable*

A V MAX. (Audio Video) see *MUSIC*

A V STATE OF THE ART. see *ELECTRONICS*

384.55 USA ISSN 1533-5992
ADAM BLACK VIDEO DIRECTORY OF ADULT FILM. Text in English. 1998. a. USD 10.95 per issue (effective 2001). **Document type:** *Directory, Consumer.*
Published by: Knight Publishing Corporation, 8060 Melrose Ave, Los Angeles, CA 90046. TEL 323-653-8060, FAX 323-655-9452, psi@loop.com, http://www.adultplayground.com/. R&P Mitcheall Neal. Adv. contact Timothy Connelly.

ADAM FILM WORLD DIRECTORY OF ADULT FILM & VIDEO. see *MOTION PICTURES*

ADAM GAY VIDEO DIRECTORY. see *HOMOSEXUALITY*

ADAM GAY VIDEO EROTICA. see *HOMOSEXUALITY*

ADAM GAY VIDEO XXX SHOWCASE. see *HOMOSEXUALITY*

384.55 USA ISSN 0883-7090
ADULT VIDEO NEWS; the adult entertainment monthly. Abbreviated title: A V N. Text in English. 1982. m. USD 78 domestic; USD 198 foreign (effective 2003). adv. illus. reprints avail. **Document type:** *Magazine, Trade.*
Published by: A V N Publications Inc., 9414 Eton Ave, Chatsworth, CA 91311. TEL 818-718-5788, FAX 818-718-5799, info@avn.com, http://www.avn.com. Ed. Mike Ramone. adv.: B&W page USD 2,180, color page USD 3,790; trim 8.375 x 10.875. Circ: 45,000 (paid).

AFTERIMAGE; the journal of media arts and cultural criticism in the social and decision sciences. see *PHOTOGRAPHY*

ALT OM FOTO & VIDEO. see *PHOTOGRAPHY*

ALTA FIDELIDAD EN AUDIO Y VIDEO. see *SOUND RECORDING AND REPRODUCTION*

384.55 USA
ALTERNATIVE CINEMA MAGAZINE; the magazine of independent and underground movie making. Text in English. 1993. s-a. USD 10 domestic; USD 15 foreign; USD 4.95 newsstand/cover (effective 2000). adv. video rev. back issues avail. **Document type:** *Consumer.* **Description:** Devoted to low-budget independent "B" cult and underground filmmaking from a fan and filmmaker's perspective.
Published by: Alternative Cinema, Inc., PO Box 371, Glenwood, NJ 07418-0371. TEL 973-509-1616, FAX 973-746-6464, eicinema@aol.com, http://www.alternativecinema.com, http://www.eicinema.com. Ed., R&P Jeffrey Faoro TEL 973-509-9352. Pub. Michael L Raso. adv.: B&W page USD 225; trim 10 x 8. Circ: 5,000.

AMERICAN FILM & VIDEO REVIEW. see *MOTION PICTURES*

ANNUAIRE DU CINEMA TELEVISION VIDEO. see *MOTION PICTURES*

AUDIO VIDEO. see *SOUND RECORDING AND REPRODUCTION*

384.558 DEU
▼ **AUDIO VIDEO FOTO BILD.** Text in German. 2003 (Dec.). m. EUR 2 newsstand/cover (effective 2004). adv. **Document type:** *Magazine, Consumer.* **Description:** Provides information and reviews on a wide range of consumer electronics and media including DVDs, televisions, digital photography, audio components and music.
Published by: Axel Springer Verlag AG, Axel-Springer-Platz 1, Hamburg, 20350, Germany. TEL 49-40-34700, FAX 49-40-34725540, information@axelspringer.de, http://www.asv.de. Ed. Harald Kuppek. Adv. contact Joerg Herms. color page EUR 10,240; trim 230 x 319.

AUGEN-BLICK; Marburger Hefte zur Medienwissenschaft. see *MOTION PICTURES*

AUSTRALIA. BUREAU OF STATISTICS. FILM AND VIDEO PRODUCTION AND DISTRIBUTION, AUSTRALIA. see *COMMUNICATIONS—Abstracting, Bibliographies, Statistics*

AUSTRALIA. BUREAU OF STATISTICS. VIDEO HIRE OUTLETS, AUSTRALIA. see *COMMUNICATIONS—Abstracting, Bibliographies, Statistics*

384.558 AUS ISSN 1327-0338
AUSTRALIAN VIDEOCAMERA:; and desktop video. Text in English. 1991. m. **Document type:** *Magazine, Consumer.*
Former titles (until 1996): Australian Videocamera and Electronic Imaging (1324-6321); (until 1995): Videocamera and Electronic Imaging (1035-9508)
Published by: VideoCamera Publications Pty. Ltd., PO Box 473, Dee Why, NSW 2099, Australia. TEL 61-2-99385344, FAX 61-2-99385311, rachel@videocamera.com.au, http://www.videocamera.com.au.

384.55 AUS
AUSTRALIAN VIDEOGRAPHY. Text in English. 6/yr. AUD 23; AUD 70 foreign (effective Aug. 1992). **Document type:** *Consumer.* **Description:** Appeals to users and prospective purchasers of video camcorders, amateur video editing equipment, and high-band (super VHS and Hi 8) TV sets.
Published by: Gareth Powell Pty Ltd., 21 Darley Rd, Randwick, NSW 2031, Australia. TEL 02-398-5111. adv.: B&W page AUD 1,070, color page AUD 1,530; trim 210 x 273.

384.55 GBR
BEST HOME CINEMA MAG ... EVER!. Text in English. a. GBP 3.50 (effective 1998). adv. **Document type:** *Consumer.*
Published by: Highbury - WV (Subsidiary of: Highbury House Communications PLC), 53-79 Highgate Rd, London, NW5 1TW, United Kingdom. TEL 44-20-7485-0011, FAX 44-20-7482-6269. Ed. Steve May. Adv. contact Caroline Padley. **Orders to:** ASM Ltd., Unit 6, Pipewell Rd Industrial Estate, Desborough, Northants NN14 2SW, United Kingdom. TEL 44-1536-762860, FAX 44-1536-760306.

BLUE LIGHTS. see *COMMUNICATIONS—Television And Cable*

BOTEIN'S REGULATION OF THE ELECTRONIC MASS MEDIA: LAW AND POLICY FOR RADIO, TELEVISION, CABLE AND NEW VIDEO TECHNOLOGIES. see *COMMUNICATIONS—Television And Cable*

BOWKER'S AUDIO & VIDEO DATABASE. see *MOTION PICTURES*

778.53 USA ISSN 1051-290X
PN1992.95
BOWKER'S COMPLETE VIDEO DIRECTORY; combining Variety's extensive listing of currently available entertainment titles with education and special interest videos for home, school, and business. Text in English. 1988. a. (in 4 vols.). USD 380 for complete set (effective 2004). **Document type:** *Directory.* **Description:** Offer reference librarians in public, school, and research libraries and at video resource centers coverage of more than 169,000 videotapes in every format available, including VHS, Beta, 3/4", U-matic, 8-mm, and laser disc.
Formerly (until 1998): Variety's Complete Home Video Directory
Related titles: ♦ CD-ROM ed.: Bowker's Audio & Video Database. ISSN 1542-6041.
—CCC.
Published by: R.R. Bowker LLC (Subsidiary of: Cambridge Information Group), 630 Central Ave., New Providence, NJ 07974. TEL 908-286-1090, 800-526-9537, FAX 908-219-0098, info@bowker.com, http://www.bowker.com. Pub. Marin Mixon. **Subscr. to:** Order Dept., PO Box 32, New Providence, NJ 07974-9903. TEL 800-521-8110.

C E MARKT; das Consumer-Electronics-Magazin fuer den Handel. (Consumer Electronics) see *ELECTRONICS*

384.558 USA
C V C REPORT. Text in English. 1983. s-m. USD 225; USD 275 foreign (effective 1999). adv. **Document type:** *Trade.*
Published by: Creative Video Consulting, Inc., 5195, Saratoga Spgs, NY 12866-8038. TEL 212-533-9870, FAX 212-473-3772. Ed., Pub. Mitchell Rowen. Circ: 800.

CABLE VIDEO BRIEFS. see *COMMUNICATIONS—Television And Cable*

621.388 USA ISSN 1091-0441
TR882
CAMCORDER & COMPUTERVIDEO. Text in English. 1985. m. USD 23; USD 4.99 per issue (effective 2005). adv. back issues avail. **Document type:** *Magazine, Trade.*
Former titles: Camcorder (1048-8804); (until 1989): Camcorder Report (1047-8787); (until 1988): Super Television; (until 1987): Home Satellite TV (0890-3549)
Related titles: Online - full text ed.: (from Gale Group).
Indexed: CompD.
Published by: Miller Magazines, Inc, 290 Maple Ct., # 232, Ventura, CA 93003-3517. http://www.candcv.com. Eds. Bob Wolenik, James L Miller. Adv. contact Jim Messing. Circ: 115,000.

CAMCORDER USER & DVD MOVIE MAKER. see *ELECTRONICS*

384.55 FRA ISSN 1289-527X
CAMERA VIDEO ET MULTIMEDIA. Text in French. 1987. m. EUR 5.50 newsstand/cover (effective 2004). **Document type:** *Magazine, Consumer.* **Description:** Reports on the latest equipment and rates its performance.
Formerly (until 1998): Camera Video (0986-2889)
Published by: Emap France (Subsidiary of: Emap Media Ltd.), 150-152 Rue Gallieni, Boulogne, 92644, France. TEL 33-1-41334961, FAX 33-1-41335010, info@emapfrance.com, http://www.emapmedia.com.

CANADIAN JOURNAL OF FILM STUDIES/REVUE CANADIENNE D'ETUDES CINEMATOGRAPHIQUES. see *MOTION PICTURES*

CARLTON COMMUNICATIONS PLC. ANNUAL REPORT AND ACCOUNTS. see *COMMUNICATIONS—Television And Cable*

384.5 FRA
CHAMPS DE L'AUDIOVISUELS. Text in French. 1996. q. **Document type:** *Journal, Trade.*
Formerly: Champs Visuels (Paris, 1996) (1272-839X)
Published by: L' Harmattan, 5 rue de l'Ecole Polytechnique, Paris, 75005, France. TEL 33-1-43257651, FAX 33-1-43258203, http://www.editions-harmattan.fr.

028.5 USA ISSN 0883-6922
PN1992.945
CHILDREN'S VIDEO REPORT. Text in English. 1985. 8/yr. USD 60. **Document type:** *Newsletter.* **Description:** Reports on children and video from experts on child development and media.
Address: 370 Court St, 76, Brooklyn, NY 11231-4331. TEL 718-935-0600, FAX 718-243-0959, CVReport@AOL.COM. Ed. Martha Dewing. Circ: 1,200.

CINEMA BLUE. see *MEN'S INTERESTS*

CINEMA IN CASA; la prima rivista di audio e video ad alta fedelta. see *COMMUNICATIONS—Television And Cable*

CINEMA STUDIO. see *MOTION PICTURES*

CINEMEDIA ACCESS COLLECTION. VIDEO CATALOG. see *MOTION PICTURES*

791.45 ESP ISSN 0212-0143
CINEVIDEO 20. Text in Spanish. 1982. m. adv. **Description:** Reports on the latest in software and hardware, technology and business related to film, video, television and the multimedia.
Published by: Comunicacion Audiovisual Iberoamericana S.A., Apartado 2016, Madrid, 28080, Spain. TEL 91-5196586, FAX 91-5195119. Ed. Fernando Campos. Adv. contact Victoria Vallejo. Circ: 7,000.

384.55 USA
COMING ATTRACTIONS. Text in English. 1984. m. USD 43 (effective 2005). adv. bk.rev. illus. **Document type:** *Magazine, Consumer.* **Description:** Provides a comprehensive guide to new releases on videocassette.
Published by: Connell Communications, Inc. (Subsidiary of: International Data Group), 86 Elm St, Peterborough, NH 03458-1009. TEL 603-924-7271, 800-216-2225, FAX 603-924-7013. Ed. Grace Miller. Pub. Jim Connell. Circ: 100,000,000.

COMING SOON MAGAZINE. see *COMPUTERS—Computer Games*

COMPUTER GAZETTE. see *COMPUTERS—Personal Computers*

COMPUTER VIDEO. see *COMMUNICATIONS—Computer Applications*

COMPUTERVIDEO. see *COMPUTERS—Computer Graphics*

621.388 USA
CONSUMER INFORMATION SERIES. Text in English. 1989. irreg. free. **Document type:** *Consumer.* **Description:** Covers topics of interest to everyone who uses captioning, including information on solving caption problems, getting local news captioned, and the new captioning mandates now in effect for broadcast and cable networks.
Related titles: Online - full text ed.
Published by: Caption Center, 125 Western Ave, Boston, MA 02134. TEL 617-492-9225, FAX 617-562-0590, caption@wgbh.org, http://www.wgbh.org/caption. R&P Mary Watkins.

CONTEMPORARY. see *ART*

CREWFINDER CYMRU WALES. see *COMMUNICATIONS—Television And Cable*

621.38 CZE ISSN 1214-6692
▼ **D V.** (Digital Video) Text in Czech. 2004. q. CZK 135 (effective 2005). adv. **Document type:** *Magazine, Consumer.*
Published by: Vogel Burda Communications s.r.o., Sokolovska 73, Prague 8, 18621, Czech Republic. TEL 42-2-21808566, FAX 42-2-21808500, http://www.dvmagazine.cz, http://www.vogel.cz. Ed. Ondrej Hokr. Adv. contact Miloslav Nepokoj. page CZK 42,000; trim 210 x 297. Circ: 12,000 (paid and controlled).

D V. (Digital Video) see *COMMUNICATIONS—Television And Cable*

791 DEU
D V D & SURROUND TEST. Text in German. bi-m. EUR 2.90 newsstand/cover (effective 2003). adv. **Document type:** *Magazine, Consumer.*
Published by: Reiner H. Nitschke Verlags GmbH, Eifelring 28, Euskirchen, 53879, Germany. TEL 49-2251-650460, FAX 49-2251-6504699, service@nitschke-verlag.de. adv.: B&W page EUR 3,000, color page EUR 5,000. Circ: 100,000 (controlled).

791.45 DEU ISSN 1614-2500
D V D & VIDEO-MARKT. (Digital Video Disc) Text in German. 1982. fortn. EUR 69.50 for 6 mos. (effective 2005). adv. **Document type:** *Magazine, Consumer.*
Formerly (until 2004): D V D & VideoReport (1618-4211); Which superseded in part (in 2002): Entertainment-Markt (0949-3891); Which was formerly (until 1995): Video-Markt (0723-077X)
Published by: Entertainment Media Verlag GmbH und Co. oHG, Einsteinring 24, Dornach, 85609, Germany. TEL 49-89-451140, FAX 49-89-45114444, emv@e-media.de, http://www.mediabiz.de. adv.: B&W page EUR 2,350, color page EUR 2,950. Circ: 5,450 (controlled).

384.558 ITA
D V D BUSINESS. (Digital Video Disc) Text in Italian. m. (11/yr.). EUR 15 (effective 2005). **Document type:** *Magazine, Consumer.*
Published by: Editoriale Duesse SpA, Via Donatello 5b, Milan, 20131, Italy. TEL 39-02-277961, FAX 39-02-27796300, e-duesse@e-duesse.it, http://www.e-duesse.it.

004.565 GBR ISSN 1468-1250
D V D BUYER. Text in English. 1999. s-a. GBP 3.99 newsstand/cover (effective 2001). 116 p./no.; back issues avail. **Document type:** *Magazine, Consumer.*
Published by: Paragon Publishing Ltd., Paragon House, 10 St Peters Rd, Bournemouth, Dorset BH1 2JS, United Kingdom. TEL 44-1202-299900, FAX 44-1202-299955, 44-1202-200217, subs@paragon.co.uk, http://www.paragon.co.uk. Ed. Paul Morgan. Adv. contact Jonathan Ginger TEL 44-1202-200555.

384.588 USA ISSN 1543-6144
TK7882.D93
D V D ETC. (Digital Video Disc) Text in English. 2002 (May). 10/yr. USD 19.95 domestic; USD 35.95 in Canada; USD 39.95 elsewhere; USD 4.95 newsstand/cover (effective 2002). adv. **Document type:** *Magazine, Consumer.* **Description:** Covers the entire spectrum of DVD products including software, hardware,home theater, video, mobile, and computer.
Published by: Avodah Publishing, LLC TEL 818-707-1747, FAX 818-707-8950, info@dvdetc.com, terence@dvdetc.com, http://dvdetc.com. Pub. Terence Carroll.

384.55 USA
D V D GUIDE. (Digital Video Disc) Text in English. 2000. q. USD 19.95; USD 5.95 newsstand/cover (effective 2001). adv. **Document type:** *Magazine, Consumer.*
Published by: N V I Publishing Group, 10 Forest Ave., Paramus, NJ 07652-5214. Pub. Ron Rich.

338.4762 GBR ISSN 1367-4498
D V D INTELLIGENCE. (Digital Video Disc) Text in English. 1997. m. GBP 195, EUR 295 (effective 2003). adv. **Document type:** *Magazine, Trade.*
Related titles: Online - full text ed.: (from Gale Group, O C L C Online Computer Library Center, Inc.).
Published by: Globalcom Publications, 26 Midway, St Albans, AL3 4BQ, United Kingdom. TEL 44-1727-851761, FAX 44-1727-753454, jean-luc@dvd-intelligence.com, sales@dvd-intelligence.com, http://www.dvd-intelligence.com.

791.43 FRA ISSN 1628-870X
D V D MAGAZINE. (Digital Video Disc) Text in French. 2001. m. adv. **Document type:** *Magazine, Consumer.*
Published by: Future France, 101-109 Rue Jean Jaures, Levallois Perret, 92300, France. TEL 33-1-41273838, yveline.duville@futurenet.fr.

384.558 DEU
DER D V D MARKT UND MEDIEN INSIGHT VIDEO. (Digital Video Disc) Text in German. 1998. w. EUR 120 (effective 2004). adv. **Document type:** *Magazine, Trade.*
Published by: Mediatainment Publishing GmbH, Kolbergerstr 11, Sehnde, 31319, Germany. TEL 49-5138-70010, FAX 49-5138-700129, ad@mediatainmentpublishing,de, http://www.mpnow.de. Ed. Claas Wolter. Adv. contact Jeannine Konrad. color page EUR 1,917; trim 210 x 280. Circ: 6,500 (paid and controlled).

384.558 USA ISSN 1098-2523
D V D NEWS; a weekly news in brief for the video industry. (Digital Video Disc) Text in English. 1997. w. looseleaf. USD 647 (effective 2005). adv. charts; mkt.; stat.; tr.lit. 6 p./no.; back issues avail.; reprints avail. **Document type:** *Newsletter, Trade.* **Description:** Covers the DVD video industry.
Related titles: Diskette ed.; E-mail ed.: USD 500 (effective 2005); Online - full text ed.: (from bigchalk, Florida Center for Library Automation, ProQuest Information & Learning).
Indexed: ABIn.
Published by: Corbell Publishing Company, 11500 W Olympic Blvd, Ste 400, Los Angeles, CA 90064. TEL 310-444-3048, FAX 310-312-4551, mhealy@corbell.com, http://www.corbell.com. Ed. Deborah Rolfe. Pub. Maureen A. Healey. adv.: B&W page USD 2,500; 8.5 x 11. Circ: 2,000 (paid and controlled).

791 DEU ISSN 1610-7330
D V D PREMIERE. (Digital Video Disc) Text in German. 1998. 10/yr. free newsstand/cover. adv. **Document type:** *Magazine, Consumer.* **Description:** Provides news and information on the latest DVD movie releases and special features.
Published by: Entertainment Media Verlag GmbH und Co. oHG, Einsteinring 24, Dornach, 85609, Germany. TEL 49-89-45114-0, FAX 49-89-45114444, emv@e-media.de, http://www.mediabiz.de. adv.: B&W page EUR 6,750, color page EUR 8,280. Circ: 450,000 (controlled).

384.558 USA
D V D PREVIEW; with Leonard Maltin. (Digital Video Disc) Text in English. 2001. bi-m. USD 14.95; USD 3.95 newsstand/cover; USD 5.50 newsstand/cover in Canada (effective 2001). adv. **Document type:** *Magazine, Consumer.* **Description:** Covers the latest in DVD movie and hardware reviews, entertainment news and revealing behind-the-scenes interviews.
Media: Optical Disk - DVD. **Related titles:** Online - full text ed.
Published by: DVD Preview, Inc., 1950 Sawtelle Blvd, Ste 282, Los Angeles, CA 90024. TEL 310-479-4918, FAX 310-996-2392, editorial@dvdpreview.tv, http://www.dvdpreview.tv. Ed. Stephanie Counts. Pub. Patrick Graham. Adv. contact Ron Ossea.

384 USA
D V D REPLICATION DIRECTORY. Text in English. a. USD 292 domestic; USD 337 foreign (effective 2001). **Document type:** *Directory.*

Published by: Corbell Publishing Company, 11500 W Olympic Blvd, Ste 400, Los Angeles, CA 90064. TEL 310-444-3048, FAX 310-312-4551, info@corbell.com, mhealy@corbell.com, http://www.corbell.com. Pub. Maureen Healy.

004.565   USA
D V D RESOURCES DIRECTORY. (Digital Video Disc) Text in English. irreg., latest 3rd Ed. USD 29.95 domestic; USD 39.95 foreign (effective 2000). **Document type:** *Directory, Trade.* **Description:** Contains a comprehensive reference guide covering all stages of the DVD production process.
Published by: Knowledge Industry Publications, Inc. (Subsidiary of: Access Intelligence, LLC), 701 Westchester Ave, White Plains, NY 10604. TEL 914-328-9157, 800-800-5474, FAX 914-328-9093, http://www.kipinet.com.

791.45   ITA   ISSN 1592-8772
D V D REVIEW. (Digital Video Disc) Text in Italian. 2001. m. EUR 89; EUR 8.90 newsstand/cover (effective 2003). adv. **Document type:** *Magazine, Consumer.*
Published by: Play Press Publishing s.r.l., Via Vitorchiano 123, Rome, RM 00189, Italy. TEL 39-06-33221250, FAX 39-06-33221235, abbonamenti@playpress.com, http://www.playpress.com. Ed. Carlo Chericoni. Pub. Alessandro Ferri. Circ: 70,000 (paid and controlled).

791.45   ITA   ISSN 1722-0300
▼ **D V D REVIEW PRESENTA.** (Digital Video Disc) Text in Italian. 2003. m. **Document type:** *Magazine, Consumer.*
Published by: Play Press Publishing s.r.l., Via Vitorchiano 123, Rome, RM 00189, Italy. TEL 39-06-33221250, FAX 39-06-33221235, abbonamenti@playpress.com, http://www.playpress.com.

791.435   DEU
D V D SPECIAL. (Digital Video Disc) Text in German. m. EUR 36; EUR 3.60 newsstand/cover (effective 2003). adv. **Document type:** *Magazine, Consumer.*
Published by: Medien Publikations- und Werbegesellschaft, Wiehenweg 14, Hille, 32479, Germany. TEL 49-5703-95904, FAX 49-5703-95906. adv.: color page EUR 4,280. Circ: 60,000 (controlled).

D V D STATISTICAL REPORT. (Digital Video Disc Statistical Report) see *COMMUNICATIONS—Abstracting, Bibliographies, Statistics*

384.558   DEU   ISSN 1617-2175
D V D VISION. (Digital Video Disc) Text in German. 2000. m. EUR 33.60; EUR 30 to students; EUR 3 newsstand/cover (effective 2003). adv. **Document type:** *Magazine, Consumer.* **Description:** Presents information and reviews on movies available in DVD format.
Published by: CyPress GmbH, Max-Planck-Str 13, Hoechberg, 97204, Germany. TEL 49-931-406910, FAX 49-931-4069115, contact@cypress.de, http://www.cypress.de. Ed. Stefan Girlich. Adv. contact Winfried Burkard. B&W page EUR 4,500; color page EUR 4,500; trim 230 x 297. Circ: 39,695 (paid and controlled). Subscr. to: dsb Abo-Betreuung GmbH, Konrad-Zuse-Str 16, Neckarsulm 74172, Germany. cypress@dsb.net, http://www.dsb.net.

384.558   DEU
D V D WELT. (Digital Video Disc) Text in German. a. EUR 4.80 newsstand/cover (effective 2003). adv. **Document type:** *Magazine, Consumer.*
Published by: Michael E. Brieden Verlag GmbH, Gartroper Str 42, Duisburg, 47138, Germany. TEL 49-203-42920, FAX 49-203-42921149, info@brieden.de, http://www.brieden.de/dvda.html. adv.: B&W page EUR 4,299, color page EUR 6,929. Circ: 50,000 (paid and controlled).

791   CZE   ISSN 1213-8703
D V DMAG. (Digital Video Disc) Text in Czech. 2002. d. adv. **Document type:** *Consumer.*
Media: Online - full content.
Published by: Trade & Leisure Publications, s.r.o., Pernerova 35a, Prague 8, 186 00, Czech Republic. TEL 420-2-225386561, FAX 420-2-225386555, dvdmag@dvdmag.cz, tlp@tlp.cz, http://www.dvdmag.cz, http://www.tlp.cz.

THE DATA BOOK; New Zealand film, television, video, photographic stills and theatre. see *BUSINESS AND ECONOMICS—Trade And Industrial Directories*

DENMARK. DET DANSKE FILMINSTITUT. KATALOG. SUPPLEMENT. see *MOTION PICTURES*

DIGEST OF THE U F V A. see *MOTION PICTURES*

384.558   USA
DIGITAL CONTENT DELIVERY REPORT. (Digital Video Disc) Text in English. 1996. bi-w. USD 897 (effective 2005). **Document type:** *Newsletter, Trade.*
Formerly (until 2004): D V D Report (1088-7067); Which incorporated (1989-2003): Tape - Disc Business (1065-3015)
Related titles: Online - full text ed.+ (from bigchalk, Florida Center for Library Automation, Gale Group, O C L C Online Computer Library Center, Inc.).
—CCC.

Published by: Access Intelligence, LLC (Subsidiary of: Veronis, Suhler & Associates Inc.), 1201 Seven Locks Rd, Ste 300, Potomac, MD 20854. TEL 301-354-2000, 800-777-5006, FAX 301-340-1451, clientservices@accessintel.com, http://www.pbimedia.com/cgi/catalog/info?DVD. Ed. Bryant Frazer.

778.59   NLD   ISSN 1574-1281
▼ **DIGITAL MOVIE.** Text in Dutch. 2004. m. EUR 38.50 domestic; EUR 45.80 in Belgium (effective 2005). adv. film rev.; tel.rev.; video rev.; software rev. illus. back issues avail. **Document type:** *Magazine, Consumer.* **Description:** Discusses video hardware and equipment.
Formed by the merger of (1999-2004): D V D Plus (1566-4325); (1981-2004): Video Uit en Thuis (0167-7039); Which incorporated (1978-1986): Premiere (0165-5361); (1983-1984): Videoaktief (0920-8518); Which was formerly (until 1983): Film en Videotechniek (0920-850X); (until 1982): Smalfilmen (0165-5981); (until 1979): Smalfilmen als Hobby (0920-8496) —IE, Infotrieve.
Published by: Uitgeverij Scala bv, Postbus 38, Amersfoort, 3800 AA, Netherlands. TEL 31-33-4892900, FAX 31-33-4802281, info@scalapublishing.nl, http://www.scalapublishing.com/digitalmovie/index.php. Circ: 21,500.

004.565   DEU
DIGITAL VIDEO; computer - editing - camcorder - dvd. Text in German. 1998. q. EUR 24.60 domestic; EUR 28.65 foreign; EUR 6.15 newsstand/cover (effective 2003). adv. **Document type:** *Magazine, Consumer.*
Published by: Verlag B. Kaemmer, Georgenstr 19, Munich, 80799, Germany. TEL 49-89-34018900, FAX 49-89-34018901, bk@verlag-kaemmer.de, http://www.digital-video.org/index.htm, http://www.verlag-kaemmer.de. Eds. Joachim Sauer, Martin Biebel. Adv. contact Martina Lacour. B&W page EUR 2,630, color page EUR 4,010. Circ: 22,780 (paid and controlled).

004.565   SWE   ISSN 1652-5892
▼ **DIGITAL VIDEO.** Text in Swedish. 2004. 6/yr. SEK 299 (effective 2005). adv. back issues avail. **Document type:** *Magazine, Consumer.*
Published by: First Publishing Group AB, Deltavaegen 3, PO Box 3187, Vaexjoe, 35043, Sweden. TEL 46-470-762400, FAX 46-470-762425, info@firstpublishing.se, http://digitalvideo.fpgroup.se, http://www.fpgroup.se. Ed. Peter Hedenfalk. Adv. contact Andreas Bjoerck. color page SEK 25,000; 210 x 285.

384.558   ITA   ISSN 1128-4218
DIGITAL VIDEO HOME THEATER. Text in Italian. m. **Document type:** *Consumer.*
Published by: Technipress Srl, Via della Bufalotta 374, Rome, 00139, Italy. TEL 39-06-8720331, FAX 39-06-87139141, http://www.technipress.it/. Circ: 85,000.

778.59   GBR
DIGITAL VIDEO MADE EASY; the easy way to take better movies. Text in English. 2002. bi-m. GBP 4.99 newsstand/cover (effective 2003). **Document type:** *Magazine, Consumer.* **Description:** Contains in-depth step-by-step tutorials on which digital camcorders to buy, shooting and editing techniques, and then how to create professional looking videos.
Published by: Paragon Publishing Ltd., Paragon House, 10 St Peters Rd, Bournemouth, Dorset BH1 2JS, United Kingdom. TEL 44-1202-299900, FAX 44-1202-299955, subs@paragon.co.uk, http://www.paragon.co.uk/mags/dvme.html. Ed. Mark Hattersley.

DIRECTORY OF BRITISH FILM-MAKERS. see *MOTION PICTURES*

DIRECTORY OF INTERNATIONAL FILM AND VIDEO FESTIVALS (YEAR). see *MOTION PICTURES*

338.47004   USA
TS2301.A7
DIRECTORY OF VIDEO, COMPUTER AND AUDIO VISUAL PRODUCTS. Text in English. 1953. a. USD 65; to commercial non-members. charts; illus.; stat. index. **Document type:** *Directory.*
Former titles: Equipment Directory of Audio-Visual, Computer and Video Products (0884-2124); Audio-Visual Equipment Directory (0571-8759)
Media: Duplicated (not offset).
Published by: International Communications Industries Association, Inc., 11242 Waples Mill Rd, Ste 200, Fairfax, VA 22030-6079. TEL 703-273-7200, FAX 703-278-8082. Ed. Diane Smith. Circ: 12,000.

DIRECTORY OF VIDEO DEALERS. see *BUSINESS AND ECONOMICS—Trade And Industrial Directories*

791   AUS   ISSN 1443-1858
DVD NOW. Text in English. 2000. q.
Published by: NextMedia, 78 Renwick St, Redfern, NSW 2016, Australia. TEL 61-9-9699-0333, FAX 61-9-9699-0334, http://www.nexmedia.com.au/.

EDUCATORS GUIDE TO FREE VIDEOTAPES (ELEMENTARY/MIDDLE SCHOOL ED.). see *EDUCATION—Teaching Methods And Curriculum*

EDUCATORS GUIDE TO FREE VIDEOTAPES (SECONDARY ED.). see *EDUCATION—Teaching Methods And Curriculum*

ENCORE. see *MOTION PICTURES*

ENCORE DIRECTORY. see *MOTION PICTURES*

ENTERTAINMENTMARKT GUIDE. see *BUSINESS AND ECONOMICS—Trade And Industrial Directories*

ETIN. see *LIBRARY AND INFORMATION SCIENCES*

F V - FOTO VIDEO ACTUALIDAD. see *PHOTOGRAPHY*

FACETS FEATURES. see *MOTION PICTURES*

778.59   ITA   ISSN 1720-9196
FAREVIDEO; tecnica e cultura della videoregistrazione. Text in Italian. 1985. m. adv.
Formerly (until 1990): Video Parade (1720-920X)
Published by: Ediscreen s.r.l., Via Guglielmo Calderini, 68, Rome, RM 00196, Italy. TEL 06-3960328, FAX 06-390072. Ed. Enzo Perilli.

FILM; kino - televiziya - video. see *MOTION PICTURES—Abstracting, Bibliographies, Statistics*

384.55   AUT
FILM & VIDEO; Fachinformation ueber Informationsvideos und 16mm Filme. Text in German. 1980. q. **Document type:** *Newsletter, Trade.* **Description:** Contains information on educational, touristic and industrial films.
Published by: Oesterreichisches Filmservice KG, Schaumburgergasse 18, Vienna, W 1040, Austria. TEL 43-1-5055337-0, FAX 43-1-5055307, info@filmservice.at, http://www.filmservice.at. Ed. Rudolf Kammel. Adv. contact Alexander Kammel. Circ: 12,500 (paid).

FILM & VIDEO. see *MOTION PICTURES*

FILM & VIDEO FINDER. see *COMMUNICATIONS—Abstracting, Bibliographies, Statistics*

FILM CLIPS; a publication for film & video professionals. see *MOTION PICTURES*

FILM FAN SAT. see *MOTION PICTURES*

FILM & VIDEO. see *MOTION PICTURES*

FILMSCAN. see *COMMUNICATIONS—Television And Cable*

FINANCIAL SURVEY. VIDEO AND AUDIO VISUAL INDUSTRY; company data for success. see *BUSINESS AND ECONOMICS—Trade And Industrial Directories*

791.43   GBR
FIRST ON VIDEO. Text in English. m. free. adv. video rev. back issues avail. **Document type:** *Magazine, Consumer.* **Description:** Promotes movies, videos and other related items.
Related titles: Online - full content ed.
Published by: Bleeding Edge Publishing (Subsidiary of: Highbury House Communications PLC), 3rd Fl, Jordan House, 47 Brunswick Pl, London, N1 6EB, United Kingdom. TEL 44-207-6086789, FAX 44-207-6086725, bedesign@columbus-group.co.uk, http://www.firstonvideo.co.uk/, http://www.bleedingedge.co.uk/. Ed. Amanda Wells. Adv. contact Charley Race.

FOTO. see *PHOTOGRAPHY*

FOTO VIDEO AUDIO NEWS (DUTCH EDITION). see *PHOTOGRAPHY*

FOTOCOMPUTER. see *PHOTOGRAPHY*

FRAMELINE NEWS. see *MOTION PICTURES*

G P N EDUCATIONAL MEDIA CATALOG. (Great Plains National) see *EDUCATION*

GEKKAN EBUI FURONTO/AUDIO VIDEO FRONT. see *SOUND RECORDING AND REPRODUCTION*

GIORNO POETRY SYSTEMS L P'S, C D'S, CASSETTES & GIORNO VIDEO PAK SERIES. see *LITERATURE—Poetry*

621.388   USA   ISSN 1082-0493
GOVERNMENT INFORMATION AND IMAGING TECHNOLOGY. Text in English. 1992. bi-m. USD 25. adv. bk.rev. **Document type:** *Newspaper.* **Description:** Provides up-to-date information on all aspects of the application of imaging technology within government organizations.
Formerly: Government Imaging

Address: 12 Andrews St, Gloucester, MA 01930-1102. TEL 301-445-4405, FAX 301-445-5722, wminami@aol.com. Ed. Wayde R Minami. Pub., Adv. contact John McWilliams. Circ: 34,000 (controlled).

355   USA   ISSN 1087-917X
GOVERNMENT VIDEO. Text in English. 1989. m. USD 54 domestic; USD 78.50 in Canada; USD 92.50 elsewhere; USD 6 per issue (effective 2005). adv. back issues avail. **Document type:** *Magazine, Trade.* **Description:** Serves the interests of video professionals in federal, state and city government as well as the military.
Formerly: G M V - Government and Military Video (1067-3407)
Related titles: Online - full content ed.; Online - full text ed.: (from bigchalk, Gale Group, ProQuest Information & Learning).
—CCC.
Published by: C M P Information Ltd. (Subsidiary of: United Business Media), 460 Park Ave, 9th Fl, New York, NY 10016. TEL 212-378-0400, FAX 212-378-2180, http://www.GVMag.com, http://www.cmpinformation.com. Ed. Mark Pescatore. adv.: B&W page USD 2,615, color page USD 3,365; trim 8.13 x 10.88. Circ: 13,500.

791.43   ITA   ISSN 1720-7665
IL GRANDE CINEMA SU D V D. Text in Italian. 2002. bi-m. **Document type:** *Magazine, Consumer.*
Published by: Play Press Publishing s.r.l., Via Vitorchiano 123, Rome, RM 00189, Italy. TEL 39-06-33221250, FAX 39-06-33221235, abbonamenti@playpress.com, http://www.playpress.com.

384.554   USA   ISSN 1051-6050
GREAT AMERICAN VIDEO BUSINESS NEWSLETTER. Text in English. 1990. s-a. USD 20. adv. **Document type:** *Newsletter.* **Description:** Provides issue analysis, feature stories, market evaluations, business and product news, and strategies for the video businessperson.
Published by: V. Parrish Publishing, 1900 S Eads St, Arlington, VA 22202. TEL 703-892-1993. Ed. Vernon Parrish.

GUIDE TO FEDERAL PROGRAMS FOR THE FILM AND VIDEO SECTOR. see *PUBLIC ADMINISTRATION*

GUIDE TO POLITICAL VIDEOS. see *POLITICAL SCIENCE*

384.55   DEU
HITSHOP; das Magazin fuer Home Entertainment. Text in German. 1997. 10/yr. free newsstand/cover. adv. **Document type:** *Magazine, Consumer.* **Description:** Contains information on the latest videos and music.
Published by: Entertainment Media Verlag GmbH und Co. oHG, Einsteinring 24, Dornach, 85609, Germany. TEL 49-89-45114-0, FAX 49-89-45114444, emv@e-media.de, http://www.mediabiz.de. Ed. Hans Fuchs. Pub. Ulrich Scheele. R&P Otto Bachmeier. Adv. contact Stefan Lessmeier. B&W page EUR 6,400, color page EUR 8,900. Circ: 404,564.

HOLLYWOOD. see *MOTION PICTURES*

HOME CINEMA. see *COMMUNICATIONS—Television And Cable*

791.45   ITA   ISSN 1593-4349
HOME CINEMA (ROME). Text in Italian. 2001. bi-m. EUR 5.20 newsstand/cover (effective 2003). adv. **Document type:** *Magazine, Consumer.*
Published by: Play Press Publishing s.r.l., Via Vitorchiano 123, Rome, RM 00189, Italy. TEL 39-06-33221250, FAX 39-06-33221235, abbonamenti@playpress.com, http://www.playpress.com. Ed. Carlo Chericoni. Pub. Alessandro Ferri. Circ: 25,000 (paid and controlled).

621.388   GBR   ISSN 1359-6276
HOME CINEMA CHOICE. Text in English. 1995. m. GBP 32.40 domestic; GBP 46.80 in Europe; GBP 72 elsewhere; GBP 3.45 newsstand/cover (effective 2003). **Document type:** *Magazine, Consumer.*
Published by: Highbury - WV (Subsidiary of: Highbury House Communications PLC), 53-79 Highgate Rd, London, NW5 1TW, United Kingdom. TEL 44-20-73311000, FAX 44-20-73311273, http://www.homecinemachoice.com/, http://www.hhc.co.uk/. Ed., Pub. Steve May.

384.558 791.43   GBR
HOME ENTERTAINMENT IRELAND. Text in English. m. free. **Description:** Covers news and features on the Irish video industry with reviews for rental, retail, DVD and games written with the Irish trend in mind.
Published by: Bleeding Edge Publishing (Subsidiary of: Highbury House Communications PLC), 3rd Fl, Jordan House, 47 Brunswick Pl, London, N1 6EB, United Kingdom. TEL 44-207-6086789, FAX 44-207-6086725, bedesign@columbus-group.co.uk, http://www.bleedingedge.co.uk/. Ed. John Hayward.

384.558 791.43 794.8   GBR
HOME ENTERTAINMENT WEEK. Text in English. w. free. **Document type:** *Magazine, Consumer.*
Related titles: Online - full content ed.

Published by: Bleeding Edge Publishing (Subsidiary of: Highbury House Communications PLC), 3rd Fl, Jordan House, 47 Brunswick Pl, London, N1 6EB, United Kingdom. TEL 44-207-6086789, FAX 44-207-6086725, http://www.heweek.co.uk/, http://www.bleedingedge.co.uk/. Ed. Peter Dodd.

384.55   USA   ISSN 1553-491X
PN1992.93
HOME MEDIA RETAILING. Text in English. 1979. w. (52/yr.). free to qualified personnel (effective 2005). back issues avail. **Document type:** *Magazine, Trade.* **Description:** For video retailers involved in home video sales. Includes proprietary market research, aggressive management, merchandising techniques, product buying information, industry people and news.
Former titles (until 2005): Video Store Magazine (1541-1737); (until 1999): Video Store (0195-1750)
Related titles: Microform ed.: (from PQC); Online - full text ed.: (from EBSCO Publishing, Factiva, Gale Group, H.W. Wilson, Northern Light Technology, Inc., O C L C Online Computer Library Center, Inc., ProQuest Information & Learning, The Dialog Corporation).
Indexed: ABIn, ATI, B&I, BPI, BRI.
—CCC.
Published by: Advanstar Communications, Inc., 201 Sandpointe Ave, Ste 600, Santa Ana, CA 92707-8700. TEL 714-513-8400, FAX 714-513-8680, info@advanstar.com, http://www.homemediaretailing.com/, http://www.advanstar.com. Ed. Kurt Indvik. Pub., R&P Don Rosenberg. Adv. contact Kurt Wohlman. Circ: 45,000 (paid and free).

HOME THEATER. see *COMMUNICATIONS—Television And Cable*

HOME THEATER. see *COMMUNICATIONS—Television And Cable*

791.43   ITA   ISSN 1723-3488
▼ **HORROR CULT.** Text in Italian. 2003. m. **Document type:** *Magazine, Consumer.*
Published by: Play Press Publishing s.r.l., Via Vitorchiano 123, Rome, RM 00189, Italy. TEL 39-06-33221250, FAX 39-06-33221235, abbonamenti@playpress.com, http://www.playpress.com.

HUSTLER EROTIC VIDEO GUIDE. see *MEN'S INTERESTS*

I E E E TRANSACTIONS ON CIRCUITS AND SYSTEMS FOR VIDEO TECHNOLOGY. see *ELECTRONICS*

IMAGE HOME ENTERTAINMENT. see *ELECTRONICS*

THE INDEPENDENT. see *MOTION PICTURES*

INDIEZINE. see *MOTION PICTURES*

INTERNATIONAL CONTACT - PHOTO, VIDEO, LAB TECHNOLOGY; independent journal for the international photographic market. see *PHOTOGRAPHY*

INTERNATIONAL KEMPS FILM, T V AND VIDEO. see *MOTION PICTURES*

INTERNATIONAL TELEVISION & VIDEO ALMANAC; reference tool of the television and home video industries. see *COMMUNICATIONS—Television And Cable*

JAHRBUCH FUER VIDEOFILMER. see *MOTION PICTURES*

JOURNAL OF FILM AND VIDEO. see *MOTION PICTURES*

JOURNAL OF MEDIA PRACTICE. see *COMMUNICATIONS*

KEMPS FILM, TV & VIDEO HANDBOOK (UK ED.). see *MOTION PICTURES*

384.55   GBR   ISSN 1472-0116
KEY NOTE MARKET REPORT: VIDEO RETAIL & HIRE. Variant title: Video Retail & Hire. Text in English. 1995. irreg., latest 2000, Nov. GBP 340 per issue (effective 2002). **Document type:** *Trade.* **Description:** Provides an overview of a specific UK market segment and includes executive summary, market definition, market size, industry background, competitor analysis, current issues, forecasts, company profiles, and more.
Formerly (until 1995): Key Note Report: Video Retail and Hire
Related titles: CD-ROM ed.; Online - full text ed.
Published by: Key Note Ltd., Field House, 72 Oldfield Rd, Hampton, Mddx TW12 2HQ, United Kingdom. TEL 44-20-8481-8750, FAX 44-20-8783-0049, info@keynote.co.uk, http://www.keynote.co.uk. Ed. Jane Griffiths.

384.558 060   GBR   ISSN 1463-0397
KEY NOTE MARKET REPORT: VIDEOCONFERENCING. Variant title: Videoconferencing Market Report. Text in English. 1998. irreg., latest 2000, Aug. GBP 340 per issue (effective 2002). **Description:** Provides an overview of a specific UK market segment and includes executive summary, market definition, market size, industry background, competitor analysis, current issues, forecasts, company profiles, and more.
Published by: Key Note Ltd., Field House, 72 Oldfield Rd, Hampton, Mddx TW12 2HQ, United Kingdom. TEL 44-20-8481-8750, FAX 44-20-8783-0049, info@keynote.co.uk, http://www.keynote.co.uk. Ed. Nick Bardsley.

KIDSHOP; was Kinder wuenschen und Eltern wissen muessen. see *CHILDREN AND YOUTH—About*

384.558   POL   ISSN 1506-6428
KINO DOMOWE. Text in Polish. 1992. 11/yr. PLZ 474 (effective 2002). adv. **Document type:** *Magazine, Consumer.*
Formerly (until 1998): Videoman (1233-0019)
Related titles: Online - full text ed.
Published by: I D G Poland S.A., ul Jordanowska 12, PO Box 73, Warsaw, 04-204, Poland. kinodomowe@kinodomowe.idg.pl, http://www.kinodomowe.idg.pl. Ed. Jerzy Labuda. Adv. contact Magdalena Wozniak. color page PLZ 9,000; trim 225 x 275.

KINO - GLAZ. see *MOTION PICTURES*

384.558   POL
KOMPUTER SWIAT FILM. Text in Polish. 2001. 4/yr. PLZ 18.50 newsstand/cover (effective 2004). adv. **Document type:** *Magazine, Consumer.*
Published by: Axel Springer Polska, Al Jerozolimskie 181, Warsaw, 02222, Poland. TEL 48-22-6084100, FAX 48-22-6084106, asp@axelspringer.com.pl, http://www.axelspringer.com.pl. Ed. Wieslaw Malecki. Adv. contact Piotr Roszczyk. page PLZ 8,500; trim 215 x 297.

LADYSLIPPER CATALOG AND RESOURCE GUIDE OF RECORDS, TAPES, COMPACT DISCS AND VIDEOS BY WOMEN. see *WOMEN'S INTERESTS*

384.55   USA
LASER SCENE. Text in English. 1988. 10/yr. USD 25 domestic; USD 42 foreign (effective 2001). adv. bk.rev. **Document type:** *Consumer.*
Formerly: Laser Views (1077-5420)
Address: c/o Scott Hughes, 386 Noe St, San Francisco, CA 94114. lvinfo@laserviews.com. Ed., Adv. contact David Goodman. Pub., R&P Joan Goodman. Circ: 30,000 (paid).

LEONARD MALTIN'S MOVIE GUIDE. see *MOTION PICTURES*

LIFE VIDEO; przeglad sprzetu i kaset. see *ELECTRONICS*

791.43   FRA   ISSN 1269-0015
M6 CINE VIDEO. Text in French. 1995. bi-m. **Document type:** *Magazine, Consumer.*
Published by: M6 Interactions, 89 av Charles-de-Gaulle, Neuilly-sur-Seine Cedex, 92575, France. TEL 33-1-41926936, http://www.m6net.fr.

384.55 306.7662   USA
MANSHOTS. Text in English. 9/yr.
Published by: Male Media Inc., 140 East 46th St, New York, NY 10017.

MARKEE. see *MOTION PICTURES*

MEDIA DETAIL; vakblad voor de detailhandelaren in de consumentenelectronica. see *ELECTRONICS*

MEDIAMATIC OFF-LINE. see *ART*

MESH; film video - digital media - installation - performance - art. see *ART*

791.45   USA   ISSN 8750-5401
MOVIE COLLECTOR'S WORLD. Text in English. 1976. m. USD 59.95 domestic; USD 109.95 foreign (effective 2005). adv. bk.rev. **Document type:** *Newspaper, Consumer.* **Description:** Brings price results, events news, collector happenings, and the latest video releases.
Incorporates: Video Shopper (Fraser); Which was formerly: Video Swapper; Former titles (until 1984): Movie & Film Collector's World (0746-0325); Film Collector's World (0745-5097)
Related titles: Online - full text ed.: USD 20 (effective 2005).
Published by: Arena Publishing, 15767 Kingston, PO Box 309, Fraser, MI 48026. TEL 586-774-4311, FAX 703-940-4566, mcw@mcwonline.com, http://www.mcwonline.com. Ed., Pub., R&P Brian A Bukantis. Circ: 5,500 (paid).

384.55   USA
MOVIE F X VIDEO MAGAZINE. Text in English. 2000. q. USD 29.99; USD 9.99 newsstand/cover (effective 2001). adv. **Document type:** *Magazine, Consumer.*
Published by: Movie F X Media, 2327 Clipper St, San Mateo, CA 94403. http://www.movie_fxmag.com. Ed., Pub. Gary Barth.

384.558   DEU
DER MUSIK D V D MARKT. (Digital Video Disc) Text in German. m. EUR 61 (effective 2004). adv. **Document type:** *Magazine, Trade.*
Published by: Mediatainment Publishing GmbH, Kolbergerstr 11, Sehnde, 31319, Germany. TEL 49-5138-70010, FAX 49-5138-700129, ad@mediatainmentpublishing,de, http://www.mpnow.de. Ed. Claas Wolter. Adv. contact Jeannine Konrad.

384.55   USA
N V R REPORTS. Text in English. 1990. irreg. free. **Document type:** *Newsletter.* **Description:** Dedicated to increasing the public's access to quality independent works on videocassette and other formats.
Published by: National Video Resources, 73 Spring St, Ste 606, New York, NY 10012. TEL 212-274-8080, FAX 212-274-8081, nvrinfo@nvr.org. Ed. Tim Gunn. Circ: 5,700.

OFFICIAL VIDEO DIRECTORY & BUYER'S GUIDE. see *BUSINESS AND ECONOMICS—Trade And Industrial Directories*

384.55   CAN   ISSN 1194-3130
ON VIDEO. Text in English. 1992. m. CND 24.
Published by: New Image Complete Print Services, 1314 Britannia Rd E, Mississauga, ON L4W 1C8, Canada. TEL 416-564-1033, FAX 416-564-3398. Ed. Catherine Puddy. adv.: B&W page CND 7,000, color page CND 7,200; trim 10.75 x 8.13. Circ: 160,000.

384.55   USA   ISSN 1094-3676
ONVIDEO; guide to home video releases. Text in English. 1995. d. adv. video rev. **Document type:** *Consumer.* **Description:** Covers forthcoming home video releases; video industry news; complete resource guide to online and mail order home video sources.
Media: Online - full text.
Address: PO Box 17377, Beverly Hills, CA 90209. TEL 213-525-2054, onvideo@cyberpod.com, http://www.onvideo.org. Ed., Pub., Adv. contact Harley W Lond.

384.555   USA
OPERATING CAMERAMAN. Text in English. 2000. s-a. USD 12; USD 6 newsstand/cover (effective 2001). adv.
Published by: Society of Operating Cameramen, Box 2006, Toluca Lake, CA 91610. TEL 818-382-7070, http://www.soc.org. Ed. Bill Hines. Pub. Georgia Packard.

P A J; a journal of performance and art. see *THEATER*

384.55   DEU   ISSN 1430-5704
P C VIDEO; Video am Computer. Text in German. 1996. 6/yr. EUR 33.90 domestic; EUR 41.40 foreign; EUR 5.90 newsstand/cover (effective 2005). adv. **Document type:** *Magazine, Consumer.*
Related titles: Online - full text ed.
Published by: Fachverlag Schiele und Schoen GmbH, Markgrafenstr 11, Berlin, 10969, Germany. TEL 49-30-2537520, FAX 49-30-2517248, redaktion@pcvideo.de, service@schiele-schoen.de, http://www.pcvideo.de, http://www.schiele-schoen.de. Ed. E Altenmueller. Adv. contact Barbara Huth. B&W page EUR 2,864, color page EUR 5,012. Circ: 30,000 (paid and controlled).

P C VIDEOLOG. see *COMMUNICATIONS—Computer Applications*

384.55   USA   ISSN 0898-302X
P R C NEWS; a monthly news in brief for the video industry. (Pre Recorded Cassette) Text in English. 1988. m. looseleaf. USD 577 (effective 2004). adv. charts; illus. 8 p./no.; back issues avail.; reprints avail. **Document type:** *Newsletter.*
Description: Covers news, mergers and acquisitions, people on the move, calendar of events, statistics, new releases, and sell-through products.
Related titles: Diskette ed.; E-mail ed.; Fax ed.; Microform ed.; Online - full content ed.; Online - full text ed.: (from LexisNexis).
Published by: Corbell Publishing Company, 11500 W Olympic Blvd, Ste 400, Los Angeles, CA 90064. TEL 310-444-3048, FAX 310-312-4551, mhealy8136@aol.com, mhealy@corbell.com, http://www.corbell.com. Ed. Deborah Rolfe. Pub. Maureen Healy. adv.: B&W page USD 1,500. Circ: 2,000 (paid and controlled).

791.43   USA
PALMER VIDEO MAGAZINE∗. Text in English. 1981. m. USD 15. adv. video rev.
Formerly: Palmer Video News
Published by: Palmer Video Corp., 51 Mohican Dr, Westfield, NJ 07090-1006. TEL 908-686-3030, FAX 908-686-2151. Eds. Mary Schwartz, Susan Baar. Circ: 203,915 (controlled).

057.1   ARM
PEREKRESTOK. Text in Russian. w. **Description:** Summarizes events of tv show by the same name which covers the countries of Central Asia. Includes video links.
Related titles: English ed.: Crossroads.
Published by: Internews Network Armenia, Arshakuniats 3, 3rd fl, Yerevan, Armenia. TEL 374-1-583620, 374-1-525527, FAX 374-1-569041.

PERSISTENCE OF VISION. see *MOTION PICTURES*

PHOTO VIDEO AUDIO NEWS (FRENCH EDITION). see *PHOTOGRAPHY*

384.558   CAN
PREMIERE VIDEO MAGAZINE. Text in English. 1984. m. CND 20, USD 25. adv. film rev. tr.lit. back issues avail. **Document type:** *Trade.*
Formerly: Premiere
Published by: Videomania Inc., 1314 Britannia Rd East, Mississauga, ON L4W 1C8, Canada. TEL 416-564-1033, FAX 416-564-3398. Ed. Salah Bachir. Circ: 9,000.

384.55   USA
PRO VIDEO REVIEW. Text in English. bi-m. USD 35; USD 50 foreign (effective 1999). tr.lit. back issues avail.; reprints avail. **Document type:** *Trade.* **Description:** Contains equipment reviews, product news, bench tests, user reports, buyers guides, new product announcements, field reports and technical questions and answers.
Published by: I M A S Publishing Group, 5827 Columbia Pike, Ste 310, Falls Church, VA 22041. TEL 703-998-7600, FAX 703-998-2966, adsales@imaspub.com, http://www.imaspub.com. **Subscr. to:** PO Box 1214, Falls Church, VA 22041-0241.

PRODUCER'S MASTERGUIDE; the international production manual for broadcast-television, feature films, television, commercials, cable, digital and videotape industries in the United States, Canada, the United Kingdom, Bermuda, the Caribbean Islands, Mexico, South America, Europe, Israel, the Far East, Australia and New Zealand. see *MOTION PICTURES*

384.558   USA
LE PRODUCTION MAKERS SOURCE. Text in English. 1956. a. USD 44.95 (effective 1999). adv. **Description:** Specialized yellow pages for the world of advertising, commercial production, film, video, music and broadcasting.
Supersedes in part: Madison Avenue Handbook: The Image Makers Source (0076-2148)
Published by: Peter Glenn Publications, Inc., 824 E. Atlantic Ave., Ste. 7, Delray Beach, FL 33483-5300. TEL 888-332-6700, info@pgdirect.com, http://www.pgdirect.com/. Ed. Lauren Gillmore. Pub. Gregory James. Adv. contact Tricia Mazzilli-Blount. Circ: 5,000.

PRODUCTION UPDATE; pre production. post production. equipment. technology. location. see *MOTION PICTURES*

791.45   USA   ISSN 1070-4949
PN1995.9.H6
PSYCHOTRONIC VIDEO. Text in English. 1989. q. USD 25; USD 50 foreign. adv. bk.rev.; film rev.; video rev. **Description:** Covers unusual film and video releases.
Indexed by: FLI.
Address: 3309 Rte 97, Narrowsburg, NY 12764-6126. TEL 914-252-6803, FAX 914-252-3905. Ed., Pub., R&P, Adv. contact Michael Weldon. Circ: 16,000.

PYRAMID MEDIA CATALOG. see *MOTION PICTURES*

QUARTERLY REVIEW OF FILM AND VIDEO. see *MOTION PICTURES*

384.558   USA
R T S VIDEO GAZETTE. Text in English. 1985. m. USD 25 (effective 1999). **Description:** Industry insider's column of latest trends, new releases and information on pricing. Also covers obscure titles available for sale, including silents, serials, B movies in all genres, foreign and cult films.
Published by: R T S, PO Box 93997, Las Vegas, NV 89193-3897. TEL 702-896-1300, rtsvmall@anv.net, http://www.rtsvideo.qpg.com.

REAL 2 REEL. see *COMMUNICATIONS—Television And Cable*

REGENT ONLINE JOURNAL OF COMMUNICATION. see *MOTION PICTURES*

384.558   AUS
REGION 4; Australia's ultimate DVD shopper's guide. Text in English. 1999. bi-m. AUD 66 domestic; AUD 100 in Asia & the Pacific; AUD 155 elsewhere (effective 2004). **Document type:** *Magazine, Consumer.*
Published by: Scribal Holdings Pty. Ltd., PO Box 2051, Richmond South, VIC 3121, Australia. TEL 61-3-94282727, FAX 61-3-94282726, mail@r4.com.au, http://www.r4.com.au/.

384.55   USA
S H E. Text in English. irreg.
Published by: Draculina Publishing, PO Box 587, Glen Carbon, IL 62034. Ed. Cameron Scholes.

SAN JOSE FILM & VIDEO PRODUCTION HANDBOOK - DIRECTORY. see *MOTION PICTURES*

SAT - AUDIO - VIDEO; postepy w elektronice powszechnego uzytku. see *ELECTRONICS*

SCREENS. see *MOTION PICTURES*

SET; cinema & video. see *MOTION PICTURES*

SOUND & VIDEO CONTRACTOR; the international management and engineering journal for sound and video contractors. see *SOUND RECORDING AND REPRODUCTION*

384.55   USA   ISSN 0883-2560
SPEC - COM JOURNAL∗. Text in English. 1967. bi-m. USD 20. adv. bk.rev. **Document type:** *Consumer.*
Published by: Spec - Com Communications and Publishing Group, Ltd. (Subsidiary of: Donovan Group), 913 Roux St, Plant City, FL 33566-2455. TEL 319-557-8791, FAX 319-583-6462. Ed. Gary Kaiser. Adv. contact Lynn Donovan. Circ: 1,400.

384.558   USA
THE STATE OF HOME VIDEO. Text in English. a. USD 1,595 (effective 2005). **Document type:** *Directory, Trade.* **Description:** Examines home video hardware and software, sales and rental, including data and revenue for retail, wholesale and manufacturing.
Published by: Kagan Research, LLC, One Lower Ragsdale Dr, Bldg One, Ste 130, Monterey, CA 93940. TEL 831-624-1536, FAX 831-625-3225, info@kagan.com, http://www.kagan.com.

STEREO & VIDEO. see *ELECTRONICS*

STEREOPHILE ULTIMATE A V. (Audio Visual) see *ELECTRONICS*

384   USA
STUMPED AT THE VIDEO STORE. Text in English. m. **Document type:** *Magazine, Consumer.*
Published by: Nitrinium Creations, PO Box 3488, Oak Park, IL 60303-3488. TEL 708-358-0596, stumped@centerstage.net, http://www.centerstage.net/stumped. Ed. Jackson Casey. Pub. Chris Neumer.

791.43   POL   ISSN 1642-624X
SWIAT FILMU D V D. AKCJA. Text in Polish. 2001. q. **Document type:** *Magazine, Consumer.*
Published by: B F Press Sp. z o.o., ul Mianowskiego 7/2, Warsaw, 02 044, Poland. redakcja@swiatfilmu.com.

791.43   POL   ISSN 1642-2953
SWIAT FILMU D V D. FANTASTYKA. Text in Polish. 2001. q. **Document type:** *Magazine, Consumer.*
Published by: B F Press Sp. z o.o., ul Mianowskiego 7/2, Warsaw, 02 044, Poland. redakcja@swiatfilmu.com.

791.43   POL   ISSN 1642-2945
SWIAT FILMU D V D. KINO. Text in Polish. 2001. q. **Document type:** *Magazine, Consumer.*
Published by: B F Press Sp. z o.o., ul Mianowskiego 7/2, Warsaw, 02 044, Poland. redakcja@swiatfilmu.com.

791.43   POL   ISSN 1642-6231
SWIAT FILMU D V D. KINO ARTYSTYCZNE. Text in Polish. 2001. q. **Document type:** *Magazine, Consumer.*
Published by: B F Press Sp. z o.o., ul Mianowskiego 7/2, Warsaw, 02 044, Poland. redakcja@swiatfilmu.com.

791.43   POL   ISSN 1642-2961
SWIAT FILMU D V D. KOMEDIA. Text in Polish. 2001. q. **Document type:** *Magazine, Consumer.*
Published by: B F Press Sp. z o.o., ul Mianowskiego 7/2, Warsaw, 02 044, Poland. redakcja@swiatfilmu.com.

384.55   ITA
T I M TRADE INTERACTIVE MULTIMEDIA. Text in Italian. fortn. (16/yr.). EUR 25 (effective 2005). **Document type:** *Magazine, Trade.*
Published by: Editoriale Duesse SpA, Via Donatello 5b, Milan, 20131, Italy. TEL 39-02-277961, FAX 39-02-27796300, e-duesse@e-duesse.it, http://www.e-duesse.it.

T V & VIDEO WORLD. see *COMMUNICATIONS—Television And Cable*

791.43   USA
TAKE ONE; the video entertainment newspaper. Text in English. 1981. m. USD 43 (effective 2005). adv. illus. **Document type:** *Newspaper, Consumer.* **Description:** Announces new movies released on videocassette each month.
Indexed: FLI.
Published by: Connell Communications, Inc. (Subsidiary of: International Data Group), 86 Elm St, Peterborough, NH 03458-1009. TEL 603-924-7271, 800-216-2225, FAX 603-924-7013. Ed. Grace Miller. Pub. Jim Connell.

TALKING PICTURES. see *MOTION PICTURES*

621.388   USA
TECHFACTS; information about captioning for video professionals. Text in English. 1989. irreg. (2-3/yr.). looseleaf. free. back issues avail. **Document type:** *Bulletin.*

Published by: Caption Center, 125 Western Ave, Boston, MA 02134. TEL 617-492-9225, FAX 617-562-0590, caption@wgbh.org, http://www.wgbh.org/caption. R&P Mary Watkins.

LE TECHNICIEN DU FILM ET DE LA VIDEO; magazine d'information des professionnels du cinema, de la television, et de l'audio-visuel. see *MOTION PICTURES*

TELEVISUAL. see *COMMUNICATIONS—Television And Cable*

THEY WON'T STAY DEAD. see *MOTION PICTURES*

TIMECODE. see *MOTION PICTURES*

384.558 384.55 ITA
TRADE HOME ENTERTAINMENT. Text in Italian. m. (11/yr.). EUR 20 (effective 2005). **Document type:** *Magazine, Trade.*
Published by: Editoriale Duesse SpA, Via Donatello 5b, Milan, 20131, Italy. TEL 39-02-277961, FAX 39-02-27796300, e-duesse@e-duesse.it, http://www.e-duesse.it.

ULTRAHIGH SPEED AND HIGH SPEED PHOTOGRAPHY, PHOTONICS, AND VIDEOGRAPHY. see *PHOTOGRAPHY*

384.55 DEU
V K E; das Videoverzeichnis auf CD-ROM. Text in German. 3/yr. **Document type:** *Catalog.*
Media: CD-ROM.
Published by: Josef Keller Verlag GmbH & Co. KG, Seebreite 9, Berg, 82335, Germany. TEL 49-8151-771144, FAX 49-8151-771190.

V O D & I T V INVESTOR. (Video on Demand and Interactive Television) see *BUSINESS AND ECONOMICS—Investments*

778.53 ITA ISSN 0394-2384
V R; mensile di videoregistrazione creativa. (Video Registrare) Text in Italian. 1985. m. USD 100. adv. back issues avail. **Document type:** *Magazine, Consumer.* **Description:** Covers home video and personal film making.
Published by: Systems Comunicazioni, Via Olanda 6, Vigano di Gaggiano, MI 20083, Italy. TEL 39-02-92270757, FAX 39-02-90841682, info@systems.it, http://www.systems.it. Ed. L Fratti. Circ: 34,000.

384.55 USA ISSN 1063-4193
V S D A VOICE✶. Text in English. 1983. bi-m. USD 19.95; includes supplement 3/yr.. **Document type:** *Newsletter.* **Description:** Supplies information about association news, legislative and First Amendment issues, emerging technologies, and commentary.
Formerly (until 1992): V S D A Reports (0896-4939)
Published by: Video Software Dealers Association, 16530 Ventura Blvd, Encino, CA 91436-4551. TEL 609-231-7800, FAX 609-231-9791. Circ: 5,000 (controlled).

VERZEICHNIS LIEFERBARER KAUFMEDIEN. see *BUSINESS AND ECONOMICS—Trade And Industrial Directories*

384.55 DEU ISSN 0172-4010
VIDEO; das Testmagazin. Text in German. 1979. m. EUR 3.80 newsstand/cover (effective 2002). adv. **Document type:** *Magazine, Consumer.*
Indexed: RGAb.
—Infotrieve.
Published by: Vereinigte Motor-Verlage GmbH & Co. KG, Leuschnerstr 1, Stuttgart, 70174, Germany. TEL 49-711-1821481, FAX 49-711-1821013. Ed. Hans-Martin Burr. Adv. contact Michael Hackenberg. B&W page EUR 5,320, color page EUR 8,835; trim 185 x 248. Circ: 102,000. **Subscr. to:** P M S GmbH & Co. KG, Grafenberger Allee 100, Duesseldorf 40237, Germany. TEL 49-203-767080, FAX 49-203-7690830.

778.53 DEU
VIDEO AKTIV DIGITAL. Text in German. 1974-199?; resumed 1997. bi-m. EUR 54 domestic; EUR 59.70 in Austria; CHF 106 in Switzerland; EUR 7.50 newsstand/cover (effective 2002). adv. back issues avail. **Document type:** *Magazine, Consumer.* **Description:** Covers tests of digital camcorders and detailed information on digital editing equipment for amateur video film-making.
Former titles: Video Aktiv (0724-4398); (until 1982): Video Journal (0722-3889)
Related titles: Online - full text ed.
Published by: Vereinigte Motor-Verlage GmbH & Co. KG, Leuschnerstr 1, Stuttgart, 70174, Germany. TEL 49-711-18201, FAX 49-711-1821759, http://www.videoaktiv.de, http://www.motorpresse.de. Ed. Hans-Martin Burr. Adv. contact Michael Hackenberg. B&W page EUR 2,610, color page EUR 3,800. Circ: 39,200.

384.5 CHE
VIDEO & SON✶. Text in German. 8/yr.
Published by: Atema Communications, Chemin Jean Pavillard 20, Pully, 1009, Switzerland. Ed. Jean Claude Marti. Circ: 25,000.

621.388 USA ISSN 1046-3860
TK6650
VIDEO & TELEVISION (YEAR). Variant title: Orion Video & Television Blue Book. Text in English. a. USD 144 (effective 1999). **Document type:** *Directory.* **Description:** Provides information on pricing used video and television equipment from 1968 to the present.
Formerly: Video (0883-5888)
Related titles: CD-ROM ed.; Diskette ed.
Published by: Orion Research Corp., 14555 N Scottsdale Rd, Ste 330, Scottsdale, AZ 85254-3457. TEL 800-844-0759, FAX 800-375-1315, orion@bluebook.com, http://www.netzone.com/orion.

384.55 CHE
VIDEO - AUDIO - REVUE. Text in German. m. adv. **Document type:** *Trade.*
Published by: Verband Schweizerischer Radio- und Televisions-Fachgeschaefte, Niklaus Wengi Str 25, Grenchen, 2540, Switzerland. TEL 41-32-6542020, FAX 41-32-6542029.

778.59029 USA ISSN 0279-571X
HD9697.V543
VIDEO BUSINESS. Text in English. 1981. 51/yr. USD 125 domestic; USD 150 in Canada; USD 190 elsewhere; USD 4 per issue domestic; free to qualified personnel (effective 2005). adv. charts; illus.; stat. back issues avail. **Document type:** *Magazine, Trade.* **Description:** Business magazine that reaches the retailers who sell and rent prerecorded video products, and others involved in the marketing and sales of entertainment software.
Related titles: Online - full text ed.: (from EBSCO Publishing, Factiva, Gale Group, LexisNexis, O C L C Online Computer Library Center, Inc., ProQuest Information & Learning).
Indexed: ABIn, B&I.
—**CCC.**
Published by: Reed Business Information (Subsidiary of: Reed Business), 5700 Wilshire Blvd, Ste 120, Los Angeles, CA 90036. TEL 323-857-6600, 323-965-2419, reinstein@variety.cahners.com, http://www.videobusiness.com/, http://www.reedbusiness.com. Ed. Scott Hettrick TEL 323-965-2424. adv.: B&W page USD 14,235, color page USD 17,650. Circ: 47,500 (paid and controlled). **Subscr. to:** Reed Business Information, PO Box 9020, Maple Shade, NJ 08052-9020. TEL 303-470-4466, FAX 303-470-4691, http://www.pubservice.com/CH.htm.

384.5 USA ISSN 0896-2871
VIDEO CHOICE. Text in English. 1988. m. USD 24.95 (effective 2000). adv.
Published by: Connell Communications, Inc. (Subsidiary of: International Data Group), 86 Elm St, Peterborough, NH 03458-1009. TEL 603-924-7271, FAX 603-924-7013. Ed. Melissa Stevenson.

VIDEO DUPLICATION DIRECTORY. see *BUSINESS AND ECONOMICS—Trade And Industrial Directories*

384.55 FRA ISSN 1151-4760
VIDEO ECHOS. Text in French. 21/yr.
Published by: Editions du Gaillard, 5 av. de la Republique, Paris, Cedex 75130, France. TEL 33-1-53364035, FAX 33-1-53364061, courrier@editions-du-gaillard.fr, http://www.editions-du-gaillard.fr/automatisation. Ed. Bruno Delamain. Circ: 7,000.

778.59 USA ISSN 1045-2885
VIDEO EVENT. Text in English. 1988. m. adv. **Document type:** *Consumer.* **Description:** Gives reviews of the box office hits being released on video.
Published by: Connell Communications, Inc. (Subsidiary of: International Data Group), 86 Elm St, Peterborough, NH 03458-1009. TEL 603-924-7271, FAX 603-924-7013. Ed. Melissa Stephenson. Pub. Jim Connell. Circ: 400,000.

790 USA
VIDEO FILM MUSIC. Short title: V F M. Text in English. 1992. bi-m. USD 5.95. adv.
Published by: Video Film Music Communications, Inc., 5231 E Memorial Dr, Ste 136, Stone Mountain, GA 30083. TEL 404-498-1729. Ed., Adv. contact David Deaton. Circ: 20,000.

791.45 CAN ISSN 0228-6726
VIDEO GUIDE. Text in English. 5/yr. CND 16; CND 20 foreign. adv. bk.rev. back issues avail.
Published by: Satellite Video Exchange Society, 1965 Main St, Vancouver, BC V5T 1C3, Canada. FAX 604-876-1185. Circ: 2,000.

791.45 GBR ISSN 1351-3893
VIDEO HOME ENTERTAINMENT. Text in English. 1981. w. GBP 90 domestic; GBP 150 in Europe; GBP 170 in Asia. adv. back issues avail. **Document type:** *Trade.*
Formed by 1992 merger of: Video Business (0950-2327); Video Trade Weekly (0262-4982)
Indexed: B&I.
Published by: Video Business Publications Ltd., Strandgate, 18-20 York Bldgs, London, WC2H 9JG, United Kingdom. TEL 071-839-7774, FAX 071-839-4393. Ed. Sam Andrews. Adv. contact Chris Whitaker. Circ: 7,500.

384.5 332.6 USA ISSN 1042-7694
VIDEO INVESTOR. Text in English. 1984. m. USD 845 (effective 2001). **Document type:** *Newsletter.* **Description:** Covers the economics of the home video industry and its impact on pay TV. Analyzes developments in hardware, software and retailing.
Formerly (until 1988): V C R Letter (8755-9927)
Related titles: E-mail ed.: USD 845 (effective 2001); Fax ed.: USD 845 (effective 2001).
Published by: Kagan World Media (Subsidiary of: Primedia, Inc.), 1 Lower Ragsdale Dr., Ste. 130, Monterey, CA 93940-5741. TEL 831-624-1536, FAX 831-625-3225, info@kagan.com. Pub. Paul Kagan.

VIDEO LIBRARIAN; the video review guide for libraries. see *LIBRARY AND INFORMATION SCIENCES*

778.59 ITA
VIDEO LINE. Text in Italian. 6/yr.
Published by: Esse 80 s.a.s., Via Gazzoletti, 19, Trento, TN 38100, Italy. TEL 461-233936, FAX 461-236009. Ed. Marco Russolo. Circ: 20,000.

791.45 CAN
VIDEO OUT DISTRIBUTION CATALOGUE. Text in English. 1983. a. USD 25.
Published by: Satellite Video Exchange Society, 1965 Main St, Vancouver, BC V5T 1C3, Canada. Ed. Carla Wolf.

384.55 DEU ISSN 0935-803X
VIDEO PLUS. Text in German. m. adv. **Document type:** *Consumer.*
Published by: Verlagsgruppe Milchstrasse, Mittelweg 177, Hamburg, 22786, Germany. TEL 040-44198-0, FAX 040-458519. Ed. Helmut Fiebig. Pubs. Dirk Manthey, Joerg Altendorf. Adv. contact Andre Hauke. Circ: 12,193.

788.59 ESP ISSN 1133-7079
VIDEO POPULAR. Text in Spanish. 1982. bi-m. EUR 24 (effective 2004). adv. bk.rev. **Document type:** *Magazine, Consumer.*
Indexed: IECT, RILM.
Published by: Video Popular, S.A, C/ Nicaragua, 137, Of 11, Barcelona, 08029, Spain. TEL 34-93-4190413, FAX 34-93-4394914, vp@videopopular.es, http://www.videopopular.es/www/index.php. Ed. Artur Paz. Adv. contact Monica Martin. Circ: 6,077.

778.59 USA ISSN 0748-0881
PN1992.95
THE VIDEO SOURCE BOOK. Text in English. 1979. a., latest 2004, 33d ed. USD 445 (effective 2004). adv. index. back issues avail. **Description:** Describes more than 125,000 currently available videotapes and discs, including feature movies, and instructional films.
Related titles: Supplement(s):.
Published by: (National Video Clearinghouse, Inc.), Gale Group (Subsidiary of: Thomson Corporation), 27500 Drake Rd, Farmington Hills, MI 48331-3535. TEL 248-699-8061, 800-877-4253, FAX 248-699-4253, galeord@gale.com, http://www.gale.com. Ed. Jim Craddock. Circ: 6,000.

384.554 USA
VIDEO SPECIALIST - NEW TECHNOLOGY NEWSLETTER. Text in English. 1981. q. looseleaf. USD 72 domestic; USD 96 foreign (effective 2000). adv. bk.rev.; video rev. back issues avail. **Document type:** *Newsletter, Trade.* **Description:** Offers advisory news to retailers, manufacturers and executives in home video. Also covers industry trends, competitive developments, automatic merchandising systems, games, strategies, promotions, multimedia formats and new products and services.
Formerly: Video Specialist Newsletter
Published by: J. Lahm Consultants Inc., 1025 STanford Ave, Fullerton, CA 92831-2809. TEL 714-738-8422, FAX 714-738-4860, vidspecnt@home.com, videodispensing.com. Pub., Adv. contact James J Lahm. Circ: 500.

THE VIDEO STATISTICAL REPORT. see *COMMUNICATIONS—Abstracting, Bibliographies, Statistics*

384.55 USA ISSN 0361-0942
TK6680
VIDEO SYSTEMS; the magazine for video professionals. Text in English. 1975. m. USD 70 domestic; USD 90 foreign; free to qualified personnel (effective 2005). adv. bk.rev. illus. reprint service avail. from PQC. **Document type:** *Magazine, Trade.* **Description:** Focuses on the latest technologies and techniques in the full production cycle from production planning to production to post-production to video presentation.
Related titles: Microfilm ed.: (from PQC); Online - full text ed.: (from bigchalk, EBSCO Publishing, Gale Group, H.W. Wilson, O C L C Online Computer Library Center, Inc., ProQuest Information & Learning); ♦ Supplement(s): Netmedia.
Indexed: AS&TI, ETA.
—Linda Hall. **CCC.**

Published by: Primedia Business Magazines & Media, Inc. (Subsidiary of: Primedia, Inc.), 9800 Metcalf Ave, Overland Park, KS 66212-2216. TEL 913-341-1300, FAX 913-967-7276, stephen_porter@intertec.com, inquiries@primediabusiness.com, http://www.videosystems.com, http://www.primediabusiness.com. Ed. Cynthia Wisehart. Pub. Jeff Victor. Adv. contact Anna Belle Rosenberg. Circ: 50,000 (controlled and free). **Subscr. to:** PO Box 12993, Overland Park, KS 66282-2993. TEL 800-441-0294, FAX 913-967-1331.

384.55 DEU
VIDEO TIPP. Text in German. 1982. m. free newsstand/cover. adv. film rev.; play rev. back issues avail. **Document type:** *Magazine, Consumer.* **Description:** Consumer information on all the latest available videos.
Published by: Entertainment Media Verlag GmbH und Co. oHG, Einsteinring 24, Dornach, 85609, Germany. TEL 49-89-45114-0, FAX 49-89-45114444, emv@e-media.de, http://www.ebiz.de/ppages/vt/index.htm, http://www.mediabiz.de. Ed. Ulrich Hoecherl. Pub. Ulrich Scheele. R&P Otto Bachmeier. Adv. contact Stefan Lessmeier. color page EUR 7,680. Circ: 221,483.

384.554 USA
VIDEO VIEWING. Text in English. 1984. m. free. **Document type:** *Consumer.*
Published by: View Publications, 4745 N Seventh St, Ste 110, Phoenix, AZ 85014. TEL 602-279-0841, FAX 602-277-8491.

621.3 USA ISSN 0192-8899
VIDEO VOICE. Text in English. 1980. m. USD 5. adv. **Document type:** *Trade.* **Description:** Provides up-to-date information on video-telecommunications industry.
Published by: David Blumenthal Associates Inc., 30 E 37th St, New York, NY 10016. TEL 212-686-8550. Ed. Paul Blumenthal. R&P Phil Keanney. Adv. contact Renee Jarmin.

791.43 USA ISSN 1070-9991
PN1995.9.H6
VIDEO WATCHDOG; the perfectionist's guide to fantastic video. Text in English. 1990. m. USD 60 domestic; USD 75 foreign; USD 6.50 newsstand/cover (effective 2005). bk.rev.; film rev.; music rev.; video rev. bibl.; illus. back issues avail. **Document type:** *Magazine, Consumer.* **Description:** Helps consumers find the most complete version of their favorite films on videotape.
Indexed: IIFP, IITV.
Address: PO Box 5283, Cincinnati, OH 45205-0283. TEL 513-471-8989, 800-275-8395, FAX 513-471-8248, videowd@aol.com, http://www.cinemaweb.com/videowd. Ed., R&P Tim Lucas. Pub. Donna Lucas.

384.55 GBR ISSN 0265-1297
VIDEO WORLD. Text in English. 1979. m. GBP 43 in Europe; GBP 50 elsewhere. adv. **Document type:** *Consumer.*
Published by: Galaxy Publications Ltd., PO Box 312, Galaxy Publications Ltd, Witham, Essex CM8 3SZ, United Kingdom. FAX 44-1376-510680. Circ: 26,766. **Subscr. to:** World Wide Subscription Service Ltd., Unit 4, Gibbs Reed Farm, Ticehurst, E Sussex TN5 7HE, United Kingdom. TEL 44-1580-200657, FAX 44-1580-200616.

VIDEOFASHION!; news, men, specials. see *CLOTHING TRADE—Fashions*

384.55 DEU ISSN 0176-3156
VIDEOFILMEN; das Magazin fuer aktive Videofilmer. Text in German. 1984. bi-m. EUR 33.90 domestic; EUR 41.40 foreign; EUR 5.90 newsstand/cover (effective 2005). adv. **Document type:** *Magazine, Consumer.*
—CCC.
Published by: Fachverlag Schiele und Schoen GmbH, Markgrafenstr 11, Berlin, 10969, Germany. TEL 49-30-2537520, FAX 49-30-2517248, service@schiele-schoen.de, http://www.videofilmen-online.de, http://www.schiele-schoen.de. Ed. E Altenmueller. Adv. contact Barbara Huth. B&W page EUR 3,196, color page EUR 5,593. Circ: 24,000.

778.59 USA ISSN 0363-1001
TK6630.A1
VIDEOGRAPHY. Text in English. 1976. m. USD 72 domestic; USD 102 in Canada; USD 153 elsewhere; USD 6 newsstand/cover; free to qualified personnel (effective 2005). adv. illus. back issues avail.; reprints avail. **Document type:** *Magazine, Trade.* **Description:** For video professionals. Contains news, trends and analysis of the video industry, interviews with specialists, editorials, guest columns, a calendar of meetings and shows.
Related titles: Online - full text ed.: (from Gale Group, Northern Light Technology, Inc., O C L C Online Computer Library Center, Inc., ProQuest Information & Learning).
Indexed: ABIn, FLI, IPARL, MRD, SoftBase.
—Linda Hall. **CCC.**
Published by: C M P Information, Inc., Entertainment Technology Group (Subsidiary of: C M P Information Ltd.), 460 Park Ave South, 9th Fl, New York, NY 10016. TEL 212-378-0400, FAX 212-378-2160, news@creativeplanet.com, http://www.videography.com, http://www.uemedia.com. Ed. Mark J Foley. Circ: 41,000.

VIDEOHOUND'S GOLDEN MOVIE RETRIEVER (YEAR). see *MOTION PICTURES*

384.55 GBR
VIDEOLOG. Text in English. 1984. fortn. adv. **Document type:** *Catalog, Trade.* **Description:** Directory of videos currently available for rent or retail in the UK.
Related titles: CD-ROM ed.
Published by: Trade Service Information Ltd., Cherryholt Rd, Stamford, Lincs PE9 2HT, United Kingdom. TEL 44-1780-750500, FAX 44-1780-751877, info@tsidirect.co.uk, http://www.tsidirect.co.uk/. Ed., R&P Christine Morris. Adv. contact Andrew Ward. Circ: 1,570 (paid).

384.55 USA ISSN 0746-7699
VIDEOLOG. Text in English. 1981. w. looseleaf. USD 252. adv. **Description:** Bulletin of video industry news, containing reviews of video release listings.
Related titles: Online - full text ed.
Published by: Trade Service Corporation, 15445 Innovation Dr., San Diego, CA 92128-3432. TEL 619-457-5920, FAX 619-457-1320. Ed. Bonnie J Dudley. Circ: 5,250.

384.55 USA
VIDEOLOG REPORTER. Text in English. 1981. w. USD 252.
Published by: Phonolog Publishing (Subsidiary of: Trade Service Corporation), 10996 Torreyana Rd, Box 85007, San Diego, CA 92138. TEL 619-457-5920. Ed. Bonnie J Dudley.

384.55 USA ISSN 0889-4973
TR845
VIDEOMAKER; camcorders - editing - computer video - audio & video production. Variant title: Computer Videomaker. Text in English. 1986. m. USD 22.50 domestic; USD 32.50 in Canada; USD 47.50 elsewhere; USD 3.99 newsstand/cover domestic; USD 5.99 newsstand/cover in Canada (effective 2005). adv. bk.rev.; software rev.; video rev. illus. Index. reprints avail. **Document type:** *Magazine, Consumer.* **Description:** Covers camcorders, video editing, desktop video and audio production for novice and expert videographers. Surverys and reviews new technology and equipment, teaches production techniques, and shows how to get more from equipment enthusiasts already own.
Related titles: Online - full text ed.: (from Gale Group).
Indexed: IHTDI.
Published by: York Publishing, PO Box 4591, Chico, CA 95927. TEL 530-891-8410, FAX 530-891-8443, editor@videomaker.com, http://www.videomaker.com. Eds. Matthew York, Stephen Muratore. Pub. Matthew York. R&P Chuck Peters. Adv. contact George Bryant. Circ: 80,000. **Subscr. to:** PO Box 3780, Chico, CA 95927.

384.55 ITA ISSN 1121-7677
VIDEOSOFT. Text in Italian. 2/yr.
Published by: Ediscreen s.r.l., Via Guglielmo Calderini, 68, Rome, RM 00196, Italy. TEL 6-39-60-409, FAX 6-39-00-72. Ed. Paola Gabrielli. Circ: 20,000.

384.55 ITA ISSN 1120-7647
VIDEOTECNICA. Text in Italian. 1989. m. EUR 47 (effective 2005). adv. **Document type:** *Magazine, Consumer.*
Published by: Vidigest Srl, Via Brenta 13, Rome, 00198, Italy. TEL 39-06-85352431, FAX 39-06-8845585, redazione@videotecnica.it, http://www.videotecnica.it. Ed. Paolo de Petris. Circ: 76,000.

384.558 GBR
VIDEOVISTA. Text in English. m. free (effective 2004). **Document type:** *Consumer.*
Media: Online - full content.
Published by: Pigasus Press, 13 Hazely Combe, Arreton, Isel of Wight, PO30 3AJ, United Kingdom. TEL 44-1983-865668, editor@videovista.net, pigasus.press@virgin.net, http://www.videovista.net/, http://www.pigasuspress.co.uk.

384.55 DEU ISSN 0941-0562
VIDEOWOCHE; das Nachrichtenmagazin fuer den Fachhandel. Text in German. 1987. w. EUR 102.50 for 6 mos. (effective 2002). adv. film rev. charts. **Document type:** *Magazine, Trade.* **Description:** Covers all aspects of the video business.
Published by: Entertainment Media Verlag GmbH und Co. oHG, Einsteinring 24, Dornach, 85609, Germany. TEL 49-89-45114-0, FAX 49-89-45114444, emv@e-media.de, http://www.videowoche.de, http://www.mediabiz.de. Ed. Ulrich Hoecherl. Pub. Ulrich Scheele. R&P Otto Bachmeier. Adv. contact Stefan Lessmeier. B&W page EUR 2,350, color page EUR 2,950. Circ: 4,350 (controlled).

384.55 DEU
VIDI AKTUELL. (Video Digital) Text in German. 1987. q. adv. back issues avail. **Document type:** *Magazine, Trade.*
Published by: VIDI Video Digital Studio Technik GmbH, Roentgenstr 3, Darmstadt, 64291, Germany. TEL 49-6151-93850, FAX 49-6151-938535, info@vidi-studiotechnik.de, http://www.vidi.net, http://www.vidi-studiotechnik.de/. Ed., Adv. contact Eckard Gruetters. Circ: 8,000.

VIEW. see *MOTION PICTURES*

VISIO. see *COMMUNICATIONS—Television And Cable*

384.558 CAN ISSN 1480-5545
VISUAL CONVERGENCE. Text in English. 1998. m. CND 50 domestic; USD 48 foreign; CND 6.50 newsstand/cover. adv. **Document type:** *Trade.* **Description:** Addresses Canadian media communications marketing. Covers videoproduction, new media, and presentation technology.
Published by: Providea Inc., 5100 Erin Mills Pkwy, Box 53076, Mississauga, ON L5M 5H0, Canada. TEL 416-410-4524, FAX 905-814-5524. Ed. Mike Allen. Pub., Adv. contact Dea Clark. page CND 3,000; trim 11 x 8. Circ: 7,100.

WHAT CAMCORDER. see *PHOTOGRAPHY*

384.558 AUS
WHAT D V D. Text in English. 2001. bi-m. AUD 35.95 domestic; AUD 61.95 in New Zealand; AUD 91.95 elsewhere (effective 2004). **Document type:** *Magazine, Consumer.* **Description:** Contains reviews, news and interviews with the stars.
Published by: Derwent Howard, PO Box 1037, Bondi Junction, NSW 1355, Australia. TEL 61-2-93864666, 800-007-820, FAX 61-2-93864288, enquiries@derwenthoward.com.au, http://www.derwenthoward.com.au/. Ed. Kris Ashton. Adv. contact Robyn Weiss.

WHAT HOME CINEMA. see *ELECTRONICS*

621.38833 GBR ISSN 1365-8956
WHAT VIDEO & TV. Text in English. 1980. m. GBP 30.60 domestic; GBP 46.80 in Europe; GBP 72 elsewhere (effective 2003). adv. illus. **Document type:** *Magazine, Consumer.*
Former titles (until 1996): What Video and What Home Cinema (1352-6162); (until 1993): What Video? (0956-2354)
Published by: Highbury - WV (Subsidiary of: Highbury House Communications PLC), 53-79 Highgate Rd, London, NW5 1TW, United Kingdom. TEL 44-20-73311000, FAX 44-20-73311273, http://www.whatvideotv.com/, http://www.hhc.co.uk/. Circ: 43,000.

WHAT VIDEO BEST BUYS. see *ELECTRONICS*

WHAT VIDEO BOOK OF TESTS. see *ELECTRONICS*

384.55 USA
WIDESCREEN REVIEW; the essential home theatre resource. Text in English. 1993. m. USD 40 domestic; USD 50 in Canada & Mexico; USD 90 elsewhere; USD 5.99 newsstand/cover (effective 2003). adv. video rev.; software rev. illus. **Document type:** *Consumer.* **Description:** Focuses on home theatre technologies, film making, and optical video disc widescreen editions presented on widescreen digital surround home theatre systems.
Related titles: Online - full text ed.
Published by: W S R Publishing, 27645 Commerce Center Dr., Temecula, CA 92590. TEL 909-676-4914, FAX 909-693-2960, wsrgary@widescreenreview.com, http://www.widescreenreview.com. Ed. Gary Reber. Adv. contact Nick Polcino. B&W page USD 2,400, color page USD 3,400; trim 10.5 x 8.13. Circ: 48,000.

WORLDWIDE DIRECTORY OF FILM AND VIDEO FESTIVALS AND EVENTS. see *MOTION PICTURES*

384.558 USA ISSN 1546-9557
TR845
▼ **XTREME VIDEO.** Text in English. 2003 (Fall). q. **Document type:** *Magazine, Consumer.* **Description:** Covers the tips and tricks of video shooting of extreme action sports such as surfing, wakeboarding, FMX, BMX, aggressive in-line skating, sea kayaking, and more. Also covers the technical aspects of videography, including streaming video, selecting a location, editing, and the latest video, photo, and related action sports gear.
Published by: C M P Media LLC (Subsidiary of: United News & Media), 600 Harrison St, 6th Fl., San Francisco, CA 94107. TEL 415-947-6746, FAX 415-947-6041, feedback@cmp.com, http://www.cmp.com.

1000 VIDEOS. see *MOTION PICTURES*

COMPUTER APPLICATIONS

see COMPUTERS

COMPUTERS

see also COMPUTERS—Artificial Intelligence ; COMPUTERS—Automation ; COMPUTERS—Calculating Machines ; COMPUTERS—Circuits ; COMPUTERS—Computer Architecture ; COMPUTERS—Computer Assisted Instruction ; COMPUTERS—Computer Engineering ; COMPUTERS—Computer Games ; COMPUTERS—Computer Graphics ; COMPUTERS—Computer Industry ; COMPUTERS—Computer Industry Directories ; COMPUTERS—Computer Industry, Vocational Guidance ; COMPUTERS—Computer Music ;

COMPUTERS—Computer Networks ; COMPUTERS—Computer Programming ; COMPUTERS—Computer Sales ; COMPUTERS—Computer Security ; COMPUTERS—Computer Simulation ; COMPUTERS—Computer Systems ; COMPUTERS—Cybernetics ; COMPUTERS—Data Base Management ; COMPUTERS—Data Communications And Data Transmission Systems ; COMPUTERS—Electronic Data Processing ; COMPUTERS—Hardware ; COMPUTERS—Information Science And Information Theory ; COMPUTERS—Internet ; COMPUTERS—Machine Theory ; COMPUTERS—Microcomputers ; COMPUTERS—Minicomputers ; COMPUTERS—Personal Computers ; COMPUTERS—Robotics ; COMPUTERS—Software ; COMPUTERS—Theory Of Computing ; COMPUTERS—Word Processing

004 USA ISSN 1547-3716
▼ ➤ **A C E T JOURNAL OF COMPUTER EDUCATION AND RESEARCH.** (Association for Computer Education in Texas) Text in English. 2003. a. free (effective 2003). **Document type:** *Journal, Academic/Scholarly.*
Published by: Association for Computer Educators in Texas, P. O. Box 3429, Galveston, TX 77552. http://www.texas.acet.org. Ed. Charles R. B. Stowe.

004 USA
QA76.73.A35 CODEN: AALEE5
A C M ADA LETTERS (ONLINE EDITION). Text in English. q. USD 53 membership (effective 2004). **Document type:** *Journal, Academic/Scholarly.*
Former titles: A C M Ada Letters (Print Edition); (until 1993): Ada Letters (0736-721X)
Media: Online - full text.
Indexed: C&ISA, E&CAJ, Inspec, SolStAb.
—AskIEEE, CISTI, Ei, IE, Infotrieve.
Published by: Association for Computing Machinery, Inc., 1515 Broadway, 17th Fl, New York, NY 10036-5701. http://www.acm.org/sigada/ada_letters/index.html. Ed. J Kaye Grau.

004 USA ISSN 0360-0300
QA76.5
➤ **A C M COMPUTING SURVEYS**; the survey and tutorial journal of the ACM. Text in English. 1969. q. USD 175 domestic to non-members; USD 195 foreign to non-members; USD 33 domestic to members; USD 53 foreign to members; USD 28 domestic to students; USD 48 foreign to students; USD 210 combined subscription domestic to non-members print & online eds.; USD 230 combined subscription foreign to non-members print & online eds.; USD 40 combined subscription domestic to members print & online eds.; USD 60 combined subscription foreign to members print & online eds.; USD 34 combined subscription domestic to students print & online eds.; USD 54 combined subscription foreign to students print & online eds. (effective 2006). illus. Index. back issues avail.; reprints avail. **Document type:** *Journal, Academic/Scholarly.* **Description:** Publishes new perspectives on hardware and software, computer systems organization, computer science theory, artificial intelligence, applications, and a spectrum of peripheral topics.
Formerly: Computing Surveys (0010-4892)
Related titles: Microfiche ed.: (from PQC); Microfilm ed.: (from WWS); Online - full text ed.: ISSN 1557-7341. USD 140 to non-members; USD 26 to members; USD 22 to students (effective 2006) (from Association for Computing Machinery, Inc., EBSCO Publishing, Florida Center for Library Automation, Gale Group, O C L C Online Computer Library Center, Inc., ProQuest Information & Learning).
Indexed: ABIn, AHCI, AIA, AS&TI, ASCA, BrCerAb, C&CSA, C&ISA, CADCAM, CIS, CMCI, CerAb, CompAb, CompC, CompD, CompLI, CompR, CorrAb, CurCont, E&CAJ, EMA, EngInd, ErgAb, IAA, ISR, Inspec, M&TEA, MBF, METADEX, MathR, ORMS, QC&AS, RASB, RefZh, SCI, SolStAb, WAA.
—BLDSC (3395.130000), AskIEEE, CISTI, Ei, IDS, IE, Infotrieve, ingenta, Linda Hall. **CCC.**
Published by: Association for Computing Machinery, Inc., 1515 Broadway, 17th Fl, New York, NY 10036-5701. TEL 212-626-0520, 800-342-6626, FAX 212-944-1318, acmhelp@acm.org, sigs@acm.org, usacm@acm.org, http://www.acm.org/surveys. Ed. Peter Wegner. Pub. Jono Hardjowirogo. Circ: 4,323.

004 USA ISSN 0891-4265
A C M DISTINGUISHED DISSERTATIONS. Text in English. irreg. price varies. **Document type:** *Monographic series.*
Indexed: Inspec.
Published by: (Association for Computing Machinery, Inc.), M I T Press, 55 Hayward St, Cambridge, MA 02142-1493. TEL 617-253-5646, FAX 617-258-6779, journals-info@mit.edu, http://mitpress.mit.edu/catalog/browse/browse.asp?sid=EEE51F3B-A704-4B6D-901E-7A4DD750A47E&btype=6&serid=12. **Subscr. to:** Springer-Verlag New York, Inc., Journal Fulfillment, PO Box 2485, Secaucus, NJ 07096-2485. TEL 800-777-4643, FAX 201-348-4505, journals@springer-ny.com.

004 USA
A C M / I E E E INTERNATIONAL WORKSHOP ON TIMING ISSUES IN THE SPECIFICATION AND SYNTHESIS OF DIGITAL SYSTEMS. PROCEEDINGS. (Association for Computing Machinery / Institute of Electrical and Electronics Engineers) Text in English. 2002. a. USD 11 per issue to members; USD 22 per issue to non-members (effective 2005). **Document type:** *Proceedings, Academic/Scholarly.*
Related titles: Online - full content ed.
Published by: Association for Computing Machinery, Inc., 1515 Broadway, 17th Fl, New York, NY 10036-5701. TEL 212-626-0500, usacm@acm.org, https://campus.acm.org/public/estore_window/estore_foyer2.cfm?src=item&offering=480021&CFID=37219283&CFTOKEN=42352593, http://www.acm.org.

004.6 USA
A C M INTERNATIONAL SYMPOSIUM ON MOBILE AD HOC NETWORKING AND COMPUTING. PROCEEDING. Text in English. a. **Document type:** *Proceedings, Academic/Scholarly.*
Related titles: Online - full content ed.
Published by: Association for Computing Machinery, Inc., 1515 Broadway, 17th Fl, New York, NY 10036-5701. TEL 212-626-0500, usacm@acm.org, http://www.acm.org.

A C M INTERNATIONAL WORKSHOP ON WIRELESS MOBILE APPLICATIONS AND SERVICES ON W L A N HOTSPOTS. see *COMMUNICATIONS*

004 305.8 USA ISSN 1556-4673
▼ **A C M JOURNAL ON COMPUTING AND CULTURAL HERITAGE.** (Association for Computing Machinery) Text in English. forthcoming 2006 (Apr.). quadrennial. USD 140 to non-members; USD 40 to members (effective 2006).
Related titles: Online - full text ed.: ISSN 1556-4711. forthcoming 2006 (Apr.).
Published by: Association for Computing Machinery, Inc., 1515 Broadway, 17th Fl, New York, NY 10036-5701. TEL 212-626-0500, 800-342-6626, usacm@acm.org, http://www.acm.org.

004 USA ISSN 0572-4252
➤ **A C M MONOGRAPH SERIES.** Text in English. 1968. irreg., latest vol.21, 1981. reprint service avail. from ISI. **Document type:** *Monographic series, Academic/Scholarly.*
Published by: (Association for Computing Machinery, Inc.), Academic Press (Subsidiary of: Elsevier Science & Technology), 525 B St, Ste 1900, San Diego, CA 92101-4495. apsubs@acad.com, http://www.academicpress.com. Ed. Thomas A Standish.

004 USA ISSN 1544-3558
QA76.9.H85
▼ **A C M TRANSACTIONS ON APPLIED PERCEPTION.** Abbreviated title: T A P. Text in English. 2004 (Jan.). q. USD 140 domestic to non-members; USD 154 foreign to non-members; USD 40 domestic to members; USD 54 foreign to members; USD 35 domestic to students; USD 49 foreign to students; USD 168 combined subscription domestic to non-members print & online eds.; USD 182 combined subscription foreign to non-members print & online eds.; USD 48 combined subscription domestic to members print & online eds.; USD 62 combined subscription foreign to members print & online eds.; USD 42 combined subscription domestic to students print & online eds.; USD 56 combined subscription foreign to students print & online eds. (effective 2006). **Document type:** *Journal, Academic/Scholarly.* **Description:** Aims to bridge the gap between perception and computer science, including the disciplines of graphics, vision, acoustics, and optics. The scope of TAP includes applications and algorithms in any of these fields that incorporate elements, of perception, and research into perceptual aspects of sensory integration.
Related titles: Online - full text ed.: ISSN 1544-3965. 2004 (Jan.). USD 112 to non-members; USD 32 to members; USD 28 to students (effective 2006) (from EBSCO Publishing).
—**CCC.**
Published by: Association for Computing Machinery, Inc., 1515 Broadway, 17th Fl, New York, NY 10036-5701. TEL 212-626-0500, 212-626-0520, 800-342-6626, FAX 212-869-0481, sigs@acm.org, usacm@acm.org, http://www.acm.org/pubs/tap.html.

004 USA ISSN 1556-4665
▼ **A C M TRANSACTIONS ON AUTONOMOUS ADOPTIVE SYSTEM.** (Association for Computing Machinery) Text in English. forthcoming 2006 (Apr.). q. USD 140 to non-members; USD 40 to members (effective 2006).
Related titles: Online - full text ed.: ISSN 1556-4703. forthcoming 2006 (Apr.).
Published by: Association for Computing Machinery, Inc., 1515 Broadway, 17th Fl, New York, NY 10036-5701. TEL 212-626-0500, 800-342-6626, usacm@acm.org, http://www.acm.org.

004 USA ISSN 1529-3785
QA76.9.L63 CODEN: ATCLA8
➤ **A C M TRANSACTIONS ON COMPUTATIONAL LOGIC.** Abbreviated title: T O C L. Variant title: Computational Logic. Text in English. 2000. q. USD 168 domestic to non-members; USD 182 foreign to non-members; USD 41 domestic to members; USD 55 foreign to members; USD 36 domestic to students; USD 50 foreign to students; USD 202 combined subscription domestic to non-members print & online eds.; USD 216 combined subscription foreign to non-members print & online eds.; USD 49 combined subscription domestic to members print & online eds.; USD 63 combined subscription foreign to members print & online eds.; USD 43, USD 57 combined subscription foreign to students print & online eds. (effective 2006). 1 cols./p.; back issues avail. **Document type:** *Journal, Academic/Scholarly.* **Description:** Devoted to research concerned with all uses of logic in computer science and its important role in many areas.
Related titles: Online - full text ed.: USD 134 to non-members; USD 33 to members; USD 29 to students (effective 2006) (from Association for Computing Machinery, Inc., EBSCO Publishing).
Indexed: ABIn, BrCerAb, C&ISA, CerAb, CompAb, CompLI, CompR, CorrAb, E&CAJ, EMA, IAA, Inspec, M&TEA, MBF, METADEX, MathR, MathSciNet, RefZh, WAA.
—CISTI, IE, Linda Hall. **CCC.**
Published by: Association for Computing Machinery, Inc., 1515 Broadway, 17th Fl, New York, NY 10036-5701. TEL 212-626-0520, 800-342-6626, FAX 212-944-1318, usacm@acm.org, http://www.acm.org/pubs/tocl. Circ: 873 (paid).

621.39 USA ISSN 1539-9087
TK7895.E42
A C M TRANSACTIONS ON EMBEDDED COMPUTING SYSTEMS. Text in English. q. USD 150 domestic to non-members; USD 164 foreign to non-members; USD 41 domestic to members; USD 545 foreign to members; USD 36 domestic to students; USD 50 foreign to students; USD 180 combined subscription domestic to non-members print & online eds.; USD 194 combined subscription foreign to non-members print & online eds.; USD 49 combined subscription domestic to members print & online eds.; USD 63 combined subscription foreign to members print & online eds.; USD 43 combined subscription domestic to students print & online eds.; USD 57 combined subscription foreign to students print & online eds. (effective 2006). back issues avail. **Description:** Explores embedded computing as a discipline informed by, and reponsive to, the needs of challenging world problems.
Related titles: Online - full text ed.: USD 120 to non-members; USD 33 to members; USD 29 to students (effective 2006) (from Association for Computing Machinery, Inc., EBSCO Publishing).
Indexed: ABIn, BrCerAb, C&ISA, CerAb, CorrAb, E&CAJ, EMA, IAA, M&TEA, MBF, METADEX, RefZh, WAA.
—CISTI. **CCC.**
Published by: Association for Computing Machinery, Inc., 1515 Broadway, 17th Fl, New York, NY 10036-5701. TEL 212-626-0520, 800-342-6626, FAX 212-869-0481, sigs@acm.org, usacm@acm.org, http://www.acm.org/tecs/index.html.

004 USA ISSN 1556-4681
▼ **A C M TRANSACTIONS ON KNOWLEDGE DISCOVERY IN DATA.** (Association for Computing Machinery) Text in English. forthcoming 2006 (Apr.). q. USD 140 to non-members; USD 40 to members (effective 2006).
Related titles: Online - full text ed.: ISSN 1556-472X. forthcoming 2006 (Apr.).
Published by: Association for Computing Machinery, Inc., 1515 Broadway, 17th Fl, New York, NY 10036-5701. TEL 212-626-0500, 800-342-6626, usacm@acm.org, http://www.acm.org.

004 USA ISSN 1049-3301
QA76.9.C65 CODEN: ATMCEZ
➤ **A C M TRANSACTIONS ON MODELING AND COMPUTER SIMULATION.** Text in English. 1991. q. USD 175 domestic to non-members; USD 189 foreign to non-members; USD 48 domestic to members; USD 62 foreign to members; USD 43 domestic to students; USD 57 foreign to students; USD 210 combined subscription domestic to non-members print & online eds.; USD 224 combined subscription foreign to non-members print & online eds.; USD 58 combined subscription domestic to members print & online eds.; USD 72 combined subscription foreign to members print & online eds.; USD 52 combined subscription domestic to students print & online eds.; USD 66 combined subscription foreign to students print & online eds. (effective 2006). illus. 1 cols./p.; reprints avail. **Document type:** *Journal, Academic/Scholarly.* **Description:** Covers research on aspects of computer simulation and modeling of complex systems. Includes applications, reviews and tutorials.
Related titles: Microform ed.; Online - full text ed.: USD 140 to non-members; USD 38 to members; USD 34 to students (effective 2006) (from Association for Computing Machinery, Inc., EBSCO Publishing).
Indexed: ABIn, AS&TI, BrCerAb, C&ISA, CIS, CerAb, CompAb, CompLI, CompR, CorrAb, E&CAJ, EMA, EngInd, IAA, Inspec, M&TEA, MBF, METADEX, RefZh, SolStAb, WAA, ZentMath.
—BLDSC (0578.671000), AskIEEE, CISTI, Ei, IE, Infotrieve, ingenta, Linda Hall. **CCC.**

C

Published by: Association for Computing Machinery, Inc., 1515 Broadway, 17th Fl, New York, NY 10036-5701. TEL 212-626-0520, 800-342-6626, FAX 212-869-0481, usacm@acm.org, http://www.acm.org/tomacs. Circ: 1,193 (paid).

004 USA
A C M WASHINGTON UPDATE. Text in English. 1997. bi-w. back issues avail. **Document type:** *Newsletter.* **Description:** Provides a means for promoting dialogue on computer policy issues with US policy makers and the general public.
Media: Online - full text.
Published by: Association for Computing Machinery, Inc., 1515 Broadway, 17th Fl, New York, NY 10036-5701. TEL 212-626-0500, 212-626-0520, 800-342-6626, FAX 212-869-0481, sigs@acm.org, usacm@acm.org, http://www.acm.org/usacm/update.

A C M WORKSHOP ON PRIVACY IN THE ELECTRONIC SOCIETY. PROCEEDINGS. see *LAW—Constitutional Law*

004 USA ISSN 1097-6353
TS155.6
A-E-C SYSTEMS. (Architecture, Engineering, Construction) Text in English. 1991. q. USD 56 foreign. adv. bk.rev. Supplement avail. **Document type:** *Trade.* **Description:** Presents case studies, how-to and features to help management-level computer users in architecture, engineering, construction, facility management, and GIS mapping.
Formerly: A-E-C Systems Computer Solutions (1061-7663)
Published by: Penton Media, Inc. (Subsidiary of: Pittway Company), 1350 Connecticut Ave NW, Washington, DC 20036. TEL 216-696-7000, FAX 216-696-1267, dsofranec@penton.com, http://www.penton.com/cae/aec. Ed. Susan Smith. R&P Larry Boulden TEL 216-931-9475. Adv. contact Carol Sumers. Circ: 30,000.

004 SGP
A M A S T SERIES IN COMPUTING. (Algebraic Methodology and Software Technology) Text in English. 1993. irreg., latest vol.8. price varies. **Document type:** *Monographic series, Academic/Scholarly.* **Description:** Covers the theoretical aspects of mathematical methodology that can effectively be used as the foundation for the new software technology.
Indexed: ZentMath.
—BLDSC (0806.393000).
Published by: World Scientific Publishing Co. Pte. Ltd., 5 Toh Tuck Link, Singapore, 596224, Singapore. TEL 65-466-5775, FAX 65-467-7667, wspc@wspc.com.sg, series@wspc.com.sg, http://www.wspc.com.sg/books/series/amast_series.shtml, http://www.worldscientific.com. Ed. T Rus. **Dist. by:** World Scientific Publishing Co., Inc., 1060 Main St, River Edge, NJ 07661. TEL 201-487-9655, 800-227-7562, FAX 201-487-9656, 888-977-2665; World Scientific Publishing Ltd., 57 Shelton St, London WC2H 9HE, United Kingdom. TEL 44-20-78360888, FAX 44-20-78362020, sales@wspc.co.uk.

004 JPN ISSN 0386-5428
A S C I I; home and office computer science magazine. (American Standard Code for Information Interchange) Text in Japanese. 1977. m. JPY 13,680; JPY 870 newsstand/cover (effective 2004). adv.
Published by: ASCII Corp., JR Shinanomachi Bldg. 34 Shinanomachi, Shinjuku-ku, Tokyo, 160-8584, Japan. http://www.ascii.co.jp/books/magazines/ascii.html. Circ: 280,000.

004 DNK ISSN 1397-8640
AALBORG UNIVERSITY. DEPARTMENT OF COMPUTER SCIENCE. REPORTS. Text in English. 1997. irreg. **Document type:** *Monographic series.*
—BLDSC (0537.309910).
Published by: Aalborg Universitet, Institut for Elektroniske Systemer/Aalborg University, Department of Computer Science, Fredrik Bajers Vej 7 A 1, Aalborg, 9220, Denmark. http://ies.auc.dk.

AALBORG UNIVERSITY. DEPARTMENT OF MATHEMATICAL SCIENCES. R. see *ENGINEERING—Electrical Engineering*

004 DNK ISSN 0106-9969
AARHUS UNIVERSITET. INSTITUT FOR MATEMATISKE FAG. DATALOGISK AFDELING. DAIMI IR. Text in Danish. 1973. irreg. price varies. **Document type:** *Monographic series, Academic/Scholarly.*
Published by: (Datalogisk Afdeling), Aarhus Universitet, Institut for Matematiske Fag/Aarhus University. Department of Mathematical Sciences, Ny Munkegade, Bygning 530, Aarhus C, 8000, Denmark. TEL 45-89-423437, FAX 45-86-131769, http://www.imf.au.dk, institut@imf.au.dk.

004 DNK ISSN 0105-8525
AARHUS UNIVERSITET. INSTITUT FOR MATEMATISKE FAG. DATALOGISK AFDELING M D. Key Title: D A I M I - M D. Text in Danish. 1973. irreg. price varies. **Document type:** *Academic/Scholarly.*
Published by: (Datalogisk Afdeling), Aarhus Universitet, Institut for Matematiske Fag/Aarhus University. Department of Mathematical Sciences, Ny Munkegade, Bygning 530, Aarhus C, 8000, Denmark. TEL 45-8942-3188, FAX 45-8613-1769, institut@imf.au.dk, http://www.imf.au.dk.

004 DNK ISSN 0105-8517
AARHUS UNIVERSITET. INSTITUT FOR MATEMATISKE FAG. DATALOGISK AFDELING. P B. Key Title: D A I M I - P B. Text in Danish. 1972. irreg. price varies. **Document type:** *Academic/Scholarly.*
Published by: (Datalogisk Afdeling), Aarhus Universitet, Institut for Matematiske Fag/Aarhus University. Department of Mathematical Sciences, Ny Munkegade, Bygning 530, Aarhus C, 8000, Denmark. TEL 45-8942-3188, FAX 45-8613-1769, institut@imf.au.dk, http://www.imf.au.dk.

004 IRL ISSN 0791-1254
ABAKUS. Text in English. 1989. a. **Document type:** *Academic/Scholarly.*
Published by: (University College Cork, Computer Science Department), Micromail, 7 Crawford Park, Bishop St, Cork, Ireland. TEL 353-121-317686, FAX 353-121-310756, willy@micromail.ie, http://www.cis.ie/micromail. Eds. Brian Dowd, Colin McCormack.

004 USA
ACADEMY COMPUTING TIMES. Text in English. 1986. 10/yr. free.
Published by: Indiana University, Wrubel Computing Center, 10th St & State Rd 46 Bypass, Bloomington, IN 47405. TEL 812-855-9255. Ed. Janet Holloway Smith.

004 USA ISSN 0163-6774
ACRONYMS. Text in English. 1971. 7/yr. free. **Description:** Addresses current mainframe, network and microcomputer topics of interest to MSU users; includes topics of more general appeal as well.
Indexed: CompC, EIA, EnerInd, ICEA, ManagCont, SoftAbEng.
Published by: Michigan State University, Computer Laboratory, Computing Information Center, East Lansing, MI 48824. TEL 517-353-1800, FAX 517-353-9847. Ed. Linda Dunn. Circ: 3,000.

▼ **AD-HOC & SENSOR WIRELESS NETWORKS**; an international journal. see *MATHEMATICS*

004 USA ISSN 1537-9310
ADVANCED TOPICS IN END USER COMPUTING. Text in English. 2002. irreg., latest vol.4, 2005. price varies. **Document type:** *Monographic series, Academic/Scholarly.* **Description:** Contains the latest research ideas and topics on how to enhance current database systems, improve information storage, refine existing database models, and develop advanced applications.
—BLDSC (0696.935610).
Published by: Idea Group Publishing (Subsidiary of: Idea Group Inc.), 701 E Chocolate Ave, Ste 200, Hershey, PA 17033-1240. TEL 717-533-8845, 866-342-6657, FAX 717-533-7115, cust@idea-group.com, http://www.idea-group.com. Ed. Mo Adam Mahmood.

004 USA ISSN 0065-2458
QA76 CODEN: ADCOA7
➤ **ADVANCES IN COMPUTERS.** Text in English. 1960. irreg., latest vol.56, 2002. USD 125 per vol. vol.62 (effective 2004). index. reprint service avail. from ISI. **Document type:** *Academic/Scholarly.* **Description:** Features new technologies for software development: agile methods, time boxing, MBASE.
Indexed: ASCA, CADCAM, CMCI, Inspec, RASB, ZentMath.
—BLDSC (0704.130000), CISTI, IE, Infotrieve, ingenta, Linda Hall. **CCC.**
Published by: Academic Press (Subsidiary of: Elsevier Science & Technology), 525 B St, Ste 1900, San Diego, CA 92101-4495. TEL 619-231-6616, 800-894-3434, FAX 619-699-6422, apsubs@acad.com, http://www.academicpress.com. Ed. Zelkowitz Marvin.

004 SGP
▼ **ADVANCES IN NATURAL COMPUTATION.** Text in English. 2004. irreg., latest vol.2, 2004. price varies. **Document type:** *Monographic series, Academic/Scholarly.* **Description:** Covers the theory and applications of natural computation, establishing the state of the art, disseminating the latest research discoveries, and providing potential textbooks to senior undergraduate and postgraduate students.
Published by: World Scientific Publishing Co. Pte. Ltd., 5 Toh Tuck Link, Singapore, 596224, Singapore. TEL 65-466-5775, FAX 65-467-7667, series@wspc.com.sg, http://www.wspc.com/books/series/anc_series.shtml, http://www.worldscientific.com. Ed. Xin Yao. **Subscr. to:** Farrer Rd, PO Box 128, Singapore 912805, Singapore. TEL 65-382-5663, FAX 65-382-5919. **Dist. by:** World Scientific Publishing Co., Inc., 1060 Main St, River Edge, NJ 07661. TEL 201-487-9655, 800-227-7562, FAX 201-487-9656, 888-977-2665, wspc@wspc.com.; World Scientific Publishing Ltd., 57 Shelton St, London WC2H 9HE, United Kingdom. TEL 44-20-78360888, FAX 44-20-78362020, sales@wspc.co.uk.

004 SGP
ADVANCES ON INFORMATICS. Variant title: Hellenic Conference on Informatics. Proceedings. (7th Hellenic Conference on Informatics (HCI '99) at University of Loannina, Greece: Advances in Informatics) Text in English. irreg., latest 1999, 7th Hellenic Conference. price varies. **Document type:** *Proceedings, Academic/Scholarly.*
Published by: World Scientific Publishing Co. Pte. Ltd., 5 Toh Tuck Link, Singapore, 596224, Singapore. TEL 65-466-5775, FAX 65-467-7667, http://www.wspc.com/books/compsci/4320.html, http://www.worldscientific.com. Eds. Dimitrios I Fotiadis, Stavros D Nikolopoulos. **Subscr. to:** Farrer Rd, PO Box 128, Singapore 912805, Singapore. **Dist. by:** World Scientific Publishing Co., Inc., 1060 Main St, River Edge, NJ 07661. TEL 201-487-9655, 800-227-7562, FAX 201-487-9656, 888-977-2665, wspc@wspc.com.; World Scientific Publishing Ltd., 57 Shelton St, London WC2H 9HE, United Kingdom. TEL 44-20-78360888, FAX 44-20-78362020, sales@wspc.co.uk.

AFRICAN-AMERICAN CAREER WORLD. see *OCCUPATIONS AND CAREERS*

004 USA ISSN 0178-4617
QA75.5 CODEN: ALGOEJ
➤ **ALGORITHMICA**; an international journal in computer science. Text in English. 1986. m. (in 3 vols., 4 nos./vol.). EUR 918 combined subscription to institutions print & online eds. (effective 2005). adv. illus. back issues avail.; reprint service avail. from PSC. **Document type:** *Journal, Academic/Scholarly.* **Description:** Publishes papers on algorithms, with a strong emphasis on practical application.
Related titles: Microform ed.: (from PQC); Online - full text ed.: ISSN 1432-0541 (from EBSCO Publishing, Springer LINK, Swets Information Services).
Indexed: ASCA, C&ISA, CCMJ, CMCI, CompAb, CompLI, CurCont, CybAb, E&CAJ, EngInd, IAOP, ISR, Inspec, MathR, MathSciNet, RefZh, SCI, SolStAb, ZentMath.
—BLDSC (0787.337000), AskIEEE, CISTI, Ei, IDS, IE, Infotrieve, ingenta, Linda Hall. **CCC.**
Published by: Springer-Verlag New York, Inc. (Subsidiary of: Springer Science+Business Media), 233 Spring St, New York, NY 10013. TEL 212-460-1500, 800-777-4643, FAX 212-473-6272, journals@springer-ny.com, http://link.springer.de/link/service/journals/00453/index.htm, http://www.springer-ny.com. Ed. C K Wong. R&P Xian Chuan Lian. Adv. contact Brian Skepton. **Subscr. outside the Americas to:** Springer GmbH Auslieferungsgesellschaft, Haberstr 7, Heidelberg 69126, Germany. TEL 49-6221-345-0, FAX 49-6221-345-4229, subscriptions@springer.de; **Subscr. to:** Journal Fulfillment, PO Box 2485, Secaucus, NJ 07096-2485. TEL 201-348-4033, FAX 201-348-4505.

004 SWE ISSN 1651-8837
▼ **ALLT OM P C.** Text in Swedish. 2003. 11/yr. SEK 349; SEK 39 per issue (effective 2005). adv. **Document type:** *Magazine, Consumer.*
Published by: First Publishing Group AB, Deltavaegen 3, PO Box 3187, Vaexjoe, 35043, Sweden. TEL 46-470-762400, FAX 46-470-762425, aopc@firstpublishing.se, info@firstpublishing.se, http://alltompc.fpgroup.se, http://www.fpgroup.se. Ed. Tommy Johansson. Adv. contact Andreas Bjoerck. color page SEK 25,000; 190 x 285. Circ: 35,000.

003 USA ISSN 0254-5330
➤ **ANNALS OF OPERATIONS RESEARCH.** Text and summaries in English. 1984. 8/yr. (in 8 vols.). EUR 2,498, USD 2,535, GBP 1,565 combined subscription to institutions print & online eds. (effective 2005). adv. reprint service avail. from PSC. **Document type:** *Journal, Academic/Scholarly.* **Description:** Presentation of trends in specific areas of operations research.
Related titles: Online - full text ed.: ISSN 1572-9338 (from EBSCO Publishing, Gale Group, IngentaConnect, Kluwer Online, O C L C Online Computer Library Center, Inc., Ovid Technologies, Inc., ProQuest Information & Learning, Springer LINK, Swets Information Services).
Indexed: ABIn, ASCA, BibLing, CCMJ, CIS, CMCI, CompAb, CompLI, CurCont, CybAb, EngInd, IAOP, ISR, Inspec, MathR, MathSciNet, ORMS, QC&AS, SCI, ST&MA, ZentMath.
—BLDSC (1043.330000), AskIEEE, CISTI, Ei, IDS, IE, Infotrieve, ingenta. **CCC.**
Published by: Springer-Verlag New York, Inc. (Subsidiary of: Springer Science+Business Media), 233 Spring St, New York, NY 10013. TEL 212-460-1500, FAX 212-460-1575, service@springer-ny.com, http://springerlink.metapress.com/openurl.asp?genre=journal&issn=0254-5330, http://www.springer-ny.com. Ed. Peter L Hammer. **Subscr. to:** Journal Fulfillment, PO Box 2485, Secaucus, NJ 07096-2485. TEL 201-348-4033, FAX 201-348-4505, journals@springer-ny.com.

➤ **THE ANNUAL A C M - S I A M SYMPOSIUM ON DISCRETE ALGORITHMS. PROCEEDINGS.** (Association for Computing Machinery - Society for Industrial and Applied Mathematics) see *MATHEMATICS*

➤ **ANNUAL CONFERENCE ON STATISTICS, COMPUTER SCIENCE AND OPERATIONS RESEARCH. PROCEEDINGS.** see *COMPUTERS—Abstracting, Bibliographies, Statistics*

004 SGP
▼ ➤ **ANNUAL REVIEW OF INTELLIGENT INFORMATICS.** Text in English. forthcoming 2006. irreg. price varies. **Document type:** *Monographic series, Academic/Scholarly.* **Description:** Covers intelligent informatics, integrating the fields of computer science and engineering, interdisciplinary computational sciences, and information technology.

Published by: World Scientific Publishing Co. Pte. Ltd., 5 Toh Tuck Link, Singapore, 596224, Singapore. TEL 65-466-5775, FAX 65-467-7667, wspc@wspc.com.sg, series@wspc.com.sg, http://www.wspc.com.sg/books/series/arii_series.shtml, http://www.worldscientific.com. Eds. Jiming Liu, Ning Zhong. **Dist. by:** World Scientific Publishing Co., Inc., 1060 Main St, River Edge, NJ 07661. TEL 201-487-9655, 800-227-7562, FAX 201-487-9656, 888-977-2665; World Scientific Publishing Ltd., 57 Shelton St, London WC2H 9HE, United Kingdom. TEL 44-20-78360888, FAX 44-20-78362020, sales@wspc.co.uk.

004 JPN
ANNUAL SURVEY OF COMPUTER USERS★. Text in Japanese. 1966. a. JPY 10,000.
Published by: Japan Management Science Institute/Nihon Keiei Kagaku Kenkyujo, 5-6-8, Miyanishi-cho, Futyu-shi, Tokyo, 183-0022, Japan. FAX 81-42-3360559, cr-info@jmsi.co.jp, http://www.jmsi.co.jp/.

004 ITA ISSN 1122-9268
APPLICANDO; la rivista per Macintosh. Text in Italian. 1983. m. (11/yr.). EUR 46 (effective 2005). back issues avail. **Document type:** *Magazine, Consumer.* **Description:** Covers Mac pc world and MacOS products, and technology around the Apple market.
Published by: Gruppo Editoriale J C E, Via Patecchio 2, Milan, MI 20141, Italy. TEL 39-02-57316011, FAX 39-02-57316291, info@jce.it, http://www.jce.it. Ed. Franco Sarcina. Pub. Jacopo Castellfranchi. Circ: 45,000.

APPLIED CATEGORICAL STRUCTURES; a journal devoted to applications of categorical methods in algebra, analysis, order, topology and computer science. see *MATHEMATICS—Computer Applications*

004 GBR ISSN 0952-3332
ARCHAEOLOGICAL COMPUTING NEWSLETTER. Text in English. 1984. q.
—BLDSC (1594.708000), IE, ingenta.
Published by: Staffordshire University, School of Computing, Trent Bldg, College Rd, Stoke on Trent, Staffordshire ST4 2DE, United Kingdom. TEL 44-1782-294000, http://www.staffs.ac.uk.

004 POL ISSN 0867-2121
QA75.5 CODEN: ATSSEB
➤ **ARCHIWUM INFORMATYKI TEORETYCZNEJ I STOSOWANEJ/ARCHIVES OF THEORETICAL AND APPLIED INFORMATICS.** Text in English; Summaries in Polish. 1971. q. EUR 42 foreign (effective 2005). abstr.; charts; illus. 100 p./no.; back issues avail. **Document type:** *Journal, Academic/Scholarly.*
Formerly (until 1989): Podstawy Sterowania (0374-4094)
Indexed: Inspec, ZentMath.
—AskIEEE, CISTI, Linda Hall.
Published by: (Polska Akademia Nauk/Polish Academy of Sciences, Instytut Informatyki Teoretycznej i Stosowanej/Institute of Theoretical and Applied Information), Centrum Elektryfikacji i Automatyzacji Gornictwa E M A G, ul Leopolda 31, Katowice, 40189, Poland. TEL 48-32-2007700, FAX 48-32-2007701, archiwum@iitis.gliwice.pl, centrum@emag.pl, http://www.iitis.gliwice.pl/en/archives_d.html, http://www.emag.katowice.pl. Ed. Stefan Wegrzyn. Adv. contact Ryszard Winiarczyk. Circ: 200 (controlled). **Dist. by:** Ars Polona, Krakowskie Przedmiescie 7, Warsaw, Poland. TEL 48-22-9263914, FAX 48-22-9265334, arspolona@arspolona.com.pl, http://www.arspolona.com.pl.

004 SGP ISSN 0129-5896
ASIA COMPUTER WEEKLY. Text in English. 1979. w. USD 180 in Asia; USD 199 elsewhere; free to qualified personnel (effective 2000). adv. back issues avail. **Document type:** *Trade.* **Description:** Reports on the latest news and happenings in the Asian computer industry.
Related titles: Online - full text ed.: (from Gale Group, ProQuest Information & Learning).
Indexed: ABIn, B&I, JOF.
Published by: C M P Business Media Pte Ltd. (Subsidiary of: United News & Media), 390 Havelock Rd, #05-00 King's Centre, Singapore, 169662, Singapore. TEL 65-735-3366, FAX 65-732-1191, info@cmpasia.com.sg, http://www.asiacomputerweekly.com/, http://www.cmpasia.com.sg/. adv.: B&W page USD 1,180, color page USD 7,680; trim 406 x 280. Circ: 19,145.

003 SGP ISSN 0217-5959
HD28 CODEN: APJRE3
➤ **ASIA PACIFIC JOURNAL OF OPERATIONAL RESEARCH.** Text in English. 1973. q. SGD 171, USD 97, EUR 94 to individuals; SGD 303, USD 172, EUR 167 combined subscription to institutions print & online eds. (effective 2006). adv. bk.rev. back issues avail. **Document type:** *Journal, Academic/Scholarly.* **Description:** Provides a forum for practitioners, academics and researchers in Operational Research and related fields, within and beyond the Asia-Pacific region.
Incorporates (1971-1984): New Zealand Operational Research (0110-6392)
Related titles: Microform ed.: (from PQC); Online - full text ed.: (from EBSCO Publishing, Factiva, O C L C Online Computer Library Center, Inc., ProQuest Information & Learning, Swets Information Services).
Indexed: ABIn, ASCA, CCMJ, CMCI, CurCont, ESPM, EngInd, IAOP, Inspec, JCQM, MathR, MathSciNet, RefZh, RiskAb, SSCI, ZentMath.
—BLDSC (1742.260750), AskIEEE, Ei, IDS, IE, ingenta. **CCC.**
Published by: (National University of Singapore, Industrial and Systems Engineering Department), World Scientific Publishing Co. Pte. Ltd., 5 Toh Tuck Link, Singapore, 596224, Singapore. TEL 65-466-5775, FAX 65-467-7667, wspc@wspc.com.sg, http://www.worldscinet.com/apjor/apjor.shtml, http://www.worldscientific.com. Ed. Zhao Gongyun. Circ: 1,100.

004 USA
ASK THE COMPUTER LADY. Text in English. 1998. w. **Document type:** *Newsletter.* **Description:** Covers basic computing and sometimes reviews freeware programs.
Media: E-mail.
Address: eboston@gwi.net, http://nospin.com/pc/complady.html. Ed. Elizabeth Boston.

005 USA
ASP.NETPRO MAGAZINE. Text in English. bi-m. **Document type:** *Magazine.*
Published by: Informant Communications Group, 5105 Florin Perkins Rd., Sacramento, CA 95826-4817. TEL 916-686-6610, FAX 916-686-8497, http://www.aspnetpro.com, http://www.informant.com.

004 DEU
▼ **ASSEMBLY PROGRAMMING JOURNAL.** Text in English. 2004. irreg. free (effective 2005). **Document type:** *Journal, Academic/Scholarly.*
Media: Online - full text.
Published by: Universitas Virtualis, Dipl. Inform. Med. Thorsten Schneider, Lange Str 33, Herford, 32051, Germany. schneider@universitas-virtualis.org, http://www.assembly-journal.com/index.php, http://www.universitas-virtualis.org.

ASSISTIVE TECHNOLOGY RESEARCH SERIES. see *HANDICAPPED—Computer Applications*

004 USA ISSN 0004-5411
QA76 CODEN: JACOAH
➤ **ASSOCIATION FOR COMPUTING MACHINERY. JOURNAL.** Text in English. 1954. bi-m. USD 235 domestic to non-members; USD 274 foreign to non-members; USD 52 domestic to members; USD 91 foreign to members; USD 47 domestic to students; USD 86 foreign to students; USD 282 combined subscription domestic to non-members print & online eds.; USD 321 combined subscription foreign to non-members print & online eds.; USD 62 combined subscription domestic to members print & online eds.; USD 101 combined subscription foreign to members print & online eds.; USD 56 combined subscription domestic to students print & online eds.; USD 95 combined subscription foreign to students print & online eds. (effective 2006). charts; illus. index. back issues avail.; reprint service avail. from PQC. **Document type:** *Journal, Academic/Scholarly.* **Description:** Papers covering research, development and applications of hardware, languages for information processing, scientific computation, automatic control and simulation of processes, artificial intelligence, operations research, computer systems and the recognition, storage and processing of data.
Related titles: Microform ed.: (from PQC, WWS); Online - full text ed.: ISSN 1557-735X. USD 188 to non-members; USD 42 to members; USD 38 to students (effective 2006) (from Association for Computing Machinery, Inc., EBSCO Publishing, Florida Center for Library Automation, Gale Group, O C L C Online Computer Library Center, Inc., ProQuest Information & Learning).
Indexed: ABIn, AS&TI, ASCA, BrCerAb, C&CSA, C&ISA, CADCAM, CCMJ, CMCI, CerAb, CompAb, CompC, CompD, CompR, CorrAb, CurCont, E&CAJ, EMA, EngInd, ErgAb, IAA, IAOP, ISR, InfoSAb, Inspec, M&TEA, MBF, METADEX, MathR, MathSciNet, RASB, RefZh, SCI, SSCI, SolStAb, WAA, ZentMath.
—AskIEEE, CISTI, Ei, IDS, IE, Infotrieve, Linda Hall. **CCC.**
Published by: Association for Computing Machinery, Inc., 1515 Broadway, 17th Fl, New York, NY 10036-5701. TEL 212-626-0520, 800-342-6626, FAX 212-944-1318, acmhelp@acm.org, sigs@acm.org, usacm@acm.org, http://www.acm.org/jacm. Ed. Joseph Y Halpern. Circ: 2,674 (paid).

004 JPN
ASUKII-.P C/ASCII .P C. Text in Japanese. m. JPY 4,250 for 6 mos.; JPY 580 newsstand/cover (effective 2004). **Document type:** *Magazine, Consumer.*
Published by: ASCII Corp., JR Shinanomachi Bldg. 34 Shinanomachi, Shinjuku-ku, Tokyo, 160-8584, Japan. http://www.ascii.co.jp/books/magazines/dotpc.html.

004.1605 CAN ISSN 0835-6661
ATOUT MICRO. Text in French. 1987. m.
Published by: P I C S H A, C P 240, St Isidore, PQ G0S 2S0, Canada. TEL 418-882-5214, FAX 418-882-5537, http://www.atoutmicro.ca/.

004 USA ISSN 1530-0900
AUSTRALASIAN COMPUTER SCIENCE CONFERENCE. PROCEEDINGS. Text in English. a. **Document type:** *Proceedings.* **Description:** Explores research, development and novel applications in computer science.
Related titles: Online - full text ed.: (from I E E E).
Published by: I E E E Computer Society, 1730 Massachusetts Ave, N W, Washington, DC 20036-1903. TEL 202-371-0101, FAX 202-728-9614, http://www.computer.org. **Subscr. addr.:** Institute of Electrical and Electronics Engineers, Inc., 445 Hoes Ln, Piscataway, NJ 08854-1331. TEL 732-981-0060, FAX 732-981-9667.

004 USA ISSN 1530-0951
AUSTRALASIAN USER INTERFACE CONFERENCE. PROCEEDINGS. Cover title: User Interface. Variant title: A U I C(Australasian User Interface Conference). Text in English. 2000. a. **Document type:** *Proceedings.* **Description:** Presents techniques, tools, and technology for constructing high-quality, innovative user interfaces over a wide range of areas including computer-supported cooperative work, virtual reality, multimedia, and the web.
Related titles: Online - full text ed.: (from I E E E).
Published by: I E E E Computer Society, 1730 Massachusetts Ave, N W, Washington, DC 20036-1903. TEL 202-371-0101, FAX 202-728-9614, http://www.computer.org. **Subscr. addr.:** Institute of Electrical and Electronics Engineers, Inc., 445 Hoes Ln, Piscataway, NJ 08854-1331. TEL 732-981-0060, FAX 732-981-9667.

AUSTRALIA. BUREAU OF STATISTICS. COMPUTING SERVICES INDUSTRY, AUSTRALIA. see *COMPUTERS—Abstracting, Bibliographies, Statistics*

004 USA ISSN 0157-3055
AUSTRALIAN COMPUTER SCIENCE COMMUNICATIONS. Text in English. 1979. q.
Indexed: Inspec.
—BLDSC (1798.192000), CISTI, IE.
Published by: (Computer Science Association of Australia AUS), I E E E Computer Society, 1730 Massachusetts Ave, N W, Washington, DC 20036-1903.

004 AUS
AUSTRALIAN DEVELOPER. Text in English. 2002. m. AUD 54.95 domestic; AUD 123.95 in New Zealand; AUD 96.95 elsewhere (effective 2004). **Description:** Provides information to Australian IT professionals and developers.
Published by: Derwent Howard, PO Box 1037, Bondi Junction, NSW 1355, Australia. TEL 61-2-93864666, 800-007-820, FAX 61-2-93864288, enquiries@derwenthoward.com.au, http://www.derwenthoward.com.au/. Ed. Lisa Mills. Adv. contact Paul Hardy.

004 NLD ISSN 0165-4683
AUTOMATISERING GIDS. Text in Dutch. 1967. w. (Fri.). EUR 98 (effective 2005). adv. bk.rev. **Document type:** *Trade.* **Description:** Reports on market developments and technological and management issues for computer industry professionals.
Related titles: CD-ROM ed.: ISSN 1566-9785.
Indexed: KES.
—IE, Infotrieve, KNAW.
Published by: Sdu Uitgevers bv, Postbus 20025, The Hague, 2500 EA, Netherlands. TEL 31-70-3789911, FAX 31-70-3854321, sdu@sdu.nl, http://www.automatiseringgids.nl/, http://www.sdu.nl/. Ed. Bas Linders. Circ: 60,524. **Subscr. to:** Postbus 20014, The Hague 2500 EA, Netherlands. TEL 31-70-3789880, FAX 31-70-3789783.

AVTOMETRIYA. see *PHYSICS—Optics*

004 DNK ISSN 1396-7002
B R I C S DISSERTATION SERIES. (Basic Research in Computer Science) Text in English. 1996. irreg. **Document type:** *Academic/Scholarly.*
Published by: Aarhus Universitet, Department of Computer Science, Ny Munkgade, Bygning 540, Aarhus C, 8000, Denmark. brics@brics.dk, http://www.brics.dk.

004 DNK ISSN 1395-2048
B R I C S LECTURES SERIES. (Basic Research in Computer Science) Text in English. 1995. irreg. **Document type:** *Academic/Scholarly.*
Published by: Aarhus Universitet, Department of Computer Science, Ny Munkgade, Bygning 540, Aarhus C, 8000, Denmark. brics@brics.dk, http://www.brics.dk.

004 DNK ISSN 0909-6043
B R I C S NEWSLETTER. (Basic Research in Computer Science) Text in English. 1994. 2/yr. **Document type:** *Academic/Scholarly.*
Published by: Aarhus Universitet, Department of Computer Science, Ny Munkgade, Bygning 540, Aarhus C, 8000, Denmark. brics@brics.dk, http://www.brics.dk.

004 DNK ISSN 0909-3206
B R I C S NOTES SERIES. (Basic Research in Computer Science) Text in English. 1994. irreg. free. **Document type:** *Academic/Scholarly.*
Indexed: Inspec.

C

▼ new title ➤ refereed ★ unverified ♦ full entry avail.

Published by: Aarhus Universitet, Department of Computer Science, Ny Munkgade, Bygning 540, Aarhus C, 8000, Denmark. brics@brics.dk, http://www.brics.dk. Ed. Uffe Henrik Engberg.

004 DNK ISSN 0909-0878
B R I C S REPORT SERIES. (Basic Research in Computer Science) Text in English. 1995. irreg. free. **Document type:** *Academic/Scholarly.*
Published by: Aarhus Universitet, Department of Computer Science, Ny Munkgade, Bygning 540, Aarhus C, 8000, Denmark. brics@brics.dk, http://www.brics.dk. Ed. Uffe Henrik Engberg.

004 USA ISSN 1542-4111
▼ **B W EXPERT.** Text in English. 2003. 10/yr. USD 595 (effective 2005). back issues avail. **Document type:** *Newsletter, Trade.*
Related titles: Online - full content ed.
Published by: Wellesley Information Services (Subsidiary of: United Communications Group), 990 Washington St, Dedham, MA 02026-6714. TEL 781-329-0419, FAX 781-320-9466, customer.service@bwexpertonline.com, customer@eview.com, http://www.bwexpertonline.com/, http://www.wispubs.com.

004 USA
BANKS OF THE BONEYARD. Variant title: Journal of the Association for Computing Machinery at UIUC. Text in English. 199?. m. free (effective 2003). **Document type:** *Newsletter, Academic/Scholarly.* **Description:** Dedicated to providing a forum for exchanging ideas related to computing professionals, both hardware and software.
Related titles: Online - full text ed.
Published by: Association for Computing Machinery, Inc., 1515 Broadway, 17th Fl, New York, NY 10036-5701. TEL 212-626-0500, 212-626-0520, 800-342-6626, FAX 212-869-0481, sigs@acm.org, usacm@acm.org, http://www.acm.org.

004 USA ISSN 1541-3004
HD30.2
BASELINE (NEW YORK). Text in English. 2001 (Oct). 18/yr. USD 6 per issue; free to qualified personnel (effective 2005). back issues avail. **Document type:** *Magazine, Trade.* **Description:** Provides information for senior-level IT and corporate executives on the management of IT solutions, cost, next generation technologies and ideas.
Related titles: Online - full content ed.; Online - full text ed.: (from bigchalk, EBSCO Publishing, Gale Group, H.W. Wilson, O C L C Online Computer Library Center, Inc.).
Indexed: BPI, CompD.
Published by: Ziff Davis Media Inc., 28 E 28th St, New York, NY 10016-7930. TEL 212-503-3500, FAX 212-503-5420, baseline@ziffdavis.com, info@ziffdavis.com, http://www.baselinemag.com/, http://www.ziffdavis.com. Ed. Tom Steinert-Threlkeld. Circ: 150,000.

004 AUS ISSN 1325-6130
BASSERNET. Text in English. bi-m.
Media: Online - full text.
Published by: University of Sydney, Basser Department of Computer Science, Madsen Bldg F09, Sydney, NSW 2006, Australia. TEL 61-2-9351-3423, FAX 61-2-9351-3838, admin@cs.usyd.edu.au, http://www.cs.su.oz.au/Bassernet.

BENCHMARK OF SALARIES AND EMPLOYMENT TRENDS IN I T (YEAR); business report. (Information Technology) see *OCCUPATIONS AND CAREERS*

004 USA ISSN 1066-0380
BENCHMARKS. Text in English. 1980. bi-m. free. bk.rev. index. back issues avail. **Document type:** *Newsletter.* **Description:** Provides timely information about topics of interest to the academic computing community at the university.
Related titles: Online - full text ed.
Published by: University of North Texas, Computing Center, PO Box 13495, Denton, TX 76203-6495. TEL 817-565-2324, FAX 817-565-4060, lynch@unt.edu. Ed. Claudia Lynch. Circ: 1,000.

BERNARDS AND BABANI PRESS RADIO & ELECTRONICS & COMPUTER BOOKS. see *COMMUNICATIONS—Radio*

004 USA ISSN 1061-9216
HC79.I55
BEYOND COMPUTING; integrating business & information technology. Text in English. 1992. 9/yr. USD 39.50 domestic; USD 49.50 in Canada; USD 59.50 elsewhere; USD 4.95 per issue domestic (effective 2001). adv. illus. back issues avail. **Document type:** *Trade.* **Description:** Dedicated to the business issues surrounding the management of information technology and is targeted at I T executives and top corporate management.
Related titles: Online - full text ed.
Indexed: CompLI, SoftBase.
—IE, Linda Hall.
Published by: International Business Machines (IBM) Corporation, 590 Madison Ave, 8th Fl, New York, NY 10022. TEL 212-745-6326, FAX 212-745-6058, jocelyng@beyondcomputingmag.com. Ed. Eileen Feretic. Pub., Adv. contact Arthur Chassen. R&P Jocelyn Glover TEL 212-745-6347. color page USD 16,200; trim 10.75 x 8.25. Circ: 150,000 (controlled). **Subscr. to:** PO Box 3014, Northbrook, IL 60065-9984.

004 ESP ISSN 0214-3844
BINARY✶. Text in Spanish. 1988. 12/yr.
Published by: Haymarket, S.A., Travesera Gracia 17-21, 5o 2o, Barcelona, 08022, Spain. TEL 3-237-22-66, FAX 1-237-66-88, TELEX 51964 INK E. Circ: 14,000.

BIOINFORM NEWS SERVICES; the integrated informatic news. see *BIOLOGY*

004 USA
BITS & BYTES ONLINE. Text in English. 1998. m. USD 30 to members (effective 2005). **Document type:** *Newsletter, Trade.*
Media: Online - full text.
Published by: Tampa Bay Computer Society, 1510 Barry Rd, Clearwater, FL 33756. TEL 727-443-4433, http://tampa-bay.org/BitsAndBytes. Ed. Cyndi Schmitt.

004 305.896073 USA ISSN 1540-2967
▼ **BLACK TECH.** Text in English. 2003 (Oct.). m. USD 19.95; USD 5.95 newsstand/cover (effective 2003).
Related titles: CD-ROM ed.: ISSN 1540-2975. USD 29.95 (effective 2002).
Published by: Kweku Publishing, 557 Main St., New Rochelle, NY 10801. TEL 914-637-3708, FAX 914-637-3709, info@kweku.com, http://www.blacktechmagazine.com, http://www.kweku.com. Pub. Kenneth G. Kweku.

004 SWE ISSN 1652-3407
BONNIER PC-TIDNINGEN. Text in Swedish. 1997. 16/yr. adv.
Formerly (until 2004): Komputer foer Alla (1403-0640)
Published by: Bonniers Kundtjaenst, Malmoe, 20550, Sweden. redaktionen@pctidningen.se, http://www.pctidningen.se.

004 AUT
BOOKS@OCG.AT. Text in German. irreg., latest vol.158, 2002. price varies. **Document type:** *Journal, Academic/Scholarly.*
Formerly (until 1999): Oesterreichische Computer Gesellschaft. Schriftenreihe
Related titles: Online - full text ed.
—BLDSC (2250.260000).
Published by: Oesterreichische Computer Gesellschaft, Wollzeile 1-3, Vienna, 1010, Austria. TEL 43-1-5120235, FAX 43-1-51202359, ocg@ocg.at, http://www.ocg.at.

004 BRA ISSN 0104-6500
QA75.5
➤ **BRAZILIAN COMPUTER SOCIETY. JOURNAL.** Text in English. 1994. q. membership. back issues avail. **Document type:** *Journal, Academic/Scholarly.*
Related titles: Online - full content ed.: free (effective 2005) (from SciELO).
Indexed: Inspec.
Published by: Sociedade Brasileira de Computacao, Caixa Postal 15064, Porto Alegre, 91501-970, Brazil. TEL 55-51-316-6835, 55-51-316-6835, http://www.scielo.br/jbcos. Ed. Marco Antonio Casanova. Circ: 2,000 (paid).

004 GBR
BRITISH COMPUTER SOCIETY WORKSHOP SERIES. Text in English. irreg., latest 1990. price varies.
Indexed: Inspec.
Published by: (British Computer Society), Cambridge University Press, The Edinburgh Bldg, Shaftesbury Rd, Cambridge, CB2 2RU, United Kingdom. TEL 44-1223-312393, FAX 44-1223-315052, information@cambridge.org, http://publishing.cambridge.org/series/bcsw.

681.3 HRV ISSN 1330-0318
BUG. Text in Croatian. 1992. 11/yr. HRK 234; HRK 295 with CD-ROM (effective 2001). adv. **Document type:** *Magazine, Consumer.*
Related titles: Online - full text ed.: ISSN 1332-6430. 1995.
Published by: Bug d.o.o., Tratinska 36, Zagreb, 10000, Croatia. TEL 385-1-3821555, FAX 385-1-3821669, pisma@bug.hr, http://www.bug.hr. Ed. Miroslav Rosandic. Adv. contact Aron Paulic. Circ: 27,000 (paid).

004 004.16 GBR ISSN 1365-6368
BUSINESS COMPUTER WORLD. Text in English. 1996. m.
Related titles: Online - full text ed.
Indexed: Inspec.
Published by: V N U Business Publications Ltd., 32-34 Broadwick St, London, W1A 2HG, United Kingdom. TEL 44-20-7316-9000, FAX 44-20-7316-9440, http://www.bcw.vnu.co.uk, http://www.vnunet.com. **Subscr. to:** PO Box 301, Sittingbourne, Kent ME9 8BN, United Kingdom.

BUSINESS INTEGRATION JOURNAL. see *BUSINESS AND ECONOMICS*

004 BGR
BYTE. Text in Bulgarian. m.
Related titles: Online - full text ed.
Published by: Top Team Co., St. Cherni Vruch 4, Sofia, 1421, Bulgaria. TEL 359-2-656764, FAX 359-2-656819, http://www.topteam.bg/byte/index.asp.

004 RUS
BYTE (RUSSIAN EDITION). Text in Russian. 1998. m. USD 96 foreign (effective 2004). adv. software rev.; Website rev. 80 p./no.; **Document type:** *Magazine, Trade.*
Published by: S K Press, Marksistkaya 34, str 10, Moscow, 109147, Russian Federation. byte@bytemag.ru, http://www.bytemag.ru, http://www.skpress.ru. Ed. Kamill Akhmetov. Pub. E Adlerov. Adv. contact O Filatov. **Dist. by:** M K - Periodica, ul Gilyarovskogo 39, Moscow 129110, Russian Federation. TEL 7-095-2845008, FAX 7-095-2813798, info@periodicals.ru, http://www.mkniga.ru.

004 USA
C A C REPORT✶. Text in English. bi-m. USD 20. **Description:** Articles and commentary on a wide range of topics in the computer field.
Related titles: Audio cassette/tape ed.
Published by: Computer Aids Corporation, PO Box 1646, Branson, MO 65616-1646.

004 USA
C & C: CREATIVITY AND COGNITION CONFERENCE. PROCEEDINGS. Text in English. irreg. price varies. **Document type:** *Proceedings, Academic/Scholarly.*
Published by: Association for Computing Machinery, Inc., 1515 Broadway, 17th Fl, New York, NY 10036-5701. TEL 212-626-0500, usacm@acm.org, http://www.acm.org.

▼ **C F O I T.** (Chief Financial Officer Information Technology) see *BUSINESS AND ECONOMICS*

004 ITA ISSN 1120-2440
C I L E A. BOLLETTINO. (Consorzio Interuniversitario Lombardo per l'Elaborazione Automatica) Text in Italian. 1984. bi-m. **Document type:** *Journal, Academic/Scholarly.* **Description:** Focuses on the studies and projects of Consorzio Interuniversitario Lombardo per l'Elaborazione Automatica.
Related titles: Online - full text ed.: 1996. free (effective 2005).
Published by: Consorzio Interuniversitario Lombardo per l'Elaborazione Automatica, Via R Sanzio 4, Segrate, 20090, Italy. TEL 39-02-26995.1, FAX 39-02-2135520, bollettino@cilea.it, http://bollettino.cilea.it.

004 AUS
C I STEMIC; a newsletter for CIS students. Text in English. 1997. irreg. (2-4/yr.). free. back issues avail. **Document type:** *Academic/Scholarly.* **Description:** Discusses issues of interest to students in computer and information science.
Media: Online - full text.
Published by: University of South Australia, School of Computer and Information Science, Advanced Computing Research Centre, UniSA Levels Campus, Mawson Lakes Blvd., Mawson Lakes, SA 5095, Australia. TEL 61-8-8302-3201, FAX 61-8-8302-3381, cis@unisa.edu.au, http://www.cis.unisa.edu.au/general/CIStemic. Ed. Karen Hughes.

621.39 004 HRV ISSN 1330-1136
➤ **C I T. JOURNAL OF COMPUTING AND INFORMATION TECHNOLOGY.** Variant title: Computing and Information Technology. Text in English. 1993. q. USD 45 to individuals; USD 195 to institutions (effective 2005). bk.rev. abstr.; bibl.; charts; illus. back issues avail. **Document type:** *Journal, Academic/Scholarly.* **Description:** Covers the methodology, practice, and theory of computer science and engineering, modelling and simulation, and information systems.
Indexed: CompLI, Inspec, LISA.
—BLDSC (4963.820000), CISTI, IE, ingenta.
Published by: Sveuciliste u Zagrebu, Sveucilisni Racunski Centar/University of Zagreb, University Computing Centre, J Marohnica bb, PO Box 741, Zagreb, 10000, Croatia. TEL 385-1-6165592, FAX 385-1-6165591, cit@srce.hr, ured@srce.hr, http://cit.srce.hr, http://www.srce.hr. Ed. Sven Loncaric.

004 USA
C M G CONFERENCE PROCEEDINGS✶. Text in English. 1976. a. USD 125 to members. **Document type:** *Proceedings.*
Indexed: Englnd.
—BLDSC (3287.228100), ingenta.
Published by: Computer Measurement Group, Inc., 151 Fries Mill Rd., Ste. 104, Turnersville, NJ 08012-2016. TEL 800-436-7264, http://www.cmg.org. **Subscr. to:** Department 77 6023, Chicago, IL 60678-6023.

004 USA
C M G TRANSACTIONS✶. Text in English. 1985. s-a. USD 125 to members. **Document type:** *Proceedings.*
Indexed: CompAb, Englnd.
Published by: Computer Measurement Group, Inc., 151 Fries Mill Rd., Ste. 104, Turnersville, NJ 08012-2016. TEL 800-436-7264, http://www.cmg.org.

004 USA
C O P I PRESS✶. (Communicator of the Electronic Printing Industry) Text in English. 1989. bi-m. free.
Published by: Computer Output Printing, Inc., 4101 Directors Row, Houston, TX 77092-8703. TEL 713-666-0911, FAX 713-666-0957. Ed. William H Young II. Circ: 11,000.

003 CAN ISSN 0315-1417
C O R S BULLETIN. Text in English. q. back issues avail.
Published by: Canadian Operational Research Society, PO Box 2225 Station D, Ottawa, ON K1P 5WP, Canada. http://www.cors.ca/bulletin/current.htm. Ed. Elkafi Hassini.

C O T S JOURNAL. (Commercial Off-the-Shelf) see *MILITARY*

004 USA ISSN 1536-7568
TK7887.5
C P U. (Computer Power User) Text in English. 2001 (Nov.). m. USD 29 domestic; USD 37 in Canada; USD 69 elsewhere; USD 5.99 newsstand/cover (effective 2004). adv. **Document type:** *Magazine, Consumer.* **Description:** Contains reviews, useful tips, and insightful commentary from world-class computing experts.
Related titles: Online - full content ed.: USD 17 worldwide (effective 2004).
Published by: Sandhills Publishing, 120 W. Harvest Dr., Lincoln, NE 68521-4408. TEL 402-479-2138, 800-848-1478, FAX 402-479-2104, editor@computerpoweruser.com, http://www.computerpoweruser.com. Ed. Ron Kobler. Pub. Mark Peery. adv.: color page USD 4,950.

004 GBR
C S G REPORT SERIES. (Computer Systems Group) Text in English. irreg.
Published by: University of Edinburgh, Computer Systems Group, Department of Computer Science, The King's Building, Edinburgh, Midlothian EH9 3JZ, United Kingdom.

004 IND ISSN 0970-647X
C S I COMMUNICATIONS✶. Text in English. 1965. m. INR 20, USD 10. adv. bk.rev.
Formerly (until 1978): C S I Newsletter
Indexed: Inspec.
—AskIEEE, Linda Hall.
Published by: Computer Society of India, S.K. Ahire Marg, 122 TV Industrial Estate, Worli-Bombay, 400 025, India. Ed. S Venkatesh. Circ: 3,000.

004 370 USA ISSN 1555-2128
▼ **C S T A VOICE.** (Computer Science Teachers Association) Text in English. 2005 (Apr.). q. free to members (effective 2005).
Related titles: Online - full text ed.: ISSN 1555-2136.
Published by: (Computer Science Teachers Association), Association for Computing Machinery, Inc., 1515 Broadway, 17th Fl, New York, NY 10036-5701. TEL 212-626-0500, 800-342-6626, usacm@acm.org, http://www.acm.org.

C W I TRACTS. see *MATHEMATICS*

004 USA
CACTUS. Text in English. 2001 (Apr.). irreg. **Document type:** *Magazine, Consumer.* **Description:** Contains articles on Unix basics, including software, equipment, hacking, and other related subjects..
Media: Online - full content.
Address: cactus@spacemail.com, http://hermes.spaceports.com/~cactus/.

004 USA
CADCAMNET. Text in English. m. USD 249 combined subscription domestic print & online eds. (effective 2005).
Document type: *Newsletter.*
Formerly: Product Data Management Report
Published by: Cyon Research Corporation, 8220 Stone Trail Dr, Bethesda, MD 20817-4556. TEL 240-425-4004, FAX 301-365-4586, wbh@wbh.com, www.cyonresearch.com.

004 USA
CALIFORNIA COMPUTER NEWS. Text in English. 1983. m. USD 30 (effective 2005). adv. bk.rev. 36 p./no. 4 cols./p.;
Document type: *Magazine, Consumer.* **Description:** Covers local and regional computer-related topics, new hardware and software products and industry news.
Published by: (G M W Communications, Inc.), ERepublic Inc., 100 Blue Ravine Rd, Folsom, CA 95630. TEL 916-932-1450, FAX 916-932-1471, cmiller@ccnmag.com, jmarcotte@cnnmag.com, http://www.ccnmag.com. Ed. John Marcotte. Pub., Adv. contact Craig Miller. B&W page USD 1,500, color page USD 2,100. Circ: 60,000 (paid).

004 GBR ISSN 0266-3236
CAMBRIDGE COMPUTER SCIENCE TEXTS. Text in English. 1972. irreg. price varies. **Document type:** *Monographic series.*
Indexed: Inspec, ZentMath.
Published by: Cambridge University Press, The Edinburgh Bldg, Shaftesbury Rd, Cambridge, CB2 2RU, United Kingdom. TEL 44-1223-312393, FAX 44-1223-315052, information@cambridge.org, http://www.cup.cam.ac.uk/. R&P Linda Nicol TEL 44-1223-325757.

004 GBR ISSN 1362-7635
CAMBRIDGE INTERNATIONAL SERIES ON PARALLEL COMPUTATION. Text in English. 1991. irreg., latest 1997. price varies. **Document type:** *Monographic series, Academic/Scholarly.*
—BLDSC (3015.954080).
Published by: Cambridge University Press, The Edinburgh Bldg, Shaftesbury Rd, Cambridge, CB2 2RU, United Kingdom. TEL 44-1223-312393, FAX 44-1223-315052, information@cambridge.org, http://publishing.cambridge.org/series/cipc.

004 150 GBR ISSN 0961-3099
CAMBRIDGE SERIES ON HUMAN-COMPUTER INTERACTION. Text in English. 1989. irreg., latest 1997. price varies. **Document type:** *Monographic series, Academic/Scholarly.*
—BLDSC (3015.990680), ingenta.
Published by: Cambridge University Press, The Edinburgh Bldg, Shaftesbury Rd, Cambridge, CB2 2RU, United Kingdom. TEL 44-1223-312393, FAX 44-1223-315052, information@cambridge.org, http://publishing.cambridge.org/series/cshc.

004 GBR ISSN 0956-9103
CAMBRIDGE TRACTS IN THEORETICAL COMPUTER SCIENCE. Text in English. 1987. irreg., latest 2002. price varies. **Document type:** *Monographic series, Academic/Scholarly.* **Description:** Covers the complete field of theoretical computer science, including mathematical foundations of computer science, formal methods of reasoning about programs and data, and formal semantics of programs and data, including formal semantics for natural language, pictures, and sound.
—BLDSC (3016.002000), IE, ingenta.
Published by: Cambridge University Press, The Edinburgh Bldg, Shaftesbury Rd, Cambridge, CB2 2RU, United Kingdom. TEL 44-1223-312393, FAX 44-1223-315052, information@cambridge.org, http://publishing.cambridge.org/series/cttc.

004 USA
CAMSOC UPDATE. (Computer Aided Ministry Society) Text in English. m. bk.rev.; software rev. **Document type:** *Newsletter.* **Description:** Contents include brief executive summary news items about the computing industry for Christians.
Media: E-mail.
Published by: C M U G, 1827 Arbucke Way, Lancaster, CA 93534. http://www.cmug.org/gs/cu/. Ed. Greg Slade.

004.092025 USA
CANADIAN DIRECTORY OF TOP COMPUTER EXECUTIVES. Text in English. 1991. s-a. USD 340; USD 520 pdf file (effective 2005). **Document type:** *Directory, Corporate.* **Description:** Listing of top DP installations in Canada, including names and titles of MIS executives.
Related titles: CD-ROM ed.; E-mail ed.
Published by: Applied Computer Research, Inc., PO Box 82266, Phoenix, AZ 85071-2266. TEL 602-216-9100, 800-234-2227, FAX 602-216-9200, tara@acrhq.com, http://www.itmarketintelligence.com, http://www.acrhq.com.

670 USA ISSN 1093-6629
CATIA SOLUTIONS. Text in English. 1997. bi-m.
Published by: ConnectPress, Ltd., 2530 Camino Entrada, Santa Fe, NM 87505-4835. TEL 505-474-5000, FAX 505-474-5001, Andrea.Braverman@connectpress.com, http://www.catiasolutions.com, http://www.connectpress.com.

003 DEU ISSN 1435-246X
➤ **CENTRAL EUROPEAN JOURNAL OF OPERATIONS RESEARCH.** Text in English. 1993. q. EUR 185.40 to institutions (effective 2005). **Document type:** *Journal, Academic/Scholarly.* **Description:** Covers the theory and practice of operations research and the relationship of operations research methods to modern quantitative economics and business administration.
Formerly (until 1998): Central European Journal for Operations Research and Economics (1335-1443)
Related titles: Online - full text ed.: (from EBSCO Publishing, ProQuest Information & Learning).
Indexed: ABIn, CCMJ, IAOP, JEL, MathR, MathSciNet, RefZh, ZentMath.
—BLDSC (3106.138090), IE. **CCC.**
Published by: (Austrian Society for Operations Research), Physica-Verlag GmbH und Co. (Subsidiary of: Springer-Verlag), Postfach 105280, Heidelberg, 69042, Germany. TEL 49-6221-487492, FAX 49-6221-487177, physica@springer.de, http://link.springer.de/link/service/journals. Eds. M Luptacik, U Leopold-Wildburger, V Mlynarovic. Adv. contact Stephan Kroeck TEL 49-30-827875739. **Subscr. in the Americas to:** Springer-Verlag New York, Inc., Journal Fulfillment, PO Box 2485, Secaucus, NJ 07096-2485. TEL 800-777-4643, 201-348-4033, FAX 201-348-4505, journals@springer-ny.com, http://www.springer-ny.com; **Subscr. to:** Springer GmbH Auslieferungsgesellschaft, Haberstr 7, Heidelberg 69126, Germany. TEL 49-6221-345-0, FAX 49-6221-345-4229, subscriptions@springer.de.

➤ **CENTRE FOR SOCIAL ANTHROPOLOGY AND COMPUTING. MONOGRAPHS.** see *ANTHROPOLOGY*

004 ISR
CHADSHOT TIKSHORET NETUNIM. Text in Hebrew. q.
Published by: Binat Co., Ramat Hachayal, 8 Hanichoshet St, Tel Aviv, 69710, Israel. TEL 03-498811.

004 ITA
IL CHI E DELL'I C T. (Information & Communication Technology) Text in Italian. 1992. a. EUR 60 (effective 2005). **Document type:** *Directory, Trade.*
Published by: Editrice il Crogiolo S.r.l., Piazza Sant' Agostino 22, Milan, MI 20123, Italy. TEL 39-02-48009805, FAX 39-02-48009745, segreteria@informatica70.com, http://www.informatica70.com. Ed. Rodolfo Grigolato. Adv. contact Roberto Zuin. Circ: 3,150 (paid); 5,850 (controlled).

004 CHN
CHINA COMPUTER RESELLER WORLD. Text in Chinese. adv.
Related titles: Online - full text ed.
Published by: I D G China, Rm. 616, Tower A, COFCO Plaza, Jianguomennei Dajie, Beijing, 100005 , China. TEL 86-10-6526-0959, FAX 86-10-6526-0866, dumin@idg.com.cn, http://www.ccrw.com.cn, http://www.idgchina.com. Ed. Weisheng Wang. Pub. Kunkun Li. adv.: color page CNY 20,000.

004 CHN
CHINA COMPUTER USERS. Text in Chinese. adv. **Document type:** *Consumer.*
Related titles: Online - full text ed.
Published by: I D G China, 5/F,Ronghua Bldg, No.B18 Xisanhuanzhong Rd, Haidian District, Beijing, 100036, China. Ed. Chao-yun Li. adv.: color page CNY 23,400.

004 CHN
CHINA COMPUTERWORLD. Variant title: Computer World - China. Text in Chinese. 1980. w. adv. **Document type:** *Magazine, Trade.* **Description:** Covers the latest developments in hardware, software, peripherals, and computer-related product news.
Related titles: Online - full text ed.
Published by: I D G China, Rm. 616, Tower A, COFCO Plaza, Jianguomennei Dajie, Beijing, 100005 , China. TEL 86-10-6526-0959, FAX 86-10-6526-0866, dumin@idg.com.cn, http://www.computerworld.com.cn/, http://www.idgchina.com. Ed. Jiuru Liu. Adv. contact Dazhi Chen. page CNY 26,800; trim 260 x 375. Circ: 179,712 (paid and controlled).

004 CHN
CHINA INFOWORLD. Text in Chinese. adv.
Related titles: Online - full text ed.
Published by: I D G China, Rm. 616, Tower A, COFCO Plaza, Jianguomennei Dajie, Beijing, 100005 , China. TEL 86-10-6526-0959, FAX 86-10-6526-0866, dumin@idg.com.cn, http://www.ciw.com.cn, http://www.idgchina.com. Ed. Chaoyun Li. adv.: page CNY 24,800.

004 UKR ISSN 1563-6518
CHIP. Text in Russian. 1996. m. UAK 16 per issue domestic (effective 2004). **Document type:** *Magazine, Trade.* **Description:** Provides readers with the latest and most crucial information on all aspects of computer technology.
Published by: Soft-Press, a/ya 618/8, Kiev, 03126, Ukraine. admin@softpress.kiev.ua, http://www.chip.kiev.ua, http://www.softpress.kiev.ua. Ed. Alexey Efetov. Pub. Ellina Shnourko Tabakova. Adv. contact Valeriy Brossel. Circ: 10,000 (controlled).

004 CZE ISSN 1210-0684
CHIP. Text in Czech. 1991. m. CZK 135 newsstand/cover (effective 2001). adv. **Document type:** *Magazine, Trade.*
Published by: Vogel Burda Communications s.r.o., Sokolovska 73, Prague 8, 18621, Czech Republic. TEL 42-2-21808566, FAX 42-2-21808500, http://www.vogel.cz. Ed. Jiri Palyza. Pub. Pavel Filipovic. Adv. contact Hana Vancurova. B&W page EUR 2,300, color page EUR 2,850; trim 210 x 297. Circ: 39,367 (paid).

004 GRC ISSN 1108-7773
CHIP. Text in Greek. 1994. fortn. **Document type:** *Magazine, Trade.* **Description:** Covers trends and important details within the field of information technology.
Published by: Computer Verlag S.A., 8 Dimokratias St, Athens, 151 27, Greece. TEL 30-1-803-3670, FAX 30-1-803-0445, chip@netor.gr, http://www.chip.gr. Pub. Petros Triantafillis. Adv. contact Vassilis Arvanitopoulos. Circ: 32,000 (paid).

004 HUN ISSN 0864-9421
CHIP; computer magazine. Text in Hungarian. 1989. m. HUF 11,424; HUF 1,196 newsstand/cover (effective 2002). adv. software rev.; tel.rev.; video rev. illus.; mkt.; stat. back issues avail. **Document type:** *Newspaper.* **Description:** Contains information for users playing a role in making decisions concerning information technology investments.
Related titles: CD-ROM ed.; Online - full text ed.
Published by: Vogel Publishing Kft, Hajdu utca 42-44, emelet 2, Budapest, 1139, Hungary. TEL 36-1-3508731, FAX 36-1-3508731, chip@vogel.hu, http://www.chipmagazin.hu. Ed., Pub., R&P Peter Ivanov. Adv. contact Gabriella Olah TEL 36-1-3508004. B&W page USD 1,800, color page USD 2,100; 266 x 185. Circ: 32,000.

004 TUR ISSN 1300-9419
CHIP. Text in Turkish. 1996. m. TRL 14,400,000, USD 100. adv. **Document type:** *Trade.* **Description:** Contains information on the Turkish software and hardware markets for beginners and professionals.

C

Published by: Vogel Publishing Ltd. Sti, Peker Sokak, Akyildiz Apt. No.26, Levent, Istanbul, Turkey. TEL 90-212-2971724, FAX 90-212-2971733, chipyaz@chip.com.tr. Ed. Gorhum Sungurtekin. R&P Paul W Hermann. Adv. contact Beste Ozerdem. B&W page USD 2,150, color page USD 2,150; 297 x 210. Circ: 60,000.

004 POL ISSN 1230-817X
CHIP; magazyn komputerowy. Text in Polish. 1993. m. PLZ 129 includes CD-ROM; PLZ 13 newsstand/cover (effective 2000). adv. bk.rev.; software rev. back issues avail. **Document type:** *Trade.* **Description:** Aims to inform readers about products, applications and novelties on the Polish and international computer markets.
Related titles: CD-ROM ed.
Published by: Vogel Publishing Sp. z o.o., Plac Czerwony 1-3-5, Wroclaw, 53661, Poland. TEL 48-71-3734475, FAX 48-71-3557361, chip@chip.pl, chip@chip.voleg.pl, http://www.chip.pl, http://www.vogel.pl. Ed. Ewa Dziekanska. Pub. Jerzy Karwelis. R&P Jaromir Lanski. Adv. contact Marcin Hutnik. color page PLZ 9,800; 297 x 210. Circ: 135,000 (controlled).

004 RUS ISSN 1609-4212
CHIP. Text in Russian. 2001. m. RUR 1,140 domestic; RUR 95 per issue domestic (effective 2004). **Document type:** *Magazine, Trade.*
Indexed: RefZh.
Published by: Izdatel'skii Dom Burda, ul Pravdy 8, Moscow, 125040, Russian Federation. TEL 7-095-7979849, FAX 7-095-2571196, vertrieb@burda.ru, http://www.burda.ru.

004 ROM ISSN 1453-7079
CHIP COMPUTER MAGAZIN. Text in Romanian. 1991. m. ROL 720,000 (effective 2005). **Document type:** *Magazine, Trade.* **Description:** Offers the latest news in the fields of computers and software.
Published by: Vogel Publishing Srl., Bd. N. D. Cocea nr. 12, et. 1-2, Brasov, 2200, Romania. TEL 40-68-415158, FAX 40-68-415158, redactie@chip.ro, http://www.chip.ro. Ed. Dan Badescu. Adv. contact Zsolt Bodola. Circ: 13,500 (controlled).

004.738 ROM ISSN 1582-1668
CHIP SPECIAL. Text in Romanian. 1996. q. adv. **Document type:** *Magazine, Trade.*
Published by: Vogel Publishing Srl., Bd. N. D. Cocea nr. 12, et. 1-2, Brasov, 2200, Romania. TEL 40-68-415158, FAX 40-68-415158.

CIBERP@IS. (Ciberpais) see *GENERAL INTEREST PERIODICALS—Spain*

004 GBR ISSN 1364-4009
CITY UNIVERSITY. COMPUTER SCIENCE TECHNICAL REPORTS. Text in English. 1996. irreg.
—BLDSC (8715.107000).
Published by: City University, Department of Computer Science, City University, Northampton Square, London, EC1V 0HB, United Kingdom.

004 DEU
▼ ➤ **CODEBREAKERS - JOURNAL.** Text in English. 2004. 3/yr. free (effective 2005). **Document type:** *Journal, Academic/Scholarly.* **Description:** It publishes articles in all aspects of computational methods used in the working fields: algorithms, virus research, software protection and reverse code engineering and cryptanalysis.
Media: Online - full text.
Published by: Universitas Virtualis, Dipl. Inform. Med. Thorsten Schneider, Lange Str 33, Herford, 32051, Germany. schneider@universitas-virtualis.org, http://www.codebreakers-journal.com/, http://www.universitas-virtualis.org.

➤ **COLIN'S MAGAZINE.** see *LITERATURE*

004 USA
COMMON.CONNECT. Text in English. bi-m. USD 125 to individual members; USD 395 to corporations (effective 2005). adv. **Document type:** *Magazine, Consumer.* **Description:** Provides relevant, timely information about the IT industry and the COMMON organization.
Formerly (until 2004): COMMONews
Published by: COMMON, 401 N Michigan Ave, Ste 2100, Chicago, IL 60611. TEL 312-279-0192, 800-777-6734, FAX 312-279-0227, vaughn_dragland@common.org, common@common.org, http://www.common.org/connect.html. Ed. Vaughn Dragland. Adv. contact Sally Cottingham. color page USD 7,900; trim 8.5 x 10.75. Circ: 85,550 (paid and controlled).

004 LBN
AL COMMUNICATIONS AND ELECTRONICS. Text in Arabic. 1984. m. LBP 50,000 domestic; USD 125 in US & Canada; USD 100 in Europe (effective 2003). adv.
Formerly: Al Computer and Electronics
Published by: Dar As-Sayad S.A.L., C/o Said Freiha, Hazmieh, P O Box 1038, Beirut, Lebanon. TEL 961-5-456373, FAX 961-5-452700, contactpr@csi.com, alanwar@alanwar.com, http://www.alanwar.com. Ed. Antoine Butros. Adv. contact Said Freiha. color page USD 3,500; bleed 215 x 285. Circ: 22,400.

004 510 USA ISSN 1526-7555
TK5101.A1
COMMUNICATIONS IN INFORMATION AND SYSTEMS. Text in English. 2001 (Jan.). q. USD 100 to individuals; USD 178 to institutions (effective 2002).
Indexed: MathR, MathSciNet, RefZh.
—BLDSC (3360.352000), CISTI.
Published by: International Press, PO Box 43502, Somerville, MA 02143-0007. TEL 617-623-3016, FAX 617-623-3101, journals@intlpress.com, http://www.ims.cuhk.edu.hk/~cis, http://www.intlpress.com. Eds. Stephen S-T. Yau, Wing-Shing Wong.

004 USA ISSN 1063-6390
CODEN: DCSIDU
COMPCON: I E E E COMPUTER SOCIETY INTERNATIONAL CONFERENCE. Variant title: Digest of Papers (Spring). Text in English. 1971. a. price varies. adv. **Document type:** *Proceedings, Trade.* **Description:** Disseminates recent advances in key computing fields.
Former titles (until 1971): I E E E International Computer Society Conference. Conference Digest; (until 1970): I E E E International Computer Group Conference. Proceedings; (until 1969): Computer Group Conference. Digest; (until 1967): I E E E Computer Conference. Digest
Related titles: Online - full text ed.: (from I E E E).
Indexed: CompC, Inspec.
—BLDSC (3363.922000), IE, ingenta. **CCC.**
Published by: (Institute of Electrical and Electronics Engineers, Inc.), I E E E Computer Society, 10662 Los Vaqueros Circle, PO Box 3014, Los Alamitos, CA 90720-1314. TEL 714-821-8380, FAX 714-821-4641, 714-821-4010, http://www.computer.org.

004 USA
COMPEURO. PROCEEDINGS. Text in English. 1987. a. price varies. adv. **Document type:** *Proceedings.* **Description:** Discusses the latest in computer technology, systems, and applications.
Indexed: Inspec.
Published by: (Institute of Electrical and Electronics Engineers, Inc.), I E E E Computer Society, 10662 Los Vaqueros Circle, PO Box 3014, Los Alamitos, CA 90720-1314. TEL 714-821-8380, FAX 714-821-4641. Ed. Cat Harris. Pub. Matt Loeb. Adv. contact Frieda Koester.

004 USA
COMPONENT DEVELOPMENT STRATEGIES. Text in English. 1991. m. USD 497 in North America; USD 567 in Europe (effective 2001). **Document type:** *Newsletter.* **Description:** Covers new technologies, new products, market developments and industry trends in the capabilities and uses of object-oriented software technologies. Includes discussions of techniques and methodologies.
Published by: Harmon Associates, 2040 Polk St, Ste 334, San Francisco, CA 94119. TEL 415-346-1425, FAX 415-346-1425. Ed. Paul Harmon.

COMPONENTS INTERNATIONAL. see *ELECTRONICS*

004 USA ISSN 1072-3544
COMPU-MART. Text in English. 1991. w. adv. **Document type:** *Magazine, Trade.*
Published by: Story Communications, 116 N Camp St, Seguin, TX 78155. TEL 830-303-3328, 800-864-1155, FAX 830-372-3011, kaw@storycomm.com, http://www.compu-mart.com/, http://www.storycomm.com. adv.: page USD 890.

004 GTM
COMPUDATA. Text in Spanish. m. USD 17 in Central America (effective 2002). **Document type:** *Magazine, Trade.*
Published by: Grupo Editorial M.A., Edificio Tikal Futura, Oficina 6B Zona 11, Torre Luna, Guatemala. TEL 502-440-4068, FAX 502-502-1207, http://www.revistacompudata.com. Ed. Patricia Mata. Circ: 5,000.

THE COMPULATELIST. see *PHILATELY*

COMPUMATH CITATION INDEX. see *COMPUTERS—Abstracting, Bibliographies, Statistics*

004 USA ISSN 0824-7935
Q334 CODEN: COMIE6
➤ **COMPUTATIONAL INTELLIGENCE/INTELLIGENCE INFORMATIQUE**; an international journal. Text mainly in English; Text occasionally in French. 1985. q. USD 162 combined subscription in the Americas to individuals & Caribbean, print & online eds.; EUR 188 combined subscription in Europe to individuals print & online eds.; GBP 125 combined subscription elsewhere to individuals print & online eds.; USD 751 combined subscription in the Americas to institutions & Caribbean, print & online eds.; GBP 540 combined subscription elsewhere to institutions print & online eds. (effective 2006). adv. abstr.; bibl.; illus. back issues avail.; reprint service avail. from PSC. **Document type:** *Journal, Academic/Scholarly.* **Description:** Serves as a forum for experimental and theoretical research, surveys, and impact studies. Coverage ranges from the tools and languages of AI to its philosophical implications.
Related titles: Online - full text ed.: ISSN 1467-8640. USD 713 in the Americas to institutions & Caribbean; GBP 513 elsewhere to institutions (effective 2006) (from Blackwell Synergy, EBSCO Publishing, Gale Group, IngentaConnect, O C L C Online Computer Library Center, Inc., Swets Information Services).
Indexed: ABIn, AHCI, AIA, ArtlAb, B&BAb, C&ISA, CADCAM, CCMJ, CMCI, CompAb, CompLI, CurCont, E&CAJ, Inspec, MathR, MathSciNet, PsycInfo, PsycholAb, RASB, SolStAb, e-psyche.
—BLDSC (3390.595000), AskIEEE, CISTI, Ei, IDS, IE, Infotrieve, ingenta. **CCC.**
Published by: Blackwell Publishing, Inc. (Subsidiary of: Blackwell Publishing Ltd.), Commerce Place, 350 Main St, Malden, MA 02148. TEL 781-388-8206, FAX 781-388-8232, subscrip@blackwellpub.com, http://www.blackwellpublishing.com/journals/COIN. Eds. Dekang Lin, Randy Goebel, Russell Greiner. Circ: 650.

004 GBR
▼ **COMPUTATIONAL STRUCTURES TECHNOLOGY.** Text in English. 2004. irreg., latest vol.1, 2004. price varies. **Document type:** *Monographic series.*
Related titles: Online - full text ed.
Published by: Research Studies Press Ltd., 16 Coach House Cloisters, 10 Hitchin St, Baldock, Hertfordshire SG7 6AE, United Kingdom. TEL 44-1462-895060, FAX 44-1462-892546, info@research-studies-press.co.uk, http://www.research-studies-press.co.uk. Ed. A Kaven.

004 ITA ISSN 1128-5575
COMPUTER. Text in Italian. 1979. d. adv. bk.rev. **Document type:** *Magazine, Consumer.*
Indexed: CMCI, Englnd, ErgAb.
Published by: Systems Comunicazioni, Via Olanda 6, Vigano di Gaggiano, MI 20083, Italy. TEL 39-02-92270757, FAX 39-02-90841682, info@systems.it, http://www.systems.it. Ed. Michele Di Pisa. Circ: 12,000.

681.3 CZE ISSN 1210-8790
COMPUTER. Text in Czech. 1994. 22/yr. CZK 690 (effective 2003). adv. **Document type:** *Magazine, Consumer.*
Related titles: Online - full text ed.
Published by: Computer Press a.s., Pod Vinici 23, Prague 4, 143 11, Czech Republic. TEL 420-2-225273930, FAX 420-2-225273934, computer@cpress.cz, webmaster@cpress.cz, http://computer.cpress.cz, http://www.cpress.cz. Ed. Michal Politzer. Adv. contact Vera Harvankova. page CZK 91,000; trim 210 x 297.

004 USA ISSN 0018-9162
TK7885.A1 CODEN: CPTRB4
➤ **COMPUTER (NEW YORK).** Variant title: I E E E Computer Magazine. Text in English. 1966. m. USD 1,185 (effective 2006). adv. bk.rev. abstr.; bibl.; charts; illus.; stat. reprints avail. **Document type:** *Journal, Academic/Scholarly.* **Description:** Contains articles and papers that cover the entire range of hardware and software design and applications. Circulates automatically to members of the IEEE Computer Society.
Formerly (until 1970): I E E E Computer Group News (0537-9229)
Related titles: CD-ROM ed.; Microfiche ed.; Online - full text ed.: ISSN 1558-0814 (from EBSCO Publishing, I E E E).
Indexed: AHCI, AIA, AS&TI, BrCerAb, C&CSA, C&ISA, CMCI, CerAb, CompAb, CompC, CompD, CompLI, CompR, CorrAb, CurCont, CybAb, E&CAJ, EEA, EMA, ErgAb, IAA, ISR, Inspec, JOF, M&MA, M&TEA, MBF, METADEX, ORMS, QC&AS, RASB, RefZh, SCI, SSCI, SoftAbEng, SoftBase, SolStAb, TelAb, WAA.
—BLDSC (3390.650000), AskIEEE, CISTI, Ei, IDS, IE, Infotrieve, ingenta, Linda Hall. **CCC.**
Published by: I E E E Computer Society, 445 Hoes Ln., Piscataway, NJ 08855-1331. TEL 732-562-5478, computer@computer.org, customer.service@ieee.org, http://www.computer.org/computer. Pub. Angela Burgess. Adv. contact Patricia Garvey. B&W page USD 4,900, color page USD 6,000. Circ: 96,859 (paid). **Subscr. to:** Maruzen Co., Ltd., 3-10 Nihonbashi 2-chome, Chuo-ku, Tokyo 103-0027, Japan. TEL 81-3-3272-0521, FAX 81-3-3272-0693; Universal Subscription Agency, Pvt. Ltd., 877, Udyog Vihar, V, Gurgoan 122001, India. TEL 91-124-347261, FAX 91-124-342496.

004 USA ISSN 0883-4881
HD9696.C63
COMPUTER (SCOTTSDALE). Variant title: Orion Computer Blue Book. Text in English. q. USD 150 per issue (effective 2005). **Document type:** *Directory.* **Description:** Provides information on pricing used computer equipment.
Related titles: CD-ROM ed.; Diskette ed.
Published by: Orion Research Corp., 14555 N Scottsdale Rd, Ste 330, Scottsdale, AZ 85254-3457. TEL 800-844-0759, FAX 800-375-1315, orion@bluebook.com, http://www.orionbluebook.com/orion/computer.asp.

COMPUTER ABSTRACTS. see *COMPUTERS—Abstracting, Bibliographies, Statistics*

004 GRC
COMPUTER AGE. Text in Greek. 1980. m. USD 60. adv.
Published by: Infopublica S A, 4 Kartali St, Athens, 115 28, Greece. Ed. Kostas Kataras. Circ: 5,000.

004 HUN ISSN 1585-8928
COMPUTER AKTIV. Text in Hungarian. 2000. fortn. adv.
Document type: *Magazine, Consumer.* **Description:** Provides information, tips and advice for beginners or users with little experience in computing.
Related titles: Online - full text ed.: ISSN 1586-4146.
Published by: Sanoma Budapest Kiadoi Rt. (Subsidiary of: Sanoma Magazines Finland Corporation), Bokor Utca 15-19, Budapest, 1037, Hungary. TEL 36-1-4371100, FAX 36-1-2502303, info@sanomabp.hu, http://www.computeraktiv.hu, http://www.sanoma.hu. adv.: page HUF 670,000; trim 220 x 295. Circ: 23,000 (paid).

COMPUTER & CONTROL ABSTRACTS. see *COMPUTERS—Abstracting, Bibliographies, Statistics*

COMPUTER AND INFORMATION SYSTEMS ABSTRACTS JOURNAL. see *COMPUTERS—Abstracting, Bibliographies, Statistics*

COMPUTER AND TELECOM NEWS. see *COMMUNICATIONS*

004 DEU ISSN 1437-6482
COMPUTER BILD. Text in German. 1996. fortn. EUR 41.60 domestic; EUR 1.50 newsstand/cover (effective 2003). adv.
Document type: *Magazine, Consumer.*
Published by: Axel Springer Verlag AG, Axel-Springer-Platz 1, Hamburg, 20350, Germany. TEL 49-40-34700, FAX 49-40-34724683, redaktion@computerbild.de, information@axelspringer.de, http://www.computerbild.de, http://www.asv.de. Ed. Harald Kuppek. adv.: page EUR 22,064. Circ: 786,565 (paid).

621.381 301 USA ISSN 1521-4303
COMPUTER BITS. Text in English. 1993. m.
Related titles: Online - full text ed.
Published by: Forest Grove, 2114 Pacific Ave, Forest Grove, OR 97116-2497. TEL 503-992-3247, FAX 503-992-3201.

004 USA
COMPUTER BOOK BYTES. Text in English. m. **Description:** Provides up-to-date information on computer book titles.
Published by: Baker & Taylor, PO Box 6885, Bridgewater, NJ 08807-0885. TEL 800-775-1800, FAX 704-329-8989.

343.0999 GBR
COMPUTER CONTRACTS. Text in English. 1994. a. looseleaf. GBP 315 (effective 2006). **Document type:** *Journal, Trade.*
Published by: Sweet & Maxwell Ltd., 100 Avenue Road, London, NW3 3PF, United Kingdom. TEL 44-20-74491111, FAX 44-20-74491144, customer.services@sweetandmaxwell.co.uk, http://www.sweetandmaxwell.co.uk. **Subscr. to:** Cheriton House, North Way, Andover, Hants SP10 5BE, United Kingdom.

343.0999 USA
COMPUTER CONTRACTS. Text in English. 1987. 5 base vols. plus a. updates. looseleaf. USD 845 base vol(s). (effective 2002). **Description:** Covers contracts for buying, selling, and leasing and licensing hardware, software, and services. Provides legal analysis and step-by-step guidance to help readers handle contracts for computer users and vendors, marketing arrangements, software development, maintenance, licensing arrangements, and telecommunication contracts.
Published by: Matthew Bender & Co., Inc. (Subsidiary of: LexisNexis North America), 1275 Broadway, Albany, NY 12204. international@bender.com, http://bender.lexisnexis.com. Ed. Esther Roditt.

COMPUTER CONTRACTS PRINCIPLES AND PRECEDENTS. see *LAW*

COMPUTER CRAFT. see *ARTS AND HANDICRAFTS*

004 USA
COMPUTER DIGEST* . Text in English. 1986. m. USD 5. bk.rev.
Formerly: Capital Computer Digest
Indexed: Inspec, SoftBase.
Published by: Clark Publishing Co., 3930 Knowles Ave, Ste 305, Kensington, MD 20895-2428. TEL 703-525-7900, FAX 703-525-9749. Ed. Bob Dietsch. adv.: B&W page USD 1,485. Circ: 50,000.

004 NLD ISSN 0924-3607
COMPUTER EXPRESS. Text in Dutch. 1988. bi-m. EUR 20 (effective 2005). bk.rev. **Document type:** *Newsletter, Consumer.* **Description:** Includes information on PCs, hardware, software, news and trends, workshops, games, and infotainment.
Related titles: Online - full text ed.
Published by: Personeelsvereniging van Computergebruikers van het Ministerie van Financien, Postbus 832, Apeldoorn, 7301 BB, Netherlands. TEL 31-55-5788584, FAX 31-45-5600863, redactie@pvcf.nl, http://www.pvcf.nl. Ed. Otto Slijkhuis. Circ: 13,750.

004 DEU ISSN 1616-0061
COMPUTER-FACHWISSEN. Text in German. 1991. m. EUR 64.80; EUR 6.50 newsstand/cover (effective 2004). adv.
Document type: *Magazine, Trade.*
Former titles (until 1999): Computer-Fachwissen fuer Betriebs- und Personalrate (1430-0400); (until 1995): Computer-Information (0941-1836)
—IE.
Published by: Bund-Verlag GmbH, Heddernheimer Landstr 144, Frankfurt Am Main, 60439, Germany. TEL 49-69-79501020, FAX 49-69-79501010, compfach@t-online.de, kontakt@bund-verlag.de, http://www.bund-verlag.de. Ed. Wolfgang Fricke. adv.: B&W page EUR 1,080. Circ: 5,671 (paid and controlled).

004 ITA ISSN 1126-5159
COMPUTER FACILE. Text in Italian. 1998. m.
Published by: Techno Publishing S.r.l., Via Tacito 5, Corsico, MI 20094, Italy. TEL 39-02-4402360, FAX 39-02-45101659, tcp@tcp.it, http://www.tcp.it.

004 GBR ISSN 1461-7765
COMPUTER FORUM. Text in English. 1997. irreg. free (effective 2003). **Document type:** *Magazine.*
Media: Online - full text.
Published by: Institution of Electrical Engineers, Michael Faraday House, Six Hills Way, Stevenage, Herts SG1 2AY, United Kingdom. TEL 44-1438-313311, FAX 44-1438-313465, inspec@iee.org, http://forum.iee.org.uk/, http://www.iee.org/.

004 CHE
COMPUTER FORUM. Text in English. m. CHF 75; CHF 95 foreign. **Document type:** *Trade.*
Published by: Diagonal Verlags AG, Industriestr 21, Mellingen, 5507, Switzerland. Circ: 18,000.

004 CAN ISSN 1192-585X
COMPUTER FREELANCER; Canada's information magazine for computing professionals. Text in English. 1993. 8/yr. CND 28, USD 28; CND 3.95 newsstand/cover. adv. **Document type:** *Trade.* **Description:** Offers independent computer professionals practical advice on sources for landing a job, technical issues, contracts, the Internet and other areas.
Address: 1800 Sheppard Ave E, P O Box 55239, North York, ON M2J 5B9, Canada. TEL 416-493-6752, FAX 416-493-7093, info@freelancer.com, http://www.freelancer.com. Ed. Jayanti Parmar. Pub. Alan Arthur.

004 GRC ISSN 1105-5464
COMPUTER GIA OLOUS/COMPUTER FOR EVERYBODY. Text in Greek. 1983. m. adv. bk.rev. back issues avail.
Description: Business systems magazine covering developments and trends in the computer marketplace.
Published by: Compupress S.A., 44 Syngrou Ave, Athens, 117 42, Greece. TEL 30-210-923-8672, FAX 30-210-921-6847, http://www.cgomag.gr, http://www.compupress.gr/default_eng.htm. Ed. George Athanasiadis. Circ: 25,000.

338 USA ISSN 1524-7910
COMPUTER GRANTS ALERT. Text in English. 1998. m. USD 205; USD 21 newsstand/cover (effective 2001). **Document type:** *Newsletter.* **Description:** Includes everything you need to apply for and win computer-related grants, including complete contact information, the scope of the grant, deadlines, and eligibility requirements.
—CCC.
Published by: Aspen Publishers, Inc. (Subsidiary of: Wolters Kluwer N.V.), 5301 Buckeystown Pike, Ste. 400, Frederick, MD 21704-8319. customer.service@aspenpubl.com, http://www.aspenpublishers.com. Ed. Michael Abshire.

004 ESP
COMPUTER HOY. Text in Spanish. fortn. adv. **Document type:** *Magazine, Consumer.*
Published by: Hobby Press S.A. (Subsidiary of: Axel Springer Verlag AG), C/ Los Vascos 17, Madrid, 28040, Spain. TEL 34-902-111315, FAX 34-902-151798, computerhoy@axelspringer.es, http://www.hobbypress.es/html/REVISTAS_PRESENTACION.HTML. Ed. Marcos Sagrados. Circ: 134,000 (paid).

621.39 ITA ISSN 1591-6960
COMPUTER IDEA. Text in Italian. 2000. 26/yr. EUR 25 (effective 2004). **Document type:** *Magazine, Consumer.*
—CCC.
Published by: V N U Business Publications (Italy), Via Gorki 69, Cinisello Balsamo, MI 20092, Italy. TEL 39-02-660341, FAX 39-02-66034238, http://www.vnu.it.

004 USA
COMPUTER INSIDER. Text in English. m.
Published by: Lewis Research Corp., 1259 El Camino Real #216, Meulo Park, CA 94025. TEL 408-730-5829. Ed. Jan Lewis.

004 PHL ISSN 0115-8686
COMPUTER ISSUES. Text in English. 1983. s-a. PHP 60, USD 4.40. bk.rev. **Document type:** *Academic/Scholarly.*
Description: Presents scholarly articles reflecting significant quantitative or qualitative research. Includes speeches, research reports, and "state of the art" papers.
Published by: (De La Salle University, College of Computer Studies), De La Salle University Press, 2401 Taft Ave, Manila, Philippines. TEL 2-59-48-32. Circ: 300.

004 USA ISSN 0010-4620
QA76 CODEN: CMPJA6
➤ **THE COMPUTER JOURNAL.** Text in English. 1958. bi-m. GBP 568, USD 1,079, USD 852 to institutions; GBP 598, USD 1,136, EUR 897 combined subscription to institutions print & online eds. (effective 2006). adv. bk.rev. illus. index. 96 p./no.; back issues avail.; reprint service avail. from PSC. **Document type:** *Journal, Academic/Scholarly.* **Description:** Publishes research papers in a full range of subject areas, as well as regular articles and occational issues to enable readers to easily access information outside their direct area of research. Provides a complete overview of developments in the field.
Related titles: Microform ed.: (from PQC); Online - full text ed.: ISSN 1460-2067. 199?. GBP 538, USD 1,022, EUR 807 to institutions (effective 2006) (from EBSCO Publishing, Gale Group, HighWire Press, IngentaConnect, O C L C Online Computer Library Center, Inc., Oxford University Press Online Journals, ProQuest Information & Learning, Swets Information Services).
Indexed: ABIn, ADPA, AHCI, AS&TI, BMT, BRI, BrCerAb, BrTechI, C&CSA, C&ISA, CIS, CMCI, CPM, CerAb, ChemAb, CompAb, CompC, CompD, CompLI, CompR, CorrAb, CurCont, CybAb, E&CAJ, EMA, ETA, EngInd, ErgAb, ExcerpMed, IAA, ISMEC, Inspec, M&MA, M&TEA, MBF, METADEX, MLA-IB, MathR, RASB, RefZh, SCI, SSCI, SolStAb, WAA, ZentMath.
—BLDSC (3394.060000), AskIEEE, CISTI, Ei, IDS, IE, Infotrieve, ingenta, Linda Hall. **CCC.**
Published by: (British Computer Society GBR), Oxford University Press (Subsidiary of: Oxford University Press), 2001 Evans Rd, Cary, NC 27513. TEL 919-677-0977, 800-852-7323, FAX 919-677-1714, jnlorders@oup-usa.org, http://www.us.oup.com. Ed. F Murtagh. Pub. Ian McIntosh. R&P Fiona Willis. adv.: B&W page USD 200. Circ: 4,500.

004 USA
COMPUTER JOURNAL (LAS VEGAS). Text in English. 1994. m. (online version d.). USD 24.95; USD 75 in Canada & Mexico; USD 120 elsewhere. adv. bk.rev.; software rev. **Document type:** *Consumer.* **Description:** Covers computer related topics.
Formerly (until 1998): Las Vegas Computer Journal (1095-1172)
Related titles: Online - full text ed.
Published by: L V C J, 2232 S Nellis Blvd, Ste 169, Las Vegas, NV 89104. TEL 702-432-6206, FAX 702-432-6204, compjour@vegas.infi.net, http://www.computerjournal.com. Ed., Pub., R&P Johanna Nezhoda. Adv. contact Rene Nezhoda. Circ: 30,000.

004 UAE
AL-COMPUTER LIL-MUBTADDI'IN/COMPUTER FOR BEGINNERS. Text in Arabic. 1986. irreg. **Description:** Information to help new computer users, especially students.
Published by: Dubai Educational Region/Mintaqat Dubai al-Ta'limiyyah, P O Box 3962, Dubai, United Arab Emirates. TEL 691405. Ed. Hamad Ahmed Al Shaibani. Circ: 1,500.

004 658 USA
COMPUTER MANAGER. Text in English. q. adv. **Document type:** *Magazine, Trade.*
Published by: Story Communications, 116 N Camp St, Seguin, TX 78155. TEL 830-303-3328, 800-864-1155, FAX 830-372-3011, kaw@storycomm.com, http://www.compumgr.com/, http://www.storycomm.com. adv.: page USD 2,000.

004.025 USA ISSN 0747-749X
COMPUTER MEDIA DIRECTORY. Text in English. 1983. q. looseleaf. USD 395 domestic; USD 419 in Canada; USD 443 elsewhere. **Document type:** *Directory.* **Description:** Lists magazines, journals, tabloids and newsletters that deal with the high technology (computer and electronics) industry.
Related titles: Diskette ed.
Published by: Morrissey Standard, 742 Gilman St, Berkeley, CA 94710-1327. TEL 510-525-4691, FAX 510-525-2501. Ed. Gary Berlind. Circ: 1,200.

004 USA ISSN 1076-027X
COMPUTER-MEDIATED COMMUNICATION MAGAZINE. Abbreviated title: C M C Magazine. Text in English. 1994. m.
Media: Online - full content.
Published by: December Communications, Inc., 154 3rd St, Troy, NY 12180-4039. http://www.december.com/cmc/mag/. Ed., Pub. John December.

530 004 LVA ISSN 1407-5806
COMPUTER MODELLING AND NEW TECHNOLOGIES. Text in English. 1996. s-a.
Formerly (until 1999): R A U Scientific Reports (1407-2742)
Indexed: Inspec.
Published by: Transporta un Sakaru Instituts, 1 Lomonosova Str, Riga, 1019, Latvia. TEL 371-7100650, FAX 371-7100660, http://www.tsi.lv, http://www.rau.lv.

004 USA
▼ **COMPUTER NEWS.** Text in English. 2005 (Jul.). m. free to qualified personnel (effective 2005). **Document type:** *Magazine, Trade.*
Media: Online - full content.

C

Published by: Possibility Media, 10400 N.W. 33rd St., Ste. 270, Miami, FL 33172. TEL 786-206-8880, FAX 786-206-8884, info@possibilitymedia.com, http://www.computernewsmagazine.com/, http://www.possibilitymedia.com/.

004 CAN ISSN 0840-3929
THE COMPUTER PAPER (B C EDITION)* ; Canada's computer information source. Text in English. 1988. m. adv. illus. **Document type:** *Newspaper, Trade.* **Description:** For IBM, Macintosh, Atari, Amiga and Unix end users. Offers news, features and reviews.
Published by: Canada Computer Paper Inc., 625 Church St 6th Fl, Toronto, ON M4Y 2GI, Canada. TEL 416-923-7100, FAX 416-923-7994, david@tcp.ca, http://www.tcp.ca. Ed. David Tanaka. Pub. David Ritter. adv.: B&W page CND 11,685, color page CND 15,165; trim 12.63 x 10.25. Circ: 400,000.

004 CAN ISSN 1195-3454
THE COMPUTER PAPER (ONTARIO EDITION)* . Text in English. m. adv. illus. **Document type:** *Newspaper, Consumer.*
Published by: Canada Computer Paper Inc., 625 Church St 6th Fl, Toronto, ON M4Y 2GI, Canada. TEL 416-588-1580, FAX 416-588-8574. Ed. Douglas Alder. Adv. contact Rob Crawford.

004 CAN ISSN 1201-429X
THE COMPUTER PAPER (PRAIRIE EDITION)* ; Canada's computer information source. Text in English. 1995. m. adv. illus. **Document type:** *Newspaper, Consumer.*
Formed by the merger of (1989-1995): Computer Paper (Alberta Edition) (1187-5259); (1991-1995): Computer Paper (Manitoba Edition) (1196-0590)
Published by: Canada Computer Paper Inc., 625 Church St 6th Fl, Toronto, ON M4Y 2GI, Canada. TEL 416-588-1580, FAX 416-588-8574. Ed. David Tanaka. Adv. contact Hari Singh Khalsa.

004.025 USA ISSN 0045-7841
COMPUTER PRICE GUIDE; the blue book of used I B M computer prices. Text in English. 1970. q. USD 495 (effective 2004). **Document type:** *Consumer.* **Description:** Provides price and market information for commonly traded IBM computers and peripherals.
Incorporates (1996-2004): Digital Systems Report (1086-9638)
Indexed: CompC.
Published by: Computer Economics, Inc., 2082 Business Center Dr., Ste 240, Irvine, CA 92612. TEL 949-831-8700, FAX 949-442-7688, custserv@compecon.com, http://www.computereconomics.com. Pub. Peter Daley. **Dist. by:** Publications Resource Group, 121 Union St., Box 792, North Adams, MA 01247. TEL 413-664-6185, FAX 413-664-9343.

621.39 THA ISSN 0858-7884
COMPUTER PROFESSIONAL INFORMATION. Text and summaries in English. 1993. a. THB 600; USD 67 foreign. adv. **Document type:** *Directory.*
Published by: Advanced Research Group Co. Ltd., AR Bldg Klongsan, 27 Charoen Nakorn 14 Rd, Bangkok, 10600, Thailand. TEL 66-2-439-4600, FAX 66-2-439-4616, http://www.ar.co.th/cpi, kid@ar.co.th. Ed., R&P Siriporn Promrat. Pub. Patchara Kiatnuntavimon. Adv. contact Vanida Siraklow. color page THB 50,000. Circ: 50,000. **Dist. by:** Current Pacific Ltd., PO Box 36-536, Northcote, Auckland, New Zealand. TEL 64-9-480-1388, FAX 64-9-480-1387, info@cplnz.com, http://www.cplnz.com.

004 JPN ISSN 0385-6658
COMPUTER REPORT* /KONPYUTA REPOTO. Text in Japanese. 1959. m. JPY 8,000.
Indexed: JCT, JTA.
Published by: Japan Management Science Institute/Nihon Keiei Kagaku Kenkyujo, 5-6-8, Miyanishi-cho, Futyu-shi, Tokyo, 183-0022, Japan. FAX 81-42-3360559, cr-info@jmsi.co.jp, http://www.jmsi.co.jp/. Ed. Kotoshi Fujimi.

621.39 USA ISSN 1089-3350
QA76.27
COMPUTER SCIENCE & ELECTRICAL ENGINEERING PROGRAMS. Text in English. 1997. a. USD 24.95. **Document type:** *Directory.* **Description:** Profiles of some 900 graduate computer science and electrical engineering programs in the U.S. and Canada.
Published by: Thomson Peterson's (Subsidiary of: Thomson Corporation), Princeton Pike Corporate Center, 2000 Lenox Dr, 3rd Fl, Lawrenceville, NJ 08648. TEL 609-243-9111, FAX 609-243-9150, http://www.petersons.com. Ed. Barbara Lawrence.

004 IND ISSN 0254-7813
QA76.5
COMPUTER SCIENCE AND INFORMATICS. Text in English. 1970. s-a. INR 20, USD 10. adv. bk.rev. charts. cum.index. back issues avail.
Formerly (until 1982): Computer Society of India. Journal (0045-7892)
Indexed: ChemAb, CompAb, Inspec.
—BLDSC (3394.265400), ingenta.
Published by: Computer Society of India, 15 Haji Park, Mumbai, Maharashtra 400 034, India. Ed. S V Rangaswamy. Circ: 3,000.

004 USA
COMPUTER SCIENCE AND SCIENTIFIC COMPUTING SERIES. Text in English. 1971. irreg., latest 1997. USD 81.95 per vol. (effective 2004). reprint service avail. from ISI. **Description:** Concerned primarily with the theory of linear and nonlinear programming, and a number of closely-related problems, and with algorithms appropriate to those problems.
Formerly: Computer Science and Applied Mathematics
Indexed: ApMecR, Inspec, MathR.
Published by: Academic Press (Subsidiary of: Elsevier Science & Technology), 525 B St, Ste 1900, San Diego, CA 92101-4495. TEL 619-231-6616, 800-894-3434, apsubs@acad.com, http://www.academicpress.com. Eds. Daniel Siewiorek, Werner Reinboldt.

COMPUTER SCIENCE AND TELECOMMUNICATIONS. see *COMMUNICATIONS*

COMPUTER SCIENCE EDUCATION. see *EDUCATION—Computer Applications*

COMPUTER SCIENCE INDEX. see *COMPUTERS—Abstracting, Bibliographies, Statistics*

004 USA
COMPUTER SCIENCE TECHNICAL REPORT ANTHOLOGY. Text in English. 1981. a. USD 7. bibl. index, cum.index: 1963-1991. back issues avail.
Related titles: Microfiche ed.
Published by: University of Maryland, Department of Computer Science, A.V. Williams Building, College Park, MD 20742. TEL 301-405-2745. Ed. Betty Kellogg. Circ: 250.

004 GBR ISSN 0953-3710
CODEN: CMSTEL
COMPUTER SCIENCE TEXTS. Text in English. 1983. irreg. price varies. **Document type:** *Monographic series.*
Indexed: Inspec.
—CCC.
Published by: Blackwell Publishing Ltd., 9600 Garsington Rd, Oxford, OX4 2ZG, United Kingdom. TEL 44-1865-776868, FAX 44-1865-714591, customerservices@oxon.blackwellpublishing.com, http://www.blackwellpublishing.com.

004 GBR ISSN 1361-4339
COMPUTER SERVICES AND SOFTWARE ASSOCIATION. REFERENCE BOOK AND BUYERS' GUIDE. Text in English. 1985. a. GBP 65. **Document type:** *Journal, Trade.*
Formerly (until 1995): Computing Services Association. Official Reference Book (0266-7916)
Published by: Computer Services and Software Association, Hanover House, 73-74 High Holborn, London, WC1V 6LE, United Kingdom. TEL 44-207-4052171. Circ: 6,000 (controlled).

COMPUTER SHOPPER; la guida piu completa al mercato dell'informatica. see *COMPUTERS—Computer Sales*

004 CHE ISSN 1017-3803
COMPUTER SPECTRUM; magazine for automation, computers and telecommunication. Text in German. bi-m. CHF 98, EUR 62. adv. bk.rev. illus. **Document type:** *Magazine, Trade.*
Related titles: Online - full text ed.
Indexed: Englnd.
Address: Aarestr 83, Umiken, 5222, Switzerland. TEL 41-56-4410043, FAX 41-56-4414854, editor@bal.ch, http://www.bal.ch. Ed., Pub. Oskar Baldinger. Circ: 10,000.

COMPUTER SPEZIAL. see *BUILDING AND CONSTRUCTION*

004.0218 NLD ISSN 0920-5489
QA76.9.S8 CODEN: CSTIEZ
➤ **COMPUTER STANDARDS & INTERFACES.** Text in English. 1986. 6/yr. EUR 895 in Europe to institutions; JPY 119,100 in Japan to institutions; USD 1,002 elsewhere to institutions (effective 2006). illus. back issues avail.; reprints avail. **Document type:** *Journal, Academic/Scholarly.* **Description:** Provides information about the impact of international and national computer standards on technology, economics and trade.
Formed by the merger of (1982-1986): Computers and Standards (0167-8051); (1983-1986): Interfaces in Computing (0252-7308)
Related titles: Microform ed.: (from PQC); Online - full text ed.: (from EBSCO Publishing, Gale Group, IngentaConnect, ScienceDirect, Swets Information Services).
Indexed: AIA, ASCA, BMT, BrCerAb, C&ISA, CADCAM, CMCI, CerAb, CompAb, CompC, CompLI, CompR, CorrAb, CurCont, E&CAJ, EMA, Englnd, IAA, Inspec, M&TEA, MBF, METADEX, RefZh, SolStAb, WAA.
—BLDSC (3394.276800), AskIEEE, CISTI, Ei, IDS, IE, Infotrieve, ingenta, Linda Hall. **CCC.**
Published by: Elsevier BV, North-Holland (Subsidiary of: Elsevier Science & Technology), Sara Burgerhartstraat 25, Amsterdam, 1055 KV, Netherlands. TEL 31-20-485-3911, FAX 31-20-485-2457, nlinfo-f@elsevier.nl, http://www.elsevier.com/locate/csi, http://www.elsevier.nl. Ed. B. Thuraisingham. **Subscr. to:** Elsevier BV, PO Box 211, Amsterdam 1000 AE, Netherlands. TEL 31-20-485-3757, FAX 31-20-485-3432, http://www.elsevier.nl.

004 GBR ISSN 1369-6246
COMPUTER SUCCESS. Text in English. 1997. w. GBP 168.50; GBP 1.75 newsstand/cover. **Document type:** *Consumer.* **Description:** Contains helpful guides and instruction for using various software, and understanding hardware.
Published by: Orbis Publishing Ltd., Griffin House, 161 Hammersmith Rd, London, W6 8SD, United Kingdom. TEL 44-181-600-2000, http://www.orbispublishing.com, computer-success.com.

004 USA ISSN 1554-7906
QA76.9.T43
COMPUTER SUPPORT SOLUTIONS. Text in English. 2001. m. USD 167 domestic; USD 177 foreign; USD 197 combined subscription print & online eds. (effective 2006).
Former titles (until 2005): Computer Support Professional (1542-2143); (until 2002): A+ Professional (1534-679X)
Related titles: Online - full content ed.: USD 197 domestic; USD 207 foreign (effective 2005).
—CCC.
Published by: Element K Journals (Subsidiary of: Eli Research, Inc.), 500 Canal View Blvd, Rochester, NY 14623. TEL 585-240-7301, 800-223-8720, 877-203-5248, FAX 585-292-4392, http://www.elementkjournals.com. Eds. Joe Froehlich, Michelle Rogers.

004 NLD ISSN 0925-9724
HD66 CODEN: CSCWEQ
➤ **COMPUTER SUPPORTED COOPERATIVE WORK**; the journal of collaborative computing. Short title: C S C W. Text in English. 1992. bi-m. EUR 558, USD 568, GBP 348 combined subscription to institutions print & online eds. (effective 2005). adv. bk.rev. back issues avail.; reprint service avail. from PSC. **Document type:** *Journal, Academic/Scholarly.* **Description:** Provides interdisciplinary forum for papers on theoretical, practical, technical and social issues in computer supported cooperative work.
Related titles: Microform ed.: (from PQC); Online - full text ed.: ISSN 1573-7551 (from EBSCO Publishing, Gale Group, IngentaConnect, Kluwer Online, O C L C Online Computer Library Center, Inc., Springer LINK, Swets Information Services).
Indexed: B&BAb, BibLing, CompAb, CompR, Englnd, ErgAb, Inspec, RefZh, SOPODA.
—BLDSC (3394.285000), AskIEEE, Ei, IE, Infotrieve, ingenta. **CCC.**
Published by: Springer-Verlag Dordrecht (Subsidiary of: Springer Science+Business Media), Van Godewijckstraat 30, Dordrecht, 3311 GX, Netherlands. TEL 31-78-6576050, FAX 31-78-6576474, http://springerlink.metapress.com/openurl.asp?genre=journal&issn=0925-9724, http://www.springeronline.com. Ed. Kjeld Schmidt.

004 SWE ISSN 0280-9982
COMPUTER SWEDEN. Text in Swedish. 1980. 3/w. SEK 1,050 (effective 2003). adv. Supplement avail. **Document type:** *Magazine, Trade.* **Description:** Covers computer systems and related products. Aimed at larger and medium sized companies.
Incorporates (1994-1997): Corporate Computing (1401-2251); (1990-1991): Mac & PC Nyheterna (1101-6760); (1982-1983): NovaGram (0280-7084)
Related titles: Online - full text ed.: ISSN 1402-4349.
Published by: (Datafoereningen i Sverige), I D G AB (Subsidiary of: I D G Communications Inc.), Sturegatan 11, Stockholm, 10678, Sweden. TEL 46-8-4536000, FAX 46-8-4536005, cs@idg.se, http://computersweden.idg.se/, http://www.idg.se. Ed. Lars Dahmen. Adv. contact Stefan Andersson. B&W page SEK 67,915, color page SEK 78,975; trim 252 x 358. Circ: 63,000 (paid).

COMPUTER TECHNOLOGY LAW REPORT. see *LAW*

004 USA ISSN 0278-9647
COMPUTER TECHNOLOGY REVIEW; technology solutions for systems integrators, VARs & OEMs. Text in English. 1981. m. USD 250 domestic; USD 300 in Canada; USD 395 elsewhere (effective 2003); free to qualified personnel. adv. bk.rev. tr.lit. back issues avail. **Document type:** *Magazine, Trade.* **Description:** Contains articles on systems, hardware and software systems integrators, OEMs, and engineering and corporate managers. Provides information on designing and utilizing computer-based systems.
Related titles: Online - full text ed.: Computer Technology News (from bigchalk, Florida Center for Library Automation, Gale Group, Northern Light Technology, Inc., O C L C Online Computer Library Center, Inc., ProQuest Information & Learning); ◆ Supplement(s): Storage Inc. ISSN 1524-6558.
Indexed: ABIn, CADCAM, CompD, CompLI, Englnd, GALA, Microcomplnd, SoftBase, TelAb.
—BLDSC (3394.305000), CISTI, Ei, IE, Infotrieve, Linda Hall. **CCC.**
Published by: West World Productions, Inc., 420 N Camden Dr, Beverly Hills, CA 90210-4507. TEL 310-276-9500, FAX 310-777-4589, http://www.wwpi.com/. Ed. Mark C. Ferelli. Pub. Yuri R Spiro. Adv. contact Lori Cole. Circ: 72,000 (controlled).

004 GBR ISSN 0268-6821
QA76.215
COMPUTER USERS YEAR BOOK. Text in English. 1969. a. (in 2 vols.). GBP 395 per issue (effective 2003). adv. bk.rev.
Document type: *Directory, Trade.* **Description:** Information source on the UK IT industry and profiles over 4,300 companies who provide IT services in the UK.
Related titles: CD-ROM ed.
—BLDSC (3394.350000).
Published by: V N U Business Publications Ltd., 32-34 Broadwick St, London, W1A 2HG, United Kingdom. TEL 44-20-73169610, FAX 44-20-73169260, directories@computing.co.uk, http://directories.computing.co.uk/directoriescuyb.htm, http://www.computing.co.uk/directories. Circ: 5,500.

004 RUS
COMPUTER WEEK - MOSCOW. Text in Russian. w.
Published by: Infoart, Pr-t Vernadskogo 82, Moscow, 117571, Russian Federation. TEL 7-095-9747238, FAX 7-095-9370293. Ed. V Shershul'skii. **US dist. addr.:** East View Information Services, 3020 Harbor Ln. N., Minneapolis, MN 55447. TEL 612-550-0961.

004 GBR ISSN 0010-4787
CODEN: COMWAA
COMPUTER WEEKLY. Text in English. 1966. w. free to qualified personnel (effective 2004). adv. bk.rev. Supplement avail.; back issues avail. **Document type:** *Magazine, Trade.* **Description:** For information technology professionals, industry analysts, OEMs, value-added resellers, and end users of micro-, mini-, and mainframe computers. Covers industry developments, new product announcements, and company profiles.
Related titles: Microform ed.: (from PQC); Online - full text ed.: (from bigchalk, EBSCO Publishing, Factiva, Florida Center for Library Automation, Gale Group, H.W. Wilson, LexisNexis, Northern Light Technology, Inc., O C L C Online Computer Library Center, Inc., ProQuest Information & Learning).
Indexed: ABIn, ADPA, BPI, BrTechI, CompC, CompD, ETA, Emerald, HECAB, Inspec, M&TEA, PROMT, RASB, RefZh.
—BLDSC (3394.360000), IE, Infotrieve, ingenta. **CCC.**
Published by: Reed Business Information Ltd. (Subsidiary of: Reed Business), Quadrant House, The Quadrant, Brighton Rd, Sutton, Surrey SM2 5AS, United Kingdom. TEL 44-208-652-3500, FAX 44-208-652-8977, cwfeedback@rbi.co.uk, http://www.computerweekly.com/, http://www.reedinfo.co.uk/. Ed. Karl Schneider TEL 44-20-8652-3043. Adv. contact Nitin Joshi TEL 44-20-8652-8804. Circ: 105,000. **Subscr. to:** Quadrant Subscription Services, Rockwood House, 9-17 Perrymount Rd, Haywards Heath, W. Sussex RH16 3DH, United Kingdom. TEL 44-1444-441212, FAX 44-1444-440620. **Dist. by:** MarketForce UK Ltd, 247 Tottenham Court Rd, London, Middx W1T 7AU, United Kingdom. TEL 44-20-72616996, FAX 44-207-2616951.

004 POL ISSN 0867-2334
COMPUTER WORLD; tygodnik menadzerow i informatykow. Text in Polish. 1990. w. PLZ 268 domestic; PLZ 536.80 foreign; PLZ 134 to students (effective 2005). adv. **Document type:** *Magazine, Consumer.*
Related titles: Online - full text ed.: free (effective 2005); ♦ Supplement(s): Computer World Top 200. ISSN 1505-456X.
Published by: I D G Poland S.A., ul Jordanowska 12, PO Box 73, Warsaw, 04-204, Poland. TEL 48-22-3217800, FAX 48-22-3217888, idg@idg.com.pl, http://www.computerworld.pl, http://www.idg.pl. Ed. Wojciech Raducha TEL 48-22-3217810. adv.: B&W page PLZ 6,300, color page PLZ 8,900; trim 270 x 342. Circ: 20,000.

004 POL ISSN 1505-456X
COMPUTER WORLD TOP 200. Text in Polish. 1998. a. adv. **Document type:** *Magazine, Consumer.*
Related titles: ♦ Supplement to: Computer World. ISSN 0867-2334.
Published by: I D G Poland S.A., ul Jordanowska 12, PO Box 73, Warsaw, 04-204, Poland. TEL 48-22-3217800, FAX 48-22-3217888, idg@idg.com.pl, http://www.idg.pl.

004 DEU ISSN 0341-5406
COMPUTER ZEITUNG; Deutschlands Zeitung fuer die Informationsgesellschaft. Text in German. 1970. w. EUR 10.85 per month domestic; EUR 12.80 per month foreign; EUR 2.70 newsstand/cover (effective 2004). adv. back issues avail.
Document type: *Newspaper, Trade.* **Description:** Features systems, software, hardware, graphic systems, applications, marketing, techniques, and management information for professionals in the computer industry. Includes listing of positions.
—IE, Infotrieve. **CCC.**
Published by: Konradin Verlag Robert Kohlhammer GmbH, Ernst Mey Str 8, Leinfelden-Echterdingen, 70771, Germany. TEL 49-711-75940, FAX 49-711-7594399, cz.redaktion@konradin.de, info@konradin.de, http://www.computer-zeitung.de, http://www.konradin.de. Ed. Peter Welchering. Adv. contact Dietmar Buettner. B&W page EUR 18,510, color page EUR 21,720; trim 295 x 420. Circ: 59,213 (paid and controlled).

004 USA
COMPUTEREPORT. Text in English. 1972. m. free.
Published by: Virginia Commonwealth University, Academic Computing, 1015 Floyd Ave, Box 174, Richmond, VA 23284. TEL 804-786-4719. Ed. R W Duvall. Circ: (controlled).

004 GBR ISSN 0268-716X
COMPUTERGRAM INTERNATIONAL; the daily newspaper for data processing, communications, and microelectronics professionals and investors. Text in English. d. (Mon.-Fri.). USD 995. back issues avail. **Document type:** *Newspaper, Trade.* **Description:** Delivers analysis of the computer industry to a global audience of senior executives in the computer vendor and user communities.
Related titles: Online - full text ed.: (from Factiva, Gale Group, O C L C Online Computer Library Center, Inc.).
Indexed: B&I, CompD.
Published by: A P T Data Group plc., 4th Fl, 12 Sutton Row, London, W1V 5FH, United Kingdom. TEL 44-171-208-4200, FAX 44-171-439-1105, http://www.computerwire.com/computergram/. Ed. Tim Palmer. **US subscr. to:** APT Data Services Inc., 828 Broadway, Ste 800, New York, NY 10010. TEL 212-677-0409, FAX 212-677-0463.

004 006.3 AUT ISSN 0946-9613
➤ **COMPUTERKULTUR.** Text in German. 1989. irreg., latest vol.13, 2001. price varies. **Document type:** *Monographic series, Academic/Scholarly.*
Indexed: ZentMath.
Published by: Springer-Verlag Wien (Subsidiary of: Springer Science+Business Media) TEL 43-1-3302415-0, FAX 43-1-330242665, books@springer.at, http://www.springer.at. Ed. R Herken. R&P Angela Foessl TEL 43-1-3302415517. **Subscr. to:** Springer-Verlag New York, Inc., 233 Spring St, New York, NY 10013. TEL 800-777-4643, FAX 201-348-4505, orders@springer-ny.com.

004 TUR
COMPUTERLIFE TURKEY. Text in Turkish. w. adv. **Document type:** *Magazine, Trade.* **Description:** Covers international and national news and trends in information technology industries and markets.
Related titles: Online - full text ed.
Published by: I M G Bilisim Yayinlari, Istiklal Caddesi, Ors Turistik is Merkezi, No. 251/253, Beyoglu-Istanbul, 80060, Turkey. TEL 90-212-292-8210, FAX 90-212-292-8211, iozdemir@computerworld.com.tr, http://www.cl.com.tr, http://www.imgbilisim.com. adv.: color page USD 1,500; trim 230 x 300. Circ: 5,000 (paid and controlled).

004 AUT ISSN 1814-8158
COMPUTERPARTNER. Text in German. 1996. m. **Document type:** *Magazine, Consumer.*
Published by: Info Technologie Verlag GmbH, Zieglergasse 6, Vienna, 1070, Austria. TEL 43-1-52305080, FAX 43-1-523050833, abo@itverlag.at, http://www.itverlag.at. Ed. Michael Reisner. Adv. contact Elfriede Slemenda.

004 NLD ISSN 0771-7784
COMPUTERRECHT; tijdschrift voor informatica, telecommunicatie en recht. Text in Dutch. 1984. bi-m. EUR 129.33 (effective 2003).
Related titles: ♦ French ed.: Droit de l'Informatique et des Telecoms. ISSN 0991-2738.
—IE, Infotrieve.
Published by: Kluwer B.V. (Subsidiary of: Wolters Kluwer N.V.), Postbus 23, Deventer, 7400 GA, Netherlands. TEL 31-570-673449, FAX 31-570-691555, juridisch@kluwer.nl, http://www.kluwer.nl.

004 GBR
COMPUTERS AND COMMUNICATIONS. Text in English. 1970. m. GBP 249 domestic; GBP 269 foreign (effective 2000); includes subscription to The Wharton Report.. **Document type:** *Corporate.* **Description:** Evaluates and analyses new products, applications and systems which will affect the users' performance at the desktop, with current focus on datawarehousing, allied to CRM (customer relations management) applications.
Formerly: Wharton Report Incorporating Computers and Communications; Which was formed by the 1992 merger of: Executive Computer Report; International Communications Report; Former titles: Business Computer Report; Computer Report
Indexed: Inspec.
Published by: Wharton Information Systems, 11 Beaumont Ave, Richmond, Surrey TW9 2HE, United Kingdom. TEL 44-20-8332-1120, n_wharton@compuserve.com. Ed. Andrea Wharton. Pub. Keith Wharton. R&P Chris Walker.

COMPUTERS AND LAW. see *LAW*

004 USA
COMPUTERS & OFFICE EQUIPMENT: LATIN AMERICAN INDUSTRIAL REPORT✶ **.** (Editions for each of 22 Latin American countries) Text in English. 1985. a. USD 435; per country report.
Published by: Aquino Productions, P O Box 15760, Stamford, CT 06901-0760.

003 GBR ISSN 0305-0548
T57.6.A1 CODEN: CMORAP
➤ **COMPUTERS & OPERATIONS RESEARCH.** Text in English. 1974. 12/yr. EUR 2,770 in Europe to institutions; JPY 368,000 in Japan to institutions; USD 3,099 to institutions except Europe and Japan (effective 2006). adv. bk.rev. charts; illus. back issues avail.; reprints avail. **Document type:** *Academic/Scholarly.* **Description:** For researchers, teachers and practitioners. Provides international papers on the methodology used for determining solutions to problems using computers.
Incorporates (1993-1998): Location Science (0966-8349)
Related titles: Microfilm ed.: (from PQC); Online - full text ed.: (from EBSCO Publishing, Gale Group, IngentaConnect, ScienceDirect, Swets Information Services).
Indexed: ABIn, ASCA, BPIA, BiolAb, BrCerAb, BusI, C&ISA, CCMJ, CIS, CLT&T, CMCI, CerAb, CompC, CompD, CompLI, CompR, CorrAb, CurCont, CybAb, E&CAJ, EMA, EngInd, ExcerpMed, F&EA, GEOBASE, HRIS, IAA, IAOP, ICEA, Inspec, M&TEA, MBF, METADEX, ManagCont, MathR, MathSciNet, ORMS, QC&AS, RefZh, SSCI, SoftAbEng, SolStAb, T&II, WAA, ZentMath, e-psyche.
—BLDSC (3394.770000), AskIEEE, CISTI, Ei, IDS, IE, Infotrieve, ingenta, Linda Hall. **CCC.**
Published by: Pergamon (Subsidiary of: Elsevier Science & Technology), The Boulevard, Langford Ln, East Park, Kidlington, Oxford OX5 1GB, United Kingdom. TEL 44-1865-843000, FAX 44-1865-843010, http://www.elsevier.com/locate/cor. Ed. Gilbert Laporte. Circ: 1,000. **Subscr. to:** Elsevier BV, PO Box 211, Amsterdam 1000 AE, Netherlands. nlinfo-f@elsevier.nl, http://www.elsevier.nl.

004 USA
COMPUTERS AND PEOPLE SERIES. Text in English. 1980. irreg., latest 1997. reprint service avail. from ISI. **Document type:** *Monographic series.*
Published by: Academic Press (Subsidiary of: Elsevier Science & Technology), 525 B St, Ste 1900, San Diego, CA 92101-4495. apsubs@acad.com, http://www.academicpress.com. Ed. B Gaines.

COMPUTERS AND THE LAW. see *LAW*

004 USA
COMPUTERS, COGNITION AND WORK. Text in English. irreg., latest 2001. price varies. **Document type:** *Monographic series, Academic/Scholarly.*
Published by: Lawrence Erlbaum Associates, Inc., 10 Industrial Ave, Mahwah, NJ 07430-2262. TEL 201-258-2200, FAX 201-236-0072, journals@erlbaum.com, http://www.erlbaum.com.

004 GBR ISSN 1359-978X
COMPUTERS IN AFRICA; the definitive guide to information technology in Africa. Text in English. 1987. m. GBP 20 (effective 2001). adv. bk.rev. stat. back issues avail.
Document type: *Magazine, Trade.* **Description:** Covers all aspects of computing, including hardware, software, LAN development, Macintosh, computer fairs, international news and analysis of the developing computer infrastructure in specific African countries.
Former titles (until 1995): Computers and Communications in Africa (1359-9771); (until 1993): Computers in Africa (0953-3257)
Published by: A I T E C, 15 High St, Graveley, Cambs PE18 6PL, United Kingdom. TEL 44-1480-831300, FAX 44-1480-831131, info@aitec.co.uk, sales@aitecafrica.com, http://www.aitecafrica.com. Eds. Bruce Conradie, Sean Moroney. Pub., R&P Sean Moroney. Adv. contact Peter Irvine. page GBP 1,750; trim 210 x 297. Circ: 14,000 (paid and controlled).

COMPUTERS IN ENGINEERING. see *ENGINEERING*

004 USA ISSN 1544-3574
QA76.9.E57
▼ **COMPUTERS IN ENTERTAINMENT.** Text in English. 2003 (Fall). q. USD 140 to libraries; USD 50 to non-members; USD 40 to members; USD 35 to students (effective 2006).
Description: Covers a wide range of theoretical and practical computer applications in the field of entertainment such as online games, CD-ROM software, CGI movies, and interactive TV. It publishers high-quality papers on the latest developments in software, hardware, and business policies that improve existing mainstream entertainment and that create new genres of entertainment.
Media: Online - full content. **Related titles:** CD-ROM ed.: ISSN 1544-3981. 2004 (Sept.); Online - full text ed.: (from Association for Computing Machinery, Inc.).
—CCC.
Published by: Association for Computing Machinery, Inc., 1515 Broadway, 17th Fl, New York, NY 10036-5701. TEL 212-626-0500, 212-626-0520, 800-342-6626, FAX 212-869-0481, sigs@acm.org, usacm@acm.org, http://www.acm.org/pubs/cie.html.

005 USA ISSN 1546-2218
QA76.9.C65
▼ **COMPUTERS, MATERIALS & CONTINUA.** Abbreviated title: C M C. Text in English. 2004. q. USD 750; USD 1,000 combined subscription print & online eds. (effective 2005).

C

Related titles: Online - full text ed.: ISSN 1546-2226. USD 600 (effective 2005).
Indexed: BrCerAb, C&ISA, CerAb, CorrAb, E&CAJ, EMA, IAA, M&TEA, MBF, METADEX, WAA.
—BLDSC (3287.196000), IE.
Published by: Tech Science Press, 81 E Main St, Forsyth 488, GA 31029 . TEL 478-992-8121, FAX 661-420-8080, sale@techscience.com, http://www.techscience.com/cmc. Eds. G S Chen, Z Z Cen.

004 ZAF ISSN 0254-2188
COMPUTERWEEK. Text in English. 1978. w. ZAR 139.65. adv. bk.rev. illus. **Document type:** *Newspaper.*
Indexed: CompC, CompD, Inspec.
Published by: Systems Publishers (Pty) Ltd., PO Box 41345, Craighall, Gauteng 2024, South Africa. TEL 27-11-789-1808, FAX 27-11-789-4725. Ed. Frank Heydenrych. Circ: 12,515.

004 DEU ISSN 0170-5121
HD9696.C6
COMPUTERWOCHE. Text in German. 1974. w. EUR 155 domestic; EUR 162 foreign; EUR 3.35 newsstand/cover (effective 2005). adv. **Document type:** *Newspaper, Trade.* **Description:** Presents information about information processing, internetworking and client-server computing in the corporate environment. Aimed at IT managers, software specialists and communications professionals.
Related titles: Online - full text ed.: (from LexisNexis); ♦ Supplement(s): Computerwoche. Extra. ISSN 0935-1310; ♦ Computerwoche. Focus. ISSN 0935-1329; ♦ Computerwoche Young Professional. ISSN 1438-1303.
Indexed: B&I, PROMT.
—IE, Infotrieve. **CCC.**
Published by: Computerwoche Verlag GmbH, Brabanter Str 4, Munich, 80805, Germany. TEL 49-89-36086-299, FAX 49-89-36086325, cw@computerwoche.de, http://www.computerwoche.de. Ed. Christoph Witte. Pub. Dieter Eckbauer. R&P Karin Griffhorn. Adv. contact Simone Fiedler. color page EUR 23,400; trim 280 x 381. Circ: 55,241 (paid and controlled).

004 DEU ISSN 0935-1310
COMPUTERWOCHE. EXTRA. Text in German. 1983. irreg.
Related titles: ♦ Supplement to: Computerwoche. ISSN 0170-5121.
Published by: Computerwoche Verlag GmbH, Brabanter Str 4, Munich, 80805, Germany. TEL 49-89-36086-299, FAX 49-89-36086325.

004 DEU ISSN 0935-1329
COMPUTERWOCHE. FOCUS. Text in German. 1988. bi-m. adv. **Document type:** *Magazine, Trade.*
Related titles: ♦ Supplement to: Computerwoche. ISSN 0170-5121.
Published by: Computerwoche Verlag GmbH, Brabanter Str 4, Munich, 80805, Germany. TEL 49-89-36086-299, FAX 49-89-36086325. adv.: page EUR 8,150. Circ: 59,425 (controlled).

004 DEU ISSN 1438-1303
COMPUTERWOCHE YOUNG PROFESSIONAL. Text in German. 1998. bi-m. adv. **Document type:** *Magazine, Trade.* **Description:** Provides information on the information technology job market, industries and career options.
Related titles: Online - full text ed.; ♦ Supplement to: Computerwoche. ISSN 0170-5121.
Published by: Computerwoche Verlag GmbH, Brabanter Str 4, Munich, 80805, Germany. TEL 49-89-36086-299, FAX 49-89-36086325, http://www.youngprofessional.de. Ed. Hans Koeniges. adv.: B&W page EUR 8,900, color page EUR 10,130. Circ: 40,224 (controlled).

004 RUS ISSN 1560-5213
COMPUTERWORLD. Text in Russian. 1995. 48/yr. RUR 396 domestic; RUR 8.25 per issue domestic (effective 2004). adv. **Document type:** *Magazine, Trade.* **Description:** Includes timely news and analysis on personal computers, workstations, midrange and central server hardware, software and networking products, in addition to issues of strategic interest to IS/IT executives.
Related titles: Online - full text ed.
Indexed: RefZh.
Published by: Izdatel'stvo Otkrytye Sistemy/Open Systems Publications, ul Rustaveli, dom 12A, komn 117, Moscow, 127254, Russian Federation. TEL 7-095-9563306, FAX 7-095-2539204, cwr@osp.ru, info@osp.ru, http://www.osp.ru/cw/. Ed. Dmitrii Gapotchenko. adv.: B&W page USD 4,400, color page USD 5,500; trim 270 x 354. Circ: 27,000 (paid and controlled). **Subscr. in US to:** East View Information Services, 3020 Harbor Ln. N., Minneapolis, MN 55447. TEL 800-477-1005, FAX 800-800-3839, eastview@eastview.com, http://www.eastview.com.

004 DNK ISSN 0906-3927
COMPUTERWORLD; Danmarks it-avis. Text in Danish. 1981. 2/w. DKK 898 (effective 2004). adv. bk.rev. reprints avail. **Document type:** *Newspaper, Consumer.* **Description:** Covers Danish and international developments in the computer world.
Formerly (until 1983): Computerworld Denmark (0107-5217); Incorporates (1988-2000): Tech World (0909-1769)
Related titles: Online - full text ed.: (from Northern Light Technology, Inc.).
Indexed: AIA, BusI, PROMT, T&II.
—Infotrieve. **CCC.**
Published by: I D G Danmark A-S, Carl Jacobsens Vej 25, Valby, 2500, Denmark. TEL 45-77-300300, FAX 45-77-300313, redaktionen@computerworld.dk, idg@idg.dk, http://www.computerworld.dk/, http://www.idg.dk. Ed. Rasmus Udsholt. R&P Arne Steinmark. adv.: B&W page USD 3,904, color page USD 4,829; trim 214 x 300. Circ: 28,500 (controlled).

004 ARG
COMPUTERWORLD ARGENTINA. Text in Spanish. 1983. fortn. adv. **Document type:** *Magazine, Consumer.*
Published by: C W Comunicaciones, Avda. Belgrano, 406 Piso 9, Capital Federal, Buenos Aires 1092, Argentina. TEL 54-11-43425583, FAX 54-11-43317672, idg@sion.com, http://www.computerworld.com.ar. Ed. Ruben Argento. adv.: B&W page USD 4,190, color page USD 6,704; trim 270 x 330. Circ: 14,150.

004 BRA
COMPUTERWORLD BRAZIL. Text in Portuguese. 1976. 26/yr. BRL 110 (effective 2002). adv. **Document type:** *Magazine, Trade.* **Description:** Provides complete coverage of computer industry news, management, software and services, networking, trends, computer careers, opinion and analyses.
Related titles: Online - full text ed.
Published by: I D G Computerworld do Brasil, Rua Tabapua, 145-3 e 4 andar, Itaim Bibi, Sao Paulo, 04533-010, Brazil. TEL 55-11-3049-2000, FAX 55-11-3071-4022, negocios@idg.com.br, http://www.computerworld.com.br, http://www.idg.com.br. adv.: B&W page BRL 17,000, color page BRL 27,000; trim 270 x 368. Circ: 30,000 (paid and controlled).

004 CRI
COMPUTERWORLD CENTRAL AMERICA. Text in Spanish. s-m. USD 13.72 (effective 2002). adv. **Document type:** *Magazine, Consumer.* **Description:** Covers the latest news and international developments on hardware (mainframes, minis, micros, workstations), communications equipment, software, services and office automation.
Related titles: Online - full text ed.
Published by: Trejos Hermanos Sucesores, S.A., Apdo. 10096, Curridabat 100 Este, Registro Nacional, San Jose, Costa Rica. TEL 506-224-2411, FAX 506-224-1528, circulacion@trejos.co.cr, http://micomputerworld.com, http://www.trejoshermanos.com. adv.: color page USD 2,675; trim 270 x 337. Circ: 10,982 (paid and controlled).

004 CHL
COMPUTERWORLD CHILE. Text in Spanish. fortn. adv. **Document type:** *Newspaper, Trade.* **Description:** Contains the latest local and international developments in hardware, software and terminals, as well as data processing, MIS and computer-related subjects.
Related titles: Online - full text ed.
Published by: Publicaciones en Computacion, Ltda., Antonio Varas 1371, Providencia, Santiago de Chile, Chile. TEL 56-2-204-2084, FAX 56-2-225-8621, http://www.cworld.cl, http://www.idgchile.cl. Ed. Jorge Espinoza. adv.: color page USD 4,160; trim 245 x 335. Circ: 12,000 (paid and controlled).

004 CZE ISSN 1210-9924
COMPUTERWORLD CZECH & SLOVAK REPUBLIC. Text in Czech, Slovak. 1990. w. CZK 599, SKK 728 (effective 2002). adv. **Document type:** *Magazine, Consumer.* **Description:** Provides information on new technology developments, hardware and software applications, industry trends and business events.
Related titles: Online - full text ed.: ISSN 1212-6810. 1996.
Published by: I D G Czech, a.s., Seydlerova 2451-11, Prague 5, 158 00, Czech Republic. TEL 420-2-57088111, FAX 420-2-6520812, info@idg.cz, http://www.cw.cz, http://www.idg.cz. Ed. Karel Taschner. Adv. contact Jitka Vyhlidkova TEL 420-2-57088181. B&W page USD 2,185, color page USD 2,855; bleed 265 x 330. Circ: 20,000 (paid and controlled).

004 ECU
COMPUTERWORLD ECUADOR. Text in Spanish. 1998. fortn. ECS 250,000, USD 25; ECS 1 newsstand/cover. adv. **Document type:** *Magazine, Consumer.* **Description:** For information professionals, managers and those who make decisions about technology acquisitions.
Published by: Ediworld, Ave. Patria 640 y Amazones, Edificio Patria, Piso 3, Apdo 17-07-8787, Quito, Ecuador. TEL 593-2220336, FAX 593-2220855, http:// www.computerworld.com.ec. Ed. Paulina Paredes. R&P Tim Clarke TEL 617-303-7820. adv.: B&W page USD 1,921, color page USD 2,077; trim 250 x 350. Circ: 1,000.

004 ESP ISSN 0212-2456
COMPUTERWORLD ESPANA. Text in Spanish. 1981. w. (44/yr.). EUR 149.47 (effective 2002). adv. **Document type:** *Magazine, Trade.* **Description:** Provides readers with vital information on optimizing information technology trends and opportunities.
Former titles (until 1981): Informatica de la Pequena y Meidana Empresa (0212-2472); (until 1977): Informatica (0212-2464)
Related titles: Online - full content ed.
—CINDOC.
Published by: I D G Communications, Fortuny, 18 4, Madrid, 28010, Spain. TEL 34-91-3496600, FAX 34-91-3196104, computerworld@idg.es, http://www.idg.es/computerworld. Ed. Maria Jose Marzal. Adv. contact Mar Cabanas TEL 34-91-3496678. color page USD 5,399; trim 277 x 365. Circ: 10,327 (paid).

004 TWN
COMPUTERWORLD - INFOWORLD TAIWAN. Text in Chinese. 1989. w. TWD 8,500. adv. **Document type:** *Newspaper, Trade.* **Description:** For MIS people and channel managers. Contains up-to-date news and comprehensive coverage of all the latest developments in hardware, software, system integrator, networking and Internet-Intranet.
Published by: I D G Communications, Taiwan, 8F, No. 131, Sec. 3, Nanking E. Rd., Taipei, 104, Taiwan. TEL 886-2-2715-3000, FAX 886-2-2547-0601, http://www.idg.com.tw/cw/index.html, http://www.infopro.com.tw. Ed. Eric Huang. Pub. James Lai. Adv. contact Lily Chou. page USD 2,733; trim 265 x 375. Circ: 20,000.

004 ITA ISSN 0392-8845
COMPUTERWORLD ITALIA. Text in Italian. 1983. w. (45 issues). EUR 11 domestic (effective 2005). adv. bk.rev. **Document type:** *Magazine, Trade.* **Description:** Covers news on PCs, workstations, mobile computing, software, LANs, and servers. Provides information on the computer industry: strategy, marketing and new products.
Related titles: Online - full text ed.
Published by: I D G Communications Italia s.r.l., Via Zante 16-2, Milano, 20138, Italy. TEL 39-02-580381, FAX 39-02-58011670, info@idg.it, http://www.cwi.it/, http://www.idgworld.it. Ed. Paolo Lombardi. Pub. Giulio Ferrari. Circ: 35,000.

004 UKR ISSN 1609-8145
COMPUTERWORLD KIEV. Variant title: Computerworld Ukraine. Text in Russian, Ukrainian. w. adv. **Document type:** *Magazine, Trade.* **Description:** Contains Ukrainian and international computer market and industry news, overviews and forecasts.
Address: Vossoedineniya pr 15, 7th Fl., Kiev, 02160, Ukraine. TEL 380-44-550-2092, FAX 380-44-294-8502. Ed. S Kostyukov. adv.: color page USD 1,900; trim 225 x 300. Circ: 12,000 (paid and controlled). **US dist. addr.:** East View Information Services, 3020 Harbor Ln. N., Minneapolis, MN 55447. TEL 612-550-0961.

004 MEX ISSN 0188-9370
COMPUTERWORLD MEXICO. Text in English. 1980. 35/yr. adv. **Document type:** *Magazine, Consumer.* **Description:** Covers the latest developments in hardware, software, peripherals, data processing and computer-related subjects.
Published by: I D G Mexico S.A. de C.V., Texas no. 66, Col Napoles, Mexico City, DF 03810, Mexico. TEL 52-5-5436821, FAX 52-5-2232909. adv.: color page USD 5,610; bleed 270 x 370. Circ: 15,000.

004 NZL ISSN 0113-1494
COMPUTERWORLD NEW ZEALAND. Text in English. 1986. w. (48/yr.). NZD 195 domestic; NZD 255 in Australasia; NZD 325 elsewhere; NZD 4.95 newsstand/cover (effective 2002). adv. **Document type:** *Magazine, Trade.* **Description:** Addresses issues related to personal computers, networking, and communications product, in addition to industry news and analysis.
Related titles: Online - full text ed.
Indexed: Inpharma, PE&ON, Reac.
Published by: I D G Communications Ltd., Wellesley St., PO Box 6813, Auckland, 1036, New Zealand. TEL 64-9-377-9902, FAX 64-9-377-4604, idg@idg.co.nz, http:// www.computerworld.co.nz, http://www.idg.net.nz. adv.: color page USD 2,158; trim 280 x 360. Circ: 8,073 (paid and controlled).

004 PER
COMPUTERWORLD PERU. Text in Spanish. fortn. adv. **Document type:** *Magazine, Consumer.* **Description:** Covers the most up-to-date technology as well as new products, studies, research, information highways, and local notes.
Published by: Empresa Editoria El Comercio, Jr A Miro Quesada, 247 Oficina 703, Lima, 1, Peru. TEL 51-14-342-5583, FAX 51-14-426-7400, editorinformaciones@comercio.com.pe, http://www.elcomercioperu.com.pe. adv.: color page USD 1,900; trim 275 x 365. Circ: 5,000 (paid and controlled).

004.692 PRT
COMPUTERWORLD PORTUGAL. Text in Portuguese. 1986. 45/yr. adv. **Document type:** *Magazine, Trade.* **Description:** Provides up-to-date information for decision-making executives in the data processing market.
Formerly: Correio Informatico (0870-8983)
Related titles: Online - full text ed.
Published by: Edicoes Expansao Economica Lda., Rue Mario Castelhano, 40-1, Queluz de Baixo, Barcarena, 2749-502, Portugal. TEL 351-21-496-95-40, FAX 351-21-436-95-39, webmaster@expansao.iol.pt, http://www.expansao.iol.pt. Ed. Idalecio Lourenco. adv.: color page USD 1,848; trim 240 x 335. Circ: 4,000.

004 CRI
COMPUTERWORLD PUERTO RICO. Text in Spanish. fortn. adv. **Document type:** *Magazine, Trade.* **Description:** Targeted at MIS/IS professionals in the Puerto Rican enterprise sector.
Published by: Trejos Hermanos Sucesores, S.A., Apdo. 10096, Curridabat 100 Este, Registro Nacional, San Jose, Costa Rica. TEL 506-224-2411, FAX 506-224-1528, circulacion@trejos.co.cr, http://www.trejoshermanos.com. adv.: B&W page USD 1,350, color page USD 1,800; trim 270 x 337. Circ: 1,000 (paid and controlled).

004 ROM ISSN 1222-4189
COMPUTERWORLD ROMANIA. Text in Romanian. 1993. fortn. ROL 400,000 domestic; USD 78.50 in Europe; USD 102.50 elsewhere (effective 2002). adv. **Document type:** *Newspaper, Trade.* **Description:** Contains analyses of the Rumanian and worldwide computer markets, news and product comparisons.
Related titles: Online - full text ed.
Published by: I D G Communications Publishing Group s.r.l., Bd. Maresal Averescu 8-10, cam. 705-708, Bucharest, 71316, Romania. TEL 40-1-224-2621, FAX 40-1-224-1132, raduc@idg.ro, http://www.computerworld.ro, http://www.idg.ro. adv.: B&W page USD 685, color page USD 900; 200 x 260. Circ: 9,600.

004 CHE ISSN 1420-5009
COMPUTERWORLD SCHWEIZ. Text in German. 1985. 50/yr. CHF 259 (effective 2003). **Document type:** *Newspaper, Trade.* **Description:** Reports in detail on all aspects of information and communications technologies available to companies.
Formerly (until 1995): Computerworld Schweiz (1421-458X)
Related titles: Online - full text ed.; Supplement(s): Computerworld Special. ISSN 1424-0882. 1999.
Published by: I D G Communications AG, Witikonerstr 15, Zuerich, 8030, Switzerland. TEL 41-1-3874444, FAX 41-1-3874584, redaktion@computerworld.ch, jacqueline.ort@idg.ch, http://www.computerworld.ch, http://www.idg.ch. Ed. Karlheinz Pichler. Adv. contact Stratos Prodromakis. Circ: 12,500.

004 SGP ISSN 0217-8362
COMPUTERWORLD SINGAPORE. Text in English. 1984. fortn. SGD 70 domestic; SGD 150 in Asia & the Pacific (effective 2002). adv. bk.rev. **Document type:** *Magazine, Trade.* **Description:** Contains up-to-the-minute news on IT products, services and strategies, with analysis that spans all computing products and platforms.
Formerly (until 1985): Asian Computerworld (0217-5665)
Related titles: Online - full text ed.: (from Northern Light Technology, Inc.).
Published by: Communications Resources Pte. Ltd., Block 1008, Toa Payoh N., #07-01, Singapore, 318996, Singapore. TEL 65-256-6201, 65-256-6201, FAX 65-251-0348, http://www.pcworld.com.sg, http://www.comres.com.sg. Ed. Gene Vallejo-Yeo. Adv. contact Melvin Ang. Circ: 11,127.

004 HUN ISSN 0237-7837
COMPUTERWORLD SZAMOTASTECHNIKA. Text in Hungarian. 1970. w. HUF 12,000 (effective 2002). adv. **Document type:** *Magazine, Consumer.* **Description:** Provides readers with market analyses, tests, reports and news on the international as well as domestic computer markets.
Formerly (until 1986): Szamotastechnika (0587-1514)
Related titles: Online - full text ed.: ISSN 1588-0265. 1998.
Published by: I D G Hungary Kft., PO Box 386, Budapest, 1537, Hungary. TEL 361-474-8850, FAX 361-269-5676, http://www.szt.hu, http://www.idg.hu. adv.: B&W page USD 2,100, color page USD 2,900; trim 233 x 301. Circ: 12,000.

004 VEN
COMPUTERWORLD VENEZUELA. Text in Spanish. s-m. VEB 29,700 domestic; USD 150 foreign (effective 2002). adv. **Document type:** *Magazine, Consumer.* **Description:** Coverage includes local and international industry and products news, reviews and features.
Related titles: Online - full text ed.
Published by: I D G Comunicaciones C.A., A.P. 61080 Chacao, Caracas, 1060-A, Venezuela. TEL 58-212-793-9262, FAX 58-212-793-7384, idg@idg.com.ve, http://www.cwv.com.ve, http://www.cwvlatin.com. adv.: color page USD 4,140; trim 266 x 370. Circ: 5,000.

004 MYS ISSN 1394-1070
COMPUTIMES SHOPPER MALAYSIA. Text in English. 1994. m. adv. **Document type:** *Magazine, Consumer.*
Related titles: Online - full text ed.: (from Gale Group).
Published by: I T Publications Sdn. Bhd. (Subsidiary of: New Straits Times Press (Malaysia) Berhad), Balai Berita 31, Jalan Riong, Kuala Lumpur, 59100, Malaysia. TEL 60-3-20569375, FAX 60-3-22840015, itp@itp.nstp.com.my.

004 GBR
COMPUTING. Text in English. 1986. w. GBP 100; GBP 1.50 newsstand/cover (effective 1999). adv. bk.rev. charts; illus.; tr.lit. **Document type:** *Trade.* **Description:** Sharply-edited mix of news, strategic analysis and technology reporting offering an unparalleled insight into the fast-moving world of enterprise technology.
Formed by the merger of (1974-1986): Computing Newspaper (0267-4769); (1974-1986): Computing Magazine (0267-4750); Which both superseded in part (in 1984): Computing (0144-3097); Which was formerly (until 1980): Computing Europe (0307-8965)
Related titles: Online - full text ed.: (from Gale Group, LexisNexis).
Indexed: B&I, BMT, BrTechI, CompD, CompR, CurCont, Emerald, EngInd, Inspec, KES, PROMT.
—BLDSC (3395.009000), IE, ingenta.
Published by: (British Computer Society), V N U Business Publications Ltd., VNU House, 32-34 Broadwick St, London, W1A 2HG, United Kingdom. TEL 44-20-7316-9000, FAX 44-20-7316-9160, http://www.vnu.co.uk. Ed. Graham Cunningham. Circ: 92,990. **Dist. by:** MarketForce UK Ltd, 247 Tottenham Court Rd, London, Middx W1T 7AU, United Kingdom. TEL 44-207-2615199, FAX 44-207-2617341.

004 AUT ISSN 0010-485X
QA76 CODEN: CMPTA2
➤ **COMPUTING;** archives for scientific computing. Text in English. 1966. 8/yr. EUR 970 combined subscription to institutions print & online eds. (effective 2005). adv. bk.rev. charts; illus.; abstr. index. back issues avail.; reprint service avail. from PSC,ISI. **Document type:** *Journal, Academic/Scholarly.* **Description:** Publishes original papers from all fields of scientific computing.
Related titles: Microform ed.: (from PQC); Online - full text ed.: ISSN 1436-5057 (from EBSCO Publishing, ProQuest Information & Learning, Springer LINK, Swets Information Services); ♦ Supplement(s): Computing Supplementum. ISSN 0344-8029.
Indexed: ABIn, ADPA, AHCI, ApMecR, CCMJ, CIS, CMCI, CompAb, CompLI, CompR, CurCont, CybAb, IAA, IAOP, ISR, Inspec, MathR, MathSciNet, PROMT, RASB, RefZh, SCI, ZentMath.
—BLDSC (3395.010000), AskIEEE, CISTI, Ei, IDS, IE, Infotrieve, ingenta, Linda Hall. **CCC.**
Published by: Springer-Verlag Wien (Subsidiary of: Springer Science+Business Media) journals@springer.at, http://www.springer.at/computing. Eds. H Brunner, R E Burkhard, Wolfgang Hackbusch. R&P Angela Foessl TEL 43-1-3302415517. Adv. contact Michael Katzenberger TEL 43-1-3302415220. B&W page EUR 1,000; 120 x 190. **Subscr. in the Americas to:** Springer-Verlag New York, Inc., Journal Fulfillment, PO Box 2485, Secaucus, NJ 07096-2485. TEL 800-777-4643, 201-348-4033, FAX 201-348-4505, journals@springer-ny.com, http://www.springer-ny.com.

004 GBR ISSN 1461-6122
COMPUTING AND INFORMATION SYSTEMS TECHNICAL REPORTS. Text in English. 1998. 3/yr. GBP 20 (effective 2003).
Related titles: Online - full content ed.
Indexed: Inspec.
—BLDSC (3395.019820).
Published by: University of Paisley, Department of Computing and Information Systems, High St, University Of Paisley, Paisley, PA1 2BE, United Kingdom. TEL 44-141-848-3300, malcolm.crowe@paisley.ac.uk, http://cis.paisley.ac.uk/research/reports/index.html. Ed. M K Crowe.

004.678 AUS ISSN 1326-2637
COMPUTING NEWS. Text in English. 1998. bi-m. **Description:** Includes articles on computing, communications and internet topics.
Media: Online - full text.
Published by: Queensland University of Technology, School of Communication, GPO Box 2434, Brisbane, QLD 4001, Australia. FAX 61-7-3864-1811, http://www.qut.edu.au/computing_services/.

016.004 USA ISSN 0010-4884
CODEN: CPGRA6
➤ **COMPUTING REVIEWS.** Text in English. 1960. m. USD 205 domestic to non-members; USD 230 foreign to non-members; USD 52 domestic to members; USD 77 foreign to members; USD 47 domestic to students; USD 72 foreign to students (effective 2006). adv. bk.rev. abstr.; illus. cum.index. reprints avail. **Document type:** *Journal, Academic/Scholarly.* **Description:** Reviews of current publications in all areas of computer science. Covers hardware, software, computer systems organization, theory of computation, information systems and computer applications.
Related titles: Microfiche ed.: (from PQC, WWS); Online - full text ed.: Computing Reviews Online. USD 118 to libraries (effective 2006) (from EBSCO Publishing, The Dialog Corporation).
Indexed: BrCerAb, C&ISA, CerAb, CorrAb, E&CAJ, EMA, IAA, M&TEA, MBF, METADEX, RASB, RefZh, WAA.
—BLDSC (3395.124000), CASDDS, Linda Hall. **CCC.**
Published by: Association for Computing Machinery, Inc., 1515 Broadway, 17th Fl, New York, NY 10036-5701. TEL 212-626-0500, 212-626-0520, 800-342-6626, FAX 212-944-1318, acmhelp@acm.org, sigs@acm.org, usacm@acm.org, http://www.acm.org/reviews. Ed. Carol Hutchins. Circ: 8,500.

004 ZAF ISSN 0254-2196
COMPUTING S A. Text in English. 1979. w. ZAR 191.67 domestic; ZAR 407.67 in Namibia; ZAR 503.67 elsewhere (effective 2000). adv. back issues avail. **Document type:** *Magazine, Trade.* **Description:** Provides comprehensive news and analysis of technology and management issues.
Formerly (until 1981): Computronics (0250-0191)
Related titles: Online - full text ed.
Indexed: ISAP, Inspec, PROMT.
Published by: T M L Business Publishing (Subsidiary of: Times Media Ltd.), PO Box 182, Pinegowrie, Gauteng 2123, South Africa. TEL 27-11-789-2144, FAX 27-11-789-3196, http://www.computingsa.co.za. Ed. Charlene Carroll. Pub. Heather Wills. Adv. contact Nicki Goosen. color page USD 1,534; trim 280 x 410. Circ: 14,200.

004 AUT ISSN 0344-8029
CODEN: COSPDM
➤ **COMPUTING SUPPLEMENTUM.** Text in English. 1977. irreg., latest vol.16, 2003. price varies. adv. abstr. reprint service avail. from ISI. **Document type:** *Monographic series, Academic/Scholarly.* **Description:** Publishes selected papers from conferences in the field of scientific computing.
Related titles: ♦ Supplement to: Computing. ISSN 0010-485X.
Indexed: CCMJ, Inspec, MathR, RASB, ZentMath.
—BLDSC (3395.128900), AskIEEE, CISTI, IE, Infotrieve, Linda Hall. **CCC.**
Published by: Springer-Verlag Wien (Subsidiary of: Springer Science+Business Media) TEL 43-1-3302415-0, FAX 43-1-330242665, books@springer.at, http://www.springer.at/computing. R&P Angela Foessl TEL 43-1-3302415517. Adv. contact Michael Katzenberger TEL 43-1-3302415220. B&W page EUR 1,000; 120 x 190. **Subscr. in the Americas to:** Springer-Verlag New York, Inc., Journal Fulfillment, PO Box 2485, Secaucus, NJ 07096-2485. TEL 800-777-4643, 201-348-4033, FAX 201-348-4505, orders@springer-ny.com.

004 JPN ISSN 0010-4906
COMPUTOPIA✶. Text in Japanese. 1966. m. adv. bk.rev.
Indexed: JCT, JTA.
Published by: Computer-Age-sha, Time 24 Bldg, 2-45 Oumi, Koutou-ku, Tokyo, 135, Japan. Eds. Teijiro Kubo, Terutaka Kawabata.

COMUNICACIONES; telecomunicaciones, comunicaciones de datos, computadoras y satelites. see *COMMUNICATIONS*

COMUNIDAD INFORMATICA. see *COMPUTERS—Abstracting, Bibliographies, Statistics*

004 USA
CONNECTED HOME. Text in English. 2002 (May). 8/yr. USD 29.95 domestic; USD 35.95 in Canada; USD 59.95 elsewhere; USD 5.95 newsstand/cover; USD 7.95 newsstand/cover in Canada (effective 2002). adv. Supplement avail. **Document type:** *Magazine, Consumer.* **Description:** Covers home computing networks for telecommuting, home entertainment equipment, multimedia and gaming components, personal digital assistant devices, Internet appliances, cellular phones and home office equipment.
Published by: Penton Media, Inc. (Subsidiary of: Pittway Company), 1300 E 9th St, Cleveland, OH 44114-1503. TEL 216-696-7000, FAX 216-696-1752, http://www.connectedhomemag.com, http://www.penton.com. Pub. Karen Forster.

CONTRACT PROFESSIONAL; the magazine for IT contractors and consultants. see *BUSINESS AND ECONOMICS—Small Business*

004 USA ISSN 0734-757X
CODEN: PCTNDC
CONTRIBUTIONS TO THE STUDY OF COMPUTER SCIENCE. Text in English. 1983. irreg., latest vol.4, 1997. price varies. **Document type:** *Monographic series, Academic/Scholarly.*
—CISTI.
Published by: Greenwood Publishing Group Inc. (Subsidiary of: Harcourt International), 88 Post Rd W, PO Box 5007, Westport, CT 06881. TEL 203-226-3571, FAX 203-226-1502, webmaster@greenwood.com, http://www.greenwood.com.

004 USA
CONVERGENCE QUARTERLY. Text in English. q. **Document type:** *Journal, Trade.* **Description:** Contains analysis and commentary on global convergence of information processing, communications, and media technologies, including trends, issues, and alliances.
Media: Online - full content.
Published by: Faulkner Information Services, Inc. (Subsidiary of: Information Today, Inc.), 116 Cooper Center, 7905 Browning Rd, Pennsauken, NJ 08109-4319. TEL 856-662-2070, 800-843-0460, FAX 856-662-3380, faulkner@faulkner.com, http://www.faulkner.com/library/showcase/cqdatasheet.htm.

004 DEU
COPERS - H R PERSONALARBEIT. Text in German. 1993. 8/yr. EUR 89; EUR 15 newsstand/cover (effective 2004). adv. **Document type:** *Magazine, Trade.*
Former titles: CoPers - Computergestuetzte und Operative Personalarbeit; CoPers - Computergestuetzte Personalarbeit (0943-6669)
Indexed: DIP, IBR, IBZ.

C

Published by: Datakontext Fachverlag GmbH, Augustinusstr 9 d, Frechen, 50226, Germany. TEL 49-2234-966100, FAX 49-2234-966109, info@datakontext.com, http://www.datakontext-press.de/COPERS/COPERS_hauptframe.htm. Adv. contact Gabriele Beuder. B&W page EUR 1,500, color page EUR 2,625; trim 185 x 270. Circ: 4,000 (paid and controlled).

004 USA ISSN 1528-4972
CROSSROADS; the ACM student magazine. Text in English. 1994. q. USD 70 combined subscription domestic to non-members print & online eds.; USD 84 combined subscription foreign to non-members print & online eds.; USD 35 combined subscription domestic to members print & online eds.; USD 49 combined subscription foreign to members print & online eds. (effective 2006). adv. **Document type:** *Journal, Academic/Scholarly.* **Description:** Provides easily accessible articles on a wide range of computer science related topics and a forum to share work with others.
Related titles: Online - full text ed.: ISSN 1528-4980. 1994. free (effective 2006).
—Linda Hall. **CCC.**
Published by: Association for Computing Machinery, Inc., 1515 Broadway, 17th Fl, New York, NY 10036-5701. TEL 212-626-0500, 800-342-6626, FAX 212-944-1318, sigs@acm.org, usacm@acm.org, http://www.acm.org/crossroads/. Ed. William Stevenson. adv.: B&W page USD 5,420. Circ: 20,000 (controlled).

004 DEU ISSN 0724-8679
C'T; Magazin fuer Computer Technik. Text in German. 1983. 26/yr. EUR 66.20 domestic; EUR 77.70 foreign; EUR 73.20 domestic with CD-ROM; EUR 84.70 foreign with CD-ROM; EUR 3 newsstand/cover (effective 2003). adv. **Document type:** *Magazine, Consumer.*
Related titles: CD-ROM ed.; Online - full text ed.: (from EBSCO Publishing).
—IE, Infotrieve. **CCC.**
Published by: Verlag Heinz Heise GmbH und Co. KG, Helstorfer Str 7, Hannover, 30625, Germany. TEL 49-511-5352-0, FAX 49-511-5352-129, ct@heise.de, abo@heise.de, http://www.heise.de/ct. Ed. Christian Persson. Adv. contact Udo Elsner. B&W page EUR 8,700, color page EUR 11,200. Circ: 390,037 (paid).

CULTIVATE INTERACTIVE. see *TECHNOLOGY: COMPREHENSIVE WORKS*

CURRENT PAPERS ON COMPUTERS & CONTROL. see *COMPUTERS—Abstracting, Bibliographies, Statistics*

004 USA ISSN 1524-6493
CURRENTS IN ELECTRONIC LITERACY. Text in English. 1999.
Media: Online - full text.
Indexed: MLA-IB.
Published by: University of Texas at Austin, Computer Writing and Research Lab, Division of Rhetoric & Composition, B5500, Austin, TX 78712-1122. http://www.cwrl.utexas.edu/currents/. Ed. John Slatin.

CUSTOMERBASE. see *BUSINESS AND ECONOMICS—Marketing And Purchasing*

004 ISR ISSN 0334-0996
D E C U S ISRAEL NEWS. Text in English, Hebrew. q.
Published by: Digital Equipment Computer Users Society, Digital House, Acadia Junction, Herzelia, 46733, Israel. TEL 052-548222.

004 USA
D E C U S MAGAZINE. Text in English. 1962. q. membership. adv. bk.rev. **Document type:** *Newsletter.* **Description:** Covers organization and committee news as well as symposia reports and technical articles of interest to the computing world.
Former titles: D E C U S '9X; DECUScope (0011-7447)
Related titles: Online - full text ed.
Indexed: Inspec.
—Linda Hall.
Published by: Digital Equipment Computer Users Society, Communications Organization, 334 South St, SHR3 1 T25, Shrewsbury, MA 01545. TEL 508-841-3584, FAX 508-841-3357, information@decus.org, http://www.decus.org. Ed., R&P Paula Morin. Circ: 25,000 (controlled).

004 USA
▼ **D S P & F P G A PRODUCT RESOURCE GUIDE.** Text in English. 2004. a. adv. **Document type:** *Trade.*
Published by: OpenSystems Publishing, 30233 Jefferson Ave, St Clair Shores, MI 48082. TEL 810-415-6500, FAX 810-415-4882, newproducts@opensystems-publishing.com, http://www.imakenews.com/opensystems/index000071570.cfm, http://www.opensystems-publishing.com/. adv.: color page USD 2,800; trim 8 x 10.875. Circ: 16,000 (paid).

004 SWE ISSN 1402-0947
DAGENS I T. Text in Swedish. 1996. 36/yr. SEK 595; SEK 20 newsstand/cover (effective 2001). adv. **Document type:** *Magazine, Trade.* **Description:** Focuses on information for decision markers who take part in the buying process of IT products and services.
Related titles: Online - full text ed.: ISSN 1402-411X.
Published by: Ekonomi och Teknik Foerlag, Maester Samuelsgatan 56, Stockholm, 10612, Sweden. TEL 46-8-796-66-50, FAX 46-8-613-30-34, redaktionen@dagensit.se, http://www.dagensit.se, http://www.et.se. Ed., Pub. Peter Pettersson. Adv. contact Carina Aakerlund. B&W page SEK 44,400, color page SEK 52,900; trim 255 x 350. Circ: 50,500.

004 NLD ISSN 0169-023X
QA76.9.D26 CODEN: DKENEW
➤ **DATA & KNOWLEDGE ENGINEERING.** Text and summaries in English. 1985. 12/yr. EUR 1,488 in Europe to institutions; JPY 197,400 in Japan to institutions; USD 1,665 to institutions except Europe and Japan (effective 2006). bk.rev. back issues avail.; reprints avail. **Document type:** *Academic/Scholarly.* **Description:** Publishes original research results, technical advances and news items concerning data engineering, knowledge engineering, and the interface of these two fields.
Related titles: Online - full text ed.: (from EBSCO Publishing, Gale Group, IngentaConnect, ScienceDirect, Swets Information Services).
Indexed: AIA, ASCA, C&ISA, CMCI, CompAb, CompLI, CompR, CurCont, CybAb, E&CAJ, EngInd, InfoSAb, Inspec, RASB, RefZh, SolStAb, ZentMath.
—BLDSC (3534.250000), AskIEEE, CISTI, Ei, IDS, IE, Infotrieve, ingenta, Linda Hall. **CCC.**
Published by: Elsevier BV, North-Holland (Subsidiary of: Elsevier Science & Technology), Sara Burgerhartstraat 25, Amsterdam, 1055 KV, Netherlands. TEL 31-20-485-3911, FAX 31-20-485-2457, nlinfo-f@elsevier.nl, http://www.elsevier.com/locate/datak, http://www.elsevier.nl. Ed. P P Chen. **Subscr. to:** Elsevier BV, PO Box 211, Amsterdam 1000 AE, Netherlands. TEL 31-20-485-3757, FAX 31-20-485-3432, http://www.elsevier.nl.

004 NOR ISSN 0806-8917
DATAMAGASINET✶. Text in Norwegian. 1983. fortn. USD 45. adv. bk.rev. **Document type:** *Magazine, Trade.*
Formerly (until 1995): C: - Privat (0805-6005); Which superseded in part: Computerworld Norge (0800-5966); Which incorporated (1993-1994): Cad - Cam World (Oslo) (0804-7480); Which was formerly (1988-1993): C - World (0802-8796)
Published by: Computer Communications Norge AS, Postboks 9090, Gronland, Oslo, 0133, Norway. TEL 47-22-05-30-00, FAX 47-22-05-30-01. Ed. Morten Hansen. Circ: 15,000.

004 NOR ISSN 0332-8171
DATATID. Text in Norwegian. 1979. m. NOK 560 domestic; NOK 935 foreign; NOK 59 newsstand/cover (effective 1999). adv. bk.rev. back issues avail. **Document type:** *Trade.* **Description:** Focuses on the needs of advanced users of computers and software.
Formerly: Teknisk Ukeblad Data (0800-532X)
Related titles: Online - full text ed.
Indexed: Inspec, PROMT.
—AskIEEE, CISTI, Linda Hall. **CCC.**
Published by: Fasit Forlag AS, Postboks 2739, St Hanshaugen, Oslo, 0131, Norway. TEL 47-22-03-22-20, FAX 47-22-03-22-21, tosterud@datatid.no, http://www.datatid.no. Ed., R&P Svein-Erik Tosterud. Pub. Svein Erik Tosterud. Adv. contact Gorm Schou. B&W page NOK 15,700, color page NOK 20,500. Circ: 11,000 (controlled).

004 DNK ISSN 0109-9213
DATATID. Text in Danish. 1984. m. (11/yr.). DKK 635 domestic; DKK 1,043 in Europe; DKK 1,180 elsewhere (effective 2001). adv. back issues avail. **Document type:** *Magazine, Trade.* **Description:** Provides current information on EDP and computers in business and in the home.
Incorporates (in 1991): Open Windows (0907-1555)
Published by: Audio Media A-S, St Kongensgade 72, Copenhagen K, 1264, Denmark. TEL 45-33-912833, FAX 45-33-910121, redaktionen@datatid.dk, http://www.datatid.dk. Ed. Michael C. Svendsen. Adv. contact Klaus Wiedemann. Circ: 35,000.

004 SWE ISSN 1650-1306
DATORMAGAZIN. Text in Swedish. 2000. m. SEK 599 (effective 2005). adv. software rev. charts; illus.; mkt.; stat. 180 p./no.; back issues avail. **Document type:** *Magazine, Consumer.* **Description:** Covers both hardware and software for professional PC users.
Incorporates (2003-2004): Naetmagazin med Saekerhet (1652-0564); Formed by the 2000 merger of: PC Plus (1402-716X); (1997-2000): PC Extra (1402-8751); Which superseded in part (1993-1997): PC & Mac Magazine (1104-1447); (1992-1995): Datormagazin (1104-3784); Which was formerly (1986-1992): Datormagazin C64-128-Amiga (0283-3379)
Published by: Hjemmet Mortensen AB (Subsidiary of: Hjemmet-Mortensen AS), Gaevlegatan 22, Stockholm, 11378, Sweden. TEL 46-8-6920100, FAX 46-8-6509705, datormagazin@datamagazin.se, info@hjemmetmortensen.se, http://www.datormagazin.se, http://www.hjemmetmortensen.se. Eds. Mats Larsson, Peter Widen. adv.: color page SEK 52,000; 190 x 285. Circ: 27,800 (controlled).

004 USA
▼ **DAYTRUM.** Text in English. 2003. irreg. free. adv. **Document type:** *Magazine, Consumer.* **Description:** Provides family-friendly information on the latest computing technologies, and the best video and computer games.
Media: Online - full content.
Address: editors@daytrum.com, http://www.daytrum.com/.

DENSANKI RIYO NI KANSURU SHINPOJUMU KOENGAIYO/SYMPOSIUM OF COMPUTER RESEARCH. PROCEEDINGS. see *ENGINEERING—Civil Engineering*

004 USA ISSN 1530-1591
DESIGN, AUTOMATION, AND TEST IN EUROPE CONFERENCE AND EXHIBITION. PROCEEDINGS. Cover title: Design, Automation and Test in Europe Conference. Variant title: D A T E - Conference. Text in English. 1998. a., latest 2003. USD 328 per vol.; USD 132 per vol. to members (effective 2004). **Document type:** *Proceedings, Trade.*
Related titles: Online - full text ed.: (from I E E E).
—BLDSC (3535.833510).
Published by: (A C M Special Interest Group on Design Automation, E D A Association), I E E E Computer Society, 1730 Massachusetts Ave, N W, Washington, DC 20036-1903. TEL 202-371-0101, FAX 202-728-9614, http://www.computer.org. **Subscr. addr.:** Institute of Electrical and Electronics Engineers, Inc., 445 Hoes Ln, Piscataway, NJ 08854-1331. TEL 732-981-0060, FAX 732-981-9667.

004 USA
DESK HELP NEWS. Text in English. irreg. **Description:** Covers the fast paced world of computing and technical support.
Media: Online - full text.
Address: Jp@helpdesknews.com, http://www.helpdesknews.com/. Ed. Jon Paul Taylor.

004 CHN ISSN 1005-0043
DIANNAO AIHAOZHE/COMPUTER FAN. Text in Chinese. 1993. s-m. CNY 110.40 (effective 2004). adv. **Document type:** *Magazine, Consumer.*
Address: PO Box 9615, Beijing, 100086, China. TEL 86-10-62161335, FAX 86-10-62162003, http://www.cfan.com.cn/index1.htm. adv.: color page USD 1,500; trim 260 x 185. Circ: 80,000.

004 CHN ISSN 1006-5202
DIANNAO JISHU/COMPUTER TECHNOLOGY. Text in Chinese. m. adv. **Document type:** *Academic/Scholarly.*
Related titles: Online - full text ed.: (from East View Information Services).
Published by: Shanghai Keji Jiaoyu Chubanshe/Shanghai Science and Technology Education Publishing House, 393 Guanshengyuan Lu, Shanghai, 200233, China. TEL 86-21-4367970, FAX 86-21-4762835. Ed. Wu Yanqi. Adv. contact Gong Qing.

004 CHN ISSN 1003-5850
TK7885.A1
DIANNAO KAIFA YU YINGYONG/COMPUTER DEVELOPMENT & APPLICATIONS. Text in Chinese. 1985. q. USD 4 per issue. adv. bk.rev. **Document type:** *Academic/Scholarly.*
Related titles: Online - full text ed.: (from East View Information Services).
Published by: Beifang Zidong Kongzhi Jishu Yanjiusuo, P.O. Box 8, Qi Xian (county), Shanxi 030900, China. TEL 86-351-7043553, FAX 86-351-7042975. Ed. Tang Pengfei. Adv. contact Song Guolao. Circ: 9,500 (paid); 500 (controlled).

▼ **DIANZI SHANGWU YANJIU/ELECTRONIC COMMERCE STUDIES.** see *BUSINESS AND ECONOMICS*

004 GBR ISSN 1461-3816
DIGIT. Text in English. 1998. m. GBP 64.87 domestic; GBP 85 in Europe; GBP 120 elsewhere; GBP 4.99 newsstand/cover (effective 2002). adv. back issues avail. **Document type:** *Magazine, Consumer.* **Description:** Contains news, reviews and tips on the latest digital technology & computer models.
Related titles: Online - full text ed.; ♦ Includes: Webcreate.
—IE. **CCC.**
Published by: I D G Media, 99 Gray's Inn Rd, London, WC1X 8UT, United Kingdom. TEL 44-20-7831-9252, http://www.digitmag.co.uk, http://www.idg.co.uk. Ed. Matthew Bath. adv.: page GBP 2,442.

DIGITAL COMMUNICATION. see *COMMUNICATIONS*

004 USA
▼ **DIGITAL E.** Text in English. 2005 (Jul.). m. free to qualified personnel (effective 2005). **Document type:** *Magazine, Consumer.*
Published by: Possibility Media, 10400 N.W. 33rd St., Ste. 270, Miami, FL 33172. TEL 786-206-8880, FAX 786-206-8884, info@possibilitymedia.com, http://www.digitalemag.com/, http://www.possibilitymedia.com/.

004 GBR
DIGITAL HOME. Text in English. 2002 (Dec.). irreg. GBP 3.50 per issue domestic; GBP 5.50 per issue in Europe; GBP 6.50 per issue elsewhere (effective 2003). **Document type:** *Magazine, Consumer.* **Description:** Contains features, articles and analysis exploring all the latest technologies and trends.

Published by: Future Publishing Ltd., Beauford Court, 30 Monmouth St, Bath, Avon BA1 2BW, United Kingdom. TEL 44-1225-442244, FAX 44-1225-446019, customerservice@futurenet.co.uk, http://www.digitalhomemag.com/, http://www.futurenet.com. Ed. Dan Hutchinson.

DIGITAL MEDIA WORLD. see *JOURNALISM*

▼ **DIGITAL MEDIEVALIST.** see *HISTORY*

004 USA
DIGITAL POWER REPORT. Text in English. m. 8 p./no.; back issues avail. **Document type:** *Newsletter, Trade.*
Related titles: Online - full content ed.
Published by: Gilder Publishing, 291A Main St, Great Barrington, MA 01230. TEL 888-484-2727, FAX 413-644-2123, hmpowerreport@gilder.com, http://www.digitalpowerreport.com. Eds. Mark Mills, Peter Huber. Adv. contact Brian Cole TEL 413-644-2127.

DIGITAL TECHNOLOGY LAW JOURNAL. see *PATENTS, TRADEMARKS AND COPYRIGHTS*

DIGITAL VIDEO MADE EASY; the easy way to take better movies. see *COMMUNICATIONS—Video*

004 DEU
DIGITAL WORLD; Technik, die Spass macht. Text in German. q. EUR 17; EUR 5 newsstand/cover (effective 2004). adv. **Document type:** *Magazine, Consumer.*
Published by: I D G Communications Verlag AG, Leopoldstr 252b, Munich, 80807, Germany. TEL 49-89-36086532, FAX 49-89-36086570, redaktion@digital-world.de, info@idg-verlag.de, http://www.digital-world.de, http://www.idg-verlag.de. Ed. Roland Bischoff. Adv. contact Reinhard Baum. B&W page EUR 5,530, color page EUR 7,900; bleed 225 x 297.

004.092 USA ISSN 0193-9920
HD9696.C63
DIRECTORY OF TOP COMPUTER EXECUTIVES. Text in English. 1972-1984; resumed. s-a. USD 370; USD 245 per issue (effective 2005). **Document type:** *Directory, Trade.* **Description:** Listing of top MIS installations in the US, including names and titles of MIS executives.
Media: Duplicated (not offset).
Published by: Applied Computer Research, Inc., PO Box 82266, Phoenix, AZ 85071-2266. TEL 602-216-9100, FAX 602-216-9200, alan@acrha.com, tara@acrhq.com, http://www.itmarketintelligence.com/, http://www.acrhq.com. Ed. Alan Howard. Circ: 3,000 (paid).

004 GBR
DIRECTORY OF TRAINING. Text in English. 1982. a. GBP 123. adv. charts; illus. index. back issues avail.
Former titles: Directory of Computer Training; Directory of Management Training
Published by: Directory of Training Ltd., 51 High St, Ruislip, Mddx HA4 7BD, United Kingdom. Ed. Colin G Steed. Circ: 3,000.

DISCRETE & COMPUTATIONAL GEOMETRY; an international journal of mathematics and computer science. see *MATHEMATICS*

DISCUSSION PAPERS IN QUANTITATIVE ECONOMICS & COMPUTING. see *BUSINESS AND ECONOMICS*

DISKRETNYI ANALIZ I ISSLEDOVANIE OPERATSII. SERIYA 1. see *MATHEMATICS*

DISKRETNYI ANALIZ I ISSLEDOVANIE OPERATSII. SERIYA 2. see *MATHEMATICS*

004 DEU ISSN 0178-2770
QA76.9.D5 CODEN: DICOEB
➤ **DISTRIBUTED COMPUTING.** Text in English. 1986. bi-m. USD 45 domestic to members; USD 59 foreign to members (effective 2006). adv. reprint service avail. from PSC. **Document type:** *Journal, Academic/Scholarly.* **Description:** Topics covered include novel architectures of distributed systems and computer networks, communication protocols and hierarchies, distributed operating systems, and formal modeling, verification and synthesis of distributed systems.
Related titles: Online - full text ed.: ISSN 1432-0452 (from EBSCO Publishing, ProQuest Information & Learning, Springer LINK, Swets Information Services).
Indexed: ASCA, BrCerAb, C&CSA, C&ISA, CMCI, CerAb, CompAb, CompLI, CompR, CorrAb, CurCont, CybAb, E&CAJ, EMA, EngInd, IAA, Inspec, M&TEA, MBF, METADEX, RefZh, SoftBase, WAA, ZentMath.
—BLDSC (3602.661200), AskIEEE, CISTI, Ei, IDS, IE, Infotrieve, ingenta, Linda Hall. **CCC.**
Published by: Springer-Verlag (Subsidiary of: Springer Science+Business Media), Tiergartenstr 17, Heidelberg, 69121, Germany. TEL 49-6221-3450, FAX 49-6221-345229, http://link.springer.de/link/service/journals/00446/index.htm, http://www.springer.de. Ed. V Hadzilacos. Adv. contact Stephan Kroeck TEL 49-30-827875739. **Subscr. in the Americas to:** Springer-Verlag New York, Inc., Journal Fulfillment, PO Box 2485, Secaucus, NJ 07096-2485. TEL 201-348-4033, FAX 201-348-4505; **Subscr. to:** Springer GmbH Auslieferungsgesellschaft, Haberstr 7, Heidelberg 69126, Germany. TEL 49-6221-345-0, FAX 49-6221-345-4229, subscriptions@springer.de.

004 FRA ISSN 0991-2738
DROIT DE L'INFORMATIQUE ET DES TELECOMS. Text in French. 4/yr.
Formerly (until 1987): Droit de l'Informatique (0772-4152)
Related titles: ♦ Dutch ed.: Computerrecht. ISSN 0771-7784.
Indexed: ELLIS, FLP.
Published by: Editions du Parques, 119 rue de Flandre, Paris, 75019, France. TEL 40-35-03-03, FAX 40-38-96-43. Circ: 3,340.

004 USA
DUMMIES DAILY COMPUTING BASICS NEWSLETTER. Text in English. 1999. d. back issues avail. **Document type:** *Newsletter.*
Media: Online - full text.
Published by: I D G Books Worldwide, Inc., 919 E. Hillsdale Blvd., Ste. 400, Foster City, CA 94404. david@mkpr.com, http://www.dummiesdaily.com/. Ed. David Hafner.

004 USA
DYNAMIC SILICON. Text in English. 2001. m.
Published by: Gilder Publishing, 291A Main St, Great Barrington, MA 01230. TEL 888-484-2727, FAX 413-644-2123, dynamicsilicon@gilder.com, http://www.dynamicsilicon.com. Ed. Nick Tredennick. Adv. contact Brian Cole TEL 413-644-2127.

004 GBR ISSN 1468-9367
CODEN: DSYYAD
➤ **DYNAMICAL SYSTEMS;** an international journal. Text in English. 1986. q. GBP 598, USD 992 combined subscription to institutions print & online eds. (effective 2006). adv. index. back issues avail.; reprint service avail. from PSC. **Document type:** *Journal, Academic/Scholarly.* **Description:** Disseminates original international research concerning the stability, instability, bifurcation and oscillatory behavior of natural and manmade systems.
Formerly (until 2000): Dynamics and Stability of Systems (0268-1110)
Related titles: Microfiche ed.; Online - full text ed.: ISSN 1468-9375. GBP 568, USD 942 to institutions (effective 2006) (from EBSCO Publishing, Gale Group, IngentaConnect, O C L C Online Computer Library Center, Inc., ProQuest Information & Learning, Swets Information Services).
Indexed: ASCA, ApMecR, BrCerAb, C&ISA, CCMJ, CerAb, CompAb, CorrAb, CurCont, E&CAJ, EMA, EngInd, IAA, ISMEC, Inspec, M&TEA, MBF, METADEX, MathR, MathSciNet, RASB, RefZh, SolStAb, WAA, ZentMath.
—BLDSC (3637.143035), AskIEEE, CISTI, Ei, IDS, IE, Infotrieve, ingenta, Linda Hall. **CCC.**
Published by: Taylor & Francis Ltd (Subsidiary of: Taylor & Francis Group), 4 Park Sq, Milton Park, Abingdon, OX14 4RN, United Kingdom. TEL 44-1235-828600, FAX 44-1235-829000, info@tandf.co.uk, http://www.tandf.co.uk/journals/titles/14689367.asp. Eds. Matthew Nicol, Peter Ashwin. Circ: 750. **Subscr. addr. in Europe:** Taylor & Francis Inc., Customer Services Dept, 325 Chestnut St, 8th Fl, Philadelphia, PA 19106. TEL 800-354-1420; **Subscr. to:** Journals Customer Service, Rankine Rd, Basingstoke, Hants RG24 8PR, United Kingdom. TEL 44-1256-813000, FAX 44-1256-330245, enquiry@tandf.co.uk.

004 USA
E A T C MONOGRAPHS IN THEORETICAL COMPUTER SCIENCE. Text in English. 1984. irreg. price varies. reprint service avail. from ISI. **Document type:** *Monographic series.*
Indexed: CCMJ.
Published by: Springer-Verlag New York, Inc. (Subsidiary of: Springer Science+Business Media), 233 Spring St, New York, NY 10013. TEL 212-460-1500, FAX 212-473-6272.

006.42 USA
E D I & BARCODING NEWS. (Electronic Data Interchange) Text in English. 1999. m. back issues avail. **Document type:** *Newsletter.* **Description:** Covers inventory management, barcoding and EDI articles, tips and news on computer software for barcoding.
Related titles: Online - full text ed.
Published by: Advanced EDI and Barcoding Corp., 10971 Park Dr., Lusby, MD 20657-2406. info@edi-barcoding.com, http://www.edi-barcoding.com/news.htm. Ed. Phyllis Davis Minik.

004 DEU ISSN 1430-2721
E D V UND KOMMUNIKATION FUER DAS HANDWERK. (Elektronische Datenverarbeitung) Text in German. 1984. bi-m. reprints avail. **Document type:** *Magazine, Trade.*
Formerly (until 1993): E D V und Handwerk (0930-5467)
Published by: Gruber und Fischer Verlags- und Beratungs-GmbH, Kapellenstr 46, Forbach, 76596, Germany. TEL 49-7220-213, FAX 49-7220-215, info@gf-vb.de, http://www.gf-vb.de. Ed. Andreas Fischer. R&P, Adv. contact Juergen Buerkel. Circ: 40,000.

E E C S - E R L NEWS. see *ENGINEERING—Electrical Engineering*

004 AUS ISSN 1443-2730
E F A UPDATE. (Electronic Frontiers Australia) Text in English. 1999. w.
Media: Online - full text.
Published by: Electronic Frontiers Australia Inc., PO Box 382, North Adelaide, SA 5006, Australia. TEL 61-2-9255-7969, FAX 61-2-9255-7736, mail@efa.org.au. Ed. Brenda Aynsley.

004 DEU
E-GUIDE. Text in German. q. **Document type:** *Magazine, Trade.* **Description:** Contains articles and information for clients of IBM Germany.
Published by: (I B M Deutschland GmbH), BurdaYukom Publishing GmbH (Subsidiary of: Hubert Burda Media Holding GmbH & Co. KG), Schleissheimer Str 141, Munich, 80797, Germany. TEL 49-89-306200, FAX 49-89-30620100, info@burdayukom.de, http://www.yukom.de. Circ: 110,000 (controlled).

E-HEALTHCARE MARKET REPORTER. see *BUSINESS AND ECONOMICS*

004 ESP ISSN 1577-5097
E L C V I A. (Electronic Letters on Computer Vision and Image Analysis) Text in English. 2002. bi-m. free (effective 2005). **Document type:** *Journal, Academic/Scholarly.* **Description:** Research and applications in computer vision and image analysis.
Media: Online - full text.
Published by: Universitat Autonoma de Barcelona, Centre de Visio per Computador, Edifici O, Campus UAB, Bellaterra (Cerdanyola), Barcelona 08193, Spain. TEL 34-93-5811828, FAX 34-93-5811670, cvc@cvc.uab.es, http://elcvia.cvc.uab.es, http://www.cvc.uab.es.

004.16 LVA ISSN 1407-7299
E-PASAULE. Variant title: P C World Latvia. Text in Latvian. 1993. m. adv. **Document type:** *Magazine, Trade.* **Description:** Contains regular reports on software and hardware products, analysis of the latest information technologies, reviews of the Latvian computer market, and practical advice in the use of hardware, software and the Internet.
Formerly (until 2000): Datorpasaule (1407-4893)
Related titles: Online - full text ed.
Published by: D T Media Group, Stabu 47-1, Riga, 1011, Latvia. TEL 371-731-4059, FAX 371-724-2397, dt@dtmedia.lv, http://www.dtmedia.lv/e-pasaule/default.stm. adv.: color page USD 1,300; trim 215 x 290. Circ: 7,500 (paid).

004 AUS ISSN 1329-8259
E R P SOFTWARE SELECTION GUIDE. Text in English. 1980. every 18 mos. looseleaf. AUD 495 domestic; AUD 450 foreign (effective 2001). software rev. 762 p./no.; **Document type:** *Catalog.* **Description:** Presents suvey data covering leading ERP and AP&S software products available in Australia and the Asia Pacific region.
Formerly (until 1998): CompMFG. MRPII Software Comparisons (1323-4374)
Media: CD-ROM.
Published by: Homer Computer Services Pty. Ltd., 31 Arnold Road, East Brighton, VIC 3187 , Australia. TEL 61-3-9592 0216, FAX 61-3-9592 5623, info@homercomputer.com.au, http://www.homercomputer.com.au, http://www.homercomputer.com.au/. Ed., Pub. Glyn G Homer.

004 USA ISSN 1541-5961
▼ **E Z TECH GUIDES.** Text in English. 2003 (Feb.). bi-m. USD 5.99 newsstand/cover (effective 2002).
Published by: Future Network USA, 150 North Hill Dr, Ste 40, Brisbane, CA 94005. TEL 415-468-4684, FAX 415-468-4686, http://www.futurenetworkusa.com/.

004 ROM ISSN 1454-8232
EASY P C. Text in Romanian. 1999. fortn. ROL 18,000 newsstand/cover. adv. **Document type:** *Magazine, Consumer.* **Description:** Provides information and advice on all aspects of personal computing.
Published by: Sanoma - Hearst Romania srl, Str. C.A. Rosetti nr. 5, sector 1, Bucharest, Romania. TEL 40-21-3138620, FAX 40-21-3138622, office@sanomahearst.ro, http://www.easypc.ro.

005.4 USA ISSN 1549-4519
HF5548.32
EDIRECTIONS; enterprise solutions for the digital age. Text in English. q. free to qualified personnel. adv. **Description:** For users of Microsoft's .NET product. Covers new applications, new tools for building them and new ways to deliver them.
Published by: I D G Communications Inc., One Exeter Plaza, 15th Fl., Boston, MA 02116-2851. editor.edirections@cxo.com. Ed. Larry Marion. Pub. Joseph L. Levy. R&P Lisa Chaffin.

004 EGY ISSN 0377-7154
QA76 CODEN: ECJODE
EGYPTIAN COMPUTER JOURNAL. Text in Arabic. 1973. 2/yr. EGP 5, USD 15 (effective 1999). bibl.; charts. back issues avail. **Document type:** *Academic/Scholarly.* **Description:** Constitutes an Egyptian Computer journal.
Indexed: CIS, CompC, CompR, Inspec.

C

▼ new title ➤ refereed ✶ unverified ♦ full entry avail.

—BLDSC (3664.234000), AskIEEE.
Published by: Cairo University, Institute of Statistical Studies and Research, Tharwat St., Orman, Cairo, Egypt. FAX 20-2-3482533, TELEX 94372, http://derp.sti.sci.eg/data/0104.htm. Ed. Ibrahim Farag Eissa.

004 EGY ISSN 1110-2586
EGYPTIAN COMPUTER SCIENCE JOURNAL/AL-MAGALLAT AL-MISSRIYYAT LIL-HASIBAT AL-ILMIYYAT. Text in English. 1971. s-a. free (effective 2004). **Document type:** *Journal, Academic/Scholarly.*
Published by: The Egyptian Computer Society, Social Works Residance, Garden City, Cairo, Egypt. TEL 20-2-7946229, http://derp.sti.sci.eg/data/0250.htm. Ed. Dr. Ahmad Ebada Sarhan.

004 CHN
ELECTRONIC & COMPUTER DESIGN WORLD. Text in Chinese. 1993. m. adv. **Document type:** *Magazine, Trade.* **Description:** Contains coverage of the latest products, technology, and market trends for electronic products both within China and worldwide.
Published by: I D G China, Rm. 616, Tower A, COFCO Plaza, Jianguomennei Dajie, Beijing, 100005 , China. TEL 86-10-6526-0959, FAX 86-10-6526-0866, dumin@idg.com.cn, http://www.edw.com.cn, http://www.idgchina.com. adv.: page CNY 5,500; trim 205 x 270. Circ: 32,000 (paid and controlled).

004 USA ISSN 1076-0490
CODEN: EINREI
ELECTRONIC INFORMATION REPORT; empowering industry decision makers since 1979. Text in English. 1979. w. (46/yr.). looseleaf. USD 685 (effective 2006). adv. charts; stat. back issues avail. **Document type:** *Newsletter, Trade.* **Description:** Monitors, analyzes, and reports on information services, including the world wide web, proprietary online services, electronic databases and more.
Former titles (until Mar. 1994): Electronic Information Week; (until Feb. 1994): I D P Report (0197-0178)
Related titles: Diskette ed.; Online - full text ed.: USD 659 (effective 2005) (from EBSCO Publishing, Factiva, Gale Group, Northern Light Technology, Inc., The Dialog Corporation).
Indexed: CompD, KES, PROMT, T&II.
—BLDSC (3702.568100). **CCC.**
Published by: SIMBA Information (Subsidiary of: R.R. Bowker LLC), 60 Long Ridge Rd., Ste 300, Stamford, CT 06902. TEL 203-325-8193, 800-307-2529, FAX 203-325-8915, info@simbanet.com, http://www.simbanet.com. Ed. Anthony Carrick TEL 443-260-2777. **Dist. by:** Publications Resource Group, 121 Union St., Box 792, North Adams, MA 01247. TEL 413-664-6185, FAX 413-664-9343.

004 HKG ISSN 1681-4835
HD30.213
THE ELECTRONIC JOURNAL OF INFORMATION SYSTEMS IN DEVELOPING COUNTRIES. Variant title: E J I S D C. Text in English. 2000. irreg. free (effective 2005). **Description:** Focuses on the design, development, implementation, management and evaluation of information systems and technologies in developing countries.
Media: Online - full text.
Indexed: Inspec.
Published by: (Erasmus Universiteit Rotterdam NLD, Technische Universiteit Delft/Delft University of Technology NLD), City University of Hong Kong, Department of Information Systems, 83 Tat Chee Ave, Kowloon Tong, Kowloon, Hong Kong. TEL 852-2788-8521, FAX 852-2788-8694, isgo@cityu.edu.hk, http://www.ejisdc.org, http://www.is.cityu.edu.hk/.

003 ARG
ELECTRONIC JOURNAL OF THE ARGENTINE SOCIETY FOR INFORMATICS AND OPERATIONS RESEARCH. Text in English, Spanish. 1998. s-a.
Formerly: S A D I O Electronic Journal of Informatics and Operations Research (1514-6774)
Media: Online - full text.
Indexed: Inspec.
Published by: Sociedad Argentina de Informatica e Investigacion Operativa/Argentine Society for Informatics and Operations Research, Uruguay 252, Piso 2 D, Buenos Aires, 1015, Argentina. TEL 54-114-3715755, FAX 54-114-3723950, http://emis.maths.adelaide.edu.au/EMIS/journals/SADIO/, http://www.sadio.org.ar/sadio.htm. Ed. Esteban Feuerstein.

004 GBR
ELECTRONIC WORKSHOPS IN COMPUTING. Text in English. irreg. **Description:** Covers proceedings of workshops and conferences on computing.
Media: Online - full text.
Indexed: Inspec.
Published by: British Computer Society, One Sanford St, Swindon, Wiltshire SN1 1HJ, United Kingdom. TEL 44-1793-417424, FAX 44-1793-480270, bcshq@hq.bcs.org.uk, http://www1.bcs.org.uk.

004 ROM ISSN 1454-2889
ELECTRONICA APLICATA. Text in Romanian. 1998. m. **Document type:** *Magazine, Trade.*
—BLDSC (3702.925000).
Published by: Intertech Press, Calea Grivitei 119, Bucharest, Sector 1, Romania. TEL 40-21-3107123, FAX 40-21-3107118, redactia@intertechpress.ro. Eds. Bogdan Alexandru Ofrim, Dragos Mihai Ofrim.

621.39 USA ISSN 1542-6408
EMBEDDED COMPUTING DESIGN. Text in English. 1997. q. free in US & Canada; USD 50 elsewhere (effective 2005). adv. **Document type:** *Magazine, Trade.* **Description:** Deals with all aspects of applied computing technologies and products.
Formerly (until 2003): Applied Computing Technologies (1531-6874)
Related titles: Online - full text ed.: ISSN 1542-6459.
Published by: OpenSystems Publishing, 30233 Jefferson Ave, St Clair Shores, MI 48082. TEL 810-415-6500, FAX 810-415-4882, http://www.embedded-computing.com, http://www.opensystems-publishing.com/. Pub. Wayne Kristoff. adv.: color page USD 3,600; trim 8 x 10.875. Circ: 21,683.

EMERSON'S DIRECTORY OF LEADING US TECHNOLOGY CONSULTING FIRMS. see *BUSINESS AND ECONOMICS—Management*

004 RUS ISSN 1729-0902
▼ **ENTER.** Text in Russian. 2003. s-m. **Document type:** *Magazine, Consumer.*
Published by: Izdatel'skii Dom Burda, ul Pravdy 8, Moscow, 125040, Russian Federation. TEL 7-095-7979849, FAX 7-095-2571196, vertrieb@burda.ru, http://www.burda.ru.

621.39 GBR
ENTERPRISE MIDDLEWARE. Text in English. 1993. m. GBP 240; USD 360 in United States. bk.rev. back issues avail. **Document type:** *Trade.*
Former titles (until 1998): Enterprise Client - Server; Mainframe Client - Server
Indexed: Inspec.
Published by: Xephon, 27-35, London Rd, Newbury, Berkshire RG14 1JL, United Kingdom. TEL 44-1635-33823, FAX 44-1635-38345, xephon@compuserve.com, http://www.xephon.com. Ed., R&P Madeleine Hudson. **Subscr. in US to:** Xephon, 9330 Lyndon B Johnson Fwy., Ste. 800, Dallas, TX 75243-4310. TEL 303-410-9344, FAX 817-455-2492.

ESHAMAN.COM. see *COMPUTERS—Abstracting, Bibliographies, Statistics*

004 NLD ISSN 0926-9762
EURO COURSES. COMPUTER AND INFORMATION SCIENCE. Text in English. 1990. irreg., latest vol.6, 1995. price varies. **Document type:** *Monographic series, Trade.* **Description:** A series devoted to the publication of courses and educational seminars organized by the European Commission's Joint Research Centre Ispra, as part of its education and training program.
Published by: (European Commission BEL), Springer-Verlag Dordrecht (Subsidiary of: Springer Science+Business Media), Van Godewijckstraat 30, Dordrecht, 3311 GX, Netherlands. TEL 31-78-6576050, FAX 31-78-6576474, http://www.springeronline.com.

004 DNK
EUROCOMPUTER; Nordens edb-avis. Text in Danish. 1995. 6/yr. adv. **Document type:** *Newspaper, Trade.*
Published by: Media-Huset ApS, Jyllingevej 57, PO Box 1670, Vanlose, 2720, Denmark. TEL 45-38-79-34-00, FAX 45-38-79-34-10. Ed., R&P Ib Helge. Adv. contact Kristian Larsen. B&W page DKK 21,600, color page DKK 24,600; trim 258 x 365. Circ: 12,810.

004 NLD
EUROPEAN CONFERENCE ON COMPUTER SUPPORTED COOPERATIVE WORK. PROCEEDINGS. Variant title: E C S C W. Text in English. irreg., latest 2003. price varies. **Document type:** *Proceedings, Academic/Scholarly.*
—BLDSC (3659.636200).
Published by: Springer-Verlag Dordrecht (Subsidiary of: Springer Science+Business Media), Van Godewijckstraat 30, Dordrecht, 3311 GX, Netherlands. TEL 31-78-6576050, FAX 31-78-6576474, http://www.springeronline.com.

EUROPEAN JOURNAL OF OPERATIONAL RESEARCH. see *BUSINESS AND ECONOMICS—Management*

004 NLD
EUROTRADE COMPUTER. Text in English. 1988. 10/yr. USD 40.
Published by: Kluwer B.V. (Subsidiary of: Wolters Kluwer N.V.), Postbus 23, Deventer, 7400 GA, Netherlands. TEL 31-570-673449, FAX 31-570-691555. adv.: B&W page USD 3,780; trim 330 x 254. Circ: 12,000.

EUROWIRED. see *BUSINESS AND ECONOMICS—Management*

570.285 USA ISSN 1063-6560
QA402.5 CODEN: EOCMEO
➤ **EVOLUTIONARY COMPUTATION.** Text in English. 1993. q. USD 66 combined subscription in US & Canada to individuals print & online eds.; USD 86 combined subscription elsewhere to individuals print & online eds.; USD 305 combined subscription in US & Canada to institutions print & online eds.; USD 325 combined subscription elsewhere to institutions print & online eds. (effective 2006). adv. **Document type:** *Journal, Academic/Scholarly.* **Description:** International forum for facilitating and enhancing the exchange of information among researchers involved in both the theoretical and practical aspects of computational systems of an evolutionary nature.
Related titles: Microfilm ed.: (from PQC); Online - full content ed.: ISSN 1530-9304. USD 59 to individuals; USD 275 to institutions (effective 2006); Online - full text ed.: (from EBSCO Publishing, Gale Group, IngentaConnect, O C L C Online Computer Library Center, Inc., Swets Information Services).
Indexed: BIOSIS Prev, BiolAb, BrCerAb, C&ISA, CMCI, CerAb, CompAb, CompLI, CorrAb, CurCont, E&CAJ, EMA, IAA, IndMed, Inspec, M&TEA, MBF, MEDLINE, METADEX, RefZh, WAA.
—BLDSC (3834.420000), CISTI, IE, Infotrieve, ingenta, Linda Hall. **CCC.**
Published by: M I T Press, 55 Hayward St, Cambridge, MA 02142-1493. TEL 617-253-5646, FAX 617-258-6779, journals-info@mit.edu, http://mitpress.mit.edu/evco. Ed. Marc Schoenauer.

004 USA
EXTREMETECH. Text in English. m. free (effective 2003).
Media: Online - full text. **Related titles:** Print ed.: ISSN 1551-8167. 2004 (Fall).
Published by: Ziff Davis Media Inc., 28 E 28th St, New York, NY 10016-7930. TEL 212-503-3500, FAX 212-503-4399, editor@extremetech.com, http://www.extremetech.com/, http://www.ziffdavis.com.

F E S P A WORLD. (Federation of European Screen Printers Associations) see *PRINTING*

004 658 USA
FEEDBACK FROM FUJITSU. Text in English. q.
Published by: (Fujitsu News Center), Michael Solomon Assoc., Inc., 516 Fifth Ave, New York, NY 10036. fnc@msapr.com, http://www.fujitsu.co.jp/index-e.html.

005.5 GBR ISSN 0934-5043
QA75.5 CODEN: FACME5
➤ **FORMAL ASPECTS OF COMPUTING**; applicable formal methods. Text in English. 1989. q. EUR 648 combined subscription to institutions print & online eds. (effective 2005). adv. bk.rev. back issues avail.; reprint service avail. from PSC. **Document type:** *Journal, Academic/Scholarly.* **Description:** Promotes growth of computer science through the application of formalisms.
Related titles: Microform ed.: (from PQC); Online - full text ed.: ISSN 1433-299X (from EBSCO Publishing, ProQuest Information & Learning, Springer LINK, Swets Information Services).
Indexed: CMCI, CompAb, CompLI, CurCont, EngInd, Inspec, ZentMath.
—BLDSC (4008.335800), AskIEEE, CISTI, Ei, IE, Infotrieve, ingenta. **CCC.**
Published by: (British Computer Society), Springer-Verlag London Ltd. (Subsidiary of: Springer Science+Business Media), Ashbourne House, The Guildway, Old Portsmouth Rd, Guildford, Surrey GU7 3DJ, United Kingdom. TEL 44-1483-734433, FAX 44-1483-734411, postmaster@svl.co.uk, http://link.springer.de/link/service/journals/00165/, http://www.springer.co.uk. Eds. Dr. J M Wing, Dr. Cliff B Jones. Adv. contact Christiane Notarmarco. Circ: 207. **Subscr. in the Americas to:** Springer-Verlag New York, Inc., Journal Fulfillment, PO Box 2485, Secaucus, NJ 07096-2485. TEL 800-777-4643, 201-348-4033, FAX 201-348-4505, journals@springer-ny.com, http://www.springer-ny.com; **Subscr. to:** Springer GmbH Auslieferungsgesellschaft, Haberstr 7, Heidelberg 69126, Germany. TEL 49-6221-345-0, FAX 49-6221-345-4229, subscriptions@springer.de.

004 USA ISSN 1551-3955
▼ ➤ **FOUNDATIONS AND TRENDS IN HUMAN COMPUTER INTERACTION.** Text in English. forthcoming 2006. 4/yr. USD 300, EUR 300 (effective 2006). **Document type:** *Journal, Academic/Scholarly.*
Related titles: Online - full text ed.: ISSN 1551-3963. forthcoming.
Published by: Now Publishers Inc., PO Box 1024, Hanover, MA 02339. TEL 781-871-0245, FAX 781-871-6172, sales@nowpublishers.com, http://www.nowpublishers.com/hci. Eds. Gegory Abowd, Jonathon Grudin. Pub. James Finlay. R&P Mike Casey.

004 GBR ISSN 1361-4436
FREELANCE INFORMER. Text in English. fortn. GBP 41 domestic; GBP 93 foreign; GBP 1.65 newsstand/cover. adv. **Document type:** *Magazine, Trade.* **Description:** For DP - IT contractors or staff who are intending to start contracting.
Indexed: M&MA.
—**CCC.**

Published by: Reed Business Information Ltd. (Subsidiary of: Reed Business), Quadrant House, The Quadrant, Brighton Rd, Sutton, Surrey SM2 5AS, United Kingdom. TEL 44-208-652-3500, FAX 44-208-652-8977, rbi.subscriptions@qss-uk.com, http://www.reedbusiness.co.uk/. Ed. John Charlton TEL 44-208-652-8693. Pub. Neil Stiles. Adv. contact Grant Allaway. **Subscr. to:** Quadrant Subscription Services, PO Box 302, Haywards Heath, W Sussex RH16 3YY, United Kingdom. TEL 44-1444-445566, FAX 44-1444-445447.

004 DEU ISSN 0016-2841
TK7800 CODEN: FUSHA2
FUNKSCHAU; die Fachzeitschrift fuer elektronische Kommunikation. Text in German. 1927. s-m. EUR 89 domestic; EUR 97.30 foreign; EUR 74.40 to students; EUR 3.60 newsstand/cover (effective 2004). adv. bk.rev. charts; illus.; mkt.; tr.lit. index. **Document type:** *Magazine, Consumer.* **Description:** Covers computers, television and telephones, with emphasis on electronic telecommunications. Includes readers' comments.
Incorporates (1951-1999): T K - Tele-Kommunikation (1615-5513); Which was formerly (until 1999): I K - Ingenieur der Kommunikationstechnik (1434-1484); (until 1996): Nachrichtentechnik, Elektronik (0323-4657); (until 1973): Nachrichtentechnik (0027-7495)
Related titles: Online - full text ed.; ♦ Supplement(s): Mobilcom. ISSN 0948-163X.
Indexed: B&I, Inspec, RefZh.
—AskIEEE, CISTI, IE, Infotrieve, Linda Hall. **CCC.**
Published by: W E K A Fachzeitschriften-Verlag GmbH, Gruberstr 46a, Poing, 85586, Germany. TEL 49-8121-950, FAX 49-8121-951396, redaktion@funkschau.de, ckasel@wekanet.de, http://www.funkschau.de, http://www.wekanet.de. Ed. Gerd O. Bausewein. Adv. contact Stefan Kroll. B&W page EUR 5,600, color page EUR 7,680; trim 185 x 260. Circ: 20,800 (paid and controlled).

004 SGP
FUZZY LOGIC SYSTEMS INSTITUTE SOFT COMPUTING SERIES. Abbreviated title: F L S I. Text in English. 2000. irreg., latest vol.6. price varies. **Document type:** *Monographic series, Academic/Scholarly.* **Description:** Covers a variety of topics in SoftComputing and will propose the emergence of a post-digital intelligent system.
Published by: World Scientific Publishing Co. Pte. Ltd., 5 Toh Tuck Link, Singapore, 596224, Singapore. TEL 65-466-5775, FAX 65-467-7667, wspc@wspc.com.sg, series@wspc.com.sg, http://www.wspc.com.sg/books/series/flsiscs_series.shtml, http://www.worldscientific.com. Ed. T Yamakawa. **Dist. by:** World Scientific Publishing Co., Inc., 1060 Main St, River Edge, NJ 07661. TEL 201-487-9655, 800-227-7562, FAX 201-487-9656, 888-977-2665; World Scientific Publishing Ltd., 57 Shelton St, London WC2H 9HE, United Kingdom. TEL 44-20-78360888, FAX 44-20-78362020, sales@wspc.co.uk.

004 DEU ISSN 0949-2283
G M D GESCHAEFTSBERICHT. Text in German. 1971. a. **Document type:** *Academic/Scholarly.*
Formerly (until 1997): G M D Jahresbericht (0948-6674)
Related titles: CD-ROM ed.
—BLDSC (4162.506700).
Published by: (Gesellschaft fuer Mathematik und Datenverarbeitung), G M D - Forschungszentrum Informationstechnik GmbH, Schloss Birlinghoven, Sankt Augustin, 53754, Germany. TEL 49-2241-14-0, FAX 49-2241-14-2889, info@gmd.de, http://www.gmd.de. Ed. Helfried Broer.

004 DEU ISSN 0724-4339
G M D - SPIEGEL. Text in English, German. 1971. q. free. adv. bk.rev. back issues avail. **Document type:** *Academic/Scholarly.* **Description:** Covers scientific research in computer science and mathematics. Includes association news, activities and projects, reports of events and exhibitions, and new publications.
Indexed: RefZh.
—CISTI.
Published by: (Gesellschaft fuer Mathematik und Datenverarbeitung), G M D - Forschungszentrum Informationstechnik GmbH, Schloss Birlinghoven, Sankt Augustin, 53754, Germany. TEL 49-2241-14-0, FAX 49-2241-14-2889, TELEX 889469-GMD-D, http://www.gmd.de/muk/gmd-spiegel.inhalt.html. Ed. Siegfried Muench. Circ: 7,000.

004 ESP
GASP. Text in Spanish. 1998. bi-w. free. back issues avail. **Document type:** *Newsletter.* **Description:** Provides news and information on computers.
Media: Online - full text.
Address: Spain. juan_diaz@seker.es, http://bbs.seker.es/~juan_diaz. Ed. Juan Diaz.

GATEWAY (NEW YORK). see *LIFESTYLE*

004 BEL ISSN 0771-713X
GENEALOGIE EN COMPUTER. Text in Dutch. 1984. bi-m. EUR 10 domestic to members; EUR 12.50 domestic to non-members; EUR 13 in Netherlands to members; EUR 15.50 in Netherlands to non-members; EUR 20 elsewhere to non-members (effective 2005). adv. bk.rev. back issues avail. **Description:** Information on the use of microcomputers for genealogical research for members of the Society.
Indexed: V&AA.
Published by: Vlaamse Vereniging voor Familiekunde, Centrum voor Familiegeschiedenis, Van Heybeeckstraat 3, Merksem (Antwerp), Belgium. http://users.skynet.be/sky60754/svvf/vvf/vvfgcmag.htm. Ed. Pieter A Donche. Circ: 300.

GEOFOCUS; revista internacional de ciencia y tecnologia de la informacion geografica. see *GEOGRAPHY*

004 DEU ISSN 0724-9764
GERMAN CHAPTER OF THE A C M. BERICHTE. (Association for Computing Machinery) Variant title: Berichte des German Chapter of the A C M. Text mainly in German. 1979. irreg. price varies.
Indexed: Inspec.
—CISTI.
Published by: B.G. Teubner Verlag (Subsidiary of: Springer Science+Business Media), Abraham-Lincoln-Str 46, Wiesbaden, 65189, Germany. TEL 49-611-78780, FAX 49-611-7878400, http://www.teubner.de.

004 USA ISSN 1097-5594
GLOBAL I T CONSULTING REPORT. Text in English. 1997. m. USD 895 (effective 2004). **Document type:** *Newsletter, Trade.* **Description:** Covers the business of IT consulting, featuring news, analysis, benchmarking data and their exclusive "Intelligence Briefings".
Related titles: Online - full text ed.
Published by: Kennedy Information Inc., One Kennedy Place, Rte 12 S, Fitzwilliam, NH 03447. TEL 212-972-3793, FAX 212-972-1002, gitcr-editor@kennedyinfo.com, http://www.kennedyinfo.com/mc/git.html. Ed. Martin Zook.

004 CAN
GOVERNMENT COMPUTING DIGEST; serving the government systems community in Canada. Text in English. 1990. 6/yr. CND 44. adv. back issues avail. **Document type:** *Trade.* **Description:** For government computing professionals, featuring articles, columns and a news section.
Published by: Synergistic Enterprises, 132 Adrian Cres, Markham, ON L3P 7B3, Canada. TEL 416-472-2801, FAX 416-472-3091. Ed. William Gadsby. Adv. contact Bill Sherman. B&W page CND 1,990, color page CND 2,590; trim 10.88 x 8.13. Circ: 4,000.

004 USA ISSN 1528-6223
GRADUATE PROGRAMS IN ENGINEERING AND COMPUTER SCIENCE. Text in English. a.
Published by: Thomson Peterson's (Subsidiary of: Thomson Corporation), Princeton Pike Corporate Center, 2000 Lenox Dr, 3rd Fl, Lawrenceville, NJ 08648. TEL 609-243-9111, FAX 609-243-9150, http://www.petersons.com.

004 DEU ISSN 1368-0110
GRADUATE TEXTS IN COMPUTER SCIENCE. Text in English. 1990. irreg., latest 2002. price varies. back issues avail. **Document type:** *Monographic series, Academic/Scholarly.*
Indexed: CCMJ, ZentMath.
Published by: Springer-Verlag (Subsidiary of: Springer Science+Business Media), Tiergartenstr 17, Heidelberg, 69121, Germany. TEL 49-6221-3450, FAX 49-6221-345229, subscriptions@springer.de, http://www.springer.de/cgi/svcat/search_book.pl?series=3191.

GRADUATING ENGINEER & COMPUTER CAREERS. see *OCCUPATIONS AND CAREERS*

004 POL ISSN 1640-7180
GRY. Text in Polish. 1999. m. PLZ 80; PLZ 7.90 newsstand/cover (effective 2004). adv. **Document type:** *Magazine, Consumer.*
Formerly (until 2000): Extra Komputer Swiat Gry (1507-5621)
Published by: Axel Springer Polska, Al Jerozolimskie 181, Warsaw, 02222, Poland. TEL 48-22-6084100, FAX 48-22-6084106, gry@komputerswiat.pl, asp@axelspringer.com.pl, http://ksgry.redakcja.pl, http://www.axelspringer.com.pl. Ed. Aleksy Uchanski.

004 ESP ISSN 0212-1549
GUIA DEL COMPRADOR DE INFORMATICA✶. Text in Spanish. 1983. 52/yr.
Published by: Haymarket, S.A., Travesera Gracia 17-21, 5o 2o, Barcelona, 08022, Spain. TEL 3-237-22-66, FAX 3-237-66-88.

004 USA ISSN 0889-4108
GUIDE TO COMPUTER LIVING. Text in English. m.
Former titles (until 1986): Guide (Portland) (0884-1446)
Published by: Aquarian Communications, 3808 S E Licyntra Ct, Portland, OR 97222. TEL 206-654-5603.

004 DEU
H M D - PRAXIS DER WIRTSCHAFTSINFORMATIK. Text in German. 1963. bi-m. EUR 114 domestic; EUR 117.40 foreign; EUR 23.50 newsstand/cover (effective 2004). adv. **Document type:** *Magazine, Trade.* **Description:** Applications of electronic data processing and its organization in business and industry.
Former titles: H M D - Zeitschrift fuer Wirtschaftsinformatik (1436-3011); (until 1999): H M D - Theorie und Praxis der Wirtschaftsinformatik (0939-2602); (until 1989): Handbuch der Modernen Datenverarbeitung (0723-5208)
Indexed: RefZh.
—IE.
Published by: dpunkt.verlag (Subsidiary of: Huethig GmbH & Co. KG), Ringstr 19, Heidelberg, 69115, Germany. TEL 49-6221-1483-0, FAX 49-6221-148399, hmd@dpunkt.de, http://hmd.dpunkt.de. Ed. Christa Preisendanz. Adv. contact Antje Niklas. B&W page EUR 590. Circ: 2,000.

378 IND
HANDBOOK OF COMPUTER EDUCATION (YEAR). Text in English. 1927. irreg., latest 1997. USD 20 (effective 2003). **Document type:** *Newsletter.* **Description:** Contains information on Computers.
Published by: Association of Indian Universities, A.I.U. House, 16 Kotla Marg, New Delhi, 110 002, India. TEL 91-11-323-0059, FAX 91-11-323-6105, aiu@del12.vsnl.net.in, http://www.aiuweb.org.

003 NLD ISSN 0927-0507
➤ **HANDBOOKS IN OPERATIONS RESEARCH AND MANAGEMENT SCIENCE.** Text in English. 1989. irreg., latest vol.9, 1995. price varies. back issues avail. **Document type:** *Monographic series, Academic/Scholarly.* **Description:** Reports on research and advances on business operations research and management science.
Related titles: Online - full text ed.: (from ScienceDirect).
Indexed: ZentMath.
—BLDSC (4250.956000), IE, ingenta.
Published by: Elsevier BV, North-Holland (Subsidiary of: Elsevier Science & Technology), Sara Burgerhartstraat 25, Amsterdam, 1055 KV, Netherlands. TEL 31-20-485-3911, FAX 31-20-485-2457, nlinfo-f@elsevier.nl, http://www.elsevier.nl. Eds. George L. Nemhauser, J. K. Lenstra. **Subscr. to:** Elsevier BV, PO Box 211, Amsterdam 1000 AE, Netherlands. TEL 31-20-485-3757, FAX 31-20-485-3432, http://www.elsevier.nl.

004 USA ISSN 1058-2444
TK7887.7
THE HARD COPY OBSERVER. Text in English. 1991. m. USD 617 in North America; USD 697 elsewhere (effective 2005). **Document type:** *Newsletter, Trade.* **Description:** It provides comprehensive reporting and analysis of new product introductions and industry events in the printer and digital copier markets.
Related titles: CD-ROM ed.
—IE, Infotrieve.
Published by: Lyra Publishing, PO Box 9143, Newtonville, MA 02160. TEL 617-454-2600, FAX 617-454-2601, clecompt@lyra.com, http://www.lyra.com/lh3m.nsf/Newsletters/HCO. Ed. Charles Lecompte.

621.39 RUS
HARD I SOFT. Text in Russian. m. USD 110 in United States.
Indexed: RefZh.
Published by: Union Publishers Ltd., A-ya 56, Moscow, 127566, Russian Federation. TEL 7-095-9036290, FAX 7-095-9036090. Ed. I V Bagrov. **US dist. addr.:** East View Information Services, 3020 Harbor Ln. N., Minneapolis, MN 55447. TEL 612-550-0961.

004 RUS
HARD 'N' SOFT; nauchno-populyarnyi komp'yuternyi zhurnal. Text in Russian. m. **Document type:** *Journal, Consumer.*
Published by: Redaktsiya Zhurnala Hard 'n' Soft, ul Rimskogo-Korsakova, dom3, ofis 409, Moscow, Russian Federation. info@hardnsoft.ru, http://www.hardnsoft.ru. Ed. Piotr Davydov.

004 USA ISSN 1072-9755
HC110.H53
HIGH-TECHNOLOGY SERVICES MANAGEMENT. Text in English. m. adv. **Document type:** *Trade.* **Description:** Covers service management: planning, marketing, technical support, field operations.
Published by: Association for Services Management International, 1342 Colonial Blvd., Ste. 25, Ft. Myers, FL 33907. TEL 941-275-7887, FAX 941-275-0794. Ed., Pub. Leonard Mafrica. R&P Leaonard Mafrica. Adv. contact Walter Donnelly. B&W page USD 2,580, color page USD 3,380; trim 10.88 x 8. Circ: 20,000.

004 621.381 USA
HIGH-TEMPERATURE ELECTRONIC MATERIALS, DEVICES & SENSORS CONFERENCE. PROCEEDINGS. Text in English. a. **Document type:** *Proceedings, Trade.*
Published by: Institute of Electrical and Electronics Engineers, Inc., 3 Park Ave, 17th Fl, New York, NY 10016-5997. TEL 800-678-4333, customer.service@ieee.org, http://www.ieee.org.

C

▼ new title ➤ refereed ✶ unverified ♦ full entry avail.

HISPANIC CAREER WORLD. see *OCCUPATIONS AND CAREERS*

004.09 GBR ISSN 0957-0144
D16.12 CODEN: HICOFM
➤ **HISTORY AND COMPUTING (EDINBURGH).** Text in English; Summaries in English, French, German. 1989. 3/yr. GBP 34 in the European Union to individuals; USD 64 in North America to individuals; GBP 37 elsewhere to individuals; GBP 75 in the European Union to institutions; USD 138 in North America to institutions; GBP 80 elsewhere to institutions (effective 2003). adv. bk.rev.; software rev. back issues avail. **Document type:** *Journal, Academic/Scholarly.* **Description:** Aimed at historians using computers for research. Covers all aspects of computer applications in the field, from quantitative methods to free-text analysis and image processing.
Related titles: Online - full text ed.: (from EBSCO Publishing).
Indexed: AmH&L, CompLI, ERA, ETA, HistAb, Inspec.
—BLDSC (4317.798020), AskIEEE, IE, Infotrieve, ingenta. **CCC.**
Published by: Edinburgh University Press, 22 George Sq, Edinburgh, Midlothian EH8 9LF, United Kingdom. TEL 44-131-650-6207, FAX 44-131-662-0053, journals@eup.ed.ac.uk, http://www.eup.ed.ac.uk/newweb/journals/Computing/. Ed. Matthew Woollard. Circ: 500.

➤ **HOME NETWORKING NEWS.** see *BUSINESS AND ECONOMICS*

004 HKG
HONG KONG COMPUTER JOURNAL. Text in English. 1985. m. adv. **Document type:** *Academic/Scholarly.*
Indexed: HongKongiana.
Published by: Arting Publications Ltd., Ste. 709 Hong Man Industrial Bldg, Chawiwan, 2 Hong Man St, Wanchai, Hong Kong, Hong Kong. TEL 852-2897-1127, FAX 852-2897-2980. Ed. Gordon Au. Adv. contact Paul Chan. Circ: 16,200.

004 JPN ISSN 0913-8420
HOSEI DAIGAKU KEISAN SENTA KENKYU HOKOKU/HOSEI UNIVERSITY. COMPUTER CENTER. BULLETIN. Text in English, Japanese. 1987. a. **Document type:** *Bulletin, Academic/Scholarly.*
Published by: Hosei Daigaku, Keisan Senta, 7-2 Kajino-cho 3-chome, Koganei-shi, Tokyo-to 184-0002, Japan.

664 USA ISSN 1520-491X
HOSPITALITY TECHNOLOGY; guiding high-growth businesses to best-choice IT solutions. Text in English. 10/yr. USD 150 domestic; USD 180 in Canada; USD 200 elsewhere (effective 2005). charts; illus.; stat. back issues avail.; reprints avail. **Document type:** *Magazine, Trade.* **Description:** Addresses the technology needs of the rapidly growing and evolving foodservice and hospitality industries.
Related titles: Online - full text ed.
Published by: Edgell Communications, Inc., 10 W Hanover Ave, Ste 107, Randolph, NJ 07869-4214. edgell@edgellmail.com, http://www.htmagazine.com, http://www.edgellcommunications.com. Eds. Joe Skorupa, Michael Kachmar. Pub. Larry Hausman. Adv. contact Helen Gurnari. Circ: 16,000 (controlled).

004 USA
▼ **HOSTING WORLD.** (delivered as a PDF file; broadband Internet connection required for subscription.) Text in English. 2005 (Jul. relaunched). m. free to qualified personnel (effective 2005). adv. **Document type:** *Magazine, Trade.* **Description:** Covers the hosting industry, technology and the business.
Media: Online - full content.
Published by: Possibility Media, 10400 N.W. 33rd St., Ste. 270, Miami, FL 33172. TEL 786-206-8880, FAX 786-206-8884, info@possibilitymedia.com, http://www.hostingworldmagazine.com/, http://www.possibilitymedia.com/. adv.: page USD 995.

004 USA ISSN 0737-0024
QA76.9.S88 CODEN: HCINE6
➤ **HUMAN - COMPUTER INTERACTION (MAHWAH)**; a journal of theoretical, empirical, and methodological issues of user psychology and of system design. Text in English. 1985. q. USD 500 in US & Canada to institutions; USD 530 elsewhere to institutions; USD 525 combined subscription in US & Canada to institutions print & online eds.; USD 555 combined subscription elsewhere to institutions print & online eds. (effective 2006). adv. bk.rev. back issues avail.; reprint service avail. from PSC. **Document type:** *Journal, Academic/Scholarly.* **Description:** Publishes theoretical, empirical and methodological articles on user psychology and computer system design as it affects the user. Reports on helping to define the issues.
Related titles: Online - full text ed.: ISSN 1532-7051. USD 475 worldwide to institutions (effective 2006) (from EBSCO Publishing, Gale Group, O C L C Online Computer Library Center, Inc., Swets Information Services).
Indexed: AHCI, ASCA, BrCerAb, C&ISA, CIJE, CMCI, CerAb, CompAb, CompLI, CorrAb, CurCont, DIP, E&CAJ, EMA, ErgAb, IAA, IBR, IBZ, ISR, Inspec, LISA, M&TEA, MBF, METADEX, PsycInfo, PsycholAb, SCI, SolStAb, WAA, e-psyche.
—BLDSC (4336.043450), AskIEEE, CASDDS, CISTI, Ei, IE, Infotrieve, ingenta, Linda Hall. **CCC.**
Published by: Lawrence Erlbaum Associates, Inc., 10 Industrial Ave, Mahwah, NJ 07430-2262. TEL 201-258-2200, 800-926-6579, FAX 201-236-0072, journals@erlbaum.com, http://www.leaonline.com/loi/hci. Ed. Thomas P Moran. adv.: page USD 500; trim 5 x 8. Circ: 1,200.

➤ **HUNGARY. KOZPONTI STATISZTIKAI HIVATAL. SZAMITASTECHNIKAI STATISZTIKAI ZSEBKONYV.** see *COMPUTERS—Abstracting, Bibliographies, Statistics*

004 CAN ISSN 1027-2666
I A S T E D INTERNATIONAL CONFERENCE. APPLIED INFORMATICS. PROCEEDINGS. Text in English. 1983. irreg. price varies. **Document type:** *Proceedings, Academic/Scholarly.*
—BLDSC (1573.200000), ingenta. **CCC.**
Published by: (International Association of Science and Technology for Development), ACTA Press, 4500-16th Ave NW, Ste 80, Calgary, AB T3B 0M6, Canada. TEL 403-288-1195, FAX 403-247-6851, journals@actapress.com, http://www.actapress.com.

004 GBR
I B M - READ ME. (International Business Machines) Text in English. 1996. every 8 wks. free. adv. bk.rev. **Document type:** *Newsletter.*
Formerly: I B M - U K News
Published by: I B M United Kingdom Ltd., North Harbour, P.O. Box 41, Portsmouth, PO6 3AU, United Kingdom. TEL 44-1705-563799, FAX 44-1705-385081, gbib1s41@ibmmail.com. Ed. Sophie Austin. Adv. contact Julian Ellison. Circ: 29,000 (controlled).

004 USA
I C I M: INTERNATIONAL CONFERENCE ON MULTIMODAL INTERFACES. PROCEEDINGS. Text in English. a. price varies. **Document type:** *Proceedings, Academic/Scholarly.*
Related titles: Online - full content ed.
Published by: Association for Computing Machinery, Inc., 1515 Broadway, 17th Fl, New York, NY 10036-5701. TEL 212-626-0500, usacm@acm.org, http://www.acm.org.

004 GBR ISSN 1364-310X
QA75.5 CODEN: ISJOF2
➤ **I C L SYSTEMS JOURNAL.** Text in English. 1978. s-a. GBP 72 in Europe; GBP 120 elsewhere (effective 1999 - 2000). adv. charts; illus. back issues avail. **Document type:** *Academic/Scholarly.* **Description:** Presents current practical applications and developments in the fields of computers and information science and technology.
Former titles (until 1996): Ingenuity (1354-9952); (until 1994): I C L Technical Journal (0142-1557)
Indexed: AHCI, C&ISA, CompAb, CompC, E&CAJ, ErgAb, Inspec, SolStAb.
—BLDSC (4362.047740), AskIEEE, CISTI, Linda Hall. **CCC.**
Published by: International Computers Ltd., Lovelace Rd, Bracknell, Berks RG12 4SN, United Kingdom. TEL 44-1344-472000, FAX 44-1344-472700, v.a.j.maller@1boro.ac.uk, victor.maller@icl.com. Ed. V A J Maller. Circ: 1,000 (paid).

004.09 USA ISSN 1058-6180
QA76.17 CODEN: IAHCEX
➤ **I E E E ANNALS OF THE HISTORY OF COMPUTING.** Text in English. 1979. q. USD 440 (effective 2006). adv. bk.rev. charts; illus.; stat. reprints avail. **Document type:** *Journal, Academic/Scholarly.* **Description:** Chronicles vital contributions in computing and their impact on society.
Formerly (until 1992): Annals of the History of Computing (0164-1239)
Related titles: CD-ROM ed.; Microfiche ed.; Online - full text ed.: (from EBSCO Publishing, I E E E).
Indexed: ASCA, AmH&L, ArtHuCI, CCMJ, CMCI, CompAb, CompC, CompLI, CompR, CurCont, EngInd, HistAb, Inspec, MathR, MathSciNet, RASB, RefZh, SSCI.
—BLDSC (4362.790000), AskIEEE, CISTI, Ei, IDS, IE, Infotrieve, ingenta, Linda Hall. **CCC.**
Published by: Institute of Electrical and Electronics Engineers, Inc., 445 Hoes Ln, Piscataway, NJ 08854-1331. TEL 732-981-0060, 800-701-4333, FAX 732-981-1721, subscription-service@ieee.org, http://www.computer.org/annals, http://www.ieee.org. Ed. Michel R Williams. R&P Bill Hagen. Adv. contact Sandy Brown. B&W page USD 750; trim 7.875 x 10.75. Circ: 4,000 (paid). **Subscr. to:** Maruzen Co., Ltd., 3-10 Nihonbashi 2-chome, Chuo-ku, Tokyo 103-0027, Japan. FAX 81-3-3275-0657; Universal Subscription Agency, Pvt. Ltd., 877, Udyog Vihar, V, Gurgoan 122001, India. TEL 91-124-347261, FAX 91-124-342496.

➤ **I E E E CONFERENCE ON COMPUTATIONAL COMPLEXITY. PROCEEDINGS.** see *MATHEMATICS*

004 570 610 USA ISSN 1049-3565
I E E E - E M B S CONFERENCE ON INFORMATION TECHNOLOGY APPLICATIONS IN BIOMEDICINE. PROCEEDINGS. (Institute of Electrical and Electronics Engineers - Engineering in Medicine and Biology Society) Text in English. 1982. a. USD 151 membership (effective 2005). **Document type:** *Proceedings, Trade.*
Former titles (until 1985): Frontiers of Engineering and Computing in Health Care (0884-9900); (until 1983): Frontiers of Engineering in Health Care (1049-3557)
—**CCC.**
Published by: Institute of Electrical and Electronics Engineers, Inc., 3 Park Ave, 17th Fl, New York, NY 10016-5997. TEL 212-419-7900, 800-678-4333, FAX 212-752-4929, customer.service@ieee.org, http://www.ieee.org.

004 621.381 USA
I E E E INTERNATIONAL INTEGRATED RELIABILITY WORKSHOP. Variant title: I E E E International Integrated Reliability Workshop Final Report. Text in English. a. USD 146 per vol.; USD 73 per vol. to members (effective 2004). **Document type:** *Proceedings, Trade.*
Published by: Institute of Electrical and Electronics Engineers, Inc., 3 Park Ave, 17th Fl, New York, NY 10016-5997. TEL 212-419-7900, 800-678-4333, FAX 212-752-4929, customer.service@ieee.org, http://www.ieee.org.

004 621.381 USA
I E E E INTERNATIONAL WORKSHOP ON INTEGRATED POWER PACKING. Text in English. a. USD 138. **Document type:** *Proceedings, Trade.*
Published by: Institute of Electrical and Electronics Engineers, Inc., 3 Park Ave, 17th Fl, New York, NY 10016-5997. TEL 212-419-7900, 800-678-4333, FAX 212-752-4929, customer.service@ieee.org, http://www.ieee.org.

004 USA
I E E E MIDNIGHT - SUN WORKSHOP ON SOFT COMPUTING METHODS IN INDUSTRIAL APPLICATIONS. Text in English. a. USD 130. **Document type:** *Proceedings, Trade.*
Published by: Institute of Electrical and Electronics Engineers, Inc., 3 Park Ave, 17th Fl, New York, NY 10016-5997. TEL 212-419-7900, 800-678-4333, FAX 212-752-4929, customer.service@ieee.org, http://www.ieee.org.

004 USA ISSN 1536-1268
TK5103.2 CODEN: IPCECF
➤ **I E E E PERVASIVE COMPUTING**; mobile, stat. for wireless and distributed applications. Text in English. 2002. q. USD 545 (effective 2006). adv. **Document type:** *Journal, Trade.* **Description:** Delivers the latest peer-reviewed developments in pervasive, mobile, and ubiquitous computing to developers, researchers, and educators who want to keep abreast of rapid technology change.
Related titles: Online - full text ed.: (from EBSCO Publishing, I E E E).
Indexed: CMCI, CompLI, CurCont, ErgAb, Inspec, RefZh.
—BLDSC (4363.012970), CISTI, IE, Infotrieve, Linda Hall. **CCC.**
Published by: I E E E Computer Society, 10662 Los Vaqueros Circle, PO Box 3014, Los Alamitos, CA 90720-1314. TEL 714-821-8380, 800-272-6657, FAX 714-821-4010, http://www.computer.org/pervasive/. Ed. M. Satyanarayanan. adv.: B&W page USD 1,050, color page USD 1,800; trim 7.875 x 10.75. **Subscr. in India to:** Universal Subscription Agency, Pvt. Ltd., 877, Udyog Vihar, V, Gurgoan 122001, India. TEL 91-124-347261, FAX 91-124-342496; **Subscr. in Japan to:** Maruzen Co., Ltd., 3-10 Nihonbashi 2-chome, Chuo-ku, Tokyo 103-0027, Japan. TEL 81-3-3272-0521, FAX 81-3-3272-0693.

005 USA
I E E E SENSORS. PROCEEDINGS. (Institute of Electrical and Electronics Engineers) Text in English. a. USD 376; USD 188 to members (effective 2004). **Document type:** *Proceedings, Trade.*
Published by: Institute of Electrical and Electronics Engineers, Inc., 445 Hoes Ln, Piscataway, NJ 08854-1331. TEL 732-981-0060, FAX 732-981-1721, customer.service@ieee.org, http://www.ieee.org.

004 USA ISSN 1051-9173
TK7895.M4
I E E E SYMPOSIUM ON MASS STORAGE SYSTEMS. DIGEST OF PAPERS. Text in English. 1980 (4th). a. USD 80 (effective 1999). adv. **Document type:** *Proceedings.* **Description:** Addresses the environments that are served by mass storage systems.
Related titles: Online - full text ed.: (from I E E E).
—BLDSC (4363.087000), Ei. **CCC.**
Published by: (Institute of Electrical and Electronics Engineers, Inc.), I E E E Computer Society, 3 Park Ave, 17th Fl, New York, NY 10017. TEL 714-821-8380, 800-678-4333, FAX 714-821-4641, customer.service@ieee.org, http://www.ieee.org. Ed. Cat Harris. Pub. Matt Loeb. Adv. contact Frieda Koester.

004 USA ISSN 0018-9340
TK7885.A1 CODEN: ITCOB4
➤ **I E E E TRANSACTIONS ON COMPUTERS.** Text in English. 1952. m. USD 1,465 (effective 2006). bk.rev. abstr.; illus. index. **Document type:** *Journal, Academic/Scholarly.* **Description:** Research and design papers in all areas of computation and information processing.
Former titles (until 1968): I E E E Transactions on Electronic Computers (0367-7508); (until 1962): I R E Transactions on Electronic Computers; (until 1954): I R E Professional Group on Electronic Computers. Transactions
Related titles: CD-ROM ed.; Microfiche ed.; Online - full text ed.: ISSN 1557-9956 (from EBSCO Publishing, I E E E, Swets Information Services).

Indexed: AIA, AS&TI, ASCA, ApMecR, C&CSA, C&ISA, CADCAM, CCMJ, CIS, CMCI, ChemAb, CompAb, CompC, CompD, CompLI, CompR, CurCont, E&CAJ, EngInd, ErgAb, IAA, ISMEC, ISR, Inspec, MathR, MathSciNet, NSCI, ORMS, QC&AS, RASB, RefZh, RoboAb, SCI, SSCI, SolStAb, TelAb, ZentMath.
—BLDSC (4363.175000), AskIEEE, CASDDS, CISTI, Ei, IDS, IE, Infotrieve, ingenta, Linda Hall. **CCC.**
Published by: Institute of Electrical and Electronics Engineers, Inc., 445 Hoes Ln, Piscataway, NJ 08854-1331. TEL 732-981-0060, 800-701-4333, FAX 732-981-1721, subscription-service@ieee.org, http://www.computer.org/tc, http://www.ieee.org. Ed. Jean Luc Gaudiot. Circ: 8,000 (paid). **Subscr. to:** Maruzen Co., Ltd., 3-10 Nihonbashi 2-chome, Chuo-ku, Tokyo 103-0027, Japan. FAX 81-3-3275-0657; Universal Subscription Agency, Pvt. Ltd., 877, Udyog Vihar, V, Gurgoan 122001, India. TEL 91-124-347261, FAX 91-124-342496. **Co-sponsor:** Computer Society.

004 USA ISSN 1089-778X
QA76.87 CODEN: ITEVF5
I E E E TRANSACTIONS ON EVOLUTIONARY COMPUTATION. Text in English. 1997. bi-m. USD 485 (effective 2006). **Document type:** *Journal, Academic/Scholarly.* **Description:** Covers specific techniques such as evolution strategies, evolutionary programming, genetic algorithms and associated methods of genetic programming and classifier systems.
Related titles: CD-ROM ed.; Microfiche ed.; Online - full text ed.: (from EBSCO Publishing).
Indexed: AS&TI, C&CSA, C&ISA, CMCI, CompAb, CompLI, CurCont, E&CAJ, EngInd, ISR, Inspec, RefZh, SCI, SolStAb.
—BLDSC (4363.187400), CISTI, IE, Infotrieve, ingenta, Linda Hall. **CCC.**
Published by: Institute of Electrical and Electronics Engineers, Inc., 445 Hoes Ln, Piscataway, NJ 08854-1331. TEL 732-981-0060, 800-701-4333, FAX 732-981-1721, subscription-service@ieee.org, http://www.ieee.org. Ed. David B Fogel. **Subscr. to:** Maruzen Co., Ltd., 3-10 Nihonbashi 2-chome, Chuo-ku, Tokyo 103-0027, Japan. FAX 81-3-3275-0657; Universal Subscription Agency, Pvt. Ltd., 877, Udyog Vihar, V, Gurgoan 122001, India. TEL 91-124-347261, FAX 91-124-342496. **Co-sponsor:** Natural Networks Council.

004 USA ISSN 1536-1233
QA76.59 CODEN: ITMCCJ
I E E E TRANSACTIONS ON MOBILE COMPUTING. Text in English. 2002. m. USD 605 (effective 2006). **Document type:** *Journal, Trade.*
Related titles: Online - full text ed.: (from EBSCO Publishing, I E E E).
Indexed: C&CSA, CMCI, CompLI, CurCont, Inspec, RefZh.
—BLDSC (4363.206600), CISTI, IE, ingenta, Linda Hall. **CCC.**
Published by: Institute of Electrical and Electronics Engineers, Inc., 445 Hoes Ln, Piscataway, NJ 08854-1331. TEL 908-981-0060, 800-701-4333, FAX 908-981-9667, customer.service@ieee.org, subscription-service@ieee.org, http://www.ieee.org. **Subscr. to:** Maruzen Co., Ltd., 3-10 Nihonbashi 2-chome, Chuo-ku, Tokyo 103-0027, Japan. FAX 81-3-3275-0657; Universal Subscription Agency, Pvt. Ltd., 877, Udyog Vihar, V, Gurgoan 122001, India. TEL 91-124-347261, FAX 91-124-342496.

004 510 USA ISSN 1092-8138
QA76.751
I E E E WORKSHOP ON PROGRAM COMPREHENSION. Text in English. 1992. a. USD 177; USD 71 to members (effective 2004). **Document type:** *Proceedings, Trade.*
Related titles: Online - full text ed.: (from I E E E).
—BLDSC (4589.123000).
Published by: Institute of Electrical and Electronics Engineers, Inc., 3 Park Ave, 17th Fl, New York, NY 10016-5997. TEL 212-419-7900, 800-678-4333, FAX 212-752-4929, customer.service@ieee.org, http://www.ieee.org.

004 GBR
I E E PROFESSIONAL APPLICATIONS OF COMPUTING. (Institution of Electrical Engineers) Text in English. 1981. irreg., latest 2003. price varies. **Document type:** *Monographic series.*
Former titles: I E E Computing Series (1351-7759); I E E Digital and Electronics and Computing Series
Indexed: Inspec, ZentMath.
Published by: Institution of Electrical Engineers, Michael Faraday House, Six Hills Way, Stevenage, Herts SG1 2AY, United Kingdom. TEL 44-1438-313311, FAX 44-1438-313465, books@iee.org, inspec@iee.org, http://www.iee.org/Publish/Books/CompApp/. Eds. B Carre, D Jacobs. R&P Michael McCabe TEL 732-321-5575.

I E I C E TRANSACTIONS ON FUNDAMENTALS OF ELECTRONICS, COMMUNICATIONS AND COMPUTER SCIENCES. see *ELECTRONICS*

004 USA ISSN 1076-7967
QA75.5
I HATE COMPUTERS. Text in English. w. **Document type:** *Newsletter.* **Description:** Contains computer and non-computer humor.
Formerly (until 1994): Bits and Bytes (1077-5838)
Related titles: Online - full text ed.
Address: 5128 S W 86th Terrace, Gainesville, FL 32608. TEL 352-392-1901, FAX 352-392-0190, fasulo@gnv.ifas.ufl.edu, http://extlab1.entnem.ufl.edu/ih8pcs/. Ed. Thomas Fasulo.

004 USA ISSN 1091-9856
CODEN: OJCOE3
➤ **I N F O R M S JOURNAL ON COMPUTING.** Text in English. 1989. q. USD 128 domestic to non-members; USD 144 foreign to non-members; USD 64 to members additonal journal; USD 168 combined subscription domestic to non-members print & online eds.; USD 202 combined subscription foreign to non-members print & online eds.; USD 84 combined subscription to members additonal journal; print & online eds.; USD 272 combined subscription domestic to institutions print &/or online eds.; USD 288 combined subscription foreign to institutions print & online eds. (effective 2004); membership includes 1 free journal. adv. charts; illus.; bibl. Index. back issues avail. **Document type:** *Journal, Academic/Scholarly.* **Description:** Dedicated to the publication of research, surveys and applied articles on the interface between operations research and computer science.
Formerly (until 1995): O R S A Journal on Computing (0899-1499)
Related titles: Online - full content ed.: ISSN 1526-5528. USD 92 to non-members; USD 46 to members additional journal (effective 2004); Online - full text ed.: (from EBSCO Publishing, Gale Group, O C L C Online Computer Library Center, Inc., ProQuest Information & Learning, Swets Information Services).
Indexed: ABIn, CCMJ, CMCI, CompAb, CurCont, IAOP, Inspec, MathR, MathSciNet, ORMS, QC&AS, ZentMath.
—BLDSC (4499.223500), AskIEEE, IE, ingenta. **CCC.**
Published by: I N F O R M S, 901 Elkridge Landing Rd., Ste. 400, Linthicum, MD 21090-2909. TEL 410-850-0300, 800-446-3676, FAX 410-684-2963, informs@informs.org, http://joc.pubs.informs.org, http://www.informs.org. Ed. W. David Kelton TEL 513-556-6834. R&P Candita Gerzevitz. Adv. contact Trish Allewalt. B&W page USD 400; trim 8.125 x 10.875. Circ: 1,800 (paid and controlled). **Subscr. to:** PO Box 631704, Baltimore, MD 631704.

➤ **I T DIRECTORY.** (Information Technology) see *BUSINESS AND ECONOMICS—Investments*

004 DEU ISSN 1611-2776
T58.5 CODEN: ITINEY
➤ **I T - INFORMATION TECHNOLOGY**; Methoden und innovative Anwendungen der Informatik und Informationstechnik. Variant title: Informationstechnik und Technische Informatik. Text in German. 1958. bi-m. EUR 248; EUR 278 combined subscription print & online eds.; EUR 48 newsstand/cover (effective 2005). adv. bk.rev. charts; illus.; tr.lit. index. back issues avail. **Document type:** *Journal, Academic/Scholarly.* **Description:** News on computer technology and application in all areas: mainframe, personal computers, hardware, software, data processing and more. Includes market news and calendar of events.
Former titles (until 2003): I T & T I (0944-2774); (until 1993): Informationstechnik - I T (0179-9738); Elektronische Rechenanlagen mit Computer-Praxis (0013-5720); Which incorporated (1968-1974): Computer Praxis (0010-4663)
Related titles: Online - full text ed.: EUR 248 (effective 2005) (from EBSCO Publishing, Swets Information Services).
Indexed: ApMecR, CompAb, EngInd, Inspec, RASB, ZentMath.
—BLDSC (4587.601000), AskIEEE, CISTI, Ei, IE, ingenta, Linda Hall. **CCC.**
Published by: (Informationstechnische Gesellschaft im VDE (ITG)), Oldenbourg Wissenschaftsverlag GmbH, Rosenheimer Str 145, Munich, 81671, Germany. TEL 49-89-450510, FAX 49-89-45051204, vertrieb-zs@verlag.oldenbourg.de, http://www.it-inftech.de, http://www.oldenbourg.de. Ed. Paul Molitor. Adv. contact Annette Finkl TEL 49-89-45051221. B&W page EUR 1,841, color page EUR 2,951. Circ: 1,750 (paid and controlled).

004 GBR
I T LEADERSHIP; leveraging business performance through technology. (Information Technology) Text in English. s-a. GBP 19.95 per issue; free (effective 2005). adv. **Document type:** *Magazine, Trade.* **Description:** Designed to help C-level executives make the right business and technology decisions, transforming the IT function from a cost center into an enabler of business value.
Published by: S P G Media Ltd. (Subsidiary of: Sterling Publishing Group Plc.), Brunel House, 55-57 North Wharf Rd, London, W2 1LA, United Kingdom. TEL 44-20-79159600, FAX 44-20-77242089, info@sterlingpublications.com, http://www.itleadership.info/, http://www.spgmedia.com/. Ed. Geraldine Lip TEL 44-20-79159695. Adv. contact Mr. Patrick Agyeman TEL 44-20-79159738. B&W page GBP 6,600, color page GBP 7,900.

621.39 USA ISSN 1520-9202
T58.5 CODEN: IPMAFM
➤ **I T PROFESSIONAL.** (Information Technology) Text in English. 1999. bi-m. USD 590 (effective 2006). adv. **Document type:** *Journal, Academic/Scholarly.* **Description:** Presents practical, tactical methodologies for information technology professionals to use and strategic information to enable careers.
Related titles: CD-ROM ed.; Microfiche ed.; Online - full text ed.: (from EBSCO Publishing, I E E E).
Indexed: CompLI, Inspec, MicrocompInd, RefZh.
—BLDSC (4587.623700), CISTI, IE, Infotrieve, Linda Hall. **CCC.**
Published by: I E E E Computer Society, 10662 Los Vaqueros Circle, PO Box 3014, Los Alamitos, CA 90720-1314. TEL 714-821-8380, 800-272-6657, FAX 714-821-4010, itpro@computer.org, http://www.computer.org/itpro/. Ed. Frank Ferrante. adv.: page USD 710. **Subscr. to:** Universal Subscription Agency, Pvt. Ltd., 877, Udyog Vihar, V, Gurgoan 122001, India. TEL 91-124-347261, FAX 91-124-342496.

004 USA
HD9696.C63
I T SUPPORT NEWS; making IT work for business. (Information Technology) Text in English. 1981. m. USD 60 in US & Canada; USD 140 foreign (effective 2001); Free to qualified subscribers.. adv. bk.rev.; software rev. charts; stat.; tr.lit. reprint service avail. from PQC. **Document type:** *Trade.* **Description:** Provides information on computer services and support systems.
Former titles: Service News (1046-1965); Computer-Electronic Service News (0744-1584)
Related titles: Online - full text ed.: (from Northern Light Technology, Inc.).
Indexed: CompC, CompD.
Published by: United Publications, Inc., 106 Lafayette St, PO Box 995, Yarmouth, ME 04096. TEL 207-846-0600, FAX 207-846-0657, info@itsupportnews.com, http://www.itsupportnews.com, http://www.unitedpublications.com/. Ed. Lynn Novak. Pub., Adv. contact Alison Harris. B&W page USD 7,245, color page USD 8,520; trim 10 x 7. Circ: 45,000 (controlled).

004 GBR
I T TODAY (ONLINE EDITION). Text in English. m. **Document type:** *Magazine, Consumer.* **Description:** Contains comment, analysis and new about the IT industry, featuring product comparisons, coverage of storage, e-business, networks, communications, mobile and desktop.
Media: Online - full content.
Published by: Reed Business Information Ltd. (Subsidiary of: Reed Business), Quadrant House, The Quadrant, Brighton Rd, Sutton, Surrey SM2 5AS, United Kingdom. http://www.ittodaymagazine.com/index.asp. Ed. Gary Flood. Adv. contact Shaun Barton.

004 DNK ISSN 1600-6100
I T UNIVERSITY. TECHNICAL REPORT SERIES. Text in English. 2000. irreg. back issues avail. **Document type:** *Monographic series, Academic/Scholarly.*
Media: Online - full content.
Published by: I T Universitetet i Koebenhavn/I T University of Copenhagen, Rued Langgaardsvej 7, Copenhagen S, 2300, Denmark. TEL 45-72-185000, FAX 45-72-185001, info@itu.dk, http://www1.itu.dk/sw27824.asp, http://www.itu.dk.

004 USA
I T WEEK. (delivered as a PDF file; broadband Internet connection required for subscription.) Text in English. w. free to qualified personnel (effective 2005). adv. **Document type:** *Magazine, Consumer.* **Description:** Covers the latest news, reviews, product information, opinion and trends for today's IT professionals.
Media: Online - full content.
Published by: Possibility Media, 10400 N.W. 33rd St., Ste. 270, Miami, FL 33172. TEL 786-206-8880, FAX 786-206-8884, info@possibilitymedia.com, http://www.itweekmagazine.com/, http://www.possibilitymedia.com/. Pub. Victor Ramos. Adv. contact Terry Logan TEL 786-206-8880 ext 103. page USD 4,110. Circ: 100,000.

004 USA
I U I: INTERNATIONAL CONFERENCE ON INTELLIGENT USER INTERFACES. PROCEEDINGS. Text in English. a. price various. **Document type:** *Proceedings, Academic/Scholarly.*
Formerly: International Workshop on Intelligent User Interfaces. Proceedings
Related titles: Online - full content ed.
Published by: Association for Computing Machinery, Inc., 1515 Broadway, 17th Fl, New York, NY 10036-5701. TEL 212-626-0500, usacm@acm.org, http://www.acm.org.

004 GBR
▼ **ICREATE.** Text in English. 2003 (Jun.). bi-m. GBP 6 newsstand/cover (effective 2003). **Document type:** *Magazine, Consumer.* **Description:** Covers Macintouch computers hardware, software programs and the latest operating systems.
Published by: Paragon Publishing Ltd., Paragon House, 10 St Peters Rd, Bournemouth, Dorset BH1 2JS, United Kingdom. TEL 44-1202-299900, FAX 44-1202-299955, http://www.paragon.co.uk/mags/icreate.html. Ed. Paul Newman.

004 GBR ISSN 1469-4166
IMPERIAL COLLEGE OF SCIENCE, TECHNOLOGY AND MEDICINE. DEPARTMENT OF COMPUTING. DEPARTMENTAL TECHNICAL REPORT. Text in English. 1992. irreg. **Document type:** *Monographic series.*
Related titles: Online - full text ed.: ISSN 1469-4174.
—BLDSC (3554.534500).

Published by: Imperial College of Science, Technology and Medicine, Department of Computing (Subsidiary of: University of London), Exhibition Rd, London, SW7 2AZ, United Kingdom. TEL 44-20-75895111, info@imperial.ac.uk, http://www.ic.ac.uk.

004 CAN ISSN 1198-8673
IN TOUCH (LONDON, ONTARIO). Text in English. 1994. q. free. index. back issues avail. **Document type:** *Newsletter, Consumer.* **Description:** Disseminates information to campus computer users regarding the activities of I.T.S. Covers areas of support for software and hardware on a wide variety of systems.
Formed by the merger of (1986-1994): I T S Focus (0840-9595); And: C C S Focus (0831-4926); Which was formerly (until 1986): Computing and Communications Services Newsletter (0831-4225); (until 1985): Computing Centre Newsletter (0706-5965); (1967-1979): University of Western Ontario Computing Centre Newsletter (0833-8108).
Published by: University of Western Ontario, Information Technology Services, Natural Sciences Centre, London, ON N6A 3B7, Canada. TEL 519-661-2151, FAX 519-661-3486, in.touch@uwo.ca, http://www.uwo.ca/its/doc/newsletters/InTouch/. Ed. Merran Neville. Circ: 2,000.

003 IND ISSN 0250-9636
INDIAN SOCIETY OF STATISTICS AND OPERATIONS RESEARCH. JOURNAL. Text in English. 1980. a. INR 150 domestic to libraries; USD 60 foreign to libraries. adv. bk.rev. abstr.; bibl.; stat. index. back issues avail.
Indexed: CCMJ, CIS, MathR, MathSciNet, ZentMath.
—CISTI.
Published by: Indian Society of Statistics and Operations Research, M.S. College, Department of Mathematics, P O Box 65, Saharanpur, 247 001, India. TEL 25407. Eds. P L Maggu, S U Khan.

004 GBR ISSN 0268-7860
CODEN: INDCE2
INDUSTRIAL COMPUTING. Text in English. 1986. m. back issues avail. **Document type:** *Trade.*
Related titles: Online - full text ed.: (from Gale Group).
Indexed: CompD, Inspec.
—CISTI. **CCC.**
Published by: E M A P Computing (Subsidiary of: E M A P Business Communications), 33-39 Bowling Green Ln, London, EC1R 0DA, United Kingdom. TEL 44-20-7837-1212, FAX 44-207-278-4008. Circ: 15,002 (controlled).

004 DEU ISSN 1434-1980
INDUSTRIE MANAGEMENT; Strategien, Organisation, Informationssystem. Text in German. 1985. bi-m. EUR 138 (effective 2003). adv. bk.rev. back issues avail. **Document type:** *Magazine, Trade.* **Description:** Covers computer applications and organization in the production and manufacturing industries.
Formerly (until 1995): C I M Management (0179-2679)
Indexed: CybAb, Inspec.
—IE, Infotrieve.
Published by: (Technische Universitaet Berlin, Systemanalyse und EDV), G I T O Verlag, Klixstr. 1A, Berlin, 13403, Germany. TEL 49-30-41938364, FAX 49-30-41938367, service@industrie-management.de, service@gito.info, http://www.industrie-management.de. Ed. Norbert Gronau. Adv. contact Andrea Gramoll. Circ: 8,000.

004 USA
INDUSTRY APPLICATIONS SOCIETY ANNUAL MEETING. Text in English. a. USD 538; USD 269 to members (effective 2004). **Document type:** *Proceedings, Trade.*
Related titles: CD-ROM ed.
Published by: Institute of Electrical and Electronics Engineers, Inc., 3 Park Ave, 17th Fl, New York, NY 10016-5997. TEL 212-419-7900, 800-678-4333, FAX 212-752-4929, customer.service@ieee.org, http://www.ieee.org. **Co-sponsor:** I E E E Industry Applications Society.

INFO BIZNES. see *BUSINESS AND ECONOMICS*

004 BRA ISSN 1415-3270
INFO EXAME. Text in Portuguese. 1986. m. BRL 107.40 domestic; USD 89.69 foreign (effective 2005). adv. charts; illus.; stat. back issues avail. **Document type:** *Magazine, Consumer.* **Description:** Contains articles and features for computer users, professionals in administration, marketing, finance, human resources and industry.
Formerly (until 1997): Informatica Exame (0103-3875)
Related titles: Online - full text ed.; ♦ Supplement to: Exame. ISSN 0102-2881.
Published by: Editora Abril, S.A., Av. das Nacoes Unidas, 7221, 11 andar Pinheiros, Sao Paulo, SP 05425-902, Brazil. TEL 55-11-50872112, FAX 55-11-50872100, atleitorinfo@abril.com.br, http://info.abril.com.br/, http://www.abril.com.br/. Ed. Antonio Machado de Barros. adv.: page BRL 50,100. Circ: 127,760.

004 BRA ISSN 1807-4545
➤ **INFOCOMP**; journal of computer science. Text in Portuguese. 1999. q. USD 5 per issue (effective 2005). **Document type:** *Journal, Academic/Scholarly.* **Description:** Publishes research articles on all aspects of computer science.
Related titles: Online - full text ed.: free (effective 2005) (from EBSCO Publishing).
Published by: Universidade Federal de Lavras, Departamento Ciencia da Computacao, Lavras, 37200-000, Brazil. TEL 55-35-38291545, FAX 55-35-38291545, infocomp@dcc.ufla.br, http://www.dcc.ufla.br/infocomp/index.eng.html. Ed. Rudini Sampaio. Circ: 300 (controlled).

004 SVN ISSN 0350-5596
QA76.5 CODEN: INFOFF
INFORMATICA; journal of computing and informatics. Text in English, Slovenian. 1977. q. USD 40 to individuals; USD 80 to institutions; USD 20 to students (effective 2004). adv. bk.rev. index. back issues avail. **Document type:** *Journal, Academic/Scholarly.*
Indexed: CCMJ, Englnd, Inspec, L&LBA, MathR, MathSciNet, RefZh, ZentMath.
—BLDSC (4481.298190), AskIEEE, Ei, IE, ingenta, KNAW.
Published by: Slovensko Drustvo Informatika, Vozarski pot 12, Ljubljana, 1000, Slovenia. info@drustvo-informatika.si, http://www.drustvo-informatika.si. Circ: 600. **Co-sponsor:** National Research Foundation.

INFORMATICS AND MEDICAL COMPUTING NEWS. see *MEDICAL SCIENCES*

004 NLD ISSN 0019-9907
INFORMATIE; maandblad voor informatievoorziening. Text in Dutch. 1958. 11/yr. EUR 161.50; EUR 24.50 newsstand/cover (effective 2005). adv. bk.rev. bibl.; charts; illus. index. reprint service avail. from PQC. **Document type:** *Trade.* **Description:** Contains information and scientific articles on computer science, systems development, and EDP management.
Related titles: CD-ROM ed.; Microform ed.: (from PQC).
Indexed: ABIn, ADPA, CybAb, Inspec.
—BLDSC (4481.300000), AskIEEE, CISTI, IE, Infotrieve, ingenta, Linda Hall. **CCC.**
Published by: Sdu Uitgevers bv, Postbus 34, The Hague, 2516 BC, Netherlands. maandblad-informatie@sdu.nl, sdu@sdu.nl, http://www.informatie.nl/, http://www.sdu.nl/. Ed. Frank Noe. Pub. Eric Mackay. adv.: B&W page EUR 1,942; trim 210 x 297. Circ: 8,348. **Co-sponsor:** Nederlands Genootschap voor Informatica, Belgisch Studiecentrum voor Automatische Informatieverwerking, Nederlands Opleidlingsinstituut voor Informatica.

004 USA ISSN 1431-472X
INFORMATIK AKTUELL. Text in English, German. 1976. irreg. price varies. reprint service avail. from ISI. **Document type:** *Academic/Scholarly.*
Formerly (until 1992): Informatik-Fachberichte (0343-3005)
Indexed: Inspec, ZentMath.
—**CCC.**
Published by: Springer-Verlag New York, Inc. (Subsidiary of: Springer Science+Business Media), 233 Spring St, New York, NY 10013. TEL 212-460-1500, FAX 212-473-6272. Ed. W Brauer.

004 USA ISSN 0890-5401
Q350 CODEN: INFCEC
➤ **INFORMATION AND COMPUTATION.** Text in English. 1957. 12/yr. EUR 1,591 in Europe to individuals; JPY 166,100 in Japan to individuals; USD 1,253 to individuals except Europe and Japan; EUR 3,351 in Europe to institutions; JPY 350,000 in Japan to institutions; USD 2,642 to institutions except Europe and Japan (effective 2006). bk.rev. bibl.; illus. index. back issues avail.; reprints avail. **Document type:** *Journal, Academic/Scholarly.* **Description:** Provides technical papers on theoretical computer sciences, information and control theory.
Formerly: Information and Control (0019-9958)
Related titles: Online - full text ed.: ISSN 1090-2651. USD 2,739 (effective 2002) (from EBSCO Publishing, Gale Group, IngentaConnect, O C L C Online Computer Library Center, Inc., ScienceDirect, Swets Information Services).
Indexed: ASCA, C&CSA, C&ISA, CCMJ, CIS, CMCI, ChemAb, CompAb, CompC, CompLI, CompR, CurCont, E&CAJ, Englnd, ExcerpMed, ISR, Inspec, MLA-IB, MathR, MathSciNet, RefZh, SCI, SSCI, SolStAb, ZentMath.
—BLDSC (4481.770000), AskIEEE, CASDDS, CISTI, Ei, IDS, IE, Infotrieve, ingenta, Linda Hall. **CCC.**
Published by: Academic Press (Subsidiary of: Elsevier Science & Technology), 525 B St, Ste 1900, San Diego, CA 92101-4495. TEL 619-231-6616, 800-894-3434, apsubs@acad.com, http://www.elsevier.com/locate/ic, http://www.academicpress.com. Ed. Dr. Albert R Meyer. **Subscr. to:** 6277 Sea Harbor Dr, Orlando, FL 32887-4800. TEL 407-345-4040, 800-545-2522, FAX 407-363-9661.

004 USA
INFORMATION DECISION AND CONTROL. Text in English. a. **Document type:** *Proceedings, Trade.*
Published by: Institute of Electrical and Electronics Engineers, Inc., 3 Park Ave, 17th Fl, New York, NY 10016-5997. TEL 800-678-4333, customer.service@ieee.org, http://www.ieee.org.

▼ **INFORMATION ECONOMICS JOURNAL.** see *BUSINESS AND ECONOMICS—Management*

INFORMATION PROCESSING LETTERS. see *COMPUTERS—Electronic Data Processing*

621.39 621.381 GBR
INFORMATION TECHNOLOGY BUYERS GUIDE. Text in English. a. GBP 125 (effective 2001). **Document type:** *Trade.* **Description:** Lists UK-based manufacturers and suppliers with a proven record for working with local government and the public service. Targeted toward officers involved in specifying and buying information technology.
Published by: Kemps Publishing Ltd., 11 Swan Courtyard, Charles Edward Rd, Birmingham, W Mids B26 1BU, United Kingdom. TEL 44-121-765-4144, FAX 44-121-706-6210.

INFORMATION TECHNOLOGY FOR DEVELOPMENT. see *BUSINESS AND ECONOMICS—International Development And Assistance*

004 PAK ISSN 1812-5638
INFORMATION TECHNOLOGY JOURNAL. Text in English. 1812. bi-m. **Document type:** *Journal, Academic/Scholarly.* **Description:** Subjects covered include computer science, information systems, computer systems and information engineering, software engineering.
Formerly: Pakistan Journal of Information & Technology
Related titles: Online - full text ed.: ISSN 1812-5646. free (effective 2005).
Indexed: C&ISA, E&CAJ, IAA.
—BLDSC (4496.368863).
Published by: Asian Network for Scientific Information, 308-Lasani Town, Sargodha Rd, Faislabad, 38090, Pakistan. TEL 92-41-2001145, FAX 92-41-731433, http://www.ansinet.org/c4p.php?j_id=itj, http://www.ansinet.net.

004 USA ISSN 1535-1556
HF5547.5.A1
➤ **INFORMATION TECHNOLOGY, LEARNING, AND PERFORMANCE JOURNAL.** Text in English. 1982. s-a. USD 55 to individual members; USD 300 to institutional members (effective 2005). adv. bk.rev. abstr.; bibl.; illus. 70 p./no. 2 cols./p.; back issues avail. **Document type:** *Journal, Academic/Scholarly.* **Description:** Articles on research of office systems technologies, problems, human factors, and office systems education.
Formerly (until 1999): Office Systems Research Journal (0737-8998)
Related titles: Microform ed.: (from PQC); Online - full text ed.: free (effective 2005) (from ProQuest Information & Learning).
Indexed: AHCI, BusEdI, CIJE, CompLI, ERA, Inspec, Microcompind.
—BLDSC (4496.368867), AskIEEE, IE.
Published by: Organizational Systems Research Association, Morehead State University, UPO 2478, Morehead, KY 40351-1689. TEL 606-783-2718, FAX 606-783-5025, e.everett@morehead-state.edu, http://www.osra.org/journal.html. Ed. R Brookshire. Circ: 450.

621.39 ZAF ISSN 1022-2057
INFORMATION TECHNOLOGY REVIEW. Short title: I T Review. Text in English. 1993. m. ZAR 118. adv. illus. **Document type:** *Journal, Trade.*
Indexed: ISAP.
Published by: Primedia Publishing, 366 Pretoria Ave, Ferndale, Randburg, Transvaal 2194, South Africa. TEL 27-11-8843857, FAX 27-11-8844677, erich@is.co.za. Ed. Erich Viedge. Adv. contact Chris Vanheusden.

004 BGR
INFOWEEK. Text in Bulgarian. w. BGL 22.20 (effective 2002). 16 p./no.; **Document type:** *Newspaper.* **Description:** Focuses on all aspects of applying IT in business and the IT market in Bulgaria, including news and research on hardware, software, the Internet, and related information.
Published by: Bulgarski Biznes Publikatsii OOD, Ul. Postoyanstvo, #67B, Sofia, 1111, Bulgaria. TEL 359-2-9714250, FAX 359-2-9714251, infoweek@infoweek.bg, http://www.infoweek.bg/about.html. Ed. Evelina Marinova. Circ: 5,000. **Dist. by:** Sofia Books, ul Silivria 16, Sofia 1404, Bulgaria. TEL 359-2-9586257, info@sofiabooks-bg.com, http://www.sofiabooks-bg.com.

004 CHE ISSN 1424-4055
INFOWEEK.CH. Text in English. 1992. bi-m. CHF 95 domestic; CHF 150 foreign (effective 2003). back issues avail.
Former titles (until 2000): P C Guide (1423-6486); (until 1998): Windows Guide (1423-6478); (until 1997): Windows-Guide Schweiz (1423-646X)
Related titles: Online - full text ed.; ♦ Supplement(s): InfoWeek.ch. Special. ISSN 1660-1149.
Published by: Compress Information Group, Seestr, 99, Thalwil, CH-8800, Switzerland. FAX 41-1-7227701, infoweek@compress.ch, http://www.infoweek.ch/. Ed. Rene Dubachi. Pub. Michael Von Babo. Circ: 14,000.

004 CHE ISSN 1660-1149
INFOWEEK.CH. SPECIAL. Text in English. 2002. q.
Related titles: ♦ Supplement to: InfoWeek.ch. ISSN 1424-4055.
Published by: Compress Information Group, Seestr, 99, Thalwil, CH-8800, Switzerland. FAX 41-1-7227701, infoweek@compress.ch, http://www.infoweek.ch.

C

004   MEX
INFOWORLD MEXICO. Text in Spanish. fortn. adv. **Document type:** *Magazine, Consumer.* **Description:** Provides information for IT executives who are responsible for purchasing enterprise-class systems in volume.
Related titles: Online - full text ed.
Published by: I D G Mexico S.A. de C.V., Texas no. 66, Col Napoles, Mexico City, DF 03810, Mexico. TEL 52-5-5436821, FAX 52-5-2232909, http://www.iworld.com.mx. Ed. Ricardo Castro Romo. adv.: color page USD 5,200; trim 240 x 290.

004   NLD   ISSN 1387-1005
INFOWORLD NETHERLANDS. Text in Dutch. 1996. bi-w. free to qualified persons. adv. software rev. illus.; mkt. back issues avail. **Document type:** *Magazine, Trade.* **Description:** Covers all aspects of computing.
Related titles: Online - full text ed.
Published by: I D G Communications Nederland BV, Postbus 5446, Haarlem, 2000 GK, Netherlands. TEL 31-23-5461111, FAX 31-23-5461155, infoworld@idg.nl, abo@idg.nl, http://www.infoworld.nl, http://www.idg.nl. Ed. Annemiek Sinnige TEL 31-23-546-1144. Pub. Paul Molenaar. Adv. contact Johan de Windt. B&W page USD 4,859, color page USD 6,495; trim 264 x 326. Circ: 23,666 (paid and controlled).

004   CHL   ISSN 0717-4195
INGENIERIA INFORMATICA. Variant title: Revista Electronica del DIICC. Text in Spanish. 1998. 3/yr.
Media: Online - full text.
Published by: Universidad de Concepcion, Departamento de Ingenieria Informatica y Ciencias de la Computacion, Edif. Central 3er. Piso, Edmundo Larenas, 215, Concepcion, Chile. TEL 56-41-204305, FAX 56-41-221770, info@inf.udec.cl, http://www.inf.udec.cl/revista.

004   FRA   ISSN 0249-6399
INSTITUT NATIONAL DE RECHERCHE EN INFORMATIQUE ET EN AUTOMATIQUE. RAPPORTS DE RECHERCHE. Text in English, French. 1974. irreg. free. bk.rev. **Document type:** *Corporate.*
Related titles: Online - full text ed.
—BLDSC (7288.126860), CISTI, Ei, IE, ingenta.
Published by: Institut National de Recherche en Informatique et en Automatique, BP 105, Le Chesnay, Cedex 78153, France. TEL 33-1-39635511, FAX 33-1-39635330, http://www.inria.fr. Ed. Bernard Larrouturou. Circ: 4,000.

INSTITUT NATIONAL DE RECHERCHE EN INFORMATIQUE ET EN AUTOMATIQUE. RAPPORTS TECHNIQUES. see *COMPUTERS—Automation*

004   USA
THE INSTITUTE. Text in English. q. free. **Document type:** *Magazine, Academic/Scholarly.*
Media: Online - full text.
Published by: Institute of Electrical and Electronics Engineers, Inc., 445 Hoes Ln, Piscataway, NJ 08854-1331. TEL 732-981-0060, FAX 732-981-9667, customer.service@ieee.org, http://www.ieee.org/theinstitute. Circ: 330,000.

004   USA   ISSN 0098-2431
QA76
INSTITUTE FOR CERTIFICATION OF COMPUTING PROFESSIONALS. ANNUAL REPORT. Key Title: Annual Report - Institute for Certification of Computing Professionals. Text in English. 1973. a. free. adv. **Document type:** *Corporate.*
Published by: Institute for Certification of Computing Professionals, 2350 E. Devon Ave., Ste. 115, Des Plaines, IL 60018-4610. TEL 847-299-4227, FAX 847-299-4280, 74040,3722@compuserve.com, http://www.iccp.org. Adv. contact Cristi Herron. Circ: 1,500.

005   USA   ISSN 1096-3553
INTEGRATED SOLUTIONS. Text in English. 1997. bi-m. free domestic to qualified personnel. adv. **Document type:** *Magazine, Trade.*
Indexed: MicrocompInd.
Published by: Corry Publishing Inc., 5539 Peach St, Erie, PA 16506. TEL 814-868-9935, FAX 814-864-2037, CarlyR@corrypub.com, http://www.integratedsolutionsmag.com/, http://www.corrypub.com. Ed. Ed Hess. adv.: page USD 8,000.

004 370   USA   ISSN 1539-364X
INTEGRATING TECHNOLOGY INTO COMPUTER SCIENCE EDUCATION, PROCEEDINGS. Text in English. 1996. a. **Document type:** *Proceedings, Academic/Scholarly.*
Published by: Association for Computing Machinery, Inc., 1515 Broadway, 17th Fl, New York, NY 10036-5701. TEL 212-626-0500, 212-626-0520, 800-342-6626, sigs@acm.org, usacm@acm.org, http://www.acm.org.

621.39   USA   ISSN 1535-864X
TK7885.A1
INTEL TECHNOLOGY JOURNAL. Text in English. 1997. irreg. free (effective 2004). **Description:** Devotes each issue to an emerging technology or to categories of products related to technology.
Media: Online - full text.
Indexed: CompLI, Inspec.

Published by: Intel Corporation, 2200 Mission College Blvd, Santa Clara, CA 95052-8119. TEL 800-628-8686, FAX 408-765-9904, http://developer.intel.com/technology/itj/index.htm, http://www.intel.com.

004   USA   ISSN 1042-4296
INTELLIGENCE; the future of computing. Text in English. 1984. m. USD 395 domestic; USD 450 foreign (effective 2004). adv. bk.rev. back issues avail. **Document type:** *Newsletter.*
Description: Covers advanced computing and communications technologies.
Address: PO Box 20008, New York, NY 10025-1510. i@eintelligence.com, http://www.eintelligence.com/i. Ed., Pub. Mr. Edward Rosenfeld.

INTELLIGENT ENGINEERING SYSTEMS THROUGH ARTIFICIAL NEURAL NETWORKS; proceedings of the A N N I E conference. see *ENGINEERING*

004   NLD   ISSN 0953-5438
QA76.9.H85   CODEN: INTCEE
➤ **INTERACTING WITH COMPUTERS.** Text in English. 1989. 6/yr. EUR 94 in Europe to individuals; JPY 12,500 in Japan to individuals; USD 105 to individuals except Europe and Japan; EUR 769 in Europe to institutions; JPY 102,400 in Japan to institutions; USD 863 to institutions except Europe and Japan (effective 2006). adv. bk.rev. abstr.; bibl.; charts; illus. index. back issues avail.; reprints avail. **Document type:** *Journal, Academic/Scholarly.* **Description:** Emphasizes interdisciplinary topics applicable to industry, including research, techniques and tools.
Related titles: Microform ed.: (from PQC); Online - full text ed.: (from EBSCO Publishing, Gale Group, IngentaConnect, ScienceDirect, Swets Information Services).
Indexed: AHCI, AIA, ASCA, B&BAb, BrCerAb, C&ISA, CMCI, CerAb, CompAb, CompLI, CorrAb, CurCont, E&CAJ, EMA, EngInd, ErgAb, IAA, ISR, InfoSAb, Inspec, L&LBA, LISA, M&TEA, MBF, METADEX, PsycInfo, PsycholAb, SCI, SOPODA, SSCI, SolStAb, WAA, e-psyche.
—BLDSC (4531.869750), AskIEEE, CISTI, Ei, IDS, IE, Infotrieve, ingenta, Linda Hall. **CCC.**
Published by: (British Computer Society GBR, H C I Specialist Group), Elsevier BV (Subsidiary of: Elsevier Science & Technology), Radarweg 29, Amsterdam, 1043 NX, Netherlands. TEL 31-20-4853911, FAX 31-20-4852457, nlinfo-f@elsevier.nl, http://www.elsevier.com/locate/intcom, http://www.elsevier.nl. Ed. Dianne Murray.

004 338.0029   USA
INTERACTIVE RESOURCES DIRECTORY. Text in English. a. (Sep.). USD 399 per issue (effective 2003). **Document type:** *Directory, Trade.* **Description:** Provides directory and information on multimedia firms, including interactive agencies, web site developers, brand marketing, multimedia design firms, POP/Kiosk Developers.
Media: CD-ROM.
Published by: V N U Business Publications (Subsidiary of: V N U Business Media), 770 Broadway, New York, NY 10003-9595. TEL 646-654-5870, bmcomm@vnuinc.com, http://www.vnubusinessmedia.com/.

004   JPN   ISSN 0387-9569
INTERFACE. Text in Japanese. m. JPY 13,920. **Description:** Provides readers with practical "how-to" articles on both hardware and software development and applications.
Indexed: AbAn, JCT, JTA, PdeR.
Published by: C Q Publishing Co., 14-2 Sugamo 1-chome, Toshima-ku, Tokyo, 170-0002, Japan. TEL 81-3-5395-2122, FAX 81-3-5395-1255. Ed. Kiyoshi Yamamoto. adv.: B&W page USD 1,800, color page USD 3,600; trim 7.19 x 10.13. Circ: 27,664. Dist. outside Japan by: Nippon IPS Co. Ltd., 11-6 Iida-Bashi 3-chome, Chiyoda-ku, Tokyo 102-0072, Japan. TEL 81-3-3238-0700.

004 614   USA   ISSN 0020-5419
INTERFACE (BETHESDA)✶. Text in English. 1968. 9/yr. looseleaf. free. bk.rev. index.
Published by: U.S. National Institutes of Health, Center for Information Technology, 10401 Fernwood Rd, Bethesda, MD 20817. TEL 301-496-5381. Ed. Joseph D Naughton. Circ: 3,000.

INTERFACE (LONDON); newsletter of the FEI. see *ELECTRONICS*

004   USA
INTERFACE (SACRAMENTO). Text in English. 1975. s-a. free. bk.rev. bibl.; illus. back issues avail. **Document type:** *Newsletter.* **Description:** Covers activities of the search membership group as well as project activities and state and national news related to criminal justice information management technology.
Published by: Search Group, Inc., 7311 Greenhaven Dr, Ste 145, Sacramento, CA 95831. TEL 916-392-2550, FAX 916-392-8440, http://www.search.org. Ed., R&P Twyla R Cunningham. Pub. Gary R Cooper. Circ: 3,500; 3,500 (controlled).

INTERFACES (LINTHICUM). see *BUSINESS AND ECONOMICS—Management*

INTERFAX. CHINA I T & TELECOM REPORT. (Information Technology) see *COMMUNICATIONS*

INTERNATIONAL ABSTRACTS IN OPERATIONS RESEARCH. see *COMPUTERS—Abstracting, Bibliographies, Statistics*

621.39   JOR   ISSN 1683-3198
➤ **THE INTERNATIONAL ARAB JOURNAL OF INFORMATION TECHNOLOGY.** Text in English. s-a. USD 30 to individuals; USD 60 to institutions; USD 20 to students (effective 2005). **Document type:** *Journal, Academic/Scholarly.* **Description:** Provides a forum for original and significant contributions in the field of information technology to promote exchange of information and knowledge in research work. Explores the new developments and inventions related to the use of information technology towards the structuring of an information society, and to assist the academic staff from local and foreign institutions on publishing research results and studies in computer science and information technology through a scholarly publication.
Published by: Zarka Private University, IAJIT, P O Box 2000, Zarka, 13110, Jordan. TEL 962-5-3821100, FAX 962-5-3821117, iajit@zpu.edu.jo, http://www.iajit.org. Ed. Emad Abuelrub.

004   USA
INTERNATIONAL CONFERENCE ON IMAGE MANAGEMENT AND COMMUNICATION IN PATIENT CARE. PROCEEDINGS. Short title: I M A C. Text in English. 1989. biennial. price varies. adv. **Document type:** *Proceedings.*
Description: Focuses on new technologies and their clinical effects on a number of different topics.
Published by: (Institute of Electrical and Electronics Engineers, Inc.), I E E E Computer Society, 10662 Los Vaqueros Circle, PO Box 3014, Los Alamitos, CA 90720-1314. TEL 714-821-8380, FAX 714-821-4641. Ed. Cat Harris. Pub. Matt Loeb. Adv. contact Frieda Koester.

INTERNATIONAL CONFERENCE ON MICROWAVE AND MILLIMETER WAVE TECHNOLOGY. PROCEEDINGS. see *ELECTRONICS*

004   USA
INTERNATIONAL CONFERENCE ON MULTIMODAL INTERFACES. PROCEEDINGS. Text in English. a. **Document type:** *Proceedings, Academic/Scholarly.*
Related titles: Online - full content ed.
Published by: I E E E Computer Society, 10662 Los Vaqueros Circle, PO Box 3014, Los Alamitos, CA 90720-1314. TEL 714-821-8380, 800-272-6657, FAX 714-821-4010, customer.service@ieee.org, http://www.computer.org.

004   AUS
▼ **INTERNATIONAL DEVELOPER.** Text in English. 2004. m. GBP 41.90 (effective 2004). **Document type:** *Magazine, Trade.* **Description:** Provides an European edition of Australian Developer, written by and for European IT professionals and developers.
Published by: Derwent Howard, PO Box 1037, Bondi Junction, NSW 1355, Australia. TEL 61-2-93864666, 800-007-820, FAX 61-2-93864288, enquiries@derwenthoward.com.au, http://www.intldeveloper.co.uk/, http://www.derwenthoward.com.au/. Ed. Lisa Mills. Adv. contact Sara Sincock. **Subscr. to:** Anthem Publishing Ltd., FreePost NATW 1280, Somerton TA11 6ZA, United Kingdom.

INTERNATIONAL DIRECTORY OF COMPUTERS AND DATA PROCESSING EQUIPMENT AND SUPPLIES IMPORTERS. see *BUSINESS AND ECONOMICS—Trade And Industrial Directories*

INTERNATIONAL DIRECTORY OF ELECTRONIC AND COMPUTER COMPONENTS & PARTS IMPORTERS. see *BUSINESS AND ECONOMICS—Trade And Industrial Directories*

006   USA   ISSN 1076-5204
QA75.5   CODEN: IJCTAG
➤ **INTERNATIONAL JOURNAL FOR COMPUTERS AND THEIR APPLICATIONS.** Abbreviated title: I J C A. Text in English. 1994. q. USD 170 (effective 2005). Index. back issues avail. **Document type:** *Journal, Academic/Scholarly.* **Description:** Provides a forum for state-of-the-art developments and research in the theory and design of computing systems, as well as current innovative activities in computer applications.
Indexed: Inspec.
—BLDSC (4542.175550), IE, ingenta.
Published by: International Society for Computers and Their Applications, 975 Walnut St, Ste 132, Cary, NC 27511. TEL 919-467-5559, FAX 919-467-3430, isca@ipass.net, http://www.isca-hq.org/journal.htm. Ed. Reda A Amar TEL 860-486-5285. Circ: 150 (paid).

004   GBR   ISSN 1741-8569
▼ ➤ **INTERNATIONAL JOURNAL OF AUTONOMIC COMPUTING.** Text in English. 2005. q. USD 450 to institutions; USD 545 to institutions print & online eds. (effective 2005). **Document type:** *Journal, Academic/Scholarly.*
Related titles: Online - full text ed.: ISSN 1741-8577. USD 450 to institutions (effective 2005).

C

Published by: Inderscience Publishers, IEL Editorial Office, PO Box 735, Olney, Bucks MK46 5WB, United Kingdom. TEL 44-1234-240519, FAX 44-1234-240515, ijac@inderscience.com, info@inderscience.com, http://www.inderscience.com/ijac. Ed. Dr. Liang-Jie Zhang. **Subscr. to:** World Trade Centre Bldg, 29 route de Pre-Bois, Case Postale 896, Geneva 15 1215, Switzerland. FAX 41-22-7910885, subs@inderscience.com.

▼ ➤ **INTERNATIONAL JOURNAL OF COGNITIVE PERFOMANCE SUPPORT.** see *BUSINESS AND ECONOMICS—Personnel Management*

343.0994 GBR ISSN 1439-6262
P87

➤ **INTERNATIONAL JOURNAL OF COMMUNICATIONS LAW AND POLICY.** Abbreviated title: I J C L P. Text in English, German. 1998. q. free (effective 2005). back issues avail. **Document type:** *Academic/Scholarly.* **Description:** Covers law and policy in the sectors of computing, telecommunications and broadcasting.

Media: Online - full text.

Published by: (Programme in Comparative Media Law & Policy), Oxford University, Centre for Socio-Legal Studies, Wolfson College, Oxford, Oxon OX2 6UD, United Kingdom. TEL 44-1865-284-220, FAX 44-1865-284-221, IJCLP@digital-law.net, http://www.digital-law.net/IJCLP/. Ed. Gunnar Bender.

➤ **INTERNATIONAL JOURNAL OF COMPUTER INTEGRATED DESIGN AND CONSTRUCTION.** see *BUILDING AND CONSTRUCTION*

004 USA ISSN 1535-6698
QA76.27

INTERNATIONAL JOURNAL OF COMPUTER RESEARCH. Text in English. 1986. q. USD 450 (effective 2005). **Document type:** *Journal, Academic/Scholarly.*

Incorporates (1993-1999): Journal of Intelligent Control, Neurocomputing and Fuzzy Logic; Former titles: Journal of Computer Abstracts and Research; (until vol.8): Computer Abstracts on Microfiche; (until vol.4): Computer Information Review (0895-6588)

Published by: Nova Science Publishers, Inc., 400 Oser Ave, Ste 1600, Hauppauge, NY 11788-3619. TEL 631-231-7269, FAX 631-231-8175, novascience@earthlink.net, http://www.novapublishers.com/journals/computer.html. Eds. Marcin Paprzycki, Frank Columbus. Circ: 700.

621.39 CAN ISSN 1708-0460

▼ **INTERNATIONAL JOURNAL OF COMPUTING AND INFORMATION SCIENCES.** Text in English. 2003. 3/yr. **Document type:** *Journal, Academic/Scholarly.*

Related titles: Online - full text ed.: ISSN 1708-0479.

Published by: A P C E P, 39 Dundas St E, Ste 202, Mississauga, ON L5A 1V9, Canada. TEL 905-290-8207, FAX 905-290-8413, info@apcep.ca, http://www31.brinkster.com/ijcis/, http://www.apcep.ca. Ed. Jehad Mohamad.

▼ **INTERNATIONAL JOURNAL OF EDUCATION AND DEVELOPMENT USING INFORMATION AND COMMUNICATION TECHNOLOGY.** see *EDUCATION*

▼ **INTERNATIONAL JOURNAL OF ELECTRONIC GOVERNMENT RESEARCH.** see *PUBLIC ADMINISTRATION*

004 GBR ISSN 1741-1068

➤ **INTERNATIONAL JOURNAL OF EMBEDDED SYSTEMS.** Text in English. q. USD 450 to institutions; USD 545 combined subscription to institutions print & online eds. (effective 2005). **Document type:** *Journal, Academic/Scholarly.* **Description:** Addresses the state of the art of all aspects of embedded computing systems with emphasis on algorithms, systems, models, compilers, architectures, tools, design methodologies, test and applications.

Related titles: Online - full text ed.: ISSN 1741-1076. USD 450 to institutions (effective 2005).

Published by: Inderscience Publishers, IEL Editorial Office, PO Box 735, Olney, Bucks MK46 5WB, United Kingdom. TEL 44-1234-240519, FAX 44-1234-240515, ijes@inderscience.com, info@inderscience.com, http://www.inderscience.com/ijes. Ed. Laurence T Yang. **Subscr. to:** World Trade Centre Bldg, 29 route de Pre-Bois, Case Postale 896, Geneva 15 1215, Switzerland. FAX 41-22-7910885, subs@inderscience.com.

➤ **INTERNATIONAL JOURNAL OF ENGINEERING EDUCATION.** see *ENGINEERING*

004 SGP ISSN 0129-0541
QA75.5 CODEN: IFCSEN

➤ **INTERNATIONAL JOURNAL OF FOUNDATIONS OF COMPUTER SCIENCE.** Abbreviated title: I J F C S. Text in English. 1990. q. SGD 395, USD 232, EUR 217 to individuals; SGD 1,087, USD 640, USD 598 combined subscription to institutions print & online eds.; SGD 660, USD 388, EUR 363 combined subscription in developing nations to institutions print & online eds. (effective 2006). cum.index every 5 yrs. back issues avail. **Document type:** *Journal, Academic/Scholarly.* **Description:** Publishes articles on all areas of the theoretical and mathematical foundations of computer science. Also publishes new results and proposals in these areas.

Related titles: Online - full text ed.: (from EBSCO Publishing, O C L C Online Computer Library Center, Inc., Swets Information Services).

Indexed: BrCerAb, C&ISA, CCMJ, CMCI, CerAb, CompAb, CompLI, CorrAb, CurCont, E&CAJ, EMA, IAA, Inspec, M&TEA, MBF, METADEX, MathR, MathSciNet, SolStAb, WAA, ZentMath.

—BLDSC (4542.258000), AskIEEE, CISTI, IE, Infotrieve, ingenta, Linda Hall. **CCC.**

Published by: World Scientific Publishing Co. Pte. Ltd., 5 Toh Tuck Link, Singapore, 596224, Singapore. TEL 65-466-5775, FAX 65-467-7667, wspc@wspc.com.sg, http://www.worldscinet.com/ijfcs/ijfcs.shtml, http://www.worldscientific.com. Ed. O H Ibarra. Circ: 150. **Subscr. to:** Farrer Rd, PO Box 128, Singapore 912805, Singapore. sales@wspc.com.sg. **Dist. by:** World Scientific Publishing Co., Inc., 1060 Main St, River Edge, NJ 07661. TEL 201-487-9655, 800-227-7562, FAX 201-487-9656, 888-977-2665.; World Scientific Publishing Ltd., 57 Shelton St, London WC2H 9HE, United Kingdom. TEL 44-20-78360888, FAX 44-20-78362020, sales@wspc.co.uk.

004 SGP ISSN 0219-8789

▼ **INTERNATIONAL JOURNAL OF INFORMATION ACQUISITION.** Text in English. 2004. q. SGD 172, USD 101, EUR 95 to individuals; SGD 429, USD 253, EUR 235 combined subscription to institutions print & online eds.; SGD 258, USD 152, EUR 141 combined subscription in developing nations to institutions print & online eds. (effective 2006).

Related titles: Online - full text ed.: (from EBSCO Publishing, O C L C Online Computer Library Center, Inc., Swets Information Services).

Indexed: C&ISA, E&CAJ, IAA.

Published by: World Scientific Publishing Co. Pte. Ltd., 5 Toh Tuck Link, Singapore, 596224, Singapore. TEL 65-466-5775, FAX 65-467-7667, wspc@wspc.com.sg, http://www.worldscinet.com/ijia/ijia.shtml, http://www.worldscientific.com. Ed. Dr. Tao Mei.

004 384.5 GBR ISSN 1742-7371

▼ ➤ **INTERNATIONAL JOURNAL OF PERVASIVE COMPUTING AND COMMUNICATIONS.** Text in English. 2004. q. GBP 175 in the European Union to institutions; GBP 235 elsewhere to institutions (effective 2005). **Document type:** *Journal, Academic/Scholarly.* **Description:** Aims to provide a high profile, leading edge forum for academics, industrial professionals, educators and policy makers working in the field to contribute, to disseminate innovative and important new work on pervasive computing and communications, eventually to achieve a world saturated with computing and communications, yet gracefully integrated with human users.

Related titles: Online - full text ed.: ISSN 1742-738X.

—BLDSC (4542.452750). **CCC.**

Published by: Troubador Publishing Limited, 9 de Montfort Mews, Leicester, LE1 7FW, United Kingdom. TEL 44-116-2559311, FAX 44-116-2559323, jpcc@troubador.co.uk, http://www.troubador.co.uk/jpcc. Eds. Dr. Laurence T Yang, Dr. Madjid Merabti. Pub. Mr. Jeremy B Thompson.

004 USA ISSN 1548-7199

▼ **INTERNATIONAL JOURNAL OF UNCONVENTIONAL COMPUTING.** Text in English. 2005. q. EUR 95 in Europe to individuals; JPY 15,932 in Japan to individuals; USD 90 elsewhere to individuals; EUR 412 combined subscription in Europe to institutions print & online; JPY 52,286 combined subscription in Japan to institutions print & online; USD 426 combined subscription elsewhere to institutions print & online (effective 2005). 80 p./no.; **Document type:** *Journal, Academic/Scholarly.* **Description:** Offers the opportunity for rapid publication of theoretical and experimental results in non-classical computing.

Related titles: Online - full text ed.: ISSN 1548-7202.

—**CCC.**

Published by: Old City Publishing, Inc., 628 N 2nd St, Philadelphia, PA 19123. TEL 215-925-4390, FAX 215-925-4371, info@oldcitypublishing.com, http://www.oldcitypublishing.com/IJUC/IJUC.html. Ed. Andrew Adamatzky.

▼ **INTERNATIONAL JOURNAL OF WAVELETS, MULTIRESOLUTION AND INFORMATION PROCESSING.** see *MATHEMATICS*

004 DEU ISSN 1433-2833

➤ **INTERNATIONAL JOURNAL ON DOCUMENT ANALYSIS AND RECOGNITION.** Text in English. 1998. q. EUR 183.40 combined subscription to institutions print & online eds. (effective 2005). adv. reprint service avail. from PSC. **Document type:** *Journal, Academic/Scholarly.* **Description:** Provides a focal point for archival literature dedicated to document analysis and recognition.

Related titles: Online - full text ed.: ISSN 1433-2825 (from EBSCO Publishing, Springer LINK, Swets Information Services).

Indexed: CompLI, Inspec.

—BLDSC (4542.186500), CISTI, IE, Infotrieve. **CCC.**

Published by: Springer-Verlag (Subsidiary of: Springer Science+Business Media), Tiergartenstr 17, Heidelberg, 69121, Germany. TEL 49-6221-3450, FAX 49-6221-345229, http://link.springer.de/link/service/journals/10032/index.htm. Eds. David S Doermann TEL 301-405-4526, Sargur N Srihari TEL 716-645-6162, Seong-Whan Lee TEL 82-2-3290-3197. Adv. contact Stephan Kroeck TEL 49-30-827875739. **Subscr. in the Americas to:** Springer-Verlag New York, Inc., Journal Fulfillment, PO Box 2485, Secaucus, NJ 07096-2485. TEL 800-777-4643, 201-348-4033, FAX 201-348-4505, journals@springer-ny.com, http://www.springer-ny.com; **Subscr. to:** Springer GmbH Auslieferungsgesellschaft, Haberstr 7, Heidelberg 69126, Germany. TEL 49-6221-345-0, FAX 49-6221-345-4229, subscriptions@springer.de.

004 USA

➤ **INTERNATIONAL LECTURE SERIES IN COMPUTER SCIENCE.** Text in English. 1981. irreg., latest vol.7, 1988. reprint service avail. from ISI. **Document type:** *Monographic series, Academic/Scholarly.*

Indexed: MathR.

Published by: Academic Press (Subsidiary of: Elsevier Science & Technology), 525 B St, Ste 1900, San Diego, CA 92101-4495. apsubs@acad.com, http://www.academicpress.com.

➤ **INTERNATIONAL MICROWAVE CONFERENCE. PROCEEDINGS.** see *ELECTRONICS*

004 USA

INTERNATIONAL SYMPOSIUM ON INFORMATION PROCESSING IN SENSOR NETWORKS. PROCEEDINGS. Text in English. a. **Document type:** *Proceedings, Academic/Scholarly.*

Related titles: Online - full content ed.

Published by: Association for Computing Machinery, Inc., 1515 Broadway, 17th Fl, New York, NY 10036-5701. TEL 212-626-0500, usacm@acm.org, http://www.acm.org.

004 USA ISSN 1530-0811

INTERNATIONAL SYMPOSIUM ON WEARABLE COMPUTERS. DIGEST OF PAPERS. Variant title: International Symposium on Wearable Computers. Proceedings. Text in English. a. USD 110. **Document type:** *Proceedings, Academic/Scholarly.*

Related titles: Online - full text ed.: (from I E E E).

Indexed: Englnd.

—BLDSC (4550.379470).

Published by: I E E E Computer Society, 3 Park Ave, 17th Fl, New York, NY 10017. customer.service@ieee.org, http://www.computer.org.

004 USA ISSN 1089-3539
CODEN: PITCFN

INTERNATIONAL TEST CONFERENCE. PROCEEDINGS. Text in English. 1972. a. price varies. **Document type:** *Proceedings, Academic/Scholarly.* **Description:** Focuses on advances in testing processes and technology.

Former titles (1981-1982): International Test Conference. Digest of Papers; (1979-1980): Test Conference. Digest of Papers (0743-1686); (until 1978): Semiconductor Test Conference. Digest of Papers; (1974-1977): Semiconductor Test Symposium. Digest of Papers; (until 1973): Symposium on Semiconductor Memory Testing. Digest of Papers; In 1972: Testing to Integrate Semiconductor Memories into Computer Mainframes. Digest of Papers

Related titles: Online - full text ed.: (from I E E E).

Indexed: Englnd, Inspec.

—BLDSC (4550.438000), IE, ingenta. **CCC.**

Published by: I E E E Computer Society, 3 Park Ave, 17th Fl, New York, NY 10017. TEL 714-821-8380, 800-678-4333, FAX 714-821-4641, customer.service@ieee.org, http://www.ieee.org.

003 GBR ISSN 0969-6016
T57.6.A1 CODEN: ITORF9

➤ **INTERNATIONAL TRANSACTIONS IN OPERATIONAL RESEARCH.** Text in English. 1994. bi-m. EUR 98 combined subscription in Europe to individuals print & online eds.; USD 109 combined subscription in the Americas to individuals & Caribbean (print & online eds.); GBP 65 combined subscription elsewhere to individuals print & online eds.; GBP 310, USD 473 combined subscription in developing nations to institutions print & online eds.; USD 1,042 combined subscription in the Americas to institutions & Caribbean (print & online eds.); GBP 620 combined subscription elsewhere to institutions print & online (effective 2006). abstr. back issues avail.; reprint service avail. from PSC. **Document type:** *Academic/Scholarly.* **Description:** Advances the practice and understanding of operational research.

Related titles: Microform ed.: (from PQC); Online - full text ed.: ISSN 1475-3995. USD 990 in the Americas to institutions & Caribbean; GBP 295, USD 449 in developing nations to institutions; GBP 589 elsewhere to institutions (effective 2006) (from Blackwell Synergy, EBSCO Publishing, Gale Group, IngentaConnect, O C L C Online Computer Library Center, Inc., ScienceDirect, Swets Information Services).
Indexed: ABIn, CCMJ, IAOP, Inspec, MathR, MathSciNet, ZentMath.
—BLDSC (4551.305950), AskIEEE, CISTI, IE, Infotrieve, ingenta. **CCC.**
Published by: (International Federation of Operational Research Societies), Blackwell Publishing Ltd., 9600 Garsington Rd, Oxford, OX4 2ZG, United Kingdom. TEL 44-1865-776868, FAX 44-1865-714591, customerservices@oxon.blackwellpublishing.com, http://www.blackwellpublishing.com/journals/ITOR.

➤ **INTERNATIONAL WORKSHOP ON COMPUTATIONAL ELECTRONICS.** see *ELECTRONICS*

➤ **INTERNATIONAL WORKSHOP ON DISCRETE ALGORITHMS AND METHODS FOR MOBILE COMPUTING AND COMMUNICATIONS. PROCEEDINGS.** see *COMMUNICATIONS*

004 USA ISSN 1530-1044
INTERNATIONAL WORKSHOP ON RECOGNITION, ANALYSIS, AND TRACKING OF FACES AND GESTURES IN REAL-TIME SYSTEMS. PROCEEDINGS. Text in English. 1999. a. **Document type:** *Proceedings, Trade.*
Related titles: Online - full text ed.: (from I E E E).
Published by: I E E E Computer Society, 10662 Los Vaqueros Circle, PO Box 3014, Los Alamitos, CA 90720-1314. TEL 714-821-8380, 800-272-6657, FAX 714-821-4010, customer.service@ieee.org, http://www.ieee.org, http://www.computer.org.

004 NLD
INTERNET PANORAMA. Text in Dutch. q. adv. bk.rev.; software rev. illus.; mkt. **Document type:** *Magazine, Trade.*
Description: Offers news, noteworthy items, tips, and behind-the-scenes stories about computers, the Internet, and everything the digital world has to offer.
Media: Online - full content.
Published by: V N U Tijdschriften B.V., Postbus 1900, Hoofddorp, 2130 JH, Netherlands. TEL 31-23-556-6770, FAX 31-23-556-6771, ServiceTeam@tijdschriften.vnu.com, http://www.panorama.nl/internet/ipano.html, http://www.vnu.nl.

004 USA ISSN 1051-9246
QA75.5
INTRODUCING COMPUTERS: CONCEPTS, SYSTEMS, AND APPLICATIONS. Text in English. 1985. a. price varies. index.
Formerly (until 1989): Computer Annual (0749-9221)
—BLDSC (4557.486700).
Published by: John Wiley & Sons, Inc., 111 River St, Hoboken, NJ 07030-5774. TEL 201-748-6000, 800-825-7550, FAX 201-748-5915, uscs-wis@wiley.com, http://www.wiley.com. Ed. Robert H Blissmer.

004 HKG
IPC PRO. Text in English. q. adv. **Description:** Contains news and information for channel and volume buyers of high grade servers, industrial grade computers, data acquisi-tion, and factory automation equipment.
Published by: Ace Marketing & Publications, Inc., 10F, Ultragrace Commercial Bldg, 5 Jordan Rd, Kowloon, Hong Kong. adv.: page USD 24,000. Circ: 28,000.

004 IRL ISSN 0332-0197
CODEN: IRCODQ
IRISH COMPUTER. Text in English. 1977. m. EUR 76 domestic; GBP 58 in United Kingdom; EUR 100 in Europe; USD 90 elsewhere (effective 2005). adv. bk.rev. **Document type:** *Consumer.* **Description:** Covers computer news specifically for the Irish industry and market.
Incorporates (1999-200?): Comms Today (1393-8932); Which was formerly (1994-1999): Communications Today (1393-0745); Incorporates (1987-199?): Telecom Report (0790-9268); And (in 1988): Micro News (0790-6323); Which was formerly (1983-1985): Micro News and Market (0790-0864)
Indexed: Inspec.
—BLDSC (4571.250000), AskIEEE.
Published by: Computer Publications Group, CPG House, Glenageary Office Park, Dun Laoghaire, Co. Dublin, Ireland. TEL 353-1-2847777, FAX 353-1-2847584, info@cpg.ie, http://www.irishcomputer.com/, http://www.cpg.ie. Ed. Eamon McGrane. Pub. Billy Huggard. Adv. contact Stephen Pearson. color page EUR 2,750; trim 210 x 297. Circ: 10,237.

004 GBR ISSN 1746-5702
QA76 CODEN: COBUAH
➤ **ITNOW.** Variant title: IT Now. Text in English. 1957; N.S. 1974; N.S. 1985. bi-m. GBP 107, USD 203, EUR 161 to institutions; GBP 113, USD 215, EUR 170 combined subscription to institutions print & online eds. (effective 2006). adv. bk.rev. illus. 32 p./no.; back issues avail.; reprint service avail. from PSC. **Document type:** *Journal, Academic/Scholarly.*
Description: Technical, commercial and academic papers on advanced programming, computer science theory, hardware and logic design, and business applications.
Formerly (until vol.47, no.2, 2005): The Computer Bulletin (0010-4531); Incorporates: Computer Newsletter (Cambridge) (0266-4631)
Related titles: Microfilm ed.: (from PQC); Online - full text ed.: ISSN 1746-5710. GBP 102, USD 194, EUR 153 to institutions (effective 2006) (from EBSCO Publishing, HighWire Press, IngentaConnect, O C L C Online Computer Library Center, Inc., Oxford University Press Online Journals, ProQuest Information & Learning, Swets Information Services).
Indexed: AHCI, BMT, C&CSA, C&ISA, CompC, CompLI, E&CAJ, ETA, EngInd, Inspec, M&MA, RASB, SolStAb, TEA.
—BLDSC (3393.745000), AskIEEE, CISTI, Ei, IE, Infotrieve, ingenta, Linda Hall. **CCC.**
Published by: (British Computer Society), Oxford University Press, Great Clarendon St, Oxford, OX2 6DP, United Kingdom. TEL 44-1865-556767, FAX 44-1865-556646, jnl.orders@oup.co.uk, http://itnow.oxfordjournals.org/, http://www.oxfordjournals.org/. Ed. John Kavanagh. Pub. Ian McIntosh. R&P Fiona Bennett. adv.: B&W page GBP 1,635, color page GBP 2,175; 241 x 186. Circ: 40,000.

004.4 CZE ISSN 1214-1917
▼ **JAK NA POCITAC.** Text in Czech. 2003. 22/yr. CZK 299 (effective 2003). adv. **Document type:** *Magazine, Consumer.*
Published by: Computer Press a.s., Pod Vinici 23, Prague 4, 143 11, Czech Republic. TEL 420-2-225273930, FAX 420-2-225273934, webmaster@cpress.cz, http://www.jnp.cz, http://www.cpress.cz. Ed. Michal Politzer. adv.: page CZK 35,000; trim 121 x 180.

004 HKG ISSN 1023-5167
JINGRI DIANNAO/COMPUTER TODAY. Text in Chinese. 1989. m. HKD 600; USD 80 foreign; HKD 30 newsstand/cover (effective 2000). adv. bk.rev. 166 p./no.; back issues avail. **Document type:** *Consumer.* **Description:** Covers computer applications; introduces computer software & hardware, networking, multimedia; buyers' guide and products review.
Published by: Modern Electronic & Computing Publishing Co. Ltd., 15 Shing Yip St, Block 1, 9/F, Rm. 1, Kwun Tong, Kowloon, Hong Kong. TEL 852-2342-9845, FAX 852-2341-4247, computertoday@electronictechnology.com, http://www.computertoday.com.hk. Ed. C C Luk. Pub. M K Luk. R&P, Adv. contact Jackio Kwok. B&W page USD 900, color page USD 1,500; trim 285 x 205. Circ: 20,000 (paid); 3,000 (controlled).

004 CHN ISSN 1007-4708
TA645
JISUAN LIXUE XUEBAO/CHINESE JOURNAL OF COMPUTATIONAL MECHANICS. Text in Chinese. 1984. q. CNY 12.50 (effective 2002). **Document type:** *Journal, Academic/Scholarly.*
Related titles: Online - full content ed.: (from WanFang Data Corp.); Online - full text ed.: (from East View Information Services).
Indexed: ApMecR, BrCerAb, C&ISA, CerAb, CorrAb, E&CAJ, EEA, EMA, IAA, M&TEA, MBF, METADEX, RefZh, SolStAb, WAA.
—BLDSC (3180.307800), Linda Hall.
Published by: Dalian Ligong Daxue/Dalian University of Technology, No.2 Linggong Road, Ganjingzi District, Dalian City, Liaoning Province 116024, China. TEL 86-411-4708744, FAX 86-411-4708400, jslxxb@dlut.edu.cn, http://jslxxb.periodicals.com.cn/default.html, http://www.dlut.edu.cn/. Ed. Mo Xie Zhong. **Dist. by:** China International Book Trading Corp, 35 Chegongzhuang Xilu, Haidian District, PO Box 399, Beijing 100044, China. TEL 86-10-68412045, FAX 86-10-68412023, cibtc@mail.cibtc.com.cn, http://www.cibtc.com.cn.

004 CHN ISSN 1000-386X
JISUANJI YINGYONG YU RUANJIAN/COMPUTER APPLICATIONS AND SOFTWARE. Text in Chinese. bi-m.
Related titles: Online - full text ed.: (from East View Information Services).
Published by: Shanghai Jisuan Jishu Yanjiusuo/Shanghai Institute of Computing Technology, 546 Yuruan Lu, Shanghai, 200040, China. TEL 520070.

004 DEU ISSN 0948-6968
QA75.5
JOURNAL FOR UNIVERSAL COMPUTER SCIENCE (ONLINE EDITION). Short title: J U C S. Text in English. 1995. m. EUR 110 to individuals; EUR 220 to institutions (effective 2004). abstr. back issues avail. **Document type:** *Academic/Scholarly.*
Description: Covers all areas of computer science.
Media: Online - full text (from EBSCO Publishing). **Related titles:** CD-ROM ed.; Print ed.: Journal for Universal Computer Science.
Indexed: CCMJ, MathR, MathSciNet.
—CCC.
Published by: Springer-Verlag (Subsidiary of: Springer Science+Business Media), Tiergartenstr 17, Heidelberg, 69121, Germany. TEL 49-6221-3450, FAX 49-6221-345229, subscriptions@springer.de, http://www.jucs.org, http://www.springer.de. Ed. H Maurer. **Subscr. in N. America to:** Springer-Verlag New York, Inc., Journal Fulfillment, PO Box 2485, Secaucus, NJ 07096-2485. TEL 212-460-1500, FAX 212-473-6272.

004 POL ISSN 1507-0360
➤ **JOURNAL OF APPLIED COMPUTER SCIENCE.** Text and summaries in English. 1991. s-a. PLZ 18 domestic (effective 2003). 150 p./no. 1 cols./p.; back issues avail. **Document type:** *Journal, Academic/Scholarly.*
Formerly: Politechnika Lodzka. Zeszyty Naukowe. Informatyka (0860-0082)
Indexed: Inspec.
Published by: (Politechnika Lodzka/Technical University of Lodz), Wydawnictwo Politechniki Lodzkiej, ul Wolczanska 223, Lodz, 93005, Poland. TEL 48-42-6312087, jacs@ics.p.lodz.pl. Ed. Andrzej Malolepszy TEL 48-42-6329757. Circ: 296. **Dist. by:** Ars Polona, Krakowskie Przedmiescie 7, Warsaw, Poland. TEL 48-22-9263914, FAX 48-22-9265334, arspolona@arspolona.com.pl, http://www.arspolona.com.pl.

▼ ➤ **JOURNAL OF COMPUTATIONAL AND THEORETICAL NANOSCIENCE.** see *PHYSICS*

621.381 USA ISSN 1569-8025
JOURNAL OF COMPUTATIONAL ELECTRONICS. Text in English. 2002. q., latest vol.2, 2003. EUR 391, USD 391, GBP 245 combined subscription to institutions print & online eds. (effective 2005). adv. reprint service avail. from PSC.
Document type: *Academic/Scholarly.* **Description:** Contains research in all areas of modeling and simulation of modern electronics, including optical, electronic, mechanical and quantum mechanical aspects, as well as research on the underlying mathematical algorithms and computational details.
Related titles: Online - full text ed.: ISSN 1572-8137 (from EBSCO Publishing, Gale Group, IngentaConnect, Kluwer Online, O C L C Online Computer Library Center, Inc., Springer LINK, Swets Information Services).
Indexed: BibLing.
—BLDSC (4963.463000), IE, ingenta. **CCC.**
Published by: Springer-Verlag New York, Inc. (Subsidiary of: Springer Science+Business Media), 233 Spring St, New York, NY 10013. TEL 212-460-1500, FAX 212-460-1575, service@springer-ny.com, http://springerlink.metapress.com/openurl.asp?genre=journal&issn=1569-8025, http://www.springer-ny.com. Eds. David K Ferry, Karl Hess. **Subscr. to:** Journal Fulfillment, PO Box 2485, Secaucus, NJ 07096-2485. TEL 201-348-4033, FAX 201-348-4505, journals@springer-ny.com.

004 USA ISSN 1549-3636
QA75.5
▼ ➤ **JOURNAL OF COMPUTER SCIENCE.** Text in English. 2005. q. USD 500; USD 175 newsstand/cover (effective 2005). adv. **Document type:** *Journal, Academic/Scholarly.*
Description: Publishes original articles, reviews and short communications of a high scientific and ethical standard in computer science.
Related titles: Online - full text ed.: ISSN 1552-6607. free (effective 2005).
Published by: Science Publications, Vails Gate Heights Dr, PO Box 879, Vails Gate, NY 12584. scipub@gmail.com, http://ansinet.org/sciencepub/c4p.php?j_id=jcs, http://www.scipub.org. Ed., R&P Muhammad S Ahmad. adv.: B&W page USD 200, color page USD 500. Circ: 175 (paid).

➤ **JOURNAL OF COMPUTER SCIENCE AND TECHNOLOGY.** see *COMPUTERS—Computer Architecture*

004.0711 USA
QA76.27
JOURNAL OF COMPUTER SCIENCE EDUCATION. Text in English. 1987. q. USD 29 domestic to non-members; USD 39 foreign to non-members; USD 20 domestic to members; USD 30 foreign to members (effective 2000). back issues avail.
Description: Information for those teaching computer science at the pre-college level.
Formerly: S I G C S Newsletter (1040-7553)
Related titles: Online - full text ed.
Indexed: CIJE, Inspec.
—CCC.
Published by: (Special Interest Groups for Computer Science), International Society for Technology in Education, 1710 Rhode Island Ave NW, Ste 900, Washington, DC 20036. FAX 541-346-5890, iste@iste.org. Ed. Phillip East. R&P Jennifer Roland TEL 541-346-2422. Circ: 450.

004 378.17334 USA ISSN 1040-2454
LB1715 CODEN: JCTEFN
➤ **JOURNAL OF COMPUTING IN TEACHER EDUCATION.** Text in English. 1983. q. USD 65 domestic membership; USD 85 in Canada membership; USD 89.55 elsewhere membership (effective 2003). adv. bk.rev.; software rev. charts. back issues avail. **Document type:** *Journal, Academic/Scholarly.*
Description: Provides research and information for teachers and educators who utilize comuters.
Indexed: CIJE, Inspec.
—BLDSC (4964.300000), IE, ingenta. **CCC.**

C

Published by: Special Interest Group for Teacher Educators (Subsidiary of: International Society for Technology in Education), 1710 Rhode Island Ave NW, Ste 900, Washington, DC 20036. TEL 202-861-7777, FAX 202-861-0888, eat@iastate.edu, http://www.iste.org/jcte/20/1/index.cfm, http://www.west.asu.edu/achristie/sigte.html. Ed. Ann Thompson.

➤ **JOURNAL OF COMPUTING SCIENCES IN COLLEGES.** see *EDUCATION—Higher Education*

004 NLD ISSN 1570-8667
JOURNAL OF DISCRETE ALGORITHMS (AMSTERDAM). Text in English. 2000; N.S. 2003. 4/yr. EUR 54 in Europe to individuals; JPY 6,400 in Japan to individuals; USD 57 elsewhere to individuals; EUR 504 in Europe to institutions; JPY 59,500 in Japan to institutions; USD 534 elsewhere to institutions (effective 2006). **Document type:** *Journal, Academic/Scholarly.* **Description:** Features new algorithms and data structures, new analyses or comparisons of known algorithms, complexity studies, and review articles of currently-active subject areas.
Formerly (until 2003): Journal of Discrete Algorithms (Stanmore) (1468-0904)
Related titles: Online - full text ed.: ISSN 1570-8675 (from EBSCO Publishing, IngentaConnect, ScienceDirect).
Indexed: Inspec, MathR, MathSciNet.
—BLDSC (4969.720000), CISTI, IE. **CCC.**
Published by: Elsevier BV (Subsidiary of: Elsevier Science & Technology), Radarweg 29, Amsterdam, 1043 NX, Netherlands. http://www.elsevier.com/locate/jda, http://www.elsevier.nl. Eds. C S Iliopoulos, D Gabbay, G F Italiano. **Subscr. to:** PO Box 211, Amsterdam 1000 AE, Netherlands. TEL 31-20-485-3757, FAX 31-20-485-3432.

JOURNAL OF EDUCATION RESOURCES IN COMPUTING. see *EDUCATION*

C

658.4 USA ISSN 1097-198X
T58.64 CODEN: JGIMFK
➤ **JOURNAL OF GLOBAL INFORMATION TECHNOLOGY MANAGEMENT.** Variant title: J G I T M. Text in English. 1998. q. USD 85 domestic to individuals; USD 105 foreign to individuals; USD 185 domestic to institutions; USD 205 foreign to institutions (effective 2004). adv. bk.rev. abstr. Index. back issues avail. **Document type:** *Journal, Academic/Scholarly.* **Description:** Multidisciplinary in scope, the journal publishes research and applied articles on all areas of MIS, as well as functional IT applications that have international focus.
Related titles: Online - full text ed.: (from O C L C Online Computer Library Center, Inc., ProQuest Information & Learning).
Indexed: ABIn, CompLI, Inspec.
—BLDSC (4996.285000), IE, ingenta.
Published by: Ivy League Publishing, 4573 Rutherford Dr, PO Box 680392, Marietta, GA 30068. TEL 770-649-6718, FAX 770-649-6719, admin@ivylp.com, http://www.uncg.edu/bae/people/palvia/jgitm.htm, http://www.ivylp.com. Ed. Prashant Palvia. adv.: B&W page USD 450; trim 6.5 x 9.75.

➤ **JOURNAL OF HEALTHCARE INFORMATION MANAGEMENT.** see *HEALTH FACILITIES AND ADMINISTRATION*

003 IND ISSN 0252-2667
QA75.5 CODEN: JIOSDC
➤ **JOURNAL OF INFORMATION & OPTIMIZATION SCIENCES.** Text in English. 1980. 3/yr. INR 900 domestic; USD 120 foreign (effective 2004). bk.rev. back issues avail. **Document type:** *Journal, Academic/Scholarly.* **Description:** Devoted to advances in information sciences, optimization sciences, and related aspects as discrete math., computer science and statistics.
Indexed: ABIn, ASFA, Biostat, CCMJ, CIS, CurCont, ESPM, EngInd, IAOP, Inspec, MathR, MathSciNet, ORMS, QC&AS, RiskAb, ST&MA, ZentMath.
—BLDSC (5006.745000), AskIEEE, CISTI, Ei, IE, Infotrieve, ingenta.
Published by: Taru Publications, G-159, Pushkar Enclave, Pashchim Vihar, New Delhi, 110 063, India. TEL 91-11-25260534, FAX 91-11-25265397, info@tarupublications.com. Ed., R&P Dr. Bal Kishan Dass. Circ: 330 (paid).

658.4 USA ISSN 1522-8053
HD30.2 CODEN: JITCAK
➤ **JOURNAL OF INFORMATION TECHNOLOGY CASES AND APPLICATIONS.** Text in English. 1999. q. USD 85 domestic to individuals; USD 105 foreign to individuals; USD 185 domestic to institutions; USD 205 foreign to institutions; USD 29 newsstand/cover to individuals; USD 49 newsstand/cover to institutions (effective 2002). adv. bk.rev. abstr. Index. back issues avail. **Document type:** *Journal, Academic/Scholarly.* **Description:** Focuses on IT cases and applications that explain existing theories and concepts or that help in building new theories and frameworks.
Related titles: Online - full text ed.: (from O C L C Online Computer Library Center, Inc., ProQuest Information & Learning).
Indexed: ABIn, CompLI, Inspec.
—BLDSC (5006.792000).
Published by: Ivy League Publishing, 4573 Rutherford Dr, PO Box 680392, Marietta, GA 30068. TEL 770-649-6718, FAX 770-649-6719, admin@ivylp.com, http://www.liu.edu/cwis/cwp/colofman/jitca/jitca.html, http://www.ivylp.com. Ed. Shailendra Palvia. Pub., R&P, Adv. contact Pankaj Palvia. B&W page USD 450; trim 6.5 x 9.75.

004 630 USA ISSN 1546-959X
▼ **JOURNAL OF INFORMATION TECHNOLOGY IN AGRICULTURE.** Text in English. forthcoming 2006. irreg. free (effective 2004).
Media: Online - full content.
Published by: World Federation of Information Technology in Agriculture, University of Florida Office of Academic Technology, 1012 Turlington, Gainesville, FL 32611. TEL 352-392-0371, http://www.jitag.org, http://www.at.ufl.edu. Ed. Fedro Zazueta.

004 USA
➤ **JOURNAL OF INSTRUCTION-LEVEL PARALLELISM.** Short title: J I L P. Text in English. 1999. a. free (effective 2005).
Media: Online - full content.
Published by: International Symposium on Microarchitecture http://www.jilp.org/. Ed. Tom Conte.

004 GBR ISSN 0955-792X
QA76.63 CODEN: JLCOEU
➤ **JOURNAL OF LOGIC AND COMPUTATION.** Text in English. 1990. bi-m. GBP 469, USD 891, EUR 704 to institutions; GBP 494, USD 939, EUR 741 combined subscription to institutions print & online eds. (effective 2006). adv. bk.rev. back issues avail.; reprint service avail. from PSC. **Document type:** *Academic/Scholarly.* **Description:** Aims to promote this new field with its comprehensive selection of technical scientific papers and regular contributions such as letters, reviews and discussions.
Related titles: Online - full text ed.: ISSN 1465-363X. GBP 445, USD 846, EUR 668 to institutions (effective 2006) (from EBSCO Publishing, Gale Group, HighWire Press, IngentaConnect, O C L C Online Computer Library Center, Inc., Oxford University Press Online Journals, ProQuest Information & Learning, Swets Information Services).
Indexed: C&ISA, CCMJ, CMCI, CompAb, CompLI, E&CAJ, EngInd, Inspec, MathR, MathSciNet, SolStAb, ZentMath.
—BLDSC (5010.552200), AskIEEE, Ei, IDS, IE, Infotrieve, ingenta. **CCC.**
Published by: Oxford University Press, Great Clarendon St, Oxford, OX2 6DP, United Kingdom. TEL 44-1865-556767, FAX 44-1865-556646, jnl.orders@oup.co.uk, http://logcom.oxfordjournals.org/, http://www.oxfordjournals.org/. Ed. Dov M. Gabbay. Pub. Ian McIntosh. R&P Fiona Bennett. adv.: B&W page GBP 225, B&W page USD 405; trim 130 x 210. Circ: 500. **U.S. subscr. to:** Oxford University Press, 2001 Evans Rd, Cary, NC 27513. jnlorders@oup-usa.org.

➤ **JOURNAL OF MACHINE LEARNING RESEARCH.** see *ENGINEERING—Mechanical Engineering*

▼ ➤ **JOURNAL OF NEGATIVE RESULTS IN SPEECH AND AUDIO SCIENCES.** see *MEDICAL SCIENCES—Otorhinolaryngology*

004 USA
JOURNAL OF OPEN COMPUTING★. Text in English. q. USD 95 to members. **Description:** Serves as the journal for the Association. Includes information on training, education, identifying issues, exploring new business models and other topics.
Media: Online - full text.
Published by: UniForum Association, PO Box 3177, Annapolis, MD 21403. TEL 410-715-9500, 800-333-8649, FAX 301-596-8803, uniforum@uniforum.or, uniforum@dkuug.dk, http://www.uniforum.org. Ed. Jim Johnson.

004 USA ISSN 0743-7315
QA76.5 CODEN: JPDCER
➤ **JOURNAL OF PARALLEL AND DISTRIBUTED COMPUTING.** Text in English. 1984. 12/yr. EUR 622 in Europe to individuals; JPY 65,000 in Japan to individuals; USD 484 to individuals except Europe and Japan; EUR 1,311 in Europe to institutions; JPY 136,900 in Japan to institutions; USD 1,019 to institutions except Europe and Japan; EUR 305 in Europe to students; JPY 31,700 in Japan to students; USD 265 to students except Europe and Japan (effective 2006). back issues avail. **Document type:** *Academic/Scholarly.* **Description:** Directed to researchers, engineers, educators, managers, programmers, and users of computers who have particular interest in parallel process and/or distributed computing. Publishes original research papers and current review articles on theory, design, evaluation, and use of parallel and/or distributed computing systems.
Related titles: Online - full text ed.: ISSN 1096-0848. USD 1,065 (effective 2002) (from EBSCO Publishing, Gale Group, IngentaConnect, O C L C Online Computer Library Center, Inc., ScienceDirect, Swets Information Services).
Indexed: ASCA, CMCI, CompAb, CompLI, CompR, CurCont, EngInd, ISR, Inspec, RefZh, SCI, ZentMath.
—BLDSC (5028.620000), AskIEEE, CISTI, Ei, IDS, IE, Infotrieve, ingenta, Linda Hall. **CCC.**
Published by: Academic Press (Subsidiary of: Elsevier Science & Technology), 525 B St, Ste 1900, San Diego, CA 92101-4495. TEL 619-231-6616, 800-894-3434, FAX 619-699-6422, apsubs@acad.com, http://www.elsevier.com/locate/jpdc, http://www.academicpress.com. Eds. A. Gottlieb, K. Hwang, S. Sahni.

004 AUS ISSN 1443-458X
QA76 CODEN: JRPTFH
➤ **JOURNAL OF RESEARCH AND PRACTICE IN INFORMATION TECHNOLOGY.** Text in English. 1967. 4/yr. AUD 66 domestic to individuals; AUD 69 foreign to individuals; USD 54 domestic to institutions; USD 81 foreign to institutions; free to members (effective 2004). adv. bk.rev. charts; illus.; stat. Index. **Document type:** *Journal, Academic/Scholarly.* **Description:** Publishes papers relating to both emerging research and to professional practice and thus contains articles that are of interest both to practicing information technology professionals and to university and industry researchers.
Formerly: Australian Computer Journal (0004-8917)
Related titles: Microform ed.: 1967 (from PQC); Online - full text ed.: 2003. free (effective 2005).
Indexed: ASCA, ApMecR, BrCerAb, C&CSA, C&ISA, CIS, CMCI, CerAb, CompAb, CompC, CompLI, CompR, CorrAb, E&CAJ, EMA, EngInd, IAA, ICEA, Inspec, M&TEA, MBF, METADEX, MathR, RefZh, SoftAbEng, WAA, ZentMath.
—BLDSC (5052.002550), AskIEEE, CISTI, Ei, IDS, IE, Infotrieve, ingenta, Linda Hall. **CCC.**
Published by: Australian Computer Society, PO Box Q534, QVB Post Office, Sydney, NSW 1230, Australia. http://www.acs.org.au/jrpit/index.html. Circ: 15,000.

004 USA ISSN 0920-8542
QA76.88 CODEN: JOSUED
➤ **JOURNAL OF SUPERCOMPUTING;** an international journal of supercomputing design, analysis and use. Text in English. 1987. 12/yr. EUR 1,178, USD 1,198, GBP 738 combined subscription to institutions print & online eds. (effective 2005). adv. illus. back issues avail.; reprint service avail. from PQC,PSC. **Document type:** *Journal, Academic/Scholarly.* **Description:** Publishes theoretical, practical,tutorial and survey papers on all aspects of supercomputing. The papers published generally fall into areas such as technology, architecture and systems algorithms, languages and programs, performance measures tecture and systems,and methods, and applications.
Related titles: Microform ed.: (from PQC); Online - full text ed.: ISSN 1573-0484 (from EBSCO Publishing, Gale Group, IngentaConnect, Kluwer Online, O C L C Online Computer Library Center, Inc., Ovid Technologies, Inc., Springer LINK, Swets Information Services).
Indexed: ASCA, BibLing, CMCI, CompAb, CompLI, CompR, CurCont, CybAb, EngInd, ISR, InfoSAb, Inspec, RefZh, SCI, ZentMath.
—BLDSC (5067.117000), AskIEEE, CISTI, Ei, IDS, IE, Infotrieve, ingenta. **CCC.**
Published by: (Supercomputing Research Center), Springer-Verlag New York, Inc. (Subsidiary of: Springer Science+Business Media), 233 Spring St, New York, NY 10013. TEL 212-460-1500, FAX 212-460-1575, service@springer-ny.com, http://springerlink.metapress.com/openurl.asp?genre=journal&issn=0920-8542, http://www.springer-ny.com. Ed. Hamid R Arabnia. **Subscr. to:** Journal Fulfillment, PO Box 2485, Secaucus, NJ 07096-2485. TEL 201-348-4033, FAX 201-348-4505, journals@springer-ny.com.

004 USA ISSN 1540-2525
LB3060.5
➤ **THE JOURNAL OF TECHNOLOGY, LEARNING, AND ASSESSMENT.** Text in English. 2002. bi-m. free (effective 2005). **Document type:** *Journal, Academic/Scholarly.*
Media: Online - full content.
Published by: Boston College, Center for the Study of Testing, Evaluation, and Educational Policy, Campion Hall, Chestnut Hill, MA 02467. TEL 617-552-4521, FAX 617-552-8419, http://www.jtla.org, http://www.csteep.bc.edu. Ed. Michael Russell.

004 AUT
JOURNAL OF UNIVERSAL COMPUTER SCIENCE. Variant title: J.UCS. Text in English. 1994. m. USD 130 to individuals and academic institutions; USD 260 to corporations (effective 2005). **Document type:** *Academic/Scholarly.* **Description:** Covers all aspects of computer sciences.
Media: Online - full text.
Published by: Institute for Information Processing and Computer Supported New Media, Inffeldgasse 16c, Graz, 8010, Austria. TEL 43-316-8735612, FAX 43-316-8735699, webmaster@iicm.edu, http://www.jucs.org, http://www.iicm.edu. Ed. Hermann Maurer.

004 USA
➤ **THE JOURNAL OF VIRTUAL ENVIRONMENTS.** Text in English. 1996. irreg. free (effective 2005). **Document type:** *Academic/Scholarly.* **Description:** Publishes research that relates to virtual environments or makes use of virtual environments, particular interest is focus on anthropological, psychological, and sociological approaches, as are the practical and technical aspects of creating, maintaining and administrating virtual environments.

Media: Online - full content.
Published by: Brandeis University, 415 South St, Waltham, MA 02254. http://www.brandeis.edu/pubs/jove. Ed. David Jacobson.

004 FIN ISSN 0357-9921
JYVASKYLA STUDIES IN COMPUTER SCIENCE, ECONOMICS AND STATISTICS. Text in English. 1980. irreg. price varies. **Document type:** *Monographic series.*
Published by: Jyvaskylan Yliopisto/University of Jyvaskyla, PO Box 35, Jyvaeskylae, 40014, Finland. TEL 941-601-211, FAX 603-371. Circ: 450.

KEY ABSTRACTS - COMPUTING IN ELECTRONICS & POWER. see *COMPUTERS—Abstracting, Bibliographies, Statistics*

KEY ABSTRACTS - HUMAN-COMPUTER INTERACTION. see *COMPUTERS—Abstracting, Bibliographies, Statistics*

KEY NOTE MARKET REPORT: MULTIMEDIA IN U K. see *COMMUNICATIONS*

004 SAU ISSN 1319-1578
➤ **KING SAUD UNIVERSITY JOURNAL. COMPUTER AND INFORMATION SCIENCES/JAMI'AT AL-MALIK SA'UD. MAJALLAH. AL-'ULUM AL-HASIB WAL-MA'LUMAT.** (Other sections avail.: Administrative Sciences, Agricultural Sciences, Architecture and Planning, Arts, Educational Sciences and Islamic Studies, Engineering Sciences, Science) Text in Arabic, English. 1993. a. USD 5 (effective 2001). **Document type:** *Journal, Academic/Scholarly.*
Indexed: Inspec.
Published by: King Saud University, University Libraries, P O Box 22480, Riyadh, 11495, Saudi Arabia. TEL 966-1-4676148, FAX 966-1-4676162, TELEX 4010190 KSU SJ. Ed. Khalid A Ad-Dobaian. R&P Dr. Sulaiman Saleh Al-Ogle. Circ: 2,000.

621.39 NLD ISSN 0893-3405
➤ **KLUWER INTERNATIONAL SERIES IN ENGINEERING AND COMPUTER SCIENCE.** Text in English. 1984. irreg., latest vol.867, 2005. price varies. back issues avail. **Document type:** *Monographic series, Academic/Scholarly.*
Indexed: CCMJ, Inspec, ZentMath.
—BLDSC (5099.730000), CISTI, IE, ingenta. **CCC.**
Published by: Springer-Verlag Dordrecht (Subsidiary of: Springer Science+Business Media), Van Godewijckstraat 30, Dordrecht, 3311 GX, Netherlands. TEL 31-78-6576050, FAX 31-78-6576474, http://www.springeronline.com.

➤ **KNJIZNICA SIGMA.** see *PHYSICS*

004 332.1 GBR ISSN 1463-1822
KNOWLEDGE MANAGEMENT; the magazine for knowledge professionals. Text in English. 1998. 10/yr. GBP 50 in United Kingdom; GBP 75 elsewhere (effective 2001). adv. bk.rev. charts; stat.; tr.lit. 36 p./no.; back issues avail.; reprints avail. **Document type:** *Magazine, Corporate.*
Related titles: Online - full text ed.: (from EBSCO Publishing).
Indexed: InfoSAb, Inspec.
—BLDSC (5100.450600).
Published by: Bizmedia, Royal Station Court, Station Rd, Twyford, Reading, Berks RG10 9NF, United Kingdom. TEL 44-118-960-2820, FAX 44-118-960-2821, admin@bizmedia.co.uk, http://www.kmmag.co.uk, http://www.bizmedia.co.uk/. Ed. Peter Williams. Pub. Melanie Williams. Adv. contact Nigel Clear TEL 44-118-960-2823. page GBP 2,800.

658 GBR ISSN 1477-8238
HD30.2
▼ ➤ **KNOWLEDGE MANAGEMENT RESEARCH & PRACTICE.** Text in English. 2003. q. USD 140 combined subscription in United States to individuals; GBP 90 combined subscription elsewhere to individuals; USD 320 combined subscription in United States to institutions; GBP 198 combined subscription elsewhere to institutions (effective 2005); includes print & online eds.. **Document type:** *Journal, Academic/Scholarly.* **Description:** Covers all aspects of managing knowledge, organizational learning, intellectual capital and knowledge economics.
Related titles: Online - full text ed.: ISSN 1477-8246. GBP 128 in Europe to institutions; USD 200 elsewhere to institutions (effective 2004) (from EBSCO Publishing, Gale Group, IngentaConnect, O C L C Online Computer Library Center, Inc., ProQuest Information & Learning, Swets Information Services).
Indexed: ABIn, IBR, IBSS, IBZ, Inspec.
—BLDSC (5100.451300), IE. **CCC.**
Published by: (Operational Research Society), Palgrave Macmillan Ltd. (Subsidiary of: Macmillan Publishers Ltd.), Houndmills, Basingstoke, Hants RG21 6XS, United Kingdom. TEL 44-1256-329242, FAX 44-1256-810526, journal-info@palgrave.com, http://www.palgrave-journals.com/kmrp/index.html. Ed. John S Edwards.

004 DNK ISSN 0107-8283
KOEBENHAVNS UNIVERSITET. DATALOGISK INSTITUT. RAPPORT. Text in Danish. irreg. free. **Document type:** *Academic/Scholarly.*
Published by: Koebenhavns Universitet, Datalogisk Institut, Universitetsparken 1, Copenhagen Oe, 2100, Denmark. TEL 45-35-32-14-00, FAX 45-35-32-14-01.

004.16 LTU ISSN 1392-3498
KOMPIUTERIJA. Variant title: P C World Lithuania. Text in Lithuanian. 1997. m. LTL 4.50 newsstand/cover (effective 2002). adv. **Document type:** *Magazine, Trade.* **Description:** Dedicated to computer hardware, software, communications, Internet, market, trends and news, programming, and entertainment.
Related titles: Online - full text ed.
Address: Laisves al. 7, Kaunas, 3000, Lithuania. TEL 370-7-400-290, FAX 370-7-400-277, kompiuterija@lrytas.lt, http://www.kompiuterija.lt. Ed. Bronislovas Burgis. Adv. contact Audrius Vaiciunas. B&W page USD 760, color page USD 912; trim 210 x 290. Circ: 11,500 (paid).

004 JPN ISSN 1340-7732
KOMPUTA SAIENSU/JAPANESE JOURNAL OF COMPUTER SCIENCE. Text in Japanese. 1994. s-a. **Document type:** *Journal, Academic/Scholarly.*
Related titles: Online - full content ed.: ISSN 1348-5172.
Published by: Nihon Komputa Saiensu Gakkai/Japanese Association of Computer Science, Department of Electrical Engineering, School of Engineering, Tokyo DENKI University, 2-2 Kanda-Nishiki-cho Chiyoda-ku, Tokyo, 101-8457, Japan. TEL 61-3-52803643, FAX 61-3-32191497, http://wwwsoc.nii.ac.jp/jacs/JJCS/, http://www.med.osaka-u.ac.jp/pub/phys1/shiga/jiba.html.

004 IDN
KOMPUTEK COMPUTERWORLD INDONESIA. Text in Indonesian. w.
Published by: P T Jawa Media Komputana, Jalan Kayun 24, Surabaya, 60271, Indonesia. TEL 31-526041, FAX 31-519806. Ed. Edi Purwono. adv.: B&W page IDR 3,800,000, color page IDR 7,600,000; trim 415 x 285. Circ: 15,000.

004 POL ISSN 1506-4026
KOMPUTER SWIAT. Text in Polish. 1998. fortn. PLZ 3.80 newsstand/cover (effective 2001). adv. **Document type:** *Magazine, Consumer.*
Related titles: Online - full text ed.: ISSN 1689-3662. 199?.
Published by: Axel Springer Polska, Al Jerozolimskie 181, Warsaw, 02222, Poland. TEL 48-22-6084100, FAX 48-22-6084106, redakcja@komputerswiat.pl, asp@axelspringer.com.pl, http://www.komputerswiat.pl, http://www.axelspringer.com.pl. Ed. Wieslaw Malecki. Circ: 130,000 (paid).

004 POL ISSN 1508-4280
KOMPUTER SWIAT BIBLIOTECZKA. Text in Polish. 1999. irreg. PLZ 9.80 newsstand/cover (effective 2001). **Document type:** *Magazine, Consumer.*
Published by: Axel Springer Polska, Al Jerozolimskie 181, Warsaw, 02222, Poland. TEL 48-22-6084100, FAX 48-22-6084106, asp@axelspringer.com.pl, http://www.axelspringer.com.pl.

004.42 POL
KOMPUTER SWIAT EKSPERT. Text in Polish. bi-m. PLZ 9.90 newsstand/cover (effective 2004). adv. **Document type:** *Magazine, Consumer.*
Published by: Axel Springer Polska, Al Jerozolimskie 181, Warsaw, 02222, Poland. TEL 48-22-6084100, FAX 48-22-6084106, redakcja@ks-ekspert.pl, asp@axelspringer.com.pl, http://www.ks-ekspert.pl, http://www.axelspringer.com.pl. Ed. Wieslaw Malecki. Adv. contact Piotr Roszczyk. page PLZ 8,500; trim 215 x 297.

004.42 POL ISSN 1640-2332
KOMPUTER SWIAT EXTRA. Text in Polish. 2000. q. PLZ 7.90 newsstand/cover (effective 2004). adv. **Document type:** *Magazine, Consumer.*
Published by: Axel Springer Polska, Al Jerozolimskie 181, Warsaw, 02222, Poland. TEL 48-22-6084100, FAX 48-22-6084106, niezbednik@komputerswiat.pl, asp@axelspringer.com.pl, http://www.axelspringer.com.pl. Ed. Wieslaw Malecki. Adv. contact Piotr Roszczyk. page PLZ 8,500; trim 215 x 297.

004 651.2 POL ISSN 1425-8250
KOMPUTERY I BIURO. Text in Polish. 1992. w.
Related titles: ♦ Supplement to: Gazeta Wyborcza. ISSN 0860-908X.
Published by: Agora S.A., ul Czerska 8/10, Warsaw, 00732, Poland. TEL 48-22-6994301, FAX 48-22-6994603, http://www.gazeta.pl.

006 BLR ISSN 1606-6464
KOMP'YUTERNAYA GAZETA/COMPUTER NEWS. Text in Russian. 1995. w. **Document type:** *Newspaper, Consumer.*
Media: Online - full content.
Published by: Izdatel'stvo Nestor, A/ya 563, Minsk, 220113, Belarus. nestorpb@nestor.minsk.by, http://www.nestor.minsk.by/kg. Ed. Svetlana Pumpur TEL 375-172-346790. Circ: 22,490.

004 UKR
KOMP'YUTERNOE OBOZRENIE/COMPUTER REVIEW. Text in Russian. 1995. w. UAK 7.10 per month domestic (effective 2004). illus. 64 p./no.; **Document type:** *Magazine, Trade.* **Description:** Designed for high-tech professionals working in the market, product and service resellers, specialists employed as IT managers in the field and non-IT companies as well as consumers interested in up-to-date news from IT field, last technology developments, new products and information concerning current marketing and sales status quo in information technologies industry.
Published by: Izdatel'skii Dom I T C, prosp Krasnozvezdnyi 51, Kiev, Ukraine. info@itc.ua, http://itc.ua/ko. Circ: 6,500 (paid); 13,300 (controlled).

004 GBR ISSN 0952-3677
L F C S REPORT SERIES. Text in English. 19??. irreg. **Document type:** *Monographic series, Academic/Scholarly.*
—BLDSC (5186.091300).
Published by: Laboratory for Foundations of Computer Science (Subsidiary of: University of Edinburgh, School of Informatics), James Clerk Maxwell Building, The King's Buildings, Mayfield Rd, Edinburgh, EH9 3JZ, United Kingdom. TEL 44-131-6505132, FAX 44-131-6677209, lfcs-admin@informatics.ed.ac.uk, http://www.lfcs.informatics.ed.ac.uk/.

004 USA ISSN 1546-4288
TK7887
LEARNING SERIES. Variant title: P C Upgrade's Learning Series. Text in English. 8/yr. USD 5.99 newsstand/cover domestic; USD 7.99 newsstand/cover in Canada (effective 2004). adv. **Document type:** *Magazine.*
Published by: Bedford Communications, Inc., 1410 Broadway, 21st Fl, New York, NY 10018. TEL 212-807-8220, http://www.techworthy.com. Ed. David Finck TEL 212-807-8220. adv.: B&W page USD 5,185, color page USD 5,700; trim 8 x 10.75.

C

004 DEU ISSN 0302-9743
TK5105.88815 CODEN: LNCSD9
➤ **LECTURE NOTES IN COMPUTER SCIENCE.** Variant title: Lecture Notes in Artificial Intelligence. Text in German. 1973. irreg., latest no.3775, 2005. price varies. back issues avail.; reprint service avail. from ISI. **Document type:** *Monographic series, Academic/Scholarly.* **Description:** Reports on leading-edge research in artificial intelligence and other areas of computer science.
Related titles: Online - full text ed.
Indexed: ASCA, CCMJ, CIS, CMCI, CompC, CybAb, Englnd, Inspec, MathR, NSCI, Philind, RefZh, SSCI, VITIS, ZentMath.
—BLDSC (5180.185000), CISTI, Ei, IDS, IE, Infotrieve, ingenta. **CCC.**
Published by: Springer-Verlag (Subsidiary of: Springer Science+Business Media), Haber Str 7, Heidelberg, 69126, Germany. TEL 49-6221-3450, FAX 49-6221-229, service@springer.de, http://www.springer.de. Eds. G Goos, J Hartmanis. **Orders in N. America to:** Springer-Verlag New York, Inc., Journal Fulfillment, PO Box 2485, Secaucus, NJ 07096-2485. TEL 201-348-4033.

004 SGP
LECTURE NOTES SERIES ON COMPUTING. Text in English. 1992. irreg., latest vol.12. price varies. **Document type:** *Monographic series, Academic/Scholarly.*
Indexed: CCMJ, ZentMath.
—BLDSC (5180.418000).
Published by: World Scientific Publishing Co. Pte. Ltd., 5 Toh Tuck Link, Singapore, 596224, Singapore. TEL 65-466-5775, FAX 65-467-7667, wspc@wspc.com.sg, series@wspc.com.sg, http://www.wspc.com.sg/books/series/lnsc_series.shtml, http://www.worldscientific.com. Ed. D T Lee. **Dist. by:** World Scientific Publishing Co., Inc., 1060 Main St, River Edge, NJ 07661. TEL 201-487-9655, 800-227-7562, FAX 201-487-9656, 888-977-2665; World Scientific Publishing Ltd., 57 Shelton St, London WC2H 9HE, United Kingdom. TEL 44-20-78360888, FAX 44-20-78362020, sales@wspc.co.uk.

004 FRA ISSN 1163-3867
LETTRE DE LA SURETE DE FONCTIONNEMENT. Text in French. 1987. bi-m. bk.rev. back issues avail. **Document type:** *Newsletter.*
Published by: E C 2, 269 rue de la Garenne, Nanterre, 92000, France. TEL 47-80-70-00, FAX 1-47-80-66-29. Ed. Jean Claude Rault.

004 MEX
EN LINEA AT 2; avances, desarrollos y novedades de la informatica. Text in Spanish. 1997. q.
Related titles: Online - full text ed.
Published by: Universidad Autonoma Metropolitana - Azcapotzalco, Ave San Pablo No 180, Col Reynosa Tamaulipas, Mexico City, DF 02200, Mexico. TEL 52-5-382-5000, http://www-azc.uam.mx/enlinea2/enlihome.htm. Ed. Rafael Lopez Bracho.

004 USA ISSN 1522-2217
LINUXWORLD (ONLINE EDITION). Text in English. 1998. irreg. USD 39.99 (effective 2005). **Document type:** *Magazine, Trade.*
Media: Online - full content. **Related titles:** ♦ Print ed.: LinuxWorld (Print Edition). ISSN 1544-4511.

Published by: I D G Communications Inc., 501 Second St, Ste 600, San Francisco, CA 94107-4133. TEL 415-348-8006, http://www.linuxworld.com/, http://www.idg.com/.

004 USA ISSN 1544-4511
▼ **LINUXWORLD (PRINT EDITION).** Text in English. 2003 (Sept./Oct.). bi-m. USD 49.99 domestic; USD 79.99 in Canada & Mexico; USD 99.99 elsewhere; USD 5.99 newsstand/cover (effective 2005). adv. **Document type:** *Magazine, Trade.* **Description:** Provides information and evaluations of Linux-based systems for Linux professionals and corporate technology managers.
Related titles: ◆ Online - full content ed.: LinuxWorld (Online Edition). ISSN 1522-2217.
Published by: SYS-CON Media, Inc., 135 Chestnut Ridge Rd, Montvale, NJ 07645. TEL 201-802-3040, 888-303-5282, FAX 201-782-9600, info@sys-con.com, http://www.linuxworld.com/, http://www.sys-con.com. adv.: B&W page USD 4,680, color page USD 4,970; trim 8.375 x 10.75. Circ: 45,000.

004 JPN ISSN 0286-486X
LOGIN. Text in Japanese. 1982. m. JPY 12,980; JPY 680 newsstand/cover (effective 2004). **Document type:** *Magazine, Consumer.*
Published by: ASCII Corp., JR Shinanomachi Bldg. 34 Shinanomachi, Shinjuku-ku, Tokyo, 160-8584, Japan. http://www.ascii.co.jp.

004 USA
M I S INFORMATION. Text in English. 1988. 10/yr. USD 20 (effective 2000). adv. bk.rev.; film rev.; software rev.; tel.rev.; Website rev. illus. back issues avail.; reprints avail. **Document type:** *Newsletter.* **Description:** Newsletter devoted to computer humor. Specializes in satire, especially relating to trends in computing.
Related titles: E-mail ed.; Online - full content ed.
Address: PO Box 755, Rochester, MN 55903-0755. misinfo@aol.com, http://members.aol.com/misinfo/misinfo.htm. Ed., Pub., R&P, Adv. contact Chris Miksanek TEL 612-833-1046. Circ: 1,000.

004 USA ISSN 0891-4702
M I T PRESS SERIES IN INFORMATION SYSTEMS. (Massachusetts Institute of Technology) Variant title: Information Systems Series. Text in English. 1985. irreg. price varies. **Document type:** *Monographic series, Academic/Scholarly.*
Indexed: Inspec.
Published by: M I T Press, 55 Hayward St, Cambridge, MA 02142-1493. TEL 617-253-5646, FAX 617-258-6779, journals-info@mit.edu, http://mitpress.mit.edu.

004 USA
M Q UPDATE. Text in English. m. USD 380 (effective 2000). **Document type:** *Trade.* **Description:** Provides information for MQ Series professionals.
Published by: Xephon, 9330 Lyndon B Johnson Fwy., Ste. 800, Dallas, TX 75243-4310. TEL 303-410-9344, FAX 303-438-0290, http://www.xephon.com/.

004 ITA ISSN 1125-4874
MAC FORMAT. Cover title: Mac Format Italia. Text in Italian. 1996. m. back issues avail. **Document type:** *Magazine, Consumer.* **Description:** Provides a guide for Macintosh users. Includes software reviews, new product announcements and hints on how to increase the computer's capabilities.
Media: Optical Disk.
Published by: Future Media Italy SpA, Via Asiago 45, Milano, MI 20128, Italy. TEL 39-02-2529161, FAX 39-02-26005520, info@futuremediaitaly.it, http://www.futuremediaitaly.it. Ed. Mietta Capasso.

004 ISR ISSN 0333-7413
MACHSHEVIM P C. Text in Hebrew. 1980. m. USD 67. adv.
Published by: Merav Publishing Industries Ltd., 27 Soutine St, Tel Aviv, 64684, Israel. TEL 972-3-5211900, FAX 972-3-5211902, merav@trendline.co.il, http://www.merav.co.il. Ed. Shlomit Miron. Circ: 8,000.

004 GBR ISSN 0950-1428
MACMILLAN COMPUTER SCIENCE SERIES. Text in English. 1975. irreg. **Document type:** *Monographic series.*
Indexed: Inspec.
Published by: Palgrave Macmillan Ltd. (Subsidiary of: Macmillan Publishers Ltd.), Houndmills, Basingstoke, Hants RG21 6XS, United Kingdom. TEL 44-1256-329242, FAX 44-1256-810526, bookenquiries@palgrave.com, http://www.palgrave.com.

MAGYAR KONYVTARI SZAKIRODALOM BIBLIOGRAFIAJA/ BIBLIOGRAPHY ON HUNGARIAN LIBRARY LITERATURE. see *COMPUTERS—Abstracting, Bibliographies, Statistics*

004.12 USA
MAINFRAME COMPUTING. Text in English. 1988. m. USD 150 in North America; USD 165 elsewhere (effective 2001). **Document type:** *Newsletter, Trade.* **Description:** Reports on computer mainframes, including supercomputers. Covers new hardware peripherals, as well as applications software, operating systems, and network systems. Emphasis is on the marketing strategies of mainframe and peripheral vendors.
Related titles: Online - full text ed.: (from Data-Star, The Dialog Corporation).

Published by: Worldwide Videotex, PO Box 3273, Boynton Beach, FL 33424-3273. TEL 561-738-2276, markedit@juno.com, http://www.wvpubs.com. Ed., Pub. Mark Wright.

004 GBR ISSN 1467-1271
MANUFACTURING AND LOGISTICS I T. Text in English. 1998. q. back issues avail. **Document type:** *Magazine, Trade.* **Description:** Provides real and relevant information about the use of information technology in manufacturing and logistics applications across Europe.
Formerly (until 1998): Logistics I T (1463-1172)
Published by: I B C Publishing (Subsidiary of: Interactive Business Communications Ltd.), Latimer House, 189 High St, Potters Bar, Herts EN6 5DA, United Kingdom. TEL 44-1707-664200, FAX 44-1707-664800, info@ibcpub.co.uk, http://www.logisticsit.com/, http://www.ibcpub.com. Ed. Ian Byfield.

004 AUS ISSN 1323-6342
THE MANUFACTURING AND LOGISTICS SOFTWARE BUYERS GUIDE (ASIA PACIFIC EDITION). Text in English. 1987. every 18 mos., latest 2000. AUD 110 per issue domestic; AUD 100 per issue foreign (effective 2001). software rev. 254 p./no.; **Document type:** *Catalog.* **Description:** Presents survey data covering leading manufacturing and logistics applications software products available in Australia and the Asia-Pacific Region.
Published by: Homer Computer Services Pty. Ltd., 31 Arnold Road, East Brighton, VIC 3187 , Australia. TEL 61-3-9592 0216, FAX 61-3-9592 5623, info@homercomputer.com.au, http://www.homercomputer.com.au, http:// www.homercomputer.com.au/. Ed., Pub. Glyn G Homer.

MATHEMATICAL METHODS OF OPERATIONS RESEARCH. see *BUSINESS AND ECONOMICS—Management*

003 USA ISSN 0364-765X
T57.6.A1 CODEN: MOREDQ
➤ **MATHEMATICS OF OPERATIONS RESEARCH.** Text in English. 1976. q. USD 138 domestic to non-members; USD 157 foreign to non-members; USD 69 to members additonal journal; USD 180 combined subscription domestic to non-members print & online eds.; USD 199 combined subscription foreign to non-members print & online eds.; USD 90 combined subscription to members additonal journal, print & online eds.; USD 272 combined subscription domestic to institutions print &/or online eds.; USD 291 combined subscription foreign to institutions print & online eds. (effective 2004). bibl.; charts; illus. back issues avail. **Document type:** *Journal, Academic/Scholarly.* **Description:** Covers continuous optimization, discrete optimization, stochastic models, game theory.
Related titles: Online - full content ed.: ISSN 1526-5471. USD 92 to non-members; USD 46 to members additional journal (effective 2004); Online - full text ed.: (from EBSCO Publishing, Gale Group, O C L C Online Computer Library Center, Inc., ProQuest Information & Learning, Swets Information Services).
Indexed: ABIn, ASCA, BPIA, BusI, CCMJ, CIS, CMCI, CPM, CompC, CompR, CurCont, CybAb, EngInd, IAOP, ISR, Inspec, JCQM, ManagCont, MathR, MathSciNet, ORMS, QC&AS, RASB, SCI, SSCI, T&II, ZentMath.
—BLDSC (5406.150000), AskIEEE, CISTI, Ei, IDS, IE, Infotrieve, ingenta, Linda Hall. **CCC.**
Published by: I N F O R M S, 901 Elkridge Landing Rd., Ste. 400, Linthicum, MD 21090-2909. TEL 410-850-0300, 800-446-3676, mathofor@sbcglobal.net, informs@informs.org, http://mor.pubs.informs.org, http://www.informs.org. Ed. Nimrod Megiddo. Circ: 2,000 (paid and controlled). **Subscr. to:** PO Box 631704, Baltimore, MD 631704.

004 ISR ISSN 0333-7685
MAYDAON; Israeli journal for information systems on EDP. Text in Hebrew. 1971. bi-m. ILS 250 (effective 1999). adv. bk.rev. **Document type:** *Proceedings, Academic/Scholarly.*
Indexed: IHP.
Published by: Israeli Chamber of Information Systems, 16 Tozereet Haaretz St, Tel Aviv, 67891, Israel. TEL 972-3-6095783, FAX 972-3-6095785, lylnan@inter.net.il. Ed., Adv. contact Benny H Raab. Circ: 3,000.

004 ISR
MEDA UNETUNIM. Text in Hebrew. 3/yr.
Published by: I.B.M. Israel, I.B.M. House, 2 Weizmann St., Tel Aviv, Israel. TEL 03-618032. Ed. Yossi Shuval.

004 PHL ISSN 0116-1792
METROPOLITAN COMPUTER TIMES✶ . Text in English. 1985. w. PHP 1,920, USD 150. adv. software rev. **Document type:** *Newspaper, Consumer.* **Description:** Covers information and computer technology issues including industry, products, services and lifestyle.
Published by: Computer Connection Inc., 29/F Philippine Stock Exchange Centre (West), Unit 2902-C, Exchange Rd, Ortigas Center, Pasig City, 1600, Philippines. TEL 632-6357306, FAX 632-6357310, mct@mozcom.com, http://www.mctimes.net/. Pub. Diana Roces Davila. adv.: B&W page PHP 60, color page PHP 96; 25 x 40.

004 JPN ISSN 0285-6425
MICOMLIFE. Text in Japanese. 1981. m. JPY 6,000.

Published by: Gakken Co. Ltd., 40-5 Kami-Ikedai 4-chome, Ota-ku, Tokyo, 145-0064, Japan. Ed. Hajime Morita.

MICRO. see *ELECTRONICS*

004 FRA ISSN 1253-1022
MICRO PRATIQUE. Text in French. 1996. m. EUR 45.90 (effective 2002). **Document type:** *Magazine, Consumer.* **Description:** Articles on domestic computers.
Published by: Editions Lariviere, Espace Clichy, 12 rue Mozart, Clichy, Cedex 92587, France. TEL 33-1-41403232, FAX 33-1-41403250, abo@editions-lariviere.fr, http://www.editions-lariviere.fr.

379.826 FRA ISSN 1163-4561
MICRO SIMULATEUR. Text in French. 1992. m. EUR 66.30 (effective 2002). adv. **Document type:** *Magazine, Consumer.*
Published by: Editions Lariviere, Espace Clichy, 12 rue Mozart, Clichy, Cedex 92587, France. TEL 33-1-41403105, FAX 33-1-41403250, abo@editions-lariviere.fr, http://www.editions-lariviere.fr.

004 CHL ISSN 0716-4777
MICROBYTE✶ ; todo computacion y telecomunicaciones. Text in Spanish. 1984. m. CLP 8,500, USD 55. back issues avail.
Published by: Editora Microbyte Ltda., Candell 1879, Nunoa, Santiago, Chile. TEL 56-2-3417507, FAX 56-2-3417504, TELEX 243259 MICRO CL. Ed. Jose Kaffman. Circ: 7,000.

004 GBR
MILCOMP EUROPE (YEAR). CONFERENCE PROCEEDINGS; military computers, systems and software. Text in English. a. **Document type:** *Proceedings.*
Published by: Nexus Media Ltd. (Subsidiary of: Highbury House Communications PLC), Nexus House, Azalea Dr, Swanley, Kent BR8 8HU, United Kingdom. TEL 44-1322-660070, FAX 44-1322-667633.

004 ITA ISSN 1124-0415
IL MIO COMPUTER. Text in Italian. m. EUR 38 (effective 2005). adv. back issues avail. **Document type:** *Magazine, Consumer.* **Description:** Discusses new software and hardware for the PC. Includes user advice, game reviews, ideas for children and news of interest to PC owners.
Published by: Future Media Italy SpA, Via Asiago 45, Milano, MI 20128, Italy. TEL 39-02-2529161, FAX 39-02-26005520, info@futuremediaitaly.it, http://www.futuremediaitaly.it. Ed. Mietta Capasso.

004 RUS ISSN 0235-3520
MIR P K. Variant title: P C World Russia. Text in Russian. m. RUR 429 domestic; RUR 33 per issue domestic (effective 2004). adv. **Document type:** *Magazine, Trade.* **Description:** Covers developments in the application and use of PC related products and services in Russia and worldwide.
Related titles: Online - full text ed.
Indexed: RASB, RefZh.
—East View.
Published by: Izdatel'stvo Otkrytye Sistemy/Open Systems Publications, ul Rustaveli, dom 12A, komn 117, Moscow, 127254, Russian Federation. TEL 7-095-9563306, FAX 7-095-2539204, info@osp.ru, http://www.osp.ru/pcworld/. adv.: B&W page USD 4,800, color page USD 6,900; trim 202 x 257. Circ: 50,000 (paid and controlled).

▼ **MOBILE INFORMATION SYSTEMS.** see *COMMUNICATIONS*

004 USA ISSN 1545-6153
QA76.59
▼ **MOBILE P C.** Text in English. 2004 (Jan.). m. USD 12 domestic; USD 26 in Canada; USD 39 elsewhere; USD 5.99 newsstand/cover (effective 2004). adv. **Document type:** *Magazine, Consumer.* **Description:** Covers all aspects of mobile and wireless computing.
Published by: Future Network USA, 150 North Hill Dr, Ste 40, Brisbane, CA 94005. TEL 415-468-4684, FAX 415-468-4686, null@mobilepcmag.com, http://www.mobilepcmag.com/, http://www.futurenetworkusa.com/. Ed. Christopher Null. Pub., Adv. contact Simon Whitcombe. color page USD 16,000; trim 8 x 10.5.

004.6 USA
MOBISYS: INTERNATIONAL CONFERENCE ON MOBILE SYSTEMS, APPLICATIONS AND SERVICES. Text in English. a.
Related titles: Online - full content ed.
Published by: Association for Computing Machinery, Inc., 1515 Broadway, 17th Fl, New York, NY 10036-5701. TEL 212-626-0500, usacm@acm.org, http://www.acm.org.

004 CAN ISSN 1025-8973
MODELLING, IDENTIFICATION, AND CONTROL. Variant title: I A S T E D International Conference. Proceedings. Modelling, Identification and Control. Text in English. 1981. a. price varies. **Document type:** *Proceedings, Academic/Scholarly.*
Published by: ACTA Press, 4500-16th Ave NW, Ste 80, Calgary, AB T3B 0M6, Canada. TEL 403-288-1195, FAX 403-247-6851, journals@actapress.com, http://www.actapress.com.

C

681.3 SVN ISSN 0352-4833
MOJ MIKRO. Text in Slovenian. 1984. m. SIT 7,480 (effective 2002). adv. **Document type:** *Magazine, Consumer.*
Related titles: Online - full text ed.: ISSN 1580-2574. 1996; Supplement(s): Telekomunikacije. ISSN 1580-1349. 1999.
Published by: Delo Revije d.o.o., Dunajska 5, Ljubljana, 1509, Slovenia. TEL 386-1-4737000, FAX 386-1-4737352, narocnine@delo-revije.si, http://www.mojmikro.delo-revije.si/, http://www.delo-revije.si. adv.: page SIT 140,000.

004 FRA ISSN 0242-5769
LE MONDE INFORMATIQUE. Text in French. 1981. w. (44/yr.). EUR 65 (effective 2005). adv. bk.rev. **Document type:** *Newspaper, Trade.* **Description:** Covers the development of new technologies, experiences of companies, and analysis and evaluation of the state of the art in software, hardware, market tendencies and manufacturing.
Related titles: Online - full text ed.; Supplement(s): Le Monde Informatique. NP Journal. ISSN 1288-3859. 1997.
Indexed: B&I.
—BLDSC (5907.030000). **CCC.**
Published by: I D G Communications France, 5 rue Chantecoq, Puteaux, 92808, France. TEL 33-1-4197-6161, FAX 33-1-4197-6160, lmihebdo@idg.fr, http://www.weblmi.com/, http://www.idg.fr. Ed. Francois Jeanne. Pub., R&P Michel Crestin. Adv. contact Pasquale Meyer. color page USD 14,449; trim 237 x 300. Circ: 62,039.

004 AUT ISSN 1021-271X
MONITOR; Das Magazin fuer Informationstechnologie. Text in German. 1983. 11/yr. EUR 33.20 domestic; EUR 59.60 foreign (effective 2005). adv. **Document type:** *Magazine, Consumer.*
Published by: Bohmann Druck und Verlag GmbH & Co. KG, Leberstr 122, Vienna, W 1110, Austria. TEL 43-1-740950, FAX 43-1-74095183, office@monitor.co.at, office.gl@bohmann.at, http://www.monitor.co.at, http://www.bohmann.at. Ed. Ruediger Maier. Adv. contact Engelbert Haidinger. color page EUR 5,030; trim 184 x 250. Circ: 15,000 (paid and controlled).

004 BRA ISSN 0103-9741
QA76.75
MONOGRAFIAS EM CIENCIA DA COMPUTACAO. Text in English, Portuguese. 1969. irreg. free. **Document type:** *Academic/Scholarly.*
Formerly (until 1975): Monographs in Computer Science and Computer Applications
Published by: (Departamento de Informatica), Pontificia Universidade Catolica do Rio de Janeiro, Rua Marques de Sao Vicente, 225,, 22 453, ZC-20, Rio De Janeiro, RJ 22451041, Brazil. FAX 55-21-511-5645, TELEX 021-31048. Ed. Carlos J P Lucena. Circ: 200.

004 USA ISSN 1431-6900
MONOGRAPHS IN COMPUTER SCIENCE. Text in English. 1975. irreg., latest 2004. price varies. **Document type:** *Monographic series, Academic/Scholarly.*
Formerly (until 1994): Texts and Monographs in Computer Science (0172-603X)
Indexed: Inspec, MathR.
Published by: Springer-Verlag New York, Inc. (Subsidiary of: Springer Science+Business Media), 233 Spring St, New York, NY 10013. TEL 212-460-1500, 800-777-4643, FAX 212-473-6272, http://www.springer-ny.com. Eds. D Gries, F L Bauer.

330 004 CHL
MOUSE. Text in Spanish. irreg.
Published by: Consorcio Periodistico de Chile S.A., Vicuna Mackenna 1870, Santiago, Chile. TEL 56-2-550-7000, FAX 56-2-550-7999, mouse@copesa.cl, http://www.mouse.cl/, http://www.copesa.cl.

004 DEU
MSTNEWS; international newsletter on microsystems and mems. Text in English. 1991. 5/yr. adv. **Document type:** *Newsletter, Trade.* **Description:** Aims to disseminate information on worldwide developments in microsystems.
Indexed: Inspec.
Published by: VDI/VDE - Technologiezentrum Informationstechnick GmbH, Rheinstrabe 10 B, Teltow, 14513, Germany. TEL 49-3328-435167, FAX 49-3328-435256, mstnews@vdivde-it.de, http://www.vdivde-it.de/mstnews. Ed. Bernhard Wybranski. adv.: color page EUR 3,800; trim 210 x 297. Circ: 12,000 (controlled).

005.1 USA ISSN 1098-7665
MULTILINGUAL COMMUNICATIONS & TECHNOLOGY. Text in English. 1992. 8/yr. USD 58 domestic; USD 78 foreign (effective 2002). adv. back issues avail. **Document type:** *Magazine.*
Formerly (until 1996): Multilingual Computing (1065-7657)
Published by: MultiLingual Computing, Inc., 319 N First Ave, Sandpoint, ID 83864. TEL 208-263-8178, FAX 208-263-6310, info@multilingual.com, http://www.multilingual.com/.

004 ESP ISSN 1577-6883
MUNDO LINUX. Variant title: Solo Programadores Mundo Linux. Text in Spanish. 199?. irreg. EUR 45 domestic; EUR 81 foreign (effective 2004). **Document type:** *Magazine, Consumer.*
Published by: Revistas Profesionales, C/ Valentin Beato 42, 3a Planta, Madrid, 28037, Spain. revistasprofesionales@revistasprofesionales.com, http://www.revistasprofesionales.com.

N A S A - D O D WORKSHOP ON EVOLVABLE HARDWARE. (National Aeronautics and Space Administration - U.S. Department of Defense) see *COMPUTERS—Computer Architecture*

004 JPN ISSN 0027-6421
N E C NEWS. Text in English. 1963. q. free. charts; illus. **Description:** Information on the new products and company's activities worldwide.
Indexed: CADCAM.
Published by: Nippon Electric Company/Nippon Denki K.K., 7-1 Shiba 5-chome, Minato-ku, Tokyo, 108-0014, Japan. FAX 3-798-1510, TELEX NECTOK J22686. Ed. Masahiro Shinoda. Circ: 23,500.

004 USA
N I C E NEWS✶. Text in English. m. adv.
Published by: (National Information Conference), ConventionNews, 4341 Montgomery Ave, Bethesda, MD 20814-4401. Ed. Jawaid Awan.

004 USA ISSN 1048-776X
QC100 CODEN: NSPUE2
N I S T SPECIAL PUBLICATION. (National Institute of Standards and Technology) Text in English. 1918. irreg. price varies. back issues avail. **Document type:** *Monographic series, Government.*
Former titles (until 1988): National Bureau of Standards. Special Publication (0083-1883); (until 1968): U.S. Department of Commerce. Buresu of Standards. Miscellaneous Publications (0096-963X)
Related titles: ♦ Series: Standards Activities of Organizations in the U.S; ♦ National Conference on Weights and Measures. Report. ISSN 0077-3964.
Indexed: BrCerAb, C&ISA, CIN, CerAb, ChemAb, ChemTitl, CorrAb, E&CAJ, EMA, IAA, Inspec, M&TEA, MBF, METADEX, RefZh, SolStAb, WAA.
—BLDSC (6113.655200), CASDDS, CISTI, IE, ingenta, Linda Hall.
Published by: U.S. National Institute of Standards and Technology, 100 Bureau Dr, Gaithersburg, MD 20899. TEL 301-975-6478, inquiries@nist.gov, http://www.nist.gov. **Subscr. to:** National Technical Information Service, Government Research Center, 5285 Port Royal Rd, Springfield, VA 22161. TEL 703-605-6060, 800-363-2068, http://www.ntis.gov.

004 621.38 USA ISSN 0895-9013
TK7870.15
NATIONAL ELECTRONIC PACKAGING AND PRODUCTION CONFERENCE (EAST). PROCEEDINGS OF THE TECHNICAL PROGRAM. Text in English. 1963. irreg. Price varies. **Document type:** *Proceedings, Trade.*
Supersedes in part (in 198?): National Electronic Packaging and Production Conference. Proceedings of the Technical Program (0470-0155)
—IE. **CCC.**
Published by: Reed Exhibitions, 383 Main Ave, Norwalk, CT 06851. TEL 203-840-4820, 888-267-3796, FAX 203-840-5580, inquiry@reedexpo.com, http://www.reedexpo.com/.

004 621.38 USA ISSN 0895-9021
TK7870.15
NATIONAL ELECTRONIC PACKAGING AND PRODUCTION CONFERENCE (WEST). PROCEEDINGS OF THE TECHNICAL PROGRAM. Abbreviated title: NEPCON West. Proceedings of the Technical Program. Text in English. 1963. irreg. Price varies. **Document type:** *Proceedings, Trade.*
Supersedes in part (in 198?): National Electronic Packaging and Production Conference. Proceedings of the Technical Program (0470-0155)
—**CCC.**
Published by: Reed Exhibitions, 383 Main Ave, Norwalk, CT 06851. TEL 203-840-4820, 888-267-3796, FAX 203-840-5580, inquiry@reedexpo.com, http://www.reedexpo.com/.

004 NLD ISSN 1567-7818
NATURAL COMPUTING; an international journal. Text in English. 2002. q. EUR 295, USD 295, GBP 194 combined subscription to institutions print & online eds. (effective 2005). adv. reprint service avail. from PSC. **Description:** Provides a publication forum for fostering links and mutual understanding between researchers from various areas of natural computing.
Related titles: Online - full text ed.: ISSN 1572-9796 (from EBSCO Publishing, Gale Group, IngentaConnect, Kluwer Online, O C L C Online Computer Library Center, Inc., Springer LINK, Swets Information Services).
Indexed: ASFA, BibLing, BrCerAb, C&ISA, CerAb, CompLI, CorrAb, E&CAJ, EMA, ESPM, ExcerpMed, IAA, Inspec, M&TEA, MBF, METADEX, MathR, MathSciNet, SolStAb, WAA.
—BLDSC (6037.112050), CISTI, IE, ingenta. **CCC.**
Published by: Springer-Verlag Dordrecht (Subsidiary of: Springer Science+Business Media), Van Godewijckstraat 30, Dordrecht, 3311 GX, Netherlands. TEL 31-78-6576050, FAX 31-78-6576474, http://springerlink.metapress.com/openurl.asp?genre=journal&issn=1567-7818, http://www.springeronline.com. Eds. G Rozenberg, Herman P Spaink.

004 GBR
NEED TO KNOW. Text in English. 1997. w. **Document type:** *Newsletter.*
Address: United Kingdom. tips@spesh.com, http://www.ntk.net/. Ed. Danny O'Brien.

004 CHE ISSN 0028-3398
TJ212 CODEN: NETEA8
NEUE TECHNIK/NEW TECHNIQUES/NOUVELLES TECHNIQUES. Text in German. 1959. m. CHF 75. adv. charts; illus. index. **Document type:** *Trade.*
Indexed: ChemAb, ExcerpMed, F&EA, Inspec.
—CISTI, Linda Hall.
Published by: Diagonal Verlags AG, Industriestr 21, Mellingen, 5507, Switzerland. Ed. Klaus Bucher. Circ: 12,000.

▼ **NEW MATHEMATICS AND NATURAL COMPUTATION.** see *MATHEMATICS*

005 NZL
NEW ZEALAND MACGUIDE. Text in English. bi-m. NZD 25 domestic; NZD 55 in Australia; NZD 75 elsewhere (effective 2003). **Document type:** *Magazine, Trade.*
Related titles: Online - full content ed.
Published by: Parkside Publishing Ltd., Herne Bay, PO Box 46-020, Auckland, New Zealand. TEL 64-9-360-1480, FAX 64-9-360-1470, http://www.macguide.co.nz/, http://www.parkside.co.nz.

NEWMEDIA; the magazine for creators of the digital future. see *COMMUNICATIONS—Television And Cable*

004 USA
NEWS DISPATCH. Text in English. w. free. adv. back issues avail. **Document type:** *Newsletter.* **Description:** Presents a summary of computer technology news.
Media: Online - full text.
Published by: C N E T, 55 Francisco St, 4th Fl, San Francisco, CA 94111. TEL 415-395-7805, FAX 415-788-1733, newsdispatch@cnet.com, http://www.news.com/searching/entry. Ed. Jai Singh.

C

004 USA ISSN 1557-2323
▼ **NEWSFACTOR MAGAZINE.** Text in English. 2005. m. USD 23.95 (effective 2006). **Document type:** *Magazine, Consumer.*
Published by: NewsFactor Network, 21700 Oxnard St, Ste 2040, Woodland Hills, CA 91367. TEL 818-593-2200, FAX 818-593-2203, http://www.newsfactor.com/. Pub. David Geller.

004 NLD ISSN 0920-1319
NIEUWS BERICHTEN INFORMATIE. Text in Dutch. 1981. 8/yr. adv. charts; abstr.; stat. **Document type:** *Newsletter.* **Description:** News on telecommunication, reviews of databases, and news of database vendors.
—IE, Infotrieve, KNAW.
Published by: Cobidoc B.V., J P Coengebouw, Kabelweg 37, Amsterdam, 1014 BA, Netherlands. TEL 31-20-6880333, FAX 31-20-6818626, info@cobidoc.nl, http://www.cobidoc.nl.

004 JPN ISSN 0285-4619
HD9696.C63
NIKKEI COMPUTER. Text in Japanese. 1981. bi-w. JPY 18,600 (effective 2000). adv. **Document type:** *Trade.* **Description:** Provides technical and general information on computers, as seen from the viewpoint of systems, products, industry, and organizational management.
Indexed: JCT, JTA.
Published by: Nikkei Business Publications Inc. (Subsidiary of: Nihon Keizai Shimbun, Inc.), 2-1-1 Hirakawa-cho, Chiyoda-ku, Tokyo, 102-8622, Japan. TEL 81-3-5210-8311, FAX 81-3-5210-8530, info@nikkeibpnyc.com, webmaster@nikkeibp.com, http://www.nikkeibp.com. Ed. Yoshiyuki Furusawa. Pub. Minoru Matsuzaki. Adv. contact Touru Kato. B&W page JPY 856,000, color page JPY 1,236,000; trim 208 x 280. Circ: 65,365. **Dist. in America by:** Nikkei Business Publications America Inc., 575 Fifth Ave, 20th Fl, New York, NY 10017.

004 JPN ISSN 1345-0182
NIKKEI LINUX/NIKKEI RINAKKUSU. Text in Japanese. 1999. m. JPY 1,280 (effective 2000). adv. **Document type:** *Trade.* **Description:** Offers practical information on use of Linux for business users, advanced users and Linus developers.
Published by: Nikkei Business Publications Inc. (Subsidiary of: Nihon Keizai Shimbun, Inc.), 2-7-6 Hirakawa-cho, Chiyoda-ku, Tokyo, 102-8622, Japan. TEL 81-3-5210-8311, FAX 81-3-5210-8530, info@nikkeibp-america.com, http://www.nikkeipb.com. Ed. Toru Tejima. Pub. Minoru Matsuzaki. adv.: B&W page JPY 200,000, color page JPY 450,000; trim 208 x 280. Circ: 50,000.

321.39 JPN ISSN 0910-7207
TK7874
NIKKEI MICRODEVICES. Text in Japanese. 1985. m. JPY 16,900. adv. **Document type:** *Trade.* **Description:** Provides specialized technical information on electronic devices and materials, detailing new trends and technologies.
—BLDSC (6113.178350), IE.

▼ *new title* ➤ *refereed* ✶ *unverified* ♦ *full entry avail.*

Published by: Nikkei Business Publications Inc. (Subsidiary of: Nihon Keizai Shimbun, Inc.), 2-7-6 Hirakawa-cho, Chiyoda-ku, Tokyo, 102-8622, Japan. TEL 81-3-5210-8311, FAX 81-3-5210-8530, info@nikkeibp-america.com, http://www.nikkeibp.com. Ed. Yousuke Mochizuki. Pub. Hirohisa Hayashi. Adv. contact Yasuhiro Gonda. B&W page JPY 370,000, color page JPY 570,000; trim 208 x 280. Circ: 16,650. **Dist. in America by:** Nikkei Business Publications America Inc., 575 Fifth Ave, 20th Fl, New York, NY 10017.

004 JPN
NIKKEI NETWORK. Text in Japanese. 2000. m. JPY 12,000 (effective 2000). adv. **Document type:** *Trade.* **Description:** Covers networking technologies ranging from the Internet to LAN, security systems and enterprise networking management.
Published by: Nikkei Business Publications Inc. (Subsidiary of: Nihon Keizai Shimbun, Inc.), 2-7-6 Hirakawa-cho, Chiyoda-ku, Tokyo, 102-8622, Japan. TEL 81-3-5210-8311, FAX 81-3-5210-8530, info@nikkeibp-america.com, http://www.nikkeipb.com. Ed. Kouji Segawa. Pub. Takuzo Niwa. adv.: B&W page JPY 400,000, color page JPY 580,000.

004 FIN ISSN 1236-6064
QA76 CODEN: NJCOFR
➤ **NORDIC JOURNAL OF COMPUTING.** Text in English. 1994. q. USD 160, EUR 160 to institutions (effective 2001). adv. back issues avail. **Document type:** *Academic/Scholarly.* **Description:** Provides an international forum for original research within informatics.
Indexed: CCMJ, CompAb, CompLI, Inspec, MathR, MathSciNet, ZentMath.
—BLDSC (6117.926050), AskIEEE, CISTI, IE, ingenta.
Published by: University of Helsinki, Department of Computer Science, Teollisuuskatu 23, PO Box 26, University of Helsinki, Helsinki, 00014, Finland. TEL 358-9-7084-4172, FAX 358-9-7084-4441, njc@cs.helsinki.fi, http://www.cs.helsinki.fi/njc/. Ed., R&P Esko Ukkonen. Circ: 150. **Subscr. to:** Allen Press Inc., PO Box 1897, Lawrence, KS 66044.

004 ESP ISSN 0211-2124
NOVATICA; revista de la Asociacion de Tecnicos de Informatica. Text in Spanish; Summaries in English, Spanish. 1970. bi-m. EUR 54.11 domestic; EUR 95 foreign (effective 2002). adv. bk.rev. illus.; tr.lit.; abstr.; bibl. 80 p./no.; back issues avail. **Document type:** *Journal, Trade.*
Formerly (until 1975): Novatecnia
Related titles: Online - full text ed.
Indexed: IECT, Inspec.
—AskIEEE, CINDOC.
Published by: Asociacion de Tecnicos de Informatica, Calle Padilla 66, 3o dcha, Madrid, 28006, Spain. TEL 34-91-402-9391, FAX 34-91-309-3685, novatica@ati.es, http://www.ati.es. Ed., R&P Rafael Fernandez Calvo. Pub. Fernando Piera. Adv. contact Adrian Cragnolini. Circ: 6,000 (paid). **Subscr. to:** Via Laietana 4, Barcelona 08003, Spain. TEL 34-93-412-5235.

NUOVE TECNOLOGIE IN MEDICINA, INFORMATICA, TELEMATICA APPLICAZIONI. see *MEDICAL SCIENCES—Experimental Medicine, Laboratory Technique*

004 SWE ISSN 1651-3169
NYHETSBREVET DATATEKNIK. Text in Swedish. 1999. 15/yr. SEK 698 (effective 2001). adv. bk.rev. index. back issues avail. **Document type:** *Magazine, Trade.* **Description:** Covers the computer industry, technology, products and software.
Formerly (until 2002): Datateknik 3.0 (1404-2991); Which was formed by the merger of (1990-1999): Natvarlden (1102-2655); (1980-1999): Datateknik (1103-095X); Which was formerly (until 1991): I D - Industriell Datateknik (0349-8476)
Indexed: Inspec.
—AskIEEE.
Published by: (Svenska Elektro- och Dataingenjoerers Riksfoerening (SER)), Ekonomi och Teknik Foerlag, Maester Samuelsgatan 56, Stockholm, 10612, Sweden. TEL 46-8-796-66-50, FAX 46-8-613-30-34, info@et.se, http://www.elektroniktidningen.se/dtnyhetsbrev, http://www.et.se. Ed., Pub. Lennart Pettersson. adv.: color page SEK 52,000; trim 180 x 260. Circ: 21,500.

003 DEU
T57.6.A1 CODEN: ORSPD5
➤ **O R SPECTRUM;** quantitative approaches in management. (Operations Research) Text in German, English. 1979. q. EUR 368 combined subscription to institutions print & online eds. (effective 2005). adv. back issues avail. **Document type:** *Journal, Academic/Scholarly.* **Description:** Contains articles on problem-solving and decision-making in management.
Formerly (until 2001): O R Spektrum (0171-6468)
Related titles: Online - full text ed.: ISSN 1436-6304 (from EBSCO Publishing, ProQuest Information & Learning, Springer LINK, Swets Information Services).
Indexed: ABIn, ASCA, CCMJ, CIS, CMCI, IAOP, Inspec, JCQM, JEL, MathR, MathSciNet, ORMS, QC&AS, ST&MA, ZentMath.
—AskIEEE, CISTI, IDS, IE. **CCC.**
Published by: (Deutsche Gesellschaft fuer Operations Research e.V.), Springer-Verlag (Subsidiary of: Springer Science+Business Media), Tiergartenstr 17, Heidelberg, 69121, Germany. TEL 49-6221-3450, FAX 49-6221-345229, http://link.springer.de/link/service/journals/00291/index.htm. Ed. K Inderfurth. Adv. contact Stephan Kroeck TEL 49-30-827875739. **Subscr. in the Americas to:** Springer-Verlag New York, Inc., Journal Fulfillment, PO Box 2485, Secaucus, NJ 07096-2485. TEL 800-777-4643, 201-348-4033, FAX 201-348-4505, journals@springer-ny.com, http://www.springer-ny.com; **Subscr. to:** Springer GmbH Auslieferungsgesellschaft, Haberstr 7, Heidelberg 69126, Germany. TEL 49-6221-345-0, FAX 49-6221-345-4229, subscriptions@springer.de.

004 RUS
OBRABOTKA SIMVOL'NOI INFORMATSII✶ . Text in Russian. 1973. irreg. illus.
Indexed: RASB.
Published by: Rossiiskaya Akademiya Nauk, Vychislitel'nyi Tsentr, Serpukhovskii raion, Pushchino, Moskovskaya Oblast' 142292, Russian Federation. TEL 234-05-84.

OFFICE PRODUCTS INTERNATIONAL. see *BUSINESS AND ECONOMICS—Office Equipment And Services*

004.3 USA ISSN 0882-8040
ONLINE INTERNATIONAL COMMAND CHART. Text in English. 1986. a.
—CISTI.
Published by: Online Inc., 88 Danbury Rd., Ste. 2C, Wilton, CT 06897-4423. TEL 800-222-3766.

003 GBR ISSN 0160-5682
Q175 CODEN: OPRQAK
OPERATIONAL RESEARCH SOCIETY. JOURNAL. Key Title: Journal of the Operational Research Society. Text in English. 1950. m. USD 1,320 combined subscription in United States to institutions print & online eds.; GBP 820 combined subscription elsewhere to institutions print & online eds. (effective 2005); includes Knowledge Management Research & Practice. adv. bk.rev. abstr.; bibl.; charts; illus. index. back issues avail.; reprints avail. **Document type:** *Journal, Academic/Scholarly.* **Description:** Includes real applications of operational research forecasting, inventory, investment, location, logistics, maintenance, marketing, packing, purchasing, production, project management, reliability and scheduling.
Former titles (until vol.29, 1978): Operational Research Quarterly (0030-3623); (until 1970): O R (1473-2858); (until 1953): Operational Research Quarterly (1473-284X)
Related titles: Online - full text ed.: ISSN 1476-9360. 1997. GBP 675 in Europe to institutions; USD 1,035 elsewhere to institutions (effective 2004) (from EBSCO Publishing, Gale Group, IngentaConnect, JSTOR (Web-based Journal Archive), O C L C Online Computer Library Center, Inc., ProQuest Information & Learning, Swets Information Services).
Indexed: ABIn, ADPA, ASCA, AgeL, ApMecR, BPI, BPIA, Biostat, BusI, C&ISA, CIS, CJA, CMCI, CPM, CivEngAb, CompAb, CompC, CompD, CompLI, CurCont, DIP, E&CAJ, ESPM, Emerald, EngInd, ExcerpMed, HRIS, IAOP, IBR, IBZ, ICEA, IMI, ISR, Inspec, JCQM, MEDLINE, MResA, ManagCont, ORMS, QC&AS, RASB, RRTA, RiskAb, SCI, SCIMP, SSCI, ST&MA, SolStAb, T&II, WAE&RSA, WBA, ZentMath.
—BLDSC (4835.900000), AskIEEE, Ei, IDS, IE, Infotrieve, ingenta, Linda Hall. **CCC.**
Published by: (Operational Research Society), Palgrave Macmillan Ltd. (Subsidiary of: Macmillan Publishers Ltd.), Houndmills, Basingstoke, Hants RG21 6XS, United Kingdom. TEL 44-1256-329242, FAX 44-1256-810526, http://www.palgrave-journals.com/jors/index.html, http://www.palgrave.com. Eds. John Wilson, Terry Williams. Pub. David Bull TEL 44-1256-329242. R&P Trace Noel. Adv. contact Robert Sloan TEL 44-20-88827199.

003 USA ISSN 0030-364X
T57.6.A1 CODEN: OPREA1
➤ **OPERATIONS RESEARCH.** Text in English. 1952. bi-m. USD 138 domestic to non-members; USD 166 elsewhere to non-members; USD 69 to members additional journal; USD 180 combined subscription domestic to non-members print & online eds.; USD 208 combined subscription elsewhere to non-members print & online eds.; USD 90 combined subscription to members additional journal; print & online eds.; USD 372 combined subscription domestic to institutions print &/or online eds.; USD 400 combined subscription elsewhere to institutions print & online eds. (effective 2004); membership includes 1 free journal. adv. bibl.; charts; stat.; illus. cum.index. back issues avail. **Document type:** *Journal, Academic/Scholarly.* **Description:** Articles address operations research in computing and decision technology; decision analysis; environment, energy, and natural resources; financial engineering; manufacturing, service, and supply chain operations; optimization; policy modeling and public sector operations research; simulation; stochastic models; telecommunications and networking; and transportation.
Formerly (until 1955): Operations Research Society of America. Journal (0096-3984)
Related titles: Microform ed.: (from PQC, WWS); Online - full content ed.: ISSN 1526-5463. USD 92 to non-members; USD 46 to members; USD 372 to institutions (effective 2004); Online - full text ed.: (from EBSCO Publishing, Gale Group, JSTOR (Web-based Journal Archive), O C L C Online Computer Library Center, Inc., ProQuest Information & Learning, Swets Information Services).
Indexed: ABIn, ASCA, ApMecR, BMT, BPI, BPIA, BRI, Biostat, BusI, C&ISA, CCMJ, CJA, CMCI, CPM, ChemAb, CivEngAb, CompC, CurCont, E&CAJ, EIA, ESPM, EnerInd, EngInd, IAOP, ISMEC, ISR, Inspec, MEDLINE, MResA, ManagCont, MathR, MathSciNet, ORMS, PAA&I, PCI, PsycholAb, QC&AS, RASB, RRTA, RefZh, RiskAb, SCI, SCIMP, SSCI, SolStAb, T&II, WAE&RSA, WildRev, ZentMath.
—BLDSC (6269.360000), AskIEEE, CISTI, Ei, IDS, IE, Infotrieve, ingenta, Linda Hall. **CCC.**
Published by: I N F O R M S, 901 Elkridge Landing Rd., Ste. 400, Linthicum, MD 21090-2909. TEL 410-850-0300, 800-446-3676, FAX 410-684-2963, informs@informs.org, http://or.pubs.informs.org, http://www.informs.org. Ed. Lawrence Wein TEL 650-724-1676. R&P Candita Gerzevitz. Adv. contact Trish Allewalt. B&W page USD 400; trim 8.125 x 10.875. Circ: 4,300 (paid). **Subscr. to:** PO Box 631704, Baltimore, MD 631704.

003 NLD ISSN 1387-666X
➤ **OPERATIONS RESEARCH/COMPUTER SCIENCE INTERFACE SERIES.** Text in English. 1993. irreg., latest vol.32, 2005. price varies. back issues avail. **Document type:** *Monographic series, Academic/Scholarly.*
Related titles: Diskette ed.
Indexed: CCMJ, ZentMath.
—BLDSC (6269.363600).
Published by: Springer-Verlag Dordrecht (Subsidiary of: Springer Science+Business Media), Van Godewijckstraat 30, Dordrecht, 3311 GX, Netherlands. TEL 31-78-6576050, FAX 31-78-6576474, http://www.springeronline.com. Eds. Ramesh Sharda, Stefan Voss.

003 DEU ISSN 0721-5924
T57.6.A1
OPERATIONS RESEARCH PROCEEDINGS. Text in German. 1972. a., latest 2003. price varies. **Document type:** *Proceedings, Academic/Scholarly.*
Formerly (until 1981): Proceedings in Operations Research (0170-088X)
Indexed: CCMJ, MathR.
—BLDSC (6269.365200).
Published by: (Deutsche Gesellschaft fuer Operations Research e.V.), Springer-Verlag (Subsidiary of: Springer Science+Business Media), Haber Str 7, Heidelberg, 69126, Germany. TEL 49-6221-3450, FAX 49-6221-229, orders@springer.de, http://www.springer.de.

OPERESHONZU RISACHI/OPERATIONS RESEARCH. see *BUSINESS AND ECONOMICS—Management*

OPTOELECTRONICS, INSTRUMENTATION AND DATA PROCESSING. see *ELECTRONICS*

004 USA
ORGANIZATIONAL SYSTEMS RESEARCH ASSOCIATION. CONFERENCE PROCEEDINGS. Text in English. 1983. a. USD 40 (effective 2000). **Document type:** *Proceedings.*
Formerly: Office Systems Research Association. Conference Proceedings
Indexed: BusEdI.
Published by: Organizational Systems Research Association, Morehead State University, UPO 2478, Morehead, KY 40351-1689. TEL 606-783-2724, FAX 606-783-5025, http://www.osra.org. Ed. Donna McAlister Kizzier. Circ: 250.

003 ZAF ISSN 0259-191X
➤ **ORION.** Text and summaries in Afrikaans, English. 1985. s-a. USD 40 (effective 2000). adv. **Document type:** *Journal, Academic/Scholarly.* **Description:** Features success stories, case studies, and methodological reviews in operations research.
Indexed: CompLI, IAOP, ISAP, Inspec, RGAb, WBA, WMB.
—BLDSC (6291.279000).
Published by: Operations Research Society of South Africa/Operasionele Navorsingsvereniging van Suid-Afrika, CSIR - Transportek, PO Box 320, Stellenbosch, 7599, South Africa. fevandyk@csir.co.za, http://www.orssa.org.za. Ed. L Paul Fatti. R&P, Adv. contact W Gevers. Circ: 450. **Subscr. to:** c/o W R Gevers, Business Editor, PO Box 610, Bellville 7535, South Africa. TEL 27-21-918-4228, FAX 27-21-918-4112.

004 USA
OTHER VOICES; viewpoints on technology. Text in English. 1998. irreg. back issues avail. **Document type:** *Newsletter.* **Description:** Features articles, tips and news on computer technology.
Media: Online - full text.
Address: othervoices@gemini.ibm.com, http://www.ibm.com/OtherVoices/Index.

004 025.04 305.896 USA ISSN 1544-6093
OURPC MAGAZINE; the computer and internet magazine for African-Americans. Text in English. 1999. 4/yr. USD 16.99 (effective 2001). adv. **Document type:** *Magazine, Consumer.* **Description:** Aims to educate the African-American community and others on the value and necessity of technology and the Internet.
Related titles: Online - full text ed.

Address: 453 Martin Luther King Jr Blvd, Detroit, MI 48201. TEL 313-833-7500, 800-390-3036, renba1@aol.com, http://www.ourpcmagazine.com. Pub. Abner McWhorter. adv.: B&W page USD 12,276, color page USD 17,186. Circ: 175,000 (paid and controlled).

004 USA
OUTSOURCING CENTER; the journal for strategic outsourcing. Text in English. 1990. m. free. adv. bk.rev. **Document type:** *Newsletter, Trade.* **Description:** For systems integrators and anyone involved in outsourcing.
Formerly: Infoserver
Media: Online - full text.
Published by: (Everest Software Corp.), InfoServer, 12700 Preston Rd, Ste 190, Dallas, TX 75230. TEL 972-980-0013, FAX 972-980-1503, info@infoserver.com, http://www.infoserver.com. Ed. Beth Ellyn Rosenthal. Circ: 8,100.

OXFORD APPLIED MATHEMATICS AND COMPUTING SERIES. see *MATHEMATICS*

681.3 HRV ISSN 1331-0542
P C CHIP. Text in Croatian. 1994. m. HRK 290 (effective 2002). adv. **Document type:** *Magazine, Consumer.*
Formerly (until 1995): Chip Exclusive (1330-6707)
Related titles: CD-ROM ed.: ISSN 1331-9426. 1996.
Published by: A1 Video d.o.o., Cvijete Zuzoric 25, Zagreb, 10000, Croatia. TEL 385-1-6117354, FAX 385-1-6154563, http://www.pcchip.hr. Ed. Dario Susanj.

004 GBR ISSN 1469-0403
P C EXPLORER ESSENTIALS SERIES. Text in English. 1999. bi-m. GBP 23.95 (effective 2002). **Document type:** *Magazine, Consumer.* **Description:** Covers a different theme with each issue dealing with a specific area of computing related issues.
Published by: Live Publishing International Ltd., Europa House, Adlington Park, Macclesfield, Cheshire SK10 4NP, United Kingdom. TEL 44-1625-855086, FAX 44-1625-855071, subs@livepublishing.co.uk, http://www.livepublishing.co.uk/pcexplorer/pageview.shtml?mainindex.html. Ed. Wayne Williams. Pub. Robin Wilkinson. Adv. contact Kenny Leslie.

004 GBR ISSN 1467-7113
P C FRIENDLY. Text in English. 1999. bi-w. GBP 2.99 newsstand/cover (effective 2001); each issues comes with CD-ROM. **Document type:** *Magazine, Consumer.* **Description:** Covers computer basics for beginning users, including topics such as the Internet, E-Mail, and softwares.
Published by: G E Fabbri Ltd., Elme House, 133 Long Acre, London, WC2E 9AW, United Kingdom. TEL 44-20-7836-0519, 44-20-7468-5600, FAX 44-20-7836-0280, mail@gefabbri.co.uk, http://www.gefabbri.co.uk/PCFriendly/. Ed. Liz Glaze.

004 GBR ISSN 1471-8243
P C HOW TO. Text in English. 2000. bi-m. GBP 35.88 (effective 2002). **Document type:** *Magazine, Consumer.* **Description:** Offers a step-by-step guides to help PC users get the most out of their computers and the Internet.
Published by: Live Publishing International Ltd., Europa House, Adlington Park, Macclesfield, Cheshire SK10 4NP, United Kingdom. TEL 44-1625-855086, FAX 44-1625-855071, subs@livepublishing.co.uk, http://www.livepublishing.co.uk/pchowto/pageview.shtml?mainindex.html. Ed. Wayne Williams. Pub. Robin Wilkinson. Adv. contact Kenny Leslie.

004 USA ISSN 1533-483X
QA76.5
P C HOW-TO GUIDE. Text in English. 2001. q. USD 8.95 newsstand/cover in United States; USD 9.95 newsstand/cover in Canada (effective 2002). adv.
Published by: Harris Publications, Inc., 800 Kennesaw Ave, Ste 220, Marietta, GA 30060. TEL 770-421-8160, 800-866-2886, http://www.harris-pub.com.

681.3 ARG ISSN 0328-7335
P C MAGAZINE. Text in Spanish. 1992. m. adv. **Document type:** *Magazine, Consumer.*
Published by: Editorial Televisa Argentina, Av Paseo Colon 275, Piso 10, Buenos Aires, Buenos Aires 1063, Argentina. TEL 54-11-4343-2225, FAX 54-11-4345-0955, http://www.pcmag.com.ar, http://www.televisa.com.ar.

681.3 ROM ISSN 1454-220X
P C MAGAZINE ROMANIA. Text in Romanian. 1998. m. ROL 264,000 (effective 2002). adv. **Document type:** *Magazine, Consumer.*
Related titles: Online - full text ed.
Published by: Agora Media, Str. Tudor Vladimirescu nr. 63, ap. 9, CP 230-1, Targu Mures, 4300, Romania. TEL 40-65-166516, FAX 40-65-166290, office@agora.ro, http://www.pcmagazine.ro, http://www.agora.ro.

004 TUR ISSN 1300-8064
P C MAGAZINE TURKIYE. Text in Turkish. 1993. m. **Document type:** *Magazine, Consumer.*
Published by: 1 Numara Hearst Yayincilik, Sabah Tesisleri, Tesvikiye Caddesi 123, Tesvikiye, Istanbul, 80200, Turkey. TEL 90-212-3158000, FAX 90-212-3159272, http://www.birnumara.com.tr.

004 794.8 GBR ISSN 0968-607X
P C MART. Text in English. 1991. bi-w. GBP 26 in United Kingdom; GBP 80 rest of Europe; GBP 140 rest of world; GBP 1 newsstand/cover (effective 2000). adv. illus.; mkt. **Document type:** *Magazine, Consumer.* **Description:** Covers all PC related subject matters. Designed to appeal to a broad cross section of the PC market from the end users to the larger corporate companies.
Published by: Trinity Publications Ltd.., 1st Fl, Edward House, 92-93 Edward St, Birmingham, B1 2RA, United Kingdom. TEL 44-121-233-8712, FAX 44-121-233-8715, circ@trinitypub.co.uk. Ed. Andrew Shorter. Pub. Wendy Wood. Adv. contact Lisa Evans. B&W page GBP 308, color page GBP 484; trim 21 x 29.7. **Dist. by:** M M C Ltd., Octagon House, White Hart Meadows, Ripley, Woking, Surrey GU23 6HR, United Kingdom. TEL 44-1483-211222, FAX 44-1483-224541.

004 TUR ISSN 1301-4773
P C NET. Text in Turkish. 1997. m. adv. **Document type:** *Magazine, Consumer.*
Published by: D B R - Dogan Burda Rizzoli Dergi Yayyncylyk ve Pazarlama A.S., Hurriyet Medya Towers, Gunesli - Istanbul, 34212, Turkey. TEL 90-212-4103111, FAX 90-212-4103112, abone@dbr.com.tr, http://www.pcnet.com.tr, http://www.dbr.com.tr.

004 AUT ISSN 1022-1611
P C NEWS. Variant title: P C News Sedu. Text in German. 1986. 5/yr. EUR 20 (effective 2005). bk.rev. bibl.; charts; illus.; mkt. **Document type:** *Magazine, Consumer.*
Related titles: Online - full text ed.
Address: Siccardsburggasse 4-1-22, Vienna, W 1100, Austria. TEL 43-1-6045070, FAX 43-1-60450702, pcnews@pcnews.at, http://pcnews.at. Ed., Pub. Franz Fiala. Circ: 4,500 (paid); 1,300 (controlled).

004 USA
▼ **P C NEWS WEEKLY**; the news weekly for everything P C. (delivered as a PDF file; broadband Internet connection required for subscription.) Text in English. 2005. w. adv. **Document type:** *Magazine, Consumer.* **Description:** Covers technology, product news, reviews and trends.
Media: Online - full content.
Published by: Possibility Media, 10400 N.W. 33rd St., Ste. 270, Miami, FL 33172. TEL 786-206-8880, FAX 786-206-8884, info@possibilitymedia.com, http://www.pcnewsweeklymag.com/, http://www.possibilitymedia.com/. Pub. Victor Ramos. adv.: B&W page USD 6,430, color page USD 7,450; 8.5 x 10.875.

004 DNK ISSN 1600-9185
P C PLANET. Text in Danish. 2000. m. adv. **Document type:** *Magazine, Consumer.*
Published by: Egmont Magasiner A/S, Hellerupvej 51, Hellerup, 2900, Denmark. TEL 45-39-457500, pc-planet@pc-planet.dk, http://www.pc-planet.dk/, http://www.egmontmagasiner.dk. Ed. Bo Andersen. Adv. contact Pia Kensoe larsen TEL 45-39-457505. page DKK 21,600. Circ: 20,000.

004 AUS ISSN 1447-1876
P C SOLUTIONS. Text in English. 2002. bi-m. AUD 59.95 domestic; AUD 81.95 in New Zealand; AUD 111.95 elsewhere (effective 2004). **Document type:** *Magazine, Consumer.* **Description:** Provides the latest tips, support, features,software, tutorials and reviews.
Published by: Derwent Howard, PO Box 1037, Bondi Junction, NSW 1355, Australia. TEL 61-2-93864666, 800-007-820, FAX 61-2-93864288, enquiries@derwenthoward.com.au, http://www.derwenthoward.com.au/. Ed. Dan Toose. Adv. contact Daniel Ferguson.

004 370 USA
P C TEACH IT; integrating technology into the classroom. Text in English. 2001. 6/yr. USD 29.99; USD 4.95 newsstand/cover; USD 6.95 newsstand/cover in Canada (effective 2003). adv. illus. **Description:** Covers computers and technology for teachers and students, including projects, assessment tools, Tips and techniques for integrating technology in the classroom and at home, and Lesson plans.
Published by: Rosewood Press, 802 A-B S Edisto Ave, Columbia, SC 29205. http://www.pcteachit.com/. Ed. Linda Dennis.

004 FRA ISSN 1264-935X
P C TEAM. Text in French. 1995. m. EUR 49.99 (effective 2003).
Related titles: Supplement(s): P C Team. Hors-Serie. ISSN 1290-5534.
Published by: Posse Press, BP 1121, Toulouse, 31036, France. TEL 33-14-9698800, http://www.possepress.com/. Ed. Arnaud Wissart.

004 GBR
P C TOOLS. Text in English. 2002. bi-m. GBP 23.88 for 2 yrs. domestic; GBP 45 for 2 yrs. in Europe; GBP 65 for 2 yrs. elsewhere (effective 2002). **Document type:** *Magazine, Consumer.* **Description:** Covers specific topics with each issue dealing with a particular area of computing.
Published by: Live Publishing International Ltd., Europa House, Adlington Park, Macclesfield, Cheshire SK10 4NP, United Kingdom. TEL 44-1625-855086, FAX 44-1625-855071, subs@livepublishing.co.uk, http://www.livepublishing.co.uk/pctools/pageview.shtml?mainindex.html. Ed. Wayne Williams. Pub. Robin Wilkinson. Adv. contact Kenny Leslie.

004 GBR ISSN 1469-042X
P C UTILITIES. Text in English. 2000. m. GBP 59.88 in Europe; GBP 77 elsewhere (effective 2002). **Document type:** *Magazine, Consumer.* **Description:** Covers all aspects of computing, including software, hardware and other related topics.
Published by: Live Publishing International Ltd., Europa House, Adlington Park, Macclesfield, Cheshire SK10 4NP, United Kingdom. TEL 44-1625-855086, FAX 44-1625-855071, subs@livepublishing.co.uk, http://www.livepublishing.co.uk/pcutilities/pageview.shtml?mainindex.html. Ed. Wayne Williams. Pub. Robin Wilkinson. Adv. contact Kenny Leslie.

004 CHN ISSN 1002-1574
P C WORLD CHINA. Text in Chinese. 1985. fortn. adv. **Document type:** *Magazine, Trade.* **Description:** Covers developments in the PC and workstation industries both domestically and worldwide, in addition to the latest technology and marketing news, and practical information on using computers in a variety of industries and enterprises.
Related titles: Online - full text ed.
Published by: I D G China, Rm. 616, Tower A, COFCO Plaza, Jianguomennei Dajie, Beijing, 100005 , China. TEL 86-10-6526-0959, FAX 86-10-6526-0866, dumin@idg.com.cn, http://www.pcworld.com.cn, http://www.idgchina.com. Ed. Wei Xiong. Adv. contact Yuxiang Gao. color page CNY 18,000; trim 185 x 260. Circ: 120,000.

004 EGY
P C WORLD EGYPT. (Personal Computer) Text in Arabic. m. adv. **Document type:** *Magazine, Consumer.* **Description:** Provides timely coverage of PC-related technology, products and services.
Related titles: Online - full text ed.
Published by: International Business Associates, 24 Syria St., Mohandessain, Cairo, 11361, Egypt. TEL 20-2-3313500, FAX 20-2-3383423, admin@pcworld.com.eg, http://www.pcworld.com.eg. adv.: B&W page USD 1,100, color page USD 1,870; trim 197 x 270. Circ: 5,000 (paid and controlled).

004 PRT ISSN 0870-161X
P C WORLD PORTUGAL. Variant title: Cerebro. Text in Portuguese. 1982. 12/yr. adv. **Document type:** *Magazine, Trade.* **Description:** Covers all news related to information technology, including personal computers, departmental systems, software and communications.
Related titles: Online - full text ed.
Indexed: e-psyche.
Published by: Edicoes Expansao Economica Lda., Rue Mario Castelhano, 40-1, Queluz de Baixo, Barcarena, 2749-502, Portugal. TEL 351-21-496-95-40, FAX 351-21-436-95-39, webmaster@expansao.iol.pt, http://www.expansao.iol.pt. adv.: color page USD 2,420; trim 205 x 275. Circ: 27,000.

621.39 GBR ISSN 1479-1293
P D A BUYER. (Personal Digital Assistant) Text in English. bi-m. GBP 3.99 newsstand/cover domestic; USD 10.50 newsstand/cover foreign (effective 2004).
Published by: Highbury Entertainment Limited, Paragon House, St. Peter's Rd, Bournemouth, Dorset BH1 2JS, United Kingdom. http://www.paragon.co.uk. Ed. David Harfield.

004 FRA
P D A MAGAZINE. (Personal Digital Assistant) Text in French. 2002 (Nov.). bi-m. **Description:** Covers PDA software, hardware, accessories and current trends.
Published by: Oracom, 30 rue Saint-Lazare, Paris, 75005, France. TEL 33-1-48740341, FAX 33-1-48740125. Ed. Frederic Botton. Circ: 27,000.

004 DEU ISSN 0930-5157
P I K: PRAXIS DER INFORMATIONSVERARBEITUNG UND KOMMUNIKATION; Fachzeitschrift fuer den Einsatz von DV-Systemen in Wirtschaft, Wissenschaft und Technik. Text in German. 1978. q. EUR 210; EUR 54 newsstand/cover (effective 2006). **Document type:** *Journal, Academic/Scholarly.*
Formerly: Rechenzentrum (0343-317X)
Indexed: IBR, IBZ.
—CCC.
Published by: K.G. Saur Verlag GmbH (Subsidiary of: Gale Group), Ortlerstr 8, Munchen, 81373, Germany. TEL 49-89-769020, FAX 49-89-76902150, info@saur.de, http://www.saur.de. Ed. Hans Meuer. Adv. contact Constanze Gueldner. Circ: 2,500.

004 BEL ISSN 0771-4157
PANINFORMATIC (EDITION FRANCAISE). Text in French. 1970; N.S. 1979. bi-m. adv. bk.rev. illus.; stat.
Former titles (until 1979): Paninforpratic (Edition Francaise) (0770-8629); (until 1977): Paninformatic (0770-8572)
Related titles: Dutch ed.: Paninformatic (Nederlandse Editie). ISSN 0771-4300.
Published by: Presselec S.P.R.L., Av FD Roosevelt 134, Brussels, 1050, Belgium. Ed. R Desoreher.

C

▼ new title ➤ refereed ✶ unverified ♦ full entry avail.

004 CAN ISSN 1027-2658
PARALLEL AND DISTRIBUTED COMPUTING AND SYSTEMS. Variant title: I A S T E D / I S M M International Conference. Proceedings. Parallel and Distributed Computing and Systems. Text in English. 1990. a. price varies. **Document type:** *Proceedings, Academic/Scholarly.*
Published by: ACTA Press, 4500-16th Ave NW, Ste 80, Calgary, AB T3B 0M6, Canada. TEL 403-288-1195, FAX 403-247-6851, journals@actapress.com, http://www.actapress.com.

004 USA ISSN 1078-7089
PEN COMPUTING MAGAZINE. Text in English. 1994. bi-m. USD 18 domestic; USD 26 in United States; USD 50 elsewhere (effective 2003). adv. back issues avail. **Document type:** *Magazine, Consumer.*
Related titles: Online - full text ed.
Published by: Pen Computing Magazine, Inc., 120 Bethpage Rd., Ste. 300, Hicksville, NY 11801-1515. TEL 516-349-9333, FAX 516-349-9334, biz@pencomputing.com, http://www.pencomputing.com. Ed. Conrad Blickenstorfer. Adv. contact Chris Sanford TEL 631-821-1565. page USD 6,500; trim 10.88 x 8.

004 ISR
PEOPLE & COMPUTERS WEEKLY. Text in English. 1980. w. USD 175.
Published by: Israel Peled Publishing, Pinsker 64, Tel Aviv, 61332, Israel. TEL 03-295145, FAX 03-295144. Ed. Israel Shalev. Circ: 7,000.

004 NLD ISSN 0166-5316
QA76.9.E95 CODEN: PEEVD9
➤ **PERFORMANCE EVALUATION.** Text in Dutch. 1981. 12/yr. EUR 1,579 in Europe to institutions; JPY 209,400 in Japan to institutions; USD 1,766 to institutions except Europe and Japan (effective 2006). back issues avail.; reprints avail. **Document type:** *Academic/Scholarly.* **Description:** For system theorists, designers, implementers and analysts who are concerned with performing aspects of computer systems, computer communications, and distributed systems.
Related titles: Microform ed.: (from PQC); Online - full text ed.: (from EBSCO Publishing, Gale Group, IngentaConnect, ScienceDirect, Swets Information Services).
Indexed: ASCA, BrCerAb, C&ISA, CMCI, CerAb, CompAb, CompC, CompLI, CompR, CorrAb, CurCont, DPD, E&CAJ, EMA, Englnd, IAA, ISR, InfoSAb, Inspec, M&TEA, MBF, METADEX, MathR, SCI, SSCI, SolStAb, WAA, ZentMath.
—BLDSC (6423.760000), AskIEEE, CISTI, Ei, IDS, IE, Infotrieve, ingenta, Linda Hall. **CCC.**
Published by: Elsevier BV, North-Holland (Subsidiary of: Elsevier Science & Technology), Sara Burgerhartstraat 25, Amsterdam, 1055 KV, Netherlands. TEL 31-20-485-3911, FAX 31-20-485-2457, nlinfo-f@elsevier.nl, http://www.elsevier.com/locate/peva, http://www.elsevier.nl/homepage/about/us/regional_sites.htt, http://www.elsevier.nl. Ed. Werner Bux. **Subscr. to:** Elsevier BV, PO Box 211, Amsterdam 1000 AE, Netherlands. TEL 31-20-485-3757, FAX 31-20-485-3432.

004 GBR ISSN 1617-4909
QA76.59 CODEN: PUCEAN
➤ **PERSONAL AND UBIQUITOUS COMPUTING.** Text in English. bi-m. EUR 408 domestic to non-members; EUR 428 foreign to non-members; EUR 78 domestic to members; EUR 98 foreign to members; EUR 62 domestic to students; EUR 82 foreign to students; EUR 95 combined subscription domestic to members print & online eds.; EUR 115 combined subscription foreign to members print & online eds.; EUR 75 combined subscription domestic to students print & online eds.; EUR 95 combined subscription foreign to students print & online eds. (effective 2006). back issues avail. **Document type:** *Journal, Academic/Scholarly.* **Description:** Focuses on issues surrounding the innovation, design, use and evaluation of new generations of handheld and mobile computers, innovative information management devices, and range of information appliances.
Formerly (until 2000): Personal Technologies (0949-2054)
Related titles: Online - full text ed.: ISSN 1617-4917. USD 62 to members; USD 50 to students (effective 2006) (from Association for Computing Machinery, Inc., EBSCO Publishing, ProQuest Information & Learning, Springer LINK, Swets Information Services).
Indexed: BrCerAb, C&ISA, CerAb, CompAb, CompLI, CorrAb, E&CAJ, EMA, ErgAb, IAA, Inspec, M&TEA, MBF, METADEX, WAA.
—BLDSC (6427.855025), IE, Infotrieve, ingenta. **CCC.**
Published by: Springer-Verlag London Ltd. (Subsidiary of: Springer Science+Business Media), Ashbourne House, The Guildway, Old Portsmouth Rd, Guildford, Surrey GU7 3DJ, United Kingdom. TEL 44-1483-734433, FAX 44-1483-734411, enquiries@personal-ubicomp.com, postmaster@svl.co.uk, http://www.personal-ubicomp.com/, http://www.springer.co.uk. Ed. Peter Thomas TEL 44-777-186-4714. Adv. contact Christiane Notarmarco. **Subscr. in the Americas to:** Springer-Verlag New York, Inc., Journal Fulfillment, PO Box 2485, Secaucus, NJ 07096-2485. TEL 800-777-4643, 201-348-4033, FAX 201-348-4505, journals@springer-ny.com, http://www.springer-ny.com; **Subscr. to:** Springer GmbH Auslieferungsgesellschaft, Haberstr 7, Heidelberg 69126, Germany. TEL 49-6221-345-0, FAX 49-6221-345-4229, subscriptions@springer.de.

004 USA
PERSPECTIVES IN COMPUTING. Text in English. irreg., latest vol.24, 1989.
Formerly: Notes and Reports in Computer Science
Indexed: Englnd, Inspec.
—BLDSC (6428.140000).
Published by: Academic Press (Subsidiary of: Elsevier Science & Technology), 525 B St, Ste 1900, San Diego, CA 92101-4495. apsubs@acad.com, http://www.academicpress.com. Ed. Werner Rheinboldt.

004 NLD ISSN 1574-1192
▼ ➤ **PERVASIVE AND MOBILE COMPUTING.** Text in English. 2005. 4/yr. EUR 400 in Europe to institutions; JPY 54,000 in Japan to institutions; USD 495 to institutions except Europe and Japan (effective 2006). **Document type:** *Journal, Academic/Scholarly.* **Description:** Publishes high-quality scientific articles, both theory and practice, covering all aspects of pervasive computing and communications.
Related titles: Online - full text ed.: (from EBSCO Publishing, ScienceDirect).
Published by: Elsevier BV (Subsidiary of: Elsevier Science & Technology), PO Box 103, Amsterdam, 1000, Netherlands. TEL 31-20-4853911, FAX 31-20-4852370, nlinfo-f@elsevier.nl, http://www.elsevier.com/locate/pmc, http://www.elsevier.nl. Eds. Behrooz Shirazi, Sajal K Das.

004 USA
POLICY MATTERS!✶**.** Text in English. 1993. q. membership. **Document type:** *Bulletin.* **Description:** Reviews the IIA's public policy and government relations council activities.
Published by: Information Industry Association, 1730 M St, N W Ste 700, Washington, DC 20036-4514. TEL 202-986-0280. Circ: 400.

004 POL ISSN 0138-0648
QA297 CODEN: PIPPE7
POLSKA AKADEMIA NAUK. INSTYTUT PODSTAW INFORMATYKI. PRACE/POLISH ACADEMY OF SCIENCES. INSTITUTE OF COMPUTER SCIENCE. REPORTS. Key Title: Prace IPI PAN. Text in English, Polish. 1970. irreg., latest no.900, 1999. free. **Description:** Covers computing systems theory, parallel computer architectures, concurrency theory, software engineering, image processing, artificial intelligence, man-machine communication, decision theory, computational statistics.
Formerly (until 1977): Polska Akademia Nauk. Centrum Obliczeniowe. Prace (0079-3175)
Indexed: GALA, MathR.
Published by: Polska Akademia Nauk, Instytut Podstaw Informatyki, ul Ordona 21, Warsaw, 01237, Poland. TEL 48-22-8362841, FAX 48-22-8376564, ipi@ipipan.waw.pl, http://www.ipipan.waw.pl. Circ: 150.

004 CHE ISSN 0254-2234
POLYSCOPE; computer - electronics - communication. Text in German. 1969. 22/yr. CHF 60 domestic; CHF 140 foreign (effective 2001). adv. bk.rev. abstr.; illus.; stat. index. **Document type:** *Journal, Trade.*
Formerly: Polyscope Automatik und Elektronik (0032-4035)
Indexed: Inspec.
Published by: Binkert Medien AG, Baslerstr 15, Laufenburg, 5080, Switzerland. TEL 41-62-8697900, FAX 41-62-8697901, binkertmedien@binkert.ch, http://www.polyscope.ch, http://www.binkertmedien.ch. Ed. Daniel Boehler. Adv. contact Ludwig Binkert. Circ: 14,850.

004 USA
▼ **PORTABLE COMPUTING MAGAZINE.** (delivered as a PDF file; broadband Internet connection required for subscription.) Text in English. forthcoming 2006 (Jan.). m. free to qualified personnel (effective 2005). adv. **Document type:** *Magazine, Trade.*
Media: Online - full content.
Published by: Possibility Media, 10400 N.W. 33rd St., Ste. 270, Miami, FL 33172. TEL 786-206-8880, FAX 786-206-8884, info@possibilitymedia.com, http://www.portablecomputingmag.com/, http://www.possibilitymedia.com/. Ed. Ken Durham. Pub. Victor Ramos. adv.: page USD 6,430; trim 7.875 x 10.75.

004 DEU ISSN 0179-1133
PRAXIS COMPUTER. Text in German. 1985. 6/yr. adv. bk.rev. **Document type:** *Magazine, Trade.*
Related titles: ◆ Supplement to: Deutsches Aerzteblatt. ISSN 0012-1207.
Indexed: RefZh.
—GNLM, IE, Infotrieve.
Published by: Deutscher Aerzte-Verlag GmbH, Dieselstr 2, Cologne, 50859, Germany. TEL 49-2234-7011-0, FAX 49-2234-7011460, praxiscomputer@aerzteblatt.de, http://www.aerzteverlag.de. Ed. Norbert Jachertz. Circ: 122,000 (controlled).

004 DEU ISSN 1434-6648
PRAXISHANDBUCH MICROSOFT ACCESS 97. Text in German. 1997. irreg. looseleaf. **Document type:** *Trade.*
Published by: W R S Verlag GmbH & Co. KG (Subsidiary of: Rudolf Haufe Verlag GmbH & Co. KG), Fraunhoferstr 5, Planegg, 82152, Germany. info@wrs.de, http://www.wrs.de.

▼ **PRESENT TECH.** see *TECHNOLOGY: COMPREHENSIVE WORKS*

004 FRA
PREVISIONS GLISSANTES DETAILLEES EN PERSPECTIVES SECTORIELLES (VOL.13): INFORMATIQUE. Text in French. 1959. irreg. charts; stat.
Supersedes in part: Economie Francaise en Perspectives Sectorielles (Vols.1-5); Which supersedes in part: Prevision a Un An de l'Economie Francaise
Published by: B I P E Conseil, L'Atrium - 6 Place Abel Gance, Boulogne-Billancourt, Cedex 92652, France. TEL 33-1-46944522, FAX 33-1-46944599.

004 USA
PRINCETON UNIVERSITY. DEPARTMENT OF COMPUTER SCIENCE. TECHNICAL REPORT SERIES. Text in English. 1960. s-a. price varies.
Former titles: Princeton University. Department of Computer Science. Technical Report Librarian; Princeton University. Computer Sciences Laboratory. Technical Report (0079-5283)
—CISTI.
Published by: Princeton University, Department of Computer Science, 35 Olden St, Princeton, NJ 08544-2087. TEL 609-258-5030, FAX 609-258-1771.

004 NLD ISSN 0921-8610
CODEN: PTPREM
➤ **PROCESS TECHNOLOGY PROCEEDINGS.** Text in Dutch. 1984. irreg., latest vol.12, 1996. price varies. back issues avail. **Document type:** *Monographic series, Academic/Scholarly.* **Description:** Examines techniques of various types of chemical engineering and processing.
Indexed: ChemAb, ChemTitl, SIA.
—BLDSC (6849.990850), CASDDS, CISTI, ingenta. **CCC.**
Published by: Elsevier BV (Subsidiary of: Elsevier Science & Technology), Radarweg 29, Amsterdam, 1043 NX, Netherlands. TEL 31-20-4853911, FAX 31-20-4852457, nlinfo-f@elsevier.nl, http://www.elsevier.nl.

004 FRA ISSN 1141-9636
PROCESSEURS. Text in French. 1989. 42/yr.
Published by: Porcedit, 182 rue du Faubourg Saint-Denis, Paris, 75010, France. TEL 40-35-09-49, FAX 40-35-08-62. Ed. Michel Ktitareff.

004 JPN ISSN 1349-8614
PROGRESS IN INFORMATICS. Text in English. 1982. s-a. **Document type:** *Journal, Academic/Scholarly.* **Description:** Covers original research, area surveys, projects and progress reports, and other topics of current interest to informaticians.
Former titles (until 2004): N I I Journal (1345-9996); (until 2000): Gakujutsu Joho Senta Kiyo/National Center for Science Information System. Research Bulletin (0913-5022); (until 1985): Tokyo Daigaku Bunken Joho Senta Kiyo/University of Tokyo. Center for Bibliographic Information. Research Bulletin (0911-3002); (until 1983): Tokyo Daigaku Joho Toshokangaku Kenkyu Senta Kiyo/University of Tokyo. Research Center for Library and Information Science. Research Bulletin (0286-7613)
Related titles: Online - full text ed.: ISSN 1349-8606.
Published by: Research Organization of Information and Systems, National Institute of Informatics, c/o Secretariat,, Editorial Committee of the "Progress in Informatics", 2-1-2 Hitotsubashi, Chiyoda-ku, Tokyo, 101-8430, Japan. TEL 81-3-42122145, FAX 81-3-42122150, pi@nii.ac.jp, http://www.nii.ac.jp/pi/.

004 SGP
PROGRESS IN NEURAL PROCESSING. Text in English. 1995. irreg., latest vol.16, 2005, May. price varies. **Document type:** *Monographic series, Academic/Scholarly.*
—ingenta.
Published by: World Scientific Publishing Co. Pte. Ltd., 5 Toh Tuck Link, Singapore, 596224, Singapore. TEL 65-466-5775, FAX 65-467-7667, wspc@wspc.com.sg, series@wspc.com.sg, http://www.wspc.com.sg/books/series/pnp_series.shtml, http://www.worldscientific.com. Eds. A Murray, Lars K Hansen. **Dist. by:** World Scientific Publishing Co., Inc., 1060 Main St, River Edge, NJ 07661. TEL 201-487-9655, 800-227-7562, FAX 201-487-9656, 888-977-2665; World Scientific Publishing Ltd., 57 Shelton St, London WC2H 9HE, United Kingdom. TEL 44-20-78360888, FAX 44-20-78362020.

004 USA
PROMPT. Text in English. 1980. m. USD 36 to members; USD 3 newsstand/cover to members. adv. back issues avail. **Document type:** *Newsletter.* **Description:** Helps users of I.B.M.-compatible computers understand the potential of their systems.
Related titles: Online - full text ed.
Published by: Pasadena I B M User Group, 2303 Glen Canyon Rd, Altadena, CA 91001-3539. TEL 818-791-1600, FAX 818-791-1600, 71333.130@compuserve.com. Ed., Adv. contact Steve Bass. page USD 400. Circ: 6,000.

004 USA
PROMPT (RALEIGH). Text in English. 1997. irreg. back issues avail. **Document type:** *Newsletter.* **Description:** Provides news briefs and tips on computer science for North Carolina State.
Media: Online - full text.

Published by: N C State, Information Technology Division, Computing Services, NC State University, Box 7109, Raleigh, NC 27695-7109. http://www.ncsu.edu/it/pub/prompt/. Ed. Sarah Noell.

PSYCOLOQUY (ONLINE EDITION); a refereed journal of peer commentary in psychology, neuroscience and cognitive science. see *PSYCHOLOGY*

004   USA

PUBLIC SECTOR (YEAR) INFORMATION SYSTEMS & E-BUSINESS SPENDING. Text in English. m. USD 695 (effective 2005). **Document type:** *Newsletter.*
Published by: Computer Economics, Inc., 2082 Business Center Dr., Ste 240, Irvine, CA 92612. TEL 949-831-8700, 800-326-8100, FAX 949-442-7688, info@compecon.com, http://www.computereconomics.com. Pub. Mark McManus.

004   GBR   ISSN 1367-2290
JN329.E4
PUBLIC SECTOR IT INSIGHT. Text in English. 1997. bi-m. GBP 250 domestic; GBP 300 foreign (effective 2000). **Description:** Attempts to explain the business of IT to both IT professionals and no-IT personnel. Provides an insight into IT related problems and solutions that affect organizations and business in all areas of the UK public sector.
Published by: Public Sector Information Ltd., Peters Gate House, St Petersgate, Stockport, SK1 1HE, United Kingdom. TEL 44-161-480-2469, FAX 44-161-292-3003, mailbox@psigroup.co.uk, http://www.psigrouop.co.uk. Circ: 17,740.

004   ITA
QUADERNI D'INFORMATICA. Text in Italian. 3/yr.
Published by: Honeywell Information Systems Italia, Pregnana Milanese, MI 20010, Italy. Ed. Franco Filippazzi.

R E D I. (Revista Electronica de Derecho Informatico) see *LAW*

004 621   USA   ISSN 1092-1524
R T C. Text in English. 1995. m. free domestic to qualified personnel (effective 2003). adv. back issues avail. **Document type:** *Journal, Trade.*
Published by: R T C Group, 927 Calle Negocio, G, San Clemente, CA 92673. TEL 949-226-2000, FAX 949-226-2050, http://www.rtcgroup.com/rtcmagazine. Ed. Tom Williams. Pub. Warren Andrews.

004 621   USA
R T C EUROPE. Text in English. m. free in Europe to qualified personnel (effective 2002). adv. **Document type:** *Journal, Trade.*
Published by: R T C Group, 927 Calle Negocio, G, San Clemente, CA 92673. TEL 949-226-2000, FAX 949-226-2050, http://www.rtcgroup.com/rtceurope. Eds. Tom Williams, Warren Andrews. Pub. Warren Andrews.

004   GRC   ISSN 1107-8618
RAM. Text in Greek. 1988. m. adv. **Document type:** *Magazine, Consumer.* **Description:** Provides information on the latest developments involving computer hardware and software products.
Published by: Lambrakis Press SA, Panepistimiou 18, Athens, 106 72, Greece. TEL 30-1-3686-452, FAX 30-1-3686-445, dolinfo@dol.gr, http://www.in.gr/ram, http://www.dol.gr. Circ: 48,195 (paid).

004   USA
RAPIDLY CHANGING FACE OF COMPUTING. Text in English. w. back issues avail. **Document type:** *Newsletter.* **Description:** Provides pragmatic, insight, analysis, and commentary on contemporary computing's innovations and trends, and on the technologies that drive them.
Media: Online - full content. **Related titles:** E-mail ed.
Published by: Compaq Computer Corportaion, Corporate Strategy Group, Box 692000, Houston, TX 77269-200. http://www.compaq.com/rcfoc/archives.html. Ed. Jeffrey R Harrow.

RECHT DER DATENVERARBEITUNG; Zeitschrift fuer Praxis und Wissenschaft. see *COMPUTERS—Computer Security*

004   ITA
▼ **RED HAT MAGAZINE.** Text in Italian. 2004. m. EUR 72 print & CD-ROM eds. (effective 2004). **Document type:** *Magazine, Trade.* **Description:** Provides technical information and editorials on open source development in both the enterprise and customer markets.
Related titles: CD-ROM ed.
Published by: BMind SpA, Via Ripamonti 129, Milan, 20141, Italy. TEL 39-02-56814487, http://www.redhat.it.

004   FRA
▼ **RED HAT MAGAZINE.** Text in French. 2003. bi-m. EUR 36 print & CD-ROM eds. (effective 2004). **Document type:** *Magazine, Trade.* **Description:** Provides technical information and editorials on open source development in both the enterprise and customer markets.
Related titles: CD-ROM ed.

Published by: BMind SaS, 11 bis Passage Dartois Bidot, Saint Maur des Fosses, 94100, France. http://www-1.redhatmagazine.com/fr/.

004   PRT
REDES. Text in Portuguese. m.
Published by: Investec Media, Ave Joao Crisostomo, 72, Lisbon, 1069-043, Portugal. TEL 351-213-307741, FAX 351-213-540643, assin@mail.fbento.pt, http://www.fbento.pt/FB/.

004   USA   ISSN 1047-935X
HD9696.C63
RELEASE 1.0; Esther Dyson's monthly report. Text in English. 1980. 15/yr. USD 795 domestic; USD 850 foreign (effective 2005). back issues avail. **Document type:** *Newsletter.* **Description:** Covers software, wide-area networking, groupware, text management, connectivity, artificial intelligence, and intellectual property law.
Formerly (until Mar. 1983): Rosen Electronics Letter (0737-6677)
Related titles: Online - full text ed.: (from Gale Group).
Indexed: CompD.
Published by: EDventure Holdings, Inc., Computer Publications Division, 104 Fifth Ave, 20th Fl, New York, NY 10011-6987. TEL 212-924-8800, FAX 212-924-0240, trista@edventura.com, us@edventure.com, http://www.edventure.com/release1/. Ed. Esther Dyson. Pub. Daphne Kis. Circ: 1,500.

004   NLD   ISSN 1385-3139
QA297.75
➤ **RELIABLE COMPUTING.** Text in English. 1996. bi-m. EUR 374, USD 374, GBP 234 combined subscription to institutions print & online eds. (effective 2005). adv. back issues avail.; reprint service avail. from PSC. **Document type:** *Academic/Scholarly.* **Description:** Covers the various aspects of interval mathematics and reliable numerical computations giving guaranteed properties of computed results; includes: original papers, surveys and tutorials, reports on new computer tools, bibliographies, reviews of new books, letters to the editor, information about scientific meeting.
Related titles: Online - full text ed.: ISSN 1573-1340 (from EBSCO Publishing, Gale Group, IngentaConnect, Kluwer Online, O C L C Online Computer Library Center, Inc., Springer LINK, Swets Information Services).
Indexed: BibLing, CCMJ, EngInd, Inspec, MathR, MathSciNet, RefZh, ZentMath.
—BLDSC (7356.424800), CISTI, IE, Infotrieve, ingenta. **CCC.**
Published by: Springer-Verlag Dordrecht (Subsidiary of: Springer Science+Business Media), Van Godewijckstraat 30, Dordrecht, 3311 GX, Netherlands. TEL 31-78-6576000, FAX 31-78-6576474, http://springerlink.metapress.com/openurl.asp?genre=journal&issn=1385-3139, http://www.springeronline.com. Ed. Vyacheslav M Nesterov.

004 300   SGP   ISSN 1793-2068
▼ **RESEARCH AND PRACTICE IN TECHNOLOGY ENHANCED LEARNING.** Text in English. forthcoming 2006. 3/yr. SGD 122, USD 72, EUR 63 to individuals; SGD 309, USD 180, EUR 158 combined subscription to institutions print & online eds.; SGD 186, USD 108, EUR 95 combined subscription in developing nations to institutions print & online eds. (effective 2006).
Published by: World Scientific Publishing Co. Pte. Ltd., 5 Toh Tuck Link, Singapore, 596224, Singapore. TEL 65-466-5775, FAX 65-467-7667, wspc@wspc.com.sg, http://www.worldscinet.com/rptel/rptel.shtml, http://www.worldscientific.com. Eds. Tak Wai Chan, Yam San Chee.

RESEARCH INSTITUTE FOR MATHEMATICAL SCIENCES. PUBLICATIONS. see *MATHEMATICS*

▼ **RESEARCH ON LANGUAGE AND COMPUTATION.** see *LINGUISTICS*

RESEARCH REPORTS ON INFORMATION SCIENCE AND ELECTRICAL ENGINEERING/KYUSHU DAIGAKU DAIGAKUIN SHISUTEMU JOHO KAGAKU KIYO. see *ENGINEERING—Electrical Engineering*

RESIDENTIAL SYSTEMS. see *ELECTRONICS*

004   FRA
▼ **REVUE INTERNATIONALE DE C F A O ET D'INFORMATIQUE GRAPHIQUE.** (Conception et Fabrication Assistees par Ordinateur) Text in French. 1986. 4/yr. EUR 280 in the European Union; EUR 315 elsewhere (effective 2003). **Description:** Covers mathematical aspects, problems of normalization, exchanges between systems, the development of databases.
Formerly (until 1994): Revue Internationale de C F A O et d'Infographie (0298-0924)
—CISTI.
Published by: (Ministere de la Recherche et de l'Espace), Lavoisier, 11 rue Lavoisier, Paris, 75008, France. TEL 33-1-42653995, FAX 33-1-42650246, info@lavoisier.fr, http://www.lavoisier.fr. Ed. Yvon Gardan. Circ: 3,000. **Subscr. to:** Lavoisier - Dept Abonnements, 14 rue de Provigny, Cachan 94236, France. TEL 33-1-47406700, FAX 33-1-47406702, abo@lavoisier.fr.

004   DNK   ISSN 0908-5491
ROSKILDE UNIVERSITETSCENTER. DATALOGISK AFDELING. DATALOGISKE NOTER. Text in Danish, English. 1993. irreg., latest vol.18, 1999. USD 10 (effective 2004). **Document type:** *Monographic series, Academic/Scholarly.* **Description:** Contains instructional material, lecture notes and textbooks.
Published by: Roskilde Universitetscenter, Datalogisk Afdeling, Bygning 42.1, Roskilde Universitetscenter, PO Box 260, Roskilde, 4000, Denmark. TEL 45-46-743839, FAX 45-46-743072, troels@ruc.dk, datalogic@ruc.dk, http://www.ruc.dk/dat. Ed. Troels Andreasen.

004   DNK   ISSN 0109-9779
ROSKILDE UNIVERSITETSCENTER. DATALOGISK AFDELING. DATALOGISKE SKRIFTER. Text in English. 1985. irreg. free. back issues avail. **Document type:** *Monographic series, Academic/Scholarly.* **Description:** Covers research activities in computer science at Roskilde University. Includes scientific papers and detailed reports.
Indexed: Inspec.
—BLDSC (3535.809800), AskIEEE.
Published by: Roskilde Universitetscenter, Datalogisk Afdeling, Bygning 42.1, Roskilde Universitetscenter, PO Box 260, Roskilde, 4000, Denmark. TEL 45-46-743839, FAX 45-46-743072, datalogic@ruc.dk, http://www.ruc.dk/dat. Ed. Troels Andreasen. Circ: 200.

004   ZAF   ISSN 1018-9564
S A COMPUTER MAGAZINE. (South Africa) Text in English. 1992. 11/yr. ZAR 163 domestic; USD 40 foreign (effective 2005). illus. **Document type:** *Magazine, Consumer.*
Formerly: S.A. Computer Buyer; Which incorporated: Cape Computer Buyer
Related titles: Online - full text ed.: ISSN 1605-6353. ZAR 80 domestic; USD 15 foreign (effective 2005).
Indexed: ISAP.
Address: PO Box 546, Constantia, Cape Town 7848, South Africa. TEL 27-21-7157134, FAX 27-21-7153873, http://www.sacm.co.za.

004   USA   ISSN 1537-145X
HD30.37
S A P INSIDER. Text in English. 2000. q. adv. back issues avail. **Document type:** *Trade.*
Related titles: Online - full content ed.
Published by: Wellesley Information Services (Subsidiary of: United Communications Group), 990 Washington St, Dedham, MA 02026-6714. Insider@WISpubs.com, customer@eview.com, http://www.sapinsideronline.com/spijsp/home1.jsp, http://www.wispubs.com. Pub. Debbie Virtue. Adv. contact Ken Kiefer TEL 781-751-8707. page USD 9,550; trim 8.125 x 10.875.

004   USA   ISSN 1524-7767
S A P PROFESSIONAL JOURNAL. Text in English. 1999. bi-m. USD 495 to individuals (effective 2005). **Document type:** *Magazine, Trade.*
Related titles: Online - full content ed.
Published by: Wellesley Information Services (Subsidiary of: United Communications Group), 11300 Rockville Pike, #1100, Rockville, MD 20852-3030. TEL 301-287-2678, 877-947-3012, FAX 301-816-8945, customer@eview.com, http://www.sappro.com/, http://www.wispubs.com.

004   USA   ISSN 1545-1372
▼ **S D S C EDUCATION NEWS.** (San Diego Supercomputer Center) Text in English. 2003 (Jun.). q. free (effective 2003).
Media: E-mail.
Published by: University of San Diego, Supercomputer Center, 9500 Gilman Dr, La Jolla, CA 92093-0505. TEL 858-534-5000, FAX 858-822-5443, http://education.sdsc.edu/index.html.

621.39   USA
S I G B E D NEWSLETTER. (Special Interest Group Embedded Systems) Text in English. s-a. USD 18 (effective 2004). **Document type:** *Newsletter.* **Description:** Provides a focal point for all aspects of embedded systems, including both software and hardware.
Published by: Association for Computing Machinery, Inc., 1515 Broadway, 17th Fl, New York, NY 10036-5701. TEL 212-626-0500, 212-626-0520, 800-342-6626, usacm@acm.org, http://www.acm.org/sigbed/.

004   USA
➤ **S I G K D D EXPLORATIONS NEWSLETTER.** (Special Interest Group on Knowledge Discovery and Data Mining) Text in English. s-a. USD 30 (effective 2004). **Document type:** *Newsletter, Academic/Scholarly.*
Related titles: Online - full text ed.
Published by: Association for Computing Machinery, Inc., 1515 Broadway, 17th Fl, New York, NY 10036-5701. TEL 212-626-0500, 212-626-0520, 800-342-6626, FAX 212-869-0481, sigs@acm.org, usacm@acm.org, http://www.acm.org/sigkdd/explorations/.

C

▼ *new title*   ➤ *refereed*   ✳ *unverified*   ◆ *full entry avail.*

004   USA
QA76.6
S I G M I C R O SYMPOSIUM PROCEEDINGS. Text in English. 1986. a. USD 35 to non-members; USD 21 to members; USD 8 student members (effective 2004). **Document type:** *Newsletter, Academic/Scholarly.* **Description:** Specializes in computer microarchitecture, especially features permitting instruction-level parallelism and their related implications on compiler design.
Former titles (until 1994): S I G M I C R O Newsletter (1050-916X); (until 1987): S I G M I C R O, T C M I C R O Newsletter (0892-3825); (until 1975): S I G M I C R O Newsletter (0163-5751)
Related titles: Online - full text ed.
Indexed: Inspec.
—CISTI, IE.
Published by: Association for Computing Machinery, Inc., 1515 Broadway, 17th Fl, New York, NY 10036-5701. TEL 212-626-0500, 212-626-0520, 800-342-6626, FAX 212-869-0481, sigs@acm.org, usacm@acm.org, http://www.acm.org.

621.39   USA
S I G M O B I L E MC2R. (Special Interest Group Mobility of Systems, Users, Data and Computing) Text in English. q. USD 20 (effective 2004). **Description:** Promotes research and development by bringing together researchers and practitioners, and fosters interest in the mobility of systems, users, data, and computing.
Published by: Association for Computing Machinery, Inc., 1515 Broadway, 17th Fl, New York, NY 10036-5701. TEL 212-626-0500, 212-626-0520, 800-342-6626, usacm@acm.org, http://www.sigmobile.org, http://www.acm.org.

004   USA   ISSN 1096-682X
QA74
S I G U C C S USER SERVICES CONFERENCE. PROCEEDINGS. (Special Interest Group on University Computing Centers) Text in English. 1990. a. USD 20 to members; USD 40 to non-members; USD 7 student members (effective 2005). **Document type:** *Proceedings, Academic/Scholarly.*
—BLDSC (0578.644000), ingenta.
Published by: Association for Computing Machinery, Inc., 1515 Broadway, 17th Fl, New York, NY 10036-5701. TEL 212-626-0500, 212-626-0520, 800-342-6626, FAX 212-869-0481, sigs@acm.org, usacm@acm.org, http://www.acm.org.

004   DNK   ISSN 0905-0167
                                       CODEN: SJITEO
SCANDINAVIAN JOURNAL OF INFORMATION SYSTEMS. Text in English. 1989. a. SEK 600 to institutions; free to members (effective 2005). **Document type:** *Magazine, Trade.* **Description:** Provides information on the use, development, and management of information systems in Scandinavia.
Indexed: CompAb, Emerald, Inspec.
—BLDSC (8087.517150), IE, ingenta.
Published by: (I R I S Association SWE), University of Aalborg, Department of Mathematical Sciences, Frederik Bajers Vej 7, Aalborg OE, 9220, Denmark. http://www.e-sjis.org. Ed. Eric Monteiro. **Co-sponsors:** Goeteborg University, Department of Informatics; Viktoria Institute.

621.39   THA   ISSN 1513-1432
QA75.5
➤ **SCHOOL OF ADVANCED TECHNOLOGIES. ELECTRONIC JOURNAL.** Text in English. 1999. s-a. free. bk.rev. back issues avail. **Document type:** *Journal, Academic/Scholarly.* **Description:** Covers computer science, information management, industrial engineering, manufacturing systems and microelectronics.
Media: Online - full text.
Published by: (School of Advanced Technologies), Asian Institute of Technology, Klong Luang, PO Box 4, Pathum Thani, 12120, Thailand. TEL 66-2-524-5853, FAX 66-2-524-5870, deansat@ait.ac.th, http://www.sat.ait.ac.th/ej-sat/. Ed. F J Devadason.

004   SGP
▼ **SCIENCE, ENGINEERING, AND BIOLOGY INFORMATICS.** Text in English. forthcoming 2006. irreg. **Document type:** *Monographic series, Academic/Scholarly.*
Published by: World Scientific Publishing Co. Pte. Ltd., 5 Toh Tuck Link, Singapore, 596224, Singapore. TEL 65-466-5775, FAX 65-467-7667, series@wspc.com.sg, http://www.wspc.com/ books/series/sebi_series.shtml, http://www.worldscientific.com. **Subscr. to:** Farrer Rd, PO Box 128, Singapore 912805, Singapore. TEL 65-382-5663, FAX 65-382-5919. **Dist. by:** World Scientific Publishing Co., Inc., 1060 Main St, River Edge, NJ 07661. TEL 201-487-9655, 800-227-7562, FAX 201-487-9656, 888-977-2665, wspc@wspc.com.; World Scientific Publishing Ltd., 57 Shelton St, London WC2H 9HE, United Kingdom. TEL 44-20-78360888, FAX 44-20-78362020, sales@wspc.co.uk.

004   CHN
T58.5   CODEN: ZYJXFK
➤ **SCIENCE IN CHINA. SERIES F: INFORMATION SCIENCES.** Text in English. bi-m. USD 312 to individuals; USD 622 to institutions; USD 1,607 to individuals for full set, series A-G; USD 2,990 to institutions for full set, series A-G (effective 2004). **Document type:** *Journal, Academic/Scholarly.*
Formerly: Science in China. Series F: Informatics (1009-2757)
Related titles: Online - full content ed.: USD 50 (effective 2004); Online - full text ed.: (from East View Information Services).
Indexed: B&BAb, BioEngAb, BrCerAb, C&ISA, CMCI, CerAb, CorrAb, CurCont, E&CAJ, EMA, IAA, M&TEA, MBF, METADEX, MathR, MathSciNet, SolStAb, WAA.
—BLDSC (8141.700000), Linda Hall. **CCC.**
Published by: Zhongguo Kexue Zazhishe/Science in China Press, 16 Donghuangchenggen North Street, Beijing, 100717, China. TEL 86-10-64019820, FAX 86-10-64031816, sale@scichina.com, http://www.scienceinchina.com/ scienceinchina_f_en.htm, http://www.scichina.com/. **Subscr. outside China to:** Maney Publishing, China Journal Distribution Services, Hudson Rd, Leeds LS9 7DI, United Kingdom. TEL 44-113-2497481, FAX 44-113-2486983, subscriptions@maney.co.uk.

004   GBR
SCOTTISH COMPUTER HEADLINE. Text in English. 1997. m. GBP 36; GBP 3 newsstand/cover (effective 2000). adv. **Description:** Dedicated to Scottish companies who purchase IT.
Related titles: Online - full text ed.
Published by: Business Publications Ltd., 3 Grosvenor Gardens, Edinburgh, EH12 5JU, United Kingdom. http://sc-headline.co.uk. Ed. Joh-Paul Cleary. Adv. contact Shona Gilhooly. page GBP 2,950. Circ: 13,000.

004   USA
SELECTED BOOK REVIEWS. Text in English. q. USD 10. bk.rev. **Document type:** *Newsletter.* **Description:** Reviews new books on software and other computer-related topics.
Related titles: Diskette ed.
Published by: Vector Graphiques, 206 Davison Ave, Lynbrook, NY 11563. Ed. John R Cartmell Jr. adv.: page USD 100. Circ: 1,000 (paid).

SEMICONDUCTOR ELECTRONICS JOURNAL. see *ELECTRONICS*

SEMICONDUCTOR MANUFACTURING MAGAZINE. see *ELECTRONICS*

SENSORS & TRANSDUCES JOURNAL. see *ENGINEERING—Engineering Mechanics And Materials*

004 621.39   USA
SERIES IN COMPUTER SCIENCE. Text in English. 1999. irreg., latest 2005. price varies. back issues avail. **Document type:** *Monographic series.* **Description:** Discusses programming and engineering topics in computer science.
Formerly: Plenum Series in Computer Science (1567-7974)
Published by: Springer-Verlag New York, Inc. (Subsidiary of: Springer Science+Business Media), 233 Spring St, New York, NY 10013. TEL 212-460-1500, FAX 212-460-1575, service@springer-ny.com, http://www.springer-ny.com. Ed. Rami Melhem.

004   SGP
SERIES IN INTELLIGENT CONTROL AND INTELLIGENT AUTOMATION. Text in English. 1996. irreg., latest vol.13. price varies. **Document type:** *Monographic series, Academic/Scholarly.*
Published by: World Scientific Publishing Co. Pte. Ltd., 5 Toh Tuck Link, Singapore, 596224, Singapore. TEL 65-466-5775, FAX 65-467-7667, wspc@wspc.com.sg, series@wspc.com.sg, http://www.wspc.com.sg/books/series/sicia_series.shtml, http://www.worldscientific.com. Ed. Fei Yue Wang. **Dist. by:** World Scientific Publishing Co., Inc., 1060 Main St, River Edge, NJ 07661. TEL 201-487-9655, 800-227-7562, FAX 201-487-9656, 888-977-2665; World Scientific Publishing Ltd., 57 Shelton St, London WC2H 9HE, United Kingdom. TEL 44-20-78360888, FAX 44-20-78362020.

004   SGP
SERIES IN NEURAL NETWORKS. Text in English. 1991. irreg. **Document type:** *Monographic series, Academic/Scholarly.*
Published by: World Scientific Publishing Co. Pte. Ltd., 5 Toh Tuck Link, Singapore, 596224, Singapore. TEL 65-466-5775, FAX 65-467-7667, wspc@wspc.com.sg, series@wspc.com.sg, http://www.wspc.com.sg/books/series/snn_series.shtml, http://www.worldscientific.com. Ed. John G Taylor.

004   SGP
▼ **SERIES ON COMPUTERS AND OPERATIONS RESEARCH.** Text in English. 2003. irreg., latest vol.4. price varies. **Document type:** *Monographic series, Academic/Scholarly.*
Published by: World Scientific Publishing Co. Pte. Ltd., 5 Toh Tuck Link, Singapore, 596224, Singapore. http://www.wspc.com.sg/books/series/scor_series.shtml. Ed. P M Pardalos. **Dist. by:** World Scientific Publishing Co., Inc., 1060 Main St, River Edge, NJ 07661; World Scientific Publishing Ltd., 57 Shelton St, London WC2H 9HE, United Kingdom.

004   SGP
SERIES ON INNOVATIVE INTELLIGENCE. Text in English. 2002. irreg., latest vol.8, 2004, Apr. price varies. **Document type:** *Monographic series, Academic/Scholarly.* **Description:** Covers advanced biology-based intelligent and knowledge processing and its design and application in business, engineering, and the sciences.
Published by: World Scientific Publishing Co. Pte. Ltd., 5 Toh Tuck Link, Singapore, 596224, Singapore. TEL 65-466-5775, FAX 65-467-7667, wspc@wspc.com.sg, series@wspc.com.sg, http://www.wspc.com/books/series/sii_series.shtml, http://www.worldscientific.com. Ed. L C Jain TEL 61-8-83023315. **Dist. by:** World Scientific Publishing Co., Inc., 1060 Main St, River Edge, NJ 07661. TEL 201-487-9655, 800-227-7562, FAX 201-487-9656, 888-977-2665; World Scientific Publishing Ltd., 57 Shelton St, London WC2H 9HE, United Kingdom. TEL 44-20-78360888, FAX 44-20-78362020.

SETSUNAN UNIVERSITY. JOURNAL OF BUSINESS ADMINISTRATION AND INFORMATION/KEIEI JOHO KENKYU. see *BUSINESS AND ECONOMICS*

004   JPN
SHUKAN COMPUTER∗ . Text in Japanese. m. adv.
Published by: Denpa Computerworld Co., 11-15 Higashi-Gotanda, Shinagawa-ku, Tokyo, 141-0022, Japan. Ed. Mr. Takahashi. Circ: 35,000.

004   JPN
SHUUKAN ASUKII/WEEKLY ASCII. Text in Japanese. w. JPY 17,640; JPY 300 base vol(s). (effective 2004). **Document type:** *Magazine, Consumer.*
Published by: ASCII Corp., JR Shinanomachi Bldg. 34 Shinanomachi, Shinjuku-ku, Tokyo, 160-8584, Japan. http://www.ascii.co.jp/books/magazines/wascii.html.

621.39   USA   ISSN 1076-366X
TK7800
SMART ELECTRONICS. Text in English. 1994. bi-m. USD 3.25 newsstand/cover.
Published by: McMullen Argus Publishing, Inc. (Subsidiary of: Primedia, Inc.), 2400 E. Katella Avenue, Suite 1100, Anaheim, CA 92806. TEL 714-572-2255, FAX 714-572-1864.

004   USA   ISSN 1546-7031
▼ **SMART TIPS AND QUICK TRICKS FOR BUSINESS PROFESSIONALS.** Text in English. 2003. a. USD 29.95 per issue domestic; USD 39.95 per issue foreign (effective 2005).
Media: CD-ROM.
Published by: Element K Journals (Subsidiary of: Eli Research, Inc.), 500 Canal View Blvd, Rochester, NY 14623. TEL 585-240-7301, 800-223-8720, 877-203-5248, FAX 585-292-4392, http://www.elementkjournals.com/store/ showAncillaryDetail.asp?prodid=159.

004   USA   ISSN 1546-7023
▼ **SMART TIPS AND QUICK TRICKS FOR I T AND WEB PROFESSIONALS.** (Information Technology) Text in English. 2003. a. USD 29.95 per issue (effective 2005).
Media: CD-ROM.
Published by: Element K Journals (Subsidiary of: Eli Research, Inc.), 500 Canal View Blvd, Rochester, NY 14623. TEL 585-240-7301, 800-223-8720, 877-203-5248, FAX 585-292-4392, http://www.elementkjournals.com/buy/ showPromo.asp?coupon=113231&m4session_id=.iBScaFAB.

004   IND
SMARTINC; technology in business. Text in English. 1985. fortn. INR 399 domestic; INR 1,100 in Bangladesh, Nepal and Buthan; GBP 63 in United Kingdom; CND 99 in Canada; USD 73 in United States; USD 89 rest of world (effective 2002). adv. **Document type:** *Magazine, Trade.* **Description:** Covers a broad spectrum of the information technology industry, including hardware and software developments, IT corporate updates and news on the industry.
Formerly: Computers Today (0970-0129)
Related titles: Online - full text ed.: (from LexisNexis).
Published by: Living Media India Pvt. Ltd., F-14-15, Connaught Place, New Delhi, India. TEL 91-11-23315801, FAX 91-11-23712998, wecare@intoday.com, http://www.smartinc-india.com/index.phtml?, http://www.indiatoday.com. Ed. J S Raju. adv.: B&W page INR 15,000, color page INR 65,000; trim 273 x 197. Circ: 52,833. **Subscr. to:** We Care, 1-A Hamilton House, New Delhi 110 001, India. TEL 91-11-23352870, FAX 91-11-23352874.

004   CHL   ISSN 0716-7784
SOCIEDAD CHILENA DE CIENCIA DE COMPUTACION. BOLETIN. Text in Spanish. 1988. q. **Document type:** *Bulletin, Academic/Scholarly.* **Description:** Covers topics in all areas of the computer sciences.
Published by: Sociedad Chilena de Ciencia de Computacion/Chilean Computer Science Society, Casilla 2777, Blanco Encalada, 2120, Santiago, Chile. TEL 56-2-6897236, FAX 56-2-6895531, sccc@dcc.uchile.cl, http://sunsite.dcc.uchile.cl/~sccc.

004 CHL ISSN 0717-4276
SOCIEDAD CHILENA DE CIENCIA DE COMPUTACION. REVISTA. Text in Spanish. 1999. irreg. free. **Document type:** *Newsletter, Academic/Scholarly.* **Description:** Provides a forum to discuss and explore all topics relevant to computer science.
Media: Online - full text.
Published by: Sociedad Chilena de Ciencia de Computacion/Chilean Computer Science Society, Casilla 2777, Blanco Encalada, 2120, Santiago, Chile. TEL 56-2-6897236, FAX 56-2-6895531, sccc@dcc.uchile.cl, http://www.ing.puc.cl/sccc/rev-sccc/objectivos.html, http://sunsite.dcc.uchile.cl/~sccc/activit.html.

SOLID SOLUTIONS. see *ENVIRONMENTAL STUDIES—Waste Management*

004 ESP ISSN 1134-4792
SOLO PROGRAMADORES. Text in Spanish. 1994. m. EUR 54 domestic (effective 2004). **Document type:** *Magazine, Consumer.*
Related titles: CD-ROM ed.: ISSN 1135-2183; Online - full text ed.: ISSN 1135-2191.
Published by: Revistas Profesionales, C/ Valentin Beato 42, 3a Planta, Madrid, 28037, Spain. revistasprofesionales@revistasprofesionales.com, http://www.revistasprofesionales.com.

004 ZAF ISSN 1015-7999
QA76 CODEN: SACJE3
➤ **SOUTH AFRICAN COMPUTER JOURNAL/SUID AFRIKAANSE REKENAARTYDSKRIF.** Text in Afrikaans, English. 1979. irreg. ZAR 40 per issue domestic to individuals; USD 20 per issue foreign to individuals; ZAR 80 per issue domestic to institutions; USD 40 per issue foreign to institutions (effective 2004). adv. bk.rev. back issues avail. **Document type:** *Academic/Scholarly.* **Description:** Publishes original research papers in the fields of computer science and information systems.
Formerly (until 1989): Questiones Informaticae (0254-2757)
Related titles: Online - full text ed.: (from International Network for the Availability of Scientific Publications, African Journals Online).
Indexed: Engind, ISAP, Inspec.
—BLDSC (8334.191000), AskIEEE, Ei, IE, ingenta.
Published by: Computer Society of South Africa, PO Box 1714, Halfway House, 1685, South Africa. TEL 27-12-420-2504, FAX 27-12-436454, http://www.journals.co.za/ej/ejour_comp.html. Ed., Adv. contact D.G. Kourie. R&P D G Kourie. Circ: 500.
Co-sponsor: South African Institute of Computer Scientists.

➤ **SOUTH CAROLINA COMPUTER AND SOFTWARE SERVICES DIRECTORY.** see *BUSINESS AND ECONOMICS—Trade And Industrial Directories*

004 USA ISSN 0177-7718
SPRINGER BOOKS ON PROFESSIONAL COMPUTING. Text in English. 1984. irreg. price varies. reprint service avail. from ISI. **Document type:** *Monographic series.*
Published by: Springer-Verlag New York, Inc. (Subsidiary of: Springer Science+Business Media), 233 Spring St, New York, NY 10013. TEL 212-460-1500, FAX 212-473-6272.

003 DEU ISSN 1431-8598
SPRINGER SERIES IN OPERATIONS RESEARCH. Text in English. 1994. irreg., latest 2003. price varies. **Document type:** *Monographic series, Academic/Scholarly.* **Description:** Contains topics of interest to operations researchers and management scientists.
Indexed: CCMJ.
Published by: Springer-Verlag (Subsidiary of: Springer Science+Business Media), Haber Str 7, Heidelberg, 69126, Germany. TEL 49-6221-3450, FAX 49-6221-229, subscriptions@springer.de, http://www.springer.de. Ed. P Glynn. **Subscr. in US to:** Springer-Verlag New York, Inc., Journal Fulfillment, PO Box 2485, Secaucus, NJ 07096-2485. TEL 212-460-1500, FAX 212-473-6272.

004 AUT ISSN 0938-9504
SPRINGERS LEHRBUECHER DER INFORMATIK. Text in German. 1990. irreg., latest 2002. price varies. **Document type:** *Monographic series, Academic/Scholarly.*
Published by: Springer-Verlag Wien (Subsidiary of: Springer Science+Business Media) TEL 43-1-3302415-0, FAX 43-1-330242665, books@springer.at, http://www.springer.at. Ed. G H Schildt. R&P Angela Foessl TEL 43-1-3302415517.
Subscr. in N. America to: Springer-Verlag New York, Inc., 233 Spring St, New York, NY 10013. TEL 800-777-4643, FAX 201-348-4505, orders@springer-ny.com.

STATISTICS AND COMPUTING. see *COMPUTERS—Abstracting, Bibliographies, Statistics*

004 USA ISSN 1549-6783
HF5548.125
STORAGE. Text in English. 2002. m. free to qualified personnel; USD 99 domestic; USD 150 in Europe, Mexico, Central & South America; USD 160 in Asia, Australia & Pacific (effective 2005). adv. back issues avail. **Document type:** *Magazine, Trade.* **Description:** Provides storage executives with in-depth analysis and forward-looking guidance on managing, storing, networking, and safeguarding the data at the core of large organizations.
Related titles: Online - full text ed.
Published by: TechTarget, 117 Kendrick St, Ste 800, Needham, MA 02494. TEL 781-657-1000, 888-274-4111, FAX 781-657-1100, info@techtarget.com, http://storagemagazine.techtarget.com/, http://www.techtarget.com/. Ed. Mark Schlack. Circ: 50,000 (controlled).

▼ **STORAGE & ENTERTAINMENT**; the storage magazine for entertainment and broadcast technologies. see *COMMUNICATIONS*

004 USA ISSN 1524-6558
QA75.5
STORAGE INC. Text in English. 1997. q.
Related titles: ♦ Supplement to: Computer Technology Review. ISSN 0278-9647.
Published by: West World Productions, Inc., 420 N Camden Dr, Beverly Hills, CA 90210-4507. TEL 310-276-9500, FAX 310-777-6670, http://www.wwpi.com.

004 USA ISSN 1097-5152
CODEN: SMSOFD
STORAGE MANAGEMENT SOLUTIONS. Abbreviated title: S M S. Text in English. 1995. bi-m. free to qualified personnel (effective 2003). adv. illus.; tr.lit. reprints avail. **Document type:** *Trade.* **Description:** Covers the enterprise storage technology information needs of end users MIS-DP.
Indexed: InfoSAb, Microcompind.
—CCC.
Published by: West World Productions, Inc., 420 N Camden Dr, Beverly Hills, CA 90210-4507. TEL 310-777-6670, FAX 310-777-6670, http://www.wwpi.com/Home_SMS.asp. Ed. Mark C. Ferelli. Pub. Yuri R Spiro. Circ: 42,000.

621.39 ROM ISSN 1220-1766
➤ **STUDIES IN INFORMATICS AND CONTROL**; with emphasis on useful applications of advanced technology. Text mainly in English; Text occasionally in French. 1992. q. USD 50 to individuals; USD 75 to institutions; USD 18.75 newsstand/cover (effective 2001). bk.rev. **Document type:** *Academic/Scholarly.* **Description:** Presents original articles, studies and technical and research reports which present work-in-progress and-or new results in information technology and computer-based control.
Related titles: CD-ROM ed.; Online - full text ed.: free (effective 2005).
Indexed: Inspec.
—BLDSC (8490.738100), AskIEEE, IE, ingenta.
Published by: National Institute for R&D in Informatics (ICI), Al. Averescu 8-10, Bucharest, 71316, Romania. TEL 40-1-2240736 ext. 289, FAX 40-1-2240539, sicbr@u3.ici.ro, http://www.ici.ro/ici/revista/sic.html. Ed. Florin-Gheorghe Filip. Pub. Brandusa Trusca. R&P Florin Gheorghe Filip. Circ: 250.
Co-sponsor: National Agency for Research, Technology and Innovation, Advisory Board for Scientific and Technological Development.

004 CZE ISSN 1214-4290
▼ **SVET POCITACU.** Text in Czech. 2003 (Oct.). fortn. CZK 35 newsstand/cover (effective 2003). adv. **Document type:** *Magazine, Consumer.*
Published by: Axel Springer Praha a.s., Strelnicna 1680/8, Prague 8, 182 21, Czech Republic. TEL 420-2-66193111, FAX 420-2-66193331, ivan.sevcik@axelspringer.cz, http://www.axelspringer.cz. Ed. Marcela Titzlova.

004 USA
SYMPOSIUM ON APPLIED COMPUTING. Abbreviated title: S A C. Text in English. 1990. a. price varies. adv. **Description:** Addresses research and conclusions on a variety of advanced applied computer science areas.
Published by: (Institute of Electrical and Electronics Engineers, Inc.), I E E E Computer Society, 10662 Los Vaqueros Circle, PO Box 3014, Los Alamitos, CA 90720-1314. TEL 714-821-8380, FAX 714-821-4010. Adv. contact Frieda Koester.

004 USA ISSN 0272-5428
CODEN: ASFPDV
SYMPOSIUM ON FOUNDATIONS OF COMPUTER SCIENCE. PROCEEDINGS. Text in English. 1960. a. USD 229; USD 92 to members (effective 2004). **Document type:** *Proceedings, Trade.* **Description:** Contains papers presented at the symposium. Subjects include computational geometry, logistics, algorithms, circuits and graph problems. May occasionally contain information on automata theory.
Former titles (until 1974): Annual Symposium on Switching and Automata Theory. Proceedings (0272-4847); Symposium on Switching and Automata Theory; Switching and Automata Theory Conference. Record (0082-0490); (until 1965): Symposium on Switching Circuit Theory and Logical Design
Related titles: Online - full text ed.: (from I E E E).
Indexed: C&ISA, E&CAJ, Engind, Inspec, SolStAb.
—BLDSC (1534.949000), Ei, IE, ingenta. **CCC.**
Published by: (Institute of Electrical and Electronics Engineers, Inc.), I E E E Computer Society, 10662 Los Vaqueros Circle, PO Box 3014, Los Alamitos, CA 90720-1314. TEL 714-821-8380, FAX 714-821-4641, customer.service@ieee.org, http://www.ieee.org.

004 CHE ISSN 0254-2226
SYSDATA. Text in German. 1901. 10/yr. CHF 61 domestic; CHF 118 foreign (effective 2001). adv. bk.rev. abstr.; illus. **Document type:** *Journal, Trade.* **Description:** Trade publication for office technology and communication. Covers computer systems, automation, information processing, software, new products. Includes reports of events, positions available.
Former titles: Sysdata und Buerotechnik; (until 1970): Buerotechnik (0006-0003)
Indexed: Inspec.
—AskIEEE.
Published by: Binkert Medien AG, Baslerstr 15, Laufenburg, 5080, Switzerland. TEL 41-62-8697900, FAX 41-62-8697901, binkertmedien@binkert.ch, http://www.sysdata.ch, http://www.binkertmedien.ch. Ed. Peter Suter. Adv. contact Bruno Schwaninger. B&W page CHF 3,585, color page CHF 4,350; trim 185 x 266. Circ: 15,000.

003 USA ISSN 0882-1666
QA75.5 CODEN: SCJAEP
SYSTEMS AND COMPUTERS IN JAPAN. Text in English. 1969. 14/yr. USD 6,430 domestic to institutions; USD 6,598 in Canada & Mexico to institutions; USD 6,696 elsewhere to institutions; USD 7,073 combined subscription domestic to institutions print & online eds.; USD 7,241 combined subscription in Canada & Mexico to institutions print & online eds.; USD 7,339 combined subscription elsewhere to institutions print & online eds. (effective 2006). adv. charts; illus. index. back issues avail. **Document type:** *Journal, Academic/Scholarly.* **Description:** Covers computing theory, algorithms, computer architecture, hardware and design, advanced digital circuitry, software theory and systems, formal languages, interface devices, automata, databases, speech and image processing, computer graphics, artificial intelligence and cognitive sciences, and computer applications.
Formerly: Systems, Computers, Control (0096-8765)
Related titles: Microfilm ed.: (from PQC); Online - full text ed.: ISSN 1520-684X. USD 6,430 to institutions (effective 2006) (from EBSCO Publishing, Swets Information Services, Wiley InterScience).
Indexed: AIA, ASCA, B&BAb, BrCerAb, C&ISA, CADCAM, CIS, CMCI, CerAb, CompAb, CompC, CompLI, CorrAb, CurCont, E&CAJ, EMA, Engind, IAA, ISMEC, Inspec, M&TEA, MBF, METADEX, MathR, RoboAb, SolStAb, TelAb, WAA.
—BLDSC (8589.292000), AskIEEE, CISTI, Ei, IDS, IE, Infotrieve, ingenta, Linda Hall. **CCC.**
Published by: (Institute of Electronics, Information and Communications Engineers of Japan JPN), John Wiley & Sons, Inc., 111 River St, Hoboken, NJ 07030-5774. TEL 201-748-6000, FAX 201-748-5915, uscs-wis@wiley.com, http://www3.interscience.wiley.com/cgi-bin/jhome/51986, http://www.wiley.com. Ed. Michiyuki Uenohara. Circ: 300.
Subscr. outside the Americas to: John Wiley & Sons Ltd., The Atrium, Southern Gate, Chichester, West Sussex PO19 8SQ, United Kingdom. TEL 44-1243-843335, 0800-243407, FAX 44-1243-843232, cs-journals@wiley.co.uk.

C

621.381 USA ISSN 0886-1420
T E N C O N (I E E E REGION 10 CONFERENCE). PROCEEDINGS; an international conference on consumer & industrial electronics & applications. Variant title: I E E E Trends in Electronics Conference. Proceedings. Text in English. 1982. irreg. USD 151 membership (effective 2005). **Document type:** *Proceedings, Trade.* **Description:** Discusses the development and application of electronics in the countries of the Western Pacific, the Indian Ocean and Oceania.
—BLDSC (6849.734000). **CCC.**
Published by: (Region 10), Institute of Electrical and Electronics Engineers, Inc., 3 Park Ave, 17th Fl, New York, NY 10016-5997. TEL 212-705-7900, 800-678-4333, FAX 212-705-7682, customer.service@ieee.org, http://www.ieee.org.

004 320 GBR ISSN 1746-4757
▼ ➤ **TANGENTIUM.** Text in English. 2003. bi-m. free (effective 2005). **Document type:** *Journal, Academic/Scholarly.* **Description:** Devoted to alternative perspectives on information technologies, democracy, and society.
Media: Online - full text.
Published by: University of Leeds, School of Computing, Leeds, LS2 9JT, United Kingdom. TEL 44-113-2334626, FAX 44-113-2334635, http://www.tangentium.org, http://www.leeds.ac.uk.

➤ **TECH COAST.** see *BUSINESS AND ECONOMICS*

➤ **TECH - N J.** see *TECHNOLOGY: COMPREHENSIVE WORKS*

004 AUS ISSN 1038-5231
TECHNICAL COMPUTING. Text in English. 1968. q. adv. illus. **Document type:** *Trade.*

Former titles (until 1991): A C A D S Quarterly (0817-072X); (until 1984): Association for Computer Aided Design. Newsletter (0818-2167)
Published by: (A C A D S Association), National Publications Pty. Ltd., PO Box 197, Cronulla, NSW 2230, Australia. TEL 02-764-111, FAX 02-763-1699.

004 GBR ISSN 1355-9907
TECHNICAL COMPUTING. Text in English. 1994. q. **Document type:** *Academic/Scholarly.*
Related titles: Online - full text ed.
Published by: Adept Scientific, United Kingdom. paul.bragg@adeptscience.co.uk, http://www.adeptscience.co.uk/as/tcm/.

005.133 USA ISSN 1523-4800
TECHNICAL GUIDE TO VISUAL PROGRAMMING. Text in English. q. USD 24.95 domestic; USD 36.95 in Canada & Mexico; USD 54.95 elsewhere (effective 2000). **Document type:** *Journal, Trade.*
Published by: Fawcette Technical Publications, 2600 S. El Camino Real., Ste. 300, San Mateo, CA 94403-2381. TEL 650-833-7100, FAX 650-853-0230, lmatthes@fawcette.com, http://www.fawcette.com. Pub. Lynne Matthes TEL 650-833-7145.

004 AUS ISSN 1326-4524
TECHNICAL REPORT. Text in English. 1987. irreg.
Media: Online - full text.
Indexed: EEA.
Published by: James Cook University of North Queensland, Department of Computer Science, Douglas Campus, Townsville, QLD 4811, Australia. TEL 61-7-4781-4111, FAX 61-7-4779-6371, tech-report@cs.jcu.edu.au, http://www.cs.jcu.edu.au.

004 DZA ISSN 1111-0902
TECHNOLOGIES AVANCEES. Text in Multiple languages. 1991. s-a. DZD 200 (effective 2004). back issues avail. **Document type:** *Academic/Scholarly.*
Related titles: Online - full text ed.: (from International Network for the Availability of Scientific Publications, African Journals Online).
Published by: Centre de Developpement des Technologies Avancees, 16303 Baba Hassen, Alger, Algeria. TEL 213-21-351018, FAX 213-21-351039, http://www.inasp.info/ajol/journals/ta/about.html. Ed. Bessalah Hamid.

TECHNOLOGY MEETINGS; meeting and incentive solutions for the high-tech industry. see *TECHNOLOGY: COMPREHENSIVE WORKS*

TELECOMMUNICATIONS DIRECTORY; an international descriptive guide to approximately 4,300 telecommunications organizations, systems, and services. see *BUSINESS AND ECONOMICS—Trade And Industrial Directories*

TELEMEDICINE LAW WEEKLY. see *LAW*

▼ **TELEMEDICINE WEEK.** see *BUSINESS AND ECONOMICS*

004 USA
THE TENAGRA APOGEE. Text in English. 1997. 2/m. **Document type:** *Bulletin.* **Description:** Daily update containing links to the latest news stories addressing the year 2000 computing crisis.
Formerly (until 2000): Year2000News
Media: Online - full text.
Published by: Year 2000 Information Center, 1100 Hercules, Ste 130, Houston, TX 77058. TEL 281-480-6300, FAX 281-480-7715, cliff@tenagra.com, http://www.apogee.tenagra.com. Ed. Cliff Kurtzman. Circ: 39,000.

004 FRA ISSN 0997-5551
TERMINAL; technologie de l'information, culture, societe. Text in French. q. EUR 39.65 to individuals; EUR 71.70 newsstand/cover to institutions (effective 2004). **Document type:** *Journal, Academic/Scholarly.*
Published by: (Centre d'Information et d'Initiatives sur l'Information), L' Harmattan, 5 rue de l'Ecole Polytechnique, Paris, 75005, France. TEL 33-1-43257651, FAX 33-1-43258203, vetois@terminal.ens-cachan.fr, http://www.weblifac.ens-cachan.fr/Terminal/., http://www.editions-harmattan.fr. Ed. Jacques Vetois.

004 USA ISSN 1557-2862
▼ **THEORY OF COMPUTING.** Text in English. 2005. irreg. **Document type:** *Journal, Academic/Scholarly.* **Description:** Dedicated to the widest dissemination of high quality research papers in all areas of Theoretical Computer Science.
Media: Online - full text.
Published by: University of Chicago, Department of Computer Science, 1100 East 58th St, Chicago, IL 60637. TEL 773-702-6614, FAX 773-702-8487, http://theoryofcomputing.org, http://www.cs.uchicago.edu. Ed. Laszlo Babai.

004 FIN ISSN 0359-8543
TIETOVIIKKO. Text in Finnish. 1983. 45/yr. EUR 119 (effective 2003). adv. bk.rev. **Document type:** *Newspaper, Trade.* **Description:** Provides essential product information for purchasing decision-makers and professionals who need to know about trends and developments in IT, telecommunications and office automation.
Indexed: RASB.
Published by: Talentum Oyj, Malminkatu 30, PO Box 920, Helsinki, 00101, Finland. TEL 358-240-4240, FAX 358-240-424130, timo.tolsa@talentum.fi, info@talentum.fi, http://www.tietoviikko.fi, http://www.talentum.fi. Ed. Kauko Ollilla TEL 358-020-4424369. Adv. contact Sanna Araviita TEL 358-40-3424230. B&W page EUR 4,880, color page EUR 7,280; trim 365 x 253. Circ: 41,000 (controlled).

TOBA SHOSEN KOTO SENMON GAKKO KIYO/TOBA NATIONAL COLLEGE OF MARITIME TECHNOLOGY. ANNUAL REPORTS. see *TRANSPORTATION—Ships And Shipping*

004 USA
HF5548 CODEN: WPITE8
TODAY (BOSTON, 1977); the journal of work process improvement. Text in English. 1977. bi-m. USD 65 foreign (effective 1999). adv. bk.rev. charts; illus.; tr.lit. cum.index 1977-1996. back issues avail. **Document type:** *Trade.* **Description:** Provides in-depth articles on topics such as applications of optical character recognition, magnetic ink character recognition, image and voice recognition and the other automated data technologies.
Former titles: Work Process Improvement Today (1073-2233); Remittance and Document Processing Today; Recognition Technologies Today (0883-5594)
Indexed: CompC, Inspec.
—BLDSC (8859.720829), AskIEEE, CASDDS, IE, ingenta.
Published by: Association for Work Process Improvement, 225 E 36th St Ste 40, New York, NY 10016. TEL 212-683-2489, FAX 212-685-3985, myoung@tawpi.org, http://www.tawpi.org. Ed., Pub., Adv. contact Mark Young. R&P W Schadt. Circ: 10,000.

004 ISL ISSN 1021-724X
TOELVUMAL; timarit Skyrslutaeknifelags Islands. Text in Icelandic. 1976. bi-m. membership. adv. bk.rev. index. **Document type:** *Trade.* **Description:** Directed to data processing professionals, computer users and computer enthusiasts.
Published by: Skyrslutaeknifelag Islands/Icelandic Society for Information Processing, Laugavegi 178, Reykjavik, 105, Iceland. TEL 354-553-2460, FAX 354-520-7171, sky@sky.is, http://www.sky.is. Ed. Einar H Reynis. R&P, Adv. contact Svanhildur Johannesdottir. Circ: 1,100.

004 330 USA
TOP TECH NEWS. Text in English. d. **Document type:** *Newsletter, Trade.*
Media: E-mail.
Published by: NewsFactor Network, 21700 Oxnard St, Ste 2040, Woodland Hills, CA 91367. TEL 818-593-2200, FAX 818-593-2203, http://www.newsfactor.com/. Pub. Richard Kern.

004 CAN ISSN 0833-3033
TORONTO COMPUTES. Text in English. 1984. m. CND 29.95 domestic; CND 75 in United States; CND 135 elsewhere (effective 1999). adv. bk.rev. **Document type:** *Newspaper, Consumer.* **Description:** Offers news, features, reviews and opinions for consumers of low-end desktop computer hardware and software.
Related titles: Online - full text ed.
Published by: Canada Computer Paper Inc., 625 Church St 6th Fl, Toronto, ON M4Y 2GI, Canada. TEL 416-588-6818, FAX 416-588-4110, http://www.torontocomputes.com. Ed. Lara King. R&P Mara Gulens. Adv. contact Frank Houston. Circ: 110,000 (controlled).

621.39 ITA
TRADE NEWS; news magazine per dealer, VAR, superstore e system integrator. Text in Italian. 1995. m. (10/yr.). adv. **Document type:** *Trade.* **Description:** Presents information about dealers, var, distributors, software houses, system integrators, franchisess and superstores.
Indexed: BrArAb.
Published by: Gruppo Editoriale J C E, Via Patecchio 2, Milan, MI 20141, Italy. TEL 39-02-57316011, FAX 39-02-57316291, info@jce.it, http://www.jce.it. Ed. Luisella Acquati. Circ: 14,800.

004 USA ISSN 1081-1109
TRI-CITY COMPUTING MAGAZINE; the Capital District's monthly computer connection. Text in English. 1994. m. USD 21. adv. bk.rev.; software rev. **Document type:** *Consumer.* **Description:** Informs computer users in the NY tri-state, NY region about industry news, local clubs and bulletin boards, and area events.
Related titles: Online - full text ed.
Published by: A J A Consulting, 5208 W Calavar Rd, Glendale, AZ 85306-4818. TEL 518-446-1944, tricity@albany.net, http://www.albany.net/~tricity/mast.html. Ed. Anthony J Ardito. Pub. Josephine Soto. R&P Anthony Ardito. Adv. contact Kevin Kiernan. Circ: 50,000.

004 USA ISSN 1542-0256
TROUBLESHOOTING & REFERENCE GUIDE FOR COMPUTER SUPPORT PROFESSIONALS. Text in English. 2001. a. USD 20 newsstand/cover (effective 2002).
Formerly (until 2002): Technician's Troubleshooting & Reference Guide for A+ Professionals
—CCC.
Published by: Element K Journals (Subsidiary of: Eli Research, Inc.), 500 Canal View Blvd, Rochester, NY 14623. TEL 585-240-7301, 800-223-8720, 877-203-5248, FAX 585-292-4392, http://www.elementkjournals.com.

621.39 TUR ISSN 1300-0632
TK1 CODEN: ELEKF8
➤ **TURKISH JOURNAL OF ELECTRICAL ENGINEERING AND COMPUTER SCIENCES.** Text and summaries in English; Abstracts in Turkish. 1993. 3/yr. USD 90 (effective 2005). abstr.; bibl.; charts; illus.; stat. **Document type:** *Journal, Academic/Scholarly.*
Formerly (until 1994): Elektrik - Doga Turkish Journal of Electrical Engineering and Computer Sciences
Related titles: Online - full text ed.: ISSN 1303-6203. free (effective 2005) (from EBSCO Publishing).
Indexed: ChemAb, CompLI, Englnd, Inspec.
—BLDSC (3710.750000), AskIEEE, CISTI.
Published by: Scientific and Technical Research Council of Turkey - TUBITAK/Turkiye Bilimsel ve Teknik Arastirma Kurumu, Ataturk Bulvari No. 221, Kavaklidere, Ankara, 06100, Turkey. TEL 90-312-468-5300, FAX 90-312-4276677, TELEX 46830 BTAK TR, bdym@tubitak.gov.tr, http://journals.tubitak.gov.tr/elektrik/index.php, http://www.tubitak.gov.tr. Ed. Kemal Leblebicioglu. Circ: 1,000.
Co-sponsor: Chamber of Electrical Engineers/Elektrik Muhendisleri Odasi.

004 MEX
U A M - AZCAPOTZALCO. COORDINACION DE SERVICIOS DE COMPUTO. BOLETIN. Text in Spanish. irreg. back issues avail.
Related titles: Online - full text ed.
Published by: Universidad Autonoma Metropolitana - Azcapotzalco, Departamento de Humanidades, Ave. San PABLO 180, Col Reynosa Tamaulipas, Mexico City, DF 02200, Mexico. TEL 52-5-382-5000, boletin@hp9000al.uam.mx, http://www-azc.uam.mx/boletin.htm/.

004 USA
U I U C D C S. REPORT SERIES. Text in English. irreg.
Indexed: Inspec.
Published by: University of Illinois at Urbana-Champaign, Department of Computer Science, 1304 W Springfield Ave, Urbana, IL 61801. TEL 217-333-3426, FAX 217-333-3501, ftp.cs.uiuc.edu:/pub/dept/tech_reports, http://www.cs.uiuc.edu.
Subscr. to: University of Illinois at Urbana Champaign, Engineering Documents Center, 155 Grainger Engineering Library, 1301 W Springfield Ave, Urbana, IL 61801.

004 GBR
THE U K DATAWAREHOUSING MARKET PERFORMANCE REPORT. Text in English. 1990. a. GBP 795 per issue (effective 2000). **Document type:** *Trade.* **Description:** Targeted at experienced users and readers who must know and understand how the market is developing.
Published by: Wharton Information Systems, 11 Beaumont Ave, Richmond, Surrey TW9 2HE, United Kingdom. TEL 44-20-8332-1120, n_wharton.compuserve.com. Ed. Andrea Wharton. Pub. Keith Wharton.

004 FRA ISSN 1292-3834
UNIVERS MACWORLD. Text in French. 1992. m. (11/yr.). adv. **Document type:** *Magazine, Consumer.* **Description:** Provides information on events and developments in the Mac world.
Formerly (until 1998): Univers Mac (1161-3157)
Published by: Editions Pressimage, 5-7 rue Raspail, Montreuil, Cedex 93108, France. TEL 33-1-49886363, FAX 33-1-49886368, umac@pressimage.fr. Ed. Bernard Le Du. adv.: color page USD 4,563; trim 210 x 285. Circ: 55,000.

UNIVERSITATEA DE VEST DIN TIMISOARA. ANALELE. SERIA MATEMATICA - INFORMATICA. see *MATHEMATICS*

UNIVERSITATEA DE VEST DIN TIMISOARA. SECTIA MATEMATICA INFORMATICA. SEMINARUL DE INFORMATICA SI MATEMATICI COMPUTATIONALE. see *MATHEMATICS*

004 HUN ISSN 0138-9491
QA297.A63
UNIVERSITATIS SCIENTIARUM BUDAPESTINENSIS DE ROLANDO EOTVOS NOMINATAE. ANNALES. SECTIO COMPUTATORICA. Text in Hungarian. 1978. a.
Indexed: MathR, MathSciNet.
—Linda Hall.
Published by: Eotvos Lorand Tudomanyegyetem, Allam- es Jogtudomanyi Kara/Eotvos Lorand University, Egyetem ter 1-3, Budapest, 1364, Hungary. TEL 1-174-930.

UNIVERSITE LIBRE DE BRUXELLES. CENTRE D'ETUDES DE RECHERCHE OPERATIONNELLE. CAHIERS/OPERATIONS RESEARCH, STATISTICS AND APPLIED MATHEMATICS. see *BUSINESS AND ECONOMICS—Management*

004 CAN ISSN 0829-5425
UNIVERSITY COMPUTING AND INFORMATION SERVICES NEWSLETTER. Text in English. 1967. irreg. looseleaf. adv. bk.rev.
Formerly: Dalhousie University. Computer Centre. Newsletter (0384-8116)
Published by: Dalhousie University, Computing Services, Halifax, NS B3H 3J5, Canada. TEL 902-424-3472. Ed. Ram Raju. Circ: 900.

004 CAN ISSN 0316-4683
UNIVERSITY OF ALBERTA. DEPARTMENT OF COMPUTING SCIENCE. TECHNICAL REPORTS. Text in English. 1965. irreg. CND 5; or on exchange.
Formerly: University of Alberta. Department of Computing Science. Publication (0065-6062)
—CISTI.
Published by: University of Alberta, Department of Computing Science, 221 Athabasca Hall, Edmonton, AB T6G 2E8, Canada. TEL 403-492-5198, FAX 403-492-1071, ftp://ftp.cs.ualberta.ca/pub/techreports/. Circ: 60.

004 CHE ISSN 0940-9580
UNIVERSITY OF FRIBOURG. SERIES IN COMPUTER SCIENCE. Text in English. 1992. irreg., latest vol.2, 1993. **Document type:** *Monographic series, Academic/Scholarly.*
Published by: University of Fribourg, Institut pour l'Automation et la Recherche Operationnelle, Misericorde, Fribourg, 1700, Switzerland. FAX 41-37-219670, Diuf-secr-pe@unifr.ch.

621.39 GBR
UNIVERSITY OF LEEDS. COMPUTING BASED LEARNING UNIT. C B L U TECHNICAL REPORTS. Text in English. irreg.
Formerly (until 2000): University of Leeds. Computing Based Learning Unit. Technical Reports
—BLDSC (3095.694000).
Published by: University of Leeds, School of Computing, Leeds, LS2 9JT, United Kingdom. TEL 44-113-2334626, FAX 44-113-2334635, K.Tait@cbl.leeds.ac.uk, http://www.leeds.ac.uk.

004 GBR ISSN 1361-6153
➤ **UNIVERSITY OF MANCHESTER. DEPARTMENT OF COMPUTER SCIENCE. TECHNICAL REPORT SERIES.** Text in English. 1986. irreg. free. **Document type:** *Monographic series, Academic/Scholarly.* **Description:** Research reprints in computer science.
Related titles: CD-ROM ed.: ISSN 1363-8378; Online - full text ed.
—BLDSC (8724.845000).
Published by: University of Manchester, Department of Computer Science, Oxford Rd, Manchester, Lancs M13 9PL, United Kingdom. TEL 44-161-275-6130, FAX 44-161-275-6236, techreports@cs.man.ac.uk, http://www.cs.man.ac.uk/cstechrep/. Ed., R&P Ulrich Nehmzow TEL 44-161-275-6169. Circ: 100 (controlled).

004 USA
UNIVERSITY OF NEW MEXICO. C I R T NEWSLETTER. (Computer & Information Resources & Technology) Text in English. 1967. 5/yr. free. bk.rev. charts; illus.; stat. index. back issues avail. **Document type:** *Newsletter.* **Description:** Provides general and higher education computer information to the computer operators of the University of New Mexico.
Former titles: University of New Mexico. C S I S Newsletter; University of New Mexico. Computing Center. Newsletter
Published by: University of New Mexico, Computer & Information Resources & Technology, 2701 Campus Blvd, N E, Albuquerque, NM 87131. TEL 505-277-8147, FAX 505-277-8101. Ed. Catherine Luther. Circ: 3,000.

004 GBR
UNIVERSITY OF NEWCASTLE-UPON-TYNE. COMPUTING SCIENCE. TECHNICAL REPORT SERIES. Text in English. 1969. irreg. GBP 30. bibl. reprint service avail. from NTI. **Document type:** *Monographic series.*
Formerly: University of Newcastle-upon-Tyne. Computing Laboratory. Technical Report Series (0963-5068)
Related titles: Microfiche ed.
—BLDSC (8724.920000), ingenta.
Published by: University of Newcastle upon Tyne, Computing Science, Claremont Tower, Newcastle upon Tyne, Tyne and Wear NE1 7RU, United Kingdom. TEL 091-222-8183, FAX 091-222-8232. Ed. I A Stewart. Circ: 112.

UNIVERSITY OF STIRLING. DEPARTMENT OF COMPUTING SCIENCE AND MATHEMATICS. TECHNICAL REPORT. see *MATHEMATICS—Computer Applications*

004 051 SGP
UPLOAD. Text in English. m. **Document type:** *Magazine, Consumer.*
Published by: Blu Inc Media Pte Ltd., 20 Martin Rd, #08-01, Singapore, 239070, Singapore. TEL 65-68794088, FAX 65-67347727, http://www.bluincmedia.com/.

004 SVN ISSN 1318-1882
UPORABNA INFORMATIKA. Text in Slovenian. 1993. q. SIT 17,800 domestic (effective 2005). **Document type:** *Journal, Academic/Scholarly.*
Indexed: Inspec.
Published by: Slovensko Drustvo Informatika, Vozarski pot 12, Ljubljana, 1000, Slovenia. info@drustvo-informatika.si, http://www.drustvo-informatika.si. Ed. Andrej Kovacic. Circ: 700.

004 USA ISSN 0894-5802
HD9696.C63
V A R BUSINESS; technology & business decisions for solutions selling. (Value Added Resellers) Text in English. 1987. bi-w. USD 120 domestic; USD 130 in Canada; USD 170 in Europe; USD 195 in Australasia (effective 2005). adv. **Document type:** *Magazine, Trade.* **Description:** Analyzes key products, technology, and business trends to help readers succeed in selling computer solutions.
Related titles: Online - full text ed.: (from EBSCO Publishing, Gale Group, LexisNexis, O C L C Online Computer Library Center, Inc., ProQuest Information & Learning); Supplement(s): Issues and Trends.
Indexed: ABIn, B&I, C&ISA, CompD, CompI, E&CAJ, IAA, MicrocompInd, SoftBase.
—BLDSC (9146.085000), IE, ingenta. **CCC.**
Published by: C M P Media LLC (Subsidiary of: United News & Media), 600 Community Dr, Manhasset, NY 11030. TEL 516-562-5000, FAX 516-733-8584, gkestin@cmp.com, http://www.varbusiness.com/, http://www.cmp.com. Pub. Robert Demarzo. adv.: B&W page USD 18,730, color page USD 22,755. Circ: 107,000 (controlled).

004 PRT
V D I. (Venda & Distribuicao Informatica) Text in Portuguese. m.
Published by: Investec Media, Ave Joao Crisostomo, 72, Lisbon, 1069-043, Portugal. TEL 351-213-307741, FAX 351-213-540643, assin@mail.fbento.pt, http://www.fbento.pt/FB/.

004 GBR
V N U NEWSWIRE. Text in English. 1995. d. free. adv. bk.rev. back issues avail. **Document type:** *Bulletin.*
Media: Online - full text.
Published by: V N U Business Publications Ltd., VNU House, 32-34 Broadwick St, London, W1A 2HG, United Kingdom. TEL 44-20-7316-9000, FAX 44-20-7316-9440, newswire@vnu.co.uk, http://www.vnu.co.uk. Ed. Jon Lambeth. Pub. Caroline Gabriel. Adv. contact Joseph Hammond Hagan.

004 MEX ISSN 1605-5780
VIRTUALIA. Text in Spanish. 1997. w. **Document type:** *Newspaper, Consumer.*
Media: Online - full text. **Related titles:** ♦ Supplement to: La Jornada (Online Edition). ISSN 1563-7476.
Published by: Jornada, FRANCISCO PETRARCA 118, Col Chapultepec Morales, Mexico City, DF 11570, Mexico. TEL 52-5-262-4300, FAX 52-5-262-4356, jornada@condor.dgsca.unam.mx, http://www.virtualia.com.mx/.

004 USA ISSN 1537-002X
VISUAL STUDIO MAGAZINE. Text in English. m. USD 27.95 (effective 2001). adv. **Document type:** *Magazine, Consumer.*
Indexed: CompLI, MicrocompInd.
—IE.
Published by: Fawcette Technical Publications, 2600 S. El Camino Real., Ste. 300, San Mateo, CA 94403-2381. TEL 800-848-5523, customerservice@fawcette.com, http://www.vbpj.com/, http://www.fawcette.com. Ed. Patrick Meader.

004 GRC ISSN 1109-2750
W S E A S TRANSACTIONS ON COMPUTERS. (World Scientific and Engineering Academy and Society) Text in English. 2002. q. EUR 100 to individuals; EUR 200 to institutions (effective 2005). **Document type:** *Journal, Academic/Scholarly.*
Indexed: BrCerAb, C&ISA, CerAb, CorrAb, E&CAJ, IAA, M&TEA, METADEX, WAA.
—BLDSC (9364.918500).
Published by: World Scientific and Engineering Academy and Society, Ag Ioannou Theologou 17-23, Zographou, Athens 15773, Greece. TEL 30-210-7473313, FAX 30-210-7473314, http://www.wseas.org. Ed. N Mastorakis.

W S E A S TRANSACTIONS ON SYSTEMS. (World Scientific and Engineering Academy and Society) see *MATHEMATICS*

004.678 FRA ISSN 1295-697X
WEB MAGAZINE. Text in French. 1999. m. **Description:** Features news and information on Internet and CD-Rom content.
Related titles: Online - full content ed.: Web Magazine.
Published by: Prisma Presse, 6 rue Daru, Paris, 75379, France. TEL 33-1-56994700, FAX 33-1-56994740, http://www.lewebmagazine.com. Eds. Ali Laidi, Yves Guittard.
Subscr. to: Service Abonnements, B 140, Sainte Genevieve Cedex 60732, France. TEL 33-3-44625202.

004 USA
▼ **WEBLOGIC PRO.** Text in English. 2004 (May). bi-m. USD 99; USD 9.99 newsstand/cover; free to qualified personnel (effective 2005). adv. **Document type:** *Magazine, Trade.* **Description:** Provides solutions for developers, architects, and administrators.
Published by: Fawcette Technical Publications, 2600 S. El Camino Real., Ste. 300, San Mateo, CA 94403-2381. TEL 800-848-5523, customerservice@fawcette.com, http://www.weblogicpro.com, http://www.fawcette.com. adv.: B&W page USD 1,800, color page USD 2,600; trim 7.875 x 10.875. Circ: 12,000.

004 USA
WHAT'S NEW (PISCATAWAY). Text in English. 1999. m. (Dec/Jan and Jul/Aug issues combined). free. **Document type:** *Newsletter, Trade.* **Description:** Informs about IEEE's library-related activities, policies, periodicals releases and technical updates.
Media: E-mail.
Published by: Institute of Electrical and Electronics Engineers, Inc., 445 Hoes Ln, Piscataway, NJ 08854-1331. TEL 908-981-0060, FAX 908-981-9667, customer.service@ieee.org, http://www.ieee.org/whats-new.

004 USA
▼ **WIDE OPEN.** Text in English. 2004. bi-m. USD 59.70 domestic; USD 83.95 foreign (effective 2004). **Document type:** *Magazine, Trade.* **Description:** Provides technical information and editorials on open source development in both the enterprise and customer markets.
Published by: Red Hat, Inc., 1801 Varsity Dr, Raleigh, NC 27606. TEL 919-754-3700, 888-733-4281, FAX 919-754-3701, http://www.wideopen.com/, http://www.redhat.com/.

004 USA
▼ **WINSTORAGE.** Text in English. 2005. q. **Document type:** *Magazine, Trade.* **Description:** Serves enterprise IT professionals responsible for purchasing and managing storage technologies for Windows-based enterprise systems.
Published by: TechTarget, 117 Kendrick St, Ste 800, Needham, MA 02494. TEL 781-657-1000, 888-274-4111, FAX 781-657-1100, info@techtarget.com, http://www.techtarget.com/. Circ: 30,000 (controlled).

WIRED. see *SOCIOLOGY*

004 621.381 USA
WORKSHOP ON HIGH PERFORMANCE ELECTRON DEVICES FOR MICROWAVE AND OPTOELECTRONIC APPLICATIONS. Text in English. a. USD 162; USD 81 to members (effective 2004). **Document type:** *Proceedings, Trade.*
Indexed: EngInd.
Published by: Institute of Electrical and Electronics Engineers, Inc., 3 Park Ave, 17th Fl, New York, NY 10016-5997. TEL 212-419-7900, 800-678-4333, FAX 212-752-4929, customer.service@ieee.org, http://www.ieee.org.

004 SGP
WORLD SCIENTIFIC SERIES IN COMPUTER SCIENCE. Text in English. 1986. irreg., latest vol.47, 1998, Aug. price varies. **Document type:** *Monographic series, Academic/Scholarly.*
Formerly (until vol.21): Series in Computer Science
Indexed: ZentMath.
—BLDSC (9360.004000).
Published by: World Scientific Publishing Co. Pte. Ltd., 5 Toh Tuck Link, Singapore, 596224, Singapore. TEL 65-466-5775, FAX 65-467-7667, wspc@wspc.com.sg, series@wspc.com.sg, http://www.wspc.com.sg/books/series/wsscs_series.shtml, http://www.worldscientific.com. **Dist. by:** World Scientific Publishing Co., Inc., 1060 Main St, River Edge, NJ 07661. TEL 201-487-9655, 800-227-7562, FAX 201-487-9656, 888-977-2665; World Scientific Publishing Ltd., 57 Shelton St, London WC2H 9HE, United Kingdom. TEL 44-20-78360888, FAX 44-20-78362020.

004 GBR ISSN 1363-9889
WORLDWIDE COMPUTER PRODUCTS NEWS. Text in English. 1995. m. GBP 50, USD 170 (effective 1999). **Document type:** *Trade.* **Description:** Monitors what new products are coming into the market within the competitive, fast-moving computer sector.
Media: Online - full text (from bigchalk, Gale Group, LexisNexis).
Indexed: CompD.
Published by: M2 Communications Ltd., PO Box 475, Coventry, W Mids CV1 2ZW, United Kingdom. TEL 44-1203-634700, FAX 44-1203-634144, M2PW@m2.com, http://www.m2.com. Ed. Darren Ingram. **Dist. in N. America by:** Publications Resource Group, 121 Union St., Box 792, North Adams, MA 01247. TEL 413-664-6185, FAX 413-664-9343.

004 USA
X S P ADVISOR. Text in English. w. free domestic to qualified personnel. **Document type:** *Newsletter, Trade.*
Published by: International Data Corp., 5 Speen St, Box 9015, Framingham, MA 01701. TEL 508-872-8200, FAX 508-935-4271, lseymour@idc.com, http://www.idc.com. Ed. Louise Seymour.

004 USA
Y2K NEWS MAGAZINE. Text in English. bi-w. USD 44.95; USD 56.95 foreign (effective 1999). adv. back issues avail. **Description:** Informs about the year 2000 problem.
Published by: Wilson Publications, LLC, 20 Our Way Dr, Crossville, TN 38555. TEL 888-925-9925, FAX 931-484-8825, info@2knews.com, http://www.y2knews.com/. Ed. James T Wilson. Pub. Tim Wilson. Adv. contact Carol Thompson.

C

004 USA ISSN 0894-4326
YANKEE INGENUITY★. Text in English. irreg.
Published by: Yankee Group, 31 Saint James Ave, Boston, MA 02116-4101. TEL 617-367-1000.

004 USA ISSN 0896-8470
CODEN: YPCSEV
YOURDON PRESS COMPUTING SERIES. Text in English. irreg. price varies. **Document type:** *Monographic series.*
Indexed: Inspec.
Published by: Prentice Hall, One Lake St, Upper Saddle River, NJ 07458. TEL 800-282-0693, http://vig.pearsoned.com/store/.

003 SCG ISSN 0354-0243
➤ **YUGOSLAV JOURNAL OF OPERATIONS RESEARCH**; an international journal dealing with theoretical and computational aspects of operations research, systems science, and management science. Text in English. 1991. s-a. (2 nos./vol.). USD 60 (effective 2001). adv. bk.rev. 160 p./no.; back issues avail. **Document type:** *Academic/Scholarly.* **Description:** Deals with all aspects of operations research, systems science, and management science.
Related titles: E-mail ed.; Online - full text ed.
Indexed: CCMJ, EngInd, IAOP, MathR, MathSciNet, RefZh, ZentMath.
—BLDSC (9421.659370), Ei, IE, ingenta.
Published by: (Laboratory for Operations Research YUG), University of Belgrade, Faculty of Organizational Sciences, Jove Ilica 154, Belgrade, 11000. TEL 381-11-3950800, FAX 381-11-461221, yujor@fon.bg.ac.yu, verakov@fon.fon.bg.ac.yu, http://www.yujor.fon.bg.ac.yu. Eds. Jovo Vuleta, Radivoj Petrovic, Vera Kovacevic-Vujcic. adv.: B&W page USD 100. Circ: 750. **Subscr. to:** Jugoslovenska Knjiga, Terazije 27-II, Belgrade 11000, Yugoslavia. TEL 381-11-625970, FAX 38-11-3231-079.

621.39 USA
Z D NET ANCHORDESK. Text in English. 1996. 3/w.
Media: Online - full text.
Published by: CNET Networks, Inc., 235 Second St, San Francisco, CA 94105. info@anchordesk.com, Janet.Chen@cnet.com., http://www.anchordesk.com, http://www.cnet.com.

004 ITA ISSN 0392-8497
ZEROUNO; mensile di informatica. Text in Italian. 1981. m. (11/yr.). EUR 22.62 (effective 2004). adv. **Document type:** *Magazine, Consumer.* **Description:** Covers client-server technology, databases and middleware.
Published by: Arnoldo Mondadori Editore SpA, Via Mondadori 1, Segrate, 20090, Italy. TEL 39-02-66814363, FAX 39-030-3198412, zerouno@mondadori.it, http://www.mondadori.com. Circ: 18,000 (controlled).

004 CZE ISSN 1212-8554
ZIVE. Text in Czech. 1996. d. adv. **Document type:** *Consumer.*
Media: Online - full content.
Published by: Computer Press a.s., Pod Vinici 23, Prague 4, 143 11, Czech Republic. TEL 420-2-225273930, FAX 420-2-225273934, webmaster@cpress.cz, http://www.zive.cz, http://www.cpress.cz. Ed. Jan Kunes. Adv. contact Jan Vobecky.

003 DEU ISSN 1619-4500
▼ ➤ **4 O R**; quarterly journal of the Belgian, French and Italian operations research societies. (Operations Research) Text in English. 2003. q. EUR 180 combined subscription to institutions print & online eds. (effective 2005). adv. back issues avail. **Document type:** *Journal, Academic/Scholarly.* **Description:** Publishes articles and research on theories and applications involving operations research.
Incorporates (1970-2002): Ricerca Operativa (0390-8127)
Related titles: Online - full content ed.: ISSN 1614-2411; Online - full text ed.: (from EBSCO Publishing, Springer LINK, Swets Information Services).
Indexed: MathR, MathSciNet.
—BLDSC (9628.850000), IE. **CCC.**
Published by: Springer-Verlag (Subsidiary of: Springer Science+Business Media), Tiergartenstr 17, Heidelberg, 69121, Germany. TEL 49-6221-3450, FAX 49-6221-345229, http://link.springer.de/link/service/journals/10288/. Eds. Denis Bouyssou, Frank Plastria, Silvano Martello. Adv. contact Stephan Kroeck TEL 49-30-827875739. **Subscr. in the Americas to:** Springer-Verlag New York, Inc., Journal Fulfillment, PO Box 2485, Secaucus, NJ 07096-2485. TEL 800-777-4643, 201-348-4033, FAX 201-348-4505, journals@springer-ny.com, http://www.springer-ny.com; **Subscr. to:** Springer GmbH Auslieferungsgesellschaft, Haberstr 7, Heidelberg 69126, Germany. TEL 49-6221-345-0, FAX 49-6221-345-4229, subscriptions@springer.de.

004 USA
21ST, THE V X M NETWORK. Text in English. 1996. bi-m. back issues avail. **Description:** Covers technology convergence, including computers, the Web, molecular computing, and more.
Media: Online - full text.
Published by: V X M Technologies, Inc., PO Box 6301, Boston, MA 02114. TEL 617-742-4422, FAX 617-248-8886, 21st@vxm.com, http://www.vxm.com. Ed. Franco Vitaliano.

24 X 7. see *HEALTH FACILITIES AND ADMINISTRATION*

COMPUTERS—Abstracting, Bibliographies, Statistics

016.004 USA ISSN 1089-5310
QA75.5
A C M ELECTRONIC GUIDE TO COMPUTING LITERATURE; bibliographic listing, author index, keyword index, category index, proper noun subject index, reviewer index, source index. Text in English. 1964. q. USD 499 to non-members; USD 175 to members (effective 2004). illus. back issues avail.; reprints avail. **Document type:** *Abstract/Index.* **Description:** Contains over 24,000 entries and listings for over 34,000 authors.
Former titles (until 1998): A C M Guide to Computing Literature (0149-1199); (until 1977): Bibliography and Subject Index of Current Computing Literature (0149-1202)
Media: CD-ROM. **Related titles:** Online - full text ed.
—IE, Linda Hall.
Published by: Association for Computing Machinery, Inc., 1515 Broadway, 17th Fl, New York, NY 10036-5701. TEL 212-626-0500, 212-626-0520, 800-342-6626, FAX 212-869-0481, sigs@acm.org, usacm@acm.org, http://www.acm.org. Ed. Aaron Finerman. Circ: 2,200.

003.021 EGY
ANNUAL CONFERENCE ON STATISTICS, COMPUTER SCIENCE AND OPERATIONS RESEARCH. PROCEEDINGS. Text and summaries in Arabic, English. a. (in 5 vols.). USD 50 (effective 1999). back issues avail. **Document type:** *Proceedings.* **Description:** Contains proceedings regarding the conferences held at Cairo University on Computer Science and Operations Research.
Published by: Cairo University, Institute of Statistical Studies and Research, Tharwat St., Orman, Cairo, Egypt. FAX 20-2-3482533. Ed. Ibrahim Farag Eissa.

621.3822021 AUS ISSN 1443-5152
AUSTRALIA. BUREAU OF STATISTICS. BUSINESS USE OF INFORMATION TECHNOLOGY. Text in English. 1994. irreg. AUD 21 (effective 2003). **Document type:** *Government.*
Published by: Australian Bureau of Statistics, PO Box 10, Belconnen, ACT 2616, Australia. TEL 61-2-6252-5249, FAX 61-2-6252-6778, http://www.abs.gov.au.

621.3822021 AUS
AUSTRALIA. BUREAU OF STATISTICS. BUSINESS USE OF INFORMATION TECHNOLOGY, PRELIMINARY. Text in English. 1998. irreg. AUD 15 (effective 2003). **Document type:** *Government.*
Published by: Australian Bureau of Statistics, PO Box 10, Belconnen, ACT 2616, Australia. TEL 61-2-6252-5249, FAX 61-2-6252-6778, http://www.abs.gov.au.

004.021 AUS
AUSTRALIA. BUREAU OF STATISTICS. COMPUTING SERVICES INDUSTRY, AUSTRALIA. Text in English. 1987. irreg., latest 1998. AUD 17.50 (effective 2003). **Document type:** *Government.* **Description:** Includes industry analysis, selected performance ratios, income and expenditure, employment, and state information.
Published by: Australian Bureau of Statistics, PO Box 10, Belconnen, ACT 2616, Australia. TEL 61-2-6252-5249, FAX 61-2-6252-6778, http://www.abs.gov.au.

621.3822021 AUS
AUSTRALIA. BUREAU OF STATISTICS. GOVERNMENT USE OF INFORMATION TECHNOLOGY, AUSTRALIA. Text in English. 1994. irreg., latest 2002. AUD 18 (effective 2003). **Document type:** *Government.*
Formerly: Australia. Bureau of Statistics. Government Information Technology, Australia
Published by: Australian Bureau of Statistics, PO Box 10, Belconnen, ACT 2616, Australia. TEL 61-2-6252-5249, FAX 61-2-6252-6778, http://www.abs.gov.au.

621.3822021 AUS ISSN 1329-4067
AUSTRALIA. BUREAU OF STATISTICS. HOUSEHOLD USE OF INFORMATION TECHNOLOGY, AUSTRALIA. Text in English. 1994. a. AUD 19 (effective 2003). **Document type:** *Government.* **Description:** Includes numbers and types of computers used, types of software and peripheral computer equipment used, expenditure on selected information technologies and source of computer training.
Published by: Australian Bureau of Statistics, PO Box 10, Belconnen, ACT 2616, Australia. TEL 61-2-6252-5249, FAX 61-2-6252-6778, http://www.abs.gov.au.

621.3822021 AUS ISSN 1442-8490
AUSTRALIA. BUREAU OF STATISTICS. INFORMATION TECHNOLOGY, AUSTRALIA. Text in English. 1993. irreg., latest 1996. AUD 23 (effective 2003). **Document type:** *Government.*
Published by: Australian Bureau of Statistics, PO Box 10, Belconnen, ACT 2616, Australia. TEL 61-2-6252-5249, FAX 61-2-6252-6778, http://www.abs.gov.au.

621.3822021 AUS
AUSTRALIA. BUREAU OF STATISTICS. INFORMATION TECHNOLOGY, AUSTRALIA, PRELIMINARY. Text in English. 1996. irreg., latest 1998. AUD 15.50 (effective 2003). **Document type:** *Government.*
Published by: Australian Bureau of Statistics, PO Box 10, Belconnen, ACT 2616, Australia. TEL 61-2-6252-5249, FAX 61-2-6252-6778, http://www.abs.gov.au.

384.33021 AUS ISSN 1443-5063
AUSTRALIA. BUREAU OF STATISTICS. INTERNET ACTIVITY, AUSTRALIA. Text in English. 2000. s-a. AUD 21 (effective 2003). **Document type:** *Government.*
Published by: Australian Bureau of Statistics, PO Box 10, Belconnen, ACT 2616, Australia. TEL 61-2-6252-5249, FAX 61-2-6252-6778, http://www.abs.gov.au.

621.3822021 AUS
AUSTRALIA. BUREAU OF STATISTICS. OCCASIONAL PAPER: INNOVATION, PRODUCTIVITY AND PROFITABILITY OF AUSTRALIAN MANUFACTURERS. Text in English. 1994. irreg. AUD 17 (effective 1998). **Document type:** *Government.*
Published by: Australian Bureau of Statistics, PO Box 10, Belconnen, ACT 2616, Australia. TEL 61-2-6252-5249, FAX 61-2-6252-6778, http://www.abs.gov.au.

621.3822021 AUS ISSN 1441-4813
AUSTRALIA. BUREAU OF STATISTICS. USE OF INFORMATION TECHNOLOGY ON FARMS, AUSTRALIA. Text in English. 2000. a. AUD 20 (effective 2003).
Published by: Australian Bureau of Statistics, PO Box 10, Belconnen, ACT 2616, Australia. TEL 61-2-6252-5249, FAX 61-2-6252-6778, http://www.abs.gov.au.

621.3822021 AUS
AUSTRALIA. BUREAU OF STATISTICS. USE OF INFORMATION TECHNOLOGY ON FARMS, AUSTRALIA, PRELIMINARY. Text in English. 1999. irreg. AUD 15.50 (effective 2003).
Published by: Australian Bureau of Statistics, PO Box 10, Belconnen, ACT 2616, Australia. TEL 61-2-6252-5249, FAX 61-2-6252-6778, http://www.abs.gov.au.

005.1021 AUS
AUSTRALIA. BUREAU OF STATISTICS. YEAR 2000 PROBLEM, AUSTRALIA. Text in English. 1998. irreg., latest 1999. AUD 15 (effective 2003). **Document type:** *Government.*
Published by: Australian Bureau of Statistics, PO Box 10, Belconnen, ACT 2616, Australia. TEL 61-2-6252-5249, FAX 61-2-6252-6778, http://www.abs.gov.au.

005.1021 AUS
AUSTRALIA. BUREAU OF STATISTICS. YEAR 2000 PROBLEM, AUSTRALIA, PRELIMINARY. Text in English. 1998. irreg., latest 1999. AUD 15 (effective 2003). **Document type:** *Government.*
Published by: Australian Bureau of Statistics, PO Box 10, Belconnen, ACT 2616, Australia. TEL 61-2-6252-5249, FAX 61-2-6252-6778, http://www.abs.gov.au.

016.0053 CAN ISSN 1181-9847
CANADA. STATISTICS CANADA. SOFTWARE DEVELOPMENT AND COMPUTER SERVICE INDUSTRY/CANADA. STATISTIQUE CANADA. INDUSTRIE DE LA PRODUCTION DE LOGICIELS ET DES SERVICES INFORMATIQUES. Text in English, French. 1972. a. CND 33; USD 33 foreign. charts. **Document type:** *Government.* **Description:** Supplies the principal statistics for businesses providing computer services as a major activity.
Formerly (until 1991): Computer Service Industry (0318-4064)
Related titles: Microform ed.: (from MML).
Published by: Statistics Canada, Operations and Integration Division, Circulation Management, Jean Talon Bldg, 2 C12, Tunney's Pasture, Ottawa, ON K1A 0T6, Canada. TEL 613-951-7277, 800-267-6677, FAX 613-951-1584, http://www.statcan.ca.

003.3021 USA ISSN 0361-0918
QA276.A1 CODEN: CSSCDB
➤ **COMMUNICATIONS IN STATISTICS: SIMULATION AND COMPUTATION.** Text in English. 1972. q. GBP 959, USD 1,599 combined subscription to institutions print & online eds. (effective 2006). adv. illus. Index. reprint service avail. from PSC. **Document type:** *Journal, Academic/Scholarly.* **Description:** Deals with problems at the interface of statistics and computer science.
Supersedes in part (with vol.5, 1976): Communications in Statistics (0090-3272)
Related titles: Microform ed.: (from RPI); Online - full text ed.: ISSN 1532-4141. GBP 921, USD 1,519 to institutions (effective 2006) (from EBSCO Publishing, O C L C Online Computer Library Center, Inc., Swets Information Services).
Indexed: ASCA, Biostat, CCMJ, CIS, CMCI, CompLI, CurCont, EngInd, ISR, Inspec, JCQM, MathR, MathSciNet, ORMS, QC&AS, RASB, RefZh, SCI, SSCI, ST&MA, ZentMath.
—BLDSC (3363.431000), AskIEEE, CISTI, Ei, IDS, IE, Infotrieve, ingenta, Linda Hall. **CCC.**
Published by: Taylor & Francis Inc. (Subsidiary of: Taylor & Francis Group), 325 Chestnut St, Ste 800, Philadelphia, PA 19016. TEL 215-625-8900, 800-354-1420, FAX 215-625-2940, info@taylorandfrancis.com, http://www.tandf.co.uk/journals/titles/03610918.asp, http://www.taylorandfrancis.com. Ed. N Balakrishnan. Adv. contact Sharon Moran. B&W page USD 600. Circ: 725.

016.0063 USA ISSN 1538-6953
HD38.7
COMPETITIVE INTELLIGENCE RESOURCES; an internet miniguide. Text in English. 2002. a. USD 95 newsstand/cover (effective 2002).
Published by: InternetMiniGuides.com, P.O. Box 220, Marco Island, FL 34146. TEL 941-434-5113, zillman@internetminiguides.com, http://www.internetminiguides.com. Pub. Marcus P. Zillma.

016.51 USA ISSN 0730-6199
Z6653
COMPUMATH CITATION INDEX. Short title: C M C I. Text in English. 1981. 3/yr. USD 1,505 for CD-ROM (effective 2005). cum.index: 1976-80. **Document type:** *Abstract/Index.* **Description:** A multidisciplinary index to the journal literature of computer science, mathematics, applications and chemistry and engineering, plus other related disciplines such as mathematical physics and econometrics.
Related titles: CD-ROM ed.: (from Thomson I S I); Magnetic Tape ed.; Online - full text ed.
Indexed: RASB.
Published by: Thomson I S I (Subsidiary of: Thomson Corporation), 3501 Market St., Philadelphia, PA 19104. TEL 215-386-0100, 800-336-4474, FAX 215-386-2911, sales@isinet.com, http://scientific.thomson.com/products/cmci/, http://www.isinet.com.

016.004 GBR ISSN 0010-4469
Z6654.C17
COMPUTER ABSTRACTS. Text in English. 1957. bi-m. EUR 6,051.24 in Europe; USD 6,029 in North America; AUD 6,799 in Australasia; GBP 4,242.22 in UK & elsewhere (effective 2006). reprint service avail. from PSC. **Document type:** *Abstract/Index.* **Description:** Presents keyworded and classified abstracts from more than 250 English-language periodicals.
Related titles: CD-ROM ed.: ISSN 1356-9821. 1995; Online - full text ed.
—BLDSC (3390.680000). **CCC.**
Published by: Emerald Group Publishing Limited, 60-62 Toller Ln, Bradford, W Yorks BD8 9BY, United Kingdom. TEL 44-1274-777700, FAX 44-1274-785200, infomation@emeraldinsight.com, http://www.emeraldinsight.com/abstracts/ca/index.htm. Ed. Dr. Rob Cameron.

016.004 GBR ISSN 0036-8113
QA76 CODEN: CCABB8
COMPUTER & CONTROL ABSTRACTS. Variant title: INSPEC Section C. Science Abstracts. Section C. Text in English. 1966. m. GBP 1,410, USD 2,400 (effective 2001). adv. abstr.; bibl.; illus. index, cum. index every 4 yrs. reprints avail. **Document type:** *Abstract/Index.* **Description:** Provides abstracts, organized by subjects, of international technological information. Listings include publication details for acquisition purposes, author and number of references cited by the author.
Related titles: CD-ROM ed.; Online - full text ed.: (from CEDOCAR, Data-Star, F I Z Technik, Questel Orbit Inc., SilverPlatter Information, Inc., The Dialog Corporation).
Indexed: ErgAb.
—BLDSC (3393.550000), CASDDS, Linda Hall. **CCC.**
Published by: INSPEC, I.E.E., Michael Faraday House, Six Hills Way, Stevenage, Herts SG1 2AY, United Kingdom. TEL 44-1438-313311, FAX 44-1438-742840, TELEX 825578 IEESTV G, inspec@iee.org.uk, http://www.iee.org.uk. **Subscr. addr. in the US:** INSPEC, Inc., 379 Thornall St, Edison, NJ 08837-2225. TEL 732-321-5575, FAX 732-321-5702.

016.004 USA ISSN 0191-9776
QA76
COMPUTER AND INFORMATION SYSTEMS ABSTRACTS JOURNAL. Text in English. 1962. m. (except Dec.). USD 1,955 combined subscription print & online eds. (effective 2006). adv. bk.rev. abstr.; illus. index on CD-ROM. back issues avail.; reprints avail. **Document type:** *Abstract/Index.* **Description:** International reference publication devoted to complete and comprehensive coverage of the international literature.
Former titles (until 1978): Computer and Information Systems (0010-4507); (until 1969): Information Processing Journal (0362-8973)
Related titles: CD-ROM ed.; Online - full text ed.: ISSN 1555-6441. USD 1,465 (effective 2006).
Indexed: RASB.
—BLDSC (3393.580000), Linda Hall.
Published by: C S A Journal Division (Subsidiary of: Cambridge Information Group), 7200 Wisconsin Ave, Ste 715, Bethesda, MD 20814. TEL 301-961-6798, 800-843-7751, FAX 301-961-6799, journals@csa.com, http://www.csa.com/factsheets/computer-set-c.php. Ed. Esther Hovis. Pub. Ted Caris. **Co-publisher:** Elsevier Engineering Information, Inc.

016.004 USA
QA76
COMPUTER SCIENCE INDEX. Text in English. 1971. q. bk.rev. illus. reprints avail. **Document type:** *Abstract/Index.* **Description:** Bibliography of books, articles, and reports relating to computers and data processing.
Former titles (until Dec.2002): Computer Literature Index (Print Edition) (0270-4846); (until 1980): Quarterly Bibliography of Computers and Data Processing (0048-6132)
Media: Online - full content.
—CCC.
Published by: EBSCO Publishing (Subsidiary of: EBSCO Industries, Inc.), 10 Estes St, PO Box 682, Ipswich, MA 01938-0682. TEL 978-356-6500, 800-653-2726, FAX 978-356-6565, ep@epnet.com, http://www.epnet.com/academic/computersci.asp. **Subscr. to:** Subscription Services, PO Box 1943, Birmingham, AL 35201-1943. TEL 205-991-6600, FAX 205-995-1518.

004.021 MEX ISSN 0185-8114
COMUNIDAD INFORMATICA. Text in Spanish. 1988. q. free or exchange basis. **Document type:** *Government.*
Published by: Instituto Nacional de Estadistica, Geografia e Informatica, Secretaria de Programacion y Presupuesto, Prol. Heroe de Nacozari 2301 Sur, Puerta 11, Acceso, Aguascalientes, 20270, Mexico. TEL 52-4-918-1948, FAX 52-4-918-0739, http://www.inegi.gob.mx. Circ: 500.

016.004 GBR ISSN 0011-3794
QA75.5
CURRENT PAPERS ON COMPUTERS & CONTROL. Abbreviated title: C P C. Text in English. 1969. m. GBP 325, USD 550 (effective 2001). index. **Document type:** *Abstract/Index.* **Description:** Contains author, title, and bibliographic details of papers published in over 4,000 international journals and conference proceedings. Covers the latest research and development and applications in all areas of computing and control.
Published by: INSPEC, I.E.E., Michael Faraday House, Six Hills Way, Stevenage, Herts SG1 2AY, United Kingdom. TEL 44-1438-313311, FAX 44-1438-742840, inspec@iee.org.uk, http://www.iee.org.uk. R&P Michael McCabe TEL 732-321-5575. **Subscr. in the US:** INSPEC, Inc., 379 Thornall St, Edison, NJ 08837-2225. TEL 732-321-5575, FAX 732-321-5702; **Subscr. to:** INSPEC, I E E, Publication Sales Dept., PO Box 96, Stevenage, Herts SG1 2SD, United Kingdom.

CURRENT POPULATION REPORTS: SPECIAL STUDIES. COMPUTER AND INTERNET USE IN THE UNITED STATES. see *POPULATION STUDIES*

016.004 USA
QA75.5 CODEN: COSLEB
ESHAMAN.COM✶. Text in English. 1988. m. bk.rev. **Document type:** *Catalog, Abstract/Index.* **Description:** Provides full text of more than 80 computer industry publications, with abstracts of articles from more than 40 other periodicals and four major newspapers. Also includes product specifications and company information for all sectors of the computer industry.
Former titles (until 2000): Computer Select (1062-8509); (until 1991): Computer Library (1062-8517)
Media: Online - full content. **Related titles:** CD-ROM ed.
—CCC.
Published by: Shaman Corporation, 1849 Sawtelle Blvd., Ste. 543, Los Angeles, CA 90025-7011. TEL 800-677-5003, info@shamancorp.com, http://www.shamancorp.com.

EXECUTIVE REPORT TO THE ELECTRONIC INDUSTRIES. see *ELECTRONICS*

004.021 HUN ISSN 0236-9842
HD9696.C63
HUNGARY. KOZPONTI STATISZTIKAI HIVATAL. SZAMITASTECHNIKAI STATISZTIKAI ZSEBKONYV. Text in Hungarian. 1984. a. HUF 156. stat. **Document type:** *Government.*
Former titles: Hungary. Kozponti Statisztikai Hivatal. Szamitastechnikai Statisztikai Evkonyv (0139-3286); Szamitastechnikai Evkonyv (0133-9559)
Published by: Kozponti Statisztikai Hivatal, Marketing Oszta'ly, Keleti Karoly utca 5-7, Budapest, 1024, Hungary. TEL 36-1-345-6000, FAX 36-1-345-6699, http://www.ksh.hu. Circ: 1,200.

016.0063 DEU
INFORMATIONSDIENST F I Z TECHNIK. BILDERKENNUNG UND -VERARBEITUNG. Variant title: Bilderkennung und -verarbeitung. Text in German. m. EUR 320 (effective 2003). **Document type:** *Journal, Abstract/Index.*
Published by: Fachinformationszentrum Technik e.V., Ostbahnhofstr 13-15, Frankfurt Am Main, 60314, Germany. TEL 49-69-4308213, kundenberatung@fiz-technik.de, http://www.fiz-technik.de.

016.62139 DEU
INFORMATIONSDIENST F I Z TECHNIK. RECHNER UND RECHNERNETZE. Variant title: Rechner und Rechnernetze. Text in German. m. EUR 290 (effective 2003). **Document type:** *Journal, Trade.*
Published by: Fachinformationszentrum Technik e.V., Ostbahnhofstr 13-15, Frankfurt Am Main, 60314, Germany. TEL 49-69-4308213, kundenberatung@fiz-technik.de, http://www.fiz-technik.de.

016.0053 DEU
INFORMATIONSDIENST F I Z TECHNIK. SOFTWARE ENGINEERING. Variant title: Software Engineering. Text in German. 1984. m. EUR 340 (effective 2003). **Document type:** *Journal, Abstract/Index.*
Formerly: Informationsdienst F I Z Technik. System-Software und Software Engineering (0176-5965)
Published by: Fachinformationszentrum Technik e.V., Ostbahnhofstr 13-15, Frankfurt Am Main, 60314, Germany. TEL 49-69-4308213, kundenberatung@fiz-technik.de, http://www.fiz-technik.de.

INFORMATIONSDIENST F I Z TECHNIK. SPRACHERKENNUNG UND -VERARBEITUNG. see *LINGUISTICS—Abstracting, Bibliographies, Statistics*

INSPEC LIST OF JOURNALS AND OTHER SERIAL SOURCES. see *ENGINEERING—Abstracting, Bibliographies, Statistics*

016.003 GBR ISSN 0020-580X
Q500
INTERNATIONAL ABSTRACTS IN OPERATIONS RESEARCH. Text in English. 1961. bi-m. USD 1,085 combined subscription in United States; GBP 680 combined subscription elsewhere (effective 2005); includes print & online eds.. adv. index, cum.index. back issues avail.; reprints avail. **Document type:** *Journal, Abstract/Index.* **Description:** Covers OR, management, decision sciences, IS, industrial engineering and related fields.
Related titles: Online - full text ed.: I A O R Online. ISSN 1476-9352.
—BLDSC (4535.580000), Linda Hall. **CCC.**
Published by: (International Federation of Operational Research Societies), Palgrave Macmillan Ltd. (Subsidiary of: Macmillan Publishers Ltd.), Houndmills, Basingstoke, Hants RG21 6XS, United Kingdom. TEL 44-1256-329242, FAX 44-1256-810526, journal-info@palgrave.com, http://www.iaor-palgrave.com/content/html/index.htm, http://www.palgrave-journals.com/. Ed. David K Smith TEL 44-1392-264478. Pub. David Bull TEL 44-1256-329242. Adv. contact Robert Sloan TEL 44-20-88827199.

629.8021 310 EGY ISSN 1110-7707
INTERNATIONAL CONGRESS FOR STATISTICS, COMPUTER SCIENCE. Text in English. a. **Document type:** *Journal, Academic/Scholarly.*
Published by: Ain Shams University, Scientific Computer Center, Abbasia, Cairo, Egypt. http://derp.sti.sci.eg/data/0352.htm.

C

016.00416 USA
INTERNET & PERSONAL COMPUTING ABSTRACTS (ONLINE EDITION). Text in English. m. index. reprints avail. **Document type:** *Abstract/Index.* **Description:** Abstracts the professional literature discussing personal computers and Internet issues. Includes products announcements, software and hardware reviews, and a buyer's guide.
Media: Online - full content (from SilverPlatter Information, Inc.).
Related titles: Magnetic Tape ed.
Published by: EBSCO Publishing (Subsidiary of: EBSCO Industries, Inc.), 10 Estes St, PO Box 682, Ipswich, MA 01938-0682. TEL 978-356-6500, 800-653-2726, FAX 978-356-6565, ep@epnet.com, http://www.epnet.com/academic/internet&personal.asp, http://www.ebsco.com. **Subscr. to:** Subscription Services, PO Box 1943, Birmingham, AL 35201-1943. TEL 205-991-6600, FAX 205-995-1518.

003.3021 GBR ISSN 0094-9655
QA276.A1 CODEN: JSCSAJ
➤ **JOURNAL OF STATISTICAL COMPUTATION AND SIMULATION.** Text in English. 1972. m. (in 3 vols., 4 nos./vol.). GBP 3,228, USD 4,729 combined subscription to institutions print & online eds. (effective 2006). adv. illus. back issues avail.; reprint service avail. from PSC. **Document type:** *Journal, Academic/Scholarly.* **Description:** Contains papers on computer algorithms related to probability or statistics, studies in statistical inference and implementation of interactive statistical systems.
Related titles: CD-ROM ed.: ISSN 1026-7778. 1995; Microform ed.; Online - full content ed.: ISSN 1563-5163. GBP 3,067, USD 4,493 to institutions (effective 2006); Online - full text ed.: (from EBSCO Publishing, Gale Group, IngentaConnect, O C L C Online Computer Library Center, Inc., Swets Information Services).
Indexed: ASCA, BrCerAb, C&ISA, CCMJ, CIS, CMCI, CerAb, CorrAb, CurCont, E&CAJ, EMA, EngInd, IAA, Inspec, JCQM, M&TEA, MBF, METADEX, MathR, MathSciNet, ST&MA, SolStAb, WAA, ZentMath.
—BLDSC (5066.820000), CISTI, Ei, IE, Infotrieve, ingenta, Linda Hall. **CCC.**
Published by: Taylor & Francis Ltd (Subsidiary of: Taylor & Francis Group), 4 Park Sq, Milton Park, Abingdon, OX14 4RN, United Kingdom. TEL 44-1235-828600, FAX 44-1235-829000, info@tandf.co.uk, http://www.tandf.co.uk/journals/titles/00949655.asp. Ed. Richard Krutchkoff. **Subscr. to:** Journals Customer Service, Rankine Rd, Basingstoke, Hants RG24 8PR, United Kingdom. TEL 44-1256-813000, FAX 44-1256-330245, enquiry@tandf.co.uk.

016.0063 GBR ISSN 0950-477X
Q334
KEY ABSTRACTS - ARTIFICIAL INTELLIGENCE. Text in English. 1975. m. GBP 145, USD 250 (effective 2001). index. **Document type:** *Abstract/Index.* **Description:** Presents abstracts on theory and applications of artificial intelligence, knowledge engineering, and expert systems.
Formerly (until 1987): Key Abstracts - Systems Theory (0306-5553)

Indexed: Inspec.
Published by: INSPEC, I.E.E., Michael Faraday House, Six Hills Way, Stevenage, Herts SG1 2AY, United Kingdom. FAX 44-1438-742840, inspec@iee.org.uk, http://www.iee.org.uk. R&P Michael McCabe TEL 732-321-5575. **Subscr. to:** INSPEC, I E E, Publication Sales Dept., PO Box 96, Stevenage, Herts SG1 2SD, United Kingdom; **US subscr. addr.:** INSPEC, Inc., 379 Thornall St, Edison, NJ 08837-2225. TEL 732-321-5575, FAX 732-321-5702.

016.62989 GBR ISSN 0954-9153
KEY ABSTRACTS - BUSINESS AUTOMATION. Text in English. 1983. m. GBP 145, USD 250 (effective 2001). **Document type:** *Abstract/Index.*
Former titles: I T Focus (INSPEC, Section D); Information Technology Update for Managers; (until 1984): I T Focus (0264-9152)
Related titles: CD-ROM ed.: (from The Dialog Corporation); Online - full text ed.: (from CEDOCAR, Data-Star, F I Z Technik, Questel Orbit Inc., The Dialog Corporation).
—Linda Hall.
Published by: INSPEC, I.E.E., Michael Faraday House, Six Hills Way, Stevenage, Herts SG1 2AY, United Kingdom. TEL 44-1438-313311, FAX 44-1438-742840, inspec@iee.org.uk, http://www.iee.org.uk. R&P Michael McCabe TEL 732-321-5575.

016.0046 GBR ISSN 0950-4788
KEY ABSTRACTS - COMPUTER COMMUNICATIONS AND STORAGE. Text in English. 1987. m. GBP 145, USD 250 (effective 2001). index. **Document type:** *Abstract/Index.* **Description:** Covers multiprocessor systems, modern storage media, including optical disc, interfaces, networks, and network equipment.
Published by: INSPEC, I.E.E., Michael Faraday House, Six Hills Way, Stevenage, Herts SG1 2AY, United Kingdom. TEL 44-1438-313311, FAX 44-1438-742840, inspec@iee.org.uk, http://www.iee.org.uk. R&P Michael McCabe TEL 732-321-5575. **Subscr. to:** Publication Sales Dept., .PO Box 96, Stevenage, Herts SG1 25D, United Kingdom

016.004 GBR ISSN 0950-4796
KEY ABSTRACTS - COMPUTING IN ELECTRONICS & POWER. Text in English. 1987. m. GBP 145, USD 250 (effective 2001). index. **Document type:** *Abstract/Index.* **Description:** Covers computer applications in communications, electrical engineering, electronics, and power engineering.
Published by: INSPEC, I.E.E., Michael Faraday House, Six Hills Way, Stevenage, Herts SG1 2AY, United Kingdom. TEL 44-1438-313311, FAX 44-1438-742840, inspec@iee.org.uk, http://www.iee.org.uk. R&P Michael McCabe TEL 732-321-5575. **Subscr. to:** INSPEC, I E E, Publication Sales Dept., PO Box 96, Stevenage, Herts SG1 2SD, United Kingdom; **US subscr. addr.:** INSPEC, Inc., 379 Thornall St, Edison, NJ 08837-2225. TEL 732-321-5575, FAX 732-321-5702.

016.62989 GBR ISSN 0960-6572
KEY ABSTRACTS - FACTORY AUTOMATION. Text in English. 1991. m. GBP 145, USD 250 (effective 2001). **Document type:** *Abstract/Index.*
Published by: INSPEC, I.E.E., Michael Faraday House, Six Hills Way, Stevenage, Herts SG1 2AY, United Kingdom. TEL 44-1438-313311, FAX 44-1438-742840, inspec@iee.org.uk, http://www.iee.org.uk. Ed. John Deaves. R&P Michael McCabe TEL 732-321-5575. **US subscr. addr.:** INSPEC, Inc., 379 Thornall St, Edison, NJ 08837-2225. TEL 732-321-5575, FAX 732-321-5702.

016.004 GBR ISSN 0964-0150
KEY ABSTRACTS - HUMAN-COMPUTER INTERACTION. Text in English. 1992. m. GBP 145, USD 250 (effective 2001). **Document type:** *Abstract/Index.*
Published by: INSPEC, I.E.E., Michael Faraday House, Six Hills Way, Stevenage, Herts SG1 2AY, United Kingdom. TEL 44-1438-313311, FAX 44-1438-742840, inspec@iee.org.uk, http://www.iee.org.uk. Ed. John Deaves. R&P Michael McCabe TEL 732-321-5575. **Subscr. to:** INSPEC, I E E, Publication Sales Dept., PO Box 96, Stevenage, Herts SG1 2SD, United Kingdom; **US subscr. addr.:** INSPEC, Inc., 379 Thornall St, Edison, NJ 08837-2225. TEL 732-321-5575, FAX 732-321-5702.

016.00637 GBR ISSN 0952-7052
KEY ABSTRACTS - MACHINE VISION. Text in English. 1989. m. GBP 145, USD 250 (effective 2001). **Document type:** *Abstract/Index.* **Description:** Summarizes recently published papers from more than 4,000 international journals and conference proceedings. Subjects covered include image processing, pattern recognition, information theory, computer vision, image-sensing devices, and applications.
Published by: INSPEC, I.E.E., Michael Faraday House, Six Hills Way, Stevenage, Herts SG1 2AY, United Kingdom. TEL 44-1438-313311, FAX 44-1438-742840, inspec@iee.org.uk, http://www.iee.org.uk. R&P Michael McCabe TEL 732-321-5575. **Subscr. to:** INSPEC, I E E, Publication Sales Dept., PO Box 96, Stevenage, Herts SG1 2SD, United Kingdom; **US subscr. addr.:** INSPEC, Inc., 379 Thornall St, Edison, NJ 08837-2225. TEL 732-321-5575, FAX 732-321-5702.

016.00632 GBR ISSN 0964-0169
CODEN: PUOGEP
KEY ABSTRACTS - NEURAL NETWORKS. Text in English. 1992. m. GBP 145, USD 250 (effective 2001). **Document type:** *Abstract/Index.*
Published by: INSPEC, I.E.E., Michael Faraday House, Six Hills Way, Stevenage, Herts SG1 2AY, United Kingdom. TEL 44-1438-313311, FAX 44-1438-742840, inspec@iee.org.uk, http://www.iee.org.uk. Ed. Bob Beasley. R&P Michael McCabe TEL 732-321-5575. **Subscr. to:** INSPEC, I E E, Publication Sales Dept., PO Box 96, Stevenage, Herts SG1 2SD, United Kingdom; **US subscr. addr.:** INSPEC, Inc., 379 Thornall St, Edison, NJ 08837-2225. TEL 732-321-5575, FAX 732-321-5702.

016.629892 GBR ISSN 0950-4842
Z5853.A8
KEY ABSTRACTS - ROBOTICS & CONTROL. Text in English. 1975. m. GBP 145, USD 250 (effective 2001). index. **Document type:** *Abstract/Index.* **Description:** Covers robots and their applications to materials handling, industrial production systems, and transportation systems.
Formerly (until 1987): Key Abstracts - Industrial Power and Control Systems (0306-5596)
Published by: INSPEC, I.E.E., Michael Faraday House, Six Hills Way, Stevenage, Herts SG1 2AY, United Kingdom. TEL 44-1438-313311, FAX 44-1438-742840, inspec@iee.org.uk, http://www.iee.org.uk. **Subscr. to:** INSPEC, I E E, Publication Sales Dept., PO Box 96, Stevenage, Herts SG1 2SD, United Kingdom; **US subscr. addr.:** INSPEC, Inc., 379 Thornall St, Edison, NJ 08837-2225. TEL 732-321-5575, FAX 732-321-5702.

016.0053 GBR ISSN 0950-4869
KEY ABSTRACTS - SOFTWARE ENGINEERING. Text in English. 1987. m. GBP 145, USD 250 (effective 2001). **Document type:** *Abstract/Index.* **Description:** Covers program support, high-level programming languages, operation systems, and database management systems.
Published by: INSPEC, I.E.E., Michael Faraday House, Six Hills Way, Stevenage, Herts SG1 2AY, United Kingdom. TEL 44-1438-313311, FAX 44-1438-742840, inspec@iee.org.uk, http://www.iee.org.uk. **Subscr. to:** INSPEC, I E E, Publication Sales Dept., PO Box 96, Stevenage, Herts SG1 2SD, United Kingdom; **US subscr. addr.:** INSPEC, Inc., 379 Thornall St, Edison, NJ 08837-2225. TEL 732-321-5575, FAX 732-321-5702.

016.014 RUS
KOMP'YUTERNYI VESTNIK/COMPUTER BULLETIN. Text in Russian. 1993. m. USD 125 (effective 1999). adv. back issues avail. **Document type:** *Abstract/Index.* **Description:** Abstracts new scientific and technical literature in the fields of computer science and technology. Covers communications, computer applications, video systems, multimedia, hypertext, numerous science disciplines, culture, art, as well as education.
Related titles: Diskette ed.
Indexed: RefZh.
Published by: Gosudarstvennaya Publichnaya Nauchno-tekhnicheskaya Biblioteka Rossii, Kuznetskii Most 12, Moscow, 103919, Russian Federation. TEL 7-095-921-2563, FAX 7-095-921-9862, info@gpntb.ru, triton@gpntb.ru. Ed. Y Shraiberg. Adv. contact Marina Zaluzhskaya. page USD 50. **Dist in US by:** International Library Information and Analytical Center, 1776 Massachusetts Ave, N W, Ste 700, Washington, DC 20036. TEL 202-463-7566, FAX 202-463-7582.

016.004 HUN ISSN 0133-736X
MAGYAR KONYVTARI SZAKIRODALOM BIBLIOGRAFIAJA/ BIBLIOGRAPHY ON HUNGARIAN LIBRARY LITERATURE. Text in Hungarian. 1965. q. exchange basis (effective 2004). back issues avail. **Document type:** *Bibliography.*
Formerly: Gyorstajekoztato a Magyar Konyvtartudomanyi Irodalomrol (0017-6052)
Indexed: RASB.
Published by: Konyvtari Intezet, Orszagos Szechenyi Konyvtar/Hungarian Library Institute, National Szechenyi Library, Budavari Palota Wing F, Budapest, 1827, Hungary. TEL 36-1-2243788, FAX 36-1-3759984, kint@oszk.hu, http://www.oszk.hu. Ed. Ferencne Javori. R&P Agnes Racz. Circ: 300.

016.6298 USA
N T I S ALERTS: COMPUTERS, CONTROL & INFORMATION THEORY. Text in English. s-m. USD 270.25 in North America; USD 345 elsewhere (effective 2005). index. back issues avail. **Document type:** *Newsletter, Bibliography.* **Description:** Contains abstracts of titles received by NTIS. Covers research and studies sponsored by the U.S. government and international sources in computer hardware, computer software, control systems and control theory, information processing, information theory, pattern recognition and image processing.
Former titles: Abstract Newsletter: Computers, Control & Information Theory; Weekly Abstract Newsletter: Computers, Control and Information Theory; Weekly Government Abstracts. Computers, Control and Information Theory (0364-796X)
Related titles: Microform ed.: (from NTI).
Published by: U.S. Department of Commerce, National Technical Information Service, 5285 Port Royal Rd, Springfield, VA 22161. TEL 703-605-6000, info@ntis.gov, http://www.ntis.gov.

621.39021 NZL
NEW ZEALAND. STATISTICS NEW ZEALAND. INFORMATION TECHNOLOGY SURVEY. Text in English. a. stat. **Document type:** *Government.* **Description:** Provides information on the total income, export income and the domestic market size of the IT industry in New Zealand.
Published by: Statistics New Zealand/Te Tari Tatau, PO Box 2922, Wellington, New Zealand. TEL 64-4-495-4600, FAX 64-4-473-2626, info@stats.govt.nz, http://www.stats.govt.nz.

016.3298 FRA ISSN 0474-5868
O E C D LIBRARY SPECIAL ANNOTATED BIBLIOGRAPHY: AUTOMATION/O C D E BIBLIOTHEQUE BIBLIOGRAPHIE SPECIALE ANALYTIQUE: AUTOMATION. Text in English, French. 1964. irreg. **Document type:** *Government.*
Related titles: Microfiche ed.
Published by: Organization for Economic Cooperation and Development, 2 Rue Andre Pascal, Paris, 75775 Cedex 16, France. TEL 33-1-45248200, FAX 33-1-45248500, http://www.oecd.org.

016.6298 RUS ISSN 0202-4101
REFERATIVNYI ZHURNAL. AVTOMATIKA I TELEMEKHANIKA. Text in Russian. 1955. m. USD 389 foreign (effective 2006). **Document type:** *Abstract/Index.*
Related titles: CD-ROM ed.; Online - full text ed.
Published by: Vserossiiskii Institut Nauchnoi i Tekhnicheskoi Informatsii (VINITI), Ul Usievicha 20, Moscow, 125190, Russian Federation. TEL 7-095-1526441, FAX 7-095-9430060, dir@viniti.ru, http://www.viniti.ru. Ed. Yurii Arskii. **Dist. by:** Informnauka Ltd., Ul Usievicha 20, Moscow 125190, Russian Federation. alfimov@viniti.ru.

016.004 RUS
REFERATIVNYI ZHURNAL. AVTOMATIKA I VYCHISLITEL'NAYA TEKHNIKA. Text in Russian. 1955. m. USD 948 foreign (effective 2006). **Document type:** *Abstract/Index.*
Formerly: Referativnyi Zhurnal. Avtomatika, Telemekhanika i Vychislitel'naya Tekhnika (0202-4098)
Related titles: CD-ROM ed.; Online - full text ed.
—East View, Linda Hall.
Published by: Vserossiiskii Institut Nauchnoi i Tekhnicheskoi Informatsii (VINITI), Ul Usievicha 20, Moscow, 125190, Russian Federation. TEL 7-095-1526441, FAX 7-095-9430060, dir@viniti.ru, http://www.viniti.ru. Ed. Yurii Arskii. **Dist. by:** Informnauka Ltd., Ul Usievicha 20, Moscow 125190, Russian Federation. alfimov@viniti.ru.

016.0051 RUS ISSN 0234-9655
REFERATIVNYI ZHURNAL. PROGRAMMNOE OBESPECHENIE. Text in Russian. 1955. m. USD 458 foreign (effective 2006). **Document type:** *Journal, Abstract/Index.*
Related titles: CD-ROM ed.; Online - full text ed.
Published by: Vserossiiskii Institut Nauchnoi i Tekhnicheskoi Informatsii (VINITI), Ul Usievicha 20, Moscow, 125190, Russian Federation. TEL 7-095-1526441, FAX 7-095-9430060, dir@viniti.ru, http://www.viniti.ru. Ed. Yurii Arskii. **Dist. by:** Informnauka Ltd., Ul Usievicha 20, Moscow 125190, Russian Federation. alfimov@viniti.ru.

016.004 RUS
REFERATIVNYI ZHURNAL. TEKHNICHESKAYA KIBERNETIKA. Text in Russian. 1965. m. USD 465 foreign (effective 2006). **Document type:** *Abstract/Index.*
Formerly: Referativnyi Zhurnal. Kibernetika (0486-2333)
Related titles: CD-ROM ed.; Online - full text ed.
—East View.
Published by: Vserossiiskii Institut Nauchnoi i Tekhnicheskoi Informatsii (VINITI), Ul Usievicha 20, Moscow, 125190, Russian Federation. TEL 7-095-1526441, FAX 7-095-9430060, dir@viniti.ru, http://www.viniti.ru. Eds. Stanislav Emelyanov, Yurii Arskii. **Dist. by:** Informnauka Ltd., Ul Usievicha 20, Moscow 125190, Russian Federation. alfimov@viniti.ru.

016.62139 RUS ISSN 0234-9663
REFERATIVNYI ZHURNAL. VYCHISLITEL'NYE MASHINY I SISTEMY. Text in Russian. 1955. m. USD 458 foreign (effective 2006).
Related titles: CD-ROM ed.; Online - full text ed.
—East View.
Published by: Vserossiiskii Institut Nauchnoi i Tekhnicheskoi Informatsii (VINITI), Ul Usievicha 20, Moscow, 125190, Russian Federation. TEL 7-095-1526441, FAX 7-095-9430060, dir@viniti.ru, http://www.viniti.ru. Ed. Yurii Arskii. **Dist. by:** Informnauka Ltd., Ul Usievicha 20, Moscow 125190, Russian Federation. alfimov@viniti.ru.

016.2139 016.51 RUS ISSN 0235-1501
REFERATIVNYI ZHURNAL. VYCHISLITEL'NYE NAUKI. Text in Russian. 1987. m. USD 640 foreign (effective 2006). **Document type:** *Journal, Abstract/Index.*
—East View.
Published by: Vserossiiskii Institut Nauchnoi i Tekhnicheskoi Informatsii (VINITI), Ul Usievicha 20, Moscow, 125190, Russian Federation. TEL 7-095-1526441, FAX 7-095-9430060, dir@viniti.ru, http://www.viniti.ru. **Dist. by:** Informnauka Ltd., Ul Usievicha 20, Moscow 125190, Russian Federation. alfimov@viniti.ru.

016.621399   USA   ISSN 0097-966X
TK7882.I6   CODEN: DTPSDS
➤ S I D INTERNATIONAL SYMPOSIUM. DIGEST OF TECHNICAL PAPERS. Text in English. 1970. a. price varies. abstr. **Document type:** *Proceedings, Academic/Scholarly.* **Description:** Publishes extended abstracts of papers presented at the annual international symposium.
Formerly: Symposium on Information Display. Digest of Technical Papers (0082-0830)
Indexed: Inspec.
—BLDSC (8271.680000), IE, ingenta, Linda Hall. **CCC.**
Published by: Society for Information Display, 610 S 2nd St, San Jose, CA 95112. TEL 408-977-1013, FAX 408-977-1531, office@sid.org, http://www.sid.org. Circ: 5,000.

016.02504   USA
▼ S I R S WEBFIND. Text in English. 2003. d. USD 400 (effective 2003). **Document type:** *Abstract/Index.*
Description: An online database of quality Web sites for younger researchers in grades 1-9 on vital issues and topics, which are evaluated for relevance and credibility.
Media: Online - full content.
Published by: S I R S Publishing, Inc., PO Box 272348, Boca Raton, FL 33427-2348. TEL 561-994-0079, FAX 561-994-4704, publisher@sirs.com, custserve@sirs.com, http://www.sirs.com/products/webfind.htm.

016.02504   USA
S K S WEBSELECT. Text in English. 2001. d. USD 850 (effective 2003). **Document type:** *Abstract/Index.* **Description:** An online database of quality Web sites on vital issues and topics, which are evaluated for relevance and credibility.
Formerly (until 2003): S I R S WebSelect
Media: Online - full content.
Published by: S I R S Publishing, Inc., PO Box 272348, Boca Raton, FL 33427-2348. TEL 561-994-0079, FAX 561-994-4704, publisher@sirs.com, custserve@sirs.com, http://www.sirs.com/products/netselect.htm.

016.003   JPN
S S O R YOKOSHU/PROCEEDINGS OF S S O R. Text in Japanese. a. abstr. **Document type:** *Proceedings.*
Published by: Summer Symposium of Operation Research/S S O R Jimu-kyoku, c/o Mr Yoshinobu Teraoka, Himeji Kogyo Daigaku Oyo Sugaku Kyoshitsu, 2167 Shoshiya, Himeji-shi, Hyogo-ken 671-2201, Japan.

003.3021   JPN
SEIKEN N S T SHINPOJUMU KOEN KOGAISHU∗ . (Numerical Simulation Turbulence) Text in English, Japanese. 1986. a. abstr. **Description:** Contains abstracts from the symposium of the group.
Published by: University of Tokyo, Institute of Industrial Science/Tokyo Daigaku Seisan Gijutsu Kenkyujo, Komaba Research Campus, 4-6-1 Komaba Meguro-ku, Tokyo, 153-8505, Japan. TEL 81-3-5452-6024, FAX 81-3-5452-6094, kokusai@iis.u-tokyo.ac.jp, http://www.iis.u-tokyo.ac.jp/index.html.

016.004   USA
SOFTBASE. Text in English. q. **Document type:** *Abstract/Index.* **Description:** Reviews some 200 trade, consumer, and academic publications, comprising more than 108,000 SoftBase records, which are divided into three main categories: technology reviews, product descriptions, and company profile.
Related titles: Online - full content ed.: (from National Information Services Corp. (N I S C)).
Published by: (Information Sources Inc), National Information Services Corp. (N I S C), Ste 6, Wyman Towers, 3100 St Paul St, Baltimore, MD 21218. TEL 410-243-0797, FAX 410-243-0982, sales@nisc.com, http://www.nisc.com.

006.6021   USA
STATISTICAL COMPUTING AND GRAPHICS. Text in English. 3/yr. **Document type:** *Newsletter.*
Related titles: Online - full text ed.
Published by: (Statistical Graphics Section), American Statistical Association, 1429 Duke St, Alexandria, VA 22314-3415. TEL 703-684-1221, FAX 703-684-2037, cocteau@bell-labs.com, http://cm.bell-labs.com/who/cocteau/newsletter/.

004.21   USA   ISSN 0960-3174
QA276.4   CODEN: STACE3
➤ STATISTICS AND COMPUTING. Text in English. 1991. q. EUR 628, USD 638, GBP 395 combined subscription to institutions print & online eds. (effective 2005). adv. bk.rev.; software rev. charts; illus. back issues avail.; reprint service avail. from PSC. **Document type:** *Journal, Academic/Scholarly.* **Description:** Addresses the use of statistical concepts in computer science and the use of in data analysis; contains original research reports, authoritative review papers, discussed papers, and occasional special issues on particular topics or carrying proceedings of relevant conferences.
Related titles: Online - full text ed.: ISSN 1573-1375 (from EBSCO Publishing, Gale Group, IngentaConnect, Kluwer Online, O C L C Online Computer Library Center, Inc., Ovid Technologies, Inc., Springer LINK, Swets Information Services).
Indexed: ASCA, BibLing, CCMJ, CIS, CMCI, CurCont, Inspec, MathR, MathSciNet, RefZh, ST&MA.

—BLDSC (8453.516500), AskIEEE, CISTI, IDS, IE, Infotrieve, ingenta. **CCC.**
Published by: Springer-Verlag New York, Inc. (Subsidiary of: Springer Science+Business Media), 233 Spring St, New York, NY 10013. TEL 212-460-1500, FAX 212-460-1575, service@springer-ny.com, http://springerlink.metapress.com/openurl.asp?genre=journal&issn=0960-3174, http://www.springer-ny.com. Ed. R W Oldford. **Subscr. to:** Journal Fulfillment, PO Box 2485, Secaucus, NJ 07096-2485. TEL 201-348-4033, FAX 201-348-4505, journals@springer-ny.com.

COMPUTERS—Artificial Intelligence

see also COMPUTERS—Cybernetics

006.3   USA
A A A I (YEAR). Text in English. 1980. a. price varies. abstr. back issues avail.; reprint service avail. from PQC. **Document type:** *Proceedings, Academic/Scholarly.* **Description:** Contains the Proceedings of the National Conference on Artificial Intelligence and the Conference on Innovative Applications of Artificial Intelligence.
Indexed: EngInd.
—BLDSC (6847.820300).
Published by: (American Association for Artificial Intelligence), M I T Press, 55 Hayward St, Cambridge, MA 02142-1493. http://mitpress.mit.edu. Circ: 3,000.

A C M SYMPOSIUM ON PRINCIPLES OF PROGRAMMING LANGUAGES. ANNUAL CONFERENCE RECORD. (Association for Computing Machinery) see *COMPUTERS—Automation*

006.3   GBR   ISSN 0951-5666
    CODEN: AISCEM
➤ A I & SOCIETY; the journal of human-centered systems and machine intelligence. (Artificial Intelligence) Text in English. 1987. q. EUR 598 combined subscription to institutions print & online eds. (effective 2005). bk.rev. back issues avail.; reprint service avail. from PSC. **Document type:** *Journal, Academic/Scholarly.* **Description:** Covers the issues, policy and management of artificial intelligence. Discusses social, economic, philosophical and political implications.
Related titles: Microform ed.: (from PQC); Online - full text ed.: ISSN 1435-5655 (from EBSCO Publishing, ProQuest Information & Learning, Springer LINK, Swets Information Services).
Indexed: AHCI, CompAb, CompR, Inspec, LISA, RASB.
—BLDSC (0772.323500), AskIEEE, CISTI, Ei, IE, Infotrieve, ingenta. **CCC.**
Published by: Springer-Verlag London Ltd. (Subsidiary of: Springer Science+Business Media), Ashbourne House, The Guildway, Old Portsmouth Rd, Guildford, Surrey GU7 3DJ, United Kingdom. TEL 44-1483-734433, FAX 44-1483-734411, postmaster@svl.co.uk, http://link.springer.de/link/service/journals/00146/, http://www.springer.co.uk. Ed. Karamjit S Gill. Adv. contact Christiane Notarmarco. Circ: 265. **Subscr. in the Americas to:** Springer-Verlag New York, Inc., Journal Fulfillment, PO Box 2485, Secaucus, NJ 07096-2485. TEL 800-777-4643, 201-348-4033, FAX 201-348-4505, journals@springer-ny.com, http://www.springer-ny.com; **Subscr. to:** Springer GmbH Auslieferungsgesellschaft, Haberstr 7, Heidelberg 69126, Germany. TEL 49-6221-345-0, FAX 49-6221-345-4229, subscriptions@springer.de.

006.3   NLD   ISSN 0921-7126
Q334   CODEN: ACMMEE
➤ A I COMMUNICATIONS; the European journal on artificial intelligence. (Artificial Intelligence) Text in English. 1988. q. EUR 392, USD 470 combined subscription print & online eds. (effective 2006). bk.rev. abstr.; bibl.; charts; stat. **Document type:** *Journal, Academic/Scholarly.* **Description:** Enhances contacts and information exchanges between artificial intelligence researchers and developers in Europe. Contains high-level background material and topics of interest to those concerned with artificial intelligence and advanced information processing, at technical levels, as well as those of opinions, policies, and news.
Related titles: Online - full text ed.: (from EBSCO Publishing, Gale Group, IngentaConnect, O C L C Online Computer Library Center, Inc., Swets Information Services).
Indexed: AIA, ASCA, B&BAb, BioEngAb, BrCerAb, C&ISA, CCMJ, CMCI, CerAb, CompAb, CompLI, CompR, CorrAb, CurCont, E&CAJ, EMA, EngInd, IAA, Inspec, LISA, M&TEA, MBF, METADEX, MSCI, MathR, MathSciNet, SCI, SolStAb, WAA, ZentMath.
—BLDSC (0772.328000), AskIEEE, CISTI, Ei, IDS, IE, Infotrieve, ingenta, Linda Hall. **CCC.**
Published by: (European Coordinating Committee for Artificial Intelligence), I O S Press, Nieuwe Hemweg 6B, Amsterdam, 1013 BG, Netherlands. TEL 31-20-6883355, FAX 31-20-6203419, info@iospress.nl, order@iospress.nl, http://www.iospress.nl/html/09217126.php. Ed. G Gottlob. R&P Ms. Carry Koolbergen TEL 31-20-6382189. Adv. contact Ms. Jolijn van Eunen. Circ: 1,000. **Subscr. to:** Kinokuniya Co. Ltd., Shinjuku 3-chome, Shinjuku-ku, Tokyo 160-0022, Japan. FAX 81-3-3439-1094, journal@kinokuniya.co.jp,

http://www.kinokuniya.co.jp; Globe Publication Pvt. Ltd., C-62 Inderpuri, New Delhi 100 012, India. TEL 91-11-579-3211, 91-11-579-3212, FAX 91-11-579-8876, custserve@globepub.com, http://www.globepub.com; I O S Press, Inc, 4502 Rachael Manor Dr., Fairfax, VA 22032-3631. iosbooks@iospress.com.

006.3   USA   ISSN 0738-4602
Q334
➤ A I MAGAZINE. (Artificial Intelligence) Text in English. 1980. q. USD 95 domestic for membership to individuals; USD 135 foreign for membership to individuals; USD 190 domestic for membership to institutions; USD 230 foreign for membership to institutions (effective 2005). adv. bk.rev. bibl.; illus. Index. 128 p./no.; back issues avail.; reprints avail. **Document type:** *Journal, Academic/Scholarly.* **Description:** Contains articles on all aspects of AI, focusing on state-of-the-art developments. Features include reports of research in progress, announcements of meetings and seminars, and information on job openings.
Related titles: CD-ROM ed.; Microform ed.; Online - full text ed.: (from bigchalk, Florida Center for Library Automation, Gale Group, H.W. Wilson, O C L C Online Computer Library Center, Inc., ProQuest Information & Learning).
Indexed: AHCI, AIA, AS&TI, ASCA, CMCI, CompAb, CompLI, CompR, CurCont, EngInd, ISR, InfoSAb, Inspec, LISA, Microcompind, ORMS, QC&AS, RefZh, RoboAb, SCI.
—BLDSC (0772.343000), AskIEEE, CISTI, Ei, IDS, IE, Infotrieve, ingenta, Linda Hall. **CCC.**
Published by: (American Association for Artificial Intelligence), A A A I Press, 445 Burgess Dr, Menlo Park, CA 94025-3442. TEL 650-328-3123, FAX 650-321-4457, aimagazine@aaai.org, info@aaai.org, http://www.aimagazine.org, http://www.aaai.org. Ed. David Leake. R&P Carol Hamilton. Adv. contact David Hamilton. B&W page USD 1,250, color page USD 1,950; trim 8.38 x 10.88. Circ: 6,000 (paid).

006.3   GBR
A I PERSPECTIVES. (Artificial Intelligence) Text in English. irreg., latest 1995, Mar. price varies. **Document type:** *Monographic series.* **Description:** Presents in-depth reports on important emerging issues in commercial artificial intelligence.
Published by: A I Intelligence, PO Box 95, Oxford, Oxon OX2 7XL, United Kingdom. TEL 44-1865-791600, FAX 44-1865-791007, aip@aiintelligence.com. Ed., Pub., R&P Alex Goodall.

006.3   GBR   ISSN 1476-3036
A I S B J. (Artificial Intelligence and Simulation of Behaviour Journal) Text in English. 2002. s-a.
Indexed: Inspec.
—BLDSC (0785.433800).
Published by: Society for the Study of Artificial Intelligence and Simulation of Behaviour, University of Sussex, School of Cognitive and Computing Sciences, Brighton, BN1 9QH, United Kingdom. admin@aisb.org.uk, http://www.aisb.org.uk. Ed. Blay Whitbey.

006.3   GBR   ISSN 0268-4179
    CODEN: AISBEJ
A I S B QUARTERLY. (Artificial Intelligence and Simulation of Behaviour) Text in English. 1964. q. **Description:** Publishes articles, features, letters, opinions and debated covering all aspects of Artificial Intelligence and Cognitive Science.
Indexed: Inspec.
—BLDSC (0785.435000), IE, ingenta.
Published by: Society for the Study of Artificial Intelligence and Simulation of Behaviour, University of Sussex, School of Cognitive and Computing Sciences, Brighton, BN1 9QH, United Kingdom. admin@aisb.org.uk, http://www.aisb.org.uk.

006.3   USA   ISSN 0893-6552
A I TODAY∗ ; the magazine of applied artificial intelligence and expert systems. (Artificial Intelligence) Text in English. 1986. bi-m. USD 95; USD 135 foreign. adv. bk.rev. back issues avail. **Description:** Covers natural language computer systems, applied expert systems, intelligent databases, robotics and artificial intelligence languages.
Related titles: Magnetic Tape ed.: 1986.
Published by: Yellowstone Information Services, R R 2, Box 42A, Bloomingdale, OH 43910-9802. TEL 304-965-5548, FAX 304-965-7785. Ed. Roger C Thibault. Circ: 5,000.

006.3   USA   ISSN 1081-6283
A I XPERT; IBM's technical magazine for AIX application developers. (Advanced Interactive Executive) Text in English. 1991. q. USD 29.95; USD 34.95 foreign. back issues avail. **Document type:** *Trade.*
Media: Online - full text. **Related titles:** CD-ROM ed.
Published by: I B M Corporation (Austin), RS-6000 Partners in Development, Izip 1007, 11400 Burnet Rd, Austin, TX 78758. TEL 512-823-6840, FAX 512-823-6520, gnoven@us.ibm.com, http://www.developer.ibm.com/library/aixpert. Ed., R&P George Noren. adv.: B&W page USD 2,795; trim 11 x 8.5. Circ: 10,000.

006.3   USA
ABLEX SERIES IN ARTIFICIAL INTELLIGENCE. Text in English. 1985. irreg., latest 1996. price varies. **Document type:** *Academic/Scholarly.*
Formerly: Advances in Artificial Intelligence
Indexed: Inspec.

C

Published by: Ablex Publishing Corporation (Subsidiary of: Greenwood Publishing Group Inc.), 88 Post Rd W, Westport, CT 06881. TEL 203-323-9606, FAX 203-357-8446. Ed. Yorick Wilks.

006.3 GBR ISSN 1059-7123
QL750 CODEN: ADBEEA

➤ **ADAPTIVE BEHAVIOR**; animals, animats, software agents, robots, adaptive systems. Text in English. 1992-1998 (vol.6, no.3-4); resumed 2001. q. GBP 230, USD 357 to institutions; GBP 240, USD 371 combined subscription to institutions print & online eds. (effective 2006). back issues avail. **Document type:** *Journal, Academic/Scholarly.* **Description:** International journal providing a forum for experimental and theoretical research on adaptive behavior in animals and autonomous artificial systems, with emphasis on mechanism, organizational principles, and architectures that can be expressed in computational, physical, or mathematical models.
Related titles: Microfilm ed.: suspended (from PQC); Online - full text ed.: ISSN 1741-2633. GBP 228, USD 353 to institutions (effective 2006) (from EBSCO Publishing, Gale Group, O C L C Online Computer Library Center, Inc., Sage Publications, Inc., Swets Information Services).
Indexed: ASFA, AnBeAb, B&BAb, BIOSIS Prev, BioEngAb, BiolAb, CMCI, CompAb, CompLI, CompR, CurCont, ESPM, EntAb, ErgAb, IAA, Inspec, PsycInfo, PsycholAb, RefZh, SSCI, WildRev, ZooRec, e-psyche.
—BLDSC (0678.309000), AskIEEE, CISTI, IDS, IE, Infotrieve, ingenta, Linda Hall. **CCC.**
Published by: (International Society for Adaptive Behavior USA), Sage Science Press (UK) (Subsidiary of: Sage Publications, Inc.), 1 Oliver's Yard, 55 City Rd, London, EC1Y 1SP, United Kingdom. TEL 44-20-73248500, FAX 44-20-73248600, info@sagepub.com, http://www.sagepub.co.uk/journal.aspx?pid=105464. Ed. Peter M Todd. **Subscr. in the Americas to:** Sage Publications, Inc., 2455 Teller Rd, Thousand Oaks, CA 91320. TEL 805-499-0721, FAX 805-499-0871, journals@sagepub.com.

006.3 GBR ISSN 1474-0346
TA345 CODEN: AIENEJ

➤ **ADVANCED ENGINEERING INFORMATICS.** Text in English. 1986. 4/yr. EUR 945 in Europe to institutions; JPY 125,400 in Japan to institutions; USD 1,056 elsewhere to institutions (effective 2006). adv. abstr. back issues avail. **Document type:** *Journal, Academic/Scholarly.* **Description:** Provides information for engineers from all disciplines who are involved in research, development and implementation of computer systems for artificial intelligence.
Former titles (until 2002): Artificial Intelligence in Engineering (0954-1810); (until 1991): International Journal for Artificial Intelligence in Engineering (0267-9264)
Related titles: Microform ed.: (from PQC); Online - full text ed.: (from EBSCO Publishing, Gale Group, IngentaConnect, ScienceDirect, Swets Information Services).
Indexed: AIA, ASCA, BrCerAb, C&ISA, CADCAM, CMCI, CerAb, CompAb, CompLI, CorrAb, CurCont, E&CAJ, EMA, ESPM, EngInd, H&SSA, IAA, Inspec, M&TEA, MBF, METADEX, SolStAb, WAA.
—BLDSC (0696.851100), AskIEEE, CISTI, Ei, IDS, IE, ingenta, Linda Hall. **CCC.**
Published by: Pergamon (Subsidiary of: Elsevier Science & Technology), The Boulevard, Langford Ln, East Park, Kidlington, Oxford OX5 1GB, United Kingdom. TEL 44-1865-843000, FAX 44-1865-843010, http://www.elsevier.com/locate/aei. Eds. I. F.C. Smith, J. C. Kunz, T. Tomiyama. **Subscr. to:** Elsevier BV, PO Box 211, Amsterdam 1000 AE, Netherlands. TEL 31-20-485-3757, FAX 31-20-485-3432, nlinfo-f@elsevier.nl, http://www.elsevier.nl.

006.3 DEU

➤ **ADVANCED MICRO- AND NANOSYSTEMS.** Text in German. 1996. 2/yr. EUR 169, USD 205 per vol. (effective 2004). adv. abstr.; charts; illus. reprints avail. **Document type:** *Journal, Academic/Scholarly.*
Formerly (until 2004): Sensors Update (1432-2404)
Related titles: Online - full text ed.: ISSN 1616-8984. EUR 438 in Europe; CHF 868 in Switzerland & Liechtenstein; USD 468 elsewhere (effective 2003) (from EBSCO Publishing, Swets Information Services, Wiley InterScience).
—BLDSC (8241.785750), CISTI, IE. **CCC.**
Published by: Wiley - V C H Verlag GmbH & Co. KGaA (Subsidiary of: John Wiley & Sons, Inc.), Boschstr 12, Weinheim, 69469, Germany. FAX 49-6201-606-117, adsales@wiley-vch.de, http://www.wiley-vch.de/books/info/amn/index.html. Ed. Henry Baltes. R&P Claudia Rutz. Adv. contact Aenne Anders TEL 49-6201-606552. Circ: 800 (paid). **Subscr. in the Americas to:** John Wiley & Sons, Inc., 111 River St, Hoboken, NJ 07030-5774. TEL 201-748-6645, FAX 201-748-6088, subinfo@wiley.com; **Subscr. outside of Germany, Austria & Switzerland to:** John Wiley & Sons Ltd., The Atrium, Southern Gate, Chichester, West Sussex PO19 8SQ, United Kingdom. TEL 44-1243-779777, FAX 44-1243-775878, cs-journals@wiley.co.uk.

006.3 SGP

ADVANCED SERIES ON ARTIFICIAL INTELLIGENCE. Text in English. 1992. irreg., latest vol.3, 1998. price varies. **Document type:** *Monographic series, Academic/Scholarly.*
Published by: World Scientific Publishing Co. Pte. Ltd., 5 Toh Tuck Link, Singapore, 596224, Singapore. TEL 65-466-5775, FAX 65-467-7667, wspc@wspc.com.sg, series@wspc.com.sg, http://www.wspc.com.sg/books/series/asai_series.shtml, http://www.worldscientific.com. Ed. Nikolaos G Bourbakis. **Dist. by:** World Scientific Publishing Co., Inc., 1060 Main St, River Edge, NJ 07661. TEL 201-487-9655, FAX 201-487-9656, 888-977-2665; World Scientific Publishing Ltd., 57 Shelton St, London WC2H 9HE, United Kingdom. TEL 44-20-78360888, FAX 44-20-78362020, sales@wspc.co.uk.

006.3 USA ISSN 1049-5258
QA76.87

ADVANCES IN NEURAL INFORMATION PROCESSING SYSTEMS. Text in English. 1989. a.
—BLDSC (0709.475500), CISTI, IE, Infotrieve, ingenta. **CCC.**
Published by: (I E E E Conference on Neural Information Processing Systems - Natural and Synthetic), Morgan Kaufmann Publishers, Inc. (Subsidiary of: Elsevier BV), 500 Sansome St, Ste 400, San Francisco, CA 94111. TEL 415-392-2665, 800-745-7323, FAX 415-982-2665, orders@mkp.com, http://www.mkp.com.

006.3 ITA

ALMA; scores of the unfinished thought. Text in Italian. 1996. irreg. **Description:** Covers artificial intelligence, neural networks and more.
Media: Online - full text.
Address: Via Tevere 68, Roges Rende, CS 87036, Italy. luigi@diemme.it, alma_mag@geocities.com, http://www.diemme.it/~luigi/alma.html. Ed. Luigi Caputo.

006.3 NLD ISSN 1012-2443
CODEN: AMAIEC

➤ **ANNALS OF MATHEMATICS AND ARTIFICIAL INTELLIGENCE.** Text in English. 1990. m. (in 3 vols.). EUR 1,095, USD 1,115, GBP 685 combined subscription to institutions print & online eds. (effective 2005). adv. back issues avail.; reprint service avail. from PSC. **Document type:** *Academic/Scholarly.* **Description:** Presents research level coverage of artificial intelligence and mathematics.
Related titles: Online - full text ed.: ISSN 1573-7470 (from EBSCO Publishing, Gale Group, IngentaConnect, Kluwer Online, O C L C Online Computer Library Center, Inc., Ovid Technologies, Inc., Springer LINK, Swets Information Services).
Indexed: ASCA, BibLing, CCMJ, CMCI, CompAb, CompLI, CurCont, EngInd, Inspec, M&GPA, MathR, MathSciNet, ZentMath.
—BLDSC (1043.005000), AskIEEE, Ei, IDS, IE, Infotrieve, ingenta. **CCC.**
Published by: Springer-Verlag Dordrecht (Subsidiary of: Springer Science+Business Media), Van Godewijckstraat 30, Dordrecht, 3311 GX, Netherlands. TEL 31-78-6576050, FAX 31-78-6576474, http://springerlink.metapress.com/openurl.asp?genre=journal&issn=1012-2443, http://www.springeronline.com. Ed. Martin Charles Golumbic.

006.33 USA

ANNUAL CONFERENCE ON A I, SIMULATION AND PLANNING IN HIGH AUTONOMY SYSTEMS. Text in English. 1990. a. price varies. adv. **Document type:** *Proceedings.* **Description:** Examines integrated methods of simulation and planning that help automate basic decision-making processes in computer systems.
Published by: (Institute of Electrical and Electronics Engineers, Inc.), I E E E Computer Society, 10662 Los Vaqueros Circle, PO Box 3014, Los Alamitos, CA 90720-1314. TEL 714-821-8380, FAX 714-821-4641. Ed. Cat Harris. Pub. Matt Loeb. Adv. contact Frieda Koester.

006.3 USA ISSN 0883-9514
Q334 CODEN: AAINEH

➤ **APPLIED ARTIFICIAL INTELLIGENCE**; an international journal. Text in English. 1987. 10/yr. GBP 721, USD 1,190 combined subscription to institutions print & online eds. (effective 2006). illus. back issues avail.; reprint service avail. from PSC. **Document type:** *Academic/Scholarly.* **Description:** Evaluates current AI systems and tools; explores theoretical research relevant to potential applications; and covers the economic, social, and cultural impacts of AI.
Related titles: Microform ed.: (from PQC); Online - full text ed.: ISSN 1087-6545. GBP 685, USD 1,131 to institutions (effective 2006) (from EBSCO Publishing, Gale Group, IngentaConnect, O C L C Online Computer Library Center, Inc., Swets Information Services).
Indexed: AHCI, AIA, ASCA, BrCerAb, C&ISA, CADCAM, CMCI, CerAb, CompAb, CompLI, CorrAb, CurCont, E&CAJ, EMA, EngInd, ErgAb, IAA, ISMEC, Inspec, M&TEA, MBF, METADEX, PsycInfo, PsycholAb, RefZh, RoboAb, SSCI, SolStAb, WAA.
—BLDSC (1571.650000), AskIEEE, CISTI, Ei, IDS, IE, Infotrieve, ingenta, Linda Hall. **CCC.**
Published by: Taylor & Francis Inc. (Subsidiary of: Taylor & Francis Group), 325 Chestnut St, Ste 800, Philadelphia, PA 19016. TEL 215-625-8900, FAX 215-625-2940, info@taylorandfrancis.com, http://www.tandf.co.uk/journals/tf/08839514.html, http://www.taylorandfrancis.com. Ed. Robert Trappl. **Subscr. addr. in Europe:** Taylor & Francis Ltd, Journals Customer Service, Rankine Rd, Basingstoke, Hants RG24 8PR, United Kingdom. TEL 44-1256-813000, FAX 44-1256-330245, enquiry@tandf.co.uk.

006.32 USA ISSN 0924-669X
Q334 CODEN: APITE4

➤ **APPLIED INTELLIGENCE**; the international journal of artificial intelligence, neural networks, and complex problem-solving technologies. Text in English. 1991. bi-m. EUR 688, USD 698, GBP 428 combined subscription to institutions print & online eds. (effective 2005). adv. back issues avail.; reprint service avail. from PSC. **Document type:** *Journal, Academic/Scholarly.* **Description:** Provides a medium for exchanging scientific research and technological achievements accomplished by the international community. Focus is on research in artificial intelligence and neural networks.
Related titles: Microform ed.: (from PQC); Online - full text ed.: ISSN 1573-7497 (from EBSCO Publishing, Gale Group, IngentaConnect, Kluwer Online, O C L C Online Computer Library Center, Inc., Ovid Technologies, Inc., Springer LINK, Swets Information Services).
Indexed: ASCA, B&BAb, BibLing, CMCI, CompAb, CompLI, CurCont, ERA, ETA, EngInd, ISR, Inspec, LISA, PsycInfo, PsycholAb, RefZh, SCI, ZentMath.
—BLDSC (1573.210000), AskIEEE, CISTI, Ei, IDS, IE, Infotrieve, ingenta. **CCC.**
Published by: Springer-Verlag New York, Inc. (Subsidiary of: Springer Science+Business Media), 233 Spring St, New York, NY 10013. TEL 212-460-1500, FAX 212-460-1575, service@springer-ny.com, http://springerlink.metapress.com/openurl.asp?genre=journal&issn=0924-669X, http://www.springer-ny.com. Ed. Moonis Ali. **Subscr. to:** Journal Fulfillment, PO Box 2485, Secaucus, NJ 07096-2485. TEL 201-348-4033, FAX 201-348-4505, journals@springer-ny.com.

006.3 NLD ISSN 0004-3702
Q335 CODEN: AINTBB

➤ **ARTIFICIAL INTELLIGENCE.** Text in English. 1970. 18/yr. EUR 2,287 in Europe to institutions; JPY 303,600 in Japan to institutions; USD 2,270 elsewhere to institutions (effective 2006). adv. bk.rev. illus. back issues avail.; reprints avail. **Document type:** *Journal, Academic/Scholarly.* **Description:** Presents technical papers for computer and research scientists and educators in AI. Includes robotics, software engineering, philosophy and logic, natural languages, cognitive psychology and vision.
Related titles: Microform ed.: (from PQC); Online - full text ed.: (from EBSCO Publishing, Gale Group, IngentaConnect, ScienceDirect, Swets Information Services).
Indexed: AHCI, AIA, AS&TI, ASCA, B&BAb, BibLing, BioEngAb, BrCerAb, C&ISA, CCMJ, CMCI, CerAb, CivEngAb, CompAb, CompC, CompLI, CompR, CorrAb, CurCont, CybAb, E&CAJ, EMA, EngInd, ErgAb, IAA, ISR, InfoSAb, Inspec, L&LBA, LISA, M&TEA, MBF, METADEX, MathR, MathSciNet, PsycholAb, RASB, RefZh, RoboAb, SCI, SSCI, SolStAb, WAA, ZentMath.
—BLDSC (1735.035000), AskIEEE, CISTI, Ei, IDS, IE, Infotrieve, ingenta, Linda Hall. **CCC.**
Published by: Elsevier BV, North-Holland (Subsidiary of: Elsevier Science & Technology), Sara Burgerhartstraat 25, Amsterdam, 1055 KV, Netherlands. TEL 31-20-485-3911, FAX 31-20-485-2457, nlinfo-f@elsevier.nl, http://www.elsevier.com/locate/artint, http://www.elsevier.nl. Eds. C. R. Perrault, E. Sandewall. Circ: 1,100. **Subscr. to:** Elsevier BV, PO Box 211, Amsterdam 1000 AE, Netherlands. TEL 31-20-485-3757, FAX 31-20-485-3432, http://www.elsevier.nl.

➤ **ARTIFICIAL INTELLIGENCE AND LAW**; an international journal. see *LAW*

006.3 GBR ISSN 0890-0604
TA174 CODEN: AIEMEG

➤ **ARTIFICIAL INTELLIGENCE FOR ENGINEERING DESIGN, ANALYSIS AND MANUFACTURING.** Abbreviated title: A I E D A M. Text in English. 4/yr. USD 452 in North America to institutions; GBP 268 elsewhere to institutions; USD 489 combined subscription in North America to institutions print & online eds.; GBP 289 combined subscription elsewhere to institutions print & online eds. (effective 2006). adv. bk.rev. back issues avail.; reprint service avail. from PSC. **Document type:** *Journal, Academic/Scholarly.* **Description:** Covers the use of artificial intelligence in planning, design, finite-element analysis, simulation spatial reasoning and graphics, process planning, optimization and manufacturing.
Related titles: Online - full text ed.: ISSN 1469-1760. USD 420 in North America to institutions; GBP 250 elsewhere to institutions (effective 2006) (from EBSCO Publishing, O C L C Online Computer Library Center, Inc., Swets Information Services).
Indexed: ASCA, ApMecR, BrCerAb, C&ISA, CMCI, CerAb, CompAb, CompLI, CorrAb, E&CAJ, EMA, EngInd, IAA, Inspec, M&TEA, MBF, METADEX, SSCI, SolStAb, WAA.
—BLDSC (1735.036200), AskIEEE, CISTI, Ei, IDS, IE, Infotrieve, ingenta, Linda Hall. **CCC.**
Published by: Cambridge University Press, The Edinburgh Bldg, Shaftesbury Rd, Cambridge, CB2 2RU, United Kingdom. TEL 44-1223-312393, FAX 44-1223-315052, journals@cambridge.org, http://uk.cambridge.org/journals/aie/. Ed. David C Brown. R&P Linda Nicol TEL 44-1223-325757. Adv. contact Rebecca Curtis TEL 44-1223-325757. **Subscr. to:** Cambridge University Press, 100 Brook Hill Dr, West Nyack, NY 10994. TEL 845-353-7500, FAX 845-353-4141, journals_subscriptions@cup.org

006.3 NLD
ARTIFICIAL INTELLIGENCE IN DESIGN (YEAR). Text in Dutch. biennial. price varies. **Document type:** *Monographic series, Academic/Scholarly.*
—BLDSC (1735.036050).
Published by: Springer-Verlag Dordrecht (Subsidiary of: Springer Science+Business Media), Van Godewijckstraat 30, Dordrecht, 3311 GX, Netherlands. TEL 31-78-6576050, FAX 31-78-6576474, http://www.springeronline.com.

006.361 NLD ISSN 0933-3657
R859.7.A78 CODEN: AIMEEW
➤ **ARTIFICIAL INTELLIGENCE IN MEDICINE.** Text in Dutch. 1989. 9/yr. EUR 188 in Europe to individuals; JPY 24,900 in Japan to individuals; USD 210 to individuals except Europe and Japan; EUR 690 in Europe to institutions; JPY 91,700 in Japan to institutions; USD 773 to institutions except Europe and Japan (effective 2006). adv. bk.rev. back issues avail. **Document type:** *Journal, Academic/Scholarly.* **Description:** Publishes original articles from a wide variety of interdisciplinary perspectives concerning the theory and practice of medical artificial intelligence.
Related titles: Microform ed.: (from PQC); Online - full text ed.: (from EBSCO Publishing, Gale Group, IngentaConnect, ScienceDirect, Swets Information Services).
Indexed: ASCA, B&BAb, BioEngAb, C&ISA, CMCI, CompAb, CompLI, CurCont, E&CAJ, ESPM, EngInd, ExcerpMed, H&SSA, INI, ISR, IndMed, Inpharma, Inspec, LISA, MEDLINE, PE&ON, Reac, SCI, SSCI, SolStAb.
—BLDSC (1735.036800), AskIEEE, CISTI, Ei, GNLM, IDS, IE, Infotrieve, ingenta. **CCC.**
Published by: Elsevier BV (Subsidiary of: Elsevier Science & Technology), Radarweg 29, Amsterdam, 1043 NX, Netherlands. TEL 31-20-4853911, FAX 31-20-4852457, nlinfo-f@elsevier.nl, http://www.elsevier.com/locate/artmed, http://www.elsevier.nl. Ed. Dr. K.-P. Adlassnig. Circ: 1,500.

006.3 NLD ISSN 0269-2821
Q334 CODEN: AIRVE6
➤ **ARTIFICIAL INTELLIGENCE REVIEW**; an international survey and tutorial journal. Text in English. 1986. 8/yr. EUR 618, USD 635, GBP 388 combined subscription to institutions print & online eds. (effective 2005). adv. bk.rev. reprint service avail. from PSC. **Document type:** *Journal, Academic/Scholarly.* **Description:** Publishes commentary on issues and developments in artificial intelligence foundations and current research.
Related titles: Microform ed.: (from PQC); Online - full text ed.: ISSN 1573-7462 (from EBSCO Publishing, Gale Group, IngentaConnect, Kluwer Online, O C L C Online Computer Library Center, Inc., Ovid Technologies, Inc., Springer LINK, Swets Information Services).
Indexed: AHCI, AIA, ASCA, ArtIAb, BibLing, BrCerAb, C&ISA, CMCI, CPE, CerAb, CompAb, CompLI, CompR, CorrAb, CurCont, E&CAJ, EMA, ERA, ETA, EngInd, IAA, ISR, Inspec, LISA, M&TEA, MBF, MEA, METADEX, PsycInfo, PsycholAb, RHEA, RefZh, SCI, SEA, SENA, SOMA, SSCI, SolStAb, TEA, WAA, ZentMath, e-psyche.
—BLDSC (1735.037300), AskIEEE, CISTI, Ei, IDS, IE, Infotrieve, ingenta, Linda Hall. **CCC.**
Published by: Springer-Verlag Dordrecht (Subsidiary of: Springer Science+Business Media), Van Godewijckstraat 30, Dordrecht, 3311 GX, Netherlands. TEL 31-78-6576050, FAX 31-78-6576474, http://springerlink.metapress.com/openurl.asp?genre=journal&issn=0269-2821, http://www.springeronline.com. Ed. Paul McKevitt.

006.3 591.5 004 USA ISSN 1064-5462
QH324.2 CODEN: ARLIEY
ARTIFICIAL LIFE. Text in English. 1993. q. USD 62 combined subscription in US & Canada to individuals print & online eds.; USD 82 combined subscription elsewhere to individuals print & online eds.; USD 270 combined subscription in US & Canada to institutions print & online eds.; USD 290 combined subscription elsewhere to institutions print & online eds. (effective 2006). **Document type:** *Academic/Scholarly.* **Description:** Acts as a primary forum for international scientific and engineering research in the new discipline of synthetic biological work. Covers topics from the origin of life, through self-reproduction, to evolution, growth and development all the way to the dynamics of whole ecosystems. Presents articles and reviews on synthetic approaches to the spectrum of biological phenomena.
Related titles: Microfiche ed.: (from PQC); Online - full content ed.: ISSN 1530-9185. USD 56 to individuals; USD 243 to institutions (effective 2006); Online - full text ed.: (from EBSCO Publishing, Gale Group, IngentaConnect, O C L C Online Computer Library Center, Inc., Swets Information Services).
Indexed: BIOSIS Prev, BiolAb, CMCI, CompAb, CompLI, CompR, CurCont, ISR, IndMed, Inspec, MEDLINE, SCI, ZooRec.
—BLDSC (1735.045000), CISTI, IE, Infotrieve, ingenta, Linda Hall. **CCC.**
Published by: (International Society of Artificial Life, Santa Fe Institute), M I T Press, 55 Hayward St, Cambridge, MA 02142-1493. TEL 617-253-5646, FAX 617-258-6779, editor@alife.org, journals-info@mit.edu, http://mitpress.mit.edu/catalog/item/default.asp?sid=27C58CFA-3776-45C8-A722-3274F8F907FC&ttype=4&tid=41. Ed. Mark A Bedau TEL 503-788-6697. Circ: 1,000 (paid).

006.3 JPN ISSN 1433-5298
➤ **ARTIFICIAL LIFE AND ROBOTICS.** Text in English. 1997. q. EUR 238 combined subscription to institutions print & online eds. (effective 2005). reprint service avail. from PSC. **Document type:** *Journal, Academic/Scholarly.* **Description:** Publishes original technical papers and reviews on the development of new technologies concerning artificial life and robotics.
Related titles: Online - full text ed.: ISSN 1614-7456 (from EBSCO Publishing, Springer LINK, Swets Information Services).
Indexed: Inspec.
—BLDSC (1735.045500), CISTI, IE, ingenta. **CCC.**
Published by: Springer-Verlag Tokyo (Subsidiary of: Springer Science+Business Media), 3-13 Hongo 3-chome, Bunkyo-ku, Tokyo, 113-0033, Japan. TEL 81-3-3812-0757, FAX 81-3-3812-0719, http://www.springer-tokyo.co.jp/. Ed. Masanori Sugisaka. Adv. contact Stephan Kroeck TEL 49-30-827875739. **Subscr. in the Americas to:** Springer-Verlag New York, Inc., Journal Fulfillment, PO Box 2485, Secaucus, NJ 07096-2485. TEL 800-777-4643, 201-348-4033, FAX 201-348-4505, journals@springer-ny.com, http://www.springer-ny.com; **Subscr. to:** Springer GmbH Auslieferungsgesellschaft, Haberstr 7, Heidelberg 69126, Germany. TEL 49-6221-345-0, FAX 49-6221-345-4229, subscriptions@springer.de.

006.3 AUS
AUSTRALASIAN COMPUTER HUMAN INTERACTION CONFERENCE. PROCEEDINGS. Text in English. a. USD 120. **Document type:** *Proceedings.*
Published by: University of South Australia, School of Computer and Information Science, Advanced Computing Research Centre, UniSA Levels Campus, Mawson Lakes Blvd., Mawson Lakes, SA 5095, Australia. TEL 61-8-8302-3201, FAX 61-8-8302-3381, cis@unisa.edu.au, http://www.cis.unisa.edu.au/~cisjfr/publications2.html.

006.3 GBR
AUSTRALIAN JOINT CONFERENCE ON ARTIFICIAL INTELLIGENCE. PROCEEDINGS. Text in English. irreg., latest 2002. price varies. **Document type:** *Proceedings, Academic/Scholarly.*
Published by: Springer-Verlag London Ltd. (Subsidiary of: Springer Science+Business Media), Ashbourne House, The Guildway, Old Portsmouth Rd, Guildford, Surrey GU7 3DJ, United Kingdom. TEL 44-1483-734433, FAX 44-1483-734411, http://www.springer.co.uk.

006.3 AUS ISSN 1321-2133
AUSTRALIAN JOURNAL OF INTELLIGENT INFORMATION PROCESSING SYSTEMS. Text in English. 1994. q. AUD 80 domestic to individuals; AUD 90 foreign to individuals; AUD 250 domestic to institutions; AUD 280 foreign to institutions (effective 2000). **Document type:** *Academic/Scholarly.* **Description:** Provides the latest information on interdisciplinary research developments and related activities in the design and implementation of intelligent information processing systems.
Indexed: Inspec.
—BLDSC (1809.105000).
Published by: Centre of Intelligent Information Processing Systems, University of Western Australia, Dept of Electrical & Electronic Engineering, Nedlands, W.A. 6907, Australia. ajiips@ee.uwa.edu.au. Ed. Yianni Attikiouzel.

006.3 NLD ISSN 0927-1023
➤ **AUTOMATED REASONING SERIES.** Text in English. 1991. irreg., latest vol.4, 1996. price varies. **Document type:** *Monographic series, Academic/Scholarly.*
Indexed: CCMJ, ZentMath.
—BLDSC (1828.379600).
Published by: Springer-Verlag Dordrecht (Subsidiary of: Springer Science+Business Media), Van Godewijckstraat 30, Dordrecht, 3311 GX, Netherlands. TEL 31-78-6576050, FAX 31-78-6576474, http://www.springeronline.com. Ed. William Pase.

006.3 USA ISSN 0928-8910
QA76.758 CODEN: ASOEEA
➤ **AUTOMATED SOFTWARE ENGINEERING**; the international journal of automated reasoning and artificial intelligence in software engineering. Text in English. 1994. q. EUR 558, USD 568, GBP 355 combined subscription to institutions print & online eds. (effective 2005). adv. reprint service avail. from PSC. **Document type:** *Academic/Scholarly.* **Description:** Publishes reports of significant industrial experience in the application of automated reasoning, knowledge representation and artificial intelligence in software engineering.
Related titles: Online - full text ed.: ISSN 1573-7535 (from EBSCO Publishing, Gale Group, IngentaConnect, Kluwer Online, O C L C Online Computer Library Center, Inc., Springer LINK, Swets Information Services).
Indexed: B&BAb, BibLing, BrCerAb, C&ISA, CerAb, CompAb, CompLI, CorrAb, E&CAJ, EMA, EngInd, IAA, Inspec, M&TEA, MBF, METADEX, RefZh, SolStAb, WAA.
—BLDSC (1828.382000), AskIEEE, CISTI, Ei, IE, Infotrieve, ingenta, Linda Hall. **CCC.**
Published by: Springer-Verlag New York, Inc. (Subsidiary of: Springer Science+Business Media), 233 Spring St, New York, NY 10013. TEL 212-460-1500, FAX 212-473-6272, journals@springer-ny.com, http://springerlink.metapress.com/openurl.asp?genre=journal&issn=0928-8910, http://www.springer-ny.com. Ed. Bashar Nuseibeh. **Subscr. to:** Journal Fulfillment, PO Box 2485, Secaucus, NJ 07096-2485. TEL 201-348-4033, FAX 201-348-4505, journals@springer-ny.com.

➤ **AUTOMATIC DOCUMENTATION AND MATHEMATICAL LINGUISTICS.** see *LINGUISTICS—Computer Applications*

006.31 USA ISSN 1387-2532
AUTONOMOUS AGENTS AND MULTI-AGENT SYSTEMS. Text in English. 1998. 6/yr. EUR 658, USD 668, GBP 298 combined subscription to institutions print & online eds. (effective 2005). adv. reprint service avail. from PSC. **Document type:** *Academic/Scholarly.* **Description:** Aims to provide a forum for disseminating significant new results in foundations, development, analysis, and applications of autonomous agents and multi-agent systems.
Related titles: Online - full text ed.: ISSN 1573-7454 (from EBSCO Publishing, Gale Group, IngentaConnect, Kluwer Online, O C L C Online Computer Library Center, Inc., Springer LINK, Swets Information Services).
Indexed: BibLing, CMCI, CompLI, CurCont, EngInd, Inspec.
—BLDSC (1835.061200), CISTI, IE, Infotrieve, ingenta. **CCC.**
Published by: Springer-Verlag New York, Inc. (Subsidiary of: Springer Science+Business Media), 233 Spring St, New York, NY 10013. TEL 212-460-1500, FAX 212-473-6272, journals@springer-ny.com, http://springerlink.metapress.com/openurl.asp?genre=journal&issn=1387-2532, http://www.springer-ny.com. Eds. Katia Sycara, Michael Wooldridge. **Subscr. to:** Journal Fulfillment, PO Box 2485, Secaucus, NJ 07096-2485. TEL 201-348-4033, FAX 201-348-4505, journals@springer-ny.com.

B@TI-COM. see *BUILDING AND CONSTRUCTION*

006.3 USA ISSN 1522-4899
BRAZILIAN SYMPOSIUM ON NEURAL NETWORKS. PROCEEDINGS. Text in English. 1997. biennial, latest vol.7, 2002. USD 155 per vol. (effective 2004). **Document type:** *Proceedings, Trade.*
Related titles: Online - full text ed.: (from I E E E).
—BLDSC (2277.427000).
Published by: Institute of Electrical and Electronics Engineers, Inc., 3 Park Ave, 17th Fl, New York, NY 10016-5997. TEL 212-419-7900, 800-678-4333, FAX 212-752-4929, customer.service@ieee.org, http://www.ieee.org.

C C A I; the journal for the integrated study of artificial intelligence, cognitive science and applied epistemology. see *LINGUISTICS—Computer Applications*

006.3 CAN ISSN 0823-9339
CODEN: CARIEZ
CANADIAN ARTIFICIAL INTELLIGENCE✶. Text in English. 1984. q. CND 10 per issue. **Document type:** *Academic/Scholarly.*
Indexed: Inspec.
—BLDSC (3017.270000), AskIEEE, CISTI, IE, ingenta.
Published by: Canadian Information Processing Society, 2800 Skymark Ave, Ste 402, Mississauga, ON L4W 5A6, Canada. info@cips.ca, http://www.cips.ca. R&P Stan Matwins.

COGNITIVE SYSTEMS RESEARCH. see *PSYCHOLOGY*

006.35 USA ISSN 0161-4126
COMMUNICATION OUTLOOK; focusing on communication aids and techniques. Text in English. 1978. q. USD 18 in the Americas; USD 24 elsewhere; USD 5 per issue (effective 2005). adv. bk.rev. back issues avail. **Document type:** *Journal, Academic/Scholarly.* **Description:** Covers technological developments for persons who experience communication handicaps due to neurological, sensory or neuromuscular conditions.
Related titles: Microform ed.: (from PQC).
Indexed: Inspec, RehabLit, YAE&RB, e-psyche.
—BLDSC (3361.600000), AskIEEE, IE, ingenta.
Published by: Michigan State University, Artificial Language Laboratory, 405 Computer Center, Michigan State University, E Lansing, MI 48824-1042. TEL 517-353-0870, FAX 517-353-4766, artlang@pilot.msu.edu, http://www.msu.edu/%7Eartlang/CommOut.html, http://www.msu.edu/~artlang. Ed., R&P John Eulenber. Adv. contact Carolyn Watt. Circ: 1,000.

COMPETITIVE INTELLIGENCE RESOURCES; an internet miniguide. see *COMPUTERS—Abstracting, Bibliographies, Statistics*

006.3 NLD
➤ **COMPUTATIONAL INTELLIGENCE.** Variant title: Proceedings of the International Symposium on Computational Intelligence. Text in English. 1990. a., latest vol.3, 1991. price varies. back issues avail. **Document type:** *Monographic series, Academic/Scholarly.*
Related titles: Online - full text ed.
Indexed: ASCA, CCMJ, CMCI, CurCont.

C

▼ new title ➤ refereed ✶ unverified ♦ full entry avail.

Published by: Elsevier BV (Subsidiary of: Elsevier Science & Technology), Radarweg 29, Amsterdam, 1043 NX, Netherlands. TEL 31-20-4853911, FAX 31-20-4852457, nlinfo-f@elsevier.nl, http://www.elsevier.nl.

➤ **COMPUTATIONAL LINGUISTICS.** see *LINGUISTICS—Computer Applications*

006.37 USA ISSN 1077-3142
TA1632 CODEN: CVIUF4
➤ **COMPUTER VISION AND IMAGE UNDERSTANDING.** Text in English. 1969. 12/yr. EUR 736 in Europe to individuals; JPY 76,800 in Japan to individuals; USD 577 to individuals except Europe and Japan; EUR 1,549 in Europe to institutions; JPY 162,000 in Japan to institutions; USD 1,215 to institutions except Europe and Japan (effective 2006). illus. reprints avail. **Document type:** *Academic/Scholarly.* **Description:** Focuses on the computer analysis of pictorial information.
Formerly (until 1995): C V G I P: Image Understanding (1049-9660); Which superseded in part (in 1991): Computer Vision, Graphics, and Image Processing (0734-189X); Which was formerly (until 1983): Computer Graphics and Image Processing (0146-664X).
Related titles: Online - full text ed.: ISSN 1090-235X. USD 1,264 (effective 2002) (from EBSCO Publishing, Gale Group, IngentaConnect, O C L C Online Computer Library Center, Inc., ScienceDirect, Swets Information Services).
Indexed: AHCI, AIA, AS&TI, ASCA, B&BAb, BioEngAb, BrCerAb, C&ISA, CADCAM, CIS, CMCI, CerAb, CompD, CompLI, CompR, CorrAb, CurCont, E&CAJ, EMA, EngInd, IAA, ISR, Inspec, M&TEA, MBF, METADEX, RASB, RefZh, RoboAb, SCI, SSCI, SolStAb, WAA, ZentMath.
—BLDSC (3394.353500), AskIEEE, CISTI, Ei, IDS, IE, Infotrieve, ingenta, Linda Hall. **CCC.**
Published by: Academic Press (Subsidiary of: Elsevier Science & Technology), 525 B St, Ste 1900, San Diego, CA 92101-4495. TEL 619-231-6616, 800-894-3434, apsubs@acad.com, http://www.elsevier.com/locate/cviu, http://www.academicpress.com. Ed. Avinash C Kak.

➤ **COMPUTERKULTUR.** see *COMPUTERS*

006.3 SVK ISSN 1335-9150
➤ **COMPUTING AND INFORMATICS.** Text and summaries in English. 1982. bi-m. USD 220 foreign (effective 2004). bk.rev. abstr.; bibl.; illus. 104 p./no.; back issues avail. **Document type:** *Journal, Academic/Scholarly.* **Description:** Covers computer architecture and networking, parallel and distributed computing, theoretical foundations, software engineering, and knowledge and information engineering.
Former titles (until 2001): Computers and Artificial Intelligence (0232-0274); (until 1982): Pocitace a Umela Inteligencia (0231-7389)
Indexed: AHCI, ASCA, CCMJ, CMCI, CompAb, CurCont, EngInd, Inspec, MathR, MathSciNet, RefZh, ZentMath.
—BLDSC (3395.019550), AskIEEE, IDS, IE, ingenta.
Published by: (Slovenska Akademia Vied, Ustav Informatiky/Slovak Academy of Sciences, Institute of Informatics), Slovak Academic Press Ltd., Nam Slobody 6, PO Box 57, Bratislava, 81005, Slovakia. sap@sappress.sk, http://www.sappress.sk. Ed., R&P Ladislav Hluchy TEL 421-2-54771004. Circ: 300 (paid). **Dist. by:** Slovart G.T.G. s.r.o., Krupinska 4, PO Box 152, Bratislava 85299, Slovakia. http://www.slovart-gtg.sk. **Co-publishers:** Slovak University of Technology, Faculty of Electrical Engineering and Information Technology; Comenius University of Bratislava, Faculty of Mathematics, Physics & Informatics; Slovak Society for Computer Science.

006.3 USA
COMPUTISTS' WEEKLY. Text in English. 1991. w. USD 95 to individuals; USD 45 to students. back issues avail. **Document type:** *Newsletter.* **Description:** News for artificial intelligence researchers, computer scientists, and software technologists.
Formerly (until 1999): Computists' Communique (1084-015X)
Media: E-mail.
Published by: Computists' International, 4064 Sutherland Dr, Palo Alto, CA 94303. TEL 650-493-4176, editor@computists.com, http://www.computists.com. Ed. Kenneth I Laws.

006.33 USA
Q334
CONFERENCE ON THE THEORETICAL ASPECTS OF REASONING ABOUT KNOWLEDGE. PROCEEDINGS. Text in English. 1986. biennial. price varies. **Document type:** *Proceedings.*
Published by: Morgan Kaufmann Publishers, Inc. (Subsidiary of: Elsevier BV), 500 Sansome St, Ste 400, San Francisco, CA 94111. TEL 415-392-2665, FAX 415-982-2665, orders@mkp.com, http://www.mkp.com. Ed. Michael B Morgan. R&P Marilyn Uffner Alan.

006.32 GBR ISSN 0954-0091
QA76.87 CODEN: CNTSEU
➤ **CONNECTION SCIENCE;** journal of neural computing, artificial intelligence, and cognitive research. Text in English. 1989. q. GBP 623, USD 1,087 combined subscription to institutions print & online eds. (effective 2006). adv. bk.rev. reprint service avail. from PSC. **Document type:** *Journal, Academic/Scholarly.* **Description:** Covers connectionist research in human and artificial intelligence, cognitive science, computational neuroscience and advanced computer science.
Related titles: Microfiche ed.; Online - full text ed.: ISSN 1360-0494. GBP 592, USD 1,033 to institutions (effective 2006) (from EBSCO Publishing, Gale Group, IngentaConnect, Northern Light Technology, Inc., O C L C Online Computer Library Center, Inc., ProQuest Information & Learning, Swets Information Services).
Indexed: ASFA, B&BAb, BioEngAb, CINAHL, CMCI, CompAb, CompLI, CurCont, EngInd, ErgAb, ISR, Inspec, L&LBA, PhilInd, PsycInfo, PsycholAb, SCI, SOPODA, e-psyche.
—BLDSC (3417.662450), AskIEEE, CISTI, Ei, GNLM, IDS, IE, Infotrieve, ingenta. **CCC.**
Published by: Taylor & Francis Ltd (Subsidiary of: Taylor & Francis Group), 4 Park Sq, Milton Park, Abingdon, OX14 4RN, United Kingdom. TEL 44-1235-828600, FAX 44-1235-829000, info@tandf.co.uk, http://www.tandf.co.uk/journals/titles/09540091.asp. Eds. Amanda J C Sharkey, Tom Ziemke, Noel E Sharkey. **Subscr. in N. America to:** Taylor & Francis Inc., Customer Services Dept, 325 Chestnut St, 8th Fl, Philadelphia, PA 19106. TEL 215-625-8900, 800-354-1420, FAX 215-625-8914, customerservice@taylorandfrancis.com; **Subscr. to:** Journals Customer Service, Rankine Rd, Basingstoke, Hants RG24 8PR, United Kingdom. TEL 44-1256-813000, FAX 44-1256-330245, enquiry@tandf.co.uk.

006 USA ISSN 1383-7133
CODEN: CNSTFT
CONSTRAINTS; an international journal. Text in English. 1996. q. EUR 411, USD 411, GBP 257 combined subscription to institutions print & online eds. (effective 2005). adv. reprint service avail. from PSC. **Document type:** *Journal, Academic/Scholarly.* **Description:** Covers the disciplines involved in constraint satisfaction and optimization, and constraint technology; also all aspects of computing with constraints such as theory and practice, algorithms and systems, reasoning and programming, logics and languages.
Related titles: Online - full text ed.: ISSN 1572-9354 (from EBSCO Publishing, Gale Group, IngentaConnect, Kluwer Online, O C L C Online Computer Library Center, Inc., Ovid Technologies, Inc., Springer LINK, Swets Information Services).
Indexed: BibLing, CCMJ, CMCI, CurCont, EngInd, Inspec, MathR, MathSciNet, RefZh, ZentMath.
—BLDSC (3420.659700), AskIEEE, CISTI, IE, Infotrieve, ingenta. **CCC.**
Published by: Springer-Verlag New York, Inc. (Subsidiary of: Springer Science+Business Media), 233 Spring St, New York, NY 10013. TEL 212-460-1500, FAX 212-460-1575, service@springer-ny.com, http://springerlink.metapress.com/openurl.asp?genre=journal&issn=1383-7133, http://www.springer-ny.com. Ed. Peter van Beek. **Subscr. to:** Journal Fulfillment, PO Box 2485, Secaucus, NJ 07096-2485. TEL 201-348-4033, FAX 201-348-4505, journals@springer-ny.com.

006.3 NLD
DECENTRALIZED A I. (Artificial Intelligence) Variant title: European Workshop on Modelling Autonomous Agents in a Multi-Agent World. Proceedings. Text in English. 1990. irreg., latest vol.3, 1992. price varies. back issues avail. **Document type:** *Proceedings.*
Published by: Elsevier BV (Subsidiary of: Elsevier Science & Technology), Radarweg 29, Amsterdam, 1043 NX, Netherlands. TEL 31-20-4853911, FAX 31-20-4852457, nlinfo-f@elsevier.nl, http://www.elsevier.nl. Ed. Yves Demazeau.

006.3 AUS ISSN 1328-8911
DESIGN COMPUTING NEWSLETTER. Text in English. 1994. irreg. back issues avail. **Document type:** *Newsletter.*
Media: Online - full text.
Published by: University of Sydney, School of Architectural and Design Science, Faculty of Architecture, Sydney, NSW 2006, Australia. TEL 61-2-9351-3605, FAX 61-2-9351-3855, http://www.arch.usyd.edu.au/kcdc/dcn/index.html.

006.35 GBR ISSN 1350-990X
E L SNEWS; the newsletter of the European Network in human language technologies. Text in English. 1992. q.
Indexed: RefZh.
Published by: (E L S N E T NLD), University of Sussex, School of Cognitive and Computing Sciences, Computer Science and Artificial Intelligence, Falmer, Brighton BN1 9QH, United Kingdom. TEL 44-01273-678195, FAX 44-01273-671320, http://www.elsnet.org/publications/elsnews/11.1.pdf.

006.3 SWE ISSN 1403-2031
ELECTRONIC NEWS JOURNAL ON REASONING ABOUT ACTIONS AND CHANGE. Text in English. m.
Related titles: Online - full text ed.: ISSN 1403-204X. free (effective 2005).
Published by: Linkoeping Universitet, Institutionen foer Tema, Linkoeping, 58183, Sweden. TEL 46-13-282286, FAX 46-13-133630, annuh@ida.liu.se, http://www.ida.liu.se. Ed. Erik Sandewall.

006.3 SWE ISSN 1403-3534
ELECTRONIC TRANSACTIONS ON ARTIFICIAL INTELLIGENCE. Abbreviated title: E T A I. Text in Swedish. q. **Document type:** *Academic/Scholarly.*
Related titles: Online - full text ed.: ISSN 1403-3526.
Indexed: CCMJ, MathSciNet.
Published by: Linkoeping Universitet, Institutionen foer Tema, Linkoeping, 58183, Sweden. TEL 46-13-282286, FAX 46-13-133630, ejs@ida.liu.se, annuh@ida.liu.se, http://www.ep.liu.se/ej/etai, http://www.ida.liu.se. Ed. Erik Sandewall. **Co-sponsors:** European Coordinating Committee for Artificial Intelligence; Kungliga Vetenskapsakademien/Royal Swedish Academy of Sciences.

006.3 GBR ISSN 0952-1976
TA345 CODEN: EAAIE6
➤ **ENGINEERING APPLICATIONS OF ARTIFICIAL INTELLIGENCE.** Text in English. 1988. 8/yr. EUR 1,124 in Europe to institutions; JPY 149,200 in Japan to institutions; USD 1,258 elsewhere to institutions; EUR 76 in Europe to qualified personnel; JPY 10,000 in Japan to qualified personnel; USD 84 elsewhere to qualified personnel (effective 2006). back issues avail. **Document type:** *Journal, Academic/Scholarly.* **Description:** Describes the practical application of AI methods in all branches of engineering.
Related titles: Microfilm ed.: (from PQC); Online - full text ed.: (from EBSCO Publishing, Gale Group, IngentaConnect, ScienceDirect, Swets Information Services).
Indexed: AHCI, AIA, ASCA, B&BAb, BrCerAb, C&ISA, CMCI, CerAb, CivEngAb, CompLI, CorrAb, CurCont, E&CAJ, EMA, EngInd, IAA, Inspec, M&TEA, MBF, METADEX, SSCI, SolStAb, WAA.
—BLDSC (3755.704500), AskIEEE, CISTI, Ei, IDS, IE, Infotrieve, ingenta, Linda Hall. **CCC.**
Published by: Pergamon (Subsidiary of: Elsevier Science & Technology), The Boulevard, Langford Ln, East Park, Kidlington, Oxford OX5 1GB, United Kingdom. TEL 44-1865-843000, FAX 44-1865-843010, eaai@wanadoo.fr, http://www.elsevier.com/locate/engappai. Eds. B Grabot, R A Vingerhoeds. **Subscr. to:** Elsevier BV, PO Box 211, Amsterdam 1000 AE, Netherlands. TEL 31-20-485-3757, FAX 31-20-485-3432, nlinfo-f@elsevier.nl, http://www.elsevier.nl.

621.399 621.3 GBR
TK1 CODEN: IJEIEV
➤ **ENGINEERING INTELLIGENT SYSTEMS;** for electrical engineering and communications. Text in English. 1993. q. GBP 152 in the European Union to institutions; GBP 162 elsewhere to institutions (effective 2002). bk.rev. Index. 64 p./no.; back issues avail. **Document type:** *Journal, Academic/Scholarly.* **Description:** Addresses computer applications in electrical engineering, communication, and electrical power systems.
Former titles: International Journal of Engineering Intelligent Systems for Electrical Engineering and Communications (1472-8915); (until 1999): Engineering Intelligent Systems for Electrical Engineering and Communications (1363-2078); (until 1996): International Journal of Engineering Intelligent Systems for Electrical Engineering and Communications (0969-1170)
Indexed: ASCA, BrCerAb, C&ISA, CMCI, CerAb, CorrAb, CurCont, E&CAJ, EMA, ESPM, EngInd, H&SSA, IAA, Inspec, M&TEA, MBF, METADEX, SolStAb, WAA.
—BLDSC (3763.150000), AskIEEE, CISTI, Ei, IDS, IE, ingenta, Linda Hall.
Published by: C R L Publishing Ltd., PO Box 31, Market Harborough, Leics LE16 9BP, United Kingdom. TEL 44-1858-469898, FAX 44-1858-431649, eis@crlpublishing.co.uk, admin@crlpublishing.co.uk, http://www.crlpublishing.co.uk. Ed., Pub. T S Dillon.

006.32 GBR ISSN 0266-4720
QA76.76.E95 CODEN: EXSYEX
➤ **EXPERT SYSTEMS;** the international journal of knowledge engineering and neural networks. Text in English. 1984. 5/yr. EUR 51 combined subscription in Europe to individuals print & online eds.; USD 57 combined subscription in the Americas to individuals & Caribbean (print & online eds.); GBP 34 combined subscription elsewhere to individuals print & online eds.; USD 590 combined subscription in the Americas to institutions & Caribbean (print & online eds.); GBP 351 combined subscription elsewhere to institutions print & online eds. (effective 2006). bk.rev. illus. Index. reprint service avail. from PSC. **Document type:** *Journal, Academic/Scholarly.* **Description:** Review of practical, technical information with papers, interviews, features, news and reviews.
Formerly: Expert Systems User; Which incorporated: Artificial Intelligence Business
Related titles: Online - full text ed.: ISSN 1468-0394. USD 559 in the Americas to institutions & Caribbean; GBP 333 elsewhere to institutions (effective 2006) (from Blackwell Synergy, EBSCO Publishing, Gale Group, IngentaConnect, O C L C Online Computer Library Center, Inc., Swets Information Services).
Indexed: ABIn, AHCI, AIA, AS&TI, ArtIAb, CADCAM, CMCI, CPM, CompAb, CompLI, CurCont, CybAb, ESPM, ErgAb, H&SSA, InfoSAb, Inspec, LISA, MicrocompInd, PsycInfo, PsycholAb, RiskAb, RoboAb.
—BLDSC (3842.004000), AskIEEE, CISTI, IDS, IE, Infotrieve, ingenta, Linda Hall. **CCC.**
Published by: Blackwell Publishing Ltd., 9600 Garsington Rd, Oxford, OX4 2ZG, United Kingdom. TEL 44-1865-776868, FAX 44-1865-714591, customerservices@oxon.blackwellpublishing.com, http://www.blackwellpublishing.com/journals/EXSY. Eds. Gordon Rugg, James L Alty TEL 44-1509-211586, Peter McGeorge TEL 44-1224-272248. Circ: 1,000.

006.3 GBR ISSN 0268-2486
EXPERT SYSTEMS APPLICATIONS. Text in English. 1985. m. GBP 395 domestic; GBP 545 foreign (effective 2000). bk.rev. **Document type:** *Newsletter.*
Indexed: CurCont, Inspec.
—AskIEEE, CISTI.
Published by: I M L Group Plc., Blair House, 184 High St, Tonbridge, Kent TN9 1BQ, United Kingdom. TEL 44-1732-359990, FAX 44-1732-770049, imlgroup@dial.pipex.com. Ed. Andrew Bond. Pub. Peter Jago. R&P Valerie Billingsby. Circ: 44 (paid).

006.33 GBR ISSN 0957-4174
QA76.76.E95 CODEN: ESAPEH
➤ **EXPERT SYSTEMS WITH APPLICATIONS.** Text in English. 1990. 8/yr. EUR 279 in Europe to individuals; JPY 37,100 in Japan to individuals; USD 314 to individuals except Europe and Japan; EUR 2,052 in Europe to institutions; JPY 272,400 in Japan to institutions; USD 2,294 to institutions except Europe and Japan (effective 2006). back issues avail. **Document type:** *Journal, Academic/Scholarly.* **Description:** For engineers, developers, researchers, scientists and consultants. Focuses on the exchange of information relating to expert systems worldwide.
Related titles: Microfilm ed.: (from PQC); Online - full text ed.: (from EBSCO Publishing, Gale Group, IngentaConnect, ScienceDirect, Swets Information Services).
Indexed: AIA, ASCA, ASFA, BrCerAb, C&ISA, CJA, CMCI, CerAb, CivEngAb, CompAb, CompLI, CorrAb, CurCont, E&CAJ, EMA, ESPM, EngInd, H&SSA, IAA, Inspec, M&TEA, MBF, METADEX, PollutAb, PsycholAb, RefZh, RiskAb, SSCI, SolStAb, WAA.
—BLDSC (3842.004220), AskIEEE, CISTI, Ei, IDS, IE, Infotrieve, ingenta, Linda Hall. **CCC.**
Published by: Pergamon (Subsidiary of: Elsevier Science & Technology), The Boulevard, Langford Ln, East Park, Kidlington, Oxford OX5 1GB, United Kingdom. TEL 44-1865-843000, FAX 44-1865-843010, http://www.elsevier.com/locate/eswa. Ed. J Liebowitz. Circ: 1,481 (paid). **Subscr. to:** Elsevier BV, PO Box 211, Amsterdam 1000 AE, Netherlands. TEL 31-20-485-3757, FAX 31-20-485-3432, nlinfo-f@elsevier.nl, http://www.elsevier.nl.

006.31 USA ISSN 1081-6593
QA402.5
FOUNDATIONS OF GENETIC ALGORITHMS. Text in English. 1991. irreg.
—BLDSC (4025.295500). **CCC.**
Published by: Morgan Kaufmann Publishers, Inc. (Subsidiary of: Elsevier BV), 500 Sansome St, Ste 400, San Francisco, CA 94111. TEL 415-392-2665, 888-864-7547, FAX 415-982-2665, mkp@mkp.com, http://www.mkp.com. Ed. Michael B Morgan.

006.3 NLD ISSN 0922-6389
FRONTIERS IN ARTIFICIAL INTELLIGENCE AND APPLICATIONS. Text in English. 1988. irreg., latest vol.63, 2000. price varies. back issues avail. **Document type:** *Monographic series, Academic/Scholarly.* **Description:** Publishes studies and papers addressing issues at the forefront of artificial intelligence.
Related titles: ♦ Series: Scandinavian Conference on Artificial Intelligence. ISSN 0927-720X.
Indexed: CCMJ, MathR, ZentMath.
—CISTI, Ei. **CCC.**
Published by: I O S Press, Nieuwe Hemweg 6B, Amsterdam, 1013 BG, Netherlands. TEL 31-20-6883355, FAX 31-20-6203419, order@iospress.nl, http://www.iospress.nl. **Subscr. to:** I O S Press, Inc, 4502 Rachael Manor Dr., Fairfax, VA 22032-3631. iosbooks@iospress.com. **Dist. by:** Ohmsha Ltd.

006.2 USA
FUZZY INFORMATION PROCESSING SOCIETY. ANNUAL MEETING. Text in English. a. **Document type:** *Proceedings, Trade.*
Published by: Institute of Electrical and Electronics Engineers, Inc., 3 Park Ave, 17th Fl, New York, NY 10016-5997. TEL 800-678-4333, customer.service@ieee.org, http://www.ieee.org.

006.2 USA ISSN 1568-4539
FUZZY OPTIMIZATION AND DECISION MAKING; a journal of modeling and computation under uncertainty. Text in English. 2002. q. EUR 343, USD 343, GBP 214 combined subscription to institutions print & online eds. (effective 2005). adv. reprint service avail. from PSC. **Document type:** *Journal, Academic/Scholarly.* **Description:** Promotes research and the development of fuzzy technology and soft-computing methodologies to enhance our ability to address complicated optimization and decision making problems involving non-probabilitic uncertainty. Covers all aspects of employing fuzzy technologies to see optimal solutions and assist in making the best possible decisions and provides a global forum for advancing the state-of-the-art theory and practice of fuzzy optimization and decision making in the presence of uncertainty.
Related titles: Online - full text ed.: ISSN 1573-2908 (from EBSCO Publishing, Gale Group, IngentaConnect, Kluwer Online, O C L C Online Computer Library Center, Inc., ProQuest Information & Learning, Springer LINK, Swets Information Services).
Indexed: ABIn, BibLing, BrCerAb, C&ISA, CerAb, CompLI, CorrAb, E&CAJ, EMA, IAA, Inspec, M&TEA, MBF, METADEX, MathR, MathSciNet, WAA.
—BLDSC (4060.739000), CISTI, IE, ingenta, Linda Hall. **CCC.**
Published by: Springer-Verlag New York, Inc. (Subsidiary of: Springer Science+Business Media), 233 Spring St, New York, NY 10013. TEL 212-460-1500, FAX 212-460-1575, service@springer-ny.com, http://springerlink.metapress.com/openurl.asp?genre=journal&issn=1568-4539, http://www.springer-ny.com. Ed. Shu-Cherng Fang. **Subscr. to:** Journal Fulfillment, PO Box 2485, Secaucus, NJ 07096-2485. TEL 201-348-4033, FAX 201-348-4505, journals@springer-ny.com.

006.31 USA ISSN 1389-2576
CODEN: GPEMFU
➤ **GENETIC PROGRAMMING AND EVOLVABLE MACHINES.** Text in English. 2000. q. EUR 386, USD 386, GBP 237 combined subscription to institutions print & online eds. (effective 2005). adv. reprint service avail. from PSC. **Document type:** *Journal, Academic/Scholarly.* **Description:** Reports innovative and significant progress in automatic evolution of software and hardware; methods for artificial evolution of active components, such as entail the development, evaluation and application of methods that mirror the process of neo-Darwinian evolution.
Related titles: Online - full text ed.: ISSN 1573-7632 (from EBSCO Publishing, Gale Group, IngentaConnect, Kluwer Online, O C L C Online Computer Library Center, Inc., Springer LINK, Swets Information Services).
Indexed: B&BAb, BibLing, BioEngAb, Inspec, RefZh.
—BLDSC (4111.890000), CISTI, IE, Infotrieve, ingenta. **CCC.**
Published by: Springer-Verlag New York, Inc. (Subsidiary of: Springer Science+Business Media), 233 Spring St, New York, NY 10013. TEL 212-460-1500, FAX 212-460-1575, service@springer-ny.com, http://springerlink.metapress.com/openurl.asp?genre=journal&issn=1389-2576, http://www.springer-ny.com. Ed. Wolfgang Banzhaf. **Subscr. to:** Journal Fulfillment, PO Box 2485, Secaucus, NJ 07096-2485. TEL 201-348-4033, FAX 201-348-4505, journals@springer-ny.com.

006.32 FRA ISSN 1166-4738
CODEN: GLSEED
GENIE LOGICIEL ET SYSTEMES EXPERTS. Text in French. 1985. q. **Document type:** *Trade.*
Formerly (until 1986): Genie Logiciel (0295-6322)
Indexed: Inspec.
—BLDSC (4116.070000), AskIEEE, CISTI, IE, ingenta. **CCC.**
Published by: E C 2, 269 rue de la Garenne, Nanterre, 92000, France. TEL 47-80-70-00, FAX 47-80-66-29. Ed. Jean Claude Rault. Circ: 2,000.

006.3 CAN ISSN 1482-7913
I A S T E D INTERNATIONAL CONFERENCE ON ARTIFICIAL INTELLIGENCE AND SOFT COMPUTING. Text in English. a. **Document type:** *Proceedings, Academic/Scholarly.*
—BLDSC (6844.164042).
Published by: (International Association of Science and Technology for Development), ACTA Press, 4500-16th Ave NW, Ste 80, Calgary, AB T3B 0M6, Canada. TEL 403-288-1195, FAX 403-247-6851, journals@actapress.com, http://www.actapress.com.

006.37 USA
I C C V - INTERNATIONAL CONFERENCE ON COMPUTER VISION. Text in English. 1982. biennial. price varies. adv. **Document type:** *Proceedings.* **Description:** Covers all areas of computer vision research including edge detection, neural networks, recognition, psychophysics and optical flow.
Former titles: I E E E Computer Society Workshop on Computer Vision; (until 1985): Workshop on Computer Vision Representation and Control. Proceedings
Published by: (Institute of Electrical and Electronics Engineers, Inc.), I E E E Computer Society, 10662 Los Vaqueros Circle, PO Box 3014, Los Alamitos, CA 90720-1314. TEL 714-821-8380, FAX 714-821-4641. Ed. Cat Harris. Pub. Matt Loeb. Adv. contact Frieda Koester.

006.3 USA ISSN 1556-603X
▼ **I E E E COMPUTATIONAL INTELLIGENCE MAGAZINE.** Text in English. forthcoming 2006 (Mar.). q. USD 375; USD 469 combined subscription print & online eds. (effective 2006). **Document type:** *Journal, Academic/Scholarly.*
Related titles: Online - full text ed.: ISSN 1556-6048. forthcoming 2006 (Mar.). USD 375 (effective 2006).
Published by: Institute of Electrical and Electronics Engineers, Inc., 445 Hoes Ln, Piscataway, NJ 08854-1331. TEL 732-981-0060, FAX 732-981-1721, customer.service@ieee.org, http://www.ieee.org.

006.37 USA ISSN 1063-6919
TA1650 CODEN: PIVRE9
I E E E COMPUTER SOCIETY CONFERENCE ON COMPUTER VISION AND PATTERN RECOGNITION. PROCEEDINGS. Text in English. 1983. a. price varies. adv. **Document type:** *Proceedings, Academic/Scholarly.* **Description:** Papers submitted at the conference on all aspects of vision, pattern recognition and image processing.
Supersedes (1977-1982): I E E E Computer Society Conference on Pattern Recognition and Image Processing. P R I P. Proceedings; Which was formerly (until 1975): Conference on Computer Graphics, Pattern Recognition, and Data Structure. Proceedings
Related titles: Online - full text ed.: (from I E E E).
Indexed: AIA, CADCAM, CompC, ISR.
—BLDSC (4362.816800), Ei, IE, ingenta. **CCC.**
Published by: (Institute of Electrical and Electronics Engineers, Inc.), I E E E Computer Society, 10662 Los Vaqueros Circle, PO Box 3014, Los Alamitos, CA 90720-1314. TEL 714-821-8380, FAX 714-821-4641, customer.service@ieee.org, http://www.computer.org.

006.37 USA ISSN 1070-2385
T385
I E E E CONFERENCE ON VISUALIZATION. Text in English. 1990. a. price varies. adv. **Document type:** *Proceedings, Academic/Scholarly.* **Description:** Explores the use of visualization strategies in a variety of applications to extract knowledge from data.
Related titles: Online - full text ed.: (from I E E E).
—BLDSC (9241.370000). **CCC.**
Published by: (Institute of Electrical and Electro), I E E E Computer Society, 3 Park Ave, 17th Fl, New York, NY 10017. TEL 714-821-8380, 800-678-4333, FAX 714-821-4641, customer.service@ieee.org, http://www.ieee.org.

006.3 USA
I E E E - I A F E - I N F O R M S CONFERENCE ON COMPUTATIONAL INTELLIGENCE FOR FINANCIAL ENGINEERING. PROCEEDINGS. (International Association of Financial Engineers - Institute for Operations Research and the Managem) Text in English. a. USD 216 per vol. (effective 2004). **Document type:** *Proceedings, Trade.*
Formerly: I E E E - I A F E Conference on Computational Intelligence for Financial Engineering. Proceedings
Indexed: EngInd.
—BLDSC (6844.167072).
Published by: Institute of Electrical and Electronics Engineers, Inc., 3 Park Ave, 17th Fl, New York, NY 10016-5997. TEL 800-678-4333, customer.service@ieee.org, http://www.ieee.org.

006.3 USA ISSN 1550-5499
TA1634
I E E E INTERNATIONAL CONFERENCE ON COMPUTER VISION. PROCEEDINGS. (Institute of Electrical and Electronics Engineers) Text in English. a. USD 348; USD 140 to members (effective 2004). **Document type:** *Proceedings, Trade.*
—BLDSC (4538.768750).
Published by: Institute of Electrical and Electronics Engineers, Inc., 3 Park Ave, 17th Fl, New York, NY 10016-5997. TEL 212-419-7900, 800-678-4333, FAX 212-752-4929, customer.service@ieee.org, http://www.ieee.org.

006.3 USA
I E E E INTERNATIONAL CONFERENCE ON EVOLUTIONARY COMPUTATION. PROCEEDINGS. Text in English. a. USD 514 per vol.; USD 257 per vol. to members (effective 2004). **Document type:** *Proceedings, Trade.*
Published by: Institute of Electrical and Electronics Engineers, Inc., 3 Park Ave, 17th Fl, New York, NY 10016-5997. TEL 212-419-7900, 800-678-4333, FAX 212-752-4929, customer.service@ieee.org, http://www.ieee.org.

511.313 USA ISSN 1544-5615
I E E E INTERNATIONAL FUZZY SYSTEMS CONFERENCE. PROCEEDINGS. Text in English. 1992. a. (in 2 vols.). USD 336 per vol.; USD 168 per vol. to members (effective 2004). **Document type:** *Proceedings, Trade.*
Formerly (until 1999): I E E E International Conference on Fuzzy Systems. Proceedings (1098-7584)
Related titles: Online - full text ed.: (from I E E E).
—**CCC.**
Published by: Institute of Electrical and Electronics Engineers, Inc., 3 Park Ave, 17th Fl, New York, NY 10016-5997. TEL 212-419-7900, 800-678-4333, FAX 212-752-4929, customer.service@ieee.org, http://www.ieee.org.

006.2 629.892 USA
I E E E INTERNATIONAL SYMPOSIUM ON COMPUTATIONAL INTELLIGENCE IN ROBOTICS AND AUTOMATION. Text in English. 1997. biennial (in 5 vols.). USD 346; USD 173 to members (effective 2004). **Document type:** *Proceedings, Trade.*
Published by: Institute of Electrical and Electronics Engineers, Inc., 3 Park Ave, 17th Fl, New York, NY 10016-5997. TEL 212-419-7900, 800-678-4333, FAX 212-752-4929, customer.service@ieee.org, http://www.ieee.org. **Co-sponsor:** I E E E Computer Society.

006.33 USA
I E E E INTERNATIONAL SYMPOSIUM ON INTELLIGENT CONTROL. PROCEEDINGS. Text in English. 1985. a. USD 244. **Description:** Examines the following intelligent-control topics: multilayer controllers for large systems, hybrid knowledge-based analytical control systems, autonomous vehicles, expert systems, robotics, vision, and more.
Formerly (until 1985): I E E E Workshop on Intelligent Control. Proceedings

Indexed: EngInd, Inspec.
—BLDSC (6844.167300).
Published by: (Institute of Electrical and Electronics Engineers, Inc.), I E E E Computer Society, 3 Park Ave, 17th Fl, New York, NY 10017. TEL 714-821-8380, 800-678-4333, FAX 714-821-4010, customer.service@ieee.org, http://www.ieee.org.

006.3   USA   ISSN 1089-3555
QA76.87
I E E E NEURAL NETWORKS FOR SIGNAL PROCESSING. Text in English. 1991. a. USD 158; USD 79 to members (effective 2004). **Document type:** *Proceedings, Trade.*
Related titles: Online - full text ed.: (from I E E E).
—BLDSC (6081.280900). **CCC.**
Published by: Institute of Electrical and Electronics Engineers, Inc., 3 Park Ave, 17th Fl, New York, NY 10016-5997. TEL 212-419-7900, 800-678-4333, FAX 212-752-4929, customer.service@ieee.org, http://www.ieee.org.

511.3223   USA   ISSN 1063-6706
QA402   CODEN: IEFSEV
➤ **I E E E TRANSACTIONS ON FUZZY SYSTEMS.** Text in English. 1993. bi-m. USD 735 (effective 2006). adv.
Document type: *Journal, Academic/Scholarly.* **Description:** Covers theories and applications of fuzzy systems with emphasis on engineering systems and scientific applications.
Related titles: CD-ROM ed.; Microfiche ed.; Online - full text ed.: (from EBSCO Publishing, Swets Information Services).
Indexed: AS&TI, ASCA, B&BAb, CMCI, CompLI, CurCont, EngInd, ISR, Inspec, RefZh, SCI.
—BLDSC (4363.187800), AskIEEE, CISTI, Ei, IDS, IE, Infotrieve, ingenta, Linda Hall. **CCC.**
Published by: Institute of Electrical and Electronics Engineers, Inc., 445 Hoes Ln, Piscataway, NJ 08854-1331. TEL 732-981-0060, 800-701-4333, FAX 732-981-1721, subscription-service@ieee.org, http://www.ieee.org. Ed. James C Bezdek. **Subscr. to:** Maruzen Co., Ltd., 3-10 Nihonbashi 2-chome, Chuo-ku, Tokyo 103-0027, Japan. FAX 81-3-3275-0657; Universal Subscription Agency, Pvt. Ltd., 877, Udyog Vihar, V, Gurgoan 122001, India. TEL 91-124-347261, FAX 91-124-342496.

006.32   USA   ISSN 1045-9227
QA76.87   CODEN: ITNNEP
➤ **I E E E TRANSACTIONS ON NEURAL NETWORKS.** Text in English. 1990. bi-m. USD 995 (effective 2006). **Document type:** *Journal, Academic/Scholarly.* **Description:** Covers self-organizing systems, neurobiological connections, network dynamics and architecture, speech recognition, electronic and photonic implementation, robotics and controls.
Related titles: CD-ROM ed.; Microfiche ed.; Online - full text ed.: (from EBSCO Publishing, Swets Information Services).
Indexed: AS&TI, ASCA, BioEngAb, C&CSA, CIS, CMCI, CompAb, CompLI, CurCont, ESPM, EngInd, H&SSA, ISMEC, ISR, Inspec, NSCI, ORMS, QC&AS, RefZh, RiskAb, SCI, SSCI.
—BLDSC (4363.207000), AskIEEE, CISTI, Ei, GNLM, IDS, IE, Infotrieve, ingenta, Linda Hall. **CCC.**
Published by: Institute of Electrical and Electronics Engineers, Inc., 445 Hoes Ln, Piscataway, NJ 08854-1331. TEL 732-981-0060, 800-701-4333, FAX 732-981-1721, subscription-service@ieee.org, http://www.ieee.org. Ed. Jacek M Zurada. **Subscr. to:** Maruzen Co., Ltd., 3-10 Nihonbashi 2-chome, Chuo-ku, Tokyo 103-0027, Japan. FAX 81-3-3275-0657; Universal Subscription Agency, Pvt. Ltd., 877, Udyog Vihar, V, Gurgoan 122001, India. TEL 91-124-347261, FAX 91-124-342496.

006.31   USA   ISSN 0162-8828
Q327   CODEN: ITPIDJ
➤ **I E E E TRANSACTIONS ON PATTERN ANALYSIS AND MACHINE INTELLIGENCE.** Short title: P A M I. Text in English. 1979. m. USD 1,415 (effective 2006). **Document type:** *Journal, Academic/Scholarly.* **Description:** Covers computer vision and image processing; knowledge representation, inference systems, and probabilistic reasoning. Extensive bibliographies.
Related titles: CD-ROM ed.; Microfiche ed.; Online - full text ed.: (from EBSCO Publishing, I E E E, Swets Information Services).
Indexed: AHCI, AIA, AS&TI, ASCA, B&BAb, C&CSA, C&ISA, CADCAM, CIS, CMCI, CompAb, CompC, CompD, CompLI, CompR, CurCont, E&CAJ, EngInd, ErgAb, IAA, ISMEC, ISR, Inspec, ORMS, RefZh, RoboAb, SCI, SSCI, ST&MA, SolStAb, ZentMath.
—BLDSC (4363.211400), AskIEEE, CISTI, Ei, IDS, IE, Infotrieve, ingenta, Linda Hall. **CCC.**
Published by: Institute of Electrical and Electronics Engineers, Inc., 445 Hoes Ln, Piscataway, NJ 08854-1331. TEL 732-981-0060, 800-701-4333, FAX 732-981-1721, subscription-service@ieee.org, http://www.computer.org/tpami, http://www.ieee.org. Ed. Kevin Bowyer. Circ: 7,000 (paid and controlled). **Subscr. to:** Maruzen Co., Ltd., 3-10 Nihonbashi 2-chome, Chuo-ku, Tokyo 103-0027, Japan. FAX 81-3-3275-0657; Universal Subscription Agency, Pvt. Ltd., 877, Udyog Vihar, V, Gurgoan 122001, India. TEL 91-124-347261, FAX 91-124-342496. **Co-sponsor:** Computer Society.

006.3   USA   ISSN 1550-5790
I E E E WORKSHOP ON APPLICATIONS OF COMPUTER VISION. PROCEEDINGS. Text in English. 1999. a. USD 155; USD 62 to members (effective 2004). **Document type:** *Proceedings, Trade.*
Indexed: EngInd.
Published by: Institute of Electrical and Electronics Engineers, Inc., 3 Park Ave, 17th Fl, New York, NY 10016-5997. TEL 212-419-7900, 800-678-4333, FAX 212-752-4929, customer.service@ieee.org, http://www.ieee.org.

006.3   USA   ISSN 1530-1842
I E E E WORKSHOP ON COMPUTER VISION BEYOND THE VISIBLE SPECTRUM. Key Title: Proceedings - IEEE Workshop on Computer Vision Beyond the Visible Spectrum. Text in English. 1999. a. USD 110. **Document type:** *Proceedings, Trade.*
Related titles: Online - full text ed.: (from I E E E).
Published by: Institute of Electrical and Electronics Engineers, Inc., 3 Park Ave, 17th Fl, New York, NY 10016-5997. TEL 212-419-7900, 800-678-4333, FAX 212-752-4929, customer.service@ieee.org, http://www.ieee.org.

006.37   USA
I E E E WORKSHOP ON PHOTOMETRIC MODELING FOR COMPUTER VISON & GRAPHICS. Text in English. a.
Document type: *Proceedings, Trade.*
Published by: Institute of Electrical and Electronics Engineers, Inc., 3 Park Ave, 17th Fl, New York, NY 10016-5997. TEL 800-678-4333, customer.service@ieee.org, http://www.ieee.org.

006.35   USA
I E E E WORKSHOP ON SPEECH CODING FOR TELECOMMUNICATIONS. Text in English. a. USD 146; USD 73 to members (effective 2004). **Document type:** *Proceedings, Trade.*
Indexed: EngInd.
Published by: Institute of Electrical and Electronics Engineers, Inc., 3 Park Ave, 17th Fl, New York, NY 10016-5997. TEL 212-419-7900, 800-678-4333, FAX 212-752-4929, customer.service@ieee.org, http://www.ieee.org.

006.3   USA
I E E E WORKSHOP ON VISUAL SURVEILLANCE. Text in English. a. USD 100 per vol.; USD 50 per vol. to members (effective 2004). **Document type:** *Proceedings, Trade.*
—BLDSC (4363.240423).
Published by: Institute of Electrical and Electronics Engineers, Inc., 3 Park Ave, 17th Fl, New York, NY 10016-5997. TEL 212-419-7900, 800-678-4333, FAX 212-752-4929, customer.service@ieee.org, http://www.ieee.org.

006.3   GBR   ISSN 1473-8716
TK7882.I6   CODEN: IVNIAK
➤ **INFORMATION VISUALIZATION.** Text in English. 2002. 4/yr. USD 262 combined subscription in United States to individuals; GBP 159 combined subscription elsewhere to individuals; USD 523 combined subscription in United States to institutions; GBP 317 combined subscription elsewhere to institutions (effective 2005); includes print & online eds.. 64 p./no.; **Document type:** *Journal, Academic/Scholarly.*
Description: Publishes articles on fundamental research and applications of information visualization, and acts as a forum for the theories, methodologies, techniques and evaluations of information visualization and its applications.
Related titles: Online - full content ed.: ISSN 1473-8724. GBP 266 in Europe to institutions; USD 383 elsewhere to institutions (effective 2004); Online - full text ed.: (from EBSCO Publishing, Gale Group, IngentaConnect, O C L C Online Computer Library Center, Inc., ProQuest Information & Learning, Swets Information Services).
Indexed: ABIn, BrCerAb, C&ISA, CerAb, CompLI, CorrAb, E&CAJ, EMA, IAA, IBR, IBZ, InfoSAb, Inspec, M&TEA, MBF, METADEX, SolStAb, WAA.
—BLDSC (4496.401000), IE, ingenta, Linda Hall. **CCC.**
Published by: Palgrave Macmillan Ltd. (Subsidiary of: Macmillan Publishers Ltd.), Houndmills, Basingstoke, Hants RG21 6XS, United Kingdom. TEL 44-1256-329242, FAX 44-1256-810526, http://www.palgrave-journals.com/ivs/index.html, http://www.palgrave.com. Ed. Chaomei Chen. Pub. Rachel Young TEL 44-1256-329242. Adv. contact Robert Sloan TEL 44-20-88827199.

006.3   ESP   ISSN 1137-3601
INTELIGENCIA ARTIFICIAL. Text in Spanish. 1994. q.
Formerly (until 1996): Boletin de la A E P I A (1135-6669)
Related titles: Online - full text ed.: free (effective 2005).
Indexed: IECT.
Published by: Asociacion Espanola de Inteligencia Artificial, Facultad de Informatica, Universidad Politecnica de Valencia, Camino de Vera s/n. Apt. 46022, Valencia, Spain. TEL 34-96-3877000, FAX 34-96-3877209, aepiaQUITAR-NO-SPAM@aepia.org, http://www.aepia.org.

006.3   GBR   ISSN 1465-4210
INTELLIGENCE IN INDUSTRY. Text in English. 1992. m. GBP 395; USD 595 foreign. back issues avail. **Document type:** *Newsletter.* **Description:** Reports on commercial developments in artificial intelligence, with emphasis on Europe.

Formerly (until 1998): A I Watch (1354-2001); Incorporates (1984-1993): Machine Intelligence News (0267-0429)
Related titles: Online - full text ed.
Published by: A I Intelligence, PO Box 95, Oxford, Oxon OX2 7XL, United Kingdom. TEL 44-1865-791600, FAX 44-1865-791007, indo@2-ins.com, http://2-ins.com/. Ed., Pub., R&P Alex Goodall. Circ: 200 (paid).

006.3   NLD   ISSN 1088-467X
QA276.4
➤ **INTELLIGENT DATA ANALYSIS.** Text in English. bi-m. EUR 798, USD 957 combined subscription print & online eds. (effective 2006). **Document type:** *Journal, Academic/Scholarly.* **Description:** Examines issues related to the research and applications of artificial intelligence techniques in data analysis across a variety of disciplines.
Media: Online - full text (from Gale Group, IngentaConnect, O C L C Online Computer Library Center, Inc., ScienceDirect, Swets Information Services).
Indexed: BrCerAb, C&ISA, CerAb, CorrAb, E&CAJ, EMA, IAA, Inspec, M&TEA, MBF, METADEX, SolStAb, WAA.
—BLDSC (4531.831573), CISTI, IE, Infotrieve, Linda Hall. **CCC.**
Published by: (National Research Council of Canada CAN), I O S Press, Nieuwe Hemweg 6B, Amsterdam, 1013 BG, Netherlands. TEL 31-20-6883355, FAX 31-20-6203419, info@iospress.nl, order@iospress.nl, http://www.iospress.nl/html/1088467x.php. Ed. A Famili. R&P Ms. Carry Koolbergen TEL 31-20-6382189. Adv. contact Ms. Jolijn van Eunen. Circ: 400.

006.32   USA   ISSN 1054-8696
Q334
INTELLIGENT SYSTEMS REPORT. Abbreviated title: I S R. Text in English. 1990. m. USD 299; USD 349 foreign (effective 1998). bk.rev. back issues avail. **Document type:** *Newsletter.* **Description:** Covers issues and events in the advanced computing field, such as expert systems, neural networks, fuzzy logic, virtual reality, speech recognition, and intelligent agents.
Formed by the merger of (1989-1990): Neural Network News (1051-5410); (1987-1990): A I Week (0897-3466); Which was formerly (1983-1987): Applied Artificial Intelligence Reporter (0887-8986)
Related titles: Online - full text ed.: (from Gale Group, ProQuest Information & Learning).
Indexed: AHCI, AIA, CADCAM, CMCI, RoboAb.
—IE, Linda Hall. **CCC.**
Published by: Lionheart Publishing, Inc., 506 Roswell St, Ste 220, Marietta, GA 30060-4101. TEL 770-431-0967, FAX 770-432-6969, lpi@lionhtpub.com, http://lionhrtpub.com/ISR/ISR-welcome.html. Ed., R&P David Blanchard. Pub. John Llewellyn.

006.31   USA   ISSN 1534-4797
INTERNATIONAL CONFERENCE ON AUTONOMOUS AGENTS. PROCEEDINGS. Text in English. 1997. a. **Document type:** *Proceedings, Academic/Scholarly.*
Published by: Association for Computing Machinery, Inc., 1515 Broadway, 17th Fl, New York, NY 10036-5701. TEL 212-626-0500, 212-626-0520, 800-342-6626, sigs@acm.org, usacm@acm.org, http://www.acm.org.

006.31   USA
INTERNATIONAL CONFERENCE ON GENETIC ALGORITHMS. PROCEEDINGS. Text in English. biennial. USD 49.95 (effective 1998). back issues avail. **Document type:** *Proceedings.* **Description:** Presents research in this area of computer algorithms.
Published by: (University of Illinois at Urbana-Champaign), Morgan Kaufmann Publishers, Inc. (Subsidiary of: Elsevier BV), 500 Sansome St, Ste 400, San Francisco, CA 94111. TEL 415-392-2665, FAX 415-982-2665, orders@mkp.com, http://www.mkp.com. Ed. Stephanie Forrest.

006.3 621.381   USA   ISSN 1097-1246
INTERNATIONAL CONFERENCE ON KNOWLEDGE - BASED INTELLIGENT ELECTRONIC SYSTEMS. PROCEEDINGS. Text in English. a. price varies. **Document type:** *Proceedings, Trade.*
Indexed: EngInd.
—BLDSC (4538.828420).
Published by: Institute of Electrical and Electronics Engineers, Inc., 3 Park Ave, 17th Fl, New York, NY 10016-5997. TEL 212-419-7900, 800-678-4333, FAX 212-752-4929, customer.service@ieee.org, http://www.ieee.org.

006.3   USA   ISSN 1098-7576
                         CODEN: ICNNF9
INTERNATIONAL CONFERENCE ON NEURAL NETWORKS. PROCEEDINGS. Text in English. 1987. a. USD 618; USD 309 to members (effective 2005). **Document type:** *Proceedings, Trade.*
Related titles: Online - full text ed.: (from I E E E).
Indexed: EngInd.
—BLDSC (4362.949600). **CCC.**
Published by: Institute of Electrical and Electronics Engineers, Inc., 3 Park Ave, 17th Fl, New York, NY 10016-5997. TEL 212-419-7900, 800-678-4333, FAX 212-752-4929, customer.service@ieee.org, http://www.ieee.org.

006.32 USA ISSN 1051-4651
Q327
INTERNATIONAL CONFERENCE ON PATTERN RECOGNITION. Text in English. 1973. biennial. price varies. adv. **Document type:** *Proceedings, Academic/Scholarly.* **Description:** Fundamental research and industrial applications in the field of pattern recognition.
Former titles (until 1991): International Conference on Pattern Recognition. Proceedings (1041-3278); (until 1978): International Joint Conference on Pattern Recognition. Proceedings (1041-326X)
Related titles: Online - full text ed.: (from I E E E).
Indexed: Englnd.
—BLDSC (4538.839560), Ei, IE, ingenta. **CCC.**
Published by: (Institute of Electrical and Electronics Engineers, Inc.), I E E E Computer Society, 3 Park Ave, 17th Fl, New York, NY 10017. TEL 714-821-8380, 800-678-4333, FAX 714-821-4641, customer.service@ieee.org, http://www.ieee.org.

006.3 USA
INTERNATIONAL JOINT CONFERENCE ON ARTIFICIAL INTELLIGENCE. ADVANCE PAPERS OF THE CONFERENCE. Text in English. 1969. s-a. price varies. adv. **Document type:** *Proceedings, Trade.*
Published by: (International Joint Conference on Artificial Intelligence), Morgan Kaufmann Publishers, Inc. (Subsidiary of: Elsevier BV), 500 Sansome St, Ste 400, San Francisco, CA 94111. TEL 415-392-2665, FAX 415-982-2665, orders@mkp.com, http://www.mkp.com. Ed. Michael B Morgan. R&P Marilyn Uffner Alan. Adv. contact Lisa Schneider.

006.3 USA ISSN 1045-0823
Q334
➤ **INTERNATIONAL JOINT CONFERENCE ON ARTIFICIAL INTELLIGENCE. PROCEEDINGS.** Text in English. 1977. biennial. USD 90 (effective 2003). adv. abstr.; bibl.; charts; illus.; stat. **Document type:** *Proceedings, Academic/Scholarly.* **Description:** Provides a forum for the exchange of current research and groundbreaking results in the field.
Indexed: Englnd.
—BLDSC (4541.440000), Ei, IE, ingenta. **CCC.**
Published by: International Joint Conference on Artificial Intelligence, Dr. Ramasamy Uthurusamy, Information Systems and Services, 200 Renaissance Center, Detroit, MI 48265-2000 . TEL 313-667-4669, FAX 313-667-4616, info@ijcai.org, http://www.ijcai.org. Ed. Denise Penrose. R&P Kate Henserson. **Dist. by:** Morgan Kaufmann Publishers, Inc., 500 Sansome St, Ste 400, San Francisco, CA 94111. TEL 415-392-2665, FAX 415-982-2665, orders@mkp.com, http://www.mkp.com.

006.33 USA ISSN 0888-613X
QA76.76.E95 CODEN: IJARE4
➤ **INTERNATIONAL JOURNAL OF APPROXIMATE REASONING.** Text in English. 1987. 9/yr. EUR 961 in Europe to institutions; JPY 127,400 in Japan to institutions; USD 1,074 elsewhere to institutions (effective 2006). bk.rev. back issues avail. **Document type:** *Journal, Academic/Scholarly.* **Description:** Represents all theoretical and applied approaches toward approximate reasoning in the design of (artificially) intelligent computer systems.
Related titles: Microform ed.: (from PQC); Online - full text ed.: (from EBSCO Publishing, Gale Group, IngentaConnect, ScienceDirect, Swets Information Services).
Indexed: AIA, ASCA, CCMJ, CMCI, CurCont, Englnd, ISR, Inspec, L&LBA, MathR, MathSciNet, SCI, ZentMath.
—BLDSC (4542.102000), AskIEEE, CISTI, Ei, IDS, IE, Infotrieve, ingenta, Linda Hall. **CCC.**
Published by: (North American Fuzzy Information Processing Society), Elsevier Inc. (Subsidiary of: Elsevier Science & Technology), 360 Park Ave. S, New York, NY 10010-1710. TEL 212-633-3730, 888-437-4636, usinfo-f@elsevier.com, http://www.elsevier.com/locate/ijar. Ed. Thierry Denoeux.

006.3 NLD ISSN 1560-4292
➤ **INTERNATIONAL JOURNAL OF ARTIFICIAL INTELLIGENCE IN EDUCATION.** Text in English. q. EUR 182, USD 218 combined subscription print & online eds. (effective 2006). **Document type:** *Journal, Academic/Scholarly.*
Related titles: Online - full content ed.: ISSN 1560-4306; Online - full text ed.: (from EBSCO Publishing, Swets Information Services).
Indexed: CPE.
—BLDSC (4542.104700). **CCC.**
Published by: I O S Press, Nieuwe Hemweg 6B, Amsterdam, 1013 BG, Netherlands. TEL 31-20-6883355, FAX 31-20-6203419, info@iospress.nl, order@iospress.nl, http://www.iospress.nl/html/15604292.php. Ed. Paul Brna. R&P Ms. Carry Koolbergen TEL 31-20-6382189. Adv. contact Ms. Jolijn van Eunen.

006.3 SGP ISSN 0218-2130
➤ **INTERNATIONAL JOURNAL OF ARTIFICIAL INTELLIGENCE TOOLS.** Short title: I J A I T. Text in English. 1992. bi-m. SGD 348, USD 205, EUR 186 to individuals; SGD 959, USD 564, EUR 512 combined subscription to institutions print & online eds.; SGD 603, USD 355, EUR 323 combined subscription in developing nations to institutions print & online eds. (effective 2006). back issues avail. **Document type:** *Journal, Academic/Scholarly.* **Description:** Provides information on design, development tests, announcements, and improvement of tools for AI.
Related titles: Online - full text ed.: (from EBSCO Publishing, O C L C Online Computer Library Center, Inc., Swets Information Services).
Indexed: CompLI, Inspec.
—BLDSC (4542.104900), AskIEEE, CISTI, IE, ingenta. **CCC.**
Published by: World Scientific Publishing Co. Pte. Ltd., 5 Toh Tuck Link, Singapore, 596224, Singapore. TEL 65-466-5775, FAX 65-467-7667, wspc@wspc.com.sg, http://www.worldscinet.com/ijait/ijait.shtml, http://www.worldscientific.com. Ed. Nikolaos G Bourbakis. **Subscr. to:** Farrer Rd, PO Box 128, Singapore 912805, Singapore. sales@wspc.com.sg. **Dist. by:** World Scientific Publishing Co., Inc., 1060 Main St, River Edge, NJ 07661. TEL 201-487-9655, 800-227-7562, FAX 201-487-9656, 888-977-2665.; World Scientific Publishing Ltd., 57 Shelton St, London WC2H 9HE, United Kingdom. TEL 44-20-78360888, FAX 44-20-78362020, sales@wspc.co.uk.

006.3 USA ISSN 1557-3958
▼ **INTERNATIONAL JOURNAL OF COGNITIVE INFORMATICS AND NATURAL INTELLIGENCE.** Text in English. forthcoming 2007 (Jan.). q. USD 85 to individuals; USD 285 to institutions (effective 2007). **Document type:** *Journal, Academic/Scholarly.*
Related titles: Online - full text ed.: ISSN 1557-3966. forthcoming 2007 (Jan.).
Published by: Idea Group Publishing (Subsidiary of: Idea Group Inc.), 701 E Chocolate Ave, Ste 200, Hershey, PA 17033-1240. TEL 717-533-8845, 866-342-6657, FAX 717-533-7115, cust@idea-group.com, http://www.idea-group.com.

006.3 USA ISSN 1542-8060
Q334
▼ ➤ **INTERNATIONAL JOURNAL OF COMPUTATIONAL COGNITION.** Text in English. 2003 (Mar.). 4/yr. USD 200; USD 60 newsstand/cover (effective 2003). **Document type:** *Journal, Academic/Scholarly.* **Description:** Provides a forum for an interdisciplinary audience, a forum accessible and affordable to scientists, educators, students and engineers working on building cognition systems into machines.
Related titles: Online - full text ed.: ISSN 1542-5908.
Published by: Yang's Scientific Research Institute, LLC, 1303 E University Blvd, #20882, Tucson, AZ 85719. TEL 520-622-7581, ijcc@yangsky.com, http://www.yangsky.com/yangijcc.htm. Ed. Tao Yang. R&P, Adv. contact Chunmei Yang.

006.3 TUR ISSN 1304-4508
▼ ➤ **INTERNATIONAL JOURNAL OF COMPUTATIONAL INTELLIGENCE.** Text in English. 2004. q. free. **Document type:** *Journal, Academic/Scholarly.* **Description:** Focuses on theories, methods and applications in computational intelligence, artificial neural networks, fuzzy systems, evolutionary computation and hybrid systems.
Related titles: Online - full text ed.: ISSN 1304-2386. 2004. free (effective 2005).
Published by: International Enformatika Society, PO Box 125, Canakkale, 17100, Turkey. TEL 90-286-2180709, FAX 90-286-2180709, ijci@ijci.org, http://www.enformatika.org/journals/1304-2386/.

006.3 GBR ISSN 1469-0268
QA76.87 CODEN: IJCICJ
➤ **INTERNATIONAL JOURNAL OF COMPUTATIONAL INTELLIGENCE AND APPLICATIONS.** Abbreviated title: I J C I A. Text in English. 2001. q. SGD 187, USD 109, EUR 103 to individuals; SGD 491, USD 284, EUR 270 combined subscription to institutions print & online eds. (effective 2006). bk.rev. back issues avail. **Document type:** *Journal, Academic/Scholarly.* **Description:** Covers the theory and applications of computational intelligence with topics such as artificial neural networks, fuzzy systems, evolutionary computation and hybrid systems.
Related titles: Online - full content ed.; Online - full text ed.: (from EBSCO Publishing, O C L C Online Computer Library Center, Inc., Swets Information Services).
Indexed: BrCerAb, C&ISA, CerAb, CompLI, CorrAb, E&CAJ, EMA, IAA, Inspec, M&TEA, MBF, METADEX, SolStAb, WAA.
—BLDSC (4542.173720), IE, ingenta, Linda Hall. **CCC.**
Published by: Imperial College Press (Subsidiary of: World Scientific Publishing Co. Pte. Ltd.), 57 Shelton St, London, WC2H 9HE, United Kingdom. TEL 44-20-7836-3954, FAX 44-20-7836-2002, edit@icpress.co.uk, geetha@icpress.co.uk, http://www.worldscinet.com/ijcia/ijcia.shtml, http://www.icpress.co.uk/. Eds. Andre C P L Ferreira de Carvalho, Antonio de Padua Braga, Brijesh Verma. **Dist. in the US by:** World Scientific Publishing Co., Inc., 1060 Main St, River Edge, NJ 07661. TEL 201-487-9655, 800-227-7562, FAX 201-487-9656, 888-977-2665, wspc@wspc.com.

006.37 USA
TA1632 CODEN: IJCVEQ
➤ **INTERNATIONAL JOURNAL OF COMPUTER VISION (VIDEO EDITION).** Text in English. 1987. 15/yr. EUR 1,698, USD 1,725, GBP 1,065 combined subscription to institutions print & online eds. (effective 2005). adv. bk.rev. back issues avail.; reprint service avail. from PQC,PSC. **Document type:** *Journal, Academic/Scholarly.* **Description:** Provides a forum for the dissemination of new research results in the field of computer vision.
Formerly (until 2004): International Journal of Computer Vision (Print Edition) (0920-5691)
Media: Video. **Related titles:** Microform ed.: (from PQC); Online - full text ed.: ISSN 1573-1405 (from Gale Group, IngentaConnect, O C L C Online Computer Library Center, Inc., Ovid Technologies, Inc., Swets Information Services).
Indexed: AHCI, AIA, AS&TI, ASCA, B&BAb, BibLing, BrCerAb, C&ISA, CMCI, CerAb, CompAb, CompLI, CompR, CorrAb, CurCont, E&CAJ, EMA, Englnd, IAA, ISR, Inspec, M&TEA, MBF, METADEX, RefZh, SCI, SolStAb, WAA.
—BLDSC (4542.175200), AskIEEE, CISTI, Ei, IDS, IE, Infotrieve, ingenta, Linda Hall. **CCC.**
Published by: Springer-Verlag New York, Inc. (Subsidiary of: Springer Science+Business Media), 233 Spring St, New York, NY 10013. TEL 212-460-1500, FAX 212-460-1575, service@springer-ny.com, http://springerlink.metapress.com/openurl.asp?genre=journal&issn=0920-5691, http://www.springer-ny.com. Eds. Christoph Schnorr, Jean Ponce, Katsushi Ikeuchi. **Subscr. to:** Journal Fulfillment, PO Box 2485, Secaucus, NJ 07096-2485. TEL 201-348-4033, FAX 201-348-4505, journals@springer-ny.com.

006.3 NLD ISSN 1448-5869
▼ ➤ **INTERNATIONAL JOURNAL OF HYBRID INTELLIGENT SYSTEMS.** Text in English. 2004. q. EUR 282, USD 338 combined subscription print & online eds. (effective 2006). **Document type:** *Journal, Academic/Scholarly.* **Description:** Provide the academic community with a medium for presenting original research and applications related to the simultaneous use of two or more intelligent techniques.
Related titles: Online - full text ed.: (from O C L C Online Computer Library Center, Inc., Swets Information Services).
—**CCC.**
Published by: I O S Press, Nieuwe Hemweg 6B, Amsterdam, 1013 BG, Netherlands. TEL 31-20-6883355, FAX 31-20-6203419, info@iospress.nl, http://www.iospress.nl/html/14485869.php. Eds. Ajith Abraham, Lakhmi C Jain, Vasile Pallade. R&P Ms. Carry Koolbergen TEL 31-20-6382189. Adv. contact Ms. Jolijn van Eunen.

006.3 USA ISSN 1548-3657
▼ ➤ **INTERNATIONAL JOURNAL OF INTELLIGENT INFORMATION TECHNOLOGIES.** Text in English. 2005. q. USD 85 to individuals print & online eds.; USD 195 to institutions print & online eds. (effective 2005). **Document type:** *Journal, Academic/Scholarly.* **Description:** Provides a forum for academics and practitioners to explore research issues related to not only the design, implementation and deployment of intelligent systems and technologies, but also economic issues and organizational impact.
Related titles: Online - full text ed.: ISSN 1548-3665. 2005. USD 145 (effective 2004).
Indexed: C&ISA, E&CAJ, IAA, Inspec.
Published by: (Information Resources Management Association), Idea Group Publishing (Subsidiary of: Idea Group Inc.), 701 E Chocolate Ave, Ste 200, Hershey, PA 17033-1240. TEL 717-533-8845, FAX 717-533-7115, cust@idea-group.com, http://www.idea-group.com/journals/details.asp?id=4295. Ed. Vijayan Sugumaran. Adv. contact Amada Phillips.

006.33 USA ISSN 0884-8173
Q334 CODEN: IJISED
➤ **INTERNATIONAL JOURNAL OF INTELLIGENT SYSTEMS.** Text in English. 1986. m. USD 2,299 domestic to institutions; USD 2,419 in Canada & Mexico to institutions; USD 2,521 elsewhere to institutions; USD 2,529 combined subscription domestic to institutions print & online eds.; USD 2,649 combined subscription in Canada & Mexico to institutions print & online eds.; USD 2,751 combined subscription elsewhere to institutions print & online eds. (effective 2006). adv. bk.rev. back issues avail. **Document type:** *Journal, Academic/Scholarly.* **Description:** Promotes the development of the theory necessary for the construction of intelligence systems. Includes developmental, as well as theoretical issues.
Related titles: Microform ed.: (from PQC); Online - full content ed.: ISSN 1098-111X. 1996. USD 2,299 to institutions (effective 2006); Online - full text ed.: (from EBSCO Publishing, Swets Information Services, Wiley InterScience).
Indexed: AHCI, AIA, ASCA, ArtHuCI, B&BAb, BrCerAb, C&ISA, CMCI, CerAb, CompLI, CorrAb, CurCont, E&CAJ, EMA, Englnd, IAA, Inspec, M&TEA, MBF, METADEX, RefZh, SSCI, SolStAb, WAA, ZentMath.
—BLDSC (4542.310500), AskIEEE, CISTI, Ei, IDS, IE, Infotrieve, ingenta, Linda Hall. **CCC.**

Published by: John Wiley & Sons, Inc., 111 River St, Hoboken, NJ 07030-5774. TEL 201-748-6000, FAX 201-748-5915, uscs-wis@wiley.com, http://www3.interscience.wiley.com/cgi-bin/jhome/36062, http://www.wiley.com. Ed. Ronald Yager. adv.: B&W page GBP 640, color page GBP 1,515. Circ: 525. **Subscr. outside the Americas to:** John Wiley & Sons Ltd., The Atrium, Southern Gate, Chichester, West Sussex PO19 8SQ, United Kingdom. TEL 44-1243-843335, 0800-243407, FAX 44-1243-843232, cs-journals@wiley.co.uk.

006.31   GBR   ISSN 1740-8865
▼ ➤ **INTERNATIONAL JOURNAL OF INTELLIGENT SYSTEMS TECHNOLOGIES AND APPLICATIONS.** Text in English. 2005. 4/yr. USD 450; USD 545 combined subscription print & online eds. (effective 2005). **Document type:** *Journal, Academic/Scholarly.* **Description:** Publishes original papers featuring innovative and practical technologies related to the design and development of intelligent systems.
Related titles: Online - full text ed.: ISSN 1740-8873. USD 450 (effective 2005).
Indexed: C&ISA, E&CAJ, IAA.
Published by: Inderscience Publishers, IEL Editorial Office, PO Box 735, Olney, Bucks MK46 5WB, United Kingdom. TEL 44-1234-240519, FAX 44-1234-240515, ijista@inderscience.com, info@inderscience.com, http://www.inderscience.com/ijista.

006.2   NLD   ISSN 1327-2314
INTERNATIONAL JOURNAL OF KNOWLEDGE-BASED IN INTELLIGENT ENGINEERING SYSTEMS. Text in English. q. EUR 393, USD 471 combined subscription print & online eds. (effective 2006). **Document type:** *Journal, Academic/Scholarly.* **Description:** Aimed at developing machines or electronic systems that can mimic aspects of the behavior of a human being.
Related titles: Online - full text ed.: (from EBSCO Publishing, O C L C Online Computer Library Center, Inc., Swets Information Services).
Indexed: Inspec.
—BLDSC (4542.311830), IE, ingenta. **CCC.**
Published by: I O S Press, Nieuwe Hemweg 6B, Amsterdam, 1013 BG, Netherlands. TEL 31-20-6883355, FAX 31-20-6203419, info@iospress.nl, order@iospress.nl, http://www.iospress.nl/html/13272314.php. Ed. R J Howlett. R&P Ms. Carry Koolbergen TEL 31-20-6382189. Adv. contact Ms. Jolijn van Eunen.

006.32   SGP   ISSN 0129-0657
QA76.87   CODEN: IJSZEG
➤ **INTERNATIONAL JOURNAL OF NEURAL SYSTEMS.** Abbreviated title: I J N S. Text in English. 1989. bi-m. SGD 379, USD 223, EUR 202 to individuals; SGD 1,062, USD 625, EUR 567 combined subscription to institutions print & online eds.; SGD 626, USD 368, EUR 333 combined subscription in developing nations to institutions print & online eds. (effective 2006). back issues avail. **Document type:** *Journal, Academic/Scholarly.* **Description:** Contains original contributions on all aspects of information processing in natural and artificial neural systems.
Related titles: Online - full text ed.: (from EBSCO Publishing, Gale Group, O C L C Online Computer Library Center, Inc., Swets Information Services).
Indexed: ASCA, ASFA, B&BAb, BioEngAb, CompAb, CompLI, IndMed, Inspec, MEDLINE, NSCI, SSCI.
—BLDSC (4542.373700), AskIEEE, CISTI, IDS, IE, Infotrieve, ingenta. **CCC.**
Published by: World Scientific Publishing Co. Pte. Ltd., 5 Toh Tuck Link, Singapore, 596224, Singapore. TEL 65-466-5775, FAX 65-467-7667, wspc@wspc.com.sg, http://www.worldscinet.com/ijns/ijns.shtml, http://www.worldscientific.com. Eds. Aapo Hyvarinen, Alan F Murray, Hojjat Adeli. Circ: 300. **Subscr. to:** Farrer Rd, PO Box 128, Singapore 912805, Singapore. sales@wspc.com.sg. **Dist. by:** World Scientific Publishing Co., Inc., 1060 Main St, River Edge, NJ 07661. TEL 201-487-9655, 800-227-7562, FAX 201-487-9656, 888-977-2665.; World Scientific Publishing Ltd., 57 Shelton St, London WC2H 9HE, United Kingdom. TEL 44-20-78360888, FAX 44-20-78362020, sales@wspc.co.uk.

006.32   SGP   ISSN 0218-0014
Q327   CODEN: IJPIEI
➤ **INTERNATIONAL JOURNAL OF PATTERN RECOGNITION AND ARTIFICIAL INTELLIGENCE.** Abbreviated title: I J P R A I. Text in English. 1987. 8/yr. SGD 572, USD 327, EUR 314 to individuals; SGD 1,578, USD 902, EUR 868 combined subscription to institutions print & online eds.; SGD 947, USD 541, EUR 521 combined subscription in developing nations to institutions print & online eds. (effective 2006). bk.rev. cum.index every 5 yrs. back issues avail. **Document type:** *Journal, Academic/Scholarly.* **Description:** Disseminates pattern recognition and artificial intelligence, in particular when the two fields intersect. Emphasis on methodology and applications.
Related titles: Online - full text ed.: (from EBSCO Publishing, O C L C Online Computer Library Center, Inc., Swets Information Services).
Indexed: ASCA, BrCerAb, C&ISA, CMCI, CerAb, CompAb, CompLI, CorrAb, CurCont, E&CAJ, EMA, EngInd, IAA, Inspec, M&TEA, MBF, METADEX, SolStAb, WAA.
—BLDSC (4542.449700), AskIEEE, CISTI, Ei, IDS, IE, Infotrieve, ingenta, Linda Hall. **CCC.**

Published by: World Scientific Publishing Co. Pte. Ltd., 5 Toh Tuck Link, Singapore, 596224, Singapore. TEL 65-466-5775, FAX 65-467-7667, wspc@wspc.com.sg, http://www.worldscinet.com/ijprai/ijprai.shtml, http://www.worldscientific.com. Eds. Patrick Shen Pei Wang, X Jiang. Circ: 250. **Subscr. to:** Farrer Rd, PO Box 128, Singapore 912805, Singapore. sales@wspc.com.sg. **Dist. by:** World Scientific Publishing Co., Inc., 1060 Main St, River Edge, NJ 07661. TEL 201-487-9655, 800-227-7562, FAX 201-487-9656, 888-977-2665.; World Scientific Publishing Ltd., 57 Shelton St, London WC2H 9HE, United Kingdom. TEL 44-20-78360888, FAX 44-20-78362020, sales@wspc.co.uk.

511.313   SGP   ISSN 0218-4885
Q375   CODEN: IJUSF6
➤ **INTERNATIONAL JOURNAL OF UNCERTAINTY, FUZZINESS AND KNOWLEDGE-BASED SYSTEMS.** Short title: I J U F K S. Text in English. 1993. bi-m. SGD 232, USD 133, EUR 128 to individuals; SGD 640, USD 366, EUR 352 combined subscription to institutions print & online eds.; SGD 384, USD 219, EUR 211 combined subscription in developing nations to institutions print & online eds. (effective 2006). back issues avail. **Document type:** *Journal, Academic/Scholarly.* **Description:** Researches the various methodologies for managing imprecise, vague, uncertain or incomplete information in neural networks and robotic systems.
Related titles: Online - full text ed.: (from EBSCO Publishing, O C L C Online Computer Library Center, Inc., Swets Information Services).
Indexed: ASCA, CCMJ, CMCI, CompLI, CompR, CurCont, EngInd, Inspec, MathR, MathSciNet.
—BLDSC (4542.696600), AskIEEE, CISTI, IDS, IE, Infotrieve, ingenta. **CCC.**
Published by: World Scientific Publishing Co. Pte. Ltd., 5 Toh Tuck Link, Singapore, 596224, Singapore. TEL 65-466-5775, FAX 65-467-7667, wspc@wspc.com.sg, http://www.worldscinet.com/ijufks/ijufks.shtml, http://www.worldscientific.com. Ed. B Bouchon-Meunier. **Subscr. to:** Farrer Rd, PO Box 128, Singapore 912805, Singapore. sales@wspc.com.sg. **Dist. by:** World Scientific Publishing Co., Inc., 1060 Main St, River Edge, NJ 07661. TEL 201-487-9655, 800-227-7562, FAX 201-487-9656, 888-977-2665.; World Scientific Publishing Ltd., 57 Shelton St, London WC2H 9HE, United Kingdom. TEL 44-20-78360888, FAX 44-20-78362020, sales@wspc.co.uk.

006.3   NLD   ISSN 1382-3434
➤ **INTERNATIONAL SERIES IN INTELLIGENT TECHNOLOGIES.** Cover title: I S I T. Text in English. 1995. irreg., latest vol.20, 2005. price varies. **Document type:** *Monographic series, Academic/Scholarly.*
Indexed: CCMJ, ZentMath.
—BLDSC (4549.257750), IE, ingenta.
Published by: Springer-Verlag Dordrecht (Subsidiary of: Springer Science+Business Media), Van Godewijckstraat 30, Dordrecht, 3311 GX, Netherlands. TEL 31-78-6576050, FAX 31-78-6576474, http://www.springeronline.com. Ed. Hans-Juergen Zimmermann.

➤ **INTERNATIONAL WORKSHOP ON CELLULAR NEURAL NETWORKS AND THEIR APPLICATIONS.** see *COMPUTERS—Circuits*

511.3   USA   ISSN 1063-6714
QA267   CODEN: PIPMFX
INTERNATIONAL WORKSHOP ON PETRI NETS AND PERFORMANCE MODELS. Abbreviated title: P N P M. Text in English. 1987. biennial. USD 102 membership (effective 2005). **Document type:** *Proceedings.*
Related titles: Online - full text ed.: (from I E E E).
Indexed: EngInd.
—BLDSC (6847.055100). **CCC.**
Published by: (Institute of Electrical and Electronics Engineers, Inc.), I E E E Computer Society, 10662 Los Vaqueros Circle, PO Box 3014, Los Alamitos, CA 90720-1314. TEL 714-821-8380, FAX 714-821-4641.

006.3   USA   ISSN 1530-1311
Q334
INTERNATIONAL WORKSHOP ON TEMPORAL REPRESENTATION AND REASONING. PROCEEDINGS. Text in English. a. USD 159; USD 64 to members (effective 2004). **Document type:** *Proceedings, Trade.*
Related titles: Online - full text ed.: (from I E E E).
Indexed: EngInd.
—BLDSC (4552.205550).
Published by: Institute of Electrical and Electronics Engineers, Inc., 3 Park Ave, 17th Fl, New York, NY 10016-5997. TEL 212-419-7900, 800-678-4333, FAX 212-752-4929, customer.service@ieee.org, http://www.ieee.org.

006.3   USA
INTERNATIONAL WORKSHOPS ON INFRASTRUCTURE FOR COLLABORATIVE RESEARCH. Text in English. irreg. price varies. **Document type:** *Proceedings, Trade.*
Published by: Institute of Electrical and Electronics Engineers, Inc., 3 Park Ave, 17th Fl, New York, NY 10016-5997. TEL 800-678-4333, customer.service@ieee.org, http://www.ieee.org.

006.3   UKR   ISSN 1561-5359
ISKUSTVENNYI INTELLEKT/ARTIFICIAL INTELLIGENCE/SHTUCHNYI INTELEKT. Text in Russian, Ukrainian, English. 1996. s-a. **Document type:** *Journal, Academic/Scholarly.*
Indexed: RefZh.
—BLDSC (0087.165000).
Published by: Natsional'na Akademiya Nauk Ukrainy, Instytut Problem Shtuchnoho Intelektu, B Hmelnitsky Ave 84, Donetsk, 83050, Ukraine. TEL 380-62-3373335, FAX 380-62-3046082, press@iai.donetsk.ua, http://www.iai.donetsk.ua. Ed. Anatolii I Shevchenko.

006.3   JPN   ISSN 0912-8085
Q334
JINKO CHINO GAKKAISHI/JAPANESE SOCIETY FOR ARTIFICIAL INTELLIGENCE. JOURNAL. Text in Japanese, English. 1986. bi-m. **Description:** Contains announcements, tutorial papers, and articles on artificial intelligence-related topics.
Indexed: INIS AtomInd, Inspec.
—BLDSC (4809.415000), IE, ingenta.
Published by: Jinkou Chinou Gakkai/Japanese Society for Artificial Intelligence, OS Bldg #402, Tsukudo-cho, Shinjuku-ku, Tokyo, 162-082, Japan. TEL 81-3-5261-3402, FAX 81-3-5261-3401, editor@ai-gakkai.or.jp, info@ai-gakkai.or.jp, http://www.ai-gakkai.or.jp/jsai, http://www.ai-gakkai.or.jp/jsai/.

006.3   JPN   ISSN 1346-0714
JINKOU CHINOU GAKKAI ROMBUNSHI/JAPANESE SOCIETY FOR ARTIFICIAL INTELLIGENCE. TRANSACTIONS. Text mainly in Japanese. a. **Document type:** *Journal, Academic/Scholarly.*
Related titles: Online - full content ed.: ISSN 1346-8030. free (effective 2005); Online - full text ed.: (from J-Stage).
Published by: Jinkou Chinou Gakkai/Japanese Society for Artificial Intelligence, OS Bldg #402, Tsukudo-cho, Shinjuku-ku, Tokyo, 162-082, Japan. info@ai-gakkai.or.jp, http://tjsai.jstage.jst.go.jp/, http://www.ai-gakkai.or.jp/jsai/.

006.3   FRA   ISSN 1166-3081
BC1
JOURNAL OF APPLIED NON-CLASSICAL LOGICS. Text in French. 1991. 4/yr. EUR 310 in the European Union; EUR 345 elsewhere (effective 2003).
Indexed: CCMJ, MathR, MathSciNet, ZentMath.
—BLDSC (4943.400000), IE, ingenta. **CCC.**
Published by: Lavoisier, 11 rue Lavoisier, Paris, 75008, France. TEL 33-1-42653995, FAX 33-1-42650246, info@lavoisier.fr, http://www.lavoisier.fr. **Subscr. to:** Lavoisier - Dept Abonnements, 14 rue de Provigny, Cachan 94236, France. TEL 33-1-47406700, FAX 33-1-47406702, abo@lavoisier.fr.

006.3   USA   ISSN 1076-9757
Q334   CODEN: JAIRFR
➤ **THE JOURNAL OF ARTIFICIAL INTELLIGENCE RESEARCH.** Variant title: J A I R. Text in English. 1994. s-a. USD 85 (effective 2005). illus.; abstr.; bibl.; charts; stat. **Document type:** *Journal, Academic/Scholarly.* **Description:** Includes all areas of artificial intelligence, automated reasoning, cognitive modeling, knowledge representation, learning, natural language, neural networks, perception and robotics.
Related titles: Online - full content ed.: free (effective 2005); Online - full text ed.: (from EBSCO Publishing).
Indexed: CCMJ, CMCI, CompAb, CurCont, EngInd, ISR, Inspec, MathR, MathSciNet, SCI, ZentMath.
—BLDSC (4947.211830), AskIEEE, CISTI. **CCC.**
Published by: (American Association for Artificial Intelligence), A I Access Foundation, Inc, Information Sciences Institute, Marina del Rey, CA 90290. http://www.jair.org/home.html. Ed. Dr. Martha E Pollack.

006.31   DEU   ISSN 1430-189X
QA76   CODEN: JICYE5
JOURNAL OF AUTOMATA, LANGUAGES AND COMBINATORICS. Text in English, German. 1965. bi-m. EUR 70 to individuals; EUR 90 to institutions (effective 2005). adv. bk.rev. charts; illus.; stat. index. **Document type:** *Journal, Academic/Scholarly.* **Description:** Provides a forum for research in all areas of the field, from theory to applications and relations to other subjects.
Former titles (until 1996): Journal of Information Processing and Cybernetics (0863-0593); (until vol.23, 1987): Elektronische Informationsverarbeitung und Kybernetik (0013-5712)
Indexed: BrCerAb, CCMJ, CompAb, CompR, CybAb, Inspec, MathR, MathSciNet, RefZh, ZentMath.
—BLDSC (4949.557000), AskIEEE, CISTI, Ei, IE, ingenta, Linda Hall. **CCC.**
Published by: Otto-von-Guericke-Universitaet Magdeburg, Fakultaet fuer Informatik, Postfach 4120, Magdeburg, 39016, Germany. TEL 49-391-6712851, FAX 49-391-6712810, jalc@irb.cs.uni-magdeburg.de, http://fuzzy.cs.uni-magdeburg.de/theo/jalc/. Ed. Juergen Dassow. Circ: 350.

006.31 NLD ISSN 0168-7433
CODEN: JAREEW
➤ **JOURNAL OF AUTOMATED REASONING.** Text in English. 1985. 8/yr. EUR 788, USD 808, GBP 498 combined subscription to institutions print & online eds. (effective 2005). adv. bk.rev. index. reprint service avail. from PSC. **Document type:** *Journal, Academic/Scholarly.* **Description:** Focuses on different theories and applications in the field of automated reasoning, the objectives being the design and implementation of a computer program to assist in solving problems and answering questions that require reasoning.
Related titles: Microform ed.: (from PQC); Online - full text ed.: ISSN 1573-0670 (from EBSCO Publishing, Gale Group, IngentaConnect, Kluwer Online, O C L C Online Computer Library Center, Inc., Ovid Technologies, Inc., Springer LINK, Swets Information Services).
Indexed: AIA, ASCA, BibLing, CCMJ, CMCI, CompAb, CompLI, CompR, CurCont, Englnd, IBR, Inspec, MathR, MathSciNet, RefZh, RoboAb, ZentMath.
—BLDSC (4949.558000), AskIEEE, CISTI, Ei, IDS, IE, Infotrieve, ingenta, Linda Hall. **CCC.**
Published by: Springer-Verlag Dordrecht (Subsidiary of: Springer Science+Business Media), Van Godewijckstraat 30, Dordrecht, 3311 GX, Netherlands. TEL 31-78-6576050, FAX 31-78-6576474, http://springerlink.metapress.com/openurl.asp?genre=journal&issn=0168-7433, http://www.springeronline.com. Ed. Deepak Kapur.

➤ **JOURNAL OF COMPUTATIONAL NEUROSCIENCE.** see *MEDICAL SCIENCES—Psychiatry And Neurology*

006.3 GBR ISSN 0952-813X
Q334 CODEN: JEAIEL
➤ **JOURNAL OF EXPERIMENTAL & THEORETICAL ARTIFICIAL INTELLIGENCE.** Short title: J E T A I. Text in English. 1989. q. GBP 446, USD 736 combined subscription to institutions print & online eds. (effective 2006). adv. reprint service avail. from PSC. **Document type:** *Journal, Academic/Scholarly.* **Description:** Focuses on problem, perception, learning, representation, memory, and neural system modeling.
Related titles: Online - full text ed.: ISSN 1362-3079. GBP 424, USD 699 to institutions (effective 2006) (from EBSCO Publishing, Gale Group, IngentaConnect, O C L C Online Computer Library Center, Inc., Swets Information Services).
Indexed: AIA, ASCA, BrCerAb, C&ISA, CMCI, CerAb, CompLI, CorrAb, E&CAJ, EMA, Englnd, IAA, Inspec, M&TEA, MBF, METADEX, PsycInfo, PsycholAb, RoboAb, SSCI, SolStAb, WAA, ZentMath.
—BLDSC (4979.780000), AskIEEE, CISTI, Ei, IDS, IE, Infotrieve, ingenta, Linda Hall. **CCC.**
Published by: Taylor & Francis Ltd (Subsidiary of: Taylor & Francis Group), 4 Park Sq, Milton Park, Abingdon, OX14 4RN, United Kingdom. TEL 44-1235-828600, FAX 44-1235-829000, info@tandf.co.uk, http://www.tandf.co.uk/journals/titles/0952813X.asp. Ed. Eric Dietrich. **Subscr. in N. America to:** Taylor & Francis Inc., Customer Services Dept, 325 Chestnut St, 8th Fl, Philadelphia, PA 19106. TEL 800-354-1420, FAX 215-625-8914; **Subscr. to:** Journals Customer Service, Rankine Rd, Basingstoke, Hants RG24 8PR, United Kingdom. TEL 44-1256-813000, FAX 44-1256-330245, enquiry@tandf.co.uk.

006.3 USA ISSN 1381-1231
T57.84 CODEN: JOHEFD
➤ **JOURNAL OF HEURISTICS.** Text in English. 1995. bi-m. EUR 638, USD 655, GBP 405 combined subscription to institutions print & online eds. (effective 2005). adv. back issues avail.; reprint service avail. from PSC. **Document type:** *Journal, Academic/Scholarly.* **Description:** Considers theoretical, empirical and experimental work relating to techniques for solving problems approximately.
Related titles: Online - full text ed.: ISSN 1572-9397 (from EBSCO Publishing, Gale Group, IngentaConnect, Kluwer Online, O C L C Online Computer Library Center, Inc., ProQuest Information & Learning, Springer LINK, Swets Information Services).
Indexed: ABIn, BibLing, CCMJ, CMCI, CompAb, CompLI, CurCont, Englnd, IAOP, Inspec, MathR, ZentMath.
—BLDSC (4998.270000), AskIEEE, CISTI, IDS, IE, Infotrieve, ingenta. **CCC.**
Published by: Springer-Verlag New York, Inc. (Subsidiary of: Springer Science+Business Media), 233 Spring St, New York, NY 10013. TEL 212-460-1500, FAX 212-460-1575, service@springer-ny.com, http://springerlink.metapress.com/openurl.asp?genre=journal&issn=1381-1231, http://www.springer-ny.com. Ed. Manuel Laguna. **Subscr. to:** Journal Fulfillment, PO Box 2485, Secaucus, NJ 07096-2485. TEL 201-348-4033, FAX 201-348-4505, journals@springer-ny.com.

006.3 NLD ISSN 0921-0296
TJ210.2 CODEN: JIRSES
➤ **JOURNAL OF INTELLIGENT AND ROBOTIC SYSTEMS;** theory and applications. Text in English. 1988. m. EUR 1,228, USD 1,258, GBP 768 combined subscription to institutions print & online eds. (effective 2005). adv. bk.rev. illus. Index. back issues avail.; reprint service avail. from PSC. **Document type:** *Journal, Academic/Scholarly.* **Description:** Provides a source linking all fields where system intelligence plays a dominant role, and promotes interaction between workers carrying out theoretical and applied research in various areas.
Incorporates (in 1994): Mechatronic Systems Engineering (0924-3992)
Related titles: Microform ed.: (from PQC); Online - full text ed.: ISSN 1573-0409 (from EBSCO Publishing, Gale Group, IngentaConnect, Kluwer Online, O C L C Online Computer Library Center, Inc., Ovid Technologies, Inc., Springer LINK, Swets Information Services).
Indexed: AIA, ASCA, ApMecR, BibLing, BrCerAb, C&ISA, CADCAM, CMCI, CerAb, CorrAb, CurCont, E&CAJ, EMA, Englnd, ErgAb, IAA, ISMEC, Inspec, M&TEA, MBF, METADEX, PsycInfo, PsycholAb, RefZh, RoboAb, SSCI, SolStAb, WAA, ZentMath, e-psyche.
—BLDSC (5007.538500), AskIEEE, CISTI, Ei, IDS, IE, Infotrieve, ingenta, Linda Hall. **CCC.**
Published by: Springer-Verlag Dordrecht (Subsidiary of: Springer Science+Business Media), Van Godewijckstraat 30, Dordrecht, 3311 GX, Netherlands. TEL 31-78-6576050, FAX 31-78-6576474, http://springerlink.metapress.com/openurl.asp?genre=journal&issn=0921-0296, http://www.springeronline.com. Ed. Spyros G Tzafestas.

006.3 USA ISSN 0925-9902
QA76.9.D3 CODEN: JIISEH
➤ **JOURNAL OF INTELLIGENT INFORMATION SYSTEMS;** integrating artificial intelligence and database technologies. Text in English. 1992. bi-m. EUR 725, USD 738, GBP 455 combined subscription to institutions print & online eds. (effective 2005). adv. illus. reprint service avail. from PSC. **Document type:** *Journal, Academic/Scholarly.* **Description:** Focuses on the creation of intelligent information systems, including reasoning processes, and their application in database management processes.
Related titles: Microform ed.: (from PQC); Online - full text ed.: ISSN 1573-7675 (from EBSCO Publishing, Gale Group, IngentaConnect, Kluwer Online, O C L C Online Computer Library Center, Inc., ProQuest Information & Learning, Springer LINK, Swets Information Services).
Indexed: ABIn, B&BAb, BibLing, CMCI, CompAb, CompLI, CompR, CurCont, Englnd, ErgAb, InfoSAb, Inspec, RefZh, ZentMath.
—BLDSC (5007.538510), AskIEEE, CISTI, Ei, IDS, IE, Infotrieve, ingenta. **CCC.**
Published by: Springer-Verlag New York, Inc. (Subsidiary of: Springer Science+Business Media), 233 Spring St, New York, NY 10013. TEL 212-460-1500, FAX 212-460-1575, service@springer-ny.com, http://springerlink.metapress.com/openurl.asp?genre=journal&issn=0925-9902, http://www.springer-ny.com. Eds. Larry Kerschberg, Maria Zemankova, Zbigniew Ras. **Subscr. to:** Journal Fulfillment, PO Box 2485, Secaucus, NJ 07096-2485. TEL 201-348-4033, FAX 201-348-4505, journals@springer-ny.com.

006.3 USA ISSN 0956-5515
TS183 CODEN: JIMNEM
➤ **JOURNAL OF INTELLIGENT MANUFACTURING.** Text in English. 1990. bi-m. EUR 868, USD 888, GBP 548 combined subscription to institutions print & online eds. (effective 2005). adv. back issues avail.; reprint service avail. from PSC. **Document type:** *Journal, Academic/Scholarly.* **Description:** provides a unique international forum for developers of intelligent manufacturing systems. By publishing quality refereed papers on the applications of artificial intelligence in manufacturing, the Journal acts as a vital link between the research community and practitioners in industry.
Related titles: Online - full text ed.: ISSN 1572-8145 (from EBSCO Publishing, Gale Group, IngentaConnect, Kluwer Online, O C L C Online Computer Library Center, Inc., Ovid Technologies, Inc., ProQuest Information & Learning, Springer LINK, Swets Information Services).
Indexed: ABIn, ASCA, ASFA, ApMecR, BibLing, CADCAM, CMCI, CurCont, ESPM, Englnd, H&SSA, Inspec, RefZh, RoboAb, SSCI.
—BLDSC (5007.538530), AskIEEE, CISTI, Ei, IDS, IE, Infotrieve, ingenta. **CCC.**
Published by: Plenum US (Subsidiary of: Springer Science+Business Media), 233 Spring St, New York, NY 10013. TEL 212-460-1500, FAX 212-460-1575, service@springer-ny.com, http://springerlink.metapress.com/openurl.asp?genre=journal&issn=0956-5515, http://www.springeronline.com. Ed. Andrew Kusiak.

➤ **JOURNAL OF MEMETICS - EVOLUTIONARY MODELS OF INFORMATION TRANSMISSION.** see *PHILOSOPHY*

006.32 GBR ISSN 1741-2560
QP363.3
▼ ➤ **JOURNAL OF NEURAL ENGINEERING.** Text in English. 2004. q. USD 570, GBP 295 combined subscription in the Americas to institutions print & online eds. (effective 2005). **Document type:** *Journal, Academic/Scholarly.* **Description:** Goal is to establish a new forum for the interdisciplinary field of neural engineering where neuroscientists, neurobiologists and engineers can publish their work in one periodical that bridges the gap between neuroscience and engineering.
Related titles: Microfiche ed.: USD 428 in North America; GBP 221 elsewhere (effective 2005); Online - full text ed.: ISSN 1741-2552 (from EBSCO Publishing, Swets Information Services).
Indexed: ExcerpMed, Inspec, RefZh.
—BLDSC (5021.416000), IE.
Published by: Institute of Physics Publishing, Dirac House, Temple Back, Bristol, BS1 6BE, United Kingdom. TEL 44-117-9297481, FAX 44-117-9294318, custserv@iop.org, http://www.iop.org/EJ/journal/JNE. Ed. Dominique M Durand.

➤ **JOURNAL OF PRAGMATICS.** see *LINGUISTICS—Computer Applications*

➤ **JOURNAL OF SEMANTICS.** see *LINGUISTICS—Computer Applications*

➤ **JOURNAL OF TELECOMMUNICATIONS AND INFORMATION TECHNOLOGY.** see *COMMUNICATIONS*

➤ **KEY ABSTRACTS - ARTIFICIAL INTELLIGENCE.** see *COMPUTERS—Abstracting, Bibliographies, Statistics*

➤ **KEY ABSTRACTS - MACHINE VISION.** see *COMPUTERS—Abstracting, Bibliographies, Statistics*

006.33 NLD ISSN 0950-7051
QA76.76.E95 CODEN: KNSYET
➤ **KNOWLEDGE-BASED SYSTEMS.** Text in English. 1987. 8/yr. EUR 942 in Europe to institutions; JPY 124,900 in Japan to institutions; USD 1,053 to institutions except Europe and Japan (effective 2006). adv. bk.rev. back issues avail. **Document type:** *Academic/Scholarly.* **Description:** Covers fifth-generation computing, expert systems, and knowledge-based methods in system design with an interdisciplinary and applications-oriented approach.
Related titles: Microform ed.: (from PQC); Online - full text ed.: (from EBSCO Publishing, Gale Group, IngentaConnect, ScienceDirect, Swets Information Services).
Indexed: AESIS, AHCI, AIA, ASCA, CMCI, CompAb, CompLI, CurCont, ESPM, Englnd, ISR, Inspec, LISA, MSB, PsycInfo, PsycholAb, RiskAb, SCI, SSCI, ZentMath.
—BLDSC (5100.442700), AskIEEE, CISTI, Ei, IDS, IE, Infotrieve, ingenta. **CCC.**
Published by: Elsevier BV (Subsidiary of: Elsevier Science & Technology), Radarweg 29, Amsterdam, 1043 NX, Netherlands. TEL 31-20-4853911, FAX 31-20-4852457, nlinfo-f@elsevier.nl, http://www.elsevier.com/locate/knosys, http://www.elsevier.nl. Ed. Ernest A Edmonds.

006.3 GBR ISSN 0269-8889
QA76.76.E95 CODEN: KEREE3
➤ **KNOWLEDGE ENGINEERING REVIEW.** Text in English. 1988 (vol.3). q. GBP 200 to institutions; USD 340 in North America to institutions; GBP 212 combined subscription to institutions print & online eds.; USD 348 combined subscription in North America to institutions print & online eds. (effective 2006). adv. reprint service avail. from PSC. **Document type:** *Journal, Academic/Scholarly.* **Description:** Monitors and promotes developments in the application of artificial intelligence techniques.
Related titles: Online - full text ed.: ISSN 1469-8005. GBP 188 to institutions; USD 308 in North America to institutions (effective 2006) (from EBSCO Publishing, O C L C Online Computer Library Center, Inc., Swets Information Services).
Indexed: ASCA, ASFA, BrCerAb, C&ISA, CMCI, CerAb, CorrAb, CurCont, E&CAJ, EMA, ESPM, Englnd, IAA, ISR, Inspec, M&TEA, MBF, METADEX, PollutAb, RefZh, SCI, WAA.
—BLDSC (5100.446000), AskIEEE, CISTI, Ei, IDS, IE, Infotrieve, ingenta, Linda Hall. **CCC.**
Published by: Cambridge University Press, The Edinburgh Bldg, Shaftesbury Rd, Cambridge, CB2 2RU, United Kingdom. TEL 44-1223-312393, FAX 44-1223-315052, journals@cambridge.org, http://uk.cambridge.org/journals/ker/. Eds. Adele E Howe, Simon Parsons. R&P Linda Nicol TEL 44-1223-325757. Adv. contact Rebecca Curtis TEL 44-1223-325757. **Subscr. to:** Cambridge University Press, 100 Brook Hill Dr, West Nyack, NY 10994. TEL 845-353-7500, FAX 845-353-4141, journals_subscriptions@cup.org

006.3 DEU ISSN 0933-1875
KUENSTLICHE INTELLIGENZ; Forschung, Entwicklung, Erfahrungen. Short title: K I. Text in German. 197?. 4/yr. EUR 56; EUR 15 newsstand/cover (effective 2005). adv. bk.rev. index. back issues avail. **Document type:** *Magazine, Trade.*
Former titles (until 1987): Gesellschaft fuer Informatik. Fachausschusses 1.2 Kuenstliche Intelligenz und Mustererkennung. Rundbrief (0935-848X); (until 198?): Gesellschaft fuer Informatik. Fachgruppe Kuenstliche Intelligenz. Rundbrief (0721-5150)
Published by: Boettcher IT Verlag, Ronzelenstr 104, Bremen, 28359, Germany. TEL 49-421-16301951, FAX 49-421-16301952, info@kuenstliche-intelligenz.de, http://xn—knstliche-intelligenz-8hc.de. Ed. Andreas Guenter. Circ: 6,000.

006.3 FRA ISSN 0767-4910
LETTRE DE L'INTELLIGENCE ARTIFICIELLE. Text in French. 11/yr. bk.rev. back issues avail. **Document type:** *Newsletter.*
Published by: E C 2, 269 rue de la Garenne, Nanterre, 92000, France. TEL 33-1-47-80-70-00, FAX 33-1-47-80-55-29. Ed. Jean Claude Rault.

006.3 USA ISSN 1061-0464
QA76.63
LOGIC PROGRAMMING. Text in English. 1982. a. price varies. **Document type:** *Proceedings.*

Formerly (until 1987): International Conference on Logic Programming. Proceedings (1061-0456)
Published by: Springer-Verlag New York, Inc. (Subsidiary of: Springer Science+Business Media), 233 Spring St, New York, NY 10013. TEL 212-460-1500, FAX 212-460-1575, service@springer-ny.com, http://www.springer-ny.com.

006.31 NLD ISSN 0923-0459
➤ **MACHINE INTELLIGENCE AND PATTERN RECOGNITION.** Text in Dutch. 1985. irreg., latest vol.4, 1986. price varies. back issues avail. **Document type:** *Monographic series, Academic/Scholarly.* **Description:** Explores developments and trends in all areas of artificial intelligence.
Related titles: Supplement(s): Parallel Processing for Artificial Intelligence.
Indexed: ZentMath.
—BLDSC (5323.610000), CISTI, IE, ingenta. **CCC.**
Published by: Elsevier BV, North-Holland (Subsidiary of: Elsevier Science & Technology), Sara Burgerhartstraat 25, Amsterdam, 1055 KV, Netherlands. TEL 31-20-485-3911, FAX 31-20-485-2457, nlinfo-f@elsevier.nl, http://www.elsevier.nl. **Subscr. to:** Elsevier BV, PO Box 211, Amsterdam 1000 AE, Netherlands. TEL 31-20-485-3757, FAX 31-20-485-3432, http://www.elsevier.nl.

006.31 USA ISSN 0885-6125
Q325.5 CODEN: MALEEZ
➤ **MACHINE LEARNING**; an international journal. Text in English. 1986. m. EUR 1,198, USD 1,215, GBP 778 combined subscription to institutions print & online eds. (effective 2005). adv. bk.rev. illus. back issues avail.; reprint service avail. from PQC,PSC. **Document type:** *Academic/Scholarly.* **Description:** Disseminates international research on computational approaches to learning, automated knowledge acquisition, and natural language processing.
Related titles: Microform ed.: (from PQC); Online - full text ed.: ISSN 1573-0565. USD 1,215 to institutions (effective 2005) (from EBSCO Publishing, Gale Group, IngentaConnect, Kluwer Online, O C L C Online Computer Library Center, Inc., Ovid Technologies, Inc., Springer LINK, Swets Information Services).
Indexed: AIA, AS&TI, ASCA, ASFA, B&BAb, BibLing, BioEngAb, BrCerAb, C&ISA, CMCI, CerAb, CompAb, CompLI, CompR, CorrAb, CurCont, E&CAJ, EMA, ESPM, Englnd, IAA, ISR, Inspec, L&LBA, M&TEA, MBF, METADEX, PsycInfo, PsycholAb, RefZh, RoboAb, SCI, SOPODA, SSCI, SolStAb, WAA, ZentMath, e-psyche.
—BLDSC (5323.870000), AskIEEE, CISTI, Ei, IDS, IE, Infotrieve, ingenta, Linda Hall. **CCC.**
Published by: Springer-Verlag New York, Inc. (Subsidiary of: Springer Science+Business Media), 233 Spring St, New York, NY 10013. TEL 212-460-1500, FAX 212-460-1575, service@springer-ny.com, http://springerlink.metapress.com/openurl.asp?genre=journal&issn=0885-6125, http://www.springer-ny.com. Ed. Foster Provost. **Subscr. to:** Journal Fulfillment, PO Box 2485, Secaucus, NJ 07096-2485. TEL 201-348-4033, FAX 201-348-4505, journals@springer-ny.com.

006.361 NLD ISSN 0928-9119
➤ **MEDICAL ARTIFICIAL INTELLIGENCE.** Text in English. 1992. irreg., latest vol.2, 1995. price varies. **Document type:** *Monographic series, Academic/Scholarly.*
—BLDSC (5526.245000).
Published by: Elsevier BV (Subsidiary of: Elsevier Science & Technology), Radarweg 29, Amsterdam, 1043 NX, Netherlands. TEL 31-20-4853911, FAX 31-20-4852457, nlinfo-f@elsevier.nl, http://www.elsevier.nl. Eds. H. U. Prokosch, J. Dudeck.

006.3 NLD ISSN 0924-6495
Q334 CODEN: MMACEO
➤ **MINDS AND MACHINES**; journal for artificial intelligence, philosophy and cognitive sciences. Text in Dutch. 1991. q. EUR 535, USD 545, GBP 338 combined subscription to institutions print & online eds. (effective 2005). adv. back issues avail.; reprint service avail. from PSC. **Document type:** *Academic/Scholarly.* **Description:** Discusses issues concerning machines and mentality, artificial intelligence, epistemology, simulation, and modeling.
Related titles: Microform ed.: (from PQC); Online - full text ed.: ISSN 1572-8641 (from EBSCO Publishing, Gale Group, IngentaConnect, Kluwer Online, O C L C Online Computer Library Center, Inc., Ovid Technologies, Inc., Springer LINK, Swets Information Services).
Indexed: ASCA, ArtHuCI, BibLing, CMCI, CompAb, CompLI, CurCont, Englnd, IPB, Inspec, NSCI, PhilInd, PsycInfo, PsycholAb, RILM, RefZh, SSCI, e-psyche.
—BLDSC (5775.593000), Ei, IDS, IE, Infotrieve, ingenta. **CCC.**
Published by: (Society for Machines and Mentality ITA), Springer-Verlag Dordrecht (Subsidiary of: Springer Science+Business Media), Van Godewijckstraat 30, Dordrecht, 3311 GX, Netherlands. TEL 31-78-6576050, FAX 31-78-6576474, http://springerlink.metapress.com/openurl.asp?genre=journal&issn=0924-6495, http://www.springeronline.com. Ed. James H Moor.

006.3 CHN ISSN 1003-6059
MOSHI SHIBIE YU RENGONG ZHINENG/PATTERN RECOGNITION AND ARTIFICIAL INTELLIGENCE. Text in Chinese. 1987. q. CNY 18 newsstand/cover (effective 2005). **Document type:** *Journal, Academic/Scholarly.*
Related titles: Online - full text ed.: (from WanFang Data Corp.).
Address: PO Box 1130, Hefei, 230031, China. bjb@iim.ac.cn, http://mssbyrgzn.periodicals.net.cn/.

006.3 USA
MULTISENSOR FUSION AND INTEGRATION FOR INTELLIGENT SYSTEMS. Text in English. 1999. a. USD 182; USD 91 to members (effective 2004). **Document type:** *Proceedings, Trade.*
Published by: Institute of Electrical and Electronics Engineers, Inc., 3 Park Ave, 17th Fl, New York, NY 10016-5997. http://www.ieee.org. **Co-sponsors:** I E E E Industrial Electronics Society; I E E E Robotics and Automation Society.

006.32 RUS
NEIROKOMP'YUTERY: RAZRABOTKA, PRIMENENIE/NEUROCOMPUTERS. Text in Russian. m. RUR 350 per issue domestic (effective 2004). **Document type:** *Journal, Academic/Scholarly.*
Related titles: ♦ Translation of: Neurocomputers. ISSN 1530-0536.
Published by: Izdatel'stvo Radiotekhnika, Kuznetskii Most 20/6, Moscow, 103031, Russian Federation. iprzhr@online.ru, http://webcenter.ru/~iprzhr/.

NETWORKS AND SPATIAL ECONOMICS; a journal of infrastructure modeling and computation. see *COMPUTERS—Computer Simulation*

006.32 616.8 USA ISSN 0899-7667
QA76.5 CODEN: NEUCEB
➤ **NEURAL COMPUTATION.** Text in English. 1989. m. USD 100 combined subscription in US & Canada to individuals print & online eds.; USD 154 combined subscription elsewhere to individuals print & online eds.; USD 730 combined subscription in US & Canada to institutions print & online eds.; USD 784 combined subscription elsewhere to institutions print & online eds. (effective 2006). back issues avail.; reprint service avail. from PQC,PSC. **Document type:** *Academic/Scholarly.* **Description:** Provides interdisciplinary forum for the dissemination of research results and for reviews of research in neural computation.
Related titles: Microform ed.: (from PQC); Online - full content ed.: ISSN 1530-888X. USD 90 to individuals; USD 657 to institutions (effective 2006) (from HighWire Press); Online - full text ed.: (from EBSCO Publishing, Gale Group, IngentaConnect, O C L C Online Computer Library Center, Inc., Swets Information Services).
Indexed: AIA, ASCA, AcoustA, B&BAb, BibInd, BioEngAb, CMCI, CompAb, CompLI, CurCont, Englnd, ISR, IndMed, Inpharma, Inspec, MEDLINE, NSA, NSCI, PsycInfo, PsycholAb, Reac, RefZh, SCI, ZentMath, e-psyche.
—BLDSC (6081.280200), AskIEEE, CISTI, Ei, GNLM, IDS, IE, Infotrieve, ingenta. **CCC.**
Published by: (Salk Institute), M I T Press, 55 Hayward St, Cambridge, MA 02142-1493. TEL 617-253-5646, FAX 617-258-6779, terry@salk.edu, journals-info@mit.edu, http://mitpress.mit.edu/neco. Ed. Terrence Sejnowski. Circ: 1,800.

006.32 GBR ISSN 0941-0643
CODEN: NCAPF5
➤ **NEURAL COMPUTING AND APPLICATIONS.** Text in English. 1992. q. EUR 538 combined subscription to institutions print & online eds. (effective 2005). back issues avail.; reprint service avail. from PSC. **Document type:** *Journal, Academic/Scholarly.* **Description:** Publishes innovations in theory and practice in the academic, commercial, and industrial fields; relates neural computing to its applications.
Related titles: Online - full text ed.: ISSN 1433-3058 (from EBSCO Publishing, Springer LINK, Swets Information Services).
Indexed: ASCA, CMCI, CompLI, CurCont, Inspec, NSCI, ZentMath.
—BLDSC (6081.280250), CISTI, IDS, IE, Infotrieve, ingenta. **CCC.**
Published by: Springer-Verlag London Ltd. (Subsidiary of: Springer Science+Business Media), Ashbourne House, The Guildway, Old Portsmouth Rd, Guildford, Surrey GU7 3DJ, United Kingdom. TEL 44-1483-734433, FAX 44-1483-734411, postmaster@svl.co.uk, http://link.springer.de/link/service/journals/00521/, http://www.springer.co.uk. Eds. H James, John MacIntyre. Adv. contact Christiane Notarmarco. **Subscr. in the Americas to:** Springer-Verlag New York, Inc., Journal Fulfillment, PO Box 2485, Secaucus, NJ 07096-2485. TEL 800-777-4643, 201-348-4033, FAX 201-348-4505, journals@springer-ny.com, http://www.springer-ny.com; **Subscr. to:** Springer GmbH Auslieferungsgesellschaft, Haberstr 7, Heidelberg 69126, Germany. TEL 49-6221-345-0, FAX 49-6221-345-4229, subscriptions@springer.de.

006.3 CZE ISSN 1210-0552
QA76.87 CODEN: NNWOFJ
➤ **NEURAL NETWORK WORLD**; international journal on non-standard computing and artificial intelligence. Text in English. 1991. bi-m. EUR 200 to individuals; EUR 100 to students (effective 2003). back issues avail. **Document type:** *Journal, Academic/Scholarly.* **Description:** Covers the latest developments in the field of information technology, focusing on neurocomputing based on applications of artificial neural networks. Also covers related fields such as brain and neurophysiological research, artificial intelligence, massive parallel information processing and soft computing.
Indexed: B&BAb, Englnd, Inspec, e-psyche.
—BLDSC (6081.280620), AskIEEE, CISTI, Ei, IE, ingenta.
Published by: Akademie Ved Ceske Republiky, Ustav Informatiky/Czech Academy of Sciences, Institute of Information and Computing Technology, Pod Vodarenskou Vezi 2, Prague 1, 18207, Czech Republic. TEL 420-2-66052080, FAX 420-2-86585789, nnw@cs.cas.cz, mirko@fd.cvut.cz, http://www.cs.cas.cz/nnw/. Ed. Mirko Novak. **Co-publisher:** Ceske Vysoke Uceni Technicke, Fakulta Dopravni/Czech Technical University in Prague, Faculty of Transportation Sciences.

006.32 GBR ISSN 0893-6080
QA76.5 CODEN: NNETEB
➤ **NEURAL NETWORKS.** Text in English. 1988. 10/yr. EUR 1,459 in Europe to institutions; JPY 193,800 in Japan to institutions; USD 1,631 to institutions except Europe and Japan; EUR 267 in Europe to qualified personnel; JPY 35,400 in Japan to qualified personnel; USD 297 to qualified personnel except Europe and Japan (effective 2006). adv. bk.rev. illus. back issues avail.; reprints avail. **Document type:** *Journal, Academic/Scholarly.* **Description:** Covers the modelling of brain and behavioral processes, and the application of these processes to computer and related technologies.
Related titles: Microfilm ed.: (from PQC); Online - full text ed.: (from EBSCO Publishing, Gale Group, IngentaConnect, ScienceDirect, Swets Information Services).
Indexed: AHCI, AIA, AS&TI, ASCA, AcoustA, B&BAb, BIOBASE, BIOSIS Prev, BioEngAb, BiolAb, Biostat, C&ISA, CIS, CMCI, CompAb, CompLI, CompR, CurCont, E&CAJ, Englnd, ExcerpMed, IABS, ISMEC, ISR, IndMed, Inspec, MEDLINE, NSCI, ORMS, PsycInfo, PsycholAb, QC&AS, RASB, RILM, RefZh, SCI, SSCI, SolStAb, Telegen, ZentMath, e-psyche.
—BLDSC (6081.280800), AskIEEE, CISTI, Ei, GNLM, IDS, IE, Infotrieve, ingenta, Linda Hall. **CCC.**
Published by: (International Neural Networks Society), Pergamon (Subsidiary of: Elsevier Science & Technology), The Boulevard, Langford Ln, East Park, Kidlington, Oxford OX5 1GB, United Kingdom. TEL 44-1865-843000, FAX 44-1865-843010, http://www.elsevier.com/locate/neunet. Eds. John Taylor TEL 44-20-7873-2214, Mitsuo Kawato, Dr. Stephen Grossberg TEL 617-353-7857. adv.: B&W page USD 600, color page USD 1,400. Circ: 1,053 (paid). **Subscr. to:** Elsevier BV, PO Box 211, Amsterdam 1000 AE, Netherlands. TEL 31-20-485-3757, FAX 31-20-485-3432, nlinfo-f@elsevier.nl, http://www.elsevier.nl. **Co-sponsors:** European Neural Networks Society; Japanese Neural Networks Society.

006.32 USA ISSN 1061-5369
QA76.87 CODEN: NPACEM
NEURAL, PARALLEL & SCIENTIFIC COMPUTATIONS. Text in English. 1993. 4/yr. USD 100 domestic to individuals; USD 130 foreign to individuals; USD 400 domestic to institutions; USD 460 foreign to institutions (effective 2005). **Document type:** *Academic/Scholarly.* **Description:** Provides an international forum to computer science, engineering, mathematical, and other applied science communities to publish research papers.
Indexed: BrCerAb, C&ISA, CCMJ, CerAb, CompAb, CompLI, CompR, CorrAb, E&CAJ, EMA, IAA, Inspec, M&TEA, MBF, METADEX, MathR, MathSciNet, RefZh, SolStAb, WAA, ZentMath.
—BLDSC (6081.281010), AskIEEE, IE, Infotrieve, ingenta, Linda Hall. **CCC.**
Published by: Dynamic Publishers, Inc., PO Box 48654, Atlanta, GA 30362. TEL 770-451-3616. Ed. M Sambandham.

006.32 USA ISSN 1370-4621
QA76.87 CODEN: NPLEFG
➤ **NEURAL PROCESSING LETTERS.** Text in English. 1994. bi-m. EUR 563, USD 563, GBP 352 combined subscription to institutions print & online eds. (effective 2005). adv. reprint service avail. from PSC. **Document type:** *Journal, Academic/Scholarly.* **Description:** Promotes fast exchange of information in the community of neural network researchers and users, and publishes research results and innovative ideas in all fields of artificial neural networks.
Related titles: Online - full text ed.: ISSN 1573-773X (from EBSCO Publishing, Gale Group, IngentaConnect, Kluwer Online, O C L C Online Computer Library Center, Inc., Ovid Technologies, Inc., Springer LINK, Swets Information Services).
Indexed: ASCA, BibLing, CMCI, CompAb, CompLI, CompR, Englnd, InfoSAb, Inspec, NSCI, RefZh, e-psyche.
—BLDSC (6081.281020), AskIEEE, IDS, IE, Infotrieve, ingenta. **CCC.**

Published by: Springer-Verlag New York, Inc. (Subsidiary of: Springer Science+Business Media), 233 Spring St, New York, NY 10013. TEL 212-460-1500, FAX 212-460-1575, service@springer-ny.com, http://springerlink.metapress.com/openurl.asp?genre=journal&issn=1370-4621, http://www.springer-ny.com. Eds. Francois Blayo, Michel Verleysen, Mohamad Hassoun. Subscr. to: Journal Fulfillment, PO Box 2485, Secaucus, NJ 07096-2485. TEL 201-348-4033, FAX 201-348-4505, journals@springer-ny.com.

006.32 USA ISSN 1530-0536
CODEN: NDAECA
➤ **NEUROCOMPUTERS**; design and applications. Text in English. 2000. q. USD 577 to institutions (effective 2002). **Document type:** *Journal, Academic/Scholarly.* **Description:** Covers all aspects of developments and applications in the field of neurocomputers.
Related titles: ♦ Russian Translation: Neirokomp'yutery: Razrabotka, Primenenie.
Indexed: Inspec.
Published by: Begell House Inc., 145 Madison Ave, New York, NY 10016-6717. TEL 212-725-1999, FAX 212-213-8368, orders@begellhouse.com, http://www.begellhouse.com/nda/nda.html. Ed. Alexander I. Galushkin.

006.32 NLD ISSN 0925-2312
QA76.87 CODEN: NRCGEO
➤ **NEUROCOMPUTING.** Text in Dutch. 1989. 18/yr. EUR 2,031 in Europe to institutions; JPY 269,400 in Japan to institutions; USD 2,271 elsewhere to institutions (effective 2006). bk.rev. back issues avail.; reprints avail. **Document type:** *Academic/Scholarly.* **Description:** Publishes articles describing recent fundamental contributions in the field of neurocomputing.
Related titles: Microform ed.: (from PQC); Online - full text ed.: (from EBSCO Publishing, Gale Group, IngentaConnect, ScienceDirect, Swets Information Services).
Indexed: ASCA, ASFA, B&BAb, BioEngAb, CMCI, CompAb, CompLI, CurCont, EngInd, ExcerpMed, IPsyAb, Inspec, NSA, NSCI, PsycInfo, PsycholAb, RefZh, SSCI, ZentMath, e-psyche.
—BLDSC (6081.365200), CISTI, Ei, GNLM, IDS, IE, Infotrieve, ingenta. **CCC.**
Published by: Elsevier BV (Subsidiary of: Elsevier Science & Technology), Radarweg 29, Amsterdam, 1043 NX, Netherlands. TEL 31-20-4853911, FAX 31-20-4852457, nlinfo-f@elsevier.nl, http://www.elsevier.com/locate/neucom, http://www.elsevier.nl. Eds. G. Dreyfus, T Heskes.

511.313 USA
NORTH AMERICAN FUZZY INFORMATION PROCESSING SOCIETY. ANNUAL MEETING. Text in English. 2000. a. USD 216; USD 108 to members (effective 2004). **Document type:** *Proceedings, Trade.*
Indexed: EngInd.
Published by: Institute of Electrical and Electronics Engineers, Inc., 3 Park Ave, 17th Fl, New York, NY 10016-5997. TEL 212-419-7900, 800-678-4333, FAX 212-752-4929, customer.service@ieee.org, http://www.ieee.org.
Co-sponsors: I E E E Systems, Man, and Cybernetics Society; I E E E Neural Networks Society.

006.3 RUS ISSN 1682-8917
NOVOSTI ISKUSTVENNOGO INTELLEKTA/A I NEWS. Text in Russian. 1990. bi-m. **Document type:** *Journal, Academic/Scholarly.*
Indexed: RefZh.
Published by: (Rossiiskaya Assotsiatsiya Isskustvennogo Intellekta), Izdatel'stvo Anakharsis, M Mogil'tsevskii per, dom 4A, kv 2, ofis 1, Moscow, 119002, Russian Federation. TEL 7-095-2415925, ainews@ainews.ru, http://www.ainews.ru/ru/main.php, http://www.anakharsis.ru. Ed. E V Popov.

006.3 AUT ISSN 0254-4326
O E G A I JOURNAL. Text in English, German; Summaries in English. 1982. q. EUR 20 domestic membership; EUR 300 foreign membership (effective 2005). adv. bk.rev. **Document type:** *Journal, Academic/Scholarly.* **Description:** Information about the field of artificial intelligence.
Indexed: Inspec, RefZh.
—AskIEEE, Ei.
Published by: Oesterreichische Gesellschaft fuer Artificial Intelligence/Austrian Society for Artificial Intelligence, Postfach 177, Vienna, W 1014, Austria. TEL 43-1-5880118824, FAX 43-1-5880118899, info@oegai.at, http://www.oegai.at/journal.shtml. Ed. Claudia Ulbricht. Pub. Anton Riegelnik. R&P, Adv. contact Silvia Miksch. Circ: 300.

006.3 USA ISSN 0894-0711
CODEN: PCAIE5
P C - A I MAGAZINE; intelligent solutions for today's computers. (Personal Computer Artificial Intelligence) Text in English. 1987. bi-m. USD 25 domestic; USD 41 in Canada & Mexico; USD 57 elsewhere (effective 2003). adv. bk.rev.; software rev. illus. back issues avail.; reprints avail. **Document type:** *Magazine, Trade.* **Description:** Topics covered include neural networks, expert systems, datamining, objected oriented development, fuzzy logic, languages and case-based reasoning.
Related titles: CD-ROM ed.
Indexed: AIA, CADCAM, CompLI, InfoSAb, Inspec, MicrocompInd, SoftBase.
—BLDSC (6413.366100), CISTI, Ei, IE, Infotrieve. **CCC.**
Published by: Knowledge Technology, P O BOX 30130, Phoenix, AZ 85046-0130. TEL 602-971-1869, info@pcai.com, http://www.pcai.com/pcai. Ed., Pub. Terry Hengl. R&P Elisa Hicks. Adv. contact Robin Okun. Circ: 10,000.

006.32 GBR ISSN 1433-7541
➤ **PATTERN ANALYSIS AND APPLICATIONS.** Short title: P A A. Text in English. 1998. q. EUR 548 combined subscription to institutions print & online eds. (effective 2005). **Document type:** *Journal, Academic/Scholarly.* **Description:** Covers research in intelligent pattern analysis and applications in computer science and engineering.
Related titles: Online - full text ed.: ISSN 1433-755X (from EBSCO Publishing, Springer LINK, Swets Information Services).
Indexed: CCMJ, CMCI, CompLI, CurCont, Inspec, MathR, MathSciNet, RefZh.
—BLDSC (6412.980451), CISTI, IE, Infotrieve, ingenta. **CCC.**
Published by: Springer-Verlag London Ltd. (Subsidiary of: Springer Science+Business Media), Ashbourne House, The Guildway, Old Portsmouth Rd, Guildford, Surrey GU7 3DJ, United Kingdom. TEL 44-1483-734433, FAX 44-1483-734411, postmaster@svl.co.uk, http://link.springer.de/link/service/journals/10044/, http://www.springer.co.uk. Ed. Sameer Singh. Adv. contact Christiane Notarmarco. **Subscr. in the Americas to:** Springer-Verlag New York, Inc., Journal Fulfillment, PO Box 2485, Secaucus, NJ 07096-2485. TEL 800-777-4643, 201-348-4033, FAX 201-348-4505, journals@springer-ny.com, http://www.springer-ny.com; **Subscr. to:** Springer GmbH Auslieferungsgesellschaft, Haberstr 7, Heidelberg 69126, Germany. TEL 49-6221-345-0, FAX 49-6221-345-4229, subscriptions@springer.de.

006.31 GBR ISSN 0031-3203
Q327 CODEN: PTNRA8
➤ **PATTERN RECOGNITION.** Text in English. 1968. 12/yr. EUR 2,559 in Europe to institutions; JPY 339,700 in Japan to institutions; USD 2,863 to institutions except Europe and Japan; EUR 330 in Europe to qualified personnel; JPY 43,600 in Japan to qualified personnel; USD 369 to qualified personnel except Europe and Japan (effective 2006). adv. bk.rev. illus. back issues avail.; reprints avail. **Document type:** *Journal, Academic/Scholarly.* **Description:** Provides a forum for the exchange of information on pattern recognition research among the many varied engineering, mathematical and applied professions which make up this unique field. Original papers cover all methods, techniques and applications of pattern recognition, artificial intelligence, image processing, 2-D and 3-D matching, expert systems and robotics.
Related titles: Microfilm ed.: (from PQC); Online - full text ed.: (from EBSCO Publishing, Gale Group, IngentaConnect, ScienceDirect, Swets Information Services).
Indexed: AHCI, AIA, ASCA, ApMecR, B&BAb, BIOSIS Prev, BiolAb, C&CSA, C&ISA, CADCAM, CIS, CMCI, CompAb, CompC, CompLI, CurCont, E&CAJ, EngInd, ExcerpMed, GEOBASE, ISMEC, ISR, Inspec, NSCI, RASB, RefZh, RoboAb, SCI, SSCI, SolStAb, ZentMath.
—BLDSC (6412.981000), AskIEEE, CINDOC, CISTI, Ei, IDS, IE, Infotrieve, ingenta, Linda Hall. **CCC.**
Published by: (Pattern Recognition Society), Pergamon (Subsidiary of: Elsevier Science & Technology), The Boulevard, Langford Ln, East Park, Kidlington, Oxford OX5 1GB, United Kingdom. TEL 44-1865-843000, FAX 44-1865-843010, http://www.elsevier.com/locate/pr. Ed. Dr. Robert S Ledley. Circ: 1,500. **Subscr. to:** Elsevier BV, PO Box 211, Amsterdam 1000 AE, Netherlands. TEL 31-20-485-3757, FAX 31-20-485-3432, nlinfo-f@elsevier.nl, http://www.elsevier.nl.

006.31 GBR
PATTERN RECOGNITION AND IMAGE PROCESSING SERIES. Text in English. irreg., latest vol.11, 2000. **Document type:** *Monographic series.*
Indexed: Inspec.
Published by: Research Studies Press Ltd., 16 Coach House Cloisters, 10 Hitchin St, Baldock, Hertfordshire SG7 6AE, United Kingdom. TEL 44-1462-895060, FAX 44-1462-892546, http://www.research-studies-press.co.uk. Ed. J Kittler.

006.31 NLD ISSN 0167-8655
TK7882.P3 CODEN: PRLEDG
➤ **PATTERN RECOGNITION LETTERS.** Text in English. 1982. 16/yr. EUR 1,828 in Europe to institutions; JPY 242,700 in Japan to institutions; USD 2,043 to institutions except Europe and Japan (effective 2006). back issues avail.; reprints avail. **Document type:** *Journal, Academic/Scholarly.* **Description:** Covers theoretical, methodological and empirical studies of image processing and pattern recognition.
Related titles: Microform ed.: (from PQC); Online - full text ed.: (from EBSCO Publishing, Gale Group, IngentaConnect, ScienceDirect, Swets Information Services).
Indexed: AEA, AHCI, AIA, ASCA, ASFA, C&CSA, CADCAM, CMCI, CompAb, CompLI, CompR, CurCont, CybAb, EngInd, GEOBASE, Inspec, RoboAb, SSCI, ZentMath.
—BLDSC (6412.981840), AskIEEE, CISTI, Ei, IDS, IE, Infotrieve, ingenta, Linda Hall. **CCC.**
Published by: (International Association for Pattern Recognition), Elsevier BV, North-Holland (Subsidiary of: Elsevier Science & Technology), Sara Burgerhartstraat 25, Amsterdam, 1055 KV, Netherlands. TEL 31-20-485-3911, FAX 31-20-485-2457, nlinfo-f@elsevier.nl, http://www.elsevier.com/locate/patrec, http://www.elsevier.nl/homepage/about/us/regional_sites.htt, http://www.elsevier.nl. Eds. G Sanniti di Baja, T K Ho. **Subscr. to:** Elsevier BV, PO Box 211, Amsterdam 1000 AE, Netherlands. TEL 31-20-485-3757, FAX 31-20-485-3432.

006.3 USA
PERSPECTIVES IN ARTIFICIAL INTELLIGENCE. Text in English. 1989. irreg., latest vol.9, 1991. back issues avail. **Document type:** *Monographic series, Academic/Scholarly.* **Description:** Focuses on artificial intelligence and attracts readers interested in cognitive science, psychology and computer science.
—BLDSC (6428.137870).
Published by: Academic Press (Subsidiary of: Elsevier Science & Technology), 525 B St, Ste 1900, San Diego, CA 92101-4495. apsubs@acad.com, http://www.academicpress.com. Ed. B Chandrasekaran.

006.32 GBR ISSN 1431-6854
PERSPECTIVES IN NEURAL COMPUTING. Text in English. 1992. irreg. **Document type:** *Monographic series.*
—BLDSC (6081.280280).
Published by: Springer-Verlag London Ltd. (Subsidiary of: Springer Science+Business Media), Ashbourne House, The Guildway, Old Portsmouth Rd, Guildford, Surrey GU7 3DJ, United Kingdom. TEL 44-1483-418800, FAX 44-1483-415144, http://www.springer.co.uk.

006.3 USA
PROGRESS IN ROBOTICS AND INTELLIGENT SYSTEMS. Text in English. 1991. a., latest 1996. price varies. **Document type:** *Academic/Scholarly.*
Published by: Ablex Publishing Corporation (Subsidiary of: Greenwood Publishing Group Inc.), 88 Post Rd W, Westport, CT 06881. TEL 203-323-9609, FAX 203-661-0792. Eds. C Y Ho, George W Zobrist.

006.3 USA ISSN 1570-0755
QA76.889
QUANTUM INFORMATION PROCESSING. Text in English. 2002. bi-m. EUR 310, USD 310, GBP 194 combined subscription to institutions print & online eds. (effective 2005). adv. reprint service avail. from PSC. **Document type:** *Journal, Academic/Scholarly.* **Description:** Provides international forum for the publication of high-quality, peer-reviewed original papers, review articles, letters, or short communications, commentary, and electronic rapid communications on all aspects, theoretical and experimental, of quantum information processing.
Related titles: Online - full text ed.: ISSN 1573-1332 (from EBSCO Publishing, Gale Group, IngentaConnect, Kluwer Online, O C L C Online Computer Library Center, Inc., Springer LINK, Swets Information Services).
Indexed: BibLing, Inspec, MathR, MathSciNet.
—BLDSC (7168.548000), IE, ingenta. **CCC.**
Published by: Springer-Verlag New York, Inc. (Subsidiary of: Springer Science+Business Media), 233 Spring St, New York, NY 10013. TEL 212-460-1500, FAX 212-460-1575, service@springer-ny.com, http://springerlink.metapress.com/openurl.asp?genre=journal&issn=1570-0755, http://www.springer-ny.com. Ed. David Cory. **Subscr. to:** Journal Fulfillment, PO Box 2485, Secaucus, NJ 07096-2485. TEL 201-348-4033, FAX 201-348-4505, journals@springer-ny.com.

006.31 IND
RECENT RESEARCH DEVELOPMENTS IN PATTERN RECOGNITION. Text in English. a., latest vol.1, 2000.
Published by: Transworld Research Network, T C 36-248 (1), Trivandrum, Kerala 695 008, India. http://www.transworldresearch.com.

006.3 USA ISSN 0268-7526
➤ **RESEARCH NOTES IN ARTIFICIAL INTELLIGENCE.** Text in English. 1984. irreg., latest 1989. price varies. abstr.; bibl.; charts; illus.; stat. **Document type:** *Proceedings, Academic/Scholarly.* **Description:** Consists of primary research works in specific areas of AI.
—CISTI.
Published by: Morgan Kaufmann Publishers, Inc. (Subsidiary of: Elsevier BV), 500 Sansome St, Ste 400, San Francisco, CA 94111. TEL 415-392-2665, FAX 415-982-2665, orders@mkp.com, http://www.mkp.com. Ed. Denise Penrose. R&P Kate Henserson. **Co-publisher:** Pitman Publishing.

006.3 FRA ISSN 0992-499X
REVUE D'INTELLIGENCE ARTIFICIELLE. Text in French. 1987. bi-m. EUR 260 in the European Union; EUR 295 elsewhere (effective 2003).
Indexed: EngInd.
—CISTI, Ei.
Published by: (Ministere de la Recherche et de l'Espace), Lavoisier, 11 rue Lavoisier, Paris, 75008, France. TEL 33-1-42653995, FAX 33-1-42650246, info@lavoisier.fr, http://www.lavoisier.fr. **Subscr. to:** Lavoisier - Dept Abonnements, 14 rue de Provigny, Cachan 94236, France. TEL 33-1-47406700, FAX 33-1-47406702, abo@lavoisier.fr.

▼ new title ➤ refereed ✶ unverified ♦ full entry avail.

ROBOTICS AND COMPUTER-INTEGRATED MANUFACTURING. see *COMPUTERS—Robotics*

006.3 USA
S I G A R T CONFERENCE PROCEEDINGS. (Special Interest Group Artifical Intelligence) Text in English. a. USD 35 (effective 2004). **Description:** Consists of the study of intelligence and its realization in computer systems.
Published by: Association for Computing Machinery, Inc., 1515 Broadway, 17th Fl, New York, NY 10036-5701. TEL 212-626-0500, 212-626-0520, 800-342-6626, usacm@acm.org, http://www.acm.org/sigart/.

006.3 NLD ISSN 0927-720X
➤ **SCANDINAVIAN CONFERENCE ON ARTIFICIAL INTELLIGENCE.** Text in English. 1987. irreg. price varies. back issues avail. **Document type:** *Proceedings, Academic/Scholarly.*
Related titles: ♦ Series of: Frontiers in Artificial Intelligence and Applications. ISSN 0922-6389.
—BLDSC (8087.473300). **CCC.**
Published by: (Scandinavian Conference on Artificial Intelligence), I O S Press, Nieuwe Hemweg 6B, Amsterdam, 1013 BG, Netherlands. TEL 31-20-6883355, FAX 31-20-6203419, order@iospress.nl, http://www.iospress.nl. **Subscr. to:** I O S Press, Inc, 4502 Rachael Manor Dr., Fairfax, VA 22032-3631. iosbooks@iospress.com. **Dist. by:** Ohmsha Ltd.

➤ **SEMIOTIC AND COGNITIVE STUDIES.** see *PHILOSOPHY*

➤ **SENSORS**; your resource for sensing, communications, and control. see *INSTRUMENTS*

006.3 SGP ISSN 1793-0839
SERIES IN MACHINE PERCEPTION AND ARTIFICIAL INTELLIGENCE. Text in English. 1992. irreg., latest vol.50. price varies. **Document type:** *Monographic series, Academic/Scholarly.* **Description:** Publishes both applications and theory-oriented articles on new developments in the fields of pattern recognition and artificial intelligence, and is of interest to both researchers in industry and academia.
Indexed: CCMJ, ZentMath.
—BLDSC (8250.163200), ingenta.
Published by: World Scientific Publishing Co. Pte. Ltd., 5 Toh Tuck Link, Singapore, 596224, Singapore. TEL 65-466-5775, FAX 65-467-7667, wspc@wspc.com.sg, series@wspc.com.sg, http://www.wspc.com.sg/books/series/wsmpai_series.shtml, http://www.worldscientific.com. Eds. Horst Bunke, Patrick Shen Pei Wang. **Dist. by:** World Scientific Publishing Co., Inc., 1060 Main St, River Edge, NJ 07661. TEL 201-487-9655, 800-227-7562, FAX 201-487-9656, 888-977-2665; World Scientific Publishing Ltd., 57 Shelton St, London WC2H 9HE, United Kingdom. TEL 44-20-78360888, FAX 44-20-78362020.

006.3 ITA ISSN 1120-9550
SISTEMI INTELLIGENTI; rivista quadrimestrale di scienze cognitive e di intelligenza artificiale. Text in Italian. 1989. 3/yr. EUR 51 domestic to individuals; EUR 84 foreign to individuals; EUR 96 domestic to institutions print & online eds.; EUR 135 foreign to institutions print & online eds. (effective 2004). adv. index. back issues avail. **Document type:** *Academic/Scholarly.*
Related titles: Online - full text ed.
Indexed: PsycInfo, PsycholAb, e-psyche.
—BLDSC (8286.420600).
Published by: Societa Editrice Il Mulino, Strada Maggiore 37, Bologna, 40125, Italy. TEL 39-051-256011, FAX 39-051-256034, riviste@mulino.it, http://www.mulino.it. Ed. Domenico Parisi. Adv. contact M Luisa Vezzali. Circ: 1,900.

006.3 NLD ISSN 0924-3542
➤ **STUDIES IN COMPUTER SCIENCE AND ARTIFICIAL INTELLIGENCE.** Text in English. 1988. irreg., latest vol.13, 1996. price varies. back issues avail. **Document type:** *Monographic series, Academic/Scholarly.* **Description:** Investigates the application of logic and logic programming in artificial intelligence and other areas of computer science.
Indexed: CCMJ, Inspec, ZentMath.
—BLDSC (8490.282000), IE.
Published by: Elsevier BV, North-Holland (Subsidiary of: Elsevier Science & Technology), Sara Burgerhartstraat 25, Amsterdam, 1055 KV, Netherlands. TEL 31-20-485-3911, FAX 31-20-485-2457, nlinfo-f@elsevier.nl, http://www.elsevier.nl. **Subscr. to:** Elsevier BV, PO Box 211, Amsterdam 1000 AE, Netherlands. TEL 31-20-485-3757, FAX 31-20-485-3432, http://www.elsevier.nl.

511.3223 DEU ISSN 1434-9922
➤ **STUDIES IN FUZZINESS AND SOFT COMPUTING.** Text in English. irreg., latest vol.192, 2005. price varies. **Document type:** *Monographic series, Academic/Scholarly.* **Description:** Covers various topics and research in the area of fuzzy logic.
Formerly (until 1996): Studies in Fuzziness (1431-9470)
Indexed: CCMJ, ZentMath.
—BLDSC (8490.579200), ingenta.
Published by: Physica-Verlag GmbH und Co. (Subsidiary of: Springer-Verlag), Postfach 105280, Heidelberg, 69042, Germany. TEL 49-6221-487492, FAX 49-6221-487177, physica@springer.de, http://www.springer.de/economics/series/sfsc.html. **Subscr. to:** Springer GmbH Auslieferungsgesellschaft, Haberstr 7, Heidelberg 69126, Germany. TEL 49-6221-345-0, FAX 49-6221-345-4229, subscriptions@springer.de.

006.3 USA ISSN 1522-371X
TECHNOLOGIES OF CREATIVITY✶. Text in Russian. 1998. q. adv. **Document type:** *Academic/Scholarly.* **Description:** Translates articles on TRIZ (theory for solving inventive problems), ARIZ (algorithm for solving inventive problems), and TDCP (theory for developing a creative personality) published in Russian academic journals.
Published by: Gregory Blake, Ed. & Pub., P O Box 7412, Americus, GA 31709-7412. TEL 530-692-2016, gblake@apollo.org. R&P, Adv. contact Gregory Blake TEL 530-692-2244.

TELEKOMUNIKACJA I TECHNIKI INFORMACYJNE. see *COMMUNICATIONS*

TRENDS IN COGNITIVE SCIENCES. see *PSYCHOLOGY*

006.3 GBR
UNCERTAINTY THEORY IN ARTIFICIAL INTELLIGENCE SERIES. Text in English. 1995. irreg., latest vol.4, 2004, Apr. price varies. **Document type:** *Monographic series.*
—BLDSC (9085.422000), ingenta.
Published by: Research Studies Press Ltd., 16 Coach House Cloisters, 10 Hitchin St, Baldock, Hertfordshire SG7 6AE, United Kingdom. TEL 44-1462-895060, FAX 44-1462-892546, http://www.research-studies-press.co.uk. Ed. J F Baldwin.

UNMANNED SYSTEMS. see *MILITARY*

006.3 FRA ISSN 1257-2748
VIGIE. INFORMATIQUE APPLIQUEE. Text in French. 1995. m. EUR 90 (effective 2004). **Document type:** *Bulletin.*
Published by: Agence pour la Diffusion de l'Information Technologique, 2, rue Brulee, Strasbourg, 67000, France. TEL 33-3-88214242, 33-1-44183139, FAX 33-1-45515096, vigies@adit.fr, info@adit.fr, http://www.vigies.com, http://www.adit.fr/.

006.3 IND ISSN 0970-8618
➤ **VIVEK**; a quarterly in artificial intelligence. Text in English. 1988. q. INR 100, USD 20. bk.rev. **Document type:** *Academic/Scholarly.* **Description:** Publishes articles on artificial intelligence and tutorials on areas of topical interest.
Indexed: Inspec.
—BLDSC (9244.428000), AskIEEE, IE, ingenta.
Published by: National Centre for Software Technology, Gulmohar Cross Rd. No. 9, Juhu, Mumbai, Maharashtra 400 049, India. TEL 91-22-620-1606, FAX 91-22-621-0139, TELEX 81-011078260 NCST IN, vivek@saathi.ncst.ernet.in, http://konark.ncst.ernet.in. Ed. S Ramani. Pub. Truptee C Shah. R&P Truptee Shah. adv.: page INR 2,000. Circ: 400.

006.3 003.5 004.01 NLD ISSN 1570-1263
▼ **WEB INTELLIGENCE AND AGENT SYSTEMS**; an international journal. Text in English. 2003. q. EUR 372, USD 446 combined subscription print & online eds. (effective 2006). **Description:** Features original research papers in all theoretical and technology areas that make up the field of Web intelligence and agent systems.
Related titles: Online - full text ed.: (from EBSCO Publishing, O C L C Online Computer Library Center, Inc., Swets Information Services).
Indexed: Inspec.
—BLDSC (9283.976500), IE. **CCC.**
Published by: I O S Press, Nieuwe Hemweg 6B, Amsterdam, 1013 BG, Netherlands. TEL 31-20-6883355, FAX 31-20-6203419, info@iospress.nl, order@iospress.nl, http://www.iospress.nl/html/15701263.php. Eds. Jiming Liu, Ning Zhong. R&P Ms. Carry Koolbergen TEL 31-20-6382189. Adv. contact Ms. Jolijn van Eunen.

006.3 USA ISSN 1550-6193
WORKSHOP ON MOBILE COMPUTING SYSTEMS AND APPLICATIONS. Text in English. a. USD 137; USD 55 to members (effective 2004). **Document type:** *Proceedings, Trade.*
Related titles: Online - full text ed.: (from I E E E).
Published by: Institute of Electrical and Electronics Engineers, Inc., 3 Park Ave, 17th Fl, New York, NY 10016-5997. TEL 212-419-7900, 800-678-4333, FAX 212-752-4929, customer.service@ieee.org, http://www.ieee.org.

WORKSHOP ON ROBOT MOTION AND CONTROL. see *COMPUTERS—Robotics*

006.3 SGP ISSN 1793-0774
WORLD SCIENTIFIC SERIES IN ROBOTICS AND INTELLIGENT SYSTEMS. Text in English. 1991. irreg., latest vol.27. price varies. **Document type:** *Monographic series, Academic/Scholarly.*
—ingenta.
Published by: World Scientific Publishing Co. Pte. Ltd., 5 Toh Tuck Link, Singapore, 596224, Singapore. TEL 65-466-5775, FAX 65-467-7667, wspc@wspc.com.sg, series@wspc.com.sg, http://www.wspc.com.sg/books/series/wssris_series.shtml, http://www.worldscientific.com. Ed. Christopher J Harris. **Dist. by:** World Scientific Publishing Co., Inc., 1060 Main St, River Edge, NJ 07661. TEL 201-487-9655, 800-227-7562, FAX 201-487-9656, 888-977-2665; World Scientific Publishing Ltd., 57 Shelton St, London WC2H 9HE, United Kingdom. TEL 44-20-78360888, FAX 44-20-78362020.

COMPUTERS—Automation

629.8 DEU
A & D KOMPENDIUM; Das Referenzbuch fuer Automatisierungs- und Antriebstechnik. (Automation and Drives) Text in German. 1998. a. EUR 100 per issue (effective 2004). adv. **Document type:** *Directory, Trade.*
Published by: Publish-Industry Verlag GmbH, Nymphenburger Str 86, Munich, 80636, Germany. TEL 49-89-5003830, FAX 49-89-50038310, info@publish-industry.net, http://www.publish-industry.net. adv.: B&W page EUR 4,330, color page EUR 5,629. Circ: 13,324 (paid and controlled).

629.8 DEU
A & D LEXIKON; Begriffe & Kurzbezeichnungen aus der Automatisierungs- & Antriebstechnik. (Automation and Drives) Text in German. a. EUR 20 per issue (effective 2004). adv. **Document type:** *Directory, Trade.*
Published by: Publish-Industry Verlag GmbH, Nymphenburger Str 86, Munich, 80636, Germany. TEL 49-89-5003830, FAX 49-89-50038310, info@publish-industry.net, http://www.publish-industry.net.

629.829 DEU ISSN 1618-2898
A & D NEWSLETTER; Das Magazin fuer Automation, Antriebstechnik und Systemintegration. (Automation and Drives) Text in German. 1999. m. EUR 95 domestic; EUR 105 in Europe; EUR 130 elsewhere; EUR 10 newsstand/cover (effective 2004). adv. **Document type:** *Magazine, Trade.*
Published by: Publish-Industry Verlag GmbH, Nymphenburger Str 86, Munich, 80636, Germany. TEL 49-89-5003830, FAX 49-89-50038310, info@publish-industry.net, http://www.publish-industry.net. adv.: B&W page EUR 4,330, color page EUR 5,629. Circ: 20,311 (paid and controlled).

629.8 DEU
A & D SOFTWARE GUIDE; Das Forum fuer Anbieter und Anwender von Automatisierungssoftware. (Automation and Drives) Text in German. a. EUR 20 per issue (effective 2004). adv. **Document type:** *Magazine, Trade.*
Published by: Publish-Industry Verlag GmbH, Nymphenburger Str 86, Munich, 80636, Germany. TEL 49-89-5003830, FAX 49-89-50038310, info@publish-industry.net, http://www.publish-industry.net. adv.: B&W page EUR 4,330, color page EUR 5,629. Circ: 20,311 (paid and controlled).

629.8 USA ISSN 0738-100X
TA174
A C M / I E E E DESIGN AUTOMATION CONFERENCE. PROCEEDINGS. Text in English. 1963. a. price varies. **Document type:** *Proceedings.* **Description:** Covers all aspects of the use of computers as aids to the design process.
Former titles (until 1981): Design Automation Conference. Proceedings (0146-7123); (until 1975): Design Automation Workshop. Proceedings (0420-0098)
Related titles: Online - full text ed.: (from I E E E).
Indexed: Inspec.
—BLDSC (3559.922500), Ei, IE, ingenta. **CCC.**
Published by: (Institute of Electrical and Electronics Engineers, Inc., Association for Computing Machinery, Inc.), I E E E Computer Society, 3 Park Ave, 17th Fl, New York, NY 10017. TEL 714-821-8380, 800-678-4333, FAX 714-821-4010, customer.service@ieee.org, http://www.ieee.org.

629.8 006.3 USA ISSN 0730-8566
A C M SYMPOSIUM ON PRINCIPLES OF PROGRAMMING LANGUAGES. ANNUAL CONFERENCE RECORD. (Association for Computing Machinery) Text in English. 1973. a., latest vol.31, 2004.
Formerly (until 1978): A C M Symposium on Principles of Programming Languages. Conference Record (0743-9016)
—BLDSC (3409.823000), IE, ingenta. **CCC.**
Published by: Association for Computing Machinery, Inc., 1515 Broadway, 17th Fl, New York, NY 10036-5701. TEL 212-626-0500, 800-342-6626, FAX 212-869-0481, sigs@acm.org, usacm@acm.org, http://www.acm.org.

629.8 USA
A D C NEWS. (Automatic Data Collection) Text in English. m. **Document type:** *Newsletter.* **Description:** Covers automatic data collection industry. Includes technical, membership and marketing events of the association.
Formerly: A I M News
Related titles: Online - full text ed.
Published by: Automatic Identification Manufacturers U.S.A., 125 Warrendale Bayne Rd., Ste. 100, Warrendale, PA 15086-7570. TEL 412-963-8588, FAX 412-963-8753, andy.lambl@aimusa.org. Ed. Andrew F Lambl. Circ: 1,000.

A F R I LIAISON. see *COMPUTERS—Robotics*

A M T ELECTRONICS. (Advanced Manufacturing Technology) see *ENGINEERING—Electrical Engineering*

629.8 DEU ISSN 1438-4531
A P L JOURNAL. (Array Programming Language) Text in German. 1982. s-a. EUR 52 domestic; EUR 55.20 foreign (effective 2002). software rev. 40 p./no.; back issues avail. **Document type:** *Journal, Trade.* **Description:** Provides readers with articles, news and reports about solutions concerning array programming language applications.
Published by: Rhombos Verlag, Kurfuerstenstr 17, Berlin, 10785, Germany. TEL 49-30-2616854, FAX 49-30-2616300, verlag@rhombos.de, http://www.rhombos.de. Ed. Dieter Lattermann. Pub. Bernhard Reiser. Circ: 500 (paid and controlled).

629.8 USA
ADVANCED DESIGN AND MANUFACTURING. Short title: A D A M. Text in English. 1998. irreg. free. **Description:** Covers automation, cell design and implementation, schedulling operation control, tooling and fixuring, robotics and concurrent-simultaneous engineering.
Media: Online - full text.
Published by: C I M ware Ltd. UK and USA Inc. ranky@admin.njit.edu, http://www.cimwareukandusa.com/ADAMmain.html. Ed. Paul G Ranky.

629.8 USA
ADVANCED INTELLIGENT MECHATRONICS. Variant title: I E E E / A S M E International Conference on Advanced Intelligent Mechatronics. Text in English. biennial. USD 470 per vol. (effective 2004). **Document type:** *Proceedings, Trade.* **Description:** Promote activities in various areas of mechatronics by providing a forum for exchange of ideas, presentation of technical achievements, and discussion of future directions.
Indexed: EngInd.
—BLDSC (4362.806150).
Published by: Institute of Electrical and Electronics Engineers, Inc., 445 Hoes Ln, Piscataway, NJ 08854-1331. TEL 732-981-0060, 800-678-4333, FAX 732-981-1721, subscription-service@ieee.org, http://www.ieee.org.

629.8 POL ISSN 1429-3447
TJ213
➤ **AKADEMIA GORNICZO-HUTNICZA IM. STANISLAWA STASZICA. AUTOMATYKA.** Text and summaries in English, Polish. 1966-1994; resumed 1997. s-a. EUR 19 foreign (effective 2005). illus. 100 p./no. 1 cols./p.; **Document type:** *Journal, Academic/Scholarly.* **Description:** Covers control theory, optimization, dynamical systems, control systems and their interdisciplinary applications. Publishes discussions, letters, reviews, accounts of scientific output of prominent specialists in the field.
Formerly: Akademia Gorniczo-Hutnicza im. Stanislawa Staszica. Zeszyty Naukowe. Automatyka (0454-4773)
Indexed: RefZh, ZentMath.
Published by: (Akademia Gorniczo-Hutnicza im. Stanislawa Staszica/University of Mining and Metallurgy), Wydawnictwo A G H, al Mickiewicza 30, Krakow, 30059, Poland. TEL 48-12-6173228, FAX 48-12-6364038, wydagh@uci.agh.edu.pl, http://www.wydawnictwoagh.pl. Ed. A J Wichur. Circ: 200 (paid). **Dist. by:** Ars Polona, Krakowskie Przedmiescie 7, Warsaw, Poland. TEL 48-22-9263914, FAX 48-22-9265334, arspolona@arspolona.com.pl, http://www.arspolona.com.pl.

629.8 USA
ANNUAL AUTOMATION REPORT TO THE ARIZONA LEGISLATURE. Text in English. a.
Published by: State Department of Administration, Data Management Division, 1616 West Adams St, Phoenix, AZ 85007. TEL 602-542-5791.

629.8 ESP
ANUARIO AUTOMATICA E INSTRUMENTACION. Text in Spanish. a. **Document type:** *Directory.* **Description:** Lists companies, products and trademarks for the automation of machines and processes.
Published by: Cetisa Editores S.A., Enrique Granados, 7, Barcelona, 08019, Spain. TEL 34-93-2431040, FAX 34-93-3492350, info@cetisa.com, http://www.cetisa.com/.

629.8312 POL ISSN 1230-2384
TJ212
ARCHIVES OF CONTROL SCIENCES. Text in English. 1956. q. EUR 122 foreign (effective 2005). bibl.; charts. index. **Document type:** *Proceedings, Academic/Scholarly.*
Former titles (until 1992): Archiwum Automatyki i Robotyki (1230-0640); (until 1991): Archiwum Automatyki i Telemechaniki (0004-072X)
Indexed: ApMecR, CCMJ, CybAb, EngInd, Inspec, MathR, MathSciNet, ZentMath.
—BLDSC (1634.115200), AskIEEE, CISTI, IE, ingenta, Linda Hall.
Published by: Politechnika Slaska, ul Akademicka 5, Gliwice, 44100, Poland. TEL 48-32-2371381, FAX 48-32-2371848, wydawnictwo_mark@polsl.pl, http://lemon.ia.polsl.gliwice.pl/ACS, http://wydawnictwo.polsl.pl. Ed. Antoni Niederlinski. R&P, Adv. contact Zbigniew Ogonowski TEL 48-32-2371084. Circ: 640. **Dist. by:** Ars Polona, Krakowskie Przedmiescie 7, Warsaw, Poland. TEL 48-22-9263914, FAX 48-22-9265334, arspolona@arspolona.com.pl, http://www.arspolona.com.pl. **Co-sponsor:** Polska Akademia Nauk, Komitet Automatyki i Cybernetyki Technicznej.

629.8 USA
ASIA AND SOUTH PACIFIC DESIGN AUTOMATION CONFERENCE. PROCEEDINGS. Text in English. a. USD 226 to institutions (effective 2004). **Document type:** *Proceedings, Trade.*
Published by: Institute of Electrical and Electronics Engineers, Inc., 3 Park Ave, 17th Fl, New York, NY 10016-5997. TEL 212-419-7900, 800-678-4333, FAX 212-752-4929, customer.service@ieee.org, http://www.ieee.org.

629.8 GBR ISSN 0144-5154
TS178.4 CODEN: ASAUDL
➤ **ASSEMBLY AUTOMATION.** Text in English. 1980. q. EUR 7,296.04 in Europe; USD 7,579 in North America; AUD 9,389 in Australasia; GBP 5,110.16 in UK & elsewhere (effective 2006). bk.rev. charts; illus.; stat. index. back issues avail.; reprint service avail. from PSC. **Document type:** *Journal, Academic/Scholarly.* **Description:** Provides up-to-date coverage of international activities related to the automation of assembly operations. Each issue is themed, ensuring that cutting edge topics are covered in depth.
Related titles: Online - full text ed.: (from EBSCO Publishing, Emerald Group Publishing Limited, Gale Group, IngentaConnect, O C L C Online Computer Library Center, Inc., ProQuest Information & Learning, Swets Information Services).
Indexed: ABIn, ASCA, BrTechI, CADCAM, CurCont, EmerIntel, Emerald, Inspec, M&TEA, RoboAb.
—BLDSC (1746.606200), AskIEEE, CISTI, Ei, IDS, IE, Infotrieve, ingenta, Linda Hall. **CCC.**
Published by: Emerald Group Publishing Limited, 60-62 Toller Ln, Bradford, W Yorks BD8 9BY, United Kingdom. TEL 44-1274-777700, FAX 44-1274-785200, infomation@emeraldinsight.com, http://www.emeraldinsight.com/aa.htm. Ed. Dr. Clive Loughlin TEL 44-1943-830399.

629.8 ITA ISSN 0005-1012
AUTOMAT; rivista italiana dell'automatico. Text in Italian. 1962. m. adv. bk.rev. index. back issues avail. **Document type:** *Trade.* **Description:** Covers industry trends, legal and fiscal problems, and association activities.
Published by: S A P A R, Sezioni Apparecchi per Pubbliche Attrazioni Ricreative, Via Di Villa Patrizi, 10, Rome, RM 00161, Italy. TEL 39-6-4403686, FAX 39-6-4402718. Ed. Maurizio Maneschi. Circ: 3,500.

629.8312 USA ISSN 0146-4116
TJ212 CODEN: ACCSCE
➤ **AUTOMATIC CONTROL AND COMPUTER SCIENCES.** Text in English. 1969. bi-m. USD 2,245 in US & Canada; USD 2,545 elsewhere (effective 2006). bk.rev. abstr.; charts; illus. index. back issues avail. **Document type:** *Journal, Academic/Scholarly.* **Description:** Offers professionals in academia, scientific research, engineering and computer design technical papers on such topics as computer networks, control strategy, data communications, software, and signal processing.
Formerly: Automatic Control (0005-1047)
Related titles: ♦ Translation of: Avtomatika i Vychislitel'naya Tekhnika. ISSN 0132-4160.
Indexed: ApMecR, CMCI, CurCont, EngInd, Inspec, MathR, ZentMath.
—BLDSC (0404.840000), AskIEEE, CISTI, Ei, IE, Infotrieve, ingenta, Linda Hall. **CCC.**
Published by: (Latvian Academy of Sciences LVA), Allerton Press, Inc., 18 W 27th St, New York, NY 10001. TEL 646-424-9686, FAX 646-424-9695, journals@allertonpress.com, http://www.allertonpress.com/journals/aut.htm. Ed. Ivars Bilinskis.

629.8 GBR ISSN 0005-1098
TJ212 CODEN: ATCAA9
➤ **AUTOMATICA.** Text in English, French, German, Russian. 1963. 12/yr. EUR 2,309 in Europe to institutions; JPY 306,600 in Japan to institutions; USD 2,583 elsewhere to institutions; EUR 83 in Europe to qualified personnel; JPY 11,100 in Japan to qualified personnel; USD 93 elsewhere to qualified personnel (effective 2006). adv. bk.rev. charts; illus. Index. back issues avail.; reprints avail. **Document type:** *Journal, Academic/Scholarly.* **Description:** Publishes papers on theoretical and experimental research and practical applications to all types of control systems.
Related titles: Microfilm ed.: (from PQC); Online - full text ed.: (from EBSCO Publishing, Gale Group, IngentaConnect, ScienceDirect, Swets Information Services).
Indexed: ABIPC, AHCI, ASCA, ApMecR, C&ISA, CCMJ, CIS, CMCI, CivEngAb, CompC, CompD, CompR, CurCont, CybAb, E&CAJ, EngInd, ErgAb, ExcerpMed, ICEA, ISMEC, ISR, InfoSAb, Inspec, MathR, MathSciNet, ORMS, QC&AS, RASB, RefZh, SCI, SoftAbEng, SolStAb, WRCInf, ZentMath.
—BLDSC (1829.450000), AskIEEE, CISTI, Ei, IDS, IE, Infotrieve, ingenta, Linda Hall. **CCC.**
Published by: (International Federation for Automatic Control NLD), Pergamon (Subsidiary of: Elsevier Science & Technology), The Boulevard, Langford Ln, East Park, Kidlington, Oxford OX5 1GB, United Kingdom. TEL 44-1865-843000, FAX 44-1865-843010, http://www.elsevier.com/locate/automatica. Ed. T. Basar. Circ: 2,000. **Subscr. to:** Elsevier BV, PO Box 211, Amsterdam 1000 AE, Netherlands. TEL 31-20-485-3757, FAX 31-20-485-3432, nlinfo-f@elsevier.nl, http://www.elsevier.nl.

629.8 ESP ISSN 0213-3113
AUTOMATICA E INSTRUMENTACION; automatizacion, medida, control, instrumentacion, sistemas, tratamiento de informacion. Text in Spanish. 1968. 11/yr. adv. bk.rev. abstr. **Document type:** *Consumer.* **Description:** Contains national and international new of the sector, technical and market trends, solutions, applications and new components and systems.
Formerly (until 1985): Tecnica de la Regulacion y Mando Automatico (0040-1722)
Indexed: IECT, Inspec.
—BLDSC (1829.500000), AskIEEE, CINDOC, CISTI, IE, Infotrieve, ingenta. **CCC.**
Published by: (International Federation of Automatic Control GBR, Comite Espanol), Cetisa Editores S.A., Enrique Granados, 7, Barcelona, 08019, Spain. TEL 34-93-2431040, FAX 34-93-3492350, info@cetisa.com, http://www.cetisa.com/. Ed. Laura Tremosa. R&P Lluis Lleida. Adv. contact Xavier Cuatracasas. Circ: 5,000.

629.8 ESP
AUTOMATICA & ROBOTICA. Text in Spanish. 12/yr.
Published by: Promotora de Tecnologia Punta, C. Espartinas, 3, 1o Dcha., Madrid, 28001, Spain. TEL 34-91-4316636, FAX 34-91-5783905. Ed. Pedro Hernanz Gomez.

C

629.8 NLD ISSN 0005-1128
CODEN: AUTOA7
AUTOMATIE; maandblad voor industriele en produktie automatisering, procestechniek en instrumentatie. Text in Dutch. 1957. 10/yr. EUR 65 domestic; EUR 90 foreign (effective 2005). adv. bk.rev. abstr.; bibl.; charts; illus. index. **Document type:** *Journal, Trade.* **Description:** Covers automation in all industries in the Netherlands and Belgium.
Indexed: ExcerpMed, Inspec, KES, PROMT.
—IE, Infotrieve.
Published by: APR Group, Postbus 2696, Amersfoort, 3800 GE, Netherlands. TEL 31-33-4567433, FAX 31-33-4567050, automatie@gmgroep.nl, apr@gmgroep.nl, http://www.periodiekenpartners.nl. Ed. W van der Bijl. Pub. J J Otto. adv.: B&W page EUR 1,490, color page EUR 2,485; trim 190 x 270. Circ: 4,100.

629.8 600 DNK ISSN 1603-3639
▼ **AUTOMATIK - TEKNISK UDVIKLING.** Text in Danish. 2003. 11/yr. adv. **Document type:** *Trade.*
Formed by the merger of (1991-2003): Automatik (0105-0168); Which incorporated (1987-1987): Produktboersen (0902-3399); (1988-2003): Teknisk Udvikling (0904-9622)
Related titles: Online - full content ed.
Published by: Forlaget Fag-Tek, Glostrup Torv 6, Glostrup, 2600, Denmark. TEL 45-43-466700, FAX 45-43-431513, http://www.teknisk-udvikling.dk/. Ed. Elo Thorndahl. Pubs. Elo Thorndahl, Joergen Blangsted. Adv. contact Joergen Blangsted. page DKK 23,100; 266 x 365. Circ: 33,471 (controlled).

629.8 HRV ISSN 0005-1144
TJ212 CODEN: ATKAAF
AUTOMATIKA; journal of the Yugoslav Committee ETAN. Text in English. 1960. bi-m. USD 50. adv. bk.rev. charts; illus.; mkt.; tr.lit. index.
Indexed: ChemAb, CompAb, CybAb, INIS AtomInd, Inspec, RefZh.
—BLDSC (1830.200000), AskIEEE, CISTI, IE, ingenta.
Published by: Jugoslovenski Savez za Elektroniku i Telekomunikacije, Automatizaciju i Nuklearnu Tehniku (ETAN), Unska 3, Zagreb, Croatia. FAX 041-611-369, TELEX 21234. Ed. Joze Cernelc. Circ: 1,000.

AUTOMATION. see *ENGINEERING—Mechanical Engineering*

629.8 DEU ISSN 1437-5435
AUTOMATION & QUALITAET. Text in German. 1994. bi-m. EUR 28 domestic; EUR 46 foreign; EUR 7 newsstand/cover (effective 2004). adv. **Document type:** *Magazine, Trade.*
Published by: Verlagsgesellschaft Gruetter GmbH & Co. KG, Postfach 910708, Hannover, 30427, Germany. TEL 49-511-4609300, FAX 49-511-4609320, info@gruetter.de, http://www.automation-qualitaet.de, http://www.gruetter.de. Ed. Ralf Hoegel. Adv. contact Werner Duda. B&W page EUR 3,620, color page EUR 4,850; trim 190 x 270. Circ: 17,864 (paid and controlled).

▼ new title ➤ refereed ✶ unverified ♦ full entry avail.

629.8 RUS ISSN 0005-1179
TJ212 CODEN: AURCAT
➤ **AUTOMATION AND REMOTE CONTROL.** Text in English. 1936. m. EUR 3,748, USD 3,758, GBP 2,348 combined subscription to institutions print & online eds. (effective 2005). charts; illus. index. back issues avail. **Document type:** *Journal, Academic/Scholarly.* **Description:** Publishes papers in the field of control theory (deterministic, stochastic, adaptive, robust, etc. formulations) and its applications (computer control, components and instruments, process control etc.).
Related titles: Online - full text ed.: ISSN 1608-3032 (from EBSCO Publishing, Gale Group, IngentaConnect, Kluwer Online, O C L C Online Computer Library Center, Inc., Ovid Technologies, Inc., Springer LINK, Swets Information Services); ♦ Translation of: Avtomatika i Telemekhanika. ISSN 0005-2310.
Indexed: ASCA, ApMecR, BibLing, CADCAM, CCMJ, CIS, CMCI, ChemAb, CompAb, CompLI, CurCont, EngInd, ISR, Inspec, MathR, MathSciNet, SCI, SSCI, ZentMath.
—BLDSC (0405.000000), AskIEEE, CISTI, Ei, IDS, IE, Infotrieve, ingenta, Linda Hall. **CCC.**
Published by: (Rossiiskaya Akademiya Nauk/Russian Academy of Sciences), M A I K Nauka - Interperiodica, Profsoyuznaya ul 90, Moscow, 117997, Russian Federation. TEL 7-095-3347420, FAX 7-095-3360666, redacsia@ipu.rssi.ru, compmg@maik.ru, www.maik.ru/journals/autorc.htm, http://www.maik.ru. Ed. Nikolai Kuznetsov. R&P Vladimir I Vasil'ev. **Subscr. to:** Springer-Verlag Dordrecht, Journals Department, PO Box 322, Dordrecht, Netherlands. TEL 31-78-6576392, FAX 31-78-6576474.

629.8 NLD ISSN 0926-5805
TH437 CODEN: AUCOES
➤ **AUTOMATION IN CONSTRUCTION.** Text in English. 1992. 6/yr. EUR 603 in Europe to institutions; JPY 80,000 in Japan to institutions; USD 674 to institutions except Europe and Japan (effective 2006). back issues avail. **Document type:** *Journal, Academic/Scholarly.* **Description:** Covers computer applications in architecture and design, in the construction, maintenance and control of intelligent structures, and the construction industry.
Related titles: Microform ed.: (from PQC); Online - full text ed.: (from EBSCO Publishing, Gale Group, IngentaConnect, ScienceDirect, Swets Information Services).
Indexed: BrCerAb, C&ISA, CerAb, CivEngAb, CorrAb, CurCont, E&CAJ, EMA, ESPM, EngInd, H&SSA, IAA, IBuildSA, ICEA, Inspec, M&TEA, MBF, METADEX, RefZh, SolStAb, WAA.
—BLDSC (1831.228000), CISTI, Ei, IE, Infotrieve, ingenta, Linda Hall. **CCC.**
Published by: Elsevier BV (Subsidiary of: Elsevier Science & Technology), Radarweg 29, Amsterdam, 1043 NX, Netherlands. TEL 31-20-4853911, FAX 31-20-4852457, nlinfo-f@elsevier.nl, http://www.elsevier.com/locate/autcon, http://www.elsevier.nl. Eds. M J Skibniewski, Y E Kalay. **Co-sponsors:** British Association for Automation and Robotics in Construction; International Association for Automation and Robotics in Construction; International Council for Building Research Studies and Documentation.

629.8 USA ISSN 1553-1244
▼ **AUTOMATION WORLD.** Text in English. 2003 (Jun.). m. USD 90 domestic; USD 130 in Canada & Mexico; USD 175 in Latin America; USD 215 in Europe; USD 325 elsewhere (effective 2005). adv. back issues avail. **Document type:** *Magazine, Trade.* **Description:** Covers the business of automation from sensor to customer.
Published by: Summit Publishing Co., One IBM Plaza, Ste 2401, 330 N Wabash Ave, Chicago, IL 60611. TEL 312-222-1010, FAX 312-222-1310, info@automationworld.com, http://www.automationworld.com/. Ed. Gary Mintchell. Pub. David Harvey. adv.: B&W page USD 6,950; trim 9 x 10.875. Circ: 70,000.

629.8 DEU ISSN 0178-2312
TJ212
➤ **AUTOMATISIERUNGSTECHNIK**; automatisierung Prozess. Short title: A T. Text in German. 1953. m. EUR 368; EUR 418 combined subscription print & online eds.; EUR 42 newsstand/cover (effective 2005). adv. bk.rev. abstr.; bibl.; charts; illus. **Document type:** *Journal, Academic/Scholarly.* **Description:** Highly technical publication containing articles about the theory of automatic controls and automation and their industrial applications. Includes dissertations.
Former titles (until 1985): Regelungstechnik (0340-434X); (until 1974): Regelungstechnik und Prozess - Datenverarbeitung (0034-3226); (until 1970): Regelungstechnik (Munich) (0370-6001)
Related titles: Online - full text ed.: EUR 368 (effective 2005) (from EBSCO Publishing, Swets Information Services).
Indexed: ApMecR, CEABA, ChemAb, CybAb, EngInd, ExcerpMed, Inspec, RefZh, ZentMath.
—BLDSC (1831.584350), AskIEEE, CISTI, IE, Infotrieve, ingenta, Linda Hall. **CCC.**
Published by: Oldenbourg Wissenschaftsverlag GmbH, Rosenheimer Str 145, Munich, 81671, Germany. TEL 49-89-450510, FAX 49-89-45051204, vertrieb-zs@verlag.oldenbourg.de, http://www.at-technik.de, http://www.oldenbourg.de. Ed. Bernd Reissenweber. Adv. contact Ulrike Staudinger. B&W page EUR 1,841, color page EUR 2,951; trim 185 x 270. Circ: 1,150 (paid and controlled).

629.8 CZE ISSN 0005-125X
CODEN: AUTMAZ
AUTOMATIZACE/AUTOMATION. Text in Czech, Slovak; Abstracts in English. 1958. m. CZK 390 domestic; EUR 50 foreign (effective 2005). adv. bk.rev. charts; illus.; mkt.; pat.; tr.mk. index. **Document type:** *Trade.* **Description:** Covers industrial measurement and control systems design and operation in general.
Indexed: ApMecR, CISA, ChemAb, CybAb, ExcerpMed, Inspec, RefZh.
—AskIEEE, CISTI, Ei, Linda Hall.
Published by: Automatizace s.r.o., Mikulandska 7, Prague 1, 110 61, Czech Republic. TEL 42-224-934513, FAX 42-224-934364, redakce@automatizace.cz, http://www.automatizace.cz. Ed. Eva Vaculikova. R&P, Adv. contact Eva Novakova. B&W page EUR 1,300; 210 x 297. Circ: 2,500. **Subscr. to:** SEND Predplatne s.r.o., PO Box 141, Prague 4 140 21, Czech Republic. TEL 42-2-267211301, FAX 42-2-267211305.

629.8 SCG ISSN 0005-1268
AUTOMATIZACIJA POSLOVANJA✶ ; unapredenje poslovne politike preduzeca. Text in Serbo-Croatian. 1960. m. YUN 500. index.
Published by: Zavod za Ekonomske Ekspertize, c/o Economical Society of Serbia, Nusiceva 6-111, P.O. Box 490, Belgrade. Ed. Branislav Bakic. Circ: 2,000.

629.8 ESP
AUTOMATIZACION. Text in Spanish. 1985. 4/yr. EUR 63 in Europe; EUR 84 in North America. **Description:** Covers robotics, numerical control and automation.
Formerly: Automatizacion de la Produccion (0213-2672)
Published by: Ediciones Tecnicas Izaro S.A., Mazustegui, 21, 4a planta, Bilbao, Vizcaya 48006, Spain. TEL 34-4-4159022, FAX 34-4-4162743. Ed. Ramon Urizar. Circ: 4,000.

629.8 ITA
AUTOMAZIONE COMPONENTI SICUREZZA. Text in Italian. 6/yr.
Address: Via Toce, 4, Varese, VA 21100, Italy. TEL 332-224-068, FAX 332-21-32-12. Ed. Franco Diari. Circ: 6,300.

629.8 ITA ISSN 0005-1284
TJ212 CODEN: ATSZAS
AUTOMAZIONE E STRUMENTAZIONE. Text in Italian. 1959. 11/yr. EUR 51 (effective 2004). adv. bk.rev. bibl.; illus.; tr.lit. index.
Formed by the merger of (1956-1959): Automazione (0567-2074); (1953-1959): Strumentazione e Automazione (1124-4844); Which was formerly (until 1957): Strumentazione. Misure e Regolazioni (1124-4720); (until 1956): Misure e Regolazioni (1124-4712)
Indexed: ApMecR, INIS AtomInd, Inspec.
—AskIEEE, CISTI, Linda Hall. **CCC.**
Published by: (Associazione Nazionale Italiana per l'Automazione), V N U Business Publications (Italy), Via Gorki 69, Cinisello Balsamo, MI 20092, Italy. TEL 39-02-660341, FAX 39-02-66034238, http://www.vnu.it.

629.8 ITA ISSN 0393-3911
AUTOMAZIONE INTEGRATA. Text in Italian. 1968. m. EUR 52 domestic; EUR 100 in Europe; EUR 130 elsewhere (effective 2005). adv. bk.rev. abstr.; charts; illus.; pat.; tr.lit. **Description:** Articles on advanced automation factories with employees, flexible working systems and robotics.
Former titles: Controlli Numerici Macchine a C N Robot Industriali (0392-6036); Controlli Numerici e Macchine (0010-8081)
Indexed: CybAb.
—CISTI.
Published by: Tecniche Nuove SpA, Via Eritrea 21, Milan, MI 201, Italy. TEL 39-02-390901, FAX 39-02-7570364, automazione.integrata@tecnichenuove.com, info@tecnichenuove.com, http://www.tecnichenuove.com/epages/tecnichenuove.storefront/4306066e0c461352273fc0a80105057f/Product/View/AI&2D3. Ed. Alessandro Garnero. adv.: B&W page ITL 2,500,000, color page ITL 4,000,000; trim 297 x 210. Circ: 6,725.

629.89 ITA ISSN 0392-8829
AUTOMAZIONE OGGI; mensile di automazione, robotica, controllo di processo, controllo numerico. Text in Italian. 1983. m. (11/yr). EUR 49.50 (effective 2005). adv. bk.rev. cum.index: 1983-1984. back issues avail. **Document type:** *Magazine, Consumer.* **Description:** Covers all aspects of industrial automation from management and production systems to process control, numerical control, robots, CAD-CAM and flexible systems.
Indexed: CybAb.
—CISTI. **CCC.**
Published by: V N U Business Publications (Italy), Via Gorki 69, Cinisello Balsamo, MI 20092, Italy. TEL 39-02-660341, FAX 39-02-66034238, http://www.jackson.it/ao/, http://www.vnu.it. Ed. Pierantonio Palerma. adv.: B&W page EUR 1,653, color page EUR 2,412; bleed 297 x 210. Circ: 11,186.

629.8 BGR ISSN 0861-7562
AVTOMATIKA I INFORMATIKA. Text in Bulgarian; Summaries in English. bi-m. USD 72 foreign (effective 2002). **Document type:** *Journal, Trade.*
Indexed: RefZh.
—CISTI.
Published by: Suiuz na Avtomatika i Informatika/Union for Automation and Informatics, Ul Rakovski 108, staya 415, Sofia, 1000, Bulgaria. TEL 359-2-9876169, FAX 359-2-9879360, sai@bgcict.acad.bg, http://hsi.iccs.bas.bg/sai/sai.html. **Dist. by:** Sofia Books, ul Silivria 16, Sofia 1404, Bulgaria. TEL 359-2-9586257, info@sofiabooks-bg.com, http://www.sofiabooks-bg.com.

629.8 RUS ISSN 0005-2310
TJ212 CODEN: AVTEAI
AVTOMATIKA I TELEMEKHANIKA. Text in Russian; Abstracts and contents page in English. 1936. m. USD 486 foreign (effective 2005). adv. bk.rev. bibl. **Document type:** *Journal, Academic/Scholarly.*
Related titles: ♦ English Translation: Automation and Remote Control. ISSN 0005-1179.
Indexed: ApMecR, BrCerAb, C&ISA, CCMJ, CerAb, ChemAb, CorrAb, CybAb, E&CAJ, EMA, EngInd, Inspec, M&TEA, MBF, METADEX, MathR, MathSciNet, RefZh, SolStAb, WAA, ZentMath.
—BLDSC (0001.060000), AskIEEE, CASDDS, CISTI, East View, Linda Hall. **CCC.**
Published by: (Rossiiskaya Akademiya Nauk/Russian Academy of Sciences, Institut Avtomatiki i Telemekhaniki), Izdatel'stvo Nauka, Profsoyuznaya ul 90, Moscow, 117864, Russian Federation. TEL 7-095-3347151, FAX 7-095-4202220, secret@naukaran.ru, http://www.naukaran.ru. **US dist. addr.:** East View Information Services; **Dist. by:** M K - Periodica, ul Gilyarovskogo 39, Moscow 129110, Russian Federation. TEL 7-095-2845008, FAX 7-095-2813798, info@periodicals.ru, http://www.mkniga.ru.

629.8 LVA ISSN 0132-4160
TJ212 CODEN: AVYTAK
➤ **AVTOMATIKA I VYCHISLITEL'NAYA TEKHNIKA.** Cover title: A V T Avtomatika i Vycislitel'naa Tehnika. Text in Russian; Text occasionally in English. 1967. bi-m. USD 400 elsewhere (effective 2004 - 2005). adv. bk.rev. charts. index. **Document type:** *Academic/Scholarly.* **Description:** Includes articles on numerous topics within the fields of automatic control, distributed information processing, and signal processing.
Formerly (until 1967): Trudy Instituta (1407-1118)
Related titles: ♦ English Translation: Automatic Control and Computer Sciences. ISSN 0146-4116.
Indexed: CurCont, CybAb, Inspec, MathR, ZentMath.
—AskIEEE, CASDDS, CINDOC, CISTI, IDS, Linda Hall. **CCC.**
Published by: Latvian University, Institute of Electronics and Computer Science, Dzerbenes iela 14, Riga, 1006, Latvia. TEL 371-7554500, FAX 371-7555337, avt@edi.lv, http://www.edi.lv/journal/journal.htm. Eds. Dr. Ivars Bilinskis, Dr. Vladimir Pelipeiko. R&P, Adv. contact Dr. Vladimir Pelipeiko. page USD 300. Circ: 200 (paid).

629.8 RUS
TF615 CODEN: ATSVAG
AVTOMATIKA, SVYAZ', INFORMATIKA. Text in Russian. 1957. m. USD 69 foreign (effective 2004). charts; illus. index.
Formerly: Avtomatika, Telemekhanika i Svyaz' (0005-2329)
Indexed: ChemAb, Inspec, RefZh.
—CASDDS, CISTI, East View, Linda Hall.
Published by: (Redaktsiya Zhurnala Avtomatika, Svyaz', Informatika), Ministerstvo Putei Soobshcheniya Rossiiskoi Federatsii, Novoryazanskaya ul 12, Moscow, 107226, Russian Federation. Circ: 3,000. **Dist. by:** Informnauka Ltd., Ul Usievicha 20, Moscow 125190, Russian Federation. alfimov@viniti.ru.

629.8 RUS ISSN 0869-4931
T58.A2 CODEN: MAVPAC
AVTOMATIZATSIYA I SOVREMENNYE TEKHNOLOGII. Abbreviated title: A S T. Text in Russian; Contents page in English. 1947. m. USD 877 foreign (effective 2004). adv. bk.rev. abstr.; bibl.; charts; illus.; stat. index. **Document type:** *Journal, Trade.* **Description:** Deals with the latest national and foreign developments in production automation and mechanization in diverse industries.
Formerly (until 1992): Mekhanizatsiya i Avtomatizatsiya Proizvodstva (0025-8873)
Indexed: ChemAb, EngInd, Inspec, RASB, RefZh.
—BLDSC (0000.610000), CASDDS, CINDOC, CISTI, Linda Hall.
Published by: (Russia. Ministerstvo Nauki i Tehnicheskoi Politiki Rossiiskoi Federatsii), Izdatel'stvo Mashinostroenie, Stromynskii per 4, Moscow, 107076, Russian Federation. TEL 7-095-2683858, mashpubl@mashin.ru, http://www.mashin.ru. Ed. V N Kalchenko. adv.: page USD 200. Circ: 1,000. **Dist. by:** Informnauka Ltd., Ul Usievicha 20, Moscow 125190, Russian Federation. alfimov@viniti.ru.

629.8 RUS ISSN 0203-2406
AVTOMATIZIROVANNYE SISTEMY UPRAVLENIYA. Text in Russian. 1974. irreg.
Indexed: MathR, RASB.
Published by: Izdatelstvo Sankt-Peterburgskogo Universiteta, Universitetskaya nab 7-9, St Petersburg, 199034, Russian Federation. **Co-sponsor:** Ministerstvo Vysshego i Srednego Spetsial'nogo Obrazovaniya.

629.8 USA ISSN 1066-8160
THE BULL BULLETIN; a semi-annual update on industrial automation. Text in English. 1992. irreg. free. bk.rev.
Document type: *Newsletter.* **Description:** Covers trends in factory automation, especially concerning controls and systems integration in discrete manufacturing.
Published by: Bull's Eye Marketing, Inc., Industrial Controls Consulting Division, N7614 State Road 149., Fond Du Lac, WI 54935-9507. TEL 920-929-6544, FAX 920-929-9344. Ed. Jonathan B Bullock. R&P Thomas B Bullock. Circ: 6,000 (controlled).

629.8 FRA ISSN 0303-1276
BULLETIN DE LIAISON DE LA RECHERCHE EN INFORMATIQUE ET EN AUTOMATIQUE. Text in French. 1973. s-m. free. adv. bk.rev. **Document type:** *Bulletin.* **Description:** Provides articles on all aspects of automation. Topics may include algorithms, transport vehicles and the integration of automation.
Related titles: Microfiche ed.
Indexed: CybAb, Inspec.
—AskIEEE, CISTI. **CCC.**
Published by: Institut National de Recherche en Informatique et en Automatique, BP 105, Le Chesnay, Cedex 78153, France. TEL 33-1-39635511, FAX 33-1-39635330, http://www.inria.fr. Circ: 5,000.

658 NLD ISSN 1567-5998
BUSINESS PROCESS MAGAZINE. Text in Dutch. 1995. 8/yr. EUR 79.50 domestic; EUR 87.50 in Belgium (effective 2005). adv. illus. back issues avail. **Document type:** *Journal, Trade.* **Description:** Covers work flow automation and management.
Formerly (until 2000): Workflow Magazine (1380-5304)
—IE.
Published by: Array Publications BV, Postbus 2211, Alphen aan den Rijn, 2400 CE, Netherlands. TEL 31-172-424177, FAX 31-172-424381, bpm@array.nl, http://www.businessprocess.nl/site/, http://www.array.nl. Ed. Esmeralda Wybrands. Adv. contact Jos Raaphorst TEL 31-172-469030. B&W page EUR 1,850, color page EUR 3,050; trim 210 x 285. Circ: 2,300 (paid).

629.8 TWN
C A D & AUTOMATION. (Computer-Aided Design) Text in Chinese. 1988. m. adv.
Published by: Acer T W P Corporation, 2-F, No 19-1 Ln 231, Fu-Hsing N. Rd, Taipei, 105, Taiwan. TEL 886-2-7136959. Ed. Wong Li Jul. Adv. contact David Tsai. B&W page USD 945, color page USD 1,890; trim 298 x 210. Circ: 10,800.

C E PRO. (Custom Electronics) see *ELECTRONICS*

629.89 USA
C I C S UPDATE. (Customer Information Control System) Text in English. m. USD 270 (effective 2000). **Document type:** *Trade.*
Published by: Xephon, 9330 Lyndon B Johnson Fwy., Ste. 800, Dallas, TX 75243-4310. TEL 303-410-9344, FAX 303-438-0290.

COMLINE: INDUSTRIAL AUTOMATION INDUSTRY OF JAPAN. see *BUSINESS AND ECONOMICS*

629.8 ESP
COMPONENTES, EQUIPOS Y SISTEMAS DE AUTOMATICA Y ROBOTICA. Text in Spanish. 1989. 16/yr.
Published by: Promotora de Tecnologia Punta, C. Espartinas, 3, 1o Dcha., Madrid, 28001, Spain. TEL 34-91-4316636, FAX 34-91-5783905. Circ: 10,000.

629.8 DEU ISSN 1615-8512
COMPUTER & AUTOMATION. Text in German. 1998. m. EUR 68.40 domestic; EUR 78 foreign; EUR 57.60 to students; EUR 7.50 newsstand/cover (effective 2004). adv. **Document type:** *Magazine, Trade.*
Related titles: Online - full text ed.; Supplement(s): Computer & Automation Product Guide. ISSN 1619-2443. 2001. EUR 7.50 newsstand/cover (effective 2003).
Published by: W E K A Fachzeitschriften-Verlag GmbH, Gruberstr 46a, Poing, 85586, Germany. TEL 49-8121-950, FAX 49-8121-951396, smatza@computer-automation.de, ckasel@wekanet.de, http://www.computer-automation.de, http://www.wekanet.de. Ed. Meinrad Happacher. Adv. contact Peter Eberhard. B&W page EUR 4,450, color page EUR 6,220; trim 210 x 297. Circ: 26,488 (paid and controlled).

COMPUTER@PRODUKTION; Computerloesungen und C-Commerce in der Industrie. see *ENGINEERING—Computer Applications*

629.8 USA
COMPUTERS IN FURNITURE AND CABINET MANUFACTURING. INTERNATIONAL SYMPOSIUM PROCEEDINGS. Text in English. 1992. biennial. USD 65; USD 85 foreign. **Document type:** *Proceedings.* **Description:** Disseminates the latest information on the use of computers in furniture and cabinet manufacturing worldwide.
Published by: Wood Machining Institute, PO Box 476, Berkeley, CA 94701. TEL 925-943-5240, FAX 925-945-0947, http://www.woodmachining.com. Ed. Ryszard Szymani. R&P R Szymani.

CONDITION MONITOR. see *ENGINEERING*

629.8 USA
CONFERENCE OF THE SOCIETY OF INSTRUMENT AND CONTROL ENGINEERS OF JAPAN. PROCEEDINGS. Text in English. a. USD 576 per vol. (effective 2004). **Document type:** *Proceedings, Trade.*
Published by: Institute of Electrical and Electronics Engineers, Inc., 3 Park Ave, 17th Fl, New York, NY 10016-5997. TEL 212-419-7900, 800-678-4333, FAX 212-752-4929, customer.service@ieee.org, http://www.ieee.org.

629.8312 GBR ISSN 0010-8022
TJ212 CODEN: CTLIAW
CONTROL AND INSTRUMENTATION. Abbreviated title: C&I. Text in English. 1958. m. adv. bk.rev. abstr.; charts; illus.; stat.; tr.lit. index. **Document type:** *Magazine, Trade.* **Description:** Covers all aspects from factory floor devices to the automation and information levels of control architecture.
Formed by the merger of: Control and Measurement; Instrument Review
Related titles: Microform ed.: (from PQC); Online - full text ed.: (from Florida Center for Library Automation, Gale Group, LexisNexis, O C L C Online Computer Library Center, Inc.).
Indexed: AEA, AESIS, ASCA, ApMecR, B&I, BMT, BrCerAb, BrTechI, C&ISA, CEA, CEABA, ChemAb, CompD, CurCont, CybAb, E&CAJ, EngInd, ErgAb, ExcerpMed, F&EA, FLUIDEX, IBuildSA, ISMEC, Inspec, LHB, PROMT, PhotoAb, RoboAb, SolStAb, TCEA, WSCA, WTA.
—BLDSC (3461.873000), AskIEEE, CISTI, Ei, IDS, IE, Infotrieve. **CCC.**
Published by: Centaur Communications Ltd., 50 Poland St, London, W1V 7AX, United Kingdom. TEL 44-20-7-970-4000, FAX 44-20-7-970-4009, customer.service@centaur.co.uk, http://www.e4engineering.com/controlandinstrumentation/home.aspx, http://www.centaur.co.uk/. Circ: 19,501.

629.8312 CAN ISSN 1480-1752
TJ212 CODEN: CISSFP
➤ **CONTROL AND INTELLIGENT SYSTEMS.** Text in English. 1972. 3/yr. USD 260 foreign (effective 2005). adv. bk.rev. charts; illus. index. back issues avail. **Document type:** *Journal, Academic/Scholarly.* **Description:** Covers control theory and its applications with emphasis on the areas of computers in control and control technology.
Former titles (until 1998): Control and Computers (0730-9538); (until 1980): Automatic Control: Theory and Applications (0315-8934)
Indexed: ASCA, BrCerAb, C&ISA, CMCI, CerAb, CompLI, CompR, CorrAb, CybAb, E&CAJ, EMA, EngInd, IAA, Inspec, M&TEA, MBF, METADEX, MathR, MathSciNet, WAA.
—BLDSC (3461.885000), AskIEEE, CISTI, Ei, IE, Infotrieve, ingenta, Linda Hall. **CCC.**
Published by: ACTA Press, 4500-16th Ave NW, Ste 80, Calgary, AB T3B 0M6, Canada. TEL 403-288-1195, FAX 403-247-6851, journals@actapress.com, http://www.actapress.com. Ed. M H Hamza. Circ: 500.

629.8 CUB
CONTROL, CIBERNETICA Y AUTOMATIZACION. Text in Spanish; Summaries in English, French. 1967. s-a. USD 24 in South America; USD 26 in North America; USD 30 elsewhere. adv. charts; illus.
Indexed: Inspec.
Published by: (Cuba. Ministerio de la Industria Basica, Instituto de Matematica, Cibernetica y Computacion), Ediciones Cubanas, Obispo No. 527, Apdo. 605, Havana, Cuba. Ed. Eduardo Canal Portuondo. Circ: 2,000.

629.8312 USA ISSN 0010-8049
TJ212 CODEN: CENGAX
CONTROL ENGINEERING; covering control, instrumentation, and automation systems worldwide. Text in English. 1954. m. USD 109.90 domestic; USD 145.90 in Canada; USD 139.90 in Mexico; USD 242.90 elsewhere; USD 15 per issue domestic; USD 25 per issue foreign (effective 2005). adv. bk.rev. illus.; mkt.; tr.lit. Supplement avail.; back issues avail.; reprint service avail. from PQC. **Document type:** *Magazine, Trade.* **Description:** Serves engineers who design and apply controls and instrumentation for the industrial marketplace. Provides facts and figures, and reports on most efficient controls and instrumentation.
Related titles: Microform ed.; Online - full text ed.: Control Engineering Online (from EBSCO Publishing, Factiva, Florida Center for Library Automation, Gale Group, H.W. Wilson, LexisNexis, Northern Light Technology, Inc., O C L C Online Computer Library Center, Inc., ProQuest Information & Learning); Supplement(s):.
Indexed: ABIn, AEA, AIA, APIAb, APICat, APIH&E, APIOC, APIPR, APIPS, APITS, AS&TI, ASCA, BMT, BrCerAb, C&ISA, CADCAM, CEA, CRIA, CRICC, CerAb, ChemAb, CompC, CorrAb, CurCont, CybAb, E&CAJ, EIA, EMA, EngInd, EnvAb, F&EA, FLUIDEX, GasAb, IAA, Inspec, M&TEA, MBF, METADEX, PROMT, RoboAb, SSCI, SolStAb, T&II, TCEA, WAA.
—BLDSC (3462.000000), AskIEEE, CISTI, Ei, IDS, IE, Infotrieve, ingenta, Linda Hall. **CCC.**
Published by: Reed Business Information (Subsidiary of: Reed Business), 2000 Clearwater Dr, Oak Brook, IL 60525. TEL 630-320-6222, FAX 630-288-8537, controlengineering@reed.com, http://www.controleng.com, http://www.reedbusiness.com. Eds. Mark T Hoske TEL 630-288-8570, David Greenfield TEL 630-288-8583. Pub. Michelle Palmer TEL 630-288-8585. adv.: B&W page USD 11,470, color page USD 13,675; trim 10.5 x 7.88. Circ: 88,085 (controlled and free). **Subscr. to:** Reed Business Information, PO Box 9020, Maple Shade, NJ 08052-9020. TEL 303-470-4466, FAX 303-470-4691.

629.89 USA
CONTROL ENGINEERING AUTOMATION INTEGRATOR GUIDE. Text in English. a. free with subscr. to Control Engineering. adv. **Document type:** *Directory, Trade.* **Description:** Surveys developments in automation integrator services, providing a directory of companies, personnel, products, and services.
Supersedes (in 1999): Control Engineering Automation Register
Related titles: Online - full text ed.
Published by: Reed Business Information (Subsidiary of: Reed Business), 2000 Clearwater Dr, Oak Brook, IL 60525. TEL 630-320-6222, FAX 630-320-6000, controleng@msn.com, http://www.reedbusiness.com. Ed. Jane Gerold. Pub. David A Harvey. adv.: B&W page USD 7,825, color page USD 8,385; trim 10.5 x 7.88.

629.89 USA
CONTROL ENGINEERING BUYERS GUIDE. Text in English. a. free with subscr. to Control Engineering. adv. bk.rev.
Document type: *Directory.* **Description:** Offers a directory listing of control engineering software.
Formed by the merger of: Control Engineering Board Level Product Guide; Control Engineering Management Series; Control Engineering Software Guide
Published by: Reed Business Information (Subsidiary of: Reed Business), 2000 Clearwater Dr, Oak Brook, IL 60525. TEL 630-320-7000, FAX 630-320-7132, http://www.controleng.com/buyersguide, http://www.reedbusiness.com. Ed. Mark T Hoske TEL 630-288-8570. Pub. David A Harvey. adv.: page USD 8,935; trim 7.875 x 10.5.

C

629.8312 GBR
CONTROL ENGINEERING EUROPE; control, instrumentation and automation in the process and manufacturing industries. Text in English. 1994. bi-m. free to qualified personnel (effective 2005). **Document type:** *Magazine, Trade.* **Description:** Provides a source of information on automation and controls within the European market.
Incorporates (1983-2004): Plant and Control Engineering (1468-344X); Formerly (until 2000): Control Engineering International (1542-5584)
Related titles: Online - full text ed.: (from Gale Group).
Indexed: Inspec.
—**CCC.**
Published by: I M L Group Plc., Blair House, 184 High St, Tonbridge, Kent TN9 1BQ, United Kingdom. TEL 44-1732-359990, FAX 44-1732-770049, imlgroup@dial.pipex.com, http://www.manufacturing.net/ctl/index.asp?layout=issueToc&CTLE=yes&pubdate=, http://www.imlgrouponthenet.net/. Pub. Peter Whitfield. Circ: 25,000.

CONTROL ENGINEERING PRACTICE. see *ENGINEERING—Computer Applications*

629.8 USA
CONTROL MAGAZINE. Text in English. 1996. m. back issues avail. **Description:** Serves the needs of automation, control, and instrumentation professionals in the process industries.
Address: 555 W Pierce Rd, Ste 301, Itasca, IL 60143. TEL 630-467-1300, FAX 630-467-1124, http://www.controlmagazine.com/. Ed. Paul Studenbacker.

629.89 DEU ISSN 0935-0381
CONTROLLING; Zeitschrift fuer erfolgsorientierte Unternehmenssteuerung. Text in German. 1989. m. EUR 140 domestic; EUR 160.50 foreign; EUR 107.50 to students; EUR 13.50 newsstand/cover (effective 2005). adv. back issues avail.; reprint service avail. from SCH. **Document type:** *Journal, Trade.* **Description:** Covers various aspects of control in computer engineering.
Indexed: IBR, IBZ.
—IE, Infotrieve.
Published by: Verlag C.H. Beck oHG, Wilhelmstr 9, Munich, 80801, Germany. TEL 49-89-38189338, FAX 49-89-38189398, abo.service@beck.de, http://www.beck.de. Eds. Peter Horvath, Thomas Reichmann. adv.: B&W page EUR 1,680, color page EUR 2,917.50; trim 186 x 260. Circ: 2,600.

CONTROLS INTELLIGENCE & PLANT SYSTEMS REPORT. see *COMPUTERS—Hardware*

621.3822 JPN ISSN 0915-1923
TK5101.A1 CODEN: DTGDE7
DENSHI JOHO TSUSHIN GAKKAI RONBUNSHI (D-II)/INSTITUTE OF ELECTRONICS, INFORMATION AND COMMUNICATION ENGINEERS. TRANSACTIONS (SECTION D-II). Text in Japanese. 1968. m. adv. bk.rev. **Document type:** *Academic/Scholarly.* **Description:** Covers topics such as: speech processing, image processing, computer graphics and pattern recognition, artificial intelligence and cognitive science, computer applications, bio-Cybernetics, medical electronics and medical information.
Supersedes in part (in 1989): Institute of Electronics, Information and Communication Engineers. Transactions (Section D) (0913-5731)
Related titles: ♦ English ed.: I E I C E Transactions on Information and Systems. ISSN 0916-8532.
Indexed: IAOP, INIS AtomInd, Inspec, JCT, RefZh.
—BLDSC (8939.442200), AskIEEE, CISTI, Linda Hall. **CCC.**
Published by: Denshi Joho Tsushin Gakkai/Institute of Electronics Information and Communication Engineers, IEICE Publishing Office, Kikai-Shinko-Kaikan Bldg., Annex 3F, 5-22, Shibakoen 3 chome, Minato-ku, Tokyo, 105-0011, Japan. TEL 81-3-3433-6692, FAX 81-3-3433-6616, shuppan@ieice.or.jp, http://www.ieice.or.jp/. Ed. Michiyuki Uenohara. Circ: 8,700.

629.8 USA ISSN 0929-5585
CODEN: DAESFC
➤ **DESIGN AUTOMATION FOR EMBEDDED SYSTEMS;** an international journal. Text in English. 1996. q. EUR 431, USD 431, GBP 270 combined subscription to institutions print & online eds. (effective 2005). adv. back issues avail.; reprint service avail. from PSC. **Document type:** *Journal, Academic/Scholarly.* **Description:** Discusses the hardware, software and host aspects of embedded systems design.
Related titles: Online - full text ed.: ISSN 1572-8080 (from EBSCO Publishing, Gale Group, IngentaConnect, Kluwer Online, O C L C Online Computer Library Center, Inc., Ovid Technologies, Inc., Springer LINK, Swets Information Services).
Indexed: BibLing, BrCerAb, C&ISA, CMCI, CerAb, CompLI, CorrAb, CurCont, E&CAJ, EMA, EngInd, IAA, Inspec, M&TEA, MBF, METADEX, RefZh, SolStAb, WAA.
—BLDSC (3559.922700), AskIEEE, CISTI, IDS, IE, Infotrieve, ingenta, Linda Hall. **CCC.**
Published by: Springer-Verlag New York, Inc. (Subsidiary of: Springer Science+Business Media), 233 Spring St, New York, NY 10013. TEL 212-460-1500, FAX 212-460-1575, service@springer-ny.com, http://springerlink.metapress.com/ openurl.asp?genre=journal&issn=0929-5585, http://www.springer-ny.com. Eds. Raul Camposano, Wayne Wolf. **Subscr. to:** Journal Fulfillment, PO Box 2485, Secaucus, NJ 07096-2485. TEL 201-348-4033, FAX 201-348-4505, journals@springer-ny.com.

629.8 CHN ISSN 1000-1026
CODEN: DXZIE9
DIANLI XITONG ZIDONGHUA/AUTOMATION OF ELECTRIC POWER SYSTEMS. Text in Chinese; Abstracts in English. 1977. bi-m. USD 192; USD 8 newsstand/cover (effective 2002). adv. 72 p./no.; **Document type:** *Journal, Academic/Scholarly.* **Description:** Covers power system analysis and control, electricity market, power dispatching automation, substation and distribution automation, protective relaying, power plant control, the application of IT and intelligent apparatuses and instruments to power system and so on.
Related titles: Online - full content ed.: 1977; Online - full text ed.: (from East View Information Services).
Indexed: C&ISA, E&CAJ, EngInd, IAA, Inspec.
—BLDSC (1831.235000), AskIEEE, CISTI, Linda Hall.
Published by: Nanjing Zidonghua Yanjiusuo/Nanjing Automation Research Institute, PO Box 323, Nanjing, Jiangsu 210003, China. TEL 86-25-3429900 ext 2055, 86-25-3429900 ext 2053, FAX 86-25-3421949, aeps@nari-china.com, http://www.aeps-info.com, http://nari-china.com. Ed. Yusheng Xue. Pub. Genfan Wu. Adv. contact Min Guo. B&W page CNY 1,000, color page CNY 15,000; 285 x 210. **Dist. outside China by:** China International Book Trading Corp, 35 Chegongzhuang Xilu, Haidian District, PO Box 399, Beijing 100044, China.

629.8 CHN ISSN 1000-3886
TK4 CODEN: DIZIE6
DIANQI ZIDONGHUA. Text in Chinese. bi-m.
Indexed: EngInd.
Published by: Shanghai Dianqi Zidonghua Yanjiusuo, 414 Xietu Lu, Shanghai, 200023, China. TEL 3779011. Ed. Li Xubao.

DIANZI YU ZIDONGHUA/ELECTRONICS AND AUTOMATION. see *ELECTRONICS*

629.8 USA ISSN 1063-6234
E C CADENCE✱. Text in English. 1992. 10/yr. GBP 44. tr.lit.
Published by: Ariel Communications, Inc., PO Box 203550, Austin, TX 78720-3550. TEL 512-250-1700, FAX 512-250-1016. Ed. Patrice Sarath. adv.: B&W page USD 8,251, color page USD 9,751; trim 10.88 x 8.25. Circ: 105,000.

629.8 NZL CODEN: AUCODR
ELECTRICAL TECHNOLOGY. Text in English. 1971. 11/yr. NZD 44.55; plus postage. adv. bk.rev. charts; illus.; tr.lit. **Document type:** *Trade.* **Description:** Contains practical information on control of industrial processes, electricity, instrumentation, computers, communications, pneumatics, and hydraulics.
Formerly (until 2001): Automation and Control (0110-6295)
Related titles: Online - full text ed.
Indexed: CompC, CompD, Inspec.
—BLDSC (1831.120000), CISTI, Ei, Linda Hall. **CCC.**
Published by: AGM Publishing Ltd., 409 New North Rd, Kingsland, Auckland, New Zealand. Ed. Sharon Newey. Circ: 6,000.

ELECTRONIC HOUSE; enhanced lifestyle through home automation. see *ELECTRONICS*

629.8 ROM ISSN 0254-2242
ELECTROTEHNICA, ELECTRONICA SI AUTOMATICA. AUTOMATICA SI ELECTRONICA. Text in Romanian; Summaries in English, French, German, Russian. 1957. q. ROL 30, USD 25. adv. bk.rev. abstr.; bibl.; charts; illus.; tr.lit. index. **Description:** Covers innovations and product development, computing techniques, computer-aided analysis, CAD, quality assurance and automation.
Formerly: Automatica si Electronica (0005-1101)
Indexed: Inspec.
—Linda Hall.
Published by: Institutul de Cercetare si Projectare pentru Electrotehnica, Splaiul Uniru 313, Bucharest, 74204, Romania. FAX 40-1-3213769, TELEX 10486. Ed. Florin Teodor Tanasescu. Circ: 300. **Subscr. to:** ILEXIM, Str. 13 Decembrie 3, PO Box 136-137, Bucharest 70116, Romania.

629.89 USA ISSN 1065-6952
ENGINEERING AUTOMATION REPORT. Text in English. 1977. m. USD 344 in US & Canada (effective 2005). bk.rev. tr.lit. 16 p./no.; back issues avail. **Document type:** *Newsletter, Trade.* **Description:** Covers computer hardware and software products used in engineering design and product data management for engineering management.
Incorporates (1977-200?): A - E - C Automation Newsletter (0277-1659); Incorporates (1978-1995): Anderson Report on Computer Graphics (0197-7040)
Related titles: Online - full text ed.
Published by: Cyon Research Corporation, 8220 Stone Trail Dr, Bethesda, MD 20817-4556. TEL 301-365-9085, FAX 301-365-4586, david.cohn@eareport.com, http:// www.eareport.com, www.cyonresearch.com. Ed., Pub. David Cohn. Circ: 7,300 (paid).

629.8 USA
TK7874.6
EUROPEAN DESIGN AUTOMATION CONFERENCE. PROCEEDINGS. Abbreviated title: E D A C. Text in English. 1990. biennial. price varies. **Document type:** *Proceedings.* **Description:** Addresses all areas of the design process from concept to manufacture and includes information on CAD and DA tools.
Formerly (until 1994): European Conference on Design Automation (1066-1409)
Related titles: CD-ROM ed.; Microfiche ed.; Online - full text ed.: (from I E E E).
Indexed: EngInd.
—Ei. **CCC.**
Published by: Institute of Electrical and Electronics Engineers, Inc., 3 Park Ave, 17th Fl, New York, NY 10016-5997. TEL 800-678-4333, customer.service@ieee.org, http://www.ieee.org.

629.8 FRA ISSN 0947-3580
EUROPEAN JOURNAL OF CONTROL. Text in English. 1996. bi-m. EUR 435 in the European Union; EUR 490 elsewhere (effective 2003). **Document type:** *Academic/Scholarly.* **Description:** Publishes papers on the theory and practice of control and systems engineering.
Indexed: ApMecR, CMCI, CurCont, EngInd, Inspec, MathR, MathSciNet, ZentMath.
—BLDSC (3829.728230), AskIEEE, CISTI, IE, Infotrieve, ingenta, Linda Hall. **CCC.**
Published by: (European Union Control Association GBR), Lavoisier, 11 rue Lavoisier, Paris, 75008, France. TEL 33-1-42653995, FAX 33-1-42650246, info@lavoisier.fr, http://www.lavoisier.fr. Ed. Sergio Bittanti. **Subscr. in N. America to:** Lavoisier - Dept Abonnements, 14 rue de Provigny, Cachan 94236, France. TEL 33-1-47406700, FAX 33-1-47406702, abo@lavoisier.fr.

629.8 DEU ISSN 0940-791X
FLEXIBLE AUTOMATION. Text in German. 1982. 6/yr. EUR 54 domestic; EUR 75 foreign; EUR 8 newsstand/cover (effective 2004). adv. **Document type:** *Magazine, Trade.* **Description:** Effects of technological innovations in industry. Features automation, flexible manufacturing systems, robots, and CIM. Includes reports of events.
Former titles: Flexible Automation Flexible Fertigung; Flexible Automation

Published by: Henrich Publikationen GmbH, Schwanheimer Str 110, Frankfurt Am Main, 60528, Germany. fa@henrich.de, fa@verlag.henrich.de, http://www.flexibleautomation.de, http://www.henrich.de. Ed. Michael Lind. R&P Willy Schweitzer. Adv. contact Ralf Schoenfeld. B&W page EUR 4,200, color page EUR 5,580; Circ: 20,180. **Subscr. to:** DataM-Services GmbH, Fichtestr 9, Wuerzburg 97074, Germany. TEL 49-931-417001, FAX 49-931-4170499, swestenberger@datam-services.de, http://www.datam-services.de.

629.8 USA ISSN 1551-3939
▼ ➤ **FOUNDATIONS AND TRENDS IN ELECTRONIC DESIGN AUTOMATION.** Text in English. forthcoming 2006. 4/yr. USD 300, EUR 300 (effective 2006). **Document type:** *Journal, Academic/Scholarly.*
Related titles: Online - full text ed.: ISSN 1551-3947. forthcoming.
Published by: Now Publishers Inc., PO Box 1024, Hanover, MA 02339. TEL 781-871-0245, FAX 781-871-6172, sales@nowpublishers.com, http://www.nowpublishers.com/eda.

629.8 USA ISSN 1528-6363
CODEN: AIDNEE
FRONTLINE SOLUTIONS. Text in English. 1986. 13/w. USD 41.50 domestic; USD 59 in Canada & Mexico; USD 79 elsewhere; USD 5 newsstand/cover domestic; USD 7.50 newsstand/cover in Canada & Mexico; USD 12 newsstand/cover elsewhere (effective 2004). adv. **Document type:** *Magazine, Trade.* **Description:** Explores how organizations are profiting by extending information throughout an enterprise. Solutions in technology are presented that enable information exchange, integrate front-end data into enterprise applications, and provide information to customers and trading partners.
Formerly (until 2000): Automatic I D News (0890-9768)
Related titles: Microfilm ed.; Online - full text ed.: (from EBSCO Publishing, Factiva, Gale Group, O C L C Online Computer Library Center, Inc., ProQuest Information & Learning); Supplement(s): Frontline Solutions Buyer'S Guide (Online). free domestic to qualified personnel; USD 34.95 domestic others.
Indexed: ABIn, B&I, EngInd, Inspec, SoftBase.
—BLDSC (4042.085780), AskIEEE, Ei, Linda Hall. **CCC.**
Published by: Questex Media Group Inc., 275 Gtrove St, Ste 2-130, Auburndale, MA 02466. TEL 617-219-8327, FAX 617-219-8310, http://www.frontlinetoday.com. Ed. George Miller. Pub. Kate Dobson. adv.: color page USD 8,530. Circ: 50,000 (paid and controlled).

629.8 USA ISSN 1470-4544
FRONTLINE SOLUTIONS EUROPE. Text in English. 1991. 9/yr. USD 95 domestic; USD 140 in Canada & Mexico; USD 185 elsewhere; USD 10 newsstand/cover domestic; USD 15 newsstand/cover in Canada & Mexico; USD 20 newsstand/cover elsewhere (effective 2004). adv. tr.lit. back issues avail. **Document type:** *Trade.* **Description:** Focuses on the use of data capture technologies in warehousing, distribution, manufacturing, and a variety of other end-user industries. Includes new-product information, educational articles, systems development and trade show coverage, and user and reseller news.
Formerly (until 2000): Automatic I.D. News Europe (1363-9765); Which Incorporated: Auto I.D. Today
Related titles: Microform ed.: (from PQC); Online - full text ed.: (from EBSCO Publishing, Gale Group).
Indexed: B&I, IPackAb, Inspec.
—BLDSC (4042.085770). **CCC.**
Published by: Advanstar Communications, Inc., 7500 Old Oak Blvd, Cleveland, OH 44130-3369. TEL 440-891-2767, FAX 440-891-2727, info@advanstar.com, http://www.flseurope.com, http://www.advanstar.com. adv.: B&W page GBP 3,165, B&W page USD 5,065, color page GBP 3,935, color page USD 6,260. Circ: 22,753. **Subscr. to:** Advanstar Marketing Services, Customer Service Department, 131 West, First St, Duluth, MN 55802. TEL 218-723-9200, 800-598-6008, FAX 218-723-9437.

629.8 ITA
FUTURA. Text in Italian. 1978. 6/yr. **Document type:** *Newsletter, Trade.* **Description:** Covers high technology for managers. Includes technology, research, science and environment.
Published by: Go Creative Group, Via Tortona, 14, Milan, MI 20144, Italy. TEL 39-2-58106415, FAX 39-2-58106428, gri@mail.sko.it. Ed. Oreste Griotti. Circ: 9,100.

629.89 CHN ISSN 1001-182X
TJ212
GONGYE KONGZHI JISUANJI/INDUSTRY CONTROL COMPUTER. Text in Chinese. bi-m. **Document type:** *Academic/Scholarly.*
Related titles: Online - full text ed.: (from East View Information Services).
Published by: Jiangsu Sheng Jisuan Jishu Yanjiusuo, Suojin Cun Taipingmen Wai, Nanjing, Jiangsu 210042, China. TEL 506450. Ed. Chan Weimin.

620 DEU ISSN 1616-4679
HALLENSER SCHRIFTEN ZUR AUTOMATISIERUNGSTECHNIK. Text in German. 2000. irreg., latest vol.3, 2002. price varies. **Document type:** *Monographic series, Academic/Scholarly.*

Published by: Logos Verlag Berlin, Comeniushof, Gubener Str 47, Berlin, 10243, Germany. TEL 49-30-42851090, FAX 49-30-42851092, redaktion@logos-verlag.de, http://www.logos-verlag.de.

629.8 DEU ISSN 0343-8759
HANDLING; Magazin fuer Automation, Handhabungstechnik und Logistik. Text in German. 1972. 7/yr. free. **Document type:** *Trade.*
Published by: Hoppenstedt Bonnier Zeitschriften GmbH, Havelstr. 9, Darmstadt, 64295, Germany. TEL 49-6151-380311, FAX 49-6151-380341. Ed. Claus Mayer. Circ: 28,000.

629.89 USA ISSN 1057-8536
HOME AUTOMATION NEWS. Text in English. 1988. bi-m. USD 125 (effective 1999). adv. tr.lit. **Document type:** *Newsletter.* **Description:** Covers current developments on the integration of home systems including electronics, security, lighting, audio, video, computers, home control.
Published by: Home Automation Association, 1444 I St N W, Ste 700, Washington, DC 20005. TEL 202-712-9050, FAX 202-216-9646, haa@bostromdc.cm. Ed., Adv. contact Mark Wright. Circ: 600 (paid).

629.8 NLD ISSN 0169-4693
I B M NIEUWS. (International Business Machines) Text in Dutch. 1964. 4/yr. free. bk.rev. charts; illus. cum.index. **Description:** For customers and prospects of IBM Nederland N.V., who use products, systems and/or services of IBM.
Former titles (until 1982): I B M Monitor (0166-0071); I B M Kwartaalschrift (0018-8654)
Indexed: KES.
Published by: I B M Nederland N.V., Johan Huizingalaan 765, PO Box 9999, Amsterdam, 1000 AG, Netherlands. TEL 31-20-5133813, FAX 31-20-6177600, MARC_BORN@NL.IBM.COM. Ed. Marc Born. Circ: 15,000 (controlled).

I D SYSTEMS BUYERS GUIDE. see *BUSINESS AND ECONOMICS—Computer Applications*

629.8 USA ISSN 1085-1992
TK7881.2
I E E E CONFERENCE ON CONTROL APPLICATIONS. PROCEEDINGS. Text in English. 1994. a. USD 330 per vol.; USD 165 per vol. to members (effective 2004). **Document type:** *Proceedings, Trade.*
Related titles: Online - full text ed.: (from I E E E).
Indexed: Engind.
—BLDSC (6844.167100). **CCC.**
Published by: Institute of Electrical and Electronics Engineers, Inc., 3 Park Ave, 17th Fl, New York, NY 10016-5997. TEL 212-419-7900, 800-678-4333, FAX 212-752-4929, customer.service@ieee.org, http://www.ieee.org.

629.8 USA
I E E E INTERNATIONAL CONFERENCE ON EMERGING TECHNOLOGIES AND FACTORY AUTOMATION. PROCEEDINGS. Text in English. a. USD 350 per vol.; USD 175 per vol. to members (effective 2004). **Document type:** *Proceedings, Trade.* **Description:** Covers newly emerging areas of technologies and their applications to factory automation. Areas discussed include innovative design and manufacturing, engineering, virtual reality, discrete-event/hybrid systems, semiconductor manufacturing.
—BLDSC (4362.948500).
Published by: Institute of Electrical and Electronics Engineers, Inc., 3 Park Ave, 17th Fl, New York, NY 10016-5997. TEL 212-419-7900, 800-678-4333, FAX 212-752-4929, customer.service@ieee.org, http://www.ieee.org. **Co-sponsor:** I E E E Industrial Electronics Society.

629.8 USA ISSN 1050-4729
TJ210.3
I E E E INTERNATIONAL CONFERENCE ON ROBOTICS AND AUTOMATION. PROCEEDINGS. Text in English. 1984. a. price varies. adv. **Document type:** *Proceedings, Academic/Scholarly.* **Description:** Covers all areas of robotics and flexible automation.
Former titles (until 1985): I E E E International Conference on Robotics and Automation (1049-3492); (until 1984): International Conference on Robotics. Proceedings (1049-3484)
Related titles: Online - full text ed.: (from I E E E).
Indexed: Engind.
—BLDSC (4362.949900), Ei, IE, ingenta. **CCC.**
Published by: (Institute of Electrical and Electronics Engineers, Inc.), I E E E Computer Society, 3 Park Ave, 17th Fl, New York, NY 10017. TEL 714-821-8380, 800-678-4333, FAX 714-821-4641, customer.service@ieee.org, http://www.ieee.org.

I E E E TRANSACTIONS ON AUTOMATIC CONTROL. see *ENGINEERING—Electrical Engineering*

I E E E TRANSACTIONS ON ROBOTICS. see *COMPUTERS—Robotics*

629.8312 GBR ISSN 1350-2379
TK1 CODEN: ICTAEX
➤ **I E E PROCEEDINGS - CONTROL THEORY AND APPLICATIONS.** Text in English. 1980. bi-m. USD 1,045 in the Americas to non-members print or online; GBP 615 elsewhere to non-members print or online; USD 1,254 combined subscription in the Americas to non-members print & online; GBP 738 combined subscription elsewhere to non-members print & online (effective 2005). adv. bk.rev. index. **Document type:** *Proceedings, Academic/Scholarly.* **Description:** Covers control systems, system modeling, design and implementation, identification, simulation, technological, economic, physiological systems, man-machine interfaces, robotics, and process control.
Formerly: I E E Proceedings D (Control Theory and Applications) (0143-7054)
Related titles: Online - full text ed.: ISSN 1359-7035 (from EBSCO Publishing); ♦ Series of: I E E Proceedings.
Indexed: AS&TI, ASCA, ApMecR, B&BAb, BMT, BrTechI, C&ISA, CEA, CMCI, Cadscan, CompC, CompD, CurCont, E&CAJ, EngInd, ExcerpMed, IAA, ISMEC, ISR, Inspec, LeadAb, MathR, RefZh, SCI, SolStAb, ZentMath, Zincscan.
—BLDSC (4362.751863), AskIEEE, CASDDS, CISTI, Ei, IDS, IE, Infotrieve, ingenta, Linda Hall. **CCC.**
Published by: Institution of Electrical Engineers, Michael Faraday House, Six Hills Way, Stevenage, Herts SG1 2AY, United Kingdom. TEL 44-1438-313311, FAX 44-1438-313465, inspec@iee.org, http://www.iee.org/Publish/Journals/Profjourn/Proc/cta/. Eds. Derek Atherton, Heinz Unbehauen, Peter Wellstead. R&P Michael McCabe TEL 732-321-5575. Circ: 3,000. **Subscr. addr. in the US:** INSPEC, Inc., 379 Thornall St, Edison, NJ 08837-2225. TEL 732-321-5575, FAX 732-321-5702; **Subscr. to:** INSPEC, I E E, Publication Sales Dept., PO Box 96, Stevenage, Herts SG1 2SD, United Kingdom. TEL 44-1438-313311, FAX 44-1438-742840.

629.89 GBR
CODEN: ISYSEK
➤ **I F A C WORKSHOP SERIES.** Text in English. 1960. irreg. price varies. bibl. back issues avail. **Document type:** *Proceedings, Academic/Scholarly.* **Description:** Publishes selected papers from international conferences pertaining to control systems, robot control, and related theoretical design and implementation issues.
Former titles (until 1994): I F A C Symposia Series (0962-9505); (until 1992): I F A C Proceedings (0742-5953); I F A C Symposium on Multivariable Control. Proceedings; Which supersedes: International Congress of Automatic Control. Proceedings (0074-3526)
Related titles: Microform ed.: (from PQC).
Indexed: CCMJ, CIN, ChemAb, ChemTitl, HRIS, IMMAb, Inspec, ZentMath.
—CASDDS. **CCC.**
Published by: (International Federation of Automatic Control), Elsevier Ltd., Books Division (Subsidiary of: Elsevier Science & Technology), Kidlington, PO Box 800, Oxford, OX2 1DX, United Kingdom. TEL 44-1865-843000, FAX 44-1865-843410. Ed. Janos Gertler. **Subscr. to:** Elsevier BV, PO Box 211, Amsterdam 1000 AE, Netherlands. TEL 31-20-485-3757, FAX 31-20-485-3432, nlinfo-f@elsevier.nl, http://www.elsevier.nl.

629.8 GBR ISSN 1472-3034
INDUSTRIAL AUTOMATION INSIDER. Text in English. 1997. m. GBP 192 (effective 2001). 12 p./no. 2 cols./p.; reprints avail. **Document type:** *Newsletter.* **Description:** Dedicated to the market and technology intelligence on industrial automation and process control.
Formerly (until 2000): S C A D A Insider (1365-9871)
Related titles: E-mail ed.; Online - full text ed.: GBP 192 (effective 1999).
Published by: Andrew Bond, Ed. & Pub., Vine House, Church Rd, Harrietsham, Maidstone, ME17 1HJ, United Kingdom. TEL 44-1622-858251, FAX 44-1622-858976, scada@abpubs.demon.co.uk, http://www.abpubs.demon.co.uk/scada.htm.

629.8 SGP ISSN 0218-3552
INDUSTRIAL AUTOMATION JOURNAL. Text in English. 1992. q. USD 44 (effective 1999). adv. **Document type:** *Journal, Trade.* **Description:** Provides information on the availability and applications of automation systems and components.
Published by: Singapore Industrial Automation Association, 151 Chin Swee Rd, 03-13 Manhattan House, Singapore, 169876, Singapore. TEL 65-734-6911, FAX 65-235-5721, sra_siaa@pacific.net.sg, http://www.asia-mfg.com.sg/siaa. Ed., R&P Stephen Teng. Pub. F A Vasenwala. Adv. contact Nicholas Neo. Circ: 5,000.

629.8 NLD ISSN 0868-4952
QA75.5 CODEN: IFOREC
INFORMATICA; international journal. Text in Lithuanian, English. 1990. q. EUR 202, USD 243 combined subscription print & online eds. (effective 2006). adv. bk.rev. 140 p./no.; back issues avail.; reprints avail. **Document type:** *Journal, Academic/Scholarly.* **Description:** Provides an international forum for high-quality original research and publishes papers on mathematical simulation and optimization, recognition and control, programming theory and systems, automation systems and elements.
Formerly (until 1990): Informatika (0134-8639)
Related titles: Online - full text ed.: EUR 160, USD 180 (effective 2005) (from Swets Information Services); Supplement(s): Informatics in Education. ISSN 1648-5831. 2002.
Indexed: CCMJ, CMCI, CurCont, Inspec, MathR, MathSciNet, RefZh.
—BLDSC (4481.298225), AskIEEE, CISTI, KNAW, Linda Hall. **CCC.**
Published by: I O S Press, Nieuwe Hemweg 6B, Amsterdam, 1013 BG, Netherlands. TEL 31-20-6883355, FAX 31-20-6203419, info@iospress.nl, http://www.iospress.nl/html/08684952.php. Eds. L Telksnys, M Sapagovas, M Sapagovas, Dr. Jonas Mockus. R&P Ms. Carry Koolbergen TEL 31-20-6382189. Adv. contact Ms. Jolijn van Eunen.

629.8 ESP ISSN 0214-932X
CODEN: INAUE7
➤ **INFORMATICA Y AUTOMATICA.** Text in Spanish. 1967. 4/yr. adv. bk.rev. **Document type:** *Academic/Scholarly.*
Former titles (until 1987): Revista de Informatica y Automatica (0210-8712); (until 1974): Revista de Automatica (0374-4205)
Indexed: IECT, Inspec, RILM.
—AskIEEE.
Published by: Asociacion Espanola de Informatica y Automatica/Spanish Association of Information Processing and Automation, Hortaleza, 104, Madrid, 28004, Spain. TEL 34-1-3192565, FAX 34-1-3083028. Ed. Juan Manuel Sanchez. Adv. contact Antonio Vaquero Sanchez. Circ: 5,000.

629.8 USA ISSN 1526-7407
HF5548.35 CODEN: ISYJFS
INFORMATION SYSTEMS CONTROL JOURNAL; a leader in I T governance and assurance. Text in English. 1976. 6/yr. USD 75 domestic; USD 90 foreign (effective 2000). adv. bk.rev. **Description:** Addresses the information systems control community; includes IS audit, computer security and related fields.
Former titles: I S Audit & Control Journal (1076-4100); (until 1994): E D P Auditor Journal (0885-0445)
Indexed: ATI, Inspec.
—BLDSC (4496.367800), AskIEEE, IE, Infotrieve, ingenta. **CCC.**
Published by: Information Systems Audit & Control Association, 3701 Algonquin Rd, Ste 1010, Rolling Meadows, IL 60008. TEL 847-253-1545, FAX 847-253-1443, publication@isaca.org, http://www.isaca.org. Ed. Michael P Cangemi. Pub. Janet K Perry. Circ: 18,160.

C

629.8 FRA
INFORMATIQUE - AUTOMATIQUE. Text in French. 1962-1980; resumed 19??. 2/yr.
Published by: Europautomation, 83-85 avenue d'Italie, Paris, 75013, France. TEL 45-87-29-22. Ed. R J Giffrain. Circ: 3,000.

629.8 004 FRA ISSN 0249-0803
INSTITUT NATIONAL DE RECHERCHE EN INFORMATIQUE ET EN AUTOMATIQUE. RAPPORTS TECHNIQUES. Text in French. 1981. irreg. **Document type:** *Monographic series, Academic/Scholarly.*
—CISTI.
Published by: Institut National de Recherche en Informatique et en Automatique, BP 105, Le Chesnay, Cedex 78153, France. TEL 33-1-39635511, FAX 33-1-39635330, http://www.inria.fr.

629.8 ROM ISSN 1223-5075
INSTITUTUL POLITEHNIC DIN IASI. BULETINUL. SECTIA 4. AUTOMATICA, CALCULATEARE. Text in English, French, German, Italian, Russian, Spanish. 1946. s-a. per issue exchange basis. bk.rev.
Related titles: Series of: Institutul Politehnic din Iasi. Buletinul.
Indexed: ZentMath.
Published by: Institutul Politehnic din Iasi "Gh Asachi", Bd Copou 11, Iasi, 6600, Romania. TEL 40-81-46577, FAX 40-81-47923. Eds. Alfred Braier, Hugo Rosman.

629.8 USA ISSN 1079-8587
INTELLIGENT AUTOMATION AND SOFT COMPUTING. Text in English. 1995. q. USD 145 to individuals; USD 390 to libraries (effective 2005).
Indexed: CMCI, CurCont.
—BLDSC (4531.831515), IE, ingenta.
Published by: AutoSoft Press, PO Box 14126, Albuquerque, NM 87191-4126. http://wacong.com/autosoft.html. Ed. Mo Jamshidi.

629.8 USA
➤ **INTERNATIONAL EMERGENCY MANAGEMENT AND ENGINEERING CONFERENCE. PROCEEDINGS.** Text in English. 1983. irreg., latest vol.10, 1993. USD 80 to non-members; USD 40 to members. adv. back issues avail. **Document type:** *Proceedings, Academic/Scholarly.* **Description:** Covers papers on automation in emergency management and engineering.
Published by: The Society for Modeling and Simulation International (SCS), Circulation Office, PO Box 17900, San Diego, CA 92177. TEL 858-277-3888, FAX 609-277-3930. Ed. James D Sullivan. R&P William Gallagher. Adv. contact Steven Branch.

629.8 GBR
INTERNATIONAL FEDERATION OF AUTOMATIC CONTROL. WORLD CONGRESS. PROCEEDINGS. Text in English. triennial. price varies. **Document type:** *Proceedings.*
Indexed: IMMAb.
—BLDSC (6849.916920).

Published by: (International Federation of Automatic Control), Pergamon (Subsidiary of: Elsevier Science & Technology), The Boulevard, Langford Ln, East Park, Kidlington, Oxford OX5 1GB, United Kingdom. TEL 44-1865-843000, FAX 44-1865-843010, http://www.elsevier.nl:80/inca/publications/store/2/7/0/270.pub.shmtl. **Subscr. to:** Elsevier BV, PO Box 211, Amsterdam 1000 AE, Netherlands. TEL 31-20-485-3757, FAX 31-20-485-3432, nlinfo-f@elsevier.nl, http://www.elsevier.nl.

629.89   GBR   ISSN 1740-7516
▼ ➤ **INTERNATIONAL JOURNAL OF AUTOMATION AND CONTROL.** Text in English. forthcoming 2006 (Oct.). q. USD 450 to institutions; USD 545 to institutions print & online eds. (effective 2005). **Document type:** *Journal, Academic/Scholarly.*
Related titles: Online - full text ed.: ISSN 1740-7524. forthcoming 2006 (Oct.). USD 450 to institutions (effective 2005).
Published by: Inderscience Publishers, IEL Editorial Office, PO Box 735, Olney, Bucks MK46 5WB, United Kingdom. TEL 44-1234-240519, FAX 44-1234-240515, ijcs@inderscience.com, info@inderscience.com, http://www.inderscience.com/ijaac. **Subscr. to:** World Trade Centre Bldg, 29 route de Pre-Bois, Case Postale 896, Geneva 15 1215, Switzerland. FAX 41-22-7910885, subs@inderscience.com.

629.89   KOR   ISSN 1598-6446
▼ **INTERNATIONAL JOURNAL OF CONTROL, AUTOMATION AND SYSTEMS.** Text in English. 2003. irreg.
Indexed: CMCI, CurCont, Inspec.
—BLDSC (4542.177500), IE.
Published by: (Institute of Control, Automation and System Engineers), Korean Institute of Electrical Engineers, Seoul, Korea, S. Ed. Jin Chung Myung. **Co-publisher:** Institute of Control, Automation and System Engineers.

▼ **INTERNATIONAL JOURNAL OF ELECTRONIC GOVERNANCE.** see *PUBLIC ADMINISTRATION*

▼ **INTERNATIONAL JOURNAL OF ELECTRONIC TRADE.** see *BUSINESS AND ECONOMICS*

629.8 003   GBR   ISSN 1746-6172
▼ ➤ **INTERNATIONAL JOURNAL OF MODELLING, IDENTIFICATION AND CONTROL.** Text in English. forthcoming 2006. q. USD 450 to institutions; USD 545 combined subscription to institutions (effective 2005). **Document type:** *Journal, Academic/Scholarly.* **Description:** Provides an international forum to report latest developments from interdisciplinary theoretical studies, computational algorithm development and applications.
Related titles: Online - full text ed.: ISSN 1746-6180. forthcoming.
Published by: Inderscience Publishers, IEL Editorial Office, PO Box 735, Olney, Bucks MK46 5WB, United Kingdom. TEL 44-1234-240519, FAX 44-1234-240515, ijmic@inderscience.com, info@inderscience.com, http://www.inderscience.com/ijmic. Ed. Quan Min Zhu.

629.892   CAN   ISSN 0826-8185
TJ210.2   CODEN: IJAUED
INTERNATIONAL JOURNAL OF ROBOTICS AND AUTOMATION. Text in English. 1986. q. USD 350 (effective 2005). adv. bk.rev. index. back issues avail. **Document type:** *Journal, Academic/Scholarly.* **Description:** Covers all aspects of robotics and automation including modelling, simulation, dynamics, design, and social implications and applications.
Indexed: AIA, ASCA, ApMecR, BrCerAb, C&ISA, CMCI, CerAb, CompAb, CompLI, CorrAb, CurCont, E&CAJ, EMA, EngInd, IAA, Inspec, M&TEA, MBF, METADEX, RefZh, RoboAb, SolStAb, WAA.
—BLDSC (4542.538400), AskIEEE, CISTI, Ei, IDS, IE, Infotrieve, ingenta, Linda Hall. **CCC.**
Published by: (International Association of Science and Technology for Development), ACTA Press, 4500-16th Ave NW, Ste 80, Calgary, AB T3B 0M6, Canada. TEL 403-288-1195, FAX 403-247-6851, journals@actapress.com, http://www.actapress.com/Editors.aspx?JournalID=5. Ed. Dr. M Kamel. Adv. contact M H Hamza.

629.8   TUR   ISSN 1304-4494
▼ ➤ **INTERNATIONAL JOURNAL OF SIGNAL PROCESSING.** Text in English. 2004. q. free. **Document type:** *Journal, Academic/Scholarly.* **Description:** Focuses on theories, methods and applications in signal processing.
Related titles: Online - full text ed.: ISSN 1304-4478. 2004. free (effective 2005).
Published by: International Enformatika Society, PO Box 125, Canakkale, 17100, Turkey. TEL 90-286-2180709, FAX 90-286-2180709, ijsp@isjp.org, http://www.enformatika.org/journals/1304-4478/.

629.8 323.4   GBR   ISSN 1745-0071
▼ ➤ **INTERNATIONAL JOURNAL OF TRANSITIONS AND INNOVATION SYSTEMS.** Text in English. forthcoming 2006. q. USD 450 to institutions; USD 545 combined subscription to institutions print & online eds. (effective 2005). **Document type:** *Journal, Academic/Scholarly.*
Related titles: Online - full text ed.: ISSN 1742-4232. forthcoming 2006. USD 450 to institutions (effective 2005).

Published by: Inderscience Publishers, IEL Editorial Office, PO Box 735, Olney, Bucks MK46 5WB, United Kingdom. TEL 44-1234-240519, FAX 44-1234-240515, ijtis@inderscience.com, info@inderscience.com, http://www.inderscience.com/ijtis. Ed. Jan Rotmans. **Subscr. to:** World Trade Centre Bldg, 29 route de Pre-Bois, Case Postale 896, Geneva 15 1215, Switzerland. FAX 41-22-7910885, subs@inderscience.com.

629.8   USA
INTERNATIONAL SYMPOSIUM ON SIGNALS, SYSTEMS, AND ELECTRONICS. Text in English. a. price varies. **Document type:** *Proceedings, Trade.*
Published by: Institute of Electrical and Electronics Engineers, Inc., 3 Park Ave, 17th Fl, New York, NY 10016-5997. TEL 212-419-7900, 800-678-4333, FAX 212-752-4929, customer.service@ieee.org, http://www.ieee.org.

629.8 531   USA
INTERNATIONAL WORKSHOP ON ADVANCED MOTION CONTROL. Text in English. a. USD 212; USD 106 to members (effective 2004). **Document type:** *Proceedings, Trade.*
Indexed: EngInd.
—BLDSC (4552.178150).
Published by: Institute of Electrical and Electronics Engineers, Inc., 3 Park Ave, 17th Fl, New York, NY 10016-5997. TEL 212-419-7900, 800-678-4333, FAX 212-752-4929, customer.service@ieee.org, http://www.ieee.org.

629.8   USA
INTERNATIONAL WORKSHOP ON ROBOT AND HUMAN INTERACTIVE COMMUNICATION. Text in English. 2000. a. USD 216; USD 108 to members (effective 2004). **Document type:** *Proceedings, Trade.*
—BLDSC (4362.973420).
Published by: Institute of Electrical and Electronics Engineers, Inc., 3 Park Ave, 17th Fl, New York, NY 10016-5997. TEL 212-419-7900, 800-678-4333, FAX 212-752-4929, customer.service@ieee.org, http://www.ieee.org. **Co-sponsor:** I E E E Robotics and Automation Society.

JISUANJI JICHENG ZHIZAO XITONG/COMPUTER INTEGRATED MANUFACTURING SYSTEMS. see *MACHINERY*

629.8   PRT
JORNAL MICRO ELECTRONICA. Text in Portuguese. 12/yr.
Address: Viv. Menela Alto dos Campitos, Sao Joao do Estoril, Estoril, 2765, Portugal. Ed. Fernando D Ferreria.

629.8   FRA   ISSN 1269-6935
QA267.5.S4   CODEN: RAPIEK
JOURNAL EUROPEEN DES SYSTEMES AUTOMATISES. Text in French, English. 1966. 24/yr. EUR 1,200 in the European Union; EUR 1,400 elsewhere (effective 2003). adv. bibl.; charts. **Description:** Covers the activities of the Association at the university and industry levels.
Formed by the merger of (1991-1996): Diagnostic et Surete de Fonctionnement (1166-3049); (1988-1996): Revue d'Automatique et de Productique Appliquees (0990-7009); (1985-1996): Automatique - Productique Informatique Industrielle (0296-1598); Former titles: R A I R O Automatique (0399-0524); (1972-1977): Revue Francaise d'Automatique, Informatique, Recherche Operationnelle. Automatique (0397-9369)
Related titles: Microfilm ed.: 1966 (from PQC).
Indexed: CIS, CMCI, CurCont, EngInd, ExcerpMed, INIS AtomInd, Inspec, MathR, RASB, ZentMath.
—BLDSC (4979.633000), AskIEEE, CISTI, Ei, IE, Infotrieve, ingenta. **CCC.**
Published by: (Association Francaise des Sciences et Technologies de l'Information et des Systemes), Lavoisier, 11 rue Lavoisier, Paris, 75008, France. TEL 33-1-42653995, FAX 33-1-42650246, info@lavoisier.fr, http://www.lavoisier.fr. Circ: 1,100. **Subscr. to:** Lavoisier - Dept Abonnements, 14 rue de Provigny, Cachan 94236, France. TEL 33-1-47406700, FAX 33-1-47406702.

629.8   USA   ISSN 1064-2315
TJ212   CODEN: JAUIEP
JOURNAL OF AUTOMATION & INFORMATION SCIENCES. Text in English. 1968 (vol.13). m. USD 2,206 (effective 2005). adv. bk.rev. abstr.; bibl.; charts; illus.; pat. index. **Document type:** *Journal, Academic/Scholarly.* **Description:** Contains translations of scholarly articles and research papers on systems analysis, digital modelling, control theory, dynamic systems, and image recognition. Papers include equations and graphs.
Former titles (until 1992): Soviet Journal of Automation and Information Sciences (0882-570X); (until 1985): Soviet Automatic Control (0038-5328)
Related titles: Microform ed.: (from PQC); Online - full text ed.: (from EBSCO Publishing); ◆ Russian Translation: Problemy Upravleniya i Informatiki. ISSN 1028-0979.
Indexed: AIA, CADCAM, CIS, CompLI, EngInd, IAA, Inspec, MathR, TelAb, ZentMath.
—BLDSC (0414.220000), AskIEEE, CISTI, IE, Infotrieve, ingenta, Linda Hall. **CCC.**

Published by: (Natsional'na Akademiya Nauk Ukrainy UKR, Institut Kibernetiki UKR), Begell House Inc., 145 Madison Ave, New York, NY 10016-6717. TEL 212-725-1999, FAX 212-213-8368, orders@begellhouse.com, http://www.begellhouse.com/jais/jais.html. Ed. V. M. Kuntsevich. Pub. Dr. William Begell. Circ: 275 (paid and controlled).

629.8   USA   ISSN 1041-4673
JOURNAL OF MANUFACTURING＊ ; issues, option and strategies. Text in English. 1989. q. USD 98. **Description:** Focuses on the dual role of technological innovation and managerial strategy in fostering business success in the automated manufacturing industry.
Published by: Frost & Sullivan, 7550 IH 10 W., Ste 400, San Antonio, TX 78229-5811. TEL 212-233-1080. Ed. Hulas H King.

JOURNAL OF SYSTEMS SCIENCE AND COMPLEXITY. see *MATHEMATICS*

KEY ABSTRACTS - BUSINESS AUTOMATION. see *COMPUTERS—Abstracting, Bibliographies, Statistics*

KEY ABSTRACTS - FACTORY AUTOMATION. see *COMPUTERS—Abstracting, Bibliographies, Statistics*

629.8   USA
LINKAGE (PHOENIX). Text in English. q.
Published by: Honeywell, 6404 N Black Canyon, Phoenix, AZ 85023. TEL 602-863-5104. Ed. Frances B Emerson.

629.8   DEU   ISSN 0935-7939
LOGISTIK SPEKTRUM; Management und Organisation. Text in German. 1988. 6/yr. adv. bk.rev. back issues avail. **Document type:** *Magazine, Trade.*
Published by: (Deutsche Gesellschaft fuer Logistik e.V.), Vereinigte Fachverlage GmbH, Lise-Meitner-Str 2, Mainz, 55129, Germany. TEL 49-6131-9920, FAX 49-6131-992100, info@vfmz.de, http://www.industrie-service.de. Ed. Michael Doeppert. Adv. contact Beatrice Thomas Meyer. B&W page EUR 7,350; trim 185 x 265. Circ: 28,000 (controlled).

531   ITA   ISSN 1126-4284
M & A. (Meccanica e Automazione) Text in Italian. 1995. 11/yr. EUR 60.50 (effective 2003). adv. **Document type:** *Magazine, Trade.*
Published by: Gruppo Editoriale Futura, Via XXV Aprile, 39, Bresso, MI 20091, Italy. TEL 39-02-665261, FAX 39-02-66526222, ma@futura-ge.com, info@futura-ge.com, http://www.futura-ge.com/prodotti/riviste/mea/profilo/.

629.8   NLD   ISSN 1572-4980
MACHINEBOUW. Text in Dutch. 1983. 10/yr. EUR 89.50 domestic; EUR 99.50 foreign (effective 2005). adv. bk.rev. charts; illus. back issues avail. **Document type:** *Journal, Trade.* **Description:** Covers practical information concerning industrial automation.
Former titles (until 2004): C A Techniek (0925-7977); (until 1991): C A Techniek in Bedrijf (0924-9605); (until 1990): C A D C A M in Bedrijf (0924-9591)
Related titles: Online - full text ed.
—IE, Infotrieve.
Published by: Array Publications BV, Postbus 2211, Alphen aan den Rijn, 2400 CE, Netherlands. TEL 31-172-469030, FAX 31-172-424381, machinebouw@array.nl, http://www.machinebouw.net, http://www.array.nl. Eds. Willem van der Velden, Mark Oosterveer. Adv. contact Eric van Wijk TEL 31-172-469030. B&W page EUR 2,150, color page EUR 3,350; 180 x 240. Circ: 5,000.

629.8   USA   ISSN 0895-3805
HD30.2
MANAGING AUTOMATION. Text in English. 1986. m. USD 60 domestic print & online eds.; USD 75 in Canada & Mexico print & online eds.; USD 125 elsewhere print & online eds.; free to qualified personnel print & online eds. (effective 2005). adv. **Document type:** *Magazine, Trade.* **Description:** Provides solutions for integrated manufacturing. Aims at managers, from the executive suite to the plant floor.
Indexed: AIA, BrCerAb, C&ISA, CADCAM, CerAb, CivEngAb, CorrAb, E&CAJ, EMA, Emerald, EngInd, IAA, Inspec, M&TEA, MBF, METADEX, RoboAb, SoftBase, SolStAb, TelAb, WAA.
—BLDSC (5359.283000), AskIEEE, CISTI, Ei, IE, ingenta, Linda Hall.
Published by: Thomas Publishing Company, Five Penn Plaza, New York, NY 10001. TEL 212-629-1546, 800-733-1127, FAX 212-629-1542, hmikisch@thomaspublishing.com, info@thomasimg.com, http://www.managingautomation.com, http://www.thomaspublishing.com. Ed. David Brousell. Pub. Heather MiKisch. adv.: B&W page USD 11,715, color page USD 14,110. Circ: 100,206 (controlled).

MANUFACTURING AUTOMATION. see *ENGINEERING—Industrial Engineering*

629.89 USA ISSN 1060-2712
MANUFACTURING AUTOMATION; the essential business resource on international manufacturing automation. Text in English. 1991. m. USD 395 domestic; USD 420 foreign (effective 2004). adv. charts. back issues avail. **Document type:** *Newsletter, Trade.* **Description:** Provides information on worldwide markets, products, technologies, and applications in key areas of manufacturing and industrial automation.
Formed by the 1991 merger of: Advanced Manufacturing; Manufacturing Automation News (0950-5113); Incorporates (in 1991): Industrial Automation Outlook (1051-9440); Advanced Manufacturing was formerly titled: Factory Automation Newsletter; Manufacturing Automation News was formed by the 1987 merger of: F M S Update (0264-889X); Robot News International (0262-1460); Industrial Automation Outlook was formerly: Factory Automation News (1045-0554)
Related titles: Online - full text ed.: (from Data-Star, Factiva, Gale Group, Northern Light Technology, Inc., The Dialog Corporation).
Indexed: CompD.
—BLDSC (5365.976000). **CCC.**
Published by: Vital Information Publications, 754 Caravel Ln., Foster City, CA 94404. FAX 614-345-7018, vip@sensauto.com, http://www.sensauto.com, http://www.automationmag.com/. Ed. Peter Adrian. Pub. Lidia Bekker TEL 650-572-0563. Circ: 500 (paid).

629.8 UKR ISSN 1028-9763
➤ **MATEMATYCHNI MASHYNY I SYSTEMY.** Text in Ukrainian, Russian, English. 1994. s-a. UAK 20 per issue (effective 2003). abstr.; bibl.; charts; illus. 200 p./no. 1 cols./p.; **Document type:** *Journal, Academic/Scholarly.* **Description:** Publishes original papers, scientific and technical reviews. Includes accounts of conferences and workshops, reports on monographs and discussions.
Indexed: RefZh.
Published by: Natsional'na Akademiya Nauk Ukrainy, Instytut Problem Matematychnykh Mashyn i System/National Academy of Sciences of Ukraine, Institute of Mathematical Machine and System Problems, 42, Academician Glushkov Ave, Kyiv, 03187, Ukraine. TEL 380-44-2664092, 380-44-2666003, FAX 380-44-2666457, mis@immsp.kiev.ua, http://www.nas.gov.ua/catalog/nas_zinf2.html, http://www.immsp.kiev.ua. Ed. Morozov Anatoliy.

629.8 USA ISSN 0195-2366
MATERIAL HANDLING PRODUCT NEWS. Text in English. 1979. m. USD 40.99 domestic; USD 47 in Canada; USD 42 in Mexico; USD 117 elsewhere; USD 4 newsstand/cover domestic; USD 6 newsstand/cover foreign (effective 2005). adv. back issues avail.; reprints avail. **Document type:** *Magazine, Trade.* **Description:** Provides a listing of equipment and systems available for the material handling industry, storage areas and warehouses.
Related titles: Online - full text ed.: (from Florida Center for Library Automation, Gale Group, O C L C Online Computer Library Center, Inc., ProQuest Information & Learning).
Indexed: ABIn, CurPA.
—**CCC.**
Published by: Reed Business Information (Subsidiary of: Reed Business), 100 Enterprise Dr, Ste 600, PO Box 912, Rockaway, NJ 07866-0912. TEL 973-920-7000, FAX 973-920-7531, http://www.mhpn.com, http://www.reedbusiness.com. Ed. Joseph Pagnotta TEL 973-292-5100 ext 272. Pub. Scott Sward TEL 973-292-5100 ext 236. adv.: B&W page USD 11,025, color page USD 11,935. Circ: 96,500. **Subscr. to:** Reed Business Information, PO Box 9020, Maple Shade, NJ 08052-9020. TEL 303-470-4466, FAX 303-470-4691.

629.8 CHE
MESS UND REGELTECHNIK. Text in German. 11/yr.
Published by: Aida AG, Postfach 1710, Rapperswil Sg, 8640, Switzerland. TEL 055-279627, FAX 055-271555. Ed. Peter Menzi. Circ: 5,000.

629.8 FRA ISSN 0755-219X
T2 CODEN: MRAUA7
MESURES. Text in French. 1936. 10/yr. EUR 135 (effective 2005). adv. bk.rev. reprints avail.
Formerly (until 1983): Mesures Regulation Automatisme (0026-0193)
Indexed: CISA, ExcerpMed, INIS AtomInd, Inspec.
—BLDSC (5682.890000), CASDDS, CISTI, IE, Infotrieve, ingenta, Linda Hall. **CCC.**
Published by: Groupe Tests, 26 rue d'Oradour-sur-Glane, Paris, Cedex 15 75504, France. TEL 33-1-44253500, http://www.mesures.com/, http://www.groupetests.fr. Ed. Jean-Francois Peyrucat. Pub. Jean-Pierre Della Mussia. Adv. contact Bernard Metier. Circ: 12,000.

629.8 RUS
MIR KOMP'YUTERNOI AVTOMATIZATSII/WORLD OF COMPUTER-AIDED AUTOMATION. Text in Russian; Abstracts in English. 1995. q.
Indexed: Inspec.
—BLDSC (0115.747000).
Published by: Asotsiatsiya V E R A, P.O. Box 159, Moscow, 105077, Russian Federation. TEL 7-095-3066749, FAX 7-095-7426829. Ed. O. Sinenko.

629.8 620.1 BEL ISSN 1379-0641
MOTION CONTROL (FRENCH EDITION). Text in French. 2002. 9/yr. EUR 51 domestic (effective 2004). **Document type:** *Magazine, Consumer.*
Related titles: Dutch ed.: Motion Control (Dutch Edition). ISSN 1379-0633.
Published by: Professional Media Group, Torhoutsesteenweg 226 bus 2/6, Zedelgem, B-8210, Belgium. TEL 32-50-240404, FAX 32-50-240445, info@pmgroup.be, http://www.pmgroup.be.

N T I S ALERTS: COMPUTERS, CONTROL & INFORMATION THEORY. see *COMPUTERS—Abstracting, Bibliographies, Statistics*

N T I S ALERTS: MANUFACTURING TECHNOLOGY. see *TECHNOLOGY: COMPREHENSIVE WORKS—Abstracting, Bibliographies, Statistics*

629.89 USA
NATIONAL MANUFACTURING WEEK. PROCEEDINGS. Text in English. 1982. a. (in 3 vols.). USD 135. **Document type:** *Proceedings.* **Description:** Publishes papers on all aspects of control engineering presented at the annual Control Engineering Conference.
Formerly: Control Engineering Conference. Proceedings
Published by: Reed Exposition Companies, Division of Reed Elsevier Inc, Box 6059, Norwalk, CT 06852-6059. TEL 203-964-8487, 800-840-0678, FAX 203-964-8287, http://www.manufacturingweek.com, http://www.reedexpo.com. Ed., R&P Maria Bradley TEL 203-840-5931.

O E C D LIBRARY SPECIAL ANNOTATED BIBLIOGRAPHY: AUTOMATION/O C D E BIBLIOTHEQUE BIBLIOGRAPHIE SPECIALE ANALYTIQUE: AUTOMATION. see *COMPUTERS—Abstracting, Bibliographies, Statistics*

OBSERVER (APTOS); office systems trends. see *BUSINESS AND ECONOMICS—Office Equipment And Services*

OFFICE AUTOMATION. see *BUSINESS AND ECONOMICS—Office Equipment And Services*

629.8 DEU ISSN 1439-9733
OPEN AUTOMATION; Maerkte - Trends - Innovationen. Text in German. 1999. bi-m. EUR 47; EUR 9.85 newsstand/cover (effective 2004). adv. 66 p./no. 3 cols./p.; back issues avail. **Document type:** *Magazine, Trade.* **Description:** Covers all aspects of automation technology and products.
Published by: V D E Verlag GmbH, Bismarckstr 33, Berlin, 10625, Germany. TEL 49-30-34800148, FAX 49-30-34800188, etz-redaktion@vde-verlag.de, zeitschriftenvertrieb@vde-verlag.de, http://www.openautomation.de, http://www.vde-verlag.de. Ed. Ronald Heinze. Adv. contact Markus Lehnert. B&W page EUR 3,315, color page EUR 4,410; trim 132 x 189. Circ: 14,155 (paid and controlled).

629.8 GBR ISSN 0143-2087
QA402.3 CODEN: OCAMD5
➤ **OPTIMAL CONTROL APPLICATIONS AND METHODS.** Text in English. 1979. bi-m. USD 2,900 to institutions; USD 3,190 combined subscription to institutions print & online eds. (effective 2006). adv. back issues avail.; reprint service avail. from PQC,PSC,ISI. **Document type:** *Journal, Academic/Scholarly.* **Description:** Presents an interdisciplinary forum for the reporting of interesting optimal control applications emphasizing both the commonality of the underlying theory and the diversity of its applications.
Related titles: Microform ed.: (from PQC); Online - full text ed.: ISSN 1099-1514. 1996. USD 2,900 (effective 2006) (from EBSCO Publishing, Swets Information Services, Wiley InterScience).
Indexed: ASCA, ApMecR, BrCerAb, C&ISA, CCMJ, CIS, CMCI, CerAb, CompAb, CorrAb, CurCont, E&CAJ, EMA, Englnd, IAA, IAOP, Inspec, M&TEA, MBF, METADEX, MathR, MathSciNet, RASB, SSCI, ST&MA, SolStAb, WAA, ZentMath.
—BLDSC (6275.070000), AskIEEE, CISTI, Ei, IDS, IE, Infotrieve, ingenta, Linda Hall. **CCC.**
Published by: John Wiley & Sons Ltd. (Subsidiary of: John Wiley & Sons, Inc.), The Atrium, Southern Gate, Chichester, West Sussex PO19 8SQ, United Kingdom. TEL 44-1243-779777, FAX 44-1243-775878, customer@wiley.co.uk, http://www3.interscience.wiley.com/cgi-bin/jhome/2133, http://www.wiley.co.uk. Ed. Bion L Pierson. adv.: B&W page GBP 650, color page GBP 1,550; trim 178 x 254. Circ: 299. **Subscr. in the Americas to:** John Wiley & Sons, Inc., 111 River St, Hoboken, NJ 07030-5774. TEL 201-748-6645, 800-225-5945, subinfo@wiley.com.

629.8 POL ISSN 0373-8698
TK5101.A1
POLITECHNIKA GDANSKA. ZESZYTY NAUKOWE. ELEKTRONIKA. Text in English, Polish; Summaries in Russian. 1967. irreg. price varies. bibl.; charts; illus. **Description:** Deals with cybernetics, automation, computer science, hydroacoustics, microwave technology, telecommunications and electronic equipment technology.
—Linda Hall.
Published by: Politechnika Gdanska, Ul G Narutowicza 11-12, Gdansk, 80952, Poland. **Dist. by:** Osrodek Rozpowszechniania Wydawnictw Naukowych PAN, Palac Kultury i Nauki, Warsaw 00901, Poland.

629.8 POL ISSN 0032-4140
TJ1313 CODEN: PAUKAP
POMIARY - AUTOMATYKA - KONTROLA. Text in Polish. 1955. m. USD 81. bk.rev. bibl.; charts; illus. index. **Description:** Covers automatics in practice and theory, measurements, controls.
Indexed: ApMecR, CISA, ChemAb, ChemTitl, CybAb, Inspec, SIA.
—AskIEEE, CASDDS, CISTI, Linda Hall.
Published by: (Polski Komitet Pomiarow i Automatyki), Oficyna Wydawnicza SIMP Press Ltd., ul Swietokrzyska 14a, Warsaw, 00050, Poland. Ed. Jan Bek. adv.: B&W page USD 1,010. Circ: 2,000. **Dist. by:** Ars Polona, Krakowskie Przedmiescie 7, Warsaw, Poland. **Co-sponsor:** Sekcja Metrologii Automatyki i Mechaniki Precyzyjnej SIMP.

PRIBORY I SISTEMY. UPRALENIE, KONTROL', DIAGNOSTIKA. see *METROLOGY AND STANDARDIZATION*

629.8 RUS ISSN 0234-6206
TJ4 CODEN: PMAVEC
PROBLEMY MASHINOSTROENIYA I AVTOMATIZATSII. Text in Russian. 1982. q. USD 90 foreign (effective 2004). 96 p./no.; **Document type:** *Journal, Academic/Scholarly.* **Description:** Publishes reviews and articles about basic researches of modern mechanical engineering, advanced experience, progressive forms and advanced technologies of mechanical engineering, including problems of management and automation.
Related titles: English Translation: Engineering and Automation Problems. 2000. UZS 10 per issue (effective 2004).
Indexed: RefZh.
—East View, Linda Hall.
Published by: Moskovskii Gorodskoi Tsentr Nauchno-Tekhnicheskoi Informatsii, Lubyanskii proezd 5, Moscow, 101990, Russian Federation. TEL 7-095-9212440, FAX 7-095-9286039, moscnti.rir@g23.relcom.ru, http://www.rosinf.ru/editions/pmea/issues. Ed. K V Frolov. **Dist. by:** M K - Periodica, ul Gilyarovskogo 39, Moscow 129110, Russian Federation. TEL 7-095-2845008, FAX 7-095-2813798, info@periodicals.ru, http://www.mkniga.ru.

629.8 UKR ISSN 1028-0979
TJ212 CODEN: AVTMA8
PROBLEMY UPRAVLENIYA I INFORMATIKI; nauchno-tekhnicheskii zhurnal. Text in Russian; Summaries in English, Russian. 1956. bi-m. **Document type:** *Academic/Scholarly.*
Formerly: Avtomatika (0572-2691)
Related titles: ♦ Translation of: Journal of Automation & Information Sciences. ISSN 1064-2315.
Indexed: C&ISA, CCMJ, CybAb, Djerelo, E&CAJ, Englnd, INIS AtomInd, Inspec, MathR, MathSciNet, RefZh, SolStAb, ZentMath.
—CASDDS, CISTI, East View, Linda Hall. **CCC.**
Published by: Natsional'na Akademiya Nauk Ukrainy, Instytut Kibernetyky im. V.M. Hlushkova, Pr Akad Glushkova 40, Kiev, 252650, Ukraine. TEL 38-44-2662229, FAX 38-44-2669064. Ed. A G Ivakhnenko. **US dist. addr.:** East View Information Services, 3020 Harbor Ln. N., Minneapolis, MN 55447. TEL 612-550-0961.

629.89 NLD ISSN 1387-5825
PROCESS CONTROL; vakblad voor procesbesturing en analysetechniek. Text in Dutch. 1996. 10/yr. EUR 61.50 domestic; EUR 71.50 in Belgium (effective 2005). adv. illus.; tr.lit. back issues avail. **Document type:** *Journal, Trade.* **Description:** Covers laboratory technology and process automation.
Formerly (until 1997): L T i P A (1385-1837); Which was formed by the 1996 merger of: I en P A (0928-1177); L T en I (0928-1185)
Published by: Array Publications BV, Postbus 2211, Alphen aan den Rijn, 2400 CE, Netherlands. TEL 31-172-424177, FAX 31-172-424381, processcontrol@array.nl, http://www.processcontrol.nl/site/, http://www.array.nl. Ed. Mark Oosterveer. Adv. contact Eric van Wijk TEL 31-172-469030. B&W page EUR 1,495, color page EUR 2,695; trim 210 x 285. Circ: 4,000 (paid).

629.8 FIN ISSN 0357-4121
PROSESSORI. Text in Finnish. 1979. m. EUR 80 (effective 2004). adv. **Document type:** *Magazine, Trade.* **Description:** Focuses on the latest development trends in electronics, data technology, telecommunications and industrial systems.
Published by: Sanoma Magazines Finland Corporation, Hoylaamotie 1 D, P.O. Box 100, Helsinki, 00040, Finland. TEL 358-9-1201, FAX 358-9-1205171, webmasteri@prosessori.fi, info@sanomamagazines.fi, http://www.prosessori.fi, http://www.sanomamagazines.fi. adv.: B&W page EUR 2,085, color page EUR 2,970. Circ: 9,626 (paid and controlled).

R I A QUARTERLY STATISTICS REPORT - ROBOTICS. see *COMPUTERS—Robotics*

REFERATIVNYI ZHURNAL. AVTOMATIKA I TELEMEKHANIKA. see *COMPUTERS—Abstracting, Bibliographies, Statistics*

REFERATIVNYI ZHURNAL. AVTOMATIKA I VYCHISLITEL'NAYA TEKHNIKA. see *COMPUTERS—Abstracting, Bibliographies, Statistics*

C

629.8 GBR ISSN 0263-1377
RETAIL AUTOMATION. Text in English. 1980. 6/yr. GBP 95; GBP 105 in Europe; GBP 115 elsewhere. adv. bk.rev. **Document type:** *Trade.* **Description:** Covers product reviews, market news, conference reports, diary and retail case studies.
Indexed: Inspec.
—AskIEEE. **CCC.**
Published by: R M D P Ltd., The Hideaway, Furze Hill, Hove, E Sussex BN3 1PA, United Kingdom. TEL 44-1273-722687, FAX 44-1273-821463. Ed., R&P Ron Condon. Adv. contact Jason Sullivan. Circ: 12,125; 375 (paid).

ROBOTICS AND AUTONOMOUS SYSTEMS. see *COMPUTERS—Robotics*

620 629.8 BRA ISSN 0103-1759
CODEN: COAUFH
S B A. (Sociedade Brasileira de Automatica) Variant title: Controle & Automacao. Text in Portuguese. 1987. 3/yr.
Related titles: Online - full text ed.: free (effective 2005).
Indexed: Inspec.
Published by: Sociedade Brasileira de Automatica, Caixa Postal 10053, Campina Grande, 58109-970, Brazil. TEL 83-310-1407, FAX 83-310-1418, http://www.fee.unicamp.br/revista_sba, http://www.sba.org.br.

629.8 SGP
S I A A'S INDUSTRIAL AUTOMATION PRODUCTS & SERVICES DIRECTORY. Text in English. 1985. a. USD 100 (effective 1999). adv. **Document type:** *Directory, Trade.* **Description:** Buyer's guide to industrial automation industry in Singapore.
Published by: Singapore Industrial Automation Association, 151 Chin Swee Rd, 03-13 Manhattan House, Singapore, 169876, Singapore. TEL 65-734-6911, FAX 65-235-5721, sra_siaa@pacific.net.sg, http://www.siaa.org.sg. R&P Stephen Teng. Adv. contact Thomas Lee. Circ: 32,000.

629.8 USA ISSN 0163-5700
QA267 CODEN: SIGNDM
S I G A C T NEWS. (Special Interest Group on Algorithms and Computation Theory) Text in English. 1969. q. USD 18 membership (effective 2005). adv. bk.rev. charts; stat. back issues avail. **Document type:** *Newsletter, Academic/Scholarly.* **Description:** Serves as a forum for issues of interest to the theoretical computer science community.
Related titles: Online - full text ed.: (from EBSCO Publishing).
Indexed: AHCI, CompR, Inspec.
—AskIEEE, CISTI, IE, Infotrieve.
Published by: Association for Computing Machinery, Inc., 1515 Broadway, 17th Fl, New York, NY 10036-5701. TEL 212-626-0500, 212-626-0520, 800-342-6626, FAX 212-944-1318, editor@sigact.acm.org, sigs@acm.org, usacm@acm.org, http://sigact.acm.org/sigactnews/, http://www.acm.org. Ed. David Haglin. Pub. Edward Grossman. adv.: page USD 1,350. Circ: 1,588 (controlled).

629.8 USA
CODEN: SIGDDQ
S I G D A NEWSLETTER (ONLINE). (Special Interest Group on Design Automation) Text in English. s-a. USD 50 (effective 2004). **Document type:** *Newsletter, Academic/Scholarly.*
Formerly (until 2002): S I G D A Newsletter (Print) (0163-5743)
Related titles: Online - full text ed.: (from EBSCO Publishing).
Indexed: AHCI, CADCAM, CompR, Inspec.
—AskIEEE, CISTI, IE.
Published by: Association for Computing Machinery, Inc., 1515 Broadway, 17th Fl, New York, NY 10036-5701. TEL 212-626-0520, 800-342-6626, FAX 212-869-0481, sigs@acm.org, usacm@acm.org, http://www.sigda.org/index.php, http://www.acm.org.

SENSOR REPORT; Sensorik Messtechnik Automatisierung. see *INSTRUMENTS*

SENSOR REVIEW. see *MACHINERY*

SENSOR TECHNOLOGY; a monthly intelligence service. see *COMPUTERS—Cybernetics*

629.8 SGP ISSN 0218-0197
SERIES IN AUTOMATION. Text in English. 1988. irreg., latest vol.4, 1992. price varies. **Document type:** *Monographic series, Academic/Scholarly.*
—CISTI.
Published by: World Scientific Publishing Co. Pte. Ltd., 5 Toh Tuck Link, Singapore, 596224, Singapore. TEL 65-466-5775, FAX 65-467-7667, wspc@wspc.com.sg, series@wspc.com.sg, http://www.wspc.com.sg/books/series/sa_series.shtml, http://www.worldscientific.com. Ed. S S Chen. **Dist. by:** World Scientific Publishing Co., Inc., 1060 Main St, River Edge, NJ 07661. TEL 201-487-9655, 800-227-7562, FAX 201-487-9656, 888-977-2665; World Scientific Publishing Ltd., 57 Shelton St, London WC2H 9HE, United Kingdom. TEL 44-20-78360888, FAX 44-20-78362020.

629.8312 JPN ISSN 0916-1600
SHISUTEMU SEIGYO JOHO/SYSTEMS, CONTROL AND INFORMATION. Text in Japanese; Summaries in English. 1957. m. JPY 10,800 membership (effective 2004). adv. bk.rev. abstr.; charts; illus. Index. back issues avail. **Document type:** *Journal, Academic/Scholarly.*
Former titles (until 1989): Shisutemu to Seigyo - Systems and Controls (0374-4507); (until 1971): Seigyo Kogaku (0021-4310)
Indexed: FLUIDEX, INIS AtomInd, Inspec, MathR, RefZh.
—BLDSC (8589.325500), AskIEEE, CISTI, IE, ingenta. **CCC.**
Published by: Shisutemu Seigyo Joho Gakkai/Institute of Systems, Control & Information Engineers, 14 Yoshidakawara-cho, Sakyo-ku, Kyoto, 606-8305, Japan. FAX 81-75-7516037. Eds. K Akazawa, M Araki. Circ: 2,500.

629.8 NLD ISSN 0165-1684
TK5102.5 CODEN: SPRODR
➤ **SIGNAL PROCESSING.** Text in English. 1979. 12/yr. EUR 2,640 in Europe to institutions; JPY 350,600 in Japan to institutions; USD 2,954 to institutions except Europe and Japan (effective 2006). adv. bk.rev. abstr.; bibl.; illus. back issues avail.; reprints avail. **Document type:** *Journal, Academic/Scholarly.* **Description:** For researchers in signal processing, computer sciences, acoustics, automatic control, and electrical and electronics engineering.
Related titles: Microform ed.: (from PQC); Online - full text ed.: (from EBSCO Publishing, Gale Group, IngentaConnect, ScienceDirect, Swets Information Services).
Indexed: AHCI, AS&TI, ASCA, AcoustA, C&ISA, CIS, CMCI, CompAb, CompLI, CompR, CurCont, CybAb, E&CAJ, EngInd, Inspec, MathR, RefZh, SolStAb, TelAb, ZentMath.
—BLDSC (8275.985300), AskIEEE, CISTI, Ei, IDS, IE, Infotrieve, ingenta, Linda Hall. **CCC.**
Published by: (European Association for Signal Processing), Elsevier BV (Subsidiary of: Elsevier Science & Technology), Radarweg 29, Amsterdam, 1043 NX, Netherlands. TEL 31-20-4853911, FAX 31-20-4852457, nlinfo-f@elsevier.nl, http://www.elsevier.com/locate/sigpro, http://www.elsevier.nl. Ed. Murat Kunt. Circ: 1,500.

629.8 DEU ISSN 1619-6864
SIGNALTHEORIE. Text in German. 2002. irreg., latest vol.4, 2002. price varies. **Document type:** *Monographic series, Academic/Scholarly.*
Published by: Bochumer Universitaetsverlag GmbH, Querenburger Hoehe 281, Bochum, 44801, Germany. TEL 49-234-9719780, FAX 49-234-9719786, bou@bou.de, http://bou.de.

629.8 POL ISSN 1642-0489
TJ225 CODEN: ZNPIET
STUDIA INFORMATICA. Text in Polish; Summaries in English, German, Russian. 1961. irreg. price varies. **Description:** For engineers and scientists. Contains papers on various aspects of automation and artificial intelligence applications.
Former titles (until 2000): Politechnika Slaska. Zeszyty Naukowe. Informatyka (0208-7286); (until 1980): Politechnika Slaska. Zeszyty Naukowe. Automatyka (0434-0760)
Indexed: ZentMath.
—Linda Hall.
Published by: Politechnika Slaska, ul Akademicka 5, Gliwice, 44100, Poland. Ed. Anna Skrzywan Kosek. Circ: 205. **Dist. by:** Ars Polona, Krakowskie Przedmiescie 7, Warsaw, Poland.

629.8 POL
➤ **STUDIA Z AUTOMATYKI I INFORMATYKI.** Text in Polish, English; Summaries in English. 1969. a., latest vol.27, 2002. price varies. bibl. **Document type:** *Bulletin, Academic/Scholarly.*
Former titles (until 1997): Studia z Automatyki; Poznanskie Towarzystwo Przyjaciol Nauk. Komisja Automatyki i Informatyki. Prace (0867-3977); (until 1989): Poznanskie Towarzystwo Przyjaciol Nauk. Komisja Automatyki. Prace (0079-4589)
Indexed: Inspec, MathR.
—AskIEEE, CISTI.
Published by: (Poznanskie Towarzystwo Przyjaciol Nauk, Komisja Automatyki i Informatyki), Poznanskie Towarzystwo Przyjaciol Nauk/Poznan Society for the Advancement of the Arts and Sciences, ul Sew Mielzynskiego 27-29, Poznan, 61725, Poland. TEL 48-61-8527441, FAX 48-61-8522205, sekretariat@ptpn.poznan.pl, wydawnictwo@ptpn.poznan.pl, http://www.ptpn.poznan.pl. Ed. Krzysztof Kozlowski. Circ: 160. **Dist. by:** Ars Polona, Krakowskie Przedmiescie 7, Warsaw, Poland. TEL 48-22-9263914, FAX 48-22-9265334, arspolona@arspolona.com.pl, http://www.arspolona.com.pl.

➤ **SUPPLY CHAIN SYSTEMS**; the resource for supply chain automation. see *BUSINESS AND ECONOMICS—Computer Applications*

629.8 USA ISSN 1043-6871
QA75.5
SYMPOSIUM ON LOGIC IN COMPUTER SCIENCE. Text in English. 1986. a. USD 140. **Document type:** *Proceedings.* **Description:** Contains computer science issues broadly relating to logic, including algebraic and topological approaches.
Related titles: Online - full text ed.: (from I E E E).
Indexed: EngInd, Inspec.
—BLDSC (1086.234500).
Published by: (Institute of Electrical and Electronics Engineers, Inc.), I E E E Computer Society, 3 Park Ave, 17th Fl, New York, NY 10017. TEL 714-821-8380, 800-678-4333, FAX 714-821-4641, customer.service@ieee.org, http://www.ieee.org.

629.8 NLD ISSN 0167-6911
T57.6 CODEN: SCLEDC
➤ **SYSTEMS & CONTROL LETTERS.** Text in English. 1981. 12/yr. EUR 1,154 in Europe to institutions; JPY 152,800 in Japan to institutions; USD 1,288 to institutions except Europe and Japan (effective 2006). adv. illus. index. reprints avail. **Document type:** *Academic/Scholarly.* **Description:** Publishes theoretical, methodological and empirical studies and applications pertaining to systems.
Related titles: Microform ed.: (from PQC); Online - full text ed.: (from EBSCO Publishing, Gale Group, IngentaConnect, ScienceDirect, Swets Information Services).
Indexed: ApMecR, C&ISA, CADCAM, CMCI, CompLI, CurCont, CybAb, E&CAJ, EngInd, IAA, ISMEC, ISR, Inspec, MathR, MathSciNet, RefZh, RoboAb, SCI, SSCI, SolStAb, ZentMath.
—BLDSC (8589.294000), AskIEEE, CISTI, Ei, IDS, IE, Infotrieve, ingenta, Linda Hall. **CCC.**
Published by: Elsevier BV, North-Holland (Subsidiary of: Elsevier Science & Technology), Sara Burgerhartstraat 25, Amsterdam, 1055 KV, Netherlands. TEL 31-20-485-3911, FAX 31-20-485-2457, nlinfo-f@elsevier.nl, http://www.elsevier.com/locate/sysconle, http://www.elsevier.nl/homepage/about/us/regional_sites.htt. Eds. A C Antoulas, I M Y Mareels. **Subscr.:** Elsevier BV, PO Box 211, Amsterdam 1000 AE, Netherlands. TEL 31-20-485-3757, FAX 31-20-485-3432.

➤ **TECHLIVING**; your hassle-free way to live. see *ELECTRONICS*

629.8 ESP ISSN 1134-2862
TECNOMARKET; nuevos productos para la automatizacion industrial. Text in Spanish. 1994. q. free (effective 2005). adv.
Published by: Cetisa Editores S.A., Enrique Granados, 7, Barcelona, 08019, Spain. TEL 34-93-2431040, FAX 34-93-3492350, info@cetisa.com, http://www.cetisa.com/tk/index.html. adv.: color page EUR 4,751, B&W page EUR 3,323; 320 x 249. Circ: 17,000 (paid).

629.8 RUS
TEKHNIKA, EKONOMIKA. SERIYA. AVTOMATIZATSIYA PROEKTIROVANIYA. Text in Russian. q. USD 99.95 in United States.
Published by: V.I.M.I., Volokolamskoe shosse 77, Moscow, 123584, Russian Federation. TEL 7-095-4911306, FAX 7-095-4916820. **US dist. addr.:** East View Information Services, 3020 Harbor Ln. N., Minneapolis, MN 55447. TEL 612-550-0961.

TRANSACTIONS ON DESIGN AUTOMATION OF ELECTRONIC SYSTEMS. see *ENGINEERING—Computer Applications*

629.89 GBR
U M I S T CONTROL SYSTEMS CENTRE SERIES. Text in English. irreg., latest vol.6, 1999. price varies. **Document type:** *Monographic series.*
Indexed: ZentMath.
Published by: (University of Manchester Institute of Science and Technology), Research Studies Press Ltd., 16 Coach House Cloisters, 10 Hitchin St, Baldock, Hertfordshire SG7 6AE, United Kingdom. TEL 44-1462-895060, FAX 44-1462-892546, http://www.research-studies-press.co.uk. Eds. M B Zarrop, P E Wellstead.

629.8 ROM ISSN 1224-600X
QA75
UNIVERSITATEA POLITEHNICA DIN TIMISOARA. BULETINUL STIINTIFIC. SERIA AUTOMATICA SI CALCULATOARE. Text in English, French, German, Romanian. 1993. s-a. USD 20 (effective 2000). bk.rev. **Document type:** *Bulletin.*
—Linda Hall.
Published by: Universitatea Politehnica din Timisoara, Piata Victoriei 2, Timisoara, 1900, Romania. TEL 40-56-200349, FAX 40-56-190321. Ed. Stefan Holban. Circ: 500.

UNIVERSITY OF SCIENCE AND TECHNOLOGY BEIJING. JOURNAL (MINERAL, METALLURGY, MATERIALS). see *MINES AND MINING INDUSTRY*

003 RUS ISSN 0130-0415
TJ212 CODEN: VTSUD9
VOPROSY TEORII SISTEM AVTOMATICHESKOGO UPRAVLENIYA. Text in Russian. 1974. irreg.
Indexed: MathR, ZentMath.
—CASDDS, Linda Hall.
Published by: Izdatelstvo Sankt-Peterburgskogo Universiteta, Universitetskaya nab 7-9, St Petersburg, 199034, Russian Federation.

629.89 CHN ISSN 1002-0411
XINXI YU KONGZHI/INFORMATION AND CONTROL. Text in Chinese. bi-m.
Related titles: Online - full text ed.: (from East View Information Services).
Indexed: AcoustA, CCMJ, Inspec, MathR.
—BLDSC (4481.800100), IE, ingenta.
Published by: Zhongguo Kexueyuan, Shenyang Zidonghua Yanjiusuo/Chinese Academy of Sciences, Shenyang Institute of Automation, 90, Sanhao Jie, Shenyang, Liaoning 110003, China. TEL 393591. Ed. Jiang Xinsong.

629.8   CHN
ZIDONGHUA JISHU YU YINGYONG/TECHNIQUES OF
AUTOMATION AND APPLICATIONS. Text in Chinese. 1982.
bi-m. CNY 4 per issue domestic (effective 2000). back issues
avail. Document type: *Academic/Scholarly.*
Formerly: Heilongjiang Zidonghua Jishu yu Yingyong (1003-7241)
Related titles: Online - full text ed.: (from East View Information
Services).
Published by: (Heilongjiang Sheng Kexueyuan Zidonghua
Yanjiusuo), Heilongjiang Zidonghua Jishu yu Yingyong, 165
Yi-shui Lu, Jingji Jizhu Kaifa qu, Ha'erbin, Heilongjiang
150090, China. Co-sponsor: Heilongjiang Sheng Zidonghua
Xiehui.

629.8   CHN   ISSN 0254-4156
TJ212   CODEN: ZIXUDZ
➤ ZIDONGHUA XUEBAO/ACTA AUTOMATICA SINICA. Text in
Chinese; Summaries in English. 1963. bi-m. CNY 150
(effective 2004). adv. Document type: *Journal,
Academic/Scholarly.* Description: Covers automation research
in mainland China, including control theory, systems science,
information science, CAD-CAM, automatic detection
instruments, and biocybernetics.
Related titles: Online - full text ed.: (from East View Information
Services).
Indexed: CCMJ, EngInd, IAA, Inspec, MathR, MathSciNet, RefZh,
ZentMath.
—BLDSC (0599.700000), AskIEEE, CISTI, IE, Infotrieve,
ingenta, Linda Hall.
Published by: (Zhongguo Zidonghua Xuehui/Chinese Association
of Automation), Kexue Chubanshe/Science Press, 16
Donghuang Cheng Genbei Jie, Beijing, 100717, China. TEL
86-10-64000246, FAX 86-10-64030255, aas@iamail.ia.ac.cn,
http://www.sciencep.com/. Circ: 11,000. Dist. by: China
International Book Trading Corp, 35 Chegongzhuang Xilu,
Haidian District, PO Box 399, Beijing 100044, China. TEL
86-10-68412045, FAX 86-10-68412023,
cibtc@mail.cibtc.com.cn, http://www.cibtc.com.cn.

➤ ZIDONGHUA YIBIAO/PROCESS AUTOMATION
INSTRUMENTATION. see *INSTRUMENTS*

COMPUTERS—Calculating Machines

➤ INSTITUTUL POLITEHNIC DIN IASI. BULETINUL. SECTIA 4.
AUTOMATICA, CALCULATEARE. see *COMPUTERS—
Automation*

➤ INTERNATIONAL CALCULATOR COLLECTOR. see
HOBBIES

COMPUTERS—Circuits

see also COMPUTERS—Computer Engineering

621.3815   USA   ISSN 0161-3626
                                          CODEN: ANDIDX
ANALOG DIALOGUE; a forum for the exchange of circuits,
systems, and software for real-world signal processing. Text in
English. 1967. q. free to institutions, libraries, and qualified
technical personnel. adv. bk.rev. bibl.; charts; illus.; tr.lit. back
issues avail. Description: Contains technical articles on
semiconductor devices used in analog and digital processing
of electrical signals in test, measurement, communications,
computer electronics, and audio-video.
Related titles: Online - full text ed.: ISSN 1552-3284.
Indexed: Inspec.
—BLDSC (0890.620000), AskIEEE, CISTI. CCC.
Published by: Analog Devices, Inc., 1 Technology Way, Box
9106, Norwood, MA 02062-9106. TEL 781-461-3392, FAX
781-326-8703, TELEX 924491, dan.sheingold@analog.com,
cammy.obrien@analog.com, http://www.analog.com/library/
analogDialogue/. Ed., Pub., R&P Daniel H Sheingold TEL
781-461-3294. Adv. contact Daniel H Sheigold. Circ: 100,000
(controlled).

621.395   USA   ISSN 0925-1030
TK7874   CODEN: AICPEF
➤ ANALOG INTEGRATED CIRCUITS AND SIGNAL
PROCESSING. Text in English. 1991. m. EUR 1,355, USD
1,378, GBP 848 combined subscription to institutions print &
online eds. (effective 2005). adv. reprint service avail. from
PSC. Document type: *Journal, Academic/Scholarly.*
Description: Research and tutorial papers on the design and
applications of analog integrated circuits and signal processing
circuits and systems.
Related titles: Microform ed.: (from PQC); Online - full text ed.:
ISSN 1573-1979 (from EBSCO Publishing, Gale Group,
IngentaConnect, Kluwer Online, O C L C Online Computer
Library Center, Inc., Ovid Technologies, Inc., Springer LINK,
Swets Information Services).
Indexed: ASCA, BibLing, BrCerAb, C&ISA, CMCI, CerAb,
CompLI, CompR, CorrAb, CurCont, E&CAJ, EMA, EngInd,
IAA, ISR, Inspec, M&TEA, MBF, METADEX, RefZh, SCI,
SSCI, SolStAb, WAA.
—BLDSC (0890.630000), AskIEEE, CISTI, Ei, IDS, IE,
Infotrieve, ingenta, Linda Hall. CCC.

Published by: Springer-Verlag New York, Inc. (Subsidiary of:
Springer Science+Business Media), 233 Spring St, New York,
NY 10013. TEL 212-460-1500, FAX 212-460-1575,
service@springer-ny.com, http://springerlink.metapress.com/
openurl.asp?genre=journal&issn=0925-1030,
http://www.springer-ny.com. Eds. David G Haigh, Mohammed
Ismail, Nobuo Fujii. Subscr. to: Journal Fulfillment, PO Box
2485, Secaucus, NJ 07096-2485. TEL 201-348-4033, FAX
201-348-4505, journals@springer-ny.com.

➤ BRAZILIAN SYMPOSIUM ON INTEGRATED CIRCUIT
DESIGN. see *COMPUTERS—Hardware*

➤ BUYER'S GUIDE TO D S P PROCESSORS. (Digital Signal
Processing) see *COMPUTERS—Computer Architecture*

621.395   USA
▼ CHIP DESIGN. Text in English. 2003. bi-m. USD 125; free in
US & Canada to qualified personnel (effective 2003). adv.
Document type: *Magazine, Trade.*
Published by: Extension Media, 1786 18th St, San Francisco, CA
94107. TEL 415-255-0390, FAX 415-255-9214,
http://www.chipdesignmag.com/, http://
www.extensionmedia.com/. Ed. Tets Maniwa. Adv. contact
Karen Murray.

D S P SITEINGS. (Digital Signal Processing) see
COMPUTERS—Computer Architecture

621.395   USA
I E E E ASIA-PACIFIC CONFERENCE ON A S I C.
PROCEEDINGS. Text in English. a. USD 168 per vol.
(effective 2004). Document type: *Proceedings, Trade.*
Description: Provides a forum for education, research, and
development of new idea related to the ASIC community in
Asia-Pacific region.
Related titles: CD-ROM ed.
Published by: Institute of Electrical and Electronics Engineers,
Inc., 3 Park Ave, 17th Fl, New York, NY 10016-5997. TEL
212-419-7900, 800-678-4333, FAX 212-752-4929,
customer.service@ieee.org, http://www.ieee.org.

621.395   USA
I E E E ASIA - PACIFIC CONFERENCE ON CIRCUITS AND
SYSTEMS. PROCEEDINGS. Text in English. a. USD 292 per
vol.; USD 146 per vol. to members (effective 2004).
Document type: *Proceedings, Trade.*
Indexed: EngInd.
—BLDSC (4362.805800).
Published by: Institute of Electrical and Electronics Engineers,
Inc., 3 Park Ave, 17th Fl, New York, NY 10016-5997. TEL
212-419-7900, 800-678-4333, FAX 212-752-4929,
customer.service@ieee.org, http://www.ieee.org.

621.3815   USA   ISSN 1531-636X
TK1
I E E E CIRCUITS AND SYSTEMS MAGAZINE (PISCATAWAY,
2000). Text in English. 2000. q. USD 430 (effective 2006).
adv. Document type: *Magazine, Trade.*
Related titles: Online - full text ed.: ISSN 1558-0830 (from
EBSCO Publishing).
Indexed: Inspec, RefZh.
—BLDSC (4362.812100), CISTI, IE, Infotrieve, Linda Hall. CCC.
Published by: Institute of Electrical and Electronics Engineers,
Inc., 445 Hoes Ln, Piscataway, NJ 08854-1331. TEL
908-981-0060, 800-701-4333, FAX 908-981-9667,
subscription-service@ieee.org, http://www.ieee.org. adv.: B&W
page USD 1,385; trim 7.875 x 10.75. Circ: 12,575. Subscr.
to: Maruzen Co., Ltd., 3-10 Nihonbashi 2-chome, Chuo-ku,
Tokyo 103-0027, Japan. FAX 81-3-3275-0657; Universal
Subscription Agency, Pvt. Ltd., 877, Udyog Vihar, V, Gurgoan
122001, India. TEL 91-124-347261, FAX 91-124-342496.

621.395   USA
I E E E CONFERENCE ON ELECTRON DEVICES AND
SOLID-STATE CIRCUITS. Text in English. irreg., latest 2003.
USD 222 newsstand/cover (effective 2004). Document type:
Proceedings, Academic/Scholarly.
—BLDSC (4362.832750).
Published by: Institute of Electrical and Electronics Engineers,
Inc., 445 Hoes Ln, Piscataway, NJ 08854-1331. TEL
732-981-0060, FAX 732-981-1721,
customer.service@ieee.org, http://www.ieee.org.
Co-sponsors: I E E E Solid-State Circuits Society; Hong
Kong University of Science & Technology; I E E E Electron
Devices Society.

621.395   USA   ISSN 1063-0988
TK7874.6   CODEN: PIAEF2
I E E E INTERNATIONAL A S I C CONFERENCE AND EXHIBIT.
PROCEEDINGS. Text in English. 1991. a. USD 186 per vol.;
USD 93 per vol. to members (effective 2004). Document
type: *Proceedings, Trade.*
Related titles: Online - full text ed.: (from I E E E).
—BLDSC (1086.233350). CCC.
Published by: Institute of Electrical and Electronics Engineers,
Inc., 3 Park Ave, 17th Fl, New York, NY 10016-5997. TEL
212-419-7900, 800-678-4333, FAX 212-752-4929,
customer.service@ieee.org, http://www.ieee.org.

I E E E INTERNATIONAL CONFERENCE ON ELECTRONICS,
CIRCUITS AND SYSTEMS. PROCEEDINGS. see
ELECTRONICS

621.395   USA   ISSN 1071-9032
I E E E INTERNATIONAL CONFERENCE ON
MICROELECTRONIC TEST STRUCTURES. PROCEEDINGS.
Text in English. 1989. a. USD 170 per vol.; USD 85 per vol. to
members (effective 2004). Document type: *Proceedings,
Trade.*
Indexed: EngInd.
—BLDSC (6844.167120). CCC.
Published by: Institute of Electrical and Electronics Engineers,
Inc., 3 Park Ave, 17th Fl, New York, NY 10016-5997. TEL
212-419-7900, 800-678-4333, FAX 212-752-4929,
customer.service@ieee.org, http://www.ieee.org.

621.395   USA   ISSN 1524-766X
TK7874
I E E E INTERNATIONAL SYMPOSIUM ON V L S I
TECHNOLOGY, SYSTEMS AND APPLICATIONS. Text in
English. a. USD 151 membership (effective 2005). Document
type: *Proceedings, Trade.*
Related titles: Online - full text ed.: (from I E E E).
—BLDSC (4550.370600), IE, ingenta. CCC.
Published by: Institute of Electrical and Electronics Engineers,
Inc., 3 Park Ave, 17th Fl, New York, NY 10016-5997. TEL
212-419-7900, 800-678-4333, FAX 212-752-4929,
customer.service@ieee.org, http://www.ieee.org.

621.395   USA
I E E E INTERNATIONAL VACUUM MICROELECTRONICS
CONFERENCE. Text in English. a. USD 176; USD 88 to
members (effective 2004). Document type: *Proceedings,
Trade.*
—ingenta.
Published by: Institute of Electrical and Electronics Engineers,
Inc., 3 Park Ave, 17th Fl, New York, NY 10016-5997. TEL
212-419-7900, 800-678-4333, FAX 212-752-4929,
customer.service@ieee.org, http://www.ieee.org.

621.395   USA   ISSN 1529-2517
TK7876
I E E E RADIO FREQUENCY INTEGRATED CIRCUITS
SYMPOSIUM. DIGEST OF PAPERS. Text in English. 1997. a.
USD 151 membership (effective 2005). Document type:
Proceedings, Trade.
Formerly (until 1998): I E E E Radio Frequency Integrated
Circuits Symposium. Digest of Technical Papers (1097-2633)
Related titles: Online - full text ed.: (from I E E E).
Indexed: EngInd.
—BLDSC (4363.038500). CCC.
Published by: Institute of Electrical and Electronics Engineers,
Inc., 3 Park Ave, 17th Fl, New York, NY 10016-5997. TEL
212-419-7900, 800-678-4333, FAX 212-752-4929,
customer.service@ieee.org, http://www.ieee.org.

006.6   USA   ISSN 1087-8270
QA76.9.H85
I E E E VIRTUAL REALITY ANNUAL INTERNATIONAL
SYMPOSIUM. Text in English. 1996. a. USD 151 membership
(effective 2005). Document type: *Proceedings, Trade.*
Related titles: Online - full text ed.: (from I E E E).
—CCC.
Published by: Institute of Electrical and Electronics Engineers,
Inc., 3 Park Ave, 17th Fl, New York, NY 10016-5997. TEL
212-419-7900, 800-678-4333, FAX 212-752-4929,
customer.service@ieee.org, http://www.ieee.org.

I E E E WORKSHOP ON APPLICATIONS OF SIGNAL
PROCESSING TO AUDIO AND ACOUSTICS. see
PHYSICS—Sound

INTEL MICROPROCESSOR FORECAST; the authoritative guide
to Intel's product strategy, unit shipments, costs, and prices.
see *COMPUTERS—Computer Architecture*

INTEL'S MERCED AND IA-64: TECHNOLOGY AND MARKET
FORECAST. see *COMPUTERS—Computer Architecture*

621.395   USA
INTERNATIONAL CONFERENCE ON ADVANCED
SEMICONDUCTOR DEVICES AND MICROSYSTEMS.
PROCEEDINGS. Text in English. a. USD 176 per vol.; USD
88 per vol. to members (effective 2004). Document type:
Proceedings, Trade.
Published by: Institute of Electrical and Electronics Engineers,
Inc., 3 Park Ave, 17th Fl, New York, NY 10016-5997. TEL
212-419-7900, 800-678-4333, FAX 212-752-4929,
customer.service@ieee.org, http://www.ieee.org.

621.395   USA   ISSN 1096-4789
INTERNATIONAL CONFERENCE ON INTEGRATED CIRCUITS
YIELDS. PROCEEDINGS. Text in English. 1998. a. price
varies. Document type: *Proceedings, Trade.*
Published by: Institute of Electrical and Electronics Engineers,
Inc., 3 Park Ave, 17th Fl, New York, NY 10016-5997. TEL
212-419-7900, 800-678-4333, FAX 212-752-4929,
customer.service@ieee.org, http://www.ieee.org.

C

621.395 338 USA
INTERNATIONAL CONFERENCE ON ION IMPLANTATION TECHNOLOGY. PROCEEDINGS. Text in English. a. USD 214; USD 107 to members (effective 2004). **Document type:** *Proceedings, Trade.*
Published by: Institute of Electrical and Electronics Engineers, Inc., 3 Park Ave, 17th Fl, New York, NY 10016-5997. TEL 212-419-7900, 800-678-4333, FAX 212-752-4929, customer.service@ieee.org, http://www.ieee.org.

INTERNATIONAL CONFERENCE ON MICROELECTRONICS. PROCEEDINGS. see *ELECTRONICS*

621.395 USA
INTERNATIONAL CONFERENCE ON SOLID-STATE AND INTEGRATED CIRCUIT TECHNOLOGY. Text in English. a. price varies. **Document type:** *Proceedings, Trade.*
Indexed: EngInd.
Published by: Institute of Electrical and Electronics Engineers, Inc., 3 Park Ave, 17th Fl, New York, NY 10016-5997. TEL 800-678-4333, customer.service@ieee.org, http://www.ieee.org.

621.395 338 USA
INTERNATIONAL INTERCONNECT TECHNOLOGY CONFERENCE. PROCEEDINGS. Text in English. a. USD 178; USD 89 to members (effective 2004). **Document type:** *Proceedings, Trade.*
Published by: Institute of Electrical and Electronics Engineers, Inc., 3 Park Ave, 17th Fl, New York, NY 10016-5997. TEL 212-419-7900, 800-678-4333, FAX 212-752-4929, customer.service@ieee.org, http://www.ieee.org.

621.3815 USA
INTERNATIONAL SYMPOSIUM ON COMPOUND SEMICONDUCTORS. Text in English. a. USD 148; USD 74 to members (effective 2004). **Document type:** *Proceedings, Trade.*
Indexed: EngInd.
Published by: Institute of Electrical and Electronics Engineers, Inc., 3 Park Ave, 17th Fl, New York, NY 10016-5997. TEL 212-419-7900, 800-678-4333, FAX 212-752-4929, customer.service@ieee.org, http://www.ieee.org.
Co-sponsors: I E E E Electron Devices Society; I E E E Lasers and Electro-Optics Society.

621.381 USA
INTERNATIONAL SYMPOSIUM ON MICRO-NANOMECHATRONICS AND HUMAN SCIENCE. PROCEEEDINGS. Text in English. a. USD 158 per vol.; USD 79 per vol. to members (effective 2004). **Document type:** *Proceedings, Trade.*
Formerly (until 2004): International Symposium on Micro Mechatronics and Human Science
—BLDSC (6846.795077).
Published by: Institute of Electrical and Electronics Engineers, Inc., 3 Park Ave, 17th Fl, New York, NY 10016-5997. TEL 212-419-7900, 800-678-4333, FAX 212-752-4929, customer.service@ieee.org, http://www.ieee.org.

621.3815 606.3 USA
INTERNATIONAL WORKSHOP ON CELLULAR NEURAL NETWORKS AND THEIR APPLICATIONS. Text in English. a. USD 228; USD 114 to members (effective 2004). **Document type:** *Proceedings, Trade.*
Published by: Institute of Electrical and Electronics Engineers, Inc., 3 Park Ave, 17th Fl, New York, NY 10016-5997. TEL 212-419-7900, 800-678-4333, FAX 212-752-4929, customer.service@ieee.org, http://www.ieee.org. **Co-sponsor:** I E E E Circuits and Systems Society.

621.3815 USA ISSN 1087-9870
INTERSOCIETY CONFERENCE ON THERMAL PHENOMENA IN ELECTRONIC SYSTEMS. PROCEEDINGS. Variant title: Thermal Phenomena in Electronic Systems. Text in English. 1990. biennial. USD 236 per issue; USD 118 per issue to members (effective 2004). **Document type:** *Proceedings, Trade.* **Description:** Covers all aspects of today's electronic systems, from pagers to cell phones, from lap-top computers to supercomputers, from consumer and automotive to satellite-based electronics.
Indexed: EngInd.
—BLDSC (4357.820000). **CCC.**
Published by: Institute of Electrical and Electronics Engineers, Inc., 3 Park Ave, 17th Fl, New York, NY 10016-5997. TEL 212-419-7900, 800-678-4333, FAX 212-752-4929, customer.service@ieee.org, http://www.ieee.org.

621.395 SGP ISSN 0218-1266
TK7800 CODEN: JCSME7
➤ **JOURNAL OF CIRCUITS, SYSTEMS AND COMPUTERS.** Text in English. 1991. bi-m. SGD 320, USD 187, EUR 176 to individuals; SGD 872, USD 508, EUR 479 combined subscription to institutions print & online eds.; SGD 525, USD 305, EUR 288 combined subscription in developing nations to institutions print & online eds. (effective 2006). back issues avail. **Document type:** *Journal, Academic/Scholarly.* **Description:** Covers a wide scope, ranging from mathematical foundations to practical engineering design in the general areas of circuits, systems and computers.
Related titles: Online - full text ed.: (from EBSCO Publishing, O C L C Online Computer Library Center, Inc., Swets Information Services).
Indexed: ASCA, CompAb, CompLI, CurCont, EngInd, Inspec.
—BLDSC (4958.368500), AskIEEE, IDS, IE, ingenta. **CCC.**
Published by: World Scientific Publishing Co. Pte. Ltd., 5 Toh Tuck Link, Singapore, 596224, Singapore. TEL 65-466-5775, FAX 65-467-7667, wspc@wspc.com.sg, http://www.worldscinet.com/jcsc/jcsc.shtml, http://www.worldscientific.com. Ed. Wai Kai Chen. **Subscr. to:** Farrer Rd, PO Box 128, Singapore 912805, Singapore. sales@wspc.com.sg. **Dist. by:** World Scientific Publishing Co., Inc., 1060 Main St, River Edge, NJ 07661. TEL 201-487-9655, 800-227-7562, FAX 201-487-9656, 888-977-2665.; World Scientific Publishing Ltd., 57 Shelton St, London WC2H 9HE, United Kingdom. TEL 44-20-78360888, FAX 44-20-78362020, sales@wspc.co.uk.

621.395 GBR
KEY NOTE MARKET REPORT: PRINTED CIRCUITS. Variant title: Printed Circuits. Text in English. irreg., latest 1993, Apr. GBP 340 per issue (effective 2002). **Document type:** *Trade.* **Description:** Provides an overview of a specific UK market segment and includes executive summary, market definition, market size, industry background, competitor analysis, current issues, forecasts, company profiles, and more.
Formerly: Key Note Report: Printed Circuits
Related titles: CD-ROM ed.; Online - full text ed.
Published by: Key Note Ltd., Field House, 72 Oldfield Rd, Hampton, Mddx TW12 2HQ, United Kingdom. TEL 44-20-8481-8750, FAX 44-20-8783-0049, info@keynote.co.uk, http://www.keynote.co.uk.

621.3815 USA
MICRO ELECTRO MECHANICAL SYSTEMS CONFERENCE. PROCEEDINGS. Text in English. a. USD 184 per issue to institutions (effective 2001).
Published by: Institute of Electrical and Electronics Engineers, Inc., 3 Park Ave, 17th Fl, New York, NY 10016-5997. TEL 800-678-4333, customer.service@ieee.org, http://www.ieee.org.

MICROPROCESSOR REPORT; the insiders' guide to microprocessor hardware. see *COMPUTERS—Computer Architecture*

621.395 USA ISSN 1548-3746
TK3226
MIDWEST SYMPOSIUM ON CIRCUITS AND SYSTEMS. CONFERENCE PROCEEDINGS. Text in English. a. USD 384; USD 192 to members (effective 2004). **Document type:** *Proceedings, Trade.*
Formerly (until 2002): Midwest Symposium on Circuits and Systems. Proceedings
Indexed: Inspec.
—BLDSC (6844.167490), ingenta.
Published by: Institute of Electrical and Electronics Engineers, Inc., 3 Park Ave, 17th Fl, New York, NY 10016-5997. TEL 212-419-7900, 800-678-4333, FAX 212-752-4929, customer.service@ieee.org, http://www.ieee.org.

621.395 ITA
P C B MAGAZINE. Text in Italian. 1987. 10/yr. EUR 42 (effective 2005). adv. **Document type:** *Magazine, Trade.* **Description:** Provides the latest technological solutions for producing printed circuit board as well as the latest applications of SMD with new component packagings.
Published by: Gruppo Editoriale J C E, Via Patecchio 2, Milan, MI 20141, Italy. TEL 39-02-57316011, FAX 39-02-57316291, info@jce.it, http://www.jce.it. Ed. Franco Borghesio. Circ: 8,000.

621.395 USA ISSN 1543-6527
▼ **PRINTED CIRCUIT DESIGN & MANUFACTURE**; the resource for electronic interconnect professionals. Text in English. 2003 (Apr.). m. USD 80 in US & Canada; USD 145 elsewhere; free to qualified personnel (effective 2005). adv. **Document type:** *Magazine, Trade.* **Description:** Covers the techniques, methodologies, processes, technologies and market conditions in the printed circuit industry.
Formed by the merger of (1978-2003): P C FAB; Which was formerly: Printed Circuit Fabrication (0274-8096); Printed Circuit Exchange (0194-9683); (1984-2003): Printed Circuit Design; Which was formerly (until 1990): Circuit Design (1047-5567); (until 1989): Printed Circuit Design (0884-9862); (until 1985): P C Design (8756-6311)
Related titles: Online - full text ed.: (from EBSCO Publishing, Gale Group, O C L C Online Computer Library Center, Inc., ProQuest Information & Learning).
Indexed: Inspec.
—BLDSC (6613.235190), CISTI, IE, ingenta, Linda Hall. **CCC.**
Published by: U P Media Group, Inc., 2018 Powers Ferry Rd, Ste 600, Atlanta, GA 30339. TEL 678-589-8800, FAX 678-589-8850, ashaughnessy@upmediagroup.com, jschuler@upmediagroup.com, http://www.pcdandm.com/pcdmag/, http://www.pcbshows.com. Eds. Andy Shaughnessy, Mike Buetow. Pub. Pete Waddell. adv.: B&W page USD 5,475; trim 8 x 10.875. Circ: 37,300 (controlled).

621.395 USA ISSN 1551-2282
TK5102.9
SENSOR ARRAY AND MULTICHANNEL SIGNAL PROCESSING. I E E E WORKSHOP. Text in English. 2000. a. USD 194 per issue; USD 97 per issue to members (effective 2004). **Document type:** *Proceedings, Trade.*
Published by: Institute of Electrical and Electronics Engineers, Inc., 3 Park Ave, 17th Fl, New York, NY 10016-5997. TEL 212-419-7900, 800-678-4333, FAX 212-752-4929, customer.service@ieee.org, http://www.ieee.org.

621.395 USA
SIGNAL PROCESSING AND ITS APPLICATIONS. Text in English. a. price varies. **Document type:** *Journal, Trade.* **Description:** Provides a forum for engineers and scientists engaged in research and development to discuss common and disparate objectives and applications of Signal Processing.
Indexed: CCMJ.
Published by: Institute of Electrical and Electronics Engineers, Inc., 3 Park Ave, 17th Fl, New York, NY 10016-5997. TEL 800-678-4333, customer.service@ieee.org, http://www.ieee.org.

621.295 USA
SOUTHWEST SYMPOSIUM ON MIXED-SIGNAL DESIGN. Text in English. a. USD 178; USD 89 to members (effective 2004). **Document type:** *Proceedings, Trade.*
—BLDSC (8356.920000).
Published by: Institute of Electrical and Electronics Engineers, Inc., 3 Park Ave, 17th Fl, New York, NY 10016-5997. TEL 212-419-7900, 800-678-4333, FAX 212-752-4929, customer.service@ieee.org, http://www.ieee.org.

621.395 USA
TOPICAL MEETING ON SILICON MONOLITHIC INTEGRATED CIRCUITS IN R F SYSTEMS. Text in English. a. USD 162; USD 81 to members (effective 2004). **Document type:** *Proceedings, Trade.*
Published by: Institute of Electrical and Electronics Engineers, Inc., 3 Park Ave, 17th Fl, New York, NY 10016-5997. TEL 212-419-7900, 800-678-4333, FAX 212-752-4929, customer.service@ieee.org, http://www.ieee.org.

621.395 USA ISSN 1095-791X
TK7800
W E S C O N CONFERENCE PROCEEDINGS. (Western Electronic Show and Convention) Text in English. 1963. a. price varies. **Document type:** *Proceedings, Trade.*
Former titles (until 1996): W E S C O N Conference Record (1044-6036); (until 1979): W E S C O N Technical Papers (0083-8837)
Related titles: Online - full text ed.: (from I E E E).
Indexed: Inspec.
—CCC.
Published by: Institute of Electrical and Electronics Engineers, Inc., 3 Park Ave, 17th Fl, New York, NY 10016-5997. TEL 212-419-7900, 800-678-4333, FAX 212-752-4929, customer.service@ieee.org, http://www.ieee.org.

621.395 CHN ISSN 1004-3365
WEIDIANZIXUE/MICROELECTRONICS. Text in Chinese. 1970. bi-m. **Document type:** *Journal, Academic/Scholarly.*
Related titles: Online - full content ed.: (from WanFang Data Corp.); Online - full text ed.: (from East View Information Services).
Indexed: Inspec, RefZh.
—BLDSC (5758.849700).
Published by: Sichuan Guti Dianlu Yanjiusuo/Sichuan Institute of Solid-State Circuits Technology, Editorial Department of Microelectronics, 14, Nanping Huayuan Lu, Dianzi 24 Suo, Chongqing, 400060, China. TEL 86-23-62839714, MINI@chinajournal.net.cn, http://mini.chinajournal.net.cn/, http://www.sisc.com.cn/.

COMPUTERS—Computer Architecture

see also COMPUTERS—Computer Engineering

004.22 USA ISSN 1544-3566
QA76.9.A73
▼ **A C M TRANSACTIONS ON ARCHITECTURE AND CODE OPTIMIZATION.** (Association for Computing Machinery) Text in English. 2004 (Apr.). q. USD 140 domestic to non-members; USD 154 foreign to non-members; USD 40 domestic to members; USD 54 foreign to members; USD 35 domestic to students; USD 49 foreign to students; USD 168 combined subscription domestic to non-members print & online eds.; USD 182 combined subscription foreign to non-members print & online eds.; USD 48 combined subscription domestic to members print & online eds.; USD 62 combined subscription foreign to members print & online eds.; USD 42 combined subscription domestic to students print & online eds. (effective 2006); USD 56 combined subscription foreign to students print & online eds. (effective 2005).
Related titles: Online - full text ed.: ISSN 1544-3973. 2004 (Jan.). USD 112 to non-members; USD 32 to members; USD 28 to students (effective 2006) (from EBSCO Publishing).
Indexed: ABIn, RefZh.
—CISTI. **CCC.**

Published by: Association for Computing Machinery, Inc., 1515 Broadway, 17th Fl, New York, NY 10036-5701. TEL 212-626-0500, 212-626-0520, 800-342-6626, FAX 212-869-0481, sigs@acm.org, usacm@acm.org, http://www.acm.org.

004.35 NLD ISSN 0927-5452
QA76.58
➤ **ADVANCES IN PARALLEL COMPUTING.** Text in English. 1990. irreg., latest vol.12, 1998. price varies. back issues avail. **Document type:** *Monographic series, Academic/Scholarly.* **Description:** Presents the theory of parallel-computing systems, including vector, pipeline, array, fifth- and future-generation computer hardware, and neural networks, along with other aspects of high-speed computing.
Indexed: ZentMath.
Published by: Elsevier BV, North-Holland (Subsidiary of: Elsevier Science & Technology), Sara Burgerhartstraat 25, Amsterdam, 1055 KV, Netherlands. TEL 31-20-485-3911, FAX 31-20-485-2457, nlinfo-f@elsevier.nl, http://www.elsevier.nl. Ed. G R Joubert. **Subscr. to:** Elsevier BV, PO Box 211, Amsterdam 1000 AE, Netherlands. TEL 31-20-485-3757, FAX 31-20-485-3432, http://www.elsevier.nl.

➤ **ARCHITECTURAL TECHNOLOGY.** see *BUILDING AND CONSTRUCTION*

004.22 621.392 USA
BUYER'S GUIDE TO D S P PROCESSORS. (Digital Signal Processing) Text in English. a. USD 2,450; USD 2,510 foreign (effective 1999). charts; stat. **Document type:** *Trade.* **Description:** Analyzes and compares 19 families of programmable digital signal processors.
Published by: Berkeley Design Technology, Inc., 2107 Dwight Way, 2nd Fl, Berkeley, CA 94704. TEL 510-665-1600, FAX 510-665-1680, info@bdti.com, cs@mdronline.com, http://www.bdti.com, http://www.mdronline.com. **Subscr. in Europe to:** Parkway Gordon, Westwood House, Elmhurst Rd, Goring, Reading, Oxon RG8 9BN, United Kingdom. TEL 44-1491-875386. **Co-publisher:** Instat - M D R.

004.22 USA
➤ **COMPUTER DESIGN AND ARCHITECTURE SERIES.** Text in English. 1976. irreg. price varies. **Document type:** *Monographic series, Academic/Scholarly.*
Indexed: Inspec.
Published by: Elsevier Inc. (Subsidiary of: Elsevier Science & Technology), 360 Park Ave. S, New York, NY 10010-1710. TEL 212-633-3730, 888-437-4636, usinfo-f@elsevier.com, http://www.elsevier.com. Ed. Edward McCluskey.

621.3822 USA
D S P SITEINGS. (Digital Signal Processing) Text in English. m. free. **Description:** Covers digital signal processing technology.
Media: Online - full text.
Address: sohie@globalinsite.com. Ed. Guy Sohie.

▼ **ENTERPRISE ARCHITECT.** see *COMPUTERS—Computer Systems*

004.22 USA ISSN 1066-6192
QA76.58
EUROMICRO WORKSHOP ON PARALLEL AND DISTRIBUTED PROCESSING. Text in English. 1993. a. USD 151 membership (effective 2005). **Document type:** *Proceedings, Trade.*
Related titles: Online - full text ed.: (from I E E E).
—BLDSC (3829.285800). **CCC.**
Published by: Institute of Electrical and Electronics Engineers, Inc., 3 Park Ave, 17th Fl, New York, NY 10016-5997. TEL 212-419-7900, 800-678-4333, FAX 212-752-4929, customer.service@ieee.org, http://www.ieee.org.

004.22 005.1 USA ISSN 1097-5209
HETEROGENEOUS COMPUTING WORKSHOP. PROCEEDINGS. Text in English. 1992. a. USD 130 per vol. (effective 2004). **Document type:** *Proceedings, Trade.*
Formerly (until 199?): Workshop on Heterogeneous Processing. Proceedings (1066-1220)
Related titles: Online - full text ed.: (from I E E E).
—BLDSC (4301.352000). **CCC.**
Published by: Institute of Electrical and Electronics Engineers, Inc., 3 Park Ave, 17th Fl, New York, NY 10016-5997. TEL 212-419-7900, 800-678-4333, FAX 212-752-4929, customer.service@ieee.org, http://www.ieee.org.

004.22 USA ISSN 1556-6056
▼ **I E E E COMPUTER ARCHITECTURE LETTERS.** Text in English. forthcoming 2006 (Sept.). s-a. USD 95 (effective 2006). **Document type:** *Journal, Academic/Scholarly.*
Related titles: Online - full text ed.: ISSN 1556-6064. forthcoming 2006 (Sept.).
Published by: Institute of Electrical and Electronics Engineers, Inc., 445 Hoes Ln, Piscataway, NJ 08854-1331. TEL 732-981-0060, FAX 732-981-1721, customer.service@ieee.org, http://www.ieee.org.

004.22 USA ISSN 1530-2032
I E E E INTERNATIONAL CONFERENCE ON MULTIMEDIA COMPUTING AND SYSTEMS. PROCEEDINGS. Text in English. 1994. a. **Document type:** *Proceedings, Trade.*
Related titles: Online - full text ed.: (from I E E E).
Indexed: Englnd.
Published by: Institute of Electrical and Electronics Engineers, Inc., 3 Park Ave, 17th Fl, New York, NY 10016-5997. TEL 212-419-7900, 800-678-4333, FAX 212-752-4929, customer.service@ieee.org, http://www.ieee.org.

004.3681 USA ISSN 1045-9219
QA76.58 CODEN: ITDSEO
➤ **I E E E TRANSACTIONS ON PARALLEL AND DISTRIBUTED SYSTEMS.** Text in English. 1990. m. USD 1,045 (effective 2006). **Document type:** *Journal, Academic/Scholarly.* **Description:** Design and implementation of multiprocessor systems, scheduling and task partitioning, performance measurement, reliability and fault tolerance, language and compilers.
Related titles: CD-ROM ed.; Microfiche ed.; Online - full text ed.: ISSN 1558-2183 (from EBSCO Publishing, I E E E).
Indexed: AS&TI, ASCA, C&ISA, CMCI, CompAb, CompLI, CompR, CurCont, E&CAJ, Englnd, ISR, Inspec, RefZh, SCI, SSCI, SolStAb.
—BLDSC (4363.209000), AskIEEE, CISTI, Ei, IDS, IE, Infotrieve, ingenta, Linda Hall. **CCC.**
Published by: Institute of Electrical and Electronics Engineers, Inc., 445 Hoes Ln, Piscataway, NJ 08854-1331. TEL 732-981-0060, 800-701-4333, FAX 732-981-1721, tpds@computer.org, subscription-service@ieee.org, http://www.computer.org/tpds, http://www.ieee.org. Ed. John A Stankovic. Circ: 5,000 (paid and free). **Subscr. to:** Maruzen Co., Ltd., 3-10 Nihonbashi 2-chome, Chuo-ku, Tokyo 103-0027, Japan. FAX 81-3-3275-0657; Universal Subscription Agency, Pvt. Ltd., 877, Udyog Vihar, V, Gurgoan 122001, India. TEL 91-124-347261, FAX 91-124-342496.

004.22 321.392 NLD ISSN 1566-2535
QA10.4
➤ **INFORMATION FUSION.** Text in English. 2000. 4/yr. EUR 102 in Europe to individuals; JPY 13,600 in Japan to individuals; USD 114 to individuals except Europe and Japan; EUR 394 in Europe to institutions; JPY 52,200 in Japan to institutions; USD 440 to institutions except Europe and Japan (effective 2006). back issues avail. **Document type:** *Journal, Academic/Scholarly.* **Description:** Reports on the developments in the field of multi-sensor, multi-source information fusion.
Related titles: Online - full text ed.: (from EBSCO Publishing, Gale Group, IngentaConnect, ScienceDirect, Swets Information Services).
Indexed: CompLI, Inspec, RefZh.
—BLDSC (4493.600850), CISTI, IE, ingenta. **CCC.**
Published by: Elsevier BV (Subsidiary of: Elsevier Science & Technology), Radarweg 29, Amsterdam, 1043 NX, Netherlands. TEL 31-20-4853911, FAX 31-20-4852457, ifjournal@yahoo.com, nlinfo-f@elsevier.nl, http://www.elsevier.com/locate/inffus, http://www.elsevier.nl. Ed. B. V. Dasarathy.

004.22 DEU
INFORMATIONSSYSTEM-ARCHITEKTUREN; Modellierung betrieblicher Informationssysteme. Text in English, German. irreg. **Description:** Covers the architecture and modelling of operational information systems.
Indexed: Inspec.
Published by: Gesellschaft fuer Informatik e.V., c/o Elmar Sinz, Otto-Friedrich-Universitaet Bamberg, Feldkirchenstr 21, Bamberg, 96045, Germany. TEL 49-951-8632512, FAX 49-951-9370412, elmar.sinz@sowi.uni-bamberg.de.

004.22 621.392 USA
INTEL MICROPROCESSOR FORECAST; the authoritative guide to Intel's product strategy, unit shipments, costs, and prices. Text in English. irreg., latest vol.4. USD 1,995; USD 1,895 with subscr. to Microprocessor Report. charts; stat. **Document type:** *Trade.* **Description:** Offers multiyear forecasts for Intel's pricing, unit shipments, manufacturing costs and capacity, and revenues and profit margins.
Related titles: Series of: Technical Library Reports.
Published by: Instat - M D R (Subsidiary of: Reed Business Information), 1101 S. Winchester Blvd., BLDG N, San Jose, CA 95128-3904. TEL 408-328-3900, 800-527-0288, FAX 408-737-2242, cs@mdr.zd.com, http://www.mdronline.com. Ed. Mel Thomsen. Pub. Linley Gwennap. **Subscr. in Europe to:** Parkway Gordon, Westwood House, Elmhurst Rd, Goring, Reading, Oxon RG8 9BN, United Kingdom. TEL 44-1491-875386.

621.392 004.22 USA
INTEL'S MERCED AND IA-64: TECHNOLOGY AND MARKET FORECAST. Text in English. a. USD 1,395; USD 1,295 with subscr. to Microprocessor Report. charts; stat. **Document type:** *Trade.* **Description:** Presents market projections for Intel's IA-64 and Merced microprocessors, providing a deep technical understanding of the pros and cons of the new technology.
Related titles: Series of: Technical Library Reports.
Published by: Instat - M D R (Subsidiary of: Reed Business Information), 1101 S. Winchester Blvd., BLDG N, San Jose, CA 95128-3904. TEL 408-328-3900, 800-527-0288, FAX 408-737-2242, cs@mdr.zd.com, http://www.mdronline.com. Ed., Pub. Linley Gwennap. **Subscr. in Europe to:** Parkway Gordon, Westwood House, Elmhurst Rd, Goring, Reading, Oxon RG8 9BN, United Kingdom. TEL 44-1491-875386.

004.33 USA
INTERFACE; journal of the Alabama Supercomputer Authority and the Alabama Research and Education Network. Text in English. 1993. q. **Document type:** *Journal, Academic/Scholarly.* **Description:** Designed to inform users and interested organizations of recent developments on supercomputing.
Media: Online - full content.
Indexed: Inspec.
Published by: Alabama Supercomputer Authority, 686 Discovery Dr., Huntsville, AL 35806. TEL 256-971-7404, FAX 256-971-7473, interface@asnmail.asc.edu, http://www.asc.edu/. Ed. Josie Morgan.

004.3681 USA ISSN 1063-6927
QA76.9.D5
INTERNATIONAL CONFERENCE ON DISTRIBUTED COMPUTING SYSTEMS. PROCEEDINGS. Text in English. 1979. a. price varies. adv. **Document type:** *Proceedings, Academic/Scholarly.* **Description:** Addresses state-of-the-art and future technical developments in the field of distributed computing systems.
Related titles: Online - full text ed.: (from I E E E).
Indexed: Englnd.
—BLDSC (4538.778900), IE, ingenta. **CCC.**
Published by: (Institute of Electrical and Electronics Engineers, Inc.), I E E E Computer Society, 3 Park Ave, 17th Fl, New York, NY 10017. TEL 714-821-8380, 800-678-4333, FAX 714-821-4641, customer.service@ieee.org, http://www.ieee.org.

004.22 621.39 USA
INTERNATIONAL CONFERENCE ON FORMAL ENGINEERING METHODS. PROCEEDINGS. Text in English. a. USD 135 per vol.; USD 50 per vol. to members (effective 2004). **Document type:** *Proceedings, Trade.*
—BLDSC (4362.949520).
Published by: Institute of Electrical and Electronics Engineers, Inc., 3 Park Ave, 17th Fl, New York, NY 10016-5997. TEL 212-419-7900, 800-678-4333, FAX 212-752-4929, customer.service@ieee.org, http://www.ieee.org.

C

004.22 005.1 USA ISSN 1530-0897
QA76.9.A73
INTERNATIONAL CONFERENCE ON HIGH - PERFORMANCE COMPUTER ARCHITECTURE. PROCEEDINGS. Variant title: H P C A. Text in English. 1995. a. USD 180; USD 72 to members (effective 2004). **Document type:** *Proceedings, Trade.*
Related titles: Online - full text ed.: (from I E E E).
—BLDSC (4550.262950).
Published by: Institute of Electrical and Electronics Engineers, Inc., 3 Park Ave, 17th Fl, New York, NY 10016-5997. TEL 212-419-7900, 800-678-4333, FAX 212-752-4929, customer.service@ieee.org, http://www.ieee.org.

004.22 USA ISSN 1094-7256
INTERNATIONAL CONFERENCE ON HIGH-PERFORMANCE COMPUTING. PROCEEDINGS. Text in English. 199?. a. USD 151 membership (effective 2005). **Document type:** *Proceedings, Trade.*
Related titles: Online - full text ed.: (from I E E E).
—**CCC.**
Published by: Institute of Electrical and Electronics Engineers, Inc., 3 Park Ave, 17th Fl, New York, NY 10016-5997. TEL 212-419-7900, 800-678-4333, FAX 212-752-4929, customer.service@ieee.org, http://www.ieee.org.

004.22 USA ISSN 1521-9097
QA76.58 CODEN: PIPSFH
INTERNATIONAL CONFERENCE ON PARALLEL AND DISTRIBUTED SYSTEMS. PROCEEDINGS. Text in English. 1992. a. USD 201; USD 81 to members (effective 2004). **Document type:** *Proceedings, Trade.*
Related titles: Online - full text ed.: (from I E E E).
Indexed: Englnd.
Published by: Institute of Electrical and Electronics Engineers, Inc., 3 Park Ave, 17th Fl, New York, NY 10016-5997. TEL 212-419-7900, 800-678-4333, FAX 212-752-4929, customer.service@ieee.org, http://www.ieee.org.

004.22 USA ISSN 1089-795X
INTERNATIONAL CONFERENCE ON PARALLEL ARCHITECTURE AND COMPILATION TECHNIQUES. PROCEEDINGS. Text in English. 1996. a. USD 178; USD 72 to members (effective 2004). **Document type:** *Proceedings, Trade.*
Related titles: Online - full text ed.: (from I E E E).
Published by: Institute of Electrical and Electronics Engineers, Inc., 3 Park Ave, 17th Fl, New York, NY 10016-5997. TEL 212-419-7900, 800-678-4333, FAX 212-752-4929, customer.service@ieee.org, http://www.ieee.org.

004.33 USA ISSN 0190-3918
QA76.6 CODEN: PCPADL
INTERNATIONAL CONFERENCE ON PARALLEL PROCESSING. PROCEEDINGS. Text in English. 1976. a. USD 145. **Document type:** *Proceedings.*
Formerly (until 1975): Sagamore Computer Conference on Parallel Processing. Proceedings
Related titles: Online - full text ed.: (from I E E E).
Indexed: Inspec.

▼ *new title* ➤ *refereed* ✶ *unverified* ♦ *full entry avail.*

—BLDSC (6844.900000), Ei, IE, ingenta. **CCC.**
Published by: (Institute of Electrical and Electronics Engineers, Inc.), C R C Press, LLC (Subsidiary of: Taylor & Francis Group), 2000 N W Corporate Blvd, Boca Raton, FL 33431. TEL 800-272-7737, journals@crcpress.com, http://www.crcpress.com/.

004.22 USA ISSN 1530-2016
QA76.58
INTERNATIONAL CONFERENCE ON PARALLEL PROCESSING WORKSHOP. PROCEEDINGS. Text in English. 19??. a. USD 217; USD 87 to members (effective 2004). **Document type:** *Proceedings, Trade.*
Related titles: Online - full text ed.: (from I E E E).
Published by: Institute of Electrical and Electronics Engineers, Inc., 3 Park Ave, 17th Fl, New York, NY 10016-5997. TEL 212-419-7900, 800-678-4333, FAX 212-752-4929, customer.service@ieee.org, http://www.ieee.org.

▼ **INTERNATIONAL JOURNAL OF ENTERPRISE INFORMATION SYSTEMS.** see *COMPUTERS—Computer Systems*

004.35 USA ISSN 1063-7133
QA76.58
INTERNATIONAL PARALLEL PROCESSING SYMPOSIUM. PROCEEDINGS. Short title: I P P S. Text in English. 1987. a. USD 102 membership (effective 2005). adv. **Document type:** *Proceedings.* **Description:** Covers new developments in parallel processing technology, including architectures, algorithms, modeling, neural networks and V L S I systems.
Formerly (until 1991): International Parallel Processing Workshop
Related titles: Online - full text ed.: (from I E E E).
—CCC.
Published by: (Institute of Electrical and Electronics Engineers, Inc.), I E E E Computer Society, 3 Park Ave, 17th Fl, New York, NY 10017. TEL 714-821-8380, 800-678-4333, FAX 714-821-4641, customer.service@ieee.org, http://www.ipdps.org, http://www.ieee.org. Ed. Cat Harris. Pub. Matt Loeb. Adv. contact Frieda Koester.

004.22 USA ISSN 1541-0056
QA76.9.D5
INTERNATIONAL SYMPOSIUM ON AUTONOMOUS DECENTRALIZED SYSTEMS. Text in English. 1993. a. USD 174; USD 70 to members (effective 2004). **Document type:** *Proceedings, Trade.*
Published by: Institute of Electrical and Electronics Engineers, Inc., 3 Park Ave, 17th Fl, New York, NY 10016-5997. TEL 212-419-7900, 800-678-4333, FAX 212-752-4929, customer.service@ieee.org, http://www.ieee.org.

004.7 USA ISSN 1082-8907
QA76.88 CODEN: PIDCFB
INTERNATIONAL SYMPOSIUM ON HIGH-PERFORMANCE DISTRIBUTED COMPUTING. PROCEEDINGS. Short title: H P D C. Text in English. 1992. a. free. adv. **Document type:** *Proceedings.* **Description:** Addresses the latest research findings in all areas of high-performance distributed computing.
Media: Online - full text (from I E E E).
Indexed: EngInd.
Published by: (Institute of Electrical and Electronics Engineers, Inc.), I E E E Computer Society, 3 Park Ave, 17th Fl, New York, NY 10017. TEL 714-821-8380, 800-678-4333, FAX 714-821-4641, customer.service@ieee.org, http://www.ieee.org. Ed. Cat Harris. Pub. Matt Loeb. Adv. contact Frieda Koester.

004.22 USA ISSN 1072-4451
QA76.6 CODEN: PSMIE7
INTERNATIONAL SYMPOSIUM ON MICROARCHITECTURE. PROCEEDINGS. Text in English. 1971 (no.4). a. price varies. adv. bibl.; charts. **Document type:** *Proceedings, Academic/Scholarly.*
Former titles: Microprogramming and Microarchitecture Workshop. Proceedings; Microprogramming Workshop. Proceedings; (until 1983): Annual Microprogramming Workshop. Proceedings (0194-1895); (1978-1982): Workshop on Microprogramming. Proceedings; (1974-1976?): Micro Proceedings (0361-2163); (until 1973): Annual Workshop on Microprogramming. Preprints; (until 1972): Annual Workshop on Microprogramming. Conference Record; (until 1969): Joint A C M - SIGMICRO - I E E E E Workshop on Microprogramming (Proceedings) ; (until 1968) : A C M Workshop on Microprogramming (Proceedings)
Related titles: Online - full text ed.: (from I E E E).
Indexed: CompC.
—BLDSC (5756.773000), Ei, IE, ingenta. **CCC.**
Published by: (Institute of Electrical and Electronics Engineers, Inc., Association for Computing Machinery, Inc.), I E E E Computer Society, 3 Park Ave, 17th Fl, New York, NY 10017. TEL 714-821-8380, 800-678-4333, FAX 714-821-4641, customer.service@ieee.org, http://www.ieee.org.

004.22 CHN ISSN 0254-4164
QA75.5 CODEN: JIXUDT
➤ **JISUANJI XUEBAO/CHINESE JOURNAL OF COMPUTERS.** Text in Chinese; Summaries in Chinese, English. 1978. m. CNY 336, USD 1,212 (effective 2003). adv. back issues avail. **Document type:** *Journal, Academic/Scholarly.* **Description:** Covers theoretical foundations and applications, hardware architecture, software, networking, CAD, and other applications.
Related titles: Online - full text ed.: (from East View Information Services).
Indexed: C&ISA, CCMJ, E&CAJ, EngInd, IAA, Inspec, MathR, MathSciNet, RefZh.
—BLDSC (3180.310000), AskIEEE, IE, ingenta, Linda Hall.
Published by: (Zhongguo Jisuanji Xuehui), Kexue Chubanshe/Science Press, 16 Donghuang Cheng Genbei Jie, Beijing, 100717, China. TEL 86-10-64000246, FAX 86-10-64030255, cjc@ict.ac.cn, http://cjc.ict.ac.cn, http://www.sciencep.com/. Ed. Paysu Shaw. Adv. contact Yuanyaun Liu. B&W page USD 500, color page USD 900; 260 x 187. Circ: 15,000. **Dist. by:** China International Book Trading Corp, 35 Chegongzhuang Xilu, Haidian District, PO Box 399, Beijing 100044, China. TEL 86-10-68412045, FAX 86-10-68412023, cibtc@mail.cibtc.com.cn, http://www.cibtc.com.cn.

004.22 CHN ISSN 1000-9000
QA75.5 CODEN: JCTEEM
➤ **JOURNAL OF COMPUTER SCIENCE AND TECHNOLOGY.** Text in English. 1986. bi-m. USD 995 in US & Canada; USD 1,210 elsewhere (effective 2004). adv. abstr.; illus. back issues avail. **Document type:** *Journal, Academic/Scholarly.* **Description:** Covers all aspects of computer science and technology, including theoretical foundations of information processing computer hardware and architecture, computer software and various computer applications.
Related titles: Online - full text ed.: ISSN 1860-4749 (from East View Information Services, Springer LINK).
Indexed: CCMJ, CMCI, CompAb, CompLI, EngInd, Inspec, MathR, MathSciNet, RefZh, ZentMath.
—BLDSC (4963.744000), AskIEEE, CISTI, Ei, IE, ingenta. **CCC.**
Published by: Zhongguo Kexueyuan, Jisuan Jishu Yanjiusuo/Chinese Academy of Sciences, Institute of Computing Technology, PO Box 2704, Beijing, 100080, China. TEL 86-10-62610746, jcst@ict.ac.cn, http://www.ict.ac.cn/. Circ: 6,000.

➤ **JOURNAL OF SYSTEMS ARCHITECTURE.** see *COMPUTERS—Computer Systems*

004.22 TWN
LING YU YI KEJI ZASHI/0 & 1 TECHNOLOGY BYTE (CHINESE EDITION). Text in Chinese. 1981. m. TWD 1,400; TWD 4,780 foreign. **Document type:** *Consumer.* **Description:** Covers computer architecture, computer and electronics industries and technology in Taiwan.
Published by: Third Wave Publishing Corp., 19-1, Ln 231, Fu-Hsing N. Rd, Taipei, Taiwan. TEL 886-2-7136959, FAX 886-2-7189467. Ed. Janet Wang. adv.: color page USD 1,800. Circ: 16,000.

004.22 621.392 USA ISSN 0899-9341
➤ **MICROPROCESSOR REPORT**; the insiders' guide to microprocessor hardware. Text in English. 1987. m. USD 895 domestic; USD 995 elsewhere (effective 2004). charts. back issues avail. **Document type:** *Newsletter, Academic/Scholarly.* **Description:** Reports on emerging microprocessor technology. Reports is exclusively subscriber-supported and dedicated to providing unbiased, in-depth and critical analysis of new high-performance microprocessor developments.
Related titles: CD-ROM ed.; Online - full text ed.: (from EBSCO Publishing, Factiva, Gale Group, Northern Light Technology, Inc.).
Indexed: CompD.
—BLDSC (5759.755000), IE, Infotrieve, ingenta. **CCC.**
Published by: Reed Business Information (Subsidiary of: Reed Business), 1101 S Winchester Blvd, Bldg N, San Jose, CA 95128-3901. TEL 408-345-1612, FAX 408-345-1650, http://www.mdronline.com, http://www.reedbusiness.com. Ed. Peter N Glaskowsky TEL 408-345-1634. Circ: 66,033. **Subscr. to:** 6909 E. Greenway Pkwy, Ste. 250, Scottsdale, AZ 85254.

004.22 004 USA
N A S A - D O D WORKSHOP ON EVOLVABLE HARDWARE. (National Aeronautics and Space Administration - U.S. Department of Defense) Text in English. a. USD 184; USD 74 to members (effective 2004). **Document type:** *Proceedings, Trade.*
Published by: Institute of Electrical and Electronics Engineers, Inc., 3 Park Ave, 17th Fl, New York, NY 10016-5997. TEL 212-419-7900, 800-678-4333, FAX 212-752-4929, customer.service@ieee.org, http://www.ieee.org.

004.35 NLD ISSN 0167-8191
CODEN: PACOEJ
➤ **PARALLEL COMPUTING.** Text in English. 1984. 12/yr. EUR 109 in Europe to individuals; JPY 14,400 in Japan to individuals; USD 121 to individuals except Europe and Japan; EUR 1,760 in Europe to institutions; JPY 233,800 in Japan to institutions; USD 1,968 to institutions except Europe and Japan (effective 2006). adv. reprints avail. **Document type:** *Journal, Academic/Scholarly.* **Description:** Presents theory and use of parallel computer systems, including vector, pipeline, array and fifth-generation computers, as well as high-speed computing.
Related titles: Online - full text ed.: (from EBSCO Publishing, Gale Group, IngentaConnect, ScienceDirect, Swets Information Services).
Indexed: AIA, ASCA, C&ISA, CMCI, CompAb, CompLI, CompR, CurCont, CybAb, E&CAJ, EngInd, Inspec, MathR, MathSciNet, RefZh, SSCI, SolStAb, ZentMath.
—BLDSC (6404.833500), AskIEEE, CISTI, Ei, IDS, IE, Infotrieve, ingenta, Linda Hall. **CCC.**
Published by: Elsevier BV, North-Holland (Subsidiary of: Elsevier Science & Technology), Sara Burgerhartstraat 25, Amsterdam, 1055 KV, Netherlands. TEL 31-20-485-3911, FAX 31-20-485-2457, nlinfo-f@elsevier.nl, http://www.elsevier.com/locate/parco, http://www.elsevier.nl. Eds. H Weberpals, D Reed. Adv. contact Tino DeCarlo. **Subscr. to:** Elsevier BV, PO Box 211, Amsterdam 1000 AE, Netherlands. TEL 31-20-485-3757, FAX 31-20-485-3432, http://www.elsevier.nl.

004.22 SGP ISSN 0129-6264
QA76.58 CODEN: PPLTEE
➤ **PARALLEL PROCESSING LETTERS.** Abbreviated title: P P L. Text in English. 1991. q. SGD 274, USD 156, EUR 151 to individuals; SGD 755, USD 431, EUR 416 combined subscription to institutions print & online eds.; SGD 450, USD 257, EUR 248 combined subscription in developing nations to institutions print & online eds. (effective 2006). back issues avail. **Document type:** *Journal, Academic/Scholarly.* **Description:** Aims to rapidly disseminate results in the field of parallel processing in the form of short letters. Covers the design and analysis of parallel and distributed algorithms, the theory of parallel computation, parallel programming languages, parallel programming environments and parallel architectures.
Related titles: Online - full text ed.: (from EBSCO Publishing, O C L C Online Computer Library Center, Inc., Swets Information Services).
Indexed: CCMJ, CompLI, EngInd, Inspec, MathR, MathSciNet.
—BLDSC (6404.833650), AskIEEE, CISTI, Ei, IE, Infotrieve, ingenta. **CCC.**
Published by: World Scientific Publishing Co. Pte. Ltd., 5 Toh Tuck Link, Singapore, 596224, Singapore. TEL 65-466-5775, FAX 65-467-7667, wspc@wspc.com.sg, http://www.worldscinet.com/ppl/ppl.shtml, http://www.worldscientific.com. Ed. Michel Cosnard. **Subscr. to:** Farrer Rd, PO Box 128, Singapore 912805, Singapore. sales@wspc.com.sg. **Dist. by:** World Scientific Publishing Co., Inc., 1060 Main St, River Edge, NJ 07661. TEL 201-487-9655, 800-227-7562, FAX 201-487-9656, 888-977-2665.; World Scientific Publishing Ltd., 57 Shelton St, London WC2H 9HE, United Kingdom. TEL 44-20-78360888, FAX 44-20-78362020, sales@wspc.co.uk.

004.33 USA ISSN 1076-4429
REAL - TIME ENGINEERING; computing with a deadline. Text in English. 1994. q. USD 24 in North America; USD 80 elsewhere. adv. illus.; tr.lit. **Document type:** *Trade.* **Description:** Covers software development tools, operating systems, libraries and trends affecting the real-time computing industry.
Published by: OpenSystems Publishing, 30233 Jefferson Ave, St Clair Shores, MI 48082. TEL 810-415-6500, FAX 810-415-4882, micrology@aol.com, http://www.realtime-engineering.com. Ed., R&P John Black. Adv. contact Pat Hopper.

004.33 NLD
➤ **REAL - TIME SAFETY CRITICAL SYSTEMS.** Text in English. 1994. irreg., latest vol.3, 1995. price varies. back issues avail. **Document type:** *Monographic series, Academic/Scholarly.* **Description:** Serves as a forum for researchers and developers to report findings in the fields of computer systems development where failure of systems or software can involve loss of life or environmental damage.
Published by: Elsevier BV (Subsidiary of: Elsevier Science & Technology), Radarweg 29, Amsterdam, 1043 NX, Netherlands. TEL 31-20-4853911, FAX 31-20-4852457, nlinfo-f@elsevier.nl, http://www.elsevier.nl. Ed. H. Zedan.

621.392 USA ISSN 0163-5964
QA76.9.A73 CODEN: CANED2
S I G A R C H COMPUTER ARCHITECTURE NEWS. (Special Interest Group on Computer Architecture) Key Title: Computer Architecture News. Text in English. 5/yr. USD 55 (effective 2004). adv. bk.rev. **Document type:** *Newsletter.*
Related titles: Online - full text ed.: (from EBSCO Publishing).
Indexed: AHCI, CompR, Inspec.
—BLDSC (3393.700000), AskIEEE, CISTI, Ei, IE, Infotrieve, ingenta, Linda Hall.

Published by: Association for Computing Machinery, Inc., 1515 Broadway, 17th Fl, New York, NY 10036-5701. TEL 212-626-0500, 212-626-0520, 800-342-6626, FAX 212-869-0481, sigs@acm.org, usacm@acm.org, http://www.acm.org/sigarch/. Circ: 5,000.

004.22 USA
SOUTH AMERICAN SYMPOSIUM ON STRING PROCESSING AND INFORMATION RETRIEVAL. Text in English. irreg., latest vol.8, 2001. price varies. **Document type:** *Proceedings, Trade.*
Published by: Institute of Electrical and Electronics Engineers, Inc., 3 Park Ave, 17th Fl, New York, NY 10016-5997. TEL 800-678-4333, customer.service@ieee.org, http://www.ieee.org.

004.33 USA
SUPERCOMPUTING AND PARALLEL PROCESSING TODAY ✶ . Text in English. 1988. bi-m. USD 195; USD 235 foreign. adv. bk.rev. index, cum.index. back issues avail. **Description:** Contains news and applications covering supercomputing and parallel processing.
Published by: Yellowstone Information Services, R R 2, Box 42A, Bloomingdale, OH 43910-9802. TEL 304-965-5548, FAX 304-965-7785. Ed. Roger C Thibault. Circ: 2,000.

T G A - REPORT. (Technische Gebaeudeausruestung) see *ENGINEERING—Mechanical Engineering*

V R NEWS. (Virtual Reality) see *COMPUTERS—Computer Graphics*

004.22 USA ISSN 1087-4097
QA76.9.C65
WORKSHOP ON PARALLEL AND DISTRIBUTED SIMULATION. PROCEEDINGS. Text in English. 199?. a. USD 165; USD 66 to members (effective 2004). **Document type:** *Proceedings, Academic/Scholarly.* **Description:** Presents state-of-the-art papers on parallel simulation technologies used to improve execution of discreet-event simulation models.
Related titles: Online - full text ed.: (from I E E E).
—BLDSC (9352.237030). **CCC.**
Published by: (Association for Computing Machinery, Inc., Institute of Electrical and Electronics Engineers, Inc.), Simulation Councils, Inc., 4838 Ronson Ct, San Diego, CA 92111. TEL 858-277-3888.

COMPUTERS—Computer Assisted Instruction

see also EDUCATION—Computer Applications

371.334 USA ISSN 1208-3658
BULLA GYMNASIA VIRTUALIS. Text in English. 1996. q. free. back issues avail. **Document type:** *Newsletter.* **Description:** Devoted to issues of online education and training.
Media: Online - full text.
Published by: CyberCorp, Inc. info@cybercorp.net, http://www.cybercorp.net/gymv/bulla/. Ed. Robert N Higgins.

371.334 USA ISSN 0742-7778
P53.28
➤ **C A L I C O JOURNAL.** Text in English. 1983. 3/yr. USD 35 domestic to individuals; USD 45 in Canada & Mexico to individuals; USD 60 elsewhere to individuals; USD 70 domestic to institutions; USD 80 in Canada & Mexico to institutions; USD 95 elsewhere to institutions (effective 2005). adv. bk.rev. back issues avail. **Document type:** *Journal, Academic/Scholarly.* **Description:** Provides information on the applications of technology in teaching and learning languages.
Related titles: Microfiche ed.: 1983.
Indexed: CIJE, Inspec, LT&LA.
—BLDSC (3010.760000), AskIEEE, IE, Infotrieve, ingenta.
Published by: Computer Assisted Language Instruction Consortium, Southwest Texas State University, 116 Centennial Hall, San Marcos, TX 78666. TEL 512-245-1417, FAX 512-245-9089, info@calico.org, http://www.calico.org. Ed. Robert Fischer. Circ: 1,000. **Subscr. to:** 214 Centennial Hall, 601 University Dr, San Marcos, TX 78666.

➤ **C A L I C O. MONOGRAPH SERIES.** see *EDUCATION—Higher Education*

371.334 DEU ISSN 0942-7430
C B T - COMPUTER BASED TRAINING. Text in German. m. adv. **Document type:** *Trade.*
Related titles: ♦ Supplement to: iBusiness.
Published by: HighText Verlag, Wilhelm-Riehl-Str 13, Munich, 80687, Germany. TEL 49-89-578387-0, FAX 49-89-57838799, info@hightext.de. Ed. Joachim Graf. R&P Daniel Treplin. Adv. contact Stefan Kratz.

C W R L E - JOURNAL: THE ELECTRONIC JOURNAL FOR COMPUTER WRITING, RHETORIC AND LITERATURE. see *LINGUISTICS—Computer Applications*

407.85 GBR ISSN 0958-8221
P53.28 CODEN: CALLEE
➤ **COMPUTER ASSISTED LANGUAGE LEARNING**; an international journal. Short title: C A L L. Text in Dutch. 1990. 5/yr. GBP 264, USD 438 combined subscription to institutions print & online eds. (effective 2006). adv. reprint service avail. from PSC. **Document type:** *Journal, Academic/Scholarly.* **Description:** Covers pedagogical principles and applications to computer-assisted language learning, computer assisted translation, applications of AI in language teaching, and related issues.
Related titles: Online - full text ed.: GBP 251, USD 416 to institutions (effective 2006) (from EBSCO Publishing, Gale Group, IngentaConnect, O C L C Online Computer Library Center, Inc., Swets Information Services).
Indexed: BrEdI, CIJE, CPE, CompLI, ERA, ETA, Inspec, L&LBA, LT&LA, MEA, MLA-IB, PsycInfo, PsycholAb, RHEA, SEA, SENA, SOMA, SOPODA, TEA.
—AskIEEE, IE, Infotrieve. **CCC.**
Published by: Routledge (Subsidiary of: Taylor & Francis Group), 4 Park Square, Milton Park, Abingdon, Oxon OX14 4RN, United Kingdom. TEL 44-1235-828600, FAX 44-1235-829000, journals@routledge.com, http://www.tandf.co.uk/journals/titles/09588221.asp, http://www.routledge.co.uk. Ed. Jozef Colpaert. adv.: page EUR 225; trim 160 x 240. Circ: 400. **Subscr. in Europe to:** Taylor & Francis Ltd, Journals Customer Service, Rankine Rd, Basingstoke, Hants RG24 8PR, United Kingdom. TEL 44-1256-813000, FAX 44-1256-330245; **Subscr. in N. America to:** Taylor & Francis Inc., Customer Services Dept, 325 Chestnut St, 8th Fl, Philadelphia, PA 19106. TEL 215-625-8900, 800-354-1420, FAX 215-625-8914.

➤ **COMPUTER EDUCATION**; a journal for teachers (especially classes of 11-18 age range) interested in computers & computing. see *EDUCATION—Computer Applications*

371.334 IND
COMPUTER EDUCATION. Text in English. 1991. bi-m. INR 580, USD 35 (effective 2000). adv. abstr.; bibl. index. **Description:** Discusses how schools and colleges are utilizing educational computer programs and systems. Describes new education software packages, including programs in sciences, social sciences, and humanities.
Published by: K.K. Roy (Private) Ltd., 55 Gariahat Rd., P O Box 10210, Kolkata, West Bengal 700 019, India. Ed. K K Roy. R&P M Misra TEL 91-33-475-4872. Circ: 1,490.

COMPUTER LEARNING. see *EDUCATION—Computer Applications*

371.334 GBR ISSN 8755-4615
LB1576.7
➤ **COMPUTERS AND COMPOSITION.** Text in English. 1983. 4/yr. EUR 66 in Europe to individuals; JPY 8,700 in Japan to individuals; USD 75 to individuals except Europe and Japan; EUR 278 in Europe to institutions; JPY 36,800 in Japan to institutions; USD 312 to institutions except Europe and Japan (effective 2006). bk.rev. back issues avail.; reprints avail. **Document type:** *Journal, Academic/Scholarly.* **Description:** For teachers of writing. Includes information on subjects related to computer use in composition classrooms and programs.
Related titles: Online - full text ed.: (from EBSCO Publishing, Gale Group, IngentaConnect, ScienceDirect, Swets Information Services).
Indexed: ABIn, CIJE, CompLI, ERA, ETA, EduInd, Inspec, MEA, MLA-IB, RHEA, SEA, SENA, SOMA, SWA, TEA.
—BLDSC (3394.671000), AskIEEE, IE, Infotrieve, ingenta. **CCC.**
Published by: Elsevier Ltd. (Subsidiary of: Elsevier Science & Technology), The Boulevard, Langford Ln, Kidlington, Oxford, OX5 1GB, United Kingdom. TEL 44-1865-843000, FAX 44-1865-843010, http://www.elsevier.com/locate/compcom. Eds. Cynthia L Selfe, Dr. Gail E. Hawisher. **Subscr. to:** Elsevier BV, PO Box 211, Amsterdam 1000 AE, Netherlands. TEL 31-20-485-3757, FAX 31-20-485-3432, nlinfo-f@elsevier.nl, http://www.elsevier.nl.

➤ **COMPUTERS IN EDUCATION JOURNAL.** see *EDUCATION—Computer Applications*

378.17334 330 GBR ISSN 1358-5363
COMPUTERS IN HIGHER EDUCATION ECONOMICS REVIEW. Text in English. 1987. s-a. free domestic to Higher Education Staff; GBP 15 domestic to Non-HE staff; GBP 25 foreign (effective 2002). adv. software rev. back issues avail. **Document type:** *Journal, Academic/Scholarly.* **Description:** Contains papers, reviews and news items relating to the use of information technology in economics education.
Related titles: Online - full content ed.
Indexed: ESPM.
Published by: (University of Portsmouth, Departmet of Economics, CALECO Research Group USA), University of Bristol, Learning and Teaching Support Network Centre for Economics, 8-10 Berkeley Sq, Bristol, BS8 1HH, United Kingdom. TEL 44-117-9287071, FAX 44-117-9287112, ltsn-econ@bristol.ac.uk, http://econltsn.ilrt.bris.ac.uk/cheer.htm. Ed. Guy Judge TEL 44-1705-844126. Adv. contact Chris Mitchell. page GBP 300. Circ: 1,250. **Co-publisher:** University of Portsmouth, Departmet of Economics, CALECO Research Group.

331.334 GBR ISSN 1460-7468
➤ **CONTINUING PROFESSIONAL DEVELOPMENT.** Text in English. q. GBP 30, USD 50; GBP 110, USD 185 with online ed. (effective 2000). bk.rev. **Document type:** *Academic/Scholarly.*
Related titles: Online - full text ed.: ISSN 1460-7476 (from EBSCO Publishing, Gale Group, IngentaConnect, Swets Information Services).
Indexed: BrEdI, Emerald.
—BLDSC (3425.688440).
Published by: Virtual University Press, Brookes University, School of Hotel and Restaurant Management, Gipsy Ln, Headington, Oxford, Oxon OX3 0BP, United Kingdom. TEL 44-1642-751168, http://www.openhouse.org.uk/virtual-university-press/cpd/welcome.htm. Ed. Nigel Hemmington. Pub., R&P Anne Christie TEL 44-1642-713530.

➤ **CURRICULUM - TECHNOLOGY QUARTERLY.** see *EDUCATION—Computer Applications*

371.344 SWE ISSN 1100-3650
➤ **DATORN I UTBILDNINGEN**; datapedagogisk tidskrift foer Svensk skola. Text in Swedish. 1987. 8/yr. SEK 350 (effective 2003). adv. back issues avail. **Document type:** *Journal, Academic/Scholarly.* **Description:** Covers computer education on every level in the Swedish school system from elementary school through university studies. Written by teachers for teachers.
Address: Frejgatan 32, Stockholm, 11326, Sweden. http://www.diu.se. Eds. Bo Andersson, Peter Becker. Adv. contact Inger Olsson. color page SEK 7,500. Circ: 4,000.

➤ **DISTANCE DEGREES.** see *EDUCATION—Guides To Schools And Colleges*

▼ ➤ **DISTANCE LEARNING.** see *EDUCATION—Teaching Methods And Curriculum*

▼ ➤ **E-LEARNING.** see *EDUCATION—Teaching Methods And Curriculum*

C

371.334 USA ISSN 0013-1962
LB1043
EDUCATIONAL TECHNOLOGY; the magazine for managers of change in education. Text in English. 1961. bi-m. USD 139 domestic; USD 159 foreign (effective 2005). adv. bk.rev.; film rev.; Website rev. charts; illus. index. 64 p./no.; back issues avail.; reprints avail. **Document type:** *Magazine, Academic/Scholarly.* **Description:** For educators at all levels involved with technology. Articles cover telecommunications, computer-aided instruction, information retrieval, educational television, the Internet in education, and electronic media in the classroom.
Indexed: ABIn, CIJE, CPE, CompC, CompD, CompLI, EAA, ECER, ERA, ETA, EduInd, HECAB, Inspec, LHTB, MRD, MicrocompInd, PsycholAb, RHEA, SOMA, SSCI, T&DA, TEA.
—BLDSC (3662.530000), AskIEEE, IE, Infotrieve, ingenta. **CCC.**
Published by: Educational Technology Publications, 700 Palisade Ave, PO Box 1564, Englewood Cliffs, NJ 07632-0564. TEL 201-871-4007, 800-952-2665, FAX 201-871-4009, edtecpubs@aol.com, http://www.bookstoread.com/etp, http://www.bookstoread.com/etp/. Pub. Lawrence Lipsitz. R&P, Adv. contact Charles Renard. Circ: 2,500 (paid).

371.334 USA ISSN 1535-394X
LB1028.3
ELEARN MAGAZINE. Text in English. 2001. irreg. **Document type:** *Magazine.* **Description:** Contains news and features written by professional journalists with expertise in education and technology, and columns and tutorials by industry leaders and stars of academia.
Media: Online - full text.
Published by: Association for Computing Machinery, Inc., 1515 Broadway, 17th Fl, New York, NY 10036-5701. TEL 212-626-0520, 800-342-6626, FAX 212-944-1318, lisa@elearnmag.org, http://www.elearnmag.org, http://www.acm.org. Ed. Lisa Neal.

371.334 USA
LB1028.5 CODEN: ELEADA
ELECTRONIC LEARNING. Text in English. 1981. 8/yr. (during school year). USD 9.99 domestic; USD 32 foreign (effective 2005). adv. bk.rev. illus. index. reprint service avail. from PQC. **Document type:** *Magazine, Consumer.* **Description:** Aimed at K-12 and college-level educators and educational administrators. Features articles on the applications and advances of technology in education.
Former titles: Electronic Learning in Your Classroom; (until 1997): Electronic Learning (0278-3258)
Related titles: Online - full text ed.: (from Gale Group, O C L C Online Computer Library Center, Inc., The Dialog Corporation); ♦ Issued with: Instructor (New York, 1999). ISSN 1532-0200.
Indexed: ABIn, CIJE, CPE, CompC, CompD, EduInd, Inspec, JHMA, LAMP, MagInd, MicrocompInd, PCR2, TOM.
—IE.
Published by: Scholastic Inc., 557 Broadway, New York, NY 10012-0399. TEL 212-343-6100, http://teacher.scholastic.com/products/instructor.htm, http://www.scholastic.com. Ed. Mickey Revenaugh. Circ: 85,000.

371.334 FRA ISSN 1162-6496
GENIE EDUCATIF. Text in French. 1991. 6/yr. back issues avail.
Published by: E C 2, 269 rue de la Garenne, Nanterre, 92000, France. TEL 33-1-47-80-70-00, FAX 33-1-47-80-66-29. Ed. Guy Gouarderes.

371.334 GBR ISSN 0267-1492
HOME COMPUTER ADVANCED COURSE. Text in English. 1984. w.
Indexed: Inspec.
Published by: Orbis Publishing Ltd., Griffin House, 161 Hammersmith Rd, London, W6 8SD, United Kingdom.

371.334 GBR
HUMAN - COMPUTER INTERACTION (NORWOOD)*. Text in English. 1982. irreg. price varies. **Document type:** *Academic/Scholarly.*
Indexed: AIA, CMCI, CompAb.
Published by: Intellect Ltd., PO Box 862, Bristol, BS99 1DE, United Kingdom. mail@intellectbooks.com. Ed. Ben Shneiderman.

I S T E UPDATE; people, events and news in education technology. see *EDUCATION—Teaching Methods And Curriculum*

INNOVATIONS IN EDUCATION AND TEACHING INTERNATIONAL. see *EDUCATION—Teaching Methods And Curriculum*

371.334 371.9 371.3 USA ISSN 1536-6324
LB1027
INSIGHT (CHARLESTON). Text in English. 2001. a., latest vol.2, 2002. USD 50 domestic (effective 2004). charts; illus.; bibl.; stat. back issues avail. **Document type:** *Journal, Academic/Scholarly.* **Description:** INSIGHT's goal is to help educators understand and plan for the use of new and emerging technologies to improve teaching, learning and school management.
Published by: Institute for the Advancement of Emerging Technologies in Education, PO Box 1348, Charleston, WV 25325-1348. TEL 304-347-0400, FAX 304-347-1847, info@iaete.org, http://www.iaete.org/insight. Ed. Tammy McGraw. R&P Krista Burdette. **Orders to:** Scarecrow Education, 4501 Forbes Blvd, Ste 200, PO Box 191, Lanham, MD 20706. TEL 800-462-6420.

INTERACTIVE MULTIMEDIA ELECTRONIC JOURNAL OF COMPUTER - ENHANCED LEARNING. see *COMPUTERS—Computer Graphics*

THE INTERNATIONAL JOURNAL FOR TECHNOLOGY IN MATHEMATICS EDUCATION. see *MATHEMATICS—Computer Applications*

INTERNATIONAL JOURNAL OF COMPUTERS FOR MATHEMATICAL LEARNING. see *MATHEMATICS—Computer Applications*

371.334 USA ISSN 1548-1093
▼ **INTERNATIONAL JOURNAL OF WEB-BASED LEARNING AND TEACHING TECHNOLOGIES.** Text in English. forthcoming 2006. q. USD 85 to individuals; USD 195 to institutions (effective 2005). **Document type:** *Journal, Academic/Scholarly.* **Description:** Provides a place for the dialogue and support of a diverse community interested in taking the challenge further.
Related titles: Online - full text ed.: ISSN 1548-1107. forthcoming 2005 (Jan.-Mar.).
Published by: (Information Resources Management Association), Idea Group Publishing (Subsidiary of: Idea Group Inc.), 701 E Chocolate Ave, Ste 200, Hershey, PA 17033-1240. TEL 717-533-8845, FAX 717-533-7115, cust@idea-group.com, http://www.idea-group.com/IJWLTT. Ed. Lilliane Esnault.

371.334 USA ISSN 1064-4326
LB1028.43
➤ **INTERPERSONAL COMPUTING AND TECHNOLOGY**; an electronic journal for the 21st century. Text in Finnish. 1993. s-a. free (effective 2003). back issues avail. **Document type:** *Journal, Academic/Scholarly.*
Media: Online - full text. **Related titles:** E-mail ed.
Indexed: CIJE.
Published by: Association for Educational Communications and Technology, 1800 N Stonelake Dr, Ste 2, Bloomington, IN 47404. TEL 812-335-7675, FAX 812-335-7678, sbbgpt@rit.edu, aect@aect.org, http://jan.ucc.nau.edu/~ipct-j/, http://www.aect.org/. Ed. Mauri Collins.

371.334 GBR ISSN 0266-4909
LB1028.5
➤ **JOURNAL OF COMPUTER ASSISTED LEARNING.** Text in English. 1985. bi-m. GBP 93, EUR 104 combined subscription in Europe to individuals print & online eds.; USD 175 combined subscription in the Americas to individuals & Caribbean (print & online eds.); GBP 104 combined subscription elsewhere to individuals print & online eds.; GBP 512 combined subscription in Europe to institutions print & online eds.; USD 944 combined subscription in the Americas to institutions & Caribbean (print & online eds.); GBP 562 combined subscription elsewhere to institutions print & online eds. (effective 2006). adv. bk.rev. illus.; charts. index. back issues avail.; reprint service avail. from PSC. **Document type:** *Journal, Academic/Scholarly.* **Description:** Covers the whole range of uses of information and communication technology to support learning and knowledge exchange.
Related titles: Microform ed.: (from PQC); Online - full text ed.: ISSN 1365-2729. GBP 486 in Europe to institutions; USD 897 in the Americas to institutions & Caribbean; GBP 534 elsewhere to institutions (effective 2006) (from Blackwell Synergy, EBSCO Publishing, Gale Group, IngentaConnect, O C L C Online Computer Library Center, Inc., Swets Information Services).
Indexed: ASCA, BrEdI, CIJE, CPE, CompAb, CompLI, CurCont, ERA, ETA, ErgAb, HRA, Inspec, L&LBA, MEA, PsycInfo, PsycholAb, RHEA, RefZh, SEA, SENA, SOMA, SOPODA, SSCI, SWA, TEA, e-psyche.
—BLDSC (4963.640000), AskIEEE, IDS, IE, Infotrieve, ingenta. **CCC.**
Published by: Blackwell Publishing Ltd., 9600 Garsington Rd, Oxford, OX4 2ZG, United Kingdom. TEL 44-1865-776868, FAX 44-1865-714591, customerservices@oxon.blackwellpublishing.com, http://www.blackwellpublishing.com/journals/JCA. Ed. Charfles Crook. Pub. Elaine Stott. R&P Sophie Savage. Adv. contact Jenny Applin. Circ: 515.

➤ **JOURNAL OF COMPUTING IN TEACHER EDUCATION.** see *COMPUTERS*

371.334 USA ISSN 1055-8896
LB1028.5 CODEN: JEMHEA
➤ **JOURNAL OF EDUCATIONAL MULTIMEDIA AND HYPERMEDIA.** Variant title: J E M H. Text in English. 1992. q. USD 130 to institutions (effective 2004). adv. back issues avail. **Document type:** *Journal, Academic/Scholarly.* **Description:** Provides a multidisciplinary, international information source to present research and applications on multimedia and hypermedia tools that allow for the integration of images, sounds, text, and data in learning and teaching software.
Related titles: Microfiche ed.; Online - full text ed.: (from Florida Center for Library Automation, Gale Group, H.W. Wilson, O C L C Online Computer Library Center, Inc., ProQuest Information & Learning).
Indexed: ABIn, BrHumI, CIJE, CPE, CommAb, CompLI, CompR, EAA, ERA, ETA, EduInd, ErgAb, Inspec, LISA, MEA, MicrocompInd, PsycInfo, PsycholAb, RHEA, SEA, SENA, SOMA, SWA, TEA.
—BLDSC (4973.170000), AskIEEE, IE, Infotrieve, ingenta. **CCC.**
Published by: Association for the Advancement of Computing in Education, PO Box 3728, Norfolk, VA 23514. TEL 757-623-7588, FAX 703-997-8760, info@aace.org, http://www.aace.org/pubs/jemh/default.htm. Ed. Gary H Marks. R&P Sarah D Williams. Adv. contact Ingrid Hoffman.

➤ **JOURNAL OF EDUCATIONAL TECHNOLOGY SYSTEMS.** see *EDUCATION—Computer Applications*

371.334 USA ISSN 1040-0370
LB1028.3
JOURNAL OF INTERACTIVE INSTRUCTION DEVELOPMENT. Text in English. 1988. q. USD 60 to non-members; USD 40 to members (effective 2004). **Document type:** *Trade.* **Description:** Articles and commentary on the development of interactive multimedia instruction materials for use in education, training and job performance improvement.
Indexed: ABIn, CIJE, CPE, ERA, ETA, EduInd, T&DA, TEA.
—BLDSC (5007.539500), IE, ingenta.
Published by: (Society for Applied Learning Technology), Learning Technology Institute, 50 Culpeper St, Warrenton, VA 20186. TEL 540-347-0055, FAX 540-349-3169, info@lti.org, http://www.lti.org. Ed. James Mohler.

JOURNAL OF RESEARCH ON TECHNOLOGY IN EDUCATION. see *EDUCATION—Computer Applications*

LEARNING AND LEADING WITH TECHNOLOGY. see *EDUCATION—Computer Applications*

371.334 GBR
MANTEX NEWSLETTER. Text in English. 1998. fortn. free. bk.rev.; software rev.; Website rev. back issues avail. **Document type:** *Newsletter.* **Description:** Provides articles about computer-based learning programs, news, free software, writing skills, topography and design.
Media: E-mail.
Published by: Mantex Information Design, Clifton Press, PO Box 100, Manchester, M20 6GZ, United Kingdom. TEL 44-161-432-5811, FAX 44-161-443-2766, roy@mantex.co.uk, info@mantex.co.uk, http://www.mantex.co.uk/. Ed., Pub., Adv. contact Dr. Roy Johnson.

371.33 USA ISSN 0025-6897
LB1043
MEDIA & METHODS; educational products, technologies & programs for schools & universities. Text in English. 1964. 5/yr. USD 35 domestic; USD 51.50 foreign (effective 2005). adv. bk.rev. illus. Index. reprints avail. **Document type:** *Magazine, Trade.* **Description:** Educational magazine devoted to the practical applications of instructional technologies. Readers include those who influence the practical uses of multimedia equipment, computers, laserdiscs, audiovisual media and library automation systems in K-12 school districts.
Formerly (until 1969): Educators Guide to Media and Methods (0013-2063)
Related titles: Microform ed.: (from PQC); Online - full text ed.: (from EBSCO Publishing, H.W. Wilson, O C L C Online Computer Library Center, Inc., ProQuest Information & Learning).
Indexed: ABIn, CIJE, CPE, CompC, CompD, ConsI, ETA, EduInd, InfoSAb, Inspec, LAMP, LHTB, MRD, MicrocompInd, RGYP.
—BLDSC (5525.250000), AskIEEE, IE, Infotrieve, ingenta. **CCC.**
Published by: American Society of Educators, 1429 Walnut St, Philadelphia, PA 19102. TEL 215-241-9201, 215-563-6005, 800-555-5657, FAX 215-587-9706, michelesok@media-methods.com, michelesok@aol.com, http://www.media-methods.com. Ed. Christine Weiser. Pub., R&P Michele Sokoloff. Circ: 50,000 (paid and controlled).

371.334 GBR ISSN 1364-3819
P C GENIUS; play & learn on your PC. Text in English. 1996. bi-w. GBP 155.48; GBP 2.99 newsstand/cover (effective 1999). back issues avail. **Document type:** *Consumer.* **Description:** Packed with exercises, quizzes, ideas and parents' notes to promote learning. Each issue comes with complete educational games, some on a disk.
Published by: Orbis Publishing Ltd., Griffin House, 161 Hammersmith Rd, London, W6 8SD, United Kingdom. subscribe@deagostini.co.uk, http://www.pcgenius.com, http://www.orbispublishing.com. **Subscr. to:** Freepost TN7 196, PO Box 1, Hastings, E Sussex TN 35 4BR, United Kingdom.

RADICAL PEDAGOGY. see *EDUCATION—Teaching Methods And Curriculum*

371.334 GBR ISSN 0958-3440
P53.28 CODEN: RCALE2
➤ **RECALL.** Text in English. 1989. s-a. GBP 90 to institutions; USD 148 in North America to institutions; GBP 98 combined subscription to institutions print & online eds.; USD 160 combined subscription in North America to institutions print & online eds. (effective 2006). adv. software rev. back issues avail. **Document type:** *Journal, Academic/Scholarly.* **Description:** Contains articles of interest to beginners in the fields of computer-assisted language learning (CALL). Includes items concerned with research and developmental work.
Related titles: Online - full text ed.: ISSN 1474-0109. GBP 82 to institutions; USD 135 in North America to institutions (effective 2006) (from EBSCO Publishing, O C L C Online Computer Library Center, Inc., Swets Information Services).
Indexed: BrEdI, CPE, ERA, ETA, Inspec, L&LBA, LT&LA, MEA, MLA-IB, PsycInfo, PsycholAb, RHEA, SEA, SENA, SOMA, SOPODA, TEA.
—BLDSC (7303.590500), AskIEEE, IE, Infotrieve, ingenta. **CCC.**
Published by: (European Association for Computer Assisted Language Learning (EUROCALL)), Cambridge University Press, The Edinburgh Bldg, Shaftesbury Rd, Cambridge, CB2 2RU, United Kingdom. TEL 44-1223-312393, FAX 44-1223-315052, journals@cambridge.org, http://uk.cambridge.org/journals. Eds. Graham Chesters, June Thompson. R&P, Adv. contact June Thompson. Circ: 2,000. **Subscr. to:** Cambridge University Press, 100 Brook Hill Dr, West Nyack, NY 10994. TEL 845-353-7500, FAX 845-353-4141, journals_subscriptions@cup.org

➤ **REVISTA IBEROAMERICANA DE EDUCACION A DISTANCIA.** see *EDUCATION—Adult Education*

➤ **SOCIETY FOR APPLIED LEARNING TECHNOLOGY. NEWSLETTER.** see *EDUCATION—Computer Applications*

➤ **TECHNOLOGY AND LEARNING**; the leading magazine of electronic education. see *EDUCATION—Computer Applications*

➤ **TECNE.** see *EDUCATION—Teaching Methods And Curriculum*

371.334 GBR ISSN 1460-7441
➤ **VIRTUAL UNIVERSITY JOURNAL.** Text in English. 1998. m. (11/yr.). GBP 40 to individuals; GBP 250 to libraries. **Document type:** *Academic/Scholarly.* **Description:** Focuses on lifelong learning research, thinking and practices.
Related titles: Online - full text ed.: ISSN 1460-745X (from EBSCO Publishing, Swets Information Services).
Indexed: BrEdI, EmerIntel, Emerald.
—BLDSC (9240.729100), Infotrieve.

Published by: Oxford Brookes University, School of Hotel and Restaurant Management, Gipsy Ln, Headington, Oxon OX3 0BP, United Kingdom. FAX 44-1642-751168, achristie9@aol.com, cr@hrm.brookes.ac.uk, http://www.openhouse.org.uk/virtual-university-press/vuj/welcome.htm. Ed. Clive Roberton. Pub. Anne Christie.

COMPUTERS—Computer Engineering

see also COMPUTERS—Computer Architecture

621.39 USA ISSN 1073-0516
QA76.9.H85 CODEN: ATCIF4
➤ **A C M TRANSACTIONS ON COMPUTER - HUMAN INTERACTION.** Abbreviated title: T O C H I. Text in English. 1994. q. USD 155 domestic to non-members; USD 169 foreign to non-members; USD 42 domestic to members; USD 56 foreign to members; USD 37 domestic to students; USD 51 combined subscription foreign to students; USD 186 combined subscription domestic to non-members print & online eds.; USD 200 combined subscription foreign to non-members print & online eds.; USD 50 combined subscription domestic to members print & online eds.; USD 64 combined subscription foreign to members print & online eds.; USD 44 combined subscription domestic to students print & online eds.; USD 58 combined subscription foreign to students print & online eds. (effective 2006). **Document type:** *Journal, Academic/Scholarly.* **Description:** Reports on research and theory on computer architecture, as it affects the end user.
Related titles: Online - full text ed.: ISSN 1557-7325. USD 124 to non-members; USD 33 to members; USD 29 to students (effective 2006) (from Association for Computing Machinery, Inc., EBSCO Publishing).
Indexed: ABIn, BrCerAb, C&ISA, CerAb, CompAb, CompLI, CompR, CorrAb, E&CAJ, EMA, ErgAb, IAA, Inspec, M&TEA, MBF, METADEX, RefZh, WAA.
—BLDSC (0578.650000), CISTI, IE, Infotrieve, ingenta, Linda Hall. **CCC.**
Published by: Association for Computing Machinery, Inc., 1515 Broadway, 17th Fl, New York, NY 10036-5701. TEL 212-626-0520, 800-342-6626, FAX 212-944-1318, dl-feedback@acm.org, sigs@acm.org, usacm@acm.org, http://www.acm.org/tochi/. Ed. Jonathan Grudin. Circ: 1,616 (paid).

➤ **ADVANCED SERIES IN ELECTRICAL AND COMPUTER ENGINEERING.** see *ENGINEERING—Electrical Engineering*

621.39 CAN ISSN 0840-8688
TK1 CODEN: CJEEEL
➤ **CANADIAN JOURNAL OF ELECTRICAL AND COMPUTER ENGINEERING.** Text and summaries in English, French. 1965. q. CND 30 domestic to members; USD 30 in United States to members; USD 60 to individuals; USD 90 to institutions (effective 2005). adv. bk.rev. back issues avail. **Document type:** *Academic/Scholarly.* **Description:** Presents scientifically reviewed papers in electrical and computer engineering.
Formerly: Canadian Electrical Engineering Journal (0700-9216)
Indexed: ASCA, BrCerAb, C&ISA, CBCARef, CMCI, CerAb, CorrAb, CurCont, CybAb, E&CAJ, EMA, EngInd, IAA, ISMEC, Inspec, M&TEA, MBF, METADEX, SCI, SolStAb, WAA.
—BLDSC (3031.320000), AskIEEE, CISTI, Ei, IDS, IE, Infotrieve, ingenta, Linda Hall.
Published by: (Universite Laval, University of Manitoba), Institute of Electrical and Electronic Engineers Canada, Departement de Genie Electrique et de Genie Informatique, Pavillon Pouliot, Bureau 1114-L, Universite Laval, Quebec, PQ G1K 7P4, Canada. TEL 403-220-6178, 800-678-4333, FAX 403-282-6855, ewh.ieee.org/reg/7/journal, http://www.gel.ulaval.ca/~mlecours/. Eds. Dr. Witold Kinsner, Dr. Xavier Maldague. Circ: 500.

➤ **COMPACTPCI SYSTEMS.** see *COMPUTERS—Personal Computers*

➤ **COMPUTER MODELING IN ENGINEERING & SCIENCES.** see *ENGINEERING*

621.3822 GBR ISSN 1063-293X
TS176 CODEN: CRAPEM
➤ **CONCURRENT ENGINEERING: RESEARCH AND APPLICATIONS.** Text in English. 1993. q. GBP 536, USD 830 to institutions; GBP 558, USD 864 combined subscription to institutions print & online eds. (effective 2006). back issues avail.; reprints avail. **Document type:** *Journal, Academic/Scholarly.* **Description:** Presents interdisciplinary research on all aspects of concurrency in computer-aided product design, engineering and manufacturing.
Related titles: E-mail ed.; Online - full content ed.; Online - full text ed.: ISSN 1531-2003. GBP 530, USD 821 to institutions (effective 2006) (from EBSCO Publishing, O C L C Online Computer Library Center, Inc., Sage Publications, Inc., Swets Information Services).
Indexed: ASCA, BrCerAb, BrTechI, C&ISA, CMCI, CerAb, CivEngAb, CompLI, CorrAb, CurCont, E&CAJ, EMA, EngInd, ErgAb, IAA, ISR, Inspec, M&TEA, MBF, METADEX, SCI, SolStAb, WAA.
—BLDSC (3405.628000), AskIEEE, CISTI, IDS, IE, Infotrieve, ingenta, Linda Hall. **CCC.**
Published by: (International Society for Productivity Enhancement USA, Concurrent Engineering Institute USA), Sage Science Press (UK) (Subsidiary of: Sage Publications, Inc.), 1 Oliver's Yard, 55 City Rd, London, EC1Y 1SP, United Kingdom. TEL 44-20-73248500, FAX 44-20-73248600, info@sagepub.com, http://www.sagepub.co.uk/journal.aspx?pid=105499. Ed. Biren Prasad. Circ: 220 (paid). **Subscr. in the Americas to:** Sage Publications, Inc., 2455 Teller Rd, Thousand Oaks, CA 91320. TEL 805-499-0721, FAX 805-499-0871, journals@sagepub.com.

621.39 NLD ISSN 1383-7575
CODEN: TOESED
➤ **CONCURRENT SYSTEMS ENGINEERING SERIES.** Text in English. 1989. irreg., latest vol.60, 2002. price varies. back issues avail. **Document type:** *Monographic series, Academic/Scholarly.* **Description:** Presents monographic studies of advanced topics in high-performance computing and communications.
Formerly (until vol.46, 1995): Transputer and Occam Engineering Series (0925-4986)
Indexed: EngInd, ZentMath.
—BLDSC (3405.653000), CISTI, Ei. **CCC.**
Published by: I O S Press, Nieuwe Hemweg 6B, Amsterdam, 1013 BG, Netherlands. TEL 31-20-6883355, FAX 31-20-6203419, market@iospress.nl, order@iospress.nl, http://www.iospress.nl. **Subscr. to:** I O S Press, Inc, 4502 Rachael Manor Dr., Fairfax, VA 22032-3631. iosbooks@iospress.com. **Dist. by:** Ohmsha Ltd.

621.39 CHE
CROSSCUTS. Text in English. 3/yr. **Document type:** *Newsletter.* **Description:** Contains articles and announcements for users.
Related titles: Online - full text ed.
Indexed: Inspec.
Published by: Centro Svizzero di Calcolo Scientifico, Galleria 2, via Cantonale, Manno, 6928, Switzerland. crosscuts-info@cscs.ch, http://www.cscs.ch. Pub. Hans-Peter Wessels.

D S P SITEINGS. (Digital Signal Processing) see *COMPUTERS—Computer Architecture*

E-LETTER ON SYSTEMS, CONTROL, & SIGNAL PROCESSING. see *COMPUTERS—Computer Systems*

ELEKTOR. see *ELECTRONICS*

621.39 USA ISSN 1558-2493
QA76.6 CODEN: EYPRE4
EMBEDDED SYSTEMS DESIGN; creative solutions for senior systems designers and their teams. Text in English. 1988. m. USD 55 domestic; USD 61 in Canada & Mexico; USD 95 elsewhere; free to qualified personnel (effective 2006). adv. back issues avail. **Document type:** *Trade.* **Description:** Provides solutions for design engineers, software designers and project managers whose daily work includes supervising, designing, writing, testing, and integrating programs used in microcontroller, embedded microprocessor, and DSP and SoC-based systems.
Formerly (until Oct. 2005): Embedded Systems Programming (1040-3272)
Related titles: Online - full text ed.: ISSN 1558-2507 (from EBSCO Publishing, Gale Group, LexisNexis, ProQuest Information & Learning).
Indexed: CompD, CompI, CompLI, CurCont, Inspec, SoftBase.
—BLDSC (3733.066000), AskIEEE, CISTI, IDS, IE, Infotrieve, ingenta. **CCC.**
Published by: C M P Media LLC (Subsidiary of: United News & Media), 600 Harrison St, 6th Fl., San Francisco, CA 94107. TEL 415-947-6746, FAX 415-947-6041, http://www.embedded.com/mag.htm, http://www.cmp.com. Ed. Jim Turlely. Pub. Eric Berg. Circ: 45,000. **Subscr. to:** PO Box 3404, Northbrook, IL 60065-9468 . TEL 847-559-7307, FAX 847-291-4816, esp@omeda.com.

621.39 NLD ISSN 0924-5375
ENGINEERING APPLICATIONS OF SYSTEMS RELIABILITY AND RISK ANALYSIS. Text in English. 1984. irreg. price varies. **Document type:** *Monographic series.*
Published by: Springer-Verlag Dordrecht (Subsidiary of: Springer Science+Business Media), Van Godewijckstraat 30, Dordrecht, 3311 GX, Netherlands. TEL 31-78-6576050, FAX 31-78-6576474, http://www.springeronline.com.

621.39 USA ISSN 1110-8657
➤ **EURASIP JOURNAL ON APPLIED SIGNAL PROCESSING;** the international journal of analog and digital signal processing. Text in English. 1994. 16/yr. USD 179.95 to individuals; USD 1,195 to institutions; USD 1,434 combined subscription to institutions print & online eds. (effective 2005). adv. Website rev. 65 p./no. 2 cols./p.; reprints avail. **Document type:** *Journal, Academic/Scholarly.* **Description:** Publishes papers on applications of signal processing in various areas and applications of new and emerging technologies to signal processing.
Formerly (until 2000): Applied Signal Processing (0941-0635)
Related titles: Microform ed.: (from PQC); Online - full text ed.: ISSN 1687-0433. USD 59.95 to individuals; USD 1,195 to institutions (effective 2005) (from EBSCO Publishing, Swets Information Services).
Indexed: AcoustA, C&CSA, C&ISA, CMCI, CurCont, E&CAJ, EngInd, IAA, Inspec, MathR, MathSciNet.
—BLDSC (3828.089200), AskIEEE, CISTI, IE, ingenta. **CCC.**
Published by: Hindawi Publishing Corporation, PO Box 1210, Sylvania, OH 43560. FAX 866-446-3294, 215-893-4392, asp@asp.hindawi.com, hindawi@hindawi.com, http://www.hindawi.com/journals/asp/index.html. Ed. K J Liu. Pub. Dr. Ahmed Abdel-Atti Ahmad Hendawi. R&P Sylvie Samir. Adv. contact Dalia Mokhtar. B&W page USD 195; 8.33 x 11.

➤ **EUROGRAPHICS.** see *COMPUTERS—Computer Graphics*

➤ **FINITE ELEMENTS IN ANALYSIS AND DESIGN.** see *ENGINEERING—Computer Applications*

681.3 DEU ISSN 0178-9627
FORTSCHRITT-BERICHTE V D I. REIHE 10: INFORMATIK - KOMMUNIKATIONSTECHNIK. Text in German. 1964. irreg., latest vol.714, 2002. price varies. **Document type:** *Monographic series, Academic/Scholarly.*
Former titles (until 1986): Fortschritt-Berichte V D I. Reihe 10: Angewandte Informatik (0933-0763); (until 1985): Fortschrittberichte der V D I Zeitschriften. Reihe 10: Angewandte Informatik (0341-1796); (until 1972): Fortschrittberichte V D I Zeitschrift. Reihe 10: Feinmechanik - Elektromechanik - Miniaturtechnik (0506-3140)
—CISTI.
Published by: V D I Verlag GmbH, Heinrichstr. 24, Duesseldorf, 40239, Germany. TEL 49-211-61880, FAX 49-211-6188112, info@vdi-nachrichten.com, http://www.vdi-verlag.de.

629.395 USA ISSN 1066-1395
TK7874.75 CODEN: PGVLEB
GREAT LAKES SYMPOSIUM ON V S L I. PROCEEDINGS. Text in English. 1991. a. USD 102 membership (effective 2005). **Document type:** *Proceedings, Trade.* **Description:** Showcases the research and development efforts in the Great Lakes region in the VLSI design field.
Related titles: Online - full text ed.: (from I E E E).
Indexed: B&BAb.
—BLDSC (4552.199400), Ei. **CCC.**
Published by: (Institute of Electrical and Electronics Engineers, Inc.), I E E E Computer Society, 10662 Los Vaqueros Circle, PO Box 3014, Los Alamitos, CA 90720-1314. TEL 714-821-8380, FAX 714-821-4641, customer.service@ieee.org, http://www.ieee.org.

621.39 USA ISSN 1552-8103
HANDHELD COMPUTING; the number one guide to handheld devices. Text in English. 1997. bi-m. USD 16.95 domestic; USD 36.95 in Canada & Mexico; USD 66.95 elsewhere (effective 2003). adv. **Document type:** *Magazine, Consumer.* **Description:** Offers news, reviews, tips and shopping advice on pocket PCs, Palm powered devices, Linux, Rim and other PDAs, smartphones, digital cameras, MP3 players and other products.
Published by: Handheld Media Group, Inc., 1670 South Amphlett Blvd Ste 105, San Mateo, CA 94402. TEL 650-378-8522, FAX 650-378-8577, comments@hhmgroup.com, https://www.pdabuzz.com/. Ed. Rick Broida. Pub. Andrew Eisenberg.

621.39 USA
HANDHELD COMPUTING'S MOBILITY. Text in English. bi-m. USD 16.95 domestic; USD 36.95 in Canada & Mexico; USD 66.95 elsewhere (effective 2003). **Description:** Designed for mobile professionals, IT executives and others who use, manage and purchase handheld and wireless products for commercial and business use.
Published by: Handheld Media Group, Inc., 1670 South Amphlett Blvd Ste 105, San Mateo, CA 94402. TEL 650-378-8522, FAX 650-378-8577, comments@hhmgroup.com, https://www.pdabuzz.com/. Ed. Rick Broida.

621.39 JPN ISSN 1342-3428
HIGH PERFORMANCE COMPUTING IN R I K E N. (Rikagaku Kenkyujo) Text in English. 1995. a.
Indexed: INIS AtomInd.
—Linda Hall.
Published by: Institute of Physical and Chemical Research, Computation Center/Rikagaku Kenkyujo. Denshi Keisankishitsu, 2-1 Hirosawa, Wako, Saitama 351-0198, Japan. TEL 81-48-4621111, FAX 81-48-4621554.

621.39 621.3 USA ISSN 0840-7789
TK7801 CODEN: CCCEFV
I E E E CANADIAN CONFERENCE ON ELECTRICAL AND COMPUTER ENGINEERING. PROCEEDINGS. Text in English. 1988. a. USD 410 per vol. to non-members; USD 205 per vol. to members (effective 2004). **Document type:** *Proceedings, Trade.*
Related titles: Online - full text ed.: (from I E E E).
—BLDSC (3019.445500). **CCC.**
Published by: Institute of Electrical and Electronics Engineers, Inc., 3 Park Ave, 17th Fl, New York, NY 10016-5997. TEL 212-419-7900, 800-678-4333, FAX 212-752-4929, customer.service@ieee.org, http://www.ieee.org.

621.39 USA ISSN 1543-4281
I E E E CONNECTIONS. (Institute of Electrical and Electronics Engineers) Text in English. 1991. q. free. **Document type:** *Newsletter, Trade.*

C

▼ new title ➤ refereed ✶ unverified ♦ full entry avail.

Formerly (until 2003): I E E E Neural Networks Society. Connections (1068-1450)
Indexed: Inspec.
Published by: I E E E Neural Networks Society, c/o Gary G. Yen, Oklahoma State University, 202 Engineering South, Stillwater, OK 74078-5032. TEL 405-744-7743, FAX 405-744-9198, a.johnston@ieee.org, http://www.okstate.edu/elec-engr/faculty/yen/nntc/new/nnc-newsletter.htm, http://www.ieee-nns.org/.

621.39 USA ISSN 0740-7475
➤ **I E E E DESIGN & TEST OF COMPUTERS.** Text in English. 1984. bi-m. USD 575 (effective 2006). adv. bk.rev. bibl.; charts; illus.; tr.lit. back issues avail.; reprints avail. **Document type:** *Journal, Academic/Scholarly.* **Description:** Covers the methods, practical experience, research ideas and products that assist in the design and testing of assemblies and systems.
Related titles: CD-ROM ed.; Microfiche ed.; Online - full text ed.: ISSN 1558-1918 (from EBSCO Publishing, I E E E).
Indexed: AHCI, ASCA, CMCI, CompAb, CompC, CompD, CompLI, CurCont, CybAb, EngInd, IAA, Inspec, ORMS, QC&AS, RASB, RefZh.
—BLDSC (4362.917500), AskIEEE, CISTI, Ei, IDS, IE, Infotrieve, ingenta, Linda Hall. **CCC.**
Published by: Institute of Electrical and Electronics Engineers, Inc., 445 Hoes Ln, Piscataway, NJ 08854-1331. TEL 732-981-0060, 800-701-4333, FAX 732-981-1721, dt@computer.org, subscription-service@ieee.org, http://www.computer.org/dt, http://www.ieee.org. Ed. Yervent Zorian. R&P Michael Spada TEL 732-981-3430. adv.: B&W page USD 990, color page USD 2,190. Circ: 6,000 (paid). **Subscr. to:** Maruzen Co., Ltd., 3-10 Nihonbashi 2-chome, Chuo-ku, Tokyo 103-0027, Japan. FAX 81-3-3275-0657; Universal Subscription Agency, Pvt. Ltd., 877, Udyog Vihar, V, Gurgoan 122001, India. TEL 91-124-347261, FAX 91-124-342496. **Co-sponsor:** Circuits and Systems Society.

005.1 USA ISSN 1541-1672
QA76.76.E95 CODEN: IISYF7
➤ **I E E E INTELLIGENT SYSTEMS;** putting A I into practice. Text in English. 1986. bi-m. USD 725 (effective 2006). adv. bk.rev. illus.; abstr. back issues avail.; reprints avail. **Document type:** *Proceedings, Academic/Scholarly.* **Description:** Covers knowledge engineering, database and data engineering, planning and problem solving, natural language processing, medical and industrial applications.
Former titles (until 2000): I E E E Intelligent Systems and Their Applications (1094-7167); (until 1997): I E E E Expert (0885-9000)
Related titles: CD-ROM ed.; Microfilm ed.; Online - full text ed.: (from EBSCO Publishing, I E E E).
Indexed: AHCI, AIA, AS&TI, ASCA, ASFA, BRI, C&ISA, CADCAM, CMCI, CompAb, CompD, CompLI, CurCont, E&CAJ, ESPM, ErgAb, ISR, Inspec, LISA, ORMS, PollutAb, QC&AS, RASB, RefZh, RiskAb, SCI, SSCI, SolStAb.
—BLDSC (4362.935620), AskIEEE, CASDDS, CISTI, Ei, IDS, IE, ingenta, Linda Hall. **CCC.**
Published by: I E E E Computer Society, 10662 Los Vaqueros Circle, PO Box 3014, Los Alamitos, CA 90720-1314. TEL 714-821-8380, FAX 714-821-4010, customer.service@ieee.org, http://computer.org/intelligent/, http://www.ieee.org. adv.: B&W page USD 2,150, color page USD 3,250. Circ: 6,864. **Subscr. to:** Maruzen Co., Ltd., 3-10 Nihonbashi 2-chome, Chuo-ku, Tokyo 103-0027, Japan. FAX 81-3-3275-0657; Universal Subscription Agency, Pvt. Ltd., 877, Udyog Vihar, V, Gurgoan 122001, India. TEL 91-124-347261, FAX 91-124-342496.

621.39 USA ISSN 1063-6404
TK7888.4
I E E E INTERNATIONAL CONFERENCE ON COMPUTER DESIGN. V L S I IN COMPUTERS & PROCESSORS. PROCEEDINGS. Short title: I C C D. Text in English. 1980. a. price varies. adv. **Document type:** *Proceedings, Academic/Scholarly.* **Description:** Details all aspects of design and implementation of VLSI computer and processor systems.
Formerly (until 1986): I E E E International Conference on Computer Design. V L S I in Computers. Proceedings; Which superseded in part (in 1983): I E E E International Conference on Circuits and Computers. I C C C Proceedings
Related titles: Online - full text ed.: (from I E E E).
Indexed: CADCAM, EngInd.
—BLDSC (4362.946100). **CCC.**
Published by: (Institute of Electrical and Electronics Engineers, Inc.), I E E E Computer Society, 10662 Los Vaqueros Circle, PO Box 3014, Los Alamitos, CA 90720-1314. TEL 714-821-8380, FAX 714-821-4641.

I E E E REAL-TIME TECHNOLOGY AND APPLICATIONS SYMPOSIUM. PROCEEDINGS. (Institute of Electrical and Electronics Engineers) see *ENGINEERING—Computer Applications*

621.39 USA
I E E E / S P WORKSHOP ON STATISTICAL SIGNAL AND ARRAY PROCESSING. Text in English. a. **Document type:** *Proceedings, Trade.*
—BLDSC (4363.066525).
Published by: (I E E E Signal Processing Society), Institute of Electrical and Electronics Engineers, Inc., 3 Park Ave, 17th Fl, New York, NY 10016-5997. TEL 800-678-4333, customer.service@ieee.org, http://www.ieee.org.

621.39 RUS
INFORMATIKA - MASHINOSTROENIE. Text in Russian. q. USD 179.95 in United States.
Indexed: Inspec.
Address: Ul Perovskaya 65, Moscow, 111394, Russian Federation. TEL 7-095-3759558, FAX 7-095-3662593. Ed. M A Menzullov. **US dist. addr.:** East View Information Services, 3020 Harbor Ln. N., Minneapolis, MN 55447. TEL 612-550-0961.

621.39 IND ISSN 0971-0469
TK7885.A1
➤ **INSTITUTION OF ENGINEERS (INDIA). COMPUTER ENGINEERING DIVISION. JOURNAL.** Text in English. 1984. s-a. INR 80, USD 25 (effective 2000). adv. charts; illus. index. **Document type:** *Academic/Scholarly.*
Indexed: EngInd, RefZh.
—CISTI, Ei, Linda Hall.
Published by: (Computer Engineering Division), Institution of Engineers (India), 8 Gokhale Rd., Kolkata, West Bengal 700 020, India. TEL 91-33-2235068, 91-33-2238314, FAX 91-33-2238345, technical@ieindia.org, http://www.ieindia.org. Ed., Pub. B C Thakurta. Adv. contact S S Basu. Circ: 2,500.

621.39 POL ISSN 0084-2788
INSTYTUT AUTOMATYKI SYSTEMOW ENERGETYCZNYCH. PRACE. Text in Polish. 1964. irreg., latest vol.44, 1996. PLZ 15 per issue. **Document type:** *Journal, Trade.* **Description:** For electrical engineers and computer specialists. Contains papers on electrical power plant automatic control and protection, electric energy transmission and distribution control and protection, electric power system operation dispatching and management, application of expert systems to power systems, the systems and devices for power energy recording, for localization of faults on branched overhead power lines.
Published by: Instytut Automatyki Systemow Energetycznych, Wystawowa 1, Wroclaw, 51618, Poland. TEL 48-71-3484221, FAX 48-71-482183, TELEX 0712773 IAS PL. Circ: 400.

621.39 NLD
INTELLIGENT AUTONOMOUS SYSTEMS. Text in English. irreg. price varies. **Document type:** *Proceedings, Academic/Scholarly.*
—BLDSC (351387).
Published by: I O S Press, Nieuwe Hemweg 6B, Amsterdam, 1013 BG, Netherlands. TEL 31-20-6883355, FAX 31-20-6203419, order@iospress.nl, http://www.iospress.nl/html/boek1078322215.html. Ed. Enrico Pagello.

621.39 USA ISSN 1084-4627
QA76.9.D3
INTERNATIONAL CONFERENCE ON DATA ENGINEERING. PROCEEDINGS. Text in English. 1984. a. price varies. adv. **Document type:** *Proceedings, Academic/Scholarly.* **Description:** Covers applications and issues in the field of data engineering.
Formerly (until 1991): Data Engineering (1063-6382)
Related titles: Online - full text ed.: (from I E E E).
Indexed: EngInd.
—BLDSC (6844.584500), Ei, IE, ingenta. **CCC.**
Published by: (Institute of Electrical and Electronics Engineers, Inc.), I E E E Computer Society, 3 Park Ave, 17th Fl, New York, NY 10017. TEL 714-821-8380, 800-678-4333, FAX 714-821-4641, customer.service@ieee.org, http://www.ieee.org.

INTERNATIONAL CONFERENCE ON FORMAL ENGINEERING METHODS. PROCEEDINGS. see *COMPUTERS—Computer Architecture*

621.39 USA
INTERNATIONAL CONFERENCE ON INFORMATION TECHNOLOGY INTERFACES. PROCEEDINGS. Text in English. a. USD 220; USD 110 to members (effective 2004). **Document type:** *Proceedings, Trade.* **Description:** Promotes the meeting of researches involved in development and application of methods and techniques from the broad framework of information technology and especially those involved in the field of computer science, information systems, operations research and statistics.
Published by: Institute of Electrical and Electronics Engineers, Inc., 3 Park Ave, 17th Fl, New York, NY 10016-5997. TEL 212-419-7900, 800-678-4333, FAX 212-752-4929, customer.service@ieee.org, http://www.ieee.org. **Co-sponsor:** I E E E Croatia.

621.39 004.678 USA ISSN 1550-6010
TA168
INTERNATIONAL CONFERENCE ON WEB INFORMATION SYSTEMS ENGINEERING WORKSHOPS. PROCEEDINGS. Text in English. 2000. a. **Document type:** *Proceedings, Trade.*
Formerly (until 200?): International Conference on Web Information Systems Engineering. Proceedings (1553-8249)
Published by: I E E E Computer Society, 10662 Los Vaqueros Circle, PO Box 3014, Los Alamitos, CA 90720-1314. TEL 714-821-8380, 800-272-6657, FAX 714-821-4010, customer.service@ieee.org, http://www.ieee.org, http://www.computer.org.

621.39 620.1 HRV ISSN 1330-1365
➤ **INTERNATIONAL JOURNAL FOR ENGINEERING MODELLING.** Text in English. 1988. q. HRK 60 domestic to individuals; HRK 250 domestic to institutions; EUR 110 in Europe; EUR 150 elsewhere (effective 2003). 64 p./no. 2 cols./p.; back issues avail.; reprints avail. **Document type:** *Journal, Academic/Scholarly.* **Description:** Covers computer aided analysis, design and research in the fields of computational mechanics, engineering modelling, numerical methods, and software development.
Formerly (until 1992): Inzenjersko Modeliranje (0352-9495)
Indexed: BrCerAb, C&ISA, CerAb, CorrAb, E&CAJ, EEA, EMA, FLUIDEX, IAA, Inspec, M&TEA, MBF, METADEX, SolStAb, WAA.
—BLDSC (4542.239500), Linda Hall.
Published by: Sveuciliste u Splitu, Gradevinski Fakultet/University of Split, Faculty of Civil Engineering, Matice Hrvatske 15, Split, 21000, Croatia. TEL 385-21-303334, 385-21-303357, FAX 385-21-465117, engmod@gradst.hr, http://www.gradst.hr/engmod/. Ed., Adv. contact Pavao Marovic. Circ: 100 (paid); 250 (controlled). **Co-publisher:** Sveuciliste u Zagrebu, Faculty of Civil Engineering/University of Zagreb.

519 006.3 POL ISSN 1641-876X
INTERNATIONAL JOURNAL OF APPLIED MATHEMATICS AND COMPUTER SCIENCE. Text in English. 1991. q. EUR 180 foreign; EUR 240 combined subscription foreign print & online eds. (effective 2005). **Document type:** *Journal, Academic/Scholarly.* **Description:** Covers applications of mathematical methods to computer science and engineering.
Formerly (until 1998): Applied Mathematics and Computer Science (0867-857X)
Related titles: Online - full text ed.: EUR 90 (effective 2005).
Indexed: Inspec, MathR, MathSciNet, RefZh.
—BLDSC (4542.089500), IE, ingenta.
Published by: University of Zielona Gora, Institute of Control and Computation Engineering, ul Podgorna 50, Zielona Gora, 65-246, Poland. TEL 48-68-3282422, 48-68-3282473, FAX 48-68-3254615, appl@issi.uz.zgora.pl, http://www.issi.uz.zgora.pl/amcs/. Ed. Jozef Korbicz. **Dist. by:** Ars Polona, Krakowskie Przedmiescie 7, Warsaw, Poland. TEL 48-22-9263914, FAX 48-22-9265334, arspolona@arspolona.com.pl, http://www.arspolona.com.pl.

621.39 GBR ISSN 1742-7185
▼ ➤ **INTERNATIONAL JOURNAL OF COMPUTATIONAL SCIENCE AND ENGINEERING.** Text in English. 2005. 4/yr. USD 450; USD 545 combined subscription print & online eds. (effective 2005). **Document type:** *Journal, Academic/Scholarly.* **Description:** Provides an international forum to report, discuss and exchange experimental results, novel designs, work-in-progress, experience, case studies, and trend-setting ideas in the area of computational science and engineering.
Related titles: Online - full text ed.: ISSN 1742-7193. USD 450 (effective 2005).
Published by: Inderscience Publishers, IEL Editorial Office, PO Box 735, Olney, Bucks MK46 5WB, United Kingdom. TEL 44-1234-240519, FAX 44-1234-240515, ijcse@inderscience.com, info@inderscience.com, http://www.inderscience.com/ijcse. Ed. Laurence T Yang.

➤ **INTERNATIONAL JOURNAL OF SPEECH TECHNOLOGY.** see *LINGUISTICS—Computer Applications*

621.39 USA ISSN 0195-623X
QA9.45 CODEN: PSMLDF
INTERNATIONAL SYMPOSIUM ON MULTIPLE-VALUED LOGIC. Text in English. 1971. a. USD 102 membership (effective 2005). adv. **Document type:** *Proceedings.* **Description:** Contains information on multiple-valued logic, including algebra.
Formerly (until 1972): Symposium on the Theory and Applications of Multiple-Valued Logic Design. Conference Record
Related titles: Online - full text ed.: (from Association for Computing Machinery, Inc., I E E E).
Indexed: B&BAb, Inspec.
—BLDSC (6846.796000), Ei, IE, ingenta. **CCC.**
Published by: (Institute of Electrical and Electronics Engineers, Inc.), I E E E Computer Society, 3 Park Ave, 17th Fl, New York, NY 10017. TEL 714-821-8380, 800-678-4333, FAX 714-821-4641, customer.service@ieee.org, http://www.ieee.org. Ed. Cat Harris. Pub. Matt Loeb. Adv. contact Frieda Koester.

629.395 USA
INTERNATIONAL SYMPOSIUM ON V L S I DESIGN. PROCEEDINGS. Text in English. 1988. a. price varies. adv. **Document type:** *Proceedings.* **Description:** Discusses the latest advances and recent technological opportunities in electronic design automation for V L S I designers, developers and users.
Published by: (Institute of Electrical and Electronics Engineers, Inc.), I E E E Computer Society, 10662 Los Vaqueros Circle, PO Box 3014, Los Alamitos, CA 90720-1314. TEL 714-821-8380, FAX 714-821-4641. Ed. Cat Harris. Pub. Matt Loeb. Adv. contact Frieda Koester.

C

621 USA ISSN 1085-9403
INTERNATIONAL VERILOG H D L CONFERENCE. PROCEEDINGS. (Hardware Description Language) Text in English. a. USD 102 membership (effective 2005). **Document type:** *Proceedings, Trade.*
Related titles: Online - full text ed.: (from I E E E).
—CCC.
Published by: I E E E Computer Society, 10662 Los Vaqueros Circle, PO Box 3014, Los Alamitos, CA 90720-1314. TEL 714-821-8380, 800-272-6657, FAX 714-821-4010, customer.service@ieee.org, http://www.ieee.org, http://www.computer.org.

INVERSE PROBLEMS; inverse problems, inverse methods and computerized inversion of data. see *MATHEMATICS—Computer Applications*

621.3 IRN ISSN 1682-0053
IRANIAN JOURNAL OF ELECTRICAL AND COMPUTER ENGINEERING. Text in Persian, Modern, English. 2002. s-a. USD 20 to individuals; USD 40 to institutional members; USD 12 to students (effective 2003).
Media: Online - full text.
Indexed: INIS AtomInd, Inspec.
—BLDSC (4567.528832), IE.
Published by: Jahad Daneshgahi, PO Box 16765-1899, Tehran, Iran. TEL 9821-745-3382, FAX 9821-745-3106, ijece@iust.ac.ir, http://www.ijece.org/. Ed. H. R. Sadegh Mohammadi.

621.39 CHN ISSN 1000-3428
TK7885.A1 CODEN: JISGEV
JISUANJI GONGCHENG/COMPUTER ENGINEERING. Text in Chinese. bi-m. USD 5. adv. **Document type:** *Academic/Scholarly.* **Description:** Covers AI theories, computer architecture, software development and applications, CAD technology, computer graphics and computer network.
Related titles: Online - full text ed.: (from East View Information Services).
Indexed: Englnd.
Published by: Shanghai Jisuanji Xuehui/Shanghai Computer Society, PO Box 800 209, Shanghai, 201800, China. TEL 9528822, FAX 9529731. Ed. Pufan Yu. Adv. contact Lieshen Diao. Circ: 10,000. **Co-sponsor:** Huadong Jisuanji Yanjiusuo - East China Research Institute of Computer Technology.

004 CHN ISSN 1000-1239
➤ **JISUANJI YANJIU YU FAZHAN/COMPUTER RESEARCH AND DEVELOPMENT.** Text in Chinese. 1958. m. CNY 576 domestic (effective 2005). adv. **Document type:** *Journal, Academic/Scholarly.* **Description:** Covers computer science theory, study of hardware and software (including applied software), computer design and implementation, networking, data base systems, Chinese character processing, and image display. Emphasis is on applications.
Related titles: Online - full text ed.: (from East View Information Services).
Indexed: C&ISA, E&CAJ, Englnd, IAA, RefZh.
—Linda Hall.
Published by: (Zhongguo Kexueyuan, Jisuan Jishu Yanjiusuo/Chinese Academy of Sciences, Institute of Computing Technology), Kexue Chubanshe/Science Press, 16 Donghuang Cheng Genbei Jie, Beijing, 100717, China. TEL 86-10-64000246, FAX 86-10-64030255, crad@ict.ac.cn, http://crad.ict.ac.cn/, http://www.sciencep.com/. Circ: 11,000. **Dist. by:** China International Book Trading Corp, 35 Chegongzhuang Xilu, Haidian District, PO Box 399, Beijing 100044, China. TEL 86-10-68412045, FAX 86-10-68412023, cibtc@mail.cibtc.com.cn, http://www.cibtc.com.cn.

621.3 USA ISSN 1540-9589
TK5105.888
➤ **JOURNAL OF WEB ENGINEERING.** Text in English. 2002 (Oct.). q. USD 384 foreign; USD 350 domestic; USD 90 per issue (effective 2005). adv. index. **Document type:** *Journal, Academic/Scholarly.* **Description:** Uses scientific, engineering and management principles and systematic approaches to successfully develop, deploy and maintain high quality Web-based systems and applications.
—BLDSC (5072.554600), IE.
Published by: Rinton Press, Inc., 565 Edmund Terrace, Paramus, NJ 07652. TEL 201-261-9408, FAX 201-261-7374, jwe@rintonpress.com, editorial@rintonpress.com, http://www.rintonpress.com/journals/jwe/. adv.: page USD 400; trim 8.5 x 11. Circ: 400.

➤ **THE KLUWER INTERNATIONAL SERIES IN SOFTWARE ENGINEERING.** see *COMPUTERS—Software*

621.39 RUS ISSN 0134-2452
KOMP'YUTERNAYA OPTIKA. Text in Russian. 1987. a. USD 98 in North America.
Indexed: Inspec.
—Linda Hall.
Address: Ul Kuusinena 21b, Moscow, 125252, Russian Federation. TEL 7-095-1987210, FAX 7-095-9430089. **Dist. by:** East View Information Services, 3020 Harbor Ln. N., Minneapolis, MN 55447. TEL 763-550-0961, FAX 763-559-2931.

621.39 RUS
KOMP'YUTERNYE INSTRUMENTY V OBRAZOVANII. Text in Russian. 1998. bi-m.
Related titles: Online - full content ed.
Published by: Rossiiskaya Akademiya Obrazovaniya, Institut Produktibnogo Obucheniya, ul. Marata, dom 25, Sankt-Peterburg, Russian Federation. TEL 7-812-1641355, http://www.ipo.spb.ru/journal/, http://www.ipo.spb.ru/center.

621.39 RUS
KOMP'YUTERRA. Text in Russian. 1992. w. USD 199 in North America.
Related titles: Online - full content ed.
Indexed: RefZh.
Address: P.O. Box 9, Moscow, 119517, Russian Federation. TEL 7-095-2322263, site@computerra.ru, http://www.computerra.ru. Ed. Yevgenii Kozlovskii. **Dist. by:** East View Information Services, 3020 Harbor Ln. N., Minneapolis, MN 55447. TEL 763-550-0961, FAX 763-559-2931.

621.39 RUS
KOMP'YUTERY V OBRAZOVANII. Text in Russian. 1994. q. USD 99 in North America.
Published by: Komp'yutery i Intellektual'nye Tekhnologii, Ul Kuusinena 21b, Moscow, 125252, Russian Federation. TEL 7-095-9168862, FAX 7-095-9168894. **Dist. by:** East View Information Services, 3020 Harbor Ln. N., Minneapolis, MN 55447. TEL 763-550-0961, FAX 763-559-2931.

621.39 DEU ISSN 1439-7358
➤ **LECTURE NOTES IN COMPUTATIONAL SCIENCE AND ENGINEERING.** Text in English. 1997. irreg., latest vol.22, 2002. **Document type:** *Monographic series, Academic/Scholarly.* **Description:** Covers monographs, lecture course material, graduate and undergraduate textbooks, and high-quality proceedings on topics from all subspecialities described by the term "computational science and engineering".
Indexed: CCMJ, MathR, ZentMath.
—BLDSC (5180.184900), CISTI, IE, ingenta. **CCC.**
Published by: Springer-Verlag Heidelberg (Subsidiary of: Springer Science+Business Media), Tiergartenstr 17, Heidelberg, 69121, Germany. TEL 49-6221-487502, FAX 49-6221-413982, subscriptions@springer.de, http://www.springer.de. Ed. Michael Griebel.

004.0688 FRA ISSN 1630-9782
LOGICIELS & SERVICES. Text in French. 1986. 10/yr. EUR 30.50 domestic; EUR 45.70 in Europe; EUR 220 elsewhere (effective 2003). **Description:** For computer engineers, distributors and enterprises.
Formerly (until 2001): Logiciels & Systemes (1267-3404); Which was formed by the 1995 merger of: Infos 3X-400 (1148-148X); (1986-1995): 9 (IX) Magazine (0980-1529); (1986-1995): Logiciels et Services (0296-8754)
Published by: Publications G R D, 85, rue du Dessous des Berges, Paris, 75013, France. TEL 33-1-5382-8253, FAX 33-1-5382-8269, http://www.grd-publications.com/grd.htm. Ed. Catherine Perzinsky. Circ: 13,000.

621.3 FRA ISSN 1295-4152
LOGIN. Text in French. 1993. m. EUR 49.99 includes CD (effective 2003). back issues avail.
Former titles (until 1999): Dream (1259-1165); (until 1994): Amiga Dream (1241-3976)
Related titles: ♦ Supplement(s): Login. Hors-Serie. ISSN 1299-6599.
Published by: Posse Press, BP 1121, Toulouse, 31036, France. TEL 33-14-9698800, http://www.possepress.com/. Ed. Arnaud Wissart.

621.3 FRA ISSN 1299-6599
LOGIN. HORS-SERIE. Text in French. 2000. quadrennial.
Related titles: ♦ Supplement to: Login. ISSN 1295-4152.
Published by: Posse Press, BP 1121, Toulouse, 31036, France. TEL 33-14-9698800, http://www.possepress.com/.

005.453 NLD ISSN 1381-1142
➤ **LOOP TRANSFORMATIONS FOR RESTRUCTURING COMPILERS.** Text in English. 1993. irreg., latest 1996. price varies. **Document type:** *Monographic series, Academic/Scholarly.*
Published by: Springer-Verlag Dordrecht (Subsidiary of: Springer Science+Business Media), Van Godewijckstraat 30, Dordrecht, 3311 GX, Netherlands. TEL 31-78-6576050, FAX 31-78-6576474, http://www.springeronline.com. Ed. Utpal Banerjee.

621.39 DEU ISSN 0946-7076
TK7874 CODEN: MCTCEF
➤ **MICROSYSTEM TECHNOLOGIES**; micro and nanosystems - information storage and processing systems. Text in English, German. 1995. 12/yr. EUR 958 combined subscription to institutions print & online eds. (effective 2005). adv. reprints avail. **Document type:** *Journal, Academic/Scholarly.* **Description:** Deals with the development and production of miniaturized systems in information technology, telecommunications, medical, biotechnological, automotive, and environmental applications.
Incorporates (1998-2001): Journal of Information Storage & Processing Systems (1099-8047)
Related titles: Microform ed.: (from PQC); Online - full text ed.: ISSN 1432-1858 (from EBSCO Publishing, Springer LINK, Swets Information Services).
Indexed: CurCont, Englnd, ISR, Inspec, SCI.
—BLDSC (5760.840000), AskIEEE, CISTI, IDS, IE, Infotrieve, ingenta. **CCC.**
Published by: Springer-Verlag (Subsidiary of: Springer Science+Business Media), Tiergartenstr 17, Heidelberg, 69121, Germany. TEL 49-6221-3450, FAX 49-6221-345229, http://link.springer.de/link/service/journals/00542/index.htm. Eds. B Bhushan, B Michel. Adv. contact Stephan Kroeck TEL 49-30-827875739. **Subscr. in the Americas to:** Springer-Verlag New York, Inc., Journal Fulfillment, PO Box 2485, Secaucus, NJ 07096-2485. TEL 800-777-4643, 201-348-4033, FAX 201-348-4505, journals@springer-ny.com, http://www.springer-ny.com; **Subscr. to:** Springer GmbH Auslieferungsgesellschaft, Haberstr 7, Heidelberg 69126, Germany. TEL 49-6221-345-0, FAX 49-6221-345-4229, subscriptions@springer.de.

621.39 USA
MIDCON CONFERENCE RECORD. Text in English. irreg. price varies. **Document type:** *Proceedings, Trade.*
Indexed: Inspec.
Published by: Institute of Electrical and Electronics Engineers, Inc., 3 Park Ave, 17th Fl, New York, NY 10016-5997. TEL 800-678-4333, customer.service@ieee.org, http://www.ieee.org.

621.399 RUS ISSN 1028-7493
OTKRYTYE SISTEMY. Text in Russian. 1994. bi-m. RUR 785.78 domestic; RUR 60.44 per issue domestic (effective 2004). **Document type:** *Magazine, Trade.* **Description:** Covers modern computer nets, hardware and software, computer graphics.
Related titles: Online - full text ed.
Indexed: RefZh.
Published by: Izdatel'stvo Otkrytye Sistemy/Open Systems Publications, ul Rustaveli, dom 12A, komn 117, Moscow, 127254, Russian Federation. TEL 7-095-9563306, FAX 7-095-2539204, info@osp.ru, http://www.osp.ru/os/.

C

621.39 GBR
P E D C NEWSLETTER. Text in English. 1998. s-a. **Document type:** *Newsletter, Academic/Scholarly.* **Description:** Focuses on evolutionary and adaptive computing in design and manufacture as well as soft computing and computational intelligence technologies.
Published by: University of Plymouth, Plymouth Engineering Design Centre, Drakes Circus, Plymouth, Devon PL4 8AA, United Kingdom. TEL 44-1752-233325, FAX 44-1752-233310, technology@plymouth.ac.uk, http://www.tech.plym.ac.uk/. Ed. Ian Parmee.

621.39 USA
PACIFIC MEDICAL TECHNOLOGY SYMPOSIUM TRANSCENDING TIME, DISTANCE AND STRUCTURAL BARRIERS. POSTPROCEEDINGS. Text in English. irreg. price varies. **Document type:** *Proceedings, Trade.*
Published by: Institute of Electrical and Electronics Engineers, Inc., 3 Park Ave, 17th Fl, New York, NY 10016-5997. TEL 800-678-4333, customer.service@ieee.org, http://www.ieee.org.

S I G A C T NEWS. (Special Interest Group on Algorithms and Computation Theory) see *COMPUTERS—Automation*

621.39 USA ISSN 0163-5999
QA76.9.E94 CODEN: PEREDN
S I G M E T R I C S PERFORMANCE EVALUATION REVIEW. (Special Interest Group on Measurement and Evaluation) Key Title: Performance Evaluation Review. Text in English. 1970. q. USD 29 to non-members; USD 25 to members; USD 10 student members (effective 2004). adv. **Document type:** *Newsletter, Academic/Scholarly.* **Description:** Fosters research in performance analysis techniques as well as the advanced and innovative use of known methods and tools, seeking a balance between theoretical, methodological, and practical issues.
Related titles: Online - full text ed.: (from EBSCO Publishing).
Indexed: CompC, CompLI, CompR, Englnd, Inspec.
—BLDSC (6423.780000), AskIEEE, CISTI, Ei, IE, Infotrieve, ingenta, Linda Hall.
Published by: Association for Computing Machinery, Inc., 1515 Broadway, 17th Fl, New York, NY 10036-5701. TEL 212-626-0500, 212-626-0520, 800-342-6626, FAX 212-869-0481, leut@cs.du.edu, sigs@acm.org, usacm@acm.org, http://www.acm.org. Circ: 2,400.

▼ **SERIES IN ELECTRICAL AND COMPUTER ENGINEERING.** see *ENGINEERING—Electrical Engineering*

621.39 SGP
SERIES ON SCALABLE COMPUTING. Text in English. 2000. irreg., latest vol.6. price varies. **Document type:** *Monographic series, Academic/Scholarly.*

Published by: World Scientific Publishing Co. Pte. Ltd., 5 Toh Tuck Link, Singapore, 596224, Singapore. TEL 65-466-5775, FAX 65-467-7667, wspc@wspc.com.sg, series@wspc.com.sg, http://www.wspc.com/books/series/ssc_series.shtml, http://www.worldscientific.com. Eds. Kai Kwang, Yuen Chung Kwong. **Dist. by:** World Scientific Publishing Co., Inc., 1060 Main St, River Edge, NJ 07661. TEL 201-487-9655, 800-227-7562, FAX 201-487-9656, 888-977-2665; World Scientific Publishing Ltd., 57 Shelton St, London WC2H 9HE, United Kingdom. TEL 44-20-78360888, FAX 44-20-78362020.

621.39 CHL
SOCIEDAD CHILENA DE CIENCIA DE COMPUTACION. CONFERENCIA INTERNACIONAL/CHILEAN COMPUTER SCIENCE SOCIETY. INTERNATIONAL CONFERENCE. Text in Spanish. 1988. a. membership. **Document type:** *Proceedings.* **Description:** Disseminates scientific and technical activities taking place in all areas of computer science in Chile.
—BLDSC (4538.739300).
Published by: Sociedad Chilena de Ciencia de Computacion/Chilean Computer Science Society, Casilla 2777, Blanco Encalada, 2120, Santiago, Chile. TEL 56-2-6897236, FAX 56-2-6895531, sccc@dcc.uchile.cl, http://sunsite.dcc.uchile.cl/~sccc.

621.39 TWN
SOLID STATE TECHNOLOGY. Text in Chinese. 6/yr. adv. **Description:** Provides information on emerging technologies and products for the production of semicon-ductors, testing, packaging and related areas.
Published by: Arco Publications Inc., 4F, No. 5, Sec. 1, Pa-Te Rd, Taipei, Taiwan. adv.: page USD 2,200. Circ: 6,000.

SOLUTIONS INTEGRATOR. see *COMPUTERS—Computer Industry*

SOLUTIONS INTEGRATOR. see *COMPUTERS—Computer Industry*

621.39 SGP
STUDIES IN JOSEPHSON SUPERCOMPUTERS. Text in English. 1991. irreg., latest 1991. price varies. **Document type:** *Monographic series, Academic/Scholarly.*
Published by: World Scientific Publishing Co. Pte. Ltd., 5 Toh Tuck Link, Singapore, 596224, Singapore. TEL 65-466-5775, FAX 65-467-7667, wspc@wspc.com.sg, series@wspc.com.sg, http://www.wspc.com.sg/books/series/sjs_series.shtml, http://www.worldscientific.com. **Dist. by:** World Scientific Publishing Co., Inc., 1060 Main St, River Edge, NJ 07661. TEL 201-487-9655, 800-227-7562, FAX 201-487-9656, 888-977-2665; World Scientific Publishing Ltd., 57 Shelton St, London WC2H 9HE, United Kingdom. TEL 44-20-78360888, FAX 44-20-78362020.

SUPERCOMPUTER EUROPEAN WATCH. see *COMPUTERS—Cybernetics*

TEST & MEASUREMENT EUROPE. see *ENGINEERING—Electrical Engineering*

TEST & MEASUREMENT WORLD; the magazine for quality in electronics. see *ENGINEERING—Electrical Engineering*

TEST & MEASUREMENT WORLD BUYER'S GUIDE. see *ENGINEERING—Electrical Engineering*

TIME-COMPRESSION TECHNOLOGIES; the magazine for fast and efficient design engineering teams. see *ELECTRONICS—Computer Applications*

621.39 AUS
UNIVERSITY OF NEWCASTLE. DEPARTMENT OF ELECTRICAL AND COMPUTER ENGINEERING. TECHNICAL REPORT EE. Text in English. 1967. irreg. free. **Document type:** *Academic/Scholarly.*
Formerly: University of Newcastle. Department of Electrical Engineering. Technical Report EE (0085-4158)
Published by: University of Newcastle, Department of Electrical and Computer Engineering, Callaghan, NSW 2308, Australia. TEL 61-49-216026, FAX 61-49-216993. Circ: 800 (controlled).

621.39 510 RUS ISSN 1560-7534
QA75.5
VYCHISLITEL'NYE TEKHNOLOGII. Text and summaries in English, Russian. 1996. q. RUR 385 for 6 mos. domestic; USD 174 foreign (effective 2005). **Document type:** *Academic/Scholarly.* **Description:** Covers mathematical models of continuous media, numerical and analytical methods for mathematical physics equations; interval analysis; application software packages and complexes; computer technologies (networks, databases, etc.); electronic publications.
Related titles: Online - full text ed.
Indexed: MathR, MathSciNet, RASB, RefZh, ZentMath.
—Linda Hall.
Published by: (Rossiiskaya Akademiya Nauk, Sibirskoe Otdelenie/Russian Academy of Sciences, Siberian Branch), Izdatel'stvo Sibirskogo Otdeleniya Rossiiskoi Akademii Nauk/Publishing House of the Russian Academy of Sciences, Siberian Branch, Morskoi pr 2, a/ya 187, Novosibirsk, 630090, Russian Federation. TEL 7-3832-300570, FAX 7-3832-333755, psb@ad-sbras.nsc.ru, http://www-psb.ad-sbras.nsc.ru. Ed. Yu I Shokin. Circ: 300. **Dist. by:** M K - Periodica, ul Gilyarovskogo 39, Moscow 129110, Russian Federation. TEL 7-095-2845008, FAX 7-095-2813798, info@periodicals.ru, http://www.mkniga.ru.

621.39 USA ISSN 1541-5848
WORKSHOP ON COMPUTERS IN POWER ELECTRONICS. PROCEEDINGS. Text in English. 1988. a. price varies. **Document type:** *Proceedings, Trade.*
Former titles (until 2000): Workshop on Computers in Power Electronics. Record (1541-583X); (until 1998): I E E E Workshop on Computers in Power Electronics (1093-5142)
Related titles: Online - full text ed.: (from I E E E).
Indexed: Englnd.
—BLDSC (4363.240125).
Published by: Institute of Electrical and Electronics Engineers, Inc., 3 Park Ave, 17th Fl, New York, NY 10016-5997. TEL 800-678-4333, customer.service@ieee.org, http://www.ieee.org.

XING DIANZI KEJI/MICRO ELECTRONICS. see *ELECTRONICS*

COMPUTERS—Computer Games

A P C T NEWS BULLETIN. see *SPORTS AND GAMES*

794.8 BRA ISSN 0104-1630
ACAO GAMES. Text in Portuguese. 1991. m. USD 65.70 (effective 2001). adv. charts; illus. **Document type:** *Magazine, Consumer.* **Description:** Covers the latest developments in the video games world, with news and articles on tips and strategies for all major systems, including PC and arcade games.
Formerly: Acao
Related titles: Special ed(s).: Computer Player.
Published by: Editora Abril, S.A., Av. das Nacoes Unidas, 7221, 11 andar Pinheiros, Sao Paulo, SP 05425-902, Brazil. benjamin.gocalves@email.abril.br.com, http://www.agames.com.br/, http://www.abril.com.br/. adv.: color page USD 7,000; trim 299 x 227. Circ: 38,361 (paid).

794.8 POL ISSN 1429-964X
ACTION PLUS. Text in Polish. 1998. m. PLZ 8.50 newsstand/cover (effective 2003). adv. software rev.; Website rev. **Document type:** *Magazine, Consumer.*
Related titles: Online - full text ed.
Published by: Wydawnictwo Bauer Sp. z o.o. (Subsidiary of: Heinrich Bauer Verlag), ul. Motorowa 1, Warsaw, 04-035, Poland. TEL 48-22-5170500, FAX 48-22-5170125, actionplus@actionplus.com.pl, kontakt@bauer.pl, http://www.actionplus.com.pl, http://www.bauer.pl. adv.: page PLZ 3,000; trim 222 x 305.

794.8 NLD
ADVANCES IN COMPUTER GAMES. Text in English. a.
—BLDSC (0704.120005).
Published by: Universiteit Maastricht, Institute for Knowledge and Agent Technology, P.O. Box 616, Maastricht, 6200 MD, Netherlands. Ed. H. J. van den Herik.

794.8 GBR
THE AMIGA ONE. Text in English. m. GBP 47.40 domestic; GBP 49 foreign. **Document type:** *Consumer.*
Former titles: One for S T Games (0962-2888); One (0955-4084)
Published by: E M A P - Images, Priory Ct, 30-32 Farringdon Ln, London, EC1R 3AU, United Kingdom. TEL 44-171-972-9700, FAX 44-171-972-6710. Circ: 52,476 (paid). **Subscr. to:** Tower Publishing Services Ltd., Tower House, Sovereign Park, Market Harborough, Leics LE16 9EF, United Kingdom. TEL 44-1858-468811, FAX 44-1858-432164.

794.8 DEU
AMIGA PLUS - POWERED BY AMIGAOS. Text in German. 2000. 11/yr. EUR 50.60 domestic; EUR 65.90 in Europe; EUR 5 newsstand/cover (effective 2003). adv. **Document type:** *Magazine, Consumer.*
Formed by the merger of (1991-2000): Amiga Plus (0942-8801); (199?-2000): AmigaOS; Which incorporated (in 1999): Amiga Fever
Published by: Falke Verlag, An der Holsatiamuehle 1, Kiel, 24149, Germany. TEL 49-431-2007660, FAX 49-431-2099035, info@amigaplus.de, info@falkemedia.de, http://www.amigaplus.de, http://www.falkemedia.de. Ed. Nico Barbat. Pub. Kassian A. Goukassian. Circ: 45,000 (paid).

794.8 GBR
ARCADE. Text in English. 1998. m. GBP 19.95 in United Kingdom; GBP 2.70 newsstand/cover; GBP 39.95 in Europe; GBP 49.95 rest of world (effective 2000). adv. **Document type:** *Consumer.* **Description:** Mixes in-depth PlayStation, PC, Nintendo 64 and Dreamcast reviews with coverage of more wide-ranging entertainment formats.
Indexed: AIAP.
Published by: Future Publishing Ltd., Beauford Court, 30 Monmouth St, Bath, Avon BA1 2BW, United Kingdom. TEL 44-1225-442244, FAX 44-1225-732285, neil.west@futurenet.co.uk, http://www.futurenet.com, http://www.futurenet.com/futureonline. Ed. Neil West. adv.: color page GBP 3,955; trim 232 x 300.

794.8 MEX
ATOMIX; la revista de videojuegos en Mexico. Text in Spanish. m.
Related titles: Online - full text ed.
Published by: Grupo Alce, Donato Guerra No. 9, Col. Juarez, Mexico, D.F., 06600, Mexico. TEL 52-55-7030172, FAX 52-55-7030180, http://www.atomix.com.mx/, http://www.grupo-alce.com/. Ed. Davo Marroquin. Circ: 90,000.

794.8 AUS ISSN 1443-6892
AUSTRALIAN STATION. Text in English. 1999. m. **Document type:** *Magazine, Consumer.*
Formerly (until 2000): Australian PlayStation (1442-0740)
Published by: NextMedia, 78 Renwick St, Redfern, NSW 2016, Australia. TEL 61-9-9699-0333, FAX 61-9-9699-0334, http://www.nexmedia.com.au/.

BECKETT ANIME UNOFFICIAL COLLECTOR. see *HOBBIES*

BECKETT DIGIMON COLLECTOR. see *HOBBIES*

794.8 USA ISSN 1541-7875
BECKETT YU-GI-OH COLLECTOR. Text in English. 2002 (Aug./Sept.). bi-m. USD 44.99; USD 9.99 newsstand/cover (effective 2004). adv. **Document type:** *Magazine, Consumer.*
Published by: Beckett Publications, 15850 Dallas Pkwy, Dallas, TX 75248. TEL 972-991-6657, FAX 972-448-9039, http://www.beckett.com/yugioh/. Pub. Claire B. Amano. Adv. contact Mike Obert TEL 972-448-9167. color page USD 4,500; trim 8 x 10.75. Circ: 133,096.

794.8 ITA
LA BIBBIA DEI CODICI. Variant title: P S Mania 2.0 La Bibbia dei Codici. Text in Italian. m. adv. **Document type:** *Magazine, Consumer.*
Published by: Play Press Publishing s.r.l., Via Vitorchiano 123, Rome, RM 00189, Italy. TEL 39-06-33221250, FAX 39-06-33221235, abbonamenti@playpress.com, http://www.playpress.com. Ed. Stefano Mancini. Pub. Alessandro Ferri. Adv. contact Lorenza Borroni TEL 39-02-45472867.

794.8 DEU
BRAVO SCREENFUN. Text in German. 1997. m. EUR 47.88; EUR 3.99 newsstand/cover (effective 2005). adv. **Document type:** *Magazine, Consumer.*
Published by: Heinrich Bauer Smaragd KG (Subsidiary of: Heinrich Bauer Verlag), Charles-de-Gaulle-Str 8, Munich, 81737, Germany. TEL 49-89-67860, FAX 49-89-6702033, stefan.karthan@screenfun.de, kommunikation@hbv.de, http://www.bravo.de/online/render.php?render=000572, http://www.hbv.de. Ed. Anatol Locker. Adv. contact Anja Visscher. page EUR 8,500. Circ: 161,201 (paid and controlled).

794.8 POL
C D ACTION. Text in Polish. 1996. m. PLZ 18.50 newsstand/cover (effective 2003). adv. **Document type:** *Magazine, Consumer.*
Related titles: Online - full text ed.
Published by: Wydawnictwo Bauer Sp. z o.o. (Subsidiary of: Heinrich Bauer Verlag), ul. Motorowa 1, Warsaw, 04-035, Poland. TEL 48-22-5170500, FAX 48-22-5170125, cdaction@cdaction.com.pl, kontakt@bauer.pl, http://www.cdaction.com.pl, http://www.bauer.pl. Eds. Jerzy Poprawa, Zbigniew Banski. Adv. contact Katarzyna Jablonska. page PLZ 9,900; trim 222 x 305.

C D AUSTRIA. (Compact Disc) see *COMPUTERS—Computer Graphics*

C D INFO. (Compact Disc) see *COMPUTERS—Computer Graphics*

794.8 POL ISSN 1426-2916
CD-ACTION. Text in Polish. 1996. m. adv. software rev.; Website rev. **Document type:** *Magazine, Consumer.*
Related titles: Online - full text ed.
Published by: Wydawnictwo Bauer Sp. z o.o. (Subsidiary of: Heinrich Bauer Verlag), ul. Motorowa 1, Warsaw, 04-035, Poland. TEL 48-22-5170500, FAX 48-22-5170125, kontakt@bauer.pl, http://www.bauer.pl.

CD-ROM ONLINE. see *COMPUTERS—Software*

794.8 USA
CHEATS!. Text in English. 2002. s-a. USD 14.99 newsstand/cover domestic; USD 19.99 newsstand/cover in Canada (effective 2004).
Published by: Future Network USA, 150 North Hill Dr, Ste 40, Brisbane, CA 94005. TEL 415-468-4684, FAX 415-468-4686, custserv@dreamcastmagazine.com, http://www.futurenetworkusa.com/. Ed. Sarah Ellerman.

C

794.8 DEU
CHEATS & MORE; das Spiele Magazin: Mit PSOne - PlayStation 2 - Game Boy Advanced. Text in German. 1998. bi-m. EUR 13.50; EUR 2.50 newsstand/cover (effective 2003). adv. **Document type:** *Magazine, Consumer.*
Published by: Schanzenstrassen Verlag GmbH, Schanzenstr 31, Cologne, 51063, Germany. info@cheats-and-more.de, http://www.cheats-and-more.de. adv.: B&W page EUR 2,400, color page EUR 3,100. Circ: 54,342 (paid and controlled).

794.1 GBR
CHESS COMPUTER WORLD. Text in English. q. USD 20. adv. **Description:** Provides players with independent information about computerized chess. Contains articles, results, games and assessment of computer playing strength.
Published by: Bryan Whitby Ed. & Pub., 16 Mansefield Rd, Kingsley, Warrington, Ches WA6 8BZ, United Kingdom.

794.8 POL ISSN 1509-0558
CLICK!. Text in Polish. 1999. m. PLZ 6.50 newsstand/cover (effective 2003). adv. **Document type:** *Magazine, Consumer.*
Published by: Wydawnictwo Bauer Sp. z o.o. (Subsidiary of: Heinrich Bauer Verlag), ul. Motorowa 1, Warsaw, 04-035, Poland. TEL 48-22-5170500, FAX 48-22-5170125, click@bauer.pl, kontakt@bauer.pl, http://www.bauer.pl. Ed. Piotr Moskal. Adv. contact Katarzyna Jablonska. page PLZ 5,000; trim 240 x 300.

794.8 ARG
CLUB NINTENDO. Text in Spanish. m. adv. **Document type:** *Magazine, Consumer.*
Published by: Editorial Televisa Argentina, Av Paseo Colon 275, Piso 10, Buenos Aires, Buenos Aires 1063, Argentina. TEL 54-11-4343-2225, FAX 54-11-4345-0955, http://www.televisa.com.ar.

794.8 ITA ISSN 1129-2393
COLLECTION. Text in Italian. 1999. 3/yr. adv. **Document type:** *Magazine, Consumer.*
Published by: Future Media Italy SpA, Via Asiago 45, Milano, MI 20128, Italy. TEL 39-02-2529161, FAX 39-02-26005520, info@futuremediaitaly.it, http://www.futuremediaitaly.it.

794.8 USA
COMING SOON MAGAZINE. Text in English. 1994. m.
Media: Online - full text.
Address: 130 Prim Rd, Ste 211, Colchester, VT 05446. t15@csoon.com, frederick@csoon.com, http://www.csoon.com. Ed. Trevor Bennicke.

794.8 GBR ISSN 1369-9253
COMPLETE GAMER✶. Text in English. 1997. bi-m. GBP 25 for 6 issues; GBP 5.99 newsstand/cover. adv. back issues avail. **Document type:** *Consumer.*
Published by: Instant Access International Ltd., 43 the Grove, London, W5 5LH, United Kingdom. TEL 44-181-205-2596, http://www.completegamer.co.uk. Ed. Dave France. Pub. Andrew Smales. Adv. contact Brett Pittam.

794.8 NLD ISSN 1384-5594
COMPUKIDS; het computerblad voor kinderen. Text in Dutch. 1996. 10/yr. EUR 50 (effective 2005). adv. software rev.; video rev.; Website rev. illus.; mkt. **Document type:** *Magazine, Consumer.* **Description:** Reviews all types of computer games for children.
Published by: Aktu Bladen Groep, Postbus 12399, Amsterdam ZO, 1100 AJ, Netherlands. TEL 31-20-5222444, FAX 31-20-6240189, redactie@compukids.nl, info@aktu.nl, http://www.compukids.nl, http://www.aktu.nl. Ed. Jetty Koster. Adv. contact Aizo Krikke.

794.8 GBR ISSN 0261-3697
COMPUTER & VIDEO GAMES. Short title: C & V Games. Text in English. 1981. m. GBP 20.28 (effective 2004). adv. illus. **Document type:** *Magazine, Consumer.* **Description:** Covers the next generation as well as older technology.
Related titles: Online - full content ed.
Published by: Future Publishing Ltd., Beauford Court, 30 Monmouth St, Bath, Avon BA1 2BW, United Kingdom. TEL 44-1225-442244, FAX 44-1225-446019, customerservice@futurenet.co.uk, http://www.computerandvideogames.com, http://www.thefuturenetwork.plc.uk. Circ: 104,000 (paid).

794.8 DEU ISSN 1439-9571
COMPUTER BILD SPIELE. Text in German. 1999. m. EUR 34.80; EUR 2.90 newsstand/cover (effective 2003). adv. **Document type:** *Magazine, Consumer.* **Description:** Contains reviews, information and advice on all aspects of PC and console gaming.
Published by: Axel Springer Verlag AG, Axel-Springer-Platz 1, Hamburg, 20350, Germany. TEL 49-40-34724300, FAX 49-40-34724683, http://www.asv.de. Ed. Frank Surholt. adv.: page EUR 10,920. Circ: 651,005 (paid).

794.1 GBR
COMPUTER CHESS NEWS SHEET. Text in English. 1985. bi-m. GBP 18 domestic; GBP 24 in North America. adv. **Document type:** *Consumer.* **Description:** Provides a survey of the chess computer scene with emphasis on realistic assessments and comparisons of the different playing strengths of many machines; includes computer results, gradings and games.
Published by: Eric Hallsworth, Ed. & Pub., The Red House, 46 High St, Wilburton, Ely, Cambs CB6, United Kingdom. ERIC@elhchess.demon.co.uk. Adv. contact Eric Hallsworth. Circ: 600.

794.8 USA ISSN 0890-2143
COMPUTER ENTERTAINER✶. Text in English. 1982. m. USD 35. bk.rev. **Description:** For computer and video game enthusiasts. Features articles on adventure, educational and quiz games, program descriptions.
Formerly: Video Game Update and Computer Entertainer
Published by: Computer Entertainer and Video Game Update, 12115 Magnolia Blvd., Ste. 189, N. Hollywood, CA 91607-2609. TEL 818-761-1561, FAX 818-904-3682. Ed. Celeste Dolan. Circ: 10,000.

794.8 USA ISSN 1546-5101
COMPUTER GAMES. Variant title: Strategy Plus. Text in English. 1990. m. USD 19.97 domestic; USD 29.97 domestic with CD-ROM (effective 2001); USD 31.97 in Canada; USD 41.97 in Canada with CD-ROM; USD 43.97 elsewhere; USD 53.97 elsewhere with CD-ROM (effective 2001). adv. **Document type:** *Consumer.* **Description:** Reviews computer games for IBM, Macintosh, and Amiga and includes information on computer hardware.
Formerly (until 1999): Strategy Plus (1078-5132)
Related titles: Online - full text ed.
Published by: Strategy Plus, Inc., 63 Millet St, Richmond, VT 05477. TEL 802-434-3060, FAX 802-434-6493, editor@cdmag.com, http://www.cgonline.com, http://www.cdmag.com. Ed. Steve Bauman. Pub., Adv. contact Russ Hoeffer. Circ: 400,000. **Subscr. to:** PO Box 1965, Marion, OH 43306. **Dist. in the UK by:** Comag, Tavistock Works, Tavistock Rd, W Drayton, Middx UB7 7QX, United Kingdom. FAX 44-1895-433801.

794.8 GRC ISSN 1108-8648
COMPUTER GAMES MAGAZINE. Text in Greek. 2000. 11/yr. EUR 5.90 newsstand/cover (effective 2002). adv. **Document type:** *Magazine, Consumer.* **Description:** Provides content that targets the 'mature' gamer with an emphasis on the more complex and demanding games.
Published by: Hyperpress S.A., 52 Dekeleias Str., N. Halkidona, Athens, 143 43, Greece. TEL 30-1-252-7000, FAX 30-1-252-5180, marketing@hyperpress.gr, http://www.hyperpress.gr. adv.: page EUR 1,470; 220 x 300. Circ: 22,000 (paid and controlled).

794.8 GRC ISSN 1109-1789
COMPUTER GAMES MAGAZINE COLLECTION. Text in Greek. 2001. irreg. **Document type:** *Magazine, Consumer.*
Published by: Hyperpress S.A., 52 Dekeleias Str., N. Halkidona, Athens, 143 43, Greece. TEL 30-1-252-7000, FAX 30-1-252-5180, marketing@hyperpress.gr, http://www.hyperpress.gr.

794.8 USA ISSN 0744-6667
GV1469.15
COMPUTER GAMING WORLD. Text in English. 1981. 12/yr. USD 19.97 domestic; USD 40.97 foreign (effective 2005). adv. **Document type:** *Magazine, Consumer.* **Description:** Contains articles on the latest developments in computer entertainment. Reviews computer hardware from a gamer's perspective.
Related titles: Online - full text ed.: (from bigchalk, EBSCO Publishing, Florida Center for Library Automation, Gale Group, ProQuest Information & Learning).
Indexed: CompD, MicrocompInd, RASB, SoftBase.
—CCC.
Published by: Ziff Davis Media Game Group (Subsidiary of: Ziff Davis Media Inc.), 28 E 28th St, New York, NY 10016-7930. info@ziffdavis.com, http://www.gamers.com/cgw/index.jsp, http://www.ziffdavis.com. Ed. John Davison. Pub. Lee Uniacke. adv.: color page USD 20,720. Circ: 300,000 (paid).

794.8 ESP
COMPUTER HOY JUEGOS. Text in Spanish. 1998. m. **Document type:** *Magazine, Consumer.*
Published by: Hobby Press S.A. (Subsidiary of: Axel Springer Verlag AG), C/ Los Vascos 17, Madrid, 28040, Spain. TEL 34-902-111315, FAX 34-902-151798, computerhoyjuegos@axelspringer.es, http://www.hobbypress.es/html/REVISTAS_PRESENTACION.HTML. Ed. Cristina Fernandez. Pub. Amalio Gomez. Circ: 41,932 (paid).

794.8 DEU ISSN 0176-2400
COMPUTER-SCHACH UND -SPIELE. Text in German. 1983. 6/yr. EUR 33.75 domestic; EUR 38.35 foreign; EUR 6.14 newsstand/cover (effective 2003). adv. bk.rev. **Document type:** *Magazine, Consumer.* **Description:** News about computer chess and other computer games.
Published by: Verlag Ernst Voegel GmbH, Kalvarienbergstr 22-30, Stamsried, 93491, Germany. TEL 49-9466-9400-0, FAX 49-9466-1276, redaktion@computerschach.de, voegel@mail.teleconsult.de, http://www.computerschach.de, http://www.verlag-voegel.de. Eds. Dieter Steinwender, Frederic Friedel. adv.: B&W page EUR 715.81, color page EUR 1,559.44; trim 176 x 247. Circ: 9,000.

794.8 DEU ISSN 0944-1743
COMPUTER-SPIELE PER POST; das Fachblatt fuer Computer- und Postspielfreunde. Text in German. 1987. q. EUR 419.30 domestic; EUR 408.20 in Germany; EUR 35.80 newsstand/cover foreign (effective 2002). adv. software rev.; bk.rev. back issues avail. **Document type:** *Newsletter, Consumer.* **Description:** Contains information for students and adults interested in playing games by mail and computer.
Published by: Verlag Computer-Spiele per Post, Alfred-Bucherer-Str 63, Bonn, 53115, Germany. TEL 49-228-621392, FAX 49-228-621332, h.topf@cspp.com, http://www.cspp.com. Ed. Harald Topf. Circ: 250.

794.1 NLD ISSN 1389-3823
COMPUTERSCHAAK. Text in Dutch. 1981. bi-m. adv. **Document type:** *Consumer.* **Description:** Contains articles, games, and problems for computer chess enthusiasts.
Published by: Computerschaak Vereniging Nederland/Computer Chess Association, c/o Theo van der Storm, Weth. Driessenstraat 5, Amsterdam (ZO), 1107 XG, Netherlands. computerschaak@aol.com, info@computerschaak.nl, redactie@computerschaak.nl, http://www.computerschaak.nl. Ed. Eric van Reem. Circ: 1,100. **Subscr. to:** C S V N, Lodewyek van Deysselhove 4, Nieuwegein 3438 HS, Netherlands.

794.8 FRA ISSN 1295-439X
CONSOLES MAX. Text in French. 1999. m. FRF 35 newsstand/cover (effective 2001). adv. software rev.; Website rev. **Document type:** *Magazine, Consumer.*
Published by: Future France, 101-109 Rue Jean Jaures, Levallois Perret, 92300, France. TEL 33-1-41273838, yveline.duville@futurenet.fr.

794 FRA ISSN 1162-8669
CONSOLES PLUS. Text in French. 1991. m. EUR 5.50 newsstand/cover (effective 2004). **Document type:** *Consumer.*
Published by: Emap France (Subsidiary of: Emap Media Ltd.), 150-152 Rue Gallieni, Boulogne, 92644, France. TEL 33-1-41334961, FAX 33-1-41335010, info@emapfrance.com, http://www.emapmedia.com.

794.8 GBR ISSN 1475-1399
CUBE. Text in English. 2002. 13/yr. GBP 3.50 newsstand/cover (effective 2002). **Document type:** *Magazine, Consumer.*
Published by: Paragon Publishing Ltd., Paragon House, 10 St Peters Rd, Bournemouth, Dorset BH1 2JS, United Kingdom. TEL 44-1202-299900, FAX 44-1202-299955, subs@paragon.co.uk, http://www.paragon.co.uk. Ed. Simon Phillips. Circ: 29,387.

794.8 DEU
CUBE; 100% unabhaengiges GameCube Magazin. Text in German. bi-m. EUR 3.90 newsstand/cover (effective 2003). adv. **Document type:** *Magazine, Consumer.*
Published by: Pro Verlag Gesellschaft fuer Publikationen mbH, Berner Str 38, Frankfurt Am Main, 60437, Germany. TEL 49-69-5008050, FAX 49-69-5008051, office@proverlag.com, http://www.proverlag.com. adv.: page EUR 4,700; trim 230 x 275.

794.8 ITA ISSN 1594-4638
CUBE. Text in Italian. 2002. m. EUR 4.50 newsstand/cover (effective 2003). adv. **Document type:** *Magazine, Consumer.*
Published by: Play Press Publishing s.r.l., Via Vitorchiano 123, Rome, RM 00189, Italy. TEL 39-06-33221250, FAX 39-06-33221235, abbonamenti@playpress.com, http://www.playpress.com. Ed. Luca Signorini. Adv. contact Lorenza Borroni TEL 39-02-45472867. Circ: 55,000 (paid and controlled).

794.8 GBR
CUBE SOLUTIONS. Text in English. 2002. bi-m. GBP 3.99 newsstand/cover (effective 2002).
Published by: Paragon Publishing Ltd., Paragon House, 10 St Peters Rd, Bournemouth, Dorset BH1 2JS, United Kingdom. TEL 44-1202-299900, FAX 44-1202-299955, subs@paragon.co.uk, http://www.paragon.co.uk. Ed. Phil King. Circ: 12,646.

794.8 USA ISSN 1524-3575
D C M; unofficial dreamcast magazine. Text in English. 1999. q. USD 9.99 newsstand/cover (effective 2000). adv. **Document type:** *Magazine, Consumer.* **Description:** To enhance the game playing on a sega dreamcast. Includes reviews, previews, strategy, tricks and tips for dreamcast games.
Published by: 2D Inc., Box 3338, Oak Brook, IL 60522-3338. Ed. Michael Shassus. Pub. Dale Strang. Adv. contact Suzie Reider. Circ: 100,000 (paid).

794.8 025.04 USA
DAILYRADAR.COM. Text in English. 2000. d. adv. **Document type:** *Consumer.* **Description:** Covers the very latest news and information on all aspects of gaming.
Incorporates (2000-2001): Totalmoviemag.com; (2000-2001): Revolution Online
Media: Online - full content.
Published by: Future Network USA, 150 North Hill Dr, Ste 40, Brisbane, CA 94005. TEL 415-468-4684, 800-234-0804, FAX 415-468-4686, info@dailyradar.com, http://www.dailyradar.com, http://www.futurenetworkusa.com/. Pub. Roddy de la Garza.

C

▼ new title ➤ refereed ✶ unverified ♦ full entry avail.

794.8 JPN
DENGEKI COMIC GAO. Text in Japanese. 1993. m. **Document type:** *Consumer.* **Description:** A computer-game entertainment magazine for media conscious youngsters. Features comics popular with boys in their mid-teens.
Published by: Kadokawa Shoten, Eigyo-bu, 2-13-3 Fujimi, Chiyoda-ku, Tokyo, 102-0071, Japan. TEL 81-3-3238-8527, FAX 81-3-3262-7765. Ed. Fujio Mano. Circ: 300,000.

794.8 JPN
DENGEKI MEGA DRIVE. Text in Japanese. 1993. bi-m. **Document type:** *Consumer.* **Description:** A computer-game magazine published specifically for users of Mega Drive.
Published by: Kadokawa Shoten, Eigyo-bu, 2-13-3 Fujimi, Chiyoda-ku, Tokyo, 102-0071, Japan. TEL 81-3-3238-8527, FAX 81-3-3262-7765. Ed. Fujio Mano. Circ: 180,000.

794.8 JPN
DENGEKI-OH. Text in Japanese. 1993. m. **Document type:** *Consumer.* **Description:** A computer-game magazine aimed at teenagers. Introduces new game software, along with tips and "secret" techniques for enhancing the game.
Published by: Kadokawa Shoten, Eigyo-bu, 2-13-3 Fujimi, Chiyoda-ku, Tokyo, 102-0071, Japan. TEL 81-3-3238-8527, FAX 81-3-3262-7765. Ed. Fujio Mano. Circ: 300,000.

794.8 JPN
DENGEKI P C ENGINE. Text in Japanese. 1993. m. **Document type:** *Consumer.* **Description:** A computer-game magazine published specifically for users of P C Engine.
Published by: Kadokawa Shoten, Eigyo-bu, 2-13-3 Fujimi, Chiyoda-ku, Tokyo, 102-0071, Japan. TEL 81-3-3238-8527, FAX 81-3-3262-7765. Ed. Fujio Mano. Circ: 220,000.

794.8 JPN
DENGEKI SUPER FAMICOM. Text in Japanese. 1993. bi-w. **Document type:** *Consumer.* **Description:** A computer-game magazine aimed at teenagers. Published specifically for users of Super Famicom.
Published by: Kadokawa Shoten, Eigyo-bu, 2-13-3 Fujimi, Chiyoda-ku, Tokyo, 102-0071, Japan. TEL 81-3-3238-8527, FAX 81-3-3262-7765. Ed. Fujio Mano. Circ: 400,000.

793.7 POL ISSN 1642-2104
DOBRA GRA. Text in Polish. 2001. q. PLZ 19.90 newsstand/cover (effective 2004). adv. **Document type:** *Magazine, Consumer.*
Published by: Axel Springer Polska, Al Jerozolimskie 181, Warsaw, 02222, Poland. TEL 48-22-6084100, FAX 48-22-6084106, listy@dobragra.pl, asp@axelspringer.com.pl, http://dobragra.redakcja.pl, http://www.axelspringer.com.pl. Ed. Aleksy Uchanski. Adv. contact Piotr Roszczyk. page PLZ 5,500; trim 215 x 297.

004 CZE ISSN 1212-8562
DOUPE. Text in Czech. 1999. d. adv. **Document type:** *Consumer.*
Media: Online - full content.
Published by: Computer Press a.s., Pod Vinici 23, Prague 4, 143 11, Czech Republic. TEL 420-2-225273930, FAX 420-2-225273934, webmaster@cpress.cz, http://www.doupe.cz, http://www.cpress.cz. Ed. Martin Zavrel.

794 FRA ISSN 1621-773X
DREAMCAST; le magazine officiel. Text in French. 1999. bi-m. adv. **Document type:** *Magazine, Consumer.*
Published by: M6 Interactions, 89 av Charles-de-Gaulle, Neuilly-sur-Seine Cedex, 92575, France. TEL 33-1-41926936, http://www.m6net.fr.

794.8 GBR ISSN 1466-2388
DREAMCAST. Variant title: Official Dreamcast Magazine. Text in English. 1999. m. GBP 39.96; GBP 4.99 newsstand/cover. adv. back issues avail. **Document type:** *Magazine, Consumer.* **Description:** Contains news, tips and advice on all aspects of Dreamcast games and gaming.
Published by: Dennis Publishing Ltd., 30 Cleveland St, London, W1P 5FF, United Kingdom. TEL 44-20-7631-1433, FAX 44-207-636-5668, http://www.dreamcastmag.co.uk, http://www.theden.co.uk.

794.8 GBR
DREAMCAST MAGAZINE; the world's most advanced console magazine. Text in English. 13/yr. GBP 17 in United Kingdom; GBP 22 in Europe; GBP 40 elsewhere; GBP 350 newsstand/cover (effective 2001). back issues avail. **Document type:** *Magazine, Consumer.* **Description:** Contains the latest news, previews and reviews of Dreamcast games.
Published by: Paragon Publishing Ltd., Paragon House, 10 St Peters Rd, Bournemouth, Dorset BH1 2JS, United Kingdom. TEL 44-1202-299900, FAX 44-1202-299955, 44-1202-200217, subs@paragon.co.uk, http://www.paragon.co.uk. Ed. Simon Phillips. Adv. contact Felicity Mead TEL 44-1202-200224.

794.8 GBR ISSN 1350-1593
EDGE. Text in English. 1993. 13/yr. GBP 34.95 in United Kingdom; GBP 3.50 newsstand/cover; GBP 59 in Europe; GBP 79 rest of world (effective 2000). adv. **Document type:** *Consumer.* **Description:** Committed to introducing future video-gaming technology for those on the leading edge of the games' frontier.
—CCC.
Published by: Future Publishing Ltd., Beauford Court, 30 Monmouth St, Bath, Avon BA1 2BW, United Kingdom. TEL 44-1225-442244, FAX 44-1225-732285, tony.mott@futurenet.co.uk, http://www.futurenet.com, http://www.futurenet.com/futureonline. Ed. Tony Mott. adv.: color page GBP 2,000; trim 210 x 280. Circ: 27,350 (paid).

794.8 USA ISSN 1063-8326
GV1469.15
ELECTRONIC GAMES✶. Text in English. 1992. bi-m. USD 24.95; USD 100 foreign. adv. software rev.
Indexed: ATI.
Published by: Decker Publications (Subsidiary of: Sendai Communications), 800 Jorie Blvd., Ste. 110, Oak Brook, IL 60523-2216. TEL 708-916-7222. Ed. Marc Camron. Circ: 250,000 (paid).

▼ **ELECTRONIC GAMING BUSINESS.** see *ELECTRONICS*

794.8 USA ISSN 1058-918X
ELECTRONIC GAMING MONTHLY. Text in English. 1986. m. USD 19.97 domestic; USD 35.97 foreign (effective 2005). adv. illus. reprints avail. **Document type:** *Magazine, Consumer.* **Description:** Covers all video games and game systems.
Related titles: Online - full text ed.: (from bigchalk, EBSCO Publishing, Gale Group, ProQuest Information & Learning).
Indexed: MicrocompInd.
—CCC.
Published by: Ziff Davis Media Game Group (Subsidiary of: Ziff Davis Media Inc.), 28 E 28th St, New York, NY 10016-7930. TEL 212-503-3500, info@ziffdavis.com, http://www.egmmag.com, http://www.ziffdavis.com. Ed. Joe Fielder. Pub. Lee Uniacke. adv.: page USD 15,975. Circ: 398,219 (paid). **Dist. in UK by:** Comag, Tavistock Works, Tavistock Rd, W Drayton, Middx UB7 7QX, United Kingdom. TEL 44-1895-444055, FAX 44-1895-433602.

794.8 GBR ISSN 1365-411X
ESSENTIAL PLAYSTATION. Text in English. 1996. q. GBP 4.99 newsstand/cover. adv. **Document type:** *Consumer.*
—CCC.
Published by: Future Publishing Ltd., Beauford Court, 30 Monmouth St, Bath, Avon BA1 2BW, United Kingdom. TEL 44-1225-442244, FAX 44-1225-732285, will.groves@futurenet.co.uk, http://www.futurenet.com, http://www.futurenet.com/futureonline. Ed. Will Groves. adv.: color page GBP 3,995. Circ: 173,412 (paid). **Subscr. to:** Freepost BS4900, Somerton, Somers TA11 6BR, United Kingdom. TEL 44-1458-271126.

EUROPE-ECHECS. see *SPORTS AND GAMES*

794.8 USA ISSN 1520-4502
EXPERT CODEBOOK. Variant title: Expert Gamer Expert Codebook. Text in English. 2/yr. USD 9.95 newsstand/cover (effective 2001). adv. software rev.; Website rev. **Document type:** *Magazine, Consumer.* **Description:** Contains tips, tricks, cheats and advice on how to reach the upper levels of various games.
Published by: Ziff Davis Media Game Group (Subsidiary of: Ziff Davis Media Inc.), 28 E 28th St, New York, NY 10016-7930. TEL 415-547-8000, FAX 415-547-8777, info@ziffdavis.com, http://www.ziffdavis.com.

794.8 USA
EXPERT GAMER BUYER'S GUIDE. Text in English. a. USD 5.99 newsstand/cover (effective 2001). adv. software rev.; Website rev. **Document type:** *Magazine, Consumer.* **Description:** Contains reviews on the best systems and games available.
Published by: Ziff Davis Media Game Group (Subsidiary of: Ziff Davis Media Inc.), 28 E 28th St, New York, NY 10016-7930. TEL 415-547-8000, FAX 415-547-8777, info@ziffdavis.com, http://www.ziffdavis.com.

794.8 ITA ISSN 1128-3858
EXTREME PLAYSTATION. Text in Italian. 1999. m. **Document type:** *Magazine, Consumer.* **Description:** Contains Playstation game reviews and strategic hints.
Related titles: ◆ English ed.: Extreme Playstation. ISSN 1369-3476.
Published by: Comic Art Publishing, Via Flavio Domiziano, 9, Rome, RM 00145, Italy. TEL 39-06-5413737, FAX 39-06-5410775, comicart@mix.it, http://www.mix.it/comicart. Ed. Roberto Genovesi. **Dist. by:** Parrini & C, Piazza Colonna 361, Rome, RM 00187, Italy. TEL 39-06-695141.

794.8 GBR ISSN 1369-3476
EXTREME PLAYSTATION. Text in English. 1997. m. GBP 26 domestic; GBP 35 in the European Union; GBP 65 elsewhere; GBP 2.95 newsstand/cover. adv. back issues avail. **Document type:** *Consumer.*
Related titles: ◆ Italian ed.: Extreme Playstation. ISSN 1128-3858.
Published by: Quay Magazine Publishing Ltd., 22 Strand St, Poole, Dorset BH15 1SB, United Kingdom. TEL 44-1202-679000, FAX 44-1202-679002. Ed. Ian Osbourne. Pub. Neil Harris. Adv. contact Jonathan Shaw. **Dist. by:** Seymour Distribution Ltd, 86 Newman St, London W1T 3EX, United Kingdom. TEL 44-20-73968000, FAX 44-20-73968002.

794.8 USA ISSN 1530-5007
FLIGHT SIMULATOR WORLD. Text in English. 1975. bi-m. USD 7.95 per issue; USD 39. adv. **Document type:** *Consumer.* **Description:** Offers users of Microsoft Flight Simulator tips on maximizing use of the software and advice on peripheral devices.
Formerly (until 2000): Full Throttle (0183-5181)
Published by: Abacus, 5130 Patterson Ave SE, # A, Grand Rapids, MI 49512-5343. editor@flightsimulatorworld.com, http://www.flightsimulatorworld.com. Ed. Tim Dickens. Pub. Arnie Lee.

794.8 USA
FOUL; videogame subculture. Text in English. 2001 (Jun.). m. USD 1 newsstand/cover (effective 2002). adv. **Document type:** *Magazine, Consumer.* **Description:** Dedicated to all aspects of the video game subculture.
Related titles: Online - full text ed.
Published by: Multimedia Empire Inc., 18 Saint Marks Pl, New York, NY 10003. TEL 212-995-8324, http://www.foulmag.com, http://www.multimedia.com. Ed. Jesse Labroca.

794.8 ISR ISSN 0792-9145
FRICK 2000. Text in Hebrew. 1992. m. USD 60 (effective 2000).
Published by: Etzb'oni Publishing House, P O Box 28110, Tel Aviv, 61280, Israel. FAX 972-3-5373906. Ed. Rami Shir. Circ: 15,000.

794.8 GBR
G-CUBE SOLUTIONZONE. Text in English. 2002 (Aug.). irreg. **Document type:** *Magazine, Consumer.* **Description:** Covers GameCube tips and guides to GameCube titles.
Published by: Live Publishing International Ltd., Europa House, Adlington Park, Macclesfield, Cheshire SK10 4NP, United Kingdom. TEL 44-1625-855086, FAX 44-1625-855071, subs@livepublishing.co.uk, http://www.livepublishing.co.uk/. Eds. Paul Roundell, Wayne Williams. Pub. Robin Wilkinson. Adv. contact Kenny Leslie.

794.8 USA ISSN 1544-6816
▼ **G M R.** Text in English. 2003 (Feb.). m. USD 4.95 newsstand/cover (effective 2003). adv. **Document type:** *Magazine, Consumer.* **Description:** Covers news and previous of the latest computer and video games.
Related titles: Online - full text ed.: (from bigchalk, ProQuest Information & Learning).
Published by: Ziff Davis Media Game Group (Subsidiary of: Ziff Davis Media Inc.), 28 E 28th St, New York, NY 10016-7930. TEL 415-547-8000, FAX 415-547-8777, info@ziffdavis.com, http://gamegroup.ziffdavis.com/about/gmr.html, http://www.ziffdavis.com. Ed. Simon Cox. adv.: B&W page USD 4,500, color page USD 5,600; trim 8.25 x 10.25. Circ: 225,000.

794.8 USA
GADGETBOY GAZETTE. Text in English. 1995. w. Free. **Description:** Provides descriptive information on new products ranging from audio and video games to small office and computer items.
Formerly: GadgetBoy
Address: http://www.gadgetboy.com. Ed. Stephen Jacobs.

794.8 ITA ISSN 1128-4412
GALAXY PLAYSTATION. Text in Italian. 1999. m. **Document type:** *Magazine, Consumer.* **Description:** Contains tips for Playstation game users.
Published by: Comic Art Publishing, Via Flavio Domiziano, 9, Rome, RM 00145, Italy.

794.8 USA ISSN 1520-9695
GV1469.15
GAME BUYER. Text in English. 1996. m. GBP 2.95 newsstand/cover (effective 2000). **Document type:** *Consumer.* **Description:** Reviews and rates every PC and video game released for every platform every month.
Formerly (until 1998): Ultra Game Players (1091-1685)
Published by: Future Network USA, 150 North Hill Dr, Ste 40, Brisbane, CA 94005. TEL 415-468-4684, FAX 415-468-4686, webmaster@imaginemedia.com, btolinski@futurenetworkusa.com, http://www.imaginemedia.com, http://www.futurenetworkusa.com/.

794.8 USA ISSN 1073-922X
GAME DEVELOPER. Text in English. 1994. bi-m. USD 49.95 domestic; USD 69.95 in Canada & Mexico; USD 99.95 elsewhere; free to qualified personnel (effective 2005). adv. bk.rev.; software rev. charts; illus.; tr.lit. back issues avail. **Document type:** *Trade.* **Description:** Covers all areas of game development from music to graphics to team management. Aimed at game developers, designers and programmers.
Related titles: Online - full text ed.: (from bigchalk, Florida Center for Library Automation, Gale Group, H.W. Wilson, LexisNexis, O C L C Online Computer Library Center, Inc., ProQuest Information & Learning).
Indexed: ABIn, BPI, CompD, MicrocompInd.
—CCC.

Published by: C M P Media LLC (Subsidiary of: United News & Media), 600 Harrison St, 6th Fl., San Francisco, CA 94107. TEL 415-947-6746, FAX 415-947-6041, http://www.gdmag.com/homepage.htm, http://www.cmp.com. Ed. Jamil Moledina. Pub. Michelle Maguire. adv.: B&W page USD 2,495; trim 10.88 x 8. Circ: 35,000.

794.8 USA ISSN 1067-6392
GAME INFORMER MAGAZINE. Text in English. 1991. m. USD 19.98 domestic; USD 4.99 newsstand/cover domestic; USD 6.99 newsstand/cover in Canada (effective 2002). adv. bk.rev. **Document type:** *Magazine, Consumer.* **Description:** Provides news, reviews and information regarding forthcoming video game hardware and software. Also provides CD-ROM and multi-media coverage.
Address: 724 N. 1st St., Flr. 4, Minneapolis, MN 55401-2885. customerservice@gameinformer.com, http://www.gameinformer.com. Ed. Andrew McNamara. Pub. Cathy Preston. R&P Vicky Valley TEL 952-946-7274. Adv. contact Rob Borm. B&W page USD 4,954, color page USD 6,140; trim 8 x 10.75. Circ: 200,000 (paid).

794.8 USA ISSN 1074-2425
GV1469.15
GAME PLAYERS SEGA NINTENDO. Text in English. 1988. m. USD 26.50 domestic; USD 41.20 in Canada. adv. **Document type:** *Consumer.* **Description:** Provides hints and strategies for video games played on Super NES, Nintendo, Game Boy, Genesis, Sega CD and Game Gear systems. Includes game descriptions and screen shots to allow readers to preview games before purchasing.
Formerly (until 1994): Game Players Nintendo Sega (1068-1809); Formed by the merger of: Game Player's Guide to Nintendo (1059-2172); Which incorporates (1990-1991): Game Player's Strategy Guide to Game Boy Games; Game Players Sega Guide (1065-3376); Which was formerly (until 1992): Game Player's Sega Genesis Strategy Guide (1052-763X)
Published by: Future Network USA, 150 North Hill Dr, Ste 40, Brisbane, CA 94005. TEL 415-468-4684, FAX 415-468-4686. Ed. Leslie Mizell. Circ: 400,000.

794.8 USA
GAME REPORT ONLINE. Text in English. 1994. q. **Document type:** *Consumer.*
Media: Online - full content.
Address: 1920 N 49th St., Seattle, WA 98103. editor@gamereport.com, http://www.gamereport.com. Ed. Peter Sarrett.

794.8 ITA ISSN 1129-0455
GAME REPUBLIC. Text in Italian. 1999. m. EUR 5 newsstand/cover (effective 2003). adv. **Document type:** *Magazine, Consumer.*
Published by: Play Press Publishing s.r.l., Via Vitorchiano 123, Rome, RM 00189, Italy. TEL 39-06-33221250, FAX 39-06-33221235, abbonamenti@playpress.com, http://www.playpress.com. Ed. Sergio Pennachini. Pub. Alessandro Ferri. Adv. contact Lorenza Borroni TEL 39-02-45472867. Circ: 50,000 (paid and controlled).

794.8 NOR
➤ **GAME STUDIES**; the international journal of computer game research. Text in English. 2001. irreg. free (effective 2005). **Document type:** *Academic/Scholarly.* **Description:** Its primary focus is aesthetic, cultural and communicative aspects of computer games.
Media: Online - full content.
Address: http://www.gamestudies.org. Ed. Dr. Espen Aarseth.

794.8 ITA
GAME ZERO MAGAZINE. Text in English. 1997. irreg.
Media: Online - full content.
Address: http://www.vol.it/team-0/contents.html.

794.8 DEU
GAMEPRO. Text in German. 2000. m. EUR 51 domestic; EUR 60 foreign; EUR 4.99 newsstand/cover (effective 2003). adv. **Document type:** *Magazine, Consumer.*
Published by: I D G Communications Verlag AG, Leopoldstr 252b, Munich, 80807, Germany. TEL 49-89-36086532, FAX 49-89-36086570, post@gamepro.de, info@idg-verlag.de, http://www.gamepro.de, http://www.idg-verlag.de. adv.: B&W page EUR 5,500, color page EUR 7,700. Circ: 205,000 (controlled).

794.8 USA ISSN 1042-8658
GAMEPRO; world's largest multiplatform gaming magazine. Text in English. 1989. m. USD 39.95 for 6 mos. (effective 2005). adv. back issues avail. **Document type:** *Magazine, Consumer.* **Description:** Information for young video game players on the newest games and the best tips for playing, with emphasis on Nintendo and Sega.
Related titles: Spanish ed.
Published by: I D G Communications Inc., 555 12TH St, Oakland, CA 94607-4002. TEL 510-768-2700, FAX 510-768-2701, comments.gamepro@gamepro.com, http://www.gamepro.com. adv.: page USD 24,185; trim 8 x 10.5. Circ: 564,702. **Dist. in UK by:** Seymour Distribution Ltd, 86 Newman St, London W1T 3EX, United Kingdom.

794.8 GRC ISSN 1109-1819
GAMEPRO COLLECTION. Text in Greek. 1998. irreg. **Document type:** *Magazine, Consumer.*
Published by: Hyperpress S.A., 52 Dekeleias Str., N. Halkidona, Athens, 143 43, Greece. TEL 30-1-252-7000, FAX 30-1-252-5180, marketing@hyperpress.gr, http://www.hyperpress.gr.

004.3 GRC ISSN 1108-863X
GAMEPRO GREECE. Text in Greek. 1996. 11/yr. EUR 3.50 newsstand/cover (effective 2002). adv. **Document type:** *Magazine, Consumer.* **Description:** Filled with reviews and news concerning the most recent developments in the field of video games worldwide.
Published by: Hyperpress S.A., 52 Dekeleias Str., N. Halkidona, Athens, 143 43, Greece. TEL 30-1-252-7000, FAX 30-1-252-5180, gamepro.mag@hyperpress.gr, http://www.hyperpress.gr/bgameproen.htm. adv.: color page EUR 1,050; trim 220 x 300. Circ: 22,000 (paid and controlled).

794.8 LBN
GAMEPRO MIDDLE EAST. Text in Arabic. 1999. m. **Document type:** *Magazine, Consumer.*
Published by: Nahas Publishing House, Radwan Ctr., 9th Fl., PO Box 11/9718, Verdun, Beirut, Lebanon. TEL 96-11-743-633, FAX 96-11-743-631, nahasleb@dm.net.lb.

794.8 TUR
GAMEPRO TURKEY. Text in Turkish. m. adv. **Document type:** *Magazine, Consumer.* **Description:** Contains game reviews, previews, strategy guides, and product information for both PC and console gaming sytems.
Related titles: Online - full text ed.
Published by: I M G Bilisim Yayinlari, Istiklal Caddesi, Ors Turistik is Merkezi, No. 251/253, Beyoglu-Istanbul, 80060, Turkey. TEL 90-212-292-8210, FAX 90-212-292-8211, mektup@gamepro.com.tr, http://www.gamepro.com.tr, http://www.imgbilisim.com. adv.: color page USD 1,400; trim 190 x 275. Circ: 15,000 (paid and controlled).

794.8 USA ISSN 1520-5169
GAMERS' REPUBLIC. Text in English. 1998. m. USD 14.99; USD 24.99 in Canada; USD 29.99 elsewhere. **Document type:** *Consumer.* **Description:** Covers all aspects of computer and console games and entertainment.
Published by: Millenium Publications, Inc. TEL 818-889-3821, subs@gamersrepublic.com, http://www.gamersrepublic.com.

794.8 GRC ISSN 1107-356X
GAMES. Text in Greek. 1996. m. USD 55 (effective 1998).
Published by: Terzopoulos Publishing Ltd., 7 Fragoklisias St, Maroussi, Athens 151 25, Greece. TEL 30-1-689-6366, FAX 30-1-680-6631, gea@compulink.gr.

▼ **GAMES AND CULTURE**; a journal of interactive media. see *SPORTS AND GAMES*

794.8 USA ISSN 1523-7516
GAMES BUSINESS. Text in English. s-m. USD 75 (effective 2000). **Document type:** *Magazine, Trade.*
Published by: Future Network USA, 150 North Hill Dr, Ste 40, Brisbane, CA 94005. TEL 415-468-4684, FAX 415-468-4686, webmaster@imaginemedia.com, btolinski@futurenetworkusa.com, http://www.imaginemedia.com, http://www.futurenetworkusa.com/.

794.8 FRA ISSN 1628-8890
GAMES COLLECTOR. Text in French. 2001. q. FRF 59 newsstand/cover (effective 2001). adv. software rev.; Website rev. **Document type:** *Magazine, Consumer.*
Published by: Future France, 101-109 Rue Jean Jaures, Levallois Perret, 92300, France. TEL 33-1-41273838, yveline.duville@futurenet.fr.

794.8 GBR
GAMES DOMAIN REVIEW. Text in English. 1994. w. **Document type:** *Consumer.*
Media: Online - full content.
Address: 435 Lichfield Rd., Aston, Birmingham, B67 SS, United Kingdom. TEL 44-121-326-0900, http://www.gamesdomain.co.uk/help/newsletter.html. Ed. Rich Greenhill.

794.8 ITA ISSN 1127-1221
THE GAMES MACHINE. Text in Italian. 1988. m. adv. **Document type:** *Magazine, Consumer.*
Related titles: Online - full content ed.
Published by: Xenia Edizioni Srl, Via Dell' Annunciata, 31, Milan, MI 20121, Italy. TEL 39-2-66804505, FAX 39-2-66804478, http://www.tgmonline.it/. Circ: 72,000.

794.8 GBR
GAMES T M; for gamers who know. (Trade Mark) Text in English. 2002. m. GBP 4 newsstand/cover (effective 2003). 180 p./no.; **Document type:** *Magazine, Consumer.* **Description:** Covers all aspects of computer & video gaming past, present & future.
Published by: Paragon Publishing Ltd., Paragon House, 10 St Peters Rd, Bournemouth, Dorset BH1 2JS, United Kingdom. TEL 44-1202-299900, FAX 44-1202-299955, subs@paragon.co.uk, http://www.paragon.co.uk/mags/gamestm.html. Ed. Simon Phillips.

794.8 DEU
GAMESHOP. Text in German. 1998. 10/yr. free newsstand/cover. adv. **Document type:** *Magazine, Consumer.* **Description:** Contains consumer information on the latest game releases.
Published by: Entertainment Media Verlag GmbH und Co. oHG, Einsteinring 24, Dornach, 85609, Germany. TEL 49-89-45114-0, FAX 49-89-45114444, emv@e-media.de, http://www.ebiz.de/ppages/gs/index.htm, http://www.mediabiz.de. Ed. Hans Fuchs. Adv. contact Matthias Teichmann. B&W page EUR 6,250, color page EUR 7,780. Circ: 257,267 (controlled).

794.8 GBR ISSN 0967-9855
GAMESMASTER. Text in English. 1993. 15/yr. GBP 24.75 in United Kingdom; GBP 2.75 newsstand/cover; GBP 36.90 in Europe; GBP 46.50 rest of world (effective 2000). adv. **Document type:** *Consumer.* **Description:** Guide to multi-format videogaming filled with news, game previews, tips, reviews, and player guides.
—CCC.
Published by: Future Publishing Ltd., Beauford Court, 30 Monmouth St, Bath, Avon BA1 2BW, United Kingdom. TEL 44-1225-442244, FAX 44-1225-732285, marcus.hawkins@futurenet.co.uk, http://www.futurenet.com, http://www.futurenet.com/futureonline. Ed. Marcus Hawkins. adv.: color page GBP 2,050. Circ: 64,565 (paid).

794.8 DEU
GAMESTAR; die ganze Welt der PC-Spiele. Text in German. 1997. m. EUR 50.04; EUR 46.68 to students; EUR 4.99 newsstand/cover (effective 2003). adv. **Document type:** *Magazine, Consumer.*
Published by: I D G Communications Verlag AG, Leopoldstr 252b, Munich, 80807, Germany. TEL 49-89-36086532, FAX 49-89-36086570, brief@gamestar.de, info@idg-verlag.de, http://www.gamestar.de, http://www.idg-verlag.de. Ed. Anita Thiel. adv.: B&W page EUR 6,900, color page EUR 8,900. Circ: 351,943 (paid and controlled). **Subscr. to:** dsb Abo-Betreuung GmbH, Konrad-Zuse-Str 16, Neckarsulm 74172, Germany. TEL 49-7132-959-0, FAX 49-7132-959105.

C

794.8 USA ISSN 1552-9738
▼ **GAMESTAR.** Text in English. 2004 (Sum). 8/yr. USD 29.97 (effective 2005). adv. **Document type:** *Magazine, Consumer.*
Published by: I D G Communications Inc., 555 12TH St, Oakland, CA 94607-4002. TEL 510-768-2700, FAX 510-768-2701, http://www.idg.com/. Ed. Wataru Maruyama. Adv. contact Greg Fox.

794.8 CZE ISSN 1212-3331
GAMESTAR CZECH REPUBLIC. Text in Czech, Slovak. 1998. m. CZK 1,176, SKK 1,404 (effective 2002). adv. **Document type:** *Magazine, Consumer.* **Description:** Provides the latest information and reviews on PC games and the gaming industry.
Related titles: Online - full text ed.: ISSN 1212-6837.
Published by: I D G Czech, a.s., Seydlerova 2451-11, Prague 5, 158 00, Czech Republic. TEL 420-2-57088111, FAX 420-2-6520812, info@idg.cz, http://www.gamestar.cz, http://www.idg.cz. Ed. Ivan Siler. adv.: color page USD 1,631; trim 210 x 295. Circ: 35,000 (paid and controlled).

794.8 HUN ISSN 1585-3187
GAMESTAR HUNGARY. Text in Hungarian. 1994. m. HUF 12,504 (effective 2002). adv. **Document type:** *Magazine, Consumer.* **Description:** Provides information and reviews on the latest games as well as all other aspects of the virtual gaming world.
Formerly (until 1999): PC-X Magazin (1218-358X)
Related titles: Online - full text ed.
Published by: I D G Hungary Kft., PO Box 386, Budapest, 1537, Hungary. TEL 361-474-8850, FAX 361-269-5676, http://www.gamestar.hu, http://www.idg.hu. adv.: color page USD 690; trim 205 x 288. Circ: 25,000 (paid and controlled).

794.8 USA ISSN 1097-394X
GAMEWEEK; the newspaper of the interactive entertainment industry. Text in English. 1985. 44/yr. USD 99 domestic; USD 149 in Europe; USD 200 elsewhere; USD 3.95 newsstand/cover domestic; USD 6.95 newsstand/cover in Canada (effective 2000). adv. software rev. illus. reprints avail. **Document type:** *Newspaper.* **Description:** Features industry news, product reviews and previews, release schedules, articles, and analysis on interactive entertainment for an audience comprised of industry participants and the retail community.
Formerly (until 1998): Videogame Advisor (1085-5130)
Related titles: Online - full text ed.: (from America Online, Inc.).
Indexed: SoftBase.
Published by: CyberActive Publishing, 64 Danbury Rd, Ste 500, Wilton, CT 06897. TEL 203-761-6150, hal@gameweek.com, jim@gameweek.com, http://www.gameweek.com/. Eds. Mike Davila, Mike Davila.

794.8 DNK ISSN 1600-2717
GAMEZONE. Text in Danish. 1995. m. DKK 685 inc. Privat Computer (effective 2004). **Document type:** *Consumer.*
Formerly (until 1999): CD-ROM Spil (1396-7541)
Related titles: ♦ Issued with: Privat Computer. ISSN 1398-7224.

Published by: Audio Media A-S, St Kongensgade 72, Copenhagen K, 1264, Denmark. TEL 45-33-912833, FAX 45-33-910121, forlaget@audio.dk, http://www.audio.dk. Ed. Torben Okholm.

794.8 USA
▼ **GAMING INDUSTRY NEWS.** Text in English. 2003. m. USD 995 (effective 2004). **Document type:** *Newsletter, Trade.* **Description:** Provides up-to-date news, inside analysis, business/technology trends and commentary on the electronic videogame industry.
Published by: Ziff Davis Media Game Group (Subsidiary of: Ziff Davis Media Inc.), 28 E 28th St, New York, NY 10016-7930. TEL 212-503-3500, gin@omeda.com, info@ziffdavis.com, https://www.zdmcirc.com/zdmcirc/gin/www/index.html, http://www.ziffdavis.com. Ed. Jimmy Guterman TEL 847-559-7339.

794.8 USA
GAMING INTELLIGENCE. Text in English. 1997. w.
Media: Online - full content.
Address: 409 Berg Ave, East Meadow, NY 11554. http://www.rpg.net/gi. Ed. Mitchell Gross.

794.8 ITA ISSN 1125-601X
GIOCHI PER IL MIO COMPUTER. Text in Italian. 1997. m. (13/yr.). EUR 67 (effective 2005). adv. **Document type:** *Magazine, Consumer.*
Published by: Future Media Italy SpA, Via Asiago 45, Milano, MI 20128, Italy. TEL 39-02-2529161, FAX 39-02-26005520, info@futuremediaitaly.it, http://www.futuremediaitaly.it.

794.8 USA ISSN 1547-6057
▼ **HARLEY HAHN'S GUIDE TO MUDS.** Text in English. 2003. a. USD 20 per issue (effective 2003).
Media: Online - full content.
Published by: Harley Hahn, 2022 Cliff Dr., Santa Barbara, CA 93109. TEL 805-564-5000, http://hhe.harley.com/gm/chapters/homepage.html, http://www.harley.com. Pub. Hahn Harley.

794.8 ESP
HOBBY CONSOLAS. Text in Spanish. 1991. 12/yr. adv. **Document type:** *Magazine, Consumer.* **Description:** Covers console video games: Sega, Nintendo, Playstation, and more.
Published by: Hobby Press S.A. (Subsidiary of: Axel Springer Verlag AG), C/ Los Vascos 17, Madrid, 28040, Spain. TEL 34-902-111315, FAX 34-902-151798, http://www.hobbypress.es. Pub. Amalio Gomez. Adv. contact Maria Perera. Circ: 73,000 (paid).

HOME ENTERTAINMENT IRELAND. see *COMMUNICATIONS—Video*

HOME ENTERTAINMENT WEEK. see *COMMUNICATIONS—Video*

794.1 NLD ISSN 1389-6911
➤ **I C G A JOURNAL.** (International Computer Games Association) Text in English. 1983. q. EUR 40 domestic to individuals; GBP 25 in United Kingdom to individuals; USD 40 elsewhere to individuals; USD 160 foreign to institutions; USD 80 foreign to libraries (effective 2001). bk.rev. back issues avail.; reprint service avail. from ISI. **Document type:** *Journal, Academic/Scholarly.* **Description:** For aficionados of computer games.
Formerly (until 2000): I C C A Journal (International Computer Chess Association) (0920-234X)
Indexed: ASCA, CMCI, SSCI.
—IDS.
Published by: International Computer Games Association, c/o H.J. van den Herik, Ed, Universiteit Maastricht, Department of Computer Science, PO Box 616, Maastricht, 6200 MD, Netherlands. TEL 31-43-3883477, FAX 31-43-3884897, info@icga.org, http://www.icga.org. Ed., R&P H J van den Herik. Circ: 500.

794.8 NLD
I M P BRIDGE MAGAZINE. Text in English. 1995. m.
Media: Online - full content.
Address: 2512 GA, The Hague, Netherlands. http://www.imp-bridge.nl. Ed. Jan Van Cleeff.

794.8 DNK ISSN 1501-8997
INCITE P C GAMES. Text in Danish. 1999. m. adv. **Document type:** *Magazine, Consumer.*
Published by: Bonnier Publications AS, Strandboulevarden 130, Copenhagen Oe, 2100, Denmark. TEL 45-39-172000, FAX 45-39-290199, bp@bp.bonnier.dk, http://www.bonnierpublications.com.

794.8 USA
INQUEST GAMER. Text in English. 1995. m. USD 28 domestic; CND 55 in Canada; USD 80 elsewhere; USD 4.99 newsstand/cover (effective 2005). adv. **Document type:** *Magazine, Consumer.* **Description:** Contains information on role-playing adventure modules, CCG players guides, and price guides that include every Magic card ever made.
Formerly (until 1999): Inquest (1081-924X)
Indexed: SoftBase.
Published by: Wizard Entertainment, 151 Wells Ave, Congers, NY 10920. TEL 914-268-2000, FAX 914-268-2392, customerservice@WizardUniverse.com, http://www.wizarduniverse.com/magazines/inquest.cfm. Ed. Patricia McCallum. Pub. Gareb S Shamus. R&P Martha Donato. Adv. contact Karen Evora.

INTERACTIVE GAMING NEWS. see *SPORTS AND GAMES*

THE INTERNATIONAL SIMULATION AND GAMING RESEARCH YEARBOOK. see *COMPUTERS—Computer Simulation*

794.8 CHE
➤ **INTERNATIONAL SOCIETY OF DYNAMIC GAMES. ANNALS.** Text in English. 1994. irreg. CHF 148. **Document type:** *Monographic series, Academic/Scholarly.* **Description:** Studies various areas of mathematical, logical, and classical mathematics.
Indexed: CCMJ, ZentMath.
—ingenta.
Published by: (International Society of Dynamic Games), Birkhaeuser Verlag AG (Subsidiary of: Springer Science+Business Media), Viaduktstr 42, Postfach 133, Basel, 4051, Switzerland. TEL 41-61-2050707, FAX 41-61-2050792, birkhauser@springer.de, http://www.birkhauser.ch. **Dist. by:** Springer GmbH Auslieferungsgesellschaft, Haberstr 7, Heidelberg 69126, Germany. TEL 49-6221-3454324, FAX 49-6221-345229; **Dist. in N. America by:** Springer-Verlag.

794.8 USA
INTROSPECTION. Text in English. 1996. irreg. **Document type:** *Newsletter.* **Description:** Dedicated to literary writing and opinion.
Media: Online - full text.
Address: 32419 Seventh Ave S W, Federal Way, WA 98023. akkbar@wa.net, http://web.wa.net/~akkbar/. Ed. Dan Hardwicke.

379.8 FRA ISSN 1625-449X
JEUX VIDEO. Text in French. 2000. m. FRF 15 newsstand/cover (effective 2001). adv. software rev.; Website rev. **Document type:** *Magazine, Consumer.*
Published by: Future France, 101-109 Rue Jean Jaures, Levallois Perret, 92300, France. TEL 33-1-41273838, yveline.duville@futurenet.fr.

681.3 SVN ISSN 1318-461X
JOKER. Text in Slovenian. 1992. m. SIT 6,912 (effective 2002). adv. **Document type:** *Magazine, Consumer.*
Published by: Delo Revije d.o.o., Dunajska 5, Ljubljana, 1509, Slovenia. TEL 386-1-4737000, FAX 386-1-4737352, joker@amadej.si, narocnine@delo-revije.si, http://joker.amadej.si, http://www.delo-revije.si. adv.: page SIT 140,000.

794.8 793 USA ISSN 1543-9399
QA76.76.C672
▼ ➤ **JOURNAL OF GAME DEVELOPMENT.** Text in English. 2004. q. USD 100 to individuals; USD 300 to institutions (effective 2004). **Document type:** *Journal, Academic/Scholarly.* **Description:** Presents original research and theoretical underpinnings that detail the most recent findings in game development related academic disciplines, hardware, software, and technology that will directly affect the way games are conceived, developed, produced, and delivered.
Published by: Charles River Media, 10 Downer Ave, Hingham, MA 02043. TEL 781-740-0400, 800-382-8505, FAX 781-740-8816, info@charlesriver.com, http://www.jogd.com/index.html, http://www.charlesriver.com. Ed. Jennifer Niles.

794.8 FRA ISSN 1163-586X
JOYPAD. Text in French. 1991. m. adv. **Document type:** *Magazine, Consumer.*
Published by: Future France, 101-109 Rue Jean Jaures, Levallois Perret, 92300, France. TEL 33-1-41273838, yveline.duville@futurenet.fr.

794.8 FRA ISSN 1145-4806
JOYSTICK. Text in French. 1988. m. adv. **Document type:** *Magazine, Consumer.*
Formerly (until 1990): Joystick Hebdo (0994-4559)
Published by: Future France, 101-109 Rue Jean Jaures, Levallois Perret, 92300, France. TEL 33-1-41273838, yveline.duville@futurenet.fr.

794.8 POL ISSN 1428-5894
KAWAII. Text in Polish. 1997. bi-m. PLZ 7.50 newsstand/cover (effective 2003). adv. software rev.; Website rev. **Document type:** *Magazine, Consumer.*
Related titles: Online - full text ed.: ISSN 1689-1554.
Published by: Wydawnictwo Bauer Sp. z o.o. (Subsidiary of: Heinrich Bauer Verlag), ul. Motorowa 1, Warsaw, 04-035, Poland. TEL 48-22-5170500, FAX 48-22-5170125, kawaii@kawaii.com.pl, kontakt@bauer.pl, http://www.kawaii.com.pl, http://www.bauer.pl. Ed. Pawel Musialowski. Adv. contact Katarzyna Jablonska. page PLZ 3,500; trim 230 x 307.

794.8 658 GBR ISSN 1465-9298
KEY NOTE MARKET REPORT: ELECTRONIC GAMES. Text in English. 1994. irreg., latest 2000, Dec. GBP 340 per issue (effective 2002). **Document type:** *Trade.* **Description:** Provides an overview of the UK electronic games market, including industry structure, market size and trends, developments, prospects, and major company profiles.
Formerly (until 1998): Key Note Report: Electronic Games (1354-3350)
Related titles: CD-ROM ed.; Online - full text ed.
Published by: Key Note Ltd., Field House, 72 Oldfield Rd, Hampton, Mddx TW12 2HQ, United Kingdom. TEL 44-20-8481-8750, FAX 44-20-8783-0049, info@keynote.co.uk, http://www.keynote.co.uk. Ed. Jacob Howard.

KIDS ZONE. see *CHILDREN AND YOUTH—For*

621.8 ROM ISSN 1582-1498
LEVEL. Variant title: Level International Games Magazine. Text in Romanian. 1997. m. adv. **Document type:** *Magazine, Consumer.*
Published by: Vogel Publishing Srl., Bd. N. D. Cocea nr. 12, et. 1-2, Brasov, 2200, Romania. TEL 40-68-415158, FAX 40-68-415158.

794.8 CZE ISSN 1211-068X
LEVEL. Text in Czech. 1995. m. CZK 480; CZK 1,992 with CD (effective 2001). adv. **Document type:** *Magazine, Consumer.* **Description:** Contains features and articles on gaming software and hardware for PCs.
Published by: Vogel Burda Communications s.r.o., Sokolovska 73, Prague 8, 18621, Czech Republic. TEL 42-2-21808566, FAX 42-2-21808500, level@vogel.cz, http://www.level.cz. Ed. Jan Herodes. Adv. contact Jana Zahalkova. color page EUR 1,950; trim 220 x 290. Circ: 46,838 (paid).

794.8 DEU
LEVEL UP!; das clevere PS2-Magazin. Text in German. bi-m. EUR 13.50; EUR 2.90 newsstand/cover (effective 2003). adv. **Document type:** *Magazine, Consumer.*
Published by: Schanzenstrassen Verlag GmbH, Schanzenstr 31, Cologne, 51063, Germany. info@levelup-magazin.de, http://www.levelup-magazin.de. adv.: B&W page EUR 2,400, color page EUR 3,100. Circ: 57,000 (paid and controlled).

794.8 USA
LICENSINGWEEK. Text in English. 1998. m. **Document type:** *Trade.* **Description:** Focuses on the licensing aspects of the interactive gaming industry.
Published by: CyberActive Publishing, 64 Danbury Rd, Ste 500, Wilton, CT 06897. TEL 203-761-6150, hal@gameweek.com, jim@gameweek.com, http://www.gameweek.com/. Eds. Mike Davila, Mike Davila.

794.8 GBR ISSN 1469-4832
M C V; the market for home computing & video games. Text in English. 1998. w. GBP 150 domestic; GBP 175 in Europe; GBP 250 elsewhere (effective 2005). adv. **Document type:** *Magazine, Consumer.* **Description:** Provides up-to-date and cutting-edge news and information on the computer gaming industry.
Published by: M C V Media UK Ltd., St Andrew House, 46-48 St Andrew St, Hertford, Herts SG14 1JA, United Kingdom. TEL 44-1992-535646, FAX 44-1992-535648, http://www.mcvuk.com/. Ed. John Minkley. Pub. Stuart Dinsey. Adv. contact Chris Buckley. **Subscr. to:** MCV Subscriptions Dept, 6 Castleham Rd, PO Box 178, St. Leonards-On-Sea, E Sussex TN38 9YT, United Kingdom. TEL 44-1424-797797, FAX 44-1424-854713, mcv.subscriptions@c-cms.com.

794.8 GBR
M C V; the market for home computing & video games. Text in English. w. (Fri.). GBP 150 domestic; GBP 175 in Europe; GBP 250 elsewhere (effective 2003). adv. **Document type:** *Newspaper, Trade.* **Description:** Offers news and expert analysis of electronic games, multimedia and related hardware, with an emphasis on product sales potential and assistance in ordering decisions the retailers need.
Published by: Intent Media Ltd., St Andrew House, 46-48 St Andrew St, Hertford, Hertfordshire SG14 1JA, United Kingdom. TEL 44-1992-535646, FAX 44-1992-535648, http://www.mcvuk.com/. Ed. Samantha Loveday. Adv. contact Chris Buckley. color page USD 5,300; trim 10.5 x 13.75. Circ: 11,500.

794.8 DEU
M C V GAMES MARKT. (Markt fuer Computer- und Videospiele) Text in German. 1994. s-m. EUR 44.50 for 6 mos. (effective 2005). adv. **Document type:** *Magazine, Trade.* **Description:** Offers retail news and expert analysis of all aspects of electronic games, multimedia and related hardware.
Formerly: M C V
Related titles: Online - full text ed.
Published by: Entertainment Media Verlag GmbH und Co. oHG, Einsteinring 24, Dornach, 85609, Germany. TEL 49-89-451140, FAX 49-89-45114444, mcv@computec.de, emv@e-media.de, http://www.mcvonline.de, http://www.mediabiz.de. Ed., Pub. Ulrich Scheele. Adv. contact Stefan Lessmeier. B&W page EUR 3,845, color page EUR 4,900; trim 210 x 297. Circ: 5,800 (paid and controlled).

794.8 DEU
M C V GAMESMARKT.DE. Text in German. 1982. 2/m. EUR 44.50 for 6 mos. (effective 2005). adv. **Document type:** *Magazine, Consumer.* **Description:** Contains the latest news and information on video games and accessories for gaming consoles and PCs.
Formerly: GamesMarkt.de (1614-2497); Which superseded in part (in 2002): Entertainment-Markt (0949-3891); Which was formerly (until 1995): Video-Markt (0723-077X)
Related titles: Online - full text ed.
Published by: Entertainment Media Verlag GmbH und Co. oHG, Einsteinring 24, Dornach, 85609, Germany. TEL 49-89-45114-0, FAX 49-89-45114444, emv@e-media.de, http://www.gamesmarkt.de, http://www.mediabiz.de. adv.: B&W page EUR 3,845, color page EUR 4,900. Circ: 5,850 (paid and controlled).

794 FRA ISSN 1628-3414
M6 TOMB RAIDER. Text in French. 1999. q. **Document type:** *Magazine, Consumer.*
Published by: M6 Interactions, 89 av Charles-de-Gaulle, Neuilly-sur-Seine Cedex, 92575, France. TEL 33-1-41926936, http://www.m6net.fr.

794.8 FRA ISSN 1633-1818
LE MAGAZINE OFFICIEL XBOX. Variant title: Xbox Magazine. Text in French. 2002. m. adv. **Document type:** *Magazine, Consumer.*
Published by: Future France, 101-109 Rue Jean Jaures, Levallois Perret, 92300, France. TEL 33-1-41273838.

794.8 DEU
MANIAC; die ganze Welt der Videospiele. Text in German. 1993. m. EUR 34 (effective 2003). adv. **Document type:** *Magazine, Consumer.*
Published by: Cybermedia Verlagsgesellschaft mbH, Wallbergstr. 10, Mering, 86415, Germany. TEL 49-8233-74010, FAX 49-8233-740117, webmaster@maniac.de, http:// www.maniac.de. Adv. contact Andreas Knauf. B&W page EUR 2,500, color page EUR 4,000. Circ: 40,000 (paid and controlled).

794.8 GBR ISSN 0967-9014
MEAN MACHINES SEGA. Text in English. 1991. m. GBP 34; GBP 40 foreign. **Document type:** *Consumer.*
Supersedes (in 1992): Mean Machines (0960-4952)
Published by: E M A P - Images, Priory Ct, 30-32 Farringdon Ln, London, EC1R 3AU, United Kingdom. TEL 44-171-972-6700, FAX 44-171-972-6710. Ed. Richard Leadbetter. Circ: 118,032 (paid). **Subscr. to:** Tower Publishing, Lathkill St, Tower House, Sovereign Park, Market Harborough, Leics LE16 9EF, United Kingdom. TEL 44-1858-468811, FAX 44-1858-432164.

▼ **MEGA HIRO GAME MASTER.** see *CHILDREN AND YOUTH—For*

794.8 GBR ISSN 0964-5764
MEGATECH. Text in English. 1991. m.?. GBP 27; GBP 38 foreign. **Document type:** *Consumer.*
Published by: E M A P - Images, Priory Ct, 30-32 Farringdon Ln, London, EC1R 3AU, United Kingdom. TEL 0171-972-6700, FAX 0171-972-6710. Ed. Steve Merrett. Circ: 44,060 (paid). **Subscr. to:** Tower Publishing, Lathkill St, Tower House, Sovereign Park, Market Harborough, Leics LE16 9EF, United Kingdom.

MICHIGAN CHESS. see *SPORTS AND GAMES*

MINNESOTA CHESS JOURNAL. see *SPORTS AND GAMES*

794.8 GBR
▼ **MOBILE GAMER.** Text in English. 2003 (Jun.). 7/yr. GBP 3.95 newsstand/cover (effective 2003). 100 p./no.; **Document type:** *Magazine, Consumer.*
Published by: Future Publishing Ltd., Beauford Court, 30 Monmouth St, Bath, Avon BA1 2BW, United Kingdom. TEL 44-1225-442244, FAX 44-1225-446019, http:// www.futurenet.com. Ed. Keith Stewart.

794.8 DEU
DER MULTIMEDIA REPORTER; aktuelles News-Magazine fuer den Multimedia Fachhandel. Text in German. 1986. w. bk.rev. **Document type:** *Magazine, Consumer.* **Description:** Contains multimedia information on all aspects of culture, education and entertainment.
Former titles (until 1999): P C Freizeit; Spiel-Ebene
Related titles: Diskette ed.
Published by: (Deutscher Software Schutz- und Forschungsverband e.V.), Boschen PR und Verlag, Amtmann-Schroeter-Str 1, Lilienthal, 28865, Germany. TEL 49-4298-5055, FAX 49-4298-5551, mmr-pressedienst@t-online.de, http://www.multimediareporter.de. Eds. Anna Gesine Seitz, Hartmuth Seitz. Circ: 50,000.

794.805 GBR
N G C. (Nintendo Gaming Consoles) Text in English. 1997. m. GBP 29 in United Kingdom; GBP 37 in Europe; GBP 55 rest of world; GBP 3.30 newsstand/cover (effective 2002). adv. **Document type:** *Magazine, Consumer.* **Description:** Focuses on games and gaming news and advice for Nintendo's two next-generation systems - Gamecube and Game Boy Advance.
Formerly: N 64 Magazine (1367-5958)
Published by: Future Publishing Ltd., Beauford Court, 30 Monmouth St, Bath, Avon BA1 2BW, United Kingdom. TEL 44-1225-442244, FAX 44-1225-732285, customerservice@futurenet.co.uk, http://www.futurenet.com/ futureonline. Ed. Tim Weaver. adv.: color page GBP 2,310. Circ: 73,210 (paid).

794.8 DEU ISSN 1433-8424
N-ZONE; das meistgekaufte Nintendo-Magazin. Text in German. 1997. m. EUR 36.60 domestic; EUR 41.60 in Austria; EUR 49.80 elsewhere; EUR 3.30 newsstand/cover (effective 2003). adv. **Document type:** *Magazine, Consumer.* **Description:** Provides articles and features on games and accessories for the Nintendo gaming system.
Published by: Computec Media AG, Dr-Mack-Str 77, Fuerth, 90762, Germany. TEL 49-911-2872100, FAX 49-911-2872200, info@computec.de, http://www.computec.de. Ed. Hans Ippisch. Adv. contact Alexander Kreis. B&W page EUR 3,400, color page EUR 4,900. Circ: 39,502 (paid and controlled).

NAUTILUS; Abenteuer & Phantastik. see *LITERATURE—Science Fiction, Fantasy, Horror*

NEW LITERACIES AND DIGITAL EPISTEMOLOGIES. see *EDUCATION*

NEW ZEALAND CHESS. see *SPORTS AND GAMES*

794.8 ITA ISSN 1129-0412
NEXT STATION. Text in Italian. 1999. m. **Document type:** *Magazine, Consumer.* **Description:** Provides reviews, hints, and descriptions of Playstation games.
Published by: Next Publishing S.r.l., Via Niccolini, 30, Milano, 20154, Italy. TEL 39-02-3191001, FAX 39-02-31910030, nextpublishing@nextpublishing.com.

794.8 ITA ISSN 1594-9389
NINTENDO; la rivista ufficiale. Text in Italian. 2002. m. (13/yr.). EUR 49; EUR 5.50 newsstand/cover (effective 2005). adv. **Document type:** *Magazine, Consumer.*
Published by: Future Media Italy SpA, Via Asiago 45, Milano, MI 20128, Italy. TEL 39-02-2529161, FAX 39-02-26005520, info@futuremediaitaly.it, http://www.futuremediaitaly.it.

794.8 GBR ISSN 1366-6266
NINTENDO 64 MAGAZINE. Key Title: 64 Magazine. Text in English. 1997. bi-m. GBP 3.99 newsstand/cover (effective 2001). adv. 100 p./no.; back issues avail. **Document type:** *Consumer.* **Description:** Offers a comprehensive guide to N64 hardware and the full range of software and peripherals available worldwide.
Published by: Paragon Publishing Ltd., Paragon House, 10 St Peters Rd, Bournemouth, Dorset BH1 2JS, United Kingdom. TEL 44-1202-299900, FAX 44-1202-299955, 64mag@paragon.co.uk, andymc@paragon.co.uk, http://www.paragon.co.uk. Ed. Roy Kimber. Adv. contact Felicity Mead TEL 44-1202-200224. Circ: 14,945. **Dist. by:** Seymour Distribution Ltd, 86 Newman St, London W1T 3EX, United Kingdom. FAX 44-207-396-8002, enquiries@seymour.co.uk.

794.8 ESP
NINTENDO ACCION. Text in Spanish. 1992. 12/yr. adv. **Document type:** *Magazine, Consumer.* **Description:** Covers Nintendo Game Boy, N.E.S. and Super Nintendo video games.
Published by: Hobby Press S.A. (Subsidiary of: Axel Springer Verlag AG), C/ Los Vascos 17, Madrid, 28040, Spain. TEL 34-902-111315, FAX 34-902-151798, http:// www.hobbypress.es. Ed. Juan Carlos Garcia. Adv. contact Maria Perera. Circ: 53,000 (paid).

794.8 FRA ISSN 1633-0684
NINTENDO MAGAZINE. Text in French. 2002. m. adv. **Document type:** *Magazine, Consumer.*
Published by: Future France, 101-109 Rue Jean Jaures, Levallois Perret, 92300, France. TEL 33-1-41273838, yveline.duville@futurenet.fr.

794.8 GBR ISSN 0965-4240
NINTENDO MAGAZINE SYSTEM. Text in English. 1992. m. GBP 34 domestic; GBP 40 foreign; GBP 2.95 newsstand/cover. **Document type:** *Consumer.*
Published by: Emap Active Ltd. (Angel House) (Subsidiary of: Emap Consumer Media), Angel House, 338-346 Goswell Rd, London, EC1V 7QP, United Kingdom. TEL 44-171-477-7399, FAX 44-171-477-7279. Ed. Tim Boone. Circ: 110,384 (paid). **Subscr. to:** Tower Publishing Services Ltd., Tower House, Sovereign Park, Market Harborough, Leics LE16 9EF, United Kingdom. TEL 44-1858-468811, FAX 44-1858-432164.

794.8 USA ISSN 1041-9551
NINTENDO POWER. Text in English. 1988. m. USD 19.95 domestic; USD 27.95 in Canada (effective 2005); USD 4.95 newsstand/cover domestic; CND 5.95 newsstand/cover in Canada (effective 2001). adv. software rev. charts; illus.; maps. back issues avail. **Document type:** *Magazine, Consumer.* **Description:** Provides tips, maps, strategies, codes and tricks for all Nintendo games.
Published by: Nintendo of America Inc., Consumer Service Department, 4820 150th Ave, N E, Redmond, WA 98052. TEL 425-882-2040, 800-255-3700, FAX 425-882-3585, http://www.nintendopower.com/power.html, http://www.nintendo.com. Ed. Yoshio Tsuboike. Pub. Minoru Arakawa. Adv. contact Jeff Bafus. color page USD 17,250; trim 10.5 x 8. Circ: 570,000 (paid).

794.8 USA
NINTENDO POWER ADVANCE. Text in English. 2001. q. USD 14.99 newsstand/cover (effective 2001). **Document type:** *Magazine, Consumer.*
Published by: Nintendo of America Inc., Consumer Service Department, 4820 150th Ave, N E, Redmond, WA 98052. TEL 800-255-3700, FAX 425-882-3585, http://www.nintendo.com.

794.8 AUS
OFFICIAL AUSTRALIAN PLAYSTATION MAGAZINE. Text in English. 1999. m. AUD 129.95; AUD 14.95 newsstand/cover (effective 2004). adv. **Document type:** *Magazine, Consumer.* **Description:** Contains the latest news and reviews on PlayStation games and products.
Published by: A C P Publishing Pty. Ltd., 54-58 Park St, Sydney, NSW 1028, Australia. TEL 61-2-92828000, FAX 61-2-92674361, playstation_support@scee.net, info@acp.com.au, http://au.playstation.com/opsm, http://www.acp.com.au. Ed. Troy Gorman. Adv. contact Samantha Liddle. Circ: 31,441 (paid and controlled). **Subscr. to:** Magshop, Reply Paid 4967, Sydney, NSW 2001, Australia. TEL 61-2-92828000, magshop@acp.com.au, http://magshop.com.au.

794.8 AUS ISSN 1446-425X
OFFICIAL AUSTRALIAN XBOX MAGAZINE. Text in English. 2002. m. AUD 124.95 domestic; AUD 148.95 in New Zealand; AUD 208.95 elsewhere (effective 2004). adv. **Document type:** *Magazine, Consumer.* **Description:** Covers all things related to Xbox and the high-tech gaming lifestyle.
Published by: Derwent Howard, PO Box 1037, Bondi Junction, NSW 1355, Australia. TEL 61-2-93864666, 800-007-820, FAX 61-2-93864288, enquiries@derwenthoward.com.au, http://www.derwenthoward.com.au/. Ed. Kevin Cheung. Adv. contact Paul Hardy.

794.8 GBR
OFFICIAL U K PLAYSTATION 2 MAGAZINE. Text in English. bi-m. GBP 26.95 domestic; GBP 36.95 in North America & Europe; GBP 46.95 elsewhere; GBP 4.99 newsstand/cover (effective 2001). adv. software rev. **Document type:** *Magazine, Consumer.* **Description:** Contains news, information, interviews, and reviews of all the latest PlayStation 2 games and developments.
Published by: Future Publishing Ltd., Beauford Court, 30 Monmouth St, Bath, Avon BA1 2BW, United Kingdom. TEL 44-1225-442244, FAX 44-1225-446019, customerservice@futurenet.co.uk, http://www.futurenet.com/ futureonline. Ed. Mike Goldsmith. Circ: 81,883 (paid).

794.8 GBR ISSN 1367-4471
OFFICIAL U K PLAYSTATION MAGAZINE. Text in English. 1995. m. GBP 34.99 domestic; GBP 59.99 in Europe; GBP 79.99 rest of world; GBP 4.99 newsstand/cover (effective 2000). adv. **Document type:** *Magazine, Consumer.* **Description:** Contains news, reviews, tips, previews, competitions, and other features on all aspects of the PlayStation market.
Formerly (until 1996): Official PlayStation Magazine (1360-2349) —CCC.
Published by: Future Publishing Ltd., Beauford Court, 30 Monmouth St, Bath, Avon BA1 2BW, United Kingdom. TEL 44-1225-442244, FAX 44-1225-732285, rob.pegley@futurenet.co.uk, http://www.futurenet.com/ futureonline. Ed. Rob Pegley. adv.: color page GBP 7,470. Circ: 380,180 (paid).

794.8 GBR ISSN 1464-9063
OFFICIAL U K PLAYSTATION SPECIALS. Text in English. 1998. q. GBP 5.99 newsstand/cover. **Document type:** *Consumer.* **Description:** Uses expertise, experience and knowledge of PlayStation gaming to take an in-depth look at a specific genre in each issue.
Published by: Future Publishing Ltd., Beauford Court, 30 Monmouth St, Bath, Avon BA1 2BW, United Kingdom. TEL 44-1225-442244, FAX 44-1225-732285, will.groves@futurenet.co.uk, http://www.futurenet.com, http://www.futurenet.com/futureonline. adv.: color page GBP 2,995; trim 232 x 280. Circ: 95,012 (paid).

794.8 USA ISSN 1094-6683
GV1469.3
OFFICIAL U.S. PLAYSTATION MAGAZINE. Text in English. 1995. m. USD 39.97 domestic; USD 59.97 foreign; USD 8.99 newsstand/cover (effective 2005). adv. **Document type:** *Magazine, Consumer.* **Description:** Provides up-to-date news and insights for PlayStation owners and users.
Formerly (until 1997): P S X (1083-1088)
Related titles: Online - full text ed.: (from EBSCO Publishing, Gale Group, ProQuest Information & Learning).
Indexed: MASUSE.
—CCC.

Published by: Ziff Davis Media Game Group (Subsidiary of: Ziff Davis Media Inc.), 28 E 28th St, New York, NY 10016-7930. TEL 212-503-3500, 212-472-4000, FAX 212-503-3599, info@ziffdavis.com, http://www.gamers.com/opm/index.jsp, http://www.ziffdavis.com. Ed. Dana Jongewaard. Pub. Lee Uniacke. adv.: color page USD 16,690. Circ: 350,000 (paid).

794.8 GBR
OFFICIAL XBOX MAGAZINE. Text in English. bi-m. GBP 5.50 newsstand/cover (effective 2001). adv. **Document type:** *Magazine, Consumer.* **Description:** Filled with exclusive reviews, news and previews as well as the best contests, tips and strategies for the Xbox gaming console.
Published by: Future Publishing Ltd., Beauford Court, 30 Monmouth St, Bath, Avon BA1 2BW, United Kingdom. TEL 44-1225-442244, FAX 44-1225-446019, customerservice@futurenet.co.uk, http://www.futurenet.com/futureonline. Ed. James Ashton.

794.8 USA ISSN 1534-7850
OFFICIAL XBOX MAGAZINE. Variant title: Xbox Magazine. Text in English. 2001 (Fall). m. USD 29.95 domestic; USD 43.95 in Canada (effective 2003). adv. **Document type:** *Magazine, Consumer.* **Description:** Provides exclusive information on the latest Xbox games and news, including game demos and interviews with game developers.
Related titles: Online - full text ed.
Published by: Future Network USA, 150 North Hill Dr, Ste 40, Brisbane, CA 94005. TEL 415-468-4684, FAX 415-468-4686, xboxmag@imaginemedia.com, http://www.oxmonline.com. Ed. Mike Salmon. Pub., Adv. contact Karen Quilantang. R&P Simon Wear. color page USD 12,500.

794 FRA ISSN 1628-8556
ONLINE GAMER. Text in French. 2000. m. FRF 49, EUR 7.47 newsstand/cover (effective 2001). adv. software rev.; Website rev. **Document type:** *Magazine, Consumer.*
Published by: Future France, 101-109 Rue Jean Jaures, Levallois Perret, 92300, France. TEL 33-1-41273838, yveline.duville@futurenet.fr.

794.8 GBR ISSN 1471-1192
P 2. Text in English. 2000. 13/yr. GBP 3.50 newsstand/cover (effective 2004). adv. 132 p./no.; back issues avail. **Document type:** *Magazine, Consumer.* **Description:** Provides information for the Play Station 2 players, covering games and DVD reviews with screenshots and high quality artwork.
Published by: Paragon Publishing Ltd., Paragon House, 10 St Peters Rd, Bournemouth, Dorset BH1 2JS, United Kingdom. TEL 44-1202-299900, FAX 44-1202-299955, 44-1202-200217, subs@paragon.co.uk, http://www.paragon.co.uk. Ed. Roy Kimber. Adv. contact Felicity Mead TEL 44-1202-200224. Circ: 19,048 (paid).

794.8 USA
P B E M; play by e-mail. Text in English. 1992. d.
Media: Online - full content.
Address: Box 3818, Charlottesville, VA 22903. http://www.pbem.com. Ed. Greg Lindahl.

P C ACTION; guida alla civilta del personal computer. see *COMPUTERS—Personal Computers*

794.8 DEU ISSN 0946-6290
P C ACTION. Text in German. 1996. m. EUR 55.20 domestic; EUR 64.20 in Austria; EUR 68.40 elsewhere; EUR 4.99 newsstand/cover (effective 2003). adv. **Document type:** *Magazine, Consumer.* **Description:** Covers all aspects of games and gaming on PCs.
Related titles: CD-ROM ed.; Online - full text ed.
Published by: Computec Media AG, Dr-Mack-Str 77, Fuerth, 90762, Germany. TEL 49-911-2872100, FAX 49-911-2872200, info@computec.de, http://www.pcaction.de, http://www.computec.de. Ed. Christian Bigge. Adv. contact Ina Willax. B&W page EUR 3,540, color page EUR 5,060. Circ: 108,835 (paid).

794.8 GBR
P C EXTREME. Text in English. 2002 (Nov.). m. **Document type:** *Magazine, Consumer.* **Description:** Covers PC gaming for hardcore gammers, including news, reviews, guides for hardware, games, gadgets, hacks and Net stuff.
Published by: Live Publishing International Ltd., Europa House, Adlington Park, Macclesfield, Cheshire SK10 4NP, United Kingdom. TEL 44-1625-855086, FAX 44-1625-855071, subs@livepublishing.co.uk, http://www.livepublishing.co.uk/pcextreme/pageview.shtml?mainindex.html. Ed. Wayne Williams. Pub. Robin Wilkinson. Adv. contact Kenny Leslie. Circ: 50,000.

794.8 GBR ISSN 1470-3815
P C GAMEPLAY. Text in English. 2000. m. GBP 45 domestic; GBP 65 in Europe; GBP 85 elsewhere; GBP 5 newsstand/cover (effective 2003). adv. **Document type:** *Magazine, Consumer.*
Incorporates (in 2001): P C Gaming World (1369-6351); Which was formerly (until 1997): C G W Computer Gaming (1365-6694)
Related titles: Online - full content ed.
Published by: Computec Media UK Ltd. (Subsidiary of: Computec Media AG), Grove House, 55 Lowlands Rd, Harrow, Mddx HA1 3AW, United Kingdom. TEL 44-208-515400, FAX 44-208-515401, pcgameplay@computecmedia.co.uk, feedback@computecmedia.co.uk, http://www.pcgameplay.co.uk/. Ed. Dave Upchurch.

794.8 004.16 SWE ISSN 1401-9922
P C GAMER. Text in Swedish. 1996. m. SEK 499 (effective 2005). adv. **Document type:** *Magazine, Consumer.*
Description: Publishes the latest information on PC games.
Published by: Hjemmet Mortensen AB (Subsidiary of: Hjemmet-Mortensen AS), Gaevlegatan 22, Stockholm, 11378, Sweden. TEL 46-8-6920100, FAX 46-8-6509705, red@pcgamer.net, info@hjemmetmortensen.se, http://www.pcgamer.net, http://www.hjemmetmortensen.se. Eds. Emil Kraftling, Anders Bjoerlin. Adv. contact Tony Gustavsson. color page SEK 34,900; trim 190 x 285. Circ: 25,200.

794.8 GBR ISSN 1351-3540
P C GAMER. Text in English. 1993. m. GBP 38.90; GBP 4.99 newsstand/cover (effective 2004). adv. **Document type:** *Magazine, Consumer.* **Description:** Contains in-depth reviews, news, exclusive updates, comprehensive tips, and special features.
—CCC.
Published by: Future Publishing Ltd., Beauford Court, 30 Monmouth St, Bath, Avon BA1 2BW, United Kingdom. TEL 44-1225-442244, FAX 44-1225-732285, james.flynn@futurenet.co.uk, http://www.pcgamer.co.uk, http://www.futurenet.com/futureonline. Ed. James Flynn. adv.: color page GBP 1,995. Circ: 65,573 (paid).

794.8 GBR
P C GAMER TIPS; strategies - maps - hints - cheats - secrets - solutions. Text in English. 1998. q. GBP 2.99 newsstand/cover. **Document type:** *Consumer.* **Description:** For hard-core gamers who want to get the best out of their games. Concentrates solely on solutions to the biggest games.
Published by: Future Publishing Ltd., Beauford Court, 30 Monmouth St, Bath, Avon BA1 2BW, United Kingdom. TEL 44-1225-442244, FAX 44-1225-446019, adam.waring@futurenet.co.uk, http://www.futurenet.com, http://www.futurenet.com/futureonline. Ed. Adam Waring. Pub. Alison Morton. Circ: 60,000 (paid).

794.8 GBR
P C GAMES. Text in English. 1994. m. GBP 47.40 domestic; GBP 55 foreign; GBP 4.95 newsstand/cover. adv. **Document type:** *Consumer.*
Media: Diskette. **Related titles:** CD-ROM ed.
Published by: E M A P - Images, Priory Ct, 30-32 Farringdon Ln, London, EC1R 3AU, United Kingdom. TEL 44-171-972-6700, FAX 44-171-972-6710. **Subscr. to:** Tower Publishing Services Ltd., Tower House, Sovereign Park, Market Harborough, Leics LE16 9EF, United Kingdom. TEL 44-1858-468811, FAX 44-1858-432164. **Dist. by:** Seymour Distribution Ltd, 86 Newman St, London W1T 3EX, United Kingdom. FAX 44-207-396-8002, enquiries@seymour.co.uk.

794.8 USA ISSN 1089-3695
GV1469.22
P C GAMES. Text in English. 1988. m. USD 24.95. **Document type:** *Consumer.* **Description:** Gives an inside look at hardware, multimedia titles and games in the market.
Former titles (until June 1996): P C Entertainment (1093-295X); (until Jan. 1996): Electronic Entertainment (1074-1356); (until 1994): P C Games (1042-2943); (until 1989): P C Resource's P C Games (1042-1351)
Indexed: CompD, SoftBase.
—CCC.
Published by: Infotainment World, Inc., 501 2nd St, Ste 500, San Francisco, CA 94107-4133. TEL 415-979-9845, FAX 415-979-5225. Circ: 180,000 (paid).

794.8 DEU ISSN 0946-6304
P C GAMES. Text in German. 1992. m. EUR 55.20 domestic; EUR 64.20 in Austria; EUR 68.40 elsewhere; EUR 2.99 newsstand/cover (effective 2003). adv. **Document type:** *Magazine, Consumer.* **Description:** Provides information and tips on all aspects of video and PC gaming.
Related titles: CD-ROM ed.; Online - full text ed.
Published by: Computec Media AG, Dr-Mack-Str 77, Fuerth, 90762, Germany. TEL 49-911-2872100, FAX 49-911-2872200, redaktion@pcgames.de, info@computec.de, http://www.pcgames.de, http://www.computec.de. Ed. Petra Mauerroeder. Adv. contact Ina Willax. B&W page EUR 7,350, color page EUR 10,500. Circ: 281,908 (paid and controlled).

794.8 AUS
P C GAMES ADDICT. Text in English. m. AUD 79.95 domestic; AUD 79.95 in New Zealand; AUD 163.95 elsewhere (effective 2004). adv. **Document type:** *Magazine, Consumer.* **Description:** Contains latest exclusive reviews, previews and in-depth features.
Media: CD-ROM.
Published by: Derwent Howard, PO Box 1037, Bondi Junction, NSW 1355, Australia. TEL 61-2-93864666, 800-007-820, FAX 61-2-93864288, enquiries@derwenthoward.com.au, http://www.derwenthoward.com.au/. Ed. Dan Toose. Adv. contact Paul Hardy.

794.8 DEU ISSN 1616-6922
P C GAMES HARDWARE; das Hardware-Magazin fuer PC-Spieler. (Personal Computer) Text in German. 2000. m. EUR 43.20 domestic; EUR 50.20 in Austria; EUR 56.40 elsewhere; EUR 3.90 newsstand/cover (effective 2003). adv. **Document type:** *Magazine, Consumer.* **Description:** Focuses on the hardware products and services available for PC gaming.
Related titles: Online - full text ed.
Published by: Computec Media AG, Dr-Mack-Str 77, Fuerth, 90762, Germany. TEL 49-911-2872100, FAX 49-911-2872200, info@computec.de, http://www.pcgameshardware.de, http://www.computec.de. Ed. Thilo Bayer. Adv. contact Wolfgang Menne. B&W page EUR 3,900, color page EUR 5,570. Circ: 105,107 (paid and controlled).

794.8 DEU
P C GAMES PLUS. Text in German. 1996. m. EUR 4.99 newsstand/cover (effective 2005). adv. **Document type:** *Magazine, Consumer.* **Description:** Provides hints and tips on all aspects of PC gaming.
Related titles: CD-ROM ed.
Published by: Computec Media AG, Dr-Mack-Str 77, Fuerth, 90762, Germany. TEL 49-911-2872100, FAX 49-911-2872200, info@computec.de, http://www.computec.de. Ed. Petra Mauerroeder. Adv. contact Thorsten Szameitat. Circ: 60,000 (paid).

794.8 FRA ISSN 1284-8611
P C JEUX. Text in French. 1997. m. FRF 38 newsstand/cover (effective 2001). adv. software rev.; Website rev. **Document type:** *Magazine, Consumer.*
Related titles: ♦ Supplement(s): P C Jeux. Hors-Serie. ISSN 1627-1009.
Published by: Future France, 101-109 Rue Jean Jaures, Levallois Perret, 92300, France. TEL 33-1-41273838, yveline.duville@futurenet.fr.

794 FRA ISSN 1627-1009
P C JEUX. HORS-SERIE. Text in French. 199?. irreg. **Document type:** *Magazine, Consumer.*
Related titles: ♦ Supplement to: P C Jeux. ISSN 1284-8611.
Published by: Future France, 101-109 Rue Jean Jaures, Levallois Perret, 92300, France. TEL 33-1-41273838, yveline.duville@futurenet.fr.

P C MART. see *COMPUTERS*

794.8 AUS ISSN 1326-5644
P C POWERPLAY. Text in English. 1996. m. AUD 48 domestic; AUD 67 in New Zealand; AUD 81 in Asia; AUD 91 elsewhere (effective 2004). **Document type:** *Magazine, Consumer.*
Published by: NextMedia, 78 Renwick St, Redfern, NSW 2016, Australia. TEL 61-9-9699-0333, FAX 61-9-9699-0334, http://www.pcpowerplay.com.au, http://www.nexmedia.com.au/. Ed. David Widgoose. Pub. Phillip Keir.

794.8 ITA ISSN 1127-6916
P C ULTRA; giochi a massima velocita. Text in Italian. 1998. m. **Document type:** *Consumer.* **Description:** Dedicated to PC platform video games. Contains articles, game reviews and tips.
Published by: Play Press Publishing s.r.l., Via Vitorchiano 123, Rome, RM 00189, Italy. TEL 39-06-3701592, FAX 39-06-3701502, playpress@uni.net, abbonamenti@playpress.com. Ed. Alessandro Ferri.

794.8 GBR ISSN 0967-8220
P C ZONE. Text in English. 1992. 13/yr. adv. back issues avail. **Document type:** *Magazine, Consumer.* **Description:** Devoted exclusively to games for IBM PC compatible computers. Contains reviews, previews and features relevant to PC games.
Related titles: CD-ROM ed.: ISSN 1354-070X; Online - full text ed.
Published by: Future Publishing Ltd., Beauford Court, 30 Monmouth St, Bath, Avon BA1 2BW, United Kingdom. TEL 44-1225-442244, FAX 44-1225-446019, customerservice@futurenet.co.uk, http://gamesradar.msn.co.uk, http://www.thefuturenetwork.plc.uk. Ed., Pub. James Ashton. Circ: 55,083 (paid).

794.1 SWE
P L Y. Text in Swedish. 1979. 4/yr. SEK 230 (effective 1997). adv. bk.rev. **Description:** Contains information about chess programs and chess computers, indluding a rating list.
Published by: Svenska Schackdatorfoereningen/Swedish Chess Computer Association, c/o Thoralf Karlsson, Ed, Uttermarksgatan 31 C, Eskilstuna, 63351, Sweden. Circ: 650. **Subscr. to:** Mr. Goeran Grottling, Diabasvaegen 3, Lindome 43732, Sweden.

C

794.8 ITA ISSN 1591-3775
P S 2. (PlayStation) Variant title: Ufficiale PlayStation 2 Magazine. Text in Italian. 2000. m. EUR 8.73 newsstand/cover (effective 2001). adv. software rev. **Document type:** *Magazine, Consumer.*
Published by: Future Media Italy SpA, Via Asiago 45, Milano, MI 20128, Italy. TEL 39-02-2529161, FAX 39-02-26005520, info@futuremediaitaly.it, http://www.futuremediaitaly.it. Ed. Claudio Tradardi.

794.8 USA
P S EXTREME. (PlayStation) Text in English. 1995. m. adv. **Document type:** *Consumer.* **Description:** Devoted entirely to the Sony PlayStation game system.
Published by: Dimension Publishing, 1175 Chess Dr., Ste. E, Foster City, CA 94404. TEL 650-372-0942, FAX 650-372-0753, d3@quake.net, http://www.psextreme.com. Ed. Greg Off. Pub. David Winding. Adv. contact Mark Winding.

794.8 GBR
▼ **P S G**; playstation gaming 24 - 7. Text in English. 2003. m. **Description:** Reviews Playstation games.
Published by: Live Publishing International Ltd., Europa House, Adlington Park, Macclesfield, Cheshire SK10 4NP, United Kingdom. TEL 44-1625-855086, FAX 44-1625-855071, subs@livepublishing.co.uk, http://www.livepublishing.co.uk/. Ed. Wayne Williams. Pub. Robin Wilkinson. Adv. contact Kenny Leslie.

794.8 USA ISSN 1095-4163
GV1469.3
P S M. (PlayStation Magazine) Text in English. 1997. m. USD 12 domestic; USD 26 in Canada; USD 39 elsewhere (effective 2003). adv. **Document type:** *Magazine, Consumer.* **Description:** Source of independent coverage for dedicated Sony PlayStation gamers.
Published by: Future Network USA, 150 North Hill Dr, Ste 40, Brisbane, CA 94005. TEL 415-468-4684, FAX 415-468-4686, http://www.psmonline.com/, http://www.futurenetworkusa.com/. Ed. Chris Slate. Pub. Dong Faust. R&P Charles Schug. Adv. contact Megan Fischer. page USD 18,694.

794.8 ITA ISSN 1126-490X
P S M; 100% indipendente PlayStation magazine. (Play Station Magazine) Text in Italian. 1996. m. EUR 37 (effective 2005). adv. software rev. **Document type:** *Magazine, Consumer.*
Formerly (until 1998): PlayStation Magazine (1125-484X)
Published by: Future Media Italy SpA, Via Asiago 45, Milano, MI 20128, Italy. TEL 39-02-2529161, FAX 39-02-26005520, info@futuremediaitaly.it, http://www.futuremediaitaly.it. Ed. Antonio Loglisci.

794.8 GBR
P S M 2. Text in English. bi-m. GBP 12.99 domestic; GBP 19.99 in Europe & N. America; GBP 24.99 elsewhere; GBP 2.99 newsstand/cover (effective 2001). adv. software rev. **Document type:** *Magazine, Consumer.* **Description:** Contains the latest news and advice on all aspects of PlayStation 2 gaming.
Published by: Future Publishing Ltd., Beauford Court, 30 Monmouth St, Bath, Avon BA1 2BW, United Kingdom. TEL 44-1225-442244, FAX 44-1225-446019, marcus.hawkins@futurenet.co.uk, customerservice@futurenet.co.uk, http://www.futurenet.com/futureonline. Ed. Marcus Hawkins. Circ: 52,439 (paid).

794.8 FRA ISSN 1624-4710
P S M 2. Variant title: PlayStation Magazine 2. Text in French. 2000. m. FRF 35 newsstand/cover (effective 2001). adv. software rev.; Website rev. **Document type:** *Magazine, Consumer.*
Published by: Future France, 101-109 Rue Jean Jaures, Levallois Perret, 92300, France. TEL 33-1-41273838, yveline.duville@futurenet.fr.

794.85 ITA ISSN 1592-4866
P S MANIA 2.0. (PlayStation) Text in Italian. 2001. m. EUR 25; EUR 4.50 newsstand/cover (effective 2003). adv. **Document type:** *Magazine, Consumer.*
Published by: Play Press Publishing s.r.l., Via Vitorchiano 123, Rome, RM 00189, Italy. TEL 39-06-33221250, FAX 39-06-33221235, abbonamenti@playpress.com, http://www.playpress.com. Ed. Daniele Cucchiarelli. Pub. Alessandro Ferri. Adv. contact Lorenza Borroni TEL 39-02-45472867. Circ: 95,000 (paid and controlled).

794.8 GBR ISSN 1468-7240
P S W. (PlayStation World) Text in English. 2000. m. GBP 3.99 newsstand/cover (effective 2003). **Document type:** *Magazine, Consumer.*
—CCC.
Published by: Computec Media UK Ltd. (Subsidiary of: Computec Media AG), Grove House, 55 Lowlands Rd, Harrow, Mddx HA1 3AW, United Kingdom. TEL 44-208-515400, FAX 44-208-515401, feedback@computecmedia.co.uk. Circ: 79,000 (paid and controlled).

681.3 HRV ISSN 1331-7849
P S X. Text in Croatian. 1999. m. adv. **Document type:** *Magazine, Consumer.*
Published by: Janus Press, Cakovecka 17, Zagreb, 10000, Croatia. TEL 385-1-3843772, FAX 385-1-3843599, psx@janus.hr, http://www.psx.janus.hr. Ed. Dario Zmo.

681.3 FIN ISSN 1235-1199
PELIT. Text in Finnish. 1992. 12/yr. EUR 66 (effective 2004). adv. **Document type:** *Magazine, Consumer.* **Description:** Covers all aspects of games and equipment for PCs, PlayStation2, Xbox, Game Cube, the Internet and mobile devices.
Incorporates (1998-2001): Peliasema (1456-0437); Formed by the merger of (1987-1992): Pelit (Helsinki, 1987) (0784-4824); (1990-1992): P C Pelit (0788-2181)
Published by: Sanoma Magazines Finland Corporation, Hoylaamotie 1 D, P.O. Box 100, Helsinki, 00040, Finland. TEL 358-9-1201, FAX 358-9-1205171, info@sanomamagazines.fi, http://www.pelit.fi, http://www.sanomamagazines.fi. adv.: B&W page EUR 2,280, color page EUR 2,920. Circ: 39,837 (paid and controlled).

794.8 GBR
PLANET. Variant title: Planet Playstation. Text in English. 1998. 13/yr. GBP 35 in United Kingdom; GBP 45 in Europe; GBP 61 rest of world; GBP 2.99 newsstand/cover (effective 2001). software rev. 100 p./no.; back issues avail. **Document type:** *Magazine, Consumer.* **Description:** Contains reviews, previews, news, cheats, tips and guides for all the latest PlayStation games.
Formerly: Playstation Planet (1465-0517)
Published by: Paragon Publishing Ltd., Paragon House, 10 St Peters Rd, Bournemouth, Dorset BH1 2JS, United Kingdom. TEL 44-1202-299900, FAX 44-1202-299955, 44-1202-200217, subs@paragon.co.uk, http://www.paragon.co.uk. Ed. Mark Hattersley. Adv. contact Felicity Mead TEL 44-1202-200224. Circ: 25,845 (paid).

794.8 ITA
PLAY. Text in Italian. m. back issues avail. **Document type:** *Consumer.* **Description:** Reviews Playstation games and provides strategic hints.
Published by: Gruppo Editoriale Futura, Via XXV Aprile, 39, Bresso, MI 20091, Italy. TEL 39-02-665261, FAX 39-02-66526222, http://www.futura-ge.com. Ed. Paolo Reina.

794.8 POL
PLAY. Text in Polish. 1999. m. **Document type:** *Magazine, Consumer.* **Description:** Provides information and advice on a wide variety of computer games.
Published by: Axel Springer Polska, Al Jerozolimskie 181, Warsaw, 02222, Poland. TEL 48-22-6084100, FAX 48-22-6084106, asp@axelspringer.com.pl, http://www.axelspringer.com.pl. Circ: 80,000 (paid).

794.8 USA
PLAY; video games - anime - movies - music - gear - toys. Text in English. 2001 (Nov.). m. USD 24.99 domestic; USD 44.99 in Canada; USD 54.99 elsewhere; USD 5.99 newsstand/cover (effective 2002). adv. film rev.; music rev.; software rev. **Document type:** *Magazine, Consumer.* **Description:** Contains in-depth coverage of the latest video games, anime, DVD releases, television programs, and music.
Published by: Fusion Entertainment Publishing, Inc., 31255 Cedar Valley Dr., Ste. 313, Westlake Village, CA 91362. TEL 818-707-7786, FAX 818-707-7212, talk@play-magazine.com, customerservice@play-magazine.com, http://www.play-magazine.com. Ed. Dave Halverson.

794.8 GBR ISSN 1358-9474
PLAY. Text in English. 1995. 14/yr. GBP 35 in United Kingdom; GBP 57 in Europe; GBP 83 rest of world; GBP 2.99 newsstand/cover (effective 2001). adv. 132 p./no.; back issues avail. **Document type:** *Magazine, Consumer.* **Description:** Unbiased and unparalleled coverage of the Sony PlayStation market as written, designed and produced by fanatical games players.
Published by: Paragon Publishing Ltd., Paragon House, 10 St Peters Rd, Bournemouth, Dorset BH1 2JS, United Kingdom. TEL 44-1202-299900, FAX 44-1202-299955, 44-1202-200217, play@paragon.co.uk, subs@paragon.co.uk, http://www.paragon.co.uk/play. Ed. Graeme Nicholson. Adv. contact Felicity Mead TEL 44-1202-200224. Circ: 66,174 (paid).

794.8 ITA ISSN 1594-9230
PLAY NATION 2 MAGAZINE. Text in Italian. 2002. m. EUR 5.99 newsstand/cover (effective 2004). adv. **Document type:** *Magazine, Consumer.*
Published by: Future Media Italy SpA, Via Asiago 45, Milano, MI 20128, Italy. TEL 39-02-2529161, FAX 39-02-26005520, info@futuremediaitaly.it, http://www.futuremediaitaly.it.

794.8 DEU ISSN 1617-2183
PLAY THE PLAYSTATION. Text in English. 1997. m. EUR 38.40 domestic; EUR 42.40 foreign; EUR 3.50 newsstand/cover (effective 2003). adv. **Document type:** *Magazine, Consumer.* **Description:** Provides informative advice and hints on all aspects of PlayStation gaming.
Published by: CyPress GmbH, Max-Planck-Str 13, Hoechberg, 97204, Germany. TEL 49-931-406910, FAX 49-931-4069115, contact@cypress.de, http://www.playplaystation.com, http://www.cypress.de. Ed. Sven Liebold. Adv. contact Winfried Burkard. B&W page EUR 3,400, color page EUR 4,600; trim 230 x 297. Circ: 54,600 (paid). **Subscr. to:** dsb Abo-Betreuung GmbH, Konrad-Zuse-Str 16, Neckarsulm 74172, Germany. cypress@dsb.net.

794.8 DEU ISSN 0946-6320
PLAY TIME. Text in German. m. adv. **Document type:** *Consumer.*
Published by: Computec Media AG, Dr-Mack-Str 77, Fuerth, 90762, Germany. TEL 49-911-96832-0, FAX 49-911-6426333. Ed. Christian Geltenpoth. Adv. contact Thorsten Szameitat. Circ: 56,002.

796.025 FRA ISSN 1626-715X
PLAYBOX. Text in French. 2000. m. EUR 49.99 (effective 2003).
Published by: Posse Press, BP 1121, Toulouse, 31036, France. TEL 33-14-9698800, http://www.possepress.com/. Ed. Arnaud Wissart.

794.8 SWE
▼ **PLAYER 1.** Text in Swedish. 2003. 6/yr. SEK 198 (effective 2003). **Document type:** *Magazine, Consumer.* **Description:** Multiplatform magazine produced by gamers for gamers.
Published by: I D G AB (Subsidiary of: I D G Communications Inc.), Sturegatan 11, Stockholm, 10678, Sweden. TEL 46-8-4536000, FAX 46-8-4536005, http://www.player1.idg.se, http://www.idg.se.

794.8 MEX
PLAYFAN. Text in Spanish. 2001. m.
Published by: Grupo Alce, Donato Guerra No. 9, Col. Juarez, Mexico, D.F., 06600, Mexico. TEL 52-55-7030172, FAX 52-55-7030180, http://www.playfan.com.mx/, http://www.grupo-alce.com/. Ed. Antonio Reyes. Circ: 90,000.

794.8 ESP
PLAYMANIA. Text in Spanish. m. adv. **Document type:** *Magazine, Consumer.*
Published by: Hobby Press S.A. (Subsidiary of: Axel Springer Verlag AG), C/ Los Vascos 17, Madrid, 28040, Spain. TEL 34-902-111315, FAX 34-902-151798, playmania@hobbypress.es, http://www.hobbypress.es/playmania. Circ: 89,000 (paid).

794.8 ESP
PLAYMANIA GUIAS & TRUCOS. Text in Spanish. m. adv. **Document type:** *Magazine, Consumer.*
Published by: Hobby Press S.A. (Subsidiary of: Axel Springer Verlag AG), C/ Los Vascos 17, Madrid, 28040, Spain. TEL 34-902-111315, FAX 34-902-151798, http://www.hobbypress.es.

794 ITA ISSN 1594-2473
PLAYPOWER STATION. Text in Italian. 1996. m. **Document type:** *Magazine, Consumer.* **Description:** Covers news of the videogame industry, game reviews and playing hints.
Formerly (until 2000): PlayStation Power (1125-4858)
Published by: Future Media Italy SpA, Via Asiago 45, Milano, MI 20128, Italy. TEL 39-02-2529161, FAX 39-02-26005520, info@futuremediaitaly.it, http://www.futuremediaitaly.it. Eds. Antonio Loglisci, Mietta Capasso.

794.8 DEU
PLAYSTATION 2. Variant title: Das Offizielle PlayStation 2 Magazin. Text in German. 2000. m. EUR 78.60 domestic; EUR 82.60 foreign; EUR 7.50 newsstand/cover (effective 2003). adv. **Document type:** *Magazine, Consumer.* **Description:** Presents official information and tips on games and accessories available for the PlayStation 2 gaming console.
Published by: CyPress GmbH, Max-Planck-Str 13, Hoechberg, 97204, Germany. TEL 49-931-406910, FAX 49-931-4069115, contact@cypress.de, http://www.opm2.de, http://www.cypress.de. Ed. Christian Blendl. Adv. contact Winfried Burkard. B&W page EUR 4,250, color page EUR 6,350; trim 230 x 297. **Subscr. to:** dsb Abo-Betreuung GmbH, Konrad-Zuse-Str 16, Neckarsulm 74172, Germany. cypress@dsb.net.

794.8 AUS ISSN 1448-6733
PLAYSTATION 2; official magazine-Australia. Text in English. 2001. m. AUD 124.95 domestic; AUD 148.95 in New Zealand; AUD 208.95 elsewhere (effective 2004). **Document type:** *Magazine, Consumer.* **Description:** Covers the latest PlayStation 2 reviews, previews and demos.
Formerly (until 2002): P S M 2 (1445-2944)
Published by: Derwent Howard, PO Box 1037, Bondi Junction, NSW 1355, Australia. TEL 61-2-93864666, 800-007-820, FAX 61-2-93864288, enquiries@derwenthoward.com.au, http://www.derwenthoward.com.au/. Ed. Richie Young. Adv. contact Paul Hardy.

794.8 FRA ISSN 1627-0983
PLAYSTATION 2 MAGAZINE. Text in French. 2000. m. adv. **Document type:** *Magazine, Consumer.*
Published by: Future France, 101-109 Rue Jean Jaures, Levallois Perret, 92300, France. TEL 33-1-41273838, yveline.duville@futurenet.fr.

C

▼ new title ➤ refereed ✶ unverified ♦ full entry avail.

794.85 ITA ISSN 1720-0989
PLAYSTATION 2 MAGAZINE UFFICIALE. Text in Italian. 2002. m. EUR 89; EUR 8.90 newsstand/cover (effective 2003). adv. **Document type:** *Magazine, Consumer.*
Published by: Play Press Publishing s.r.l., Via Vitorchiano 123, Rome, RM 00189, Italy. TEL 39-06-33221250, FAX 39-06-33221235, abbonamenti@playpress.com, http://www.playpress.com. Ed. Diego Malara. Pub. Alessandro Ferri. Adv. contact Lorenza Borroni TEL 39-02-45472867. Circ: 90,000 (paid and controlled).

794.8 AUS
PLAYSTATION 2 OFFICIAL AUSTRALIAN MAGAZINE. Text in English. 2001. m. AUD 14.95 newsstand/cover (effective 2001). adv. **Document type:** *Magazine, Consumer.* **Description:** Presents the latest information on PlayStation 2 gaming consoles and related products.
Published by: A C P Publishing Pty. Ltd., 54-58 Park St, Sydney, NSW 1028, Australia. TEL 61-2-9282-8000, FAX 61-2-9267-4361, info@acp.com.au, http://www.acp.com.au. Ed. Narayan Patterson. Adv. contact Samantha Liddle.

794.85 ITA
PLAYSTATION 2 STRATEGY MAGAZINE UFFICIALE. Text in Italian. 9/yr. EUR 5.50 newsstand/cover (effective 2003). adv. **Document type:** *Magazine, Consumer.*
Published by: Play Press Publishing s.r.l., Via Vitorchiano 123, Rome, RM 00189, Italy. TEL 39-06-33221250, FAX 39-06-33221235, abbonamenti@playpress.com, http://www.playpress.com. Ed. Carlo Chericoni. Pub. Alessandro Ferri. Adv. contact Lorenza Borroni TEL 39-02-45472867. Circ: 50,000 (paid and controlled).

794.8 USA
PLAYSTATION CODE BOOK. Text in English. 2001. a., latest 2nd Annual. USD 9.99 newsstand/cover in United States; USD 11.99 newsstand/cover in Canada (effective 2001). adv. **Document type:** *Magazine, Consumer.*
Published by: Future Network USA, 150 North Hill Dr, Ste 40, Brisbane, CA 94005. TEL 415-468-4684, FAX 415-468-4686. Ed. Bill Donohue.

C

794.8 790.1 DEU
PLAYSTATION GAMES GUIDE. Text in German. 1997. a. play rev. illus. back issues avail. **Document type:** *Consumer.* **Description:** Catalogue containing every Playstation game available in Germany.
Related titles: Online - full text ed.
Published by: X-Plain Verlag GmbH und Co. KG, Friedensallee 41, Hamburg, 22765, Germany. TEL 49-40-3988370, FAX 49-40-3988370, http://www.x-plain.de, torstenweber@x-plain.de. Circ: 250,000.

794.8 GRC ISSN 1108-8621
PLAYSTATION MAGAZINE. Text in Greek. 1997. 11/yr. EUR 5.90 newsstand/cover (effective 2002). adv. **Document type:** *Magazine, Consumer.* **Description:** Contains the latest news and reviews of PlayStation games and products.
Published by: Hyperpress S.A., 52 Dekeleias Str., N. Halkidona, Athens, 143 43, Greece. TEL 30-1-252-7000, FAX 30-1-252-5180, marketing@hyperpress.gr, http://www.hyperpress.gr. adv.: page EUR 1,470; 230 x 280. Circ: 32,000 (paid and controlled).

794.8 GRC ISSN 1109-1800
PLAYSTATION MAGAZINE COLLECTION. Text in Greek. 1999. irreg. **Document type:** *Magazine, Consumer.*
Published by: Hyperpress S.A., 52 Dekeleias Str., N. Halkidona, Athens, 143 43, Greece. TEL 30-1-252-7000, FAX 30-1-252-5180, marketing@hyperpress.gr, http://www.hyperpress.gr.

794.8 GBR
PLAYSTATION MAX. Text in English. m. GBP 19.99 in United Kingdom; GBP 34.99 in Europe; GBP 44.99 rest of world; GBP 1.70 newsstand/cover (effective 2000). **Document type:** *Consumer.* **Description:** Presents essential tips, reviews, and other gaming information for the complete PlayStation experience.
Formerly: Playstation Power
Indexed: INI.
Published by: Future Publishing Ltd., Beauford Court, 30 Monmouth St, Bath, Avon BA1 2BW, United Kingdom. TEL 44-1225-442244, FAX 44-1225-732285, andy.dyer@futurenet.co.uk, http://www.futurenet.com, http://www.futurenet.com/futureonline. Ed. Andy Dyer.

794.8 ITA
PLAYSTATION NATION. Text in Italian. 1999. m. **Document type:** *Magazine, Consumer.* **Description:** Provides Playstation news, hardware updates and game reviews.
Published by: Xenia Edizioni Srl, Via Carducci, 31, Milano, 20123, Italy. TEL 39-02-878512, FAX 39-02-878567. Ed. Alessandro Rossetto.

794.8 IRL ISSN 1393-9599
PLAYSTATION OFFICIAL MAGAZINE IRELAND. Text in English. 2000. m. adv. **Document type:** *Magazine, Consumer.*
Published by: T P Media, 12 Lower Liffey St, Dublin 1, Ireland. TEL 353-1-8748515, FAX 353-1-8720979, ivan@tpmedia.ie. adv.: page EUR 3,098; trim 230 x 280. Circ: 16,000 (paid and controlled).

794.8 ITA ISSN 1127-4956
PLAYSTATION PLUS. Text in Italian. 1998. m. adv. software rev. **Document type:** *Magazine, Consumer.*
Published by: Future Media Italy SpA, Via Asiago 45, Milano, MI 20128, Italy. TEL 39-02-2529161, FAX 39-02-26005520, info@futuremediaitaly.it, http://www.futuremediaitaly.it. Ed. Claudio Tradardi.

794.8 GBR ISSN 1362-8674
PLAYSTATION POWER. Text in English. 1996. m. GBP 29.99 in United Kingdom; GBP 49.99 in Europe; GBP 59.99 rest of world; GBP 2.50 newsstand/cover (effective 2000). **Document type:** *Consumer.* **Description:** Dedicated to full-on PlayStation gaming.
Published by: Future Publishing Ltd., Beauford Court, 30 Monmouth St, Bath, Avon BA1 2BW, United Kingdom. TEL 44-1225-442244, FAX 44-1225-732285, sean.atkins@futurenet.co.uk, http://www.futurenet.com, http://www.futurenet.com/futureonline. Ed. Sean Atkins. Circ: 94,120 (paid).

794.8 ITA ISSN 1128-3823
PLAYSTATION PRO. Text in Italian. 1999. m.
Published by: Comic Art Publishing, Via Flavio Domiziano, 9, Rome, RM 00145, Italy. TEL 39-06-5413737, FAX 39-06-5410775, comicart@mix.it, http://www.mix.it/comicart.

794.8 GBR ISSN 1364-3932
PLAYSTATION SOLUTIONS. Text in English. 1996. m. GBP 3.99 newsstand/cover. **Document type:** *Consumer.* **Description:** Contains tips, hints and strategies for games involving the PlayStation system.
Published by: E X 5 Publishing, Floor 3, Wellpark, Willeys Ave, Exeter, EX2 8BE, United Kingdom. TEL 44-1392-276340, FAX 44-1392-276325, mail@rapide.co.uk, info@ex5.co.uk, http://www.rapide.co.uk, http://www.ex5.co.uk/. **Dist. by:** M M C Ltd., Octagon House, White Hart Meadows, Ripley, Woking, Surrey GU23 6HR, United Kingdom. TEL 44-1483-211222, FAX 44-1483-224541.

794.8 ITA ISSN 1127-3518
PLAYSTATION TIPS. Text in Italian. 1998. m. adv. software rev. **Document type:** *Magazine, Consumer.*
Published by: Future Media Italy SpA, Via Asiago 45, Milano, MI 20128, Italy. TEL 39-02-2529161, FAX 39-02-26005520, info@futuremediaitaly.it, http://www.futuremediaitaly.it. Ed. Claudio Tradardi.

794.8 GRC ISSN 1108-8613
PLAYSTATION TIPS. Text in Greek. 1998. q. EUR 5.90 newsstand/cover (effective 2002). adv. **Document type:** *Magazine, Consumer.* **Description:** Provides guides, hints and advice for PlayStation games.
Published by: Hyperpress S.A., 52 Dekeleias Str., N. Halkidona, Athens, 143 43, Greece. TEL 30-1-252-7000, FAX 30-1-252-5180, marketing@hyperpress.gr, http://www.hyperpress.gr. adv.: page EUR 880; 230 x 280. Circ: 23,000 (paid and controlled).

794.8 GRC ISSN 1109-1797
PLAYSTATION TIPS COLLECTION. Text in Greek. 1999. irreg. adv. **Document type:** *Magazine, Consumer.*
Published by: Hyperpress S.A., 52 Dekeleias Str., N. Halkidona, Athens, 143 43, Greece. TEL 30-1-252-7000, FAX 30-1-252-5180, marketing@hyperpress.gr, http://www.hyperpress.gr.

794.8 ITA ISSN 1128-3815
PLAYSTATION ZONE. Text in Italian. 1999. m. **Document type:** *Magazine, Consumer.* **Description:** Contains strategies and tricks for playstation game users.
Published by: Comic Art Publishing, Via Flavio Domiziano, 9, Rome, RM 00145, Italy. TEL 39-06-5413737, FAX 39-06-5410775, comicart@mix.it, http://www.mix.it/comicart. Ed. Rinaldo Traini. **Dist. by:** Parrini & C, Piazza Colonna 361, Rome, RM 00187, Italy. TEL 39-06-695141.

794.8 DEU
PLAYZONE. Variant title: Play Zone. Text in German. 1998. m. EUR 55.20 domestic; EUR 64.20 in Austria; EUR 68.40 elsewhere; EUR 4.99 newsstand/cover (effective 2003). adv. **Document type:** *Magazine, Consumer.* **Description:** Provides tips, advice and cheat codes for all PlayStation games.
Formerly: PlayStation Zone
Published by: Computec Media AG, Dr-Mack-Str 77, Fuerth, 90762, Germany. TEL 49-911-2872100, FAX 49-911-2872200, pszone@computec.de, http://www.pszone.de, http://www.computec.de. Ed. Hans Ippisch. Adv. contact Thorsten Szameitat. B&W page EUR 4,550, color page EUR 6,500; trim 210 x 297. Circ: 255,117 (paid and controlled).

794.8 USA ISSN 1524-3567
POCKET GAMES. Text in English. 1999. 4/yr. USD 9.99 newsstand/cover; USD 13.99 newsstand/cover in Canada (effective 2001). software rev.; Website rev. **Document type:** *Magazine, Consumer.* **Description:** Provides gamers with news and reviews on the latest portable handheld gaming devices and products.
Published by: Ziff Davis Media Game Group (Subsidiary of: Ziff Davis Media Inc.), 28 E 28th St, New York, NY 10016-7930. TEL 415-547-8000, FAX 415-547-8777, info@ziffdavis.com, http://www.ziffdavis.com. Ed. Simon Cox.

794.8 USA
POLYGON. Text in English. 1997. m. USD 29.99 (effective 2003). adv. bk.rev.; software rev. index. **Document type:** *Newsletter, Consumer.* **Description:** Covers the videogames industry for age 18-35 adults.
Formerly (until 2003): Silicon Magazine (1524-2471)
Published by: Deviation LLC, 52487, Knoxville, TN 37950-2487. http://www.polygonmag.com/index.php. Ed. Dane Baker. adv.: B&W page USD 800, color page USD 950. Circ: 22,000 (controlled).

006.7 AUT
POWER NEWS; fun with electronics. Text in German. 1987. bi-m. EUR 13; EUR 2.50 newsstand/cover (effective 2002). adv. software rev. **Document type:** *Magazine, Consumer.* **Description:** Contains articles, arts, tests, cases, hardware, software, internet, digital media. Informs of the latest software and hardware for individual and business computer users.
Former titles: Multimedia Time; Multimedia Time - business and communication; Apple Time
Published by: Page Verlag Inc., Hermanngasse 18, Vienna, W 1070, Austria. TEL 43-1-52626500, FAX 43-1-526265050, multimedia@page.co.at, home@page.at, http://www.page.at. Ed. Renato Zapella. Pub., R&P Renato Zappella. Adv. contact Brigitte Zapella. Circ: 140,000.

794.8 DEU ISSN 0937-9754
POWER PLAY. Text in German. 1988. m. **Document type:** *Consumer.*
Related titles: Online - full text ed.
Published by: W E K A Computerzeitschriften-Verlag GmbH, Gruberstr 46a, Poing, 85586, Germany. TEL 49-8121-950, FAX 49-8121-951199, http://www.magnamedia.de.

794.8 GBR ISSN 1362-5047
POWERSTATION; the complete a-z of PlayStation tips. Text in English. 1996. 13/yr. GBP 3.99 newsstand/cover; GBP 36 in United Kingdom; GBP 48 in Europe; GBP 65 rest of world (effective 2001). adv. 132 p./no.; **Document type:** *Magazine, Consumer.* **Description:** Features tips, passwords, cheats and mapped solutions to all the latest PlayStation games.
Published by: Paragon Publishing Ltd., Paragon House, 10 St Peters Rd, Bournemouth, Dorset BH1 2JS, United Kingdom. TEL 44-1202-299900, FAX 44-1202-299955, powerstn@paragon.co.uk, http://www.paragon.co.uk. Ed. Phil King. Adv. contact Felicity Mead TEL 44-1202-200224. Circ: 41,854 (paid). **Dist. by:** Seymour Distribution Ltd, 86 Newman St, London W1T 3EX, United Kingdom. FAX 44-207-396-8002, enquiries@seymour.co.uk.

794.8 AUS
QUANDARY COMPUTER GAME REVIEWS. Text in English. 1995. s-a. software rev. **Document type:** *Newsletter.*
Media: Online - full text.
Address: PO Box 166, North Fremantle, W.A. 6159, Australia. TEL 61-8-9430-4602, quandary@quandaryland.com, http://www.quandaryland.com. Pubs. Gordon Aplin, Rosemary Young.

RECREATIONAL & EDUCATIONAL COMPUTING; a mathemagical panoply of computer recreations for thinking readers. see *COMPUTERS—Personal Computers*

▼ **S F T - SPIELE FILME TECHNIK.** see *MOTION PICTURES*

794.8 DEU ISSN 1437-3599
S T-COMPUTER; atari-computing heute. Text in German. 1996. 11/yr. EUR 50.10 domestic; EUR 65.40 foreign; EUR 5 newsstand/cover (effective 2003). adv. back issues avail. **Document type:** *Magazine, Consumer.* **Description:** Contains information and features for owners and users of Atari systems.
Formerly (until 1998): ST-Computer Atari Insider (1437-3580); Which was formed by the merger of (19??-1996): Atari Inside (1437-3572); (1986-1996): ST-Computer (0932-0385); Which incorporated (1987-1993): S T - Magazin (0934-3237); Which was formerly (until 1988): 6800er S T - Magazin (0933-2308)
Published by: Falke Verlag, An der Holsatiamuehle 1, Kiel, 24149, Germany. TEL 49-431-2007660, FAX 49-431-2099035, info@st-computer.net, info@falkemedia.de, http://www.st-computer.net, http://www.falkemedia.de. Ed. Thomas Raukamp. Pub. Kassian A. Goukassian. Circ: 50,000.

794.8 USA ISSN 1070-1575
S.W.A.T.PRO* ; secret weapon and tactic guide. Variant title: SwatPro. Text in English. 1991. bi-m. USD 20. **Document type:** *Consumer.*
Published by: Infotainment World, Inc., 501 2nd St, Ste 500, San Francisco, CA 94107-4133. TEL 415-349-4300.

SAKKELET. see *SPORTS AND GAMES*

SCHWEIZERISCHE SCHACHZEITUNG; revue Suisse des echecs, revista scacchistica Svizzera. see *SPORTS AND GAMES*

794.8 GBR ISSN 1352-4267
SEGA. Text in English. 1994. m. GBP 34; GBP 40 foreign. adv. **Document type:** *Consumer.*

Published by: E M A P - Images, Priory Ct, 30-32 Farringdon Ln, London, EC1R 3AU, United Kingdom. TEL 44-171-972-6700, FAX 44-171-972-6710. **Subscr. to:** Tower Publishing Services Ltd., Tower House, Sovereign Park, Market Harborough, Leics LE16 9EF, United Kingdom. TEL 44-1858-468811, FAX 44-1858-432164.

794.8 USA
SEGAVISIONS✶. Text in English. 1990. bi-m. software rev.
Published by: (Sega of America), Infotainment World, Inc., 501 2nd St, Ste 500, San Francisco, CA 94107-4133. TEL 415-349-4300. Ed. Nic Lavaroff. Circ: 1,000,000 (controlled).

SELL OUT. see *COMMUNICATIONS—Television And Cable*

794.8 GBR
LB1029.S53
SIMULATION AND GAMING YEARBOOK (YEAR). GAMES AND SIMULATIONS TO ENHANCE QUALITY LEARNING. Text in English. a. GBP 35. adv. **Document type:** *Directory.*
Formerly: Simulation and Gaming Yearbook (Year). Interactive Learning (1351-4644)
Indexed: BrEdI.
Published by: (Society for Advancement of Games and Simulations in Education and Training), Kogan Page Ltd., 120 Pentonville Rd, London, N1 9JN, United Kingdom. FAX 44-20-7837-6348. Ed. Danny Saunders. R&P Caroline Gromm. Adv. contact Linda Batham.

794.8 GBR
SOLUTIONZONE. Text in English. irreg. **Description:** Covers cheats and solutions for PC and console games.
Published by: Live Publishing International Ltd., Europa House, Adlington Park, Macclesfield, Cheshire SK10 4NP, United Kingdom. TEL 44-1625-855086, FAX 44-1625-855071, subs@livepublishing.co.uk, http://www.livepublishing.co.uk/. Ed. Wayne Williams. Pub. Robin Wilkinson. Adv. contact Kenny Leslie.

STAR WARS GAMER; the force in star wars gaming. see *SPORTS AND GAMES*

794.8 GBR ISSN 1463-6263
STATION✶. Text in English. 1998. m. GBP 4.95 newsstand/cover. adv. **Document type:** *Consumer.*
Contact Dist.: M M C Ltd., Octagon House, White Hart Meadows, Ripley, Woking, Surrey GU23 6HR, United Kingdom. TEL 44-1483-211222, FAX 44-1483-224541, mail@rapide.co.uk, http://www.rapide.co.uk. Ed., Pub. Dave Perry. Adv. contact John Massey. color page GBP 7,000; trim 230 x 300.

794.8 GBR
STATION SOLUTIONZONE. Text in English. 2002 (Sep.). irreg. **Document type:** *Magazine, Consumer.* **Description:** Covers tips and tricks for Playstation 1 and Playstation 2 games.
Published by: Live Publishing International Ltd., Europa House, Adlington Park, Macclesfield, Cheshire SK10 4NP, United Kingdom. TEL 44-1625-855086, FAX 44-1625-855071, subs@livepublishing.co.uk, http://www.livepublishing.co.uk/. Eds. Paul Roundell, Wayne Williams. Pub. Robin Wilkinson. Adv. contact Kenny Leslie.

794.8 GBR ISSN 1471-6119
STRATEGY PLAYER. Text in English. 2000. 13/yr. GBP 44 in United Kingdom; GBP 50 in Europe; GBP 63 rest of world; GBP 4.99 newsstand/cover (effective 2001); comes with a CD-ROM. 116 p./no.; back issues avail. **Document type:** *Magazine, Consumer.* **Description:** Contains features, detailed reviews and the latest news on titles that matter to the thinking gamer.
Published by: Paragon Publishing Ltd., Paragon House, 10 St Peters Rd, Bournemouth, Dorset BH1 2JS, United Kingdom. TEL 44-1202-299900, FAX 44-1202-299955, 44-1202-200217, subs@paragon.co.uk, http://www.paragon.co.uk. Ed. Mike O'Sullivan. Adv. contact Felicity Mead TEL 44-1202-200224.

794.8 USA
STREET BEAT; onestop guide to music and coin machines. Text in English. 1992. m. USD 20 (effective 1997). adv. **Document type:** *Trade.* **Description:** Covers the jukebox and coin operated entertainment industry. Includes information on pinball machines and video games as well as record reviews and guides to music programming.
Published by: Street Beat Publishing, 85 N 3rd St, Ste 6E, Brooklyn, NY 11211. TEL 718-388-4370, FAX 718-388-5859, SBeatMail@aol.com. Ed., Pub. Jeremy Tepper. Adv. contact Leslie Morrow. Circ: 5,000.

794.8 USA ISSN 1545-4142
▼ **STUFF GAMER.** Text in English. 2003. bi-m. USD 5.99 newsstand/cover (effective 2004). adv. **Document type:** *Magazine, Consumer.*
Published by: Dennis Publishing, Inc., 1040 Ave of the Americas, 23rd Fl, New York, NY 10018. TEL 212-302-2626, FAX 212-302-2635, http://www.stuffgamer.com.

SUPER. see *ELECTRONICS*

794.8 ITA ISSN 1126-3652
SUPER CONSOLE. Variant title: Super Console PlayStation. Text in Italian. 1994. 11/yr. EUR 28.60 (effective 2003). adv. **Document type:** *Magazine, Consumer.* **Description:** Covers important technical and legal events in the video game industry. Also includes reviews of the new releases, tips for players and interviews with game creators.
Published by: Gruppo Editoriale Futura, Via XXV Aprile, 39, Bresso, MI 20091, Italy. TEL 39-02-665261, FAX 39-02-66526222, superconsole@futura-ge.com, info@futura-ge.com, http://www.futura-ge.com/prodotti/riviste/SuperPlaystation. Ed. Paolo Reina.

794.8 ITA
SUPER TRIX. Text in Italian. bi-m. adv. **Document type:** *Magazine, Consumer.* **Description:** Covers all items and issues of interest to Sony PlayStation users.
Published by: Gruppo Editoriale Futura, Via XXV Aprile, 39, Bresso, MI 20091, Italy. TEL 39-02-665261, FAX 39-02-66526222, info@futura-ge.com, http://www.futura-ge.com/prodotti/riviste/Supertrix/profilo/.

794.8 USA ISSN 1547-4046
▼ **SURGE;** the pulse of gaming. Text in English. 2003 (Nov.). bi-m. (will be monthly second half of 2004). USD 5.99 per issue (effective 2003). adv. **Document type:** *Magazine, Consumer.* **Description:** Focuses on the latest gaming trends, new gear, personalities and issues in creating games.. Contains in-depth interviews with developers and celebrities, game reviews and coverage of hardware.
Published by: Bedford Communications, Inc., 1410 Broadway, 21st Fl, New York, NY 10018. TEL 212-807-8220, http://www.techworthy.com. adv.: B&W page USD 6,335, color page USD 6,970; trim 8 x 10.75.

794.8 GBR ISSN 1474-452X
TIP STATION. Text in English. 2001. bi-m. GBP 16.67 (effective 2002). **Document type:** *Magazine, Consumer.* **Description:** Covers tips and tricks for Playstation 1 and Playstation 2 games.
Published by: Live Publishing International Ltd., Europa House, Adlington Park, Macclesfield, Cheshire SK10 4NP, United Kingdom. TEL 44-1625-855086, FAX 44-1625-855071, subs@livepublishing.co.uk, http://www.livepublishing.co.uk/. Eds. Paul Roundell, Wayne Williams. Pub. Robin Wilkinson. Adv. contact Kenny Leslie.

794.8 USA ISSN 1090-641X
TIPS & TRICKS. Text in English. 1994. m. USD 19.95 (effective 2005). adv. **Document type:** *Magazine, Consumer.* **Description:** Provides hints, tips and advice on a variety of video games.
Published by: L F P, Inc., 8484 Wilshire Blvd., Ste. 900, Beverly Hills, CA 90211. TEL 323-651-5400, 800-304-1849, FAX 323-651-0651, http://www.tipstricks.com/. Ed. Chris Bieniek. Adv. contact Brian Dunn TEL 323-951-7905. B&W page USD 6,646, color page USD 7,838; trim 10.875 x 16. **Dist. in UK by:** Comag, Tavistock Works, Tavistock Rd, W Drayton, Middx UB7 7QX, United Kingdom. TEL 44-1895-444055, FAX 44-1895-433602.

794.8 GBR ISSN 1366-9532
TOTAL 64; total reading for the Nintendo generation. Text in English. 1997. m. GBP 2.99 newsstand/cover. software rev. illus. **Document type:** *Consumer.* **Description:** Reviews new computer games for the Nintendo-64 system.
Published by: E X 5 Publishing, Floor 3, Wellpark, Willeys Ave, Exeter, EX2 8BE, United Kingdom. TEL 44-1392-276340, FAX 44-1392-276325, mail@rapide.co.uk, info@ex5.co.uk, http://www.rapide.co.uk, http://www.ex5.co.uk/. **Dist. by:** Magazine Marketing Co.. TEL 44-1483-211222, FAX 44-1483-224541.

794.8 GBR
TOTAL GAME BOY. Text in English. 1998. bi-m. GBP 2.99 newsstand/cover (effective 2001). adv. 84 p./no.; back issues avail. **Document type:** *Magazine, Consumer.* **Description:** Provides news, previews, reviews, hints and tips, competitions and more relating to Nintendo's new color portable gaming platform.
Former titles: Total Game Boy Color; Total Games Guide to Game Boy Color (1464-5904)
Published by: Paragon Publishing Ltd., Paragon House, 10 St Peters Rd, Bournemouth, Dorset BH1 2JS, United Kingdom. TEL 44-1202-299900, FAX 44-1202-299955, gecko@paragon.co.uk, http://www.paragon.co.uk. Ed. Nick Roberts. Adv. contact Felicity Mead TEL 44-1202-200224. **Dist. by:** Seymour Distribution Ltd, 86 Newman St, London W1T 3EX, United Kingdom. FAX 44-207-396-8002, enquiries@seymour.co.uk.

794.8 GBR ISSN 1361-7036
TOTAL PLAYSTATION. Text in English. 1996. bi-m. GBP 29.50; GBP 2.99 newsstand/cover (effective 1999). adv. **Document type:** *Consumer.*
Published by: E X 5 Publishing, Floor 3, Wellpark, Willeys Ave, Exeter, EX2 8BE, United Kingdom. TEL 44-1392-276340, FAX 44-1392-276325, info@ex5.co.uk, http://www.ex5.co.uk/. adv.: color page GBP 1,604; trim 230 x 300. Circ: 67,741 (paid). **Dist. by:** M M C Ltd., Octagon House, White Hart Meadows, Ripley, Woking, Surrey GU23 6HR, United Kingdom. TEL 44-1483-211222, FAX 44-1483-224541.

794.8 ITA
TUTTO CODICI; bimestrale a carattere di informazioni programmi e giochi per computer. Text in Italian. 1999. bi-m. **Document type:** *Magazine, Consumer.* **Description:** Contains tricks and passwords for playstation games.
Published by: Tattilo Editrice SpA, Via degli Olmetti 18, Formello, RM 00060, Italy. TEL 39-06-9040701, FAX 39-06-90407030, il.tattilo.editrice@tattilo.it, http://www.tattilo.it. Ed. Roberto Balsamo. **Affiliate:** Marco Andrea Celegato.

794.8 ITA
TUTTO PLAYSTATION; mensile a carattere di informazioni programmi e giochi per computer. Text in Italian. 1999. m. **Document type:** *Magazine, Consumer.* **Description:** Provides reviews and ratings of new games. Also includes tricks and strategies for players.
Published by: Tattilo Editrice SpA, Via degli Olmetti 18, Formello, RM 00060, Italy. TEL 39-06-9040701, FAX 39-06-90407030, il.tattilo.editrice@tattilo.it, http://www.tattilo.it. Ed. Roberto Balsamo. **Affiliate:** Marco Andrea Celegato.

794.8 GBR ISSN 1368-5317
ULTIMATE P C. Text in English. 1997. m. GBP 35.55; GBP 3.95 newsstand/cover (effective 1999). adv. **Document type:** *Consumer.* **Description:** Contains a wide variety of PC games reviews and solutions.
Published by: E X 5 Publishing, Floor 3, Wellpark, Willeys Ave, Exeter, EX2 8BE, United Kingdom. TEL 44-1392-276340, FAX 44-1392-276325, info@ex5.co.uk, http://www.ex5.co.uk/. Circ: 60,882 (paid). **Dist. by:** M M C Ltd., Octagon House, White Hart Meadows, Ripley, Woking, Surrey GU23 6HR, United Kingdom. TEL 44-1483-211222, FAX 44-1483-224541.

794.8 GBR
ULTIMATE P C STRATEGIES. Text in English. 1998. m. GBP 4.99 newsstand/cover. adv. **Document type:** *Consumer.* **Description:** Filled with solutions, guides, tips and cheats for all types of PC games.
Published by: E X 5 Publishing, Floor 3, Wellpark, Willeys Ave, Exeter, EX2 8BE, United Kingdom. TEL 44-1392-276340, FAX 44-1392-276325, info@ex5.co.uk, http://www.ex5.co.uk/. **Dist. by:** M M C Ltd., Octagon House, White Hart Meadows, Ripley, Woking, Surrey GU23 6HR, United Kingdom. TEL 44-1483-211222, FAX 44-1483-224541.

794.8 GBR ISSN 1367-2533
ULTIMATE SOLUTIONS✶. Text in English. 1997. q. GBP 4.99 newsstand/cover. **Document type:** *Consumer.*
Contact Dist.: M M C Ltd., Octagon House, White Hart Meadows, Ripley, Woking, Surrey GU23 6HR, United Kingdom. TEL 44-1483-211222, FAX 44-1483-224541.

VERZEICHNIS LIEFERBARER KAUFMEDIEN. see *BUSINESS AND ECONOMICS—Trade And Industrial Directories*

794.8 USA
VIDEO GAMES UNDERGROUND. Text in English. 19??-2001; resumed 2002 (Mar.). bi-m. **Document type:** *Magazine, Consumer.*
Formerly (until 2001): Video Games Review
Published by: Kappa Publishing Group, Inc., 6198 Butler Pike., Ste. 200, Blue Bell, PA 19422-2606.

794.8 ITA ISSN 1723-3348
▼ **VIDEOGIOCHI (MILAN, 2003).** Text in Italian. 2003. m. EUR 26 (effective 2005). **Document type:** *Magazine, Consumer.*
Published by: Future Media Italy SpA, Via Asiago 45, Milano, MI 20128, Italy. TEL 39-02-2529161, FAX 39-02-26005520, info@futuremediaitaly.it, http://www.futuremediaitaly.it.

794.8 USA
VOODOO (FOSTER CITY); the official 3Dfx interactive magazine. Text in English. 1998. q. USD 12.95; USD 5.99 newsstand/cover (effective 1998). **Document type:** *Consumer.* **Description:** Focuses on all things related to or impacted by 3Dfx graphics technology, including software and hardware reviews and previews, arcade games and location based entertainment, and developer interviews.
Published by: Dimension Publishing, 1175 Chess Dr., Ste. E, Foster City, CA 94404. TEL 650-372-0942, FAX 650-372-0753, d3@quake.net, http://www.3dfx.com. Ed. Chris Kramer.

794.8 GBR ISSN 1475-1429
X B M; the hardcore videogames magazine. (X Box Magazine) Text in English. 2001. m. (13/yr.). GBP 3.20 newsstand/cover (effective 2003). **Document type:** *Magazine, Consumer.* **Description:** Covers Xbox software from in-depth work in progress features, extensive previews and interviews with developers, to accurate and honest reviews.
Published by: Paragon Publishing Ltd., Paragon House, 10 St Peters Rd, Bournemouth, Dorset BH1 2JS, United Kingdom. TEL 44-1202-299900, FAX 44-1202-299955, subs@paragon.co.uk, http://www.paragon.co.uk/mags/xbm.html. Ed. Nick Jones. Circ: 21,993.

794.8 DEU
X B M; das XBox-Mag im XXL-Format. (XBox Magazin) Text in German. bi-m. EUR 5.90 newsstand/cover (effective 2003). adv. **Document type:** *Magazine, Consumer.*

C

▼ new title ➤ refereed ✶ unverified ♦ full entry avail.

Published by: Pro Verlag Gesellschaft fuer Publikationen mbH, Berner Str 38, Frankfurt Am Main, 60437, Germany. TEL 49-69-5008050, FAX 49-69-5008051, office@proverlag.com, http://www.proverlag.com. adv.: page EUR 4,900; trim 230 x 297.

794.85   ITA   ISSN 1594-4670
X B M. Text in Italian. 2002. m. EUR 4.50 newsstand/cover (effective 2003). adv. **Document type:** *Magazine, Consumer.*
Published by: Play Press Publishing s.r.l., Via Vitorchiano 123, Rome, RM 00189, Italy. TEL 39-06-33221250, FAX 39-06-33221235, abbonamenti@playpress.com, http://www.playpress.com. Ed. Alberto Belli. Pub. Alessandro Ferri. Adv. contact Lorenza Borroni TEL 39-02-45472867. Circ. 70,000 (paid and controlled).

794.8   DEU
X ZONE; das unabhaengige XBox-Magazin. Text in German. 2002. bi-m. EUR 6.99 newsstand/cover (effective 2003). adv. **Document type:** *Magazine, Consumer.*
Published by: Computec Media AG, Dr-Mack-Str 77, Fuerth, 90762, Germany. TEL 49-911-2872100, FAX 49-911-2872200, info@computec.de, http://www.computec.de. Ed. Hans Ippisch. Adv. contact Ina Willax. B&W page EUR 4,130, color page EUR 5,900; trim 210 x 297. Circ. 75,000 (paid and controlled).

794.8   DEU
XBOX; das offizielle XBox-Magazin. Variant title: Das Offizielle XBox-Magazin. Text in German. 2002. m. EUR 88.20 domestic; EUR 101.40 in Austria; EUR 97.20 elsewhere; EUR 7.99 newsstand/cover (effective 2003). adv. **Document type:** *Magazine, Consumer.*
Published by: Computec Media AG, Dr-Mack-Str 77, Fuerth, 90762, Germany. TEL 49-911-2872100, FAX 49-911-2872200, info@computec.de, http://www.computec.de. Ed. Hans Ippisch. Adv. contact Ina Willax. B&W page EUR 4,130, color page EUR 5,900; trim 210 x 297. Circ. 75,000 (paid and controlled).

794.8   ITA   ISSN 1594-2546
XBOX. Variant title: Xbox Magazine Ufficiale. Text in Italian. 2002. m. EUR 79 (effective 2005). adv. **Document type:** *Magazine, Consumer.*
Published by: Future Media Italy SpA, Via Asiago 45, Milano, MI 20128, Italy. TEL 39-02-2529161, FAX 39-02-26005520, info@futuremediaitaly.it, http://www.futuremediaitaly.it.

794.8   USA   ISSN 1538-9723
XBOX NATION. Abbreviated title: X B N. Text in English. 2001 (Dec.). m. (q. until Nov. 2002; bi-m until Mar. 2004). USD 19.97 domestic; USD 35.97 foreign; USD 5.99 newsstand/cover domestic; USD 6.99 newsstand/cover in Canada (effective 2003). adv. 48 p./no.; **Document type:** *Magazine, Consumer.* **Description:** Covers Xbox games and accessories, offering news, game reviews and previews, along with targeted tips and strategies.
Related titles: Online - full text ed.: (from bigchalk, EBSCO Publishing, ProQuest Information & Learning).
Indexed: MASUSE.
Published by: Ziff Davis Media Game Group (Subsidiary of: Ziff Davis Media Inc.), 28 E 28th St, New York, NY 10016-7930. TEL 415-547-8000, FAX 415-547-8777, info@ziffdavis.com, http://www.ziffdavis.com. Ed. Simon Cox. Circ. 20,000.

794.8   GBR
XPERT; xbox tips cheats and solutions. Text in English. 2002. bi-m. GBP 3.99 newsstand/cover (effective 2003). **Document type:** *Magazine, Consumer.* **Description:** Contains Xbox tips, cheats and solutions.
Published by: Paragon Publishing Ltd., Paragon House, 10 St Peters Rd, Bournemouth, Dorset BH1 2JS, United Kingdom. TEL 44-1202-299900, FAX 44-1202-299955, subs@paragon.co.uk, http://www.paragon.co.uk/mags/xpert.html. Ed. Phil King. Circ. 8,338.

794.8   USA
2 X S; an ezine by and for roll - role players. Text in English. 1996. q.
Media: Online - full text.
Address: PO Box 392, Ector, TX 75439. aramus@netexas.net, http://www.netexas.net/rglaser/2xs/. Ed. Aramus Hudra.

794.8   GBR   ISSN 1461-2828
64 GAME BUSTER ✶ . Text in English. 1998. m. GBP 3.95 newsstand/cover. adv. **Document type:** *Consumer.*
Contact Dist.: M M C Ltd., Octagon House, White Hart Meadows, Ripley, Woking, Surrey GU23 6HR, United Kingdom. TEL 44-1483-211222, FAX 44-1483-224541. Ed. Simon Philips. Pub. Andrew Collins. Adv. contact Gerard Richardson.

COMPUTERS—Computer Graphics

see also PRINTING—Computer Applications

006.6   USA
A C M - I E E E SYMPOSIUM ON VOLUME VISUALIZATION. (Association for Computing Machinery - Institute of Electrical and Electronics Engineers) Text in English. a., latest 2002. price varies. **Document type:** *Proceedings, Academic/Scholarly.*

Published by: Institute of Electrical and Electronics Engineers, Inc., 3 Park Ave, 17th Fl, New York, NY 10016-5997. TEL 212-419-7900, 800-678-4333, FAX 212-752-4929, customer.service@ieee.org, http://www.ieee.org.

006.6   USA   ISSN 1551-1669
T385
A C M SIGGRAPH SYMPOSIUM ON INTERACTIVE 3D GRAPHICS. PROCEEDINGS. Text in English. a. price varies. **Document type:** *Proceedings, Academic/Scholarly.*
Former titles: (until 2003): A C M Symposium on Interactive 3D Graphics. Proceedings (1541-0390); (until 1999): Symposium on Interactive 3D Graphics (1551-1642)
—BLDSC (0578.647).
Published by: Association for Computing Machinery, Inc., 1515 Broadway, 17th Fl, New York, NY 10036-5701. TEL 212-626-0500, 212-626-0520, FAX 212-869-0481, sigs@acm.org, usacm@acm.org, http://www.acm.org.

006.6   USA   ISSN 1548-4580
A C M SPECIAL INTEREST GROUP IN COMPUTER GRAPHICS / EUROGRAPHICS SYMPOSIUM ON COMPUTER ANIMATION. PROCEEDINGS. Text in English. a. **Document type:** *Proceedings, Trade.*
Related titles: Online - full content ed.
Published by: (A C M Special Interest Group in Computer Graphics), Association for Computing Machinery, Inc., 1515 Broadway, 17th Fl, New York, NY 10036-5701. TEL 212-626-0500, 800-342-6626, usacm@acm.org, http://portal.acm.org/toc.cfm?id=SERIES10768, http://www.acm.org.

006.6   USA   ISSN 0730-0301
T385   CODEN: ATGRDF
➤ **A C M TRANSACTIONS ON GRAPHICS.** Text in English. 1982. q. USD 185 domestic to non-members; USD 199 foreign to non-members; USD 48 domestic to members; USD 43 foreign to members; USD 43 domestic to students; USD 57 foreign to students; USD 222 combined subscription domestic to non-members print & online eds.; USD 236 combined subscription foreign to non-members print & online eds.; USD 58 combined subscription domestic to members print & online eds.; USD 72 combined subscription foreign to members print & online eds.; USD 52 combined subscription domestic to students print & online eds.; USD 66 combined subscription foreign to students print & online eds. (effective 2006). bk.rev. charts; illus. index. back issues avail.; reprints avail. **Document type:** *Journal, Academic/Scholarly.*
Description: Provides coverage of various forms of graphics applications including geometric modeling, design and analysis of algorithms, person-machine interaction techniques and computer graphics hardware.
Related titles: Microform ed.; Online - full text ed.: ISSN 1557-7368. USD 148 to non-members; USD 38 to members; USD 34 to students (effective 2006) (from Association for Computing Machinery, Inc., EBSCO Publishing).
Indexed: ABIn, AHCI, AIA, AS&TI, ASCA, BrCerAb, C&ISA, CADCAM, CIS, CMCI, CerAb, CompAb, CompC, CompD, CompLI, CompR, CorrAb, CurCont, E&CAJ, EMA, EngInd, ErgAb, IAA, ISMEC, ISR, Inspec, M&TEA, MBF, METADEX, RefZh, SCI, SolStAb, WAA, ZentMath.
—BLDSC (0578.665000), AskIEEE, CISTI, Ei, IDS, IE, Infotrieve, ingenta, Linda Hall. **CCC.**
Published by: Association for Computing Machinery, Inc., 1515 Broadway, 17th Fl, New York, NY 10036-5701. TEL 212-626-0520, 800-342-6626, FAX 212-944-1318, usacm@acm.org, http://www.acm.org/tog/. Ed. John Hart. Pub. Jono Hardjowirogo. Circ. 2,025 (paid).

006.7   LUX
A C T S NEWS CLIPS. (Advanced Communications Technologies & Services) Text in Multiple languages. bi-w. **Document type:** *Newsletter.* **Description:** Covers advances communications technologies and services, multimedia computer systems and information technology.
Media: Online - full text.
Published by: European Commission, Office for Official Publications of the European Union, 2 Rue Mercier, Luxembourg, L-2985, Luxembourg. FAX 352-2929-1, newclips@newmedia.at, http://www.uk.infowin.org/ACTS/IENM/NEWSCLIPS/. Ed. Robert Verrue.

A G D QUARTAL. see *ART*

621.399   NLD   ISSN 0926-9622
ADVANCES IN DESIGN AND MANUFACTURING. Text in English. 1991. irreg., latest vol.8, 1998. price varies. back issues avail. **Document type:** *Monographic series, Academic/Scholarly.* **Description:** Discusses the impact of computer and information technology on all sectors of the manufacturing industry.
—CISTI. **CCC.**
Published by: I O S Press, Nieuwe Hemweg 6B, Amsterdam, 1013 BG, Netherlands. TEL 31-20-6883355, FAX 31-20-6203419, market@iospress.nl, order@iospress.nl, http://www.iospress.nl. **Subscr. to:** I O S Press, Inc, 4502 Rachael Manor Dr., Fairfax, VA 22032-3631. iosbooks@iospress.com. **Dist. by:** Ohmsha Ltd.

006.6   NLD   ISSN 0928-1479
ADVANCES IN IMAGE COMMUNICATION. Text in English. 1993. irreg., latest vol.9, 2000. price varies. back issues avail. **Document type:** *Monographic series, Academic/Scholarly.* **Description:** Discusses research and applications in image communication.
—BLDSC (0709.086000), ingenta.
Published by: Elsevier BV, North-Holland (Subsidiary of: Elsevier Science & Technology), Sara Burgerhartstraat 25, Amsterdam, 1055 KV, Netherlands. TEL 31-20-485-3911, FAX 31-20-485-2457, nlinfo-f@elsevier.nl, http://www.elsevier.nl. Ed. J Biemond. **Subscr. to:** Elsevier BV, PO Box 211, Amsterdam 1000 AE, Netherlands. http://www.elsevier.nl.

ATLAS MAGAZINE. see *ART*

006.7   USA
AUTHORWARE ✶ . Text in English. 1988. q. USD 20; USD 30 foreign. adv. bk.rev. **Description:** Focuses on interactive multi-media authoring software, computer-aided instruction (CAI), and computer-based training (CBT).
Formerly: Co Action Magazine.
Published by: Authorware, Inc., 600 Townsend St, San Francisco, CA 94103-4945. TEL 415-595-3101, FAX 415-595-3077. Ed. Kathy Nordgaard. Circ. 5,000.

620.00420258   USA
AUTOCAD E-NEWS. Text in English. irreg. free. adv. back issues avail. **Document type:** *Newsletter.* **Description:** Provides latest news from CAD and computers in the world, including questions and answers from AutoCAD users.
Media: Online - full text.
Address: ktrelski@aol.com, http://members.aol.com/cadnews. Ed., Pub. Krzysztof Trelski.

B I C A. (Bulletin of Information on Computing in Anthropology) see *ANTHROPOLOGY*

B V S REVIEWS. (Bruce Von Stiers) see *COMPUTERS— Software*

BASELINE (EAST MALLING). see *PRINTING*

006.6   USA   ISSN 1049-0035
NC998.5.A1
BEFORE & AFTER ✶ ; how to design cool stuff. Text in English. 1990. 4/yr. USD 36 domestic; USD 40 in Canada; USD 54 elsewhere. **Document type:** *Trade.* **Description:** Practical graphic design advice, with particular emphasis on techniques and applications of Aldus PageMaker and FreeHand design software.
Published by: PageLab, Inc., 2007 Opportunity Dr Ste 10, Roseville, CA 95678-3007. TEL 916-784-3880, FAX 916-784-3995, pagelab@quiknet.com. Ed. Gaye McWade.

BRAINBOX. see *COMPUTERS—Internet*

006.6   USA   ISSN 1530-1834
BRAZILIAN SYMPOSIUM ON COMPUTER GRAPHICS AND IMAGE PROCESSING. PROCEEDINGS. Text in English. 1992. a. USD 195 per vol. (effective 2004). **Document type:** *Proceedings, Trade.*
Related titles: Online - full text ed.: (from I E E E).
Published by: Institute of Electrical and Electronics Engineers, Inc., 3 Park Ave, 17th Fl, New York, NY 10016-5997. TEL 212-419-7900, 800-678-4333, FAX 212-752-4929, customer.service@ieee.org, http://www.ieee.org.

006.6   NLD   ISSN 1386-1689
C A D MAGAZINE. Text in Dutch. 1990. 8/yr. EUR 55 domestic; EUR 95 foreign (effective 2003).
—Infotrieve.
Published by: CMedia Productions B.V., Postbus 231, Emmeloord, 8300 AE, Netherlands. TEL 31-527-619000, FAX 31-527-620989, services@cadmag.nl, http://www.cadplaza.nl.

006.7   AUT
C D AUSTRIA. (Compact Disc) Text in German. 11/yr. EUR 49.90 (effective 2005). adv. **Document type:** *Magazine, Consumer.* **Description:** Contains news and reviews on a wide variety of multimedia applications and software.
Published by: C D A Verlags- und Handelsgesellschaft mbH, Tobra 9, Perg, 4320, Austria. TEL 43-7262-57557-0, FAX 43-7262-5755744, redaktion@cda-verlag.com, http://www.cd-austria.at, http://www.cda-verlag.com. Ed. Karl Strasser. Pub. Harald Gutzelnig. Adv. contact Marianne Gutzelnig. B&W page EUR 3,390, color page EUR 3,990; trim 210 x 297. Circ. 17,491 (paid and controlled).

006.7   AUT
C D INFO. (Compact Disc) Text in German. 1997. m. EUR 42.90; EUR 4.95 newsstand/cover (effective 2005). adv. **Document type:** *Magazine, Consumer.* **Description:** Provides news and information on the latest multimedia applications and software available for the whole family.

Published by: C D A Verlags- und Handelsgesellschaft mbH, Tobra 9, Perg, 4320, Austria. TEL 43-7262-57557-0, FAX 43-7262-5755744, redaktion@cda-verlag.com, http://cd-info.cda-verlag.com, http://www.cda-verlag.com. Ed. Karl Strasser. Pub. Harald Gutzelnig. Adv. contact Marianne Gutzelnig. B&W page EUR 2,490, color page EUR 2,990; trim 210 x 297. Circ: 48,000 (paid and controlled).

006.6 TWN ISSN 1609-0004
C G MAGAZINE. Text in Chinese. 2001. s-a. **Document type:** *Magazine, Consumer.* **Description:** Contains the latest information on computer graphics technology, graphic designers, the Internet and other related topics.
Published by: Jianduan Chuban Qufen Youxian Gongsi/Sharp Point Publishing Ltd., Inc., 231 Xindiansi, Fuyu-Lu 43-Hao 8-Lou, Taipei, Taiwan. TEL 886-2-2218-1582, FAX 886-2-2218-1583, janey@spp.com.tw, http://www.spp.com.tw/asp/mag/cgm/index.asp.

006.7 621.399 CAN ISSN 1487-7554
CANADIAN NEW MEDIA. Text in English. 1998. 24/yr. CND 695 domestic; CND 745 foreign; CND 50 newsstand/cover (effective 2003). **Document type:** *Newsletter, Trade.* **Description:** Reports and analyzes developments in the emerging interactive digital and multimedia technologies and the delivery of content and services in Canada.
Related titles: E-mail ed.; Online - full text ed.: ISSN 1700-5086.
Published by: Decima Publishing Inc., 1800-160 Elgin St, Ottawa, ON K2P 2C4, Canada. TEL 613-230-1984, FAX 613-230-9048, cjeffrey@decima.ca, http://www.decima.com/publishing. Ed. Jeff Leiper. Pub. Mario Mota.

006.7 DEU
CHIP SONDERHEFTE. Text in German. 1980. 3/yr. price varies. adv. **Document type:** *Magazine, Trade.*
Former titles: Chip Multimedia; (until 1993): Chip Sonderhefte; Chip Special
Published by: Vogel Verlag und Druck GmbH & Co. KG, Max-Planck-Str 7-9, Wuerzburg, 97064, Germany. TEL 49-931-418-2335, FAX 49-931-4182090, http://www.chip.de. Adv. contact Joachim Berger. Circ: 60,000. **Subscr. in US to:** Vogel Europublishing Inc.; **Subscr. to:** DataM-Services GmbH, Fichtestr 9, Wuerzburg 97074, Germany. TEL 49-931-417001, FAX 49-931-4170499, swestenberger@datam-services.de, http://www.datam-services.de.

006.68 CAN ISSN 1190-8874
Z286.D47
CHRIS DICKMAN'S COREL DRAW JOURNAL. Text in English. 1993. 10/yr. CND 47. bk.rev. back issues avail. **Document type:** *Consumer.* **Description:** Devoted solely to providing hands-on tips and techniques for those using the CorelDRAW graphics suite of applications.
Formerly (until 1994): Chris Dickman's Mastering Corel Draw (1192-9006)
Related titles: Diskette ed.
Published by: Kazak Communications, 16 Ottawa St, Toronto, ON M4T 2B6, Canada. TEL 416-924-0759, FAX 416-924-4875. Ed. Chris Dickman. Circ: 5,000 (paid).

006 FRA
CLONE. Text in French. 1994. q. **Description:** Covers virtual reality and cyberculture.
Media: Online - full text.
Published by: Alpha du Centaure, France. clone@imaginet.fr.

006.6 686.2 USA ISSN 1055-3339
COLOR BUSINESS REPORT. Text in English. 1991. m. USD 545 domestic to individuals; USD 595 foreign to individuals; USD 605 domestic to institutions; USD 655 foreign to institutions; USD 30 newsstand/cover (effective 2001). charts; illus.; mkt.; stat. back issues avail. **Document type:** *Newsletter, Trade.* **Description:** Offers product managers, strategic planners, and research and development executives in the computer industry information on computer peripheral product introductions, hands-on product evaluations, end-user reactions to new products, printing technology and computer graphics.
Published by: Blackstone Research Associates, 10 River Rd, Ste 104, Uxbridge, MA 01569-2245. TEL 508-278-3449, FAX 508-278-7975, mike@blackstoneresearch.com, http://www.blackstoneresearch.com. Ed., R&P Michael Zeis.

COLOR SLIDES NEWSLETTER. see *COMPUTERS—Software*

006.6 NLD ISSN 1381-6446
➤ **COMPUTATIONAL IMAGING AND VISION.** Text in English. 1994. irreg., latest vol.30, 2005. price varies. **Document type:** *Monographic series, Academic/Scholarly.*
Indexed: BIOSIS Prev, CCMJ, ZentMath.
—BLDSC (3390.594000), IE, ingenta. **CCC.**
Published by: Springer-Verlag Dordrecht (Subsidiary of: Springer Science+Business Media), Van Godewijckstraat 30, Dordrecht, 3311 GX, Netherlands. TEL 31-78-6576050, FAX 31-78-6576474, http://www.springeronline.com. Ed. Max A Viergever.

▼ ➤ **COMPUTER-AIDED DESIGN AND APPLICATIONS.** see *ENGINEERING—Computer Applications*

006.6 NLD ISSN 0167-8396
T385 CODEN: CAGDEX
➤ **COMPUTER-AIDED GEOMETRIC DESIGN.** Text in English. 1984. 9/yr. EUR 697 in Europe to institutions; JPY 92,600 in Japan to institutions; USD 780 elsewhere to institutions; EUR 73 in Europe to qualified personnel; JPY 9,800 in Japan to qualified personnel; USD 82 elsewhere to qualified personnel (effective 2006). adv. illus. back issues avail.; reprints avail. **Document type:** *Academic/Scholarly.* **Description:** Reports on computer-aided geometric design applications in the design of automobiles, planes and ships, mathematical foundations, geometric aspects of CAD-CAM, and robot cinematics.
Related titles: Online - full text ed.: (from EBSCO Publishing, Gale Group, IngentaConnect, ScienceDirect, Swets Information Services).
Indexed: ApMecR, BrCerAb, C&ISA, CADCAM, CCMJ, CMCI, CerAb, CivEngAb, CompAb, CompLI, CompR, CorrAb, CurCont, CybAb, E&CAJ, EMA, EngInd, IAA, ISMEC, ISR, Inspec, M&TEA, MBF, METADEX, MathR, MathSciNet, SCI, SolStAb, WAA, ZentMath.
—BLDSC (3393.541500), AskIEEE, CISTI, Ei, IDS, IE, Infotrieve, ingenta, Linda Hall. **CCC.**
Published by: Elsevier BV, North-Holland (Subsidiary of: Elsevier Science & Technology), Sara Burgerhartstraat 25, Amsterdam, 1055 KV, Netherlands. TEL 31-20-485-3911, FAX 31-20-485-2457, nlinfo-f@elsevier.nl, http://www.elsevier.com/locate/cagd, http://www.elsevier.nl/homepage/about/us/regional_sites.htt. Eds. G. E. Farin, H. Prautzsch. **Subscr. to:** Elsevier BV, PO Box 211, Amsterdam 1000 AE, Netherlands. TEL 31-20-485-3757, FAX 31-20-485-3432.

776.6 GBR ISSN 1546-4261
TR897.5 CODEN: JVCAEO
➤ **COMPUTER ANIMATION AND VIRTUAL WORLDS.** Text in English. 1990. 5/yr. USD 1,315 to institutions; USD 1,447 combined subscription to institutions print & online eds. (effective 2006). adv. back issues avail.; reprints avail. **Document type:** *Journal, Academic/Scholarly.* **Description:** Includes topics that range from scenario making to postproduction for those who apply animation techniques to science and art.
Formerly (until 2004): The Journal of Visualisation and Computer Animation (1049-8907)
Related titles: Microform ed.: (from PQC); Online - full content ed.: ISSN 1546-427X. 1997. USD 1,315 to institutions (effective 2006); Online - full text ed.: (from EBSCO Publishing, Gale Group, IngentaConnect, Swets Information Services, Wiley InterScience).
Indexed: ASCA, BrCerAb, C&ISA, CMCI, CerAb, CompLI, CorrAb, CurCont, E&CAJ, EMA, EngInd, ErgAb, IAA, ISR, Inspec, M&TEA, MBF, METADEX, SCI, SolStAb, WAA.
—BLDSC (3393.596700), AskIEEE, Ei, IDS, IE, Infotrieve, ingenta. **CCC.**
Published by: John Wiley & Sons Ltd. (Subsidiary of: John Wiley & Sons, Inc.), The Atrium, Southern Gate, Chichester, West Sussex PO19 8SQ, United Kingdom. TEL 44-1243-779777, FAX 44-1243-775878, customer@wiley.co.uk, http://www.interscience.wiley.com/jpages/1049-8907/, http://www.wiley.co.uk. adv.: B&W page GBP 650, color page GBP 1,550; trim 210 x 297. **Subscr. in the Americas to:** John Wiley & Sons, Inc., 111 River St, Hoboken, NJ 07030-5774. TEL 201-748-6645, FAX 201-748-6088, subinfo@wiley.com.

006.6 GBR ISSN 1360-5372
COMPUTER ARTS. Text in English. 1995. 13/yr. GBP 54 combined subscription domestic print & CD-ROM eds.; GBP 73.53 combined subscription in US & Canada print & CD-ROM eds.; GBP 86.53 combined subscription elsewhere print & CD-ROM eds. (effective 2003). adv. **Document type:** *Magazine, Consumer.* **Description:** Reports on, encourages, nurtures and facilitates creativity using the latest technology.
Indexed: DAAI.
—**CCC.**
Published by: Future Publishing Ltd., Beauford Court, 30 Monmouth St, Bath, Avon BA1 2BW, United Kingdom. TEL 44-1225-442244, FAX 44-1225-732285, bob.abbott@futurenet.co.uk, http://www.computerarts.co.uk, http://www.futurenet.com/futureonline. Ed. Gillian Roach. adv.: color page GBP 2,565; trim 232 x 280. Circ: 34,710 (paid).

681.31 FRA ISSN 1288-1333
COMPUTER ARTS. Text in French. 1998. m. FRF 45 newsstand/cover (effective 2001). adv. software rev.; Website rev. **Document type:** *Magazine, Consumer.*
Indexed: DAAI.
Published by: Future France, 101-109 Rue Jean Jaures, Levallois Perret, 92300, France. TEL 33-1-41273838, yveline.duville@futurenet.fr.

681.36 ITA ISSN 1127-8919
COMPUTER ARTS; la revista di grafica per mac & pc. Text in Italian. 1999. m. (13/yr.). EUR 48 (effective 2005). adv. **Document type:** *Magazine, Trade.*
Published by: Future Media Italy SpA, Via Asiago 45, Milano, MI 20128, Italy. TEL 39-02-2529161, FAX 39-02-26005520, info@futuremediaitaly.it, http://www.futuremediaitaly.it.

621.399 CZE ISSN 1212-4389
COMPUTER DESIGN. Text in Czech. 1995. q. CZK 352 (effective 2003). adv. **Document type:** *Magazine, Trade.*
Formerly (until 1997): C A D and Graphics (1211-1082)
Published by: Computer Press a.s., Pod Vinici 23, Prague 4, 143 11, Czech Republic. TEL 420-2-225273930, FAX 420-2-225273934, design@cpress.cz, webmaster@cpress.cz, http://design.cpress.cz, http://www.cpress.cz. Ed. David Nemec. adv.: page CZK 63,000; trim 210 x 297.

006.6 ITA
COMPUTER GRAFICA; tecniche & applicazioni. Text in Italian. 1995. 10/yr. back issues avail. **Document type:** *Consumer.* **Description:** Covers a wide range of information on the field of computer graphics, including news, technical advice and software reviews.
Published by: Edizioni Imago International Srl, Corso Indipendenza 6, Milan, 20129, Italy. TEL 39-02-70009474, FAX 39-02-70009480, edizionimago@tin.it.

006.6 ZAF ISSN 1025-2738
COMPUTER GRAPHICS; CAD, CAD/CAM, CAE and GIS in Southern Africa. Text in English. 1990. bi-m. ZAR 90 (effective 2001). adv. bk.rev.; software rev. illus. back issues avail. **Document type:** *Trade.* **Description:** Covers computer graphics technology and applications, including design, manufacture, mapping, construction and illustration.
Related titles: Online - full text ed.
Indexed: EngInd, ErgAb, ISAP.
Published by: Technews (Pty.) Ltd., PO Box 626, Kloof, 3640, South Africa. TEL 27-31-764-0593, FAX 27-31-764-0386, cgraphics@technews.co.za, technews@iafrica.com.za. Ed. Graeme Bell. Pub. Kevin Beaumont. Adv. contact Jane Fortmann TEL 27-31-764-5316. B&W page ZAR 5,480, color page ZAR 7,120; 180 x 260. Circ: 4,800 (controlled).

006.6 USA
COMPUTER GRAPHICS (SAN DIEGO). Text in English. 1988. irreg., latest vol.3, 1991. back issues avail. **Document type:** *Monographic series.*
Published by: Academic Press (Subsidiary of: Elsevier Science & Technology), 525 B St, Ste 1900, San Diego, CA 92101-4495. apsubs@acad.com, http://www.academicpress.com. Ed. Sol Sherr.

006.6 ITA ISSN 1127-8544
COMPUTER GRAPHICS & PUBLISHING. Text in Italian. 1998. 6/yr. EUR 28 (effective 2005). bk.rev.; Website rev. 96 p./no.; back issues avail. **Document type:** *Magazine, Consumer.* **Description:** Contains articles on the technological and artistic components of computer graphics. Provides lengthy descriptions of new products and software.
Published by: I H T Gruppo Editoriale, Via Monte Napoleone 9, Milan, MI 20121, Italy. TEL 39-02-794181, FAX 39-02-784021, cgp@iht.it, http://www.iht.it. Ed. Alfredo Distefano. Adv. contact Massimiliano Lisa. Circ: 20,000 (paid). **Dist. in Italy by:** Messaggerie Periodici SpA, Via Giulio Carcano 32, Milano 20141, Italy.

006.6 GBR ISSN 0167-7055
T385
➤ **COMPUTER GRAPHICS FORUM;** the international journal of the Eurographics Association. Text in English. 1982. q. USD 996 combined subscription in the Americas to institutions & Caribbean (print & online eds.); GBP 593 combined subscription elsewhere to institutions print & online eds. (effective 2006). bk.rev. reprint service avail. from PSC. **Document type:** *Journal, Academic/Scholarly.* **Description:** Provides coverage of developments in the international computer graphics industry.
Related titles: Online - full text ed.: ISSN 1467-8659. USD 946 in the Americas to institutions & Caribbean; GBP 563 elsewhere to institutions (effective 2006) (from Blackwell Synergy, EBSCO Publishing, Gale Group, IngentaConnect, O C L C Online Computer Library Center, Inc., Swets Information Services).
Indexed: ABIn, ASCA, BrTechI, CADCAM, CMCI, CompAb, CompLI, CurCont, CybAb, DPD, EngInd, ErgAb, Inspec.
—BLDSC (3393.982000), AskIEEE, CISTI, Ei, IDS, IE, Infotrieve, ingenta, Linda Hall. **CCC.**
Published by: (European Association for Computer Graphics CHE, Eurographics Association), Blackwell Publishing Ltd., 9600 Garsington Rd, Oxford, OX4 2ZG, United Kingdom. TEL 44-1865-776868, FAX 44-1865-714591, customerservices@oxon.blackwellpublishing.com, http://www.blackwellpublishing.com/journals/CGF. Eds. David Duke TEL 44-1225-323407, Roberto Scopigno TEL 39-050-3152929.

006.6 USA ISSN 1530-1052
COMPUTER GRAPHICS INTERNATIONAL. PROCEEDINGS. Text in English. 199?. a. USD 115. **Document type:** *Proceedings, Academic/Scholarly.*
Related titles: Online - full text ed.: (from I E E E).
—BLDSC (3393.982300).
Published by: I E E E Computer Society, 10662 Los Vaqueros Circle, PO Box 3014, Los Alamitos, CA 90720-1314. TEL 714-821-8380, 800-272-6657, FAX 714-821-4010, customer.service@ieee.org, http://www.ieee.org.

006.6 USA ISSN 1069-529X
T385 CODEN: CGPSFU
COMPUTER GRAPHICS PROCEEDINGS. ANNUAL CONFERENCE SERIES. Text in English. a. USD 45 to non-members; USD 35 to members (effective 2004). **Document type:** *Proceedings, Academic/Scholarly.*

C

Formerly (until 1993): Computer Graphics (New York) (0097-8930)
Related titles: CD-ROM ed.: ISSN 1069-9236. 1993; Online - full text ed.: (from EBSCO Publishing).
Indexed: AHCI, CMCI, CompC, CompR, CurCont, ErgAb, Inspec, PROMT, RASB.
—BLDSC (3393.970000), AskIEEE, CISTI, Ei, IE, ingenta, Linda Hall.
Published by: Association for Computing Machinery, Inc., 1515 Broadway, 17th Fl, New York, NY 10036-5701. TEL 212-626-0500, 212-626-0520, 800-342-6626, FAX 212-869-0481, sigs@acm.org, usacm@acm.org, http://www.acm.org. Ed. Sue Mair.

006.6 USA ISSN 0271-4159
T385 CODEN: CGWODH
COMPUTER GRAPHICS WORLD. Text in English. 1978. m. USD 55 domestic; USD 75 in Canada & Mexico; USD 115 elsewhere; USD 10 per issue; free to qualified personnel (effective 2005). adv. bk.rev. illus. reprints avail. **Document type:** *Magazine, Trade.* **Description:** Publishes articles covering image processing, CAD-CAM, graphic arts, computerized modeling and software, multimedia and animation, for users and vendors of computer graphics software, hardware and services.
Formerly: Computer Graphics (Eugene) (0162-3273)
Related titles: Microform ed.: (from PQC); Online - full text ed.: (from EBSCO Publishing, Florida Center for Library Automation, Gale Group, Northern Light Technology, Inc., O C L C Online Computer Library Center, Inc., ProQuest Information & Learning, The Dialog Corporation); ♦ Partial Italian translation(s): Computer Gazette. ISSN 1123-4253.
Indexed: AHCI, AS&TI, ASCA, BrTechI, CADCAM, CMCI, CompC, CompD, EngInd, GALA, Inspec, LAMP, M&TEA, MASUSE, MicrocompInd, PROMT, SoftBase.
—BLDSC (3393.985000), AskIEEE, CISTI, Ei, IDS, IE, Infotrieve, ingenta, Linda Hall. **CCC.**
Published by: PennWell Corp., 1421 S Sheridan Rd, Tulsa, OK 74112. TEL 918-835-3161, 800-331-4463, FAX 918-831-9497, cgw@omeda.com, Headquarters@PennWell.com, http://www.cgw.com, http://www.pennwell.com. Ed. Phil LoPiccolo. adv.: B&W page USD 10,920, color page USD 12,915; trim 11 x 8.5. Circ: 63,915.

006.6 USA ISSN 0895-2760
T385
COMPUTER GRAPHICS WORLD BUYERS GUIDE. Text in English. 1983. a. USD 118 domestic; USD 158 in Canada & Mexico; USD 204 in Europe. adv. **Document type:** *Directory.*
Formerly: Computer Graphics Directory (0743-2836)
Related titles: Microform ed.: (from PQC).
—Linda Hall. **CCC.**
Published by: PennWell Corp., 98 Spit Brook Rd, Nashua, NH 03062-5737. TEL 603-891-0123, http://www.pennwell.com. Circ: 2,000.

006.6 JPN
COMPUTER GRAPHICS WORLD JAPAN. Text in Japanese. m. adv. **Document type:** *Magazine, Trade.* **Description:** Covers a wide range of digital media and graphics topics, including product reviews, industry trends, software tips and the introduction of top creators' works.
Related titles: Online - full text ed.
Published by: I D G Japan, Inc., Hongo 3-4-5, Bunkyo-ku, Tokyo, 1130033, Japan. TEL 81-3-5800-3111, FAX 81-3-5800-3590, http://www.idg.co.jp/gw/. adv.: B&W page USD 2,204, color page USD 4,171; trim 277 x 420. Circ: 50,000 (paid).

681.31 DEU ISSN 0932-7924
COMPUTER-GRAPHIK-MARKT. Text in German. 1985. a. EUR 46 domestic; EUR 54 in Europe (effective 2004). adv. **Document type:** *Journal, Trade.*
Published by: Dressler Verlag GmbH, Gaisbergstr 55-57, Heidelberg, 69115, Germany. TEL 49-6221-91130, FAX 49-6221-911321, info@dressler-verlag.de, http://www.dressler-verlag.de/cgm/index.htm.

006.6 DEU ISSN 0936-2770
COMPUTER GRAPHIK TOPICS; reports of the INI-GraphicsNet. Text in English, German. 1989. 6/yr. back issues avail. **Document type:** *Journal, Academic/Scholarly.*
Related titles: Diskette ed.; Online - full text ed.
Address: Fraunhoferstr. 5, Darmstadt, 64283, Germany. TEL 49-6151-155146, FAX 49-6151-155446, bernad.lukacin@igd.fraunhofer.de, http://www.inigraphics.net/press. Ed., R&P Bernad Lukacin. Pub. Jose Encarnacao.

006.6 GBR ISSN 0097-8493
T385 CODEN: COGRD2
➤ **COMPUTERS & GRAPHICS.** Text in English. 1975. 6/yr. EUR 1,744 in Europe to institutions; JPY 231,600 in Japan to institutions; USD 1,949 to institutions except Europe and Japan; EUR 175 in Europe to qualified personnel; JPY 23,300 in Japan to qualified personnel; USD 195 to qualified personnel except Europe and Japan (effective 2006). adv. bk.rev. illus. back issues avail.; reprints avail. **Document type:** *Academic/Scholarly.* **Description:** Contains papers on the utilization of computer interactive graphics applications in industrial problem solving. Articles cover computer-aided design, person-machine communication techniques, and information systems.
Related titles: Microfilm ed.: (from PQC); Online - full text ed.: (from EBSCO Publishing, Gale Group, IngentaConnect, ScienceDirect, Swets Information Services).
Indexed: AHCI, ASCA, ASFA, ApMecR, BMT, BrCerAb, C&ISA, CIS, CMCI, CerAb, CompAb, CompC, CompLI, CompR, CorrAb, CurCont, CybAb, E&CAJ, EMA, EngInd, ErgAb, FLUIDEX, IAA, ISMEC, Inspec, LAMP, M&TEA, MBF, METADEX, MathSciNet, RASB, SSCI, SolStAb, WAA.
—BLDSC (3394.700000), AskIEEE, CISTI, Ei, IDS, IE, Infotrieve, ingenta, Linda Hall. **CCC.**
Published by: Pergamon (Subsidiary of: Elsevier Science & Technology), The Boulevard, Langford Ln, East Park, Kidlington, Oxford OX5 1GB, United Kingdom. TEL 44-1865-843000, FAX 44-1865-843010, http://www.elsevier.com/locate/cag. Ed. Jose L. Encarnacao. Circ: 1,050. **Subscr. to:** Elsevier BV, PO Box 211, Amsterdam 1000 AE, Netherlands. TEL 31-20-485-3757, FAX 31-20-485-3432, nlinfo-f@elsevier.nl, http://www.elsevier.nl.

006.7 DEU
COMPUTERVIDEO. Text in German. 1997. bi-m. EUR 35.40 domestic; EUR 37.40 foreign; EUR 5.90 newsstand/cover (effective 2004). adv. **Document type:** *Magazine, Trade.*
Published by: Fascination Verlagsgesellschaft mbH, Baumschulenweg 12a, Muenster, 48159, Germany. TEL 49-251-2652744, FAX 49-251-2652745, info@computervideo.de, http://www.computervideo.de. Ed., Pub. Roland Schaefer. adv.: B&W page EUR 2,225, color page EUR 3,150. Circ: 28,000 (paid and controlled).

006.6 DEU ISSN 0949-8958
COREL DRAW. Text in German. 1995. bi-m. looseleaf. **Document type:** *Trade.*
Published by: W R S Verlag GmbH & Co. KG (Subsidiary of: Rudolf Haufe Verlag GmbH & Co. KG), Fraunhoferstr 5, Planegg, 82152, Germany. info@wrs.de, http://www.wrs.de.

006.6 USA ISSN 1063-7591
T385
COREL MAGAZINE USA. Text in English. 1992. m. USD 39.95 (effective 2001). adv. back issues avail. **Document type:** *Trade.* **Description:** For users of CorelDraw, Photo-Paint and other graphics software from Corel Corp. Includes tutorials, technical and product solutions of interest to graphic design desktop publishing professionals.
Related titles: CD-ROM ed.; Online - full text ed.: USD 14.95 (effective 2001).
Published by: Omray Inc., 9801 Anderson Mill Rd, Ste 207, Austin, TX 78750. TEL 512-250-3112, FAX 512-219-3156, daveb@corelmag.com, http://www.corelmag.com. Ed., R&P D Scott Campbell. Pub. Dave Baceski. Adv. contact Cynthia McGrail. B&W page USD 4,750, color page USD 5,725. Circ: 30,000.

006.68 USA ISSN 1550-4352
NX260
CREATIVE DESIGNER. Text in English. 2000. m. USD 107 domestic; USD 117 foreign (effective 2005).
Formerly (until 2004): The Design Authority (1530-5988)
Related titles: Online - full text ed.: ISSN 1539-0217.
—CCC.
Published by: Element K Journals (Subsidiary of: Eli Research, Inc.), 500 Canal View Blvd, Rochester, NY 14623. TEL 585-240-7301, 800-223-8720, 877-203-5248, FAX 585-292-4392, http://www.elementkjournals.com. Eds. Amy Courtwright, Michelle Rogers.

CREATIVE FOTOSTAMPA. see *PHOTOGRAPHY*

006.6 GBR ISSN 1355-4638
CREATIVE TECHNOLOGY. Text in English. m. GBP 27.50 domestic; GBP 40 in Europe; GBP 52 elsewhere; GBP 2.50 newsstand/cover. adv. software rev. illus. **Description:** Covers the creation and application of graphic design and illustration on the computer. Reviews software and hardware.
Formerly (until Sept. 1994): X Y Z Direction (0965-3848); Which was formed by the merger of (1991-1992): X Y Z (1356-0441); Direction (Teddington) (0952-7508); Which was formerly (1982-1986): Design and Art Direction
Indexed: DAAI, Inspec.
Address: c/o Debbie Brown, Ed, 10 Barley Mow Passage, London, W4 4PH, United Kingdom. TEL 44-171-742-2885, FAX 44-171-995-3633, creaT@cix.compulink.co.uk. Pub., R&P Kevin Marriot TEL 44-171-995-3632. Adv. contact Will Harries. **Subscr. to:** Creative Technology Subscriptions, Goldworth Industrial Park, Fulham House, Goldsworth Rd, Woking, Surrey GU21 1LY, United Kingdom. TEL 44-1483-733800.

006 ESP ISSN 1133-3030
CUADERNOS DE DOCUMENTACION MULTIMEDIA. Text in Spanish. 1992. a. back issues avail.
Formerly (until 1992): Cuadernos de Documentacion Audiovisual (1133-3022)
Related titles: CD-ROM ed.: ISSN 1575-9725; Online - full text ed.: ISSN 1575-9733.
—CINDOC.
Published by: Universidad Complutense de Madrid, Facultad de Ciencias de la Informacion, Ave. Complutense, s-n, Madrid, 28040, Spain. http://www.ucm.es/info/multidoc/multidoc/revista. Ed. Alfonso Lopez Yepes.

006.42 DEU
D B S IMAGE PROCESSING NEWSLETTER. Text in German. m. free. **Document type:** *Newsletter.* **Description:** Targeted at all those who want to keep up to date with the latest developments in image processing.
Media: E-mail.
Published by: D B S GmbH, Kohlhoekerstr 61, Bremen, 28203, Germany. TEL 49-421-3359122, FAX 49-412-3359180, h.bassmann@dbs.de, http://www.dbs-imaging.com/. Ed. Henning Bassmann.

006.68 USA
D T & G JOURNAL OF DESIGN, TYPOGRAPHY & GRAPHICS. Text in English. 1989. m. free. **Description:** For people who use computers for graphics, publishing, art, or communications.
Media: Online - full text.
Published by: Design & Publishing Center, 15 Southgate, Harrisonburg, VA 22801. showker@graphic-design.com, http://www.graphic-design.com/DTG/. Ed. Fred Showker.

006.6 USA ISSN 1441-5585
DESIGN DRAWING. Text in English. 1998. m.
Media: Online - full text.
Published by: Cybereps, 80 Liberty Ship Way, Sausalito, CA 94965. TEL 415-289-5040, FAX 415-289-1589, http://www.design-drawing.com/.

006.6 AUS ISSN 1320-3088
DESIGN GRAPHICS. Text in English. m. AUD 92.40 domestic; NZD 128 in New Zealand; USD 83.60 in United States; CND 118.70 in Canada; GBP 53.20 in United Kingdom; EUR 78.32 in Europe; AUD 132 elsewhere (effective 2005). adv. software rev.; bk.rev. 96 p./no.; back issues avail. **Document type:** *Magazine, Trade.* **Description:** Devoted to all aspects of graphic design and digital imaging.
Indexed: ABM, DAAI.
Published by: D G International Pty. Ltd., PO Box 10, Ferny Creek, VIC 3786, Australia. TEL 61-3-97601200, FAX 61-3-97551155, email@designgraphics.com.au, http://www.designgraphics.com.au. Ed. Loueze Harper. Pub., R&P Colin Wood. Adv. contact Colleen Bate. Circ: 32,000 (paid).

006.6 USA ISSN 1549-9235
DESIGNER. Text in English. q. USD 60 (effective 2001). **Document type:** *Newsletter.*
Indexed: DAAI.
Published by: University & College Designer's Association, 199 Enon Springs Rd W., Ste. 300, Smyrna, TN 37167-3047. TEL 815-754-4112, FAX 815-754-0801, info@ucda.com, http://www.ucda.com/publications/index.html. Ed. Tadson Bussey. Circ: 12,000 (paid).

DESKTOP. see *PUBLISHING AND BOOK TRADE—Computer Applications*

006.6 POL
DIGIT. Text in Polish. 10/yr. PLZ 99; PLZ 9.90 newsstand/cover (effective 2002). adv. **Document type:** *Magazine, Consumer.*
Related titles: Online - full text ed.
Published by: I D G Poland S.A., ul Jordanowska 12, PO Box 73, Warsaw, 04-204, Poland. TEL 48-22-3217800, FAX 48-22-3217888, idg@idg.com.pl, http://www.digit.pl, http://www.idg.pl. Ed. Tomasz Bitner. Adv. contact Joanna Fiala. B&W page PLZ 4,100, color page PLZ 6,100; trim 203 x 288.

006.6 GBR ISSN 1462-6268
CODEN: ITMEER
➤ **DIGITAL CREATIVITY.** Text in English. 1990. q. GBP 214, USD 367 combined subscription to institutions print & online eds. (effective 2006). adv. bk.rev. reprint service avail. from PSC. **Document type:** *Journal, Academic/Scholarly.* **Description:** Publishes advanced-level articles and reviews for persons involved in graphic art and design.
Supersedes (in 1997): Intelligent Tutoring Media (0957-9133)
Related titles: Online - full text ed.: GBP 203, USD 349 to institutions (effective 2006) (from EBSCO Publishing, Gale Group, IngentaConnect, O C L C Online Computer Library Center, Inc., Swets Information Services).
Indexed: ABM, ArtHuCI, CPE, CurCont, ERA, ETA, ErgAb, Inspec, MEA, MicrocompInd, RHEA, SEA, SENA, SOMA, TEA.
—BLDSC (3588.395200), AskIEEE, IE, ingenta. **CCC.**
Published by: Routledge (Subsidiary of: Taylor & Francis Group), 4 Park Sq, Milton Park, Abingdon, Oxon OX14 4RN, United Kingdom. TEL 44-1235-828600, FAX 44-1235-829000, info@routledge.co.uk, http://www.tandf.co.uk/journals/titles/14626268.asp, http://www.routledge.com. Eds. Colin Beardon, Lone Malmborg. adv.: page EUR 225; trim 210 x 297.

➤ **DIGITAL GRAPHICS MAGAZINE.** see *ART—Computer Applications*

006.6 USA ISSN 1557-2811
DIGITAL IMAGING TECHNIQUES; an advanced tool for commercial & creative pros. Text in English. 1999 (Mar.). 9/yr. USD 55 (effective 2005). adv. **Document type:** *Magazine, Trade.* **Description:** Covers digital imaging technology, creative concepts, production, and other related fields.

C

Formerly (until 2005): Digital Imaging (1084-5119); Which incorporated (in June 2001): Micro Publishing News (1523-5203); Which was formerly: Digital Imaging Report; Which incorporated: Corporate Publishing
Related titles: Online - full text ed.: (from Gale Group).
Indexed: SoftBase.
—CCC.
Published by: Cygnus Business Media, Inc., 3 Huntington Quadrangle, Ste 301N, Melville, NY 11747-3601. TEL 631-856-2700, FAX 631-845-2723, info@imaginginfo.com, http://www.imaginginfo.com. Ed. Andrew Darlow. Circ: 48,000 (controlled). **Subscr. to:** 1233 Janesville Ave, Fort Atkinson, WI 53538-0803.

DIGITAL PHOTOGRAPHY & DESIGN. see *PHOTOGRAPHY*

006.47 DEU
DIGITAL PRODUCTION. Text in German. 1997. bi-m. EUR 82 domestic; EUR 97 foreign; EUR 13 newsstand/cover (effective 2005). adv. **Document type:** *Magazine, Trade.* **Description:** Reports on leading-edge computer graphics technologies and their creative uses.
Related titles: Online - full text ed.
Published by: Reed Business Information GmbH (Subsidiary of: Reed Business Information International), Gabrielenstr 9, Munich, 80636, Germany. TEL 49-89-898170, FAX 49-89-89817300, info@digitalproduction.com, mg@rbi.de, http://www.digitalproduction.com, http://www.reedelsevier.de. Ed. Michael Klein. Pub. Hendrik van der Vliet. Adv. contact Uwe Mark. B&W page EUR 3,914, color page EUR 4,584; trim 190 x 270. Circ: 11,595 (paid and controlled).

004 NLD ISSN 0141-9382
TK7882.I6 CODEN: DISPDP
➤ **DISPLAYS.** Text in English. 1979. 5/yr. EUR 63 in Europe to individuals; JPY 8,400 in Japan to individuals; USD 71 elsewhere to individuals; EUR 632 in Europe to institutions; JPY 83,900 in Japan to institutions; USD 706 elsewhere to institutions (effective 2006). adv. bk.rev. abstr.; illus.; pat. index. back issues avail. **Document type:** *Academic/Scholarly.* **Description:** Covers research and commercial development of display technology, including digital, alphanumeric, graphic and pictorial displays.
Related titles: Microform ed.: (from PQC); Online - full text ed.: (from EBSCO Publishing, Gale Group, IngentaConnect, ScienceDirect, Swets Information Services).
Indexed: AHCI, ASCA, B&BAb, CADCAM, CIN, CMCI, ChemAb, ChemTitl, CompAb, CompLI, CurCont, CybAb, EngInd, ErgAb, IAA, Inspec, MSB, PsycInfo, PsycholAb, RefZh, SSCI.
—BLDSC (3598.721500), AskIEEE, CASDDS, CISTI, Ei, IDS, IE, Infotrieve, ingenta, Linda Hall. **CCC.**
Published by: Elsevier BV (Subsidiary of: Elsevier Science & Technology), Radarweg 29, Amsterdam, 1043 NX, Netherlands. TEL 31-20-4853911, FAX 31-20-4852457, nlinfo-f@elsevier.nl, http://www.elsevier.com/locate/displa, http://www.elsevier.nl. Ed. C. M. Lampert.

➤ **DOCUMENT DESIGN.** see *PRINTING*

006.6 USA ISSN 1094-2548
Z253.53
DYNAMIC GRAPHICS MAGAZINE; quick, cool, creative ideas for Mac & PC. Text in English. 1996. bi-m. USD 36 domestic; USD 48.15 in Canada; USD 60 elsewhere (effective 2005). back issues avail. **Document type:** *Magazine, Trade.* **Description:** Focuses on practical solutions to design questions.
Related titles: Online - full content ed.: USD 36 (effective 2005).
Indexed: DAAI.
Published by: Dynamic Graphics Group, PO Box 9007, Maple Shade, NJ 08052. TEL 856-380-4122, 856-380-4101, http://www.dgusa.com/PUBS/DGM/dgm.aspx.

006 USA
ED-MEDIA (YEAR) WORLD CONFERENCE ON EDUCATIONAL MULTIMEDIA, HYPERMEDIA & TELECOMMUNICATIONS. PROCEEDINGS. Text in English. a. **Document type:** *Proceedings.*
Formerly: Educational Multimedia Hypermedia and Telecommunications
—BLDSC (3659.744800).
Published by: Association for the Advancement of Computing in Education, PO Box 3728, Norfolk, VA 23514. TEL 757-623-7588, FAX 703-997-8760, info@aace.org, http://www.aace.org. Ed. Betty Collins.

ELECTRONIC & ELECTRICAL ENGINEERING RESEARCH STUDIES. PATTERN RECOGNITION AND IMAGE PROCESSING SERIES. see *ENGINEERING—Electrical Engineering*

006.693 USA ISSN 1537-0755
ELECTRONIC DEVICE FAILURE ANALYSIS; a resource for technical information and industry developments. Text in English. q. USD 90 to non-members; USD 60 to members (effective 2003).
Indexed: BrCerAb, C&ISA, CerAb, CorrAb, E&CAJ, EMA, IAA, M&TEA, MBF, METADEX, WAA.
—BLDSC (3700.815000), IE, Linda Hall.
Published by: A S M International, 9639 Kinsman Rd, Materials Park, OH 44073. TEL 877-983-3327, http://www.edfas.org. Ed. Charles F Hawkins.

621.367 GBR ISSN 1356-5397
ELECTRONIC IMAGING; digital capture, manipulation and output. Text in English. 1994. m. GBP 30; GBP 2.95 newsstand/cover (effective 1999). **Document type:** *Consumer.* **Description:** Features news and information about graphic software, scanners, digital cameras and photography.
Published by: Archant Specialist Ltd. (Subsidiary of: Archant), The Mill, Bearwalden Business Park, Royston Rd, Wendens Ambo, Essex CB11 4GB, United Kingdom. TEL 44-1799-544200, farine.clarke@archant.co.uk, http://www.archant.co.uk/.

006.6 621.39 AUT ISSN 0946-2767
EUROGRAPHICS. Text in English. 1994. irreg., latest 2001. price varies. **Document type:** *Monographic series, Academic/Scholarly.*
Published by: Springer-Verlag Wien (Subsidiary of: Springer Science+Business Media) TEL 43-1-3302415-0, FAX 43-1-330242665, books@springer.at, http://www.springer.at. Eds. F Sillion, W Hausmann, W Purgathofer. R&P Angela Foessl TEL 43-1-3302415517. **Subscr. in N. America to:** Springer-Verlag New York, Inc., 233 Spring St, New York, NY 10013. TEL 800-777-4643, FAX 201-348-4505, orders@springer-ny.com.

EXPOSURE (OXFORD). see *PHOTOGRAPHY*

621.399 USA ISSN 1572-2740
▼ ➤ **FOUNDATIONS AND TRENDS IN COMPUTER GRAPHICS AND VISION.** Text in English. 2004. 4/yr. USD 300 domestic; EUR 300 foreign; USD 340 combined subscription domestic print & online eds.; EUR 340 combined subscription foreign print & online eds. (effective 2006). **Document type:** *Journal, Academic/Scholarly.* **Description:** Provides tutorial coverage of subjects, research retrospectives as well as survey papers that offer state-of-the-art reviews in computer graphics.
Related titles: Online - full text ed.: ISSN 1572-2759. USD 300 domestic; EUR 300 foreign (effective 2005).
Published by: Now Publishers Inc., PO Box 1024, Hanover, MA 02339. TEL 781-871-0245, FAX 781-871-6172, sales@nowpublishers.com, http://www.nowpublishers.com/pages/8/index.htm. Eds. Brian Curless, Luc van Gool. Pub., R&P James Finlay.

➤ **FRESHFACE.** see *COMPUTERS—Internet*

006.6 DEU
GRAFIK & VIDEO. Variant title: PC Go Grafik & Video. Text in German. 4/yr. EUR 25.05 domestic; EUR 29 in Europe; EUR 7.80 newsstand/cover (effective 2003). adv. **Document type:** *Magazine, Consumer.* **Description:** Contains articles, advice and tips on graphics software and hardware.
Related titles: Online - full text ed.
Published by: W E K A Computerzeitschriften-Verlag GmbH, Gruberstr 46a, Poing, 85586, Germany. TEL 49-8121-951001, FAX 49-8121-951199, guv@wekanet.de, http://www.grafik-video.de, http://www.wekanet.de. Ed. Stephan Quinkertz. Adv. contact Roy Decker. B&W page EUR 2,600, color page EUR 3,100; trim 185 x 266.

GRAPH CREATIVE. see *PRINTING*

▼ **GRAPHIC & DESIGN BUSINESS.** see *ART*

006.42 USA ISSN 1524-0703
T385 CODEN: GRMOFM
➤ **GRAPHICAL MODELS.** Text in English. 1969. 6/yr. EUR 409 in Europe to individuals; JPY 42,700 in Japan to individuals; USD 321 to individuals except Europe and Japan; EUR 861 in Europe to institutions; JPY 90,000 in Japan to institutions; USD 674 to institutions except Europe and Japan (effective 2006). illus. Index. back issues avail.; reprints avail. **Document type:** *Journal, Academic/Scholarly.* **Description:** Focuses on the synthesis methods and computational models underlying computer-generated or -processed imagery.
Former titles (until 1998): Graphical Models and Image Processing (1077-3169); (until 1995): C V G I P: Graphical Models and Image Processing (1049-9652); Which supersedes in part (in 1991): Computer Vision, Graphics, and Image Processing (0734-189X); Which was formerly (until 1983): Computer Graphics and Image Processing (0146-664X)
Related titles: Online - full text ed.: ISSN 1524-0711. USD 702 (effective 2002) (from EBSCO Publishing, Gale Group, IngentaConnect, O C L C Online Computer Library Center, Inc., ScienceDirect, Swets Information Services).
Indexed: AHCI, AIA, AS&TI, ASCA, B&BAb, C&ISA, CADCAM, CIS, CMCI, CompC, CompD, CompR, CurCont, CybAb, E&CAJ, EngInd, ErgAb, GEOBASE, IAA, ISMEC, ISR, Inspec, RoboAb, SCI, SSCI, SolStAb, ZentMath.
—BLDSC (4212.350000), AskIEEE, CISTI, Ei, IDS, IE, Infotrieve, ingenta, Linda Hall. **CCC.**
Published by: Academic Press (Subsidiary of: Elsevier Science & Technology), 525 B St, Ste 1900, San Diego, CA 92101-4495. TEL 619-231-6616, 800-894-3434, apsubs@acad.com, http://www.elsevier.com/locate/gmod, http://www.academicpress.com. Eds. Ingrid Carlbom, Dr. Norman I. Badler.

006.6 CAN ISSN 0713-5424
QA76.9.I58
➤ **GRAPHICS INTERFACE. PROCEEDINGS✶ /INTERFACE GRAPHIQUE. COMPTES RENDUS.** Variant title: Graphic Interface Conference. Proceedings. Text in English, French. 1969. a. CND 45; to non-members; members $35. back issues avail. **Document type:** *Proceedings, Academic/Scholarly.*
Indexed: C&ISA, E&CAJ, EngInd, ISMEC, SolStAb.
—BLDSC (4212.513000), Ei, IE, ingenta. **CCC.**
Published by: Canadian Information Processing Society, 2800 Skymark Ave, Ste 402, Mississauga, ON L4W 5A6, Canada. TEL 905-602-1370, FAX 905-602-7884, info@cips.ca, http://www.cips.ca. Circ: 500. **Co-sponsors:** Canadian Man-Computer Communications Society; National Computer Graphics Association of Canada.

006.68 USA
GRAPHING AND CHARTING, SIMPLIFIED. Text in English. 1976. irreg. USD 12.95 (effective 2000). **Document type:** *Trade.* **Description:** Provides an indispensable tool in the study for promotion examinations. Contains test material with questions and answers on interpreting graphs and charts.
Published by: Gould Publications, Inc. (Subsidiary of: LexisNexis), 1333 North US Hwy 17-92, Longwood, FL 32750-3724. TEL 407-695-9500, 800-717-7917, FAX 407-695-2906, info@gouldlaw.com, http://www.gouldlaw.com.

006.42 USA
▼ **H D MAGAZINE.** (High Definition) (delivered as a PDF file; broadband Internet connection required for subscription.) Text in English. forthcoming 2006 (Jan.). m. free to qualified personnel (effective 2005). **Document type:** *Magazine, Consumer.* **Description:** Covers the latest information, technology and news on high definition television displays.
Media: Online - full content.
Published by: Possibility Media, 10400 N.W. 33rd St., Ste. 270, Miami, FL 33172. TEL 786-206-8880, FAX 786-206-8884, info@possibilitymedia.com, http://www.hdmagonline.com/, http://www.possibilitymedia.com/.

006.6 USA ISSN 1541-5864
HIGHEND MAGAZINE. Text in English. 2002. q. USD 45 domestic; USD 50 elsewhere (effective 2003). adv.
Published by: D M G Publishing, 2756 N. Green Valley Pkwy. Ste. 26, Henderson, NV 89014-2120. TEL 702-990-8656, 888-778-9283, FAX 702-616-9647, info@dmgpublishing.com, http://www.highend3d.com/mag/, http:// www.dmgpublishing.com. Pubs. Alice M. Edgin, Charles A. Edgin.

006.6 USA ISSN 1388-3690
QA76.73.L23 CODEN: LSCOEX
➤ **HIGHER-ORDER AND SYMBOLIC COMPUTATION**; an international journal. Text in English. 1988. q. EUR 498, USD 508, GBP 315 combined subscription to institutions print & online eds. (effective 2005). adv. reprint service avail. from PQC,PSC. **Document type:** *Journal, Academic/Scholarly.* **Description:** Presents a forum for current and evolving symbolic computing, focusing on LISP and object-oriented programming.
Formerly (until 1998): L I S P and Symbolic Computation (0892-4635)
Related titles: Microform ed.: (from PQC); Online - full text ed.: ISSN 1573-0557 (from EBSCO Publishing, Gale Group, IngentaConnect, Kluwer Online, O C L C Online Computer Library Center, Inc., Ovid Technologies, Inc., Springer LINK, Swets Information Services).
Indexed: AIA, ASCA, ChemAb, CompAb, CompR, EngInd, Inspec.
—BLDSC (4307.399600), AskIEEE, CISTI, Ei, IE, Infotrieve, ingenta. **CCC.**
Published by: Springer-Verlag New York, Inc. (Subsidiary of: Springer Science+Business Media), 233 Spring St, New York, NY 10013. TEL 212-460-1500, FAX 212-460-1575, service@springer-ny.com, http://springerlink.metapress.com/openurl.asp?genre=journal&issn=1388-3690, http://www.springer-ny.com. Eds. Carolyn L Talcott, Olivier Danvy. **Subscr. to:** Journal Fulfillment, PO Box 2485, Secaucus, NJ 07096-2485. TEL 201-348-4033, FAX 201-348-4505, journals@springer-ny.com.

006.6 USA ISSN 0272-1716
T385 CODEN: ICGADZ
➤ **I E E E COMPUTER GRAPHICS AND APPLICATIONS.** (Institute of Electrical and Electronics Engineers) Text in English. 1981. bi-m. USD 795 in North America; USD 830 elsewhere (effective 2006). adv. bk.rev. charts; illus.; stat. 96 p./no.; back issues avail.; reprints avail. **Document type:** *Journal, Academic/Scholarly.* **Description:** For professional users. Articles and columns present timely information on computer graphics research, technology and applications.
Related titles: CD-ROM ed.; Microfiche ed.; Online - full text ed.: (from EBSCO Publishing, I E E E).
Indexed: AHCI, AIA, AS&TI, ASCA, B&BAb, CADCAM, CMCI, CompAb, CompC, CompD, CompLI, CurCont, CybAb, EngInd, ErgAb, IAA, ICEA, ISR, Inspec, MicrocompInd, RASB, RefZh, SCI, SSCI, SoftAbEng, SoftBase.
—BLDSC (4362.814300), AskIEEE, CISTI, Ei, IDS, IE, Infotrieve, ingenta, Linda Hall. **CCC.**

C

Published by: Institute of Electrical and Electronics Engineers, Inc., 445 Hoes Ln, Piscataway, NJ 08854-1331. TEL 732-981-0060, 800-701-4333, FAX 732-981-1721, kkelly@computer.org, subscription-service@ieee.org, http://www.computer.org/cga. Pub. Angela Burgess. adv.: B&W page USD 2,150, color page USD 3,350. Circ: 8,000 (paid). **Subscr. to:** Maruzen Co., Ltd., 3-10 Nihonbashi 2-chome, Chuo-ku, Tokyo 103-0027, Japan. FAX 81-3-3275-0657; Universal Subscription Agency, Pvt. Ltd., 877, Udyog Vihar, V, Gurgoan 122001, India. TEL 91-124-347261, FAX 91-124-342496. **Co-sponsor:** Computer Society.

006.6 USA
TA1634
I E E E INTERNATIONAL CONFERENCE ON INFORMATION VISUALISATION (YEAR). Text in English. 1996. a. USD 192; USD 77 to members (effective 2004). **Document type:** *Proceedings, Trade.* **Description:** Covers information visualization, applied visualization, augmented and virtual reality, graphical modelling, etc.
Formerly: I E E E Conference on Information Visualization (1522-404X)
Related titles: Online - full text ed.: (from I E E E).
—BLDSC (4363.086650).
Published by: Institute of Electrical and Electronics Engineers, Inc., 445 Hoes Ln, Piscataway, NJ 08854-1331. TEL 908-981-0060, FAX 908-981-9667, customer.service@ieee.org, http://www.computer.org/.

006.6 USA
➤ **I E E E JOURNAL OF TECHNOLOGY COMPUTER AIDED DESIGN.** Text in English. 1996. irreg. free. back issues avail. **Document type:** *Monographic series, Academic/Scholarly.* **Description:** Covers modeling and simulation of basic semiconductor devices, materials and processes.
Media: Online - full text. **Related titles:** CD-ROM ed.; Microfiche ed.
Indexed: Inspec.
Published by: Institute of Electrical and Electronics Engineers, Inc., 3 Park Ave, 17th Fl, New York, NY 10016-5997. TEL 800-678-4333, customer.service@ieee.org, http://www.ieee.org/journal/tcal. Ed. Mark Law.

C

006.7 USA ISSN 1070-986X
QA76.575 CODEN: IEMUE4
➤ **I E E E MULTIMEDIA MAGAZINE.** Text in English. 1994. q. USD 615 (effective 2006). adv. illus. reprints avail. **Document type:** *Journal, Academic/Scholarly.* **Description:** Feature articles and papers covering hardware and software for media compression, media storage and transport, workstation support for multimedia, data modeling, and abstractions to embed multimedia in application programs.
Related titles: CD-ROM ed.; Microfiche ed.; Online - full text ed.: (from EBSCO Publishing, I E E E).
Indexed: ASCA, B&BAb, CMCI, CompAb, CompLI, CurCont, EngInd, ErgAb, ISR, Inspec, RefZh, SCI.
—BLDSC (4363.006400), AskIEEE, CISTI, Ei, IDS, IE, Infotrieve, ingenta, Linda Hall. **CCC.**
Published by: Institute of Electrical and Electronics Engineers, Inc., 445 Hoes Ln, Piscataway, NJ 08854-1331. TEL 732-981-0060, 800-701-4333, FAX 732-981-1721, mm@computer.org, subscription-service@ieee.org, http://www.computer.org/multimedia, http://www.ieee.org. Ed. William Grosky. adv.: B&W page USD 1,350, color page USD 3,350. Circ: 10,000 (paid). **Subscr. to:** Maruzen Co., Ltd., 3-10 Nihonbashi 2-chome, Chuo-ku, Tokyo 103-0027, Japan. FAX 81-3-3275-0657; Universal Subscription Agency, Pvt. Ltd., 877, Udyog Vihar, V, Gurgoan 122001, India. TEL 91-124-347261, FAX 91-124-342496. **Co-sponsor:** Computer Society.

006.6 USA ISSN 1093-9547
I E E E SYMPOSIUM ON INFORMATION VISUALIZATION. Text in English. a. USD 151 membership (effective 2005). **Document type:** *Proceedings, Trade.*
Related titles: Online - full text ed.: (from I E E E).
—BLDSC (4363.086650). **CCC.**
Published by: Institute of Electrical and Electronics Engineers, Inc., 3 Park Ave, 17th Fl, New York, NY 10016-5997. TEL 212-419-7900, 800-678-4333, FAX 212-752-4929, customer.service@ieee.org, http://www.ieee.org.

006.6 USA ISSN 1072-4354
I E E E SYMPOSIUM ON VISUAL LANGUAGES. PROCEEDINGS. Text in English. 1993. a. USD 138; USD 55 to members (effective 2004). **Document type:** *Proceedings, Trade.*
Indexed: EngInd.
—**CCC.**
Published by: Institute of Electrical and Electronics Engineers, Inc., 3 Park Ave, 17th Fl, New York, NY 10016-5997. TEL 212-419-7900, 800-678-4333, FAX 212-752-4929, customer.service@ieee.org, http://www.ieee.org.

006.42 USA ISSN 1057-7149
TA1632 CODEN: IIPRE4
➤ **I E E E TRANSACTIONS ON IMAGE PROCESSING.** Text in English. 1992. 13/yr. USD 1,140 (effective 2006). **Document type:** *Journal, Academic/Scholarly.* **Description:** Covers the signal processing aspects of image processing, computed imaging, image scanning, display and printing.
Related titles: CD-ROM ed.; Microform ed.; Online - full text ed.: (from EBSCO Publishing, Swets Information Services).
Indexed: AS&TI, ASCA, C&CSA, C&ISA, CCMJ, CMCI, CompAb, CompLI, CurCont, E&CAJ, EngInd, ISR, Inspec, MathR, MathSciNet, RefZh, SCI, SolStAb.
—BLDSC (4363.190900), AskIEEE, CISTI, Ei, IDS, IE, Infotrieve, ingenta, Linda Hall. **CCC.**
Published by: Institute of Electrical and Electronics Engineers, Inc., 445 Hoes Ln, Piscataway, NJ 08854-1331. TEL 732-981-0060, 800-701-4333, FAX 732-981-1721, customer.service@ieee.org, subscription-service@ieee.org, http://www.ieee.org. Ed. A C Bovik. **Subscr. to:** Maruzen Co., Ltd., 3-10 Nihonbashi 2-chome, Chuo-ku, Tokyo 103-0027, Japan. FAX 81-3-3275-0657; Universal Subscription Agency, Pvt. Ltd., 877, Udyog Vihar, V, Gurgoan 122001, India. TEL 91-124-347261, FAX 91-124-342496. **Co-sponsor:** Signal Processing Society.

006.6 USA ISSN 1077-2626
T385 CODEN: ITVGEA
➤ **I E E E TRANSACTIONS ON VISUALIZATION AND COMPUTER GRAPHICS.** Text in English. 1995. bi-m. USD 750 (effective 2006). **Document type:** *Journal, Academic/Scholarly.* **Description:** Combines the field of scientific visualization with the technologies of computer graphics, image, and signal processing, computer vision, CAD and user interfaces.
Related titles: CD-ROM ed.; Microfiche ed.; Online - full text ed.: (from EBSCO Publishing, I E E E).
Indexed: AS&TI, ASCA, B&BAb, CMCI, CompAb, CompLI, CurCont, EngInd, ISR, Inspec, RefZh, SCI.
—BLDSC (4363.231400), AskIEEE, CISTI, IDS, IE, Infotrieve, Linda Hall. **CCC.**
Published by: Institute of Electrical and Electronics Engineers, Inc., 445 Hoes Ln, Piscataway, NJ 08854-1331. TEL 732-981-0060, 800-701-4333, FAX 732-981-1721, tvcg@computer.org, customer.service@ieee.org, subscription-service@ieee.org, http://www.computer.org/tvcg, http://www.ieee.org. Ed. Hans Hagen. Circ: 4,500 (controlled and free). **Subscr. to:** Maruzen Co., Ltd., 3-10 Nihonbashi 2-chome, Chuo-ku, Tokyo 103-0027, Japan. FAX 81-3-3275-0657; Universal Subscription Agency, Pvt. Ltd., 877, Udyog Vihar, V, Gurgoan 122001, India. TEL 91-124-347261, FAX 91-124-342496.

006.6 USA
I E E E WORKSHOP ON MULTI - VIEW MODELING AND ANALYSIS OF VISUALS. Text in English. a. USD 100. **Document type:** *Proceedings, Trade.*
Published by: Institute of Electrical and Electronics Engineers, Inc., 3 Park Ave, 17th Fl, New York, NY 10016-5997. TEL 212-419-7900, 800-678-4333, FAX 212-752-4929, customer.service@ieee.org, http://www.ieee.org.

006.6 USA
I E E E WORKSHOP ON VISUAL MOTION. Text in English. 1990. biennial. price varies. adv. **Document type:** *Proceedings.* **Description:** Examines key issues in the field, such as image-flow, optical flow, 3D motion, active vision and statistical estimation.
Published by: (Institute of Electrical and Electronics Engineers, Inc.), I E E E Computer Society, 10662 Los Vaqueros Circle, PO Box 3014, Los Alamitos, CA 90720-1314. TEL 714-821-8380, FAX 714-821-4641. Ed. Cat Harris. Pub. Matt Loeb. Adv. contact Frieda Koester.

I P ENEWS. (Interactive Publications) see *LITERATURE*

621.399 USA ISSN 1083-1304
I S & T - S I D COLOR IMAGING CONFERENCE. FINAL PROGRAM AND PROCEEDINGS. Text in English. 1993. a. USD 85 to non-members; USD 65 to members (effective 2005). **Document type:** *Proceedings, Academic/Scholarly.*
—**CCC.**
Published by: International Society for Imaging Science and Technology, 7003 Kilworth Ln, Springfield, VA 22151. TEL 703-642-9090, FAX 703-642-9094, info@imaging.org. **Co-sponsor:** Society for Information Display.

006.7 DEU
IBUSINESS. Text in German. 1991. s-m. looseleaf. adv. bk.rev. charts; illus.; mkt.; maps. index. back issues avail. **Document type:** *Magazine, Trade.*
Formerly: Multimedia (0940-5577); Which incorporated (1993-1997): T V Interaktiv (0947-1677); (1993-1994): Virtual Realities (0946-5456)
Related titles: Online - full text ed.; ♦ Supplement(s): C B T - Computer Based Training. ISSN 0942-7430; ♦ Multimedia Magazin. ISSN 0946-4581; ♦ Point of Sale. ISSN 0944-4033.
Published by: HighText Verlag, Wilhelm-Riehl-Str 13, Munich, 80687, Germany. TEL 49-89-5783870, FAX 49-89-57838799, redaktion@hightext.de, info@hightext.de, http://www.ibusiness.de, http://www.hightext.de. Ed., Pub. Joachim Graf. R&P Daniel Treplin. Adv. contact Stefan Kratz. color page EUR 1,850; trim 177 x 250. Circ: 2,000 (paid).

006.6 USA ISSN 1536-3430
IC3D; the definitive Maya resource. Text in English. bi-m. USD 65 domestic; USD 85 in Canada & Mexico; USD 95 elsewhere; USD 12.95 newsstand/cover (effective 2002). adv. **Document type:** *Magazine, Trade.*
Published by: D M G Publishing, 2756 N. Green Valley Pkwy. Ste. 26, Henderson, NV 89014-2120. TEL 702-990-8656, 888-778-9283, FAX 702-616-9647, info@ic3dmag.com, info@dmgpublishing.com, http://www.ic3dmag.com, http://www.dmgpublishing.com.

006.42 NLD ISSN 0262-8856
TA1632
➤ **IMAGE AND VISION COMPUTING.** Text in English. 1982. 12/yr. EUR 84 in Europe to individuals; JPY 11,200 in Japan to individuals; USD 94 to individuals except Europe and Japan; EUR 1,270 in Europe to institutions; JPY 168,700 in Japan to institutions; USD 1,419 to institutions except Europe and Japan (effective 2006). adv. bk.rev. abstr.; illus. index. back issues avail.; reprints avail. **Document type:** *Journal, Academic/Scholarly.* **Description:** Focuses on the applications of electronically generated images on astronomy, biomedicine, robotics, remote sensing, broadcasting, metallurgy, seismology and radar.
Related titles: Microform ed.: (from PQC); Online - full text ed.: (from EBSCO Publishing, Gale Group, IngentaConnect, ScienceDirect, Swets Information Services).
Indexed: AHCI, ASCA, B&BAb, BioEngAb, C&ISA, CADCAM, CMCI, CompAb, CompC, CompD, CompLI, CurCont, CybAb, E&CAJ, EngInd, ISMEC, ISR, Inspec, LAMP, RefZh, RoboAb, SCI, SSCI, SolStAb.
—BLDSC (4368.991400), AskIEEE, Ei, IDS, IE, Infotrieve, ingenta, Linda Hall. **CCC.**
Published by: Elsevier BV (Subsidiary of: Elsevier Science & Technology), Radarweg 29, Amsterdam, 1043 NX, Netherlands. TEL 31-20-4853911, FAX 31-20-4852457, keith.baker@reading.ac.uk, nlinfo-f@elsevier.nl, http://www.elsevier.com/locate/imavis, http://www.elsevier.nl. Ed. Keith D. Baker.

006 USA
IMAGES NEWSLETTER. Text in English. irreg. free. bk.rev. back issues avail. **Document type:** *Newsletter.* **Description:** Covers visual simulation and related virtual reality technologies, and their applications.
Related titles: Online - full text ed.
Published by: Image Society, Inc., PO Box 6221, Chandler, AZ 85246-6221. image@asu.edu, http://www.public.asu.edu/~image/newsltr/newsltr.html.

621.399 USA ISSN 0362-0972
TK7882.I6 CODEN: INFDAB
INFORMATION DISPLAY. Abbreviated title: I D. Text in English. 1963. m. free domestic to qualified personnel (effective 2000). adv. bk.rev. charts; illus.; tr.lit. reprints avail. **Document type:** *Academic/Scholarly.*
Formerly (until 1975): S I D Journal (0092-4342); Which incorporated (in 1972): Information Display (0020-0042)
Indexed: ABIn, ArtInd, B&BAb, C&ISA, CompC, CompLI, E&CAJ, EngInd, Inspec, RASB, SolStAb.
—BLDSC (4493.560000), AskIEEE, CISTI, IE, Infotrieve, ingenta, Linda Hall. **CCC.**
Published by: Society for Information Display, 610 S 2nd St, San Jose, CA 95112. TEL 408-977-1013, FAX 408-977-1531, http://www.sid.org. Ed. Ken Werner. Circ: 14,000 (controlled).

006.68 USA ISSN 1095-4961
T385
INSIDE ILLUSTRATOR. Text in English. 1997. m. USD 137; USD 167 combined subscription print & online eds. (effective 2005). **Document type:** *Magazine, Consumer.* **Description:** Contains tips, shortcuts and techniques for Adobe Illustrator.
—**CCC.**
Published by: Element K Journals (Subsidiary of: Eli Research, Inc.), 500 Canal View Blvd, Rochester, NY 14623. TEL 585-240-7301, 800-223-8720, 877-203-5248, FAX 585-292-4392, http://www.elementkjournals.com/products/showProduct.asp?prodID=33&catId=3. Eds. G. H. Cloutier, Michelle Rogers.

006.68 USA ISSN 1094-0774
T385
INSIDE PHOTOSHOP. Text in English. 1997. m. USD 139 domestic; USD 149 foreign; USD 169 combined subscription print & online eds. (effective 2005). **Document type:** *Magazine, Consumer.* **Description:** Contains tips, shortcuts and techniques for Adobe Photoshop users.
Related titles: Online - full text ed.: USD 169 domestic; USD 179 foreign (effective 2005) (from ProQuest Information & Learning).
—**CCC.**
Published by: Element K Journals (Subsidiary of: Eli Research, Inc.), 500 Canal View Blvd, Rochester, NY 14623. TEL 585-240-7301, 800-223-8720, 877-203-5248, FAX 585-292-4392, http://www.elementkjournals.com/products/showProduct.asp?prodID=29&catId=1. Eds. Amy Courtwright, Michelle Rogers.

371.33467 USA ISSN 1525-9102
LB1028.55
➤ **INTERACTIVE MULTIMEDIA ELECTRONIC JOURNAL OF COMPUTER - ENHANCED LEARNING.** Abbreviated title: I M E J of C E L. Text in English. 1999. irreg. free (effective 2005). bk.rev. back issues avail. **Document type:** *Journal, Academic/Scholarly.*
Media: Online - full text.

Published by: Wake Forest University, 1834 Wake Forest Rd, Winston Salem, NC 27106. TEL 336-758-5255, imej@wfu.edu, http://imej.wfu.edu/. Eds. Anne Boyle, Jennifer J Burg.

006.7 CAN ISSN 1206-9361
INTERACTIVE VOICE. Text in English. 1997. q. back issues avail. **Document type:** *Trade.* **Description:** Provides a framework and structure to develop the effective use and understanding of new media technology.
Related titles: Online - full text ed.: ISSN 1206-937X.
Published by: Canadian Institute for New Media, Research and Development, P O Box 8500, Cranbrook V1C , BC, Canada. TEL 250-489-8278, FAX 250-489-8253, cinmrd@cotr.bc.ca, http://mediavision.cotr.bc.ca/. Ed. Jeffrey Hunt.

776.6 USA ISSN 1550-3623
TR897.7
INTERNATIONAL CONFERENCE ON COMPUTER ANIMATION AND SOCIAL AGENTS. PROCEEDINGS. Text in English. 1994. a. USD 152 per vol.; USD 61 per vol. to members (effective 2004). **Document type:** *Proceedings, Trade.*
Formerly (until 2003): Computer Animation. Proceedings (1087-4844)
Related titles: Online - full text ed.: (from I E E E).
Indexed: Englnd.
—BLDSC (3393.596000). **CCC.**
Published by: Institute of Electrical and Electronics Engineers, Inc., 3 Park Ave, 17th Fl, New York, NY 10016-5997. TEL 212-419-7900, 800-678-4333, FAX 212-752-4929, customer.service@ieee.org, http://www.ieee.org.

006.6 USA ISSN 1522-4880
INTERNATIONAL CONFERENCE ON IMAGE PROCESSING. PROCEEDINGS. Text in English. a. USD 626; USD 313 to members (effective 2004). **Document type:** *Proceedings, Trade.*
Related titles: Online - full text ed.: (from I E E E).
Indexed: Englnd.
—BLDSC (4538.826075). **CCC.**
Published by: Institute of Electrical and Electronics Engineers, Inc., 3 Park Ave, 17th Fl, New York, NY 10016-5997. TEL 212-419-7900, 800-678-4333, FAX 212-752-4929, customer.service@ieee.org, http://www.ieee.org.

INTERNATIONAL DIRECTORY OF DESIGN. see *ART*

INTERNATIONAL DIRECTORY OF PRINTING AND GRAPHIC ARTS EQUIPMENT AND SUPPLIES IMPORTERS. see *BUSINESS AND ECONOMICS—Trade And Industrial Directories*

006.6 AUS ISSN 1329-7147
➤ **INTERNATIONAL JOURNAL OF DESIGN COMPUTING.** Text in English. 1997. a. free (effective 2005). back issues avail. **Document type:** *Journal, Academic/Scholarly.* **Description:** Promotes research and technology transfer in design computing through the publications of interactive, multimedia journal articles within the general topic of design computing.
Media: Online - full text.
Published by: University of Sydney, Faculty of Architecture, Sydney, NSW 2006, Australia. TEL 61-2-9351-5933, FAX 61-2-9351-3031, ijdc@arch.usyd.edu.au, http://www.arch.usyd.edu.au/kcdc/journal/index.html. Ed. Mary Lou Maher.

621.399 SGP ISSN 0219-4678
T385
➤ **INTERNATIONAL JOURNAL OF IMAGE AND GRAPHICS.** Abbreviated title: I J I G. Text in Chinese. 2001. q. SGD 258, USD 147, EUR 142 to individuals; SGD 515, USD 295, EUR 283 combined subscription to institutions print & online eds.; SGD 309, USD 176, EUR 170 combined subscription in developing nations to institutions print & online eds. (effective 2006). back issues avail. **Document type:** *Journal, Academic/Scholarly.* **Description:** Emphasizes on efficient and effective image and graphics technologies and systems, and provide a central forum for scientists, researchers, engineers and vendors from different disciplines to exchange ideas, identify problems, investigate relevant issues, share common interests, explore new directions, and initiate possible collaborative research and system development.
Related titles: Online - full text ed.: (from EBSCO Publishing, O C L C Online Computer Library Center, Inc., Swets Information Services).
Indexed: BrCerAb, C&ISA, CerAb, CorrAb, E&CAJ, EMA, IAA, M&TEA, MBF, METADEX, SolStAb, WAA.
—BLDSC (4542.298500), CISTI, IE, Linda Hall. **CCC.**
Published by: World Scientific Publishing Co. Pte. Ltd., 5 Toh Tuck Link, Singapore, 596224, Singapore. TEL 65-466-5775, FAX 65-467-7667, http://www.worldscinet.com/ijig/ijig.shtml, http://www.worldscientific.com. Ed. David Zhang TEL 852-2766-7271. **Subscr. to:** Farrer Rd, PO Box 128, Singapore 912805, Singapore. sales@wspc.com.sg. **Dist. in the US by:** World Scientific Publishing Co., Inc., 1060 Main St, River Edge, NJ 07661. TEL 201-487-9655, 800-227-7562, FAX 201-487-9656, 888-977-2665, wspc@wspc.com.; **Dist. by:** World Scientific Publishing Ltd., 57 Shelton St, London WC2H 9HE, United Kingdom. TEL 44-20-78360888, FAX 44-20-78362020, sales@wspc.co.uk.

006.6 GBR ISSN 0958-9961
Z265 CODEN: IMOTEX
➤ **INTERNATIONAL JOURNAL OF MICROGRAPHICS & OPTICAL TECHNOLOGY**; including all aspects of electronic information transfer. Text in English. 1982. bi-m. GBP 250, USD 550 (effective 2005). 20 p./no.; reprint service avail. from PQC. **Document type:** *Academic/Scholarly.* **Description:** Contains news and new product information in the fields of micrographics, electronic information transfer, and workflow.
Formerly: International Journal of Micrographics and Video Technology (0743-9636); Incorporates: Microdoc; Which was formerly (until 1982): Micropublishing of Current Periodicals (0364-3999)
Related titles: Microfilm ed.: (from PQC); Online - full text ed.: (from ProQuest Information & Learning).
Indexed: ADPA, ASCA, BrArAb, BrCerAb, C&ISA, CerAb, CompC, CorrAb, E&CAJ, EMA, Englnd, IAA, Inspec, LIMI, M&TEA, MBF, METADEX, PhotoAb, RASB, SolStAb, WAA.
—BLDSC (4542.354300), AskIEEE, Ei, IDS, IE, ingenta, Linda Hall. **CCC.**
Published by: Research Information Ltd., Grenville Court, Britwell Rd, Burnham, Bucks SL1 8DF, United Kingdom. TEL 44-1628-600499, FAX 44-1628-600488, info@researchinformation.co.uk, http://www.researchinformation.co.uk/. Ed. Bob Yorke. Pub. Kumar Patel TEL 44-20-8328-2470. Circ: 300.

006.6 SGP ISSN 0218-6543
QA448.D38 CODEN: IJSMFC
➤ **INTERNATIONAL JOURNAL OF SHAPING MODELING.** Short title: I J S M. Text in English. 1994. s-a. SGD 109, USD 63, EUR 60 to individuals; SGD 272, USD 160, EUR 149 combined subscription to institutions print & online eds.; SGD 167, USD 98, EUR 91 combined subscription in developing nations to institutions print & online eds. (effective 2006). back issues avail. **Document type:** *Journal, Academic/Scholarly.* **Description:** Aims at creating a suitable environment for exchanging research results obtained in advanced theories and techniques devised for handling the shape of objects, pointing out the three main aspects of modeling: disciplines, roles and applications.
Related titles: Online - full text ed.: (from EBSCO Publishing).
Indexed: CompLI, ESPM, Inspec, SWRA, ZentMath.
—BLDSC (4542.546000), AskIEEE, IE, ingenta. **CCC.**
Published by: World Scientific Publishing Co. Pte. Ltd., 5 Toh Tuck Link, Singapore, 596224, Singapore. TEL 65-466-5775, FAX 65-467-7667, wspc@wspc.com.sg, http://www.worldscinet.com/ijsm/ijsm.shtml, http://www.worldscientific.com. Ed. Bianca Falcidieno. **Subscr. to:** Farrer Rd, PO Box 128, Singapore 912805, Singapore. sales@wspc.com.sg. **Dist. by:** World Scientific Publishing Co., Inc., 1060 Main St, River Edge, NJ 07661. TEL 201-487-9655, 800-227-7562, FAX 201-487-9656, 888-977-2665.; World Scientific Publishing Ltd., 57 Shelton St, London WC2H 9HE, United Kingdom. TEL 44-20-78360888, FAX 44-20-78362020, sales@wspc.co.uk.

006.6 620.00420285 CHN ISSN 1003-9775
CODEN: JFTXFX
JISUANJI FUZHU SHEJI YU TUXINGXUE XUEBAO/JOURNAL OF COMPUTER-AIDED DESIGN & COMPUTER GRAPHICS. Text in Chinese, English. 1989. bi-m. CNY 252 (effective 2004). **Document type:** *Journal, Academic/Scholarly.*
Related titles: Online - full text ed.: (from East View Information Services).
Indexed: Inspec, RefZh.
—BLDSC (4963.555000), IE, ingenta.
Published by: (Chinese Academy of Sciences, Institute of Computing Technology), Kexue Chubanshe/Science Press, 16 Donghuang Cheng Genbei Jie, Beijing, 100717, China. TEL 86-10-64000246, FAX 86-10-64030255, http://www.sciencep.com/. **Dist. by:** China International Book Trading Corp, 35 Chegongzhuang Xilu, Haidian District, PO Box 399, Beijing 100044, China. TEL 86-10-68412045, FAX 86-10-68412023, cibtc@mail.cibtc.com.cn, http://www.cibtc.com.cn.

006.7 FRA ISSN 1263-5251
LE JOURNAL DU MULTIMEDIA ET DES NOUVELLES TECHNOLOGIES; regards sur la formation des adultes. Text in French. 1972. m. adv. bk.rev.
Former titles: Journal de la Formation Continuee et de l'E.A.O. (0761-9863); (until 1983): Journal de la Formation Continuee (0761-9855)
Published by: Journal du Multimedia et des Nouvelles Technologies, 2 rue d'Amsterdam, Paris, 75009, France. TEL 33-1-47640757. Ed. Roger Christophe. Pub. Liliane Errera. Circ: 21,000.

006.6 AUS
➤ **JOURNAL OF AUSTRALASIAN GRAPHICS IMAGERY.** Text in English. 1997. irreg. **Document type:** *Academic/Scholarly.* **Description:** Contains scientific papers dealing with any area of computer graphics or computer vision research.
Media: Online - full text.
Published by: Curtin University of Technology, School of Computing, Hayman Rd, Bentley, W.A. 6102, Australia. TEL 619-351-7680, raytrace@cs.curtin.edu.au, http://www.cs.curtin.edu.au/jagi/. Ed. Andrew Marriott.

➤ **JOURNAL OF DESIGN COMMUNICATION.** see *ENGINEERING—Computer Applications*

006.6 USA ISSN 1086-7651
T385 CODEN: JGTOFD
➤ **JOURNAL OF GRAPHICS TOOLS.** Text in English. 1996. q. USD 70 domestic to individuals; USD 95 foreign to individuals; USD 160 domestic to institutions; USD 185 foreign to institutions (effective 2005). cum.index. 48 p./no.; back issues avail. **Document type:** *Journal, Trade.* **Description:** Reports techniques, research results and tricks of the trade of interest to computer graphics professionals.
Indexed: CompR, Inspec, ZentMath.
—BLDSC (4996.462000), IE, ingenta.
Published by: A K Peters, Ltd., 888 Worcester St, Ste 230, Wellesley, MA 02482. TEL 781-416-2888, FAX 781-416-2889, service@akpeters.com, http://www.acm.org/jgt, http://www.akpeters.com. Eds. Alice Peters, Ronen Barzel. Pubs. Alice Peters, Klaus Peters.

006.6 USA
THE JOURNAL OF IMAGING SERVICES. Text in English. 1986. bi-m. USD 275 (effective 2003). adv. bk.rev. charts; illus. **Document type:** *Journal, Trade.* **Description:** Contains professional development information for production document imaging operations.
Former titles: Imaging Service Bureau News (1055-8098); Service Bureau Newsletter (0892-5631)
Related titles: Online - full text ed.: (from Northern Light Technology, Inc.).
Indexed: ABIn.
Published by: Image Publishing, L L C, 871 Ethan Allen Hwy, Ste 204, Ridgefield, CT 06877. TEL 203-431-3270, 800-347-9310, pub@imagepub.net, http://www.imagepub.net/. Ed., Pub. David Miles. Adv. contact Valerie Mazur. page USD 960. Circ: 1,200.

006.7 USA
LB1028.3
JOURNAL OF INSTRUCTION DELIVERY SYSTEMS. Text in English. 1987. q. USD 60 domestic; USD 80 foreign; USD 20 per issue (effective 2005). back issues avail. **Document type:** *Journal, Trade.* **Description:** Articles and commentary on uses of interactive multimedia to enhance productivity through appropriate applications of technology in education, training and job performance.
Formerly (until 1992): Instruction Delivery System (0892-4872)
Indexed: AIA, CIJE, CPE, ERA, ETA, T&DA.
—BLDSC (5007.508000), ingenta.
Published by: (Society for Applied Learning Technology), Learning Technology Institute, 50 Culpeper St, Warrenton, VA 20186. TEL 540-347-0055, FAX 540-349-3169, info@lti.org, http://www.salt.org/salt.asp?ss=l&pn=jids, http://www.lti.org. Ed. Dr. Gertrude Abramson. Circ: 300 (paid).

004 DEU ISSN 1860-2037
▼ ➤ **JOURNAL OF VIRTUAL REALITY AND BROADCASTING.** Text in English. 2004. irreg. free. **Document type:** *Journal, Academic/Scholarly.* **Description:** Covers topics related to the fields of virtual reality, interface techniques, computer graphics and interactive broadcasting.
Media: Online - full content.
Published by: Di P P - N R W, Postfach 270451, Cologne, 50510, Germany. TEL 49-221-40075124, FAX 49-221-40075190, dipp@hbz-nrw.de, http://www.jvrb.org, http://www.dipp.nrw.de. Ed. Jens Herder.

006.42 USA ISSN 1047-3203
P93.5 CODEN: JVCRE7
➤ **JOURNAL OF VISUAL COMMUNICATION AND IMAGE REPRESENTATION.** Text in English. 1990. 6/yr. EUR 325 in Europe to individuals; JPY 34,000 in Japan to individuals; USD 254 to individuals except Europe and Japan; EUR 888 in Europe to institutions; JPY 92,600 in Japan to institutions; USD 696 to institutions except Europe and Japan (effective 2006). back issues avail. **Document type:** *Academic/Scholarly.* **Description:** Publishes papers on the state-of-the-art of visual communication and image representation with emphasis on novel technologies and theoretical work in this multidisciplinary area of pure and applied research.
Related titles: Online - full text ed.: ISSN 1095-9076. USD 558 (effective 2002) (from EBSCO Publishing, Gale Group, IngentaConnect, O C L C Online Computer Library Center, Inc., ScienceDirect, Swets Information Services).
Indexed: ASCA, CMCI, CompLI, CurCont, Englnd, Inspec.
—BLDSC (5072.493000), AskIEEE, CISTI, Ei, IDS, IE, Infotrieve, ingenta. **CCC.**
Published by: Academic Press (Subsidiary of: Elsevier Science & Technology), 525 B St, Ste 1900, San Diego, CA 92101-4495. TEL 619-231-6616, 800-894-3434, FAX 619-699-6422, apsubs@acad.com, http://www.elsevier.com/locate/jvci, http://www.academicpress.com. Eds. C.-C. J. Kuo, Yehoshua Y Zeevi.

C

006.6 005.1   CZE   ISSN 1213-6972
➤ **JOURNAL OF W S C G.** (Winter School of Computer Graphics) Text in English. 1992. a., latest vol.12, 2003. EUR 45 to individuals; EUR 75 to institutions (effective 2003). index. back issues avail. **Document type:** *Journal, Academic/Scholarly.* **Description:** Covers levels of details (algorithms etc.), parallel & distributed graphics computer aided geometric design, graphics architecture & visualization HW image based rendering, mathematical aspects of graphics, global illumination, ray tracing radiosity, computational geometry surface meshing, etc.
Related titles: CD-ROM ed.: ISSN 1213-6980; Online - full text ed.: ISSN 1213-6964.
Indexed: Inspec.
Published by: (Zapadoceska Univerzita v Plzni, Katedra Informatiky a Vypocetni Techniky/University of West Bohemia in Pilsen, Department of Computer Science and Engineering), Vaclav Skala - Union Agency, Na Mazinach 9, Plzen, 32200, Czech Republic. unionagency@volny.cz, http://wscg.zcu.cz, http://www.volny.cz/unionagency. Ed., Pub. Vaclav Skala.

006.42   USA   ISSN 1099-8284
HF5736
K M WORLD; creating and managing the knowledge-based enterprise. (Knowledge Management) Text in English. 1992. m. USD 63.95 domestic; USD 86 in Canada & Mexico; USD 116 elsewhere; free to qualified personnel (effective 2005). adv. back issues avail. **Document type:** *Magazine, Trade.* **Description:** Reports on new technologies, chronicles and evaluates them and delivers practical solutions.
Former titles (until 1997): I W (1099-8276); (until 1996): Imaging World (1060-894X)
Related titles: Online - full text ed.: (from EBSCO Publishing, Florida Center for Library Automation, Gale Group, O C L C Online Computer Library Center, Inc., ProQuest Information & Learning).
Indexed: ABIn, MicrocompInd, SoftBase.
—CCC.
Published by: Information Today, Inc., 143 Old Marlton Pike, Medford, NJ 08055-8750. TEL 609-654-6266, FAX 609-654-4309, custserv@infotoday.com, http://www.kmworld.com/, http://www.infotoday.com. Ed. Hugh McKellar. Pub. Andy Moore. Adv. contacts Cathy Rogals, David Panara. page USD 7,850; trim 9.5 x 11.75. Circ: 56,000.

006.6   RUS   ISSN 1609-0284
KAK. Text in Russian. 1997. q. USD 154 in United States (effective 2004). **Document type:** *Magazine, Trade.*
Related titles: Online - full content ed.: ISSN 1609-1280. 1998.
Published by: Redaktsiya Zhurnala Kak, Smolenskii Bul'var, dom 4, ofis 30, Moscow, 119034, Russian Federation. TEL 7-095-7839790, FAX 7-095-5029068, studio@kak.ru, http://www.kak.ru. **Dist. by:** East View Information Services, 3020 Harbor Ln. N., Minneapolis, MN 55447. TEL 800-477-1005, FAX 800-800-3839, eastview@eastview.com, http://www.eastview.com.

006.6   USA   ISSN 1536-3112
KEYFRAME MAGAZINE. Text in English. bi-m. USD 54, USD 72, USD 84 (effective 2002). adv. **Document type:** *Magazine, Trade.*
Published by: D M G Publishing, 2756 N. Green Valley Pkwy. Ste. 26, Henderson, NV 89014-2120. TEL 702-990-8656, 888-778-9283, FAX 702-616-9647, info@dmgpublishing.com, http://www.keyframemag.com, http://www.dmgpublishing.com.

KOG. see *MATHEMATICS*

006.6   RUS
KOMPYUART. Text in Russian. 1997. m. USD 145 in North America.
Indexed: RefZh.
Published by: Komp'yuter Press, Gorokhovskii Per 7, A-ya 37, Moscow, 113093, Russian Federation. TEL 7-095-2004686, FAX 7-095-9253821. **Dist. by:** East View Information Services, 3020 Harbor Ln. N., Minneapolis, MN 55447. TEL 763-550-0961, FAX 763-559-2931.

006.6   USA
TK6680.5
LAYERS; the graphics magazine for Macintosh users. Text in English. 1992. bi-m. USD 19.95 domestic; USD 39.95 foreign; USD 6.95 newsstand/cover domestic; USD 7.95 newsstand/cover in Canada (effective 2005). adv. software rev.; video rev. back issues avail.; reprints avail. **Document type:** *Magazine, Consumer.* **Description:** Covers all aspects of graphics software and products for the Macintosh.
Former titles (until 2005): Mac Design (1550-7726); (until 2001): Mac Today (1535-1378)
Related titles: Online - full text ed.
Published by: K W Media Group, Inc., 333 Douglas Rd E., Oldsmar, FL 34677-2922. TEL 813-433-5010, 877-622-8632, FAX 813-433-5015, http://www.layersmagazine.com. Ed. Scott Kelby. Pub. Jim Workman. R&P Chris Main. Adv. contact Kevin Agren. **Dist. by:** International Publishers Direct, 27500 Riverview Center Blvd, Bonita Springs, FL 34134. TEL 858-320-4563, FAX 858-677-3220.

006.76   USA   ISSN 1534-0295
A LIST APART. Text in English. irreg. free (effective 2004). back issues avail.
Media: Online - full text.
Published by: American Library Association, 50 E Huron St, Chicago, IL 60611-2795. TEL 312-280-4216, 800-545-2433, FAX 312-944-8741, http://www.alistapart.com/, http://www.ala.org.

741.6   MEX
LUDICA; arte y cultura del diseno. Text in Spanish. 1998. q. MXP 150 domestic; MXP 350 foreign (effective 2000). adv. **Document type:** *Consumer.*
Published by: Collage Editores S.A. de C.V., Alvaro Obregon No 71, Colonia Roma, Mexico, D.F., 06700, Mexico. TEL 52-5-514-4367. Ed. Francisco Avila.

621.399   USA
M C N: COMPUTER AUTOMATED SOLUTIONS FOR DESIGN ENGINEERING✱. Text in English. m.
Published by: Ariel Communications, Inc., PO Box 203550, Austin, TX 78720-3550. TEL 512-250-1700, FAX 512-250-1016. Ed. Dave Baceski. adv.: page USD 4,700. Circ: 55,000.

M.E.L.O.N. (Multimedia & Entertainment Law Online News) see *LAW*

006.6 776   USA   ISSN 1546-2242
TK5105.8883
➤ **M X DEVELOPER'S JOURNAL.** Text in English. 2003 (Nov.). m. USD 39.99 domestic; USD 49.99 in Canada & Mexico; USD 59.99 elsewhere (effective 2005). **Document type:** *Magazine, Trade.*
Published by: SYS-CON Media, Inc., 135 Chestnut Ridge Rd, Montvale, NJ 07645. TEL 201-802-3040, 888-303-5282, FAX 201-782-9600, info@sys-con.com, http://www.mxdj.com, http://www.sys-con.com. Ed. Jeremy Geelan. Adv. contact Robyn Forma.

006.42   POL   ISSN 1230-0535
T385
MACHINE GRAPHICS & VISION. Text in English. 1992. q. EUR 162 foreign (effective 2005). **Document type:** *Journal, Academic/Scholarly.* **Description:** Covers research and applications on image synthesis, analysis and processing; tutorial papers in the area of machine vision and visualization; state-of-the art papers of various aspects of vision and visualization; information on innovative uses of various graphic and vision devices and systems.
Indexed: ApMecR, Inspec, RefZh.
—BLDSC (5323.280000), IE, ingenta.
Published by: Polska Akademia Nauk, Instytut Podstaw Informatyki, ul Ordona 21, Warsaw, 01237, Poland. TEL 48-22-8362841, FAX 48-22-8376564, ipi@ipipan.waw.pl, http://www.ipipan.waw.pl/MGV/MGV.html. Ed. Wojciech Mokrzycki. Circ: 250. **Dist. by:** Ars Polona, Krakowskie Przedmiescie 7, Warsaw, Poland. TEL 48-22-9263914, FAX 48-22-9265334, arspolona@arspolona.com.pl, http://www.arspolona.com.pl.

006.68   USA   ISSN 1533-0281
MACROMEDIA SOLUTIONS. Text in English. 2001. m. USD 157 domestic; USD 177 foreign (effective 2002).
Related titles: Online - full text ed.: ISSN 1539-0225.
—CCC.
Published by: Element K Journals (Subsidiary of: Eli Research, Inc.), 500 Canal View Blvd, Rochester, NY 14623. Eds. Stephen Dow, Michelle Rogers.

006.7   GRC
MULTIMEDIA & CD-ROM. Text in Greek. 1995. m. adv. software rev. **Document type:** *Consumer.* **Description:** Covers multimedia technology.
Related titles: CD-ROM ed.
Published by: Compupress S.A., 44 Syngrou Ave, Athens, 117 42, Greece. TEL 30-210-923-8672, FAX 30-210-921-6847, http://www.compupress.gr/default_eng.htm. Ed. John Patrikos. Pub. N O Manousos. Adv. contact V Giakamozis. Circ: 16,000 (paid).

006.7   GBR
MULTIMEDIA & CD-ROM DIRECTORY (YEAR); the global source of information for the multimedia and CD-ROM industries. Text in English. 1997. a. (in 2 vols.). USD 195 per vol. in United States. adv. bk.rev. **Document type:** *Directory.* **Description:** Lists CD-ROM and multimedia CD titles, companies, and related products and services worldwide.
Formed by the 1997 merger of: Multimedia Yearbook (1358-6394); Which was formerly (1992-1995): European Multimedia Yearbook (0966-7709); CD-ROM Directory (0957-2686); Which was formerly (1986-1987): International Directory of Information Products on CD-ROM (0951-3418)
Related titles: CD-ROM ed.: Multimedia & CD-ROM Directory on CD-ROM.
Published by: Waterlow New Media Information, 6-14 Underwood St, London, N1 9NF, United Kingdom. TEL 44-171-324-2366. **Dist. in US by:** Omnigraphics, Inc., 615 Griswold St, Detroit, MI 48226. TEL 313-961-1340, FAX 313—961-1383.

MULTIMEDIA & INTERNET@SCHOOLS; the media and technology specialist's guide to electronic tools and resources for K-12. see *EDUCATION—Computer Applications*

006.7   USA   ISSN 1051-953X
MULTIMEDIA COMPUTING & PRESENTATIONS✱. Text in English. 1988. bi-m. USD 449; USD 499 foreign. bk.rev. **Document type:** *Trade.* **Description:** For high-level executives who make decisions about emerging multimedia technologies. Covers the opportunities and challenges these new technologies present in communications, entertainment, publishing, advertising, education, and other areas.
Related titles: CD-ROM ed.: 1988; Online - full text ed.: 1988 (from Gale Group).
Indexed: CompD.
—CCC.
Published by: Multimedia Computing Corp., 894 Ross Dr, Sunnyvale, CA 94089-1443. TEL 408-737-7575, FAX 408-739-8019. Ed. Nick Arnett.

006.7   USA   ISSN 1079-4212
MULTIMEDIA DAILY. Text in English. 1994. d.
Published by: Pasha Publications Inc., 1600 Wilson Blvd, Ste 600, Arlington, VA 22209. TEL 703-528-1244, FAX 703-528-3742.

006.7   USA   ISSN 1085-1453
HD9696.M843
THE MULTIMEDIA DIRECTORY✱; software producers, publishers & tele-media firms. Text in English. 1994. s-a. **Document type:** *Directory.*
Published by: Carronade Group, 2355 Francisco St, 6, San Francisco, CA 94123. TEL 415-474-3500. Eds. Clancy Fort, Jon Samsel.

006.7   DEU   ISSN 0946-4581
MULTIMEDIA MAGAZIN. Text in German. m. adv. **Document type:** *Trade.*
Formerly (until 1993): M P C Multimedia Magazin (0942-7449)
Related titles: ♦ Supplement to: iBusiness.
Published by: HighText Verlag, Wilhelm-Riehl-Str 13, Munich, 80687, Germany. TEL 49-89-578387-0, FAX 49-89-57838799, info@hightext.de. Ed. Joachim Graf. R&P Daniel Treplin. Adv. contact Stefan Kratz.

006.6   USA
MULTIMEDIA MODELING. Text in English. irreg. price varies. **Document type:** *Proceedings, Trade.*
Published by: Institute of Electrical and Electronics Engineers, Inc., 3 Park Ave, 17th Fl, New York, NY 10016-5997. TEL 800-678-4333, customer.service@ieee.org, http://www.ieee.org.

006.7   USA
MULTIMEDIA PUBLISHER. Text in English. m. USD 150 in North America; USD 165 elsewhere (effective 2001). bk.rev. **Document type:** *Newsletter, Trade.* **Description:** Covers all facets of multimedia publishing, exploring trends and marketing strategies.
Related titles: Online - full text ed.
Published by: Worldwide Videotex, PO Box 3273, Boynton Beach, FL 33424-3273. TEL 561-738-2276, markedit@juno.com, http://www.wvpubs.com. Ed., Pub. Mark Wright.

006.7   DEU   ISSN 0942-4962
QA76.575   CODEN: MUSYEW
➤ **MULTIMEDIA SYSTEMS.** Text in English. 1993. bi-m. EUR 448 combined subscription to institutions print & online eds. (effective 2005). adv. back issues avail.; reprint service avail. from PSC. **Document type:** *Journal, Academic/Scholarly.* **Description:** Serves as a forum for innovative research, emerging technologies, and state-of-the-art methods in all aspects of multimedia computing, communication, storage, and applications among researchers, engineers, and users.
Related titles: Microform ed.: (from PQC); Online - full text ed.: ISSN 1432-1882 (from EBSCO Publishing, Springer LINK, Swets Information Services).
Indexed: AS&TI, ASCA, CMCI, CompLI, CurCont, EngInd, ISR, Inspec, SCI.
—BLDSC (5983.148500), AskIEEE, CISTI, IDS, IE, Infotrieve, ingenta. CCC.
Published by: (Association for Computing Machinery, Inc. USA), Springer-Verlag (Subsidiary of: Springer Science+Business Media), Tiergartenstr 17, Heidelberg, 69121, Germany. TEL 49-6221-3450, FAX 49-6221-345229, http://link.springer.de/link/service/journals/00530/index.htm. Ed. Klara Nahrstedt. Adv. contact Stephan Kroeck TEL 49-30-827875739. **Subscr. in the Americas to:** Springer-Verlag New York, Inc., Journal Fulfillment, PO Box 2485, Secaucus, NJ 07096-2485. TEL 800-777-4643, 201-348-4033, FAX 201-348-4505, journals@springer-ny.com, http://www.springer-ny.com; **Subscr. to:** Springer GmbH Auslieferungsgesellschaft, Haberstr 7, Heidelberg 69126, Germany. TEL 49-6221-345-0, FAX 49-6221-345-4229, subscriptions@springer.de.

006.7   USA   ISSN 1380-7501
➤ **MULTIMEDIA TOOLS AND APPLICATIONS**; an international journal. Text in English. 1995. 9/yr. EUR 1,298, USD 1,368, GBP 808 combined subscription to institutions print & online eds. (effective 2005). adv. reprint service avail. from PSC. **Document type:** *Journal, Academic/Scholarly.* **Description:** Publishes original research articles on multimedia development and performance measurement tools, user interfaces, and case studies of multimedia applications.

Related titles: Online - full text ed.: ISSN 1573-7721 (from EBSCO Publishing, Gale Group, IngentaConnect, Kluwer Online, O C L C Online Computer Library Center, Inc., Springer LINK, Swets Information Services).
Indexed: B&BAb, BibLing, CMCI, CompLI, CurCont, EngInd, ErgAb, Inspec, RefZh.
—BLDSC (5983.148820), AskIEEE, CISTI, IDS, IE, Infotrieve, ingenta. **CCC.**
Published by: Springer-Verlag New York, Inc. (Subsidiary of: Springer Science+Business Media), 233 Spring St, New York, NY 10013. TEL 212-460-1500, FAX 212-460-1575, service@springer-ny.com, http://springerlink.metapress.com/openurl.asp?genre=journal&issn=1380-7501, http://www.springer-ny.com. Ed. Borko Furht. **Subscr. to:** Journal Fulfillment, PO Box 2485, Secaucus, NJ 07096-2485. TEL 201-348-4033, FAX 201-348-4505, journals@springer-ny.com.

006.7   DEU   ISSN 1434-596X
MULTIMEDIA UND RECHT. Abbreviated title: M M R. Text in German. 1998. m. EUR 294 domestic; EUR 314.50 foreign; EUR 27.50 newsstand/cover (effective 2005). **Document type:** *Journal, Trade.*
Indexed: IBR, IBZ.
Published by: Verlag C.H. Beck oHG, Wilhelmstr 9, Munich, 80801, Germany. TEL 49-89-38189338, FAX 49-89-38189398, abo.service@beck.de, http://www.beck.de.

006.7   GBR   ISSN 1361-4568
QA76.76.I59   CODEN: NRHMFY
➤ **NEW REVIEW OF HYPERMEDIA AND MULTIMEDIA.** Text in English. 1989. s-a. GBP 159, USD 262 combined subscription to institutions print & online eds. (effective 2006). adv. back issues avail.; reprint service avail. from PSC. **Document type:** *Journal, Academic/Scholarly.* **Description:** Discusses the conceptual basis of hypertext systems: cognitive aspects, design strategies, knowledge representation, and link dynamics.
Formerly (until 1995): Hypermedia (0955-8543)
Related titles: Online - full text ed.: ISSN 1740-7842. GBP 151, USD 249 to institutions (effective 2006) (from EBSCO Publishing, Gale Group, IngentaConnect, O C L C Online Computer Library Center, Inc., Swets Information Services).
Indexed: AHCI, BrHumI, C&ISA, CompLI, E&CAJ, ERA, ETA, EngInd, ErgAb, IAA, InfoSAb, Inspec, LISA, MEA, RHEA, SEA, SENA, SOMA, TEA.
—BLDSC (6087.764530), AskIEEE, CINDOC, CISTI, IE, Infotrieve, ingenta.
Published by: Taylor & Francis Ltd (Subsidiary of: Taylor & Francis Group), 4 Park Sq, Milton Park, Abingdon, OX14 4RN, United Kingdom. TEL 44-1235-828600, FAX 44-1235-829000, info@tandf.co.uk, http://www.tandf.co.uk/journals/titles/13614568.asp. Ed. Douglas Tudhope. **Subscr. to:** Journals Customer Service, Rankine Rd, Basingstoke, Hants RG24 8PR, United Kingdom. TEL 44-1256-813000, FAX 44-1256-330245, enquiry@tandf.co.uk.

006.6   JPN   ISSN 0912-1609
NIKKEI COMPUTER GRAPHICS. Key Title: Nikkei C G. Text in Japanese. 1986. m. JPY 13,860 (effective 1999). adv. **Document type:** *Trade.* **Description:** Contains comprehensive information on computer graphics and CG systems, and their applications in business.
Published by: Nikkei Business Publications Inc. (Subsidiary of: Nihon Keizai Shimbun, Inc.), 2-1-1 Hirakawa-cho, Chiyoda-ku, Tokyo, 102-8622, Japan. TEL 81-3-5210-8311, FAX 81-3-5210-8530, info@nikkeibpnyc.com, webmaster@nikkeibp.com, http://www.nikkeibp.com. Ed. Hideo Anpo. Pub. Minora Matsuzaki. Adv. contact Touru Kato. B&W page JPY 391,000, color page JPY 548,000; trim 208 x 280. Circ: 20,211. **Dist. in America by:** Nikkei Business Publications America Inc., 575 Fifth Ave, 20th Fl, New York, NY 10017.

OTKRYTYE SISTEMY. see *COMPUTERS—Computer Engineering*

006.6   USA
PACIFIC CONFERENCE ON COMPUTER GRAPHICS AND APPLICATIONS. PROCEEDINGS. Text in English. a. USD 209; USD 84 to members (effective 2004). **Document type:** *Proceedings, Trade.*
Indexed: EngInd.
Published by: Institute of Electrical and Electronics Engineers, Inc., 3 Park Ave, 17th Fl, New York, NY 10016-5997. TEL 212-419-7900, 800-678-4333, FAX 212-752-4929, customer.service@ieee.org, http://www.ieee.org.

006.6   USA   ISSN 1543-4346
PARALLEL AND LARGE-DATA VISUALIZATION AND GRAPHICS SYMPOSIUM. PROCEEDINGS. Text in English. 1999. a. USD 154; USD 77 to members (effective 2004). **Document type:** *Proceedings, Trade.*
Published by: Institute of Electrical and Electronics Engineers, Inc., 3 Park Ave, 17th Fl, New York, NY 10016-5997. TEL 212-419-7900, 800-678-4333, FAX 212-752-4929, customer.service@ieee.org, http://www.ieee.org. **Co-sponsor:** I E E E Communications Society.

006.6   USA
PHILLIPS DOCUMENT MANAGEMENT SOURCE BOOK. Text in English. 1985. a. USD 199; USD 223 foreign (effective 1999). **Document type:** *Directory.* **Description:** Provides over 400 pages of product and service information, competitive profiles, current market research, financial and operating facts, and access to executive personnel.
Formerly: International Imaging Sourcebook
Published by: Access Intelligence, LLC (Subsidiary of: Veronis, Suhler & Associates Inc.), 1201 Seven Locks Rd, Ste 300, Potomac, MD 20854. TEL 301-354-2000, 800-777-5006, FAX 301-424-2058, pbi@phillips.com, clientservices@accessintel.com, http://www.pbimedia.com.

▼ **PHOTOSHOP FIX.** see *PHOTOGRAPHY*

006.68   USA   ISSN 1536-2620
PHOTOSHOP FUNDAMENTALS. Text in English. 2001. m. USD 139; USD 169 combined subscription print & online eds. (effective 2005). **Document type:** *Magazine, Consumer.*
Related titles: Online - full text ed.: ISSN 1539-039X. USD 169 domestic; USD 179 foreign (effective 2005).
—CCC.
Published by: Element K Journals (Subsidiary of: Eli Research, Inc.), 500 Canal View Blvd, Rochester, NY 14623. TEL 585-240-7301, 800-223-8720, 877-203-5248, FAX 585-292-4392, http://www.elementkjournals.com/products/showProduct.asp?prodID=11&catId=3. Ed. Michelle Rogers.

006.68   USA
PHOTOSHOP TIPS & TRICKS. Text in English. 1995. m. USD 39.95; includes DT&G Journal of Design, Topography & Graphics. **Description:** Focuses on the process involved in using computers to create digital art for publishing.
Media: Online - full text.
Published by: Design & Publishing Center, 15 Southgate, Harrisonburg, VA 22801. showker@graphic-desig.com, http://www.graphic-design.com/Photoshop. Ed. Fred Showker.

006.6   USA   ISSN 1535-4687
PHOTOSHOP USER; the adobe photoshop how-to magazine. Text in English. 1998. 8/yr. USD 99 membership; USD 9.95 per issue (effective 2005). adv. **Document type:** *Magazine, Trade.* **Description:** Addresses the techniques, issues and concerns of Photoshop users.
Related titles: Online - full text ed.
—Linda Hall.
Published by: National Association of Photoshop Professionals, 333 Douglas Rd East, Oldsmar, FL 34677. TEL 813-433-5006, 800-738-8513, FAX 813-433-5015, info@photoshopuser.com, http://www.photoshopuser.com. adv.: color page USD 7,665; trim 8.125 x 10.875.

006.6   TWN   ISSN 1024-8307
POWER MEDIA. Text in Chinese. 1995. m. adv.
Published by: Acer T W P Corporation, 2-F, No 19-1 Ln 231, Fu-Hsing N. Rd, Taipei, 105, Taiwan. TEL 886-2-7136959, FAX 886-2-7189467. Adv. contact David Tsai. B&W page USD 860, color page USD 1,720; trim 298 x 210. Circ: 10,000.

---

006   USA   ISSN 1054-7460
TA167   CODEN: PSENEG
➤ **PRESENCE;** teleoperators and virtual environments. Text in English. 1992. bi-m. USD 90 combined subscription in US & Canada to individuals print & online eds.; USD 120 combined subscription elsewhere to individuals print & online eds.; USD 535 combined subscription in US & Canada to institutions print & online eds.; USD 565 combined subscription elsewhere to institutions print & online eds. (effective 2006). **Document type:** *Academic/Scholarly.* **Description:** Contains research and designs applicable to advanced eletromechanical and computer systems, incorporating perspectives from physics to philosophy.
Related titles: Online - full content ed.: ISSN 1531-3263. USD 80 to individuals; USD 482 to institutions (effective 2006); Online - full text ed.: (from EBSCO Publishing, Gale Group, IngentaConnect, O C L C Online Computer Library Center, Inc., Swets Information Services).
Indexed: BrCerAb, C&ISA, CMCI, CerAb, CompAb, CompLI, CorrAb, CurCont, E&CAJ, EMA, ErgAb, IAA, ISR, InfoSAb, Inspec, M&TEA, MBF, METADEX, SCI, WAA.
—BLDSC (6609.709700), CISTI, IDS, IE, Infotrieve, ingenta, Linda Hall. **CCC.**
Published by: M I T Press, 55 Hayward St, Cambridge, MA 02142-1493. TEL 617-253-5646, FAX 617-258-6779, presence@mit.edu, journals-info@mit.edu, http://mitpress.mit.edu/presence. Eds. Mel Slater, Nathaniel I Durlach TEL 617-253-2534.

006.6   USA   ISSN 0032-8510
Z119
PRINT; design - culture. Text in English. 1940. bi-m. USD 57 domestic; USD 72 in Canada; USD 98 elsewhere (effective 2005). adv. bk.rev. illus. index. back issues avail.; reprint service avail. from PQC. **Document type:** *Magazine, Trade.* **Description:** Disseminates various aspects of graphic design programs with professional input on visual communication: film, animation, environmental and computer graphics.
Incorporates (in 1976): Packaging Design (0030-9109)

Related titles: Microform ed.: (from PQC); Online - full text ed.: (from bigchalk, EBSCO Publishing, Florida Center for Library Automation, Gale Group, H.W. Wilson, Northern Light Technology, Inc., O C L C Online Computer Library Center, Inc., ProQuest Information & Learning).
Indexed: ABIn, ABM, ABS&EES, ArtInd, DAAI, FLI, IBRH, PCI, RASB.
—BLDSC (6612.995000), CISTI, IE, Infotrieve, ingenta, Linda Hall.
Published by: F & W Publications, Inc., 38 E 29th St, 3rd Fl, New York, NY 10016. TEL 212-447-1400, FAX 212-447-5231, info@printmag.com, wds@fwpubs.com, http://www.printmag.com, http://www.fwpublications.com. Ed. Joyce Rutter Kaye. Pub. Joel Toner. adv.: B&W page USD 4,485, color page USD 6,100; trim 9 x 10.75. Circ: 56,788.

PRINT ACTION. see *ART*

PRINTACTION NATIONAL DIRECTORY OF SERVICES & EQUIPMENT FOR THE TRADE. see *BUSINESS AND ECONOMICS—Trade And Industrial Directories*

006.68   ITA   ISSN 1594-4654
PROGETTI PRATICI. Text in Italian. 2002. bi-m. EUR 7.90 newsstand/cover (effective 2003). adv. **Document type:** *Magazine, Consumer.*
Published by: Play Press Publishing s.r.l., Via Vitorchiano 123, Rome, RM 00189, Italy. TEL 39-06-33221250, FAX 39-06-33221235, abbonamenti@playpress.com, http://www.playpress.com. Ed. Manuel Serrenti. Pub. Alessandro Ferri. Circ: 40,000 (paid and controlled).

006.6   GBR
▼ **QERCUS: GRAPHICS & DESIGN.** Text in English. 2004. bi-m. GBP 29.95 domestic; GBP 38.84 in Europe; GBP 41.15 elsewhere (effective 2004). **Document type:** *Magazine, Trade.*
Formed by the merger of (in 2004): Acorn Publisher (1356-1537); Acorn User (1471-1001); Which had former titles (until 1983): B B C Acorn User (0962-9475); (until 1988): Acorn User (0263-7456)
Published by: Finnybank Ltd., 30 Finnybank Rd, Cheshire, M33 6LR, United Kingdom. TEL 44-161-9699820, FAX 44-8700-519527, info@finnybank.com, http://www.finnybank.com/.

QUICK ANSWERS FOR DIGITAL PHOTOGRAPHY. see *PHOTOGRAPHY*

006.6   GBR   ISSN 1077-2014
TA1637   CODEN: REIMFQ
➤ **REAL - TIME IMAGING.** Text in English. 1995. bi-m. EUR 158 in Europe to individuals; JPY 17,000 in Japan to individuals; USD 145 to individuals except Europe and Japan; EUR 474 in Europe to institutions; JPY 51,300 in Japan to institutions; USD 421 to institutions except Europe and Japan (effective 2005). adv. reprints avail. **Document type:** *Journal, Academic/Scholarly.* **Description:** For researchers, technologists, and practitioners involved in fundamental real-time imaging technologies and applications.
Related titles: Online - full text ed.: ISSN 1096-116X. USD 469 (effective 2002) (from EBSCO Publishing, Gale Group, IngentaConnect, O C L C Online Computer Library Center, Inc., ScienceDirect, Swets Information Services).
Indexed: B&BAb, CMCI, CompLI, CompR, CurCont, EngInd, Inspec, ZentMath.
—BLDSC (7303.282648), AskIEEE, CISTI, IDS, IE, Infotrieve, ingenta, Linda Hall. **CCC.**
Published by: Academic Press (Subsidiary of: Elsevier Science & Technology), Harcourt Pl, 32 Jamestown Rd, London, NW1 7BY, United Kingdom. TEL 44-20-7424-4200, FAX 44-20-7483-2293, apsubs@acad.com, http://www.academicpress.com/rti, http://www.elsevier.com/. Ed. N. Kehtarnavaz. R&P Catherine John. Adv. contact Nik Screen.

006.6 770   NLD   ISSN 1567-3200
REMOTE SENSING AND DIGITAL IMAGE PROCESSING. Text in English. 1999. irreg., latest vol.8, 2005. price varies. **Document type:** *Monographic series, Trade.*
—BLDSC (7356.815350).
Published by: Springer-Verlag Dordrecht (Subsidiary of: Springer Science+Business Media), Van Godewijckstraat 30, Dordrecht, 3311 GX, Netherlands. TEL 31-78-6576050, FAX 31-78-6576474, http://www.springeronline.com. Ed. Freek D van der Meer.

006.6   RUS   ISSN 1560-4640
S A P R I GRAFIKA. (Sistemy Avtomatizirovannogo Proektirovaniya) Text in Russian. 1996. m. USD 159 in United States. 96 p./no.; **Document type:** *Journal.*
Indexed: RefZh.
Published by: Komp'yuter Press, Gorokhovskii Per 7, A-ya 37, Moscow, 113093, Russian Federation. cad@compress.ru, http://www.sapr.ru/. Ed. D G Kraskovskii. **US dist. addr.:** East View Information Services, 3020 Harbor Ln. N., Minneapolis, MN 55447. TEL 612-550-0961.

S B S DIGITAL DESIGN; the how-to newsletter for electronic designers. (Step by Step) see *PUBLISHING AND BOOK TRADE—Computer Applications*

C

006.68 USA
S I D INTERNATIONAL SYMPOSIUM. APPLICATIONS SEMINAR NOTES. Text in English. a. USD 60 (effective 2000). **Document type:** *Proceedings, Academic/Scholarly.*
Published by: Society for Information Display, 610 S 2nd St, San Jose, CA 95112. TEL 408-977-1013, FAX 408-977-1531, office@sid.org, http://www.sid.org.

621.399 001.53 USA ISSN 0887-915X
TK7882.I6
S I D INTERNATIONAL SYMPOSIUM. SEMINAR LECTURE NOTES. (Society for Information Display) Text in English. a. price varies. **Document type:** *Monographic series, Academic/Scholarly.*
—BLDSC (8239.405000), IE, ingenta, Linda Hall. **CCC.**
Published by: (Palisades Institute for Research Services), Society for Information Display, 610 S 2nd St, San Jose, CA 95112. TEL 408-977-1013, FAX 408-977-1531, office@sid.org, http://www.sid.org.

006.6 USA
S I G G R A P H COMPUTER GRAPHICS AND INTERACTIVE TECHNIQUES. (Special Interest Group Graphics) Text in English. q. USD 85 (effective 2004). **Description:** Promotes the generation and dissemination of information on computer graphics and interactive techniques. Members include researchers, developers and users from the technical, academic, business, and artistic communities.
Published by: Association for Computing Machinery, Inc., 1515 Broadway, 17th Fl, New York, NY 10036-5701. TEL 212-626-0500, 212-626-0520, 800-342-6626, usacm@acm.org, http://www.acm.org/siggraph/.

776.6 USA ISSN 1098-6138
T385
S I G G R A P H CONFERENCE ABSTRACTS AND APPLICATIONS. (Special Interest Group on Computer Graphics and Interactive Techniques) Text in English. irreg.
Related titles: CD-ROM ed.: ISSN 1098-6146.
Published by: Association for Computing Machinery, Inc., 1515 Broadway, 17th Fl, New York, NY 10036-5701. TEL 212-626-0500, FAX 212-869-0481.

006.7 USA
S I G M M CONFERENCE PROCEEDINGS. (Special Interest Group Multimedia) Text in English. a. USD 60 (effective 2004). **Document type:** *Proceedings.* **Description:** Interdisciplinary forum on multimedia, sponsoring the ACM Multimedia Conference series, held in collaboration with SIGs interested in specific aspects of multimedia.
Published by: Association for Computing Machinery, Inc., 1515 Broadway, 17th Fl, New York, NY 10036-5701. TEL 212-626-0500, 212-626-0520, 800-342-6626, usacm@acm.org, http://www.acm.org/sigmm/.

006.6 USA
S I G W E B NEWSLETTER. Text in English. 1992. 3/yr. USD 34 (effective 2004). **Document type:** *Newsletter, Academic/Scholarly.* **Description:** Covers the multi-disciplinary field of hypertext and hypermedia, facilitating its application both on the World Wide Web and also in independent, distributed and stand-alone environments.
Formerly (until 1998): S I G Link Review
Published by: Association for Computing Machinery, Inc., 1515 Broadway, 17th Fl, New York, NY 10036-5701. TEL 212-626-0500, 212-626-0520, 800-342-6626, FAX 212-869-0481, sigs@acm.org, usacm@acm.org, http://www.acm.org.

SERIF; the magazine of type and typography. see *PRINTING*

006.6 USA ISSN 1057-7041
T385
SILICON GRAPHICS WORLD✶ . Text in English. 1991. bi-m. USD 45; USD 75 foreign (effective 1998). illus. **Document type:** *Trade.*
Indexed: SoftBase.
Published by: Publications & Communications, Inc., 505 Cypress Creek Rd, Ste B, Cedar Park, TX 78613-4429. TEL 512-250-9023, 800-678-9724, FAX 512-678-9724. adv.; B&W page USD 3,202, color page USD 3,952; trim 14.5 x 10.75.

006.7 CAN ISSN 0846-3131
SILVER SCREEN. Text in English. 1988. q. CND 53.50. adv. bk.rev. **Document type:** *Newsletter.* **Description:** Targeted towards multimedia and entertainment finance and investment, specifically video, television and film. For readers in Canada, the US, Europe and the Pacific Rim.
Published by: Malcolm Silver & Co. Ltd., 194 Merton St, Ste 210, Toronto, ON M4S 3B5, Canada. TEL 416-488-3393, FAX 416-488-5217, msilver@davisville.ca, http://www.davisville.ca/ msilver. Ed., R&P Jill Battson. Adv. contact Keith Cole. Circ: 1,300 (paid).

006.6 USA ISSN 1546-7015
▼ **SMART TIPS AND QUICK TRICKS FOR GRAPHIC AND DIGITAL DESIGNERS.** Text in English. 2003. a. USD 29.95 per issue (effective 2005).
Media: CD-ROM.

Published by: Element K Journals (Subsidiary of: Eli Research, Inc.), 500 Canal View Blvd, Rochester, NY 14623. TEL 585-240-7301, 800-223-8720, 877-203-5248, FAX 585-292-4392, http://www.elementkjournals.com/store/showAncillaryDetail.asp?prodid=161.

621.399 USA ISSN 1071-0922
TK7882.I6 CODEN: JSIDE8
SOCIETY FOR INFORMATION DISPLAY. JOURNAL. Text in English. 1963. q. free to members (effective 2004). bk.rev. abstr.; charts; illus. index. back issues avail. **Document type:** *Journal, Academic/Scholarly.* **Description:** Presents original work dealing with the theory and practice of information display.
Former titles (until 1991): Society for Information Display. Proceedings (0734-1768); (until 1976): S I D Proceedings (0036-1496)
Indexed: C&ISA, CompC, E&CAJ, EngInd, ISMEC, Inspec, SolStAb.
—BLDSC (4889.100000), AskIEEE, CISTI, Ei, IE, Infotrieve, Linda Hall. **CCC.**
Published by: Society for Information Display, 610 S 2nd St, San Jose, CA 95112. TEL 408-977-1013, FAX 408-977-1531, office@sid.org, http://www.sid.org. Ed. Alan Sobel. Circ: 4,500.

STATISTICAL COMPUTING AND GRAPHICS. see
COMPUTERS—Abstracting, Bibliographies, Statistics

006.7 USA ISSN 1554-3412
TK7881.4
STUDIO/MONTHLY; shoot post deliver. Text in English. 1996. m. USD 89; free to qualified personnel (effective 2005). adv. illus. back issues avail.; reprints avail. **Document type:** *Magazine, Trade.* **Description:** Covers all facets of the audio-video, multi-media interactive industry: video, presentation media, computer-graphics and audio services, with special emphasis on practical "how to" information.
Formerly (until 2005): A V Video & Multimedia Producer (1090-7459); Which was formed by the merger of (1995-1996): Multimedia Producer (1079-4689); (1978-1996): A V Video (0747-1335); Which incorporated (19??-1990): Video Management (1047-7713); Which was formerly (until 1989): Video Manager (0747-3745); (until 1984): Video User (0273-7817); (until 1980): V U Marketplace (0149-6832); A V Video was formerly (until 1984): Audio Visual Directions (0746-8989); (until 1980): Audio Visual Product News (0164-6834)
Related titles: Online - full text ed.: (from Gale Group).
Indexed: CompD, SoftBase.
—IE. **CCC.**
Published by: Access Intelligence, LLC (Subsidiary of: Veronis, Suhler & Associates Inc.), 701 Westchester Ave, White Plains, NY 10604. TEL 914-328-9157, FAX 914-328-7107, bmarchant@pbmedi.com, clientservices@accessintel.com, http://www.avvideo.com, http://www.pbimedia.com. Pub., Adv. contact Laurie Corn. B&W page USD 10,200, color page USD 11,900. Circ: 80,000 (paid and controlled).

006.7 NLD ISSN 1571-9839
T V M. (Tijdschrift voor Multimedia) Text in Dutch. 1988. m. EUR 69 (effective 2005). adv. bk.rev. back issues avail. **Document type:** *Trade.* **Description:** Covers new media developments on the Internet and in e-commerce, virtual reality, and digital video discs (DVDs).
Former titles (until 2001): Tijdschrift voor Multimedia (1385-7703); (until 1997): Multi Media Computing Magazine (0923-8182); Which incorporated (in 1991): Mini - Microcomputer (0167-6547); Which was formed by the merger of (1979-1981): Microcomputer (0167-3343); (1980-1981): Compu-techniek (0165-9758); And incorporated (in 1985): Informatronica (0167-7225); Which superseded (1976-1983): Electronica Top International (0166-2961); Incorporates (1987-2001): A V Prof (0923-7054)
Published by: Magenta Communicatie Projecten, Postbus 134, Groesbeek, 6560 AC, Netherlands. TEL 31-24-3454150, FAX 31-24-3976071, info@multimediagids.nl, http://www.tvm.info. Circ: 4,800.

TECHNICAL GUIDE TO VISUAL PROGRAMMING. see
COMPUTERS

006.6 USA
TECHNOLOGY WATCH; for the graphic arts and information industries. Text in English. 1980. m. USD 95. adv. bk.rev. **Document type:** *Newsletter.*
Related titles: Online - full text ed.
Indexed: GALA.
Published by: Technology Watch, Inc., PO Box 2206, Springfield, VA 22152. Ed., Pub., Adv. contact Henry B Freedman.

006.6 USA ISSN 1534-2832
TK8315 CODEN: TMRAB7
TRANSFORM; reinventing business with content and collaboration technologies. Text in English. 1992. m. free to qualified subscribers. adv. software rev. **Document type:** *Magazine, Trade.* **Description:** For professionals who buy, implement and manage imaging products and services.
Former titles (until 2001): Imaging and Document Solutions (1522-6085); (until vol.7, no.10, 1998): Imaging Magazine (1083-2912)

Related titles: Online - full text ed.: (from EBSCO Publishing, Florida Center for Library Automation, Gale Group, H.W. Wilson, O C L C Online Computer Library Center, Inc., ProQuest Information & Learning).
Indexed: BPI, CompD, CompLI, EngInd, IAA, InfoSAb, Inspec, MicrocompInd, SoftBase.
—AskIEEE, Ei, IE, Linda Hall. **CCC.**
Published by: C M P Media LLC (Subsidiary of: United News & Media), 11 W 19th St, New York, NY 10011-4280. TEL 917-305-3361, 888-824-9792, http://www.transformmag.com, http://www.cmp.com. Ed. Doug Henschen. adv.: B&W page USD 9,799, color page USD 11,269. Circ: 62,103.

TYPOFILE. see *PRINTING*

006 GBR ISSN 1360-3485
V R NEWS. (Virtual Reality) Text in English. 1992. m. (10/yr.). GBP 95; USD 150 foreign (effective 2000). adv. bk.rev.; software rev. bibl.; charts; illus.; mkt.; pat.; stat. back issues avail. **Document type:** *Newsletter, Trade.* **Description:** Covers virtual reality research, technology, products, applications, markets, businesses and events.
Indexed: Inspec.
Published by: Cydata Ltd., PO Box 2515, London, N4 4JW, United Kingdom. TEL 44-181-292-1498, FAX 44-181-292-1346, info@vrnews.com, http://www.vrnews.com. Ed., Pub., R&P, Adv. contact Mike Bevan. B&W page USD 1,600, color page USD 2,400; trim 210 x 297. Circ: 1,100.

006.6 USA
▼ **VECTORS: JOURNAL OF CULTURE AND TECHNOLOGY IN A DYNAMIC VERNACULAR.** Text in English. 2004 (Fall). s-a.
Description: Dedicated to expanding the potentials of academic publication via emergent and transitional media.
Media: Online - full content.
Published by: University of Southern California, Institute for Multimedia Literacy, 746 W Adams Blvd, Los Angeles, CA 90089-7727. TEL 213-743-4768, http:// vectors.iml.annenberg.edu/. Eds. Steve Anderson, Tara McPherson.

VIDEO LINE. see *COMMUNICATIONS—Video*

006 GBR ISSN 1359-4338
QA76.9.H85 CODEN: VIREFH
➤ **VIRTUAL REALITY**; research, development and applications. Text in English. 1995. q. EUR 388 combined subscription to institutions print & online eds. (effective 2005). adv. **Document type:** *Journal, Academic/Scholarly.* **Description:** Provides a forum for academics, researchers and technicians to share papers on issues relevant to virtual reality and virtual environment systems.
Related titles: Online - full text ed.: ISSN 1434-9957 (from EBSCO Publishing, ProQuest Information & Learning, Springer LINK, Swets Information Services).
Indexed: CompAb, CompLI, ErgAb, Inspec.
—IE, Infotrieve. **CCC.**
Published by: (Virtual Reality Society), Springer-Verlag London Ltd. (Subsidiary of: Springer Science+Business Media), Ashbourne House, The Guildway, Old Portsmouth Rd, Guildford, Surrey GU7 3DJ, United Kingdom. TEL 44-1483-734433, FAX 44-1483-734411, postmaster@svl.co.uk, http://www.springer.co.uk. Eds. Daniel Ballin, John Vince, Rae Earnshaw, Robert Macredie. Adv. contact Christiane Notarmarco. **Subscr. in the Americas to:** Springer-Verlag New York, Inc., Journal Fulfillment, PO Box 2485, Secaucus, NJ 07096-2485. TEL 800-777-4643, 201-348-4033, FAX 201-348-4505, journals@springer-ny.com, http://www.springer-ny.com; **Subscr. to:** Springer GmbH Auslieferungsgesellschaft, Haberstr 7, Heidelberg 69126, Germany. TEL 49-6221-345-0, FAX 49-6221-345-4229, subscriptions@springer.de.

006.68 USA
VISUAL BASIC PROGRAMMERS JOURNAL ON CD-ROM. Text in English. m. USD 99.95 domestic; USD 129.95 foreign (effective 2000). software rev. **Document type:** *Trade.*
Media: CD-ROM.
Published by: Fawcette Technical Publications, 2600 S. El Camino Real., Ste. 300, San Mateo, CA 94403-2381. TEL 650-833-7100, FAX 650-853-0230, lmatthes@fawcette.com, http://www.fawcette.com.

006.6 DEU ISSN 0178-2789
T385 CODEN: VICOE5
➤ **THE VISUAL COMPUTER**; international journal of computer graphics. Text in English. 1985. 10/yr. EUR 898 combined subscription to institutions print & online eds. (effective 2005). adv. back issues avail.; reprint service avail. from ISI. **Document type:** *Journal, Academic/Scholarly.* **Description:** Reports on the state-of-the-art technology in the fields of computer vision, graphics, and imaging, with a specific focus on applications.
Related titles: Microform ed.: (from PQC); Online - full text ed.: ISSN 1432-2315 (from EBSCO Publishing, Springer LINK, Swets Information Services).
Indexed: ASCA, CMCI, CompAb, CompLI, CurCont, CybAb, EngInd, Inspec, RefZh, ZentMath.
—BLDSC (9241.235000), AskIEEE, CISTI, Ei, IDS, IE, Infotrieve, ingenta, Linda Hall. **CCC.**

Published by: (International Computer Graphics Society), Springer-Verlag (Subsidiary of: Springer Science+Business Media), Tiergartenstr 17, Heidelberg, 69121, Germany. TEL 49-6221-3450, FAX 49-6221-345229, http://link.springer.de/link/service/journals/00371/index.htm. Ed. Nadia Magnenat-Thalmann. Adv. contact Stephan Kroeck TEL 49-30-827875739. **Subscr. in the Americas to:** Springer-Verlag New York, Inc., Journal Fulfillment, PO Box 2485, Secaucus, NJ 07096-2485. TEL 800-777-4643, 201-348-4033, FAX 201-348-4505, journals@springer-ny.com, http://www.springer-ny.com; **Subscr. to:** Springer GmbH Auslieferungsgesellschaft, Haberstr 7, Heidelberg 69126, Germany. TEL 49-6221-345-0, FAX 49-6221-345-4229, subscriptions@springer.de.

006.693 004.3 USA ISSN 1552-9886
QA76.76.H94
WEB3D (YEAR) SYMPOSIUM. PROCEEDINGS. Text in English. a. **Document type:** *Proceedings.*
Former titles (until 2001): Web3D - V R M L Symposium. Proceedings (1551-4404); (until 2000): V R M L Symposium. Proceedings (1534-939X)
—BLDSC (9283.983250).
Published by: Association for Computing Machinery, Inc., 1515 Broadway, 17th Fl, New York, NY 10036-5701. TEL 212-626-0520, FAX 212-869-0481, sigs@acm.org, usacm@acm.org, http://www.acm.org. Ed. Stephen N Spencer. **Subscr. to:** ACM Order Department, P O Box 11405, Church St. Sta., New York, NY 10286-1405. TEL 800-342-6626.

WORKING SMARTER WITH MICROSOFT POWERPOINT. see *COMPUTERS—Software*

006.693 GBR ISSN 0953-2331
3 D. Text in English. m. GBP 36 domestic; GBP 59 in Europe; GBP 68 elsewhere. **Document type:** *Trade.*
Supersedes in part (in 1990): C A D - C A M International (0261-6920)
Related titles: Online - full text ed.: (from Gale Group).
Indexed: CompD.
—CISTI.
Published by: E M A P Computing (Subsidiary of: E M A P Business Communications), 33-39 Bowling Green Ln, London, EC1R 0DA, United Kingdom. TEL 44-20-7837-1212, FAX 44-20-7578-4008.

006.42 USA ISSN 1058-9503
3 D ARTIST. Text in English. 1991. 5/yr. USD 19 domestic; USD 26 foreign; USD 5 newsstand/cover foreign (effective 2001). back issues avail. **Document type:** *Magazine, Trade.* **Description:** Provides practical information for working 3D artists and all who use affordable desktop 3D graphics.
Published by: Columbine, Inc., PO Box 4787, Santa Fe, NM 87502. TEL 505-424-8945, FAX 505-424-8946, webmaster@3dartist.com, ballen@3dartist.com, http://www.3dartist.com/3dasubs.htm. Ed., Pub., R&P Bill Allen. Adv. contact Sally Beach. Circ: 25,000. **Dist. by:** International Publishers Direct, 27500 Riverview Center Blvd, Bonita Springs, FL 34134. TEL 858-320-4563.

006.693 GBR
3 D WORLD. Text in English. m. GBP 44.99 domestic; GBP 56 foreign (effective 2005). adv. **Document type:** *Magazine, Consumer.* **Description:** Contains practical tips and creative advice as well as reviews of the latest computer graphics hardware and software for PCs and Macs.
Incorporates (1996-2003): Computer Generated Imaging (1361-7737)
Related titles: Online - full text ed.
Published by: Future Publishing Ltd., Beauford Court, 30 Monmouth St, Bath, Avon BA1 2BW, United Kingdom. TEL 44-1225-442244, FAX 44-1225-446019, 3dworld@futurenet.co.uk, customerservice@futurenet.co.uk, http://www.computerarts.co.uk/3dworld, http://www.futurenet.co.uk. Ed. Ed Ricketts. Circ: 14,652 (paid).

COMPUTERS—Computer Industry

338.47004 USA ISSN 1557-0169
KF390.5.C6
ANDREWS LITIGATION REPORTER: COMPUTER & INTERNET. Text in English. 1983. bi-w. looseleaf. USD 1,226 (effective 2005). adv. bibl.; stat. cum.index every 6 mos. back issues avail. **Document type:** *Newsletter, Trade.* **Description:** Reports on copyright, patent and trademark claims, theft of secret cases, significant user - vendor contract-misrepresentation claims, consultant liability questions, and other evolving issues as they relate to the computer industry.
Former titles (until 2004): Computer & Internet Litigation Reporter (1546-704X); (until 2003): Computer & Online Industry Litigation Reporter (1091-7810); (until 1996): Computer Industry Litigation Reporter (0740-1469)
Related titles: Online - full text ed.
—CCC.
Published by: Andrews Publications (Subsidiary of: Thomson West), 175 Strafford Ave, Ste 140, Wayne, PA 19087. TEL 610-225-0510, 800-345-1101, FAX 610-225-0501, http://www.andrewsonline.com. Ed. Donna Higgins.

338 BRA
ANUARIO DE INFORMATICA. Text in Portuguese. a. adv. **Document type:** *Directory, Trade.*
Related titles: CD-ROM ed.
Published by: I D G Computerworld do Brasil, Rua Tabapua, 145-3 e 4 andar, Itaim Bibi, Sao Paulo, 04533-010, Brazil. TEL 55-11-3049-2000, FAX 55-11-3071-4022, negocios@idg.com.br, http://www.idg.com.br. adv.: B&W page USD 4,000, color page USD 6,700; trim 210 x 280. Circ: 55,000 (paid and controlled).

338.47004 SGP ISSN 0254-5586
HD9696.C63
ASIAN SOURCES COMPUTER PRODUCTS. Short title: Computer Products. Text in English. 1983. m. USD 75 (effective 2005). **Document type:** *Catalog.* **Description:** Covers Asian made computer products, computers and peripherals, subassemblies and manufacturing.
Related titles: CD-ROM ed.; Online - full text ed.
Indexed: HongKongiana, Inspec.
Published by: Global Sources, c/o Media Data Systems Pte Ltd, PO Box 0203, Raffles City, 911707, Singapore. TEL 65-65472800, FAX 65-65472888, service@globalsources.com, http://www.globalsources.com/MAGAZINE/BUYERS/CPBR.HTM?pi_proj=GSOLHP. Circ: 24,600.

338.47004 GBR
BUSINESS MONITOR: COMPUTER SERVICES. Text in English. q. charts; stat. back issues avail. **Document type:** *Government.*
Related titles: Series of: Service and Distributive Monitors Series.
Published by: (C.S.O. Library), Office for National Statistics, Government Buildings, Cardiff Rd, Newport, Gwent NP9 1XG, United Kingdom. TEL 44-1633-812973, FAX 44-1633-812599, library@onls.gov.uk. **Subscr. to:** Stationery Office, PO Box 276, London SW8 5DT, United Kingdom. TEL 44-20-7873-9090, FAX 44-207-873-8200.

338.47004 GBR ISSN 1354-8700
BUSINESS RATIO PLUS: COMPUTER EQUIPMENT DISTRIBUTORS. Text in English. 1978. a. GBP 275 (effective 2001). charts; stat. **Document type:** *Trade.*
Formerly (until 1994): Business Ratio Report. Computer Equipment Distributors (0267-8551)
Published by: The Prospect Shop Ltd., Field House, 72 Oldfield Rd, Hampton, Middx TW12 2HQ, United Kingdom. TEL 44-20-8461-8730, 44-20-8481-8720, FAX 44-20-8783-1940, info@theprospectshop.co.uk.

338.47004 GBR ISSN 1358-3697
BUSINESS RATIO PLUS: COMPUTER SERVICES; an industry sector analysis. Text in English. 1979. a. charts; stat. **Document type:** *Trade.*
Formerly (until 1994): Business Ratio Report. Computer Services (0261-7676)
Published by: The Prospect Shop Ltd., Field House, 72 Oldfield Rd, Hampton, Middx TW12 2HQ, United Kingdom. TEL 44-20-8461-8730, 44-20-8481-8720, FAX 44-20-8783-1940, info@theprospectshop.co.uk.

▼ **BUSINESS VIEW**; the H P magazine of business and technology. (Hewlett-Packard) see *BUSINESS AND ECONOMICS—Investments*

338.47004 NLD ISSN 1388-218X
C B M. (Computer Business Magazine) Text in Dutch. 1997. m. EUR 51 domestic; EUR 60 foreign (effective 2005). adv. software rev. illus. **Document type:** *Trade.* **Description:** Covers various aspects of the computer industry.
Published by: Magenta Communicatie Projecten, Postbus 134, Groesbeek, 6560 AC, Netherlands. TEL 31-24-3454150, FAX 31-24-3976071, cbm@kantoorweb.nl, http://www.kantoorweb.nl. Ed. Yvonne Keijzers TEL 31-24-3454157. Pub. Joost Heessels. Adv. contacts Annet Poelen, Paqui Tamayo. B&W page EUR 1,690, color page EUR 2,785; trim 214 x 300. Circ: 5,000.

338.47004 USA ISSN 0893-4843
C D COMPUTING NEWS. (Compact Disc) Text in English. 1987. m. USD 150 in North America; USD 165 elsewhere (effective 2005). back issues avail. **Document type:** *Newsletter, Trade.* **Description:** Covers CD-ROM technology, products, and news, with emphasis on marketing strategies.
Related titles: Online - full text ed.: (from bigchalk, EBSCO Publishing, Factiva, Gale Group, LexisNexis, ProQuest Information & Learning, The Dialog Corporation).
Indexed: ABIn, CompD.
—CCC.
Published by: Worldwide Videotex, PO Box 3273, Boynton Beach, FL 33424-3273. TEL 561-738-2276, markedit@juno.com, http://www.wvpubs.com. Ed., Pub. Mark Wright.

338.47004 USA
C T O MAGAZINE. (Chief Technology Officer) Text in English. 2001. q. **Document type:** *Magazine, Trade.* **Description:** Contains information and insight on e-business technology and trends of interest to technology management executives.
Published by: InfoWorld Media Group (Subsidiary of: I D G Communications), 501 Second St, San Francisco, CA 94107. TEL 415-243-4344, 800-227-8365, FAX 415-978-3120, http://www.infoworld.com/cto/cto_magazine.html. Ed. Michael Vizard. Adv. contact Steve Martin.

004.16 VEN
C W CANALES. (Computer World) Text in Spanish. q. adv. **Document type:** *Magazine, Trade.* **Description:** Provides resellers, VARs, consultants, network and systems integrators, dealers, OEMs, retailers, mass merchants, wholesalers, distributors, manufacturers and other influential channel decision makers with knowledge and insights into the technology and general marketing dynamics that will help them manage and grow their businesses.
Related titles: Online - full text ed.
Published by: I D G Comunicaciones C.A., A.P. 61080 Chacao, Caracas, 1060-A, Venezuela. TEL 58-212-793-9262, FAX 58-212-793-7384, idg@idg.com.ve, http://www.cwv.com.ve/canales, http://www.cwvlatin.com. adv.: B&W page USD 2,300, color page USD 3,450; trim 266 x 370. Circ: 6,200 (controlled).

338.47004 GBR
CE B I T NEWS. Text in English. 1986. 3/yr. adv. bk.rev.; software rev. charts; stat.; tr.lit. 140 p./no. 4 cols./p.; **Document type:** *Trade.*
Published by: Portman Communications Ltd., 52 Foundling Ct, London, WC1N 1AN, United Kingdom. TEL 44-171-837-0815, FAX 44-171-278-9917. Ed. Philip Gallagher. Pub., R&P, Adv. contact Jim Charos. B&W page USD 11,125, color page USD 12,370; trim 11.88 x 8.88. Circ: 50,000 (controlled).

338.47004 USA ISSN 1529-6903
CERTIFICATION MAGAZINE. Text in English. 1999. bi-m. adv. **Document type:** *Magazine, Trade.* **Description:** Provides IT professionals interested in technical certifications with the most comprehensive resources for news, information and opinion.
Related titles: Online - full text ed.: (from EBSCO Publishing).
Indexed: MicrocompInd.
Published by: MediaTec Publishing, Inc., 444 N Michigan Ave, Chicago, IL 60611. TEL 312-828-2800, editor@certmag.com, http://www.certmag.com. Pub. Norman B Kamikow.

C

338.47004 USA
CERTIFICATION NEWS. Text in English. 1975. q. USD 50. **Document type:** *Newsletter, Consumer.* **Description:** Offers updated information pertinent to the computer industry and international certification.
Published by: Institute for Certification of Computing Professionals, 2350 E. Devon Ave., Ste. 115, Des Plaines, IL 60018-4610. TEL 847-299-4227, FAX 847-299-4280, 74040,3722@compuserve.com, http://www.iccp.org. Ed. Cristi Herron. Circ: 25,000 (controlled).

338.47004 USA ISSN 1045-2990
CHANNELMARKER LETTER✶. Text in English. 1989. m. USD 499; USD 599 foreign (effective 1997). index, cum index: vols.1-7. back issues avail. **Document type:** *Newsletter.*
Published by: Merrin Information Services, Inc., 560 Los Nidos Drive, Santa Fe, NM 8750-8356. TEL 415-493-5050, FAX 415-493-5480. Ed. Terry Walton. Pub. Seymour Merrin.

338 GBR ISSN 1474-1725
CH@NNEL. Text in English. 2000. m. GBP 40 (effective 2002). adv. **Document type:** *Magazine, Trade.* **Description:** Covers and comments on trends within the IT solutions and services industry while reporting on the issues facing traditional VAR's systems integrators and network resellers.
Formed by the merger of (1990-2000): V A R (0960-8427); (199?-2000): Network Reseller Magazine (1461-8885)
Published by: Reed Business Information Ltd. (Subsidiary of: Reed Business), Quadrant House, The Quadrant, Brighton Rd, Sutton, Surrey SM2 5AS, United Kingdom. TEL 44-20-8652-4021, FAX 44-208-652-8977, http://www.reedinfo.co.uk/. Ed. Dominic Turnbull. Adv. contact Shaun Barton.

338.47004 JPN
COMLINE: COMPUTER INDUSTRY OF JAPAN. Text in English. irreg. **Document type:** *Trade.*
Media: Online - full content.
Published by: O D S Corp., Kuyo Bldg, 5-10-5 Minami-Aoyama, Minato-ku, Tokyo, 107, Japan. TEL 81-3-3486-2676, http://www.ods.co.jp/. **Dist. by:** COMLINE International Corp., 10601 South DeAnza Blvd Ste 216, Cupertino, CA 95014. TEL 408-257-9956.

338 CHN
COMPUTER BUSINESS NEWS CHINA. Text in Chinese. 1998. w. adv. **Document type:** *Newspaper, Trade.* **Description:** Focuses on the commercial channels and purchasing customers of the information technology industry.
Published by: I D G China, Rm. 616, Tower A, COFCO Plaza, Jianguomennei Dajie, Beijing, 100005 , China. TEL 86-10-6526-0959, FAX 86-10-6526-0866, dumin@idg.com.cn, http://www.idgchina.com. adv.: B&W page USD 3,480, color page USD 3,980; trim 260 x 375. Circ: 95,000 (paid and controlled).

338.47004 GBR ISSN 1350-4665
T58.64
COMPUTER BUSINESS REVIEW. Text in English. 1993. m. GBP 75 domestic; GBP 125 in Europe (effective 2003). bk.rev. back issues avail. **Document type:** *Trade.* **Description:** Examines the business side of the computer industry in depth. Analyzes corporate and market strategies, financial performances, M & A activities and other trends.
Related titles: Online - full text ed.: GBP 100 (effective 2003) (from Gale Group, Northern Light Technology, Inc., O C L C Online Computer Library Center, Inc.).
Indexed: B&I, C&CSA, Inspec.
—BLDSC (3393.770200), AskIEEE, IE, ingenta.
Published by: ComputerWire Plc., 12 Sutton Row, London, W1V 5FH, United Kingdom. TEL 44-171-208-4200, FAX 44-171-439-1105, cbred@computerwire.com, http://www.cbronline.com/cbr.nsf/home, http:// www.computerwire.com. Ed. Joanna Mancey. Pub., R&P Peter White. Adv. contact Bill Hammond.

COMPUTER BUYER; what to buy - how to buy it. see *COMPUTERS—Personal Computers*

338.47004 USA ISSN 1090-7602
COMPUTER CURRENTS. BOSTON. Text in English. 1987. m. USD 19.95 (effective 1999). adv. software rev. illus. **Document type:** *Trade.* **Description:** Directed to business and personal users of microcomputers in the Boston area.
Formerly: Boston Computer Currents (0897-9324)
Related titles: Online - full text ed.
Published by: ComputerUser.com, Inc., 1563 Solano Ave, Berkeley, CA 94707-2116. TEL 510-527-0333, 800-365-7773, FAX 510-527-4106, editorial@computercurrrents.com, http://www.computercurrents.com, http:// www.computeruser.com. Pub., Adv. contact Stan Politi.

338.47004 USA ISSN 1097-8461
COMPUTER CURRENTS. CHICAGO. Text in English. 1997. m. USD 19.95 (effective 1999). adv. software rev. illus. **Document type:** *Trade.* **Description:** Dedicated to personal and professional users of computers in the Chicago metropolitan area.
Published by: ComputerUser.com, Inc., 1563 Solano Ave, Berkeley, CA 94707-2116. TEL 510-527-0333, 800-365-7773, FAX 510-527-4106, editorial@computercurrents.com, http://www.computercurrents.com, http:// www.computeruser.com. Pub., Adv. contact Stan Politi.

338.47004 USA ISSN 1097-847X
COMPUTER CURRENTS. DALLAS - FT. WORTH. Text in English. 1987. m. USD 19.95 (effective 1999). adv. bk.rev.; film rev.; software rev. charts. back issues avail. **Document type:** *Trade.* **Description:** Directed to business and professional personal computer users for the Dallas - Ft. Worth area.
Formerly (until 1988): Texas Computing
Related titles: Microfiche ed.; Online - full text ed.
Published by: ComputerUser.com, Inc., 1563 Solano Ave, Berkeley, CA 94707-2116. TEL 510-527-0333, 800-365-7773, FAX 510-527-4106, editorial@computercurrents.com, http://www.computercurrents.com, http:// www.computeruser.com. Pub., Adv. contact Stan Politi. Circ: 70,000.

338.47004 USA ISSN 1097-8453
COMPUTER CURRENTS. HOUSTON. Text in English. 1989. m. USD 19.95 (effective 1999). adv. software rev. illus. **Document type:** *Trade.* **Description:** Covers news, issues and trends in personal computers for professional users and laypersons in the metropolitan Houston area.
Published by: ComputerUser.com, Inc., 1563 Solano Ave, Berkeley, CA 94707-2116. TEL 510-527-0333, 800-365-7773, FAX 510-527-4106, edit@compcurr.com, http:// www.computercurrents.com, http://www.computeruser.com. Pub., Adv. contact Stan Politi.

338.47004 USA
COMPUTER CURRENTS. NORTHERN CALIFORNIA. Text in English. bi-w. USD 29.95 (effective 1999). adv. software rev. illus. **Document type:** *Trade.* **Description:** Covers news and events for personal and professional computer users in northern California.
Former titles: Computer Currents. Bay Area (1090-7572); Bay Area Computer Currents (8756-0046)
Related titles: Microfiche ed.: (from PQC); Online - full text ed.: (from Gale Group).
Indexed: SoftBase.
Published by: ComputerUser.com, Inc., 1563 Solano Ave, Berkeley, CA 94707-2116. TEL 510-527-0333, 800-365-7773, FAX 510-527-4106, editorial@computercurrents.com, http://www.computercurrents.com, http:// www.computeruser.com. Pub., Adv. contact Stan Politi.

338.47004 USA ISSN 1090-7599
COMPUTER CURRENTS. SOUTHERN CALIFORNIA. Text in English. m. USD 19.95 (effective 1999). adv. **Document type:** *Trade.* **Description:** Dedicated to personal and professional users of microcomputers in the greater Los Angeles and southern California region.
Formerly: Computer Currents. Los Angeles (0897-9308)
Published by: ComputerUser.com, Inc., 1563 Solano Ave, Berkeley, CA 94707-2116. TEL 510-527-0333, 800-365-7773, FAX 510-527-4106, editorial@computercurrents.com, http://www.computercurrents.com, http:// www.computeruser.com. Pub., Adv. contact Stan Politi.

338.47004 USA
COMPUTER ENTREPRENEUR. Text in English. 1983. m. USD 36. adv. bk.rev.
Published by: Computer Entrepreneur Publishing Company, PO Box 456, Grand Central Sta, New York, NY 10163. Ed. Richard Holt. Circ: 10,000.

338.47004 USA
COMPUTER INDUSTRY DAILY. Text in English. 1994. d. USD 495 (effective 1998). **Document type:** *Bulletin.* **Description:** Delivers daily news briefs on the latest technologies, vendor announcements, vendor strategies, and industry trends.
Media: Online - full text. **Related titles:** Diskette ed.
Published by: Computer Economics, Inc., 2082 Business Center Dr., Ste 240, Irvine, CA 92612. TEL 949-831-8700, FAX 949-442-7688, info@compecon.com, http:// www.computereconomics.com. Ed. Anne Zalatan.

338 NZL ISSN 1172-0220
COMPUTER INDUSTRY DIRECTORY NEW ZEALAND. Variant title: Computerworld Computer Industry Directory New Zealand. Text in English. 1993. a. adv. **Document type:** *Directory, Trade.* **Description:** Provides a source of business information for computer and communication product buyers.
Published by: I D G Communications Ltd., Wellesley St., PO Box 6813, Auckland, 1036, New Zealand. TEL 64-9-377-9902, FAX 64-9-377-4604, idg@idg.co.nz, http://www.idg.net.nz. adv.: B&W page USD 791, color page USD 1,041; trim 205 x 275. Circ: 9,000 (paid and controlled).

338.47004 USA
COMPUTER INDUSTRY WEEK✱. Text in English. w.
Published by: Insight in Action, 15845 Cumberland Dr, Poway, CA 92064-2346. TEL 503-697-1136, FAX 503-638-7799. Ed. Tom Clarkson.

343.73 DEU
COMPUTER LAW REVIEW INTERNATIONAL; a journal of information law and technology. Text in English. bi-m. EUR 149; EUR 28 newsstand/cover (effective 2005). adv. **Document type:** *Magazine, Trade.* **Description:** Presents and discusses the essential developments in computer, telecommunications and media law worldwide.
Formerly (until 2000): Computer und Recht International
Related titles: Online - full text ed.
—BLDSC (3394.075820).
Published by: Verlag Dr. Otto Schmidt KG, Gustav-Heinemann-Ufer 58, Cologne, 50968, Germany. TEL 49-221-93738460, FAX 49-221-93738943, cr-international@otto-schmidt.de, info@otto-schmidt.de, http://www.cr-international.com/ home.html, http://www.otto-schmidt.de. adv.: color page EUR 1,671, B&W page EUR 955.

338.47004 UAE ISSN 0964-5861
COMPUTER NEWS MIDDLE EAST/AKHBAR AL-HISAB AL-ALI AL-SHARQ AL-AWSAT. Text in Arabic, English, Persian, Modern. 1991. m. USD 150 (effective 2002). adv. software rev. back issues avail. **Document type:** *Magazine, Trade.* **Description:** Aimed at the Middle East corporate computing market. Reviews hardware and software, contains company profiles, and features articles on technology and market developments for MIS professionals, agents and distributors, and public- and private-sector decision makers.
Related titles: Online - full text ed.
Published by: Corporate Publishing International, PO Box 13700, Dubai, United Arab Emirates. TEL 971-4-351-5316, FAX 971-4-359-8486, cpi@emirates.net.ae, http:// www.compnewsme.com, http://www.cpilive.net. adv.: B&W page USD 4,500, color page USD 5,000; trim 235 x 330. Circ: 10,240.

338.47004 USA
COMPUTER OPERATIONS MANAGEMENT COMMUNIQUE. Text in English. 1987. bi-m. USD 155. **Document type:** *Newsletter.* **Description:** Provides data processing industry news, hardware and software product announcements, and AFCOM news.
Published by: (Association for Computer Operations Management), D C M S, Inc., 742 E Chapman Ave, Orange, CA 92666. TEL 714-997-9743, FAX 714-997-9743. Ed. John J Adams. Circ: 2,600 (paid).

338.47004 USA ISSN 0886-0556
QA76.5
COMPUTER SHOPPER; the computer magazine for direct buyers. Text in English. 1979. m. USD 19.99 (effective 2005). adv. bk.rev. charts; illus. reprints avail. **Document type:** *Magazine, Consumer.* **Description:** For individuals and companies interested in buying, reselling and using computer hardware, software and peripherals. Articles offer information on popular models of computers, software, new products, club news, network news and magazine reviews.
Related titles: Online - full text ed.: (from Florida Center for Library Automation, Gale Group).
Indexed: CompD, CompI, LRI, MicrocompInd, PCR2, SoftBase.
—BLDSC (3394.275280), IE. **CCC.**
Published by: Ziff Davis Media Inc., 28 E 28th St, New York, NY 10016-7930. TEL 212-472-4000, 800-999-7476, FAX 902-563-4807, http://shopper.cnet.com/4002-7409_9-5510693.html. Ed. Janice J Chen. adv.: B&W page USD 17,690, color page USD 21,980. Circ: 500,000 (paid). **Dist. in UK by:** Seymour Distribution Ltd, 86 Newman St, London W1T 3EX, United Kingdom. TEL 44-20-73968000, FAX 44-20-73968002.

338.470 GBR
COMPUTER SHOPPER.CO.UK. Text in English. 1988. m. GBP 23.97 domestic; GBP 95 in Europe; GBP 110 elsewhere (effective 2003). adv. **Document type:** *Magazine, Consumer.*
Incorporates: Internet Shopper; Software Shopper; Portable Shopper; P C Shopper; Mobile Shopper; Games Shopper; Formerly: Computer Shopper (0955-8578)
Related titles: CD-ROM ed.: Computer Shopper (CD-ROM Edition). ISSN 1357-0846. 1995; Online - full text ed.
—BLDSC (3394.275282). **CCC.**
Published by: Dennis Publishing Ltd., 30 Cleveland St, London, W1P 5FF, United Kingdom. TEL 44-20-79076000, editorial.shopper@dennis.co.uk, http:// www.computershopper.co.uk/. Ed. Jeremy Spencer. Adv. contact Mike Shepherd. Circ: 171,105 (paid).

338 DEU
COMPUTER TRADE/HANDEL MIT COMPUTERN. Text in English, German. q. EUR 40 (effective 2001). adv. **Document type:** *Magazine, Trade.*
Published by: Zeitungs- und Zeitschriftenverlag Heinrichs, Brueggekamp 1, Barsinghausen, 30890, Germany. TEL 49-5105-2289. Ed., Pub. Gerhard Heinrichs.

338 GBR ISSN 1463-3906
COMPUTER TRADE SHOPPER. Text in English. 1998. fortn. GBP 25 domestic; USD 38 elsewhere (effective 2002). adv. **Document type:** *Trade.* **Description:** Keeps resellers, VARs, integrators and distributors who assemble PCs and systems up-to-date with the best selling products in the market, who stocks them, and at what price.
Related titles: Online - full text ed.: (from Gale Group, ProQuest Information & Learning).
Indexed: CompD.
—**CCC.**
Published by: Reed Business Information Ltd. (Subsidiary of: Reed Business), Quadrant House, The Quadrant, Brighton Rd, Sutton, Surrey SM2 5AS, United Kingdom. TEL 44-208-652-3500, http://www.reedinfo.co.uk/. Eds. Joe Fay TEL 44-20-8652-2069, Nick Booth. Adv. contact Paddy Lynch TEL 44-20-8652-2052. color page USD 2,263; trim 284 x 384. Circ: 16,000 (paid and controlled). **Subscr. to:** Quadrant Subscription Services, PO Box 302, Haywards Heath, W Sussex RH16 3YY, United Kingdom. TEL 44-1444-445566, FAX 44-1444-445447.

343.0999 DEU ISSN 0179-1990
KK164.C66 CODEN: CRECE3
COMPUTER UND RECHT; Forum fuer die Praxis des Rechts der Datenverarbeitung, Kommunikation und Automation. Text in German. 1986. m. EUR 309; EUR 30.90 newsstand/cover (effective 2005). adv. index. reprints avail. **Document type:** *Magazine, Trade.*
Incorporates (in 1989): Informatik und Recht (0179-0463); Which was formerly (1972-1986): Datenverarbeitung im Recht (0301-2980)
Indexed: ELLIS, FLP, IBR, IBZ, Inspec.
—AskIEEE, IE, Infotrieve. **CCC.**
Published by: (Graefe und Partner Verlagsgesellschaft mbH), Verlag Dr. Otto Schmidt KG, Gustav-Heinemann-Ufer 58, Cologne, 50968, Germany. TEL 49-221-93738460, FAX 49-221-93738943, info@otto-schmidt.de, http:// www.computerundrecht.de, http://www.otto-schmidt.de. adv.: B&W page EUR 1,450, color page EUR 2,537.50. Circ: 2,292 (paid and controlled).

338.47004 USA
COMPUTERCREDIBLE MAGAZINE. Text in English. 1995. m.
Published by: Assimilations, Inc., 1249 W Jordan River Dr., South Jordan, UT 84095-8250. TEL 801-254-5432, FAX 801-253-0914, computer@credible.com, http:// www.computer.com. Ed. Rick Simi. Circ: 35,000.

338 DEU
DER COMPUTERHANDEL. Text in German. q. EUR 40 (effective 2001). adv. **Document type:** *Magazine, Trade.*
Published by: Zeitungs- und Zeitschriftenverlag Heinrichs, Brueggekamp 1, Barsinghausen, 30890, Germany. TEL 49-5105-2289. Ed., Pub. Gerhard Heinrichs.

338 DEU
COMPUTERPARTNER. Text in German. 1996. w. adv. **Document type:** *Magazine, Trade.* **Description:** Provides its readers with up-to-date news and reports about IT trends and the newest developments on the market.
Related titles: Online - full text ed.
Published by: I D G Communications Verlag AG, Brabanter Str 4, Munich, 80805, Germany. TEL 49-89-36086299, FAX 49-89-36086325, online@computerpartner.de, info@idg-verlag.de, http://www.computerpartner.de, http://www.idg-verlag.de. Ed. Damian Sicking. adv.: color page EUR 9,650; trim 235 x 315. Circ: 35,965 (controlled).

338 IRL
COMPUTERSCOPE CHANNELS; the magazine for ireland's computer industry. Text in English. 2001. 2/yr. free to qualified personnel. adv. **Document type:** *Magazine, Trade.*
Description: Covers trends and technologies that will have the greatest impact on personal computing for business and home use in Ireland.
Published by: Scope Communications Ltd., Prospect House, 3 Prospect Rd., Glasnevin, Dublin, 9, Ireland. TEL 353-1-8824407, FAX 353-1-8300888, info@scope.ie, http://www.channels.ie, http://www.techcentral.ie. Ed. Gordon Smith. Pub. Frank Quinn. R&P, Adv. contact Brenda Smith. page EUR 2,920.

338.47004 USA ISSN 1533-5585
COMPUTERUSER TWIN CITIES. (Regional editions avail.: Atlanta, Boston, Chicago, Dallas-Ft. Worth, Houston, Los Angeles, San Francisco, New York, Philadelphia, Baltimore, Washington D.C., Minneapolis, Detroit, Columbus, Kansas City) Text in English. 1983. m. USD 24.99 (effective 2005). adv. bk.rev.; software rev. illus. back issues avail.; reprints avail. **Document type:** *Magazine, Trade.* **Description:** Directed to personal and professional computer users in major metropolitan areas.
Formerly (until 199?): Computer User (0742-5902)
Related titles: Online - full text ed.: (from Gale Group).
Indexed: CompD.
Published by: ComputerUser.com, Inc., 220 S. 6th St, Ste 500, Minneapolis, MN 55402. TEL 612-336-9279, FAX 612-339-5806, editorial@computercurrents.com, http://www.computeruser.com. Ed. James Mathewson. adv.: B&W page USD 36,900; trim 10 x 12. Circ: 900,000.

338.47004 BGR ISSN 1311-2171
COMPUTERWORLD. Text in Bulgarian. 48/yr. USD 160 foreign (effective 2002). adv. **Document type:** *Newspaper, Consumer.*
Description: Provides executives, managers and professionals with national and international business oriented information.
Related titles: Online - full text ed.: (from Northern Light Technology, Inc.); ♦ Supplement(s): NetworkWorld Bulgaria. ISSN 1311-3151.
Published by: I D G Bulgaria Ltd., 1 Hristo Smirnenski blvd, etazh 11, Sofia, 1421, Bulgaria. TEL 359-2-9630886, FAX 359-2-9632841, idg@mbox.digsys.bg, http://www.idg.bg. Ed. Vladimir Vladkov. Pub. Tatiana Hinova. Adv. contact Yanka Petrouska. B&W page USD 1,590, color page USD 2,200; 280 x 380. Circ: 8,500 (paid and controlled).

338 DNK
COMPUTERWORLD DENMARK ANNUAL. Text in Danish. 1992. a. adv. **Document type:** *Directory, Trade.* **Description:** Contains information on managerial level position changes, IT scandals, and trends in technology, telecommunications, and e-commerce.
Published by: I D G Danmark A-S, Carl Jacobsens Vej 25, Valby, 2500, Denmark. TEL 45-77-30-03-00, FAX 45-77-30-03-02, idg@idg.dk, http://www.idg.dk. adv.: B&W page USD 4,196, color page USD 5,320; trim 266 x 365. Circ: 30,000 (paid and controlled).

338.47004 HKG ISSN 1023-4934
COMPUTERWORLD HONG KONG. Text in English. 1984. w. HKD 200; USD 122 in Asia; USD 180 elsewhere (effective 2000). adv. bk.rev. back issues avail.; reprints avail.
Document type: *Magazine, Trade.* **Description:** Provides information for technical professionals throughout Hong Kong and Asia.
Related titles: Online - full text ed.
Published by: I D G Communications (HK) Ltd., Ste. 1701, K WAH Center, 191 Java Rd, North Point, Hong Kong, Hong Kong. TEL 852-2861-3238, FAX 852-2861-0953, infohk@idg.com.hk, http://www.cw.com.hk, http://www.idg.com.hk. Ed. Don Tennant. Pub. Melvyn Bennett. R&P Karman Cheng. Adv. contact Vera Chan. B&W page HKD 39,100, color page HKD 47,600; trim 292 x 407. Circ: 11,800 (controlled).

338.47004 MYS
COMPUTERWORLD MALAYSIA. Text in English. 1984. m. adv.
Document type: *Magazine, Trade.* **Description:** Covers the latest trends and technologies for information services management, professionals, industry consultants and vendors working in Malaysia.
Related titles: Online - full text ed.
Published by: I D G Communications (S) Pte. Ltd., Unit 612, Block A, Kelana Business Centre, 97 Jalan SS7/2 Kelana Jaya, Selangor Darul Ehsan, Petaling Jaya, 47301, Malaysia. TEL 60-03-7043692, FAX 60-03-7044026, http://www.computerworld.com.my. Ed. Justin Then. Pub. Choong Chau Sim. Adv. contact Jimmy Yu. B&W page USD 1,565, color page USD 1,941; trim 260 x 345. Circ: 8,434 (paid).

338 NOR ISSN 1501-6595
COMPUTERWORLD NORWAY. Text in Norwegian. 1983. 2/w. NOK 1,188 (effective 2002). adv. **Document type:** *Newspaper, Trade.*
Formerly (until 1998): Computerworld Norge (0800-5966)
Related titles: Online - full text ed.: ISSN 1501-6609.
Published by: I D G Communications Norge, PO Box 9090, Gronland, Oslo, 0133, Norway. TEL 47-22-053000, FAX 47-22-053001, http://web1.computerworld.no, http://www.idg.no. adv.: color page USD 6,256; trim 280 x 398. Circ: 26,000 (paid).

338 PAK
COMPUTERWORLD PAKISTAN. Text in English. 1995. fortn. PKR 800 (effective 2002). adv. **Document type:** *Magazine, Trade.* **Description:** Contains coverage of the latest developments worldwide in computer hardware, software, internet, networking, product reviews, computer careers, viewpoints, and market trends.
Related titles: Online - full text ed.
Published by: OMAG Enterprises, 1st Fl., Lotia Bldg., Club Rd., Karachi, 75530, Pakistan. TEL 92-21-568-6368, FAX 92-21-568-0384, info@pakworld.com, http://www.pakworld.com/cw. adv.: B&W page PKR 24,360, color page PKR 36,540; bleed 270 x 342. Circ: 5,000 (paid).

COMPUTRADE INTERNATIONAL. see *BUSINESS AND ECONOMICS*

004 USA CODEN: PEMZES
CONFERENCE ANALYSIS IN-DEPTH REPORTS ON LEADING IT CONFERENCES. Text in English. 1989. irreg. **Document type:** *Newsletter, Trade.*
Formerly: The Computer Conference Analysis Newsletter (1071-2216)
Related titles: Online - full text ed.: (from EBSCO Publishing).
Indexed: CompD.
Published by: Giga Information Group, 400 Technology Sq, Cambridge, MA 02139. TEL 617-613-5731, http://www.gigaweb.com/.

338.47004 330 BEL ISSN 1378-5079
[CORPORATE] SOLUTIONS. Text in Flemish. 1992. bi-m.
Former titles (until 2002): C M Corporate.net (1377-0020); (until 2000): C M Corporate (0779-1828)
Related titles: French ed.: ISSN 1378-5060.
Published by: V N U Business Publications (Belgium), Hulstlaan 42, Brussels, 1170, Belgium. http://www.vnunet.be/corporatesolutions.

338.47004 USA ISSN 1542-1376
QA76.9.M3
DATA CENTER MANAGEMENT. Abbreviated title: D C M. Text in English. 1981. bi-m. USD 184 domestic; USD 204 in Canada; USD 236 elsewhere (effective 2002). adv. **Document type:** *Trade.* **Description:** Contains articles addressing technical and management issues for managers of integrated mainframe, midrange and client-server data center environments.
Former titles (until 2002): Enterprise Management Issues (1542-1384); (until 1997): Computer Operations Manager (1061-1401)
Indexed: CompLI.
Published by: (Association for Computer Operations Management), Atwood Publishing, LLC (Subsidiary of: Gem Communications), 380 Wright Rd, PO Box 400, Norwalk, IA 50211. TEL 913-469-1110, FAX 913-469-0806, http://www.atwood.com. Adv. contact Tom Bauchard. Circ: 4,000.

338.47004 NLD ISSN 0167-9759
DATA-INFO; nieuwsbrief voor de automatisering. Text in Dutch. 1990. 20/yr. USD 160 elsewhere (effective 2000). back issues avail. **Document type:** *Newsletter, Trade.* **Description:** Contains news, analysis, and commentary dealing with and oriented toward the IT industry.
Related titles: CD-ROM ed.: Mark.It.
Published by: Marketons BV, Postbus 1310, Nijmegen, 6501 BH, Netherlands. TEL 31-24-322-4200, FAX 31-24-360-3176, redactie@marketons.nl, http://www.marketons.nl/producten/datainfo. Ed., Pub., R&P Willem J Veldkamp. Circ: 1,500 (paid).

338 PRT
DEALER WORLD PORTUGAL. Text in Portuguese. 1996. 11/yr. adv. **Document type:** *Magazine, Trade.* **Description:** Provides analysis of major market trends, revealing the strategies of the major manufacturers and distributors, and presents product news and practical answers in areas of interest to distribution managers.
Published by: Edicoes Expansao Economica Lda., Rue Mario Castelhano, 40-1, Queluz de Baixo, Barcarena, 2749-502, Portugal. TEL 351-21-496-95-40, FAX 351-21-436-95-39, webmaster@expansao.iol.pt, http://www.expansao.iol.pt. adv.: color page USD 1,644; trim 210 x 297. Circ: 5,000 (paid and controlled).

338 ESP ISSN 1135-3805
DEALER WORLD SPAIN. Text in Spanish. 1995. m. free to qualified personnel. adv. **Document type:** *Magazine, Trade.*
Description: Contains information for professionals working within IT distribution channels.
Related titles: Online - full text ed.
Published by: I D G Communications, Fortuny, 18 4, Madrid, 28010, Spain. TEL 34-91-3496600, FAX 34-91-3496100, dealer@idg.es, http://www.idg.es/dealer. Ed. Juan Ramon Melara. Adv. contact Yolanda Martinez TEL 34-91-3496684. color page USD 1,819; trim 210 x 280. Circ: 13,826 (controlled).

DIRECTIONS ON MICROSOFT; the independent view of Microsoft technology & strategy. see *COMPUTERS—Software*

338 FRA ISSN 0757-309X
DISTRIBUTIQUE. Text in French. 1983. w. (42/yr.). EUR 50 (effective 2005). adv. **Document type:** *Magazine, Trade.*
Description: Analyzes the main trends of the market, exposes the strategies of the major manufacturers, presents a panorama of commercial offers for each category of products and brings practical answers in all the areas of interest to distribution managers.
Related titles: Online - full text ed.; Supplement(s): Les Guides des Grossistes Informatiques. ISSN 1261-9086. 1995.
Published by: I D G Communications France, 5 rue Chantecoq, Puteaux, 92808, France. TEL 33-1-4197-6161, FAX 33-1-4197-6160, http://www.distributique.com/, http://www.idg.fr. Ed. Frabrice Alessi. Pub., R&P Gerard Adamis. Adv. contact Sylvie Neuhoff. color page USD 4,157; trim 230 x 300. Circ: 21,000.

338.47004 CHE
E C M A MEMENTO. Text in English. a. free. **Document type:** *Academic/Scholarly.* **Description:** Covers standardization information and communication systems.
Formerly: E C M A Technical Report
Related titles: CD-ROM ed.; Online - full text ed.
—BLDSC (3648.101500).
Published by: European Computer Manufacturers Association, 114 Rue du Rhone, Geneva, 1204, Switzerland. TEL 41-22-8496000, FAX 41-22-8496001, helpdesk@ecma.ch, http://www.ecma.ch. Ed. Jan W van den Beld.

EUROPEAN SERVICES INDUSTRY. see *BUSINESS AND ECONOMICS—Production Of Goods And Services*

338 CAN ISSN 1180-3711
CODEN: EIDRE2
EVANS REPORT. Text in English. 1971. 25/yr. looseleaf. CND 15,000. index, cum.index every 3 yrs. **Document type:** *Trade.*
Description: Focuses on key market statistics and trends in the Canadian information technology market.
Formerly: E D P In-Depth Reports (0315-3819)
Related titles: Microfiche ed.; Online - full text ed.
Indexed: CompC, CompLI, Inspec.
—AskIEEE. **CCC.**
Published by: Evans Research Corporation of Canada, 1 Eva Rd, Ste 309, Etobicoke, ON M9C 4Z5, Canada. TEL 416-621-8814, FAX 416-621-8031, http://www.evansresearch.com. Ed. Bill Fournier. Circ: 700.

338.47004 USA
TK5101.A1 CODEN: ASOCF5
FORBES - ANDREW SEYBOLD'S WIRELESS OUTLOOK; a monthly perspective of issues affecting the mobile computer and communications industries. Text in English. 1981. m. USD 299 (effective 2001). bk.rev. **Document type:** *Magazine, Trade.* **Description:** Newsletter for and about the mobile computer industry, with emphasis on data communications, including wireless technologies. Provides in-depth, hands-on evaluations, technology tutorials and analyses.
Former titles (until 2000): Andrew Seybold's Outlook (1095-2551); (until June 1997): Andrew Seybold's Outlook on Communications and Computing (1080-4056); Which was formed by the 1995 merger of: Andrew Seybold's Outlook on Mobile Computing (1066-8845); Andrew Seybold's Outlook on Professional Computing (0895-3821); Which was formerly (until 1987): Seybold Outlook on Professional Computing (0887-5758); (until May 1986): Seybold Report on Professional Computing (0736-5314)
Related titles: Online - full text ed.: USD 249 (effective 1999) (from Gale Group).
Indexed: CMCI, CompB, CompC, CompD, Inspec.
—AskIEEE, IE.
Published by: Andrew Seybold's Outlook, Inc., 980 A University Ave, Los Gatos, CA 95032. TEL 408-354-7900, FAX 408-354-7980, http://www.andyseybold.com/index.htm. Ed., Pub. Andrew M Seybold. R&P Linda M Seybold. Circ: 2,500 (paid). **Subscr. in Japan to:** Takashi Kimura, TPI J Net Corp, Schon Lebrn Yoshida 203, 3-9-15 Nishi-Gotanda, Shinagawa-ku, Tokyo 141-0031, Japan. TEL 81-3-3492-1341, 81-3-3492-0760.

338 DEU ISSN 1433-7924
FREIBERUFLER INFO. Text in German. 1997. bi-m. EUR 36 domestic; EUR 38 foreign; EUR 8 newsstand/cover (effective 2002). adv. **Document type:** *Magazine, Trade.* **Description:** Aimed at independent professionals from the information technology and communications industry, consultants and freelancers in the new economy.
Related titles: Online - full text ed.

C

▼ new title ➤ refereed ✶ unverified ♦ full entry avail.

Published by: Computerwoche Verlag GmbH, Brabanter Str 4, Munich, 80805, Germany. TEL 49-89-360860, FAX 49-89-36086118, http://www.freiberufler.de. Ed. Wolf-Dietrich Lorenz. Adv. contact Inge Schmid. B&W page USD 2,088, color page USD 2,291; trim 184 x 258. Circ: 4,316 (controlled).

338.47004 ESP ISSN 1138-8218
GRAN CUENTA; informatica y comunicaciones para la empresa. Abbreviated title: G C. Text in Spanish. 1997. m. adv. back issues avail. **Document type:** *Trade.*
Published by: Kunzer International, rancisco Sancha, 4 2o. Fl, Madrid, 28034, Spain. TEL 34-91-729-0444, FAX 34-91-729-3090, pvd@pvd.com, http://www.pvd.com. Ed. Gemma Sahagun. Pub. Javier Moreno Lago. R&P Javier Moreno. Adv. contact Paul Brazell. B&W page USD 1,480, color page USD 1,900; trim 285 x 210.

338.47004 USA
I D C JAPAN REPORT. Text in English. 1974. m. looseleaf. USD 495 domestic; USD 535 foreign (effective 2005). adv. back issues avail. **Document type:** *Magazine.* **Description:** News and information on the fast-paced Japanese information technology market.
Formerly (until April 1989): E D P Japan Report
Related titles: Online - full text ed.
Published by: International Data Corporation, 5 Speen St, Framingham, MA 01701. TEL 508-872-8200, FAX 508-935-4015, http://www.idcresearch.com. Ed. Yugi Ogino.

338.47004 DEU
I D G NEWSLINE; newsletter for the German computer market. Text in English. q. **Document type:** *Newsletter.*
Published by: I D G Communications Verlag AG, Rheinstr 28, Munich, 80803, Germany. TEL 089-36086-0, FAX 089-36086325.

C

338 IND
I S COMPUTERWORLD INDIA. Text in English. fortn. adv. **Document type:** *Magazine, Trade.* **Description:** Provides the Indian market with coverage of native IS management-related issues, technology solutions, product availability and pricing information.
Published by: Technology Media Group Pvt. Ltd., No. 3540, Hal II Stage, Indiranagar, Bangalore, 560 038, India. TEL 91-80-521-0309, FAX 91-80-521-0362, click@tmgpower.com, http://www.tmgpower.com. adv.: color page USD 1,500; trim 200 x 265. Circ: 30,000 (paid and controlled).

338 DNK
I T BRANCHEN TOP 100. (Information Technology) Text in Danish. a. adv. **Document type:** *Magazine, Trade.* **Description:** Contains analyses, evaluations, trends, interviews, and articles on the top IT companies in Denmark.
Published by: I D G Danmark A-S, Carl Jacobsens Vej 25, Valby, 2500, Denmark. TEL 45-77-30-03-00, FAX 45-77-30-03-02, idg@idg.dk, http://www.idg.dk. adv.: page DKK 28,850; trim 189 x 277. Circ: 42,000 (controlled).

381.45004 NOR ISSN 1500-9920
I T BRANSJEN. Text in Norwegian. 1997. 11/yr. adv. **Document type:** *Magazine, Trade.* **Description:** Contains news and analysis from the local and international IT markets, information on the latest market trends, updates about product launches and successful marketing stories, creative sales tips and business advice.
Published by: I D G Communications Norge, PO Box 9090, Gronland, Oslo, 0133, Norway. TEL 47-22-053000, FAX 47-22-053001, http://www.idg.no. adv.: B&W page USD 3,823, color page USD 4,611; trim 210 x 297. Circ: 9,500 (paid and controlled).

338.47004 USA ISSN 1538-5930
I T CONTRACTOR; the business magazine for contractors and consultants. Text in English. 2001. bi-m. free to qualified personnel. adv. **Document type:** *Magazine, Trade.* **Description:** Contains the latest news, information, advice and resources for starting out and ssurviving in the expanding contracting and consulting markets.
Published by: MediaTec Publishing, Inc., 444 N Michigan Ave, Chicago, IL 60611. TEL 312-828-2800, editor@itcmagazine.com, http://www.itcmagazine.com. Ed., Pub. Norman B Kamikow. Adv. contact John Taggart.

338 NZL
I T CONTRACTORS HANDBOOK. (Information Technology) Text in English. 2000. a. NZD 15.95 newsstand/cover. adv. **Document type:** *Directory, Trade.* **Description:** Provides practical advice on the right steps to take - and the traps to avoid - for people seeking to advance themselves in the IT contracting market.
Published by: I D G Communications Ltd., Wellesley St., PO Box 6813, Auckland, 1036, New Zealand. TEL 64-9-377-9902, FAX 64-9-377-4604, idg@idg.co.nz, http://www.idg.net.nz. adv.: color page USD 1,297; trim 205 x 275. Circ: 6,000 (paid and controlled).

338.47004 DEU
I T DIALOG. (Information Technology) Text in German. q. **Document type:** *Magazine, Trade.*
Related titles: English ed.

Published by: (debis Systemhaus GmbH), BurdaYukom Publishing GmbH (Subsidiary of: Hubert Burda Media Holding GmbH & Co. KG), Schleissheimer Str 141, Munich, 80797, Germany. TEL 49-89-306200, FAX 49-89-30620100, info@burdayukom.de, http://www.yukom.de. Circ: 10,000 (controlled).

338 NOR
I T KURS. (Information Technology) Text in Norwegian. q. adv. **Document type:** *Magazine, Trade.* **Description:** Provides an overview of information technology resources in Norway as well as listings of classroom, corporate and interactive courses.
Related titles: Online - full text ed.
Published by: I D G Communications Norge, PO Box 9090, Gronland, Oslo, 0133, Norway. TEL 47-22-053000, FAX 47-22-053001, http://www.itkurs.no, http://www.idg.no. adv.: color page USD 5,387; trim 210 x 297. Circ: 53,000 (controlled).

338 GBR ISSN 1475-3332
I T RESELLER. (Information Technology) Text in English. 1997. bi-m. adv. **Document type:** *Magazine, Trade.* **Description:** Provides information and resources for professional resellers, distributors, system integrators and OEMs to build and inform the 'channel' in Europe.
Formerly (until 2001): I T Reseller Magazine (1369-880X)
Related titles: E-mail ed.; Fax ed.; Online - full text ed.
Published by: I B C Publishing (Subsidiary of: Interactive Business Communications Ltd.), Latimer House, 189 High St, Potters Bar, Herts EN6 5DA, United Kingdom. TEL 44-1707-664200, FAX 44-1707-664800, info@ibcpub.co.uk, http://www.it-reseller.com/, http://www.ibcpub.com. Ed. Ian Byfield. Adv. contact Roy Stokes. color page GBP 3,750; trim 210 x 297. Circ: 13,300.

338.47004 USA
I T SERVICES BUSINESS REPORT (ONLINE). (Information Technology) Text in English. 1998. m. USD 495 in US & Canada; USD 559 elsewhere (effective 2004). adv. **Document type:** *Trade.* **Description:** Reports on all sectors of the IT services industry. Covers staffing, contracting and project management issues.
Formerly: I T Services Business Report (Print) (1097-7708)
Media: Online - full content.
Published by: Staffing Industry Analysts, Inc., 881 Fremont Ave, Los Altos, CA 94024. TEL 650-948-9303, 800-950-9496, FAX 650-948-9345, http://www.staffingindustry.com/. Ed., Pub. Peter Yessne. R&P Joanne Jaime TEL 650-948-9303 ext. 216. Adv. contact Grant Landes.

621.29 USA
INDUSTRY APPLICATIONS SOCIETY CONFERENCE. PROCEEDINGS. Text in English. a. **Document type:** *Proceedings, Trade.*
Published by: Institute of Electrical and Electronics Engineers, Inc., 3 Park Ave, 17th Fl, New York, NY 10016-5997. TEL 212-419-7900, 800-678-4333, FAX 212-752-4929, customer.service@ieee.org, http://www.ieee.org.

338 MAR
INFOMAGAZINE - P C WORLD. Text in French. 22/yr. MAD 299 (effective 2002). adv. **Document type:** *Magazine, Trade.* **Description:** Covers the complete scope of information technology and computer products, related events, buyers guides, customer satisfaction surveys and market surveys.
Related titles: Online - full text ed.
Address: 39, Rue Al Banafsaj Beausejour, Casablanca, Morocco. TEL 212-2-366239, FAX 212-2-395431, infomag@marocnet.net.ma, http://www.infomagazine.ma. adv.: color page USD 2,030; trim 200 x 280. Circ: 10,000 (paid).

INFORMATION TECHNOLOGY LAW REPORTS. see *LAW—Corporate Law*

338.47004 USA ISSN 1526-9892
HD9696.C6
INFOTECH TRENDS; source for market data on the information technology industry. Text in English. 1984. bi-w. USD 600 to individuals single user; USD 1,200 to corporations up to 10 users; 1 IP address; USD 3,000 to corporations up to 50 users; 5 IP addresses (effective 2005). abstr.; charts; stat. cum.index. back issues avail. **Document type:** *Trade.*
Former titles (until Sep.1999): Computer Industry Forecasts (0894-6213); (until 1987): Computer Industry Abstracts (0883-931X); Which incorporated (1984-1985): Computer Industry Forecast (0883-9301)
Media: Online - full content.
—CCC.
Published by: Information Technology Trends, 8378 Moller Ranch Dr, Pleasanton, CA 94588. TEL 925-462-1202, FAX 925-462-1225, support@infott.com, http://www.infotechtrends.com. Ed. Reny Parker.

338.47004 USA ISSN 0199-6649
QA75.5 CODEN: INWODU
INFOWORLD; defining technology for business. Text in English. 1979. w. USD 195 domestic; USD 215 in Canada & Mexico; USD 495 in Europe; USD 335 elsewhere; free in US & Canada to qualified personnel (effective 2005). adv. bk.rev. illus.; stat. Index. back issues avail.; reprint service avail. from PQC. **Document type:** *Magazine, Trade.* **Description:** Serves the needs of IT professionals who drive technology buying decisions for today's businesses.
Formerly (until 1981): Intelligent Machines Journal (0164-3878)
Related titles: Microfilm ed.: (from PQC); Online - full text ed.: (from bigchalk, EBSCO Publishing, Florida Center for Library Automation, Gale Group, H.W. Wilson, LexisNexis, Micromedia ProQuest, Northern Light Technology, Inc., O C L C Online Computer Library Center, Inc., ProQuest Information & Learning); Arabic ed.: Electronica. 2001.
Indexed: ABIn, BPI, BrCerAb, C&ISA, CADCAM, CBCARef, CBPI, CerAb, CompB, CompC, CompD, CompIU, ConsI, CorrAb, E&CAJ, EMA, IAA, InfoSAb, Inspec, LAMP, M&TEA, MASUSE, MBF, METADEX, MagInd, MicrocompInd, PROMT, PSI, PersLit, ResCtrInd, RoboAb, SoftBase, SolStAb, TelAb, WAA.
—BLDSC (4499.360000), AskIEEE, CASDDS, IDS, IE, Infotrieve, Linda Hall. **CCC.**
Published by: InfoWorld Media Group (Subsidiary of: I D G Communications), 501 Second St, San Francisco, CA 94107. TEL 415-243-4344, 800-227-8365, FAX 415-978-3120, http://www.infoworld.com/. Ed. Kevin S McKean. adv.: B&W page USD 31,245, color page USD 39,495. Circ: 370,000.

INSTITUTE FOR CERTIFICATION OF COMPUTING PROFESSIONALS. ANNUAL REPORT. see *COMPUTERS*

338.47004 GBR
INTERNATIONAL SMART CARD INDUSTRY GUIDE. Text in English. 1995. a. GBP 125. adv. back issues avail. **Document type:** *Directory.*
Published by: Smart Card News Ltd., 31 Ashdown Ave, Saltdean, Brighton, E Sussex BN2 8AH, United Kingdom. TEL 44-1273-302503, FAX 44-1273-300991, 44-1273-516518, 44-1273-516510, scn@pavilion.co.uk, http://www.smartcard.co.uk. Ed. Jack Smith. Pub., R&P Patsy Everett TEL 44-1273-515651. Adv. contact Albert Andoh.

338.47004 USA ISSN 1050-9070
CODEN: ISPEEZ
INTERNATIONAL SPECTRUM✱; the business person's computer magazine. Text in English. 1984. bi-m. USD 40; USD 50 foreign (effective 1999). adv. bk.rev. index. back issues avail. **Document type:** *Trade.* **Description:** Covers software-hardware products for the business person using Pick-Unix - DOS.
Indexed: CompI, Inspec, SoftBase.
Published by: International Database Management Association, 7596 Eads Ave 140, La Jolla, CA 92037-4813. TEL 858-551-7855, FAX 858-551-7866, multi-value@intl-spectrum.com, http://www.intl-spectrum.com. Ed. Hollie Johnson. Pub. Monica Giobbi. R&P Gus Giobbi. Adv. contact Suzanne Hauser. Circ: 50,000.

338.47004 USA ISSN 1073-1385
INTERVUE. Text in English. 1984. q. free to qualified personnel. **Document type:** *Consumer.* **Description:** Presents current trends in computer graphics hardware and software applications and information management technology.
Published by: Intergraph Corporation, LR24C2, Huntsville, AL 35894. TEL 205-730-8172, FAX 205-730-9508. Ed. Thomas Gates. Circ: 60,000 (controlled).

JISUANJI JICHENG ZHIZAO XITONG/COMPUTER INTEGRATED MANUFACTURING SYSTEMS. see *MACHINERY*

KARRIEREFUEHRER INFORMATIONSTECHNOLOGIE; Berufseinstieg fuer Hochschulabsolventen. see *OCCUPATIONS AND CAREERS*

338.47004 GBR ISSN 1366-6371
KEY NOTE MARKET REPORT: COMPUTER SERVICES. Variant title: Computer Services Marketing Report. Text in English. 1993. irreg., latest 2001, Oct. GBP 340 per issue (effective 2002). **Document type:** *Trade.* **Description:** Provides an overview of the UK computer services market, including industry structure, market size and trends, developments, prospects, and major company profiles.
Formerly (until 1995): Key Note Report: Computer Services (1352-6553)
Related titles: CD-ROM ed.; Online - full text ed.
Published by: Key Note Ltd., Field House, 72 Oldfield Rd, Hampton, Mddx TW12 2HQ, United Kingdom. TEL 44-20-8481-8750, FAX 44-20-8783-0049, info@keynote.co.uk, http://www.keynote.co.uk. Ed. Jacob Howard.

338.47004 338 GBR ISSN 1356-6229
KEY NOTE MARKET REVIEW: U K COMPUTER MARKET. Variant title: Computer Market (UK) Market Review. Key Note Market Review: Computer Market (UK). U K Computer Market. Text in English. 1991. irreg., latest 2002, Feb. GBP 565 per issue (effective 2002). **Document type:** *Trade.* **Description:** Provides an overview of the UK computer market, including industry structure, market size and trends, developments, prospects, and major company profiles.
Related titles: CD-ROM ed.; Online - full text ed.
Published by: Key Note Ltd., Field House, 72 Oldfield Rd, Hampton, Mddx TW12 2HQ, United Kingdom. TEL 44-20-8481-8750, FAX 44-20-8783-0049, info@keynote.co.uk, http://www.keynote.co.uk/showReport.asp?report=ComputerMa144. Ed. Dominic Fenn.

LING YU YI KEJI ZASHI/0 & 1 TECHNOLOGY BYTE (CHINESE EDITION). see *COMPUTERS—Computer Architecture*

338.47004 USA
MAINFRAME MARKET MONITOR. Text in English. 1991. q. USD 1,830 (effective 2000). **Document type:** *Trade.*
Published by: Xephon, 9330 Lyndon B Johnson Fwy., Ste. 800, Dallas, TX 75243-4310. TEL 817-455-7050, FAX 303-438-0290. Ed. Dave Bates.

338.47004 USA ISSN 1083-396X
MICROSTATION WORLD. Text in English. 1995. q. USD 12.95; USD 4.95 newsstand/cover. adv. back issues avail. **Document type:** *Trade.* **Description:** Serves the information needs of managers, engineers, and users of the MicroStation line of computer-aided design products. Describes customer success in implementing technology and how to manage new technology.
Related titles: Microfilm ed.; Online - full text ed.: (from Northern Light Technology, Inc., ProQuest Information & Learning).
Published by: Bentley Systems, Inc., 690 Pennsylvania Dr, Exton, PA 19341. TEL 610-458-2758, FAX 610-458-6284, world@bentley.com, http://www.bentley.com. Ed., R&P Rachael Dalton. Adv. contact Byron Mitchell. Circ: 110,000.

338.47004 USA
NEW EQUIPMENT REPORTER∗; new products industrial news. Text in English. 1943. m.
Published by: De Roche Publications, 12 Del Italia, Irvine, CA 92714-5355. Ed. David De Roche. Circ: 18,034.

004.05 NZL ISSN 1174-3719
NEW ZEALAND RESELLER NEWS. Text in English. 1997. fortn. NZD 118.80; NZD 4.95 newsstand/cover (effective 2002). adv. **Document type:** *Magazine, Trade.* **Description:** Contains news and information directed towards technology products resellers, dealers, network and system integrators, consultants, agents and distributors.
Related titles: Online - full text ed.
Published by: I D G Communications Ltd., Wellesley St., PO Box 6813, Auckland, 1036, New Zealand. TEL 64-9-377-9902, FAX 64-9-377-4604, idg@idg.co.nz, http://reseller.co.nz, http://www.idg.net.nz. adv.: B&W page NZD 1,990, color page NZD 2,990; trim 185 x 260. Circ: 2,876 (controlled).

338.47004 JPN
NIKKEI SYSTEM PROVIDER. Text in Japanese. 1996. bi-w. JPY 18,000 (effective 2000). adv. **Document type:** *Trade.* **Description:** Provides information useful in surviving computer industries to managers and sales persons at resellers, solution providers,etc.
Formerly: Nikkei Watcher Computer Market
Published by: Nikkei Business Publications Inc. (Subsidiary of: Nihon Keizai Shimbun, Inc.), 2-1-1 Hirakawa-cho, Chiyoda-ku, Tokyo, 102-8622, Japan. TEL 81-3-5210-8311, FAX 81-3-5210-8530, info@nikkeibpnyc.com, webmaster@nikkeibp.com, http://www.nikkeibp.com. Ed. Katsumi Tanaka. Pub. Minoru Matsuzaki. Adv. contact Masayuki Tsuta. B&W page JPY 275,000, color page JPY 473,000; trim 210 x 280. Circ: 13,468. **Dist. in America by:** Nikkei Business Publications America Inc., 575 Fifth Ave, 20th Fl, New York, NY 10017.

338.47004 USA
OFFICE - DATA PROCESSING MACHINES: LATIN AMERICAN INDUSTRIAL REPORT∗. Text in English. 1985. a. USD 235; per country report.
Published by: Aquino Productions, P O Box 15760, Stamford, CT 06901-0760. Ed. Andres C Aquino.

338 MMR
P C WORLD MYANMAR. Text in English. m. adv. **Document type:** *Magazine, Trade.* **Description:** Contains local news, up-to-date information on world wide computer science and industry, new product reports, and special reports.
Published by: Today Publishing House Ltd., Bldg. C-2, Nyaung Tan Housing Estate, Pazundaung Township, Yangon, Myanmar. TEL 95-1-295-886, FAX 95-1-294-092, today@today.com.mm. adv.: color page USD 900; trim 6 x 8. Circ: 4,000 (paid).

004.16 NOR ISSN 0801-5236
P C WORLD NORGE. Text in Norwegian. 1985. m. NOK 995 (effective 2003). adv. **Document type:** *Magazine, Trade.* **Description:** Contains information on comparative tests of PCs, software and peripherals, as well as buyer information on LANs and communications equipment.
Formerly (until 1987): P C Mikrodata (0800-9465); Which was formed by the merger of (1984-1985): P C World Norge (0800-9902); (1982-1985): Mikrodata (0800-269X); Which was formerly (until 1983): Hobbydata (0800-353X)
Related titles: Online - full text ed.: ISSN 0807-2728.
Published by: I D G Communications Norge, PO Box 9090, Gronland, Oslo, 0133, Norway. TEL 47-22-053000, FAX 47-22-053001, http://www.pcworld.no, http://www.idg.no. adv.: B&W page USD 4,402, color page USD 5,723; trim 210 x 297. Circ: 38,000 (paid).

004.16 NOR ISSN 0803-4494
P C WORLD NORGE EKSPRESS. Text in Norwegian. 1991. w. adv. **Document type:** *Bulletin, Trade.* **Description:** Contains news and information for computer equipment buyers, professional PC users and PC enthusiasts.
Related titles: Online - full text ed.
Published by: I D G Communications Norge, PO Box 9090, Gronland, Oslo, 0133, Norway. TEL 47-22-053000, FAX 47-22-053001, http://www.pcworld.no/ekspress/, http://www.idg.no. adv.: B&W page USD 2,804, color page USD 3,765; trim 184 x 268. Circ: 24,500 (controlled).

338.47004 ESP
P V D. (Publicacion del Distribuidor de Informatica) Text in Spanish. 1999. m. adv. back issues avail. **Document type:** *Trade.* **Description:** Designed for computer store dealers, manufactures and computer wholesalers.
Published by: Kunzer International, rancisco Sancha, 4 2o. Fl, Madrid, 28034, Spain. TEL 34-91-729-0444, FAX 34-91-729-3090, pvd@pvd.com, http://www.pvd.com. Ed. Gemma Sahagun. Pub., R&P Javier Moreno. Adv. contact Paul Brazell. B&W page USD 1,480, color page USD 1,900; trim 285 x 210.

338.47004 USA
HF5415.5
THE PROFESSIONAL JOURNAL; for executives, managers, and professionals in the high-technology services industry. Text in English. 1975. m. USD 65 domestic; USD 89 foreign. adv. bk.rev. back issues avail. **Description:** For executives, managers and professionals of the high-technology services industry.
Former titles: A F S M International (1049-2135); (until 1988): The Field Service Manager (0199-8889)
Related titles: Microfiche ed.; Online - full text ed.
Published by: Association for Services Management International, 1342 Colonial Blvd, Ste 28, Fort Myers, FL 33907. TEL 813-275-7887, FAX 813-275-0794. Ed. Joseph Tiepik. adv.: B&W page USD 1,090, color page USD 1,800. Circ: 5,800.

338.47004 ESP
QUIEN ES QUIEN EN INFORMATICA Y TELECOMUNICACIONES. Variant title: Anuario del Sector de la Informatica y Telecomunicaciones. Text in Spanish. 1999. a. adv. back issues avail. **Document type:** *Directory.*
Published by: Kunzer International, rancisco Sancha, 4 2o. Fl, Madrid, 28034, Spain. TEL 34-91-729-0444, FAX 34-91-729-3090, pvd@pvd.com, http://www.pvd.com. Pub., R&P Javier Moreno. Adv. contact Paul Brazell. B&W page USD 1,000, color page USD 1,400; trim 285 x 210.

THE REPORT ON I B M. see *COMPUTERS—Hardware*

338.47004 USA ISSN 1072-9453
REPORT ON MICROSOFT; independent biweekly news and analysis of Microsoft Corporation. Text in English. 1993. bi-w. USD 395 in North America; USD 443 elsewhere.
Related titles: Online - full text ed.: (from Factiva, Northern Light Technology, Inc.).
—CCC.
Published by: DataTrends Publications, Inc., PO Box 4460, Leesburg, VA 20177-8541. TEL 703-779-0574, 800-766-8130, FAX 703-779-2267. Pub. Paul G Ochs.

338 UAE
RESELLER WORLD MIDDLE EAST. Text in English. m. USD 150 (effective 2002). adv. **Document type:** *Magazine, Trade.* **Description:** Contains news, analysis, features and reviews on all aspects of the information technology channel industry.
Published by: Corporate Publishing International, PO Box 13700, Dubai, United Arab Emirates. TEL 971-4-351-5316, FAX 971-4-359-8486, cpi@emirates.net.ae, http://www.cpilive.net. adv.: B&W page USD 4,000, color page USD 4,500; trim 235 x 330. Circ: 7,170 (paid and controlled).

338.47004 USA ISSN 1048-3462
SERVICE INDUSTRY NEWSLETTER∗. Text in English. 1980. m.
Formerly (until 1989): Field Service Newsletter (0889-3624)
Published by: Ledgeway Publications, c/o Dataquest, 900 Chelmsford St, No T2, 9th Fl, Lowell, MA 01851-8100. TEL 508-370-5555, FAX 508-370-6262. Ed. Jean Kane. Circ: 800.

338.47004 600 USA ISSN 1091-9503
HC79.H53
SILICONINDIA; technology and business magazine. Text in English. 199?. m. USD 24 domestic; CND 32 in Canada; USD 48 elsewhere; USD 2.95 newsstand/cover domestic; USD 3.95 newsstand/cover in Canada (effective 2000). back issues avail.; reprints avail. **Document type:** *Magazine.* **Description:** Features Information Technology news on software, stocks, strategy, legal advices, management.
Related titles: Online - full text ed.: (from EBSCO Publishing).
Address: 37600 Central Ct., Newark, CA 94560-3455. http://www.siliconindia.com. Ed. Yogesh Sharma. Pub. Mona Sharma.

338.47004 GBR ISSN 0967-196X
SMART CARD NEWS. Text in English. 1992. m. GBP 375; GBP 395 foreign. adv. **Document type:** *Newsletter.*
Published by: Smart Card News Ltd., 40 Arundel Pl, Brighton, E Sussex BN2 1GO, United Kingdom. TEL 44-1273-302503, FAX 44-1273-300991. Ed. Jack Smith. Pub., R&P Patsy Everett TEL 44-1273-515651. Adv. contact Albert Andoh. Circ: 1,000 (controlled).

338.47004 USA ISSN 1097-5667
SOLUTIONS INTEGRATOR∗. Text in English. 1997. s-m. adv. **Document type:** *Magazine, Trade.* **Description:** Concerned with the computer industry and computer technology.
Related titles: Online - full text ed.
Indexed: SoftBase.
—IE.
Published by: International Data Group, I D G Channel Services, 2200 Jackson St Apt 203, San Francisco, CA 94115-1362. TEL 650-294-7800, FAX 650-294-7801. Ed. John Russell. Adv. contact Keith Newman. B&W page USD 12,600, color page USD 15,900; trim 10.88 x 8.25. Circ: 90,000 (controlled).

338.47004 BRA ISSN 1415-8884
SOLUTIONS INTEGRATOR. Text in Portuguese. 1998. fortn. adv. **Document type:** *Magazine, Trade.*
Related titles: Online - full text ed.
Published by: I D G Computerworld do Brasil, Rua Tabapua, 145-3 e 4 andar, Itaim Bibi, Sao Paulo, 04533-010, Brazil. TEL 55-11-3049-2000, FAX 55-11-3071-4022, negocios@idg.com.br, http://www.solutionsintegrator.com.br, http://www.idg.com.br. adv.: color page USD 14,000; trim 270 x 368. Circ: 30,000 (controlled).

338.47004 THA
THAI COMPUTERWORLD. Text in English. 1991. s-m. THB 30. adv. bk.rev. **Document type:** *Magazine, Consumer.* **Description:** Provides up-to-date information on national and international happenings in the computer industry.
Published by: Media Transasia (Thailand) Ltd., 14th Fl., Ocena Tower II, 75/8 Soi Sukhumvit, 19 Sukhumvit Rd., Klongtoeynue, Wattana, Bangkok, 10110, Thailand. TEL 662-204-2320, FAX 662-204-2391, tcw1@internet.ksc.net.th. Ed. Pravir Ganguly. Adv. contact Pramodh Noronha. B&W page THB 24,000, color page THB 35,000. Circ: 28,500.

338.47004 DEU
TIPS & TRENDS. Text in German. 1982. 4/yr. membership. bk.rev. **Document type:** *Newsletter.* **Description:** Trends and news for consumer electronics retailers on new products and their use.
Formerly (until 1994): D V I - Infos
Published by: Deutsches Video Institut e.V., Budapester Str 44, Berlin, 10787, Germany. TEL 49-30-230896-0, FAX 49-30-23089621, info@dvi.de, http://www.dvi.de. Ed. Marietta Puder. Circ: 5,200.

338.47004 TWN
TRADE WINNERS; the international trade weekly from Asia to the world. Text in English. w. TWD 2,400, USD 80 (effective 2000). adv. **Description:** Presents information and advertising for a wide range of Taiwan-made computers and peripherals, electronic components, and electrical appliances.
Related titles: Online - full content ed.
Address: 4F-2, No 190, Keelung Rd, Sec 2, PO Box 7-250, Taipei, Taiwan. TEL 886-2-27333988, FAX 886-2-27333990, service@twinner.com.tw, http://www.twinner.com.tw. Ed. Kay K Chen. **Subscr. to:** P O Box 2868, Vancouver, WA 98668.

338.47004 JPN ISSN 0915-051X
UNISYS NEWS. Text in Japanese. 1961. m. **Document type:** *Consumer.*
Formerly (until 1988): Univac News (0388-6883)
Published by: Nihon Unisys Ltd., 1-1-1 Toyosu, Koto-ku, Tokyo, 135-0061, Japan. TEL 81-3-5546-4111. Ed. Hiroshi Takei. Pub. Munehisa Yamashita.

VENTUREWIRE PROFESSIONAL. see *BUSINESS AND ECONOMICS*

338.47 USA ISSN 1530-7034
TK5105.8885.W43
WEBSPHERE ADVISOR. Text in English. 2000. s-m. USD 99 domestic; USD 119 in Canada; USD 139 elsewhere (effective 2005). **Document type:** *Magazine, Trade.*
Published by: Advisor Media, Inc., 4849 Viewridge Ave, San Diego, CA 92123-1643. TEL 858-278-5600, FAX 858-278-0300, advisor@advisor.com, http://www.advisor.com.

C

338.47004 TWN ISSN 1022-9698
0 YU 1 BYTE KEJI ZAZHI/0 & 1 TECHNOLOGY BYTE. Variant title: 0 & 1 Byte Magazine. Text in Chinese. 1981. m. adv.
Published by: Acer T W P Corporation, 2-F, No 19-1 Ln 231, Fu-Hsing N. Rd, Taipei, 105, Taiwan. TEL 886-2-7136959, FAX 886-2-7189467. Ed. Angel Chen. Adv. contact David Tsai. B&W page USD 1,042, color page USD 2,175; trim 298 x 210. Circ: 16,000.

COMPUTERS—Computer Industry Directories

338 384 GBR
AFRICAN COMPUTING & COMMUNICATIONS YEARBOOK; key information for Africa's IT managers. Text in English. a., latest 1999. GBP 10 per issue (effective 2001). adv. back issues avail. **Document type:** *Directory.* **Description:** Contains a listing of leading computer and telecoms suppliers and essays on IT development in Africa.
Related titles: Online - full content ed.
Published by: A I T E C, 15 High St, Graveley, Cambs PE18 6PL, United Kingdom. TEL 44-1480-831300, FAX 44-1480-831131, info@aitec.co.uk, admin@aitecafrica.com, http://www.aitecafrica.com/yearbook2/yearbook.html. Ed., Pub., R&P Sean Moroney. Adv. contact Peter Irvine. B&W page GBP 2,000, color page GBP 2,800. Circ: 5,000.

338.47004 CAN
COMPUTER DEALER NEWS SOURCE GUIDE. Text in English. 1985. a., latest 2003. adv. **Document type:** *Directory.* **Description:** Provides Canada's computer resellers with information on sources, trade names, products, manufacturers and services.
Related titles: Online - full text ed.
Published by: Transcontinental Media, Inc. (Subsidiary of: Transcontinental, Inc.), 25 Sheppard Ave West, Ste 100, Toronto, ON M2N 6S7, Canada. TEL 416-733-7600, FAX 416-218-3544, info@transcontinental.ca, http://www.transcontinental-gtc.com/en/home.html, http://www.itbusiness.ca. adv.: B&W page CND 2,467.

658.0029 GBR
COMPUTER FEATURES DIRECTORY. Text in English. 1993. m. GBP 295 (effective 1999). **Document type:** *Directory.* **Description:** Targets public relations and marketing agencies, consultants and vendors that focus on information technology.
Related titles: Diskette ed.; Online - full text ed.
Published by: Insight Marketing Concepts, Somerset House, The Old Court House, London Rd, Ascot, Berks SL5 7EN, United Kingdom. TEL 44-1344-874004, FAX 44-1344-874100, cfd@insightgroup.co.uk, http://www.insightgroup.co.uk. Ed. Stuart Sykes. Circ: 100 (paid).

338 GBR
COMPUTER SITES; UK company sites, systems and contacts. Text in English. a., latest 2003, May. GBP 295 per issue (effective 2003). **Document type:** *Directory, Trade.* **Description:** Contains essential profiles of the IT resources of thousands of UK companies.
Related titles: CD-ROM ed.; Online - full text ed.
—BLDSC (3395.128750).
Published by: V N U Business Publications Ltd., 32-34 Broadwick St, London, W1A 2HG, United Kingdom. TEL 44-20-73169610, FAX 44-20-73169260, directories@computing.co.uk, http://directories.computing.co.uk/directoriessites.htm, http://www.computing.co.uk/directories.

338 MEX
DIRECTORIO DE COMPUTO. Text in Spanish. 1998. irreg., latest vol.4, 2001. USD 300 (effective 2001). **Document type:** *Directory.* **Description:** Lists computing departments in Mexico City in business and government (by top executive, company, address, phone and fax numbers, e-mail); vendors (listing hardware, software, consumibles, services, with trademarks); associations, publishers, and information centers.
Published by: Ibcon S.A., Gutenberg 224, Col Anzures, Mexico City, DF 11590, Mexico. TEL 52-5-2554577, FAX 52-5-2554577, ibcon@infosel.net.mx, http://www.ibcon.com.mx.

338.47004 USA ISSN 1067-1072
HD9696.C63
DIRECTORY OF COMPUTER AND CONSUMER ELECTRONICS RETAILERS. Text in English. 1983. a. USD 290 (effective 1999). **Document type:** *Directory.* **Description:** Profiles on more than 2,200 computer retailers and dealers. Includes more than 400 computer and software distributors. Names and titles of over 8,000 key personnel and decision makers are listed. Listings identify sales volume, hardware brands carried, and vertical market operations served.
Former titles: Directory of Computer Retailers, Dealers and Distributors (Year); (until 1988): Directory of Computer and Software Retailers (0738-839X)
Related titles: CD-ROM ed.; Diskette ed.; Magnetic Tape ed.
Published by: C S G Information Services (Subsidiary of: Lebhar-Friedman, Inc.), 3922 Coconut Palm Dr, Tampa, FL 33619. TEL 813-664-6800, FAX 813-664-6882. Ed. Ashley Valdes.

DIRECTORY OF U.S. GOVERNMENT DATAFILES FOR MAINFRAMES AND MICROCOMPUTERS. see *BUSINESS AND ECONOMICS—Trade And Industrial Directories*

DIRECTORY OF VIDEO, COMPUTER AND AUDIO VISUAL PRODUCTS. see *COMMUNICATIONS—Video*

338.47004 ESP ISSN 0211-8688
GUIA CHIP. Text in Spanish. 1981. a. EUR 69.90 (effective 2005).
Description: Covers computers and communications. Includes a company directory and products available.
Published by: V N U Business Publications (Spain), San Sotero 8 4a Planta, Madrid, 28037, Spain. TEL 34-91-3137900, FAX 34-91-3273704, http://www.guiachip.com/, http://www.vnubp.es. Ed. Oscar Guijaro. Circ: 7,000.

338 USA
INFORMATION STRATEGIES RESOURCE GUIDE. Text in English. a. **Document type:** *Directory, Trade.* **Description:** Provides information on products and services for the data warehousing industry.
Media: Online - full text.
Published by: Data Warehousing Institute, 5200 Southcenter Blvd, Ste 250, Seattle, WA 98188-2356. TEL 206-246-5059, FAX 206-246-5952, ehobbs@dw-institute.com, info@dw-institute.com, http://www.dw-institute.com/resourceguide2000/index.html. Ed. E Hobbs.

338 GBR
MAJOR IT COMPANIES OF THE WORLD (YEAR). Text in English. a. GBP 490 (effective 2001). **Document type:** *Directory.* **Description:** Provides key data on the world's largest IT and dot com companies.
Published by: Graham & Whiteside Ltd (Subsidiary of: Gale Group), Tuition House, 5-6 Francis Grove, London, SW19 4DT, United Kingdom. TEL 44-20-8947-1011, FAX 44-20-8947-1163, galeord@gale.com, http://www.galegroup.com/graham&whiteside/.

338.47004 SGP
MALAYSIA TIMES GUIDE TO COMPUTERS. Text in English. a. USD 35 (effective 2000). adv. **Document type:** *Directory.* **Description:** Lists computer manufacturers, distributors, agents and dealers in Malaysia and Thailand. Also serves as a guide to buying computer hardware, software, networking systems, peripherals and other computer related products and services.
Formerly: Times Guide to Computers (Malaysia - Thailand Edition) (1394-1305)
Published by: Times Media Pte Ltd, Directories Division, 1 New Industrial Rd, Times Centre, Singapore, 536196, Singapore. TEL 65-2848844, FAX 65-2850161, ttdmktg@cop.tpl.com.sg, http://www.timesbiz.com.sg. Pub., R&P Leslie Lim. Adv. contact Joseph Liang.

338.47004 GBR
MICROINFO ELECTRONIC MEDIA DIRECTORY. Abbreviated title: M E M D. Text in English. 3/yr. GBP 25 in British Isles; GBP 40 in Europe; GBP 45 elsewhere (effective 2000). **Document type:** *Directory.* **Description:** Provides a directory of providers, titles, forthcoming titles, contents and price updates of products in the electronic media industry.
Published by: Microinfo Ltd., PO Box 3, Alton, Hants GU34 2PG, United Kingdom. TEL 44-1420-86848, FAX 44-1420-89889, emedia@microinfo.co.uk, http://www.microinfo.co.uk.

338.47004 USA
MICROLEADS RESELLER DIRECTORY ON DISK*. Text in English. 1985. a. USD 595 (effective 1999). **Document type:** *Directory.*
Formerly: Microleads Dealer Directory
Media: Diskette.
Published by: Chromatic Communications Enterprises, Inc., PO Box 1728, Benicia, CA 94510-4728. TEL 800-782-3475, FAX 707-746-0542. Pub., R&P Michael Shipp.

338.47004 USA ISSN 1056-0386
HD9696.C63
MICROLEADS VENDOR DIRECTORY*. Text in English. 1983. a. USD 495 (effective 1999). **Document type:** *Directory.* **Description:** Offers a directory for the microcomputer industrylisting over 11,000 companies, 35,000 products, and 30,000 executives. Listings are arranged under eight cross-references sections: hardware, software, accessories, distributors, franchisors, support services, publishers and periodicals.
Formerly: Personal Computer - An Industry Source Book (0739-3687)
Media: Diskette.
Published by: Chromatic Communications Enterprises, Inc., PO Box 1728, Benicia, CA 94510-4728. TEL 800-782-3475, FAX 707-746-0542. Ed., Pub., R&P Michael Shipp.

338.47004 USA
HD9696.C63
NORTHWEST HIGH TECH DATABASE. Text in English. irreg. (approx. d.). USD 79.95 (effective 2000). **Document type:** *Directory.* **Description:** Profiles more than 2000 software, hardware, sales and service companies in the Pacific Northwest and Western Canada.
Media: Online - full content. **Related titles:** CD-ROM ed.: USD 149.95 per issue (effective 2000); E-mail ed.: USD 140 per issue (effective 2000); Print ed.: Northwest High Tech on the Web. ISSN 1053-6809. 1988.
Published by: Northwest High Tech, 12307 NE 149th Ct., Kirkland, WA 98034-1120. TEL 425-823-9338, 877-804-8324, info@nwhtweb.com, http://www.nwhtweb.com.

REAL ESTATE SOFTWARE GUIDE. see *REAL ESTATE—Computer Applications*

338 SGP ISSN 0218-1002
TIMES GUIDE TO COMPUTERS. Text in English. 1985. a. USD 35 (effective 2000). adv. **Document type:** *Directory.* **Description:** Directory of computer manufacturers, agents, distributors and dealers in Singapore.
Published by: Times Media Pte Ltd, Directories Division, 1 New Industrial Rd, Times Centre, Singapore, 536196, Singapore. TEL 65-2848844, FAX 65-2850161, ttdmktg@cop.tpl.com.sg, http://www.timesbiz.com.sg. Pub., R&P Leslie Lim. Adv. contact Joseph Liang.

COMPUTERS—Computer Industry, Vocational Guidance

see also EDUCATION ; OCCUPATIONS AND CAREERS

371.425 GBR ISSN 1367-9643
COMPUTER CONTRACTOR. Text in English. 1989. fortn. GBP 70; GBP 2.80 newsstand/cover (effective 1999). **Document type:** *Trade.* **Description:** Covers industry issues, views, comment and advice on legal and financial issues for contractors, as well as on the IT marketplace.
Published by: V N U Business Publications Ltd., VNU House, 32-34 Broadwick St, London, W1A 2HG, United Kingdom. TEL 44-20-7316-9000, FAX 44-20-7316-9160, http://www.computercontractor.vnu.co.uk.

371.425 USA
THE INDEPENDENT (ST. LOUIS). Text in English. 1977. 6/yr. membership. adv. bk.rev. **Document type:** *Newsletter.*
Published by: Independent Computer Consultants Association, 11131 S. Towne Sq., Ste. F, St. Louis, MO 63123-7817. TEL 314-892-1675, FAX 314-487-1345, execdirector@icca.org, http://www.icca.org. Ed. Joyce Burkard. Circ: 2,600.

371.425 USA
NETWORK CONTRACTS REPORT. Text in English. bi-w. USD 385. **Document type:** *Trade.* **Description:** Aimed at computing and communications industry executives worldwide. Includes business news on major contract awards for network hardware, software, and services.
Published by: Worldnet News Group, 27475 Ynez Rd, Ste 290, Temecula, CA 92591-4632. TEL 909-672-3575, 800-539-NEWS, FAX 909-672-8058.

SPORTWISSENSCHAFT. see *SPORTS AND GAMES*

STRATEGIC NEWS SERVICE. see *COMMUNICATIONS*

COMPUTERS—Computer Music

see also MUSIC—Computer Applications

786.76 USA
ARRAY; communications of the I C M A. Text in English. bi-m.
Indexed: RILM.
Published by: International Computer Music Association, 1100 Baits Dr, Ann Arbor, MI 48109-2085. TEL 734-936-0425, FAX 734-818-3031.

B U G MAGAZINE; the magazine for the electronic musician. (Boss Users Group) see *MUSIC—Computer Applications*

786.76 GBR ISSN 1463-6875
COMPUTER MUSIC; the complete music making guide for mac and pc. Text in English. 1998. m. GBP 44 in United Kingdom; GBP 5 newsstand/cover; GBP 65 in Europe; GBP 65 in North America; GBP 85 rest of world (effective 2000). adv. **Document type:** *Consumer.* **Description:** Tests the latest computer music products and offers tutorials on the most current software, enabling computer owners to develop their musical interests and expertise.
—CCC.
Published by: Future Publishing Ltd., Beauford Court, 30 Monmouth St, Bath, Avon BA1 2BW, United Kingdom. TEL 44-1225-442244, FAX 44-1225-732285, andy.jones@futurenet.co.uk, http://www.futurenet.com, http://www.futurenet.com/futureonline. Ed. Andy Jones. adv.: color page GBP 2,565; trim 232 x 280. Circ: 27,740 (paid).

787.76 GBR
CUBASE. Text in English. USD 14.99 newsstand/cover (effective 2004).
Published by: Future Publishing Ltd., Beauford Court, 30 Monmouth St, Bath, Avon BA1 2BW, United Kingdom. TEL 44-1225-442244, FAX 44-1225-446019, http://www.futurenet.co.uk. Ed. Ronan MacDonald.

786.76 GBR ISSN 0929-8215
ML5 CODEN: JNEMEE
➤ **JOURNAL OF NEW MUSIC RESEARCH.** Abbreviated title: J N M R. Text in English. 1972. q. GBP 370, USD 630 combined subscription to institutions print & online eds. (effective 2006). adv. bk.rev. abstr.; bibl.; charts. back issues avail.; reprint service avail. from PSC. **Document type:** *Journal, Academic/Scholarly.* **Description:** Discusses developments in news music, including instrumental and electronic music, computer, interactive and multimedia systems, music-related DSP, psychoacoustics, and related topics such as music perception and music history.
Formerly (until 1993): Interface (0303-3902); Which was formed by the 1972 merger of: Electronic Music Reports; Instituut voor Psychoakoestiek en Elektronische Muziek. Jaarboek
Related titles: Online - full text ed.: Journal of New Music Research. Electronic Appendix. GBP 352, USD 599 (effective 2006) (from EBSCO Publishing, Gale Group, IngentaConnect, O C L C Online Computer Library Center, Inc., Swets Information Services).
Indexed: ASCA, ArtHuCI, CMCI, CurCont, IIMP, Inspec, MusicInd, PCI, RILM.
—BLDSC (5022.750000), AskIEEE, IDS, IE, Infotrieve, ingenta. **CCC.**
Published by: Routledge (Subsidiary of: Taylor & Francis Group), 4 Park Sq, Milton Park, Abingdon, Oxon OX14 4RN, United Kingdom. TEL 44-1235-828600, FAX 44-1235-829000, info@routledge.co.uk, http://www.tandf.co.uk/journals/titles/09298215.asp, http://www.routledge.co.uk. Ed. Alan Marsden. adv.: page EUR 225; trim 210 x 297. Circ: 1,000. **Subscr. in N. America to:** Taylor & Francis Inc.

786.76 USA ISSN 0748-2043
SMALL COMPUTERS IN THE ARTS NEWS✶. Abbreviated title: S C A N. Text in English. 1982. 3/yr. USD 15. adv. bk.rev. **Description:** Contains articles about music and graphics education, music synthesis and composition, and each issue features an artist and his or her work.
Published by: Small Computers in the Arts Network, Inc., 209 Upland Rd., Merton Sta., PA 19066-1821. Ed. Dick Moberg. Circ: 350.

781.34 NLD ISSN 1384-1203
➤ **STUDIES ON NEW MUSIC RESEARCH.** Text in English. 1996. irreg., latest vol.5, 2001. price varies. back issues avail. **Document type:** *Monographic series, Academic/Scholarly.* **Description:** Publishes research in computer-generated electronic music.
Published by: Taylor & Francis The Netherlands (Subsidiary of: Taylor & Francis Group), Schipolweg 107 C, PO Box 447, Leiden, 2316 XC, Netherlands. TEL 31-715-243080, FAX 31-715-234571, pub@swets.nl, http://www.tandf.co.uk/swets.asp.

786.76 781.34 SWE
▼ **STUDIO.** Text in Swedish. 2003. 11/yr. SEK 474 (effective 2003). **Description:** Focuses on the software and accessories required to produce music with the computer.
Related titles: Online - full content ed.
Published by: I D G AB (Subsidiary of: I D G Communications Inc.), Sturegatan 11, Stockholm, 10678, Sweden. TEL 46-8-4536000, FAX 46-8-4536005, http://www.studio.idg.se, http://www.idg.se. Ed. Bjoern E. Olsberg TEL 46-8-4536214. Adv. contact Martin Ekman.

COMPUTERS—Computer Networks

see also COMPUTERS—Internet

004.6 USA ISSN 1550-4859
▼ ➤ **A C M TRANSACTIONS ON SENSOR NETWORKS.** Variant title: Association for Computing Machinery Transactions on Sensor Networks. Text in English. 2005 (Jan.). q. USD 140 domestic to non-members; USD 154 foreign to non-members; USD 40 domestic to members; USD 54 foreign to members; USD 35 domestic to students; USD 49 foreign to students; USD 168 combined subscription domestic to non-members print & online eds.; USD 182 combined subscription foreign to non-members print & online eds.; USD 48 combined subscription domestic to members print & online eds.; USD 62 combined subscription foreign to members print & online eds.; USD 42 combined subscription domestic to students print & online eds.; USD 56 combined subscription foreign to students print & online eds. (effective 2006). **Document type:** *Journal, Academic/Scholarly.* **Description:** Covers results in the research and applications of distributed, wireless or wireline sensor and actuator networks.
Related titles: Online - full text ed.: ISSN 1550-4867. 2005 (Jan.). USD 112 to non-members; USD 32 to members; USD 28 to students (effective 2006).
Published by: Association for Computing Machinery, Inc., 1515 Broadway, 17th Fl, New York, NY 10036-5701. TEL 212-626-0500, 800-342-6626, FAX 212-944-1318, sigs@acm.org, http://www.acm.org.

004.65 370 USA ISSN 1092-7131
➤ **A L N MAGAZINE.** (Asynchronous Learning Networks) Text in English. irreg. free (effective 2003). **Document type:** *Academic/Scholarly.*
Media: Online - full content.
Published by: Sloan Consortium, Olin College of Engineering and Babson College, 1735 Great Plain Ave., Needham, MA 02492. TEL 781-292-2524, FAX 781-292-2505, publisher@sloan-c.org, http://www.sloan-c.org/publications/magazine/index.asp. Ed. John R. Bourne.

004.66 USA ISSN 1093-6696
A T M WORLD. (Asynchronous Transfer Mode) Text in English. 1997. 3/yr. USD 36 (effective 2000). adv. **Document type:** *Journal, Trade.* **Description:** Covers Asynchronous Transfer Mode success stories.
Published by: Broadband Publishing Corp, 200 W Rivers St, Ste 201, PO Box 6535, Ketchum, ID 83340. TEL 208-725-0600, FAX 208-725-0854, karenh@broadbandpub.com, http://www.atmworldmag.com, http://www.broadbandpub.com. Ed. David F Hold. Pub., R&P Karen P Hold. Adv. contact Amanda F Seasard.

004.6 NLD ISSN 1570-8705
TK7872.D48
▼ ➤ **AD HOC NETWORKS.** Text in English. 2003. 6/yr. EUR 387 in Europe to institutions; JPY 45,800 in Japan to institutions; USD 410 to institutions except Europe and Japan (effective 2006). adv. **Document type:** *Journal, Academic/Scholarly.* **Description:** Provides coverage of all topics of interest to those involved in ad hoc and sensor networking areas.
Related titles: Online - full text ed.: (from EBSCO Publishing, IngentaConnect, ScienceDirect, Swets Information Services).
Indexed: C&CSA, Inspec.
—BLDSC (0678.173700), IE. **CCC.**
Published by: Elsevier BV (Subsidiary of: Elsevier Science & Technology), Radarweg 29, Amsterdam, 1043 NX, Netherlands. TEL 31-20-4853911, FAX 31-20-4852457, nlinfo-f@elsevier.nl, http://www.elsevier.com/locate/adhoc, http://www.elsevier.nl. Ed. I.F. Akyildiz.

004.6 GBR
APACHE WEEK. Text in English. 1999. w. free (effective 2003). **Document type:** *Journal.* **Description:** Provides timely information, mainly new product releases and bug fixes, to the Apache community. The featured articles are basically abstracts of some of the publications on the web that are of interest to Apache users. Covers from general articles about servers and web technology through to detailed technical articles about 'how to' use Apache's advanced features.
Media: Online - full text.
Address: Red Hat Europe, 10 Alan Turing Way, Guildford, GU2 7YF, United Kingdom. editors@apacheweek.com, http://www.apacheweek.com.

004.6 AUS ISSN 1038-359X
AUSTRALIAN & NEW ZEALAND L A N MAGAZINE. Variant title: L A N Magazine. Text in English. m. AUD 45. adv. **Description:** Covers local networking industry - networking news, product updates, relevant business news and coverage of industry events.
Published by: A C P Computer Publications, 54-58 Park St., Level 6, Sydney, NSW 1028, Australia. TEL 61-2-2889168, FAX 61-2-2674909, lanmag@acp.com.au. Ed. Ben Gerholt. Pub. Paul Dykzeul. Adv. contact M Chivers. B&W page AUD 2,700, color page AUD 3,600; trim 210 x 275. Circ: 15,250.

004.6 FIN ISSN 1456-5579
BISNES.FI. Text in Finnish. 1991. m. EUR 75 domestic; EUR 85 elsewhere (effective 2005). adv. **Document type:** *Magazine, Trade.* **Description:** Deals exclusively with organization performance and system integration from the point of view of telecommunications. Scope comprises the whole field from networking to transmission of data, text, speech and visual images and their integrated functions.
Formerly (until 1999): Tietoverkko (0788-6381)
Related titles: Online - full text ed.
Published by: Kulttuuritehdas Korjaamo, Toolonkatu 51 b, Helsinki, 00250, Finland. TEL 358-20-7417002, FAX 358-20-7417001, info@kulttuuritehdaskorjaamo.fi, http://www.bisnes.fi, http://www.korjaamo.fi. Ed. Jaakko Lyytinen. adv.: page EUR 4,270; 230 x 300.

004.6 USA
BLINK NEWSLETTER. Text in English. 199?. bi-m. free to qualified personnel. adv. **Document type:** *Newsletter, Consumer.* **Description:** Provides helpful and fun articles on the Internet for Earthlink users.
Published by: EarthLink Network, Inc., 3100 New York Dr, Pasadena, CA 91107. elnblink@earthlink.net, http://www.earthlink.net/blink/. Ed. Thomas Sullivan. Pub. Mike Brown. Adv. contact Nancy Carol Inguanzo.

004.6 USA
BROADBAND BUSINESS FORECAST. Text in English. 1991. bi-w. USD 1,097 (effective 2005). tr.lit. **Document type:** *Newsletter, Trade.* **Description:** Covers developments, trends and applications of high-bandwidth data transmission and communications.
Former titles: Broadband Business Report; (until 2002): Broadband Networking News (1059-0544); Incorporates (1996-2001): Cable Europe (1364-5617); (1995-2001): I S P Business News; (2000-2001): Internet Protocol I Q; (1991-2000): Advanced Intelligent Network News (1072-0030); (1997-1998): Managed Network Services News (1092-292X); (1988-1998): I S D N News (0899-9554)
Related titles: Online - full text ed.: (from Gale Group, LexisNexis, Northern Light Technology, Inc.).
Indexed: CompD.
—**CCC.**
Published by: Access Intelligence, LLC (Subsidiary of: Veronis, Suhler & Associates Inc.), 1201 Seven Locks Rd, Ste 300, Potomac, MD 20854. TEL 301-354-2000, 800-777-5006, FAX 301-340-1451, clientservices@accessintel.com, http://www.phillips.com, http://www.pbimedia.com. Ed. Eric Ladley.

004.66 USA ISSN 1529-1391
TK5103.4+in process
BROADBAND WORLD. Text in English. 1999. every 3 yrs. USD 36 (effective 2000). adv. **Document type:** *Journal, Trade.* **Description:** Reports on successes in broadband communications.
Published by: Broadband Publishing Corp, 200 W Rivers St, Ste 201, PO Box 6535, Ketchum, ID 83340. TEL 208-725-0600, FAX 208-725-0854, karenh@broadbandpub.com, http://www.broadbandpub.com. Ed. David F Hold. Pub., R&P Karen P Hold. Adv. contact Amanda F Seasard.

004.6 USA
BURTON GROUP NEWS ANALYSIS. Text in English. 1989. s-m. looseleaf. price varies. cum.index: 1992-1994. **Document type:** *Newsletter.* **Description:** Analyzes significant events and products in the PC network industry.
Formerly: Clarke Buton News Analysis (1051-0915)
Related titles: CD-ROM ed.; Online - full text ed.
Published by: Burton Group, PO Box 3448, Salt Lake City, UT 84110-3448. TEL 801-943-1966, FAX 801-943-2425, info@tbg.com. Ed. Jamie Lewis. Pub. Judith Burton. Circ: 2,000 (paid).

004.6 USA
BURTON GROUP REPORT. Text in English. m. price varies. cum.index: 1992-1994. **Document type:** *Newsletter.* **Description:** Contains in-depth technology analysis of LAN architecture issues.
Formerly: Clarke Burton Report (1048-4620)
Related titles: CD-ROM ed.; Diskette ed.; Online - full text ed.
Published by: Burton Group, PO Box 3448, Salt Lake City, UT 84110-3448. TEL 801-943-1966, FAX 801-943-2425, info@tbg.com. Ed. Jamie Lewis. Pub. Judith Burton. Circ: 1,500 (paid).

C C S U LIBRARY NEWSLETTER; bulletin of the Elihu Burritt Library. (Central Connecticut State University) see *LIBRARY AND INFORMATION SCIENCES*

658.3 CAN ISSN 1495-5482
C X O CANADA. Text in English. 2000. bi-m. CND 23.70 domestic; CND 30 foreign (effective 2002). adv. **Document type:** *Magazine, Trade.* **Description:** Offers a Canadian perspective on the people, companies and trends driving e-business.
Related titles: Online - full text ed.
Published by: I T World Canada, Inc., No.302 - 55 Town Centre Court, Scarborough, ON M1P 4X4, Canada. TEL 416-290-0240, FAX 416-290-0238, info@itworldcanada.com, http://www.itworldcanada.com/cxo/. Circ: 5,000 (paid and controlled).

004.6 FRA
CALCULATEURS PARALLELES RESEAUX ET SYSTEMES REPARTIS. Text in French. 1989. q. EUR 290 in Europe; EUR 350 elsewhere (effective 2002).
Former titles: Calculateurs Paralleles (1260-3198); (until 1994): La Lettre du Transputer et des Calculateurs Paralleles (1246-502X); (until 1992): La Lettre du Transputer et des Calculateurs Distribues (1145-4458); (until 1990): La Lettre du Transputer (0997-7392)
—BLDSC (7777.084000), ingenta.
Published by: Hermes Science Publications, 8, quai du Marche-Neuf, Paris, 75004, France. FAX 33-1-53101521, hermes@iway.fr, http://lifc.univ-fcomte.fr/revue/CPRSR, http://www.hermes-science.com.

004.68 GBR ISSN 1065-0741
Z678.93.L63 CODEN: CISYF9
➤ **CAMPUS-WIDE INFORMATION SYSTEMS**; the journal of technology on campus. Text in English. 1984. 5/yr. EUR 1,597.54 in Europe; USD 1,569 in North America; AUD 2,049 in Australasia; GBP 1,119.04 in UK & elsewhere (effective 2006). a.index. back issues avail.; reprint service avail. from PSC. **Document type:** *Journal, Academic/Scholarly.* **Description:** Covers the use of campus-wide information systems, the use of computer networks on campus and online public-access catalogs.
Former titles: Academic and Library Computing (1055-4769); (until 1991): Library Workstation Report (1041-7923); (until 1989): Library Workstation and P C Report (0894-9158); (until vol.4, no.7, 1987): M300 and P C Report (0743-7633)
Related titles: Online - full text ed.: (from EBSCO Publishing, Emerald Group Publishing Limited, Gale Group, IngentaConnect, O C L C Online Computer Library Center, Inc., ProQuest Information & Learning, Swets Information Services).
Indexed: ABIn, C&CSA, CompD, CompLI, EmerIntel, Emerald, Inspec, LISA, MicrocompInd.

C

—BLDSC (3506.283000), AskIEEE, IE, Infotrieve, ingenta, Linda Hall. **CCC.**
Published by: Emerald Group Publishing Limited, 60-62 Toller Ln, Bradford, W Yorks BD8 9BY, United Kingdom. TEL 44-1274-777700, FAX 44-1274-785200, infomation@emeraldinsight.com, http://www.emeraldinsight.com/cwis.htm. Ed. Glenn Hardaker. Pub., R&P Vicky Williams. **Subscr. addr. in N America:** Emerald Group Publishing Ltd., 44 Brattle St, 4th Fl, Cambridge, MA 02138. TEL 617-497-2175, 888-622-0075, FAX 617-354-6875.

004.6 USA ISSN 1093-1279
HD9696.S58
CARD TECHNOLOGY; tracking the future of card systems and applications. Text in English. m. USD 98 in US & Canada; USD 148 elsewhere (effective 2005). adv. back issues avail. **Document type:** *Newsletter, Trade.* **Description:** Developed and written by independent journalists. Takes you inside the smart card industry, spotlighting the market trends, new technologies and news that is shaping the industry.
Related titles: Online - full text ed.: (from Florida Center for Library Automation, Gale Group, Northern Light Technology, Inc., O C L C Online Computer Library Center, Inc., ProQuest Information & Learning).
Indexed: B&I, BLI, CompD, HRIS.
—**CCC.**
Published by: Source Media, Inc., One State St Plaza, 27th Fl, New York, NY 10004. TEL 212-803-6077, 800-221-1809, FAX 212-747-1154, custserv@sourcemedia.com, http://www.cardtechnology.com/, http://www.sourcemedia.com. Eds. Daniel Balaban TEL 33-6-74-49-77-68, Donald Davis TEL 312-983-6152. Pub. Andrew Rowe. Adv. contact Jim Baker TEL 312-983-6179. color page USD 3,760. Circ: 25,047.

004.16 AUS
CHANNEL X AUSTRALIA. Text in English. m. AUD 56; AUD 6.95 newsstand/cover (effective 2002). adv. **Document type:** *Magazine, Trade.* **Description:** Covers current IT channel business challenges by addressing technology and new-market issues in an analytical and targeted fashion.
Related titles: Online - full text ed.
Published by: I D G Communications Pty. Ltd., 88 Christie St, St Leonards, NSW 2065, Australia. TEL 61-2-94395133, FAX 61-2-94395512, http://www.idg.com.au. adv.: color page USD 2,169; trim 210 x 297.

004 USA ISSN 1079-6606
CHERYL WATSON'S TUNING LETTER. Text in English. 1991. bi-m. USD 765 (effective 2004). **Document type:** *Newsletter, Trade.*
Published by: Watson & Walker, Inc., 2130 Bispham Rd, Sarasota, FL 34231. TEL 941-924-6565, 800-553-4562, FAX 941-924-4892, http://www.watsonwalker.com/TUNING.html. Ed., Pub. Cheryl Watson.

004.6 CHN
CHINA NETWORKWORLD. Text in Chinese. 1984. w. adv. **Document type:** *Newspaper, Consumer.* **Description:** Covers the latest news, worldwide and domestic, and provides an in-depth look at technology, new products, and leading industry figures within the computer and networked systems industries.
Formerly: Computer and Communication
Published by: I D G China, Rm. 616, Tower A, COFCO Plaza, Jianguomennei Dajie, Beijing, 100005 , China. TEL 86-10-6526-0959, FAX 86-10-6526-0866, dumin@idg.com.cn, http://www.cnw.com.cn/, http://www.idgchina.com. Ed. Guangpu Cai. Adv. contact Weijuan Chu. page CNY 19,800; trim 260 x 356. Circ: 97,840.

004.6 USA
CHIPNET ELECTRONIC MAGAZINE. Text in English. 1994. every 6 wks. **Document type:** *Newsletter.*
Media: Online - full text.
Published by: ChipNet Publications, 650 Stadler Rd, Helena, MT 59602. chipnet@aol.com, http://www.tybee.com/chipnet. Ed. John Peck.

004.6 USA
CLIENT SERVER NEWS; the new weekly newsletter for the windows NT marketplace worldwide. Text in English. 1993. w. USD 595 (effective 1999). adv. **Document type:** *Newsletter.* **Description:** For industry executives, analysts and major end-users affiliated with the Windows NT operating system.
Published by: G2 Computer Intelligence Inc., PO Box 7, Glen Head, NY 11545-0007. TEL 516-759-7025, FAX 516-759-7028. Ed., Pub. Maureen O'Gara. R&P, Adv. contact Charles Hall.

004.6 GBR ISSN 0968-2082
HD66 CODEN: COLCEH
➤ **COLLABORATIVE COMPUTING.** Text in English. 1994. q. GBP 55, USD 99 domestic to individuals; GBP 130 domestic to institutions; USD 225 in North America to institutions. charts; illus. **Document type:** *Academic/Scholarly.* **Description:** Publishes innovative research in computer-supported cooperative work and computer-mediated communications, with emphasis on the development of computer and communication technologies to support group work.
Related titles: Online - full text ed.
Indexed: Inspec.
—AskIEEE. **CCC.**
Published by: Chapman & Hall, Journals Department (Subsidiary of: International Thomson Publishing Group), Chapman & Hall, 2-6 Boundary Row, London, SE1 8HN, United Kingdom. TEL 44-20-7865-0066, FAX 44-20-7522-9623, jhelp@chall.co.uk, http://www.chaphall.com/chaphall/journals.html. **Dist. by:** International Thompson Publishing Services Ltd., Cheriton House, North Way, Walworth Industrial Estate, Andover, Hants SP10 5BE, United Kingdom. TEL 44-1264-342713, FAX 44-1264-342807.

004.6 CAN ISSN 1484-9739
COMMUNICATIONS & NETWORKING. Text in English. 1997. m. CND 80 domestic; USD 115 in United States; USD 155 elsewhere; free to qualified personnel (effective 2003). **Document type:** *Magazine, Trade.*
Published by: Transcontinental Media, Inc. (Subsidiary of: Transcontinental, Inc.), 25 Sheppard Ave West, Ste 100, Toronto, ON M2N 6S7, Canada. TEL 416-733-7600, FAX 416-218-3544, gmeckbach@itbusiness.ca, info@transcontinental.ca, http://www.transcontinental-gtc.com/en/home.html, http://www.itbusiness.ca. Circ: 20,000 (controlled).

004.6 GBR ISSN 0966-4882
COMMUNICATIONS NETWORKS. Text in English. 1984. m. GBP 30. adv. **Document type:** *Trade.*
Formerly (until 1991): Communications (0266-8009)
Indexed: B&I, Inspec.
—AskIEEE. **CCC.**
Published by: E M A P Computing (Subsidiary of: E M A P Business Communications), 33-39 Bowling Green Ln, London, EC1R 0DA, United Kingdom. TEL 44-20-7837-1212, FAX 44-207-278-4008. Ed. Maxwell Cooter. Circ: 20,000.

004.68 GBR ISSN 1077-4696
COMMUNICATIONS STANDARDS NEWS; tcp/ip - lans - wans - multimedia - wireless - osi. Text in English. 1982. bi-w. looseleaf. USD 497 domestic; USD 530 foreign. cum.index: 1982-1988. back issues avail. **Document type:** *Newsletter.*
Incorporates (in July 1994): Open Systems Communications (0741-2851); Incorporates (1990-1992): Open Systems Report (1052-701X); Supersedes: Gateway (Ann Arbor) (0890-2526); Formerly: O S I Communication (0740-4433)
Related titles: Online - full text ed.: (from LexisNexis, ProQuest Information & Learning).
—**CCC.**
Published by: Omnicom P B I, Rosemount House, Rosemount Ave, W Byfleet, Surrey KT14 6NP, United Kingdom. TEL 44-1932-355515, FAX 44-1932-355962. Ed. Mary Crowley. Circ: 800.

004.6 GBR
COMMUNICATIONSWEEK INTERNATIONAL. Text in English. 199?. w. **Document type:** *Trade.* **Description:** Cover computer networks, ATM technology, ISDN broadband wireless network technologies and related issues.
Related titles: Online - full text ed.
Published by: Emap Media Ltd. (Subsidiary of: Emap Business Communications Ltd.), 33-39 Bowling Green Ln, London, EC1R 0DA, United Kingdom. TEL 44-20-7505-8000, FAX 44-20-7505-8504, andrew@cwi.emap.com, http://www.totaltele.com/, http://www.totaltele.com/cilive/. Ed. Anne Morris.

384.3 025.4 USA
COMMWEB. Text in English. d. adv. **Document type:** *Trade.* **Description:** Complete, focused, one-stop information resource that guides business and service-provider organizations in evaluating, purchasing and implementing advanced communications systems and networks.
Published by: C M P Media LLC (Subsidiary of: United News & Media), 600 Community Dr, Manhasset, NY 11030. TEL 516-562-5000, FAX 516-562-5036, http://www.commweb.com.

384 NLD ISSN 1389-1286
TK5105.5
➤ **COMPUTER NETWORKS.** Text in English. 1976. 18/yr. EUR 1,789 in Europe to institutions; JPY 237,800 in Japan to institutions; USD 2,000 to institutions except Europe and Japan (effective 2006). illus. Index. back issues avail.; reprints avail. **Document type:** *Journal, Academic/Scholarly.* **Description:** Covers all aspects of the design, implementation, use and management of computer networks, communications subsystems and all other supporting activities.
Former titles (until 1999): Computer Networks and ISDN Systems (0169-7552); (until 1985): Computer Networks (0376-5075)
Related titles: Microform ed.: (from PQC); Online - full text ed.: (from EBSCO Publishing, Gale Group, IngentaConnect, ScienceDirect, Swets Information Services); ♦ Supplement(s): Computer Networks for Research in Europe. ISSN 1389-1308.
Indexed: ABIn, AIA, ASCA, B&BAb, BrCerAb, BrHumI, C&CSA, C&ISA, CADCAM, CMCI, CerAb, CommAb, CompAb, CompC, CompD, CompLI, CompR, CorrAb, CurCont, CybAb, E&CAJ, EMA, EngInd, ErgAb, IAA, Inspec, LISA, M&TEA, MBF, METADEX, MathR, RASB, RefZh, SSCI, SolStAb, TelAb, WAA, ZentMath.
—BLDSC (3394.114900), AskIEEE, CISTI, Ei, IDS, IE, Infotrieve, ingenta, Linda Hall. **CCC.**
Published by: (International Council for Computer Communications), Elsevier BV, North-Holland (Subsidiary of: Elsevier Science & Technology), Sara Burgerhartstraat 25, Amsterdam, 1055 KV, Netherlands. TEL 31-20-485-3911, FAX 31-20-485-2457, nlinfo-f@elsevier.nl, http://www.elsevier.com/locate/comnet, http://www.elsevier.nl. Eds. H. Rudin, I. F. Akyildiz. Circ: 2,500. **Subscr.:** Elsevier BV, PO Box 211, Amsterdam 1000 AE, Netherlands. TEL 31-20-485-3757, FAX 31-20-485-3432, http://www.elsevier.nl.

004.62 USA ISSN 0899-126X
COMPUTER PROTOCOLS. Text in English. 1988. m. USD 150 in North America; USD 165 elsewhere (effective 2001). bk.rev. **Document type:** *Newsletter, Trade.* **Description:** Contains news and information about computer protocols and their related products, including LANs, gateways, and bridges.
Related titles: Online - full text ed.: (from bigchalk, Data-Star, EBSCO Publishing, Factiva, Gale Group, LexisNexis, ProQuest Information & Learning, The Dialog Corporation).
Indexed: CompD.
—**CCC.**
Published by: Worldwide Videotex, PO Box 3273, Boynton Beach, FL 33424-3273. TEL 561-738-2276, markedit@juno.com, http://www.wvpubs.com. Ed., Pub. Mark Wright.

004 COL ISSN 0122-2961
COMPUTERWORLD COLOMBIA. Text in Spanish. 1989. s-m. COP 70,000 domestic; USD 80 foreign; COP 3,500 newsstand/cover (effective 2000). adv. bk.rev. bibl. 28 p./no. 4 cols./p.; **Document type:** *Magazine, Consumer.* **Description:** Covers computer systems applications, networking, the internet and computer related news.
Published by: Iviarco Ltda., Carrera 90 No. 156-19 Piso 4, Bogota, CUND, Colombia. TEL 57-1-6800399, FAX 57-1-6800399, http://www.computerworld.com.co. Ed., Adv. contact Ciro Villate. color page USD 2,400; trim 350 x 498. Circ: 5,000.

004.65 USA
CONFERENCE ON LOCAL COMPUTER NETWORKS. PROCEEDINGS. Text in English. 1976. a. USD 145. adv. **Document type:** *Proceedings.* **Description:** Topics include basic LAN issues: broadband, software, token rings, management and future directions.
Former titles (until 1979): Conference on Local Computer Networking (0742-1303); (until 1976): Conference on Experiments in New Approaches to Local Computer Networking
Related titles: Online - full text ed.: (from I E E E).
Indexed: EngInd.
—BLDSC (3409.635200), IE, ingenta. **CCC.**
Published by: (Institute of Electrical and Electronics Engineers, Inc.), I E E E Computer Society, 3 Park Ave, 17th Fl, New York, NY 10017. TEL 714-821-8380, 800-678-4333, FAX 714-821-4641, customer.service@ieee.org, http://www.ieee.org. Ed. Cat Harris. Pub. Matt Loeb. Adv. contact Frieda Koester. **Co-sponsor:** University of Minnesota. Computer Center.

004.64 USA ISSN 1070-0994
QA76.55
CONNECT (ANN ARBOR)✶; the modem user's resources. Text in English. 1993. 9/yr. USD 18 (effective 1994). adv. bk.rev. back issues avail. **Document type:** *Consumer.* **Description:** Covers commercial on-line services, the Internet, and bulletin board systems and networks from a user's perspective.
Related titles: Online - full text ed.
Indexed: SoftBase.
Published by: Pegasus Press, Inc., 523 Sanford St, Covington, KY 41011-2529. TEL 313-973-8825, FAX 313-973-0411. Ed. William Rail. Adv. contact Mary Caro. Circ: 65,000.

CONNECT (LONDON). see *COMMUNICATIONS*

004.6 ITA
CONNESSIONI & CABLAGGI. Text in Italian. 1989. 9/yr. EUR 41 (effective 2005). **Description:** Devoted to the area of cabling and networking.
Published by: Gruppo Editoriale J C E, Via Patecchio 2, Milan, MI 20141, Italy. TEL 39-02-57316011, FAX 39-02-57316291, info@jce.it, http://www.jce.it. Ed. Gioiella Campelli. Pub. Jacopo Castelfranchi. Circ: 11,000.

004.6 GBR
CONNEXION; the networking newspaper. Text in English. 1988. fortn. GBP 60; GBP 80 foreign. adv.
Indexed: B&I, Inspec.
Published by: V N U Business Publications Ltd., 32-34 Broadwick St, London, W1A 2HG, United Kingdom. TEL 44-20-7316-9000, FAX 44-20-7316-9003. Ed. John Caffrey. Pub. Tony Faure. Adv. contact Richard Beagley. B&W page USD 4,920, color page USD 6,310; trim 15.25 x 11. Circ: 29,460.

004.6 GBR ISSN 1461-0493
CORPORATE INTRANET REVIEW (YEARS). Text in English. a. GBP 45, USD 80 (effective 1998). **Description:** Focuses on managing and developing corporate intranets. Examines new techniques and how to integrate them with existing legacy applications.

Published by: Euromoney Publications plc, Nestor House, Playhouse Yard, London, EC4V 5EX, United Kingdom. TEL 44-207-7798673, FAX 44-20-77798541.

004.6 USA
CORPORATE INTRANET SOLUTIONS. Text in English. m. USD 395 (effective 1999). **Document type:** *Newsletter, Trade.* **Description:** Provides advice on how to maximize a company's intranet as a business tool. Discusses options in important areas, including knowledge management, browser selection and standardization, security and software solutions.
Published by: Gartner Inc., 56 Top Gallant Rd, Stamford, CT 06904-2212. TEL 203-316-1111, 800-544-7337, FAX 203-316-6300, jwhitney@info-edge.com, http://www.gartner3.gartnerweb.com, http://www.info-edge.com.

004.68 GBR ISSN 1369-7382
CORPORATE NETWORKS. Text in English. 1995. 10/yr. GBP 47; GBP 57 foreign. **Document type:** *Trade.* **Description:** Provides news, updates and analysis, boardroom briefings and case studies to reflect the increasing use of client-servers to deliver corporate networks in the fast expanding networked computer industry.
Formerly: Client - Server Magazine (1358-6505)
Related titles: ♦ Supplement to: Business & Technology Magazine. ISSN 1351-3680.
—CCC.
Published by: Reed Business Information Ltd. (Subsidiary of: Reed Business), Quadrant House, The Quadrant, Brighton Rd, Sutton, Surrey SM2 5AS, United Kingdom. TEL 44-20-8652-4800, FAX 44-20-8652-4748.

004.6 GBR ISSN 0265-4490
DATABASE AND NETWORK JOURNAL; an international journal of database and network practice. Text in English. 1974. bi-m. GBP 122 domestic; GBP 147, USD 291 foreign (effective 2003). bk.rev. bibl.; charts; tr.lit. 28 p./no.; back issues avail.; reprints avail. **Document type:** *Academic/Scholarly.*
Incorporates in part (in 1994): P C Business Software (0954-2833); Former titles (until 1983): Database Journal (0141-0849); Mini Micro Software (0265-6760); Small Systems Software
Related titles: Online - full text ed.: (from Florida Center for Library Automation, Gale Group).
Indexed: AEA, BMT, CADCAM, CompC, CompD, EngInd, Inspec, TelAb.
—BLDSC (3535.802700), AskIEEE, CISTI, Ei, IE, Infotrieve, ingenta.
Published by: A.P. Publications Ltd., Old Exchange House, Marford Rd, Wheathampstead, Herts AL4 8AY, United Kingdom. TEL 44-1582-833504, FAX 44-1582-832327, 106142.1713@compuserve.com, http://www.ap-publications.co.uk. Ed. Ed Patterson. Circ: 1,400.

004.6 GBR ISSN 0955-7415
DATACOM; the internetworking magazine. Text in English. 1989. m. GBP 48. adv. **Document type:** *Trade.* **Description:** For specifiers and purchasers of networking hard- and software products and services. Supplies strategic management information on all areas of voice and data communications.
Indexed: B&I, Inspec.
—AskIEEE, Infotrieve.
Published by: E M A P Computing, E M A P Business Communications, 33-39 Bowling Green Ln, London, WC1R ODA, United Kingdom. TEL 44-20-7388-2430, FAX 44-20-7388-2480. Ed. Jim Hayes. Pub. Danny Phillips. Adv. contact Peter Garner. page GBP 2,756; trim 210 x 297. Circ: 21,000 (controlled). **Subscr. to:** Ferrari House, 258 Field End Rd, Ruislip, Mddx HA4 9UX, United Kingdom. TEL 44-181-868-4499.

004.6 384.3 GBR
DATACOM EUROPE. Text in English. 2000. q. adv. back issues avail. **Document type:** *Magazine, Trade.* **Description:** Helps readers understand real life in the developing networks and Internet channels in Europe.
Formerly: DataCom Reseller (1472-8109)
Published by: I B C Publishing (Subsidiary of: Interactive Business Communications Ltd.), Latimer House, 189 High St, Potters Bar, Herts EN6 5DA, United Kingdom. TEL 44-1707-664200, FAX 44-1707-664800, info@ibcpub.co.uk, http://www.datacomeurope.com/, http://www.ibcpub.com. Ed. Ian Byfield.

DEVELOPPEUR REFERENCE. see *COMPUTERS—Computer Programming*

005.5 USA
DOMINO UPDATE. Text in English. m. USD 255; USD 510 includes Notes version (effective 2000). **Document type:** *Trade.* **Description:** Contains information on Domino, an applications and messaging server program for the Lotus Corporation's Lotus Notes product.
Published by: Xephon, 9330 Lyndon B Johnson Fwy., Ste. 800, Dallas, TX 75243-4310. TEL 303-410-9344, FAX 303-438-0290, http://www.xephon.com/.

004.66 USA
DOW JONES BANDWIDTH INTELLIGENCE ALERT. Variant title: Bandwidth Intelligence Alert. Text in English. 2001. w. USD 900 (effective 2001). adv. **Document type:** *Newsletter, Trade.* **Description:** Provides current information on the companies, trading activity and issues shaping the nascent broadband market.
Published by: Dow Jones Company, 1250 H St, NW, 7th Fl, Washington, DC 20005. TEL 202-393-7400, FAX 202-393-0974. Ed. Michael Rieke. R&P, Adv. contact Carlos Mesa.

323.445 AUS ISSN 1329-6906
E F A NEWS. Text in English. q. **Document type:** *Newsletter.* **Description:** Aims to protect and promote the civil liberties of users of computer-based communications systems and those affected by their use.
Related titles: Online - full text ed.
Published by: Electronic Frontiers Australia Inc., PO Box 382, North Adelaide, SA 5006, Australia. TEL 61-8-83578844, FAX 61-8-83733829, editor@efa.org.au, http://www.efa.org.au/efa/news. Ed. Brenda Aynsley.

E T H O S NEWSLETTER. (European Telematics Horizontal Observatory Service) see *COMMUNICATIONS—Computer Applications*

▼ **EI MAGAZINE.** see *COMPUTERS—Internet*

004.6 USA ISSN 1054-1055
QA75.5 CODEN: EOURER
EJOURNAL. Text in English. 1991. m. free. **Description:** Explores the theory and practice of providing information in an electronic format.
Media: Online - full text.
Published by: State University of New York at Albany, Computing and Network Services, 1400 Washington Ave, Albany, NY 12222. Ejournal@albany.edu, http://www.hanover.edu/philos/ejournal. Ed. Ted Jennings.

004.6 FRA ISSN 1262-3261
TK5105.5
ELECTRONIC JOURNAL ON NETWORKS AND DISTRIBUTED PROCESSING. Text in French, English. 1995. s-a. free. back issues avail. **Document type:** *Academic/Scholarly.* **Description:** For managers, designers and operators ofcomputer networks.
Media: Online - full content.
Published by: Laboratoire T A S C, Av. de l'Universite, Pau, 64000, France. TEL 33-5-59923128, FAX 33-5-59808374, annig.leparc@univ-pau.fr, http://rerir.univ-pau.fr, http://rerir.univ-pau.fr/. Ed. Annig Lacayrelle.

621.3692 USA
ELECTRONICAST PHOTONICS. Text in English. 1999. bi-m. USD 775 (effective 2000). **Document type:** *Newsletter.* **Description:** Includes current news of the global fiber optics communication industry.
Related titles: E-mail ed.
Published by: ElectroniCast Corporation, 1923 Bayview Ave., Belmont, CA 94002-1616. electronicast@msn.com, http://www.electronicast.com. Ed. Stephen ontgomery.

004 USA
ENTERPRISE NETWORKS & SERVERS; a chronicle of information for networks and servers in the enterprise. Text in Spanish. 2002. m. USD 45 (effective 2005). back issues avail. **Document type:** *Magazine, Trade.*
Formed by the merger of (1988-2002): Serverworld (1535-6531); (1987-2002): Enterprise Networking Magazine (1076-1462); Which was formerly (until 1999): A B U I Network News (1061-5547); (until 1991): Network News (Sudbury) (1057-2082)
Published by: Publications & Communications, Inc., 11675 Jollyville Rd Ste 150, Austin, TX 78759. TEL 512-637-0353, FAX 512-331-3900, mikey@pcinews.com, http://www.enterprisenetworksandservers.com/, http://www.pcinews.com/. Eds. Larry Storer TEL 254-399-6484, Robert Martin. Adv. contact Mike Yokom. Circ: 17,000 (controlled).

621.3962 USA
EUROPEAN FIBER OPTICS REPORT. Text in English. 2000. biennial. USD 8,750 to corporations (effective 2000). **Description:** Provides an analysis and forecast of European consumption of fiber optic communication components.
Published by: ElectroniCast Corporation, 1923 Bayview Ave., Belmont, CA 94002-1616. electronicast@msn.com, http://www.electronicast.com. Ed. Stephen ontgomery.

004.6 DEU ISSN 1617-1683
EXPERT'S INSIDE. NETWARE. Text in German. 2001. m. EUR 116.40; EUR 9.70 newsstand/cover (effective 2003). adv. **Document type:** *Magazine, Trade.*
Published by: redtec publishing GmbH, Gruber Str 46a, Poing, 85586, Germany. TEL 49-8121-951850, FAX 49-8121-951880, info@redtec.de, http://www.experts-inside.de/netware, http://www.redtec.de. Adv. contact Guido Klausbruckner. B&W page EUR 1,000, color page EUR 1,500; trim 210 x 297.

004.6 USA
FAULKNER'S ENTERPRISE COMMUNICATIONS. Text in English. 1965. d. **Document type:** *Trade.* **Description:** Covers all of the areas of vital interest and importance to today's telecommunications and data communications manager, specialist, and end-user.
Former titles: Faulkner's Enterprise Networking; Data Communications Reports; Auerbach Data Communications Reports (0004-7724)
Media: Online - full content. **Related titles:** CD-ROM ed.: USD 1,507.
Published by: Faulkner Information Services, Inc. (Subsidiary of: Information Today, Inc.), 116 Cooper Center, 7905 Browning Rd, Pennsauken, NJ 08109-4319. TEL 856-662-2070, 800-843-0460, FAX 856-662-3380, faulkner@faulkner.com, http://www.faulkner.com.

621.3692 USA
FIBER OPTIC INDUSTRY GLOBAL QUARTERLY REVIEW. Text in English. q. USD 4,000 to corporations (effective 2000). **Description:** Includes information on fiber optic component and system deployments, new product announcements, and market forecast summaries.
Published by: ElectroniCast Corporation, 1923 Bayview Ave., Belmont, CA 94002-1616. electronicast@msn.com, http://www.electronicast.com. Ed. Stephen ontgomery.

621.3692 USA ISSN 0275-0457
FIBER OPTICS AND COMMUNICATIONS. Text in English. 1978. m. USD 695 in US & Canada; USD 745 elsewhere (effective 2004). back issues avail. **Document type:** *Newsletter.* **Description:** Covers domestic and international news on fiber optics, communications and related fields.
Formerly: Fiber Optics and Communications Newsletter (0274-6271)
Indexed: CompC.
—CCC.
Published by: Information Gatekeepers, Inc., 320 Washington St, Ste 302, Brighton, MA 02135. TEL 617-782-5033, 800-323-1088, FAX 617-782-5735, info@igigroup.com, http://www.igigroup.com/nl/pages/focomm.html. Ed. Sebastian Wargacki. Pub. Dr. Paul Polishuk. Circ: 350.

621.3692 USA ISSN 8756-2049
FIBER OPTICS NEWS. Text in English. 1981. bi-w. USD 997 (effective 2005). back issues avail. **Document type:** *Newsletter, Trade.*
Formerly: Fiber - Laser News (0275-6099)
Related titles: Online - full text ed.: (from Gale Group, LexisNexis, The Dialog Corporation).
Indexed: ABIn, PROMT.
—CCC.
Published by: Access Intelligence, LLC (Subsidiary of: Veronis, Suhler & Associates Inc.), 1201 Seven Locks Rd, Ste 300, Potomac, MD 20854. TEL 301-354-2000, 800-777-5006, FAX 301-340-1451, jschwartz@pbimedia.com, clientservices@accessintel.com, http://www.pbimedia.com/cgi/catalog/info?FON.

621.3692 USA ISSN 1051-189X
FIBER OPTICS WEEKLY UPDATE. Short title: F O W U. Text in English. 1978. w. USD 695 in US & Canada; USD 745 elsewhere (effective 2004). back issues avail. **Document type:** *Newsletter, Trade.* **Description:** Covers news, information and market trends on fiber optics.
Formerly: Fiber Optics and Communications Weekly News Service (0732-9407)
Related titles: Online - full text ed.: (from Factiva, Florida Center for Library Automation, Gale Group, Northern Light Technology, Inc., O C L C Online Computer Library Center, Inc., ProQuest Information & Learning).
Indexed: ABIn.
—CCC.
Published by: Information Gatekeepers, Inc., 320 Washington St, Ste 302, Brighton, MA 02135. TEL 617-782-5033, 800-323-1088, FAX 617-782-5735, info@igigroup.com, http://www.igigroup.com. Ed. Sebastian Wargacki. Pub. Dr. Paul Polishuk.

004.6 USA ISSN 1554-057X
▼ ➤ **FOUNDATIONS AND TRENDS IN NETWORKING.** Text in English. forthcoming 2006. 4/yr. USD 300 in North America; EUR 300 elsewhere; USD 340 combined subscription in North America print & online eds.; EUR 340 combined subscription elsewhere print & online eds. (effective 2006). **Document type:** *Journal, Academic/Scholarly.* **Description:** Publishes high-quality survey and tutorial monographs on all aspects of networking.
Related titles: Online - full text ed.: ISSN 1554-0588. forthcoming 2006. USD 300 in North America; EUR 300 elsewhere (effective 2006).
Published by: Now Publishers Inc., PO Box 1024, Hanover, MA 02339. TEL 781-871-0245, FAX 781-871-6172, sales@nowpublishers.com, http://www.nowpublishers.com/net. Ed. Anthony Ephremides. Pub., R&P Mike Casey.

004.6 USA ISSN 1083-3501
FRONTIERS IN NETWORKING. Text in English. q. USD 89.95. **Document type:** *Academic/Scholarly.*
Media: CD-ROM.

Published by: Academic Press (Subsidiary of: Elsevier Science & Technology), 525 B St, Ste 1900, San Diego, CA 92101-4495. TEL 619-231-6616, 800-894-3434, FAX 619-699-6422, apsubs@acad.com, http://www.academicpress.com.

004.65 USA ISSN 1541-1222
GIGABIT / A T M. Text in English. 1991. m. USD 695 in US & Canada; USD 745 elsewhere (effective 2004). back issues avail. **Document type:** *Newsletter.* **Description:** Looks at products, trends, and industry news relating to ATM and its technology.
Formerly: Asynchronous Transfer Mode Newsletter (1067-5221)
Related titles: E-mail ed.: USD 695 worldwide (effective 2003); Online - full text ed.: (from ProQuest Information & Learning).
Indexed: ABIn.
Published by: Information Gatekeepers, Inc., 320 Washington St, Ste 302, Brighton, MA 02135. TEL 617-782-5033, 800-323-1088, FAX 617-782-5735, info@igigroup.com, http://www.igigroup.com/nl/pages/atmtelecom.html. Pub. Dr. Paul Polishuk. **Dist. by:** Publications Resource Group, 121 Union St., Box 792, North Adams, MA 01247. TEL 413-664-6185, FAX 413-664-9343.

004.6 USA ISSN 1067-8719
THE GILBANE REPORT; newsletter on content management and information technology. Text in English. 1993. 10/yr. USD 249 combined subscription print & online eds. (effective 2005). **Document type:** *Journal, Trade.* **Description:** Covers technology and trends in content management technologies.
Related titles: Online - full text ed.: USD 99 (effective 2005).
Published by: Bluebill Advisors, Inc, 763 Massachusetts Ave, Cambridge, MA 02139. TEL 617-497-9443, FAX 617-497-5256, info@gilbane.com, customerservice@gilbane.com, http://www.gilbane.com/, http://www.bluebilladvisors.com/. Ed. Frank Gilbane TEL 617-497-9443.

004.6 USA
H E P NET NEWS NEWSLETTER. (High Energy Physics) Text in English. 1993. irreg. back issues avail. **Document type:** *Newsletter.* **Description:** Topics range from tools and methods used to optimize the network to innovations in video-conferencing.
Published by: H E P Network Resource Center, PO Box 500, Sta 368, Batavia, IL 60515. marcia@hep.net, http://www.hep.net/hepnrc/hepnetnews/. Ed. Marcia Knauf.

004.6 USA
HELP DESK SOLUTIONS. Text in English. m. USD 395 (effective 1999). **Document type:** *Newsletter, Trade.* **Description:** Discusses ways to transform your help desk into a smooth-running operation that gets problems solved with minimal disruption.
Published by: Gartner Inc., 56 Top Gallant Rd, Stamford, CT 06904-2212. TEL 203-316-1111, 800-544-7337, FAX 203-316-6300, jwhitney@info-edge.com, http://www.gartner3.gartnerweb.com, http://www.info-edge.com.

004.6 KOR
HI-TECH INFORMATION. Text in Korean. 1989. bi-w. adv. **Document type:** *Magazine, Trade.* **Description:** Aimed at management decision makers who make or influence purchasing decisions in the hardware, software, telecommunications, semiconductor, networking, and internet industries.
Related titles: Online - full text ed.
Published by: Hi-Tech Information Inc., 494-65 Yonggang-Dong, Mapo-Gu, Daeho Bldg., 3rd Fl., Seoul, 121070, Korea, S. TEL 82-2-3257300, FAX 82-2-7196409, webmaster@hitech.co.kr, http://www.hitech.co.kr. Ed. Y S Gimm. Adv. contact Junbin Kim. B&W page USD 1,500, color page USD 3,000; trim 270 x 380. Circ: 30,000.

HIGH POTENTIAL. see *OCCUPATIONS AND CAREERS*

HIGH POTENTIAL CHANCES. see *OCCUPATIONS AND CAREERS*

004.16 GBR
HOTSPOT MARKETS. Text in English. 2002. m. GBP 495, USD 940, EUR 743 (effective 2004). **Document type:** *Newsletter, Trade.* **Description:** Covers Wi-Fi hotspot operators, suppliers and end-users as well as data and analysis on the public WLAN business cases, rollout strategies and services of mobile, fixed-line and start up operators.
Related titles: Online - full content ed.: ISSN 1478-8403. 2002. GBP 1,485, USD 2,821, EUR 2,228 (effective 2004); Online - full text ed.: (from Gale Group).
Published by: Baskerville (Subsidiary of: T & F Informa plc), Sheepen Place, Colchester, Essex C03 3LP, United Kingdom. TEL 44-20-70175537, FAX 44-20-70174783, telecoms.enquiries@informa.com, http://baskerville.telecoms.com/NASApp/cs/ContentServer?pagename=marlin/home&siteid=20001000863&MarlinViewType=MARKT_EFFORT&marketingid=20001127204, http://www.baskerville.telecoms.com/.

004.6 USA ISSN 1063-6692
TK5105.5 CODEN: IEANEP
➤ **I E E E - A C M TRANSACTIONS ON NETWORKING.** (Institute of Electrical and Electronics Engineers - Association for Computing Machinery) Text in English. 1993. bi-m. USD 475 domestic to non-members; USD 516 foreign to non-members; USD 46 domestic to members; USD 87 foreign to members; USD 23 domestic to students; USD 64 foreign to students; USD 571 combined subscription domestic to non-members print & online eds.; USD 612 combined subscription foreign to non-members print & online eds.; USD 55 combined subscription domestic to members print & online eds.; USD 96 combined subscription foreign to members print & online eds.; USD 28 combined subscription domestic to students print & online eds.; USD 69 combined subscription foreign to students print & online eds. (effective 2006). adv. illus. reprints avail. **Document type:** *Journal, Academic/Scholarly.* **Description:** Contains high-quality papers on network architecture and design, communication protocols, network software, network technologies, services, operations and management.
Related titles: CD-ROM ed.; Microfiche ed.; Online - full text ed.: ISSN 1558-2566. USD 379 to non-members; USD 37 to members; USD 18 to students (effective 2006) (from Association for Computing Machinery, Inc., EBSCO Publishing, Swets Information Services).
Indexed: AS&TI, ASCA, BrCerAb, C&CSA, C&ISA, CMCI, CerAb, CompAb, CompLI, CompR, CorrAb, CurCont, E&CAJ, EMA, EngInd, IAA, ISR, Inspec, M&TEA, MBF, METADEX, RefZh, SCI, SolStAb, WAA.
—BLDSC (4362.787550), AskIEEE, CISTI, Ei, IDS, IE, Infotrieve, ingenta, Linda Hall. **CCC.**
Published by: Institute of Electrical and Electronics Engineers, Inc., 445 Hoes Ln, Piscataway, NJ 08854-1331. TEL 732-981-0060, FAX 732-981-1721, subscription-service@ieee.org, http://www.comsoc.org/livepubs/net, http://www.ieee.org. Ed. Ellen Zegurba. R&P Michael Spada TEL 732-981-3430. **Subscr. to:** Maruzen Co., Ltd., 3-10 Nihonbashi 2-chome, Chuo-ku, Tokyo 103-0027, Japan. TEL 81-3-3272-0521, FAX 81-3-3272-0693; Universal Subscription Agency, Pvt. Ltd., 877, Udyog Vihar, V, Gurgoan 122001, India. TEL 91-124-347261, FAX 91-124-342496. **Co-sponsors:** Special Interest Group on Data Communication; Association for Computing Machinery, Inc.

004.6 003 USA ISSN 1098-7789
TK5105.35
I E E E - A T M WORKSHOP. PROCEEDINGS. Text in English. 1995. a. **Document type:** *Proceedings, Trade.*
Related titles: Online - full text ed.: (from I E E E).
Indexed: EngInd.
—BLDSC (4362.807045).
Published by: Institute of Electrical and Electronics Engineers, Inc., 3 Park Ave, 17th Fl, New York, NY 10016-5997. TEL 212-419-7900, 800-678-4333, FAX 212-752-4929, customer.service@ieee.org, http://www.ieee.org.

I E E E CANADIAN CONFERENCE ON ELECTRICAL AND COMPUTER ENGINEERING. PROCEEDINGS. see *COMPUTERS—Computer Engineering*

I E E E INTELLIGENT NETWORKS WORKSHOP. see *COMMUNICATIONS*

I E E E INTERNATIONAL PERFORMANCE, COMPUTING, AND COMMUNICATIONS CONFERENCE. PROCEEDINGS. see *COMPUTERS—Data Communications And Data Transmission Systems*

I E E E INTERNATIONAL TELECOMMUNICATIONS SYMPOSIUM. see *COMMUNICATIONS*

004.6 USA ISSN 0890-8044
TK5105.5
➤ **I E E E NETWORK**; the magazine of global information exchange. Text in English. 1987. bi-m. USD 310 (effective 2006). adv. illus. reprints avail. **Document type:** *Journal, Academic/Scholarly.* **Description:** Covers network protocols and architecture: protocol design and validation, communications software, network control, signaling and management, network implementation (LAN,MAN,WAN) and micro-to-host communications.
Related titles: CD-ROM ed.; Microfiche ed.; Online - full text ed.: (from EBSCO Publishing).
Indexed: ASCA, C&CSA, C&ISA, CompD, CompLI, CurCont, CybAb, E&CAJ, EngInd, ISR, Inspec, RefZh, SCI, SolStAb, TelAb.
—BLDSC (4363.007500), AskIEEE, CISTI, Ei, IDS, IE, Infotrieve, ingenta, Linda Hall. **CCC.**
Published by: Institute of Electrical and Electronics Engineers, Inc., 445 Hoes Ln, Piscataway, NJ 08854-1331. TEL 732-981-0060, 800-701-4333, FAX 732-981-1721, subscription-service@ieee.org, http://www.ieee.org. Ed. Jorg Leibeherr. **Subscr. to:** Maruzen Co., Ltd., 3-10 Nihonbashi 2-chome, Chuo-ku, Tokyo 103-0027, Japan. FAX 81-3-3275-0657; Universal Subscription Agency, Pvt. Ltd., 877, Udyog Vihar, V, Gurgoan 122001, India. TEL 91-124-347261, FAX 91-124-342496. **Co-sponsor:** Communications Society.

➤ **I E E E OPEN ARCHITECTURES AND NETWORK PROGRAMMING.** see *COMMUNICATIONS*

004.6 USA
I E E E WORKSHOP ON LOCAL AND METROPOLITAN AREA NETWORK. Text in English. a. **Document type:** *Proceedings, Trade.*
Published by: Institute of Electrical and Electronics Engineers, Inc., 3 Park Ave, 17th Fl, New York, NY 10016-5997. TEL 800-678-4333, customer.service@ieee.org, http://www.ieee.org.

004.6 USA
I F I P - I E E E INTERNATIONAL SYMPOSIUM ON INTEGRATED NETWORK MANAGEMENT. Text in English. a. USD 195 (effective 2004). **Document type:** *Proceedings, Trade.*
Published by: Institute of Electrical and Electronics Engineers, Inc., 3 Park Ave, 17th Fl, New York, NY 10016-5997. TEL 212-419-7900, 800-678-4333, FAX 212-752-4929, customer.service@ieee.org, http://www.ieee.org.

004.6 DEU ISSN 1614-063X
I S D N & D S L. (Integrated Services Digital Network) Text in German. 1995. 4/yr. EUR 17; EUR 2.95 newsstand/cover (effective 2005). adv. **Document type:** *Magazine, Consumer.* **Description:** Contains information and resources for people who would like to learn more about digital networks.
Former titles (until 2002): I S D N & D S L fuer Einsteiger (1619-5876); (until 2002): I S D N fuer Einsteiger (0948-6712)
Published by: Neue Mediengesellschaft Ulm mbH, Konrad-Celtis-Str 77, Munich, 81369, Germany. TEL 49-89-74117-0, FAX 49-89-74117787, isdn.einsteiger@nmg.de, empfang@nmg.de, http://www.isdn-einsteiger.de, http://www.nc-online.de. Ed. Markus Selinger. Adv. contact Ulrike Schauf. page EUR 4,500. Circ: 110,000 (controlled).

004.6 DEU ISSN 0931-0827
I S D N REPORT. (Integrated Services Digital Network) Text in German. 1987. m. **Document type:** *Magazine, Trade.*
Indexed: DSA.
Published by: Neue Mediengesellschaft Ulm mbH, Konrad-Celtis-Str 77, Munich, 81369, Germany. TEL 49-89-74117190, FAX 49-89-74117195, bettina.guenther@nmg.de. Circ: 3,050.

004.6 USA
TK5105.7
I T ARCHITECT; strategies & solutions for the network professional. Text in English. 1986. 13/yr. free in US & Canada to qualified personnel; USD 135 domestic; USD 175 foreign (effective 2005). adv. bk.rev. illus. reprints avail. **Document type:** *Magazine, Trade.* **Description:** Devoted to products and solutions for the networking industry.
Incorporates: Data Communications (0363-6399); Former titles (until Aug. 2005): Network Magazine (1539-8137); (until 1998): Network (1093-8001); (until 1997): L A N Magazine (1069-5621); (until 1993): Local Area Network Magazine (0898-0012); Which incorporated (1985-1993): L A N Technology (1042-4695); Which was formerly (until 1989): Micro-Systems Journal (8750-9482)
Related titles: Online - full text ed.: (from bigchalk, EBSCO Publishing, Factiva, Gale Group, H.W. Wilson, LexisNexis, O C L C Online Computer Library Center, Inc., ProQuest Information & Learning).
Indexed: ABIn, BPI, CompD, CompI, CompLI, InfoSAb, Inspec, MicrocompInd, PCR2, RefZh, SoftBase, TelAb.
—BLDSC (6077.203236), CISTI, IE, ingenta, Linda Hall. **CCC.**
Published by: C M P Media LLC (Subsidiary of: United News & Media), 600 Harrison St, 6th Fl., San Francisco, CA 94107. TEL 415-947-6000, FAX 415-947-6022, jsiefert@cmp.com, http://www.itarchitect.com. Ed. Art Wittman. Pub. John Siefert. adv.: B&W page USD 13,560, color page USD 16,560; trim 10.88 x 8.75. Circ: 210,000 (controlled).

004.6 DNK
I T BRANCHEN. (Information Technology) Text in Danish. 1999. 18/yr. adv. **Document type:** *Magazine, Trade.* **Description:** Contains articles and features on information technology news, sales and marketing, products, and trends.
Published by: I D G Danmark A-S, Carl Jacobsens Vej 25, Valby, 2500, Denmark. TEL 45-77-30-03-00, FAX 45-77-30-03-02, itbranchen@idg.dk, idg@idg.dk, http://www.itbranchen.dk, http://www.idg.dk. Ed. Finn Morsing. Adv. contact Lars Ostermann. B&W page USD 2,905, color page USD 3,532; 266 x 365. Circ: 14,500 (controlled).

004.6 DEU
I T - DIRECTOR; Business - People - Companies. Text in German. 1995. m. EUR 70 domestic; EUR 92 in Europe; EUR 125 elsewhere (effective 2002). adv. **Document type:** *Magazine, Trade.* **Description:** Provides market and technical information for IT managers.
Formerly: Client Server Computing (0947-5419)
Related titles: ♦ Supplement(s): SAPlement.
Published by: Medienhaus Verlag GmbH, Bertram-Blank-Str. 8, Bergisch Gladbach, 51427, Germany. TEL 49-2204-9214-0, FAX 49-2204-921430, redaktion@it-director.de, http://www.it-director.de, http://www.medienhaus-verlag.de. Eds. Berthold Wesseler, Guido Piech. Pub. Klaus Dudda. Adv. contact Hendrik Dreisbach. B&W page EUR 5,300, color page EUR 6,950. Circ: 25,220 (paid and controlled).

004.16 DNK
I T PARTNER DENMARK. (Information Technology) Text in Danish. 18/yr. adv. **Document type:** *Newspaper, Trade.* **Description:** Provides comprehensive coverage on sales and marketing within the Danish IT industry.
Published by: I D G Danmark A-S, Carl Jacobsens Vej 25, Valby, 2500, Denmark. TEL 45-77-30-03-00, FAX 45-77-30-03-02, idg@idg.dk, http://www.idg.dk. adv.: B&W page USD 2,793, color page USD 3,408; 266 x 365. Circ: 12,700 (controlled).

004.6 NLD ISSN 1566-5275
I T SERVICE MAGAZINE. (Information Technology) Text in Dutch. 1992. 8/yr. EUR 67.50 domestic; EUR 75.50 in Belgium (effective 2005). adv. illus. **Document type:** *Journal, Trade.* **Description:** Covers IT management.
Former titles (until 2000): Open Computing (1383-648X); (until 1995): P C Werkstation (0927-7595)
—Infotrieve.
Published by: Array Publications BV, Postbus 2211, Alphen aan den Rijn, 2400 CE, Netherlands. TEL 31-172-469030, FAX 31-172-424381, itservice@array.nl, http://www.itservice.nl, http://www.array.nl. Eds. Floris Hulshoff Pol, Dick Schievels. Adv. contact Jos Raaphorst TEL 31-172-469030. B&W page EUR 1,995, color page EUR 3,195; 190 x 265. Circ: 4,700.

004.68 GBR
THE INDUSTRIAL ETHERNET BOOK. Text in English. 1999. s-a. adv. **Description:** Aims to increase the awarness and usage of industrial ethernet.
Related titles: Online - full text ed.
Published by: Fieldbus.com, 1 W St, Titchfield, Hants, PO14 4DH, United Kingdom. TEL 44-132-984-6166, FAX 44-132-951-2063, adrian@fieldbus.com, http://ethernet.industrial-networking.com. Ed. Bill George. adv.: page GBP 1,800. Circ: 10,000.

004.68 GBR ISSN 1464-6056
INDUSTRIAL NETWORKING + OPEN CONTROL. Text in English. 1998. bi-m. adv. **Description:** Designed for users and specifiers of digital networking technology. Features products and services for manufacturing and process automation throughout the world.
Published by: Fieldbus.com, 1 W St, Titchfield, Hants, PO14 4DH, United Kingdom. TEL 44-173-274-1162, FAX 44-173-274-1163, http://www.fieldbus.com. Ed. Andy Pye. Pub. Geoff Hidgkinson. adv.: page GBP 2,745; 395 x 295. Circ: 12,000.

INFORMATION COMMUNICATIONS WORLD. see *COMMUNICATIONS—Computer Applications*

004.6 AUS ISSN 1324-5945
INFORMATIONAGE. Text in English. 1993. 10/yr. adv. **Document type:** *Magazine, Trade.* **Description:** Provides insight into career-focused feature articles, benchmark reviews and in-depth analysis of industry and government news.
Formerly (until 1995): Informatics (1039-5008)
Related titles: Online - full text ed.
Published by: I D G Communications Pty. Ltd., 88 Christie St, St Leonards, NSW 2065, Australia. TEL 61-2-94395133, FAX 61-2-94395512, heidi_woof@idg.com.au, http://www.infoage.idg.com.au, http://www.idg.com.au. Ed. Peter Davidson. Adv. contact Mark Hobson. page AUD 4,675. Circ: 14,477 (paid and controlled).

INFOSYS; the electronic newsletter for information systems. see *COMPUTERS—Information Science And Information Theory*

004.678 USA ISSN 1097-5276
TK5105.8885.M53
INSIDE MICROSOFT FRONTPAGE. Text in English. m. USD 137 domestic; USD 147 foreign; USD 167 combined subscription print & online eds. (effective 2005). **Document type:** *Magazine, Consumer.* **Description:** Contains tips, techniques and how-to articles about designing and managing Web sites using Microsoft FrontPage.
Related titles: Online - full text ed.: ISSN 1539-0349. USD 167 domestic; USD 177 foreign (effective 2005).
—CCC.
Published by: Element K Journals (Subsidiary of: Eli Research, Inc.), 500 Canal View Blvd, Rochester, NY 14623. TEL 585-240-7301, 800-223-8720, 877-203-5248, FAX 585-292-4392, http://www.elementkjournals.com/products/showProduct.asp?prodID=32&catId=2. Eds. Mark Ray, Michelle Rogers.

004.6 USA ISSN 1061-7647
QA76.76.O63
INSIDE NETWARE. Text in English. 1992. m. USD 147; USD 177 combined subscription print & online eds. (effective 2005). **Document type:** *Consumer.*
Related titles: Online - full text ed.: ISSN 1539-0411. USD 177 domestic; USD 187 foreign (effective 2005) (from ProQuest Information & Learning).
—CCC.
Published by: Element K Journals (Subsidiary of: Eli Research, Inc.), 500 Canal View Blvd, Rochester, NY 14623. TEL 585-240-7301, 800-223-8720, 877-203-5248, FAX 585-292-4392, http://www.elementkjournals.com/products/showProduct.asp?prodID=16&catId=2. Eds. Jutta VanStean, Michelle Rogers.

INTEGRATED DEALER NEWS. see *COMMUNICATIONS*

004.6 GBR
INTEGRATION. Text in English. 1992. m. GBP 50; GBP 70 foreign. **Document type:** *Trade.*
Indexed: CMCI.
Published by: V N U Business Publications Ltd., 32-34 Broadwick St, London, W1A 2HG, United Kingdom. TEL 44-207-4394242, FAX 44-20-7437-4841.

004.68 USA
TK5101.A1
INTENET. Text in English. 1990. m. adv. **Description:** Covers the local area network, wide area network and all aspects of internetworking.
Former titles: Communications and Computer News (1057-0071); Communications and Computer Product and Software News (1059-5465)
Related titles: Microfilm ed.: (from PQC).
Indexed: SoftBase.
Published by: Horizon House Publications, 685 Canton St, Norwood, MA 02062. TEL 781-769-9750, FAX 781-762-9071. Circ: 40,000.

004.6 USA
INTERACTIVE CONTENT; consumer media strategies monthly. Text in English. m. USD 675; USD 775 with online ed.. back issues avail. **Document type:** *Newsletter.* **Description:** Tracks business developments in consumer online services for the mass market.
Related titles: Online - full text ed.
Published by: Jupiter Communications, 627 Broadway, New York, NY 10012. TEL 212-780-6060, 800-488-4345, FAX 212-780-6075, http://www.jup.com. Ed. Mark Mooradian. Pub. Gene Derose. **Dist. by:** Publications Resource Group, 121 Union St., Box 792, North Adams, MA 01247. TEL 413-664-6185, FAX 413-664-9343.

004.6 USA ISSN 1089-2540
HE8700.6
(YEAR) INTERACTIVE SOURCEBOOK. Text in English. 1995. a. USD 495 (effective 1998). adv. **Document type:** *Directory.* **Description:** Lists suppliers of cable modems, interactive video systems, Internet and website software, merger and acquisition consultants, Internet home page designers, and others.
Related titles: CD-ROM ed.
Published by: North American Publishing Co., 1500 Spring Garden St., Ste 1200, Philadelphia, PA 19130-4094. TEL 215-238-5300, FAX 215-238-5457, http://www.napco.com. Ed. Robin Whitmire. **Dist. by:** Publications Resource Group, 121 Union St., Box 792, North Adams, MA 01247. TEL 413-664-6185, FAX 413-664-9343.

004.6 003 USA
INTERNATIONAL CONFERENCE ON A T M. PROCEEDINGS. Text in English. a. **Document type:** *Proceedings, Trade.*
—BLDSC (4362.943770).
Published by: Institute of Electrical and Electronics Engineers, Inc., 3 Park Ave, 17th Fl, New York, NY 10016-5997. TEL 800-678-4333, customer.service@ieee.org, http://www.ieee.org.

004.6 384 USA ISSN 1095-2055
INTERNATIONAL CONFERENCE ON COMPUTER COMMUNICATIONS AND NETWORKS. PROCEEDINGS. Text in English. 1992. a. USD 151 (effective 2005). **Document type:** *Proceedings, Academic/Scholarly.*
Related titles: Online - full text ed.: (from I E E E).
—BLDSC (4538.768620). **CCC.**
Published by: Institute of Electrical and Electronics Engineers, Inc., 445 Hoes Ln, Piscataway, NJ 08854-1331. TEL 732-981-0060, 800-678-4333, FAX 732-981-1721, customer.service@ieee.org, http://www.ieee.org.

004.6 USA ISSN 1530-1095
INTERNATIONAL CONFERENCE ON COOPERATIVE INFORMATION SYSTEMS. PROCEEDINGS. Text in English. a. USD 135 per vol. (effective 2004). **Document type:** *Proceedings, Trade.*
Related titles: Online - full text ed.: (from I E E E).
—BLDSC (6844.169450).
Published by: Institute of Electrical and Electronics Engineers, Inc., 3 Park Ave, 17th Fl, New York, NY 10016-5997. TEL 212-419-7900, 800-678-4333, FAX 212-752-4929, customer.service@ieee.org, http://www.ieee.org.

004.6 USA ISSN 1092-1648
TK5105.55
INTERNATIONAL CONFERENCE ON NETWORK PROTOCOLS. PROCEEDINGS. Text in English. 1993. a. USD 185; USD 74 to members (effective 2004). **Document type:** *Proceedings, Trade.*
Related titles: Online - full text ed.: (from I E E E).
Indexed: Englnd.
—BLDSC (4538.838460). **CCC.**
Published by: Institute of Electrical and Electronics Engineers, Inc., 3 Park Ave, 17th Fl, New York, NY 10016-5997. TEL 212-419-7900, 800-678-4333, FAX 212-752-4929, customer.service@ieee.org, http://www.ieee.org.

004.6 USA
INTERNATIONAL CONFERENCE ON TELECOMMUNICATIONS IN MODERN SATELLITE, CABLE AND BROADCASTING SERVICES. PROCEEDINGS. Text in English. irreg. (in 2 vols.). USD 250 per issue; USD 125 per issue to members (effective 2004). **Document type:** *Proceedings, Trade.* **Description:** Aimed at the efficient exchange of results in the area of telecommunications through presentation of current scientific results and development trends.
Published by: Institute of Electrical and Electronics Engineers, Inc., 3 Park Ave, 17th Fl, New York, NY 10016-5997. TEL 212-419-7900, 800-678-4333, FAX 212-752-4929, customer.service@ieee.org, http://www.ieee.org.

004.6 USA
INTERNATIONAL JOINT CONFERENCE ON NEURAL NETWORKS. PROCEEDINGS. Text in English. a. price varies. **Document type:** *Proceedings, Academic/Scholarly.*
Published by: Institute of Electrical and Electronics Engineers, Inc., 445 Hoes Ln, Piscataway, NJ 08854-1331. TEL 732-981-0060, FAX 732-981-1721, customer.service@ieee.org, http://www.ieee.org.

004.6 384.53 GBR ISSN 1743-8225
▼ ➤ **INTERNATIONAL JOURNAL OF AD HOC AND UBIQUITOUS COMPUTING.** Text in English. 2005. q. USD 450 to institutions print or online; USD 545 combined subscription to institutions print & online (effective 2005). **Document type:** *Journal, Academic/Scholarly.* **Description:** Publishes papers that address networking or computing problems in the context of mobile and wireless ad hoc networks, wireless sensor networks, ad hoc computing systems, and ubiquitous computing systems.
Related titles: Online - full content ed.: ISSN 1743-8233.
Published by: Inderscience Publishers, IEL Editorial Office, PO Box 735, Olney, Bucks MK46 5WB, United Kingdom. TEL 44-1234-240519, FAX 44-1234-240515, ijahuc@inderscience.com, http://www.inderscience.com/ijahuc. Eds. Han-Chieh Chao, Dr. Yuh-Shyan Chen.

004.6 USA ISSN 1550-1329
▼ **INTERNATIONAL JOURNAL OF DISTRIBUTED SENSOR NETWORKS.** Text in English. 2005. q. USD 299 combined subscription to institutions print & online eds.; GBP 182 combined subscription to individuals print & online eds. (effective 2006). **Document type:** *Journal, Academic/Scholarly.* **Description:** Provides a forum for the publication of important research contributions in developing high performance computing solutions to problems arising from the complexities of these sensor network systems.
Related titles: Online - full content ed.: ISSN 1550-1477. 2005. USD 284, GBP 173 to institutions (effective 2006); Online - full text ed.: (from EBSCO Publishing, Swets Information Services).
Indexed: C&ISA, E&CAJ, IAA.
Published by: Taylor & Francis Inc. (Subsidiary of: Taylor & Francis Group), 325 Chestnut St, Ste 800, Philadelphia, PA 19016. TEL 215-625-8900, 800-354-1420, FAX 215-625-2940, info@taylorandfrancis.com, http://www.tandf.co.uk/journals/titles/15501329.asp, http://www.taylorandfrancis.com. Ed. Dr. S S Iyengar TEL 225-578-1252.

004.6 GBR ISSN 1740-0562
▼ ➤ **INTERNATIONAL JOURNAL OF HIGH PERFORMANCE COMPUTING AND NETWORKING.** Text in English. 2004. bi-m. USD 540 to institutions; USD 685 combined subscription to institutions print & online eds. (effective 2005). **Document type:** *Journal, Academic/Scholarly.* **Description:** Addresses the most innovative developments in high-performance computing and networking.
Related titles: Online - full text ed.: ISSN 1740-0570. USD 540 to institutions (effective 2005).
—BLDSC (4542.280460).
Published by: Inderscience Publishers, IEL Editorial Office, PO Box 735, Olney, Bucks MK46 5WB, United Kingdom. TEL 44-1234-240519, FAX 44-1234-240515, ijhpcn@inderscience.com, info@inderscience.com, http://www.inderscience.com/ijhpcn. **Subscr. to:** World Trade Centre Bldg, 29 route de Pre-Bois, Case Postale 896, Geneva 15 1215, Switzerland. FAX 41-22-7910885, subs@inderscience.com.

004.68 GBR ISSN 1470-9503
➤ **INTERNATIONAL JOURNAL OF NETWORKING AND VIRTUAL ORGANISATIONS.** Text in English. 2001. 4/yr. USD 450 to institutions; USD 545 combined subscription to institutions pirnt & online eds. (effective 2005). **Document type:** *Journal, Academic/Scholarly.* **Description:** Provides a refereed source of information in the field of Networking and Virtual Organizations.
Related titles: Online - full text ed.: ISSN 1741-5225. USD 450 (effective 2005).
Indexed: BrCerAb, C&ISA, CerAb, CorrAb, E&CAJ, EMA, ErgAb, IAA, Inspec, M&TEA, MBF, METADEX, SolStAb, WAA.
—BLDSC (4542.373350), IE, ingenta, Linda Hall.
Published by: Inderscience Publishers, IEL Editorial Office, PO Box 735, Olney, Bucks MK46 5WB, United Kingdom. TEL 44-1234-240519, FAX 44-1234-240515, ijnvo@inderscience.com, editor@inderscience.com, http://www.inderscience.com/ijnvo. Ed. Dr. Mohammed A Dorgham. **Subscr. to:** World Trade Centre Bldg, 29 route de Pre-Bois, Case Postale 896, Geneva 15 1215, Switzerland. FAX 41-22-7910885, subs@inderscience.com.

▼ new title ➤ refereed ✶ unverified ♦ full entry avail.

004.678 384.53 005.8 GBR ISSN 1747-8405
▼ ➤ **INTERNATIONAL JOURNAL OF SECURITY AND NETWORKS.** Text in English. forthcoming 2006 (Sept.). q. USD 450 to institutions; USD 545 combined subscription to institutions (effective 2005). **Document type:** *Journal, Academic/Scholarly.* **Description:** Aims to establish an effective channel of communication between industry, government agencies, academic and research institutions and persons concerned with network security related problems. It also aims to promote and coordinate developments in the field of wireless/wired network security.
Related titles: Online - full content ed.: ISSN 1747-8413. forthcoming.
Published by: Inderscience Publishers, IEL Editorial Office, PO Box 735, Olney, Bucks MK46 5WB, United Kingdom. TEL 44-1234-240519, FAX 44-1234-240515, ijsn@inderscience.com, info@inderscience.com, http://www.inderscience.com/ijsn. Ed. Dr. Yang Xiao.

➤ **INTERNATIONAL WORKSHOP ON QUALITY OF SERVICE.** see *COMMUNICATIONS*

➤ **INTERNET HOMESTEADER. SERIES A: LIBRARY AND INFORMATION SCIENCE.** see *LIBRARY AND INFORMATION SCIENCES*

➤ **INTERNET TELEPHONY MAGAZINE**; the authority on voice, video, fax and data convergence. see *COMMUNICATIONS—Telephone And Telegraph*

➤ **INTRANET DIGEST.** see *COMPUTERS—Internet*

004.6 USA
J U G NEWSLETTER✶. Text in English. m. membership. adv. **Description:** For Jefferson State Computer Users Group members. Features articles, news briefs and meeting notes.
Published by: Jefferson State Computer Users Group, 1140 Sweet Rd, Medford, OR 97501-1849. Ed. John Newman. **Subscr. to:** PO Box 457, Gold Hill, OR 97525-0457.

621.3692 USA
JAPAN/PACIFIC RIM FIBER OPTICS REPORT. Text in English. 2000. biennial. USD 8,750 to corporations (effective 2000). **Description:** Provides a detailed, quantitative analysis of the use of each signigicant type of fiber optic component in each significant application, in Japan, Korea, Taiwan, China and other Pacific Rim countries.
Published by: ElectroniCast Corporation, 1923 Bayview Ave., Belmont, CA 94002-1616. electronicast@msn.com, http://www.electronicast.com. Ed. Stephen ontgomery.

004.16 USA ISSN 1097-4946
THE JEFFRIES LETTER. Text in English. 1982. m. USD 495 in US & Canada; USD 520 elsewhere (effective 1999). bk.rev. **Document type:** *Newsletter.* **Description:** Features reports and reviews on the use of asynchronous transfer mode (ATM) for LANs and internetworks.
Former titles (until 1998): A T M User (1068-5189); (until 1993): Jeffries Report (0734-4589)
Published by: Jeffries Research, 2263 Callender Rd, Arroyo Grande, CA 93420. TEL 805-343-5444, FAX 805-343-2118, info@jeffriesletter.com, http://www.jeffriesletter. Ed. Ron Jeffries. Circ: 1,000.

JISUANJI XUEBAO/CHINESE JOURNAL OF COMPUTERS. see *COMPUTERS—Computer Architecture*

004.65 370 USA ISSN 1092-8235
LC5803.C65
➤ **JOURNAL OF ASYNCHRONOUS LEARNING NETWORKS.** Abbreviated title: J A L N. Text in English. irreg. free (effective 2005). **Document type:** *Journal, Academic/Scholarly.* **Description:** Aim to describe original work in asynchronous learning networks (ALN), including experimental results.
Media: Online - full content.
Published by: Sloan Consortium, Olin College of Engineering and Babson College, 1735 Great Plain Ave., Needham, MA 02492. TEL 781-292-2524, FAX 781-292-2505, publisher@sloan-c.org, http://www.sloan-c.org/publications/jaln/index.asp.

004.6 KOR ISSN 1229-2370
TK5101.A1
JOURNAL OF COMMUNICATIONS AND NETWORKS. Text in English. 1999. q. KRW 20,000 domestic to members; USD 138 foreign to members; USD 150 domestic to non-members; USD 158 foreign to non-members (effective 2000). **Document type:** *Journal, Academic/Scholarly.*
Indexed: CurCont, SCI.
—BLDSC (4961.661000), IE, ingenta, Linda Hall.
Published by: Korean Institute of Communication Sciences, Hyundai Kirim Officetel No 1504-6, 1330-18 Seochodong, Seochoku, Seoul, 137-070, Korea, S. FAX 82-2-539-5588, office@jcn.snu.ac.kr, http://jcn.kics.or.kr. Ed. Stephen Weinstein.

004.6 NLD ISSN 0926-6801
CODEN: JHSNEB
➤ **JOURNAL OF HIGH SPEED NETWORKS.** Text in English. 1992. q. EUR 447, USD 538 combined subscription print & online eds. (effective 2006). back issues avail. **Document type:** *Journal, Academic/Scholarly.* **Description:** Publishes work on theoretical and technical issues related to very-high-speed computer networks, optical networks and the control, management and operation of very-high-speed networks.
Related titles: Online - full text ed.: (from EBSCO Publishing, Gale Group, IngentaConnect, O C L C Online Computer Library Center, Inc., Swets Information Services).
Indexed: ASCA, BrCerAb, C&ISA, CMCI, CerAb, CompAb, CompLI, CompR, CorrAb, CurCont, E&CAJ, EMA, EngInd, IAA, Inspec, M&TEA, MBF, METADEX, MSCI, SolStAb, WAA.
—BLDSC (4998.560000), AskIEEE, CISTI, Ei, IDS, IE, Infotrieve, ingenta, Linda Hall. **CCC.**
Published by: I O S Press, Nieuwe Hemweg 6B, Amsterdam, 1013 BG, Netherlands. TEL 31-20-6883355, FAX 31-20-6203419, info@iospress.nl, order@iospress.nl, http://www.iospress.nl/html/09266801.php. Ed. Deepinder Sidhu TEL 410-455-3028. R&P Ms. Carry Koolbergen TEL 31-20-6382189. Adv. contact Ms. Jolijn van Eunen. Circ: 200. **Subscr. to:** I O S Press, Inc, 4502 Rachael Manor Dr., Fairfax, VA 22032-3631. iosbooks@iospress.com; Globe Publication Pvt. Ltd., C-62 Inderpuri, New Delhi 100 012, India. TEL 91-11-579-3211, 91-11-579-3212, FAX 91-11-579-8876, custserve@globepub.com, http://www.globepub.com; Kinokuniya Co. Ltd., Shinjuku 3-chome, Shinjuku-ku, Tokyo 160-0022, Japan. FAX 81-3-3439-1094, journal@kinokuniya.co.jp, http://www.kinokuniya.co.jp.

004.6 SGP ISSN 0219-2659
TK5101.A1 CODEN: JINOBR
➤ **JOURNAL OF INTERCONNECTION NETWORKS.** Abbreviated title: J O I N. Text in English. 2000. q. SGD 223, USD 128, EUR 123 to individuals; SGD 525, USD 301, EUR 288 combined subscription to institutions print & online eds.; SGD 316, USD 181, EUR 173 combined subscription in developing nations to institutions print & online eds. (effective 2006). back issues avail. **Document type:** *Journal, Academic/Scholarly.* **Description:** Addresses all aspects of interconnection networks including their theory, analysis, design, implementation and application, and corresponding issues of communication and computing.
Related titles: Online - full text ed.: (from EBSCO Publishing, O C L C Online Computer Library Center, Inc., Swets Information Services).
Indexed: CompLI, Inspec.
—BLDSC (5007.542000), IE, Infotrieve, ingenta. **CCC.**
Published by: World Scientific Publishing Co. Pte. Ltd., 5 Toh Tuck Link, Singapore, 596224, Singapore. TEL 65-466-5775, FAX 65-467-7667, http://www.worldscinet.com/join/join.shtml, http://www.worldscientific.com. Eds. C T Howard Ho, Friedhelm Meyer auf der Heide, Kei Hirako. **Subscr. to:** Farrer Rd, PO Box 128, Singapore 912805, Singapore. sales@wspc.com.sg. **Dist. in the US by:** World Scientific Publishing Co., Inc., 1060 Main St, River Edge, NJ 07661. TEL 201-487-9655, 800-227-7562, FAX 201-487-9656, 888-977-2665, wspc@wspc.com.; **Dist. by:** World Scientific Publishing Ltd., 57 Shelton St, London WC2H 9HE, United Kingdom. TEL 44-20-78360888, FAX 44-20-78362020, sales@wspc.co.uk.

004.6 GBR ISSN 1084-8045
QA76.5 CODEN: JNCAF3
➤ **JOURNAL OF NETWORK AND COMPUTER APPLICATIONS.** Text in English. 1977. 4/yr. EUR 213 in Europe to individuals; JPY 22,900 in Japan to individuals; USD 222 elsewhere to individuals; EUR 860 in Europe to institutions; JPY 92,900 in Japan to institutions; USD 765 elsewhere to institutions (effective 2006). adv. reprints avail. **Document type:** *Academic/Scholarly.* **Description:** Provides an interdisciplinary forum for the presentation of full-length papers and shorter communications on software engineering and on hardware design.
Formerly (until vol.19, 1996): Journal of Microcomputer Applications (0745-7138)
Related titles: Online - full text ed.: ISSN 1095-8592. USD 738 (effective 2002) (from EBSCO Publishing, Gale Group, IngentaConnect, O C L C Online Computer Library Center, Inc., ScienceDirect, Swets Information Services).
Indexed: AHCI, ASCA, ASFA, BMT, BrCerAb, C&CSA, CMCI, CompAb, CompC, CompLI, CompR, CurCont, CybAb, ESPM, EngInd, Inspec, PollutAb, RASB, RefZh, SSCI.
—BLDSC (5021.410600), AskIEEE, CISTI, Ei, IDS, IE, Infotrieve, ingenta, Linda Hall. **CCC.**
Published by: Academic Press (Subsidiary of: Elsevier Science & Technology), Harcourt Pl, 32 Jamestown Rd, London, NW1 7BY, United Kingdom. TEL 44-20-7424-4200, FAX 44-20-7483-2293, apsubs@acad.com, http://www.elsevier.com/locate/jnca. Ed. J B Thompson.

004.6 USA ISSN 1064-7570
TK5105.5 CODEN: JNSMEG
➤ **JOURNAL OF NETWORK AND SYSTEMS MANAGEMENT.** Text in English. 1993. q. EUR 538, USD 555, GBP 338 combined subscription to institutions print & online eds. (effective 2005). adv. reprint service avail. from PSC. **Document type:** *Journal, Academic/Scholarly.* **Description:** Publishes original research, surveys and case studies discussing architecture, analysis, design, software, standards and migration issues related to the operation, management and control of distributed systems and communication networks for voice, data, image and networked computing.
Related titles: Microfilm ed.: (from PQC); Online - full text ed.: ISSN 1573-7705 (from EBSCO Publishing, Gale Group, IngentaConnect, Kluwer Online, O C L C Online Computer Library Center, Inc., Ovid Technologies, Inc., ProQuest Information & Learning, Springer LINK, Swets Information Services).
Indexed: ABIn, BibLing, BrCerAb, C&ISA, CerAb, CompLI, CorrAb, E&CAJ, EMA, EngInd, IAA, Inspec, LISA, M&TEA, MBF, METADEX, RefZh, SolStAb, WAA.
—BLDSC (5021.410700), AskIEEE, CISTI, Ei, IE, Infotrieve, ingenta, Linda Hall. **CCC.**
Published by: Plenum US (Subsidiary of: Springer Science+Business Media), 233 Spring St, New York, NY 10013. TEL 212-460-1500, FAX 212-460-1575, service@springer-ny.com, http://springerlink.metapress.com/openurl.asp?genre=journal&issn=1064-7570, http://www.springeronline.com. Ed. Manu Malek.

➤ **JOURNAL OF NETWORK INDUSTRIES.** see *LAW—Corporate Law*

004.6 USA ISSN 1041-8334
TK5105.5 CODEN: JNMAEI
JOURNAL OF NETWORK MANAGEMENT✶. Text in English. 1989. q. USD 98.
Indexed: CompAb.
—Linda Hall.
Published by: Frost & Sullivan, 7550 IH 10 W., Ste 400, San Antonio, TX 78229-5811. TEL 212-233-1080.

JOURNAL OF TECHNOLOGY LAW & POLICY. see *PATENTS, TRADEMARKS AND COPYRIGHTS*

004.6 TWN ISSN 1022-968X
KAIFANG XITONG YU WANGLU/OPEN SYSTEMS & NETWORK. Text in Chinese. 1991. m. TWD 1,350; TWD 2,950 foreign. back issues avail. **Document type:** *Consumer.* **Description:** Covers technical reports, market trends, product reviews, and new technologies.
Published by: Third Wave Publishing Corp., 19-1, Ln 231, Fu-Hsing N. Rd, Taipei, Taiwan. TEL 886-2-7136959, FAX 886-2-7189467. Ed. Samuel Huang. adv.: color page USD 2,180. Circ: 9,200.

KEY ABSTRACTS - NEURAL NETWORKS. see *COMPUTERS—Abstracting, Bibliographies, Statistics*

004.6 GBR ISSN 1366-1949
KEY NOTE MARKET REPORT: NETWORKS. Variant title: Networks. Text in English. irreg. (1st Edition), latest 1996, Sept. GBP 340 per issue (effective 2002). **Document type:** *Trade.* **Description:** Provides an overview of a specific UK market segment and includes executive summary, market definition, market size, industry background, competitor analysis, current issues, forecasts, company profiles, and more.
Published by: Key Note Ltd., Field House, 72 Oldfield Rd, Hampton, Mddx TW12 2HQ, United Kingdom. TEL 44-20-8481-8750, FAX 44-20-8783-0049, info@keynote.co.uk, http://www.keynote.co.uk. Ed. Donna Jones.

004.16 RUS ISSN 1027-0868
L A N; zhurnal setevykh reshenii. (Local Area Network) Text in Russian. 1995. m. RUR 396 domestic; RUR 33 per issue domestic (effective 2004). adv. **Document type:** *Magazine, Trade.*
Related titles: Online - full text ed.
Indexed: RefZh.
Published by: Izdatel'stvo Otkrytye Sistemy/Open Systems Publications, ul Rustaveli, dom 12A, komn 117, Moscow, 127254, Russian Federation. TEL 7-095-9563306, FAX 7-095-2539204, info@osp.ru, http://www.osp.ru/lan/.

004.68 NLD
L A N INTERNETWORKING BUYERS GUIDE. (Local Area Network) Text in Dutch. 1998. 3/yr. mkt. **Document type:** *Directory, Trade.*
Formerly: L A N Internetworking Product Guide (1389-1677)
Related titles: ♦ Supplement to: NetworkWorld. ISSN 1572-0357.
Published by: I D G Communications Nederland BV, Postbus 5446, Haarlem, 2000 GK, Netherlands. TEL 31-23-5461111, FAX 31-23-5461155, abo@idg.nl, http://www.lanmagazine.nl, http://www.idg.nl. Adv. contact Fred Driessen.

004.68 USA
L A N MANAGEMENT NEWS AND ANALYSIS. (Local Area Network) Text in English. m. USD 395 (effective 1999). **Document type:** *Newsletter, Trade.* **Description:** Provides practical information for LAN managers to optimize the use, performance, and efficiency of their LAN.

Published by: Gartner Inc., 56 Top Gallant Rd, Stamford, CT 06904-2212. TEL 203-316-1111, 800-544-7337, FAX 203-316-6300, jwhitney@info-edge.com, http://www.gartner3.gartnerweb.com, http://www.info-edge.com.

004.68 USA
L A N PRODUCT NEWS. (Local Area Network) Text in English. 1989. m. USD 165 in North America; USD 180 elsewhere (effective 2005). bk.rev. back issues avail. **Document type:** *Newsletter, Trade.* **Description:** Provides news and information on the computer local area network industry. Covers new hardware and software products, as well as research and development, with special emphasis on the marketing strategies of LAN manufacturers and vendors, user applications, and development of industry standards.
Related titles: Online - full text ed.: (from Data-Star, The Dialog Corporation).
Published by: Worldwide Videotex, PO Box 3273, Boynton Beach, FL 33424-3273. TEL 508-477-8979, 561-738-2276, markedit@juno.com, http://www.wvpubs.com. Ed., Pub. Mark Wright. Circ: 60,000 (paid).

621.3692 USA
LAN/PREMISES COMPONENTS QUARTERLY REPORTS. (Local Area Networks) Text in English. q. **Description:** Provides independent information of high value to equipment and system manufacturers, component vendors and distributors, LAN suppliers, business and agency communications managers.
Published by: ElectroniCast Corporation, 1923 Bayview Ave., Belmont, CA 94002-1616. electronicast@msn.com, http://www.electronicast.com. Ed. Stephen ontgomery.

004.68 DEU ISSN 0942-4172
LANLINE. Text in German. 1989. m. EUR 88.20 domestic; EUR 100.20 foreign; EUR 9 newsstand/cover (effective 2005). adv. **Document type:** *Magazine, Trade.* **Description:** Provides information on products and resources of interest to network and IT professionals.
—IE, Infotrieve.
Published by: Aktuelles Wissen Verlagsgesellschaft mbH, Bretonischer Ring 13, Grasbrunn, 85630, Germany. TEL 49-89-456160, FAX 49-89-45616100, rhh@lanline.awi.de, sm@lanline.awi.de, http://www.lanline.de, http://www.awi.de. Ed. Joerg Schroeper. Adv. contact Cornelia Jacobi. B&W page EUR 4,696, color page EUR 7,100.

621.3692 USA
LATIN AMERICAN FIBER OPTICS REPORT. Text in English. 1998. a. USD 8,750 to corporations (effective 2000). **Description:** Resents a detailed forecast of consumption of fiber optic communication components.
Published by: ElectroniCast Corporation, 1923 Bayview Ave., Belmont, CA 94002-1616. electronicast@msn.com, http://www.electronicast.com. Ed. Stephen ontgomery.

LAW AND ELECTRONIC COMMERCE. see *LAW*

004.6 DEU ISSN 1613-2033
LINUX JOURNAL. Text in German. 1993. 10/yr. adv. **Document type:** *Magazine, Trade.*
Formerly (until 2003): UNIX Open (0943-8416)
Published by: Aktuelles Wissen Verlagsgesellschaft mbH, Bretonischer Ring 13, Grasbrunn, 85630, Germany. TEL 49-89-456160, FAX 49-89-45616100, http://www.awi.de. Ed. Joerg Schroeper. Pub. Eduard Heilmayr. Adv. contact Wolfgang Zielke.

004.68 USA ISSN 1073-0958
MATRIX MAPS QUARTERLY. Text in English. 1993. q. back issues avail. **Description:** Describes network sizes and locations by demographic analysis and graphical presentation.
Related titles: Online - full text ed.
Published by: Matrix.Net, 1106 Clayton Ln Ste 501W, Austin, TX 78723. TEL 512-451-7602, FAX 512-452-0127, webmaster@matrix.net, http://www.matrix.net/publications/mmq/index.html.

004.6 USA
MICHNET NEWS. Text in English. 1986. q. free. bk.rev. back issues avail. **Document type:** *Newsletter.* **Description:** Publishes information and documentation on MICHNET, feature articles on interesting network applications, the computing environments at the Merit member institutions, and information about recent developments in networking technology.
Formerly: Merit Network News
Related titles: Online - full text ed.
Published by: Merit Network, Inc., c/o Mariella Wells, Ed, 4251 Plymouth Rd, Ann Arbor, MI 48105-2785. TEL 734-764-9430, FAX 734-647-3185, info@merit.edu, http://www.merit.edu/michnet/michnet.news/. R&P Mariella Wells. Circ: 16,000.

004.6 USA ISSN 1383-469X
TK5103.2 CODEN: MNAOCV
➤ **MOBILE NETWORKS AND APPLICATIONS.** Key Title: Journal on Special Topics in Mobile Networks & Applications. Abbreviated title: M O N E T. Text in English. 1996. bi-m. USD 64 domestic to members; USD 84 foreign to members; USD 77 combined subscription domestic to members print & online eds.; USD 97 combined subscription foreign to members print & online eds. (effective 2006). adv. reprint service avail. from PSC. **Document type:** *Journal, Academic/Scholarly.* **Description:** Publishes significant research in the area of mobile networking, nomadic computing, and related topics.
Related titles: Online - full text ed.: ISSN 1572-8153. USD 51 (effective 2006) (from Association for Computing Machinery, Inc., EBSCO Publishing, Gale Group, IngentaConnect, Kluwer Online, O C L C Online Computer Library Center, Inc., Ovid Technologies, Inc., ProQuest Information & Learning, Springer LINK, Swets Information Services).
Indexed: ABIn, BibLing, BrCerAb, C&CSA, C&ISA, CMCI, CerAb, CompAb, CompLI, CompR, CorrAb, CurCont, E&CAJ, EMA, EngInd, IAA, Inspec, M&TEA, MBF, METADEX, WAA.
—BLDSC (5879.953540), AskIEEE, CISTI, IE, Infotrieve, ingenta. **CCC.**
Published by: (Association for Computing Machinery, Inc.), Springer-Verlag New York, Inc. (Subsidiary of: Springer Science+Business Media), 233 Spring St, New York, NY 10013. TEL 212-460-1500, FAX 212-460-1575, service@springer-ny.com, http://springerlink.metapress.com/openurl.asp?genre=journal&issn=1383-469X, http://www.springer-ny.com. Ed. Imrich Chlamtac. **Subscr. to:** Journal Fulfillment, PO Box 2485, Secaucus, NJ 07096-2485. TEL 201-348-4033, FAX 201-348-4505, journals@springer-ny.com.

004.64 USA
MODEM USER NEWS. Text in English. 1989. m. USD 150 in North America; USD 165 elsewhere (effective 2001). bk.rev. back issues avail. **Document type:** *Newsletter, Trade.* **Description:** Provides the latest news and information on software, hardware, supplies, and services for individuals and companies who communicate via modems in computer or facsimile applications.
Related titles: Online - full text ed.: (from Data-Star, The Dialog Corporation).
Published by: Worldwide Videotex, PO Box 3273, Boynton Beach, FL 33424-3273. TEL 561-738-2276, markedit@juno.com, http://www.wvpubs.com. Ed., Pub. Mark Wright.

004.6 USA ISSN 1076-2442
CODEN: ECCOEE
MULTIMEDIA WIRE. Text in English. 1993. d. USD 495 (effective 1999). **Document type:** *Newsletter.*
Incorporates (1995-1997): Interactive Daily (1083-141X)
Media: Fax. **Related titles:** Fax ed.; Online - full text ed.: (from bigchalk, LexisNexis, ProQuest Information & Learning).
Indexed: ABIn.
Published by: Warren Communications News, Inc., 2115 Ward Ct, N W, Washington, DC 20037.

004.6 DEU ISSN 0946-7513
N & C - NETWORKS UND COMMUNICATIONS. Text in German. 1993. m. bk.rev.; software rev. mkt. back issues avail. **Document type:** *Magazine, Trade.*
Formerly (until 1993): N & C - Netware und Communication (0943-7509); Incorporates (1991-1996): NetWorks (0939-6675); (1991-1995): I S D N Business (0943-6723)
Related titles: Online - full text ed.
—IE.
Published by: Neue Mediengesellschaft Ulm mbH, Konrad-Celtis-Str 77, Munich, 81369, Germany. TEL 49-89-74117233, FAX 49-89-74117159, nundc@nmg.de, http://www.nc-online.de. Ed., R&P Stefan Rubner. Pub. Guenter Goetz. Adv. contact Marcus Plantenberg. Circ: 15,000 (paid); 10,000 (controlled).

004.6 DEU
N T ADMINISTRATOR. Text in German. m. EUR 160.20 domestic; EUR 184.20 foreign; EUR 16 newsstand/cover (effective 2005). adv. **Document type:** *Magazine, Trade.* **Description:** Covers all aspects and configurations involving Windows NT.
Published by: Aktuelles Wissen Verlagsgesellschaft mbH, Bretonischer Ring 13, Grasbrunn, 85630, Germany. TEL 49-89-456160, FAX 49-89-45616100, http://www.awi.de. Ed. Frank-Martin Binder. Pub. Eduard Heilmayr. Adv. contact Cornelia Jacobi.

005.43 USA
N T UPDATE. Text in English. m. USD 255 (effective 2000). **Document type:** *Trade.* **Description:** Provides information for Windows NT & Windows 2000 professionals .
Published by: Xephon, 9330 Lyndon B Johnson Fwy., Ste. 800, Dallas, TX 75243-4310. TEL 303-410-9344, FAX 303-438-0290, http://www.xephon.com/.

004.6 SWE ISSN 1103-6931
NAETVERK & KOMMUNIKATION. Text in Swedish. 1991. 20/yr. SEK 716 (effective 2003). adv. **Document type:** *Magazine, Trade.* **Description:** Contains comprehensive tests and news reports that provide EDP and network managers with qualified decision-making material for future product investments and advice on how to make a company's communication solutions more efficient.
Formerly (until 1993): Lokala Naetverk (1102-5115); Incorporates (1984-1997): Svenska P C World (0281-9015); (1998-2001): Win2000 World (1650-1365); Which was formerly (until 2000): NTWorld (1403-6495)
Related titles: CD-ROM ed.: N & K Plus. SEK 625 (effective 2002); Online - full text ed.: ISSN 1402-4853.
Published by: I D G AB (Subsidiary of: I D G Communications Inc.), Sturegatan 11, Stockholm, 10678, Sweden. TEL 46-8-4536000, FAX 46-8-4536005, nok@idg.se, http://nok.idg.se, http://www.idg.se. Ed. Fredrik Bernsel TEL 46-8-4536230. adv.: color page SEK 64,800; trim 185 x 260. Circ: 23,000 (paid).

004.68 USA
NATIONAL LABORATORY FOR APPLIED NETWORK RESEARCH PACKETS. Text in English. 1999. q.
Media: Online - full text.
Published by: (National Laboratory for Applied Network Research), University of San Diego, Supercomputer Center, 9500 Gilman Dr, La Jolla, CA 92093-0505. TEL 619-534-5000, FAX 619-534-5113, packets_editor@nlanr.net, http://www.nlanr.net/NLANRPackets/. Ed. Mike Gannis.

004.6 GBR ISSN 0268-5531
NETLINK✶ . Text in English. 1984. bi-m. GBP 24 to non-members. bibl. back issues avail. **Description:** Covers all aspects of local area computer networking.
Indexed: Inspec.
—AskIEEE.
Published by: Aslib, Association for Information Management, Publications Department, Staple Hall, Stone House Court, London, EC3A 7PB, United Kingdom. TEL 44-20-7903-0000, FAX 44-20-7903-0011, pubs@aslib.com, http://www.aslib.com. Eds. Joyce Copeland, W Tuck. Circ: 500.

004.6 PAK ISSN 1561-3550
NETMAG. Variant title: Network Magazine. Text in English. 1998. bi-m. PKR 600; USD 65 foreign. adv. back issues avail.
Related titles: Online - full text ed.: ISSN 1561-3569.
Published by: NetMag Magazine Publishers, Ltd., 7-10 Birdwood Rd., Lahore 3, Pakistan. TEL 92-042-7550577, FAX 92-042-7552759, subscribe@netmag.com.pk, http://www.netmag.com.pk/.

004.6 330 USA ISSN 1385-9587
➤ **NETNOMICS.** Text in Dutch. 1999. 3/yr. EUR 224, USD 224, GBP 120 combined subscription to institutions print & online eds. (effective 2005). adv. illus. reprint service avail. from PSC. **Document type:** *Academic/Scholarly.* **Description:** Serves as an outlet for research in economics, particularly as related to computer hardware and software.
Related titles: Online - full text ed.: ISSN 1573-7071 (from EBSCO Publishing, Gale Group, IngentaConnect, O C L C Online Computer Library Center, Inc., Springer LINK, Swets Information Services).
Indexed: BibLing, Inspec, JEL, RefZh.
—BLDSC (6077.136000), IE, Infotrieve, ingenta. **CCC.**
Published by: Springer-Verlag New York, Inc. (Subsidiary of: Springer Science+Business Media), 233 Spring St, New York, NY 10013. TEL 212-460-1500, FAX 212-460-1575, service@springer-ny.com, http://springerlink.metapress.com/openurl.asp?genre=journal&issn=1385-9587, http://www.springer-ny.com. Eds. Anna Nagurney, Hans M Amman. **Subscr. to:** Journal Fulfillment, PO Box 2485, Secaucus, NJ 07096-2485. TEL 201-348-4033, FAX 201-348-4505, journals@springer-ny.com.

004.65 NOR ISSN 1501-0333
NETTVERK & KOMMUNIKASJON. Text in Norwegian. 1993. 10/yr. NOK 695 (effective 2002). adv. **Document type:** *Magazine, Trade.* **Description:** Contains information for network administrators and managers, MIS directors and data processing and telecom managers.
Formerly (until 1998): P C World Norge Nettverk (0806-9174)
Related titles: Online - full text ed.: ISSN 1502-6809.
Published by: I D G Communications Norge, PO Box 9090, Gronland, Oslo, 0133, Norway. TEL 47-22-053000, FAX 47-22-053001, http://www.idg.no. adv.: B&W page USD 4,194, color page USD 5,480; trim 210 x 297. Circ: 20,000 (paid and controlled).

004.6 USA ISSN 1040-5747
NETWARE ADVISOR. Text in English. m.
Published by: Business Systems Group, 1510 Eldridge Parkway, Ste 110-106, Houston, TX 77077-1760. TEL 713-397-2184.

006.32 GBR ISSN 0954-898X
QA76.87 CODEN: NEWKEB
➤ **NETWORK (ABINGDON)**; computation in neural systems. Text in English. 1990. q. GBP 325, USD 536 combined subscription to institutions print & online eds. (effective 2006). bk.rev. illus. index. back issues avail.; reprint service avail. from PSC. **Document type:** *Journal, Academic/Scholarly.* **Description:** Subject coverage includes experimental neuroscience; physics; computer science; applied mathematics and engineering; proposing, analyzing, simulating and designing models with the aim of synthesizing the biological results.
Related titles: Microfiche ed.: USD 439 in the Americas; GBP 224 elsewhere (effective 2004); Online - full text ed.: ISSN 1361-6536. GBP 342 to institutions (effective 2006) (from EBSCO Publishing, Gale Group, IngentaConnect, Swets Information Services).
Indexed: ASCA, ASFA, CMCI, CompAb, CompLI, CurCont, ISR, IndMed, Inspec, MEDLINE, NSA, NSCI, RefZh, SCI, ZentMath.
—BLDSC (6077.203005), AskIEEE, CISTI, GNLM, IDS, IE, Infotrieve, ingenta, Linda Hall. **CCC.**
Published by: Taylor & Francis Ltd (Subsidiary of: Taylor & Francis Group), 4 Park Sq, Milton Park, Abingdon, OX14 4RN, United Kingdom. TEL 44-1235-828600, FAX 44-1235-829000, info@tandf.co.uk, http://www.tandf.co.uk/journals/titles/0954898X.asp. Ed. Geoffrey J Goodhill. **Subscr. in N America to:** Taylor & Francis Inc., Customer Services Dept, 325 Chestnut St, 8th Fl, Philadelphia, PA 19106. TEL 215-625-8900, 800-354-1420, FAX 215-625-8914, customerservice@taylorandfrancis.com; **Subscr. outside N America to:** Journals Customer Service, Rankine Rd, Basingstoke, Hants RG24 8PR, United Kingdom. TEL 44-1256-813000, FAX 44-1256-330245, enquiry@tandf.co.uk.

004.6 BEL ISSN 1374-8114
NETWORK & TELECOM. Text in French. 1999. 8/yr. EUR 44.25 (effective 2002). adv. **Document type:** *Magazine, Trade.* **Description:** Contains information and support for Belgian telecommunications networking professionals and decision-makers.
Related titles: Dutch ed.: ISSN 1374-8106.
Published by: Best Of Publishing, Rodenbachstraat 70, Brussels, 1190, Belgium. TEL 32-2-346-4850, FAX 32-2-346-4365, jp@best.be, http://www.best.be. Pub. Jean-Paul De Clerk. adv.: color 1/8 page USD 3,603; trim 206 x 297. Circ: 20,000 (paid and controlled).

004.6 GBR
NETWORK COMPUTING; the independent Novel Network solutions. Text in English. m. adv. **Document type:** *Trade.*
Indexed: B&I, Inspec, MicrocompInd.
Published by: Business and Technical Communications Ltd. (BTC), 25 Station Sq, Petts Wood, Kent BR5 1LZ, United Kingdom. TEL 44-1689-616000, FAX 44-1689-826622, netcomputing@btc.co.uk, http://www.networkcomputing.co.uk. Ed. Geoff Marshall. Adv. contact Keith Pegg TEL 44-1689-616000.

004.6 DEU ISSN 1435-2524
NETWORK COMPUTING. Text in German. 1989. 20/yr. EUR 101.10 domestic; EUR 131.95 foreign (effective 2005). adv. **Document type:** *Magazine, Trade.* **Description:** Covers important trends, developments and topics involving PC networks and professionals.
Formerly (until 1997): P C Netze (0936-4315)
—IE, Infotrieve.
Published by: C M P - W E K A Verlag GmbH & Co. KG, Gruber Str 46a, Poing, 85586, Germany. TEL 49-8121-951512, FAX 49-8121-951597, kontakt@cmp-weka.de, http://www.networkcomputing.de, http://www.cmp-weka.de. Ed. Ralf Ladner. Adv. contact Fritz Fischbacher. B&W page EUR 5,350, color page EUR 7,700; trim 180 x 272. Circ: 20,240 (controlled).

004.6 USA ISSN 1046-4468
TK5105.5 CODEN: NETCF7
NETWORK COMPUTING (MANHASSET). Text in English. 1990. bi-w. USD 95; free to qualified personnel (effective 2005). adv. software rev. illus. **Document type:** *Magazine, Trade.* **Description:** For purchasers of computers, peripherals and software used in network environment. Focuses on the network as the basic business environment for computing. Articles cover connecting computers, networking opportunities and technical solutions for networking problems.
Related titles: Online - full text ed.: (from bigchalk, EBSCO Publishing, Florida Center for Library Automation, Gale Group, H.W. Wilson, LexisNexis, O C L C Online Computer Library Center, Inc., ProQuest Information & Learning).
Indexed: ABIn, BPI, BrCerAb, C&ISA, CerAb, CompD, CompI, CompLI, CorrAb, CurCont, E&CAJ, EMA, IAA, Inspec, M&TEA, MASUSE, MBF, METADEX, MicrocompInd, RefZh, SoftBase, WAA.
—BLDSC (6077.203190), CISTI, IDS, IE, Infotrieve, ingenta, Linda Hall. **CCC.**
Published by: C M P Media LLC (Subsidiary of: United News & Media), 600 Community Dr, Manhasset, NY 11030. TEL 516-562-5000, FAX 516-562-5036, pschnaidt@nwc.com, http://www.networkcomputing.com. Ed. Mike Lee. adv.: B&W page USD 25,280, color page USD 29,985; trim 10.5 x 7.88. Circ: 220,000 (controlled).

004.6 HKG
NETWORK COMPUTING ASIA. Text in English. m. free to qualified personnel. **Document type:** *Journal, Trade.*
Published by: C M P Asia Ltd. (Subsidiary of: United News & Media), 17/F China Resources Bldg, 26 Harbour Rd, Wanchai, Hong Kong. TEL 852-2827-6211, FAX 852-2827-7831, info@cmpasia.com, http://www.ncasia.com/, http://www.mfasia.com.sg/.

004.6 GBR ISSN 1361-892X
CODEN: NWRKEA
NETWORK NEWS. Text in English. 1995. w. **Document type:** *Trade.* **Description:** Services industry decision makers responsible for the management, development and purchasing of networking products and services.
Formed by the merger of (1985-1995): Network (0269-3089); Connexion
Related titles: Online - full text ed.: (from Northern Light Technology, Inc.).
Indexed: B&I, Inspec.
—BLDSC (6077.203319), AskIEEE. **CCC.**
Published by: V N U Business Publications Ltd., VNU House, 32-34 Broadwick St, London, W1A 2HG, United Kingdom. TEL 44-20-7316-9000, FAX 44-20-7316-9160, http://www2.vnu.co.uk.

NETWORK OPERATIONS AND MANAGEMENT SYMPOSIUM. see *COMPUTERS—Computer Systems*

004.6 GBR ISSN 1353-4858
TK5105.59 CODEN: NTSCF5
NETWORK SECURITY. Text in English. 1994. 12/yr. EUR 883 in Europe to institutions; JPY 117,200 in Japan to institutions; USD 988 to institutions except Europe and Japan (effective 2006). abstr. **Document type:** *Newsletter.* **Description:** Addresses technical and management issues relating to international network security problems.
Related titles: Microform ed.: (from PQC); Online - full text ed.: (from EBSCO Publishing, Gale Group, IngentaConnect, ScienceDirect, Swets Information Services); Supplement(s): Netsec News.
Indexed: C&CSA, Inspec.
—BLDSC (6077.203970), AskIEEE, IE, Infotrieve, ingenta.
Published by: Elsevier Advanced Technology (Subsidiary of: Elsevier Science & Technology), The Boulevard, Langford Ln, Kidlington, Oxon OX5 2BG, United Kingdom. TEL 44-1865-843750, FAX 44-1865-843971, http://www.elsevier.com/locate/compseconline. **Subscr. to:** Elsevier BV, PO Box 211, Amsterdam 1000 AE, Netherlands. TEL 31-20-485-3757, FAX 31-20-485-3432, nlinfo-f@elsevier.nl, http://www.elsevier.nl.

004.6 GBR ISSN 1367-9678
NETWORK SOLUTIONS. Text in English. 1997. m. **Document type:** *Trade.* **Description:** Technical monthly for network professionals. Delivers detailed, independent product reviews from respected IT testing facilities.
Related titles: Online - full text ed.: (from LexisNexis).
Published by: V N U Business Publications Ltd., VNU House, 32-34 Broadwick St, London, W1A 2HG, United Kingdom. TEL 44-20-7316-9000, FAX 44-20-7316-9160, http://www.vnu.co.uk. Circ: 40,000 (controlled).

004.66 USA ISSN 1542-6009
NETWORK TECHNOLOGY REPORT. (Asynchronos Transfer Mode and Internet Protocol Report) Text in English. 1993. 10/yr. USD 448 (effective 2002). adv. **Document type:** *Newsletter, Trade.*
Former titles (until 2002): The A T M & I P Report (1529-1383); (until 1999): A T M Report (1072-981X)
Related titles: Online - full text ed.
Published by: Broadband Publishing Corp, 200 W Rivers St, Ste 201, PO Box 6535, Ketchum, ID 83340. TEL 208-725-0600, FAX 208-725-0854, http://www.broadbandpub.com. Ed. David F Hold. Pub., R&P Karen P Hold. Adv. contact Amanda F Seasard.

004.6 USA ISSN 0887-7661
QA76
NETWORK WORLD. Text in English. 1983. w. (Mon.). free to qualified personnel; USD 129 domestic; USD 160.50 in Canada; USD 150 in South America; USD 150 in Central America; USD 205 in Europe; USD 300 elsewhere (effective 2005). adv. bk.rev. illus. back issues avail.; reprints avail. **Document type:** *Magazine, Trade.* **Description:** Covers news, new technologies, products and services, trends, applications, electronic commerce, management strategies relating to network computing in the enterprise.
Incorporates (in 1991): Connect; Former titles (until 1986): On Communications (8750-7854); Computerworld on Communications
Related titles: CD-ROM ed.; Microform ed.; Online - full text ed.: Network World Fusion (from EBSCO Publishing, Florida Center for Library Automation, Gale Group, LexisNexis, Northern Light Technology, Inc., O C L C Online Computer Library Center, Inc., ProQuest Information & Learning).
Indexed: ABIn, B&I, CompD, CompIU, LRI, MicrocompInd, PSI, SoftBase, TelAb.
—BLDSC (6077.204380), IE. **CCC.**
Published by: Network World Inc., 118 Turnpike Rd, Southborough, MA 01772. TEL 508-460-3333, 800-622-1108, FAX 508-460-1192, jdix@nww.com, http://www.networkworld.com/, http://www.nwfusion.com. Ed. John Dix. Pub. Evilee Thibeault. Adv. contact Karen Wallace. B&W page USD 37,245, color page USD 45,598; trim 10.25 x 12. Circ: 170,072 (controlled). **Subscr. to:** PO Box 3091, Northbrook, IL 60065-9928.

004.6 ITA
NETWORK WORLD ITALIA. Text in Italian. 1992. m. EUR 30.90 domestic; EUR 51.65 foreign (effective 2002). **Document type:** *Magazine, Trade.* **Description:** Devoted to the world of computer networks and telecommunications.
Formerly (until 2001): NetWorking Italia (1121-5267)
Related titles: Online - full text ed.
Indexed: B&I.
Published by: I D G Communications Italia s.r.l., Via Zante 16-2, Milano, 20138, Italy. TEL 39-02-580381, FAX 39-02-58011670, info@idg.it, http://www.nwi.it, http://www.idgworld.it. Ed. Alessandro Degli Occhi. Pub. Giulio Ferrari. Adv. contact Marco Bertolotti. Circ: 17,400.

004.6 UAE
NETWORK WORLD MIDDLE EAST. Text in English. m. USD 150 (effective 2002). adv. **Document type:** *Magazine, Trade.* **Description:** Provides up-to-date news, features and facts about the networking industry.
Published by: Corporate Publishing International, PO Box 13700, Dubai, United Arab Emirates. TEL 971-4-351-5316, FAX 971-4-359-8486, cpi@emirates.net.ae, http://www.cpilive.net. adv.: B&W page USD 4,500, color page USD 5,000; trim 235 x 330. Circ: 12,417 (paid and controlled).

004.6 PRT
NETWORK WORLD PORTUGAL. Text in Portuguese. 11/yr. adv. **Document type:** *Magazine, Trade.* **Description:** Contains information aimed at directors and chief information officers, networking managers and people from public and local administration as well as outsourcing enterprise and networking installers.
Published by: Edicoes Expansao Economica Lda., Rue Mario Castelhano, 40-1, Queluz de Baixo, Barcarena, 2749-502, Portugal. TEL 351-21-496-95-40, FAX 351-21-436-95-39, webmaster@expansao.iol.pt, http://www.expansao.iol.pt. adv.: color page USD 1,894; trim 210 x 297. Circ: 10,000 (controlled).

004.6 ZAF
NETWORK WORLD S A; enterprise network strategies. Text in English. 1993. m. ZAR 82.50 domestic; ZAR 190.50 foreign (effective 2000). adv. software rev. **Document type:** *Magazine, Trade.*
Published by: T M L Business Publishing (Subsidiary of: Times Media Ltd.), PO Box 182, Pinegowrie, Gauteng 2123, South Africa. TEL 27-11-789-2144, FAX 27-11-789-3196. Ed. Jocelyn Bayer. Adv. contact Jackie Renwick. B&W page USD 726, color page USD 791; trim 280 x 410. Circ: 4,000 (paid and controlled).

004.6 USA ISSN 1091-3556
TK5105.5
➤ **NETWORKER**; the craft of network computing. Text in English. q. USD 80 domestic to non-members; USD 110 foreign to non-members; USD 52 domestic to members; USD 72 foreign to members; USD 47 domestic to students; USD 67 foreign to students; USD 114 combined subscription domestic to non-members print & online eds.; USD 134 combined subscription foreign to non-members print & online eds.; USD 62 combined subscription domestic to members print & online eds.; USD 82 combined subscription foreign to members print & online eds.; USD 56 combined subscription domestic to students print & online eds.; USD 76 combined subscription foreign to students print & online eds. (effective 2006). adv. **Document type:** *Journal, Academic/Scholarly.* **Description:** Dedicated to advancing the art, science, engineering, and application of information technology.
Related titles: Online - full text ed.: USD 76 to non-members; USD 42 to members; USD 38 to students (effective 2006) (from EBSCO Publishing).
Indexed: BrCerAb, C&ISA, CerAb, CompR, CorrAb, E&CAJ, EMA, IAA, Inspec, M&TEA, MBF, METADEX, WAA.
—IE. **CCC.**
Published by: Association for Computing Machinery, Inc., 1515 Broadway, 17th Fl, New York, NY 10036-5701. TEL 212-626-0500, 800-342-6626, FAX 212-944-1318, usacm@acm.org, http://www.acm.org/networker/. adv.: B&W page USD 1,375.

004.6 USA
NETWORKS UPDATE. Text in English. 1989. m. USD 150 in North America; USD 165 elsewhere (effective 2001). bk.rev. back issues avail. **Document type:** *Newsletter, Trade.* **Description:** Includes national, international, public, private, and military network products, services, companies, marketing strategies, and research and development with specific applications items spanning a range of subjects such as ISDN, LANs, WANs, X.25, X.400, and OSI.
Related titles: Online - full text ed.: (from Data-Star, The Dialog Corporation).

Published by: Worldwide Videotex, PO Box 3273, Boynton Beach, FL 33424-3273. TEL 561-738-2276, markedit@juno.com, http://www.wvpubs.com. Ed., Pub. Mark Wright.

004.68   NLD   ISSN 1572-0357
NETWORKWORLD. Text in Dutch. 1989. 11/yr. EUR 92.50 (effective 2003). adv. illus. back issues avail. **Document type:** *Magazine, Trade.* **Description:** Covers all aspects of managing, creating, and using computer networks.
Former titles (until 2003): L A N Internetworking Magazine (1385-7797); (until 1995): L A N Magazine (0926-308X)
Related titles: Online - full text ed.; ♦ Supplement(s): L A N Internetworking Buyers Guide.
—IE.
Published by: I D G Communications Nederland BV, Postbus 5446, Haarlem, 2000 GK, Netherlands. TEL 31-23-5461111, FAX 31-23-5461155, dschievels@idg.nl, abo@idg.nl, http://www.networkworld.nl/, http://www.idg.nl. Ed. Dick Schievels. Pub. Raimon Gort. Adv. contact Fred Driessen. B&W page USD 2,457, color page USD 3,737; trim 210 x 285. Circ: 100,267.

004.6   ARG
NETWORKWORLD ARGENTINA. Text in Spanish. m. USD 50; USD 5 newsstand/cover (effective 2002). adv. **Document type:** *Magazine, Trade.* **Description:** Focuses on offering information on the new business economy as driven by both e-business and Internet-integrated digital networks.
Published by: C W Comunicaciones, Avda. Belgrano, 406 Piso 9, Capital Federal, Buenos Aires 1092, Argentina. TEL 54-11-43425583, FAX 54-11-43317672, idg@sion.com. adv.: color page USD 4,000; trim 200 x 280. Circ: 16,000 (paid and controlled).

004.6   BGR   ISSN 1311-3151
NETWORKWORLD BULGARIA. Text in Bulgarian. 1993. q. adv. back issues avail. **Document type:** *Magazine, Trade.* **Description:** Focuses on renovation of Bulgarian telecommunications, LAN implementations and services.
Related titles: ♦ Supplement to: Computerworld. ISSN 1311-2171.
Published by: I D G Bulgaria Ltd., 1 Hristo Smirnenski blvd, etazh 11, Sofia, 1421, Bulgaria. TEL 359-2-9630886, FAX 359-2-9632841, idg@mbox.digsys.bg, http://www.idg.bg. Ed. Vladimir Vladkov. Pub. Tatiana Hinova. Adv. contact Yanka Petrouska. B&W page USD 345, color page USD 620; trim 205 x 285.

004.6   ROM   ISSN 1454-4997
NETWORKWORLD ROMANIA. Text in Romanian. 1994. m. ROL 110,000 domestic; USD 38 in Europe; USD 49 elsewhere (effective 2002). adv. **Document type:** *Magazine, Trade.* **Description:** Covers issues such as architecture and administration of networks, transmission of data, voice and images, reviews and comparative analyses of specific product categories, as well as case studies and up-to-date specialist information services.
Related titles: Online - full text ed.
Published by: I D G Communications Publishing Group s.r.l., Bd. Maresal Averescu 8-10, cam. 705-708, Bucharest, 71316, Romania. TEL 40-1-224-2621, FAX 40-1-224-1132, http://www.networkworld.ro, http://www.idg.ro. adv.: B&W page USD 543, color page USD 714; 175 x 250. Circ: 5,000 (paid and controlled).

006.32   USA   ISSN 1548-5986
QA76.87
➤ **NEURAL COMPUTING SURVEYS (ONLINE).** Text in English. 1998. q. **Document type:** *Journal, Academic/Scholarly.* **Description:** Aims to bring the second view-point on neural networks.
Formerly (until 1999): Neural Computing Surveys (Print) (1093-7609)
Media: Online - full content.
Indexed: Inspec.
Published by: Neural Computing Surveys jagota@icsi.berkeley.edu, http://www.dcs.rhbnc.ac.uk/NCS. Ed. Arun Jagota.

004.6   GBR   ISSN 1361-4576
TK5105.5   CODEN: NRINF8
➤ **THE NEW REVIEW OF INFORMATION NETWORKING.** Text in English. 1993; N.S. 1995. s-a. GBP 130, USD 228 combined subscription to institutions print & online eds. (effective 2006). back issues avail.; reprint service avail. from PSC. **Document type:** *Journal, Academic/Scholarly.* **Description:** Provides a source on the needs and behaviour of the network user; the role of networks in teaching, learning, research and scholarly communication; the implications of networks for library and information services; the development of campus and other information strategies; the role of information publishers on the networks; policies for funding and charging for network and information services; and standards and protocols for network applications.
Formerly (until 1994): Journal of Information Networking (0966-9248)
Related titles: Online - full text ed.: ISSN 1740-7869. GBP 124, USD 217 to institutions (effective 2006) (from EBSCO Publishing, Gale Group, IngentaConnect, O C L C Online Computer Library Center, Inc., Swets Information Services).
Indexed: ERA, ETA, EngInd, InfoSAb, Inspec, LISA.

—BLDSC (6087.764555), AskIEEE, IE, ingenta.
Published by: Routledge (Subsidiary of: Taylor & Francis Group), 4 Park Sq, Milton Park, Abingdon, Oxon OX14 4RN, United Kingdom. TEL 44-1235-828600, FAX 44-1235-829000, info@routledge.co.uk, http://www.tandf.co.uk/journals/titles/13614576.asp, http://www.routledge.co.uk. Ed. Michael Breaks. **Subscr. to:** Taylor & Francis Ltd, Journals Customer Service, Rankine Rd, Basingstoke, Hants RG24 8PR, United Kingdom. TEL 44-1256-813000, FAX 44-1256-330245, enquiry@tandf.co.uk.

004.6   NZL   ISSN 1173-9738
NEW ZEALAND NETGUIDE MAGAZINE. Variant title: NetGuide. Text in English. 1996. m. (except Jan.). NZD 39.50 domestic; NZD 74.90 in Australia; NZD 105.90 elsewhere (effective 2004). adv. **Document type:** *Consumer.* **Description:** Includes feature articles, tutorials, columns, reviews and guidelines for the newcomer and the more experienced user of the Internet.
Published by: A C P Media Ltd., 100 Westhaven Dr, Westhaven, Private Bag 92512, Auckland, New Zealand. jewer@acpmedia.co.nz, http://www.netguide.co.nz. Circ: 22,338 (paid). **Subscr. to:** Magshop, Reply Paid 4967, Sydney, NSW 2001, Australia. TEL 61-2-92828000, magshop@acp.com.au, http://magshop.com.au.

004.68   USA   ISSN 1533-7960
        CODEN: NCONFZ
NOVELL CONNECTION; the magazine for networking professionals. Text in English. 1990. m. USD 36; USD 3 newsstand/cover. software rev. illus. back issues avail. **Document type:** *Trade.* **Description:** Enables newtworking professionals using Novell software to work and solve problems more efficiently.
Formerly (until 2001): NetWare Connection (1076-3422)
Related titles: Online - full text ed.
Indexed: EngInd, InfoSAb, MicrocompInd.
Published by: Connection Newspapers, LLC, PO Box 5200, Provo, UT 84605-2000. TEL 801-228-4576, FAX 801-228-4540, editors@ncmag.com, http://www.ncmag.com. Ed., R&P Debi Pearson. Pub., Adv. contact Ted Lloyd. Circ: 140,000 (controlled). **Co-sponsor:** Novell Inc.

004.6   DEU   ISSN 0945-0491
OBJEKTSPEKTRUM; die Computer-Zeitschrift fuer Objektorientierung und Componentware. Text in German. 1994. bi-m. EUR 45.10 domestic; EUR 48 in Europe; EUR 52 elsewhere; EUR 40.60 to students; EUR 7.80 newsstand/cover (effective 2005). adv. **Document type:** *Magazine, Trade.*
—CCC.
Published by: SIGS Datacom GmbH (Subsidiary of: 101 Communications, Llc.), Lindlaustr 2c, Troisdorf, 53842, Germany. TEL 49-2241-2341100, FAX 49-2241-2341199, info@sigs-datacom.de, http://www.sigs-datacom.de/sd/publications/os/. adv.: B&W page EUR 3,005, color page EUR 4,365.

004.68   USA   ISSN 0731-8367
ON-LINE (DURHAM). Text in English. 1975. q. USD 10 to non-members. bk.rev. index. back issues avail. **Description:** Information on the local campus computing environment.
Indexed: MagInd, PROMT.
Published by: University of New Hampshire, University Computing Department, Hamilton Smith Hall, Durham, NH 03824. TEL 603-862-3058. Circ: 1,500.

004.6   DEU   ISSN 1616-6795
OPENSOURCE; das Netzwerkmagazin fuer wissenschaftliche Mitarbeiter. Text in German. 1999. 4/yr. adv. **Document type:** *Magazine, Trade.*
Published by: Evoluzione Media AG, Plinganserstr 150, Munich, 81369, Germany. TEL 49-89-76900030, FAX 49-89-76900340, redaktion@evoluzione.de, http://www.evoluzione.de. Ed. Patrick Meidel. Adv. contact Mareike Jung. page EUR 5,568. Circ: 44,000 (controlled).

OPTICAL NETWORKS DAILY. see *COMMUNICATIONS— Telephone And Telegraph*

004.6   NLD   ISSN 1573-4277
▼ ➤ **OPTICAL SWITCHING AND NETWORKING.** Text in English. 2004. 4/yr. EUR 337 in Europe to institutions; JPY 39,800 in Japan to institutions; USD 337 to institutions except Europe and Japan (effective 2006). **Document type:** *Journal, Academic/Scholarly.* **Description:** Provides complete coverage of all topics of interest to those involved in the optical and opto-electronic networking areas.
Related titles: Online - full text ed.: (from EBSCO Publishing, ScienceDirect).
—CCC.
Published by: Elsevier BV (Subsidiary of: Elsevier Science & Technology), Radarweg 29, Amsterdam, 1043 NX, Netherlands. TEL 31-20-4853911, FAX 31-20-4852457, nlinfo-f@elsevier.nl, http://www.elsevier.com/locate/osn, http://www.elsevier.nl. Eds. F Neri, G Rouskas.

004.68   GBR
P C LAN. Text in English. m. GBP 50; GBP 70 foreign. adv. **Document type:** *Trade.* **Description:** Provides products, server and company reviews from the networker's point of view.

Published by: V N U Business Publications Ltd., 32-34 Broadwick St, London, W1A 2HG, United Kingdom. TEL 44-207-4394242, FAX 44-20-7437-4841. adv.: B&W page USD 4,190, color page USD 4,580; trim 297 x 210. Circ: 25,000.

004.16   USA
P C MAGAZINE LATIN AMERICA. Text in Spanish. 1989. m. USD 33.50 (effective 2005). adv. software rev. back issues avail. **Document type:** *Magazine, Trade.*
Published by: Editorial Televisa, 6355 N W 36th St, Miami, FL 33166. TEL 305-871-6400, 800-288-6677, FAX 305-871-7146, 305-871-5026, subscriptions@editorialtelevisa.com, http://www.editorialtelevisa.us/contenido/articulo.asp?chapter=140&article=227. Ed. Fernando Castellanos. Adv. contact Juan Alduncin. Circ: 217,000 (controlled).

004.68   USA
P C NETGUIDE. Text in English. 1996. m. USD 9.95 (effective 1999). back issues avail. **Document type:** *Trade.*
Related titles: Online - full text ed.: P C NetGuide On-line.
Published by: P C Net Guides of America, Inc., 3511 W. Commercial Blvd., Ste. 305, Ft. Lauderdale, FL 33309. http://www.pcnetguide.com. Ed., Pub. Harvey Gordon. adv.: page USD 975; trim 11.5 x 9.25.

004.16   ARG   ISSN 0328-4255
P C WORLD ARGENTINA. Text in Spanish. m. USD 50 (effective 2002). adv. **Document type:** *Magazine, Consumer.* **Description:** Includes articles on computer networks, computer systems, data communications, software and word processing.
Published by: Avenue S.A., 25 de Mayo 432, 4o Piso, Buenos Aires, 1002, Argentina. TEL 54-11-4315-2244, FAX 54-11-4315-2244, info@pcw.com.ar, http://www.pcw.com.ar. Ed. David Exposito. adv.: B&W page ARS 2,700, color page ARS 3,600; trim 203 x 273.

004.16   CRI
P C WORLD CENTRO AMERICA. Text in Spanish. m. adv. **Document type:** *Magazine, Consumer.* **Description:** Includes articles on computer networks, computer systems, data communications, software and word processing.
Published by: Trejos Hermanos Sucesores, S.A., Apdo. 10096, Curridabat 100 Este, Registro Nacional, San Jose, Costa Rica. TEL 506-224-2411, FAX 506-224-1528, http://www.trejoshermanos.com. adv.: B&W page CRC 2,400, color page CRC 2,720; trim 203 x 273. Circ: 15,000 (paid and controlled).

004.16   CHL
P C WORLD CHILE. Text in Spanish. m. adv. **Document type:** *Magazine, Consumer.* **Description:** Publishes articles on computer networks, computer systems, data communications, software, word processing and information technology.
Related titles: Online - full text ed.
Published by: Publicaciones en Computacion, Ltda., Antonio Varas 1371, Providencia, Santiago de Chile, Chile. TEL 56-2-204-2084, FAX 56-2-225-8621, http://www.pcworld.cl, http://www.idgchile.cl. adv.: B&W page CLP 1,875, color page CLP 2,500; trim 205 x 273. Circ: 8,000 (paid and controlled).

004.16   COL   ISSN 0122-3135
P C WORLD COLOMBIA. Text in Spanish. m. adv. **Document type:** *Magazine, Consumer.* **Description:** Publishes articles on computer networks, computer systems, data communications, software, word processing and information technology.
Published by: Iviarco Ltda., Carrera 90 No. 156-19 Piso 4, Bogota, CUND, Colombia. TEL 57-1-6800399, FAX 57-1-6800399, http://www.pc-world.com.co. adv.: B&W page VEB 1,725, color page VEB 2,300; trim 203 x 273. Circ: 10,000 (paid and controlled).

004.16   ECU
P C WORLD ECUADOR. Text in Spanish. 1992. m. ECS 336,000, USD 29; USD 2.80 newsstand/cover. adv. **Document type:** *Magazine, Consumer.* **Description:** Publishes articles on computer networks, computer systems, data communications, microcomputers, software, word processing and information technology.
Published by: Ediworld, Ave. Patria 640 y Amazones, Edificio Patria, Piso 3, Apdo 17-07-8787, Quito, Ecuador. TEL 593-2220336, FAX 593-2220855, pcworld@pcworld.com.ec, http://www.pcworld.com.ec. Ed. Paulina Paredes. R&P Tim Clark TEL 617-303-7820. adv.: B&W page USD 2,350, color page USD 2,500; trim 203 x 273. Circ: 10,000.

004.16   IND
P C WORLD INDIA. Text in English. 1995. m. INR 2,251, USD 50; INR 251 newsstand/cover (effective 1999). adv. bk.rev. index. back issues avail. **Document type:** *Magazine, Consumer.* **Description:** Publishes articles on computer networks, news for PC users, products, technology and software.
Published by: Media Tranasia (India) Pvt. Ltd., K-35 Green Park, New Delhi, 110 016, India. TEL 91-11-6960926, FAX 91-11-686-7641, pcworld@giasdl01.vsnl.net.in, http://www.pcwindia.com. Ed. Ashish Bhatia. Pub. Xavier Collaco TEL 91-11-6960926. Adv. contact R Lalit Kumar. B&W page USD 950, color page USD 1,500; trim 200 x 265. Circ: 270,000.

▼ *new title*   ➤ *refereed*   ✳ *unverified*   ♦ *full entry avail.*

004.16 MEX ISSN 0188-932X
P C WORLD MEXICO. Text in Spanish. 1987. m. adv. **Document type:** *Magazine, Consumer.* **Description:** Features articles on computer networks, computer systems, data communications, software, wordprocessing and information technology.
Related titles: Online - full text ed.: ISSN 1605-5551. 1999.
Published by: I D G Mexico S.A. de C.V., Texas no. 66, Col Napoles, Mexico City, DF 03810, Mexico. TEL 52-5-5436821, FAX 52-5-2232909, http://www.pcworld.com.mx. adv.: B&W page USD 3,371, color page USD 4,494; trim 203 x 273. Circ: 25,000 (paid and controlled).

004.16 PER
P C WORLD PERU. (Personal Computer) Text in Spanish. fortn. adv. **Document type:** *Magazine, Consumer.* **Description:** Publishes articles on computer networks, computer systems, data communications, software, word processing and information technology.
Published by: Empresa Editoria El Comercio, Jr A Miro Quesada, 247 Oficina 703, Lima, 1, Peru. TEL 51-14-342-5583, FAX 51-14-426-7400, editorinformaciones@comercio.com.pe, http://www.elcomercioperu.com.pe. adv.: B&W page PEN 2,700, color page PEN 4,260; trim 180 x 245. Circ: 300,000 (paid and controlled).

004.16 PER
P C WORLD PROFESSIONAL. (Personal Computer) Text in Spanish. m. adv. **Document type:** *Magazine, Trade.* **Description:** Contains information and advice on increasing user productivity and awareness of new products.
Published by: Empresa Editoria El Comercio, Jr A Miro Quesada, 247 Oficina 703, Lima, 1, Peru. TEL 51-14-342-5583, FAX 51-14-426-7400, editorinformaciones@comercio.com.pe, http://www.elcomercioperu.com.pe. adv.: B&W page USD 1,725, color page USD 2,300; trim 203 x 273. Circ: 6,000 (paid and controlled).

004.16 VEN
P C WORLD VENEZUELA. Text in Spanish. m. adv. **Document type:** *Magazine, Consumer.* **Description:** Includes articles on computer networks, computer systems, data communications, software, word processing and information technology.
Published by: Grupo Editorial Producto, Ave. Ppal de Las Mercedes, Edif. Aco Piso 7, Caracas, DF 1060, Venezuela. TEL 58-212-993-5633, FAX 58-212-993-0644, gep@infoline.wtfe.com, http://www.pcworld.com.ve. adv.: B&W page VEB 1,725, color page VEB 2,300; trim 203 x 273.

004.6 USA
PUBLISHING FOR INTRANETS: MONEY MAKING STRATEGIES FOR REACHING THE CORPORATE DESKTOP. Text in English. 1997. irreg. USD 1,295 (effective 2000). **Description:** Features 20 in-depth case studies of Fortune 500 companies, which examine the information needs and the names of key information buyers within the company.
Published by: SIMBA Information (Subsidiary of: R.R. Bowker LLC), 60 Long Ridge Rd., Ste 300, Stamford, CT 06902. TEL 203-325-8193, 800-307-2529, 888-269-5372, FAX 203-325-8915, info@simbanet.com, http://www.simbanet.com.

QUIEN ES QUIEN EN INFORMATICA Y TELECOMUNICACIONES. see *COMPUTERS—Computer Industry*

343.0994 ESP ISSN 1139-482X
R E D E T I. (Revista del Derecho de las Telecomunicaciones e Infraestructuras) Key Title: REDETI. Revista del Derecho de las Telecomunicacions e Infraestructuras. Text in Spanish. 1998. 3/yr. EUR 90 (effective 2002). back issues avail.
Published by: Editorial Montecorvo, Doctor Esquedo, 47, Madrid, 28028, Spain. TEL 34-91-5746411, FAX 34-91-5041558, editorial@montecorvo.com.

004.6 BRA
R T I: REDES, TELECOM E INSTALACOES; voice, data and image - networks, infraestrrctures and technologies. Text in Portuguese, English. 2000. m. adv. **Description:** Aimed at the telecom and datacom markets, covering both technologies and infrastructure of communications networks.
Published by: Aranda Editora Ltda., AL OLGA, 315, Perdizes, Sao Paulo, SP 01155-900, Brazil. TEL 55-11-38245300, FAX 55-11-3662-0103, info@arandanet.com.br, http://www.arandanet.com.br. Pub., Adv. contact Jose Roberto Goncalves. B&W page USD 1,930, color page USD 2,881; trim 18 x 25.

004.6 USA ISSN 1553-7560
REDMOND; the independent voice of the Microsoft IT community. Text in English. 1995. m. USD 39.95 domestic; USD 54.95 in Canada & Mexico; USD 64.95 elsewhere; free to qualified personnel (effective 2005). adv. illus.; tr.lit. back issues avail. **Document type:** *Magazine, Consumer.* **Description:** Provides technical tips and career advice for networking professionals.
Formerly (until Oct. 2004): Microsoft Certified Professional Magazine (1081-3497)
Related titles: Supplement(s): 101 Solutions.
—CCC.
Published by: 101 Communications, Llc., 9121 Oakdale Ave, Ste 101, Chatsworth, CA 91311. TEL 818-734-1520, FAX 818-734-1522, mail@mcpmag.com, info@101com.com, http://redmondmag.com, http://www.101com.com. Ed. Doug Barney. Pub. Henry Allain. adv.: B&W page USD 10,290; trim 7.75 x 10.5. Circ: 80,000.

004.6 FRA ISSN 1285-8749
RESEAUX (PARIS). Text in French. 1989. m. FRF 1,800.
Formerly (until 1997): La Lettre des Reseaux (0996-8210)
Indexed: Inspec.
Published by: A Jour (Subsidiary of: Groupe Tests), 26 Rue d'Oradour-sur-Glane, Paris, 75504, France. TEL 33-1-44253500, redac.ajour@groupe-tests.fr, http://www.01net.com, http://www.ajour.fr. Ed. Jean Claude Streicher.

RESEAUX & TELECOMS. see *COMMUNICATIONS*

004.6 AUS ISSN 1446-9022
➤ **THE REVIEW OF NETWORK ECONOMICS.** Text in English. 2002. q. free (effective 2005). **Description:** Publishes papers on the economics of network industries that have the primary purpose of reviewing, or providing a fresh perspective on the existing literature.
Media: Online - full content.
Published by: Network Economics Consulting Group, Level 7, 90 Mount St, North Sydney, NSW 2060, Australia. TEL 61-2-9965-4199, FAX 61-2-9954-4284, http://www.rnejournal.com/. Ed. Julian Wright.

➤ **REVISTA DIGITAL UNIVERSITARIA.** see *COMPUTERS—Internet*

004.6 MEX
REVISTA RED. Text in Spanish. 1990. m. free to qualified personnel. **Document type:** *Trade.* **Description:** Publishes articles, notes and news on networks and telecommunications.
Related titles: Online - full text ed.: ISSN 1605-4075. 1998.
Published by: Editorial Red, HOMERO 109, Desp. 301,, Col Polanco, Mexico City, DF 11560, Mexico. TEL 52-5-5458186, FAX 52-5-5458194, ppayro@red.com.mx, http://www.revistared.com/. Ed. Pablo Payro. Circ: 24,000.

REVUSER; an independent journal for advanced Revelation and Revelation users. see *COMPUTERS—Minicomputers*

004.68 USA
S A N / L A N; newsletter covering worldwide technology trends, applications, and markets. (Storage Area Network / Local Area Network) Text in English. 1982. m. looseleaf. USD 695 in US & Canada; USD 745 elsewhere (effective 2005). back issues avail. **Document type:** *Newsletter, Trade.* **Description:** Covers worldwide technology trends, applications, products, developments, and markets for LANs.
Former titles (until 2001): Local Area Networks (1051-1962); Local Area Networks Newsletter (0897-3210)
Related titles: Online - full text ed.: (from Factiva).
Indexed: PROMT.
—CCC.
Published by: Information Gatekeepers, Inc., 320 Washington St, Ste 302, Brighton, MA 02135. TEL 617-782-5033, 800-323-1088, FAX 617-782-5735, info@igigroup.com, http://www.igigroup.com/nl/pages/lan.html. Ed. Tony Carmona. Pub. Dr. Paul Polishuk. Circ: 1,000 (paid).

004.6 ITA
S M A U NEWS. Text in Italian. 1994. 7/yr. **Description:** Informs about new communications technology market.
Published by: Gruppo Editoriale J C E, Via Patecchio 2, Milan, MI 20141, Italy. TEL 39-02-57316011, FAX 39-02-57316291, info@jce.it, http://www.jce.it. Ed. Annamaria Tasca. Pub. Jacopo Castelfranchi. Circ: 300,000.

004.6 DEU
SAPLEMENT. Text in German. bi-m. adv. **Document type:** *Magazine, Trade.*
Related titles: ♦ Supplement to: I T - Director.
Published by: Aktuelles Wissen Verlagsgesellschaft mbH, Bretonischer Ring 13, Grasbrunn, 85630, Germany. TEL 49-89-456160, FAX 49-89-45616100, ap@clientserver.awi.de, ra@clientserver.awi.de, http://www.clientserver.de. Eds. Albert Probst, Rainer Annuscheit. Pub. Eduard Heilmayr. Adv. contact Sybille Reed.

▼ **SECURE ENTERPRISE.** see *COMPUTERS—Computer Security*

004.6 USA
SELLING NETWORKS✶. Text in English. 1994. bi-m. **Document type:** *Trade.*
Published by: McGraw-Hill Companies, Inc., 1221 Ave of the Americas, New York, NY 10020. http://www.mcgraw-hill.com. **Subscr. to:** 1900 O Farrell St, San Mateo, CA 94403.

004.6 RUS ISSN 1560-5191
SETI/NETWORK WORLD. Text in Russian. 1996. 16/yr. RUR 198 domestic; RUR 11 per issue domestic (effective 2004). adv. **Document type:** *Magazine, Trade.* **Description:** Contains product reviews, analysis of technology trends, new application and industry news that are designed to help users with the selection and application of network technology.
Related titles: Online - full text ed.
Published by: Izdatel'stvo Otkrytye Sistemy/Open Systems Publications, ul Rustaveli, dom 12A, komn 117, Moscow, 127254, Russian Federation. TEL 7-095-9563306, FAX 7-095-2539204, nets@networld.ru, info@osp.ru, http://www.osp.ru/nets/. adv.: B&W page USD 2,800, color page USD 4,000; trim 202 x 257. Circ: 15,000 (paid and controlled).

SETI I SISTEMY SVYAZI. see *COMMUNICATIONS*

004.6 USA ISSN 1538-8298
SMART TIPS AND QUICK TRICKS FOR MACROMEDIA PRODUCTS. Text in English. 2002. a. USD 10 per issue domestic; USD 20 per issue foreign (effective 2005).
—CCC.
Published by: Element K Journals (Subsidiary of: Eli Research, Inc.), 500 Canal View Blvd, Rochester, NY 14623. TEL 585-240-7301, 800-223-8720, 877-203-5248, FAX 585-292-4392, http://www.elementkjournals.com. Eds. Stephen Dow, Michelle Rogers.

004.6 USA ISSN 1538-8344
SMART TIPS AND QUICK TRICKS FOR MICROSOFT ACTIVE SERVER PAGES. Text in English. 2002. a. USD 10 per issue domestic; USD 20 per issue foreign (effective 2005).
—CCC.
Published by: Element K Journals (Subsidiary of: Eli Research, Inc.), 500 Canal View Blvd, Rochester, NY 14623. TEL 585-240-7301, 800-223-8720, 877-203-5248, FAX 585-292-4392, http://www.elementkjournals.com. Eds. Jan Mater-Cavagnaro, Jason Fisher, Michelle Rogers.

004.6 USA ISSN 1538-8360
SMART TIPS AND QUICK TRICKS FOR NOVELL NETWARE. Text in English. 2002. a. USD 10 per issue domestic; USD 20 per issue foreign (effective 2005).
—CCC.
Published by: Element K Journals (Subsidiary of: Eli Research, Inc.), 500 Canal View Blvd, Rochester, NY 14623. TEL 585-240-7301, 800-223-8720, 877-203-5248, FAX 585-292-4392, http://www.elementkjournals.com. Eds. Jutta VanStean, Michelle Rogers.

004.6 USA ISSN 1091-8914
SUNWORLD; I D G's magazine for the Sun community. Text in English. 1988. m. free. adv. bk.rev.; software rev. charts. index. reprints avail. **Document type:** *Trade.* **Description:** Offers system administrators, IT professionals, and UNIX developers articles on applications of Unix technologies, the computer industry, programming, and systems. Delivers strategic market and technical analysis to UNIX and Internet-network professionals.
Former titles (until 1995): Advanced Systems (1074-9306); (until 1994): SunWorld (1054-5980); (until 1991): SunTech Journal (1046-5456); SunTechnology (0896-8950)
Media: Online - full text.
Indexed: Microcompind, SoftBase.
—CISTI.
Published by: Web Publishing Inc (Subsidiary of: I D G Communications Inc.), 501 Second St, Ste 310, San Francisco, CA 94107. TEL 415-243-4188, FAX 415-267-1732, carolyn.wong@sunworld.com, http://www.sunworld.com. Ed. Carolyn Wong. Pub., Adv. contact Colette McMullen. B&W page USD 6,375; trim 10.75 x 8. Circ: 100,000.

004.68 DEU ISSN 0943-4941
SYSTEME. Variant title: Electronic Embedded Systeme. Text in German. 1987. m. EUR 82.50 domestic; EUR 94.60 foreign (effective 2005). adv. bk.rev. back issues avail. **Document type:** *Magazine, Trade.*
Formerly (until 1993): V M E-bus (0931-5101)
—IE, Infotrieve.
Published by: Aktuelles Wissen Verlagsgesellschaft mbH, Bretonischer Ring 13, Grasbrunn, 85630, Germany. TEL 49-89-456160, FAX 49-89-45616100, http://www.systeme-online.de. Ed. Wolfgang Patelay. Pub. Eduard Heilmayr. Adv. contact Cornelia Jacobi.

004.6 USA
SYSTEMS & NETWORK MANAGEMENT JOURNAL. Text in English. 1996. bi-w. USD 495 (effective 2005). bk.rev. **Document type:** *Journal, Trade.* **Description:** Provides news on computer hardware and software products that work toward multivendor networking, and distributed networks and systems.
Formerly: Systems & Network Management Report (1087-4933); Which was formed by the merger of (1989-1996): Network Management Systems and Strategies (1043-1217); (1988-1996): Distributed Systems Management Report (1079-4727); Which was formerly: O P E N (1072-7760); (until 1992): O S I Product and Equipment News (0898-0489)
Related titles: Online - full text ed.: (from Factiva).
—CCC.

Published by: DataTrends Publications, Inc., PO Box 4460, Leesburg, VA 20177-8541. TEL 703-779-0574, 800-766-8130, FAX 703-779-2267, dtrends@ix.netcom.com, http://www.datatrendspublications.com/SNMJ.htm, http://www.datatrendspublications.com/default.htm. Pub. Paul G Ochs.

004.6 POL ISSN 1428-6394
QA76.88 CODEN: TASKFU
T A S K QUATERLY. (Trojmiejska Akademicka Siec Komputerowa) Text in English. 1997. q. USD 92 foreign to individuals; USD 108 foreign to institutions (effective 2004). **Document type:** *Bulletin, Academic/Scholarly.* **Description:** Provides a common platform for the presentation of papers and exchange of views on numerical methods in their applications to solve a variety of problems in science and engineering with the aid of high performance computers.
Indexed: Inspec, RefZh.
—BLDSC (8606.667150), CISTI.
Published by: Trojmiejska Akademicka Siec Komputerowa, Centrum Informatyczne/Academic Computer Center in Gdansk TASK, Gdansk University of Technology, ul. G. Narutowicza 11/12, Gdansk, 80952, Poland. TEL 48-58-3472411, quarterly@task.gda.pl, office@task.gda.pl, http://www.task.gda.pl/quart/. Ed. Piotr Doerffer.

004.6 USA
T C P - S N A UPDATE. (Transmission Control Protocol - Systems Network Architecture) Text in English. q. USD 190 (effective 2000). **Document type:** *Trade.*
Formerly: S N A Update
Published by: Xephon, 9330 Lyndon B Johnson Fwy., Ste. 800, Dallas, TX 75243-4310. TEL 817-455-7050, FAX 303-438-0290.

004.6 USA
T C PMAG.COM; for Cisco internetworking experts. Text in English. free (effective 2005). adv. **Document type:** *Magazine, Trade.* **Description:** Provides training information for computer professionals using Cisco technologies.
Media: Online - full text.
Published by: 101 Communications, Llc., 16271 Laguna Canyon Rd, Irvine, CA 92618. TEL 949-754-6700, FAX 949-453-1369, editor@tcpmag.com, info@101com.com, http://www.tcpmag.com, http://www.101com.com.

004.6 USA
TASTY BITS FROM THE TECHNOLOGY FRONT. Text in English. w. **Document type:** *Newsletter.* **Description:** Presents bellwethers in computer and communications technology, with special attention to commerce on the Internet.
Media: Online - full text.
Address: dawson@world.std.com, http://www.tbtf.com/.

004.6 AUS
TELCO COMPANY PROFILES AUSTRALIA. Text in English. 1984. a., latest 2002, July, 7th Edition. USD 700 domestic; USD 730 foreign (effective 2001). **Document type:** *Directory.* **Description:** Lists over 100 telecommunications carriers and major service providers, Internet service providers, callback operators, MDS and pay TV license holders in Australia.
Former titles: Carriers and Service Providers Australia (1329-9077); (until 1998): Telecommunications Carriers and Service Providers Market (1326-6810); Which superseded in part: Directory of Electronic Services and Communications Networks in Australia and New Zealand (1322-350X)
Published by: Paul Budde Communication Pty. Ltd., 2643 George Downes Dr, Bucketty, NSW 2250, Australia. TEL 61-2-4998-8144, FAX 61-2-4998-8247, sally@budde.com.au, pbc@budde.com.au, http://www.budde.com.au. Ed. Paul Budde. Circ: 200.

004.6 USA ISSN 1081-5074
TELECOM & NETWORK SECURITY REVIEW. Text in English. 1993. m. USD 290; USD 320 foreign. **Document type:** *Newsletter.* **Description:** Covers security of long-distance commercial telecommunications systems and computer networks that may be penetrated via telephone service.
Related titles: Online - full text ed.
—CCC.
Published by: Pasha Publications Inc., 1600 Wilson Blvd, Ste 600, Arlington, VA 22209. TEL 703-528-1244, FAX 703-528-3742. Ed. Beth McConnell.

004.6 GBR ISSN 1363-9900
TELECOMWORLDWIRE. Text in English. 1994. d. GBP 200 (effective 1999). bk.rev. **Document type:** *Trade.* **Description:** International news service covering telecommunications and IT sectoral news and developments.
Incorporates (1992-199?): Data Broadcasting News
Media: Online - full text (from Gale Group, LexisNexis).
Published by: M2 Communications Ltd., PO Box 475, Coventry, W Mids CV1 2ZW, United Kingdom. TEL 44-1203-634700, FAX 44-1203-634144, M2PW@m2.com, http://www.m2.com. Ed. Darren Ingram. **Dist. in N. America by:** Publications Resource Group, 121 Union St., Box 792, North Adams, MA 01247. TEL 413-664-6185, FAX 413-664-9343.

TELETRAFFIC SCIENCE AND ENGINEERING. see *COMMUNICATIONS—Computer Applications*

004.6 ITA
TRADE ITALIA. Text in Italian. 1995. 10/yr. **Description:** For dealers, distributors, software houses, system integrators, franchisees and superstores.
Published by: Gruppo Editoriale J C E, Via Patecchio 2, Milan, MI 20141, Italy. TEL 39-02-57316011, FAX 39-02-57316291, info@jce.it, http://www.jce.it. Ed. Luisella Acquati. Pub. Jacopo Castelfranchi. Circ: 10,000.

005 USA ISSN 1049-5606
U S E N I X CONFERENCE PROCEEDINGS. Text in English. 198?. irreg. price varies. **Document type:** *Proceedings, Academic/Scholarly.*
Published by: U S E N I X Association, 2560 Ninth St, Ste 215, Berkeley, CA 94710. TEL 510-528-8649, FAX 510-548-5738, conference@usenix.org, office@usenix.org, http://www.usenix.org/publications/library/proceedings/.

004.6 CAN ISSN 0843-803X
VISION INTERFACE CONFERENCE PROCEEDINGS - COMPTE RENDU∗. Text in English, French. 1981. a. USD 45 to non-members; USD 35 to members. **Document type:** *Proceedings.*
Indexed: Englnd.
Published by: Canadian Information Processing Society, 2800 Skymark Ave, Ste 402, Mississauga, ON L4W 5A6, Canada. info@cips.ca, http://www.cips.ca.

004.6 USA
W2K NEWS. Text in English. 1996. w. free. **Description:** Designed for Win NT/2000 professionals that have the job to get and keep this platform up and running.
Formerly: Ntools E-newsflash (1527-3407)
Media: Online - full content.
Published by: Sunbelt Software TEL 727-562-0101, http://www.sunbelt-software.com/w2knews.cfm. Ed. Stu Sjouwerman. Circ: 600,000 (free).

004.68 GBR
WEB AND OPEN TECHNOLOGIES JOURNAL. Text in English. 1997. m. (10/yr.). GBP 545 (effective 1997). bk.rev. **Document type:** *Bulletin.*
Formed by the 1997 merger of: Information Interchange Report; Which was formerly: O I I Spectrum (1351-0096); Distributed Computing Directories (1359-4699); Which was formerly: Open Systems Networking and Computing (1359-4702); (until 1993): Open Systems Newsletter (0952-1992)
Published by: Technology Appraisals Ltd., 82 Hampton Rd, Twickenham, Mddx TW2 5QS, United Kingdom. TEL 44-181-893-3986, FAX 44-181-744-1149, techapp@cix.compulink.co.uk. Ed. Peter Judge. Pub. Alan Paton.

WEB3D (YEAR) SYMPOSIUM. PROCEEDINGS. see *COMPUTERS—Computer Graphics*

004.6 USA ISSN 1537-4475
QA76.76.O63 CODEN: WNMAFQ
WINDOWS & .NET MAGAZINE. Text in English. 1995. 14/yr. USD 49.95 domestic; USD 59 in Canada; USD 99 elsewhere (effective 2003). adv. back issues avail. **Document type:** *Magazine, Consumer.* **Description:** Provides hands-on information for deploying business-critical applications based on Windows NT Server and Workstation.
Former titles (until 2001): Windows 2000 Magazine (1527-1552); (until 2000): Windows N T Magazine (1083-138X)
Related titles: Online - full text ed.: (from EBSCO Publishing).
Indexed: CompLI, Inpharma, MicrocompInd, PE&ON, Reac.
—BLDSC (9319.3322), IE. **CCC.**
Published by: Penton Technology Media (Subsidiary of: Penton Media, Inc.), 221 E 29th St, Ste 242, Loveland, CO 80538. TEL 970-663-4700, 800-621-1544, FAX 970-663-3285, karen@windowsmag.com, subs@winntmag.com, http://www.winnetmag.com, http://www.winntmag.com. Ed. Kathy Blomstrom. Adv. contact Bart Taylor. **Dist. in UK by:** Comag, Tavistock Works, Tavistock Rd, W Drayton, Middx UB7 7QX, United Kingdom. TEL 44-1895-444055, FAX 44-1895-433602.

004.6 NLD ISSN 1566-2950
WINDOWS & NETWERKEN; onafhankelijke nieuwsbrief voor Windows professionals. Text in Dutch. 1996. 10/yr. EUR 133.90; EUR 14 per issue (effective 2003).
Formerly (until 1999): N T Today (1385-1691)
—Infotrieve.
Published by: Ten Hagen & Stam b.v. (Subsidiary of: Sdu Uitgevers bv), Postbus 34, Den Haag, 2501 AG, Netherlands. http://www.tenhagenstam.nl.

004.6 USA ISSN 1537-4483
WINDOWS SCRIPTING SOLUTIONS. Text in English. m. USD 129 domestic; USD 135 foreign (effective 2002). adv. **Document type:** *Magazine, Trade.* **Description:** Provides practical advice, code modules, and scripts for systems administrators and others who use code at the command line and in scripts to automate tasks and create utilities.
Related titles: Online - full text ed.
—CCC.
Published by: Penton Technology Media (Subsidiary of: Penton Media, Inc.), 221 E 29th St, Ste 242, Loveland, CO 80538. TEL 970-663-4700, 800-621-1544, FAX 970-663-3285, http://www.winscriptingsolutions.com.

WINDOWS WEB SOLUTIONS. see *COMPUTERS—Internet*

384.5 GBR ISSN 1472-7226
WIRELESS EVOLUTION. Variant title: Evolution. Text in English. 2001. s-a. (Jun. & Oct.). adv. **Document type:** *Magazine, Trade.*
Related titles: Online - full text ed.: (from Gale Group); ♦ Supplement to: Mobile Communications International. ISSN 1352-9226.
Published by: Informa Telecoms & Media (Subsidiary of: T & F Informa plc), 37-41 Mortimer St, London, W1T 3JH, United Kingdom. TEL 44-20-7017-4278, FAX 44-20-7017-4698, http://www.mobilecomms.com/NASApp/cs/ContentServer?pagename=marlin/home&siteid=30000000121&MarlinViewType=MARKT_EFFORT&marketingid=30000060229&forcedB, http://www.telecoms.com/.

COMPUTERS—Computer Programming

see also COMPUTERS—Software

005.13 USA ISSN 1523-2867
QA76.7
A C M / S I G P L A N NOTICES. (Association for Computing Machinery / Special Interest Group on Programming Languages) Text in English. 1965. m. USD 62 (effective 2004). bk.rev. charts; illus.; stat. back issues avail. **Document type:** *Bulletin, Academic/Scholarly.* **Description:** Explores programming language concepts and tools, focusing on design, implementation, and efficient use.
Formerly (until 1991): S I G P L A N Notices (0362-1340)
Related titles: Online - full text ed.: (from Association for Computing Machinery, Inc.).
Indexed: AHCI, ASCA, CMCI, CompAb, CompR, CurCont, Englnd, ErgAb, Inspec, RASB.
—BLDSC (0578.640500), AskIEEE, CISTI, IDS, IE, ingenta.
Published by: Association for Computing Machinery, Inc., 1515 Broadway, 17th Fl, New York, NY 10036-5701. TEL 212-626-0500, 212-626-0520, 800-342-6626, FAX 212-869-0481, sig.not@acm.org, sigs@acm.org, usacm@acm.org, http://www.cs.appstate.edu/~sigplan, http://www.acm.org. Ed. Jay Fenwick. Circ: 11,600 (controlled).

005.1 USA
A C M / S I G P L A N WORKSHOP ON PARTIAL EVALUATION AND SEMANTICS-BASED PROGRAM MANIPULATION. PROCEEDINGS. (Association for Computing Machinery/Special Interest Group on Programming Languages) Text in English. a. **Document type:** *Proceedings, Academic/Scholarly.*
Related titles: Online - full content ed.
Published by: Association for Computing Machinery, Inc., 1515 Broadway, 17th Fl, New York, NY 10036-5701. TEL 212-626-0500, 800-342-6626, FAX 212-869-0481, http://www.acm.org.

005.1 USA ISSN 0164-0925
QA76.7 CODEN: ATPSDT
➤ **A C M TRANSACTIONS ON PROGRAMMING LANGUAGES AND SYSTEMS.** Text in English. 1979. bi-m. USD 240 domestic to non-members; USD 260 foreign to non-members; USD 56 domestic to members; USD 76 foreign to members; USD 51 domestic to students; USD 71 foreign to students; USD 288 combined subscription domestic to non-members print & online eds.; USD 308 combined subscription foreign to non-members print & online eds.; USD 67 combined subscription domestic to members print & online eds.; USD 87 combined subscription foreign to members print & online eds.; USD 61 combined subscription domestic to students print & online eds.; USD 81 combined subscription foreign to students print & online eds. (effective 2006). charts; illus. index. reprints avail. **Document type:** *Journal, Academic/Scholarly.* **Description:** Provides a forum for the research in computer science areas. Publishes research and algorithms, programming languages and systems.
Incorporates (1992-1993): Letters on Programming Languages and Systems (1057-4514)
Related titles: Microform ed.: (from WWS); Online - full text ed.: USD 192 to non-members; USD 45 to members; USD 41 to students (effective 2006) (from Association for Computing Machinery, Inc., EBSCO Publishing, Florida Center for Library Automation, Gale Group).
Indexed: ABIn, AIA, AS&TI, ASCA, BMT, BrCerAb, C&CSA, C&ISA, CADCAM, CIS, CMCI, CerAb, CompAb, CompC, CompD, CompLI, CompR, CorrAb, CurCont, E&CAJ, EMA, ETA, Englnd, ErgAb, IAA, ISR, Inspec, M&TEA, MBF, METADEX, RefZh, SCI, SolStAb, WAA, ZentMath.
—BLDSC (0578.675000), AskIEEE, CISTI, Ei, IDS, IE, Infotrieve, ingenta, Linda Hall. **CCC.**
Published by: Association for Computing Machinery, Inc., 1515 Broadway, 17th Fl, New York, NY 10036-5701. TEL 212-626-0500, 800-342-6626, FAX 212-944-1318, usacm@acm.org, http://www.acm.org/toplas. Ed. Ron Cytron. Circ: 7,077 (paid).

➤ **A C M TRANSACTIONS ON SOFTWARE ENGINEERING AND METHODOLOGY.** see *COMPUTERS—Software*

005.1 USA ISSN 1550-4875
▼ **A C M TRANSACTIONS ON SPEECH AND LANGUAGE PROCESSING.** (Association for Computing Machinery) Text in English. 2005. a. USD 140 domestic to non-members; USD 154 foreign to non-members; USD 40 domestic to members; USD 54 foreign to members; USD 35 domestic to students; USD 49 foreign to students; USD 168 combined subscription domestic to non-members print & online eds.; USD 182 combined subscription foreign to non-members print & online eds.; USD 48 combined subscription domestic to members print & online eds.; USD 62 combined subscription foreign to members print & online eds.; USD 42 combined subscription domestic to students print & online eds.; USD 56 combined subscription foreign to students print & online eds. (effective 2006). **Description:** Focuses on practical areas of the design, devleopment, and evaluation of speech-and text-processing systems along with their associated theory.
Related titles: Online - full text ed.: ISSN 1550-4883. 2005. USD 112 to non-members; USD 32 to members; USD 28 to students (effective 2006).
Published by: Association for Computing Machinery, Inc., 1515 Broadway, 17th Fl, New York, NY 10036-5701. TEL 212-626-0500, 800-342-6626, FAX 212-944-1318, sigs@acm.org, http://www.acm.org.

005.13 USA
A C M WORKSHOP ON X M L SECURITY. PROCEEDINGS. Text in English. a. **Document type:** *Proceedings, Academic/Scholarly.*
Published by: Association for Computing Machinery, Inc., 1515 Broadway, 17th Fl, New York, NY 10036-5701. TEL 212-626-0500, usacm@acm.org, http://www.acm.org.

005.1 USA ISSN 0067-2483
CODEN: ASDPDL
A.P.I.C. STUDIES IN DATA PROCESSING. Variant title: A.P.I.C. Series. Text in English. 1961. irreg., latest vol.37, 1991. reprint service avail. from ISI.
Indexed: Inspec, ZentMath.
—CISTI. **CCC.**
Published by: (Automatic Programming Information Centre), Academic Press (Subsidiary of: Elsevier Science & Technology), 525 B St, Ste 1900, San Diego, CA 92101-4495. apsubs@acad.com, http://www.academicpress.com. Eds. I Wand, M Shave.

A P L QUOTE QUAD. see *COMPUTERS—Personal Computers*

005.117 FRA ISSN 1102-593X
➤ **A S U NEWSLETTER.** Text in English. 1991. irreg. (3-4/yr.). adv. bk.rev. **Document type:** *Newsletter, Academic/Scholarly.* **Description:** Forum for news, reviews, articles and editorials in the field of advanced object oriented programming as applied to modeling complex systems.
Formerly (until 1991): Simula Newsletter (0800-0069)
Indexed: Inspec.
—BLDSC (1765208000), AskIEEE, IE.
Published by: Association of Simula Users, c/o Alain Tanguy, Laboratoire d'Informatique, LIMOS, Universite Pascal, Clement-Ferrard II, 63177, France. TEL 33-0-473 40 50 16, FAX 33-0-473 40 50 01, http://www.isima.fr/asu/wn10.html. adv.: B&W page SEK 5,000. Circ: 70.

005.13 USA ISSN 1064-1505
CODEN: AICNE9
ADA IC NEWS. Text in English. q. **Document type:** *Newsletter.* **Description:** Provides news, conference reports, and articles about projects programmed in Ada.
Formerly: Ada Information Clearinghouse Newsletter
Media: E-mail.
Indexed: Inspec.
Published by: Ada Information Clearinghouse, PO Box 1866, Falls Church, VA 22041. TEL 703-681-2466, 800-232-4211, FAX 703-681-2869, adainfo@sw-eng.falls-church.va.us, http://www.adaic.org.

005.13 USA ISSN 1094-3641
QA76.73.A35
ADA LETTERS. Text in English. 1997. q. **Document type:** *Journal, Trade.* **Description:** Provides an information interchange forum on all aspects of the Ada language and Ada-related technologies.
Related titles: Online - full text ed.: (from EBSCO Publishing).
Indexed: CompR.
—BLDSC (0678.245400), CISTI, IE, ingenta.
Published by: Association for Computing Machinery, Inc., 1515 Broadway, 17th Fl, New York, NY 10036-5701. TEL 212-626-0500, 800-342-6626, FAX 212-869-0481, sigs@acm.org, usacm@acm.org, http://www.acm.org/sigada.

005.13 GBR ISSN 1381-6551
ADA USER JOURNAL. Text in English. q. GBP 125 (effective 2000). adv. bk.rev. **Document type:** *Academic/Scholarly.* **Description:** Publishes material which promotes the effective development and use of the ADA language; includes news reports on significant ADA events and a calendar of activities.
Formerly (until 1994): Ada User (0268-652X)
Indexed: EngInd, Inspec.
—BLDSC (0678.248120), AskIEEE, CISTI, Ei, IE, Infotrieve. **CCC.**
Published by: Ada Language UK Ltd., PO Box 322, York, YO10 3GY, United Kingdom. TEL 44-1904-412740, FAX 44-1904-426702, admin@adauk.org.uk, http://www.adauk.org.uk. Ed. J S Briggs. R&P J.S. Briggs TEL 44-2392-846438. Adv. contact H S Byard.

005.117 GBR
AGENTLINK NEWSLETTER. Text in English. 1998. irreg. **Document type:** *Newsletter.* **Description:** Provides a relatively informal way of communicating what is happening in the agent world and agent-based computer systems.
Media: Online - full text.
Published by: (Department of Electronic Engineering), University of London, Queen Mary College, London, E1 4NS, United Kingdom. Paul.Davidsson@ide.hk-r.se, http://www.agentlink.org. Ed. Paul Davidsson.

005.1 USA ISSN 1540-6768
AGILE PROJECT MANAGEMENT ADVISORY SERVICE EXECUTIVE REPORT. Text in English. 1994. m. USD 2,400 (effective 2005). charts; illus. back issues avail. **Document type:** *Newsletter, Trade.* **Description:** Contains management and technology advice for developing and delivering software applications in today's fast paced e-business economy.
Former titles: E-project Management Advisory Service Executive Report (1536-299X); (until 2000): E-business Application Delivery (1530-3489); (until 1999): Application Development Strategies (1087-6243); Which was formed by the merger of (1989-1994): C A S E Strategies (1045-1986); (1987-1994): C A S E Outlook (0895-2108)
Related titles: Online - full text ed.: ISSN 1554-706X; Supplement(s): Agile Project Management Advisory Service E-mail Advisor; Agile Project Management Advisory Service Executive Summary; Agile Project Management Advisory Service Executive Update.
Indexed: CurCont.
—IDS. **CCC.**
Published by: Cutter Information Corp., 37 Broadway, Ste 1, Arlington, MA 02474. TEL 781-648-8700, FAX 781-648-1950, http://www.cutter.com/project/abstracts.html. Ed. Jim Highsmith. Pub. Karen Fine Coburn.

ANNUAL N A S A GODDARD SOFTWARE ENGINEERING WORKSHOP. PROCEEDINGS. see *COMPUTERS—Software*

005.1 GBR ISSN 1367-5788
QA76 CODEN: ARCOF8
➤ **ANNUAL REVIEWS IN CONTROL.** Text in English. 1960. 2/yr. EUR 466 in Europe to institutions; JPY 61,900 in Japan to institutions; USD 522 to institutions except Europe and Japan; EUR 76 in Europe to qualified personnel; JPY 10,000 in Japan to qualified personnel; USD 84 to qualified personnel except Europe and Japan (effective 2006). abstr. back issues avail. **Document type:** *Journal, Academic/Scholarly.* **Description:** Provides substantive review articles on topics of interest to professionals in the field of computer software. Topics covered include distributed control systems, automation, software and real time systems, programming and applications.
Formerly (until 1996): Annual Review in Automatic Programming (0066-4138)
Related titles: Microform ed.: (from PQC); Online - full text ed.: (from EBSCO Publishing, Gale Group, IngentaConnect, ScienceDirect, Swets Information Services).
Indexed: CMCI, CompC, CompLI, CurCont, EngInd, Inspec, ZentMath.
—BLDSC (1522.256000), CISTI, Ei, IE, Infotrieve, ingenta, Linda Hall. **CCC.**
Published by: Pergamon (Subsidiary of: Elsevier Science & Technology), The Boulevard, Langford Ln, East Park, Kidlington, Oxford OX5 1GB, United Kingdom. TEL 44-1865-843000, FAX 44-1865-843010, http://www.elsevier.com/locate/arcontrol, http://www.elsevier.nl. Ed. J J Gertler. **Subscr. to:** Elsevier BV, PO Box 211, Amsterdam 1000 AE, Netherlands. TEL 31-20-485-3757, FAX 31-20-485-3432, nlinfo-f@elsevier.nl.

005.11 USA
APPLIED COMPUTING REVIEW. Text in English. s-a. USD 30 (effective 2004). **Description:** Covers development of new computing applications.
Related titles: Online - full text ed.
Indexed: Inspec.
Published by: Association for Computing Machinery, Inc., 1515 Broadway, 17th Fl, New York, NY 10036-5701. TEL 212-626-0500, 212-626-0520, 800-342-6626, usacm@acm.org, http://www.acm.org.

ASIA PACIFIC SOFTWARE ENGINEERING CONFERENCE. PROCEEDINGS. see *COMPUTERS—Software*

005.115 USA
ASSOCIATION OF LOGIC PROGRAMMING. NEWSLETTER. Short title: ALP Newsletter. Text in English. q. free to members. back issues avail. **Document type:** *Newsletter.* **Description:** Contains news, net postings, calls for papers, comments, conference announcements, and news about the association.
Related titles: Online - full text ed.
Published by: (Association of Logic Programming), Elsevier Inc. (Subsidiary of: Elsevier Science & Technology), 360 Park Ave. S, New York, NY 10010-1710. TEL 212-633-3730, 888-437-4636, ad@ratree.psu.ac.th, usinfo-f@elsevier.com, http://www-lp.doc.ic.ac.uk/alp/archive.html, http://www.elsevier.com. Ed. Andrew Davison.

AUSTRALIA. BUREAU OF STATISTICS. YEAR 2000 PROBLEM, AUSTRALIA. see *COMPUTERS—Abstracting, Bibliographies, Statistics*

AUSTRALIA. BUREAU OF STATISTICS. YEAR 2000 PROBLEM, AUSTRALIA, PRELIMINARY. see *COMPUTERS—Abstracting, Bibliographies, Statistics*

AUSTRALIAN SOFTWARE ENGINEERING CONFERENCE. PROCEEDINGS. see *COMPUTERS—Software*

005.117 USA ISSN 1535-9581
B E A WEBLOGIC DEVELOPER'S JOURNAL. Text in English. 2001 (Dec.). m. USD 49.99 for 2 yrs. domestic; USD 69.99 for 2 yrs. in Canada & Mexico; USD 79.99 for 2 yrs. elsewhere; USD 12 newsstand/cover (effective 2005). adv. software rev. **Document type:** *Magazine, Trade.* **Description:** Contains articles and features written exclusively by and for the international community of developers who design, build, customize, deploy, and administer WebLogic application server software.
Related titles: Online - full text ed.: USD 19.99 (effective 2005) (from Factiva, Gale Group).
Indexed: CompD.
Published by: SYS-CON Media, Inc., 135 Chestnut Ridge Rd, Montvale, NJ 07645. TEL 201-802-3040, 888-303-5282, FAX 201-782-9600, info@sys-con.com, http://wldj.sys-con.com, http://www.sys-con.com. Ed. Jason Westra. R&P Fuat Kircaali. Adv. contact Carmen Gonzalez. Circ: 25,000 (controlled).

005.12 NLD ISSN 0006-3835
QA76 CODEN: NBITAB
➤ **BIT (LISSE);** numerical mathematics. Variant title: B I T (Nordisk Tidskrift for Informationsbehandling). Text in English. 1961. q. EUR 348, USD 355, GBP 218 combined subscription to institutions print & online eds. (effective 2005). bk.rev. bibl.; charts; illus. index, cum.index: 1961-1973, 1980-1989. back issues avail.; reprint service avail. from ISI,PSC. **Document type:** *Journal, Academic/Scholarly.* **Description:** Concentrates on the design and analysis of algorithms, programming languages, computer systems and numerical, as well as non-numerical computation.
Formerly (until 1967): Nordisk Tidskrift for Informationsbehandling (0901-246X)
Related titles: Online - full text ed.: ISSN 1572-9125 (from EBSCO Publishing, Gale Group, IngentaConnect, Kluwer Online, O C L C Online Computer Library Center, Inc., Springer LINK, Swets Information Services).
Indexed: ApMecR, BibLing, CCMJ, CIS, CMCI, CompAb, CompC, CompLI, CompR, CurCont, ISR, Inspec, MathR, MathSciNet, SCI, ZentMath.
—BLDSC (2095.400000), AskIEEE, CISTI, IDS, IE, Infotrieve, ingenta, Linda Hall. **CCC.**
Published by: (BIT Foundation SWE), Springer-Verlag Dordrecht (Subsidiary of: Springer Science+Business Media), Van Godewijckstraat 30, Dordrecht, 3311 GX, Netherlands. TEL 31-78-6576050, FAX 31-78-6576474, http://springerlink.metapress.com/openurl.asp?genre=journal&issn=0006-3835, http://www.springeronline.com. Ed. Axel Ruhe. Circ: 1,000.

005.13 USA ISSN 1063-7273
BORLAND LANGUAGE EXPRESS★. Text in English. 1990. q.
Formerly (until vol.2, no.1, 1992): Turbo Technix (0893-827X)
Published by: Borland International, Inc., 100 Borland Way, Scotts Valley, CA 95066-3249. TEL 408-438-8400, FAX 408-439-9119. Ed. David Intersimone.

005.5 USA
BUILDER.COM; beyond the code. Text in English. w. free (effective 2003). back issues avail.
Media: Online - full text. **Related titles:** E-mail ed.
Published by: CNET Networks, Inc., 235 Second St, San Francisco, CA 94105. TEL 415-344-2000, FAX 415-395-9254, Janet.Chen@cnet.com., http://builder.com.com/, http://www.cnet.com.

005.13 USA
C++ BUILDER DEVELOPER'S JOURNAL. Variant title: C Plus Plus Builder Developer's Journal. Text in English. 1990. m. USD 79; USD 99 foreign (effective 1999). **Document type:** *Consumer.* **Description:** Offers fresh ideas, shortcuts, and advice from software experts who explore every aspect of C Plus Plus Builder.
Former titles: Inside Microsoft Visual C Plus Plus (1082-3743); (until 1995): Microsoft C - C Plus Plus Developer's Journal (1068-5669); (until 1993): Inside Microsoft C (1047-6075)
Published by: Reisdorph Publishing, PO Box 50213, Colorado Springs, CO 80919. TEL 719-266-0736, FAX 719-260-7151, customer_relations@reisdorph.com, http://www.zdjournals.com.

005.1 USA ISSN 1534-1852
C - C++ CODER MAGAZINE. Variant title: C - C Plus Plus Coder Magazine. Text in English. 1999. m. back issues avail. **Document type:** *Newsletter.* **Description:** Dedicated to help programmers with code problems, offering workaround solutions.
Media: Online - full text.
Published by: Mega Tech Software, 51 Whitman Ave, Staten Island, NY 10308. codermag@megatechsoftware.com, http://www.megatechsoftware.com/codermag.htm.

005.115 USA ISSN 1075-2838
QA76.73.C15 CODEN: CCUJEX
C/C++ USERS JOURNAL; advanced solutions for C/C++ programmers. Variant title: C/C Plus Plus. Text in English. 1981. m. USD 29.95 domestic; USD 46 in Canada & Mexico; USD 65 elsewhere; free to qualified personnel (effective 2005). adv. bk.rev.; software rev. back issues avail. **Document type:** *Trade.* **Description:** Discusses C and C Plus Plus programming at all levels, in addition to related software tools, books, public domain software and other products.
Formerly (until 1994): C Users Journal (0898-9788); Which was formed by the Dec. 1987 merger of: C Journal (8756-9736); C Users Group Newsletter
Related titles: CD-ROM ed.; Online - full text ed.: (from Gale Group).
Indexed: CompD, CompR, EngInd, Inspec, MicrocompInd, SoftBase.
—BLDSC (2943.175250), CISTI, IE, Infotrieve, ingenta. **CCC.**
Published by: C M P Media LLC (Subsidiary of: United News & Media), 2800 Campus Dr, San Mateo, CA 94403. TEL 650-513-4300, FAX 650-513-4618, http://www.cuj.com/, http://www.cmp.com. Ed. Jonathan Erickson TEL 650-513-4578. adv.: B&W page USD 2,500, color page USD 3,045. Circ: 39,048.

005.13 USA ISSN 1093-2097
C++ DEVELOPERS JOURNAL. Text in English. 199?. m. USD 19.95 domestic; USD 37.95 in Canada & Mexico; USD 63.95 elsewhere (effective 2000). adv. back issues avail. **Document type:** *Magazine, Trade.* **Description:** Provides independent and practical hands-on advice and perspective to professional Windows programmers.
Formerly (until 1997): Visual C++ Developers Journal (1089-9715)
Related titles: Online - full text ed.: (from ProQuest Information & Learning).
Published by: Fawcette Technical Publications, 2600 S. El Camino Real., Ste. 300, San Mateo, CA 94403-2381. TEL 650-833-7100, 800-848-5523, FAX 650-853-0230, feedback@fawcette.com, http://www.fawcette.com. adv.: B&W page USD 5,238, color page USD 6,966; trim 7 x 10. Circ: 45,000 (paid).

CD-ROM ONLINE. see *COMPUTERS—Software*

005.1 USA ISSN 1547-5166
QA76.76.D47
CODE (HOUSTON); component developer magazine. Text in English. 2000. bi-m. USD 19.99 (effective 2003). adv. **Document type:** *Magazine.*
Published by: E P S Software, 13810 Champion Forest Dr. Ste. 202, Houston, TX 77069. TEL 281-866-7444, FAX 281-866-7466, info@eps-software.com, http://www.code-magazine.com, http://www.eps-software.com. Ed. Rod Paddock.

005.13 GBR ISSN 1477-8424
QA76.7 CODEN: COLADA
➤ **COMPUTER LANGUAGES, SYSTEMS AND STRUCTURES.** Text in English. 1976. 4/yr. EUR 259 in Europe to individuals; JPY 27,000 in Japan to individuals; USD 225 to individuals except Europe and Japan; EUR 942 in Europe to institutions; JPY 130,300 in Japan to institutions; USD 1,054 to institutions except Europe and Japan (effective 2006). adv. bk.rev. illus. back issues avail.; reprints avail. **Document type:** *Academic/Scholarly.* **Description:** Presents original and review articles on programming systems and structures, programming languages and their theory. Contains abstract and full text of papers pertinent to the subject.
Formerly (until 2003): Computer Languages (0096-0551)
Related titles: Microfilm ed.: (from PQC); Online - full text ed.: (from EBSCO Publishing, Gale Group, IngentaConnect, ScienceDirect, Swets Information Services).
Indexed: AHCI, ASCA, BrCerAb, C&ISA, CMCI, CerAb, CompAb, CompC, CompLI, CompR, CorrAb, CurCont, E&CAJ, EMA, EngInd, ErgAb, IAA, Inspec, M&TEA, MBF, METADEX, RefZh, SolStAb, WAA, ZentMath.
—BLDSC (3394.071000), AskIEEE, CISTI, Ei, IDS, IE, ingenta, Linda Hall. **CCC.**
Published by: Pergamon (Subsidiary of: Elsevier Science & Technology), The Boulevard, Langford Ln, East Park, Kidlington, Oxford OX5 1GB, United Kingdom. TEL 44-1865-843000, FAX 44-1865-843010, http://www.elsevier.com/locate/comlan. Ed. Dr. Robert S Ledley. Circ: 1,025. **Subscr. to:** Elsevier BV, PO Box 211, Amsterdam 1000 AE, Netherlands. TEL 31-20-485-3757, FAX 31-20-485-3432, nlinfo-f@elsevier.nl, http://www.elsevier.nl.

➤ **COMPUTER NEWS.** see *COMPUTERS—Software*

005.11 005.15 ITA ISSN 1123-8526
COMPUTER PROGRAMMING; il primo mensile di programmazione. Text in Italian. 1991-1995; resumed 199?. m. EUR 50 (effective 2005). **Document type:** *Magazine, Consumer.* **Description:** Provides information on C++, databases, Delphi, JAVA, Visual Basic and Windows. Specifically concerned with new software offered in Italian.
Related titles: Online - full text ed.
Published by: Gruppo Editoriale Infomedia Srl, Via Valdera P 116, Ponsacco, PI 56038, Italy. TEL 39-0587-736460, FAX 39-0587-732232, http://www.infomedia.it. Ed. Alessadro Pedone.

COMPUTER RESELLER NEWS (RUSSIAN EDITION). see *COMPUTERS—Software*

005.1 GBR ISSN 0885-2308
TK7882.S65 CODEN: CSPLEO
➤ **COMPUTER SPEECH AND LANGUAGE.** Text in English. 1996. 4/yr. EUR 152 in Europe to individuals; JPY 16,400 in Japan to individuals; USD 155 elsewhere to individuals; EUR 443 in Europe to institutions; JPY 47,900 in Japan to institutions; USD 396 elsewhere to institutions (effective 2006). adv. reprints avail. **Document type:** *Academic/Scholarly.* **Description:** Publishes papers of original research related to quantitative description of the recognition, understanding, production, and coding of speech by humans or machines.
Related titles: Online - full text ed.: ISSN 1095-8363. USD 417 (effective 2002) (from EBSCO Publishing, Gale Group, IngentaConnect, O C L C Online Computer Library Center, Inc., ScienceDirect, Swets Information Services).
Indexed: AHCI, ASCA, ArtlAb, B&BAb, BibLing, BrCerAb, C&ISA, CMCI, CerAb, CompAb, CompLI, CorrAb, E&CAJ, EMA, IAA, Inspec, L&LBA, LingAb, M&TEA, MBF, METADEX, PCI, SOPODA, SolStAb, WAA, e-psyche.
—BLDSC (3394.276600), AskIEEE, CISTI, Ei, IDS, IE, Infotrieve, ingenta. **CCC.**
Published by: Academic Press (Subsidiary of: Elsevier Science & Technology), Harcourt Pl, 32 Jamestown Rd, London, NW1 7BY, United Kingdom. TEL 44-20-7424-4200, FAX 44-20-7483-2293, apsubs@acad.com, http://www.elsevier.com/locate/csl. Eds. A. Stolcke, E. Briscoe, R. Moore.

005.1 GBR ISSN 1532-0626
QA76.58 CODEN: CCPEBO
➤ **CONCURRENCY AND COMPUTATION: PRACTICE & EXPERIENCE.** Text in English. 1989. 15/yr. USD 3,170 to institutions; USD 3,487 combined subscription to institutions print & online eds. (effective 2006). adv. back issues avail.; reprint service avail. from PSC. **Document type:** *Journal, Academic/Scholarly.* **Description:** Relays practical experience of concurrent machines and focuses especially on concurrent solutions to specific probems, concurrent algorithms and computational methods, as well as programming environments and more.
Formerly (until 2000): Concurrency: Practice and Experience (1040-3108)
Related titles: Microform ed.: (from PQC); Online - full content ed.: ISSN 1532-0634. USD 3,170 to institutions (effective 2006); Online - full text ed.: (from EBSCO Publishing, Swets Information Services, Wiley InterScience).
Indexed: ASCA, ASFA, BrCerAb, C&ISA, CMCI, CerAb, CompAb, CompLI, CorrAb, CurCont, E&CAJ, EMA, ESPM, IAA, ISMEC, Inspec, M&TEA, MBF, METADEX, SolStAb, WAA.
—BLDSC (3405.622000), AskIEEE, CISTI, Ei, IDS, IE, ingenta. **CCC.**
Published by: John Wiley & Sons Ltd. (Subsidiary of: John Wiley & Sons, Inc.), The Atrium, Southern Gate, Chichester, West Sussex PO19 8SQ, United Kingdom. TEL 44-1243-779777, FAX 44-1243-775878, customer@wiley.co.uk, http://www.interscience.wiley.com/jpages/1532-0626/, http://www.wiley.co.uk. adv.: B&W page GBP 650, color page GBP 1,550; trim 200 x 260. Circ: 500. **Subscr. to:** John Wiley & Sons, Inc., 111 River St, Hoboken, NJ 07030-5774. TEL 201-748-6645, FAX 201-748-6088, subinfo@wiley.com.

➤ **CONFERENCE ON SOFTWARE ENGINEERING EDUCATION AND TRAINING. PROCEEDINGS.** see *COMPUTERS—Software*

005.114 USA
CRAY CHANNELS. Text in English. irreg.
Indexed: Inspec.
Published by: Cray Research, Inc., Distribution Center, 2360 Pilot Knob Rd, Mendota Heights, MN 55120. TEL 612-683-5907, FAX 612-452-0141, http://www.cray.com.

005.1 USA ISSN 1522-7383
CUTTER I T JOURNAL; the journal of information technology management. (Information Technology) Text in English. 1988. m. USD 485 domestic; USD 585 foreign (effective 2000). back issues avail. **Description:** Covers high-level computer software, trends and forecasts; includes commentary.
Formerly (until vol. 11, no. 3, 1998: American Programmer (1048-5600)
Related titles: Online - full text ed.: ISSN 1554-5946.
Indexed: CompLI, EngInd, Inspec, MicrocompInd, PAIS.
—BLDSC (3506.198200), AskIEEE, Ei, IDS, IE, ingenta, Linda Hall.
Published by: Cutter Information Corp., 37 Broadway, Ste 1, Arlington, MA 02474. TEL 781-648-8702, 800-964-8702, FAX 781-648-1950, http://www.cutter.com/consortium/. Ed. Edward Yourdon. Pub. Karen Fine Coburn.

005.1 DEU ISSN 0930-1054
DIE DATENSCHLEUDER; das wissenschaftliche Fachblatt fuer Datenreisende. Text in German. 1984. 4/yr. EUR 32 for 2 yrs.; EUR 16 for 2 yrs. to students (effective 2005). bk.rev. charts; illus. back issues avail. **Document type:** *Bulletin.*
Published by: Chaos Computer Club e.V., Lokstedter Weg 72, Hamburg, 20251, Germany. TEL 49-40-4018010, FAX 49-40-40180141, ds@ccc.de, mail@ccc.de, http://www.ccc.de. Ed. A Mueller Maguhn. Circ: 2,000.

005.11 005.15 ITA ISSN 1124-5468
DEV. DEVELOPING SOFTWARE SOLUTIONS; la rivista che ti insegna a programmare. Text in Italian. 1993. m. EUR 50 (effective 2005). **Document type:** *Magazine, Consumer.* **Description:** Covers new software product applications and offers instructions in developing programming skills.
Related titles: Online - full text ed.: ISSN 1721-1301. 1998.
Published by: Gruppo Editoriale Infomedia Srl, Via Valdera P 116, Ponsacco, PI 56038, Italy. TEL 39-0587-736460, FAX 39-0587-732232, http://www.infomedia.it. Ed. Alessandro Pedone.

681.3 FRA ISSN 1628-3368
DEVELOPPEUR REFERENCE. Text in French. 1991. 20/yr. EUR 200 (effective 2002). adv. **Document type:** *Magazine, Trade.* **Description:** Contains information aimed at programmers, analyst programmers, project leaders, IT managers, and professional developers.
Formerly (until 2001): Langages et Systemes (1167-2145)
Related titles: Online - full text ed.
Published by: I D G Communications France, 5 rue Chantecoq, Puteaux, 92808, France. TEL 33-1-4197-6161, FAX 33-1-4197-6160, devreference@idg.fr, http://www.devreference.net, http://www.idg.fr. Ed. Pierre Tran. Pub. Michel Crestin. adv.: color page USD 4,741; bleed 230 x 300. Circ: 20,000 (paid and controlled).

C

DOTNETPRO; das .Net-Magazin fuer Entwickler. see *COMPUTERS—Internet*

005.117 USA
▼ **ECLIPSE DEVELOPER'S JOURNAL**; the resource for developers using the eclipse platform. Text in English. 2004. m. USD 39.99 (effective 2005). **Document type:** *Magazine, Trade.*
Media: Online - full content.
Published by: SYS-CON Media, Inc., 135 Chestnut Ridge Rd, Montvale, NJ 07645. TEL 201-802-3040, 888-303-5282, FAX 201-782-9600, info@sys-con.com, http://eclipse.sys-con.com, http://www.sys-con.com.

005.117 USA
▼ **ECLIPSE NEWSLETTER.** Text in English. 2004. w. **Document type:** *Newsletter, Trade.*
Media: Online - full content.
Published by: SYS-CON Media, Inc., 135 Chestnut Ridge Rd, Montvale, NJ 07645. TEL 888-303-5282, FAX 201-782-9600, info@sys-con.com, http://www.eclipsenewsletter.com, http://www.sys-con.com.

005.11 NLD ISSN 0921-2787
P98 CODEN: LANTEB
ELECTRIC WORD✶. Text in Dutch. 1983. bi-m. USD 50 to individuals; USD 80 to institutions. adv. bk.rev. **Description:** Informs professionals working with natural language about the current changes in their industry.
Formerly: Language Technology; Incorporates (1983-1988): Language Monthly
Indexed: Inspec, SoftBase.
—AskIEEE.
Published by: Language Technology B.V., Emmalaan 21, Amsterdam, 1075 AT, Netherlands. TEL 20-188225, FAX 20-838616. Ed. Louis Rossetto. Circ: 1,000.

005.1 USA ISSN 1074-4916
EMBEDDED SYSTEMS PROGRAMMING PRODUCT NEWS. Text in English. 1994. q. adv. **Document type:** *Trade.*
Published by: C M P Media LLC (Subsidiary of: United News & Media), 600 Harrison St, 6th Fl., San Francisco, CA 94107. TEL 415-947-6746, FAX 415-947-6041, http://www.cmp.com.

EMPIRICAL SOFTWARE ENGINEERING; an international journal. see *COMPUTERS—Software*

▼ **ENTERPRISE ARCHITECT.** see *COMPUTERS—Computer Systems*

ENTERPRISE PARTNER. see *COMPUTERS—Software*

005.1 USA
FILEMAKER ADVISOR. Text in English. 1997. bi-m. USD 49 domestic; USD 59 in Canada; USD 69 elsewhere (effective 2005). adv. software rev. illus.; tr.lit. back issues avail.
Document type: *Magazine, Trade.* **Description:** Provides a wide array of articles, including user spotlight stories, how-to columns, and comprehensive product information, all serving the needs of power users and application developers.
Formerly: FileMaker Pro Advisor (1093-6963)
Related titles: CD-ROM ed.
Published by: Advisor Media, Inc., 4849 Viewridge Ave, San Diego, CA 92123-1643. TEL 858-278-5600, FAX 858-278-0300, pr@advisor.com, subscribe@advisor.com, http://filemakeradvisor.com/, http://www.advisor.com. adv.: B&W page USD 2,005, color page USD 2,995; trim 10.88 x 8. Circ: 26,000 (paid). **Subscr. to:** PO Box 469003, Escondido, CA 92046-9003. **Dist. by:** International Publishers Direct, 27500 Riverview Center Blvd, Bonita Springs, FL 34134. TEL 858-320-4563.

005.13 DEU ISSN 1435-6287
FORSCHUNGSERGEBNISSE PROGRAMMENTWICKLUNG. Text in German. 1997. irreg., latest vol.13, 2002. price varies.
Document type: *Monographic series, Academic/Scholarly.*
Published by: Verlag Dr. Kovac, Arnoldstr 49, Hamburg, 22763, Germany. TEL 49-40-3988800, FAX 49-40-3988055, info@verlagdrkovac.de, http://www.verlagdrkovac.de/4-3.htm.

005.112 USA ISSN 0884-0822
QA76.73.F24 CODEN: FODMD5
FORTH DIMENSIONS* . Text in English. 1979. bi-m. USD 40 domestic; USD 46 in Canada & Mexico; USD 52 elsewhere. adv. bk.rev. index. back issues avail. **Document type:** *Trade.* **Description:** For Forth programming language users and developers. Features articles on language implementation and optimization, applications incorporating Forth. Includes regular columns covering standards, new product announcements and reviews.
Indexed: EngInd, Inspec.
—BLDSC (4017.670000), AskIEEE, CISTI, Ei.
Published by: Forth Interest Group, 100 Dolores St 183, Carmel, CA 93923-8665. TEL 510-893-6784, FAX 510-535-1295. Ed. Marlin Ouverson. Adv. contact Mike Elola. Circ: 2,000.

005.13 USA ISSN 1061-7264
QA76.73.F25
FORTRAN FORUM. Text in English. 1982. 3/yr. USD 20 (effective 2005). **Document type:** *Journal, Academic/Scholarly.*
Formerly (until 1984): ForTec Forum (0735-3731)
Related titles: Online - full text ed.
—CISTI, IE, Infotrieve.
Published by: Association for Computing Machinery, Inc., 1515 Broadway, 17th Fl, New York, NY 10036-5701. TEL 212-626-0500, 212-626-0520, 800-342-6626, FAX 212-869-0481, sigs@acm.org, usacm@acm.org, http://www.acm.org.

005.1 USA
GARTNERCONNECT. Text in English. d. **Document type:** *Trade.*
Media: Online - full text.
Published by: Gartner Inc., 56 Top Gallant Rd, Stamford, CT 06904-2212. TEL 203-316-1111, 800-544-7337, FAX 203-316-6300, jwhitney@info-edge.com, http://www.gartner3.gartnerweb.com.

GENETIC PROGRAMMING AND EVOLVABLE MACHINES. see *COMPUTERS—Artificial Intelligence*

005.13 USA ISSN 1098-4054
GETTING STARTED WITH VISUAL BASIC. Text in English. s-a. USD 24.95 domestic; USD 36.95 in Canada & Mexico; USD 39.95 elsewhere (effective 2000). adv. **Document type:** *Magazine, Trade.*
Published by: Fawcette Technical Publications, 2600 S. El Camino Real., Ste. 300, San Mateo, CA 94403-2381. TEL 650-833-7100, FAX 650-853-0230, jhadfield@fawcette.com, http://www.fawcette.com. Ed., Pub. Jeff Hadfield. Adv. contact Sean Raman. B&W page USD 3,300, color page USD 4,300.

005.117 USA ISSN 1543-1282
HARDCORE DELPHI. Text in English. 1995. m. USD 179 domestic; USD 199 in Canada; USD 204 elsewhere (effective 2003). adv. **Document type:** *Newsletter, Trade.* **Description:** Contains insightful articles, undocumented techniques, trouble-shooting suggestions from Delphi experts, and step-by-step instructions for Delphi development.
Formerly (until 2002): Delphi Developer (1082-4375)
Published by: Pinnacle Publishing, Inc. (Subsidiary of: Lawrence Ragan Communications, Inc.), 316 N. Michigan Ave, Ste 300, Chicago, IL 60601. TEL 312-960-4209, 800-493-4867, FAX 312-960-4106, pinpub@ragan.com, http://www.pinpub.com. Ed. Lloyd Work. adv.: page USD 1,200. Circ: 5,200 (paid).

005.13 USA ISSN 1543-1290
HARDCORE VISUAL BASIC. Text in English. 1994. m. USD 179 domestic; USD 199 in Canada; USD 204 elsewhere (effective 2003). adv. **Document type:** *Newsletter, Trade.* **Description:** For software developers using Visual Basic.
Formerly (until 2002): Visual Basic Developer (1077-6087)
—IE.
Published by: Pinnacle Publishing, Inc. (Subsidiary of: Lawrence Ragan Communications, Inc.), 316 N. Michigan Ave, Ste 300, Chicago, IL 60601. TEL 312-960-4209, 800-493-4867, FAX 312-960-4106, pinpub@ragan.com, http://www.pinpub.com. Ed. Karen Watterson. adv.: page USD 1,200. Circ: 4,500 (paid).

005 USA ISSN 1543-0987
HARDCORE VISUAL STUDIO.NET. Text in English. 2001. m. USD 219 domestic; USD 239 in Canada; USD 244 elsewhere (effective 2003). **Document type:** *Newsletter, Trade.*
Formerly (until 2002): Net Developer (1534-4517)
Published by: Pinnacle Publishing, Inc. (Subsidiary of: Lawrence Ragan Communications, Inc.), 316 N. Michigan Ave, Ste 300, Chicago, IL 60601. TEL 312-960-4209, 800-493-4867, FAX 312-960-4106, pinpub@ragan.com, http://www.pinpub.com. Ed. Bill Hatfield.

HARDCORE WEB SERVICES. see *COMPUTERS—Software*

I E E E INTERNATIONAL SYMPOSIUM ON COMPUTERS AND COMMUNICATIONS. see *COMPUTERS—Software*

005.13 USA
I E E E INTERNATIONAL WORKSHOP ON SOURCE CODE ANALYSIS AND MANIPULATION. PROCEEDINGS. Text in English. irreg. **Document type:** *Proceedings, Academic/Scholarly.*
Published by: I E E E Computer Society, 10662 Los Vaqueros Circle, PO Box 3014, Los Alamitos, CA 90720-1314. TEL 714-821-8380, FAX 714-821-4010, http://www.ieee.org.

I E E E WORKSHOP ON APPLICATION - SPECIFIC SOFTWARE ENGINEERING AND TECHNOLOGY. see *COMPUTERS—Software*

I E E SOFTWARE ENGINEERING SERIES. (Institution of Electrical Engineers) see *COMPUTERS—Software*

005.1 USA
I T JOURNAL. Text in English. w. **Document type:** *Trade.* **Description:** Delivers analysis of events in the IT industry and a strategic overview of major trends and directions in technology.
Media: Online - full text.
Published by: Gartner Inc., 56 Top Gallant Rd, Stamford, CT 06904-2212. TEL 203-316-1111, 800-544-7337, FAX 203-316-6300, jwhitney@info-edge.com, http://www.gartner3.gartnerweb.com.

005.1 USA
➤ **I T JOURNAL ON-LINE.** Text in English. a. **Document type:** *Journal, Academic/Scholarly.*
Related titles: Online - full text ed.
Published by: University of Virginia, Curry School of Education, Instructional Technology Program, 405 Emmet St, Charlottesville, VA 22903. http://etext.virginia.edu/journals/itjournal/. Ed. Susannah McGowan.

005.118 USA
ICON NEWSLETTER. Text in English. 1978. 3/yr. free. back issues avail. **Document type:** *Newsletter.* **Description:** Provides information about the implementation and application of the Icon programming language.
Published by: (Icon Project), University of Arizona, Department of Computer Science, Gould-Simpson 725, 1040 E Fourth St, Tucson, AZ 85721-0077. TEL 602-621-8448. Eds. Madge T Griswold, Ralph E Griswold. Circ: 1,500.

INFOCUS (PHILADELPHIA); the technical journal for Prime Information, Universe and Unidata. see *COMPUTERS—Computer Systems*

005.13 DEU ISSN 0942-8682
INFORMATIK UND SPRACHE. Text in German, English. 1992. irreg., latest vol.6, 2000. price varies. **Document type:** *Monographic series, Academic/Scholarly.* **Description:** Provides information on studies and research in the field of computer linguistics and data processing.
Published by: Georg Olms Verlag, Hagentorwall 7, Hildesheim, 31134, Germany. TEL 49-5121-1501-0, FAX 49-5121-150150, info@olms.de, http://www.olms.de. Ed. Pius Ten Hacken. R&P Christiane Busch.

▼ **INNOVATIONS IN SYSTEMS AND SOFTWARE ENGINEERING.** see *COMPUTERS—Software*

005.13 USA ISSN 1081-3667
INSIDE MICROSOFT OFFICE. Text in English. 1995. m. USD 117 domestic; USD 127 foreign; USD 147 combined subscription print & online eds. (effective 2005). **Document type:** *Magazine, Consumer.*
Related titles: Online - full content ed.: USD 147 domestic; USD 157 foreign (effective 2005); Online - full text ed.: (from ProQuest Information & Learning).
—CCC.
Published by: Element K Journals (Subsidiary of: Eli Research, Inc.), 500 Canal View Blvd, Rochester, NY 14623. TEL 585-240-7301, 800-223-8720, 877-203-5248, FAX 585-292-4392, http://www.elementkjournals.com/products/showProduct.asp?prodID=207&catId=1.

005.1 USA ISSN 1539-0403
INSIDE MICROSOFT VISUAL BASIC. Text in English. 1991. m. USD 147 domestic; USD 157 foreign; USD 177 combined subscription print & online eds. (effective 2005). **Document type:** *Magazine, Consumer.* **Description:** Contains tips and techniques exclusively aimed at programmers using VisualBASIC.
Former titles: Inside Visual Basic (1093-8745); (until 1997): Inside Visual Basic for Windows (1066-7555); (until 1993): Inside VisualBASIC (1059-1788)
Related titles: Online - full text ed.: 1991. USD 177 domestic; USD 187 foreign (effective 2005).
—IE. CCC.
Published by: Element K Journals (Subsidiary of: Eli Research, Inc.), 500 Canal View Blvd, Rochester, NY 14623. TEL 585-240-7301, 800-223-8720, 877-203-5248, FAX 585-292-4392, http://www.elementkjournals.com/products/showProduct.asp?prodID=15&catId=2. Eds. Mike D. Jones, Michelle Rogers.

005.72 USA ISSN 1527-0270
TK5105.888
INSIDE WEB DESIGN. Text in English. m. USD 177; USD 207 combined subscription print & online eds. (effective 2005). **Document type:** *Magazine, Consumer.*
Related titles: Online - full text ed.: ISSN 1539-0438.
—CCC.
Published by: Element K Journals (Subsidiary of: Eli Research, Inc.), 500 Canal View Blvd, Rochester, NY 14623. TEL 585-240-7301, 800-223-8720, 877-203-5248, FAX 585-292-4392, http://www.elementkjournals.com/products/showProduct.asp?prodID=18&catId=3. Ed. Michelle Rogers.

005.72 USA ISSN 1527-5361
QA76.625 CODEN: IWDNBR
INSIDE WEB DEVELOPMENT. Text in English. 2000. m. USD 187 domestic; USD 197 foreign; USD 217 combined subscription print & online eds. (effective 2005). **Document type:** *Magazine, Consumer.*
Related titles: Online - full text ed.: ISSN 1539-0209. USD 217 domestic; USD 227 foreign (effective 2005).
—CCC.
Published by: Element K Journals (Subsidiary of: Eli Research, Inc.), 500 Canal View Blvd, Rochester, NY 14623. TEL 585-240-7301, 800-223-8720, 877-203-5248, FAX 585-292-4392, http://www.elementkjournals.com/products/showProduct.asp?prodID=3&catId=2. Eds. Mike D. Jones, Michelle Rogers.

005.1 USA ISSN 1072-5520
QA76.9.H85 CODEN: IERAE3
➤ **INTERACTIONS (NEW YORK)**; new visions of human-computer interactions. Text in English. 1994. bi-m. USD 90 domestic to non-members; USD 112 foreign to non-members; USD 52 domestic to members; USD 74 foreign to members; USD 15 domestic to students; USD 37 foreign to students; USD 210 combined subscription domestic to non-members print & online eds.; USD 232 combined subscription foreign to non-members print & online eds.; USD 62 combined subscription domestic to members print & online eds.; USD 84 combined subscription foreign to members print & online eds.; USD 18 combined subscription domestic to students print & online eds.; USD 40 combined subscription foreign to students print & online eds. (effective 2006). adv. **Document type:** *Journal, Academic/Scholarly.* **Description:** Communicates ideas, standards, practices, research results and case studies to the practitioner.
Related titles: Online - full text ed.: USD 140 to non-members; USD 42 to members; USD 12 to students (effective 2006) (from Association for Computing Machinery, Inc., EBSCO Publishing, ProQuest Information & Learning).
Indexed: ABIn, CompR, ErgAb, Inspec.
—BLDSC (4531.871765), AskIEEE, IE, Infotrieve, ingenta, Linda Hall. **CCC.**
Published by: Association for Computing Machinery, Inc., 1515 Broadway, 17th Fl, New York, NY 10036-5701. TEL 212-626-0500, 212-626-0520, 800-342-6626, FAX 212-869-0481, interactions@acm.org, sigs@acm.org, usacm@acm.org, http://www.acm.org/interactions. Ed. John Rheinfrank. Pub. James Maurer. adv.: page USD 5,420.

➤ **INTERACTIVE MAGAZINE.** see *COMPUTERS—Software*

005.13 USA
THE INTERNATIONAL CONFERENCE ON ARRAY-PROG LANGUAGE. PROCEEDINGS. Text in English. a. **Document type:** *Proceedings, Academic/Scholarly.*
Related titles: Online - full content ed.
Published by: Association for Computing Machinery, Inc., 1515 Broadway, 17th Fl, New York, NY 10036-5701. TEL 212-626-0500, usacm@acm.org, http://www.acm.org.

INTERNATIONAL CONFERENCE ON AUTOMATED SOFTWARE ENGINEERING. PROCEEDINGS. see *COMPUTERS—Software*

INTERNATIONAL CONFERENCE ON ENGINEERING OF COMPLEX COMPUTER SYSTEMS. PROCEEDINGS. see *COMPUTERS—Software*

005.13 USA
INTERNATIONAL CONFERENCE ON INFORMATION TECHNOLOGY: CODING AND COMPUTING. PROCEEDINGS. Text in English. irreg. **Document type:** *Proceedings, Academic/Scholarly.*
Published by: I E E E Computer Society, 10662 Los Vaqueros Circle, PO Box 3014, Los Alamitos, CA 90720-1314. TEL 714-821-8380, FAX 714-821-4010, http://www.ieee.org.

INTERNATIONAL CONFERENCE ON SOFTWARE ENGINEERING: EDUCATION AND PRACTICE. PROCEEDINGS. see *COMPUTERS—Software*

▼ **INTERNATIONAL JOURNAL OF AGILE AND EXTREME SOFTWARE DEVELOPMENT.** see *COMPUTERS—Software*

▼ **INTERNATIONAL JOURNAL OF ENTERPRISE INFORMATION SYSTEMS.** see *COMPUTERS—Computer Systems*

005.1 SGP ISSN 0129-0533
QA76.5 CODEN: IHSCEZ
➤ **INTERNATIONAL JOURNAL OF HIGH SPEED COMPUTING.** Abbreviated title: I J H S C. Text in English. 1990. q. SGD 152, USD 92, EUR 83 to individuals; SGD 417, USD 253, EUR 229 combined subscription to institutions print & online eds.; SGD 250, USD 152, EUR 138 combined subscription in developing nations to institutions print & online eds. (effective 2005). back issues avail. **Document type:** *Journal, Academic/Scholarly.* **Description:** Covers parallel computation, algorithms, program restructuring, and compiler technology, performance evaluation, scheduling and resource allocation. Provides insight into the fields of supercomputing and other high speed parallel computing for computer scientists, electrical engineers, and physicists.
Related titles: Online - full text ed.: (from EBSCO Publishing, O C L C Online Computer Library Center, Inc., Swets Information Services).
Indexed: ASCA, CMCI, CompAb, CompLI, CurCont, EngInd, Inspec, ZentMath.
—BLDSC (4542.280500), AskIEEE, CISTI, IDS, IE, Infotrieve, ingenta. **CCC.**
Published by: World Scientific Publishing Co. Pte. Ltd., 5 Toh Tuck Link, Singapore, 596224, Singapore. TEL 65-466-5775, FAX 65-467-7667, wspc@wspc.com.sg, http://www.worldscinet.com/ijhsc/ijhsc.shtml, http://www.worldscientific.com. Eds. E G Ng, I S Duff, Y Muroaka. Circ: 200. **Subscr. to:** Farrer Rd, PO Box 128, Singapore 912805, Singapore. sales@wspc.com.sg. **Dist. by:** World Scientific Publishing Co., Inc., 1060 Main St, River Edge, NJ 07661. TEL 201-487-9655, 800-227-7562, FAX 201-487-9656, 888-977-2665.; World Scientific Publishing Ltd., 57 Shelton St, London WC2H 9HE, United Kingdom. TEL 44-20-78360888, FAX 44-20-78362020, sales@wspc.co.uk.

005.1 GBR ISSN 1744-5760
QA76.9.A43 CODEN: PAAPEC
➤ **INTERNATIONAL JOURNAL OF PARALLEL, EMERGENT AND DISTRIBUTED SYSTEMS.** Text in English. 1993. 6/yr. GBP 939, USD 1,229 combined subscription to institutions print & online eds. (effective 2006). reprint service avail. from PSC. **Document type:** *Journal, Academic/Scholarly.* **Description:** Publishes papers relating to parallel and multiprocessor computer systems covering the areas of parallel algorithms and parallel applications.
Formerly (until 2005): Parallel Algorithms and Applications (1063-7192)
Related titles: CD-ROM ed.: ISSN 1026-7689. 1995; Microform ed.; Online - full text ed.: ISSN 1744-5779. 1996. GBP 892, USD 1,168 (effective 2006) (from EBSCO Publishing, Gale Group, IngentaConnect, O C L C Online Computer Library Center, Inc., Swets Information Services).
Indexed: CCMJ, MathR, MathSciNet, ZentMath.
—BLDSC (6404.833020), CISTI, IE, Infotrieve, ingenta. **CCC.**
Published by: Taylor & Francis Ltd (Subsidiary of: Taylor & Francis Group), 4 Park Sq, Milton Park, Abingdon, OX14 4RN, United Kingdom. TEL 44-1235-828600, FAX 44-1235-829000, http://www.tandf.co.uk/journals/titles/17445760.asp. Ed. Ivan Stojmenovic. **Subscr. to:** Journals Customer Service, Rankine Rd, Basingstoke, Hants RG24 8PR, United Kingdom. TEL 44-1256-813000, FAX 44-1256-330245, enquiry@tandf.co.uk.

005.11 USA ISSN 0885-7458
QA76.5 CODEN: IJPPE5
➤ **INTERNATIONAL JOURNAL OF PARALLEL PROGRAMMING.** Text in English. 1972. bi-m. EUR 1,088, USD 1,118, GBP 685 combined subscription to institutions print & online eds. (effective 2005). adv. bibl.; charts; illus.; stat. back issues avail.; reprint service avail. from PSC. **Document type:** *Journal, Academic/Scholarly.* **Description:** Publishes original papers in the computer and information sciences, with emphasis on the programming of parallel systems.
Formerly (until 1987): International Journal of Computer and Information Sciences (0091-7036)
Related titles: Microfilm ed.: (from PQC); Online - full text ed.: ISSN 1573-7640 (from EBSCO Publishing, Gale Group, IngentaConnect, Kluwer Online, O C L C Online Computer Library Center, Inc., Ovid Technologies, Inc., Springer LINK, Swets Information Services).
Indexed: ABIn, ASCA, BibLing, BrCerAb, C&ISA, CADCAM, CIS, CMCI, CerAb, ChemAb, CompAb, CompC, CompD, CompLI, CompR, CorrAb, CurCont, CybAb, E&CAJ, EMA, EngInd, ErgAb, IAA, InfoSAb, Inspec, M&TEA, MBF, METADEX, MLA, MLA-IB, MathR, RASB, RefZh, SCI, SoftAbEng, SolStAb, WAA, ZentMath.
—BLDSC (4542.441500), AskIEEE, CISTI, Ei, IDS, IE, Infotrieve, ingenta, Linda Hall. **CCC.**
Published by: Plenum US (Subsidiary of: Springer Science+Business Media), 233 Spring St, New York, NY 10013. TEL 212-460-1500, FAX 212-460-1575, service@springer-ny.com, http://springerlink.metapress.com/openurl.asp?genre=journal&issn=0885-7458, http://www.springeronline.com. Eds. Alexandru Nicolau, Nicholas Carriero, Utpal Banerjee, Wen-Mei Hwu.

➤ **INTERNATIONAL JOURNAL OF SOFTWARE ENGINEERING AND KNOWLEDGE ENGINEERING.** see *COMPUTERS—Software*

➤ **INTERNATIONAL SYMPOSIUM ON REQUIREMENTS ENGINEERING. PROCEEDINGS.** see *COMPUTERS—Software*

➤ **INTERNATIONAL SYMPOSIUM ON SOFTWARE ENGINEERING FOR PARALLEL AND DISTRIBUTED SYSTEMS.** see *COMPUTERS—Software*

➤ **INTERNATIONAL SYMPOSIUM ON SOFTWARE ENGINEERING STANDARDS.** see *COMPUTERS—Software*

➤ **INTERNATIONAL SYMPOSIUM ON SOFTWARE RELIABILITY ENGINEERING. PROCEEDINGS.** see *COMPUTERS—Software*

➤ **JAPANESE SOCIETY OF COMPUTATIONAL STATISTICS. JOURNAL.** see *STATISTICS*

005.117 USA ISSN 1087-6944
QA76.73.J38 CODEN: JDJOFA
JAVA DEVELOPER'S JOURNAL. Abbreviated title: J D J. Variant title: Internet Developer's Journal. Text in English. 1996. m. USD 69.99 domestic; USD 89.99 in Canada & Mexico; USD 99 elsewhere; USD 5.99 newsstand/cover (effective 2005). adv. bk.rev.; software rev. illus. reprints avail. **Document type:** *Magazine, Trade.* **Description:** Looks at techniques and tools for developing webpages with Java.
Related titles: Online - full text ed.: USD 39.99 (effective 2005) (from Florida Center for Library Automation, Gale Group).
Indexed: CompD.
—IE.
Published by: SYS-CON Media, Inc., 135 Chestnut Ridge Rd, Montvale, NJ 07645. TEL 201-802-3040, 888-303-5282, FAX 201-782-9600, info@sys-con.com, http://java.sys-con.com, http://www.sys-con.com. Ed. Sean Rhody. Pub., R&P Fuat Kircaali. Adv. contact Carmen Gonzalez. Circ: 110,000 (paid).

005.117 USA ISSN 1531-1228
JAVA ENTERPRISE DEVELOPER. Text in English. 2000. m. adv. **Document type:** *Newsletter, Trade.* **Description:** Focuses on Java and the Java Enterprise platform and the tools and technology created by Sun to support that platform.
Published by: Pinnacle Publishing, Inc. (Subsidiary of: Lawrence Ragan Communications, Inc.), 316 N. Michigan Ave, Ste 300, Chicago, IL 60601. TEL 312-960-4209, 800-493-4867, FAX 312-960-4106, pinpub@ragan.com, http://www.pinpub.com.

005.1 DEU ISSN 1619-795X
JAVA MAGAZIN. Text in German. 1998. m. EUR 69; EUR 6.50 newsstand/cover (effective 2005). adv. **Document type:** *Magazine, Trade.*
Published by: Software & Support Verlag GmbH, Kennedyallee 87, Frankfurt am Main, 60596, Germany. TEL 49-69-63008890, FAX 49-69-63008989, redaktion@javamagazin.de, info@software-support.biz, http://www.javamagazin.de, http://www.software-support.biz. Adv. contact Patrik Baumann. Circ: 30,000 (controlled).

005.117 USA ISSN 1096-4495
QA76.73.J38
JAVA PRO. Text in English. 1997. m. USD 19.95 domestic; USD 37.95 in Canada & Mexico; USD 63.95 rest of world (effective 2005). adv. **Document type:** *Magazine, Trade.* **Description:** Offers solutions for serious developers using Java.
—IE.
Published by: Fawcette Technical Publications, 2600 S. El Camino Real., Ste. 300, San Mateo, CA 94403-2381. TEL 650-833-7144, FAX 650-853-0230, javapro@fawcette.com, http://www.java-pro.com. Ed. Sean Gallagher. Pub. Jeff Miller. Adv. contact Shana Deane. B&W page USD 4,760, color page USD 6,350. Circ: 35,000 (paid).

005.117 DEU ISSN 1431-4436
JAVA SPEKTRUM; das Computermagazin rund um JAVA. Text in German. 1996. bi-m. EUR 32.20 domestic; EUR 36.50 in Europe; EUR 52 elsewhere; EUR 29.50 to students; EUR 5.50 newsstand/cover (effective 2005). adv. **Document type:** *Magazine, Trade.* **Description:** Contains information and articles on all things related to the JAVA programming language.
Published by: SIGS Datacom GmbH (Subsidiary of: 101 Communications, Llc.), Lindlaustr 2c, Troisdorf, 53842, Germany. TEL 49-2241-2341100, FAX 49-2241-2341199, info@sigs-datacom.de, javaspektrum@sigs.com, http://www.sigs-datacom.de/sd/publications/js/. Ed. Michael Stal. adv.: B&W page EUR 3,005, color page EUR 4,365. Circ: 16,000 (paid and controlled).

005.117 USA ISSN 1091-8906
JAVAWORLD; fueling innovation. Text in English. 1996. m. adv. bk.rev.; software rev. charts; illus. index. reprints avail. **Document type:** *Journal, Trade.* **Description:** Covers computer applications related to Java technologies, the computer industry, computer programming, and computer systems. Aimed at Java technology developers and enterprise managers who are planning, developing and delivering real-world applications. Intends to help readers understand and effectively use Java and related technologies.
Media: Online - full text (from LexisNexis, Northern Light Technology, Inc., ProQuest Information & Learning).
Published by: (International Data Group), Web Publishing Inc (Subsidiary of: I D G Communications Inc.), 501 Second St, Ste 310, San Francisco, CA 94107. TEL 415-267-4518, FAX 415-267-1732, carolyn_wong@itworld.com, http://www.javaworld.com. Ed. Carolyn Wong. Pub., Adv. contact Colette McMullen. Circ: 140,000.

005.13 JPN
JAVAWORLD JAPAN. Text in Japanese. m. adv. **Document type:** *Magazine, Trade.* **Description:** Focuses on the JAVA computing environment where new hardware, middleware and applications have been, and are being, developed.
Related titles: Online - full text ed.
Published by: I D G Japan, Inc., Hongo 3-4-5, Bunkyo-ku, Tokyo, 1130033, Japan. TEL 81-3-5800-3111, FAX 81-3-5800-3590, http://www.idg.co.jp/jw/. adv.: B&W page USD 2,361, color page USD 4,407; trim 210 x 282. Circ: 50,000 (paid).

JET INFO. see *COMPUTERS—Computer Security*

005.1 USA ISSN 1084-6654
QA9.A1
➤ **JOURNAL OF EXPERIMENTAL ALGORITHMICS.** Text in English. 1996. q. USD 164 to non-members; USD 29 to members; USD 24 to students (effective 2006). illus. back issues avail.; reprints avail. **Document type:** *Journal, Academic/Scholarly.* **Description:** Dedicated entirely to experimental work in algorithms and data structures.
Media: Online - full text (from Association for Computing Machinery, Inc.).
Indexed: CCMJ, CompAb, CompLI, Inspec, MathR, MathSciNet.
Published by: Association for Computing Machinery, Inc., 1515 Broadway, 17th Fl, New York, NY 10036-5701. TEL 212-626-0500, 212-626-0520, 800-342-6626, FAX 212-869-0481, editor@jea.acm.org, sigs@acm.org, usacm@acm.org, http://www.jea.acm.org, http://www.acm.org. Ed. Bernard M E Moret.

005.115 USA ISSN 1080-5230
CODEN: CDREFB
➤ **JOURNAL OF FUNCTIONAL AND LOGIC PROGRAMMING.** Text in English. 1995. irreg. (1 vol./yr.). free. reprints avail. **Document type:** *Academic/Scholarly.* **Description:** Publishes original research on functional and logic programming, including theoretical foundations. Articles are published on an article by article basis.
Media: Online - full text.
Indexed: CCMJ, MathR, MathSciNet.
Published by: European Association for Programming Languages and Systems kuchen@uni-muenster.de, http://danae.uni-muenster.de/lehre/kuchen/JFLP/, http://homepages.cwi.nl/~paulk/eapls/.

005.114 GBR ISSN 0956-7968
QA76.62 CODEN: JFPRES
➤ **JOURNAL OF FUNCTIONAL PROGRAMMING.** Text in English. 1991. bi-m. GBP 240 to institutions; USD 390 in North America to institutions; GBP 250 combined subscription to institutions print & online eds.; USD 415 combined subscription in North America to institutions print & online eds. (effective 2006). adv. back issues avail.; reprint service avail. from PSC. **Document type:** *Journal, Academic/Scholarly.* **Description:** Covers new languages and extensions, reasoning, proof and program transformation, program synthesis, implementation techniques, type theory, and parallelism.
Related titles: Microform ed.: (from PQC); Online - full text ed.: ISSN 1469-7653. GBP 210 to institutions; USD 352 in North America to institutions (effective 2006) (from EBSCO Publishing, O C L C Online Computer Library Center, Inc., Swets Information Services).
Indexed: CCMJ, CMCI, CompLI, CurCont, Inspec, MathR, MathSciNet, RefZh, ZentMath.
—BLDSC (4986.820000), AskIEEE, CISTI, IE, Infotrieve, ingenta. **CCC.**

C

Published by: Cambridge University Press, The Edinburgh Bldg, Shaftesbury Rd, Cambridge, CB2 2RU, United Kingdom. TEL 44-1223-312393, FAX 44-1223-315052, journals@cambridge.org, http://uk.cambridge.org/journals/JFP/. Eds. Greg Morrisett, Paul Hudak. R&P Linda Nicol TEL 44-1223-325757. Adv. contact Rebecca Curtis TEL 44-1223-325757. **Subscr. to:** Cambridge University Press, 100 Brook Hill Dr, West Nyack, NY 10994. TEL 845-353-7500, FAX 845-353-4141, journals_subscriptions@cup.org

005.1   USA   ISSN 1526-1719
QA166   CODEN: JGAAA7
➤ **JOURNAL OF GRAPH ALGORITHMS AND APPLICATIONS.** Abbreviated title: J G A A. Text in English. 1997. irreg. free (effective 2005); free. illus. reprints avail. **Document type:** *Journal, Academic/Scholarly.* **Description:** Provides the graph algorithms research community with an opportunity to undertake a pioneering role in the development of electronic publishing standards in the field.
Media: Online - full text.
Indexed: CCMJ, Inspec, MathR, MathSciNet, ZentMath.
Published by: Brown University, Department of Computer Science, 115 Waterman St, Providence, RI 02912-1910. TEL 401-863-7639, FAX 401-863-7657, jgaa@cs.brown.edu, rt@cs.brown.edu, tollis@utdallas.edu, http:// www.emis.ams.org/journals/JGAA, http://www.cs.brown.edu/ publications/jgaa/. Eds. Ioannis G Tollis, Roberto Tamassia.

005.1   NLD   ISSN 1570-7873
▼ **JOURNAL OF GRID COMPUTING.** Text in English. 2003. q. EUR 310, USD 310, GBP 194 combined subscription to institutions print & online eds. (effective 2005). adv. reprint service avail. from PSC. **Document type:** *Journal, Academic/Scholarly.*
Related titles: Online - full text ed.: ISSN 1572-9184 (from EBSCO Publishing, Gale Group, IngentaConnect, Kluwer Online, O C L C Online Computer Library Center, Inc., Springer LINK, Swets Information Services).
Indexed: BibLing.
—BLDSC (4996.520502), CISTI, IE. **CCC.**
Published by: Springer-Verlag Dordrecht (Subsidiary of: Springer Science+Business Media), Van Godewijckstraat 30, Dordrecht, 3311 GX, Netherlands. TEL 31-78-6576050, FAX 31-78-6576474, http://springerlink.metapress.com/openurl.asp? genre=journal&issn=1570-7873, http://www.springeronline.com. Eds. Ian Foster, Peter Kacsuk.

005   NLD   ISSN 1567-8326
QA76.6   CODEN: JLAPAJ
➤ **THE JOURNAL OF LOGIC AND ALGEBRAIC PROGRAMMING.** Text in English. 1984. 8/yr. EUR 1,087 in Europe to institutions; JPY 144,600 in Japan to institutions; USD 1,215 to institutions except Europe and Japan (effective 2006). bibl.; charts; illus. back issues avail.; reprints avail. **Document type:** *Academic/Scholarly.* **Description:** Contains original research papers, survey and review articles, tutorial expositions and historical studies in logic programming.
Formerly (until vol.46): Journal of Logic Programming (0743-1066)
Related titles: Microform ed.: (from PQC); Online - full text ed.: (from EBSCO Publishing, Gale Group, IngentaConnect, ScienceDirect, Swets Information Services).
Indexed: AIA, ASCA, CADCAM, CCMJ, CMCI, CompAb, CompLI, CompR, CurCont, EngInd, ISR, Inspec, MathR, MathSciNet, RefZh, SCI, SSCI, ZentMath.
—BLDSC (5010.552100), AskIEEE, CISTI, Ei, IDS, IE, Infotrieve, ingenta, Linda Hall. **CCC.**
Published by: Elsevier BV, North-Holland (Subsidiary of: Elsevier Science & Technology), Sara Burgerhartstraat 25, Amsterdam, 1055 KV, Netherlands. TEL 31-20-485-3911, FAX 31-20-485-2457, nlinfo-f@elsevier.nl, http://www.elsevier.com/ locate/jlap, http://www.elsevier.nl. Eds. J. A. Bergstra, J. V. Tucker. Circ: 1,000. **Subscr. outside the Americas to:** Elsevier BV, PO Box 211, Amsterdam 1000 AE, Netherlands. TEL 31-20-485-3757, FAX 31-20-485-3432, http://www.elsevier.nl.

➤ **JOURNAL OF MULTIPLE-VALUED LOGIC AND SOFT COMPUTING.** see *MATHEMATICS*

005.117   CHE   ISSN 1660-1769
JOURNAL OF OBJECT TECHNOLOGY. Text in English. 2002. bi-m. free (effective 2005). bk.rev. back issues avail.
Media: Online - full text.
Address: EtH Zurich, RZ Bldg, Clausiusstrasse, 59, Zurich, 8092, Switzerland. TEL 41-1-6325277, FAX 41-1-6321435, http://www.jot.fm/. Ed. Richard Wiener.

005.1   USA
KERMIT NEWS. Text in English. 1986. irreg., latest vol.6, 1995. free (effective 2005). **Document type:** *Newsletter.* **Description:** Contains news about the university's Kermit communications software.
Formerly (until 1995): Kermit News (Print) (0899-9309)
Media: Online - full content.
Published by: Columbia University Academic Information Systems, Kermit Development and Distribution, 612 W 115th St, New York, NY 10025. TEL 212-854-3703, FAX 212-663-8202, kermit@columbia.edu, cmg@columbia.edu, http://www.columbia.edu/kermit/news.html. Ed., R&P Christine M Gianone. Circ: 40,000.

005.11   RUS   ISSN 0868-6157
KOMP'YUTER PRESS. Text in Russian. m. USD 169.95 in United States.
Indexed: Inspec, RefZh.
—East View.
Address: Gorokhovskii Per 7, A-ya 37, Moscow, 113093, Russian Federation. TEL 7-095-2004686, FAX 7-095-9253821. Ed. B M Molchanov. **US dist. addr.:** East View Information Services, 3020 Harbor Ln. N., Minneapolis, MN 55447. TEL 612-550-0961.

005.11   RUS
KOMP'YUTERNAYA KHRONIKA - ITERSOTSIOINFORM. Text in Russian. m. USD 960 in United States.
Address: Kashirskoe shosse 102, korp 2, kv 248, Moscow, 115551, Russian Federation. TEL 7-095-3915442, FAX 7-095-3915449. Ed. A N Krivomazov. **US dist. addr.:** East View Information Services, 3020 Harbor Ln. N., Minneapolis, MN 55447. TEL 612-550-0961.

005.117   RUS
KOMP'YUTERNYE UCHEBNYE PROGRAMMY I INNOVATSII. Text in Russian. q. RUR 100 for 6 mos. (effective 2002). 200 p./no.;
Related titles: Online - full text ed.
Published by: Redaktsiya Zhurnala Komp'yuternye Uchebnye Programmy i Innovatsii, B. Cheremuchkinskaya 17a, Moscow, 113447, Russian Federation. TEL 7-095-1276171, FAX 7-095-1272653, AlexandraG@rui.ru, http://www.informika.ru/ text/magaz/innovat, http://www.rui.ru. Ed. A Galkina.
Co-publisher: Russkii Universitet Innovatsii.

005.11   UKR
KOMP'YUTERY I PROGRAMMY. Text in Ukrainian. 9/yr. USD 95 in United States.
Published by: Komizdat, Pr Vozzednannya 15, Kiev, Ukraine. TEL 550-62-23. **US dist. addr.:** East View Information Services, 3020 Harbor Ln. N., Minneapolis, MN 55447. TEL 612-550-0961.

005.11   FRA   ISSN 0981-0455
LETTRE ADA. Text in French. 1987. 10/yr. bk.rev. back issues avail. **Document type:** *Newsletter.* **Description:** Dedicated to the Ada computer programming language.
Published by: E C 2, 269 rue de la Garenne, Nanterre, 92000, France. TEL 47-80-70-00, FAX 47-80-66-29. Ed. Jean Claude Rault. Circ: 300.

005.13   USA   ISSN 1536-4674
LINUX MAGAZINE; open source. open standards. Text in English. 1999. m. USD 29.95 domestic; USD 59.95 in Canada; USD 89.95 elsewhere; USD 4.95 newsstand/cover (effective 2004). adv. **Document type:** *Magazine, Consumer.*
Related titles: Online - full text ed.
Indexed: CompLI, MicrocompInd.
Address: 330 Townsend St, Ste 112, San Francisco, CA 94107. TEL 415-764-1617, FAX 415-764-1615, http:// www.linuxmagazine.com/. Ed., Pub. Adam M Goodman. **Subscr. to:** Box 56535, Boulder, CO 80323. linuxmag@neodata.com.

LOOP TRANSFORMATIONS FOR RESTRUCTURING COMPILERS. see *COMPUTERS—Computer Engineering*

005.1   USA   ISSN 1072-3226
QA76.73.M15   CODEN: MCPUEF
➤ **M COMPUTING.** Text in English. 1978. 5/yr. adv. **Document type:** *Academic/Scholarly.* **Description:** Describes advances in M Technology, including systems, installations and programming techniques. Presents new product and industry information; announces meetings for M software users.
Former titles (until Feb. 1993): M U M P S Computing (Massachusetts General Hospital Utility Multi-Programming System) (1060-7684); M U G Quarterly (0193-0885)
Indexed: Inspec.
—BLDSC (5313.580000), AskIEEE, CISTI.
Published by: M Technology Association, 1738 Elton Rd, Ste 205, Silver Spring, MD 20903. TEL 301-431-4070, FAX 301-431-0017, MTA@mtechnology.org, http:// jacquardsystems.com/MComputing/issn.htm. Ed. Pam McIntyre. Adv. contact Marlo Brown. Circ: 4,000.

005.12 004.678   USA   ISSN 1528-4859
QA76.75   CODEN: MMSAC4
M S D N MAGAZINE. Text in English. 1986. 12/yr. USD 45 domestic; USD 60 in Canada & Mexico; USD 70 elsewhere; USD 5.95 newsstand/cover; free to qualified personnel (effective 2005). **Document type:** *Magazine, Trade.* **Description:** Provides detailed information on emerging Microsoft Internet technologies and the tools that allow developers to use them, as well as the latest Internet products from other companies.
Incorporates (in 2000): Microsoft Internet Developer; (1986-2000): Microsoft Systems Journal (0889-9932)
Related titles: Online - full text ed.
Indexed: CompD, CompLI, CurCont, Inspec, MicrocompInd, RefZh.
—BLDSC (5980.862600), CISTI, IE, Infotrieve. **CCC.**

Published by: C M P Media LLC (Subsidiary of: United News & Media), 600 Harrison St, 6th Fl., San Francisco, CA 94107. TEL 415-947-6746, http://msdn.microsoft.com/msdnmag/. Ed. Joshua Trupin. Pub. Kerry Gates. Adv. contact Jonathan Sawyer TEL 603-924-8400. Circ: 75,365.

005.1   DEU
▼ **M S D N MAGAZINE EUROPE.** (Microsoft Developers Network) Text in German. 2005. 10/yr. EUR 7.90 newsstand/cover (effective 2005). adv. **Document type:** *Magazine, Trade.* **Description:** Provides the most comprehensive development information available on Microsoft technologies.
Published by: Software & Support Verlag GmbH, Kennedyallee 87, Frankfurt am Main, 60596, Germany. TEL 49-69-6300890, FAX 49-69-63008989, fschrader@msdnmag-europe.net, info@software-support.biz, http://www.msdnmag-europe.net, http://www.software-support.biz. Adv. contact Kathrin Arndt. B&W page EUR 3,120, color page EUR 4,350. Circ: 27,000 (controlled).

005.13   MLT   ISSN 1093-5193
M WEB MAGAZINE. Text in English. 1996. q. free. adv. bk.rev. **Document type:** *Academic/Scholarly.* **Description:** Contains programming tutorials, interviews, projects, shareware, humor and more.
Media: Online - full text.
Address: 1 Triq il-Kosbor, Zonqor, Marsascala, ZBR 09, Malta. FAX 356-639740, mwm@mcenter.com, chrisb@4u.net, http://www.geocities.com/SiliconValley/7041/mwm.html. Ed., Pub., R&P, Adv. contact Chris Bonnici. Circ: 8,000.

005.1   USA
MCARTHUR BUSINESS SYSTEMS DEVELOPER NEWSLETTER. Text in English. w. free.
Media: Online - full text.
Published by: McArthur Business Systems, 152 Chestnut Dr, Richboro, PA 18954. TEL 215-355-1291, FAX 215-322-5977, kmcarthur@mbsinternet.com. Ed. Kenneth McArthur.

005.117   USA   ISSN 1538-599X
MICROSOFT OFFICE SOLUTIONS. Text in English. 1997. m. USD 29.95 domestic; USD 34.95 in Canada; USD 59.95 elsewhere (effective 2000); USD 4.95 newsstand/cover. adv. back issues avail.
Former titles (until 2002): Microsoft Office PRO (1535-4865); Microsoft Office & Visual Basic for Applications Developer (1093-9016)
Related titles: CD-ROM ed.: USD 39.95.
Indexed: CompLI.
Published by: Informant Communications Group, 5105 Florin Perkins Rd., Sacramento, CA 95826-4817. TEL 916-686-6610, FAX 916-686-8497, circulation@informant, advertising@informant, http://www.msofficemag.net, http://www.informant.com. Ed. Jerry Coffrey. R&P Mark Wiseman. Adv. contact Jack Krack.

005.1   USA   ISSN 1547-8165
▼ **MICROSOFT WINDOWS SERVER 2003 SOLUTIONS.** Text in English. 2004 (Apr.). m. USD 197 domestic; USD 217 foreign; USD 227 combined subscription print & online eds. (effective 2005). **Document type:** *Magazine, Consumer.*
Published by: Element K Journals (Subsidiary of: Eli Research, Inc.), 500 Canal View Blvd, Rochester, NY 14623. TEL 800-223-8720, 877-203-5248, FAX 585-292-4392, http://www.elementkjournals.com/products/showProduct.asp? prodID=189&catID=2. Eds. Mike D. Jones, Rozanne Whalen.

005.11   USA   ISSN 1079-3135
QA76.76.O63
NATIONAL SYSTEMS PROGRAMMERS ASSOCIATION TECHNICAL SUPPORT. Key Title: NaSPA Technical Support. Variant title: Technical Support. Text in English. 1994. m. USD 29.98 domestic; USD 44.98 in Canada; USD 54.98 elsewhere. adv. **Document type:** *Trade.* **Description:** Serves and supports enterprise networks and operating ennvironments i.e. MVS, VM, VSE, LANs, etc.
Formed by the Oct. 1994 merger of: In-Depth Report. 370-390 Operating Systems (1072-7647); In-Depth Report. Computing Solutions (1072-9100); Which incorporated (in Jun. 1993): Information Technologies (1069-8140); Both of which superseded (in Apr. 1993): Technical Support (1052-2581)
Indexed: CompLI.
Published by: Technical Enterprises, Inc., 7044 S 13th St, Oak Creek, WI 53154-1429. TEL 414-768-8000, FAX 414-768-8001, market@naspa.net, http://www.naspa.net. Ed. Amy Novotny. Pub., R&P, Adv. contact Jerry Seefeldt. Circ: 45,000.

005.11 GBR ISSN 1351-3249
QA76.9.N38 CODEN: NLENFE
➤ **NATURAL LANGUAGE ENGINEERING.** Text in English. 1995. q. GBP 152 to institutions; USD 236 in North America to institutions; GBP 166 combined subscription to institutions print & online eds.; USD 265 combined subscription in North America to institutions print & online eds. (effective 2006). bk.rev. tr.lit. back issues avail.; reprint service avail. from PSC,ISI. **Document type:** *Journal, Academic/Scholarly.* **Description:** Offers broad coverage of such topics as machine translation, information retrieval, speech recognition and generation, dialogue systems, knowledge bases for natural language processing, text analysis, and integrated systems.
Related titles: Online - full text ed.: ISSN 1469-8110. GBP 145 to institutions; USD 230 in North America to institutions (effective 2006) (from EBSCO Publishing, O C L C Online Computer Library Center, Inc., Swets Information Services).
Indexed: CompAb, CompLI, EngInd, Inspec, L&LBA, PsycInfo, PsycholAb, SOPODA.
—BLDSC (6040.728100), AskIEEE, CISTI, IE, Infotrieve, ingenta. **CCC.**
Published by: Cambridge University Press, The Edinburgh Bldg, Shaftesbury Rd, Cambridge, CB2 2RU, United Kingdom. TEL 44-1223-312393, FAX 44-1223-315052, journals@cambridge.org, http://uk.cambridge.org/journals/nle/. Eds. B K Boguraev, Christian Jacquemin, John I. Tait. R&P Linda Nicol TEL 44-1223-325757. **Subscr. addr. in N America:** Cambridge University Press, 100 Brook Hill Dr, West Nyack, NY 10994. TEL 845-353-7500, FAX 845-353-4141, journals_subscriptions@cup.org

005.13 USA ISSN 1541-2849
.NET DEVELOPER'S JOURNAL; world's leading .net resource. Text in English. 2002 (Mar.). m. USD 69.99 domestic; USD 89.99 in Canada & Mexico; USD 99.99 elsewhere; USD 6.99 newsstand/cover (effective 2005). software rev. **Document type:** *Magazine, Trade.*
Formerly (until Jan. 2003): .Net Programmer's Journal
Related titles: Online - full content ed.: USD 39.99 (effective 2005).
Published by: SYS-CON Media, Inc., 135 Chestnut Ridge Rd, Montvale, NJ 07645. TEL 201-802-3040, 888-303-5282, FAX 201-782-9600, info@sys-con.com, http://dotnet.sys-con.com, http://www.sys-con.com. Pub. Fuat Kircaali. Adv. contact Carmen Gonzalez.

005.1 JPN
NIKKEI SOFTWARE. Text in Japanese. 1998. m. JPY 960 newsstand/cover. adv. **Document type:** *Trade.* **Description:** Focuses on practical information for creating quality application programs and hints for application developments.
Published by: Nikkei Business Publications Inc. (Subsidiary of: Nihon Keizai Shimbun, Inc.), 2-1-1 Hirakawa-cho, Chiyoda-ku, Tokyo, 102-8622, Japan. TEL 81-3-5210-8311, FAX 81-3-5210-8530, info@nikkeibpnyc.com, webmaster@nikkeibp.com, http://www.nikkeibp.com. Ed. Toshihiko Yanagida. Pub. Minoru Matsuzaki. adv.: B&W page JPY 300,000, color page JPY 500,000; trim 208 x 280. Circ: 43,959. **Dist. in America by:** Nikkei Business Publications America Inc., 575 Fifth Ave, 20th Fl, New York, NY 10017.

005.117 USA
O M G IN MOTION. (Object Management Group) Text in English. m.
Related titles: Online - full text ed.
Published by: O M G, First Needham Place, 250 First Ave Ste 201, Needham, MA 02494. TEL 781-444-0404, FAX 781-444-0320, info@omg.org, http://www.omg.org. Ed. Chris Vander Rhodes.

005.117 USA
O M G NEWS. (Object Management Group) Text in English. q. free to qualified personnel (effective 2000).
Published by: O M G, First Needham Place, 250 First Ave Ste 201, Needham, MA 02494. TEL 781-444-0404, FAX 781-444-0320, info@omg.org, http://www.omg.org. Ed. Chris Vander Rhodes.

005.1 USA
ONLINE HELP JOURNAL. Text in English. 1994. q. USD 99 (effective 1999). **Description:** Includes articles with code samples and live demos.
Formerly (until 1998): WinHelp Journal
Media: Online - full text.
Published by: WinWriters, 2529 Perkins Ln W., Seattle, WA 98199-3603. TEL 206-285-2605, 800-838-8999, FAX 206-216-0322, http://www.ohs.com. Pub. Joe Welinske.

ORACLE INTERNALS. see *COMPUTERS—Data Base Management*

005.1 GBR ISSN 0964-8836
P C W PLUS. Text in English. 1987. m. GBP 26.95. adv. charts; illus. back issues avail. **Description:** Covers general-interest, programming, product reviews, business uses, and news.
Formerly (until 1992): 8000 Plus (0952-505X)
Published by: Future Publishing Ltd., Beauford Court, 30 Monmouth St, Bath, Avon BA1 2BW, United Kingdom. TEL 44-1224-442244, FAX 44-1224-462986. Pub. Simon Stansfield. Circ: 30,583. **Subscr. to:** Future Publishing, Somerton, Somers TA11 6BR, United Kingdom. TEL 44-1225-822511.

THE P H O E N I C S JOURNAL OF COMPUTATIONAL FLUID DYNAMICS & ITS APPLICATIONS. (Parabolic Hyperbolic Or Elliptic Numerical Integration Code Series) see *ENGINEERING—Engineering Mechanics And Materials*

005.12 USA ISSN 1096-9764
PC / 104 EMBEDDED SOLUTIONS. Text in English. 1997. 3/yr. free domestic; USD 50 foreign (effective 2002).
Related titles: Online - full text ed.: ISSN 1550-0373.
Published by: OpenSystems Publishing, 30233 Jefferson Ave, St Clair Shores, MI 48082. TEL 810-415-6500, FAX 810-415-4882, http://www.pc104-embedded-solns.com, http://www.opensystems-publishing.com/.

005.117 USA ISSN 1545-7567
CODEN: PEJOFF
THE PERL JOURNAL (ONLINE EDITION). Text in English. 1996. m. USD 12 (effective 2003). adv. bk.rev. index. back issues avail. **Document type:** *Consumer.* **Description:** Deals with programming for the world wide web and applications. Includes columns on CGI scripting, Windows, networking, and regular expressions; contests; features; and tips, tricks, and traps.
Formerly: The Perl Journal (Print Edition) (1087-903X)
Media: Online - full content.
Published by: C M P Media LLC (Subsidiary of: United News & Media), 600 Community Dr, Manhasset, NY 11030. TEL 516-562-5000, http://tpj.com/, http://www.cmp.com. Ed. Jon Orwant. adv.: B&W page USD 1,320, color page USD 1,980; trim 9.75 x 7.25. Circ: 16,000 (paid).

005.11 RUS
PERSONAL'NYE PROGRAMMY. Text in Russian. 1990. m. USD 131 in North America (effective 2000).
Indexed: RefZh.
Address: Chapaevskii per 14, Moscow, 125252, Russian Federation. TEL 7-095-1570384. **Dist. by:** East View Information Services, 3020 Harbor Ln. N., Minneapolis, MN 55447. TEL 763-550-0961, FAX 763-559-2931.

005.1 UKR ISSN 1727-4907
PROBLEMY PROGRAMMIROVANIYA/PROBLEMS OF PROGRAMMING. Text in Russian; Summaries in English, Russian, Ukrainian. 1999. q. **Description:** Covers various aspects of computer programming, including software engineering, data processing techniques in parallel and distributed computer systems and networks, and the theory and methods of system analysis and decision making.
Indexed: MathR, MathSciNet.
Published by: Natsional'na Akademiya Nauk Ukrainy, Instytut Programnykh System, Prosp. Academika Glushkova, 40, Kiev, 03680, Ukraine. TEL 380-44-2662148, FAX 380-44-2666263, iss@isofts.kiev.ua. Ed. Pylyp I Andon.

005.1 USA
PROGRAMMER'S MEGADECK. Text in English. s-a. adv. **Document type:** *Trade.*
Published by: Fawcette Technical Publications, 2600 S. El Camino Real., Ste. 300, San Mateo, CA 94403-2381. TEL 650-833-7104, FAX 650-853-0230, http://www.fawcette.com. Adv. contact Dan Reback. Circ: 175,000 (controlled).

005.11 USA
PROGRAMMERS TRENDS E-NEWSLETTER. Text in English. 2002 (Jan.). bi-m. free (effective 2005). **Document type:** *Newsletter, Trade.*
Formerly: Programmers Report; Supersedes (1996-Oct. 2001): Java Report; (1988-Dec. 2001): Journal of Object-Oriented Programming
Media: Online - full text.
Published by: 101 Communications, Llc., 9121 Oakdale Ave, Ste 101, Chatsworth, CA 91311. TEL 818-734-1520, FAX 818-734-1522, info@101com.com, http://www.101com.com. Ed. Jack Vaughan. Circ: 100,000 (controlled).

005.1 RUS ISSN 0132-3474
QA76 CODEN: PROGD3
➤ **PROGRAMMIROVANIE.** Text in Russian. 1975. bi-m. USD 150 foreign (effective 2005). back issues avail. **Document type:** *Journal, Academic/Scholarly.* **Description:** Publishes theoretical and practical papers addressing all areas of computer science.
Related titles: Microfilm ed.: (from PQC); Online - full text ed.; ♦ English Translation: Programming and Computer Software. ISSN 0361-7688.
Indexed: CCMJ, EngInd, Inspec, MathR, MathSciNet, RASB, RefZh, ZentMath.
—CISTI, Linda Hall. **CCC.**
Published by: (Moskovskii Gosudarstvennyi Universitet im. M.V. Lomonosova, Fakul'tet Vychislitel'noi Matematiki i Kibernetiki/M.V. Lomonosov Moscow State University, Faculty of Computing Mathematics and Cybernetics), Izdatel'stvo Nauka, Profsoyuznaya ul 90, Moscow, 117864, Russian Federation. TEL 7-095-3347151, FAX 7-095-4202220, secret@naukaran.ru, http://www.maik.rssi.ru/cgi-bin/list.pl?page=prog, http://www.naukaran.ru. **Dist. by:** M K - Periodica, ul Gilyarovskogo 39, Moscow 129110, Russian Federation. TEL 7-095-2845008, FAX 7-095-2813798, info@periodicals.ru, http://www.mkniga.ru.

005.1 GBR
➤ **PSYCHOLOGY OF PROGRAMMING INTEREST GROUP. PROCEEDINGS.** Text in English. 1988. a. GBP 20. **Document type:** *Proceedings, Academic/Scholarly.*
—BLDSC (6848.855150).
Published by: Psychology of Programming Interest Group, Computing Research Centre, Sheffield Hallam University, Harmer Bldg., Sheffield, S Yorks S11 8HD, United Kingdom. b.khazaei@shu.ac.uk. Eds. Babak Khazaei, Rick Osborn.

005.1 RUS ISSN 0234-6621
R S D N MAGAZINE. (Russian Software Developer Network) Text in Russian. bi-m. **Document type:** *Magazine, Trade.*
Indexed: RefZh.
Published by: Optim.Ru, ul Amundsena, 15/ 1-7, Moscow, 129343, Russian Federation. TEL 7-095-1800201, mag@rsdn.ru, audit@optim.ru, http://www.rsdn.ru, http://www.optim.ru.

005 USA ISSN 1540-3114
QA76.8.M3
REALBASIC DEVELOPER. Text in English. 2002. bi-m. USD 32 domestic; USD 40 in Canada; USD 47 elsewhere (effective 2002).
Related titles: Online - full text ed.: ISSN 1540-3122.
Published by: DesignWrite, 872, Lafayette, OR 97127-0872. http://www.rbdeveloper.com.

REFERATIVNYI ZHURNAL. PROGRAMMNOE OBESPECHENIE. see *COMPUTERS—Abstracting, Bibliographies, Statistics*

▼ **S A P NETWEAVER.** (System Application Programming) see *COMPUTERS—Computer Systems*

005.1 USA ISSN 1551-3688
TK7895.E42
▼ ➤ **S I G B E D REVIEW.** (Special Interest Group on Embedded Systems) Variant title: A C M S I G B E D Review. Text in English. 2004 (Apr.). q. **Document type:** *Newsletter, Academic/Scholarly.*
Media: Online - full content.
Published by: Association for Computing Machinery, Inc., 1515 Broadway, 17th Fl, New York, NY 10036-5701. TEL 212-869-7440, FAX 212-944-1318, sigs@acm.org, http://www.cs.virginia.edu/sigbed/index.html, http://www.acm.org.

005.1 DEU ISSN 1611-4647
S Q L SERVER MAGAZIN. (Structured Query Language) Text in German. 1999. q. EUR 20 newsstand/cover (effective 2005). adv. **Document type:** *Magazine, Trade.*
Formerly (until 2002): S Q L Server (1617-0075)
Published by: H & T Verlag GmbH & Co. KG (Subsidiary of: Verlagsgruppe Handelsblatt GmbH), Konrad-Zuse-Platz 1, Munich, 81829, Germany. TEL 49-89-4447870, FAX 49-89-44478710, rm@verlags.de, info@htverlag.de, http://www.sql-news.de, http://www.htverlag.de. Ed. Rainer Mueller. adv.: page EUR 4,000.

005.1 USA ISSN 1522-2187
S Q L SERVER MAGAZINE. Text in English. 1999. m. USD 49.95 domestic; USD 59 in Canada; USD 99 elsewhere (effective 2003). back issues avail.; reprints avail. **Document type:** *Magazine, Trade.* **Description:** Provides an independent guide to using SQL Server as a business application-development platform.
Related titles: CD-ROM ed.; Online - full content ed.; Online - full text ed.: (from ProQuest Information & Learning).
—**CCC.**
Published by: Penton Technology Media (Subsidiary of: Penton Media, Inc.), 221 E 29th St, Ste 242, Loveland, CO 80538. TEL 970-663-4700, 800-621-1544, FAX 970-663-3285, kathy@sqlmag.com, http://www.sqlmag.com/. Ed. Kathy Blomstrom. Pub. Mike Whited. Adv. contact Richard Resnick.

005.1 USA ISSN 1536-2612
S Q L SERVER SOLUTIONS. (Structured Query Language) Text in English. 2001. m. USD 187 domestic; USD 197 foreign; USD 217 combined subscription print & online eds. (effective 2005). **Description:** Provides coverage of Microsoft SQL Server in all its flavors, from the scaled down to Embedded SQL Server and SQL Server for Windows CE to the desktop version of MSDE all the way up to the largest server clusters.
Related titles: Online - full content ed.: USD 217 domestic; USD 227 foreign (effective 2005).
—**CCC.**

Published by: Element K Journals (Subsidiary of: Eli Research, Inc.), 500 Canal View Blvd, Rochester, NY 14623. TEL 585-240-7301, 800-223-8720, 877-203-5248, FAX 585-292-4392, http://www.elementkjournals.com/products/showProduct.asp?prodID=36&catID=2. Eds. Jason Fisher, Michelle Rogers.

005.1 005.74 USA ISSN 1526-4041
S Q L SERVER UPDATE. (Structured Query Language) Text in English. 1998. m. USD 49.95 domestic; USD 59 in Canada (effective 2004). **Document type:** *Magazine, Trade.* **Description:** Provides information on SQL Servers.
Related titles: Online - full text ed.
Published by: Windows I T Pro Magazine Network (Subsidiary of: Penton Media, Inc.), 221 E 29th St, Loveland, CO 80538. TEL 970-663-4700, 800-621-1544, FAX 970-667-2321, http://www.sqlmag.com, http://www.windowsitpro.com.

005.1 NLD ISSN 0167-6423
QA76.6 CODEN: SCPGD4
➤ **SCIENCE OF COMPUTER PROGRAMMING.** Text in English. 1981. 15/yr. EUR 1,432 in Europe to institutions; JPY 190,400 in Japan to institutions; USD 1,603 elsewhere to institutions (effective 2006). bk.rev. index. back issues avail.; reprints avail. **Document type:** *Journal, Academic/Scholarly.* **Description:** Publishes research in requirements analysis and the mathematics of computer programming.
Related titles: Microform ed.: (from PQC); Online - full text ed.: (from EBSCO Publishing, Gale Group, IngentaConnect, ScienceDirect, Swets Information Services).
Indexed: ASCA, BrCerAb, C&ISA, CCMJ, CMCI, CerAb, CompAb, CompC, CompD, CompLI, CompR, CorrAb, CurCont, CybAb, E&CAJ, EMA, Englnd, IAA, IAOP, Inspec, M&TEA, MBF, METADEX, MathR, MathSciNet, SolStAb, WAA, ZentMath.
—BLDSC (8141.808000), AskIEEE, CISTI, Ei, IDS, IE, Infotrieve, ingenta, Linda Hall. **CCC.**
Published by: Elsevier BV, North-Holland (Subsidiary of: Elsevier Science & Technology), Sara Burgerhartstraat 25, Amsterdam, 1055 KV, Netherlands. TEL 31-20-485-3911, FAX 31-20-485-2457, nlinfo-f@elsevier.nl, http://www.elsevier.com/locate/scico, http://www.elsevier.nl/homepage/about/us/regional_sites.htt, http://www.elsevier.nl. Ed. J Bergstra. **Subscr. to:** Elsevier BV, PO Box 211, Amsterdam 1000 AE, Netherlands. TEL 31-20-485-3757, FAX 31-20-485-3432.

005.11 USA ISSN 0894-2226
QA76.58
SERLIN REPORT ON PARALLEL PROCESSING. Text in English. 1987. m. USD 695 (effective 2000). index. back issues avail. **Document type:** *Trade.* **Description:** Reports on and analyzes business and technical developments in massively-parallel systems, supercomputers and workstation clusters used mainly in technical applications.
Published by: I T O M International Co., 22676 Royal Oak Way, Cupertino, CA 94014. TEL 408-253-2580, FAX 408-253-2580, omri@svpal.org. Ed. Omri Serlin.

005.115 USA
SIGMAPASCAL. Text in English. 1997. m. free. back issues avail. **Document type:** *Newsletter.* **Description:** Contains Pascal sources, discussion forum and links on Pascal programming.
Media: Online - full text.
Address: webmaster@sigmanet.hypermart.net, http://sigmanet.hypermart.net.

SIGNAL PROCESSING: IMAGE COMMUNICATION. see *COMPUTERS—Data Communications And Data Transmission Systems*

005.1 USA ISSN 1543-1142
▼ **SMART TIPS AND QUICK TRICKS FOR S Q L SERVER SOLUTIONS.** (Structured Query Language) Text in English. 2003. irreg. USD 10 per issue domestic; USD 20 per issue foreign (effective 2005).
—**CCC.**
Published by: Element K Journals (Subsidiary of: Eli Research, Inc.), 500 Canal View Blvd, Rochester, NY 14623. TEL 585-240-7301, 800-223-8720, 877-203-5248, FAX 585-292-4392, http://www.elementkjournals.com.

005.72 USA ISSN 1538-8301
SMART TIPS AND QUICK TRICKS FOR WEB DESIGN. Text in English. 2002. a. USD 10 per issue domestic; USD 20 per issue foreign (effective 2005).
—**CCC.**
Published by: Element K Journals (Subsidiary of: Eli Research, Inc.), 500 Canal View Blvd, Rochester, NY 14623. TEL 585-240-7301, 800-223-8720, 877-203-5248, FAX 585-292-4392, http://www.elementkjournals.com. Eds. Ron Wilder, Michelle Rogers.

005.72 USA ISSN 1538-8328
SMART TIPS AND QUICK TRICKS FOR WEB DEVELOPMENT. Text in English. 2002. a. USD 10 per issue domestic; USD 20 per issue foreign (effective 2005).
—**CCC.**
Published by: Element K Journals (Subsidiary of: Eli Research, Inc.), 500 Canal View Blvd, Rochester, NY 14623. TEL 585-240-7301, 800-223-8720, 877-203-5248, FAX 585-292-4392, http://www.elementkjournals.com. Eds. Mike D. Jones, Michelle Rogers.

SOFTWARE AND SYSTEMS MODELING. see *COMPUTERS—Software*

SOFTWARE ENGINEERING. see *COMPUTERS—Software*

005.1 RUS
TEKHNOLOGIYA KLIENT-SERVER. Text in Russian. 1994. q. **Document type:** *Magazine, Trade.*
Published by: Optim.Ru, ul Amundsena, 15/ 1-7, Moscow, 129343, Russian Federation. TEL 7-095-1800201, audit@optim.ru, http://www.optim.ru/cs. Ed. M F Kupaev. Circ: 5,000.

005.115 GBR ISSN 1471-0684
THEORY AND PRACTICE OF LOGIC PROGRAMMING. Text in English. 2001. bi-m. GBP 222 to institutions; USD 360 in North America to institutions; GBP 242 combined subscription to institutions print & online eds.; USD 395 combined subscription in North America to institutions print & online eds. (effective 2006). reprint service avail. from PSC. **Description:** Topics covered are applications of artificial intelligence that use logic programming, natural language processing, knowledge representation, nonmonotic reasoning, databases, implementations and architectures and constraint logic programming.
Related titles: Online - full text ed.: ISSN 1475-3081. GBP 205 to institutions; USD 335 in North America to institutions (effective 2006) (from EBSCO Publishing, O C L C Online Computer Library Center, Inc., Swets Information Services).
Indexed: CurCont.
—BLDSC (8814.628440), CISTI, IE, Infotrieve, Linda Hall. **CCC.**
Published by: (Association for Logic Programming USA), Cambridge University Press, The Edinburgh Bldg, Shaftesbury Rd, Cambridge, CB2 2RU, United Kingdom. TEL 44-1223-312393, FAX 44-1223-315052, journals@cambridge.org, http://titles.cambridge.org/journals/journal_catalogue.asp?historylinks=ALPHA&mnemonic=TLP, http://www.cup.cam.ac.uk/. Ed. Maurice Bruynooghe. **Subscr. to:** Cambridge University Press, 100 Brook Hill Dr, West Nyack, NY 10994. TEL 845-353-7500, FAX 845-353-4141, journals_subscriptions@cup.org

005.1 USA ISSN 1537-0291
V B NET ADVISOR. (Visual Basic) Text in English. 2001. bi-m. USD 99 domestic; USD 109 in Canada; USD 119 elsewhere (effective 2002).
Published by: Advisor Media, Inc., 4849 Viewridge Ave, San Diego, CA 92123-1643. TEL 858-278-5600, FAX 858-278-0300, http://www.advisor.com. Ed. John L Hawkins.

005.13 USA
V S A M UPDATE. (Virtual Storage Access Method) Text in English. q. USD 185 (effective 2000). **Document type:** *Trade.*
Published by: Xephon, 9330 Lyndon B Johnson Fwy., Ste. 800, Dallas, TX 75243-4310. TEL 817-455-7050, FAX 303-438-0290.

005.1 ITA ISSN 1123-8534
VISUAL BASIC JOURNAL. Text in Italian. 1995. bi-m. EUR 44 (effective 2005). **Document type:** *Magazine, Consumer.*
Related titles: Online - full text ed.: ISSN 1721-9736. 1996.
Published by: Gruppo Editoriale Infomedia Srl, Via Valdera P 116, Ponsacco, PI 56038, Italy. TEL 39-0587-736460, FAX 39-0587-732232, http://www.infomedia.it.

VISUAL BASIC PROGRAMMERS JOURNAL ON CD-ROM. see *COMPUTERS—Computer Graphics*

005.13 USA ISSN 1079-0608
VISUAL C++ DEVELOPER. Variant title: Visual C Plus Plus Developer. Text in English. 1994. m. USD 149 (effective 2004). adv. **Document type:** *Newsletter, Trade.* **Description:** Presents information for Visual C++ developers on a wide range of topics, including validation, adding serial numbers to EXEs, high-resolution timers for Windows, static and dynamic MFC libraries, HTML, editing, and security.
—IE.
Published by: Pinnacle Publishing, Inc. (Subsidiary of: Lawrence Ragan Communications, Inc.), 316 N. Michigan Ave, Ste 300, Chicago, IL 60601. TEL 312-960-4209, 800-493-4867, FAX 312-960-4106, pinpub@ragan.com, http://www.pinpub.com. adv.: page USD 800. Circ: 2,000 (paid).

005.117 USA
VISUAL J PLUS PLUS INFORMANT. Text in English. 1997. m. USD 29.95 domestic; USD 59.95 foreign; USD 4.95 newsstand/cover. adv. back issues avail.
Published by: Informant Communications Group, 5105 Florin Perkins Rd., Sacramento, CA 95826-4817. TEL 916-686-6610, FAX 916-686-8497, jcoffey@informant.com. Ed. Jerry Coffrey. Pub., R&P Michael Koulouris. Adv. contact Debby Curry.

VISUAL STUDIO MAGAZINE. see *COMPUTERS*

005.118 GBR ISSN 1369-2992
VISUAL SYSTEMS JOURNAL; the indpendent source for software developers. Abbreviated title: V S J. Text in English. 1997. 11/yr. GBP 60 foreign (effective 2000); free to qualified personnel in UK. adv. software rev. back issues avail. **Document type:** *Magazine, Trade.* **Description:** Offers professionals in visual programming up-to-the-minute advice and ideas.
—BLDSC (9241.365000). **CCC.**
Published by: Bearpark Publishing, Long Island House, 1-4 Warple Way, London, W3 0RG, United Kingdom. TEL 44-120-8600-9400, FAX 44-120-8600-9401, vsjmag@bearpark.co.uk, http://www.vsj.co.uk, http://www.bearpark.co.uk. Ed. Mike James. Adv. contact Jon Walford. B&W page GBP 1,890, color page GBP 2,915. Circ: 9,800 (paid and controlled).

005.1 RUS ISSN 0507-5386
QA76
VYCHISLITEL'NYE METODY I PROGRAMIROVANIYE/ NUMERICAL METHODS AND PROGRAMMING. Text in Russian. 2000. s-a. (in 1 vol., 2 nos./vol.). **Document type:** *Journal, Academic/Scholarly.*
Related titles: Online - full content ed.: ISSN 1726-3522.
Indexed: Inspec, RefZh.
—CISTI.
Published by: (Moskovskii Gosudarstvennyi Universitet im. M.V. Lomonosova, Nauchno-Issledovatel'skii Vychislitel'nyi Tsentr), Izdatel'stvo Moskovskogo Gosudarstvennogo Universiteta im. M. V. Lomonosova/Publishing House of Moscow State University, B Nikitskaya 5/7, Moscow, 103009, Russian Federation. TEL 7-095-2295091, FAX 7-095-2036671, num-meth@srcc.msu.su, kd_mgu@rambler.ru, http://num-meth.srcc.msu.su, http://www.msu.ru/depts/MSUPubl. Ed. T E Vasil'eva. Circ: 300 (paid).

005.117 USA ISSN 1535-6906
WEB SERVICES JOURNAL. Text in English. 2001 (Sep.). m. USD 69.99 domestic; USD 89.99 in Canada & Mexico; USD 99.99 elsewhere; USD 6.99 newsstand/cover (effective 2005). adv. software rev. illus. **Document type:** *Magazine, Trade.* **Description:** Provides accurate, insightful information to the information technologist working with Web Services, from developer to CIO.
Incorporates (in 2004): X M L Journal
Related titles: Online - full text ed.: (from Factiva, Gale Group).
Indexed: CompD.
Published by: SYS-CON Media, Inc., 135 Chestnut Ridge Rd, Montvale, NJ 07645. TEL 201-802-3040, 888-303-5282, FAX 201-782-9600, info@sys-con.com, http://www.webservices.sys-con.com, http://www.sys-con.com. Ed. Sean Rhody. R&P Fuat Kircaali. Adv. contact Carmen Gonzalez. Circ: 30,000 (paid and controlled).

005.117 USA ISSN 1542-3336
WEB SERVICES STRATEGIES. Text in English. 1991. m. USD 497 domestic; USD 567 foreign (effective 2005). back issues avail. **Document type:** *Newsletter, Trade.* **Description:** Covers new technologies, new products, market developments and industry trends in the capabilities and uses of distributed component architectures & technologies and e-business. Includes discussion of techniques and methodologies.
Former titles (until 2002): Component - Development Strategies (1522-7391); (until 1999): Object - Oriented Strategies (1059-4108)
Related titles: Online - full text ed.: ISSN 1554-592X.
Indexed: CurCont.
—IDS.
Published by: Cutter Information Corp., 37 Broadway, Ste 1, Arlington, MA 02474. TEL 781-641-9876, 800-492-1650, FAX 800-888-1816, http://www.cutter.com/webservices/index.html. Ed. Tom Welsh. Pub. Karen Fine Coburn. R&P Megan Nields.

005.117 USA ISSN 1535-6914
WEBSPHERE DEVELOPER'S JOURNAL. Text in English. 2001 (Sep.). m. USD 89 domestic; USD 99 in Canada & Mexico; USD 129 elsewhere; USD 8.99 newsstand/cover (effective 2005). adv. software rev. **Document type:** *Magazine, Trade.* **Description:** Contains articles and information those who design, build, customize, deploy, or administer IBM's WebSphere suite of software products for developing, testing, and deploying interoperable e-business applications - from simple Web serving to the most sophisticated transaction-based solutions.
Related titles: Online - full text ed.: USD 39.99 (effective 2005) (from Factiva, Gale Group).
Indexed: CompD.
Published by: SYS-CON Media, Inc., 135 Chestnut Ridge Rd, Montvale, NJ 07645. TEL 201-802-3040, 888-303-5282, FAX 201-782-9600, info@sys-con.com, http://websphere.sys-con.com, http://www.sys-con.com. Ed. Jack Martin. R&P Fuat Kircaali. Adv. contact Carmen Gonzalez. Circ: 25,000 (paid and controlled).

WORKING CONFERENCE ON REVERSE ENGINEERING. PROCEEDINGS. see *COMPUTERS—Software*

005.117 USA ISSN 1537-2421
X M L DEVELOPER. Text in English. 2000. m. adv. **Document type:** *Newsletter, Trade.* **Description:** Offers technical advice and how-tos written by high-end professional developers- for high-end professional developers.

Related titles: Online - full text ed.: ISSN 1537-2413.
Published by: Pinnacle Publishing, Inc. (Subsidiary of: Lawrence Ragan Communications, Inc.), 316 N. Michigan Ave, Ste 300, Chicago, IL 60601. pinpub@ragan.com, http://www.pinpub.com.

005.1 USA ISSN 1534-9780
QA76.76.H94
X M L JOURNAL. Text in English. 2000. m. free with subscr. to Web Services Journal. adv. **Document type:** *Consumer.*
Related titles: CD-ROM ed.; ♦ Online - full text ed.: X M L Journal (Online).
Indexed: CompD.
Published by: SYS-CON Media, Inc., 135 Chestnut Ridge Rd, Montvale, NJ 07645. info@sys-con.com, http://xml.sys-con.com, http://www.sys-con.com. Ed. Ajit Sagar. Pub. Fuat Kircaali. Adv. contact Megan Ring. Circ: 55,000 (paid).

005.1 004.678 USA
X M L JOURNAL (ONLINE). Text in English. m. USD 39.99 (effective 2005). adv. **Document type:** *Magazine, Trade.* **Description:** Resource for Internet technology professionals involved with leveraging XML into the international business e-marketplace.
Media: Online - full text (from Gale Group). **Related titles:** CD-ROM ed.; ♦ Print ed.: X M L Journal. ISSN 1534-9780.
Published by: SYS-CON Media, Inc., 135 Chestnut Ridge Rd, Montvale, NJ 07645. TEL 201-802-3040, 888-303-5282, FAX 201-782-9600, info@sys-con.com, http://xml.sys-con.com, http://www.sys-con.com. Ed. Sean Rhody.

005.1 USA
XCELL JOURNAL; the online journal for programmable logic. Text in English. q. **Document type:** *Trade.* **Description:** Contains features on comprehensive design solutions for both high-performance and low-cost applications.
Media: Online - full content.
Published by: Xilinx, Inc., PO Box 240010, San Jose, CA 95154-2410. http://www.xilinx.com/publications/xcellonline/index.htm.

COMPUTERS—Computer Sales

see also BUSINESS AND ECONOMICS—Marketing And Purchasing

004.0688 AUS ISSN 1326-5822
AUSTRALIAN RESELLER NEWS. Text in English. 1991. 48/yr. AUD 71.50 domestic; AUD 250 in New Zealand; AUD 375 elsewhere (effective 2002). adv. **Document type:** *Newspaper, Trade.* **Description:** Dedicated to delivering timely and accurate information about products, services, business and the information technology marketplace to Australia's IT distribution channel.
Formerly (until 1996): Reseller (1037-132X)
Related titles: Online - full text ed.
Published by: I D G Communications Pty. Ltd., 88 Christie St, St Leonards, NSW 2065, Australia. TEL 61-2-94395133, FAX 61-2-94395512, http://www.arnnet.com.au, http://www.idg.com.au. Ed. Gerard Norsa. Adv. contact Glen Myles. B&W page AUD 5,450, color page AUD 5,950; trim 235 x 300.

004.0688 USA ISSN 1539-7343
HD9696.C6
C R N; vital information for VARs and technology integrators. Abbreviated title: C R N. Text in English. 1982. w. (Mon.). USD 220 domestic; free to qualified personnel (effective 2005). adv. back issues avail. **Document type:** *Newspaper, Trade.* **Description:** Offers dealers, VARS, distributors and vendors of microcomputer products news and comprehensive analysis on emerging market trends.
Former titles (until 2000): Computer Reseller News (0893-8377); Which Incorporates (1991-1992): Computer Reseller Sources (1060-1376); Macintosh News; (until 1986): Computer Retail News (0744-673X)
Related titles: Online - full text ed.: C R N Online (from bigchalk, EBSCO Publishing, Florida Center for Library Automation, Gale Group, LexisNexis, Northern Light Technology, Inc., O C L C Online Computer Library Center, Inc.); ♦ Regional ed(s).: C R N Canada; ♦ Supplement(s): Computer Retail Week. ISSN 1066-7598; Benchmarks (Manhasset). ISSN 1059-7573.
Indexed: ABIn, B&I, C&ISA, CompC, CompD, CompIU, E&CAJ, Englnd, IAA, LRI, MCIU, Microcomplnd, SoftBase.
—BLDSC (3394.257200). **CCC.**
Published by: C M P Media LLC (Subsidiary of: United News & Media), 600 Community Dr, Manhasset, NY 11030. TEL 516-562-5000, FAX 516-562-5036, feedback@cmp.com, http://www.crn.com/, http://www.cmp.com. Eds. Heather Cicincy, Michael Vizard, Robert DeMarzo. Pub. Lisa MacKenzie TEL 949-223-3627. adv.: B&W page USD 19,350, color page USD 23,465; trim 14.38 x 10.75. Circ: 117,501 (controlled).

004.0688 CAN
C R N CANADA. (Computer Reseller News) Text in English. 2001. bi-w. adv. **Document type:** *Magazine, Trade.* **Description:** Covers Canadian computer industry news and events, addressing critical topics, trends and emerging technology.
Related titles: Online - full content ed.; ♦ Regional ed(s).: C R N. ISSN 1539-7343.
Published by: Q M P Media Inc., 1 Director Court, Ste 201, Woodbridge, Ontario, ON L4L 4S5, Canada. TEL 905-851-8391, FAX 905-851-8482, http://www.crncanada.ca/. Ed. Ian L Masters. Pub. Douglas A Munroe. Adv. contact Pauline Reel. B&W page CND 3,495, color page CND 1,200; trim 10 x 12.

004.0688 USA
COMPUTER CONNECTION✶. Text in English. 1993. m. USD 13.
Address: 11065 N.W. 21st. Pl., Coral Springs, FL 33071-5744. Ed. Sorensen. adv.: B&W page USD 210; trim 10 x 7.

004.0688 ITA ISSN 1122-3227
COMPUTER DEALER & V A R. Text in Italian. m. (11/yr.). EUR 32 domestic; EUR 64 foreign (effective 2005). adv. **Document type:** *Magazine, Trade.*
Indexed: B&I.
Published by: Gruppo Editoriale A G E P E Srl, Via G Patecchio 2, Milan, MI 20141, Italy. TEL 39-02-399861, FAX 39-02-39844800, mbox@gruppoagepe.it, http://www.agepe.it. Ed. Mauro Bellini. Pub., R&P Roberto Avanzo. Adv. contact Roberto Lenzi. Circ: 11,780.

004.0688 CAN ISSN 1184-2369
COMPUTER DEALER NEWS. Text in English. 1985. bi-w. free to qualified personnel (effective 2005). adv. **Document type:** *Magazine, Consumer.* **Description:** Provides Canadian computer resellers with critical market information.
Formerly: Canadian Computer Dealer News (0834-4612)
Related titles: Microfilm ed.: (from MML); Microform ed.: (from MML); Online - full text ed.: (from EBSCO Publishing, Florida Center for Library Automation, Gale Group, Micromedia ProQuest, Northern Light Technology, Inc., ProQuest Information & Learning).
Indexed: ABIn, CBCABus, CBCARef, CBPI, CompD, CompIU.
—CCC.
Published by: Transcontinental Media, Inc. (Subsidiary of: Transcontinental, Inc.), 25 Sheppard Ave West, Ste 100, Toronto, ON M2N 6S7, Canada. TEL 416-733-7600, FAX 416-218-3544, mslofstra@itbusiness.ca, info@transcontinental.ca, http://www.itbusiness.ca/, http://www.transcontinental-gtc.com/en/home.html. adv.: B&W page CND 3,795, color page CND 4,990; trim 12.25 x 9.5. Circ: 16,692.

004.0688 DEU ISSN 1619-1102
COMPUTER RESELLER NEWS; die Zeitschrift fuer Fachhaendler, VARs und OEMs. Text in German. 1994. w. adv. **Document type:** *Magazine, Trade.*
Related titles: Online - full text ed.
Published by: W E K A Computerzeitschriften-Verlag GmbH, Gruberstr 46a, Poing, 85586, Germany. TEL 49-8121-950, FAX 49-8121-951199, cradzwil@cmp.com, http://www.crn-online.de/, http://www.magnamedia.de/crn/. Ed. Thorsten Koster. adv.: B&W page EUR 7,300, color page EUR 9,300. Circ: 33,725 (paid and controlled).

004.0688 USA ISSN 1066-7598
COMPUTER RETAIL WEEK. Text in English. 1990. fortn. USD 179.95; USD 189.95 in Canada; USD 230 in Europe; USD 300 in Australasia. back issues avail. **Document type:** *Trade.* **Description:** Covers news and trends in the computer retail industry.
Related titles: Online - full text ed.: (from EBSCO Publishing, Gale Group, Northern Light Technology, Inc., O C L C Online Computer Library Center, Inc.); ♦ Supplement to: C R N. ISSN 1539-7343.
Indexed: ABIn, B&I, CompD, Microcomplnd, SoftBase.
—CCC.
Published by: C M P Net, 600 Community Dr, Manhasset, NY 11030. crw@halldata.com, http://www.crw.com, http://www.cmp.com. Ed. Keith Newman.

004.068 ITA
COMPUTER SHOPPER; la guida piu completa al mercato dell'informatica. Text in Italian. m. **Document type:** *Consumer.* **Description:** Provides information to consumers of computer software and hardware.
Published by: A G E M SpA, Via Anton Giulio Bragaglia, 33, Rome, RM 00123, Italy. TEL 39-06-30884122. Ed. Enrico Morelli. **Dist. by:** A. Pieroni S.r.l., Viale Vittorio Veneto, 28, Milan, MI 20124, Italy. TEL 39-02-632461, FAX 39-02-63246232.

004.0688 NLD
COMPUTERPARTNER; vaktijdschrift voor de ICT-handel. Text in Dutch. 2000. bi-w. free to qualified persons. adv. illus.; mkt. **Document type:** *Magazine, Trade.* **Description:** Discusses computer and data telecommunications sales.
Related titles: Online - full text ed.
Published by: I D G Communications Nederland BV, Postbus 5446, Haarlem, 2000 GK, Netherlands. TEL 31-23-5461111, FAX 31-23-5461155, computerpartner@idg.nl, abo@idg.nl, http://www.computerpartner.nl, http://www.idg.nl. Eds. Flory Hartog TEL 31-23-546-1193, Marcel Roozeboom TEL 31-23-546-1130. Adv. contact Fred Driessen. B&W page USD 3,086, color page USD 4,365; trim 250 x 315. Circ: 12,159 (paid and controlled).

004.0688 CAN ISSN 1484-9089
COMPUTERWORLD. Text in English. 1985. 2/m. CND 55 domestic; CND 75 in United States; CND 95 elsewhere; free to qualified personnel (effective 2003). adv. **Document type:** *Magazine, Trade.* **Description:** Presents news and analysis of all aspects of computer and networking technology trends and issues.
Former titles (until 1996): Computerworld Canada (1195-6100); (until 1993): Direct Access (0827-5033); Incorporates (1976-1997): Info World Canada (1208-4182); Which was formerly (until 1996): Info Canada (1187-7081); (until 1991): Computer Data (0383-7319); Which incorporated (1993-1994): I T Magazine (1196-4715)
Related titles: Microform ed.: (from MML); Online - full text ed.: (from bigchalk, Micromedia ProQuest, ProQuest Information & Learning).
Indexed: ABIn, CompD, Inspec, SoftBase.
—BLDSC (3394.981000), CISTI. **CCC.**
Published by: I T World Canada, Inc., No.302 - 55 Town Centre Court, Scarborough, ON M1P 4X4, Canada. TEL 416-290-0240, FAX 416-290-0238, info@itworldcanada.com, http://www.itworldcanada.com/cw/. Ed. Gail Balfour. Pub., R&P John Jones. Adv. contact Stephen Kranabetter. B&W page CND 7,816, color page CND 9,266; trim 10.5 x 13.5. Circ: 45,100.

004.0688 DEU
DEALERS ONLY. Text in German. 22/yr. free to qualified personnel. adv. **Document type:** *Magazine, Trade.*
Published by: up2media AG, Quellenstr 32, Neustadt, 67433, Germany. TEL 49-6321-89980, FAX 49-6321-899899, dealers-only@up2media.de, info@up2media.de, http://www.dealers-only.biz, http://www.up2media.de. adv.: color page EUR 3,210; trim 210 x 297.

004.0688 USA
EASY DATA COMPUTER COMPARISONS✶. Text in English. 1982. q. USD 120. stat.; charts. index. back issues avail.
Published by: (Easy Data Corporation), Dykstra Consultants, 545 Baywood Dr, Newport Beach, CA 92660-7141.

004.0688 USA
FREQUENT BUYER. Text in English. 1988. m. free to qualified personnel. adv. **Description:** Designed to support the Merisel frequent buyer program.
Formerly: Softsell Reseller
Published by: Merisel, 200 Continental Blvd, El Segundo, CA 90245. TEL 213-615-3080, FAX 213-615-1263. Ed. W Bryan Wadsworth. Circ: 13,000.

LOGICIELS & SERVICES. see *COMPUTERS—Computer Engineering*

MICRO MONEY NEWSLETTER. see *COMPUTERS—Microcomputers*

P C MART. see *COMPUTERS*

004.16 USA ISSN 0736-0894
HD9696.C63
P C RETAILING✶. (Personal Computer) Text in English. 1983. m. free to qualified personnel. adv. bk.rev. **Description:** Aimed at IBM retailers.
Formerly (until 1984): Digital Retailing
Published by: Bartex Publishing Group, 74 Sargent Beechwood, Brookline, MA 02445-7542. TEL 617-890-5124. Ed. Neil Spann. Circ: 45,000.

659.131 ITA ISSN 1594-4018
RESELLER BUSINESS. Text in Italian. 1997. w. **Document type:** *Magazine, Trade.* **Description:** Contains news on the I.T. sector for trade operators.
Formerly (until 2002): Reseller Weekly (1594-4026)
Published by: Gruppo Editoriale A G E P E Srl, Via G Patecchio 2, Milan, MI 20141, Italy. TEL 39-02-399861, FAX 39-02-39844800, mbox@gruppoagepe.it, http://www.agepe.it. Ed. Mauro Bellini. Pub. Roberto Avanzo. Circ: 15,500.

004.0688 USA
RESELLER QUARTERLY. Text in English. 1991. q. free to qualified personnel. adv. **Description:** Designed to support the Merisel customer base.
Published by: Merisel, 200 Continental Blvd, El Segundo, CA 90245. TEL 213-615-3080, FAX 213-615-1263. Ed. W Bryan Wadsworth. Circ: 25,000.

SOFTWARE MAGAZINE. see *COMPUTERS—Software*

004.0688 FRA ISSN 0762-5669
VENTE INFORMATIQUE✶. Text in French. 10/yr.
Published by: L.N.E., 1, rue Gaston Boissier, Paris, 75015, France. TEL 33-5-45654400, TELEX 202 548 F. Ed. Yves Dupre. Circ: 12,000.

▼ *new title* ➤ *refereed* ✶ *unverified* ♦ *full entry avail.*

COMPUTERS—Computer Security

005.8 384 USA ISSN 1543-7221
A C M CONFERENCE ON COMPUTER AND COMMUNICATIONS SECURITY. PROCEEDINGS. Text in English. 2000. a. price varies. **Document type:** *Proceedings, Academic/Scholarly.*
Published by: Association for Computing Machinery, Inc., 1515 Broadway, 17th Fl, New York, NY 10036-5701. TEL 212-626-0500, 800-342-6626, FAX 212-869-0481, usacm@acm.org, http://www.acm.org.

005.8 USA ISSN 1094-9224
QA76.9.A25 CODEN: ATISBQ
➤ **A C M TRANSACTIONS ON INFORMATION AND SYSTEM SECURITY.** Short title: T I S S E C. Variant title: Information and System Security. Transactions on Information and System Security. Text in English. 1998. q. USD 170 domestic to non-members; USD 184 foreign to non-members; USD 41 domestic to members; USD 55 foreign to members; USD 36 domestic to students; USD 50 foreign to students; USD 204 combined subscription domestic to non-members print & online eds.; USD 218 combined subscription foreign to non-members print & online eds.; USD 49 combined subscription domestic to members print & online eds.; USD 63 combined subscription foreign to members print & online eds.; USD 43 combined subscription domestic to students print & online eds.; USD 57 combined subscription foreign to students print & online eds. (effective 2006). abstr. back issues avail. **Document type:** *Journal, Academic/Scholarly.* **Description:** Publishes original archival-quality research papers and technical notes in all areas of information and system security including technologies, systems, applications, and policies.
Related titles: Online - full text ed.: ISSN 1557-7406. USD 136 to non-members; USD 33 to members; USD 29 to students (effective 2006) (from Association for Computing Machinery, Inc., EBSCO Publishing).
Indexed: ABIn, BrCerAb, C&CSA, C&ISA, CerAb, CompLI, CompR, CorrAb, E&CAJ, EMA, IAA, Inspec, M&TEA, MBF, METADEX, RefZh, WAA.
—BLDSC (0578.666000), CISTI, IE. **CCC.**
Published by: Association for Computing Machinery, Inc., 1515 Broadway, 17th Fl, New York, NY 10036-5701. TEL 212-626-0500, 212-626-0520, 800-342-6626, FAX 212-869-0481, sigs@acm.org, usacm@acm.org, http://www.acm.org/tissec/. Ed. Ravi Sandhu.

658.478 USA ISSN 1568-2633
ADVANCES IN INFORMATION SECURITY. Text in English. 2001. irreg., latest vol.17, 2005. price varies. **Document type:** *Monographic series, Academic/Scholarly.* **Description:** Covers all aspects of computer and network security, including related areas such as fault tolerance and software assurance.
—BLDSC (0709.149500), CISTI.
Published by: Springer-Verlag New York, Inc. (Subsidiary of: Springer Science+Business Media), 233 Spring St, New York, NY 10013. TEL 212-460-1500, FAX 212-460-1575, service@springer-ny.com, http://www.springer-ny.com. Ed. Sushil Jajodia.

005.8 USA ISSN 1063-9527
QA76.9.A25
ANNUAL CONFERENCE COMPUTER SECURITY APPLICATIONS. PROCEEDINGS. Text in English. 1989. a. price varies. adv. **Document type:** *Proceedings, Academic/Scholarly.* **Description:** Covers various methods, issues, systems, designs and applications that contribute to the field of information security.
Related titles: Online - full text ed.: (from I E E E).
—BLDSC (1081.907000). **CCC.**
Published by: (Institute of Electrical and Electronics Engineers, Inc.), I E E E Computer Society, 10662 Los Vaqueros Circle, PO Box 3014, Los Alamitos, CA 90720-1314. TEL 714-821-8380, FAX 714-821-4641.

005.8 USA ISSN 0746-7281
AUERBACH DATA SECURITY MANAGEMENT. Text in English. 1981. bi-m. looseleaf. USD 495 (effective 2000 - 2001). back issues avail.; reprints avail. **Document type:** *Journal, Trade.* **Description:** Provides information on protecting data resources from human and computer error. Covers implementation of security measures, software packages, disaster-recovery planning, and security hardware.
Formerly (until 1983): Data Security Management (0736-363X)
Related titles: CD-ROM ed.: USD 450 (effective 2001); Online - full text ed.: (from EBSCO Publishing).
—CCC.
Published by: Auerbach Publications (Subsidiary of: C R C Press, LLC), 2000 Corporate Blvd., NW, Boca Raton, FL 33431. TEL 561-994-0555, FAX 561-374-3401, orders@crcpress.com, http://www.auerbach-publications.com, http://www.auerbach-publications.com/home.asp. Ed. Harold F. Tipton. Pub. Richard O'Hanley TEL 212-845-4017. R&P Jamie Sigal TEL 561-994-0555.

005.8 658.478 USA ISSN 1546-4105
▼ **BANK FRAUD AND I T SECURITY REPORT.** (Information Technology) Text in English. 2003 (Aug.). m. USD 425 (effective 2005). **Document type:** *Newsletter, Trade.* **Description:** Provides expert coverage of the most important trends and hot issues in bank fraud and IT security.
Indexed: C&CSA.
Published by: A.S. Pratt & Sons, Inc., 1911 Fort Myer Dr, Arlington, VA 22209. TEL 703-528-0145, FAX 703-528-1736, http://www.sheshunoff.com/store/H27.html.

005.8 DEU ISSN 0933-4033
BUNDESDATENSCHUTZGESETZ. Text in German. 1977. irreg. looseleaf. price varies. **Document type:** *Monographic series, Trade.*
Published by: Erich Schmidt Verlag GmbH & Co. (Berlin), Genthiner Str 30G, Berlin, 10785, Germany. TEL 49-30-250085-0, FAX 49-30-2500521, vertrieb@esvmedien.de, http://www.erich-schmidt-verlag.de.

658.478 USA ISSN 0899-4595
C P R - J. (Contingency Planning & Recovery Journal) Text in English. 1987. q. USD 65 domestic; USD 83 foreign (effective 2000). adv. bk.rev. **Document type:** *Trade.* **Description:** Devoted to issues of development, implementation, documentation and testing of computer contingency and recovery plans to protect business and critical process continuity and minimizing loss from computer and business disruptions. Includes tutorials and a thorough digest of literature sources published on the subject. Practical guidelines and practices are featured regularly.
Formerly: C P R - R (0899-4994)
Published by: (Contingency Planning & Recovery Institute), Management Advisory Publications, 57 Greylock Rd, Wellesley, MA 02481. TEL 617-235-2895, http://www.masp.com. Ed. J F Kuong. Adv. contact N Lagos.

005.8 USA
C=HACKING; welcome to the cutting edge. Text in English. 1992. irreg. back issues avail. **Description:** Contains contributed articles covering the Commodore 8-bit technical developments from its most innovative and productive members.
Media: Online - full content.
Address: sjudd@ffd2.com, http://www.ffd2.com/fridge/chacking/. Ed., Pub. Stephen L Judd.

COMMUNICATOR (PHOENIX, 1986). see *COMMUNICATIONS*

005.8 GBR ISSN 1468-1714
➤ **COMPUTER & COMMUNICATIONS SECURITY ABSTRACTS.** Text in English. 1992. bi-m. EUR 959.22 in Europe; USD 979 in North America; AUD 1,159 in Australasia; GBP 668.88 in UK & elsewhere (effective 2006). back issues avail.; reprint service avail. from PSC. **Document type:** *Journal, Abstract/Index.* **Description:** Contains indexed and keyworded abstracts from over 100 computer security journals.
Formerly (until 1999): Computer & Communications Security Reviews (1352-6278)
Related titles: Online - full text ed.
—CCC.
Published by: Emerald Group Publishing Limited, 60-62 Toller Ln, Bradford, W Yorks BD8 9BY, United Kingdom. TEL 44-1274-777700, FAX 44-1274-785200, infomation@emeraldinsight.com, http://www.emeraldinsight.com/abstracts/ccsa/index.htm. Ed. Chris Mitchell. Pub. Lynn Thorley.

005.8 340 USA ISSN 1556-5718
▼ **COMPUTER CRIMES LAW BULLETIN.** Text in English. 2005 (May). m. USD 147 (effective 2006). **Document type:** *Newsletter.*
Related titles: Online - full content ed.: ISSN 1556-570X.
Published by: Quinlan Publishing Group, Marine Industrial Park, 23 Drydock Ave, 6th Fl, Boston, MA 02210-2387. TEL 617-542-0048, 800-229-2084, FAX 617-507-1079, info@quinlan.com, http://www.quinlan.com. Pub. Dennis Hofmaier.

658.478 GBR ISSN 1361-3723
CODEN: CFSBEK
COMPUTER FRAUD & SECURITY. Text in English. 1979. 12/yr. EUR 906 in Europe to institutions; JPY 120,500 in Japan to institutions; USD 982 elsewhere to institutions (effective 2006). bk.rev. charts. back issues avail. **Document type:** *Newsletter.* **Description:** Provides information and advice on methods to combat computer crime and minimize risks.
Formerly (until Oct. 1995): Computer Fraud and Security Bulletin (0142-0496)
Related titles: Microform ed.: (from PQC); Online - full text ed.: (from Data-Star, EBSCO Publishing, Factiva, Gale Group, IngentaConnect, ScienceDirect, Swets Information Services, The Dialog Corporation).
Indexed: C&CSA, CompLI, CurCont, Inspec.
—BLDSC (3393.964600), AskIEEE, CISTI, IDS, IE, Infotrieve, ingenta. **CCC.**
Published by: Pergamon (Subsidiary of: Elsevier Science & Technology), The Boulevard, Langford Ln, East Park, Kidlington, Oxford OX5 1GB, United Kingdom. TEL 44-1865-843000, FAX 44-1865-843010, http://www.elsevier.com/locate/compseconline. Ed. S. Hilley. **Subscr. to:** Elsevier BV, PO Box 211, Amsterdam 1000 AE, Netherlands. TEL 31-20-485-3757, FAX 31-20-485-3432, nlinfo-f@elsevier.nl, http://www.elsevier.nl.

658.478 GBR ISSN 0267-3649
➤ **COMPUTER LAW & SECURITY REPORT.** Text in English. 1985. 6/yr. EUR 1,021 in Europe to institutions; JPY 135,600 in Japan to institutions; USD 1,104 to institutions except Europe and Japan (effective 2006). adv. index. back issues avail. **Document type:** *Academic/Scholarly.* **Description:** Covers information technology law and computer security for general and financial managers.
Related titles: Microform ed.: (from PQC); Online - full text ed.: (from EBSCO Publishing, Gale Group, IngentaConnect, ScienceDirect, Swets Information Services).
Indexed: C&CSA, CLI, ELJI, ESPM, EngInd, ILP, Inspec, LJI, LRI, RiskAb.
—BLDSC (3394.074900), AskIEEE, IE, Infotrieve, ingenta. **CCC.**
Published by: Pergamon (Subsidiary of: Elsevier Science & Technology), The Boulevard, Langford Ln, East Park, Kidlington, Oxford OX5 1GB, United Kingdom. TEL 44-1865-843000, FAX 44-1865-843010, http://www.elsevier.com/locate/compseconline. Circ: 500. **Subscr. to:** Elsevier BV, PO Box 211, Amsterdam 1000 AE, Netherlands. TEL 31-20-485-3757, FAX 31-20-485-3432, nlinfo-f@elsevier.nl, http://www.elsevier.nl.

005.8 USA ISSN 0742-0633
QA76.9.A25
COMPUTER SECURITY ALERT. Text in English. 1973. m. USD 197 domestic membership; USD 237 foreign membership (effective 2002). adv. 10 p./no.; **Document type:** *Newsletter, Trade.*
Formerly: Computer Security Newsletter
Published by: Computer Security Institute, 600 Harrison St, San Francisco, CA 94107. TEL 415-905-2670, FAX 415-905-2234, csi@mfi.com, http://www.gocsi.com.

005.8 USA ISSN 0738-4262
COMPUTER SECURITY, AUDITING AND CONTROLS. Short title: Com - S A C. Text in English. 1974. q. USD 98 in North America; USD 118 in Europe; USD 120 elsewhere (effective 2005). bk.rev. **Document type:** *Trade.* **Description:** Tutorials on computer security, audit and controls and comprehensive digest of all key articles and literature on the title subjects. Summary of new developments and product announcements in the field.
Indexed: ATI, DPD, Inspec.
—BLDSC (3394.274910), AskIEEE, IE, ingenta.
Published by: Management Advisory Publications, 57 Greylock Rd, Wellesley, MA 02481. TEL 781-235-2895, FAX 781-235-5446, jaykmasp@aol.com, http://www.masp.com/publications/MAP-2.html. Ed. J F Kuong. Adv. contact N Lagos. Circ: 1,000 (paid).

005.8029 USA ISSN 1059-5317
QA76.9.A25
COMPUTER SECURITY BUYER'S GUIDE. Text in English. a. looseleaf. adv. **Document type:** *Directory.* **Description:** Describes products and services designed for computer security practitioners.
Published by: Computer Security Institute, 600 Harrison St, San Francisco, CA 94107. TEL 415-905-2670, FAX 415-905-2234, csi@mfi.com, http://www.gocsi.com. Pub. Patrice Rapdlus. Adv. contact Whitney Wilson. Circ: 4,000.

005.8 USA ISSN 1530-1869
COMPUTER SECURITY, DEPENDABILITY AND ASSURANCE. Key Title: Proceedings - Computer Security, Dependability and Assurance. Text in English. a. price varies. **Document type:** *Proceedings, Trade.*
Related titles: Online - full text ed.: (from I E E E).
Published by: Institute of Electrical and Electronics Engineers, Inc., 3 Park Ave, 17th Fl, New York, NY 10016-5997. TEL 212-419-7900, 800-678-4333, FAX 212-752-4929, customer.service@ieee.org, http://www.ieee.org.

658.478 USA ISSN 0882-1453
QA76.9.A25
COMPUTER SECURITY DIGEST✶. Text in English. 1983. m. looseleaf. USD 125. bk.rev. index. **Document type:** *Newsletter.* **Description:** Provides digests of current incidents involving computer security breaches and computer-related crime.
Formerly: Corporate and Computer Fraud Digest
Related titles: Online - full text ed.: (from Northern Light Technology, Inc., ProQuest Information & Learning).
Published by: Computer Protection Systems, Inc., 12275 Appletree Dr, Plymouth, MI 48170-3739. TEL 313-459-8787, FAX 313-459-2720. Ed., Pub. Jack Bologna.

005.8 USA ISSN 1063-6900
COMPUTER SECURITY FOUNDATIONS WORKSHOP. PROCEEDINGS. Text in English. 1988. a. USD 110 (effective 2005). adv. **Document type:** *Proceedings.* **Description:** Explores fundamental issues in computer security.
Related titles: Online - full text ed.: (from I E E E).
Indexed: EngInd.
—BLDSC (3394.274918). **CCC.**
Published by: (Institute of Electrical and Electronics Engineers, Inc.), I E E E Computer Society, 10662 Los Vaqueros Circle, PO Box 3014, Los Alamitos, CA 90720-1314. TEL 714-821-8380, FAX 714-821-4641. Ed. Cat Harris. Pub. Matt Loeb. Adv. contact Frieda Koester.

658.478 005.8 USA ISSN 0277-0865
QA76.9.A25 CODEN: CSJLDR
COMPUTER SECURITY JOURNAL. Text in English. 1981. q. USD 197 domestic membership; USD 237 foreign membership (effective 2004). bk.rev. **Document type:** *Trade.* **Description:** Presents ideas and information about current security practices and products.
Related titles: Online - full text ed.
Indexed: ATI, C&CSA, CJPI, CompD, DPD, Engind, Inspec.
—BLDSC (3394.274920), AskIEEE, CASDDS, CISTI, Ei, IE, Infotrieve, ingenta, Linda Hall.
Published by: Computer Security Institute, 600 Harrison St, San Francisco, CA 94107. TEL 818-487-8529, FAX 818-487-4550, 866-721-8529, csimember@espcomp.com, http://www.gocsi.com. Circ: 3,000.

005.8 USA
COMPUTER SECURITY UPDATE. Text in English. m. USD 165 in US & Canada; USD 180 elsewhere; USD 25 per issue in US & Canada; USD 30 per issue elsewhere (effective 2003). **Document type:** *Newsletter, Trade.* **Description:** Provides news and information on computer security worldwide. This includes the latest hardware and software products available to protect all computers and networks from hackers, viruses, and all international and domestic threats.
Published by: Worldwide Videotex, PO Box 3273, Boynton Beach, FL 33424-3273. TEL 561-738-2276, markedit@juno.com, http://www.wvpubs.com.

005.8 GBR ISSN 0167-4048
QA76.9.A25 CODEN: CPSEDU
➤ **COMPUTERS & SECURITY.** Text in English. 1982. 8/yr. EUR 779 in Europe to institutions; JPY 103,500 in Japan to institutions; USD 842 to institutions except Europe and Japan (effective 2006). adv. bk.rev. abstr.; bibl. index. back issues avail. **Document type:** *Academic/Scholarly.* **Description:** Provides information about all phases of computer security.
Related titles: Online - full text ed.: (from EBSCO Publishing, Gale Group, IngentaConnect, ScienceDirect, Swets Information Services).
Indexed: ABIn, ADPA, ASCA, BrCerAb, C&CSA, C&ISA, CJA, CJPI, CMCI, CerAb, CompAb, CompC, CompD, CompLI, CorrAb, CurCont, E&CAJ, EMA, ESPM, Emerald, Engind, IAA, Inspec, M&TEA, MBF, METADEX, RiskAb, SolStAb, WAA.
—BLDSC (3394.781000), AskIEEE, CASDDS, CISTI, Ei, IDS, IE, Infotrieve, ingenta, Linda Hall. **CCC.**
Published by: (International Federation for Information Processing AUT, Technical Committee on Computer Security), Pergamon (Subsidiary of: Elsevier Science & Technology), The Boulevard, Langford Ln, East Park, Kidlington, Oxford OX5 1GB, United Kingdom. TEL 44-1865-843000, FAX 44-1865-843010, http://www.elsevier.com/locate/compseconline. Ed. E. Schultz. **Subscr. to:** Elsevier BV, PO Box 211, Amsterdam 1000 AE, Netherlands. TEL 31-20-485-3757, FAX 31-20-485-3432, nlinfo-f@elsevier.nl, http://www.elsevier.nl.

658.478 USA
HV8290
COMPUTING & COMMUNICATIONS: LAW & PROTECTION REPORT. Text in English. 1975. m. USD 84 domestic; USD 96 in Canada & Mexico (effective 2000); USD 116 elsewhere (effective 2003). bk.rev. tr.lit. back issues avail. **Document type:** *Newsletter.* **Description:** Devoted to the legal liability risks of inadequate or absent computer and telecommunications security, and civil and criminal laws affecting breaches of computer security.
Former titles: Computing and Communications Protection; Data Processing and Communications Security (0749-1484)
Related titles: Microfiche ed.: (from PQC); Microfilm ed.: (from PQC).
Indexed: CJPI.
Published by: Assets Protection Publishing, 5029 Sheboygan Ave #201, Madison, WI 53705. Ed., R&P Paul Shaw. Circ: 2,000.

005.8 USA
CRYPTO-GRAM. Text in English. m. free. software rev.; Website rev. back issues avail. **Document type:** *Newsletter, Trade.* **Description:** Covers computer security and cryptography.
Media: E-mail.
Published by: Counterpane Internet Security, Inc., 19050 Pruneridge Ave, Cupertino, CA 95014. TEL 408-777-3600, FAX 408-777-3601, info@counterpane.com, http://www.counterpane.com/crypto-gram.html. Ed. Bruce Schneier.

005.8 USA ISSN 0161-1194
Z102.5 CODEN: CRYPE6
➤ **CRYPTOLOGIA**; a quarterly journal devoted to all aspects of cryptology. Text in English. 1977. q. USD 48 domestic; USD 60 foreign (effective 2004). adv. bk.rev. illus.; pat.; stat. index. back issues avail.; reprint service avail. from PQC. **Document type:** *Journal, Academic/Scholarly.* **Description:** Scholarly journal on aspects of cryptology including computer security, mathematics, codes, cryptanalysis, history, the military, literature, and language.
Related titles: Microform ed.: (from PQC); Online - full text ed.: (from bigchalk, Northern Light Technology, Inc., ProQuest Information & Learning).
Indexed: C&CSA, CompC, CurCont, Inspec, MathR, RefZh, ZentMath.
—BLDSC (3490.155480), AskIEEE, CISTI, IDS, IE, Infotrieve, ingenta, Linda Hall. **CCC.**
Address: c/o Department of Mathematical Sciences, United States Military Academy, West Point, NY 10996. TEL 845-938-3200, cryptologia@usma.edu, brian-winkel@usma.edu, http://www.dean.usma.edu/math/pubs/cryptologia/. Ed., Pub., R&P Brian J Winkel. Circ: 1,000.

005.8 323 070 USA ISSN 1540-3327
▼ **CRYPTORIGHTS JOURNAL**; the security quarterly for human rights & journalism. Text in English. 2003 (Fall). q. **Document type:** *Newsletter.*
Related titles: Online - full text ed.: ISSN 1540-3335.
Indexed: C&CSA.
Published by: The CryptoRights Foundation, 80 Alviso St., San Francisco, CA 94127. TEL 415-334-5533, FAX 415-334-2346, info@cryptorights.org, http://www.cryptorights.org/journal. Ed. Jeff Milstead.

005.8 USA ISSN 1540-0891
CYBER-CRIME FIGHTER; success secrets for security managers and investigators. Text in English. 2002. m. USD 297 domestic; USD 357 foreign (effective 2003).
Published by: White-Collar Crime 101, LLC, 213 Ramapoo Rd., Ridgefield, CT 06877. TEL 800-440-2261, FAX 203-431-6054, http://www.cybercrimefighter.com. Ed. Peter Goldmann.

CYBERCRIME LAW REPORT. see *LAW—Computer Applications*

658.4 DNK ISSN 0907-5437
DANSK SECURITY. Text in Danish. 199?. 5/yr. DKK 240 (effective 2001).
Address: Vedelsgade 46, Vejle, 7100, Denmark. TEL 45-76-40-00-14, FAX 45-76-40-00-86, adm@dansksecurity.dk, http://www.dansksecurity.dk.

005.8 USA ISSN 1065-9986
➤ **DATA SECURITY LETTER.** Text in English. 1988. 11/yr. USD 89 domestic to individuals; USD 114 foreign to individuals; USD 345 domestic to institutions; USD 370 foreign to institutions. bk.rev. bibl. index. back issues avail. **Document type:** *Newsletter, Academic/Scholarly.* **Description:** Focuses on information systems security, with emphasis on trends, research and development, and new technologies.
Published by: Trusted Information Systems, Inc., 1145 Herndon Pkwy., Ste. 500, Herndon, VA 20170-5535. TEL 301-854-6889, FAX 301-854-5363, dsl@tis.com, http://www.tis.com/. Ed. Sharon Osuna. Circ: 350 (paid).

005.8 NLD
DATABASE SECURITY. Text in English. irreg. price varies. **Document type:** *Monographic series, Trade.*
—BLDSC (3535.803590), ingenta.
Published by: Springer-Verlag Dordrecht (Subsidiary of: Springer Science+Business Media), Van Godewijckstraat 30, Dordrecht, 3311 GX, Netherlands. TEL 31-78-6576050, FAX 31-78-6576474, http://www.springeronline.com.

005.8 DNK ISSN 0906-642X
DATASIKKERHEDSBLADET. Text and summaries in Danish. 1990. q. DKK 960 (effective 2001). **Document type:** *Magazine, Trade.* **Description:** Covers all aspects of information technology security and related applications.
Published by: UNI-C, Vermundsgade 5, Copenhagen OE, 2100, Denmark. TEL 45-35-87-88-89, FAX 45-35-87-88-90, redaktion@datasb.dk, http://www.datasb.dk. Ed. Jan Carlsen.

658.478 DEU ISSN 0170-7256
DATENSCHUTZ-BERATER; Informationsdienst der Verlagsgruppe Handelsblatt. Text in German. 1978. m. EUR 192; EUR 96 to students; EUR 17 newsstand/cover (effective 2004). adv. **Document type:** *Magazine, Trade.*
—**CCC.**
Published by: Verlagsgruppe Handelsblatt GmbH, Kasernenstr 67, Duesseldorf, 40213, Germany. TEL 49-211-8870, FAX 49-211-371792, leser-service@vhb.de, http://www3.vhb.de/datenschutz-berater/, http://www.vhb.de. adv.: B&W page EUR 1,246, color page EUR 2,325. Circ: 2,600 (paid and controlled).

005.8 DEU ISSN 0173-7767
DATENSCHUTZ NACHRICHTEN. Text in German. 1978. 6/yr. EUR 32; EUR 9 newsstand/cover (effective 2004). bk.rev. index. back issues avail. **Document type:** *Journal, Trade.*
Published by: Deutsche Vereinigung fuer Datenschutz, Bonner Talweg 33-35, Bonn, 53113, Germany. TEL 49-228-222498, FAX 49-228-2438470, dvd@datenschutzverein.de, http://www.datenschutzverein.de. Ed. Heinz Alenfelder. Circ: 500 (controlled).

658.478 DEU
DATENSCHUTZ UND DATENSICHERUNG; Recht und Sicherheit der Informations und Kommunikationssysteme. Short title: D u D. Text in German. 1978. m. EUR 237; EUR 118.80 to students; EUR 26 newsstand/cover (effective 2005). adv. **Document type:** *Magazine, Trade.* **Description:** Provides a forum for legal and technical questions involving data protection and data integrity in information processing and communications.
Former titles: Datenschutz und Datensicherung - Informationsrecht - Kommunikationssysteme; Datenschutz und Datensicherung Zugleich der Datenschutzbeauftragte (0724-4371)
Indexed: DIP, ELLIS, IBR, IBZ.
—IE.
Published by: Friedr. Vieweg und Sohn Verlagsgesellschaft mbH (Subsidiary of: Springer Science+Business Media), Abraham-Lincoln-Str 46, Wiesbaden, 65189, Germany. TEL 49-611-78780, FAX 49-611-7878400, vieweg.service@bertelsmann.de, http://www.dud.de, http://www.vieweg.de. Adv. contact Christian Kannenberg. B&W page EUR 1,380, color page EUR 2,280. Circ: 1,850 (paid and controlled).

005.8 AUT ISSN 1014-9333
DATENSCHUTZ UND INFORMATIONSRECHT. Text in German. 1988. q. bk.rev. back issues avail. **Document type:** *Journal, Academic/Scholarly.*
Related titles: Online - full text ed.
Published by: ARGE DATEN - Oesterreichische Gesellschaft fuer Datenschutz, Redtenbachergasse 20, Vienna, W 1160, Austria. TEL 43-676-9107032, FAX 43-1-4803209, webmaster@argedaten.at, http://www2.argedaten.at. Ed. Hans Zeger. Circ: 800 (controlled).

658.478 CHE ISSN 1424-9944
DIGMA; Zeitschrift fuer Datenrecht und Informationssicherheit. Text in German. 2001. q. CHF 138, EUR 87 (effective 2001). adv. **Document type:** *Magazine, Trade.* **Description:** Covers all legal and technological aspects of information and communications security and privacy.
Related titles: Online - full text ed.
Published by: Schulthess Juristische Medien AG, Zwinglipiatz 2, Zuerich, 8022, Switzerland. TEL 41-1-2519336, FAX 41-1-2616394, zs.verlag@schulthess.com, http://www.e-digma.ch, http://www.schulthess.com. Eds. Alex Piazza, Lukas Faessler.

C

658.478 USA ISSN 0736-6981
CODEN: EDPCDF
E D P A C S; the E D P audit, control and security newsletter. (Electronic Data Processing) Text in English. 1973. m. USD 245 domestic (effective 2005); USD 285 foreign (effective 2001). bk.rev. index. 20 p./no. 2 cols./p.; back issues avail.; reprints avail. **Document type:** *Newsletter.* **Description:** Enables electronic data processing professionals to keep abreast of important topics and developments in computer audit, security, and control.
Related titles: Online - full text ed.: (from EBSCO Publishing, O C L C Online Computer Library Center, Inc., ProQuest Information & Learning).
Indexed: ABIn, ATI, C&CSA, CompC, DPD, Inspec.
—BLDSC (3661.115000), AskIEEE. **CCC.**
Published by: (E D P Auditors Association), Auerbach Publications (Subsidiary of: C R C Press, LLC), 2000 Corporate Blvd., NW, Boca Raton, FL 33431. TEL 561-994-0555, 800-272-7737, FAX 561-374-3401, auerbach@crcpress.com, http://www.auerbach-publications.com/ejournals/product_info/product_detail.asp?id=146, http://www.auerbach-publications.com/home.asp. Ed. Belden Menkus. Pub. Richard O'Hanley TEL 212-845-4017. Circ: 5,000.

006 ZAF
ESECURE. Text in English. m. adv. **Document type:** *Journal, Trade.* **Description:** Addresses online security issues for business information systems. Topics include, but are not limited to, access control and authentication; biometric devices; business liability issues; certification, standards and legal issues; data and application security; digital certificates, CAs and PKI; disaster recovery and incident response plans; eCommerce, eBusiness, eServices, eSecurity; encryption technologies; security and firewall implementation and management; mobile code security; virus protection; system logging; internet and network security.
Published by: Technews (Pty.) Ltd., PO Box 626, Kloof, 3640, South Africa. TEL 27-31-764-0593, FAX 27-31-764-0386, http://www.technews.co.za. Adv. contact Jane Fortmann TEL 27-31-764-5316. B&W page ZAR 8,400, color page ZAR 10,150; 180 x 260. Circ: 7,500.

658.478 USA ISSN 1042-721X
FEDERAL COMPUTER MARKET REPORT; intelligence and strategies for executives in government procurement. Text in English. 1977. s-m. USD 495 (effective 2005). back issues avail. **Document type:** *Newsletter.* **Description:** Analyzes government procurement regulations, technical evaluation criteria, minority subcontracting, RFP Instructions and other issues of interest to vendors and government buyers.
Formerly: Procurement Systems Digest (0163-1489)
Related titles: Online - full text ed.: (from Northern Light Technology, Inc.).
—**CCC.**
Published by: Computer Age & E D P News Services (Subsidiary of: Millin Publishing Group, Inc.), 1150 Connecticut Ave. NW, 900, Washington, DC 20036. TEL 202-862-4375, FAX 202-659-3493, millin@aol.com, http://www.millinpubs.com. Pub. S L Millin. Circ: 975 (paid).

005.8 USA ISSN 1547-6030
HARLEY HAHN'S INTERNET INSECURITY. Text in English. 2001. a. USD 20 per issue (effective 2003).
Media: Online - full content.
Published by: Harley Hahn, 2022 Cliff Dr., Santa Barbara, CA 93109. TEL 805-564-5000, http://hhe.harley.com/is/chapters/chapter-list.html, http://www.harley.com. Pub. Hahn Harley.

HEALTHCARE DATA SECURITY MANUAL. see *HEALTH FACILITIES AND ADMINISTRATION*

658.478 362.11068 USA ISSN 1539-7653
HEALTHCARE INFORMATION SECURITY; the newsletter for it professionals. Text in English. 2001 (Dec.). m. USD 297 (effective 2002). **Document type:** *Newsletter.*
—CCC.
Published by: H C Pro, Inc., 200 Hoods Ln, Marblehead, MA 01945. TEL 781-639-1872, FAX 781-639-7857, hcprocustomerservice@hcpro.com, http://www.hcpro.com. Ed. Dan Landriqan. Pub. Suzanne Perney.

005.8 USA ISSN 1540-7993
QA76.9.A25
▼ I E E E SECURITY & PRIVACY MAGAZINE. (Institute of Electrical and Electronics Engineers) Text in English. 2003 (Feb.). bi-m. USD 565 (effective 2006). **Document type:** *Magazine, Trade.* **Description:** Contains research articles, case studies, tutorials, and regular departments covering diverse aspects of information assurance such as legal and ethical issues, privacy concerns, tools to help secure information, analysis of vulnerabilities and attacks, trends and new developments, pedagogical and curricular issues in educating the next generation of security professionals, secure operating systems and applications, security issues in wireless networks, design and test strategies for secure and survivable systems, and cryptology.
Related titles: Online - full text ed.: (from I E E E).
Indexed: CMCI, CurCont, Inspec, RefZh.
—BLDSC (4363.063300), CISTI, IE, Linda Hall. **CCC.**
Published by: I E E E Computer Society, 1730 Massachusetts Ave, N W, Washington, DC 20036-1903. TEL 202-371-0101, FAX 202-728-9614, mis.custserv@computer.org, http://www.computer.org/security/. Ed. George Cybenko. Pub. Angela Burgess.

005.8 USA ISSN 1081-6011
QA76.9.A25
I E E E SYMPOSIUM ON SECURITY AND PRIVACY. PROCEEDINGS. Text in English. 1980. a. USD 165; USD 66 to members (effective 2004). adv. **Document type:** *Proceedings, Trade.* **Description:** Covers advances in design, implementation, and application of secure computer systems.
Former titles (until 1995): I E E E Computer Society Symposium on Research in Security and Privacy. Proceedings (1063-7109); (until 1990): I E E E Symposium on Security and Privacy. Proceedings (1063-9578); (until 1986): Symposium on Security and Privacy. Proceedings (0278-7032)
Related titles: Online - full text ed.: (from I E E E).
—BLDSC (4363.088000), IE, ingenta. **CCC.**
Published by: (I E E E Computer Society), Institute of Electrical and Electronics Engineers, Inc., 3 Park Ave, 17th Fl, New York, NY 10016-5997. TEL 800-678-4333, customer.service@ieee.org, http://www.ieee.org. Eds. Cat Harris, Cat Harris. Pubs. Matt Loeb, Matt Loeb. Adv. contacts Frieda Koester, Frieda Koester.

005.8 USA ISSN 1545-5971
QA76.9.F38
▼ I E E E TRANSACTIONS ON DEPENDABLE AND SECURE COMPUTING. Text in English. 2004 (Jan.). q. USD 285 (effective 2006). **Document type:** *Journal, Academic/Scholarly.*
Related titles: Online - full text ed.: (from EBSCO Publishing, I E E E).
Indexed: C&CSA, Inspec, RefZh.
—BLDSC (4363.176700), CISTI, Linda Hall.
Published by: Institute of Electrical and Electronics Engineers, Inc., 3 Park Ave, 17th Fl, New York, NY 10016-5997. TEL 212-419-7900, FAX 212-752-4929, customer.service@ieee.org, http://www.ieee.org.

005.8 USA ISSN 1556-6013
▼ I E E E TRANSACTIONS ON INFORMATION FORENSICS AND SECURITY. Text in English. forthcoming 2006 (Mar.). q. USD 810 combined subscription print & online eds. (effective 2006). **Document type:** *Journal, Academic/Scholarly.*
Related titles: Online - full content ed.: ISSN 1556-6021. forthcoming 2006 (Mar.). USD 648 (effective 2006).
Published by: Institute of Electrical and Electronics Engineers, Inc., 445 Hoes Ln, Piscataway, NJ 08854-1331. TEL 732-981-0060, FAX 732-981-1721, customer.service@ieee.org, http://www.ieee.org.

658.478 USA
I S S A JOURNAL. Variant title: The I S S A Password. Text in English. s-m. membership. adv. **Document type:** *Newsletter, Trade.* **Description:** Provides members with up-to-date industry information and association news.
Former titles (until 2003): Password; I S S A Journal; (until 1993): I S S A Access
Published by: Information Systems Security Association, 7044 S 13th St, Oak Creek, WI 53154. TEL 414-768-8000, 800-370-ISSA, FAX 414-768-8001, http://www.issa.org/cgi/journallibrary.cgi. Ed. Meta Levin. Pub. Scott Sherer. Adv. contact Denise Rockhill. Circ: (controlled).

005.8 DEU ISSN 1617-1527
DER I T - RECHTSBERATER. Text in German. 1998. m. EUR 169; EUR 16.90 newsstand/cover (effective 2005). adv. **Document type:** *Magazine, Trade.*
Formerly (until 2001): Computerrecht Intern (1434-8802)
Published by: Verlag Dr. Otto Schmidt KG, Gustav-Heinemann-Ufer 58, Cologne, 50968, Germany. TEL 49-221-93738460, FAX 49-221-93738943, itrb@otto-schmidt.de, info@otto-schmidt.de, http://www.computerrechtintern.de, http://www.otto-schmidt.de.

005.8 USA ISSN 1096-8903
INFORMATION SECURITY. Text in English. 1997. m. free in US & Canada; USD 99 in US & Canada; USD 210 elsewhere (effective 2005). adv. **Document type:** *Magazine, Trade.* **Description:** Covers news, analysis, insight, and commentary on today's information security marketplace.
Related titles: Online - full content ed.; Online - full text ed.: (from LexisNexis).
Indexed: C&CSA, MicrocompInd, SoftBase.
—BLDSC (4494.313500).
Published by: TechTarget, 117 Kendrick St, Ste 800, Needham, MA 02494. TEL 781-657-1000, 888-274-4111, FAX 781-657-1100, info@techtarget.com, http://www.infosecuritymag.com, http://www.techtarget.com/. Ed. Lawrence Walsh TEL 781-657-1665. adv.: B&W page USD 6,300, color page USD 8,700; bleed 8.25 x 11.125.

005.8 USA ISSN 1549-8654
▼ INFORMATION SECURITY & PRODUCT DESTRUCTION NEWS. Text in English. 2004 (Jan./Feb.). bi-m. USD 19.95 domestic; USD 39.95 foreign (effective 2004).
Published by: Downing & Associates, Inc., 6075 Hopkins Rd, Mentor, OH 44060. TEL 440-257-6453, FAX 440-257-6459, downassoc1@aol.com. Ed., Pub. Rick Downing.

INFORMATION SECURITY MANAGEMENT. see *BUSINESS AND ECONOMICS—Computer Applications*

005.8 GBR ISSN 1363-4127
QA76.9.A25 CODEN: ISTRFR
➤ INFORMATION SECURITY TECHNICAL REPORT. Text in English. 1996. 4/yr. EUR 1,761 in Europe to institutions; JPY 233,900 in Japan to institutions; USD 1,905 elsewhere to institutions (effective 2006). back issues avail. **Document type:** *Journal, Academic/Scholarly.* **Description:** Devoted to recent or newly emerging information technology security issues.
Related titles: Online - full text ed.: (from EBSCO Publishing, Gale Group, IngentaConnect, ScienceDirect, Swets Information Services).
Indexed: C&CSA, EngInd, Inspec.
—BLDSC (4494.317500), IE, Infotrieve, ingenta. **CCC.**
Published by: Elsevier Advanced Technology (Subsidiary of: Elsevier Science & Technology), The Boulevard, Langford Ln, Kidlington, Oxon OX5 2BG, United Kingdom. TEL 44-1865-843750, FAX 44-1865-843971, http://www.elsevier.com/locate/compseconline. Ed. F. Piper. **Subscr. to:** Elsevier BV, PO Box 211, Amsterdam 1000 AE, Netherlands. TEL 31-20-485-3757, FAX 31-20-485-3432, nlinfo-f@elsevier.nl, http://www.elsevier.nl.

▼ ➤ INFORMATION STORAGE + SECURITY JOURNAL. see *COMPUTERS—Information Science And Information Theory*

658.478 USA ISSN 1065-898X
QA76.9.A25 CODEN: ISSEFH
INFORMATION SYSTEMS SECURITY. Text in English. 1991. bi-m. USD 175 (effective 2005). adv. index. 56 p./no. 2 cols./p.; back issues avail.; reprints avail. **Document type:** *Journal, Trade.* **Description:** Covers information security issues such as security planning and awareness, network security and access control, Internet security, end-user authentication, business continuity, and resumption planning.
Formerly (until 1991): Journal of Information Systems Security
Related titles: Online - full text ed.: (from EBSCO Publishing, H.W. Wilson, O C L C Online Computer Library Center, Inc., ProQuest Information & Learning).
Indexed: ABIn, BPI, C&CSA, CompAb, InfoSAb, Inspec, MicrocompInd.
—BLDSC (4496.368602), AskIEEE, IE, Infotrieve, ingenta. **CCC.**
Published by: Auerbach Publications (Subsidiary of: C R C Press, LLC), 2000 Corporate Blvd., NW, Boca Raton, FL 33431. TEL 561-994-0555, 800-272-7737, FAX 561-374-3401, auerbach@crcpress.com, http://www.auerbach-publications.com/ejournals/issues/issue_archive.asp?section=1086, http://www.auerbach-publications.com/home.asp. Ed. Jeffrey L Ott. Pub., Adv. contact Richard O'Hanley TEL 212-845-4017. R&P Jamie Sigal TEL 561-994-0555. B&W page USD 2,000; trim 10 x 7. Circ: 500.

004.056 NLD ISSN 1568-3672
INFOSECURITY.NL (HAARLEM). Text in Dutch. 2000. q. EUR 44.92; EUR 11.32 per issue (effective 2003). adv. **Document type:** *Magazine, Trade.* **Description:** Provides news on information security and company critical aspects of corporate ICT security.
Published by: I D G Communications Nederland BV, Postbus 5446, Haarlem, 2000 GK, Netherlands. TEL 31-23-5461111, FAX 31-23-5461155, abo@idg.nl, http://www.infosecurity.nl, http://www.idg.nl. adv.: B&W page USD 2,155; trim 8.25 x 11.25. Circ: 10,500 (controlled).

005.8 GBR ISSN 1742-6847
▼ ➤ INFOSECURITY TODAY. Text in English. 2004. 6/yr. EUR 172 in Europe to institutions; JPY 22,800 in Japan to institutions; USD 193 to institutions except Europe and Japan (effective 2006). **Document type:** *Journal, Academic/Scholarly.* **Description:** Provides in-depth analysis of specific business and management issues relating to information security.
Related titles: Online - full text ed.: (from EBSCO Publishing, ScienceDirect, Swets Information Services).
Indexed: Inspec.
—IE.
Published by: Elsevier Advanced Technology (Subsidiary of: Elsevier Science & Technology), The Boulevard, Langford Ln, Kidlington, Oxon OX5 2BG, United Kingdom. TEL 44-1865-843750, FAX 44-1865-843971, eatsales@elsevier.co.uk, http://www.elsevier.com/locate/inftod, http://www.elsevier.nl.

005.8 USA ISSN 1553-832X
▼ INSIDE MICROSOFT WINDOWS SERVER SECURITY. Text in English. 2005 (Apr.). m. USD 207; USD 237 combined subscription print & online eds. (effective 2005). **Document type:** *Magazine, Consumer.*
Published by: Element K Journals (Subsidiary of: Eli Research, Inc.), 500 Canal View Blvd, Rochester, NY 14623. TEL 585-240-7301, 800-223-8720, 877-203-5248, FAX 585-292-4392, http://www.elementkjournals.com/products/showProduct.asp?prodID=244&catId=2.

005.8 GBR ISSN 1744-1765
INTERNATIONAL JOURNAL OF INFORMATION AND COMPUTER SECURITY. Text in English. q. USD 450 to institutions; USD 545 combined subscription to institutions print & online eds. (effective 2005). **Document type:** *Journal, Academic/Scholarly.* **Description:** Aims to promote and coordinate developments of information and computer security in the fields of information technology, political science, informatics, sociology, engineering and science.
Related titles: Online - full text ed.: ISSN 1744-1773. USD 450 to institutions (effective 2005).
Published by: Inderscience Publishers, IEL Editorial Office, PO Box 735, Olney, Bucks MK46 5WB, United Kingdom. TEL 44-1234-240519, FAX 44-1234-240515, ijics@inderscience.com, info@inderscience.com, http://www.inderscience.com/ijics. Ed. Dr. Eldon Y Li TEL 805-756-2964. **Subscr. to:** World Trade Centre Bldg, 29 route de Pre-Bois, Case Postale 896, Geneva 15 1215, Switzerland. FAX 41-22-7910885, subs@inderscience.com.

005.8 DEU ISSN 1615-5262
➤ INTERNATIONAL JOURNAL OF INFORMATION SECURITY. Abbreviated title: I J I S. Text in English. 2001. q. EUR 130 combined subscription to institutions print & online eds. (effective 2005). adv. reprint service avail. from PSC. **Document type:** *Journal, Academic/Scholarly.* **Description:** Provides prompt publication of important technical work in information security, whether theoretical, applicable, or related to implementation.
Related titles: Online - full content ed.: ISSN 1615-5270. 2001; Online - full text ed.: (from EBSCO Publishing, ProQuest Information & Learning, Springer LINK, Swets Information Services).
Indexed: C&CSA, CompLI, Inspec.
—BLDSC (4542.304963), Infotrieve. **CCC.**
Published by: Springer-Verlag (Subsidiary of: Springer Science+Business Media), Tiergartenstr 17, Heidelberg, 69121, Germany. TEL 49-6221-3450, FAX 49-6221-345229, http://link.springer.de/link/service/journals/10207/index.htm. Eds. Catherine A Meadows, Dieter Gollmann, Eiji Okamoto. Adv. contact Stephan Kroeck TEL 49-30-827875739. **Subscr. in the Americas to:** Springer-Verlag New York, Inc., Journal Fulfillment, PO Box 2485, Secaucus, NJ 07096-2485. TEL 800-777-4643, 201-348-4033, FAX 201-348-4505, journals@springer-ny.com, http://www.springer-ny.com; **Subscr. to:** Springer GmbH Auslieferungsgesellschaft, Haberstr 7, Heidelberg 69126, Germany. TEL 49-6221-345-0, FAX 49-6221-345-4229, subscriptions@springer.de.

▼ ➤ INTERNATIONAL JOURNAL OF SECURITY AND NETWORKS. see *COMPUTERS—Computer Networks*

005.8 USA
INTERNET SECURITY ADVISOR. Text in English. 1998. 6/yr. USD 59 domestic; USD 69 in Canada; USD 79 elsewhere; USD 4.99 newsstand/cover; CND 6.99 newsstand/cover in Canada (effective 2000). adv. software rev. illus. back issues avail. **Document type:** *Trade.* **Description:** Focuses on IT professionals who use Microsoft Windows NT and Internet Computering, and who protect the safety of the organization's computer network from breaches and failures.
Formerly: Security Advisor (1095-2942)
Related titles: Online - full text ed.
Indexed: MicrocompInd, SoftBase.
Published by: Advisor Media, Inc., 4849 Viewridge Ave, San Diego, CA 92123-1643. TEL 858-278-5600, FAX 858-278-0300, advisor@advisor.com, http://www.advisor.com. Ed. John L Hawkins. Pub. B J Ghiglione. R&P David Kodama. Adv. contact Sheri Ogletree. B&W page USD 5,900, color page USD 6,900; trim 10.88 x 8. Circ: 40,000 (paid). **Subscr. to:** PO Box 469003, Escondido, CA 92046-9003. **Dist. by:** International Publishers Direct, 27500 Riverview Center Blvd, Bonita Springs, FL 34134.

005.8 005.74 005.1 RUS
JET INFO. Text in Russian. 1995. bi-w. **Document type:** *Journal, Trade.*
Published by: Redaktsiya Zhurnala Jet Info, ul Bol'shaya Novodmitrovskaya, dom 14, str 1, Moscow, 127015, Russian Federation. TEL 7-095-4117601, FAX 7-095-4117602, JetInfo@jet.msk.su, http://www.jetinfo.ru.

005.8 NLD ISSN 0926-227X
QA76.9.A25 CODEN: JCSIET
➤ **JOURNAL OF COMPUTER SECURITY.** Text in English. 1992. 6/yr. EUR 648, USD 777 combined subscription print & online eds. (effective 2006). **Document type:** *Journal, Academic/Scholarly.* **Description:** Publishes advances in theory, architecture, design, implementation, analysis and application of secure computer and communication systems.
Related titles: Online - full text ed.: (from EBSCO Publishing, Gale Group, IngentaConnect, O C L C Online Computer Library Center, Inc., Swets Information Services).
Indexed: BrCerAb, C&CSA, C&ISA, CerAb, CompAb, CompLI, CompR, CorrAb, E&CAJ, EMA, Emerald, EngInd, IAA, Inspec, M&TEA, MBF, METADEX, SolStAb, WAA.
—BLDSC (4963.746000), AskIEEE, CISTI, IE, Infotrieve, ingenta, Linda Hall. **CCC.**
Published by: I O S Press, Nieuwe Hemweg 6B, Amsterdam, 1013 BG, Netherlands. TEL 31-20-6883355, FAX 31-20-6203419, info@iospress.nl, order@iospress.nl, http://www.iospress.nl/html/09266801.php. Eds. Jonathan Millen TEL 650-859-2358, Sushil Jajodia TEL 703-993-1653. R&P Ms. Carry Koolbergen TEL 31-20-6382189. Adv. contact Ms. Jolijn van Eunen. Circ: 250. **Subscr. to:** I O S Press, Inc, 4502 Rachael Manor Dr., Fairfax, VA 22032-3631. iosbooks@iospress.com; Kinokuniya Co. Ltd., Shinjuku 3-chome, Shinjuku-ku, Tokyo 160-0022, Japan. FAX 81-3-3439-1094, journal@kinokuniya.co.jp, http://www.kinokuniya.co.jp; Globe Publication Pvt. Ltd., C-62 Inderpuri, New Delhi 100 012, India. TEL 91-11-579-3211, 91-11-579-3212, FAX 91-11-579-8876, custserve@globepub.com, http://www.globepub.com.

005.8 USA ISSN 1553-6548
▼ **JOURNAL OF INFORMATION PRIVACY & SECURITY.** Abbreviated title: J I P S. Text in English. 2005. q. USD 85 to individuals; USD 185 to institutions (effective 2005).
Published by: Ivy League Publishing, 4573 Rutherford Dr, PO Box 680392, Marietta, GA 30068. TEL 770-649-6718, FAX 770-649-6719, admin@ivylp.com, http://academics.uww.edu/business/gbrc/jips/, http://www.ivylp.com.

005.8 DEU ISSN 0177-4565
CODEN: KZKEED
K E S. (Kommunikations- und EDV Sicherheit) Text in German. 1985. bi-m. EUR 122; EUR 23 newsstand/cover (effective 2004). adv. bk.rev. bibl.; charts; illus.; stat. index. back issues avail. **Document type:** *Journal, Trade.* **Description:** Covers issues relating to communications and electronic data security.
Indexed: Inspec.
—AskIEEE, IE, Infotrieve. **CCC.**
Published by: SecuMedia Verlags GmbH, Lise-Meitner-Str 4, Gau-Algesheim, 55435, Germany. TEL 49-6725-9304-0, FAX 49-6725-5994, info@secumedia.de, http://www.kes.de, http://www.secumedia.de. Ed. Norbert Luckhardt. Pub. Peter Hohl. Adv. contact Veronika Laufersweiler TEL 49-6725-930414. B&W page EUR 1,880, color page EUR 2,830; trim 210 x 297. Circ: 6,960 (paid and controlled).

KEY NOTE MARKET REPORT: ACCESS CONTROL. see *CRIMINOLOGY AND LAW ENFORCEMENT—Security*

658.478 GBR
KEY NOTE MARKET REPORT: I T SECURITY. Text in English. 1998. irreg., latest 2002, Mar. GBP 340 per issue (effective 2002). **Description:** Provides an overview of a specific UK market segment and includes executive summary, market definition, market size, industry background, competitor analysis, current issues, forecasts, company profiles, and more.
Published by: Key Note Ltd., Field House, 72 Oldfield Rd, Hampton, Mddx TW12 2HQ, United Kingdom. TEL 44-20-8481-8750, FAX 44-20-8783-0049, info@keynote.co.uk, http://www.keynote.co.uk. Ed. Jacob Howard.

LAW OF INTERNET SECURITY AND PRIVACY. see *LAW*

005.8 DEU
▼ **P C SECURITY**; das Magazin fuer Sicherheit. Text in German. 2003. 4/yr. EUR 24.60 domestic; EUR 28.65 foreign; EUR 6.15 newsstand/cover (effective 2003). adv. **Document type:** *Magazine, Consumer.* **Description:** Covers all aspects of security hardware and software for computer systems, networks and applications.
Published by: Verlag B. Kaemmer, Georgenstr 19, Munich, 80799, Germany. TEL 49-89-34018900, FAX 49-89-34018901, bk@verlag-kaemmer.de, http://www.pc-secure.org/index.html, http://www.verlag-kaemmer.de. Ed. Christian Galuschka. Adv. contact Martina Lacour. B&W page EUR 2,630, color page EUR 4,010; trim 185 x 263. Circ: 20,000 (paid and controlled).

005.8 340 USA ISSN 0145-7659
KF1262.A15
PRIVACY JOURNAL; an independent monthly on privacy in a computer age. Text in English. 1974. m. looseleaf. USD 125 (effective 2004). bk.rev. tr.lit. index, cum.index. back issues avail.; reprint service avail. from PQC. **Document type:** *Journal.* **Description:** Reports on legislation, legal trends, new technology, and public attitudes affecting the confidentiality of personal information and the individual's right to privacy.
Related titles: Microform ed.: (from PQC); Online - full text ed.: (from bigchalk, Northern Light Technology, Inc., ProQuest Information & Learning).
Indexed: BLI.
Address: PO Box 28577, Providence, RI 02908. TEL 401-274-7861, 800-621-1031, FAX 401-274-4747, orders@privacyjournal.net, http://www.privacyjournal.net. Ed., Pub. Mr. Robert Ellis Smith. Circ: 2,100.

005.8 USA ISSN 1541-5244
▼ **PRIVACY, SECURITY & TRUST REPORT.** Text in English. 2004. 10/yr.
Published by: Assets Protection Publishing, 5029 Sheboygan Ave #201, Madison, WI 53705. Ed. Paul Shaw.

▼ **PRODUCT ID**; the journal of automatic prodict id technolgy. see *BUSINESS AND ECONOMICS—Production Of Goods And Services*

005.8 USA
R A C F UPDATE. (Resource Access Control Facility) Text in English. q. USD 290 (effective 2000). **Document type:** *Trade.* **Description:** Provides information on Resource Access Control Facility, the IBM security management product.
Published by: Xephon, 9330 Lyndon B Johnson Fwy., Ste. 800, Dallas, TX 75243-4310. TEL 303-410-9344, FAX 303-438-0290, http://www.xephon.com/.

658.478 DEU ISSN 0178-8930
KK6071.5.A13
RECHT DER DATENVERARBEITUNG; Zeitschrift fuer Praxis und Wissenschaft. Short title: R D V. Text in German. 1985. 6/yr. EUR 120; EUR 25 newsstand/cover (effective 2004). adv. index. **Document type:** *Magazine, Trade.*
Indexed: DIP, IBR, IBZ.
—IE, Infotrieve.
Published by: (Gesellschaft fuer Datenschutz und Datensicherung e.V.), Datakontext Fachverlag GmbH, Augustinusstr 9 d, Frechen, 50226, Germany. TEL 49-2234-966100, FAX 49-2234-966109, info@datakontext.com, http://www.datakontext-press.de/rdv/recht_hauptframe.htm. Ed. Georg Wronka. Adv. contact Gabriele Beuder. B&W page EUR 1,125, color page EUR 1,968.75; trim 186 x 255. Circ: 4,070 (paid and controlled).

005.8 USA
THE RISKS DIGEST. Text in English. irreg. back issues avail. **Document type:** *Newsletter.* **Description:** A forum on risks to the public in computers and related systems.
Media: Online - full text. **Related titles:** E-mail ed.
Published by: A C M, Committe on Computers and Public Policy, Computer Science Laboratory, 333 Ravenswood Ave EL-243, Menlo Pank, CA 94025-3493. http://catless.ncl.ac.uk/Risks. Ed. Peter G Neumann.

658.478 GBR
S C MAGAZINE (ASIA PACIFIC EDITION). Text in English. m. free to qualified personnel (effective 2005). **Document type:** *Magazine, Trade.*
Media: Online - full content. **Related titles:** ♦ International ed. of: S C Magazine (UK / Europe Edition). ISSN 1479-9200; ♦ International ed.: S C Magazine (US Edition). ISSN 1547-6693.
Published by: Haymarket Publishing Ltd., 174 Hammersmith Rd, London, W6 7JP, United Kingdom. TEL 44-20-82675000, FAX 44-20-82674268, hpg@haymarketgroup.com, http://www.scmagazine.com/home/index.cfm?regionpref=Asia-Pacific, http://www.haymarketgroup.co.uk/.

005.8 GBR ISSN 1479-9200
S C MAGAZINE (UK / EUROPE EDITION); the international journal of computer security. Text in English. 1994. m. GBP 59 (effective 2005). adv. bk.rev. back issues avail. **Document type:** *Magazine, Trade.* **Description:** News, product reviews, features, in-depth articles and editorial on all aspects of computer security.
Former titles (until 2001): S C infosecurity News Magazine (International Edition) (1352-4097); (until 1994): Virus News International (0960-3921)
Related titles: ♦ International ed.: S C Magazine (Asia Pacific Edition); ♦ S C Magazine (US Edition). ISSN 1547-6693.
Indexed: Inspec, MicrocompInd.
—BLDSC (8087.448400), AskIEEE, IE, ingenta.
Published by: Haymarket Publishing Ltd., 174 Hammersmith Rd, London, W6 7JP, United Kingdom. TEL 44-20-82675000, FAX 44-20-82674268, hpg@haymarketgroup.com, http://www.scmagazine.com/home/index.cfm?regionpref=UK, http://www.haymarketgroup.co.uk/. Ed. Ron Condon TEL 44-208-2678016. adv.: page USD 2,486; trim 206 x 275. Circ: 5,000 (paid).

005.8 USA ISSN 1547-6693
QA76.9.A25
S C MAGAZINE (US EDITION). Variant title: Secure Computing Infosecurity News Magazine. Text in English. 1990. m. USD 60 domestic; USD 75 in Canada & Mexico; USD 160 elsewhere; free to qualified personnel (effective 2004). adv. **Document type:** *Magazine, Trade.* **Description:** Provides information on security products and services, market trends and industry developments.
Former titles (until 2002): S C Infosecurity News Magazine (1096-7974); Secure Computing (1095-0893); Info Security News (1066-7822); I S P News (1051-2500)
Related titles: Online - full text ed.; ♦ International ed.: S C Magazine (Asia Pacific Edition); ♦ International ed. of: S C Magazine (UK / Europe Edition). ISSN 1479-9200.
Indexed: MicrocompInd, SoftBase.
Published by: Haymarket Media Inc. (Subsidiary of: Haymarket Group Ltd.), 114 W 26th St., 3rd Fl, New York, NY 10001. TEL 646-638-6000, FAX 646-638-6117, http://www.scmagazine.com/index2.html, http://www.haymarketgroup.com/. Ed. Illena Armstrong TEL 508-278-9768. adv.: page USD 6,989; bleed 8.375 x 11.125. Circ: 50,100 (controlled).

C

005.8 ESP ISSN 1136-0623
S I C - SEGURIDAD EN INFORMATICA Y COMUNICACIONES. Text in Spanish. 1992. bi-m. EUR 46.63 domestic; EUR 84.14 in Europe; EUR 110.70 elsewhere (effective 2005). adv. bk.rev.; software rev. back issues avail. **Document type:** *Trade.* **Description:** Dedicated to all aspects of security in computing and communication systems.
Formerly (until 1995): Seguridad Informatica (1136-0615)
Published by: Ediciones Coda S.L., Goya 39, Madrid, 28001, Spain. TEL 34-91-5758324, FAX 34-91-5777047, info@revistasic.com, http://www.revistasic.com/. Ed., R&P Luis G Fernandez. Pub. Jose de la Pena. Adv. contact Victoria Colino. color page EUR 1,352.28; trim 297 x 210. Circ: 4,000.

005.8 SWE ISSN 1404-7365
SAEKERHET & SEKRETESS. Text in Swedish. 1998. 9/yr. SEK 464; SEK 223 to students (effective 2003). adv. **Document type:** *Magazine, Trade.* **Description:** Contains articles and features on IT security, new products, new technologies and current events in the information security business.
Related titles: Online - full text ed.
Published by: I D G AB (Subsidiary of: I D G Communications Inc.), Sturegatan 11, Stockholm, 10678, Sweden. TEL 46-8-4536000, FAX 46-8-4536005, sakerhet@idg.se, http://sakerhet.idg.se, http://www.idg.se. Ed. Fredrik Bernsel TEL 46-8-4536230. adv.: page SEK 64,800; trim 185 x 260.

SECOM ANNUAL REPORT (YEAR). see *CRIMINOLOGY AND LAW ENFORCEMENT—Security*

658.478 004.6 USA ISSN 1547-3953
QA76.9.A25
▼ **SECURE ENTERPRISE.** Text in English. 2004. 9/yr. **Document type:** *Magazine, Trade.*
Published by: (Computer Security Institute), C M P Media LLC (Subsidiary of: United News & Media), 600 Community Dr, Manhasset, NY 11030. TEL 516-562-5000, FAX 516-562-5036, http://www.cmp.com.

005.8 FRA ISSN 0297-9101
SECURITE INFORMATIQUE. Text in French. 1986. m. (11/yr.). EUR 523 domestic; EUR 556 foreign (effective 2000). **Document type:** *Newsletter.* **Description:** Contains information on technology products, trends, users, security strategy and law.
Published by: Publi-News, 47 rue Aristide Briand, Levallois-Perret, 92300, France. TEL 33-1-41499360, FAX 33-1-47573725, publi.news@wanadoo.fr. Ed. Ange Galula.

SECURITY; the magazine for buyers of security products, systems and service. see *CRIMINOLOGY AND LAW ENFORCEMENT—Security*

▼ new title ➤ refereed ✶ unverified ♦ full entry avail.

005.8 USA
SECURITY ADMINISTRATOR. Text in English. m. USD 129 domestic; USD 135 foreign (effective 2002). **Document type:** *Magazine, Trade.* **Description:** Contains articles and features on how to make your system secure with expert tips, tactics, and defenses.
Published by: Penton Technology Media (Subsidiary of: Penton Media, Inc.), 221 E 29th St, Ste 242, Loveland, CO 80538. TEL 970-663-4700, 800-621-1544, FAX 970-663-3285, http://www.secadministrator.com.

005.8 AUS
SECURITY ELECTRONICS MAGAZINE. Text in English. 11/yr. AUD 105; AUD 140 for 2 yrs. 23 issues (effective 2000). **Document type:** *Trade.* **Description:** Covers issues in computer security, access control, and the future of electronics.
Address: Ste 6, 586-590 Parramatta Rd, Petersham, NSW 2049, Australia. TEL 61-2-95600749, FAX 61-2-95600849, bridge@hotlinks.net.au, http://www.safecity.com.au/secele.htm. Ed. John Adams. Adv. contact Monique Keatinge.

005.8021 USA
SECURITY MANAGEMENT PRACTICES. Variant title: Faulkner's Security Management Practices. Text in English. m. USD 595 (effective 2004). **Document type:** *Trade.* **Description:** Covers all aspects of facility security, data security, network security, financial and legal security, e-mail security, and web site security.
Media: Online - full content.
Published by: Faulkner Information Services, Inc. (Subsidiary of: Information Today, Inc.), 116 Cooper Center, 7905 Browning Rd, Pennsauken, NJ 08109-4319. TEL 856-662-2070, 800-843-0460, FAX 856-662-3380, faulkner@faulkner.com, http://www.faulkner.com.

005.8 USA ISSN 1539-9885
TK5105.59
SECURITY RESOURCES; an internet miniguide. Text in English. 2002. a. USD 95 newsstand/cover (effective 2002).
Published by: InternetMiniGuides.com, P.O. Box 220, Marco Island, FL 34146. TEL 941-434-5113, FAX 941-642-9115, zillman@internetminiguides.com, http://www.internetminiguides.com. Pub. Marcus P. Zillma.

005.8 USA
SECURITY WIRE DIGEST. Text in English. bi-w. free to qualified personnel. back issues avail. **Document type:** *Trade.*
Media: E-mail.
Published by: TruSecure Corp., 8 N. Main St., Ste. 403, Attleboro, MA 02703-2282. Info@trusecure.com, http://www.TruSecure.com.

005.82 SGP ISSN 1793-2238
▼ **SERIES ON CODING THEORY AND CRYPTOLOGY.** Text in English. 2005. irreg. price varies. **Document type:** *Monographic series, Academic/Scholarly.*
Published by: World Scientific Publishing Co. Pte. Ltd., 5 Toh Tuck Link, Singapore, 596224, Singapore. TEL 65-466-5775, FAX 65-467-7667, wspc@wspc.com.sg, http://www.worldscibooks.com/series/sctc_series.shtml, http://www.worldscientific.com. **Subscr. to:** Farrer Rd, PO Box 128, Singapore 912805, Singapore. TEL 65-382-5663, FAX 65-382-5919. **Dist. by:** World Scientific Publishing Co., Inc., 1060 Main St, River Edge, NJ 07661. TEL 201-487-9655, 800-227-7562, FAX 201-487-9656, 888-977-2665, wspc@wspc.com.

352.379 RUS ISSN 1562-7128
SISTEMY BEZOPASNOSTI. Text in Russian. 1995. bi-m. **Document type:** *Journal, Trade.*
Published by: Groteck, 7 Miusskaya sq, 4th Fl, PO Box 53, Moscow, 103030, Russian Federation. TEL 7-095-2516845, FAX 7-095-2513389, groteck@groteck.ru, http://www.groteck.ru/security_ru.php#1, http://www.groteck.net. Circ: 25,000.

▼ **STORAGE & GOVERNMENT**; the storage magazine for government, military and aerospace technologies. see *COMPUTERS—Data Base Management*

TELECOM & NETWORK SECURITY REVIEW. see *COMPUTERS—Computer Networks*

005.8 GBR ISSN 0956-9979
QA76.76.C68 CODEN: VBULE3
VIRUS BULLETIN; the international publication on computer virus prevention, recognition and removal. Text in English. 1989. m. GBP 195 (effective 2005). software rev. back issues avail. **Document type:** *Bulletin, Trade.* **Description:** Dedicated to reporting and analyzing malicious computer programs.
Indexed: Inspec.
—BLDSC (9240.850300), AskIEEE, IE. **CCC.**
Address: The Pentagon, Abingdon Science Park, Abingdon, Oxon OX14 3YP, United Kingdom. TEL 44-1235-555139, FAX 44-1235-531889, editorial@virusbtn.com, ah@virusbtn.com, http://www.virusbtn.com/. Ed. Helen Martin TEL 44-1235-544036.

005.8 AUS
VIRUS WATCH. Text in English. 1989. q. AUD 14, USD 10. software rev. back issues avail. **Document type:** *Newsletter.* **Description:** Provides product details, technical tips, and virus information.
Related titles: Diskette ed.
Published by: Leprechaun Software Pty. Ltd., PO Box 826, Capalaba, QLD 4157, Australia. TEL 61-7-38231300, FAX 61-7-38231233, intl@leprechaun.com.au, http://www.leprechaun.com.au/. Circ: 9,500.

338.47004 USA ISSN 0749-3851
QA76.9.A25
2600; the quarterly journal of the American hacker. Text in English. 1984. q. USD 20 in US & Canada; USD 30 elsewhere (effective 2005). adv. bk.rev. index. back issues avail. **Document type:** *Consumer.* **Description:** Covers news, events and technical information on computer security, hacking, the laws, and other related subjects.
Published by: 2600 Enterprises, Inc., PO Box 752, Middle Island, NY 11953-0752. TEL 516-751-2600, FAX 516-474-2677, info@2600.com, http://www.2600.com/magazine/. Ed. Emanuel Golstein. Pub. Emanuel Goldstein. Circ: 30,000.

COMPUTERS—Computer Simulation

003.3 USA
A B S E L NEWS & VIEWS. Text in English. s-a. adv. **Description:** Published as a service to ABSEL members and others interested in simulation and experiential learning.
Published by: Association for Business Simulation and Experiential Learning, University of Utah, Dept of Management, Salt Lake City, UT 84112. Ed. Susan Chesteen. Adv. contact Susan A Chesteen.

003.3 USA
➤ **ANNUAL SIMULATION SYMPOSIUM. PROCEEDINGS.** Text in English. 1967. a. USD 80 to non-members; USD 40 to members. back issues avail. **Document type:** *Proceedings, Academic/Scholarly.* **Description:** Includes papers dealing with various techniques and applications of computer simulation.
Published by: The Society for Modeling and Simulation International (SCS), Circulation Office, PO Box 17900, San Diego, CA 92177. TEL 858-277-3888, FAX 858-277-3930. Ed. Hildy Linn.

➤ **AUDIOTEX UPDATE.** see *COMMUNICATIONS—Computer Applications*

003.3 DNK ISSN 0106-357X
COMBINED SIMULATION. Text in Danish. 1978. irreg.
Published by: Koskilde Universitetscenter, Datalogi, Roskilde, 4000, Denmark.

COMMUNICATIONS IN STATISTICS: SIMULATION AND COMPUTATION. see *COMPUTERS—Abstracting, Bibliographies, Statistics*

COMPLEXITY. see *MATHEMATICS*

D B S IMAGE PROCESSING NEWSLETTER. see *COMPUTERS—Computer Graphics*

003.3 USA ISSN 0278-2375
➤ **DEVELOPMENTS IN BUSINESS SIMULATION & EXPERIENTIAL EXERCISES.** Variant title: A B S E L Conference Proceedings. Text in English. 1974. a. USD 15. back issues avail. **Document type:** *Proceedings, Academic/Scholarly.*
Published by: (Association for Business Simulation and Experiential Learning), Oklahoma State University, Stillwater, College of Business Administration, 201 Business, Stillwater, OK 74078-4011. TEL 405-744-8647, FAX 405-744-5180. Eds. John D Overby, Precha Thavikulwat. Circ: 300 (paid). **Subscr. to:** ABSEL, c/o Robert A Wells, LB8152, Georgia Southern University, Statesboro, GA 30460-8152. TEL 916-681-5216.

003.3025 USA
DIRECTORY OF SIMULATION SOFTWARE. Text in English. 1993. a. USD 40 to non-members; USD 20 to members. **Document type:** *Directory.* **Description:** Provides a comprehensive listing of simulation-oriented software, with contact names, platforms, and prices.
Published by: The Society for Modeling and Simulation International (SCS), Circulation Office, PO Box 17900, San Diego, CA 92177. TEL 858-277-3888, FAX 858-277-3930. Ed. Hildy Linn. R&P William Gallagher.

003.3 USA ISSN 0924-6703
CODEN: DEDAEE
➤ **DISCRETE EVENT DYNAMIC SYSTEMS: THEORY AND APPLICATIONS.** Text in English. 1991. q. EUR 578, USD 588, GBP 365 combined subscription to institutions print & online eds. (effective 2005). adv. back issues avail.; reprint service avail. from PSC. **Document type:** *Journal, Academic/Scholarly.* **Description:** Publishes papers on the modeling and control of discrete event dynamic systems (DEDS), including engineering and mathematical models of manufacturing plants, communication and computer networks, management information databases, command-control-communication systems, and other man-made operational systems.
Related titles: Microform ed.: (from PQC); Online - full text ed.: ISSN 1573-7594 (from EBSCO Publishing, Gale Group, IngentaConnect, Kluwer Online, O C L C Online Computer Library Center, Inc., Ovid Technologies, Inc., Springer LINK, Swets Information Services).
Indexed: ASCA, BibLing, CCMJ, CMCI, CurCont, EngInd, Inspec, MathR, MathSciNet, RefZh, ZentMath.
—BLDSC (3597.028000), AskIEEE, CISTI, Ei, IDS, IE, Infotrieve, ingenta. **CCC.**
Published by: Springer-Verlag New York, Inc. (Subsidiary of: Springer Science+Business Media), 233 Spring St, New York, NY 10013. TEL 212-460-1500, FAX 212-460-1575, service@springer-ny.com, http://springerlink.metapress.com/openurl.asp?genre=journal&issn=0924-6703, http://www.springer-ny.com. Ed. Yu-Chi (Larry) Ho. **Subscr. to:** Journal Fulfillment, PO Box 2485, Secaucus, NJ 07096-2485. TEL 201-348-4033, FAX 201-348-4505, journals@springer-ny.com.

003.3 USA
DISTRIBUTED SIMULATION. PROCEEDINGS. Text in English. irreg., latest 1990. price varies. back issues avail. **Document type:** *Proceedings.* **Description:** Covers the latest developments in distributed simulation technologies.
Published by: The Society for Modeling and Simulation International (SCS), Circulation Office, PO Box 17900, San Diego, CA 92177. TEL 858-277-3888, FAX 858-277-3930. Ed. Hildy Linn.

003.3 UKR ISSN 0204-3572
QA75.5 CODEN: ELMODO
➤ **ELEKTRONNOE MODELIROVANIE**; mezhdunarodni naucho-teoreticheskii zhurnal. Text in Russian, English; Summaries in English, Russian, Ukrainian. 1979. bi-m. USD 240 foreign (effective 2002). adv. bk.rev. **Document type:** *Academic/Scholarly.* **Description:** Informs about the newest achievements in theoretical and applied computer simulation.
Formerly: Matematicheskoe Modelirovanie i Teoriya Elektricheskikh Tsepei
Indexed: BrCerAb, C&ISA, CerAb, CorrAb, CybAb, Djerelo, E&CAJ, EMA, IAA, INIS AtomInd, Inspec, M&TEA, MBF, METADEX, RefZh, WAA.
—AskIEEE, CASDDS, CISTI, East View, Linda Hall. **CCC.**
Published by: Natsional'na Akademiya Nauk Ukrainy, Instytut Problem Modelyuvannya v Enerhetytsi, Ul Generala Naumova 15, Kiev, 03680, Ukraine. TEL 380-44-4441063, FAX 380-44-4440586, svetlana@ipme.kiev.ua, http://www.rql.kiev.ua/e-modeling. Ed., Pub. V F Evdokimov. R&P, Adv. contact E P Semagina. Circ: 200 (paid and controlled). **Dist. by:** Ukrposhta, Khreschatyk 22, Kiev 01001, Ukraine. TEL 38-44-2287969, 38-44-2297754.

003.3 NLD ISSN 0929-2268
EUROSIM - SIMULATION NEWS EUROPE; a European forum on simulation activities. Short title: S N E. Variant title: Simulation News Europe. Text in German. 1990. 3/yr. EUR 10 (effective 2004). bk.rev.; software rev. back issues avail. **Document type:** *Newsletter, Academic/Scholarly.* **Description:** Disseminates information on simulation to members of European simulation societies, interested research and development institutions, companies, and libraries.
Related titles: ♦ English ed.: Simulation Modelling Practice and Theory. ISSN 1569-190X.
Published by: (Technische Universitaet Wien/Vienna University of Technology AUT), Elsevier BV (Subsidiary of: Elsevier Science & Technology), Radarweg 29, Amsterdam, 1043 NX, Netherlands. TEL 31-20-4853911, FAX 31-20-4852457, argesim@argesim.tuwien.ac.at, nlinfo-f@elsevier.nl, http://argesim.tuwien.ac.at/sne/sne_main.html, http://www.elsevier.nl. Eds. F Breitenecker, I Husinsky. Circ: 3,000.

003.3 CHE ISSN 1463-9963
TA347.B69
➤ **INTERFACES AND FREE BOUNDARIES.** Text in English. 1999. q. EUR 390 combined subscription print & online eds. (effective 2003). adv. back issues avail. **Document type:** *Journal, Academic/Scholarly.* **Description:** Aims to be a forum where mathematical analysis, partial differential equations, modelling, scientific computing and the various applications which involve mathematical modelling meet.
Related titles: Online - full text ed.: ISSN 1463-9971. GBP 205, USD 350 to institutions Online only (effective Mar. 2002) (from EBSCO Publishing, Gale Group, O C L C Online Computer Library Center, Inc., ProQuest Information & Learning).
Indexed: CCMJ, MathR, MathSciNet.
—BLDSC (4533.462700), IE, ingenta.

Published by: European Mathematical Society Publishing House, c/o Dr. Thomas Hinterman, Seminar for Applied Mathematics, ETH-Zentrum FLI C1, Zurich, 8092, Switzerland. TEL 41-1-6323436, subscriptions@ems-ph.org, hintermann@ems-ph.org, ifbj@ptmat.fc.ul.pt, http://www.ams.org/distribution/ifb/, http://www.ems-ph.org. Eds. Charles M Elliott, Jose Francisco Rodrigues, Robert V Kohn. adv.: page GBP 170, page USD 395. Circ: 300.

➤ **INTERNATIONAL JOURNAL OF NONLINEAR MODELLING IN SCIENCE AND ENGINEERING.** see *MATHEMATICS*

003.3 794.8 GBR
THE INTERNATIONAL SIMULATION AND GAMING RESEARCH YEARBOOK. Text in English. a. **Document type:** *Yearbook, Academic/Scholarly.*
Formerly: International Simulation and Gaming Yearbook
—BLDSC (4549.404550), ingenta.
Published by: (The Society for the Advancement of Games and Simulations in Education), Kogan Page Ltd., 120 Pentonville Rd, London, N1 9JN, United Kingdom.

003.3 USA
INTERNATIONAL SIMULATORS CONFERENCE. PROCEEDINGS. Text in English. 1984. a. price varies. adv. back issues avail. **Document type:** *Proceedings.*
Description: Includes papers on simulation technology and methods in training, especially in the nuclear power industry.
Published by: The Society for Modeling and Simulation International (SCS), Circulation Office, PO Box 17900, San Diego, CA 92177. TEL 858-277-3888, FAX 858-277-3930. Ed. Ariel Sharon. R&P William Gallagher. Adv. contact Steven Branch.

INTERNATIONAL WORKSHOP ON DISTRIBUTED INTERACTIVE SIMULATION AND REAL - TIME APPLICATIONS. see *COMPUTERS—Computer Systems*

JAPANESE SOCIETY OF COMPUTATIONAL STATISTICS. JOURNAL. see *STATISTICS*

JOURNAL OF COMPUTATIONAL METHODS IN SCIENCES AND ENGINEERING. see *MATHEMATICS*

003.3 USA ISSN 1533-3825
QA76.9.D26
THE JOURNAL OF CONCEPTUAL MODELING. Text in English. irreg. free. bk.rev. back issues avail. **Description:** Dedicated to data modeling, design, simulation, and implementation issues.
Media: Online - full text.
Published by: Information Conceptual Modeling, Inc., 8171 Hidden Bay Trail N, Lake Elmo, MN 55042. TEL 651-777-8494, FAX 651-777-9634, scotb@inconcept.com, http://www.inconcept.com/JCM/. Ed. Scot Becker.

003.3 USA ISSN 1548-5129
▼ **JOURNAL OF DEFENSE MODELING AND SIMULATION.** Text in English. 2004 (Jan). q. free (effective 2004).
Related titles: Online - full text ed.: ISSN 1557-380X.
Published by: The Society for Modeling and Simulation International (SCS), Circulation Office, PO Box 17900, San Diego, CA 92177. TEL 858-277-3888, FAX 858-277-3930, info@scs.org, http://www.scs.org/pubs/jdms/jdms.html.

003.3 USA ISSN 1524-2021
JOURNAL OF MODELING AND SIMULATION OF MICROSYSTEMS. Text in English. 1999. q. USD 85 to individuals; USD 100 to individuals print & online eds.; USD 395 to institutions; USD 495 to institutions print & online eds. (effective 2003). **Description:** Contains records of state-of-the-art research in computational capabilities applied towards advanced technologies.
Related titles: Online - full text ed.
Indexed: Inspec.
Published by: Applied Computational Research Society, One Kendall Sq, PMB 308, Cambridge, MA 02139. info@cr.org, http://www.cr.org.

JOURNAL OF STATISTICAL COMPUTATION AND SIMULATION. see *COMPUTERS—Abstracting, Bibliographies, Statistics*

MANUTENTION ET SYSTEMES. see *TECHNOLOGY: COMPREHENSIVE WORKS*

003.3 NLD ISSN 0378-4754
QA76.4 CODEN: MCSIDR
➤ **MATHEMATICS AND COMPUTERS IN SIMULATION.** Text and summaries in English, French. 1959. 18/yr. EUR 1,851 in Europe to institutions; JPY 245,800 in Japan to institutions; USD 2,071 to institutions except Europe and Japan (effective 2006). adv. bk.rev. charts; illus. index every 2 yrs. back issues avail. **Document type:** *Proceedings, Academic/Scholarly.*
Description: Provides an international forum for the dissemination of up-to-date information in the field of the computer simulation of systems.
Incorporates (in 1988): I M A C S News; Which was formerly: A I C A News; International Association for Mathematics and Computers in Simulation. Transactions (0377-9114); (until 1975): International Association for Analog Computation. Proceedings (0020-594X)
Related titles: Microform ed.: (from PQC); Online - full text ed.: (from EBSCO Publishing, Gale Group, IngentaConnect, ScienceDirect, Swets Information Services).
Indexed: ASCA, ApMecR, Biostat, C&ISA, CCMJ, CIS, CMCI, ChemAb, CompAb, CompC, CompLI, CompR, CurCont, CybAb, E&CAJ, Englnd, IAA, IAOP, Inspec, MathR, MathSciNet, ORMS, QC&AS, RASB, RefZh, SSCI, ST&MA, SolStAb, ZentMath.
—BLDSC (5405.180000), AskIEEE, CISTI, Ei, IDS, IE, Infotrieve, ingenta, Linda Hall. **CCC.**
Published by: (International Association for Mathematics and Computers in Simulation USA), Elsevier BV, North-Holland (Subsidiary of: Elsevier Science & Technology), Sara Burgerhartstraat 25, Amsterdam, 1055 KV, Netherlands. TEL 31-20-485-3911, FAX 31-20-485-2457, nlinfo-f@elsevier.nl, http://www.elsevier.com/locate/matcom, http://www.elsevier.nl. Eds. A. Preumont, R Vichnevetsky. Circ: 1,000. **Subscr. to:** Elsevier BV, PO Box 211, Amsterdam 1000 AE, Netherlands. TEL 31-20-485-3757, FAX 31-20-485-3432, http://www.elsevier.nl.

003.3 USA ISSN 0198-0092
TA343 CODEN: MSPCD4
MODELING AND SIMULATION. Text in English. 1969. a. price varies. reprint service avail. from PQC,ISI. **Document type:** *Proceedings.*
Indexed: Inspec.
—CASDDS. **CCC.**
Published by: University of Pittsburgh, c/o Dr Marlin Mickle, 348 Benedum Engineering Hall, Pittsburgh, PA 15261.

003.3 NOR ISSN 0332-7353
QA401 CODEN: MIDCDA
MODELING, IDENTIFICATION AND CONTROL. Abbreviated title: M I C. Text in English. 1980. q. NOK 180 to individuals; NOK 600 to institutions; NOK 90 to students (effective 2004). adv. back issues avail. **Document type:** *Bulletin, Academic/Scholarly.* **Description:** Aims to present a review of Norwegian research activities in the field of modeling, identification and control to the international scientific community.
Related titles: Online - full text ed.: (from EBSCO Publishing).
Indexed: ApMecR, CCMJ, CMCI, CompLI, CurCont, Englnd, INIS AtomInd, ISR, Inspec, MathR, MathSciNet, RefZh, SCI, ZentMath.
—BLDSC (5883.525500), CISTI, IE, Infotrieve, ingenta, Linda Hall. **CCC.**
Published by: Norges Forskningsraad/The Research Council of Norway, P O Box 2700, St Hanshaugen, Oslo, 0131, Norway. TEL 47-22-037000, FAX 47-22-037001, post@forskningsradet.no, http://www.itk.ntnu.no/publikasjoner/mic, http://www.forskningsradet.no. Ed. Jens G Balchen TEL 47-73-594382. R&P Lars Imsland TEL 47-73-594392. adv.: B&W page NOK 15,000.

003.3 USA ISSN 1566-113X
NETWORKS AND SPATIAL ECONOMICS; a journal of infrastructure modeling and computation. Text in English. 2001. q. EUR 348, USD 348, GBP 218 combined subscription to institutions print & online eds. (effective 2005). adv. reprint service avail. from PSC. **Document type:** *Journal, Academic/Scholarly.* **Description:** Devoted to the mathematical and numerical study of economic activities facilitated by human infrastructure.
Related titles: Online - full text ed.: ISSN 1572-9427 (from EBSCO Publishing, Gale Group, IngentaConnect, Kluwer Online, O C L C Online Computer Library Center, Inc., ProQuest Information & Learning, Springer LINK, Swets Information Services).
Indexed: ABIn, BibLing, CMCI, CurCont.
—BLDSC (6077.206220), IE, Infotrieve, ingenta. **CCC.**
Published by: Springer-Verlag New York, Inc. (Subsidiary of: Springer Science+Business Media), 233 Spring St, New York, NY 10013. TEL 212-460-1500, FAX 212-460-1575, service@springer-ny.com, http://springerlink.metapress.com/openurl.asp?genre=journal&issn=1566-113x, http://www.springer-ny.com. Ed. Terry L Friesz. **Subscr. to:** Journal Fulfillment, PO Box 2485, Secaucus, NJ 07096-2485. TEL 201-348-4033, FAX 201-348-4505, journals@springer-ny.com.

003.3 NLD ISSN 0928-2149
➤ **PROCESS SIMULATION & MODELING.** Text in English. 1992. irreg., latest vol.1, 1992. price varies. **Document type:** *Monographic series, Academic/Scholarly.*
—BLDSC (6849.990580).
Published by: Elsevier BV (Subsidiary of: Elsevier Science & Technology), Radarweg 29, Amsterdam, 1043 NX, Netherlands. TEL 31-20-4853911, FAX 31-20-4852457, nlinfo-f@elsevier.nl, http://www.elsevier.nl.

➤ **SEIKEN N S T SHINPOJUMU KOEN KOGAISHU.** (Numerical Simulation Turbulence) see *COMPUTERS—Abstracting, Bibliographies, Statistics*

511.8 JPN
SEIKEN N S T SHINPOJUMU KOEN RONBUNSHU. (Numerical Simulation Turbulence) Text in Japanese. 1986. a. **Document type:** *Proceedings, Academic/Scholarly.* **Description:** Contains proceedings of the group's symposium.
Published by: University of Tokyo, Institute of Industrial Science/Tokyo Daigaku Seisan Gijutsu Kenkyujo, Komaba Research Campus, 4-6-1 Komaba Meguro-ku, Tokyo, 153-8505, Japan. TEL 81-3-5452-6024, FAX 81-3-5452-6094, ntani@iis.u-tokyo.ac.jp, kokusai@iis.u-tokyo.ac.jp, http://www.iis.u-tokyo.ac.jp, http://www.iis.u-tokyo.ac.jp/index.html.

003.3 JPN ISSN 0285-9947
SHIMYURESHON/JAPAN SOCIETY FOR SIMULATION TECHNOLOGY. JOURNAL. Text in Japanese. 1973. 4/yr. membership. adv. back issues avail. **Document type:** *Journal, Academic/Scholarly.* **Description:** Research papers on the use of simulation methods in physical science and engineering.
Former titles (until 1981): Shimyureshon Gijutsu Kenkyukai Ronbunshu/Japan Society for Simulation Technology. Research Papers (0288-3198); (until 1974): Shimyureshon Gijutsu Kenkyukai Shiryo (0288-318X)
Related titles: Online - full text ed.: (from JICST).
Indexed: Inspec.
—BLDSC (4808.143000), AskIEEE, IE, ingenta, Linda Hall. **CCC.**
Published by: Nihon Shimyureshon Gakkai/Japan Society for Simulation Technology, 1- 6 Kojimachi, Sogo Kojimachi #3 Bldg. 6 Fl Chiyoda-ku, Tokyo, 102-0083, Japan. TEL 81-3-32394738, FAX 81-3-32394714, simul@pp.iij4u.or.jp, http://wwwsoc.nii.ac.jp/jsst/backnum/backnum.html. Circ: 1,800.

620.0044 USA
SHORT CIRCUIT; the newsletter of engineer empowerment. Text in English. 1992. USD 175; USD 200 foreign (effective 1998). bk.rev. illus. **Document type:** *Newsletter.* **Description:** Includes problem-solving science, technology and sociology, humor.
Related titles: Online - full text ed.
Published by: F E S Ltd. Publishing, PO Box 158, Stuart, FL 34995. FAX 772-229-5636, statewav@metrolink.net. Ed. Carolyn Bonnie Crosby. Pub. William Livingston.

C

SIMULATION; transactions of the Society for Modeling and Simulation International. see *ENGINEERING*

003.3 USA ISSN 1046-8781
H62 CODEN: SIGAEI
➤ **SIMULATION & GAMING;** an international journal of theory, design and research. Text in English. 1970. q. USD 552, GBP 356 to institutions; USD 574, GBP 371 combined subscription to institutions print & online eds. (effective 2006). adv. bk.rev. charts; abstr.; illus. index. back issues avail.; reprint service avail. from PQC. **Document type:** *Journal, Academic/Scholarly.* **Description:** Publishes theoretical and empirical papers related to man, man-machine, and machine simulations of social processes.
Formerly (until 1990): Simulation and Games (0037-5500)
Related titles: Microform ed.: (from PQC); Online - full text ed.: ISSN 1552-826X. USD 546, GBP 352 to institutions (effective 2006) (from C S A, EBSCO Publishing, Gale Group, Northern Light Technology, Inc., O C L C Online Computer Library Center, Inc., Sage Publications, Inc., Swets Information Services).
Indexed: ABCPolSci, ABIn, ABS&EES, AMB, AMHA, ASCA, AgeL, BRI, CIJE, CIS, CommAb, CompC, CompLI, CompR, CurCont, EAA, ERA, ESPM, ETA, HRA, IBSS, IPSA, Inspec, JCQM, LAMP, LRI, MEA&I, MRD, PAIS, PCI, PRA, PSA, PsycInfo, PsycholAb, RASB, RHEA, RiskAb, SOPODA, SSA, SSCI, SSI, SociolAb, TEA, e-psyche.
—BLDSC (8285.161000), AskIEEE, IDS, IE, Infotrieve, ingenta. **CCC.**
Published by: (Association for Business Simulation and Experiential Learning), Sage Publications, Inc., 2455 Teller Rd, Thousand Oaks, CA 91320. TEL 805-499-0721, 800-818-7243, FAX 805-499-8096, 800-583-2665, info@sagepub.com, http://www.sagepub.com/journal.aspx?pid=34. Ed. David Crookall. Pub. Sara Miller McCune. R&P Tanya Udin TEL 805-499-0721 ext 7716. Adv. contact Kirsten Beaulieu TEL 805-499-0721 ext 7160. page USD 350. Circ: 500 (paid). **Subscr. overseas to:** Sage Publications Ltd., 1 Oliver's Yard, 55 City Rd, London EC1 1SP, United Kingdom. TEL 44-20-73740645, FAX 44-20-73748741, subscription@sagepub.co.uk. **Co-sponsors:** North American Simulation and Gaming Association; Japan Association of Business and Gaming; International Simulation and Gaming Association.

003.3 USA ISSN 1060-3689
QA76.9.C65 CODEN: SIMUD5
SIMULATION DIGEST. Variant title: S I G S I M Newsletter. Text in English. 1968. s-a. USD 25 to members; USD 34 to non-members (effective 2005). bk.rev. **Document type:** *Newsletter.* **Description:** Provides information on modeling, simulation, and systems analysis.
Formerly (until 1988): Simuletter (0163-6103)
Related titles: Online - full text ed.: (from Association for Computing Machinery, Inc., EBSCO Publishing).
Indexed: Inspec.
—CISTI. **CCC.**

Published by: Association for Computing Machinery, Inc., 1515 Broadway, 17th Fl, New York, NY 10036-5701. TEL 212-626-0500, 212-626-0520, 800-342-6626, FAX 212-869-0481, sigs@acm.org, usacm@acm.org, http://www.acm.org/sigsim/. Ed. Dana Wyatt. Circ: 2,400.

003.3 NLD ISSN 1569-190X
QA76.9.C65 CODEN: SMPTCA
➤ **SIMULATION MODELLING PRACTICE AND THEORY.** Text in English. 1993. 8/yr. EUR 845 in Europe to institutions; JPY 112,100 in Japan to institutions; USD 944 elsewhere to institutions (effective 2006). software rev. abstr. reprints avail. **Document type:** *Journal, Academic/Scholarly.* **Description:** Publishes original research and tutorial papers in the field of simulation.
Formerly (until 2002): Simulation Practice and Theory (0928-4869)
Related titles: Microform ed.: (from PQC); Online - full text ed.: (from EBSCO Publishing, Gale Group, IngentaConnect, ScienceDirect, Swets Information Services); ♦ German ed.: EUROSIM - Simulation News Europe. ISSN 0929-2268.
Indexed: C&ISA, CompAb, CompLI, CurCont, E&CAJ, EngInd, Inspec, SolStAb, ZentMath.
—BLDSC (8285.164320), AskIEEE, CISTI, Ei, IE, ingenta. **CCC.**
Published by: (Federation of European Simulation Societies - EUROSIM), Elsevier BV (Subsidiary of: Elsevier Science & Technology), Radarweg 29, Amsterdam, 1043 NX, Netherlands. TEL 31-20-4853911, FAX 31-20-4852457, nlinfo-f@elsevier.nl, http://www.elsevier.com/locate/simpat, http://www.elsevier.nl. Ed. H J Halin.

651.8 621.319 USA ISSN 0735-9276
CODEN: SMCPAX
➤ **SIMULATION SERIES.** Text in English. 1971. q. index. reprint service avail. from PQC. **Document type:** *Proceedings, Academic/Scholarly.* **Description:** Covers papers on special topic conferences.
Formerly: Simulation Councils Proceedings (0037-5519)
Indexed: ApMecR, CompC, CompR, CurCont, EngInd, IAA, Inspec.
—BLDSC (8285.164800), CISTI, Ei, IE, ingenta, Linda Hall. **CCC.**
Published by: The Society for Modeling and Simulation International (SCS), Circulation Office, PO Box 17900, San Diego, CA 92177. TEL 858-277-3888, FAX 858-277-3930. Ed. Hildy Linn. R&P William Gallaghere.

003.3 USA ISSN 1080-241X
T57.62 CODEN: RASSDU
SIMULATION SYMPOSIUM. PROCEEDINGS. Text in English. 1968. a. USD 181; USD 73 to members (effective 2004). adv. **Document type:** *Proceedings, Trade.* **Description:** Provides information on the field of simulation with the primary focus on digital discrete simulation.
Formerly (until 1992): Simulation Symposium. Record of Proceedings (0272-4715)
Related titles: Online - full text ed.: (from I E E E).
Indexed: Inspec.
—BLDSC (1530.850000), Ei, IE, ingenta. **CCC.**
Published by: (Institute of Electrical and Electronics Engineers, Inc.), I E E E Computer Society, 10662 Los Vaqueros Circle, PO Box 3014, Los Alamitos, CA 90720-1314. TEL 714-821-8380, FAX 714-821-4641, customer.service@ieee.org, http://www.ieee.org. Adv. contact Frieda Koester. **Co-sponsors:** Annual Simulation Symposium, Inc.; The Society for Modeling and Simulation International (SCS).

003.3 USA ISSN 0740-6797
CODEN: TSCSEV
➤ **SOCIETY FOR MODELING AND SIMULATION INTERNATIONAL. TRANSACTIONS.** Text in English. 1984. q. USD 175 (effective 2004). adv. back issues avail. **Document type:** *Journal, Academic/Scholarly.* **Description:** It is a highly referred scholarly journal of archival value that has been published since 1984, Transactions contains mathematical and scientific theoretical technical papers that are widely indexed and abstracted.
Indexed: AIA, ASCA, B&BAb, Biostat, C&ISA, CADCAM, CMCI, CompAb, CurCont, E&CAJ, EngInd, Inspec, SolStAb.
—BLDSC (9006.410000), AskIEEE, CISTI, Ei, IDS, IE, Infotrieve, Linda Hall. **CCC.**
Published by: The Society for Modeling and Simulation International (SCS), Circulation Office, PO Box 17900, San Diego, CA 92177. TEL 858-277-3888, FAX 858-277-3930, info@scs.org, http://www.scs.org. Ed. Tag Gon Kim. Circ: 1,000. **Subscr. to:** Allen Press Inc., PO Box 7075, Lawrence, KS 66044-7075. TEL 785-843-1235, FAX 785-843-1274.

003.3 USA ISSN 0094-7474
QA76 CODEN: PSCCD6
SUMMER COMPUTER SIMULATION CONFERENCE. PROCEEDINGS. (Winter Simulation Conference. Proceedings also published annually; sponsoring body and publisher vary) Text in English. 1967. a. price varies. adv. bk.rev. illus. index, cum.index. back issues avail. **Document type:** *Proceedings, Trade.*
Indexed: ApMecR, ChemAb, ChemTitl, CompC, CompD, Inspec.
—BLDSC (8533.410000), CASDDS, IE, ingenta. **CCC.**
Published by: The Society for Modeling and Simulation International (SCS), Circulation Office, PO Box 17900, San Diego, CA 92177. TEL 858-277-3888, FAX 858-277-3930. Ed. Hildy Linn. R&P William Gallagher. Adv. contact Steven Branch.

006 USA
V R IN THE SCHOOLS. (Virtual Reality) Text in English. 1995. q.
Related titles: Online - full text ed.
Published by: East Carolina University, School of Education, Virtual Reality and Education Laboratory, Speight Building, Greenville, NC 27858. TEL 252-328-6621, FAX 252-328-4368, http://www.soe.ecu.edu/vr. Ed. Lawrence Auld.

V R NEWS. (Virtual Reality) see *COMPUTERS—Computer Graphics*

003.3 USA ISSN 0891-7736
T57.62
WINTER SIMULATION CONFERENCE. PROCEEDINGS. (Earlier papers published in: IEEE Transactions on Systems Science and Cybernetics) Text in English. a. USD 418; USD 209 to members (effective 2004). adv. **Document type:** *Proceedings, Trade.*
Former titles (until 1979): Winter Simulation Conference (0743-1902); (until 1970): Conference on the Applications of Simulation; (until 1967): Conference on the Applications of GPSS
Related titles: Online - full text ed.
Indexed: C&ISA, E&CAJ, EngInd, SolStAb.
—BLDSC (9319.550000), IE, ingenta. **CCC.**
Published by: Institute of Electrical and Electronics Engineers, Inc., 3 Park Ave, 17th Fl, New York, NY 10016-5997. TEL 800-678-4333, FAX 619-277-3930, customer.service@ieee.org, http://www.ieee.org. Ed. Hildy Linn. R&P William Gallagher. Adv. contact Steven Branch. Circ: 1,050.

COMPUTERS—Computer Systems

see also COMPUTERS—Computer Architecture

003 CHE ISSN 0254-3133
A C C I S NEWSLETTER. (Advisroy Committee for the Coordination of Information Systems) Text in English. 1983. bi-m.
Published by: Information Systems Coordination Committe, Palais des Nations C552, Geneva, 1211, Switzerland. TEL 44-22-9172804, FAX 44-22-9170248.

003 USA ISSN 0734-2071
QA76.9.S88 CODEN: ACSYEC
➤ **A C M TRANSACTIONS ON COMPUTER SYSTEMS.** Short title: T O C S. Variant title: Transactions on Computer Systems. Text in English. 1983. q. USD 185 domestic to non-members; USD 199 foreign to non-members; USD 44 domestic to members; USD 58 foreign to members; USD 39 domestic to students; USD 53 foreign to students; USD 222 combined subscription domestic to non-members print & online eds.; USD 236 combined subscription foreign to non-members print & online eds.; USD 53 combined subscription domestic to members print & online eds.; USD 67 combined subscription foreign to members print & online eds.; USD 47 combined subscription domestic to students print & online eds.; USD 61 combined subscription foreign to students print & online eds. (effective 2006). illus. back issues avail.; reprints avail. **Document type:** *Journal, Academic/Scholarly.* **Description:** Publishes the newest findings of the computing research field. Includes theoretical and conceptual explorations of operating systems, distributed systems and networks.
Related titles: Microform ed.; Online - full text ed.: ISSN 1557-7333. USD 148 to non-members; USD 35 to members; USD 31 student members (effective 2006) (from Association for Computing Machinery, Inc., EBSCO Publishing, Florida Center for Library Automation, Gale Group, ProQuest Information & Learning).
Indexed: ABIn, AHCI, AIA, AS&TI, BrCerAb, C&CSA, C&ISA, CADCAM, CMCI, CerAb, CompAb, CompD, CompLI, CompR, CorrAb, CurCont, E&CAJ, EMA, EngInd, IAA, ISR, Inspec, M&TEA, MBF, METADEX, RefZh, SCI, SolStAb, TelAb, WAA.
—BLDSC (0578.657000), AskIEEE, CISTI, Ei, IDS, IE, Infotrieve, ingenta, Linda Hall. **CCC.**
Published by: Association for Computing Machinery, Inc., 1515 Broadway, 17th Fl, New York, NY 10036-5701. TEL 212-626-0520, 800-342-6626, FAX 212-869-0481, carla@cs.duke.edu, sigs@acm.org, usacm@acm.org, http://www.acm.org/tocs/. Ed. Carla Ellis TEL 919-660-6523. Circ: 1,851 (paid).

004.5 USA ISSN 1553-3077
Z699.A1
▼ **A C M TRANSACTIONS ON STORAGE.** (Association for Computing Machinery) Text in English. 2004. q. USD 140 domestic to non-members; USD 154 foreign to non-members; USD 40 domestic to members; USD 54 foreign to members; USD 35 domestic to students; USD 49 foreign to students; USD 168 combined subscription domestic to non-members print & online eds.; USD 182 combined subscription foreign to non-members print & online eds.; USD 48 combined subscription domestic to members print & online eds.; USD 62 combined subscription foreign to members print & online eds.; USD 42 combined subscription domestic to students print & online eds.; USD 56 combined subscription foreign to students print & online eds. (effective 2006). **Description:** Covers research contributions that introduce new concepts, techniques, analysis, architectures, and devices, as well as applied contributions that report on development of new tools and systems.
Related titles: Online - full text ed.: ISSN 1553-3093. 2004 (Dec.). USD 112 to non-members; USD 32 to members; USD 28 to students (effective 2006) (from EBSCO Publishing).
Published by: Association for Computing Machinery, Inc., 1515 Broadway, 17th Fl, New York, NY 10036-5701. TEL 212-626-0500, 800-342-6626, usacm@acm.org, http://www.acm.org.

003 AUS ISSN 0819-2898
A F M INFORMATION SYSTEMS SERIES (NO.). (Accounting and Financial Management) Text in English. 1987. irreg. **Document type:** *Academic/Scholarly.*
Published by: University of New England, Armidale, NSW 2351, Australia. TEL 61-67-73221, FAX 61-67-733122. R&P J J Staunton TEL 61-67-733276.

004 USA
A M - F M - G I S NETWORKS. Text in English. 1984. bi-m. USD 95 to members (effective 2001). back issues avail. **Document type:** *Newsletter.* **Description:** Provides association members with technical news and association updates.
Published by: Geospatial Information & Technology Association (GITA), 14456 E Evans Ave, Aurora, CO 80014. TEL 303-337-0513, FAX 303-337-1001, info@gita.org, http://www.gita.org. Ed. Elizabeth Roberts. R&P Molly Sausaman. Circ: 2,300 (paid).

003 USA ISSN 1532-5806
➤ **ACADEMY OF INFORMATION AND MANAGEMENT SCIENCES JOURNAL.** Text in English. s-a. **Document type:** *Journal, Academic/Scholarly.*
Related titles: Online - full text ed.
Published by: (Academy of Information and Management Sciences), Allied Academies, 145 Travis Rd., P. O. Box 2689, Cullowhee, NC 28723. http://www.alliedacademies.org/ims/index.html. Ed. Chris Lee.

003 SGP
ADVANCES IN FUZZY SYSTEMS-APPLICATIONS AND THEORY. Text in English. 1994. irreg., latest vol.22. price varies. **Document type:** *Monographic series, Academic/Scholarly.* **Description:** Provides an up-to-date picture of developments in fuzzy logic, ranging from the strictly theoretical to the latest applications. Topics covered will include fuzzy mathematical theory, soft computing, hardware implementations, and industrial applications.
Published by: World Scientific Publishing Co. Pte. Ltd., 5 Toh Tuck Link, Singapore, 596224, Singapore. TEL 65-466-5775, FAX 65-467-7667, wspc@wspc.com.sg, series@wspc.com.sg, http://www.wspc.com.sg/books/series/afsat_series.shtml, http://www.worldscientific.com. **Dist. by:** World Scientific Publishing Co., Inc., 1060 Main St, River Edge, NJ 07661. TEL 201-487-9655, 800-227-7562, FAX 201-487-9656, 888-977-2665; World Scientific Publishing Ltd., 57 Shelton St, London WC2H 9HE, United Kingdom. TEL 44-20-78360888, FAX 44-20-78362020, sales@wspc.co.uk.

ANNUAL BATTERY CONFERENCE ON APPLICATIONS AND ADVANCES. see *AERONAUTICS AND SPACE FLIGHT*

003 USA ISSN 1060-3425
TA168 CODEN: PHISD7
ANNUAL HAWAII INTERNATIONAL CONFERENCE ON SYSTEM SCIENCES. PROCEEDINGS. Short title: H I C S S. Text in English. 1968. a. price varies. adv. **Document type:** *Proceedings, Academic/Scholarly.* **Description:** Presents ideas, advances, and applications among academicians and practitioners in the information, computer and systems science fields.
Formerly (until 1988): Hawaii International Conference on System Sciences. Proceedings (0073-1129)
Related titles: Online - full text ed.: (from I E E E).
Indexed: Inspec.
—BLDSC (6841.157550), IE, ingenta. **CCC.**
Published by: (Institute of Electrical and Electronics Engineers, Inc.), I E E E Computer Society, 10662 Los Vaqueros Circle, PO Box 3014, Los Alamitos, CA 90720-1314. TEL 714-821-8380, FAX 714-821-4641, cs.books@computer.org, mis.custserv@computer.org. Circ: 400. **Subscr. to:** IEEE Service Center, 445 Hoes Lane, PO Box 1331, Piscataway, NJ 08855-1331. TEL 732-981-1393, FAX 732-981-9667.

003 SGP ISSN 0218-2599
ASIA - PACIFIC I.T. TIMES; today's technologies for the systems integration marketplace. Text in English. 1991. s-m. USD 48. adv. **Document type:** *Trade.* **Description:** Provides the latest, well-researched technology information and features that address aspects of today's systems integration marketplace.
Published by: R M Technology Media Pte. Ltd., 1 North Bridge Rd, 24-06 High St Ctr, Singapore, 179094, Singapore. TEL 65-3340393, FAX 65-3343097. Ed. Lim Fung Meng. Adv. contact Lynn Loke. B&W page USD 4,180, color page USD 4,780; trim 375 x 275. Circ: 21,468 (controlled).

003 JPN ISSN 1561-8625
ASIAN JOURNAL OF CONTROL. Text in English. 1993. q.
Formerly (until 1999): Journal of Control Systems and Technology (1022-2812)
Indexed: CMCI, CurCont, EngInd, Inspec.
—BLDSC (1742.478500), IE, ingenta.
Published by: Chinese Automatic Control Society, c/o Prof. Hidenori Kimura, Dept. of Mathematics Eng and Information Physics, University of Tokyo 7-3-1 Hongo, Tokyo, Bunkyo-ku 113-8656, Japan. Ed. Li-Chen Fu.

003 USA ISSN 1058-6393
TK7801 CODEN: CCSCE2
ASILOMAR CONFERENCE ON SIGNALS, SYSTEMS AND COMPUTERS. CONFERENCE RECORD. Text in English. 1967. a. price varies. adv. **Document type:** *Proceedings, Academic/Scholarly.* **Description:** Presents new ideas and preliminary research results in the general areas of signal, systems, and computers.
Former titles (until 1986): Asilomar Conference on Circuits, Systems and Computers. Conference Record; (until 1972): Asilomar Conference on Circuits and Systems. Conference Record (0571-3218)
Related titles: Online - full text ed.: (from I E E E).
Indexed: B&BAb, EngInd, Inspec.
—BLDSC (1742.787170), Ei, IE, ingenta. **CCC.**
Published by: (Institute of Electrical and Electronics Engineers, Inc.), I E E E Computer Society, 10662 Los Vaqueros Circle, PO Box 3014, Los Alamitos, CA 90720-1314. TEL 714-821-8380, FAX 714-821-4641.

003 USA ISSN 0735-9985
AUERBACH SYSTEMS DEVELOPMENT MANAGEMENT. Text in English. 1976. bi-m. looseleaf. USD 495 (effective 2000 - 2001). software rev. back issues avail.; reprints avail. **Document type:** *Journal, Trade.* **Description:** Presents advice on how to develop, organize and implement the appropriate system for the user's needs. Contains information on cost-effective and efficient design techniques and tools, evaluating software, choosing hardware, and training personnel.
Related titles: CD-ROM ed.: 1996. USD 450 (effective 2001).
—CCC.
Published by: Auerbach Publications (Subsidiary of: C R C Press, LLC), 2000 Corporate Blvd., NW, Boca Raton, FL 33431. TEL 212-286-1010, FAX 212-297-9176, orders@crcpress.com, http://www.auerbach-publications.com, http://www.auerbach-publications.com/home.asp. Ed. Janet Butler. Pub. Richard O'Hanley TEL 212-845-4017. R&P Jamie Sigal TEL 561-994-0555.

003 AUS
➤ **AUSTRALASIAN JOURNAL OF INFORMATION SYSTEMS.** Text in English. 1993. s-a. AUD 44 domestic; AUD 45 New Zealand & SE Asia; AUD 55 elsewhere (effective 2005). 200 p./no.; back issues avail. **Document type:** *Journal, Academic/Scholarly.* **Description:** Covers information systems theory and practice.
Formerly: Australian Journal of Information Systems (1039-7841)
Related titles: Online - full text ed.: ISSN 1326-2238. 1993.
Indexed: CompLI, InfoSAb, Inspec.
—BLDSC (1794.945000), IE, ingenta.
Published by: University of Wollongong, Department of Information Systems, Northfields Ave, Wollongong, NSW 2522, Australia. TEL 61-2-42214919, FAX 61-4-42214474, r.macgregor@uow.edu.au, http://www.aaisnet.org/ajis/. Ed. Robert MacGregor.

003 BGR ISSN 1310-8255
COMPLEX CONTROL SYSTEMS. Text in English. 1984. a.
Formerly (until 1996): Kompleksni Sistemi za Upravlenie (0205-1605)
Indexed: Inspec.
—Linda Hall.
Published by: Bulgarska Akademiya na Naukite/Bulgarian Academy of Sciences, 6 Moskovska St, Sofia, 1000, Bulgaria. TEL 359-2-981-33-47, FAX 359-2-979-34-67, http://www.pensoft.net.

003 AUS ISSN 1320-0682
QA267.7 CODEN: COINF2
➤ **COMPLEXITY INTERNATIONAL.** Text in English. 1994. a. free. bk.rev.; software rev. illus. cum.index: 1993-1999. back issues avail.; reprints avail. **Document type:** *Academic/Scholarly.* **Description:** Publishes papers dealing with complex systems research on any aspect of complexity. Relevant topics include: artificial life, chaos, evolutionary programming (including genetic algorithms) neural networks, self-organization, and applications.
Related titles: Online - full text ed.: free (effective 2005).
Indexed: CCMJ, CIN, ChemAb, ChemTitl, MathR, MathSciNet, ZentMath, ZooRec.
—CASDDS.
Published by: Charles Sturt University, PO Box 789, Albury, NSW 2640, Australia. TEL 61-2-6051-9730, FAX 61-2-6051-9897, ci-editor@csu.edu.au, http://www.csu.edu.au/ci/ci/. Ed., Pub. David Green.

003 USA
CODEN: MPCSEZ
COMPUTER SYSTEMS SERIES. (Some vols. out of print) Text in English. 1984. irreg., latest 1990. price varies. **Document type:** *Monographic series, Academic/Scholarly.*
Formerly: M I T Press Series in Computer Systems (0891-4710)
Indexed: Inspec.
Published by: M I T Press, 55 Hayward St, Cambridge, MA 02142-1493. TEL 617-253-5646, FAX 617-258-6779, http://mitpress.mit.edu/catalog/browse/browse.asp?sid=7D2C307E-BE20-41E6-BE65-CADF54522348&btype=6&serid=121. R&P Paul Dzus.

003 GBR ISSN 1352-9404
➤ **COMPUTING AND INFORMATION SYSTEMS.** Text in English. 1994. 3/yr. GBP 50 (effective 2003). **Document type:** *Academic/Scholarly.* **Description:** Publishes contributions to research and occasional articles on development of academic subdisciplines.
Related titles: Online - full content ed.
Indexed: Inspec.
—BLDSC (3395.019800), AskIEEE, IE, ingenta.
Published by: University of Paisley, Department of Computing and Information Systems, High St, University Of Paisley, Paisley, PA1 2BE, United Kingdom. TEL 44-141-848-3301, FAX 44-141-848-3542, mkc@paisley.ac.uk, malcolm.crowe@paisley.ac.uk, http://www-cis.paisley.ac.uk/research/journal/. Ed., R&P M K Crowe. Circ: 120.

003 USA ISSN 1542-0906
CUTTER BENCHMARK REVIEW. Text in English. 1995. m. USD 295 in North America; USD 355 elsewhere (effective 2002).
Formerly (until 2001): I T Metric Strategies from Cutter Information Corporation (1080-8647)
Related titles: Online - full text ed.: ISSN 1554-5938.
Indexed: CompLI.
Published by: Cutter Information Corp., 37 Broadway, Ste 1, Arlington, MA 02474. TEL 781-648-8700, 800-964-5118, FAX 781-648-1950, 800-888-1816, http://www.cutter.com. Ed. Robert D. Austin. Pub. Karen Fine Coburn.

CYBERNETICS AND SYSTEMS. see *COMPUTERS—Cybernetics*

003 DEU
D V DIALOG; die Welt der iSeries und der AS-400. Text in German. 1985. 10/yr. EUR 75 domestic; EUR 99 in Europe; EUR 135 elsewhere (effective 2005). adv. charts; illus. back issues avail. **Document type:** *Magazine, Trade.*
Published by: Medienhaus Verlag GmbH, Bertram-Blank-Str. 8, Bergisch Gladbach, 51427, Germany. TEL 49-2204-9214-0, FAX 49-2204-921430, http://www.dv-dialog.de, http://www.medienhaus-verlag.de. adv.: B&W page EUR 9,000, color page EUR 10,650. Circ: 16,420 (paid and controlled).

003 BEL ISSN 1375-6753
DEDICATED SYSTEMS MAGAZINE. Text in English. 1987-2002; resumed 2003. q. EUR 209, USD 270 (effective 2004). adv. **Document type:** *Magazine, Trade.* **Description:** Focuses on state of the art hardware and software for dedicated systems, including real-time systems, embedded systems and fault tolerant systems.
Former titles (until 2000): Real-Time Magazine (1018-0303); (until 1991): V M E Bus Applications (1013-364X)
Related titles: ♦ Online - full text ed.: Dedicated Systems Magazine (Online).
Indexed: Inspec.
—BLDSC (3540.826000), IE, Infotrieve, ingenta.
Published by: Dedicated Systems Experts, Rue de la Justice 21, Brussels, 1070, Belgium. TEL 32-2-5205577, FAX 32-2-5208309, http://www.dedicated-systems.com/magazine. Ed., Pub. Martin Timmerman. adv.: B&W page EUR 1,365, color page EUR 2,110; trim 210 x 297.

005 BEL
DEDICATED SYSTEMS MAGAZINE (ONLINE). Text in English. 1993. q. back issues avail.
Media: Online - full text. **Related titles:** ♦ Print ed.: Dedicated Systems Magazine. ISSN 1375-6753.
Published by: Dedicated Systems Experts, Bergensesteenweg 421 B12, St. Pieters-Leeuw, 1600, Belgium. TEL 32-2-3311284, http://www.dedicated-systems.com/magazine/magazine.htm. Ed. Martin Timmerman.

355 USA
UC263
DEFENCE A T & L. Text in English. 1972. bi-m. bk.rev. charts; illus.; stat. back issues avail. **Document type:** *Government.* **Description:** Serves as a vehicle for transmitting information on policies, trends, events, and current thinking affecting program management and defense systems acquisition.
Formerly (until 2004): Program Manager (0199-7114)
Related titles: Microfiche ed.; Online - full text ed.: (from EBSCO Publishing, Gale Group).
Indexed: AUNI, LID&ISL.
—BLDSC (3546.213080), IE, ingenta.
Published by: Defense Systems Management College, Research and Information Division, c/o Superintendent of Documents, U S Government Printing Office, Box 371954, Pittsburgh, PA 15250-7954. TEL 202-512-1800, FAX 202-512-2250, gpoacess@gpo.gor, http://www.access.gpo.gov. Ed. Catherine M Clark. Circ: 11,599.

320.001171 JPN ISSN 0915-1915
TK5101.A1 CODEN: DJTJEK
DENSHI JOHO TSUSHIN GAKKAI RONBUNSHI (D-I)/INSTITUTE OF ELECTRONICS, INFORMATION AND COMMUNICATION ENGINEERS. TRANSACTIONS (SECTION D-I). Text in Japanese. 1968. m. **Document type:** *Academic/Scholarly.* **Description:** Covers topics such as: Automation, language and theory of computing, algorithm and computation complexity, computer hardware and design, computer systems, software theory, software systems, databases, computer networks, fault tolerant computing, information security.
Supersedes in part (in 1989): Institute of Electronics, Information and Communication Engineers. Transactions (Section D) (0913-5731); Which was formerly (until 1986): Denshi Tsushin Gakkai Ronbunshi. D (0374-468X)
Related titles: ♦ English ed.: I E I C E Transactions on Information and Systems. ISSN 0916-8532.
Indexed: CybAb, IAOP, INIS AtomInd, Inspec, JCT, RefZh, TelAb.
—BLDSC (8939.442100), AskIEEE, CISTI, Linda Hall. **CCC.**
Published by: Denshi Joho Tsushin Gakkai/Institute of Electronics Information and Communication Engineers, IEICE Publishing Office, Kikai-Shinko-Kaikan Bldg., Annex 3F, 5-22, Shibakoen 3 chome, Minato-ku, Tokyo, 105-0011, Japan. TEL 81-3-3433-6692, FAX 81-3-3433-6616, shuppan@ieice.or.jp, http://www.ieice.or.jp/. Ed. Shigeo Tsujii.

DISTRIBUTED AND PARALLEL DATABASES; an international journal. see *COMPUTERS—Data Base Management*

003 USA ISSN 1068-6266
TK5105.5
DISTRIBUTED COMPUTING MONITOR. Text in English. 1986. m. USD 595 domestic; USD 615 in Canada; USD 630 elsewhere (effective 2003). back issues avail. **Document type:** *Newsletter.* **Description:** Provides comprehensive analysis and objective evaluation of LAN products and vendor strategies. Takes a look ahead at advanced distributed computing technologies and implementation issues for objects, advanced client-server development tools, object request brokers, message-oriented middleware, and integrated distributed systems management.
Former titles: Distributed Computing (1058-4153); Patricia Seybold's Network Monitor (0890-4685)
Related titles: CD-ROM ed.; Online - full text ed.
—IE.
Published by: Patricia Seybold Group, 110 Commercial St, Boston, MA 02109. TEL 617-742-5200, 800-826-2424, info@psgroup.comm, http://www.psgroup.com. Ed. Anne Thomas. Pub. Patricia B Seybold.

003 NLD
E-LETTER ON SYSTEMS, CONTROL, & SIGNAL PROCESSING. Text in English. 1986. m. free. adv. back issues avail. **Document type:** *Newsletter, Academic/Scholarly.*
Media: Online - full text.
Published by: Eindhoven University of Technology, Department of Mathematics & Computing Science, PO Box 513, Eindhoven, 5600 MB, Netherlands. TEL 31-10-472378, FAX 31-40-465995, eletter-request@win.tue.nl, http://scad.utdallas.edu/eletter/eletter.html. Eds. Anton A Stoorvogel, Siep Weiland. Circ: 3,000.

005.42 004.22 USA ISSN 1547-4569
▼ **ENTERPRISE ARCHITECT.** Text in English. 2003 (Sum.). q.
Published by: Fawcette Technical Publications, 2600 S. El Camino Real., Ste. 300, San Mateo, CA 94403-2381. TEL 800-848-5523, http://www.fawcette.com/ea/. Eds. Kay Keppler, Dan Ruby. Pub. Lynne Matthes TEL 650-833-7145.

004 USA ISSN 0740-4980
F T SYSTEMS. (Fault Tolerant) Text in English. 1982. m. USD 695 (effective 2000). index. back issues avail. **Document type:** *Trade.* **Description:** Reports on and analyzes business and technical developments in on-line transaction processing (OLTP), fault-tolerant systems and parallel commercial systems.
Published by: I T O M International Co., 22676 Royal Oak Way, Cupertino, CA 94014. TEL 408-253-2580, FAX 408-253-2580, omri@svpal.org. Ed. Omri Serlin.

003 USA ISSN 0925-9856
QA76.9.S88 CODEN: FMSDE6
➤ **FORMAL METHODS IN SYSTEM DESIGN**; an international journal. Text in English. 1992. bi-m. EUR 748, USD 768, GBP 468 combined subscription to institutions print & online eds. (effective 2005). adv. back issues avail.; reprint service avail. from PSC. **Document type:** *Journal, Academic/Scholarly.* **Description:** Provides international forum for research in the development and application of formal methods in VLSI hardware and software system design.

C

Related titles: Microform ed.: (from PQC); Online - full text ed.: ISSN 1572-8102 (from EBSCO Publishing, Gale Group, IngentaConnect, Kluwer Online, O C L C Online Computer Library Center, Inc., Ovid Technologies, Inc., Springer LINK, Swets Information Services).
Indexed: ASCA, BibLing, BrCerAb, C&CSA, C&ISA, CMCI, CerAb, CompLI, CompR, CorrAb, E&CAJ, EMA, EngInd, IAA, Inspec, M&TEA, MBF, METADEX, RefZh, SolStAb, WAA, ZentMath.
—BLDSC (4008.337500), AskIEEE, CISTI, Ei, IDS, IE, Infotrieve, ingenta, Linda Hall. **CCC.**
Published by: Springer-Verlag New York, Inc. (Subsidiary of: Springer Science+Business Media), 233 Spring St, New York, NY 10013. TEL 212-460-1500, FAX 212-460-1575, service@springer-ny.com, http://springerlink.metapress.com/openurl.asp?genre=journal&issn=0925-9856, http://www.springer-ny.com. Ed. Edmund M Clarke. **Subscr. to:** Journal Fulfillment, PO Box 2485, Secaucus, NJ 07096-2485. TEL 201-348-4033, FAX 201-348-4505, journals@springer-ny.com.

003 NLD ISSN 0167-739X
QA75.5
➤ **FUTURE GENERATION COMPUTER SYSTEMS.THE INTERNATIONAL JOURNAL OF GRID COMPUTING: THEORY, METHODS AND APPLICATIONS.** Text in English. 1985. 8/yr. EUR 874 in Europe to institutions; JPY 116,100 in Japan to institutions; USD 978 elsewhere to institutions (effective 2006). adv. bk.rev. illus. back issues avail. **Document type:** *Journal, Academic/Scholarly.* **Description:** Presents new developments in the field of computer systems. Includes models for new architectures and their analysis, as well as their hardware and software implementations.
Formerly: Fifth Generation Computer Systems
Related titles: Online - full text ed.: (from EBSCO Publishing, Gale Group, IngentaConnect, ScienceDirect, Swets Information Services).
Indexed: AIA, ASCA, ArtIAb, BrCerAb, C&ISA, CADCAM, CMCI, CerAb, CompAb, CompLI, CompR, CorrAb, CurCont, CybAb, E&CAJ, EMA, EngInd, IAA, Inspec, M&TEA, MBF, METADEX, RefZh, SolStAb, WAA.
—BLDSC (4060.570000), AskIEEE, CISTI, Ei, IDS, IE, Infotrieve, ingenta, Linda Hall. **CCC.**
Published by: Elsevier BV, North-Holland (Subsidiary of: Elsevier Science & Technology), Sara Burgerhartstraat 25, Amsterdam, 1055 KV, Netherlands. TEL 31-20-485-3911, FAX 31-20-485-2457, nlinfo-f@elsevier.nl, http://www.elsevier.com/locate/fgcs, http://www.elsevier.nl. Ed. Peter Sloot. **Subscr. to:** Elsevier BV, PO Box 211, Amsterdam 1000 AE, Netherlands. TEL 31-20-485-3757, FAX 31-20-485-3432, http://www.elsevier.nl.

003 GBR ISSN 0950-303X
CODEN: ISYUEQ
I B M SYSTEM USER. (International Business Machines) Text in English. 1981. m. GBP 100, USD 180 (effective 1999). adv. bk.rev. **Document type:** *Trade.* **Description:** For IT executives with both IBM and IBM-compatible systems. Totally independent of IBM, it provides technical insight in every area of the IT environment from the desktop to the mainframe, from the departmental network to the internet, and from word processors to integrated business suites.
Formerly: I B M User (0261-3654)
Related titles: Online - full text ed.: (from Gale Group); ♦ Supplement(s): Node. ISSN 0960-3786.
Indexed: CompC, CompD, ICEA, Inspec, SoftAbEng.
—AskIEEE, CISTI, IE. **CCC.**
Published by: I B C Business Publishing Ltd., 69-77 Paul St, London, EC2A 4LQ, United Kingdom. TEL 44-20-7553-1000, FAX 44-20-7553-1593. Circ: 11,000.

I E E E - A T M WORKSHOP. PROCEEDINGS. see *COMPUTERS—Computer Networks*

003 USA ISSN 1541-4922
QA76.9.D5
I E E E DISTRIBUTED SYSTEMS ONLINE. Text in English. 2000. m. free to members (effective 2006). **Document type:** *Trade.*
Media: Online - full content. **Related titles:** Online - full text ed.: (from I E E E).
Indexed: Inspec.
—BLDSC (4362.917650), Linda Hall.
Published by: I E E E Computer Society, 10662 Los Vaqueros Circle, PO Box 3014, Los Alamitos, CA 90720-1314. TEL 714-821-8380, FAX 714-821-4010, customer.service@ieee.org, http://dsonline.computer.org, http://www.computer.org. Ed. Jean Bacon.

005 020 USA
I E E E INFORMATION TECHNOLOGY CONFERENCE. PROCEEDINGS. Text in English. a. USD 118. **Document type:** *Proceedings, Trade.*
Published by: Institute of Electrical and Electronics Engineers, Inc., 3 Park Ave, 17th Fl, New York, NY 10016-5997. TEL 212-419-7900, 800-678-4333, FAX 212-752-4929, customer.service@ieee.org, http://www.ieee.org.

I E E E INTELLIGENT NETWORKS WORKSHOP. see *COMMUNICATIONS*

004 USA ISSN 1094-7116
TK7874 CODEN: PIISFG
I E E E INTERNATIONAL CONFERENCE ON INNOVATIVE SYSTEMS IN SILICON. Text in English. 1989. a. USD 151 membership (effective 2005). **Document type:** *Proceedings, Trade.* **Description:** Reports on the progress made in all aspects, including theory, technology, applications and products.
Formerly (until 1996): International Conference on Wafer Scale Integration. Proceedings (1063-2204)
Related titles: CD-ROM ed.; Microfiche ed.; Online - full text ed.: (from I E E E).
—Ei. **CCC.**
Published by: Institute of Electrical and Electronics Engineers, Inc., 3 Park Ave, 17th Fl, New York, NY 10016-5997. TEL 800-678-4333, customer.service@ieee.org, http://www.ieee.org.

003 USA ISSN 1554-8422
TK6590.A6
I E E E INTERNATIONAL SYMPOSIUM ON PHASED ARRAY SYSTEMS AND TECHNOLOGY. Text in English. 2000. a. USD 216; USD 108 to members (effective 2004). **Document type:** *Proceedings, Trade.*
Related titles: CD-ROM ed.
Indexed: EngInd.
Published by: Institute of Electrical and Electronics Engineers, Inc., 3 Park Ave, 17th Fl, New York, NY 10016-5997. TEL 212-419-7900, 800-678-4333, FAX 212-752-4929, customer.service@ieee.org, http://www.ieee.org.

I E E E OPEN ARCHITECTURES AND NETWORK PROGRAMMING. see *COMMUNICATIONS*

003 USA ISSN 1530-132X
I E E E REAL - TIME SYSTEMS EDUCATION WORKSHOP. Text in English. 1996. a. USD 185; USD 74 to members (effective 2004). **Document type:** *Proceedings, Trade.*
Related titles: Online - full text ed.: (from I E E E).
Published by: Institute of Electrical and Electronics Engineers, Inc., 3 Park Ave, 17th Fl, New York, NY 10016-5997. TEL 212-419-7900, 800-678-4333, FAX 212-752-4929, customer.service@ieee.org, http://www.ieee.org.

I E E E SYMPOSIUM ON AUTONOMOUS UNDERWATER VEHICLE TECHNOLOGY. see *EARTH SCIENCES—Oceanography*

003 USA ISSN 1063-8210
TK7874 CODEN: IEVSE9
➤ **I E E E TRANSACTIONS ON VERY LARGE SCALE INTEGRATION SYSTEMS.** Text in English. 1993. m. USD 845 (effective 2006). adv. **Document type:** *Journal, Academic/Scholarly.* **Description:** Design and implementation of VLSI and microelectronic systems, system specifications, design and partitioning, high performance computing and communication systems.
Related titles: CD-ROM ed.; Microfiche ed.; Online - full text ed.: ISSN 1557-9999 (from EBSCO Publishing).
Indexed: AS&TI, ASCA, C&ISA, CMCI, CompR, CurCont, E&CAJ, EngInd, Inspec, RefZh, SolStAb.
—BLDSC (4363.231300), AskIEEE, CISTI, Ei, IDS, IE, Infotrieve, ingenta, Linda Hall. **CCC.**
Published by: Institute of Electrical and Electronics Engineers, Inc., 445 Hoes Ln, Piscataway, NJ 08854-1331. TEL 732-981-0060, 800-701-4333, FAX 732-981-1721, subscription-service@ieee.org, http://www.computer.org, http://www.ieee.org. Ed. Bing Sheu. **Subscr. to:** Maruzen Co., Ltd., 3-10 Nihonbashi 2-chome, Chuo-ku, Tokyo 103-0027, Japan. FAX 81-3-3275-0657; Universal Subscription Agency, Pvt. Ltd., 877, Udyog Vihar, V, Gurgoan 122001, India. TEL 91-124-347261, FAX 91-124-342496.

519 DEU ISSN 1612-2461
I G E L NEWSLETTER. Text in English. 2002. irreg. **Document type:** *Newsletter, Trade.*
Published by: I G E L Technology GmbH, Schlacte 39-40, Bremen, 28195, Germany. TEL 49-421-1769390, FAX 49-421-1769302, marketing@igel.de, info@igel.de, http://www.igel.de/newsletter.

005.42 USA ISSN 0889-6836
INFOCUS (PHILADELPHIA); the technical journal for Prime Information, Universe and Unidata. Text in English. bi-m. USD 48 domestic; USD 58 in Canada; USD 75 elsewhere. **Description:** Covers programming methodology, system administration, and discussions of programming tools.
Incorporates (in 1992): S Select (0895-7746)
Published by: Infocus, Inc., 37 S. Main St., Yardley, PA 19067. TEL 215-321-2200, FAX 215-321-2205. Ed. Lee J Leitner.

004 NLD ISSN 0378-7206
HD28 CODEN: IMANDC
➤ **INFORMATION & MANAGEMENT.** Text in English. 1968. 8/yr. EUR 640 in Europe to institutions; JPY 84,900 in Japan to institutions; USD 716 to institutions except Europe and Japan (effective 2006). adv. bk.rev. abstr.; illus. index. back issues avail.; reprints avail. **Document type:** *Journal, Academic/Scholarly.* **Description:** For managers of information systems, researchers and systems designers. Provides information on new developments in applied information systems.
Incorporates (1981-1985): Systems, Objectives, Solutions (0165-7747); Former titles (until 1977): Management Datamatics (0579-5486); (until 1975): Management Informatics; I A G Journal (0018-8387)
Related titles: Microform ed.: (from PQC); Online - full text ed.: (from EBSCO Publishing, Gale Group, IngentaConnect, O C L C Online Computer Library Center, Inc., ScienceDirect, Swets Information Services).
Indexed: ABIn, ADPA, APEL, AS&TI, ASCA, BPIA, CMCI, CPM, CompAb, CompC, CompD, CompLI, CompR, CurCont, CybAb, Emerald, EngInd, IAOP, ICEA, InfoSAb, Inspec, RASB, SSCI, SoftAbEng.
—BLDSC (4481.835000), AskIEEE, CISTI, Ei, IDS, IE, Infotrieve, ingenta, Linda Hall. **CCC.**
Published by: (International Federation for Information Processing AUT, Applied Information Processing Group), Elsevier BV, North-Holland (Subsidiary of: Elsevier Science & Technology), Sara Burgerhartstraat 25, Amsterdam, 1055 KV, Netherlands. TEL 31-20-485-3911, FAX 31-20-485-2457, nlinfo-f@elsevier.nl, http://www.elsevier.com/locate/im, http://www.elsevier.nl. Ed. E H Sibley. Circ: 2,500. **Subscr. to:** Elsevier BV, PO Box 211, Amsterdam 1000 AE, Netherlands. TEL 31-20-485-3757, FAX 31-20-485-3432, http://www.elsevier.nl.

003 USA ISSN 1092-0374
HF5548.2
INFORMATION EXECUTIVE. Text in English. 1951. 10/yr. USD 45 domestic to non-members; USD 75 foreign to non-members (effective 2005). adv. bk.rev. charts; illus.; stat. index. reprint service avail. from PQC. **Document type:** *Magazine, Trade.* **Description:** For mid and upper-level managers in information systems management. Articles focus on the manager's involvement in a computer environment.
Former titles (until 1998): Inside D P M A (0898-171X); (until 1988): Data Management (0148-5431); (until 1970): Journal of Data Management (0449-2412)
Related titles: Microfilm ed.: (from PQC); Online - full text ed.: (from EBSCO Publishing, Factiva, ProQuest Information & Learning).
Indexed: ABIn, BPI, BusI, CMCI, CompB, CompC, CurCont, DPD, Inspec, LHTB, RASB, ResCtrInd, TelAb.
—Linda Hall. **CCC.**
Published by: A I T P - Association of Information Technology Professionals, 401 N Michigan Ave, Ste 2400, Chicago, IL 60611-4267. TEL 312-245-1070, 800-224-9371, FAX 312-527-6636, http://www.aitp.org. adv.: page USD 1,700; 10 x 14. Circ: 6,000 (controlled).

003 GBR ISSN 0306-4379
QA76.9.D3 CODEN: INSYD6
➤ **INFORMATION SYSTEMS.** Text in English. 1975. 8/yr. EUR 1,539 in Europe to institutions; JPY 204,400 in Japan to institutions; USD 1,722 elsewhere to institutions (effective 2006). adv. bk.rev. illus. back issues avail.; reprint service avail. from PQC. **Document type:** *Journal, Academic/Scholarly.* **Description:** Publishes articles concerning the design and implementation of languages, data models, and software and hardware for information systems.
Incorporates (1988-1992): Database Technology (0951-9327)
Related titles: Microfilm ed.: (from PQC); Online - full text ed.: (from EBSCO Publishing, Gale Group, IngentaConnect, ScienceDirect, Swets Information Services).
Indexed: ASCA, B&BAb, BioIAb, C&ISA, CIJE, CMCI, CompAb, CompC, CompLI, CompR, CurCont, E&CAJ, EngInd, ExcerpMed, ISR, InfoSAb, Inspec, LISA, RASB, RefZh, SCI, SolStAb, ZentMath.
—BLDSC (4496.367300), AskIEEE, CINDOC, Ei, IDS, IE, Infotrieve, ingenta, Linda Hall. **CCC.**
Published by: Pergamon (Subsidiary of: Elsevier Science & Technology), The Boulevard, Langford Ln, East Park, Kidlington, Oxford OX5 1GB, United Kingdom. TEL 44-1865-843000, FAX 44-1865-843010, http://www.elsevier.com/locate/is. Eds. Dr. Dennis Shasha, Gottfried Vossen. Circ: 1,200. **Subscr. to:** Elsevier BV, PO Box 211, Amsterdam 1000 AE, Netherlands. TEL 31-20-485-3757, FAX 31-20-485-3432, nlinfo-f@elsevier.nl, http://www.elsevier.nl.

003 GBR ISSN 1350-1917
T58.6 CODEN: ISYJER
➤ **INFORMATION SYSTEMS JOURNAL**; an international journal promoting the study and practice of information systems. Text in English. 1991. q. GBP 98, EUR 147 combined subscription in Europe to individuals print & online eds.; USD 181 combined subscription in the Americas to individuals & Caribbean, print & online eds.; GBP 108 combined subscription elsewhere to individuals print & online eds.; GBP 423 combined subscription in Europe to institutions print & online eds.; USD 781 combined subscription in the Americas to institutions & Caribbean, print & online eds.; GBP 465 combined subscription elsewhere to institutions print & online eds. (effective 2006). adv. bk.rev. bibl.; illus. index. reprint service avail. from PSC. **Document type:** *Journal, Academic/Scholarly.* **Description:** Aims to promote the study of, and interest in, information systems and to publish articles that reflect the wide and interdisciplinary nature of the subject.
Formerly (until 1994): Journal of Information Systems (0959-2954)
Related titles: Microform ed.: (from PQC); ♦ Online - full text ed.: Information Systems Journal Online. ISSN 1365-2575.
Indexed: ABIn, ASCA, CompAb, CompLI, CurCont, ERA, ETA, Emerald, ErgAb, InfoSAb, Inspec, PsycInfo, PsycholAb, SSCI, TEA.

C

—BLDSC (4496.368300), AskIEEE, IDS, IE, Infotrieve, ingenta. **CCC.**
Published by: Blackwell Publishing Ltd., 9600 Garsington Rd, Oxford, OX4 2ZG, United Kingdom. TEL 44-1865-776868, FAX 44-1865-714591, customerservices@oxon.blackwellpublishing.com, http://www.blackwellpublishing.com/journals/ISJ. Eds. David Avison, Guy Fitzgerald. Pub. Elaine Stott. R&P Sophie Savage. Adv. contact Jenny Applin. Circ: 400.

003 GBR ISSN 1365-2575
➤ **INFORMATION SYSTEMS JOURNAL ONLINE.** Text in English. 1999. q. GBP 402 in Europe to institutions; USD 743 in the Americas to institutions & Caribbean; GBP 442 elsewhere to institutions (effective 2006). **Document type:** *Academic/Scholarly.*
Media: Online - full text (from Blackwell Synergy, EBSCO Publishing, Gale Group, IngentaConnect, O C L C Online Computer Library Center, Inc., Swets Information Services). **Related titles:** Microform ed.: (from PQC); ♦ Print ed.: Information Systems Journal. ISSN 1350-1917.
Published by: Blackwell Publishing Ltd., 9600 Garsington Rd, Oxford, OX4 2ZG, United Kingdom. TEL 44-1865-776868, FAX 44-1865-714591, customerservices@oxon.blackwellpublishing.com, http://www.blackwellpublishing.com.

➤ **INTERNATIONAL CONFERENCE ON A T M. PROCEEDINGS.** see *COMPUTERS—Computer Networks*

003 020 USA
INTERNATIONAL CONFERENCE ON DATABASE SYSTEMS FOR ADVANCED APPLICATIONS. PROCEEDINGS. Text in English. a. USD 120. **Document type:** *Proceedings, Trade.*
Published by: Institute of Electrical and Electronics Engineers, Inc., 3 Park Ave, 17th Fl, New York, NY 10016-5997. TEL 800-678-4333, customer.service@ieee.org, http://www.ieee.org.

003 USA ISSN 1533-9610
QA76.9.D5
INTERNATIONAL CONFERENCE ON DISTRIBUTED COMPUTING SYSTEMS WORKSHOP. PROCEEDINGS. Text in English. a. USD 256; USD 103 to members (effective 2004). **Document type:** *Proceedings, Trade.*
Published by: Institute of Electrical and Electronics Engineers, Inc., 3 Park Ave, 17th Fl, New York, NY 10016-5997. TEL 212-419-7900, 800-678-4333, FAX 212-752-4929, customer.service@ieee.org, http://www.ieee.org.

INTERNATIONAL CONFERENCE ON ENGINEERING OF COMPLEX COMPUTER SYSTEMS. PROCEEDINGS. see *COMPUTERS—Software*

003 USA ISSN 1530-1427
INTERNATIONAL CONFERENCE ON REAL-TIME COMPUTING SYSTEMS AND APPLICATIONS. PROCEEDINGS. Text in English. 1998. irreg. price varies. **Document type:** *Proceedings, Trade.*
Related titles: Online - full text ed.: (from I E E E).
Published by: Institute of Electrical and Electronics Engineers, Inc., 3 Park Ave, 17th Fl, New York, NY 10016-5997. TEL 212-419-7900, 800-678-4333, FAX 212-752-4929, customer.service@ieee.org, http://www.ieee.org.

003 020 USA ISSN 1098-8068
QA76.9.D3
INTERNATIONAL DATABASE ENGINEERING AND APPLICATIONS SYMPOSIUM. Key Title: Proceedings - International Database Engineering and Applications Symposium. Text in English. 199?. a. USD 184; USD 74 to members (effective 2004). **Document type:** *Proceedings, Trade.*
Related titles: Online - full text ed.: (from I E E E).
Indexed: CIS.
—BLDSC (4539.503250).
Published by: Institute of Electrical and Electronics Engineers, Inc., 3 Park Ave, 17th Fl, New York, NY 10016-5997. TEL 212-419-7900, 800-678-4333, FAX 212-752-4929, customer.service@ieee.org, http://www.ieee.org.

003 USA ISSN 1541-7719
QA76.9.O35
INTERNATIONAL ENTERPRISE DISTRIBUTED OBJECT COMPUTING CONFERENCE. PROCEEDINGS. Text in English. 1997. a. USD 183; USD 74 to members (effective 2004). **Document type:** *Proceedings, Trade.*
Formerly (until 1999): International Enterprise Distributed Object Computing Workshop. Proceedings (1541-7700)
Related titles: Online - full text ed.: (from I E E E).
—BLDSC (4540.008600).
Published by: Institute of Electrical and Electronics Engineers, Inc., 3 Park Ave, 17th Fl, New York, NY 10016-5997. TEL 212-419-7900, 800-678-4333, FAX 212-752-4929, customer.service@ieee.org, http://www.ieee.org.

▼ **INTERNATIONAL JOURNAL OF AD HOC AND UBIQUITOUS COMPUTING.** see *COMPUTERS—Computer Networks*

620.001171 GBR ISSN 0267-6192
QA75.5 CODEN: CSSEEI
➤ **INTERNATIONAL JOURNAL OF COMPUTER SYSTEMS SCIENCE AND ENGINEERING.** Short title: C S S E Journal. Text in English. 1985. bi-m. GBP 250 in the European Union to institutions; GBP 260 elsewhere to institutions (effective 2002). bk.rev. charts; illus. index. 64 p./no.; back issues avail. **Document type:** *Journal, Academic/Scholarly.* **Description:** Focuses on theory and applications in such areas as fault-tolerant systems, LAN engineering, parallel-processing, and multiple cooperating processor systems.
Related titles: Microform ed.: (from PQC).
Indexed: AIA, BrCerAb, C&ISA, CADCAM, CMCI, CerAb, CompAb, CompLI, CorrAb, CurCont, E&CAJ, EMA, IAA, Inspec, M&TEA, MBF, METADEX, TelAb, WAA, ZentMath.
—BLDSC (3394.291700), AskIEEE, CISTI, Ei, IDS, IE, Infotrieve, ingenta, Linda Hall.
Published by: C R L Publishing Ltd., PO Box 31, Market Harborough, Leics LE16 9BP, United Kingdom. TEL 44-1858-469898, FAX 44-1858-431649, csse@crlpublishing.co.uk, admin@crlpublishing.co.uk, http://www.crlpublishing.co.uk. Ed. T.S. Dillon. Pub. T S Dillon. Adv. contact J Thompson. Circ: 300 (paid).

➤ **THE INTERNATIONAL JOURNAL OF DIGITAL ACCOUNTING RESEARCH.** see *BUSINESS AND ECONOMICS—Accounting*

005.42 004.22 USA ISSN 1548-1115
▼ **INTERNATIONAL JOURNAL OF ENTERPRISE INFORMATION SYSTEMS.** Text in English. 2005. q. USD 85 to individuals; USD 195 to institutions (effective 2005). **Document type:** *Journal, Academic/Scholarly.* **Description:** Provides comprehensive coverage and understanding of various Enterprise Information Systems (EIS) such as Enterprise Resource Planning (ERP) and Electronic Commerce (EC) and their implications on supply chain management and organizational competitiveness.
Related titles: Online - full text ed.: ISSN 1548-1123. 2005.
Indexed: C&ISA, E&CAJ, IAA.
Published by: Idea Group Publishing (Subsidiary of: Idea Group Inc.), 701 E Chocolate Ave, Ste 200, Hershey, PA 17033-1240. TEL 717-533-8845, FAX 717-533-7115, cust@idea-group.com, http://www.idea-group.com/journals/details.asp?id=4292. Ed. Angappa Gunasekaran.

004.01 TWN ISSN 1562-2479
INTERNATIONAL JOURNAL OF FUZZY SYSTEMS. Text in English. 1995. q. TWD 1,000 domestic to individuals; USD 50 foreign to individuals; TWD 2,500 domestic to institutions; USD 120 foreign to institutions (effective 2002). **Description:** Covers the theory, design, and application of fuzzy systems, soft computing systems, grey systems, and extension theory systems.
Formerly (until 1999): Mohu Xitong Xuekan (1026-2474)
Indexed: ASFA, BrCerAb, C&ISA, CerAb, CorrAb, E&CAJ, EMA, ESPM, FS&TA, IAA, Inspec, M&TEA, MBF, METADEX, MathR, MathSciNet, WAA.
—BLDSC (4542.260600), IE, ingenta, Linda Hall.
Published by: Chinese Fuzzy Systems Association, c/o Han-Pang Huang, Robotics Laboratory, Department of Mechanical Engineering, National Taiwan University, Taipei, 10674, Taiwan. TEL 886-2-2363-3875, FAX 886-2-2363-1755, http://www.fuzzy.org.tw/ijfs.htm. Ed. Han-Pang Huang.

003 GBR ISSN 0308-1079
Q295 CODEN: IJGSAX
➤ **INTERNATIONAL JOURNAL OF GENERAL SYSTEMS;** a comprehensive periodical devoted to general systems methodology, applications and education. Text in French. 1974. bi-m. GBP 1,752, USD 2,297 combined subscription to institutions print & online eds. (effective 2006). adv. bk.rev. abstr.; bibl.; charts; illus. index. back issues avail.; reprint service avail. from PSC. **Document type:** *Journal, Academic/Scholarly.* **Description:** Devoted primarily to the publication of original research and educational contributions relevant to general systems.
Incorporates (1997-2003): International Journal of Smart Engineering System Design (1025-5818)
Related titles: CD-ROM ed.: ISSN 1026-7492. 1995; Microform ed.: (from MIM, PQC); Online - full text ed.: ISSN 1563-5104. GBP 1,664, USD 2,182 to institutions (effective 2006) (from EBSCO Publishing, Gale Group, IngentaConnect, O C L C Online Computer Library Center, Inc., Swets Information Services).
Indexed: ASCA, BiolAb, BrCerAb, C&ISA, CCMJ, CIS, CMCI, CerAb, CompAb, CompLI, CompR, CorrAb, CurCont, E&CAJ, EMA, EngInd, HRA, IAA, ISR, Inspec, M&TEA, MBF, METADEX, MathR, MathSciNet, SCI, SSCI, SolStAb, WAA, ZentMath.
—BLDSC (4542.266000), AskIEEE, CISTI, IE, Infotrieve, ingenta. **CCC.**
Published by: Taylor & Francis Ltd (Subsidiary of: Taylor & Francis Group), 4 Park Sq, Milton Park, Abingdon, OX14 4RN, United Kingdom. TEL 44-1235-828600, FAX 44-1235-829000, info@tandf.co.uk, http://www.tandf.co.uk/journals/titles/03081079.asp. Ed. George J Klir. **Subscr. in N. America to:** Taylor & Francis Inc., Customer Services Dept, 325 Chestnut St, 8th Fl, Philadelphia, PA 19106. TEL 215-625-8900, 800-354-1420, FAX 215-625-8914, customerservice@taylorandfrancis.com; **Subscr. to:** Journals Customer Service, Rankine Rd, Basingstoke, Hants RG24 8PR, United Kingdom. TEL 44-1256-813000, FAX 44-1256-330245, enquiry@tandf.co.uk.

004 362.11068 USA ISSN 1555-3396
▼ ➤ **INTERNATIONAL JOURNAL OF HEALTHCARE INFORMATION SYSTEMS AND INFORMATICS.** Text in English. forthcoming 2006 (Jan.). q. USD 85 to individuals; USD 195 to institutions (effective 2006). **Document type:** *Journal, Academic/Scholarly.* **Description:** Promotes advance research in the application of information systems and informatics to the health care arena.
Related titles: Online - full text ed.: ISSN 1555-340X. forthcoming 2006 (Jan.).
Published by: Idea Group Publishing (Subsidiary of: Idea Group Inc.), 701 E Chocolate Ave, Ste 200, Hershey, PA 17033-1240. TEL 717-533-8845, FAX 717-533-7115, cust@idea-group.com, http://www.idea-group.com/IJHISI. Ed. Joseph Tan.

003 TWN ISSN 1017-1819
T58.6 CODEN: IIMSEQ
INTERNATIONAL JOURNAL OF INFORMATION AND MANAGEMENT SCIENCES. Text in English. q. TWD 800, USD 60 (effective 1999). abstr.; bibl.; charts; stat. **Document type:** *Academic/Scholarly.* **Description:** Publishes original contributions on information systems, general systems, stochastic systems, transportation systems, industrial management, industrial engineering, management sciences, regional science, decision science, operations research, and applied statistics.
Formed by the 1990 merger of: Tamkang Journal of Management Sciences (0255-6863); International Journal on Policy and Information
Indexed: CCMJ, CurCont, EngInd, Inspec, MathR, MathSciNet, ZentMath.
—BLDSC (4542.304850), AskIEEE, Ei, IE, ingenta.
Published by: (Graduate Institute of Management Sciences), Tamkang University, 151 Ying Chuan Rd Tamsui, Taipei, 25137, Taiwan. Ed. C L Sheng. Circ: 400.

003 IND
INTERNATIONAL JOURNAL OF SYSTEM. Text in English. s-a. USD 55 per issue (effective 2003).
Published by: Scientific Publishers, 5-A New Pali Rd., Near Hotel Taj Hari Mahal, PO Box 91, Jodhpur, Rajasthan 342 003, India. TEL 91-291-2433323, FAX 91-291-2512580, info@scientificpub.com, http://www.scientificpub.com.

INTERNATIONAL SYMPOSIUM ON OBJECT-ORIENTED REAL-TIME DISTRIBUTED COMPUTING. see *COMPUTERS—Data Base Management*

003 USA ISSN 1087-4089
QA76.58
INTERNATIONAL SYMPOSIUM ON PARALLEL ARCHITECTURES, ALGORITHMS, AND NETWORKS. Text in English. 1994. a. USD 204; USD 82 to members (effective 2005). **Document type:** *Proceedings, Trade.*
Related titles: Online - full text ed.: (from I E E E).
Indexed: EngInd.
—**CCC.**
Published by: Institute of Electrical and Electronics Engineers, Inc., 3 Park Ave, 17th Fl, New York, NY 10016-5997. TEL 212-419-7900, 800-678-4333, FAX 212-752-4929, customer.service@ieee.org, http://www.ieee.org.

003 USA ISSN 1529-4188
QA76.9.D3
INTERNATIONAL WORKSHOP ON DATABASE AND EXPERT SYSTEMS APPLICATIONS. Text in English. 1996. a. USD 230; USD 92 to members (effective 2004). **Document type:** *Proceedings, Trade.*
Related titles: Online - full text ed.: (from I E E E).
Indexed: EngInd.
—BLDSC (4552.178915).
Published by: Institute of Electrical and Electronics Engineers, Inc., 3 Park Ave, 17th Fl, New York, NY 10016-5997. TEL 800-678-4333, customer.service@ieee.org, http://www.ieee.org.

003 620.004 USA ISSN 1530-1990
INTERNATIONAL WORKSHOP ON DISTRIBUTED INTERACTIVE SIMULATION AND REAL - TIME APPLICATIONS. Text in English. 1997. a. USD 166; USD 67 to members (effective 2004). **Document type:** *Proceedings, Trade.*
Related titles: Online - full text ed.: (from I E E E).
Published by: Institute of Electrical and Electronics Engineers, Inc., 3 Park Ave, 17th Fl, New York, NY 10016-5997. TEL 800-678-4333, customer.service@ieee.org, http://www.ieee.org.

INTERNATIONAL WORKSHOP ON OBJECT ORIENTED REAL TIME DEPENDABLE SYSTEMS. PROCEEDINGS. see *COMPUTERS—Data Base Management*

C

▼ *new title* ➤ *refereed* ✶ *unverified* ♦ *full entry avail.*

JISUANJI JICHENG ZHIZAO XITONG/COMPUTER INTEGRATED MANUFACTURING SYSTEMS. see *MACHINERY*

003 USA ISSN 0022-0000
QA76.5 CODEN: JCSSBM
➤ **JOURNAL OF COMPUTER AND SYSTEM SCIENCES.** Text in English. 1967. 8/yr. EUR 128 in Europe to individuals; JPY 13,300 in Japan to individuals; USD 104 to individuals except Europe and Japan; EUR 2,326 in Europe to institutions; JPY 242,900 in Japan to institutions; USD 1,890 to institutions except Europe and Japan (effective 2006). illus. Index. back issues avail.; reprints avail. **Document type:** *Academic/Scholarly.* **Description:** Publishes original research papers on computer science and in system science, with emphasis on pertinent mathematical theory and its applications.
Related titles: Online - full text ed.: ISSN 1090-2724. USD 1,929 (effective 2002) (from EBSCO Publishing, Gale Group, IngentaConnect, O C L C Online Computer Library Center, Inc., ScienceDirect, Swets Information Services).
Indexed: ASCA, BiolAb, C&CSA, CCMJ, CMCI, CompAb, CompC, CompLI, CompR, CurCont, CybAb, EngInd, ExcerpMed, IAOP, ISR, Inspec, MathR, MathSciNet, RASB, RefZh, SCI, SSCI, ZentMath.
—BLDSC (4963.600000), AskIEEE, CISTI, Ei, IDS, IE, Infotrieve, ingenta, Linda Hall. **CCC.**
Published by: Academic Press (Subsidiary of: Elsevier Science & Technology), 525 B St, Ste 1900, San Diego, CA 92101-4495. TEL 619-231-6616, 800-894-3434, FAX 619-699-6422, apsubs@acad.com, http://www.elsevier.com/locate/jcss, http://www.academicpress.com.

003.0711 USA ISSN 0887-4417
QA76.27 CODEN: JCISE9
➤ **JOURNAL OF COMPUTER INFORMATION SYSTEMS.** Text in English. 1960. q. free to individual members; USD 175 to institutions (effective 2004). adv. bk.rev.; film rev. Index. back issues avail.; reprint service avail. from PQC. **Document type:** *Journal, Academic/Scholarly.* **Description:** For collegiate information systems educators. Features articles on instruction, research, trends and information in information systems fields.
Formerly (until 1985): Journal of Data Education (0022-0310)
Related titles: Microform ed.: (from PQC); Online - full text ed.: (from bigchalk, EBSCO Publishing, Northern Light Technology, Inc., ProQuest Information & Learning).
Indexed: ABIn, ASCA, BusEdI, CMCI, CompC, CompLI, Inspec.
—BLDSC (4963.730000), AskIEEE, IDS, IE, ingenta.
Published by: International Association for Computer Information Systems, c/o G. Daryl Nord, 217 College of Business, Oklahoma State University, Stillwater, OK 74078. TEL 405-744-8632, FAX 405-744-5180, jnord@okstate.edu, http://www.fgcu.edu/rboggs/jcis/index.asp, http://www.iacis.org/. Ed. Jeretta Horn Nord. R&P G Daryl Nord TEL 405-744-8632. Adv. contact G. Daryl Nord. Circ: 1,000 (controlled).

003 FRA ISSN 1246-0125
JOURNAL OF DECISION SYSTEMS. Text in English, French. 1992. q. EUR 280 in the European Union; EUR 315 elsewhere (effective 2003). **Document type:** *Academic/Scholarly.*
Formerly (until 1997): Revue des Systemes de Decision (1166-8636)
Related titles: Online - full text ed.
—BLDSC (4967.880000). **CCC.**
Published by: Lavoisier, 11 rue Lavoisier, Paris, 75008, France. TEL 33-1-42653995, FAX 33-1-42650246, info@lavoisier.fr, http://www.lavoisier.fr. Ed. Frederic Adam. **Subscr. to:** Lavoisier - Dept Abonnements, 14 rue de Provigny, Cachan 94236, France. TEL 33-1-47406700, FAX 33-1-47406702, abo@lavoisier.fr.

003 NLD ISSN 0963-8687
HD30.213 CODEN: JSIYE3
➤ **THE JOURNAL OF STRATEGIC INFORMATION SYSTEMS.** Text in English. 1978. 4/yr. EUR 134 in Europe to individuals; JPY 17,700 in Japan to individuals; USD 150 to individuals except Europe and Japan; EUR 416 in Europe to institutions; JPY 55,200 in Japan to institutions; USD 465 to institutions except Europe and Japan (effective 2006). adv. bk.rev. abstr. index. back issues avail. **Document type:** *Academic/Scholarly.* **Description:** Integrates academic findings and research with the practical needs of professionals attempting to create functional information systems.
Incorporates: International Information Systems; Former titles (until 1992): Journal of Strategic I T; (until 1990): Information Age (0261-4103); (until Jan. 1982): Information Privacy (0141-3406)
Related titles: Microform ed.: (from PQC); Online - full text ed.: (from EBSCO Publishing, Gale Group, IngentaConnect, ScienceDirect, Swets Information Services).
Indexed: ABIn, ADPA, AHCI, ASCA, BPIA, CMCI, CommAb, CompAb, CompD, CompLI, CurCont, Emerald, EngInd, ICEA, InfoSAb, Inspec, LISA, SSCI, SoftAbEng, TelAb.
—BLDSC (5066.872880), AskIEEE, CISTI, Ei, IDS, IE, Infotrieve, ingenta. **CCC.**
Published by: Elsevier BV, North-Holland (Subsidiary of: Elsevier Science & Technology), Sara Burgerhartstraat 25, Amsterdam, 1055 KV, Netherlands. TEL 31-20-485-3911, FAX 31-20-485-2457, nlinfo-f@elsevier.nl, http://www.elsevier.com/locate/jsis, http://www.elsevier.nl. Eds. Robert D. Galliers, Sirkka Jarvenpaa. **Subscr. to:** Elsevier BV, PO Box 211, Amsterdam 1000 AE, Netherlands. TEL 31-20-485-3757, FAX 31-20-485-3432, http://www.elsevier.nl.

➤ **JOURNAL OF SYSTEMS AND SOFTWARE.** see *COMPUTERS—Software*

003 NLD ISSN 1383-7621
QA76.5 CODEN: MMICDT
➤ **JOURNAL OF SYSTEMS ARCHITECTURE.** Text in Dutch. 1975. 12/yr. EUR 1,175 in Europe to institutions; JPY 155,900 in Japan to institutions; USD 1,312 elsewhere to institutions (effective 2006). adv. bk.rev. index. back issues avail.; reprints avail. **Document type:** *Academic/Scholarly.* **Description:** Publishes papers presenting the results of original research and technological progress.
Former titles (until 1996): Microprocessing and Microprogramming (0165-6074); Euromicro Journal (0167-3858); Euromicro Newsletter (0303-1268)
Related titles: Microform ed.: (from PQC); Online - full text ed.: (from EBSCO Publishing, Gale Group, IngentaConnect, ScienceDirect, Swets Information Services).
Indexed: ABIn, AHCI, AIA, ASCA, B&BAb, C&ISA, CADCAM, CMCI, CompAb, CompD, CompLI, CompR, CurCont, E&CAJ, EngInd, ICEA, Inspec, RefZh, SoftAbEng, SolStAb.
—BLDSC (5068.066000), AskIEEE, CISTI, Ei, IDS, IE, Infotrieve, ingenta, Linda Hall. **CCC.**
Published by: (European Association for Micro-Processing and Micro-Programming), Elsevier BV, North-Holland (Subsidiary of: Elsevier Science & Technology), Sara Burgerhartstraat 25, Amsterdam, 1055 KV, Netherlands. TEL 31-20-485-3911, FAX 31-20-485-2457, nlinfo-f@elsevier.nl, http://www.elsevier.com/locate/sysarc, http://www.elsevier.nl. Eds. Krzysztof Kuchcinski, P Cremonesi. Circ: 1,250. **Subscr. to:** Elsevier BV, PO Box 211, Amsterdam 1000 AE, Netherlands. TEL 31-20-485-3757, FAX 31-20-485-3432, http://www.elsevier.nl.

003 CHN ISSN 1004-3756
Q295 CODEN: JSSEER
JOURNAL OF SYSTEMS SCIENCE AND SYSTEMS ENGINEERING. Text in English. 1992. q. USD 140 (effective 2000). **Document type:** *Academic/Scholarly.* **Description:** Carries papers on both theories and applications of SS and SE in management and planning of R&D, production, economy, education, demography, military activities involving various interdisciplinary theories, methodologies and techniques ranging from natural science to social science.
Related titles: Online - full text ed.: (from East View Information Services).
Indexed: Inspec.
—BLDSC (5068.095500), AskIEEE, CISTI, IE, ingenta.
Published by: (Systems Engineering Society of China), International Academic Publishers, 137 Chaonei Dajie, Beijing, 100010, China. TEL 86-10-4038366, FAX 86-10-6401-4877. Ed. Liu Bao.

003 USA ISSN 1044-6397
QA76.76.O63 CODEN: LOGNEM
;LOGIN:; the magazin of the USENIX Association. Variant title: Semicolon Login Colon. Text in English. 1997. bi-m. USD 110 to individual members; USD 230 to institutional members; USD 40 to students (effective 2004). adv. back issues avail. **Document type:** *Journal, Consumer.*
Related titles: Online - full text ed.
Published by: The Usenix Association, 2560 Ninth Street, Suite 215, Berkeley, CA 94710. TEL 510-528-8649, FAX 510-548-5738, office@usenix.org, http://www.usenix.org/publications/login/, http://www.usenix.com. adv.: B&W page USD 1,700, color page USD 1,900; 7 x 10.

LOGISTIK HEUTE. see *BUSINESS AND ECONOMICS—Computer Applications*

003 USA ISSN 0276-7783
T58.6 CODEN: MISQDP
➤ **M I S QUARTERLY.** (Management Information Systems) Text in English. 1977. q. USD 85 domestic to individuals; USD 95 foreign to individuals; USD 105 domestic to institutions; USD 115 foreign to institutions; USD 75 domestic to students; USD 85 foreign to students (effective 2004). adv. illus.; abstr. Index. back issues avail.; reprints avail. **Document type:** *Journal, Academic/Scholarly.*
Related titles: Microfiche ed.; Online - full text ed.: (from EBSCO Publishing, Florida Center for Library Automation, Gale Group, H.W. Wilson, JSTOR (Web-based Journal Archive), O C L C Online Computer Library Center, Inc., ProQuest Information & Learning).
Indexed: ABIn, ASCA, BPI, BPIA, CMCI, CPM, CompC, CompD, CompLI, CurCont, Emerald, InfoSAb, Inspec, RefZh, SSCI.
—BLDSC (5359.039000), AskIEEE, CISTI, IDS, IE, Infotrieve, ingenta.
Published by: (University of Minnesota, School of Management), M I S Research Center, University of Minnesota, Carlson School of Management, 321 19th Ave S, Minneapolis, MN 55455. TEL 612-624-2035, 612-624-2029, FAX 612-624-2056, misq@csom.umn.edu, http://www.misq.org/. Ed. Ron Weber. Pub. Alok Gupta. R&P, Adv. contact Jan DeGross TEL 612-624-5043. page USD 300. Circ: 3,000. **Subscr. to:** Allen Press Inc. **Co-sponsor:** Association for Information Systems.

003 JPN
MACPEOPLE. Text in Japanese. m. JPY 9,360; JPY 830 newsstand/cover (effective 2004). **Document type:** *Magazine, Consumer.*
Published by: ASCII Corp., JR Shinanomachi Bldg. 34 Shinanomachi, Shinjuku-ku, Tokyo, 160-8584, Japan. http://www.ascii.co.jp/books/magazines/macpeople.html.

005.5 338 004 USA ISSN 1534-6803
MANUFACTURING I T. Text in English. a. USD 45 per issue (effective 2003). **Document type:** *Proceedings.*
Published by: The Instrumentation, Systems and Automation Society, 67 Alexander Dr, Research Triangle Park, NC 27709. TEL 919-549-8411, FAX 919-549-8288, info@isa.org, http://www.isa.org.

005.5 USA
MERRILL'S EDGAR ADVISOR; a publication for participants in the EDGAR and SEDAR systems for securities reporting. Text in English. 1991. q. free. **Document type:** *Newsletter.*
Related titles: Online - full text ed.
Published by: Merrill Corporation, One Merrill Circle, St. Paul, MN 55108. TEL 800-688-1933, FAX 612-644-1633, edgar@merrillcorp.com, http://www.merrillcorp.com. Ed., R&P Richard Dargis. Circ: 18,950.

004.2 GBR ISSN 1352-7312
MICRO TECHNOLOGY EUROPE. Text in English. 1991. m. free (effective 2005). adv. software rev.; Website rev. tr.lit. 36 p./no.; back issues avail.; reprints avail. **Document type:** *Magazine, Trade.* **Description:** Provides one stop solution to key areas of embedded design, hardware, and software in system design.
Formerly (until 1993): Micro Technology
Related titles: CD-ROM ed.; E-mail ed.; Fax ed.; Special ed(s).: Micro Technology Europe: Media Pack (Year).
Published by: M T Publications Ltd., 1st Fl, 95a Rivington St, London, EC2A 3AY, United Kingdom. TEL 44-20-77393841, FAX 44-20-77393897, mte@microtechnology.co.uk, http://www.mtemag.com/, http://www.microtechnology.co.uk. Ed. Paul Gregg. Pub. Maurice A Cantwell. Adv. contact Colin Campbell. Circ: 15,500 (controlled).

MICROSYSTEMS. see *COMPUTERS—Microcomputers*

003 USA ISSN 0923-6082
TK5102.5 CODEN: MUSPE5
➤ **MULTIDIMENSIONAL SYSTEMS AND SIGNAL PROCESSING**; an international journal. Text in English. 1990. q. EUR 528, USD 538, GBP 328 combined subscription to institutions print & online eds. (effective 2005). adv. reprint service avail. from PQC,PSC. **Document type:** *Journal, Academic/Scholarly.* **Description:** Publishes survey papers and original studies in fundamental and applied research in multidimensional systems, including mathematical modeling and the application of neural networks and artificial intelligence in signal and data processing.
Related titles: Microform ed.: (from PQC); Online - full text ed.: ISSN 1573-0824 (from EBSCO Publishing, Gale Group, IngentaConnect, Kluwer Online, O C L C Online Computer Library Center, Inc., Ovid Technologies, Inc., Springer LINK, Swets Information Services).
Indexed: ASCA, BibLing, CCMJ, CMCI, CompR, CurCont, EngInd, ISR, InfoSAb, Inspec, MathR, MathSciNet, RefZh, SCI, ZentMath.
—BLDSC (5983.088000), AskIEEE, CISTI, Ei, IDS, IE, Infotrieve, ingenta. **CCC.**
Published by: Springer-Verlag New York, Inc. (Subsidiary of: Springer Science+Business Media), 233 Spring St, New York, NY 10013. TEL 212-460-1500, FAX 212-460-1575, service@springer-ny.com, http://springerlink.metapress.com/openurl.asp?genre=journal&issn=0923-6082, http://www.springer-ny.com. Ed. Nirmal K Bose. **Subscr. to:** Journal Fulfillment, PO Box 2485, Secaucus, NJ 07096-2485. TEL 201-348-4033, FAX 201-348-4505, journals@springer-ny.com.

003 NLD ISSN 0258-1248
CODEN: NASFEG
➤ **N A T O ADVANCED SCIENCE INSTITUTES SERIES F: COMPUTER AND SYSTEMS SCIENCES.** (North Atlantic Treaty Organization) Text in English. 1983. irreg., latest vol.181, 2001. price varies. **Document type:** *Monographic series, Academic/Scholarly.* **Description:** Publishes cutting-edge research in various areas of computer systems science.
Formerly: N A T O Advanced Study Institute Series F: Computer and System Sciences
Related titles: Online - full text ed.
Indexed: CCMJ, Inspec, ZentMath.
—CISTI. **CCC.**

C

Published by: (North Atlantic Treaty Organization BEL, North Atlantic Treaty Organization, Scientific Affairs Division BEL), I O S Press, Nieuwe Hemweg 6B, Amsterdam, 1013 BG, Netherlands. TEL 31-20-6883355, FAX 31-20-6203419, order@iospress.nl, http://www.iospress.nl/site/navfr/navframe2.html.

003 004.6 USA
NETWORK OPERATIONS AND MANAGEMENT SYMPOSIUM. Text in English. 1998. biennial. price varies. **Document type:** *Proceedings, Trade.*
—BLDSC (4363.007550).
Published by: Institute of Electrical and Electronics Engineers, Inc., 3 Park Ave, 17th Fl, New York, NY 10016-5997. TEL 800-678-4333, customer.service@ieee.org, http://www.ieee.org.

620.001171 FRA ISSN 1290-2926
NETWORKING AND INFORMATION SYSTEMS JOURNAL. Text in French. 1993. 6/yr. EUR 54.15 (effective 2003). adv.
Formerly (until 1998): Ingenierie des Systemes d'Information (1247-0317)
—IE, ingenta. **CCC.**
Published by: Editions Hermes, 8 quai du Marche-Neuf, Paris, 75004, France. TEL 33-1-53101520, FAX 33-1-53101521, http://www.editions-hermes.fr. Eds. Arnold Rochfeld, Mokrane Bouzeghoub. Adv. contact Jean Philippe.

003 JPN ISSN 0917-5342
NIKKEI INFORMATION STRATEGY/NIKKEI JOHO SUTORATEJI. Text in Japanese. 1992. m. JPY 12,000 (effective 2000). adv. **Document type:** *Trade.* **Description:** Contains detailed information for successful construction and utilization of information systems in corporate management.
Published by: Nikkei Business Publications Inc. (Subsidiary of: Nihon Keizai Shimbun, Inc.), 2-1-1 Hirakawa-cho, Chiyoda-ku, Tokyo, 102-8622, Japan. TEL 81-3-5210-8311, FAX 81-3-5210-8530, info@nikkeibpnyc.com, webmaster@nikkeibp.com, http://www.nikkeibp.com. Ed. Yuzuru Uesato. Pub. Minoru Matsuzaki. Adv. contact Toshio Takamine. B&W page JPY 490,000, color page JPY 700,000; trim 208 x 280. Circ: 23,892. **Dist. in America by:** Nikkei Business Publications America Inc., 575 Fifth Ave, 20th Fl, New York, NY 10017.

003 GBR ISSN 0960-3786
NODE. Text in English. 1990. m.
Related titles: ♦ Supplement to: I B M System User. ISSN 0950-303X.
Published by: I B C Business Publishing Ltd., 69-77 Paul St, London, EC2A 4LQ, United Kingdom. TEL 44-20-7553-1567, FAX 44-20-7553-1593, http://www.bankingtech.com.

003 USA ISSN 1048-8928
TK7885.A1
O E M INTEGRATOR✶. Text in English. 1990. m. free to qualified personnel. adv. **Document type:** *Trade.*
Published by: Johnson Hill Press, Inc., 1233 Janesville Ave, Box 803, Fort Atkinson, WI 53538. TEL 920-563-6388. Ed. W Arnold. Adv. contact Barbara Arnold.

003 USA
THE ONLINE JOURNAL OF COMPUTER CONTROLLED SYSTEMS; products, vendors, and technical information. Text in English. 1996. free. adv. tr.lit. **Document type:** *Trade.* **Description:** Offers technical data, articles, news, products, and vendor listing. Covers computer systems on factory automation, medical equipment, laboratory instruments, vending machines and home automation.
Media: Online - full text.
Published by: Arrick Publishing, 10768 County Road 2335., Tyler, TX 75707-3328. TEL 817-571-0595, FAX 817-571-2317, editor@controlled.com, http://www.controlled.com/. Ed., Adv. contact Roger Arrick.

003 NLD ISSN 1230-1612
QC174.85.O6
OPEN SYSTEMS AND INFORMATION DYNAMICS. Text in English. 1993. q. EUR 342, USD 342, GBP 214 combined subscription to institutions print & online eds. (effective 2005). adv. reprint service avail. from PSC. **Description:** Promotes interdisciplinary research in mathematics, physics, engineering and life sciences. Of particular interest is a system and information-theoretic approach to phenomena dealing with control, filtering, communication, pattern recognition chaotic dynamics, memory and cooperative behaviour in open complex systems, classical and quantum, living and artificial.
Related titles: Online - full text ed.: ISSN 1573-1324 (from EBSCO Publishing, Gale Group, IngentaConnect, Kluwer Online, O C L C Online Computer Library Center, Inc., Springer LINK, Swets Information Services).
Indexed: BibLing, CCMJ, CMCI, CurCont, Inspec, MathR, MathSciNet, RefZh.
—BLDSC (6266.183560), CISTI, IE, Infotrieve, ingenta. **CCC.**
Published by: (Uniwersytet Mikolaja Kopernika/Nicolaus Copernicus University POL), Springer-Verlag Dordrecht (Subsidiary of: Springer Science+Business Media), Van Godewijckstraat 30, Dordrecht, 3311 GX, Netherlands. TEL 31-78-6576050, FAX 31-78-6576474, http://springerlink.metapress.com/openurl.asp?genre=journal&issn=1230-1612, http://www.springeronline.com. Eds. A Jamiolkowski, Luigi Accardi, M Ohya, Roman S Ingarden.

P C WORLD INDIA. see *COMPUTERS—Computer Networks*

620.001171 USA ISSN 0892-4252
CODEN: PSCEED
PRENTICE-HALL INTERNATIONAL SERIES IN SYSTEMS AND CONTROL ENGINEERING. Text in English. irreg. **Document type:** *Monographic series.*
Indexed: Inspec.
Published by: Prentice Hall, One Lake St, Upper Saddle River, NJ 07458. TEL 800-282-0693, FAX 800-835-5327, http://www.prenhall.com.

003 USA ISSN 0922-6443
QA76.54 CODEN: RESYE9
➤ **REAL-TIME SYSTEMS**; the international journal of time-critical computing systems. Text in English. 1989. 9/yr. EUR 878, USD 898, GBP 548 combined subscription to institutions print & online eds. (effective 2005). adv. reprint service avail. from PSC. **Document type:** *Journal, Academic/Scholarly.* **Description:** Consists of research papers, invited papers, reports on projects and case studies, standards and corresponding proposals for general discussion.
Related titles: Microform ed.: (from PQC); Online - full text ed.: ISSN 1573-1383 (from EBSCO Publishing, Gale Group, IngentaConnect, Kluwer Online, O C L C Online Computer Library Center, Inc., Ovid Technologies, Inc., Springer LINK, Swets Information Services).
Indexed: AIA, ASCA, BibLing, BrCerAb, C&ISA, CADCAM, CMCI, CerAb, CompAb, CompLI, CompR, CorrAb, CurCont, E&CAJ, EMA, Englnd, IAA, InfoSAb, Inspec, M&TEA, MBF, METADEX, MathR, PsycholAb, RefZh, SolStAb, WAA, ZentMath.
—BLDSC (7303.282660), AskIEEE, CISTI, Ei, IDS, IE, Infotrieve, ingenta, Linda Hall. **CCC.**
Published by: Springer-Verlag New York, Inc. (Subsidiary of: Springer Science+Business Media), 233 Spring St, New York, NY 10013. TEL 212-460-1500, FAX 212-460-1575, service@springer-ny.com, http://springerlink.metapress.com/openurl.asp?genre=journal&issn=0922-6443, http://www.springer-ny.com. Eds. John A Stankovic, Kim-Fung Man, Wolfgang A Halang. **Subscr. to:** Journal Fulfillment, PO Box 2485, Secaucus, NJ 07096-2485. TEL 201-348-4033, FAX 201-348-4505, journals@springer-ny.com.

003.3 USA ISSN 1052-8725
QA76.54
REAL - TIME SYSTEMS SYMPOSIUM. Variant title: I E E E Real - Time Systems Symposium. Proceedings. Text in English. 1981. a. price varies. **Document type:** *Proceedings, Academic/Scholarly.* **Description:** Focuses on computer systems in charge of real-time applications.
Related titles: Online - full text ed.: (from I E E E).
Indexed: Englnd.
—BLDSC (4363.039000). **CCC.**
Published by: (Institute of Electrical and Electronics Engineers, Inc.), I E E E Computer Society, 3 Park Ave, 17th Fl, New York, NY 10017. TEL 714-821-8380, 800-678-4333, FAX 714-821-4641, customer.service@ieee.org, http://www.ieee.org. **Orders in Europe to:** I E E E Computer Society, Ave de l'Aquilon 13, Brussels 1200, Belgium. TEL 32-2-770-2198, 32-2-770-8505.

003 FRA ISSN 1260-5875
G70.212
REVUE INTERNATIONALE DE GEOMATIQUE. Text in French. 1991. 4/yr. EUR 275 in the European Union; EUR 305 elsewhere (effective 2003).
Former titles (until 1994): Revue de Geomatique (1247-0589); (until 1992): Revue des Sciences de l'Information Geographique et de l'Analyse Spatiales (1166-9624)
Published by: (Ministere de la Recherche et de l'Espace), Lavoisier, 11 rue Lavoisier, Paris, 75008, France. TEL 33-1-42653995, FAX 33-1-42650246, info@lavoisier.fr, http://www.lavoisier.fr. Ed. Jean-Paul Cheylan. **Subscr. to:** Lavoisier - Dept Abonnements, 14 rue de Provigny, Cachan 94236, France. TEL 33-1-47406700, FAX 33-1-47406702, abo@lavoisier.fr.

005.42 USA ISSN 1554-365X
➤ **S A P FINANCIALS EXPERT.** (System Application Programming) Text in English. 2002. 10/yr. USD 595 (effective 2005). **Document type:** *Newsletter, Trade.*
Formerly (until 2005): F I / C O Expert (1537-9922)
Related titles: Online - full content ed.
Published by: Wellesley Information Services (Subsidiary of: United Communications Group), 990 Washington St, Dedham, MA 02026-6714. TEL 781-329-0419, FAX 781-320-9466, customer.service@sapfinancialsexpert.com, customer@eview.com, http://www.ficoexpertonline.com/, http://www.wispubs.com.

005.42 USA ISSN 1555-4856
▼ **S A P NETWEAVER.** (System Application Programming) Text in English. 2005 (Spr.). q. free to qualified personnel (effective 2006).
Published by: Wellesley Information Services (Subsidiary of: United Communications Group), 11300 Rockville Pike, #1100, Rockville, MD 20852-3030. TEL 301-287-2700, FAX 301-816-8945, info@wispubs.com, http://www.sapnetweavermagazine.com, http://www.wispubs.com.

003 USA ISSN 1060-1074
QA76.75
S C O MAGAZINE✶. (Santa Cruz Operation) Text in English. 1991. bi-m.
Related titles: ♦ Supplement to: Information Week (US Edition). ISSN 8750-6874.
Indexed: SoftBase.
Published by: C M P Media LLC (Subsidiary of: United News & Media), 600 Community Dr, Manhasset, NY 11030. TEL 516-562-5000, FAX 516-365-4601.

003 USA ISSN 1075-3265
S C O WORLD✶. (Santa Cruz Operation) Text in English. 1994. 6/yr. USD 21.95; USD 28 in Canada; USD 49 elsewhere. adv. bk.rev. **Document type:** *Trade.*
Published by: Venture Publishing, Inc., 2893 El Camino Real #2, Redwood City, CA 94061-4001. TEL 650-941-1550, FAX 650-941-1504, bob@scoworld.com, http://scoworld.com. Ed. Robert Billhimer. Pub. Bob Billhimer. R&P Jeanne Ketchum. adv.: B&W page USD 6,995, color page USD 8,050; trim 10.75 x 8. Circ: 50,000 (paid).

003 USA
S I G D O C NEWSLETTER. (Special Interest Group for Documentation) Text in English. q. USD 45 (effective 2004). **Document type:** *Newsletter, Academic/Scholarly.*
—BLDSC (8275.267900).
Published by: Association for Computing Machinery, Inc., 1515 Broadway, 17th Fl, New York, NY 10036-5701. TEL 212-626-0500, 212-626-0520, 800-342-6626, FAX 212-869-0481, sigs@acm.org, usacm@acm.org, http://www.acm.org/sigdoc/.

003 USA
HF5547.5.A1 CODEN: SIGBEL
S I G GROUP BULLETIN. (Special Interest Group) Text in English. 3/yr. USD 48 (effective 2004). **Document type:** *Newsletter, Academic/Scholarly.*
Former titles (until 1997): S I G O I S Bulletin (0894-0819); (until 1986): S I G O A Bulletin (0893-2867); (until 1985): S I G O A Newsletter (0737-819X)
Related titles: Online - full text ed.
Indexed: Inspec.
—BLDSC (8275.269700), AskIEEE, IE.
Published by: Association for Computing Machinery, Inc., 1515 Broadway, 17th Fl, New York, NY 10036-5701. TEL 212-626-0500, 212-626-0520, 800-342-6626, FAX 212-869-0481, group-editors@acm.org, sigs@acm.org, usacm@acm.org, http://www.acm.org/siggroup/.

003 USA
SEMAPHORE SIGNAL. Text in English. 1983. m. USD 10. adv. **Description:** For Apple Lisa and Apple Macintosh computer users. Provides news and information on current products.
Formerly: Signal
Published by: Semaphore Corp., 6325, Santa Barbara, CA 93160-6325. TEL 408-688-9200. Ed. Mike Gabrielson. Circ: 7,000 (controlled).

SHISUTEMU SEIGYO JOHO/SYSTEMS, CONTROL AND INFORMATION. see *COMPUTERS—Automation*

003 ITA ISSN 0394-929X
SISTEMI E IMPRESA. Text in Italian. 1955. m. (10/yr.). adv. bk.rev. charts; illus. index. **Description:** For systems technology managers.
Former titles (until 1988): Sistemi e Automazione (0037-5896); (until 1967): Schede Perforate e Calcolo Elettronico
Indexed: CybAb, Inspec.
—BLDSC (8286.420400), AskIEEE, IE, ingenta.
Published by: Edizioni Scientifiche Tecniche Europee s.r.l., Via Giorgio Vasari, 15, Milan, MI 20135, Italy. TEL 39-02-55018039, FAX 39-02-5455644, edizioni.este@iol.it. Ed. Franco Rebuffo. R&P Gianni Ceriani. Adv. contact Emma Samarati. Circ: 6,500 (paid); 3,000 (controlled).

003 USA ISSN 0094-2898
QA402 CODEN: PASTDB
SOUTHEASTERN SYMPOSIUM ON SYSTEM THEORY. PROCEEDINGS. Key Title: Proceedings of the Annual Southeastern Symposium on System Theory. Text in English. 1969. a. price varies. adv. **Document type:** *Proceedings, Academic/Scholarly.* **Description:** Covers system modeling, analysis, simulation and control.
Related titles: Online - full text ed.: (from I E E E).
Indexed: Inspec.
—BLDSC (8352.497000), IE, ingenta. **CCC.**
Published by: (Institute of Electrical and Electronics Engineers, Inc.), I E E E Computer Society, 10662 Los Vaqueros Circle, PO Box 3014, Los Alamitos, CA 90720-1314. TEL 714-821-8380, FAX 714-821-4641, customer.service@ieee.org, http://www.computer.org.
Co-sponsor: Computer Society.

SPROUTS; working papers on information environments, systems and organizations. see *COMPUTERS—Information Science And Information Theory*

STUDIES IN COMPUTER AND COMMUNICATIONS SYSTEMS. see *COMMUNICATIONS—Computer Applications*

C

▼ new title ➤ refereed ✶ unverified ♦ full entry avail.

003 USA ISSN 1063-9535
QA76.88
SUPERCOMPUTING PROCEEDINGS. Text in English. 1988. a. price varies. adv. **Document type:** *Proceedings, Academic/Scholarly.* **Description:** Provides future directions and exchange information on supercomputing.
Related titles: CD-ROM ed.; Online - full text ed.: (from I E E E).
Indexed: Inspec.
—Ei. **CCC.**
Published by: (Institute of Electrical and Electronics Engineers, Inc.), I E E E Computer Society, 10662 Los Vaqueros Circle, PO Box 3014, Los Alamitos, CA 90720-1314. TEL 714-821-8380, FAX 714-821-4641.

003 USA ISSN 1060-9857
QA76.9.D5 CODEN: PRDSFK
SYMPOSIUM ON RELIABLE DISTRIBUTED SYSTEMS. PROCEEDINGS. Text in English. 1981. a. USD 102 membership (effective 2005). **Document type:** *Proceedings.*
Formerly (until 1987): Symposium on Reliability in Distributed Software and Database Systems. Proceedings (1073-4899)
Related titles: Online - full text ed.: (from I E E E).
—BLDSC (6849.629000), Ei, IE, ingenta. **CCC.**
Published by: (Institute of Electrical and Electronics Engineers, Inc.), I E E E Computer Society, 3 Park Ave, 17th Fl, New York, NY 10017. TEL 714-821-8380, 800-678-4333, FAX 714-821-4641, customer.service@ieee.org, http://www.ieee.org. **Co-sponsors:** University of Pittsburgh; Association for Computing Machinery, Inc.

SYSTEMS CONTRACTOR NEWS; serving the electronic systems industry. see *ELECTRONICS*

005.42 658 USA ISSN 1096-7893
SYSTEMS DEVELOPMENT MANAGEMENT. Text in English. 199?. bi-m.
Related titles: Online - full text ed.: (from EBSCO Publishing).
Published by: Auerbach Publications (Subsidiary of: C R C Press, LLC), 2000 Corporate Blvd., NW, Boca Raton, FL 33431. TEL 212-286-9404, FAX 212-297-9176, orders@crcpress.com, http://www.auerbach-publications.com/home.asp.

003 GBR ISSN 1092-7026
BF1 CODEN: SRBSF9
➤ **SYSTEMS RESEARCH AND BEHAVIORAL SCIENCE.** Text in English. 1984. bi-m. USD 595 to institutions; USD 655 combined subscription to institutions print & online eds. (effective 2006). adv. bk.rev. charts; illus. reprints avail. **Document type:** *Journal, Academic/Scholarly.* **Description:** Provides a forum for the exchange of new ideas and knowledge relating to the use of systems thinking in the development, management and assessment of activities, programs and organizations.
Formed by the merger of (1984-1997): Systems Research (0731-7239); 1956-1997): Behavioral Science (0005-7940)
Related titles: Microform ed.: (from PQC); Online - full text ed.: ISSN 1099-1743. 1996. USD 595 to institutions (effective 2006) (from EBSCO Publishing, Florida Center for Library Automation, Gale Group, ProQuest Information & Learning, Swets Information Services, Wiley InterScience).
Indexed: ABIn, ASCA, AgeL, BAS, CMCI, CompAb, CompC, CurCont, ExcerpMed, IAOP, IBSS, IPSA, Inspec, RASB, RHEA, SSCI, SSI, ZentMath, e-psyche.
—BLDSC (8589.424650), AskIEEE, CISTI, IDS, IE, Infotrieve, ingenta, Linda Hall. **CCC.**
Published by: (International Federation for Systems Research), John Wiley & Sons Ltd. (Subsidiary of: John Wiley & Sons, Inc.), The Atrium, Southern Gate, Chichester, West Sussex PO19 8SQ, United Kingdom. TEL 44-1243-779777, FAX 44-1243-775878, customer@wiley.co.uk, http://www.interscience.wiley.com/jpages/0731-7239/, http://www.wiley.co.uk. Ed. Mike C Jackson. Pub. Diane Taylor. R&P Diane Southern TEL 44-1243-770347. adv.: B&W page GBP 650, color page GBP 1,550; trim 200 x 260. **Subscr. in the America to:** John Wiley & Sons, Inc., 111 River St, Hoboken, NJ 07030-5774. TEL 201-748-6645, 800-225-5945, subinfo@wiley.com

003 USA ISSN 0199-8951
SYSTEMS USER. Text in English. 1980. m. USD 62; USD 98 foreign. adv. bk.rev.
Indexed: CompC, CompD, Inspec.
Published by: Caulfield Publishing Ltd., 308 E Van Buren St, Janesville, WI 53545-4047. Ed. Susan Lindsay. Circ: 37,668.

005.432 USA
▼ **T U X.** (Torvolds Unix) Text in English. 2004. m. USD 35.99 domestic; USD 45.99 in Canada & Mexico; USD 69.99 elsewhere (effective 2005). **Description:** Provides information for new Linux users and is dedicated to promoting and simplifying the use of Linux on the desktop.
Published by: Specialized Systems Consultants Publishing, Ltd., PO Box 55759, Seattle, WA 98155. info@tuxmagazine.com, http://www.tuxmagazine.com/, http://www.ssc.com. Eds. Marjorie Richardson, Marcel Gagne. Pub. Phil Hughes.

003 USA
TORONTO SYSTEMS LETTER✱. Text in English. 1960. bi-m. membership. adv. bk.rev. **Description:** Delves into technical and management issues of information systems management.
Published by: Association for Systems Management, Toronto Chapter, 6289 Hastings Dr, Cleveland, OH 44131-2958. TEL 416-364-4018, FAX 416-862-0315. Ed. Jon Witteker. Circ: 400.

UNIXNT. see *COMPUTERS—Software*

003.5 UKR ISSN 0130-5395
T58.6 CODEN: UPSMBC
UPRAVLYAYUSHCHIE SISTEMY I MASHINY. Short title: U S i M. Text and summaries in English, Russian, Ukrainian. 1972. bi-m. USD 115. illus. **Document type:** *Proceedings, Academic/Scholarly.* **Description:** Covers theories and methods of informatics, information technologies and real-time systems.
Indexed: ApMecR, ChemAb, Djerelo, EngInd, INIS AtomInd, Inspec, RefZh.
—AskIEEE, CASDDS, CISTI, Linda Hall.
Published by: Natsional'na Akademiya Nauk Ukrainy, Instytut Kibernetyky im. V.M. Hlushkova, Pr Akad Glushkova 40, Kiev, 252650, Ukraine. TEL 38-44-2660009, FAX 38-44-2669001. Ed. V I Skurikhin. Pub. V I Gritsenko. Circ: 859. **US dist. addr.:** East View Information Services, 3020 Harbor Ln. N., Minneapolis, MN 55447. TEL 763-550-0961, FAX 763-559-2931, eastview@eastview.com, http://www.eastview.com.

003 USA ISSN 0884-1357
TK7895.B87
V M E BUS SYSTEMS. Key Title: VMEbus Systems. Text in English. 1984. bi-m. free in US & Canada; USD 60 elsewhere (effective 2002). bk.rev. charts; illus.; tr.lit. back issues avail. **Document type:** *Trade.* **Description:** For hardware and system engineers involved in the development and use of VMEbus and VXIbus Systems.
Incorporates: V X I Journal (1072-9933)
Related titles: Online - full text ed.: ISSN 1550-0403.
—CISTI.
Published by: OpenSystems Publishing, 30233 Jefferson Ave, St Clair Shores, MI 48082. TEL 810-415-6500, FAX 810-415-4882, http://www.vmebus-systems.com. Ed., R&P John Black. Adv. contact Pat Hopper. Circ: 18,000.

V R NEWS. (Virtual Reality) see *COMPUTERS—Computer Graphics*

VOICE AND DATA. see *COMMUNICATIONS*

VOPROSY TEORII SISTEM AVTOMATICHESKOGO UPRAVLENIYA. see *COMPUTERS—Automation*

005.43 USA ISSN 1552-3136
WINDOWS I T PRO. Text in English. m. USD 49.95 domestic; USD 59 in Canada; GBP 59 elsewhere (effective 2005). **Document type:** *Magazine, Trade.*
Related titles: Online - full text ed.: (from ProQuest Information & Learning).
Published by: Penton Media, Inc. (Subsidiary of: Pittway Company), 221 E. 29th St., Loveland, CO 80538. TEL 970-663-4700, 800-621-1544, FAX 970-667-2321, http://www.windowsitpro.com/, http://www.pentonmedia.com. Ed. Janet Robbins. Pub. Kim Paulsen.

WIRELESS COMMUNICATIONS AND MOBILE COMPUTING. see *COMMUNICATIONS*

003 USA ISSN 1071-0485
WORKSHOP ON FUTURE TRENDS OF DISTRIBUTED COMPUTING SYSTEMS. PROCEEDINGS. Text in English. irreg. USD 102 membership (effective 2005). **Document type:** *Proceedings, Trade.*
Related titles: Online - full text ed.: (from I E E E).
—BLDSC (6844.166760). **CCC.**
Published by: I E E E Computer Society, 10662 Los Vaqueros Circle, PO Box 3014, Los Alamitos, CA 90720-1314. TEL 714-821-8380, 800-272-6657, FAX 714-821-4010, customer.service@ieee.org, http://www.computer.org.

620.001171 CHN ISSN 1000-6788
TA168 CODEN: XGLSE2
➤ **XITONG GONGCHENG LILUN YU SHIJIAN/SYSTEM ENGINEERING THEORY AND PRACTICE.** Text in Chinese; Summaries in Chinese, English. 1981. m. CNY 96 (effective 2001). bk.rev.; software rev. abstr.; bibl.; charts; illus.; pat. Index. back issues avail. **Document type:** *Journal, Academic/Scholarly.* **Description:** Aims at publishing the new results on the theory of system science and the applicaiton of a variety of areas.
Related titles: CD-ROM ed.; Online - full content ed.; Online - full text ed.: (from East View Information Services).
Indexed: EngInd.
Published by: Zhongguo Xitong Gongcheng Xuehui/Systems Engineering Society of China, Xitong Yanjiusuo, Zhongguancun, Beijing, 100080, China. TEL 81-1-2541828, FAX 81-1-2568364, xtll@chinajournal.net.cn. Ed. Gu Jifa. Circ: 2,300 (paid).

003 CHN ISSN 1000-0577
Q295 CODEN: XKSHEW
➤ **XITONG KEXUE YU SHUXUE/JOURNAL OF SYSTEMS SCIENCE AND MATHEMATICAL SCIENCES.** Text in Chinese; Summaries in English. 1981. q. CNY 112 (effective 2004). adv. **Document type:** *Journal, Academic/Scholarly.* **Description:** Presents original papers in mathematics from mainland China, including systems theory, system modeling, and system control.
Related titles: Online - full text ed.: (from East View Information Services, WanFang Data Corp.); ♦ Chinese Translation: Journal of Systems Science and Complexity. ISSN 1009-6124.
Indexed: CCMJ, CIS, IAOP, MathR, MathSciNet, RefZh, ZentMath.
—Linda Hall.
Published by: (Zhongguo Kexueyuan, Xitong Kexue Yanjiusuo/Chinese Academy of Sciences, Institute of System Science), Kexue Chubanshe/Science Press, 16 Donghuang Cheng Genbei Jie, Beijing, 100717, China. TEL 86-10-64000246, FAX 86-10-64030255, jssms@slaff.iss.ac.cn, http://xtkxysx-z.periodicals.net.cn/default.html, http://www.sciencep.com/. Circ: 6,000. **Dist. by:** China International Book Trading Corp, 35 Chegongzhuang Xilu, Haidian District, PO Box 399, Beijing 100044, China. TEL 86-10-68412045, FAX 86-10-68412023, cibtc@mail.cibtc.com.cn, http://www.cibtc.com.cn.

COMPUTERS—Cybernetics

see also COMPUTERS—Artificial Intelligence

➤ **BULLETIN OF INFORMATICS AND CYBERNETICS.** see *MATHEMATICS*

510 001.6 USA
➤ **COMPUTATIONAL MATHEMATICS AND APPLICATIONS.** Text in English. 1977. irreg., latest 1994. USD 105 per vol. vol.10 (effective 2004). reprint service avail. from ISI. **Document type:** *Academic/Scholarly.* **Description:** Presents state-of-the-art theories, methods, algorithms, and applications of mathematical extensions for classical wavelet analysis.
Indexed: MathR.
Published by: Academic Press (Subsidiary of: Elsevier Science & Technology), 525 B St, Ste 1900, San Diego, CA 92101-4495. TEL 619-231-6616, 800-894-3434, apsubs@acad.com, http://www.academicpress.com. Ed. J R Whiteman.

003.5 POL ISSN 0324-8569
QA402.3 CODEN: CCYBAP
➤ **CONTROL AND CYBERNETICS.** Text in English. 1972. q. EUR 120; EUR 40 per issue (effective 2005). adv. bk.rev.; software rev. bibl. back issues avail. **Document type:** *Journal, Academic/Scholarly.* **Description:** Publishes papers dealing with systems and control theory and systems control and management.
Indexed: ApMecR, CCMJ, CMCI, CompC, CurCont, CybAb, Inspec, MathR, MathSciNet, RefZh, ZentMath.
—BLDSC (3461.856000), AskIEEE, CISTI, IE, ingenta.
Published by: Polska Akademia Nauk, Instytut Badan' Systemowych/Polish Academy of Sciences, Systems Research Institute, ul Newelska 6, Warsaw, 01447, Poland. TEL 48-22-8373578, FAX 48-22-8372772, control@ibspan.waw.pl, owsinski@ibspan.waw.pl, http://control.ibspan.waw.pl, http://www.ibspan.waw.pl. Ed. Zbigniew Nahorski. R&P, Adv. contact Jan W Owsinski TEL 48-22-8364414. Circ: 600.

003.5 BEL ISSN 0011-4227
Q350 CODEN: CYBEA5
CYBERNETICA. Text in English, French. 1958. q. USD 120 (effective 1998). bk.rev. charts; illus. index. back issues avail. **Document type:** *Academic/Scholarly.*
Indexed: ASCA, ASFA, AnBeAb, CCMJ, CMCI, CompC, CurCont, ESPM, EngInd, ExcerpMed, H&SSA, Inspec, MathR, SSCI, ZentMath.
—AskIEEE, CISTI, Linda Hall.
Published by: International Association for Cybernetics/Association Internationale de Cybernetique, Palais des Expositions, Av Sergent Vrithoff 2, Namur, 5000, Belgium. TEL 32-81-735209, FAX 32-81-742045.

003.5 GBR ISSN 0907-0877
Q300
➤ **CYBERNETICS & HUMAN KNOWING**; a journal of second order cybernetics, autopoiesis and cyber-semiotics. Text in English. 1994. q. GBP 46 combined subscription domestic to individuals print & online eds.; USD 87.50 combined subscription foreign to individuals print & online eds.; GBP 99 combined subscription domestic to institutions print & online eds.; USD 188 combined subscription foreign to institutions print & online eds.; GBP 18.50 per issue domestic to individuals; USD 35 per issue foreign to individuals; GBP 37.50 per issue domestic to institutions; USD 71.50 per issue foreign to institutions (effective 2006). bk.rev. back issues avail. **Document type:** *Journal, Academic/Scholarly.* **Description:** Acts as an international, trans-disciplinary journal examining and reconceptualizing the emerging constellation of human understanding and practices of living in a post-modern information environment, drawing largely on the cybernetics of cybernetics.

Related titles: Online - full text ed.: (from EBSCO Publishing, Gale Group, IngentaConnect, O C L C Online Computer Library Center, Inc., Swets Information Services).
Indexed: RILM, e-psyche.
—BLDSC (3506.390300), IE, ingenta. **CCC.**
Published by: Imprint Academic, PO Box 200, Exeter, Devon EXS 5YX, United Kingdom. TEL 44-1392-841600, FAX 44-1392-841478, sandra@imprint.co.uk, http://www.imprint.co.uk/C&HK/cyber.htm. Ed. Soren Brier. Pub., R&P, Adv. contact Mr. Keith Sutherland. Circ: 200.

003.54 BGR ISSN 1311-9702
Q300 CODEN: CITYBA
CYBERNETICS AND INFORMATION TECHNOLOGIES. Abbreviated title: C I T. Text in English, Bulgarian. q. **Document type:** *Journal, Academic/Scholarly.*
Indexed: BrCerAb, C&ISA, CerAb, CorrAb, E&CAJ, EMA, IAA, Inspec, M&TEA, MBF, METADEX, MathR, MathSciNet, WAA.
—BLDSC (3506.390500), Linda Hall.
Published by: Bulgarska Akademiya na Naukite, Institut po Informatsionni Tekhnologii/Bulgarian Academy of Sciences, Institute of Information Technologies, 2, Acad. G Bonchev, Sofia, 1113, Bulgaria. Ed. Danail Dochev.

003.5 USA ISSN 0196-9722
Q300 CODEN: CYSYDH
➤ **CYBERNETICS AND SYSTEMS.** Text in English. 1971. 8/yr. GBP 1,098, USD 1,813 combined subscription to institutions print & online eds. (effective 2006). adv. bk.rev. abstr.; bibl.; charts; illus. index. back issues avail.; reprint service avail. from PQC,PSC. **Document type:** *Journal, Academic/Scholarly.* **Description:** Provides information on cybernetics applications for the scientific community. Topics covered include machine science, production systems, problem-solving in games, systems methodology and information systems.
Formerly (until 1980): Journal of Cybernetics (0022-0280)
Related titles: Microform ed.: (from PQC); Online - full text ed.: ISSN 1087-6553. GBP 1,043, USD 1,722 to institutions (effective 2006) (from EBSCO Publishing, Gale Group, IngentaConnect, O C L C Online Computer Library Center, Inc., Swets Information Services).
Indexed: AHCI, ApMecR, BIOSIS Prev, BiolAb, BrCerAb, C&ISA, CIS, CMCI, CerAb, CompAb, CompLI, CorrAb, CurCont, CybAb, E&CAJ, EMA, EngInd, IAA, IPSA, ISMEC, Inspec, M&TEA, MBF, METADEX, MathR, SolStAb, WAA, ZentMath.
—BLDSC (3506.391000), AskIEEE, CISTI, Ei, IDS, IE, Infotrieve, ingenta, Linda Hall. **CCC.**
Published by: (Austrian Society for Cybernetic Studies AUT), Taylor & Francis Inc. (Subsidiary of: Taylor & Francis Group), 325 Chestnut St, Ste 800, Philadelphia, PA 19016. TEL 215-625-8900, 800-354-1420, FAX 215-625-2940, 215-625-8914, info@taylorandfrancis.com, http://www.tandf.co.uk/journals/titles/01969722.asp, http://www.taylorandfrancis.com. Ed. Robert Trappl. Circ: 450. **Subscr. outside N. America to:** Taylor & Francis Ltd, Journals Customer Service, Rankine Rd, Basingstoke, Hants RG24 8PR, United Kingdom. TEL 44-1256-813000, FAX 44-1256-330245, enquiry@tandf.co.uk.

003.5 USA ISSN 1060-0396
Q300 CODEN: CYASEC
➤ **CYBERNETICS AND SYSTEMS ANALYSIS.** Text in English. 1965. bi-m. EUR 2,785, USD 2,835, GBP 1,735 combined subscription to institutions print & online eds. (effective 2005). adv. back issues avail. **Document type:** *Journal, Academic/Scholarly.* **Description:** Contains scholarly papers on all aspects of cybernetics. Topics include mathematical tools and models, computing algorithms, numeric software, specifications, computer applications and theorems.
Formerly: Cybernetics (0011-4235)
Related titles: Microfilm ed.: (from PQC); Online - full text ed.: ISSN 1573-8337 (from EBSCO Publishing, Gale Group, IngentaConnect, Kluwer Online, O C L C Online Computer Library Center, Inc., Ovid Technologies, Inc., ProQuest Information & Learning, Springer LINK, Swets Information Services); ♦ Translation of: Kibernetika i Sistemnyi Analiz. ISSN 1019-5262.
Indexed: ABIn, ASCA, ApMecR, BibLing, CCMJ, CMCI, CompAb, CompC, CompLI, CurCont, EngInd, Inspec, MathR, MathSciNet, SCI, ZentMath.
—BLDSC (0411.087800), AskIEEE, CISTI, IDS, IE, Infotrieve, ingenta, Linda Hall. **CCC.**
Published by: (Natsional'na Akademiya Nauk Ukrainy UKR), Consultants Bureau (Subsidiary of: Springer-Verlag New York, Inc.), 233 Spring St, New York, NY 10013. TEL 212-460-1500, FAX 212-460-1575, service@springer-ny.com, http://springerlink.metapress.com/openurl.asp?genre=journal&issn=1060-0396, http://www.springeronline.com. Ed. I V Sergienko.

003.5 BEL
CYBERNETICS: WORKS IN PROGRESS/CYBERNETICS: DOCUMENTS DE TRAVAIL. Text in Multiple languages. irreg., latest vol.5. price varies. **Document type:** *Monographic series.*
Published by: International Association for Cybernetics/ Association Internationale de Cybernetique, Palais des Expositions, Av Sergent Vrithoff 2, Namur, 5000, Belgium. TEL 32-81-735209, FAX 32-81-742045.

GEEKGIRL. see *WOMEN'S INTERESTS*

003.5 UKR ISSN 0207-0111
QA76.38 CODEN: GVMKD2
GIBRIDNYE VYCHISLITEL'NYE MASHINY I KOMPLEKSY; respublikanskii mezhvedomstvennyi sbornik nauchnykh trudov. Text in Russian. 1979. a.
—CASDDS, Linda Hall. **CCC.**
Published by: (Institut Problem Modelirovaniya v Energetike), Natsional'na Akademiya Nauk Ukrainy, vul Volodymyrs'ka 54, Kyiv, 01601, Ukraine. TEL 380-44-2352239, FAX 380-44-2343243, prez@nas.gov.ua, http://www.nas.gov.ua. **Dist. by:** M K - Periodica, ul Gilyarovskogo 39, Moscow 129110, Russian Federation.

003.5 DEU ISSN 0723-4899
➤ **GRUNDLAGENSTUDIEN AUS KYBERNETIK UND GEISTESWISSENSCHAFT;** Humankybernetik. Text in German, Esperanto, French, English, Italian. 1960. q. EUR 40 (effective 2003). adv. bk.rev. bibl.; charts. Supplement avail.; back issues avail. **Document type:** *Journal, Academic/Scholarly.* **Description:** Covers the aesthetics of information, cybernetic educational theory, cybernetic linguistics, biocybernetics, as well as economic and juridical cybernetics.
Indexed: DIP, IBR, IBZ, Inspec, L&LBA, PhilInd, SOPODA.
—**CCC.**
Published by: (Institut fuer Kybernetik), Akademia Libroservo - IfK Paderborn, Kleinenberger Weg 16, Paderborn, 33100, Germany. TEL 49-5251-163530, FAX 49-5251-163533, bbara1@hrz.upb.de, http://www.grkg.126.com. Ed. Dr. Helmar Frank. R&P Vera Barandovska TEL 49-5251-163522. Adv. contact Baerbel Ehmke TEL 49-5251-64200. Circ: 300.

➤ **I E E E TRANSACTIONS ON SIGNAL PROCESSING.** see *ENGINEERING—Electrical Engineering*

003.5 USA ISSN 1083-4427
TA167 CODEN: ITSHFX
➤ **I E E E TRANSACTIONS ON SYSTEMS, MAN AND CYBERNETICS, PART A: SYSTEMS & HUMANS.** Text in English. 1971. bi-m. USD 425 (effective 2006). bk.rev. abstr.; illus. index. **Document type:** *Journal, Academic/Scholarly.* **Description:** Contains papers on the theoretical and practical considerations of natural and synthetic systems involving people and machines.
Supersedes in part (in 1996): I E E E Transactions on Systems, Man and Cybernetics (0018-9472); Which was formed by the merger of (1968-1971): I E E E Transactions on Man-Machine Systems (0536-1540); Which was formerly (1963-1967): I E E E Transactions on Human Factors in Electronics (0096-249X); (1965-1971): I E E E Transactions on Systems Science and Cybernetics (0536-1567)
Related titles: CD-ROM ed.; Microfiche ed.; Online - full text ed.: (from EBSCO Publishing, Swets Information Services).
Indexed: AHCI, AIA, AS&TI, BibInd, Biostat, CADCAM, CMCI, ChemAb, CompAb, CompC, CompD, CompLI, CurCont, CybAb, DIP, ESPM, EngInd, ErgAb, ExcerpMed, H&SSA, HRIS, IAA, IBR, IBZ, ISR, Inspec, MathR, NSCI, ORMS, PsySCAP, PsycInfo, PsycholAb, QC&AS, RefZh, RiskAb, RoboAb, SCI, SSCI, TelAb, ZentMath.
—BLDSC (4363.225000), AskIEEE, CISTI, Ei, IDS, IE, Infotrieve, ingenta, Linda Hall. **CCC.**
Published by: Institute of Electrical and Electronics Engineers, Inc., 445 Hoes Ln, Piscataway, NJ 08854-1331. TEL 732-981-0060, 800-701-4333, FAX 732-981-1721, subscription-service@ieee.org, http://www.ieee.org. Ed. Chelsea C White III. **Subscr. to:** Maruzen Co., Ltd., 3-10 Nihonbashi 2-chome, Chuo-ku, Tokyo 103-0027, Japan. FAX 81-3-3275-0657; Universal Subscription Agency, Pvt. Ltd., 877, Udyog Vihar, V, Gurgoan 122001, India. TEL 91-124-347261, FAX 91-124-342496. **Co-sponsor:** Systems, Man and Cybernetics Society.

003.5 USA ISSN 1083-4419
Q300 CODEN: ITSCFI
➤ **I E E E TRANSACTIONS ON SYSTEMS, MAN AND CYBERNETICS, PART B: CYBERNETICS.** Text in English. 1971. bi-m. USD 445 (effective 2006). **Document type:** *Journal, Academic/Scholarly.* **Description:** Deals with computational intelligence including communication and control across humans, machines, and organizations at the structural or neural level, as well as functional and purposeful ones.
Supersedes in part (in 1996): I E E E Transactions on Systems, Man and Cybernetics (0018-9472); Which was formed by the merger of (1968-1971): I E E E Transactions on Man-Machine Systems (0536-1540); Which was formerly (1963-1967): I E E E Transactions on Human Factors in Electronics (0096-249X); (1965-1971): I E E E Transactions on Systems Science and Cybernetics (0536-1567)
Related titles: CD-ROM ed.; Microfiche ed.; Online - full text ed.: (from EBSCO Publishing, Swets Information Services).
Indexed: AS&TI, CMCI, CompAb, CompD, CompLI, CurCont, ESPM, EngInd, ErgAb, H&SSA, IAA, ISR, Inspec, RefZh, RiskAb, SCI, ZentMath.
—BLDSC (4363.225050), AskIEEE, CISTI, IDS, IE, Infotrieve, ingenta, Linda Hall. **CCC.**

Published by: Institute of Electrical and Electronics Engineers, Inc., 445 Hoes Ln, Piscataway, NJ 08854-1331. TEL 732-981-0060, 800-701-4333, FAX 732-981-1721, subscription-service@ieee.org, http://www.ieee.org. Ed. Krishna Pattipati. **Subscr. to:** Maruzen Co., Ltd., 3-10 Nihonbashi 2-chome, Chuo-ku, Tokyo 103-0027, Japan. FAX 81-3-3275-0657; Universal Subscription Agency, Pvt. Ltd., 877, Udyog Vihar, V, Gurgoan 122001, India. TEL 91-124-347261, FAX 91-124-342496. **Co-sponsor:** Systems, Man and Cybernetics Society.

003.5 USA ISSN 1094-6977
TA168 CODEN: ITCRFH
➤ **I E E E TRANSACTIONS ON SYSTEMS, MAN AND CYBERNETICS, PART C: APPLICATIONS AND REVIEWS.** Text in English. 1971. bi-m. USD 275 (effective 2006). adv. bk.rev. illus. Index. reprints avail. **Document type:** *Journal, Academic/Scholarly.* **Description:** Presents overview, tutorial, and application papers on all aspects of systems engineering, cybernetics and computational intelligence, and human machine systems.
Supersedes in part (in 1996): I E E E Transactions on Systems, Man and Cybernetics (0018-9472); Which was formed by the merger of (1968-1971): I E E E Transactions on Man-Machine Systems (0536-1540); Which was formerly (1963-1967): I E E E Transactions on Human Factors in Electronics (0096-249X); (1965-1971): I E E E Transactions on Systems Science and Cybernetics (0536-1567)
Related titles: CD-ROM ed.; Microfiche ed.; Online - full text ed.: (from EBSCO Publishing, Swets Information Services).
Indexed: AS&TI, C&ISA, CMCI, CompLI, CurCont, E&CAJ, EngInd, ErgAb, ISR, InfoSAb, Inspec, RefZh, SCI, SolStAb.
—BLDSC (4363.225070), AskIEEE, CISTI, IDS, IE, Infotrieve, ingenta, Linda Hall.
Published by: Institute of Electrical and Electronics Engineers, Inc., 445 Hoes Ln, Piscataway, NJ 08854-1331. TEL 732-981-0060, 800-701-4333, FAX 732-981-1721, smcc-eic@labe.felk.cvut.cz, subscription-service@ieee.org, http://ieeexplore.ieee.org/xpl/RecentIssue.jsp?punumber=5326, http://www.ieee.org. Ed. Vladimir Marik. **Subscr. to:** Maruzen Co., Ltd., 3-10 Nihonbashi 2-chome, Chuo-ku, Tokyo 103-0027, Japan. FAX 81-3-3275-0657; Universal Subscription Agency, Pvt. Ltd., 877, Udyog Vihar, V, Gurgoan 122001, India. TEL 91-124-347261, FAX 91-124-342496. **Co-sponsor:** Systems, Man and Cybernetics Society.

C

003 DEU ISSN 0178-3564
CODEN: IFENEI
➤ **INFORMATIK - FORSCHUNG UND ENTWICKLUNG.** Key Title: Informatik. Text in German. 1986. q. EUR 348 combined subscription to institutions print & online eds. (effective 2005). adv. **Document type:** *Journal, Academic/Scholarly.* **Description:** Covers all aspects of informatics and information systems.
Related titles: Online - full text ed.: ISSN 0949-2925 (from EBSCO Publishing, Springer LINK, Swets Information Services).
Indexed: BMT, EngInd, Inspec, ZentMath.
—BLDSC (4481.366000), AskIEEE, Ei, IE, Infotrieve, ingenta. **CCC.**
Published by: (Gesellschaft fuer Informatik e.V.), Springer-Verlag (Subsidiary of: Springer Science+Business Media), Tiergartenstr 17, Heidelberg, 69121, Germany. TEL 49-6221-3450, FAX 49-6221-345229, http://link.springer.de/link/service/journals/00450/index.htm. Eds. S Jaehnichen, T Haerder. Adv. contact Stephan Kroeck TEL 49-30-827875739. **Subscr. in the Americas to:** Springer-Verlag New York, Inc., Journal Fulfillment, PO Box 2485, Secaucus, NJ 07096-2485. TEL 800-777-4643, 201-348-4033, FAX 201-348-4505, journals@springer-ny.com, http://www.springer-ny.com; **Subscr. to:** Springer GmbH Auslieferungsgesellschaft, Haberstr 7, Heidelberg 69126, Germany. TEL 49-6221-345-0, FAX 49-6221-345-4229, subscriptions@springer.de.

003.5 BEL ISSN 0074-3380
INTERNATIONAL CONGRESS FOR CYBERNETICS. PROCEEDINGS/CONGRES INTERNATIONAL DE CYBERNETIQUE. ACTES. Text in English. 1956. triennial. **Document type:** *Proceedings.*
Related titles: French ed.: Association Internationale de Cybernetique. Congres International de Cybernetique. Actes. ISSN 0538-6675. 1956.
Published by: International Association for Cybernetics/ Association Internationale de Cybernetique, Palais des Expositions, Av Sergent Vrithoff 2, Namur, 5000, Belgium. TEL 32-81-717171, FAX 32-81-717100.

003.5 GBR ISSN 1071-5819
TA167 CODEN: IHSTEI
➤ **INTERNATIONAL JOURNAL OF HUMAN-COMPUTER STUDIES.** Text in English. 1969. 12/yr. EUR 659 in Europe to individuals; JPY 71,200 in Japan to individuals; USD 690 elsewhere to individuals; EUR 2,327 in Europe to institutions; JPY 251,400 in Japan to institutions; USD 2,069 elsewhere to institutions (effective 2006). adv. illus. reprints avail. **Document type:** *Journal, Academic/Scholarly.* **Description:** Aimed at engineers, researchers, psychologists, and computer scientists. Contains articles on a broad range of pertinent topics, from person-machine interaction to management and medical information systems.
Incorporates (1989-1995): Knowledge Acquisition (1042-8143); Formerly (1969-1993): International Journal of Man-Machine Studies (0020-7373)

Related titles: Online - full text ed.: ISSN 1095-9300. USD 2,182 (effective 2002) (from EBSCO Publishing, Gale Group, IngentaConnect, O C L C Online Computer Library Center, Inc., ScienceDirect, Swets Information Services).
Indexed: AHCI, AIA, AS&TI, ASCA, BiolAb, C&ISA, CADCAM, CMCI, ChemAb, CommAb, CompAb, CompC, CompD, CompLI, CompR, CurCont, CybAb, E&CAJ, ETA, EngInd, ErgAb, ExcerpMed, IAA, ISR, Inspec, LISA, LingAb, PsySCAP, PsycInfo, PsycholAb, RoboAb, SCI, SSCI, TEA, ZentMath, e-psyche.
—BLDSC (4542.288100), AskIEEE, CISTI, Ei, IDS, IE, Infotrieve, ingenta, Linda Hall. **CCC.**
Published by: Academic Press (Subsidiary of: Elsevier Science & Technology), Harcourt Pl, 32 Jamestown Rd, London, NW1 7BY, United Kingdom. TEL 44-20-7424-4200, FAX 44-20-7483-2293, apsubs@acad.com, http://www.elsevier.com/locate/ijhcs. Eds. E. Motta, S. Wiedenbeck. **Subscr. to:** Harcourt Publishers Ltd., Foots Cray High St, Sidcup, Kent DA14 5HP, United Kingdom. TEL 44-208-3085700, FAX 44-20-83090807.

➤ **JOURNAL OF AUTOMATION & INFORMATION SCIENCES.** see *COMPUTERS—Automation*

003.5 RUS ISSN 1064-2307
QA75.5 CODEN: JSSIE5
➤ **JOURNAL OF COMPUTER AND SYSTEM SCIENCES INTERNATIONAL.** Text in English. 1963. bi-m. USD 2,889 in North America; USD 3,322 elsewhere (effective 2004). adv. bk.rev. abstr.; bibl.; charts; illus.; pat.; stat. index. **Document type:** *Journal, Academic/Scholarly.* **Description:** Contains papers on computer and systems science, control theory, and optimization studies. Specific topics include algorithms, design of computer and control systems, data processing, robotics, pattern recognition and applied mathematics.
Former titles (until 1992): Soviet Journal of Computer and Systems Sciences (0882-4002); (until 1984): Engineering Cybernetics (0013-788X)
Related titles: Microform ed.: (from PQC); ♦ Translation of: Rossiiskaya Akademiya Nauk. Izvestiya. Teoriya i Systemy Upravleniya. ISSN 1029-3620.
Indexed: AIA, ASCA, ArtHuCI, C&ISA, CADCAM, CIS, CMCI, CivEngAb, CurCont, E&CAJ, EngInd, ISMEC, Inspec, MathR, RoboAb, SSCI, SolStAb, ZentMath.
—BLDSC (0414.230000), AskIEEE, CISTI, Ei, IDS, IE, Infotrieve, ingenta, Linda Hall. **CCC.**
Published by: (Rossiiskaya Akademiya Nauk/Russian Academy of Sciences), M A I K Nauka - Interperiodica, Profsoyuznaya ul 90, Moscow, 117997, Russian Federation. TEL 7-095-3347420, FAX 7-095-3360666, compmg@maik.ru, http://www.maik.rssi.ru/journals/compsys.htm, http://www.maik.ru. Ed. Evgenii A Fedosov. R&P Vladimir I Vasil'ev. **Subscr. to:** Interperiodica, PO Box 1831, Birmingham, AL 35201-1831. TEL 205-995-1567, 800-633-4931, FAX 205-995-1588.

006.3 ISR ISSN 0334-1860
CODEN: JISYEH
JOURNAL OF INTELLIGENT SYSTEMS. Text in English. 1986. 6/yr. USD 330 (effective 2006). adv. abstr. **Document type:** *Academic/Scholarly.*
Indexed: ArtIAb, B&BAb, EngInd, Inspec, PsycholAb, ZentMath.
—BLDSC (5007.538600), AskIEEE, CISTI, IE, Infotrieve, ingenta.
Published by: Freund Publishing House, Ltd., P O Box 35010, Tel Aviv, 61350, Israel. TEL 972-3-5628540, FAX 972-3-5628538, h_freund@netvision.net.il, http://www.freundpublishing.com/Journal_Intelligent_Systems/IntelliPrev.htm. Ed. M Wright. Circ: 1,000.

003.5 UKR ISSN 1019-5262
TJ212 CODEN: KBRNA5
KIBERNETIKA I SISTEMNYI ANALIZ; nauchno-teoreticheskii zhurnal. Text in Russian; Summaries in English, Ukrainian. 1965. bi-m. USD 234 foreign (effective 2003). index. **Document type:** *Academic/Scholarly.*
Formerly (until 1991): Kibernetika (0023-1274)
Related titles: ♦ English Translation: Cybernetics and Systems Analysis. ISSN 1060-0396.
Indexed: BiolAb, CCMJ, CIS, CybAb, Djerelo, EngInd, INIS AtomInd, Inspec, MathR, MathSciNet, RASB, RefZh, ZentMath.
—BLDSC (0088.726500), CASDDS, CINDOC, CISTI, East View, KNAW, Linda Hall.
Published by: Natsional'na Akademiya Nauk Ukrainy, Instytut Kibernetyky im. V.M. Hlushkova, Pr Akad Glushkova 40, Kiev, 252650, Ukraine. TEL 380-44-2660059. Ed. V S Mikhalevich. **Dist. by:** M K - Periodica, ul Gilyarovskogo 39, Moscow 129110, Russian Federation. TEL 7-095-2845008, FAX 7-095-2813798, info@periodicals.ru, http://www.mkniga.ru; **US dist. addr.:** East View Information Services, 3020 Harbor Ln. N., Minneapolis, MN 55447. TEL 612-550-0961.

003.5 UKR ISSN 0454-9910
Q300 CODEN: KVYTAS
KIBERNETIKA I VYCHISLITEL'NAYA TEKHNIKA; respublikanskii mezhvedomstvennyi sbornik nauchnykh trudov. Text in Russian. 1965. 4/yr.
Indexed: CybAb, EngInd, Inspec, MathR, ZentMath.
—AskIEEE, CASDDS, CISTI, Linda Hall. **CCC.**
Published by: Natsional'na Akademiya Nauk Ukrainy, Instytut Kibernetyky im. V.M. Hlushkova, Pr Akad Glushkova 40, Kiev, 252650, Ukraine. TEL 38-44-2652494. Ed. V S Mikhalevich.

003 GBR ISSN 0368-492X
Q300 CODEN: KBNTA3
➤ **KYBERNETES.** Text in English. 1970. 10/yr. EUR 9,938.66 in Europe; USD 10,229 in North America; AUD 12,559 in Australasia; GBP 6,958.91 in UK & elsewhere (effective 2006). bk.rev. index. reprint service avail. from PSC. **Document type:** *Journal, Academic/Scholarly.* **Description:** Concerned with the interdisciplinary study of cybernetics and systems. Topics covered include artificial intelligence, automation, cybernetic modelling, the philosophy of cybernetics and its interrelations with other sciences.
Related titles: Online - full text ed.: (from EBSCO Publishing, Emerald Group Publishing Limited, Gale Group, IngentaConnect, O C L C Online Computer Library Center, Inc., ProQuest Information & Learning, Swets Information Services).
Indexed: AHCI, ASCA, BIOSIS Prev, BiolAb, BrCerAb, C&ISA, CCMJ, CMCI, CerAb, ChemAb, CompAb, CompLI, CorrAb, CurCont, CybAb, E&CAJ, EMA, EmerIntel, EngInd, IAA, Inspec, M&TEA, MBF, METADEX, MathR, MathSciNet, RefZh, SSCI, SolStAb, WAA, ZentMath.
—BLDSC (5134.840000), AskIEEE, CISTI, Ei, IDS, IE, Infotrieve, ingenta, Linda Hall. **CCC.**
Published by: Emerald Group Publishing Limited, 60-62 Toller Ln, Bradford, W Yorks BD8 9BY, United Kingdom. TEL 44-1274-777700, FAX 44-1274-785200, infomation@emeraldinsight.com, http://www.emeraldinsight.com/kyb.htm. Ed. Brian Rudall. Pub. Vicky Williams. Circ: 750.

➤ **KYBERNETIKA/CYBERNETICS.** see *MATHEMATICS*

003.5 DEU ISSN 0932-8092
TA1632 CODEN: MVAPEO
➤ **MACHINE VISION & APPLICATIONS**; an international journal. Text in English. 1988. bi-m. EUR 348 combined subscription to institutions print & online eds. (effective 2005). adv. back issues avail.; reprint service avail. from PSC. **Document type:** *Journal, Academic/Scholarly.* **Description:** Covers applications and engineering aspects of image-related computing including original contributions dealing with scientific, commercial, industrial, military and biomedical applications.
Related titles: Microform ed.: (from PQC); Online - full text ed.: ISSN 1432-1769 (from EBSCO Publishing, Springer LINK, Swets Information Services).
Indexed: AHCI, ASCA, B&BAb, BrCerAb, C&ISA, CMCI, CerAb, CompAb, CompLI, CompR, CorrAb, CurCont, E&CAJ, EMA, EngInd, IAA, ISMEC, Inspec, M&TEA, MBF, METADEX, SolStAb, WAA.
—BLDSC (5326.570000), AskIEEE, CISTI, Ei, IDS, IE, Infotrieve, ingenta, Linda Hall. **CCC.**
Published by: (International Association for Pattern Recognition NLD), Springer-Verlag (Subsidiary of: Springer Science+Business Media), Tiergartenstr 17, Heidelberg, 69121, Germany. TEL 49-6221-3450, FAX 49-6221-345229, http://link.springer.de/link/service/journals/00138/index.htm. Ed. Mohan M Trivedi TEL 619-534-0415. Adv. contact Stephan Kroeck TEL 49-30-827875739. Circ: 1,480. **Subscr. in the Americas to:** Springer-Verlag New York, Inc., Journal Fulfillment, PO Box 2485, Secaucus, NJ 07096-2485. TEL 800-777-4643, 201-348-4033, FAX 201-348-4505, journals@springer-ny.com, http://www.springer-ny.com; **Subscr. to:** Springer GmbH Auslieferungsgesellschaft, Haberstr 7, Heidelberg 69126, Germany. TEL 49-6221-345-0, FAX 49-6221-345-4229, subscriptions@springer.de.

003.5 513.5 USA ISSN 0278-6419
QA1 CODEN: MUCTD4
➤ **MOSCOW STATE UNIVERSITY COMPUTATIONAL MATHEMATICS AND CYBERNETICS.** Text in English. 1977. q. USD 1,960 per vol. in US & Canada; USD 2,240 per vol. elsewhere (effective 2006). abstr.; charts; illus. index. back issues avail. **Document type:** *Journal, Academic/Scholarly.* **Description:** Publishes papers that report on the theoretical research of practical problems in computer technology, artificial intelligence, computation algorithms, and system dynamics.
Related titles: ♦ Russian ed.: Moskovskii Gosudarstvennyi Universitet. Vestnik. Seriya 15. Vychislitel'naya Matematika i Kibernetika. ISSN 0137-0782.
Indexed: CCMJ, Inspec, MathR, MathSciNet, ZentMath.
—BLDSC (0416.238300), AskIEEE, CISTI, IE, Infotrieve, Linda Hall. **CCC.**
Published by: (Moskovskii Gosudarstvennyi Universitet im. M.V. Lomonosova/M.V. Lomonosov Moscow State University RUS), Allerton Press, Inc., 18 W 27th St, New York, NY 10001. TEL 646-424-9686, FAX 646-424-9695, journals@allertonpress.com, http://www.allertonpress.com/journals/muk.htm. Ed. Dmitry P Kostomarov.

003.5 RUS ISSN 0137-0782
QA75.5 CODEN: VMUKD8
MOSKOVSKII GOSUDARSTVENNYI UNIVERSITET. VESTNIK. SERIYA 15. VYCHISLITEL'NAYA MATEMATIKA I KIBERNETIKA. Text in Russian. 1977. q. USD 28 foreign (effective 2004). **Document type:** *Journal, Academic/Scholarly.*
Related titles: ♦ English ed.: Moscow State University Computational Mathematics and Cybernetics. ISSN 0278-6419.
Indexed: C&ISA, CIS, E&CAJ, MathR, MathSciNet, RefZh, SolStAb, ZentMath.
—CISTI, Linda Hall.
Published by: (Moskovskii Gosudarstvennyi Universitet im. M.V. Lomonosova, Fakul'tet Vychislitel'noi Matematiki i Kibernetiki/M.V. Lomonosov Moscow State University, Faculty of Computing Mathematics and Cybernetics), Izdatel'stvo Moskovskogo Gosudarstvennogo Universiteta im. M. V. Lomonosova/Publishing House of Moscow State University, B Nikitskaya 5/7, Moscow, 103009, Russian Federation. TEL 7-095-2295091, FAX 7-095-2036671, kd_mgu@rambler.ru, http://www.msu.ru/depts/MSUPubl. **Dist. by:** M K - Periodica, ul Gilyarovskogo 39, Moscow 129110, Russian Federation. TEL 7-095-2845008, FAX 7-095-2813798, info@periodicals.ru, http://www.mkniga.ru.

003.5 BEL ISSN 1374-2876
➤ **PRINCIPIA CYBERNETICA NEWS.** Text and summaries in English. 1990. bi-w. free. **Document type:** *Newsletter, Academic/Scholarly.* **Description:** Aims at the computer-supported collaborated development of an evolutionary-systemic world view.
Media: Online - full text. **Related titles:** E-mail ed.
Published by: Principia Cybernetica Project, c/o Francis Heylighen, Free University of Brussels, Pleinlaan, Brussels, 1050, Belgium. TEL 32-2-6442677, FAX 32-2-6440744, pcp@vub.ac.be, http://pespmc1.vub.ac.be/. Ed. Francis Heylighen. Circ: 600.

003.5 BGR ISSN 0204-9848
TJ212 CODEN: PTKRDU
PROBLEMI NA TEKHNICHESKATA KIBERNETIKA I ROBOTIKA/PROBLEMS OF ENGINEERING CYBERNETICS AND ROBOTICS. Text in Multiple languages. 1975. irreg. BGL 0.89 per issue. reprint service avail. from IRC. **Description:** Provides scholarly papers on all aspects of robotics and cybernetics. Topics may include grippers, algorithms, automatic learning, and industrial and measuring robots.
Indexed: CCMJ, CybAb, IAA, Inspec, MathR, MathSciNet, RefZh, ZentMath.
—BLDSC (0133.124500), AskIEEE, CISTI, Linda Hall.
Published by: (Bulgarska Akademiya na Naukite, Institut po Tehniceska Kibernetika i Robotika/Bulgarian Academy of Sciences, Central Laboratory of Mechatronics and Instrumentation), Universitetsko Izdatelstvo Sv. Kliment Okhridski/Publishing House of the Sofia University St. Kliment Ohridski, Akad G Bonchev 6, Sofia, 1113, Bulgaria. Circ: 470.

003.5 FRA ISSN 0399-0559
T57.6 CODEN: RSROD3
➤ **R A I R O - OPERATIONS RESEARCH/R A I R O - RECHERCHE OPERATIONELLE.** Text in English, French. 1966. q. EUR 282 combined subscription domestic print & online eds.; EUR 354 combined subscription in the European Union print & online eds.; EUR 367 combined subscription elsewhere print & online eds. (effective 2006). adv. bk.rev. bibl.; charts. **Document type:** *Academic/Scholarly.* **Description:** Covers all branches of operations research and scientific management. Includes all practical and theoretical aspects pertaining to mathematical theories, as well as modeling, algorithms and computer science.
Incorporates (1972-1977): Revue Francaise d'Automatique, Informatique et de Recherche Operationnelle; Supersedes in part (in 1972): Revue Francaise d'Informatique et de Recherche Operationnelle (0035-3035)
Related titles: Microfilm ed.: (from PQC); Online - full text ed.: ISSN 1290-3868. EUR 235 (effective 2006) (from EBSCO Publishing, Swets Information Services).
Indexed: ASCA, BrCerAb, C&ISA, CCMJ, CIS, CMCI, CerAb, CorrAb, CurCont, CybAb, E&CAJ, EMA, EngInd, IAA, IAOP, ISR, Inspec, M&TEA, MBF, METADEX, MathR, MathSciNet, RASB, SSCI, WAA, ZentMath.
—BLDSC (7307.310000), AskIEEE, CISTI, Ei, IDS, IE, Infotrieve, ingenta, Linda Hall. **CCC.**
Published by: (Association Francaise des Sciences et Technologies de l'Information et des Systemes), E D P Sciences, 17 Ave du Hoggar, Parc d'Activites de Courtaboeuf, BP 112, Cedex A, Les Ulis, F-91944, France. TEL 33-1-69187575, FAX 33-1-69860678, subscribers@edpsciences.org, http://www.edpsciences.org/journal/index.cfm?edpsname=ro. Eds. A Billionnet, P Chretienne, P Mahey. Circ: 1,025.

003.5 FRA ISSN 0752-4072
QA75.5 CODEN: TTSIDJ
R A I R O - TECHNIQUE ET SCIENCES INFORMATIQUES. Text in English, French. 1967. 24/yr. EUR 310 domestic; EUR 368 in the European Union; EUR 378 elsewhere (effective 2005). bibl.; charts. **Description:** Information on software engineering and programming; languages and compilers; operating, information and distributed systems; artificial intelligence as well as pattern recognition.
Former titles: R A I R O Informatique - Computer Science (0399-0532); (until 1977): Revue Francaise d'Automatique, Informatique et de Recherche Operationnelle. Informatique; Supersedes in part (in 1972): Revue Francaise d'Informatique et de Recherche Operationnelle (0035-3035)
Related titles: Microfilm ed.: (from PQC).
Indexed: CIS, CurCont, INIS AtomInd, Inspec, MathR, RASB, ZentMath.

C

—BLDSC (8740.008000), AskIEEE, CISTI, IE, Infotrieve, ingenta, Linda Hall. **CCC.**
Published by: Lavoisier, 11 rue Lavoisier, Paris, 75008, France. TEL 33-1-42653995, FAX 33-1-42650246, info@lavoisier.fr, http://www.lavoisier.fr. Ed. Jean-Louis Giavitto. Circ: 4,000. **Subscr. to:** Lavoisier - Dept Abonnements, 14 rue de Provigny, Cachan 94236, France. TEL 33-1-47406700, FAX 33-1-47406702, abo@lavoisier.fr.

003.5 FRA ISSN 0988-3754
QA1 CODEN: RITAE4
➤ **R A I R O - THEORETICAL INFORMATICS AND APPLICATIONS/INFORMATION THEORIQUE ET APPLICATIONS.** (Revue Francaise d'Automatique, Informatique, Recherche Operationnelle) Variant title: R A I R O Informatique Theorique et Applications. Text in English, French. 1966. q. EUR 326 combined subscription domestic print & online eds.; EUR 386 combined subscription in the European Union print & online eds.; EUR 397 combined subscription elsewhere print & online eds. (effective 2006). bibl.; charts. **Document type:** *Academic/Scholarly.* **Description:** Contains research of high scientific level in theoretical computer science and its applications.
Formerly (until 1986): R A I R O Informatique Theorique - Theoretical Informatics (0399-0540); Which superseded in part (in 1972): Revue Francaise d'Informatique et de Recherche Operationnelle (0035-3035)
Related titles: Microfilm ed.: (from PQC); Online - full text ed.: ISSN 1290-385X. EUR 271 (effective 2006) (from EBSCO Publishing, Swets Information Services).
Indexed: ASCA, BrCerAb, C&ISA, CIS, CMCI, CerAb, CompAb, CorrAb, CurCont, CybAb, E&CAJ, EMA, IAA, Inspec, M&TEA, MBF, METADEX, MathR, MathSciNet, SSCI, WAA, ZentMath.
—BLDSC (8814.559300), AskIEEE, CISTI, Ei, IDS, IE, Infotrieve, ingenta, Linda Hall. **CCC.**
Published by: (Association Francaise des Sciences et Technologies de l'Information et des Systemes), E D P Sciences, 17 Ave du Hoggar, Parc d'Activites de Courtaboeuf, BP 112, Cedex A, Les Ulis, F-91944, France. TEL 33-1-69187575, FAX 33-1-69860678, subscribers@edpsciences.org, http://www.edpsciences.org/journal/index.cfm?edpsname=ita. Ed. C Choffrut. Circ: 1,025.

➤ **REFERATIVNYI ZHURNAL. TEKHNICHESKAYA KIBERNETIKA.** see *COMPUTERS—Abstracting, Bibliographies, Statistics*

003.5 RUS ISSN 1029-3620
ROSSIISKAYA AKADEMIYA NAUK. IZVESTIYA. TEORIYA I SISTEMY UPRAVLENIYA. Text in Russian. 1963. bi-m. RUR 1,190 for 6 mos. domestic (effective 2004). **Document type:** *Journal, Academic/Scholarly.* **Description:** Contains papers on computer and systems science, control theory, and optimization studies. Specific topics include algorithms, design of computer and control systems, data processing, robotics, pattern recognition and applied mathematics.
Former titles (until 1994): Rossiiskaya Akademiya Nauk. Izvestiya. Tekhnicheskaya Kibernetika (1026-3497); (until 1992): Akademiya Nauk S.S.S.R. Izvestiya. Tekhnicheskaya Kibernetika (0002-3388)
Related titles: Online - full text ed.; ♦ English Translation: Journal of Computer and System Sciences International. ISSN 1064-2307.
Indexed: BrCerAb, C&ISA, CCMJ, CerAb, ChemAb, CompR, CorrAb, CurCont, CybAb, E&CAJ, EMA, Inspec, M&TEA, MBF, METADEX, MathR, MathSciNet, RefZh, SolStAb, WAA, ZentMath.
—BLDSC (0178.155000), CINDOC, CISTI, East View, KNAW, Linda Hall.
Published by: (Rossiiskaya Akademiya Nauk, Otdelenie Mekhaniki i Protsessov Upravleniya), Izdatel'stvo Nauka, Profsoyuznaya ul 90, Moscow, 117864, Russian Federation. TEL 7-095-3347151, FAX 7-095-4202220, info@gosniias.msk.ru, secret@naukaran.ru, http://www.maik.rssi.ru/cgi-bin/list.pl?page=teorsist, http://www.naukaran.ru.

629.8 USA ISSN 8756-4017
CODEN: ASBOE9
SENSOR TECHNOLOGY; a monthly intelligence service. Text in English. 1985. m. USD 1,152 (effective 2005). bibl.; charts; pat.; stat.; tr.lit. back issues avail. **Document type:** *Newsletter, Trade.* **Description:** Follows rapidly evolving technological research and details complete advances.
Incorporates (in 2005): Sensor Business Digest (1060-1902)
Related titles: E-mail ed.: USD 960 (effective 2005); Online - full text ed.: (from Factiva, Gale Group).
—CCC.
Published by: Technical Insights (Subsidiary of: Frost & Sullivan), 7550 IH 10 West, Ste 400, San Antonio, TX 78229. TEL 212-850-8600, FAX 212-850-8800, technicalinsights@frost.com, http://www.frost.com/prod/servlet/ti-home.pag. Ed. Peter Savage. Pub. Paul Majchrzyk.

SENSORS; your resource for sensing, communications, and control. see *INSTRUMENTS*

SENSOR'S BUYERS GUIDE. see *INSTRUMENTS*

STUDII SI CERCETARI DE CALCUL ECONOMIC SI CIBERNETICE ECONOMICE. see *BUSINESS AND ECONOMICS—Economic Situation And Conditions*

003.5 NLD ISSN 0924-5553
SUPERCOMPUTER EUROPEAN WATCH. Text in Dutch. 1989. 11/yr. USD 328 elsewhere. **Document type:** *Academic/Scholarly.*
Published by: ASFRA B.V., Voorhaven 33, Edam, 1135 BL, Netherlands. TEL 31-2993-72751, FAX 31-2993-72877, asfra@pi.net.

003.5 USA ISSN 1063-6889
QA76.9.C62
➤ **SYMPOSIUM ON COMPUTER ARITHMETIC. PROCEEDINGS.** Text in English. 1975 (3rd). biennial. USD 102 membership (effective 2005). **Document type:** *Proceedings, Academic/Scholarly.* **Description:** Describes new and theoretical developments in computer arithmetic.
Related titles: Online - full text ed.: (from I E E E).
Indexed: Englnd.
—BLDSC (8585.163300). **CCC.**
Published by: (Institute of Electrical and Electronics Engineers, Inc.), I E E E Computer Society, 10662 Los Vaqueros Circle, PO Box 3014, Los Alamitos, CA 90720-1314. TEL 714-821-8380, FAX 714-821-4641.

003.5 POL ISSN 0239-8044
TECHNIKI KOMPUTEROWE; biuletyn informacyjny. Text in Polish; Summaries in English, Polish. 1962-1989; resumed 1993. a. per issue exchange basis. adv. charts; illus. **Document type:** *Bulletin.*
Indexed: Inspec.
—AskIEEE.
Published by: Instytut Maszyn Matematycznych, Ul Krzywickiego 34, Warsaw, 02078, Poland. TEL 48—22-6218441, FAX 48-22-6299270, czajkowski@imm.org.pl, r.czajkowski@imm.org.pl, http://imm.org.pl. Ed. Roman Czajkowski. Circ: 100.

003.5 JPN
TETSUDO SAIBANE. SHINPOJUMU RONBUNSHU (CD-ROM EDITION)/RAILWAY CYBERNETICS. SYMPOSIUM. PAPERS. Text in Japanese. 1964. a. JPY 10,000 (effective 2001).
Formerly (until Nov. 2000): Tetsudo ni Okeru Saibanetikkusu Riyo Kokunai Shinpojumu Ronbunshu (Print Edition)/Symposium on the Use of Cybernetics on the Railway. Papers
Media: CD-ROM.
—BLDSC (8798.282500).
Published by: Nihon Tetsudo Saibanetikkusu Kyogikai/Japan Railway Cybernetics Association, 28-6 Kamei-Do 1-chome, Koto-ku, Tokyo, 136-0071, Japan. TEL 81-3-5626-2324, FAX 81-3-5626-2325.

020 NLD ISSN 0921-3406
➤ **THEORY AND DECISION LIBRARY. SERIES D: SYSTEM THEORY, KNOWLEDGE ENGINEERING AND PROBLEM SOLVING.** Text in English. 1973; N.S. 1987. irreg., latest vol.16, 1996. price varies. **Document type:** *Monographic series, Academic/Scholarly.* **Description:** Covers the design, study and development of structures, organizations and systems aimed at formal applications mainly in the social and human sciences, but also relevant to the information sciences.
Supersedes in part (in 1987): Theory and Decision Library (0921-3376)
Indexed: ZentMath.
Published by: Springer-Verlag Dordrecht (Subsidiary of: Springer Science+Business Media), Van Godewijckstraat 30, Dordrecht, 3311 GX, Netherlands. TEL 31-78-6576050, FAX 31-78-6576474, http://www.springeronline.com. Ed. R Lowen.

003.5 HUN ISSN 0324-721X
Q300 CODEN: ACCYDX
UNIVERSITY OF SZEGED. ACTA CYBERNETICA. Text in English, French, German, Russian. 1969. s-a. bk.rev. index. back issues avail. **Document type:** *Journal, Academic/Scholarly.* **Description:** Presents scholarly papers on various aspects and applications of cybernetics. Covers such areas as rewriting systems, automata, attributed transformation, algebraic theories and mathematical systems theories.
Indexed: CCMJ, CIS, CMCI, CompR, Englnd, Inspec, MathR, MathSciNet, RASB, RefZh, ZentMath.
—AskIEEE, Ei, Linda Hall.
Published by: (Szegedi Tudomanyegyetem, Informatikai Tanszekcsoport/University of Szaged, Department of Informatics), Szegedi Tudomanyegyetem/University of Szeged, c/o E Szabo, Exchange Librarian, Dugonics ter 13, PO Box 393, Szeged, 6701, Hungary. TEL 36-62-544009, FAX 36-62-420895, csirik@inf.u-szeged.hu, http://www.inf.u-szeged.hu/local/acta, http://www.u-szeged.hu. Ed. Janos Csirik. Circ: 400.

UPRAVLYAYUSHCHIE SISTEMY I MASHINY. see *COMPUTERS—Computer Systems*

▼ **WEB INTELLIGENCE AND AGENT SYSTEMS**; an international journal. see *COMPUTERS—Artificial Intelligence*

COMPUTERS—Data Base Management

025.04 USA
A C M INTERNATIONAL WORKSHOP ON MULTIMEDIA DATABASES. PROCEEDINGS. Text in English. a. USD 14 per issue to members; USD 7 per issue to non-members (effective 2005). **Document type:** *Proceedings, Academic/Scholarly.*
Related titles: Online - full content ed.
Published by: Association for Computing Machinery, Inc., 1515 Broadway, 17th Fl, New York, NY 10036-5701. TEL 212-626-0500, usacm@acm.org, http://www.acm.org.

005.74 USA ISSN 1055-6338
QA76.9.D3
A C M SIGACT-SIGMOD-SIGART SYMPOSIUM ON PRINCIPLES OF DATABASE SYSTEMS. PROCEEDINGS. Text in English. 1987. a. price varies. **Document type:** *Proceedings.*
Former titles (until 1986): A C M SIGACT-SIGMOD Symposium on Principles of Database Systems. Proceedings; A C M Symposium on Principles of Database Systems. Proceedings
—BLDSC (6836.150780), IE, ingenta.
Published by: Association for Canadian Studies in the United States, 1424 16th St NW, Ste 502, Washington, DC 20036-2238. info@acsus.org, http://www.acsus.org.

005.74 USA ISSN 0362-5915
QA76.9.D3 CODEN: ATDSD3
➤ **A C M TRANSACTIONS ON DATABASE SYSTEMS.** Text in English. 1976. q. USD 184 domestic to non-members; USD 198 foreign to non-members; USD 43 domestic to members; USD 57 foreign to members; USD 38 domestic to students; USD 52 foreign to students; USD 221 combined subscription domestic to non-members print & online eds.; USD 235 combined subscription foreign to non-members print & online eds.; USD 52 combined subscription domestic to members print & online eds.; USD 66 combined subscription foreign to members print & online eds.; USD 46 combined subscription domestic to students print & online eds.; USD 60 combined subscription foreign to students print & online eds. (effective 2006). charts; illus. index. back issues avail.; reprints avail. **Document type:** *Journal, Academic/Scholarly.* **Description:** Reports on work in database management and design. Covers the development and validation of abstractions and models to describe database applications, formalization and design methods which exploit the knowledge for effective processing of data.
Related titles: Microfiche ed.: (from PQC); Microform ed.: (from WWS); Online - full text ed.: USD 147 to non-members; USD 34 to members; USD 30 student members (effective 2006) (from Association for Computing Machinery, Inc., EBSCO Publishing, Florida Center for Library Automation, Gale Group).
Indexed: ABIn, AIA, AS&TI, ASCA, BrCerAb, C&ISA, CADCAM, CMCI, CerAb, CompAb, CompC, CompD, CompLI, CompR, CorrAb, CurCont, E&CAJ, EMA, Englnd, ErgAb, IAA, ISR, InfoSAb, Inspec, M&TEA, MBF, METADEX, MathR, RASB, RefZh, SCI, SSCI, SolStAb, TelAb, WAA, ZentMath.
—BLDSC (0578.660000), AskIEEE, CISTI, Ei, IDS, IE, Infotrieve, ingenta, Linda Hall. **CCC.**
Published by: Association for Computing Machinery, Inc., 1515 Broadway, 17th Fl, New York, NY 10036-5701. TEL 212-626-0520, 800-342-6626, FAX 212-869-0481, usacm@acm.org, http://www.acm.org/tods. Ed. Richard T. Snodgrass. Pub. Jono Hardjowirogo. Circ: 3,300.

005.74 CAN
A I X CASE NEWSLETTER∗. Text in English. 1992. 3/yr. **Document type:** *Newsletter.*
Published by: (I B M Software Solutions Division), I B M Canada Ltd., 3600 Steeles Ave., East F2/270, Markham, ON I3R 9Z7, Canada. TEL 416-448-2170, FAX 416-448-2114, patsmith@vnet.ibm.com. Ed. Patti Smith.

ACCESS (ROCKVILLE). see *COMPUTERS—Microcomputers*

005.74 SGP
ADVANCED DATABASE RESEARCH AND DEVELOPMENT SERIES. (vol.10: Advances in Multimedia and Databases for the New Century; a Swiss-Japanese perspective) Text in English. 1993. irreg., latest vol.10, 2000. prices varies. **Document type:** *Monographic series, Academic/Scholarly.* **Description:** Provides information for researchers in multimedia, databases and virtual reality.
—BLDSC (0696.844000).
Published by: (Ochanomizu University JPN), World Scientific Publishing Co. Pte. Ltd., 5 Toh Tuck Link, Singapore, 596224, Singapore. TEL 65-466-5775, FAX 65-467-7667, series@wspc.com.sg, http://www.wspc.com.sg/books/series/adrds_series.shtml, http://www.worldscientific.com. **Subscr. to:** Farrer Rd, PO Box 128, Singapore 912805, Singapore. **Dist. in the US by:** World Scientific Publishing Co., Inc., 1060 Main St, River Edge, NJ 07661. TEL 201-487-9655, 800-227-7562, FAX 201-487-9656, 888-977-2665, wspc@wspc.com.; **Dist. by:** World Scientific Publishing Ltd., 57 Shelton St, London WC2H 9HE, United Kingdom. TEL 44-20-78360888, FAX 44-20-78362020, sales@wspc.co.uk. **Co-sponsor:** Ecole Polytechnique Federale de Lausanne.

C

005.74 USA ISSN 0197-1476
TK5105
ADVANCES IN DATA COMMUNICATIONS MANAGEMENT. Text in English. irreg.
—CISTI.
Published by: Heyden & Sons, Inc., c/o John Wiley & Sons, 605 Third Ave, New York, NY 10016. TEL 215-382-6673.

ADVANCES IN DATA PROCESSING MANAGEMENT. see *COMPUTERS—Electronic Data Processing*

025.04 USA
ADVANCES IN DATABASE SYSTEMS. Text in English. 1996. irreg., latest vol.29, 2005. price varies. **Document type:** *Monographic series, Academic/Scholarly.*
Formerly (until vol.29, 2005): Kluwer International Series on Advances in Database Systems (1386-2944)
—BLDSC (5099.729000).
Published by: Springer Science+Business Media, Inc., 233 Spring St, New York, NY 10013. TEL 212-460-1500, FAX 212-473-6272. Ed. Ahmed K Elmagarmid.

005.74 USA ISSN 0197-1433
QA76.9.D5
ADVANCES IN DISTRIBUTED PROCESSING MANAGEMENT. Text in English. irreg.
—CISTI.
Published by: Heyden & Sons, Inc., c/o John Wiley & Sons, 605 Third Ave, New York, NY 10016.

▼ **ADVANCES IN MANAGEMENT INFORMATION SYSTEMS.** see *LIBRARY AND INFORMATION SCIENCES—Computer Applications*

005.74 USA ISSN 1073-9564
QA76.76.A65 CODEN: ADTRF4
APPLICATION DEVELOPMENT TRENDS; development solutions for corporate software managers. Variant title: A D Trends. Text in English. 1989. m. USD 49 domestic; USD 89 in Canada & Mexico; USD 129 elsewhere (effective 2005). adv. bk.rev. Supplement avail.; back issues avail. **Document type:** *Magazine, Trade.* **Description:** Provides comprehensive coverage of developments in application development software technology.
Formerly (until Jan. 1994): C A S E Trends (1046-5944)
Related titles: Online - full text ed.: ADTmag.com. 1989; Supplement(s): 101 Solutions.
Indexed: CADCAM, InfoSAb, Inspec, MicrocompInd, SoftBase.
—BLDSC (1570.511470), IE, ingenta. **CCC.**
Published by: 101 Communications, Llc., 600 Worcester Rd., Ste 301, Framingham, MA 01702. TEL 508-875-6644, FAX 508-875-6622, mmadden@adtmag.com, info@101com.com, http://www.adtmag.com, http://www.101com.com. Ed. Michael W. Bucken. Pub. Mark Sande. Adv. contact Navid Davani. Circ: 57,000.

005.74 USA
ASSOCIATION FOR COMPUTING MACHINERY. SPECIAL INTEREST GROUP FOR MANAGEMENT INFORMATION SYSTEMS. CONFERENCE PROCEEDINGS. Text in English. 1969. irreg. price varies. adv. **Document type:** *Proceedings, Academic/Scholarly.*
Formerly: Association for Computing Machinery. Special Interest Group for Business Processing and Management. Conference Proceedings.
Published by: Association for Computing Machinery, Inc., 1515 Broadway, 17th Fl, New York, NY 10036-5701. TEL 212-626-0500, 212-626-0520, 800-342-6626, FAX 212-869-0481, sigs@acm.org, usacm@acm.org, http://www.acm.org. Eds. Detmar Straub, Ephraim McLean.

005.74 USA ISSN 0730-8078
QA76.9.D3
ASSOCIATION FOR COMPUTING MACHINERY. SPECIAL INTEREST GROUP ON MANAGEMENT OF DATA. INTERNATIONAL CONFERENCE PROCEEDINGS. Text in English. 1976. a. USD 146 per issue to non-members (effective 2004).
—BLDSC (6836.150900). **CCC.**
Published by: Association for Computing Machinery, Inc., 1515 Broadway, 17th Fl, New York, NY 10036-5701. TEL 212-626-0500, 800-342-6626, FAX 212-869-0481, usacm@acm.org, http://www.acm.org/sigmod.

025.04 USA ISSN 1530-0919
AUSTRALASIAN DATABASE CONFERENCE. PROCEEDINGS. Text in English. 199?. a. **Document type:** *Proceedings.* **Description:** Explores emerging themes, including: managing Internet-based information, handling the temporal aspects of data, index structures, data mining and querying techniques.
Related titles: Online - full text ed.: (from I E E E).
Published by: I E E E Computer Society, 1730 Massachusetts Ave, N W, Washington, DC 20036-1903. TEL 202-371-0101, FAX 202-728-9614, http://www.computer.org. **Subscr. to:** Institute of Electrical and Electronics Engineers, Inc., 445 Hoes Ln, Piscataway, NJ 08854-1331. TEL 732-981-0060, FAX 732-981-9667, http://www.ieee.org.

658.1 USA
C A F M SYSTEM & STRATEGIES (YEAR); a manager's guide to facility management automation. Text in English. 1983. a. USD 99. adv. index. **Description:** Guide to the automation of facility management functions, written especially for the facility manager considering automation or maintaining an automated system.
Formerly (until 1986): Design Compudata (Year)
Published by: Graphic Systems Inc., 52 JFK St, Ste 3, Cambridge, MA 02138-4953. TEL 617-492-1148, FAX 617-492-4044. Ed. Eric Teicholz. Circ: 1,000.

005.74 GBR ISSN 1363-2353
C M I TECHNOLOGY WATCH, DATA WAREHOUSING. Text in English. 1996. m.
Published by: Cambridge Market Intelligence, The Quadrangle, 49, Atalanta St, London, SW6 6TR, United Kingdom. TEL 44-20-75657900, FAX 44-20-75657938, jonathan.sjiemfat@cmi.co.uk, http://www.insidecareer.co.uk.

COMPLEX CONTROL SYSTEMS. see *COMPUTERS—Computer Systems*

005.74 USA
COMPUTER DATABASE. Text in English. m. price varies. **Document type:** *Database, Abstract/Index.* **Description:** Provides access to today's most well-read and influential periodicals on the computer, telecommunications and electronics industries.
Media: Online - full text (from Data-Star).
Published by: Gale Group (Subsidiary of: Thomson Corporation), 27500 Drake Rd, Farmington Hills, MI 48331-3535. TEL 248-699-4253, 800-877-4253, FAX 248-699-8035, galeord@gale.com, http://www.gale.com.

025.04 USA ISSN 1089-019X
COMPUTING NEWS & REVIEW; the managers' publication of database trends. Text in English. 1987. m. free. adv. bk.rev. 52 p./no. 4 cols./p.; **Document type:** *Trade.* **Description:** Provides in-depth news and information on the latest techniques for data delivery, availability and analysis of database industries.
Indexed: SoftBase.
Published by: Thurman Marketing Services Inc., 92 Argonaut, Ste 275, Aliso Viejo, CA 92656. TEL 949-581-3993, FAX 949-581-3399, compnews@newsrev.com, http://www.news.rev.com. Ed., R&P Scott Thurman. Pub. Phyllis Thurman. Adv. contact Donna Lejeune. Circ: 30,000.

005.74 GBR ISSN 1475-7443
CONTENT AND DOCUMENT MANAGEMENT GUIDE AND DIRECTORY. Text in English. 1994. a., latest 13th ed. GBP 45 per issue to non-members; GBP 30 per issue to members (effective 2003). **Document type:** *Directory.*
Former titles (until 2002): Document Management Guide and Directory (1475-8903); (until 1999): Document Management Directory (1464-7583); (until 1997): Document Management Guide and Directory (1366-6584); (until 1996): Document Management Guide & Year Book (1365-0793); (until 1995): Document Management Year Book (1354-0114)
Related titles: CD-ROM ed.: GBP 50 per issue to non-members; GBP 35 per issue to members (effective 2003).
—BLDSC (3425.326000).
Published by: Cimtech Ltd., University of Hertfordshire, 45 Grosvenor Rd, St Albans, Herts AL1 3AW, United Kingdom. TEL 44-1727-813651, FAX 44-1727-813649, c.cimtech@herts.ac.uk, http://www.cimtech.co.uk. Eds. Roger Broadhurst, Tom Hendley. Adv. contact Roger Broadhurst.

005.74 USA
D B 2 UPDATE. Text in English. m. USD 380 (effective 2000). **Document type:** *Trade.*
Published by: Xephon, 9330 Lyndon B Johnson Fwy., Ste. 800, Dallas, TX 75243-4310. TEL 817-455-7050, FAX 303-438-0290.

005.74 330 USA ISSN 1521-2912
QA76.9.D3
D M REVIEW; covering business intelligence, integration, & analytics. (Data Management) Text in English. 1991. m. USD 35 domestic; USD 49 in Canada; USD 79 elsewhere; free to qualified personnel (effective 2005). adv. back issues avail. **Document type:** *Magazine, Trade.* **Description:** Covers topics relating to data warehousing issues and solutions.
Former titles (until 1997): Data Management Review (1067-3717); (until 1993): Data Base Management (Milwaukee) (1066-5498); (until 1991): 370 - 390 Data Base Management (1056-974X)
Related titles: Online - full text ed.: (from EBSCO Publishing, Gale Group, O C L C Online Computer Library Center, Inc.).
Indexed: Inspec, SoftBase.
—BLDSC (3605.700700), IE, ingenta.
Published by: Source Media, Inc., One State St Plaza, 27th Fl, New York, NY 10004. TEL 212-803-6077, 800-221-1809, FAX 212-747-1154, info@dmreview.com, custserv@sourcemedia.com, http://www.dmreview.com, http://www.sourcemedia.com. Circ: 59,308 (controlled).

005.74 USA
THE DATA ADMINISTRATION NEWSLETTER. Text in English. q. **Document type:** *Newsletter.* **Description:** Directed at individuals who manage data as a valued corporate asset.
Media: Online - full text.
Published by: Data Administration Newsletter, PO Box 112571, Upper St. Clair, PA 15241. rseiner@tdan.com, http://www.tdan.com. Ed., Pub. Robert S Seiner.

005.74 USA ISSN 1532-0936
QA76 CODEN: DTBSAN
DATA BASE FOR ADVANCES IN INFORMATION SYSTEMS. Text in English. 1968. q. USD 49 (effective 2004). illus. **Document type:** *Journal, Academic/Scholarly.* **Description:** Covers information systems and technologies for management, and the management of these systems and technologies.
Formerly (until 1995): Data Base (0095-0033); Which superseded: S I G B D P Newsletter
Related titles: Online - full text ed.: (from EBSCO Publishing, O C L C Online Computer Library Center, Inc., ProQuest Information & Learning).
Indexed: ABIn, CMCI, CompAb, CompC, CompLI, CompR, CurCont, DPD, EngInd, ErgAb, Inspec, RASB, RILM.
—BLDSC (3534.311000), AskIEEE, CISTI, Ei, IDS, IE, ingenta.
Published by: Association for Computing Machinery, Inc., 1515 Broadway, 17th Fl, New York, NY 10036-5701. TEL 212-626-0500, 212-626-0520, 800-342-6626, FAX 212-869-0481, sigs@acm.org, usacm@acm.org, http://www.acm.org.

005.74 USA ISSN 1096-7575
DATA BASE MANAGEMENT. Text in English. 1976. bi-m. looseleaf. USD 495 (effective 2000 - 2001). back issues avail.; reprints avail. **Document type:** *Trade.* **Description:** Provides current guidance on how to select, install, implement, and maintain data base management systems and keep abreast of trends.
Formerly (until 199?): Auerbach Data Base Management (0735-9977)
Related titles: CD-ROM ed.: 1997. USD 450 (effective 2001).
—**CCC.**
Published by: Auerbach Publications (Subsidiary of: C R C Press, LLC), 2000 Corporate Blvd., NW, Boca Raton, FL 33431. TEL 561-994-0555, FAX 561-374-3401, orders@crcpress.com, http://www.auerbach-publications.com/home.asp. Ed. Sanjiv Purba. Pub. Richard O'Hanley TEL 212-845-4017. R&P Jamie Sigal TEL 561-994-0555.

025.04 NLD ISSN 0922-3487
CODEN: DHSTEV
➤ **DATA HANDLING IN SCIENCE AND TECHNOLOGY.** Text in Dutch. 1984. irreg., latest vol.22, 2000. price varies. back issues avail. **Document type:** *Monographic series, Academic/Scholarly.* **Description:** Discusses data handling in all areas of chemical research and engineering.
Indexed: Inspec, ZentMath.
—BLDSC (3534.588000), CASDDS, CISTI, IE, ingenta. **CCC.**
Published by: Elsevier BV (Subsidiary of: Elsevier Science & Technology), Radarweg 29, Amsterdam, 1043 NX, Netherlands. TEL 31-20-4853911, FAX 31-20-4852457, nlinfo-f@elsevier.nl, http://www.elsevier.nl. Ed. S C Rutan.

005.74 ITA
DATA MANAGER; la rivista di information & communication technology. Text in Italian. 1975. 10/yr. EUR 61 domestic; EUR 81 foreign (effective 2005). adv. bk.rev. back issues avail. **Document type:** *Magazine, Trade.* **Description:** Includes interviews with managers of leading companies. Offers developments in the art of Italian informatics, its applications, future trends and prospectives.
Related titles: Online - full text ed.
Published by: Datamanager, Via L B Alberti 10, Milan, MI 20149, Italy. TEL 39-02-33101836, FAX 39-02-3450749, http://www.datamanager.it. Circ: 20,000.

342.0858 USA
DATA PRIVACY LAW. Text in English. irreg. USD 90.
Published by: LexisNexis (Subsidiary of: LexisNexis North America), PO Box 7587, Charlottesville, VA 22906-7587. TEL 804-972-7600, 800-562-1197, FAX 804-972-7666, llp.customer.support@lexis-nexis.com, http://www.lexislawpublishing.com. Eds. Joel R Reidenberg, Paul Schwartz.

005.74 FRA ISSN 1683-1470
Q183.9
➤ **DATA SCIENCE JOURNAL.** Text in English. 2002. q. free (effective 2005). **Document type:** *Journal, Academic/Scholarly.* **Description:** Publishes papers about data and data systems.
Media: Online - full text.
Published by: International Council for Science/Conseil International pour la Science, 51 bd. de Montmorency, Paris, 75016, France. TEL 33-1-45250329, FAX 33-1-42889431, secretariat@icsu.org, http://www.datasciencejournal.org/, http://www.icsu.org. Ed. F.J. Smith.

005.74 USA
CODEN: DBNEDK
DATA TO KNOWLEDGE NEWSLETTER. Text in English. 1973. bi-m. looseleaf. USD 129; USD 156 foreign (effective 1999). bk.rev. charts; illus. back issues avail. **Document type:** *Newsletter.* **Description:** Covers various current information technology topics in data, information, business rules, knowledge management, and enterprise architecture.

Formerly (until 1998): Data Base Newsletter (0735-3677)
Indexed: Inspec.
—AskIEEE, CASDDS.
Published by: Business Rule Solutions, Inc., 2476 Bolsover St, Ste 488, Houston, TX 77005-2518. datatoknow@brsolutions.com. Ed. Ronald G Ross. Pub. Gladys S W Lam. R&P Esther Tse TEL 604-899-5452. Circ: 1,750.

DATABASE AND NETWORK JOURNAL; an international journal of database and network practice. see *COMPUTERS—Computer Networks*

005.74 USA
DATABASE DISCUSSION. Text in English. 1992. irreg. (2-3/yr.). **Document type:** *Bibliography.* **Description:** For subscribers to ISI databases.
Published by: Thomson I S I (Subsidiary of: Thomson Corporation), 3501 Market St., Philadelphia, PA 19104. TEL 215-386-0100, 800-336-4474, FAX 215-386-2911, sales@isinet.com, http://www.isinet.com. Ed. Michelle Brown.

005.74 NLD ISSN 0925-6911
DATABASE MAGAZINE. Text in Dutch. 1990. 8/yr. EUR 77.50 domestic; EUR 85.50 in Belgium (effective 2005). adv. bk.rev. illus. index. back issues avail. **Document type:** *Journal, Trade.* **Description:** Covers applications, development and database management for systems developers, information managers and database administrators.
—IE, Infotrieve, KNAW.
Published by: Array Publications BV, Postbus 2211, Alphen aan den Rijn, 2400 CE, Netherlands. TEL 31-172-424177, FAX 31-172-424381, dbm@array.nl, http://www.dbm.nl/site/, http://www.array.nl. Ed. Hans Lamboo. Adv. contact Will Manusiwa TEL 31-172-469030. B&W page EUR 1,995, color page EUR 3,195; trim 210 x 285. Circ: 4,000 (paid).

DATABASE MARKETER. see *BUSINESS AND ECONOMICS—Marketing And Purchasing*

025.04 USA
DATABASE TRENDS AND APPLICATIONS. Text in English. m. free to qualified personnel. **Description:** Provides information to corporate information project teams, IS and line-of-business managers, covering the solutions for conceptualizing, specifying, implementing and maintaining large-scale, organization-wide information projects including the full range of enterprise applications.
Published by: Unisphere Media, LLC, 500 Madison Ave, Morristown, NJ 07960. TEL 973-285-3305, http://www.databasetrends.com/.

025.04 658 JPN ISSN 0918-6484
DATABASES IN JAPAN. Text in English. 1986. a.
Former titles (until 1992): Database in Japan (0915-5686); (until 1989): Database Services in Japan (0914-1243); (until 1987): Database White Paper (0914-1235)
Published by: Detabesu Shinko Senta/Database Promotion Center, 5th Flr., Shinbashi-Towa Bldg., 2-13-8 Shinbashi, Minato-ku, Tokyo, 105-0004, Japan. TEL 81-3-35082430, FAX 81-3-35082440, pubs@dpc.or.jp, http://www.dpc.or.jp.

005.74 JPN ISSN 0912-5833
DATANET. Text in Japanese. 1986. s-m. USD 550. **Document type:** *Newsletter.*
Published by: PenLogue Publishing Corp., Futaba Building, 3-4-18 Mita, Minato-ku, Tokyo, 108-0073, Japan. TEL 81-3-3452-8080, FAX 81-3-3452-5728, pdb01343@nifty-serve.com. Ed. Minoru Nakamura.

005.74 IND
DATAQUEST (ONLINE EDITION); the business of infotech. Text in English. 1982. m. USD 50 (effective 2000). adv. bk.rev. **Document type:** *Trade.*
Published by: Cyber Media India Ltd., Cyber House, B-35 Sector 32-Institutional, Gurgaon, Haryana 122022, India. TEL 91-11-26381673, FAX 91-11-26380694, naveencs@cmil.com, http://www.dqindia.com. Ed. Shyam Malhotra. Pub. Pradeep Gupta. R&P Prasanth Kumar Roy. Adv. contact Akhila Doraswamy. B&W page USD 1,364, color page USD 1,848; trim 266 x 196. Circ: 40,000.

005.74 USA ISSN 1556-3235
QA76.9.D3 CODEN: DBMAF5
DB2 MAGAZINE. Text in English. 1996. q. adv. **Document type:** *Trade.*
Related titles: Online - full text ed.: ISSN 1556-3251.
Indexed: Inspec.
—BLDSC (3535.900370).
Published by: C M P Media LLC (Subsidiary of: United News & Media), 2800 Campus Dr, San Mateo, CA 94403. TEL 650-513-4300, FAX 650-513-4618, webmaster@db2mag.com, http://www.db2mag.com.

005.74 AUT ISSN 0419-9081
DIAGRAMM; Fachzeitschrift fuer Datenverarbeitung und Organisation. Text in German. 1969. 10/yr. EUR 12; EUR 1.45 newsstand/cover (effective 2001). adv. 16 p./no. 4 cols./p.; **Document type:** *Journal, Trade.*
Indexed: FS&TA, MLA-IB.
Published by: E D V - Verlag H. Munk, Rechte Wienzeile 85/4-6, Vienna, 1050, Austria. TEL 43-1-5818182, FAX 43-1-9695611, diagramm@chello.at. Ed., Pub. Herbert O. Munk. Circ: 10,000.

005.74 USA ISSN 0926-8782
QA76.9.D5 CODEN: DAATES
➤ **DISTRIBUTED AND PARALLEL DATABASES**; an international journal. Text in English. 1993. bi-m. EUR 685, USD 698, GBP 418 combined subscription to institutions print & online eds. (effective 2005). adv. back issues avail.; reprint service avail. from PSC. **Document type:** *Journal, Academic/Scholarly.* **Description:** Presents new research results, systems developments and experiences in distributed and parallel database systems.
Related titles: Microform ed.: (from PQC); Online - full text ed.: ISSN 1573-7578 (from EBSCO Publishing, Gale Group, IngentaConnect, Kluwer Online, O C L C Online Computer Library Center, Inc., Ovid Technologies, Inc., Springer LINK, Swets Information Services).
Indexed: ASCA, BibLing, CMCI, CompLI, CompR, CurCont, EngInd, InfoSAb, Inspec, RefZh.
—BLDSC (3602.660800), AskIEEE, CISTI, Ei, IDS, IE, Infotrieve, ingenta. **CCC.**
Published by: Springer-Verlag New York, Inc. (Subsidiary of: Springer Science+Business Media), 233 Spring St, New York, NY 10013. TEL 212-460-1500, FAX 212-460-1575, service@springer-ny.com, http://springerlink.metapress.com/openurl.asp?genre=journal&issn=0926-8782, http://www.springer-ny.com. Ed. Ahmed K Elmagarmid. **Subscr. to:** Journal Fulfillment, PO Box 2485, Secaucus, NJ 07096-2485. TEL 201-348-4033, FAX 201-348-4505, journals@springer-ny.com.

005.74 GBR ISSN 1360-6786
DOCUMENT MANAGEMENT UPDATE. Text in English. 1995. fortn. (20/yr.). GBP 397, USD 647. bk.rev. **Document type:** *Newsletter.* **Description:** Covers knowledge management, workflow, business process automation, groupware, internet and intranet technologies, recognition technologies and data capture, work management software, voice processing, and data storage.
Address: 1-1A, Brockley Cross Business Center, 96 Endwell Rd, London, SE4 2PD, United Kingdom. TEL 44-171-635-8886, FAX 44-171-277-6911, dmu@newsletterinteractive.com, info@pressfactory.co.uk. Ed. Stuart Draper.

005.74 658.8 GBR ISSN 1365-6619
DOCUMENT SYSTEMS OUTLOOK; the newsletter for senior I T decision makers. Text in English. 1996. m.?. **Document type:** *Newsletter.*
—BLDSC (3609.194300).
Published by: Mitre House Publishing Ltd., 154 Graham Rd, Wimbledon, London, SW19 3SJ, United Kingdom. http://www.mitrehousepublishing.co.uk/. Ed. Richard Blausten.

Z699.A1 DEU
E D M REPORT; Data-Management-Magazin. Text in German. 1995. q. EUR 50; EUR 15 newsstand/cover (effective 2005). adv. **Document type:** *Magazine, Trade.*
Published by: Dressler Verlag GmbH, Gaisbergstr 55-57, Heidelberg, 69115, Germany. TEL 49-6221-91130, FAX 49-6221-911321, info@dressler-verlag.de, http://www.edm-report.de, http://www.dressler-verlag.de. adv.: B&W page EUR 5,420, color page EUR 7,220. Circ: 19,653 (paid and controlled).

005.74 CHE
E T H INSTITUT FUER INFORMATIONSSYSTEME. DEPARTEMENT INFORMATIK. Text in German. irreg. **Document type:** *Bulletin, Academic/Scholarly.*
Published by: Eidgenoessische Technische Hochschule Zuerich, Institut fuer Informationssysteme, ETH Zentrum, Zurich, 8092, Switzerland. TEL 41-1-6322756, FAX 41-1-2523404. Ed. H. J. Schek.

025.04 USA ISSN 1525-2531
Z699.A1 CODEN: ECONF4
ECONTENT; digital content strategies & resources. Text in English. 1978. 10/yr. USD 115 domestic; USD 126 in Canada & Mexico; USD 151 elsewhere (effective 2005). adv. illus. index. back issues avail.; reprints avail. **Document type:** *Magazine, Trade.* **Description:** Features articles on a variety of topics of interest to online database users, and electronic content providers and users. Includes database search aids.
Formerly (until Jun. 1999): Database (0162-4105)
Related titles: E-mail ed.: EContent Xtra; Online - full text ed.: (from bigchalk, EBSCO Publishing, Factiva, Gale Group, H.W. Wilson, O C L C Online Computer Library Center, Inc., ProQuest Information & Learning); Print ed.
Indexed: ABIn, AS&TI, B&I, BPI, CIJE, CINAHL, CMCI, CompC, CompD, CurCont, EngInd, InfoSAb, Inspec, KES, LHTB, LIMI, LISA, LRI, LibLit, Microcompind, SSCI, SoftBase, T&II, WBA, WMB.
—BLDSC (3659.530425), AskIEEE, CASDDS, CINDOC, Ei, IDS, IE, Infotrieve, ingenta, Linda Hall. **CCC.**
Published by: Information Today, Inc., 143 Old Marlton Pike, Medford, NJ 08055-8750. TEL 609-654-6266, FAX 609-654-4309, custserv@infotoday.com, http://www.econtentmag.com, http://www.infotoday.com. Ed. Michelle Manafy. Circ: 4,500 (paid). **Dist. by:** International Publishers Direct, 27500 Riverview Center Blvd, Bonita Springs, FL 34134. TEL 858-320-4563, FAX 858-677-3220.

025.04 CAN ISSN 1207-8603
ELECTRONIC INFORMATION PARTNERSHIPS. Text in English. 1992. q. **Document type:** *Journal, Trade.*
Formerly: Electronic Dissemination Partnerships (1194-3750)
Related titles: Diskette ed.: ISSN 1208-6460. 199?; Online - full text ed.: (from Micromedia ProQuest).
Published by: (Interdepartmental Working Group on Database Industry Support), Sysnovators Ltd., 17 Taunton Place, Gloucester, ON K1J 7J7, Canada. TEL 613-746-5150, FAX 613-746-9757, pbrandon@fox.nstn.ns.ca.

005.74 USA ISSN 1061-9550
ENGINEERING DOCUMENT MANAGEMENT SYSTEM COMPARISON REPORT. Text in English. 1988. q. USD 490 (effective 2000). bibl.; charts; tr.lit. back issues avail.; reprints avail. **Document type:** *Newsletter.* **Description:** Reports on and compares all major electronic engineering document management, archive, and distribution systems currently available.
Formerly: Comparison Report on Engineering Scanning Systems (1056-182X)
Published by: International Imaging, Inc., 1147 Manhattan Ave, Ste 322, Manhattan Beach, CA 90266. TEL 310-937-7000, FAX 310-937-7001. Ed. Stephen J Gilheany. **Subscr. to:** 701 W Foothill Blvd, Azusa, CA 91702.

005.74 USA ISSN 1521-9518
QA76.9.A73
ENTERPRISE DEVELOPMENT. Text in English. 1998. m. adv. **Document type:** *Trade.*
Related titles: ♦ Supplement to: Visual Basic Programmer's Journal. ISSN 1075-1955.
Indexed: CompLI, SoftBase.
—IE.
Published by: Fawcette Technical Publications, 2600 S. El Camino Real., Ste. 300, San Mateo, CA 94403-2381. TEL 650-833-7100, FAX 650-853-0230, sgallagher@fawcette.com, http://www.fawcette.com, http://www.alimage.com/fawcet/., http://www.windx.com. Ed. Sean Gallagher. Pub. Jeff Miller. Adv. contact Stephen Shore. B&W page USD 8,160, color page USD 9,760. Circ: 70,000.

C

005.74 USA ISSN 1098-4755
QA76.9.D3 CODEN: EOXRA4
EXPLORING ORACLE. Text in English. 1996. m. USD 187 domestic; USD 197 foreign; USD 217 combined subscription print & online eds. (effective 2005). **Document type:** *Magazine, Consumer.* **Description:** Offers fresh ideas, shortcuts, and advice from computer experts for Oracle DBMS developers.
Formerly: Exploring Oracle D B M S (1089-344X)
Related titles: Online - full text ed.: USD 217 domestic; USD 227 foreign (effective 2005) (from ProQuest Information & Learning).
—**CCC.**
Published by: Element K Journals (Subsidiary of: Eli Research, Inc.), 500 Canal View Blvd, Rochester, NY 14623. TEL 585-240-7301, 800-223-8720, 877-203-5248, FAX 585-292-4392, http://www.elementkjournals.com/products/showProduct.asp?prodID=28&catId=2. Eds. Lisa Lenos, Michelle Rogers.

005.74025 USA ISSN 0897-4810
QA76.9.D32
FEDERAL DATA BASE FINDER. Text in English. 1984. every 18 mos. USD 125. **Description:** A directory of free and fee-based data bases and files available from the federal government.
Published by: Information U S A, Inc., PO Box E, Kensington, MD 20895-0418. TEL 301-924-0556, FAX 301-929-8907. Ed. Matthew Lesko. Circ: 5,000.

FILEMAKER ADVISOR. see *COMPUTERS—Computer Programming*

005.741 USA ISSN 1554-0669
▼ ➤ **FOUNDATIONS AND TRENDS IN INFORMATION RETRIEVAL.** Text in English. forthcoming 2006. q. USD 300 in North America; EUR 300 elsewhere; USD 340 combined subscription in North America print & online eds.; EUR 340 combined subscription elsewhere print & online eds. (effective 2006). **Document type:** *Journal, Academic/Scholarly.* **Description:** Publishes high-quality survey and tutorial monographs on all aspects of information retrieval.
Related titles: Online - full text ed.: ISSN 1554-0677. forthcoming 2006. USD 300 in North America; EUR 300 elsewhere (effective 2006).
Published by: Now Publishers Inc., PO Box 1024, Hanover, MA 02339. TEL 781-871-0245, FAX 781-871-6172, sales@nowpublishers.com, http://www.nowpublishers.com/ir. Eds. Fabrizio Sebastiani, Jamie Callan. Pub., R&P James Finlay.

005.74 USA ISSN 1042-6302
FOXTALK; solutions for Microsoft FoxPro and Visual FoxPro developers. Text in English. 1989. m. looseleaf. USD 149 domestic includes diskette; USD 159 in Canada includes diskette; USD 169 elsewhere includes diskette (effective 2004). adv. back issues avail. **Document type:** *Newsletter, Trade.* **Description:** Offers a variety of tips and in-depth articles on topics such as FoxPro language, systems analysis and design, cross-platform development, optimization, user interface design, and more.
Related titles: CD-ROM ed.: 1989.
—CISTI.
Published by: Pinnacle Publishing, Inc. (Subsidiary of: Lawrence Ragan Communications, Inc.), 316 N. Michigan Ave, Ste 300, Chicago, IL 60601. TEL 312-960-4209, 800-493-4867, FAX 312-960-4106, pinpub@ragan.com, http://www.pinpub.com. Ed. Whil Hentzen. Pub. Mickey Friedman. adv.: page USD 1,200. Circ: 4,000 (paid).

025.04 USA ISSN 1066-8934
QA76.9.D32 CODEN: GDDAE6
GALE DIRECTORY OF DATABASES. Text in English. a. (in 2 vols.), latest 2004. USD 540 per vol. (effective 2005). charts; stat. **Document type:** *Directory.* **Description:** Identifies 8,550 databases. Contains information on database selection and database descriptions, including producers and their addresses.
Formed by the merger of (1979-1992): Directory of Online Databases (0193-6840); (1990-1992): Directory of Portable Databases (1045-8352); (1978-1992): Computer Readable Databases (0271-4477); Which was formerly: Computer Readable Bibliographic Data Bases
Related titles: CD-ROM ed.: (from SilverPlatter Information, Inc.); Diskette ed.; Magnetic Tape ed.; Online - full text ed.: (from Data-Star, Questel Orbit Inc.).
—BLDSC (4066.773000), CINDOC, GNLM, Linda Hall. **CCC.**
Published by: Gale Group (Subsidiary of: Thomson Corporation), 27500 Drake Rd, Farmington Hills, MI 48331-3535. TEL 248-699-8061, 800-877-4253, FAX 248-699-4253, galeord@gale.com, http://www.gale.com. Ed. Kathleen Young Marcaccio.

H D M WEEK. (Health Data Management) see *HEALTH FACILITIES AND ADMINISTRATION*

HEALTH DATA MANAGEMENT (NEW YORK). see *HEALTH FACILITIES AND ADMINISTRATION*

I C A S A NEWS. see *AGRICULTURE—Crop Production And Soil*

025.04 004.5 USA
I E E E INTERNATIONAL NONVOLATILE MEMORY TECHNOLOGY CONFERENCE. PROCEEDINGS. Text in English. a. USD 116 per vol.. **Document type:** *Proceedings, Trade.*
—BLDSC (2023.760000).
Published by: Institute of Electrical and Electronics Engineers, Inc., 3 Park Ave, 17th Fl, New York, NY 10016-5997. TEL 800-678-4333, customer.service@ieee.org, http://www.ieee.org.

020 GBR
I M I S JOURNAL. Text in English. 1980. 6/yr. free. adv. bk.rev. **Document type:** *Trade.* **Description:** Discusses advances, implications and potential in information systems.
Former titles (until 1997): I D P M Journal (0969-823X); (until 1992): I D P M Information Management (1351-6035); (until 1992): Information Management Journal (0265-5306); (until 1984): Institute of Data Processing Management. Members Journal (0143-5132)
Indexed: Inspec.
—BLDSC (4369.510000).
Published by: Institute for the Management of Information Systems, IMIS House, 5 Kingfisher House, New Mill Rd, Orpington, Kent BR5 3QG, United Kingdom. TEL 44-700-00-23456, FAX 44-700-00-23023, central@imis.org.uk, http://www.imis.org.uk. Ed. Robin Bradford. R&P V J Hymas. adv.: B&W page GBP 800, color page GBP 1,200; trim 210 x 297. Circ: 12,000.

INDUSTRIAL MANAGEMENT & DATA SYSTEMS. see *BUSINESS AND ECONOMICS—Computer Applications*

005.74 USA ISSN 8750-6874
QA75.5 CODEN: INFWE4
INFORMATION WEEK (US EDITION); business innovation powered by technology. Variant title: InformationWeek. Text in English. 1979. w. USD 199 domestic; USD 219 in Canada; USD 459 in Europe, Mexico, Central & South America; USD 489 in Asia, Australia & Pacific; USD 4.95 newsstand/cover domestic; CND 5.95 newsstand/cover in Canada (effective 2005). adv. **Document type:** *Magazine, Trade.* **Description:** Includes news and analysis about cutting-edge products, technology, and notable vendors for people who manage technology in business.
Incorporates (in 1994): Open Systems Today (1061-0839); Which was formerly (1988-1992): UNIX Today (1040-5038); (until 1984): Information Systems News (0199-0691)
Related titles: Online - full text ed.: Information Week Online (from bigchalk, EBSCO Publishing, Florida Center for Library Automation, Gale Group, H.W. Wilson, Northern Light Technology, Inc., O C L C Online Computer Library Center, Inc., ProQuest Information & Learning); ♦ Supplement(s): S C O Magazine. ISSN 1060-1074.
Indexed: ABIn, AgeL, B&I, BPI, BrCerAb, C&ISA, CerAb, CompB, CompC, CompD, CompIU, CorrAb, E&CAJ, EMA, GALA, IAA, ISAP, InfoSAb, Inspec, M&TEA, MBF, METADEX, Microcompind, PROMT, ResCtrInd, SoftBase, SolStAb, WAA.
—BLDSC (4496.410100), AskIEEE, CASDDS, IE, Infotrieve, ingenta, Linda Hall. **CCC.**
Published by: C M P Media LLC (Subsidiary of: United News & Media), 600 Community Dr, Manhasset, NY 11030. TEL 516-562-5000, 800-292-3642, FAX 516-562-5036, iweekletters@cmp.com, bevans@cmp.com, http://www.informationweek.com/. Ed. Bob Evans. Pub. Scott Vaughan. Adv. contact Patricia Mayer. B&W page USD 39,065, color page USD 47,815; trim 10.5 x 15.75. Circ: 440,000 (paid and controlled).

005.74 USA ISSN 1524-3621
QA75.5 CODEN: INENF7
INTELLIGENT ENTERPRISE; enterprise solutions for business intelligence. Text in English. 1998. 18/yr. USD 95 domestic; USD 125 in Canada & Mexico; USD 175 elsewhere (effective 2005). adv. back issues avail.; reprint service avail. from PQC. **Document type:** *Magazine, Trade.* **Description:** Focuses on practical solutions for designing, using and maintaining database management systems.
Formed by the merger of (1987-1998): Database Programming and Design (0895-4518); (1986-1998): D B M S (1041-5173); Which was formerly (until 1988): Business Software
Related titles: Microfilm ed.: (from PQC); Online - full text ed.: IntelligenceEnterprise.com (from EBSCO Publishing, Gale Group, H.W. Wilson, LexisNexis, O C L C Online Computer Library Center, Inc.).
Indexed: BPI, CompD, CompLI, EngInd, InfoSAb, Inspec, Microcompind, RILM, RefZh, SoftBase.
—BLDSC (4531.831590), AskIEEE, CASDDS, Ei, IE, ingenta, Linda Hall. **CCC.**
Published by: C M P Media LLC (Subsidiary of: United News & Media), 600 Harrison St, 6th Fl., San Francisco, CA 94107. TEL 415-947-6746, FAX 415-947-6041, iemagazine@mfi.com, http://www.intelligententerprise.com. Ed. David B Stodder. Pub., Adv. contact David Kalman. B&W page USD 15,288, color page USD 17,138; bleed 8.25 x 11. Circ: 80,000 (paid).

005.74 USA ISSN 1047-7349
QA76.9.D3
➤ **INTERNATIONAL CONFERENCE ON VERY LARGE DATA BASES. PROCEEDINGS.** Text in English. 1983. a. USD 50 (effective 2003). abstr.; charts; stat.; illus. **Document type:** *Proceedings, Academic/Scholarly.* **Description:** Forum for research in database system management design and programming.
Former titles (until 1987): Very Large Data Bases. Proceedings (0730-9317); (until 1977): International Conference on Very Large Data Bases. Proceedings (0278-2596)
—BLDSC (6845.076000), IE, ingenta. **CCC.**
Published by: (V L D B Endowment DEU, International Conference on Very Large Data Bases), Morgan Kaufmann Publishers, Inc. (Subsidiary of: Elsevier BV) orders@mkp.com, http://www.mkp.com. Ed. Diavie Cerra. R&P Kate Henserson.

005.74 USA ISSN 1548-3924
▼ ➤ **INTERNATIONAL JOURNAL OF DATA WAREHOUSING AND MINING.** Text in English. 2005. q. USD 85 to individuals; USD 195 to institutions (effective 2005). **Document type:** *Journal, Academic/Scholarly.* **Description:** Aims to provide a forum for state-of-the-art developments and research, as well as current innovative activities in data warehousing and mining.
Related titles: Online - full text ed.: ISSN 1548-3932. 2005.
Indexed: C&ISA, E&CAJ, IAA.
Published by: Idea Group Publishing (Subsidiary of: Idea Group Inc.), 701 E Chocolate Ave, Ste 200, Hershey, PA 17033-1240. TEL 717-533-8845, FAX 717-533-7115, cust@idea-group.com, http://www.idea-group.com/journals/details.asp?id=4291. Ed. David Taniar.

025.04 003 USA ISSN 1555-0885
INTERNATIONAL SYMPOSIUM ON OBJECT-ORIENTED REAL-TIME DISTRIBUTED COMPUTING. Text in English. 1998. a. USD 188 to members (effective 2004). **Document type:** *Proceedings, Trade.*
Published by: Institute of Electrical and Electronics Engineers, Inc., 3 Park Ave, 17th Fl, New York, NY 10016-5997. TEL 212-419-7900, 800-678-4333, FAX 212-752-4929, customer.service@ieee.org, http://www.ieee.org.

025.04 003 USA ISSN 1530-1443
INTERNATIONAL WORKSHOP ON OBJECT ORIENTED REAL TIME DEPENDABLE SYSTEMS. PROCEEDINGS. Text in English. 1994. a. USD 173; USD 70 to members (effective 2004). **Document type:** *Proceedings, Trade.*
Related titles: Online - full text ed.: (from I E E E).
Indexed: EngInd.
—BLDSC (4552.196100).
Published by: Institute of Electrical and Electronics Engineers, Inc., 3 Park Ave, 17th Fl, New York, NY 10016-5997. TEL 212-419-7900, 800-678-4333, FAX 212-752-4929, customer.service@ieee.org, http://www.ieee.org.

INTERNET SECURITY ADVISOR. see *COMPUTERS—Computer Security*

JEONGBO GWAHAGHOE NONMUNJI. DEI'TA'BEI'SEU/KOREA INFORMATION SCIENCE SOCIETY. JOURNAL. DATABASE. see *COMPUTERS—Information Science And Information Theory*

JET INFO. see *COMPUTERS—Computer Security*

005.74 USA ISSN 1384-5810
CODEN: DMKDFD
➤ **THE JOURNAL OF DATA MINING AND KNOWLEDGE DISCOVERY.** Text in English. 1997. bi-m. EUR 588, USD 598, GBP 378 combined subscription to institutions print & online eds. (effective 2005). adv. reprint service avail. from PSC. **Document type:** *Journal, Academic/Scholarly.* **Description:** Publishes articles on all aspects of knowledge discovery in databases and data mining methods for extracting high-level representations from data.
Related titles: Online - full text ed.: ISSN 1573-756X (from Association for Computing Machinery, Inc., EBSCO Publishing, Gale Group, IngentaConnect, Kluwer Online, O C L C Online Computer Library Center, Inc., Springer LINK, Swets Information Services).
Indexed: BibLing, CMCI, CompAb, CompLI, CurCont, ISR, InfoSAb, Inspec, MathR, MathSciNet, RefZh, SCI, ST&MA.
—BLDSC (3534.726000), CISTI, IDS, IE, Infotrieve, ingenta. **CCC.**
Published by: Springer-Verlag New York, Inc. (Subsidiary of: Springer Science+Business Media), 233 Spring St, New York, NY 10013. TEL 212-460-1500, FAX 212-460-1575, service@springer-ny.com, http://springerlink.metapress.com/openurl.asp?genre=journal&issn=1384-5810, http://www.springer-ny.com. Ed. Geoffrey I Webb. **Subscr. to:** Journal Fulfillment, PO Box 2485, Secaucus, NJ 07096-2485. TEL 201-348-4033, FAX 201-348-4505, journals@springer-ny.com.

005.74 USA ISSN 1063-8016
QA76.9.D3 CODEN: JDAMEQ
➤ **JOURNAL OF DATABASE MANAGEMENT.** Text in English. 1990. q. USD 95 combined subscription to individuals print & online eds.; USD 315 combined subscription to institutions print & online eds. (effective 2005). 48 p./no.; **Document type:** *Journal, Academic/Scholarly.* **Description:** Provides those who design, develop, and administer DBMS-based information systems with state-of-the-art research.
Formerly: Journal of Database Administration (1047-9430)
Related titles: Online - full text ed.: ISSN 1533-8010. USD 68 to individuals; USD 212 to institutions (effective 2004) (from EBSCO Publishing, Florida Center for Library Automation, Gale Group, O C L C Online Computer Library Center, Inc., ProQuest Information & Learning).
Indexed: ABIn, BrCerAb, BusEdI, C&ISA, CMCI, CerAb, CompD, CompLI, CorrAb, CurCont, E&CAJ, EMA, Emerald, IAA, InfoSAb, Inspec, LISA, M&TEA, MBF, METADEX, Microcompind, SolStAb, WAA.
—BLDSC (4967.815000), AskIEEE, IE, Infotrieve, ingenta, Linda Hall. **CCC.**
Published by: (Information Resources Management Association), Idea Group Publishing (Subsidiary of: Idea Group Inc.), 701 E Chocolate Ave, Ste 200, Hershey, PA 17033-1240. TEL 717-533-8845, 866-342-6657, FAX 717-533-7115, jtravers@idea-group.com, http://www.idea-group.com/journals/details.asp?id=198. Ed. Keng Siau. Circ: 350 (controlled).

➤ **JOURNAL OF GLOBAL INFORMATION TECHNOLOGY MANAGEMENT.** see *COMPUTERS*

➤ **JOURNAL OF INFORMATION TECHNOLOGY CASES AND APPLICATIONS.** see *COMPUTERS*

005.74 USA
KNOWLEDGE DISCOVERY NUGGETS NEWS. Text in English. 1997. m. adv. back issues avail. **Document type:** *Newsletter.* **Description:** Contains articles and news about data mining and knowledge discovery.
Media: Online - full text. **Related titles:** E-mail ed.
Published by: Knowledge Discovery Nuggets FAX 413-828-0271, gps@kdnuggets.com, http://www.kdnuggets.com/. Ed. Gregory Piatetsky-Shapiro.

005.74 005.72 GBR ISSN 1369-1368
KNOWLEDGE MANAGEMENT (LONDON). Text in English. 1997. 10/yr. GBP 345 domestic; EUR 550 in Europe; USD 500 elsewhere (effective 2004). adv. **Description:** Covers all aspects of intellectual capital management.
Related titles: Online - full content ed.: GBP 195 domestic; EUR 305 in Europe; USD 345 elsewhere (effective 2004); Online - full text ed.: (from EBSCO Publishing).
—IE.

C

Published by: Ark Group Ltd, 86-88 Upper Richmond Rd, London, SW15 2UR, United Kingdom. TEL 44-20-87852700, FAX 44-20-87859373, info@ark-group.com, http://www.kmmagazine.com, http://www.ark-group.com. Ed. Simon Lelic TEL 44-20-87855939. Pub., Adv. contact Luis Keats.

005.74 DEU ISSN 1432-1564
HD30.213
KOELNER INFORMATIONS MANAGEMENT. Text in German. 1996. irreg. **Document type:** *Trade.* **Description:** Contains news about data base management.
Published by: Stadt Koeln, Amt fuer Stadtentwicklung und Statistik, Athener Ring 4, Cologne, 50765, Germany. TEL 49-221-21887, FAX 49-221-2211900.

005.74 AUS
M I S (NEW ZEALAND EDITION). Text in English. 1997. m. (except Jan.). NZD 69.95 domestic; NZD 103 foreign (effective 2002). adv. **Document type:** *Trade.* **Description:** Business issues ralating to strategic IT implementations.
Formerly: M I S New Zealand (1174-3506)
Related titles: ♦ Regional ed(s).: M I S (Australian Edition). ISSN 1445-5382; M I S (UK Edition). GBP 49 domestic; GBP 85 in Europe (effective 2002); M I S (Asia Edition). SGD 63 (effective 2002).
Published by: Fairfax Business Media (Subsidiary of: John Fairfax Holdings Ltd.), 201 Sussex St, Sydney, NSW 2000, Australia. TEL 61-2-9282-2822, rob@industrial.co.nz, http://www.misweb.com.au, http://www.fxj.com.au/. Circ: 1,928.

005.74 USA ISSN 0891-4699
CODEN: MHSSEP
MCGRAW-HILL SERIES IN MANAGEMENT INFORMATION SYSTEMS. Text in English. 1982. irreg. **Document type:** *Monographic series.*
Indexed: Inspec.
Published by: McGraw-Hill Higher Education, 1221 Ave. of the Americas, New York, NY 10020. TEL 212-512-2000, http://www.mhhe.com.

005.74 GBR ISSN 1361-4584
QA76.9.T48 CODEN: JDTMEJ
NEW REVIEW OF DOCUMENT AND TEXT MANAGEMENT. Text in English. 1993. 3/yr. GBP 65, USD 125. adv. bk.rev. back issues avail. **Document type:** *Academic/Scholarly.*
Formerly (until 1995): Journal of Document and Text Management (0969-9325)
Indexed: ETA, Inspec.
—AskIEEE.
Published by: Taylor Graham Publishing, 48 Regent St, Cambridge, CB2 1FD, United Kingdom. Ed. Forbes Gibb.

005.74 USA
O A U G CONFERENCE PROCEEDINGS. Text in English. irreg. USD 50. **Document type:** *Proceedings.*
Related titles: CD-ROM ed.
Published by: Oracle Applications User Group, 1 Piedmont Ctr NE, Ste. 400, Atlanta, GA 30305-1501. TEL 404-240-0999, FAX 404-240-0998, oaug@mindspring.com, http://www.oaug.org.

005.74 USA
O A U G FORUM. Text in English. s-a. adv. **Document type:** *Newsletter.*
Related titles: Online - full text ed.
Published by: Oracle Applications User Group, 1 Piedmont Ctr NE, Ste. 400, Atlanta, GA 30305-1501. TEL 404-240-0999, FAX 404-240-0998, oaug@mindspring.com, http://www.oaug.org.

005.74 USA
O A U G INSIGHT. Text in English. q. **Document type:** *Newsletter.*
Related titles: Online - full text ed.
Published by: Oracle Applications User Group, 1 Piedmont Ctr NE, Ste. 400, Atlanta, GA 30305-1501. TEL 404-240-0999, FAX 404-240-0998, oaug@mindspring.com, http://www.oaug.org.

OEKONOMISTYRING OG INFORMATIK. see *BUSINESS AND ECONOMICS—Management*

020 AUS ISSN 0816-956X
CODEN: ONCUEF
ONLINE CURRENTS. Text in English. 1986. 10/yr. AUD 231 domestic; AUD 250 foreign; AUD 297 combined subscription print & online eds. (effective 2004). adv. bk.rev. index. back issues avail. **Document type:** *Journal.* **Description:** Provides information about the online industry and electronic information, including both Australian and overseas news.
Related titles: Online - full text ed.
Indexed: ABIX, AESIS, CINAHL, InfoSAb.
—CASDDS.
Published by: Enterprise Information Management Pty. Ltd., PO Box 215, Lindfield, NSW 2070, Australia. TEL 61-2-98809000, FAX 61-2-98809001, olc@pnc.com.au, http://www.onlinecurrents.com.au. Eds. Elizabeth Drynan, Pamela Johnstone. R&P, Adv. contact Elizabeth Drynan. Circ: 1,000.

005.74 NLD ISSN 1389-1383
OPTIMIZE; onafhankelijk vaktijdschrift voor de Oracle-professional. Text in Dutch. 1998. bi-m. EUR 59.50 domestic; EUR 65.50 in Belgium (effective 2005). adv. bk.rev.; software rev. charts; illus. 60 p./no.; back issues avail. **Document type:** *Journal, Trade.* **Description:** Offers the Oracle database professional news and articles on the latest developments in the Oracle market, with reviews, first looks, opinion, product news, and interviews.
Published by: Array Publications BV, Postbus 2211, Alphen aan den Rijn, 2400 CE, Netherlands. TEL 31-172-424177, FAX 31-172-424381, optimize@array.nl, http://www.optimize.nl/site/, http://www.array.nl. Ed. Dre de Man. Adv. contacts Jos Raaphorst TEL 31-172-469030, Will Manusiwa TEL 31-172-469030. B&W page EUR 1,995, color page EUR 3,195; trim 210 x 285. Circ: 3,500 (paid).

005.74 005.1 USA ISSN 1522-8584
ORACLE INTERNALS. Text in English. 1999. m. USD 145 (effective 1999). adv. index. 20 p./no. 2 cols./p.; back issues avail.; reprints avail. **Document type:** *Newsletter, Trade.* **Description:** Provides database administrators with technical tips and techniques.
Related titles: Online - full text ed.: (from O C L C Online Computer Library Center, Inc.).
Published by: Auerbach Publications (Subsidiary of: C R C Press, LLC), 2000 Corporate Blvd., NW, Boca Raton, FL 33431. TEL 212-297-9176, FAX 212-297-9176, orders@crcpress.com, http://www.auerbach-publications.com, http://www.auerbach-publications.com/home.asp. Ed. Donald Burleson. Pub., Adv. contact Richard O'Hanley TEL 212-845-4017. R&P Jamie Sigal TEL 561-994-0555. B&W page USD 2,000; trim 10 x 7.

005.74 USA ISSN 1065-3171
ORACLE MAGAZINE. Text in English. 1987. bi-m. free to qualified personnel; USD 4.95 newsstand/cover domestic (effective 2004). adv. **Document type:** *Magazine, Trade.* **Description:** Publishes practical, technical articles relating to applications of Oracle-based information management technology, as well as in-depth overviews and analysis of trends and issues affecting information managers.
Related titles: Online - full text ed.
Indexed: BrCerAb, C&ISA, CerAb, CorrAb, E&CAJ, EMA, IAA, M&TEA, MBF, METADEX, SoftBase, WAA.
—IE.
Published by: Oracle Corporation, 500 Oracle Pkwy., 8BP1, Redwood Shores, CA 94065. TEL 1-847-6479630, FAX 1-847-6479735, jgibbs@us.oracle.com, http://www.oramag.com/. Ed. Jeff Spicer. adv.: B&W page USD 9,450, color page USD 10,500; trim 10.88 x 8. Circ: 120,126 (controlled).

005.74 USA ISSN 1525-1756
ORACLE PROFESSIONAL. Text in English. 1994. m. USD 199 (effective 2004). adv. **Document type:** *Newsletter, Trade.* **Description:** Offers tips, insights, and solutions for a variety of Oracle development tasks, including DBMS SQL enhancements, architecture servers, application servers, Web servers, security, and analyzing schemas.
—IE.
Published by: Pinnacle Publishing, Inc. (Subsidiary of: Lawrence Ragan Communications, Inc.), 316 N. Michigan Ave, Ste 300, Chicago, IL 60601. TEL 312-960-4209, 800-493-4867, FAX 312-960-4106, pinpub@ragan.com, http://www.pinpub.com. adv.: page USD 1,200. Circ: 3,500 (paid).

005.74 USA
ORACLE UPDATE. Text in English. m. USD 255 (effective 2000). **Document type:** *Trade.* **Description:** Provides information on Oracle relational database systems.
Published by: Xephon, 9330 Lyndon B Johnson Fwy., Ste. 800, Dallas, TX 75243-4310. TEL 303-410-9344, FAX 303-438-0290, http://www.xephon.com/.

005.74 USA ISSN 0163-5808
QA76.9.D3 CODEN: SRECD8
S I G M O D RECORD. (Special Interest Group on Management of Data) Text in English. q. USD 35 to non-members; USD 23 to members; USD 8 student members (effective 2004). bk.rev. **Document type:** *Newsletter, Academic/Scholarly.*
Formerly: S I G F I D E T Record
Related titles: Online - full text ed.: (from EBSCO Publishing).
Indexed: CMCI, CompAb, CompR, CurCont, EngInd, Inspec.
—BLDSC (8275.570000), AskIEEE, CISTI, Ei, IE, Infotrieve, ingenta, Linda Hall.
Published by: Association for Computing Machinery, Inc., 1515 Broadway, 17th Fl, New York, NY 10036-5701. TEL 212-626-0500, 212-626-0520, 800-342-6626, FAX 212-869-0481, sigs@acm.org, usacm@acm.org, http://www.acm.org.

S Q L SERVER MAGAZIN. (Structured Query Language) see *COMPUTERS—Computer Programming*

S Q L SERVER MAGAZINE. see *COMPUTERS—Computer Programming*

S Q L SERVER UPDATE. (Structured Query Language) see *COMPUTERS—Computer Programming*

005.74 USA ISSN 1070-4795
Z699.A1 CODEN: SMDPE8
SEARCHER (MEDFORD); the magazine for database professionals. Text in English. 1993. 10/yr. USD 86.95 domestic; USD 111 in Canada & Mexico; USD 118 elsewhere (effective 2005). adv. illus. reprints avail. **Document type:** *Magazine, Trade.* **Description:** Explores and deliberates on a comprehensive range of issues important to the professional database searcher. Includes all electronic media: online, CD-ROM, diskette, tape leasing.
Related titles: Online - full text ed.: (from EBSCO Publishing, Florida Center for Library Automation, Gale Group, H.W. Wilson, O C L C Online Computer Library Center, Inc., ProQuest Information & Learning).
Indexed: ABIn, BrCerAb, BrHumI, C&ISA, CIJE, CINAHL, CerAb, CompD, CorrAb, DIP, E&CAJ, EMA, IAA, IBR, IBZ, InfoSAb, Inpharma, Inspec, LISA, LRI, LibLit, M&TEA, MBF, METADEX, MicrocompInd, PE&ON, Reac, SoftBase, WAA.
—BLDSC (8214.625500), Ei, IDS, IE, Infotrieve, ingenta, Linda Hall. **CCC.**
Published by: Information Today, Inc., 143 Old Marlton Pike, Medford, NJ 08055-8750. TEL 609-654-6266, FAX 609-654-4309, custserv@infotoday.com, http://www.infotoday.com/searcher/default.htm. Ed. Barbara Quint. Adv. contact Michael Zarrello. Circ: 3,000 (paid). **Outside N. America subscr. to:** Learned Information Europe Ltd.

005.74 USA ISSN 1066-7911
QA76.9.D3
SMART ACCESS. Text in English. 1993. m. USD 149 (effective 2004). adv. back issues avail. **Document type:** *Newsletter, Trade.* **Description:** For developers and power users working with Microsoft Access.
Related titles: Online - full text ed.: (from Northern Light Technology, Inc.).
—IE, Infotrieve.
Published by: Pinnacle Publishing, Inc. (Subsidiary of: Lawrence Ragan Communications, Inc.), 316 N. Michigan Ave, Ste 300, Chicago, IL 60601. TEL 312-960-4209, 800-493-4867, FAX 312-960-4106, pinpub@ragan.com, http://www.pinnaclepublishing.com/sa, http://www.pinpub.com. adv.: page USD 1,200. Circ: 7,000 (paid).

C

005.74 USA ISSN 1538-8379
SMART TIPS AND QUICK TRICKS FOR ORACLE. Text in English. 2002. a. USD 10 per issue domestic; USD 20 per issue foreign (effective 2005).
—**CCC.**
Published by: Element K Journals (Subsidiary of: Eli Research, Inc.), 500 Canal View Blvd, Rochester, NY 14623. TEL 585-240-7301, 800-223-8720, 877-203-5248, FAX 585-292-4392, http://www.elementkjournals.com. Eds. Lisa Lenos, Michelle Rogers.

005.74 005.8 USA ISSN 1547-4682
JK468.A8
▼ **STORAGE & GOVERNMENT**; the storage magazine for government, military and aerospace technologies. Text in English. 2003. bi-m. USD 300 domestic (effective 2003). adv. **Document type:** *Magazine, Trade.*
Published by: West World Productions, Inc., 420 N Camden Dr, Beverly Hills, CA 90210-4507. TEL 310-276-9500, FAX 310-246-1405, http://www.wwpi.com. Eds. Christine Taylor Chudnow, George McNamara. Pub. Yuri R Spiro.

005.74 RUS
STORAGE NEWS. Text in Russian. 1999. bi-m. free to qualified personnel (effective 2004). **Document type:** *Journal, Trade.*
Published by: Redaktsiya Zhurnala Storage News, a/ya 57, Moscow, 115516, Russian Federation. TEL 7-095-2334935, FAX 7-095-9574899, info@storagenews.ru, http://www.storagenews.ru. Circ: 5,000.

025.04 DEU ISSN 1435-6279
STUDIEN ZUR DATENBANKFORSCHUNG. Text in German. 1991. irreg., latest vol.7, 1999. price varies. **Document type:** *Monographic series, Academic/Scholarly.*
Published by: Verlag Dr. Kovac, Arnoldstr 49, Hamburg, 22763, Germany. TEL 49-40-3988800, FAX 49-40-39888055, info@verlagdrkovac.de, http://www.verlagdrkovac.de/4-2.htm.

005.74 020 USA ISSN 1530-2067
QA76.64
TECHNOLOGY OF OBJECT ORIENTED LANGUAGES AND SYSTEMS. Text in English. 1989. irreg., latest vol.39, 2001. price varies. **Document type:** *Proceedings, Trade.*
Related titles: Online - full text ed.: (from I E E E).
Published by: Institute of Electrical and Electronics Engineers, Inc., 3 Park Ave, 17th Fl, New York, NY 10016-5997. TEL 212-419-7900, 800-678-4333, FAX 212-752-4929, customer.service@ieee.org, http://www.ieee.org.

005.74 USA
TECHREPUBLIC. Text in English. d. free to qualified personnel (effective 2003). adv. **Document type:** *Trade.* **Description:** Covers news and issues about information technology for executives, managers, system administrators, support personnel and consultants.
Media: Online - full text.

Published by: TechRepublic, Inc. (Subsidiary of: Gartner Inc.), 9900 Corporate Campus Dr, Louisville, KY 40223. TEL 502-992-8000, 800-217-4339, FAX 502-992-8001, home@techrepublic.com, customers@techrepublic.com, http://www.techrepublic.com.

005.74 020 USA ISSN 1530-1893
USER INTERFACES TO DATA INTENSIVE SYSTEMS. PROCEEDINGS. Text in English. irreg. price varies. **Document type:** *Proceedings, Trade.*
Related titles: Online - full text ed.: (from I E E E).
Published by: Institute of Electrical and Electronics Engineers, Inc., 3 Park Ave, 17th Fl, New York, NY 10016-5997. TEL 212-419-7900, 800-678-4333, FAX 212-752-4929, customer.service@ieee.org, http://www.ieee.org.

005.74 DEU ISSN 1066-8888
QA76.9.D3 CODEN: VLDBFR
➤ **THE V L D B JOURNAL**; the international journal of very large data bases. (Very Large Data Bases) Text in German. 1992. q. USD 248 domestic to non-members; USD 262 foreign to non-members; USD 48 domestic to members; USD 62 foreign to members; USD 43 domestic to students; USD 57 foreign to students; USD 58 combined subscription domestic to members print & online eds.; USD 72 combined subscription foreign to members print & online eds.; USD 52 combined subscription domestic to students print & online eds.; USD 66 combined subscription foreign to students print & online eds. (effective 2005). adv. abstr. back issues avail. **Document type:** *Journal, Academic/Scholarly.* **Description:** Dedicated to publishing scholarly contributions from around the world to the advancement of information system architectures, the effect of emerging technologies on information systems, and the development of novel applications.
Related titles: Online - full text ed.: ISSN 0949-877X. USD 34 to students (effective 2005) (from EBSCO Publishing, Springer LINK, Swets Information Services).
Indexed: C&ISA, CMCI, CurCont, E&CAJ, IAA, Inspec.
—BLDSC (9246.037000), AskIEEE, CISTI, IDS, IE, Infotrieve. **CCC.**
Published by: (V L D B Endowment), Springer-Verlag (Subsidiary of: Springer Science+Business Media), Tiergartenstr 17, Heidelberg, 69121, Germany. TEL 49-6221-3450, FAX 49-6221-345229, http://link.springer.de/link/service/journals/00778/index.htm. Eds. Elisa Bertino TEL 39-2-5500-6227, Kyu-Young Whang TEL 82-42-869-3522. Adv. contact Stephan Kroeck TEL 49-30-827875739. **Subscr. in the Americas to:** Springer-Verlag New York, Inc., Journal Fulfillment, PO Box 2485, Secaucus, NJ 07096-2485. TEL 800-777-4643, 201-348-4033, FAX 201-348-4505, journals@springer-ny.com, http://www.springer-ny.com; **Subscr. to:** Springer GmbH Auslieferungsgesellschaft, Haberstr 7, Heidelberg 69126, Germany. TEL 49-6221-345-0, FAX 49-6221-345-4229, subscriptions@springer.de.

025.74 USA
WORLDWIDE DATABASES. Text in English. 1990. m. USD 150 in North America; USD 165 elsewhere (effective 2001). bk.rev. back issues avail. **Document type:** *Newsletter, Trade.* **Description:** Reports on news and information dealing with online computer databases around the world. Includes articles on new database products and enhancements, developments, distribution agreements, and user applications.
Related titles: Online - full text ed.: (from Data-Star, The Dialog Corporation).
Published by: Worldwide Videotex, PO Box 3273, Boynton Beach, FL 33424-3273. TEL 561-738-2276, markedit@juno.com, http://www.wvpubs.com. Ed., Pub. Mark Wright.

COMPUTERS—Data Communications And Data Transmission Systems

004.6 USA ISSN 1551-6857
QA76.575
▼ ➤ **A C M TRANSACTIONS ON MULTIMEDIA COMPUTING COMMUNICATIONS AND APPLICATIONS.** (Association for Computing Machinery) Text in English. 2005 (Feb.). 4/yr. USD 140 domestic to non-members; USD 154 foreign to non-members; USD 40 domestic to members; USD 54 foreign to members; USD 35 domestic to students; USD 49 foreign to students; USD 168 combined subscription domestic to non-members print & online eds.; USD 182 combined subscription foreign to non-members print & online eds.; USD 48 combined subscription domestic to members print & online eds.; USD 62 combined subscription foreign to members print & online eds.; USD 42 combined subscription domestic to students print & online eds.; USD 56 combined subscription foreign to students print & online eds. (effective 2006). **Document type:** *Journal, Academic/Scholarly.*
Related titles: Online - full text ed.: ISSN 1551-6865. USD 112 to non-members; USD 32 to members; USD 28 to students (effective 2006) (from EBSCO Publishing).
Published by: Association for Computing Machinery, Inc., 1515 Broadway, 17th Fl, New York, NY 10036-5701. TEL 212-869-7440, 800-342-6626, FAX 212-944-1318, usacm@acm.org, http://www.acm.org.

➤ **A F M INFORMATION SYSTEMS SERIES (NO.).** (Accounting and Financial Management) see *COMPUTERS—Computer Systems*

362 004.6 USA
ADVANCE FOR HEALTH INFORMATION EXECUTIVES. Text in English. m. Free to qualified subscribers. adv. **Document type:** *Magazine, Trade.* **Description:** Publishes solutions and strategies for health information systems, such as computer-based patient records systems.
Related titles: Online - full content ed.
Published by: Merion Publications, Inc., 2900 Horizon Dr, King of Prussia, PA 19406. TEL 800-355-5627, FAX 610-278-1421, 610-278-1425, firving@merion.com, http://www.advanceforhie.com, http://www.advanceweb.com.

004.6 USA
ADVANCED TECHNOLOGY FOR DEVELOPERS✶ ; a monthly how-to newsletter for developers. Text in English. m. USD 198. **Document type:** *Newsletter.*
Published by: High-Tech Communications, 2407 Pennsylvania, West Mifflin, PA 15122. TEL 412-749-8299, FAX 412-741-6094. Ed. Jane Klimasauskas.

004.6 USA
ASSOCIATION FOR COMPUTING MACHINERY. ANNUAL REPORT (YEAR). Text in English. a. **Document type:** *Yearbook, Academic/Scholarly.*
Related titles: ♦ Supplement to: Association for Computing Machinery. Communications. ISSN 0001-0782.
Published by: Association for Computing Machinery, Inc., 1515 Broadway, 17th Fl, New York, NY 10036-5701. TEL 212-626-0500, 212-626-0520, 800-342-6626, FAX 212-869-0481, sigs@acm.org, usacm@acm.org, http://www.acm.org.

004.6 USA ISSN 0001-0782
CODEN: CACMA2
➤ **ASSOCIATION FOR COMPUTING MACHINERY. COMMUNICATIONS.** Text in English. 1958. m. USD 184 domestic to non-members; USD 223 foreign to non-members; USD 221 combined subscription domestic to non-members; USD 260 combined subscription foreign to non-members; free membership (effective 2006). adv. charts; illus. index. back issues avail.; reprints avail. **Document type:** *Journal, Academic/Scholarly.* **Description:** Articles on all aspects of computing, including artificial intelligence, programming, human and social aspects of computing, operations research and management applications. Covers industry and ACM news.
Formerly (until 1959): Communications of the Association for Computing Machinery
Related titles: Microfiche ed.: (from PQC); Online - full text ed.: ISSN 1557-7317. USD 143 to non-members (effective 2004) (from Association for Computing Machinery, Inc., EBSCO Publishing, Florida Center for Library Automation, Gale Group, O C L C Online Computer Library Center, Inc., ProQuest Information & Learning); ♦ Supplement(s): MemberNet; ♦ Association for Computing Machinery. Annual Report (Year).
Indexed: ABIn, ABS&EES, AHCI, AIA, AS&TI, ASCA, ApMecR, BMT, BPI, BrCerAb, C&CSA, C&ISA, CADCAM, CIS, CMCI, CerAb, CompAb, CompC, CompD, CompLI, CompR, CorrAb, CurCont, E&CAJ, EMA, EngInd, ErgAb, IAA, IAOP, ISR, InfoSAb, Inspec, M&TEA, MBF, METADEX, MLA-IB, MathR, ORMS, QC&AS, RASB, RefZh, RoboAb, SCI, SolStAb, WAA.
—BLDSC (3344.250000), AskIEEE, CASDDS, CISTI, Ei, IDS, IE, Infotrieve, ingenta, Linda Hall. **CCC.**
Published by: Association for Computing Machinery, Inc., 1515 Broadway, 17th Fl, New York, NY 10036-5701. TEL 212-626-0500, 212-869-7440, 800-342-6626, FAX 212-944-1318, acmhelp@acm.org, sigs@acm.org, usacm@acm.org, http://www.acm.org/cacm/. Ed. Diane Crawford. adv.: B&W page USD 5,420, color page USD 5,420. Circ: 85,000 (paid).

➤ **BROADBAND ADVERTISING.** see *ADVERTISING AND PUBLIC RELATIONS*

004.6 USA ISSN 1544-2756
HE9715.U6
BROADBAND WIRELESS DATA REVIEW. Variant title: Kagan's Broadband Wireless Data Review. Text in English. a. USD 995 newsstand/cover (effective 2003).
Published by: Kagan Research, LLC, One Lower Ragsdale Dr, Bldg One, Ste 130, Monterey, CA 93940. TEL 831-624-1536, FAX 831-625-3225, info@kagan.com, http://www.kagan.com.

004.6 GBR ISSN 1740-4495
▼ **BROADBAND WORLD.** Text in English. 2003 (Jul.). m. GBP 24 domestic; GBP 29 in Europe & Ireland; GBP 34 elsewhere (effective 2003). **Document type:** *Magazine, Consumer.* **Description:** Covers the major issues in the broadband market & service industry, including reviews on the latest gadgets and also step-by-step users guides.
Published by: Optimum Publications, 90 Walcot St, Bath, BA1 5BG, United Kingdom. TEL 44-1225-339977, feedback@broadbandworldmagazine.co.uk, http://www.broadbandworldmagazine.co.uk/. Ed. Chris James.

004.6 ZAF
CABLETALK. Text in English. 1999. bi-m. adv. **Document type:** *Magazine, Trade.* **Description:** Aimed at cabling professionals who are responsible for the design, integration, installation, testing and maintanence of a cabling infrastructure.
Published by: T M L Business Publishing (Subsidiary of: Times Media Ltd.), PO Box 182, Pinegowrie, Gauteng 2123, South Africa. TEL 27-11-789-2144, FAX 27-11-789-3196. adv.: B&W page USD 691, color page USD 756; 210 x 297. Circ: 5,500 (controlled).

004.6 384 CHN
CHINA I T AND TELECOM TIMES. (Information Technology) Text in English. adv. **Document type:** *Newsletter, Trade.* **Description:** Provides news and analysis of China's information technology and telecommunications industries.
Published by: Clear Thinking Corp., 2-F Profit Tower, 17 Chaoyangmenwai Ave, Beijing, 100020, China. TEL 86-1-65991631, 86-1-65991634, FAX 86-1-65991639, marketing@clearthinking.com, http://www.clearthinking.com/publications/default.asp.

COMMUNICATIONS & NETWORKING. see *COMPUTERS—Computer Networks*

004.6 NLD ISSN 0140-3664
TK5105.5 CODEN: COCOD7
➤ **COMPUTER COMMUNICATIONS.** Text in English. 1978. 18/yr. EUR 1,522 in Europe to institutions; JPY 202,200 in Japan to institutions; USD 1,703 elsewhere to institutions (effective 2006). adv. bk.rev. bibl.; illus. index. back issues avail.; reprints avail. **Document type:** *Academic/Scholarly.* **Description:** Focuses on networking and distributed computing techniques, communications hardware and software, and standardization.
Related titles: Microform ed.: (from PQC); Online - full text ed.: (from EBSCO Publishing, Gale Group, IngentaConnect, ScienceDirect, Swets Information Services).
Indexed: ASCA, BrCerAb, C&CSA, C&ISA, CADCAM, CMCI, CerAb, CompAb, CompC, CompD, CompLI, CorrAb, CurCont, CybAb, E&CAJ, EMA, EngInd, IAA, Inspec, KES, LISA, M&MA, M&TEA, MBF, METADEX, Microcompind, PROMT, RASB, RefZh, SSCI, SolStAb, TelAb, WAA.
—BLDSC (3393.831000), AskIEEE, CISTI, Ei, IDS, IE, Infotrieve, ingenta, Linda Hall. **CCC.**
Published by: Elsevier BV (Subsidiary of: Elsevier Science & Technology), Radarweg 29, Amsterdam, 1043 NX, Netherlands. TEL 31-20-4853911, FAX 31-20-4852457, nlinfo-f@elsevier.nl, http://www.elsevier.com/locate/comcom, http://www.elsevier.nl. Eds. Jeremy B. Thompson, M. Atiquzzaman.

004.6 USA ISSN 0146-4833
TK5105.5 CODEN: CCRED2
➤ **COMPUTER COMMUNICATIONS REVIEW.** Text in English. 1978 (vol.8). 5/yr. USD 40 (effective 2004). **Document type:** *Journal, Academic/Scholarly.*
Related titles: Online - full text ed.: (from EBSCO Publishing).
Indexed: C&CSA, CMCI, CompC, CompR, CurCont, EngInd, Inspec, TelAb.
—BLDSC (3393.830000), AskIEEE, CISTI, IE, Infotrieve, ingenta, Linda Hall.
Published by: Association for Computing Machinery, Inc., 1515 Broadway, 17th Fl, New York, NY 10036-5701. TEL 212-626-0500, 212-626-0520, 800-342-6626, FAX 212-869-0481, sigs@acm.org, usacm@acm.org, http://www.acm.org. Ed. David Oran.

004.6 GBR ISSN 0306-6886
COMPUTER REPORT. Text in English. 1974. w. GBP 49, USD 110. bk.rev.
Indexed: Emerald.
Published by: European Communications Consultants Ltd., 2 Duncan Terr, London, N1 8BZ, United Kingdom. Ed. Stacey Tanner. Circ: 800.

COMPUTER SCIENCE AND TELECOMMUNICATIONS. see *COMMUNICATIONS*

004.6 AUT ISSN 1814-814X
COMPUTERWELT. Text in German. 1986. w. EUR 67 domestic; EUR 151 foreign; EUR 39 to students (effective 2005). adv. **Document type:** *Magazine, Consumer.* **Description:** Information for data processing managers, engineers and students.
Related titles: Online - full text ed.
Published by: Info Technologie Verlag GmbH, Zieglergasse 6, Vienna, 1070, Austria. TEL 43-1-52305080, FAX 43-1-523050833, abo@itverlag.at, http://www.computerwelt.at, http://www.itverlag.at. Ed. Edmund Lindau. Adv. contact Elfriede Slemenda. page EUR 10,590; trim 199 x 270. Circ: 18,000.

004.6 AUT
COMPUTERWELT TOP 500. Text in German. 1991. a. adv. **Document type:** *Directory, Trade.* **Description:** Contains a ranking of the top 500 information technology companies in Austria as well as sales figures and background information on the Austrian IT market.
Related titles: Online - full text ed.
Published by: Info Technologie Verlag GmbH, Zieglergasse 6, Vienna, 1070, Austria. TEL 43-1-52316310, FAX 43-1-523050833, abo@itverlag.at, http://www.top500.at, http://www.itverlag.at. adv.: B&W page USD 4,626, color page USD 6,014; trim 228 x 300. Circ: 40,000 (controlled).

CORPORATE I T UPDATE. see *BUSINESS AND ECONOMICS*

C

004.6 DEU ISSN 0177-6894
D F N MITTEILUNGEN. Text in English, German. 1985. q. free. bk.rev. **Document type:** *Newsletter, Trade.* **Description:** Examines data communication in science.
Indexed: RefZh.
Published by: Verein zur Foerderung eines Deutschen Forschungsnetzes, Anhalter Str 1, Berlin, 10963, Germany. TEL 49-30-88429924, FAX 49-30-884299-70, dfn-verein@dfn.de, http://www.dfn.de. Ed. K E Maass. Circ: 7,000.

004.6 GBR
DATA COMMUNICATIONS INTERNATIONAL. Text in English. m.
Indexed: C&CSA.
Address: Wimbledon Bridge House, Hartfield Rd, London, SW19 3RU, United Kingdom. TEL 081-545-6265, FAX 081-540-3833, TELEX 892191. Ed. Peter Heywood. Circ: 80,000.

004.6 USA ISSN 1096-7567
DATA COMMUNICATIONS MANAGEMENT. Text in English. 1975. bi-m. looseleaf. USD 495 (effective 2000 - 2001). back issues avail.; reprints avail. **Document type:** *Journal, Trade.* **Description:** Contains more than 85 articles on all areas of data communications and networking. Provides how-to information.
Formerly (until 199?): Auerbach Data Communications Management (0736-0002)
Related titles: CD-ROM ed.: 1996. USD 450 (effective 2001); Online - full text ed.: (from EBSCO Publishing).
—CCC.
Published by: Auerbach Publications (Subsidiary of: C R C Press, LLC), 2000 Corporate Blvd., NW, Boca Raton, FL 33431. TEL 212-286-1010, FAX 212-297-9176, orders@crcpress.com, http://www.auerbach-publications.com, http://www.auerbach-publications.com/home.asp. Ed. John Lusa. Pub. Richard O'Hanley TEL 212-845-4017. R&P Jamie Sigal TEL 561-994-0555.

004.6 USA
DATA COMPRESSION CONFERENCE. PROCEEDINGS. Text in English. 1991. a. USD 102 membership (effective 2005). adv. **Document type:** *Proceedings.* **Description:** Presents current research, new techniques, and important studies on data compression and related areas.
Formerly (until 1993): I E E E Computer Society. D C C (1068-0314)
Related titles: Online - full text ed.: (from I E E E).
Indexed: B&BAb, Englnd.
—BLDSC (3534.455000). **CCC.**
Published by: (Institute of Electrical and Electronics Engineers, Inc.), I E E E Computer Society, 3 Park Ave, 17th Fl, New York, NY 10017. TEL 714-821-8380, 800-678-4333, FAX 714-821-4641, customer.service@ieee.org, http://www.ieee.org. Ed. Cat Harris. Pub. Matt Loeb. Adv. contact Frieda Koester.

004.6 DEU ISSN 0176-3288
DATACOM. Text in German. 1984. m. bk.rev. back issues avail. **Document type:** *Magazine, Trade.* **Description:** Special-interest magazine for data communication professionals covering topics such as in-house data transmission, the problems of LAN and WAN cabling, and long distance data transmission.
—IE.
Published by: Datacom Zeitschriften Verlag GmbH, Elbestr 7, Krefeld, 47800, Germany. TEL 49-2151-51920, FAX 49-2151-519234, info@datacom-verlag.de, http://www.datacom-verlag.de. Eds. Reinhold Hoelbling, Stefan Lueschow. Pub. Klaus Lipinski. Adv. contact Andrea Schmidt Dietrich. Circ: 10,951.

004.6 GBR ISSN 0959-6429
DATACOMMS BOOK (YEAR). Text in English. 1986. a. GBP 74. adv. **Document type:** *Trade.*
Media: Magnetic Tape.
Published by: V N U Business Publications Ltd., 32-34 Broadwick St, London, W1A 2HG, United Kingdom. TEL 44-207-4394242, FAX 44-20-7437-9638. Ed. Peter Chare.

004.6 USA ISSN 1071-1295
TK7882.C6 CODEN: DOIREO
DOCUMENT IMAGING REPORT. Text in English. 1991. bi-w. USD 597 domestic; USD 630 foreign (effective 2005). charts; illus.; stat. back issues avail. **Document type:** *Newsletter.* **Description:** Discusses strategies and applications of imaging technology of interest to executives and corporate planners.
Formed by the 1993 merger of: Document Management Technology (1051-2217); (1990-1993): Imaging Business Report (1050-7019); (1991-1993): Electronic Imaging Report (1057-0942); Document Image & Automation Update (1071-6149); Which was formerly (until 1993): Document Image Automation Update (1054-9706); (until 1986): Videodisc and Optical Disk Update (0742-5732); (until 1991): Optical Information Systems Update (0887-5162)
Related titles: CD-ROM ed.: USD 109 per issue domestic; USD 130 per issue foreign (effective 2000); Online - full text ed.: (from Factiva, Gale Group, LexisNexis, Northern Light Technology, Inc., ProQuest Information & Learning).
Indexed: ABIn, CompD.
—CCC.
Published by: R M G Enterprises, Inc., 5905 Beacon Hill Ln, Erie, PA 16509. TEL 412-480-5116, FAX 412-291-1352, http://www.documentimagingreport.com. Ed. Ralph Gammon. Pub. Larry W Roberts.

004.6 GBR ISSN 1466-545X
E-COMMERCE IN FINANCE. Text in English. 1988. 10/yr. looseleaf. GBP 340, USD 595 domestic; GBP 350 foreign. bk.rev. back issues avail. **Document type:** *Trade.* **Description:** Covers the most recent international developments for electronic data interchange. Concentrates on the news, analysis, case studies, marketplace information, and a diary of major events.
Former titles (until 1999): E D I Update (1463-239X); (until vol.10, no.4, 1998): E D I Update International (1366-4751); (until 1996): E D I Update (0954-6154); Which incorporated (1984-199?): Cash Management News (0268-6635)
Related titles: Online - full text ed.: (from O C L C Online Computer Library Center, Inc.).
Indexed: ABIn.
—BLDSC (3637.718500).
Published by: I B C Business Publishing Ltd., 69-77 Paul St, London, EC2A 4LQ, United Kingdom. TEL 44-20-7553-1000, FAX 44-20-7553-1593, http://www.bankingtech.com. Ed. Sherree DeCovny. Pub. John Foley. **Subscr. in the U.S. to:** I B C (USA), 290 Eliot St, Box 91004, Ashland, MA 01721-9104. TEL 508-881-2800, FAX 508-881-0982.

ELECTRIC WORD. see *COMPUTERS—Computer Programming*

004.6 NLD ISSN 1570-2294
K5 CODEN: EDLRE7
➤ **ELECTRONIC COMMUNICATION LAW REVIEW;** legal aspects of paperless communication. Text in English. 1994. q. EUR 267, USD 267 to institutions for print or online ed. (effective 2003). bk.rev. abstr. reprints avail. **Document type:** *Journal, Academic/Scholarly.* **Description:** Publishes studies and review articles addressing the legal ramifications of the increased use of EDI, including analysis of current and evolving legislation, and responses to unexpected legal consequences.
Formerly (until 2002): E D I Law Review (0929-2233)
Related titles: Online - full text ed.: (from EBSCO Publishing, Kluwer Online, O C L C Online Computer Library Center, Inc., Swets Information Services).
Indexed: ESPM, Englnd, Inspec, RASB, RiskAb, SWRA.
—BLDSC (3700.288000), AskIEEE, Ei, IE, Infotrieve, ingenta. **CCC.**
Published by: Unversiteit van Tilburg, Faculty of Law, PO Box 90153, Tilburg, 5000 LE, Netherlands. TEL 31-13-4668199, FAX 31-13-4668149.

004.6 USA ISSN 1099-4971
ENTERPRISE OPERATIONS MANAGEMENT. Text in English. 1977. bi-m. looseleaf. USD 495 (effective 2000 - 2001). back issues avail.; reprints avail. **Document type:** *Journal, Trade.* **Description:** Contains more than 85 articles on all areas of data center operations. Provides how-to information for data center operations, computer centers, and data processing operations managers.
Former titles (until 1998): Data Center Operations Management (1096-7885); (until 199?): Auerbach Data Center Operations Management (0736-3648)
Related titles: CD-ROM ed.: 1996. USD 450 (effective 2001); Online - full text ed.: (from EBSCO Publishing).
—CCC.
Published by: Auerbach Publications (Subsidiary of: C R C Press, LLC), 2000 Corporate Blvd., NW, Boca Raton, FL 33431. TEL 212-286-1010, FAX 212-297-9176, orders@crcpress.com, http://www.auerbach-publications.com, http://www.auerbach-publications.com/home.asp. Ed. Steven Blanding. Pub. Richard O'Hanley TEL 212-845-4017. R&P Jamie Sigal TEL 561-994-0555.

004.6 USA
EXCHANGE & OUTLOOK ADMINISTRATOR. Text in English. 1998. m. USD 129 domestic; USD 135 foreign (effective 2003). **Document type:** *Magazine, Trade.*
Formerly: Exchange Administrator (1097-704X)
Related titles: Online - full text ed.: (from EBSCO Publishing).
—CCC.
Published by: Penton Technology Media (Subsidiary of: Penton Media, Inc.), 221 E 29th St, Ste 242, Loveland, CO 80538. http://www.exchangeadmin.com/.

004.6 USA
FEDERAL A D P AND TELECOMMUNICATIONS STANDARDS INDEX. Text in English. s-a. USD 19.50. **Document type:** *Abstract/Index.* **Description:** Contains revised standards requirements.
Former titles (until 1995): A D P and Telecommunications Standards Index; Federal Information Resources Management Regulations
Published by: U.S. General Services Administration, Office of Public Affairs, 18th and F Sts, N W, Washington, DC 20405. TEL 202-501-1231. **Subscr. to:** Department of Commerce, National Technical Information Service, Springfield, VA 22161. TEL 703-487-4650.

004.6 USA ISSN 1526-839X
GLOBAL TECHNOLOGY BUSINESS. Text in English. 1998. m. **Document type:** *Trade.*
Indexed: CompLI.
—IE.
Published by: Dasar, Inc., 1157 San Antonio Rd, Mountain View, CA 94043. TEL 650-934-2300, FAX 650-934-2306, http://www.gtbusiness.com. Ed. Laurence Scott. Circ: 60,000.

004.6 HKG
I D N. Text in English. 1994. bi-m. HKD 480, USD 108. adv. **Document type:** *Journal, Trade.*
Related titles: Chinese ed.
Published by: Systems Design Ltd., Shop C, 5-9 Gresson St, Wanchai, Hong Kong, Hong Kong. TEL 852-2528-5744, FAX 852-2529-1296, info@idnworld.com, http://www.idnworld.com. Ed., Pub. Laurence Ng. Adv. contact Amy Cheung. Circ: 27,300.

004.6 USA ISSN 1097-2641
TK5105.5
I E E E INTERNATIONAL PERFORMANCE, COMPUTING, AND COMMUNICATIONS CONFERENCE. PROCEEDINGS. Text in English. 1997. a. USD 202; USD 101 to members (effective 2004). **Document type:** *Proceedings, Trade.*
Related titles: Online - full text ed.: (from I E E E).
Indexed: Englnd.
—BLDSC (4362.963650).
Published by: Institute of Electrical and Electronics Engineers, Inc., 3 Park Ave, 17th Fl, New York, NY 10016-5997. TEL 212-419-7900, 800-678-4333, FAX 212-752-4929, customer.service@ieee.org, http://www.ieee.org.

004.6 004 USA
I E E E - S P INTERNATIONAL SYMPOSIUM ON TIME-FREQUENCY AND TIME-SCALE ANALYSIS. Text in English. a. USD 166. **Document type:** *Proceedings, Trade.*
Published by: Institute of Electrical and Electronics Engineers, Inc., 3 Park Ave, 17th Fl, New York, NY 10016-5997. TEL 800-678-4333, customer.service@ieee.org, http://www.ieee.org.

004.6 SGP ISSN 1012-8328
I T ASIA. Text in English. 1987. m. adv.
Published by: Newscom Pte. Ltd., 105 Boon Keng Rd 04-17, Singapore, 339776, Singapore. TEL 2919861, FAX 2931445. Ed. Austin Morais. Adv. contact Desmond Wong. B&W page USD 6,545, color page USD 7,415; trim 356 x 261. Circ: 22,266.

004.6 IND
INFORMATION SYSTEMS COMPUTERWORLD. Text in English. 1987. fortn. INR 15 newsstand/cover. adv. **Description:** Provides the Indian market with native IS management issues, technology solutions, availability and pricing information. Targeted at MIS, EDP, IT professionals in the country.
Formerly: C and C
Published by: Media Transasia India Ltd., K-35 Green Park (Main), New Delhi, 110 016, India. TEL 91-11-6960926, FAX 91-11-686-7641, TELEX 031-73262, iscw@del2.vsnl.net.in, mtilit@ndf.vsnl.net.in. Ed. Vinita Chawla. Pub. Xavier Collaco. Adv. contact Hara Prasanna. B&W page USD 950, color page USD 1,300; trim 26.5 x 20. Circ: 18,000. **Subscr. to:** 808, Dalamal Towers, 211 Nariman Point, Mumbai, Maharashtra, India.

004.6 GBR ISSN 0959-4116
INFORMATION TECHNOLOGY REVIEW. Short title: I T Review. Text in English. 1989. a. **Document type:** *Bulletin.* **Description:** Annual review of IT budget and expenditure trends.
Published by: Price Waterhouse, 32 London Bridge St, London, SE1 9SY, United Kingdom. TEL 44-171-939-6283, FAX 44-171-403-5265, brian_martin@europe.notes.pw.com. Ed. Brian Martin. Circ: 25,000 (controlled).

004.6 330 USA ISSN 1548-0631
▼ ➤ **INTERNATIONAL JOURNAL OF BUSINESS DATA COMMUNICATIONS AND NETWORKING.** Text in English. 2005. q. USD 85 to individuals; USD 195 to institutions (effective 2005). **Document type:** *Journal, Academic/Scholarly.* **Description:** Covers both guided and wireless communications of voice, data, images and video and their impact on the organizations in which they are used. The journal aims to address the key issues for businesses utilizing data communications and the increasing importance of networking technologies in business.
Related titles: Online - full text ed.: ISSN 1548-064X. 2005.
Indexed: C&ISA, E&CAJ, IAA.
Published by: (Information Resources Management Association), Idea Group Publishing (Subsidiary of: Idea Group Inc.), 701 E Chocolate Ave, Ste 200, Hershey, PA 17033-1240. TEL 717-533-8845, FAX 717-533-7115, cust@idea-group.com, http://www.idea-group.com/journals/details.asp?id=4293. Ed. Jairo A Gutierrez. R&P Jan Travers.

004.6 USA ISSN 1548-369X
▼ **INTERNATIONAL JOURNAL OF MOBILE COMPUTING AND COMMERCE.** Text in English. forthcoming 2006 (Jan-Mar). q. USD 85 to individuals; USD 195 to institutions (effective 2005). **Document type:** *Journal, Academic/Scholarly.* **Description:** Provides an enabling forum for academics and professionals to discuss and publish on these issues.
Related titles: Online - full text ed.: ISSN 1548-3703. forthcoming 2005 (Jan.-Mar.).

C

▼ *new title* ➤ *refereed* ✱ *unverified* ♦ *full entry avail.*

Published by: (Information Resources Management Association), Idea Group Publishing (Subsidiary of: Idea Group Inc.), 701 E Chocolate Ave, Ste 200, Hershey, PA 17033-1240. TEL 717-533-8845, FAX 717-533-7115, cust@idea-group.com, http://www.idea-group.com/journals/details.asp?id=4296. Ed. Sherif Kamel.

004.6   USA
INTERNATIONAL ZURICH SEMINAR ON BROADBAND COMMUNICATIONS: ACCESSING, TRANSMISSION, NETWORKING. PROCEEDINGS. Text in English. biennial. USD 170 per vol.; USD 85 per vol. to members (effective 2004). **Document type:** *Proceedings, Trade.*
Former titles: International Zurich Seminar on Digital Communications. Proceedings; (until 1972): International Zurich Seminar on Integrated Systems for Speech, Video and Data Communications. Proceedings; (until 1970): International Seminar on Digital Processing of Analog Signals (Proceedings)
Indexed: EngInd.
—BLDSC (4552.601000), ingenta.
Published by: (Switzerland Chapter on Digital Communication Systems), Institute of Electrical and Electronics Engineers, Inc., 345 E 47th St, New York, NY 10017-2394. customer.service@ieee.org, http://www.ieee.org.

JOURNAL OF END USER COMPUTER SUPPORT; innovations for business & nonprofit environments. see *COMPUTERS—Personal Computers*

004.6   USA   ISSN 1387-5485
TK5102.5   CODEN: JVSPED
➤ **JOURNAL OF V L S I SIGNAL PROCESSING SYSTEMS FOR SIGNAL, IMAGE, AND VIDEO TECHNOLOGY;** the journal of DSP technologies. Text in English. 1989. 9/yr. EUR 1,298, USD 1,355, GBP 815 combined subscription to institutions print & online eds. (effective 2005). adv. reprint service avail. from PQC,PSC. **Document type:** *Journal, Academic/Scholarly.* **Description:** Publishes research and survey papers on the design and implementation of signal processing systems with VLSI circuits.
Formerly (until 1995): Journal of V L S I Signal Processing (0922-5773)
Related titles: Microform ed.: (from PQC); Online - full text ed.: ISSN 1573-109X (from EBSCO Publishing, Gale Group, IngentaConnect, Kluwer Online, O C L C Online Computer Library Center, Inc., Ovid Technologies, Inc., Springer LINK, Swets Information Services).
Indexed: ASCA, ASFA, BibLing, BrCerAb, C&ISA, CMCI, CerAb, CompR, CorrAb, CurCont, E&CAJ, EMA, EngInd, IAA, Inspec, M&TEA, MBF, METADEX, RefZh, SolStAb, WAA, ZentMath.
—BLDSC (5072,504500), AskIEEE, CISTI, Ei, IDS, IE, ingenta. **CCC.**
Published by: Springer-Verlag New York, Inc. (Subsidiary of: Springer Science+Business Media), 233 Spring St, New York, NY 10013. TEL 212-460-1500, FAX 212-460-1575, service@springer-ny.com, http://springerlink.metapress.com/openurl.asp?genre=journal&issn=0922-5773, http://www.springer-ny.com. Ed. S Y Kung. **Subscr. to:** Journal Fulfillment, PO Box 2485, Secaucus, NJ 07096-2485. TEL 201-348-4033, FAX 201-348-4505, journals@springer-ny.com.

➤ **JOURNAL ON APPLIED INFORMATION TECHNOLOGY.** see *COMPUTERS—Information Science And Information Theory*

004.6   USA   ISSN 1544-2748
HE8700.72.L29
KAGAN'S LATIN AMERICAN BROADBAND. Variant title: Latin American Broadband. Text in English. a. USD 675 newsstand/cover (effective 2003). **Description:** Contains comprehensive economic, technological and regulatory analysis of 20 Latin American markets and in-depth profiles of major operators. Exclusive 10-year multichannel growth and revenue projections, plus multichannel subs, TVHH and total revenue for each country and each region, plus more.
Published by: Kagan Research, LLC, One Lower Ragsdale Dr, Bldg One, Ste 130, Monterey, CA 93940. TEL 831-624-1536, FAX 831-625-3225, info@kagan.com, http://www.kagan.com.

KEY ABSTRACTS - COMPUTER COMMUNICATIONS AND STORAGE. see *COMPUTERS—Abstracting, Bibliographies, Statistics*

MEALEY'S LITIGATION REPORT: CYBER TECH & E-COMMERCE. see *LAW—Corporate Law*

004.6   USA
MEMBERNET; your key to the world of ACM...and beyond. Text in English. bi-m. **Document type:** *Newsletter, Academic/Scholarly.* **Description:** Aims to keep members and others in the computing community up-to-date on current ACM activities, people, and publications relating to the computing field.
Media: Online - full text. **Related titles:** ◆ Supplement to: Association for Computing Machinery. Communications. ISSN 0001-0782.

Published by: Association for Computing Machinery, Inc., 1515 Broadway, 17th Fl, New York, NY 10036-5701. TEL 212-626-0500, 212-626-0520, 800-342-6626, FAX 212-869-0481, mn-editor@acm.org, sigs@acm.org, usacm@acm.org, http://www.acm.org/membernet/. Ed. Carol Wierzbicki.

004.6   GBR
N P L REPORT C I S E. Text in English. irreg. **Document type:** *Monographic series.*
Former titles (until 1995): N P L Report D I T C (0262-5369); (until 1982): N P L Report D N A C S (0143-7348)
Indexed: Inspec.
—CISTI.
Published by: (Centre for Information Systems Engineering), National Physical Laboratory, Queens Rd, Teddington, Middlesex TW11 0LW, United Kingdom. TEL 44-181-943-7002, FAX 44-181-977-7091, cisegen@cise.npl.co.uk.

004.6   RUS   ISSN 0032-9460
Q350   CODEN: PRITA9
➤ **PROBLEMS OF INFORMATION TRANSMISSION.** Text in English. 1965. q. EUR 2,498, USD 2,288, GBP 1,558 combined subscription to institutions print & online eds. (effective 2005). back issues avail. **Document type:** *Journal, Academic/Scholarly.* **Description:** Covers statistical information theory; coding theory and techniques; noisy channels; error detection and correction; signal detection, extraction, and analysis; analysis of communication networks; optimal processing and routing; random process theory; and bionics.
Related titles: Microfilm ed.: (from PQC); Online - full text ed.: ISSN 1608-3253 (from EBSCO Publishing, Gale Group, IngentaConnect, Kluwer Online, O C L C Online Computer Library Center, Inc., Ovid Technologies, Inc., Springer LINK, Swets Information Services); ◆ Translation of: Problemy Peredachi Informatsii. ISSN 0555-2923.
Indexed: BibLing, CCMJ, CIS, CompC, EngInd, Inspec, MathR, MathSciNet, ZentMath.
—BLDSC (0416.933000), AskIEEE, CISTI, IE, Infotrieve, ingenta, Linda Hall. **CCC.**
Published by: (Rossiiskaya Akademiya Nauk/Russian Academy of Sciences), M A I K Nauka - Interperiodica, Profsoyuznaya ul 90, Moscow, 117997, Russian Federation. TEL 7-095-3347420, FAX 7-095-3360666, compmg@maik.ru, http://www.maik.ru/cgi-bin/journal.pl?name=inftr&page=main. Ed. Leonid A Bassalygo. **Subscr. to:** Springer-Verlag Dordrecht, Journals Department, PO Box 322, Dordrecht, Netherlands. TEL 31-78-6576392, FAX 31-78-6576474.

004.6   RUS   ISSN 0555-2923
Q350   CODEN: PPDIA5
PROBLEMY PEREDACHI INFORMATSII. Text in Russian. 1965. q. USD 124 foreign (effective 2005). **Document type:** *Journal, Academic/Scholarly.* **Description:** Covers statistical information theory; coding theory and techniques; noisy channels; error detection and correction; signal detection, extraction, and analysis; analysis of communication networks; optimal processing and routing; random process theory; and bionics.
Related titles: ◆ English Translation: Problems of Information Transmission. ISSN 0032-9460.
Indexed: CCMJ, CIS, EngInd, Inspec, MathR, MathSciNet, RASB, RefZh, ZentMath.
—CISTI, Linda Hall. **CCC.**
Published by: Izdatel'stvo Nauka, Profsoyuznaya ul 90, Moscow, 117864, Russian Federation. TEL 7-095-3347151, FAX 7-095-4202220, secret@naukaran.ru, http://www.naukaran.ru.
Dist. by: M K - Periodica, ul Gilyarovskogo 39, Moscow, 129110, Russian Federation. TEL 7-095-2845008, FAX 7-095-2813798, info@periodicals.ru, http://www.mkniga.ru.

S T P MAGAZINE. (Straight Through Processing) see *BUSINESS AND ECONOMICS—Banking And Finance*

SCAN: THE DATA CAPTURE REPORT. see *COMPUTERS—Hardware*

004.6   NLD   ISSN 0923-5965
TA1632   CODEN: SPICEF
➤ **SIGNAL PROCESSING: IMAGE COMMUNICATION.** Text in English; Summaries in English, French, German. 1989. 10/yr. EUR 870 in Europe to institutions; JPY 115,600 in Japan to institutions; USD 974 to institutions except Europe and Japan (effective 2006). illus. cum.index. back issues avail.; reprints avail. **Document type:** *Journal, Academic/Scholarly.*
Description: Details all aspects of the design, implementation, and use of image transmission, storage, and display systems.
Related titles: Microform ed.: (from PQC); Online - full text ed.: (from EBSCO Publishing, Gale Group, IngentaConnect, ScienceDirect, Swets Information Services).
Indexed: ASCA, B&BAb, BrCerAb, C&ISA, CMCI, CerAb, CompAb, CompLI, CorrAb, CurCont, E&CAJ, EMA, EngInd, IAA, Inspec, M&TEA, MBF, METADEX, RefZh, SolStAb, WAA.
—BLDSC (8275.985600), AskIEEE, CISTI, Ei, IDS, IE, Infotrieve, ingenta, Linda Hall. **CCC.**

Published by: (European Association for Signal Processing), Elsevier BV (Subsidiary of: Elsevier Science & Technology), Radarweg 29, Amsterdam, 1043 NX, Netherlands. TEL 31-20-4853911, FAX 31-20-4852457, nlinfo-f@elsevier.nl, http://www.elsevier.com/locate/image, http://www.elsevier.nl. Eds. L Chiariglione, M Tekalp.

004.6   USA   ISSN 0896-4068
SILVERPLATTER EXCHANGE. Text in English. 1988. irreg. free. **Description:** Contains information for and about CD-ROM users.
Published by: SilverPlatter Information, Incorporated (Subsidiary of: Ovid Technologies, Incorporated), 100 River Ridge Dr., Norwood, MA 02062. TEL 800-343-0064, FAX 781-769-87632, http://www.silverplatter.com, http://www.ovid.com. Ed. Elizabeth Morley. Circ: 31,000.

SOLARIS INFORMATION COMMUNICATION. see *LIBRARY AND INFORMATION SCIENCES—Computer Applications*

TECHREPUBLIC. see *COMPUTERS—Data Base Management*

TELCO COMPANY PROFILES AUSTRALIA. see *COMPUTERS—Computer Networks*

004.6   HKG
TELCOM ASIA. Text in Chinese, English. 1989. m.
Published by: C C I Asia-Pacific Ltd., 23/F Tianjin Bldg, 167 Connaught Rd W, Hong Kong, Hong Kong. TEL 852-2858-0789, FAX 852-2857-6309. Ed. Brian Washburn. Pub. Tom Gorman. adv.: B&W page USD 4,800, color page USD 6,150; trim 279 x 203. Circ: 20,750.

TELECOM WEB NEWS DIGEST. see *COMMUNICATIONS*

004.6   NLD   ISSN 0920-413X
TELECOMMAGAZINE; toonaangevend vaktijdschrift over telecommunicatie. Text in Dutch. 1986. 10/yr. EUR 69.50 domestic; EUR 79.50 in Belgium (effective 2005). adv. bk.rev. charts; illus. back issues avail. **Document type:** *Magazine, Trade.* **Description:** Publishes studies of data communications geared to the layperson.
Incorporates (1989-1990): P C Netwerk (0924-9737)
Indexed: TelAb.
—IE, Infotrieve, KNAW. **CCC.**
Published by: Array Publications BV, Postbus 2211, Alphen aan den Rijn, 2400 CE, Netherlands. TEL 31-172-469030, FAX 31-172-424381, telecommagazin@array.nl, http://www.telecommagazine.nl, http://www.array.nl. Eds. Floris Hulshoff Pol, Rene Frederick. Adv. contact Sander Corneus. B&W page EUR 2,900, color page EUR 4,275; 185 x 265. Circ: 8,137.

621.3823   USA
TELESPAN (E-MAIL EDITION); a bulletin on teleconferencing. Text in English. 40/yr. USD 377 (effective 2000). bk.rev. index. back issues avail. **Document type:** *Newsletter.*
Former titles: TeleSpan (Print Edition) (0743-2283); (until 1981): TeleSpan Newsletter (0749-9922)
Media: E-mail. **Related titles:** Microform ed.: (from PQC).
Published by: TeleSpan Publishing Corporation, 50 W Palm St, Altadena, CA 91001-4337. TEL 626-797-5482, FAX 626-797-2035, telespanpb@aol.com, http://www.telespan.com. Ed. Shirley Singletary. Pub. Elliot Gold.

004.6   DNK   ISSN 0108-5220
VISUELT∗ . Text in Danish. 1983. 4/yr. DKK 150. illus.
Indexed: ABM, DAAI.
Published by: Blanketfolket Forening for Visuel Data-Medie Kommunikation, c/o Bent Osholm, Ed, Lavager 15, Albertslund, 2620, Denmark. TEL 42-648927, FAX 42-64-89-27. Circ: 1,000.

VOICE & DATA. see *COMMUNICATIONS*

VOICE AND DATA. see *COMMUNICATIONS*

004.6   USA   ISSN 1069-3416
WIRELESS DATA NEWS. Text in English. 1993. bi-w. USD 1,097 (effective 2005). back issues avail. **Document type:** *Newsletter, Trade.* **Description:** Covers the mobile and wireless data industry, including new products and technologies, market trends, and company news.
Incorporates (in 2001): Wireless Insider (1526-6389); Which Incorporated (in 1995): Personal Devices Report; Which incorporated (1993-1994): Wireless Media and Messaging
Related titles: Online - full text ed.: (from bigchalk, Gale Group, LexisNexis, Northern Light Technology, Inc., O C L C Online Computer Library Center, Inc., ProQuest Information & Learning).
Indexed: ABIn.
—CCC.
Published by: Access Intelligence, LLC (Subsidiary of: Veronis, Suhler & Associates Inc.), 1201 Seven Locks Rd, Ste 300, Potomac, MD 20854. TEL 301-354-2000, 800-777-5006, FAX 301-424-2058, clientservices@accessintel.com, http://www.pbimedia.com/cgi/catalog/info?WDN. Ed. Mary McCormick. Pub. Joelle M Martin.

004.6 USA
WORKSHOP ON MULTIMEDIA SIGNAL PROCESSING. Text in English. a. USD 202; USD 101 to members (effective 2004). **Document type:** *Proceedings, Trade.*
Related titles: CD-ROM ed.
—BLDSC (4363.240185).
Published by: Institute of Electrical and Electronics Engineers, Inc., 3 Park Ave, 17th Fl, New York, NY 10016-5997. TEL 212-419-7900, 800-678-4333, FAX 212-752-4929, customer.service@ieee.org, http://www.ieee.org.

COMPUTERS—Electronic Data Processing

see also BUSINESS AND ECONOMICS—Banking And Finance—Computer Applications

004 USA
A M R A NEWS. (Automatic Meter Reading Association) Text in English. 1987. m. USD 275 (effective 2005). 20 p./no. 3 cols./p.; back issues avail.; reprints avail. **Document type:** *Magazine, Trade.* **Description:** Features articles, product information, industry news and case studies related to the utility automation field.
Published by: A M R A, 60 Revere Dr., Ste. 500, Northbrook, IL 60062. TEL 847-480-9628, FAX 847-480-9282, amra@amra-intl.org, http://www.amra-intl.org. Circ: 1,500 (paid and free).

A P D U NEWSLETTER. see *ENGINEERING—Computer Applications*

A P L JOURNAL. (Array Programming Language) see *COMPUTERS—Automation*

004 USA
ACTIVITIES. Text in English. 1993. q. **Document type:** *Newsletter.* **Description:** Provides information about developments in the color printer business with a special focus on thermal transfer technology.
Published by: Association of Color Thermal Transfer Technology, Inc., 310 Commerce Dr., Amherst, NY 14228. TEL 716-691-5817, FAX 716-691-3395.

005.74 USA ISSN 0196-8696
HF5548.125
ADVANCES IN DATA PROCESSING MANAGEMENT. Text in English. irreg.
Indexed: Inspec.
Published by: Heyden & Sons, Inc., c/o John Wiley & Sons, 605 Third Ave, New York, NY 10016. TEL 215-382-6673.

004 DNK ISSN 0109-2847
ALT OM DATA. Text in Danish. 1983. m. DKK 825 domestic; DKK 1,501 in Europe; DKK 1,740 elsewhere (effective 2002). adv. bk.rev. **Document type:** *Magazine, Consumer.* **Description:** Covers all aspects of the Danish PC market, including reviews of hardware and software.
Related titles: Online - full text ed.
Published by: Audio Media A-S, St Kongensgade 72, Copenhagen K, 1264, Denmark. TEL 45-33-91-28-33, FAX 45-33-91-01-21, redaktion@altomdata.dk, http://www.altomdata.dk/. Ed. Jesper Kofoed. Adv. contact Klaus Wiedemann. Circ: 45,000 (controlled).

004 GBR ISSN 0953-4474
APPLE BUSINESS. Text in English. m. **Document type:** *Trade.*
Published by: E M A P Computing (Subsidiary of: E M A P Business Communications), 33-39 Bowling Green Ln, London, EC1R 0DA, United Kingdom. TEL 44-20-7837-1212, FAX 44-207-278-4008.

004 USA ISSN 0746-7265
AUERBACH E D P AUDITING. (Electronic Data Processing) Text in English. 1978. bi-m. looseleaf. USD 495 (effective 2000 - 2001). charts. back issues avail.; reprints avail. **Document type:** *Journal, Trade.* **Description:** Provides a comprehensive and referenceable desktop aid for the working audit professional.
Formerly (until 1983): E D P Auditing (0736-3656)
Related titles: CD-ROM ed.: 1996. USD 450 (effective 2001).
Indexed: ATI.
—CCC.
Published by: Auerbach Publications (Subsidiary of: C R C Press, LLC), 2000 Corporate Blvd., NW, Boca Raton, FL 33431. TEL 212-286-1010, FAX 212-297-9176, orders@crcpress.com, http://www.auerbach-publications.com/home.asp. Ed. Belden Menkus. Pub. Richard O'Hanley TEL 212-845-4017. R&P Jamie Sigal TEL 561-994-0555.

004 USA
BLACK DATA PROCESSING ASSOCIATES. JOURNAL✶. Text in English. q. adv. **Document type:** *Trade.* **Description:** Includes information on word processing and data communications.
Formerly: Black Data Processing Associates. Data News
Published by: National Black Data Processing, 8401 Corporate Dr., Ste. 405, Landover, MD 20785-2224. TEL 202-789-1540, FAX 202-789-1592, http://www.bdpa.org. Ed., Adv. contact Pat Drumming. R&P George Williams.

004 USA
BLACK DATA PROCESSING ASSOCIATES. NATIONAL JOURNAL✶. Text in English. q. adv. **Document type:** *Trade.* **Description:** Includes word processing and data communications.
Published by: National Black Data Processing, 8401 Corporate Dr., Ste. 405, Landover, MD 20785-2224. TEL 202-789-1540, FAX 202-789-1592, http://www.bdpa.org. R&P George Williams. Adv. contact Pat Drumming.

651.8 IRL
BUSINESS SOLUTIONS. Text in English. bi-m. adv. **Document type:** *Magazine, Trade.*
Indexed: Inspec.
Address: 52-53 Morrison Chambers, Nassau St., Dublin, 2, Ireland. TEL 353-1-6796700, FAX 353-1-6796737, maree@prempbl.com. adv.: B&W page EUR 1,898.96, color page EUR 2,787.08; bleed 210 x 297. Circ: 15,000.

004 NLD ISSN 0169-3786
COMPUTABLE; Het ict vakblad van nederland. Text in Dutch. 1968. w. (Fri.). adv. bk.rev. illus. index. **Document type:** *Newspaper, Trade.*
Former titles (until 1984): Weekblad Computable (0165-5450); (until 1979): Computable (0010-4450)
Related titles: Online - full text ed.
Indexed: KES.
—IE. **CCC.**
Published by: V N U Business Publications (Netherlands), Ceylonpoort 5-25, Haarlem, 2037 AA, Netherlands. TEL 31-23-5463463, FAX 31-23-5463931, http://www.computable.nl/. Ed. Ferdinand Sennema. Pub. Roderick Wijsmuller. adv.: B&W page EUR 10,945; trim 250 x 315. Circ: 47,960.

004 IND
COMPUTER DIGEST AND DATA PROCESSING. Text in English. w. INR 715, USD 85 (effective 1999). index. **Document type:** *Newsletter.* **Description:** Covers topics in computer and data processing industry in India.
Formerly: Computer World - Data Processing - Accounting
Media: Duplicated (not offset).
Published by: International Press Cutting Service, PO Box 121, Allahabad, Uttar Pradesh 211 001, India. TEL 91-532-622392. Circ: 1,200.

004 USA ISSN 0739-0874
CODEN: CERTDR
COMPUTER ECONOMICS REPORT; the financial advisor of data processing users. Text in English. 1979. m. USD 695 (effective 2004). charts; stat. index. back issues avail. **Document type:** *Newsletter, Consumer.* **Description:** Provides financial advice for data processing users. Offers information on lease provisions, used and new equipment systems and management techniques.
Incorporates (in 1996): Computer Economics Report International (1054-5026)
Related titles: Online - full text ed.: (from Florida Center for Library Automation, Gale Group, Northern Light Technology, Inc., ProQuest Information & Learning).
Indexed: CompC, Inspec.
—BLDSC (3393.915000), AskIEEE, CASDDS, IE, ingenta. **CCC.**
Published by: Computer Economics, Inc., 2082 Business Center Dr., Ste 240, Irvine, CA 92612. TEL 949-831-8700, FAX 949-442-7688, info@compecon.com, http://www.computereconomics.com. Ed. Beverly Waite. Pub. Peter Daley.

651.8 USA ISSN 1051-6476
COMPUTERS, FOODSERVICE & YOU✶. Text in English. 1990. bi-m. USD 149 (effective 1998). software rev. index. **Document type:** *Newsletter.* **Description:** Provides computer information for the foodservice industry.
Address: 400 E Gude Dr, Rockville, MD 20850. TEL 301-926-3726. Ed. Mike J Pappas. Pub. Ellen Stuhlmann. Circ: 400 (paid).

004 AUS ISSN 0813-295X
COMPUTERWORLD AUSTRALIA. Text in English. 1978. w. ((46/yr.)). AUD 127 domestic; AUD 250 in New Zealand; AUD 375 elsewhere (effective 2002). adv. **Document type:** *Magazine, Trade.* **Description:** Contains a balance of news, analysis, product and technology reviews, e-commerce and business information.
Formerly (until 1984): Australasian Computerworld (0156-2231)
Related titles: Online - full text ed.
Indexed: CompD.
Published by: I D G Communications Pty. Ltd., 88 Christie St, St Leonards, NSW 2065, Australia. TEL 61-9-2439-5133, FAX 61-2-94395512, http://www.computerworld.idg.com.au. Ed. John Costello. Pub. Steve Ireland. Adv. contact Barry Sanders. color page USD 4,734; trim 235 x 300. Circ: 11,431.

004 GBR
CORPORATE I T STRATEGY; using information for business performance. (Information Technology) Text in English. m. GBP 35; GBP 60 in Europe; GBP 90 elsewhere. adv. **Document type:** *Trade.*
Published by: V N U Business Publications Ltd., 32-34 Broadwick St, London, W1A 2HG, United Kingdom. TEL 44-20-7316-9000, FAX 44-20-7316-9380. Ed. Caroline Gabriel. Pub. Iain Blackhall. Adv. contact Brin Bucknor.

▼ **COURTS TODAY.** see *LAW—Judicial Systems*

004 DEU ISSN 0341-5449
D S W R; Zeitschrift fuer Praxisorganisation, Betriebswirtschaft und elektronische Datenverarbeitung. (Datenverarbeitung - Steuer - Wirtschaft - Recht) Text in German. 1971. m. EUR 48 domestic; EUR 108.20 foreign; EUR 4.50 newsstand/cover (effective 2005). adv. back issues avail. **Document type:** *Journal, Trade.* **Description:** Covers organizational practice, management research, and the processing of electronic data.
Indexed: DIP, IBR, IBZ.
—IE, Infotrieve.
Published by: Verlag C.H. Beck oHG, Wilhelmstr 9, Munich, 80801, Germany. TEL 49-89-38189338, FAX 49-89-38189398, abo.service@beck.de, http://www.beck.de. adv.: B&W page EUR 3,900, color page EUR 6,825; trim 186 x 260. Circ: 35,900 (controlled).

005.72029 USA ISSN 1057-2554
HD9696.C63
DATA ENTRY - DATA CONVERSION SERVICES DIRECTORY✶. Text in English. 1988. irreg. USD 33.95. adv. **Description:** Lists over 600 companies worldwide that provide data entry and data conversion services. Indexed geographically, by services provided and areas of specialization.
Formerly: Data Entry Services Directory (0899-4579)
Published by: Morgan-Rand Inc., 1 Sentry Pkwy, 1000, Blue Bell, PA 19422. TEL 215-938-5500, FAX 215-938-5549. Ed. Shawn Phillips. Circ: 3,000.

004 USA ISSN 0744-1673
HD9696.C63 CODEN: DASODY
DATA SOURCES; the comprehensive guide to the data processing industry: hardware, data communications products, software, company profiles. Text in English. 1981. 2/yr., latest 2002. USD 455 (effective 2003). **Description:** Provides listings of over 43,000 hardware, software and data communications products as well as profiles on 10,000 companies.
—CASDDS. **CCC.**
Published by: Gale Group (Subsidiary of: Thomson Corporation), 27500 Drake Rd, Farmington Hills, MI 48331-3535. TEL 248-699-4253, 800-347-4253, FAX 248-699-8035, gale.galeord@thomson.com, http://www.galegroup.com.

004 GBR
DATACOMS. Text in English. m. **Document type:** *Trade.*
Published by: E M A P Computing (Subsidiary of: E M A P Business Communications), 33-39 Bowling Green Ln, London, EC1R 0DA, United Kingdom. TEL 44-20-7837-1212, FAX 44-207-278-4008.

004 ESP ISSN 0213-022X
DATAMATION (EDICION ESPANOLA)✶. Text in Spanish. 1985. 11/yr.
Published by: Haymarket, S.A., Travesera Gracia 17-21, 5o 2o, Barcelona, 08022, Spain. TEL 3-237-22-66, FAX 1-237-66-88. Ed. J M Vila Solanes. Circ: 10,000.

004 USA
DATAMATION (ONLINE EDITION). (print ed. published m.) Text in English. 1959. d. free (effective 2005). back issues avail. **Document type:** *Magazine, Trade.*
Formerly (until 1998): Datamation (Print Edition) (0011-6963)
Indexed: C&CSA.
—CISTI, IE.
Published by: Jupitermedia Corp., 23 Old Kings Hwy South, Darien, CT 06820. TEL 203-662-2800, FAX 203-655-4686, info@jupitermedia.com, http://www.datamation.com, http://www.jupitermedia.com. Circ: 200,420 (controlled).

DATENSCHUTZ UND DATENSICHERUNG; Recht und Sicherheit der Informations und Kommunikationssysteme. see *COMPUTERS—Computer Security*

004.025 CAN ISSN 0842-1951
DIRECTION INFORMATIQUE. Text in English. 1988. m. CND 80 domestic; USD 115 in United States; USD 155 elsewhere; free to qualified personnel (effective 2003). adv. **Document type:** *Magazine, Trade.*
Indexed: CPerI, PdeR.
Published by: Transcontinental Media, Inc. (Subsidiary of: Transcontinental, Inc.), 25 Sheppard Ave West, Ste 100, Toronto, ON M2N 6S7, Canada. TEL 416-733-7600, FAX 416-218-3544, info@transcontinental.ca, http://www.directioninformatique.com, http://www.transcontinental-gtc.com/en/home.html, http://www.itbusiness.ca. adv.: B&W page USD 4,535. Circ: 20,000 (controlled).

651.5 GBR ISSN 1351-3222
DOCUMENT MANAGER; document management, document imaging, intra/internet, workgroup computing. Text in English. 1994. bi-m. GBP 29 in United Kingdom; GBP 35 elsewhere (effective 2001). **Document type:** *Trade.*
Related titles: Online - full text ed.
Indexed: Inspec.
—BLDSC (3609.113024). **CCC.**

C

Published by: Business and Technical Communications Ltd. (BTC), 25 Station Sq, Petts Wood, Kent BR5 1LZ, United Kingdom. TEL 44-1689-616000, FAX 44-1689-826622, http://www.document-manager.com. Ed. Dave Tyler. Pub. John Jageurs. Adv. contact Craig Molloy TEL 44-1689-616000.

004   USA   ISSN 1553-8664
E D P WEEKLY; the leading information technology news summary. (Electronic Data Processing) Text in English. 1958. w. (Mon.). USD 495 domestic; USD 542 foreign (effective 2005). bk.rev. back issues avail.; reprint service avail. from PQC. **Document type:** *Newsletter*. **Description:** Reports industry-wide corporate and governmental announcements, developments and strategies, with special features on mini and micro computers, electronic commerce, world trade, and market research.
Former titles (until 1987): Computer Age E D P Weekly (0884-206X); (until 1982): E D P Weekly (0012-7558); Incorporates (1976-1989): Data - Comm Industry Report (0149-9556); Which was formerly: Computer Age - Data Communications; Incorporates (1975-1989): E F T S Industry Report; Which was formerly: E F T S Report (0360-3784); Incorporates (1976-1989): Mini-Micro Computer Report (0363-7905); (1982-1989): Robotics Report (0889-5759); (1970-1989): World Trade Report (Springfield); Which was formerly: Computer Age: World Trade (0010-4477)
Related titles: Microform ed.: (from PQC); Online - full text ed.
Indexed: CompC, CompR, PROMT.
—CCC.
Published by: Computer Age & E D P News Services (Subsidiary of Millin Publishing Group, Inc.), 1150 Connecticut Ave. NW, 900, Washington, DC 20036. TEL 202-862-4375, FAX 202-659-3493, millin@erols.com, http://www.millinpubs.com. Pub. S L Millin. Circ: 2,400.

ELECTRONIC RETAILING. see *BUSINESS AND ECONOMICS—Marketing And Purchasing*

004   CUB
ELECTRONICA Y PROCESOS DE DATOS EN CUBA. Text in Spanish. 3/yr. USD 26 in South America; USD 28 in North America; USD 34 elsewhere.
Published by: (C I D), Ediciones Cubanas, Obispo No. 527, Apdo. 605, Havana, Cuba.

651.8   USA   ISSN 1528-2813
ENTERPRISE SOLUTIONS FOR MICROSOFT BACKOFFICE & WINDOWS N T. Text in English. 1995. q. USD 59.95 domestic; USD 79.95 foreign (effective 2001). **Document type:** *Trade.* **Description:** Designed to satisfy the needs of Information Technology professionals building and implementing client - server applications in a Windows NT server environment.
Former titles (until 1999): BackOffice C T O Magazine (1527-8921); (until 1998): BackOffice Magazine (1084-6433)
Related titles: Online - full text ed.: (from Gale Group, O C L C Online Computer Library Center, Inc.).
Indexed: SoftBase.
—CCC.
Published by: PennWell Corp., 98 Spit Brook Rd, Nashua, NH 03062-5737. TEL 603-891-0123, http://www.pennwell.com.

005.5   USA   ISSN 1533-8983
ENTERPRISE SYSTEMS. Text in English. 1987. m. free to qualified personnel (effective 2005). adv. bk.rev. **Document type:** *Magazine, Trade.* **Description:** Provides technical and information systems management information oriented to professionals associated directly with enterprisewide information systems.
Formerly (until 2001): Enterprise Systems Journal (1053-6566); Incorporates (1990-1991): Contingency Journal (1050-2122); Which was formerly (until vol.5, no.9, 1990): Mainframe Journal (0895-5751)
Related titles: Online - full text ed.: (from Factiva, Gale Group, Northern Light Technology, Inc.); Supplement(s): 101 Solutions.
Indexed: ABIn, CompD, CompLI, InfoSAb, Inspec, MicrocompInd, SoftBase.
—BLDSC (3776.630500), CISTI, IE. **CCC.**
Published by: 101 Communications, Llc., 1300 Virginia Dr, Ste 400, Fort Washington, PA 19034. TEL 215-643-8000, FAX 215-643-3901, info@101com.com, http://www.esj.com, http://www.101com.com. Ed. Linda Briggs. Circ: 83,500 (controlled). **Subscr. to:** Enterprise Systems Journal, PO Box 3055, Northbrook, IL 60065-3055. TEL 800-306-6332, FAX 847-564-9002.

004   USA
QA76.54
EUROMICRO CONFERENCE ON REAL-TIME SYSTEMS. PROCEEDINGS. Text in English. 1989. a. USD 169 per vol.; USD 68 per vol. to members (effective 2004). adv. **Document type:** *Proceedings, Trade.* **Description:** Presents current research, new techniques and important studies on data compression and related areas.
Formerly: Euromicro Workshop on Real-Time Systems. Proceedings (1068-3070)
Related titles: Online - full text ed.: (from I E E E).
—BLDSC (6843.724570). **CCC.**

Published by: (Institute of Electrical and Electronics Engineers, Inc.), I E E E Computer Society, 10662 Los Vaqueros Circle, PO Box 3014, Los Alamitos, CA 90720-1314. TEL 714-821-8380, FAX 714-821-4641, customer.service@ieee.org, http://www.ieee.org. Ed. Cat Harris. Pub. Matt Loeb. Adv. contact Frieda Koester.

004   DEU   ISSN 0947-4862
HC240.9.I55
EUROPEAN INFORMATION TECHNOLOGY OBSERVATORY (YEAR). Text in English. 1993. a. EUR 80 (effective 2005). **Document type:** *Yearbook, Academic/Scholarly.* **Description:** Covers all aspects of information and communications technology in Europe.
Published by: European Information Technology Observatory, Hahnstr 70, Frankfurt am Main, W 60528, Germany. TEL 49-69-2424160, FAX 49-69-24241616, info@eito.com, http://www.eito.com.

004   CAN   ISSN 1483-4405
GOVERNMENT COMPUTER MAGAZINE. Text in English. 1991. 11/yr. CND 34.95; CND 89.95 in United States; CND 120 elsewhere. adv. bk.rev. **Document type:** *Trade.*
Formerly (until 1996): Hum Magazine (1188-522X)
Address: 303 260 St Patrick St, Ottawa, ON K1N 5K5, Canada. TEL 613-789-6431, FAX 613-789-6433. Ed. Lee Hunter. Pub. David Ritter. Adv. contact Chris Cole. B&W page CND 1,910, color page CND 2,790; trim 10.75 x 8. Circ: 13,000 (controlled).

I E E E - S P INTERNATIONAL SYMPOSIUM ON TIME-FREQUENCY AND TIME-SCALE ANALYSIS. see *COMPUTERS—Data Communications And Data Transmission Systems*

004   USA   ISSN 1063-6374
QA76.58   CODEN: PSPDF8
I E E E SYMPOSIUM ON PARALLEL AND DISTRIBUTED PROCESSING. PROCEEDINGS. Short title: S P D P. Text in English. 1989. a. price varies. adv. **Document type:** *Proceedings, Academic/Scholarly.* **Description:** Details important studies on subjects such as distributed programming, programming languages, modeling, scheduling, algorithms, fault tolerance and architectures.
Related titles: Online - full text ed.: (from I E E E).
—Ei. **CCC.**
Published by: (Institute of Electrical and Electronics Engineers, Inc.), I E E E Computer Society, 10662 Los Vaqueros Circle, PO Box 3014, Los Alamitos, CA 90720-1314. TEL 714-821-8380, FAX 714-821-4641.

004   CAN   ISSN 0315-5986
T57.6.A1   CODEN: INFRCL
➤ **I N F O R JOURNAL**; information systems and operational research/systemes d'information et recherche operationnelle. Text in English, French. 1963. q. CND 55 domestic to individuals; CND 60 foreign to individuals; CND 80 domestic to institutions; CND 85 foreign to institutions (effective 2004). adv. bk.rev. charts; illus. index. 160 p./no.; back issues avail.; reprints avail. **Document type:** *Journal, Academic/Scholarly.*
Formerly (until 1970): Canadian Operational Research Society Journal (0574-9638)
Related titles: Online - full text ed.: (from EBSCO Publishing, Micromedia ProQuest, O C L C Online Computer Library Center, Inc., ProQuest Information & Learning).
Indexed: ABIn, CBCARef, CIS, CMCI, CPM, CompC, CompR, CurCont, CybAb, EngInd, IAOP, Inspec, JCQM, ORMS, QC&AS, RASB, RefZh, ZentMath.
—BLDSC (4478.880000), AskIEEE, CISTI, Ei, IDS, IE, Infotrieve, ingenta, Linda Hall. **CCC.**
Published by: (Institute of Computer Science), University of Toronto Press, Journals Division, 5201 Dufferin St, Toronto, ON M3H 5T8, Canada. TEL 416-667-7810, FAX 416-667-7881, journals@utpress.utoronto.ca, http://www.utpjournals.com. Ed., Adv. contact Michel Gendreau. Circ: 400. **Co-sponsors:** Canadian Operational Research Society; Canadian Information Processing Society.

004   JPN
QA75.5
➤ **I P S J JOURNAL.** Text in Japanese, English. m. JPY 17,010 to non-members; JPY 6,930 to members (effective 2001). 300 p./no.; **Document type:** *Academic/Scholarly.* **Description:** Contains original research papers and review articles in the field of computer, information science and technology.
Formerly (until Apr. 2000): Joho Shori Gakkai Rombunshi/Information Processing Society of Japan. Transactions (0387-5806); Which superseded in part: Joho Shori (0447-8053)
Related titles: Online - full content ed.: 2001.
Indexed: CCMJ, CompAb, IAOP, Inspec, MathR, MathSciNet, RefZh, ZentMath.
—BLDSC (4567.476620), AskIEEE, CISTI. **CCC.**
Published by: Information Processing Society of Japan/Joho Shori Gakkai, 7th Fl Shibaura-Maekawa Bldg, 3-16-20 Shibaura, Minato-ku, Tokyo, 108-0023, Japan. TEL 81-3-5484-3535, FAX 81-3-5484-3534, editt@ipsj.or.jp, http://www.ipsj.or.jp. Ed. Katsumi Tanaka. Pub. Takayuki Yanagawa. R&P Hideki Shimanuki. Circ: 6,000.

004   JPN
QA75.5
➤ **I P S J MAGAZINE.** Text in Japanese. 1960. m. JPY 13,860 to non-members (effective 2001). adv. bk.rev. 120 p./no.; **Document type:** *Academic/Scholarly.* **Description:** Presents papers and results of research on the theoretical fundamentals and applications of computers, with emphasis on information processing. Aims to promote the international exchange of information processing.
Supersedes in part: Joho Shori (0447-8053)
Related titles: Online - full content ed.
Indexed: Inspec, JCT, JTA, RASB.
—AskIEEE, CISTI.
Published by: Information Processing Society of Japan/Joho Shori Gakkai, 7th Fl Shibaura-Maekawa Bldg, 3-16-20 Shibaura, Minato-ku, Tokyo, 108-0023, Japan. TEL 81-3-5484-3535, FAX 81-3-5484-3534, editj@ipsj.or.jp, http://www.ipsj.or.jp. Ed. Haruhisa Ishida. Pub. Takayuki Yanagawa. R&P Keiko Ushiro. adv.: page JPY 135,000. Circ: 30,000.

004   USA
I T A A DATA NEWSLETTER. Text in English. 1987. m. membership.
Formerly: A D A S P O Data
Published by: Information Technology Association of America, 1401 Wilson Blvd., Ste. 1100, Arlington, VA 22209-2318. TEL 703-522-5055, FAX 703-525-2279. Ed. Robert Cohen. Circ: 3,000.

004.025   USA   ISSN 1071-6629
T58.5
I T A A MEMBERSHIP DIRECTORY. Text in English. 1963. a. USD 150 to non-members. **Document type:** *Directory.* **Description:** Lists I.T.A.A. members involved in micro-, mini-, mainframe computer software, system integration, professional consulting services, data processing and network services. Cross-indexed by geographic regions served.
Former titles: A D A P S O Membership Directory; A D A P S O Membership; A D A P S O Directory; Directory of Data Processing Service Organizations (0084-9901)
Published by: Information Technology Association of America, 1401 Wilson Blvd., Ste. 1100, Arlington, VA 22209-2318. TEL 703-522-5055, FAX 703-525-2279. Circ: 10,000 (controlled).

I T A A TECHNICAL INFORMATION SERIES. see *COMPUTERS—Software*

004   USA
I T COST MANAGEMENT SOURCEBOOK. (Information Technology) Text in English. 1996. base vol. plus m. updates. USD 2,500 (effective 1998). **Document type:** *Directory.* **Description:** Provides current financial guide to data processing equipment acquisition and control of data processing expenses.
Formed by the merger of (1987-1996): Computer Economics Sourcebook; (1990-1996): Residual Value Forecasts for D E C Systems and Peripherals; (1989-1996): Residual Value Forecasts for I B M Systems and Peripherals
Published by: Computer Economics, Inc., 2082 Business Center Dr., Ste 240, Irvine, CA 92612. TEL 949-831-8700, FAX 949-442-7688, info@compecon.com, http://www.computereconomics.com. Ed. Terrin Lovett. Pub. Anne Zalatan.

004   USA   ISSN 1091-1820
CODEN: ICMSFJ
I T COST MANAGEMENT STRATEGIES; the planning assistant for IT directors. (Information Technology) Text in English. 1982. m. USD 495 (effective 1998). charts; stat. index. back issues avail. **Document type:** *Newsletter.* **Description:** Provides financial advice and analyses to IT executives in charge of data processing budgets. Reports on and evaluates the financial management of IT operations, IT equipment acquisition methods and more.
Incorporates (in 1996): Systems Reengineering Economics Letter (1074-732X); Former titles (until Aug. 1996): I S Budget (Information Systems) (1076-2620); (until 1994): D P Budget (0890-4316); (until 1986): Computer Executive Letter (0739-2265)
Related titles: Online - full text ed.: (from Florida Center for Library Automation, Gale Group, ProQuest Information & Learning).
Indexed: CompC, Inspec.
—AskIEEE. **CCC.**
Published by: Computer Economics, Inc., 2082 Business Center Dr., Ste 240, Irvine, CA 92612. editor@compecon.com, http://www.computereconomics.com. Eds. Beverly Waite, Edward Pesabew, Anne Zalatan. Pubs. Anne Zalatan, Bruno Bassi. **Dist. by:** Publications Resource Group.

004   DEU   ISSN 1432-3559
IDENT; das Forum fuer automatische Datenerfassung und Prozessinformatik. Text in German. 1996. 8/yr. adv. **Document type:** *Magazine, Trade.*
Published by: Umschau Zeitschriftenverlag Breidenstein GmbH, Brueningstr 580, Frankfurt Am Main, 65929, Germany. TEL 49-69-26000, FAX 49-69-2600609. Ed. Thorsten Aha. Adv. contact Bernd Pohl TEL 49-69-2600621. B&W page EUR 2,715, color page EUR 3,890; trim 186 x 252. Circ: 11,870 (paid).

004 GBR ISSN 1367-966X
INFOMATICS DIGEST. Text in English. 1980. m. GBP 33; GBP 2.80 newsstand/cover (effective 1999). **Document type:** *Trade.* **Description:** Provides the people who are selling the IT dream with a sharp blend of news and comment.
Formerly: Infomatics (0260-7247)
Indexed: CompC, CompD, Inspec, LISA, M&MA, PROMT, WTA.
Published by: V N U Business Publications Ltd., VNU House, 32-34 Broadwick St, London, W1A 2HG, United Kingdom. TEL 44-20-7316-9000, FAX 44-20-7316-9160, http://webserv.vnunet.com. Ed. David Bannister. Circ: 20,000.

INFORMAA QUARTERLY. see *BUSINESS AND ECONOMICS—Office Equipment And Services*

004 HUN ISSN 0019-9753
INFORMACIO-ELEKTRONIKA. Text in Hungarian; Summaries in English, Russian. 1966. bi-m. HUF 300. adv. bk.rev. stat. **Document type:** *Government.*
Indexed: CompR, DPD, Inspec.
—AskIEEE, CISTI.
Published by: Kozponti Statisztikai Hivatal, Marketing Oszta'ly, Keleti Karoly utca 5-7, Budapest, 1024, Hungary. TEL 31-1-345-6000, FAX 36-1-345-6699, http://www.ksh.hu. Circ: 1,820.

004 SVK ISSN 0323-1984
INFORMACNE SYSTEMY. Text in Czech, Slovak; Summaries in English, Russian. 1972. bi-m. USD 14. illus.
Indexed: Inspec, RASB.
Published by: Institut Informatiky a Statistiky (INFOSTAT), Dubravska cesta 3, Bratislava, 84221, Slovakia. **Dist. by:** Slovart G.T.G. s.r.o., Krupinska 4, PO Box 152, Bratislava 85299, Slovakia. TEL 421-2-63839472, FAX 421-2-63839485, http://www.slovart-gtg.sk.

004 ITA
INFORMATICA* . Text in Italian. 11/yr.
Address: Via Valdonega, 117, San Salvatore Monferrato, AL 15046, Italy. TEL 2-58-11-12-83. Ed. Rodolfo Grigolato. Circ: 21,894.

004 USA ISSN 1096-8024
INFORMATION MANAGEMENT (WASHINGTON, D.C.); strategy, systems, and technologies. Text in English. 1973. bi-m. looseleaf. USD 495 (effective 2000 - 2001). back issues avail.; reprints avail. **Document type:** *Journal, Trade.* **Description:** Covers more than 150 topics pertaining to all aspects of data processing management. Provides latest information on current technology and management practices.
Former titles (until 199?): Auerbach Information Management (1045-7879); (until 1991): Auerbach Data Processing Management (0735-9993)
Related titles: CD-ROM ed.: 1996. USD 450 (effective 2001).
—CCC.
Published by: Auerbach Publications (Subsidiary of: C R C Press, LLC), 2000 Corporate Blvd., NW, Boca Raton, FL 33431. TEL 212-286-1010, FAX 212-297-9176, orders@crcpress.com, http://www.auerbach-publications.com, http://www.auerbach-publications.com/home.asp. Ed. Janet Butler. Pub. Richard O'Hanley TEL 212-845-4017. R&P Jamie Sigal TEL 561-994-0555.

004 NLD ISSN 0020-0190
QA76 CODEN: IFPLAT
➤ **INFORMATION PROCESSING LETTERS.** Text in English. 1971. 24/yr. EUR 1,727 in Europe to institutions; JPY 229,300 in Japan to institutions; USD 1,931 to institutions except Europe and Japan (effective 2006). bk.rev. bibl.; charts. back issues avail.; reprints avail. **Document type:** *Journal, Academic/Scholarly.* **Description:** Presents concise reports of interesting results in the field of information processing.
Related titles: Microform ed.: (from PQC); Online - full text ed.: (from EBSCO Publishing, Gale Group, IngentaConnect, ScienceDirect, Swets Information Services).
Indexed: ABIn, ASCA, C&CSA, C&ISA, CCMJ, CIS, CMCI, CompAb, CompC, CompD, CompLI, CompR, CurCont, CybAb, E&CAJ, EngInd, ExcerpMed, IAOP, Inspec, MathR, MathSciNet, RASB, RefZh, SSCI, SolStAb, ZentMath.
—BLDSC (4493.898000), AskIEEE, Ei, IDS, IE, Infotrieve, ingenta, Linda Hall. **CCC.**
Published by: Elsevier BV (Subsidiary of: Elsevier Science & Technology), Radarweg 29, Amsterdam, 1043 NX, Netherlands. TEL 31-20-4853911, FAX 31-20-4852457, dehne@scs.carleton.ca, nlinfo-f@elsevier.nl, http://www.elsevier.com/locate/ipl, http://www.elsevier.nl.

➤ **INFORMATION STRATEGY: THE EXECUTIVE'S JOURNAL.** see *BUSINESS AND ECONOMICS—Management*

004 USA
INFORMATION SYSTEMS SPENDING; an analysis of trends and strategies. Text in English. 1990. a. USD 1,595. **Document type:** *Newsletter.* **Description:** Provides an inside look at the complexities and successful strategies of information systems budget management.
Published by: Computer Economics, Inc., 2082 Business Center Dr., Ste 240, Irvine, CA 92612. TEL 949-831-8700, FAX 949-442-7688, info@compecon.com, http://www.computereconomics.com. Pub. Anne Zalatan.

651.8 FRA ISSN 0299-0733
INSTITUT NATIONAL DE RECHERCHE EN INFORMATIQUE ET EN AUTOMATIQUE. COLLECTION DIDACTIQUE. Text in French. irreg. price varies.
Indexed: ZentMath.
—CISTI.
Published by: Institut National de Recherche en Informatique et en Automatique, BP 105, Le Chesnay, Cedex 78153, France. TEL 33-1-39635511, FAX 33-1-39635330, http://www.inria.fr. Ed. Bernard Larrouturou.

INTERNATIONAL GEOSCIENCE AND REMOTE SENSING SYMPOSIUM DIGEST. see *GEOGRAPHY*

004.69 USA ISSN 1548-3673
▼ **INTERNATIONAL JOURNAL OF E-COLLABORATION.** Text in English. 2005. q. USD 85 to individuals; USD 195 to institutions (effective 2005). **Document type:** *Journal, Academic/Scholarly.* **Description:** Addresses the design and implementation of e-collaboration technologies, assess the behavioral impacts of e-collaboration technologies on individuals and groups, and present theoretical considerations on links between the use of e-collaboration technologies and behavioral patterns.
Related titles: Online - full text ed.: ISSN 1548-3681. 2005.
Indexed: C&ISA, E&CAJ, IAA.
Published by: (Information Resources Management Association), Idea Group Publishing (Subsidiary of: Idea Group Inc.), 701 E Chocolate Ave, Ste 200, Hershey, PA 17033-1240. TEL 717-533-8845, FAX 717-533-7115, cust@idea-group.com, http://www.idea-group.com/journals/details.asp?id=4297. Ed. Ned Kock.

004 USA ISSN 1539-3062
T58.5 CODEN: IJISBA
▼ ➤ **INTERNATIONAL JOURNAL OF I T STANDARDS AND STANDARDIZATION RESEARCH**; the international source for advances in IT standards and standardization research. (Information Technology) Text in English. 2003. s-a. USD 85 combined subscription to individuals print & online eds.; USD 205 combined subscription to institutions print & online eds. (effective 2005). adv. Index. **Document type:** *Journal, Academic/Scholarly.* **Description:** Publishes research findings that advance knowledge and research in all aspects of IT standards and standardization in modern organizations.
Related titles: Online - full text ed.: ISSN 1539-3054. USD 68 to individuals; USD 116 to institutions (effective 2004) (from O C L C Online Computer Library Center, Inc., ProQuest Information & Learning).
Indexed: ABIn, BrCerAb, C&ISA, CerAb, CompLI, CorrAb, E&CAJ, EMA, IAA, Inspec, M&TEA, MBF, METADEX, SolStAb, WAA.
—BLDSC (4542.311740), IE, Linda Hall. **CCC.**
Published by: (Information Resources Management Association), Idea Group Publishing (Subsidiary of: Idea Group Inc.), 701 E Chocolate Ave, Ste 200, Hershey, PA 17033-1240. TEL 717-533-8845, 866-342-6657, FAX 717-533-7115, cust@idea-group.com, http://www.idea-group.com/journals/details.asp?id=497. Ed. Kai Jakobs. Pub., R&P Jan Travers. adv.: B&W page USD 350; trim 7 x 10.

004 TUR ISSN 1305-239X
▼ ➤ **INTERNATIONAL JOURNAL OF INFORMATION TECHNOLOGY.** Text in German. 2004. q. free. **Document type:** *Journal, Academic/Scholarly.* **Description:** Focuses on theories, methods and applications in information technology.
Related titles: Online - full text ed.: ISSN 1305-2403. 2004. free (effective 2005).
Published by: International Enformatika Society, PO Box 125, Canakkale, 17100, Turkey. TEL 90-286-2180709, FAX 90-286-2180709, ijit@ijit.org, http://www.enformatika.org/journals/1305-2403/.

004 GBR ISSN 1461-4111
T58.5 CODEN: IJITAC
➤ **INTERNATIONAL JOURNAL OF INFORMATION TECHNOLOGY AND MANAGEMENT.** Abbreviated title: I J I T M. Text in English. 2001. 4/yr. USD 450 to institutions; USD 545 combined subscription to institutions print & online eds. (effective 2005). **Document type:** *Journal, Academic/Scholarly.* **Description:** Covers technological, managerial, political, economic and organizational aspects of information technology applications.
Related titles: Online - full content ed.: ISSN 1741-5179. USD 450 to institutions (effective 2005); Online - full text ed.: (from EBSCO Publishing).
Indexed: BrCerAb, C&ISA, CerAb, CompLI, CorrAb, E&CAJ, EMA, IAA, Inspec, M&TEA, MBF, METADEX, RefZh, SolStAb, WAA.
—BLDSC (4542.304990), IE, ingenta, Linda Hall.
Published by: Inderscience Publishers, IEL Editorial Office, PO Box 735, Olney, Bucks MK46 5WB, United Kingdom. TEL 44-1234-240519, FAX 44-1234-240515, ijitm@inderscience.com, editor@inderscience.com, http://www.inderscience.com/ijitm. Ed. Dr. Mohammed A Dorgham. **Subscr. to:** World Trade Centre Bldg, 29 route de Pre-Bois, Case Postale 896, Geneva 15 1215, Switzerland. FAX 41-22-7910885, subs@inderscience.com.

004 651.8 SWE
▼ **I T & CO.** Text in Swedish. 2003. 10/yr. **Description:** Aimed at decision makers in companies with less than 50 employees. Tips for small entrepreneurs.
Published by: I D G AB (Subsidiary of: I D G Communications Inc.), Sturegatan 11, Stockholm, 10678, Sweden. TEL 46-8-4536000, FAX 46-8-4536005, http://www.itco.idg.se, http://www.idg.se. Ed. Fredrik Agren.

004 USA ISSN 1048-5120
ITEM PROCESSING REPORT. Text in English. 1990. bi-w. USD 995 (effective 2004). **Document type:** *Newsletter, Trade.*
Incorporates (in 1992): Powell Report
Related titles: Online - full text ed.: (from Data-Star, LexisNexis, Northern Light Technology, Inc., ProQuest Information & Learning, The Dialog Corporation).
Indexed: ABIn, BLI.
—CCC.
Published by: Access Intelligence, LLC (Subsidiary of: Veronis, Suhler & Associates Inc.), 1201 Seven Locks Rd, Ste 300, Potomac, MD 20854. TEL 301-354-2000, FAX 301-424-2058, clientservices@accessintel.com, http://www.pbimedia.com. Ed. Susan Aluise.

004 USA ISSN 1556-6587
▼ **JOURNAL OF AUTONOMIC AND TRUSTED COMPUTING.** Text in English. forthcoming 2006 (May). 3/yr. USD 380 (effective 2006).
Related titles: Online - full text ed.: ISSN 1556-6595. forthcoming 2006 (May).
Published by: American Scientific Publishers, 25650 N Lewis Way, Stevenson Ranch, CA 91381-1439. TEL 661-254-0807, FAX 661-254-1207, http://www.aspbs.com/joatc.

004 USA
JOURNAL OF I T FINANCIAL MANAGEMENT. Text in English. 1990. 3/yr. USD 75 membership to individuals; USD 400 membership to corporations with 15 or less members; USD 800 membership to corporations with 30 or less members; USD 1,200 membership to corporations with 45 or less members (effective 2003). bibl. back issues avail. **Document type:** *Journal, Trade.* **Description:** Provides specialized financial literature for this unique profession. Informs on association activities.
Formerly: Journal of Financial Management for Data Processing (1078-5736)
Published by: I T Financial Management Association, PO Box 30188, Santa Barbara, CA 93130. TEL 805-687-7390, FAX 805-687-7382, info@itfma.com, http://www.itfma.com/. Ed. Susan J Quinlan. R&P Terence A Quinlan. Circ: 1,000 (paid).

JOURNAL OF INFORMATION SYSTEMS EDUCATION. see *EDUCATION—Computer Applications*

004 GBR ISSN 0959-1524
TS156.8 CODEN: JPCOEO
➤ **JOURNAL OF PROCESS CONTROL.** Text in English. 1990. 10/yr. EUR 1,068 in Europe to institutions; JPY 142,000 in Japan to institutions; USD 1,195 to institutions except Europe and Japan; EUR 76 in Europe to qualified personnel; JPY 10,000 in Japan to qualified personnel; USD 84 to qualified personnel except Europe and Japan (effective 2006). back issues avail. **Document type:** *Academic/Scholarly.* **Description:** Covers the application of control theory, operations research, computer science and engineering principles to the solution of process-control problems.
Related titles: Microform ed.: (from PQC); Online - full text ed.: (from EBSCO Publishing, Gale Group, IngentaConnect, ScienceDirect, Swets Information Services).
Indexed: ASCA, B&BAb, CEABA, CIN, CMCI, ChemAb, ChemTitl, CurCont, EngInd, ISR, Inspec, SCI.
—BLDSC (5042.645000), AskIEEE, CASDDS, CISTI, Ei, IDS, IE, Infotrieve, ingenta. **CCC.**
Published by: Elsevier Ltd. (Subsidiary of: Elsevier Science & Technology), The Boulevard, Langford Ln, Kidlington, Oxford, OX5 1GB, United Kingdom. TEL 44-1865-843000, FAX 44-1865-843010, http://www.elsevier.com/locate/jprocont. Ed. T. J. McAvoy. **Subscr. to:** Elsevier BV, PO Box 211, Amsterdam 1000 AE, Netherlands. TEL 31-20-485-3757, FAX 31-20-485-3432, nlinfo-f@elsevier.nl, http://www.elsevier.nl.

004 GBR
KEY NOTE MARKET REPORT: I T TRAINING. Variant title: I T Training. Text in English. a., latest 2001, Sept. GBP 340 per issue (effective 1999). **Document type:** *Trade.* **Description:** Provides an overview of a specific UK market segment and includes executive summary, market definition, market size, industry background, competitor analysis, current issues, forecasts, company profiles, and more.
Published by: Key Note Ltd., Field House, 72 Oldfield Rd, Hampton, Mddx TW12 2HQ, United Kingdom. TEL 44-20-8481-8750, FAX 44-20-8783-0049, info@keynote.co.uk, http://www.keynote.co.uk. Ed. Dominic Fenn.

004 JPN
KYOTO UNIVERSITY. DATA PROCESSING CENTER. REPORT/KYOTO DAIGAKU OGATA KEISANKI SENTA EIBUN REPOTO. Text in English. irreg. per issue exchange basis.
Published by: Kyoto University, Data Processing Center/Kyoto Daigaku Ogata Keisanki Senta, Yoshida Hon-cho, Sakyo-ku, Kyoto-shi, 606, Japan.

C

▼ new title ➤ refereed ✱ unverified ♦ full entry avail.

004 ITA ISSN 0392-9027
LINEA E D P; settimanale di informatica. (Entry Data Products) Text in Italian. 1978. w. (43 issues). EUR 30 domestic; EUR 80 foreign (effective 2005). adv. **Document type:** *Magazine, Trade.*
Published by: Gruppo Editoriale A G E P E Srl, Via G Patecchio 2, Milan, MI 20141, Italy. TEL 39-02-399861, FAX 39-02-39844800, mbox@gruppoagepe.it, http://www.agepe.it. Ed. Roberto Bonino. Pub., R&P Roberto Avanzo. Adv. contact Roberto Lenzi. Circ: 40,670.

LOV & DATA. see *LAW*

004 ISR
MA'ASEH HOSHEV. Text in English, Hebrew. 1976 (vol.4). bi-m. USD 10. adv.
Published by: Information Processing Association of Israel, Kfar Hamakabia, Ramat Gan, 52109, Israel. Ed. Batsheva Shezaf.

MANUFACTURING I T. see *COMPUTERS—Computer Systems*

MARKETONS I T DATABANK. see *COMPUTERS—Information Science And Information Theory*

004 ITA ISSN 0393-0599
MEDIA DUEMILA. Text in Italian. 1983. 11/yr.
Related titles: Online - full text ed.
Address: Corso Duca degli Abbruzzi 42, Turin, TO 10129, Italy. TEL 39-011-504995, FAX 39-011-503646, http://www.media2000.it. Circ: 24,000.

P M S TODAY. see *BUSINESS AND ECONOMICS—Computer Applications*

004.16 USA ISSN 1063-9470
PC-TRANS; the resource for personal computing in transportation. Text in English. 1991. q. free. adv. software rev. mkt. back issues avail. **Document type:** *Directory, Trade.*
Indexed: HRIS.
Published by: Kansas University Transportation Center, 2011 Learned Hall, Lawrence, KS 66045. TEL 785-864-5655, FAX 785-864-3199, pctrans@kuhub.cc.ukans.edu, http://kuhub.cc.ukans.edu. Ed., R&P Lisa Harris. Adv. contact Mehrdad Givechi. B&W page USD 600; trim 9.19 x 7. Circ: 15,000.

004 GBR ISSN 1356-0336
PERWILL UPDATE. Text in English. 1989. irreg.
Indexed: Inspec.
Published by: Perwill plc, 13A Market Square, Alton, Hampshire GU34 1UR, United Kingdom. TEL 44-1420-545000, FAX 44-1420-545001, info@perwill.com, http://www.perwill.com.

PHARMACY ELECTRONIC COMMUNICATIONS STANDARD. see *PHARMACY AND PHARMACOLOGY*

004 USA
T175 CODEN: DTMNAT
PLUGIN DATAMATION; profit and value from information technology. Text in English. 1957. m. free (effective 2005). adv. bk.rev. charts; illus. index. reprint service avail. from PQC. **Document type:** *Magazine, Trade.* **Description:** Covers analysis, evaluation, implementation, and selection of technologies needed for companies to keep a competitive advantage with a focus on being the IT survival guide for today's IS management.
Formerly (until 1998): Datamation (0011-6963)
Media: Online - full text (from Factiva, Gale Group, H.W. Wilson, O C L C Online Computer Library Center, Inc., ProQuest Information & Learning, The Dialog Corporation). **Related titles:** Microfiche ed.: (from CIS); Microform ed.
Indexed: AAR, ABIn, ADPA, AESIS, AIA, AS&TI, ASCA, ASEANManA, ATI, Acal, ApMecR, BMT, BPI, BrCerAb, C&CSA, C&ISA, CADCAM, CMCI, ChemAb, CompC, CompD, Compl, CompIU, CurCont, CybAb, DPD, E&CAJ, Emerald, ErgAb, ExcerpMed, GALA, IMI, ISR, Inspec, LHTB, LOIS, LRI, M&MA, MagInd, MicrocompInd, ORMS, PAIS, PROMT, QC&AS, RASB, RoboAb, SCI, SCIMP, SRI, SSCI, SoftBase, SolStAb, T&II, TelAb.
—AskIEEE, CASDDS, CISTI, Ei, IDS, IE, Linda Hall.
Published by: EarthWeb, 23 Old Kings Hwy, Darien, CT 06820. TEL 617-303-7906, FAX 617-345-5486, info@earthweb.com, http://www.datamation.com, http://www.earthweb.com/. Ed. Sharon Gaudin. Pub. Marty Moore. Circ: 200,300.

004 USA
PROCESSOR. Text in English. 1979. w. USD 59. adv. **Document type:** *Trade.*
Published by: Sandhills Publishing Co., 120 W Harvest Dr, Lincoln, NE 68521. TEL 402-479-2181, 800-331-1978, FAX 402-479-2195, feedback@sandhills.com, http://www.sandhills.com. Circ: 180,000. **Subscr. to:** PO Box 86510, Lincoln, NE 68501-5673. TEL 800-334-7445, FAX 402-479-2193.

PROF I T DATENBANK CD-ROM. see *COMPUTERS—Information Science And Information Theory*

004 USA ISSN 0898-8439
RETAIL SYSTEMS ALERT; a monthly update on automation news and trends for retailers. Text in English. 1987. m. USD 295 (effective 2000). bk.rev. charts; stat. Index. back issues avail. **Document type:** *Newsletter, Trade.* **Description:** Focuses on how retailers are using information technology systems to streamline their operations.
Published by: Retail Systems Alert Group, 332, Newton U F, MA 02464-0002. info@retailsystems.com, http://www.retailsystems.com/. Ed. Eric L Olson. Pub. Thomas H Friedman. R&P Karen Eaton. Circ: 700.

004 GBR
▼ **RETAIL SYSTEMS ALERT EXECUTIVE LETTER.** Text in English. 2004 (Jun.). m. free. **Document type:** *Newsletter, Trade.* **Description:** Examines issues related to forward-thinking views and trends of inventory management, store management, buying, sourcing, IT systems, and supply chain/logistics.
Media: Online - full content.
Published by: Retail Systems Alert Europe Inc. (Subsidiary of: Retail Systems Alert Group), 53 Coleridge St, Hove, East Sussex BN3 5AB, United Kingdom. TEL 44-1273-722687, FAX 44-1273-821463, info@retailsystems.com, http://www.retailsystems.com. Ed. Greg Belkin.

004 PRT
RS232 INFORMATICA. Text in Portuguese. 11/yr.
Address: Calcada de Palma de Baixo, 15 c-c Dnta, Lisbon, 1600, Portugal. TEL 726-46-52, TELEX 13011 VASSIS P. Ed. Carlos M S Aguda. Circ: 15,000.

114 510 USA ISSN 1530-6429
SAMPLING THEORY IN SIGNAL AND IMAGE PROCESSING; an international journal. Text in English. 2001. 3/yr. USD 100 to individuals; USD 180 to libraries (effective 2005). **Document type:** *Journal, Academic/Scholarly.*
Related titles: Online - full text ed.
Indexed: Inspec, MathR, MathSciNet.
—BLDSC (8072.495000).
Published by: Sampling Publishing, 60 Leroy St, Potsdam, NY 13676. TEL 315-265-2755, FAX 315-268-2371, http://www.stsip.org, http://www.cu.clarkson.edu/~jerria/SAMPLING_PUBLISHING.html.

004 PRT ISSN 0871-6218
SEMANA INFORMATICA. Text in Portuguese. 1989. 4/m. illus. back issues avail. **Document type:** *Magazine, Consumer.*
Related titles: Online - full text ed.
Published by: Investec Media, Ave Joao Crisostomo, 72, Lisbon, 1069-043, Portugal. TEL 351-213-307741, FAX 351-213-540643, assin@mail.fbento.pt, http://semanainformatica.xl.pt/, http://www.fbento.pt/FB/. Ed. Nuno Ribeiro. Circ: 308,000.

SEMAPHORE SIGNAL. see *COMPUTERS—Computer Systems*

SOUTH AFRICA. STATISTICS SOUTH AFRICA. CENSUS OF PROFESSIONAL AND BUSINESS SERVICES - DATA PROCESSING SERVICES. see *BUSINESS AND ECONOMICS—Abstracting, Bibliographies, Statistics*

004 DEU ISSN 0343-5202
P98 CODEN: SPDADH
SPRACHE UND DATENVERARBEITUNG; international journal for language data processing. Text in English, German. 1977. 2/yr. EUR 43.46 (effective 2003). adv. bk.rev. **Document type:** *Journal, Academic/Scholarly.*
Indexed: BibLing, DIP, IBR, IBZ, Inspec, MLA-IB, PCI, SOPODA.
—BLDSC (8419.868500), AskIEEE, IE, ingenta.
Published by: Institut fuer Kommunikationsforschung und Phonetik, Poppelsdorfer Allee 47, Bonn, 53115, Germany. TEL 49-228-735621, FAX 49-228-735639, b.schroeder@uni-bonn.de, http://www.linse.uni-essen.de.

004 AUT ISSN 0178-0069
SPRINGERS ANGEWANDTE INFORMATIK. Text in German. 1985. irreg., latest 1996. price varies. **Document type:** *Monographic series, Academic/Scholarly.*
Published by: Springer-Verlag Wien (Subsidiary of: Springer Science+Business Media) TEL 43-1-3302415-0, FAX 43-1-330242665, books@springer.at, http://www.springer.at. Ed. H Schauer. R&P Angela Foessl TEL 43-1-3302415517. **Subscr. in N. America to:** Springer-Verlag New York, Inc., 233 Spring St, New York, NY 10013. TEL 800-777-4643, FAX 201-348-4505, orders@springer-ny.com.

004 USA ISSN 1090-0799
CODEN: MFSMER
STORAGE MANAGEMENT. Text in English. m. USD 495; USD 545 foreign (effective 1999). **Document type:** *Newsletter.*
Indexed: Inspec.
Published by: Institute for Computer Capacity Management, 1020 8th Ave S, Ste 6, Naples, FL 34102. TEL 239-261-8945, FAX 239-261-5456.

TAIWAN COMPUTER; providing the latest Taiwan trade information. see *COMPUTERS—Hardware*

004 PRT
VIDA INFORMATICA. Text in Portuguese. w. **Description:** Contains news on all aspects of computers.
Address: Travessa de Santo Ildefonso, 1, Lisbon, 1200, Portugal. TEL 676315, FAX 66-74-20, TELEX 66036. Ed. J E Aparicio. Circ: 10,000.

004 DEU ISSN 0937-6429
QA76.5 CODEN: WIINE9
➤ **WIRTSCHAFTSINFORMATIK.** Text in German; Summaries in English. 1959. 10/yr. EUR 228; EUR 114 to students; EUR 48 newsstand/cover (effective 2004). adv. bk.rev. index. **Document type:** *Journal, Academic/Scholarly.*
Former titles (until 1990): Angewandte Informatik (0013-5704); (until 1971): Elektronische Datenverarbeitung (0374-3012)
Related titles: Online - full text ed.: (from Swets Information Services).
Indexed: ASCA, CMCI, CompAb, CompR, CurCont, CybAb, DIP, EngInd, ExcerpMed, IAOP, IBR, IBZ, Inspec, RASB, SSCI.
—BLDSC (9325.524500), AskIEEE, CISTI, Ei, IDS, IE, ingenta, Linda Hall. **CCC.**
Published by: Friedr. Vieweg und Sohn Verlagsgesellschaft mbH (Subsidiary of: Springer Science+Business Media), Abraham-Lincoln-Str 46, Wiesbaden, 65189, Germany. TEL 49-611-7878151, FAX 49-611-7878423, redaktion@wirtschaftsinformatik.de, vieweg.service@bertelsmann.de, http://www.wirtschaftsinformatik.de, http://www.vieweg.de. Adv. contact Christian Kannenberg. B&W page EUR 1,700, color page EUR 2,930. Circ: 4,700 (paid and controlled).

005.52 USA ISSN 1068-9699
HF5548.125 CODEN: WOCREX
WORKGROUP COMPUTING REPORT; applying technology to business processes. Text in English. 1978. m. looseleaf. USD 595 domestic; USD 615 in Canada; USD 630 elsewhere (effective 2003). software rev. charts; illus. back issues avail. **Document type:** *Newsletter, Trade.* **Description:** Provides in-depth coverage of office and word processing systems; occasionally contains articles on automation applications.
Former titles: Office Computing Report (1057-8889); Patricia Seybold's Office Computing Report (0894-9921); Patricia Seybold's Office Systems Report (1040-2594); (until 1986): Patty Seybold's Office Computing Report (0887-3062); (until 1985): Seybold Report Office Systems (0736-7279); (until 1982): Seybold Report on Word Processing (0160-9572)
Related titles: CD-ROM ed.; Online - full text ed.: (from LexisNexis).
Indexed: CompB, CompC, CompD, Inspec.
—AskIEEE, IE.
Published by: Patricia Seybold Group, 110 Commercial St, Boston, MA 02109. TEL 617-742-5200, 800-826-2424, TELEX 6503122583, info@psgroup.comm, http://www.psgroup.com. Ed. Ronni T Marshak. Pub. Patricia B Seybold.

004 FRA ISSN 0997-654X
HD9696.C63
ZERO UN REFERENCES. Text in French. 1965. w. adv.
Former titles (until 1988): Zero - Un Informatique Magazine (0985-2999); (until 1986): Zero un Informatique Mensuel (1243-2636); (until 1981): Zero un Informatique (0398-1185); (until 1974): Zero un Informatique Management (0374-1230); (until 1970): Zero un Informatqiue. Etudes (0245-9248); (until 1967): Zero un Informatique (0044-4359)
Related titles: ♦ Supplement to: Zero - Un Informatique (Hebdomadaire). ISSN 0298-2285.
Indexed: Inspec.
—**CCC.**
Published by: Groupe Tests, 26 rue d'Oradour-sur-Glane, Paris, Cedex 15 75504, France. TEL 33-1-44253500, http://www.groupetests.fr. Circ: 45,114.

COMPUTERS—Hardware

Includes: Analog Computers, Digital Computers. Disk Drives, Input-Output Systems, Laser Printers, Memory Structures, Modems, Monitors, Peripherals, Printers, Tape Decks, Terminals

004 USA ISSN 1081-7735
TK7888.4
ASIAN TEST SYMPOSIUM. PROCEEDINGS. Text in English. 1992. a., latest vol.12, 2003. USD 210 per vol. (effective 2004). **Document type:** *Proceedings, Trade.*
Related titles: Online - full text ed.: (from I E E E).
—BLDSC (6842.486140). **CCC.**
Published by: Institute of Electrical and Electronics Engineers, Inc., 3 Park Ave, 17th Fl, New York, NY 10016-5997. TEL 212-419-7900, 800-678-4333, FAX 212-752-4929, customer.service@ieee.org, http://www.ieee.org.

621.39 USA
ASSOCIATION FOR COMPUTING MACHINERY. COMPUTER SERVICE. Text in English. q. **Document type:** *Journal, Academic/Scholarly.*
Published by: Association for Computing Machinery, Inc., 1515 Broadway, 17th Fl, New York, NY 10036-5701. TEL 212-626-0500, 212-626-0520, 800-342-6626, FAX 212-869-0481, sigs@acm.org, usacm@acm.org, http://www.acm.org.

621.39 USA
ASSOCIATION FOR COMPUTING MACHINERY. CONFERENCE PROCEEDINGS. Text in English. a. price varies. **Document type:** *Proceedings, Academic/Scholarly.*
Formerly (until 1980): Association for Computing Machinery. Proceedings of the Annual Conference (0730-8329)
Related titles: Online - full text ed.
—BLDSC (0578.626070). **CCC.**
Published by: Association for Computing Machinery, Inc., 1515 Broadway, 17th Fl, New York, NY 10036-5701. TEL 212-626-0500, 212-626-0520, 800-342-6626, FAX 212-869-0481, sigs@acm.org, usacm@acm.org, http://www.acm.org.

004 621.395 USA
BRAZILIAN SYMPOSIUM ON INTEGRATED CIRCUIT DESIGN. Text in English. a. USD 188 per vol. (effective 2004). **Document type:** *Proceedings, Trade.*
Published by: Institute of Electrical and Electronics Engineers, Inc., 3 Park Ave, 17th Fl, New York, NY 10016-5997. TEL 212-419-7900, 800-678-4333, FAX 212-752-4929, customer.service@ieee.org, http://www.ieee.org.

004 USA
BUZZBYTES. Text in English. 1989. s-w. bk.rev.; Website rev.; software rev. **Document type:** *Newspaper, Consumer.*
Published by: American Newsfeatures Syndicate, 113 Wattenbarger Rd, Sweetwater, TN 37874-6135. cybercast@bigfoot.com. Ed. C W Mann. R&P Tom Call. Circ: 487.

CHIPS MAGAZINE. see *MILITARY*

004.7025 USA
COMPULIFE'S MICROMARKET BLUE DISC. Text in English. 1982. q. USD 75. **Description:** Used microcomputer price guide for hardware and peripherals.
Published by: Compulife, 5101 164th Ave SE, Bellevue, WA 98006-5703. TEL 206-641-6101. Ed. Steve Sharp.

004.5 FRA ISSN 0988-3452
COMPUTER DATA STORAGE NEWSLETTER; the monthly news report on the worldwide magnetic and optical disk and tape industry. Text in English. 1988. 12/yr. bk.rev. back issues avail. **Document type:** *Newsletter.* **Description:** News report on the international computer data storage industry; includes new products, new technologies, marketing and distribution trends, market studies, reports of major industry events, and worldwide developments.
Published by: Micro Journal, 11 rue de Provence, Paris, 75009, France. TEL 33-1-42463056, FAX 33-1-48242276, maleval@compuserve.com, http://www.mosarca.com/storagenews. Ed. Jean-Jacques Maleval. R&P Jean Jacques Maleval. Circ: 500 (paid).

004 USA
THE COMPUTER HARDWARE INDUSTRY. Text in English. 1990. a. USD 395. **Description:** Covers super computers, mainframes, mid-ranges, workstations and personal computers. Analyzes the future and new technological advances.
Published by: Dun & Bradstreet Information Services (Murray Hill) (Subsidiary of: Dun & Bradstreet, Inc.), 103 John F Kennedy Pkwy., Short Hills, NJ 07078-2708. TEL 908-665-5224, FAX 908-771-7599. Ed. Matthew Gowen.

004 005 ITA ISSN 1125-7857
COMPUTER MAGAZINE. Text in Italian. 1997. m. EUR 39 (effective 2005). adv. **Document type:** *Magazine, Consumer.* **Description:** Informs on new hardware and software products. Provides purchasing advice and includes articles on how to maximize your computer capabilities.
Published by: Future Media Italy SpA, Via Asiago 45, Milano, MI 20128, Italy. TEL 39-02-2529161, FAX 39-02-26005520, info@futuremediaitaly.it, http://www.futuremediaitaly.it. Ed. Mietta Capasso.

004.7 GBR
COMPUTER PERIPHERALS. Text in English. 2/yr. adv.
Published by: Peripheral Suppliers Association, Owles Hall, Owles Ln, Buntingford, Herts SG9 9PL, United Kingdom. Ed. H M W Gibbons.

004 USA ISSN 0093-416X
TK7885.A1 CODEN: CMRVCK
COMPUTER REVIEW. Text in English. 1961. a. USD 495 domestic; USD 520 foreign (effective 2005). charts. index. **Document type:** *Directory.* **Description:** Profiles computer, telecommunications, and Internet solution providers and reviews their products and services.
Incorporates (1983-1991): Microcomputer Review (8755-7525); (1973-1991): Computer Terminals Review (0147-9415); Which was formerly (until 1976): Terminals Review (0093-2337); (1974-1991): Computer Peripherals Review (0149-5054); Which was formerly: Peripherals Review; (1988-1991): Computer-Specs; Former titles (until 1973): Computer Characteristics Review (0010-454X); (until 1969): Computer Characteristics Quarterly
Related titles: Diskette ed.
Indexed: CompR, Inspec.
—Linda Hall.
Address: 19 Pleasant St, Box 260, Gloucester, MA 01930. TEL 978-283-2100, FAX 978-281-3125, info@computerreview.com, http://www.computerreview.com. Ed. Alexander Luhowy. Pub. George Luhowy. Circ: 1,000.

621.39 USA ISSN 1522-869X
TK7874
CONFERENCE ON ADVANCED RESEARCH IN V L S I. PROCEEDINGS. (Very Large Scale Integration) Text in English. 1979. a. USD 140 per vol.. **Document type:** *Proceedings, Trade.*
Related titles: Online - full text ed.: (from I E E E).
—BLDSC (3408.775640).
Published by: Institute of Electrical and Electronics Engineers, Inc., 3 Park Ave, 17th Fl, New York, NY 10016-5997. TEL 212-419-7900, 800-678-4333, FAX 212-752-4929, customer.service@ieee.org, http://www.ieee.org.

CONSTRUCTION BUSINESS COMPUTING. see *COMPUTERS—Software*

621.39 USA ISSN 1528-6312
CONTROLS INTELLIGENCE & PLANT SYSTEMS REPORT. Text in English. 1981. m. looseleaf. USD 195 domestic (effective 2005). bk.rev. **Document type:** *Newsletter, Consumer.* **Description:** Offers advice to marketing and other executives who make and sell industrial controls, peripherals, and industrial computers.
Former titles (until 2000): Industrial Controls Intelligence and the P L C Insider's Newsletter (1074-0511); (until 1994): Controls Digest (1067-3121); (until 1993): P L C Insider's Newsletter (1040-9718)
Related titles: Diskette ed.; Online - full content ed.: ISSN 1529-4013.
Published by: Controls Intelligence, Inc., P O Box 550, Chelsea, MI 48118-0208. TEL 734-475-9400, FAX 734-475-8860, editors@KVQuest.com, http://www.controlsintelligence.com. Eds. Audra Lungo, Katrina Snyder. Circ: 10,000 (paid).

DATA NEWS; l'actualite informatique. see *COMMUNICATIONS—Computer Applications*

005.5 DEU ISSN 0933-8667
DESIGN & ELEKTRONIK. Text in German. 1985. fortn. EUR 68.40 domestic; EUR 78 foreign; EUR 57.60 to students; EUR 7.50 newsstand/cover (effective 2005). adv. back issues avail. **Document type:** *Magazine, Trade.*
Related titles: Online - full text ed.
—CCC.
Published by: W E K A Fachzeitschriften-Verlag GmbH, Gruberstr 46a, Poing, 85586, Germany. TEL 49-8121-950, FAX 49-8121-951396, redaktion@design-elektronik.de, ckasel@wekanet.de, http://www.elektroniknet.de/design-elektronik.de, http://www.wekanet.de. Ed. Caspar Grote. Adv. contact Christian Stadler. B&W page EUR 4,530, color page EUR 6,350; trim 186 x 260. Circ: 21,913 (paid and controlled).

DISPLAYS. see *COMPUTERS—Computer Graphics*

DOCUMENT IMAGING REPORT. see *COMPUTERS—Data Communications And Data Transmission Systems*

004.36 USA ISSN 1094-2793
GIGABIT NEWS; covering worldwide developments in fiber distributed data interface. Text in English. 1989. m. USD 695 in US & Canada; USD 745 elsewhere (effective 2004). **Document type:** *Newsletter, Trade.* **Description:** Covers FDDI and GIGABIT technology, markets, applications, products, standards, and business developments.
Formerly (until 1997): F D D I News (1051-1903)
—CCC.
Published by: Information Gatekeepers, Inc., 320 Washington St, Ste 302, Brighton, MA 02135. TEL 617-782-5033, 800-323-1088, FAX 617-782-5735, info@igigroup.com, http://www.igigroup.com/nl/pages/giganews.html. Ed. Tony Carmona. Pub. Dr. Paul Polishuk.

004 USA
GREAT LAKES SYMPOSIUM ON V L S I. (Very Large Scale Integration) Text in English. a. USD 125. **Document type:** *Proceedings.*
Published by: Institute of Electrical and Electronics Engineers, Inc., 3 Park Ave, 17th Fl, New York, NY 10016-5997. TEL 800-678-4333, customer.service@ieee.org, http://www.ieee.org.

004 USA
GREGORY'S CLEARPATH - A-SERIES TECHNICAL JOURNAL. Text in English. 1986. 9/yr. USD 235; USD 270 foreign (effective 1999). tr.lit. back issues avail. **Document type:** *Trade.* **Description:** Provides technical information for Unisys A-Series computer users.
Formerly (until 1998): Gregory's A-Series Technical Journal (0892-4856)
Related titles: CD-ROM ed.
Published by: Gregory Publishing Company, 333 Cobalt Way, Ste 107, Sunnyvale, CA 94086. TEL 408-727-4660, FAX 408-492-1948, joyce@gregpub.com, http://www.gregpub.com. Ed. Don Gregory. Circ: 500 (paid).

004 USA ISSN 1530-082X
TK7874
I E E E COMPUTER SOCIETY WORKSHOP ON V L S I. PROCEEDINGS. (Very Large Scale Integration) Text in English. a. USD 166 per vol.; USD 67 per vol. to members (effective 2004). **Document type:** *Proceedings, Trade.*
Related titles: Online - full text ed.: (from I E E E).
Published by: Institute of Electrical and Electronics Engineers, Inc., 3 Park Ave, 17th Fl, New York, NY 10016-5997. TEL 212-419-7900, 800-678-4333, FAX 212-752-4929, customer.service@ieee.org, http://www.ieee.org.

I E E E INTERNATIONAL NONVOLATILE MEMORY TECHNOLOGY CONFERENCE. PROCEEDINGS. see *COMPUTERS—Data Base Management*

004 621.39 USA
I E E E INTERNATIONAL WORKSHOP ON DEFECT BASED TESTING. Text in English. a. USD 100; USD 45 to members. **Document type:** *Proceedings.*
Formerly: I E E E International Workshop on I D D Q Testing
Indexed: Englnd.
—BLDSC (4362.973260).
Published by: Institute of Electrical and Electronics Engineers, Inc., 3 Park Ave, 17th Fl, New York, NY 10016-5997. TEL 212-419-7900, 800-678-4333, FAX 212-752-4929, customer.service@ieee.org, http://www.ieee.org.

004 005.1 USA ISSN 1092-6100
QA76.9.S88
I E E E INTERNATIONAL WORKSHOP ON HARDWARE - SOFTWARE CODESIGN. Text in English. 19??. a. USD 176; USD 88 to members (effective 2004). **Document type:** *Proceedings, Trade.*
Related titles: Online - full text ed.: (from I E E E).
—BLDSC (4552.190500). **CCC.**
Published by: Institute of Electrical and Electronics Engineers, Inc., 3 Park Ave, 17th Fl, New York, NY 10016-5997. TEL 212-419-7900, 800-678-4333, FAX 212-752-4929, customer.service@ieee.org, http://www.ieee.org.

C

004 USA ISSN 1087-4852
TK7895.M4
I E E E INTERNATIONAL WORKSHOP ON MEMORY TECHNOLOGY, DESIGN AND TESTING. Text in English. 19??. a. USD 151 membership (effective 2005). **Document type:** *Proceedings, Trade.*
Related titles: Online - full text ed.: (from I E E E).
Indexed: Englnd.
—BLDSC (7325.719000). **CCC.**
Published by: Institute of Electrical and Electronics Engineers, Inc., 3 Park Ave, 17th Fl, New York, NY 10016-5997. TEL 212-419-7900, 800-678-4333, FAX 212-752-4929, customer.service@ieee.org, http://www.ieee.org.

004 621.382 USA
I E E E SIGNAL PROCESSING ON HIGHER ORDER STATISTICS. Text in English. a. USD 130. **Document type:** *Proceedings, Trade.*
—BLDSC (4363.066522).
Published by: Institute of Electrical and Electronics Engineers, Inc., 3 Park Ave, 17th Fl, New York, NY 10016-5997. TEL 212-419-7900, 800-678-4333, FAX 212-752-4929, customer.service@ieee.org, http://www.ieee.org.

004 USA
I E E E SYMPOSIUM ON F P G AS FOR CUSTOM COMPUTING MACHINES. Text in English. 1991. a. USD 170 per vol.; USD 68 per vol. to members (effective 2004). **Document type:** *Proceedings, Trade.*
Former titles (until 199?): International Conference on Tools with Artificial Intelligence. Proceedings (1082-3409); (until 1991): International Conference on Tools for Artificial Intelligence (1063-6730)
Related titles: Online - full text ed.: (from I E E E).
Indexed: Englnd.
—BLDSC (4362.949970). **CCC.**
Published by: Institute of Electrical and Electronics Engineers, Inc., 3 Park Ave, 17th Fl, New York, NY 10016-5997. TEL 212-419-7900, 800-678-4333, FAX 212-752-4929, customer.service@ieee.org, http://www.ieee.org.

004 USA ISSN 0743-1562
I E E E SYMPOSIUM ON V L S I TECHNOLOGY. Text in English. a. USD 168; USD 84 to members (effective 2004). **Document type:** *Proceedings, Trade.*
—BLDSC (8585.837580). **CCC.**
Published by: Institute of Electrical and Electronics Engineers, Inc., 3 Park Ave, 17th Fl, New York, NY 10016-5997. TEL 212-419-7900, 800-678-4333, FAX 212-752-4929, customer.service@ieee.org, http://www.ieee.org.

004 USA ISSN 1093-0167
TK7874
I E E E - V L S I TEST SYMPOSIUM. Text in English. 1994. a. USD 211 per vol.; USD 85 per vol. to members (effective 2004). **Document type:** *Proceedings, Trade.*
Related titles: Online - full text ed.: (from I E E E).
—BLDSC (4363.236500).

Published by: Institute of Electrical and Electronics Engineers, Inc., 3 Park Ave, 17th Fl, New York, NY 10016-5997. TEL 212-419-7900, 800-678-4333, FAX 212-752-4929, customer.service@ieee.org, http://www.ieee.org.

004 USA
I E E E WORKSHOP ON INDUSTRIAL STRENGTH FORMAL SPECIFICATION TECHNIQUES. Text in English. a. **Document type:** *Proceedings, Trade.*
Indexed: Englnd.
Published by: Institute of Electrical and Electronics Engineers, Inc., 3 Park Ave, 17th Fl, New York, NY 10016-5997. TEL 800-678-4333, customer.service@ieee.org, http://www.ieee.org.

005.5 GBR ISSN 1350-2387
TK1 CODEN: ICDTEA
➤ **I E E PROCEEDINGS - COMPUTERS AND DIGITAL TECHNIQUES.** Text in English. 1978. bi-m. USD 1,045 in the Americas to non-members print or online; GBP 615 elsewhere to non-members print or online; USD 1,254 combined subscription in the Americas to non-members print & online; GBP 738 combined subscription elsewhere to non-members print & online; USD 174 per issue in the Americas to non-members; GBP 103 per issue elsewhere to non-members (effective 2005). adv. bk.rev. index. **Document type:** *Proceedings, Academic/Scholarly.* **Description:** Covers hardware and software for digital systems, theory design and application of computers, minicomputers, microprocessors, computer languages, computer architecture, VLSI and CAD of VLSI, logic circuits, and digital subsystems.
Former titles (until 1994): I E E Proceedings E (Computers and Digital Techniques) (0143-7062); (until 1980): I E E Journal on Computers and Digital Techniques (0140-1335)
Related titles: Online - full text ed.: ISSN 1359-7027 (from EBSCO Publishing); ♦ Series of: I E E Proceedings.
Indexed: AS&TI, ASCA, BMT, BrTechI, C&CSA, C&ISA, CMCI, CompAb, CompC, CompD, CompLI, CurCont, E&CAJ, Englnd, ExcerpMed, IAA, Inspec, MathR, RefZh, SCI, SolStAb, ZentMath.
—BLDSC (4362.751860), AskIEEE, CISTI, Ei, IDS, IE, Infotrieve, ingenta, Linda Hall. **CCC.**
Published by: Institution of Electrical Engineers, Michael Faraday House, Six Hills Way, Stevenage, Herts SG1 2AY, United Kingdom. TEL 44-1438-313311, FAX 44-1438-313465, inspec@iee.org, http://www.iee.org/Publish/Journals/Profjourn/Proc/cdt/. Ed. Bashir Al-Hashimi. R&P Michael McCabe TEL 732-321-5575. Circ: 4,000. **Subscr. in the US:** INSPEC/I E E, 379 Thornall St., Edison, NJ 08837. TEL 732-321-5575, FAX 732-321-5702; **Subscr. to:** INSPEC, I E E, Publication Sales Dept., PO Box 96, Stevenage, Herts SG1 2SD, United Kingdom. TEL 44-1438-313311, FAX 44-1438-742840.

004.7 GBR ISSN 0960-6645
IN HAND. Text in English. 1985. bi-m. GBP 98; GBP 108 in North America. adv. back issues avail. **Document type:** *Trade.* **Description:** Covers hand-held computer devices used for bar-code scanning.
Related titles: Online - full text ed.
Address: 31 Randolph Dr, Farnborough, Hants GU14 0QQ, United Kingdom. TEL 01252-518960, FAX 01252-518960. Ed., Adv. contact Keith Goodyear. page GBP 770; 190 x 268. Circ: 10,000.

004 USA
INTEL CHANNEL NEWS. Text in English. bi-m. **Document type:** *Newsletter.* **Description:** Designed specifically for resellers, retailers and Intel product dealers.
Media: Online - full text.
Published by: Intel Corporation, 2200 Mission College Blvd, Santa Clara, CA 95052-8119. TEL 800-628-8686, FAX 408-765-9904, channel.news@intel.com, http://channel.intel.com/business/cicnews/index.htm/, http://www.intel.com.

004 USA
INTERNATIONAL CONFERENCE ON MICROELECTRONICS FOR NEURAL, FUZZY, AND BIO-INSPIRED SYSTEMS. PROCEEDINGS. Text in English. a. price varies. **Document type:** *Proceedings, Trade.*
Published by: Institute of Electrical and Electronics Engineers, Inc., 3 Park Ave, 17th Fl, New York, NY 10016-5997. TEL 212-419-7900, 800-678-4333, FAX 212-752-4929, customer.service@ieee.org, http://www.ieee.org.

004 USA ISSN 1530-2024
TK7874
INTERNATIONAL CONFERENCE ON MICROELECTRONICS SYSTEMS EDUCATION. PROCEEDINGS. Text in English. 1994. a. USD 151; USD 61 to members (effective 2004). **Document type:** *Proceedings, Trade.*
Related titles: Online - full text ed.: (from I E E E).
Published by: Institute of Electrical and Electronics Engineers, Inc., 3 Park Ave, 17th Fl, New York, NY 10016-5997. TEL 212-419-7900, 800-678-4333, FAX 212-752-4929, customer.service@ieee.org, http://www.ieee.org.

004 USA ISSN 1063-9667
INTERNATIONAL CONFERENCE ON V L S I DESIGN. PROCEEDINGS. (Very Large Scale Integration) Text in English. a. USD 290; USD 116 to members (effective 2004). **Document type:** *Proceedings, Trade.*
Related titles: Online - full text ed.: (from I E E E).
—**CCC.**
Published by: (I E E E Computer Society), Institute of Electrical and Electronics Engineers, Inc., 445 Hoes Ln, Piscataway, NJ 08854-1331. TEL 732-981-0060, FAX 732-981-1721, customer.service@ieee.org, http://www.ieee.org.

004 USA
INTERNATIONAL MICROPROCESSES AND NANOTECHNOLOGY CONFERENCE. PROCEEDINGS. Text in English. a. price varies. **Document type:** *Proceedings, Trade.*
Published by: Institute of Electrical and Electronics Engineers, Inc., 3 Park Ave, 17th Fl, New York, NY 10016-5997. TEL 212-419-7900, 800-678-4333, FAX 212-752-4929, customer.service@ieee.org, http://www.ieee.org.

621.39 USA ISSN 1550-5774
TK7874
INTERNATIONAL SYMPOSIUM ON DEFECT AND FAULT - TOLERANCE IN V L S I SYSTEMS. PROCEEDINGS. (Very Large Scale Integration) Variant title: I E E E International Symposium on Defect and Fault - Tolerance in V L S I Systems. Proceedings. Text in English. 1989. irreg. USD 120. **Document type:** *Proceedings, Academic/Scholarly.*
Former titles (until 1996): International Workshop on Defect and Fault - Tolerance in V L S I Systems. Proceedings (1063-6722); (until 1991): Defect and Fault Tolerance in V L S I Systems (1055-9329)
Related titles: Online - full text ed.: (from I E E E).
Indexed: Englnd.
—BLDSC (4362.967800). **CCC.**
Published by: I E E E Computer Society, 10662 Los Vaqueros Circle, PO Box 3014, Los Alamitos, CA 90720-1314. TEL 714-821-8380, 800-272-6657, FAX 714-821-4010, http://www.computer.org.

004 USA
INTERNATIONAL SYMPOSIUM ON ENVIRONMENTALLY CONSCIOUS DESIGN AND INVERSE MANUFACTURING. Text in English. irreg. price varies. **Document type:** *Proceedings, Trade.*
Published by: Institute of Electrical and Electronics Engineers, Inc., 3 Park Ave, 17th Fl, New York, NY 10016-5997. TEL 212-419-7900, 800-678-4333, FAX 212-752-4929, customer.service@ieee.org, http://www.ieee.org.

INTERNATIONAL VERILOG H D L CONFERENCE. PROCEEDINGS. (Hardware Description Language) see *COMPUTERS—Computer Engineering*

004 USA
ISERIES NEWS. Text in English. 1982. m. USD 149 (effective 2003). adv. bk.rev. index. reprints avail. **Document type:** *Magazine, Trade.* **Description:** Publishes technical articles explaining and interpreting AS-400, with coverage of new releases.
Former titles: News - 400 (1084-7626); News 3X-400 (1040-6093); News 34-38 (8750-1678)
Related titles: Online - full content ed.; Online - full text ed.
Indexed: SoftBase.
—CISTI, IE. **CCC.**
Published by: Penton Technology Media (Subsidiary of: Penton Media, Inc.), 221 E 29th St, Ste 242, Loveland, CO 80538. TEL 970-663-4700, FAX 970-663-3285, editors@iseriesnetwork.com, http://www.iseriesnetwork.com. Ed., R&P Kathy Nelson. Pub. Wayne Madden. Adv. contact Kim Hansen. Circ: 30,500.

004 GBR ISSN 1475-9128
ISERIES NEWS U K. Text in English. 1996. 11/yr. adv. **Document type:** *Magazine, Trade.* **Description:** Focuses exclusively on iSeries (AS/400) business and technology.
Formerly (until 2001): News - 400 (1465-9964)
Published by: Penton Media Europe (Subsidiary of: Penton Media, Inc.), Penton House, 288-290 Worton Rd, Isleworth, Mddx TW7 6EL, United Kingdom. TEL 44-20-8232-1600, FAX 44-20-8232-1650, information@penton.com, http://www.penton.com. Adv. contact Kathie Cutter. color page GBP 2,563; trim 210 x 297. Circ: 11,000 (controlled).

004 ITA
ISERIESNEWS; mensile per utenti di sistemi IBM 34-36-38 e AS-400. Text in Italian. 1988. m. EUR 94 domestic; EUR 113.62 in Europe; EUR 165.27 elsewhere (effective 2005). adv. **Document type:** *Magazine, Consumer.*
Formerly: News 3X-400 (1121-8649)
Published by: Gruppo Editoriale Duke Italia, Via Melchiorre Gioia 55/B, Milan, 2020124, Italy. TEL 39-02-6748001, FAX 39-02-67073071, http://www.iseries.it/index.shtml, http://dossier.duke.it. Circ: 21,415.

004.3 DEU ISSN 0935-9680
IX; Magazin fuer professionelle Informationstechnik. Text in German. 1988. m. adv. **Document type:** *Magazine, Trade.*
Incorporates (1988-1992): UNIX-Magazin (0934-8476)
Related titles: CD-ROM ed.
—GNLM, IE.
Published by: Verlag Heinz Heise GmbH und Co. KG, Helstorfer Str 7, Hannover, 30625, Germany. TEL 49-511-5352-0, FAX 49-511-5352-129, ix@heise.de, abo@heise.de, http://www.heise.de/ix. Ed. Juergen Seeger. Adv. contact Michael Hanke TEL 49-511-5352167. Circ: 56,229 (paid).

JISUANJI YANJIU YU FAZHAN/COMPUTER RESEARCH AND DEVELOPMENT. see *COMPUTERS—Computer Engineering*

621.39 GBR ISSN 0278-6125
CODEN: JMSYEB
➤ **JOURNAL OF MANUFACTURING SYSTEMS.** Text in English. 1982. 4/yr. EUR 714 in Europe to institutions; JPY 94,800 in Japan to institutions; USD 799 elsewhere to institutions (effective 2006). adv. bk.rev. illus. Index. back issues avail.; reprints avail. **Document type:** *Journal, Academic/Scholarly.* **Description:** For members of the Society and other practicing manufacturing engineers, researchers and educators. Covers such topics as integrating manufacturing processes into systems, hardware and component research and development, computer-aided manufacturing, as well as sensors.
Related titles: Online - full text ed.: (from Northern Light Technology, Inc., O C L C Online Computer Library Center, Inc., ProQuest Information & Learning, ScienceDirect).
Indexed: ABIn, AIA, ASCA, ApMecR, CADCAM, CivEngAb, CurCont, Englnd, Inspec, ORMS, QC&AS, RefZh, RoboAb, SCI, TTI.
—BLDSC (5011.650000), AskIEEE, CISTI, IDS, IE, Infotrieve, ingenta, Linda Hall. **CCC.**
Published by: (Society of Manufacturing Engineers USA, Computer and Automated Systems Association USA), Elsevier Ltd. (Subsidiary of: Elsevier Science & Technology), The Boulevard, Langford Ln, Kidlington, Oxford, OX5 1GB, United Kingdom. TEL 44-1865-843000, FAX 44-1865-843010, nlinfo-f@elsevier.nl, http://www.elsevier.com/locate/jmansys. Ed. J T Black. Circ: 1,000. **Subscr. in the US & Canada to:** Society of Manufacturing Engineers, Customer Service, PO Box 6020, Dearborn, MI 48121. TEL 800-733-4763, FAX 313-240-8252.

004 338 GBR ISSN 1365-8123
KEY NOTE MARKET REPORT: COMPUTER HARDWARE. Variant title: Computer Hardware Market Report. Text in English. 1996. irreg., latest 2001, Oct. GBP 340 per issue (effective 2002). **Document type:** *Trade.* **Description:** Provides an overview of the UK computer hardware sector, including industry structure, market size and trends, developments, prospects, and major company profiles.
Published by: Key Note Ltd., Field House, 72 Oldfield Rd, Hampton, Mddx TW12 2HQ, United Kingdom. TEL 44-20-8481-8750, FAX 44-20-8783-0049, info@keynote.co.uk, http://www.keynote.co.uk. Ed. Jacob Howard.

004.7 USA
M V S UPDATE. (Multiple Virtual Storage) Text in English. m. USD 505 (effective 2000). **Document type:** *Trade.*
Published by: Xephon, 9330 Lyndon B Johnson Fwy., Ste. 800, Dallas, TX 75243-4310. TEL 817-455-7050, FAX 303-438-0290.

004 005 ITA ISSN 1120-8465
MACINTOSH MAGAZINE. Cover title: Macintosh & Internet Magazine. Text in Italian. m. **Description:** Provides information for Macintosh users and enthusiasts. Contains articles on maximizing the computer's capabilities.
Published by: M G E Communications, Via Cola di Rienzo, 163, Roma, 00192, Italy. TEL 39-06-3243289, FAX 39-06-3243088.

004.7 USA
CODEN: OMNEEF
MASS STORAGE NEWS; opportunities and trends in data storage & retrieval. Text in English. 1982. 24/yr. USD 597 (effective 2003). charts; illus.; stat. back issues avail. **Document type:** *Newsletter.* **Description:** Covers the optical storage marketplace from the vendor perspective, including industry trends, new products, and corporate alliances and partnerships.
Formerly (until Apr. 1998): Optical Memory News (0741-5869); Incorporates (1990-1991): Optical and Magnetic Report (1047-5117); Optical Memory Newsletter
Related titles: CD-ROM ed.: USD 109 per issue domestic; USD 130 per issue foreign (effective 2000); Online - full text ed.: (from LexisNexis, ProQuest Information & Learning).
Indexed: ABIn.
—CASDDS. **CCC.**
Published by: Corry Publishing Inc., 5905 Beacon Hill Ln, Erie, PA 16509. TEL 814-868-9935, FAX 814-835-0441, edm@corrypub.com, CarlyR@corrypub.com, http://www.massstoragenews.com/, http://www.corrypub.com. Ed. Mike Downing. Pub. Terry Peterson. R&P Ed Miseta. Circ: 1,000.

004 GBR ISSN 1355-1507
MEDIA INDUSTRIES TRENDS✶. Text in English. s-a. (in 2 vols., 3 nos./vol.). GBP 105 per issue.
Former titles (until 1993): Trend Monitor Reports (0963-0325); Trend Monitor (0954-7479)

Published by: Aslib, Association for Information Management, Publications Department, Staple Hall, Stone House Court, London, EC3A 7PB, United Kingdom. TEL 44-20-7903-0000, FAX 44-20-7903-0011, pubs@aslib.co.uk, pubs@aslib.com, http://www.aslib.co.uk/aslib/, http://www.aslib.com/aslib. Ed. Jan Wyllie.

004.3 CAN ISSN 0849-8180
MICRO CONTROL JOURNAL. Text in English. 1989. 6/yr. CND 17.50, USD 17.50. adv. bk.rev. back issues avail.
Description: Covers applications of computers to real time control systems, data acquisitions, sensors and motor controls.
Address: 27 Penrith Crescent, London, ON N6G 4M8, Canada. TEL 519-434-6904, FAX 519-668-1450. Ed. S Gupta. Circ: 5,000.

004 USA ISSN 1040-0966 CODEN: MODIE3
MONOSSON REPORT ON D E C AND I B M. (Digital Equipment Corporation and International Business Machines) Text in English. 1981. m. index. **Document type:** *Trade.*
Formerly (until June 1988): Monosson on D E C (0884-4097)
Published by: Monosson Technology Enterprise, 1260 Boylston St., Boston, MA 02215-4401. TEL 617-267-2900, FAX 617-2672370. Ed. Sheila Osmundsen. Circ: 400.

621.39 USA
OPTICAL DATA STORAGE TOPICAL MEETING. Text in English. 2000. a. USD 182; USD 91 to members (effective 2004). **Document type:** *Proceedings, Trade.*
Published by: Institute of Electrical and Electronics Engineers, Inc., 3 Park Ave, 17th Fl, New York, NY 10016-5997. TEL 212-419-7900, 800-678-4333, FAX 212-752-4929, customer.service@ieee.org, http://www.ieee.org.

P C GAMES HARDWARE; das Hardware-Magazin fuer PC-Spieler. (Personal Computer) see *COMPUTERS—Computer Games*

P C MARKET; la prima grande guida all'acquisto dei prodotti informatici. see *COMPUTERS—Personal Computers*

P C MART. see *COMPUTERS*

338.47004 USA ISSN 0742-5341
THE REPORT ON I B M. Text in English. 1984. w. USD 495 (effective 2005). **Document type:** *Newsletter, Trade.*
Description: Independent newsletter reporting and providing analysis on the activities and plans of the IBM Corporation.
Incorporates (in 1992): A D - Solutions Report; Mainframe Communications Report
Related titles: Online - full text ed.: (from Factiva).
—CCC.
Published by: DataTrends Publications, Inc., PO Box 4460, Leesburg, VA 20177-8541. dtrends@ix.netcom.com, info@datatrendspublications.com, http://www.datatrendspublications.com/default.htm. Pub. Paul G Ochs. **Dist. by:** Publications Resource Group, 121 Union St., Box 792, North Adams, MA 01247. TEL 413-664-6185, FAX 413-664-9343.

004 USA
SCAN: THE DATA CAPTURE REPORT. Text in English. 1977. bi-m. USD 497 domestic; USD 530 foreign (effective 1999). charts; illus.; stat. back issues avail. **Document type:** *Newsletter.* **Description:** Management and marketing newsletter covering automatic data capture, bar coding and related technologies.
Related titles: CD-ROM ed.: USD 109 per issue domestic; USD 130 per issue foreign (effective 2000).
Published by: Corry Publishing Inc., 5539 Peach St, Erie, PA 16506. TEL 814-868-9935, FAX 814-835-0441, edm@corrypub.com, CarlyR@corrypub.com, http://www.corrypub.com. Ed. Rick Morgan. Pub. Terry Peterson.

004 AUS ISSN 1030-2662
SILICON CHIP. Text in English. 1987. m. AUD 76 domestic; AUD 85 in New Zealand; AUD 129 elsewhere (effective 2004). adv. **Document type:** *Magazine, Trade.* **Description:** Directed towards professionals, trades people and enthusiasts in the electronics, electrical, computer and related fields.
Published by: Silicon Chip Publications Pty Ltd., Unit 8, 101 Darley St, Mona Vale, NSW 2103, Australia. TEL 61-2-99795644, FAX 61-2-99796503, silchip@siliconchip.com.au, http://www.siliconchip.com.au/. Ed., Pub. Leo Simpson.

621.39 TWN
TAIWAN COMPUTER; providing the latest Taiwan trade information. Cover title: T C. Text in Chinese. m. TWD 2,200. adv. **Document type:** *Trade.* **Description:** Contains information and advertising on Taiwan-made computers and Taiwan's computer industry. Mainly concerned with IBM-compatible PCs. Includes a trade-show calendar.
Formerly (until Mar. 1990): Target Electronics Industry Computer
Published by: United Pacific International Inc., P.O. Box 81-417, Taipei, Taiwan. TEL 866-2-715-0751, FAX 866-2-7125591, TELEX 28784 UNIPAINC. **Dist. in US by:** Perfect Seller Mr. John Huang, 5422 Commercial Drive, Huntington Beach, CA 92649.

004 DNK ISSN 0900-3762
TECHNICAL PRODUCT UPDATE. Text in Danish. m. free.
Published by: Digital Equipment Corporation A-S, Aadalsvej 99, Horsholm, 2970, Denmark.

004 USA
TEST & MEASUREMENT NEWS. Text in English, French, German, Italian, Spanish. q. **Document type:** *Newsletter.*
Description: Describes the newest products and applications from HP, such as hardware, including telecommunications news.
Media: Online - full text.
Published by: Hewlet- Packard, Test and Measurement Call Center, 9780 S Meridian Blvd, Englewood, CO 80112. http://tmo.hp.com/tmo/events, http://www.tmo.hp.com/tmo/events.

004 USA
THE VIEW (FEDERAL WAY)✶ . Text in English. 1996. d.
Description: Covers computer hardwares for those interested in buying hardware.
Media: Online - full text.
Published by: View (Federal Way), 1031 SW 334th St, Federal Way, WA 98023-5313. danielf@the-view.com, http://www.the-view.com. Ed. Daniel W Finley.

621.39 USA ISSN 1051-9637
TK5105.5
3 TECH. Variant title: 3 Tech 3 Com's Technical Journal. Text in English. 1990. q.
Published by: 3 Com Corp., 540 Bayfront Plaza, Box 58145, Santa Clara, CA 95052-8145.

COMPUTERS—Information Science And Information Theory

see also COMPUTERS

A C M / I E E E JOINT CONFERENCE ON DIGITAL LIBRARIES. PROCEEDINGS. see *LIBRARY AND INFORMATION SCIENCES*

020 USA ISSN 1527-6805
QA76.9.D6 CODEN: AJCDBH
➤ **A C M JOURNAL OF COMPUTER DOCUMENTATION.** (Association of Computing Machinery) Text in English. 1974. q. USD 45 to non-members; USD 30 to members (effective 2004). **Document type:** *Journal, Academic/Scholarly.*
Description: Provides a forum for discussion conceptual, practical, research and policy issues in computers documentation for practitioners, analysts and teachers of documentation.
Former titles (until 2000): Journal of Computer Documentation; Asterisk (0731-1001); (until 1981): Systems Documentation Newsletter (0163-5956)
Related titles: Online - full text ed.: (from Association for Computing Machinery, Inc., EBSCO Publishing).
Indexed: CompR, ErgAb, Inspec, RefZh.
—BLDSC (0578.628500), CISTI, IE, ingenta.
Published by: Association for Computing Machinery, Inc., 1515 Broadway, 17th Fl, New York, NY 10036-5701. TEL 212-626-0500, 212-626-0520, 800-342-6626, FAX 212-869-0481, sigs@acm.org, usacm@acm.org, http://www.acm.org/sigdoc/journal.html. Ed. Russell Borland.

003.54 USA ISSN 1544-3647
HF5737 CODEN: DOWOFI
A I I M E-DOC MAGAZINE; enterprise content magazine at work. Text in English. 2000. bi-m. USD 90; free to qualified personnel (effective 2005). adv. back issues avail. **Document type:** *Magazine, Trade.* **Description:** Reports on developments affecting the document imaging and information management sector.
Formerly (until Mar. 2003): E-doc (1529-0484); Which was formed by the merger of (1996-2000): Document World (1025-9228); (1987-2000): Inform (Silver Spring) (0892-3876); Which was formerly (until 1986): Journal of Information and Image Management (0745-9963); (until 1983): Journal of Micrographics (0022-2712); N M A Journal; Which incorporated (as of vol.15): Micrographics Today (0149-9300); Which was formerly (until 1975): Micro News Bulletin (0026-2544); Which incorporated: N M A Annual Report
Related titles: Online - full text ed.: (from EBSCO Publishing, H.W. Wilson, Northern Light Technology, Inc., O C L C Online Computer Library Center, Inc., ProQuest Information & Learning); ♦ Regional ed(s).: e-doc (European Edition). ISSN 1470-4900.
Indexed: ABIn, Inspec, LibLit, RefZh.
—BLDSC (0773.138550), AskIEEE, CISTI, IE, Infotrieve. **CCC.**
Published by: Association for Information and Image Management, 1100 Wayne Ave, Ste 1100, Silver Spring, MD 20910. TEL 301-587-8202, FAX 301-587-2711, docuworld@aol.com, http://www.edocmagazine.com. Ed. Bryant Duhon. Adv. contact Amy Michalski. Circ: 30,000.
Subscr. to: Powerhouse Solutions Ltd., 19-21 High St, Sutton, Surrey SM1 1DJ, United Kingdom. TEL 44-181-6610449, FAX 44-181-6439846. **Co-sponsor:** International Information Management Congress.

020 USA
A S I S & T MONOGRAPH SERIES. Text in English. irreg., latest 1997. price varies. **Document type:** *Monographic series.*
Formerly (until 2000): A S I S Monograph Series
Indexed: SSCI.
Published by: (American Society for Information Science & Technology), Information Today, Inc., 143 Old Marlton Pike, Medford, NJ 08055-8750. TEL 609-654-6266, FAX 609-654-4309, custserv@infotoday.com, http://www.infotoday.com.

A S O R BULLETIN. see *BUSINESS AND ECONOMICS—Management*

003.54 DEU ISSN 0001-5903
QA76 CODEN: AINFA2
➤ **ACTA INFORMATICA.** Text in English. 1971. 9/yr., latest vol.40. EUR 768 combined subscription to institutions print & online eds. (effective 2005). adv. illus. back issues avail.; reprint service avail. from ISI,PSC. **Document type:** *Journal, Academic/Scholarly.* **Description:** Provides international dissemination of contributions on the art, discipline and science of informatics. Covers the design, description, presentation and analysis of programs, information structures, computing systems and interaction between components.
Related titles: Microform ed.: (from PQC); Online - full text ed.: ISSN 1432-0525 (from EBSCO Publishing, ProQuest Information & Learning, Springer LINK, Swets Information Services).
Indexed: ABIn, ASCA, CCMJ, CIS, CMCI, CompAb, CompC, CompLI, CompR, CurCont, EngInd, IAOP, ISR, Inspec, MathR, MathSciNet, RASB, RefZh, SCI, ZentMath.
—BLDSC (0627.850000), AskIEEE, CASDDS, Ei, IDS, IE, Infotrieve, ingenta, Linda Hall. **CCC.**
Published by: Springer-Verlag (Subsidiary of: Springer Science+Business Media), Tiergartenstr 17, Heidelberg, 69121, Germany. TEL 49-6221-3450, FAX 49-6221-345229, http://link.springer.de/link/service/journals/00236/index.htm. Ed. Ernst-Ruediger Olderog. Adv. contact Stephan Kroeck TEL 49-30-827875739. **Subscr. in the Americas to:** Springer-Verlag New York, Inc., Journal Fulfillment, PO Box 2485, Secaucus, NJ 07096-2485. TEL 201-348-4033, FAX 201-348-4505, journals@springer-ny.com, http://www.springer-ny.com; **Subscr. to:** Springer GmbH Auslieferungsgesellschaft, Haberstr 7, Heidelberg 69126, Germany. FAX 49-6221-345-4229, subscriptions@springer.de.

➤ **ADVANCES IN ACCOUNTING INFORMATION SYSTEMS.** see *BUSINESS AND ECONOMICS—Accounting*

003 DEU ISSN 0938-5495
ADVANCES IN KNOWLEDGE ORGANIZATION. Text in German. 1990. irreg., latest vol.9, 2004. price varies. **Document type:** *Monographic series, Academic/Scholarly.*
—BLDSC (0709.254500), IE, ingenta. **CCC.**
Published by: (International Society for Knowledge Organization), Ergon Verlag, Grombuehlstr 7, Wuerzburg, 97080, Germany. TEL 49-931-280084, FAX 49-931-282872, service@ergon-verlag.de, http://www.ergon-verlag.de/index.html?information-_library-sciences_advances_in_knowledge_organization.htm.

003.54 USA
HD30.3
ADVANCES IN MANAGERIAL COGNITION AND ORGANIZATIONAL INFORMATION. Text in English. 1984. irreg., latest vol.6, 1999. price varies. back issues avail. **Document type:** *Monographic series, Academic/Scholarly.*
Former titles: Advances in Managerial Cognition and Organizational Information Processing (1080-7772); (until 1992): Advances in Information Processing in Organizations (0747-9778)
—BLDSC (0709.339300). **CCC.**
Published by: J A I Press Inc. (Subsidiary of: Elsevier Science & Technology), 360 Park Ave S, New York, NY 10010-1710. TEL 212-989-5800, FAX 212-633-3990, usinfo-f@elsevier.com, http://www.elsevier.com/wps/find/bookseriesdescription.cws_home/BS_AMCO/description. Eds. Dr. James R Meindl, Joseph F Porac.

003 POL ISSN 1508-2806
QA75.5
➤ **AKADEMIA GORNICZO-HUTNICZA IM. STANISLAWA STASZICA. ROCZNIK. COMPUTER SCIENCE.** Key Title: Computer Science. Variant title: Informatyka. Text and summaries in English, Polish. 1997. a., latest vol.3, 2001. EUR 10 per issue foreign (effective 2005). abstr.; bibl. 120 p./no. 1 cols./p.; back issues avail. **Document type:** *Journal, Academic/Scholarly.* **Description:** Covers theoretical aspects of computer science, pattern recognition and processing, evolutionary algorithms and neural networks, database systems, knowledge engineering and automated reasoning, computer networks and distributed systems, algorithms for large scale computaitions and their implementation, multimedia systems and computer graphics.
Indexed: RefZh.

C

▼ new title ➤ refereed ✶ unverified ♦ full entry avail.

Published by: (Akademia Gorniczo-Hutnicza im. Stanislawa Staszica/University of Mining and Metallurgy), Wydawnictwo A G H, al Mickiewicza 30, Krakow, 30059, Poland. TEL 48-12-6173228, FAX 48-12-6364038, wydagh@uci.agh.edu.pl, http://www.wydawnictwoagh.pl. Ed. A J Wichur. Circ: 200 (paid). **Dist. by:** Ars Polona, Krakowskie Przedmiescie 7, Warsaw, Poland. TEL 48-22-9263914, FAX 48-22-9265334, arspolona@arspolona.com.pl, http://www.arspolona.com.pl.

➤ **AMERICAN SOCIETY FOR INFORMATION SCIENCE AND TECHNOLOGY. JOURNAL.** see *LIBRARY AND INFORMATION SCIENCES*

020 USA
AMERICAN SOCIETY OF INFORMATION SCIENCE AND TECHNOLOGY. BULLETIN. Text in English. 1995. bi-m. back issues avail.
Media: Online - full text.
Published by: American Society of Information Science and Technology, 1320 Fenwick Ln, Ste. 510, Silver Spring, MD 20910. TEL 301-495-0900, FAX 301-495-0810, asis@asis.org, http://www.asis.org/Bulletin/index.html. Ed. Richard B Hill.

ANNALS OF LIBRARY AND INFORMATION STUDIES. see *LIBRARY AND INFORMATION SCIENCES*

ARCHIWUM INFORMATYKI TEORETYCZNEJ I STOSOWANEJ/ARCHIVES OF THEORETICAL AND APPLIED INFORMATICS. see *COMPUTERS*

003.54 USA ISSN 1529-3181
T58.5
ASSOCIATION FOR INFORMATION SYSTEMS. COMMUNICATIONS. Text in English. irreg. USD 50 to non-members; free to members (effective 2005). **Document type:** *Corporate.*
Media: Online - full content.
Indexed: ABIn, CompR.
Published by: Association for Information Systems, PO Box 2712, Atlanta, GA 30301-2712. TEL 404-651-0348, FAX 404-651-4938, Membership@aisnet.org, http://cais.isworld.org/, http://www.aisnet.org. Ed. Paul Gray.

003.54 USA ISSN 1536-9323
T58.5
ASSOCIATION OF INFORMATION SYSTEMS. JOURNAL. Text in English. irreg. USD 40 combined subscription to non-members (effective 2005). **Document type:** *Journal, Academic/Scholarly.*
Media: Online - full content.
Indexed: ABIn, CompR.
Published by: Association for Information Systems, PO Box 2712, Atlanta, GA 30301-2712. TEL 404-651-0348, FAX 404-651-4938, Membership@aisnet.org, http://jais.aisnet.org/, http://www.aisnet.org. Ed. Sirkka L Jarvenpaa TEL 512-471-1751.

020 USA
HD30.2
AUERBACH INFORMATION MANAGEMENT SERIES. Text in English. 1972. 7 base vols. plus bi-m. updates. looseleaf. USD 2,995 (effective 2001). back issues avail. **Document type:** *Journal, Trade.* **Description:** Addresses all critical management and technical issues involved in starting up and running a successful information center.
Incorporates (in 1989): Managing the Information System Resource; End-User Computing Management; Which was formerly: Managing the Information Center Resource
Related titles: CD-ROM ed.: 1996. USD 2,995 (effective 2001).
Published by: Auerbach Publications (Subsidiary of: C R C Press, LLC), 2000 Corporate Blvd., NW, Boca Raton, FL 33431. TEL 212-286-1010, FAX 212-297-9176, orders@crcpress.com, http://www.auerbach-publications.com, http://www.auerbach-publications.com/home.asp. Ed., Pub. Richard O'Hanley TEL 212-845-4017. R&P Jamie Sigal TEL 561-994-0555.

AUSTRALIA. BUREAU OF STATISTICS. BUSINESS USE OF INFORMATION TECHNOLOGY. see *COMPUTERS—Abstracting, Bibliographies, Statistics*

AUSTRALIA. BUREAU OF STATISTICS. BUSINESS USE OF INFORMATION TECHNOLOGY, PRELIMINARY. see *COMPUTERS—Abstracting, Bibliographies, Statistics*

AUSTRALIA. BUREAU OF STATISTICS. GOVERNMENT USE OF INFORMATION TECHNOLOGY, AUSTRALIA. see *COMPUTERS—Abstracting, Bibliographies, Statistics*

AUSTRALIA. BUREAU OF STATISTICS. HOUSEHOLD USE OF INFORMATION TECHNOLOGY, AUSTRALIA. see *COMPUTERS—Abstracting, Bibliographies, Statistics*

AUSTRALIA. BUREAU OF STATISTICS. INFORMATION TECHNOLOGY, AUSTRALIA. see *COMPUTERS—Abstracting, Bibliographies, Statistics*

AUSTRALIA. BUREAU OF STATISTICS. INFORMATION TECHNOLOGY, AUSTRALIA, PRELIMINARY. see *COMPUTERS—Abstracting, Bibliographies, Statistics*

AUSTRALIA. BUREAU OF STATISTICS. OCCASIONAL PAPER: INNOVATION, PRODUCTIVITY AND PROFITABILITY OF AUSTRALIAN MANUFACTURERS. see *COMPUTERS—Abstracting, Bibliographies, Statistics*

AUSTRALIA. BUREAU OF STATISTICS. USE OF INFORMATION TECHNOLOGY ON FARMS, AUSTRALIA. see *COMPUTERS—Abstracting, Bibliographies, Statistics*

AUSTRALIA. BUREAU OF STATISTICS. USE OF INFORMATION TECHNOLOGY ON FARMS, AUSTRALIA, PRELIMINARY. see *COMPUTERS—Abstracting, Bibliographies, Statistics*

003 DEU
BIBLIOGRAPHIE INFORMATIK, DIDAKTIK UND ELEMENTARE COMPUTERANWENDUNGEN FUER SCHULE, HOCHSCHULE UND WEITERBILDUNG. Text in English, German. 1987. bi-m. EUR 35 (effective 2003). abstr. 60 p./no. 2 cols./p.; back issues avail. **Document type:** *Journal, Abstract/Index.*
Formerly: Bibliographie Informatik fuer Schule, Hochschule und Weiterbildung (0935-8757)
Published by: Fachinformationszentrum Karlsruhe, Gesellschaft fuer wissenschaftlich-technische Information mbH (Subsidiary of: STN Service Center Europe), Eggenstein Leopoldshafen, 76344, Germany. TEL 49-7247-808240, FAX 49-7247-808461, helpdesk@fiz-karlsruhe.de, http://www.fiz-karlsruhe.de. Adv. contact Gerhard Koenig.

003.54 GBR
BRITISH COMPUTER SOCIETY. MONOGRAPHS IN INFORMATICS. Text in English. irreg., latest 1992. price varies. **Document type:** *Monographic series.*
Indexed: Inspec.
Published by: (British Computer Society), Cambridge University Press, The Edinburgh Bldg, Shaftesbury Rd, Cambridge, CB2 2RU, United Kingdom. TEL 44-1223-312393, FAX 44-1223-315052, information@cambridge.org, http://publishing.cambridge.org/series/bcsm.

020 330 BRA ISSN 1415-2061
CENTRO DE CIENCIAS DA ECONOMIA E INFORMATICA. REVISTA. Text in Portuguese. 1997. irreg.
Published by: Universidade da Regiao da Campanha, Centro de Ciencias da Economia e Informatica, Campus Central - Av Tupy Silveira 2099, Bage, RS 96400-110, Brazil. TEL 55-53-2428244, ccei@ccei.urcamp.tche.br, http://www.urcamp.tche.br/site/ccei/ccei.html.

THE CHARLESTON ADVISOR; critical reviews of Web products for information professionals. see *LIBRARY AND INFORMATION SCIENCES—Computer Applications*

CHEM-BIO INFORMATICS JOURNAL. see *CHEMISTRY—Computer Applications*

003.54 020 KOR ISSN 1015-9908
CHONGBO KWAHAK HOECHI/KOREA INFORMATION SCIENCE SOCIETY REVIEW. Text in English, Korean. 1983. m. **Description:** Covers technological trends and announcements of the society.
Indexed: Inspec.
Published by: Korea Information Science Society/Han'guk Chongbo Kwahakhoe, No. 401 Murijae Bldg, 984-1 Bangbae-3dong Secho-du, Seoul, 137-063 , Korea, S. TEL 82-2-5889246, FAX 82-2-5211352, kiss@kiss.or.kr, http://www.kiss.or.kr/.

003.54 IRL
THE CLICKONOMIST. Text in English. 1998. m. free. adv. **Document type:** *Newsletter.* **Description:** Examines the issues in developing an online presence.
Media: Online - full text. **Related titles:** E-mail ed.
Published by: Nua Ltd., Merrion House, Merrion Road, Dublin, 4, Ireland. TEL 353-1-676-8996, FAX 353-1-283-9988, eamonn@nua.ie, http://www.nua.ie/nuathinking. Ed., R&P Eamonn O'Shea. Adv. contact Oriana LoLacona.

003.54 USA ISSN 1543-5970
COMMUNICATIONS OF THE I I M A. (International Information Management Association) Text in English. 2002. q.
Published by: International Information Management Association, Department of Information and Decision Sciences, California State University, San Bernardino, CA 92407. TEL 909-880-5786, FAX 909-880-7176, http://www.iima.org. Ed. Rob Harris.

COMPUTER ISSUES. see *COMPUTERS*

003.54 PHL ISSN 0117-3308
COMPUTERWORLD PHILIPPINES; journal of information systems management. Text in English. 1991. fortn. PHP 2,600 (effective 2002). adv. back issues avail. **Document type:** *Newspaper, Trade.* **Description:** Covers local and international news and analysis of interest to Philippine information technology professionals and observers.
Related titles: Online - full text ed.: (from Florida Center for Library Automation, Gale Group, LexisNexis, ProQuest Information & Learning).
Indexed: ABIn.
Published by: W S Computer Publishing Corp., 5/F SEDCCO I Bldg., Rada St., Legaspi Village, Makati City, 1200, Philippines. TEL 632-812-8401, FAX 632-894-2487, http://www.itnetcentral.com/computerworld/. Ed. Chin Wah Wong. Adv. contact Delia C Gutierree. B&W page USD 2,820, color page USD 4,512; trim 280 x 430. Circ: 15,500.

CONCURRENT ENGINEERING: RESEARCH AND APPLICATIONS. see *COMPUTERS—Computer Engineering*

CORPORATE LIBRARY BENCHMARKS. see *LIBRARY AND INFORMATION SCIENCES*

CREATING THE DIGITAL LIBRARY. see *LIBRARY AND INFORMATION SCIENCES*

CYBERNETICS AND INFORMATION TECHNOLOGIES. see *COMPUTERS—Cybernetics*

D I M A C S SERIES IN DISCRETE MATHEMATICS AND THEORETICAL COMPUTER SCIENCE. (Discrete Mathematics and Theoretical Computer Science) see *MATHEMATICS*

025.04 DNK ISSN 0107-7481
DISPLAY; oplysning om elektronisk informationssoegning. Text in Danish. 1982. 10/yr. DKK 350 (effective 2001). adv. bk.rev.; Website rev. abstr.; illus. 16 p./no.; back issues avail.; reprints avail. **Document type:** *Newsletter.*
Related titles: Online - full text ed.
Published by: I N F O S C A N, Statens Information, Kigkurren 10, Copenhagen, 2300, Denmark. TEL 45-33-37-91-11, FAX 45-33-37-91-17, infoscan@si.dk, http://www.infoscan.dk/display. Ed. Karen Bonnis. Adv. contact Peter Raben. Circ: 600.

003 ESP ISSN 0210-4210
Z1007
DOCUMENTACION DE LAS CIENCIAS DE LA INFORMACION. Text in Spanish. 1976. a., latest vol.24, 2001. EUR 18 in the European Union; EUR 25 elsewhere (effective 2004). back issues avail. **Document type:** *Journal, Academic/Scholarly.* **Description:** Publishes theoretical work on documentation and information sciences. Includes also journalism, mass media and up-to-date technology as a tool.
Related titles: CD-ROM ed.: EUR 50 to individuals; EUR 66 to institutions (effective 2003).
Indexed: RASB.
—CINDOC.
Published by: (Universidad Complutense de Madrid, Facultad de Ciencias de la Informacion), Universidad Complutense de Madrid, Servicio de Publicaciones, C Isaac Peral s/n, Ciudad Universitaria, Madrid, 28040, Spain. TEL 34-91-3946934, FAX 34-91-3946978, carquero@ccinf.ucm.es, servicio@publicaciones.ucm.es, http://www.ucm.es/publicaciones. Eds. Felix Sagredo, Jose Lopez Yepes.

003.54 GBR ISSN 1470-4900
E-DOC (EUROPEAN EDITION). Text in English. 2000. bi-m.
Related titles: ♦ Regional ed(s).: A I I M E-doc Magazine. ISSN 1544-3647.
Indexed: Inspec.
Published by: Highbury House Communications PLC, 13 The Publishing House, 1-3 Highbury Station Rd, London, N1 1SE, United Kingdom. TEL 44-20-7226-2222, FAX 44-20-7704-3151.

020 USA ISSN 1528-8226
HF5548.32
➤ **E-SERVICE JOURNAL.** Text in English. 2001. 3/yr. USD 45 domestic to individuals; USD 57.50 foreign to individuals; USD 125 domestic to institutions .; USD 137.50 foreign to institutions (effective 2006). abstr.; charts; illus. 100 p./no.; back issues avail.; reprints avail. **Document type:** *Journal, Academic/Scholarly.* **Description:** Covers the research on the design, delivery, and impact of electronic services.
Related titles: Online - full content ed.: ISSN 1528-8234. USD 40.50 (effective 2003); Online - full text ed.: (from EBSCO Publishing, Gale Group, H.W. Wilson, IngentaConnect, O C L C Online Computer Library Center, Inc., Project MUSE, ProQuest Information & Learning, Swets Information Services).
Indexed: ABIn.
—BLDSC (3638.645000), IE, Infotrieve. **CCC.**
Published by: Indiana University Press, 601 N Morton St, Bloomington, IN 47404. TEL 812-855-9449, 800-842-6796, journals@indiana.edu, http://iupjournals.org/eservice/, http://www.indiana.edu/~iupress/journals/. Eds. Carol Saunders, Laku Chidambaram. Circ: 200 (paid).

➤ **E T R I JOURNAL.** see *ELECTRONICS*

▼ ➤ **ECOLOGICAL INFORMATICS**; an international journal on ecoinformatics and computational ecology. see *ENVIRONMENTAL STUDIES*

➤ **EDUCATION AND INFORMATION TECHNOLOGIES.** see *EDUCATION—Teaching Methods And Curriculum*

➤ **ELECTRONIC COMMERCE & LAW REPORT.** see *LAW—Civil Law*

003.54 330.9 NLD ISSN 1567-4223
HF5548.32
ELECTRONIC COMMERCE RESEARCH AND APPLICATIONS. Text in English. 2002. 4/yr. EUR 442 in Europe to institutions; JPY 46,100 in Japan to institutions; USD 384 elsewhere to institutions (effective 2006). **Description:** Aims to create and disseminate enduring knowledge in the fast changing e-commerce environment.
Related titles: Online - full text ed.: (from EBSCO Publishing, Gale Group, IngentaConnect, ScienceDirect).
Indexed: Inspec.
—BLDSC (3700.282500), IE, ingenta. **CCC.**
Published by: Elsevier BV (Subsidiary of: Elsevier Science & Technology), Radarweg 29, Amsterdam, 1043 NX, Netherlands. TEL 31-20-4853911, FAX 31-20-4852457, nlinfo-f@elsevier.nl, http://www.elsevier.com/locate/elerap, http://www.elsevier.nl. Ed. Dr. Jae Kyu Lee.

003.54 020 SWE ISSN 1400-6529
TH215
➤ **ELECTRONIC JOURNAL OF INFORMATION TECHNOLOGY IN CONSTRUCTION.** Key Title: Electronic Journal of Information Technologies in Construction. Text in English. 1995. every 2 yrs. (in 2 vols.). free (effective 2005). 150 p./no.; **Document type:** *Journal, Academic/Scholarly.* **Description:** Covers the use of IT in construction.
Media: Online - full content. **Related titles:** Print ed.: ISSN 1403-6835. 1998. USD 60 per issue for 2 vols. (effective 2003); limited copies of the print ed.
Indexed: Inspec.
—CISTI.
Published by: Kungliga Tekniska Hoegskolan/Royal Institute of Technology, Valhallavagen 79, Stockholm, 10044, Sweden. TEL 46-8-7906000, FAX 46-8-7906500, http://www.itcon.org, http://www.kth.se. Ed. Bo-Christer Bjork.

020 GBR ISSN 0960-085X
T58.5 CODEN: EISYEU
➤ **EUROPEAN JOURNAL OF INFORMATION SYSTEMS.** Text in English. 1991. 5/yr. GBP 161 combined subscription in Europe to individuals; USD 225 combined subscription elsewhere to individuals; GBP 401 combined subscription in Europe to institutions; USD 596 combined subscription elsewhere to institutions (effective 2005); Combined subscr. includes print & online. bk.rev. abstr.; illus. index. back issues avail. **Document type:** *Journal, Academic/Scholarly.* **Description:** Provides information on theory and practice of information systems for professionals in academia, industry, commerce and government.
Incorporates (1969-1991): Journal of Applied Systems Analysis (0308-9541); Which was formerly (until 1976): Journal of Systems Engineering (0022-4820)
Related titles: Online - full text ed.: ISSN 1476-9344. GBP 289 in Europe; USD 405 elsewhere (effective 2004) (from EBSCO Publishing, Gale Group, IngentaConnect, O C L C Online Computer Library Center, Inc., ProQuest Information & Learning, Swets Information Services).
Indexed: ABIn, ASCA, CMCI, CPM, CompAb, CompLI, CompR, CurCont, ERA, ETA, Emerald, IAOP, IBR, IBSS, IBZ, InfoSAb, Inspec, LISA, MEA, RASB, RHEA, SEA, SENA, SOMA, ST&MA, TEA.
—BLDSC (3829.730400), AskIEEE, CISTI, IDS, IE, Infotrieve, ingenta, Linda Hall. **CCC.**
Published by: (Operational Research Society), Palgrave Macmillan Ltd. (Subsidiary of: Macmillan Publishers Ltd.), Houndmills, Basingstoke, Hants RG21 6XS, United Kingdom. TEL 44-1256-329242, FAX 44-1256-810526, EJIS@brunel.ac.uk, http://www.palgrave-journals.com/ejis/index.html, http://www.palgrave.com. Eds. Bob O'Keefe, Ray Paul, Richard Baskerville. Pub. Rachel Young TEL 44-1256-329242. R&P Trace Noel. Adv. contact Robert Sloan TEL 44-20-88827199.

020 USA
EXECUTIVE BRIEF. Text in English. 1987 (vol.3). q. membership.
Formerly (until 1990): S I M Spectrum
Related titles: Online - full text ed.
Published by: Society for Information Management, 401 N Michigan Ave, Chicago, IL 60611-4267. TEL 312-644-6610, FAX 312-245-1083, http://www.simnet.org. Ed. Lisa Suarez. Circ: 2,700.

003 DEU ISSN 0172-2204
F I Z - K A BERICHTE. Text in German. 1979. irreg., latest vol.23, 2003. price varies. **Document type:** *Monographic series, Trade.*
Published by: Fachinformationszentrum Karlsruhe, Gesellschaft fuer wissenschaftlich-technische Information mbH (Subsidiary of: STN Service Center Europe), Eggenstein Leopoldshafen, 76344, Germany. TEL 49-228-9237917, FAX 49-228-9237929, helpdesk@fiz-karlsruhe.de, http://www.fiz-karlsruhe.de.

FACTA UNIVERSITATIS. SERIES MATHEMATICS AND INFORMATICS. see *MATHEMATICS*

▼ **FOUNDATIONS AND TRENDS IN COMMUNICATIONS AND INFORMATION THEORY.** see *COMMUNICATIONS—Computer Applications*

003.54 USA ISSN 1571-9545
▼ ➤ **FOUNDATIONS AND TRENDS IN TECHNOLOGY, INFORMATION AND OPERATIONS MANAGEMENT.** Text in English. 2004. 4/yr. USD 300 domestic; EUR 300 foreign; USD 340 combined subscription domestic print & online eds.; EUR 340 combined subscription foreign print & online eds. (effective 2006). **Document type:** *Journal, Academic/Scholarly.* **Description:** Provides tutorial coverage of subjects, research retrospectives as well as survey papers that offer state-of-the-art reviews in technology and information theory.
Related titles: Online - full text ed.: ISSN 1571-9553. USD 300 domestic; EUR 300 foreign (effective 2005).
Published by: Now Publishers Inc., PO Box 1024, Hanover, MA 02339. TEL 781-871-0245, FAX 781-871-6172, uday.karmarkar@anderson.ucla.edu, sales@nowpublishers.com, http://www.nowpublishers.com/pages/7/index.htm. Ed. Uday Karmarkar. Pub., R&P Zac Rolnik.

➤ **FUNDAMENTA INFORMATICAE.** see *MATHEMATICS—Computer Applications*

003.54 USA
GARTNER GROUP. RESEARCH REVIEW. Text in English. m. USD 500. **Document type:** *Trade.* **Description:** Synopsis of key research analysis conducted by GartnerGroup analysts on current information technology issues.
Indexed: AgeL.
Published by: Gartner Inc., 56 Top Gallant Rd, Stamford, CT 06904-2212. TEL 203-316-1111, 800-544-7337, FAX 203-316-6300, jwhitney@info-edge.com, http://www.gartner3.gartnerweb.com, http://www.info-edge.com.

020 CHL
GERENCIA & SISTEMAS; la revista de informacion para la gerencia. Text in Spanish. m. free. adv.
Published by: Editora Microbyte Ltda., Candell 1879, Nunoa, Santiago, Chile. TEL 56-2-3417507, FAX 56-2-3417504, garanci@gerencia.cl, http://www.gerencia.cl/. adv.: color page CLP 600,000; 20.5 x 27.5. Circ: 7,000.

GLOBAL TECHNOLOGY BUSINESS. see *COMPUTERS—Data Communications And Data Transmission Systems*

HEALTH INFORMATICS CONFERENCE. see *MEDICAL SCIENCES—Computer Applications*

003 NLD ISSN 0923-8433
➤ **HUMAN FACTORS IN INFORMATION TECHNOLOGY.** Text in English. 1989. irreg., latest vol.13, 1999. price varies. back issues avail. **Document type:** *Monographic series, Academic/Scholarly.* **Description:** Surveys a wide range of topics dealing with all aspects of human factors in the application of information technology.
Indexed: ZentMath, e-psyche.
—BLDSC (4336.081300), IE, ingenta.
Published by: Elsevier BV, North-Holland (Subsidiary of: Elsevier Science & Technology), Sara Burgerhartstraat 25, Amsterdam, 1055 KV, Netherlands. TEL 31-20-485-3911, FAX 31-20-485-2457, nlinfo-f@elsevier.nl, http://www.elsevier.nl. Eds. Hans Bullinger, Peter Polson. **Subscr. to:** Elsevier BV, PO Box 211, Amsterdam 1000 AE, Netherlands. TEL 31-20-485-3757, FAX 31-20-485-3432, http://www.elsevier.nl.

004 SWE ISSN 1402-151X
➤ **HUMAN I T (ONLINE EDITION)**; tidskrift foer studier av IT ur ett humanvetenskapligt perspektiv / journal of information technology studies as a human science. Text in English, Swedish. 1997. 3/yr. free (effective 2005). back issues avail. **Document type:** *Journal, Academic/Scholarly.*
Media: Online - full content.
Published by: Hoegskolan i Boraas, Centrum foer Studier av IT ur ett Humanvetenskapligt Perspektiv/University College of Boraas, Centre for Information Technology Studies as a Human Science, Boraas, 50190, Sweden. TEL 46-33-164320, FAX 46-33-164045, humanIT@hb.se, http://www.hb.se/bhs/ith. Eds. Helena Francke, Mats Dahlstroem TEL 46-33-164421.

▼ ➤ **HUMAN TECHNOLOGY**; an interdisciplinary journal on humans in I C T environments. see *COMMUNICATIONS*

621.381 USA
I B M DIRECTIONS. (International Business Machines) Text in English. 1987. q.
Published by: I B M Corp., 1133 Westchester Ave, White Plains, NY 10604. TEL 914-945-3837.

621.381 001.6 USA ISSN 0018-8646
TK7800 CODEN: IBMJAE
➤ **I B M JOURNAL OF RESEARCH AND DEVELOPMENT.** Text in English. 1957. bi-m. USD 260 in North America; USD 275 elsewhere; USD 65 newsstand/cover in North America; USD 70 newsstand/cover elsewhere (effective 2004). abstr.; bibl. Index. back issues avail.; reprint service avail. from PQC. **Document type:** *Journal, Academic/Scholarly.*
Related titles: Microform ed.: (from PQC); Online - full text ed.: free (effective 2005) (from bigchalk, EBSCO Publishing, H.W. Wilson, O C L C Online Computer Library Center, Inc., ProQuest Information & Learning).
Indexed: ABIPC, ABIn, AIA, AS&TI, ASCA, ApMecR, BMT, BrCerAb, C&ISA, CADCAM, CCI, CIS, CMCI, CerAb, ChemAb, CompAb, CompC, CompD, CompLI, CompR, CorrAb, CurCont, CybAb, DPD, E&CAJ, EIA, EMA, EngInd, ErgAb, ExcerpMed, GALA, IAA, ISMEC, ISR, InfoSAb, Inspec, M&TEA, MBF, METADEX, MSCI, MathR, ORMS, PROMT, PhysBer, QC&AS, RASB, RefZh, RoboAb, S&VD, SCI, SolStAb, TelAb, WAA, ZentMath.
—BLDSC (4360.070000), AskIEEE, CASDDS, CISTI, Ei, IDS, IE, Infotrieve, ingenta, Linda Hall. **CCC.**
Published by: I B M Corp., 1133 Westchester Ave, White Plains, NY 10604. TEL 914-945-3837, FAX 914-945-2018, ritsko@watson.ibm.com, http://www.research.ibm.com/journal/rd/. Ed. John J Ritsko. Circ: 17,000. **Subscr. to:** PO Box 500, Missouri City, TX 77459-9903 . TEL 800-426-5687.

003 USA ISSN 0018-8670
TA168 CODEN: IBMSA7
➤ **I B M SYSTEMS JOURNAL.** Text in English. 1962. q. USD 115 in North America; USD 130 elsewhere (effective 2005). bk.rev. abstr.; bibl.; charts; illus. cum.index. 200 p./no. 2 cols./p.; back issues avail.; reprints avail. **Document type:** *Journal, Academic/Scholarly.* **Description:** Provides a bridge between computer science and the practical application of computing through referred technical papers in software, software systems and architecture.
Related titles: Microform ed.: (from PQC); Online - full text ed.: free (effective 2005) (from EBSCO Publishing, Florida Center for Library Automation, Gale Group, H.W. Wilson, O C L C Online Computer Library Center, Inc., ProQuest Information & Learning).
Indexed: ABIn, AIA, AS&TI, ASCA, AcoustA, B&BAb, BMT, BrTechI, C&CSA, C&ISA, CADCAM, CIS, CMCI, ChemAb, CompAb, CompC, CompD, CompLI, CompR, CurCont, CybAb, DPD, E&CAJ, EngInd, ErgAb, ExcerpMed, ISR, InfoSAb, Inspec, MathR, ORMS, PCR2, QC&AS, RefZh, SCI, SSCI, SolStAb, TelAb, ZentMath.
—BLDSC (4360.090000), AskIEEE, CASDDS, CISTI, Ei, IDS, IE, Infotrieve, ingenta, Linda Hall. **CCC.**
Published by: I B M Corp., 1101 Kitchawan Rd, Yorktown Heights, NY 10598-0218. TEL 914-945-3831, FAX 914-945-2018, http://www.research.ibm.com/journal/sj/. Ed., R&P John J Ritsko. Circ: 30,000 (paid).

➤ **I E E E INFORMATION TECHNOLOGY CONFERENCE. PROCEEDINGS.** see *COMPUTERS—Computer Systems*

003.54 USA
I E E E INFORMATION THEORY AND COMMUNICATIONS WORKSHOP. Text in English. a. USD 194 per vol.; USD 97 per vol. to members (effective 2004). **Document type:** *Proceedings, Trade.*
Published by: Institute of Electrical and Electronics Engineers, Inc., 3 Park Ave, 17th Fl, New York, NY 10016-5997. TEL 212-419-7900, 800-678-4333, FAX 212-752-4929, customer.service@ieee.org, http://www.ieee.org.

003.54 USA
I E E E INTERNATIONAL INFORMATION THEORY WORKSHOP. Text in English. a. USD 184 per vol.; USD 92 per vol. to members (effective 2004). **Document type:** *Proceedings, Trade.*
Published by: Institute of Electrical and Electronics Engineers, Inc., 3 Park Ave, 17th Fl, New York, NY 10016-5997. TEL 212-419-7900, 800-678-4333, FAX 212-752-4929, customer.service@ieee.org, http://www.ieee.org.

003.54 USA ISSN 0271-4655
Q350
I E E E INTERNATIONAL SYMPOSIUM ON INFORMATION THEORY. Text in English. 1967. a. USD 208; USD 104 to members (effective 2004). **Document type:** *Proceedings, Trade.* **Description:** Recent advances in areas such as coding, Shannon theory, modulation and stochastic processes.
Related titles: CD-ROM ed.; Microfiche ed.
Indexed: EngInd.
—BLDSC (4362.972000), IE, ingenta. **CCC.**
Published by: Institute of Electrical and Electronics Engineers, Inc., 3 Park Ave, 17th Fl, New York, NY 10016-5997. TEL 212-419-7900, 800-678-4333, FAX 212-752-4929, customer.service@ieee.org, http://www.ieee.org. **Co-sponsor:** Information Theory Group.

003.54 USA ISSN 0018-9448
Q350 CODEN: IETTAW
➤ **I E E E TRANSACTIONS ON INFORMATION THEORY.** Text in English. 1953. m. USD 775 (effective 2006). bk.rev. abstr.; illus. index. **Document type:** *Journal, Academic/Scholarly.* **Description:** Theoretical and experimental aspects of transmission, processing and utilization.
Former titles (until 1962): I R E Transactions on Information Theory (0096-1000); (until 1955): I R E Professional Group on Information Theory Transactions
Related titles: CD-ROM ed.; Microfiche ed.; Online - full text ed.: (from EBSCO Publishing, Swets Information Services).
Indexed: AS&TI, ASCA, AcoustA, ApMecR, BMT, C&CSA, CADCAM, CCMJ, CIS, CMCI, ChemAb, CompAb, CompC, CompD, CompLI, CurCont, CybAb, EngInd, ErgAb, ExcerpMed, IAA, ISR, InfoSAb, Inspec, MathR, MathSciNet, ORMS, QC&AS, RASB, RefZh, SCI, TelAb, ZentMath.
—BLDSC (4363.197500), AskIEEE, CISTI, Ei, IDS, IE, Infotrieve, ingenta, Linda Hall. **CCC.**

C

▼ *new title* ➤ *refereed* ✶ *unverified* ♦ *full entry avail.*

Published by: Institute of Electrical and Electronics Engineers, Inc., 445 Hoes Ln, Piscataway, NJ 08854-1331. TEL 732-981-0060, 800-701-4333, FAX 732-981-1721, poor@princeton.edu, subscription-service@ieee.org, http://ieeexplore.ieee.org/xpl/RecentIssue.jsp?puNumber=18, http://www.ieee.org. Ed. H Vincent Poor. **Subscr. to:** Maruzen Co., Ltd., 3-10 Nihonbashi 2-chome, Chuo-ku, Tokyo 103-0027, Japan. FAX 81-3-3275-0657; Universal Subscription Agency, Pvt. Ltd., 877, Udyog Vihar, V, Gurgoan 122001, India. TEL 91-124-347261, FAX 91-124-342496. **Co-sponsor:** Information Theory Group.

020 025.26 USA ISSN 1538-1897
TA1637
I E E E WORKSHOP CONTENT - BASED ACCESS OF IMAGE AND VIDEO LIBRARIES. Text in English. a. USD 100. **Document type:** *Proceedings, Trade.*
Published by: Institute of Electrical and Electronics Engineers, Inc., 3 Park Ave, 17th Fl, New York, NY 10016-5997. TEL 800-678-4333, customer.service@ieee.org, http://www.ieee.org.

621.3822 JPN ISSN 1349-2543
▼ ➤ **I E I C E ELECTRONICS EXPRESS.** Variant title: E L E X. Institute of Electronics Information and Communication Engineers Electronics Express. Text in English. 2004. s-m. free (effective 2004). **Document type:** *Journal, Academic/Scholarly.* **Description:** Publishes original papers that embrace the entire field of modern electronics, including: electron devices; integrated circuits; photonic devices, circuits and systems; electromagnetic theory; microwave and millimeter-wave devices, circuits and systems; micro- or nano-electromechanical systems; new functional devices and materials; and all other science and engineering for electronics.
Media: Online - full content.
Indexed: Inspec.
Published by: Denshi Joho Tsushin Gakkai/Institute of Electronics Information and Communication Engineers, IEICE Publishing Office, Kikai-Shinko-Kaikan Bldg., Annex 3F, 5-22, Shibakoen 3 chome, Minato-ku, Tokyo, 105-0011, Japan. TEL 81-3-3433-6692, FAX 81-3-3433-6616, elex@ieice.org, shuppan@ieice.or.jp, http://www.elex.ieice.org/, http://www.ieice.or.jp/. Ed. Takeshi Kamiya.

003.54 GBR ISSN 0916-8532
QA75.5 CODEN: ITISEF
➤ **I E I C E TRANSACTIONS ON INFORMATION AND SYSTEMS.** Variant title: Institute of Electronics Information and Communication Engineers Transactions on Information and Systems. Text in English. 1976. m. GBP 207, USD 352, EUR 311 to institutions; GBP 119, USD 202, EUR 179 in developing nations to institutions; GBP 218, USD 371, EUR 327 combined subscription to institutions print & online eds. (effective 2006). back issues avail. **Document type:** *Journal, Academic/Scholarly.* **Description:** Covers topics such as: Automation, language and theory of computing, algorithm and computational complexity, computer hardware and design, computer systems, software theory, software systems, databases, computer networks, fault tolerant computing, information security, speech processing, imaging processing, computer graphics and pattern recognition, artificial intelligence and cognitive science, computer applications, bio-cybernetics and neurocomputing, medical electronics, and medical information.
Supersedes in part (in 1991): I E I C E Transactions on Communications Electronics Information and Systems (0917-1673); Former titles (until 1991): Transactions of the Institute of Electronics, Information and Communication Engineers (0913-574X); (until 1987): Transactions of the Institute of Electronics and Communication Engineers of Japan. Section E (0387-236X); (until 1976): Transactions of the Institute of Electronics and Communication Engineers of Japan. Abstracts (0418-6869); (until 1956): Journal of the Institute of Electrical Communication Engineers of Japan. Abstracts (0914-5273)
Related titles: Online - full text ed.: ISSN 1745-1361. GBP 196, USD 333, EUR 294 to institutions (effective 2006) (from HighWire Press); ♦ Japanese ed.: Denshi Joho Tsushin Gakkai Ronbunshi (D-I). ISSN 0915-1915; ♦ Japanese ed.: Denshi Joho Tsushin Gakkai Ronbunshi (D-II). ISSN 0915-1923.
Indexed: ASCA, B&BAb, C&ISA, CMCI, CurCont, CybAb, E&CAJ, EngInd, IAOP, INIS AtomInd, ISMEC, Inspec, JCT, SolStAb, TelAb.
—BLDSC (4363.240675), AskIEEE, CISTI, Ei, IDS, IE, Infotrieve, ingenta, Linda Hall. **CCC.**
Published by: (Denshi Joho Tsushin Gakkai/Institute of Electronics Information and Communication Engineers JPN), Oxford University Press, Great Clarendon St, Oxford, OX2 6DP, United Kingdom. TEL 44-1865-556767, FAX 44-1865-556646, jnl.orders@oup.co.uk, http://ietisy.oxfordjournals.org/, http://www.oxfordjournals.org/. R&P Fiona Bennett.

020 AUT ISSN 1024-8102
I F I P NEWSLETTER; the leading edge of information technology. Text in English. 1984. q. free membership. **Document type:** *Newsletter, Academic/Scholarly.*
Published by: International Federation for Information Processing, IFIP Secretariat, Hofstr 3, Laxenburg, 2361, Austria. TEL 43-2236-73616, FAX 43-2236-736169, ifip@ifip.or.at, http://www.ifip.org/newsletters/newsl.html.

I M I S JOURNAL. see *COMPUTERS—Data Base Management*

003 NLD ISSN 1387-0068
I T LOGISTIEK. (Informatie Technologie) Key Title: I T L. Text in Dutch. 1997. m. EUR 105.95 (effective 2005). adv. **Document type:** *Trade.*
Published by: Reed Business Information bv (Subsidiary of: Reed Business), Postbus 4, Doetinchem, 7000 BA, Netherlands. TEL 31-314-349911, FAX 31-314-343991, info@reedbusiness.nl, http://www.productonline.reedbusiness.nl/product.asp?catalog%5Fname=RBI&category%5Fname=&product%5Fid=653%28Octopus%29, http://www.reedbusiness.nl. Ed. H Beerens. Pub. Martine L Lofvers. Adv. contact Cor van Nek. B&W page EUR 2,306, color page EUR 3,759; trim 285 x 215. Circ: 8,500.

003.54 USA
I T MANAGER'S JOURNAL✶. (Information Technology) Text in English. d. back issues avail. **Document type:** *Trade.* **Description:** Includes survey questions with live results, and discussions of a broad range of information technology issues.
Media: Online - full text.
Published by: Adover News Network, Andover Advanced Tech, 50 Nagog Park No 2FL, Acton, MA 01720-3409. TEL 978-635-5300, FAX 978-635-5326, http://www.ITManagersJournal.com/. Ed. Stephen Heiser.

004 020 USA
▼ **I T SOLUTIONS GUIDE.** (Information Technology) Text in English. 2004 (May). q. USD 19.99 domestic; USD 29.99 in Canada & Mexico; USD 39.99 elsewhere; USD 5.99 newsstand/cover (effective 2005). **Document type:** *Magazine, Trade.*
Related titles: Online - full text ed.: USD 9.99 (effective 2005).
Published by: SYS-CON Media, Inc., 135 Chestnut Ridge Rd, Montvale, NJ 07645. TEL 201-802-3040, 888-303-5282, FAX 201-782-9600, info@sys-con.com, http://www.sys-con.com.

351.0285 GBR
I T TRENDS IN LOCAL GOVERNMENT. (Information Technology) Text in English. 1987. a. GBP 35 for government & academic organizations; GBP 250 for society members; GBP 300 commercial (effective 2000). 100 p./no.; **Document type:** *Academic/Scholarly.*
Related titles: CD-ROM ed.: Local Authority Application Software Index. 1999. GBP 75 for government & academic institutions; GBP 350 for society members; GBP 400 commercial (effective 2000); for CD-ROM plus report.
—BLDSC (4587.695000).
Published by: Society of Information Technology Management, PO Box 121, Northampton, Northants NN4 6TG, United Kingdom. TEL 44-121-414-6665, 44-604-674800, FAX 44-121-414-4989, bwestcott@socitm.gov.uk, http://www.socitm.gov.uk. Ed. Brian Westcott.

020 658 RUS
IBUSINESS. Text in Russian. bi-m. **Document type:** *Journal, Trade.*
Published by: Groteck, 7 Miusskaya sq, 4th Fl, PO Box 53, Moscow, 103030, Russian Federation. TEL 7-095-2516845, FAX 7-095-2513389, groteck@groteck.ru, http://www.groteck.net. Circ: 10,000.

INDILINGA: AFRICAN JOURNAL OF INDIGENOUS KNOWLEDGE SYSTEMS. see *LIBRARY AND INFORMATION SCIENCES*

020 DEU ISSN 1433-7150
INFO21. Text in German. 6/yr. EUR 7,679 domestic; EUR 10,124 foreign; EUR 15 newsstand/cover domestic; EUR 20 newsstand/cover foreign (effective 2004). **Description:** Features the latest news, hard facts and analysis for document management, workflow, groupware, content creation, distribution, data processing and archiving.
Published by: Informations-GmbH & Co. KG, Landsberger Strasse 101, Essen, 45219, Germany. TEL 49-2054-104890, FAX 49-2054-1048929, http://www.info21.de/. **Subscr. to:** Advanstar Communications, Inc., Advanstar Marketing Services, Customer Service Department, 131 West, First St, Duluth, MN 55802. TEL 218-723-9200, 888-527-7008.

003 USA ISSN 1070-0013
INFOMANAGE; the international management newsletter for the information services professional. Text in English. 1993. m. USD 97.50 domestic; USD 117.50 foreign (effective 2005). bk.rev.; software rev. index. Supplement avail. **Document type:** *Newsletter.*
—CCC.
Published by: S M R Publishing (Subsidiary of: S M R International), 14 Mamaronek Ave, Unite Plains, NY 10601. TEL 914-328-5434, FAX 914-328-6154, questions@infomanage.net, smrintl@mindspring.com, http://www.mindspring.com/~smrintl/smr.html. Ed. Guy St Clair. Pub. Guy St. Clair. Circ: 1,400 (paid).

020 ZAF
INFORM. Text in English. 1964. m. free. adv. back issues avail. **Document type:** *Trade.*
Indexed: LibLit.
Published by: I S M, PO Box 1419, Johannesburg, 2000, South Africa. Ed. Mark Ingle. Circ: 13,000.

INFORMAA QUARTERLY. see *BUSINESS AND ECONOMICS—Office Equipment And Services*

020 POL ISSN 1230-2090
Z699.4.C17
INFORMACJA NAUKOWA/INFORMATION SCIENCE. Text in Polish; Summaries in English, French, Russian. 1991. irreg. **Document type:** *Monographic series.* **Description:** Covers computer science, information science, computer information systems, and information-retrieval languages.
Published by: Instytut Informacji Naukowej Technicznej i Ekonomicznej, Ul Zurawia 4 a, Warsaw, 00503, Poland. TEL 48-22-6295624, FAX 48-22-6297989, iinte@cc.cup.gov.pl, http://www.cup.gov.pl/iinte/iinte-oo.htm.

INFORMATICA; revista de computacion y sistemas. see *LIBRARY AND INFORMATION SCIENCES—Computer Applications*

INFORMATICS IN HEATHCARE AUSTRALIA. see *MEDICAL SCIENCES—Computer Applications*

004 DEU ISSN 0934-4721
INFORMATIK BETRIFFT UNS. Text in German. 1988. q. **Document type:** *Journal, Academic/Scholarly.*
Published by: Bergmoser und Hoeller Verlag GmbH, Karl-Friedrich-Str 76, Aachen, 52072, Germany. TEL 49-241-93888123, FAX 49-241-93888134, kontakt@buhv.de, http://www.buhv.de.

INFORMATION & SECURITY/INFORMATSIYA I BEZOPASNOST'/INFORMATSIYA I SIGURNOST; an international journal. see *CRIMINOLOGY AND LAW ENFORCEMENT—Security*

003 GBR ISSN 1369-118X
HM851 CODEN: ICSOF3
➤ **INFORMATION, COMMUNICATION AND SOCIETY.** Text in English. 1998. bi-m. GBP 391, USD 647 combined subscription to institutions print & online eds. (effective 2006). back issues avail.; reprint service avail. from PSC. **Document type:** *Journal, Academic/Scholarly.* **Description:** Transcends cultural and geographical boundaries as it explores a diverse range of issues relating to the development and application of information and communications technologies.
Related titles: Online - full text ed.: ISSN 1468-4462. GBP 371, USD 615 to institutions (effective 2006) (from EBSCO Publishing, Gale Group, IngentaConnect, O C L C Online Computer Library Center, Inc., Swets Information Services).
Indexed: CompLI, ESPM, ErgAb, IBSS, Inspec, PSA, PhilInd, RiskAb, SSA, SociolAb.
—BLDSC (4493.322000), IE, Infotrieve, ingenta. **CCC.**
Published by: Routledge (Subsidiary of: Taylor & Francis Group), 4 Park Square, Milton Park, Abingdon, Oxon OX14 4RN, United Kingdom. TEL 44-1235-828600, FAX 44-1235-829000, http://www.tandf.co.uk/journals/titles/1369118X.asp, http://www.routledge.co.uk. Eds. Barry Wellman, Brian D Loader, William H Dutton. R&P Sally Sweet. **Subscr. to:** Taylor & Francis Ltd, Journals Customer Service, Rankine Rd, Basingstoke, Hants RG24 8PR, United Kingdom. TEL 44-1256-813000, FAX 44-1256-330245, enquiry@tandf.co.uk.

003.54 FRA ISSN 1630-649X
Q350
INFORMATION INTERACTION INTELLIGENCE. Text in French. 2001. s-a. EUR 30 (effective 2005). 340 p./no.; **Document type:** *Magazine, Trade.*
Published by: Cepadues Editions, 111 Rue Nicolas Vauquelin, Toulouse, 3100, France. TEL 33-5-6140-5736, FAX 33-5-6141-7989, cepadues@cepadues.com, http://www.cepadues.com.

003.54 NLD ISSN 1389-1995
➤ **INFORMATION - KNOWLEDGE - SYSTEMS MANAGEMENT.** Abbreviated title: I K S M. Text in English. 1999. q. EUR 305, USD 348 combined subscription print & online eds. (effective 2006). adv. bk.rev. back issues avail. **Document type:** *Journal, Academic/Scholarly.* **Description:** Offers a primary source of information for persons responsible for engineering and managing information, knowledge, and systems.
Related titles: E-mail ed.; Online - full text ed.: (from EBSCO Publishing, Gale Group, IngentaConnect, O C L C Online Computer Library Center, Inc., Swets Information Services).
Indexed: BrCerAb, C&ISA, CerAb, CompLI, CompR, CorrAb, E&CAJ, EMA, IAA, IBR, IBZ, InfoSAb, Inspec, M&TEA, MBF, METADEX, SolStAb, WAA.
—BLDSC (4493.607970), CISTI, IE, Infotrieve, ingenta, Linda Hall. **CCC.**
Published by: I O S Press, Nieuwe Hemweg 6B, Amsterdam, 1013 BG, Netherlands. TEL 31-20-6883355, FAX 31-20-6203419, info@iospress.nl, order@iospress.nl, http://www.iospress.nl/html/13891995.php. Eds. Andrew P Sage, W B Rouse. R&P Ms. Carry Koolbergen TEL 31-20-6382189. Adv. contact Ms. Jolijn van Eunen. Circ: 150. **Subscr. to:** I O S Press, Inc, 4502 Rachael Manor Dr., Fairfax, VA 22032-3631. iosbooks@iospress.com; Kinokuniya Co. Ltd., Shinjuku 3-chome, Shinjuku-ku, Tokyo 160-0022, Japan. FAX 81-3-3439-1094, journal@kinokuniya.co.jp, http://www.kinokuniya.co.jp; Globe Publication Pvt. Ltd., C-62 Inderpuri, New Delhi 100 012, India. TEL 91-11-579-3211, 91-11-579-3212, FAX 91-11-579-8876, custserve@globepub.com, http://www.globepub.com.

➤ **INFORMATION LANDSCAPES FOR A LEARNING SOCIETY.** see *LIBRARY AND INFORMATION SCIENCES*

003.54 USA ISSN 1098-4798
INFORMATION MANAGEMENT (NEW YORK, 1998). Text in English. 1998. m. **Document type:** *Journal, Academic/Scholarly.*
Related titles: Online - full text ed.: (from ProQuest Information & Learning).
Indexed: ABIn.
Published by: American Management Association International, 1601 Broadway, New York, NY 10019. TEL 212-586-8100, 800-262-9699, 800-714-6395, FAX 212-903-8168, 518-891-3653, 212-903-8168, pubs_cust_serv@amanet.org, customerservice@amanet.org, http://www.amanet.org.

003.54 USA ISSN 0961-7612
T58.64 CODEN: IMRPE2
INFORMATION MANAGEMENT REPORT; an international newsletter for information professionals and librarians. Text in English. 1991. m. GBP 325 combined subscription domestic print & online eds.; EUR 525 combined subscription in Europe print & online eds.; USD 505 combined subscription elsewhere print & online eds. (effective 2003). bk.rev. charts; illus.; stat. back issues avail. **Document type:** *Newsletter, Trade.* **Description:** Reports on and analyses the latest technical and strategic initiatives in the management of information worldwide. Covers such topics as knowledge management, corporate intranets, electronic access and delivery, storage and retrieval systems, document management, copyright and electronic publishing.
Incorporates (1978-1991): Outlook on Research Libraries (0165-2818); (1988-1991): Advanced Information Report (0953-8712); Which was formerly (1979-1988): Communication Technology Impact (0142-5854)
Related titles: Online - full text ed.: (from Data-Star, Gale Group).
Indexed: Inspec, LISA, PROMT, RASB.
—BLDSC (4493.687155), CASDDS, IE, Infotrieve. **CCC.**
Published by: C S A Journal Division (Subsidiary of: Cambridge Information Group), 7200 Wisconsin Ave, Ste 715, Bethesda, MD 20814. TEL 301-961-6798, 800-843-7751, FAX 301-961-6799, journals@csa.com, http://www.csa.com.

651.8 ISR ISSN 0073-7879
INFORMATION PROCESSING ASSOCIATION OF ISRAEL. NATIONAL CONFERENCE ON DATA PROCESSING. PROCEEDINGS. Text in Hebrew, English. 1964. a. **Document type:** *Proceedings.*
Published by: Information Processing Association of Israel, Kfar Hamakabia, Ramat Gan, 52109, Israel.

003 GBR
INFORMATION PROCESSING REPORT. Text in English. 1975. m. GBP 249 domestic; GBP 269 foreign (effective 2000); includes subscription to The Wharton Report.. **Document type:** *Corporate.* **Description:** Covers new products, systems and applications in printing, desktop publishing, word processing, document management, work flow and computer telephone integration. Written for MIS and administration managers, with current focus on web phones.
Former titles: Text and Image News; Information Processing Report (0958-6512); International Information and Word Processing Report (0958-6504); International Word Processing Report
Indexed: Inspec.
Published by: Wharton Information Systems, 11 Beaumont Ave, Richmond, Surrey TW9 2HE, United Kingdom. TEL 44-20-8332-1120, n_wharton@compuserve.com. Ed. Andrea Wharton.

025.04 NLD ISSN 1386-4564
QA76.9.T48 CODEN: IFRTFY
INFORMATION RETRIEVAL. Text in English. 1998. q. EUR 419, USD 419, GBP 262 combined subscription to institutions print & online eds. (effective 2005). adv. bk.rev. reprint service avail. from PSC. **Document type:** *Journal, Academic/Scholarly.* **Description:** Provides international forum for theory and experiment in information retrieval and its application in the networked information environment.
Related titles: Online - full text ed.: ISSN 1573-7659 (from EBSCO Publishing, Gale Group, IngentaConnect, Kluwer Online, O C L C Online Computer Library Center, Inc., ProQuest Information & Learning, Springer LINK, Swets Information Services).
Indexed: ABIn, BibLing, CMCI, ErgAb, InfoSAb, Inspec, RefZh.
—BLDSC (4494.146000), IE, Infotrieve, ingenta. **CCC.**
Published by: Springer-Verlag Dordrecht (Subsidiary of: Springer Science+Business Media), Van Godewijckstraat 30, Dordrecht, 3311 GX, Netherlands. TEL 31-78-6576050, FAX 31-78-6576474, http://springerlink.metapress.com/openurl.asp?genre=journal&issn=1386-4564, http://www.springeronline.com. Eds. Josiane Mothe, Justin Zobel, Paul B Kantor.

INFORMATION SCIENCE AND KNOWLEDGE MANAGEMENT. see *LIBRARY AND INFORMATION SCIENCES*

020 USA ISSN 0020-0255
Z699.A1 CODEN: ISIJBC
➤ **INFORMATION SCIENCES.** (In 3 sections, A: Informatics and Computer Science, B: Intelligent Systems, C: Applications) Text in English. 1969. 24/yr. EUR 103 in Europe to individuals; JPY 14,100 in Japan to individuals; USD 115 elsewhere to individuals; EUR 3,848 in Europe to institutions; JPY 511,400 in Japan to institutions; USD 4,306 elsewhere to institutions (effective 2006). adv. bk.rev. abstr.; charts; illus. back issues avail.; reprints avail. **Document type:** *Journal, Academic/Scholarly.* **Description:** Designed to inform researchers, developers, managers, strategic planners, and others interested in state-of-the-art research activities in intelligent systems and engineering.
Incorporates (1994-1995): Information Sciences - Applications (1069-0115)
Related titles: Microform ed.: (from PQC); Online - full text ed.: (from EBSCO Publishing, Gale Group, IngentaConnect, ScienceDirect, Swets Information Services).
Indexed: ASCA, B&BAb, BrCerAb, C&ISA, CCMJ, CIS, CMCI, CerAb, ChemAb, CompAb, CompC, CompLI, CompR, CorrAb, CurCont, CybAb, E&CAJ, EMA, EngInd, IAA, ICEA, ISR, InfoSAb, Inspec, L&LBA, M&TEA, MBF, METADEX, MLA, MLA-IB, MathR, MathSciNet, RASB, SCI, SSCI, SoftAbEng, SolStAb, WAA, WTA, ZentMath.
—BLDSC (4494.250000), AskIEEE, CISTI, Ei, IDS, IE, Infotrieve, ingenta, Linda Hall. **CCC.**
Published by: Elsevier Inc. (Subsidiary of: Elsevier Science & Technology), 360 Park Ave. S, New York, NY 10010-1710. TEL 212-633-3730, 888-437-4636, usinfo-f@elsevier.com, http://www.elsevier.com/locate/ins. Ed. W. Pedrycz. **Subscr. outside the Americas to:** Elsevier BV, PO Box 211, Amsterdam 1000 AE, Netherlands. TEL 31-20-485-3757, FAX 31-20-485-3432.

020 NLD ISSN 0167-5265
Z699.A1 CODEN: ISUDX8
➤ **INFORMATION SERVICES & USE.** Text in English. 1981. q. EUR 357, USD 428 combined subscription print & online eds. (effective 2006). adv. bk.rev. illus. reprints avail. **Document type:** *Journal, Academic/Scholarly.* **Description:** Contains data on international developments in information management and its applications. Articles cover online systems, library automation, word processing, micrographics, videotex, and telecommunications.
Incorporates (1987-1993): Infomediary (0169-2763)
Related titles: Microform ed.: (from PQC); Online - full text ed.: (from EBSCO Publishing, Gale Group, IngentaConnect, O C L C Online Computer Library Center, Inc., Swets Information Services).
Indexed: AESIS, BPIA, BrCerAb, BrHumI, BusI, C&ISA, CIJE, CIN, CerAb, ChemAb, ChemTitl, CompAb, CompC, CompLI, CompR, CorrAb, DIP, DPD, E&CAJ, EMA, EngInd, FLUIDEX, IAA, IBR, IBZ, InfoSAb, Inspec, KES, LHTB, LIMI, LISA, LRI, LibLit, M&MA, M&TEA, MBF, METADEX, ManagCont, RASB, SolStAb, T&II, WAA.
—BLDSC (4495.950000), AskIEEE, CASDDS, CINDOC, Ei, IE, Infotrieve, ingenta, Linda Hall. **CCC.**
Published by: I O S Press, Nieuwe Hemweg 6B, Amsterdam, 1013 BG, Netherlands. TEL 31-20-6883355, FAX 31-20-6203419, info@iospress.nl, order@iospress.nl, http://www.iospress.nl/html/01675265.php. Eds. T Cawkell TEL 44-175-365-3967, A W Elias TEL 812-246-5497. R&P Ms. Carry Koolbergen TEL 31-20-6382189. Adv. contact Ms. Jolijn van Eunen. Circ: 500. **Subscr. to:** Globe Publication Pvt. Ltd., C-62 Inderpuri, New Delhi 100 012, India. TEL 91-11-579-3211, 91-11-579-3212, FAX 91-11-579-8876, custserve@globepub.com, http://www.globepub.com; Kinokuniya Co. Ltd., Shinjuku 3-chome, Shinjuku-ku, Tokyo 160-0022, Japan. FAX 81-3-3439-1094, journal@kinokuniya.co.jp, http://www.kinokuniya.co.jp; I O S Press, Inc, 4502 Rachael Manor Dr., Fairfax, VA 22032-3631. iosbooks@iospress.com.

003.54 USA ISSN 0197-2243
Z668 CODEN: INSCD8
➤ **THE INFORMATION SOCIETY**; an international journal. Text in English. 1981. 5/yr. GBP 222, USD 366 combined subscription to institutions print & online eds. (effective 2006). adv. bk.rev. abstr.; illus. Index. reprint service avail. from PSC. **Document type:** *Journal, Academic/Scholarly.* **Description:** Provides a forum for such topics on information as transborder flow and regulatory issues.
Related titles: Online - full text ed.: ISSN 1087-6537. GBP 211, USD 348 to institutions (effective 2006) (from EBSCO Publishing, Gale Group, IngentaConnect, O C L C Online Computer Library Center, Inc., Swets Information Services).
Indexed: ABIn, AHCI, CADCAM, CommAb, CompC, CompLI, CurCont, EAA, ErgAb, FamI, InfoSAb, Inspec, M&MA, PAIS, PRA, RASB, SSA, SSCI, SociolAb, TelAb, V&AA.
—BLDSC (4496.310000), AskIEEE, CISTI, IDS, IE, Infotrieve, ingenta, Linda Hall. **CCC.**
Published by: Taylor & Francis Inc. (Subsidiary of: Taylor & Francis Group), 325 Chestnut St, Ste 800, Philadelphia, PA 19016. TEL 215-625-8900, 800-354-1420, FAX 215-625-2940, info@taylorandfrancis.com, http://www.tandf.co.uk/journals/titles/01972243.asp, http://www.taylorandfrancis.com. Ed. Dr. Harmeet Sawhney. **Subscr. outside N. America to:** Taylor & Francis Ltd, Journals Customer Service, Rankine Rd, Basingstoke, Hants RG24 8PR, United Kingdom. TEL 44-1256-813000, FAX 44-1256-330245, enquiry@tandf.co.uk.

003.54 BEL ISSN 1026-6186
INFORMATION SOCIETY NEWS. Text in English. 1996. irreg.
Related titles: Online - full text ed.: ISSN 1560-8603.
—BLDSC (4496.312000).
Published by: European Commission, Directorate General - Information Society, Rue de la Loi 200, Brussels, 1049, Belgium. TEL 32-2-2968800, FAX 32-2-2994170, http://europa.eu.int/information_society/.

003 DEU
INFORMATION SOURCES IN INFORMATION TECHNOLOGY. Text in English. 1991. irreg. GBP 60 (effective 2001). **Document type:** *Directory, Trade.* **Description:** Enables information professionals and librarians to evaluate information sources in information technology.
Published by: K.G. Saur Verlag GmbH (Subsidiary of: Gale Group), Ortlerstr 8, Munchen, 81373, Germany. TEL 49-89-769020, FAX 49-89-76902150, info@saur.de, http://www.saur.de. Ed. David Haynes.

621.3822 USA ISSN 1549-1331
▼ **INFORMATION STORAGE + SECURITY JOURNAL.** Text in English. 2004 (May). 9/m. USD 39.99 domestic; USD 49.99 in Canada & Mexico; USD 59.99 elsewhere; USD 5.99 newsstand/cover (effective 2005). adv. back issues avail. **Document type:** *Journal, Trade.* **Description:** Covers major infosecurity issues of the day - identity theft, cyber-terrorism, encryption, perimeter defense, and more.
Related titles: Online - full text ed.: USD 19.99 (effective 2005).
Published by: SYS-CON Media, Inc., 135 Chestnut Ridge Rd, Montvale, NJ 07645. TEL 201-802-3040, 888-303-5282, FAX 201-782-9600, info@sys-con.com, http://www.issjournal.com, http://www.sys-con.com. adv.: B&W page USD 5,710, color page USD 7,137; trim 8.375 x 10.75. Circ: 35,000.

C

003.54 USA ISSN 1387-3326
T58.64 CODEN: ISFRFP
INFORMATION SYSTEMS FRONTIERS; a journal of research and innovation. Text in English. 1999. 5/yr. EUR 400, USD 400, GBP 251 combined subscription to institutions print & online eds. (effective 2005). adv. reprint service avail. from PSC. **Document type:** *Journal, Academic/Scholarly.* **Description:** Aims to provide a common forum of dissemination of frontline industrial developments of substantial academic value and pioneering academic research of significant practical impact.
Related titles: Online - full text ed.: ISSN 1572-9419 (from EBSCO Publishing, Gale Group, IngentaConnect, Kluwer Online, O C L C Online Computer Library Center, Inc., ProQuest Information & Learning, Springer LINK, Swets Information Services).
Indexed: ABIn, BibLing, CMCI, CompLI, CurCont, ESPM, Inspec, RefZh, RiskAb.
—BLDSC (4496.368170), IE, Infotrieve, ingenta. **CCC.**
Published by: Springer-Verlag New York, Inc. (Subsidiary of: Springer Science+Business Media), 233 Spring St, New York, NY 10013. TEL 212-460-1500, FAX 212-460-1575, service@springer-ny.com, http://springerlink.metapress.com/openurl.asp?genre=journal&issn=1387-3326, http://www.springer-ny.com. Eds. H Raghav Rao, Ram Ramesh. **Subscr. to:** Journal Fulfillment, PO Box 2485, Secaucus, NJ 07096-2485. TEL 201-348-4033, FAX 201-348-4505, journals@springer-ny.com.

003 USA ISSN 1047-7047
QA76.27 CODEN: ISYREH
➤ **INFORMATION SYSTEMS RESEARCH.** Text in English. 1990. q. USD 128 domestic to non-members; USD 144 foreign to non-members; USD 64 to members additional journal; USD 168 combined subscription domestic to non-members print & online eds.; USD 184 combined subscription foreign to non-members print & online eds.; USD 84 combined subscription to members additional journal; print & online eds.; USD 272 combined subscription domestic to institutions print &/or online eds.; USD 288 combined subscription foreign to institutions print & online eds. (effective 2004); membership includes 1 free journal. adv. bibl.; charts; illus. **Document type:** *Journal, Academic/Scholarly.*
Related titles: Online - full content ed.: ISSN 1526-5536. USD 92 to non-members; USD 46 to members additional journal (effective 2004); Online - full text ed.: (from EBSCO Publishing, Gale Group, ProQuest Information & Learning, Swets Information Services).
Indexed: ABIn, ASCA, BPI, CMCI, CompLI, CurCont, Emerald, Inspec, PsycInfo, PsycholAb, SSCI.
—BLDSC (4496.368601), AskIEEE, IDS, IE, Infotrieve, ingenta. **CCC.**
Published by: I N F O R M S, 901 Elkridge Landing Rd., Ste. 400, Linthicum, MD 21090-2909. TEL 410-850-0300, 800-446-3676, FAX 410-684-2963, informs@informs.org, http://isr.pubs.informs.org, http://www.informs.org. Ed. Chris F. Kemerer. R&P Candita Gerzevitz. Adv. contact Trish Allewalt. B&W page USD 400; trim 8.125 x 10.875. Circ: 2,000 (paid and controlled). **Subscr. to:** PO Box 631704, Baltimore, MD 631704.

003.54 338.91 USA ISSN 1544-7529
HD76
▼ ➤ **INFORMATION TECHNOLOGIES AND INTERNATIONAL DEVELOPMENT.** Text in English. 2003. q. USD 95 combined subscription in US & Canada to individuals print & online eds.; USD 115 combined subscription elsewhere to individuals print & online eds.; USD 208 combined subscription in US & Canada to institutions print & online eds.; USD 228 combined subscription elsewhere to institutions print & online eds. (effective 2005). **Document type:** *Journal, Academic/Scholarly.* **Description:** Focuses on the intersection of information and communication technologies with international development.
Related titles: Online - full text ed.: ISSN 1544-7537. USD 85 to individuals; USD 187 to institutions (effective 2005) (from EBSCO Publishing, Gale Group, IngentaConnect, O C L C Online Computer Library Center, Inc., Swets Information Services).
Indexed: BrCerAb, C&ISA, CerAb, CorrAb, E&CAJ, EMA, IAA, M&TEA, MBF, METADEX, WAA.
—BLDSC (4496.368614).
Published by: M I T Press, 55 Hayward St, Cambridge, MA 02142-1493. TEL 617-253-5646, FAX 617-258-6779, itid-ed@mit.edu, journals-info@mit.edu, http://www.mitpress.mit.edu/itid, http://mitpress.mit.edu. Eds. Ernest J Wilson III, Michael L Best.

➤ **INFORMATION TECHNOLOGY AND LIBRARIES.** see *LIBRARY AND INFORMATION SCIENCES*

003 USA ISSN 1098-3058
G155.A1
➤ **INFORMATION TECHNOLOGY AND TOURISM**; application - methodology - techniques. Text in English. 1998. q. USD 375 combined subscription domestic print & online eds.; USD 405 combined subscription foreign print & online eds. (effective 2005). back issues avail. **Document type:** *Journal, Academic/Scholarly.* **Description:** Devoted to the relationship between information and communication systems and tourism.
Related titles: Online - full text ed.: (from EBSCO Publishing, Gale Group, IngentaConnect).
Indexed: AbHyg, H&TI, RDA, RRTA, WAE&RSA.
—BLDSC (4496.368745). **CCC.**
Published by: Cognizant Communication Corporation, 3 Hartsdale Rd, Elmsford, NY 10523-3701. TEL 914-592-7720, FAX 914-592-8981, cogcomm@aol.com, http://www.cognizantcommunication.com. Ed. Hannes Werthner.

➤ **INFORMATION TECHNOLOGY CATALOGUE.** see *TRANSPORTATION—Air Transport*

➤ **INFORMATION TECHNOLOGY, EDUCATION AND SOCIETY.** see *EDUCATION*

020 USA ISSN 1545-9535
INFORMATION TECHNOLOGY IN HOSPITALITY. Text in English. 1999. s-a. USD 175 domestic; USD 195 foreign (effective 2005).
Formerly (until 2003): International Journal of Hospitality Information Technology (1533-7340)
—BLDSC (4542.282950).
Published by: Cognizant Communication Corporation, 3 Hartsdale Rd, Elmsford, NY 10523-3701. TEL 914-592-7720, FAX 914-592-8981, cogcomm@aol.com, http://www.cognizantcommunication.com.

658 020 374.4 USA ISSN 1057-7939
Z678.9.A1
INFORMATION TECHNOLOGY NEWSLETTER; international newsletter of information technology and libraries. Text in English. 1990. s-a. USD 30 to individuals; USD 45 to institutions (effective 2005). 20 p./no.; **Document type:** *Newsletter, Trade.* **Description:** Designed to help librarians strategically plan aspects of implementing information technology resources.
Related titles: Online - full text ed.: (from O C L C Online Computer Library Center, Inc., ProQuest Information & Learning).
Indexed: ABIn, EngInd, InfoSAb.
—Linda Hall. **CCC.**
Published by: Idea Group Publishing (Subsidiary of: Idea Group Inc.), 701 E Chocolate Ave, Ste 200, Hershey, PA 17033-1240. TEL 717-533-8845, 866-342-6657, FAX 717-533-7115, jtravers@idea-group.com, cust@idea-group.com, http://www.idea-group.com/journals/details.asp?id=201. Ed. Rabbi Mehdi Khosrow-Pour. Circ: 750.

INFORMATION TECHNOLOGY REVIEW. see *COMPUTERS—Data Communications And Data Transmission Systems*

020 USA
INFORMATION TECHNOLOGY SERIES. Text in English. 1976. irreg., latest vol.6. price varies. **Document type:** *Monographic series.*
Published by: (American Federation of Information Processing Societies), Springer-Verlag New York, Inc. (Subsidiary of: Springer Science+Business Media), 233 Spring St, New York, NY 10013. TEL 212-460-1500, FAX 212-473-6272.

020 IND ISSN 0971-7102
INFORMATION TODAY & TOMORROW. Text in English. q.
Description: Includes information on new tools and techniques, events concluded and announcements, interesting Internet sites, new database products and services.
Indexed: InfoSAb, RefZh.
Published by: National Information System for Science and Technology (NISSAT), Department of Scientific & Industrial Research (DSIR), Government of India, Technology Bhawan, New Mehrauli Rd, New Delhi, 110 016, India. TEL 91-11-6567373, FAX 91-11-6170420, vkv@alpha.nic.in, http://itt.nissat.tripod.com/.

003.54 AUS ISSN 1442-5734
INFORMATION WEEK AUSTRALIA; business innovation powered by technology. Text in English. 1999. bi-w. AUD 109.45 (effective 2004). **Document type:** *Journal, Trade.*
Description: Presents business information technology, explain the issues and jargon for executives with varying levels of IT understanding.
Related titles: Online - full content ed.
Published by: A J B Publishing, PO Box 2286, Strawberry Hills, NSW 2016, Australia. TEL 61-2-83993611, FAX 61-2-83993622, enquiries@authoritynetwork.com, http://www.itnews.com.au/infoweek/, http://www.ajb.com.au/.

INFORMATIONSSPECIALISTEN. see *LIBRARY AND INFORMATION SCIENCES*

INFORMATSIONNOE OBSHCHESTVO. see *SOCIAL SCIENCES: COMPREHENSIVE WORKS*

003 RUS ISSN 1684-6400
INFORMATSIONNYE TEKHNOLOGII. Text in Russian. 1995. m. USD 641 foreign (effective 2004). **Document type:** *Journal, Trade.*
Indexed: Inspec, RefZh.
—BLDSC (0086.786500), CISTI.
Published by: Izdatel'stvo Mashinostroenie, Stromynskii per 4, Moscow, 107076, Russian Federation. TEL 7-095-2683858, mashpubl@mashin.ru, http://www.informika.ru/text/magaz/it, http://www.mashin.ru. Ed. I P Norenkov. **Dist. by:** Informnauka Ltd., Ul Usievicha 20, Moscow 125190, Russian Federation. alfimov@viniti.ru.

003 RUS
INFORMATSIONNYE TEKHNOLOGII I VYCHISLITEL'NYE SISTEMY. Text in Russian. q. USD 99.95 in United States.
Address: Leninskii pr-t 32-a, Moscow, 117334, Russian Federation. TEL 7-095-9381749. **US dist. addr.:** East View Information Services, 3020 Harbor Ln. N., Minneapolis, MN 55447. TEL 612-550-0961.

003 RUS
INFORMATSIONNYE TEKHNOLOGII PROEKTIROVANIYA I PROIZVODSTVA. Text in Russian. q. USD 109.95 in United States.
Indexed: RefZh.
Address: Volokolamskoe shosse 77, Moscow, 123584, Russian Federation. TEL 7-095-4911306. **US dist. addr.:** East View Information Services, 3020 Harbor Ln. N., Minneapolis, MN 55447. TEL 612-550-0961.

003 RUS
INFORMATSIONNYE TEKHNOLOGII V OBRAZOVANII. Text in Russian. 1996. a. **Document type:** *Journal, Academic/Scholarly.*
Media: Online - full content.
Published by: Moskovskii Gosudarstvennyi Universitet im. M.V. Lomonosova, Tsentr Novykh Informatsionnykh Tekhnologii/M.V. Lomonosov Moscow State University, Center of New Information Technologies, Vorob'evy Gory, Moscow, 119992, Russian Federation. TEL 7-095-9392343, FAX 7-095-9390713, http://mech.math.msu.su/InfTech/titl_jr1.htm. Ed. A. Mikhalev.

004 USA ISSN 1097-2501
INFOSTOR. Text in English. 1997. m. USD 120 domestic; CND 155 in Canada; USD 190 elsewhere; USD 12 per issue (effective 2005). adv. **Document type:** *Magazine, Trade.*
Related titles: Online - full text ed.: (from EBSCO Publishing, Factiva, Gale Group, O C L C Online Computer Library Center, Inc., ProQuest Information & Learning).
Indexed: CompD.
—**CCC.**
Published by: PennWell Corp., 98 Spit Brook Rd, Nashua, NH 03062-5737. TEL 603-891-0123, FAX 603-891-9177, 603-891-9146, http://is.pennnet.com/home.cfm, http://www.pennwell.com. Ed. David Simpson TEL 949-497-7377. Pub. Mark Finkelstein TEL 603-891-9133. Adv. contact Kathy Poggi. B&W page USD 10,835, color page USD 12,650; trim 11 x 14.25. Circ: 30,000.

004 USA
INFOSTOR EUROPE. Text in English. q. USD 30 in Europe; USD 60 elsewhere; USD 7.50 per issue (effective 2004). **Document type:** *Magazine, Trade.*
Published by: PennWell Corp., 1421 S Sheridan Rd, Tulsa, OK 74112. TEL 918-835-3161, 800-331-4463, FAX 918-831-9804, Headquarters@PennWell.com, http://www.pennwell.com. Ed. David Simpson TEL 949-497-7377.

003 NZL ISSN 1173-3764
INFOSYS; the electronic newsletter for information systems. Text in English. 1994. w. free. **Document type:** *Newsletter.*
Description: For faculty, students, and practitioners in the field of information systems. Publishes news items, announcements, requests for assistance, calls for papers, notices of professional meetings and conferences, position announcements, and other items of interest to the global information systems community.
Media: Online - full text.
Published by: Massey University, Information Systems Department, Albany, New Zealand. TEL 64-9-4418150, FAX 64-9-4418181, d.viehland@massey.ac.nz. Ed. Dennis Viehland. Circ: 5,200.

020 GBR ISSN 1473-7507
QA76
➤ **INNOVATIONS IN TEACHING AND LEARNING IN INFORMATION AND COMPUTER SCIENCES.** Text in English. s-a. bk.rev. back issues avail. **Document type:** *Journal, Academic/Scholarly.*
Media: Online - full text.
Indexed: InfoSAb.
Published by: Loughborough University, Department of Information Science, Medway Bldg, Loughborough, LE11 3TU, United Kingdom. TEL 44-1509-223078, FAX 44-1509-223994, ltsn-ics@lboro.ac.uk, http://www.ics.ltsn.ac.uk/pub/italics. Ed. Peter Enser.

003.54 USA
INSIDE (STAMFORD). Text in English. w. USD 500 (effective 1999). **Document type:** *Trade.* **Description:** A weekly look at the industry's most important IT issues being discussed at GartnerGroup Analysis meetings. Provides advice to senior executives on how IT can be developed to achieve enterprise goals and objectives.
Published by: Gartner Inc., 56 Top Gallant Rd, Stamford, CT 06904-2212. TEL 203-316-1111, 800-544-7337, FAX 203-316-6300, jwhitney@info-edge.com, http://www.gartner3.gartnerweb.com, http://www.info-edge.com.

020 BRA ISSN 0104-4869
➤ **INSTITUTO DE INFORMATICA DA PUC CAMPINAS. REVISTA.** Text in Portuguese, English; Summaries in Portuguese, English. 1992. 2/yr., latest vol.5, no.1, 1997. **Document type:** *Magazine, Academic/Scholarly.* **Description:** Provides research and technical articles developed by the Institutes professors and researchers.
Published by: Pontificia Universidade Catolica de Campinas, Instituto de Informatica, Rod. D. Pedro I, Km 136, CP 317, Campinas, SP 13020-904, Brazil. TEL 55-19-7567094, informat@zeus.puccamp.br, http://www.puccamp.br. Ed. Dr. Frank Herman Behrens. Circ: 3,000 (controlled).

020 JPN ISSN 1340-9050
Z671
INTERDISCIPLINARY INFORMATION SCIENCES. Text in English. 1994. s-a. **Description:** Covers information and communication, computer science, information systems, and their impacts on the behavior and system of individual, groups, and society.
Related titles: Online - full text ed.: ISSN 1347-6157. 2002. free (effective 2005) (from J-Stage).
Indexed: MathR, MathSciNet, ZooRec.
—BLDSC (4533.356455), IE.
Published by: Tohoku University, Graduate School of Information Sciences, Aramaki aza Aoba 09, Aoba-ku, Sendai, Miyagi 980-8579, Japan. TEL 81-22-2175813, FAX 81-22-2175815, http://iis.jstage.jst.go.jp/, http://www.is.tohoku.ac.jp/. Ed. Hajime Urakawa.

INTERNATIONAL CONFERENCE ON DATABASE SYSTEMS FOR ADVANCED APPLICATIONS. PROCEEDINGS. see *COMPUTERS—Computer Systems*

INTERNATIONAL DATABASE ENGINEERING AND APPLICATIONS SYMPOSIUM. see *COMPUTERS—Computer Systems*

003 DEU
INTERNATIONAL HANDBOOKS ON INFORMATION SYSTEMS. Text in English. 1998. irreg., latest 2003. price varies. **Document type:** *Monographic series, Academic/Scholarly.* **Description:** Dedicated to selected topics of information theory and applications.
Related titles: Online - full text ed.
Published by: Springer-Verlag (Subsidiary of: Springer Science+Business Media), Haber Str 7, Heidelberg, 69126, Germany. TEL 49-6221-3450, FAX 49-6221-229, subscriptions@springer.de, http://www.itm.uni-sb.de/ihis/, http://www.springer.de.

INTERNATIONAL JOURNAL OF COMPUTER APPLICATIONS IN TECHNOLOGY. see *COMPUTERS—Software*

003 SGP ISSN 0218-8430
QA76.9.D3
➤ **INTERNATIONAL JOURNAL OF COOPERATIVE INFORMATION SYSTEMS.** Abbreviated title: I J C I S. Text in English. 1992. q. SGD 311, USD 177, EUR 171 to individuals; SGD 858, USD 490, EUR 472 combined subscription to institutions print & online eds.; SGD 512, USD 292, EUR 282 combined subscription in developing nations to institutions print & online eds. (effective 2006). back issues avail. **Document type:** *Journal, Academic/Scholarly.* **Description:** Provides a forum where both the AI and DBS research communities can come to understand the intricacies of intelligent cooperative work.
Formerly (until vol.4, no.1, 1995): International Journal of Intelligent and Cooperative Information Systems (0218-2157)
Related titles: Online - full text ed.: (from EBSCO Publishing, O C L C Online Computer Library Center, Inc., Swets Information Services).
Indexed: ASCA, BrCerAb, C&ISA, CMCI, CerAb, CompLI, CorrAb, CurCont, E&CAJ, EMA, IAA, Inspec, M&TEA, MBF, METADEX, SolStAb, WAA.
—BLDSC (4542.178300), AskIEEE, CISTI, IDS, IE, Infotrieve, ingenta, Linda Hall. **CCC.**
Published by: World Scientific Publishing Co. Pte. Ltd., 5 Toh Tuck Link, Singapore, 596224, Singapore. TEL 65-466-5775, FAX 65-467-7667, wspc@wspc.com.sg, http://www.worldscinet.com/ijcis/ijcis.shtml, http://www.worldscientific.com. Eds. G Schlageter, M P Papazoglou. **Subscr. to:** Farrer Rd, PO Box 128, Singapore 912805, Singapore. sales@wspc.com.sg. **Dist. by:** World Scientific Publishing Co., Inc., 1060 Main St, River Edge, NJ 07661. TEL 201-487-9655, 800-227-7562, FAX 201-487-9656, 888-977-2665.; World Scientific Publishing Ltd., 57 Shelton St, London WC2H 9HE, United Kingdom. TEL 44-20-78360888, FAX 44-20-78362020, sales@wspc.co.uk.

▼ ➤ **INTERNATIONAL JOURNAL OF INFORMATION AND COMMUNICATION TECHNOLOGY EDUCATION.** see *EDUCATION*

003.54 GBR ISSN 0268-4012
H61.9
➤ **INTERNATIONAL JOURNAL OF INFORMATION MANAGEMENT.** Text in English. 1980. 6/yr. EUR 231 in Europe to individuals; JPY 30,600 in Japan to individuals; USD 258 elsewhere to individuals; EUR 695 in Europe to institutions; JPY 92,300 in Japan to institutions; USD 778 elsewhere to institutions (effective 2006). index. back issues avail. **Document type:** *Journal, Academic/Scholarly.* **Description:** Promotes corporate efficiency and individual productivity by addressing questions of information, systems, organization and management, planning and decision-making, and interpersonal communications.
Formerly (until 1985): Social Science Information Studies (0143-6236)
Related titles: Microform ed.: (from PQC); Online - full text ed.: (from EBSCO Publishing, Gale Group, IngentaConnect, ScienceDirect, Swets Information Services).
Indexed: ABIn, ASCA, B&BAb, CPM, CompD, CompLI, CurCont, ERA, ETA, Emerald, EngInd, ILD, IPSA, InfoSAb, Inspec, LISA, MEA, PAIS, RASB, RHEA, RefZh, SEA, SENA, SOMA, SSCI, TEA.
—BLDSC (4542.304900), AskIEEE, CINDOC, Ei, IDS, IE, Infotrieve, ingenta. **CCC.**
Published by: Pergamon (Subsidiary of: Elsevier Science & Technology), The Boulevard, Langford Ln, East Park, Kidlington, Oxford OX5 1GB, United Kingdom. TEL 44-1865-843000, FAX 44-1865-843010, http://www.elsevier.com/locate/ijinfomgt. Ed. Philip Hills. **Subscr. to:** Elsevier BV, PO Box 211, Amsterdam 1000 AE, Netherlands. TEL 31-20-485-3757, FAX 31-20-485-3432, nlinfo-f@elsevier.nl, http://www.elsevier.nl.

020 FRA ISSN 1290-2942
INTERNATIONAL JOURNAL OF INFORMATION SCIENCES FOR DECISION MAKING. Text in English. 1997. irreg.
Related titles: Online - full text ed.: ISSN 1265-499X.
—BLDSC (4542.304960).
Published by: Centre de Recherche Retrospective de Marseille, Faculte des Sciences et Techniques de St Jerome, Marseille, Cedex 20 13397, France. TEL 33-4-91-28-87-40, FAX 33-4-91-28-87-12, crrm@crrm.univ-mrs.fr, http://crrm.univ-mrs.fr. Eds. Henri Dou, Dr. Luc Quoniam.

621.3822 SGP ISSN 0219-6220
T58.62 CODEN: IJITBD
➤ **INTERNATIONAL JOURNAL OF INFORMATION TECHNOLOGY AND DECISION MAKING.** Abbreviated title: I J I T D M. Text in English. 2002. q. SGD 206, USD 118, EUR 114 to individuals; SGD 515, USD 295, EUR 283 combined subscription to institutions print & online eds.; SGD 309, USD 176, EUR 170 combined subscription in developing nations to institutions print & online eds. (effective 2006). back issues avail. **Document type:** *Journal, Academic/Scholarly.* **Description:** Provides a global forum for exchanging research findings and case studies which bridge the latest information technology and various decision-making techniques.
Related titles: Online - full text ed.: (from EBSCO Publishing, O C L C Online Computer Library Center, Inc., Swets Information Services).
Indexed: BrCerAb, C&ISA, CMCI, CerAb, CompLI, CorrAb, E&CAJ, EMA, IAA, Inspec, M&TEA, MBF, METADEX, SolStAb, WAA.
—BLDSC (4542.304980), IE, ingenta, Linda Hall. **CCC.**
Published by: World Scientific Publishing Co. Pte. Ltd., 5 Toh Tuck Link, Singapore, 596224, Singapore. wspc@wspc.com.sg, http://www.worldscinet.com/ijitdm/ijitdm.shtml, http://www.worldscientific.com. Ed. Yong Shi TEL 402-554-3652. **Subscr. in the US to:** Farrer Rd, PO Box 128, Singapore 912805, Singapore. TEL 65-382-5663, FAX 65-382-5919, sales@wspc.com.sg. **Dist. by:** World Scientific Publishing Co., Inc., 1060 Main St, River Edge, NJ 07661. TEL 201-487-9655, 800-227-7562, FAX 201-487-9656, 888-977-2665.; World Scientific Publishing Ltd., 57 Shelton St, London WC2H 9HE, United Kingdom. TEL 44-20-78360888, FAX 44-20-78362020, sales@wspc.co.uk.

▼ ➤ **INTERNATIONAL JOURNAL OF KNOWLEDGE MANAGEMENT.** see *BUSINESS AND ECONOMICS—Management*

621.3822 GBR ISSN 1476-1289
▼ ➤ **INTERNATIONAL JOURNAL OF WEB ENGINEERING AND TECHNOLOGY.** Text in English. 2003. q. USD 450 to institutions; USD 545 combined subscription to institutions print & online eds. (effective 2005). **Document type:** *Journal, Academic/Scholarly.* **Description:** Provides information in the fields of Web Engineering and Web technology.
Related titles: Online - full content ed.: ISSN 1741-9212. USD 450 to institutions (effective 2005); Online - full text ed.: (from EBSCO Publishing).
Indexed: BrCerAb, C&ISA, CerAb, CorrAb, E&CAJ, EMA, ErgAb, IAA, Inspec, M&TEA, MBF, METADEX, WAA.
—BLDSC (4542.701150), IE, Linda Hall.
Published by: Inderscience Publishers, IEL Editorial Office, PO Box 735, Olney, Bucks MK46 5WB, United Kingdom. TEL 44-1234-240519, FAX 44-1234-240515, ijwet@inderscience.com, editor@inderscience.com, http://www.inderscience.com/ijwet. Ed. Lorna Uden. **Subscr. to:** World Trade Centre Bldg, 29 route de Pre-Bois, Case Postale 896, Geneva 15 1215, Switzerland. FAX 41-22-7910885, subs@inderscience.com.

020 USA ISSN 1552-6283
TK5105.88815
▼ **INTERNATIONAL JOURNAL ON SEMANTIC WEB AND INFORMATION SYSTEMS.** Text in English. 2005 (Jan). q. USD 85 to individuals; USD 195 to institutions (effective 2005). **Document type:** *Journal, Academic/Scholarly.* **Description:** Promotes a knowledge transfer channel where academics, practictioners and researchers can discuss, analyze, criticize, synthesize, communicate, elaborate, and simplify the more than promising technology of the Semantic Web in the context of Information Systems. Aims to establish value-adding knowledge transfer and personal development channels in three distinctive areas: Academia, Industry, and Government.
Related titles: Online - full text ed.: ISSN 1552-6291.
Indexed: C&ISA, E&CAJ, IAA.
Published by: Idea Group Publishing (Subsidiary of: Idea Group Inc.), 701 E Chocolate Ave, Ste 200, Hershey, PA 17033-1240. TEL 717-533-8845, 866-342-6657, FAX 717-533-7115, mkurtz@idea-group.com, cust@idea-group.com, http://www.idea-group.com/ijswis. Ed. Amit Sheth.

020 USA
INTERNATIONAL WORKSHOP ON MULTIMEDIA DATA BASE MANAGEMENT SYSTEMS. Text in English. a. price varies. **Document type:** *Proceedings, Trade.*
—BLDSC (4552.195040).
Published by: Institute of Electrical and Electronics Engineers, Inc., 3 Park Ave, 17th Fl, New York, NY 10016-5997. TEL 212-419-7900, 800-678-4333, FAX 212-752-4929, customer.service@ieee.org, http://www.ieee.org.

020 USA ISSN 1097-8585
INTERNATIONAL WORKSHOP ON RESEARCH ISSUES IN DATA ENGINEERING. PROCEEDINGS. Text in English. '19??. a. USD 142; USD 57 to students (effective 2004). **Document type:** *Proceedings, Trade.*
Published by: Institute of Electrical and Electronics Engineers, Inc., 3 Park Ave, 17th Fl, New York, NY 10016-5997. TEL 212-419-7900, 800-678-4333, FAX 212-752-4929, customer.service@ieee.org, http://www.ieee.org.

▼ **THE INTERNET JOURNAL OF INFORMATION SYSTEMS.** see *BUSINESS AND ECONOMICS*

IRYO JOHO SHISUTEMU KENKYU KAIHATSU HOKOKUSHO/REPORT OF RESEARCH AND DEVELOPMENT OF MEDICAL INFORMATION SYSTEM. see *MEDICAL SCIENCES*

003.54 020 FRA ISSN 1299-9547
IT-EXPERT. Text mainly in French. 1996. bi-m.
Formerly (until 1999): Databases Journal (1270-4881)
Indexed: Inspec.
Published by: Press & Communication France, 3 rue Marcel Allegot, Meudon, 92190, France. TEL 33-1-46902121, FAX 33-1-46902120, redaction@it-expertise.com, http://www.it-expertise.com.

020 331.1 USA
ITRECRUITERMAG.COM; employment opportunities and career news for information technology professionals. Text in English. 1998. bi-m. **Document type:** *Trade.*
Published by: Quantum Communications Group, Inc., 1493 Chain Bridge Rd, No 100, McLean, VA 22101. TEL 703-714-9462, FAX 708-714-9482, articles@itrecruitermag.com, http://www.itrecruitermag.com. Ed. Loretta W Prencipe.

003.54 HKG ISSN 1532-4516
T1
➤ **J I T T A**; an information systems journal. (Journal of Information Technology Theory & Application) Text in English. 1999. irreg. **Document type:** *Journal, Academic/Scholarly.*
Media: Online - full content. **Related titles:** Online - full text ed.: (from bigchalk, O C L C Online Computer Library Center, Inc., ProQuest Information & Learning); Print ed.: ISSN 1552-6496.
Indexed: ABIn.
—IE.
Address: Hong Kong University of Science and Technology, Clear Water Bay, Kowloon, Hong Kong. editor@jitta.org, http://www.jitta.org/. Ed., Pub. Ken Peffers.

005.7 KOR ISSN 1229-7739
JEONGBO GWAHAGHOE NONMUNJI. DEI'TA'BEI'SEU/KOREA INFORMATION SCIENCE SOCIETY. JOURNAL. DATABASE. Text in Korean. 1995. q. **Document type:** *Journal, Academic/Scholarly.*
—BLDSC (4811.108000).
Published by: Korea Information Science Society/Han'guk Chongbo Kwahakhoe, No. 401 Murijae Bldg, 984-1 Bangbae-3dong Secho-du, Seoul, 137-063 , Korea, S. TEL 82-2-5889246, FAX 82-2-5211352, kiss@kiss.or.kr, http://www.kiss.or.kr/.

621.38 KOR ISSN 1229-7720
JEONGBO GWAHAGHOE NONMUNJI. JEONGBO TONGSIN/KOREA INFORMATION SCIENCE SOCIETY. JOURNAL. INFORMATION NETWORKING. Text in Korean. 1995. q. **Document type:** *Journal, Academic/Scholarly.*
—BLDSC (4811.109000).
Published by: Korea Information Science Society/Han'guk Chongbo Kwahakhoe, No. 401 Murijae Bldg, 984-1 Bangbae-3dong Secho-du, Seoul, 137-063 , Korea, S. TEL 82-2-5889246, FAX 82-2-5211352, kiss@kiss.or.kr, http://www.kiss.or.kr/.

020 KOR ISSN 1229-7712
JEONGBO GWAHAGHOE NONMUNJI. KEOMPYUTING UI SILJE/JOURNAL OF K I S S. COMPUTING PRACTICES. Text in Korean. 1974. bi-m. KRW 40,000 to individuals For membership; KRW 20,000 to students For membership; KRW 200,000 to institutions For membership (effective 2000). **Document type:** *Journal, Academic/Scholarly.*
Formerly (until 2000): Jeongbo Gwahaghoe Nonmunji (C) (1226-2293); Which superseded in part (in 1995): Jeongbo Gwahaghoe Nonmunji (0258-9125)
Indexed: Inspec.
—BLDSC (4811.107500).
Published by: Korea Information Science Society/Han'guk Chongbo Kwahakhoe, No. 401 Murijae Bldg, 984-1 Bangbae-3dong Secho-du, Seoul, 137-063 , Korea, S. TEL 82-2-5889246, FAX 82-2-5211352, kiss@kiss.or.kr, http://www.kiss.or.kr/.

020 KOR ISSN 1229-683X
JEONGBO GWAHAGHOE NONMUNJI. SI'SEU'TEM MICH I'LON/JOURNAL OF K I S S. COMPUTER SYSTEMS AND THEORY. Text in Korean. 1974. m. KRW 40,000 to individuals For membership; KRW 20,000 to students For membership; KRW 200,000 to institutions For membership (effective 2000). **Document type:** *Journal, Academic/Scholarly.*
Formerly (until 2000): Jeongbo Gwahaghoe Nonmunji (A) (1226-2315); Which superseded in part (in 1995): Jeongbo Gwahaghoe Nonmunji (0258-9125)
Indexed: Inspec.
—BLDSC (4811.105000).
Published by: Korea Information Science Society/Han'guk Chongbo Kwahakhoe, No. 401 Murijae Bldg, 984-1 Bangbae-3dong Secho-du, Seoul, 137-063 , Korea, S. TEL 82-2-5889246, FAX 82-2-5211352, kiss@kiss.or.kr, http://www.kiss.or.kr/.

020 KOR ISSN 1229-6848
JEONGBO GWAHAGHOE NONMUNJI. SO'PEUTEUWEEO MICH EUNG'YONG/JOURNAL OF K I S S. SOFTWARE AND APPLICATIONS. Text in Korean. 1974. m. KRW 40,000 to individuals For membership; KRW 20,000 to students For membership; KRW 200,000 to institutions For membership (effective 2000). **Document type:** *Academic/Scholarly.*
Formerly (until 2000): Jeongbo Gwahaghoe Nonmunji (B) (1226-2285); Which superseded in part (in 1995): Jeongbo Gwahaghoe Nonmunji (0258-9125)
Indexed: Inspec.
—BLDSC (4811.110000).
Published by: Korea Information Science Society/Han'guk Chongbo Kwahakhoe, No. 401 Murijae Bldg, 984-1 Bangbae-3dong Secho-du, Seoul, 137-063 , Korea, S. TEL 82-2-5889246, FAX 82-2-5211352, kiss@kiss.or.kr, http://www.kiss.or.kr/.

C

020 CHN ISSN 1671-5896
JILIN DAXUE XUEBAO (XINXI KEXUE BAN)/JILIN UNIVERSITY. JOURNAL (INFORMATION SCIENCE EDITION). Text in Chinese. 1983. bi-m. CNY 5 per issue domestic (effective 2000). back issues avail. **Document type:** *Journal, Academic/Scholarly.*
Formerly: Changchun Youdian Xueyuan Xuebao/Changchun Institute of Posts and Telecommunications. Journal (1000-1794)
Related titles: Online - full content ed.: (from WanFang Data Corp.); Online - full text ed.: (from East View Information Services).
Indexed: BrCerAb, C&ISA, CerAb, CorrAb, E&CAJ, EMA, IAA, Inspec, M&TEA, MBF, METADEX, RefZh, WAA.
Published by: Jilin Daxue/Jilin University, Editorial Dept. of Journal of Jilin University (Information Science Ed.), 20, Nanhou Dalou, Changchun, 1671-5896, China. TEL 85-431-5151027, 86-431-5152552, ccyd@chinajournal.net.cn, http://ccyd.chinajournal.net.cn/. **Dist. by:** China International Book Trading Corp, 35 Chegongzhuang Xilu, Haidian District, PO Box 399, Beijing 100044, China. TEL 86-10-68412045, FAX 86-10-68412023, cibtc@mail.cibtc.com.cn, http://www.cibtc.com.cn.

JOHN MARSHALL JOURNAL OF COMPUTER & INFORMATION LAW. see *LAW*

003.54 JPN
JOHO RIRON TO SONO OYO SHINPOJUMU YOKOSHU/SYMPOSIUM ON INFORMATION THEORY AND ITS APPLICATIONS. PROCEEDINGS. Text in English, Japanese. a. **Document type:** *Proceedings.*
Published by: Joho Riron to Sono Oyo Gakkai/Society of Information Theory and Its Applications, c/o Prof. Suguru Arimoto, Ritsumeikan University, Department of Robotics Faculty of Science and Engineering, 1-1-1 Noji-Higashi, Kusatsu-shi, Shiga-ken 525-0058, Japan. TEL 81-775-61-2664, FAX 81-775-61-2665.

003.54 JPN ISSN 1343-0130
➤ **JOURNAL OF ADVANCED COMPUTATIONAL INTELLIGENCE.** Text and summaries in English. bi-m. JPY 66,000; USD 660 foreign. back issues avail. **Document type:** *Academic/Scholarly.*
Formerly (until 1997): Journal of Advanced Automation Technology
—BLDSC (4918.945750).
Published by: Fuji Technology Press Ltd., 4F Toranomon Sangyo Bldg, 2-29, Toranomon 1-chome, Minato-ku, Tokyo, 105-0001, Japan. TEL 81-3-35080051, FAX 81-3-35920648, tae00762@niftyserve.or.jp. Pub. Keiji Hayashi.

020 USA ISSN 1553-9105
QA75.5
JOURNAL OF COMPUTATIONAL INFORMATION SYSTEMS. Text in English. q. USD 600 to individuals; USD 1,200 to institutions (effective 2005). **Document type:** *Journal, Academic/Scholarly.* **Description:** Designed to be of broad interest and use to both researchers and engineers of information systems. Publishes original papers in areas of computer science and computational applications of information systems.
Published by: Binary Information Press, PO Box 162, Bethel, CT 06801-0162. http://www.jofcis.com/. Ed. X N Luo.

JOURNAL OF CRYPTOLOGY. see *MATHEMATICS*

020 USA ISSN 1368-7506
ZA4060
➤ **JOURNAL OF DIGITAL INFORMATION.** Abbreviated title: J o D I. Text in English. 1997. q. free (effective 2005). back issues avail. **Document type:** *Journal, Academic/Scholarly.* **Description:** Covers digital libraries, hypermedia systems, information management, intelligent agents, interfaces to digital information, and the social consequences of digital information.
Media: Online - full text.
Indexed: CINAHL, InfoSAb, Inspec.
Published by: Texas A & M University Libraries, College Station, TX 77843. TEL 409-845-5741, http://jodi.tamu.edu. Circ: 6,005 (controlled).

020 IND ISSN 0972-7272
▼ ➤ **JOURNAL OF DIGITAL INFORMATION MANAGEMENT.** Text in English. 2003. 4/yr. INR 900, USD 42, EUR 42 combined subscription to individuals print & online eds.; INR 1,400, USD 54, EUR 54 combined subscription to institutions print & online eds. (effective 2004). **Document type:** *Journal, Academic/Scholarly.* **Description:** Aims to identify the optimum strategy and best practice for the ideal digital information management.
Related titles: Online - full text ed.: INR 800, USD 32, EUR 32 to individuals; INR 1,200, USD 44, EUR 44 to institutions (effective 2003) (from EBSCO Publishing).
Indexed: Inspec.
—BLDSC (4969.617000), IE.
Published by: Digital Information Research Foundation, 3/76 Vanchinathan St, Periyar Salai, Palavakkam, Chennai, 600 041, India. http://www.dirf.org. Eds. Daisy Jacobs, P. Pichappan.

020 USA ISSN 1548-7741
THE JOURNAL OF INFORMATION AND COMPUTATIONAL SCIENCE. Text in English. q. **Document type:** *Journal, Academic/Scholarly.* **Description:** Publishes original papers of scientific value in all areas of information and computational science.
Published by: Binary Information Press, PO Box 162, Bethel, CT 06801-0162. http://www.joics.com/. Ed. Ren-Hong Wang.

003.54 USA
JOURNAL OF INFORMATION POLICY. Text in English. 1998. q. USD 5. adv. **Document type:** *Trade.* **Description:** Reprints speeches and position papers on public policy affecting all types of information transfer.
Published by: Silverberg Independent Media, 1310 Millfarm Dr, Vienna, VA 22182. TEL 703-757-0520, FAX 703-757-0555, SiMedia@erols.com, http://www.Infopolicy.com. Ed., Pub. David Silverberg. Adv. contact Cindy McConnel.

003.54 JPN ISSN 0021-7298
T58.6 CODEN: JOKAAB
JOURNAL OF INFORMATION PROCESSING AND MANAGEMENT/JOHO KANRI. Text in Japanese; Summaries in English. 1958. m. USD 175. adv. bk.rev. abstr.; charts; illus. index.
Formerly: Information and Documentation
Related titles: Online - full content ed.: ISSN 1347-1597; Online - full text ed.: (from J-Stage).
Indexed: CIN, ChemAb, ChemTitl, INIS AtomInd, InfoSAb, Inspec, JTA, MathR, RASB, RefZh.
—BLDSC (5006.772200), AskIEEE, CASDDS, IE, ingenta.
Published by: Japan Science and Technology Corporation, Information Center for Science and Technology/Kagaku Gijutsu Shinko Jigyodan, 5-3 Yonban-cho, Chiyoda-ku, Tokyo, 102-0081, Japan. TEL 81-3-5214-8413, FAX 81-3-5214-8410, http://johokanri.jstage.jst.go.jp/. Circ: 5,000.

020 USA ISSN 0888-7985
CODEN: JINFE3
THE JOURNAL OF INFORMATION SYSTEMS. Text in English. 1986. s-a. USD 35; USD 140 combined subscription print & online eds. (effective 2005). reprint service avail. from PSC. **Document type:** *Journal, Academic/Scholarly.* **Description:** Aims to improve accounting information systems research, education and practice.
Related titles: Online - full text ed.: (from EBSCO Publishing, Florida Center for Library Automation, Gale Group, O C L C Online Computer Library Center, Inc., ProQuest Information & Learning).
Indexed: ABIn, CompLI, Inspec.
—BLDSC (5006.777000), AskIEEE, IE. **CCC.**
Published by: American Accounting Association, 5717 Bessie Dr, Sarasota, FL 34233-2399. TEL 941-921-7747, FAX 941-923-4093, dstone@uky.edu, office@aaahq.org, http://www.acct.tamu.edu/jis, http://aaahq.org. Ed. Dan Stone. R&P Mary Cole.

JOURNAL OF INFORMATION TECHNOLOGY EDUCATION. see *EDUCATION—Teaching Methods And Curriculum*

003.54 USA ISSN 1042-1319
T58.64
JOURNAL OF INFORMATION TECHNOLOGY MANAGEMENT. Text in English. 1990. q. USD 111 domestic to individuals; USD 231 domestic to institutions; USD 156 foreign to individuals; USD 276 foreign to institutions (effective 2005). adv. **Document type:** *Academic/Scholarly.*
Indexed: Inspec.
—BLDSC (5006.795000), IE.
Published by: (Association of Management), Maximilian Press, PO Box 64841, Virginia Beach, VA 23464-0841. http://www.aom-iaom.org/j-two-jitm.html. Ed. Dr. Al Bento. Adv. contact Willem A Hamel. Circ: 1,500.

JOURNAL OF INTERNATIONAL SELLING & SALES MANAGEMENT. see *BUSINESS AND ECONOMICS—Marketing And Purchasing*

JOURNAL OF INTERNATIONAL TECHNOLOGY AND INFORMATION MANAGEMENT. see *BUSINESS AND ECONOMICS—Management*

JOURNAL OF LAW AND INFORMATION SCIENCE. see *LAW*

020 USA ISSN 0742-1222
CODEN: JMISEB
➤ **JOURNAL OF MANAGEMENT INFORMATION SYSTEMS.** Abbreviated title: J M I S. Text in English. 1984. q. USD 99 domestic to individuals; USD 127 foreign to individuals; USD 780 combined subscription domestic to institutions print & online eds.; USD 886 combined subscription foreign to institutions print & online eds. (effective 2006). adv. bk.rev. charts; illus. index. back issues avail.; reprint service avail. from PSC. **Document type:** *Journal, Academic/Scholarly.* **Description:** Presents research that advances the practice and understanding of organizational information systems. Aims to serve those investigating new models of information delivery and the changing landscape of information policy making, as well as practitioners and executives managing information resources.
Related titles: Online - full text ed.: 2000 (June) (from EBSCO Publishing, Gale Group, H.W. Wilson, Northern Light Technology, Inc., O C L C Online Computer Library Center, Inc., ProQuest Information & Learning, Swets Information Services).
Indexed: ABIn, ADPA, BPI, CMCI, CompLI, CurCont, Emerald, EngInd, IBR, Inspec, ORMS, QC&AS, RASB, RefZh, SCIMP, SSCI.
—BLDSC (5011.350000), AskIEEE, IE, Infotrieve, ingenta. **CCC.**
Published by: M.E. Sharpe, Inc., 80 Business Park Dr, Armonk, NY 10504. TEL 914-273-1800, 800-541-6563, FAX 914-273-2106, custserv@mesharpe.com, http://www.mesharpe.com/mall/results1.asp. Ed. Vladimir Zwass. adv.: page USD 300; 9 x 6. **Subscr. to:** Allen Press Inc., PO Box 1897, Lawrence, KS 66044.

020 AUS ISSN 1328-7265
JOURNAL OF SYSTEMS AND INFORMATION TECHNOLOGY. Text in English. 1997. s-a. AUD 80 (effective 2002). **Document type:** *Journal, Academic/Scholarly.* **Description:** Provides an avenue for scholarly work that takes a systemic or holistic perspective in relation to areas such as information systems development, information technology, information systems management and electronic commerce.
—BLDSC (5068.064500).
Published by: Edith Cowan University, c/o Dr. Craig Standing. Ed., Joondalup, W.A. 6027, Australia. FAX 61-08-9400-5633, c.standing@ecu.edu.au, http://www.bs.ac.ecu.edu.au/josit/.

003.54 004.6 AUT ISSN 1683-1373
JOURNAL ON APPLIED INFORMATION TECHNOLOGY. Abbreviated title: J A P I T. Text in English. 2002. q.
Indexed: Inspec.
Published by: Technische Universitaet Wien, Institut fuer Industrielle Elektronik und Materialwissenschaften/Vienna University of Technology, Institute of Industrial Electronics and Material Science, Gusshausstrasse 27-29, Vienna, 1040, Austria. TEL 43-1-5880136601, FAX 43-1-5880136699, http://www.iemw.tuwien.ac.at/.

THE JOURNAL ON INFORMATION TECHNOLOGY IN HEALTHCARE. see *MEDICAL SCIENCES*

KANKYO JOHO KAGAKU/ENVIRONMENTAL INFORMATION SCIENCE. see *ENVIRONMENTAL STUDIES*

003 GBR ISSN 0219-1377
➤ **KNOWLEDGE AND INFORMATION SYSTEMS.** Text in English. 1999. 8/yr. EUR 588 combined subscription to institutions print & online eds. (effective 2005). back issues avail.; reprint service avail. from PSC. **Document type:** *Journal, Academic/Scholarly.* **Description:** Provides an international forum for researchers and professionals to share their knowledge and report new advances on all topics related to knowledge systems and advanced information systems.
Related titles: Online - full text ed.: ISSN 0219-3116 (from EBSCO Publishing, ProQuest Information & Learning, Springer LINK, Swets Information Services).
Indexed: ABIn, CMCI, CompAb, CompLI, CurCont, Inspec.
—BLDSC (5100.437300), CISTI, IE, Infotrieve. **CCC.**
Published by: Springer-Verlag London Ltd. (Subsidiary of: Springer Science+Business Media), Ashbourne House, The Guildway, Old Portsmouth Rd, Guildford, Surrey GU7 3DJ, United Kingdom. TEL 44-1483-734433, FAX 44-1483-734411, postmaster@svl.co.uk, http://link.springer.de/link/service/journals/10115/, http://www.springer.co.uk. Eds. Benjamin Wah, Xindong Wu. Adv. contact Christiane Notarmarco. **Subscr. in the Americas to:** Springer-Verlag New York, Inc., Journal Fulfillment, PO Box 2485, Secaucus, NJ 07096-2485. TEL 800-777-4643, 201-348-4033, FAX 201-348-4505, journals@springer-ny.com, http://www.springer-ny.com; **Subscr. to:** Springer GmbH Auslieferungsgesellschaft, Haberstr 7, Heidelberg 69126, Germany. TEL 49-6221-345-0, FAX 49-6221-345-4229, subscriptions@springer.de.

➤ **KOMP'YUTERY V UCHEBNOM PROTSESSE.** see *LIBRARY AND INFORMATION SCIENCES*

➤ **L I T A-L.** (Library and Information Technology Association) see *LIBRARY AND INFORMATION SCIENCES—Computer Applications*

➤ **L I T A NEWSLETTER (ONLINE EDITION).** (Library and Information Technology Association) see *LIBRARY AND INFORMATION SCIENCES*

➤ **LLOYD: INFORMATION TECHNOLOGY LAW.** see *LAW*

020 352 072 GBR
LOCAL GOVERNMENT I T IN USE. (Information Technology) Text in English. 1997. 8/yr. free to qualified personnel (effective 2005). adv. bk.rev.; software rev. tr.lit.; illus. 24 p./no.; back issues avail. **Document type:** *Newsletter.*
Published by: Informed Publications Ltd., 95 Ditchling Rd, Brighton, Sussex BN1 4ST, United Kingdom. TEL 44-1273-277110, FAX 44-1273-623338, lgito@infopub.co.uk, http://www.infopub.co.uk/xhtml/lgitu.asp. Ed., Pub. Helen Olsen. Adv. contact Ann-Marie Campbell-Smith. B&W page GBP 1,200, color page GBP 1,800. Circ: 8,500.

C

020 GBR ISSN 1860-5974
▼ ➤ **LOGICAL METHODS IN COMPUTER SCIENCE.** Text in English. 2004 (July). irreg. free (effective 2005). **Document type:** *Journal, Academic/Scholarly.* **Description:** Covers theoretical and practical areas in computer science involving logical methods.
Media: Online - full content.
Published by: International Federation for Computational Logic http://www.lmcs-online.org/. Ed. Dana S Scott TEL 412-268-3881.

020 MYS ISSN 0127-9084
QA75.5 CODEN: MJCSFS
➤ **MALAYSIAN JOURNAL OF COMPUTER SCIENCE.** Text in English. 1985. s-a. USD 40 (effective 2003). abstr. back issues avail. **Document type:** *Journal, Academic/Scholarly.* **Description:** Promotes the exchange of information on the use of information technology. Covers research work, new inventions and developments in computer science.
Related titles: Online - full text ed.
Indexed: Inspec, RILM.
Published by: University of Malaya, Faculty of Computer Science and Information Technology, Kuala Lumpur, 50603, Malaysia. TEL 60-3-79676361, FAX 60-3-79579249, edzan@um.edu.my, saipeck@um.edu.my, http://ejum.fsktm.um.edu.my, http://www.fsktm.um.edu.my. Eds. Chiew Thiarr Kiar, Koh Swee Neo, Lee Sai Peck. R&P Nor Edzan Nasir.

658 GBR ISSN 1470-6326
MANAGEMENT INFORMATION SYSTEMS. Text in English. 2000. irreg., latest vol.4, 2002. price varies. **Document type:** *Monographic series.*
Published by: WIT Press, Ashurst Lodge, Ashurst, Southampton, Hants SO40 7AA, United Kingdom. TEL 44-238-029-3223, FAX 44-238-029-2853, marketing@witpress.com, http://www.witpress.com.

338 003.54 USA ISSN 1547-6731
▼ **MANUFACTURING I T (CAROL STREAM)**; the source for information technology in manufacturing. (Information Technology) Text in English. 2003 (Dec.). a. free (effective 2004).
Published by: Specialty Publishing Co., 135 E Saint Charles Rd, Carol Stream, IL 60188. TEL 630-933-0844, FAX 630-933-0845, http://www.specialtypub.com.

003.54 NLD
MARKETONS I T DATABANK. Text in Dutch. m. charts. **Document type:** *Directory, Trade.* **Description:** Offers an historic overview of the IT market while keeping up to date with the latest developments. Each month, the database of 16,000 records is updated with some 500 new articles concerning all relevent developments in the marketplace.
Media: CD-ROM. **Related titles:** ♦ CD-ROM ed.: Prof I T Datenbank CD-ROM.
Published by: Marketons BV, Postbus 1310, Nijmegen, 6501 BH, Netherlands. TEL 31-24-322-4200, FAX 31-24-360-3176, redactie@marketons.nl, http://www.marketons.nl/producten/itdb.

NATIONAL ELECTRONIC PACKAGING AND PRODUCTION CONFERENCE (EAST). PROCEEDINGS OF THE TECHNICAL PROGRAM. see *COMPUTERS*

NATIONAL ELECTRONIC PACKAGING AND PRODUCTION CONFERENCE (WEST). PROCEEDINGS OF THE TECHNICAL PROGRAM. see *COMPUTERS*

O E C D INFORMATION TECHNOLOGY OUTLOOK/ PERSPECTIVES DES TECHNOLOGIES DE L'INFORMATION. see *LIBRARY AND INFORMATION SCIENCES—Computer Applications*

020 DNK ISSN 1603-2551
ON EDGE. Text in Danish. 2002. 3/yr. back issues avail. **Document type:** *Academic/Scholarly.*
Media: Online - full content.
Published by: Syddansk Universitet, Knowledge Lab, Campusvej 55, Odense M, 5230, Denmark. med@knowledgelab.sdu.dk, http://www.knowledgelab.dk.

025.04 GBR ISSN 0263-2187
ON LINE (SUNBURY-ON-THAMES). Text in English. 1978. 3/yr. charts; illus.
Indexed: RASB.
Published by: B O C Computer Services, 99 Staines Rd W., Sunbury-on-thames, Mddx, United Kingdom.

003.54 351 USA
OPEN FORUM; innovations in information resource management to support government. Text in English. m. **Document type:** *Bulletin, Government.*
Published by: Nelson A. Rockefeller Institute of Government, 411 State St, Albany, NY 12203-1003. TEL 518-443-5258, FAX 518-443-5788, cooperm@rockinst.org, http://www.rockinst.org. Pub. Michael Cooper.

DER ORGANISATOR. see *BUSINESS AND ECONOMICS—Management*

P X I TECHNOLOGY REVIEW. see *COMPUTERS—Minicomputers*

003.54 PAK ISSN 1682-6027
PAKISTAN JOURNAL OF INFORMATION TECHNOLOGY. Text in English. 2002. q. USD 200 (effective 2003). **Document type:** *Journal.*
Indexed: Inspec.
—BLDSC (6341.450000).
Published by: Asian Network for Scientific Information, 308-Lasani Town, Sargodha Rd, Faislabad, 38090, Pakistan. TEL 92-41-2001145, FAX 92-41-731433, http://www.pjas.pjit, http://www.ansinet.net.

PERFORMANCE MEASUREMENT AND METRICS; the international journal for library and information services. see *LIBRARY AND INFORMATION SCIENCES*

003.54 PHL
PHILIPPINE I.T. JOURNAL. (Information Technology) Text in English. m.?. PHP 320; USD 80 foreign. **Document type:** *Trade.* **Description:** A technical journal for Philippine information technology professionals.
Published by: (Department of Science and Technology), Science and Technology Information Institute, P.O. Box 3596, Manila, Philippines. TEL 822-0954. **Subscr. to:** Dept. of Science and Technology, Bicutan, Taguig, P.O. Box 2131, Manila, Philippines.

020 USA
PLANET I T; the community of I T professionals. Text in English. 1998. d. **Document type:** *Trade.*
Media: Online - full content.
Published by: C M P Media LLC (Subsidiary of: United News & Media), 600 Community Dr, Manhasset, NY 11030. pkrass@cmp.com, http://www.PlanetIT.com. Ed. Joy Blake. Circ: 140,000.

020 003.54 USA ISSN 0891-4559
PRENTICE-HALL INFORMATION AND SYSTEM SCIENCES SERIES. Text in English. irreg. **Document type:** *Monographic series.*
Indexed: Inspec.
Published by: Prentice Hall, One Lake St, Upper Saddle River, NJ 07458. TEL 800-282-0693, FAX 800-835-5327, http://vig.prenhall.com, http://www.prenhall.com.

PROBABILITY IN THE ENGINEERING AND INFORMATIONAL SCIENCES. see *ENGINEERING—Abstracting, Bibliographies, Statistics*

003.54 NLD
PROF I T DATENBANK CD-ROM. Text in Dutch. irreg. **Document type:** *Directory.* **Description:** Lists the names and addresses and provides information on the 500 most important Dutch and foreign IT suppliers and contactors.
Media: CD-ROM. **Related titles:** ♦ CD-ROM ed.: Marketons I T Databank.
Published by: Marketons BV, Postbus 1310, Nijmegen, 6501 BH, Netherlands. TEL 31-24-322-4200, FAX 31-24-360-3176, redactie@marketons.nl, http://www.marketons.nl/producten/profit.

621.3822 USA ISSN 0743-1597
PROGRESS IN COMPUTER SCIENCE. Text in English. 1981. irreg. **Document type:** *Monographic series.*
Indexed: Inspec.
Published by: Birkhaeuser Boston (Subsidiary of: Springer Science+Business Media), 675 Massachusetts Ave, Cambridge, MA 02139-3309. TEL 617-876-2333, FAX 617-876-1272, info@birkhauser.com, http://www.birkhauser.com.

020 CHN ISSN 1007-7634
Z671 CODEN: QKJIEF
QINGBAO KEXUE (CHANGCHUN)✶ /INFORMATION SCIENCE. Text in Chinese; Abstracts and contents page in English. 1980. bi-m. CNY 2.60. adv. bk.rev. bibl.; charts. **Description:** Reports on the theory method and technology of information collecting, processing, searching, analyzing, and transmitting, as well as the construction of information systems and networks, and the management of information work and policy.
Formerly (until 1998): Qingbao Kexue (Ha'erbin) (1000-8489)
Related titles: Online - full text ed.: (from East View Information Services).
Indexed: RASB.
—CASDDS.
Published by: Qingbao Kexue Zazhishe, 142 Renmin Dajie, Changchun, 130022, China. TEL 86-431-5705200, http://qbkx.periodicals.net.cn/default.html. Circ: 5,000. **Dist. outside China by:** China International Book Trading Corp, 35 Chegongzhuang Xilu, Haidian District, PO Box 399, Beijing 100044, China.

R M MAGAZINE. (Read Me) see *COMMUNICATIONS—Computer Applications*

RESEARCH IN STRATEGIC MANAGEMENT AND INFORMATION TECHNOLOGY. see *BUSINESS AND ECONOMICS—Management*

020 JPN ISSN 0912-2370
RESEARCH REPORTS ON INFORMATION SCIENCES. SERIES A, MATHEMATICAL SCIENCE. Text and summaries in English. 1974. irreg. price varies. **Document type:** *Monographic series, Academic/Scholarly.*
Indexed: Inspec.
—AskIEEE.
Published by: (Joho Kagakka), Tokyo Kogyo Daigaku, Rigakubu/Tokyo Institute of Technology, Faculty of Science, Department of Information Sciences, 12-1 Okayama 2-chome, Meguro-ku, Tokyo, 152-0033, Japan.

003 JPN ISSN 1342-2804
RESEARCH REPORTS ON MATHEMATICAL AND COMPUTING SCIENCES. SERIES B, OPERATIONS RESEARCH. Text and summaries in English. 1974. irreg. price varies. **Document type:** *Monographic series, Academic/Scholarly.*
Formerly (until 1995): Research Reports on Information Sciences. Series B, Operations Research (0912-2389)
Indexed: Inspec.
—AskIEEE.
Published by: (Joho Kagakka), Tokyo Kogyo Daigaku, Rigakubu/Tokyo Institute of Technology, Faculty of Science, Department of Information Sciences, 12-1 Okayama 2-chome, Meguro-ku, Tokyo, 152-0033, Japan.

003.54 JPN ISSN 1342-2812
RESEARCH REPORTS ON MATHEMATICAL AND COMPUTING SCIENCES. SERIES C, COMPUTER SCIENCES. Text and summaries in English. 1974. irreg. price varies. **Document type:** *Monographic series, Academic/Scholarly.*
Formerly (until 1995): Research Reports on Information Sciences. Series C, Computer Sciences (0912-2397)
Indexed: Inspec.
—BLDSC (7769.541727), AskIEEE.
Published by: (Joho Kagakka), Tokyo Kogyo Daigaku, Rigakubu/Tokyo Institute of Technology, Faculty of Science, Department of Information Sciences, 12-1 Okayama 2-chome, Meguro-ku, Tokyo, 152-0033, Japan.

003 GBR ISSN 1740-1402
RETHINK I T. (Information Technology) Text in English. m. USD 410 (effective 2000). **Document type:** *Journal, Trade.*
Former titles (until 2003): Insight I S (1356-5478); (until 1994): Insight I B M
Related titles: Online - full text ed.: (from Gale Group).
Indexed: CompD.
Published by: Xephon, 27-35, London Rd, Newbury, Berkshire RG14 1JL, United Kingdom. TEL 44-1635-33823, FAX 44-1635-38345, xephon@compuserve.com.

REVISTA MACKENZIE DE ENGENHARIA E COMPUTACAO. see *ENGINEERING*

621.3822 CHE ISSN 0254-6213
S E A S ANNIVERSARY MEETING. PROCEEDINGS. Variant title: Share European Association. Anniversary Meeting. Proceedings. Text in English. 1983. a.
Indexed: Inspec.
Published by: Guide Share Europe, Hinterbergstrasse 9, PO Box 5127, Cham, 6330, Switzerland. TEL 41-41-748-70-20, FAX 41-41-748-70-35, gsehq@gse.org, http://www.gse.org.

003.54 USA ISSN 0163-5840
Z699.5.E6 CODEN: FASRDV
S I G I R FORUM. (Special Interest Group on Information Retrieval) Text in English. 196?. 3/yr. USD 20 (effective 2004). **Document type:** *Newsletter, Academic/Scholarly.* **Description:** Welcomes members working in all aspects of information storage, retrieval, and dissemination, including research strategies, output schemes, and system evaluation.
Related titles: Online - full text ed.: (from EBSCO Publishing).
Indexed: EngInd, InfoSAb, Inspec.
—BLDSC (8275.330000), AskIEEE, Ei, IE, Infotrieve, ingenta.
Published by: Association for Computing Machinery, Inc., 1515 Broadway, 17th Fl, New York, NY 10036-5701. TEL 212-626-0500, 212-626-0520, 800-342-6626, FAX 212-869-0481, sigs@acm.org, usacm@acm.org, http://www.acm.org/sigir/.

S I G I T E NEWSLETTER. (Special Interest Group Information Technology Education) see *EDUCATION—Teaching Methods And Curriculum*

020 USA
S I M NETWORK. Text in English. bi-m. membership.
Related titles: Online - full text ed.
Published by: Society for Information Management, 401 N Michigan Ave, Chicago, IL 60611-4267. TEL 312-644-6610, FAX 312-245-1083, http://www.simnet.org. Ed. Mary Rose Mazza. Circ: 2,700.

003 DEU ISSN 0931-4326
S T NEWS. Text in English. 1985. bi-m. **Document type:** *Newsletter, Academic/Scholarly.*
Related titles: Online - full text ed.
—BLDSC (8465.077000).
Published by: Fachinformationszentrum Karlsruhe, Gesellschaft fuer wissenschaftlich-technische Information mbH (Subsidiary of: STN Service Center Europe), Eggenstein Leopoldshafen, 76344, Germany. TEL 49-7247-808555, FAX 49-7247-808131, helpdesk@fiz-karlsruhe.de, http://www.fiz-karlsruhe.de.

C

003 GBR ISSN 1364-5064
Z286.S37
SCHOLARLY COMMUNICATIONS REPORT; news and updates on key issues in the changing scholarly communications process. Text in English. 1996. 11/yr. GBP 225, USD 380 to institutions; GBP 250, USD 420 combined subscription to institutions print & online (effective 2005). **Document type:** *Newsletter, Academic/Scholarly.* **Description:** Keep abreast of developments in scholarly communications, and in particular the impact of electronic publishing.
Related titles: Online - full content ed.
—BLDSC (8092.540230), IE, Infotrieve.
Published by: S C R Publishing Ltd., 94 Mill St, Kidlington, Oxford OX5 2EF, United Kingdom. TEL 44-1865-370845, albertjprior@aol.com, http://www.scrpublishing.com/si_pd.cfm. Eds. Albert Prior, David Brown. **Subscr. to:** Portland Customer Services, Commerce Way, Colchester CO2 8HP, United Kingdom. TEL 44-1206-796351, FAX 44-1206-799331, sales@portland-services.com, http://www.portland-services.com.

621.3822 CHE ISSN 1028-284X
SHARE EUROPE SPRING CONFERENCE. PROCEEDINGS. Text in English. 1984. a.
Formerly (until 1990): S E A S Spring Meeting. Proceedings (0255-6464)
Indexed: Inspec.
Published by: Guide Share Europe, Hinterbergstrasse 9, PO Box 5127, Cham, 6330, Switzerland. TEL 41-41-748-70-20, FAX 41-41-748-70-35, gsehq@gse.org, http://www.gse.org.

THE SOFTWARE QUALITY ADVISOR; the "how-to" newsletter of software quality assurance. see *COMPUTERS—Software*

621.3822 FRA ISSN 1683-2418
SOURCE O C D E. SCIENCE ET TECHNOLOGIES DE L'INFORMATION. (Organisation de Cooperation et de Developpement Economiques) Text in French. irreg. EUR 750, USD 862, GBP 496, JPY 101,300 (effective 2005).
Related titles: Online - full content ed.: ISSN 1684-3061. EUR 525, USD 603, GBP 348, JPY 70,900 (effective 2005); Online - full text ed.: (from EBSCO Publishing, Gale Group, IngentaConnect, Swets Information Services); ♦ English ed.: Source O E C D. Science & Information Technology. ISSN 1608-0270.
Published by: Organization for Economic Cooperation and Development, 2 Rue Andre Pascal, Paris, 75775 Cedex 16, France. TEL 33-1-45248200, FAX 33-1-45248500, http://www.oecd.org. **Dist. by:** Extenza - Turpin, Pegasus Dr, Stratton Business Park, Biggleswade, Beds SG18 8TQ, United Kingdom. TEL 44-1462-687552, FAX 44-1462-480947, subscriptions@extenza-turpin.com; O E C D Turpin North America, PO Box 194, Downingtown, PA 19335-0194. TEL 610-524-5361, 800-456-6323, FAX 610-524-5417, journalscustomer@turpinna.com.

621.3822 FRA ISSN 1608-0270
SOURCE O E C D. SCIENCE & INFORMATION TECHNOLOGY. Text in English. irreg. EUR 750, USD 862, GBP 496, JPY 101,300 (effective 2005).
Related titles: Online - full content ed.: 2000. EUR 525, USD 603, GBP 348, JPY 70,900 (effective 2005); Online - full text ed.: ISSN 1681-5416 (from EBSCO Publishing, Gale Group, IngentaConnect, Swets Information Services); ♦ French ed.: Source O C D E. Science et Technologies de l'Information. ISSN 1683-2418.
Published by: Organization for Economic Cooperation and Development, 2 Rue Andre Pascal, Paris, 75775 Cedex 16, France. TEL 33-1-45248200, FAX 33-1-45248500, http://www.oecd.org. **Dist. by:** Extenza - Turpin, Pegasus Dr, Stratton Business Park, Biggleswade, Beds SG18 8TQ, United Kingdom. TEL 44-1462-687552, FAX 44-1462-480947, subscriptions@extenza-turpin.com; O E C D Turpin North America, PO Box 194, Downingtown, PA 19335-0194. TEL 610-524-5361, 800-456-6323, FAX 610-524-5417, journalscustomer@turpinna.com.

SOUTH AMERICAN SYMPOSIUM ON STRING PROCESSING AND INFORMATION RETRIEVAL. see *COMPUTERS—Computer Architecture*

003.54 USA ISSN 1535-6078
➤ **SPROUTS**; working papers on information environments, systems and organizations. Text in English. 2001. q. free (effective 2005). cum.index. back issues avail. **Document type:** *Journal, Academic/Scholarly.* **Description:** Geared for any interesting theory driven or theory building work in the context of information environments, systems and organizations, with no limitation of size, genre, or method. Innovative and challenging work is especially encouraged. The journal is open for interdisciplinary work that broadens the base of scholarship in management, design, and information systems through linkages with the full breadth of arts and sciences.
Media: Online - full text.
Published by: Case Western Reserve University, Weatherhead School of Management, PBL 525, 10900 Euclid Ave, Cleveland, OH 44106-7235. TEL 216-368-2144, sprouts@cwru.edu, http://weatherhead.cwru.edu/sprouts/, http;//weatherhead.cwru.edu. Eds. Kalle Lyytinen, Michael Avital. R&P Colleen Gepperth TEL 216-368-2144.

➤ **STUDIES IN VISUAL INFORMATION PROCESSING.** see *MEDICAL SCIENCES—Psychiatry And Neurology*

020 HRV ISSN 0351-1804
➤ **SVEUCILISTE U ZAGREBU. FAKULTET ORGANIZACIJE I INFORMATIKE VARAZDIN. ZBORNIK RADOVA.** Text in Serbo-Croatian. 1977. s-a. HRK 100 (effective 2002). **Document type:** *Journal, Academic/Scholarly.* **Description:** Publishes original scientific papers, preliminary communications, review articles, conference papers, and professional papers in the field of information and organizational sciences.
Indexed: Inspec, RefZh.
Published by: Sveuciliste u Zagrebu, Fakultet Organizacije i Informatike Varazdin/University of Zabreb, Faculty of Organization and Informatics in Varazdin, Pavlinska 2, Varazdin, 42000, Croatia. TEL 385-42-213777, FAX 385-42-213413, zbornik@foi.hr, http://www.foi.hr/znanstruc/zbornik/zbornik_instructions.html. Eds. Stjepo Vojvoda, Boris Aurer.

621.3822 USA ISSN 1550-6533
SYMPOSIUM ON COMPUTER ARCHITECTURE AND HIGH PERFORMANCE COMPUTING. PROCEEDINGS. Text in English. 1987. a. **Document type:** *Proceedings, Academic/Scholarly.*
Related titles: Online - full text ed.: (from I E E E).
Published by: I E E E Computer Society, 10662 Los Vaqueros Circle, PO Box 3014, Los Alamitos, CA 90720-1314. TEL 714-821-8380, FAX 714-821-4010, http://www.ieee.org.

TECHNOLOGY OF OBJECT ORIENTED LANGUAGES AND SYSTEMS. see *COMPUTERS—Data Base Management*

621.3822 DEU
TERMINOLOGY AND KNOWLEDGE ENGINEERING. Text in English. irreg., latest vol.99, 1999. price varies. **Document type:** *Monographic series, Academic/Scholarly.*
Published by: (International Society for Knowledge Organization), Ergon Verlag, Grombuehlstr 7, Wuerzburg, 97080, Germany. TEL 49-931-280084, FAX 49-931-282872, ergon-verlag@t-online.de, service@ergon-verlag.de, http://www.ergon-verlag.de.

THEORY AND DECISION LIBRARY. SERIES D: SYSTEM THEORY, KNOWLEDGE ENGINEERING AND PROBLEM SOLVING. see *COMPUTERS—Cybernetics*

621.3822 JPN ISSN 1347-2666
TOUKAI DAIGAKU KIYOU. DENSHI JOUHOU GAKUBU/TOKAI UNIVERSITY. SCHOOL OF INFORMATION TECHNOLOGY AND ELECTRONICS. PROCEEDINGS. Text in Japanese. 2002. s-a. **Document type:** *Proceedings, Academic/Scholarly.*
Indexed: BrCerAb, C&ISA, CerAb, CorrAb, E&CAJ, EMA, IAA, M&TEA, MBF, METADEX, WAA.
—Linda Hall.
Published by: Toukai Daigaku, Denshi Jouhou Gakubu/Tokai University, School of Information Technology and Electronics, 1117 Kitakaname, Hiratsuka, Kanagawa 259-1292, Japan. http://www.ite.u-tokai.ac.jp/.

U E TODAY. see *EDUCATION*

363.700285 USA ISSN 1045-8077
HT390 CODEN: URJOEO
➤ **U R I S A JOURNAL.** Text in English. 1989. s-a. USD 295 to institutions (effective 2005). bk.rev. maps. **Document type:** *Academic/Scholarly.* **Description:** Covers electronic information systems for managers, users, developers, and educators. Discusses improved systems that can be developed and used effectively and equitably at all levels of government.
Related titles: Online - full text ed.: free (effective 2005).
Indexed: Inspec.
—BLDSC (9124.328000), AskIEEE, IE, ingenta.
Published by: Urban and Regional Information Systems Association, 1460 Renaissance Dr, Ste 305, Park Ridge, IL 60068-1348. TEL 847-824-6300, FAX 847-824-6363, info@urisa.org, http://www.urisa.org/journal.htm, http://www.urisa.org/index.htm. Circ: 3,800. **Subscr. to:** Dept. 77-6100, Chicago, IL 60678-6100. TEL 847-824-6300, FAX 847-824-6363.

003 USA ISSN 0749-9531
HT390
U R I S A NEWS. Text in English. 1982. bi-m. USD 165 for membership to individuals; USD 625 for membership to corporations w/ 10 or fewer employees; USD 2,000 for membership to corporations w/ more than 10 employees (effective 2002); membership c/w URISA News, Marketplace and the URISA Journal.. adv. **Document type:** *Newsletter, Trade.* **Description:** Covers association news and events.
Published by: Urban and Regional Information Systems Association, 1460 Renaissance Dr, Ste 305, Park Ridge, IL 60068-1348. TEL 847-824-6300, FAX 847-824-6363, info@urisa.org, http://www.urisa.org/NEWS/Newset.htm, http://www.urisa.org/index.htm.

U.S. BUREAU OF THE CENSUS. (YEAR) ECONOMIC CENSUS. INFORMATION. see *COMMUNICATIONS—Abstracting, Bibliographies, Statistics*

020 ROM ISSN 1224-2268
UNIVERSITATEA "AL. I. CUZA" DIN IASI. ANALELE STIINTIFICE. INFORMATICA. Text in English, French, German, Russian. 1989. a.
Supersedes in part (1900-1988): Universitatea "Al. I. Cuza" din Iasi. Analele Stiintifice. Sectiunea 1a: Matematica (0041-9109)
Indexed: MathR, MathSciNet, RefZh.
—CISTI, Linda Hall.
Published by: Universitatea "Al. I. Cuza" din Iasi/"Alexandru Ioan Cuza" University of Iasi, Carol I Boulevard, Iasi, 6600, Romania. TEL 40-032-201000, FAX 40-032-201201, sysadmin@uaic.ro, http://www.uaic.ro.

003 GBR
UNIVERSITY OF CENTRAL ENGLAND IN BIRMINGHAM. FACULTY OF COMPUTING & INFORMATION STUDIES. RESEARCH PAPERS. Text in English. 1996. irreg. GBP 10.
Related titles: Diskette ed.
—BLDSC (7755.005415).
Published by: University of Central England in Birmingham, Faculty of Computing & Information Studies, University Of Central England, Perry Barr, Birmingham, B42 2SU, United Kingdom. TEL 44-121-331-5300, FAX 44-121-356-2875, TELEX 334684 UCEBIR.

003 ZAF ISSN 1021-1500
UNIVERSITY OF TRANSKEI. DEPARTMENT OF INFORMATION SCIENCE. OCCASIONAL PAPERS. Text in English. 1993. irreg. **Document type:** *Academic/Scholarly.*
Published by: University of Transkei, Department of Information Science, Private Bag X1, Umtata, 5100, South Africa.

020 USA
URBAN & REGIONAL INFORMATION SYSTEMS ASSOCIATION. ANNUAL CONFERENCE PROCEEDINGS. Text in English. 1980. a., latest 2001. USD 99 to non-members; free to members (effective 2002). adv. abstr. **Document type:** *Proceedings, Trade.* **Description:** Includes papers on the use of information systems technology in all facets of land-use planning.
Related titles: CD-ROM ed.: USD 45 to non-members; USD 39 to members (effective 2002).
Published by: Urban and Regional Information Systems Association, 1460 Renaissance Dr, Ste 305, Park Ridge, IL 60068-1348. http://www.urisa.org/store/urisa_conference_proceedings.htm. Adv. contact Tegan Parodi.

USER INTERFACES TO DATA INTENSIVE SYSTEMS. PROCEEDINGS. see *COMPUTERS—Data Base Management*

020 FRA ISSN 1257-273X
VIGIE. TECHNOLOGIES DE L'INFORMATION. Text in French. 1995. m. EUR 90 (effective 2004). **Document type:** *Bulletin.*
Published by: Agence pour la Diffusion de l'Information Technologique, 2, rue Brulee, Strasbourg, 67000, France. TEL 33-3-88214242, 33-1-44183139, FAX 33-1-45515096, vigies@adit.fr, info@adit.fr, http://www.vigies.com, http://www.adit.fr/.

621.3822 500 GRC ISSN 1790-0832
W S E A S TRANSACTIONS ON INFORMATION SCIENCE AND APPLICATIONS. Text in English. a. EUR 100 to individuals; EUR 200 to institutions (effective 2005).
Indexed: C&ISA, E&CAJ, IAA.
—BLDSC (9364.918700).
Published by: World Scientific and Engineering Academy and Society, Ag Ioannou Theologou 17-23, Zographou, Athens 15773, Greece. TEL 30-210-7473313, FAX 30-210-7473314, http://www.wseas.org. Ed. Zoran Bojkovic.

020 CHN
XINXI CHANYE BAO/INFORMATION INDUSTRY. Text in Chinese. 1984. m. CNY 108 (effective 2004). **Document type:** *Newspaper, Academic/Scholarly.*
Published by: Sichuan Sheng Dianzi Xuehui, 66, Guiwangqiao Xijie, Chengdu, 610017, China. TEL 86-28-86081617 ext 823, http://www.scie-sc.com/. **Dist. by:** China International Book Trading Corp, 35 Chegongzhuang Xilu, Haidian District, PO Box 399, Beijing 100044, China. TEL 86-10-68412045, FAX 86-10-68412023, cibtc@mail.cibtc.com.cn, http://www.cibtc.com.cn.

020 FRA ISSN 0298-2285
ZERO - UN INFORMATIQUE (HEBDOMADAIRE); les technologies de l'information au service de l'entreprise. Text in French. 1966. w. EUR 125. adv.
Formerly (until 1986): Zero - Un Hebdo (0398-1169); Which was formed by the 1969 merger of: Zero un Informatique. Ed. Actualites (0044-4367); (1968-1969): Zero un Informatique. Profession (1243-2628); Which was formerly (until 1968): Zero un Actualites de l'Informatique (1243-261X)
Related titles: Online - full text ed.: (from O C L C Online Computer Library Center, Inc.); ♦ Supplement(s): Zero un References. ISSN 0997-654X.
Indexed: PdeR, RefZh.
—CCC.
Published by: Groupe Tests, 26 rue d'Oradour-sur-Glane, Paris, Cedex 15 75504, France. TEL 33-1-44253500, redaction@01informatique.presse.fr, http://www.01net.com/01informatique/, http://www.groupetests.fr. Ed. Jean Francois Ruiz. Adv. contact Jean Weiss. Circ: 52,552.

C

COMPUTERS—Internet

see also COMPUTERS—Computer Networks

383.34 USA
A & E PUBLISHING WORLDWIDE E-MAGAZINE. Text in English. bi-w. free. adv. **Description:** Covers marketing strategies, tips and articles for online entrepreneurs.
Media: Online - full text. **Related titles:** E-mail ed.
Published by: A & E Publishing, 21520 G Yorba Linda Blvd PMB 427, Yorba Linda, CA 92887. ezine-mlm-info@aepublishing.com, http://www.aepublishing.com. Ed. Ed Justice. Circ: 5,000.

384.33 USA
A B C'S OF MAKING MONEY ONLINE. Text in English. w. free. adv. **Document type:** *Newsletter.* **Description:** Provides simple ideas on how to make money online.
Media: Online - full text.
Published by: Grafica Design webmaster@graphicadesign.com, http://www.graficadesign.com/free.htm.

658.8 USA
A B C'S OF NET MARKETING E-ZINE. Text in English. m. free. **Document type:** *Newsletter.* **Description:** Includes web design and promotional marketing tips.
Media: Online - full text.
Published by: A B C's of Net Marketing E-zine news@thisandthatmall.com, http://www.thisandthatmall.com/marketing_newsletter.htm. Ed. Robert Fox.

004.678 USA
A C M SIGCOMM INTERNET MEASURMENT CONFERENCE. PROCEEDINGS. Text in English. a. **Document type:** *Proceedings, Academic/Scholarly.*
Published by: Association for Computing Machinery, Inc., 1515 Broadway, 17th Fl, New York, NY 10036-5701. TEL 212-626-0500, usacm@acm.org, http://www.acm.org.

004.678 USA ISSN 1533-5399
TK5105.875.I57
➤ **A C M TRANSACTIONS ON INTERNET TECHNOLOGY.** Text in English. 2001 (Aug.). q. USD 160 domestic to non-members; USD 174 foreign to non-members; USD 39 domestic to members; USD 53 foreign to members; USD 34 domestic to students; USD 48 foreign to students; USD 192 combined subscription domestic to non-members print & online eds.; USD 206 combined subscription foreign to non-members print & online eds.; USD 47 combined subscription domestic to members print & online eds.; USD 61 combined subscription foreign to members print & online eds.; USD 41 combined subscription domestic to students print & online eds.; USD 55 combined subscription foreign to students print & online eds. (effective 2006). **Document type:** *Journal, Academic/Scholarly.* **Description:** Covers diverse aspects of the social impact of the Internet and web technology as well as public policy issues guiding the development and application of the technology.
Related titles: Online - full text ed.: ISSN 1557-6051. USD 128 to non-members; USD 31 to members; USD 27 student members (effective 2006) (from Association for Computing Machinery, Inc., EBSCO Publishing).
Indexed: ABIn, BrCerAb, C&ISA, CerAb, CompR, CorrAb, E&CAJ, EMA, IAA, Inspec, M&TEA, MBF, METADEX, RefZh, WAA.
—CISTI, Linda Hall. **CCC.**
Published by: Association for Computing Machinery, Inc., 1515 Broadway, 17th Fl, New York, NY 10036-5701. TEL 212-626-0500, 212-626-0520, 800-342-6626, FAX 212-869-0481, sigs@acm.org, usacm@acm.org, http://www.acm.org/pubs/periodicals/toit. Ed. Won Kim.

025.04 DEU
DAS A O L - MAGAZIN. Text in German. 1999. q. EUR 1.80 newsstand/cover (effective 2004). adv. **Document type:** *Magazine, Consumer.*
Published by: Magazin Verlag am Fleetrand GmbH, Griegstr 75, Hamburg, 22763, Germany. TEL 49-40-37037914, FAX 49-40-37037845. adv.: page EUR 5,900. Circ: 100,000 (controlled).

004.678 USA
A V E W D NEWSLETTER. Text in English. 1994. m. free. **Description:** Includes Web events and trends, e-articles on theory about main Web issues.
Media: Online - full text.
Published by: A V E W D Newsletter novsoft@cam.org, http://www.cam.org/~novsoft/index.html. Ed. Alex Vasilesco.

005 384.558 USA ISSN 1525-3880
HQ471
A V N ONLINE MAGAZINE; adult internet news & webmaster resource. (Adult Video News) Text in English. 1999. m. USD 72 domestic; CND 200 in Canada (effective 2002). bk.rev. **Document type:** *Consumer.*
Related titles: Online - full content ed.
Published by: A V N Publications Inc., 9414 Eton Ave, Chatsworth, CA 91311. erik@avn.com, http://www.avnonline.com. Ed. Erik McFarland. Pub. Paul Fishbein. Circ: 13,000.

▼ **ACADEMY OF BUSINESS AND ECONOMICS. JOURNAL**; JABE. see *BUSINESS AND ECONOMICS—International Commerce*

383.34 USA
ACCUSUBMIT!; mercenary Internet marketing. Text in English. bi-w. **Document type:** *Newsletter.* **Description:** Features articles geared toward increasing website's visibility and traffic. Designed for entrepreneurs and Internet marketers.
Media: E-mail.
Address: webmaster@accusubmit.com, subscribe@accusubmit.com, http://accusubmit.com. Ed. J Gregory Wilson.

004.678 USA
AD NAUSEAM. Text in English. irreg. back issues avail. **Description:** Covers the rantings and blatherings on the Internet and its tremendous growth.
Media: Online - full text. Ed. Jim Nelson.

383.34 TON
ADVANCE CONSULTANCY NEWS. Text in English. w. free. **Document type:** *Newsletter.* **Description:** Dedicated to everyone who wants to utilize the powers of the Internet to maximize their business profit potential.
Media: E-mail.
Address: Tonga. news@advance.to, paul@advance.to. Ed. Paul Graham.

658.8 USA
ADVERTISING SUCCESS. Text in English. m. free. **Document type:** *Newsletter.* **Description:** Provides marketing reports on how to succeed on the Internet.
Media: Online - full text.
Address: danlowe@earthlink.net, http://succeed.webjump.com. Pub. Dan Lowe.

ADVISING EBUSINESSES. see *LAW—Corporate Law*

025.0434 USA
ALERT (WASHINGTON, 1995). Text in English. 1995. irreg. back issues avail. **Document type:** *Newsletter.* **Description:** Provide timely information on specific topics related to law & legal issues.
Media: Online - full text.
Published by: Arent Fox Kintner Plotkin & Kahn PLLC, 1050 Connecticut Ave, NW, Washington, DC 20036-5339. TEL 202-827-6000, FAX 202-857-6395, infolaw@arentfox.com, http://www.arentfox.com/publications/alerts/alerts.html.

383.34 AUS
ALL THE SECRETS. Text in English. w. free. adv. **Document type:** *Newsletter.* **Description:** Offers advice for Internet entrepreneurs.
Media: Online - full text.
Published by: Deer Park Press, PO Box 1269, Rockhampton, QLD 4700, Australia. TEL 61-7-4936-2692, FAX 61-7-4930-4366, wiley@reporters.net, http://www.networx.com.au/mall/secrets. Ed. Phil Wiley.

384.33 USA
AMERICA'S LOCAL BUSINESS NEWS NETWORK✶. Text in English. d. adv. bk.rev. **Document type:** *Trade.* **Description:** Covers the Internet, finance and general business news.
Media: Online - full text.
Published by: American Digital Media, 6424 N W Fifth Way, Fort Lauderdale, FL 33309-6112. TEL 561-809-9505, FAX 561-804-9050, gferber@dbusiness.com, http://washington.dbusiness.com/.

ANDREWS LITIGATION REPORTER: E-BUSINESS LAW BULLETIN. see *BUSINESS AND ECONOMICS—Computer Applications*

004.678 330 USA
ANNUAL EDITIONS: INTERNET AND BUSINESS. Text in English. 2001. a. USD 20.31 per vol. (effective 2004). **Document type:** *Academic/Scholarly.* **Description:** Compilation of current, carefully selected articles from Business Week. Provides effective and useful perspectives on today's important topics concerning the Internet and business.
Published by: McGraw-Hill - Dushkin (Subsidiary of: McGraw-Hill Higher Education), 2460 Kerper Blvd, Dubuque, IA 52001. TEL 800-243-6532, customer.service@mcgraw-hill.com, http://www.dushkin.com/text-data/catalog/0072396245.mhtml. Ed. Robert W Price.

004.678 ITA
ANOTHER WIN95.COM NEWSLETTER. Text in English. 1997. irreg. **Document type:** *Newsletter.* **Description:** Reviews a Windows 95 related web resource to allow readers a brief introduction.
Formerly: Another Windows 95 Links and Resources Newsletter
Media: Online - full text.
Address: Via Madonna del Pantano 55, Lago Patria, NA, Italy. TEL 39-81-5092318, webmaster@anotherwin95.com, http://www.anotherwin95.com. Ed., Pub. Richard Hay.

384.33 USA
ANSURNEWS SITE PROMOTION NEWSLETTER. Text in English. m. adv. **Document type:** *Newsletter.* **Description:** Dedicated to educating readers on all aspects of Internet marketing and advertising.
Media: Online - full text.
Published by: AnsurNews Services, 1108 Cardinal Dr, Paige, TX 78659. TEL 512-321-4332, ansurnet@ansur.net, http://www.ansur.net.

025.04 USA
ANSWERS (LA HABRA). Text in English. w. **Document type:** *Newsletter.* **Description:** Provides information on Internet marketing & advertising; topics include online promotion, marketing, e-commerce, web design, affiliate programs and more.
Formerly: Ads and Things
Media: E-mail.
Published by: K & D Publishing, 4040 Leigh St., Riverside, CA 92509-6637. answers-on@mail-list.com, http://www.advertisingtips.net/, http://www.kndpublishing.com. Ed. Kim Skinner.

004.678 ARG ISSN 0329-3068
LOS ARCHIVOS DE INTERNET WORLD. Text in Spanish. 1997. m.
Related titles: ♦ Supplement to: Internet World. ISSN 0329-2967.
Published by: Avenue S.A., 25 de Mayo 432, 4o Piso, Buenos Aires, 1002, Argentina. TEL 54-11-4315-2244, info@iworld.com.ar, http://www.iworld.com.ar. Ed. David Exposito.

025.04 330 USA
ARIBA B2B UPDATE. Text in English. m. **Document type:** *Trade.* **Description:** Focuses on educational content, news and upcoming events for business-to-business online e-commerce.
Media: E-mail.
Published by: Ariba, Inc., 175 Bleecker St, Ste 8, New York, NY 10012. TEL 212-982-0665, FAX 215-794-5062, lindad@ariba.com. Ed. Linda DiBiasio. Pub., Adv. contact Jeff Berman.

025.04 330 USA
ARIBA MAGAZINE; the magazine for business-to-business ecommerce. Text in English. 2000. 2/yr. adv. **Document type:** *Magazine, Trade.* **Description:** Packed with interesting and interest generating information on all aspects of business to business e-commerce.
Published by: Ariba, Inc., 175 Bleecker St, Ste 8, New York, NY 10012. TEL 212-982-0665, FAX 215-794-5062, info@aribamag.com, lindad@ariba.com, http://www.aribamag.com/, http://www.ariba.com. Ed. Linda DiBiasio. Pub., Adv. contact Jeff Berman.

025.04 USA ISSN 1540-1995
ZA4201
ARTICLES, ABSTRACTS, DOCUMENTS, PAPERS, REPORTS AND LITERATURE RESOURCES; an internet miniguide. Text in English. 2002 (June). a. USD 95 newsstand/cover (effective 2002).
Published by: InternetMiniGuides.com, P.O. Box 220, Marco Island, FL 34146. TEL 941-434-5113, FAX 941-642-9115, zillman@internetminiguides.com, http://www.internetminiguides.com. Pub. Marcus P. Zillma.

ASIAN E-BANKER. see *BUSINESS AND ECONOMICS—Banking And Finance*

004.678 AUS
ASSOCIATE PROGRAMS NEWSLETTER; successful affiliate marketing. Text in English. 1998. w. free. adv. bk.rev.; software rev.; Website rev. back issues avail. **Document type:** *Newsletter, Consumer.* **Description:** Aimed to people who want to add another income stream to their web site.
Media: Online - full text.
Address: 12 Esplanade, Tuan, QLD 4650, Australia. TEL 61-741-298233, allan@associateprograms.com, http://www.associateprograms.com/search/newsletter.shtml. Ed., Pub., R&P, Adv. contact Allan Gardyne TEL 61-741-298233. Circ: 16,400.

AUCTION BYTES - UPDATE; the buyers and sellers guide to online auctions. see *HOBBIES*

AUSTRALIA. BUREAU OF STATISTICS. INTERNET ACTIVITY, AUSTRALIA. see *COMPUTERS—Abstracting, Bibliographies, Statistics*

AUTO RETAILING ON THE WEB. see *TRANSPORTATION—Automobiles*

004.693 USA
B B S MAGAZINE. (Bulletin Board Systems) Text in English. 1990. m. USD 26 to individuals; USD 30 foreign to individuals; USD 31 to institutions; USD 41 foreign to institutions. adv. bk.rev. back issues avail. **Document type:** *Consumer.* **Description:** Used by modem owners to call local bulletin board systems.
Formerly: B B S Callers Digest (1055-2812)

C

▼ new title ➤ refereed ✶ unverified ♦ full entry avail.

Published by: Callers Digest, Inc., 701 Stokes Rd, Medford, NJ 08055. TEL 609-953-9110, FAX 609-953-7961, http://www.bbsmag.com. Ed. Rick Robinson. Pub. Richard Paguette. Adv. contact John Carcione. Circ: 46,000. **Subscr. to:** The National Interest, PO Box 622, Shrub Oak, NY 10588.

B E A WEBLOGIC DEVELOPER'S JOURNAL. see *COMPUTERS—Computer Programming*

BACKBONE MAGAZINE; the strength of e-business. see *BUSINESS AND ECONOMICS*

025.04   USA   ISSN 1533-4317
BACON'S INTERNET MEDIA DIRECTORY. Variant title: Internet Media Directory. Text in English. 2000. a. USD 395 (effective 2005). **Document type:** *Directory, Trade.*
Published by: Bacon's Information, Inc., 332 S Michigan Ave, Ste 900, Chicago, IL 60604. TEL 312-922-2400, 800-621-0561, FAX 312-987-9773, directories@bacons.com, http://www.bacons.com.

BANKING ONLINE. see *BUSINESS AND ECONOMICS—Banking And Finance—Computer Applications*

BEAUTY & MORE. see *BEAUTY CULTURE*

384.33   USA
BIZ - E. Text in English. 1998. irreg. adv. back issues avail. **Document type:** *Trade.* **Description:** Offers information to help promote Web sites and e-commerce.
Media: Online - full text.
Published by: S W Domains editor@bizwizard.com, http://www.bizwizard.com/biz-e. Ed. L Browne.

005.276   CAN
BIZ TIPS NEWSLETTER. Text in English. m. free. **Document type:** *Newsletter.* **Description:** Provides support and information to small business owners and aspiring entrepreneurs.
Media: Online - full text.
Published by: Biz Resource Group, 33119 S Fraser Way, No. 208, Abbotsford, BC V2S 2B1, Canada. TEL 604-850-6908, FAX 604-855-0363, wendyweb@bizresource.com, http://www.bizresource.com. Ed. Wendy McClelland.

004.6780688   USA
BIZNEWS. Text in English. **Description:** For North Carolina businesses that want to leverage the web to make an impact on their business. Provides information, biznews, and Internet marketing techniques.
Media: Online - full text.
Address: http://www.biznexus.com/nesletters/.

004.6780688   USA
BIZREPORT NEWSLETTER. Text in English. w. **Document type:** *Newsletter.* **Description:** Presents information and articles on Internet marketing, network marketing, advertising tips, business start-up ideas, new business trends and advertising techniques.
Media: Online - full text.
Address: http://www.bizreport.com.

384.33   USA
BIZWIZE. Text in English. m. free. **Document type:** *Newsletter.* **Description:** Keeps up-to-date with information on small business, home business opportunities on and of the Net. Lists both new and successfully established busines opportunitites available with low and no start-up costs.
Media: Online - full text. Ed. Kenneth Turbin.

004.678   USA
QA76.9.B84
BOARDWATCH (ONLINE EDITION); analysis of telecom software, services and strategy. Text in English. 1987. m. adv. bk.rev. illus. back issues avail.; reprints avail. **Document type:** *Magazine, Trade.* **Description:** Covers Internet access and the World Wide Web.
Former titles: Boardwatch (Print Edition) (1054-2760); Incorporates (1999-2000): C L E C Magazine (1530-2148); (until 1989): Denver P C Boardwatch (0894-5209)
Media: Online - full text (from Gale Group, O C L C Online Computer Library Center, Inc., ProQuest Information & Learning).
Indexed: CompD.
—CCC.
Published by: Penton Media, Inc. (Golden), 13949 W Colfax Ave, Ste 250, Golden, CO 80401-3209. TEL 303-235-9510, 800-933-6038, FAX 303-235-9502, subscriptions@boardwatch.com, http://www.boardwatch.com, http://www.penton.com. Ed. Todd Erickson. Pub. Randy Goldner. Adv. contact Larry Robinson. page USD 6,945; trim 10.75 x 7.88. Circ: 11,200; 12,400 (paid).

025.04   USA
BOTSPOT. Text in English. m. free. adv. **Document type:** *Newsletter.* **Description:** Presents a platform to use bots and intelligent agents in your searches concerning hobbies, special interests, and business.
Media: Online - full text.

Published by: BotSpot, Inc., PO Box 220, Marco Island, FL 34146-0220. TEL 239-434-3850, FAX 239-642-9115, team@botspot.com, http://www.botspot.com/newsletter.

005.72   USA
BRAINBOX✳**.** Text in English. 1998. bi-w. free. back issues avail. **Document type:** *Newsletter.* **Description:** Designed for people interested in the user experience of interative media, the Internet, e-commerce, and design.
Related titles: Online - full text ed.
Published by: HannaHodge, Inc., 310 S Michigan Ave #2, Chicago, IL 60604-4207. TEL 312-397-9020, FAX 312-397-9019, owner-brainbox@hannahodge.com, http://www.hannahodge.com/brainbox.htm. Ed. Challis Hodge.

BROADBAND ACCESS EUROPE; essential intelligence on Europe's broadband industry. see *COMMUNICATIONS*

004.6   USA   ISSN 1542-569X
▼ **BROADBAND ACCESS REPORT.** Text in English. 2003 (Mar.). 10/yr. USD 448 (effective 2002).
Published by: Broadband Publishing Corp, 200 W Rivers St, Ste 201, PO Box 6535, Ketchum, ID 83340. TEL 208-725-0600, FAX 208-725-0854, bpc@broadbandpub.com, http://www.broadbandpub.com.

006 330   USA
BROADBAND HOUSE. Text in English. q. USD 19.99 for 18 mos.; USD 4.95 newsstand/cover (effective 2002). adv. **Description:** Features the realm where business, technology and design meet, focusing on those who work from home and use advanced computer and telecommunications technology.
Published by: Broadband House Magazine, 1545 Waukegan Rd, 6, Glenview, IL 60025. TEL 847-998-8501, FAX 847-998-8511, editor@bbhmag.com, publisher@bbhmag.com, http://www.bbhmag.com. Adv. contact Christopher Chalk. B&W page USD 16,035, color page USD 19,320; 8.875 x 10.75.

BROADBAND WORLD. see *COMPUTERS—Computer Networks*

BROADCAST & BROADBAND ASIA PACIFIC. see *COMMUNICATIONS—Television And Cable*

004.678   USA   ISSN 1538-1730
BUSINESS 2.0. Text in English. N.S. 2001. m. USD 9.99 domestic; CND 9.65 in Canada; USD 3.99 newsstand/cover (effective 2004). adv. illus. reprints avail. **Document type:** *Magazine, Consumer.* **Description:** Provides a steady source of insight and perspective on the ideas, people, and driving principles of today's business economy.
Formed by the merger of (2000-2001): eCompany Now (1528-9265); (1995-2001): Business 2.0 (Brisbane) (1524-9824); Which was formerly (until 1998): The Net - Your Cyberspace Companion (1080-2681)
Related titles: Online - full text ed.: Business 2.0 Online (from EBSCO Publishing, Gale Group); ♦ Supplement(s): Motion.
Indexed: MicrocompInd, SoftBase.
—IE.
Published by: Time Inc., Fortune Group, 1 California St., San Francisco, CA 94111. TEL 415-293-4800, FAX 415-293-5900, forwardslash@business2.com, http://www.business2.com. Ed. Ned Desmond. Pub. Lisa T Bentley. adv.: B&W page USD 23,995, color page USD 31,306; trim 10.75 x 17.13. Circ: 550,000.

BUSINESS ADVANTAGE NEWSLETTER. see *BUSINESS AND ECONOMICS—Marketing And Purchasing*

384.33   GRC
THE BUSINESS INTERNET NEWSLETTER. Text in Greek. 1995. m. adv. **Document type:** *Newsletter.* **Description:** Covers topics on integrating business and the Internet and World Wide Web. Examines new opportunities or new ways of doing business with these online services. For entrepreneurs, marketers, and advertising professionals.
Published by: Compupress S.A., 44 Syngrou Ave, Athens, 117 42, Greece. TEL 30-210-923-8672, FAX 30-210-921-6847, http://www.compupress.gr/default_eng.htm. Ed. M Nikolaou. Pub. N O Manousos. Adv. contact V Giakamozis. Circ: 6,000 (paid).

659.13   IRL   ISSN 1649-0738
THE BUSINESS OF E-MAIL. Text in English. 2000. m. **Document type:** *Trade.* **Description:** Aimed at persons who want to maximize their business.
Media: Online - full text.
Published by: E-Search Ltd., The Weir Centre, Weir St., Bandon, Cork 6, Ireland. TEL 353-23-29880, FAX 353-23-52535, info@allrealgood.com, admin@esearch.ie, http://www.allrealgood.com/business_of_email.shtml, http://www.esearch.ie. Ed. Denise Cox. Circ: 2,345.

384.33   USA
BUSINESS TECH. Text in English. m. USD 99. **Description:** Focuses on Internet business, emerging technology, and strategic planning.
Media: Online - full text.
Address: btech@businesstech.com, http://businesstech.com.

BUSINESSFINANCEMAG.COM. see *BUSINESS AND ECONOMICS—Management*

BUSY MARKETING TIPS. see *BUSINESS AND ECONOMICS—Marketing And Purchasing*

659.13   USA
C C I E CENTRAL. (Cisco Certified Internetwork Experts) Text in English. 1998. q. free to qualified personnel. **Document type:** *Magazine, Trade.* **Description:** Provides program updates and other information of interest to Cisco Certified Internetwork Experts.
Published by: Cisco Systems, Inc., 170 W Tasman Dr, San Jose, CA 95134. TEL 408-526-7208, 800-553-6387, info@cisco.com, http://www.cisco.com/warp/public/625/ccie/ccie_program/ccie_central.html.

025.04   SWE   ISSN 1651-3118
C I O SWEDEN. (Chief Information Officer) Text in Swedish. 2002. 10/yr. SEK 595 (effective 2003). adv. **Document type:** *Magazine, Trade.* **Description:** Covers the people, companies and new technology that make up the new economy.
Formed by the merger of (2001-2002): C R Manager (1651-1115); (2000-2002): Industry Standard Sverige (1650-2566); Which was formed by the merger of (2000-2000): D N E (1404-9228); (1998-2000): ITaffaerer (1403-3054); (1999-2000): Nollett (1404-1510); (1998-2000): TeleAffaerer (1404-7381); Incorporates (2000-2001): Evaerlden (1650-1705)
Related titles: Online - full text ed.
Published by: I D G AB (Subsidiary of: I D G Communications Inc.), Sturegatan 11, Stockholm, 10678, Sweden. TEL 46-8-4536000, FAX 46-8-4536005, cio@idg.se, http://cio.idg.se, http://www.idg.se. Ed. Alexandra Heymowska TEL 46-8-453-64-15. adv.: page SEK 36,500; 185 x 260. Circ: 25,000 (paid).

004.678   USA
C O O L DOCTOR - COMPUTING ONLINE DOCTOR. Text in English. 1996. w. **Description:** Covers topics related to computer use, hardware, software, programming, Internet and web.
Media: Online - full text.
Published by: Kissware Works! cool@kww.com, http://kww.com/cool/. Ed. Robert Zee.

C O R E-HEALTH TREND WATCH. see *MEDICAL SCIENCES*

C O R HEALTHCARE STRATEGIST TREND WATCH. see *HEALTH FACILITIES AND ADMINISTRATION*

025.04   GBR   ISSN 1360-6875
CAFE MAGAZINE. Text in English. 1995. q. **Document type:** *Newsletter.* **Description:** Social history of coffee, cafes, and cybercafes.
Related titles: Online - full text ed.
Address: Box 173, Cambridge, CB5 8YB, United Kingdom. bapollo@cityscape.co.uk, http://www.gold.net/users/fy15. Ed. Bob Biderman.

CALL MAGAZIN; das Infosystem fuer Festnetz, Mobilfunk, Internet, WAP. see *COMMUNICATIONS*

004.678   CAN
CAPITAL MAGAZINE. Text in English. w. **Description:** Contains web-based editorial and media content to promote and assist in the development of independent media publications, producers, and projects.
Media: Online - full content.
Address: editor@capitalmag.com, http://www.capitalmag.com/. Ed. Jarrett Martineau.

CATALOGUE & MAIL ORDER BUSINESS. see *BUSINESS AND ECONOMICS—Marketing And Purchasing*

CATALYST (FAIRFAX). see *BUSINESS AND ECONOMICS—Management*

CD-ROM ONLINE. see *COMPUTERS—Software*

THE CHARLESTON ADVISOR; critical reviews of Web products for information professionals. see *LIBRARY AND INFORMATION SCIENCES—Computer Applications*

004.678   CHN
CHINA INTERNET TIMES. Text in Chinese. m. adv. **Document type:** *Magazine, Consumer.* **Description:** Contains news of current network technologies as they apply to the national economy and people's daily life, in addition to industry events, market trends, and new product information.
Published by: I D G China, Rm. 616, Tower A, COFCO Plaza, Jianguomennei Dajie, Beijing, 100005 , China. TEL 86-10-6526-0959, FAX 86-10-6526-0866, dumin@idg.com.cn, http://www.ciworld.com.cn, http://www.idgchina.com. Ed. Li-Ying Chen. adv.: color page CNY 15,000; trim 210 x 285. Circ: 30,000 (paid and controlled).

CHINA TELECOM WEEKLY. see *COMMUNICATIONS*

004.678   USA
CHIPNET READINGS. Text in English. 1997. fortn. **Document type:** *Newsletter.* **Description:** Provides useful and entertaining information to Internet users.
Media: Online - full text.

Published by: ChipNet Publications, 650 Stadler Rd, Helena, MT 59602. cnreadings@hotmail.com, http://www.tybee.com/chipnet. Ed. John Peck.

004 CAN
CINFOLINK CHINA INTERNET DIRECTORY. Text in English. 1996. biennial. CND 25, USD 20 (effective 2002). **Document type:** *Directory, Government.* **Description:** Covers selected electronic national information networks and 350 key sources of current online services in the People's Republic of China and Hong Kong. Contains review articles by leading members of information industry in China.
Former titles (until 1997): Cinfolink Annual Review of Information Services and the Internet in China; Cinfolink Directory of Information Services in China
Related titles: Online - full text ed.
Published by: Cinfolink Services, 301 10 Malta Ave, Brampton, ON L6Y 4G6, Canada. TEL 905-456-3801, FAX 905-458-8292, cinfo@ican.net, http://www.woodmedia.com/cinfolink. Ed. Harry C Campbell. Circ: 700; 200 (paid).

384.33 USA
THE CLASSIC INSIDER NEWSLETTER. Text in English. irreg. free. **Document type:** *Newsletter.* **Description:** Includes surveys and evaluation of programs in telecommunications, travel, internet services and related business opportunitites.
Media: Online - full text.
Published by: Classic Insider Newsletter signal@mwci.net. Pub. Anthony Bulloch.

384.33 USA
CLASSIFIEDS, LINKS AND MORE... Text in English. irreg. **Document type:** *Newsletter.* **Description:** Offers reviews of classified ad sites, and useful links for marketing goods and services on the Internet.
Media: E-mail.
Address: subscribe@getrealproductions.com, ruth@getrealproductions.com. Ed. Ruth Farmer.

384.33 USA
THE CLICK QUICK FILES. Text in English. bi-w. free. **Document type:** *Newsletter.* **Description:** Designed for webmaster and online entrepreneurs.
Media: Online - full text.
Published by: Click Quick Files rja@clickquick.com, http://www.clickquick.com. Ed. Ryan Adams.

CLONE. see *COMPUTERS—Computer Graphics*

025.04 378.154 USA
COLLEGE NEWS. Text in English. 1991. m. free (effective 2003). **Document type:** *Newsletter.* **Description:** Campus newswire and student service dedicated to meeting the Internet needs of students, graduates and others interested in higher education.
Related titles: Online - full text ed.
Address: publishr@collegenews.com, http://www.collegenews.com.

025.04 DEU
COM-ONLINE.DE. Text in German. d. adv. **Document type:** *Consumer.*
Media: Online - full content. **Related titles:** ♦ Print ed.: com!online. ISSN 1437-3432.
Published by: Neue Mediengesellschaft Ulm mbH, Konrad-Celtis-Str 77, Munich, 81369, Germany. TEL 49-89-74117-0, FAX 49-89-74117787, redaktion@com-online.de, empfang@nmg.de, http://www.com-online.de, http://www.nc-online.de.

COMMERCE EXTRA. see *BUSINESS AND ECONOMICS*

025.04 DEU ISSN 1437-3432
COM!ONLINE; Internet & Computer. Text in German. 1980. m. EUR 25.80; EUR 3.30 newsstand/cover (effective 2003). adv. **Document type:** *Magazine, Consumer.* **Description:** Provides the latest news, links and trends from the online world.
Former titles (until 1999): Com! (0948-6844); (until 1995): Btx-Magazin (0947-8981); (until 1994): Bildschirmtext-Magazin (0930-5556); (until 1985): Bildschirmtext-Magazin fuer Teleleser (0174-3473)
Related titles: ♦ Online - full content ed.: com-online.de.
Published by: Neue Mediengesellschaft Ulm mbH, Konrad-Celtis-Str 77, Munich, 81369, Germany. TEL 49-89-74117-0, FAX 49-89-74117787, redaktion@com-online.de, empfang@nmg.de, http://www.com-online.de, http://www.nc-online.de. Adv. contact Bettina Guenther. page EUR 11,600. Circ: 277,224 (paid).

004.678 USA
COMPUTER CORNER. Text in English. w. **Document type:** *Bulletin.* **Description:** Weekly look at news from the digital domain.
Media: Online - full text.
Address: news8@wfaa.com, http://www.wfaa.com/ccindex.html.

004 621.39 USA ISSN 1524-1211
COMPUTER LINK MAGAZINE; western NY's computer magazine. Text in English. 1997. m. USD 25 domestic; USD 35 foreign (effective 2001). adv. bk.rev.; software rev. illus.; tr.lit. 44 p./no.; back issues avail. **Document type:** *Newspaper, Trade.* **Description:** Seeks to inform big business as well as the general computer user about the computer industry.
Related titles: Online - full text ed.
Published by: Millenium Publishing, Inc., 2117 Buffalo Road, 290, Rochester, NY 14624. TEL 716-244-2290, FAX 716-244-2391, info@computerlinkmag.com, http://www.computerlinkmag.com. Ed., Pub., R&P Justin E Ziemniak. Adv. contact Justin E Ziemiak. B&W page USD 900, color page USD 1,200; trim 9.38 x 7.13. Circ: 35,000.

004.678 GBR
COMPUTER PUBLISHING; the easy way to better dtp. Text in English. 1999. bi-m. GBP 18 in United Kingdom; GBP 5 newsstand/cover; GBP 24 in Europe; GBP 34 rest of world (effective 2000). adv. **Document type:** *Consumer.*
Published by: Future Publishing Ltd., Freepost BS4900, Somerton, Somers TA11 6BR, United Kingdom. TEL 44-145-827-1157, FAX 44-145-827-4378, computerpublishing@futurenet.co.uk, http://www.computerpublishing.co.uk. Ed. Nick Veitch. Pub. Jon Bickley. adv.: color page GBP 2,565; trim 232 x 280. Circ: 40,000 (paid).

COMPUTING JAPAN. see *BUSINESS AND ECONOMICS—Computer Applications*

COMPUTING NEWS. see *COMPUTERS*

CONNECT. see *COMMUNICATIONS*

CONNECT; revija za digitalno prihodnost. see *COMMUNICATIONS*

CONNECT (LONDON). see *COMMUNICATIONS*

CONSUMER REPORTS GUIDE TO ONLINE SHOPPING. see *CONSUMER EDUCATION AND PROTECTION*

CONTEXTO EDUCATIVO; revista digital de educacion y nuevas technologias. see *EDUCATION*

COOL ENGLISH - DAS KINDERWEB. see *CHILDREN AND YOUTH—For*

025.04 346 USA ISSN 1534-4568
KF242.C68
CORPORATE COUNSEL'S WEB SITE REVIEW. Text in English. 1999. m. USD 180 (effective 2001).
—CCC.
Published by: Business Laws, Inc., 11630 Chillicothe Rd, Chesterland, OH 44026. TEL 440-729-7996, FAX 440-729-0645, http://www.businesslaws.com.

384.33 USA
A CREATIVE NEWSLETTER. Text in English. w. free. adv. **Document type:** *Newsletter.* **Description:** Provides information on topics such as Internet business and marketing.
Media: Online - full text.
Published by: Creative Newsletter crvisions@aol.com, http://www.creativevisions.net. Ed. Joe Casale.

025.04 GBR
CREATIVE SERVICES INDEX (YEAR). Text in English. a. adv. **Document type:** *Directory, Trade.* **Description:** Geared to buyers and co-ordinators in leading companies who need to know where to find services that support them in their creative production process.
Related titles: Online - full content ed.
Published by: The Publishing Factory Ltd., 32 Queensway, London, W2 3RX, United Kingdom. TEL 44-20-77274232, FAX 44-20-77924236, production@creativecityonline.com, http://www.creaticeproductiononline.com, http://www.creativecityonline.com/. adv.: color page GBP 525.

384.34 USA
CREATIVE WEB TRAFFIC IDEAS. Text in English. 1996. irreg. free. **Description:** Discusses current hot topics in Web promotions and innovative techniques being tried to increase the number of Web visitors. Helpful guidelines and tips, valuable tools and resources.
Media: Online - full text.
Address: http://www.trafficplan.com/newsletter.htm. Ed. Bob Elston.

004.678 GBR
CRE@TE ONLINE; the Web Designer's bible. Text in English. 2000. bi-m. GBP 19.99 in United Kingdom; GBP 24.99 in Europe; GBP 29.99 in North America; GBP 34.99 rest of world; GBP 5 newsstand/cover (effective 2001). **Document type:** *Consumer.*
Related titles: Online - full content ed.
Published by: Future Publishing Ltd., Beauford Court, 30 Monmouth St, Bath, Avon BA1 2BW, United Kingdom. TEL 44-1225-442244, FAX 44-1225-446019, customerservice@futurenet.co.uk, http://www.createonline.co.uk/, http://www.futurenet.com/futureonline. Ed. Mark Higham. Pub. Richard Wilson.

CUT; Journalismus, Fiction & Teknik bei elektronische Medien. see *JOURNALISM*

005.72 GBR
CYBER ASPECT; web builder bulletin. Text in English. 1999. bi-w. **Document type:** *Bulletin, Trade.*
Media: Online - full text.
Address: Website Designs, 31 Medina, Tamworth, Staffs, B772JL, United Kingdom. TEL 44-1827-251918, FAX 44-1827-261869, steve@cyber-aspect.com, http://www.cyber-aspect.com. Ed. Steve Cartwright.

004.68 CAN
CYBER REVIEW. Text in English. bi-m. abstr. back issues avail. **Document type:** *Newsletter, Trade.* **Description:** Addresses the needs of business executives and senior managers in the cyber space environment.
Media: Online - full text. **Related titles:** E-mail ed.
Published by: CYBER Management, Inc, 151 Bloor St W, Ste 470, Toronto, ON M5S 1S4, Canada. TEL 416-929-1014, FAX 416-929-1552, cyber@cyberm.com, http://www.cyberm.com/CyberR.html. Ed. Linda Wilson.

384.3 USA
CYBERONLINE. Text in English. m. free. **Document type:** *Newsletter.* **Description:** Features tips, tricks and ponters on how to promote your web site, doing business on Internet, accepting credit cards on the Internet, conducting sweepstakes to promote your business and using utmost the WWW.
Media: Online - full text.
Address: newsletter@cyberonline.com, http://www.resoluteinc.com/cyberonline/.

CYBERPHILOSOPHY. see *PHILOSOPHY*

616.8584 USA ISSN 1094-9313
HM851 CODEN: CYBEFA
➤ **CYBERPSYCHOLOGY & BEHAVIOR**; the impact of the Internet, multi-media & virtual reality on behavior & society. Text in English. 1998. bi-m. USD 481 domestic to institutions; USD 570 foreign to institutions; USD 566 combined subscription domestic to institutions print & online eds.; USD 658 combined subscription foreign to institutions print & online eds. (effective 2006). adv. back issues avail.; reprint service avail. from PSC. **Document type:** *Journal, Academic/Scholarly.* **Description:** Explores the impact of the Internet, multimedia, and virtual reality on behavior and society.
Related titles: Online - full text ed.: ISSN 1557-8364. USD 194 to individuals; USD 372 to institutions (effective 2005) (from EBSCO Publishing, Gale Group, O C L C Online Computer Library Center, Inc., Swets Information Services).
Indexed: CurCont, ESPM, ErgAb, ExcerpMed, H&SSA, PsycInfo, PsycholAb, RiskAb, SSCI, e-psyche.
—BLDSC (3506.400270), IE, Infotrieve, ingenta. **CCC.**
Published by: Mary Ann Liebert, Inc. Publishers, 140 Huguenot St 3rd Fl, New Rochelle, NY 10801-5215. TEL 914-740-2100, FAX 914-740-2101, 800-654-3237, info@liebertpub.com, http://www.liebertpub.com/cpb. Ed. Dr. Mark Wiederhold. adv.: B&W page USD 1,150; trim 8.5 x 11. Circ: 1,261 (paid).

025.04 CAN
CYBERPULSE. Text in English. q. free. **Document type:** *Newsletter.* **Description:** Aims to internet serching and training.
Media: E-mail.
Published by: Workingfaster.com, 1235 Bay St, Ste 1000, Toronto, ON M5R 3K4, Canada. TEL 416-928-1405, FAX 416-928-2903, http://www.imr.on.ca/cyberpulse/, http://www.workingfaster.com. Ed. Rita Vine.

025.04 USA ISSN 1085-2417
ZA4375 CODEN: CYGUFF
THE CYBERSKEPTIC'S GUIDE TO INTERNET RESEARCH. Text in English. 1995. 10/yr. USD 164.95 domestic; USD 175 in Canada & Mexico; USD 195 elsewhere; USD 112.95 domestic to non-profit organizations; USD 123 in Canada & Mexico to non-profit organizations; USD 143 elsewhere to non-profit organizations (effective 2005). Website rev. charts; illus.; mkt.; stat. s-a index. 8 p./no.; back issues avail.; reprints avail. **Document type:** *Newsletter, Consumer.* **Description:** Aimed at business librarians, market researchers and persons using the Internet for serious purposes. Analyses various sites and compares using the Internet to using traditional online versions of those same sources.
Indexed: CINAHL, InfoSAb, MicrocompInd.
—CISTI. **CCC.**
Published by: Information Today, Inc., 143 Old Marlton Pike, Medford, NJ 08055-8750. TEL 609-654-6266, FAX 609-654-4309, custserv@infotoday.com, http://www.infotoday.com/cyberskeptics.htm. Ed. Sheri Lanza.

CYBERSOCIOLOGY; magazine for social-scientific researchers of cyberspace. see *SOCIOLOGY*

C

▼ *new title* ➤ *refereed* ✶ *unverified* ♦ *full entry avail.*

343 USA
▼ **CYBERSPACE INFRINGEMENT LITIGATION REPORTER.** Text in English. 2004. m. USD 1,350 (effective 2004). **Document type:** *Newsletter, Trade.*
Published by: Computer Law Reporter, Inc., 1601 Connecticut Ave, N W, Ste 602, Washington, DC 20009. TEL 202-462-5755, FAX 202-328-2430, crl@reporters.com, http://www.lawreporters.com.

025.0434 USA ISSN 1088-0593
KF390.5.C6
CYBERSPACE LAWYER. Text in English. 1996 (Apr.). 11/yr. USD 287 (effective 2004). **Document type:** *Newsletter, Trade.* **Description:** Focuses on the practical use of the Internet by members of the legal profession.
Published by: Glasser LegalWorks (Subsidiary of: West Publishing Co.), 150 Clove Rd, Little Falls, NJ 07424. TEL 973-890-0008, 800-308-1700, FAX 973-890-0042, legalwks@aol.com, http://www.legalwks.com/newsletters.

005.276 USA
CYBERWIRE DISPATCH. Text in English. 1994. w. free.
Media: Online - full content.
Address: http://cyberwerks.com/cyberwire. Ed. Brock N Meeks.

CYBIZ; das Fachmagazin fuer Erfolg mit E-Commerce. see *BUSINESS AND ECONOMICS—Computer Applications*

CYBIZ. see *BUSINESS AND ECONOMICS—Computer Applications*

CYBIZ.DE. see *BUSINESS AND ECONOMICS—Computer Applications*

D M M V SPECIAL. (Deutscher Multimedia Verband) see *BUSINESS AND ECONOMICS—Marketing And Purchasing*

DAILYRADAR.COM. see *COMPUTERS—Computer Games*

004.6 GBR
DANTE. ANNUAL REPORT. Text in English. 1993. a. back issues avail.
Media: Online - full text.
Published by: Dante, Francis House, 112 Hills Rd, Cambridge, CB2 1PQ, United Kingdom. TEL 44-1223-302992, FAX 44-1223-303005, dante@dante.org.uk, http://www.dante.net/. Ed. Josefien Bersee.

004.678 USA
DARWIN (ONLINE EDITION). Text in English. 2000. irreg. free. back issues avail. **Document type:** *Magazine, Consumer.* **Description:** Explains technology to non-technology oriented business people.
Media: Online - full content. **Related titles:** Online - full text ed.: (from bigchalk, O C L C Online Computer Library Center, Inc., ProQuest Information & Learning).
Published by: C X O Media Inc. (Subsidiary of: I D G Communications Inc.), 492 Old Connecticut Path, PO Box 9208, Framingham, MA 01701-9208. TEL 508-872-0080, FAX 508-879-7784, letters@darwinmag.com, http://www.darwinmag.com, http://www.cxo.com/. Ed. Janice Brand. Pub. Gary J Beach.

025.0634 GBR
DATA PROTECTION: LAWS OF THE WORLD. Text in English. 1998. 2 base vols. plus updates 2/yr. looseleaf. GBP 445 base vol(s).; GBP 440, EUR 662 updates in Europe; GBP 450, USD 818 updates elsewhere (effective 2006). **Document type:** *Journal, Trade.*
Published by: Sweet & Maxwell Ltd., 100 Avenue Road, London, NW3 3PF, United Kingdom. TEL 44-20-74491111, FAX 44-20-74491144, customer.services@sweetandmaxwell.co.uk, http://www.sweetandmaxwell.co.uk. **Subscr. to:** Cheriton House, North Way, Andover, Hants SP10 5BE, United Kingdom.

004.678 GBR ISSN 1362-2765
DEMON DISPATCHES; the demon internet customer magazine. Text in English. 1996. bi-m. membership. adv. **Document type:** *Consumer.* **Description:** Provides a guide to making the most of the Net and reflects the way the Internet mixes with everyday life.
Related titles: Online - full text ed.
Published by: (Demon Internet), Dispatch Publishing Ltd., 11 Clerkenwell Green, London, EC1R 0DN, United Kingdom. TEL 44-181-371-1234, FAX 44-171-251-6699, magazine@demon.net, http://www.dispatches.demon.net.

004.678 DEU ISSN 1438-0161
DENT-ONLINE. Text in German. q. EUR 23.36 to institutions (effective 2005). adv. **Document type:** *Journal, Trade.* **Description:** Provides information on the latest software and Internet dental resources and technology available.
Related titles: Online - full text ed.
—IE. **CCC.**
Published by: Urban und Vogel Medien und Medizin Verlagsgesellschaft mbH (Subsidiary of: Springer Science+Business Media), Neumarkter Str 43, Munich, 81673, Germany. TEL 49-89-4372-1411, FAX 49-89-4372-1410, verlag@urban-vogel.de, http://www.multimedica.de/public/html/uvogel/ZE/FUFZE220X/index.html, http://www.urban-vogel.de. Ed. Friederike Klein. Adv. contact Peter Urban. B&W page EUR 2,600, color page EUR 3,850. Circ: 25,500.

004.678 USA
DESIGN LAB JOURNAL. Text in English. w. **Description:** Covers all facets of online marketing and Web site promotion.
Media: Online - full text.
Address: kwojcie@hotmail.com, http://www.kjdm.com/journal.html. Pub. Kajetan Wojciechowski.

004.68 MEX
DIARIO DE LA COLONIA. Text in Spanish. 2000. bi-m. back issues avail.
Related titles: Online - full text ed.
Published by: Sociedad de Fomento a la Educacion, el Comercio Electronico y la Informacion por Internet, 1o. de Mayo Oriente No. 106-A, Desp. 7 Col. Centro, Tulancingo, Hidalgo, 43600, Mexico. TEL 52-77-536455, cartas@diariolacolonia.com, http://www.diariodelacolonia.com/. Ed. Leonardo Ortiz Vallejo.

004.678 AUS ISSN 1442-7613
DIGIHOUSE NEWSLETTER. Text in English. 1999. m. back issues avail. **Document type:** *Newsletter.*
Media: Online - full text.
Published by: Digihouse Pty ltd, 5 Fuller Crt, Sunbury, VIC 3429, Australia. TEL 61-5-0084-4950, FAX 61-3-9744-4035, http://www.digihouse.com.au.

025.4 658 USA
DIGITAL COAST DAILY. Text in English. 1999. d. adv. **Document type:** *Trade.* **Description:** Provides information and coverage of West Coast-based convergence activities.
Media: Online - full text.
Published by: Rising Tide Studios, 307 W 36th St, 10th Fl, New York, NY 10018-6403. TEL 646-473-2222, FAX 646-473-2223, subscribe@digitalcoastdaily.com, http://www.digitalcoastdaily.com. Ed. Jason McCabe Calacanis. Pub. Karol Martesko-Fenster. Adv. contact Keith Long.

025.4 USA ISSN 1531-1015
DIGITAL COAST REPORTER. Text in English. 5/yr. adv. **Document type:** *Magazine, Trade.*
Published by: Rising Tide Studios, 307 W 36th St, 10th Fl, New York, NY 10018-6403. TEL 646-473-2222, FAX 646-473-2223, http://www.siliconalleyreporter.com. Ed. Jason McCabe Calacanis. Pub. Karol Martesko-Fenster. Adv. contact Keith Long.

▼ **DIGITAL FORMATIONS.** see *COMMUNICATIONS*

DIGITAL FORTUNE CHINA. see *BUSINESS AND ECONOMICS—Computer Applications*

025.04 DEU
DIGITAL MIRROR. Text in German. 1995. w. free. back issues avail. **Document type:** *Consumer.*
Media: Online - full text.
Published by: Infinite Tools Medienproduktions- und Vertriebs GmbH, Gedonstr 2, Munich, 80802, Germany. TEL 49-89-33040755, FAX 49-89-33040752, md@infinite.de, http://www.digitalmirror.de/. Ed., Pub. Matthias Ditsch.

025.4 USA
DIGITAL MUSIC WEEKLY. Text in English. 2000. d. adv. **Document type:** *Trade.* **Description:** Provides insight into the rapidly emerging issues and technologies in the music industry.
Media: Online - full text.
Published by: Rising Tide Studios, 307 W 36th St, 10th Fl, New York, NY 10018-6403. TEL 646-473-2222, FAX 646-473-2223, letters@digitalmusicweekly.com, http://www.digitalmusicweekly.com. Ed. Jason McCabe Calacanis. Pub. Karol Martesko-Fenster. Adv. contact Keith Long.

005.72 USA
DIGITAL PRODUCER MAGAZINE; news, tools & techniques for content creation. Text in English. d. adv. **Document type:** *Trade.* **Description:** Contains news and information on events, products and technology for digital media production and professionals.
Media: Online - full content.
Published by: Digital Media Online, Inc., 1508 Brookhollow Dr, Ste 360, Santa Ana, CA 92705. TEL 714-424-6100, FAX 714-424-6101, editor@digitalmedianet.com, http://www.digitalproducer.com. Pub. John Virata.

DIGITAL WEB MAGAZINE. see *ART—Computer Applications*

THE DIGITAL WOMAN ONLINE; women with their modems running. see *BUSINESS AND ECONOMICS—Management*

383.33 USA
DIRECT EMAIL BUSINESS. Text in English. m. free. **Document type:** *Bulletin.* **Description:** Provides site updates, specials, marketing ideas, tips and promotional tools.
Media: Online - full text.
Published by: NetMark Communications TEL 561-641-9887, FAX 561-433-3979, http://www.finsave.com.

DIRECTORY OF ENVIRONMENTAL WEBSITES ON THE INTERNET. see *ENVIRONMENTAL STUDIES*

DIRECTORY OF GHOSTLY WEBSITES. see *PARAPSYCHOLOGY AND OCCULTISM*

025.04 USA ISSN 1081-2024
KF242.A1
DIRECTORY OF ONLINE SERVICES. Text in English. 1994. a. free. **Document type:** *Directory.* **Description:** Lists sources contained in Lexis-Nexis online services.
Formerly (until 1995): Lexis-Nexis Library Contents, Alphabetical List, Quick Reference (1078-3245)
Related titles: Online - full text ed.
Published by: LexisNexis (Subsidiary of: Reed Elsevier plc), 9443 Springboro Pike, Miamisburg, OH 45342. TEL 937-865-6800, http://www.lexis-nexis.com/lnce/literature/directory, http://www.lexisnexis.com. Ed. Lorraine Gongla Coppinger. Circ: 225,000.

004.678 DEU
▼ **DISINFOJOURNAL**; the first international e-journal of disinformation on the net. Text in English. 2003. irreg.
Media: Online - full content.
Published by: Institute for the Examination of Information Behavior at the Internet http://www.disinfojournal.net/index.html. Ed. Alan Springer.

DOCTOR EBIZ; helping small business succeed online. see *BUSINESS AND ECONOMICS—Small Business*

004.6 USA
THE DOCULABS REPORT. Text in English. 2002. s-a. USD 175 per issue (effective 2003).
Related titles: Online - full text ed.
Published by: Doculabs, Inc, 120 S La Salle St Ste 2300, Chicago, IL 60603. TEL 312-433-7793, FAX 312-433-7795, info@doculabs.com, http://www.doculabs.com/.

DOCUMENTING E-COMMERCE TRANSACTIONS. see *LAW—Corporate Law*

025.0634 GBR
DOMAIN NAMES; global practice and procedure. Text in English. 2000. 2 base vols. plus updates 2/yr. looseleaf. GBP 454 base vol(s).; GBP 345, EUR 519 updates in Europe; GBP 355, USD 645 updates elsewhere (effective 2006). **Document type:** *Journal, Trade.*
Published by: Sweet & Maxwell Ltd., 100 Avenue Road, London, NW3 3PF, United Kingdom. TEL 44-20-74491111, FAX 44-20-74491144, customer.services@sweetandmaxwell.co.uk, http://www.sweetandmaxwell.co.uk. **Subscr. to:** Cheriton House, North Way, Andover, Hants SP10 5BE, United Kingdom.

004.67 IRL ISSN 1393-3167
DOT.IE. Text in English. 1996. m. adv. **Document type:** *Magazine, Consumer.*
Published by: Hoson Company, 3-7 Camden Pl., Dublin, 2, Ireland. TEL 353-1-4784322, FAX 353-1-4781055, editor@hoson.com, http://www.hoson.com. Ed. Roisin Dwyer. Adv. contact Pete Wilson. color page EUR 3,237. Circ: 15,000 (paid and controlled).

025.04 DEU ISSN 1619-7933
DOT.NET MAGAZIN. Text in German. 2002. m. EUR 76.50; EUR 8.50 newsstand/cover (effective 2005). adv. **Document type:** *Magazine, Trade.*
Published by: Software & Support Verlag GmbH, Kennedyallee 87, Frankfurt am Main, 60596, Germany. TEL 49-69-6300890, FAX 49-69-63008989, info@dotnet-magazin.de, info@software-support.biz, http://www.dotnet-magazin.de, http://www.software-support.biz. Ed. Sarah Metzger. adv.: B&W page EUR 3,150, color page EUR 4,350. Circ: 30,000 (controlled).

DOTCEO. see *BUSINESS AND ECONOMICS—Management*

005.276 DEU ISSN 1610-1553
DOTNETPRO; das .Net-Magazin fuer Entwickler. Text in German. 2002. 10/yr. EUR 127 domestic; EUR 139.40 in Austria; EUR 215.30 in Switzerland; EUR 139 elsewhere; EUR 14.90 newsstand/cover (effective 2003). adv. **Document type:** *Magazine, Trade.*
Formed by the merger of (1998-2002): V B A Magazin (1610-1537); (1995-2002): Basic Pro (1610-1545); (1988-2002): System Journal (1616-8097); Which was formerly (until 2000): Microsoft System Journal (0933-9434)
Related titles: Online - full text ed.
—IE.
Published by: redtec publishing GmbH, Gruber Str 46a, Poing, 85586, Germany. TEL 49-8121-951850, FAX 49-8121-951880, info@dotnetpro.de, info@redtec.de, http://www.dotnetpro.de, http://www.redtec.de. Ed. Cordula Lochmann. Adv. contact Guido Klausbruckner. B&W page EUR 3,900, color page EUR 4,900; trim 210 x 297. Circ: 13,551 (paid and controlled).

C

DOW JONES BANDWIDTH INTELLIGENCE ALERT. see *COMPUTERS—Computer Networks*

004.678 USA
DUMMIES DAILY AMERICA ONLINE NEWSLETTER. Text in English. 1999. d. back issues avail. **Document type:** *Newsletter.*
Media: Online - full text.
Published by: I D G Books Worldwide, Inc., 919 E. Hillsdale Blvd., Ste. 400, Foster City, CA 94404. david@mkpr.com, http://www.dummiesdaily.com/. Ed. David Hafner.

005.276 USA
DUMMIES DAILY FRONTPAGE NEWSLETTER. Text in English. 1999. d. **Document type:** *Newsletter.*
Media: Online - full text.
Published by: I D G Books Worldwide, Inc., 919 E. Hillsdale Blvd., Ste. 400, Foster City, CA 94404. david@mkpr.com, http://www.dummiesdaily.com/. Ed. David Hafner.

025.04 USA
DUMMIES DAILY INTERNET SEARCH TIPS NEWSLETTER. Text in English. 1999. d. back issues avail. **Document type:** *Newsletter.*
Media: Online - full text.
Published by: I D G Books Worldwide, Inc., 919 E. Hillsdale Blvd., Ste. 400, Foster City, CA 94404. david@mkpr.com, http://www.dummiesdaily.com/. Ed. David Hafner.

004.678 USA
DUMMIES DAILY INTERNET TIPS NEWSLETTER. Text in English. 1999. d. **Document type:** *Newsletter.*
Media: Online - full text.
Published by: I D G Books Worldwide, Inc., 919 E. Hillsdale Blvd., Ste. 400, Foster City, CA 94404. david@mkpr.com, http://www.dummiesdaily.com/. Ed. David Hafner.

025.04 USA
DUMMIES DAILY ONLINE SHOPPING TIPS NEWSLETTER. Text in English. 1999. d. **Document type:** *Newsletter.*
Media: Online - full text.
Published by: I D G Books Worldwide, Inc., 919 E. Hillsdale Blvd., Ste. 400, Foster City, CA 94404. david@mkpr.com, http://www.dummiesdaily.com/. Ed. David Hafner.

004.692 USA
DUMMIES DAILY OUTLOOK EXPRESS NEWSLETTER. Text in English. 1999. d. back issues avail. **Document type:** *Newsletter.*
Media: Online - full text.
Published by: I D G Books Worldwide, Inc., 919 E. Hillsdale Blvd., Ste. 400, Foster City, CA 94404. david@mkpr.com, http://www.dummiesdaily.com/. Ed. David Hafner.

004.678 USA
DUMMIES DAILY WEB AFTER FIVE: REVIEWS NEWSLETTER. Text in English. 1999. d. back issues avail. **Document type:** *Newsletter.*
Media: Online - full text.
Published by: I D G Books Worldwide, Inc., 919 E. Hillsdale Blvd., Ste. 400, Foster City, CA 94404. david@mkpr.com, http://www.dummiesdaily.com/. Ed. David Hafner.

658.054678 DEU
E-BUSINESS. Variant title: Wirtschaftswoche e-Business. Text in German. 2001. fortn. **Document type:** *Magazine, Trade.* **Description:** Provides information and content on new strategies and technologies within the e-business world.
Related titles: Online - full text ed.: 2001.
Published by: H & T Verlag GmbH & Co. KG (Subsidiary of: Verlagsgruppe Handelsblatt GmbH), Konrad-Zuse-Platz 1, Munich, 81829, Germany. TEL 49-89-4447870, FAX 49-89-44478710, info@htverlag.de, http://www.e-business.de, http://www.htverlag.de.

659.13 GBR
E.BUSINESS; today's strategies for tomorrow's business. Text in English. 1999. m. GBP 28.80; GBP 48.80 in Europe; GBP 58.80 rest of world; GBP 3 newsstand/cover (effective 2000). adv. **Description:** Provides high-tech coverage in low-tech language for business decision-makers. Reports on the effects of the electronic world on all business processes and reflects on how business is being shaped by the Internet.
Published by: Crimson Publishing, Vigilant House, 120 Wilton Rd, London, SW1V 1JZ, United Kingdom. TEL 44-20-78087141, FAX 44-20-78087142, enquiries@crimsonpublishing.co.uk, http://www.ebusiness.uk.com, http://www.crimsonpublishing.co.uk. Adv. contact Tony Jee. color page GBP 3,200; trim.

004.678 GBR
E-BUSINESS PARTNER; for resellers, distributors and other channel specialists working to supply and support internet users. Text in English. 1999. bi-m. adv. **Document type:** *Magazine, Trade.* **Description:** Provides information and product news for Internet customers of resellers and other specialists involved with electronic networks.
Published by: Business Publications Ltd., Brooklyn House, 22 The Green, West Drayton, Middlesex UB7 7PQ, United Kingdom. TEL 44-1895-421111, FAX 44-1895-431252, info@e-businesspartner.com, http://www.channelbusiness.com.

E-BUSINESS WORLD. see *BUSINESS AND ECONOMICS*

384.33 USA
E C MGT.COM EZINE. (Electronic Commerce Management) Text in English. 1999. m. free. **Document type:** *Newsletter.* **Description:** Focuses on e-commerce trends.
Formerly: E C M Ezine
Media: Online - full text.
Published by: E C M Ezine, 19672 Stevens Creek Blvd, Ste 200, Cupertino, CA 95014. TEL 408-257-3000, FAX 603-843-0769, mitchell.levy@ecnow.com, http://ecnow.com/ec.edge/. Ed. Mitchell Levy.

025.4 658 USA ISSN 1526-3622
E-COM. Text in English. 1999. m. USD 39.95 (effective 2001). adv. **Document type:** *Magazine, Trade.* **Description:** Provides information and advice to the people who need to make the business of e-commerce work.
Media: Online - full text.
Published by: Specialty Publishing Co., 135 E Saint Charles Rd, Carol Stream, IL 60188. TEL 630-933-0844, FAX 630-933-0845, http://www.e-commag.com. Ed., Pub. Peggy Smedley. Adv. contact Robert Parzy.

340 USA ISSN 1536-2698
KF390.5.C6
E-COMMERCE LAW & STRATEGY. Text in English. 1994. m. USD 365 combined subscription print & online eds. (effective 2005). **Document type:** *Newsletter, Trade.*
Incorporates (in 2003): E-Securities Newsletter; Formed by the merger of (1984-1999): Computer Law Strategist (0747-8933); (1994-1999): Multimedia & Web Strategist (1092-3446); Which was formerly (until 1996): Multimedia Strategist (1080-3904)
Related titles: Online - full content ed.: USD 245 (effective 2003).
—CCC.
Published by: Law Journal Newsletters (Subsidiary of: A L M), 1617 JFK Blvd, Ste 1750, Philadelphia, PA 19103. TEL 800-888-8300, lawcatalog@amlaw.com, http://www.ljnonline.com/pub/ljn_ecommerce/. Ed. Michael Lear-Olimpi.

E-COMMERCE LAW DAILY. see *LAW*

025.04 330 USA
E-COMMERCE LAW REPORT; buying and selling on the Internet. Text in English. 11/yr. USD 287 (effective 2005). **Document type:** *Newsletter, Trade.*
Published by: Glasser LegalWorks (Subsidiary of: West Publishing Co.), 150 Clove Rd, Little Falls, NJ 07424. TEL 973-890-0008, 800-308-1700, FAX 973-890-0042, legalwks@aol.com, http://www.legalwks.com/newsletters.

384.33 USA ISSN 1098-5654
E-COMMERCE MARKET REPORTER. Text in English. 1997. 24/yr. USD 547 (effective 2000). adv. index. back issues avail. **Document type:** *Newsletter, Trade.* **Description:** Covers strategies, new products, innovation, privacy issues, business solutions, services available, vendor news and comparative information for implementing sales and marketing on the Internet.
—CCC.
Published by: E-Commerce Information Center, 1913 Atlantic Ave, Ste F4, Manasquan, NJ 08736. TEL 732-292-1100, FAX 732-292-1111, ecic@thecic.com, http://www.theecic.com. Ed. Jodi Kastel. Pub. Robert K Jenkins. Adv. contact Samuel DePalma.

E-COMMERCE PRACTITIONER. see *BUSINESS AND ECONOMICS—Marketing And Purchasing*

384.33 GBR ISSN 1464-9578
E-COMMERCE QUARTERLY. Text in English. q.
—BLDSC (3637.718870), ingenta.
Published by: Lasersurf Multimedia, 5 The Old Grammar, Bungay, Suffolk, NR35 1PU, United Kingdom. TEL 44-1986-892284, info@ecommercequarterly.com. Pub. Roy Williams.

E-COMMERCE TAX ALERT. see *BUSINESS AND ECONOMICS—Public Finance, Taxation*

E-COMMERCE TAX REPORT. see *BUSINESS AND ECONOMICS—Public Finance, Taxation*

E-COMMERCE TAX REPORT (ONLINE EDITION). see *BUSINESS AND ECONOMICS—Public Finance, Taxation*

E-COMMERCE TIMES. see *BUSINESS AND ECONOMICS—Marketing And Purchasing*

E F A UPDATE. (Electronic Frontiers Australia) see *COMPUTERS*

E-JAY. see *MUSIC*

004.692 USA ISSN 1540-3882
▼ **E-MAIL MALEDICTA**; how to avoid E-mail messages that wound, embarrass, and lead to lawsuits. Text in English. 2004. 10/yr. USD 56 domestic; USD 68 in Canada; USD 88 elsewhere (effective 2005). software rev. illus. **Document type:** *Newsletter.* **Description:** Improving E-mail usage, how to avoid legal problems by careless or deliberate misuse of e-mail systems.
Published by: Assets Protection Publishing, 5029 Sheboygan Ave #201, Madison, WI 53705. Ed., Pub., R&P Paul Shaw.

025.04 AUT
E-MEDIA. Text in German. 2000. fortn. EUR 99.90 (effective 2003). adv. **Document type:** *Magazine, Consumer.*
Related titles: Online - full text ed.
Published by: Verlagsgruppe News Gesellschaft mbH (Subsidiary of: Gruner und Jahr AG & Co.), Alfred-Feierfeil-Str. 3, Perchtoldsdorf, N 2380, Austria. TEL 43-1-863315340, FAX 43-1-86331590, http://www.news.at/emedia/. Circ: 189,000 (paid and controlled).

E-MERGING BUSINESS; taking your business to the next level. see *BUSINESS AND ECONOMICS—Small Business*

E-MMERCE. see *BUSINESS AND ECONOMICS*

025.04 346 USA ISSN 1055-5307
E R I S A LITIGATION REPORTER. (Employee Retirement Income Security Act) Text in English. bi-m. USD 334 (effective 2005). **Document type:** *Newsletter, Trade.*
Related titles: Online - full text ed.: (from ProQuest Information & Learning).
Indexed: ABIn.
—CCC.
Published by: Glasser LegalWorks (Subsidiary of: West Publishing Co.), 150 Clove Rd, Little Falls, NJ 07424. TEL 973-890-0008, 800-308-1700, FAX 973-890-0042, legalwks@aol.com, http://www.legalwks.com/newsletters/#erisa.

C

384.54 USA
E-RADIO; the business of audio on the internet. Text in English. m. USD 59; USD 89 foreign (effective 2000). adv. **Document type:** *Magazine, Trade.* **Description:** Covers the evolving world of radio and audio on the Internet.
Published by: Streamline Publishing, Inc., 224 Datura St, Ste 701, West Palm Beach, FL 33401. TEL 561-655-8778, FAX 561-655-6164, edryan@eradiomag.com, http://www.eradiomag.com.

E-SERVICE JOURNAL. see *COMPUTERS—Information Science And Information Theory*

004.678 GBR ISSN 1744-0882
▼ **E-SIGNATURE LAW JOURNAL.** Text in English. 2004. s-a. GBP 120 (effective 2005). bk.rev. **Document type:** *Journal, Academic/Scholarly.*
—BLDSC (3638.645500). CCC.
Published by: Pario Communications Ltd, 19a Church St, Langford, Biggleswade, Beds SG18 9QT, United Kingdom. TEL 44-1462-701098, information@pariocommunications.co.uk. Ed. Stephen Mason.

004.678 USA
EAI JOURNAL; the resource for e-business and application integration. Text in English. m. USD 12 in Canada & Mexico; USD 36 elsewhere (effective 2000); free to qualified personnel. adv. **Document type:** *Magazine, Trade.* **Description:** Looks at the technical issues surrounding strategic e-business deployment, including the integration of applications and middleware, and features all the latest breaking news in the market.
Related titles: ♦ Online - full text ed.: eAI Journal Online.
Address: 9330 Lyndon B Johnson Fwy., Ste. 800, Dallas, TX 75243-4310. TEL 214-340-2147, FAX 214-341-7081, info@eaijournal.com, http://www.eaijournal.com. Ed. Tony Brown. Adv. contacts Karin Altonaga, Leslie Ringe.

004.678 USA
EAI JOURNAL ONLINE. Text in English. d. adv. **Document type:** *Trade.* **Description:** Contains information that helps companies develop long-term architectural strategies to integrate the best available technologies with existing e-business systems.
Media: Online - full text. **Related titles:** ♦ Print ed.: eAI Journal.
Published by: eAI Journal, 9330 Lyndon B Johnson Fwy., Ste. 800, Dallas, TX 75243-4310. TEL 214-340-2147, FAX 214-341-7081, info@eaijournal.com, http://www.eaijournal.com. Ed. Tony Brown. Adv. contacts Karin Altonaga, Leslie Ringe.

025.04 USA
EASY INTERNET✶. Text in English. 4/yr. USD 3.99 newsstand/cover (effective 2001). adv. **Document type:** *Magazine, Consumer.* **Description:** Provides a complete guide to all aspects of the Web.
Published by: Ziff-Davis Publishing Co. (Subsidiary of: Softbank), 28 E 28th St, 14th Fl., New York, NY 10016-7922. TEL 212-503-4783, 800-950-0484, FAX 212-503-4703, http://www.zdnet.com.

004.6   USA
EBIZCHRONICLE; the business of e-business. Text in English.
3/w.
Media: E-mail.
Published by: EbizChronicle, 274 Madison Ave Ste 1102, New
York, NY 10016. TEL 212-686-4408, FAX 212-686-4408,
http://www.ebizchronicle.com., http://www.ebizchronicle.com/.
Ed. Zuhair Kashmeri.

ECOMPANY. see *BUSINESS AND ECONOMICS—Computer
Applications*

025.4   USA
ECOMPANY.COM. Text in English. d. adv. **Document type:**
Trade.
Media: Online - full content. **Related titles:** ♦ Print ed.:
eCompany Now.
Published by: eCompany Now, One California St, 29th Fl, San
Francisco, CA 94111. TEL 415-293-4811, FAX 415-293-5290,
http://www.ecompany.com. Ed. Ned Desmond.

025.4   USA   ISSN 1548-5234
LB1044.87
**EDUCATORS GUIDE TO FREE INTERNET RESOURCES
(ELEMENTARY-MIDDLE SCHOOL EDITION).** Text in English.
2002. irreg. (1st Edition), latest 2002-2003. USD 39.95 per
issue (effective 2003). 291 p./no.; **Document type:** *Directory.*
Description: Lists free programs, lesson plans, articles,
tutorials, teacher's guides, web sites, and more-nearly 1800 of
them are fully described in this must-have Guide to the
Internet and it's vast store of educational resources. More
than 1100 listings are new to this edition. Subjects covered
include, geography, language arts, science, geography, going
online, consumer education, and more.
Published by: Educators Progress Service, Inc., 214 Center St,
Randolph, WI 53956. TEL 920-326-3126, 888-951-4469, FAX
920-326-3127, questions@freeteachingaids.com,
http://www.freeteachingaids.com/vfc_877083320.html. Ed.
Kathleen Suttles Nehmer.

025.04   USA   ISSN 1549-6996
LB1044.87
**EDUCATORS GUIDE TO FREE INTERNET RESOURCES
(SECONDARY EDITION).** Text in English. 1983. a., latest 20th
Edition, 2002-2003. USD 39.95 per issue (effective 2003). 317
p./no.; **Document type:** *Directory, Academic/Scholarly.*
Description: Covers free films, videotapes, pamphlets, charts
and disks.
Supersedes in part (in 2002): Educators Guide to Free Computer
Materials and Internet Resources; Which was formerly (until
2001): Guide to Free Computer Materials and Internet
Resources (1530-6828); (until 2000): Guide to Free Computer
Materials (0748-6235)
Published by: Educators Progress Service, Inc., 214 Center St,
Randolph, WI 53956. TEL 920-326-3126, 888-951-4469, FAX
920-326-3127, questions@freeteachingaids.com,
http://www.freeteachingaids.com/vfc_877083320.html. Ed.
Kathleen Suttles Nehmer.

EHEALTHCARE STRATEGY & TRENDS. see *HEALTH
FACILITIES AND ADMINISTRATION*

004.68   GBR
▼ **EI MAGAZINE.** Text in English. 2004. 10/yr. GBP 195
domestic; EUR 305 in Europe; USD 345 elsewhere; GBP 540
combined subscription domestic print & online eds; EUR 295
combined subscription in Europe print & online eds; USD 440
combined subscription elsewhere print & online eds (effective
2004). adv. back issues avail. **Document type:** *Magazine,
Trade.* **Description:** Aimed exclusively at intranet, extranet
and enterprise portal professionals.
Formed by the merger of (2001-2004): C M Focus (1475-0759);
(1996-2004): Intranet Strategist (1477-5964); Which was
formerly (until 2002): Virtual Business (1467-0534); (until
1999): Intranet Communicator (1365-7011)
Related titles: Online - full content ed.
—BLDSC (3664.734000), IE.
Published by: Ark Group Ltd, 86-88 Upper Richmond Rd,
London, SW15 2UR, United Kingdom. TEL 44-20-87852700,
FAX 44-20-87859373, info@ark-group.com,
http://www.eimagazine.com/, http://www.ark-group.com. Ed.
Layisha Laypang. Adv. contact Melissa Midgley.

EL.PUB WEEKLY; interactive electronic publishing R & D news
and resources. see *PUBLISHING AND BOOK
TRADE—Computer Applications*

004.678 025.04 070.5   GBR
**THE ELECTRONIC AFRICAN BOOKWORM: A WEB
NAVIGATOR.** Text in English. 1998. irreg., latest vol.2, 2000.
GBP 8.95, USD 15 (effective 2001). **Description:** Serves as a
quick access guide to some of the best Internet sites on
Africa, African publishing and the African book trade.
Related titles: Online - full text ed.
Published by: African Books Collective Ltd., The Jam Factory, 27
Park End St, Oxford, Oxon OX1 1HU, United Kingdom. FAX
44-1865-793298, abc@africanbookscollective.com,
http://www.africanbookscollective.com. Ed. Hans M Zell. Pub.
Ros Sherwin.

025.04 346   USA   ISSN 1090-8420
ELECTRONIC BANKING LAW AND COMMERCE REPORT. Text
in English. 1996. 10/yr. USD 287 (effective 2005). **Document
type:** *Newsletter, Trade.*
Indexed: BLI.
Published by: Glasser LegalWorks (Subsidiary of: West
Publishing Co.), 150 Clove Rd, Little Falls, NJ 07424. TEL
973-890-0008, 800-308-1700, FAX 973-890-0042,
legalwks@aol.com, http://www.legalwks.com/newsletters/
#electronic. Ed. David E Brown.

ELECTRONIC BUSINESS LAW. see *LAW—Corporate Law*

384.33   GBR   ISSN 1361-2727
ELECTRONIC COMMERCE AND COMMUNICATIONS. Text in
English. 1990. 10/yr. USD 150. bk.rev. **Document type:**
Consumer. **Description:** For users and suppliers of products
and services for electronic data interchange and electronic
commerce.
Formerly (until 1995): E D I Analysis (0958-5052)
Address: 10 Fourways, Canning Rd, Croydon, CR0 6QB, United
Kingdom. TEL 44-181-655-4354,
johnkav@cix.compulink.co.uk. Pub. Terry Benson. Circ:
10,000.

383.33   USA   ISSN 1389-5753
ELECTRONIC COMMERCE RESEARCH. Text in Spanish. 2001.
q. EUR 384, USD 384, GBP 240 combined subscription to
institutions print & online eds. (effective 2005). adv. reprint
service avail. from PSC. **Document type:** *Academic/Scholarly.*
Related titles: Online - full text ed.: ISSN 1572-9362 (from
EBSCO Publishing, Gale Group, IngentaConnect, Kluwer
Online, O C L C Online Computer Library Center, Inc.,
ProQuest Information & Learning, Springer LINK, Swets
Information Services).
Indexed: ABIn, BibLing, CompR, Inspec, RefZh.
—BLDSC (3700.282400), IE, Infotrieve, ingenta. **CCC.**
Published by: Springer-Verlag New York, Inc. (Subsidiary of:
Springer Science+Business Media), 233 Spring St, New York,
NY 10013. TEL 212-460-1500, FAX 212-460-1575,
service@springer-ny.com, http://springerlink.metapress.com/
openurl.asp?genre=journal&issn=1389-5753,
http://www.springer-ny.com. Ed. Bezalel Gavish. **Subscr. to:**
Journal Fulfillment, PO Box 2485, Secaucus, NJ 07096-2485.
TEL 201-348-4033, FAX 201-348-4505, journals@springer-
ny.com.

ELECTRONIC EDUCATION REPORT; business intelligence on
opportunities in the educational software industry. see
EDUCATION—Computer Applications

004.678   CHE   ISSN 1422-9331
HD58.7
**ELECTRONIC JOURNAL OF ORGANIZATIONAL
VIRTUALNESS.** Text in English. 1999. q.
Media: Online - full content.
Published by: Virtual Organization Network ps@pascal-sieber.net,
http://www.virtual-organization.net/. Ed. Pascal Sieber.

004.678   USA   ISSN 1081-3055
QA76.9.H85
► **THE ELECTRONIC JOURNAL OF VIRTUAL CULTURE.** Text
in English. 1993. q. back issues avail. **Document type:**
Academic/Scholarly. **Description:** Covers the emerging social
and cultural aspects of the internet and related computer
applications.
Formerly (until 1996): Arachnet Electronic Journal on Virtual
Culture (1068-5723)
Media: Online - full text.
Published by: Electronic Journal of Virtual Culture TEL
330-273-5932, diane@kovacs.com, http://rdz.stjohns.edu/ejvc/
ejvc.html. Ed. Diane K Kovacs.

384.33   USA   ISSN 1087-7843
HF5415.1265
THE ELECTRONIC MARKETPLACE (YEAR); strategies for
connecting buyers & sellers. Text in English. 1995. a. USD
1,695 (effective 2000). **Document type:** *Trade.* **Description:**
Offers an in-depth analysis of the emerging business of
electronic commerce and shopping from a marketer's
perspective.
Published by: SIMBA Information (Subsidiary of: R.R. Bowker
LLC), 60 Long Ridge Rd., Ste 300, Stamford, CT 06902. TEL
203-325-8193, 800-307-2529, 888-269-5372, FAX
203-325-8915, info@simbanet.com, http://www.simbanet.com.

004.678   USA
ELECTRONIC RECRUITING NEWS. Text in English. 1995. d.
free. adv. **Document type:** *Newsletter.* **Description:** Targeted
at human resource professionals, headhunters, placement
firms and recruiting agencies on the Net.
Media: Online - full text.
Published by: Internet Business Network, PO Box 637, Mill
Valley, CA 94942-0637. TEL 415-389-6493, FAX
415-383-8676, jrs@interbiznet.com, http://www.interbiznet.com.
Ed. John Sumser. Adv. contact Colleen Gildea.

ELECTRONIC TRADING MARKETS. see *BUSINESS AND
ECONOMICS—Computer Applications*

004.692   USA
THE EMAILIAN. Text in English. 1997. m. **Document type:**
Bulletin. **Description:** Newsletter for publishers of all sizes
who deliver publications via e-mail.
Media: Online - full text.
Published by: MessageMedia, Inc., 11101 W. 120th Ave.,
Broomfield, CO 80021-3453. TEL 303-440-7550, FAX
303-440-0303, support@messagemedia.com,
http://www.messagemedia.com. MARKET; Webmagazin fuer
Online-Marketing und E-Commerce. see *BUSINESS AND
ECONOMICS—Marketing And Purchasing*

004.678   USA
EMARKETECT MAGAZINE; the journal for emarketplace builders,
owners and operators. Text in English. 2001. bi-m. USD 36
domestic; USD 48 in Canada; USD 60 elsewhere (effective
2001). adv. **Document type:** *Magazine, Trade.* **Description:**
Provides extensive coverage of online exchanges, trading
communities, vortals, hubs and other technologies and
services to the architects, developers, investors and managers
of emarketplaces.
Related titles: Online - full text ed.
Published by: Group IV Inc., PO Box 50040, Phoenix, AZ
85076-0040. TEL 602-631-9880, FAX 602-631-9958,
info@marketect.com, http://www.emarketect.com. adv.: B&W
page USD 2,610, color page USD 3,585; trim 8.125 x 10.875.

025.04   USA
EMEDIA BUYER'S GUIDE. Text in English. a. USD 7.95
newsstand/cover (effective 2001). **Document type:** *Magazine,
Trade.* **Description:** Provides information and reviews on
products and services used to produce digital output and
content.
Published by: Online, Inc. (Subsidiary of: Information Today, Inc.),
88 Danbury Rd., Ste. 2C, Wilton, CT 06897-4423. TEL
203-761-1466, 800-248-8466, FAX 203-761-1444,
emedia@onlineinc.com, http://www.emedialive.com. **Dist. by:**
International Publishers Direct, 27500 Riverview Center Blvd,
Bonita Springs, FL 34134. TEL 858-320-4563, FAX
858-677-3220.

659.13 330   MEX
EMPRESA E. (Empresa Electronica) Text in Spanish. 2001. m.
MXP 360; MXP 760 Including Hecho en Mexico (effective
2001). **Document type:** *Trade.*
Related titles: Online - full text ed.
Published by: Grupo Internacional Editorial S A de C V, Rio
Nazas 34, Col. Cuahutemoc, Mexico D F, 06500, Mexico. TEL
52-5-2099930, FAX 52-5-5660564,
buzon@intermundo.com.mx, http://www.empresa-e.com. Ed.
Ana Luisa Ochoa. Circ: 15,000.

384.33 340   GBR
▼ **ENCYCLOPEDIA OF E-COMMERCE LAW.** Text in English.
2003. 2 base vols. plus updates 3/yr. looseleaf. GBP 485
(effective 2005). **Document type:** *Trade.*
Published by: Sweet & Maxwell Ltd., 100 Avenue Road, London,
NW3 3PF, United Kingdom. TEL 44-20-74491111, FAX
44-20-74491144, customer.services@sweetandmaxwell.co.uk,
http://www.sweetandmaxwell.co.uk. **Subscr. to:** Cheriton
House, North Way, Andover, Hants SP10 5BE, United
Kingdom.

ENTDECKUNGEN - DAS KINDERWEB. see *CHILDREN AND
YOUTH—For*

025.4   JPN
ENTERPRISE SERVERS WORLD JAPAN. Text in Japanese. m.
adv. **Document type:** *Magazine, Trade.*
Published by: I D G Japan, Inc., Hongo 3-4-5, Bunkyo-ku, Tokyo,
1130033, Japan. TEL 81-3-5800-3111, FAX 81-3-5800-3590,
http://www.idg.co.jp. adv.: B&W page USD 2,046, color page
USD 3,778; trim 210 x 277. Circ: 25,000.

025.4 338   USA
ENTREPRENEUR'S NETPRENEUR. Variant title: Netpreneur.
Text in English. 2000. m. adv. **Document type:** *Magazine,
Trade.* **Description:** Provides insight and information on
setting up and maintaining e-businesses.
Media: Online - full content.
Published by: Entrepreneur Media, Inc., 2445 McCabe Way, Ste
400, Irvine, CA 92614. TEL 949-261-2325, 800-926-6995, FAX
949-261-0234, subscribe@entrepreneurmag.com,
http://www.entrepreneur.com/netpreneur, http://
www.entrepreneurmag.com.

004.678   USA
ENTREPRENEURS NEWSLETTER. Text in English. 1994. d.
Media: Online - full content.
Published by: Internet Entrepreneurs Support Service
Association, 4040 Towhee Dr, Calabasas, CA 91302.
http://www.entrepreneurs.com. Ed. Ron Ehrens.

004.678   USA
ESERVICE PROVIDER; the magazine for web and application
hosting executives. Text in English. 2001. m. **Document type:**
Magazine, Trade. **Description:** Provides insight and
perspective on the strategies, companies, technologies and
people leading the service provider market.

C

Published by: Penton Media, Inc. (Golden), 13949 W Colfax Ave, Ste 250, Golden, CO 80401-3209. TEL 303-235-9510, 800-933-6038, FAX 303-235-9502. Pub. Randy Goldner. Adv. contact Larry Robinson. Circ: 30,000 (controlled).

004.678 CHE
ETOY TANKSYSTEM. Text in German. 1994. 4/yr.
Media: Online - full text.
Address: PO Box 3365, Zuerich, 8049, Switzerland. mailme@etoy.com, http://www.etoy.com.

025.4 AUT
E!TREND. Text in German. 4/yr. adv. **Document type:** *Magazine, Consumer.*
Published by: Wirtschafts-Trend Zeitschriftenverlagsgesellschaft mbH, Lindengasse 52, Vienna, W 1070, Austria. TEL 43-1-53470-0, FAX 43-1-5353250, http://www.etrend.at, http://trend.at. Pub. Christian Rainer. R&P Helmut Hanusch.

004.692 USA
EUDORA NEWS. Text in English. q. **Document type:** *Newsletter.* **Description:** Contains tips, success stories and product news concerning Eudora Internet e-mail software.
Media: Online - full text.
Published by: Qualcomm Inc., 10185 Mckellar Ct., San Diego, CA 92121-4233. eudora-news-feedback@eudora.com, http://www.eudora.com/.

EV; entertainment and the digital economy. see *THEATER*

025.04 USA ISSN 1554-2009
TA1635 CODEN: CNEEEF
EVENT D V; the event videographer's resource. Text in English. 1988. m. free domestic; USD 50 foreign (effective 2005). adv. bk.rev. illus. Index. back issues avail.; reprints avail. **Document type:** *Magazine, Trade.* **Description:** Offers meaningful analyses, unique case studies, critical reviews, and comprehensive new products and emerging technology reporting involving optical storage, CD-ROM, and DVD technologies for developers and end-users.
Former titles (until 2004): EMedia: The Digital Studio Magazine (1529-7306); (until 2000): EMedia Magazine (1525-4658); (until 1999): E Media Professional (1090-946X); (until 1997): CD-ROM Professional (1049-0833); Which incorporated (1993-1994): CD-ROM News Extra (1075-1106); (until 1990): Laserdisk Professional (0896-4149)
Related titles: Online - full text ed.: (from bigchalk, EBSCO Publishing, Florida Center for Library Automation, Gale Group, H.W. Wilson, O C L C Online Computer Library Center, Inc., ProQuest Information & Learning); Supplement(s): EMedia Xtra.
Indexed: ABIn, ASCA, B&I, BPI, CIJE, CINAHL, CompD, CurCont, Inspec, LISA, LibLit, MicrocompInd, SoftBase, T&II. —BLDSC (3830.772547), AskIEEE, CASDDS, CINDOC, CISTI, Ei, IDS, IE, ingenta, Linda Hall. **CCC.**
Published by: Online, Inc. (Subsidiary of: Information Today, Inc.), 88 Danbury Rd., Ste. 2C, Wilton, CT 06897-4423. TEL 203-761-1466, FAX 203-761-1444, emedia@onlineinc.com, http://www.emedialive.com, http://www.emediapro.net. Ed. Stephen F. Nathans. R&P Jenny Pemberton. adv.: B&W page USD 3,875, color page USD 4,960; trim 10.88 x 8.25. Circ: 17,000 (paid). **Dist. by:** International Publishers Direct, 27500 Riverview Center Blvd, Bonita Springs, FL 34134. TEL 858-320-4563, FAX 858-677-3220.

004.16 USA ISSN 1530-6283
QA75.5
EWEEK; the enterprise newsweekly. Text in English. 1984. w. USD 195 domestic; USD 295 in Canada & Mexico; USD 395 elsewhere (effective 2005); free domestic to qualified personnel. adv. software rev. illus.; tr.lit. reprints avail. **Document type:** *Magazine, Trade.* **Description:** Covers all aspects of computers for corporate users. Covers a wide variety of topics, including software, hardware, industry news, and business strategies and hardware.
Incorporates (1994-2001): Inter@ctive Week (1078-7259); Formerly (until 2000): P C Week (0740-1604)
Related titles: CD-ROM ed.; Microform ed.: (from PQC); Online - full text ed.: (from America Online, Inc., bigchalk, CompuServe Inc., EBSCO Publishing, Florida Center for Library Automation, Gale Group, H.W. Wilson, O C L C Online Computer Library Center, Inc.).
Indexed: BPI, BrCerAb, BusI, C&ISA, CerAb, CompD, CompIU, ConsI, CorrAb, CurCont, E&CAJ, EMA, IAA, InfoSAb, LRI, M&TEA, MBF, METADEX, MagInd, MicrocompInd, PAIS, PCR2, RASB, SoftBase, SolStAb, T&II, WAA. —BLDSC (3834.465450), CISTI, IDS, IE, Linda Hall. **CCC.**
Published by: Ziff Davis Media Inc., 28 E 28th St, New York, NY 10016-7930. TEL 212-503-3500, FAX 212-503-4399, eweek@ziffdavis.com, info@ziffdavis.com, http://www.eweek.com/, http://www.ziffdavis.com. Pub. Chris Dobbrow. Circ: 445,000 (paid and controlled).

621.3 ROM ISSN 1582-5434
EWEEK. Text in Romanian. 2001. w. adv. **Document type:** *Magazine, Consumer.*
Published by: Agora Media, Str. Tudor Vladimirescu nr. 63, ap. 9, CP 230-1, Targu Mures, 4300, Romania. TEL 40-65-166516, FAX 40-65-166290, office@agora.ro, http://www.agora.ro.

384.33 USA
EXPERTBIZ INSIGHTS. Text in English. irreg. free. adv. **Document type:** *Newsletter.* **Description:** For anyone who seeks to profit from their own expertise through consulting, teaching, and self-publishing.
Media: Online - full text.
Address: editor@expertbiz.com, http://www.expertbiz.com/insights.htm. Ed. Carole Lipski.

004.692 DEU ISSN 1617-1675
EXPERT'S INSIDE. EXCHANGE. Text in German. 2001. m. EUR 10.20 newsstand/cover. **Document type:** *Magazine, Trade.*
Published by: redtec publishing GmbH, Gruber Str 46a, Poing, 85586, Germany. TEL 49-8121-951850, FAX 49-8121-951880, info@redtec.de, http://www.redtec.de.

EXPERT'S INSIDE. VISUAL BASIC - VB.NET. see *COMPUTERS—Software*

FAMILY MEDICINE NET GUIDE; your guide to the internet. see *MEDICAL SCIENCES*

FAMILY MEDICINE NET GUIDE ENEWSLETTER. see *MEDICAL SCIENCES*

FAMILY MEDICINE NET GUIDE ONLINE. see *MEDICAL SCIENCES*

FASTCOMPANY.COM. see *BUSINESS AND ECONOMICS—Management*

384.33 USA
FIERCE VO I P; the voip business & technology report. (Voice Internet Provider) Text in English. d. free. **Document type:** *Newsletter, Trade.* **Description:** Reports on the latest developments in VoIP technology and business.
Media: E-mail.
Published by: FierceMarkets, Inc., 1319 F St, NW, Ste 604, Washington, DC 20004. TEL 202-628-8778, info@fiercemarkets.com, http://www.fiercevoip.com, http://www.fiercemarkets.com. Ed. John Edwards. Adv. contact Ryan Willumson.

025.04 CAN
THE FINGER SEARCHER SCIENCE SEEKER. Text in English. 1998. w. adv. index. back issues avail. **Document type:** *Newsletter.* **Description:** Presents information over the Internet for science students.
Media: Online - full text.
Published by: Finger Searcher Science Seeker, Canada. TEL 403-451-7756, martin@connect.ab.ca, http://www.connect.ab.ca/~xdr/fsearch/fsindex.html. Ed. Martin H Badke.

004.678 USA ISSN 1396-0466
ZA3201
➤ **FIRST MONDAY.** Text in English. 1996 (May). m. free (effective 2005). illus. back issues avail. **Document type:** *Journal, Academic/Scholarly.* **Description:** Publishes original articles about the Internet and the global information infrastructure, including political and regulatory issues, economic, technical and social factors, reports on standards and discussions of the contents of the Internet.
Media: Online - full text. **Related titles:** CD-ROM ed.: ISSN 1396-0458. 1996.
Indexed: BRI, C&CSA, CBRI, CommAb, InfoSAb, Inspec, LISA, LibLit, PAIS.
Published by: (University of Illinois at Chicago Library), First Monday Editorial Group, c/o Edward Valauskas, Chief Editor, PO Box 87636, Chicago, IL 60680-0636. ejv@uic.edu, http://www.firstmonday.org. Ed., Pub., R&P Edward J Valauskas. Circ: 314,559.

025.04 DEU
FIRSTSURF. Text in German. 1996. w. adv. **Document type:** *Consumer.* **Description:** Presents up-to-date information on all aspects and trends relating to the Internet.
Media: Online - full text.
Published by: Symposion Publishing GmbH, Werdener Str. 4, Duesseldorf, 40227, Germany. TEL 49-211-866930, FAX 49-211-8669323, klietmann@symposion.de, http://www.firstsurf.com. Ed., Adv. contact Markus Klietmann TEL 49-211-8669319.

004.6 USA ISSN 1541-1206
FIXED WIRELESS MONTHLY NEWSLETTER. Text in English. 1993. m. USD 695 in US & Canada; USD 745 elsewhere (effective 2005). adv. illus. reprints avail. **Document type:** *Newsletter, Trade.*
Formerly (until 2005): Information Superhighways (1078-6589)
Related titles: Online - full text ed.: (from Florida Center for Library Automation, Gale Group).
Indexed: CompD.
Published by: Information Gatekeepers, Inc., 320 Washington St, Ste 302, Brighton, MA 02135. TEL 617-782-5033, 800-323-1088, FAX 617-734-8562, info@igigroup.com, http://www.igigroup.com. Ed. Tony Carmona. Pub. Dr. Paul Polishuk.

004.678 AUS ISSN 1329-8526
➤ **FLEXIBLE ONLINE LEARNING.** Text in English. 1998. q. abstr. back issues avail. **Document type:** *Academic/Scholarly.* **Description:** Publishes articles regarding the delivery of educational programs through the medium of the Internet.
Media: Online - full text.
Published by: University of Technology, Sydney, Institute for Interactive Multimedia, PO Box 123, Broadway, NSW 2007, Australia. TEL 61-2-9514-2000, http://www.lib.uts.edu.au/folp/journal/index.html. Ed. Shirley Alexander.

➤ **FOCUS MONEY.** see *BUSINESS AND ECONOMICS—Investments*

➤ **FORBIDDEN INTERNET.** see *LIFESTYLE*

004.678 USA ISSN 1555-077X
▼ **FOUNDATIONS AND TRENDS IN WEB SCIENCE.** Text in English. forthcoming 2006. q.
Related titles: Online - full text ed.: ISSN 1555-0788. forthcoming 2006.
Published by: Now Publishers Inc., PO Box 1024, Hanover, MA 02339. TEL 781-871-0245, FAX 781-871-6172, http://www.nowpublishers.com. Pub., R&P Mike Casey.

004.16 AUS ISSN 1440-7949
FREE ACCESS. Text in English. 1998. 6/yr. AUD 26 (effective 2001). **Description:** Presents articles on home computing, the Internet, communications and technology.
Related titles: Online - full text ed.
Published by: Media Advantage Communications, PO Box 124, Coogee, NSW 2034, Australia. TEL 61-2-9664-5611, FAX 61-2-9664-5633, info@mediaadvantage.com, http://www.freeaccess.com.au. Pubs. John Pospisil, Tom Crawley.

025.04 GBR ISSN 1460-7239
FREE PINT; helping you use the web for your work. Text in English. 1997. fortn. free (effective 2002). adv. bk.rev.; Website rev. 17 p./no.; back issues avail. **Document type:** *Newsletter.* **Description:** Written for people who use the Internet to obtain business information. Informs readers how to find reliable information on the web.
Media: Online - full text.
Indexed: Inpharma, PE&ON, Reac.
Published by: Free Pint Ltd, 4 - 6 Station Approach, Ashford, Mddx TW15 2QN, United Kingdom. TEL 44-1784-420044, FAX 44-1784-420033, info@freepint.com, http://www.freepint.com. Eds. Rex Cooke, William Hann TEL 44-1784-455435. Adv. contact William Hann TEL 44-1784-455435. Circ: 49,000 (controlled).

004.678 USA
FRESHFACE. Text in English. irreg. adv. bk.rev. **Description:** Provides a web multimedia magazine for creative people on the Internet.
Media: Online - full text.
Address: freshface@webskills.com, http://www.freshface.com.

THE FUTURE PROFIT NEWSLETTER. see *BUSINESS AND ECONOMICS—Marketing And Purchasing*

G INFO - GAZETA DE INFORMATICA. see *BUSINESS AND ECONOMICS—Computer Applications*

GHOST SITES. see *PARAPSYCHOLOGY AND OCCULTISM*

025.04 GBR ISSN 1468-7178
GOING ONLINE, CD-ROM AND THE INTERNET. Text in English. 1980. irreg., latest vol.10, 1997. GBP 32.99 per vol. to non-members; GBP 26.50 per vol. to members (effective 2001). **Document type:** *Trade.*
Former titles (until 1994): Going Online and CD-ROM; (until 1992): Going Online (0953-3753)
—BLDSC (4201.132450).
Published by: Aslib, Association for Information Management, Publications Department, Staple Hall, Stone House Court, London, EC3A 7PB, United Kingdom. TEL 44-20-7903-0000, FAX 44-20-7430-0514, pubs@aslib.com, http://www.aslib.co.uk/pubs/2001/01/07.html, http://www.aslib.com. Eds. Phil Bradley, Terry Hanson.

GRAFIK & VIDEO. see *COMPUTERS—Computer Graphics*

GRAN CUENTA; informatica y comunicaciones para la empresa. see *COMPUTERS—Computer Industry*

384.44 ITA
GRATIS. Text in Italian. irreg. free. **Description:** Provides news and tips about business on the Internet.
Media: Online - full text.
Address: Italy. musictus@musictus.com, http://www.gratis.it.

004.678 378 AUS
GUIDE TO USING THE INTERNET AND THE WORLD WIDE WEB. Text in English. a. **Document type:** *Bulletin.*
Published by: Queensland Board of Senior Secondary School Studies, P.O. Box 307, Spring Hill, QLD 4101, Australia. TEL 61-7-3864-0299, FAX 61-7-3221-2553, office@qbssss.edu.au.

▼ *new title* ➤ *refereed* ✶ *unverified* ♦ *full entry avail.*

THE H R INTERNET AND TECHNOLOGY LETTER. see *BUSINESS AND ECONOMICS—Computer Applications*

005.276   USA   ISSN 1543-0995
HARDCORE A S P.NET. (Application Service Provider) Text in English. 1999. m. USD 199 domestic; USD 219 in Canada; USD 224 elsewhere (effective 2003). adv. **Document type:** *Newsletter, Trade.* **Description:** Focuses exclusively on the complete suite of Web tools and technologies Microsoft offers. **Formerly** (until 2002): ActiveWeb Developer (1525-1705)
Published by: Pinnacle Publishing, Inc. (Subsidiary of: Lawrence Ragan Communications, Inc.), 316 N. Michigan Ave, Ste 300, Chicago, IL 60601. TEL 312-960-4209, 800-493-4867, FAX 312-960-4106, pinpub@ragan.com, http://www.pinpub.com. Ed. Bill Hatfield. adv.: page USD 800. Circ: 1,500 (paid).

004.678   USA   ISSN 1547-6049
HARLEY HAHN'S INTERNET ADVISOR. Text in English. 2002. a. USD 20 per issue (effective 2003).
Media: Online - full content.
Published by: Harley Hahn, 2022 Cliff Dr., Santa Barbara, CA 93109. TEL 805-564-5000, http://hhe.harley.com/ia/chapters/chapter-list.html, http://www.harley.com. Pub. Hahn Harley.

025.04   USA   ISSN 1546-4148
ZA4201
HARLEY HAHN'S INTERNET YELLOW PAGES. Text in English. 1994. a. USD 29.99 per issue (effective 2003). **Document type:** *Directory.* **Description:** Contains useful advice and guides to exploring interesting sites on the Internet.
Former titles (until 2002): Harley Hahn's Internet and Web Yellow Pages (1091-0204); (until 1997): Internet Yellow Pages (1089-9065)
Related titles: CD-ROM ed.; Online - full text ed.: ISSN 1547-5999.
Published by: Osborne - McGraw Hill, 2600 Tenth St, 6th Fl, Berkeley, CA 94710. TEL 800-227-0900, http://www.osborne.com. Ed. Harley Hahn.

HE@LTH INFORMATION ON THE INTERNET. see *MEDICAL SCIENCES*

004.678   TWN   ISSN 1561-0438
HELLO! NET/DAJIA LAI SHANG WANG. Text in English. 1999 (Mar.). m. TWD 1,535; TWD 139 newsstand/cover (effective 2001). **Description:** Contains information on the internet, solutions for frequently encountered problems online, tools and software.
Published by: Jianduan Chuban Qufen Youxian Gongsi/Sharp Point Publishing Ltd., Inc., 231 Xindiansi, Fuyu-Lu 43-Hao 8-Lou, Taipei, Taiwan. TEL 886-2-2218-1582, FAX 886-2-2218-1583, hellonet@spp.com.tw, janey@spp.com.tw, http://www.spp.com.tw/asp/mag/hellonet/index.asp.

THE HERSH WEB SITE OBSERVER ONLINE. see *JOURNALISM*

005.72   USA
HOMEPAGE HELPERS. Text in English. w. free. **Document type:** *Newsletter.* **Description:** Shares tips on site promotion and web design.
Media: Online - full text.
Address: http://www.homepagenow.com.

005.72   DEU
HOMEP@GE MAGAZIN; die perfekte Web-Werkstatt. Text in German. m. adv. **Document type:** *Magazine, Consumer.* **Description:** Provides basic and practical information and advice to those who would like to install, design and maintain their own web site.
Related titles: Online - full content ed.
Published by: Neue Mediengesellschaft Ulm mbH, Konrad-Celtis-Str 77, Munich, 81369, Germany. TEL 49-89-74117-0, FAX 49-89-74117787, redaktion@homepagemagazin.de, empfang@nmg.de, http://www.homepagemagazin.de, http://www.nc-online.de. Ed. Markus Selinger. Pub. Guenter Goetz. Adv. contact Bettina Guenther. Circ: 45,891 (paid).

004.678   USA
HOSTINGTECH. Text in English. 2000-2002 (Jan.10th); resumed 2003. m. **Document type:** *Magazine, Trade.*
Published by: Everyones Internet, Inc., 835 Greens Pkwy., Ste. 150, Houston, TX 77067-4450. customerservice@ev1.net, http://www.hostingtech.com/, http://www.ev1.net/.

004.678   USA   ISSN 1089-7801
TK5105.875.I57   CODEN: IICOFX
▶ **I E E E INTERNET COMPUTING.** Text in English. 1997. bi-m. USD 735 (effective 2006). adv. bk.rev. illus. Index. back issues avail.; reprints avail. **Document type:** *Journal, Academic/Scholarly.* **Description:** Covers internet technologies and their effect on engineers and engineering.
Related titles: CD-ROM ed.; Microfiche ed.; Online - full text ed.: (from EBSCO Publishing, I E E E).
Indexed: C&CSA, C&ISA, CMCI, CompAb, CompLI, CurCont, E&CAJ, ESPM, EngInd, Inspec, MicrocompInd, RefZh, RiskAb, SolStAb.
—BLDSC (4362.973900), CISTI, IDS, IE, Infotrieve, ingenta, Linda Hall. **CCC.**

Published by: Institute of Electrical and Electronics Engineers, Inc., 445 Hoes Ln, Piscataway, NJ 08854-1331. TEL 732-981-0060, 800-701-4333, FAX 732-981-1721, subscription-service@ieee.org, http://www.computer.org/internet, http://www.ieee.org. Ed. Munindar P Singh. Adv. contact Patricia Garvey. Circ: 20,000 (paid). **Subscr. to:** Maruzen Co., Ltd., 3-10 Nihonbashi 2-chome, Chuo-ku, Tokyo 103-0027, Japan. FAX 81-3-3275-0657; Universal Subscription Agency, Pvt. Ltd., 877, Udyog Vihar, V, Gurgoan 122001, India. TEL 91-124-347261, FAX 91-124-342496.

004.678   DEU   ISSN 1616-1017
I M; die Fachzeitschrift fuer Information Management & Consulting. Variant title: I M - Information Management. Text in German, English. 1997. q. EUR 99; EUR 50 to students; EUR 25 newsstand/cover (effective 2005). adv. **Document type:** *Magazine, Trade.* **Description:** Covers information processing, internet networking, and client-server computing in the corporate environment.
Formed by the merger of (1986-1997): I M - die Fachzeitschrift fuer Information Management (1616-1009); Which was formerly (until 1992): Information Management (0930-5181); (1993-1997): M & C - Management & Computer (0943-4763)
Indexed: Inspec.
—BLDSC (4368.585000), AskIEEE, IE, ingenta. **CCC.**
Published by: Information Multimedia Communication AG, Altenkesseler Str 17, Gebaeude B2, Saarbruecken, 66115, Germany. TEL 49-681-94760, FAX 49-681-9476530, imc@im-c.de, http://www.im-c.de/im/. Ed. Wolfgang Kraemer. Adv. contact Peter Sprenger. B&W page EUR 1,400, color page EUR 1,850; trim 170 x 230. Circ: 2,855 (paid and controlled).

I S P BUSINESS NEWSLETTER. (Internet Service Providers) see *COMMUNICATIONS—Telephone And Telegraph*

004.678   GBR   ISSN 1475-4061
I S P WORLD. (Internet Service Provider) Text in English. 2000. m. **Document type:** *Magazine, Trade.*
Published by: Penton Media Europe (Subsidiary of: Penton Media, Inc.), Penton House, 288-290 Worton Rd, Isleworth, Mddx TW7 6EL, United Kingdom. TEL 44-20-8232-1600, FAX 44-20-8232-1650, information@penton.com, http://www.penton.com.

025.04   USA
I-STREET MAGAZINE. Text in English. m. adv. **Document type:** *Magazine, Trade.* **Description:** Contains news and networking information on challenges associated with starting and growing a sustainable Internet business.
Formerly: Chicago Software News
Published by: i-Street, Inc., 68 E Wacker Pl, Ste 800, Chicago, IL 60601. TEL 312-263-4159, FAX 312-263-4510, editor@i-street.com, info@i-street.com, http://www.i-street.com. Ed. Gary Ruderman.

I T & SOCIETY. see *SOCIOLOGY*

I T WEEK (ONLINE EDITION). (Information Technology) see *BUSINESS AND ECONOMICS—Computer Applications*

I T WEEK (PRINT EDITION); the newsweekly for the connected enterprise. (Information Technology) see *BUSINESS AND ECONOMICS—Computer Applications*

004.678   USA
I-TIPS NEWSLETTER. Text in English. 1998. bi-m. free. back issues avail. **Document type:** *Newsletter.* **Description:** Covers market trends, marketing channels, web site development, marketing on the internet, and traditional marketing techniques such as direct mail, catalogs, advertising and exhibits.
Media: Online - full text.
Published by: Internet Monitor, 1807 Pearl St., Denver, CO 80210-3136. TEL 303-778-8311, 888-534-3322, FAX 303-778-8311, cwaugh@sni.net, http://www.internet-monitor.com/. Ed. Carol Ann Waugh.

004.678   AUS
I - WATCH NEWSLETTER. Text in English. 1996. w. **Document type:** *Newsletter.* **Description:** Provides internet users with a brief review of two useful internet sites each week.
Media: Online - full text.
Published by: Exton Enterprises, PO Box 394, Mount Ommaney, QLD 4074, Australia. exton@gil.com.au, http://www.gil.com.au/comm/eemall/iwatch/. Ed. Rohan Exton.

338.47004678   NLD   ISSN 1084-4678
QA76.9.A25   CODEN: TDCREP
I-WAYS; digest of electronic commerce policy and regulation. Text in English. 1984. q. EUR 397, USD 478 combined subscription print & online eds. (effective 2006). adv. bk.rev. bibl.; charts; illus.; stat.; tr.lit. index. back issues avail.; reprints avail. **Document type:** *Magazine, Trade.* **Description:** Focuses on the policies, politics, and technologies of all that moves across borders electronically.
Formerly (until Mar 1995): Transnational Data and Communications Report (0892-399X); Which was formed by the merger of (1980-1984): Chronicle of International Communication (0278-0011); (1978-1984): Transnational Data Report (0167-6962)

Related titles: Online - full text ed.: (from EBSCO Publishing, O C L C Online Computer Library Center, Inc., Swets Information Services).
Indexed: CommAb, CompC, CompD, ELLIS, Inspec, KES, PAIS. —BLDSC (4357.837000), AskIEEE, IE, Infotrieve, ingenta. **CCC.**
Published by: I O S Press, Nieuwe Hemweg 6B, Amsterdam, 1013 BG, Netherlands. TEL 31-20-6883355, FAX 31-20-6203419, info@iospress.nl, order@iospress.nl, http://www.iospress.nl/html/10844678.php. Ed. Russell Pipe. R&P Ms. Carry Koolbergen TEL 31-20-6382189. Adv. contact Ms. Jolijn van Eunen.

025.4 600   USA
IHEALTHCARE WEEKLY. Text in English. 2000. d. adv. **Document type:** *Trade.* **Description:** Covers news and events affecting traditional and Internet healthcare services and providers.
Media: Online - full text.
Published by: Rising Tide Studios, 307 W 36th St, 10th Fl, New York, NY 10018-6403. TEL 646-473-2222, FAX 646-473-2223, subscribe@ihealthcareweekly.com, http://www.ihealthcareweekly.com. Ed. Jason McCabe Calacanis. Pub. Karol Martesko-Fenster. Adv. contact Keith Long.

IM WEBLAND. see *CHILDREN AND YOUTH—For*

004.692   USA
IN SIGHT OF THE BIG EYE. Text in English. 1997. m. **Description:** For E-Mail Club subscribers and friends and fans of the Big Eye.
Media: Online - full text.
Published by: E-Mail Club, Inc., PO Box 2776, Sarasota, FL 34230. emailclub@mailback.com, http://www.bigeye.com. Ed. Charles Arnold.

384.33   USA
INET-EXEC. Text in English. w. USD 149; USD 2.95 newsstand/cover (effective 2000). adv. illus. **Document type:** *Newspaper, Trade.* **Description:** For professional and amateur operators of online information services including Internet, World Wide Web and BBS.
Former titles (until 1999): Sysop News and Cyber World Report; (until 1998): Info-Mat Magazine
Published by: B B S Press Service Inc, P O Box 367209, Bonita Spgs, FL 34136-7209. FAX 239-992-4862, support@sysop.com, http://www.sysop.com. Ed., Pub., R&P Alan R Bechtold. Adv. contact Debie D Bechtold. Circ: 35,000.

004.678   AUS
INFO. Text in English. 1985. q. **Document type:** *Newsletter.* **Description:** Provides full-text articles and information about the internet and technology in general.
Media: Online - full text.
Published by: University of Tasmania, Information Services Division, GPO Box 252-69, Hobart, TAS 7109, Australia. TEL 61-3-6226-7408, FAX 61-3-6226-7669, tony.ryan@its.utas.edu.au, http://info.utas.edu.au/docs/info/index.html. Ed. Tony Ryan.

004.6   MEX
INFOCHANNEL; semanario del canal de distribucion de TI. Text in Spanish. 1994. w. MXP 499 (effective 2001).
Related titles: Online - full text ed.: ISSN 1607-1093. 1999.
Published by: High Tech Editores, S.A. de C.V., Ave Tres No 51, Col San Pedro de los Pinos, Mexico, D.F. 03800, Mexico. TEL 52-5-278-8110, FAX 52-5-272-1640, htech@htech.com.mx, http://www.infochannel.com.mx. Ed. Ramon Chomina-Lopez. Circ: 10,000.

INFORMATION COMMMONS; an online publication advocating acces to ideas. see *LIBRARY AND INFORMATION SCIENCES*

004.692   USA   ISSN 1078-4942
THE INFORMATION FREEWAY REPORT; free business and government information via modem. Text in English. 1994. m. USD 160 (effective 1999). s-a. index. **Document type:** *Newsletter.* **Description:** Shows managers how to obtain free business information available online from electronic bulletin boards, databases and internet files.
Related titles: Online - full text ed.: (from Florida Center for Library Automation, Gale Group).
Published by: Washington Researchers, Ltd., 1655 Fort Myer Dr., Ste. 800, Arlington, VA 22209-3119. TEL 703-312-2863, FAX 703-527-4586, research@researchers.com, http://www.researchers.com, http://www.washingtonresearchers.com. Ed. Laurie Schlagel. R&P Ellen O'Kane.

025.04   USA   ISSN 1055-3916
Z699.A1
INFORMATION SEARCHER; the newsletter for CD-ROM, online searching and the Internet in schools. Text in English. 1988. q. USD 34 domestic; USD 39 in Canada; USD 42 in Asia; USD 40 in Europe (effective 2003). adv. bk.rev. illus. reprints avail. **Document type:** *Newsletter.* **Description:** Dedicated to online and CD-ROM searching and Internet in schools.
Formerly: Online Searcher
Related titles: Online - full text ed.: (from H.W. Wilson, O C L C Online Computer Library Center, Inc.).
Indexed: LibLit.

Published by: Datasearch Group, Inc., 14 Hadden Rd, Scarsdale, NY 10583. TEL 914-723-1995, FAX 914-723-1995, billberger@yahoo.com, http://www.infosearcher.com. Ed., Pub. Pam Berger. Adv. contact Bill Berger.

658.054678   DEU   ISSN 1617-9846
➤ **INFORMATION SYSTEMS AND E-BUSINESS MANAGEMENT.** Text in English. 2002. q. (in 1 vol., 4 nos./vol.). EUR 133.90 combined subscription to institutions print & online eds. (effective 2005). reprint service avail. from PSC. **Document type:** *Journal, Academic/Scholarly.*
Related titles: Online - full text ed.: ISSN 1617-9854. 2002 (from EBSCO Publishing, ProQuest Information & Learning, Springer LINK).
Indexed: ABIn.
—BLDSC (4496.367357), IE. **CCC.**
Published by: Springer-Verlag (Subsidiary of: Springer Science+Business Media), Tiergartenstr 17, Heidelberg, 69121, Germany. TEL 49-6221-3450, FAX 49-6221-345229. Eds. Joerg Becker, Michael J Shaw. Adv. contact Stephan Kroeck TEL 49-30-827875739. **Subscr. to:** Springer GmbH Auslieferungsgesellschaft, Haberstr 7, Heidelberg 69126, Germany. TEL 49-6221-345-0, FAX 49-6221-345-4229, subscriptions@springer.de; Springer-Verlag New York, Inc., Journal Fulfillment, PO Box 2485, Secaucus, NJ 07096-2485. TEL 201-348-4033, journals@springer-ny.com.

004.678   DEU   ISSN 1436-0829
HF5548.2
INFORMATION WEEK (GERMAN EDITION); Das Praxismagazin fuer CIOs und IT-Manager. Text in German. 1962. bi-w. EUR 113 domestic; EUR 164 foreign; EUR 94.60 domestic to students; EUR 144.70 foreign to students (effective 2005). adv. bk.rev. charts; illus. **Document type:** *Magazine, Trade.* **Description:** Reports on the strategic planning concepts of information management: outsourcing, downsizing and distributed systems.
Incorporates (1977-1997): Online (0342-9393); Which incorporated (1985-1992): Topix (0179-8014); (1977-1985): O V D (0342-9407); Which was formed by the merger of (1956-1977): A D L Nachrichten (0514-9061); (1971-1977): Oeffentliche Verwaltung und Datenverarbeitung (0340-3262); (1963-1977): Online (0340-1545); Which was formerly (until 1973): Zeitschrift fuer Datenverarbeitung (0044-2453); (until 1966): Datentraeger (0340-1693)
Related titles: Online - full text ed.: (from Northern Light Technology, Inc.).
Indexed: CMCI, Inspec, PROMT, RASB, SSCI, T&II, TelAb.
—CISTI, Infotrieve, Linda Hall.
Published by: C M P - W E K A Verlag GmbH & Co. KG, Gruber Str 46a, Poing, 85586, Germany. TEL 49-8121-951512, FAX 49-8121-951597, kontakt@cmp-weka.de, http://www.informationweek.de, http://www.cmp-weka.de. Ed. Markus Bereszewski. Adv. contact Fritz Fischbacher. page EUR 9,500; trim 181 x 230. Circ: 12,963.

INFOSAT; die Multimedia-Illustrierte. see *COMMUNICATIONS—Television And Cable*

INFOSAT ONLINE. see *COMMUNICATIONS—Television And Cable*

025.04   GRC   ISSN 1108-8192
INLIFE. Text in Greek. 1997. m. adv. **Document type:** *Magazine, Consumer.* **Description:** Contains news and information for multimedia and Internet users and enthusiasts.
Formerly (until 2000): Rom (1108-6300)
Related titles: Online - full text ed.
Published by: Lambrakis Press SA, Panepistimiou 18, Athens, 106 72, Greece. TEL 30-1-3686-452, FAX 30-1-3686-445, dolinfo@dol.gr, http://www.in.gr/inlife, http://www.dol.gr. Circ: 13,234 (paid).

025.4   BEL   ISSN 1371-3965
INSIDE INTERNET. Text in French. 1996. 10/yr. EUR 34.50 (effective 2002). adv. **Document type:** *Magazine, Consumer.*
Related titles: Dutch ed.: ISSN 1372-8679.
Published by: Best Of Publishing, Rodenbachstraat 70, Brussels, 1190, Belgium. TEL 32-2-346-4850, FAX 32-2-346-4365, jp@best.be, http://www.internetaddict.be/, http://www.best.be. Pub. Jean-Paul De Clerk.

004.678   USA   ISSN 1075-7902
TK5105.875.I57   CODEN: ININFR
INSIDE THE INTERNET; Internet tips for DOS, Macintosh and Windows. Text in English. 1994. m. USD 97 domestic; USD 107 foreign (effective 2005). adv. illus. reprints avail.
Document type: *Newsletter, Trade.* **Description:** Each issue offers a feature story highlighting the newest and most exciting "stops" on the network; includes practical tips on how to retrieve information from the Internet, as well as coverage of the wide range of Internet tools available.
Related titles: Online - full text ed.: USD 117 domestic; USD 127 foreign (effective 2005) (from ProQuest Information & Learning).
Indexed: MicrocompInd.
—IE, Infotrieve. **CCC.**
Published by: Element K Journals (Subsidiary of: Eli Research, Inc.), 500 Canal View Blvd, Rochester, NY 14623. TEL 585-240-7301, 800-223-8720, 877-203-5248, FAX 585-292-4392, http://www.elementkjournals.com. Ed. Darrell Ray Elmore.

004.678   USA
INTELLIGENT E A I. (Enterprise Application Integration) Variant title: IntelligentEAI. Text in English. 2000. bi-m. adv. **Document type:** *Magazine, Trade.* **Description:** Contains articles and features that examine solutions to a wide variety of information technology strategies and projects.
Published by: C M P Media LLC (Subsidiary of: United News & Media), 600 Harrison St, 6th Fl., San Francisco, CA 94107. TEL 415-905-2200, 800-250-2429, FAX 415-905-2233, http://www.intelligenteai.com, http://www.cmp.com. Adv. contact David Kalman.

INTERACTIVE TRAVEL REPORT. see *TRAVEL AND TOURISM*

004.678   GBR   ISSN 1463-662X
INTERCHANGE (SWINDON). Text in English. 1986. q. GBP 40, USD 62 to individual members; GBP 80, USD 125 to institutional members (effective 2000). adv. **Document type:** *Newsletter, Trade.* **Description:** Contains articles and news relating to the development and use of Standard Generalized Markup Language (SGML) and related standards.
Formerly (until 1996): International S G M L Users' Group Newsletter (0952-8008)
Indexed: Inspec.
—BLDSC (4532.560000).
Published by: International S G M L X M L Users' Group, PO Box 361, Swindon, Wilts SN2 3ZT, United Kingdom. info@isgmlug.org, http://www.isgmlug.org. Ed. Eamonn Neylon. Adv. contact Yvonne Vine.

INTERNATIONAL CONFERENCE ON WEB INFORMATION SYSTEMS ENGINEERING WORKSHOPS. PROCEEDINGS. see *COMPUTERS—Computer Engineering*

▼ **INTERNATIONAL JOURNAL OF E-BUSINESS RESEARCH.** see *BUSINESS AND ECONOMICS—Computer Applications*

INTERNATIONAL JOURNAL OF ELECTRONIC BUSINESS. see *BUSINESS AND ECONOMICS—Computer Applications*

004.678   USA   ISSN 1554-1045
▼ **INTERNATIONAL JOURNAL OF INFORMATION TECHNOLOGY AND WEB ENGINEERING.** Text in English. forthcoming 2006 (Jan.). q. USD 85 to individuals; USD 195 to institutions (effective 2006). **Document type:** *Journal, Academic/Scholarly.* **Description:** Organizations are continuously overwhelmed by a variety of new information technologies, many are Web based. These new technologies are capitalizing on the widespread use of network and communication technologies for seamless integration of various issues in information and knowledge sharing within and among organizations. This emphasis on integrated approaches is unique to this journal and dictates cross platform and multidisciplinary strategy to research and practice.
Related titles: Online - full text ed.: ISSN 1554-1053. forthcoming 2006 (Jan.).
Published by: Idea Group Publishing (Subsidiary of: Idea Group Inc.), 701 E Chocolate Ave, Ste 200, Hershey, PA 17033-1240. TEL 717-533-8845, 866-342-6657, FAX 717-533-7115, cust@idea-group.com, http://www.idea-group.com/ijitwe. Eds. David Rine, Ghazi Alkhatib. R&P, Adv. contact Hannah Gordon.

▼ **INTERNATIONAL JOURNAL OF INTERNET AND ENTERPRISE MANAGEMENT.** see *BUSINESS AND ECONOMICS—Management*

025.04   GBR   ISSN 1477-5212
▼ **INTERNATIONAL JOURNAL OF INTERNET MARKETING AND ADVERTISING.** Abbreviated title: I J I M A. Text in English. 2003. q. USD 450 to institutions; USD 545 combined subscription to institutions print & online eds. (effective 2005). **Document type:** *Journal, Trade.* **Description:** Provides information on the use of the Internet and its applications in marketing and advertising.
Related titles: Online - full text ed.: ISSN 1741-8100. USD 450 to institutions (effective 2005) (from EBSCO Publishing).
Indexed: BrCerAb, C&ISA, CerAb, CorrAb, E&CAJ, EMA, IAA, Inspec, M&TEA, MBF, METADEX, WAA.
—BLDSC (4542.311200), IE, Linda Hall.
Published by: Inderscience Publishers, IEL Editorial Office, PO Box 735, Olney, Bucks MK46 5WB, United Kingdom. TEL 44-1234-240519, FAX 44-1234-240515, ijima@inderscience.com, editor@inderscience.com, http://www.inderscience.com/ijima. Ed. Dr. Eldon Y Li TEL 805-756-2964. **Subscr. to:** World Trade Centre Bldg, 29 route de Pre-Bois, Case Postale 896, Geneva 15 1215, Switzerland. FAX 41-22-7910885, subs@inderscience.com.

004.678   GBR   ISSN 1743-8209
▼ ➤ **INTERNATIONAL JOURNAL OF INTERNET PROTOCOL TECHNOLOGY.** Text in English. 2005. 4/yr. USD 450; USD 545 combined subscription print & online eds. (effective 2005). **Document type:** *Journal, Academic/Scholarly.* **Description:** Provides an open forum for researchers, academics, engineers, network managers, and service providers in internet protocol technology.
Related titles: Online - full text ed.: ISSN 1743-8217. USD 450 (effective 2005).

Published by: Inderscience Publishers, IEL Editorial Office, PO Box 735, Olney, Bucks MK46 5WB, United Kingdom. TEL 44-1234-240519, FAX 44-1234-240515, ijipt@inderscience.com, info@inderscience.com, http://www.inderscience.com/ijipt. Ed. Han-Chieh Chao.

025.04   GBR   ISSN 1744-2621
▼ ➤ **INTERNATIONAL JOURNAL OF METADATA, SEMANTICS AND ONTOLOGIES.** Text in English. 2005. q. USD 450; USD 545 combined subscription print & online eds. (effective 2005). **Document type:** *Journal, Academic/Scholarly.* **Description:** Aims to provide an open forum in which several disciplines converge and provide their perspectives regarding the complex topic of metadata creation, use and assessment.
Related titles: Online - full text ed.: ISSN 1744-263X. USD 450 (effective 2005).
Published by: Inderscience Publishers, IEL Editorial Office, PO Box 735, Olney, Bucks MK46 5WB, United Kingdom. TEL 44-1234-240519, FAX 44-1234-240515, ijmso@inderscience.com, info@inderscience.com, http://www.inderscience.com/ijmso. Ed. Miguel-Angel Sicilia.

▼ ➤ **INTERNATIONAL JOURNAL OF SECURITY AND NETWORKS.** see *COMPUTERS—Computer Networks*

025.04   GBR   ISSN 1741-1106
▼ ➤ **INTERNATIONAL JOURNAL OF WEB AND GRID SERVICES.** Text in English. 2005. 4/yr. USD 450; USD 545 combined subscription print & online eds. (effective 2005). **Document type:** *Journal, Academic/Scholarly.* **Description:** Devoted to publishing papers on theoretical developments and practical applications in web services and grid services.
Related titles: Online - full text ed.: ISSN 1741-1114. USD 450 (effective 2005).
Published by: Inderscience Publishers, IEL Editorial Office, PO Box 735, Olney, Bucks MK46 5WB, United Kingdom. TEL 44-1234-240519, FAX 44-1234-240515, ijwgs@inderscience.com, info@inderscience.com, http://www.inderscience.com/ijwgs. Ed. David Taniar.

004.678   GBR   ISSN 1477-8394
▼ **INTERNATIONAL JOURNAL OF WEB BASED COMMUNITIES.** Text in English. 2003. q. USD 450 to institutions; USD 545 combined subscription to institutions print & online eds. (effective 2005). **Document type:** *Journal, Academic/Scholarly.*
Related titles: Online - full text ed.: ISSN 1741-8216. USD 450 to institutions (effective 2005) (from EBSCO Publishing).
Indexed: BrCerAb, C&ISA, CerAb, CorrAb, E&CAJ, EMA, IAA, Inspec, M&TEA, MBF, METADEX, WAA.
—BLDSC (4542.701130), IE.
Published by: Inderscience Publishers, IEL Editorial Office, PO Box 735, Olney, Bucks MK46 5WB, United Kingdom. TEL 44-1234-240519, FAX 44-1234-240515, ijwbc@inderscience.com, editor@inderscience.com, http://www.inderscience.com/ijwbc. Ed. Dr. Piet Kommers.
Subscr. to: World Trade Centre Bldg, 29 route de Pre-Bois, Case Postale 896, Geneva 15 1215, Switzerland. FAX 41-22-7910885, subs@inderscience.com.

▼ **INTERNATIONAL JOURNAL OF WEB ENGINEERING AND TECHNOLOGY.** see *COMPUTERS—Information Science And Information Theory*

678   GBR   ISSN 1744-0084
➤ **INTERNATIONAL JOURNAL OF WEB INFORMATION SYSTEMS.** Text in English. q. GBP 175 in the European Union to institutions; GBP 235 elsewhere to institutions (effective 2005). **Document type:** *Journal, Academic/Scholarly.* **Description:** Aims to be a source for Web Information Systems research and development, and to serve as an outlet for facilitating communication and networking among Web Information Systems researchers and professionals across academics, government, industry, researchers, and students.
Related titles: Online - full text ed.: ISSN 1744-0092.
—CCC.
Published by: Troubador Publishing Limited, 9 de Montfort Mews, Leicester, LE1 7FW, United Kingdom. TEL 44-116-2559311, FAX 44-116-2559323, ijwis@troubador.co.uk, http://www.troubador.co.uk/ijwis. Eds. Dr. David Taniar, Dr. Ismail Khalil Ibrahim. Pub. Mr. Jeremy B Thompson.

004.678   USA   ISSN 1545-7362
▼ ➤ **INTERNATIONAL JOURNAL OF WEB SERVICES;** an international source for researchers and engineers in the field of web services. Text in English. 2004 (Jan.). q. USD 90 to individuals; USD 225 to institutions (effective 2005). **Document type:** *Journal, Academic/Scholarly.* **Description:** Provides a source for Web Services research and engineering that serves as an outlet for facilitating communication and networking among Web Services/e-business researchers and engineers.
Related titles: Online - full text ed.: ISSN 1546-5004. 2004 (Jan.) (from O C L C Online Computer Library Center, Inc., ProQuest Information & Learning).
Indexed: ABIn, BrCerAb, C&ISA, CerAb, CorrAb, E&CAJ, EMA, IAA, Inspec, M&TEA, MBF, METADEX, WAA.

C

▼ *new title*   ➤ *refereed*   * *unverified*   ♦ *full entry avail.*

Published by: (Information Resources Management Association), Idea Group Publishing (Subsidiary of: Idea Group Inc.), 701 E Chocolate Ave, Ste 200, Hershey, PA 17033-1240. TEL 717-533-8845, FAX 717-533-7115, IJWS@idea-group.com, cust@idea-group.com, http://www.idea-group.com/journals/details.asp?id=4138. Ed. Liang-Jie Zhang.

004.678 USA ISSN 1537-2456
LB1044.84
➤ **INTERNATIONAL JOURNAL ON E-LEARNING**; corporate, government, healthcare & higher education. Text in English. 1999. q. USD 55 domestic to individual members; USD 70 foreign to individual members; USD 140 domestic to institutions; USD 155 foreign to institutions; USD 40 domestic to students; USD 55 foreign to students (effective 2005). adv. bk.rev. illus. back issues avail.; reprints avail. **Document type:** *Journal, Academic/Scholarly.* **Description:** Designed for researchers, developers, and Internet users in educational, business, and professional environments.
Formed by the 2002 merger of: Webnet Journal (1522-192X); International Journal of Educational Telecommunications (1077-9124)
Related titles: Online - full text ed.: (from Florida Center for Library Automation, Gale Group, O C L C Online Computer Library Center, Inc., ProQuest Information & Learning).
Indexed: ABIn, CompD, EduInd, InfoSAb, MicrocompInd, PsycInfo, PsycholAb.
—BLDSC (4542.189800), IE. **CCC.**
Published by: Association for the Advancement of Computing in Education, PO Box 3728, Norfolk, VA 23514. TEL 757-623-7588, FAX 703-997-8760, info@aace.org, http://www.aace.org/pubs/ijel/default.htm. Ed. Gary Marks. R&P Marianne Williams. Adv. contact Ingrid L Hoffman.

C

025.04 GBR
INTERNATIONAL ONLINE INFORMATION MEETING (PROCEEDINGS). Text in English. 1977. a. USD 135 (effective 2001). back issues avail. **Document type:** *Proceedings.*
Published by: Learned Information Europe Ltd. (Subsidiary of: V N U Business Publications Ltd.), Woodside, Hinksey Hill, Oxford, Oxon OX1 5BE, United Kingdom. FAX 44-1865-388056. **Dist. in N. America by:** Information Today, Inc., 143 Old Marlton Pike, Medford, NJ 08055-8750.

025.04 USA ISSN 1530-1354
INTERNATIONAL WORKSHOP ON ADVANCE ISSUES OF E-COMMERCE AND WEB-BASED INFORMATION SYSTEMS. PROCEEDINGS. Text in English. 1999. a. USD 151; USD 61 to members (effective 2004). **Document type:** *Proceedings, Trade.*
Related titles: Online - full text ed.: (from I E E E).
Published by: Institute of Electrical and Electronics Engineers, Inc., 3 Park Ave, 17th Fl, New York, NY 10016-5997. TEL 212-419-7900, 800-678-4333, FAX 212-752-4929, customer.service@ieee.org, http://www.ieee.org.

681.3 CZE ISSN 1211-6351
INTERNET. Text in Czech. 1996. m. CZK 79 newsstand/cover (effective 2003). adv. **Document type:** *Magazine, Consumer.*
Related titles: Online - full text ed.
Published by: Trade & Leisure Publications, s.r.o., Pernerova 35a, Prague 8, 186 00, Czech Republic. TEL 420-2-225386551, FAX 420-2-225386555, internet@tlp.cz, tlp@tlp.cz, http://inetmag.cz, http://www.tlp.cz. Ed. Lukas Rous. Adv. contact Ivo Keilwerth.

004.678 GBR
INTERNET ACCESS MADE EASY GUIDE TO A O L. (America Online) Text in English. 1997. irreg., latest vol.3, 1999. GBP 2.95 newsstand/cover (effective 2001). adv. 84 p./no.; back issues avail. **Document type:** *Consumer.* **Description:** Offers newcomers to the Internet advice on how to get the most of the World Wide Web and America Online.
Published by: Paragon Publishing Ltd., Paragon House, 10 St Peters Rd, Bournemouth, Dorset BH1 2JS, United Kingdom. TEL 44-1202-299900, aol.mag@paragon.co.uk, http://www.paragon.co.uk/aol. Ed. Geoff Harris. Adv. contact Jennie Brown TEL 44-1202-200212. **Dist. by:** Seymour Distribution Ltd, 86 Newman St, London W1T 3EX, United Kingdom. TEL 44-20-7396-8002, enquiries@seymour.co.uk.

384.33 GBR
INTERNET ADVISOR; your easy guide to the internet. Text in English. 1999. bi-m. GBP 3.99 newsstand/cover; GBP 21.89 in United Kingdom; GBP 36.99 in Europe; GBP 51.99 rest of world (effective 2000). **Document type:** *Consumer.* **Description:** Promotes the idea that the Internet is easy to use and that it provides excellent resources for education, entertainment and communication.
Published by: Future Publishing Ltd., Beauford Court, 30 Monmouth St, Bath, Avon BA1 2BW, United Kingdom. TEL 44-1225-442244, FAX 44-1225-446019, john.weir@futurenet.co.uk, http://www.futurenet.com, http://www.futurenet.com/futureonline. Pub. John Weir.

383.33 USA ISSN 1092-1303
HF5548.32
INTERNET AND ELECTRONIC COMMERCE STRATEGIES. Text in English. 1997. m. **Document type:** *Newsletter.* **Description:** Focuses on the computer industry and Internet market. Articles cover electronic data interchange and electronic commerce, specifically transactions over the Internet, and examine legislation and security issues.
Related titles: Online - full text ed.: (from Florida Center for Library Automation, Gale Group).
—**CCC.**
Published by: Computer Economics, Inc., 2082 Business Center Dr., Ste 240, Irvine, CA 92612. Ed. Anne Zalatan. Pub. Bruno Bassi.

004.678 378 GBR ISSN 1096-7516
LB2395.7 CODEN: IHEDF3
THE INTERNET AND HIGHER EDUCATION. Text in English. 1984. 4/yr. EUR 84 in Europe to individuals; JPY 11,200 in Japan to individuals; USD 94 to individuals except Europe and Japan; EUR 270 in Europe to institutions; JPY 35,900 in Japan to institutions; USD 303 to institutions except Europe and Japan (effective 2006). adv. abstr.; bibl.; illus. 100 p./no.; back issues avail.; reprints avail. **Document type:** *Journal, Academic/Scholarly.* **Description:** Publishes scholarly papers dealing with any aspect of enhancing instruction and learning outcomes via the deployment of coursework in digital form via the Internet.
Formerly: Microcomputers for Information Management (0742-2342)
Related titles: Online - full text ed.: (from EBSCO Publishing, Gale Group, IngentaConnect, ScienceDirect, Swets Information Services).
Indexed: CIJE, CINAHL, CompAb, CurCont, EngInd, InfoSAb, Inspec, LibLit, MicrocompInd, RASB.
—BLDSC (4557.199717), AskIEEE, IE, ingenta, Linda Hall. **CCC.**
Published by: Pergamon (Subsidiary of: Elsevier Science & Technology), The Boulevard, Langford Ln, East Park, Kidlington, Oxford OX5 1GB, United Kingdom. TEL 44-1865-843000, FAX 44-1865-843010, http://www.elsevier.com/locate/iheduc. Ed. Dr. Laurie P. Dringus. Circ: 500. **Subscr. to:** Elsevier BV, PO Box 211, Amsterdam 1000 AE, Netherlands. TEL 31-20-485-3757, FAX 31-20-485-3432, nlinfo-f@elsevier.nl, http://www.elsevier.nl.

004.678 AUS ISSN 1444-0717
INTERNET AND ONLINE MARKET. Text in English. 1984. a., latest 2001. USD 425 domestic; USD 445 in United States; USD 450 in Europe (effective 2001). stat. **Document type:** *Directory.* **Description:** Covers online, Internet, bulletin boards and audiotex services. Includes information on developments and trends in Australia.
Former titles (until 1999): Internet and Online Services Markets Australia (1444-0709); (until 1997): Internet and Online Services Markets in Australia and New Zealand (1326-6799); (until 1997): Electronic Information Sevices Market; Which superseded in part: Directory of Electronic Services and Communications Networks in Australia and New Zealand (1322-350X)
Published by: Paul Budde Communication Pty. Ltd., 2643 George Downes Dr, Bucketty, NSW 2250, Australia. TEL 61-2-4998-8144, FAX 61-2-4998-8247, sally@budde.com.au, http://www.budde.com.au. Ed. Paul Budde.

INTERNET & TECHNOLOGY FINANCE. see *COMMUNICATIONS*

025.04 USA
INTERNET ATLAS OF WEBSITES; 150,000 city, state & country Web sites. Text in English. 2001 (Feb). q. USD 59.95; USD 19.95 newsstand/cover (effective 2001). **Document type:** *Directory, Consumer.*
Published by: Web Bound Inc., 715 Lago Circle, Knoxville, TN 37922. http://www.webbound.com.

004.678 AUS ISSN 1324-7999
INTERNET.AU. Text in English. 1994. m. AUD 58 domestic; AUD 90 in New Zealand; AUD 116 in Asia; AUD 132 elsewhere (effective 2004).
Supersedes (in 1997): Internet Australia (1323-0484)
Related titles: Online - full text ed.
Indexed: WBA.
Published by: NextMedia, 78 Renwick St, Redfern, NSW 2016, Australia. TEL 61-9-9699-0333, FAX 61-9-9699-0334, http://www.internetau.com/magazine_index.cfm?id=8, http://www.nexmedia.com.au/.

INTERNET BANKING GROWTH STRATEGIES. see *BUSINESS AND ECONOMICS—Banking And Finance—Computer Applications*

384.5402854678 GBR ISSN 1470-4188
INTERNET BROADCASTER. Text in English. 2000. bi-m. GBP 495 (effective 2000). **Description:** Covers all aspects of the broadcasting on broadband Internet systems.
Published by: PS Publishing, Old Ale House, 129 Bengeo St, Hertford, Herts, SG14 3EX, United Kingdom. TEL 44-1992-410487, FAX 44-1992-410487, pbright@dial.pipex.com. Pub. Peter Bright.

384.33 004.678 GBR ISSN 1366-2821
INTERNET BUSINESS; the magazine for business on the net. Text in English. 1997. m. GBP 24.95; GBP 3.95 newsstand/cover (effective 1999). adv. software rev. illus.; mkt. **Document type:** *Trade.* **Description:** Reports on ways to use the Internet as a prime business tool. It is the comprehensive source of business information for companies looking to exploit the Internet.
Related titles: Online - full text ed.: (from EBSCO Publishing).
Indexed: Inspec, M&MA, MicrocompInd.
—BLDSC (4557.199735), IE.
Published by: Internet Business Magazine Ltd., Regent House, Hove St, Hove, East Sussex BN3 2DW, United Kingdom. TEL 44-1273-773224, FAX 44-1273-749189, t_wilson@ibmag.co.uk, http://www.ibmag.co.uk. Ed. Tim Wilson. Pub. Russell Church. Adv. contact Neil Vardy. **Subscr. to:** Internet Business Magazine, Domino House, Morris Close, Park Farm, Industrial Estate, ., Wellingborough, Northants NN8 8BR, United Kingdom. TEL 44-1933-405400, FAX 44-1933-402377. **Dist. by:** Comag, Tavistock Works, Tavistock Rd, W Drayton, Middx UB7 7QX, United Kingdom. TEL 44-1895-444055, FAX 44-1895-433602.

384.33 GBR ISSN 1363-9919
INTERNET BUSINESS NEWS. Text in English. 1994. m. GBP 100, USD 170 (effective 1998). **Document type:** *Trade.* **Description:** Provides key insights into the commercial activities and benefits available through the Internet to companies worldwide.
Media: Online - full text (from bigchalk, Gale Group, LexisNexis).
Indexed: CompD.
Published by: M2 Communications Ltd., PO Box 475, Coventry, W Mids CV1 2ZW, United Kingdom. TEL 44-1203-634700, FAX 44-1203-634144, M2PW@m2.com, http://www.m2.com. Ed. Darren Ingram. **Dist. in N. America by:** Publications Resource Group, 121 Union St., Box 792, North Adams, MA 01247. TEL 413-664-6185, FAX 413-664-9343.

INTERNET BUSINESS NEWSLETTER. see *COMMUNICATIONS—Telephone And Telegraph*

384.34 USA
INTERNET BUSINESS REPORT; software, tools & platforms. Text in English. s-m. USD 695; USD 795 with electronic ed.. software rev. back issues avail. **Document type:** *Newsletter.* **Description:** Provides insight into the events and technologies transforming the Internet.
Related titles: Online - full text ed.
Published by: Jupiter Communications, 627 Broadway, New York, NY 10012. TEL 516-780-6060, 800-488-4345, FAX 212-780-6075, http://www.jup.com. **Dist. by:** Publications Resource Group, 121 Union St., Box 792, North Adams, MA 01247. TEL 413-664-6185, FAX 413-664-9343.

384.33 USA
INTERNET BUSINESS STRATEGIES. Text in English. m. USD 395 (effective 1999). **Document type:** *Newsletter, Trade.* **Description:** Presents precise information about Internet developments, trends and strategies as they continually evolve. Covers the approaches to Internet marketing, technology, electronic commerce and standards that work best and how to strategically implement them.
Published by: Gartner Inc., 56 Top Gallant Rd, Stamford, CT 06904-2212. TEL 203-316-1111, 800-544-7337, FAX 203-316-6300, jwhitney@info-edge.com, http://www.gartner3.gartnerweb.com, http://www.info-edge.com.

004.678 RUS
INTERNET.BY. Text in Russian. m. adv.
Published by: Izdatel'stvo Yunipak, Ul. Mel'nikaite, 2-708, Minsk, Russian Federation. TEL 226-84-26, edward@open.by, al@solo.by. Ed. Andrei Lankin. Pub. Edvard Zhilinskii. Adv. contact Alesya Krivitskaya.

004.678 USA ISSN 1080-8493
TK5105.875.I57
INTERNET CONNECTION (LITTLE FALLS); your guide to government resources. Text in English. 1995. 10/yr. USD 114 (effective 2005). **Document type:** *Newsletter, Trade.*
—CISTI. **CCC.**
Published by: Glasser LegalWorks (Subsidiary of: West Publishing Co.), 150 Clove Rd, Little Falls, NJ 07424. TEL 973-890-0008, 800-308-1700, FAX 973-890-0042, legalwks@aol.com, http://www.legalwks.com/newsletters/#internet. Ed. Don MacLeod.

005.276 USA
INTERNET DAILY NEWS. Text in English. d.
Media: Online - full content.
Address: http://www.tvpress.com/idn/idnfp.html. Ed. William R Stanek.

025.04 USA ISSN 1542-8699
ZA4235
INTERNET DIMENSIONS. Text in English. bi-m. USD 350 newsstand/cover (effective 2001).
Published by: Media Dynamics, Inc., 570 7th Ave Rm 1906, New York, NY 10018-1619. TEL 212-704-0024, FAX 212-704-0023, info@mediadynamicsinc.com, http://www.mediadynamicsinc.com/pub06.htm.

052   AUS
INTERNET DIRECTORY. Text in English. bi-m. **Document type:**
Directory, Consumer.
Published by: Emap Australia Pty. Ltd. (Subsidiary of: Emap
International), 187 Thomas St., Level 6, Haymarket, NSW
2000, Australia. TEL 61-2-9581-9555, FAX 61-2-9581-9556.

025.4   BEL   ISSN 1375-3991
INTERNET EN BELGIQUE. Text in French. 1998. a. **Document
type:** *Magazine, Trade.*
Related titles: Dutch ed.: Internet in Belgie. ISSN 1375-4009.
Published by: Best Of Publishing, Rodenbachstraat 70, Brussels,
1190, Belgium. TEL 32-2-346-4850, FAX 32-2-346-4365,
jp@best.be, http://www.best.be. Pub. Jean-Paul De Clerk.

681.3   ITA   ISSN 1127-1663
INTERNET FACILE. Text in Italian. 1998. m. EUR 34; EUR 5
newsstand/cover (effective 2003). adv. **Document type:**
Magazine, Consumer.
Published by: Play Press Publishing s.r.l., Via Vitorchiano 123,
Rome, RM 00189, Italy. TEL 39-06-33221250, FAX
39-06-33221235, abbonamenti@playpress.com,
http://www.playpress.com. Ed. Giulia Gatti. Pub. Alessandro
Ferri. Circ: 50,000 (paid and controlled).

384.33   GBR   ISSN 1363-2922
INTERNET FOR BUSINESS. Text in English. 1996. bi-m.
Document type: *Newsletter, Trade.*
Indexed: B&I.
Published by: Financial Times Telecoms & Media Publishing
(Subsidiary of: Financial Times Group), Maple House, 149
Tottenham Court Rd, London, W1P 9LL, United Kingdom. TEL
44-171-896-2234, FAX 44-171-896-2256.

025.4   DEU
INTERNET FUER EINSTEIGER. Text in German. 2000. a. EUR
7.60 newsstand/cover (effective 2003). adv. **Document type:**
Magazine, Consumer.
Published by: Data Becker GmbH & Co. KG, Merowingerstr 30,
Duesseldorf, 40223, Germany. TEL 49-211-933470, FAX
49-211-9334710, thapp@databecker.de, http://
www.databecker.de. adv.: page EUR 4,200. Circ: 48,280 (paid
and controlled).

384.33   USA   ISSN 1533-1377
THE INTERNET GAZETTE NEWSLETTER. Text in English. w.
adv. **Document type:** *Newsletter.* **Description:** Includes
information about web marketing and Internet promotion with
tips on search engine relevancy techniques, strategic linking,
site announcement and more.
Media: Online - full text.
Published by: Write For You, Inc, 8 Hummingbird Ct., Marlboro,
NJ 07746-2511. info@wrte4u.com, http://
www.internetgazette.net/. Pub. Monica Fersht. Circ: 50,000.

025.4   DEU   ISSN 1431-7346
INTERNET INTERN. Text in German. 1999. q. EUR 7.60
newsstand/cover (effective 2003). adv. **Document type:**
Magazine, Consumer.
Published by: Data Becker GmbH & Co. KG, Merowingerstr 30,
Duesseldorf, 40223, Germany. TEL 49-211-933470, FAX
49-211-9334710, thapp@databecker.de, http://
www.databecker.de. Adv. contact Volker Boerdeling. page
EUR 4,200; trim 180 x 274. Circ: 40,180 (paid and controlled).

025.0634   USA   ISSN 1529-6369
INTERNET LAW AND BUSINESS. Text in English. 2000. m. USD
1,050 (effective 2005). **Document type:** *Newsletter, Trade.*
Published by: Computer Law Reporter, Inc., 1601 Connecticut
Ave, N W, Ste 602, Washington, DC 20009. TEL
202-462-5755, FAX 202-328-2430, crl@reporters.com,
http://www.lawreporters.com/NewFiles/ILBx.html. Ed. H Tiller.

INTERNET LAW & REGULATION. see *LAW—Computer
Applications*

384.33   USA   ISSN 1544-1911
KF390.5.C6
▼ **INTERNET LAW & STRATEGY.** Text in English. 2003 (Jan.).
m. USD 279 combined subscription print & online eds.
(effective 2005). **Document type:** *Newsletter, Trade.*
Description: Contains news, advice and analysis for lawyers
and their clients who are involved with the Internet.
Formed by the merger of (1996-2003): Internet Newsletter
(1088-0615); (1998-2003): E-Securities (1522-5070)
Related titles: Online - full content ed.: USD 199 (effective 2003).
—CCC.
Published by: Law Journal Newsletters (Subsidiary of: A L M),
1617 JFK Blvd, Ste 1750, Philadelphia, PA 19103. TEL
800-888-8300, catalog@ljx.com, lawcatalog@amlaw.com,
http://www.ljnonline.com/pub/ljn_internetlaw/. Ed. Janine M
Sagar.

340 384.330   AUS   ISSN 1329-9735
➤ **INTERNET LAW BULLETIN.** Text in English. 1998. 10/yr. AUD
620.40 (effective 2005). **Document type:** *Bulletin,
Academic/Scholarly.* **Description:** Addresses laws and
regulations governing the Internet.
Incorporates (1994-1998): Convergence Reporter (1323-2339)

Published by: LexisNexis Butterworths (Subsidiary of: LexisNexis
Asia Pacific), Tower 2, 475-495 Victoria Ave, Chatswood,
NSW 2067, Australia. TEL 61-2-94222189, FAX
61-2-94222406, customer.relations@lexisnexis.com.au,
http://www.lexisnexis.com.au/aus/products/catalog/current_htm/
INT.asp?productid=INT&jurisdiction=0&category=8&medium=
0&author=&title=&overview=, http://www.lexisnexis.com.au/aus/
default.asp.

025.0434   USA   ISSN 1087-7703
KF242.A1
INTERNET LAW RESEARCHER. Text in English. 1996. 11/yr.
USD 172 (effective 2005). **Document type:** *Newsletter, Trade.*
Published by: Glasser LegalWorks (Subsidiary of: West
Publishing Co.), 150 Clove Rd, Little Falls, NJ 07424. TEL
973-890-0008, 800-308-1700, FAX 973-890-0042,
legalwks@aol.com, orders@glasserlegalworks.com,
http://www.internetlawresearcher.com, http://
www.legalwks.com. Ed. Don MacLeod.

025.0434   USA   ISSN 1087-7223
KF242.A1
INTERNET LAWYER. Text in English. 1995. m. USD 149
(effective 2002). back issues avail. **Document type:**
Newsletter.
Media: Online - full text.
Published by: The Daily Record Company, 11 East Saratoga St,
Baltimore, MD 21202-2199. TEL 800-296-8181, FAX
410-752-2894, staff@internetlawyer.com, http://
www.internetlawyer.com/. Pub. Keith A Rosenbaum.

004.678   GBR   ISSN 1465-6965
INTERNET MADE EASY; the magazine for total internet
beginners. Text in English. 1999. m. GBP 29 in United
Kingdom; GBP 48 in Europe; GBP 69 rest of world; GBP 3.99
newsstand/cover (effective 2002). 116 p./no.; back issues
avail. **Document type:** *Magazine, Consumer.* **Description:**
Provides information on accessing the Internet for beginners
with step by step guides and advise.
Published by: Paragon Publishing Ltd., Paragon House, 10 St
Peters Rd, Bournemouth, Dorset BH1 2JS, United Kingdom.
TEL 44-1202-299900, FAX 44-1202-299955, 44-1202-200217,
subs@paragon.co.uk, http://www.paragon.co.uk. Ed. Dominic
Brookman. Adv. contact Jennie Brown TEL 44-1202-200212.
Circ: 17,361.

004.678   DEU
INTERNET MAGAZIN. Text in German. 1996. m. EUR 41
domestic; EUR 57.90 foreign; EUR 36.60 to students; EUR
3.80 newsstand/cover (effective 2003). adv. **Document type:**
Magazine, Consumer.
Related titles: Online - full text ed.
Published by: W E K A Computerzeitschriften-Verlag GmbH,
Gruberstr 46a, Poing, 85586, Germany. TEL 49-8121-950,
FAX 49-8121-951199, redaktion@internet-magazin.de,
http://www.internet-magazin.de, http://www.wekanet.de. Ed.
Daniela Schrank. Adv. contact Gisela Nerke. B&W page EUR
4,630, color page EUR 5,900; trim 185 x 266. Circ: 40,598
(paid).

004.678   THA
INTERNET MAGAZINE; Thailand's leading Internet magazine.
Text and summaries in English, Thai. 1996. m. THB 540; THB
45 newsstand/cover. adv. bk.rev.; software rev. bibl.; charts;
illus.; mkt.; maps; stat.; tr.lit. Index. back issues avail.
Document type: *Magazine, Consumer.*
Published by: Se - Education Public Company Ltd.,
Asok-Dindang Rd, Dindang, 800-43-45 Soi Trakulsuk,
Bangkok, 10320, Thailand. TEL 66-2-6429800, FAX
66-2-6429866, se-ed@loxinfo.co.th. Ed. Mongkol Kaewchan.
Adv. contact Saipin Chantrakes.

004.67805   GBR   ISSN 1460-2555
INTERNET MAGAZINE. Text in English. 1994. m. GBP 34.65
domestic; GBP 81.97 in Europe; GBP 97.97 elsewhere; GBP
2.47 newsstand/cover (effective 2004). adv. back issues avail.
Document type: *Consumer.* **Description:** Provides the latest
news and analysis of events shaping the Internet industry in
the UK and abroad.
Formerly (until 1997): Internet (1355-6428)
Related titles: Online - full text ed.: (from Gale Group).
Indexed: CompD.
—IE.
Published by: Emap Active Ltd. (Angel House) (Subsidiary of:
Emap Consumer Media), Angel House, 338-346 Goswell Rd,
London, EC1V 7QP, United Kingdom. TEL 44-171-477-7399,
FAX 44-171-8807441, http://www.internet-magazine.com. Ed.
Martyn Moore. Pub. Sonja Woolley. Adv. contact Nigel Ashton.
color page USD 4,300. **Subscr. to:** Tower House, Tower
House, Sovereign Park, Market Harborough, Leics LE16 9EF,
United Kingdom. TEL 44-1858-435338, FAX 44-1858-435958.
Dist. by: Frontline, Park House, 117 Park Rd, Peterborough,
Cambs PE1 2TS, United Kingdom. TEL 44-1733-555161, FAX
44-1733-562788.

025.4   NZL   ISSN 1175-3811
INTERNET MAGAZINE. Text in English. 2000. 11/yr. NZD 36.50
domestic; NZD 54.50 in Australasia; NZD 74.50 elsewhere;
NZD 3.95 newsstand/cover (effective 2002). adv. **Document
type:** *Magazine, Consumer.* **Description:** Offers practical
advice on using the Internet both as a tool for personal and
professional gain and for entertainment and enjoyment.

Related titles: Online - full text ed.
Published by: I D G Communications Ltd., Wellesley St., PO Box
6813, Auckland, 1036, New Zealand. TEL 64-9-377-9902, FAX
64-9-377-4604, idg@idg.co.nz, http://imag.co.nz,
http://www.idg.net.nz. adv.: B&W page NZD 2,230; trim 148 x
210. Circ: 30,000 (paid and controlled).

004.678   USA   ISSN 1082-1945
INTERNET MARKETING & TECHNOLOGY REPORT. Text in
English. 1995. m. USD 387 (effective 1998). **Document type:**
Newsletter. **Description:** Provides marketing, sales, and
corporate executives with marketing success stories,
demographic trends, sales tactics. Includes insider analyses
from top business marketers and technical experts.
—CCC.
Published by: Computer Economics, Inc., 2082 Business Center
Dr., Ste 240, Irvine, CA 92612. TEL 949-831-8700, FAX
949-442-7688, info@compecon.com, http://
www.computereconomics.com. Pub. Anne Zalatan.

004.678   USA   ISSN 1099-0143
INTERNET MARKETING REPORT. Abbreviated title: I M R. Text
in English. 1998. s-m. USD 299. software rev. charts.
Document type: *Newsletter.* **Description:** News and advice
to help companies harness the power of the Internet.
Published by: Progressive Business Publications, 370 Technology
Dr, Malvern, PA 19355-1315. TEL 610-695-8600,
800-220-5000, FAX 610-647-8089, editor@pbp.com,
http://www.pbp.com. Ed. Alan Field. R&P Curt Brown. Circ:
1,500 (paid).

INTERNET MARKETING TIPS. see *CERAMICS, GLASS AND
POTTERY—Abstracting, Bibliographies, Statistics*

383.33 658.8   USA
INTERNET MARKETING UPDATE. Text in English. 1998. m. free.
Document type: *Newsletter.* **Description:** Provides marketing
trends, updates, ideas, tips, and promotional tools for online
success and general business.
Media: Online - full text.
Published by: NetMark Communications TEL 561-641-9887, FAX
561-433-3979, http://www.finsave.com/mnet/.

004.678 510   USA   ISSN 1542-7951
QA1
▼ **INTERNET MATHEMATICS.** Text in English. 2003. q. USD 100
domestic to individuals; USD 120 foreign to individuals; USD
275 domestic to institutions; USD 295 foreign to institutions
(effective 2003). **Document type:** *Journal,
Academic/Scholarly.*
Indexed: MathR, MathSciNet.
Published by: A K Peters, Ltd., 888 Worcester St, Ste 230,
Wellesley, MA 02482. TEL 508-655-9933, FAX 508-655-5847,
service@akpeters.com, http://www.internetmathematics.org,
http://www.akpeters.com. Ed. Fan Chung Graham.

659.13   USA
▼ **INTERNET MEDIA REVIEW.** Text in English. 2004. w. USD
297 (effective 2005). **Document type:** *Journal, Trade.*
Description: Contains the latest information and research on
website publishing and Internet marketing.
Media: Online - full content.
Published by: Digital Media Advisors, LLC, 121 Boston Post Rd,
Sudbury, MA 01776. TEL 800-901-3556, FAX 508-881-5604,
don@digitalmediaadvisors.com, http://
www.internetmediareview.com, http://
www.digitalmediaadvisors.com. Ed., Pub. Don Nicholas.

025.04   GBR
THE INTERNET MOLE. Text in English. m. GBP 20 domestic new
subscriber; GBP 30 domestic; GBP 36 in Europe; GBP 42
elsewhere (effective 2000); Subscription includes free online
archive access and issues posted to your account..
Description: Aims at providing resourceful information on
searching the internet and making the most of online
information.
Media: Online - full content.
Published by: The Internet Mole, PO Box 329, Bury St.
Edmunds, IP31 3EZ, United Kingdom. mole@molemag.net,
http://www.molemag.net.

004.678   ITA   ISSN 1123-6027
INTERNET NEWS. Text in Italian. 1995. m. EUR 31 domestic
(effective 2004). adv.
Published by: Tecniche Nuove SpA, Via Eritrea 21, Milan, MI
201, Italy. TEL 39-02-390901, FAX 39-02-7570364,
info@tecnichenuove.com, http://www.tecnichenuove.com.

004.678   USA   ISSN 1542-5312
ZA3201
INTERNET NEWSROOM. Text in English. 1995. m. USD 149
domestic; USD 174 foreign (effective 2002). illus.; tr.lit. back
issues avail. **Document type:** *Newsletter, Trade.*
Related titles: Online - full text ed.
Published by: Bergman Publishing, LLC, P. O. Box 2625, Glen
Allen, VA 23058-2625. TEL 804-762-7115, FAX 804-762-7112.
Ed. Ronald P. Bergman. Circ: 500.

025.04   USA
INTERNET-ON-A-DISK. Text in English. 1994. m. USD 10 by
e-mail. software rev. back issues avail.
Related titles: Diskette ed.; E-mail ed.; Online - full text ed.

C

Published by: B & R Samizdat Express, PO Box 161, W Roxbury, MA 02132. TEL 617-469-2269, seltzer@samizdat.com, http://www.samizdat.com. Ed., Pub., R&P Richard Seltzer.

681.3 ITA ISSN 1591-6995
INTERNET PRATICO. Text in Italian. 1999. bi-m. EUR 17.55 (effective 2003). adv. **Document type:** *Magazine, Consumer.*
Published by: Gruppo Editoriale Futura, Via XXV Aprile, 39, Bresso, MI 20091, Italy. TEL 39-02-665261, FAX 39-02-66526222, internetpratico@futura-ge.com, info@futura-ge.com, http://www.futura-ge.com/prodotti/riviste/internetPratico.

025.4 FRA
INTERNET PRATIQUE. Text in French. m. FRF 29 newsstand/cover (effective 2001). adv. software rev.; Website rev. **Document type:** *Magazine, Consumer.*
Published by: Future France, 101-109 Rue Jean Jaures, Levallois Perret, 92300, France. TEL 33-1-41273838, yveline.duville@futurenet.fr.

025.4 DEU ISSN 1611-8634
▼ **INTERNET - PRAXIS UND ZUKUNFTSANWENDUNGEN.** Text in German. 2003. irreg. price varies. **Document type:** *Monographic series, Academic/Scholarly.*
Published by: Verlag Dr. Kovac, Arnoldstr 49, Hamburg, 22763, Germany. TEL 49-40-3988800, FAX 49-40-39888055, info@verlagdrkovac.de, http://www.verlagdrkovac.de/4-5.htm.

025.04 DEU ISSN 1619-6481
INTERNET PROFESSIONELL. Text in German. m. EUR 48; EUR 4.05 newsstand/cover (effective 2005). adv. **Document type:** *Magazine, Trade.* **Description:** Contains information and insight into products, services and trends of interest to professionals working with the Internet.
Related titles: Online - full text ed.
—CCC.
Published by: V N U Business Publications Deutschland GmbH, Riesstr 25, Munich, 80992, Germany. TEL 49-89-143120, FAX 49-89-14312740, interpro@vnu.de, redaktion_vnunet@vnu.de, http://www.vnunet.de/ipro/default.asp. Ed. Karen Heidl. Adv. contact Katja Mueller. B&W page EUR 3,980, color page EUR 5,050; trim 210 x 297. Circ: 15,876 (paid and controlled).

C

659.13 USA
INTERNET PROTOCOL JOURNAL. Text in English. q. **Document type:** *Magazine, Trade.* **Description:** Serves as an information and educational resource for engineering professionals in the design, development and operation of public and private internets and intranets.
Published by: Cisco Systems, Inc., 170 W Tasman Dr, San Jose, CA 95134. TEL 408-526-7208, 800-553-6387, info@cisco.com, http://www.cisco.com.

004.678 USA ISSN 1087-5301
Z674.75.I58 CODEN: IRSQFC
➤ **INTERNET REFERENCE SERVICES QUARTERLY;** a journal of innovative information practice, technologies and resources. Abbreviated title: I R S Q. Text in English. 1996. q. USD 95 combined subscription domestic to institutions print & online eds.; USD 128.25 combined subscription in Canada to institutions print & online eds.; USD 137.75 combined subscription elsewhere to institutions print & online eds. (effective 2006). adv. bk.rev. 120 p./no. 1 cols./p.; reprint service avail. from HAW. **Document type:** *Academic/Scholarly.* **Description:** Highlights theoretical, research and practical application of internet-related information services, sources and resources.
Related titles: Microform ed.: (from PQC); Online - full text ed.: ISSN 1540-4749. free to institutions (effective 2003); free with print subs. (from EBSCO Publishing, O C L C Online Computer Library Center, Inc., Swets Information Services).
Indexed: BrCerAb, C&ISA, CINAHL, CerAb, CommAb, CompR, CorrAb, DIP, E&CAJ, EMA, ESPM, IAA, IBR, IBZ, InfoSAb, Inspec, LISA, LibLit, M&TEA, MBF, METADEX, MicrocompInd, SWRA, WAA.
—BLDSC (4557.199825), AskIEEE, Haworth, IE, Infotrieve, ingenta. **CCC.**
Published by: Haworth Information Press (Subsidiary of: Haworth Press, Inc.), 10 Alice St, Binghamton, NY 13904. TEL 607-722-5857, 800-429-6784, FAX 607-771-0012, 800-895-0582, getinfo@haworthpress.com, http://www.haworthpress.com/web/IRSQ. Eds. Jane Schillie, Margaret K Scharf. Pub. William Cohen. R&P Ruth Ann Heath TEL 607-722-5857 ext 316. Adv. contact Rebecca Miller-Baum TEL 607-722-5857 ext 337. B&W page USD 315, color page USD 550; trim 4.375 x 7.125. Circ: 654 (paid).

004.678 GBR ISSN 1066-2243
TK5105.5 CODEN: IRESEF
➤ **INTERNET RESEARCH.** Text in English. 1991. 5/yr. EUR 2,173.91 in Europe; USD 2,229 in North America; AUD 2,499 in Australasia; GBP 1,521.41 in UK & elsewhere (effective 2006). adv. illus. Index. reprint service avail. from PSC. **Document type:** *Journal, Academic/Scholarly.* **Description:** Covers developments in information technology and communication, focusing on the use of telecommunications networks to provide information services and products. Publishes papers on policy and technical issues affecting electronic networks and potential applications.
Formerly (until 1993): Electronic Networking (1051-4805)
Related titles: Online - full text ed.: GBP 209 (from EBSCO Publishing, Emerald Group Publishing Limited, Gale Group, IngentaConnect, O C L C Online Computer Library Center, Inc., ProQuest Information & Learning, Swets Information Services).
Indexed: ABIn, ASCA, C&CSA, CIJE, CMCI, CommAb, CompAb, CompLI, CurCont, EAA, ESPM, EmerIntel, Emerald, HRA, InfoSAb, Inspec, LISA, LibLit, MicrocompInd, PAIS, PRA, RASB, RefZh, RiskAb, SSCI.
—BLDSC (4557.199827), AskIEEE, IDS, IE, Infotrieve, ingenta. **CCC.**
Published by: Emerald Group Publishing Limited, 60-62 Toller Ln, Bradford, W Yorks BD8 9BY, United Kingdom. TEL 44-1274-777700, FAX 44-1274-785200, infomation@emeraldinsight.com, http://www.emeraldinsight.com/intr.htm. Ed. Dr. David G Schwartz TEL 972-54-890-060.

383.33 USA ISSN 1084-5798
THE INTERNET RESOURCE DIRECTORY FOR K-12 TEACHERS AND LIBRARIANS. Text in English. 1995. a.
Published by: Libraries Unlimited, Inc. (Subsidiary of: Greenwood Publishing Group Inc.), 88 Post Road W, Westport, CT 06881. TEL 800-225-5800, FAX 203-222-1502, lu-books@lu.com, http://www.lu.com/.

383.33 GBR ISSN 1361-9381
INTERNET RESOURCES NEWSLETTER; the free, monthly newsletter for academics, students, engineers, scientists and social scientists. Text in English. 1994. m. free (effective 2003). bk.rev. **Document type:** *Newsletter, Academic/Scholarly.*
Media: Online - full text.
Indexed: LISA.
Published by: Heriot-Watt University, Internet Resource Centre, Riccarton, Edinburgh EH14 4AS, United Kingdom. TEL 44-131-451-3576, FAX 44-131-451-3164, r.a.macleod@hw.ac.uk, http://www.hw.ac.uk/libwww/irn/irn.html. Eds. Catherine Ferguson, Catherine Ure, Roddy MacLeod.

004.678 USA
INTERNET ROADSTOP: MAC ZINE AND INFORMATION. Text in English. m. **Description:** Provides articles, reviews, columns focusing on the upgrading of the Macintosh, pros and cons of different operating systems, and internet tools.
Media: Online - full text.
Address: roadstop@digiserve.com, http://macstop.com. Ed. Ben Wilson.

004.678 USA
INTERNET SCAMBUSTERS. Text in English. 1995. m. free. back issues avail.
Related titles: Online - full text ed.: ISSN 1522-3701.
Published by: Netrageous Inc., 18113 Town Center Dr, Ste 114, Olney, MD 20832. TEL 301-570-5400, 800-780-0090, scambusters@scambusters.org, http://www.scambusters.org/. Ed. Audri Lanford.

364.163 USA
INTERNET SCAMS EZINE; the business opportunist's protection against online fraud. Text in English. bi-w. free. **Description:** Designed to give you the only defense you can have against a scam.
Address: inetscams@cp-tel.net, http://www.bcity.com/newsletter/. Ed. Jonathan Leger.

INTERNET SECURITY ADVISOR. see *COMPUTERS—Computer Security*

025.04 POL
INTERNET STANDARD. Text in Polish. m. adv. **Document type:** *Magazine, Trade.*
Related titles: Online - full text ed.
Published by: I D G Poland S.A., ul Jordanowska 12, PO Box 73, Warsaw, 04-204, Poland. TEL 48-22-3217800, FAX 48-22-3217888, istandard@idg.com.pl, idg@idg.com.pl, http://www.internetstandard.com.pl, http://www.idg.pl.

025.04 USA
INTERNET SURFER. Text in English. 1998. m. USD 24.95; USD 75 in Canada & Mexico; USD 120 elsewhere. adv. bk.rev. **Description:** Dedicated to the Internet and the World Wide Web.
Related titles: Online - full text ed.
Published by: Las Vegas Computer Journal Publications, 2232 S Nellis Blvd, Las Vegas, NV 89104. TEL 702-432-6206, FAX 702-432-6204, http://www.internetsurfer.com. Ed. Johanna Nezhoda. Circ: 30,000.

004.678 USA
INTERNET SURVEYS. Text in English. m. **Document type:** *Newsletter.* **Description:** A digest of the most interesting surveys containing data relating to the Internet.
Media: Online - full text.
Address: web@nua.ie, http://www.nua.ie/choice/surveys.

004.678 USA
INTERNET TEACHER. Text in English. 1996. w. **Document type:** *Newsletter, Academic/Scholarly.* **Description:** Contains information on general resources for teaching on the Internet.
Media: E-mail.
Published by: Regulus Communications yam@regulus.com.

INTERNET TELEPHONY MAGAZINE; the authority on voice, video, fax and data convergence. see *COMMUNICATIONS—Telephone And Telegraph*

004.678 USA
THE INTERNET TIMES. Text in English. 1996. s-m. **Description:** Covers the latest in Internet technology advances and their marketing applications, especially for the European market.
Media: Online - full text.
Published by: Euro-Marketing Associates, 1850 Union St, Ste 1229, San Francisco, CA 94123. TEL 415-680-2423, ema@euromktg.com, http://www.euromktg.com/eng/ed/it.html.

004.678 NLD ISSN 1570-9175
INTERNET TIPS & TRUCS. Text in Dutch. 2001. m. adv. **Document type:** *Magazine, Consumer.*
Related titles: ◆ Supplement to: Tips & Trucs. ISSN 1566-5518.
Published by: I D G Communications Nederland BV, Richard Holkade 8, Haarlem, 2033 PZ, Netherlands. tips_trucs@idg.nl, http://www.idg.nl/producten/prod.phtml?prod=tt&type=print. adv.: color page EUR 1,275; trim 210 x 285.

INTERNET TRAVEL PLANNER; how to plan trips and save money online. see *TRAVEL AND TOURISM*

025.04 USA
INTERNET TREND WATCH FOR LIBRARIES. Text in English. 1996. m. USD 30. **Description:** Provides up-to-date information on how libraries are integrating the Internet technology into their setting.
Media: Online - full text.
Published by: Librarians and Educators Online leo@leonline.com, http://www.leonline.com. Eds. Jennifer Fleming, Linda W Braun.

364.163 CAN
INTERNET WATCHDOG. Text in English. m. back issues avail. **Document type:** *Newsletter.* **Description:** Covers topics related to Internet fraud and scams.
Media: Online - full text.
Published by: E-Commerce Reporting Association, 908 Fern Glen Rd, Emsdale, ON, Canada. FAX 800-665-2723, http://ecra-net.com. Ed. Bernard Balan.

371.42 025.04 USA
THE INTERNET WEB SOURCE. Text in English. 1993. 15/yr. USD 49 (effective 1998). adv. **Document type:** *Bulletin.* **Description:** Provides profiles of top Internet companies, reviews of useful websites and special coverage of America Online.
Former titles (until 1999): The Internet Job Source; (until 1997): Job Source (1091-7160)
Related titles: Online - full text ed.
Published by: Shieh Communications, PO Box 45, Guilderland, NY 12084. TEL 518-869-9279, jobsource@aol.com, http://www.statejobs.com. Ed., Pub. Joseph Shieh.

004.678 USA ISSN 1081-2474
INTERNET WEEK; news and analysis of internet business opportunities. Text in English. 1995. 53/yr. USD 175; USD 395 in Europe; USD 425 in Asia. adv. illus. reprints avail. **Document type:** *Newsletter, Consumer.*
Incorporates (1993?-1995): Internet Letter (1070-9851)
Related titles: Online - full text ed.: (from LexisNexis, Northern Light Technology, Inc., ProQuest Information & Learning).
Indexed: ABIn.
—CCC.
Published by: Access Intelligence, LLC (Subsidiary of: Veronis, Suhler & Associates Inc.), 1201 Seven Locks Rd, Ste 300, Potomac, MD 20854. TEL 301-354-2000, FAX 301-762-4196, http://www.internetweek.com/.

384.33 658.054 GBR ISSN 1460-1214
INTERNET WORKS. Text in English. 1997. 13/yr. GBP 39.99 in United Kingdom; GBP 79.99 in Europe; GBP 89.99 rest of world (effective 2003). adv. **Document type:** *Trade.* **Description:** Designed to help the business Internet user benefit from all aspects of the Internet, from setting up an online business to finding an ISP.
—CCC.
Published by: Future Publishing Ltd., Beauford Court, 30 Monmouth St, Bath, Avon BA1 2BW, United Kingdom. TEL 44-1225-442244, FAX 44-1225-732285, marcus.austin@futurenet.co.uk, http://www.iwks.com/, http://www.futurenet.com. Ed. Marcus Austin. Pub. John Weir. adv.: color page GBP 2,050. Circ: 21,820 (paid).

004.678 ARG ISSN 0329-2967
INTERNET WORLD. Text in Spanish. 1997. m. ARS 50 (effective 2001). **Document type:** *Trade.*
Related titles: Online - full text ed.; ◆ Supplement(s): Los Archivos de Internet World. ISSN 0329-3068.
Published by: Avenue S.A., 25 de Mayo 432, 4o Piso, Buenos Aires, 1002, Argentina. TEL 54-11-4315-2244, info@iworld.com.ar, http://www.iworld.com.ar. Ed. David Exposito.

025.04   DEU   ISSN 1433-3309
INTERNET WORLD; for internet professionals. Text in German. 1997. m. EUR 40.80; EUR 3.95 newsstand/cover (effective 2005). adv. **Document type:** *Magazine, Consumer.* **Description:** Provides articles and features on available Internet resources from a technical and business-oriented point-of-view.
Incorporates (1996-1998): Global Online (1431-2778)
Related titles: ♦ Print ed.: Internet World Online.
Published by: Neue Mediengesellschaft Ulm mbH, Konrad-Celtis-Str 77, Munich, 81369, Germany. TEL 49-89-74117-0, FAX 49-89-74117787, mail@internetworld.de, empfang@nmg.de, http://www.internetworld.de, http://www.nc-online.de. Ed. Peter Klein. Pub. Guenter Goetz. Adv. contact Bettina Guenther. page EUR 7,110. Circ: 49,679 (paid).

025.04   GBR   ISSN 1365-439X
INTERNET WORLD. Text in English. 1996. m. adv. **Document type:** *Magazine, Trade.* **Description:** Analyses the technology and business solutions coming to the market that will revolutionize a company's approach to the Internet, profiles of those driving the Internet both in the UK and around the world, and vertical coverage of key market sectors and factors driving e-business.
Formerly (until 1999): Internet Advisor (1363-349X)
Published by: Penton Media Europe (Subsidiary of: Penton Media, Inc.), Penton House, 288-290 Worton Rd, Isleworth, Mddx TW7 6EL, United Kingdom. TEL 44-20-8232-1600, FAX 44-20-8232-1650, information@penton.com, http://www.internetworld.co.uk, http://www.penton.com. Adv. contact Steve Rivers. B&W page GBP 2,750, color page GBP 3,250; trim 210 x 297. Circ: 35,000 (controlled).

004.678   MEX
INTERNET WORLD EN ESPANOL. Text in Spanish. m. adv. **Document type:** *Magazine, Consumer.* **Description:** Presents features and articles on all aspects of the Internet.
Published by: Editorial Ness, S.A. de C.V., Renacimiento, no 180, Col San Juan Tlihuaca, Mexico, 02400, Mexico. TEL 52-5-561-8333, FAX 52-5-561-9122, csansor@mpsnet.com.mx. adv: color page MXP 3,577. Circ: 35,000 (paid and controlled).

025.04   DEU
INTERNET WORLD ONLINE. Text in German. d. adv. **Document type:** *Consumer.*
Related titles: ♦ Print ed.: Internet World. ISSN 1433-3309.
Published by: Neue Mediengesellschaft Ulm mbH, Konrad-Celtis-Str 77, Munich, 81369, Germany. TEL 49-89-74117-0, FAX 49-89-74117787, mail@internetworld.de, empfang@nmg.de, http://www.internetworld.de, http://www.nc-online.de.

004.678   SWE   ISSN 1401-6125
INTERNET WORLD SWEDEN. Text in Swedish. 1996. 11/yr. SEK 369; SEK 34 newsstand/cover (effective 2003). adv. **Document type:** *Magazine, Consumer.* **Description:** Contains information and reviews on the latest and most interesting sites on the Internet.
Related titles: Online - full text ed.: ISSN 1402-4675.
Indexed: M&MA.
Published by: I D G AB (Subsidiary of: I D G Communications Inc.), Sturegatan 11, Stockholm, 10678, Sweden. TEL 46-8-4536000, FAX 46-8-4536005, iw@iwred.idg.se, http://internetworld.idg.se, http://www.idg.se. Ed. Mikael Zackrisson. Adv. contact Sofia Pettersson. color page SEK 51,900; trim 185 x 260. Circ: 109,600 (paid).

025.04   ISL   ISSN 1024-8730
INTERNETID. Text in Icelandic. 1995. 6/yr.
Published by: Lindin hf., Krokhals 4, Reykjavik, Iceland. TEL 354-567-1030, FAX 354-567-1824.

004.678   USA
INTERNETMERCADO. Text in English, Spanish. m. adv. **Description:** Promotes internet & e-commerce usage among Hispanics.
Published by: Internet Mercado, 2329 South Purdue, Los Angeles, CA 90064. TEL 310-914-3007, FAX 310-914-0607, servicioalcliente@internetmercado.com, http://www.internetmercado.com. Pub. Marcelino Miyares. Adv. contact Jeri Lawrence.

004.6   USA
INTRANET DIGEST. Text in English. 1999. m. bk.rev. back issues avail. **Document type:** *Trade.* **Description:** Focuses on the creation, development and deployment of corporate intranets.
Media: Online - full text.
Address: 18 Commerce Way, Ste 2050, Woburn, MA 01801. TEL 781-932-0960, eviscosi@intranetics.com, http://www.intranetdigest.com/. Ed. Elaine Viscosi.

004.68   GBR
INTRANET MANAGEMENT; a T F P L guide to best practice. Text in English. 1998. irreg. GBP 85.
Published by: T F P L Publishing, 17-18 Britton St, London, EC1M 5NQ, United Kingdom. TEL 44-171-251-5522, FAX 44-171-251-8318, central@tfpl.com, http://www.tfpl.com.

383.33   USA
INTRANETS AND ADVANCED NETWORKING. Text in English. 1996. m. USD 1,075 (effective 1998). **Document type:** *Newsletter.* **Description:** News and analysis of technologies, products and services for in-company intranets, plus regulatory issues.
Published by: Computer Economics, Inc., 2082 Business Center Dr., Ste 240, Irvine, CA 92612. TEL 949-831-8700, FAX 949-442-7688, http://www.computereconomics.com. Ed. Bob Emmerson. Pub., R&P Philip Gallagher.

INVESTMENT.COM. see *BUSINESS AND ECONOMICS—Investments*

659.13   USA
IPROSPERITY WEB BUSINESS E-ZINE. Text in English. 1999. w. back issues avail. **Document type:** *Newsletter.* **Description:** Provides web marketing information articles by major webmarketing experts.
Media: Online - full text.
Address: 2009 N 14th, Ste 612, Arlington, VA 22201. bnbpubs@aol.com, http://members.aol.com/bnbpubs/iprosperity.html. Ed. Mary Benzinger.

659.13   USA
IQ: THE FASTEST WAY TO INCREASE YOUR INTERNET QUOTIENT. Text in English. 2000. bi-m. free to qualified personnel. adv. **Document type:** *Magazine, Trade.* **Description:** Provides content, news, and analyses of current trends in conducting business within the Internet economy.
Published by: (Cisco Systems, Inc.), Hachette Filipacchi Media U.S., Inc. (Subsidiary of: Hachette Filipacchi Medias S.A.), 1633 Broadway, New York, NY 10019. TEL 212-767-6000, iq-editorial@cisco.com, http://www.cisco.com/go/iqmagazine, http://www.hfmus.com. adv.: B&W page USD 7,200, color page USD 10,000; trim 8.5 x 10.875.

025.4   USA
ISOURCE BUSINESS. Text in English. 2000. m. free (effective 2003). adv. **Document type:** *Magazine, Trade.* **Description:** Aims to educate and inform top-level executives, purchasing and supply management professionals about B2B e-commerce, specifically e-procurement.
Related titles: ♦ Online - full text ed.: iSource Business Online.
Published by: Grand View Media Group, Inc. (Subsidiary of: EBSCO Industries, Inc.), 200 Croft St., # 1, Birmingham, AL 35242-1824. TEL 888-431-2877, webmaster@grandviewmedia.com, http://www.isourceonline.com/, http://www.grandviewmedia.com. Ed. Julie Murphree. Pub. Doug Moore. Adv. contact Val Carrier.

025.4   USA
ISOURCE BUSINESS ONLINE. Text in English. 2000. d. adv. **Document type:** *Trade.* **Description:** Provides hard-hitting analysis and viewpoints on Internet-based business-to-business commerce and procurement to top-level industry executives and supply chain management professionals.
Media: Online - full text. **Related titles:** ♦ Print ed.: iSource Business.
Published by: Grand View Media Group, Inc. (Subsidiary of: EBSCO Industries, Inc.), 200 Croft St., # 1, Birmingham, AL 35242-1824. TEL 888-431-2877, webmaster@grandviewmedia.com, http://www.grandviewmedia.com. Ed. Julie Murphree.

025.04   GBR   ISSN 1472-6297
IT'S ON THE NET. Text in English. 2001. q. GBP 3.75 newsstand/cover (effective 2003). Website rev. **Document type:** *Magazine, Consumer.* **Description:** Contains more than 10,000 website reviews in every issue and 26 color-coded subject categories.
Published by: S P L (Subsidiary of: Highbury House Communications PLC), Berwick House, 8-10 Knoll Rise, Orpington, Kent BR6 0PS, United Kingdom. TEL 44-1689-887200, email@splpublishing.co.uk, http://www.iotn.co.uk/, http://www.hhc.co.uk/. Ed. Andrew Noakes. Adv. contact Melanie Latimer TEL 44-1689-887292.

681.324   ESP   ISSN 1139-0859
IWORLD; the internet magazine. Text in Spanish. 1998. m. EUR 44 (effective 2002). adv. **Document type:** *Magazine, Consumer.* **Description:** Covers everything that happens on the Internet.
Related titles: Online - full content ed.: ISSN 1139-1111. 1997.
Published by: I D G Communications, Fortuny, 18 4, Madrid, 28010, Spain. TEL 34-91-3496600, FAX 34-91-3496100, iworld@idg.es, http://www.idg.es/iworld. Ed. Fernando Cabello. Adv. contact Lola Rubio TEL 34-91-3496682. color page USD 2,541; bleed 210 x 280. Circ: 25,000 (paid and controlled).

JACK. see *MEN'S INTERESTS*

659.13   JPN   ISSN 1345-4846
J@PAN INC.; business - technology - people. Text in English. 1994. m. JPY 8,000; USD 80.55 elsewhere; JPY 800 newsstand/cover; USD 8.95 newsstand/cover elsewhere (effective 2000). adv. bk.rev.; software rev. charts; illus.; stat.; tr.lit.; maps; mkt. **Document type:** *Magazine, Trade.* **Description:** Chronicles the rise of e-business in Japan while focusing on e-commerce, venture capital, investment, the Internet, technology, people and enterprises.

Formerly (until 1999): Computing Japan (Print) (1340-7228)
Related titles: Online - full text ed.: 1999. JPY 5,600; USD 49.95 elsewhere (effective 2000) (from EBSCO Publishing, Florida Center for Library Automation, Gale Group).
Indexed: MicrocompInd.
—BLDSC (3395.064000).
Published by: LINC Media Inc., Odakyu Minami-Aoyama Bldg 8F, 7-8-1 Minami Aoyama, Minato-ku, Tokyo, 107-0062, Japan. TEL 81-3-3499-2099, FAX 81-3-3499-2199, steve@japaninc.net, http://www.japaninc.net. Ed. Steve Mollman. Pub. Terrie Lloyd. R&P Robert Jamison TEL 480-775-1912. Adv. contact John Muehling. color page USD 4,783; trim 211 x 277.

025.04362   USA   ISSN 1539-8285
RA773.6   CODEN: HCINF7
JOURNAL OF CONSUMER HEALTH ON THE INTERNET. Text in English. 1997. q. USD 180 combined subscription domestic to institutions print & online eds.; USD 243 combined subscription in Canada to institutions print & online eds.; USD 261 combined subscription elsewhere to institutions print & online eds. (effective 2006). adv. back issues avail.; reprint service avail. from HAW. **Document type:** *Journal, Academic/Scholarly.* **Description:** Discusses topics relating to internet-accessible materials on health care.
Formerly (until 2003): Health Care on the Internet (1089-4187)
Related titles: Microform ed.: (from PQC); Online - full text ed.: ISSN 1539-8293. free with print ed. (effective 2001) (from EBSCO Publishing, O C L C Online Computer Library Center, Inc., Swets Information Services).
Indexed: AgeL, BrCerAb, C&ISA, CINAHL, CerAb, CompR, CorrAb, E&CAJ, EMA, ESPM, H&SSA, IAA, IBR, IBZ, InfoSAb, Inspec, LISA, M&TEA, MBF, METADEX, MicrocompInd, PEI, RefZh, SWR&A, WAA, e-psyche.
—BLDSC (4274.942510), AskIEEE, Haworth, IE, ingenta. **CCC.**
Published by: Haworth Information Press (Subsidiary of: Haworth Press, Inc.), 10 Alice St, Binghamton, NY 13904. TEL 607-722-5857, 800-429-6784, FAX 607-771-0012, 800-895-0582, getinfo@haworthpress.com, http://www.haworthpress.com/web/JCHI/. Ed. Sandra M Wood TEL 717-531-8630. Pub. William Cohen. R&P Ruth Ann Heath TEL 607-722-5857 ext 316. Adv. contact Rebecca Miller-Baum TEL 607-722-5857 ext 337. B&W page USD 315, color page USD 550; trim 4.375 x 7.125. Circ: 600.

▼ **JOURNAL OF DIGITAL FORENSIC PRACTICE.** see *CRIMINOLOGY AND LAW ENFORCEMENT—Security*

▼ **JOURNAL OF E-GOVERNMENT.** see *PUBLIC ADMINISTRATION*

▼ **JOURNAL OF INTERNATIONAL BUSINESS AND ECONOMICS.** see *BUSINESS AND ECONOMICS—International Commerce*

JOURNAL OF INTERNET BANKING AND COMMERCE. see *BUSINESS AND ECONOMICS—Banking And Finance*

004.678   USA   ISSN 1091-1367
Z695.24   CODEN: JICTFP
JOURNAL OF INTERNET CATALOGING; the international quarterly of digital organization, classification, and access. Text in English. 1997. q. USD 170 combined subscription domestic to institutions print & online eds.; USD 229.50 combined subscription in Canada to institutions print & online eds.; USD 246.50 combined subscription elsewhere to institutions print & online eds. (effective 2006). adv. back issues avail.; reprint service avail. from HAW. **Document type:** *Journal, Academic/Scholarly.* **Description:** Focuses on the organization, access, and bibliographic control of Internet resources.
Related titles: Microform ed.: (from PQC); Online - full text ed.: ISSN 1528-7017. free with subscr. to the print ed. (from EBSCO Publishing, O C L C Online Computer Library Center, Inc., Swets Information Services).
Indexed: BrCerAb, C&ISA, CerAb, CorrAb, E&CAJ, EMA, IAA, IBR, IBZ, InfoSAb, Inspec, LISA, M&TEA, MBF, METADEX, MicrocompInd, PAIS, RefZh, SWR&A, WAA.
—BLDSC (5007.693100), Haworth, IE, Infotrieve, ingenta, KNAW, Linda Hall.
Published by: Haworth Information Press (Subsidiary of: Haworth Press, Inc.), 10 Alice St, Binghamton, NY 13904. TEL 607-722-5857, 800-429-6784, FAX 607-771-0012, 800-895-0582, getinfo@haworthpress.com, http://www.haworthpress.com/web/JIC. Ed. Ruth Carter TEL 724-940-4192. Pub. William Cohen. R&P Ruth Ann Heath TEL 607-722-5857 ext 316. Adv. contact Rebecca Miller-Baum TEL 607-722-5857 ext 337. B&W page USD 315, color page USD 550; trim 7.375 x 7.125. Circ: 556 (paid).

JOURNAL OF INTERNET COMMERCE. see *BUSINESS AND ECONOMICS—Computer Applications*

JOURNAL OF INTERNET LAW. see *LAW*

004.678   CAN   ISSN 1206-4890
JOURNAL OF INTERNET PURCHASING. Text in English. 1997. bi-m. free (effective 2004). **Description:** Informs purchasing professionals and executives on principal developments, benchmark practices, and future trends in the Internet-based purchasing practices of governments and industry.
Media: Online - full text.

C

Indexed: ESPM, RiskAb.
Address: PO Box 5145, Sta F, Ottawa, ON K2C 3H3, Canada. sollish@worldnet.att.net, http://www.arraydev.com/commerce/jip/. Ed. Fred Sollish. Pub. Nahum Goldmann.

384 TWN ISSN 1607-9264
➤ **JOURNAL OF INTERNET TECHNOLOGY.** Text in Chinese. 1999. q. USD 100 (effective 2004). **Document type:** *Journal, Academic/Scholarly.* **Description:** Contains original technical articles in all disciplines of Internet technology and applications.
Related titles: Online - full text ed.
Indexed: C&ISA, E&CAJ, IAA, Inspec.
Published by: National Dong Hwa University, Computer Center, 1, Sec 2, Da Hsueh Rd, Shou-Feng, Hualien, Taiwan. TEL 886-3-8635000, FAX 886-3-8632700, jit@mail.ndhu.edu.tw, http://jit.ndhu.edu.tw. Ed. Kim-Joan Chen. Pub. Wen-Shu Hwang. R&P Reen-Cheng Wang. Adv. contact Han-Chieh Chao. Circ: 200 (paid and controlled).

▼ ➤ **JOURNAL OF MOBILE MULTIMEDIA.** see *COMMUNICATIONS—Telephone And Telegraph*

➤ **JOURNAL OF ONLINE BEHAVIOR**; dedicated to the empirical study of human behavior online. see *SOCIOLOGY*

➤ **JOURNAL OF TECHNOLOGY IN COUNSELING.** see *PSYCHOLOGY*

004.678 USA
JOURNAL OF WEB PROMOTION. Text in English. s-a. USD 45 to individuals; USD 85 to institutions; USD 250 to libraries (effective 2005). **Document type:** *Trade.* **Description:** Carries information on planning and applied research relevant to website promotion management.
Published by: Haworth Press, Inc., 10 Alice St, Binghamton, NY 13904-1580. TEL 607-722-5857, 800-429-6784, FAX 607-722-1424, 800-895-0582.

004.678 NLD ISSN 1570-8268
▼ **JOURNAL OF WEB SEMANTICS.** Text in English. 2003. 4/yr. EUR 356 in Europe to institutions; JPY 42,000 in Japan to institutions; USD 377 to institutions except Europe and Japan (effective 2006). **Description:** Covers research and applications of various subject areas that contribute to the development of a knowledge-intensive and intelligent service Web, including knowledge technologies, ontology, agents, databases and the semantic grid, information retrieval, language technology, and human-computer interaction.
Media: Online - full content. **Related titles:** Online - full text ed.: (from ScienceDirect, Swets Information Services).
—IE.
Published by: Elsevier BV (Subsidiary of: Elsevier Science & Technology), Radarweg 29, Amsterdam, 1043 NX, Netherlands. nlinfo-f@elsevier.nl, http://www.elsevier.com/locate/websem, http://www.elsevier.nl. Ed. Carole Goble.

025.04 USA ISSN 1553-3611
▼ ▼ **JOURNAL OF WEBSITE PROMOTION**; innovations in internet business research, theory, and practice. Text in English. 2005. s-a. USD 250 combined subscription domestic to institutions print & online eds.; USD 337.50 combined subscription in Canada to institutions print & online eds.; USD 362.50 combined subscription elsewhere to institutions print & online eds. (effective 2006). adv. reprint service avail. from HAW. **Document type:** *Journal, Trade.* **Description:** Provides up-to-date research and immediately useful information about website promotion.
Related titles: Online - full content ed.; Online - full text ed.: ISSN 1553-362X (from EBSCO Publishing).
Indexed: C&ISA, E&CAJ, IAA.
—Haworth.
Published by: Internet Practice Press (Subsidiary of: Haworth Press, Inc.), 10 Alice St, Binghamton, NY 13904. TEL 607-722-5857, 800-429-6784, FAX 607-771-0012, 800-895-0582, getinfo@haworthpress.com, http://www.haworthpress.com/web/JWP/. Ed. Richard Alan Nelson. Pub. William Cohen. R&P Ruth Ann Heath TEL 607-722-5857 ext 316. Adv. contacts Christine Miner, Rebecca Miller-Baum TEL 607-722-5857 ext 337.

004.678 USA ISSN 1525-9366
K G B REPORT. (Keving G. Barkes) Text in English. 1999. w. adv. back issues avail. **Document type:** *Newsletter.* **Description:** Reports internet technology and the media in general.
Related titles: Online - full content ed.: ISSN 1525-898X.
Published by: K G B Consulting, Inc., 1512 Annette Ave., Library, PA 15129-9735. TEL 412-854-4707, FAX 412-854-2550, http://www.kgb.com/kgbrep.shtml. Ed. Kevin G Barkes.

025.04 028.5 USA
K I D S REPORT. (Kids Identifying and Discovering Sites) Text in English. 1997. fortn. **Document type:** *Bulletin.* **Description:** Produced by K-12 students as an Internet resource guide for other K-12 students.
Media: Online - full text.
Published by: University of Wisconsin at Madison, Computer Sciences Department, 5355a Computer Sciences and Statistics, 1210 West Dayton St, Madison, WI 53706. TEL 608-262-1204, FAX 608-262-9777, scout@cs.wisc.edu, http://scout.cs.wisc.edu/scout/kids/index.html, http://scout.wisc.edu/.

004.56 GRC ISSN 1108-6866
KAFENIO; where Europe is only a mouseclick away. Text in English. 2000. m. adv. **Document type:** *Consumer.* **Description:** Contains information, resources and communications on all aspects of Europe.
Media: Online - full content.
Published by: Meier & Jacobson Editorial Services, PO Box 142, Karpathos, Greece. TEL 30-245-31716, FAX 30-245-31716, editor@kafeniocom.com, http://www.kafeniocom.com. Ed. Roberta Beach Jacobson. Pub., Adv. contact Alf B. Meier.

KEY NOTE MARKET ASSESSMENT. BOOK RETAILING ON THE INTERNET. see *PUBLISHING AND BOOK TRADE*

KEY NOTE MARKET ASSESSMENT. E-COMMERCE: THE INTERNET GROCERY MARKET. see *FOOD AND FOOD INDUSTRIES—Grocery Trade*

KEY NOTE MARKET ASSESSMENT. INTERNET ADVERTISING. see *ADVERTISING AND PUBLIC RELATIONS*

384.33 607 GBR
KEY NOTE MARKET ASSESSMENT. INTERNET SERVICE PROVIDERS. Text in English. 2001. irreg., latest 2001, Aug. GBP 730 per issue (effective 2002). **Description:** Provides an in-depth strategic analysis across a broad range of industries and contains an examination on the scope, dynamics and shape of key UK markets in the consumer, financial, lifestyle and business to business sectors.
Published by: Key Note Ltd., Field House, 72 Oldfield Rd, Hampton, Mddx TW12 2HQ, United Kingdom. TEL 44-20-8481-8750, FAX 44-20-8783-0049, info@keynote.co.uk, http://www.keynote.co.uk. Ed. Simon Taylor.

KEY NOTE MARKET ASSESSMENT. NEW MEDIA MARKETING. see *COMMUNICATIONS*

004.678 338 GBR
KEY NOTE MARKET REPORT: CONSUMER INTERNET USAGE. Text in English. 1996. irreg., latest 2000, Sept. GBP 340 per issue (effective 2002). **Document type:** *Trade.* **Description:** Provides an overview of the UK computer internet usage market, including industry structure, market size and trends, developments, prospects, and major company profiles.
Formerly (until 1999): Key Note Market Report. Internet Usage In the Home (1367-2401)
Published by: Key Note Ltd., Field House, 72 Oldfield Rd, Hampton, Mddx TW12 2HQ, United Kingdom. TEL 44-20-8481-8750, FAX 44-20-8783-0049, info@keynote.co.uk, http://www.keynote.co.uk. Ed. Nick Bardsley.

658 GBR ISSN 1461-5134
KEY NOTE MARKET REPORT: INTERNET USAGE IN BUSINESS. Text in English. 1997. irreg., latest 2001, July. GBP 340 per issue (effective 2002). **Description:** Provides an overview of a specific UK market segment and includes executive summary, market definition, market size, industry background, competitor analysis, current issues, forecasts, company profiles, and more.
—CCC.
Published by: Key Note Ltd., Field House, 72 Oldfield Rd, Hampton, Mddx TW12 2HQ, United Kingdom. TEL 44-20-8481-8750, FAX 44-20-8783-0049, info@keynote.co.uk, http://www.keynote.co.uk. Ed. Jacob Howard.

025.04 GBR
KEY NOTE MARKET REPORT: ONLINE DATABASES. Variant title: Online Databases. Text in English. irreg., latest vol.5, 1990. GBP 265 (effective 1999). **Document type:** *Trade.*
Published by: Key Note Ltd., Field House, 72 Oldfield Rd, Hampton, Mddx TW12 2HQ, United Kingdom. TEL 44-20-8481-8750, FAX 44-20-8783-0049, info@keynote.co.uk, http://www.keynote.co.uk.

KIDSPOTS. see *CHILDREN AND YOUTH—For*

004.678 USA
THE KLEINMAN REPORT. Text in English. 1995. w. **Description:** Covers Internet related topics.
Media: Online - full text.
Published by: Kleinman Report geoff@kleinman.com, http://www.kleinman.com. Ed. Geoffrey Kleinman.

KNOWLEDGE MANAGEMENT (LONDON). see *COMPUTERS—Data Base Management*

686.2 005 USA ISSN 1095-3248
LABEL & NARROW WEB. Text in English. 1996. 8/yr. USD 50 domestic; USD 75 foreign; free to qualified personnel (effective 2005). adv. back issues avail. **Document type:** *Magazine, Trade.*
Related titles: Online - full text ed.: (from Gale Group, O C L C Online Computer Library Center, Inc.).
—CCC.
Published by: Rodman Publications, Inc., 70 Hilltop Rd, 3rd Fl, Ramsey, NJ 07446. TEL 201-825-2552, FAX 201-825-0553, label@rodpub.com, http://www.labelandnarrowweb.com. Ed. Jack Kenny. Pubs. Kathleen Scully, Matthew Montgomery. Circ: 11,000 (paid and controlled).

▼ **LANGUAGE@INTERNET.** see *LINGUISTICS*

004.678 USA
LEARN IT ON THE WEB. Text in English. 199?. 2/w. back issues avail. **Document type:** *Newsletter.* **Description:** Contains reviews of educational web resources.
Media: Online - full text.
Address: 739 N Main St, Mocksville, NC 27028. mxs@learnitontheweb.com, http://www.learnitontheweb.com/. Ed. Mark X Schambach.

004.678 USA
LEARNING FOUNTAINS MAGAZINE. Text in English. m. free. bk.rev. back issues avail. **Description:** Dedicated to helping learn new techniques for corporate promotion over the Internet, website design, advertising and everything related to the Internet.
Media: Online - full text.
Address: paul@learningfountain.com, http://www.learningfountain.com/fountain.htm. Ed. Paul Siegel.

025.04 USA ISSN 1098-6898
LIBRARIAN NET NEWS; a librarians online companion. Text in English. 1996. 5/yr., latest vol.4, no.3. USD 49.95 (effective 2001). Website rev. 16 p./no.; **Document type:** *Newsletter.* **Description:** Contains interviews with librarians concerning various challenges posed in providing public access to the Internet. Includes reference sites, and success stories from librarians and Internet users.
Formerly: Net Connect (1093-2380)
Published by: Research Communications Inc, 3724 Jefferson St, 318, Austin, TX 78732. TEL 512-458-2021, 800-331-5076, FAX 512-458-2059, researchcomm@austin.rr.com. Ed. Craig Gowen.

025.04 USA ISSN 1066-5293
Z678.892.U6
THE LIBRARIAN'S YELLOW PAGES. Text in English. 1993. a.
—Linda Hall.
Published by: The Librarian's Yellow Pages, 2089 Post Rd, Larchmont, NY 10538. TEL 800-235-9723, FAX 914-833-3053, info@librariansyellowpages.com, http://www.librariansyellowpages.com. Pub. Raissa Fomerand.

659.13 USA
LINE56.COM. Text in English. 2000. d. adv. **Document type:** *Trade.*
Media: Online - full content. **Related titles:** ♦ Print ed.: Line56 E-Business Journal.
Published by: B2B E-Commerce International, Inc., 10940 Wilshire Blvd, Ste 600, Los Angeles, CA 90024. TEL 310-443-4226, FAX 310-443-4230, info@line56.com, webmaster@line56.com, http://www.line56.com. Adv. contact Pat Ashby.

659.13 USA
LINE56 E-BUSINESS JOURNAL. Text in English. 2000. q. adv. **Document type:** *Magazine, Trade.* **Description:** Provides strategic guidance for those seeking maximum advantage from the dynamic advances and alliances of global business-to-business e-commerce.
Supersedes (in 2002): Line56 (1534-5408)
Related titles: ♦ Online - full content ed.: Line56.com.
Indexed: ABIn, CompLI.
Published by: B2B E-Commerce International, Inc., 10940 Wilshire Blvd, Ste 600, Los Angeles, CA 90024. TEL 310-443-4226, FAX 310-443-4230, info@line56.com, http://www.line56.com. Ed. Lester Craft. adv.: B&W page USD 11,500, color page USD 13,500; trim 9 x 10.75. Circ: 100,000 (controlled).

004.678 MEX
LINK. Text in Spanish. m. USD 71 (effective 1997). adv. **Document type:** *Consumer.* **Description:** Presents an internet guide that help users to find information in a faster and easier way.
Published by: Consorcio Sayrols, Mier y Pesado 126, Mexico, Col del Valle, Mexico City, DF 03100, Mexico. TEL 52-5-6874699, FAX 525-523-7045, beatrizc@spin.com.mx, http://www.sayrols.com.mx. Ed. Monica Mistretta. Adv. contact Beatriz Coria. B&W page USD 1,600, color page USD 2,080; trim 270 x 205. Circ: 20,000.

A LIST APART. see *COMPUTERS—Computer Graphics*

THE LITTLE NEWSLETTER. see *BUSINESS AND ECONOMICS—Marketing And Purchasing*

▼ **THE LITTLE NIPPER'S INTERNET CLUBHOUSE.** see *CHILDREN AND YOUTH—For*

C

004.678 ITA ISSN 1720-5301
LOGIN; building the information highway. Text in Italian. 1996. bi-m. EUR 44 (effective 2005). **Document type:** *Magazine, Trade.*
Related titles: Online - full text ed.: ISSN 1720-531X.
Published by: Gruppo Editoriale Infomedia Srl, Via Valdera P 116, Ponsacco, PI 56038, Italy. TEL 39-0587-736460, FAX 39-0587-732232, http://www.infomedia.it.

384.33 USA
M & A E-NEWS. Text in English. w. free. adv. **Document type:** *Newsletter.* **Description:** Designed to help everyone to be profitable on the Internet.
Related titles: E-mail ed.; Online - full text ed.
Address: 808 S Clayton Rd, 19, New Lebanon, OH 45345. TEL 937-687-1328, FAX 937-687-1328, info@manda1.com, http://www.manda1.com. Ed. Mike Rogers. Circ: 25,450.

035.0434 USA ISSN 1093-3255
K13
THE M & A LAWYER. Text in English. 1997 (Apr.). 10/yr. USD 325 (effective 2005). **Document type:** *Newsletter, Trade.* **Description:** Provides coverage of developments which affect all types of mergers and acquisitions transactions including securities law, state law, international, taxation, accounting, and practice areas such as intellectual property, employee benefits/compensation, antitrust, and environmental.
Published by: Glasser LegalWorks (Subsidiary of: West Publishing Co.), 150 Clove Rd, Little Falls, NJ 07424. TEL 973-890-0008, 800-308-1700, FAX 973-890-0042, legalwks@aol.com, http://www.malawyerreport.com/malawyerreport/, http://www.legalwks.com. Ed. Broc Romanek.

025.04 USA ISSN 1532-3137
HE9713
M-BUSINESS; the voice of the next mobile economy. Text in English. 2000. m. qualified personnel. adv. **Document type:** *Magazine, Trade.* **Description:** Clarifies issues, analyzes developments and guides new strategies related to the mobile business economy.
Indexed: CompLI, MicrocompInd.
Published by: C M P Media LLC (Subsidiary of: United News & Media), 600 Harrison St, 6th Fl., San Francisco, CA 94107. TEL 415-947-6746, FAX 415-947-6041, http://www.mbizcentral.com. Ed. Morwenna Marshall. Pub. Eric Bergman. R&P Fred Wood. Adv. contact Joe Siart. Circ: 100,000 (controlled).

004.678 GBR
M-COMMERCE WORLD. Text in English. 2000. m. adv. **Document type:** *Magazine, Trade.* **Description:** Contains news, analysis, interviews, market research, case studies and features on every aspect of the business of wireless Internet.
Published by: Hillgate Communications Ltd., Shand House, 14-20 Shand St, London, SE1 2ES, United Kingdom. TEL 44-207-645-3600, FAX 44-207-407-7771, http://www.m-commercesource.com/magazine.htm, http://www.hillgate.com.

M D NET GUIDE; physician's internet directory. see *MEDICAL SCIENCES*

M D NET GUIDE ENEWSLETTER. see *MEDICAL SCIENCES*

M D NET GUIDE ONLINE; physician's internet directory. see *MEDICAL SCIENCES*

M S D N MAGAZINE. see *COMPUTERS—Computer Programming*

004.678 USA
MAC NET JOURNAL. Text in English. 1995. m. **Description:** Contains informative articles on how to get more out of Macintosh computers for home and business use.
Media: Online - full text.
Published by: (Bottom Line Online), White Rabbit Publishing, 3711 N Mullen St, Tacoma, WA 98407. TEL 206-752-6402, mchuff@wolfenet.com, http://www.blol.com/web_mnj/. Ed. Rob McNair Huff.

004.678 POL
MAGAZYN INTERNET. Text in Polish. m. PLZ 174.90 domestic; EUR 99 in Europe; EUR 119 elsewhere (effective 2005). 116 p./no.; **Document type:** *Magazine, Consumer.*
Related titles: CD-ROM ed.
Published by: A V T- Korporacja Sp. z o. o., ul Burleska 9, Warsaw, 01939, Poland. TEL 48-22-5689941, FAX 48-22-5689944, redakcja@ep.com.pl, http://www.mi.com.pl, http://www.avt.pl. Ed. Krystian Grzenkowicz. Circ: 27,000.

MAJOR TELECOMMUNICATIONS COMPANIES OF THE WORLD (YEAR). see *COMMUNICATIONS*

MAMAMEDIA. see *CHILDREN AND YOUTH—For*

MARKETING ST. KILDA. see *BUSINESS AND ECONOMICS—Computer Applications*

384.33 USA
MARKETING BONANZA NEWSLETTER. Text in English. m. free. **Document type:** *Newsletter.* **Description:** Presents direct-marketing resources and new direct marketing methods that anyone can use on or off line.
Media: E-mail.
Address: peeryj@cougar.netutah.net. Ed. Jason Peery.

658 USA
MARKETING SMARTER WITH SEARCH ENGINES. Text in English. m. USD 297 (effective 2005). **Document type:** *Newsletter, Trade.* **Description:** Contains the latest marketing news involving search engines.
Published by: McMurry Publishing, 1010 E Missouri Ave, Phoenix, AZ 85014-2601. TEL 602-395-5850, 888-626-8779, FAX 602-395-5853, info@mcmurry.com, http://www.mcmurry.com/newsletters/msse/.

MASSON NEWSLETTER DE INTERNET MEDICINA. see *MEDICAL SCIENCES—Computer Applications*

MATRIX MAPS QUARTERLY. see *COMPUTERS—Computer Networks*

004.68 USA
MATRIX.NET WHITE PAPERS. Text in English. irreg. back issues avail. **Description:** Provides an in-depth discussion of topics related to the Internet and networking.
Media: Online - full text.
Published by: Matrix.Net, 1106 Clayton Ln Ste 501W, Austin, TX 78723. TEL 512-451-7602, FAX 512-452-0127, webmaster@matrix.net, http://www.matrix.net/.

004.68 USA ISSN 1059-0749
MATRIX NEWS. Text in English. 1991. m. **Document type:** *Newsletter.* **Description:** Presents articles of interest to those who follow the Internet with topics ranging from the history to the development of new Internet protocols.
Related titles: Online - full text ed.
Published by: Matrix.Net, 1106 Clayton Ln Ste 501W, Austin, TX 78723. TEL 512-451-7602, FAX 512-452-0127, webmaster@matrix.net, http://www.matrix.net/.

384.34 AUS
MCGUIRE'S HOME BUSINESS NEWSLETTER. Text in English. m. free. adv. **Document type:** *Newsletter.* **Description:** Includes informative articles, marketing tips, business opportunities and free advertising opportunitites for the Internet entrepreneur.
Media: Online - full text.
Address: Australia. mcguires@forfree.at, http://come.to/mcguires, http://www.ebquarry.com/~mcquires. Ed., Pub. John McGuire.

004.6 USA ISSN 1090-4255
MEDIA COMPUTING; email report on emerging media markets. Text in English. 1989. m. USD 495 (effective 1998). charts; illus.; stat. index. **Document type:** *Newsletter.* **Description:** Offers an analysis of emerging technology and business trends in the multimedia and Internet markets.
Former titles (until 1996): Pacific Rim Media (1085-519X); (until 1994): NeoJapan
Media: Online - full text. **Related titles:** E-mail ed.
Published by: Dreamscape Net, 509 Meder St., Santa Cruz, CA 95060-2309. TEL 408-685-8818, statsuno@aol.com. Ed. Sheridan M Tatsuno.

MEDIA UK INTERNET DIRECTORY. see *JOURNALISM*

658.8 USA
MERLE'S MISSION. Text in English. m. **Document type:** *Newsletter.* **Description:** For people interested in the Internet, promotion and marketing.
Media: Online - full text.
Address: msmerle@stratos.net, http://www.merlesworld.com/newsletter.htm. Ed. Merle Stinnett.

025.04 USA
THE MESH. Text in English. m. **Document type:** *Newsletter.* **Description:** Features articles, reviews, columns, listings, and what's hot about the online world.
Media: Online - full text.
Published by: Mesh themesh@aol.com, http://www.albany.globalone.net/themesh/.

004.678 USA
MESSAGES FROM THE FUTURE. Text in English. 1994. w. **Description:** Features Internet investigative reporting.
Media: Online - full text.
Address: rhb@islandnet.com, http://www.islandnet.com/~rhb/future_page.html.

MICRO HEBDO. see *COMPUTERS—Personal Computers*

004.678 RUS
MIR INTERNET. Text in Russian. 1997. m. 96 p./no.; back issues avail.
Address: Vyborgskaya Naberezhnaya 27/6, St Petersburg, Russian Federation. TEL 7-812-3271311, FAX 7-812-3271315, editors@iworld.ru, http://www.iworld.ru. Ed. Maria Govorun.

004.678 USA ISSN 1542-1457
QA76.9.D3
MOBILE BUSINESS ADVISOR. Text in English. 1988. bi-m. USD 39 domestic; USD 59 in Canada; USD 79 elsewhere; USD 4.99 newsstand/cover (effective 2005). adv. bk.rev. reprints avail. **Document type:** *Magazine, Trade.* **Description:** Provides guidance for designing, deploying and maintaining on-line applications. Includes articles on such vital topics as database security; distributed data; data warehouse and mart; client-server and other Web database related topics.
Formerly: E-Business Advisor (1098-8912); Formed by the 1998 merger of: Internet, Java and Active X Advisor (1093-9083); Which was formerly (until 1997): Internet and Java Advisor (1090-6452); Internet Advisor (1084-158X); And: Databased Web Advisor (1093-9091); Which was formerly (until 1997): Databased Advisor (1090-6436); (until 1996): Data Based Application Advisor (1082-1252); (1983-1995): Data Based Advisor (0740-5200)
Related titles: Online - full text ed.: (from Florida Center for Library Automation, Gale Group, LexisNexis).
Indexed: CompD, CompLI, CompR, EngInd, InfoSAb, Inspec, MicrocompInd, SoftBase, TTI.
—BLDSC (5879.953131), CISTI, Ei, IE, ingenta.
Published by: Advisor Media, Inc., 4849 Viewridge Ave, San Diego, CA 92123-1643. TEL 858-278-5600, FAX 858-278-0300, subscribe@advisor.com, http://mobilebusinessadvisor.com/, http://www.advisor.com. Ed. John L Hawkins. Pub. Jeanne Banfield Hawkins. R&P David Kodama. Adv. contacts Sheri Ogletree, Michael Callan. B&W page USD 3,450, color page USD 5,185. Circ: 35,556 (paid). **Dist. by:** International Periodical Distributors, 674 Via de la Valle, Ste 204, Solana Beach, CA 92075.

384.5 004.678 USA ISSN 1541-1281
MOBILE INTERNET. Text in English. m. USD 695 in US & Canada; USD 745 elsewhere (effective 2004). **Document type:** *Newsletter, Trade.*
Formerly: Wireless Internet Newsletter
Related titles: E-mail ed.: ISSN 1541-129X.
Published by: Information Gatekeepers, Inc., 320 Washington St, Ste 302, Brighton, MA 02135. TEL 617-782-5033, 800-323-1088, FAX 617-734-8562, info@igigroup.com, http://www.igigroup.com/nl/pages/wiretel.html. Pub. Dr. Paul Polishuk.

C

384.535 GBR ISSN 1479-6511
HE9713
MOBILE MEDIA. Text in English. 2000. fortn. **Document type:** *Newsletter, Trade.* **Description:** Covers mobile media news, analysis and statistics, including fortnightly examination of the Asian market, monthly review of the North America market, coverage of entertainment, enterprise, mobile Java, media and marketing and regulation.
Formerly (until 2002): Mobile Internet (1470-8841)
Related titles: Online - full content ed.; Online - full text ed.: (from Gale Group).
Published by: Baskerville (Subsidiary of: T & F Informa plc), Sheepen Place, Colchester, Essex C03 3LP, United Kingdom. TEL 44-20-70175537, FAX 44-20-70174783, telecoms.enquiries@informa.com, http://www.baskerville.telecoms.com/. Ed. Jessica Sandin.

004.678 USA ISSN 0741-580X
QA76.55
MODEM NOTES; on line to the business community. Text in English. 1983. m. USD 36. adv. bk.rev. **Description:** For personal computer users. Features articles on modems and their applications. Offers information and reviews of databases that can be accessed online.
Published by: Cache Data Products, Inc., 403 Oxford Rd, E, Lansing, MI 48823-2628. Ed. Katherine Ackerman.

658.8 USA
MOM'S OLD-FASHIONED INTERNET GAZETTE. Text in English. m. free. **Description:** Features articles on Web site promotion, design and marketing tips.
Media: Online - full text.
Address: TEL 250-752-4536, 800-619-2559, moms@bcsupernet.com, http://www.bcsupernet.com/users/e-mall/moms.htm. Ed. Ingela F Hyatt.

MULTIMEDIA & INTERNET@SCHOOLS; the media and technology specialist's guide to electronic tools and resources for K-12. see *EDUCATION—Computer Applications*

MUSIC.COM MAGAZINE. see *MUSIC*

MYNEWS@SABRE.COM. see *TRAVEL AND TOURISM*

NATUR - DAS KINDERWEB. see *CHILDREN AND YOUTH—For*

004.6 NLD ISSN 1381-5857
NET. Text in Dutch. 1994. 11/yr. EUR 31.50 (effective 2002). adv. software rev. illus. **Document type:** *Magazine, Trade.* **Description:** Discusses all issues pertaining to the Internet.
Related titles: Online - full text ed.
—IE, Infotrieve, KNAW.

▼ new title ➤ refereed ✶ unverified ♦ full entry avail.

Published by: I D G Communications Nederland BV, Postbus 5446, Haarlem, 2000 GK, Netherlands. TEL 31-23-5461111, FAX 31-23-5461155, redactie@net-magazine.nl, abo@idg.nl, http://www.net-magazine.nl, http://www.idg.nl. Ed. Rogier Mostert. Pub. Paul Molenaar. Adv. contact Johan de Windt. B&W page USD 1,945, color page USD 3,224; trim 210 x 285. Circ: 13,284.

004.678 GBR ISSN 1466-3619
THE NET✱. Text in English. 1999. m. GBP 1.99 newsstand/cover. adv. **Document type:** *Consumer.* **Description:** Designed to help Internet surfers and consumers find the sites and products they want and need.
Published by: Haymarket Magazines Ltd. (Subsidiary of: Haymarket Publishing Ltd.), 174 Hammersmith Rd, London, W6 7JP, United Kingdom. http://www.haymarketgroup.com/.

025.4 FRA ISSN 1278-6098
.NET. Text in French. 1996. m. adv. **Document type:** *Magazine, Consumer.*
Published by: Future France, 101-109 Rue Jean Jaures, Levallois Perret, 92300, France. TEL 33-1-41273838, yveline.duville@futurenet.fr.

384.33 GBR ISSN 1355-7602
NET (BATH); the Internet magazine. Text in English. 1994. m. GBP 44.99 in United Kingdom; GBP 3.99 newsstand/cover; GBP 59.99 in Europe; GBP 79.99 rest of world (effective 2000). adv. illus. reprints avail. **Document type:** *Consumer.* **Description:** Provides news, reviews, features and interviews on the wonder and excitement of the rapidly expanding online world.
Related titles: CD-ROM ed.: ISSN 1365-4977.
Indexed: BrHumI, LISA.
—BLDSC (6076.627000), IE, Infotrieve. **CCC.**
Published by: Future Publishing Ltd., Beauford Court, 30 Monmouth St, Bath, Avon BA1 2BW, United Kingdom. TEL 44-1225-442244, FAX 44-1225-442244, dave.taylor@futurenet.co.uk, http://www.futurenet.com, http://www.futurenet.com/futureonline. Ed. Dave Taylor. adv.: color page GBP 2,850; trim 232 x 280. Circ: 49,190 (paid).

004.678 MEX
NET AT. Text in Spanish. fortn. USD 25 (effective 1997). adv. **Document type:** *Newspaper.* **Description:** Includes news about internet, nets, and telecommunications and their impact in the business world.
Published by: Consorcio Sayrols, Mier y Pesado 126, Mexico, Col del Valle, Mexico City, DF 03100, Mexico. TEL 52-5-6874699, FAX 525-523-7045, beatrizc@spin.com.mx, http://www.sayrols.com.mx. Ed. Monica Mistretta. Adv. contact Beatriz Coria. B&W page USD 2,682, color page USD 3,447; trim 260 x 320. Circ: 5,000.

THE NET MARKET NEWS. see *BUSINESS AND ECONOMICS—Marketing And Purchasing*

384.33 USA
NET MARKETING INFO. Text in English. irreg. free. **Document type:** *Newsletter.* **Description:** Keeps up-to-date on the latest marketing trends and opportunities available on the Internet.
Media: Online - full text.
Address: timshank@geocities.com, http://www.netmarketinginfo.com/. Ed. Tim Shank.

681.3 ROM ISSN 1582-4497
NET REPORT. Text in Romanian. 1999. m. ROL 300,000; ROL 150,000 to students (effective 2002). adv. **Document type:** *Magazine, Trade.*
Formerly (until 2001): P C Report und Byte (1454-3990); Which was formed by the merger of (1992-1998): P C Report (1220-9856); (1995-1999): Byte Romania (1223-9801)
Related titles: Online - full text ed.
Published by: Agora Media, Str. Tudor Vladimirescu nr. 63, ap. 9, CP 230-1, Targu Mures, 4300, Romania. TEL 40-65-166516, FAX 40-65-166290, office@agora.ro, http://www.netreport.ro, http://www.agora.ro.

025.04 USA ISSN 1529-9007
NET SHOPPING GUIDE. Text in English. 2000. 4/yr. USD 14.95 (effective 2000). adv. **Document type:** *Magazine, Consumer.* **Description:** Contains listings and reviews of hundreds of shops and shopping resources on the Web as well as feature articles that will help prepare one for the online shopping experience.
Published by: W S Guide, Inc., 526 Boston Post Rd, Wayland, MA 91778. TEL 508-358-3434, FAX 508-358-5195, editor@webguidemag.com, http://www.webguidemag.com. Ed. Perry Glasser. Pub. Michael Siggins. Adv. contact Arthur Rosenberg.

025.04 USA
NET.TECH INTERNET TECHNICAL NEWSLETTER. Text in English. m.
Published by: Penton Technology Media (Subsidiary of: Penton Media, Inc.), 221 E 29th St, Ste 242, Loveland, CO 80538. TEL 800-621-1544, FAX 970-663-3285.

384.33 USA ISSN 1078-7593
NETCETERA. Text in English. 1994. m. free. **Description:** Offers updates on new resources, services, and developments on the Internet, especially those that impact businesses.
Media: Online - full text.
Address: 15400 S E 30th Pl, Ste 202, Bellevue, WA 98007. netcetera-feedback@nwnet.net, http://www.nwnet.net/netcetera/. Ed., Pub., R&P Jan Eveleth. Circ: 1,000.

004.678 USA
NETFUTURE. Text in English. 1995. s-m. free. **Document type:** *Newsletter.* **Description:** Seeks to address those deep levels at which we half-consciously shape technology and are shaped by it.
Media: Online - full text.
Address: 169 Rte 21C, Ghent, NY 12075. TEL 518-672-5103, FAX 518-672-5103, stevet@oreilly.com, http://www.oreilly.com/~steve/netfuture/. Ed., R&P Steve Talbott.

005.276 USA
NETMEDIA; streaming content creation and delivery. Text in English. 2000. irreg., latest 2001, Apr. adv. back issues avail. **Document type:** *Magazine, Trade.* **Description:** Provides comprehensive coverage of streaming content creation and delivery, from new technology and applications to industry data and research.
Related titles: Online - full content ed.; ♦ Supplement to: Video Systems. ISSN 0361-0942.
Published by: Primedia Business Magazines & Media, Inc. (Subsidiary of: Primedia, Inc.), 9800 Metcalf Ave, Overland Park, KS 66212-2216. TEL 913-341-1300, inquiries@primediabusiness.com, http://www.industryclick.com/magazine.asp?magazineid=127&SiteID=15, http://www.primediabusiness.com. adv.: B&W page USD 9,995, color page USD 11,995; trim 8 x 10.75. **Subscr. to:** PO Box 12993, Overland Park, KS 66282-2993. TEL 800-441-0294, FAX 913-967-1331.

383.33 USA
NETPROFESSIONAL. Text in English. 1997. bi-m. USD 19.95; USD 25.95 in Canada; USD 44.95 elsewhere. **Document type:** *Trade.* **Description:** News and information source for web developers and network administrators.
Related titles: Online - full text ed.
Address: PO Box 5200, Westlake Village, CA 91359-5200. TEL 805-494-9797, 800-622-3381, FAX 805-494-9798, cust_service@devdepot.com, http://www.netprolive.com.

004.6 USA
NETSCAPEPRESS.COM. Text in English. irreg. adv. back issues avail. **Document type:** *Newsletter.* **Description:** Offers a wide variety of information for anyone on the web.
Media: Online - full content.
Published by: Netscape, 466 Ellis St, Montain View, CA 94043-4042. TEL 650-254-1900, FAX 650-528-4124, pradmin@netscape.com, http://www.netscapepress.com/. Ed. Pat Gowdy.

025.04 781.64 DEU
NETSPOTTING; das Magazin fuer Musik und Popkultur im Internet. Text in English, German. 2000. m. adv. **Document type:** *Magazine, Consumer.* **Description:** Provides insight and information on the latest music and pop culture trends and events on the Internet.
Published by: Netspotting Verlag GmbH, Im Bruehl 1-5, Duesseldorf, 40625, Germany. TEL 49-211-2807120, FAX 49-211-28071229, news@netspotting.de, anzeigen@netspotting.de, http://www.netspotting.de. Ed. Sascha Krueger. Pubs. Michael Lohrmann, Philipp Huberty.

004.678 USA
NETSURFER DIGEST. Text in English. 1994. w. free. **Description:** Guide to interesting news, places and resources online.
Media: Online - full text.
Address: 333 Cobalt Way, Ste 107, Sunnyvale, CA 94086. editor@netsurf.com, http://www.netsurf.com/nsd/. Eds. Arthur Bebak, Lawrence Nyveen.

004.678 USA
NETWATCHERS CYBERZINE. Text in English. 1995. m. back issues avail. **Description:** Covers developments in the law of cyberspace and the online world.
Media: Online - full text.
Published by: Eminent Technologies Ltd., 319 W Washington, Broken Arrow, OK 74012. TEL 918-451-2711, mdyer@ionet.net, http://www.emitech.com/netwatchers/front.htm. Ed. Marshall Dyer. Circ: 100.

025.04 USA ISSN 1093-7951
NETWORK (YEAR). Text in English. m. free. **Document type:** *Bulletin.* **Description:** Contains the latest news, ideas, and trends affecting the business of web development and internet marketing.
Media: Online - full text.
Published by: Professional Presence Network ppn@ppn.com, http://www.ppn.org/net98/. Ed. Sean Cafferky.

NETWORK TECHNOLOGY REPORT. (Asynchronos Transfer Mode and Internet Protocol Report) see *COMPUTERS—Computer Networks*

681.324 POL ISSN 1232-8723
NETWORLD. Text in Polish. 1994. 10/yr. PLZ 140; PLZ 70 to students (effective 2002). adv. **Document type:** *Magazine, Consumer.*
Related titles: Online - full text ed.
Published by: I D G Poland S.A., ul Jordanowska 12, PO Box 73, Warsaw, 04-204, Poland. TEL 48-22-3217800, FAX 48-22-3217888, idg@idg.com.pl, http://www.networld.pl, http://www.idg.pl. Ed. Bronislaw Piwowar. Adv. contact Agata Mysluk. B&W page PLZ 4,700, color page PLZ 7,200; trim 203 x 288.

025.04 USA ISSN 1095-1180
NEVADA WEB PAGES. Text in English. 1997. s-a. USD 3.50. adv.
Related titles: Online - full text ed.
Published by: Las Vegas Computer Journal Publications, 2232 S Nellis Blvd, Las Vegas, NV 89104. TEL 702-432-6206, FAX 702-432-6204, compjour@vegas.infi.net, http://www.computerjournal.com/nvpages.htm. Ed. Johanna Nezhoda. Circ: 50,000.

NEW LITERACIES AND DIGITAL EPISTEMOLOGIES. see *EDUCATION*

NEW MEDIA INVESTOR. see *BUSINESS AND ECONOMICS—Investments*

025.4 USA
NEW PRODUCT NEWS (ALBUQUERQUE)✱. Text in English. w. **Document type:** *Newsletter.* **Description:** Quick and easy reference site to find out about the latest brand new products and services.
Media: Online - full text.
Published by: Multimedia Internet Services, Inc., 6616 Gulton CT N E, Albuquerque, NM 87109-4452. TEL 505-275-6418, FAX 505-298-3939, npn@newproductnews.com, http://www2.newproductnews.com/npn/. Ed. Chuck Mooney.

THE NEW REVIEW OF INFORMATION NETWORKING. see *COMPUTERS—Computer Networks*

NEW YORK METRO COMPUTERUSER; for business & IT professionals. see *BUSINESS AND ECONOMICS—Computer Applications*

025.04 USA
NEWSWEEK E-LIFE. Variant title: e-Life. Text in English. 1999. q. adv. **Document type:** *Magazine, Consumer.* **Description:** Provides practical advice on how to cope with services and products from the digital world.
Related titles: ♦ Supplement(s): Newsweek. ISSN 0028-9604.
Published by: Newsweek, Inc. (Subsidiary of: Washington Post Co.), 251 W 57th St, New York, NY 10019-1894. customer.care@newsweek.com, http://www.newsweek.com.

025.04 JPN
NIKKEI ENTERTAINMENT!. Text in Japanese. 1997. m. adv. **Document type:** *Consumer.* **Description:** Covers entertainment industry: movies, music, CDs, PC games, the Internet and digital TV programs.
Published by: Nikkei Business Publications Inc. (Subsidiary of: Nihon Keizai Shimbun, Inc.), 2-7-6 Hirakawa-cho, Chiyoda-ku, Tokyo, 102-8622, Japan. TEL 81-3-5210-8311, FAX 81-3-5210-8530, info@nikkeibpnyc.com, info@nikkeibp-america.com, http://www.nikkeibp.com. Ed. Hideo Shinada. Pub. Ginjiro Takahashi. Adv. contact Hajime Takao. B&W page JPY 760,000, color page JPY 1,100,000; trim 210 x 280. Circ: 119,260. **Dist. in America by:** Nikkei Business Publications America Inc., 575 Fifth Ave, 20th Fl, New York, NY 10017.

004.678 JPN
NIKKEI INTERNET TECHNOLOGY. Text in Japanese. 1997. m. JPY 10,200 (effective 2000). adv. **Document type:** *Trade.* **Description:** Focuses on how to use the Internet to create a new communications environment. Includes recent trends, new technology and products from the U.S., and evaluation reports on the latest software.
Published by: Nikkei Business Publications Inc. (Subsidiary of: Nihon Keizai Shimbun, Inc.), 2-1-1 Hirakawa-cho, Chiyoda-ku, Tokyo, 102-8622, Japan. TEL 81-3-5210-8311, FAX 81-3-5210-8530, info@nikkeibpnyc.com, http://www.nikkeibp.com. Ed. Norio Inaba. Pub. Minoru Matsuzaki. adv.: B&W page JPY 270,000, color page JPY 540,000; trim 208 x 280. Circ: 27,604. **Dist. in America by:** Nikkei Business Publications America Inc., 575 Fifth Ave, 20th Fl, New York, NY 10017.

025.04 JPN ISSN 1342-0100
NIKKEI NETNAVIGATOR. Text in Japanese. 1996. m. JPY 790 newsstand/cover. adv. **Document type:** *Consumer.* **Description:** Offers how-to and whereabouts information for internet surfers.
Published by: Nikkei Business Publications Inc. (Subsidiary of: Nihon Keizai Shimbun, Inc.), 2-7-6 Hirakawa-cho, Chiyoda-ku, Tokyo, 102-8622, Japan. TEL 81-3-5210-8311, FAX 81-3-5210-8530, info@nikkeibpnyc.com, info@nikkeibp-america.com, http://www.nikkeibp.com. Ed. Hirokazu Tsuchiya. Pub. Minoru Inaba. Adv. contact Akira Kimura. B&W page JPY 420,000, color page JPY 700,000; trim 210 x 280. Circ: 130,012. **Dist. in America by:** Nikkei Business Publications America Inc., 575 Fifth Ave, 20th Fl, New York, NY 10017.

NONPROFIT ONLINE NEWS; news of the online nonprofit community. see *SOCIAL SERVICES AND WELFARE*

NORTH CAROLINA JOURNAL OF LAW & TECHNOLOGY. see *LAW*

NOVOSTI E-KOMMERTSII. see *BUSINESS AND ECONOMICS—Computer Applications*

004.678 IRL
NUA INTERNET SURVEYS. Text in English. 1996. m. free. adv. **Document type:** *Newsletter.* **Description:** Contains digests of the most important surveys and reports on the Internet.
Media: Online - full text.
Published by: Nua Ltd., Westland Court, S. Cumberland St., Dublin, 2, Ireland. TEL 353-1-676-8996, FAX 353-1-283-9988, sorcha@nua.ie, http://www.nua.ie/surveys/. Ed. Soecha Nieilidhe. R&P Sorcha Nieilidhe. Adv. contact Orian Lolacona.

ONCOLOGY NET GUIDE; internet guide to cancer sites. see *MEDICAL SCIENCES—Oncology*

ONCOLOGY NET GUIDE ENEWSLETTER. see *MEDICAL SCIENCES—Oncology*

ONCOLOGY NET GUIDE ONLINE; internet guide to cancer sites. see *MEDICAL SCIENCES—Oncology*

004.678 USA ISSN 0146-5422
Z699.A1 CODEN: ONLIDN
ONLINE; the leading magazine for information professionals. Text in English. 1977. bi-m. USD 115 domestic; USD 126 in Canada & Mexico; USD 151 elsewhere (effective 2005). adv. bk.rev. illus. index. back issues avail.; reprint service avail. from PQC. **Document type:** *Magazine, Trade.* **Description:** Provides practical, hands-on commentary and analysis of information industry trends and products.
Related titles: Microform ed.: 1977 (from PQC); Online - full text ed.: 1977 (from EBSCO Publishing, Factiva, Florida Center for Library Automation, Gale Group, H.W. Wilson, O C L C Online Computer Library Center, Inc., ProQuest Information & Learning).
Indexed: ABIn, ABS&EES, AESIS, BPI, CIJE, CINAHL, CMCI, ChemAb, ChemTitl, CompC, CurCont, EngInd, IAA, InfoSAb, Inspec, LHTB, LIMI, LISA, LRI, LibLit, MagInd, MicrocompInd, PCI, PROMT, RAPRA, RefZh, SSCI, SoftAbEng, SoftBase, TelAb.
—BLDSC (6260.755000), AskIEEE, CASDDS, CINDOC, CISTI, Ei, GNLM, IDS, IE, Infotrieve, ingenta, KNAW, Linda Hall. **CCC.**
Published by: Information Today, Inc., 143 Old Marlton Pike, Medford, NJ 08055-8750. TEL 609-654-6266, FAX 609-654-4309, info@onlineinc.com, custserv@infotoday.com, http://www.infotoday.com/online/default.shtml. Ed. Marydee Ojala. Circ: 6,000 (paid).

659.13 IRL
ONLINE BUSINESS ANALYST. Text in English. 1999. bi-m. back issues avail. **Document type:** *Newsletter.* **Description:** Dedicated to business strategy for online businesses.
Media: Online - full text.
Address: 20 Knocklyon Heights, Templeogue, Dublin, 16, Ireland. TEL 353-1-53012870, FAX 353-1-6335-921, oba@capitalexpertise.com, http://www.capitalexpertise.com/oba. Ed. Stephane Giraud.

ONLINE COURSES NEWSLETTER. see *EDUCATION—Computer Applications*

ONLINE CURRENTS. see *COMPUTERS—Data Base Management*

004.678 USA ISSN 1040-6646
Z699
ONLINE HOTLINE NEWS SERVICE - ARCHIVE EDITION. Text in English. 1980. irreg. USD 10 newsstand/cover (effective 2001). bk.rev. index, cum.index. **Document type:** *Newsletter.* **Description:** Covers the online and CD-ROM fields.
Formerly: Information Intelligence Online Hotline (0277-9250)
Media: CD-ROM. **Related titles:** Online - full text ed.: (from Factiva, Gale Group).
—Infotrieve. **CCC.**
Published by: Information Intelligence, Inc., PO Box 31098, Phoenix, AZ 85046-1098. TEL 602-996-2283, order@infointelligence.com, info@infointelligence.com, http://www.infointelligence.com. Ed. Richard S. Huleatt.

ONLINE INFORMATION REVIEW; the international journal of digital information, research and use. see *LIBRARY AND INFORMATION SCIENCES*

004.678 USA
ONLINE INSIDER. Text in English, Japanese. 1994. w. back issues avail. **Document type:** *Newsletter.* **Description:** Focuses on the current news in the online - Internet world with analysis and commentary.
Formerly (until 1998): Seidman's Online Insider
Media: Online - full text.
Address: 2754 Pierce St 3, San Francisco, CA 94123. TEL 404-685-0835, robert@onlineinsider.com, http://www.onlineinsider.com/. Ed. Robert Seidman.

ONLINE INVESTOR. see *BUSINESS AND ECONOMICS—Investments*

004.678 USA
ONLINE MARKETPLACE. Text in English. m. USD 695; USD 795 with online ed.. **Document type:** *Newsletter, Trade.* **Description:** Tracks consumer trends in banking, retailing, financial services, travel, grocery and catalog sales online.
Related titles: Online - full text ed.
Published by: Jupiter Communications, 627 Broadway, New York, NY 10012. TEL 212-780-6060, FAX 212-780-6075, http://www.jup.com/newsletter/.

004.678 USA
CODEN: IIONDK
ONLINE NEWSLETTER. Text in English. 1980. 10/yr. looseleaf. USD 43.75 in North America to individuals; USD 75 elsewhere to individuals; USD 62.50 in North America to libraries; USD 87.50 elsewhere to libraries; USD 25 in North America to students; USD 43.75 elsewhere to students (effective 2001). bk.rev. index. back issues avail. **Document type:** *Newsletter.* **Description:** Covers all aspects of online use; features events, mergers, acquisitions, new products and relevant news.
Formerly: Information Intelligence Online Newsletter (0194-0694)
Related titles: CD-ROM ed.; Microform ed.: (from PQC); Online - full text ed.: (from Data-Star, EBSCO Publishing, ProQuest Information & Learning, The Dialog Corporation).
Indexed: ABIn, Inspec, LISA, MicrocompInd.
—AskIEEE, CASDDS. **CCC.**
Published by: Information Intelligence, Inc., PO Box 31098, Phoenix, AZ 85046-1098. TEL 602-996-2283, order@infointelligence.com, http://www.infointelligence.com. Ed. Richard S. Huleatt.

ONLINE PC. see *COMPUTERS—Personal Computers*

ONLINE PC ZEITUNG. see *COMPUTERS—Personal Computers*

025.04 USA
ONLINE PRODUCT NEWS. Text in English. 1981. m. USD 150 in North America; USD 165 elsewhere (effective 2001). bk.rev. back issues avail. **Document type:** *Newsletter, Trade.* **Description:** Provides information and news on online services and on computer products, such as software and modems, used in accessing them. Focuses on industry trends and technology to help the online user.
Related titles: Online - full text ed.
Published by: Worldwide Videotex, PO Box 3273, Boynton Beach, FL 33424-3273. TEL 561-738-2276, markedit@juno.com, http://www.wvpubs.com. Ed., Pub. Mark Wright.

004.678 NOR ISSN 0805-6315
ONLINE WORLD MONITOR NEWSLETTER. Text in Norwegian. 1994. bi-m. NOK 175 (effective 1998). **Document type:** *Newsletter.* **Description:** For supporters of the online world shareware book.
Media: Online - full text.
Address: Saltrod, 4815, Norway. presno@grida.no, http://login.eunet.no/~presno/monitor.html. Ed. Odd de Presno.

004.678 ITA ISSN 1723-7041
OPEN SOURCE. Text in Italian. 1995. m. USD 44 (effective 1997). adv. back issues avail. **Document type:** *Magazine, Consumer.*
Formerly (until 2003): Inter.net (1128-4471)
Related titles: Online - full text ed.
Published by: Systems Comunicazioni, Via Olanda 6, Vigano di Gaggiano, MI 20083, Italy. TEL 39-02-92270757, FAX 39-02-90841682, info@systems.it, http://www.systems.it. Ed. M Di Pisa. Adv. contact Lilia Pini.

OURPC MAGAZINE; the computer and internet magazine for African-Americans. see *COMPUTERS*

P C FORMAT. see *COMPUTERS—Personal Computers*

P H P MAGAZIN. (Personal Home Page) see *COMPUTERS—Software*

659.13 USA
PACKET; cisco systems users magazine. Text in English. q. free to qualified personnel. adv. **Document type:** *Magazine, Trade.* **Description:** Contains complete coverage of cutting-edge networking trends and innovations.
Published by: Cisco Systems, Inc., 170 W Tasman Dr, San Jose, CA 95134. TEL 408-526-7208, 800-553-6387, info@cisco.com, http://www.cisco.com/warp/public/784/packet/. Ed. David Ball. Adv. contact Kristen Bergamn. color page USD 13,675.

681.3 FRA ISSN 1628-8971
PAGES WEB PRATIQUES. Text in French. 2001. q. FRF 45 newsstand/cover (effective 2001). adv. software rev.; Website rev. **Document type:** *Magazine, Consumer.*
Published by: Future France, 101-109 Rue Jean Jaures, Levallois Perret, 92300, France. TEL 33-1-41273838, yveline.duville@futurenet.fr.

681.3 ITA ISSN 1591-2515
PAGINE WEB FACILE. Text in Italian. 2000. 8/yr. EUR 37; EUR 5.20 newsstand/cover (effective 2003). adv. **Document type:** *Magazine, Consumer.*
Published by: Play Press Publishing s.r.l., Via Vitorchiano 123, Rome, RM 00189, Italy. TEL 39-06-33221250, FAX 39-06-33221235, abbonamenti@playpress.com, http://www.playpress.com. Ed. Alessandra Spadano. Pub. Alessandro Ferri. Circ: 40,000 (paid and controlled).

PARTNERSHIP ONLINE. see *BUSINESS AND ECONOMICS*

658.8 USA
PEERLESS EXPRESS ZINE. Text in English. bi-m. free. **Description:** Publishes articles on marketing and promotion strategies on the Internet.
Media: Online - full text.
Published by: Collex Resource Management, Inc. mnixon14@bellsouth.net, http://opportunitywealth.web2010.com/freenewsletter.news.htm. Ed. Michael Nixon.

PERVASIVE WEEKLY. see *COMMUNICATIONS*

004.678 RUS
PLANETA INTERNET. Text in Russian. m. USD 125 in United States.
Published by: Mamont-1, Usievicha ul 16-2, Moscow, 125315, Russian Federation. TEL 7-095-3241842, http://www.netplanet.ru. **US dist. addr.:** East View Information Services, 3020 Harbor Ln. N., Minneapolis, MN 55447. TEL 612-550-0961.

384.33029 USA ISSN 1548-5447
HF5548.325.U6
PLUNKETT'S E-COMMERCE & INTERNET BUSINESS ALMANAC. Text in English. biennial. USD 249.99 (effective 2005); includes CD-ROM. **Document type:** *Directory, Trade.* **Description:** Contains profiles of leading corporations in e-commerce, online services, equipment for internet communications, internet services and more. Also includes chapters on trends, careers, finance, mergers, acquisitions, stocks and investments.
Supersedes (in 1999): Plunkett's Internet and Web Industry Almanac
Related titles: CD-ROM ed.
Published by: Plunkett Research, Ltd, PO Drawer 541737, Houston, TX 77254-1737. TEL 713-932-0000, FAX 713-932-7080, info@plunkettresearch.com, http://www.plunkettresearch.com. Ed., Pub. Jack W Plunkett.

PLUNKETT'S ON-LINE TRADING, FINANCE & INVESTMENT WEB SITES ALMANAC. see *BUSINESS AND ECONOMICS—Public Finance, Taxation*

004.678 USA
THE POCKET NEWSLETTER. Text in English. 1988. m. **Document type:** *Newsletter, Consumer.*
Media: Online - full text.
Published by: Pocket Internet, 266 Main St, Medfield, MA 02052. http://www.thepocket.com/index.htm. Ed. George Dillon.

659.13 USA
PODER. Text in Spanish, Portuguese. 2000. m. USD 55; USD 5 newsstand/cover (effective 2002). adv. stat.; maps. 118 p./no.; back issues avail.; reprints avail. **Document type:** *Magazine, Consumer.* **Description:** Provides news, information and analysis on all aspects of the Latin American economy.
Formerly (until 2001): Punto-Com (1533-3205)
Related titles: Online - full content ed.
Published by: Zoom Media Group, 309 23rd St, Ste 212, Miami Beach, FL 33139. TEL 305-535-3125, FAX 305-535-3126, http://www.punto-com.com, http://www.zoommg.com. Ed. Isaac Lee. Pub., Adv. contact Jose Chao. B&W page USD 9,921, color page USD 13,000; trim 8 x 10.875. Circ: 70,000 (controlled).

004.678 GBR ISSN 1366-7661
PRACTICAL INTERNET; getting online cheaper, faster and easier. Text in English. 1997. 13/yr. GBP 36 in United Kingdom; GBP 55 in Europe; GBP 81 rest of world; GBP 4.99 newsstand/cover (effective 2003). 164 p./no.; back issues avail. **Document type:** *Magazine, Consumer.*
Published by: Paragon Publishing Ltd., Paragon House, 10 St Peters Rd, Bournemouth, Dorset BH1 2JS, United Kingdom. TEL 44-1202-299900, 44-1202-299955, FAX 44-1202-299955, 44-1202-200217, subs@paragon.co.uk, http://www.paragon.co.uk/mags/practicali.html. Ed. Mark Newman. Adv. contact Jennie Brown TEL 44-1202-200212. Circ: 13,265 (paid).

004.678 GBR
PRACTICAL WEB PROJECTS. Text in English. 2002. 9/yr. GBP 5.99 newsstand/cover (effective 2003). **Description:** Covers web designs and creative software like Photoshop and Flash.
Published by: Paragon Publishing Ltd., Paragon House, 10 St Peters Rd, Bournemouth, Dorset BH1 2JS, United Kingdom. TEL 44-1202-299900, FAX 44-1202-299955, subs@paragon.co.uk, http://www.paragon.co.uk/mags/pwp.html. Ed. Paul Newman.

025.04 USA
PREMIUM LINKS. Text in English. w. free. **Document type:** *Newsletter.* **Description:** Presents five great websites that are appropriate for all ages.
Media: E-mail.

C

▼ new title ➤ refereed ✶ unverified ♦ full entry avail.

Address: byron@premiumlinks.net, http://premiumlinks.net/newsletter.htm/. Ed. Byron Bytesworth.

PROFIT (REDWOOD SHORES); business to e-business. see *BUSINESS AND ECONOMICS*

658.8 USA
PROSPERITY BUILDER NEWSLETTER. Text in English. irreg. free. adv. **Document type:** *Newsletter.* **Description:** Publishes articles on Internet business marketing strategies.
Media: Online - full text.
Address: TEL 805-721-8101, FAX 805-725-2126, webmaster@prosperitybuilder.com, http://www.prosperitybuilder.com. Ed. John Fleeman.

070.5797 USA
PUBLISHER PLUG-IN. Text in English. m. **Document type:** *Newsletter.* **Description:** Designed to help email newsletter publishers produce the best quality ezine.
Media: E-mail.
Published by: Ezine Publishers Association, Box 21143, Eugene, OR 97402-2481. plug-in@ezinepublisher.org, http://www.ezinepublisher.org.

004.678 USA
PULSE OF THE INTERNET✶. Text in English. 1997. q. USD 19.95; USD 25.95 in Canada; USD 35.95 elsewhere. adv.
Related titles: Online - full text ed.
Published by: Virtual Press, Inc., 1516 1/2 Boyd Ave, Racine, WI 53405-3526. william@aloha.com, http://www.tvpress.com/pin.html. Ed. William R Stanek.

004.6 USA
THE PULVER REPORT. Text in English. irreg. back issues avail. **Document type:** *Newsletter.* **Description:** Provides news and short articles about the emerging net technologies.
Media: Online - full text.
Published by: Pulver Report, 115 Broadhollow Rd, Ste 225, Melvine, NY 11747. TEL 631-547-0800, FAX 631-293-3996, http://www.pulver.com/reports/. Ed. Jeff Pulver.

C

384.33 USA ISSN 1533-1369
QUESTFINDER NEWS. Text in English. adv. **Description:** Designed for webmasters and experts in the field of web design and the Internet.
Media: Online - full text.
Published by: Write For You, Inc, 8 Hummingbird Ct., Marlboro, NJ 07746-2511. info@wrte4u.com, http://www.questfinder.net. Pub. Monica Fersht. Circ: 110,000.

R T I: REDES, TELECOM E INSTALACOES; voice, data and image - networks, infraestrrctures and technologies. see *COMPUTERS—Computer Networks*

RADIO H.F. INTERNET NEWSLETTER. see *COMMUNICATIONS—Radio*

004.678 USA
RAGAN'S INTERACTIVE PUBLIC RELATIONS. Text in English. 1995. bi-w. USD 279. **Document type:** *Newsletter.* **Description:** Helps PR people navigate cyberspace.
Published by: Lawrence Ragan Communications, Inc., 316 N Michigan Ave, Ste 300, Chicago, IL 60601. TEL 312-960-4140, 800-878-5331, FAX 312-960-4106, 71154.2605@compuserve.com, cservice@ragan.com, http://www.ragan.com. Ed. Steve Crescenzo.

004.6 USA
RAGAN'S INTRANET REPORT. Text in English. m. USD 229. **Document type:** *Newsletter.* **Description:** For communicators responsible for creating and maintaining the content of their company's intranet. Teaches communicators how intranet works, and how to use it to communicate.
Published by: Lawrence Ragan Communications, Inc., 316 N Michigan Ave, Ste 300, Chicago, IL 60601. TEL 312-960-4106, 800-878-5331, FAX 312-960-4106, http://www.ragan.com.

340 004.678 DEU ISSN 1616-9603
RECHT DER NEUEN MEDIEN. Text in German. 2001. irreg., latest vol.21, 2005. price varies. **Document type:** *Monographic series, Academic/Scholarly.*
Published by: Verlag Dr. Kovac, Arnoldstr 49, Hamburg, 22763, Germany. TEL 49-40-3988800, FAX 49-40-39888055, info@verlagdrkovac.de, http://www.verlagdrkovac.de/12-9.htm.

004.6 ESP ISSN 1576-7930
REDMARKET; informe confidencial de los negocios de Internet. Text in Spanish. 2000. w. EUR 240.40 domestic Combined print & online eds.; EUR 294.50 in Europe Combined print & online eds. (effective 2001). back issues avail. **Document type:** *Newsletter.*
Related titles: CD-ROM ed.; Online - full text ed.
Published by: Publicaciones Alimarket S.A., Albasanz 14 3o, Madrid, 28037, Spain. TEL 34-91-3274340, FAX 34-91-3274522, informa@alimarket.es, http://www.alimarket.es. Ed. Francisco Mota. Adv. contact Isabel Bajo.

025.04 FRA ISSN 1147-7814
REPERTOIRE DES BANQUES DE DONNEES PROFESSIONNELLES/PROFESSIONAL DATABASES DIRECTORY. Text in French. irreg. **Document type:** *Directory.* **Description:** Describes 2000 professional databases available online in France, indexed by subject, producer and vendor.
Formerly (until 1989): Repertoire des Banques de Donnees en Conversationnel (0758-816X)
Related titles: Online - full text ed.
Published by: Association des Professionnels de l'Information et de la Documentation (ADBS)/Association of Information and Documentation Professionals, 25 rue Claude Tillier, Paris, 75012, France. TEL 33-01-43722525, FAX 33-01-43723041, adbs@adbs.fr, http://www.adbs.fr. Ed. Jean Michel Rauzier.

384.33 380.1 USA
REPORT ON ELECTRONIC COMMERCE; online business, financial and consumer strategies and trends. Text in English. 1995. bi-w. (23/yr.). USD 745 domestic; USD 910 foreign (effective 2005). mkt.; stat. back issues avail. **Document type:** *Newsletter.* **Description:** Covers trends in business and consumer transactions on the internet. Includes details on business models, regulation and standards applying to e-commerce.
Incorporates: Interactive Services Report; Which was formerly: Information and Interactive Services Report (1059-731X); Which was formed by the merger of (1987-1991): Electronic Shopping News (0893-0333); (1987-1991): Interactivity Report (0893-0325); Which was formed by the merger of (1980-1987): International Videotex Teletext News (0197-677X); (1982-1987): Teleservices Report (0730-0263)
Related titles: Online - full text ed.
Published by: Telecommunications Reports (Subsidiary of: Aspen Publishers, Inc.), 1333 H St, N W, Ste 100, Washington, DC 20005. TEL 202-312-6060, FAX 202-312-6111, customerservice@tr.com, http://www.tr.com. Ed. Jerry Ashworth. Pub. Victoria Mason.

004.678 COL ISSN 0123-5338
EL REPORTE DELTA; hacemos la diferencia agregando valor. Text in Spanish. 1997. w. free. **Document type:** *Newsletter.* **Description:** Specializes in the strategic use of information technology in general and Internet technology in particular.
Media: E-mail.
Published by: Jose Camilo Daccach Ed. & Pub., Calle 8, 2-N-47, Cali, VALLE, Colombia. TEL 57-2-6674820, http://delta.hypermart.net. Circ: 3,200.

▼ **REVIEW OF BUSINESS RESEARCH.** see *BUSINESS AND ECONOMICS—International Commerce*

004.6 MEX ISSN 1607-6079
REVISTA DIGITAL UNIVERSITARIA. Abbreviated title: R D U. Text in Spanish. 2000. q. back issues avail.
Media: Online - full text.
Indexed: ZooRec.
Published by: Universidad Nacional Autonoma de Mexico, Direccion General de Servicios de Computo Academico, Circuito Exterior, Ciudad Universitaria, Mexico, D.F., 04510, Mexico. denisc@servidor.unam.mx, http://www.revista.unam.mx/. Ed. Carlos Vizcaino Sahagun.

REVISTA RED. see *COMPUTERS—Computer Networks*

REVISTA VIRTUAL MATEMATICA, EDUCACION E INTERNET. see *MATHEMATICS*

004.678 AUS
ROY MORGAN INTERNET MONITOR. Text in English. d. NZD 9,800 (effective 2000). **Document type:** *Trade.*
Media: Online - full content.
Published by: Roy Morgan Research, PO Box 2282 U, Melbourne, VIC 3001, Australia. TEL 61-3-96296888, FAX 61-3-96291250, http://www.roymorgan.com.

▼ **S I R S WEBFIND.** see *COMPUTERS—Abstracting, Bibliographies, Statistics*

S K S WEBSELECT. see *COMPUTERS—Abstracting, Bibliographies, Statistics*

005.72 USA ISSN 1064-0851
S T A T NEWS. (Site Tips and Tricks) Text in English. 1999. bi-m. back issues avail. **Description:** Provides ideas and short articles on how to use and improve the performance of web sites.
Media: Online - full content.
Published by: Tip Top Services, 5092 - A Tip Top Rd, Mariposa, CA 95338. TEL 209-742-6783, bob@sitetipsandtricks.com, http://www.sitetipsandtricks.com. Ed. Bob McElwain.

004.678 USA ISSN 1526-2286
SAY WHAT YOU MEAN ON THE WEB. Variant title: Say What You Mean Report. Text in English. irreg. free. **Document type:** *Newsletter.* **Description:** Published for people in business who want to make their web sites easier to use and understand.
Media: Online - full text.
Address: c/o Ron Scheer, PO Box 131, Marina del Rey, CA 90292. TEL 310-358-7620, ronscheer@ronscheer.com, http://ronscheer.com/. Pub. Ron Scheer.

025.04 USA ISSN 1092-3861
ZA4201
THE SCOUT REPORT. Text in English. w. **Document type:** *Bulletin.* **Description:** Provides a fast, convenient way to stay informed of valuable resources on the Internet.
Media: Online - full text.
Published by: University of Wisconsin at Madison, Computer Sciences Department, 5355a Computer Sciences and Statistics, 1210 West Dayton St, Madison, WI 53706. TEL 608-262-1204, FAX 608-262-9777, scout@cs.wisc.edu, http://scout.wisc.edu/report/sr/current/. **Co-sponsor:** National Science Foundation.

THE SCOUT REPORT FOR BUSINESS & ECONOMICS. see *BUSINESS AND ECONOMICS*

THE SCOUT REPORT FOR SCIENCE & ENGINEERING. see *SCIENCES: COMPREHENSIVE WORKS*

THE SCOUT REPORT FOR SOCIAL SCIENCES. see *SOCIAL SCIENCES: COMPREHENSIVE WORKS*

025.04 USA
SEARCH ENGINE REPORT. Text in English. m. free. adv. **Document type:** *Newsletter, Trade.* **Description:** Keeps Web developers and search engine users informed of changes to the site and provides general useful search engine news.
Media: Online - full text.
Published by: Jupitermedia Corp., 23 Old Kings Hwy South, Darien, CT 06820. TEL 203-662-2800, FAX 203-655-4686, info@jupitermedia.com, http://searchenginewatch.com/sereport/, http://www.jupitermedia.com. Ed. Danny Sullivan.

025.04 USA
SEARCH ENGINE WATCH. Text in English. m. USD 89 (effective 2002). **Document type:** *Newsletter, Consumer.* **Description:** Contains detailed information on all the major search engines, including submission tips, what's considered spamming, important design issues relating to relevancy, and other topics.
Media: Online - full content.
Published by: Jupitermedia Corp., 23 Old Kings Hwy South, Darien, CT 06820. TEL 203-662-2800, FAX 203-655-4686, info@jupitermedia.com, http://www.jupitermedia.com.

004.678 USA
SENIORNET NEWSLINE. Text in English. 1986. q. membership. software rev. illus. **Document type:** *Newsletter.* **Description:** Informs and inspires older adults about the use of computers and the internet. Provides updates on the activities of the Seniornet nonprofit organization.
Published by: Seniornet, 121 Second St, 7th Fl, San Francisco, CA 94105. seniornet@seniornet.org, http://www.seniornet.org. Ed., Pub. Marcie Schwarz. Circ: 28,000 (controlled).

384.33 USA
▼ **SERVICE PROVIDER MAGAZINE.** Text in English. 2004 (Sep.). m. free to qualified personnel (effective 2005). **Document type:** *Magazine, Trade.*
Media: Online - full content.
Published by: Possibility Media, 10400 N.W. 33rd St., Ste. 270, Miami, FL 33172. TEL 786-206-8880, FAX 786-206-8884, info@possibilitymedia.com, http://www.serviceprovidermagazine.com/, http://www.possibilitymedia.com/. Adv. contact Terry Logan TEL 786-206-8880 ext 103.

SERVICE PROVIDER WEEKLY. see *BUSINESS AND ECONOMICS*

025.4 658 USA
SILICON ALLEY DAILY. Text in English. 1998. d. adv. **Document type:** *Trade.* **Description:** Provides coverage of breaking Internet industry news.
Media: Online - full text.
Published by: Rising Tide Studios, 307 W 36th St, 10th Fl, New York, NY 10018-6403. TEL 646-473-2222, FAX 646-473-2223, service@siliconalleydaily.com, editor@siliconalleyreporter.com, http://www.siliconalleydaily.com, http://www.siliconalleyreporter.com. Ed. Jason McCabe Calacanis. Pub. Karol Martesko-Fenster. Adv. contact Keith Long.

025.04 035.89155 USA
SILICON IRAN. Text in English, Persian, Modern. 2001 (Mar). bi-m. **Document type:** *Magazine, Trade.* **Description:** Provides insight and information into the inner workings of Silicon Valley for Iranian-Americans.
Published by: Iran Today Publishing, 1177 Branham Ln, Ste 388, San Jose, CA 95123. TEL 408-323-3169, FAX 408-323-3168. Ed. Sima Hashem Far.

025.4 BEL ISSN 1376-4411
SKYNET WEB MAGAZINE. Text in French. 2000. m. **Document type:** *Magazine, Consumer.*
Related titles: Dutch ed.: ISSN 1376-4403.
Published by: Best Of Publishing, Rodenbachstraat 70, Brussels, 1190, Belgium. TEL 32-2-346-4850, FAX 32-2-346-4365, jp@best.be, http://magazine.skynet.be, http://www.best.be. Pub. Jean-Paul De Clerk.

SMART COMPANY; business technology & the internet made easy. see *BUSINESS AND ECONOMICS—Computer Applications*

SMART T V & SOUND; interactive T V & D V D - MP3 - Internet audio & video - satellite tv. see *COMMUNICATIONS—Television And Cable*

004.678 USA ISSN 1538-828X
SMART TIPS AND QUICK TRICKS FOR INTERNET USERS. Text in English. 2002. a. USD 10 per issue domestic; USD 20 per issue foreign (effective 2005).
—CCC.
Published by: Element K Journals (Subsidiary of: Eli Research, Inc.), 500 Canal View Blvd, Rochester, NY 14623. TEL 585-240-7301, 800-223-8720, 877-203-5248, FAX 585-292-4392, http://www.elementkjournals.com. Eds. T. L. Aardsma, Michelle Rogers.

SMART TIPS AND QUICK TRICKS FOR MICROSOFT VISUAL BASIC. see *COMPUTERS—Software*

004.678 USA ISSN 1526-2340
SPENCER'S INTERNET GAZETTE. Text in English. 1999. bi-m. adv. **Document type:** *Newsletter.* **Description:** Includes marketing ideas for the Internet.
Media: Online - full text.
Address: 630 Robert Taylor Rd., La Grange, GA 30240. spencerpub@mindspring.com, http://www.spencerpub.com. Ed. Jayne Spencer.

025.4 SVN ISSN 1580-3457
SPLETKA.NET. Text in Slovenian. 2000. m. adv. **Document type:** *Magazine, Consumer.*
Published by: Delo Revije d.o.o., Dunajska 5, Ljubljana, 1509, Slovenia. TEL 386-1-4737000, FAX 386-1-4737352, spletka@spletka.net, narocnine@delo-revije.si, http://www.spletka.net, http://www.delo-revije.si.

004.68 MEX ISSN 1405-6658
SPUTNIK. Text in Spanish. 1998. m. adv.
Related titles: Online - full text ed.: ISSN 1607-128X. 1998.
Published by: Grupo Alce, Donato Guerra No. 9, Col. Juarez, Mexico, D.F., 06600, Mexico. TEL 52-55-7030172, FAX 52-55-7030180, http://www.sputnik.com.mx/, http://www.grupo-alce.com/. Ed. Antonio Reyes.

STANDARD TIME & FREQUENCY SERVICE BULLETIN. see *METROLOGY AND STANDARDIZATION*

005.276 USA
STREAMING MEDIA. Text in English. 2000. m. USD 29.95 domestic; USD 60 foreign (effective 2001); free to qualified personnel. adv. **Document type:** *Magazine, Trade.*
Media: Online - full content.
Published by: Streaming Media, Inc. (Subsidiary of: Penton Media, Inc.), 710 Florida St, Ste 200, San Francisco, CA 94110. TEL 415-593-4800, 888-301-8895, FAX 415-641-4445, info@streamingmedia.com, http://www.streamingmedia.com/magazine. Ed. Greg Frame. Pub. Stuart Sheldon. Adv. contact Alec Dinner TEL 415-593-7310. color page USD 9,495, B&W page USD 6,364; trim 8.25 x 10.875. Circ: 30,000.

005.276 USA
▼ **STREAMING MEDIA INDUSTRY SOURCEBOOK.** Text in English. 2004. a. USD 20 (effective 2005). **Document type:** *Directory, Trade.* **Description:** Contains a comprehensive directory of solution provider companies as well as practical articles on choosing, installing and maintaining a streaming initiative.
Published by: Information Today, Inc., 143 Old Marlton Pike, Medford, NJ 08055-8750. TEL 609-654-6266, FAX 609-654-4309, custserv@infotoday.com, http://www.infotoday.com. Ed. Mark Fritz.

005.276 USA
STREAMING MEDIA XTRA. Text in English. w. free. **Document type:** *Newsletter, Trade.* **Description:** Provides real-world solutions for the implementation of streaming media technology and applications.
Media: E-mail.
Published by: Information Today, Inc., 143 Old Marlton Pike, Medford, NJ 08055-8750. TEL 609-654-6266, FAX 609-654-4309, custserv@infotoday.com, http://www.streamingmedia.com/subscribe.asp, http://www.infotoday.com.

004.678 USA
SUCCESS ONLINE WEEKLY. Text in English. w. **Document type:** *Newsletter.*
Media: Online - full text.
Published by: K & D Publishing, 4040 Leigh St., Riverside, CA 92509-6637. webmaster@kndpublishing.com, http://www.kndpublishing.com.

SUPPORT INSIGHT; the first place for training news. see *BUSINESS AND ECONOMICS—Computer Applications*

004.678 NLD ISSN 0921-5387
SURFNET BULLETIN. Text in Dutch. 1987. 4/yr.
—IE, Infotrieve.
Published by: SURFnet bv, Postbus 19035, Utrecht, 3501 DA, Netherlands. TEL 31-30-2305305, FAX 31-30-2305329, redactie@surfnet.nl, www.surfnet.nl/publicaties/bulletin, http://www.surfnet.nl. Ed. Mariska Herweijer.

004.678 USA ISSN 1557-1823
TK5105.875.I57
SURVEYING THE DIGITAL FUTURE. Variant title: Digital Future Report. U C L A Internet Report. Text in English. 2000. a.
Media: Online - full content.
Published by: University of Southern California, Center for the Digital Future, 300 S Grand Ave Ste 3950, Los Angeles, CA 90071. TEL 213-437-4433, digitalcenter@digitalcenter.org, http://www.digitalcenter.org/downloads/DigitalFutureReport-Year4-2004.pdf.

004.678 CHE ISSN 1422-5662
SWITCH-JOURNAL. Text in English, French, German. 1989. s-a. CHF 40 (effective 2002). **Description:** Reports on the activities and projects of the foundation.
Indexed: Inspec.
—BLDSC (8577.173200).
Published by: SWITCH, Teleinformatikdienste fuer Lehre und Forschung, Geschaeftsstelle, Limmatquai 138, Zurich, 8001, Switzerland. info@switch.ch, http://www.switch.ch.

004.678 USA
SYMPOSIUM ON APPLICATIONS AND THE INTERNET. PROCEEDINGS. Text in English. irreg. **Document type:** *Proceedings, Academic/Scholarly.*
Published by: I E E E Computer Society, 10662 Los Vaqueros Circle, PO Box 3014, Los Alamitos, CA 90720-1314. TEL 714-821-8380, FAX 714-821-4010, http://www.ieee.org.

TAEGLICH KRESS. see *COMMUNICATIONS*

004.678 GBR ISSN 1467-338X
TALES FROM THE TERMINAL ROOM. Text in English. 1999. m. free (effective 2003). Website rev. back issues avail. **Document type:** *Newsletter, Trade.*
Media: Online - full text. **Related titles:** E-mail ed.
Published by: R B A Information Services, 88 Star Rd, Caversham, Reading, RG4 5BE, United Kingdom. TEL 44-118-947-2256, FAX 44-870-056-8547, tfttr@rba.co.uk, info@rba.co.uk, http://www.rba.co.uk/tfttr/. Ed. Karen Blakeman.

TASTY BITS FROM THE TECHNOLOGY FRONT. see *COMPUTERS—Computer Networks*

384.33 USA
TECH TIPS MONTHLY. Text in English. 1998. m. back issues avail. **Document type:** *Newsletter.*
Related titles: Online - full text ed.
Published by: Lacy Internet Development, 933 15th Ave. N., South Sain Paul, MN 55075. TEL 651-552-9117, FAX 651-455-2251, todd@lacy-internet.com, http://www.lacy-interent.com/newsletter/index.html. Ed. Todd Lacy.

383.34 USA
TECHCAPITAL; technology, business and finance. Text in English. bi-m. free. **Document type:** *Trade.* **Description:** Provides sources of financing for Internet and technology entrepreneurs, including venture capital, commercial and investment banks.
Media: Online - full text.
Address: shannonh@technews.com, http://www.techcapital.com/. Ed. Shannon Henry.

004.678 USA ISSN 1089-2176
TECHKNOW TIMES. Text in English. 1996. irreg. free. **Document type:** *Newsletter.* **Description:** Covers news related to Internet and online marketing, WWW sites and design, and online technology and culture.
Media: Online - full text.
Address: techknow-request@techknowtimes.com, http://www.techknowtimes.com.

384.33 USA
TECHNO - BIZ DIGEST. Text in English. bi-w. free. **Document type:** *Newsletter.* **Description:** Dedicated to people who are thinking about, just starting, or already have experience running an Internet home business.
Media: Online - full text.
Address: sales@interfocus.com, http://www.interfocus.com/.

004.678 USA
TECHNO - FILE NEWS. Abbreviated title: T F N. Text in English. d. adv. **Document type:** *Newsletter.* **Description:** Informs listeners on 95 radio stations worldwide about the new media revolution, computers, the Internet and more.
Media: Online - full text.
Address: 1103 Stewart Ave, Garden City, NY 11530. TEL 516-222-1103, FAX 516-222-1391, lazlow@lazlow.com, http://www.lazlow.com/. Ed. Laslow Jones.

025.04 USA
THESTANDARD.COM. Text in English. d. adv. **Document type:** *Trade.* **Description:** Contains daily updates and insights on the information economy.
Media: Online - full content (from Florida Center for Library Automation). **Related titles:** Online - full text ed.: (from Gale Group, LexisNexis, O C L C Online Computer Library Center, Inc.).
Published by: Standard Media International, 100 Pine St., Ste. 475, San Francisco, CA 94111-5120. info@thestandard.com, http://www.thestandard.com.

004.678 USA ISSN 1090-7017
TK 7889.M33
TIDBITS (ISSAQUAH). Text in Dutch, English, French, German, Japanese. 1990. w. **Document type:** *Newsletter.* **Description:** Provides analysis and commentary on events, products, and issues surrounding the Macintosh Internet world.
Media: Online - full text.
Published by: TidBits Electronic Publishing, 50 Hickory Rd., Ithaca, NY 14850-9606. TEL 425-392-0553, editors@tidbits.com, http://www.tidbits.com/. Ed., Pub., R&P, Adv. contact Adam C Engst. Circ: 150,000.

659.13 ITA ISSN 1594-9168
TIMER MAGAZINE. Text in Italian. 2002. 9/yr. EUR 49.50 (effective 2003). adv. **Document type:** *Magazine, Trade.*
Published by: Gruppo Editoriale Futura, Via XXV Aprile, 39, Bresso, MI 20091, Italy. TEL 39-02-665261, FAX 39-02-66526222, info@futura-ge.com, http://www.futura-ge.com/prodotti/riviste/timer/profilo/.

025.04 GBR ISSN 1461-5533
TIPS & ADVICE INTERNET. Text in English. 1997. fortn. (22/yr). GBP 79 (effective 2003). **Description:** Points the reader to new sites and Internet software, features practical, jargon-free tips on how to find specific information, and helps make the most of the time spent surfing the Internet.
—Infotrieve.
Published by: Indicator Advisors & Publishers, Calgarth House, 39-41 Bank St, Ashford, Kent, United Kingdom. TEL 44-1233-653500, FAX 44-1233-647100, http://www.indicator.co.uk.

C

025.04 053.1 DEU
TOMORROW; Deutschlands grosse Internet Illustrierte. Text in German. 1998. m. EUR 30; EUR 2.80 newsstand/cover (effective 2003). adv. software rev. **Document type:** *Magazine, Consumer.* **Description:** Provides access and insight into the hottest sites and services on the Internet.
Related titles: Online - full text ed.
Published by: Verlagsgruppe Milchstrasse, Mittelweg 177, Hamburg, 22786, Germany. TEL 49-40-41311310, FAX 49-40-41312015, service@tomorrow.de, abo@milchstrasse.de, http://www.tomorrow.de, http://www.milchstrasse.de. Adv. contact Stephanie Haller TEL 49-40-41311214. page EUR 10,900. Circ: 178,340 (paid and controlled). **Subscr. to:** Postfach 302, Offenburg 77649, Germany. TEL 49-781-6396997.

TOO COOL FOR GROWNUPS; bringing the power of the Internet into the classroom. see *EDUCATION*

TRAVELERS' USE OF THE INTERNET. see *TRAVEL AND TOURISM*

383.33 USA
TRENDSETTERS.COM. Text in English. w. free. adv. **Document type:** *Consumer.* **Description:** Chronicles the Internet's impact on traditional marketing. Contains data-rich market overviews designed to help readers understand key trends.
Formerly (until 2003): Iconocast
Media: Online - full text.
Published by: Iconocast Inc., 470 Third St 102, San Francisco, CA 94107. TEL 415-778-0800, FAX 415-778-0808, http://www.iconocast.com/. Ed. Michael Tchong. Adv. contact Greg Ogarrio. Circ: 10,000.

004.692 USA
ULTIMATE E-MAIL. Text in English. 1997. w. **Document type:** *Bulletin.* **Description:** Aimed at simplifying and enhancing the Net for the everyday business user.
Media: Online - full text.
Address: charnoff@netogether.com, http://www.ultimate-mail.com. Ed. Lenny Charnoff.

025.04 USA
UNDERGROUNDONLINE. Text in English. 1997. d. adv. **Document type:** *Consumer.* **Description:** Provides a launching point for visitors to shop, play games, listen to music, watch video clips and catch up on the latest in entertainment news.
Media: Online - full content.
Address: 395 Hudson St, New York, NY 10014. TEL 212-624-3300, FAX 212-624-3310, webmasters@ugo.com, http://www.ugo.com. Adv. contact Greg Martin.

004.678 GBR
USERLINK MAGAZINE. Text in English. bi-m.
Formerly: C U A Userlink Magazine
Indexed: Inspec.
Published by: Easypublishing Ltd., Vigilant House, 120 Wilton Rd., London, SW1V 1JZ, United Kingdom. TEL 44-20-7808-7520, FAX 44-20-7808-7520, http://www.easypublishing.co.uk.

V I P NEWSLETTER. (Virtual Intellectual Property) see *PATENTS, TRADEMARKS AND COPYRIGHTS*

025.04 USA ISSN 1547-6251
▼ **V O N MAGAZINE.** (Voice on the Net) Text in English. 2004. m. USD 29; USD 4.95 newsstand/cover; free to qualified personnel (effective 2005). adv. back issues avail. **Document type:** *Magazine, Trade.* **Description:** Provides information and buying advice for end users, resellers and decision makers in the IP communications field.
Related titles: Online - full text ed.
Published by: V O N Publishing LLC, 115 Broadhollow Rd, Ste 225, Melville, NY 11747. TEL 631-961-8950, FAX 631-293-3996, http://www.vonmag.com. Ed. Richard Grigonis. Pub. Jeff Pulver. Adv. contact Maury Kauffman. color page USD 9,410; trim 8.375 x 10.875. Circ: 29,740 (paid and controlled).

378 USA
V U - OWNERS. Text in English. irreg. **Document type:** *Newsletter.*
Media: Online - full text.
Address: chris@christopher-knight.com, join-vu-owners@sparklist.com, http://www.christopher-knight.com. Ed. Christopher M Knight.

004.678 AUS
VICNET ZINE. Text in English. 1996. m. free. adv. back issues avail. **Document type:** *Newsletter.* **Description:** Provides information about local events, as well as full-text editorials and news about internet development in the region.
Media: Online - full text.
Published by: VicNet - Victoria's Network, 328 Swanston St, Melbourne, VIC 3000, Australia. TEL 61-3-96699710, FAX 61-3-96699805, neils@vicnet.net.au, http://www.vicnet.net.au/zine/. Ed., Adv. contact Richard Hayward. R&P Neil Shedden.

C

VICTORIAN G U M INC. NEWS. see *GENEALOGY AND HERALDRY*

▼ **VO I P MONITOR.** (Voice Over Internet Provider) see *COMMUNICATIONS—Computer Applications*

W A P MAGAZIN. (Wireless Application Protocol) see *COMMUNICATIONS*

004.738 POL ISSN 1428-2879
W W W; Magazyn Internetowy. (World Wide Web) Text in Polish. 1997. m. PLZ 89; PLZ 8.90 newsstand/cover (effective 2003). adv. **Document type:** *Magazine, Consumer.*
Related titles: Online - full text ed.: ISSN 1689-0515.
Published by: Wydawnictwo Murator Sp. z o.o., ul Kamionkowska 45, Warsaw, 03812, Poland. TEL 48-22-5905000, FAX 48-22-5905444, www@murator.com.pl, wydawnictwo@murator.com.pl, http://www-mag.com.pl, http://www.murator.com.pl. Ed. Mariusz Sawicki. Adv. contact Anna Piela. page PLZ 10,000.

025.04 346 USA ISSN 1095-2985
KF1066.A3
WALLSTREETLAWYER.COM. Text in English. 1997 (Jun.). m. USD 340 (effective 2005). **Document type:** *Newsletter, Trade.*
Published by: Glasser LegalWorks (Subsidiary of: West Publishing Co.), 150 Clove Rd, Little Falls, NJ 07424. TEL 973-890-0008, 800-308-1700, FAX 973-890-0042, legalwks@aol.com, http://www.legalwks.com/newsletters/wallstreet/index.shtml.

025.04 659.1 USA ISSN 1541-5392
WEB AD MONTHLY; the technology and business of web advertising. Text in English. 2001 (Dec.). m. USD 347 in North America; USD 427 elsewhere (effective 2002).
Published by: Lyra Research, Inc., P. O. Box 9143, Newtonville, MA 02460-9143. TEL 617-454-2600, FAX 617-454-2601, mail@lyra.com, http://www.webadmonthly.com, http://www.lyra.com. Pub. Frank Stefansson.

005.276 USA ISSN 1098-7754
HF6146.I58
WEB ADVERTISING (YEAR); market analysis & forecast. Text in English. a., latest vol.4, 2000. USD 1,695 (effective 2000). **Description:** Surveys top advisors and web sites to construct an accurate and informed analysis of the industry's structure and dynamics.
Published by: SIMBA Information (Subsidiary of: R.R. Bowker LLC), 60 Long Ridge Rd., Ste 300, Stamford, CT 06902. TEL 203-325-8193, 800-307-2529, 888-269-5372, FAX 203-325-8915, info@simbanet.com, http://www.simbanet.com.

005.276 USA
WEB BOUND✶. Text in English. 1996. q. USD 29.95 domestic; USD 49.95 foreign (effective 2000). adv. illus.
Published by: N.A. International, 1525 Westport Dr, Knoxville, TN 37922-8046.

004.678 790.1 USA
WEB BOUND SPECIAL EDITION: TOP 12,000 SPORTS WEBSITES. Text in English. 2001. m. USD 49.95; USD 5.95 newsstand/cover (effective 2001). **Document type:** *Consumer.*
Published by: Web Bound Inc., 715 Lago Circle, Knoxville, TN 37922. TEL 865-692-0389, FAX 865-690-1639, http://www.webbound.com. Pub. Art McCammon.

004.678 USA ISSN 1098-5271
WEB BUILDER CD-ROM. Text in English. q. USD 29.95 domestic; USD 35.95 in Canada & Mexico; USD 44.95 elsewhere (effective 2000). **Document type:** *Trade.*
Media: CD-ROM.
Published by: Fawcette Technical Publications, 2600 S. El Camino Real., Ste. 300, San Mateo, CA 94403-2381. TEL 650-833-7100, FAX 650-853-0230, http://www.fawcette.com. Pub. Lynne Matthes TEL 650-833-7145.

WEB COMMERCE TODAY. see *BUSINESS AND ECONOMICS*

004.678 USA ISSN 1099-7202
WEB CONTENT REPORT. Text in English. m. USD 299 (effective 2002). **Document type:** *Newsletter.* **Description:** Source of information for people who create and maintain the content of their organization's World Wide Web site. Includes information on how to attract visitors to your organization's Web site, how to monitor and evaluate the traffic on your home page, new developments in WWW technology, and how to sell products on your site.
Published by: Lawrence Ragan Communications, Inc., 316 N Michigan Ave, Ste 300, Chicago, IL 60601. TEL 312-960-4106, 800-878-5331, FAX 312-960-4106, cservice@ragan.com, http://www.ragan.com.

025.04 USA
WEB DESIGNERS GAZETTE. Text in English. m. free. adv. back issues avail. **Document type:** *Trade.* **Description:** Focuses on web design issues.
Media: Online - full text.
Published by: E & G Internet Marketing Services webmaster@eg-web.com, http://www.eg-web.com/gazette.shtml.

005.276 GBR
WEB DEVELOPER'S JOURNAL. Text in English. 1994. w.
Media: Online - full content.
Published by: internet.com Corp., 75 Leonard St, London, EC2A 4QS, United Kingdom. http://www.WebDevelopersJournal.com. Ed. Bruce Morris.

005.276 USA
THE WEB DEVELOPER'S JOURNAL✶. Text in English. 1992. d. bk.rev. **Document type:** *Bulletin.* **Description:** Contains software downloads, articles on web techniques and trends in software and hardware. Aims to the intermediate to advanced web developer.
Media: Online - full text.
Published by: Markland Communities, Inc., National Computer Tectonics, 109 Willow Ln, Oak Ridge, TN 37830-8240. bmorris@usit.net, cmorris@webdevelopersjournal, http://nctweb.com/webdev. Eds. Bruce Morris, Charlie Morris.

005.276 USA
WEB DEVELOPER'S VIRTUAL LIBRARY. Text in English. 1994. w. free.
Media: Online - full content.
Published by: Spectrum, 530 Bercut Dr, Ste E, Sacramento, CA 95814. http://www.wdvl.com/, http://www.stars.com. Ed. Scott Clark.

025.04 USA ISSN 1097-4210
ZA4225
WEB FEET; the Internet traveler's desk reference. Text in English. 1998. m. looseleaf. USD 165 (effective 2000). **Document type:** *Consumer.* **Description:** Recommends the best Web sites in all subject areas.
Published by: RockHill Communications, 522, Bala Cynwyd, PA 19004-0522. TEL 610-667-2040, 888-762-5445, FAX 610-667-2291, info@webfeetguides.com, http://www.rockhillcommunications.com/webfeet. Ed. Terry Schneider. Pub. Matt DeJulio.

383.33 USA
WEB GOLD. Text in English. w. USD 149. **Document type:** *Newsletter.* **Description:** Contains timely business development and marketing information.
Related titles: Online - full text ed.
Published by: Bizpromo webmaster@bizpromo.com, http://www.bizpromo.com.

025.04 USA ISSN 1524-2609
WEB GUIDE. Text in English. 1998. bi-m. USD 23.95; USD 33.95 in Canada; USD 43.95 elsewhere (effective 2000). adv. Website rev. illus. **Document type:** *Magazine, Consumer.* **Description:** Aims to be an authoritative, entertaining and attractive guide to Internet content. Also contains several in-depth single-topic features that explore Web resources for entertainment, research, shopping and work.
Published by: W S Guide, Inc., 526 Boston Post Rd, Wayland, MA 91778. TEL 508-358-3434, FAX 508-358-5195, editor@webguidemag.com, http://www.webguidemag.com. Ed. Perry Glasser. Pub. Michael Siggins. Adv. contact Arthur Rosenberg.

004.678 USA ISSN 1087-7711
WEB INFORMANT (ELK GROVE); the complete monthly guide to web development. Text in English. 1996. m. USD 39.95 (effective 1997). adv. bk.rev. illus. reprints avail. **Document type:** *Consumer.* **Description:** Publishes programming for the World Wide Web with Java, Perl and other languages.
Published by: Informant Communications Group, 5105 Florin Perkins Rd., Sacramento, CA 95826-4817. TEL 916-686-6610, FAX 916-686-8497, circulation@informant.com, http://www.informant.com/wi/index.HTM. Ed. Jerry Coffey. Circ: 18,000 (paid).

004.678 USA ISSN 1524-6353
WEB INFORMANT (PORT WASHINGTON). Text in English. 1995. 3/m. **Description:** Analyzes recent trends with using the Internet and the web for public relations, advertising, and marketing communications.
Media: Online - full text.
Address: 938 Port Washington Blvd, Port Washington, NY 11050. TEL 516-944-3407, david@strom.com, http://www.webinformant.com. Ed. David Strom.

WEB MARKETING TODAY. see *BUSINESS AND ECONOMICS—Marketing And Purchasing*

005.276 USA ISSN 1549-3288
HD9999.I49
WEB - ONLINE SERVICES (YEAR); market analysis and forecast. Text in English. 1990. a. USD 1,895 (effective 2000). charts; stat. back issues avail. **Document type:** *Trade.* **Description:** Analyzes and forecasts online services including legal, brokerage, credit, marketing intelligence, financial news and research, agribusiness, and healthcare.
Former titles (until 1998): Web - Online Services (Year): Business Professional Market Analysis and Forecast; Web - Online Services (Year): Business Professional Analysis and Forecast; Which superseded in part (in 1997): Online Services: Review, Trends and Forecast (1057-3666)
Published by: SIMBA Information (Subsidiary of: R.R. Bowker LLC), 60 Long Ridge Rd., Ste 300, Stamford, CT 06902. TEL 203-325-8193, 800-307-2529, 888-269-5372, FAX 203-325-8915, info@simbanet.com, http://www.simbanet.com.

004.678 GBR ISSN 1464-7427
WEB PAGES MADE EASY. Text in English. 1998. m. GBP 29 in United States; GBP 35 in Europe; GBP 46 rest of world; GBP 3.99 newsstand/cover (effective 2001). adv. 100 p./no.; back issues avail. **Document type:** *Magazine, Consumer.* **Description:** Covers step-by-step, beginner-oriented guide to making a Web site.
Published by: Paragon Publishing Ltd., Paragon House, 10 St Peters Rd, Bournemouth, Dorset BH1 2JS, United Kingdom. TEL 44-1202-299900, FAX 44-1202-299955, 44-1202-200217, subs@paragon.co.uk, http://www.paragon.co.uk. Ed. Rob Clymo. Adv. contact Jennie Brown TEL 44-1202-200212. Circ: 14,744 (paid).

025.4 PHL
THE WEB PHILIPPINES. Text in English. bi-m. PHP 900 (effective 2002). adv. **Document type:** *Magazine, Consumer.* **Description:** Contains articles and features for active online users who have turned to the Internet for their mainstream entertainment and information needs.
Related titles: Online - full text ed.
Published by: W S Computer Publishing Corp., 5/F SEDCCO I Bldg., Rada St., Legaspi Village, Makati City, 1200, Philippines. TEL 632-812-8401, FAX 632-894-2487, http://www.itnetcentral.com/theweb/. adv.: B&W page USD 1,005, color page USD 1,608; trim 215 x 280. Circ: 10,000 (paid).

005.276 USA
WEB REVIEW; for people who make the Web work. Text in English. w. back issues avail. **Document type:** *Trade.* **Description:** Provides information about the world wide web and the people who work for it, in it, and with it.
Media: Online - full text.
Address: wr-info@webreview.com, http://www.webreview.com. Ed. David Sims.

WEB SERVICES JOURNAL. see *COMPUTERS—Computer Programming*

004.678 USA
WEB SIGHT DIRECTORY MAGAZINE. Text in English. 2000. m. USD 24.99; USD 3.95 newsstand/cover (effective 2001). adv. **Document type:** *Consumer.*
Published by: Net Directors, Inc., 3550 Wilshire Blvd, Ste 835, Los Angeles, CA 90010. TEL 213-252-1269, FAX 213-252-1277, webmag@pacbell.com, http://www.websitedirect-mag.com. Ed. Leslie Small.

004.678 051 079.5957 SGP
THE WEB SINGAPORE. Text in English. 1997. m. SGD 42; SGD 5 newsstand/cover (effective 1999). music rev.; software rev.; video rev. back issues avail. **Document type:** *Consumer.* **Description:** Combines discussion of the popular culture of the Internet with information about how to use it.
Related titles: Online - full text ed.

Published by: Communication Resources Pte. Ltd., Blk. 1008, Tao Payoh North, No. 07-01, Singapore, 318996, Singapore. TEL 65-12-256-6201, FAX 65-12-251-0348. Ed. Joseph Lim. Pub. Tan Tee Seng. adv.: B&W page SGD 2,200, color page SGD 3,000; trim 279 x 210. Circ: 15,000.

025.04 USA ISSN 1089-4861
ZA4226
WEB SITE SOURCE BOOK (YEAR); a guide to major US businesses, organizations, agencies, institutions, and other information resources on the World Wide Web. Text in English. 1996. a., latest 2002, 7th ed. USD 135 (effective 2001). Index. **Document type:** *Directory, Trade.* **Description:** Provides World Wide Web addresses and other key contact information for major businesses, agencies, and institutions throughout the United States and Canada. Entries are presented in two sections: an alphabetical index arranged by organization name and a classified section arranged by subject headings.
Published by: Omnigraphics, Inc., 615 Griswold St, Detroit, MI 48226. TEL 313-961-1341, 800-234-1340, FAX 313-961-1383, 800-875-1340, info@omnigraphics.com, http://www.omnigraphics.com. Ed. Darren L Smith. Pub. Frederick G Ruffner Jr.

004.678 USA
WEB SOLUTIONS. Text in English. 1995. m. **Description:** Covers Internet related topics.
Media: Online - full text.
Published by: I S - O O P Group, 175 Osborn Ave, New Haven, CT 06511. ssteinhardt@online-magazine.com, http://www.online-magazine.com. Ed. Steve Steinhardt.

004.693 CAN
WEB TIMES. Text in English. 1995. d. **Description:** Lists live Internet broadcasts and chats.
Related titles: Online - full text ed.; International ed.: Web Times (International Edition).
Address: 516 Centennial Pkwy, Delta, BC V4L 1L1, Canada. djohnsto@unixg.ubc.ca, http://www.webtimes.com. Ed. Devin Johnston.

025.4 GBR
WEB USER. Text in English. 2001. fortn. GBP 23.17 domestic; USD 67.50 in United States (effective 2004). adv. **Document type:** *Magazine, Consumer.* **Description:** Offers support, advice and information on how to navigate through the complexities of the Web.
Published by: I P C Country & Leisure Media Ltd. (Subsidiary of: I P C Media Ltd.), King's Reach Tower, Stamford St, London, SE1 9LS, United Kingdom. FAX 44-20-72617900, http://www.web-user.co.uk/, http://www.ipcmedia.com. Ed. Colin Tough. **Subscr. to:** I P C Media Ltd., Perrymount Rd, Haywards Heath RH16 3DA, United Kingdom. TEL 44-1444-475675, FAX 44-1444-445599.

384.33 USA
WEB WEEK. (delivered as a PDF file; broadband Internet connection required for subscription.) Text in English. w. free to qualified personnel (effective 2005). adv. **Document type:** *Magazine, Trade.* **Description:** Covers the Internet business market.
Media: Online - full content.
Published by: Possibility Media, 10400 N.W. 33rd St., Ste. 270, Miami, FL 33172. TEL 786-206-8880, FAX 786-206-8884, info@possibilitymedia.com, http://www.possibilitymedia.com/. adv.: page USD 2,055; trim 8.5 x 10.875. Circ: 125,000.

005.276 USA
WEB - ZINE; the Internet & Web magazine. Text in English. m. **Description:** For internet users.
Media: Online - full text.
Address: chadz@nmsu.edu, http://www.nmsu.edu/~czimmerm/Web-Zine/.

THE WEBBIZ TELEGRAM. see *BUSINESS AND ECONOMICS—Marketing And Purchasing*

025.04 USA ISSN 1527-2508
ZA4201
WEBBOUND. Text in English. 1996. q. USD 9.95 newsstand/cover domestic; USD 13.95 newsstand/cover in Canada (effective 2003). **Document type:** *Directory.*
Published by: Web Bound Inc., 715 Lago Circle, Knoxville, TN 37922. TEL 865-692-0389, FAX 865-690-1639, http://www.webbound.com. Pub. Art McCammon.

025.4 AUS ISSN 1444-1241
WEBBUSINESS. Text in English. 2000. m. adv. **Document type:** *Magazine, Trade.* **Description:** Reports on trends and issues that are shaping the strategic use of the Internet, intranet and extranets.
Published by: I D G Communications Pty. Ltd., 88 Christie St, St Leonards, NSW 2065, Australia. TEL 61-2-94395133, FAX 61-2-94395512, heidi_woof@idg.com.au, http://www.web-business.com.au, http://www.idg.com.au. adv.: color page USD 3,163; trim 205 x 275. Circ: 10,000 (controlled).

004.678 GBR
WEBCREATE. Text in English. m. free with subscr. to Digit or Macworld. **Document type:** *Magazine, Consumer.* **Description:** Contains information on online design, graphics, animation, movies and other related technology, providing showcase for new products and other issues relevant to the UK design community.
Related titles: Online - full content ed.; ♦ Issued with: Macworld. ISSN 0957-2341; ♦ Issued with: Digit. ISSN 1461-3816.
Published by: I D G Media, 99 Gray's Inn Rd, London, WC1X 8UT, United Kingdom. TEL 44-20-7831-9252, webeditor@webcreate.co.uk, http://www.webcreate.co.uk/, http://www.idg.co.uk. Ed. Gillian Thompson.

005.72 USA
WEBDESIGN & REVIEW. Text in English. 1997. m. USD 39.95; includes DT&G Journal of Design, Typography & Graphics. **Description:** Focuses on design issues for producing web pages and web sites.
Media: Online - full text.
Published by: Design & Publishing Center, 15 Southgate, Harrisonburg, VA 22801. showker@graphic-design.com, http://www.graphic-design.com/WEB/. Ed. Fred Showker.

025.4 CHE ISSN 1422-2728
WEBDO. Text in French. 1995. q. adv. **Document type:** *Consumer.* **Description:** Reports on entertaining and informative sites and sources on the Web.
Media: Online - full text. **Related titles:** ♦ Print ed.: Webdo Mag. ISSN 1423-8705.
Published by: Ringier Romandie, Pont Bessieres 3, Case postale 3733, Lausanne, 1002, Switzerland. TEL 41-21-3317130, FAX 41-21-3317121, info@webdo.ch, info@ringier.ch, http://www.webdo.ch, http://www.ringier.ch.

025.4 CHE ISSN 1423-8705
WEBDO MAG; magazine suisse d'infos et de services. Text in French. 1997. q. CHF 20 (effective 2000). adv. **Document type:** *Magazine, Consumer.*
Formerly (until 1998): Webdo (1422-2736)
Related titles: ♦ Online - full text ed.: Webdo. ISSN 1422-2728.
Published by: Ringier Romandie, Pont Bessieres 3, Case postale 3733, Lausanne, 1002, Switzerland. TEL 41-21-3317130, FAX 41-21-3317121, info@webdo.ch, info@ringier.ch, http://www.webdo.ch, http://www.ringier.ch. Ed. Nicolas Willemin.

005.276 USA
THE WEBMASTER TRIBUNE. Text in English. 1998. w. free. adv. **Document type:** *Newsletter.* **Description:** Each issue offers information regarding Web site design and promotion.
Media: Online - full text.
Published by: Webmaster Tribune webmaster@webmaster-resources.com, http://www.webmaster-resources.com. Ed. Matt Mickiewicz.

004.678 USA
WEBMASTERS EZINE. Text in English. 1998. bi-w. **Document type:** *Trade.* **Description:** Designed to help webmasters improve both the content and promotion of their sites.
Media: E-mail.
Address: subscribe@notts.net, ezine@notts.net. Ed. Greg Matthews.

004.678 SGP
WEBNEWZ. Text in English. 1997. fortn. adv. **Document type:** *Bulletin.* **Description:** Covers products and technologies involving networking and the Web for the Asian market.
Media: Online - full text.
Address: 105 Boon Keng Rd 04-17, Singapore, 339776, Singapore. TEL 65-2919861, FAX 65-2931445, siddha@singnet.com.sg, http://wn.newscom.asia.com. Ed. A. Siddhartha. Pub. Austin Morais. R&P A Siddhartha. Adv. contact Bernie Lim.

384.33 USA
WEBPROFESSIONS MONTHLY UPDATE. Text in English. 1998. m. adv. **Document type:** *Newsletter.* **Description:** Designed to online business owners, including links to products and services on how to grow an Internet business.
Media: Online - full text.
Address: webprofessions@yahoo.com, http://www.webprofessions.com. Ed. Lawrence Manning.

025.04 USA
WEBREFERENCE UPDATE. Text in English. w. **Document type:** *Newsletter.* **Description:** Highlights what's new on the Web.
Media: Online - full text.
Address: aking@webreference.com, http://www.webreference.com/new/.

383.33 USA ISSN 1529-0409
WEBSITE SUCCESS MONTHLY. Text in English. m. free. **Document type:** *Trade.* **Description:** Provides tips on website design, hosting, promotion, and important internet industry news.
Media: Online - full text.
Published by: L R S Marketing subscribe@lrsmarketing.com, http://www.lrsmarketing.com/newsletter_home.htm. Ed. Lisa Schmeckpeper.

025.04 GBR
WEBSITE WEEKLY. Text in English. w. free. **Document type:** *Newsletter.* **Description:** Offers tips for promoting and making money from one's Web site.
Media: Online - full text.
Address: Southcote, Belgrave Rd, Bath, BA1 6LU, United Kingdom. chris.gibbs@connect-2.co.uk, http://chrisgibbs.connect-2.co.uk/. Ed. Chris Gibbs.

WEBSPHERE DEVELOPER'S JOURNAL. see *COMPUTERS—Computer Programming*

025.04 USA
WEBSURFERS BIWEEKLY EARTH SCIENCE REVIEW. Text in English. 1996. bi-w. bk.rev. **Document type:** *Trade.* **Description:** Allows one to retrieve earth science related Web sites and materials.
Media: Online - full text.
Address: TEL 303-763-8270, michaelg@rmi.com, http://shell.rmi.net/~michaelg/index.html. Ed. Mike Garrison.

004.678 USA
WEBTRACK. Text in English. m. USD 195; USD 595 with online ed.. **Document type:** *Newsletter, Trade.* **Description:** Features data and analyses on buyers, sellers and trends, as well as discussion about new approaches to driving traffic and usage on consumer oriented Web sites and online services.
Related titles: Online - full text ed.
Published by: Jupiter Communications, 627 Broadway, New York, NY 10012. TEL 212-780-6060, FAX 212-780-6075, http://www.jup.com/newsletter/.

659.13 DEU
WEBTRADE. Text in German. 2000. m. EUR 4.50 newsstand/cover (effective 2001). adv. **Document type:** *Magazine, Trade.* **Description:** Provides the latest news and information on all aspects of e-commerce.
Related titles: Online - full text ed.
Published by: TargetPress Publishing GmbH, Enzianstr 2-6, Starnberg, 82319, Germany. TEL 49-8151-265170, FAX 49-8151-265211, redaktion@webtrade-online.de, http://www.webtrade-online.de. Ed. Herbert Sebald. Adv. contact Angus G Spelthahn. page EUR 5,200; trim 181 x 267. Circ: 118,650 (paid).

004.678 USA ISSN 1524-0010
WEEKEND WEB PICKS. Text in English. w. (Fri.).
Media: Online - full text.
Address: wwp@netogether.com, http://www.netogether.com/picks.html.

WHAT SA CELLPHONE SATELLITE INTERNET. see *ELECTRONICS*

659.13 USA ISSN 1534-7265
WHAT'S WORKING ONLINE. Text in English. 2/m. **Document type:** *Newsletter, Trade.* **Description:** Presents articles and information on more efficient methods of marketing and conducting business on the Internet.
Published by: Briefings Publishing Group (Subsidiary of: Douglas Publications, Inc.), 1101 King St, Ste 110, Alexandria, VA 22314. TEL 703-518-2343, 800-722-9221, FAX 703-684-2136, customerservice@briefings.com, http://www.briefings.com.

004.678 CAN ISSN 1183-7837
WHO'S WHO IN SUPER SITES. Text in English. 1992. a. CND 1,294.70 domestic. **Document type:** *Directory.* **Description:** Lists the top 2,500 Canadian IT computing sites.
Related titles: CD-ROM ed.: CND 2,010 per vol. domestic (effective 2000).
Published by: Whitsed Publishing, 268 Lakeshore Rd E, Ste 510, Mississauga, ON L5G 1H1, Canada. TEL 905-271-1601, FAX 905-271-4522. Ed. Roy Whitsed. **Dist. by:** International Press Publications Inc, 90 Nolan Ct, Ste 21, Markham, ON L3R 4L9, Canada. TEL 800-679-2514, FAX 905-946-9590.

004.678 USA ISSN 1548-8926
TK5105.8885.M57
WINDOWS SERVER SYSTEM MAGAZINE. Text in English. 2001 (Fall/Winter, vol.1, no.1). bi-m. free to qualified personnel (effective 2004). adv. **Document type:** *Magazine, Consumer.*
Formerly (until 2003): .net Magazine (1539-5251)
Related titles: Online - full content ed.
Indexed: MicrocompInd.
Published by: Fawcette Technical Publications, 2600 S. El Camino Real., Ste. 300, San Mateo, CA 94403-2381. TEL 800-848-5523, lmatthes@fawcette.com, customerservice@fawcette.com, http://www.ftponline.com/dotnetmag/, http://www.fawcette.com. Ed. Patrick Meader. Pub. Lynne Matthes TEL 650-833-7145. Adv. contact Kent Wu TEL 650-833-7127.

025.4 USA ISSN 1537-825X
WINDOWS WEB SOLUTIONS. Text in English. 1999. m. USD 129 domestic; USD 135 foreign (effective 2002). adv. **Document type:** *Magazine, Trade.* **Description:** Contains practical, in-depth articles to help deploy, manage, optimize, and secure Web-enabled enterprises.
Formerly (until 2001): I I S Administrator (1526-808X)
Related titles: Online - full text ed.

▼ new title ➤ refereed ✶ unverified ♦ full entry avail.

Published by: Penton Technology Media (Subsidiary of: Penton Media, Inc.), 221 E 29th St, Ste 242, Loveland, CO 80538. TEL 970-663-4700, 800-621-1544, FAX 970-663-3285, http://www.windowswebsolutions.com.

004.678 384.5 USA ISSN 1544-1695
WIRELESS INTERNET MAGAZINE. Text in English. 2001. s-m. (bi-m. until 2002). free to qualified personnel. adv. back issues avail. **Document type:** *Magazine, Trade.* **Description:** Features articles on trends, global industry news coverage, the latest developments, breakthrough technologies and other related topics.
Related titles: Online - full content ed.
Published by: Reed Business Information (Subsidiary of: Reed Business), PO Box 266008, Highlands Ranch, CO 80163-6008. http://www.wirelessinternetmag.com/, http://www.reedbusiness.com. Ed. Bill Menezes. Pub. Debby Denton TEL 303-470-4867.

004.678 USA
WOMEN ONLINE. Text in English. m. **Description:** Contains news, reviews and other information about women online.
Media: Online - full text.
Address: agoodloe@women-online.com, http://www.women-online.com. Ed. Amy Goodloe.

004.6 GBR
THE WORKS OF DANTE. Text in English. 1993. bi-m. back issues avail. **Document type:** *Newsletter.*
Media: Online - full text.
Published by: Dante, Francis House, 112 Hills Rd, Cambridge, CB2 1PQ, United Kingdom. TEL 44-1223-302992, FAX 44-1223-303005, dante@dante.org.uk, http://www.dante.net/. Ed. Josefien Bersee.

025.0634 USA ISSN 1473-3579
WORLD DATA PROTECTION REPORT. Text in English. 2001. m. **Document type:** *Newsletter.*
Related titles: Online - full text ed.: (from The Bureau of National Affairs, Inc.).
—CCC.
Published by: The Bureau of National Affairs, Inc., 1231 25th St., NW, Washington, DC 20037. TEL 800-372-1033. **Subscr. to:** 9435 Key West Ave, Rockville, MD 20850.

025.04 382.029 GBR
WORLD DIRECTORY OF BUSINESS INFORMATION WEBSITES. Text in English. 1998. 2/yr., latest 2003, Feb. GBP 425, USD 690, EUR 690 per issue (effective 2003). **Document type:** *Directory, Trade.* **Description:** Provides details on where to find more than 1,200 sources of business information on the Internet.
Published by: Euromonitor, 60-61 Britton St, London, EC1 5UX, United Kingdom. TEL 44-20-7251-8024, FAX 44-20-7608-3149, info@euromonitor.com, http://www.euromonitor.com. **Dist. by:** Current Pacific Ltd., PO Box 36-536, Northcote, Auckland, New Zealand. TEL 64-9-480-1388, FAX 64-9-480-1387, info@cplnz.com, http://www.cplnz.com.

WORLD E-COMMERCE & I P REPORT. see *LAW—Corporate Law*

025.0634 USA
WORLD INTERNET LAW REPORT. Text in English. 2001. m. **Document type:** *Newsletter.*
Published by: The Bureau of National Affairs, Inc., 1231 25th St., NW, Washington, DC 20037. TEL 800-372-1033, http://www.bna.com. **Subscr. to:** 9435 Key West Ave, Rockville, MD 20850.

004.678 GRC
THE WORLD OF INTERNET. Text in Greek. 1995. m. adv. **Document type:** *Consumer.* **Description:** Covers the Internet and the World Wide Web.
Published by: Compupress S.A., 44 Syngrou Ave, Athens, 117 42, Greece. TEL 30-210-923-8672, FAX 30-210-921-6847, http://www.compupress.gr/default_eng.htm. Ed. George Saklabanakis. Pub. N O Manousos. Adv. contact V Giakamozis. Circ: 12,000 (paid).

004.678 USA ISSN 1386-145X
TK5105.888
➤ **WORLD WIDE WEB.** Text in Dutch. q. EUR 392, USD 392, GBP 245 combined subscription to institutions print & online eds. (effective 2005). adv. reprint service avail. from PSC. **Document type:** *Journal, Academic/Scholarly.* **Description:** Publishes research results, case studies, project experiences, surveys, and tutorials related to the World Wide Web.
Related titles: Online - full text ed.: ISSN 1573-1413 (from EBSCO Publishing, Gale Group, IngentaConnect, Kluwer Online, O C L C Online Computer Library Center, Inc., Springer LINK, Swets Information Services).
Indexed: BibLing, C&CSA, CMCI, CompLI, CurCont, InfoSAb, Inspec, RefZh.
—BLDSC (9360.222000), IE, Infotrieve, ingenta. **CCC.**
Published by: Springer-Verlag New York, Inc. (Subsidiary of: Springer Science+Business Media), 233 Spring St, New York, NY 10013. TEL 212-460-1500, FAX 212-460-1575, service@springer-ny.com, http://springerlink.metapress.com/openurl.asp?genre=journal&issn=1386-145x, http://www.springer-ny.com. Eds. Marek Rusinkiewicz, Yanchun Zhang. **Subscr. to:** Journal Fulfillment, PO Box 2485, Secaucus, NJ 07096-2485. TEL 201-348-4033, FAX 201-348-4505, journals@springer-ny.com.

004.696 USA ISSN 0731-7891
WORLDWIDE VIDEOTEX UPDATE. Text in English. 1981. m. USD 150 in North America; USD 165 elsewhere (effective 2001). back issues avail. **Document type:** *Newsletter, Trade.* **Description:** Reports news and information on videotex, online services, electronic mail, satellite communications, and television-related technologies, such as teleconferencing and teletext.
Related titles: Online - full text ed.: (from bigchalk, Data-Star, EBSCO Publishing, Factiva, Gale Group, LexisNexis, ProQuest Information & Learning, The Dialog Corporation).
—CCC.
Published by: Worldwide Videotex, PO Box 3273, Boynton Beach, FL 33424-3273. TEL 561-738-2276, markedit@juno.com, http://www.wvpubs.com. Ed., Pub. Mark Wright.

004.68 MEX
WWW; para vivir en Internet. (World Wide Web) Text in Spanish. 2000. m. MXP 20 newsstand/cover (effective 2000).
Related titles: Online - full text ed.
Published by: Grupo Alce, Donato Guerra No. 9, Col. Juarez, Mexico, D.F., 06600, Mexico. TEL 52-55-7030172, FAX 52-55-7030180, http://www.revistawww.com.mx/, http://www.grupo-alce.com/. Ed. Antonio Reyes. Circ: 90,000.

004.678 USA
WWWIZ. Text in English. 1995. m. USD 28 domestic; USD 50 foreign (effective 2000). **Document type:** *Consumer.* **Description:** Provides general interest stories on and about the World Wide Web.
Related titles: Online - full text ed.: 1995.
Address: 280 White Cap Ln, Newport Beach, CA 92657-1089. wiz@wwwiz.com, http://wwwiz.com. Ed., Pub., R&P Don Hamilton. Adv. contact Mike Noon. Circ: 120,000 (free).

004.6 BOL ISSN 1609-6673
X-EXTR@INTERNET. Text in Spanish. irreg. adv.
Media: Online - full text.
Published by: Khainata-Web Designers, C. Fernando Guachalla No. 452, Ed. Guachalla Piso 6, Dept. 603, La Paz, Bolivia. info@khainata.com, http://x-extrainternet.com/, http://www.hkainata.com/.

X M L & WEB SERVICES MAGAZIN. see *COMPUTERS—Software*

X M L JOURNAL (ONLINE). see *COMPUTERS—Computer Programming*

XNET. see *MEN'S INTERESTS*

025.04 IND
ZANY ZINE. Text in English. 1996. w. free. adv. **Document type:** *Bulletin.* **Description:** Source of online entertainment and information.
Media: Online - full text.
Address: 2-421 Girja Bhavan, Bhaudaji Rd., Matunga, Mumbai, Maharashtra 400 019, India. TEL 91-22-4025448, rashmin@giasbm01.vsnl.net.in, http://www.geocities.com/SouthBeach/4195. Ed., Pub., R&P, Adv. contact Nikunj Sanghvi.

384.33 USA
ZCOMMERCE. Text in English. 1998. irreg.?. free. adv. **Document type:** *Newsletter.* **Description:** Covers electronic commerce on the Internet.
Media: Online - full text.
Published by: Cybereps, 80 Liberty Ship Way, Sausalito, CA 94965. TEL 415-289-5040, FAX 415-289-1589.

004.678 USA
1ST STEPS: DAILY MARKETING AND DESIGN. Text in English. 1995. d. **Document type:** *Newsletter.* **Description:** Focuses on tips, techniques, tools and resources for on-line marketing, advertising, customer service and promotion.
Media: Online - full text.
Published by: Internet Business Network, PO Box 637, Mill Valley, CA 94942-0637. FAX 415-383-8676, staff@interbiznet.com, http://www.interbiznet.com/nomad.html. Ed., Pub., R&P John Sumser.

004.678 USA
1ST STEPS IN THE HUNT. Text in English. 1995. d. **Document type:** *Newsletter, Consumer.* **Description:** Provides tips and techniques for successful job hunting. Covers topics ranging from resume preparation and distribution to specific reviews of job sites.
Media: Online - full text.
Published by: Internet Business Network, PO Box 637, Mill Valley, CA 94942-0637. TEL 415-389-6493, FAX 415-383-8676, staff@interbiznet.com, http://www.interbiznet.com/hunt. Ed. John Sumser.

004.678 330 TWN ISSN 1608-9383
3 C MALL/E-SHIDAI QUANFANGWEI QINGBAO ZHI. Text in Chinese. 2001 (May). m. TWD 1,356; TWD 119 newsstand/cover (effective 2001). **Document type:** *Magazine, Consumer.* **Description:** Cover internet commerce, including the latest electronic products, reviews, and softwares.
Published by: Jianduan Chuban Qufen Youxian Gongsi/Sharp Point Publishing Ltd., Inc., 231 Xindiansi, Fuyu-Lu 43-Hao 8-Lou, Taipei, Taiwan. TEL 886-2-2218-1582, FAX 886-2-2218-1583, ching@spp.com.tw, janey@spp.com.tw, http://www.spp.com.tw/asp/mag/3cMall/index.asp.

COMPUTERS—Machine Theory

621.39 USA ISSN 1550-4832
▼ **A C M JOURNAL ON EMERGING TECHNOLOGIES.** (Association for Computing Machinery) Text in English. 2005. q. USD 140 to non-members; USD 40 to members (effective 2004).
Related titles: Online - full text ed.: ISSN 1550-4840. forthcoming 2005 (from EBSCO Publishing).
Published by: Association for Computing Machinery, Inc., 1515 Broadway, 17th Fl, New York, NY 10036-5701. TEL 212-626-0500, 800-342-6626, FAX 212-944-1318, sigs@acm.org, http://www.acm.org.

621.39 004 FIN ISSN 1458-6401
HELSINKI UNIVERSITY OF TECHNOLOGY. SIGNAL PROCESSING LABORATORY. REPORT. Text in English. 1989. irreg., latest vol.52, 2005. **Document type:** *Monographic series, Academic/Scholarly.*
Former titles (until 2001): Helsinki University of Technology. Laboratory of Signal Processing and Computer Technology. Report (1456-6907); (until 1999): Helsinki University of Technology. Department of Electrical and Communications Engineering. Laboratory of Signal Processing and Computer Technology. Report (1239-9434); (until 1996): Helsinki University of Technology. Faculty of Electrical Engineering. Laboratory of Signal Processing and Computer Technology. Report (0787-7374)
Published by: Helsinki University of Technology, Signal Processing Laboratory, PO Box 3000, Espoo, 02015, Finland. TEL 358-9-4512486, FAX 358-9-4523614, http://wooster.hut.fi.

THEORETICAL COMPUTER SCIENCE. see *COMPUTERS—Theory Of Computing*

004 USA ISSN 1078-2192
3 C ON-LINE. Text in English. 1994. q.
Related titles: Online - full text ed.: (from EBSCO Publishing).
Indexed: CompR.
Published by: Association for Computing Machinery, Inc., 1515 Broadway, 17th Fl, New York, NY 10036-5701. TEL 212-626-0500, 212-626-0520, 800-342-6626, FAX 212-869-0481, sigs@acm.org, usacm@acm.org, http://www.acm.org.

COMPUTERS—Microcomputers

see also COMPUTERS—Personal Computers

004.16 USA ISSN 0741-997X
ABSOLUTE REFERENCE; the journal for 1-2-3 and Symphony users. Text in English. 1983. m. USD 60. adv. back issues avail. **Description:** For 1-2-3 and Symphony users. Features instructional articles as well as columns on spreadsheets and product reviews.
Published by: Que Publishing Corporation, PO Box 90, Carmel, IN 46032-0090. TEL 800-428-8331. Ed. David Maguiness.

004.16 USA
ACCESS (NEW YORK, 1983)✶; the consulting services newsletter. Text in English. 1983. m. USD 24. adv. bk.rev. back issues avail. **Description:** Primarily for Charles River Computers clients. Offers evaluations and comparisons of different software, hardware and peripheral packages for personal computer.
Published by: Charles River Computers, 1290 Avenue Of The Americas, 39th Fl, New York, NY 10104-0101. TEL 212-371-3500. Ed. Mark Dobson. Circ: 9,706.

005.74 USA ISSN 1050-1878
ACCESS (ROCKVILLE). Text in English. m.
Published by: United Communications Group, 11300 Rockville Pike Ste 1100, Rockville, MD 20852-3030. TEL 301-816-8950. Ed. Doug O'Boyle. adv.: page USD 1,130.

005.5 USA ISSN 1043-0768
ACKNOWLEDGE THE WINDOW LETTER. Text in English. 1989. m. looseleaf. USD 245 domestic; USD 275 in Canada; USD 330 elsewhere. bk.rev. **Description:** Covers news, product reviews, and presents information on new software applications for users of Microsoft Windows and Presentation Manager.

C

Related titles: CD-ROM ed.; Online - full text ed.: (from Gale Group).
Indexed: CompD.
Published by: Mendham Technology Group, 144 Talmadge Rd, Box 11, Mendham, NJ 07945. TEL 201-543-2273, FAX 201-543-6033. Ed. Carole Patton. Circ: 2,500.

APPLE EDUCATION NEWS; an information service for educators and trainers. see *EDUCATION—Computer Applications*

AUSTRALIAN MACWORLD. see *COMPUTERS—Personal Computers*

AUSTRALIAN P C USER. see *COMPUTERS—Personal Computers*

AUSTRALIAN PERSONAL COMPUTER. see *COMPUTERS—Personal Computers*

621.3916 ESP ISSN 0210-3923
B I T. (Boletin Informativo de Telecomunicacion) Text in Spanish. 1976. bi-m.
Related titles: Online - full text ed.; Italian ed.; Japanese ed.
Indexed: IECT.
—CINDOC.
Published by: Asociacion Espanola de Ingenieros de Telecomunicacion/Spanish Association of Telecommunications Engineers, General Arrando, 38, Madrid, 28010, Spain. TEL 34-91-4197418, FAX 34-91-4101155, http://www.iies.es/teleco/. Ed. Carmen Fernandez Ruiz. Circ: 6,000.

B U G NEWSLETTER. see *COMPUTERS—Personal Computers*

BUG REPORT. see *COMPUTERS—Personal Computers*

BUILDERS' COMPUTER NEWSLETTER. see *BUILDING AND CONSTRUCTION*

004.16 USA
QA76.5
BYTE.COM. Text in English. 1975. w. membership. adv. bk.rev. illus. Index. reprint service avail. from PQC. **Document type:** *Magazine, Trade.* **Description:** Covers topics in microcomputers for business and professional users emphasizing technical information, applications and products.
Supersedes (1975-1999): Byte (Print Edition) (0360-5280); (1995-1999): Byte on CD-ROM (1082-7838)
Media: Online - full text (from Gale Group). **Related titles:** Microform ed.: (from PQC).
Indexed: ABIn, ABS&EES, AIA, AS&TI, ASCA, Acal, B&I, BMT, BPI, BRI, BusI, C&ISA, CADCAM, CBPI, CBRI, CMCI, CPerI, CompC, CompD, CompI, ConsI, CurCont, CybAb, E&CAJ, ErgAb, GALA, IHTDI, Inspec, LAMP, LRI, MASUSE, MCIU, MELSA, MRD, MagInd, MicrocompInd, PCAb, PCR2, PMR, RASB, RGAb, RGPR, RILM, RoboAb, SCI, SoftAbEng, SoftBase, SolStAb, T&II, TOM, TelAb.
—AskIEEE, CASDDS, CISTI, Ei, IDS, Linda Hall. **CCC.**
Published by: C M P Media LLC (Subsidiary of: United News & Media), 600 Community Dr, Manhasset, NY 11030. http://www.byte.com. Ed. Jonathan Erickson. Circ: 500,000.

004.16 TUR ISSN 1300-6711
BYTE TUERKIYE. Text in Turkish. 1995. m. TRL 9,000,000 domestic; USD 100 in United States; TRL 750,000 newsstand/cover. **Document type:** *Consumer.* **Description:** Computer magazine oriented towards professional IT managers and users.
Supersedes in part (1993-1995): Ihlas Bilgi Islem (1300-672X)
Published by: Ihlas Gaz Mat Yay A.S., Kocaoglu Is Mrk. K.S.N. 8, Mehmet Murat Sk., Sirkeci - Istanbul, 34400, Turkey. TEL 90-212-5129271, FAX 90-212-5140656. Ed. Kerem Kocer. Circ: 25,000 (paid).

C U AMIGA. see *COMPUTERS—Personal Computers*

CALL - A.P.P.L.E. (Apple Pugetsound Program Library Exchange) see *COMPUTERS—Personal Computers*

004.16 USA ISSN 1071-7749
CHICAGO COMPUTER GUIDE✶. Text in English. m.
Indexed: SoftBase.
Published by: Micro Computer Learning Center, Inc., 954 W Washington Blvd, Ste 510, Chicago, IL 60607-2224. TEL 312-332-0419. Ed. Armond Mussey. adv.: page USD 1,400. Circ: 50,000.

004.16 DEU ISSN 0170-6632
CODEN: CHIPDP
CHIP; das Mikrocomputer-Magazin. Text in German. 1978. m. EUR 45.60 domestic; EUR 61.20 foreign; EUR 3.99 newsstand/cover (effective 2004). adv. bk.rev. back issues avail. **Document type:** *Magazine, Trade.*
Incorporates (1983-1986): H C - Mein Home Computer (0176-1021); Which incorporated (in 1983): P E - Populaere Elektronik (0724-2581); Which was formerly (1976-1982): Populaere Elektronik (0342-2437)
Related titles: ♦ CD-ROM ed.: Chip CD Plus; Online - full text ed.: (from EBSCO Publishing).
Indexed: Inspec, RefZh.
—BLDSC (3181.123600), AskIEEE, CISTI, IE, Infotrieve. **CCC.**
Published by: Vogel Verlag und Druck GmbH & Co. KG, Max-Planck-Str 7-9, Wuerzburg, 97064, Germany. TEL 49-931-4180, FAX 49-931-4182100, info@chip.de, marliese_bernhardt@vogel-medien.de, http://www.chip.de, http://www.vogel-medien.de. Ed. Thomas Pyczak. Adv. contact Gabriele Groitzsch. B&W page EUR 10,570, color page EUR 14,400; trim 185 x 266. Circ: 417,047 (paid). **Subscr. to:** Vogel Verlag, Max-Planck-Str 7-9, Wuerzburg 97064, Germany. **Dist. in US by:** Vogel Europublishing Inc., 632 Sunflower Ct., San Ramos, CA 94583. TEL 510-803-1266, 510-803-1265.

004.16 DEU
CHIP CD PLUS. Text in German. m. adv. **Document type:** *Trade.*
Media: CD-ROM. **Related titles:** Online - full text ed.: (from EBSCO Publishing); ♦ Print ed.: Chip. ISSN 0170-6632.
Published by: Vogel Verlag und Druck GmbH & Co. KG, Max-Planck-Str 7-9, Wuerzburg, 97064, Germany. TEL 49-931-418-2335, FAX 49-931-4182905, http://www.chip.de, http://www.vogel-medien.de. Circ: 3,500 (controlled). **Subscr. to:** DataM-Services GmbH, Fichtestr 9, Wuerzburg 97074, Germany. TEL 49-931-417001, FAX 49-931-4170499, swestenberger@datam-services.de, http://www.datam-services.de.

004.16 USA ISSN 1528-0608
QA76.76.A65 CODEN: CCINFK
CIRCUIT CELLAR; the magazine for computer applications. Text in English. 1988. m. USD 21.95 domestic; USD 31.95 in Canada & Mexico; USD 49.95 elsewhere (effective 2005). adv. illus. index. back issues avail.; reprints avail. **Document type:** *Trade.* **Description:** Dedicated to high-tech hardware design and software applications.
Formerly (until 1999): Circuit Cellar Ink (0896-8985)
Related titles: CD-ROM ed.: ISSN 1528-0810. 2000; Online - full text ed.: ISSN 1527-8131.
Indexed: CompI, Inspec.
—BLDSC (3198.835586), IE, Infotrieve, ingenta.
Published by: Circuit Cellar, Inc., 4 Park St., Ste. 20, Vernon, CT 06066. TEL 860-875-2199, http://www.circuitcellar.com/. Pub. Daniel Rodrigues. Adv. contact Sue Hodge. B&W page USD 2,100, color page USD 2,350; trim 10 x 7. Circ: 35,000 (paid).

004.16 USA ISSN 1053-752X
COMMUNAL COMPUTING NEWS. Text in English. 1987. q. USD 18 (effective 1999). **Document type:** *Newsletter.*
Published by: Communal Computing, Inc., 3222 Brooklawn Court, Chevy Chase, MD 20815. TEL 301-656-9524, FAX 301-656-9564. Ed. Glenn S Easton. adv.: page USD 695. Circ: 3,500.

COMPUTER (NEW YORK). see *COMPUTERS*

004.16 USA ISSN 1067-389X
CODEN: FIMIEV
COMPUTER JOURNAL (TULSA)✶. Text in English. 1989. m. USD 24; USD 36 foreign. adv. **Document type:** *Trade.* **Description:** Shows business people how computing technology can address their business needs. Presents the latest technology and trends in a non-technical way.
Published by: Adventure Publishing (Tulsa), 4941 S 78th E Ave, Tulsa, OK 74145-6410. TEL 918-621-2131, 800-726-7667, FAX 918-621-2134, tcj@tcpi.com. Ed., R&P, Adv. contact Cheryl Cooper. Circ: 70,000.

004.16 USA
COMPUTER LETTER; business issues in technology. Text in English. 1985. 40/yr. looseleaf. USD 595; USD 695 foreign. back issues avail. **Document type:** *Newsletter.* **Description:** Guide to business issues in computing and examines strategic planning.
Published by: Dow Jones Newsletters (Subsidiary of: Dow Jones Newswires), 1155 Av of the Americas, New York, NY 10036. TEL 212-597-5716.

COMPUTER RETAILERS' GUIDE. see *COMPUTERS—Personal Computers*

004.16 GBR ISSN 0010-4760
TK7885.A1 CODEN: COSVA3
COMPUTER SURVEY; list of digital computer installations world-wide. Text in English. 1962. bi-m. GBP 282. **Document type:** *Directory, Trade.*
Related titles: Diskette ed.
Indexed: BusI, CompC, CurCont, Inspec.
Published by: Inn Data Ltd., Wimbledon, PO Box 372, London, SW19 6LH, United Kingdom. TEL 44-181-780-2095, FAX 44-181-788-5243. Ed. Georgina A Dodd. Pub., R&P Barrie Lomas. Circ: 2,500.

025 USA ISSN 1041-7915
Z678.9.A1 CODEN: CPLIE8
COMPUTERS IN LIBRARIES. Variant title: C I L. Text in English. 1981. 10/yr. USD 99.95 domestic; USD 114 in Canada & Mexico; USD 124 elsewhere (effective 2005). bk.rev.; software rev. bibl.; illus. Index. back issues avail.; reprint service avail. from WSH. **Document type:** *Magazine, Trade.* **Description:** Provides complete coverage of the news and issues in the rapidly evolving field of library information technology.
Formerly (until 1989): Small Computers in Libraries (0275-6722); Which incorporated (1986-1988): Systems Librarian and Automation Review (0890-8354); (1985-1987): Bulletin Board Systems (0882-990X); And (1986-1987): Public Computing (0884-9498)
Related titles: Online - full text ed.: (from bigchalk, EBSCO Publishing, Florida Center for Library Automation, Gale Group, H.W. Wilson, Northern Light Technology, Inc., O C L C Online Computer Library Center, Inc., ProQuest Information & Learning).
Indexed: ABIn, B&I, CIJE, CINAHL, CLI, CompC, CompD, CompR, EngInd, IBR, IBZ, ILP, InfoSAb, Inspec, LHTB, LIMI, LISA, LibLit, MRD, MagInd, MicrocompInd, PCI, PCR2, SoftBase, T&II, WBA, WMB.
—BLDSC (3394.924000), AskIEEE, CINDOC, CISTI, IE, Infotrieve, ingenta, Linda Hall. **CCC.**
Published by: Information Today, Inc., 143 Old Marlton Pike, Medford, NJ 08055-8750. TEL 609-654-6266, FAX 609-654-4309, custserv@infotoday.com, http://www.infotoday.com/cilmag/default.shtml. Ed. Kathy Dempsey. Adv. contact Michael Zarrello. Circ: 6,000. **Subscr. outside US to:** Learned Information Europe Ltd., Woodside, Hinksey Hill, Oxford, Oxon OX1 5BE, United Kingdom. TEL 44-1865-388000, FAX 44-1865-736354.

COMPUTERTALK; for contemporary pharmacy management. see *PHARMACY AND PHARMACOLOGY—Computer Applications*

COMPUTERTALK PHARMACY SYSTEMS BUYERS GUIDE. see *PHARMACY AND PHARMACOLOGY—Computer Applications*

004.16 USA ISSN 0010-4841
CODEN: CMPWAB
COMPUTERWORLD; newsweekly for information technology leaders. Text in English. 1967. w. (Mon.). USD 99 domestic; USD 130 in Canada; USD 250 in Central America; USD 295 elsewhere (effective 2005). adv. bk.rev. bibl.; charts; illus.; mkt.; pat.; stat.; abstr. back issues avail.; reprint service avail. from PQC. **Document type:** *Magazine, Trade.* **Description:** Covers every aspect of the computer community and industry. Features in-depth reports, news, software, networking, systems, peripherals, and editorials.
Related titles: Microform ed.: (from PQC); Online - full text ed.: (from bigchalk, EBSCO Publishing, Florida Center for Library Automation, Gale Group, H.W. Wilson, LexisNexis, Northern Light Technology, Inc., O C L C Online Computer Library Center, Inc., ProQuest Information & Learning).
Indexed: ABIn, AIA, BPI, BusI, CADCAM, CompC, CompD, CompIU, InfoSAb, Inspec, LRI, MASUSE, MCIU, MagInd, MicrocompInd, PROMT, RASB, ResCtrInd, SoftBase, TelAb, WBA, WMB.
—BLDSC (3394.980000), CASDDS, CISTI, IE. **CCC.**
Published by: Computerworld, Inc. (Subsidiary of: I D G Communications Inc.), 500 Old Connecticut Path, Box 9171, Framingham, MA 01701-9171. TEL 508-879-0700, 800-669-1002, FAX 508-875-8931, maryfran_johnson@computerworld.com, http://www.computerworld.com. Ed. Don Tennant. Pub. Robert Carrigan. Adv. contact Dave Peterson. B&W page USD 22,930, color page USD 30,880. Circ: 250,707. **Subscr. to:** PO Box 2043, Marion, OH 43305-2043.

004.16 USA
COMPUTING TIMES. Text in English. m. USD 10.50. adv. bk.rev. **Document type:** *Trade.*
Related titles: Online - full text ed.
Published by: Triad Publications, PO Box 14018, Tulsa, OK 74159-1018. TEL 918-585-8564. Ed., Pub. Brent Morrison. Adv. contact Paul Karady. Circ: 40,000.

004.16 USA
COMPUTING UNPLUGGED. Text in English. m. free. adv. **Document type:** *Consumer.* **Description:** Offers ideas and techniques designed to help PalmPilot users get the most out of their devices.
Formerly (until 2003): PalmPower Magazine
Related titles: Online - full text ed.: ISSN 1554-5660.
Published by: ZATZ Publishing, PO Box 201, Rocky Hill, NJ 08553. TEL 609-497-4501, FAX 609-497-4008, david@palmpower.com, http://www.computingunplugged.com/, http://www.palmpower.com. Ed. David Gewirtz.

004.16 USA
COMPUTOREDGE. Text in English. 1982. w. USD 85 (effective 1999). adv. **Document type:** *Consumer.* **Description:** Contains non-technical, entertaining articles on all aspects of computers: hardware, software, technology, productivity, advice, and personal experience.
Related titles: Online - full text ed.
Published by: Byte Buyer, Inc., PO Box 83086, San Diego, CA 92138-1833. TEL 619-573-0315, FAX 619-573-0205, editor@computoredge.com, http://www.computoredge.com/. Ed. Leah Steward. Pub. John Dunning. R&P Patrica Smith. Adv. contact Elvira Phipps. page USD 1,157. Circ: 250,000.

CYBERLOG; library of applied medical software. see *MEDICAL SCIENCES—Computer Applications*

D E C U S MAGAZINE. see *COMPUTERS*

005.36 GBR
D N J (ONLINE). Text in English. 1997. bi-m. GBP 29, USD 42 (effective 2002). **Description:** Covers applications on the Windows platform.
Media: Online - full text.
Indexed: Inspec.
Published by: Matt Publishing Ltd., 7 Unity St, Bristol, BS1 5HH, United Kingdom. TEL 44-117-930-0255, FAX 44-117-930-0245, http://www.dnjonline.com. Ed., Pub. Matt Nicholson.

070.5797 USA
D T P TECHNIQUES. Text in English. m. **Document type:** *Newsletter.* **Description:** Electronic newsletter for NT desktop publishing.
Media: Online - full text.
Published by: Advanced Firmware, 235685, Encinitas, CA 92023-5685. TEL 619-756-5702, FAX 619-756-5702, support@advfirmware.com, http://www.advfirmware.com.

004.16 USA
D XERS MAGAZINE✶. Text in English. m. USD 15.
Address: RR 1 Box 121 A, Elloree, SC 29047-9801. Ed. Gus Browning.

004.16 FRA ISSN 1148-4675
DECISION MICRO. Text in French. 1982. w. EUR 39 domestic; EUR 48.30 foreign (effective 2003).
Formerly (until 1990): Decision Informatique (0293-3896)
—IE, Infotrieve. **CCC.**
Published by: Groupe Tests, 26 rue d'Oradour-sur-Glane, Paris, Cedex 15 75504, France. TEL 33-1-44253176, FAX 33-1-45580216, redaction@decision-micro_presse.fr, http://www.groupetests.fr. Ed. Jean Francois Ruiz. Circ: 25,474.

DEMOLETTER. see *COMPUTERS—Personal Computers*

DENTAL COMPUTER NEWSLETTER. see *MEDICAL SCIENCES—Computer Applications*

004.16 DEU ISSN 0936-8833
DESKTOP DIALOG. Text in German. 1987. m. EUR 66.34 domestic; EUR 76 foreign; EUR 6 newsstand/cover (effective 2004). adv. back issues avail. **Document type:** *Magazine, Trade.* **Description:** Provides information for digital publishing and multimedia users.
Related titles: Supplement(s): Desktop Dialog Special. ISSN 1434-9825. 1995.
Published by: Druckspiegel Verlagsgesellschaft mbH und Co., Industriestr 2, Heusenstamm, 63150, Germany. TEL 49-6104-606303, FAX 49-6104-606399, mdiehl@desktop-dialog.de, info@kepplermediengruppe.de, http://www.desktop-dialog.de, http://www.kepplermediengruppe.de. Ed. Manfred Diehl. adv.: color page EUR 4,250; trim 188 x 270. Circ: 14,800 (paid and controlled).

004.16 780 USA
DESKTOP MUSIC; production guide. Text in English. 2001. a., latest 2002. USD 6.95 newsstand/cover (effective 2001). adv. **Document type:** *Consumer.*
Published by: Primedia Business Magazines & Media, Inc. (Subsidiary of: Primedia, Inc.), 9800 Metcalf Ave, Overland Park, KS 66212-2216. TEL 913-341-1300, inquiries@primediabusiness.com, http://images.industryclick.com/files/33/DMPGframe.html, http://www.primediabusiness.com.

686.22544416 USA
DESKTOP PUBLISHING. Text in English. w. **Document type:** *Newsletter.* **Description:** Targets anyone involved in desktop publishing from novice to professional, for fun or for profit.
Media: Online - full text.
Published by: The Mining Company, PO Box 6572, New York, NY 10128-0006. TEL 212-876-3512, FAX 212-876-3512, desktoppub.guide@miningco.com, http://desktoppub.miningco.com/mbody.htm. Ed. Jacci Howard Bear.

004.16 USA
DIGITAL CHICAGO; the resource for Chicagoland's creative community. Text in English. 1989. bi-m. USD 22 (effective 1999). adv. bk.rev.; software rev. back issues avail. **Document type:** *Trade.* **Description:** Provides local and regional information, including news and reviews of software and hardware, profiles of local users, and a resource directory.
Formerly (until 1996): Mac - Chicago (1045-5825)
Published by: Digital Chicago, Inc., 401 N Wabash Ave, Ste 513, Chicago, IL 60611-5660. TEL 312-321-3229, FAX 312-329-9416, info@digitalchiago.com, info@digitalchiago.com, http://www.digitalchicago.com. Ed., Pub. Fred Lebolt. R&P, Adv. contact Phyllis Wier. Circ: 25,000.

004.16 USA ISSN 1547-8610
Z681.3.D53
DIGITAL DOCUMENT QUARTERLY. Text in English. 2002. q.
Media: Online - full content.
Published by: H M G Consulting, Inc., 20044 Glen Brae Dr, Saratoga, CA 95070. http://home.pacbell.net/hgladney/ddq.htm.

070.5797 ZAF ISSN 1024-8552
DIGITAL IMAGING & PUBLISHING. Text in English. 1988. 9/yr. ZAR 104; ZAR 170 in southern Africa; ZAR 540 elsewhere. adv. **Document type:** *Trade.* **Description:** Covers electronic publishing and pre-press.
Formerly: D T P Today (1016-1287)
Published by: Graphix Publications (Pty) Ltd., PO Box 751119, Garden View, 2047, South Africa. TEL 27-11-622-4800, FAX 27-11-622-2480, graphix@aztec.co.za. Ed. Colleen Bate. Pub. Brian Strickland. Adv. contact Dyelan Copeland.

004.16 USA ISSN 1056-7038
CODEN: DMEDEG
DIGITAL MEDIA: A SEYBOLD REPORT. Text in English. m. USD 395; USD 401 in Canada; USD 413 elsewhere. **Document type:** *Trade.*
Related titles: Online - full text ed.: (from EBSCO Publishing, Florida Center for Library Automation, Gale Group).
Indexed: CompD, Inspec, MicrocompInd.
—AskIEEE, IE.
Published by: Seybold Publications, 999 Oakmont Plaza Drive, Westmont, IL 60559. TEL 610-565-6864, 800-325-3830, FAX 610-565-1858. Ed. Mitch Radcliffe. Pub. Jonathan Seybold.

004.16 USA
DISKETTE GAZETTE. Text in English. 1986. m. free. bk.rev.
Published by: International Datawares Inc., 2150 A Oakland Rd, San Jose, CA 95131. TEL 408-943-1233, FAX 408-943-1002. Ed. Delfina Daves. Circ: 75,000.

DR. DOBB'S JOURNAL; software tools for the professional programmer. see *COMPUTERS—Software*

DR. DOBB'S JOURNAL ESPANA. see *COMPUTERS—Software*

631.3916 GBR
EMBEDDED SYSTEMS. Text in English. 1980. 8/yr. EUR 114; USD 15 newsstand/cover foreign (effective 2000). adv. back issues avail. **Document type:** *Trade.* **Description:** Provides in-depth technical information and news to embedded systems designers working in a range of vertical markets.
Former titles (until 1999): Embedded Systems Engineering (0969-8825); (until 1993): Microsystem Design (0269-1477); (until 1985): Micro Forecast (0144-1132)
Indexed: Inspec.
—BLDSC (3733.065500), IE, ingenta.
Published by: Electronic Design Automation Ltd., 63-66 Hatton Garden, London, EC1N 8SR, United Kingdom. TEL 44-20-76811000, FAX 44-20-72425124, afitzpatric@unmf.com, eda@edaltd.co.uk, http://qqq.es-mag.com, http://www.edaltd.co.uk/. adv.: B&W page GBP 3,500, color page GBP 5,600;. Circ: 17,983.

621.381 USA ISSN 1541-7956
EMBEDDED SYSTEMS DEVELOPMENT. Text in English. m. USD 60 domestic; USD 70 in Canada; USD 90 elsewhere; USD 7 newsstand/cover domestic; USD 8 newsstand/cover in Canada; USD 9 newsstand/cover elsewhere (effective 2000). **Document type:** *Trade.* **Description:** Provides up-to-date technical information and analysis to the engineers and engineering managers responsible for developing today's microprocessor and microcontroller-based embedded and real-time systems.
Formerly (until 2000): Penton's Embedded Systems Development (1099-4157)
Related titles: Online - full text ed.
Published by: Penton Media, Inc. (Hasbrouck Heights) (Subsidiary of: Pittway Company), 611 Rte 46 W, Hasbrouck Heights, NJ 07604. TEL 201-393-6057, FAX 201-393-6043, corpcomm@penton.com, http://www.penton.com. Circ: 50,000 (controlled).

004.16 USA
FLEXLINES. Text in English. 1984. 6/yr. USD 30; USD 60 foreign. adv. bk.rev. **Document type:** *Trade.*
Published by: Data Access Corporation, 14000 S W 119th Ave, Miami, FL 33186. TEL 305-238-0012, FAX 305-238-0017, TELEX 469021 DATA ACCESS CI. Ed. Beverly Horning Gore. Pub. C L Casanave. Circ: 5,000.

FORBES - ANDREW SEYBOLD'S WIRELESS OUTLOOK; a monthly perspective of issues affecting the mobile computer and communications industries. see *COMPUTERS—Computer Industry*

004.16 USA
FROBBER✶. Text in English. q. USD 195. adv. **Description:** Instructs Atari computer users.
Published by: (Tri-Comp Polytechnical Inc.), FROBCO, c/o Embarcadero Venture, Box 2600, Menlo Park, CA 94026-2600. Ed. Candace L Brown. Circ: 200 (controlled).

G R M U G NEWSLETTER. see *COMPUTERS—Personal Computers*

004.16 USA
GREATER KANSAS CITY COMPUTER USER MAGAZINE. Text in English. 1990. m. USD 12 (effective 2005). **Document type:** *Newspaper, Trade.*
Formerly: K C Computer User
Address: d/b/a A&W Publishing, P O Box 26025, Overland Park, KS 66225-6025. TEL 913-345-2675, FAX 913-451-1698, contact@kccomputeruser.com, http://www.kccomputeruser.com/. Ed. James Mathewson. Pub. Ron Goertzen. R&P Angie Fitzsimmons TEL 913-341-6881. Adv. contact Kathy Boos. Circ: 40,000.

H A L - P C MAGAZINE. see *COMPUTERS—Personal Computers*

004.16 USA ISSN 0892-2829
QA76.8.H48
THE H P CHRONICLE✶; the independent newspaper for Hewlett-Packard computers users. (Hewlett-Packard) Text in English. 1983. m. USD 45; USD 75 foreign (effective 1999). back issues avail. **Document type:** *Trade.*
Formerly: Chronicle (Austin) (0741-0522)
Related titles: Online - full text ed.: (from ProQuest Information & Learning).
—IE, Infotrieve.
Published by: Publications & Communications, Inc., 505 Cypress Creek Rd, Ste B, Cedar Park, TX 78613-4429. TEL 512-250-9023, 800-678-9724, FAX 512-331-3900. adv.: B&W page USD 3,586, color page USD 4,336; trim 14.5 x 10.75. Circ: 17,000.

004.16 USA ISSN 0747-055X
HOME COMPUTER MAGAZINE✶. Text in English. 1981. 10/yr. USD 25. bk.rev. back issues avail.
Former titles: 99'er Home Computer Magazine; 99'er Magazine
Indexed: CompD.
Published by: Emerald Valley Publishing Co., PO Box 860, Gleneden Beach, OR 97388-0860. TEL 503-485-8796. Ed. Gary Kaplan. Circ: 250,000.

004.16 USA ISSN 0272-1732
CODEN: IEMIDZ
➤ **I E E E MICRO.** Text in English. 1981. bi-m. USD 710 (effective 2006). adv. bk.rev. bibl.; charts; illus.; tr.lit. index. reprints avail. **Document type:** *Journal, Academic/Scholarly.* **Description:** For advanced microcomputer users. Articles on chips, systems, applications, software, hardware design, new technical developments and microcomputer law and standards.
Related titles: CD-ROM ed.; Microfiche ed.; Online - full text ed.: (from EBSCO Publishing, I E E E).
Indexed: AIA, AS&TI, ASCA, CMCI, CompAb, CompB, CompC, CompD, CompLI, CurCont, CybAb, EngInd, ErgAb, ISMEC, ISR, Inspec, PCR2, RASB, RILM, RefZh, RoboAb, SCI, SSCI.
—BLDSC (4362.999500), AskIEEE, CISTI, Ei, IDS, IE, Infotrieve, ingenta, Linda Hall. **CCC.**
Published by: Institute of Electrical and Electronics Engineers, Inc., 445 Hoes Ln, Piscataway, NJ 08854-1331. TEL 732-981-0060, 800-701-4333, FAX 732-981-1721, micro-ma@computer.org, subscription-service@ieee.org, http://www.computer.org/micro, http://www.ieee.org. Ed. Stephen L Diamond. adv.: B&W page USD 2,290, color page USD 3,490. Circ: 6,246 (paid). **Subscr. to:** Maruzen Co., Ltd., 3-10 Nihonbashi 2-chome, Chuo-ku, Tokyo 103-0027, Japan. FAX 81-3-3275-0657; Universal Subscription Agency, Pvt. Ltd., 877, Udyog Vihar, V, Gurgoan 122001, India. TEL 91-124-347261, FAX 91-124-342496. **Co-sponsor:** Computer Society.

004.16 USA ISSN 1536-125X
T174.7 CODEN: IWCEAS
I E E E TRANSACTIONS ON NANOTECHNOLOGY. Text in English. 2002. bi-m. USD 590 combined subscription print & online eds. (effective 2006). **Document type:** *Journal, Trade.*
Related titles: Online - full content ed.: USD 475 (effective 2006); Online - full text ed.: (from EBSCO Publishing).
Indexed: CurCont, Inspec, MSCI, RefZh.
—BLDSC (4363.206900), CISTI, IE, Linda Hall. **CCC.**
Published by: Institute of Electrical and Electronics Engineers, Inc., 445 Hoes Ln, Piscataway, NJ 08854-1331. TEL 908-981-0060, FAX 908-981-9667, subscription-service@ieee.org, http://www.ieee.org. Ed. Sandip Tiwari. **Subscr. to:** Universal Subscription Agency, Pvt. Ltd., 877, Udyog Vihar, V, Gurgoan 122001, India. TEL 91-124-347261, FAX 91-124-342496.

I E E PROCEEDINGS - SOFTWARE. see *COMPUTERS—Software*

INDIVIDUAL INVESTOR'S GUIDE TO COMPUTERIZED INVESTING. see *BUSINESS AND ECONOMICS—Investments*

004.16 DEU ISSN 0941-6048
INFODOC; Technologien fuer Information und Dokumentation. Text in German. 1992. 6/yr. adv. bk.rev. back issues avail. **Document type:** *Journal, Academic/Scholarly.*
Formed by the merger of (1990-1992): Gigatrend (0178-7853); (1975-1992): Mikrodok (0344-8010); Which was formerly (until 1978): Mikrodok-Informations-Dienst (0343-0286)
Indexed: Inspec.
—AskIEEE.
Published by: F B O - Fachverlag fuer Buero- und Organisationstechnik GmbH, Taunusstr 54, Wiesbaden, 65183, Germany. TEL 49-611-534-0, FAX 49-611-534430. Ed. Heinz Scharfenberg. Adv. contact Cornelia Maschke.

004.16 USA ISSN 0895-8726
INFONETICS. Text in English. 1987. irreg.
Published by: Infonetics Research Institute, 900 E. Hamilton Ave., Ste. 230, Campbell, CA 95008-0665. TEL 408-298-7999, FAX 408-298-2073. Ed. Michael Howard. R&P Larry Howard.

686.22 USA
INSIDE REPORT ON NEW MEDIA. Text in English. 1986. m. USD 395. **Document type:** *Newsletter, Trade.*
Former titles: Bove & Rhodes Inside Report on Desktop Publishing and Multimedia (1043-6065); (until 1988): Bove and Rhodes Inside Report
Published by: Conference Communications Ireland, 1320 18th St, San Francisco, CA 94107. TEL 415-776-8667, FAX 415-431-9368, cci@ireland.com, http://www.webcom.com/insrep/. Ed. Tom Hargadon.

INTEL OWNER'S CLUB. see *COMPUTERS—Software*

004.16 CAN ISSN 1206-212X
QA76.5 CODEN: IJCAFW
INTERNATIONAL JOURNAL OF COMPUTERS AND APPLICATIONS. Text in English. 1979. 3/yr. USD 80 membership individual; USD 175 membership corporate (effective 2005). adv. bk.rev. index. back issues avail. **Document type:** *Journal, Academic/Scholarly.* **Description:** Covers all aspects of mini and microcomputers including technology, hardware, software, systems, education, networks, distributed processing and applications.
Formerly (until 1997): International Journal of Mini and Microcomputers (0702-0481)
Indexed: BrCerAb, C&ISA, CerAb, ChemAb, CompAb, CompC, CompLI, CompR, CorrAb, CybAb, E&CAJ, EMA, EngInd, IAA, Inspec, M&TEA, MBF, METADEX, WAA.
—BLDSC (4542.175480), AskIEEE, CISTI, Ei, IE, Infotrieve, ingenta, Linda Hall. **CCC.**
Published by: ACTA Press, 4500-16th Ave NW, Ste 80, Calgary, AB T3B 0M6, Canada. TEL 403-288-1195, FAX 403-247-6851, journals@actapress.com, http://www.actapress.com/Editors.aspx?JournalID=2.

004.14 SGP ISSN 0219-581X
QC176.8.N35 CODEN: IJNNAJ
➤ **INTERNATIONAL JOURNAL OF NANOSCIENCE.** Text in English. 2002. bi-m. SGD 369, USD 217, EUR 197 to individuals; SGD 921, USD 542, EUR 491 combined subscription to institutions print & online eds.; SGD 552, USD 325, EUR 295 combined subscription in developing nations to institutions print & online eds. (effective 2006). back issues avail. **Document type:** *Journal, Academic/Scholarly.* **Description:** Covers all aspects of nanometer scale science and technology, including subjects from basic science of nanoscale physics and chemistry to nanostructured materials and applications in nanodevices, quantum engineering and quantum computing.
Related titles: Online - full content ed.; Online - full text ed.: (from EBSCO Publishing, O C L C Online Computer Library Center, Inc., Swets Information Services).
Indexed: BrCerAb, C&ISA, CerAb, CorrAb, E&CAJ, EMA, IAA, Inspec, M&TEA, MBF, METADEX, SolStAb, WAA.
—BLDSC (4542.369250), CISTI, IE, ingenta, Linda Hall. **CCC.**
Published by: World Scientific Publishing Co. Pte. Ltd., 5 Toh Tuck Link, Singapore, 596224, Singapore. wspc@wspc.com.sg, http://www.worldscinet.com/journals/ijn/ijn.shtml, http://www.worldscientific.com. **Subscr. in the US to:** Farrer Rd, PO Box 128, Singapore 912805, Singapore. TEL 65-382-5663, FAX 65-382-5919. **Dist. by:** World Scientific Publishing Ltd., 57 Shelton St, London WC2H 9HE, United Kingdom. TEL 44-20-78360888, FAX 44-20-78362020, sales@wspc.co.uk.; World Scientific Publishing Co., Inc., 1060 Main St, River Edge, NJ 07661. TEL 201-487-9655, FAX 201-487-9656, 888-977-2665, wspc@wspc.com.

➤ **INTERNATIONAL SYMPOSIUM ON MINI AND MICROCOMPUTERS. PROCEEDINGS.** see *COMPUTERS—Minicomputers*

➤ **INTERNET & PERSONAL COMPUTING ABSTRACTS (ONLINE EDITION).** see *COMPUTERS—Abstracting, Bibliographies, Statistics*

➤ **J U G NEWSLETTER.** see *COMPUTERS—Computer Networks*

384 004.16 ESP ISSN 1696-313X
▼ ➤ **JOURNAL OF DIGITAL CONTENTS;** an international journal. Abbreviated title: J D C. Text in Multiple languages. 2004. q. back issues avail. **Document type:** *Journal, Academic/Scholarly.* **Description:** Covers the management, presentation and uses of contents in digital environments including research, technical, design and practical issues aimed at researchers, developers and teachers.
Related titles: Online - full text ed.: ISSN 1697-4735. free (effective 2005).
Published by: Formatex Research Centre, C/ Zurbaran 1, 2o(Office1), Badajoz, 06001, Spain. jdc@formatex.org, http://www.formatex.org/jdc/jdc.htm.

004.16 USA ISSN 1546-2234
CODEN: JEUCEZ
➤ **JOURNAL OF ORGANIZATIONAL AND END USER COMPUTING;** the international journal of information user management. Text in English. 1989. q. USD 95 combined subscription to individuals print & online eds.; USD 315 combined subscription to institutions print & online eds. (effective 2005). adv. bk.rev. 48 p./no.; **Document type:** *Journal, Academic/Scholarly.* **Description:** Provides a forum to both academics and information technology practitioners to advance the practice and understanding of end-user computing in organizations.
Former titles (until 2004): Journal of End User Computing (1063-2239); (until 1992): Journal of Microcomputer Systems Management (1043-6464)
Related titles: Online - full text ed.: ISSN 1533-7987 (from bigchalk, EBSCO Publishing, Factiva, Florida Center for Library Automation, Gale Group, O C L C Online Computer Library Center, Inc., ProQuest Information & Learning).
Indexed: ABIn, BPI, BrCerAb, BusEdI, C&ISA, CerAb, CompD, CompLI, CorrAb, E&CAJ, EMA, Emerald, EngInd, IAA, InfoSAb, Inspec, LISA, M&TEA, MBF, METADEX, MicrocompInd, ORMS, QC&AS, SolStAb, WAA.
—BLDSC (5027.058000), AskIEEE, Ei, IE, Infotrieve, ingenta, Linda Hall. **CCC.**
Published by: (Information Resources Management Association), Idea Group Publishing (Subsidiary of: Idea Group Inc.), 701 E Chocolate Ave, Ste 200, Hershey, PA 17033-1240. TEL 717-533-8845, 866-342-6657, FAX 717-533-7115, cust@idea-group.com, jtravers@idea-group.com, http://www.idea-group.com/journals/details.asp?id=130. Ed. Mo Adam Mahmood. R&P Jan Travers. Circ: 250.

➤ **KOMPUTER FOR ALLE.** see *COMPUTERS—Minicomputers*

➤ **L T WORLD.** (Library Technology) see *LIBRARY AND INFORMATION SCIENCES—Computer Applications*

➤ **LANGUAGE RESOURCES AND EVALUATION.** see *HUMANITIES: COMPREHENSIVE WORKS—Computer Applications*

➤ **LAWYER'S P C.** see *LAW—Computer Applications*

004.16 USA ISSN 1523-0422
LONG DISTANCE COMPETITION REPORT. Text in English. 1983. s-m. USD 697 in North America; USD 721 elsewhere (effective 2005). index, cum.index. **Document type:** *Newsletter.* **Description:** Independent "business intelligence" on all of AT&T's activities. Briefings on new products and services, computers and networking equipment, prices and marketing. Full coverage of long-distance activities, joint ventures, regulatory action, personnel decisions.
Formerly (until 1999): Report on A T and T (0741-8361)
Related titles: Online - full text ed.: (from Factiva).
Published by: Warren Communications News, Inc., 2115 Ward Ct, N W, Washington, DC 20037. TEL 202-872-9200, 800-327-7205, FAX 202-293-3435, info@warren-news.com, http://www.telecommunications.com, http://www.warren-news.com. Ed. Michael Feazel. Pub. Albert Warren. **Dist. by:** Publications Resource Group, 121 Union St., Box 792, North Adams, MA 01247. TEL 413-664-6185, FAX 413-664-9343.

004.16 CHE
M & K COMPUTERMARKT; Schweizer Fachzeitschrift fuer Computer und Kommunikation. Text in German. 1979. m. CHF 75; CHF 85 foreign. **Document type:** *Trade.*
Formed by the merger of: Mikro- und Klein-Computer (0251-0006); Computermarkt (0254-5012); Mikro-Klein Computer
Indexed: Inspec.
—AskIEEE.
Published by: M & K Computer Verlag AG, Seeburgstr 12, Luzern 15, 6000, Switzerland. TEL 041-3701846, FAX 041-307268. Ed. Daniel Schwarzentruber. adv.: B&W page CHF 3,570, color page CHF 4,470; trim 285 x 185. Circ: 15,000.

004.16 SWE ISSN 1650-5786
M3; maxi mobile magazine. Text in Swedish. 2001. 11/yr. SEK 399 (effective 2003). adv. **Document type:** *Magazine, Consumer.* **Description:** Provides information and advice for purchasers and users of data, IT and mobile products such as laptops, desktop computers, computer components, palm computers, digital cameras, and mobile phones.
Formed by the merger of (1991-2001): Maxidata (1102-7029); (2000-2001): Mobile World (1650-0415)
Related titles: Online - full text ed.
Published by: I D G AB (Subsidiary of: I D G Communications Inc.), Sturegatan 11, Stockholm, 10678, Sweden. TEL 46-8-4536000, FAX 46-8-4536005, m3@idg.se, http://m3.idg.se, http://www.idg.se. Ed. Daniel Sjoeholm. adv.: color page SEK 43,100; 185 x 260. Circ: 26,100.

004.16 USA ISSN 1065-3929
MACROMEDIA USER JOURNAL (GUALALA); for multimedia developers and users of macromedia programs. Text in English. m.
Formerly (until 1992): Macromind
Published by: Bove & Rhoades, PO Box 1289, Gualala, CA 95445-1289. TEL 707-884-4413, 800-222-4863, FAX 707-884-4421. Eds. Cheryl Rhodes, Tony Bove.

004.16 USA
MACS U N I T E. (Users Network for Integrating Technology into Education) Text in English. irreg. free. **Document type:** *Newsletter.* **Description:** Includes news on Mac related products.
Media: E-mail.
Address: 15016 W 150th St, Olathe, KS 66062. KCStarguy@aol.com, http://members.aol.com/kcstarguy/camp/. Ed. Eric Flescher.

MACWORLD; the Macintosh magazine for the network professional. see *COMPUTERS—Personal Computers*

MACWORLD SWEDEN. see *COMPUTERS—Personal Computers*

004.16 JPN ISSN 1343-8565
TS540
MAIKUROMEKATORONIKUSU/MICROMECHATRONICS. Text in Japanese; Summaries in English. 1957. q. JPY 500 membership (effective 2003). adv. **Document type:** *Bulletin, Academic/Scholarly.* **Description:** Covers the development of micro and wearable information devices.
Formerly (until 1997): Nihon Tokei Gakkaishi (Tokyo, 1957)/Horological Institute of Japan. Journal (Tokyo, 1957) (0029-0416)
Indexed: Inspec, JTA, RefZh.
—BLDSC (5759.191000), AskIEEE, Linda Hall.
Published by: Nihon Tokei Gakkai/Horological Institute of Japan, HIJ Secretariat Office, Business Center for Academic Societies, 5-16-9 Honkomagome, Bunkyo Ward, Tokyo, 113-0021, Japan. TEL 81-3-5814-5801, FAX 81-3-5814-5820, hij@wwwsoc.nii.ac.jp, http://wwwsoc.nii.ac.jp/hij/.

MAPLE ORCHARD; Canadian publication on Apple and Macintosh computing. see *COMPUTERS—Personal Computers*

004.16 GBR ISSN 0956-3881
MICRO COMPUTER MART; the bargain buy for bargain buys. Text in English. 1985. w. GBP 80 in United Kingdom; GBP 150 rest of Europe; GBP 250 rest of world; GBP 1.10 newsstand/cover (effective 2000). adv. bk.rev.; software rev. back issues avail. **Document type:** *Consumer.* **Description:** Contains news, reports and information on available new and used computers.
Published by: Trinity Publications Ltd.., 1st Fl, Edward House, 92-93 Edward St, Birmingham, B1 2RA, United Kingdom. TEL 44-121-233-8712, FAX 44-121-233-8715, editorial@microcomputermart.co.uk, http://micromart.co.uk/. Ed., R&P Andrew Shorter. Pub. Sara Wilde. Adv. contact Lisa Evans. B&W page GBP 417.35; trim 210 x 297. **Dist. by:** M M C Ltd., Octagon House, White Hart Meadows, Ripley, Woking, Surrey GU23 6HR, United Kingdom. TEL 44-1483-211222, FAX 44-1483-224541.

MICRO MEDICAL NEWSLETTER. see *MEDICAL SCIENCES—Computer Applications*

004.16 USA ISSN 0742-9398
MICRO MONEY NEWSLETTER✶. Text in English. 1983. 10/yr. looseleaf. USD 55. back issues avail. **Description:** Explains how to make money with microcomputers and their related products.
Published by: H O W Publishing Company Inc., 232 Briargate Rd, Washington, IL 61571-3118. Ed. Harry Wahl.

004.16 FRA ISSN 0765-2887
MICRO P C. Text in French. m.
Published by: Editions Verona, 69 rue de Rome, Paris, 75008, France. TEL 45-22-55-33. Ed. Eric von Ascheberg. Circ: 40,000.

004.16 FRA ISSN 0183-5084
MICRO SYSTEMES. Text in French. 11/yr.
Indexed: Inspec.
—CISTI.
Address: 2-12 rue de Bellevue, Paris, 75019, France. TEL 42-00-33-05, FAX 42-41-89-40. Ed. Pascal Rosier. Circ: 96,000.

MICROBANKER BANKING TECHNOLOGY STRATEGIES NEWSLETTER; the research letter on financial end-user computing. see *BUSINESS AND ECONOMICS—Banking And Finance—Computer Applications*

004.16 THA ISSN 0857-0140
MICROCOMPUTER; for general P C user. Variant title: Microcomputer Magazine. Text and summaries in English, Thai. 1983. m. THB 720; THB 60 newsstand/cover. adv. software rev. charts; illus.; mkt.; stat.; tr.lit. Index. back issues avail. **Document type:** *Consumer.*
Published by: Se - Education Public Company Ltd., Asok-Dindang Rd, Dindang, 800-43-45 Soi Trakulsuk, Bangkok, 10320, Thailand. TEL 66-2-6429800, FAX 66-2-6429866, se-ed@loxinfo.co.th. Ed. Mongkol Kaewchan. Adv. contact Kriangkrai Cheepcharoenrath.

▼ new title ➤ refereed ✶ unverified ♦ full entry avail.

004.16 USA ISSN 1076-8289
TK7800
MICROCOMPUTER JOURNAL; the magazine for computer enthusiasts. Text in English. 1984. bi-m. USD 24; USD 29 in Canada & Mexico; USD 49 elsewhere. adv. **Document type:** *Consumer.* **Description:** For readers actively involved in upgrading and expanding personal computer, microcontrollers and related equipment for both home and work.
Former titles (until Dec. 1993): Computercraft (1055-5072); (until 1992): Modern Electronics (0149-2357)
Indexed: IHTDI, MicrocompInd.
—CISTI.
Published by: Midnight Engineering, 103 8th St., Fowler, CO 81039-1003. TEL 719-254-4558, FAX 719-254-4517. Ed. Arthur Salsberg. Pub. William E Gates. Adv. contact Donald Allen. Circ: 50,000.

004.16 USA ISSN 1066-1824
QA76.215
MICROCOMPUTER MARKET PLACE (YEAR); the complete guide to PC software and hardware vendors, service providers, and information sources. Text in English. 1993. a. USD 29.95. **Document type:** *Directory.* **Description:** Lists major companies and providers of software, hardware, and microcomputer service.
Published by: Random House Inc. (Subsidiary of: W. Bertelsmann Verlag GmbH & Co. KG), 201 East 50th St, New York, NY 10022. **Dist. by:** Reference Press Inc.. TEL 512-454-7778, FAX 512-454-9401.

004.16 USA ISSN 1055-3258
THE MICROCOMPUTER TRAINER. Text in English. 1991. m. (11/yr.). USD 195. bk.rev. back issues avail. **Document type:** *Newsletter.* **Description:** Offers practical solutions and strategies for professional trainers and technical support staff responsible for building end-user skills.
Published by: Systems Literacy Inc., PO Box 1032, Hopatcong, NJ 07843-0832. TEL 201-330-8963, FAX 201-330-0163. Ed. Loretta Weiss Morris. Pub. Loretta Weiss-Morris. R&P Barbara Schinke.

C

004.16 THA
MICROCOMPUTER USER; for PC buyers and general public. Text and summaries in English, Thai. 1993. m. THB 600; THB 50 newsstand/cover. adv. bk.rev.; software rev. charts; illus.; mkt.; maps; stat.; tr.lit. Index. back issues avail. **Document type:** *Consumer.* **Description:** Provides information for PC buyers and general users.
Published by: Se - Education Public Company Ltd., Asok-Dindang Rd, Dindang, 800-43-45 Soi Trakulsuk, Bangkok, 10320, Thailand. TEL 66-2-6429800, FAX 66-2-6429866, se-ed@loxinfo.co.th. Ed. Wirath Winijwatanawong. Adv. contact Patcharin Preuthikul.

MICROELECTRONICS AND SIGNAL PROCESSING. see *ELECTRONICS*

MICROPROCESSOR-BASED AND INTELLIGENT SYSTEMS ENGINEERING. see *ENGINEERING*

004.16 USA ISSN 1049-2445
MICROPROCESSOR I C'S D.A.T.A. DIGEST. (Integrated Circuits) Text in English. 1981. a. USD 205. adv. **Description:** Reference guide covering up to 20 technical parameters on over 20,300 devices from more than 185 manufacturers.
Formerly: Microprocessor I C's D.A.T.A. Book (0276-511X)
Related titles: CD-ROM ed.
Published by: D.A.T.A. Business Publishing (Subsidiary of: I H S Energy), 15 Inverness Way E, Box 6510, Englewood, CO 80155-6510. TEL 800-447-4666, FAX 303-799-4082. Ed. Walt Bryant. Adv. contact Laura Burrell.

004.16 NLD ISSN 0141-9331
QA76.5 CODEN: MIMID5
➤ **MICROPROCESSORS AND MICROSYSTEMS.** Text in Dutch. 1976. 8/yr. EUR 678 in Europe to institutions; JPY 90,100 in Japan to institutions; USD 758 to institutions except Europe and Japan (effective 2006). bk.rev. abstr.; illus. index. back issues avail. **Document type:** *Academic/Scholarly.* **Description:** Serves the professional computing and engineering community with practical papers on the design and implementation of microprocessor-based computer and control systems.
Formerly: Microprocessors (0308-5953)
Related titles: Microform ed.: (from PQC); Online - full text ed.: (from EBSCO Publishing, Gale Group, IngentaConnect, ScienceDirect, Swets Information Services).
Indexed: AIA, ASCA, BMT, BrCerAb, BrTechI, CADCAM, CMCI, CompAb, CompC, CompD, CompLI, CurCont, EngInd, ICEA, Inspec, LAMP, RefZh, RoboAb, SoftAbEng.
—BLDSC (5759.771000), AskIEEE, CISTI, Ei, IDS, IE, Infotrieve, ingenta, Linda Hall. **CCC.**
Published by: Elsevier BV (Subsidiary of: Elsevier Science & Technology), Radarweg 29, Amsterdam, 1043 NX, Netherlands. TEL 31-20-4853911, FAX 31-20-4852457, nlinfo-f@elsevier.nl, http://www.elsevier.com/locate/micpro, http://www.elsevier.nl. Eds. A K Somani, J E Cooling. **Subscr.:** PO Box 211, Amsterdam 1000 AE, Netherlands. TEL 31-20-485-3757, FAX 31-20-485-3432.

004.16 GBR ISSN 0269-5766
MICROSCOPE. Text in English. 1982. w. GBP 49 domestic; USD 82 in United States; GBP 49.90 elsewhere (effective 2005). adv. **Document type:** *Magazine, Trade.* **Description:** Covers the latest news and analysis and assesses how issues impact on the marketplace involving computer manufacturers, distributors and resellers.
Related titles: Online - full text ed.: (from Gale Group, ProQuest Information & Learning).
Indexed: CompD, PhotoAb, WSCA.
—CCC.
Published by: Reed Business Information Ltd. (Subsidiary of: Reed Business), Quadrant House, The Quadrant, Brighton Rd, Sutton, Surrey SM2 5AS, United Kingdom. TEL 44-20-86523500, FAX 44-20-86528932, rbi.subscriptions@qss-uk.com, http://www.microscope.co.uk/, http://www.reedbusiness.co.uk/. Ed. Billy MacInnes TEL 44-208-652-2069. Adv. contact Paul Shapiro. Circ: 10,289.

004.16 003 USA ISSN 1389-2134
MICROSYSTEMS. Text in English. irreg., latest vol.15, 2005. price varies. **Description:** Provides an outstanding library of research, text, and reference materials in the field of Microsystems.
—BLDSC (5760.880000).
Published by: Springer-Verlag New York, Inc. (Subsidiary of: Springer Science+Business Media), 233 Spring St, New York, NY 10013. TEL 212-460-1500, FAX 212-460-1575, service@springer-ny.com, http://www.springer-ny.com. Ed. Stephen D Senturia.

004.16 CAN ISSN 0836-5482
MICROVIEW; journal for micro users in business. Text in English. 10/yr. CND 149 domestic; CND 161 foreign (effective 2000). **Document type:** *Newsletter.* **Description:** Informative publication on microcomputers. Covers applications, reviews and evaluations of new products.
Published by: Canadian Institute of Chartered Accountants, 277 Wellington St W, Toronto, ON M5V 3H2, Canada. TEL 416-977-3222, FAX 416-977-8585. Eds. Blair Whelan, Hugh Hardie.

004.16 SWE ISSN 0348-4009
MIKRODATORN. Text in Swedish. 15/yr. SEK 645 (effective 2003). adv. **Document type:** *Magazine, Trade.* **Description:** Contains product reviews, comparisons, and the latest news on all professional microcomputers, including IBM compatibles and Macintoshes.
Related titles: Audio cassette/tape ed.; Online - full text ed.: ISSN 1402-4802.
Published by: I D G AB (Subsidiary of: I D G Communications Inc.), Sturegatan 11, Stockholm, 10678, Sweden. TEL 46-8-4536000, FAX 46-8-4536005, http://mikrodatorn.idg.se, http://www.idg.se. Ed. Torgny Palm. Pub. Bengt A Marnfeldt. Adv. contact Thomas Nyhlen. color page SEK 64,000; trim 185 x 260. Circ: 31,200 (paid).

621.3916 621.3914 USA
MINI/MICRO CONFERENCE RECORD. Text in English. irreg. price varies. **Document type:** *Proceedings, Trade.*
Indexed: Inspec.
Published by: Institute of Electrical and Electronics Engineers, Inc., 3 Park Ave, 17th Fl, New York, NY 10016-5997. TEL 212-419-7900, 800-678-4333, FAX 212-752-4929, customer.service@ieee.org, http://www.ieee.org.

681.3 ITA ISSN 1723-0683
▼ **IL MIO PALMARE.** Text in Italian. 2003. 8/yr. EUR 5.20 newsstand/cover (effective 2003). adv. **Document type:** *Magazine, Consumer.*
Published by: Play Press Publishing s.r.l., Via Vitorchiano 123, Rome, RM 00189, Italy. TEL 39-06-33221250, FAX 39-06-33221235, abbonamenti@playpress.com, http://www.playpress.com. Ed. Diego Magnani. Pub. Alessandro Ferri. Circ: 50,000 (paid and controlled).

004.16 USA ISSN 1070-2792
MONITOR (BROOKEVILLE). Text in English. 1982. 12/yr. USD 42 membership (effective 2005). adv. bk.rev. **Document type:** *Magazine, Trade.* **Description:** News, announcements, advertisements, and special features for users of IBM personal computers and compatibles.
Formerly: Capital P C Monitor (0884-0830)
Published by: Capital P C User Group, Inc., 19209 Mt Airey Rd, Brookeville, MD 20833. TEL 301-762-9372, FAX 301-762-9375, editor@cpcug.org, http://cpcug.org. Ed., R&P, Adv. contact Susan Kousek. Circ: 1,500 (controlled).

N O H U G NEWS. see *COMPUTERS—Personal Computers*

NEW ENGLAND WORLD OF SANYO. see *COMPUTERS—Personal Computers*

004.16 JPN ISSN 0288-3635
QA76.5
➤ **NEW GENERATION COMPUTING**; computing paradigms and computational intelligence. Text in Japanese. 1983. q. EUR 388 to institutions (effective 2005). illus. reprint service avail. from PSC,ISI. **Document type:** *Journal, Academic/Scholarly.* **Description:** Covers the fields of programming (logic, constraint, functional, and object-oriented); distributed and parallel computing; knowledge-based systems; agent-oriented systems; learning; knowledge discovery; evolutionary mechanisms; and emergent systems.
Related titles: Microfiche ed.: (from PQC); Online - full text ed.: (from EBSCO Publishing).
Indexed: AHCI, AIA, ASCA, CADCAM, CMCI, CompAb, CompLI, CompR, CurCont, CybAb, EngInd, Inspec, SSCI, ZentMath.
—BLDSC (6084.211200), AskIEEE, CISTI, Ei, IDS, IE, Infotrieve, ingenta, Linda Hall. **CCC.**
Published by: Springer-Verlag Tokyo (Subsidiary of: Springer Science+Business Media), 3-13 Hongo 3-chome, Bunkyo-ku, Tokyo, 113-0033, Japan. TEL 81-3-38120331, FAX 81-3-38187454, http://www.springer-tokyo.co.jp/. Ed. Koichi Furukawa. **Subscr. in the Americas to:** Springer-Verlag New York, Inc., Journal Fulfillment, PO Box 2485, Secaucus, NJ 07096-2485. TEL 201-348-4033, FAX 201-348-4505; **Subscr. to:** Springer GmbH Auslieferungsgesellschaft, Haberstr 7, Heidelberg 69126, Germany. TEL 49-6221-345-0, FAX 49-6221-345-4229, subscriptions@springer.de.

004.16 USA
NEWS & REVIEW. Text in English. 1987. m. USD 35; USD 75 foreign. adv. bk.rev. **Document type:** *Newspaper.* **Description:** Aimed at mainstream computer users worldwide. Focuses on DBMS news with other departments on client-server computing, networking and the internet.
Published by: Thurman Marketing Services Inc., 145 Columbia, Ste 100, Aliso Viejo, CA 92656-1490. TEL 714-362-3993, FAX 714-362-4151, compnews@newsrev.com, http://www.hewsrev.com. Ed. Stanley Goodrich. R&P Phyllis Thurman. Adv. contact Scott Thurman. B&W page USD 1,650, color page USD 2,680. Circ: 25,000.

004.16 GBR
NEWS I S. Text in English. w. USD 540 (effective 2000). bk.rev. **Document type:** *Trade.*
Formerly: News I B M
Media: Online - full text.
Published by: Xephon plc, 27-35 London Rd, Newbury, Berks RG14 1JL, United Kingdom. info@xephon.com, http://www.xephon.com. Ed. Trevor Eddolls. Circ: 1,500 (paid).

NEWSLINK (WESTERVILLE). see *COMPUTERS—Personal Computers*

004.16 JPN ISSN 0918-581X
NIKKEI OPEN SYSTEMS. Text in Japanese. 1993. m. JPY 10,700 (effective 2000). adv. **Document type:** *Trade.* **Description:** Offers practical information for construction and utilization of open systems consisting of workstations, PCs, and LANs.
Published by: Nikkei Business Publications Inc. (Subsidiary of: Nihon Keizai Shimbun, Inc.), 2-1-1 Hirakawa-cho, Chiyoda-ku, Tokyo, 102-8622, Japan. TEL 81-3-5210-8311, FAX 81-3-5210-8530, info@nikkeibpnyc.com, webmaster@nikkeibp.com, http://www.nikkeibp.com. Ed. Nozomu Inoue. Pub. Minoru Matsuzaki. Adv. contact Satoru Inomoto. B&W page JPY 286,000, color page JPY 528,000; trim 210 x 280. Circ: 30,344. **Dist. in America by:** Nikkei Business Publications America Inc., 575 Fifth Ave, 20th Fl, New York, NY 10017.

004.16 USA
NORTH TEXAS P C NEWS. Text in English. 1982. m. USD 24. adv. bk.rev. **Description:** Each issue includes feature articles, special interest groups' reports, software reviews and a directory of key group officials.
Published by: North Texas P C Users Group Inc., 2025 Rockcreek Dr, Arlington, TX 76010. TEL 817-275-4109. Ed. J P Pribyl. Circ: 1,500.

004.16 AUT
OESTERREICHISCHE MIKRO COMPUTER MAGAZIN. Text in German. q.
Published by: Johann L. Bondi und Sohn, Industriestrasse 2, Perchtoldsdorf, N 2380, Austria. TEL 01-864921, FAX 01-86492144, TELEX 131136. Circ: 40,500.

004.16 ZAF
P C & OFFICE TECHNOLOGY∗. Text in English. 1982. m. ZAR 25. adv. bk.rev.
Incorporates: Microcomputer Owner
Indexed: CompC.
Published by: Systems Publishers (Pty) Ltd., PO Box 41345, Craighall, Gauteng 2024, South Africa. Ed. David Briston. Circ: 7,500.

P C CHRONICLES. see *COMPUTERS—Personal Computers*

004.16 USA ISSN 1042-3575
QA76.9.E94
P C DIGEST RATINGS REPORT∗. Text in English. 1987. m. USD 450; USD 470 foreign. index. **Description:** Reports test ratings of microcomputer systems and peripherals.

Formerly (until 1989): P C Digest (0891-575X)
—CCC.
Published by: National Software Testing Laboratories, Inc. (Subsidiary of: McGraw-Hill, Inc.), Plymouth Corporate Center, 625 W Ridge Pike, No 6D, Conshohocken, PA 19428-1180. TEL 215-941-9600, FAX 215-941-9952. Pub. Linda Dibasio.

P C M; premier personal computer magazine for Tandy computer users. see *COMPUTERS—Personal Computers*

004.16 ITA ISSN 1128-8760
P C MAGAZINE. Text in Italian. 1984. m. (11/yr.). EUR 34.30 (effective 2005). adv. **Document type:** *Magazine, Consumer.* **Description:** Analyzes news concerning both hardware and software of computer products, specifically dedicated to standard IBM computers, MS-DOS-OS2 and Olivetti N24, as well as other compatibles.
Former titles (until 1988): P C World Magazine (1128-8752); (until 1985): P C Magazine (1121-2055)
—CCC.
Published by: V N U Business Publications (Italy), Via Gorki 69, Cinisello Balsamo, MI 20092, Italy. TEL 39-02-660341, FAX 39-02-66034238, http://www.jackson.it/pcm/, http://www.vnu.it. Eds. Pierantonio Palerma, Fabio Bossi. adv.: B&W page EUR 4,130, color page EUR 5,783; bleed 210 x 275. Circ: 52,387 (controlled).

P C MAGAZINE; the independent guide to personal computing and the Internet. see *COMPUTERS—Personal Computers*

004 ISR
P C MAGAZINE ISRAEL. Text in Hebrew. 1992. m. ILS 259; USD 135 in United States. adv. bk.rev. 140 p./no. 3 cols./p.; back issues avail. **Document type:** *Newspaper.* **Description:** Includes news and in-depth reviews of hardware, software, communication, and Internet applications.
Related titles: Online - full text ed.
Published by: P C Media Ltd., 13 Yad Harutzim St, P O Box 11438, Tel Aviv, 61114, Israel. TEL 972-3-6385810, FAX 972-3-6889207, http://www.goldenpc.co.il. Ed. Yehuda Elyada. Pub. Dahlia Pelled. Adv. contact Y Yosefi. color page USD 1,395; trim 21 x 27. Circ: 13,600 (paid).

004.16 GBR ISSN 0969-1839
P C MARKETPLACE. Text in English. 1991. m.
Related titles: ♦ Supplement to: What Personal Computer?. ISSN 0956-5248.
Published by: E M A P Computing (Subsidiary of: E M A P Business Communications), 33-39 Bowling Green Ln, London, EC1R 0DA, United Kingdom. TEL 44-20-7837-1212, FAX 44-20-7578-4008.

P C NETGUIDE. see *COMPUTERS—Computer Networks*

P C RETAILING. (Personal Computer) see *COMPUTERS—Computer Sales*

P.C. REVIEW; evaluations of new personal computer products. see *COMPUTERS—Software*

004.16 GBR ISSN 0964-4547
P C REVIEW (LONDON). Text in English. m. GBP 47.40; GBP 55 foreign. **Document type:** *Consumer.*
Media: Diskette. **Related titles:** CD-ROM ed.
Published by: E M A P - Images, Priory Ct, 30-32 Farringdon Ln, London, EC1R 3AU, United Kingdom. TEL 44-171-972-6710, FAX 44-171-972-6710. Ed. Christina Erskine. Circ: 45,000 (paid). **Subscr. to:** Tower Publishing Services Ltd., Tower House, Sovereign Park, Market Harborough, Leics LE16 9EF, United Kingdom. TEL 44-1858-468811, FAX 44-1858-432164.

P C TIP. see *COMPUTERS—Personal Computers*

P C UPDATE. see *COMPUTERS—Personal Computers*

P C WELT. see *COMPUTERS—Personal Computers*

P C WORKS - NEWS. see *COMPUTERS—Personal Computers*

P C WORLD DENMARK. (Personal Computer) see *COMPUTERS—Personal Computers*

004.16 GBR
P C YEAR BOOK. HARDWARE VOLUME. Text in English. 1985. a. **Document type:** *Trade.*
Supersedes: P C Year Book; Microcomputer User's Year Book
Published by: V N U Business Publications Ltd., 32-34 Broadwick St, London, W1A 2HG, United Kingdom. TEL 44-207-4394242, FAX 44-20-7734-5510. Ed. Peter Chave. Circ: 3,500.

005.36 GBR
P C YEAR BOOK. SOFTWARE VOLUME. Text in English. 1985. a. **Document type:** *Trade.*
Supersedes: P C Year Book
Published by: V N U Business Publications Ltd., 32-34 Broadwick St, London, W1A 2HG, United Kingdom. TEL 44-207-4394242, FAX 44-20-7734-5510. Circ: 3,500.

PERSONAL COMPUTER MAGAZINE; het computerblad voor Nederland en Belgie. see *COMPUTERS—Personal Computers*

338.47004 USA
HD9696.C63
PLUNKETT'S INFOTECH INDUSTRY ALMANAC. Text in English. 1996. a. USD 249.99 (effective 2005); includes CD-ROM. **Document type:** *Directory, Trade.* **Description:** Provides an in-depth analysis of the burgeoning InfoTech revolution, each industry segment, and the most outstanding corporations within those industries.
Related titles: CD-ROM ed.
Published by: Plunkett Research, Ltd, PO Drawer 541737, Houston, TX 77254-1737. TEL 713-932-0000, FAX 713-932-7080, info@plunkettresearch.com, http://www.plunkettresearch.com. Ed., Pub. Jack W Plunkett.

004.16 USA ISSN 1528-5456
POCKETPC. (Personal Computer) Text in English. 1997. bi-m. USD 19.95 domestic; USD 25.95 in Canada & Mexico; USD 37.95 elsewhere (effective 2004). adv. illus. **Document type:** *Magazine.* **Description:** Covers computer hardware and software with the Windows C E operating system.
Formerly: Handheld P C Magazine (1093-2585)
Related titles: Online - full text ed.: USD 19.95 (effective 2003) (from EBSCO Publishing); Special ed(s).: Pocket PC Ultimate Buyer's Guide (Year). free with Pocket PC (effective 2004).
Published by: Thaddeus Computing, Inc., c/o Wayne Kneeskern, Controller, Box 869, Fairfield, IA 52556-0869. TEL 515-472-6330, FAX 515-472-1879, wayne@thaddeus.com, http://www.pocketpcmag.com/, http://www.thaddeus.com, http://www.hpcmag.com/. Eds. Hal Goldstein, Richard Hall. Pub., R&P Hal Goldstein. Adv. contact Wayne Kneeskern.

004.16 USA ISSN 0732-7501
PORTABLE COMPANION✶; for Osborne computer users. Text in English. 1982-1983; N.S. 1984. bi-m. USD 25. adv. bk.rev. **Description:** For Osborne computer users. Features articles on hardware, peripherals, programs and applications. Includes a column by Adam Osborne as well as new product announcements.
Indexed: CompC.
Published by: Osborne Computer Corp., c/o Ed Walsh, 1255 Post St, 948, San Francisco, CA 94109-6712. Ed. Tony Bove. Circ: 18,000. **Co-sponsor:** T U G Inc.

THE PORTABLE COMPUTING LETTER. see *COMPUTERS—Personal Computers*

004.16 DNK ISSN 1398-7224
PRIVAT COMPUTER. Text in Danish. 1990. m. DKK 685 domestic inc. GameZone (effective 2004). adv. back issues avail. **Document type:** *Magazine, Consumer.*
Former titles (until 1998): Computer PC (1398-4578); (until 1998): Privat Computer (0909-1777); Which incorporated (1994-1995): PC Professeonal (1395-5551); (until 1993): Det Nye Computer (0905-6009); Which was formed by the merger of (1989-1990): Computer Action (0904-6011); Which incorporated (in 1989): Games Prewiew (0905-0582); Which was formerly (until 1988): C64-128 Club (0904-8650); (1985-1990): Computer Commodore Magazine (0900-8284); Which incorporated (in 1989): Amiga Interface (0904-8774); Which was formerly (in 1988): AmigaClub Magazine (0903-840X)
Related titles: Online - full text ed.; ♦ Includes: GameZone. ISSN 1600-2717.
Published by: Audio Media A-S, St Kongensgade 72, Copenhagen K, 1264, Denmark. TEL 45-33-912833, FAX 45-33-910121, redaktionen@pricom.dk, forlaget@audio.dk, http://www.privatcomputer.dk, http://www.audio.dk. Ed. Jeppe Christensen. Adv. contact Peter Kirkegard Alfier. Circ: 30,000.

004.16 GBR ISSN 0966-1913
R I S C USER. (Reduced Instruction Set Computer) Text in English. 1987. 10/yr. adv. bk.rev. index. **Document type:** *Consumer.*
Published by: R I S C O S Ltd., 3 Clarendon Rd, Cyncoed, Cardiff, CF23 9JD, United Kingdom. TEL 44-29-20492324, FAX 44-29-20492326, Editor@riscos.com, http://foundation.riscos.com/fru.htm, http://www.riscos.com/. Ed. Richard Hallas. Circ: 7,000.

004.16 USA ISSN 1538-7542
HD9696.S58
REPORT ON SMART CARDS✶. Text in English. 1987. m. USD 595; USD 655 foreign. bk.rev. back issues avail. **Document type:** *Newsletter.* **Description:** Covers the technology, applications and markets of smart cards, memory cards and optical cards.
Formerly: Smart Card Monthly (0893-9462)
Published by: Telecommunications Reports (Subsidiary of: Aspen Publishers, Inc.), 1333 H St, N W, Ste 100, Washington, DC 20005. http://www.tr.com/rsc. Ed., Pub. Stephan Seidman. Circ: 300 (paid).

ROOT DIRECTORY. see *COMPUTERS—Personal Computers*

S V M MAC. (Science et Vie Micro) see *COMPUTERS—Personal Computers*

SAN FRANCISCO BAY AREA SANYO GROUP NEWSLETTER. see *COMPUTERS—Personal Computers*

SANYO SOURCE. see *COMPUTERS—Personal Computers*

004.16 USA
SAWTOOTH NEWS. Text in English. 1985. 3/yr. free. **Document type:** *Newsletter.* **Description:** Covers topics of interest to persons in P.C. interviewing and analysis, such as computer interviewing, conjoint analysis, and data clustering.
Related titles: Online - full text ed.
Published by: Sawtooth Technologies, 1500 Skokie Blvd., Ste. 510, Northbrook, IL 60062-4116. TEL 847-866-0870, FAX 847-866-0876, info@sawtooth.com, http://www.sawtooth.com. Ed., R&P Suzanne Weiss. Circ: 8,000.

004.16 USA
SCARLETT✶. Text in English. 1982. m. USD 12. adv. bk.rev. **Description:** For club members as well as owners of Apple, Franklin and Basis computers. Covers current news and trends.
Formerly: Scarlett Letter
Published by: Big Red Apple Club, 1401 Charolais Dr, Norfolk, NE 68701-2348. TEL 402-379-4680. Ed. John Wrenholt. Circ: 9,000.

004.16 FRA ISSN 0760-6516
SCIENCE ET VIE MICRO. Short title: S V M. Text in French. 1983. 11/yr. EUR 30 domestic; EUR 44 foreign (effective 2003). adv. bk.rev. Supplement avail. **Document type:** *Trade.* **Description:** For the professional end-user.
Related titles: ♦ Supplement to: Science & Vie. ISSN 0036-8369.
Indexed: PdeR, RefZh.
—CISTI, IE, Infotrieve.
Published by: Emap France (Subsidiary of: Emap Media Ltd.), 150-152 Rue Gallieni, Boulogne, 92644, France. TEL 33-1-41334961, FAX 33-1-41335010, info@emapfrance.com, http://www.emapmedia.com. Circ: 121,981.

SMALL BUSINESS COMPUTING & COMMUNICATIONS. see *COMPUTERS—Personal Computers*

SMALL OFFICE. see *COMPUTERS—Personal Computers*

621.3916 USA ISSN 1536-7673
HD9696.M49
SMALL TIMES; the business of micro & nanotechnology. Text in English. 2001 (Sep.). bi-m. free in US & Canada to qualified personnel; USD 30 in US & Canada; USD 60 elsewhere (effective 2005). adv. 60 p./no.; **Document type:** *Magazine, Trade.* **Description:** Covers MEMS, microsystems and nanotechnologies industries.
Related titles: Online - full content ed.; Supplement(s): Small Tech Business Directory.
Indexed: BrCerAb, C&ISA, CerAb, CorrAb, E&CAJ, EMA, IAA, M&TEA, MBF, METADEX, WAA.
—Linda Hall.
Published by: SmallTimes Media, 655 Phoenix Dr, Ann Arbor, MI 48108. TEL 734-994-1106, FAX 734-994-1554, info@smalltimes.com, jimdozois@smalltimes.com, http://www.smalltimes.com, http://www.smalltimes.com/. adv.: color page USD 5,470. Circ: 26,614 (controlled and free).

SOFT - LETTER; trends & strategies in software publishing. see *COMPUTERS—Software*

SOFTWARE DIGEST; the independent, comparative ratings report for PC and LAN software. see *COMPUTERS—Software*

005.36 USA ISSN 0734-0125
SPREADSHEET. Text in English. m. USD 52.
Published by: International Electronic Spreadsheet Users Group (InterCalc), 25 Roxbury Rd, Scarsdale, NY 10583. TEL 914-472-0038. Ed. Roger Clark. Circ: 2,500.

STACK (HICKSVILLE). see *COMPUTERS—Personal Computers*

004.16 USA
TARGET AN AIM 65 NEWSLETTER. Text in English. bi-m. USD 7. adv.
Published by: Target Publications, 1176 Bay Circle, Lima, OH 45801. Circ: 500.

TECHNOLOGY & BUSINESS. see *COMPUTERS—Personal Computers*

004.16 USA
TRULY PORTABLE. Text in English. irreg. bk.rev.
Published by: Rachel Holmen, Ed. & Pub., Oakland, P O Box 2916, Oakland, CA 94618-0116. TEL 510-845-5274. Circ: 1,000.

004.16 HUN ISSN 1217-7598
UJ ALAPLAP; computing. Text in Hungarian. 1983. m. USD 58 (effective 1993). bk.rev. **Document type:** *Trade.* **Description:** Covers mainly software information and general computing topics for programmers and advanced computer users.
Former titles (until 1993): Alaplap (0865-9788); (until 1990): Mikroszamitogep Magazin (0236-6088)
Related titles: CD-ROM ed.

C

▼ *new title* ➤ *refereed* ✶ *unverified* ♦ *full entry avail.*

Published by: Uj Alaplap Kiado Kft., PO Box 571, Budapest, 1539, Hungary. TEL 36-1-3224417, alaplap@mail.datanet.hu, http://www.alaplap.hu. Ed. Pal Faklen. adv.: B&W page USD 1,000; trim 295 x 203. Circ: 11,000.

USER MAGAZIN. see *COMPUTERS—Personal Computers*

VICTORIAN G U M INC. NEWS. see *GENEALOGY AND HERALDRY*

004.16 CHN
WEI JISUANJI XINXI/INFORMATION ON MICROCOMPUTERS. Text in Chinese. q.
Published by: China INTEL Computer Users Association, Changzhi, PO Box 20, Taiyuan, 046000, China. Ed. Zhuang Zixin.

004.16 CHN ISSN 1008-0570
WEIJISUANJI XINXI/CONTROL & AUTOMATION. Text in Chinese. 1984. m. CNY 10, USD 4.20 newsstand/cover (effective 2003). **Document type:** *Journal, Academic/Scholarly.*
Formerly (until 1990): Weixingji Xinxi/Microcomputer Information (1000-7016)
Related titles: Online - full text ed.: (from East View Information Services).
Indexed: Inspec.
—BLDSC (3461.845000), IE.
Address: PO Box 8712, Beijing, 100080, China. control@public.fhnet.cn.net, http://wjsjxx.periodicals.net.cn/default.html. **Dist. by:** China International Book Trading Corp, 35 Chegongzhuang Xilu, Haidian District, PO Box 399, Beijing 100044, China. TEL 86-10-68412045, FAX 86-10-68412023, cibtc@mail.cibtc.com.cn, http://www.cibtc.com.cn.

004.16 CHN ISSN 1003-1944
WEIJISUANJI YINGYONG/MICROCOMPUTER APPLICATIONS. Text in Chinese. 1980. bi-m. adv.
Related titles: Online - full text ed.: (from East View Information Services).
Address: PO Box 2712, Beijing, 100080, China. TEL 86-10-284573, FAX 86-10-256-1457, TELEX 222525 IOAAS CN. Adv. contact Xiaoxia Wang. Circ: 50,000.

005.36 GBR
WHAT P C? (ONLINE EDITION); the essential buyer's guide. Text in English. 1982. w. adv. bk.rev. back issues avail. **Document type:** *Magazine, Trade.* **Description:** Buyers' guide to business microcomputers and software; includes tables on products available in the UK.
Former titles: What P C? (Print Edition) (1466-7878); (until 1999): What P C? and Software (1367-9686); (until 1995): What P C? (0967-490X); (until 1992): What Micro? (0264-441X)
Media: Online - full content.
Indexed: Inspec, RAPRA.
—BLDSC (9309.757430), AskIEEE, IE, Infotrieve.
Published by: V N U Business Publications Ltd., VNU House, 32-34 Broadwick St, London, W1A 2HG, United Kingdom. TEL 44-20-7316-9000, FAX 44-20-7316-9160, whatpc@vnu.co.uk, http://www.whatpc.co.uk, http://www.vnunet.com. Ed. Chris Cain. Pub. Juliet Parker. Adv. contact Victoria Shaw. Circ: 56,679. **Subscr. in US to:** Global Media Representatives Inc., 611 Veterans Blvd, Ste 205, Redwood City, CA 94063. TEL 415-306-0880, FAX 415-306-0890. **Dist. by:** MarketForce UK Ltd, 247 Tottenham Court Rd, London, Middx W1T 7AU, United Kingdom. TEL 44-207-2615199, FAX 44-207-2617341.

004.16 USA
THE YELLOWSTONE WINDOWS LETTER★. Text in English. 1991. bi-m. USD 49.95; USD 89.95 foreign.
Published by: Yellowstone Information Services, R R 2, Box 42A, Bloomingdale, OH 43910-9802. TEL 304-965-5548, FAX 304-965-7785. Ed. Roger Thibault.

COMPUTERS—Minicomputers

004.14 USA ISSN 1086-881X
QA75.5
A S - 400 SYSTEMS MANAGEMENT. Text in English. 1973. m. USD 42; USD 54 in Canada; USD 102 in Europe; USD 198 elsewhere (effective 1999). adv. bk.rev. **Document type:** *Trade.* **Description:** For managers of IBM minicomputers, RS-6000 workstations and related products.
Former titles (until 1995): 3 X - 400 Systems Management (1070-6097); Systems 3X - 400 (1055-7768); Systems 3X and A S World (1044-1239); Small System World (0272-5444); System - 3 World
Related titles: Online - full text ed.: (from O C L C Online Computer Library Center, Inc., ProQuest Information & Learning).
Indexed: ABIn, CompC, CompD, GALA, Inspec, ResCtrInd, SoftBase.
—CISTI. **CCC.**
Published by: Adams Business Media, 2101 S Arlington Heights Rd, 150, Arlington, IL 60005. TEL 847-427-9512, FAX 847-882-6842, 71333.730@compuserve.com, http://www.abm.net. Ed. Renee Robbins. Circ: 55,279.

AMY D. WOHL'S OPINIONS. see *COMPUTERS—Personal Computers*

004.14 USA ISSN 0899-9783
COMPUTER WORKSTATIONS. Text in English. 1988. m. USD 150 in North Africa; USD 165 elsewhere (effective 2001). bk.rev. **Document type:** *Newsletter, Trade.* **Description:** Provides information on computer workstations used in network applications, computer-aided design, computer-aided engineering, and other business and industrial applications to improve productivity.
Related titles: Online - full text ed.: (from bigchalk, EBSCO Publishing, Factiva, Gale Group, LexisNexis, ProQuest Information & Learning).
Indexed: CompD, MicrocompInd.
Published by: Worldwide Videotex, PO Box 3273, Boynton Beach, FL 33424-3273. TEL 561-738-2276, markedit@juno.com, http://www.wvpubs.com. Ed., Pub. Mark Wright.

004.14 GBR ISSN 0950-5482
D E C COMPUTING; midrange newspaper. (Digital Equipment Corporation) Text in English. 1985. w. GBP 60; GBP 80 foreign. adv. bk.rev. **Document type:** *Trade.* **Description:** Contains news coverage and analysis, features on industry developments, a buyer's guide and product reviews.
Indexed: Inspec.
—AskIEEE.
Published by: V N U Business Publications Ltd., 32-34 Broadwick St, London, W1A 2HG, United Kingdom. TEL 44-207-4394242, FAX 44-20-7437-4841. Ed. C Gabriel. Adv. contact David Weekes. B&W page USD 4,590, color page USD 5,790; trim 15.25 x 11. Circ: 15,717.

004.14 GBR ISSN 0269-0489
CODEN: DETOEY
D E C TODAY. (Digital Equipment Corporation) Text in English. 1986. m. GBP 30; GBP 50 foreign. charts; illus.; pat.; stat.; tr.lit. back issues avail.
Indexed: Inspec.
—AskIEEE.
Published by: C.W. Communications Ltd., 99 Grays Inn Rd, London, WC1X 8UT, United Kingdom. Ed. Charlie Brown. Circ: 12,501.

004.14 USA ISSN 1065-6189
THE H P PALMTOP PAPER. (Hewlett-Packard) Text in English. 1986. bi-m. USD 39 domestic; USD 45 in Canada & Mexico; USD 57 elsewhere (effective 2000); subscr. includes one Subscribers Disk and 2 bonus issues. adv. cum.index: 1986-1996. back issues avail. **Document type:** *Newsletter.* **Description:** Covers computer hardware and software for Hewlett Packard 95 LX, 100 LX, and 200 LX palmtop computers.
Related titles: Diskette ed.: USD 100; USD 118 foreign.
Published by: Thaddeus Computing, Inc., c/o Wayne Kneeskern, Controller, Box 869, Fairfield, IA 52556-0869. TEL 515-472-6330, FAX 515-472-1879, wayne@thaddeus.com, http://www.palmtoppaper.com, http://www.thaddeus.com. Ed. Ed Keefe. R&P Hal Goldstein. Circ: 10,000.

004.14 USA
H P - U X - USR. Text in English. bi-m. USD 49.50; USD 99.50 foreign. adv.
Published by: (International Association of Hewlett-Packard Computer Users), Interex, Publications Department, 1192 Borregas Ave, Sunnyvale, CA 94089. TEL 408-747-0227, FAX 408-747-0947. Ed. Michael Ehrhardt. Adv. contact Brian Hallin.

004.14025 USA ISSN 0733-9305
INFOPERSPECTIVES★. Text in English. 1980. m. USD 595; USD 630 foreign (effective 1997). **Description:** Follows the use of mainframe and other large information processing devices at Fortune 1000 companies. Helps give MIS directors guidance in developing budgets and technical strategies for data processing.
Incorporates (1979-1997): Computer and Communications Buyer (0272-4553)
Related titles: Online - full text ed.: (from Gale Group).
Published by: Technology News of America Co., Inc., 123 Seventh Ave 171, Brooklyn, NY 11215-1301. TEL 212-334-9750. Ed. Hesh Weiner.

004.14 USA ISSN 0279-2664
INTERACT; the magazine for users of HP3000 computers. Text in English. 1981. m. USD 49.50. adv. tr.lit. **Document type:** *Consumer.*
Indexed: AHCI.
Published by: (H P 3000 International Users Group), Interex, Publications Department, 1192 Borregas Ave, Sunnyvale, CA 94089. TEL 408-747-0227, FAX 408-747-0947, TELEX 4971527. Ed. Connie Wright. Circ: 14,000.

004.14 USA ISSN 1049-8982
INTEREXPRESS; the news publication for HP users worldwide. Text in English. 1980. m. USD 30.50. **Document type:** *Consumer.* **Description:** Examines the HP role in industry.
Formerly: Interrupt
Published by: Interex, Publications Department, 1192 Borregas Ave, Sunnyvale, CA 94089. TEL 408-747-0227, FAX 408-747-0947. Ed. Connie Wright. Circ: 8,000.

004.14 CAN
INTERNATIONAL SYMPOSIUM ON MINI AND MICROCOMPUTERS. PROCEEDINGS. Text in English. 1975. a. price varies. **Document type:** *Proceedings, Academic/Scholarly.*
Published by: International Society for Mini and Microcomputers (ISMM), 4500 16th Ave, NW, Ste 80, Calgary, AB T3B 0M6, Canada. TEL 403-288-1195, FAX 403-247-6851. Ed. M H Hamza.

004.16 DNK ISSN 1396-0342
KOMPUTER FOR ALLE. Text in Danish. 1996. m. adv. **Document type:** *Magazine, Consumer.*
Published by: Bonnier Publications AS, Strandboulevarden 130, Copenhagen Oe, 2100, Denmark. TEL 45-39-172000, FAX 45-39-290199, red@komputer.dk, http://www.komputer.dk, http://www.bonnierpublications.com. Ed. Leif Jonasson. Adv. contact Lars Grindsted. page DKK 60,050. Circ: 63,564.

▼ **MICROTEC;** miniature technology and design. see *ENGINEERING*

004.14 USA
MIDRANGE CHANNELS. Text in English. bi-m. USD 24 in North America; USD 43 elsewhere. **Document type:** *Trade.* **Description:** Provides sales and marketing information to resellers of midrange systems.
Published by: Boucher Communications, Inc., 1300 Virginia Dr, Ste 400, Fort Washington, PA 19034-3221. TEL 215-643-8000, FAX 215-643-8099. **Subscr. to:** Midrange Channels, PO Box 3055, Northbrook, IL 60065-3055. TEL 800-306-6332, FAX 847-564-9002.

MINI/MICRO CONFERENCE RECORD. see *COMPUTERS—Microcomputers*

004.14 DEU ISSN 1615-8288
NOTEBOOK ORGANIZER & HANDY. Text in German. 1997. m. EUR 52.80; EUR 5 newsstand/cover (effective 2003). adv. **Document type:** *Magazine, Consumer.*
Formerly (until 1999): Notebook & Organizer (1436-8838)
Published by: Bikini Verlag GmbH, St.-Emmeram-Str. 28, Aschheim, 85609, Germany. TEL 49-89-9097980, FAX 49-89-90979811, gb@nouh.de, http://www.nouh.de, http://www.bikini-verlag.de. Ed., Pub. Gerhard Bauer. Adv. contact Gert Winkelmeier TEL 49-2684-6107. B&W page EUR 2,965, color page EUR 3,988. Circ: 25,000 (paid and controlled).

004.14 USA ISSN 1537-1069
P X I TECHNOLOGY REVIEW. Text in English. q. free domestic; USD 50 foreign (effective 2005). adv. **Document type:** *Magazine, Trade.*
Related titles: Online - full text ed.: ISSN 1550-039X.
Published by: OpenSystems Publishing, 30233 Jefferson Ave, St Clair Shores, MI 48082. TEL 810-415-6500, FAX 810-415-4882, http://www.pxionline.com, http://www.opensystems-publishing.com/. Ed. Rosemary Kristoff. adv.: color page USD 3,250; trim 8 x 10.875. Circ: 21,941.

004.14 USA ISSN 1051-8118
REVUSER; an independent journal for advanced Revelation and Revelation users. Text in English. bi-m. USD 35. **Description:** For users of Revelation and Advanced Revelation. Publishes technical information about personal computers, workstations, networking and applications.
Published by: Infocus, Inc., 37 S. Main St., Yardley, PA 19067. TEL 215-321-2200, FAX 215-321-2205. Ed. Lee J Leitner.

005.34 USA ISSN 0736-2730
SOFTWARE CATALOG: MINICOMPUTERS. Text in English. 1983. irreg., latest 1987. price varies. **Document type:** *Catalog.* **Description:** Contains in-depth descriptions including the availability, applications, price and compatibility of over 7,800 programs for minicomputers.
Published by: Elsevier Inc. (Subsidiary of: Elsevier Science & Technology), 360 Park Ave. S, New York, NY 10010-1710. TEL 212-633-3730, 888-437-4636, usinfo-f@elsevier.com, http://www.elsevier.com.

004.12 JPN ISSN 0918-5453
SUNWORLD/SANWARUDO. Variant title: Independent Journal of Sun and S P A R C Systems. Text in Japanese. 1991. m. adv. **Document type:** *Magazine, Trade.* **Description:** Introduces all the latest Sun/SPARC Systems applications as well as providing articles and new product news.
Related titles: Online - full text ed.
Published by: I D G Japan, Inc., Hongo 3-4-5, Bunkyo-ku, Tokyo, 1130033, Japan. TEL 81-3-5800-3111, FAX 81-3-5800-3590, http://www.idg.co.jp/sw/. Pub. Kazuhiko Kajihara. adv.: B&W page USD 3,542, color page JPY 4,565; trim 210 x 282. Circ: 28,000.

SUNWORLD; I D G's magazine for the Sun community. see *COMPUTERS—Computer Networks*

004.14 USA ISSN 1059-9959
WORKSTATION✶; independent news magazine for H P Apollo workstation and server users. Text in English. 1985. m. USD 45; USD 75 foreign (effective 1999). bk.rev. reprints avail. **Document type:** *Trade.* **Description:** Contains in-depth articles and editorials about new and enhanced products from Hewlett-Packard, Apollo, and third-party companies.
Former titles: H P Design and Automation (0896-212X); H P Design and Manufacturing (0892-2810); Chronicle Magazine
Indexed: Inspec, SoftBase.
Published by: Publications & Communications, Inc., 505 Cypress Creek Rd, Ste B, Cedar Park, TX 78613-4429. TEL 512-250-9023, 800-678-9724, FAX 512-331-3900. Ed. John Mitchell. adv.: B&W page USD 3,401, color page USD 4,201. Circ: 10,000.

004.14 CHN ISSN 1000-1220
XIAOXING WEIXING JISUANJI XITONG/MICROCOMPUTER SYSTEMS. Text in Chinese. m. **Document type:** *Academic/Scholarly.*
Related titles: Online - full text ed.: (from East View Information Services).
Indexed: Englnd, Inspec, MicrocompInd. —BLDSC (5797.755000), AskIEEE, IE, ingenta.
Published by: Zhongguo Kexueyuan, Shenyang Jisuan Jishu Yanjiusuo/Chinese Academy of Sciences, Shenyang Institute of Computing Technology, 18 Sanhao Jie, Heping-qu, Shenyang, Liaoning 110003, China. TEL 86-24-392758. Ed. Luan Guixing. adv.: B&W page USD 1,000. Circ: 23,000.

COMPUTERS—Personal Computers

see also COMPUTERS—Microcomputers

A C E INTERNATIONAL. see *COMMUNICATIONS—Television And Cable*

004.16 USA ISSN 0884-7975
A M U S LOG✶. Text in English. 1978. m. USD 75. adv. back issues avail. **Document type:** *Trade.* **Description:** For Alpha Micro computer users - beginners through advanced.
Formerly (until 1985): A M U S Newsletter (0273-8708)
Related titles: Online - full text ed.: (from ProQuest Information & Learning).
Published by: Alpha Micro User Society, 210 N Iris Ave, Rialto, CA 92376-5727. TEL 303-678-7066, FAX 303-678-9420, slg@indra.com. Ed. Claudia Previn. Adv. contact Jim Randazzo. Circ: 1,400 (paid).

004.16 USA
A P H TECHNOLOGY UPDATE; technology for people who are visually impaired. Text in English. 1985. s-a. free. **Document type:** *Newsletter.* **Description:** Contains articles about computer products designed for visually impaired users.
Former titles: Access Abilities; Micro Materials Update (1081-518X)
Related titles: Audio cassette/tape ed.; Braille ed.; CD-ROM ed.
Published by: American Printing House for the Blind, Inc., 1839 Frankfort Ave, Louisville, KY 40206. TEL 502-895-2405, FAX 502-899-2274, info@aph.org, http://www.aph.org/techup. Ed. Larry Skutchan. Circ: 8,800.

005.26 USA ISSN 0163-6006
QA76.73.A27 CODEN: APLQD9
➤ **A P L QUOTE QUAD.** Text in English. 1970. q. USD 45 to non-members; USD 30 to members; USD 15 student members (effective 2005). bk.rev. **Document type:** *Newsletter, Academic/Scholarly.*
Formerly: S I G P L A N - S T A P L Quote Quad
Related titles: Online - full text ed.: (from EBSCO Publishing).
Indexed: C&ISA, CompR, E&CAJ, ISMEC, Inspec, SolStAb. —BLDSC (1568.579000), AskIEEE, CISTI, IE, Infotrieve, ingenta.
Published by: Association for Computing Machinery, Inc., 1515 Broadway, 17th Fl, New York, NY 10036-5701. TEL 212-626-0520, 800-342-6626, FAX 212-869-0481, sigs@acm.org, usacm@acm.org, http://www.acm.org/sigapl/qq.htm. Circ: 1,600.

004.16 AUS ISSN 1329-2641
A U S O M NEWS; Power Mac, Macintosh, Newton & Apple II computers. Text in English. 1979. m. (except Jan.). AUD 50 to members. adv. **Description:** Contains information about installing, operating and general use of Apple computers and the activities of AUSOM.
Published by: Apple Users Group of Melbourne Inc., Room 2.7, Ross Huse, 247 Flinders Lane, Melbourne, VIC 3000, Australia. TEL 61-3-96541924, secretary@ausom.net.au, http://www.ausom.net.au. Ed. Pam Doughty. Adv. contact Gary Lowen. page AUD 130; trim 210 x 297. Circ: 1,400.

004.165 USA ISSN 1093-2909
ABOUT THIS PARTICULAR MACINTOSH. Abbreviated title: A T P M. Text in English. 1995. m. bk.rev. back issues avail. **Description:** Devoted to the personal computing experience, the Macintosh experience, including tales from Mac users.
Media: Online - full text.
Address: subscriptions@atpm.com, editor@atpm.com, http://www.atpm.com/. Pubs. Michael Tsai, Robert Paul Leitao.

ABSOLUTE REFERENCE; the journal for 1-2-3 and Symphony users. see *COMPUTERS—Microcomputers*

004.16 GBR ISSN 0957-4867
AMIGA FORMAT. Text in English. 1988. m. GBP 39.95 in United Kingdom; GBP 49.95 in Europe; GBP 56.95 rest of world; GBP 5.99 newsstand/cover (effective 2000). adv. back issues avail. **Document type:** *Consumer.* **Description:** Enables readers to get the most out of their Amiga machines and keeps them in touch with industry news and product information.
Supersedes in part (in 1989): S T Amiga Format (0954-805X) **—CCC.**
Published by: Future Publishing Ltd., Beauford Court, 30 Monmouth St, Bath, Avon BA1 2BW, United Kingdom. TEL 44-1225-442244, FAX 44-1225-732285, ben.vost@futurenet.co.uk, http://www.futurenet.com, http://www.futurenet.com/futureonline. Ed. Ben Vost. Pub. Dominic Beaven. Adv. contact Rob Bennett. Circ: 14,644.

004.16 DEU
AMIGA MAGAZIN. Text in German. m. adv. **Document type:** *Magazine, Consumer.*
Related titles: Online - full text ed.
Published by: W E K A Computerzeitschriften-Verlag GmbH, Gruberstr 46a, Poing, 85586, Germany. TEL 49-81-21951141, FAX 49-81-21952114, http://www.amiga-magazin.de, http://www.wekanet.de. Ed. Stephan Quinkertz. Adv. contact Alan Markovic. Circ: 212,969.

004.16 USA
AMIGA REPORT MAGAZINE. Text in English. 1993. bi-w. **Document type:** *Trade.* **Description:** Contains information, news, reviews, and views directed at users of the Amiga computer.
Media: Online - full text.
Address: 1203 Alexander Ave, Streamwood, IL 60107. FAX 847-741-0689, jcompton@xnet.com, http://www.cucug.org/ar/. Ed. Jason Compton.

004.16 ESP ISSN 1130-1074
AMIGA WORLD. Text in Spanish. 11/yr.
Address: Rafael Calvo, 18 4oB, Madrid, 28010, Spain. TEL 1-319-40-14, FAX 1-319-61-04. Ed. Juan Miguel Urraca. Circ: 18,000.

004.16 USA
AMY D. WOHL'S OPINIONS. Text in English. m. USD 395 (effective 2000). bk.rev. **Document type:** *Newsletter.*
Former titles: Amy D. Wohl's Trends Letter; (until 1991): Wohl Report on End User Computing
Media: Online - full content.
Published by: Wohl Associates, 915, Montgomery, PA 19072. TEL 610-667-4842, FAX 610-667-3081, opinions@wohl.com, http://www.wohl.com. Ed., Pub., R&P Amy D Wohl.

004.16 USA
APPLE DIRECT; an information resource from Apple developers services. Text in English. m. **Description:** For Apple users. Feature articles on pertinent software, hardware, new product developments, marketing and news clips as well as listings of upcoming events pertinent to developers.
Published by: Apple Computer, Inc., 1 Infinite Loop, Cupertino, CA 95014. TEL 408-974-2552.

APPLE EDUCATION NEWS; an information service for educators and trainers. see *EDUCATION—Computer Applications*

004.16 AUS ISSN 1328-3049
APPLESAUCE. Text in English. 1980. m. (except Jan.). AUD 30 to members (effective 2000). adv. **Document type:** *Newsletter.* **Description:** Contains club news, product reviews, hints and tips for club members.
Related titles: Online - full text ed.: ISSN 1328-3057.
Published by: South Australian Apple Users Club, PO Box 3129, Unley, SA 5061, Australia. TEL 61-8-84434298, pcarter@acslink.net.au, http://www.saauc.org.au/AppleSauce/. Ed., R&P P.J. Carter. Adv. contact P J Carter.

004.16 JPN ISSN 0916-0302
ASAHI PASOKON/ASAHI PERSONAL COMPUTERS. Text in Japanese. 1988. s-m. USD 150.50.
Published by: Asahi Shimbun Publishing Co., 5-3-2 Tsukiji, Chuo-ku, Tokyo, 104-8011, Japan. Ed. Keijiro Mori. **Dist. by:** Japan Publications Trading Co., Ltd., Book Export II Dept, PO Box 5030, Tokyo International, Tokyo 101-3191, Japan. TEL 81-3-32923753, FAX 81-3-32920410, infoserials@jptco.co.jp, http://www.jptco.co.jp.

004.16 AUS ISSN 1034-3806
AUSTRALIAN COMMODORE AND AMIGA REVIEW. Text in English. 1984. m. AUD 34. adv. bk.rev. back issues avail.
Formerly: Australian Commodore Review
Published by: Gareth Powell Pty Ltd., 21 Darley Rd, Randwick, NSW 2031, Australia. TEL 02-398-511. Ed. Andrew Farrell. Circ: 11,500.

004.16 AUS ISSN 1329-9484
AUSTRALIAN MACWORLD. Text in English. 1994. m. AUD 75 domestic; AUD 120 foreign; AUD 6.95 newsstand/cover (effective 2004). adv. **Document type:** *Magazine, Consumer.* **Description:** Aimed at users and potential users of the Apple Macintosh; primarily for people in business and professions.
Formerly (until 1998): Australian MacUser (1322-9753); Which was formed by the merger of (1991-1994): Australian & New Zealand MacUser (1037-4353); (1989-1994): MacNews (1039-2238)
Published by: Niche Media Pty Ltd (Subsidiary of: Waivcom Worldwide Ltd.), 165 Fitzroy St, St Kilda, VIC 3182, Australia. TEL 61-3-95255566, 800-804-160, FAX 61-3-95255628, subscription@niche.com.au, http://niche.com.au/mw/general.html, http://www.niche.com.au. Ed. Matthew J C Powell. Adv. contact Joanne Davies. color page AUD 3,685; trim 206 x 275. Circ: 12,000.

004.16 AUS ISSN 1329-2978
AUSTRALIAN P C AUTHORITY. Text in English. 1997. m. AUD 66.80 domestic; AUD 91.50 in New Zealand; AUD 109 in Asia; AUD 127 elsewhere (effective 2004).
Published by: AJB Publishing, Unit2-5, 44-70 Rosehill St, Redfern, NSW 2016, Australia. TEL 61-2-8399-3611, FAX 61-2-8399-3622, http://www.pcauthority.com.au/. Ed. Adrian Jenkins.

004.16 AUS ISSN 1322-3712
AUSTRALIAN P C USER. Variant title: P C User. Text in English. m. AUD 73 (effective 2004). adv. **Document type:** *Magazine, Consumer.* **Description:** For the business user and other end users of personal computers. Ideal companion for the small office, home office computer user.
Former titles (until 1994): Australian and New Zealand P C User (1039-2149); (until 1992): Australian P C User (1034-4705)
Related titles: Online - full text ed.: (from EBSCO Publishing).
Published by: A C P Computer Publications, 54-58 Park St., Level 6, Sydney, NSW 1028, Australia. TEL 61-2-928989137, FAX 61-2-92674909, pcuser@acp.com.au, http://www.pcuser.com.au, http://www.acp.com.au. Ed. Glenn Rees. Adv. contact Simon Smith. B&W page AUD 2,595, color page AUD 3,440; trim 210 x 275. Circ: 58,665.

004.16 AUS ISSN 0813-1384
AUSTRALIAN P C WORLD. Text in English. 1984. m. AUD 66 domestic; AUD 150 in New Zealand; AUD 200 elsewhere (effective 2004). adv. **Document type:** *Magazine, Consumer.* **Description:** Contains articles and features on the business use of new products and technologies, product comparisons, best buys and a help screen section, with particular emphasis on how the user can increase productivity with their existing systems and how new products and services can help their business.
Related titles: Online - full text ed.: (from Gale Group).
Indexed: CompD.
Published by: I D G Communications Pty. Ltd., 88 Christie St, St Leonards, NSW 2065, Australia. TEL 61-2-94395133, FAX 612-9439-5512, http://www.pcworld.idg.com.au, http://www.idg.com.au. Ed. Robert Thirlwell. adv.: color page USD 2,883; trim 205 x 275. Circ: 42,700.

004.16 AUS ISSN 0725-4415
AUSTRALIAN PERSONAL COMPUTER. Text in English. 1980. m. AUD 79; AUD 9.80 newsstand/cover (effective 2004). adv. bk.rev. back issues avail. **Document type:** *Magazine, Consumer.*
Related titles: Online - full text ed.: (from EBSCO Publishing).
Indexed: MicrocompInd, WBA, WMB.
Published by: A C P Computer Publications, 54-58 Park St., Level 6, Sydney, NSW 1028, Australia. TEL 61-2-92889123, FAX 61-2-92674909, apc@acp.com.au, http://apcmag.com, http://www.acp.com.au. Ed. David Flynn. Adv. contact Cameron Curtis. B&W page AUD 3,200, color page AUD 4,280; trim 210 x 275. Circ: 65,398.

004.16 SWE
▼ **AV - MAGASINET.** Text in Swedish. 2003. 6/yr. adv. **Description:** Focuses on IT home electronics integration and provides sales tips.
Related titles: ♦ Supplement to: I T.Branschen. ISSN 1402-0963.
Published by: I D G AB (Subsidiary of: I D G Communications Inc.), Sturegatan 11, Stockholm, 10678, Sweden. TEL 46-8-4536000, FAX 46-8-4536005, http://www.idg.se. Ed. Maya Uusitalo. adv.: page SEK 46,500;. Circ: 21,000.

004.16 USA
B A U D. (Big Apple Users Digest) Text in English. 1979. m. membership. adv. **Description:** Provides news, information and commentary for users of Apple II computers.
Published by: Big Apple Users Group, 345 W 58th St, Apt 5L, New York, NY 10019-1132. TEL 212-606-2297, baug@dorsai.org. Ed. Polly Bookhout. Circ: 25.

004.16 USA ISSN 1076-089X
B U G NEWSLETTER. Text in English. 1983. m. USD 25 membership (effective 2000). adv. bk.rev. **Document type:** *Newsletter.*
Published by: Brevard Users Group, PO Box 2456, Melbourne, FL 32902-2456. TEL 407-253-2793. Ed., R&P Jack Nash. Adv. contact Ted Glaser. Circ: 350.

C

004.16 USA
BIGSKYMAC EZINE. Text in English. 1995. m. **Description:** Covers Macintosh computer related topics.
Formerly: Big Sky Mac E - Zine
Media: Online - full text.
Address: bgskymac@imt.net, http://www.imt.net/~bgskymac/BigSky_MacEzine.html. Ed., Pub. Bud Henley.

004.16 USA
THE BITSIFTER DIGEST. Text in English. 1996. w. free. adv. back issues avail. **Document type:** *Newsletter.* **Description:** Includes commentary, editorials, reviews, and gossip.
Media: Online - full text. **Related titles:** E-mail ed.
Published by: Pandora Productions, 24985 Soquel Rd, Los Gatos, CA 95030. editor@bitsifter.com, http://www.bitsifter.com. Ed., R&P, Adv. contact Michael Lopp TEL 408-353-3530.

004.16 USA
BUG REPORT. Text in English. 1983. m. USD 12.50. adv. bk.rev. **Description:** For IBM and clone computer users.
Formerly: G S B U G
Published by: Greater South Bay P C Users Group, PO Box 6950, Torrance, CA 90504-6950. TEL 310-329-2804. Ed. Lindsey Barlow. Circ: 400.

004.16 USA
BUGNET. Text in English. 1994. m. **Document type:** *Newsletter.* **Description:** Global resource for PC bugs, glitches, incompatibilities, and their fixes.
Media: Online - full text.
Address: PO Box 393, Sumas, WA 98295. bugnet@bugnet.com, cb@bugnet.com, http://www.bugnet.com/free1.html. Ed. Bruce Brown.

BYTE.COM. see *COMPUTERS—Microcomputers*

BYTE TUERKIYE. see *COMPUTERS—Microcomputers*

004.16 GBR
C E M A PERSONAL COMPUTERS AND PERIPHERALS. Text in English. 1986. m. GBP 2,000, USD 3,500 (effective 1999). bk.rev.; software rev. charts; stat. **Document type:** *Newsletter.*
Published by: (Cores European Market Analysis), Portman Communications Ltd., 52 Foundling Ct, London, WC1N 1AN, United Kingdom. TEL 44-171-837-0815, FAX 44-171-278-9917, 100141.676@compuserve. Ed. Keith Waller. Pub., R&P Philip Gallagher. Circ: 400 (paid).

004.16 GBR ISSN 0963-0090
C U AMIGA. Text in English. 1981. m. GBP 47.40 domestic; GBP 55 foreign. adv. **Document type:** *Consumer.*
Former titles (until 1991): C U Amiga-64 (0957-5103); (until 1989): Commodore User (0265-721X)
Indexed: CompD, Inspec.
Published by: E M A P - Images, Priory Ct, 30-32 Farringdon Ln, London, EC1R 3AU, United Kingdom. TEL 44-171-972-6700, FAX 44-171-972-6710. Circ: 111,400. **Subscr. to:** Tower Publishing Services Ltd., Tower House, Sovereign Park, Market Harborough, Leics LE16 9EF, United Kingdom. TEL 44-1858-468811, FAX 44-1858-432164.

004.16 JPN ISSN 8755-4909
CALL - A.P.P.L.E. (Apple Pugetsound Program Library Exchange) Text in English. 1978. m. USD 25 membership (effective 2005). adv. bk.rev. back issues avail.; reprints avail. **Document type:** *Magazine, Consumer.* **Description:** For advanced Apple IIGS and II users. Feature articles cover hardware, programming in a variety of languages, software and applications as well as other topics and editorials.
Indexed: CompC, CompD, Inspec, LAMP, MicrocompInd, SoftBase.
Published by: Apple PugetSound Program Library Exchange, 290 S W 43rd, Renton, WA 98055-4936. info@callapple.org, editor@callapple.org, http://www.callapple.org/. Ed. Kathryn Hallgrimson Suther. Circ: 30,000.

CHANNELMARKER LETTER. see *COMPUTERS—Computer Industry*

CHEMICAL ENGINEERING PROGRESS SOFTWARE DIRECTORY. see *CHEMISTRY—Computer Applications*

004.16 USA ISSN 1063-7672
CHRISTIAN COMPUTING MAGAZINE; applying tomorrow's technology to today's ministries. Text in English, Portuguese. 1989. m. USD 14.95; USD 33 foreign (effective 1999). adv. **Document type:** *Consumer.* **Description:** Contains information on the developments of new digital Christian resources and the application of technology to the ministry.
Formerly: Christian Computing (1047-1847)
Related titles: Online - full text ed.
Address: PO Box 198, 309 S Washington, Raymore, MO 64083. TEL 816-331-3881, 800-456-1868, FAX 816-331-5510, steve@ccmag.com, http://www.gospelcom.net/ccmag/. Ed., Pub. Steve Hewitt. R&P Kevin Cross. Adv. contact Gary Geib.

005.446 621.39 USA ISSN 1098-7622
COMPACTPCI SYSTEMS. Text in English. 1997. 9/yr. free domestic; USD 90 foreign (effective 2002).
Related titles: Online - full text ed.: ISSN 1550-0381.
Published by: OpenSystems Publishing, 30233 Jefferson Ave, St Clair Shores, MI 48082. TEL 810-415-6500, FAX 810-415-4882, http://www.compactpci-systems.com, http://www.opensystems-publishing.com/.

004.16 FRA ISSN 0985-7443
COMPATIBLES P C MAGAZINE. Text in French. 1987. 11/yr.
Published by: Societe Europeenne de Presse et de Communication (SEPCOM), 5-7 rue de l'Amiral Courbet, St-Mande, 94160, France. TEL 33-1-43984383, FAX 33-1-43287212. Ed. Michel Barreau. Circ: 82,142.

004.16 338 GBR ISSN 0962-1989
COMPUTER BUYER; what to buy - how to buy it. Text in English. 1991. m. GBP 23.97 domestic; GBP 70 in Europe; GBP 90 elsewhere (effective 2003). adv. back issues avail. **Document type:** *Consumer.* **Description:** Assists the non-technical user to make buying decisions on computers and products with greater confidence.
Related titles: Online - full text ed.
Published by: Dennis Publishing Ltd., 30 Cleveland St, London, W1P 5FF, United Kingdom. TEL 44-20-7971-7728, FAX 44-20-7917-5732, editorial.buyer@dennis.co.uk, http://www.computerbuyer.co.uk. Ed. Paul Sanders. Pub. Adrian Finnis. R&P Bruce Sanford TEL 44-171-917-7658. Adv. contact Pete Wooton. Circ: 53,000; 51,737 (paid). **Overseas subscr. to:** Computer Buyer Subscriptions, Freepost WD7, Bristol, Avon BS12 0BR, United Kingdom. **Dist. by:** Seymour Distribution Ltd, 86 Newman St, London W1T 3EX, United Kingdom. TEL 44-20-73968000, FAX 44-20-73968002.

004.16 USA ISSN 0738-9213
QA76.5
COMPUTER BUYER'S GUIDE AND HANDBOOK. Text in English. 1982. m. USD 24.95 domestic; USD 31.95 foreign (effective 2001). adv. **Document type:** *Magazine, Consumer.*
Indexed: RASB, SoftBase.
—CASDDS. **CCC.**
Published by: Bedford Communications, Inc., 1410 Broadway, 21st Fl, New York, NY 10018. TEL 212-807-8220, FAX 212-807-1098, http://www.bedfordmags.com/cbg/. Ed. David Finck TEL 212-807-8220. Pub. Edward Brown. Adv. contact Carol Berman. B&W page USD 5,760, color page USD 6,895. Circ: 45,000.

004.16 AUS ISSN 1327-2004
COMPUTER CHOICE. Text in English. 1996. bi-m. AUD 41.80 to individuals; AUD 66 to institutions (effective 2003). **Document type:** *Magazine, Consumer.* **Description:** Contains consumer information about personal computers and related equipment and programs for the home user.
Published by: Australian Consumers' Association, 57 Carrington Rd, Marrickville, NSW 2204, Australia. TEL 61-2-95773399, FAX 61-2-95773377, ausconsumer@choice.com.au, http://www.choice.com.au. Ed. Rohan Hills. Circ: 10,000.

004.16 DEU ISSN 1617-3333
COMPUTER EASY. Text in German. 1998. fortn. **Document type:** *Magazine, Consumer.*
Published by: Vogel Verlag und Druck GmbH & Co. KG, Max-Planck-Str 7-9, Wuerzburg, 97064, Germany. TEL 49-931-45353-0, FAX 49-931-4535399, http://www.chip.de/c_navseite_9738446.html, http://www.vogel-medien.de. Circ: 154,307 (paid). **Subscr. to:** DataM-Services GmbH, Fichtestr 9, Wuerzburg 97074, Germany. TEL 49-931-417001, FAX 49-931-4170499, swestenberger@datam-services.de, http://www.datam-services.de.

004.16 ITA ISSN 1123-4253
COMPUTER GAZETTE. Short title: C G. Variant title: C G Computer Gazette. Text in Italian. 1986. m. EUR 53.50 (effective 2005). adv. bk.rev.; software rev.; Website rev. 96 p./no.; back issues avail. **Document type:** *Magazine, Consumer.* **Description:** Focuses on digital video, Web casting, DVD, CAD/CAM/CAE, computer graphics and animation.
Formerly (until 1994): Commodore Gazette (0394-6991)
Related titles: ♦ Partial translation of: Computer Graphics World. ISSN 0271-4159.
Published by: I H T Gruppo Editoriale, Via Monte Napoleone 9, Milan, MI 20121, Italy. TEL 39-02-794181, FAX 39-02-784021, cgp@iht.it, http://www.iht.it. Pub., Adv. contact Massimiliano Lisa. B&W page USD 2,400, color page USD 3,400; trim 210 x 285. Circ: 20,000.

004.16 NLD ISSN 1388-2376
COMPUTER IDEE. Text in Dutch. 1998. bi-w. EUR 48.10; EUR 2.10 newsstand/cover (effective 2005). adv. **Description:** Provides readers with information on PCs, peripherals, software and applications, hi-fi, and telecommunications.
—CCC.
Published by: V N U Business Publications (Netherlands), Ceylonpoort 5-25, Haarlem, 2037 AA, Netherlands. TEL 31-23-5463463, FAX 31-23-5463931, http://www.computeridee.nl/, http://www.vnubp.nl. Ed. Mark Friederichs. Pub. Anita van der Aa. adv.: color page EUR 6,134; trim 215 x 285. Circ: 132,426.

004.16 USA ISSN 0748-8610
QA76.5
COMPUTER RETAILERS' GUIDE. Text in English. 1984. q.
Formerly (until 1985): Computer Retail News. Retailers Guide (0884-7444)
Published by: C M P Media LLC (Subsidiary of: United News & Media), 600 Community Dr, Manhasset, NY 11030. TEL 516-562-5000, FAX 516-365-4601.

004.16 USA
COMPUTER SURVIVAL REPORT. Text in English. 1980. m. USD 350 (effective 2005). bk.rev.; software rev.; Website rev. **Document type:** *Magazine, Consumer.*
Formerly (until 1990): Computer User's Survival Magazine (1053-3834)
Related titles: E-mail ed.; Online - full text ed.
Published by: Enterprises Publishing, 400 E 59th St, Ste 9F, New York, NY 10022. TEL 212-755-4363, FAX 212-755-4365, punchin@usa.net, http://www.computersurvivaljournal.com. Ed. John Edwards. Circ: 200,000 (controlled); 100,000 (free).

004.16 NLD ISSN 0927-2739
COMPUTER! TOTAAL. Text in Dutch. 1992. 11/yr. EUR 41.95 (effective 2005). adv. software rev. illus.; mkt. back issues avail. **Document type:** *Magazine, Trade.* **Description:** Offers an overview and understanding of hardware and software with reports and tests on new products, product comparisons and an indication of trends and future developments.
Formed by the merger of (1984-1991): P C World Benelux (0169-3417); (1977-1992): H C C Nieuwsbrief (0928-2688); (1990-1991): P C Thuis (0926-3101)
Related titles: Online - full text ed.
—IE, Infotrieve.
Published by: (Hobby Computer Club), I D G Communications Nederland BV, Postbus 5446, Haarlem, 2000 GK, Netherlands. TEL 31-23-5461111, FAX 31-23-5461155, redactie@computertotaal.nl, abo@idg.nl, http://www.computertotaal.nl, http://www.idg.nl. Ed. Eric Verweij. Pub. Raimon Gort. Adv. contact Fred Driessen. Circ: 200,000.

004.16 GBR
COMPUTERACTIVE. Text in English. 1998. fortn. GBP 24.99 domestic; GBP 100 foreign (effective 2003). adv. back issues avail. **Document type:** *Magazine, Consumer.* **Description:** The plain-speaking guide to computers for people who don't want to get a science degree to use computers at home for work or play.
Published by: V N U Business Publications Ltd., VNU House, 32-34 Broadwick St, London, W1A 2HG, United Kingdom. TEL 44-20-7316-9000, FAX 44-20-7316-9160, letters@computeractive.co.uk, http://www.computeractive.co.uk/. Ed. Jim Lennox. Pub. Juliet Parker. Adv. contact Nigel Taylor. color page GBP 5,513; trim 230 x 320. Circ: 325,836 (paid). **Dist. by:** MarketForce UK Ltd, 247 Tottenham Court Rd, London, Middx W1T 7AU, United Kingdom. TEL 44-207-2615199, FAX 44-207-2617341.

004.16 DEU
COMPUTERFOTO. Text in German. 1996. m. EUR 84; EUR 7.60 newsstand/cover (effective 2003). adv. back issues avail. **Document type:** *Magazine, Consumer.* **Description:** All about digital photography and electronic image processing.
Related titles: Online - full text ed.
Published by: redtec publishing GmbH, Gruber Str 46a, Poing, 85586, Germany. TEL 49-8121-951850, FAX 49-8121-951880, redaktion@computerfoto.de, computerfoto@macup.com, info@redtec.de, http://www.computerfoto.de, http://www.redtec.de. Ed. Richard Joerges. Adv. contact Monika Zachacker. B&W page EUR 3,200, color page EUR 4,200; trim 185 x 265. Circ: 23,761 (paid).

004.16 USA ISSN 8756-7911
COMPUTERITER; microcomputer news and views for the writer-editor. Text in English. 1984. m. looseleaf. USD 40. bk.rev. back issues avail.
Published by: Creative Business Communications, PO Box 476, Columbia, MD 21045. TEL 301-596-5591, FAX 301-997-7946. Ed. Linda J Elengold. Circ: 7,000.

COMPUTERLAND MAGAZINE. see *BUSINESS AND ECONOMICS—Computer Applications*

004.16 USA
COMPUTERS IN LIBRARIES: BUYERS GUIDE & CONSULTANT DIRECTORY. Text in English. 1986. a. reprint service avail. from WSH. **Document type:** *Directory.* **Description:** Lists products and services available to libraries and information centers, broken down by computers, peripherals, software, consultants, online database systems and services; covers furniture and other products as well.
Formerly (until 1988): Small Computers in Libraries: Buyers Guide and Consultant Directory (0896-9485)
Published by: Information Today, Inc., 143 Old Marlton Pike, Medford, NJ 08055-8750. TEL 609-654-6266, FAX 609-654-4309, custserv@infotoday.com, http://www.infotoday.com. Circ: 30,000.

COMPUTERWORLD; newsweekly for information technology leaders. see *COMPUTERS—Microcomputers*

004.16 USA ISSN 1530-3713
CONSUMER REPORTS HOME COMPUTER BUYING GUIDE. Variant title: Home Computer Buying Guide. Text in English. 199?. a. USD 9.95 newsstand/cover; USD 12.95 newsstand/cover in Canada (effective 2001). **Document type:** *Magazine, Consumer.*
Formerly (until 1998): Consumer Reports Guide to Personal Computers (1091-8051)
Published by: Consumers Union of the United States, Inc., 101 Truman Ave, Yonkers, NY 10703-1057. TEL 914-378-2000, 800-234-1645, FAX 914-378-2900, http://www.consumerreports.org.

004.16 USA ISSN 0899-8159
QA76.9.A25
CRYPTOSYSTEMS JOURNAL. Text in English. 1988. irreg. USD 45; USD 65 foreign (effective 1999). bk.rev. back issues avail. **Document type:** *Academic/Scholarly.* **Description:** Covers the implementation of cryptographic systems (encryption, decryption, key generation) on IBM-PCs. Includes one or more diskettes or CD-ROM with complete source code.
Related titles: CD-ROM ed.; Diskette ed.
Published by: Tony Patti, Ed. & Pub., 485 Middle Holland Rd., Holland, PA 18966. TEL 215-579-9888, crypto@compuserve.com, http://ourworld.compuserve.com/homepages/crypto.

621.3916 GBR
▼ **CUSTOM P C.** Text in English. 2003 (Aug.). m. GBP 3.50 newsstand/cover (effective 2003). adv. **Document type:** *Magazine, Consumer.* **Description:** Aimed at the performance hardware and customization markets among computer enthusiasts.
Published by: Dennis Publishing Ltd., 30 Cleveland St, London, W1P 5FF, United Kingdom. TEL 44-20-79076000, FAX 44-20-7907-6439, http://www.custompc.co.uk, http://www.theden.co.uk. Ed. Gareth Ogden. Pub. Pete Wooton. R&P Rob Willis. Adv. contact Julie Boland. color page GBP 1,985.

CYBERLOG; library of applied medical software. see *MEDICAL SCIENCES—Computer Applications*

004.16 DEU ISSN 0933-1557
D O S INTERNATIONAL✶ ; das Magazine fuer aktive PC-Anwender. (Disk Operating System) Text in German. 1987. m. adv. back issues avail. **Document type:** *Consumer.*
—IE.
Published by: Daten- und Medienverlag GmbH, Dornacherstr 3, Feldkirchen, 85622, Germany. Ed. Ralf Ockenfelds. Pub. Michael Scharfenberger. Adv. contact Stefan Grajer. Circ: 176,958.

D XERS MAGAZINE. see *COMPUTERS—Microcomputers*

004.16 USA
DEMOLETTER. Text in English. 1985. m. USD 495; USD 575 foreign. **Document type:** *Newsletter.* **Description:** Covers emerging issues and new-product trends and technologies in the personal computing industry.
Formerly: Stewart Alsop's P C Letter (8756-7822)
Related titles: CD-ROM ed.; E-mail ed.: DemoWeekly; Online - full text ed.
Published by: I D G Executive Forums, Network World Events & Executive Forums, 118 Turnpike Rd, Southborough, MA 01772. TEL 508-490-6545, 800-643-4668, FAX 508-460-1385, registrar@idgexecforums.com, http://www.idgexecforums.com/demoletter/. Circ: 1,200.

004.16 TWN ISSN 1024-3879
DIANNAO SHIJIE ZAZHI/P C WORLD TAIWAN. Text in Chinese. 1988. m. TWD 5,000. adv. **Document type:** *Magazine, Consumer.* **Description:** Provides analysis and reports on software, hardware, market development, and operations for audience in sectors such as IT, service, manufacturing, military, public service, academics, and students.
Published by: I D G Communications, Taiwan, 8F, No. 131, Sec. 3, Nanking E. Rd., Taipei, 104, Taiwan. TEL 886-2-2715-3000, FAX 886-2-2547-0601, http://www.idg.com.tw/pcw/index.html. Ed. Daniel Wang. Pub. Jack Wang. Adv. contact Lily Chou. B&W page TWD 50,000, color page TWD 84,000; trim 210 x 280. Circ: 30,000.

004 FRA ISSN 1764-5719
▼ **DIGITAL WORLD.** Text in French. 2003. bi-m. EUR 17 (effective 2005). adv. **Document type:** *Magazine, Consumer.*
Published by: I D G Communications France, 5 rue Chantecoq, Puteaux, 92808, France. TEL 33-1-4197-6161, FAX 33-1-4197-6160, http://www.digitalworld.fr/, http://www.idg.fr. adv.: color page USD 9,125; trim 210 x 297. Circ: 60,000 (controlled).

004 USA
▼ **DIGITAL WORLD.** Text in English. 2004 (Oct.). bi-m. **Document type:** *Magazine, Consumer.* **Description:** Contains information on the latest in consumer electronics and computing.
Published by: I D G Communications Inc., 501 Second St, Ste 600, San Francisco, CA 94107-4133. TEL 415-348-8006, FAX 415-442-1891, http://www.idg.com/.

004.1605 ESP
▼ **DIGITAL WORLD.** Text in Spanish. 2003. m. adv. **Document type:** *Magazine, Consumer.*
Published by: I D G Communications, Fortuny, 18 4, Madrid, 28010, Spain. TEL 34-91-3496600, FAX 34-91-3496100, idg_nt@idg.es, http://www.idg.es. adv.: color page USD 7,821; trim 210 x 280. Circ: 200,000 (controlled).

338.47621382 GBR ISSN 1366-9486
DIGITAL WORLD. Variant title: Go Digital. Text in English. 1997. q. adv. **Document type:** *Magazine, Consumer.* **Description:** Focuses on the use of the PC as a digital hub in the home and small office environment.
Published by: I D G Media, 5th Fl, 85 Tottenham Court Rd, London, W1T 4TQ, United Kingdom. TEL 44-20-72915920, FAX 44-20-75801935, http://www.idg.co.uk. Circ: 150,000 (controlled).

004.16 RUS
DOMASHNII KOMP'YUTER. Text in Russian. m.
Address: A-ya 9, Moscow, 119517, Russian Federation. TEL 7-095-2322263, FAX 7-095-2322261. Ed. A V Petrachenkov. Pub. Dmitrii Mendrelyuk. **US dist. addr.:** East View Information Services, 3020 Harbor Ln. N., Minneapolis, MN 55447. TEL 612-550-0961.

004.16 UKR
DOMASHNII P K/HOME P C. Text in Russian. 1998. m. UAK 6.68 per issue domestic (effective 2004). illus. 100 p./no.; **Document type:** *Magazine, Consumer.* **Description:** Targeted on home users of personal computers. Aims to help users overcome obstacles related to installing and running new equipment and software. The subjects covered include, but are not limited to, Internet, computer gaming, multimedia products and software that comes on accompanying CD.
Published by: Izdatel'skii Dom I T C, prosp Krasnozvezdnyi 51, Kiev, Ukraine. info@itc.ua, http://itc.ua/dpk. Circ: 17,600.

004.16 USA
DVORAK DIRECTORY. Text in English. a. USD 4 (effective 1999). **Document type:** *Directory.* **Description:** Comprehensive listing of sources for Dvorak related products.
Former titles: Dvorak Products List; Dvorak International. Typing Manual for Computer and Typewriter
Published by: Dvorak International, PO Box 11985, Eugene, OR 97440. TEL 802-287-2343, DvorakInt@aol.com. Ed. Steve Ingram.

FREE ACCESS. see *COMPUTERS—Internet*

004.16 USA
G R M U G NEWSLETTER. Text in English. irreg.
Published by: Great River Microcomputer Users Group, 47 Lake Dr S, Rte 9, Quincy, IL 62301. Ed. David N Wexler.

004.16 USA
GW2K: THE GATEWAY MAGAZINE. Text in English. q. adv. **Document type:** *Newsletter.*
Published by: Gateway 2000, Inc., 610 Gateway Dr, North Sioux City, SD 57049. TEL 800-846-2000, FAX 605-232-2023, editor@gw2k.com. Adv. contact Nick Hofer.

004.16 USA
H A L - P C MAGAZINE. Text in English. 1983. m. USD 40 to members (effective 2003). adv. bk.rev. **Document type:** *Magazine, Trade.*
Former titles: H A L - P C User Journal (1069-3467); H A L - P C Newsletter
Published by: Houston Area League of P C Users, Inc., 4543 Post Oak Place Dr, Ste 200, Houston, TX 77027-3103. TEL 713-993-3300, FAX 713-993-3333, cevans@hal-pc.org, http://www.hal-pc.org. Ed. Charles W Evans. R&P Charles Evans. Adv. contact D.J. Jennings. Circ: 20,000 (paid).

004.16 384 USA ISSN 1069-2096
HIGH PERFORMANCE COMPUTING AND COMMUNICATIONS WEEK. Text in English. 1992. w.
Related titles: Online - full text ed.: (from Florida Center for Library Automation, Gale Group).
—CCC.
Published by: King Communications Group, Inc., 627 National Press Bldg, Washington, DC 20045. TEL 202-638-4260, 202-662-9748, FAX 202-662-9744.

004.16 CHN
HOME P C WORLD CHINA. Text in Chinese. m. adv. **Document type:** *Magazine, Consumer.* **Description:** Contains reports on new technologies, products and digital solutions for the home PC user.
Published by: I D G China, Rm. 616, Tower A, COFCO Plaza, Jianguomennei Dajie, Beijing, 100005 , China. TEL 86-10-6526-0959, FAX 86-10-6526-0866, dumin@idg.com.cn, http://www.idgchina.com. adv.: color page USD 5,600. Circ: 120,000 (paid and controlled).

I E E E MICRO. see *COMPUTERS—Microcomputers*

004.16 USA ISSN 1520-9210
QA76.575 CODEN: ITMUF8
➤ **I E E E TRANSACTIONS ON MULTIMEDIA.** (Institute of Electrical and Electronic Engineers) Text in English. 1999. bi-m. USD 520 (effective 2006). **Document type:** *Journal, Academic/Scholarly.* **Description:** Seeks to integrate all aspects of multimedia systems and technology, signal processing, and applications.
Related titles: CD-ROM ed.; Online - full text ed.: (from EBSCO Publishing).
Indexed: CMCI, CurCont, ErgAb, Inspec, RefZh.
—BLDSC (4363.206700), CISTI, IE, Infotrieve, ingenta, Linda Hall. **CCC.**
Published by: Institute of Electrical and Electronics Engineers, Inc., 445 Hoes Ln, Piscataway, NJ 08854-1331. TEL 732-981-0060, 800-701-4333, FAX 732-981-1721, tmm.info@ieee.org, subscription-service@ieee.org, http://www.ieee.org/organizations/tab/tmm.html. Ed. Bing J Sheu. **Subscr. to:** Maruzen Co., Ltd., 3-10 Nihonbashi 2-chome, Chuo-ku, Tokyo 103-0027, Japan. FAX 81-3-3275-0657; Universal Subscription Agency, Pvt. Ltd., 877, Udyog Vihar, V, Gurgoan 122001, India. TEL 91-124-347261, FAX 91-124-342496. **Co-sponsors:** I E E E Circuits and Systems Society; I E E E Signal Processing Society; I E E E Communications Society; I E E E Computer Society.

➤ **I E E E WIRELESS COMMUNICATIONS MAGAZINE.** see *COMMUNICATIONS*

004.16 AUT
I S S B AMIGA MAGAZINE. Text in German. bi-m.
Address: Kirchengasse 27, Vienna, W 1070, Austria. TEL 02732-853273, FAX 02732-85327. Ed. Marcello Isidori. Circ: 30,000.

004.16 BEL ISSN 1371-3817
INFO MEDIA NET (NEDERLANDSE EDITION). Text in Dutch. 1986. 10/yr.
Formerly (until 1995): Samsom Personal Computer (Vlaamse Editie) (0774-9929)
Related titles: Ed.: Info Media Net (Edition Francaise). ISSN 1371-3809. BEF 4,770.
Published by: C E D Samsom (Subsidiary of: Wolters Samsom Belgie n.v.), Kouterveld 14, Diegem, 1831, Belgium. TEL 32-2-7231111.

INSIDE MARKET DATA; the newsletter of real-time market data. see *BUSINESS AND ECONOMICS—Banking And Finance—Computer Applications*

INSIDE MICROSOFT WINDOWS; tips and tricks for Microsoft Windows. see *COMPUTERS—Software*

INSIDE MICROSOFT WINDOWS. see *COMPUTERS—Software*

004.16 USA ISSN 1081-3314
QA76.76.O63 CODEN: INSOFC
INSIDE SOLARIS. Text in English. 1995. m. USD 177 domestic; USD 187 foreign; USD 207 combined subscription print & online eds. (effective 2005). **Document type:** *Magazine, Consumer.* **Description:** Helps to establish and maintain an efficient operating environment.
Related titles: Online - full text ed.: USD 207 domestic; USD 217 foreign (effective 2005) (from ProQuest Information & Learning).
—IE. **CCC.**
Published by: Element K Journals (Subsidiary of: Eli Research, Inc.), 500 Canal View Blvd, Rochester, NY 14623. TEL 585-240-7301, 800-223-8720, 877-203-5248, FAX 585-292-4392, http://www.elementkjournals.com/products/showProduct.asp?prodID=26&catId=2.

THE INSIDE WORD (P C EDITION - MICROSOFT WORD 5.5 & 6.0). see *COMPUTERS—Word Processing*

J U G NEWSLETTER. see *COMPUTERS—Computer Networks*

004.16 USA ISSN 1533-2721
JOURNAL OF END USER COMPUTER SUPPORT; innovations for business & nonprofit environments. Text in English. 2002. q. USD 60 domestic to individuals; USD 81 in Canada to individuals; USD 87 elsewhere to individuals; USD 95 domestic to institutions; USD 128 in Canada to institutions; USD 138 elsewhere to institutions (effective 2004). adv. reprint service avail. from HAW. **Document type:** *Journal, Trade.* **Description:** Publishes theoretical and practical application material aimed at increasing awareness of the dynamic nature of systems support.
Related titles: Online - full text ed.: ISSN 1533-273X. 2004.
Published by: Internet Practice Press (Subsidiary of: Haworth Press, Inc.), 10 Alice St, Binghamton, NY 13904. TEL 607-722-5857, 800-429-6784, FAX 607-771-0012, 800-895-0582, getinfo@haworthpress.com, http://www.haworthpressinc.com/store/product.asp?sku=J178, http://www.haworthpress.com/. Ed. W Simmons. Pub. William Cohen. R&P Ruth Ann Heath TEL 607-722-5857 ext 316. Adv. contact Rebecca Miller-Baum TEL 607-722-5857 ext 337. B&W page USD 315, color page USD 550; trim 6 x 8.5.

C

004.16 GBR
KEY NOTE MARKET REPORT: PERSONAL COMPUTERS & WORKSTATIONS. Variant title: Personal Computers & Workstations. Text in English. irreg., latest vol.8, 1990. GBP 265 (effective 1999).
Published by: Key Note Ltd., Field House, 72 Oldfield Rd, Hampton, Mddx TW12 2HQ, United Kingdom. TEL 44-20-8481-8750, FAX 44-20-8783-0049, info@keynote.co.uk, http://www.keynote.co.uk.

KOMPUTER FOR ALLE. see *COMPUTERS—Minicomputers*

004.16 USA ISSN 1535-4857
LAPTOP; mobile solutions for business and life. Text in English. 1989. m. USD 18 domestic; USD 30 foreign (effective 2005). adv. **Document type:** *Magazine, Consumer.*
Formerly (until 2000): Laptop Buyer's Guide and Handbook (1089-036X)
Related titles: Online - full text ed.
Indexed: SoftBase.
—CCC.
Published by: Bedford Communications, Inc., 1410 Broadway, 21st Fl, New York, NY 10018. TEL 212-807-8220, FAX 212-807-1098, mspoonauer@bedfordmags.com, http://www.techworthy.com/magazines/laptop/. Ed. Mark Spoonauer. Pub. Edward Brown. Adv. contact Melissa Rocco. B&W page USD 10,980. Circ: 70,000 (paid). **Dist. in UK by:** Comag, Tavistock Works, Tavistock Rd, W Drayton, Middx UB7 7QX, United Kingdom. TEL 44-1895-433600, FAX 44-189-543-3606.

004.6 DEU
LAPTOP GUIDE. Text in German. 2/yr. adv. **Document type:** *Magazine, Consumer.* **Description:** Contains detailed product reviews and information on a wide variety of portable computers.
Published by: Komunik Verlag & Marketing GmbH, Konrad-Celtis-Str 77, Munich, 81369, Germany. TEL 49-89-74117233, FAX 49-89-74117178, coroli@komunik.de, http://www.komunik.de.

004.16 USA
LAPTOP NEWSLETTER. Text in English. m. **Document type:** *Newsletter.* **Description:** Contains a summary of notebook news, reviews, and opinions.
Media: Online - full text.
Address: info@notebookmall.com, http://www.notebookmall.com. Ed. Alex Botezatu.

004.16 ITA
LIST SOLUZIONI PER INFORMATICA✶. Text in Italian. 11/yr.
Published by: Edicomp Holding SpA, Piazza San Lorenzo in Lucina 26, Rome, 00186, Italy. TEL 39-06-68809644, FAX 39-06-6873645, direzione@edicomp.it, http://www.edicomp.net. Circ: 34,580.

LOADSTAR; the monthly software collection for people who love their Commodores. see *COMPUTERS—Software*

004.16 USA
LOADSTAR QUARTERLY. Text in English. q. USD 24.95; USD 28.95 foreign (effective 1998). **Description:** For owners of Commodore 128 computers.
Media: Diskette.
Published by: J & F Publishing, Inc., PO Box 30008, Shreveport, LA 71130-0008. TEL 318-221-8718, judi@loadstar.com, http://www.loadstar.com.

LONG DISTANCE COMPETITION REPORT. see *COMPUTERS—Microcomputers*

004 USA
LONGWORDS NEWSLETTER. Text in English. m. back issues avail. **Document type:** *Newsletter.*
Media: Online - full content.
Published by: Dallas - Fort Worth Compaq Users Group, 5430 LBJ Freeway, Ste 900, Dallas, TX 75240. TEL 972-702-4500, dfwlug@dfwlug.decus.org, http://www.dfwcug.org/. Ed. Pat Jankowiak.

681.3 FRA ISSN 1287-6364
M6 MULTIMEDIA. Text in French. 1997. bi-m. **Document type:** *Magazine, Consumer.*
Published by: M6 Interactions, 89 av Charles-de-Gaulle, Neuilly-sur-Seine Cedex, 92575, France. TEL 33-1-41926936, http://www.m6net.fr.

004.16 USA ISSN 1088-548X
QA76.8.M3
MAC ADDICT; a better machine. a better magazine. Text in English. 1996. m. USD 29.95 combined subscription domestic includes CD-ROM; USD 45 combined subscription in Canada includes CD-ROM; USD 58 combined subscription elsewhere includes CD-ROM (effective 2005). adv. bk.rev.; software rev. charts; illus. back issues avail. **Document type:** *Magazine, Consumer.* **Description:** Provides hands-on tutorials, reviews, regular columns, and news coverage on the latest-breaking technology in the Mac market.
Related titles: Online - full text ed.
Indexed: MicrocompInd.
Published by: Future Network USA, 150 North Hill Dr, Ste 40, Brisbane, CA 94005. TEL 415-468-4684, FAX 415-468-4686, letters@macaddict.com, http://www.macaddict.com/magazine/index.html, http://www.futurenetworkusa.com/. Ed. Rik Myslewski. Pub. Bernie Lanigan TEL 646-723-5405. R&P Charles Schug. Adv. contact Ben Grasso. color page USD 15,450; trim 8 x 10.5. **Subscr. to:** PO Box 58251, Boulder, CO 80328-8251. **Dist. in UK by:** Seymour Distribution Ltd, 86 Newman St, London W1T 3EX, United Kingdom. FAX 44-207-396-8002, enquiries@seymour.co.uk.

004.16 USA ISSN 1074-0392
MAC HOME JOURNAL. Variant title: MacHome Journal. Text in English. 1993. m. USD 29.95 domestic; USD 39.95 in Canada; USD 49.95 newsstand/cover elsewhere; USD 4.95 newsstand/cover (effective 2005). adv. bk.rev. **Document type:** *Magazine, Consumer.* **Description:** For the home Mac user.
Indexed: MicrocompInd.
Address: 200 Folsom St, San Francisco, CA 94105. TEL 415-957-1911, 800-800-6542, FAX 415-882-9502, editor@machome.com, http://www.machome.com. Ed. Amy Wood. Pub. Kevin Octavio. Adv. contact Tim Urlaub. Circ: 65,000.

004.16 DEU
MAC LIFE. Text in German. 2000. m. EUR 60 domestic; EUR 70 foreign; EUR 5.90 newsstand/cover (effective 2003). adv. **Document type:** *Magazine, Consumer.*
Related titles: Online - full text ed.
Published by: Falke Verlag, An der Holsatiamuehle 1, Kiel, 24149, Germany. TEL 49-431-2007660, FAX 49-431-2099035, redaktion@mac-life.de, info@falkemedia.de, http://www.mac-life.de, http://www.falkemedia.de. Ed., Pub. Kassian A. Goukassian. adv.: B&W page EUR 2,200, color page EUR 2,500. Circ: 13,500 (paid and controlled).

MAC NET JOURNAL. see *COMPUTERS—Internet*

004.16 JPN
MAC POWER. Text in Japanese. 1990. m. JPY 13,200; JPY 1,000 newsstand/cover (effective 2004).
Published by: ASCII Corp., JR Shinanomachi Bldg. 34 Shinanomachi, Shinjuku-ku, Tokyo, 160-8584, Japan. http://www.ascii.co.jp/books/magazines/macpower.html.

004.16 USA ISSN 1062-452X
QA76.76.O63
THE MACAUTHORITY. Text in English. 1992. m. USD 107; USD 137 combined subscription print & online eds. (effective 2005). **Document type:** *Consumer.*
Related titles: Online - full text ed.: ISSN 1539-042X. USD 137 domestic; USD 147 foreign (effective 2005) (from ProQuest Information & Learning).
Indexed: InfoSAb, MicrocompInd.
—CCC.
Published by: Element K Journals (Subsidiary of: Eli Research, Inc.), 500 Canal View Blvd, Rochester, NY 14623. TEL 585-240-7301, 800-223-8720, 877-203-5248, FAX 585-292-4392, http://www.elementkjournals.com/products/showProduct.asp?prodID=17&catId=1. Ed. Michelle Rogers.

004.16 CAN
MACCENTRAL. Text in English. 1995. d. **Document type:** *Bulletin.* **Description:** Provides a platform from which to promote, discuss, inform, and generally wonder at the world which is Macintosh.
Media: Online - full text.
Address: 6526 Roslyn Rd, Halifax, NS B3L 2M9, Canada. TEL 902-455-9169, email@maccentral.com, http://www.maccentral.com. Ed. Stan Flack.

004.16 USA
MACCOM. Text in English. 1996. m. **Description:** Macintosh e-mail magazine with reviews, articles, ads, tips, contests and more.
Media: Online - full text.
Address: maccom@maccom.net, http://www.maccom.net. Ed. Aaron Gibbons.

004.16 GBR ISSN 0968-3305
MACFORMAT. Text in English. 1993. 13/yr. GBP 49.95 domestic; GBP 64 in Europe; GBP 78 rest of world (effective 2003). adv. software rev. back issues avail. **Document type:** *Consumer.* **Description:** Provides balanced application coverage, from graphics and games to spreadsheets and multimedia, for the active, hands-on Macintosh user.
Related titles: CD-ROM ed.: ISSN 1353-8519; Online - full text ed.
—CCC.
Published by: Future Publishing Ltd., Beauford Court, 30 Monmouth St, Bath, Avon BA1 2BW, United Kingdom. TEL 44-1225-442244, FAX 44-1225-732285, macformat@futurenet.co.uk, http://www.macformat.com/, http://www.futurenet.co.uk. Ed., R&P Alex Summersby. Pub. Jon Bickley. Adv. contact Rob Bennett. color page GBP 1,995; trim 210 x 297. Circ: 35,650 (paid).

004.16 USA ISSN 1070-7425
MACINTOSH TIPS & TRICKS. Text in English. irreg. free. bk.rev. **Document type:** *Newsletter.* **Description:** News and productivity for the Apple Macintosh computer.
Media: Online - full text.
Published by: Giles Road Press, PO Box 20337, Wickenburg, AZ 85358-0337. TEL 520-684-1011, FAX 520-684-3965, info@gilesrd.com, http://www.gilesrd.com. Ed., Pub., R&P Maria Langer.

004.16 CHE
MACINTOUCH. Text in German. 1987. bi-m. CHF 48; CHF 54 foreign (effective 1998). adv. bk.rev. **Document type:** *Consumer.* **Description:** Provides information for users of Apple Macintosh systems.
Related titles: Online - full text ed.
Published by: Macintouch Verlag, Birkenweg 2, Wallisellen, 8304, Switzerland. TEL 41-1-8305600, FAX 41-1-8305458, ricford@macintouch.com, http://www.macintouch.com. Ed. Heinz Stucki. Pub. Hans Ruedi Roth. Adv. contact Juerg Kaiser. Circ: 11,000.

004.16 DEU
MACMAGAZIN UND MACEASY. Text in German. 1995. m. **Document type:** *Magazine, Consumer.*
Formerly: MACeasy
Published by: redtec publishing GmbH, Gruber Str 46a, Poing, 85586, Germany. TEL 49-40-85183250, FAX 49-40-85183299, macmags@macup.com, http://www.macup.com/macmags. Eds. Claus Heitmann, Frank Lohstoeter. Adv. contact Ingo Hoelters. Circ: 29,467 (paid).

004.16 DEU
MACPROFILER. Text in German. m. EUR 59.90; EUR 5.30 newsstand/cover (effective 2003). adv. **Document type:** *Magazine, Consumer.*
Related titles: Online - full text ed.
Published by: Publishing Port Hamburg GmbH, Feldstr 66, Hamburg, 20359, Germany. TEL 49-40-80818780, FAX 49-40-808187899, http://www.macprofiler.de. Ed. Volker Riebartsch. Adv. contact Barbara Herpich. B&W page EUR 3,000, color page EUR 3,900. Circ: 12,700 (paid and controlled).

MACS U N I T E. (Users Network for Integrating Technology into Education) see *COMPUTERS—Microcomputers*

004.16 USA ISSN 1067-8360
QA76.8.M3 CODEN: MCMGEQ
MACTECH MAGAZINE; for Macintosh programmers & developers. Text in English. 1984. m. USD 47 domestic; USD 59 in Canada; USD 97 elsewhere; USD 124 combined subscription domestic print & disk; USD 136 combined subscription in Canada print & disk; USD 194 combined subscription elsewhere print & disk (effective 2003). adv. **Document type:** *Trade.* **Description:** Strives to deliver the latest information to all developers and to provide a forum where programmers and developers can exchange ideas and breakthroughs.
Formerly (until 1992): MacTutor (8756-8810)
Related titles: CD-ROM ed.; Online - full text ed.
Indexed: SoftBase.
—IE.
Address: PO Box 5200, Westlake Village, CA 91359-5200. TEL 805-494-9797, FAX 805-494-9798, info@devdepot.com, cust_serv@devdepot.com, ad_sales@mactech.com, http://www.mactech.com. Ed. Nick De Mello. Pub. Neil Ticktin. adv.: B&W page USD 1,045, color page USD 2,250; trim 11 x 8.5. Circ: 13,500 (paid).

004.16 DEU ISSN 0935-6282
MACUP. Text in German. 1985. m. EUR 64.80 domestic; EUR 74.80 foreign; EUR 4.90 newsstand/cover (effective 2003). adv. back issues avail. **Document type:** *Magazine, Consumer.* **Description:** Contains information and reviews on Mac computers and related accessories and products.
—IE, Infotrieve.
Published by: redtec publishing GmbH, Gruber Str 46a, Poing, 85586, Germany. TEL 49-8121-951850, FAX 49-8121-951880, macup@macup.com, info@redtec.de, http://www.macup.com, http://www.redtec.de. Ed. Martin Stein. Adv. contact Monika Zachacker. B&W page EUR 4,200, color page EUR 5,600; trim 203 x 245. Circ: 40,665.

004.16 RUS
MACUP. Text in Russian. m. RUR 66 per issue domestic; RUR 111 per issue in the CIS; RUR 165 per issue foreign (effective 2004). **Document type:** *Journal, Trade.*
Published by: Redaktsiya Zhurnala MACup, pr-kt Marshala Zhukova, 1, Moscow, 123308, Russian Federation. macup@macup.ru, http://www.macup.ru. Ed. Sergey Khimchenko. Pub. Anna Biryuleva.

004.16 DEU ISSN 0935-6290
MACUP EXTRA. Text in German. q. EUR 9.90 newsstand/cover (effective 2005). **Document type:** *Magazine, Consumer.* **Description:** Highlights one area of special interest to Macintosh users.
Published by: redtec publishing GmbH, Gruber Str 46a, Poing, 85586, Germany. TEL 49-8121-951850, FAX 49-8121-951880, info@redtec.de, http://www.redtec.de.

004.16 GBR ISSN 0269-3275
MACUSER. Text in English. 1985. 25/yr. GBP 47 domestic; GBP 65 in Europe; GBP 122 elsewhere; GBP 2.99 newsstand/cover. adv. **Document type:** *Consumer.*

C

Related titles: Online - full text ed.
Indexed: MRD, MicrocompInd, SoftBase.
—BLDSC (5330.796200), IE, Infotrieve.
Published by: Dennis Publishing Ltd., 30 Cleveland St, London, W1P 5FF, United Kingdom. TEL 44-20-7917-7728, FAX 44-20-7917-5732, edit@macuser.co.uk, http:// www.macuser.co.uk. Ed. Adam Banks. Circ: 32,522 (paid).
Subscr. to: MacUser, FREEPOST WD7, Bristol, Avon BS32 0ZZ, United Kingdom. TEL 44-1454-620070, FAX 44-1454-620080. **Dist. by:** USM Distribution Ltd., U S M Distribution, 85-86 Newman St, London W1P 3LD, United Kingdom. TEL 44-20-7396-8000, FAX 44-20-7396-8002.

004.16   DEU   ISSN 0937-4906
MACWELT. Text in German. 1990. m. EUR 59.40 domestic; EUR 68.76 foreign; EUR 5.40 newsstand/cover (effective 2005). adv. **Document type:** *Magazine, Consumer.* **Description:** Provides information to Macintosh users at home, in business, research, design publishing and media.
Related titles: Online - full text ed.; ♦ Supplement to: P C Welt. ISSN 0175-0496.
—IE, Infotrieve.
Published by: I D G Communications Verlag AG, Leopoldstr 252b, Munich, 80807, Germany. TEL 49-89-36086532, FAX 49-89-36086570, webmaster@macwelt.de, info@idg-verlag.de, http://www.macwelt.de, http://www.idg-verlag.de. Ed. Sebastian Hirsch. Pub. Stephan Scherzer. Adv. contact Marion Aschenbrenner. B&W page EUR 4,900, color page EUR 6,500; trim 185 x 266. Circ: 40,679 (paid and controlled).
Subscr. to: dsb Abo-Betreuung GmbH, Konrad-Zuse-Str 16, Neckarsulm 74172, Germany. TEL 49-7132-959-0, FAX 49-7132-959105.

004.16   USA   ISSN 0741-8647
QA76.8.M3   CODEN: MACWEA
MACWORLD; the Macintosh magazine for the network professional. Text in English. 1984. m. USD 19.97 domestic; CND 29.97 in Canada; USD 44.97 foreign; USD 7.99 newsstand/cover (effective 2005). adv. software rev. illus.; tr.lit. back issues avail.; reprints avail. **Document type:** *Magazine, Consumer.* **Description:** Provides for Macintosh personal computer users. Features articles on applications and hardware. Regular columns include new products, questions and answers, hardware and software reviews.
Incorporates (1985-1997): MacUser (0884-0997); Which was formerly: MacLetter
Related titles: Microfiche ed.: (from NBI, PQC); Online - full text ed.: (from America Online, Inc., bigchalk, EBSCO Publishing, Florida Center for Library Automation, Gale Group, Northern Light Technology, Inc., O C L C Online Computer Library Center, Inc., ProQuest Information & Learning).
Indexed: ABIn, B&I, BPI, CompD, Compl, ConsI, InfoSAb, Inspec, MASUSE, MRD, MagInd, MicrocompInd, PCR2, RGAb, RGPR, SoftBase, TOM.
—BLDSC (5330.796300), CASDDS, CISTI, Ei, IDS, IE, Infotrieve, ingenta. **CCC.**
Published by: Mac Publishing, L.L.C. (Subsidiary of: I D G Communications Inc.), 501 Second St, 5th Fl, San Francisco, CA 94107. TEL 415-243-0505, FAX 415-243-3544, kgalang@macworld.com, customer_service@macworld.com, http://www.macworld.com/magazine. Ed. Jason Snell. Pub. Cynthia Ramsey. adv.: B&W page USD 26,025, color page USD 33,830. Circ: 405,000 (paid). **Subscr. to:** Macworld Subscription Services, PO Box 37781, Boone, IA 50037-0781. TEL 800-288-6848.

004.16   GBR   ISSN 0957-2341
                                   CODEN: MAWRER
MACWORLD; the essential Macintosh resource. Text in English. 1989. m. GBP 49.66 domestic; GBP 90 in Europe; GBP 120 rest of world (effective 2005). adv. software rev. **Document type:** *Magazine, Consumer.* **Description:** Takes a solutions-oriented approach to Mac computing, giving you the technical know-how to get the most from your system.
Related titles: CD-ROM ed.: ISSN 1356-9503. 1995; Online - full text ed.: (from Northern Light Technology, Inc.); ♦ Includes: Webcreate.
Indexed: Inspec.
—IE, Infotrieve.
Published by: I D G Media, Media House, Adlington Park, Macclesfield, Ches SK10 4PZ, United Kingdom. TEL 44-1625-878888, FAX 44-1625-879966, editor@macworld.co.uk, http://www.macworld.co.uk/. Ed. Simon Jary. Pub. Guy Eaton. Adv. contact Anne Ridyard. Circ: 33,012 (paid). **Subscr. to:** Freepost WC4336, Leicester, Leics LE87 4DE, United Kingdom. **Dist. by:** Comag, Tavistock Works, Tavistock Rd, W Drayton, Middx UB7 7QX, United Kingdom. TEL 44-1895-433600, FAX 44-189-543-3606.

681.31   ESP   ISSN 1132-1156
MACWORLD ESPANA; magazine for macintosh users. Text in Spanish. 1992. m. EUR 59.20 (effective 2002). adv. **Document type:** *Magazine, Consumer.* **Description:** Contains news, tips, product reviews and solutions designed to help Macintosh users enhance personal productivity.
Related titles: Online - full text ed.
Published by: I D G Communications, Fortuny, 18 4, Madrid, 28010, Spain. TEL 34-91-3496600, FAX 34-91-3496100, macworld@idg.es, http://www.idg.es/macworld. Ed. Daniel de Blas. Adv. contact Natacha Parron TEL 34-91-3496679. color page USD 2,772; trim 210 x 280. Circ: 9,021 (paid and controlled).

004.16   ITA
MACWORLD ITALIA; tutto il mondo MacIntosh. Text in Italian. 1991. m. (11/yr. plus 1 special issue). EUR 34 (effective 2005). adv. **Document type:** *Magazine, Consumer.* **Description:** Provides the latest news from Italy and the world. Contains reviews of single products, advice, tips, tricks and explanations.
Related titles: Online - full text ed.
Published by: I D G Communications Italia s.r.l., Via Zante 16-2, Milano, 20138, Italy. TEL 39-02-580381, FAX 39-02-58011670, macworld@idg.it, info@idg.it, http://www.macworld.it, http://www.idgworld.it. Ed. Enrico Lotti. Pub. Mario Toffoletti. Adv. contact Gianluca Soravia. Circ: 16,500.

004.16   KOR
MACWORLD KOREA. Text in Korean. m. adv.
Published by: Hi-Tech Information Inc., 494-65 Yonggang-Dong, Mapo-Gu, Daeho Bldg., 3rd Fl., Seoul, 121070, Korea, S. TEL 82-2-3257300, FAX 82-2-7196409. Pub. Y S Gimm. Adv. contact Junbin Kim. B&W page USD 1,800, color page USD 2,100; trim 277 x 213. Circ: 30,000.

004.16   SWE   ISSN 0284-3005
MACWORLD SWEDEN. Text in Swedish. 1986. 10/yr. SEK 595 Print Edition; SEK 430 Online Edition; SEK 790 combined subscription Print & Online Eds (effective 2005). adv. **Document type:** *Magazine, Consumer.* **Description:** Focuses on tests of products and services. Reports on news and provides articles on how-to in the Mac-World.
Incorporates Svenska Macpressen (1101-1416)
Related titles: Online - full text ed.: ISSN 1402-4756 (from Northern Light Technology, Inc.).
Published by: I D G AB (Subsidiary of: I D G Communications Inc.), Sturegatan 11, Stockholm, 10678, Sweden. TEL 46-8-4536000, FAX 46-8-4536005, macworld@macworld.se, http://macworld.idg.se, http://www.idg.se. Eds. Pernilla Norin TEL 47-8-4536247, Andreas Leijen TEL 47-8-4536248. Adv. contact Jesper Landen TEL 47-8-4536178. color page SEK 51,000; trim 185 x 260. Circ: 12,400 (paid).

004.16   TUR   ISSN 1300-6169
MACWORLD TURKEY. Text in Turkish. 1992. m. TRL 30,000,000 (effective 2002). adv. **Document type:** *Magazine, Trade.* **Description:** Contains information on products and services available to the users of Macintosh computers.
Related titles: Online - full text ed.
Published by: Globus Dunya Basinevi, 100 Yil Mahallesi, Bagcilar - Istanbul, 34440, Turkey. TEL 90-212-6290808, FAX 90-212-6294628, http://www.macworld.com.tr. adv.: color page USD 1,300; trim 195 x 272. Circ: 10,000 (paid and controlled).

MAKINTOSH. see *PUBLISHING AND BOOK TRADE—Computer Applications*

004.16   CAN   ISSN 0827-1755
MAPLE ORCHARD; Canadian publication on Apple and Macintosh computing. Text in English. 1982. m. CND 15 to non-members. adv. bk.rev. **Document type:** *Newsletter.*
Related titles: Online - full text ed.
Published by: Loyal Ontario Group Interested in Computers Inc. (LOGIC), P O Box 958, Thornhill, ON L3T 4A5, Canada. TEL 416-323-0828. Ed. Ken Nelson. Circ: 350.

004.16   USA   ISSN 1522-4279
QA75.5
MAXIMUM P C. (Personal Computer) Text in English. 1993. m. USD 29.95 combined subscription domestic includes CDs; USD 37 in Canada includes CDs; USD 53 elsewhere includes CDs (effective 2005). adv. illus. reprints avail. **Document type:** *Magazine, Consumer.* **Description:** Offers unique, real-world reviews of all the PC gear money can buy.
Formed by the merger of (1994-1998): Home P C (1073-1784); (1993-1998): Boot (1088-5439); Which was formerly (until 1996): CD-ROM Today (1069-4099)
Related titles: CD-ROM ed.; Online - full text ed.: (from EBSCO Publishing, Gale Group).
Indexed: CompD, MASUSE, MicrocompInd, SoftBase.
—IE. **CCC.**
Published by: Future Network USA, 150 North Hill Dr, Ste 40, Brisbane, CA 94005. TEL 415-468-4684, FAX 415-468-4686, http://www.maximumpc.com/, http://www.futurenetworkusa.com. Ed. Will Smith. Pub. Chris Coelho. adv.: B&W page USD 7,140, color page USD 8,920; trim 10.88 x 8.38. Circ: 123,000 (paid).

681.3   FRA   ISSN 1628-1632
MICRO DINGO. Text in French. 199?. m. adv. **Document type:** *Magazine, Consumer.*
Published by: Ixo Publishing, 16 rue Hoche, Quartier des Bouvets, Puteaux, 92800, France. TEL 33-1-41028000, info@ixo.com, http://www.ixo.com.

004.16   FRA   ISSN 1276-549X
MICRO HEBDO. Text in French. 1998. w. adv. **Document type:** *Newspaper, Consumer.* **Description:** Contains articles and features that make new IT and PC technologies accessible to all.
Published by: I D G Communications France, 5 rue Chantecoq, Puteaux, 92808, France. TEL 33-1-4197-6161, FAX 33-1-4197-6160, http://www.idg.fr. adv.: color page USD 8,407; trim 220 x 285. Circ: 141,800 (paid and controlled).

MICRO MEDICAL NEWSLETTER. see *MEDICAL SCIENCES—Computer Applications*

MICROBANKER BANKING TECHNOLOGY STRATEGIES NEWSLETTER; the research letter on financial end-user computing. see *BUSINESS AND ECONOMICS—Banking And Finance—Computer Applications*

MICROLEADS RESELLER DIRECTORY ON DISK. see *COMPUTERS—Computer Industry Directories*

004.16   ESP
MICROMANIA. Text in Spanish. 1982. 12/yr. adv. **Document type:** *Magazine, Consumer.* **Description:** Covers computer games, music, software and personal computers.
Published by: Hobby Press S.A. (Subsidiary of: Axel Springer Verlag AG), C/ Los Vascos 17, Madrid, 28040, Spain. TEL 34-902-111315, FAX 34-902-151798, http:// www.hobbypress.es/micromania/. Ed. Domingo Gomez. Adv. contact Maria Perera. Circ: 38,000 (paid).

004.16   FIN   ISSN 0785-9988
MIKRO P C. Key Title: Mikro PC. Text in Finnish. 1983. 15/yr. EUR 90 (effective 2005). adv. bk.rev. index. **Document type:** *Magazine, Trade.* **Description:** Reports on extensive product tests in concrete user situations and carries out broad product comparisons on PCs, peripherals and software.
Formerly (until 1988): Mikro (0780-6663)
Related titles: Online - full text ed.
Published by: Talentum Oyj, Malminkatu 30, PO Box 920, Helsinki, 00101, Finland. TEL 358-240-4240, FAX 358-240-424130, mikropc@talentum.fi, info@talentum.fi, http://www.mikropc.fi, http://www.talentum.fi. Ed. Kauko Ollilla TEL 358-020-4424369. Adv. contact Sanna Araviita TEL 358-40-3424230. B&W page EUR 5,990, color page EUR 4,050; trim 210 x 297. Circ: 30,015 (controlled).

004.6   SCG
MIKRO P C WORLD YUGOSLAVIA. Text in Serbian. m. YUN 1,089 (effective 2002). adv. **Document type:** *Magazine, Trade.* **Description:** Contains news and product reviews of PC hardware and software and covers Internet and desktop publishing topics.
Related titles: Online - full text ed.
Published by: Mikro Knjiga Publishing Company, Pozeska 81A, Belgrade, 11030. TEL 381-11-543-593, FAX 381-11-542-516, http://www.mikro.co.yu. Ed. Milenko Vasic. Adv. contact Marija Soldatovic. B&W page USD 670, color page USD 900; trim 201 x 267. Circ: 9,000 (paid and controlled).

004.16   FIN   ISSN 0781-2078
MIKROBITTI. Text in Finnish. 1984. 11/yr. EUR 73 (effective 2004). adv. **Document type:** *Magazine, Consumer.*
Published by: Sanoma Magazines Finland Corporation, Hoylaamotie 1 D, P.O. Box 100, Helsinki, 00040, Finland. TEL 358-9-1201, FAX 358-9-1205171, info@sanomamagazines.fi, http://www.mikrobitti.fi, http://www.sanomamagazines.fi. adv.: B&W page EUR 3,610, color page EUR 4,590. Circ: 86,688 (paid and controlled).

MIKRODATORN. see *COMPUTERS—Microcomputers*

004.16   USA
MINI' APP'LES. Text in English. m. USD 25. adv. **Document type:** *Newsletter.*
Published by: Minnesota Apple Computer User's Group, Inc., PO Box 796, Hopkins, MN 55343. TEL 612-229-6952. Ed., Adv. contact John Hunkins Sr. Circ: 500.

004.6   DEU   ISSN 1436-7130
MOBILE COMPUTER & KOMMUNIKATION. Text in German. 1998. 10/yr. EUR 45.60; EUR 4 newsstand/cover (effective 2003). adv. **Document type:** *Magazine, Consumer.* **Description:** Covers news, trends and products on the cutting edge of mobile computing and telecommunications technology.
Published by: Komunik Verlag & Marketing GmbH, Konrad-Celtis-Str 77, Munich, 81369, Germany. TEL 49-89-74117233, FAX 49-89-74117178, coroli@komunik.de, http://www.komunik.de. Ed. Ralf Hinnenberg. Adv. contact Alicia Clees. B&W page EUR 3,200, color page EUR 3,900. Circ: 13,144 (paid and controlled).

004.16   CHE   ISSN 1424-7305
MOBILE WORLD. Text in German. 1990. 4/yr. CHF 15; CHF 5 newsstand/cover (effective 2001). adv. **Document type:** *Magazine, Trade.*
Former titles (until 2000): Portable Systems (1424-1102); (until 1997): Laptop Magazin (1424-1072)
Published by: B & L Verlags AG, Steinwiesenstr 3, Schlieren, 8952, Switzerland. TEL 41-1-7333999, FAX 41-1-7333989, info@blverlag.ch, http://www.blverlag.ch. Ed. Volker Richert. Circ: 40,000.

MONITOR (BROOKEVILLE). see *COMPUTERS—Microcomputers*

004.16   GRC   ISSN 1107-065X
MONITOR P C. Text in Greek. 1996. m. USD 110 (effective 1998). **Document type:** *Consumer.*
Published by: Terzopoulos Publishing Ltd., 7 Fragoklisias St, Maroussi, Athens 151 25, Greece. TEL 30-1-689-6366, FAX 30-1-680-6631, tpc@terz.hol.gr.

C

▼ *new title*   ➤ *refereed*   ✳ *unverified*   ♦ *full entry avail.*

004.16 ESP ISSN 1134-2749
MUY ESPECIAL. Text in Spanish. 1990. bi-m. EUR 12.48 domestic; EUR 24.63 in Europe; EUR 30.93 elsewhere (effective 2004). adv. **Document type:** *Magazine, Consumer.*
Published by: G y J Espana Ediciones S.L., Albasanz, 15 Edificio A, Madrid, 28037, Spain. TEL 34-91-4369800, FAX 34-91-5751280, http://www.gyj.es. Ed. Miguel Ruiz. Adv. contact Elena Sanchez Fabres. page EUR 5,364; bleed 224 x 285. Circ: 150,000.

004.16 SGP
N I I SCAN✶ . Text in English. 1994. m.
Media: Online - full content.
Published by: Infocomm Development Authority of Singapore, 8 Temasek Blvd, #14-00 Suntec Tower 3, Singapore, 038988, Singapore. TEL 65-211-0888, FAX 65-211-2222, info@ida.gov.sg, http://www.ncb.gov.sg/nii/scan.html, http://www.ida.gov.sg/.

004.16 USA
N O H U G NEWS✶ . Text in English. m.
Published by: New Orleans Heath Users Group, Heathkit Electronics Center, 1 Packard Bell Way, Sacramento, CA 95828-0903.

004.16 USA
THE NAKED P C NEWSLETTER; what you need to know about all things P C. Text in English. 1998. irreg., latest vol.14. free. adv. back issues avail. **Document type:** *Newsletter.* **Description:** Covers all aspects of computing and owning a PC.
Media: Online - full text.
Published by: Naked P C Newsletter tnpc@primeconsulting.com, http://www.thenakedpc.com. Ed. Dan Butler. Pubs. Lee Hudspeth, T J Lee.

NETWORK COMPUTING. see *COMPUTERS—Computer Networks*

004.16 USA
NEW ENGLAND WORLD OF SANYO. Text in English. 1984. m. USD 15. adv. bk.rev.
Published by: Sanyo New England Users Club, 46 Asbury St, Lexington, MA 02173. Ed. R E Zapolin. Circ: 250.

004.16 USA
NEWSLINK (WESTERVILLE)✶ . Text in English. 1984. m. USD 20. adv. bk.rev.
Formerly: Link (Westerville)
Published by: Sanyo Users of Central Ohio, 6128 Headington Pl., Gahanna, OH 43230-6329. Ed. Tom Peet. Circ: 100.

004.16 USA
NEWTNEWS. Text in English. 1994. w. **Document type:** *Newsletter.* **Description:** A weekly freeware newsletter that focuses on the Apple Newton and related technologies.
Media: Online - full text.
Address: 5375 Hewlett Dr, San Diego, CA 92115. newtnews@pobox.com, http://www.ridgecrest.ca.us/NewtNews. Ed. Steve Holden.

004.16 JPN ISSN 1341-9919
NIKKEI BEST P C. Text in Japanese. 1996. m. JPY 680 newsstand/cover. adv. **Document type:** *Consumer.* **Description:** Assists consumers in their purchase of PCs, peripherals and software. Includes extensive coverage on retail prices and best buys.
Published by: Nikkei Business Publications Inc. (Subsidiary of: Nihon Keizai Shimbun, Inc.), 2-1-1 Hirakawa-cho, Chiyoda-ku, Tokyo, 102-8622, Japan. TEL 81-3-5210-8311, FAX 81-3-5210-8530, info@nikkeibpnyc.com, webmaster@nikkeibp.com, http://www.nikkeibp.com. Ed., Pub. Kazuo Kuniya. Adv. contact Jun Mimura. B&W page JPY 200,000, color page JPY 550,000; trim 208 x 210. Circ: 86,894. **Dist. in America by:** Nikkei Business Publications America Inc., 575 Fifth Ave, 20th Fl, New York, NY 10017.

004.16 JPN ISSN 0289-6508
NIKKEI BYTE. Text in Japanese. 1984. m. JPY 11,800 (effective 1999). adv. **Document type:** *Trade.* **Description:** Contains updates and reviews of advanced technologies in personal computing for both professionals and general users.
Published by: Nikkei Business Publications Inc. (Subsidiary of: Nihon Keizai Shimbun, Inc.), 2-7-6 Hirakawa-cho, Chiyoda-ku, Tokyo, 102-8622, Japan. TEL 81-3-5210-8311, FAX 81-3-5210-8530, info@nikkeibpnyc.com, info@nikkeibp-america.com, http://www.nikkeibp.com. Ed., Pub. Shigeru Ishii. Adv. contact Zenta Kishi. B&W page JPY 485,000, color page JPY 947,000; trim 208 x 280. Circ: 79,533. **Dist. in America by:** Nikkei Business Publications America Inc., 575 Fifth Ave, 20th Fl, New York, NY 10017.

004.16 JPN ISSN 1340-8372
NIKKEI CLICK. Text in Japanese. 1994. m. JPY 490 newsstand/cover (effective 2000). adv. **Document type:** *Consumer.* **Description:** Offers an easy guide to enjoying PCs as a multimedia tool, introducing electronic communication and CD-ROM.
Published by: Nikkei Business Publications Inc. (Subsidiary of: Nihon Keizai Shimbun, Inc.), 2-1-1 Hirakawa-cho, Chiyoda-ku, Tokyo, 102-8622, Japan. TEL 81-3-5210-8311, FAX 81-3-5210-8530, info@nikkeibpnyc.com, webmaster@nikkeibp.com, http://www.nikkeibp.com. Ed. Akira Suzuki. Pub. Tamio Ota. Adv. contact Noriyuki Obara. B&W page JPY 410,000, color page JPY 700,000; trim 210 x 280. Circ: 171,327. **Dist. in America by:** Nikkei Business Publications America Inc., 575 Fifth Ave, 20th Fl, New York, NY 10017.

004.16 JPN ISSN 0918-8894
NIKKEI MAC. Text in Japanese. 1993. m. JPY 12,900. adv. **Document type:** *Trade.* **Description:** Focuses on the efficient use of Apple Computer's Macintosh in business fields.
Published by: Nikkei Business Publications Inc. (Subsidiary of: Nihon Keizai Shimbun, Inc.), 2-1-1 Hirakawa-cho, Chiyoda-ku, Tokyo, 102-8622, Japan. TEL 81-3-5210-8311, FAX 81-3-5210-8530, webmaster@nikkeibp.com, http://www.mac.nikkeibp.com, http://www.nikkeibp.com. Ed. Shinichi Yokota. Pub. Tamio Ota. Adv. contact Haruo Isonuma. B&W page JPY 220,000, color page JPY 496,000; trim 208 x 280. Circ: 69,153. **Dist. in US by:** Nikkei Business Publications America Inc.

NIKKEI OPEN SYSTEMS. see *COMPUTERS—Microcomputers*

004.16 JPN ISSN 1341-9900
NIKKEI P C 21. Text in Japanese. 1996. m. JPY 590 newsstand/cover (effective 2001). adv. 300 p./no.; **Document type:** *Consumer.* **Description:** Targets businesspeople working at the front lines of the information society with reports on the inner workings of PCs and how to make the most of this key business tool.
Published by: Nikkei Business Publications Inc. (Subsidiary of: Nihon Keizai Shimbun, Inc.), 2-1-1 Hirakawa-cho, Chiyoda-ku, Tokyo, 102-8622, Japan. TEL 81-3-5210-8311, FAX 81-3-5210-8530, info@nikkeibp-america.com, webmaster@nikkeibp.com, http://www.nikkeibp.com. Ed. Sakae Kato. Pub. Tamio Ota. Adv. contact Naoya Nakamura. B&W page JPY 410,000, color page JPY 700,000; trim 210 x 280. Circ: 195,889. **Dist. in America by:** Nikkei Business Publications America Inc., 575 Fifth Ave, 20th Fl, New York, NY 10017. TEL 212-867-3278.

004.16 JPN
NIKKEI P C BEGINNERS 21. Text in Japanese. 1999. m. JPY 680 (effective 2000). adv. **Document type:** *Consumer.* **Description:** Guides novice PC users in marking use of PCs and the internet.
Published by: Nikkei Business Publications Inc. (Subsidiary of: Nihon Keizai Shimbun, Inc.), 2-7-6 Hirakawa-cho, Chiyoda-ku, Tokyo, 102-8622, Japan. TEL 81-3-5210-8311, FAX 81-3-5210-8530, info@nikkeibp-america.com, http://www.nikkeipb.com. Ed. Yuji Saeki. Pub. Tamio Oota. adv.: B&W page JPY 300,000, color page JPY 540,000; trim 210 x 280. Circ: 120,000.

004.16 JPN ISSN 0287-9506
NIKKEI PERSONAL COMPUTING. Text in Japanese. 1983. bi-w. JPY 11,800 (effective 2000). adv. **Document type:** *Trade.* **Description:** Provides practical guidelines on the use of personal computers, as well as related business opportunities and applications.
Published by: Nikkei Business Publications Inc. (Subsidiary of: Nihon Keizai Shimbun, Inc.), 2-1-1 Hirakawa-cho, Chiyoda-ku, Tokyo, 102-8622, Japan. TEL 81-3-5210-8311, FAX 81-3-5210-8530, info@nikkeibpnyc.com, webmaster@nikkeibp.com, http://www.nikkeibp.co.jp/npc. Ed. Shunich Fujita. Pub. Tamio Ohta. Adv. contact Kazuhiko Yahiro. B&W page JPY 1,007,000, color page JPY 1,460,000; trim 208 x 280. Circ: 269,236. **Dist. in America by:** Nikkei Business Publications America Inc., 575 Fifth Ave, 20th Fl, New York, NY 10017.

004.16 JPN ISSN 1341-1497
NIKKEI WINPC. Text in Japanese. 1995. m. JPY 890 newsstand/cover. adv. **Document type:** *Consumer.* **Description:** Provides Window users "how-to" information on Windows and detailed and practical tips for immediate application.
Published by: Nikkei Business Publications Inc. (Subsidiary of: Nihon Keizai Shimbun, Inc.), 2-1-1 Hirakawa-cho, Chiyoda-ku, Tokyo, 102-8622, Japan. TEL 81-3-5210-8311, FAX 81-3-5210-8530, info@nikkeibpnyc.com, webmaster@nikkeibp.com, http://www.nikkeibp.com. Ed. Makoto Kawakami. Pub. Tamio Ota. Adv. contact Shunich Ono. B&W page JPY 250,000, color page JPY 450,000; trim 208 x 280. Circ: 92,009. **Dist. in America by:** Nikkei Business Publications America Inc., 575 Fifth Ave, 20th Fl, New York, NY 10017.

NORTH TEXAS P C NEWS. see *COMPUTERS—Microcomputers*

004.6 CHE
ONLINE PC. Text in German. d. adv. **Document type:** *Consumer.*
Media: Online - full content. **Related titles:** ♦ Print ed.: Online PC Zeitung.
Published by: Neue Mediengesellschaft GmbH, Kirchweg 129, Oberengstringen, 8102, Switzerland. TEL 41-1-7511616, FAX 41-1-7751242, redaktion@onlinepc.ch, verlag@onlinepc.ch, http://www.onlinepc.ch.

004.16 CHE
ONLINE PC ZEITUNG. Text in German. m. CHF 20; CHF 3 newsstand/cover (effective 2000). adv. **Document type:** *Magazine, Consumer.* **Description:** Provides information and content about current topics on computers, telecommunications and the Internet.
Related titles: ♦ Online - full content ed.: Online PC.
Published by: Neue Mediengesellschaft GmbH, Kirchweg 129, Oberengstringen, 8102, Switzerland. TEL 41-1-7511616, FAX 41-1-7751242, redaktion@onlinepc.ch, verlag@onlinepc.ch, http://www.onlinepc.ch. Ed. Rolf Baur. Pub. Ingo Rausch. Adv. contact Adrian Dahinden. B&W page CHF 9,942.60. Circ: 63,794 (paid and controlled).

004.16 ESP ISSN 0211-9579
ORDENADOR PERSONAL. Text in Spanish. 1982. m. adv. bk.rev.
Published by: P C Disc S.A., Ferraz, 11 Piso 1, Madrid, 28008, Spain. TEL 541 34 00, FAX 248-11-23. Ed. Francisco Javier San Roman y Perez. Circ: 20,000.

004.16 FRA ISSN 0183-570X
ORDINATEUR INDIVIDUEL. Text in French. 1978. m. adv. **Document type:** *Magazine, Consumer.* **Description:** Contains information on current and future technological innovations as well as comprehensive information about existing products and internet sites.
—IE, Infotrieve.
Published by: I D G Communications France, 5 rue Chantecoq, Puteaux, 92808, France. TEL 33-1-4197-6161, FAX 33-1-4197-6160, http://www.idg.fr. adv.: color page USD 5,451; trim 208 x 284. Circ: 141,415.

004.16 GBR ISSN 1467-2057
P C ACE. Text in English. 1999. fortn. GBP 1.60 newsstand/cover (effective 2001). **Document type:** *Magazine, Consumer.* **Description:** Provides a step-by-step guide to cool computing with easy to follow instructions and examples.
Published by: Eaglemoss Publications Ltd., 5 Cromwell Rd, London, SW7 2HR, United Kingdom. TEL 44-20-7590-8300, FAX 44-20-7590-8301, hjames@woodgt.co.uk, http://www.pcace.co.uk, http://www.eaglemoss.co.uk.

681.3 FRA ISSN 1278-6101
P C ACHAT. Text in French. 1996. m. FRF 20 newsstand/cover (effective 2003). adv. software rev.; Website rev. **Document type:** *Magazine, Consumer.*
Published by: Future France, 101-109 Rue Jean Jaures, Levallois Perret, 92300, France. TEL 33-1-41273838, yveline.duville@futurenet.fr, http://www.futurenet.fr/. Ed. Alivier Derracol.

004.16 005.36 ITA ISSN 1127-1248
P C ACTION; guida alla civilta del personal computer. Text in Italian. 1992. 11/yr. **Document type:** *Magazine, Consumer.* **Description:** Provides information for PC users on such topics as the Internet, software, hardware accessories and games.
Published by: Xenia Edizioni Srl, Via Dell' Annunciata, 31, Milan, MI 20121, Italy.

004.16 NLD ISSN 0925-5745
P C - ACTIVE. Text in Dutch. 1987. 11/yr. EUR 66 domestic; EUR 66 in Belgium (effective 2005). adv. software rev. illus. **Document type:** *Journal, Trade.* **Description:** Covers PC hardware and software.
Incorporated (in 1998): Link (1384-2285); Which was formerly (until 1996): Modem Magazine (0929-8878); Former titles (until 1989): P C Amstrad (0925-5737); (until 1989): P C Amstrad: Computerblad voor de Amstrad/Schneider Wereld (0922-3002); (until 1988): P C Amstrad: Schneider Computerblad (0921-2957)
—IE, Infotrieve.
Published by: Aktu Bladen Groep, Postbus 12399, Amsterdam ZO, 1100 AJ, Netherlands. TEL 31-20-5222444, FAX 31-20-6240189, pca.redactie@pc-active.nl, info@aktu.nl, http://www.pc-active.nl/, http://www.aktu.nl. Ed. Frank Meurs. adv.: color page EUR 2,610; 184 x 260. Circ: 54,716.

004.16 ESP ISSN 1130-9954
P C ACTUAL; personal computer professional magazine. Text in Spanish. 1984. m. EUR 40 per issue (effective 2005). adv. **Document type:** *Trade.* **Description:** Offers a global and deep survey of the personal computer industry.
Former titles (until 1991): P C Magazine Actual (0214-9931); (until 1988): P C Magazine (0213-0831)
Related titles: Optical Disk - DVD ed.: ISSN 1695-8055. 2001.
Indexed: CRIA.
—IE, Infotrieve. **CCC.**
Published by: V N U Business Publications (Spain), San Sotero 8 4a Planta, Madrid, 28037, Spain. TEL 34-91-3137900, FAX 34-91-3273704, http://www.vnubp.es/. Ed. Oscar Guijaro. Circ: 22,650.

004.16 GBR ISSN 1359-804X
P C ADVISOR; expert advice in plain English. Text in English. m. GBP 23.97 (effective 2002). adv. software rev. back issues avail. **Document type:** *Magazine, Consumer.* **Description:** Offers expert advice in plain English about all aspects of buying and using PCs and PC software.
Related titles: Online - full text ed.

C

Published by: I D G Media, 5th Fl, 85 Tottenham Court Rd, London, W1T 4TQ, United Kingdom. TEL 44-20-72915920, pcadvisor_online@idg.com, http://www.pcadvisor.co.uk/, http://www.idg.co.uk. Ed. Andrew Charlesworth. Pub. David Fernando. Circ: 120,010 (paid).

004.16 GBR ISSN 0962-1466
P C ANSWERS. Text in English. 1991. 13/yr. GBP 44.99 in United Kingdom; GBP 51.99 in Europe; GBP 69.99 rest of world (effective 2003). adv. **Document type:** *Consumer.* **Description:** Aims to educate readers about the finer points of PC ownership by using hands-on projects.
Related titles: Online - full text ed.
—CCC.
Published by: Future Publishing Ltd., Beauford Court, 30 Monmouth St, Bath, Avon BA1 2BW, United Kingdom. TEL 44-1225-442244, FAX 44-1225-732285, nick.merritt@futurenet.co.uk, http://www.pcanswers.co.uk/ magazine/, http://www.futurenet.com/futureonline. Ed. Nick Merritt. Circ: 31,190 (paid).

004.16 GBR ISSN 1461-7900
P C BASICS. Text in English. 1998. 13/yr. GBP 39 in United Kingdom; GBP 59 in Europe; GBP 85 rest of world; GBP 3.99 newsstand/cover (effective 2001). 116 p./no.; back issues avail. **Document type:** *Magazine, Consumer.* **Description:** Covers both software and hardware in plain language for beginning PC users, providing step by step guides, tips and monthly focus on specific aspects of computing.
Published by: Paragon Publishing Ltd., Paragon House, 10 St Peters Rd, Bournemouth, Dorset BH1 2JS, United Kingdom. TEL 44-1202-299900, FAX 44-1202-299955, 44-1202-200217, subs@paragon.co.uk, http://www.paragon.co.uk. Ed. Dave Harfield. Adv. contact Jennie Brown TEL 44-1202-200212. Circ: 18,200 (paid).

P C BUSINESS; Produkte und Loesungen fuer Ihr Unternehmen. see *BUSINESS AND ECONOMICS—Computer Applications*

004.16 USA
P C CHRONICLES✶. Text in English. 1982. m. membership. adv. bk.rev. **Description:** Instructs IBM PC users.
Published by: Greater Cleveland P C Users Group, c/o Roy McCartney, 6542 Carter Blvd, Mentor, OH 44060. TEL 216-944-5173. Ed. Ward Larkin. Circ: 350.

004 CZE ISSN 1212-3110
P C DEALER. (Personal Computer) Text in Czech. 1998. m. adv. **Document type:** *Magazine, Trade.*
Published by: Vogel Burda Communications s.r.o., Sokolovska 73, Prague 8, 18621, Czech Republic. TEL 42-2-21808566, FAX 42-2-21808500, http://www.vogel.cz. Pub. Pavel Filipovic.

004.16 FRA ISSN 1164-6977
P C DIRECT. Text in French. 1992. m. (11/yr.). EUR 27 (effective 2005). adv. **Document type:** *Magazine, Trade.*
Related titles: ♦ Supplement to: P C Expert. ISSN 1164-6969.
Published by: V N U Business Publications (France), 2-6 Rue Bourets, Le Ventose, Suresnes, 92154, France. TEL 33-1-41444000, FAX 33-1-41444001, http://www.vnunet.fr. Ed. Patrick Scherrer. Adv. contact Frank Surena. B&W page USD 4,302, color page USD 4,780; trim 11.25 x 8.25. Circ: 87,501.

004.16 DEU ISSN 0943-4038
P C DIREKT; the up-to-date buyer's magazine. Text in German. 1991. m. EUR 33 domestic; EUR 36 foreign; EUR 3 newsstand/cover (effective 2003). adv. **Document type:** *Magazine, Consumer.* **Description:** For active buyers of PC hardware and software.
Related titles: Online - full text ed.
Published by: V N U Business Publications Deutschland GmbH, Riesstr 25, Munich, 80992, Germany. TEL 49-89-143120, FAX 49-89-14312740, pcd_feedback@vnu.de, redaktion_vnunet@vnu.de, http://www.pcdirekt.de, http://www.vnunet.de. Ed. Thomas Jannot. Pub. Jens Dhein. adv.: B&W page EUR 5,080, color page EUR 5,895; bleed 210 x 297. Circ: 132,000 (paid and controlled).

004.16 ESP
P C DISC; publicacion con programas para P C compatibles. Text in Spanish. 1987. m. (10/yr.). adv. bk.rev.
Published by: P C Disc S.A., Ferraz, 11 Piso 1, Madrid, 28008, Spain. TEL 541 34 00, FAX 248-11-23. Ed. Gilberto Sanchez. Circ: 13,000.

004.16 ITA
P C DISK MAGAZINE. Text in Italian. 10/yr.
Address: Via Ferri, 6, Cinisello Balsamo, MI 20092, Italy. TEL 2-660-251, FAX 2-660-103-53, TELEX 352-376 JCE MIL I. Ed. Silvia Vigano. Circ: 17,000.

004.16 COL
P C DISTRIBUTOR. Text in English, Portuguese, Spanish. 1990. bi-m. free. **Document type:** *Trade.* **Description:** For distributors of personal computers in Latin America.
Published by: Empresar Editores Ltda., Carrera 11 No. 94-02 L-123, Bogota, CUND, Colombia. TEL 57-1-218-2730, FAX 57-1-610-1958. Ed. Hernando Bahamon. Circ: 5,000 (controlled).

621.381 ESP
P C DOS DISK MAGAZINE✶. Text in Spanish. 12/yr.
Description: For users of IBM, Amstrad and compatibles.
Published by: Infodisc Informatica S.L., Ferraz, 11 1o, Madrid, 28008, Spain. TEL 3-347-92-79, FAX 3-433-05-92. Ed. Alberto Rodriguez.

681.3 FRA ISSN 1628-3457
P C DRIVER. Text in French. 199?. bi-m. adv. **Document type:** *Magazine, Consumer.*
Published by: Ixo Publishing, 16 rue Hoche, Quartier des Bouvets, Puteaux, 92800, France. TEL 33-1-41028000, info@ixo.com, http://www.ixo.com.

004.16 GBR ISSN 1471-7425
P C ESSENTIALS. Text in English. 2000. 9/yr. GBP 5.99 newsstand/cover (effective 2003). **Document type:** *Magazine, Consumer.* **Description:** Covers PC programs, shareware and free applications.
Published by: Paragon Publishing Ltd., Paragon House, 10 St Peters Rd, Bournemouth, Dorset BH1 2JS, United Kingdom. TEL 44-1202-299900, FAX 44-1202-299955, subs@paragon.co.uk, http://www.paragon.co.uk/mags/ pcessentials.html. Ed. Geoff Spick.

004.16 FRA ISSN 1164-6969
P C EXPERT. Text in French. 1992. m. EUR 38 domestic; EUR 50.60 foreign (effective 2005). **Document type:** *Magazine, Consumer.*
Related titles: ♦ Supplement(s): P C Direct. ISSN 1164-6977.
—CISTI, IE, Infotrieve.
Published by: V N U Business Publications (France), 2-6 Rue Bourets, Le Ventose, Suresnes, 92154, France. TEL 33-1-41444000, FAX 33-1-41444001, http://pcexpert.vnunet.fr/, http://www.vnunet.fr. Ed. Thierry Derouet. Adv. contact Philip Dersahaguian. Circ: 150,000 (paid).

004.16 GBR ISSN 1472-9377
P C FIRST AID. Text in English. 2001. 9/yr. GBP 4.99 newsstand/cover (effective 2003). **Document type:** *Magazine, Consumer.* **Description:** Offers practical advice and step by step guide on PC problems from BIOS to Windows problems, from driver conflicts to failing hard drives. Also provides software to protect PC against bugs, viruses and further trouble.
Published by: Paragon Publishing Ltd., Paragon House, 10 St Peters Rd, Bournemouth, Dorset BH1 2JS, United Kingdom. TEL 44-1202-299900, FAX 44-1202-299955, subs@paragon.co.uk, http://www.paragon.co.uk/mags/ pcfirstaid.html. Ed. Geoff Spick.

004.16 SWE ISSN 1402-6139
P C FOER ALLA. Text in Swedish. 1997. 11/yr. SEK 495 (effective 2003). adv. **Document type:** *Magazine, Consumer.* **Description:** Publishes information of interest to personal computer users at home and in the workplace.
Related titles: Online - full text ed.
Published by: I D G AB (Subsidiary of: I D G Communications Inc.), Sturegatan 11, Stockholm, 10678, Sweden. TEL 46-8-4536000, FAX 46-8-4536005, http://pcforalla.idg.se, http://www.idg.se. Ed. Fredrik Agren. Pub. Bengt A Marnfeldt. Adv. contact Henrik Olsson. color page SEK 64.90; trim 185 x 260. Circ: 102,700 (paid).

004.16 025.04 GBR ISSN 1353-6583
P C FORMAT. Text in English. 1994. 13/yr. GBP 49.99 domestic with CD-ROM; GBP 69.99 in Europe with CD-ROM; GBP 89.99 rest of world with CD-ROM; GBP 54.99 domestic with DVD; GBP 74.99 in Europe with DVD; GBP 94.99 rest of world with DVD (effective 2003). adv. **Document type:** *Consumer.* **Description:** Covers all aspects of home-leisure computing: games, music, desktop publishing, graphics, animation, the Internet, and multimedia.
Related titles: CD-ROM ed.; Online - full text ed.; Optical Disk - DVD ed.
—CCC.
Published by: Future Publishing Ltd., Beauford Court, 30 Monmouth St, Bath, Avon BA1 2BW, United Kingdom. TEL 44-1225-442244, FAX 44-1225-732285, james.binns@futurenet.co.uk, http://www.pcformat.co.uk/, http://www.futurenet.com/futureonline. Ed. James Binns. Circ: 95,330 (paid).

004.16 PRT
P C FORMAT. Text in Portuguese. m. PTE 7,480. software rev. illus.
Published by: Investec Media, Ave Joao Crisostomo, 72, Lisbon, 1069-043, Portugal. TEL 351-213-307741, FAX 351-213-540643, assin@mail.fbento.pt, http://www.fbento.pt/ FB/.

004.16 POL ISSN 1640-7776
P C FORMAT. Text in Polish. 1994. m. PLZ 16.50 newsstand/cover (effective 2003). adv. software rev.; Website rev. **Document type:** *Magazine, Consumer.*
Formerly (until 2000): P C Shareware (1232-938X)
Related titles: Online - full text ed.
Published by: Wydawnictwo Bauer Sp. z o.o. (Subsidiary of: Heinrich Bauer Verlag), ul. Motorowa 1, Warsaw, 04-035, Poland. TEL 48-22-5170500, FAX 48-22-5170125, pcformat@pcformat.com.pl, kontakt@bauer.pl, http://www.pcformat.com.pl, http://www.bauer.pl. Ed. Mariusz Turowski. Adv. contact Katarzyna Jablonska. page PLZ 7,700.

004.16 ESP ISSN 0214-1434
P C FORUM✶. Text in Spanish. 1987. 11/yr.
Published by: Editorial Planeta S.A., Corsega, 273-277, Barcelona, 08008, Spain. TEL 3-433-12-28, FAX 3-433-00-86. Circ: 20,000.

004.16 DEU ISSN 0934-7186
P C FUER EINSTEIGER. Text in German. 1989. 2/yr. EUR 7.60 newsstand/cover (effective 2003). adv. **Document type:** *Magazine, Consumer.*
Published by: Data Becker GmbH & Co. KG, Merowingerstr 30, Duesseldorf, 40223, Germany. TEL 49-211-933470, FAX 49-211-9334710, thapp@databecker.de, http:// www.databecker.de. Adv. contact Volker Boerdeling. page EUR 4,200; trim 180 x 274.

004.16 794.8 USA ISSN 1080-4471
GV1469.2
P C GAMER. (Personal Computer) Text in English. 1988. m. USD 24.95 domestic includes m. CD-ROM; USD 39.95 in Canada includes m. CD-ROM; USD 54.95 elsewhere includes m. CD-ROM (effective 2005). adv. back issues avail. **Document type:** *Magazine, Consumer.* **Description:** Covers computer games and educational products for IBM PC and compatible computers. Includes hints and tips to improve readers' scores, coverage of popular PC games, and previews of forthcoming games.
Former titles (until May 1994): Game Player's P C Entertainment (1059-2180); (until 1991): Game Player's P C Strategy Guide (1056-6414); Game Player's M S - D O S Strategy Guide (1041-5424)
Related titles: CD-ROM ed.: ISSN 1353-8500.
Indexed: SoftBase.
Published by: Future Network USA, 150 North Hill Dr, Ste 40, Brisbane, CA 94005. TEL 415-468-4684, FAX 415-468-4686, editor@pcgamer.com, http://www.pcgamer.com, http://www.futurenetworkusa.com/. Ed. George Jones. adv.: page USD 13,982. Circ: 250,000 (paid). **Subscr. to:** PO Box 51199, Boulder, CO 80322.

P C GAMER. see *COMPUTERS—Computer Games*

004.16 GBR
P C GAMES SOLUTIONS. Text in English. m. GBP 3.99 newsstand/cover. adv. **Document type:** *Consumer.* **Description:** Provides gaming tips and solutions as well as recommending which games to purchase.
Published by: I D G Media, Media House, Adlington Park, Macclesfield, Ches SK10 4PZ, United Kingdom. TEL 44-1625-878888, FAX 44-1625-879966, pcgs@idg.co.uk, http://www.idg.co.uk/pcgs/. Ed. Wayne Williams. Adv. contact Lisa Bracewell. **Dist. by:** Comag, Tavistock Works, Tavistock Rd, W Drayton, Middx UB7 7QX, United Kingdom.

004.16 PRT
P C GUIA. Text in Portuguese. m. EUR 57.60 with CD; EUR 73 with DVD (effective 2005). illus. back issues avail. **Document type:** *Magazine, Consumer.*
Published by: Investec Media, Ave Joao Crisostomo, 72, Lisbon, 1069-043, Portugal. TEL 351-213-307741, FAX 351-213-540643, assin@mail.fbento.pt, http://pcguia.xl.pt/pcg/, http://www.fbento.pt/FB/.

004.16 GBR ISSN 1358-5967
P C GUIDE. Text in English. 1995. m. GBP 45 in United Kingdom; GBP 58.95 in Europe; GBP 78.95 rest of world; GBP 4.99 newsstand/cover (effective 2000). adv. **Document type:** *Consumer.* **Description:** Aims to help PC owners get more out of their machines in a jargon-free, easy-to-understand fashion.
Related titles: CD-ROM ed.: ISSN 1358-5975.
—CCC.
Published by: Future Publishing Ltd., Beauford Court, 30 Monmouth St, Bath, Avon BA1 2BW, United Kingdom. TEL 44-1225-442244, FAX 44-1225-732285, matthew.richards@futurenet.co.uk, http://www.futurenet.com, http://www.futurenet.com/futureonline. Ed. Matthew Richards. Circ: 23,753 (paid).

004.16 SWE ISSN 1400-4828
P C HEMMA. Text in Swedish. 1986. m. SEK 499; SEK 49 per issue (effective 2005). adv. **Document type:** *Magazine, Consumer.* **Description:** Focuses on the home user and the use of the PC in the home environment.
Former titles (until 1994): Svenska Hemdatornytt (1100-5467); (until 1988): Svenska Hemdator Hacking (0283-3115)
Related titles: Includes: PC Hemma Special.
Published by: Hjemmet Mortensen AB (Subsidiary of: Hjemmet-Mortensen AS), Gaevlegatan 22, Stockholm, 11378, Sweden. TEL 46-8-6920100, FAX 46-8-6509705, info@hjemmetmortensen.se, http://www.pchemma.net, http://www.hjemmetmortensen.se. Eds. Anders Oehman, Jenny Floden, Robert Laangstroem. adv.: color page SEK 34,900; trim 190 x 285. Circ: 60,100.

C

004.16 GBR ISSN 1355-2384
P C HOME; the essential guide to home computing. Text in English. 1992. 13/yr. GBP 4.99 newsstand/cover includes CD-ROM (effective 2003). adv. 134 p./no.; back issues avail.
Document type: *Magazine, Consumer.* **Description:** Essential guide to home computing that includes practical advice on what to buy and how to get the best results from hardware and software.
Related titles: CD-ROM ed.: ISSN 1351-5373.
—CCC.
Published by: Paragon Publishing Ltd., Paragon House, 10 St Peters Rd, Bournemouth, Dorset BH1 2JS, United Kingdom. TEL 44-1202-299900, FAX 44-1202-299955, 44-1202-200217, subs@paragon.co.uk, http://www.paragon.co.uk/mags/pchome.html. Ed. John Taylor. Adv. contact Lee Jensen TEL 44-1202-200236. Circ: 25,452 (paid).

004.16 ITA ISSN 1594-4646
P C HOME. (Personal Computer) Text in Italian. 2002. m. EUR 33; EUR 5.50 newsstand/cover (effective 2003). adv.
Document type: *Magazine, Consumer.*
Published by: Play Press Publishing s.r.l., Via Vitorchiano 123, Rome, RM 00189, Italy. TEL 39-06-33221250, FAX 39-06-33221235, abbonamenti@playpress.com, http://www.playpress.com. Ed. Lorenzo Ermigiotti. Pub. Alessandro Ferri. Circ: 70,000 (paid and controlled).

004.16 CAN
P C IMPROVEMENT NEWS. (Personal Computer) Text in English. 1998. w. back issues avail. **Description:** Includes a collection of some of the highlights from the week in the PC industry, as well as some tips and tricks.
Media: E-mail.
Published by: P C Improvements, Inc., 6 Hilda St, St Catharines, ON, Canada. TEL 905-682-6401, http://www.pcimprovements.com/pci_news/index.html/. Circ: 240.

004.16 DEU ISSN 0949-2461
P C INTERN. (Personal Computer) Text in German. 1995. q. EUR 7.60 newsstand/cover (effective 2003). adv. **Document type:** *Magazine, Consumer.* **Description:** Provides regular information on the latest developments in the computer market and the specialist areas of networking, programming and multimedia.
Related titles: Online - full text ed.
Published by: Data Becker GmbH & Co. KG, Merowingerstr 30, Duesseldorf, 40223, Germany. TEL 49-211-933470, FAX 49-211-9334710, pcintern@pcintern.de, thapp@databecker.de, http://www.pcintern.de/, http://www.databecker.de. Ed. Harald Feldkamp. Pub. Achim Becker. Adv. contact Volker Boerdeling. page EUR 4,200; trim 180 x 274. Circ: 65,765 (paid).

004.16 GBR ISSN 1460-0234
P C KNOWHOW. Text in English. 1997. w. GBP 1.65 newsstand/cover (effective 2001). **Document type:** *Magazine, Consumer.* **Description:** Provides a comprehensive and up-to-date source of information on computer software, hardware and the Internet.
Published by: Eaglemoss Publications Ltd., 5 Cromwell Rd, London, SW7 2HR, United Kingdom. TEL 44-20-7590-8300, FAX 44-20-7590-8301, hjames@woodgt.co.uk, http://www.pcknowhow.co.uk, http://www.eaglemoss.co.uk.

P C LAN. see *COMPUTERS—Computer Networks*

004.16 TUR
P C LIFE TURKEY. Text in Turkish. m. adv. **Document type:** *Magazine, Trade.* **Description:** Contains news about the information technology sector as well as reviews of hardware and software products.
Related titles: Online - full text ed.
Published by: I M G Bilisim Yayinlari, Istiklal Caddesi, Ors Turistik is Merkezi, No. 251/253, Beyoglu-Istanbul, 80060, Turkey. TEL 90-212-292-8210, FAX 90-212-292-8211, mcelik@pcworld.com.tr, http://www.pclife.com.tr, http://www.imgbilisim.com. adv.: color page USD 2,000; trim 190 x 275. Circ: 40,000 (paid and controlled).

004.16 USA
P C LIFEBOAT. Text in English. 1983. irreg. (6-10/yr.). USD 26. adv. bk.rev. back issues avail. **Description:** Provides a communication network for Epson and MS-DOS clone owners interested in new hardware and software products, and programming tips.
Formerly: Epson LifeBoat; Incorporates: Amigahelp
Related titles: Diskette ed.
Published by: National P C Users Group, 273 Woodland, State College, PA 16803. TEL 814-237-5511, lifeboatpc@aol.com. Ed. Richard Shoemaker. Circ: 5,000.

004.16 USA ISSN 0747-0460
QA76.5
P C M; premier personal computer magazine for Tandy computer users. Text in English. m. USD 34. software rev. index. back issues avail. **Document type:** *Consumer.* **Description:** For Tandy MS-DOS and portable computer users. Covers languages, business, communications, education, games, graphics, and desktop publishing.
Indexed: CompD, MicrocompInd, PCR2, SoftBase.
Published by: Falsoft, Inc., 5803 Timber Ridge Dr., Prospect, KY 40059-9317. TEL 502-228-4492, FAX 502-228-5121. Ed. Lawrence C Falk. Circ: 87,046.

004.16 DEU ISSN 0177-0977
P C MAGAZIN. Text in German. m. EUR 48 domestic; EUR 64.20 foreign; EUR 40.80 to students; EUR 4.30 newsstand/cover (effective 2003). adv. **Document type:** *Magazine, Consumer.* **Description:** Contains articles and product information for professional PC users.
Related titles: Online - full text ed.: (from The Dialog Corporation).
—IE.
Published by: W E K A Computerzeitschriften-Verlag GmbH, Gruberstr 46a, Poing, 85586, Germany. TEL 49-81-21951141, FAX 49-81-21952114, redaktion@pc-magazin.de, http://www.pc-magazin.de. Ed. David Goehler. adv.: B&W page EUR 7,450, color page EUR 11,100.

004.16 GRC
P C MAGAZINE. Text in Greek. m. adv. **Document type:** *Magazine, Consumer.* **Description:** Contains information on available products and services in all sectors of the PC and information technology markets.
Published by: Liberis Publications S.A./Ekdoseon Lymperi A.E., Ioannou Metaxa 80, Karelas, Koropi 19400, Greece. TEL 30-1-6198000, FAX 30-1-6198608, pcmag@pcmag.gr, info@liberis.gr, http://www.liberis.gr. Circ: 30,000.

004.165 SVN
P C MAGAZINE. Text in Slovenian. m. SIT 7,452 (effective 2002). adv. **Document type:** *Magazine, Consumer.*
Published by: Burda d.o.o., Dunajska 106, Ljubljana, 1000, Slovenia. TEL 386-1-5604350, FAX 386-1-5604351, info@burda.si, http://www.burda.si.

004.165 USA ISSN 0888-8507
P C MAGAZINE; the independent guide to personal computing and the Internet. Text in English. 1982. bi-w. (22/yr.). USD 25 domestic; USD 66 foreign (effective 2005). adv. bk.rev.; software rev. illus. back issues avail.; reprints avail.
Document type: *Magazine, Consumer.* **Description:** For IBM personal computer users. Feature articles are comparative reviews of computer hardware and general business software programs such as word processing, spreadsheets, graphics, CAD and communications.
Formerly (until 1986): P C: The Independent Guide to I B M Personal Computers (0745-2500)
Related titles: CD-ROM ed.: P C Magazine C D. ISSN 1078-8085; Online - full text ed.: (from bigchalk, EBSCO Publishing, Florida Center for Library Automation, Gale Group, H.W. Wilson, O C L C Online Computer Library Center, Inc., ProQuest Information & Learning); Spanish ed.: P C Magazine en Espanol. ISSN 1069-9953; Ed.: PC Magazine (Serbia). 2004.
Indexed: ABIX, Acal, CADCAM, CompB, CompC, CompD, ConsI, EngInd, InfoSAb, Inpharma, Inspec, LRI, MASUSE, MRD, MagInd, MicrocompInd, PCR2, PE&ON, RASB, Reac, RefZh, SoftBase, T&II, TOM, WBA, WMB.
—BLDSC (6413.367600), CASDDS, CISTI, Ei, IE, Infotrieve, ingenta, KNAW, Linda Hall. **CCC.**
Published by: Ziff Davis Media Inc., 28 E 28th St, New York, NY 10016-7930. TEL 212-503-3500, FAX 212-503-4399, pcmag@ziffdavis.com, info@ziffdavis.com, http://www.pcmag.com, http://www.ziffdavis.com. Ed. Michael J Miller. adv.: B&W page USD 57,845, color page USD 70,860; trim 10.5 x 7.88. Circ: 1,225,000.

004.16 PRT ISSN 0871-6625
P C MAGAZINE (PORTUGUESE EDITION). Text in Portuguese. 1990. m. software rev. illus. **Document type:** *Magazine, Consumer.*
Published by: Investec Media, Ave Joao Crisostomo, 72, Lisbon, 1069-043, Portugal. TEL 351-213-307741, FAX 351-213-540643, assin@mail.fbento.pt, http://www.fbento.pt/FB/.

004.16 RUS ISSN 0869-4257
P C MAGAZINE (RUSSIAN EDITION). Text in Russian. m. RUR 330; USD 196 in North America (effective 2004). adv.
Document type: *Magazine, Consumer.*
Indexed: RefZh.
—East View.
Published by: S K Press, Marksistkaya 34, str 10, Moscow, 109147, Russian Federation. newsdesk@pcmag.ru, deliver@skpress.ru, http://www.pcmag.ru, http://www.skpress.ru. Ed. R G Gerr. Pub. N Fedulov. **Subscr. in US to:** East View Information Services, 3020 Harbor Ln. N., Minneapolis, MN 55447. TEL 800-477-1005, FAX 800-800-3839, eastview@eastview.com, http://www.eastview.com.

004.16 ITA
P C MARKET; la prima grande guida all'acquisto dei prodotti informatici. Text in Italian. 1998. m. **Description:** Provides a consumer guide for technology products. Contains tables of information that compare various models and brands of hardware.
Published by: Techno Publishing S.r.l., Via Tacito 5, Corsico, MI 20094, Italy. TEL 39-02-4402360, FAX 39-02-45101659, tcp@tcp.it, http://www.tcp.it.

004.16 AUT
P C MARKT. Text in German. m.
Address: Sommerhaidenweg 124, Vienna, W 1190, Austria. TEL 01-4432950, FAX 01-442825. Circ: 42,000.

004.16 BRA ISSN 1414-3828
P C MASTER; informacao e lazer para usuarios avancados, com o melhor da PC format. Text in Burmese. 1997. m. USD 144; includes a CD-ROM. adv. **Document type:** *Magazine, Consumer.* **Description:** Provides information on new software, hardware, and the Internet for advanced users.
Published by: Editora Europa Ltda., Rua MMDC 121, Butanta, Sao Paulo, SP 05510-021, Brazil. TEL 55-11-30385050, FAX 55-11-38190538, pcmaster@europanet.com.br, http://www.europanet.com.br. Ed. Aydano Roriz. Adv. contact Givaldo Fernandez. color page USD 9,605; trim 288 x 210. Circ: 20,600 (paid).

004.16 GRC ISSN 1105-5472
P C MASTER. Text in Greek. 1989. m. adv. **Document type:** *Consumer.* **Description:** Covers topics and applications relevant to the low-end PC market.
Published by: Compupress S.A., 44 Syngrou Ave, Athens, 117 42, Greece. TEL 30-210-923-8672, FAX 30-210-921-6847, pcmaster@compupress.gr, http://www.compupress.gr/entypa_pcm_eng.htm, http://www.compupress.gr/default_eng.htm. Ed. Vangelis Kratsas. Pub. N O Manousos. Adv. contact Alexis Kanavos. Circ: 20,000.

681.3 FRA ISSN 1290-3159
P C MAX. HORS-SERIE. Text in French. 1999. irreg. FRF 45 newsstand/cover (effective 2001). adv. **Document type:** *Magazine, Consumer.*
Published by: Future France, 101-109 Rue Jean Jaures, Levallois Perret, 92300, France. TEL 33-1-41273838, yveline.duville@futurenet.fr.

004.16 MEX
P C MEDIA. Text in Spanish. m. adv. **Document type:** *Magazine, Consumer.* **Description:** Provides information and content for buyers and users of PCs and related products and services.
Published by: Editorial Ness, S.A. de C.V., Renacimiento, no 180, Col San Juan Tlihuaca, Mexico, 02400, Mexico. TEL 52-5-561-8333, FAX 52-5-561-9122, csansor@mpsnet.com.mx. adv.: color page MXP 3,577. Circ: 35,000 (paid and controlled).

004.16 BEL ISSN 0771-4254
P C MICRO MAGAZINE✶. Text in French. 1982. m. adv. back issues avail.
Related titles: Dutch ed.: ISSN 0771-4408.
Published by: Ecopress S.A., Rue Gabrielle 114, Brussels, 1180, Belgium. FAX 32-2-3442451. Ed. Renee Baguette. Circ: 15,000 (controlled). **Subscr. to:** A M P Abonnements, 1 Rue de la Petite Ile, Brussels 1170, Belgium.

004.16 ISR
P C MONTHLY; Israeli monthly for PC computers. Text in Hebrew. m. ILS 56.60. **Description:** For owners of personal computers.
Published by: Technosdar Inc., P O Box 31684, Tel Aviv, Israel. TEL 03-622418. Ed. Dan Halevy.

004.16 ITA ISSN 1123-7600
P C OPEN. Text in Italian. 1995. m. (11/yr.). EUR 36 domestic; EUR 63 foreign (effective 2005). **Document type:** *Magazine, Consumer.*
Published by: Gruppo Editoriale A G E P E Srl, Via G Patecchio 2, Milan, MI 20141, Italy. TEL 39-02-399861, FAX 39-02-39844800, mbox@gruppoagepe.it, http://www.agepe.it. Ed. Roberto Mazzoni. Pub. Roberto Avanzo. Adv. contact Roberto Lenzi.

004.16 USA
P C OPPORTUNITIES. Text in English. 1984. m. USD 25. adv.
Published by: Opportunities Publishing, Inc., 305 W Jackson Ave, Oxford, MS 38655. TEL 601-236-5510. Circ: 19,102.

004.16 ISR
P C PLUS/ANASHIM UMACHSHEVIM; people and computers magazine weekly. Text in Hebrew. 1981. m. USD 135.
Formerly: People and Computers Magazine
—BLDSC (6422.872200).
Published by: Israel Peled Publishing, P O Box 33325, Tel Aviv, 61332, Israel. TEL 03-295145, FAX 03-295144. Ed. Israel Peled. Circ: 9,500.

004.16 GBR ISSN 0952-2565
P C PLUS. Text in English. 1986. 13/yr. EUR 49.99 in United Kingdom; EUR 80.99 in Europe; EUR 94.99 rest of world (effective 2003). adv. **Document type:** *Consumer.*
Description: Provides news, reviews, and in-depth group tests of new PCs, hardware, and software.
Related titles: CD-ROM ed.: ISSN 1353-8527. 1994. GBP 49.99 domestic; GBP 80.99 in Europe; GBP 80.99 in US & Canada; GBP 94.99 elsewhere (effective 2003); Online - full text ed.; Optical Disk - DVD ed.: EUR 54.99 in United Kingdom; EUR 89.99 in Europe; EUR 99.99 elsewhere (effective 2003).
—BLDSC (6413.371000), IE, Infotrieve, ingenta. **CCC.**
Published by: Future Publishing Ltd., Beauford Court, 30 Monmouth St, Bath, Avon BA1 2BW, United Kingdom. TEL 44-1225-442244, FAX 44-1225-732285, dave.pearman@futurenet.co.uk, http://www.pcplus.co.uk/, http://www.futurenet.com/futureonline. Ed. Dave Pearman. Circ: 120,260 (paid).

004.16 005.36 ITA ISSN 1122-911X
P C PRATICO. Text in Italian. 1994. m. EUR 35.04 (effective 2003). adv. **Document type:** *Magazine, Consumer.* **Description:** Provides information on hardware and software available on the market. Also contains articles for technology pc users.
Published by: Gruppo Editoriale Futura, Via XXV Aprile, 39, Bresso, MI 20091, Italy. TEL 39-02-665261, FAX 39-02-66526222, pcpratico@futura-ge.com, info@futura-ge.com, http://www.futura-ge.com/prodotti/riviste/pcpratico. Ed. Paolo Reina.

004.16 DEU ISSN 0940-6743
P C PRAXIS. Text in German. 1984. m. EUR 40.80; EUR 3.60 newsstand/cover (effective 2003). adv. bk.rev. **Document type:** *Magazine, Consumer.* **Description:** Aims to provide professional PC users, decision makers and dealers with articles concerning the practical side of computing.
Former titles (until 1989): Data Welt (0930-4975); (until 1985): Neue Datawelt (0176-4187)
Related titles: Online - full text ed.
Published by: Data Becker GmbH & Co. KG, Merowingerstr 30, Duesseldorf, 40223, Germany. TEL 49-211-933470, FAX 49-211-9334710, pcpraxis@pcpraxis.de, thapp@databecker.de, http://www.pcpraxis.de, http://www.databecker.de. Ed. Juergen Grollius. Pub. Achim Becker. Adv. contact Volker Boerdeling. B&W page EUR 6,200, color page EUR 7,800; trim 180 x 274. Circ: 368,423 (paid).

004.16 GBR ISSN 1355-4603
P C PRO; computing in the real world. Text in English. 1994. m. GBP 19.99 (effective 2003). adv. software rev. cum.index. back issues avail. **Document type:** *Magazine, Consumer.* **Description:** Covers all aspects of computing for PC users, including product reviews.
Related titles: CD-ROM ed.: ISSN 1357-0854; Online - full text ed.
Indexed: Inspec.
—BLDSC (6413.371300), AskIEEE.
Published by: Dennis Publishing Ltd., 30 Cleveland St, London, W1P 5FF, United Kingdom. TEL 44-20-7917-7728, FAX 44-20-7917-5732, avrilw@pcpro.co.uk, http://www.pcpro.co.uk. Ed. Avril Williams. Pub. James Tye. Adv. contact Ian Westwood. page GBP 2,650. Circ: 80,000 (paid). **Subscr. to:** Subscriptions Department, FREEPOST WD7, Patchway, Bristol BS32 0ZZ, United Kingdom. TEL 44-1454-620070, FAX 44-1454-622080. **Dist. by:** Seymour Distribution Ltd, 86 Newman St, London W1T 3EX, United Kingdom. FAX 44-207-396-8002, enquiries@seymour.co.uk.

004.16 ITA ISSN 1121-3337
P C PROFESSIONALE. Text in Italian. 1991. m. EUR 39.78 (effective 2004). adv. **Document type:** *Magazine, Consumer.*
Published by: Arnoldo Mondadori Editore SpA, Via Mondadori 1, Segrate, 20090, Italy. TEL 39-02-66814363, FAX 39-030-3198412, pcpro@mondadori.it, http://www.mondadori.com. Circ: 101,878.

004.16 DEU ISSN 0939-5822
P C PROFESSIONELL; the independent magazine for PC specialists. Text in German. 1991. m. EUR 48, EUR 54; EUR 4.50 newsstand/cover (effective 2003). adv. **Document type:** *Magazine, Consumer.* **Description:** Contains articles and features for professional computer buyers and users.
Related titles: Online - full text ed.
—IE, Infotrieve. **CCC.**
Published by: V N U Business Publications Deutschland GmbH, Riesstr 25, Munich, 80992, Germany. TEL 49-89-143120, FAX 49-89-14312740, redaktion_vnunet@vnu.de, http://www.vnunet.de/pc-pro/default.asp. Ed. Franz Neumeier. Pub. Jon Ross. Adv. contact Joerg Muehle. B&W page EUR 8,652, color page EUR 11,551. Circ: 239,478 (paid and controlled).

004.16 IND ISSN 0971-216X
P C QUEST. Text in English. 1987. m. INR 240, USD 60 (effective 2000). adv. **Document type:** *Consumer.*
Related titles: Online - full text ed.: (from LexisNexis).
Published by: Cyber Media India Ltd., Cyber House, B-35 Sector 32-Institutional, Gurgaon, Haryana 122022, India. TEL 91-11-6433999, FAX 91-11-6475765, pcq@pobox.com, naveencs@cmil.com, http://www.pcquest.com, http://www.dqindia.com. Ed. Shyam Malhotra. Pub. Pradeep Gupta. R&P Hoshie Ghaswalla. Adv. contact Akhila Doraswamy. B&W page USD 1,100, color page USD 1,535; trim 266 x 296. Circ: 38,076.

004.16 COL
P C REGIONAL. Text in English, Portuguese, Spanish. 1990. bi-m. COP 9,600; COP 14,000 foreign (effective 1992). adv. back issues avail. **Document type:** *Consumer.* **Description:** For users of personal computers.
Published by: Empresar Editores Ltda., Carrera 11 No. 94-02 L-123, Bogota, CUND, Colombia. TEL 57-1-218-2730, FAX 57-1-610-1958. Ed. Hernando Bahamon. Circ: 10,000.

004.16 ZAF
P C REPORT; South Africa's independent information source for PC professionals. Text in English. 1993. m. ZAR 96. adv. illus. **Document type:** *Trade.*
Published by: Systems Publishers (Pty) Ltd., PO Box 41345, Craighall, Gauteng 2024, South Africa. TEL 27-11-789-1808, FAX 27-11-789-4725.

P C RETAILING. (Personal Computer) see *COMPUTERS—Computer Sales*

P.C. REVIEW; evaluations of new personal computer products. see *COMPUTERS—Software*

004.16 USA
P C S ADVISOR. (Progressive Computer Software) Text in English. 3/yr.
Published by: P C S Technologies, 4250 Wissahickon Ave, Philadelphia, PA 19129-1215. TEL 215-226-2222, FAX 215-225-2339. Ed. Robert J Evans.

004.16 MEX
P C SEMANAL. Text in Spanish. w. USD 100 (effective 1997). adv. **Document type:** *Newspaper.* **Description:** Includes news, new products, information regarding the Mexican computer market.
Related titles: Online - full text ed.: ISSN 1605-4113. 1998 (from Gale Group).
Published by: Consorcio Sayrols, Mier y Pesado 126, Mexico, Col del Valle, Mexico City, DF 03100, Mexico. TEL 52-5-6874699, FAX 525-523-7045, beatrizc@spin.com.mx, http://www.sayrols.com.mx. Ed. Monica Mistretta. R&P Roberto Davo TEL 52-5-5236714. Adv. contact Beatriz Coria. B&W page USD 2,235, color page USD 2,873; 260 x 320. Circ: 15,000.

004.16 DEU ISSN 0943-5948
P C SHOPPING. Text in German. 1993. m. EUR 30; EUR 5 newsstand/cover (effective 2003). adv. **Document type:** *Magazine, Consumer.* **Description:** Contains the latest information and advice on purchasing PCs and related products and services.
Related titles: Online - full text ed.
Published by: Vogel IT-Medien GmbH, Gutermannstr 25, Augsburg, 86154, Germany. TEL 49-821-21770, FAX 49-821-2177150, http://www.pc-shopping.de. Eds. Andreas Donner, Juergen Paukner. Adv. contact Sebastian Maindok. B&W page EUR 4,590, color page EUR 5,290; trim 185 x 260. Circ: 65,620 (paid and controlled).

681.3 ITA ISSN 1720-7649
P C SOLUZIONI. Text in Italian. 2002. m. adv. **Document type:** *Magazine, Consumer.*
Published by: Gruppo Editoriale Futura, Via XXV Aprile, 39, Bresso, MI 20091, Italy. TEL 39-02-665261, FAX 39-02-66526222, pcs@futura-ge.com, info@futura-ge.com, http://www.futura-ge.com/prodotti/riviste/PcSoluzioni.

004.16 USA ISSN 1081-7026
P C SUPPORT EXPERT. Text in English. 1993. bi-m. USD 89; USD 109 in Canada & Mexico; USD 129 elsewhere. **Document type:** *Newsletter.* **Description:** Contains information on IBM's PC Support-400 and Client Access-400 products.
Published by: M C Press, LLC, 5650 El Camino Real, Ste 225, Carlsbad, CA 92008. TEL 619-931-8615, FAX 619-931-9935. Ed. Craig Pelkie.

004.16 CHE ISSN 1422-4704
P C TIP. Text in German. 1994. m. CHF 34; CHF 3.40 newsstand/cover (effective 2001). adv. bk.rev.; software rev. charts; stat. back issues avail. **Document type:** *Magazine, Consumer.* **Description:** Consumer oriented tips, tricks and news for interested PC users.
Related titles: Online - full text ed.
Published by: I D G Communications AG, Witikonerstr 15, Zuerich, 8030, Switzerland. TEL 41-1-3874444, FAX 41-1-3874584, redaktion@pctip.ch, jacqueline.ort@idg.ch, http://www.pctip.ch, http://www.idg.ch. Ed. Sonja Wunsch. Pub. Martin Meier. R&P Gebhard Osterwalder. Adv. contact Stratos Prodromakis. page CHF 6,500. Circ: 70,000 (paid); 22,807 (controlled).

004.16 GBR ISSN 0960-0124
P C TODAY. Text in English. 1987. 13/yr. adv. illus.; tr.lit. back issues avail. **Document type:** *Consumer.* **Description:** Covers all business aspects of computing with a personal computer.
Formerly: Personal Computing with the I B M - P C Compatibles
Indexed: MicrocompInd.
Published by: Europress Publications Ltd., Europa House, Adlington Park, Adlington, Macclesfield, Ches SK10 4NP, United Kingdom. TEL 44-1625-878888, FAX 44-1625-879966. Ed. Alex France. Adv. contact John Singh. Circ: 35,779. **Subscr. to:** Europress Direct, PO Box 2, Ellesmere Port, S Wirral L65 3EA, United Kingdom.

004.16 ESP
P C TODAY. (Personal Computer) Text in Spanish. 2000. fortn. **Document type:** *Magazine, Consumer.*
Published by: Hobby Press S.A. (Subsidiary of: Axel Springer Verlag AG), C/ Los Vascos 17, Madrid, 28040, Spain. TEL 34-902-111315, FAX 34-902-151798, pctoday@axelspringer.es, http://www.hobbypress.es. Ed. Ricardo Nieto. Adv. contact Blanca Samperiz. Circ: 79,000 (paid).

004.16 USA ISSN 1040-6484
QA76.5
P C TODAY; computing for small business. Text in English. 1987. m. USD 29 domestic; USD 37 in Canada; USD 69 foreign (effective 2005). adv. software rev. illus. **Document type:** *Magazine, Consumer.* **Description:** Shows how to increase productivity and decrease costs, maximize return on investment, utilize software more effectively; presents new technology.
Formerly: P C Catalog
Indexed: MicrocompInd, SoftBase.
—IE. **CCC.**
Published by: Sandhills Publishing Co., 120 W Harvest Dr, Lincoln, NE 68521. TEL 402-479-2181, 800-331-1978, FAX 402-479-2195, editor@pctoday.com, feedback@sandhills.com, http://www.pctoday.com/, http://www.sandhills.com. Circ: 44,183.

004.16 AUS ISSN 1031-8208
P C UPDATE. Text in English. 1983. 11/yr. AUD 55 to individuals; AUD 132 to institutions (effective 2004). **Document type:** *Magazine, Consumer.*
Formerly (until 1984): Melb - P C
Published by: Melbourne PC User Group, Inc, PO Box 283, South Melbourne, VIC 3205, Australia. TEL 61-3-9699-6222, FAX 61-3-9699-6499, office@melbpc.org.au, http://www.melbpc.org.au/pcupdate/. Ed. Ash Nallawalla. Adv. contact Gary Taig.

004.16 USA ISSN 1067-0998
TK7887.5
P C UPGRADE; the guide to building and expanding computer systems. Text in English. 6/yr. USD 14.97 (effective 2001). adv. **Document type:** *Magazine, Consumer.*
Formerly: Desktop Publishing - Office Automation Buyer's Guide and Handbook
Indexed: InfoSAb, MicrocompInd, SoftBase.
—**CCC.**
Published by: Bedford Communications, Inc., 1410 Broadway, 21st Fl, New York, NY 10018. TEL 212-807-8220, FAX 212-807-1098, http://www.bedfordmags.com/pcu/. Ed. David Finck TEL 212-807-8220. Pub. Edward Brown. Adv. contact Carol Berman. B&W page USD 3,745, color page USD 4,970.

681.3 FRA ISSN 1628-3376
P C UTILITIES. Text in French. 200?. bi-m. adv. **Document type:** *Magazine, Consumer.*
Published by: Ixo Publishing, 16 rue Hoche, Quartier des Bouvets, Puteaux, 92800, France. TEL 33-1-41028000, info@ixo.com, http://www.ixo.com.

004.16 ESP ISSN 1136-4769
P C WEEK. Text in Spanish. 1989. w.
Formerly: eWeek
Related titles: Online - full text ed.
—CINDOC.
Published by: ZDNet Espana, C. Miguel Yuste, 26, Madrid, 28037, Spain. TEL 34-91-3277950, zdnet@zdnet-es.com, http://www.zdnet-es.com/. Ed. Juanjo Jimenez.

004.16 GBR ISSN 0269-3011
CODEN: PCWKEJ
P C WEEK; first for technology news. Text in English. 1985. w. adv. **Document type:** *Trade.* **Description:** Serves the information needs of corporate IT decision makers and purchasers in large companies throughout the UK.
Indexed: Inspec.
—**CCC.**
Published by: V N U Business Publications Ltd., VNU House, 32-34 Broadwick St, London, W1A 2HG, United Kingdom. TEL 44-20-7316-9360, FAX 44-20-7316-9160, martin_lynch@vnu.co.uk, http://www.pcweek.vnu.co.uk. Ed. Martin Lynch. Adv. contact Richard Beagley. Circ: 50,675.

004.16 RUS ISSN 1560-6929
P C WEEK (RUSSIAN EDITION). Text in Russian. 1995. w. RUR 420; USD 220 in United States (effective 2004). adv. **Document type:** *Magazine, Consumer.*
Related titles: CD-ROM ed.; Online - full content ed.
Published by: S K Press, Marksistkaya 34, str 10, Moscow, 109147, Russian Federation. deliver@skpress.ru, http://www.pcweek.ru, http://www.skpress.ru. Ed. E M Proidakov. Pub. E Adlerov. **Subscr. in US to:** East View Information Services, 3020 Harbor Ln. N., Minneapolis, MN 55447. TEL 800-477-1005, FAX 800-800-3839, eastview@eastview.com, http://www.eastview.com.

004.16 DEU ISSN 0175-0496
P C WELT. Text in German. 1983. m. EUR 42 domestic; CHF 82.20 in Switzerland; EUR 51 elsewhere; EUR 2 newsstand/cover (effective 2005). adv. **Document type:** *Magazine, Consumer.* **Description:** Aimed specifically at PC experts. Reports feature systems operating under MS-DOS, Windows and OS-2.
Incoprorates (1981-1985): Micro-Computerwelt (0721-6432)
Related titles: Online - full text ed.; ♦ Supplement(s): Macwelt. ISSN 0937-4906.
Indexed: Inspec.
—IE, Infotrieve. **CCC.**

C

Published by: I D G Communications Verlag AG, Leopoldstr 252b, Munich, 80807, Germany. TEL 49-89-36086532, FAX 49-89-36086570, redaktion@pcwelt.de, info@idg-verlag.de, http://www.pcwelt.de, http://www.idg-verlag.de. Ed. Michael Lohmann. Adv. contact Reinhard Baum. B&W page EUR 14,990, color page EUR 16,790; trim 180 x 264. Circ: 470,815 (paid). **Subscr. to:** dsb Abo-Betreuung GmbH, Konrad-Zuse-Str 16, Neckarsulm 74172, Germany. TEL 49-7132-959-0, FAX 49-7132-959105.

P C WINDOWS. see *COMPUTERS—Software*

004.16 USA
P C WORKS - NEWS. Text in English. w. adv. back issues avail. **Document type:** *Newsletter.* **Description:** Offers tips about pc software and freeware reviews.
Media: Online - full text.
Address: owner-pcworksnews@mailinglist.net, http://pcworkers.com/newsletter.html. Ed. Marlene Coldwell.

004.16 USA ISSN 0737-8939
CODEN: PCWDDV
P C WORLD. (Personal Computer) Text in English. 1982. m. USD 19.97 domestic; CND 34.97 elsewhere; USD 6.99 newsstand/cover (effective 2005). adv. software rev. illus. back issues avail.; reprints avail. **Document type:** *Magazine, Consumer.* **Description:** Ranks top hardware products and features news, articles, features, and special reports to help PC-proficient managers plan effectively for computer purchases, buy wisely, and use their investments in computers and technology to maximize personal and workgroup productivity.
Incorporates (1985-1995): P C World. Lotus Edition (1073-0621); Which was formerly (until 1992): Lotus (8756-7334); (1987-1990): P C Resource (0892-0575)
Related titles: Microform ed.; (from PQC); Online - full text ed.: (from bigchalk, CompuServe Inc., EBSCO Publishing, Factiva, Florida Center for Library Automation, Gale Group, H.W. Wilson, O C L C Online Computer Library Center, Inc., ProQuest Information & Learning).
Indexed: ABIPC, BPI, CPerl, CRIA, CompB, CompC, CompD, CompI, CompIU, ConsI, InfoSAb, Inspec, LHTB, LRI, MASUSE, MCIU, MagInd, Microcompind, PCAb, PCR2, RASB, RGAb, RGPR, RefZh, SoftBase, WBA, WMB.
—BLDSC (6413.375000), AskIEEE, CASDDS, CISTI, Ei, IE, Infotrieve, ingenta, Linda Hall. **CCC.**
Published by: I D G Communications Inc., 501 Second St, Ste 600, San Francisco, CA 94107-4133. TEL 415-243-0500, FAX 415-442-1891, letters@pcworld.com, http://www.pcworld.com/, http://www.idg.com/. Eds. Ramon G. McLeod, Harry McCracken. Pub. Bob Ostrow. adv.: B&W page USD 59,830, color page USD 73,280; trim 7875 x 10.5. Circ: 1,103,839 (paid).

004.16 BGD
P C WORLD BANGLADESH. (Personal Computer) Text in English. m. adv. **Document type:** *Magazine, Trade.*
Published by: Information Services Network Ltd., 52 New Eskaton Rd., Dhaka, 1000, Bangladesh. TEL 880-2-842785, FAX 880-2-831939, pcworld@bangla.net, http://home.bangla.net/pcwbd. Ed. A.K. Sayeedul Huq. adv.: color page USD 450. Circ: 1,500 (paid and controlled).

004.16 BLR
P C WORLD BELARUS. Text in Belorussian. bi-m. adv. **Document type:** *Magazine, Consumer.* **Description:** Provides up-to-date coverage of information technology, products, and industry news and trends.
Related titles: Online - full text ed.
Published by: Z A O Komputerny Mir, Smoljachkova str. 21-55, Minsk, 220071, Belarus. TEL 375-17-284-5577, FAX 375-17-284-5577, pc-world@nsys.by, http://www.pcworld.by. adv.: color page USD 1,635; trim 225 x 303. Circ: 5,000 (paid and controlled).

004.16 BEL
P C WORLD BELGIUM. (Personal Computer) Text in French, Flemish. 10/yr. EUR 36.80 (effective 2002). adv. **Document type:** *Magazine, Consumer.* **Description:** Provides information and content for professional computer users.
Published by: Best Of Publishing, Rodenbachstraat 70, Brussels, 1190, Belgium. TEL 32-2-346-4850, FAX 32-2-346-4365, jp@best.be, http://www.best.be. Ed. Jean-Claude Verset. Pub. Jean-Paul De Clerk. adv.: B&W page USD 3,326; trim 206 x 297. Circ: 28,000 (paid and controlled).

004.16 BRA ISSN 1413-9367
QA76.8.I2594
P C WORLD BRAZIL. (Personal Computer) Text in Portuguese. 1992. m. BRL 76.90 (effective 2002). adv. **Document type:** *Magazine, Consumer.* **Description:** Addresses the information and technical needs of business users of PCs in Brazil.
Related titles: Online - full text ed.
Published by: I D G Computerworld do Brasil, Rua Tabapua, 145-3 e 4 andar, Itaim Bibi, Sao Paulo, 04533-010, Brazil. TEL 55-11-3049-2000, FAX 55-11-3071-4022, negocios@idg.com.br, http://www.pcworld.com.br, http://www.idg.com.br. adv.: color page USD 7,650; trim 210 x 280. Circ: 60,000 (paid and controlled).

004.16 BGR ISSN 1311-3127
P C WORLD BULGARIA. (Personal Computer) Text in Bulgarian. m. USD 50. adv. back issues avail. **Document type:** *Magazine, Trade.* **Description:** Covers developments in the applications of PCs in Bulgaria and worldwide.
Published by: I D G Bulgaria Ltd., 1 Hristo Smirnenski blvd, etazh 11, Sofia, 1421, Bulgaria. TEL 359-2-9630886, FAX 359-2-9632841, idg@mbox.digsys.bg, http://www.idg.bg. Ed. Bistra Papazova. Pub. Tatiana Hinova. R&P Yanka Petrovska. Adv. contact Yanka Petrouska. B&W page USD 780, color page USD 1,210; bleed 200 x 280. Circ: 4,000 (paid).

004.16 CZE ISSN 1210-1079
P C WORLD CZECH & SLOVAK REPUBLIC. (Personal Computer) Text in Czech, Slovak. 1991. m. CZK 950, SKK 1,244 (effective 2002). adv. **Document type:** *Magazine, Consumer.* **Description:** Provides coverage of information technology products, trends, markets, and industry news.
Related titles: Online - full text ed.: ISSN 1212-6829. 1997.
Published by: I D G Czech, a.s., Seydlerova 2451-11, Prague 5, 158 00, Czech Republic. TEL 420-2-57088111, FAX 420-2-6520812, pcworld@idg.cz, info@idg.cz, http://www.pcworld.cz, http://www.idg.cz. Ed. Jana Pelikanova. Adv. contact Katerina Reblova. color page USD 2,301; trim 210 x 295. Circ: 46,000 (paid and controlled).

004.16 DNK ISSN 0904-4191
P C WORLD DENMARK. (Personal Computer) Text in Danish. 1985. 22/yr. DKK 897 (effective 2002). adv. reprints avail. **Document type:** *Magazine, Consumer.* **Description:** Provides up-to-date news and information on the IT industry and related products and services.
Related titles: Online - full text ed.
Indexed: CompIU, RGAb.
Published by: I D G Danmark A-S, Carl Jacobsens Vej 25, Valby, 2500, Denmark. TEL 45-77-30-03-00, FAX 45-77-30-03-02, pcworld@pcworld.dk, idg@idg.dk, http://www.pcworld.dk, http://www.idg.dk. Ed. David Kjaergaard. Adv. contact Birgitte Rygaard. B&W page USD 2,868, color page USD 3,538; trim 210 x 297. Circ: 16,500.

004.16 KEN
P C WORLD EAST AFRICA. Text in English. m. adv. **Document type:** *Magazine, Trade.* **Description:** Contains reviews on the latest technology and provides insights into local and international market trends.
Published by: P C World Kenya, Yaya Centre, 3rd Fl., POB 76170, Nairobi, Kenya. TEL 254-2-571-589, FAX 254-2-714-018, pcworld@nbi.ispkenya.com. adv.: B&W page USD 700, color page USD 900; trim 210 x 297. Circ: 5,000 (paid and controlled).

004.16 ESP ISSN 0213-1307
P C WORLD ESPANA; la revista profesional para los usuarios de ordenadores personales. Text in Spanish. 1983. m. EUR 59.18 (effective 2002). adv. **Document type:** *Magazine, Trade.* **Description:** Covers all professional computers using MS-DOS software and peripherals, software, supplies, and products.
Formerly (until 1988): MicroSistemas
Related titles: Online - full content ed.
—CINDOC, IE, Infotrieve.
Published by: I D G Communications, Fortuny, 18 4, Madrid, 28010, Spain. TEL 34-91-3496600, FAX 34-91-3496100, pcworld@idg.es, http://www.idg.es/pcworld. Ed. Isabel Campo. Adv. contact Sergio Saenz TEL 34-91-3496681. color page USD 5,948; trim 210 x 280. Circ: 71,498 (paid).

004.16 HKG ISSN 1023-4942
P C WORLD HONG KONG. Text in English. 1992. m. HKD 350; USD 85 in Asia; USD 95 elsewhere. adv. **Document type:** *Consumer.* **Description:** Provides products and PC productivity hints for PC users in Hong Kong.
Published by: I D G Communications (HK) Ltd., Ste. 1701, K WAH Center, 191 Java Rd, North Point, Hong Kong, Hong Kong. TEL 852-2861-3238, FAX 852-2861-0953. Ed. Peter Gloster. Pub. Melvyn Bennett. R&P Karman Cheng. Adv. contact Vera Chan. B&W page HKD 20,200, color page HKD 26,100; trim 205 x 277. Circ: 9,500.

004.16 HUN ISSN 1215-5055
P C WORLD HUNGARY. Text in Hungarian. 1992. m. HUF 9,960 (effective 2002). adv. **Document type:** *Magazine, Consumer.* **Description:** Contains coverage of products, applications and trends in the international personal computer market.
Related titles: Online - full text ed.
Published by: I D G Hungary Kft., PO Box 386, Budapest, 1537, Hungary. TEL 361-474-8850, FAX 361-269-5676, http://www.pcworld.hu, http://www.idg.hu. adv.: page HUF 350,000; 210 x 307. Circ: 35,000 (paid and controlled).

004.16 ITA ISSN 1120-8066
P C WORLD ITALIA; il mensile guida nel mondo del computer. Text in Italian. m. (11/yr. plus 2 special issues). EUR 27 (effective 2005). adv. back issues avail. **Document type:** *Magazine, Consumer.* **Description:** Helps PC users buy and use Personal Computer hardware and software. Contains previews, trials and comparisons of products from Italian and international companies.
Related titles: Online - full text ed.
Indexed: B&I.
Published by: I D G Communications Italia s.r.l., Via Zante 16-2, Milano, 20138, Italy. TEL 39-02-580381, FAX 39-02-58011670, pcwww@idg.it, info@idg.it, http://www.pcw.it, http://www.idgworld.it. Ed. Paolo Galvani. Pub. Mario Toffoletti. Adv. contact Mauro Buccola. Circ: 83,000.

005.43 JPN ISSN 1344-4751
P C WORLD JAPAN/GEKKAN PISHI WARUDO JAPAN. Text in Japanese. 1993. m. **Document type:** *Magazine, Trade.*
Formerly (until 1998): Windows World Japan (1340-4857)
Published by: I D G Japan, Inc., Hongo 3-4-5, Bunkyo-ku, Tokyo, 1130033, Japan. TEL 81-3-5800-3111, FAX 81-3-5800-3590, http://www.idg.co.jp. Ed. Junichi Togashi. Pub. Yoshimoto Matsuura. adv.: B&W page JPY 280,000; trim 277 x 210. Circ: 80,000.

681.32 POL ISSN 1232-3004
P C WORLD KOMPUTER. Text in Polish. 1986. m. adv. **Document type:** *Magazine, Consumer.*
Formerly (until 1992): Komputer (0860-2514)
Related titles: Online - full text ed.; Supplement(s): P C World Komputer Special. ISSN 1507-8558. 1999; P C World Komputer Extra. ISSN 1507-7640. 1999; P C World Komputer na Gwiazdke. ISSN 1509-0213. 1999.
Published by: I D G Poland S.A., ul Jordanowska 12, PO Box 73, Warsaw, 04-204, Poland. TEL 48-22-3217800, FAX 48-22-3217888, pcwk@idg.com.pl, idg@idg.com.pl, http://www.pcworld.pl, http://www.idg.pl. Adv. contact Malgorzata Brudniak. B&W page PLZ 9,000, color page PLZ 11,800; trim 203 x 288.

004.16 KOR
P C WORLD KOREA. Text in Korean. 1990. m.
Published by: Hi-Tech Information Inc., 494-65 Yonggang-Dong, Mapo-Gu, Daeho Bldg., 3rd Fl., Seoul, 121070, Korea, S. TEL 82-2-3257300, FAX 82-2-7196409. adv.: B&W page USD 1,500, color page USD 2,500; trim 258 x 190. Circ: 40,000.

004.16 MYS ISSN 1511-404X
P C WORLD MALAYSIA. Text in English. 1992. m. MYR 89 domestic; MYR 168 in Asia & the Pacific (effective 2002). adv. **Document type:** *Magazine, Consumer.* **Description:** Provides latest product information and PC productivity hints for PC users in Malaysia.
Related titles: Online - full text ed.
Published by: Digital Access Sdn. Bhd., P5-2 Podium Block, Plaza Dwitasik, No. 21 Jalan 5/106, Bandar Sri Permaisuri, Kuala Lumpur, 56000, Malaysia. TEL 60-3-973-5669, FAX 60-3-973-6040, http://www.pcw.com.my. Ed. Terence Stephen. adv.: B&W page USD 576, color page USD 753; trim 215 x 279. Circ: 17,000.

004.16 MLT
P C WORLD MALTA. Text in English. bi-m. MTL 8 domestic; USD 40 in the European Union; USD 47 elsewhere (effective 2002). adv. **Document type:** *Magazine, Trade.* **Description:** Targets professional PC users and those with responsibility for the purchase of PC-related products and services.
Related titles: Online - full text ed.: ISSN 1607-1751.
Published by: Business Marketing Services Ltd., Flat 7, Cambridge Ct., Achille Ferris St., Msida, 04, Malta. TEL 356-21-320-336, FAX 356-21-319-255, pcweditor@bms.com.mt, info@bms.com.mt, http://www.bms.com.mt/pcworld. adv.: B&W page USD 700, color page USD 800; trim 210 x 297. Circ: 1,500 (paid).

004.16 NZL ISSN 0114-7285
P C WORLD NEW ZEALAND. Text in English. 1988. 11/yr. NZD 79.95 domestic; NZD 95 in Australasia; NZD 110 elsewhere; NZD 8.95 newsstand/cover (effective 2002). adv. **Document type:** *Magazine, Trade.* **Description:** Covers the spectrum of business PC usage, keeping readers abreast of the latest hardware, software, Internet and networking products and techniques.
Formerly (until 1989): Infoworld New Zealand (0113-9797)
Related titles: Online - full text ed.
Indexed: Inpharma, PE&ON, Reac.
Published by: I D G Communications Ltd., Wellesley St., PO Box 6813, Auckland, 1036, New Zealand. TEL 64-9-377-9902, FAX 64-9-377-4604, idg@idg.co.nz, http://pcworld.co.nz, http://www.idg.net.nz. adv.: color page NZD 3,982; trim 205 x 275. Circ: 21,131 (paid and controlled).

004.16 NOR
P C WORLD NORGE PRODUKTGUIDE. Text in Norwegian. 2/yr. adv. **Document type:** *Magazine, Consumer.* **Description:** Contains information and advice for Norwegian PC users and buyers.
Published by: I D G Communications Norge, PO Box 9090, Gronland, Oslo, 0133, Norway. TEL 47-22-053000, FAX 47-22-053001, http://www.idg.no. adv.: B&W page USD 4,402, color page USD 5,723; trim 210 x 297. Circ: 38,000 (paid and controlled).

004.16 PAK
P C WORLD PAKISTAN. Text in English. m.
Published by: Micro Publications, 33-C Main Gulberg, Lahore, Pakistan. TEL 42-5711147, FAX 42-5760277. adv.: B&W page USD 950, color page USD 1,350; trim 275 x 205. Circ: 5,000.

004.16 PAN
P C WORLD PANAMA. (Personal Computer) Text in Spanish. m. adv. **Document type:** *Magazine, Consumer.* **Description:** Contains information, news, reviews and comparisons on personal computer products and services.
Related titles: Online - full text ed.
Published by: Edicomputo, S.A., PO Box 832-0055, World Trade Ctr. Bldg. Marbella, 53rd St., 1st Fl., Panama, Panama. TEL 507-223-6145, FAX 507-264-0174, pcworld@pcworld.com.pa, pcworld@cwp.net.pa, http://www.pcworld.com.pa. adv.: color page USD 980; trim 203 x 273. Circ: 4,000 (paid and controlled).

004.16 PHL ISSN 0118-1882
P C WORLD PHILIPPINES. Text in English. 1989. m. PHP 1,200 (effective 2002). adv. bk.rev.; software rev. index. back issues avail. **Document type:** *Magazine, Trade.* **Description:** Contains articles on personal computing, industry trends, in-depth reports on specialized markets, LANs, networking, telecomputing, new product reviews, and detailed features on PC applications and utilities.
Formerly: P C Digest (0117-0996)
Related titles: Online - full text ed.
Published by: W S Computer Publishing Corp., 5/F SEDCCO I Bldg., Rada St., Legaspi Village, Makati City, 1200, Philippines. TEL 632-812-8401, FAX 632-894-2487, http://www.itnetcentral.com/pcworld. Ed. P W Wong. Adv. contact Delia C Gutierree. B&W page USD 1,165, color page USD 1,865; trim 215 x 280. Circ: 12,500.

004.16 ROM
P C WORLD ROMANIA. (Personal Computer) Text in Romanian. 1990. m. ROL 400,000 domestic; USD 88 in Europe; USD 135 elsewhere (effective 2002). adv. **Document type:** *Magazine, Trade.* **Description:** Contains reviews and ratings of the latest PCs, peripheral and software products.
Formerly (until 1993): Infoclub (1220-8639)
Related titles: Online - full text ed.
Published by: I D G Communications Publishing Group s.r.l., Bd. Maresal Averescu 8-10, cam. 705-708, Bucharest, 71316, Romania. TEL 40-1-224-2621, FAX 40-1-224-1132, http://www.pcworld.ro, http://www.idg.ro. Ed. Ion Diamandi. adv.: B&W page USD 1,230, color page USD 1,550; trim 175 x 250. Circ: 15,000.

004.16 SGP
P C WORLD SINGAPORE. Text in English. 1992. m. SGD 70 domestic; SGD 150 in Asia & the Pacific (effective 2002). adv. **Document type:** *Magazine, Consumer.* **Description:** Provides latest product information and PC productivity hints for PC users in Singapore.
Related titles: Online - full text ed.
Published by: Communication Resources Pte. Ltd., Blk. 1008, Tao Payoh North, No. 07-01, Singapore, 318996, Singapore. TEL 65-256-6201, FAX 65-251-0348, marketing@comres.com.sg, http://www.pcworld.com.sg. Ed. Steven Ray Wemple. Pub. Tan Tee Seng. Adv. contact Jane Leong. B&W page SGD 2,560, color page SGD 3,380; trim 215 x 279. Circ: 17,000.

004.16 UKR
P C WORLD UKRAINE. Text in Ukrainian. m. adv. **Document type:** *Magazine, Trade.*
Address: 18/14 V. Khvoyko St., Kiev, 04080, Ukraine. TEL 380-44-201-4977, FAX 380-44-201-4966, pcw@pcworld.kiev.ua, http://www.pcworld.kiev.ua.

004.16 VNM
P C WORLD VIETNAM. Text in Vietnamese. m. adv. **Document type:** *Magazine, Trade.* **Description:** Contains information on computer product development, IT strategies, assessments and evaluations, learning and exchanging experiences, and buyer's guides.
Published by: H C M City Information and Telecommunications, 79 Truong Dinh District, Ho Chi Minh City 1, Viet Nam. TEL 84-8-822-5096, FAX 84-8-822-0742, pcworldvn@hcm.vnn.vn, http://www.idgvietnam.com. Ed. Le Trung Viet. Pub. Nguyen Trong. adv.: B&W page USD 860, color page USD 1,810; trim 200 x 280. Circ: 44,000. **Co-sponsor:** H C M City Committee for Sciences & Technology.

004.16 NGA
P C WORLD WEST AFRICA. Text in English. 1991. m. NGN 300, USD 30. adv. bk.rev. back issues avail. **Document type:** *Magazine, Trade.* **Description:** Examines computer products and applications, communications systems, and telecommunications as they relate to African businesses and education.
Formerly: P C World Africa (0795-4077)
Published by: Microbyte International Nigeria Ltd., 2A Allen Ave., Buffalo House, 3rd Fl., Lagos, Nigeria. TEL 234-1-493-9835, FAX 234-1-493-9837. adv.: color page USD 1,500; trim 200 x 268. Circ: 10,000.

004.16 ZWE
P C WORLD ZIMBABWE. Text in English. m. adv. **Document type:** *Magazine, Trade.* **Description:** Filled with news, buyers' guides, features, columns, and reviews that enable business managers to stay abreast of the latest hardware and software products and computing techniques.
Related titles: Online - full text ed.
Address: 3 Boundry Rd., Box 2361, Eastlea, Harare, Zimbabwe. TEL 263-91-700-300, FAX 263-4-870969, sales@cyberm.co.zw, http://www.samara.co.zw/pcworld/, http://www.samara.co.zw/pcworld/. adv.: B&W page USD 981, color page USD 1,795; 210 x 290. Circ: 5,000 (paid and controlled).

004.38 GBR
P D A ESSENTIALS; helping you get more from your handheld. (Personal Digital Assistant) Text in English. 9/yr. GBP 4.99 newsstand/cover (effective 2003). **Document type:** *Magazine, Consumer.* **Description:** Covers all the major brands of Personal Digital Assistant, includes a CD of valuable programs.
Published by: Paragon Publishing Ltd., Paragon House, 10 St Peters Rd, Bournemouth, Dorset BH1 2JS, United Kingdom. TEL 44-1202-299900, FAX 44-1202-299955, subs@paragon.co.uk, http://www.paragon.co.uk/mags/pdaessentials.html. Ed. Dave Harfield.

004.16 DEU ISSN 0935-6274
PAGE; das Magazin fuer Kreative und Medienprofis. Text in German. 1986. m. EUR 96; EUR 7.60 newsstand/cover (effective 2005). adv. back issues avail. **Document type:** *Magazine, Consumer.* **Description:** Provides information on creative multiplatform publishing on PCs.
Related titles: Online - full text ed.
Published by: redtec publishing GmbH, Gruber Str 46a, Poing, 85586, Germany. TEL 49-8121-951850, FAX 49-8121-951880, info@page-online.de, info@redtec.de, http://www.page-online.de/magazin/, http://www.redtec.de. Ed. Gabriele Guender. Adv. contact Guido Klausbruckner. B&W page EUR 3,500, color page EUR 4,700. Circ: 24,522 (paid and controlled).

004.16 PRT
PC GUIA. Text in Portuguese. 1987. m. EUR 57.60 with CD; EUR 73 with DVD (effective 2005). adv. software rev. illus. **Document type:** *Magazine, Consumer.*
Formerly (until 2000): Personal Computer World (0871-6161)
Indexed: EngInd.
Published by: Investec Media, Ave Joao Crisostomo, 72, Lisbon, 1069-043, Portugal. TEL 351-213-307741, FAX 351-213-540643, http://www.pcguia.pt/, http://www.investec.pt. Ed. Nuno Ribeiro.

004.16 ITA ISSN 1128-5567
PERSONAL COMPUTER; mensile d'informatica. Text in Italian. 1984. m. USD 80. adv. reprints avail. **Document type:** *Magazine, Consumer.*
Published by: Systems Comunicazioni, Via Olanda 6, Vigano di Gaggiano, MI 20083, Italy. TEL 39-02-92270757, FAX 39-02-90841682, info@systems.it, http://www.systems.it. Ed. Michele Di Pisa. Circ: 24,000.

004.16 ESP
PERSONAL COMPUTER & INTERNET. Text in Spanish. 1992. 12/yr. **Document type:** *Magazine, Consumer.* **Description:** Covers games, music, and software for personal computers.
Formerly (until 2003): P C Mania
Related titles: CD-ROM ed.; Diskette ed.
Published by: Hobby Press S.A. (Subsidiary of: Axel Springer Verlag AG), C/ Los Vascos 17, Madrid, 28040, Spain. personalcomputer@axelspringer.es, http://www.hobbypress.es. Ed. Pio Sierra. Circ: 82,126 (paid).

004.16 ITA
PERSONAL COMPUTER - ANNUARIO. Text in Italian. s-a. **Document type:** *Directory, Consumer.*
Published by: Systems Comunicazioni, Via Olanda 6, Vigano di Gaggiano, MI 20083, Italy. TEL 39-02-92270757, FAX 39-02-90841682, info@systems.it, http://www.systems.it. Ed. Agostina Ronchetti.

004.16 GBR ISSN 0957-2279
PERSONAL COMPUTER MAGAZINE. Text in English. 1984. m. GBP 24; GBP 50 foreign. adv. **Document type:** *Trade.* **Description:** Covers Unix and OS-2, and mini and mainframe connectivity.
Former titles (until 1988): P C Magazine (0953-7708); (until 1987): P C. U K Edition (0267-4815)
Indexed: Inspec, MicrocompInd.
—CCC.
Published by: V N U Business Publications Ltd., 32-34 Broadwick St, London, W1A 2HG, United Kingdom. TEL 44-207-4394242, FAX 44-20-7437-7906. adv.: B&W page GBP 3,035, color page GBP 3,735; trim 210 x 297. Circ: 100,552.

004.16 NLD ISSN 0772-8077
PERSONAL COMPUTER MAGAZINE; het computerblad voor Nederland en Belgie. Text in Dutch. 1983. m. EUR 4.50 newsstand/cover (effective 2005). adv. **Document type:** *Trade.* **Description:** Independent and professional special interest magazine on personal computers and software.
Incorporates (1995-1998): Tele-PC (1383-8091)
—IE, Infotrieve, KNAW. **CCC.**
Published by: V N U Business Publications (Netherlands), Ceylonpoort 5-25, Haarlem, 2037 AA, Netherlands. TEL 31-23-5463463, FAX 31-23-5463931, http://www.pcmweb.nl/. Ed. Ferdinand Sennema. adv.: B&W page EUR 5,860; trim 210 x 285. Circ: 125,000 (paid).

004.16 GBR ISSN 0142-0232
CODEN: PCWODU
PERSONAL COMPUTER WORLD. Text in English. 1978. m. GBP 24.97; GBP 45 in Europe; GBP 125 elsewhere (effective 2003). adv. bk.rev. **Document type:** *Trade.* **Description:** First with the news, first to test products, first to give readers the information they need to make informed decisions for their business and home computing.
Related titles: Online - full text ed.: (from Gale Group).
Indexed: BldManAb, BrTechI, CompD, Inspec, LAMP, MicrocompInd, RASB.
—BLDSC (6427.860000), AskIEEE, Ei, IE, Infotrieve, ingenta. **CCC.**
Published by: V N U Business Publications Ltd., VNU House, 32-34 Broadwick St, London, W1A 2HG, United Kingdom. TEL 44-20-7316-9000, FAX 44-20-7316-9160, gordon_laing@vnu.co.uk, http://www.pcw.vnunet.com/, http://www.pcw.co.uk. Ed. Gordon Laing. Pub. Mick Andon. Adv. contact Chantelle Johnson. B&W page GBP 2,255, color page GBP 2,955; trim 210 x 297. Circ: 147,381. **Subscr. to:** PO Box 301, Sittingbourne, Kent ME9 8BN, United Kingdom. **Dist. by:** MarketForce UK Ltd, 247 Tottenham Court Rd, London, Middx W1T 7AU, United Kingdom. TEL 44-207-2615199, FAX 44-207-2617341.

004.16 MEX
PERSONAL COMPUTING MEXICO; la revista de los sistemas personales. Text in Spanish. m. USD 71 (effective 1997). **Document type:** *Consumer.* **Description:** Includes a buyer's guide of products available in Mexico. Contains news on new products, LAN, and Macintosh.
Published by: Consorcio Sayrols, Mier y Pesado 126, Mexico, Col del Valle, Mexico City, DF 03100, Mexico. TEL 52-5-6874699, FAX 525-523-7045, beatrizc@spin.com.mx, http://www.sayrols.com.mx. Ed. Monica Mistretta. R&P Roberto Davo TEL 52-5-5236714. adv.: B&W page USD 3,465, color page USD 4,500; trim 270 x 205. Circ: 25,000.

004.16 USA
PERSONAL COMPUTING NEWS AND ANALYSIS. Text in English. m. USD 395. **Document type:** *Newsletter, Trade.* **Description:** Provides analysis of PCs, Macs, software, and telecommunications that helps you evaluate and select the products that best meet your needs and will result in solutions that are the best and the most cost-effective.
Published by: Gartner Inc., 56 Top Gallant Rd, Stamford, CT 06904-2212. TEL 203-316-1111, 800-544-7337, FAX 203-316-6300, jwhitney@info-edge.com, http://www.gartner3.gartnerweb.com.

PINKERTON EYE ON TRAVEL. see *TRAVEL AND TOURISM*

004.16 USA
PLANET P D A. (Personal Digital Assistant) Text in English. d. adv. **Document type:** *Magazine, Consumer.*
Media: Online - full content. **Related titles:** E-mail ed.: Planet P D A eNews.
Published by: Technology Marketing Corporation, One Technology Plaza, Norwalk, CT 06854. TEL 203-852-6950, 800-243-6002, FAX 203-853-2845, tmc@tmcnet.com, http://www.planetpdamag.com, http://www.tmcnet.com. Ed. Laura Guevin. Adv. contact Michelle Tehrani.

681.3 CZE ISSN 1212-0723
POCITAC PRO KAZDEHO/COMPUTER EASY. Text in Czech. 1998. fortn. CZK 800 (effective 2001). adv. **Document type:** *Magazine, Consumer.*
Published by: Vogel Burda Communications s.r.o., Sokolovska 73, Prague 8, 18621, Czech Republic. TEL 42-2-21808566, FAX 42-2-21808500, http://www.vogel.cz/ppk. Ed. Ivan Heisler. Pub. Pavel Filipovic. Adv. contact Hoskova Zuzana. color page EUR 2,300; trim 210 x 297. Circ: 29,483 (paid).

004.16 DEU
POCKET P C MAGAZIN. Text in German. bi-m. EUR 26.40 (effective 2003). adv. **Document type:** *Magazine, Consumer.*
Published by: Bikini Verlag GmbH, St.-Emmeram-Str. 28, Aschheim, 85609, Germany. TEL 49-89-9097980, FAX 49-89-90979811, redaktion@pocket-pc-magazin.de, gb@nouh.de, http://www.pocket-pc-magazin.de, http://www.bikini-verlag.de. Ed., Pub. Gerhard Bauer. Adv. contact Gert Winkelmeier TEL 49-2684-6107. B&W page EUR 2,965, color page EUR 3,988.

PORTABLE COMPANION; for Osborne computer users. see *COMPUTERS—Microcomputers*

004.16 USA ISSN 1096-1968
PORTABLE COMPUTING DIRECT SHOPPER. Text in English. 1997. m. back issues avail. **Document type:** *Consumer.*
Indexed: MicrocompInd.
Published by: Freedom Technology Media Group, 156 W 56th St, 3rd Fl, New York, NY 10019. TEL 212-333-7600, FAX 212-333-7874, circulation@curtco.com, http://www.curtco.com. **Subscr. to:** 29160 Heathercliff Rd., Suite 200, Malibu, CA 90265.

004.16 USA
THE PORTABLE COMPUTING LETTER★. Text in English. 1991. bi-m. USD 49.95; USD 89.95 foreign.

C

▼ new title ➤ refereed ★ unverified ♦ full entry avail.

Published by: Yellowstone Information Services, R R 2, Box 42A, Bloomingdale, OH 43910-9802. TEL 304-965-5548, FAX 304-965-7785. Ed. Roger Thibault.

004.6 ITA ISSN 1722-8891
PORTATILE & WIRELESS. Text in Italian. 1998. m. EUR 39 (effective 2005). adv. **Document type:** *Magazine, Consumer.*
Formerly (until 2003): Il Mio Portatile (1127-1728)
Published by: Future Media Italy SpA, Via Asiago 45, Milano, MI 20128, Italy. TEL 39-02-2529161, FAX 39-02-26005520, info@futuremediaitaly.it, http://www.futuremediaitaly.it. Ed. Sonia Iacona.

004 GBR ISSN 1466-0458
PRINT IT MAGAZINE; regular updates on PC and Mac driven printers. Text in English. 1999. q. GBP 10 domestic; GBP 25 foreign; GBP 2.75 newsstand/cover (effective 2001). adv. software rev.; bk.rev. back issues avail. **Document type:** *Magazine, Consumer.* **Description:** Provides a practical guide to the equipment, services and skills that everyday computer users need to produce better quality printed communications.
Published by: Paper Trail Trading Ltd., Apsley Mills Cottage, London Rd, Hemel Hempstead, Herts HP3 9RY, United Kingdom. TEL 44-1442-234600, FAX 44-1442-275749, printit-mag@paper-pub.co.uk, papertrail@paper-pub.co.uk. adv.: color page GBP 2,000; trim 210 x 297. Circ: 20,000.

PRIVAT COMPUTER. see *COMPUTERS—Microcomputers*

PROMPT; P C Zeitschrift. see *HANDICAPPED—Visually Impaired*

004.16 NLD ISSN 1566-1474
PUBLISH. Text in Dutch. 1990. 11/yr. adv. **Document type:** *Trade.*
Former titles (until 1998): MacWorld Magazine (0927-1066); (until 1991): Macintosh Magazine (0926-3098)
—Infotrieve.
Published by: Wegener Tijdschriften Groep BV (Subsidiary of: Wegener NV), Postbus 1860, Diemen, 1110 CD, Netherlands. TEL 31-20-6603402, FAX 31-20-6606354. Circ: 10,600.

004.16 USA ISSN 0886-8174
QA75.5
PUGET SOUND COMPUTERUSER; business technology, office automation, computers. Key Title: Puget Sound Computer User. Text in English. 1986. m. USD 12 domestic (effective 1999); USD 36 in Canada. adv. index. back issues avail. **Document type:** *Consumer.* **Description:** Covers new developments in computer hardware and software, industry trends, personnel and management issues, consumer electronics, and more.
Published by: K F H Publications, Inc., 2511 25th Ave E., Seattle, WA 98112-2259. TEL 206-547-4950, FAX 206-545-6591. Ed. Sharon Baerny. Pub. Ray Kehl. Adv. contact Gil Podolinsky. B&W page USD 2,860, color page USD 3,510; trim 15 x 11. Circ: 100,000.

R I S C USER. (Reduced Instruction Set Computer) see *COMPUTERS—Microcomputers*

004.16 USA ISSN 0899-014X
RECREATIONAL & EDUCATIONAL COMPUTING; a mathemagical panoply of computer recreations for thinking readers. Key Title: The R E C Newsletter. Text in English. 1986 (Jan.). bi-m. USD 28 domestic; USD 32 in Canada & Mexico; USD 36 elsewhere; USD 5 per issue domestic (effective 2005). bk.rev.; software rev. 20 p./no.; Supplement avail.; back issues avail. **Document type:** *Newsletter.* **Description:** Features applications of mathematics and computers in recreational format, reviews of games and correspondence, programs, puzzles, graphics, humor, news and trends, editorials, and reader letters and solutions.
Address: C/o Dr. Michael W. Ecker, REC Editor, c/o Penn State University, W-B Campus, Lehman, PA 18627. DrMWEcker@aol.com, MWE1@psu.edu, http://members.aol.com/DrMWEcker/main.html. Ed., Pub. Dr. Michael W Ecker.

004.16025 USA
ROOT DIRECTORY. Text in English. 1985. m. USD 20. adv. bk.rev.
Formerly (until 1989): Letter (Bradenton)
Published by: (Manatee P C User's Group, Inc.), Daniel L. Crumpler, Ed. & Pub., 411 67th St, N W, Bradenton, FL 34209-1652. TEL 813-795-0063. Circ: 1,000.

004.16 NLD ISSN 0923-2214
S T; onafhankelijk tijdschrift van en voor gebruikers van Atari ST computers. Text in Dutch. 1986. q. EUR 22 domestic; USD 40 in United States (effective 2000). software rev. 48 p./no.; back issues avail. **Document type:** *Magazine, Consumer.* **Description:** For serious Atari ST users and programmers.
Published by: Stichting S T, Bakkersteeg 9A, Leiden, 2311 RH, Netherlands. TEL 31-71-5130045, ataristxs4all.nl, atarist@xs4all.nl, http://www.xs4all.nl/~atarist. Ed. Han Driesen. Circ: 1,000 (paid).

004.16 GBR ISSN 0957-4859
S T FORMAT. Text in English. 1988. m. GBP 33; GBP 45 in Europe; GBP 54.95 elsewhere. adv. back issues avail. **Document type:** *Consumer.* **Description:** Covers Amiga ST computing, programming and games.
Supersedes in part (in 1989): S T Amiga Format (0954-805X)
—CCC.
Published by: Future Publishing Ltd., Beauford Court, 30 Monmouth St, Bath, Avon BA1 2BW, United Kingdom. TEL 44-1224-442244, FAX 44-1224-462986. Ed. Karen Levell. Pub. Simon Stansfield. Circ: 38,671 (paid). **Subscr. to:** Future Publishing, Somerton, Somers TA11 6BR, United Kingdom. TEL 44-1225-822511.

004.16 FRA ISSN 1166-4770
S V M MAC. (Science et Vie Micro) Text in French. 1988. 11/yr. EUR 30 domestic; EUR 44 foreign (effective 2003). adv.
Formerly (until 1991): S V M Macintosh (0992-5120)
Related titles: Online - full text ed.
Indexed: PdeR.
—IE, Infotrieve.
Published by: Excelsior Publications (Subsidiary of: Emap France), 1 rue du Colonel Pierre Avia, Paris, 75503 Cedex 15, France. Ed. Andreas Pfeiffer. Adv. contact Gilles Dekeranflech. Circ: 64,414.

S.W.A.T.PRO; secret weapon and tactic guide. see *COMPUTERS—Computer Games*

004.16 USA
SAN FRANCISCO BAY AREA SANYO GROUP NEWSLETTER. Text in English. m.
Published by: San Francisco Bay Area Sanyo Group, 1260 Westwood St, Redwood City, CA 94061. Ed. Barbara Valley.

004.16 USA
SANYO SOURCE. Text in English. s-m. USD 32.
Published by: Computer User Services, 230 Anderson St, Hackensack, NJ 07601.

SCARLETT. see *COMPUTERS—Microcomputers*

SCIENCE ET VIE MICRO. see *COMPUTERS—Microcomputers*

004.16 HKG
SING TAO P C MARKET. Text in Chinese, English. 1993. w. HKD 5 newsstand/cover. adv. **Description:** Introduces new electronic and telecommunication technologies, innovative computing techniques as well as advanced computing accessories.
Related titles: Online - full text ed.
Published by: Sing Tao Ltd., 2B, Sing Tao Bldg, 1 Wang Kwong Rd, Kowloon Bay, Kowloon, Hong Kong. TEL 852-2798-2442, FAX 852-2795-3007. Ed. Thomas Wong. Adv. contact Cathy Tang. color page HKD 28,000; trim 340 x 260.

004.16 USA ISSN 1523-3057
SMALL BUSINESS COMPUTING & COMMUNICATIONS. Text in English. m. USD 19.97 domestic; USD 32.97 in Canada; USD 36.97 elsewhere; USD 3.99 newsstand/cover. adv. **Document type:** *Trade.* **Description:** Reference for businesspeople and executives who are expanding small businesses through the use of technology.
Indexed: CompLI, MicrocompInd, SoftBase.
Published by: Freedom Technology Media Group, 156 W 56th St, 3rd Fl, New York, NY 10019. TEL 310-589-3100, 800-537-4638, FAX 310-589-3131, nsullivan@smalloffice.com, http://www.smalloffice.com. Eds. Cathy Grayson Brower, Michael Warshaw.

004 USA
SMALL OFFICE. Text in English. w. adv. **Document type:** *Trade.*
Media: Online - full text.
Published by: Freedom Technology Media Group, 156 W 56th St, 3rd Fl, New York, NY 10019. TEL 212-333-7600, FAX 212-333-7874, nsullivan@smalloffice.com, http://www.smalloffice.com, http://www.hoc.smalloffice.com. Ed. Nick Sullivan.

004.16 USA ISSN 1093-4170
QA76.5
SMART COMPUTING. Variant title: Smart Computing in Plain English. Text in English. 1990. m. USD 29 domestic; USD 37 in Canada; USD 69 elsewhere; USD 4.95 per issue (effective 2005). adv. illus. reprints avail. **Document type:** *Magazine, Consumer.* **Description:** Provides step-by-step instructions and how-to solutions for various day-to-day computer tasks and applications.
Formerly (until May 1997): P C Novice (1052-1186)
Related titles: Online - full text ed.: (from EBSCO Publishing).
Indexed: ARG, InfoSAb, MicrocompInd, RGAb, RGPR, SoftBase.
—BLDSC (8310.193234), IE, ingenta. **CCC.**
Published by: Sandhills Publishing Co., 120 W Harvest Dr, Lincoln, NE 68521. TEL 402-479-2181, 800-331-1978, FAX 402-479-2195, editor@smartcomputing.com, http://www.smartcomputing.com/. Ed. Ronald D Kobler. adv.: page USD 6,960. Circ: 205,837. **Subscr. to:** PO Box 86510, Lincoln, NE 68501-5673. TEL 800-334-7445, FAX 402-479-2193.

004.6 USA
SMART COMPUTING GUIDE SERIES. Text in English. m. USD 7.99 newsstand/cover (effective 2004). **Document type:** *Magazine, Consumer.* **Description:** Provides in-depth information and details on a different computing topic each month.
Published by: Sandhills Publishing Co., 120 W Harvest Dr, Lincoln, NE 68521. TEL 402-479-2181, 800-331-1978, FAX 402-479-2195, feedback@sandhills.com, http://www.smartcomputing.com.

004.16 USA
SMART COMPUTING LEARNING SERIES. Text in English. m. USD 7.99 newsstand/cover (effective 2004). **Document type:** *Magazine, Consumer.* **Description:** Contains detailed how-to articles and advice on how to get the most out of today's computing technology.
Published by: Sandhills Publishing Co., 120 W Harvest Dr, Lincoln, NE 68521. TEL 402-479-2181, 800-331-1978, FAX 402-479-2195, feedback@sandhills.com, http://www.smartcomputing.com.

004.16 USA ISSN 1551-2592
QA76
SMART COMPUTING REFERENCE SERIES. Text in English. q. USD 9.99 newsstand/cover (effective 2004). **Document type:** *Magazine, Consumer.* **Description:** Provides quick and easy solutions to computing questions and problems.
Published by: Sandhills Publishing Co., 120 W Harvest Dr, Lincoln, NE 68521. TEL 402-479-2181, 800-331-1978, FAX 402-479-2195, feedback@sandhills.com, http://www.smartcomputing.com.

004.16 USA ISSN 1538-8387
SMART TIPS AND QUICK TRICKS FOR SOLARIS. Text in English. 2002. irreg. USD 10 per issue domestic; USD 20 per issue foreign (effective 2005).
—CCC.
Published by: Element K Journals (Subsidiary of: Eli Research, Inc.), 500 Canal View Blvd, Rochester, NY 14623. TEL 585-240-7301, 800-223-8720, 877-203-5248, FAX 585-292-4392, http://www.elementkjournals.com. Eds. Debra Seiloff, Michelle Rogers.

004.16 USA ISSN 1538-8352
SMART TIPS AND QUICK TRICKS FOR YOUR MACINTOSH. Text in English. 2002. a. USD 10 per issue domestic; USD 20 per issue foreign (effective 2005).
—CCC.
Published by: Element K Journals (Subsidiary of: Eli Research, Inc.), 500 Canal View Blvd, Rochester, NY 14623. TEL 585-240-7301, 800-223-8720, 877-203-5248, FAX 585-292-4392, http://www.elementkjournals.com. Eds. Ron Wilder, Michelle Rogers.

SOFT - LETTER; trends & strategies in software publishing. see *COMPUTERS—Software*

SOFTWARE DIGEST; the independent, comparative ratings report for PC and LAN software. see *COMPUTERS—Software*

SPREADSHEET. see *COMPUTERS—Microcomputers*

004.16 USA
STACK (HICKSVILLE). Text in English. 1975. m. USD 25 membership. adv. bk.rev. **Document type:** *Bulletin.*
Related titles: Diskette ed.
Published by: Long Island Computer Association, Inc., PO Box 71, Hicksville, NY 11802. TEL 516-293-9368. Ed. Al Levy. Circ: 5,000.

004.16 USA ISSN 1093-8923
STRIKING HOME. Text in English. q. USD 15. **Description:** Contains studies comparing the Dvorak keyboard layout to Qwerty, product reviews, first person accounts from Dvorak typists.
Formerly: Dvorak International. Quarterly
Published by: Dvorak International, PO Box 11985, Eugene, OR 97440. TEL 541-302-6441, DvorakInt@aol.com.

004.16 USA
SURVEY (LA JOLLA)✶. Text in English. 1984. bi-m.
Indexed: CERDIC.
Published by: K V A Associates, c/o Amatneek, 2356 Torrey Pines Rd 17, La Jolla, CA 92037-3412.

004.16 AUS ISSN 1445-8675
TECHNOLOGY & BUSINESS. Text in English. 1994. m. AUD 65 domestic; AUD 115 foreign (effective 2004). adv. **Description:** Provides comprehensive product information.
Former titles (until 2001): P C Magazine Australia (1329-3532); (until 1997): Windows Sources Australia (1322-0071)
Indexed: ABIX.
Published by: ZDNet Australia, Level 4, 45 Murray St, Pyrmont, NSW 2009, Australia. TEL 61-2-85149999, FAX 61-2-85149950, info@zdnet.com.au, http://web.zdnet.com.au/technologyandbusiness/, http://www.zdnet.com.au/. adv.: color page AUD 1,840. Circ: 35,767 (paid).

004.16 USA
TECHWEB. Text in English. w. illus.

Media: Online - full content.
Address: http://www.techweb.com. Ed. Jeff Pundyk.

004.16 FIN ISSN 0359-4947
TIETOKONE. Text in Finnish. 1982. 14/yr. EUR 82 (effective 2005). adv. **Document type:** *Magazine, Consumer.* **Description:** Offers well-tested and comparative information on new IT products and techniques.
Incorporates (1989-2003): Macmaailma (0786-3683)
Related titles: CD-ROM ed.: ISSN 1238-7584; Online - full text ed.: ISSN 1238-7606.
Published by: Sanoma Magazines Finland Corporation, Hoylaamotie 1 D, P.O. Box 100, Helsinki, 00040, Finland. TEL 358-9-1201, FAX 358-9-1205171, toimitus@tietokone.fi, info@sanomamagazines.fi, http://www.tietokone.fi, http://www.sanomamagazines.fi. Ed. Hannu Jaervinen. adv.: color page EUR 6,190. Circ: 45,106 (paid and controlled).

004.16 NLD ISSN 1566-5518
TIPS & TRUCS. Variant title: Computer! Totaal Tips & Trucs. Text in Dutch. 1997. 10/yr. adv. **Document type:** *Magazine, Consumer.* **Description:** Aimed at helping people to work more efficiently and easily on their personal computers.
Related titles: ♦ Supplement(s): Internet Tips & Trucs. ISSN 1570-9175.
Published by: I D G Communications Nederland BV, Postbus 5446, Haarlem, 2000 GK, Netherlands. TEL 31-23-5461111, FAX 31-23-5461155, abo@idg.nl, http://www.idg.nl/producten/prod.phtml?prod=tt&type=print. Ed. Hans Doorn. Adv. contact Erwin van Faassen. B&W page USD 1,898, color page USD 3,178; trim 210 x 285. Circ: 77,541 (paid and controlled).

004.16 ISL ISSN 1025-5516
TOLVUHEIMUR. Variant title: P C World Island. Text in Icelandic. 1995. 10/yr. ISK 7,290 (effective 2002). adv. **Document type:** *Magazine, Consumer.* **Description:** Dedicated to computers and information technology.
Published by: Heimur hf., Borgartuni 23, Reykjavik, 105, Iceland. TEL 354-512-7575, FAX 354-561-8646, http://www.heimur.is. adv.: page ISK 101,700.

004.16 USA
ULTIMATE MOBILITY. Text in English. q. USD 5.99 newsstand/cover domestic; USD 7.99 newsstand/cover in Canada (effective 2004).
Published by: Bedford Communications, Inc., 1410 Broadway, 21st Fl, New York, NY 10018. TEL 212-807-8220, http://www.techworthy.com. Ed. Mark Spoonauer.

004.16 JPN
UPLINK✶; personal computer magazine with a 3.5" companion disk. Text in Japanese. 1993. m. JPY 9,360.
Published by: ASCII Corp., JR Shinanomachi Bldg. 34 Shinanomachi, Shinjuku-ku, Tokyo, 160-8584, Japan. http://www.ascii.co.jp.

004.16 DEU
USER MAGAZIN✶. Text in German. 1979. 8/yr. adv. bk.rev. **Document type:** *Newsletter.* **Description:** For Apple, Macintosh, and AT computer users.
Published by: J.P. Kern, Schwannstr 28, Neuss, 41460, Germany. Ed. Rolf Hermann. Circ: 1,200.

004.16 ITA ISSN 1592-4378
WEEK.IT. Text in Italian. 1987. 42/yr. EUR 49.90 (effective 2004). adv. **Document type:** *Magazine, Consumer.* **Description:** Contains worldwide news, product tests, market and company analyses.
Formerly (until 2000): P C Week Italia (1120-5172)
Published by: Arnoldo Mondadori Editore SpA, Via Mondadori 1, Segrate, 20090, Italy. TEL 39-02-66814363, FAX 39-030-3198412, pcweek@mondadori.it, http://www.mondadori.com. Ed. Riccardo Cervelli. Circ: 30,464.

004.16 GBR
WHAT LAPTOP & HANDHELD PC. Text in English. 1999. m. GBP 28.20 in United Kingdom; GBP 48.20 in Europe; GBP 58.20 rest of world; GBP 2.99 newsstand/cover in United Kingdom (effective 2000). adv. software rev. back issues avail. **Document type:** *Magazine, Consumer.* **Description:** Presents clear and unbiased information about laptops and handheld PCs.
Published by: Crimson Publishing, Vigilant House, 120 Wilton Rd, London, SW1V 1JZ, United Kingdom. TEL 44-20-78087141, FAX 44-20-78087142, info@whatlaptop.co.uk, enquiries@crimsonpublishing.co.uk, http://www.whatlaptop.co.uk, http://www.crimsonpublishing.co.uk.

004.16 GBR ISSN 0956-5248
WHAT PERSONAL COMPUTER?. Text in English. m. GBP 24 domestic; GBP 35 foreign. **Document type:** *Trade.*
Related titles: ♦ Supplement(s): P C Marketplace. ISSN 0969-1839.
Indexed: Inspec.
—AskIEEE. **CCC.**
Published by: E M A P Computing (Subsidiary of: E M A P Business Communications), 33-39 Bowling Green Ln, London, EC1R 0DA, United Kingdom. TEL 44-20-7837-1212, FAX 44-207-278-4008.

005.469 GBR
WINDOWS ANSWERS. Text in English. 1998. bi-m. GBP 3.99 newsstand/cover. **Document type:** *Consumer.* **Description:** Complete guide to the world's most popular operating system. Written by experts and shows its readers how to use Windows more effectively both at work and at home.
Published by: Future Publishing Ltd., Beauford Court, 30 Monmouth St, Bath, Avon BA1 2BW, United Kingdom. TEL 44-1225-442244, FAX 44-1225-446019, john.weir@futurenet.co.uk, http://www.futurenet.com, http://www.futurenet.com/futureonline. Pub. John Weir. Circ: 30,000 (paid).

005.446 GBR ISSN 1463-8452
WINDOWS EXPERT. Text in English. 1997. bi-m. GBP 11.94 domestic; GBP 29.94 in Europe; GBP 41.94 elsewhere; GBP 3.99 newsstand/cover. adv. **Document type:** *Consumer.* **Description:** Keeps users up to date and informed about the world of Windows by providing the latest software, hardware, and technology news and reviews.
Formerly (until 1998): Windows 95 Utilities (1360-5887)
Published by: I D G Media, Media House, Adlington Park, Macclesfield, Ches SK10 4PZ, United Kingdom. TEL 44-1625-878888, FAX 44-1625-879966, windows@idg.co.uk, http://www.idg.co.uk/windows. Ed. Neil Mohr. Pub. Robin Wilkinson. Adv. contact Barbara Newall. Circ: 24,031 (paid). **Dist. by:** Comag, Tavistock Works, Tavistock Rd, W Drayton, Middx UB7 7QX, United Kingdom. TEL 44-1895-433600, FAX 44-189-543-3606.

005.446 ITA ISSN 1127-168X
WINDOWS FACILE. Text in Italian. 1998. m. EUR 38; EUR 5.50 newsstand/cover (effective 2003). adv. **Document type:** *Magazine, Consumer.*
Published by: Play Press Publishing s.r.l., Via Vitorchiano 123, Rome, RM 00189, Italy. TEL 39-06-33221250, FAX 39-06-33221235, abbonamenti@playpress.com, http://www.playpress.com. Ed. Fabio Valenza. Pub. Alessandro Ferri. Circ: 55,000 (paid and controlled).

005.4469 GBR ISSN 1461-2631
WINDOWS MADE EASY; all you need to know about windows explained in english. Text in English. 1997. m. GBP 36 in United Kingdom; GBP 55 in Europe; GBP 81 rest of world; GBP 4.99 newsstand/cover (effective 2001). adv. 116 p./no.; back issues avail. **Document type:** *Magazine, Consumer.* **Description:** Takes new PC owners through the rigors of setting up the machine, working with Windows, and solves any rudimentary problems that might be encountered.
Published by: Paragon Publishing Ltd., Paragon House, 10 St Peters Rd, Bournemouth, Dorset BH1 2JS, United Kingdom. TEL 44-1202-299900, FAX 44-1202-299955, 44-1202-200217, subs@paragon.co.uk, http://www.paragon.co.uk. Ed. John Taylor. Adv. contact Jennie Brown TEL 44-1202-200212.

681.3 FRA ISSN 1266-8044
WINDOWS NEWS. Text in French. 199?. m. FRF 38 newsstand/cover (effective 2001). adv. software rev.; Website rev. **Document type:** *Magazine, Consumer.*
—Infotrieve.
Published by: Future France, 101-109 Rue Jean Jaures, Levallois Perret, 92300, France. TEL 33-1-41273838, yveline.duville@futurenet.fr.

THE YELLOWSTONE WINDOWS LETTER. see *COMPUTERS—Microcomputers*

COMPUTERS—Robotics

see also COMPUTERS—Artificial Intelligence

629.892 FRA
A F R I LIAISON. Text in French. 1982. q. membership. bk.rev. **Description:** Contains international coverage of the industrial robotics industry. Articles cover product developments, automation, systems design and market news. Features include a calendar of events, employment opportunities and a listing of available literature.
Published by: Association Francaise de Robotique Industrielle, 4 Place Jussieu, Tour 66, Paris, Cedex 5 75252, France. TEL 43-54-71-70, FAX 43-54-71-70. Ed. Gerard Bourgeois. Circ: 2,000.

629.892 USA ISSN 0885-5684
ADVANCED MANUFACTURING TECHNOLOGY; monthly report. Text in English. 1979. m. USD 695 in North America to institutions; USD 755 elsewhere to institutions (effective 2004). pat.; stat. back issues avail. **Document type:** *Newsletter.* **Description:** Focuses on technological advances that can ensure manufacturing competitiveness, e.g., desktop manufacturing, computer graphics, flexible automation, computer-integrated manufacturing, and other techniques for cutting costs, improving the quality of manufactured products, and increasing productivity.
Formerly: Industrial Robots International (0197-9280)
Related titles: Online - full text ed.: (from Factiva, Florida Center for Library Automation, Gale Group).
Published by: Technical Insights (Subsidiary of: Frost & Sullivan), PO Box 190, Churchton, MD 20733. TEL 301-889-0562, FAX 301-889-0564, sgr@nasw.org, technicalinsights@frost.com, http://www.ti.frost.com, http://www.frost.com/prod/servlet/ti-home.pag. Ed. Peter Savage. Pub. Paul Majchrzyk. Circ: 1,000 (paid).

629.892 NLD ISSN 0169-1864
TJ210.2 CODEN: ADROEI
➤ **ADVANCED ROBOTICS.** Text in English. 1986. m. EUR 1,200, USD 1,500 combined subscription to institutions print & online eds. (effective 2006). adv. illus. back issues avail.; reprint service avail. from PSC. **Document type:** *Journal, Academic/Scholarly.* **Description:** Interdisciplinary coverage of research on robotics science and engineering.
Related titles: Online - full content ed.: 2000; Online - full text ed.: ISSN 1568-5535. EUR 1,080, USD 1,350 to institutions (effective 2006) (from EBSCO Publishing, Gale Group, IngentaConnect, Kluwer Online, O C L C Online Computer Library Center, Inc., Springer LINK, Swets Information Services).
Indexed: AHCI, AIA, ASCA, ApMecR, B&BAb, BrCerAb, C&ISA, CADCAM, CMCI, CerAb, CorrAb, CurCont, E&CAJ, EMA, Englnd, IAA, ISMEC, Inspec, M&TEA, MBF, METADEX, RoboAb, SolStAb, WAA.
—BLDSC (0696.926500), AskIEEE, CISTI, Ei, IDS, IE, Infotrieve, ingenta, Linda Hall. **CCC.**
Published by: (Robotics Society of Japan), V S P (Subsidiary of: Brill Academic Publishers), Brill Academic Publishers, PO Box 9000, Leiden, 2300 PA, Netherlands. TEL 31-71-5353500, FAX 31-71-5317532, vsppub@brill.nl, http://www.vsppub.com/journals/jn-AdvRob.html. Ed. K Kosuge. **Dist. by:** Extenza - Turpin, Pegasus Dr, Stratton Business Park, Biggleswade, Beds SG18 8TQ, United Kingdom. TEL 44-1767-604954, FAX 44-1767-601640, marketing@extenza-turpin.com, http://www.extenza-turpin.com.

➤ **ADVANCES IN DESIGN AND MANUFACTURING.** see *COMPUTERS—Computer Graphics*

➤ **AKADEMIA GORNICZO-HUTNICZA IM. STANISLAWA STASZICA. AUTOMATYKA.** see *COMPUTERS—Automation*

629.892 USA
ANNUAL IDEAS IN SCIENCE AND ELECTRONICS EXPOSITION AND SYMPOSIUM. Text in English. a. **Document type:** *Academic/Scholarly.*
—BLDSC (1086.232500).
Published by: Carnegie Mellon University, Robotics Institute, 5000 Forbes Ave, Pittsburgh, PA 15213-3890. TEL 412-268-3818, FAX 412-268-6436, robotics@ri.cmu.edu, http://www.ri.cmu.edu.

ARTIFICIAL LIFE. see *COMPUTERS—Artificial Intelligence*

ARTIFICIAL LIFE AND ROBOTICS. see *COMPUTERS—Artificial Intelligence*

629.892 USA
ASSEMBLY AND TASK PLANNING. Text in English. 1999. irreg., latest vol.5, 2003. USD 202 per vol. (effective 2004). **Document type:** *Proceedings, Trade.* **Description:** Addresses issues ranging from the research of efficient assembly sequences to the detailed robot instructions that carry out the assembly sequences or other manufacturing tasks.
Published by: Institute of Electrical and Electronics Engineers, Inc., 445 Hoes Ln, Piscataway, NJ 08854-1331. TEL 732-981-0060, 800-678-4333, FAX 732-981-1721, subscription-service@ieee.org, http://www.ieee.org.

629.892 USA ISSN 1535-5535
RB37.A1 CODEN: JALAFP
THE ASSOCIATION FOR LABORATORY AUTOMATION. JOURNAL. Variant title: J A L A. Text in English. 1997. 6/yr. USD 194 domestic to individuals; USD 219 foreign to individuals; USD 266 domestic to institutions; USD 292 foreign to institutions (effective 2006). adv. **Document type:** *Journal, Academic/Scholarly.* **Description:** Covers the advancement of technology in the laboratory.
Related titles: Online - full text ed.: ISSN 1540-2452 (from EBSCO Publishing, Gale Group, ScienceDirect, Swets Information Services).
Indexed: AnalAb, CINAHL, ExcerpMed, Inspec, MSB.
—BLDSC (4704.340000), IE. **CCC.**
Published by: Association for Laboratory Automation, Health Science Center, University of Virginia, Box 572, Charlottesville, VA 22908. FAX 804-924-5718, conal@virginia.edu, http://www.elsevier.com/locate/jala. adv.: B&W page USD 1,825; trim 8.5 x 11. Circ: 1,200 (paid). **Subscr. to:** Elsevier Inc., 360 Park Ave. S, New York, NY 10010-1710. elspcs@elsevier.com, http://www.elsevier.com/homepage/about/us/regional_sites.htt.

629.892 AUS ISSN 0726-3716
AUSTRALIAN ROBOTICS AND AUTOMATION ASSOCIATION. NEWSLETTER. Text in English. 1982. q. AUD 50 (effective 1999). adv. bk.rev. stat. back issues avail. **Document type:** *Newsletter.* **Description:** Covers robotics in Australia and New Zealand.

Published by: Australian Robotics and Automation Association Inc., GPO Box 1527, Sydney, NSW 2001, Australia. TEL 61-2-99675755, FAX 61-2-99675892, MichaelK@zip.com.au, http://www.araa.asn.au. Ed., Adv. contact Michael Kassler. page AUD 275. Circ: 500.

AUTOMATICA & ROBOTICA. see *COMPUTERS—Automation*

629.892 GBR ISSN 1364-2561
AUTOMATION. Text in English. 1996. bi-m. GBP 38; GBP 53 in Europe; USD 82 in US & Canada; GBP 66 elsewhere. **Document type:** *Trade.*
Related titles: Online - full text ed.: (from Gale Group, O C L C Online Computer Library Center, Inc.).
Published by: Wilmington Publishing Ltd. (Subsidiary of: Wilmington Group Plc), Apex House, London Rd, Northfleet, Gravesend, Kent DA11 9JA, United Kingdom. TEL 44-1322-277788, FAX 44-1474-534944, wbp@wilmington.co.uk.

003 629.892 USA ISSN 0929-5593
TJ211.495
➤ **AUTONOMOUS ROBOTS.** Text in English. 1994. bi-m. EUR 748, USD 768, GBP 458 combined subscription to institutions print & online eds. (effective 2005). adv. back issues avail.; reprint service avail. from PSC. **Document type:** *Academic/Scholarly.* **Description:** Publishes papers on the theory and application of robotic systems incorporating self-sufficiency.
Related titles: Online - full text ed.: ISSN 1573-7527 (from EBSCO Publishing, Gale Group, IngentaConnect, Kluwer Online, O C L C Online Computer Library Center, Inc., Ovid Technologies, Inc., Springer LINK, Swets Information Services).
Indexed: ApMecR, BibLing, CMCI, CompLI, CurCont, EngInd, ISR, Inspec, RefZh, SCI.
—BLDSC (1835.061600), AskIEEE, CISTI, Ei, IDS, IE, Infotrieve, ingenta, Linda Hall. **CCC.**
Published by: Springer-Verlag New York, Inc. (Subsidiary of: Springer Science+Business Media), 233 Spring St, New York, NY 10013. TEL 212-460-1500, FAX 212-473-6272, journals@springer-ny.com, http://springerlink.metapress.com/openurl.asp?genre=journal&issn=0929-5593, http://www.springer-ny.com. Ed. George A Bekey. **Subscr. to:** Journal Fulfillment, PO Box 2485, Secaucus, NJ 07096-2485. TEL 201-348-4033, FAX 201-348-4505, journals@springer-ny.com.

629.892 JPN
CHINO IDO ROBOTTO SHINPOJUMU SHIRYO/INTELLIGENT ROBOT SYMPOSIUM. PROCEEDINGS. Text in Japanese. 1982. biennial. JPY 2,500 per issue. **Document type:** *Proceedings.*
Published by: Nihon Kikai Gakkai/Japan Society of Mechanical Engineers, Shinanomachi-Rengakan Bldg, Shinanomachi 35, Shinjuku-ku, Tokyo, 160, Japan.

COMPONENTES, EQUIPOS Y SISTEMAS DE AUTOMATICA Y ROBOTICA. see *COMPUTERS—Automation*

621.892 USA ISSN 0069-8644
TK9151.6 CODEN: CRSTBJ
➤ **CONFERENCE ON REMOTE SYSTEMS TECHNOLOGY. PROCEEDINGS.** Text in English. 1951. a. USD 110 (effective 1998). back issues avail.; reprints avail. **Document type:** *Proceedings, Academic/Scholarly.* **Description:** Presents full scientific papers on robotics and other remote technologies used in the context of nuclear engineering.
Indexed: BiolAb, CIN, ChemAb, ChemTitl, Inspec.
—CASDDS, Ei. **CCC.**
Published by: American Nuclear Society, Inc., 555 N Kensington Ave, La Grange Park, IL 60526-5592. TEL 708-352-6611, FAX 708-352-0499. R&P Mary Beth Gardner. Circ: 500.

➤ **FACTA UNIVERSITATIS. SERIES MECHANICS, AUTOMATIC CONTROL AND ROBOTICS.** see *PHYSICS—Mechanics*

629.892 004.01 USA ISSN 1545-1143
QA76.9.H85
HAPTICS-E; the electronic journal of haptics research. Text in English. 1999. irreg.
Address: Biorobotics Lab Dept. of Electrical Engineering, Box 352500 University of Washington, Seattle, WA 98195-2500. http://www.haptics-e.org. Ed. Blake Hannaford. **Co-sponsor:** I E E E Robotics and Automation Society.

629.892 USA
I E E E INTERNATIONAL CONFERENCE ON INTELLIGENT ROBOTS AND SYSTEMS. PROCEEDINGS. Text in English. a. USD 662 per vol.; USD 331 per vol. to members (effective 2004). **Document type:** *Proceedings, Trade.*
Indexed: EngInd.
Published by: Institute of Electrical and Electronics Engineers, Inc., 3 Park Ave, 17th Fl, New York, NY 10016-5997. TEL 212-419-7900, 800-678-4333, FAX 212-752-4929, customer.service@ieee.org, http://www.ieee.org.

I E E E INTERNATIONAL CONFERENCE ON ROBOTICS AND AUTOMATION. PROCEEDINGS. see *COMPUTERS—Automation*

I E E E INTERNATIONAL SYMPOSIUM ON COMPUTATIONAL INTELLIGENCE IN ROBOTICS AND AUTOMATION. see *COMPUTERS—Artificial Intelligence*

629.892 USA ISSN 1070-9932
TJ210.2 CODEN: IRAMEB
➤ **I E E E ROBOTICS AND AUTOMATION MAGAZINE.** Text in English. 1994. q. USD 315 (effective 2006). adv. illus. Index. reprints avail. **Document type:** *Journal, Academic/Scholarly.* **Description:** Prototyping, demonstration and evaluation, and commercialization of robotic and automation technology and systems, application of theory to real-world systems, with emphasis on implementation.
Media: Microform. **Related titles:** CD-ROM ed.; Microfiche ed.; Online - full text ed.
Indexed: AS&TI, ASCA, CMCI, CurCont, EngInd, IAA, Inspec, RefZh.
—BLDSC (4363.062300), AskIEEE, CISTI, Ei, IDS, IE, Infotrieve, ingenta, Linda Hall. **CCC.**
Published by: Institute of Electrical and Electronics Engineers, Inc., 445 Hoes Ln, Piscataway, NJ 08854-1331. TEL 732-981-0060, 800-701-4333, FAX 732-981-1721, subscription-service@ieee.org, http://www.ncsu.edu/IEEE-RAS/RAM/RAM.html, http://www.ieee.org. Ed. Kimon P Valavanis. **Subscr. to:** Maruzen Co., Ltd., 3-10 Nihonbashi 2-chome, Chuo-ku, Tokyo 103-0027, Japan. FAX 81-3-3275-0657; Universal Subscription Agency, Pvt. Ltd., 877, Udyog Vihar, V, Gurgoan 122001, India. TEL 91-124-347261, FAX 91-124-342496.

629.892 USA ISSN 1552-3098
TJ210.2 CODEN: IRAUEZ
➤ **I E E E TRANSACTIONS ON ROBOTICS.** Text in English. 1985. bi-m. USD 660 (effective 2006). bk.rev. illus. Index. reprints avail. **Document type:** *Journal, Academic/Scholarly.* **Description:** Features theory and applications in robotic dynamics and control.
Supersedes in part (in 2004): I E E E Transactions on Robotics and Automation (1042-296X); Which was formerly (until 1988): I E E E Journal of Robotics and Automation (0882-4967)
Related titles: CD-ROM ed.; Microfiche ed.; Online - full text ed.: (from EBSCO Publishing, Swets Information Services).
Indexed: AIA, AS&TI, ASCA, B&BAb, C&ISA, CADCAM, CMCI, CivEngAb, CompD, CurCont, CybAb, E&CAJ, EngInd, ISMEC, Inspec, RefZh, RoboAb, SCI, SSCI, SolStAb.
—BLDSC (4363.219600), AskIEEE, CISTI, Ei, IDS, IE, Infotrieve, ingenta, Linda Hall.
Published by: Institute of Electrical and Electronics Engineers, Inc., 445 Hoes Ln, Piscataway, NJ 08854-1331. TEL 732-981-0060, 800-701-4333, FAX 732-981-1721, subscription-service@ieee.org, http://www.ieee.org. Ed. Richard A Volz. **Subscr. to:** Maruzen Co., Ltd., 3-10 Nihonbashi 2-chome, Chuo-ku, Tokyo 103-0027, Japan. FAX 81-3-3275-0657; Universal Subscription Agency, Pvt. Ltd., 877, Udyog Vihar, V, Gurgoan 122001, India. TEL 91-124-347261, FAX 91-124-342496. **Co-sponsor:** Robotics and Automation Council.

629.892 SWE ISSN 1400-5972
HD9696.R62
I F R ROBOTICS NEWSLETTER. (International Federation of Robotics) Text in English. 1989. 4/yr. EUR 90 (effective 2001). adv. back issues avail. **Document type:** *Newsletter, Trade.* **Description:** News about industrial and service robots.
Indexed: RoboAb.
Published by: International Federation of Robotics, Secretariat, c/o Sveriges Verkstadsindustrier, Fack 5510, Stockholm, 11485, Sweden. TEL 46-8-782-08-00, FAX 46-8-660-33-78, http://www.ifr.org. Ed. Kerstin Tegloef Delgado. adv.: B&W page USD 1,000. Circ: 2,000.

629.892 USA ISSN 0745-8088
INDUSTRIAL NEWS (MONTROSE). Text in English. m. USD 5. adv. **Document type:** *Newspaper.* **Description:** Covers robot design, CAD-CAM, worker safety, flexible assembly, machining and electronic manufacturing in the robotics industry.
Published by: Industrial News Co., 2155 Verdugo, Montrose, CA 91020. TEL 818-957-4329. Ed. Tom Clement.

629.892 GBR ISSN 0143-991X
CODEN: IDRBAT
➤ **INDUSTRIAL ROBOT;** an international journal. Text in English. 1973. bi-m. EUR 9,155.66 in Europe; USD 9,559 in North America; AUD 11,359 in Australasia; GBP 6,415.16 in UK & elsewhere (effective 2006). bk.rev. charts; illus.; pat. index. reprint service avail. from PSC. **Document type:** *Journal, Academic/Scholarly.* **Description:** Keeps industry practitioners and academics up-to-date with new international developments that relate to the design and application of industrial robot systems. Each issue is themed to ensure that cutting edge topics are covered ion depth.
Incorporates: Service Robot (1356-3378)
Related titles: Online - full text ed.: (from EBSCO Publishing, Emerald Group Publishing Limited, Gale Group, IngentaConnect, O C L C Online Computer Library Center, Inc., ProQuest Information & Learning, Swets Information Services).
Indexed: ABIn, AIA, AS&TI, ASCA, ApMecR, BrCerAb, BrTechI, C&ISA, CADCAM, CMCI, CerAb, CivEngAb, CompC, CompD, CorrAb, CurCont, E&CAJ, EMA, EmerIntel, EngInd, FLUIDEX, IAA, IPackAb, ISMEC, ISR, Inspec, M&TEA, MBF, METADEX, P&BA, RefZh, SCI, SolStAb, WAA.
—BLDSC (4462.200000), AskIEEE, CISTI, Ei, IDS, IE, Infotrieve, ingenta, Linda Hall. **CCC.**
Published by: Emerald Group Publishing Limited, 60-62 Toller Ln, Bradford, W Yorks BD8 9BY, United Kingdom. TEL 44-1274-777700, FAX 44-1274-785200, infomation@emeraldinsight.com, http://www.emeraldinsight.com/ir.htm. Ed. Dr. Clive Loughlin TEL 44-1943-830399.

629.892 AUT ISSN 1729-8806
▼ ➤ **INTERNATIONAL JOURNAL OF ADVANCED ROBOTIC SYSTEMS.** Text in English. 2004. q. EUR 220 to individuals; EUR 280 to institutions; EUR 60 newsstand/cover (effective 2005). adv. bk.rev. charts; illus. back issues avail. **Document type:** *Journal, Academic/Scholarly.*
Indexed: Inspec.
—BLDSC (4541.572500).
Address: Gusshausstr 27-29, Vienna, 1040, Austria. info@ars-journal.com, lazinica@ars-journal.com, http://www.ars-journal.com. Eds. Alexandar Lazinica, Merdan Munir, Vedran Kordic. Pub. Alen Doganac. R&P Vedran Kordic. Adv. contact Alexandar Lazinica. color page EUR 500; trim 205 x 290. Circ: 400 (paid and controlled).

629.892 SGP ISSN 0219-8436
TJ210.2
▼ ➤ **INTERNATIONAL JOURNAL OF HUMANOID ROBOTICS.** Text in English. 2004 (Mar.). q. SGD 202, USD 119, EUR 111 to individuals; SGD 507, USD 299, EUR 280 combined subscription to institutions print & online eds.; SGD 306, USD 180, EUR 168 combined subscription in developing nations to institutions print & online eds. (effective 2006). back issues avail. **Document type:** *Journal, Academic/Scholarly.* **Description:** Covers the theory, the development and application of advanced humanoid robot, including both the artificial body and artificial intelligence, investigation of mind-body interaction, or psycho-somatic engineering such as artificial psychology, and the science of learning.
Related titles: Online - full content ed.; Online - full text ed.: (from EBSCO Publishing, O C L C Online Computer Library Center, Inc., Swets Information Services).
Indexed: BrCerAb, C&ISA, CerAb, CorrAb, E&CAJ, EMA, IAA, M&TEA, MBF, METADEX, WAA.
—BLDSC (4542.288650), IE.
Published by: World Scientific Publishing Co. Pte. Ltd., 5 Toh Tuck Link, Singapore, 596224, Singapore. TEL 65-466-5775, FAX 65-467-7667, wspc@wspc.com.sg, wspc@wspc.com.sg, http://www.worldscinet.com/ijhr/ijhr.shtml, http://www.worldscientific.com. Eds. Jean-Guy Fontaine, Juyang (John) Weng, Ming Xie. **Dist. by:** World Scientific Publishing Co., Inc., 1060 Main St, River Edge, NJ 07661. TEL 201-487-9655, FAX 201-487-9656, 888-977-2665, wspc@wspc.com; World Scientific Publishing Ltd., 57 Shelton St, London WC2H 9HE, United Kingdom. TEL 44-20-78360888, FAX 44-20-78362020, sales@wspc.co.uk.

➤ **INTERNATIONAL JOURNAL OF NANOSCIENCE.** see *COMPUTERS—Microcomputers*

➤ **INTERNATIONAL JOURNAL OF ROBOTICS AND AUTOMATION.** see *COMPUTERS—Automation*

629.892 GBR ISSN 0278-3649
TJ211
➤ **INTERNATIONAL JOURNAL OF ROBOTICS RESEARCH.** Text in English. 1982. m. GBP 864, USD 1,340 to institutions; GBP 900, USD 1,395 combined subscription to institutions print & online eds. (effective 2006). bk.rev. illus. Index. 112 p./no.; back issues avail.; reprint service avail. from PQC. **Document type:** *Journal, Academic/Scholarly.* **Description:** Interdisciplinary approach to the study of robotics for researchers, scientists and students.
Related titles: Microform ed.: (from PQC); Online - full text ed.: ISSN 1741-3176. GBP 855, USD 1,326 to institutions (effective 2006) (from bigchalk, EBSCO Publishing, O C L C Online Computer Library Center, Inc., Sage Publications, Inc., Swets Information Services).
Indexed: AIA, AS&TI, ASCA, ASFA, ApMecR, BrCerAb, BrTechI, C&ISA, CADCAM, CMCI, CerAb, CivEngAb, CompAb, CompLI, CompR, CorrAb, CurCont, E&CAJ, EMA, EngInd, ErgAb, IAA, ISMEC, ISR, Inspec, M&TEA, MBF, METADEX, OceAb, RefZh, RoboAb, SCI, SolStAb, WAA, ZooRec.
—BLDSC (4542.538500), AskIEEE, CISTI, Ei, IDS, IE, Infotrieve, ingenta, Linda Hall. **CCC.**
Published by: Sage Science Press (UK) (Subsidiary of: Sage Publications, Inc.), 1 Oliver's Yard, 55 City Rd, London, EC1Y 1SP, United Kingdom. TEL 44-20-73248500, FAX 44-20-73248600, info@sagepub.com, http://www.sagepub.co.uk/journal.aspx?pid=105596. Ed. John M Hollerbach. Pub. Sara Miller McCune. Circ: 1,340. **Subscr. in the Americas to:** Sage Publications, Inc., 2455 Teller Rd, Thousand Oaks, CA 91320. TEL 805-499-0721, 800-818-7243, FAX 805-499-0871, 800-583-2665, info@sagepub.com, journals@sagepub.com, http://www.sagepub.com.

➤ **INTERNATIONAL WORKSHOP ON ROBOT AND HUMAN INTERACTIVE COMMUNICATION.** see *COMPUTERS—Automation*

629.892 CHN ISSN 1002-0446
JIQIREN/ROBOT. Text in Chinese. bi-m.

Related titles: Online - full text ed.: (from East View Information Services).
Indexed: C&ISA, E&CAJ, EngInd, IAA, Inspec.
Published by: Zhongguo Kexueyuan, Shenyang Zidonghua Yanjiusuo/Chinese Academy of Sciences, Shenyang Institute of Automation, 90, Sanhao Jie, Shenyang, Liaoning 110003, China. TEL 393591. Ed. Jiang Xinsong.

JOURNAL OF INTELLIGENT AND ROBOTIC SYSTEMS; theory and applications. see COMPUTERS—Artificial Intelligence

JOURNAL OF MICROMECHATRONICS. see ENGINEERING—Electrical Engineering

629.892   USA   ISSN 0741-2223
TJ210.3
➤ **JOURNAL OF ROBOTIC SYSTEMS.** Text in English, Japanese; Summaries in English, Japanese. 1984. m. USD 2,499 domestic to institutions; USD 2,619 in Canada & Mexico to institutions; USD 2,721 elsewhere to institutions; USD 2,749 combined subscription domestic to institutions print & online eds.; USD 2,869 combined subscription in Canada & Mexico to institutions print & online eds.; USD 2,971 combined subscription elsewhere to institutions print & online eds. (effective 2006). adv. bk.rev. illus. Index. back issues avail.; reprint service avail. from PSC. **Document type:** Journal, Academic/Scholarly. **Description:** For computer scientists, electrical, mechanical, manufacturing and industrial engineers. Presents research results on all aspects of design, realization and use of robots, robot components and systems.
Related titles: Microform ed.: (from PQC); Online - full text ed.: ISSN 1097-4563. 1996. USD 2,499 to institutions (effective 2006) (from EBSCO Publishing, Swets Information Services, Wiley InterScience).
Indexed: AIA, AS&TI, ASCA, ApMecR, C&ISA, CADCAM, CMCI, CivEngAb, CompLI, CurCont, E&CAJ, EngInd, IAA, ISMEC, ISR, Inspec, RoboAb, SCI, SolStAb, ZentMath.
—BLDSC (5052.110000), AskIEEE, CISTI, Ei, IDS, IE, Infotrieve, ingenta, Linda Hall. **CCC.**
Published by: John Wiley & Sons, Inc., 111 River St, Hoboken, NJ 07030-5774. TEL 800-825-7550, FAX 201-748-5915, uscs-wis@wiley.com, http://www.interscience.wiley.com/jpages/0741-2223/, http://www.wiley.com. Eds. Gerardo Beni, Susan Hackwood. adv.: B&W page USD 1,080, color page EUR 2,420; trim 8.25 x 11. Circ: 750. **Subscr. outside the Americas to:** John Wiley & Sons Ltd., The Atrium, Southern Gate, Chichester, West Sussex PO19 8SQ, United Kingdom. TEL 44-1243-779777, FAX 44-1243-775878, cs-journals@wiley.co.uk.

629.892   JPN   ISSN 0915-3942
➤ **JOURNAL OF ROBOTICS AND MECHATRONICS.** Text and summaries in English. 1989. bi-m. JPY 72,000 to non-members; JPY 24 to members (effective 2004). back issues avail. **Document type:** Journal, Academic/Scholarly. **Description:** Focuses on advanced computational intelligence, including the synergetic integration of neural networks, fuzzy logic and evolutionary computation.
Indexed: INIS AtomInd, RefZh.
—BLDSC (5052.112000), CISTI, IE, ingenta. **CCC.**
Published by: (Japan Society of Mechanical Engineers/Nihon Kikai Gakkai, Robotics and Mechatronics Division), Fuji Technology Press Ltd., 4F Toranomon Sangyo Bldg, 2-29, Toranomon 1-chome, Minato-ku, Tokyo, 105-0001, Japan. TEL 81-3-35080051, FAX 81-3-35920648, http://www.fujipress.jp/. Ed. Makoto Kaneko.

➤ **KEY ABSTRACTS - ROBOTICS & CONTROL.** see COMPUTERS—Abstracting, Bibliographies, Statistics

629.892   USA   ISSN 0896-0348
MILITARY ROBOTICS NEWSLETTER; covering government and defense applications of robotics. Text in English. 1987. bi-w. USD 375 in US & Canada; USD 400 elsewhere (effective 2005). reprints avail. **Document type:** Newsletter, Trade. **Description:** Covers military and government use of robotics and unmanned vehicles.
Related titles: Online - full text ed.: (from Factiva, Gale Group).
Published by: L & B Limited, 19 Rock Creek Church Rd, N W, Washington, DC 20011-6005. TEL 202-723-1600, http://www2.dgsys.com/~jlovece. Ed. Joseph A Lovece. Circ: 250 (paid).

MOBILE ROBOTS. see PHYSICS—Optics

629.892   GBR
NEW FRONTIERS IN ROBOTICS. Text in English. irreg. price varies. **Document type:** Monographic series, Academic/Scholarly.
Published by: Imperial College Press (Subsidiary of: World Scientific Publishing Co. Pte. Ltd.), 57 Shelton St, London, WC2H 9HE, United Kingdom. TEL 44-20-7836-3954, FAX 44-20-7836-2002, edit@icpress.co.uk, http://www.wspc.com/books/series/acoe_series.shtml, http://www.icpress.co.uk/. Eds. Miomir Vukobratovic, Xie Ming.

PROBLEMI NA TEKHNICHESKATA KIBERNETIKA I ROBOTIKA/PROBLEMS OF ENGINEERING CYBERNETICS AND ROBOTICS. see COMPUTERS—Cybernetics

PROGRESS IN ROBOTICS AND INTELLIGENT SYSTEMS. see COMPUTERS—Artificial Intelligence

629.892   USA
R I A QUARTERLY STATISTICS REPORT - ROBOTICS. Text in English. q. USD 50 (effective 1999).
Published by: Robotic Industries Association, 900 Victors Way, Box 3724, Ann Arbor, MI 48106. TEL 734-994-6088, FAX 734-994-3338, ria@robotics.org, http://www.robotics.org. R&P Jeff Burnstein.

629.892   GBR   ISSN 1474-1512
REAL ROBOTS. Key Title: Ultimate Real Robots. Text in English. fortn. **Document type:** Magazine, Consumer.
Published by: Eaglemoss Publications Ltd., 5 Cromwell Rd, London, SW7 2HR, United Kingdom. TEL 44-8707-270160, http://www.realrobots.co.uk/magazine.html, http://www.eaglemoss.co.uk.

629.892   USA   ISSN 1060-4375
ROBOT EXPLORER. Text in English. 1992. 8/yr. USD 14.95 in North America; USD 29.95 elsewhere. adv. bk.rev. **Document type:** Newsletter. **Description:** Targets the non-industrial usages of robotics. Topics include commercial, research, and educational projects.
Published by: Appropriate Solutions, Inc., 145 Grove St, Box 458, Peterborough, NH 03458. TEL 603-924-6079, FAX 603-525-4923, apsol@apsol.com. Ed. Ray Cote. Pub. Andrew Taylor. R&P Raymond Cote. Adv. contact Elizabeth S Alpaugh Cote. Circ: 500 (paid).

629.892   USA
ROBOT TIMES. Text in English. q. membership. **Document type:** Newsletter. **Description:** Contains information for members about workshops, conferences, symposia, industry standards, publications and trade shows.
Indexed: CADCAM.
Published by: Robotic Industries Association, 900 Victors Way, Box 3724, Ann Arbor, MI 48106. TEL 734-994-6088, FAX 734-994-3338, ria@robotics.org, http://www.robotics.org. Ed., R&P Jeff Burnstein.

629.892   AUS
ROBOTIC AGE. Text in English. 1983. q.
Address: PO Box 1024, Richmond North, VIC 3121, Australia. TEL 03-429-5599, FAX 03-427-0332. Ed. Geoffrey M Gold. Circ: 8,000.

629.892   GBR   ISSN 0263-5747
TJ210.2
➤ **ROBOTICA.** Text in English. 1983. bi-m. GBP 390 to institutions; USD 645 in North America to institutions; GBP 420 combined subscription to institutions print & online eds.; USD 696 combined subscription in North America to institutions print & online eds. (effective 2006). adv. bk.rev. illus. Index. back issues avail.; reprint service avail. from PSC. **Document type:** Journal, Academic/Scholarly. **Description:** Contains robotics, automation industrial research and educational programs results for students and professionals.
Related titles: Online - full text ed.: ISSN 1469-8668. GBP 360 to institutions; USD 600 in North America to institutions (effective 2006) (from EBSCO Publishing, O C L C Online Computer Library Center, Inc., Swets Information Services).
Indexed: AHCI, AIA, ASCA, BRI, BrCerAb, BrTechI, C&ISA, CADCAM, CBRI, CMCI, CerAb, CivEngAb, CompC, CompLI, CorrAb, CurCont, E&CAJ, EMA, EngInd, ErgAb, IAA, ISMEC, Inspec, M&TEA, MBF, METADEX, RefZh, RoboAb, SolStAb, WAA.
—BLDSC (8000.452300), AskIEEE, CISTI, Ei, IDS, IE, Infotrieve, ingenta, Linda Hall. **CCC.**
Published by: Cambridge University Press, The Edinburgh Bldg, Shaftesbury Rd, Cambridge, CB2 2RU, United Kingdom. TEL 44-1223-312393, FAX 44-1223-315052, journals@cambridge.org, http://uk.cambridge.org/journals/journal_catalogue.asp?historylinks=ALPHA&mnemonic=ROB. Ed. J Rose. R&P Linda Nicol TEL 44-1223-325757. Adv. contact Rebecca Curtis TEL 44-1223-325757. Circ: 650. **Subscr. to:** Cambridge University Press, 100 Brook Hill Dr, West Nyack, NY 10994. TEL 845-353-7500, FAX 845-353-4141, journals_subscriptions@cup.org

629.892   CAN
ROBOTICS AND APPLICATIONS. Text in English. 1991. a. price varies. **Document type:** Proceedings, Academic/Scholarly.
Formerly: Robotics and Manufacturing (1027-264X)
Published by: ACTA Press, 4500-16th Ave NW, Ste 80, Calgary, AB T3B 0M6, Canada. TEL 403-288-1195, FAX 403-247-6851, journals@actapress.com, http://www.actapress.com.

629.892   DEU
ROBOTICS & AUTOMATION. Text in English, German. 1999. q. EUR 40 (effective 2001). adv. bk.rev.; software rev. bibl.; charts; illus.; pat.; mkt.; stat.; tr.lit. **Document type:** Magazine, Trade. **Description:** Covers all aspects of robotics and automation.
Published by: Zeitungs- und Zeitschriftenverlag Heinrichs, Brueggekamp 1, Barsinghausen, 30890, Germany. TEL 49-5105-2289. Ed., Pub. Gerhard Heinrichs. adv.: B&W page EUR 4,000, color page EUR 6,000; trim 192 x 295.

629.892   NLD   ISSN 0921-8890
TJ210.2   CODEN: RASOEJ
➤ **ROBOTICS AND AUTONOMOUS SYSTEMS.** Text in English. 1985. 12/yr. EUR 1,563 in Europe to institutions; JPY 207,400 in Japan to institutions; USD 1,749 to institutions except Europe and Japan (effective 2006). adv. bk.rev. illus. Index. back issues avail.; reprints avail. **Document type:** Academic/Scholarly. **Description:** Provides information on the international robotics industry. Focuses on applications in business and technology.
Formerly (until 1988): Robotics (0167-8493)
Related titles: Online - full text ed.: (from EBSCO Publishing, Gale Group, IngentaConnect, ScienceDirect, Swets Information Services).
Indexed: AHCI, AIA, ASCA, ApMecR, C&ISA, CADCAM, CMCI, CivEngAb, CompAb, CompLI, CurCont, E&CAJ, EngInd, IPackAb, ISMEC, Inspec, RefZh, RoboAb, SolStAb, TTI.
—BLDSC (8000.453180), AskIEEE, CISTI, Ei, IDS, IE, Infotrieve, ingenta, Linda Hall. **CCC.**
Published by: Elsevier BV, North-Holland (Subsidiary of: Elsevier Science & Technology), Sara Burgerhartstraat 25, Amsterdam, 1055 KV, Netherlands. TEL 31-20-485-3911, FAX 31-20-485-2457, nlinfo-f@elsevier.nl, http://www.elsevier.com/locate/robot, http://www.elsevier.nl/homepage/about/us/regional_sites.htt, http://www.elsevier.nl. Eds. T C Henderson, R. Dillmann, T. Arai. Circ: 1,200. **Subscr.:** Elsevier BV, PO Box 211, Amsterdam 1000 AE, Netherlands. TEL 31-20-485-3757, FAX 31-20-485-3432.

629.892   GBR   ISSN 0736-5845
➤ **ROBOTICS AND COMPUTER-INTEGRATED MANUFACTURING.** Text in English. 1984. 6/yr. EUR 1,087 in Europe to institutions; JPY 144,100 in Japan to institutions; USD 1,217 to institutions except Europe and Japan (effective 2006). adv. bk.rev. bibl.; pat.; abstr.; illus. Index. reprints avail. **Document type:** Journal, Academic/Scholarly. **Description:** Features original international papers on theoretical, experimental and applied robotics and on computer-integrated manufacturing, with an emphasis on flexible manufacturing systems.
Incorporates (1988-1998): Computer Integrated Manufacturing Systems (0951-5240); Which incorporated (1988-1991): Advanced Manufacturing Engineering (0951-5232)
Related titles: Microfilm ed.: (from PQC); Online - full text ed.: (from EBSCO Publishing, Gale Group, IngentaConnect, ScienceDirect, Swets Information Services).
Indexed: AIA, AS&TI, ASCA, BrCerAb, C&ISA, CADCAM, CMCI, CerAb, CompC, CompLI, CorrAb, CurCont, E&CAJ, EMA, EngInd, ErgAb, IAA, Inspec, M&TEA, MBF, METADEX, ManagCont, RASB, RefZh, RoboAb, SolStAb, WAA.
—BLDSC (8000.453200), AskIEEE, CISTI, Ei, IDS, IE, Infotrieve, ingenta, Linda Hall. **CCC.**
Published by: Pergamon (Subsidiary of: Elsevier Science & Technology), The Boulevard, Langford Ln, East Park, Kidlington, Oxford OX5 1GB, United Kingdom. TEL 44-1865-843000, FAX 44-1865-843010, http://www.elsevier.com/locate/rcim, http://www.elsevier.nl. Eds. A Sharon, G Lin. Circ: 2,500. **Subscr. to:** Elsevier BV, PO Box 211, Amsterdam 1000 AE, Netherlands. TEL 31-20-485-3757, FAX 31-20-485-3432, nlinfo-f@elsevier.nl, http://www.elsevier.nl.

629.892   GBR
ROBOTICS AND MECHATRONICS SERIES. Text in English. 1993. irreg., latest vol.6, 2003. price varies. **Document type:** Monographic series.
Related titles: CD-ROM ed.
—BLDSC (8000.453460).
Published by: Research Studies Press Ltd., 16 Coach House Cloisters, 10 Hitchin St, Baldock, Hertfordshire SG7 6AE, United Kingdom. TEL 44-1462-895060, FAX 44-1462-892546, http://www.research-studies-press.co.uk. Ed. J Billingsley.

629.892   USA
ROBOTICS INSTITUTE. TECHNICAL REPORTS. Text in English. 1980. a.
Related titles: Online - full text ed.
Published by: Carnegie Mellon University, Robotics Institute, 5000 Forbes Ave, Pittsburgh, PA 15213-3890. TEL 412-268-3818, FAX 412-268-6436, robotics@ri.cmu.edu, http://www.ri.cmu.edu/cgi-bin/tech_reports.cgi.

629.892   USA   ISSN 0193-6913
TS191   CODEN: ROTODJ
ROBOTICS TODAY. Text in English. 1979. q. USD 85 to non-members (effective 2005). adv. bk.rev. charts; illus.; stat.; tr.lit. **Document type:** Newsletter. **Description:** Offers comprehensive information on the application of robotics in automated manufacturing.
Media: Online - full text (from O C L C Online Computer Library Center, Inc., ProQuest Information & Learning). **Related titles:** Microfiche ed.; Microform ed.: (from PQC); Online - full text ed.: (from Northern Light Technology, Inc.).
Indexed: ABIn, AIA, ApMecR, CADCAM, CompC, CompD, CompLI, CybAb, EngInd, Inspec, PROMT, RASB, RoboAb.
—AskIEEE, Linda Hall. **CCC.**
Published by: Society of Manufacturing Engineers, One SME Dr, PO Box 930, Dearborn, MI 48121-0930. TEL 313-425-3267, FAX 313-425-3417, dhelka@sme.org, http://www.sme.org/. Ed. Ms. Dianna L Helka TEL 313-425-3267. Circ: 15,000.
Co-sponsor: Composites Manufacturing Association of S M E.

629.892 USA ISSN 0737-7908
TS191.8
ROBOTICS WORLD; the end users magazine of flexible automation. Text in English. 1982. 10/yr. USD 50 domestic; USD 72 in Canada & Mexico; USD 99 elsewhere; USD 6 newsstand/cover domestic; USD 9 newsstand/cover foreign (effective 2005). adv. software rev.; Website rev. illus.; abstr.; pat.; stat.; tr.lit. Index. 48 p./no. 3 cols./p.; back issues avail.; reprint service avail. from PQC. **Document type:** *Magazine, Trade.* **Description:** Provides comprehensive coverage of the robotics industry. Articles report on robotics applications in the assembly, flexible automation, coating, tracking, welding and computer-integrated manufacturing industries.
Incorporates (1990-200?): Motion Control (1053-4644)
Related titles: Microform ed.: (from PQC); Online - full text ed.: (from bigchalk, Factiva, Florida Center for Library Automation, Gale Group, Northern Light Technology, Inc., O C L C Online Computer Library Center, Inc., ProQuest Information & Learning); Supplement(s): Robotics World. Worldwide Directory. USD 52.95 domestic; USD 67.95 foreign (effective 2004).
Indexed: ABIn, AIA, AS&TI, CADCAM, CompD, CybAb, EngInd, Inspec, PROMT, RoboAb.
—BLDSC (8000.456000), AskIEEE, CISTI, Ei, IE, Infotrieve, ingenta, Linda Hall. **CCC.**
Published by: (Robotic Industries Association), Douglas Publications, Inc., 2807 N Parham Rd, Ste 200, Richmond, VA 23294. TEL 804-762-9600, FAX 804-217-8999, info@douglaspublications.com, http://www.roboticsworld.com/, http://www.douglaspublications.com. Ed. Janine Nunes TEL 815-282-5076. adv.: B&W page USD 5,265; trim 7 x 10. Circ: 24,000 (paid).

629.892 621 JPN
ROBOTIKUSU MEKATORONIKUSU KOENKAI KOEN RONBUNSHU/ANNUAL CONFERENCE ON ROBOTICS AND MECHATRONICS. PROCEEDINGS. Text in English. 1989. a. JPY 14,000.
Published by: Nihon Kikai Gakkai/Japan Society of Mechanical Engineers, Shinanomachi-Rengakan Bldg, Shinanomachi 35, Shinjuku-ku, Tokyo, 160, Japan.

629.892 JPN ISSN 0387-1940
CODEN: ROBBDQ
ROBOTTO/ROBOT. Text in Japanese. 1971. bi-m. JPY 1,300 per issue (effective 2000). **Document type:** *Academic/Scholarly.*
Indexed: B&BAb, CivEngAb, Inspec.
—BLDSC (8000.467000), AskIEEE, Ei, Linda Hall.
Published by: Japan Robot Association/Nihon Robotto Kogyokai, Kikaishinko Bldg, 3-5-8 Shibakoen, Minato-ku, Tokyo, 105-0011, Japan. TEL 81-3-3434-2919, FAX 81-3-3578-1404, jara@jade.dti.ne.jp, http://www.jade.dti.net/jp/~jara.

629.892 JPN
ROBOTTO SENSA SHINPOJUMU YOKOSHU/ROBOT SENSOR SYMPOSIUM. PREPRINTS. Text in Japanese; Summaries in English. 1988. biennial.
Published by: Keisoku Jido Seigyo Gakkai/Society of Instrument and Control Engineers, 1-35-28-303 Hongo, Bunkyo-ku, Tokyo, 113-0033, Japan.

629.892 RUS ISSN 0869-7566
CODEN: STINA4
S T I N. Text in Russian. 1930. m. USD 565. adv. bk.rev. bibl.; charts; illus. index. **Document type:** *Academic/Scholarly.* **Description:** Publishes articles about the development and installation of all-around automated bays, and about the design and use of industrial robots.
Formerly (until 1993): Stanki i Instrumenty (0038-9811)
Indexed: BrCerAb, C&ISA, CerAb, ChemAb, CorrAb, E&CAJ, EMA, EngInd, Inspec, M&TEA, MBF, METADEX, RefZh, SolStAb, WAA.
—BLDSC (0169.481000), AskIEEE, CASDDS, CISTI, East View, Linda Hall.
Published by: (Russia. Ministerstvo Nauki i Tekhnologii), Izdatel'stvo TOO Stin, Donskoi pr-t 5-i 21b, Moscow, 117334, Russian Federation. TEL 7-095-9555202. Ed. Igor A Novosel'skii. adv.: page MRK 4,000. Circ: 13,600. **US dist. addr.:** East View Information Services, 3020 Harbor Ln. N., Minneapolis, MN 55447. TEL 612-550-0961.

629.892 SGP
SERIES IN ROBOTICS AND AUTOMATED SYSTEMS. Text in English. 1991. irreg., latest vol.11, 1993. price varies. **Document type:** *Monographic series.*
Published by: World Scientific Publishing Co. Pte. Ltd., 5 Toh Tuck Link, Singapore, 596224, Singapore. TEL 65-466-5775, FAX 65-467-7667. Ed. T Husband.

629.892 600 USA ISSN 1546-0592
▼ **SERVO.** Text in English. 2003. m. USD 24.95 (effective 2004).
Related titles: Online - full text ed.
Published by: T & L Publications, 430 Princeland Ct, Corona, CA 92879. TEL 909-371-8497, 800-783-4624, FAX 909-371-3052, http://www.servomagazine.com. Ed. Dan Danknick.

629.892 DEU ISSN 1610-7438
▼ ➤ **SPRINGER TRACTS IN ADVANCED ROBOTICS.** Text in English. 2003. irreg., latest vol.22, 2006. price varies. **Document type:** *Monographic series, Academic/Scholarly.* **Description:** Covers all the technical contents, applications, and multidisciplinary aspects of robotics.
Related titles: Online - full text ed.: ISSN 1610-742X.
—BLDSC (8424.795000), CISTI.
Published by: Springer-Verlag (Subsidiary of: Springer Science+Business Media), Tiergartenstr 17, Heidelberg, 69121, Germany. TEL 49-6221-3450, FAX 49-6221-345229, orders@springer.de, http://www.springer.de.

629.892 006.3 USA
WORKSHOP ON ROBOT MOTION AND CONTROL. Text in English. 1999. a. USD 182; USD 91 to members (effective 2004). **Document type:** *Proceedings, Trade.*
Published by: Institute of Electrical and Electronics Engineers, Inc., 3 Park Ave, 17th Fl, New York, NY 10016-5997. TEL 212-419-7900, 800-678-4333, FAX 212-752-4929, customer.service@ieee.org, http://www.ieee.org.

629.892 CHE
WORLD ROBOTICS; statistics, market analysis, forecasts, case studies and profitability of robot investment. Text in English. 1989. a. USD 120 (effective 2003). charts; illus.; stat. 380 p./no.; **Document type:** *Monographic series, Academic/Scholarly.* **Description:** Contains a collection of data from more than 20 national robotics associations. Provides statistics, by application areas, industrial branches and types of robots, from 1983 to 2002 and forecasts to 2006. Analyzes both industrial and service robots.
Former titles: World Industrial Robots; World Robot Statistics; I F R World Industrial Robot Statistics (1020-1076)
Indexed: IIS.
Published by: United Nations, Economic Commission for Europe (ECE), Palais des Nations, Geneva 10, 1211, Switzerland. TEL 41-22-9174444, FAX 41-22-9170505, info.ece@unece.org, http://www.unece.org. Ed. Jan Karlsson. R&P Anne Cunningham TEL 212-963-0869. **Co-sponsor:** International Federation of Robotics.

WORLD SCIENTIFIC SERIES IN ROBOTICS AND INTELLIGENT SYSTEMS. see *COMPUTERS—Artificial Intelligence*

COMPUTERS—Software

see also COMPUTERS—Computer Programming

A & D SOFTWARE GUIDE; Das Forum fuer Anbieter und Anwender von Automatisierungssoftware. (Automation and Drives) see *COMPUTERS—Automation*

A B A - UNIX - GROUP NEWSLETTER. see *LAW—Computer Applications*

005.43 USA ISSN 0736-6663
A C M SYMPOSIUM ON OPERATING SYSTEMS PRINCIPLES. PROCEEDINGS. Text in English. 1967. irreg., latest 2001. USD 18 per issue to members; USD 36 per issue to non-members (effective 2005).
—**CCC.**
Published by: Association for Computing Machinery, Inc., 1515 Broadway, 17th Fl, New York, NY 10036-5701. TEL 212-626-0500, 800-342-6626, FAX 212-869-0481, sigs@acm.org, usacm@acm.org, http://www.acm.org.

005.5 USA ISSN 0098-3500
QA76.6 CODEN: ACMSCU
➤ **A C M TRANSACTIONS ON MATHEMATICAL SOFTWARE.** Text in English. 1975. q. USD 184 domestic to non-members; USD 198 foreign to non-members; USD 44 domestic to members; USD 58 foreign to members; USD 39 domestic to students; USD 53 foreign to students; USD 221 combined subscription domestic to non-members print & online eds.; USD 235 combined subscription foreign to non-members print & online eds.; USD 53 combined subscription domestic to members print & online eds.; USD 67 combined subscription foreign to members print & online eds.; USD 47 combined subscription domestic to students print & online eds.; USD 61 combined subscription foreign to students print & online eds. (effective 2006). adv. charts; illus. back issues avail.; reprints avail. **Document type:** *Journal, Academic/Scholarly.* **Description:** Disseminates the original work of computer scientists that forms the theoretical foundations of subsequent applications.
Related titles: Microfiche ed.: (from PQC); Microfilm ed.: (from WWS); Online - full text ed.: ISSN 1557-7295. USD 147 to non-members; USD 35 to members; USD 31 to students (effective 2006) (from Association for Computing Machinery, Inc., EBSCO Publishing, Florida Center for Library Automation, Gale Group).
Indexed: ABIn, AS&TI, ASCA, BrCerAb, C&ISA, CCMJ, CIS, CMCI, CerAb, CompAb, CompC, CompD, CompLI, CompR, CorrAb, CurCont, CybAb, E&CAJ, EMA, EngInd, IAA, IAOP, ISR, Inspec, M&TEA, MBF, METADEX, MathR, MathSciNet, RASB, RefZh, SCI, SolStAb, WAA, ZentMath.
—BLDSC (0578.670000), AskIEEE, CISTI, Ei, IDS, IE, Infotrieve, ingenta, Linda Hall. **CCC.**
Published by: Association for Computing Machinery, Inc., 1515 Broadway, 17th Fl, New York, NY 10036-5701. TEL 212-626-0520, 800-342-6626, FAX 212-944-1318, acmhelp@acm.org, sigs@acm.org, usacm@acm.org, http://www.acm.org/toms/. Ed. Richard T. Snodgrass. Pub. Jono Hardjowirogo. adv.: B&W page USD 4,870, color page USD 6,700; trim 8.13 x 10.88. Circ: 3,114 (paid).

005.1 USA ISSN 1049-331X
QA76.758 CODEN: ATSMER
➤ **A C M TRANSACTIONS ON SOFTWARE ENGINEERING AND METHODOLOGY.** Abbreviated title: T O S E M. Text in English. 1992. q. USD 165 domestic to non-members; USD 179 foreign to non-members; USD 40 domestic to members; USD 54 foreign to members; USD 35 domestic to students; USD 49 foreign to students; USD 198 combined subscription domestic to non-members print & online eds.; USD 212 combined subscription foreign to non-members print & online eds.; USD 48 combined subscription domestic to members print & online eds.; USD 62 combined subscription foreign to members print & online eds.; USD 42 combined subscription domestic to students print & online eds.; USD 56 combined subscription foreign to students print & online eds. (effective 2006). illus. reprints avail. **Document type:** *Journal, Academic/Scholarly.* **Description:** Publishes research on the mechanisms, tools and processes involved in supporting complex systems of scale and longevity that require substantial investments in definition, design, development, maintenance, and related support activities.
Related titles: Microform ed.; Online - full text ed.: ISSN 1557-7392. USD 132 to non-members; USD 32 to members; USD 28 student members (effective 2006) (from Association for Computing Machinery, Inc., EBSCO Publishing).
Indexed: ABIn, AS&TI, BrCerAb, C&CSA, C&ISA, CMCI, CerAb, CompAb, CompLI, CompR, CorrAb, CurCont, E&CAJ, EMA, EngInd, IAA, ISR, Inspec, M&TEA, MBF, METADEX, RefZh, SCI, SolStAb, WAA.
—BLDSC (0578.675100), AskIEEE, CISTI, Ei, IE, Infotrieve, ingenta, Linda Hall. **CCC.**
Published by: Association for Computing Machinery, Inc., 1515 Broadway, 17th Fl, New York, NY 10036-5701. TEL 212-626-0520, 800-342-6626, FAX 212-944-1318, usacm@acm.org, http://www.acm.org/tosem. Circ: 2,234 (paid).

005.43 USA
A I X UPDATE. Text in English. m. USD 275 (effective 2000). **Document type:** *Trade.* **Description:** Provides information on AIX, an open operating system from IBM that is based on a version of UNIX.
Published by: Xephon, 9330 Lyndon B Johnson Fwy., Ste. 800, Dallas, TX 75243-4310. TEL 303-410-9344, FAX 303-438-0290, http://www.xephon.com/.

005.43 USA ISSN 1527-5515
A M F E-ZINE; windows and technology news, tips, tricks and more. (Andrew M. Freeman) Text in English. 1998. m. free. adv. back issues avail. **Document type:** *Newsletter.* **Description:** Provides short articles and tips and tricks for Windows office users.
Media: E-mail.
Published by: Andrew M. Freeman, PO Box 189, Holbrook, NY 11741-0189. amf1@amfsoftware.com, ezine@amfsoftware.com, http://amfsoftware.com/subscribe.html. Ed. Andrew M Freeman. Circ: 7,000.

005.16 USA
A S P ISLAND. (Application Service Provider) Text in English. w. adv. **Document type:** *Trade.* **Description:** Covers news and trends of the Application Server Provider industry.
Media: Online - full text.
Published by: Jupitermedia Corp., 23 Old Kings Hwy South, Darien, CT 06820. TEL 203-662-2800, FAX 203-655-4686, info@aspisland.com, info@jupitermedia.com, http://www.aspisland.com, http://www.jupitermedia.com. Ed. Mike Mathewson TEL 949-487-1488.

ABSOLUTE REFERENCE; the journal for 1-2-3 and Symphony users. see *COMPUTERS—Microcomputers*

005.5 USA ISSN 1528-7203
QA76.9.D3
ACCESS - V B - S Q L ADVISOR. Text in English. 1992. m. USD 99 combined subscription domestic; USD 169 combined subscription in Canada; USD 189 combined subscription elsewhere (effective 2005). **Document type:** *Magazine, Trade.* **Description:** Explains how to build business solutions with Microsoft application development tools. For users of Microsoft Access, Visual Basic, Office, Internet, Windows 95 - NT and SQL Server.
Former titles (until 2000): Access - Office -V B Advisor (1099-7555); (until 1997): Access - Office - V B A Advisor (1093-9105); (until 1997): Access - Visual Basic Advisor (1078-2990); (until 1995): Access Advisor (1066-7253)
Related titles: Online - full text ed.
Indexed: CompLI, SoftBase.
—IE, Infotrieve.
Published by: Advisor Media, Inc., 4849 Viewridge Ave, San Diego, CA 92123-1643. TEL 858-278-5600, FAX 858-278-0300, advisor@advisor.com, http://accessvbsqladvisor.com, http://www.advisor.com. Pub. B J Ghiglione. Adv. contact Sheri Ogletree. Circ: 40,000. **Dist. by:** International Periodical Distributors, 674 Via de la Valle, Ste 204, Solana Beach, CA 92075.

ACKNOWLEDGE THE WINDOW LETTER. see *COMPUTERS—Microcomputers*

C

005.5 GBR ISSN 1362-962X
ADVANCED SOFTWARE DEVELOPMENT SERIES. Text in English. 1989. irreg., latest vol.6, 1998. price varies. **Document type:** *Monographic series.*
—BLDSC (0696.928900), ingenta.
Published by: Research Studies Press Ltd., 16 Coach House Cloisters, 10 Hitchin St, Baldock, Hertfordshire SG7 6AE, United Kingdom. TEL 44-1462-895060, FAX 44-1462-892546, http://www.research-studies-press.co.uk. Ed. J Kramer.

ADVANCED TECHNOLOGY IN WASHINGTON STATE. see *BUSINESS AND ECONOMICS—Trade And Industrial Directories*

ADVANCES IN ENGINEERING SOFTWARE. see *ENGINEERING—Computer Applications*

005.5 USA ISSN 1044-7997
QA76.75
➤ **ADVANCES IN SOFTWARE SCIENCE AND TECHNOLOGY.** Text in English. 1989. irreg., latest vol.5, 1994. back issues avail. **Document type:** *Monographic series, Academic/Scholarly.*
—CISTI. **CCC.**
Published by: (Japanese Society for Software Science and Technology JPN), Academic Press (Subsidiary of: Elsevier Science & Technology), 525 B St, Ste 1900, San Diego, CA 92101-4495. TEL 619-231-6616, 800-894-3434, apsubs@acad.com, http://www.academicpress.com.

005.5 USA ISSN 1524-6388
ADVISOR EXPERT: LOTUS NOTES AND DOMINO ADMINISTRATION. Text in English. 1999. 6/yr. USD 99 domestic; USD 109 in Canada; USD 119 elsewhere (effective 2000). **Document type:** *Trade.* **Description:** Contains Lotus Domino codes, articles, sample solutions, and exclusive files.
Related titles: Online - full text ed.
Published by: Advisor Media, Inc., 4849 Viewridge Ave, San Diego, CA 92123-1643. TEL 858-278-5600, FAX 858-278-0300, subscribe@advisor.com, http://www.advisor.com. Ed. John L Hawkins. Pub. B J Ghiglione. Adv. contact Sheri Ogletree.

005.5 USA ISSN 1524-6396
ADVISOR EXPERT: LOTUS NOTES & DOMINO R5. Text in English. 1999. m. USD 199 domestic; USD 219 in Canada; USD 239 elsewhere (effective 2000). **Document type:** *Trade.* **Description:** Contains Lotus Notes codes, articles, sample solutions, and exclusive files.
Related titles: Online - full text ed.
Published by: Advisor Media, Inc., 4849 Viewridge Ave, San Diego, CA 92123-1643. TEL 858-278-5600, FAX 858-278-0300, subscribe@advisor.com, http://www.advisor.com. Ed. John L Hawkins. Pub. B J Ghiglione. Adv. contact Sheri Ogletree.

005.5 USA ISSN 1524-8887
ADVISOR EXPERT: MICROSOFT S Q L SERVER. Text in English. 1999. 6/yr. USD 99 domestic; USD 109 in Canada; USD 119 elsewhere (effective 2000). **Document type:** *Trade.* **Description:** Explores and explains SQL Server development and administration.
Related titles: Online - full text ed.
Published by: Advisor Media, Inc., 4849 Viewridge Ave, San Diego, CA 92123-1643. TEL 858-278-5600, FAX 858-278-0300, subscribe@advisor.com, http://www.advisor.com. Ed. John L Hawkins. Pub. B J Ghiglione. Adv. contact Sheri Ogletree.

005.5 USA ISSN 1090-3062
AGENTNEWS WEBLETTER. Text in English. 1996. irreg. **Document type:** *Newsletter.*
Media: Online - full text.
Published by: University of Maryland Baltimore County, Laboratory of Advanced Information Technology, 5401 Wilkens Ave, Baltimore, MD 21228. TEL 410-455-3000, FAX 410-455-3969, http://www.cs.umbc.edu/agentnews/. Ed. Tim Finn.

AGILE PROJECT MANAGEMENT ADVISORY SERVICE EXECUTIVE REPORT. see *COMPUTERS—Computer Programming*

AIR QUALITY DATA MANAGEMENT SOFTWARE REPORT. see *ENVIRONMENTAL STUDIES—Computer Applications*

005.5 USA ISSN 1557-0479
KF390.5.C6
ANDREWS LITIGATION REPORTER: SOFTWARE LAW BULLETIN. Text in English. 1988. m. USD 500 (effective 2005). bk.rev. index. **Document type:** *Bulletin, Trade.* **Description:** Examines software legal issues. Analyzes the most recent cases, state regulations and statutes, U.S. government documents and international issues.
Formerly (until 2004): Software Law Bulletin (0897-2680)
Related titles: Online - full text ed.
—**CCC.**
Published by: Andrews Publications (Subsidiary of: Thomson West), 175 Strafford Ave, Ste 140, Wayne, PA 19087. TEL 610-225-0510, 800-345-1101, FAX 610-225-0501, west.customer.service@thomson.com, http://www.andrewsonline.com. Ed. Donna Higgins. Circ: 250.

005.1 USA
ANNUAL N A S A GODDARD SOFTWARE ENGINEERING WORKSHOP. PROCEEDINGS. Variant title: Software Engineering Workshop. Proceedings. Text in English. a. **Document type:** *Proceedings, Trade.*
Published by: I E E E Computer Society, 10662 Los Vaqueros Circle, PO Box 3014, Los Alamitos, CA 90720-1314. TEL 714-821-8380, 800-272-6657, FAX 714-821-4010, customer.service@ieee.org, http://www.ieee.org, http://www.computer.org.

005.15 NLD ISSN 1568-4946
➤ **APPLIED SOFT COMPUTING.** Text in English. 2001 (Jun). 4/yr. EUR 460 in Europe to institutions; JPY 48,000 in Japan to institutions; USD 400 to institutions except Europe and Japan (effective 2006). **Document type:** *Journal, Academic/Scholarly.* **Description:** Promotes an integrated view of soft computing to solve real life problems.
Media: Online - full content. **Related titles:** Online - full text ed.: (from Gale Group, IngentaConnect, ScienceDirect); Print ed.
Indexed: C&ISA, CMCI, CompLI, CurCont, E&CAJ, IAA, Inspec.
—BLDSC (1578.350000), IE. **CCC.**
Published by: (World Conference on Soft Computing JPN), Elsevier BV (Subsidiary of: Elsevier Science & Technology), Radarweg 29, Amsterdam, 1043 NX, Netherlands. TEL 31-20-4853911, FAX 31-20-4852457, asoc@cranfield.ac.uk, nlinfo-f@elsevier.nl, http://www.elsevier.com/locate/asoc, http://www.elsevier.nl. Ed. R. Roy.

005.5 AUS
AQUARIAN NEWS. Text in English. 1998. m. bk.rev. back issues avail. **Document type:** *Newsletter.* **Description:** Covers computer software tools.
Media: Online - full text.
Address: PO Box 820, Castlemaine, VIC 3450, Australia. TEL 61-3-54706812, feedback@aquatee.com, http://www.aquatee.com/news/newsletters/index.htm/. Ed. Tim Jones.

005.5 910.285 USA ISSN 1534-5467
G70.212
ARCUSER. Text in English. 1998. q. free (effective 2003). adv.
Published by: Environmental Systems Research Institute, Inc., 380 New York St, Redlands, CA 92373. TEL 909-793-2853, FAX 909-307-3051, http://www.esri.com/news/arcuser/index.html. Ed. Monica Pratt. Adv. contact Cindy Everett.

005.12 USA ISSN 1530-1362
ASIA PACIFIC SOFTWARE ENGINEERING CONFERENCE. PROCEEDINGS. Cover title: A P S E C. Text in English. 1994. a., latest vol.10, 2003. USD 218 per vol. (effective 2004). **Document type:** *Proceedings, Trade.*
Related titles: Online - full text ed.: (from I E E E).
—BLDSC (1742.261630).
Published by: Institute of Electrical and Electronics Engineers, Inc., 3 Park Ave, 17th Fl, New York, NY 10016-5997. TEL 212-419-7900, 800-678-4333, FAX 212-752-4929, customer.service@ieee.org, http://www.ieee.org.

ASIAN CLASSICS INPUT PROGRAM. see *RELIGIONS AND THEOLOGY—Buddhist*

005.1 USA
ASPECT-ORIENTED SOFTWARE DEVELOPMENT. Variant title: International Conference on Aspect-Oriented Software Development. Proceedings. Text in English. a. **Document type:** *Proceedings, Academic/Scholarly.*
Related titles: Online - full content ed.
Published by: (Aspect-Oriented Software Association), Association for Computing Machinery, Inc., 1515 Broadway, 17th Fl, New York, NY 10036-5701. TEL 212-626-0500, 800-342-6626, FAX 212-869-0481, sigs@acm.org, http://www.acm.org.

ASTROTALK BULLETIN. see *ASTROLOGY*

005.12 USA ISSN 1530-0803
AUSTRALIAN SOFTWARE ENGINEERING CONFERENCE. PROCEEDINGS. Abbreviated title: A S W E C. Text in English. 198?. a. USD 191 per vol. (effective 2004). **Document type:** *Proceedings, Trade.*
Related titles: Online - full text ed.: (from I E E E).
Indexed: Englnd.
—BLDSC (1820.660000).
Published by: Institute of Electrical and Electronics Engineers, Inc., 3 Park Ave, 17th Fl, New York, NY 10016-5997. TEL 212-419-7900, 800-678-4333, FAX 212-752-4929, customer.service@ieee.org, http://www.ieee.org.

005.446 AUS
▼ **AUSTRALIAN WINDOWS XP;** Australia's official monthly magazine. Variant title: Microsoft Windows XP. Text in English. 2004 (Jul.). m. AUD 99.95 (effective 2004). **Document type:** *Magazine, Trade.*
Published by: Derwent Howard, PO Box 1037, Bondi Junction, NSW 1355, Australia. TEL 61-2-93864666, 800-007-820, FAX 61-2-93864288, enquiries@derwenthoward.com.au, http://www.derwenthoward.com.au/. Ed. David Flynn. Adv. contact Gary Angus.

005.5 DEU ISSN 0934-1749
AUTOCAD MAGAZIN; das unabhaengige Magazin der C A - Techniken. Text in German. 1988. 7/yr. EUR 57.40; EUR 45.50 to students; EUR 9.50 newsstand/cover (effective 2004). adv. back issues avail. **Document type:** *Magazine, Trade.* **Description:** For those interested in CAD systems.
—IE, Infotrieve.
Published by: W I N - Verlag GmbH & Co. KG, Johann-Sebastian-Bach Str 5, Vaterstetten, 85591, Germany. TEL 49-8106-3500, FAX 49-8106-350190, info@win-verlag.de, http://www.autocad-magazin.de, http://www.win-verlag.de. Ed. Rainer Trummer. Pub. Hans-J. Grohmann. Adv. contact Sandra Brietzke TEL 49-8106-350230. color page EUR 6,820. Circ: 9,313 (paid and controlled).

005.5 CAN ISSN 1198-0869
AUTOCAD USER. Text in English. 1993. 4/yr. CND 18 domestic; USD 20 in United States; USD 25 elsewhere (effective 2000). adv. **Document type:** *Trade.*
Published by: CAD Communications Inc., 338 4195 Dundas St W, Toronto, ON M8X 1Y4, Canada. TEL 416-236-5856, FAX 416-236-5219. Ed. Ralph Grabowski. Pub., R&P, Adv. contact Arvid Stonkus. B&W page CND 2,600, color page CND 3,400; trim 10.88 x 8.13.

005.5 ESP
AUTODESK NOTICIAS. Text in Spanish. q. adv.
Related titles: Supplement(s): Guia de Soluciones.
Published by: Edimicros, S.L., C/ Seneca, 31 Pral, Barcelona, 08006, Spain. TEL 34-93-368-3800, FAX 34-93-415-2071. Circ: 12,000 (paid).

B I T. (Boletin Informativo de Telecomunicacion) see *COMPUTERS—Microcomputers*

005.5 USA
B V S REVIEWS. (Bruce Von Stiers) Text in English. 1997. m. free. bk.rev. back issues avail. **Description:** Covers software, computer graphics and digital media.
Media: Online - full text.
Address: 939 N E Wabash, Topeka, KS 66616. TEL 785-357-7313, bvonstiers@aol.com, http://members.aol.com/bvonstiers/. Pub. Bruce Von Stiers.

005.1 USA ISSN 1553-1929
BETTER SOFTWARE. Text in English. 9/yr. USD 75 domestic; USD 110 foreign (effective 2005). back issues avail. **Document type:** *Trade.*
Formerly (until 200?): Software Testing & Quality Engineering (1532-3579)
Related titles: Online - full content ed.
Indexed: CompLI.
—BLDSC (1947.111500), IE, ingenta.
Published by: Software Quality Engineering, Inc., 330 Corporate Way, Ste 300, Orange Park, FL 32073. TEL 904-278-0707, 800-423-8378, FAX 904-278-4380, info@stqemagazine.com, http://www.stqemagazine.com. Pub. Jim DeWolf. Adv. contact Lynn MacEwen.

005.5 GBR ISSN 0264-1283
BRITISH MICRO SOFTWARE NEWS. Text in English. 1984. fortn. GBP 135, USD 250. **Document type:** *Newsletter.* **Description:** Lists new software products for the business microcomputer.
Published by: Ferndown Publications, 302 Bramhill Ln S., Bramhill, Stockport, Ches SK7 3DL, United Kingdom. TEL 0161-439-4926. Ed. P Smith.

005.5 GBR ISSN 1356-7551
BUSINESS RATIO PLUS: COMPUTER SOFTWARE HOUSES. Text in English. 1986. a. charts; stat. **Document type:** *Trade.*
Formerly (until 1994): Business Ratio Report. Computer Software Houses (0950-6543)
Published by: The Prospect Shop Ltd., Field House, 72 Oldfield Rd, Hampton, Middx TW12 2HQ, United Kingdom. TEL 44-20-8461-8730, 44-20-8481-8720, FAX 44-20-8783-1940, info@theprospectshop.co.uk.

005.5 GBR
C A D DES. (Computer-Aided Design) Text in English. 1990. m. GBP 30 (effective 1999). back issues avail. **Document type:** *Trade.* **Description:** Covers Auto CAD for managers and other design professionals.
Published by: Electronic Design Automation Ltd., 63-66 Hatton Garden, London, EC1N 8SR, United Kingdom.

C A F M SYSTEM & STRATEGIES (YEAR); a manager's guide to facility management automation. see *COMPUTERS—Data Base Management*

C++ BUILDER DEVELOPER'S JOURNAL. see *COMPUTERS—Computer Programming*

CALL CENTRE FOCUS. see *COMMUNICATIONS—Telephone And Telegraph*

CANADA. STATISTICS CANADA. SOFTWARE DEVELOPMENT AND COMPUTER SERVICE INDUSTRY/CANADA. STATISTIQUE CANADA. INDUSTRIE DE LA PRODUCTION DE LOGICIELS ET DES SERVICES INFORMATIQUES. see *COMPUTERS—Abstracting, Bibliographies, Statistics*

C

CATALOGUE OF SOFTWARE FOR RADIO SPECTRUM MANAGEMENT. see *COMMUNICATIONS*

005.36 GBR ISSN 1355-0659
CD-ROM MAGAZINE. Text in English. 1994. m. GBP 4.99 newsstand/cover. adv. **Document type:** *Consumer.*
Description: Covers various aspects of the business and leisure multimedia market.
Published by: Maverick Magazines, 16-17 Hollybush Row, Oxford, OX1 1JH, United Kingdom. TEL 44-1865-202770, FAX 44-1865-202771. Ed. Guy Sneesby. **Dist. by:** Seymour Distribution Ltd, 86 Newman St, London W1T 3EX, United Kingdom. TEL 44-20-73968000.

005.16 794.8 USA
CD-ROM ONLINE. Text in English. 1995. q. free. adv. software rev. back issues avail. **Document type:** *Newsletter.*
Description: Constitutes a multimedia PC resource, containing reviews of the newest technology.
Published by: CD-ROM Publications, 162 Milbar Blvd, Farmingdale, NY 11735. TEL 516-847-0201, FAX 516-847-0308, editor@nsiweb.com, http://www.nsiweb.com/cdrom. Ed., R&P, Adv. contact Tracy Jacks. Pub. Sanjeev Manucha.

005.5 USA
CD-ROM REVIEW MAGAZINE. Text in English. irreg. free. software rev. back issues avail. **Description:** Includes monthly reviews of the latest CD-ROMs, reader requested reviews, and the top 20 best-seller list.
Media: Online - full text.
Published by: C D - R O M Review Magazine cdrmag@nsiweb.com, http://www.nsiweb.com/cdrom. Ed. Tracy Jacks.

004.56 GBR ISSN 1353-1034
CD-ROM TODAY. Text in English. 1994. m. GBP 4.95 newsstand/cover. adv. **Document type:** *Consumer.*
—CCC.
Published by: Future Publishing Ltd., Beauford Court, 30 Monmouth St, Bath, Avon BA1 2BW, United Kingdom. TEL 44-1225-442244, FAX 44-1225-732285, gill.stevenson@futurenet.co.uk, http://www.futurenet.co.uk, http://www.futurenet.com/futureonline.

CHEMICAL ENGINEERING PROGRESS SOFTWARE DIRECTORY. see *CHEMISTRY—Computer Applications*

371.334 USA ISSN 1555-242X
QA76.76.C54
CHILDREN'S TECHNOLOGY REVIEW. Text in English. 1993. 4/yr. USD 26 domestic; USD 42 in Canada; USD 59 elsewhere (effective 2005). **Document type:** *Consumer.*
Description: Covers software and hardware for parents and teachers of children 3 to 14 years old.
Former titles (until 2005): Children's Software & New Media Revue; (until 2001): Children's Software Revue (1069-9430)
Related titles: Online - full text ed.: ISSN 1555-2470.
Indexed: MRD.
Published by: Active Learning Associates, 120 Main St., Flemington, NJ 08822-1617. TEL 800-993-9499, http://www.childrenssoftware.com. Ed. Warren Buckleitner. R&P, Adv. contact Ellen Wolock. Circ: 4,400 (paid).

005.5 POL ISSN 1427-7301
CHIP SPECIAL. Text in Polish. 1995. 5/yr. PLZ 120 (effective 2005). adv. software rev. back issues avail. **Document type:** *Magazine, Consumer.* **Description:** Every issue is dedicated to one topic and includes CD-ROM with software concerning the overall subject.
Related titles: CD-ROM ed.
Indexed: RefZh.
Published by: Vogel Publishing Sp. z o.o., Plac Czerwony 1-3-5, Wroclaw, 53661, Poland. TEL 48-71-3734475, FAX 48-71-3557361, chip@chip.pl, special@vogel.pl, http://special.chip.pl. Ed. Romuald Gnitecki. Adv. contact Marcin Hutnik. color page PLZ 3,500; 297 x 210.

CHURCH BUSINESS. PRODUCTS & TECHNOLOGY. see *RELIGIONS AND THEOLOGY*

005.1 USA ISSN 1523-9101
QA76.9.W43 CODEN: CDJOAU
COLDFUSION DEVELOPER'S JOURNAL. Variant title: Cold Fusion Developer's Journal. Text in English. 1999. m. USD 89.99 domestic; USD 99.99 in Canada & Mexico; USD 129.99 elsewhere; USD 9.99 newsstand/cover (effective 2005). adv. back issues avail. **Document type:** *Magazine, Trade.*
Description: Provides up-to-the minute information on what is happening in the ColdFusion and web application industries.
Related titles: Online - full text ed.: USD 39.99 (effective 2005) (from Factiva, Gale Group).
Indexed: CompD.
Published by: SYS-CON Media, Inc., 135 Chestnut Ridge Rd, Montvale, NJ 07645. TEL 201-802-3040, 888-303-5282, FAX 201-782-9600, info@sys-con.com, http://cfdj.sys-con.com, http://www.sys-con.com. Ed. Robert Diamond. Adv. contact Robyn Forma. Circ: 30,000 (paid).

006.68 USA
COLOR SLIDES NEWSLETTER. Text in English. 1997. m. free. adv. software rev. back issues avail. **Document type:** *Newsletter.* **Description:** Provides helpful tips and design suggestions for users of presentation graphics programs such as PowerPoint, Corel Presentations, WordPerfect Presentations, and Harvard Graphics.
Media: Online - full text.
Published by: Konold Kreations, 2963 Reynard Rd, Columbus, OH 43232. TEL 614-866-4376, FAX 614-866-4376, george@colorslide.com, http://www.colorslide.com/instruct/newsletr.html. Ed., Pub., R&P George E Konold Jr. Circ: 600.

005.5 USA
COMING TO ORDER. Text in English. 1989. bi-m. USD 55. back issues avail.
Published by: EyeOn Associates, Inc., 660 Fairmont Ave, Westfield, NJ 07090. TEL 908-232-4674. Ed. Lauren Flast. Circ: 1,000.

005.5 USA ISSN 1524-4059
COMPONENT ADVISOR. Text in English. 1999. m. USD 99 domestic; USD 119 in Canada; USD 139 elsewhere (effective 2000). **Document type:** *Trade.* **Description:** Provides practical how-to information on component-based software development and IT management.
Related titles: Online - full text ed.
Published by: Advisor Media, Inc., 4849 Viewridge Ave, San Diego, CA 92123-1643. TEL 858-278-5600, FAX 858-278-0300, subscribe@advisor.com, http://www.advisor.com. Ed. John L Hawkins. Pub. B J Ghiglione. Adv. contact Sheri Ogletree.

COMPUTER-AIDED CIVIL AND INFRASTRUCTURE ENGINEERING. see *ENGINEERING—Computer Applications*

COMPUTER MAGAZINE. see *COMPUTERS—Hardware*

005.5 005.1 RUS
COMPUTER NEWS. Text in Russian. m.
Published by: Vse dlya P.K., Ul Krasnokazarmennaya 17-a, kv 114, Moscow, 111250, Russian Federation. TEL 7-095-3625332. **US dist. addr.:** East View Information Services, 3020 Harbor Ln. N., Minneapolis, MN 55447. TEL 612-550-0961.

COMPUTER PROGRAMMING; il primo mensile di programmazione. see *COMPUTERS—Computer Programming*

005.5 005.1 RUS ISSN 1560-6910
COMPUTER RESELLER NEWS (RUSSIAN EDITION). Text in Russian. 24/yr. RUR 630 (effective 2004). adv. 4 cols./p.; **Document type:** *Newspaper, Trade.*
Related titles: Online - full text ed.
Published by: S K Press, Marksistkaya 34, str 10, Moscow, 109147, Russian Federation. deliver@skpress.ru, http://www.crn.ru, http://www.skpress.ru. Ed. A D Pittman. Pub. E Adlerov. **US dist. addr.:** East View Information Services, 3020 Harbor Ln. N., Minneapolis, MN 55447. TEL 612-550-0961.

006.3 004 MDA ISSN 1561-4042
➤ **COMPUTER SCIENCE JOURNAL OF MOLDOVA.** Text in English. 1993. 3/yr. USD 90; USD 30 per issue (effective 2003). bk.rev.; software rev. charts; illus. 120 p./no.; **Document type:** *Journal, Academic/Scholarly.* **Description:** Covers a number of research topics including software, mathematical linguistics, artificial intelligence, operations research, computer simulation, computer algebra and others. Intended for scientific researchers, undergraduates and post-graduates. The journal looks to gather the main results on Computer Science research in Moldova and abroad.
Indexed: CCMJ, MathR, MathSciNet, RefZh, ZentMath.
—CISTI, Linda Hall.
Published by: Academia de Stiinte a Moldovej, Institutul de Matematica si Informatica, Academiei 5, Chisinau, 2028, Moldova. TEL 373-2-725982, FAX 373-2-738027, csjmol@mat.moldova.su. Ed. Dr. Constantin Gaindric.

005.5 GBR ISSN 1366-3224
COMPUTER SOFTWARE AND SERVICES CD-ROM; a complete overview of the UK IT industry. Variant title: C S S C D. Text in English. 1996. s-a. GBP 575 (effective 2001). **Document type:** *Directory.* **Description:** Provides detailed information on over 10,000 UK IT companies, the services they provide, and 15,000 software products.
Media: CD-ROM.
Published by: Learned Information Europe Ltd. (Subsidiary of: V N U Business Publications Ltd.), Woodside, Hinksey Hill, Oxford, Oxon OX1 5BE, United Kingdom. TEL 44-1865-388100, FAX 44-1865-388056, customerservice@cssonline.co.uk, http://www.cssonline.co.uk.

COMPUTERS, FOODSERVICE & YOU. see *COMPUTERS—Electronic Data Processing*

005.5 CAN ISSN 0319-0161
COMPUTING CANADA. Text in English. 1975. bi-w. CND 80 domestic; USD 115 in United States; USD 155 elsewhere; free to qualified personnel (effective 2005). adv. bk.rev. back issues avail. **Document type:** *Magazine, Consumer.*
Description: Devoted to coverage of information technology in Canada.
Related titles: Microfilm ed.: (from MML); Microform ed.: (from MML); Online - full text ed.: (from bigchalk, EBSCO Publishing, Florida Center for Library Automation, Gale Group, Micromedia ProQuest, Northern Light Technology, Inc., ProQuest Information & Learning).
Indexed: ABIn, CBCABus, CBCARef, CBPI, CPerI, CompC, CompD, LRI, MicrocompInd, PROMT, PSI, SoftBase.
—BLDSC (3395.031000). **CCC.**
Published by: Transcontinental Media, Inc. (Subsidiary of: Transcontinental, Inc.), 25 Sheppard Ave West, Ste 100, Toronto, ON M2N 6S7, Canada. TEL 416-733-7600, FAX 416-218-3544, pmacinnis@itbusiness.ca, info@transcontinental.ca, http://www.itbusiness.ca/index.asp?layid=69, http://www.transcontinental-gtc.com/en/home.html. Circ: 40,000.

005.12 USA ISSN 1093-0175
QA76.758
CONFERENCE ON SOFTWARE ENGINEERING EDUCATION AND TRAINING. PROCEEDINGS. Text in English. 1997. a. USD 174 per vol.; USD 70 per vol. to members (effective 2004). **Document type:** *Proceedings, Trade.*
Related titles: Online - full text ed.: (from I E E E).
—BLDSC (3410.070000).
Published by: Institute of Electrical and Electronics Engineers, Inc., 3 Park Ave, 17th Fl, New York, NY 10016-5997. TEL 212-419-7900, 800-678-4333, FAX 212-752-4929, customer.service@ieee.org, http://www.ieee.org.

005.16 004 USA ISSN 1098-6057
CONSTRUCTION BUSINESS COMPUTING. Text in English. 1998. m. USD 199 (effective 2003). **Document type:** *Trade.*
Description: Reviews new software and hardware, with in-the-field tests by contractors, not techies. Offers solutions to common hardware and software compatibility problems. Includes specific ideas to reduce paperwork, strenghten financial controls, and improve profitability.
—CCC.
Published by: Institute of Management & Administration, Inc., 3 Park Ave, New York, NY 10016-5902. TEL 212-244-0360, FAX 212-564-0465, subserve@ioma.com, http://www.ioma.com.

CONSULTANTS ADVISORY. see *BUSINESS AND ECONOMICS—Management*

CONTROLS INTELLIGENCE & PLANT SYSTEMS REPORT. see *COMPUTERS—Hardware*

005.5 USA
CROSSTALK (HILL AFB); the journal of defense software engineering. Text in English. m.
Related titles: Online - full text ed.: free (effective 2005).
Published by: U.S. Department of Defense, Software Technology Support Center, Ogden ALC-MASE, 7278 Fourth St, Hill AFB, UT 84056-5205. http://www.stsc.hill.af.mil/CrossTalk/2004/04/index.html. Ed. Pamela Bowers.

CYBERLOG; library of applied medical software. see *MEDICAL SCIENCES—Computer Applications*

005.43 USA
D O S WORLD. (Disk Operating System) Text in English. 1991. bi-m. USD 23.70. adv. illus. **Document type:** *Trade.*
Formerly: D O S Resource Guide (1056-7364)
Published by: Connell Communications, Inc. (Subsidiary of: International Data Group), 86 Elm St, Peterborough, NH 03458-1009. Ed. Jeff Detray.

DATA NEWS; l'actualite informatique. see *COMMUNICATIONS—Computer Applications*

DESIGN & ELEKTRONIK. see *COMPUTERS—Hardware*

DEV. DEVELOPING SOFTWARE SOLUTIONS; la rivista che ti insegna a programmare. see *COMPUTERS—Computer Programming*

005.5 TWN ISSN 1022-2901
DI SAN BO/THIRD WAVE MAGAZINE. Text in Chinese. 1982. m. TWD 1,350; TWD 2,950 foreign. adv. **Document type:** *Consumer.* **Description:** Introduces PC software and hardware of all brands.
Published by: Third Wave Publishing Corp., 19-1, Ln 231, Fu-Hsing N. Rd, Taipei, Taiwan. TEL 886-2-7136959, FAX 886-2-7189467. Ed. Corena Lee. Adv. contact Janet Wang. B&W page USD 1,077, color page USD 2,112; trim 260 x 190. Circ: 27,000 (paid).

DIGITAL KIDS. see *COMMUNICATIONS*

005.5 USA ISSN 1077-4394
DIRECTIONS ON MICROSOFT; the independent view of Microsoft technology & strategy. Text in English. 1992. 20/yr. USD 1,390 domestic print & online eds.; USD 1,450 foreign print & online eds. (effective 2004). abstr. index. back issues avail. **Document type:** *Newsletter, Consumer.* **Description:** Provides news and analysis of business and technology issues relating to the Microsoft Corporation.
Formerly: Microsoft Directions
Related titles: Online - full text ed.
—IE.
Published by: Redmond Communications Inc., 15127 N E 24th, Ste 293, Redmond, WA 98052. TEL 206-882-3396, FAX 206-885-0848, directions@redcomm.com, http://www.directionsonmicrosoft.com/. Ed. Robert Horwitz. Pub., R&P Jeff Parker. Circ: 4,000 (paid).

005.13 USA ISSN 1085-3200
DO IT WITH LOTUS 1-2-3 FOR WINDOWS✶. Text in English. 1991. m. looseleaf. USD 69; USD 89 in Canada; USD 99 elsewhere. adv. **Document type:** *Newsletter.* **Description:** Tips and techniques for users of Lotus 1-2-3 software.
Formerly (until 1995): 1-2-3 for Windows Report (1057-2333)
Published by: I D G Newsletter Corporation, PO Box 92880, Rochester, NY 14692. TEL 617-482-8785, 800-807-0771, FAX 617-338-0164, idgcust@pcworld.com, http://idgnews.com. Ed. Richard Cranford. Pub. Craig Pierce. Adv. contact Scott Tharler. Circ: 10,000.

005.5 USA ISSN 1078-795X
DO IT WITH LOTUS SMARTSUITE✶. Text in English. 1994. m. looseleaf. USD 69; USD 89 in Canada; USD 109 elsewhere. adv. **Document type:** *Consumer.* **Description:** Tips and techniques for users of Lotus SmartSuite.
Published by: I D G Newsletter Corporation, PO Box 92880, Rochester, NY 14692. TEL 617-482-8785, 800-807-0771, FAX 617-338-0164, idgcust@pcworld.com, http://idgnews.com. Ed. Valerie Murray. Pub. Craig Pierce. Adv. contact Scott Tharler.

005.5 USA ISSN 1081-7905
DO IT WITH MACINTOSH SYSTEM 7.5✶. Text in English. 1995. m. looseleaf. USD 69; USD 89 in Canada; USD 109 elsewhere. adv. **Document type:** *Consumer.* **Description:** Tips, advice and hands-on guidance on Macintosh System 7.5.
Published by: I D G Newsletter Corporation, PO Box 92880, Rochester, NY 14692. TEL 617-482-8785, 800-807-0771, FAX 617-338-0164, idgcust@pcworld.com, http://idgnews.com. Ed. Scott Fields. Pub. Craig Pierce. Adv. contact Scott Tharler.

005.5 USA ISSN 1080-398X
DO IT WITH MICROSOFT OFFICE✶. Text in English. 1995. m. looseleaf. USD 69; USD 89 in Canada; USD 109 elsewhere. adv. **Document type:** *Consumer.* **Description:** Tips and techniques for Microsoft Office users.
Published by: I D G Newsletter Corporation, PO Box 92880, Rochester, NY 14692. TEL 617-482-8785, 800-807-0771, FAX 617-338-0164, idgcust@pcworld.com, http://idgnews.com. Ed. Jim Pile. Pub. Craig Pierce. Adv. contact Scott Tharler.

005.5 USA ISSN 1078-7968
DO IT WITH MICROSOFT PUBLISHER✶. Text in English. 1994. m. looseleaf. USD 69; USD 89 in Canada; USD 109 elsewhere. adv. **Document type:** *Consumer.* **Description:** Tips and techniques for Microsoft Publisher users.
Published by: I D G Newsletter Corporation, PO Box 92880, Rochester, NY 14692. TEL 617-482-8785, 800-807-0771, FAX 617-338-0164, idgcust@pcworld.com, http://idgnews.com. Ed. Scott Fields. Pub. Craig Pierce. Adv. contact Scott Tharler.

005.5 USA
DO IT WITH WINDOWS 95✶. Text in English. 1995. m. looseleaf. USD 69; USD 89 in Canada; USD 109 elsewhere. adv. **Document type:** *Consumer.*
Published by: I D G Newsletter Corporation, PO Box 92880, Rochester, NY 14692. TEL 617-482-8785, 800-707-8065, FAX 617-338-0164, idgcust@pcworld.com, http://idgnews.com. Ed. Valerie Murray. Pub. Craig Pierce. Adv. contact Scott Tharler.

DOMINO UPDATE. see *COMPUTERS—Computer Networks*

005.5 USA
DOMINOPOWER MAGAZINE; the power magazine for Lotus Notes and Domino users. Text in English. m. adv. back issues avail. **Document type:** *Trade.*
Related titles: Online - full text ed.: ISSN 1554-5687.
Published by: ZATZ Publishing, PO Box 201, Rocky Hill, NJ 08553. TEL 609-497-4501, FAX 609-497-4008, denise@dominopower.com, http://www.dominopower.com. Ed. David Gewirtz. Adv. contact Stephen Amontis.

005.36 USA ISSN 1044-789X
QA76.5 CODEN: DDJOEB
DR. DOBB'S JOURNAL; software tools for the professional programmer. Text in English. 1977. m. USD 25 (effective 2005). adv. bk.rev. charts; illus.; stat. back issues avail.; reprints avail. **Document type:** *Magazine, Trade.* **Description:** Delivers the latest programming languages, algorithms, program listings, operating systems, and more.
Former titles (until 1989): Dr. Dobb's Journal of Software Tools for the Professional Programmer (0888-3076); (until 1985): Dr. Dobb's Journal (8750-0264); (until 1984): Dr. Dobb's Journal for the Experienced in Microcomputing (0748-6987); (until 1984): Dr. Dobb's Journal for Users of Small Computer Systems (0278-6508); (until 1981): Dr. Dobb's Journal of Computer Calisthenics and Orthodontia (0190-1435)
Related titles: CD-ROM ed.; Microform ed.: (from PQC); Online - full text ed.: (from EBSCO Publishing, O C L C Online Computer Library Center, Inc., ProQuest Information & Learning); ♦ Regional ed(s).: Dr. Dobb's Journal Espana.
Indexed: AS&TI, ASCA, C&ISA, CMCI, CompC, CompD, CompI, CompR, E&CAJ, EngInd, IAA, InfoSAb, Inspec, MicrocompInd, PMR, RefZh, SoftBase.
—BLDSC (3606.590000), AskIEEE, CISTI, Ei, IDS, IE, Infotrieve, ingenta, Linda Hall. **CCC.**
Published by: (Markt and Technik Verlag Akiengeselltschaft DEU), C M P Media LLC (Subsidiary of: United News & Media), 600 Harrison St, 6th Fl., San Francisco, CA 94107. TEL 415-947-6746, FAX 415-947-6041, editors@ddj.com, http://www.ddj.com/, http://www.cmp.com. Ed. Jonathan Erickson TEL 650-513-4578. adv.: B&W page USD 12,750, color page USD 14,950. Circ: 117,039 (paid).

005.36 ESP
DR. DOBB'S JOURNAL ESPANA. Text in Spanish. 2002. m. EUR 5.95 newsstand/cover (effective 2002).
Related titles: ♦ Regional ed(s).: Dr. Dobb's Journal. ISSN 1044-789X.
Published by: M K M Publicaciones, Avenida del Generalisimo 14, Boadilla del Monte (Madrid), 28660, Spain. TEL 34-91-6333953, FAX 34-91-6332564, http://www.mkm-pi.com. Circ: 15,000 (controlled).

005.5 USA
DR. EXCEL NEWSLETTER. Text in English. 1999. m. free. adv. **Document type:** *Newsletter.* **Description:** Offers tips, tricks and ideas about Excel.
Media: Online - full text.
Address: drexcel@drexcel.com, http://drexcel.com/.

005.5 USA
DUMMIES DAILY MICROSOFT EXCEL 97 NEWSLETTER. Text in English. 1999. d. **Document type:** *Newsletter.*
Media: Online - full text.
Published by: I D G Books Worldwide, Inc., 919 E. Hillsdale Blvd., Ste. 400, Foster City, CA 94404. david@mkpr.com, http://www.dummiesdaily.com/. Ed. David Hafner.

DUMMIES DAILY QUICKEN NEWSLETTER. see *BUSINESS AND ECONOMICS—Banking And Finance*

005.43 USA
DUMMIES DAILY WINDOWS NEWSLETTER. Text in English. 1999. d. back issues avail. **Document type:** *Newsletter.*
Media: Online - full text.
Published by: I D G Books Worldwide, Inc., 919 E. Hillsdale Blvd., Ste. 400, Foster City, CA 94404. david@mkpr.com, http://www.dummiesdaily.com/. Ed. David Hafner.

E H & S SOFTWARE NEWS. (Environmental, Health and Safety) see *ENVIRONMENTAL STUDIES—Computer Applications*

005.5 USA ISSN 1085-2395
E N T (ONLINE EDITION). Variant title: Enterprise Solutions for Managers of Windows N T. Text in English. 1996. 20/yr. free (effective 2005). **Document type:** *Magazine, Trade.* **Description:** Identifies industry trends as they relate to the Windows NT environment.
Formerly: E N T (Print Edition)
Media: Online - full text (from Factiva, Gale Group). **Related titles:** Supplement(s): 101 Solutions.
Indexed: ABIn, CompD, MicrocompInd, SoftBase.
—IE. **CCC.**
Published by: 101 Communications, Llc., 1300 Virginia Dr, Ste 400, Fort Washington, PA 19034. TEL 215-643-8000, FAX 215-643-3901, http://www.entmag.com. Ed. Scott Bekker. Pub. Mark Durrick. Circ: 80,025. **Subscr. to:** E N T, PO Box 3055, Northbrook, IL 60065-3055. TEL 847-291-5212, FAX 847-564-9002.

005.5 USA
E-PRO MAGAZINE; the magazine for Lotus and websphere professionals. Text in English. 1996. m. free (effective 2003). adv. **Document type:** *Magazine, Trade.* **Description:** Helps IT professionals with a commitment to Lotus technologies select the best tools, make well-informed decisions, and get the highest return on their investment.
Formerly: Group Computing (1521-1282)
Indexed: SoftBase.
Published by: Penton Technology Media (Subsidiary of: Penton Media, Inc.), 221 E 29th St, Ste 242, Loveland, CO 80538. TEL 970-663-4700, 800-621-1544, FAX 970-663-3285, http://www.e-promag.com, http://www.duke.com. Ed. Libby Ingrassia Schwarz. Pub., Adv. contact Wayne Madden. B&W page USD 4,095, color page USD 5,525; trim 8.125 x 10.75.

005.43 DEU
▼ **ECLIPSE MAGAZIN.** Text in German. 2004. q. EUR 34.90; EUR 9.80 newsstand/cover (effective 2005). adv. **Document type:** *Magazine, Trade.*
Published by: Software & Support Verlag GmbH, Kennedyallee 87, Frankfurt am Main, 60596, Germany. TEL 49-69-6300890, FAX 49-69-63008989, redaktion@eclipse-magazin.de, info@software-support.biz, http://www.eclipse-magazin.de, http://www.software-support.biz. Adv. contact Patrik Baumann.

EDUCATIONAL SOFTWARE REVIEW. see *EDUCATION—Computer Applications*

ELECTRONIC EDUCATION REPORT; business intelligence on opportunities in the educational software industry. see *EDUCATION—Computer Applications*

▼ **ELECTRONICS SYSTEMS & SOFTWARE.** see *ELECTRONICS*

005.5 USA ISSN 1534-083X
EMBEDDED LINUX JOURNAL. Abbreviated title: E L J. Text in English. 2001. bi-m. free in North America; USD 27 elsewhere. adv. **Document type:** *Magazine, Trade.* **Description:** Focuses on Linux and other open-source operating systems.
Published by: Specialized Systems Consultants Publishing, Ltd., PO Box 55549, Seattle, WA 98155-0549. eljeditor@ssc.com, http://embedded.linuxjournal.com, http://www.ssc.com. Ed. Don Marti. Pub. Phil Hughes. Adv. contact Carlie Fairchild. Circ: 80,000 (controlled).

005.1 USA ISSN 1382-3256
QA76.758 CODEN: ESENFW
➤ **EMPIRICAL SOFTWARE ENGINEERING**; an international journal. Text in English. 1996. q. EUR 411, USD 411, GBP 257 combined subscription to institutions print & online eds. (effective 2005). adv. reprint service avail. from PSC. **Document type:** *Journal, Academic/Scholarly.* **Description:** Covers the collection and analysis data and experience that can be used to characterize, evaluate and reveal relationships between software engineering artifacts.
Related titles: Online - full text ed.: ISSN 1573-7616 (from EBSCO Publishing, Gale Group, IngentaConnect, Kluwer Online, O C L C Online Computer Library Center, Inc., Ovid Technologies, Inc., Springer LINK, Swets Information Services).
Indexed: BibLing, BrCerAb, C&ISA, CMCI, CerAb, CompAb, CompLI, CorrAb, CurCont, E&CAJ, EMA, EngInd, IAA, Inspec, M&TEA, MBF, METADEX, RefZh, SolStAb, WAA.
—BLDSC (3737.024150), AskIEEE, CISTI, IE, Infotrieve, ingenta, Linda Hall. **CCC.**
Published by: Springer-Verlag New York, Inc. (Subsidiary of: Springer Science+Business Media), 233 Spring St, New York, NY 10013. TEL 212-460-1500, FAX 212-460-1575, service@springer-ny.com, http://springerlink.metapress.com/openurl.asp?genre=journal&issn=1382-3256, http://www.springer-ny.com. Eds. Lionel C Briand, Victor R Basili. **Subscr. to:** Journal Fulfillment, PO Box 2485, Secaucus, NJ 07096-2485. TEL 201-348-4033, FAX 201-348-4505, journals@springer-ny.com.

➤ **ENGINEERING & INDUSTRIAL SOFTWARE DIRECTORY.** see *BUSINESS AND ECONOMICS—Trade And Industrial Directories*

004 RUS ISSN 1606-0229
ENTERPRISE PARTNER. Text in Russian. 1999. s-m. RUR 300 (effective 2004). adv. software rev.; Website rev. **Document type:** *Magazine, Trade.*
Published by: S K Press, Marksistkaya 34, str 10, Moscow, 109147, Russian Federation. deliver@skpress.ru, http://www.skpress.ru. Ed. Kamill Akhmetov. Pub. E Adlerov.

ENTERPRISE SYSTEMS. see *COMPUTERS—Electronic Data Processing*

ENVIRONMENTAL COST ESTIMATING SOFTWARE REPORT. see *ENVIRONMENTAL STUDIES—Computer Applications*

ENVIRONMENTAL MODELLING & SOFTWARE. see *ENVIRONMENTAL STUDIES—Computer Applications*

ENVIRONMENTAL SOFTWARE GUIDE. see *ENVIRONMENTAL STUDIES—Computer Applications*

005.5 USA ISSN 1542-2801
THE ESSENTIAL PC SUPPORT GUIDE FOR WINDOWS XP USERS. Text in English. 2002. a. USD 84.90 per issue domestic; USD 94.90 per issue foreign (effective 2005).
—**CCC.**
Published by: Element K Journals (Subsidiary of: Eli Research, Inc.), 500 Canal View Blvd, Rochester, NY 14623. TEL 585-240-7301, 800-223-8720, 877-203-5248, FAX 585-292-4392, http://www.elementkjournals.com/store/showAncillaryDetail.asp?prodid=52.

005.1 USA ISSN 1089-6503
QA76.9.A73 CODEN: EROMF4
EUROMICRO CONFERENCE. PROCEEDINGS. Text in English. 19??. a. USD 169 per vol.; USD 68 per vol. to members (effective 2004). **Document type:** *Proceedings, Trade.*
Related titles: Online - full text ed.: (from I E E E).
Indexed: EngInd.
—BLDSC (3829.285100).

C

Published by: Institute of Electrical and Electronics Engineers, Inc., 3 Park Ave, 17th Fl, New York, NY 10016-5997. TEL 212-419-7900, 800-678-4333, FAX 212-752-4929, customer.service@ieee.org, http://www.ieee.org.

005.12   USA   ISSN 1534-5351
QA76.76.S64
EUROPEAN CONFERENCE ON SOFTWARE MAINTENANCE AND REENGINEERING. PROCEEDINGS. Text in English. 1999. a. USD 185 per vol.; USD 74 per vol. to members (effective 2004). **Document type:** *Proceedings, Trade.*
Related titles: Online - full text ed.: (from I E E E).
—BLDSC (6843.743300).
Published by: Institute of Electrical and Electronics Engineers, Inc., 3 Park Ave, 17th Fl, New York, NY 10016-5997. TEL 212-419-7900, 800-678-4333, FAX 212-752-4929, customer.service@ieee.org, http://www.ieee.org.

005.5   DEU   ISSN 0946-6800
EXCEL. Text in German. 1994. bi-m. looseleaf. **Document type:** *Trade.*
Published by: W R S Verlag GmbH & Co. KG (Subsidiary of: Rudolf Haufe Verlag GmbH & Co. KG), Fraunhoferstr 5, Planegg, 82152, Germany. info@wrs.de, http://www.wrs.de.

005.34   DEU   ISSN 1617-1624
EXPERT'S INSIDE. ACCESS. Text in German. 2001. m. EUR 72.60; EUR 6.90 newsstand/cover (effective 2003). adv. **Document type:** *Magazine, Trade.*
Published by: redtec publishing GmbH, Gruber Str 46a, Poing, 85586, Germany. TEL 49-8121-951850, FAX 49-8121-951880, info@redtec.de, http://www.experts-inside.de/access, http://www.redtec.de. Adv. contact Guido Klausbruckner. B&W page EUR 1,000, color page EUR 1,500; trim 210 x 297. Circ: 3,000 (paid and controlled).

005.369   DEU   ISSN 1617-1608
EXPERT'S INSIDE. EXCEL. Text in German. 2001. m. EUR 72.60; EUR 6.90 newsstand/cover (effective 2003). adv. **Document type:** *Magazine, Trade.*
Published by: redtec publishing GmbH, Gruber Str 46a, Poing, 85586, Germany. TEL 49-8121-951850, FAX 49-8121-951880, info@redtec.de, http://www.experts-inside.de/excel, http://www.redtec.de. Adv. contact Guido Klausbruckner. B&W page EUR 1,000, color page EUR 1,500; trim 210 x 297.

005.34   DEU   ISSN 1617-1659
EXPERT'S INSIDE. LOTUS NOTES - DOMINO. Text in German. 2001. m. EUR 147; EUR 12.25 newsstand/cover (effective 2003). adv. **Document type:** *Magazine, Trade.*
Published by: redtec publishing GmbH, Gruber Str 46a, Poing, 85586, Germany. TEL 49-8121-951850, FAX 49-8121-951880, info@redtec.de, http://www.experts-inside.de/lotus, http://www.redtec.de. Adv. contact Guido Klausbruckner. B&W page EUR 1,000, color page EUR 1,500; trim 210 x 297.

004.678   DEU   ISSN 1610-1324
EXPERT'S INSIDE. VISUAL BASIC - VB.NET. Text in German. 2001. m. EUR 72.60; EUR 6.90 newsstand/cover (effective 2003). adv. **Document type:** *Magazine, Trade.*
Formerly (until 2001): Expert's Inside. Visual Basic (1617-1691)
Published by: redtec publishing GmbH, Gruber Str 46a, Poing, 85586, Germany. TEL 49-8121-951850, FAX 49-8121-951880, info@redtec.de, http://www.experts-inside.de/visualbasic, http://www.redtec.de. Adv. contact Guido Klausbruckner. B&W page EUR 1,000, color page EUR 1,500; trim 210 x 297.

005.43   DEU   ISSN 1617-1640
EXPERT'S INSIDE. WINDOWS NT/2000. Text in German. 2001. m. EUR 132.60; EUR 11.75 newsstand/cover (effective 2003). adv. **Document type:** *Magazine, Trade.*
Published by: redtec publishing GmbH, Gruber Str 46a, Poing, 85586, Germany. TEL 49-8121-951850, FAX 49-8121-951880, info@redtec.de, http://www.experts-inside.de/windows, http://www.redtec.de. Adv. contact Guido Klausbruckner. B&W page EUR 1,000, color page EUR 1,500; trim 210 x 297.

FAIRPLAY MARINE COMPUTING & INTERNET GUIDE. see *TRANSPORTATION—Ships And Shipping*

005.5   GBR
FINANCIAL SOFTWARE AND SYSTEMS GUIDE. Text in English. 1986. biennial. GBP 85.
Formerly: Software Guide for Accountants
Published by: V N U Business Publications Ltd., 32-34 Broadwick St, London, W1A 2HG, United Kingdom. TEL 44-207-4394242, FAX 44-20-7734-5510. Ed. Ann Maher.

005.5   USA
FINESSE MARKETPLACE JOURNAL. Text in English. 1995. bi-m. free. software rev. **Description:** Includes Mac and Windows tips and tricks.
Media: Online - full text.
Address: webmaster@fingraphics.com, http://www.fingraphics.com. Ed. Leon Fainbuch.

FORBES - ANDREW SEYBOLD'S WIRELESS OUTLOOK; a monthly perspective of issues affecting the mobile computer and communications industries. see *COMPUTERS—Computer Industry*

005   CHE   ISSN 1023-0114
FORUM LOGICIEL. Text in French. 1991. bi-m.
Media: Online - full text. **Related titles:** ♦ English ed.: Methods & Tools. ISSN 1023-4918.
Published by: Martinig & Associates, Rue des Marronniers 25, Vevey, 1800, Switzerland. TEL 41-21-922-1300, FAX 41-21-921-2353, franco@martinig.ch, http://www.martinig.ch. Ed. Franco Martinig.

005.5   USA   ISSN 1066-7261
QA76.9.D3
FOXPRO ADVISOR; the magazine for using microsoft FoxPro. Text in English. 1993. m. USD 99 domestic; USD 119 in Canada; USD 139 elsewhere (effective 2005). adv. back issues avail. **Document type:** *Magazine, Trade.* **Description:** Explains how build database solutions with Microsoft FoxPro. For users of Microsoft FoxPro, ranging from new users to advanced developers.
—IE, Infotrieve.
Published by: Advisor Media, Inc., 4849 Viewridge Ave, San Diego, CA 92123-1643. TEL 858-278-5600, FAX 858-278-0300, advisor@advisor.com, http://foxproadvisor.com, http://www.advisor.com. Ed. John L Hawkins. R&P Patrice Quinn. Circ: 8,000 (paid). **Dist. by:** International Periodical Distributors, 674 Via de la Valle, Ste 204, Solana Beach, CA 92075.

005.5   ITA
FREE SOFTWARE COMPUTER MAGAZINE. Text in Italian. 6/yr.
Address: Via Ferri, 6, Cinisello Balsamo, MI 20092, Italy. TEL 2-66-02-51, FAX 2-612-76-20, TELEX 352376 JCE MIL I. Ed. Marinella Zetti.

005.5   RUS   ISSN 0320-7420
G P N T B ROSSII. ALGORITMY I PROGRAMMY. Text in Russian. m. USD 129.95 in United States.
Indexed: RASB.
—East View.
Published by: Gosudarstvennaya Publichnaya Nauchno-tekhnicheskaya Biblioteka Rossii, Kuznetskii Most 12, Moscow, 103919, Russian Federation. TEL 7-095-2925570, FAX 7-095-921-9862. Ed. A I Zemskov. **US dist. addr.:** East View Information Services, 3020 Harbor Ln. N., Minneapolis, MN 55447. TEL 612-550-0961.

005.5   USA
G U I PROGRAM NEWS. (Graphic User Interface) Text in English. m. USD 150 in North America; USD 165 elsewhere (effective 2001). bk.rev. **Document type:** *Newsletter, Trade.* **Description:** Reports on the popular graphic user interfaces and the growing number of associated applications for microcomputers and workstations.
Related titles: Online - full text ed.
Published by: Worldwide Videotex, PO Box 3273, Boynton Beach, FL 33424-3273. TEL 561-738-2276, markedit@juno.com, http://www.wvpubs.com. Ed., Pub. Mark Wright.

GENETIC PROGRAMMING AND EVOLVABLE MACHINES. see *COMPUTERS—Artificial Intelligence*

005.5   DEU
GO! LINUX; starten - nutzen - tunen. Text in German. m. **Document type:** *Magazine, Consumer.* **Description:** Contains advice and tips on using the Linux operating system.
Published by: W E K A Computerzeitschriften-Verlag GmbH, Gruberstr 46a, Poing, 85586, Germany. TEL 49-8121-951001, FAX 49-8121-951199, golinux@wekanet-team.de, http://www.golinux.de, http://www.wekanet.de. Ed. Ulrich Rohde.

GOVERNMENT WINDOWS N T; the enterprise networking magazine from Government Computer News. see *PUBLIC ADMINISTRATION—Computer Applications*

005.5   USA   ISSN 1544-127X
▼ **GROUPWISE ADVISOR.** Text in English. 2003 (Spr.). q. USD 49 combined subscription domestic print & online; USD 69 combined subscription in Canada print & online; USD 89 combined subscription elsewhere print & online (effective 2003).
Related titles: Online - full text ed.
Published by: Advisor Media, Inc., 4849 Viewridge Ave, San Diego, CA 92123-1643. TEL 858-278-5600, FAX 858-278-0300, http://gwadvisor.com/, http://www.advisor.com. Ed. John L Hawkins. Pub. Jeanne Banfield Hawkins.

005.5   ITA
GUIDA ALLE APPLICAZIONI OS-2 WARP. Text in Italian. 1996. s-a. adv. **Document type:** *Trade.* **Description:** Provides an overview of OS/2 Warp platform products, IBM operative system with special focus on workgroup, network management and the Internet.
Published by: Gruppo Editoriale J C E, Via Patecchio 2, Milan, MI 20141, Italy. TEL 39-02-57316011, FAX 39-02-57316291, info@jce.it, http://www.jce.it. Ed. Fausto Gimondi. Circ: 35,000.

681.3   ITA   ISSN 1592-3487
GUIDA SOFTWARE. Text in Italian. 2001. q. EUR 5.20 newsstand/cover (effective 2003). adv. **Document type:** *Magazine, Consumer.*

Published by: Play Press Publishing s.r.l., Via Vitorchiano 123, Rome, RM 00189, Italy. TEL 39-06-33221250, FAX 39-06-33221235, abbonamenti@playpress.com, http://www.playpress.com. Ed. Diego Magnani. Pub. Alessandro Ferri. Circ: 40,000 (paid and controlled).

HARDCORE A S P.NET. (Application Service Provider) see *COMPUTERS—Internet*

005.1   USA   ISSN 1543-222X
HARDCORE WEB SERVICES. Text in English. 2002. m. **Document type:** *Newsletter, Trade.*
Published by: Pinnacle Publishing, Inc. (Subsidiary of: Lawrence Ragan Communications, Inc.), 316 N. Michigan Ave, Ste 300, Chicago, IL 60601. TEL 312-960-4209, 800-493-4867, FAX 312-960-4106, pinpub@ragan.com, http://www.pinpub.com. Ed. Mike Gunderloy.

HETEROGENEOUS COMPUTING WORKSHOP. PROCEEDINGS. see *COMPUTERS—Computer Architecture*

HONG KONG COMPUTER DIRECTORY (YEAR). see *BUSINESS AND ECONOMICS—Trade And Industrial Directories*

005.5   GBR
HOT ECHO; the journal of the Scottish software community. Text in English. 1997. m. free.
Media: Online - full text.
Published by: (Scottish Enterprise), Editions Publishing, 24 Alva St, Edinburgh, EH2 4QD, United Kingdom. FAX 0131-2262317, comments@hotecho.org, http://www.hotecho.org/index.html.

005.5   MYS   ISSN 0116-6964
I C L A R M SOFTWARE. Text in English. 1987. irreg.
Indexed: ASFA, ESPM.
Published by: WorldFish Center, PO Box 500 GPO, Penang, 10670, Malaysia. TEL 60-4-641-4623, FAX 60-4-643-4463, http://www.cgiar.org/iclarm/.

I D I I SOFTWARE NEWSLETTER. see *BUSINESS AND ECONOMICS—Production Of Goods And Services*

005.5   USA   ISSN 1078-8093
I D U G SOLUTIONS JOURNAL; for users of DB2 technology. Text in English. 1994. q. USD 3.95 newsstand/cover. adv. illus. **Document type:** *Journal, Trade.*
Published by: (International DB2 Users Group), Design Liberte, 5048 W Coyle Ave, Skokie, IL 60077. TEL 847-677-9326. Eds. Doug Stacey, Michael Cotignola. Pub. Linda Pearlstein. Adv. contact Shawn Rogers. Circ: 30,000.

005.1   USA   ISSN 1530-2059
TA168
I E E E HIGH - ASSURANCE SYSTEMS ENGINEERING SYMPOSIUM. Text in English. 1998. a. USD 150 per vol.; USD 60 per vol. to members (effective 2004). **Document type:** *Proceedings, Trade.*
Related titles: Online - full text ed.: (from I E E E).
—BLDSC (4540.722180). **CCC.**
Published by: Institute of Electrical and Electronics Engineers, Inc., 3 Park Ave, 17th Fl, New York, NY 10016-5997. TEL 212-419-7900, 800-678-4333, FAX 212-752-4929, customer.service@ieee.org, http://www.ieee.org.

I E E E INTELLIGENT SYSTEMS; putting A I into practice. see *COMPUTERS—Computer Engineering*

005.1   USA   ISSN 0730-3157
QA76.6
I E E E INTERNATIONAL COMPUTER SOFTWARE AND APPLICATIONS CONFERENCE. PROCEEDINGS. Abbreviated title: I E E E - C O M P S A C. Text in English. 1977. a. USD 256 per vol.; USD 106 per vol. to members (effective 2004). **Document type:** *Proceedings, Trade.* **Description:** Provides papers primarily dealing with software engineering and developmental themes, along with major applications areas.
Related titles: Online - full text ed.: (from I E E E).
—BLDSC (3368.300000), IE, ingenta. **CCC.**
Published by: Institute of Electrical and Electronics Engineers, Inc., 3 Park Ave, 17th Fl, New York, NY 10016-5997. TEL 212-419-7900, 800-678-4333, FAX 212-752-4929, customer.service@ieee.org, http://www.ieee.org.

005.1   USA   ISSN 1530-1346
QA75.5
I E E E INTERNATIONAL SYMPOSIUM ON COMPUTERS AND COMMUNICATIONS. Text in English. 1995. a. USD 151 membership (effective 2005). **Document type:** *Proceedings, Trade.*
Related titles: Online - full text ed.: (from I E E E).
—BLDSC (4363.086350). **CCC.**
Published by: Institute of Electrical and Electronics Engineers, Inc., 3 Park Ave, 17th Fl, New York, NY 10016-5997. TEL 212-419-7900, 800-678-4333, FAX 212-752-4929, customer.service@ieee.org, http://www.ieee.org.

I E E E INTERNATIONAL WORKSHOP ON HARDWARE - SOFTWARE CODESIGN. see *COMPUTERS—Hardware*

005.5 USA ISSN 0740-7459
CODEN: IESOEG
➤ **I E E E SOFTWARE.** Text in English. 1984. bi-m. USD 77 (effective 2006). adv. bk.rev. illus.; tr.lit. reprints avail. **Document type:** *Journal, Academic/Scholarly.* **Description:** Covers programming, methodology, software project management, programming environment, hardware and software monitoring, and programming tools.
Related titles: CD-ROM ed.; Microfiche ed.; Microfilm ed.; Online - full text ed.: (from EBSCO Publishing, I E E E).
Indexed: AHCI, AS&TI, ASCA, B&BAb, BMT, C&CSA, CMCI, CompAb, CompC, CompD, CompLI, CurCont, CybAb, EngInd, ErgAb, ISR, Inspec, ORMS, QC&AS, RASB, RefZh, SCI, SSCI, SoftBase.
—BLDSC (4363.066560), AskIEEE, CISTI, Ei, IDS, IE, Infotrieve, ingenta, Linda Hall. **CCC.**
Published by: Institute of Electrical and Electronics Engineers, Inc., 445 Hoes Ln, Piscataway, NJ 08854-1331. TEL 732-981-0060, 800-701-4333, FAX 732-981-1721, software@computer.org, subscription-service@ieee.org, http://www.computer.org/software, http://www.ieee.org. Circ: 23,000 (controlled and free). **Subscr. to:** Maruzen Co., Ltd., 3-10 Nihonbashi 2-chome, Chuo-ku, Tokyo 103-0027, Japan. FAX 81-3-3275-0657; Universal Subscription Agency, Pvt. Ltd., 877, Udyog Vihar, V, Gurgoan 122001, India. TEL 91-124-347261, FAX 91-124-342496. **Co-sponsor:** Computer Society.

005.1 USA ISSN 0098-5589
QA76.6 CODEN: IESEDJ
➤ **I E E E TRANSACTIONS ON SOFTWARE ENGINEERING.** Text in English. 1975. m. USD 1,350 (effective 2006). **Document type:** *Journal, Academic/Scholarly.* **Description:** Details specification, development, management, test, maintenance and documentation of computer programs.
Related titles: CD-ROM ed.; Microfiche ed.; Online - full text ed.: (from EBSCO Publishing, I E E E).
Indexed: ABIn, AIA, AS&TI, ASCA, BMT, C&CSA, C&ISA, CADCAM, CIS, CMCI, CompAb, CompC, CompD, CompLI, CompR, CurCont, CybAb, E&CAJ, EngInd, IAA, ISMEC, ISR, Inspec, MathR, ORMS, QC&AS, RefZh, SCI, SolStAb, TelAb, ZentMath.
—BLDSC (4363.220500), AskIEEE, CISTI, Ei, IDS, IE, Infotrieve, ingenta, Linda Hall. **CCC.**
Published by: Institute of Electrical and Electronics Engineers, Inc., 445 Hoes Ln, Piscataway, NJ 08854-1331. TEL 732-981-0060, 800-701-4333, FAX 732-981-1721, subscription-service@ieee.org, http://www.computer.org/tse, http://www.ieee.org. Ed. Richard A Kemmerer. Circ: 11,000 (paid). **Subscr. to:** Maruzen Co., Ltd., 3-10 Nihonbashi 2-chome, Chuo-ku, Tokyo 103-0027, Japan. FAX 81-3-3275-0657; Universal Subscription Agency, Pvt. Ltd., 877, Udyog Vihar, V, Gurgoan 122001, India. TEL 91-124-347261, FAX 91-124-342496. **Co-sponsor:** Computer Society.

005.1 USA
I E E E WORKSHOP ON APPLICATION - SPECIFIC SOFTWARE ENGINEERING AND TECHNOLOGY. Text in English. a. USD 105. **Document type:** *Proceedings, Trade.*
Published by: Institute of Electrical and Electronics Engineers, Inc., 3 Park Ave, 17th Fl, New York, NY 10016-5997. TEL 800-678-4333, customer.service@ieee.org, http://www.ieee.org.

I E E PROCEEDINGS - COMPUTERS AND DIGITAL TECHNIQUES. see *COMPUTERS—Hardware*

005.36 GBR ISSN 1462-5970
QA76.758
I E E PROCEEDINGS - SOFTWARE. Text in English. 1981. bi-m. USD 1,045 in the Americas print or online; GBP 615 elsewhere print or online; USD 1,254 combined subscription in the Americas print & online; GBP 738 combined subscription elsewhere print & online; USD 174 per issue in the Americas; GBP 103 per issue elsewhere (effective 2005). **Document type:** *Proceedings, Academic/Scholarly.* **Description:** Covers all aspects of the software cycle, including design, development, implementation and maintenance.
Former titles (until 1997): I E E Proceedings - Software Engineering (1364-5080); (until 1996): Software Engineering Journal (0268-6961); Which incorporated: Software and Microsystems (0261-3182)
Related titles: Online - full text ed.: ISSN 1463-9831 (from EBSCO Publishing).
Indexed: AHCI, ASCA, BrTechI, C&CSA, C&ISA, CADCAM, CIS, CMCI, CompAb, CompC, CompLI, CurCont, E&CAJ, EngInd, ICEA, Inspec, PAA&I, RefZh, SolStAb.
—BLDSC (4362.755590), AskIEEE, CISTI, Ei, IDS, IE, Infotrieve, ingenta, Linda Hall. **CCC.**
Published by: Institution of Electrical Engineers, Michael Faraday House, Six Hills Way, Stevenage, Herts SG1 2AY, United Kingdom. TEL 44-1438-313311, FAX 44-1438-313465, inspec@iee.org, http://www.iee.org/Publish/Journals/Profjourn/Proc/sen/. Ed. Judith Bishop. R&P Michael McCabe TEL 732-321-5575. **Subscr. in the US to:** INSPEC/I E E, 379 Thornall St., Edison, NJ 08837. TEL 732-321-5575, FAX 732-321-5702; **Subscr. to:** INSPEC, I E E, Publication Sales Dept., PO Box 96, Stevenage, Herts SG1 2SD, United Kingdom. TEL 44-1438-313311, FAX 44-1438-742840. **Co-sponsor:** British Computer Society.

005.1 GBR ISSN 0269-3062
CODEN: ISESEM
I E E SOFTWARE ENGINEERING SERIES. (Institution of Electrical Engineers) Text in English. 1985. irreg. **Document type:** *Monographic series.*
Indexed: Inspec.
—CCC.
Published by: Institution of Electrical Engineers, Michael Faraday House, Six Hills Way, Stevenage, Herts SG1 2AY, United Kingdom. TEL 44-1438-313311, FAX 44-1438-313465, inspec@iee.org, http://www.iee.org/.

I T A A MEMBERSHIP DIRECTORY. see *COMPUTERS—Electronic Data Processing*

005.5 USA
I T A A NEW PRODUCTS AND SERVICES GUIDE. Text in English. 3/yr. **Description:** Highlights new and established software products, computer services and business support services for high technology companies.
Published by: Information Technology Association of America, 1401 Wilson Blvd., Ste. 1100, Arlington, VA 22209-2318. TEL 703-522-5055, FAX 703-525-2279.

005.5 USA
I T A A SOFTWARE INDUSTRY REPORTS. Text in English. irreg. price varies.
Published by: Information Technology Association of America, 1401 Wilson Blvd., Ste. 1100, Arlington, VA 22209-2318. TEL 703-522-5055, FAX 703-525-2279.

005.5 USA
I T A A TECHNICAL INFORMATION SERIES. Text in English. irreg.
Formerly: A D A S P O Technology Papers
Published by: Information Technology Association of America, 1401 Wilson Blvd., Ste. 1100, Arlington, VA 22209-2318. TEL 703-522-5055, FAX 703-525-2279.

005.5 USA
THE ICON ANALYST. Text in English. 1990. bi-m. USD 25; USD 35 foreign. index. back issues avail. **Document type:** *Academic/Scholarly.* **Description:** Covers the Icon programming language, along with techniques and implementation. Aimed at high-level computer programmers.
Published by: Icon Project, Department of Computer Science, University of Arizona, Tucson, AZ 85721. TEL 602-621-6609, FAX 602-621-4426. Ed. Madget Griswold. Circ: 160 (paid).

005.5 NLD ISSN 0950-5849
HF5548.2 CODEN: ISOTE7
➤ **INFORMATION AND SOFTWARE TECHNOLOGY.** Text in English. 1959. 12/yr. EUR 878 in Europe to institutions; JPY 116,500 in Japan to institutions; USD 983 elsewhere to institutions (effective 2006). adv. bk.rev. abstr.; illus. index. back issues avail.; reprint service avail. from PQC. **Document type:** *Journal, Academic/Scholarly.* **Description:** Bridges the gap between software theory and application. Covers research, developments and implementation, and information systems management.
Formerly: Data Processing (0011-684X)
Related titles: Microform ed.: (from PQC); Online - full text ed.: (from EBSCO Publishing, Gale Group, IngentaConnect, ScienceDirect, Swets Information Services).
Indexed: ABIn, ADPA, AHCI, AIA, AS&TI, ASCA, BMT, C&ISA, CMCI, CompAb, CompC, CompD, CompLI, CurCont, E&CAJ, EngInd, ErgAb, ICEA, Inspec, LISA, M&MA, PROMT, RefZh, SSCI, SoftAbEng, SolStAb, TelAb.
—BLDSC (4481.865000), AskIEEE, CISTI, Ei, IDS, IE, Infotrieve, ingenta, Linda Hall. **CCC.**
Published by: Elsevier BV (Subsidiary of: Elsevier Science & Technology), Radarweg 29, Amsterdam, 1043 NX, Netherlands. TEL 31-20-4853911, FAX 31-20-4852457, nlinfo-f@elsevier.nl, http://www.elsevier.com/locate/infsof, http://www.elsevier.nl. Eds. C. Wohlin, M Shepperd, S. Elbaum.

005.5 NLD ISSN 1386-3681
INFORMATION SYSTEMS. Text in English. 1948. irreg. price varies. abstr. **Document type:** *Journal, Academic/Scholarly.*
Supersedes in part (in Feb. 1997): Centrum voor Wiskunde in Informatica. Department of Computer Science. Report (0169-118X); Which was formerly (until 1984): Stichting Mathematisch Centrum. Afdeling Informatica. Rapport (0376-4028); (until 1973): Stichting Mathematisch Centrum. Rekenafdeling. Rapport (0517-6417)
Indexed: RefZh.
—BLDSC (7259.125000), CISTI.
Published by: (Stichting Mathematisch Centrum), Centrum voor Wiskunde en Informatica, Department of Computer Science/National Research Institute for Mathematics and Computer Science (Subsidiary of: Stichting Mathematisch Centrum), PO Box 94079, Amsterdam, 1090 GB, Netherlands. TEL 31-20-592-4128, FAX 31-20-592-4199, tamende@cwi.nl, http://www.cwi.nl.

005.1 GBR ISSN 1614-5046
▼ ➤ **INNOVATIONS IN SYSTEMS AND SOFTWARE ENGINEERING.** Text in English. 2005. 2/yr. EUR 198 (effective 2005). **Document type:** *Journal, Academic/Scholarly.*
Related titles: Online - full text ed.: ISSN 1614-5054.
Published by: Springer-Verlag London Ltd. (Subsidiary of: Springer Science+Business Media), Ashbourne House, The Guildway, Old Portsmouth Rd, Guildford, Surrey GU7 3DJ, United Kingdom. TEL 44-1483-734433, FAX 44-1483-734411, postmaster@svl.co.uk, http://www.springer.co.uk.

005.5 USA ISSN 1533-9009
INSIDE ADOBE INDESIGN. Text in English. 2001. m. USD 117; USD 147 combined subscription print & online eds. (effective 2005). **Document type:** *Magazine, Consumer.*
Related titles: Online - full text ed.: ISSN 1539-0241.
—CCC.
Published by: Element K Journals (Subsidiary of: Eli Research, Inc.), 500 Canal View Blvd, Rochester, NY 14623. TEL 585-240-7301, 800-223-8720, 877-203-5248, FAX 585-292-4392, http://www.elementkjournals.com/products/showProduct.asp?prodID=215&catId=3. Eds. Renee Dustman, Michelle Rogers.

005.5 USA ISSN 1071-0728
T385
INSIDE AUTO C A D; tips & techniques for users of AutoCAD. (Computer Aided Design) Text in English. 1993. m. USD 107; USD 137 print & online eds. (effective 2005). adv. back issues avail. **Document type:** *Magazine, Consumer.* **Description:** Offers fresh ideas, shortcuts, and advice from experts who explore every aspect of AutoCAD.
Related titles: Online - full text ed.: (from ProQuest Information & Learning).
—CCC.
Published by: Element K Journals (Subsidiary of: Eli Research, Inc.), 500 Canal View Blvd, Rochester, NY 14623. TEL 585-240-7301, 800-223-8720, 877-203-5248, FAX 585-292-4392, http://www.elementkjournals.com/products/showProduct.asp?prodID=21&catId=3. Ed. Michelle Rogers.

C

005.52 USA ISSN 1526-9477
INSIDE COREL WORDPERFECT SUITE. Text in English. 1996. m. USD 107; USD 137 combined subscription print & online eds. (effective 2005). **Description:** Offers fresh ideas, shortcuts, and advice from computer experts who explore every aspect of WordPerfect Suite.
Formerly (until 1999): Inside Corel WordPerfect Suite 7 (1090-0470)
Related titles: Online - full text ed.: ISSN 1539-0314. USD 137 domestic; USD 147 foreign (effective 2005).
—CCC.
Published by: Element K Journals (Subsidiary of: Eli Research, Inc.), 500 Canal View Blvd, Rochester, NY 14623. TEL 585-240-7301, 800-223-8720, 877-203-5248, FAX 585-292-4392, http://www.elementkjournals.com/premier/journal_archive.asp?vwJournalID=CW7. Eds. Christine Spencer, Michelle Rogers.

005.5 USA ISSN 1067-8204
QA76.9.D3
INSIDE MICROSOFT ACCESS. Text in English. 1993. m. USD 117 domestic; USD 127 foreign; USD 147 combined subscription print & online eds. (effective 2005). adv. back issues avail. **Document type:** *Magazine, Consumer.*
Related titles: Online - full text ed.: ISSN 1539-0446. USD 147 domestic; USD 157 foreign (effective 2005) (from ProQuest Information & Learning).
—CCC.
Published by: Element K Journals (Subsidiary of: Eli Research, Inc.), 500 Canal View Blvd, Rochester, NY 14623. TEL 585-240-7301, 800-223-8720, 877-203-5248, FAX 585-292-4392, http://www.elementkjournals.com/products/showProduct.asp?prodID=19&catId=1. Eds. Sean Kavanagh, Michelle Rogers.

005.5 USA ISSN 1075-1580
HF5548.4.M523
INSIDE MICROSOFT EXCEL. Text in English. 1994. m. USD 117 domestic; USD 127 foreign; USD 147 combined subscription print & online eds. (effective 2005). **Document type:** *Magazine, Consumer.* **Description:** Contains tips, shortcuts and techniques for using Microsoft Excel.
Related titles: Online - full text ed.: USD 147 domestic; USD 157 foreign (effective 2005) (from ProQuest Information & Learning).
—IE. **CCC.**
Published by: Element K Journals (Subsidiary of: Eli Research, Inc.), 500 Canal View Blvd, Rochester, NY 14623. TEL 585-240-7301, 800-223-8720, 877-203-5248, FAX 585-292-4392, http://www.elementkjournals.com/products/showProduct.asp?prodID=24&catId=1.

INSIDE MICROSOFT OFFICE. see *COMPUTERS—Computer Programming*

005.5 USA ISSN 1546-7007
▼ **INSIDE MICROSOFT OUTLOOK.** Text in English. 2004 (Mar.). m. USD 107 domestic; USD 117 foreign; USD 137 combined subscription print & online eds. (effective 2005). **Document type:** *Magazine, Consumer.*
Related titles: Online - full text ed.: USD 137 domestic; USD 147 foreign (effective 2005).

Published by: Element K Journals (Subsidiary of: Eli Research, Inc.), 500 Canal View Blvd, Rochester, NY 14623. TEL 585-240-7301, 800-223-8720, 877-203-5248, FAX 585-292-4392, http://www.elementkjournals.com/products/showProduct.asp?prodID=188&catId=1. Ed. Michelle Rogers.

005.5   USA   ISSN 1076-8106
T385
INSIDE MICROSOFT POWERPOINT. Text in English. 1994. m. USD 117; USD 147 combined subscription print & online eds. (effective 2005). **Description:** Contains tips, shortcuts and techniques for Microsoft PowerPoint.
Related titles: Online - full text ed.: USD 147 domestic; USD 157 foreign (effective 2005) (from ProQuest Information & Learning).
—IE. CCC.
Published by: Element K Journals (Subsidiary of: Eli Research, Inc.), 500 Canal View Blvd, Rochester, NY 14623. TEL 585-240-7301, 800-223-8720, 877-203-5248, FAX 585-292-4392, http://www.elementkjournals.com/products/showProduct.asp?prodID=23&catId=1.

005.43   USA   ISSN 1051-9734
QA76.76.O63
INSIDE MICROSOFT WINDOWS. Text in English. 1990. m. USD 107; USD 137 combined subscription print & online eds. (effective 2005). **Document type:** *Magazine, Consumer.* **Description:** Contains tips and techniques aimed exclusively to users of Windows.
Related titles: Online - full text ed.: (from ProQuest Information & Learning).
—CCC.
Published by: Element K Journals (Subsidiary of: Eli Research, Inc.), 500 Canal View Blvd, Rochester, NY 14623. TEL 585-240-7301, 800-223-8720, 877-203-5248, FAX 585-292-4392, http://www.elementkjournals.com. Ed. Curt Havlin.

005.43   GBR   ISSN 0966-968X
INSIDE MICROSOFT WINDOWS; tips and tricks for Microsoft Windows. Text in English. 1992. m. GBP 39; GBP 42 in the European Union; GBP 45 elsewhere. illus. **Document type:** *Newsletter.* **Description:** Informs users how to best employ and operate Microsoft Windows; offers time-saving tips.
—IE.
Published by: Cobb Group U K, Cottons Centre, Hay's Ln, London, SE1 2QT, United Kingdom. TEL 0171-378-6800, FAX 0171-378-8779. Ed. Elisa Williams. **Subscr. to:** Tower House, Tower House, Sovereign Park, Market Harborough, Leics LE16 9EF, United Kingdom. TEL 0158-468888, FAX 0158-434958.

005.43   USA   ISSN 1532-1207
INSIDE MICROSOFT WINDOWS 2000. Text in English. 2000. m. USD 207; USD 237 combined subscription print & online eds. (effective 2005). **Document type:** *Magazine, Consumer.*
Related titles: Online - full text ed.: ISSN 1539-0276. USD 237 domestic; USD 247 foreign (effective 2005).
—IE. CCC.
Published by: Element K Journals (Subsidiary of: Eli Research, Inc.), 500 Canal View Blvd, Rochester, NY 14623. TEL 585-240-7301, 800-223-8720, 877-203-5248, FAX 585-292-4392, http://www.elementkjournals.com/products/showProduct.asp?prodID=9&catId=2. Eds. Rozanne Whalen, Michelle Rogers.

005.5   USA   ISSN 1543-0812
▼ **INSIDE MICROSOFT WINDOWS X P.** Text in English. 2003. m. USD 127 domestic; USD 137 foreign; USD 157 combined subscription print & online eds. (effective 2005). **Document type:** *Magazine, Consumer.*
Related titles: Online - full content ed.: USD 157 domestic; USD 167 foreign (effective 2005).
—CCC.
Published by: Element K Journals (Subsidiary of: Eli Research, Inc.), 500 Canal View Blvd, Rochester, NY 14623. TEL 585-240-7301, 800-223-8720, 877-203-5248, FAX 585-292-4392, http://www.elementkjournals.com/products/showProduct.asp?prodID=13&catId=2.

005.52   USA   ISSN 1090-476X
Z52.5.M52
INSIDE MICROSOFT WORD. Text in English. m. USD 107 domestic; USD 117 foreign; USD 137 combined subscription print & online eds. (effective 2005). **Document type:** *Magazine, Consumer.* **Description:** Contains tips, shortcuts, and techniques for Microsoft Word users.
Related titles: Online - full text ed.: ISSN 1539-0470. USD 137 domestic; USD 147 foreign (effective 2005) (from ProQuest Information & Learning).
—IE. CCC.
Published by: Element K Journals (Subsidiary of: Eli Research, Inc.), 500 Canal View Blvd, Rochester, NY 14623. TEL 585-240-7301, 800-223-8720, 877-203-5248, FAX 585-292-4392, http://www.elementkjournals.com/products/showProduct.asp?prodID=22&catId=1. Eds. T. L. Aardsma, Michelle Rogers.

005.1   USA   ISSN 1071-8168
INSIDE NATURAL. Text in English. 1991. q. USD 95 in US & Canada; USD 110 elsewhere (effective 2003).
—IE, Infotrieve.

Published by: S L Robinson & Associates, 28 Teal Dr, Langhorne, PA 19047. TEL 215-741-0820, FAX 215-741-1351, slrinc@aol.com, http://members.aol.com slrinc. Ed. Steve Robinson.

686.22544416   USA   ISSN 1083-1754
Z286.D47
INSIDE PAGEMAKER. Text in English. 1995. m. USD 117; USD 147 combined subscription print & online eds. (effective 2005). **Description:** Contains tips, shortcuts and techniques for Adobe PageMaker users.
Related titles: Online - full text ed.: (from ProQuest Information & Learning).
—CCC.
Published by: Element K Journals (Subsidiary of: Eli Research, Inc.), 500 Canal View Blvd, Rochester, NY 14623. TEL 585-240-7301, 800-223-8720, 877-203-5248, FAX 585-292-4392, http://www.elementkjournals.com/products/showProduct.asp?prodID=27&catId=3.

686.22544416   USA   ISSN 1097-5772
Z253.532.Q37
INSIDE QUARKXPRESS. Text in English. m. USD 137 domestic; USD 147 foreign; USD 167 combined subscription print & online eds. (effective 2005). **Document type:** *Magazine, Consumer.* **Description:** Contains tips, shortcuts and techniques for QuarkXPress users.
Related titles: Online - full text ed.: ISSN 1539-0365.
Published by: Element K Journals (Subsidiary of: Eli Research, Inc.), 500 Canal View Blvd, Rochester, NY 14623. TEL 585-240-7301, 800-223-8720, 877-203-5248, FAX 585-292-4392, http://www.elementkjournals.com/products/showProduct.asp?prodID=34&catId=3. Eds. Renee Dustman, Michelle Rogers.

005.36   USA
INTEL OWNER'S CLUB. Text in English. bi-m. back issues avail. **Document type:** *Newsletter.* **Description:** Includes the latest Intel technologies, tips on how to get the most from your system, free downloadable demos of hot new applications, etc.
Related titles: E-mail ed.
Published by: Intel Corporation, 2200 Mission College Blvd, Santa Clara, CA 95052-8119. TEL 800-628-8686, FAX 408-765-9904, http://www.intel.com/home/club/newsltr.htm.

005.5   USA
INTERACTION (SAN FRANCISCO). Text in English. 1994. q. free. **Document type:** *Trade.*
Published by: (Sierra On-Line), I D G Communications Inc., 501 Second St, Ste 600, San Francisco, CA 94107-4133. TEL 415-281-8650, FAX 415-281-3915.

005.5   USA
INTERACTIVE MAGAZINE. Text in English. m. **Description:** Provides software for evaluation and guest columns views on Java integration.
Media: Online - full text.
Published by: S A S Institute, Inc., 100 SAS Campus Dr, Cary, NC 27513-2414. TEL 919-677-8000, FAX 919-677-4444, links@sas.com, http://www.sas.com/software/sas/com/interactive/current/noshock/index.html.

005.1   USA   ISSN 1087-2191
INTERNATIONAL COMPUTER PERFORMANCE AND DEPENDABILITY SYMPOSIUM. Text in English. 1995. a. USD 151 membership (effective 2005). **Document type:** *Proceedings, Trade.*
Related titles: Online - full text ed.: (from I E E E).
Indexed: EngInd.
—BLDSC (4362.940700). CCC.
Published by: Institute of Electrical and Electronics Engineers, Inc., 3 Park Ave, 17th Fl, New York, NY 10016-5997. TEL 800-678-4333, customer.service@ieee.org, http://www.ieee.org.

005.1   USA   ISSN 1527-1366
QA76.758
INTERNATIONAL CONFERENCE ON AUTOMATED SOFTWARE ENGINEERING. PROCEEDINGS. Variant title: I E E E International Automated Software Engineering Conference. Text in English. a. USD 194; USD 78 to members (effective 2004). **Document type:** *Proceedings, Trade.*
Related titles: Online - full text ed.: (from I E E E).
—BLDSC (4362.943800).
Published by: Institute of Electrical and Electronics Engineers, Inc., 3 Park Ave, 17th Fl, New York, NY 10016-5997. TEL 212-419-7900, 800-678-4333, FAX 212-752-4929, customer.service@ieee.org, http://www.ieee.org.

005.1 003   USA
INTERNATIONAL CONFERENCE ON ENGINEERING OF COMPLEX COMPUTER SYSTEMS. PROCEEDINGS. Text in English. irreg., latest vol.8, 2002. USD 150 per vol.; USD 60 per vol. to members (effective 2004). **Document type:** *Proceedings, Trade.*
—BLDSC (4362.949000).
Published by: Institute of Electrical and Electronics Engineers, Inc., 3 Park Ave, 17th Fl, New York, NY 10016-5997. TEL 212-419-7900, 800-678-4333, FAX 212-752-4929, customer.service@ieee.org, http://www.ieee.org.

INTERNATIONAL CONFERENCE ON HIGH - PERFORMANCE COMPUTER ARCHITECTURE. PROCEEDINGS. see *COMPUTERS—Computer Architecture*

005.1 568.568   USA   ISSN 1551-6393
QA76.9.D3
INTERNATIONAL CONFERENCE ON SCIENTIFIC AND STATISTICAL DATABASE MANAGEMENT. PROCEEDINGS. Text in English. 1996. a. USD 194; USD 78 to members (effective 2004). **Document type:** *Proceedings, Trade.*
Formerly (until 2003): International Conference on Scientific and Statistical Database Systems. Proceedings (1099-3371)
Related titles: Online - full text ed.: (from I E E E).
Indexed: EngInd.
—BLDSC (4538.874870).
Published by: Institute of Electrical and Electronics Engineers, Inc., 3 Park Ave, 17th Fl, New York, NY 10016-5997. TEL 212-419-7900, 800-678-4333, FAX 212-752-4929, customer.service@ieee.org, http://www.ieee.org.

005.12   USA   ISSN 1523-4479
INTERNATIONAL CONFERENCE ON SOFTWARE ENGINEERING: EDUCATION AND PRACTICE. PROCEEDINGS. Text in English. a. price varies. **Document type:** *Proceedings, Trade.*
Published by: Institute of Electrical and Electronics Engineers, Inc., 3 Park Ave, 17th Fl, New York, NY 10016-5997. TEL 212-419-7900, 800-678-4333, FAX 212-752-4929, customer.service@ieee.org, http://www.ieee.org.

005.1   USA   ISSN 0270-5257
QA76.6   CODEN: PCSEDE
INTERNATIONAL CONFERENCE ON SOFTWARE ENGINEERING. PROCEEDINGS. Text in English. 1975. a. price varies. adv. **Document type:** *Proceedings, Academic/Scholarly.* **Description:** Covers advances in the software and hardware of methodological and linguistic tools.
Formerly: National Conference on Software Engineering. Proceedings
Related titles: Online - full text ed.: (from Association for Computing Machinery, Inc., I E E E).
Indexed: EngInd.
—BLDSC (4538.883800), Ei, IE, ingenta. CCC.
Published by: I E E E Computer Society, 10662 Los Vaqueros Circle, PO Box 3014, Los Alamitos, CA 90720-1314. TEL 714-821-8380, 800-272-6657, FAX 714-821-4010, http://www.computer.org.

005.1 658.568   USA
INTERNATIONAL CONFERENCE ON SOFTWARE MAINTENANCE. PROCEEDINGS. Text in English. a. USD 203; USD 82 to members (effective 2004). **Document type:** *Proceedings, Trade.*
—BLDSC (4538.883910).
Published by: Institute of Electrical and Electronics Engineers, Inc., 3 Park Ave, 17th Fl, New York, NY 10016-5997. TEL 212-419-7900, 800-678-4333, FAX 212-752-4929, customer.service@ieee.org, http://www.ieee.org.

005.1   GBR   ISSN 1746-1375
▼ ► **INTERNATIONAL JOURNAL OF AGENT-ORIENTED SOFTWARE ENGINEERING.** Text in English. forthcoming 2006. q. USD 450, USD 545 to institutions (effective 2005). **Document type:** *Journal, Academic/Scholarly.* **Description:** Fosters discussion on all software engineering aspects of the use of agent technology for the development of IT systems.
Related titles: Online - full content ed.: ISSN 1746-1383. forthcoming 2006.
Published by: Inderscience Publishers, IEL Editorial Office, PO Box 735, Olney, Bucks MK46 5WB, United Kingdom. TEL 44-1234-240519, FAX 44-1234-240515, ijaose@inderscience.com, info@inderscience.com, http://www.inderscience.com/ijaose. Eds. Brian Henderson-Sellers, Paolo Giorgini.

005.1   GBR   ISSN 1743-5137
▼ ► **INTERNATIONAL JOURNAL OF AGILE AND EXTREME SOFTWARE DEVELOPMENT.** Text in English. 2005. q. USD 450 to institutions print or online; USD 545 combined subscription to institutions print & online (effective 2005). **Document type:** *Journal, Academic/Scholarly.* **Description:** Offers a forum for discussion and sharing of ideas related to agile methods and practices.
Related titles: Online - full content ed.: ISSN 1743-5145.
Published by: Inderscience Publishers, IEL Editorial Office, PO Box 735, Olney, Bucks MK46 5WB, United Kingdom. TEL 44-1234-240519, FAX 44-1234-240515, ijased@inderscience.com, info@inderscience.com, http://www.inderscience.com/ijaesd. Ed. Darren Dalcher.

005.5   GBR   ISSN 0952-8091
                                          CODEN: IJCTEK
► **INTERNATIONAL JOURNAL OF COMPUTER APPLICATIONS IN TECHNOLOGY.** Text in English. 1988. 6/yr. USD 930 to institutions; USD 1,215 combined subscription to institutions print & online eds. (effective 2005). adv. bk.rev. abstr.; charts; illus. back issues avail. **Document type:** *Journal, Academic/Scholarly.* **Description:** Information on computer applications: advanced manufacturing systems and technology, information technology and systems, software engineering and management, communications, as well as computer-aided learning.

Related titles: Online - full text ed.: ISSN 1741-5047. USD 930 (effective 2005).
Indexed: ABIn, AHCI, AIA, AS&TI, ASCA, BrCerAb, BrTechI, C&ISA, CADCAM, CMCI, CerAb, CivEngAb, CompLI, CorrAb, CurCont, E&CAJ, EMA, ErgAb, IAA, ISMEC, Inspec, M&TEA, MBF, METADEX, RoboAb, SolStAb, WAA.
—BLDSC (4542.174400), AskIEEE, CISTI, Ei, IDS, IE, Infotrieve, ingenta, Linda Hall. **CCC.**
Published by: (International Network of Centres for Computer Applications CHE), Inderscience Publishers, IEL Editorial Office, PO Box 735, Olney, Bucks MK46 5WB, United Kingdom. TEL 44-1234-240519, FAX 44-1234-240515, ijcat@inderscience.com, editor@inderscience.com, http://www.inderscience.com/ijcat. Ed. Dr. Mohammed A Dorgham. R&P Jeanette Brooks. Circ: 10,000. **Subscr. to:** World Trade Centre Bldg, 29 route de Pre-Bois, Case Postale 896, Geneva 15 1215, Switzerland. FAX 41-22-7910885, subs@inderscience.com. **Co-sponsor:** UNESCO.

005.1 GBR ISSN 1743-5099
▼ ➤ **INTERNATIONAL JOURNAL OF FORENSIC SOFTWARE ENGINEERING.** Text in English. 2005. 4/yr. USD 450; USD 545 combined subscription print & online eds. (effective 2005). **Document type:** *Journal, Academic/Scholarly.* **Description:** Aims to facilitate improvement in software development practice and to foster debate and discussion in the community about the factors connected with success and failure and the steps needed to rescue a failing project, improve current practice and develop a responsive approach to failure prevention.
Related titles: Online - full text ed.: ISSN 1743-5102. USD 450 (effective 2005).
Published by: Inderscience Publishers, IEL Editorial Office, PO Box 735, Olney, Bucks MK46 5WB, United Kingdom. TEL 44-1234-240519, FAX 44-1234-240515, ijfse@inderscience.com, info@inderscience.com, http://www.inderscience.com/ijfse. Ed. Darren Dalcher.

005.5 GBR ISSN 1094-3420
QA76.5 CODEN: IHPCFL
➤ **THE INTERNATIONAL JOURNAL OF HIGH PERFORMANCE COMPUTING APPLICATIONS.** Variant title: S A H P C. Text in English. 1987. q. GBP 552, USD 855 to institutions; GBP 575, USD 890 combined subscription to institutions print & online eds. (effective 2006). adv. bk.rev. 96 p./no.; back issues avail.; reprint service avail. from PQC. **Document type:** *Journal, Academic/Scholarly.* **Description:** Interdisciplinary forum for the exchange of experiences in supercomputing, with emphasis on software techniques.
Former titles (until 1999): International Journal of Supercomputer Applications and High-Performance Computing (1078-3482); (until 1994): International Journal of Supercomputer Applications (0890-2720)
Related titles: Microform ed.: (from PQC); Online - full text ed.: ISSN 1741-2846. GBP 546, USD 846 to institutions (effective 2006) (from EBSCO Publishing, O C L C Online Computer Library Center, Inc., Sage Publications, Inc., Swets Information Services, The Dialog Corporation).
Indexed: AIA, ASCA, ASFA, ApMecR, BrCerAb, C&ISA, CADCAM, CMCI, CerAb, CivEngAb, CompAb, CompLI, CorrAb, CurCont, CybAb, E&CAJ, EMA, EngInd, IAA, ISR, InfoSAb, Inspec, M&TEA, MBF, METADEX, SCI, SSCI, SolStAb, WAA.
—BLDSC (4542.280470), AskIEEE, CISTI, Ei, IDS, IE, Infotrieve, ingenta, Linda Hall. **CCC.**
Published by: Sage Publications Ltd. (Subsidiary of: Sage Publications, Inc.), 1 Oliver's Yard, 55 City Rd, London, EC1 1SP, United Kingdom. TEL 44-20-73248500, FAX 44-20-73248600, info@sagepub.co.uk, http://www.sagepub.co.uk/journal.aspx?pid=105593. Eds. David E Keyes, Jack Dongarra. Circ: 650. **Subscr. in the Americas to:** Sage Publications, Inc., 2455 Teller Rd, Thousand Oaks, CA 91320. TEL 805-499-0721, 805-499-0721, FAX 805-499-0871, 805-499-0871, info@sagepub.com, journals@sagepub.com, http://www.sagepub.com.

005.1 SGP ISSN 0218-1940
QA76.758 CODEN: ISEKEW
➤ **INTERNATIONAL JOURNAL OF SOFTWARE ENGINEERING AND KNOWLEDGE ENGINEERING.** Short title: S E K E. Text in English. 1991. bi-m. SGD 333, USD 196, EUR 178 to individuals; SGD 943, USD 555, EUR 503 combined subscription to institutions print & online eds.; SGD 566, USD 333, EUR 302 combined subscription in developing nations to institutions print & online eds. (effective 2006). index. back issues avail. **Document type:** *Journal, Academic/Scholarly.* **Description:** Serves as a forum for researchers, practitioners, and developers to exchange ideas and results for the advancement of software engineering and knowledge engineering.
Related titles: Online - full text ed.: (from EBSCO Publishing, O C L C Online Computer Library Center, Inc., Swets Information Services).
Indexed: ASCA, ASFA, BrCerAb, C&ISA, CMCI, CerAb, CompAb, CompLI, CorrAb, CurCont, E&CAJ, EMA, EngInd, IAA, Inspec, M&TEA, MBF, METADEX, SSCI, SolStAb, WAA.
—BLDSC (4542.585000), AskIEEE, CISTI, IDS, IE, Infotrieve, ingenta, Linda Hall. **CCC.**
Published by: World Scientific Publishing Co. Pte. Ltd., 5 Toh Tuck Link, Singapore, 596224, Singapore. TEL 65-466-5775, FAX 65-467-7667, wspc@wspc.com.sg, http://www.worldscinet.com/ijseke/ijseke.shtml, http://www.worldscientific.com. Ed. S K Chang. **Subscr. to:** Farrer Rd, PO Box 128, Singapore 912805, Singapore. sales@wspc.com.sg. **Dist. by:** World Scientific Publishing Co., Inc., 1060 Main St, River Edge, NJ 07661. TEL 201-487-9655, 800-227-7562, FAX 201-487-9656, 888-977-2665.; World Scientific Publishing Ltd., 57 Shelton St, London WC2H 9HE, United Kingdom. TEL 44-20-78360888, FAX 44-20-78362020, sales@wspc.co.uk.

005.5 DEU ISSN 1433-2779
QA76.75
➤ **INTERNATIONAL JOURNAL ON SOFTWARE TOOLS FOR TECHNOLOGY TRANSFER.** Text in German. 1997. q. EUR 300 combined subscription to institutions print & online eds. (effective 2005). adv. reprint service avail. from PSC. **Document type:** *Journal, Academic/Scholarly.* **Description:** Provides a forum for research and design professionals to discuss all aspects of tools that assist in the development of reliable and correct computer systems.
Incorporates (1982-2000): Software - Concepts & Tools (0945-8115)
Related titles: Online - full text ed.: ISSN 1433-2787 (from EBSCO Publishing, ProQuest Information & Learning, Springer LINK, Swets Information Services).
Indexed: CompAb, CompLI, Inspec.
—BLDSC (4542.586000), CISTI, IE, Infotrieve, ingenta. **CCC.**
Published by: Springer-Verlag (Subsidiary of: Springer Science+Business Media), Tiergartenstr 17, Heidelberg, 69121, Germany. TEL 49-6221-3450, FAX 49-6221-345229, http://link.springer.de/link/service/journals/10009/index.htm. Eds. Bernhard Steffen, Matthew Dwyer. Adv. contact Stephan Kroeck TEL 49-30-827875739. **Subscr. in the Americas to:** Springer-Verlag New York, Inc., Journal Fulfillment, PO Box 2485, Secaucus, NJ 07096-2485. TEL 800-777-4643, 201-348-4033, FAX 201-348-4505, journals@springer-ny.com, http://www.springer-ny.com; **Subscr. to:** Springer GmbH Auslieferungsgesellschaft, Haberstr 7, Heidelberg 69126, Germany. TEL 49-6221-345-0, FAX 49-6221-345-4229, subscriptions@springer.de.

➤ **INTERNATIONAL SMART CARD INDUSTRY GUIDE.** see *COMPUTERS—Computer Industry*

005.1 658.568 USA ISSN 1530-1435
QA76.76.Q35
INTERNATIONAL SOFTWARE METRICS SYMPOSIUM. Text in English. 1993. a. USD 151 membership (effective 2005). **Document type:** *Proceedings, Trade.*
Related titles: Online - full text ed.: (from I E E E).
Indexed: EngInd.
—BLDSC (6846.736400). **CCC.**
Published by: Institute of Electrical and Electronics Engineers, Inc., 3 Park Ave, 17th Fl, New York, NY 10016-5997. TEL 212-419-7900, 800-678-4333, FAX 212-752-4929, customer.service@ieee.org, http://www.ieee.org.

005.1 USA
INTERNATIONAL SYMPOSIUM ON FAULT-TOLERANT COMPUTING FAST ABSTRACTS. Text in English. a. price varies. **Document type:** *Proceedings, Abstract/Index.*
Published by: Institute of Electrical and Electronics Engineers, Inc., 3 Park Ave, 17th Fl, New York, NY 10016-5997. TEL 212-419-7900, 800-678-4333, FAX 212-752-4929, customer.service@ieee.org, http://www.ieee.org.

005.1 USA ISSN 1090-705X
INTERNATIONAL SYMPOSIUM ON REQUIREMENTS ENGINEERING. PROCEEDINGS. Text in English. 1993. a. USD 180; USD 72 to members (effective 2004). **Document type:** *Proceedings, Trade.*
Related titles: Online - full text ed.: (from I E E E).
—BLDSC (7300.254200).
Published by: Institute of Electrical and Electronics Engineers, Inc., 3 Park Ave, 17th Fl, New York, NY 10016-5997. TEL 212-419-7900, 800-678-4333, FAX 212-752-4929, customer.service@ieee.org, http://www.ieee.org.

005.12 USA
INTERNATIONAL SYMPOSIUM ON SOFTWARE ENGINEERING FOR PARALLEL AND DISTRIBUTED SYSTEMS. Text in English. irreg. price varies. **Document type:** *Proceedings, Trade.*
—BLDSC (4550.346400).
Published by: Institute of Electrical and Electronics Engineers, Inc., 3 Park Ave, 17th Fl, New York, NY 10016-5997. TEL 212-419-7900, 800-678-4333, FAX 212-752-4929, customer.service@ieee.org, http://www.ieee.org.

005.12 USA ISSN 1530-1613
QA76.758
INTERNATIONAL SYMPOSIUM ON SOFTWARE ENGINEERING STANDARDS. Text in English. 1995. a. price varies. **Document type:** *Proceedings, Trade.*
Published by: Institute of Electrical and Electronics Engineers, Inc., 3 Park Ave, 17th Fl, New York, NY 10016-5997. TEL 212-419-7900, 800-678-4333, FAX 212-752-4929, customer.service@ieee.org, http://www.ieee.org.

005.12 USA ISSN 1071-9458
QA76.76.R44 CODEN: PSSRFV
INTERNATIONAL SYMPOSIUM ON SOFTWARE RELIABILITY ENGINEERING. PROCEEDINGS. Text in English. a. USD 206; USD 83 to members (effective 2004). **Document type:** *Proceedings, Trade.*
Related titles: Online - full text ed.: (from I E E E).
—BLDSC (4550.346500). **CCC.**
Published by: Institute of Electrical and Electronics Engineers, Inc., 3 Park Ave, 17th Fl, New York, NY 10016-5997. TEL 212-419-7900, 800-678-4333, FAX 212-752-4929, customer.service@ieee.org, http://www.ieee.org.

005.1 658.568 USA ISSN 1080-1820
INTERNATIONAL SYMPOSIUM ON SYSTEM SYNTHESIS. PROCEEDINGS. Text in English. 1995. a. USD 151 membership (effective 2005). **Document type:** *Proceedings, Trade.*
Related titles: Online - full text ed.: (from I E E E).
—BLDSC (4550.351450). **CCC.**
Published by: Institute of Electrical and Electronics Engineers, Inc., 3 Park Ave, 17th Fl, New York, NY 10016-5997. TEL 212-419-7900, 800-678-4333, FAX 212-752-4929, customer.service@ieee.org, http://www.ieee.org.

005.5 USA ISSN 1074-6005
CODEN: PWRPED
INTERNATIONAL WORKSHOP IN RAPID SYSTEM PROTOTYPING. PROCEEDINGS. Short title: R S P. Text in English. 1990. a. price varies. adv. **Document type:** *Proceedings, Academic/Scholarly.* **Description:** Documents current research trends and reports on system specifications, system modeling, system design and design validation.
Related titles: Online - full text ed.: (from I E E E).
—BLDSC (4362.973415), Ei. **CCC.**
Published by: (Institute of Electrical and Electronics Engineers, Inc.), I E E E Computer Society, 3 Park Ave, 17th Fl, New York, NY 10017. TEL 714-821-8380, 800-678-4333, FAX 714-821-4641, customer.service@ieee.org, http://www.ieee.org.

C

005.1 USA
INTERNATIONAL WORKSHOP ON INNOVATIVE ARCHITECTURE. POSTPROCEEDING. Text in English. a. USD 135; USD 54 to members (effective 2004). **Document type:** *Proceedings, Trade.*
Published by: Institute of Electrical and Electronics Engineers, Inc., 3 Park Ave, 17th Fl, New York, NY 10016-5997. TEL 800-678-4333, customer.service@ieee.org, http://www.ieee.org.

005.1 USA
INTERNATIONAL WORKSHOP ON MULTIMEDIA SOFTWARE ENGINEERING. Text in English. a. USD 183; USD 74 to members (effective 2004). **Document type:** *Proceedings, Trade.*
Published by: Institute of Electrical and Electronics Engineers, Inc., 3 Park Ave, 17th Fl, New York, NY 10016-5997. TEL 212-419-7900, 800-678-4333, FAX 212-752-4929, customer.service@ieee.org, http://www.ieee.org.

005.5 USA ISSN 1521-852X
QA76.758 CODEN: PIWEE9
INTERNATIONAL WORKSHOP ON SOFTWARE TECHNOLOGY AND ENGINEERING PRACTICE. PROCEEDINGS. Short title: C A S E. Text in English. 1992. biennial. price varies. adv. **Document type:** *Proceedings, Trade.* **Description:** Covers the overriding issues of software engineering and CASE.
Formerly (until 1997): International Workshop on Computer-Aided Software Engineering. Proceedings (1066-1387)
Related titles: Online - full text ed.: (from I E E E).
—**CCC.**
Published by: (Institute of Electrical and Electronics Engineers, Inc.), I E E E Computer Society, 10662 Los Vaqueros Circle, PO Box 3014, Los Alamitos, CA 90720-1314. TEL 714-821-8380, FAX 714-821-4641, customer.service@ieee.org, http://www.ieee.org. Ed. Cat Harris. Pub. Matt Loeb. Adv. contact Frieda Koester.

INTERNATIONAL WORKSHOPS ON INFRASTRUCTURE FOR COLLABORATIVE RESEARCH. see *COMPUTERS—Artificial Intelligence*

005.5 DEU
INVENTOR MAGAZIN; Schneller Konstruieren. Text in German. 2002. bi-m. EUR 20; EUR 4 newsstand/cover (effective 2002). adv. **Document type:** *Magazine, Trade.*
Related titles: Online - full text ed.
Published by: W I N - Verlag GmbH & Co. KG, Johann-Sebastian-Bach Str 5, Vaterstetten, 85591, Germany. TEL 49-8106-350-0, FAX 49-8106-350190, info@win-verlag.de, http://www.inventor-magazin.de, http://www.win-verlag.de. Ed. Rainer Trummer. Pub. Hans-J. Grohmann. Adv. contact Gabi Koenig TEL 49-8106-350100. page EUR 6,820; trim 210 x 297. Circ: 21,000 (paid and controlled).

005 USA ISSN 1541-843X
ITERATIONS; an interdisciplinary journal of software history. Text in English. 2002 (Sept.). irreg.
Media: Online - full content.

Published by: University of Minnesota, Charles Babbage Institute, 211 Andersen Library, 222 21st Ave. S., Minneapolis, MN 55455. TEL 612-624-5050, FAX 612-624-8054, cbi@tc.umn.edu, http://www.cbi.umn.edu/iterations. Ed. Jeffrey R. Yost.

JISUANJI YANJIU YU FAZHAN/COMPUTER RESEARCH AND DEVELOPMENT. see *COMPUTERS—Computer Engineering*

JISUANJI YINGYONG YU RUANJIAN/COMPUTER APPLICATIONS AND SOFTWARE. see *COMPUTERS*

LE JOURNAL DU MULTIMEDIA ET DES NOUVELLES TECHNOLOGIES; regards sur la formation des adultes. see *COMPUTERS—Computer Graphics*

005.5 USA ISSN 1094-6136
TS157.5 CODEN: JSCHFP
➤ **JOURNAL OF SCHEDULING.** Text in English. 1998. 6/yr. EUR 484, USD 484, GBP 303 combined subscription to institutions print & online eds. (effective 2005). adv. reprint service avail. from PSC. **Document type:** *Journal, Academic/Scholarly.* **Description:** Provides a forum for publication of all forms of scheduling-oriented research.
Related titles: Online - full text ed.: ISSN 1099-1425. 1998. USD 484 (effective 2005) (from EBSCO Publishing, Gale Group, IngentaConnect, Kluwer Online, O C L C Online Computer Library Center, Inc., Springer LINK, Swets Information Services, Wiley InterScience).
Indexed: BibLing, BrCerAb, C&ISA, CCMJ, CerAb, CompAb, CompLI, CorrAb, CurCont, E&CAJ, EMA, IAA, IAOP, Inspec, M&TEA, MBF, METADEX, MathR, MathSciNet, WAA.
—BLDSC (5052.620000), IE, Infotrieve, ingenta, Linda Hall. **CCC.**
Published by: Plenum US (Subsidiary of: Springer Science+Business Media), 233 Spring St, New York, NY 10013. TEL 212-460-1500, FAX 212-460-1575, service@springer-ny.com, http://springerlink.metapress.com/openurl.asp?genre=journal&issn=1094-6136, http://www.springeronline.com. Ed. Edmund Burke.

005.1 GBR ISSN 1532-060X
QA76.76.S64 CODEN: JSMECT
➤ **JOURNAL OF SOFTWARE MAINTENANCE AND EVOLUTION**; research and practice. Text in English. 1989. bi-m. USD 1,935 to institutions; USD 2,129 combined subscription to institutions print & online eds. (effective 2006). adv. back issues avail.; reprint service avail. from PSC. **Document type:** *Journal, Academic/Scholarly.* **Description:** Covers the viability of software and conveys the results of academic research and practical experience into the computing community.
Formerly: Journal of Software Maintenance (1040-550X).
Related titles: Microform ed.: (from PQC); Online - full text ed.: ISSN 1532-0618. USD 1,935 to institutions (effective 2006) (from EBSCO Publishing, Swets Information Services, Wiley InterScience).
Indexed: ASCA, BrCerAb, C&ISA, CMCI, CerAb, CompAb, CompLI, CompR, CorrAb, CurCont, E&CAJ, EMA, EngInd, IAA, Inspec, M&TEA, MBF, METADEX, SolStAb, WAA.
—BLDSC (5064.938300), AskIEEE, CISTI, Ei, IDS, IE, ingenta. **CCC.**
Published by: John Wiley & Sons Ltd. (Subsidiary of: John Wiley & Sons, Inc.), The Atrium, Southern Gate, Chichester, West Sussex PO19 8SQ, United Kingdom. TEL 44-1243-779777, FAX 44-1243-775878, customer@wiley.co.uk, http://www.wiley.com/WileyCDA/WileyTitle/productCd-SMR.html, http://www.wiley.co.uk. Eds. Aniello Cimitile, Ned Chapin. adv.: B&W page GBP 650, color page GBP 1,550; trim 260 x 200. Circ: 400. **Subscr. outside the Americas to:** John Wiley & Sons, Inc., 111 River St, Hoboken, NJ 07030-5774. TEL 201-748-6645, FAX 201-748-6088, subinfo@wiley.com.

➤ **JOURNAL OF STATISTICAL SOFTWARE.** see *STATISTICS*

005.5 USA ISSN 0164-1212
QA76.5 CODEN: JSSODM
➤ **JOURNAL OF SYSTEMS AND SOFTWARE.** Text in English. 1979. 12/yr. EUR 1,766 in Europe to institutions; JPY 234,200 in Japan to institutions; USD 1,976 to institutions except Europe and Japan (effective 2006). illus. back issues avail.; reprints avail. **Document type:** *Academic/Scholarly.* **Description:** Covers all aspects of programming methodology, software engineering, and related hardware topics.
Related titles: Microform ed.: (from PQC); Online - full text ed.: (from EBSCO Publishing, Gale Group, IngentaConnect, ScienceDirect, Swets Information Services).
Indexed: ABIn, AS&TI, ASCA, B&BAb, BrCerAb, C&ISA, CMCI, CerAb, CompAb, CompD, CompLI, CompR, CorrAb, CurCont, CybAb, E&CAJ, EMA, EngInd, IAA, ICEA, ISMEC, Inspec, M&TEA, MBF, METADEX, RefZh, SoftAbEng, SolStAb, WAA.
—BLDSC (5068.065000), AskIEEE, CISTI, Ei, IDS, IE, Infotrieve, ingenta, Linda Hall. **CCC.**
Published by: Elsevier Inc. (Subsidiary of: Elsevier Science & Technology), 360 Park Ave. S, New York, NY 10010-1710. TEL 212-633-3730, 888-437-4636, usinfo-f@elsevier.com, http://www.elsevier.com/locate/jss. Ed. D. N. Card.

➤ **JOURNAL OF W S C G.** (Winter School of Computer Graphics) see *COMPUTERS—Computer Graphics*

005.1 JPN ISSN 1341-870X
KENKYUKAI SHIRYO SHIRIZU/JAPAN SOCIETY FOR SOFTWARE SCIENCE AND TECHNOLOGY. INTERNET CONFERENCE. PROCEEDINGS. Text in English. 1995. irreg. **Document type:** *Proceedings, Academic/Scholarly.*
Published by: Nihon Sofutowea Kagakukai/Japan Society for Software Science and Technology, Gakkai-Center Bildg, 2-4-16 Yayoi, Bunkyo-ku, Tokyo, 113-0032, Japan. TEL 81-3-58022060, FAX 81-3-58023007, http://www.jssst.or.jp/jssst/.

KEY ABSTRACTS - SOFTWARE ENGINEERING. see *COMPUTERS—Abstracting, Bibliographies, Statistics*

005.5 GBR ISSN 1464-1259
KEY NOTE MARKET REPORT: COMPUTER SOFTWARE. Variant title: Computer Software Marketing Report. Text in English. 1993. irreg., latest 2001, May. GBP 340 per issue (effective 1999). **Document type:** *Trade.* **Description:** Provides an overview of the UK computer software sector, including industry structure, market size and trends, developments, prospects, and major company profiles.
Formerly (until 1998): Key Note Report: Computer Software (1352-6936)
Related titles: CD-ROM ed.; Online - full text ed.
Published by: Key Note Ltd., Field House, 72 Oldfield Rd, Hampton, Mddx TW12 2HQ, United Kingdom. TEL 44-20-8481-8750, FAX 44-20-8783-0049, info@keynote.co.uk, http://www.keynote.co.uk. Ed. Jacob Howard.

005.5 USA ISSN 0197-7342
HA32
KEYWORDS (CHICAGO); for users of S P S S software products. Text in English. 1974. q. free. **Description:** For SPSS software users. Articles mainly cover specific applications. Regular columns contain questions-and-answers and new product announcements.
Published by: S P S S Inc., 444 N Michigan Ave, Chicago, IL 60611. TEL 312-329-2400, FAX 312-329-3668. Ed. David Pittman. Circ: 25,000.

005.5 USA
KITSOFT'S OFFICIAL E-NEWS✶. Text in English. irreg. (1-2/mo.). free. back issues avail. **Document type:** *Newsletter.* **Description:** Presents tips and news with the latest software, desktop themes, screen savers and more.
Media: Online - full text.
Published by: KitSoft, 3540 W Sahara Ave, Ste 240, Las Vegas, NV 89102. TEL 702-282-1539, ken@kitsoft.com, http://www.kitsoft.com/. Ed. Kenneth Lamug.

005.5 NLD ISSN 1384-6469
➤ **THE KLUWER INTERNATIONAL SERIES IN SOFTWARE ENGINEERING.** Text in English. 1996. irreg., latest vol.10, 2005. price varies. **Document type:** *Monographic series, Academic/Scholarly.* **Description:** Publishes important research and applications in the field of software engineering.
—BLDSC (5099.731000), IE, ingenta.
Published by: Springer-Verlag Dordrecht (Subsidiary of: Springer Science+Business Media), Van Godewijckstraat 30, Dordrecht, 3311 GX, Netherlands. TEL 31-78-6576050, FAX 31-78-6576474, http://www.springeronline.com. Ed. Victor R Basili.

005.5 JPN ISSN 0289-6540
KONPYUTA SOFUTOWEA/COMPUTER SOFTWARE. Text in Japanese. 1984. q. JPY 5,500. adv. bk.rev. charts. **Document type:** *Journal, Academic/Scholarly.*
Related titles: Online - full content ed.: free (effective 2005); Online - full text ed.: (from J-Stage).
Published by: (Nihon Sofutowea Kagakukai/Japan Society for Software Science and Technology), Iwanami Shoten, Publishers, 2-5-5 Hitotsubashi, Chiyoda-ku, Tokyo, 101-0003, Japan. FAX 81-3-3239-9618, editor@jssst.or.jp. **Dist. overseas by:** Japan Publications Trading Co., Ltd., Book Export II Dept, PO Box 5030, Tokyo International, Tokyo 101-3191, Japan. TEL 81-3-32923753, FAX 81-3-32920410, infoserials@jptco.co.jp, http://www.jptco.co.jp.

004.1 JPN ISSN 1341-8718
. **KOSHUKAI SHIRYO SHIRIZU.** Text in Japanese. 1996. irreg. **Document type:** *Academic/Scholarly.*
Published by: Nihon Sofutowea Kagakukai/Japan Society for Software Science and Technology, Gakkai-Center Bildg, 2-4-16 Yayoi, Bunkyo-ku, Tokyo, 113-0032, Japan. TEL 81-3-58022060, FAX 81-3-58023007, http://www.jssst.or.jp/jssst/.

005.43 DEU ISSN 1619-7968
LINUX ENTERPRISE. Text in German. 2000. bi-m. EUR 29.50; EUR 5.80 newsstand/cover (effective 2005). adv. **Document type:** *Magazine, Trade.*
Published by: Software & Support Verlag GmbH, Kennedyallee 87, Frankfurt am Main, 60596, Germany. TEL 49-69-6300890, FAX 49-69-63008989, redaktion@linuxenterprise.de, info@software-support.biz, http://www.linuxenterprise.de, http://www.software-support.biz. adv.: B&W page EUR 3,150, color page EUR 4,350. Circ: 40,000 (controlled).

005.5 GBR ISSN 1470-4234
LINUX FORMAT. Text in English. 1999. m. GBP 49.90 domestic; GBP 73.53 in North America & Europe; GBP 86.53 elsewhere; GBP 4.99 newsstand/cover (effective 2002). adv. **Document type:** *Magazine, Consumer.* **Description:** Contains informative features, news, tutorials, reviews, previews, and technical Q&As on all aspects of the Linux OS.
Formerly (until 2000): Linux Answers (1468-7844)
Related titles: Online - full text ed.
—CCC.
Published by: Future Publishing Ltd., Beauford Court, 30 Monmouth St, Bath, Avon BA1 2BW, United Kingdom. TEL 44-1225-442244, FAX 44-1225-446019, customerservice@futurenet.co.uk, http://www.linuxformat.co.uk, http://www.futurenet.com/futureonline. Ed. Nick Veitch.

005.5 USA
LINUX GAZETTE. Text in English. m. software rev. **Document type:** *Journal, Trade.* **Description:** Dedicated to making Linux more fun, and to sharing ideas and discoveries.
Media: Online - full text.
Published by: Specialized Systems Consultants Publishing, Ltd., PO Box 85867, Seattle, WA 98145. TEL 206-297-7514, 888-666-4689, FAX 206-297-7515, linux@ssc.com, http://www.linuxjournal.com/. Pub. Phil Hughes. Adv. contact Carlie Fairchild.

005.43 DEU
LINUX INTERN. Text in German. 1999. 2/yr. EUR 9.90 newsstand/cover (effective 2003). adv. **Document type:** *Magazine, Consumer.*
Published by: Data Becker GmbH & Co. KG, Merowingerstr 30, Duesseldorf, 40223, Germany. TEL 49-211-933470, FAX 49-211-9334710, thapp@databecker.de, http://www.databecker.de. Adv. contact Volker Boerdeling. page EUR 2,700; trim 180 x 274. Circ: 47,680 (paid and controlled).

005.5 USA ISSN 1075-3583
QA76.76.O63 CODEN: LIJOFX
LINUX JOURNAL. Text in English. 1994. m. USD 22 domestic; USD 47 foreign (effective 2006). adv. software rev. back issues avail. **Document type:** *Magazine, Trade.* **Description:** Offers articles that appeal to newcomers as well as serious technical articles for long-time Unix users. Also icludes articles on commercial uses for Linux.
Incorporates (1996-1997): Websmith (1086-1890)
Related titles: CD-ROM ed.; Online - full text ed.: (from Association for Computing Machinery, Inc., EBSCO Publishing).
Indexed: BrCerAb, C&ISA, CerAb, CompLI, CompR, CorrAb, E&CAJ, EMA, IAA, Inspec, M&TEA, MBF, METADEX, MicrocompInd, SoftBase, WAA.
—BLDSC (5221.637220), IE, Infotrieve.
Published by: Specialized Systems Consultants Publishing, Ltd., PO Box 55549, Seattle, WA 98155-0549. http://www.linuxjournal.com/, http://www.ssc.com. Ed. Don Marti. Adv. contact Carlie Fairchild. Circ: 93,000 (paid).

005.5 USA
LINUX JOURNAL BUYER'S GUIDE. Text in English. a. USD 7 newsstand/cover (effective 2001). **Document type:** *Magazine, Trade.* **Description:** Provides listings and reviews of products and services available for users of Linux.
Published by: Specialized Systems Consultants Publishing, Ltd., PO Box 85867, Seattle, WA 98145. TEL 206-297-7514, 888-666-4689, FAX 206-297-7515, linux@ssc.com, http://www2.linuxjournal.com/bg/index.html, http://www.ssc.com. **Dist. by:** International Publishers Direct, 27500 Riverview Center Blvd, Bonita Springs, FL 34134. TEL 858-320-4563, FAX 858-677-3220.

005.43 ITA ISSN 1722-6163
▼ **LINUX PRO.** Text in Italian. 2003. m. EUR 47 (effective 2005). adv. **Document type:** *Magazine, Consumer.*
Published by: Future Media Italy SpA, Via Asiago 45, Milano, MI 20128, Italy. TEL 39-02-2529161, FAX 39-02-26005520, info@futuremediaitaly.it, http://www.futuremediaitaly.it.

005.5 USA
LINUX RESOURCES. Text in English. w. software rev. **Document type:** *Journal, Trade.* **Description:** Provides late-breaking news on the Linux operating system plus general information about Linux, where to get it, and how to install it.
Media: Online - full text.
Published by: Specialized Systems Consultants Publishing, Ltd., PO Box 85867, Seattle, WA 98145. TEL 206-297-7514, 888-666-4689, FAX 206-297-7515, linux@ssc.com, http://www.linuxjournal.com/. Pub. Phil Hughes.

005.5 USA
LINUX TODAY. Text in English. 2002. w.
Media: Online - full text.
Published by: Linux Today Management, 23 Old Kings Hwy S, Darien, CT 06820. http://www.linuxtoday.com/.

005.5 SWE
LINUX WORLD✶. Text in Swedish. 4/yr. adv. **Document type:** *Magazine, Consumer.* **Description:** Targets professional and technical users that are open to new operating system solutions such as Linux.

C

Published by: I D G AB (Subsidiary of: I D G Communications Inc.), Sturegatan 11, Stockholm, 10678, Sweden. FAX 46-8-453-62-40, http://www.idg.se. Ed. Fredrik Bernsel TEL 46-8-4536230. Adv. contact Michael Schebesta. page SEK 59,800; trim 185 x 260. Circ: 23,000 (paid and controlled).

005.43   USA
LINUXGRAM. Text in English. w. USD 100, GBP 70 per reader; USD 12, GBP 8 per month per reader (effective 2003). **Document type:** *Trade.* **Description:** Supplies strategic intelligence weekly to the computer industry and its customers about the Operating Systems wars.
Media: Online - full content.
Published by: G2 Computer Intelligence Inc., 323 Glen Cove Ave, Sea Cliff, NY 11579. TEL 516-759-7028, 877-426-3971, FAX 516-759-7025, paperboy@g2news.com, http://www.g2news.com. Eds. Maureen O'Gara, Stuart Zipper TEL 303-759-9256.

LITIGATION APPLICATIONS. see *LAW—Computer Applications*

005.36   USA   ISSN 0886-4144
QA76.8.C64
LOADSTAR; the monthly software collection for people who love their Commodores. Text in English. 1984. m. USD 69.95; USD 75 foreign. **Description:** For owners of Commodore 64 or 128 computers.
Media: Diskette.
Published by: J & F Publishing, Inc., PO Box 30008, Shreveport, LA 71130-0008. TEL 318-221-8718. Ed. Fender Tucker. Circ: 1,500.

005.5   USA   ISSN 1095-3965
LOCKERGNOME'S FREE WINDOWS 95 - N T E-ZINE. Text in English. 1996. w. free. adv. **Document type:** *Newsletter.*
Description: For Windows 95/NT users, with information about software, web sites, themes, fonts, updates and patches, tips and tricks, news and more.
Media: Online - full text.
Published by: Lockergnome, 108 3d St, Ste 305A, Des Moines, IA 50309. TEL 515-288-9578, chris@lockergnome.com, http://www.lockergnome.com/. Ed., Pub., Adv. contact Christopher Pirillo.

005.5   CAN   ISSN 0836-6853
LOGIBASE; repertoire quebecois des logiciels et documents electroniques. Text in French. 1985. a. adv. back issues avail.
Document type: *Directory.* **Description:** Directory of software developed in Quebec or available in French, for all computer systems and-or applications: 6000 detailed descriptions from 750 software firms, with complete Canadian addresses.
Related titles: CD-ROM ed.; Online - full text ed.
Published by: Services Documentaires Multimedia Inc., 75 Port Royal E, bureau 300, Montreal, PQ H3L 3T1, Canada. TEL 514-382-0895, FAX 514-384-9139, info@sdm.qc.ca, logibase@sdm.qc.ca, http://www.sdm.qc.ca. Circ: 700.

005.5   USA   ISSN 1534-9632
LOTUS ADVISOR. Text in English. 1995. m. USD 99 domestic; USD 119 in Canada; USD 139 elsewhere (effective 2005). adv. **Document type:** *Magazine, Trade.* **Description:** Technical publication that explains how to take advantage of the power of Lotus Notes and Domino. For developers and power users who are customizing Lotus Notes to serve their organizations.
Former titles: Lotus Notes & Domino Advisor (1521-1851); Lotus Notes Advisor (1079-235X)
Published by: Advisor Media, Inc., 4849 Viewridge Ave, San Diego, CA 92123-1643. TEL 858-278-5600, FAX 858-278-0300, advisor@advisor.com, http://www.advisor.com. Ed. John L Hawkins. R&P David Kodama. Adv. contact Sheri Ogletree. **Dist. by:** International Periodical Distributors, 674 Via de la Valle, Ste 204, Solana Beach, CA 92075.

005.5   ITA
M C - MICROCOMPUTER SOFTWARE. Text in Italian. 1990. m. (11/yr.). adv. back issues avail.
Published by: Technipress Srl, Via della Bufalotta 374, Rome, 00139, Italy. TEL 39-06-8720331, FAX 39-06-87139141, http://www.technipress.it/. Ed. Marco Marinacci. Circ: 15,000.

005.1   SGP
▼ **M S D N MAGAZINE. AUSTRALIA - NEW ZEALAND EDITION.** Text in English. 2004. bi-m. USD 40 (effective 2005). adv. **Document type:** *Magazine, Trade.*
Published by: Charlton Media Group, 9B Stanley St, Singapore, 068728, Singapore. TEL 65-6223-7660, admin@charltonmedia.com, http://www.charltonmedia.com. Ed. Angela McFeeters. Pub. Timothy Charlton.

005.1   SGP
▼ **M S D N MAGAZINE. INDIA EDITION.** Text in English. 2004. bi-m. USD 40 (effective 2005). adv. **Document type:** *Magazine, Trade.*
Published by: Charlton Media Group, 9B Stanley St, Singapore, 068728, Singapore. TEL 65-6223-7660, admin@charltonmedia.com, http://www.charltonmedia.com. Ed. Angela McFeeters. Pub. Timothy Charlton.

005.1   SGP
▼ **M S D N MAGAZINE. SOUTHEAST ASIA EDITION.** Text in English. 2004. bi-m. USD 40 (effective 2005). adv. **Document type:** *Magazine, Trade.*
Published by: Charlton Media Group, 9B Stanley St, Singapore, 068728, Singapore. TEL 65-6223-7660, admin@charltonmedia.com, http://www.charltonmedia.com. Ed. Angela McFeeters. Pub. Timothy Charlton.

M S D S SOFTWARE REPORT. (Materials Safety Data Sheets) see *ENVIRONMENTAL STUDIES—Computer Applications*

▼ **M X MAGAZIN.** see *COMMUNICATIONS—Computer Applications*

005.5   USA   ISSN 1533-9122
MAC ADMINISTRATION. Text in English. 2001. m. USD 177 domestic; USD 187 foreign; USD 207 combined subscription print & online eds. (effective 2005). **Document type:** *Magazine, Consumer.*
Related titles: Online - full text ed.: ISSN 1539-0233. USD 207 domestic; USD 217 foreign (effective 2005).
—CCC.
Published by: Element K Journals (Subsidiary of: Eli Research, Inc.), 500 Canal View Blvd, Rochester, NY 14623. TEL 585-240-7301, 800-223-8720, 877-203-5248, FAX 585-292-4392, http://www.elementkjournals.com/products/showProduct.asp?prodID=6&catID=2. Eds. Joe Froehlich, Michelle Rogers.

MAC FORMAT. see *COMPUTERS*

MAC POWER. see *COMPUTERS—Personal Computers*

MACINTOSH MAGAZINE. see *COMPUTERS—Hardware*

005.43   FRA   ISSN 1638-072X
LE MAGAZINE OFFICIEL WINDOWS X P. Text in French. 2002. m. adv. **Document type:** *Magazine, Consumer.*
Published by: Future France, 101-109 Rue Jean Jaures, Levallois Perret, 92300, France. TEL 33-1-41273838, yveline.duville@futurenet.fr.

005.5   USA   ISSN 1097-5241
TJ153
MECHANICAL SOLUTIONS; the independent resource for Autodesk mechanical users. Text in English. 1997. q. USD 20; USD 25 in Canada; USD 30 elsewhere; USD 7 newsstand/cover domestic; USD 8 newsstand/cover in Canada; USD 9 newsstand/cover elsewhere (effective 2000). adv. back issues avail. **Document type:** *Trade.* **Description:** Provides information, advice, and opinions to those working to solve their organization's mechanical engineering, product development, and business problems with software, hardware, services, support, and content related to Autodesk and its partners.
Related titles: Microfilm ed.; Online - full text ed.
—Linda Hall.
Published by: Penton Media, Inc. (Subsidiary of: Pittway Company), 1300 E 9th St, Cleveland, OH 44114-1503. TEL 216-696-7000, FAX 216-696-1267, rmills@penton.com, http://www.penton.com. Ed. Robert Mills. Pub. Larry Boulden TEL 216-931-9475. R&P Diane Sofranec. Adv. contact Peter Mullins. page USD 6,500; trim 10.75 x 7.75. Circ: 60,000 (controlled).

MEDICAL COMPUTING REVIEW; by physicians, for physicians: articles on software & computer technology. see *MEDICAL SCIENCES—Computer Applications*

MERRILL'S EDGAR ADVISOR; a publication for participants in the EDGAR and SEDAR systems for securities reporting. see *COMPUTERS—Computer Systems*

005   CHE   ISSN 1023-4918
METHODS & TOOLS. Text in English. 1993. 10/yr. **Description:** Provides practical knowledge for software development professionals.
Media: Online - full text. **Related titles:** ◆ French ed.: Forum Logiciel. ISSN 1023-0114.
Published by: Martinig & Associates, Rue des Marronniers 25, Vevey, 1800, Switzerland. TEL 41-21-922-1300, FAX 41-21-921-2353, franco@martinig.ch, http://www.martinig.ch/mt/index.html. Ed. Franco Martinig.

MICRO SYSTEMES. see *COMPUTERS—Microcomputers*

MICROLEADS RESELLER DIRECTORY ON DISK. see *COMPUTERS—Computer Industry Directories*

005.5   USA   ISSN 1538-8271
MICROSOFT ACCESS FUNDAMENTALS. Text in English. 2002 (May). m. USD 117 domestic; USD 127 foreign; USD 147 combined subscription (effective 2005). **Document type:** *Magazine, Consumer.* **Description:** Designed to build reader's Access skills from the ground up.
Related titles: Print ed.: USD 147 domestic; USD 157 foreign (effective 2005).
—CCC.

Published by: Element K Journals (Subsidiary of: Eli Research, Inc.), 500 Canal View Blvd, Rochester, NY 14623. TEL 585-240-7301, 800-223-8720, 877-203-5248, FAX 585-292-4392, http://www.elementkjournals.com/products/showProduct.asp?prodID=12&catID=1. Eds. Christine Spencer, Michelle Rogers.

005.5   BRA
MICROSOFT BUSINESS JOURNAL. Text in Portuguese. q. adv. **Document type:** *Magazine, Trade.* **Description:** Provides updated information on Microsoft's corporate products, success cases in significant users, technical articles and industry trends presented by renowned specialists.
Published by: I D G Computerworld do Brasil, Rua Tabapua, 145-3 e 4 andar, Itaim Bibi, Sao Paulo, 04533-010, Brazil. TEL 55-11-3049-2000, FAX 55-11-3071-4022, negocios@idg.com.br, http://www.idg.com.br. adv.: color page USD 9,000; trim 210 x 280. Circ: 30,000 (controlled).

005.5   USA   ISSN 1540-840X
MICROSOFT EXCEL FUNDAMENTALS. Text in English. 2002 (Nov.). m. USD 107 domestic; USD 117 foreign; USD 137 combined subscription print & online eds. (effective 2005).
Document type: *Magazine, Consumer.* **Description:** Designed to help the reader to build Excel skills by starting with the basics.
Related titles: Online - full content ed.: USD 137 domestic; USD 147 foreign (effective 2005).
—CCC.
Published by: Element K Journals (Subsidiary of: Eli Research, Inc.), 500 Canal View Blvd, Rochester, NY 14623. TEL 585-240-7301, 800-223-8720, 877-203-5248, FAX 585-292-4392, http://www.elementkjournals.com/products/showProduct.asp?prodID=1&catID=1. Eds. T. L. Aardsma, Michelle Rogers.

005.5   USA   ISSN 1542-2798
MICROSOFT OFFICE X P QUICK REFERENCE GUIDE. Text in English. 2002. a. USD 47.90 per issue (effective 2005); includes subscr. to Microsoft Office XP Quick Reference Card & a Smart Tips and Quick Tricks Booklet.
—CCC.
Published by: Element K Journals (Subsidiary of: Eli Research, Inc.), 500 Canal View Blvd, Rochester, NY 14623. TEL 585-240-7301, 800-223-8720, 877-203-5248, FAX 585-292-4392, http://www.elementkjournals.com.

005.5   USA   ISSN 1542-278X
MICROSOFT OFFICE XP QUICK REFERENCE CARD. Text in English. 2002. a. USD 47.90 per issue (effective 2005); includes subscr. to Microsoft Office X P Quick Reference Guide & a Smart Tips and Quick Tricks Booklet.
—CCC.
Published by: Element K Journals (Subsidiary of: Eli Research, Inc.), 500 Canal View Blvd, Rochester, NY 14623. TEL 585-240-7301, 800-223-8720, 877-203-5248, FAX 585-292-4392, http://www.elementkjournals.com.

005.5   USA
MICROSOFT TRACKER. Text in English. m. USD 395 (effective 1999). **Document type:** *Newsletter, Trade.* **Description:** For today's corporate IS managers, CEOs, CFOs, and other top executives who must monitor Microsoft's initiatives in all areas - operating systems, Internet, networking and applications - to plan their own long-term strategy.
Published by: Gartner Inc., 56 Top Gallant Rd, Stamford, CT 06904-2212. TEL 203-316-1111, 800-544-7337, FAX 203-316-6300, jwhitney@info-edge.com, http://www.gartner3.gartnerweb.com, http://www.info-edge.com.

005.15   USA
MICROSOFT WINDOWS X P QUICK REFERENCE GUIDE. Text in English. a. USD 34.90 per issue domestic; USD 44.90 per issue foreign (effective 2005).
Published by: Element K Journals (Subsidiary of: Eli Research, Inc.), 500 Canal View Blvd, Rochester, NY 14623. TEL 585-240-7301, 800-223-8720, 877-203-5248, FAX 585-292-4392, http://www.elementkjournals.com.

005.43   GBR
MICROSOFT WINDOWS XP. Text in English. m. GBP 69.96 domestic; GBP 94.94 in Europe; GBP 96.44 elsewhere (effective 2005). adv. **Document type:** *Magazine, Consumer.* **Description:** Provides guides and information on all aspects of the Windows XP operating system.
Published by: Future Publishing Ltd., Beauford Court, 30 Monmouth St, Bath, Avon BA1 2BW, United Kingdom. TEL 44-1225-442244, FAX 44-1225-446019, editor@windowsxpmagazine.co.uk, customerservice@futurenet.co.uk, http://www.windowsxpmagazine.co.uk/, http://www.futurenet.co.uk. Ed. David Bradley.

005   USA
MIDRANGE DEVELOPER. Text in English. m.
Published by: M C Press, LLC, 125 N. Woodland, Double Oak, TX 75077. TEL 817-961-0660. Pub. David Uptmor TEL 760-438-2793.

MOODY'S COMPANY DATA. see *BUSINESS AND ECONOMICS—Computer Applications*

C

MORTGAGE TECHNOLOGY. see *REAL ESTATE*

005.5 CAN
MUGSHOTS; the Medianet Users Group newsletter. Text in English. q. looseleaf. free. **Document type:** *Newsletter.*
Published by: Dymaxion Research Ltd., 5515 Cogswell St, Halifax, NS B3J 1R2, Canada. TEL 902-422-1973, FAX 902-421-1267, info@medianet.ns.ca, http://www.medianet.ns.ca. Ed. Nancy Cowper. R&P Peter Mason.

MULTIMEDIA TOOLS AND APPLICATIONS; an international journal. see *COMPUTERS—Computer Graphics*

005.5 SWE
THE MULTISIMPLEX NEWSLETTER. Text in Swedish. 1997. irreg. (4-6/yr.). **Document type:** *Newsletter.* **Description:** Covers the theoretical and practical aspects of the MultiSimplex experimental design and optimization software package.
Media: Online - full text.
Published by: MultiSimplex AB, Stenbergsgrand 9, Karlskrona, 37132, Sweden. TEL 46-455-279-70, FAX 46-455-279-22, info@multisimplex.com, http://www.multisimplex.com/newsl.htm. Ed., R&P Tomas Oberg.

N T UPDATE. see *COMPUTERS—Computer Networks*

NEW GENERATION COMPUTING; computing paradigms and computational intelligence. see *COMPUTERS—Microcomputers*

NIKKEI CLICK. see *COMPUTERS—Personal Computers*

005.5 JPN
NIKKEI WINDOWS N T. Text in Japanese. 1997. m. JPY 12,000; JPY 1,100 newsstand/cover (effective 2000). adv. **Document type:** *Trade.* **Description:** Covers the latest Windows NT products; explains the usage of Windows NT in business.
Published by: Nikkei Business Publications Inc. (Subsidiary of: Nihon Keizai Shimbun, Inc.), 2-1-1 Hirakawa-cho, Chiyoda-ku, Tokyo, 102-8622, Japan. TEL 81-3-5210-8311, FAX 81-3-5210-8530, info@nikkeibpnyc.com, webmaster@nikkeibp.com, http://www.nikkeibp.com. Ed. Hideki Shinde. Pub. Minoru Matsuzaki. Adv. contact Tetsuhiro Yamaoka. B&W page JPY 320,000, color page JPY 550,000; trim 208 x 280. Circ: 32,601. **Dist. in America by:** Nikkei Business Publications America Inc., 575 Fifth Ave, 20th Fl, New York, NY 10017.

005.5 DEU ISSN 1431-1798
NOTES MAGAZIN; erfolgreiches Informationsmanagement. Text in German. 1996. 8/yr. adv. **Document type:** *Magazine, Trade.* **Description:** For existing and potential Lotus Notes users.
—IE, Infotrieve.
Published by: W I N - Verlag GmbH & Co. KG, Johann-Sebastian-Bach Str 5, Vaterstetten, 85591, Germany. TEL 49-8106-350-0, FAX 49-8106-350190, info@win-verlag.de, http://www.notes-magazin.de, http://www.win-verlag.de. Ed. Peter von Bechen. Pub. Hans-J. Grohmann. Adv. contact Dagmar Horsch TEL 49-8106-350227. Circ: 20,251 (paid).

005.5 CAN ISSN 1203-5696
O S/2 E-ZINE!. Text in English. 1995. m. **Description:** Contains news, reviews, tips and interviews for novice and experienced OS-2 users.
Media: Online - full text.
Published by: Haligonian Media, 26 Victoria Rd, Dartmouth, NS B2Y 2V9, Canada. editor@haligonian.com, http://www.os2ezine.com/, http://www.haligonian.com/os2/. Ed. Trevor Smith.

005.5 USA ISSN 1530-9495
OPEN; linux and open source for e-business. Text in English. 2000. m. USD 4.95 newsstand/cover (effective 2001). adv. software rev. illus. **Document type:** *Magazine, Trade.* **Description:** Aims to help IT professionals and corporate managers buy Linux and other open source products, tools, and services to build and deploy open source solutions in the enterprise.
Indexed: Microcomplnd.
Published by: Open Source Development Network, 50 Nagog Park, Acton, MA 01720. TEL 978-635-5300, FAX 978-635-5326, http://www.openmagazine.net, http://www.osdn.com. Eds. Jack Fegreus, Lisa Daigle. Pub. Michael Lamattina.

005.43 USA ISSN 0163-5980
QA76.6 CODEN: OSRED8
OPERATING SYSTEMS REVIEW. Text in English. 1970 (vol.4). 5/yr. USD 30 (effective 2004). adv. bk.rev. bibl.; charts; illus. Index. reprints avail. **Document type:** *Newsletter, Academic/Scholarly.*
Related titles: Online - full text ed.: (from EBSCO Publishing).
Indexed: AHCI, C&CSA, C&ISA, CompC, CompR, E&CAJ, Englnd, Inspec, SolStAb.
—BLDSC (6267.895000), AskIEEE, CISTI, IE, Infotrieve, ingenta, Linda Hall. **CCC.**
Published by: Association for Computing Machinery, Inc., 1515 Broadway, 17th Fl, New York, NY 10036-5701. TEL 212-626-0500, 212-626-0520, 800-342-6626, FAX 212-869-0481, sigs@acm.org, usacm@acm.org, http://www.acm.org/sigops/osr.html. Ed. William Waite. R&P Debbie Cotton TEL 212-626-0652. Circ: 8,000.

005.5 USA ISSN 1080-0654
ORACLE INFORMANT; the independent monthly guide to Oracle development. Text in English. 1996. m. USD 49.95. bk.rev.; software rev. back issues avail. **Document type:** *Trade.* **Description:** Covers technical issues facing the Oracle developer.
Related titles: CD-ROM ed.
Published by: Informant Communications Group, 5105 Florin Perkins Rd., Sacramento, CA 95826-4817. TEL 916-686-6610, FAX 916-686-8497, circulation@informant.com. Ed. Jerry Coffey. Adv. contact Lynn Beaudoin. page USD 2,000; trim 10.75 x 8. Circ: 15,000 (paid).

ORACLE PROFESSIONAL. see *COMPUTERS—Data Base Management*

ORACLE UPDATE. see *COMPUTERS—Data Base Management*

P C ACTION; guida alla civilta del personal computer. see *COMPUTERS—Personal Computers*

005.5 DEU ISSN 0948-2873
P C GO!. Text in German. m. EUR 54.90 domestic; EUR 67.20 foreign; EUR 48.20 to students; EUR 5 newsstand/cover (effective 2003). adv. **Document type:** *Magazine, Consumer.* **Description:** Contains articles and features on all aspects of PC products and applications written in a clear and understandable style.
Incorporates (in 1993): P C Windows (0946-8668)
Related titles: CD-ROM ed.: ISSN 1432-5357; Online - full text ed.: ISSN 1432-5349.
—IE, Infotrieve.
Published by: W E K A Computerzeitschriften-Verlag GmbH, Gruberstr 46a, Poing, 85586, Germany. TEL 49-8121-950, FAX 49-8121-951199, redaktion@pcgo.de, http://www.pcgo.de, http://www.wekanet.de. Ed. Jobst-Hendrick Kehrhahn. adv.: B&W page EUR 6,630, color page EUR 9,900; trim 185 x 266. Circ: 278,080 (paid). **Subscr. to:** Postfach 1163, Neckarsulm 74168, Germany.

005.43 DEU
P C LINUX; Linux starten, nutzen tunen. Text in German. q. EUR 35.10; EUR 10 newsstand/cover (effective 2003). adv. **Document type:** *Magazine, Trade.*
Related titles: Online - full text ed.
Published by: W E K A Computerzeitschriften-Verlag GmbH, Gruberstr 46a, Poing, 85586, Germany. TEL 49-8121-950, FAX 49-8121-951621, redaktion@pc-magazin.de, http://www.pc-magazin.de/pclinux, http://www.wekanet.de. Ed. Ulrich Rohde. Pub. Stephan Quinkertz. Adv. contact Roy Decker. B&W page EUR 2,600, color page EUR 3,100; trim 185 x 266.

P C MART. see *COMPUTERS*

P C PRATICO. see *COMPUTERS—Personal Computers*

005.5 USA ISSN 1052-357X
P.C. REVIEW✶; evaluations of new personal computer products. Text in English. m. USD 195.
Published by: Amanda C. Hixson, Ed. & Pub., c/o Amanda Hixson, 365 Monroe Dr, Palo Alto, CA 94306-4418. **Subscr. to:** 50 West Palm St, Altadena, CA 91001.

005.5 FRA
P C T E NEWSLETTER. Text in French. 1989. q. back issues avail. **Document type:** *Newsletter.*
Published by: E C 2, 269 rue de la Garenne, Nanterre, 92000, France. TEL 33-1-47-80-70-00, FAX 33-1-47-80-66-29. Ed. Ian Campbell.

005.43 ITA
P C WINDOWS. Text in Italian. 1991. m. adv. **Document type:** *Consumer.*
Published by: G R Edizioni s.r.l., Viale Carlo Espinasse, 93, Milan, MI 20156, Italy. TEL 39-2-38010030, FAX 39-2-38010028. Ed. Gianluigi Zanfrognini.

P C WORLD JAPAN/GEKKAN PISHI WARUDO JAPAN. see *COMPUTERS—Personal Computers*

P C YEAR BOOK. SOFTWARE VOLUME. see *COMPUTERS—Microcomputers*

005.43 DEU ISSN 1619-7976
P H P MAGAZIN. (Personal Home Page) Text in German. 2002. bi-m. EUR 52; EUR 9.80 newsstand/cover (effective 2005). **Document type:** *Magazine, Trade.*
Published by: Software & Support Verlag GmbH, Kennedyallee 87, Frankfurt am Main, 60596, Germany. TEL 49-69-6300890, FAX 49-69-63008989, redaktion@phpmag.de, info@software-support.biz, http://www.phpmag.de, http://www.software-support.biz.

P M S TODAY. see *BUSINESS AND ECONOMICS—Computer Applications*

005.5 DEU ISSN 1434-2308
P P S MANAGEMENT. Text in German. 1998. q. EUR 54 (effective 2003). adv. bk.rev.; software rev. back issues avail. **Document type:** *Magazine, Trade.* **Description:** Focuses all aspects of the encouragement of PPC - Systems. It offers managers and users criteria to select PPC - Software.
Indexed: Inspec.
Published by: G I T O Verlag, Klixstr. 1A, Berlin, 13403, Germany. TEL 49-30-41938364, FAX 49-30-41938367, service@pps-management.de, service@gito.info, http://www.pps-management.de. Ed. Norbert Gronau. Adv. contact Andrea Gramoll. Circ: 11,800.

005.43 USA
PACIFIC NORTHWEST SOFTWARE QUALITY CONFERENCE PROCEEDINGS. Text in English. a.
—BLDSC (1089.593000).
Published by: Pacific Northwest Software Quality Conference, P.O. Box 10733, Portland, OR 97296-0733. pnsqc@pnsqc.org, http://www.pnsqc.org.

PERSONAL COMPUTER MAGAZINE; het computerblad voor Nederland en Belgie. see *COMPUTERS—Personal Computers*

005.5 USA ISSN 1078-1889
POWERBUILDER DEVELOPER'S JOURNAL. Abbreviated title: P B D J. Text in English. 1994. m. USD 149 domestic; USD 169 in Canada & Mexico; USD 189 elsewhere; USD 15 newsstand/cover (effective 2005). adv. software rev. illus. back issues avail. **Document type:** *Magazine, Trade.*
Related titles: Online - full text ed.
—IE.
Published by: SYS-CON Media, Inc., 135 Chestnut Ridge Rd, Montvale, NJ 07645. TEL 201-802-3040, 888-303-5282, FAX 201-782-9600, info@sys-con.com, http://pbdj.sys-con.com, http://www.sys-con.com. Ed. John Olson. Pub. Fuat A Kircaali. R&P Fuat Kircaali. Adv. contact Carmen Gonzalez. Circ: 37,000 (paid).

005.5 USA
PRAGMA'S PRODUCT PROFILES. Text in English. 1984. m. free to qualified personnel. adv. **Description:** For Pick Operating Systems users. Provides news and information on current systems. Also covers hardware and user groups.
Published by: Semaphore Corp., 6325, Santa Barbara, CA 93160-6325. TEL 408-688-9200. Ed. Mike Gabrielson. Circ: 4,000 (controlled).

005.52 DEU ISSN 1615-2646
PRAXISHANDBUCH WORD 2000. Text in German. 1993. bi-m. looseleaf. EUR 49.80 (effective 2005). **Document type:** *Magazine, Trade.*
Former titles: Praxishandbuch WinWord (1436-6436); (until 1997): Word fuer Windows (0945-4322)
Published by: W R S Verlag GmbH & Co. KG (Subsidiary of: Rudolf Haufe Verlag GmbH & Co. KG), Fraunhoferstr 5, Planegg, 82152, Germany. info@wrs.de, http://www.wrs.de.

005.1 USA ISSN 0891-4516
PRENTICE-HALL SOFTWARE SERIES. Text in English. irreg. **Document type:** *Monographic series.*
Indexed: Inspec.
Published by: Prentice Hall, One Lake St, Upper Saddle River, NJ 07458. TEL 800-282-0693, FAX 800-835-5327, http://www.prenhall.com.

005.5 USA ISSN 1040-1482
PRODUCTIVITY SOFTWARE. Text in English. 1988. m. USD 150 in North America; USD 165 elsewhere (effective 2001). bk.rev. back issues avail. **Document type:** *Newsletter, Trade.* **Description:** Provides information and news on the latest business software products for microcomputers, minicomputers, and mainframes to increase productivity and cost-effectiveness. Covers the vendors who develop and market the programs and the end user.
Related titles: Online - full text ed.: (from bigchalk, Data-Star, EBSCO Publishing, Factiva, Gale Group, LexisNexis, ProQuest Information & Learning, The Dialog Corporation).
Published by: Worldwide Videotex, PO Box 3273, Boynton Beach, FL 33424-3273. TEL 561-738-2276, markedit@juno.com, http://www.wvpubs.com. Ed., Pub. Mark Wright.

PROGRAMMERS TRENDS E-NEWSLETTER. see *COMPUTERS—Computer Programming*

005.5 RUS ISSN 0361-7688
QA76 CODEN: PCSODA
➤ **PROGRAMMING AND COMPUTER SOFTWARE.** Text in English. 1975. bi-m. EUR 1,768, USD 1,628, GBP 1,098 combined subscription to institutions print & online eds. (effective 2005). back issues avail. **Document type:** *Journal, Academic/Scholarly.* **Description:** Publishes theoretical and practical papers addressing all areas of computer science.

Related titles: Microfilm ed.: (from PQC); Online - full text ed.: ISSN 1608-3261 (from EBSCO Publishing, Gale Group, IngentaConnect, Kluwer Online, O C L C Online Computer Library Center, Inc., Springer LINK, Swets Information Services); ♦ Translation of: Programmirovanie. ISSN 0132-3474.
Indexed: ASCA, BibLing, CCMJ, CMCI, CompAb, CompC, CompLI, CurCont, Englnd, ICEA, InfoSAb, Inspec, MathR, MathSciNet, SoftAbEng, ZentMath.
—BLDSC (0420.420000), AskIEEE, CISTI, Ei, IDS, IE, Infotrieve, ingenta, Linda Hall. **CCC.**
Published by: (Rossiiskaya Akademiya Nauk/Russian Academy of Sciences), M A I K Nauka - Interperiodica, Profsoyuznaya ul 90, Moscow, 117997, Russian Federation. TEL 7-095-3347420, FAX 7-095-3360666, compmg@maik.ru, http://www.maik.rssi.ru/journals/procom.htm, http://www.maik.ru. Ed. Viktor P Ivannikov. **Subscr. to:** Springer-Verlag Dordrecht.

005.5 JPN ISSN 0910-7223
PROMPT. Text in Japanese. 1985. m. **Description:** For personal computers users.
Published by: Nikkan Kogyo Shimbun, Ltd., 14-1 Nihonbashikoamicho, Chuo-ku, Tokyo, 103-8548, Japan. TEL 03-263-2311, FAX 03-262-4603, TELEX NIKKANKO J29687. Ed. Norio Shishido. Circ: 50,000.

005.43 GBR
▼ **QERCUS: THE WHOLE PICTURE FOR R I S C O S USERS.** (Reduced Instruction Set Computer Operating System) Text in English. 2004. m. (13/yr.). GBP 45.95 domestic; GBP 55.05 in Europe; GBP 66.75 elsewhere (effective 2004). **Document type:** *Magazine, Trade.*
Formed by the merger of (in 2004): Acorn Publisher (1356-1537); Acorn User (1471-1001); Which had former titles (until 1993): BBC Acorn User (0962-9475); (until 1988): Acorn User (0263-7456)
Published by: Finnybank Ltd., 30 Finnybank Rd, Cheshire, M33 6LR, United Kingdom. TEL 44-161-9699820, FAX 44-8700-519527, info@finnybank.com, http://www.finnybank.com/.

QUANTUM P C REPORT FOR C P AS. see *BUSINESS AND ECONOMICS—Accounting*

005.5 USA ISSN 1542-7730
QA76.758 CODEN: AQCUAE
▼ ➤ **QUEUE**; tomorrow's computing today. Variant title: A C M Queue. Text in English. 2003 (Mar.). 10/yr. USD 34 combined subscription domestic to non-members print & online eds.; USD 66 combined subscription foreign to non-members print & online eds.; USD 24 combined subscription domestic to members print & online eds.; USD 56 combined subscription foreign to members print & online eds.; USD 24 combined subscription domestic to students print & online eds.; USD 56 combined subscription foreign to students print & online eds. (effective 2006). adv. back issues avail.; reprints avail. **Document type:** *Journal, Academic/Scholarly.* **Description:** Focuses on defining the challenges and problems software developers and programmers face as technologies continue to change and evolve.
Related titles: Online - full text ed.: ISSN 1542-7749. 2003. free (effective 2006) (from Association for Computing Machinery, Inc., EBSCO Publishing, ProQuest Information & Learning).
Indexed: ABIn, BrCerAb, C&ISA, CerAb, CorrAb, E&CAJ, EMA, IAA, Inspec, M&TEA, MBF, METADEX, RefZh, WAA.
—Linda Hall. **CCC.**
Published by: Association for Computing Machinery, Inc., 1515 Broadway, 17th Fl, New York, NY 10036-5701. TEL 212-626-0520, 800-342-6626, FAX 212-944-1318, sigs@acm.org, usacm@acm.org, http://www.acmqueue.org, http://www.acm.org. Ed. Edward Grossman. adv.: B&W page USD 2,415, color page USD 3,450. Circ: 30,000 (paid and controlled).

005.5 USA ISSN 1544-6522
▼ **QUICK ANSWERS FOR A S P.** (Active Server Pages) Variant title: Element K Journals' Quick Answers for A S P. Text in English. 2003. a. USD 89 per issue domestic; USD 99 per issue foreign (effective 2005). **Description:** Contains two full years' worth of articles published in Active Server Developer's Journal.
Media: CD-ROM.
Published by: Element K Journals (Subsidiary of: Eli Research, Inc.), 500 Canal View Blvd, Rochester, NY 14623. TEL 585-240-7301, 800-223-8720, 877-203-5248, FAX 585-292-4392, http://www.elementkjournals.com.

005.15 USA ISSN 1543-821X
QA76.9.D3
QUICK ANSWERS FOR MICROSOFT ACCESS. Text in English. a. USD 89 per issue domestic; USD 99 per issue foreign (effective 2005). **Description:** Includes a collection of Inside Microsoft Access articles.
Media: CD-ROM.
Published by: Element K Journals (Subsidiary of: Eli Research, Inc.), 500 Canal View Blvd, Rochester, NY 14623. TEL 585-240-7301, 800-223-8720, 877-203-5248, FAX 585-292-4392, http://www.elementkjournals.com/store/showAncillaryDetail.asp?prodid=46.

005.15 USA ISSN 1543-8228
QUICK ANSWERS FOR MICROSOFT EXCEL. Text in English. a. USD 89 per issue domestic; USD 99 per issue foreign (effective 2005).
Media: CD-ROM.
Published by: Element K Journals (Subsidiary of: Eli Research, Inc.), 500 Canal View Blvd, Rochester, NY 14623. TEL 585-240-7301, 800-223-8720, 877-203-5248, FAX 585-292-4392, http://www.elementkjournals.com/store/showAncillaryDetail.asp?prodid=46.

005.5 USA ISSN 1544-6530
▼ **QUICK ANSWERS FOR MICROSOFT FRONTPAGE.** Variant title: Element K Journals' Quick Answers for Microsoft FrontPage. Text in English. 2003. a. USD 89 per issue domestic; USD 99 per issue foreign (effective 2005).
Media: CD-ROM.
Published by: Element K Journals (Subsidiary of: Eli Research, Inc.), 500 Canal View Blvd, Rochester, NY 14623. TEL 585-240-7301, 800-223-8720, 877-203-5248, FAX 585-292-4392, http://www.elementkjournals.com.

005.5 USA ISSN 1544-6506
HF5548.4.M525
▼ **QUICK ANSWERS FOR MICROSOFT OFFICE 2000.** Variant title: Element K Journals' Quick Answers for Office 2000. Text in English. 2003. a. USD 89 per issue domestic; USD 99 per issue foreign (effective 2005).
Media: CD-ROM.
Published by: Element K Journals (Subsidiary of: Eli Research, Inc.), 500 Canal View Blvd, Rochester, NY 14623. TEL 585-240-7301, 800-223-8720, 877-203-5248, FAX 585-292-4392, http://www.elementkjournals.com/store/showAncillaryDetail.asp?prodID=133.

005.5 USA ISSN 1544-6484
▼ **QUICK ANSWERS FOR MICROSOFT POWERPOINT.** Variant title: Element K Journals' Quick Answers for Microsoft Power Point. Text in English. 2003. a. USD 89 per issue domestic; USD 99 per issue foreign (effective 2005).
Media: CD-ROM.
Published by: Element K Journals (Subsidiary of: Eli Research, Inc.), 500 Canal View Blvd, Rochester, NY 14623. TEL 585-240-7301, 800-223-8720, 877-203-5248, FAX 585-292-4392, http://www.elementkjournals.com.

005.15 USA ISSN 1543-7655
QA76.65
▼ **QUICK ANSWERS FOR MICROSOFT VISUAL BASIC.** Text in English. 2003. a. USD 89 per issue domestic; USD 99 per issue foreign (effective 2005).
Media: CD-ROM.
Published by: Element K Journals (Subsidiary of: Eli Research, Inc.), 500 Canal View Blvd, Rochester, NY 14623. TEL 585-240-7301, 800-223-8720, 877-203-5248, FAX 585-292-4392, http://www.elementkjournals.com/store/showAncillaryDetail.asp?prodid=45.

005.5 USA ISSN 1544-6492
QA76.76
▼ **QUICK ANSWERS FOR MICROSOFT WINDOWS 2000.** Variant title: Element K Journals' Quick Answers for Microsoft Windows 2000. Text in English. 2003. a. USD 89 per issue domestic; USD 99 per issue foreign (effective 2005).
Media: CD-ROM.
Published by: Element K Journals (Subsidiary of: Eli Research, Inc.), 500 Canal View Blvd, Rochester, NY 14623. TEL 585-240-7301, 800-223-8720, 877-203-5248, FAX 585-292-4392, http://www.elementkjournals.com/store/showAncillaryDetail.asp?prodID=131.

005.15 USA
QUICK ANSWERS FOR MICROSOFT WINDOWS X P. Text in English. a. USD 89 per issue domestic; USD 99 per issue foreign (effective 2005). **Description:** Gives you hundreds of tips, techniques, illustrations, and step-by-step "how-to" articles on Windows XP in an easy-to-use, electronically searchable format.
Media: CD-ROM.
Published by: Element K Journals (Subsidiary of: Eli Research, Inc.), 500 Canal View Blvd, Rochester, NY 14623. TEL 585-240-7301, 800-223-8720, 877-203-5248, FAX 585-292-4392, http://www.elementkjournals.com.

005.15 USA ISSN 1543-8236
QUICK ANSWERS FOR MICROSOFT WORD. Text in English. a. USD 89 per issue domestic; USD 99 per issue foreign (effective 2005).
Media: CD-ROM.
Published by: Element K Journals (Subsidiary of: Eli Research, Inc.), 500 Canal View Blvd, Rochester, NY 14623. TEL 585-240-7301, 800-223-8720, 877-203-5248, FAX 585-292-4392, http://www.elementkjournals.com.

005.5 USA ISSN 1544-6514
▼ **QUICK ANSWERS FOR WEB DESIGN.** Variant title: Element K Journals' Quick Answers for Web Design. Text in English. 2003. a. USD 89 per issue domestic; USD 99 per issue foreign (effective 2005).
Media: CD-ROM.
Published by: Element K Journals (Subsidiary of: Eli Research, Inc.), 500 Canal View Blvd, Rochester, NY 14623. TEL 585-240-7301, 800-223-8720, 877-203-5248, FAX 585-292-4392, http://www.elementkjournals.com.

REQUIREMENTS ENGINEERING. see *ENGINEERING—Computer Applications*

REVISTA CANARIA DE ESTUDIOS INGLESES. see *LINGUISTICS*

005.5 BRA ISSN 0104-8732
REVISTA DO CD-ROM; informatica pratica e descomplicada. Text in Portuguese. 1995. m. USD 110 with CD-ROM. adv. **Description:** For people who do not want to read complicated computer book guides. Covers games, computing tips, new computing programs, service features for PC users, and the latest software and hardware.
Published by: Editora Europa Ltda., Rua MMDC 121, Butanta, Sao Paulo, SP 05510-021, Brazil. TEL 55-11-30385050, FAX 55-11-38190538, revista.cd-rom@europanet.com.br, http://www.europanet.com.br. Ed. Aydano Roriz. Adv. contact Givaldo Fernandez. B&W page USD 9,028, color page USD 12,475; trim 275 x 205. Circ: 80,500 (paid).

005.5 CHN ISSN 1003-6970
RUANJIAN/SOFTWARE. Text in Chinese. 1979. m. CNY 264 to individuals; USD 42 foreign to individuals. adv. **Description:** Introduces update softwares domestic and foreign and famous software manufactures in the world.
Related titles: CD-ROM ed.; Online - full text ed.
Published by: Tianjin Dianzi Xuehui/Tianjin Electronics Society, 151 Jiefang Beilu, Tianjin 300040, China. TEL 86-22-3112605, FAX 86-22-3112605, swjour@public.tpt.tj.cn, http://www.softmag.com. Ed. Zhang Shangren.

005.5 CHN ISSN 1005-2348
QA76.75
RUANJIAN SHIJIE/SOFTWARE WORLD. Text in Chinese. 1993. m.
Related titles: Online - full text ed.: (from East View Information Services).
Published by: Software World Magazine Agency, P.O. Box 162, Beijing, China. TEL 86-10-821-2233, FAX 86-10-821-1386. Circ: 50,000.

005.5 CHN ISSN 1000-9825
CODEN: RUXUEW
➤ **RUANJIAN XUEBAO/JOURNAL OF SOFTWARE.** Text in Chinese; Summaries in English. 1990. m. CNY 240 (effective 2000). **Document type:** *Academic/Scholarly.* **Description:** Covers research in both theoretical and applied aspects of computer science and software techniques.
Related titles: Online - full text ed.: (from East View Information Services).
Indexed: C&ISA, E&CAJ, Englnd, IAA, Inspec, MathR, MathSciNet, RefZh, SolStAb.
Published by: Chinese Academy of Sciences, Institute of Software, PO Box 8718, Beijing, 100080, China. TEL 86-10-6256-2563, FAX 86-10-64887716, jos@ns.ict.ac.cn, http://www.cos.ac.cn/xuebao/sye.html. Ed. Feng Yu Lin. Adv. contact Yulan Ju. Circ: 3,000. **Dist. by:** PO Box 399, Beijing 100044, China.

005.1 330 USA ISSN 1532-3986
S A S COM. Text in English. q.
Formerly (until 2001): S A S Communications (0270-9422)
Published by: S A S Institute, Inc., 100 SAS Campus Dr, Cary, NC 27513-2414. TEL 919-677-8000, FAX 919-677-4444, links@sas.com, http://www.sas.com/news/sascom/index.html, http://www.sas.com/corporate/publications/index.html.

005.5 USA ISSN 1528-1965
S D TIMES; the industry newspaper for software development managers. (Software Development) Text in English. 2000. s-m. USD 179 domestic; USD 189 in Canada; USD 229 elsewhere; free to qualified personnel (effective 2004). adv. **Document type:** *Newspaper, Trade.* **Description:** Contains news and news analysis of important and relevant issues of interest to people managing software and application development projects.
Related titles: Online - full text ed.: (from ProQuest Information & Learning).
Indexed: ABIn, BrCerAb, C&ISA, CerAb, CorrAb, E&CAJ, EMA, IAA, M&TEA, MBF, METADEX, SolStAb, WAA.
—Linda Hall.
Published by: B Z Media LLC, Seven High St, Huntington, NY 11743. TEL 631-421-4158, FAX 631-421-4045, info@sdtimes.com, info@bzmedia.com, http://www.sdtimes.com/, http://www.bzmedia.com. Ed. Alan Zeichick. Adv. contact Ted Bahr. B&W page USD 5,560, color page USD 6,995; trim 10.375 x 13. Circ: 45,000 (paid and controlled).

005.5 USA
S I G ADA ANNUAL INTERNATIONAL CONFERENCE. PROCEEDINGS. (Special Interest Group on Ada) Text in English. a. software rev. **Document type:** *Proceedings, Academic/Scholarly.*
Formerly (until 1998): Tri - Ada Conference. Proceedings
Related titles: Online - full text ed.
—BLDSC (0578.637000).

C

▼ new title ➤ refereed ✶ unverified ♦ full entry avail.

Published by: Association for Computing Machinery, Inc., 1515 Broadway, 17th Fl, New York, NY 10036-5701. TEL 212-626-0500, 212-626-0520, 800-342-6626, FAX 212-869-0481, sigs@acm.org, usacm@acm.org, http://www.acm.org/sigada/.

005.16 USA
S R M. (Software Risk Management) Text in English. 2000. q. **Document type:** *Magazine, Trade.* **Description:** Covers software risk management related topics of interest to CEOs and managers in virtually every industry that relies on essential software.
Published by: Cigital, 21351 Ridgetop Circle, Ste 400, Dulles, VA 20166-6503. TEL 703-404-9293, 800-824-0022, FAX 703-404-9295, editor@srmmagazine.com, info@cigital.com, http://www.srmmagazine.com, http://www.cigital.com. Ed. Steve Goodwin.

005.5 USA
THE S T LABS REPORT. Text in English. bi-m. **Document type:** *Trade.*
Published by: S T Labs, Inc., Sterling Plaza, 3rd Fl, 3535 128th Ave, S E, Bellevue, WA 98006. pruec@stlabs.com.

005.1 658.568 USA
SCIENCE AND ENGINEERING IN SOFTWARE DEVELOPMENT. Text in English. a. price varies. **Document type:** *Proceedings, Trade.*
Published by: Institute of Electrical and Electronics Engineers, Inc., 3 Park Ave, 17th Fl, New York, NY 10016-5997. TEL 800-678-4333, customer.service@ieee.org, http://www.ieee.org.

005.1 620 NLD ISSN 1058-9244
QA76.6 CODEN: SCIPEV
➤ **SCIENTIFIC PROGRAMMING.** Text in English. 1992. q. EUR 477, USD 573 combined subscription print & online eds. (effective 2006). adv. back issues avail. **Document type:** *Journal, Academic/Scholarly.* **Description:** Provides a meeting ground for research in, and practical experience with, software engineering environments, tools, languages, and models of computation aimed specifically at supporting scientific and engineering computing.
Related titles: Microform ed.: (from PQC); Online - full text ed.: (from EBSCO Publishing, Gale Group, IngentaConnect, O C L C Online Computer Library Center, Inc., Swets Information Services).
Indexed: BrCerAb, C&ISA, CerAb, CompAb, CompLI, CorrAb, E&CAJ, EMA, EngInd, IAA, Inspec, M&TEA, MBF, METADEX, SolStAb, WAA.
—BLDSC (8190.220000), AskIEEE, CISTI, Ei, IE, Infotrieve, ingenta, Linda Hall. **CCC.**
Published by: I O S Press, Nieuwe Hemweg 6B, Amsterdam, 1013 BG, Netherlands. TEL 31-20-6883355, FAX 31-20-6203419, info@iospress.nl, order@iospress.nl, http://www.iospress.nl/html/10589244.html. Eds. Boleslaw Szymanski TEL 518-276-2714, Ronald H Perrott TEL 44-1232-335463. R&P Ms. Carry Koolbergen TEL 31-20-6382189. Adv. contact Ms. Jolijn van Eunen. Circ: 400.
Subscr. to: I O S Press, Inc, 4502 Rachael Manor Dr., Fairfax, VA 22032-3631. iosbooks@iospress.com; Kinokuniya Co. Ltd., Shinjuku 3-chome, Shinjuku-ku, Tokyo 160-0022, Japan. FAX 81-3-3439-1094, journal@kinokuniya.co.jp, http://www.kinokuniya.co.jp; Globe Publication Pvt. Ltd., C-62 Inderpuri, New Delhi 100 012, India. TEL 91-11-579-3211, 91-11-579-3212, FAX 91-11-579-8876, custserve@globepub.com, http://www.globepub.com.

005.5 USA
SEARCH SOFT BASE. Text in English. 1991. m. looseleaf. software rev.; Website rev. abstr.; bibl.; mkt. **Document type:** *Directory, Bibliography.*
Formerly: Search Software
Related titles: Online - full content ed.
Published by: Information Sources Inc, 1173 Colusa Ave, Box 8120, Berkeley, CA 94707. TEL 510-525-6220, FAX 510-525-1568, info@searchsoftbase.com, http://www.searchsoftbase.com. Ed., Pub., R&P Ruth K Koolish.

005 SGP
▼ **SERIES ON COMPONENT-BASED SOFTWARE DEVELOPMENT.** Text in English. 2004. irreg., latest vol.1. price varies. **Document type:** *Monographic series, Academic/Scholarly.* **Description:** Explores software assembled by components. Creates a forum for CBD researchers, practitioners and students. Includes related surveys, reports, proceedings, monographs, and textbooks.
Published by: World Scientific Publishing Co. Pte. Ltd., 5 Toh Tuck Link, Singapore, 596224, Singapore. TEL 65-466-5775, FAX 65-467-7667, wspc@wspc.com.sg, series@wspc.com.sg, http://www.wspc.com/books/series/scbsd_series.shtml, http://www.worldscientific.com. Ed. Kung-Kiu Lau TEL 44-161-2755716. **Dist. by:** World Scientific Publishing Co., Inc., 1060 Main St, River Edge, NJ 07661. TEL 201-487-9655, 800-227-7562, FAX 201-487-9656, 888-977-2665; World Scientific Publishing Ltd., 57 Shelton St, London WC2H 9HE, United Kingdom. TEL 44-20-78360888, FAX 44-20-78362020.

005.1 SGP ISSN 1793-0995
SERIES ON SOFTWARE ENGINEERING & KNOWLEDGE ENGINEERING. Text in English. 1993. irreg., latest vol.17. price varies. **Document type:** *Monographic series, Academic/Scholarly.*
—BLDSC (8250.202340), ingenta.
Published by: World Scientific Publishing Co. Pte. Ltd., 5 Toh Tuck Link, Singapore, 596224, Singapore. TEL 65-466-5775, FAX 65-467-7667, wspc@wspc.com.sg, series@wspc.com.sg, http://www.wspc.com.sg/books/series/sseke_series.shtml, http://www.worldscientific.com. Ed. S K Chang. **Dist. by:** World Scientific Publishing Co., Inc., 1060 Main St, River Edge, NJ 07661. TEL 201-487-9655, 800-227-7562, FAX 201-487-9656, 888-977-2665; World Scientific Publishing Ltd., 57 Shelton St, London WC2H 9HE, United Kingdom. TEL 44-20-78360888, FAX 44-20-78362020.

005.5 USA
SHAREPAPER✶. Text in English. 1996. d. software rev. **Description:** Contains reviews of low cost, high quality software, tips and related links.
Media: Online - full text.
Published by: (Snail Mail), ZCO, Inc., 3550 General Atomics Ct no.14, San Diego, CA 92121-1122. mgersh@sharepaper.com, http://www.sharepaper.com. Ed. Lars Mathiassen.

005.5 USA ISSN 1554-7833
▼ **SHAREPOINT ADVISOR.** Text in English. 2005. m. USD 99 (effective 2005). **Document type:** *Magazine, Trade.* **Description:** Covers all the issues related to Microsoft Sahrepoint products and technologies. Includes advice on creating, customizing, integrating and managing collabortion sites with Sharepoint products and technologies, including Wondows SharePoint Services and Microsoft SharePoint Portal Server.
Published by: Advisor Media, Inc., 4849 Viewridge Ave, San Diego, CA 92123-1643. TEL 858-278-5600, FAX 858-278-0300, advisor@advisor.com, subscribe@advisor.com, http://sharepointadvisor.com, http://www.advisor.com.

005.5 GBR
THE SITES DIRECTORY (YEAR). Text in English. 1985. a. GBP 295 per issue (effective 2003). **Document type:** *Directory, Trade.* **Description:** Profiles the IT used at 14,000 company sites with over 20,000 named contacts. This directory provides company data together with the systems used, operating systems installed and communications information.
Former titles: Computing Software; (until 2004): The Software Users Year Book (0268-6708); Which was formed by the merger of (1983-1985): Microcomputer Software Directory (0267-6818); (1977-1985): International Directory of Software (0260-3438)
Related titles: CD-ROM ed.
—BLDSC (3395.128800), IE, Infotrieve.
Published by: V N U Business Publications Ltd., 32-34 Broadwick St, London, W1A 2HG, United Kingdom. TEL 44-20-73169610, FAX 44-20-73169260, directories@computing.co.uk, http://www.bcs.org/BCS/Products/Publications/Offers/vnu.htm, http://www.computing.co.uk/directories. Ed. Geoff Knott.

005.437 USA
SKEEVIS!; windows 95/98 e-zine. Text in English. 1998. w. free. **Document type:** *Newsletter.* **Description:** Includes tips, news and articles about Windows 95 and 98.
Media: Online - full text.
Address: skeevis@skeevis.com, http://www.skeevis.com. Ed. Zvi Band. Pub. Grand Poobah.

SMART CARD NEWS. see *COMPUTERS—Computer Industry*

005.15 USA
SMART TIPS AND QUICK TIPS FOR OFFICE X P. Text in English. a. USD 10 per issue domestic; USD 20 per issue foreign (effective 2005). **Description:** Offers more than 45 timesaving tips, tricks, and techniques designed to increase your productivity with the applications you use within Office XP, including Microsoft Word, Excel, PowerPoint, Access, and Outlook all in one convenient resource.
Published by: Element K Journals (Subsidiary of: Eli Research, Inc.), 500 Canal View Blvd, Rochester, NY 14623. TEL 585-240-7301, 800-223-8720, 877-203-5248, FAX 585-292-4392, http://www.elementkjournals.com.

005.5 USA ISSN 1537-6982
SMART TIPS AND QUICK TRICKS FOR ADOBE ILLUSTRATOR. Text in English. 2002. irreg. USD 11.50 per issue (effective 2005).
—**CCC.**
Published by: Element K Journals (Subsidiary of: Eli Research, Inc.), 500 Canal View Blvd, Rochester, NY 14623. TEL 585-240-7301, 800-223-8720, 877-203-5248, FAX 585-292-4392, http://www.elementkjournals.com. Eds. Stephen Dow, Michelle Rogers.

005.5 USA ISSN 1537-6990
SMART TIPS AND QUICK TRICKS FOR ADOBE INDESIGN. Text in English. 2002. a. USD 11.50 per issue (effective 2005).
—**CCC.**
Published by: Element K Journals (Subsidiary of: Eli Research, Inc.), 500 Canal View Blvd, Rochester, NY 14623. TEL 585-240-7301, 800-223-8720, 877-203-5248, FAX 585-292-4392, http://www.elementkjournals.com. Eds. Renee Dustman, Michelle Rogers.

005.5 USA ISSN 1537-6974
SMART TIPS AND QUICK TRICKS FOR ADOBE PAGEMAKER. Text in English. 2002. a. USD 11.50 per issue (effective 2005).
—**CCC.**
Published by: Element K Journals (Subsidiary of: Eli Research, Inc.), 500 Canal View Blvd, Rochester, NY 14623. TEL 585-240-7301, 800-223-8720, 877-203-5248, FAX 585-292-4392, http://www.elementkjournals.com. Eds. Katherine McRay, Michelle Rogers.

005.5 USA ISSN 1537-6966
SMART TIPS AND QUICK TRICKS FOR ADOBE PHOTOSHOP. Text in English. 2002. irreg. USD 11.50 per issue (effective 2005).
—**CCC.**
Published by: Element K Journals (Subsidiary of: Eli Research, Inc.), 500 Canal View Blvd, Rochester, NY 14623. TEL 585-240-7301, 800-223-8720, 877-203-5248, FAX 585-292-4392, http://www.elementkjournals.com. Eds. Amy Courtwright, Michelle Rogers.

005.5 USA ISSN 1537-7016
SMART TIPS AND QUICK TRICKS FOR AUTOCAD. Text in English. 2002. irreg. USD 11.50 per issue (effective 2005).
—**CCC.**
Published by: Element K Journals (Subsidiary of: Eli Research, Inc.), 500 Canal View Blvd, Rochester, NY 14623. TEL 585-240-7301, 800-223-8720, 877-203-5248, FAX 585-292-4392, http://www.elementkjournals.com. Ed. Michelle Rogers.

005.5 USA ISSN 1543-1959
▼ **SMART TIPS AND QUICK TRICKS FOR COREL WORDPERFECT SUITE.** Text in English. 2003. irreg. USD 10 per issue domestic; USD 20 per issue foreign (effective 2005).
—**CCC.**
Published by: Element K Journals (Subsidiary of: Eli Research, Inc.), 500 Canal View Blvd, Rochester, NY 14623. TEL 585-240-7301, 800-223-8720, 877-203-5248, FAX 585-292-4392, http://www.elementkjournals.com.

005.5 USA ISSN 1537-6885
SMART TIPS AND QUICK TRICKS FOR MICROSOFT ACCESS. Text in English. 2002. a. USD 10 per issue domestic; USD 20 per issue foreign (effective 2005).
—**CCC.**
Published by: Element K Journals (Subsidiary of: Eli Research, Inc.), 500 Canal View Blvd, Rochester, NY 14623. TEL 585-240-7301, 800-223-8720, 877-203-5248, FAX 585-292-4392, http://www.elementkjournals.com. Eds. Sean Kavanagh, Michelle Rogers.

005.5 USA ISSN 1537-6877
SMART TIPS AND QUICK TRICKS FOR MICROSOFT EXCEL. Text in English. 2002. a. USD 10 per issue domestic; USD 20 per issue foreign (effective 2005).
—**CCC.**
Published by: Element K Journals (Subsidiary of: Eli Research, Inc.), 500 Canal View Blvd, Rochester, NY 14623. TEL 585-240-7301, 800-223-8720, 877-203-5248, FAX 585-292-4392, http://www.elementkjournals.com. Eds. Sean Kavanagh, Michelle Rogers.

005.5 USA ISSN 1537-6907
SMART TIPS AND QUICK TRICKS FOR MICROSOFT FRONTPAGE. Text in English. 2002. a. USD 10 per issue domestic; USD 20 per issue foreign (effective 2005).
—**CCC.**
Published by: Element K Journals (Subsidiary of: Eli Research, Inc.), 500 Canal View Blvd, Rochester, NY 14623. TEL 585-240-7301, 800-223-8720, 877-203-5248, FAX 585-292-4392, http://www.elementkjournals.com. Eds. Mark Ray, Michelle Rogers.

005.5 USA ISSN 1537-6923
SMART TIPS AND QUICK TRICKS FOR MICROSOFT OFFICE 2000. Text in English. 2002. a. USD 10 per issue domestic; USD 20 per issue foreign (effective 2005).
—**CCC.**
Published by: Element K Journals (Subsidiary of: Eli Research, Inc.), 500 Canal View Blvd, Rochester, NY 14623. TEL 585-240-7301, 800-223-8720, 877-203-5248, FAX 585-292-4392, http://www.elementkjournals.com. Ed. Michelle Rogers.

005.5 USA ISSN 1539-946X
SMART TIPS AND QUICK TRICKS FOR MICROSOFT OFFICE X P. Text in English. 2002. a. USD 10 per issue domestic; USD 20 per issue foreign (effective 2005).
—**CCC.**
Published by: Element K Journals (Subsidiary of: Eli Research, Inc.), 500 Canal View Blvd, Rochester, NY 14623. TEL 585-240-7301, 800-223-8720, 877-203-5248, FAX 585-292-4392, http://www.elementkjournals.com. Eds. Matt Gebhardt, Sean Kavanagh, T. L. Aardsma, Michelle Rogers.

C

005.5 USA ISSN 1537-6893
SMART TIPS AND QUICK TRICKS FOR MICROSOFT POWERPOINT. Text in English. 2002. a. USD 10 per issue domestic; USD 20 per issue foreign (effective 2005).
—CCC.
Published by: Element K Journals (Subsidiary of: Eli Research, Inc.), 500 Canal View Blvd, Rochester, NY 14623. TEL 585-240-7301, 800-223-8720, 877-203-5248, FAX 585-292-4392, http://www.elementkjournals.com. Eds. Matt Gebhardt, Michelle Rogers.

005.5 004.678 USA ISSN 1538-831X
SMART TIPS AND QUICK TRICKS FOR MICROSOFT VISUAL BASIC. Text in English. 2002. a. USD 10 per issue domestic; USD 20 per issue foreign (effective 2005).
—CCC.
Published by: Element K Journals (Subsidiary of: Eli Research, Inc.), 500 Canal View Blvd, Rochester, NY 14623. TEL 585-240-7301, 800-223-8720, 877-203-5248, FAX 585-292-4392, http://www.elementkjournals.com. Eds. Mike D. Jones, Michelle Rogers.

005.43 USA ISSN 1537-6931
SMART TIPS AND QUICK TRICKS FOR MICROSOFT WINDOWS 2000. Text in English. 2002. a. USD 10 per issue domestic; USD 20 per issue foreign (effective 2005).
Related titles: CD-ROM ed.
—CCC.
Published by: Element K Journals (Subsidiary of: Eli Research, Inc.), 500 Canal View Blvd, Rochester, NY 14623. TEL 585-240-7301, 800-223-8720, 877-203-5248, FAX 585-292-4392, http://www.elementkjournals.com. Eds. Rozanne Whalen, Michelle Rogers.

005.43 USA ISSN 1537-6958
SMART TIPS AND QUICK TRICKS FOR MICROSOFT WINDOWS N T. Text in English. 2002. a. USD 10 per issue domestic; USD 20 per issue foreign (effective 2005).
—CCC.
Published by: Element K Journals (Subsidiary of: Eli Research, Inc.), 500 Canal View Blvd, Rochester, NY 14623. TEL 585-240-7301, 800-223-8720, 877-203-5248, FAX 585-292-4392, http://www.elementkjournals.com. Eds. John Garrett, Michelle Rogers.

005.5 USA ISSN 1543-1134
▼ **SMART TIPS AND QUICK TRICKS FOR MICROSOFT WINDOWS X P.** Text in English. 2003. irreg. USD 10 per issue domestic; USD 20 per issue foreign (effective 2005).
—CCC.
Published by: Element K Journals (Subsidiary of: Eli Research, Inc.), 500 Canal View Blvd, Rochester, NY 14623. TEL 585-240-7301, 800-223-8720, 877-203-5248, FAX 585-292-4392, http://www.elementkjournals.com.

005.5 USA ISSN 1537-6869
SMART TIPS AND QUICK TRICKS FOR MICROSOFT WORD. Text in English. 2002. a. USD 10 per issue domestic; USD 20 per issue foreign (effective 2005).
—CCC.
Published by: Element K Journals (Subsidiary of: Eli Research, Inc.), 500 Canal View Blvd, Rochester, NY 14623. TEL 585-240-7301, 800-223-8720, 877-203-5248, FAX 585-292-4392, http://www.elementkjournals.com. Eds. T. L. Aardsma, Michelle Rogers.

SMART TIPS AND QUICK TRICKS FOR QUARKXPRESS. see *PUBLISHING AND BOOK TRADE—Computer Applications*

005.36 USA ISSN 0882-3499
SOFT - LETTER; trends & strategies in software publishing. Text in English. 1983. s-m. looseleaf. USD 395. bk.rev. index. back issues avail. **Document type:** *Newsletter.* **Description:** For managers of software companies. Covers news, trends and strategies in the software publishing field.
Related titles: Online - full text ed.: (from Factiva, Gale Group, Northern Light Technology, Inc.).
Indexed: CompD.
Published by: U C G Technologies, 11300 Rockville Pike, Ste 1100, Rockville, MD 20852-3030. TEL 301-287-2718, 301-924-3944, jtarter@softletter.com, http://www.softletter.com. Ed. Jeffrey Tarter. Pub. Carol Crowell. R&P Jane Farber. Circ: 1,500 (paid).

005.5 USA ISSN 1087-6367
QA76.75
SOFTWARE & CD-ROM REVIEWS ON FILE. Text in English. 1985. m. looseleaf. USD 249. cum.index. **Description:** For library, business, school or home use. Contains condensed versions of software reviews that appeared in any of over 150 publications. Features software for all major microcomputer systems and programming languages.
Formerly: Software Reviews on File (8755-7169)
Published by: Facts on File, Inc. (Subsidiary of: W R C Media Inc.), 132 W 31st St, 17th Fl, New York, NY 10001. TEL 212-967-8800. Circ: 1,300.

005.1 DEU ISSN 1619-1366
➤ **SOFTWARE AND SYSTEMS MODELING.** Text in English. 2002. q. EUR 250 combined subscription to institutions print & online eds. (effective 2005). adv. back issues avail. **Document type:** *Journal, Academic/Scholarly.* **Description:** Aims to further the understanding of the theoretical underpinnings and industrial applications of systems modeling languages and techniques.
Related titles: Online - full text ed.: ISSN 1619-1374 (from EBSCO Publishing, ProQuest Information & Learning, Springer LINK, Swets Information Services).
Indexed: CompLI.
—BLDSC (8321.450255), IE. **CCC.**
Published by: Springer-Verlag (Subsidiary of: Springer Science+Business Media), Tiergartenstr 17, Heidelberg, 69121, Germany. TEL 49-6221-3450, FAX 49-6221-345229, http://link.springer.de/link/service/journals/10270. Eds. Bernhard Rumpe TEL 49-89-289-28129, Robert France TEL 970-491-6356. Adv. contact Stephan Kroeck TEL 49-30-827875739. **Subscr. in the Americas to:** Springer-Verlag New York, Inc., Journal Fulfillment, PO Box 2485, Secaucus, NJ 07096-2485. TEL 800-777-4643, 201-348-4033, FAX 201-348-4505, journals@springer-ny.com, http://www.springer-ny.com; **Subscr. to:** Springer GmbH Auslieferungsgesellschaft, Haberstr 7, Heidelberg 69126, Germany. TEL 49-6221-345-0, FAX 49-6221-345-4229, subscriptions@springer.de.

004 330 USA
SOFTWARE BUSINESS. Text in English. bi-m. free domestic; USD 50 domestic; USD 65 elsewhere (effective 2005). **Document type:** *Magazine, Trade.*
Published by: Webcom Communications Corp., 7355 E Orchard Rd, Ste 100, Greenwood Village, CO 80111. TEL 720-528-3770, 800-803-9488, FAX 720-528-3771, johncg@infowebcom.com, http://www.softwarebusinessonline.com, http://www.infowebcom.com.

SOFTWARE CATALOG: MINICOMPUTERS. see *COMPUTERS—Minicomputers*

005.5 USA ISSN 1070-8588
QA76.76.D47
SOFTWARE DEVELOPMENT. Text in English. 1993. m. USD 39 domestic; USD 45 in Canada & Mexico; USD 54 elsewhere (effective 2003); USD 7 newsstand/cover; GBP 3.20 newsstand/cover in Canada. adv. **Document type:** *Trade.* **Description:** Focuses on products to streamline the development process and increase productivity and practices for the corporate developer.
Related titles: Online - full text ed.: (from bigchalk, ProQuest Information & Learning).
Indexed: CompD, CompLI, Inspec, MicrocompInd, SoftBase.
—BLDSC (8321.450660), IE, Infotrieve, ingenta. **CCC.**
Published by: C M P Media LLC (Subsidiary of: United News & Media), 600 Harrison St, 6th Fl., San Francisco, CA 94107. TEL 415-947-6746, FAX 415-947-6041, http://www.sdmagazine.com/, http://www.cmp.com. Ed. Alexandra Weber Morales. Pub. Stan Barnes. adv.: B&W page USD 8,646. Circ: 100,000.

005.5 GBR ISSN 0964-6841
➤ **SOFTWARE DEVELOPMENT MONITOR.** Text in English. 1992. 12/yr. GBP 495, USD 738 (effective 1995). bk.rev.; software rev. back issues avail. **Document type:** *Academic/Scholarly.* **Description:** In-depth analysis of emerging technologies and market trends relevant to commercial software development.
Related titles: Microform ed.: (from PQC).
—CCC.
Published by: Pergamon (Subsidiary of: Elsevier Science & Technology), The Boulevard, Langford Ln, East Park, Kidlington, Oxford OX5 1GB, United Kingdom. TEL 44-1865-843000, FAX 44-1865-843010. Ed. Tina Monk. **Subscr. to:** Elsevier BV, PO Box 211, Amsterdam 1000 AE, Netherlands. TEL 31-20-485-3757, FAX 31-20-485-3432, nlinfo-f@elsevier.nl, http://www.elsevier.nl.

005.36 USA ISSN 1084-7790
QA76.76.E93
SOFTWARE DIGEST✶; the independent, comparative ratings report for PC and LAN software. Text in English. 1983. 12/yr. USD 450. cum.index.
Former titles (until Mar. 1995): Software Digest Ratings Report (0893-6455); Software Digest Ratings Newsletter (0742-0676); Which supersedes in part: Software Digest
—CCC.
Published by: National Software Testing Laboratories, Inc. (Subsidiary of: McGraw-Hill, Inc.), Plymouth Corporate Center, 625 W Ridge Pike, No 6D, Conshohocken, PA 19428-1180. TEL 215-941-9600, 800-257-9402, FAX 215-941-9950. Pub. Linda Dibasio.

005.5 USA ISSN 1065-6146
CODEN: SECLE3
SOFTWARE ECONOMICS LETTER; maximizing your return on corporate software. Text in English. 1992. m. USD 395 (effective 1998). back issues avail. **Document type:** *Newsletter.* **Description:** Provides the corporate and IS communities with a concise analysis of software issues and enables them to stay informed of the latest trends in software and software licensing.
Incorporates (in 1996): Client - Server Economics Letter (1074-3138)
Indexed: Inspec.
—BLDSC (8321.451187), AskIEEE. **CCC.**
Published by: Computer Economics, Inc., 2082 Business Center Dr., Ste 240, Irvine, CA 92612. TEL 949-831-8700, FAX 949-442-7688, info@compecon.com, http://www.computereconomics.com. Pubs. Anne Zalatan, Mark McManus. **Dist. by:** Publications Resource Group, 121 Union St., Box 792, North Adams, MA 01247.

005.36 USA ISSN 0000-006X
QA76.753
SOFTWARE ENCYCLOPEDIA; a guide for personal, professional, and business users. Text in English. 1985. a. (in 2 vols.). USD 355 (effective 2004). **Document type:** *Directory, Bibliography.* **Description:** Provides annotated listings for microcomputer software, along with contact information. Indexed by title, compatible systems, and applications.
Related titles: Magnetic Tape ed.; Online - full text ed.
—BLDSC (8321.451190).
Published by: R.R. Bowker LLC (Subsidiary of: Cambridge Information Group), 630 Central Ave., New Providence, NJ 07974. TEL 908-286-1090, 800-526-9537, FAX 908-219-0098, info@bowker.com, http://www.bowker.com. **Subscr. to:** Order Dept., PO Box 32, New Providence, NJ 07974-9903. TEL 800-521-8110.

005.1 NLD ISSN 1386-369X
SOFTWARE ENGINEERING. Variant title: Centrum voor Wiskunde en Informatica. S E N Report Series: Software Engineering. S E N Report Series: Software Engineering. Text in English. 1948. irreg. price varies. abstr. back issues avail. **Document type:** *Monographic series, Academic/Scholarly.*
Supersedes in part (in Feb 1997): Centrum voor Wiskunde en Informatica. Department of Computer Science. Report (0169-118X); Which was formerly (until 1984): Stichting Mathematisch Centrum. Afdeling Informatica. Rapport (0376-4028); (until 1973): Stichting Mathematisch Centrum. Rekenafdeling. Rapport (0517-6417)
Indexed: RefZh.
—BLDSC (7259.135000), CISTI.
Published by: (Stichting Mathematisch Centrum), Centrum voor Wiskunde en Informatica, Department of Computer Science/National Research Institute for Mathematics and Computer Science (Subsidiary of: Stichting Mathematisch Centrum), PO Box 94079, Amsterdam, 1090 GB, Netherlands. TEL 31-20-592-4128, FAX 31-20-592-4199, cwi-buro@cwi.nl, tamende@cwi.nl, http://www.cwi.nl/static/publications/reports/reports.html.

C

005.1 USA ISSN 0163-5948
QA76.758 CODEN: SFENDP
SOFTWARE ENGINEERING NOTES. Text in English. bi-m. USD 35 to non-members; USD 25 to members; USD 12 student members (effective 2004). **Document type:** *Journal, Academic/Scholarly.* **Description:** Contains information on cost-effective, timely development and maintenance of high-quality software.
Related titles: Online - full text ed.: (from EBSCO Publishing).
Indexed: AHCI, C&CSA, CompAb, CompLI, CompR, EngInd, ErgAb, Inspec.
—BLDSC (8321.451500), AskIEEE, CISTI, Ei, IE, Infotrieve, ingenta.
Published by: Association for Computing Machinery, Inc., 1515 Broadway, 17th Fl, New York, NY 10036-5701. TEL 212-626-0500, 212-626-0520, 800-342-6626, FAX 212-869-0481, sigs@acm.org, usacm@acm.org, http://www.acm.org/sigsoft/SEN/.

005.5 GBR ISSN 0965-6545
SOFTWARE FUTURES. Text in English. 1991. m. GBP 395; GBP 495 in North America. back issues avail. **Document type:** *Newsletter.* **Description:** Enables software developers to keep abreast of all developments, from CASE to 4GLs to object orientation and software quality. Aimed at professional package authors and user-based development teams on diverse platforms.
Related titles: Diskette ed.; Online - full text ed.: (from Factiva).
Published by: A P T Data Group plc., 4th Fl, 12 Sutton Row, London, W1V 5FH, United Kingdom. TEL 44-171-528-7083, FAX 44-171-439-1105, sfutures@power.globalnews.com. Ed. Clare Haney. Pub. Dominic Sharp. Circ: 2,000. **US subscr. to:** APT D Services Inc., 828 Broadway, Ste 800, New York, NY 10010. TEL 212-677-0409, FAX 212-677-0463.

005.5 USA
SOFTWARE INDUSTRY BUSINESS PRACTICE SURVEY. Text in English. a. USD 400. **Description:** Includes information about products, pricing, development and testing, types of support, methods of maintenance, marketing, strategic alliances, management, growth and finance.
Indexed: ATI.
Published by: Information Technology Association of America, 1401 Wilson Blvd., Ste. 1100, Arlington, VA 22209-2318. TEL 703-522-5055, FAX 703-525-2279.

▼ new title ➤ refereed ✶ unverified ♦ full entry avail.

005.5 338.4 USA ISSN 1042-7252
SOFTWARE INDUSTRY REPORT; a comprehensive information management analysis of the computer software industry. Text in English. 1968. s-m. USD 495 domestic; USD 519 foreign (effective 2005). bk.rev. back issues avail. **Document type:** *Newsletter.* **Description:** Tracks worldwide industry and government software activities and opportunities, with an emphasis on innovative strategies for MIS executives, market research and new developments in systems technology.
Former titles: Computer Age - Software Digest; Software Digest (Annandale) (0038-0636)
Related titles: Online - full text ed.: (from Factiva, Gale Group, Northern Light Technology, Inc.).
Indexed: CompC, CompD.
—CCC.
Published by: Computer Age & E D P News Services (Subsidiary of: Millin Publishing Group, Inc.), 1150 Connecticut Ave. NW, 900, Washington, DC 20036. TEL 202-862-4375, FAX 202-659-3493, millin@erols.com, millin@aol.com, http://www.millinpubs.com. Ed., R&P Michael E Cotter. Pub. S L Millin. Circ: 900 (paid).

005.5 USA ISSN 0897-8085
QA76.75 CODEN: SMWMEQ
SOFTWARE MAGAZINE. Text in English. 1981. bi-m. USD 42 domestic; USD 58 in Canada; USD 140 elsewhere; USD 7 domestic; free to qualified personnel (effective 2005). adv. bk.rev. back issues avail.; reprint service avail. from PQC. **Document type:** *Magazine, Trade.* **Description:** For business and professional users. Feature articles offer information on software applications and industry developments. Also contains news briefs and new software package announcements for mainframe, mini- and microcomputers.
Formerly (until 1987): Software News (Hudson) (0279-9782)
Related titles: E-mail ed.; Microform ed.: 1981 (from PQC); Online - full text ed.: Softwaremag.com. 1981 (from EBSCO Publishing, Florida Center for Library Automation, Gale Group, Northern Light Technology, Inc., O C L C Online Computer Library Center, Inc., ProQuest Information & Learning).
Indexed: ABIn, CompC, CompD, CompI, CompIU, EngInd, InfoSAb, Inspec, MASUSE, Microcompind, PCR2, PROMT, SoftBase.
—BLDSC (8321.451700), CISTI, Ei, IE, Infotrieve, ingenta. **CCC.**
Published by: King Content Co., 233 Needham St, Ste 300, Newton, MA 02464. TEL 508-668-1150, softwaremagazine@mcimail.com, http://www.softwaremag.com/. Ed. John P Desmond. adv.: B&W page USD 8,200, color page USD 9,120. Circ: 75,000 (controlled).

005.5 GBR ISSN 0038-0644
QA76.5 CODEN: SPEXBL
➤ **SOFTWARE: PRACTICE & EXPERIENCE.** Text in English. 1971. 15/yr. USD 3,345 to institutions; USD 3,680 combined subscription to institutions print & online eds. (effective 2006). adv. bk.rev. illus.; abstr. index. back issues avail.; reprint service avail. from PQC,ISI. **Document type:** *Journal, Academic/Scholarly.* **Description:** Provides the details and experience of the tools or methods used to achieve the results for all those who design, implement, or maintain software.
Related titles: Microform ed.: (from PQC); Online - full text ed.: ISSN 1097-024X. 1998. USD 3,345 to institutions (effective 2006) (from EBSCO Publishing, Swets Information Services, Wiley InterScience).
Indexed: AHCI, AS&TI, ASCA, BMT, BrCerAb, BrTechI, C&ISA, CMCI, CerAb, CompAb, CompC, CompD, CompLI, CompR, CorrAb, CurCont, CybAb, E&CAJ, EMA, ETA, EngInd, IAA, ICEA, InfoSAb, Inspec, JOF, M&TEA, MBF, METADEX, SoftAbEng, SolStAb, WAA, ZentMath.
—BLDSC (8321.453000), AskIEEE, CISTI, Ei, IDS, IE, Infotrieve, ingenta, Linda Hall. **CCC.**
Published by: John Wiley & Sons Ltd. (Subsidiary of: John Wiley & Sons, Inc.), The Atrium, Southern Gate, Chichester, West Sussex PO19 8SQ, United Kingdom. TEL 44-1243-779777, FAX 44-1243-775878, customer@wiley.co.uk, http://www.interscience.wiley.com/jpages/0038-0644/, http://www.wiley.co.uk. Eds. A Wellings, Douglas E Comer. Pub. Anne Marie Halligan. adv.: B&W page GBP 650, color page GBP 1,550; trim 200 x 260. Circ: 1,800. **Subscr. in the Americas to:** John Wiley & Sons, Inc., 111 River St, Hoboken, NJ 07030-5774. TEL 800-225-5945, subinfo@wiley.com.

005.5 GBR ISSN 1077-4866
QA76.75 CODEN: SPIPFL
➤ **SOFTWARE PROCESS IMPROVEMENT AND PRACTICE.** Text in English. 1995. 6/yr. USD 540 to institutions; USD 594 combined subscription to institutions print & online eds. (effective 2006). adv. abstr. back issues avail. **Document type:** *Journal, Academic/Scholarly.* **Description:** Aims to foster improvement in the quality, productivity, performance and assessment of the software development process.
Related titles: Microform ed.: (from PQC); Online - full text ed.: ISSN 1099-1670. 1997. USD 540 to institutions (effective 2006) (from EBSCO Publishing, Swets Information Services, Wiley InterScience).
Indexed: BrCerAb, C&ISA, CerAb, CompLI, CorrAb, E&CAJ, EMA, IAA, Inspec, M&TEA, MBF, METADEX, SolStAb, WAA.
—BLDSC (8321.453300), IE, Infotrieve, ingenta. **CCC.**
Published by: John Wiley & Sons Ltd. (Subsidiary of: John Wiley & Sons, Inc.), The Atrium, Southern Gate, Chichester, West Sussex PO19 8SQ, United Kingdom. TEL 44-1243-779777, FAX 44-1243-775878, customer@wiley.co.uk, http://www.interscience.wiley.com/jpages/1077-4866, http://www.wiley.co.uk. Eds. Darren Dalcher, David Raffo. Pub. Anne Marie Halligan. adv.: B&W page GBP 650, color page GBP 1,550; trim 210 x 297. **Subscr. in the Americas to:** John Wiley & Sons, Inc., 111 River St, Hoboken, NJ 07030-5774. TEL 201-748-6645, 800-225-5945, subinfo@wiley.com.

005.1 DEU ISSN 1617-6006
SOFTWARE-QUALITAETSMANAGEMENT; Theorie & Praxis. Text in German. 2001. irreg., latest vol.2, 2002. price varies. **Document type:** *Monographic series, Academic/Scholarly.*
Published by: Logos Verlag Berlin, Comeniushof, Gubener Str 47, Berlin, 10243, Germany. TEL 49-30-42851090, FAX 49-30-42851092, redaktion@logos-verlag.de, http://www.logos-verlag.de. Ed. Roland Petrasch.

005.5 USA ISSN 1068-400X
CODEN: UQUAEU
THE SOFTWARE QUALITY ADVISOR; the "how-to" newsletter of software quality assurance. Text in English. 1991. q. USD 36 (effective 1998). bk.rev.; software rev. back issues avail. **Document type:** *Newsletter.* **Description:** Focuses on software testing and quality assurance. Aims to provide practical and proven methods for ensuring quality for software testers, QA analysts, developers, and end-users.
Published by: Rice Consulting Services, Inc., 6127, Moore, OK 73153-0127. TEL 405-692-7331, FAX 405-692-7570, rcs@telepath.com, http://www.telepath.com/rcs. Ed., Pub., R&P Randall W Rice. Circ: 500 (paid).

005.14 USA ISSN 0963-9314
QA76.76.Q35 CODEN: SQJOET
➤ **SOFTWARE QUALITY JOURNAL.** Text in English. 1992. q. EUR 518, USD 528, GBP 328 combined subscription to institutions print & online eds. (effective 2005). adv. bk.rev.; software rev. back issues avail.; reprint service avail. from PSC. **Document type:** *Academic/Scholarly.* **Description:** Contains practical and researched-based material on software-quality and related issues.
Related titles: Online - full text ed.: ISSN 1573-1367 (from EBSCO Publishing, Gale Group, IngentaConnect, Kluwer Online, O C L C Online Computer Library Center, Inc., Springer LINK, Swets Information Services).
Indexed: ASCA, BibLing, CIS, CMCI, CompAb, CompLI, Inspec, RefZh.
—BLDSC (8321.453530), AskIEEE, CISTI, IDS, IE, Infotrieve, ingenta. **CCC.**
Published by: Springer-Verlag New York, Inc. (Subsidiary of: Springer Science+Business Media), 233 Spring St, New York, NY 10013. TEL 212-460-1500, FAX 212-460-1575, service@springer-ny.com, http://springerlink.metapress.com/openurl.asp?genre=journal&issn=0963-9314, http://www.springer-ny.com. Ed. James Bieman. **Subscr. to:** Journal Fulfillment, PO Box 2485, Secaucus, NJ 07096-2485. TEL 201-348-4033, FAX 201-348-4505, journals@springer-ny.com.

005.14 USA ISSN 1522-0540
SOFTWARE QUALITY PROFESSIONAL. Text in English. q. USD 40 domestic to members; USD 60 foreign to members; USD 70 domestic to non-members; USD 95 foreign to non-members; USD 120 domestic to institutions; USD 150 foreign to institutions (effective 2003). **Document type:** *Journal, Trade.* **Description:** Provides readers with an understanding of software quality practices that have been proven effective in a wide range of industries, applications, and organizational settings.
Related titles: Online - full text ed.: (from O C L C Online Computer Library Center, Inc., ProQuest Information & Learning).
—IE. **CCC.**
Published by: American Society for Quality Control, 600 N Plankinton Ave, Milwaukee, WI 53203-2914. TEL 414-272-8575, FAX 414-272-1734, http://www.asq.org.

005.5 NLD ISSN 1386-6036
SOFTWARE RELEASE MAGAZINE; het vakblad voor software. Text in Dutch. 1996. 8/yr. EUR 72.50 domestic; EUR 82.50 in Belgium (effective 2005). adv. software rev. charts; illus.; tr.lit. **Document type:** *Journal, Trade.* **Description:** Covers issues and techniques in corporate software development.
Formerly (until 1996): Software Release (1385-1659)
Published by: Array Publications BV, Postbus 2211, Alphen aan den Rijn, 2400 CE, Netherlands. TEL 31-172-424177, FAX 31-172-424381, release@array.nl, http://www.release.nl/site/, http://www.array.nl. Ed. Dre de Man. Adv. contact Will Manusiwa TEL 31-172-469030. B&W page EUR 1,995, color 1/2 page EUR 3,195; trim 210 x 285. Circ: 4,100 (paid).

005.5 GBR ISSN 1462-611X
➤ **SOFTWARE STUDIES.** Text in English. 1998. irreg., latest vol.3, 2001. **Document type:** *Proceedings, Academic/Scholarly.* **Description:** Consists of books concerned with the state-of-the-art developments in software design, and applications for engineering. Each volume is composed of authored works or edited volumes of several chapters written by leading researchers in the field, covers areas of current interest or active research.
—CISTI.
Published by: WIT Press, Ashurst Lodge, Ashurst, Southampton, Hants SO40 7AA, United Kingdom. TEL 44-238-029-3223, FAX 44-238-029-2853, marketing@witpress.com, http://www.witpress.com. **Dist. by:** Computational Mechanics Inc., 25 Bridge St, Billerica, MA 01821-1007. TEL 978-667-5841, FAX 978-667-7582, marketing@compmech.com, http://www.compmech.com/witpress.

005.5 USA ISSN 1068-8544
CODEN: SOSUEA
SOFTWARE SUCCESS; increasing profits for software entrepreneurs. Text in English. 1988. m. USD 395 (effective 2003). index. back issues avail. **Document type:** *Newsletter.* **Description:** Offers advice on software sales and marketing, covering management and finance tactics software entrepreneurs can use to increase profits.
Former titles (until 1992): David H. Bowen's Software Success (0896-4386); (until 1987): David H. Bowen's Software Strategies (0896-4378)
—CCC.
Published by: United Communications Group, 11300 Rockville Pike Ste 1100, Rockville, MD 20852-3030. TEL 617-444-5755, FAX 617-444-8958, http://www.softwaresuccess.com. Ed. Jeffrey Tarter. Circ: 2,500.

005.5 USA
SOFTWARE TECH NEWS. Text in English. 1993. 4/yr. free in United States. back issues avail. **Document type:** *Newsletter, Government.* **Description:** Publishes technical reports, current awareness, and information on software technology.
Related titles: Online - full text ed.
Published by: U.S. Department of Defense, Data and Analysis Center for Software, PO Box 1400, Rome, NY 13442-1400. TEL 315-334-4905, 800-214-7921, FAX 315-334-4964, dacs-newsletter@rome.ittssc.com, http://www.dacs.dtic.mil/awareness/newsletters/listing.shtml. Ed., R&P Lon R Dean. Circ: 6,000.

005.5 USA ISSN 1548-3460
▼ **SOFTWARE TEST & PERFORMANCE.** Text in English. 2004. m. free to qualified personnel. adv. **Document type:** *Magazine, Trade.* **Description:** Aims to improve the efficiency of individual and team software quality assurance and testing processes.
Indexed: C&ISA, E&CAJ, IAA.
Published by: B Z Media LLC, Seven High St, Huntington, NY 11743. TEL 631-421-4158, FAX 631-421-4045, info@bzmedia.com, http://www.stpmag.com, http://www.bzmedia.com. Ed. Alan Zeichick. Adv. contact Ted Bahr. B&W page USD 3,595, color page USD 4,490.

005.5 GBR ISSN 0960-0833
QA76.76.T48 CODEN: JTREET
➤ **SOFTWARE TESTING, VERIFICATION AND RELIABILITY.** Text in English. 1991. q. USD 765 to institutions; USD 842 combined subscription to institutions print & online eds. (effective 2006). adv. bk.rev. back issues avail.; reprints avail. **Document type:** *Journal, Academic/Scholarly.* **Description:** Provides information on research and experience for those who wish to measure the progress in the important fields of software testing and reliability.
Related titles: Microform ed.: (from PQC); Online - full text ed.: ISSN 1099-1689. 1997. USD 765 to institutions (effective 2006) (from EBSCO Publishing, Swets Information Services, Wiley InterScience).
Indexed: BrCerAb, C&ISA, CMCI, CerAb, CompAb, CompLI, CorrAb, CurCont, E&CAJ, EMA, IAA, Inspec, M&TEA, MBF, METADEX, SolStAb, WAA.
—BLDSC (8321.457500), AskIEEE, CISTI, Ei, IE, Infotrieve, ingenta, Linda Hall. **CCC.**
Published by: John Wiley & Sons Ltd. (Subsidiary of: John Wiley & Sons, Inc.), The Atrium, Southern Gate, Chichester, West Sussex PO19 8SQ, United Kingdom. TEL 44-1243-779777, FAX 44-1243-775878, customer@wiley.co.uk, http://www3.interscience.wiley.com/cgi-bin/jhome/13635, http://www.wiley.co.uk. Ed. Martin Woodward. Pub. Anne Marie Halligan. adv.: B&W page GBP 650, color page GBP 1,550; 170 x 230. Circ: 420. **Subscr. in the Americas to:** John Wiley & Sons, Inc., 111 River St, Hoboken, NJ 07030-5774. TEL 201-748-6645, 800-225-5945, subinfo@wiley.com.

005.1 USA
SOFTWARE VISUALIZATION: A C M SYMPOSIUM ON SOFTWARE VISUALIZATION. PROCEEDINGS. Text in English. a. **Document type:** *Proceedings, Academic/Scholarly.*
Related titles: Online - full content ed.
Published by: Association for Computing Machinery, Inc., 1515 Broadway, 17th Fl, New York, NY 10036-5701. TEL 212-626-0500, usacm@acm.org, http://www.acm.org.

C

005.5 CHN
SOFTWARE WORLD. Text in Chinese. adv.
Related titles: Online - full text ed.
Published by: I D G China, Rm. 616, Tower A, COFCO Plaza, Jianguomennei Dajie, Beijing, 100005 , China. TEL 86-10-6526-0959, FAX 86-10-6526-0866, dumin@idg.com.cn, http://www.swm.com.cn, http://www.idgchina.com. Ed. Xu Guo. adv.: page CNY 29,500.

005.5 GBR ISSN 0038-0652
QA76 CODEN: SOFWBG
SOFTWARE WORLD; an international journal of computer programs and packages. Text in English. 1969. bi-m. GBP 122 domestic; GBP 147, USD 291 foreign (effective 2003). adv. bk.rev.; software rev. illus.; tr.lit. 28 p./no.; back issues avail.; reprint service avail. from PQC. **Document type:** *Academic/Scholarly.* **Description:** Discusses software programs and packages for use in many installations. Includes business news.
Incorporates in part (in 1994): P C Business Software (0954-2833); Which was formerly: Mini Micro Software (0265-6760); Small Systems Software (0308-3314)
Related titles: Microform ed.: (from PQC); Online - full text ed.: (from Gale Group).
Indexed: AEA, BMT, CompC, CompD, Inspec, MicrocompInd.
—BLDSC (8321.460000), AskIEEE, CISTI, Ei, IE, Infotrieve, Linda Hall.
Published by: A.P. Publications Ltd., Old Exchange House, Marford Rd, Wheathampstead, Herts AL4 8AY, United Kingdom. TEL 44-1582-833504, FAX 44-1582-832327, 106142.1713@compuserve.com, http://www.ap-publications.co.uk. Ed. Ed Patterson. Circ: 1,033.

005.36 USA
SOURCEVIEW JOURNAL OF SOFTWARE EVALUATIONS, REVIEWS & RATINGS✶. Text in English. 1985. m. USD 36. adv. bk.rev.; software rev. **Description:** For professional software developers and users. Features articles on industry trends, copyright laws and manufacturing.
Former titles: Sourceview (0742-3772); Sourceview Magazine
Published by: SourceView Software International (Subsidiary of: SourceView Corporation), PO Box 4713, Walnut, CA 94596-0713. TEL 800-929-8117. Ed. Paul Elmore. Circ: 50,000.

SOUTH CAROLINA COMPUTER AND SOFTWARE SERVICES DIRECTORY. see *BUSINESS AND ECONOMICS—Trade And Industrial Directories*

SPREADSHEET. see *COMPUTERS—Microcomputers*

005.5 DEU ISSN 1618-2723
STREAMING BUSINESS MAGAZIN. Text in German. 1996. 6/yr. **Document type:** *Magazine, Trade.* **Description:** For professional multimedia users.
Formerly (until 2001): 3 D Live (Drei Dimensiona) (1432-1734)
Published by: W I N - Verlag GmbH & Co. KG, Johann-Sebastian-Bach Str 5, Vaterstetten, 85591, Germany. TEL 49-8106-350-0, FAX 49-8106-350190, info@win-verlag.de, http://www.streamingbusiness-magazin.de, http://www.win-verlag.de. Ed. Rainer Miserre. Pub. Hans-J. Grohmann. Adv. contact Oskar Fromm. Circ: 20,000 (paid).

005.5 USA
SWIFT'S DIRECTORY OF EDUCATIONAL SOFTWARE FOR THE I B M - P C✶. Text in English. a. (plus s-a. updates). USD 19.95.
Published by: D.C. Heath & Company, 222 Berkeley St, Boston, MA 02116-3748. TEL 617-862-6650.

005.5 USA ISSN 1054-3902
SYMANTEC. Text in English. 1990. q. USD 16. adv. **Description:** Directed to owners of Symantec and Peter Norton personal computer software.
Published by: Symantec Corporation, 10201 Torre Ave, Cupertino, CA 95014-2132. TEL 408-253-9600, FAX 408-253-3968. Ed. Hugh R Bethell. Circ: 650,000 (controlled).

005.43 384.53 USA
▼ **SYMBIAN DEVELOPER'S JOURNAL.** Abbreviated title: S D J. Text in English. 2005. irreg. **Description:** Covers developments related to the Symbian operating system, an open platform for advanced mobile phones and devices.
Media: Online - full content.
Published by: SYS-CON Media, Inc., 135 Chestnut Ridge Rd, Montvale, NJ 07645. TEL 201-802-3040, 888-303-5282, FAX 201-782-9600, info@sys-con.com, http://symbian.sys-con.com, http://www.sys-con.com. Ed. Jim Liddle.

005.1 USA ISSN 1088-4955
SYMPOSIUM ON THE FRONTIERS OF MASSIVELY PARALLEL PROCESSING. PROCEEDINGS. Text in English. 1988. a. price varies. **Document type:** *Proceedings, Trade.*
Related titles: Online - full text ed.: (from I E E E).
—BLDSC (8585.237700).
Published by: Institute of Electrical and Electronics Engineers, Inc., 3 Park Ave, 17th Fl, New York, NY 10016-5997. TEL 800-678-4333, customer.service@ieee.org, http://www.ieee.org.

005.43 USA ISSN 1061-2688
QA76.76.063 CODEN: SYADE7
SYS ADMIN; the journal for UNIX systems administrators. Variant title: Systems Administration. Text in English. 1992. m. USD 39 domestic; USD 58 in Canada & Mexico; USD 69 elsewhere; free to qualified personnel (effective 2005). adv. back issues avail. **Document type:** *Magazine, Trade.* **Description:** Provides technical information for UNIX administrators who seek to improve the performance or extend the capabilities of their UNIX systems. Focuses on system-level processes.
Related titles: CD-ROM ed.; Online - full text ed.: (from bigchalk).
Indexed: CompD, SoftBase.
—IE, Infotrieve. **CCC.**
Published by: C M P Media LLC (Subsidiary of: United News & Media), 600 Harrison St, 6th Fl., San Francisco, CA 94107. TEL 415-947-6746, FAX 415-947-6041, aankerholz@cmp.com, http://www.sysadminmag.com/, http://www.cmp.com. Ed. Amber Ankerholz TEL 785-838-7528. adv.: B&W page USD 1,515; trim 8 x 10.88. Circ: 29,121 (paid).

T E Q. see *TECHNOLOGY: COMPREHENSIVE WORKS*

T E S S. (The Educational Software Selector) see *EDUCATION—Computer Applications*

005.1 USA
T S O / I S P F UPDATE. (Time Sharing Option / Interactive System Productivity Facility) Text in English. q. USD 250 (effective 2000). **Document type:** *Trade.* **Description:** Provides information on TSO (The main MVS systems user interface), and ISPF (A set of menus for compiling & managing programs & configuring the system).
Published by: Xephon, 9330 Lyndon B Johnson Fwy., Ste. 800, Dallas, TX 75243-4310. TEL 303-410-9344, FAX 303-438-0290, http://www.xephon.com/.

T W I C E. (This Week in Consumer Electronics) see *ELECTRONICS*

005.43 USA ISSN 1551-2770
▼ **TECHNET MAGAZINE**; the Microsoft journal for IT professionals. Text in English. 2005. s-a. (Spring & Winter). free domestic to qualified personnel; USD 55 in Canada; USD 70 elsewhere (effective 2005). adv. **Document type:** *Magazine, Trade.* **Description:** Contains technical information for IT Professionals using Microsoft products and technologies.
Published by: (Microsoft Corp.), C M P Media LLC (Subsidiary of: United News & Media), 600 Harrison St, 6th Fl., San Francisco, CA 94107. TEL 415-947-6746, FAX 415-947-6041, tnmag@microsoft.com, http://www.microsoft.com/technet/technetmag/default.aspx, http://www.cmp.com. Ed. Joshua Trupin. Pub. Kerry Gates. adv.: B&W page USD 14,450, color page USD 12,075; trim 8 x 10.5.

005.5 USA ISSN 1548-5374
▼ **TEKKA.** Text in English. 2003. q. USD 50 (effective 2004). **Document type:** *Academic/Scholarly.* **Description:** It is about enjoying new media and creating beautiful software. Intricate databases, catchy hypertext fictions.
Published by: Eastgate Systems, Inc., 134 Main St, Watertown, MA 02172. TEL 617-924-9044, FAX 617-924-9051, info@eastgate.com, http://www.eastgate.com. Eds. Anja Rav, Elin Sjursen. Pub. Mark Bernstein.

005.5 USA
THE TESTERS' NETWORK. Text in English. 1996. m. **Document type:** *Trade.* **Description:** Contains articles, links, product reviews, and other information for software quality assurance professionals.
Media: Online - full text.
Published by: S T Labs, Inc., Sterling Plaza, 3rd Fl, 3535 128th Ave, S E, Bellevue, WA 98006. pruec@stlabs.com, http://www.stlabs.com/testnet.htm. Ed. Prue Cuper.

005.34 DEU
DER TITELSCHUTZ ANZEIGER MIT SOFTWARE TITEL. Text in German. m. adv. **Document type:** *Magazine, Trade.*
Related titles: ♦ Supplement to: Der Titelschutz Anzeiger.
Published by: Presse Fachverlag GmbH & Co. KG, Eidelstedter Weg 22, Hamburg, 20255, Germany. TEL 49-40-57009-0, FAX 49-40-57009300, titelschutz-anzeiger@presse-fachverlag.de, info@presse-fachverlag.de, http://www.titelschutzanzeiger.de, http://www.presse-fachverlag.de.

005.5 USA
U M B C AGENTNEWS. Text in English. w. **Description:** Includes short news items, announcements and articles about intelligent software agents and related technologies.
Media: E-mail.
Published by: University of Maryland Baltimore County, Laboratory of Advanced Information Technology, 5401 Wilkens Ave, Baltimore, MD 21228. TEL 410-455-3000, FAX 410-455-3969, http://www.cs.umbc.edu/agentnews/current/. Ed. Tim Finn.

005.43 USA
U N I X REVIEW'S PERFORMANCE COMPUTING. Text in English. m. USD 55; USD 60 in Canada; USD 75 elsewhere (effective 2001). **Document type:** *Trade.* **Description:** Publishes two types of feature articles: analysis of technology trends and standards and pragmatic tutorial articles.
Formerly: Performance Computing
Related titles: Online - full text ed.
Address: 411 Borel Ave, Ste 100, San Mateo, CA 94402. TEL 650-338-9500, 888-847-6188, FAX 650-338-9739, http://www.performancecomputing.com. Ed. Mark Hall. Pub. John Keough.

005.5 USA ISSN 1537-0305
UNICENTER ADVISOR. Text in English. 1995. q. USD 39 domestic; USD 49 in Canada; USD 59 elsewhere (effective 2002). adv. **Document type:** *Trade.*
Former titles (until 2001): Unicenter T N G Advisor; C A - Unicenter Advisor (1090-6444); (until 1996): Visual Objects Advisor (1076-9927)
Published by: Advisor Media, Inc., 4849 Viewridge Ave, San Diego, CA 92123-1643. TEL 858-278-5600, FAX 858-278-0300, subscribe@advisor.com, http://www.advisor.com/. Ed. John L Hawkins. Pub. B J Ghiglione. R&P David Kodama. Adv. contact Sheri Ogletree.

005.42 USA ISSN 0952-3359
UNIGRAM.X; the weekly information newsletter for the UNIX community worldwide. Text in English. 1984. w. USD 495 (effective 1999). adv. cum.index. **Document type:** *Newsletter.* **Description:** Directed at UNIX hardware and software marketers.
Related titles: Online - full text ed.
Published by: G2 Computer Intelligence Inc., PO Box 7, Glen Head, NY 11545-0007. TEL 516-759-7025, FAX 516-759-7028. Ed., Pub. Maureen O'Gara. R&P, Adv. contact Charles Hall. Circ: 100,000.

C

005 GBR
UNIVERSAL NET.CONNECT. Text in English. 1996. bi-m. GBP 150 (effective 1999). adv. tr.lit. back issues avail. **Document type:** *Magazine, Trade.* **Description:** Specializing in groupware and workflow technology.
Published by: NetConnections Ltd, Cromwell House, 14 Fulwood Pl, London, WC1V 6HZ, United Kingdom. TEL 44-171-405-7222, FAX 44-171-242-2766, sdutta@netconnections.co.uk, http://www.netconnections.co.uk. Ed., Pub., R&P Soman Dutta. Adv. contact Robert Glazier. B&W page GBP 1,450, color page GBP 1,800; trim 21 x 29.7. Circ: 35,000.

005.43 PRT
UNIX COMPUTER WORLD. Text in Portuguese. 12/yr.
Published by: Oceanus - Publicacoes e Edicoes Ltda., RUA QUINTA DAS PALMIERAS, 76-4, Oeiras, 2780, Portugal. TEL 2466072, FAX 246-61-22, TELEX 63840 OCEANU P. Ed. Maria Diniz. Circ: 15,000.

005.43 JPN ISSN 0913-0748
UNIX MAGAZINE. Text in Japanese. 1986. m. JPY 13,200 (effective 2004).
Published by: ASCII Corp., JR Shinanomachi Bldg. 34 Shinanomachi, Shinjuku-ku, Tokyo, 160-8584, Japan. http://www.ascii.co.jp/books/magazines/unix.html.

005.43 USA
UNIX SOFTWARE JOURNAL✶. Text in English. 1988. q. USD 15. adv. **Description:** Covers the latest software technology, applications, and issues of interest to users in the Unix marketplace.
Formerly (until 1990): Unix Journal
Published by: FourGen Software Inc., 115 N E 100th St, Seattle, WA 98125-8013. TEL 206-774-9209, 206-528-4000, FAX 206-672-4950. Ed. Gary Gagliardi. Circ: 15,000.

005.43 USA
UNIX UPDATE. Text in English. m. USD 150 in North America; USD 165 elsewhere (effective 2001). **Document type:** *Newsletter, Trade.* **Description:** Provides news and information on UNIX-based computer systems and products around the world. Covers research and development, as well as new hardware and software products and enhancements.
Related titles: Online - full text ed.
Published by: Worldwide Videotex, PO Box 3273, Boynton Beach, FL 33424-3273. TEL 561-738-2276, markedit@juno.com, http://www.wvpubs.com. Ed., Pub. Mark Wright.

005.43 USA
UNIX VIDEO QUARTERLY. Text in English. q. USD 195; USD 310 foreign. bk.rev. **Description:** Covers products, companies, people, and trade shows in the UNIX industry. Subscribers can watch hardware and software products in use, as well as see and hear interviews with vendor representatives.
Published by: Infopro Systems, PO Box 220, Rescue, CA 95672. TEL 916-677-5870, FAX 916-677-5873.

▼ *new title* ➤ *refereed* ✶ *unverified* ♦ *full entry avail.*

005.43   GBR   ISSN 1473-0693
UNIXNT. Text in English. 1989. m. GBP 100, USD 180 (effective 1999). adv. **Document type:** *Trade.* **Description:** Provides commercial users with insight and analysis into vendor strategies, the value of product announcements, and real life experiences of IT managers.
Former titles (until 2000): Unix & NT News (1369-7099); (until 1997): Unix News (0956-2753)
Related titles: Online - full text ed.: (from Gale Group).
Indexed: Inspec.
—BLDSC (9120.490100), IE.
Published by: I B C Business Publishing Ltd., 69-77 Paul St, London, EC2A 4LQ, United Kingdom. TEL 44-20-7553-1000, FAX 44-20-7553-1593. Ed. Alison Hawkings. Pub. Beverly Harper. Adv. contact Oren Wolf.

005.5   USA
THE UPDATE. Text in English. m. free. adv. **Document type:** *Newsletter.* **Description:** Contains information on software and computers.
Media: E-mail.
Published by: Update sdown12@hotmail.com.

005.1   USA
UPGRADE. Text in English. 1984. m. USD 79 (effective 2002). adv. charts; illus.; stat.; tr.lit. **Document type:** *Trade.* **Description:** Serves the education and information needs of members by presenting timely, factual and complete information on subjects of pressing importance to its readers.
Formerly: Software Publishers Association. News (1083-4605)
Published by: Software and Information Industry Association, 1090 Vermont Ave NW, # 6, Washington, DC 20005-4905. TEL 202-452-1600, FAX 202-223-8756, orders@siia.net, http://www.siia.net. Ed. Kathleen Rakestraw. R&P Kathleen M Rakestraw. Adv. contact Heather Henderson. B&W page USD 1,375, color page USD 2,075.

V S D A VOICE. see *COMMUNICATIONS—Video*

005.16   USA   ISSN 1083-7213
THE VIEW; technical journal for Lotus Notes and Domino. Text in English. 1995. bi-m. USD 374 domestic; USD 399 foreign (effective 2005). **Document type:** *Magazine, Trade.*
—Infotrieve.
Published by: Wellesley Information Services (Subsidiary of: United Communications Group), 990 Washington St, Dedham, MA 02026-6714. TEL 781-407-0360, FAX 781-329-9186, customer@eview.com, http://www.eview.com, http://www.wispubs.com.

VIRUS WATCH. see *COMPUTERS—Computer Security*

005.5   NLD   ISSN 0921-0490
W G S NEWSLETTER. Text in Dutch. 1985. s-a. **Document type:** *Newsletter.*
Related titles: Online - full text ed.
—BLDSC (9309.553500).
Published by: Working Group on Software, c/o Ruth Kool, Sec, Eindhoven University of Technology, Dept of Mathematics and Computing Science, PO Box 513, Eindhoven, 5600 MB, Netherlands. FAX 31-40-2465995, rkool@win.tue.nl.

W S S RESEARCH SERIES. (Water Software Systems) see *ENGINEERING—Electrical Engineering*

WASTE MANIFEST SOFTWARE REPORT. see *ENVIRONMENTAL STUDIES—Computer Applications*

005.26   CAN   ISSN 0828-5624
WATCOM NEWS. (Waterloo Computing) Text in English. 1982. q. CND 10, USD 10. **Description:** Newsletter featuring information on Watcom software.
Formerly: Infowat
Published by: W A T C O M Products Inc., 415 Phillip St, Waterloo, ON N2L 3X2, Canada. TEL 519-886-3700. Ed. Janet Cater. Circ: 6,000.

WATER SOFTWARE SYSTEMS RESEARCH REPORTS. see *ENGINEERING—Electrical Engineering*

WHAT P C? (ONLINE EDITION); the essential buyer's guide. see *COMPUTERS—Microcomputers*

005.5   DEU   ISSN 0941-9209
WIN; Alles ueber Windows. Text in German. 1991. m. **Document type:** *Magazine, Consumer.* **Description:** Offers tips on using Windows programs.
—IE.
Published by: Vogel Verlag und Druck GmbH & Co. KG, Max-Planck-Str 7-9, Wuerzburg, 97064, Germany. TEL 49-931-418-2335, FAX 49-931-4182908, http://www.vogel-medien.de. Ed. Reinhard Gloggengiesser. Adv. contact Gabriele Groitzsch. Circ: 125,638.

005.43   DEU   ISSN 1616-2269
WINDOWS 2000 MAGAZIN. Text in German. 1993. m. EUR 61.80 domestic; EUR 73.80 foreign; EUR 6 newsstand/cover (effective 2005). adv. **Document type:** *Magazine, Trade.* **Description:** Contains features and articles with information and resources related to all aspects of the Windows 2000 operating system.

Formerly (until 2000): N T Magazin (New Technology) (1438-4353)
Published by: Aktuelles Wissen Verlagsgesellschaft mbH, Bretonischer Ring 13, Grasbrunn, 85630, Germany. TEL 49-89-456160, FAX 49-89-45616100, http://www.win2000mag.de, http://www.awi.de. Ed. Frank-Michael Schlede. Pub. Eduard Heilmayr. Adv. contact Cornelia Jacobi. B&W page EUR 4,172, color page EUR 5,840.

005.43   JPN
WINDOWS 2000 WORLD JAPAN. Text in Japanese. m. adv. **Document type:** *Magazine, Trade.* **Description:** Presents articles on both the client and server aspects of the Windows 2000 network system, including Intranet/Internet environments.
Formerly (until 2000): Windows N T World
Related titles: Online - full text ed.
Published by: I D G Japan, Inc., Hongo 3-4-5, Bunkyo-ku, Tokyo, 1130033, Japan. TEL 81-3-5800-3111, FAX 81-3-5800-3590, http://www.idg.co.jp/win2000/. adv.: B&W page USD 2,282, color page USD 4,407; trim 210 x 277. Circ: 80,000 (paid and controlled).

005.43   RUS
WINDOWS & .NET MAGAZINE. Text in Russian. 1999. bi-m. RUR 1,210 domestic; RUR 110 per issue domestic (effective 2004). adv. **Document type:** *Magazine, Trade.*
Formerly: Windows 2000 Magazine (1563-101X)
Related titles: Online - full text ed.
Published by: Izdatel'stvo Otkrytye Sistemy/Open Systems Publications, ul Rustaveli, dom 12A, komn 117, Moscow, 127254, Russian Federation. TEL 7-095-9563306, FAX 7-095-2539204, letters@win2000mag.ru, info@osp.ru, http://www.osp.ru/win2000/. Ed. Dmitrii Toropov. Circ: 10,000.

005.43   USA   ISSN 1543-6454
QA76.5   CODEN: WDJOFH
WINDOWS DEVELOPER NETWORK; application development from windows to web. Text in English. 1990. m. USD 34.99 domestic; USD 45 in Canada & Mexico; USD 64 elsewhere (effective 2003). adv. bk.rev. back issues avail. **Document type:** *Magazine, Trade.* **Description:** Provides practical, highly technical information for Windows developers.
Former titles (until 2003): Windows Developer Magazine (1537-2014); (until 2001): Windows Developer's Journal (1083-9887); (until 1995): Windows - D O S Developers Journal (1059-2407); (until Dec. 1991): Tech Specialist (1049-913X)
Related titles: CD-ROM ed.; Online - full text ed.: ISSN 1543-6462 (from Gale Group).
Indexed: CompD, CompLI, Inspec, MicrocompInd, SoftBase.
—BLDSC (9319.332265), IE. **CCC.**
Published by: C M P Media LLC (Subsidiary of: United News & Media), 1601 W 23rd St, Ste 200, Lawrence, KS 66046. TEL 785-841-1631, FAX 785-841-3565, http://www.wd-mag.com. Ed. John Dorsey. Pub. Kerry Gates. Adv. contact Amy Phalen. B&W page USD 1,950, color page USD 2,495. Circ: 25,000 (paid).

005.5   USA   ISSN 1051-6425
WINDOWS JOURNAL. Text in English. 1990. bi-m. USD 99 domestic; USD 145 in Europe; USD 165 in Asia & the Pacific. adv. bk.rev.
Formerly: Wugnet Journal
Related titles: Online - full text ed.: (from CompuServe Inc.).
Published by: Wugnet Publications, Inc., PO Box 1967, Media, PA 19063. TEL 215-565-1861, FAX 215-565-7106. Ed. Howard Sobel. Circ: 10,000.

005.43   USA   ISSN 1526-9388
QA76.76.O63
WINDOWS PROFESSIONAL. Text in English. 1996. m. USD 167 domestic; USD 177 foreign (effective 2005). **Description:** Contains tips, shortcuts and techniques for Windows 95.
Formerly (until 1999): Windows 95 Professional (1085-1291)
Related titles: Online - full text ed.: USD 197 domestic; USD 207 foreign (effective 2005).
—CCC.
Published by: Element K Journals (Subsidiary of: Eli Research, Inc.), 500 Canal View Blvd, Rochester, NY 14623. TEL 585-240-7301, 800-223-8720, 877-203-5248, FAX 585-292-4392, http://www.elementkjournals.com.

005   ESP
WINDOWS TI MAGAZINE. Text in Spanish. m. EUR 70 domestic; EUR 165 foreign (effective 2004).
—CINDOC.
Published by: NewTec Ediciones, S.L., Ave. Diagonal, 468, 5o. A, Barcelona, 08006, Spain. TEL 34-93-2386290, FAX 34-93-2386295, info@windowstimag.com, http://www.windowstimag.com, http://www.wntmag.com/. Ed. Carlos Del Collado.

005.5   USA
WINSURFER*. Text in English. 1995. m. USD 49. adv. **Document type:** *Consumer.* **Description:** Systems-level tips, bug reports, networking advice about Windows 95 and Windows NT.
Published by: I D G Newsletter Corporation, PO Box 92880, Rochester, NY 14692. TEL 617-482-8785, 800-807-0771, FAX 617-338-0164, idgcust@pcworld.com, http://idgnews.com. Ed. Jim Pile. Pub. Craig Pierce. Adv. contact Scott Tharler.

WORD PROGRESS. see *LAW—Computer Applications*

005.52   USA
WORDPERFECT SUITE NEWSLETTER ONLINE. Text in English. 1998. m. USD 19.95 (effective 1999). **Document type:** *Newsletter.* **Description:** Aims to promote the growth of the WordPerfect processing program and its use in homes and offices.
Media: Online - full text.
Published by: Web Information Services editor@wpsuitenews.com, http://www.wpsuitenews.com. Ed. Allen Clark.

005.1 005.12   USA   ISSN 1095-1350
QA76.758
WORKING CONFERENCE ON REVERSE ENGINEERING. PROCEEDINGS. Text in English. 199?. a. USD 189; USD 76 to members (effective 2004). **Document type:** *Proceedings, Trade.*
Related titles: Online - full text ed.: (from I E E E).
—BLDSC (6849.902600). **CCC.**
Published by: Institute of Electrical and Electronics Engineers, Inc., 3 Park Ave, 17th Fl, New York, NY 10016-5997. TEL 212-419-7900, 800-678-4333, FAX 212-752-4929, customer.service@ieee.org, http://www.ieee.org.

005.7565   USA   ISSN 1530-4353
WORKING SMARTER WITH MICROSOFT ACCESS. (Avail. in 2 versions: Access 2000 and Access 2002) Text in English. 1999. bi-w. USD 4.27 per issue (effective 2005). **Document type:** *Newsletter, Consumer.* **Description:** Contains time-saving tips.
—CCC.
Published by: Mosaic Media, Inc., OneOnOne Computer Training (Subsidiary of: Mosaic Media, Inc.), 751 Roosevelt Rd, Ste 108, Glen Ellyn, IL 60137-5905. TEL 800-424-8668, FAX 630-628-0550, oneonone@pincom.com, http://www.oootraining.com. Eds. Kimi Nance, Natalie Young.

005.369   USA   ISSN 1530-4337
WORKING SMARTER WITH MICROSOFT EXCEL. (Avail. in 3 Versions: Excel 2000, Excel 2002 and Excel 2003.) Text in English. 1999. bi-w. USD 4.27 per issue (effective 2005). **Document type:** *Newsletter, Consumer.* **Description:** Contains time-saving tips.
—CCC.
Published by: Mosaic Media, Inc., OneOnOne Computer Training (Subsidiary of: Mosaic Media, Inc.), 751 Roosevelt Rd, Ste 108, Glen Ellyn, IL 60137-5905. TEL 800-424-8668, FAX 630-628-0550, oneonone@pincom.com, http://www.oootraining.com. Ed. B Alan August.

005.369   USA   ISSN 1530-4345
T385
WORKING SMARTER WITH MICROSOFT POWERPOINT. (Avail. in 2 versions: Powerpoint 2000 and PowerPoint 2002) Text in English. 1999. bi-w. USD 4.27 per issue (effective 2005). **Document type:** *Newsletter, Consumer.* **Description:** Contains time-saving tips.
—CCC.
Published by: Mosaic Media, Inc., OneOnOne Computer Training (Subsidiary of: Mosaic Media, Inc.), 751 Roosevelt Rd, Ste 108, Glen Ellyn, IL 60137-5905. TEL 800-424-8668, FAX 630-628-0550, oneonone@pincom.com, http://www.oootraining.com. Ed. B Alan August.

005.5   USA   ISSN 1530-4329
WORKING SMARTER WITH OFFICE 2000. Text in English. 199?. bi-w. USD 4.27 per issue (effective 2005). **Document type:** *Newsletter.*
—CCC.
Published by: Mosaic Media, Inc., OneOnOne Computer Training (Subsidiary of: Mosaic Media, Inc.), 751 Roosevelt Rd, Ste 108, Glen Ellyn, IL 60137-5905. TEL 800-424-8668, FAX 630-628-0550, oneonone@pincom.com, http://www.oootraining.com. Ed. Helen Bradley.

005.1 005.16   USA   ISSN 1530-1621
QA76.76.O63
WORKSHOP ON HOT TOPICS IN OPERATING SYSTEMS. Text in English. 1995. a. USD 135; USD 50 to members (effective 2004). **Document type:** *Proceedings, Trade.*
Related titles: Online - full text ed.: (from I E E E).
—BLDSC (9352.231659).
Published by: Institute of Electrical and Electronics Engineers, Inc., 3 Park Ave, 17th Fl, New York, NY 10016-5997. TEL 212-419-7900, 800-678-4333, FAX 212-752-4929, customer.service@ieee.org, http://www.ieee.org.

WRITER'S N W; news and reviews for the community of the printed word. see *PUBLISHING AND BOOK TRADE*

005.43   DEU
X M L & WEB SERVICES MAGAZIN. Text in German. 2002. q. EUR 35; EUR 9.80 newsstand/cover (effective 2005). adv. **Document type:** *Magazine, Trade.*
Published by: Software & Support Verlag GmbH, Kennedyallee 87, Frankfurt am Main, 60596, Germany. TEL 49-69-6300890, FAX 49-69-63008989, redaktion@xmlmagazin.de, info@software-support.biz, http://www.xmlmagazin.de, http://www.software-support.biz. adv.: B&W page EUR 2,340, color page EUR 3,360. Circ: 25,000 (controlled).

005.5 DEU
ZIMPEL. SOFTWARE: Z DATA. Text in German. 1996. base vol. plus m. updates. **Document type:** *Directory.*
Related titles: CD-ROM ed.
Published by: Verlag Dieter Zimpel (Subsidiary of: Springer Science+Business Media), Angererstr 36, Munich, 80796, Germany. TEL 49-89-3073445, FAX 49-89-302409. Eds. Ingrid Finsterwald, Petra Baumgartner. **Subscr. to:** Gabler Verlag, Abraham-Lincoln-Str 46, Wiesbaden 65189, Germany. TEL 49-611-7878297, FAX 49-611-7878466.

COMPUTERS—Theory Of Computing

004.01 USA ISSN 0737-8017
QA267 CODEN: CATCDQ
➤ **ANNUAL A C M SYMPOSIUM ON THE THEORY OF COMPUTING. PROCEEDINGS.** Text in English. 1969. a., latest 2004. USD 46 per issue to members; USD 92 per issue to non-members (effective 2005). bibl.; charts. 652 p./no.; **Document type:** *Proceedings, Academic/Scholarly.*
Former titles (until 1982): Annual A C M Symposium on Theory of Computing. Conference Proceedings (0734-9025); (until 1980): Annual A C M Symposium on Theory of Computing. Conference Record (0277-0261)
Related titles: Online - full text ed.: (from Association for Computing Machinery, Inc.).
—BLDSC (1073.870000), Ei, IE, ingenta. **CCC.**
Published by: Association for Computing Machinery, Inc., 1515 Broadway, 17th Fl, New York, NY 10036-5701. TEL 212-869-7440, 800-342-6626, FAX 212-869-0481, sigs@acm.org, http://www.acm.org.

➤ **DISCRETE MATHEMATICS AND THEORETICAL COMPUTER SCIENCE (ONLINE EDITION).** see *MATHEMATICS*

004.01 NLD ISSN 1571-0661
QA75.5
ELECTRONIC NOTES IN THEORETICAL COMPUTER SCIENCE. Text in English. 1995. irreg. free to qualified personnel (effective 2006). **Document type:** *Journal, Trade.* **Description:** Publishes proceedings, lecture notes, monographs, and other similar material in the field of theoretical computer science.
Media: Online - full text (from IngentaConnect, ScienceDirect).
Indexed: Inspec.
—BLDSC (3702.660700), IE.
Published by: Elsevier BV (Subsidiary of: Elsevier Science & Technology), Radarweg 29, Amsterdam, 1043 NX, Netherlands. TEL 31-20-4853911, FAX 31-20-4852457, nlinfo-f@elsevier.nl, http://www.elsevier.com/locate/entcs, http://www.elsevier.nl.

004.01 NLD ISSN 0252-9742
EUROPEAN ASSOCIATION FOR THEORETICAL COMPUTER SCIENCE. BULLETIN. Text in English. 1995. 3/yr. bk.rev. **Document type:** *Bulletin.* **Description:** Reports on computer science and technical issues.
Indexed: Inspec, MathR, MathSciNet.
—BLDSC (2505.719300), IE, ingenta. **CCC.**
Published by: European Association for Theoretical Computer Science, c/o G. Rozenberg, University of Leiden, Dept. of Math & Computer Science, PO Box 9512, Leiden, 2300, Netherlands. http://www.liacs.nl/~beatcs/, http://www.eatcs.org. Ed. G. Rosenberg.

004.01 USA ISSN 1551-305X
▼ ➤ **FOUNDATIONS AND TRENDS IN THEORETICAL COMPUTER SCIENCE.** Text in English. 2005. 4/yr. USD 300, EUR 300; USD 340, EUR 340 combined subscription print & online eds. (effective 2006). **Document type:** *Journal, Academic/Scholarly.*
Related titles: Online - full text ed.: ISSN 1551-3068. 2005. USD 300, EUR 300 (effective 2005).
Published by: Now Publishers Inc., PO Box 1024, Hanover, MA 02339. TEL 781-871-0245, FAX 781-871-6172, sales@nowpublishers.com, http://www.nowpublishers.com/tcs. Ed. Madhu Sedan. Pub. James Finlay. R&P Mike Casey.

➤ **GENETIC PROGRAMMING AND EVOLVABLE MACHINES.** see *COMPUTERS—Artificial Intelligence*

➤ **INTERNATIONAL JOURNAL OF FUZZY SYSTEMS.** see *COMPUTERS—Computer Systems*

➤ **J C M C C.** (Journal of Combinatorial Mathematics and Combinatorial Computing) see *MATHEMATICS*

▼ ➤ **JOURNAL OF COGNITIVE ENGINEERING AND DECISION MAKING.** see *PSYCHOLOGY*

004.01 NLD ISSN 0304-3975
CODEN: TCSCDI
➤ **THEORETICAL COMPUTER SCIENCE.** Text in Dutch. 1975. 60/yr. EUR 5,562 in Europe to institutions; JPY 738,200 in Japan to institutions; USD 6,224 to institutions except Europe and Japan (effective 2006). back issues avail.; reprints avail. **Document type:** *Journal, Academic/Scholarly.* **Description:** Presents research papers on theoretical and mathematical aspects of computer science. Focuses on the problems of practical computation. Subjects covered include automata, formal languages, semantics of programming languages and algorithms.
Related titles: Microform ed.: (from PQC); Online - full text ed.: (from EBSCO Publishing, Gale Group, IngentaConnect, ScienceDirect, Swets Information Services).
Indexed: B&BAb, BrCerAb, C&CSA, C&ISA, CMCI, CerAb, CompAb, CompC, CompD, CompLI, CompR, CorrAb, CurCont, CybAb, E&CAJ, EMA, EngInd, IAA, ISR, Inspec, M&TEA, MBF, METADEX, MathR, MathSciNet, RefZh, SCI, SSCI, SolStAb, WAA, ZentMath.
—BLDSC (8814.556000), AskIEEE, CISTI, Ei, IDS, IE, Infotrieve, ingenta, Linda Hall. **CCC.**
Published by: Elsevier BV, North-Holland (Subsidiary of: Elsevier Science & Technology), Sara Burgerhartstraat 25, Amsterdam, 1055 KV, Netherlands. TEL 31-20-485-3911, FAX 31-20-485-2457, nlinfo-f@elsevier.nl, http://www.elsevier.com/locate/entcs, http://www.elsevier.nl/homepage/about/us/regional_sites.htt, http://www.elsevier.nl. Eds. G Ausiello, M W Mislove, M Nivat. **Subscr. to:** Elsevier BV, PO Box 211, Amsterdam 1000 AE, Netherlands. TEL 31-20-485-3757, FAX 31-20-485-3432.

004.01 USA ISSN 1432-4350
QA75.5 CODEN: TCSYFI
➤ **THEORY OF COMPUTING SYSTEMS;** an international journal. Text in English. 1966. bi-m. (in 1 vol., 6 nos./vol.). EUR 558 combined subscription to institutions print & online eds. (effective 2005). adv. back issues avail.; reprint service avail. from ISI. **Document type:** *Journal, Academic/Scholarly.* **Description:** Features original research from all areas of theoretical computer science.
Formerly (until 1997): Mathematical Systems Theory (0025-5661)
Related titles: Microform ed.: (from PQC); Online - full text ed.: ISSN 1433-0490 (from EBSCO Publishing, ProQuest Information & Learning, Springer LINK, Swets Information Services).
Indexed: ABIn, ASCA, CIS, CMCI, CompAb, CompLI, CurCont, ISR, Inspec, MathR, MathSciNet, RASB, RefZh, SCI, ZentMath.
—BLDSC (8814.631250), AskIEEE, CISTI, IDS, IE, Infotrieve, ingenta, Linda Hall. **CCC.**
Published by: Springer-Verlag New York, Inc. (Subsidiary of: Springer Science+Business Media), 233 Spring St, New York, NY 10013. TEL 212-460-1500, 800-777-4643, FAX 212-473-6272, journals@springer-ny.com, http://link.springer.de/link/service/journals/00224/, http://www.springer-ny.com. Ed. Alan L Selman. R&P Xian Chuan Lian. Adv. contact Brian Skepton. B&W page USD 575; 5 x 8. **Subscr. outside the Americas to:** Springer GmbH Auslieferungsgesellschaft, Haberstr 7, Heidelberg 69126, Germany. TEL 49-6221-345-0, FAX 49-6221-345-4229, subscriptions@springer.de; **Subscr. to:** Journal Fulfillment, PO Box 2485, Secaucus, NJ 07096-2485. TEL 800-777-4643, 201-348-4033, FAX 201-348-4505.

▼ ➤ **WEB INTELLIGENCE AND AGENT SYSTEMS;** an international journal. see *COMPUTERS—Artificial Intelligence*

COMPUTERS—Word Processing

➤ **ARCHIV FUER STENOGRAFIE, TEXTVERARBEITUNG, BUEROTECHNIK.** see *EDUCATION—Teaching Methods And Curriculum*

005.52 USA
DUMMIES DAILY MICROSOFT WORD 97 NEWSLETTER. Text in English. 1999. d. **Document type:** *Newsletter.*
Media: Online - full text.
Published by: I D G Books Worldwide, Inc., 919 E. Hillsdale Blvd., Ste. 400, Foster City, CA 94404. david@mkpr.com, http://www.dummiesdaily.com/. Ed. David Hafner.

005.52 USA
DUMMIES DAILY NERD WORD OF THE DAY NEWSLETTER. Text in English. 1999. d. back issues avail. **Document type:** *Newsletter.*
Media: Online - full text.
Published by: I D G Books Worldwide, Inc., 919 E. Hillsdale Blvd., Ste. 400, Foster City, CA 94404. david@mkpr.com, http://www.dummiesdaily.com/. Ed. David Hafner.

005.52 DEU ISSN 1617-1616
EXPERT'S INSIDE. WORD. Text in German. 2001. m. EUR 72.60; EUR 6.90 newsstand/cover (effective 2003). adv. **Document type:** *Magazine, Trade.*
Published by: redtec publishing GmbH, Gruber Str 46a, Poing, 85586, Germany. TEL 49-8121-951850, FAX 49-8121-951880, info@redtec.de, http://www.experts-inside.de/word, http://www.redtec.de. Adv. contact Guido Klausbruckner. B&W page EUR 1,000, color page EUR 1,500; trim 210 x 297.

INSIDE COREL WORDPERFECT SUITE. see *COMPUTERS—Software*

INSIDE MICROSOFT WORD. see *COMPUTERS—Software*

005.52 USA ISSN 1052-7605
THE INSIDE WORD (P C EDITION - MICROSOFT WORD 5.5 & 6.0). Text in English. 1991. m. USD 69; USD 89 foreign. **Document type:** *Consumer.*
—CCC.
Published by: Element K Journals (Subsidiary of: Eli Research, Inc.), 500 Canal View Blvd, Rochester, NY 14623.

PRAXISHANDBUCH WORD 2000. see *COMPUTERS—Software*

005.52 USA
WORD TIPS* . Text in English. w. **Description:** Designed to help you learn how to effectively use and master Microsoft Word for Windows.
Media: Online - full text.
Published by: Discovery Computing, Inc., P O Box 11356, Cincinnati, OH 45211-0356. TEL 800-628-8280, FAX 307-283-2714, awyatt@dcomp.com, http://www.dcomp.com/WordTips/. Ed. Allen Wyatt.

WORDPERFECT SUITE NEWSLETTER ONLINE. see *COMPUTERS—Software*

005.52 USA ISSN 0890-524X
WORDSTAR SCROLL. Text in English. 1985. bi-m. looseleaf. USD 30 (effective 1996). adv. bk.rev. back issues avail. **Document type:** *Newsletter.* **Description:** Serves as the official publication for the WordStar Processing Users' Group.
Published by: WordStar Processing Users' Group, Inc., 7958 S W 105th Pl, Miami, FL 33173. TEL 305-274-0099, FAX 305-271-8904, cbabbage@gix.netcom.com. Ed. Emerson Boardman. Pub., R&P, Adv. contact David Rafky. Circ: 4,000. **Subscr. to:** PO Box 16 1443, Miami, FL 33116-1443.

WORKGROUP COMPUTING REPORT; applying technology to business processes. see *COMPUTERS—Electronic Data Processing*

005.52 USA ISSN 1530-4299
WORKING SMARTER WITH MICROSOFT WORD. (Avail. in 3 versions: Word 2000, Word 2002 and Word 2003) Text in English. 199?. bi-w. USD 4.27 per issue (effective 2005). **Document type:** *Newsletter, Consumer.* **Description:** Contains time-saving tips.
—CCC.
Published by: Mosaic Media, Inc., OneOnOne Computer Training (Subsidiary of: Mosaic Media, Inc.), 751 Roosevelt Rd, Ste 108, Glen Ellyn, IL 60137-5905. TEL 800-424-8668, FAX 630-628-0550, oneonone@pincom.com, http://www.oootraining.com. Ed. Herb Tyson.

005.52 USA ISSN 1530-4280
WORKING SMARTER WITH WORDPERFECT. (Avail. in 2 versions: WordPerfect 9 and WordPerfect 10.) Text in English. 199?. bi-w. USD 4.27 per issue (effective 2005). **Document type:** *Consumer.* **Description:** Includes time-saving tips.
—CCC.
Published by: Mosaic Media, Inc., OneOnOne Computer Training (Subsidiary of: Mosaic Media, Inc.), 751 Roosevelt Rd, Ste 108, Glen Ellyn, IL 60137-5905. TEL 800-424-8668, FAX 630-628-0550, oneonone@pincom.com, http://www.oootraining.com. Ed. Sara Thornbury.

CONSERVATION

see also ENERGY ; ENVIRONMENTAL STUDIES ; FISH AND FISHERIES ; FORESTS AND FORESTRY ; WATER RESOURCES

A C A REVIEW. see *FISH AND FISHERIES*

A I C C M BULLETIN. see *ART*

A I C C M NATIONAL NEWSLETTER. see *HUMANITIES: COMPREHENSIVE WORKS*

333.72 USA ISSN 1538-0742
A N J E C REPORT. Text in English. 1969. q. USD 15 (effective 2000). adv. bk.rev. **Document type:** *Newsletter, Academic/Scholarly.* **Description:** Contains information on a variety of environmental subjects with a special focus on New Jersey.
Former titles (until 1977): Association of New Jersey Environmental Commissions Newsletter; Association of New Jersey Conservation Commissions Newsletter (0044-9636)
Published by: Association of New Jersey Environmental Commissions, PO Box 157, Mendham, NJ 07945. TEL 973-539-7547, FAX 973-539-7713, anjec@aol.com, anjec@aol.com. Ed., R&P Sandy Batty. Adv. contact Margaret Davey. Circ: 2,200.

C

▼ *new title* ➤ *refereed* * *unverified* ◆ *full entry avail.*

C

333.72   USA   ISSN 1062-6190
A P T COMMUNIQUE. Text in English; Text occasionally in
Multiple languages. 1972. bi-m. free to members (effective
2004). adv. bk.rev. cum.index.
Former titles (until 1989): Association for Preservation
Technology. Communique (0319-4558); (until 1975):
Association for Preservation Technology. Newsletter
(0319-454X)
Indexed: AIAP.
Published by: Association for Preservation Technology
International, 4513 Lincoln Ave, Ste 213, Lisle, IL 60532-1290.
TEL 630-968-6400, information@apti.org, http://www.apti.org.
Circ: 2,000.

333.7   IDN
A S E A N REVIEW OF BIODIVERSITY AND ENVIRONMENTAL
CONSERVATION. Text in English. m. USD 215.
Media: Online - full content.
Published by: Association of South East Asian Nations (ASEAN),
ASEAN Secretariat, Jalan Sisingamangaraja 70 A, Jakarta,
12110, Indonesia. TEL 62-21-7262991, FAX 62-21-7398234,
limster@pop.jaring.my, public@aseansec.org,
http://www.arbec.com.my/index.htm.

A S P I TECHNICAL SERIES. see ENVIRONMENTAL STUDIES

333.72   POL   ISSN 0208-6131
ACTA UNIVERSITATIS LODZIENSIS: FOLIA SOZOLOGICA. Text
in Polish. 1955-1974; N.S. 1983. irreg. Document type:
Academic/Scholarly. Description: Devoted to problems of
theory and practice of biological conservation in Poland.
Supersedes in part: Uniwersytet Lodzki. Zeszyty Naukowe. Seria
2: Nauki Matematyczno-Przyrodnicze (0076-0366)
—CISTI, Linda Hall.
Published by: Wydawnictwo Uniwersytetu Lodzkiego/Lodz
University Press, ul Jaracza 34, Lodz, 90262, Poland. TEL
331671. Dist. by: Ars Polona, Krakowskie Przedmiescie 7,
Warsaw, Poland.

333.72   POL   ISSN 0208-533X
NA109.P7
ACTA UNIVERSITATIS NICOLAI COPERNICI. NAUKI
HUMANISTYCZNO-SPOLECZNE. ZABYTKOZNAWSTWO I
KONSERWATORSTWO. Text in Polish. 1966. irreg. price
varies. Document type: Academic/Scholarly.
Formerly (until 1973): Uniwersytet Mikolaja Kopernika. Nauki
Humanistyczno-Spoleczne. Zeszyty Naukowe.
Zabytkoznawstwo i Konserwatorstwo (0563-9506)
Indexed: BHA.
Published by: Uniwersytet Mikolaja Kopernika/Nicolaus
Copernicus University, Wydawnictwo, ul Gagarina 39, Torun,
87100, Poland. TEL 48-56-14295. Dist. by: Osrodek
Rozpowszechniania Wydawnictw Naukowych PAN, Palac
Kultury i Nauki, Warsaw 00901, Poland.

ACTION ALERT (SAN FRANCISCO). see ENVIRONMENTAL
STUDIES

ADIRONDAC. see SPORTS AND GAMES—Outdoor Life

599 346.044   USA   ISSN 0194-1488
ADMINISTRATION OF THE MARINE MAMMAL PROTECTION
ACT OF 1972 (UNITED STATES, FISH AND WILDLIFE
SERVICE). Text in English. 1973. a.
Published by: U.S. Fish and Wildlife Service, 1201 Oak Ridge
Dr., Ste. 200, Ft. Collins, CO 80525-5589.

AELVRAEDDAREN. see ENVIRONMENTAL STUDIES

AFRICAN JOURNAL OF ECOLOGY. see BIOLOGY

AFRICAN JOURNAL OF ECOLOGY ONLINE. see BIOLOGY

AFRICAN JOURNAL OF RANGE & FORAGE SCIENCE. see
AGRICULTURE—Crop Production And Soil

333.72 634.9   USA   ISSN 1093-8966
QL737.P9
➤ AFRICAN PRIMATES. Text in English, French. 1995. 2/yr.
USD 20 domestic Voluntary contribution (effective 2000).
bk.rev. bibl.; illus.; maps; stat. back issues avail. Document
type: Academic/Scholarly. Description: Caters to field
primatologists and conservationists involved in the
conservation of African Primates.
Indexed: ZooRec.
Published by: Zoo Atlanta, 800 Cherokee Ave SE, Atlanta, GA
30315-1440. TEL 404-624-5808, FAX 404-627-7514,
forthmand@mindspring.com, http://www.primate.wisc.edu/pin/.
Ed. T M Butynski. Circ: 1,200.

333.95416 363.7   ZAF   ISSN 0256-6273
                                       CODEN: ICOAB5
➤ AFRICAN WILDLIFE. Variant title: African Wildlife (Multilingual
Edition). Text in English. 1983. q. ZAR 185 domestic (effective
2004). adv. bk.rev. charts; illus. index. back issues avail.
Document type: Magazine, Academic/Scholarly.

Formed by the merger of (1946-1983): African Wildlife (English
Edition) (0256-6257); Which was formerly (until 1982): African
Wildlife (International Edition); (1946-1983): Afrika-Natuurlewe
(Afrikaanse Edition) (0256-6265); Which was formerly (until
1982): African Wildlife (Afrikaanse Edition) (0256-6249); Both
of which superseded in part (in 1979): African Wildlife
(Multilanguage Edition) (0002-0273)
Related titles: Microform ed.: (from PQC).
Indexed: ASFA, BiolAb, EPB, EnvAb, ISAP, KWIWR, SFA, WBA,
WMB, WildRev, ZooRec.
—BLDSC (0735.000000), IE, Linda Hall.
Published by: Wildlife and Environment Society of South Africa,
PO Box 394, Howick, 3290, South Africa. TEL 27-33-3303931,
FAX 27-33-3304576, wildmag@yebo.co.za,
http://www.wildlifesociety.org.za. Ed. Sandie Anderson. Circ:
15,000.

333.95416   USA
KF5640.A15
AFRICAN WILDLIFE NEWS. Text in English. 1963. 5/yr. USD 25.
bk.rev. Document type: Newsletter.
Former titles: Wildlife News (0270-0360); African Wildlife News
(0065-4086)
Published by: African Wildlife Foundation, 1400 16th St, NW, Ste
120, Washington, DC 20036. TEL 202-939-3333, FAX
202-265-2361, TELEX 1504TEMBO, http://www.awf.com. Ed.,
R&P Rebecca Villarreal. Circ: 40,000.

333.95416   USA   ISSN 1058-9805
AFRICAN WILDLIFE UPDATE; the independent source for news.
Text in English. 1991. irreg. bk.rev. back issues avail.
Document type: Newsletter, Academic/Scholarly.
Description: Reports current news on African wildlife and
keeps people informed about events affecting its conservation.
Media: Online - full text.
Address: PO Box 546, Olympia, WA 98507-0546.
awnews@aol.com, http://www.africanwildlife.org/.

333.72   ETH
AGAZEN; environment and population. Text in Amharic, English.
1986. s-a. USD 1 per issue. adv. bk.rev. charts; illus. back
issues avail. Document type: Bulletin. Description: Publishes
short articles on conservation and environmental issues for a
secondary school and undergraduate audience.
Published by: Ethiopian Wildlife and Natural History Society, PO
Box 13303, Addis Ababa, Ethiopia. TEL 251-1-183520. Ed.
Zewditu Tessema. Circ: 15,000.

AGRO-ECOLOGY NEWS AND PERSPECTIVES; science and
education for a sustanaible agriculture. see
ENVIRONMENTAL STUDIES

333.95416   USA   ISSN 0894-8356
ALABAMA WILDLIFE. Text in English. 1985. q. USD 25. adv.
Description: Covers outdoors, wildlife and related topics.
Address: PO Box 1109, Montgomery, AL 36102. FAX
334-832-9454. Ed., R&P Dan Dumont. Adv. contact Barbara
Harrington.

333.72   USA
ALASKA CENTER FOR THE ENVIRONMENT. CENTER NEWS.
Text in English. 1972. q. USD 35 (effective 1999). adv. bk.rev.
Document type: Newsletter.
Published by: Alaska Center for the Environment, 519 W 8th
Ave, Ste 201, Anchorage, AK 99501-3549. TEL 907-274-3621,
FAX 907-274-8733. Ed. Cliff Eames. Circ: 9,000.

ALASKA DEPARTMENT OF FISH AND GAME. DIVISION OF
COMMERCIAL FISHERIES. SPECIAL PUBLICATION. see
FISH AND FISHERIES

ALASKA DEPARTMENT OF FISH AND GAME. DIVISION OF
WILDLIFE CONSERVATION. FEDERAL AID IN WILDLIFE
RESTORATION. ANNUAL MONITORING REPORT. see FISH
AND FISHERIES

ALASKA DEPARTMENT OF FISH AND GAME. DIVISION OF
WILDLIFE CONSERVATION. FEDERAL AID IN WILDLIFE
RESTORATION. ANNUAL PERFORMANCE REPORT OF
SURVEY. see FISH AND FISHERIES

ALASKA DEPARTMENT OF FISH AND GAME. DIVISION OF
WILDLIFE CONSERVATION. FEDERAL AID IN WILDLIFE
RESTORATION. ANNUAL RESEARCH PERFORMANCE
REPORT. see FISH AND FISHERIES

ALASKA DEPARTMENT OF FISH AND GAME. DIVISION OF
WILDLIFE CONSERVATION. FEDERAL AID IN WILDLIFE
RESTORATION. RESEARCH PROGRESS REPORT. see
FISH AND FISHERIES

ALASKA DEPARTMENT OF FISH AND GAME. DIVISION OF
WILDLIFE CONSERVATION. FEDERAL AID IN WILDLIFE
RESTORATION. SURVEY-INVENTORY MANAGEMENT
REPORT. see FISH AND FISHERIES

ALASKA DEPARTMENT OF FISH AND GAME. DIVISION OF
WILDLIFE CONSERVATION. FEDERAL AID IN WILDLIFE
RESTORATION. WILDLIFE TECHNICAL BULLETIN. see
FISH AND FISHERIES

ALASKA DEPARTMENT OF FISH AND GAME. DIVISION OF
WILDLIFE CONSERVATION. FINAL REPORT. see FISH AND
FISHERIES

333.95416   USA
ALASKA. DEPARTMENT OF FISH AND GAME. WILDLIFE
NOTEBOOK SERIES. Text in English. irreg.
Formerly: Alaska. Department of Fish and Game. Wildlife Booklet
Series (0084-0130)
Published by: Department of Fish and Game, Division of Wildlife
Conservation, PO Box 22526, Juneau, AK 99802-2526. TEL
907-465-4190, http://www.state.ak.us/local/akpages/fish.game/
wildlife/wildmain.htm.

333.95416   USA   ISSN 0362-6962
SK367
ALASKA. DIVISION OF WILDLIFE CONSERVATION. ANNUAL
REPORT OF SURVEY - INVENTORY ACTIVITIES. Key Title:
Annual Report of Survey - Inventory Activities. Text in English.
1970. a. (biennial, triennial). free. illus. Document type:
Government.
Formerly (until 1991): Alaska. Division of Game. Annual Report of
Survey - Inventory Activities
Published by: Department of Fish and Game, Division of Wildlife
Conservation, PO Box 22526, Juneau, AK 99802-2526. TEL
907-465-4190. Ed. Mary Hicks. Circ: 350.

639.2 333.72   USA
ALASKA WILDLIFE NEWS. Text in English. m.
Media: Online - full text.
Published by: Alaska Department of Fish and Game, 1255 West
8th St, Juneau, AK 99801. TEL 907-465-4256,
http://www.wildlife.alaska.gov/pubs/wildlife_news/index.cfm. Ed.
Michelle Sydeman.

333.7   CAN
ALBERTA GAME WARDEN. Text in English. q. CND 12, CND 17
domestic (effective 2002). Document type: Magazine.
Published by: Alberta Fish & Wildlife Officers Association, c/o
Gazette Press Ltd, 25 Chisholm Ave, PO Box 263, St Albert,
AB T8N 1N3, Canada. gamewarden@wtc.ab.ca,
http://www.gamewarden.ab.ca. Ed. Daniel Boyco.

333.7   CAN   ISSN 1205-8734
ALBERTA'S ENERGY RESOURCES IN REVIEW. Text in English.
1967. a. free.
Former titles (until 1995): Energy Alberta (0833-3505); (until
1984): Alberta Energy (0825-1525); Which superseded in part
(in 1982): Conservation in Alberta (0380-4496)
Published by: Energy and Utilities Board, 640 5th Ave, S W,
Calgary, AB T2P 3G4, Canada. TEL 403-297-8190, FAX
403-297-7040, eub.info_services@eub.gov.ab.ca,
http://www.eub.gov.ab.ca.

ALBURY & DISTRICT HISTORICAL SOCIETY. BULLETIN. see
HISTORY—History Of Australasia And Other Areas

ALISO; a journal of taxonomic and evolutionary botany. see
BIOLOGY—Botany

ALIVE (MILWAUKEE). see ANIMAL WELFARE

333.7845   USA
ALONG THE TOWPATH. Text in English. 1969. q. looseleaf.
membership. bk.rev. charts; illus.; stat.
Published by: Chesapeake & Ohio Canal Association, Inc., PO
Box 366, Glen Echo, MD 20812-0366. Ed. Donald Besom.
Circ: 800.

ALPINE GARDENER. see BIOLOGY—Botany

AMERICAN HAWKWATCHER; a journal devoted to raptors &
raptor migration. see BIOLOGY—Ornithology

333.95416   USA   ISSN 0065-9150
AMERICAN LITTORAL SOCIETY. SPECIAL PUBLICATIONS.
Text in English. 1962. irreg. (approx. 2-3/yr). USD 25 to
individuals; USD 30 to institutions (effective 1999). adv. bk.rev.
reprint service avail. from PQC.
Indexed: ASFA, BiolAb.
—Linda Hall.
Published by: American Littoral Society, Sandy Hook, Highlands,
NJ 07732. TEL 908-291-0055. Ed. D W Bennett. Circ: 7,500.

333.72 551.4   USA
AMERICAN RIVERS; bringing rivers to life. Text in English. 1973.
3/yr. USD 20 to individual members; USD 15 to individual
members students & seniors (effective 2005). Document
type: Newsletter. Description: Dedicated to protecting and
restoring healthy natural rivers, and the variety of life they
sustain, for the benefit of people, fish and wildlife. It informs
and educate members, friends, and the general public about
river conservation issues.
Address: 1025 Vermont Ave., NW., Ste 720, Washington, DC
20005. TEL 202-347-7550, 877-347-7550, FAX 202-347-9240,
jsenn@americanrivers.org, http://www.americanrivers.org.

AMERICAN SHORE AND BEACH PRESERVATION
ASSOCIATION. NEWSLETTER. see ENVIRONMENTAL
STUDIES

AMERICAN SOCIETY FOR CONSERVATION ARCHAEOLOGY REPORT. see *ARCHAEOLOGY*

AMERICAN UNIVERSITY STUDIES. SERIES 21. REGIONAL STUDIES. see *ETHNIC INTERESTS*

AMERICAN WHITEWATER. see *SPORTS AND GAMES—Boats And Boating*

AMOEBA. see *BIOLOGY*

ANBLICK; Zeitschrift fuer Jagd und Natur in den Alpen. see *SPORTS AND GAMES—Outdoor Life*

333.9 GBR ISSN 1367-9430
QH75.A1
ANIMAL CONSERVATION; a journal of ecology, evolution and genetics. Text in English. q. USD 208 in North America to institutions; GBP 132 elsewhere to institutions; USD 230 combined subscription in North America to institutions print & online eds.; GBP 145 combined subscription elsewhere to institutions print & online eds. (effective 2005). **Document type:** *Journal, Academic/Scholarly.* **Description:** Contains new research into the factors which influence the conservation of animal species and their habitats.
Related titles: Online - full text ed.: ISSN 1469-1795. USD 195 in North America to institutions; GBP 124 elsewhere to institutions (effective 2005) (from EBSCO Publishing, O C L C Online Computer Library Center, Inc., Swets Information Services).
Indexed: ASFA, AgBio, AnBrAb, ApEcolAb, B&BAb, BIOSIS Prev, BiolAb, CurCont, ESPM, EntAb, ForAb, GEOBASE, GenetAb, HGA, IndVet, SeedAb, VetBull, ZooRec.
—BLDSC (0903.230000), IE, Infotrieve, ingenta, Linda Hall.
Published by: Blackwell Publishing Ltd., 9600 Garsington Rd, Oxford, OX4 2ZG, United Kingdom. TEL 44-1865-776868, FAX 44-1865-714591, customerservices@oxon.blackwellpublishing.com, http://www.blackwellpublishing.com. Eds. E J Milner-Gullard, John Gittleman, Keith Crandall.

ANNUAL DEPARTMENTAL REPORT BY THE DIRECTOR OF AGRICULTURE AND FISHERIES. see *AGRICULTURE*

ANNUAL REPORT ON THE ENVIRONMENT AND NATURAL RESOURCES. see *ENVIRONMENTAL STUDIES*

333.72 USA
THE ANTARCTICA PROJECT. Text in English. 1982. q. looseleaf. USD 20 membership minimum (effective 2002). illus. **Document type:** *Newsletter.* **Description:** Covers current events of Antarctica and the international campaign for its protection. It is a non-governmental conservation organization in the world that works full-time on the protection of Antarctica and its dependent and associated ecosystems.
Published by: (Antarctic & Southern Ocean Coalition), Antarctica Project, 1630 Connecticut Ave, Ste 300, Washington, DC 20009. TEL 202-234-2480, FAX 202-387-4823, antarctica@igc.org, http://www.asoc.org. Ed. Beth Clark. R&P Scott Altmann TEL 202-234-2480. Circ: 1,000.

APPALACHIAN ALTERNATIVES. see *ENVIRONMENTAL STUDIES*

333.9 GBR ISSN 1052-7613
QH541.5.W3 CODEN: AQCOEY
➤ **AQUATIC CONSERVATION**; marine and freshwater ecosystems. Text in English. 1991. 7/yr. USD 995 to institutions; USD 1,095 combined subscription to institutions print & online eds. (effective 2006). adv. bk.rev. illus. back issues avail.; reprint service avail. from PSC. **Document type:** *Journal, Academic/Scholarly.* **Description:** Dedicated to publishing original papers that relate specifically to freshwater, brackish or marine habitats and encouraging work that spans these ecosystems.
Related titles: Microform ed.: (from PQC); Online - full content ed.: ISSN 1099-0755. 1997. USD 995 to institutions (effective 2006); Online - full text ed.: (from EBSCO Publishing, Swets Information Services, Wiley InterScience).
Indexed: ASCA, ASFA, ApEcolAb, BIOBASE, BIOSIS Prev, BiolAb, CivEngAb, CurCont, EPB, ESPM, EntAb, EnvEAb, FLUIDEX, GEOBASE, IABS, ISR, M&TEA, OceAb, PollutAb, RRTA, RefZh, S&F, SCI, SFA, SWRA, WAE&RSA, WRCInf, WildRev, ZooRec.
—BLDSC (1582.371000), CISTI, IDS, IE, Infotrieve, ingenta. **CCC.**
Published by: John Wiley & Sons Ltd. (Subsidiary of: John Wiley & Sons, Inc.), The Atrium, Southern Gate, Chichester, West Sussex PO19 8SQ, United Kingdom. TEL 44-1243-779777, FAX 44-1243-775878, customer@wiley.co.uk, http://www.interscience.wiley.com/jpages/1052-7613/, http://www.wiley.co.uk. Ed. Philip Boon. adv.: B&W page GBP 650, color page GBP 1,550; trim 200 x 260. Circ: 500. **Subscr. in the Americas to:** John Wiley & Sons, Inc., 111 River St, Hoboken, NJ 07030-5774. TEL 201-748-6645, 800-225-5945, subinfo@wiley.com.

➤ **AQUATIC ENVIRONMENT PROTECTION**; analytical methods. see *ENVIRONMENTAL STUDIES*

333.72 USA
ARBOR DAY. Text in English. bi-m. membership. **Document type:** *Newsletter.* **Description:** Serves as a communication link for members, promoting tree-planting projects throughout the United States.
Formerly: Arbor Day News
Published by: National Arbor Day Foundation, 100 Arbor Ave, Nebraska City, NE 68410. TEL 402-474-5655, FAX 402-474-0820. Ed. James R Fazio. Pub. John E Rosenow. R&P Gary Brienzo.

333.75 634.96 GBR
ARBORVITAE. Text in English. q. **Document type:** *Newsletter.*
—BLDSC (1594.015000), ingenta.
Published by: I U C N - World Conservation Union, 23 Bath Bldgs, Montpelier, Bristol, Avon BS6 5PT, United Kingdom. TEL 44-117-942-8674, FAX 44-117-942-8674, equilibrium@compuserve.com. Eds. Nigel Dudley, Sue Stolton.

ARID LAND RESEARCH AND MANAGEMENT. see *AGRICULTURE—Crop Production And Soil*

557.54 USA ISSN 0277-9455
CODEN: ALABDH
ARID LANDS NEWSLETTER (ABRIDGED PRINT EDITION). Text in English. 1975. s-a. free (effective 2005). 4 p./no.; **Document type:** *Newsletter, Abstract/Index.* **Description:** Contains abstracts & summaries of the online edition.
Related titles: ♦ Abridged ed. of: Arid Lands Newsletter (Online Edition). ISSN 1092-5481.
Indexed: Agr, EPB, SFA, WAE&RSA, WildRev.
—BLDSC (1668.270000).
Published by: University of Arizona, Office of Arid Lands Studies, 1955 E Sixth St, Tucson, AZ 85719-5224. TEL 520-621-8584, FAX 520-621-3816, kwaser@ag.arizona.edu, http://ag.arizona.edu/OALS/ALN/ALNHome.html. Ed., R&P Katherine Waser. Circ: 1,000 (free).

557.54 USA ISSN 1092-5481
ARID LANDS NEWSLETTER (ONLINE EDITION). Text in English. s-a. free. bk.rev. back issues avail. **Document type:** *Newsletter, Academic/Scholarly.* **Description:** Publishes articles about problems, potential, and sustainable development of arid and semiarid lands worldwide, for an audience of researchers, land managers, policy makers and dry lands inhabitants.
Media: Online - full content. **Related titles:** E-mail ed.; ♦ Abridged ed.: Arid Lands Newsletter (Abridged Print Edition). ISSN 0277-9455.
Published by: University of Arizona, Office of Arid Lands Studies, 1955 E Sixth St, Tucson, AZ 85719-5224. TEL 520-621-8584, FAX 520-621-3816, kwaser@ag.arizona.edu, http://ag.arizona.edu/OALS/ALN/ALNHome.html. Ed., R&P Katherine Waser.

333.75416 USA ISSN 0882-5572
SK51
ARIZONA WILDLIFE VIEWS. Text in English. 1953. bi-m. USD 8.50 (effective 2002). charts; illus.; stat. **Document type:** *Journal, Government.* **Description:** Articles on Arizona wildlife, hunting, fishing and boating.
Indexed: WildRev.
Published by: Game and Fish Department, 2221 W Greenway Rd, Phoenix, AZ 85023-4399. TEL 602-942-3000, http://www.gf.state.az.us. Circ: 17,000 (paid).

333.9 GBR ISSN 0306-8870
THE ARK (FAVERSHAM). Text in English. 1974. q. GBP 18; GBP 30 foreign (effective 2000). adv. bk.rev. index. **Document type:** *Bulletin, Academic/Scholarly.* **Description:** Promotes conservation of endangered breeds of British farm animals.
Indexed: NumL.
—BLDSC (1668.750000), IE, ingenta.
Published by: (Rare Breeds Survival Trust), A F L Deeson Partnership Ltd., Ewell House, Faversham, Kent ME13 8UP, United Kingdom. TEL 44-1795-535468, FAX 44-1795-535469. Ed., R&P Richard Lutwyche TEL 44-1203-696551. Adv. contact Julie Billings. Circ: 10,000 (controlled).

333.72 USA ISSN 0884-9145
ARKANSAS OUTDOORS. Text in English. 1946. w. free to qualified personnel. **Document type:** *Newsletter.*
Published by: Game and Fish Commission, 2 Natural Resource Dr, Little Rock, AR 72205. TEL 501-223-6342, FAX 501-223-6447, jhmosby@agfc.state.ar.us. Ed. Joe Mosby. Circ: 1,300.

333.95416 USA ISSN 1063-0953
SK371
ARKANSAS WILDLIFE. Text in English. 1967. q. USD 8 (effective 2000). charts; illus.; stat. **Document type:** *Consumer.*
Formerly (until 1992): Arkansas Game & Fish Magazine (0004-1807)
Indexed: RefZh, SFA, WildRev.
Published by: Game and Fish Commission, 2 Natural Resource Dr, Little Rock, AR 72205. TEL 501-223-6331, FAX 501-223-6447. Ed., R&P Keith Sutton TEL 501-223-6406. Circ: 72,000.

333.72 USA
THE ARROW (CEDAR KNOLLS). Text in English. 1989. q. **Document type:** *Newsletter.* **Description:** Presents information on public policy issues in Morris County on which Morris 2000 is currently working.
Published by: Morris 2000, 2 Ridgedale Ave, Cedar Knolls, NJ 07927. TEL 201-984-2000. Ed. Carol J Rufener.

333.72 DEU ISSN 0940-8215
ARTENSCHUTZREPORT. Text in German. 1991. irreg. **Document type:** *Journal, Academic/Scholarly.* **Description:** Concerned with scientific and scholarly research on the conservation of plants and animals in Germany.
Indexed: ESPM, ZooRec.
Address: Thymianweg 25, Jena, 07745, Germany. Eds., Pubs. Martin Goerner, Peter Kneis.

333.72 500 SGP
ASIAN GEOGRAPHIC. Cover title: AsianGeographic. Text in English. bi-m. SGD 32 domestic (effective 2002). **Description:** Covers the natural history, environment and culture of Asia.
Published by: Asian Geographic Magazines Pte Ltd, 45A Haji Ln, Singapore, 189238, Singapore. TEL 65-298-3241, FAX 65-291-2068, info@asiangeographic.org, http://www.asiangeographic.org.

ASIAN - PACIFIC ENVIRONMENT; newsletter of the Asia Pacific people's environment network. see *ENVIRONMENTAL STUDIES*

333.95416 USA
ASSOCIATION OF MIDWEST FISH AND WILDLIFE AGENCIES. PROCEEDINGS✶. (Notes: Publisher varies according to host state.) Text in English. 1934. a. price varies. **Document type:** *Proceedings.*
Former titles: Association of Midwest Fish and Wildlife Commissioners. Proceedings; Association of Midwest Fish and Game Commissioners. Proceedings (0066-9601)
Published by: Association of Midwest Fish and Wildlife Agencies, 444 N Capitol St N W, Washington, DC 20001. Circ: 25.

333.95416 333.72 ITA
ATTENZIONE; rivista WWF per l'ambiente e il territorio. (World Wildlife Fund) Text in Italian. 1998. irreg. **Document type:** *Monographic series, Consumer.* **Description:** Addresses and gives information on environmental issues, land conservation, climatic changes, ecosystems, as well as commercial uses of wild plant species.
Published by: Fondo Mondiale per la Natura/World Wildlife Fund, Via Po 25c, Rome, 00198, Italy. TEL 39-06-852492, FAX 39-06-8554410, wwf@wwf.it, http://www.wwf.it. Ed. Fulco Pratesi.

333.95416 USA ISSN 0097-7136
QL671 CODEN: AUDUAD
AUDUBON. Text in English. 1899. bi-m. USD 20 domestic; USD 45 in Canada; USD 50 elsewhere (effective 2004); includes membership. adv. bk.rev. charts; illus. index. back issues avail.; reprints avail. **Document type:** *Magazine, Consumer.* **Description:** Covers environment, wildlife and preservation of wildlife habitat.
Formerly (until 1961): Audubon Magazine (0004-7694); (until 1940): Bird Lore (1059-8626)
Related titles: CD-ROM ed.: (from ProQuest Information & Learning); Microform ed.: (from PMC, PQC); Online - full text ed.: (from Florida Center for Library Automation, Gale Group, Northern Light Technology, Inc., O C L C Online Computer Library Center, Inc.).
Indexed: ABS&EES, ASFA, Acal, BRI, BiolAb, BiolDig, CBRI, CPerl, ChPerl, EIA, EPB, ESPM, EnerRev, EnvAb, GSI, GardL, KWIWR, MASUSE, MagInd, PMR, RGAb, RGPR, RI-1, RI-2, SWRA, TOM, WildRev.
—BLDSC (1789.850000), IE, Infotrieve, ingenta, Linda Hall.
Published by: National Audubon Society, 700 Broadway, New York, NY 10003. TEL 212-979-3000, FAX 212-979-3188, editor@audubon.org, http://magazine.audubon.org/index.html, http://www.audubon.org. Ed. David Seideman. Pub. Patrick Downes. adv.: B&W page USD 18,135, color page USD 29,985; trim 10.81 x 8.25. Circ: 425,000 (paid). **Subscr. to:** PO Box 52529, Boulder, CO 80322.

333.95416 USA ISSN 0571-8805
AUDUBON CONSERVATION REPORT. Text in English. 1964. irreg.
—Linda Hall.
Published by: National Audubon Society, 700 Broadway, New York, NY 10003. TEL 212-979-3000, FAX 212-979-3188, http://www.audubon.org.

333.72 USA ISSN 0274-502X
AUDUBON SOCIETY OF RHODE ISLAND. REPORT. Text in English. 1966. 6/yr. USD 10 to non-members (effective 2000). bk.rev. **Document type:** *Newsletter.* **Description:** Articles focus on natural history and environmental issues in Rhode Island.
Formerly: Rhode Island Audubon Report (0556-8587)
Published by: Audubon Society of Rhode Island, 12 Sanderson Rd, Smithfield, RI 02917-2606. TEL 401-949-5454, FAX 401-949-5788. Ed. Ken Weber. R&P, Adv. contact Eugenia Marks. Circ: 5,000.

C

333.72 USA ISSN 1097-1548
AULLWOOD NOTES. Text in English. 1962. bi-m. membership. bk.rev. **Document type:** *Newsletter.*
Media: Duplicated (not offset).
Published by: (Friends of Aullwood, Inc.), Aullwood Audubon Center and Farm, 1000 Aullwood Rd, Dayton, OH 45414. TEL 937-890-7360. Ed. John C Ritzenthaler. Circ: 1,500.

346.044 AUS ISSN 1320-5323
K1
➤ **AUSTRALASIAN JOURNAL OF NATURAL RESOURCES LAW AND POLICY.** Text in English. 1994. s-a. AUD 150 (effective 2002). adv. **Document type:** *Academic/Scholarly.* **Description:** Publishes articles and information on all aspects of natural resources.
—BLDSC (1794.970000), IE, ingenta.
Published by: (University of Wollongong), University of Wollongong, Faculty of Law, Centre for Natural Resources Law and Policy, Northfields Ave, Wollongong, NSW 2522, Australia. maria_agnew@uow.edu.au. Ed. Martin Tsamenyi.

➤ **AUSTRALASIAN PARKS AND LEISURE.** see *LEISURE AND RECREATION*

➤ **AUSTRALASIAN PRIMATOLOGY.** see *BIOLOGY—Zoology*

333.72 AUS ISSN 0587-5846
AUSTRALIAN CONSERVATION FOUNDATION. ANNUAL REPORT. Text in English. 1968. a. illus. **Document type:** *Corporate.* **Description:** Annual report of the Australian Conservation Foundation.
Published by: Australian Conservation Foundation, 340 Gore St, Fitzroy, VIC 3065, Australia. TEL 61-3-94161166, FAX 61-3-94160767. R&P Louise Ray.

333.72 AUS ISSN 1035-137X
CODEN: ANEVEA
AUSTRALIAN ENVIRONMENT REVIEW. Text in English. 1982. m. AUD 481.80 (effective 2004). bk.rev. **Document type:** *Newsletter.* **Description:** Features highlights on water management, waste management, the greenhouse debate, transport, energy, and environmental law.
Formerly (until 1990): Australian Environment Management Review Newsletter (0728-7593)
Indexed: INIS AtomInd.
—IE.
Published by: LexisNexis Butterworths (Subsidiary of: LexisNexis Asia Pacific), Tower 2, 475-495 Victoria Ave, Chatswood, NSW 2067, Australia. TEL 61-2-94222189, FAX 61-2-94222406, customer.relations@lexisnexis.com.au, http://www.lexisnexis.com.au/default.asp. **Subscr. to:** Locked Bag 2222, Chatswood, NSW 2047, Australia. TEL 1800-772-772, FAX 61-2-94222405.

AUSTRALIAN GEOGRAPHIC. see *GEOGRAPHY*

333.72071 AUS ISSN 0814-0626
AUSTRALIAN JOURNAL OF ENVIRONMENTAL EDUCATION. Text in English. 1984. a. AUD 15. **Document type:** *Academic/Scholarly.* **Description:** Presents information and arguments that will stimulate debate about educational activities to enhance environmental awareness, understanding and action among all Australians.
Indexed: AEI, CIJE.
—BLDSC (1807.650000), IE, ingenta.
Published by: Australian Association for Environmental Education, c/o I. Robottom, Ed., Faculty of Education, Geelong, Deakin University, VIC 3217, Australia.

333.7 AUS ISSN 1440-4397
S494.5.S86
AUSTRALIAN LANDCARE. Text in English. 1996. q. AUD 28.10 (effective 2005). **Document type:** *Magazine, Trade.* **Description:** Promotes management and practices which farmers can adopt to bring about improvement to the soil, water, vegetation, habitat and wildlife resources on their properties while at the same time operating profitable businesses.
Formerly (until 1998): Australian Farm Journal Sustainable Agriculture (1328-6536)
Indexed: AEA, AgrForAb, FCA, FPA, ForAb, HerbAb, I&DA, IndVet, NutrAb, PBA, PGegResA, RDA, S&F, VetBull, WAE&RSA, WeedAb.
—BLDSC (1813.272000), CISTI.
Published by: Rural Press Ltd. (Subsidiary of: Agricultural Publishers Pty. Ltd.), 10 Sydenham St., PO Box 254, Moonee Ponds, VIC 3039, Australia. FAX 61-3-93705622, http://landcare.farmonline.com.au/, http://www.ruralpress.com/. Ed. Patrick Francis. Adv. contact Donna Clarke.

333.72 AUS ISSN 1320-9736
AUSTRALIAN NATURE CONSERVATION AGENCY. ANNUAL REPORT. Text in English. 1976. a. illus. **Document type:** *Government.*
Formerly: Australian National Parks and Wildlife Service. Report (0314-1322)
—CCC.
Published by: (Australia. Australian Nature Conservation Agency), AusInfo, GPO Box 1920, Canberra Mc, ACT 2610, Australia. TEL 61-2-6295-4512, FAX 61-2-6295-4455.

333.95416 AUS
AUSTRALIAN WILDLIFE MAGAZINE✶. Text in English. 1966. q. included in membership. bk.rev. **Document type:** *Magazine, Academic/Scholarly.*
Formerly (until 2003): Australian Wildlife Newsletter (0155-266X)
Published by: Wildlife Preservation Society of Australia, PO Box 42, Brighton Le Sands, NSW 2216, Australia. TEL 61-2-95561537, FAX 61-2-95990000, wildlifepreservation@optusnet.com.au, http://www.wpsa.org.au/default2.asp?contentID=11. Ed. Pat Medway. Circ: 1,000 (paid).

B B C WILDLIFE. see *BIOLOGY—Zoology*

333.72 DEU
B U N D MAGAZIN. Text in German. q. adv. **Document type:** *Magazine, Consumer.*
Published by: (Bund fuer Umwelt und Naturschutz Deutschland), Natur und Umwelt Verlag GmbH, Am Koellnischen Park 1, Berlin, 10179, Germany. TEL 49-30-2758640, FAX 49-30-27586440, bund@bund.net, http://www.bund.net. Adv. contact Kalina Otte. B&W page EUR 6,260, color page EUR 7,050; trim 188 x 242. Circ: 250,000 (controlled).

346.044 USA ISSN 1049-3972
BACK FORTY. Text in English. 1990. bi-m. looseleaf. USD 110 (effective 1998). adv. index. back issues avail. **Document type:** *Newsletter, Academic/Scholarly.*
Address: c/o Hastings College of Law, 200 McAllister St, San Francisco, CA 94102. TEL 415-565-4857, FAX 415-565-4818. Ed. William T Hutton. R&P David Shapiro. Adv. contact Dana M Landrum. Circ: 500.

333.7 USA
BACKYARD WILDLIFE HABITAT. Text in English. 1997. q. **Document type:** *Newsletter, Consumer.*
Media: Online - full content.
Published by: National Wildlife Federation, 11100 Wildlife Center Dr., Reston, VA 20190-5362. TEL 703-438-6284, 800-822-9919, FAX 703-438-6349, pubs@nwf.org, http://www.nwf.org/habitats/index.html.

BAT NEWS. see *BIOLOGY—Zoology*

BAY NATURE. see *ENVIRONMENTAL STUDIES*

BEAR NEWS. see *BIOLOGY—Zoology*

333.72 BEL ISSN 0771-355X
BEENBREEK; Natuur 2000. Text in Dutch; Summaries in English. 1969. bi-m. EUR 12.39 membership (effective 2005). bk.rev. illus. index. back issues avail. **Document type:** *Bulletin, Academic/Scholarly.* **Description:** Includes articles on the study and conservation of nature in Belgium and the world, coming events agenda, new products information, etc.
Published by: Natuur 2000, Bervoetstraat 33, Antwerp, 2000, Belgium. TEL 32-3-231-2604, FAX 32-3-233-6499, natuur2000@telenet.be, http://home.scarlet.be/~na983929. Ed. Julius Anton Smeyers. Adv. contact Jan Voet. Circ: 2,500.

BEFRIENDING CREATION. see *RELIGIONS AND THEOLOGY*

BEIJING JIENENG. see *ENERGY*

333.72 DEU ISSN 0525-4736
BEITRAEGE ZUR LANDESENTWICKLUNG. Text in German. 1966. irreg., latest vol.54, 1999. price varies. **Document type:** *Monographic series, Academic/Scholarly.*
Published by: (Landschaftsverband Rheinland, Umweltamt), Rheinland Verlag GmbH, Abtei Brauweiler, Postfach 2140, Pulheim, 50250, Germany. TEL 49-2234-9854265, FAX 49-2234-82503. **Dist. by:** Dr. Rudolf Habelt GmbH, Am Buchenhang 1, Bonn 53115, Germany. TEL 49-228-232016, FAX 49-228-9238322.

577.51 DEU ISSN 0949-5681
TC273.9.L68
BERICHTE DER FORSCHUNGSSTELLE KUESTE. Text in German. 1970. irreg. **Document type:** *Monographic series, Academic/Scholarly.*
Former titles (until 1996): Niedersaechsisches Landesamt fuer Wasser und Abfall. Forschungsstelle Kueste. Jahresbericht (0939-785X); (until 1990): Niedersaechsisches Landesamt fuer Wasserwirtschaft. Forschungsstelle Kueste. Jahresbericht (0179-5384); (until 1985): Forschungsstelle fuer Insel- und Kuestenschutz der Niedersaechsischen Wasserwirtschaftsverwaltung. Jahresbericht (0340-4323)
Indexed: ESPM.
Published by: Niedersaechsisches Landesamt fuer Oekologie, Postfach 101062, Hildesheim, 31110, Germany. TEL 49-5121-509-0, FAX 49-5121-509196, poststelle@nloe.niedersachsen.de, http://jupiter.nloe.de.

333.72 DEU
BERLIN - BRANDENBURGER NATURMAGAZIN; Naturschutz in Berlin und Brandenburg. Text in German. 1987. bi-m. EUR 24.50; EUR 4.30 newsstand/cover (effective 2005). bk.rev. 48 p./no.; back issues avail. **Document type:** *Magazine, Consumer.* **Description:** Contains articles and features about nature conservation in East Germany, Berlin and Brandenburg with some articles about European countries.
Formerly (until 1998): Oekowerkmagazin (0935-7602)
Related titles: E-mail ed.; Fax ed.
Indexed: ZooRec.
Published by: (Naturschutzbund Deutschland), Natur und Text in Brandenburg GmbH, Friedensallee 21, Rangsdorf, 15834, Germany. TEL 49-708-20432, FAX 49-708-20433, nut-brandenburg@t-online.de, http://www.naturmagazin.net/naturmagazin_aktuell.html. Ed., R&P, Adv. contact Christof Ehrentraut TEL 49-708-73801. Pub. Reinhard Baier. Circ: 10,000.

333.7 GBR
BEST PRACTICE PROTECTED AREA GUIDELINES SERIES. Text in English.
Indexed: ZooRec.
—BLDSC (1942.327866).
Published by: I U C N - World Conservation Union, 219c Huntingdon Rd, Cambridge, CB3 0DL, United Kingdom. TEL 44-1223-277894, FAX 44-1223-277175. Ed. Adrian Phillips.

346.044 DEU ISSN 0405-6779
BEWAEHRUNGSHILFE; Fachzeitschrift fuer Bewaehrungs-, Gerichts- und Straffaelligenhilfe. Text in German. 1953. q. **Document type:** *Newspaper, Trade.*
Indexed: AC&P, DIP, IBR, IBZ.
Published by: (Deutsche Bewaehrungshilfe e.V.), Forum Verlag Godesberg GmbH, Ferdinandstr 16, Moenchengladbach, 41061, Germany. TEL 49-2161-206669, FAX 49-2161-209183, forumverlaggodesberg.gmbh@t-online.de.

333.72 DEU ISSN 0342-8095
BIMBO; der kleine Tierfreund. Text in German. 1977. m. EUR 22.80 (effective 2003). bk.rev. illus. **Document type:** *Magazine, Consumer.* **Description:** Information about nature, animals and environmental protection for children aged 6-8.
Published by: Johann Michael Sailer Verlag GmbH & Co. KG, Aeusserer Laufer Platz 17, Nuernberg, 90403, Germany. TEL 49-911-53960, FAX 49-911-5396912, sailer@sailer-verlag.de, http://www.sailer-verlag.de. Ed. Andrea Hoesel. Circ: 75,000 (paid).

333.95 CRI ISSN 0250-6963
BIOCENOSIS. Text in Spanish. 1979. 2/yr. CRC 1,700; USD 13 in Central America; USD 15 in North America; USD 20 in Europe; USD 21 in Africa. adv. **Document type:** *Academic/Scholarly.*
Indexed: ASFA, ESPM, INIS AtomInd.
Published by: (Oficina de Extencion Comunitaria y Conservacion del Medio Ambiente), Universidad Estatal a Distancia, Apdo. 474, San Pedro de Montes de Oca, San Jose, 2050, Costa Rica. TEL 506-2532121, FAX 506-2346547, biocenos@arenal.uned.ac.cr. Ed. Martha Camacho. Adv. contact Oscar Raul Hernandez.

BIODIVERSITY. see *ENVIRONMENTAL STUDIES*

333.95 NLD ISSN 0960-3115
QH75.A1 CODEN: BONSEU
➤ **BIODIVERSITY AND CONSERVATION.** Text in Dutch. 1991. 14/yr. EUR 1,998, USD 2,068, GBP 1,318 combined subscription to institutions print & online eds. (effective 2005). adv. illus. reprint service avail. from PSC. **Document type:** *Journal, Academic/Scholarly.* **Description:** Contains papers on biological diversity in all its aspects, its description, analysis and conservation, and its controlled and rational use by man.
Related titles: Online - full text ed.: ISSN 1572-9710 (from EBSCO Publishing, Gale Group, IngentaConnect, Kluwer Online, O C L C Online Computer Library Center, Inc., Ovid Technologies, Inc., Springer LINK, Swets Information Services).
Indexed: AEA, ASCA, ASFA, AgBio, Agr, AgrForAb, AnBrAb, ApEcolAb, B&BAb, BIOBASE, BIOSIS Prev, BibAg, BibLing, BioCN&I, BiolAb, CPA, CivEngAb, CurCont, DSA, EPB, ESPM, EntAb, EnvAb, EnvEAb, FCA, FPA, ForAb, GEOBASE, GardL, GenetAb, HGA, HelmAb, HerbAb, HortAb, I&DA, IABS, ISR, IndVet, MaizeAb, NemAb, NutrAb, OrnHort, PBA, PGegResA, PGrRegA, PN&I, PlantSci, PollutAb, PoultAb, ProtozoAb, RA&MP, RDA, RPP, RRTA, RefZh, RevApplEntom, RiceAb, S&F, SCI, SFA, SSCI, SWRA, SeedAb, TDB, TriticAb, VITIS, VetBull, WAE&RSA, WeedAb, WildRev, ZooRec.
—BLDSC (2071.700000), CISTI, IDS, IE, Infotrieve, ingenta. CCC.
Published by: Springer-Verlag Dordrecht (Subsidiary of: Springer Science+Business Media), Van Godewijckstraat 30, Dordrecht, 3311 GX, Netherlands. TEL 31-78-6576050, FAX 31-78-6576474, http://springerlink.metapress.com/openurl.asp?genre=journal&issn=0960-3115, http://www.springeronline.com. Ed. Alan T Bull.

➤ **BIODIVERSITY NEWS;** the newsletter for biodiversity action planners. see *BIOLOGY*

➤ **BIODYNAMICS;** a periodical furthering soil conservation and increased fertility in order to improve nutrition and health. see *AGRICULTURE—Crop Production And Soil*

333.95 NLD ISSN 0006-3207
S900 CODEN: BICOBK
➤ **BIOLOGICAL CONSERVATION.** Text in English. 1969. 28/yr. EUR 2,344 in Europe to institutions; JPY 311,100 in Japan to institutions; USD 2,624 to institutions except Europe and Japan (effective 2006). adv. bk.rev. charts; illus.; abstr. back issues avail.; reprints avail. **Document type:** *Journal, Academic/Scholarly.* **Description:** Publishes original papers dealing with the preservation of wildlife and the conservation or wise use of biological and allied natural resources.
Related titles: Microform ed.: (from PQC); Online - full text ed.: (from EBSCO Publishing, Gale Group, IngentaConnect, ScienceDirect, Swets Information Services).
Indexed: AEA, AESIS, APD, ASCA, ASFA, AbHyg, AgBio, Agr, AgrForAb, AnBrAb, ApEcolAb, B&AI, B&BAb, BIOBASE, BIOSIS Prev, BioCN&I, BiolAb, CPA, CurCont, EIA, EPB, ESPM, EnerInd, EnerRev, EntAb, EnvAb, ExcerpMed, FCA, FPA, ForAb, GEOBASE, GardL, GenetAb, HGA, HelmAb, HerbAb, HortAb, I&DA, IABS, ISR, IndVet, KWIWR, M&TEA, MaizeAb, NutrAb, OceAb, OrnHort, PBA, PGegResA, PGrRegA, PN&I, PotatoAb, PoultAb, RA&MP, RDA, RM&VM, RPP, RRTA, RevApplEntom, RiceAb, S&F, SCI, SFA, SSCI, SWRA, SeedAb, TDB, TriticAb, VetBull, WAE&RSA, WeedAb, WildRev, ZooRec.
—BLDSC (2075.100000), CISTI, IDS, IE, Infotrieve, ingenta, Linda Hall. **CCC.**
Published by: Elsevier BV (Subsidiary of: Elsevier Science & Technology), Radarweg 29, Amsterdam, 1043 NX, Netherlands. TEL 31-20-4853911, FAX 31-20-4852457, nlinfo-f@elsevier.nl, http://www.elsevier.com/locate/biocon, http://www.elsevier.nl. Ed. R Marrs. **Subscr. to:** Elsevier, Subscription Customer Service, 6277 Sea Harbor Dr, Orlando, FL 32887-4800. TEL 407-345-4020, 877-839-7126, FAX 407-363-1354.

333.72 577 GBR
BIOLOGICAL CONSERVATION, RESTORATION AND SUSTAINABILITY. Text in English. 1999. irreg., latest vol.1, 1999. price varies. **Document type:** *Monographic series, Academic/Scholarly.* **Description:** Covers scientific and cultural issues facing those who are interested in improving the ecological conditions, biological diversity, or productivity of damaged wildlands.
Indexed: BIOSIS Prev, ZooRec.
Published by: Cambridge University Press, The Edinburgh Bldg, Shaftesbury Rd, Cambridge, CB2 2RU, United Kingdom. TEL 44-1223-312393, FAX 44-1223-315052, information@cambridge.org, http://publishing.cambridge.org/series/bcrs, http://www.cup.cam.ac.uk/.

333.95 CAN ISSN 0824-1600
QH75.A1
BIOSPHERE. Text in French. 1985. 5/yr. USD 26.75 (effective 1999). adv. bk.rev. **Description:** Full-colour magazine dealing with the environment, wildlife, and the conservation of natural resources.
Incorporates: Biosphere en Bref
Related titles: Online - full text ed.
Indexed: CPerI, PdeR.
Published by: (Canadian Wildlife Federation), Malcolm Publishing Inc., 11 450 Albert Hudon Blvd, Montreal, PQ H1G 3J9, Canada. TEL 514-327-4464, FAX 514-327-7592. Ed. Martin Silverstone. Circ: 20,000.

BIRDLIFE INTERNATIONAL. STUDY REPORT. see *BIOLOGY—Ornithology*

BIRDWATCHER'S YEARBOOK AND DIARY. see *BIOLOGY—Ornithology*

BLUE BILL. see *BIOLOGY—Ornithology*

333.95416 USA ISSN 0196-3430
BLUE GOOSE FLYER. Text in English. 1975. q. USD 25 to members (effective 2005). bk.rev. **Document type:** *Newsletter, Consumer.* **Description:** Provides informational and educational material on issues concerning the National Wildlife Refuge System and individual refuge units.
Published by: National Wildlife Refuge Association, 1010 Wisconsin Ave N W, Ste 200, Washington, DC 20007. TEL 202-333-9075, FAX 202-333-9077, nwra@refugenet.org, http://www.refugenet.org/new-publications/blue-goose-flyer.html, http://www.RefugeNET.org. Circ: 1,500 (paid and controlled).

333.95416 USA ISSN 1050-0715
THE BLUEBIRD. Text in English. 1937. q.
—Linda Hall.
Published by: Audubon Society of Missouri, 1800 S Roby Farm Rd, Rocheport, MO 65279. TEL 573-698-2855, palmer1076@aol.com, http://www.mobirds.org.

BOARD OF THE BOTANIC GARDENS AND STATE HERBARIUM. ANNUAL REPORT. see *BIOLOGY—Botany*

333.72 DEU ISSN 1432-170X
BODENSCHUTZ. Text in German. 1988. q. looseleaf. EUR 49.60; EUR 14.90 newsstand/cover (effective 2006). adv. **Document type:** *Journal, Trade.*
Published by: Erich Schmidt Verlag GmbH & Co. (Berlin), Genthiner Str 30G, Berlin, 10785, Germany. TEL 49-30-2500850, FAX 49-30-250085305, esv@esvmedien.de, http://www.erich-schmidt-verlag.de. Eds. Rainer Schmidt, Wilhelm Koenig. adv.: B&W page EUR 840, color page EUR 1,710. Circ: 1,400 (paid and controlled).

333.72 AUS ISSN 0159-6586
BOGONG. Text in English. 1980. q. AUD 15 to individuals; AUD 18 to libraries; AUD 20 to institutions (effective 2000). adv. bk.rev. back issues avail. **Document type:** *Magazine, Academic/Scholarly.* **Description:** Covers primarily local and regional with some national and international environmental and related social issues.
Indexed: AltPI.
Published by: Canberra Environment Centre, GPO Box 1875, Canberra, ACT 2601, Australia. TEL 61-2-62480885, FAX 61-2-62473064, caserec@peg.apc.org, envcentre.act@ecoaction.net.au, http://www.spirit.net.au/envoz/eccser/core.html, http://www.ecoaction.net.au. Ed., R&P Tasmin Sowoen. Circ: 500.

BOMENNIEUWS. see *GARDENING AND HORTICULTURE*

333.91 USA ISSN 0899-2681
BOUNDARY WATERS JOURNAL; the magazine of America's favorite wilderness area. Text in English. 1987. q. USD 21 domestic; USD 25 in Canada; USD 26 elsewhere; USD 4.95 per issue (effective 2005). adv. bk.rev. back issues avail. **Document type:** *Magazine, Consumer.* **Description:** Covers canoeing, camping, fishing, and natural resource management for both the expert, as well as the novice.
Published by: Boundary Waters Journal Publishing Co, 9396 Rocky Ledge Rd, Ely, MN 55731. TEL 218-365-6184, 800-548-7319, bwjournal@boundarywatersjournal.com, http://www.boundarywatersjournal.com. Ed., Pub., R&P Stuart Osthoff. Adv. contact Anne Moravitz. B&W page USD 600, color page USD 1,080; trim 9.63 x 7.25. Circ: 32,000 (paid).

333.72 GBR ISSN 1362-6094
BOURNEMOUTH UNIVERSITY. SCHOOL OF CONSERVATION SCIENCES. OCCASIONAL PAPER. Text in English. 1995. irreg. **Document type:** *Monographic series, Academic/Scholarly.*
Indexed: NumL.
—BLDSC (6212.660000).
Published by: Bournemouth University, School of Conservation Sciences, Talbot Campus, Fern Barrow, Poole, Dorset BH12 5BB, United Kingdom.

333.72 GBR
BOURNEMOUTH UNIVERSITY. SCHOOL OF CONSERVATION SCIENCES. RESEARCH REPORTS. Text in English. irreg. **Document type:** *Monographic series, Academic/Scholarly.*
—BLDSC (7760.343000).
Published by: Bournemouth University, School of Conservation Sciences, Talbot Campus, Fern Barrow, Poole, Dorset BH12 5BB, United Kingdom. TEL 44-1202-595178, FAX 44-1202-515707, consci@bmth.ac.uk, http://csweb.bournemouth.ac.uk/consci/text/. Ed. Timothy Darvill.

363.7 CAN ISSN 0824-5126
BRANTA; Canada's forum for environmental awareness. Text in English. 1983. q. CND 40 to individual members; CND 2.50 newsstand/cover. adv. illus. **Document type:** *Newsletter.* **Description:** Covers environmental, wildlife and nature themes.
Published by: Fort Whyte Foundation Inc., 1961 McCreary Rd, Winnipeg, MB R3P 2K9, Canada. TEL 204-989-8355, FAX 202-895-4700, fwc@fortwhyte.mb.ca, http://www.mbnet.mb.ca/fortwhyte. Ed., R&P, Adv. contact Graham Wren. Circ: 1,000; 3,000 (paid).

333.78 CAN ISSN 1195-4825
GE190.C2
BRITISH COLUMBIA. MINISTRY OF ENVIRONMENT, LANDS AND PARKS. ANNUAL REPORT. Text in English. 1964. a. free. **Document type:** *Government.*
Former titles (until 1992): British Columbia. Ministry of Environment. Annual Report (1181-8336); (until 1989): British Columbia. Ministry of Environment and Parks. Annual Report (0838-1933); British Columbia. Ministry of Environment. Annual Report (0227-7506); British Columbia. Department of Lands, Forests and Water Resources. Water Resources Service. Report (0068-1873)
—BLDSC (1352.878000), CISTI.
Published by: Ministry of Environment, Lands and Parks, Communications Branch, Sta Provincial Government, PO Box 9360, Victoria, BC V8W 9M2, Canada. TEL 250-387-9422, FAX 250-356-6464. Circ: 3,000.

333.95416 USA
BROADSIDES. Text in English. 4/yr. USD 30 membership (effective 2000). **Document type:** *Newsletter, Consumer.*
Published by: Great Old Broads for Wilderness, PO Box 2924, Durango, CO 81302-2924. TEL 801-487-9898, broads@greatoldbroads.org, http://www.greatoldbroads.org. Ed. Erin Moore. R&P Liz McCay.

BROOKER'S RESOURCE MANAGEMENT GAZETTE. see *LAW*

333.95416 USA ISSN 0889-6445
SK303
BUGLE (MISSOULA); journal of elk and the hunt. Text in English. 1984. bi-m. free to members. adv. illus. reprints avail. **Document type:** *Magazine, Consumer.* **Description:** Focuses on conserving elk, other wildlife and their habitat, from the viewpoints of hunters, naturalists and all those who care about elk and the land.
Indexed: WildRev.
Published by: Joy Publications, LLC, 2291 W Broadway, PO Box 8249, Missoula, MT 59807-8249. TEL 406-523-4500, 800-225-5355, FAX 406-523-4550, bugle@rmef.org, http://www.elkfoundation.org. Ed. Dan Crockett. R&P Lee Cromrich. Adv. contact Tara Sheridan. Circ: 195,000 (paid).

333.72 COL
BULLETIN: ALERT BIOLOGICAL AND CULTURAL DIVERSITY. Text in Spanish. 1999. m. free. **Document type:** *Bulletin.*
Related titles: Online - full text ed.
Published by: Instituto Latinoamericano de Servicios Legales Alternativos/Inter-American Legal Services Association, Apartado Aereo 077844, Bogota, CUND, Colombia. TEL 57-1-2884437, FAX 57-1-2884854, silsa@coll.telecom.com.co, http://www.ilsa.org.co.

333.9 FRA ISSN 0767-2861
CODEN: BFPPE2
➤ **BULLETIN FRANCAIS DE LA PECHE ET DE LA PISCICULTURE**; connaissance et gestion du patrimoine aquatique. Short title: B F P P. Text and summaries in English, French. 1928. q. EUR 43 domestic; EUR 51 foreign (effective 2005). bk.rev. bibl.; illus. index. back issues avail. **Document type:** *Journal, Academic/Scholarly.* **Description:** Publishes scientific articles concerning all problems of fishery management and, more generally, of aquatic ecosystems.
Formerly (until 1985): Bulletin Francais de Pisciculture (0373-0514)
Indexed: ASCA, ASFA, AgBio, AgrForAb, AnBrAb, BIOSIS Prev, BiolAb, CRFR, CurCont, ESPM, ExcerpMed, HelmAb, HortAb, IndVet, NutrAb, ProtozoAb, RA&MP, RM&VM, RRTA, RefZh, SFA, VetBull, WAE&RSA, WeedAb, WildRev, ZooRec.
—CASDDS, IDS.
Published by: Conseil Superieur de la Peche, Immeuble Le Pericentre, 16 Avenue Louison Bobet, Fontenay sous Bois, 94120, France. TEL 33-31-45143600, FAX 33-31-45143660, csp.bfpp@csp.ecologie.gouv.fr, csp.bfpp@csp.environnement.gouv.fr, http://www.csp.ecologie.gouv.fr/pages/publications/bfpp/findex.htm, http://www.csp.environnement.gouv.fr/pages/publications/bfpp/index.fr. Ed., R&P Valerie Maniglier. Circ: 1,300.

C

333.72 AUT
BURGENBOTE; Oesterreichs Bindenschild. Text in German. 1973 (vol.5). 4/yr. membership. adv. illus. **Document type:** *Bulletin.*
Published by: Burgen- und Schloesserer haltungsverein, Stadtamt, Retz, N 2070, Austria. Ed. Fred Borth. Circ: 1,000.

333.73 USA
BUSINESS ASSOCIATE; partners in land conservation. Text in English. 1984. s-a. membership. back issues avail. **Document type:** *Newsletter.* **Description:** Reports on various environmental activities of member companies for the corporate members of the Western Pennsylvania Conservancy.
Published by: Western Pennsylvania Conservancy, 209 Fourth Ave, Pittsburgh, PA 15222-1707. TEL 412-288-2777, FAX 412-281-1792. Ed. Bill Randour. Circ: 1,000.

333.9 GBR ISSN 0254-0878
CODEN: BUSTEW
BUSTARD STUDIES. Text in English. 1983. a. GBP 10. **Document type:** *Academic/Scholarly.*
Published by: BirdLife International, Wellbrook Ct, Girton Rd, Cambridge, CB3 ONA, United Kingdom.

BUTTERFLY. see *BIOLOGY—Entomology*

333.72 SWE ISSN 0345-7982
BYGD OCH NATUR (TIDSKRIFT); tidskrift foer hembygdsvaard. Text in Swedish. 1920. 5/yr. SEK 100 (effective 2004). adv. bk.rev. cum index:1939-1983, 1984-1989. **Document type:** *Magazine, Consumer.*
Formerly (until 1939): Tidskrift foer Hembygdsvaard; Incorporates (1933-1996): Bygd och Natur (Aarsbok) (0007-7453)
Indexed: NAA, RILM.
Published by: Sveriges Hembygdsfoerbund S H F/Swedish Local Heritage Federation, PO Box 6167, Stockholm, 10233, Sweden. TEL 46-8-345511, FAX 46-8-347474, kansli@hembygd.se, http://www.hembygd.se. Ed. Peter Johansson. Circ: 12,000.

333.72 UKR
BYULETEN' EKOLOHICHNOHO STANU ZONY VIDCHUZHENNYA. Text in Ukrainian, Russian. s-a. USD 65 in the Americas (effective 2000).
Published by: Chernobyl'interinform, Ul B Khmel'nitskogo 1-a, Chernobyl, Ukraine. TEL 380-37-52098, FAX 380-37-52205. **Dist. by:** East View Information Services, 3020 Harbor Ln. N., Minneapolis, MN 55447. TEL 763-550-0961, FAX 763-559-2931.

333.72 USA ISSN 0886-8298
C B E ENVIRONMENTAL REVIEW. Text in English. 1972. 3/yr. USD 30 to individuals; USD 20 to students (effective 2000). bk.rev. **Document type:** *Newsletter.*
Indexed: AltPI.
Published by: Citizens for a Better Environment, 1845 N. Farwell Ave., Ste. 220, Milwaukee, WI 53202-1715. TEL 414-271-7280, FAX 414-271-5904, http://www.cbemw.org. Ed. Sara Daleiden. R&P Marilyn Goris TEL 414-271-7280. Circ: 48,000.

333.9 CHE
C B S G NEWS. (Conservation Breeding Specialist Group) Text in English. 4/yr. USD 25 (effective 2000). **Document type:** *Newsletter.*
Indexed: SFA.
Published by: (Species Survival Commission), International Union for Conservation of Nature and Natural Resources, Rue Mauverney 28, Gland, 1196, Switzerland. TEL 41-22-9990001, FAX 41-22-9990002, mail@hq.iucn.org, http://www.cbsg.org. **Subscr. to:** 12101 Johnny Cake Ridge Rd., Apple Valley, MN 55124.

C C I NEWSLETTER/BULLETIN DE L'I C C. see *MUSEUMS AND ART GALLERIES*

C C I NOTES/NOTES DE L'I C C. see *MUSEUMS AND ART GALLERIES*

C C I TECHNICAL BULLETINS/I C C BULLETINS TECHNIQUES. see *MUSEUMS AND ART GALLERIES*

333.72 USA
C E A S E NEWS. Text in English. 1980. 3/yr. USD 10 (effective 1999). bk.rev. **Document type:** *Newsletter.* **Description:** Provides a forum for the exchange of ideas on how to help children become peaceful and constructive citizens, with a sense of responsibility towards one another and their environment.
Published by: Concerned Educators Allied for a Safe Environment, c/o Peggy Schirmer, Ed, 17 Gerry St, Cambridge, MA 02138. TEL 617-864-0999, FAX 617-864-0999. Ed. Peggy Schirmer. Circ: 900.

C E L S S JOURNAL/C E L S S GAKKAISHI. see *BIOLOGY*

C E L S S NEWS. see *BIOLOGY*

577.22 GBR
C L I V A R NEWSLETTER EXCHANGES. Text in English. 1996. q. **Description:** Includes articles on global climate, El Nino phenomenon and environmental issues in general.
Published by: Climate Variability and Predictability Programme, Southampton Oceanographic Center, Empress Dock, Southampton, S014 32H, United Kingdom. TEL 44-1703-596-777, FAX 44-1703-596-204, icpo@soc.soton.ac.uk, http://www.dkrz.de/clivar/publications.html. Ed. Andreas Villwock.

C N P S INVENTORY OF RARE AND ENDANGERED VASCULAR PLANTS OF CALIFORNIA. see *BIOLOGY—Botany*

333.783 USA ISSN 0887-9176
C S P R A NEWSLETTER. Text in English. 1968. bi-m. USD 36 (effective 1999). adv. bk.rev. back issues avail. **Document type:** *Newsletter.*
Published by: California State Park Rangers Association, PO Box 292010, Sacramento, CA 95829-2010. TEL 916-558-3734, FAX 916-387-1179, dugbryce@earthlink.net, http://members.aol.com/cspraweb. Ed. Doug Bryce. R&P, Adv. contact Carol Boyce. Circ: 700 (paid).

333.9 USA ISSN 1052-5823
CALIFORNIA COAST & OCEAN. Text in English. 1985. q. USD 18 domestic; USD 33 foreign (effective 2004). bk.rev. illus. index. **Document type:** *Government.* **Description:** Covers California coastal environmental issues.
Formerly (until 1990): California WaterfrontAge (8756-0852)
Indexed: ASFA, BiolDig, EPB, ESPM, EnvAb, PollutAb.
Published by: California State Coastal Conservancy, 1330 Broadway, Ste 1100, Oakland, CA 94612-2530. TEL 510-286-0934, FAX 510-286-0470, calcoast@igc.org, http://www.coastalconservancy.ca.gov/coast&ocean/summer2004/index.html. Ed., R&P Rasa Gustaitis. Circ: 10,000.

333.72 USA
CALIFORNIA FISH AND GAME CODE. SUPPLEMENT. Text in English. a. looseleaf. USD 24.95 (effective 2000). index.
Published by: (California. Department of Fish and Game), Gould Publications, Inc. (Subsidiary of: LexisNexis), 1333 North US Hwy 17-92, Longwood, FL 32750-3724. TEL 407-695-9500, 800-717-7917, FAX 407-695-2906, info@gouldlaw.com, http://www.gouldlaw.com.

333.783 USA
CALIFORNIA PARKLANDS. Text in English. q. USD 40 membership (effective 2001). **Document type:** *Newsletter, Consumer.*
Published by: California State Parks Foundation, Box 548, Kentfield, CA 94914-0548. TEL 415-258-9975, FAX 415-258-9930, calpark@calparks.org, http://www.calparks.org. Ed. Bill Cullison.

CALIFORNIA PARKS & RECREATION. see *LEISURE AND RECREATION*

CALIFORNIA TODAY. see *ENVIRONMENTAL STUDIES*

333.9 CAN ISSN 1194-2258
CALL OF THE LOON. Text in English. 1991. m. adv. charts; illus.; maps; stat.; tr.lit. 8 p./no. 5 cols./p.; back issues avail. **Document type:** *Newsletter.* **Description:** Disseminates club project news, issues and event information.
Published by: Ontario Federation of Anglers & Hunters, 4601 Guthrie Dr, P O Box 2800, Peterborough, ON K9J 8L5, Canada. TEL 705-748-6324, FAX 705-748-9577, ofah@ofah.org, http://www.ofah.org. Ed., R&P, Adv. contact Mark Holmes. page CND 500. Circ: 1,300 (controlled).

333.72 USA ISSN 1074-9209
THE CALLER. Text in English. 1990. q. USD 25 to members. adv. stat. back issues avail. **Document type:** *Newsletter.* **Description:** Includes articles submitted by volunteer members and state conservation agencies.
Published by: National Wild Turkey Federation, Inc., 770 Augusta Rd, PO Box 530, Edgefield, SC 29824-0530. TEL 803-637-3106, FAX 803-637-0034, nwtf@nwtf.net, kroop@nwtf.net, http://www.nwtf.net. Ed. Russ Lumpkin. Adv. contact Jenny Johnson. Circ: 160,000 (paid).

CALYPSO LOG. see *ENVIRONMENTAL STUDIES*

333.72 BRA ISSN 0104-1541
OS CAMINHOS DA TERRA. Variant title: Terra. Text in Portuguese. 1992. m. BRL 76.80; BRL 6.40 newsstand/cover (effective 2002). adv. illus. back issues avail. **Document type:** *Magazine, Consumer.* **Description:** Covers nature, ecology, adventure travel, and exotic places.
Related titles: E-mail ed.
Published by: Editora Abril, S.A., Av. das Nacoes Unidas, 7221, 11 andar Pinheiros, Sao Paulo, SP 05425-902, Brazil. TEL 55-011-30372000, FAX 55-011-30375638, terra.atleitor@email.abril.com.br, relacoes.corporativas@abril.com.br, http://www.revistaterra.com.br/, http://www.abril.com.br/. adv.: color page USD 11,500; trim 202 x 266. Circ: 112,482 (paid).

CANADIAN ARCTIC RESOURCES COMMITTEE. MEMBERS' UPDATE. see *ENVIRONMENTAL STUDIES*

333.95416 CAN ISSN 1196-6432
CANADIAN SPECIES AT RISK. Text in English. 1992. a.
Published by: Committee on the Status of Endangered Wildlife in Canada, COSEWIC Secretariat, c/o Canadian Wildlife Service, Environment Canada, Ottawa, ON K1A 0H3, Canada. TEL 819-953-3215, FAX 819-994-3684.

333.95416 CAN ISSN 1201-673X
CANADIAN WILDLIFE. Text in English. 1965. 5/yr. CND 26.75 to members (effective 1999). bk.rev. **Description:** Contains wide range of subjects including articles on wildlife, wild areas, nature-related research, endangered species, wildlife management, land use issues, character profiles and the science and politics of conservation.
Formerly: International Wildlife (Canadian Edition); Incorporates: Wildlife Update; Formerly: Canadian Chronicle; Supersedes: Wildlife News (0043-5503)
Related titles: Online - full text ed.: (from EBSCO Publishing).
Indexed: CBCARef, CPerl, MASUSE.
Published by: (Canadian Wildlife Federation), Malcolm Publishing Inc., 11 450 Albert Hudon Blvd, Montreal, PQ H1G 3J9, Canada. TEL 514-327-4464, FAX 514-327-7592. Ed. Martin Silverstone. Circ: 77,000.

333.95416 CAN ISSN 0576-6370
CODEN: CWOPAL
➤ **CANADIAN WILDLIFE SERVICE. OCCASIONAL PAPERS.** Text in English. 1966. irreg., latest vol.102, 2000. free. illus. **Document type:** *Monographic series, Academic/Scholarly.* **Description:** Contains research results of major CWS wildlife studies.
Formerly: Fisheries and Environment Canada. Occasional Paper
Related titles: Online - full text ed.; French ed.: Service Canadien de la Faune. Publications Hors Serie. 1966.
Indexed: ASFA, BiolAb, ESPM, GEOBASE, KWIWR, NutrAb, RRTA, SFA, WAE&RSA, WildRev, ZooRec.
—BLDSC (6215.500000), CISTI, IE, ingenta, Linda Hall. **CCC.**
Published by: Canadian Wildlife Service/Service Canadien de la Faune, Environment Canada, Ottawa, ON K1A 0H3, Canada. TEL 819-997-1095, FAX 819-997-2756, cws-scf@ec.gc.ca, http://www.cws-scf.ec.gc.ca/pub/ops/intro.html, http://ec.gc.ca/cws-scf/pub/ops/intro.html. R&P Patricia Logan. Circ: 2,000.

333.95416 CAN ISSN 0069-0023
S964.C2 CODEN: CWPNBL
➤ **CANADIAN WILDLIFE SERVICE. PROGRESS NOTES.** Text in English. 1967. irreg., latest vol.216, 2000. free. **Document type:** *Academic/Scholarly.* **Description:** Contains data and conclusions from C.W.S. wildlife studies.
Related titles: French ed.: Service Canadien de la Faune. Cahiers de Biologie. ISSN 0703-0967.
Indexed: ASFA, BiolAb, ESPM, IBR, KWIWR, SFA, WildRev, ZooRec.
—CISTI, Linda Hall.
Published by: Canadian Wildlife Service/Service Canadien de la Faune, Environment Canada, Ottawa, ON K1A 0H3, Canada. TEL 819-997-1095, FAX 819-997-2756, cws-scf@ec.gc.ca, mark.hickson@ec.gc.ca, http://www.cws-scf.ec.gc.ca, http://www.ec.gc.ca/cws-scf/. Ed. Patricia Logan. Circ: 2,000.

333.95 CAN
CANADIAN WILDLIFE SERVICE. R E N E W REPORT. (Recovery of Nationally Endangered Wildlife) Text in English. 1988. a. free. illus.; maps. back issues avail. **Document type:** *Bulletin, Government.* **Description:** Discusses actions CWS is taking to protect Canada's wildlife.
Former titles (until 1997): Canadian Wildlife Service. R E N E W Annual Report; (until 1995): Canadian Wildlife Service. R E N E W Report (1484-1681); (until 1994): Canadian Wildlife Service. Annual Report - R E N E W (1484-1665); (until 1993): Canadian Wildlife Service. Report - R E N E W (1190-9323); Which superseded in part (in 1990): Canadian Wildlife Service. Annual Report - R E N E W (1187-3876)
Related titles: Online - full text ed.; ♦ French ed.: Service Canadien de la Faune. Rescape Rapport.
Published by: Canadian Wildlife Service/Service Canadien de la Faune, Environment Canada, Ottawa, ON K1A 0H3, Canada. TEL 819-997-1095, FAX 819-997-2756, http://www.ec.gc.ca.

333.95416 CAN ISSN 0384-1480
CANADIAN WOLF DEFENDERS. NEWSLETTER✱. Text in English. 1963. q. membership. bk.rev. bibl.; illus.; stat.; tr.lit.
Published by: Canadian Wolf Defenders, 3819 112 A St, Edmonton, AB T6J 1K4, Canada. Ed. Dick Dekker. Circ: 900.

333.7 NZL ISSN 0528-0311
CANTERBURY MUSEUM. BULLETIN. Text in English. 1950. irreg.
Indexed: ZooRec.
Published by: Canterbury Museum, Rolleston Ave, Christchurch, New Zealand. TEL 64-3-3665000, FAX 64-3-3665622.

333.7 NZL ISSN 0370-3878
CANTERBURY MUSEUM. RECORDS. Text in English. 1907. irreg.
—BLDSC (7317.000000), CISTI. **CCC.**
Published by: Canterbury Museum, Rolleston Ave, Christchurch, New Zealand. TEL 64-3-3665000, FAX 64-3-3665622.

333.72 CHE
CAPRINAE NEWS. Text in English. a. USD 10 (effective 2000). **Document type:** *Newsletter.*
Published by: (Species Survival Commission - Caprinae Specialist Group), International Union for Conservation of Nature and Natural Resources, Rue Mauverney 28, Gland, 1196, Switzerland. TEL 41-22-9990001, FAX 41-22-9990002, mail@hq.iucn.org. **Subscr. to:** Dr. David Shackelton, Dept of Animal Sc, University of British Columbia, V6T 124, Vancouver, BC, Canada.

333.95416 BRB
CARIBBEAN CONSERVATION ASSOCIATION. ANNUAL REPORT. Text in English. 1991. a. free to members (effective 2001). Website rev. **Document type:** *Corporate.* **Description:** Compilation of Annual General Meeting activities including speeches, reports, members' workshop process and outcomes, participants' lists. Financial report (confidential) is not included.
Related titles: E-mail ed.
Published by: Caribbean Conservation Association, "Chelford", Bush Hill, The Garrison, St Michael, Barbados. TEL 246-426-5373, FAX 246-429-8483, cca@caribsurf.com, http://www.ccanet.net/.

CARIBBEAN RESEARCH INSTITUTE. REPORT. see *HISTORY—History Of North And South America*

333.72 CHE ISSN 1027-2992
CAT NEWS. Text in English. 2/yr. CHF 50, USD 40 (effective 2004). **Document type:** *Newsletter, Academic/Scholarly.*
Indexed: KWIWR, WildRev, ZooRec.
—BLDSC (3064.514000).
Published by: Species Survival Commission - Cat Specialist Group (Subsidiary of: International Union for Conservation of Nature and Natural Resources), Bougy, 1172, Switzerland. TEL 41-21-8086012, FAX 41-21-8086012, pjackson@sefanet.ch. Ed. Peter Jackson.

CENTER VIEW. see *ENVIRONMENTAL STUDIES*

333.70025 USA ISSN 1087-8491
GE20
CENTRAL ATLANTIC ENVIRONMENTAL DIRECTORY. Text in English. 1996. biennial. USD 18.50 (effective 2001). index. **Document type:** *Directory.* **Description:** Annotated listings of citizen groups and government agencies in New Jersey, New York and Pennsylvania.
Media: CD-ROM. **Related titles:** Diskette ed.; Online - full text ed.
Published by: Harbinger Communications, 616 Sumner St, Santa Cruz, CA 95062. TEL 406-721-0440, FAX 406-721-0440, ned@ism.net, http://eelink.net/gaindirectories.html.

333.783 USA
CENTRAL PARK CONSERVANCY. Text in English. a. **Document type:** *Corporate.*
Address: The Arsenal, Central Park, New York, NY 10021.

333.9 USA ISSN 1071-8443
QL666.C5 CODEN: CCOBED
➤ **CHELONIAN CONSERVATION BIOLOGY.** Text in English. s-a. USD 50 per vol. to individuals; USD 100 per vol. to institutions (effective 2005). **Document type:** *Academic/Scholarly.* **Description:** Covers all aspects of turtle and tortoise research, particularly concerning their conservation, systemic relationships, diversity, geographic distribution, natural history, reproduction, and morphology.
Indexed: ASFA, BIOSIS Prev, BiolAb, ESPM, OceAb, WildRev, ZooRec.
—BLDSC (3133.451900), IE, ingenta, Linda Hall.
Published by: Chelonian Research Foundation, 168 Goodrich St, Lunenberg, MA 01462. Ed. Anders G J Rhodin.

➤ **CHILDREN'S WHALEWATCH.** see *CHILDREN AND YOUTH—For*

➤ **CHILEANS.** see *GARDENING AND HORTICULTURE*

➤ **CHIROPTERA NEOTROPICAL.** see *BIOLOGY—Zoology*

➤ **CHRIS AND TILDE STUART'S GUIDE TO SOUTHERN AFRICAN GAME & NATURE RESERVES.** see *TRAVEL AND TOURISM*

333.72 POL ISSN 0009-6172
CODEN: CPZOAO
➤ **CHRONMY PRZYRODE OJCZYSTA.** Text in Polish; Summaries in English. 1945. bi-m. EUR 15 foreign (effective 2005). bk.rev. bibl.; charts; illus. index. 100 p./no. 1 cols./p.; back issues avail. **Document type:** *Journal, Academic/Scholarly.*
Indexed: AgrLib, BiolAb, SFA, WildRev, ZooRec.
Published by: Polska Akademia Nauk, Instytut Ochrony Przyrody, al A Mickiewicza 33, Krakow, 31120, Poland. TEL 48-12-6320549, FAX 48-12-6322432, chronmy@iop.krakow.pl, http://www.iop.krakow.pl. Ed. Zygmunt Denisiuk. R&P Elzbieta Skorek. Circ: 1,000. **Dist. by:** Ars Polona, Krakowskie Przedmiescie 7, Warsaw, Poland. TEL 48-22-9263914, FAX 48-22-9265334, arspolona@arspolona.com.pl, http://www.arspolona.com.pl. **Co-sponsor:** Panstwowa Rada Ochrony Przyrody.

➤ **CINCLUS.** see *BIOLOGY—Ornithology*

➤ **CITES NEWS - PLANTS**; a newsletter for the European region of the CITES plants. see *BIOLOGY—Botany*

➤ **CIVIC FOCUS.** see *ENVIRONMENTAL STUDIES*

711 GBR
CIVIC TRUST AWARDS. Text in English. 1959. a. GBP 10 (effective 2000). back issues avail.
—BLDSC (3268.580000).
Published by: Civic Trust, 17 Carlton House Terr, London, SW1 5AW, United Kingdom. TEL 44-171-930-0914, FAX 44-171-321-0180, pride@civictrust.org.uk, http://www.civictrust.org.uk.

333.78 USA
CLEARING HOUSE NEWSLETTER. Text in English. 1975. m. membership only. adv. **Document type:** *Newsletter.* **Description:** Provides information on large outdoor grounds management.
Published by: National Institute on Park & Grounds Management, 5162, De Pere, WI 54115-5162. TEL 414-733-2301. Ed. Erik Madisen. Circ: 1,100.

CLEARWATER NAVIGATOR. see *ENVIRONMENTAL STUDIES*

333.72 USA
COASTAL AMERICA PROGRESS REPORT. Text in English. a. **Document type:** *Corporate.*
Related titles: Online - full content ed.
Published by: Coastal America, Coastal America Reporters Bldg, 300 7th St, SW Ste 680, Washington, DC 20250. TEL 202-401-9928, FAX 202-401-9821, http://www.coastalamerica.gov/.

333.72 USA
COASTAL AMERICA UPDATE. Text in English. 3/yr. back issues avail. **Document type:** *Newsletter, Academic/Scholarly.*
Related titles: Online - full content ed.
Published by: Coastal America, Coastal America Reporters Bldg, 300 7th St, SW Ste 680, Washington, DC 20250. TEL 202-401-9928, FAX 202-401-9821, http://www.coastalamerica.gov/.

COASTAL SOCIETY. ANNUAL CONFERENCE. PROCEEDINGS. see *ENVIRONMENTAL STUDIES*

COASTAL SOCIETY BULLETIN. see *ENVIRONMENTAL STUDIES—Pollution*

COASTLINES (STONY BROOK). see *EARTH SCIENCES—Oceanography*

333.72 AUS ISSN 1325-3336
COLONG BULLETIN. Text in English. 1968. bi-m. AUD 25 (effective 2001). bk.rev. abstr.; charts; illus. 10 p./no.; back issues avail. **Document type:** *Bulletin.*
Published by: Colong Foundation for Wilderness, 2-362 Kent St, Sydney, NSW 2000, Australia. TEL 9299-7341, FAX 9299-5713, foundation@colongwilderness.org, http://www.colongwilderness.org.au. Ed., Pub. Alex Colley. Circ: 500.

COLORADO. DIVISION OF WILDLIFE. DIVISION REPORT. see *ENVIRONMENTAL STUDIES*

333.95416 USA ISSN 0084-8875
SK375 CODEN: CWSPA7
COLORADO. DIVISION OF WILDLIFE. SPECIAL REPORT. Text in English. 1962. irreg., latest vol.67, 1991. USD 2. bibl.; charts; illus.; stat. back issues avail.
Indexed: BIOSIS Prev, BiolAb, KWIWR, SFA, WLR, WildRev, ZooRec.
—Linda Hall.
Published by: Division of Wildlife, 317 W. Prospect, Ft. Collins, CO 80526. TEL 303-484-2836. Ed. Nancy W McEwen. Circ: 1,200.

333.95416 USA ISSN 0084-8883
COLORADO. DIVISION OF WILDLIFE. TECHNICAL PUBLICATION. Text in English. 1955. irreg., latest vol.39, 1991. USD 2 per issue (effective 2005). bibl.; charts; illus.; stat.
Indexed: BiolAb, SFA, WLR, WildRev, ZooRec.
—BLDSC (8706.180000), Linda Hall.
Published by: Division of Wildlife, 317 W. Prospect, Ft. Collins, CO 80526. TEL 303-484-2836. Ed. Nancy W McEwen. Circ: 1,200.

COLORADO. DIVISION OF WILDLIFE. TERRESTRIAL AND AQUATIC WILDLIFE RESEARCH. RESEARCH REVIEW. see *FISH AND FISHERIES*

COLORADO OUTDOORS. see *SPORTS AND GAMES—Outdoor Life*

333.95416 USA ISSN 0164-3193
COLORADO WILDLIFE. Text in English. 1981. bi-m. USD 35 domestic membership; USD 40 foreign membership (effective 2000). adv. bk.rev. **Document type:** *Newsletter.* **Description:** Updates on wildlife-related and natural resource conservation issues in Colorado, particularly issues of interest to Colorado Wildlife Federation members.
Published by: Colorado Wildlife Federation, 4045 Wadsworth Blvd., Ste. 20, Wheat Ridge, CO 80033-4625. TEL 303-987-0400, FAX 303-987-0200, cwfed@aol.com, http://www.coloradowildlife.com. Ed., R&P Diane Gansauer. Adv. contact Phillip Ill. Circ: 5,500 (paid and controlled).

333.72 USA ISSN 0893-276X
COLUMBIANA; bioregional journal for the Intermountain Northwest. Text in English. 1987. bi-m. USD 15 domestic; USD 17 in Canada. adv. bk.rev. **Description:** Lifestyle and ecology of the intermountain Northwest region.
Supersedes (1978-1986): Okanogan Natural News
Published by: Columbia Bioregional Education Project, Chesaw Rte, Box 83F, Oroville, WA 98844. TEL 509-485-3844. Ed. Geraldine Payton. Adv. contact Stuart R Gillespie. Circ: 6,000.

333.7845 DEU ISSN 1607-3649
COMMISSION INTERNATIONALE POUR LA PROTECTION DU RHIN. RAPPORT D'ACTIVITE. Text in French. 1971. a. **Document type:** *Journal, Academic/Scholarly.*
Supersedes in part: Internationale Kommission zum Schutze des Rheins gegen Verunreinigung. Taetigkeitsbericht (0173-6531)
Related titles: ♦ French ed.: Internationale Kommission zum Schutze des Rheins. Taetigkeitsbericht. ISSN 1607-3657.
Published by: Internationale Kommission zum Schutze des Rheins/Commission Internationale pour la Protection du Rhin - Internationale Commissie ter Bescherming van de Rijn, Hohenzollernstr. 18, Koblenz, 56068, Germany. TEL 49-261-12495, FAX 49-261-36572, sekretariat@iksr.de, http://www.iksr.org.

COMPARATIVE PHYSIOLOGY AND ECOLOGY. see *BIOLOGY—Physiology*

333.72 USA ISSN 0198-9103
COMPENDIUM NEWSLETTER; Your Guide to the World's Environmental Crisis. Text in English. 1972. bi-m. USD 20 (effective 2000). adv. bk.rev.; dance rev.; film rev.; tel.rev.; video rev. illus. 20 p./no.; **Document type:** *Newsletter.* **Description:** Contains ecological news and information.
Published by: Educational Communications, Inc. (Los Angeles), PO Box 351419, Los Angeles, CA 90035-9119. TEL 310-559-9160, ecnp@aol.com, http://www.ecoprojects.org. Ed. Nancy Pearlman. Circ: 800.

665.5 USA ISSN 1060-8907
TJ163.4.P3
CON.WEB. Text in English. 1996. m. free (effective 2004). back issues avail.; reprints avail. **Document type:** *Trade.* **Description:** Information resource on energy conservation, energy efficiency and renewable energy in the Pacific northwest of the United States.
Media: Online - full content.
Published by: NewsData Corporation, PO Box 900928, Seattle, WA 98109-9228. TEL 206-285-4848, FAX 206-281-8035, marko@newsdata.com, newsdata@newsdata.com, http://www.newsdata.com/enernet/conweb/index.html. Ed., R&P Mark Chrenschall. Pub. Mr. Cyrus Noe. **Co-sponsor:** Northwest Energy Efficiency Alliance.

333.72 USA
CONDOR CALL; journal of the Los Padres Chapter, Sierra Club. Text in English. 6/yr. USD 5. 8 p./no. 5 cols./p.; back issues avail.; reprints avail. **Document type:** *Newsletter.*
Published by: Sierra Club, 1056 Eugenia Pl, A, Carpinteria, CA 93013. gnusman@aol.com, http://www.sierraclub.org/chapters/lospadres. Ed., Adv. contact John Hankins. Circ: 6,500 (paid).

333.7845 363.7 USA
CONNECTICUT RIVER ENVIRONMENT. Text in English. 1998. biennial. USD 15 (effective 1999). **Document type:** *Directory.* **Description:** Contains a listing of environmental, conservation citizen groups and agencies working in the Connecticut river watershed on conservation, recreation and access.
Related titles: Online - full text ed.
Published by: Connecticut River Watershed Council, Inc., 15 Bank Row St., Greenfield, MA 01301-3511. TEL 413-529-9500, FAX 413-529-9501, crwc@crocker.com, http://www.ctriver.com.

C

333.95416 USA ISSN 1087-7525
CONNECTICUT WILDLIFE. Text in English. 1993. bi-m. USD 6 (effective 2002). **Document type:** *Magazine, Consumer.* **Description:** Contains information about wildlife habitat improvement techniques.
Published by: Connecticut Department of Environmental Protection, 79 Elm St., Hartford, CT 06106-5127. TEL 860-424-3540, FAX 860-424-4058, dep.webmaster@po.state.ct.us, http://dep.state.ct.us/burnatr/wildlife/geninfo/cw.htm.

CONOPID RECORDING SCHEME NEWSLETTER. see *BIOLOGY—Entomology*

CONSCIENCE CANADA NEWSLETTER. see *POLITICAL SCIENCE—Civil Rights*

CONSERVATION; G C I newsletter. see *ART*

CONSERVATION AERONAUTICS. see *ENVIRONMENTAL STUDIES*

333.72 639.9 IND ISSN 0972-4923
➤ **CONSERVATION AND SOCIETY.** Text in English. s-a. INR 425 domestic to individuals; USD 17 SAARC to individuals; INR 750 domestic to institutions; USD 28 SAARC to institutions; GBP 102 in UK, Europe, Middle East, Africa & Australasia; USD 168 elsewhere (effective 2004). **Description:** Dedicated to the theory and practice of the conservation of natural resources, particularly as mediated by the conflicts and tensions that accompany societal claims on these resources.
—BLDSC (3417.985000), IE.
Published by: Sage Publications India Pvt. Ltd. (Subsidiary of: Sage Publications, Inc.), M-32 Market, Greater Kailash-I, PO Box 4215, New Delhi, 110 048, India. TEL 91-11-6444958, FAX 91-11-6472426, sageind@nda.vsnl.net.in, http://www.indiasage.com/. Ed. Kamaljit S Bawa.

577 USA ISSN 0888-8892
QH75.A1 CODEN: CBIOEF
➤ **CONSERVATION BIOLOGY.** Text in English; Abstracts in Spanish. 1986. bi-m. USD 636 combined subscription in the Americas to institutions & Caribbean (print & online eds.); USD 652 combined subscription in Canada & Mexico to institutions print & online eds.; GBP 499 combined subscription elsewhere to institutions print & online eds. (effective 2006). adv. illus. index. back issues avail.; reprints avail. **Document type:** *Journal, Academic/Scholarly.*
Related titles: Online - full text ed.: ISSN 1523-1739. USD 604 in the Americas to institutions & Caribbean; USD 619 in Canada & Mexico to institutions; GBP 474 elsewhere to institutions (effective 2006) (from Blackwell Synergy, EBSCO Publishing, Gale Group, IngentaConnect, JSTOR (Web-based Journal Archive), O C L C Online Computer Library Center, Inc., Ovid Technologies, Inc., Swets Information Services).

Indexed: AEA, ASCA, ASFA, AgBio, Agr, AgrForAb, AnBeAb, AnBrAb, ApEcolAb, B&AI, B&BAb, BIOBASE, BIOSIS Prev, BibAg, BioCN&I, BiolAb, BiolDig, CBA, CPA, CurCont, DSA, EPB, ESPM, EntAb, EnvAb, EnvInd, FCA, FPA, ForAb, GEOBASE, GSI, GardL, GenetAb, HGA, HelmAb, HerbAb, HortAb, I&DA, IABS, ISR, IndVet, KWIWR, M&TEA, MaizeAb, NutrAb, OceAb, OrnHort, PBA, PGegResA, PHN&I, PN&I, PlantSci, PotatoAb, PoultAb, ProtozoAb, RA&MP, RDA, RM&VM, RPP, RRTA, RefZh, RevApplEntom, RiceAb, S&F, SCI, SFA, SIA, SSCI, SWRA, SeedAb, SoyAb, TDB, VetBull, W&CBA, WAE&RSA, WeedAb, WildRev, ZooRec.
—BLDSC (3417.999000), CISTI, IDS, IE, Infotrieve, ingenta, Linda Hall. **CCC.**
Published by: (Society for Conservation Biology), Blackwell Publishing, Inc. (Subsidiary of: Blackwell Publishing Ltd.), Commerce Place, 350 Main St, Malden, MA 02148. TEL 781-388-8206, FAX 781-388-8232, subscrip@blackwellpub.com, http://www.blackwellpublishing.com/journals/CBI. Ed. Gary K Meffe. R&P Tracey Davies. Adv. contact Jenny Applin. Circ: 5,000.

333.95 GBR ISSN 1363-3090
CONSERVATION BIOLOGY SERIES. Text in English. 1993. latest no.8, 2002. price varies. **Document type:** *Monographic series, Academic/Scholarly.*
Indexed: BIOSIS Prev, ZooRec.
—BLDSC (3417.999200), IE, ingenta.
Published by: Cambridge University Press, The Edinburgh Bldg, Shaftesbury Rd, Cambridge, CB2 2RU, United Kingdom. TEL 44-1223-312393, FAX 44-1223-315052, information@cambridge.org, https://booktrade.cambridge.org/series.asp?series=CBS, http://www.cup.cam.ac.uk/. Eds. Morris L Gosling, William J Sutherland.

333.72 USA ISSN 0027-6537
CONSERVATION COMMISSION NEWS. Text in English. 1967. q. USD 5. adv. bk.rev. charts; illus. **Document type:** *Newsletter.* **Description:** Deals with matters of interest to municipal conservation commissioners.
Published by: New Hampshire Association of Conservation Commissions, 54 Portsmouth St, Concord, NH 03301. TEL 603-224-7867, FAX 603-228-0423. Ed. Marjory M Swope. Circ: 1,650.

C

333.72025 USA ISSN 0069-911X
S920
CONSERVATION DIRECTORY; a listing of organizations, agencies and officials concerned with natural resource use and management. Text in English. 1955. a. USD 61. **Document type:** *Directory.*
Published by: National Wildlife Federation, 11100 Wildlife Center Dr., Reston, VA 20190-5362. TEL 703-790-4000, FAX 703-790-4468, gordonr@nwf.org, http://www.nwf.org. Ed. Rue Gordon. Circ: 6,000.

333.72 GBR ISSN 0262-2203
CONSERVATION EDUCATION; a bulletin for teachers and youth leaders. Text in English. 1981. 2/yr. GBP 1. bk.rev. illus. **Document type:** *Bulletin.* **Description:** A bulletin for teachers, youth leaders and young people.
Published by: Young People's Trust for the Environment and Nature Conservation, 8 Leapale Rd, Guildford, GU1 4JX, United Kingdom. TEL 44-1483-39600, FAX 44-1483-301992. Ed. Cyril Littlewood. Circ: 40,000.

CONSERVATION GENETICS. see *BIOLOGY—Genetics*

577 USA ISSN 1539-6827
QH75.A1
CONSERVATION IN PRACTICE. Text in English. 2000. q. USD 75 in the Americas; GBP 45 elsewhere (effective 2006). adv. Index. back issues avail. **Document type:** *Magazine, Academic/Scholarly.* **Description:** A magazine of science, practice and policy that presents cutting-edge research from every field of conservation.
Formerly (until 2001): Conservation Biology in Practice (1526-4629)
Related titles: Online - full text ed.: ISSN 1552-5228. USD 71 in the Americas to institutions; GBP 43 elsewhere to institutions (effective 2005) (from Blackwell Synergy, EBSCO Publishing).
Indexed: ASFA, ApEcolAb, ESPM, ForAb, GardL, HortAb, OrnHort, PGegResA, RDA, RRTA, SWRA, WAE&RSA, WRCInf, WeedAb.
—BLDSC (3418.077500), IE. **CCC.**
Published by: Society for Conservation Biology, 4245 N Fairfax Dr, Suite 400, Arlington, VA 22203-1651. TEL 703-276-2384, FAX 703-995-4633, InPractice@conbio.org, info@conbio.org, http://www.conbio.org/CIP. Ed. Kathryn A Kohm TEL 206-685-4724. Adv. contact Rebecca Gamboa TEL 206-616-2958. B&W page USD 525; 8.25 x 10.875.

333 USA ISSN 1521-9941
GE140
CONSERVATION MATTERS. Text in English. 1994. q. c/w membership. **Document type:** *Magazine, Consumer.*
Related titles: Online - full content ed.: (from Florida Center for Library Automation); Online - full text ed.: (from Gale Group).
Published by: Conservation Law Foundation, 62 Summer St, Boston, MA 02110-1016. TEL 617-350-0990, FAX 617-350-4030, http://www.clf.org/.

333.72 GBR ISSN 0309-2224
AM141
CONSERVATION NEWS. Text in English. 1976. 3/yr. GBP 2.50 per issue (effective 2003). adv. bk.rev. 56 p./no.; back issues avail. **Document type:** *Newsletter, Academic/Scholarly.* **Description:** Keeps the members up to date with current events, discusses new methods and techniques and acts as a forum on conservation issues.
Related titles: Online - full text ed.
Indexed: A&ATA, AIAP, BrArAb, NumL, RILM.
—BLDSC (3418.071000).
Published by: United Kingdom Institute for Conservation of Historic and Artistic Works, 3rd Fl, Downstream Building, 1 London Bridge, London, SE1 9BG, United Kingdom. TEL 44-20-77853805, FAX 44-20-77853806, ukic@ukic.org.uk, http://www.ukic.org.uk. Adv. contact Lyndsay Piper TEL 44-353-95-41073. Circ: 2,000.

CONSERVATION NEWS DIGEST; news briefs for non-industrial private woodland owners across the nation. see *FORESTS AND FORESTRY*

333.72 AUS ISSN 0816-875X
CONSERVATION NORTH QUEENSLAND. Text in English. 1975. m. AUD 15 (effective 2001). bk.rev. back issues avail. **Document type:** *Newsletter.* **Description:** Focuses on North Queensland environmental issues and concerns.
Published by: North Queensland Conservation Council Inc., PO Box 364, Townsville, QLD 4810, Australia. TEL 61-7-47716226, FAX 61-7-477121713, nqcc@beyond.net.au, http://www.nqcc.org.au. Ed. Carolyn Pike. R&P Margaret Moorhouse. Circ: 250.

577 AUS ISSN 1447-3682
➤ **CONSERVATION SCIENCE WESTERN AUSTRALIA.** Variant title: CALMScience. Text in English. 1993. irreg. (approx. 2/yr.). Supplement avail.; back issues avail. **Document type:** *Academic/Scholarly.* **Description:** For those interested in nature conservation, sustainable utilization and land management.
Formerly: C A L M Science (1320-145X); Which was formed by the merger of (1985-1993): Western Australia. Department of Conservation and Land Management. Technical Report (0816-6757); (1988-1993): Western Australia. Department of Conservation and Land Management. Occasional Paper (1031-4865); (1985-1993): Western Australia. Department of Conservation and Land Management. Research Bulletin (1032-8106); Which was formerly: Western Australia. Department of Conservation and Land Management. Bulletin (0816-9675); Which was formed by the merger of (1919-1985): Western Australia. Forest Department. Bulletin (0085-8129); (1976-1985): Western Australia. Department of Fisheries and Wildlife. Wildlife Research Bulletin (0726-0725)
Related titles: Online - full content ed.
Indexed: ASI, AgBio, AgrForAb, BIOSIS Prev, BiolAb, FPA, ForAb, GEOBASE, HerbAb, PBA, PGegResA, PGrRegA, PoultAb, RPP, RRTA, S&F, SFA, SeedAb, WildRev, ZooRec.
—BLDSC (3015.446000), CISTI, IE, ingenta.
Published by: Department of Conservation and Land Management, Locked Bag 104, Bentley Delivery Centre, W.A. 6893, Australia. TEL 61-89334-0324, FAX 61-89334-0498, http://science.calm.wa.gov.au/cswajournal/, http://www.calm.wa.gov.au. Circ: 500.

333.72 USA
CONSERVATION SCIENCES. Text in English. q. USD 13 (effective 1999). back issues avail. **Document type:** *Academic/Scholarly.* **Description:** Dedicated to promoting informed conservation policy and natural resource management through applied research.
Indexed: ZooRec.
Published by: Manomet Center for Conservation Sciences, PO Box 1770, Manomet, MA 02345. TEL 508-224-6521, FAX 508-224-9220, web.response@manomet.org, http://www.manomet.org/quarterly/csqrt.htm.

333.72 USA ISSN 1520-0639
S930
CONSERVATION VOICES. Text in English. 1998 (Feb./Mar.). bi-m. USD 24 (effective 2001).
Published by: Soil and Water Conservation Society, 945 SW Ankeny Rd., Ankeny, IA 50021-9764. TEL 515-289-2331, FAX 515-289-1227, http://www.swcs.org/. Ed. Deb Happe. Adv. contact Karen Howe.

CONSERVATION VOTER. see *ENVIRONMENTAL STUDIES*

333.72 GBR ISSN 0140-0096
N8554
➤ **THE CONSERVATOR.** Text in English. 1977. a. price varies. bk.rev. back issues avail. **Document type:** *Journal, Academic/Scholarly.* **Description:** Aim of the journal is to help improve the practice of conservation by communicating information and ideas relating to the conservation of objects and collections of cultural value.
Indexed: A&ATA, ABM, AIAP, BHA, BrArAb, KES, NumL, RILM.
Published by: United Kingdom Institute for Conservation of Historic and Artistic Works, 3rd Fl, Downstream Building, 1 London Bridge, London, SE1 9BG, United Kingdom. TEL 44-20-77853805, FAX 44-20-77853806, ukic@ukic.org.uk, http://www.ukic.org.uk. Ed. Janey Croyn. Adv. contact Lyndsay Piper TEL 44-353-95-41073. Circ: 1,400.

333.78 USA
CONSERVE* ; water, land, life. Text in English. 1971. s-a. membership. **Document type:** *Newsletter.*
Published by: Western Pennsylvania Conservancy, 209 Fourth Ave, Pittsburgh, PA 15222-1707. Ed. Bill Randour. Circ: 20,000.

333.95416 USA ISSN 1093-1007
CONSERVE WILDLIFE NEWSLETTER. Text in English. 1978. q. free. back issues avail. **Document type:** *Newsletter, Consumer.* **Description:** Contains articles pertaining to the research, protection and management of native endangered, threatened and nongame wildlife in N.J., with occasional coverage of relevant national and international topics.
Formerly: Nongame News (1061-0928)
Published by: Department of Environmental Protection, Division of Fish, Game and Wildlife, PO Box 400, Trenton, NJ 08625-0400. TEL 609-292-9400, FAX 609-984-1414, njwildlife@nac.net, Http://www.njfishandwildlife.com, http://www.njfishandwildlife.com. Ed., R&P Linda Tesauro TEL 609-292-1276. Circ: 49,000 (free).

333.72 GBR ISSN 0143-4144
CONSERVER; the magazine for people working for a better environment. Text in English. 1972. 3/yr. membership. adv. bk.rev. 3 cols./p.; **Document type:** *Newsletter.* **Description:** Aims to keep the members and everyone interested in practical conservation up-to-date with news and issues.
Published by: B T C V, 36 St Marys St, Wallingford, Oxon OX10 0EU, United Kingdom. TEL 44-1491-821600, FAX 44-1491-839646, information@btcv.org, http://www.btcv.org. Ed., R&P, Adv. contact Katherine Taylor. Circ: 10,000 (controlled).

333.7 GRC ISSN 1108-4146
CONTRIBUTIONS TO THE ZOOGEOGRAPHY AND ECOLOGY OF THE EASTERN MEDITERRANEAN REGION. Text in English. 1999. triennial.
Indexed: ZooRec.
Published by: Hellenic Zoological Society, P.O. Box 3249, Athens, 10210, Greece.

333.9 USA ISSN 0886-8441
CODEN: CHHSEU
CORRIE HERRING HOOKS SERIES. Text in English. irreg., latest vol.47. price varies. charts; illus. back issues avail. **Document type:** *Monographic series, Academic/Scholarly.* **Description:** Discusses efforts in conservation worldwide.
Indexed: BIOSIS Prev, ZooRec.
—BLDSC (3472.270000).
Published by: University of Texas Press, Books Division, PO Box 7819, Austin, TX 78713-7819. TEL 512-471-7233, 800-252-3206, FAX 512-232-7178, 800-687-6046, utpress@uts.cc.utexas.edu, http://www.utexas.edu/utpress/subjects/chh.html, http://www.utexas.edu/utpress/subjects/series.html.

333.72 IND
CORSONAT. Text in English. 1979. q. INR 10, USD 2. adv. bk.rev. **Description:** Discusses conservation and all aspects of animal and plant life in India.
Published by: Corbett Society of Naturalists, 342 Shivaji Rd., Meerut, Uttar Pradesh 250 001, India. Ed. Y M Rai. Circ: 300.

COUNTRY ROAD CHRONICLES. see *NATIVE AMERICAN STUDIES*

333.78 333.73 GBR ISSN 1466-2531
COUNTRYSIDE FOCUS; working for people and places in rural England. Text in English. 1983. bi-m. free. illus.; maps. 8 p./no. 4 cols./p.; back issues avail. **Document type:** *Newspaper, Government.* **Description:** Focuses on the work and policies of the Commission and presents debates on issues affecting the countryside.
Former titles (until 1999): Countryside (0964-2455); (until 1991): Countryside Commission News (0264-8822)
Related titles: Online - full text ed.; Supplement(s):.
Indexed: H&TI.
—**CCC.**
Published by: Countryside Agency, John Dower House, Crescent Pl Cheltenham, Glos, GL50 3RA, United Kingdom. TEL 44-1242-521381, FAX 44-1242-584270, jonn@paperspublishing.co.uk, http://www.countryside.gov.uk. Ed., R&P Suzanne Bennett TEL 44-1242-533302. Circ: 19,500.

333.72 GBR
COUNTRYSIDE VOICE. Text in English. 1962. 3/yr. free to members. adv. bk.rev. illus. **Document type:** *Newsletter.* **Description:** Covers issues and activities for people who want to protect rural England.
Former titles (until 002): C P R E Voice (1366-8676); (until 1996): Countryside Campaigner (0268-5795); Council for the Protection of Rural England. Quarterly Bulletin (0010-9916); Council for the Preservation of Rural England. Monthly Bulletin
Indexed: RICS.
—BLDSC (3482.088000).

Published by: (Council for the Protection of Rural England), Think Publishing, The Pall Mall Deposit, 124-128 Barlby Rd, London, W10 6BL, United Kingdom. TEL 44-20-8962-3020, FAX 44-20-8962-8689, info@cpre.org.uk, cpre@thinkpublishing.co.uk. Ed. Jo Bourne. Pub. Ian McAuliffe. Adv. contact David Trafford. Circ: 34,000.

COVERED BRIDGE TOPICS. see *HISTORY—History Of North And South America*

639.9 597.9 USA ISSN 1542-1562
QL666.C925
CROCODILE SPECIALIST GROUP. NEWSLETTER. Text in English. 1971. q. USD 40 (effective 2002).
Published by: I U C N - World Conservation Union, Species Survival Commission Crocodile Specialist Group, Dept. of Natural Science, Florida Museum of Natural History, Gainesville, FL 32611. FAX 352-392-9367. Ed. J. P. Ross.

333.7845 USA
CURRENTS & EDDIES. Text in English. 1952. q. membership. bk.rev. **Document type:** *Newsletter.*
Formerly: Valley Newsletter
Published by: Connecticut River Watershed Council, Inc., 15 Bank Row St., Greenfield, MA 01301-3511. TEL 413-529-9500, FAX 413-529-9501. Ed. Whitty Sanford. Circ: 2,000 (controlled).

CYPRUS. DEPARTMENT OF FISHERIES. ANNUAL REPORT ON THE DEPARTMENT OF FISHERIES AND THE CYPRUS FISHERIES. see *FISH AND FISHERIES*

DAL COMUNE-NOTIZIE. see *ENVIRONMENTAL STUDIES*

333.72 580 AUS ISSN 1039-6500
➤ **DANTHONIA.** Text in English. 1991. q. AUD 40 for membership to individuals; AUD 300 for membership to corporations with annual budget of less than AUD500,000; AUD 400 for membership to corporations with annual budget of more than AUD500,000 (effective 2002). software rev. bibl.; charts; illus. 20 p./no.; back issues avail. **Document type:** *Newsletter, Academic/Scholarly.* **Description:** Promotes the plant conservation issues to academics, community groups, etc. Also aims to communicate recent research and provide resources, e.g. publications lists & online titles.
Published by: Australian Network for Plant Conservation Inc., G.P.O. Box 1777, Canberra, ACT 2601, Australia. TEL 61-2-6250-9509, FAX 61-2-6250-9528, anpc@anbg.gov.au, http://www.anbg.gov.au/anpc. Eds. Jeanette Mill, Laura Vallee TEL 61-2-6250-9523. Adv. contact Laura Vallee TEL 61-2-6250-9523. Circ: 1,000.

➤ **THE DEFENDER.** see *ENVIRONMENTAL STUDIES*

333.95416 USA ISSN 0162-6337
S960 CODEN: DEFEDZ
DEFENDERS. Text in English. 1930. q. USD 20 to members. bk.rev. illus. back issues avail. **Description:** Features in-depth report on wildlife conservation issues, primarily in the U.S.
Former titles (until 1975): Defenders of Wildlife Magazine (0162-6329); (until Dec. 1974): Defenders of Wildlife International (0162-6310); (until Aug. 1974): Defenders of Wildlife News (0011-7528)
Indexed: ASFA, BiolAb, BiolDig, EPB, ESPM, EnvAb, SFA, WildRev, ZooRec.
—CIS.
Published by: Defenders of Wildlife, 1130 17th St NW, Washington, DC 20036-4604. TEL 202-682-9400, FAX 202-682-1331, info@defenders.org, http://www.defenders.org/defendersmag/issues/summer04/. Ed., R&P Mark Cheater. Circ: 130,000.

333.91 USA
DELAWARE SEA GRANT REPORTER. Text in English. 1982. s-a. single copies free. bk.rev. back issues avail. **Document type:** *Newsletter.* **Description:** Informs the public of marine research, issues and events that affect Delaware.
Indexed: ASFA, BiolDig, Inspec.
Published by: University of Delaware, Sea Grant College Program, Marine Public Education Office, 103 General Services Bldg., 222 S Chapel St., Newark, DE 19716-3530. TEL 302-831-8083, FAX 302-831-2005, marinecom@udel.edu, http://www.ocean.udel.edu. Ed., R&P Tracey Bryant TEL 302-831-8185. Circ: 5,600.

333.72 551.46 USA ISSN 0886-8476
A DELAWARE SEA GRANT TECHNICAL REPORT. Text in English. irreg. **Document type:** *Monographic series.*
Published by: University of Delaware, Sea Grant College Program, Marine Public Education Office, 103 General Services Bldg., 222 S Chapel St., Newark, DE 19716-3530. TEL 302-831-8083, FAX 302-831-2005, marinecom@udel.edu, http://www.ocean.udel.edu/publications/tech.html.

333.95416 USA ISSN 0418-7598
SK305.M6
➤ **DESERT BIGHORN COUNCIL. TRANSACTIONS.** Text in English. 1957. a. USD 26; USD 28 foreign (effective 2000). bk.rev. cum.index. back issues avail. **Document type:** *Proceedings, Academic/Scholarly.*
Indexed: SFA, WildRev, ZooRec.
Published by: Desert Bighorn Council, c/o Bighorn Institute, Box 262, Palm Desert, CA 92261-0262. TEL 760-346-7334, FAX 760-340-3987, BI@BighornInstitute.org, birhrist@aol.com, divined@nevada.edu. Ed. Ray Lee. R&P Darren Devine TEL 702-895-1564. Circ: 300 (paid).

333.72 DEU ISSN 0939-3501
DEUTSCHER JUGENDBUND FUER NATURBEOBACHTUNG. NATURKUNDLICHE BEITRAEGE. Text in German. 1978. s-a. EUR 2 per issue (effective 2005). bk.rev. back issues avail. **Document type:** *Bulletin, Consumer.*
Published by: Deutscher Jugendbund fuer Naturbeobachtung, Justus-Strandes-Weg 14, Hamburg, 22337, Germany. info@naturbeobachtung.de, http://www.naturbeobachtung.de.

DEUTSCHER RAT FUER LANDESPFLEGE. SCHRIFTENREIHE. see *ENVIRONMENTAL STUDIES*

333.7845 DEU ISSN 0417-3430
DEUTSCHES GEWAESSERKUNDLICHES JAHRBUCH. WESER- UND EMSGEBIET. Text in German. 1959. a. **Document type:** *Monographic series, Academic/Scholarly.*
Published by: Niedersaechsisches Landesamt fuer Oekologie, Postfach 101062, Hildesheim, 31110, Germany. TEL 49-5121-509-0, FAX 49-5121-509196, poststelle@nloe.niedersachsen.de, http://jupiter.nloe.de.

DIPTERISTS FORUM. BULLETIN. see *BIOLOGY—Entomology*

333.72025 USA ISSN 0270-1111
GE1
DIRECTORY OF ENVIRONMENTAL ORGANIZATIONS. Text in English. 1975. s-a. USD 30; USD 5 directory index (effective 2000). 325 p./no.; **Document type:** *Directory.* **Description:** Contains a comprehensive, alphabetical, zip or subject list of more than 6,500 names, addresses, and telephone numbers of international, national, state, regional, and local organizations concerned with environmental issues.
Related titles: Diskette ed.: USD 300 (effective 2000).
Published by: Educational Communications, Inc. (Los Angeles), PO Box 351419, Los Angeles, CA 90035-9119. TEL 310-559-9160, FAX 310-559-9160, http://www.ecoprojects.org. Ed. Nancy Pearlman Lynn Cason. Circ: 500.

DIRECTORY OF ENVIRONMENTAL WEBSITES ON THE INTERNET. see *ENVIRONMENTAL STUDIES*

DISCOVERY. see *SCIENCES: COMPREHENSIVE WORKS*

333.72 USA
DISORDERLY CONDUCT; an insurrectionary green-anarchist quarterly. Text in English. q. USD 3 newsstand/cover. **Document type:** *Newsletter, Consumer.* **Description:** Contains original writings, action updates, news, rants and reprints from an anti-authoritarian and anti-industrial viewpoint.
Published by: Green Anarchy, PO Box 11331, Eugene, OR 97440.

333.95416 GBR ISSN 0265-5640
QL76.5.C55 CODEN: DODODN
➤ **DODO**; journal of the wildlife conservation trusts. Text in English. 1977. a. GBP 15 (effective 1999). bibl.; charts; illus. reprints avail. **Document type:** *Journal, Academic/Scholarly.* **Description:** Covers conservation, breeding and husbandry of endangered species, field studies, capture expeditions and re-introduction programs, behavioral studies, reporductive biology, and population management.
Indexed: ASFA, CurCont, IndVet, NutrAb, PsycInfo, PsycholAb, SFA, WildRev, ZooRec, e-psyche.
—BLDSC (3614.290000), IDS, IE, ingenta.
Published by: Currell Wildlife Preservation Trust, Les Augres Manor, Trinity, Jersey Channel Isl JE3 5BP, United Kingdom. TEL 44-1534-860000, FAX 44-1534-860001, afeistner@durrell.org. Ed. Jeremy J C Mallinson. Pub. J Mallinson. R&P Anna T C Feistner. Circ: 2,000.

333.72 DEU
DOKUMENTATION NATUR UND LANDSCHAFT. SONDERHEFTE. Text in German. irreg. price varies. **Document type:** *Monographic series, Government.*
Published by: (Germany. Bundesanstalt fuer Naturschutz), W. Kohlhammer GmbH, Hessbruehlstr 69, Stuttgart, 70565, Germany. TEL 49-711-7863-0, FAX 49-711-7863263, info@kohlhammer-katalog.de, http://www.kohlhammer.de.

DOLPHIN LOG. see *CHILDREN AND YOUTH—For*

333.7 RUS
DOM PRIRODY. Text in Russian. m. USD 99.95 in United States.
Published by: Soyuz Ekologicheskikh Organizatsii Moskvy, Volkonskii per 8, str 1, Moscow, 103473, Russian Federation. TEL 7-095-2819356, FAX 7-095-2819004. Ed. A N Frolov. **US dist. addr.:** East View Information Services, 3020 Harbor Ln. N., Minneapolis, MN 55447. TEL 612-550-0961.

DROUGHT NETWORK NEWS. see *WATER RESOURCES*

DRYLANDS PROGRAMME. ISSUE PAPER. see *ENVIRONMENTAL STUDIES*

333.95416 USA ISSN 0012-6950
DUCKS UNLIMITED. Text in English. 1938. bi-m. USD 35 membership (effective 2004). adv. bk.rev. illus.; stat. **Document type:** *Magazine, Consumer.* **Description:** Highlights the efforts of the organization to restore wildlife habitats throughout North America, for both their natural value and their recreational merits. Features articles and essays on techniques and gear for the waterfowl sportsman.
Indexed: WildRev.
Published by: Ducks Unlimited, Inc., 1 Waterfowl Way, Memphis, TN 38120-2351. TEL 901-758-3825, FAX 901-758-3909, http://www.ducks.org/. Ed. Tom Fulgham. adv.: B&W page USD 15,855, color page USD 22,660; trim 8.125 x 10.75. Circ: 640,000 (paid).

333.9 NLD ISSN 0168-7948
DUIN. Text in Dutch. 1978. q. bk.rev. illus. index. 4 p./no. 2 cols./p.; **Document type:** *Journal, Consumer.* **Description:** Covers dune and coastal conservation.
—IE, Infotrieve.
Published by: Stichting Duinbehoud, Postbus 664, Leiden, 2300 AR, Netherlands. TEL 31-71-5160490, FAX 31-71-5160499, stichting@duinbehoud.nl, http://www.duinbehoud.nl. Ed. H Wijkhuisen.

E A N H S BULLETIN. see *BIOLOGY*

E - SCRAP NEWS; North America's recycling and composting journal. see *ENVIRONMENTAL STUDIES—Waste Management*

E-SCRAP NEWS. see *ENVIRONMENTAL STUDIES—Waste Management*

EAGLE (GALENA). see *ENVIRONMENTAL STUDIES*

333.72 USA ISSN 1055-8411
HC110.E5
EARTH FIRST!; the radical environmental journal. Text in English. 1980. 8/yr. USD 30 domestic; USD 40 foreign; USD 4 newsstand/cover domestic; USD 6 newsstand/cover in Canada (effective 2003). adv. bk.rev. illus. back issues avail.; reprints avail. **Document type:** *Newspaper, Consumer.* **Description:** Covers the cutting edge of radical environmental action and thought.
Former titles (until 1990): Earth First! Journal (1055-8845); (until 1989): Earth First! (1047-7195)
Related titles: Online - full text ed.: (from ProQuest Information & Learning, SoftLine Information).
Indexed: AltPI, EnvAb, PerIslam.
Published by: Daily Planet Publishing, PO Box 3023, Tucson, AZ 85702. TEL 520-620-6900, FAX 413-254-0057, collective@earthfirstjournal.org, http://www.snet.co.uk/ef, http://www.earthfirstjouranl.org. Adv. contact Jim Flynn. Circ: 15,000.

333.72 GBR
EARTH HERITAGE. Text in English. 1968. s-a. free. **Document type:** *Academic/Scholarly.* **Description:** Earth Heritage Journal is produced twice a year for the geological and landscape conservation community by English Nature, Scottish Nature Heritage, and_countryside council for Wa les.
Formerly (until Jan. 1994): Earth Science Conservation (0142-2324)
Indexed: RefZh.
Published by: English Nature, Northminster House, Peterborough, Cambs PE1 1UA, United Kingdom. TEL 44-1733-455000, FAX 44-1733-568834, TELEX 931 2130132 NC G, http://www.english-nature.org.uk. Ed., R&P Stuart Campbell TEL 44-1248-385500.

EARTH ISLAND JOURNAL; an international environmental news magazine. see *ENVIRONMENTAL STUDIES*

EARTH NEWS. see *ENVIRONMENTAL STUDIES*

EARTH QUARTERLY; living in harmony with the Earth and each other. see *GENERAL INTEREST PERIODICALS—United States*

EARTHLIGHT; the magazine of spirituality ecology. see *RELIGIONS AND THEOLOGY*

910 USA ISSN 1526-4092
EARTHWATCH INSTITUTE. RESEARCH & EXPLORATION. Text in English. 1999. a. USD 45 membership (effective 2003). **Document type:** *Journal, Academic/Scholarly.*
Related titles: Online - full text ed.: (from EBSCO Publishing).
Indexed: MASUSE, WBA.
Published by: Earthwatch Expeditions, Inc., 3 Clock Tower Pl., Maynard, MA 01754-2574. TEL 978-461-0081, FAX 978-461-2332, info@earthwatch.org, http://www.earthwatch.org.

333.72 AUS
ECO ECHO; the green voice of the Sunshine Coast. Text in English. 1984. 3/yr. free to members. adv. bk.rev. back issues avail. **Document type:** *Magazine, Academic/Scholarly.* **Description:** Contains issues, articles and news pertaining to the Sunshine Coast and South East Queensland.

C

Published by: Sunshine Coast Environmental Council, PO Box 269, Nambour, QLD 4560, Australia. TEL 61-7-54415747, FAX 61-7-54417478, scec@scec.org.au, http://www.scec.org.au/main/publications.html. adv.: page AUD 140. Circ: 600.

333.72   USA
ECO-HUMANE LETTER. Text in English. 1976. irreg. USD 15 (effective 2000). adv. bk.rev. **Document type:** *Newsletter.*
Formerly: Eco-Letter.
Published by: International Ecology Society, 1471 Barclay St., St. Paul, MN 55106-1405. Ed. R J F Kramer. Circ: 17,000.

333.72   DEU
ECO-WORLD - DAS ALTERNATIVE BRANCHENBUCH. Text in German. 1985. a. EUR 5 (effective 2005). adv. **Document type:** *Directory, Consumer.*
Published by: A L T O P Verlags- und Vertriebsgesellschaft mbH, Gotzinger Str 48, Munich, 81371, Germany. TEL 49-89-7466110, FAX 49-89-74661160, info@eco-world.de, http://www.oneworld.de, http://www.eco-world.de.

ECOLOGIA. see *BIOLOGY*

ECOLOGIA AUSTRAL. see *BIOLOGY*

ECOLOGICAL ECONOMICS. see *ENVIRONMENTAL STUDIES*

ECOLOGICAL ECONOMICS BULLETIN. see *ENVIRONMENTAL STUDIES*

ECOLOGICAL PSYCHOLOGY. see *PSYCHOLOGY*

333.72   USA   ISSN 1543-4060
QH76   CODEN: RMNOEA
➤ **ECOLOGICAL RESTORATION.** Text in English. 1981. q. USD 48 combined subscription to individuals print & online eds.; USD 180 combined subscription to institutions print & online eds. (effective 2006). adv. bk.rev. back issues avail.; reprint service avail. from PQC. **Document type:** *Journal, Academic/Scholarly.*
Former titles (until 2000): Ecological Restoration, North America (1522-4740); (until 1999): Restoration and Management Notes (0733-0707)
Related titles: Microform ed.: (from PQC); Online - full text ed.: ISSN 1543-4079. USD 171 to institutions (effective 2006) (from EBSCO Publishing, Gale Group, IngentaConnect).
Indexed: ASFA, Agr, ApEcolAb, BIOBASE, BiolDig, CTO, CivEngAb, EPB, ESPM, EnerRev, EnvAb, EnvEAb, GardL, M&TEA, PollutAb, SFA, SWRA, WildRev, ZooRec.
—BLDSC (3649.225000), CIS, CISTI, IE, ingenta, Linda Hall. **CCC.**
Published by: (University of Wisconsin at Madison), University of Wisconsin Press, Journal Division, 1930 Monroe St, 3rd Fl, Madison, WI 53711-2059. TEL 608-263-0668, FAX 608-263-1173, journals@uwpress.wisc.edu, http://www.wisc.edu/wisconsinpress/journals/journals/er.html. Ed. Dave Egan. adv.: page USD 315; trim 8.5 x 11. Circ: 2,000.

➤ **THE ECOLOGIST ASIA.** see *BIOLOGY*

➤ **THE ECOLOGISTS.** see *BIOLOGY*

333.72   GBR   ISSN 0144-6258
ECOLOGY & CONSERVATION STUDIES. Text in English. 1980. q. membership. bk.rev.
—BLDSC (3650.040500).
Published by: Ecology and Conservation Studies Society, c/o J. Gadsby, GeN Sec., 36 The Windings, Sanderstead, South Croydon, Surrey CR2 0HU, United Kingdom. Ed. Shirley Goodwin. Circ: 250.

333.72   CAN   ISSN 1708-3087
QH75.A1
➤ **ECOLOGY AND SOCIETY.** Text in English. 1997. 2/yr. free (effective 2005). illus. reprints avail. **Document type:** *Journal, Academic/Scholarly.* **Description:** Covers the conservation of ecosystems, landscapes, species, populations and genetic diversity; restoration of ecosystems and habitats; and the management of natural resources.
Formerly: Conservation Ecology (1195-5449)
Media: Online - full text.
Indexed: ASFA, AgBio, AgrForAb, ApEcolAb, BIOSIS Prev, BiolAb, CPA, CurCont, EA, ESPM, ForAb, GEOBASE, GSI, HerbAb, I&DA, MaizeAb, PAIS, PBA, PGegResA, PoultAb, S&F, SWRA, SeedAb, TriticAb, WAE&RSA, ZooRec.
—**CCC.**
Published by: Resilience Alliance Publications, PO Box 40037, Waterloo Square PO, Waterloo, ON N2J 4V1, Canada. TEL 902-542-2201, FAX 902-585-1059, info@consecol.org, questions@consecol.org, http://www.ecologyandsociety.org/, http://www.consecol.org.

➤ **ECOLOGY, ECONOMY & ENVIRONMENT.** see *ENVIRONMENTAL STUDIES*

333.72   GBR   ISSN 0143-9073
ECOS; a review of conservation. Text in English. 1980. q. GBP 19 domestic membership; GBP 29 foreign membership; GBP 12.50 foreign to students (effective 1999). adv. bk.rev. back issues avail.

Indexed: AgBio, AgrForAb, AnBrAb, EPB, EnvAb, FPA, ForAb, GEOBASE, HerbAb, HortAb, I&DA, IndVet, MaizeAb, PGegResA, PN&I, REE&TA, RRTA, S&F, SeedAb, TriticAb, VetBull, WAE&RSA, WeedAb.
—BLDSC (3659.531300), CISTI, IE, ingenta.
Published by: British Association of Nature Conservationists, Nature Conservation Bureau, 36 Kingfisher Court, Hambridge Rd, Newbury, Berks RG14 5SJ, United Kingdom. Ed., R&P Rick Minter. Circ: 900.

ECOSPHERE; the world in your hands. see *ENVIRONMENTAL STUDIES*

ECOTHEOLOGY. see *RELIGIONS AND THEOLOGY*

ECOTONE; Newsletter of the Cairns & Far North Environment Centre Inc. see *ENVIRONMENTAL STUDIES*

ECOUILLAGES. see *ENVIRONMENTAL STUDIES*

ECOVILLAGE NEWSLETTER. see *HOUSING AND URBAN PLANNING*

EDIZIONI PER LA CONSERVAZIONE; periodico internazionale di prevenzione e conservazione. see *ENVIRONMENTAL STUDIES*

EDUCATION PAR LE JEU ET L'ENVIRONNEMENT. see *ENVIRONMENTAL STUDIES*

639.9 634.9   EGY   ISSN 1110-113X
EGYPTIAN JOURNAL OF WILDLIFE AND NATURAL RESOURCES. Text in English. 1979. a. free (effective 2004). **Document type:** *Journal, Academic/Scholarly.*
Published by: Egyptian Association for Conservation of Natural Resources, 22 Murad Str, Giza Zoo, Giza, Egypt. TEL 20-2-5708895, http://derp.sti.sci.eg/data/0139.htm. Ed. Dr. Muhammad Abdel-Aziz Zaher.

333.72   CHE   ISSN 1016-3174
EIDGENOESSISCHE FORSCHUNGSANSTALT FUER WALD, SCHNEE UND LANDSCHAFT. JAHRESBERICHT. Text in German, French. 1946. a. free. bk.rev. back issues avail. **Document type:** *Monographic series, Trade.*
Former titles (until 1989): Eidgenoessische Anstalt fuer das Forstliche Versuchswesen. Jahresbericht (1011-9124); (until 1956): Jahresbericht ueber die Taetigkeit der Eidgenoessische Anstalt fuer das Forstliche Versuchswesen (1423-3096)
Indexed: FPA.
Published by: Eidgenoessische Forschungsanstalt fuer Wald Schnee und Landschaft, Zuercherstr 111, Birmensdorf ZH, 8903, Switzerland. TEL 41-1-7392111, FAX 41-1-7392215, bibliothek@wsl.ch, http://www.wsl.ch. Ed. Mario Broggi. Circ: 7,000.

333.7   RUS
EKOLOGICHESKAYA SITUATSIYA. Text in Russian. w.
Address: A-ya 90, Moscow, 113191, Russian Federation. TEL 7-095-9552950, FAX 7-095-9552927. **US dist. addr.:** East View Information Services, 3020 Harbor Ln. N., Minneapolis, MN 55447. TEL 612-550-0961.

333.7   RUS   ISSN 0868-7420
QH77.R8
EKOLOGICHESKII VESTNIK ROSSII. Text in Russian. m.
Indexed: RefZh.
—East View.
Published by: Rossiiskii Ekologicheskii Soyuz, Ul Kedrova 8, k 1, Moscow, 117874, Russian Federation. TEL 7-095-3320765, FAX 7-095-2182983. Ed. B G Tril'. **US dist. addr.:** East View Information Services, 3020 Harbor Ln. N., Minneapolis, MN 55447. TEL 612-550-0961.

333.7   RUS
EKOLOGIYA I PROMYSHLENNOST' ROSSII. Text in Russian. m.
Indexed: RefZh.
Published by: Izdatel'stvo Mashinostroenie, Stromynskii per 4, Moscow, 107076, Russian Federation. TEL 7-095-2683858, mashpubl@mashin.ru, http://www.mashin.ru. **US dist. addr.:** East View Information Services, 3020 Harbor Ln. N., Minneapolis, MN 55447.

EKOLOGIYA PROMYSHLENNOGO PROIZVODSTVA. see *ENVIRONMENTAL STUDIES*

EKONOMICHESKIE I PRAVOVYE VOPROSY NEDROPOL'ZOVANIYA V ROSSII. see *BUSINESS AND ECONOMICS*

333.72   SLV
EL SALVADOR. MINISTERIO DE AGRICULTURA Y GANADERIA. DIRECCION GENERAL DE RECURSOS NATURALES RENOVABLES. PLAN ANUAL OPERATIVO∗. Text in Spanish. a.
Published by: (El Salvador. Direccion General de Recursos Naturales Renovables), Ministerio de Agricultura y Ganaderia, c/o OSPA 31, Avda. del Sur, 627, San Salvador, El Salvador.

333.95416   GBR   ISSN 0969-1340
ENACT; managing land for wildlife. Text in English. 1993. q. GBP 12; GBP 15 foreign. adv. back issues avail. **Document type:** *Consumer.* **Description:** ENACT is English Nature's way of encouraging land managers to practice nature conservation. No lectures, just useful advice from fellow practitioners. Articles focus on the problems of managing different sites, using case studies to suggest practical solutions.
—BLDSC (3738.230000), IE, ingenta.
Published by: English Nature, Northminster House, Peterborough, Cambs PE1 1UA, United Kingdom. TEL 44-1733-455000, FAX 44-1733-568834, TELEX 931-2130132 NC G, http://www.english-nature.org.uk. Ed. David Henshilwood. R&P Doris Butler TEL 44-1635-268881. **Subscr. to:** British Wildlife Publishing, Lower Barn, Rooks Farm, Rotherwick, Basingstoke, Harts RG27 9AY, United Kingdom.

333.95416   USA   ISSN 1077-1352
QH75.A1
ENCYCLOPEDIA OF ENDANGERED SPECIES. Text in English. 1994. biennial.
Published by: Gale Research Co. (Subsidiary of: Gale Group), 220 Book Tower, Detroit, MI 48226. TEL 248-699-4253, FAX 248-699-8035, 800-414-5043.

333.95416   USA   ISSN 1091-7314
QL84.2
ENDANGERED SPECIES BULLETIN. Text in English. 1976. 6/yr. illus. reprints avail. **Document type:** *Bulletin, Government.*
Formerly (until 1994): Endangered Species Technical Bulletin (0145-9236)
Related titles: Online - full text ed.: (from Florida Center for Library Automation, Gale Group); ◆ Supplement(s): Endangered Species Update. ISSN 1081-3705.
Indexed: Agr, EPB, EnvAb, GardL, SFA, WildRev.
—BLDSC (3739.663000), IE.
Published by: U.S. Fish and Wildlife Service, Division of Endangered Species, 452 Arlington Sq, Washington, DC 20240. TEL 703-358-2390, esb@fws.gov, http://www.fws.gov. Ed. Michael Bender.

333.95416   USA   ISSN 1081-3705
QL81.5   CODEN: ESUPEF
ENDANGERED SPECIES UPDATE; science, policy & emerging issues. Text in English; Abstracts in Spanish, French. 1983. 4/yr. looseleaf. USD 33 domestic to individuals; USD 38 foreign to individuals; USD 78 domestic to institutions; USD 83 foreign to institutions; USD 25 domestic to students; USD 30 foreign to students (effective 2004). bk.rev. back issues avail. **Document type:** *Newsletter, Academic/Scholarly.* **Description:** Reprints the Endangered Species Bulletin with additional material on endangered species. Provides a forum for the exchange of information and ideas on endangered species issues, management and conservation.
Formerly (until Jul. 1987): Endangered Species Technical Bulletin Reprint
Related titles: Online - full text ed.: (from bigchalk, Florida Center for Library Automation, Gale Group, O C L C Online Computer Library Center, Inc., ProQuest Information & Learning); ◆ Supplement to: Endangered Species Bulletin. ISSN 1091-7314.
Indexed: EPB, EnvAb, GardL, RefZh, WildRev, ZooRec.
Published by: University of Michigan, School of Natural Resources & Environment, 430 E University, Dana Bldg, Ann Arbor, MI 48109-1115. TEL 734-764-6453, esupdate@umich.edu, http://www.umich.edu/~esupdate. Ed. Andrea Krafjevic TEL 734-763-3243. Circ: 1,200.

333.95416   ZAF   ISSN 1016-1902
ENDANGERED WILDLIFE. Text in English. 1983. 3/yr. USD 55, GBP 35 membership includes Vision of Wildlife (effective 2000); i. adv. bk.rev. back issues avail. **Document type:** *Journal, Academic/Scholarly.* **Description:** Studies conservation of wildlife in Africa, with a focus on endangered species.
Formerly (until 1990): Quagga
Indexed: ISAP, SFA, WildRev.
Published by: Endangered Wildlife Trust, Private Bag X11, Parkview, Johannesburg 2122, South Africa. TEL 27-11-486-1102, FAX 27-11-486-1506, ewtsa@global.co.za, http://ewt.org.za. Ed. David Holt Biddle. Adv. contact Lynn Ras. Circ: 6,000.

333.79   CHE
ENERGIE EXTRA. Text in French, German. 1977. bi-m. free. charts; stat. **Document type:** *Government.* **Description:** Covers political and technical aspects of energy ical aspects of energy with special emphasis on savings.
Formerly (until 1996): Courrier de l'Antigaspillage
Indexed: RefZh.
Published by: Office Federal de l'Energie, Bern, 3003, Switzerland. TEL 41-31-3225664, FAX 41-31-3232510. Circ: 35,000.

ENERGIYA: EKONOMIKA, TEKHNIKA, EKOLOGIYA. see *ENERGY*

ENERGY AND HOUSING REPORT; the national newsletter on residential energy conservation and consumption trends. see *ENERGY*

ENERUGI SHIGEN/ENERGY AND RESOURCES. see *ENERGY*

333.72   GBR   ISSN 0967-876X
ENGLISH NATURE RESEARCH REPORTS. Text in English. 1992. irreg., latest vol.18, 1993. **Document type:** *Monographic series.*
Indexed: ForAb, HerbAb, PGegResA, RPP, RevApplEntom, S&F, ZooRec.
—BLDSC (3775.106070).
Published by: English Nature, Northminster House, Peterborough, Cambs PE1 1UA, United Kingdom. TEL 44-1733-340345, FAX 44-1733-68834, http://www.english-nature.org.uk.

333.72   GBR   ISSN 1363-3015
ENGLISH NATURE SCIENCE. Text in English. 1992. irreg.
Indexed: ZooRec.
—BLDSC (3775.106080), ingenta.
Published by: English Nature, Northminster House, Peterborough, Cambs PE1 1UA, United Kingdom. TEL 44-1733-340345, FAX 44-1733-68834, http://www.english-nature.org.uk.

346.044   USA
S930
ENVIROACTION. Text in English. 1980. m. USD 10 membership; USD 13 foreign membership. index. **Document type:** *Newsletter.*
Supersedes: National Wildlife's Conservation (0736-9522); Which was formerly (1938-1983): Conservation Report (0010-6488)
Related titles: Microform ed.: (from PQC).
Published by: National Wildlife Federation, 11100 Wildlife Center Dr., Reston, VA 20190-5362. TEL 703-790-4000, 800-822-9919, FAX 703-772-7332, mclean@nwf.org, http://www.nwf.org. Ed. Tim McLean. Circ. 32,000.

333.72   ZAF
ENVIROKIDS. Text in English. 1979. q. ZAR 120 (effective 2003). adv. bk.rev. back issues avail. **Document type:** *Consumer.* **Description:** Constitutes an environmental magazine for the youth and for environmental clubs.
Formerly: Toktokkie (0256-0437).
Indexed: ISAP.
Published by: Wildlife and Environment Society of South Africa, PO Box 394, Howick, 3290, South Africa. TEL 27-33-3303931, FAX 27-33-3304576, rgriffs@iafrica.com, http:// www.wildlifesociety.org.za. R&P Roberta Griffiths TEL 27-21-7011397. Adv. contact Robert Griffiths. Circ. 12,000.

ENVIRONMENT ABSTRACTS. see *CONSERVATION— Abstracting, Bibliographies, Statistics*

333.95   AUS
ENVIRONMENT N S W. Text in English. q. membership. back issues avail. **Document type:** *Newsletter.* **Description:** Discusses the organization's conservation efforts in New South Wales.
Published by: Nature Conservation Council of N.S.W., Level 5, 362 Kent St, Sydney, NSW 2000, Australia. TEL 61-2-9279-2466, FAX 61-2-9279-2499, ncc@nccnsw.org.au, http://www.nccnsw.org.au. Ed. Kathy Ridge. Circ. 1,000.

ENVIRONMENT NEW JERSEY; news of New Jersey's natural and historic resources. see *ENVIRONMENTAL STUDIES*

ENVIRONMENT NEWSLETTER. see *ENVIRONMENTAL STUDIES*

ENVIRONMENT SOUTH AUSTRALIA. see *ENVIRONMENTAL STUDIES*

ENVIRONMENTAL AND RESOURCE ECONOMICS. see *ENVIRONMENTAL STUDIES*

ENVIRONMENTAL AND RESOURCE ECONOMICS. see *ENVIRONMENTAL STUDIES*

ENVIRONMENTAL AWARENESS. see *ENVIRONMENTAL STUDIES*

ENVIRONMENTAL CONSERVATION; an international journal of environmental science . see *ENVIRONMENTAL STUDIES*

ENVIRONMENTAL HISTORY. see *HISTORY*

ENVIRONMENTAL LANDSCAPE NEWS. see *GARDENING AND HORTICULTURE*

ENVIRONMENTAL NEWS DIGEST. see *ENVIRONMENTAL STUDIES*

ENVIRONMENTAL OPPORTUNITIES NEWSLETTER. see *ENVIRONMENTAL STUDIES*

ENVIRONMENTAL PROGRESS (SPRINGFIELD). see *ENVIRONMENTAL STUDIES*

ENVIRONMENTAL TRENDS IN BRITISH COLUMBIA. see *ENVIRONMENTAL STUDIES*

333.72   ISR   ISSN 0334-9578
ERETZ MAGAZINE. Text in English. 1985. bi-m. USD 52.50 (effective 2001). adv. **Document type:** *Magazine, Consumer.* **Description:** Covers the culture, geography, history, nature, archaeology and people of Israel.
Incorporates (1976-1991): Israel - Land and Nature (0333-6867)
Related titles: Hebrew ed.: Eretz Va-Teva. 1985. USD 52.50 (effective 2001).
Indexed: IHP, IJP, SFA, ZooRec.
Published by: Eretz Ha-Tzvi Inc., 5 Ma'avar Yabok St, Tel Aviv, 67440, Israel. TEL 972-3-6912211, FAX 972-3-6091890. Ed., R&P Yadin Roman. Pubs. Dita Kohl, Yadin Ronan. Adv. contact Dita Kohl. Circ. 15,000. **Subscr. in US to:** SFC, 100 Cooper Center, 7905 Browning Rd, Pennsauken, NJ 08109-4319. TEL 609-488-1881.

333.72   USA   ISSN 1073-7227
TA760
EROSION CONTROL; the journal for erosion & sediment control professionals. Text in English. 1973. 9/yr. USD 36 domestic; USD 75 foreign (effective 2000); free to qualified personnel (effective 2005). adv. bk.rev. bibl.; illus. back issues avail. **Document type:** *Journal, Trade.* **Description:** Features articles on erosion-control techniques and technologies, problems and solutions, national programs around the world, and member profiles, as well as association news, and information on new products.
Formerly (until 1993): I E C A Report (0733-8910)
Indexed: EPB, EnvAb, FLUIDEX, GEOBASE, RefZh.
—CISTI, Linda Hall.
Published by: (International Erosion Control Association), Forester Communications, Inc., PO Box 3100, Santa Barbara, CA 93130. TEL 805-682-1300, FAX 805-682-0200, http://www.erosioncontrol.com/ec.html, http://www.forester.net. Ed. Janice Kasperson TEL 805-681-1300 ext 12. Pub., R&P, Adv. contact Daniel Waldman. Circ. 20,000 (controlled).

333.95416   GBR   ISSN 0961-6004
ESSEX WILDLIFE MAGAZINE. Text in English. 1982. w. (48/yr.). membership. adv. bk.rev. illus. reprint service avail. from PQC. **Document type:** *Consumer.*
Formerly (until 1991): Watch Over Essex (0264-2700); Supersedes: Essex Naturalists' Trust Bulletin
Published by: Essex Wildlife Trust Ltd., Wick Nature Reserve, S. Green Rd, Essex, Fingringhoe Rd, Fingringhoe, Colchester, Essex CO2 8DZ, United Kingdom. TEL 01206-729678. Ed. Sue Newton. Adv. contact Kevin Davis. Circ. 12,000.

333.95416   ETH
ETHIOPIAN WILDLIFE AND NATURAL HISTORY SOCIETY. NEWSLETTER. Text in English. m. membership. **Document type:** *Newsletter.* **Description:** Presents news of society meetings and outdoor activities and conservation news affecting Ethiopia.
Indexed: RefZh, SFA, WildRev, ZooRec.
Published by: Ethiopian Wildlife and Natural History Society, PO Box 13303, Addis Ababa, Ethiopia. Ed. Zewditu Tessema.

333.9   USA
EVERGLADES REPORTER∗ . Text in English. 1969. a. USD 1 membership. bk.rev. back issues avail. **Document type:** *Newsletter.* **Description:** Dedicated to the restoration and protection of the Everglades and associated natural systems.
Published by: Friends of the Everglades, Inc., 244 Westward Dr, Ste A, Miami, FL 33166-5260. TEL 305-888-1230. Ed. Joe Podgor. Circ. 5,000 (paid).

EXPLORER (CLEVELAND). see *SCIENCES: COMPREHENSIVE WORKS*

333.72   USA
F R P A JOURNAL. (Florida Recreation and Park Association) Text in English. q. free membership (effective 2004). adv. **Document type:** *Journal, Trade.*
Published by: (Florida Recreation and Park Association), Naylor Publications, Inc., 5950 NW 1st Pl, Gainesville, FL 32607-6018. TEL 800-369-6220, http://www.naylor.com. Pub. Steve Stramm. Adv. contact Jim Dielschneider. B&W page USD 1,019.50; trim 8.375 x 10.875. Circ. 2,300.

FAELTBIOLOGEN. see *ENVIRONMENTAL STUDIES*

333.72   USA   ISSN 1077-3274
FAIR CHASE. Text in English. 1986. q. USD 25 (effective 1999). adv. bk.rev. illus. **Document type:** *Newsletter.* **Description:** Features hunting stories, conservation topics, and recently accepted trophies.
Former titles (until 1994): Boone and Crockett Club News Journal (1067-2958); (until 1993): Boone and Crockett Club Associates Newsletter
Published by: Boone and Crockett Club, 250 Station Dr, Missoula, MT 59801-2753. TEL 406-542-1888, FAX 406-542-0784, bcclub@montana.com, http://www.boone-crockett.org. Ed. George Bettas. R&P, Adv. contact Julie L Tripp.

333.72   CHE   ISSN 0014-715X
FAMILIENBLATT; Monatszeitschrift des Blauen Kreuzes. Text in German. 1885. m. CHF 30 (effective 1999). illus. reprint service avail. from SCH. **Document type:** *Newsletter, Consumer.*

Former titles (until 1956): Arbeiterfreund (1421-6981); (until 1950): Der Illustrierte Arbeiterfreund (1421-6973)
Published by: Blaukreuz Verlag, Lindenrain 5 A, Bern, 3001, Switzerland. TEL 41-31-3005866, FAX 41-31-3005869. Ed. Else Schoenthal. Circ. 4,000.

FAUNE SAUVAGE; bulletin technique et juridique de l'Office National de la Chasse et de la Faune Sauvage. see *BIOLOGY—Zoology*

333.783   USA   ISSN 0740-3690
FEDERAL PARKS & RECREATION. Text in English. 1983. fortn. looseleaf. USD 207 (effective 2005). back issues avail. **Document type:** *Newsletter.*
Related titles: E-mail ed.
Published by: Resources Publishing Co., P O Box 41320, Arlington, VA 22204-8320. TEL 703-553-0552, FAX 703-553-0558, coffinj@clark.net, http://www.plnfpr.com. Ed., Pub., R&P James B Coffin.

FENGNIAN/HARVEST; friend to the farmers. see *AGRICULTURE*

333.73   AUS
FIELD NATS NEWS. Text in English. m. free. back issues avail. **Document type:** *Newsletter, Academic/Scholarly.*
Published by: Field Naturalists Club of Victoria, 1 Gardenia St., Locked Bag 3, Blackburn, VIC 3130, Australia. fncv@vicnet.net.au, http://home.vicnet.au/~fncv/. Eds. Joan Broadberry, Noel Schleiger.

333.783   USA
FIELD NOTES (FRAMINGHAM)∗ . Text in English. 1981. s-a. bk.rev. **Document type:** *Newsletter.* **Description:** News, events and financial matters pertaining to parks and landscapes throughout the US and Canada designed by Frederick Law Olmsted and Olmsted Brothers..
Formerly: National Association for Olmsted Parks. Newsletter (0895-819X)
Published by: National Association for Olmsted Parks, Inc., 19 Harrison St, Framingham, MA 01702. TEL 508-820-7676, FAX 508-879-4888, naop@resource-network.com, http://www.olmsted.org. Circ. 1,100.

372.357   ESP   ISSN 1136-5552
THE FIRST WORD BULLETIN. Text in English. 1995. s-a. USD 24; USD 3.50 per issue (effective 1999). adv. back issues avail. **Document type:** *Bulletin, Consumer.* **Description:** Covers environmental studies, problems with aging, youth education, and human relationships with animals. Target audience - general public. Self-help, poetry, humor, nature, alternative medicine, young adult and senior citizens.
Related titles: Diskette ed.
Published by: First Word Bulletin Associates, Domingo Fernandez, 5, Apartado 500, Madrid, 28036, Spain. TEL 34-91-3596418, FAX 34-91-3208961, http://www.interlink.es/peraso/first. Ed., Pub., R&P G.W. Amick TEL 34-91-3596418. Adv. contact G W Amick. B&W page USD 200, color page USD 350. Circ. 3,000.

FISCH UND UMWELT MECKLENBURG-VORPOMMERN. JAHRESHEFT. see *ENVIRONMENTAL STUDIES*

FISH & FISHERIES. see *FISH AND FISHERIES*

577 639.2   CAN
FISHERIES RESOURCE CONSERVATION COUNCIL. REPORT. Text in English. irreg.
Published by: Fisheries Resource Conservation Council, PO Box 2001, Sta D, Ottawa, ON K1P 5W3, Canada. TEL 613-998-0433, FAX 613-998-1146, http://www.frcc-ccrh.ca/Press7.htm.

FISHERIES WESTERN AUSTRALIA. FISHERIES RESEARCH REPORTS. see *FISH AND FISHERIES*

333.9   FRA   ISSN 1680-1857
FLAMINGO SPECIALIST GROUP NEWSLETTER. Text in French. 1980. a. **Document type:** *Newsletter.*
Formerly: Flamingo Research
Published by: Flamingo Research, c/o Dr. Alan Johnson, Station Biologique de la Tour du Valat, Aries, Le Sambuc, Arles, 13200, France.

333.95416   USA   ISSN 1520-8214
FLORIDA FISH AND WILDLIFE NEWS. Text in English. 1979 (vol.7). m. USD 15. reprints avail.
Former titles: Wildlife Notes; Florida Out of Doors
Published by: Florida Wildlife Federation, PO Box 6870, Tallahassee, FL 32314-6870. TEL 904-656-7113. Ed. Richard Farren. Circ. 9,500.

FLORIDA LAND USE AND GROWTH MANAGEMENT LAW. see *LAW*

▼ *new title*   ➤ *refereed*   ∗ *unverified*   ◆ *full entry avail.*

333.95416 USA ISSN 0015-4369
SK1
FLORIDA WILDLIFE. Text in English. 1947. bi-m. USD 12 (effective 2001). bk.rev. illus. 32 p./no. 3 cols./p.; **Document type:** *Magazine, Government.* **Description:** Presents informational articles on state wildlife conservation and its interaction with fishing and hunting. Includes news on legislative and regulatory developments and provides legal guidance in the practice of these sports; natural history and status of threatened and endangered species.
Indexed: SFA, WildRev.
Published by: Fish & Wildlife Conservation Commission, 620 S Meridian St, Tallahassee, FL 32399-1600. TEL 850-488-9453, FAX 850-488-8974, subletr@gfc.state.fl.us, http://www.floridaconservation.org. Ed. Dick Sublette. Circ: 20,000 (paid).

333.72 USA ISSN 0744-3315
QL81.5
FOCUS (WASHINGTON, D.C. 1977). Text in English. 1977. bi-m. USD 15 to members (effective 2005). bk.rev. **Document type:** *Newsletter, Consumer.* **Description:** Discusses World Wildlife Fund conservation activities worldwide.
Indexed: MEA&I.
Published by: World Wildlife Fund, 1250 24th St, N W, Washington, DC 20037. TEL 202-293-4800, FAX 202-293-9211, membership@wwfus.org, https://secure.worldwildlife.org/about/focus.cfm, http://www.worldwildlife.org/. Ed., R&P Ann Felber TEL 202-778-9546. Circ: 1,000,000.

FOCUS ON FISH AND WILDLIFE. see *SPORTS AND GAMES—Outdoor Life*

598 333.95416 NZL ISSN 0015-7384
CODEN: FRBDAK
FOREST & BIRD. Text in English. 1923. q. avail. by membership only. adv. bk.rev. illus.; maps. Index. 48 p./no.; **Document type:** *Magazine, Consumer.* **Description:** Covers New Zealand natural history and conservation.
Indexed: EPB, INZP, SFA, WildRev, ZooRec.
—BLDSC (3989.115000), IE, ingenta. **CCC.**
Published by: Royal Forest and Bird Protection Society of New Zealand Inc., 172 Taranaki St, PO Box 631, Wellington, New Zealand. TEL 64-4-3857374, FAX 64-4-3857373, office@forestandbird.org.nz, http://www.forestandbird.org.nz/Magazines/index.asp. Ed. Miachael Szabo. Circ: 18,000 (controlled).

FOREST HISTORY TODAY. see *FORESTS AND FORESTRY*

FOREST NOTES; New Hampshire's conservation magazine. see *FORESTS AND FORESTRY*

333.72 CHE ISSN 1424-5108
SD1 CODEN: MEFLEK
➤ **FOREST SNOW AND LANDSCAPE RESEARCH.** Text in German; Summaries in English, French, German, Italian. 1891. 3/yr. CHF 28 per issue (effective 2005). bk.rev. charts; illus.; stat. index, cum.index. back issues avail. **Document type:** *Journal, Academic/Scholarly.*
Former titles (until 1999): Eidgenoessische Forschungsanstalt fuer Wald, Schnee und Landschaft. Mitteilungen (1016-3158); (until 1990): Switzerland. Eidgenoessische Anstalt fuer das Forstliche Versuchswesen. Mitteilungen (0251-4133); Switzerland. Schweizerische Anstalt fuer das Forstliche Versuchswesen. Mitteilungen (0080-7257)
Indexed: AgrForAb, ForAb, SeedAb.
—BLDSC (3998.850000).
Published by: Eidgenoessische Forschungsanstalt fuer Wald Schnee und Landschaft, Zuercherstr 111, Birmensdorf ZH, 8903, Switzerland. TEL 41-1-7392111, FAX 41-1-7392215, bibliothek@wsl.ch, http://www.wsl.ch. Ed. Mario Broggi. Circ: 750.

➤ **FORTH NATURALIST AND HISTORIAN SERIES.** see *SCIENCES: COMPREHENSIVE WORKS*

333.72 CHE ISSN 1021-2256
FORUM FUER WISSEN. Text in German. 1991. a. free. back issues avail. **Document type:** *Proceedings, Academic/Scholarly.*
Indexed: FPA, ForAb, HortAb, OrnHort, RDA, RRTA, S&F, WAE&RSA.
Published by: Eidgenoessische Forschungsanstalt fuer Wald Schnee und Landschaft, Zuercherstr 111, Birmensdorf ZH, 8903, Switzerland. TEL 41-1-7392111, FAX 41-1-7392215, bibliothek@wsl.ch, http://www.wsl.ch. Ed. Mario Broggi.

333.95416 CAN ISSN 0822-7284
FRANC - VERT. Text in French. 1984. q. CND 23. adv. bk.rev. **Document type:** *Consumer.* **Description:** Discusses the conservation of wilderness areas, parklands, waterways, and other natural resources in Quebec.
Formerly (until 1990): Franc - Nord
Indexed: CBPI, CPerl, PdeR.
—CISTI.
Published by: Union Quebecoise Pour la Conservation de la Nature, 690 Grande Allee Est, Quebec, PQ G1R 2K5, Canada. TEL 418-648-2104, FAX 418-648-0991. Ed. Karen Grislis. Adv. contact Helene Savard. Circ: 6,000.

FRENCH INSTITUTE, PONDICHERRY. PONDY PAPERS IN ECOLOGY. see *BIOLOGY*

333.95416 USA ISSN 0016-1284
FRIEND O'WILDLIFE. Text in English. 1959. bi-m. USD 5. adv. bk.rev. illus.
Published by: North Carolina Wildlife Federation, Inc., PO Box 10626, Raleigh, NC 27605. TEL 919-833-1923, FAX 919-829-1192. Ed. Eddie Nickens. Circ: 40,000.

333.783 USA
FRIENDS OF ACADIA JOURNAL; the magazine of Acadia National Park and surrounding communities. Text in English. 1996. 3/yr. USD 35 to members; USD 2.50 newsstand/cover to members. **Document type:** *Consumer.* **Description:** Dedicated to preserving and protecting the natural beauty, ecological vitality and cultural distinctiveness of Acadia National Park and surrounding communities, thereby ensuring a high quality experience for visitors and residents.
Published by: Friends of Acadia, 43 Cottage St, PO Box 725, Bar Harbor, ME 04609. TEL 207-288-3340, 800-914-4415, FAX 207-288-8938, marla@acadia.net, http://www.foacadia.org. Ed. Marla Major. Pub. W Kent Olson.

333.783 USA
FRIENDS OF PARKS & RECREATION. Text in English. 1990. q. USD 15 (effective 1999). **Description:** Covers topics of interest to volunteers and participants in parks, recreation and leisure services.
Published by: National Recreation and Park Association, 22377 Belmont Ridge Rd, Ashburn, VA 20148-4501. Ed. Sylvia Somerville. **Co-sponsor:** National Recreation Foundation.

333.9 CHE
FROGLOG. Text in English. q. **Document type:** *Newsletter.*
Published by: (Species Survival Commission - Task Force on Declining Amphibians Populations), International Union for Conservation of Nature and Natural Resources, Rue Mauverney 28, Gland, 1196, Switzerland. TEL 41-22-9990001, FAX 41-22-9990002, mail@hq.iucn.org. **Subscr. to:** J. Wilkinson, Dept. of Biology, The Open University, Walton Hall, Milton Keynes, Bucks MK7 6AA, United Kingdom.

333.75 USA
FRONTIER NEWS. Text in English. w. back issues avail. **Document type:** *Government.* **Description:** Presents news stories about natural forests.
Related titles: Online - full text ed.
Published by: World Resources Institute, 10 G St, N E, Ste 800, Washington, DC 20002. TEL 202-729-7600, FAX 202-729-7610, lauralee@wri.org, http://www.wri.org/ffi/news/. **Co-sponsor:** Forest Frontiers Initiative.

570 UGA
FRONTIER-UGANDA WILDLIFE PROTECTED AREAS PROJECT. BASELINE SURVEYS PROGRAMME REPORT. Text in English. 1993. irreg.
Formerly (until 1997): Frontier-Uganda Game Reserves Project. Technical Report (1369-0485)
—BLDSC (1863.863000).
Published by: Frontier - Uganda, PO Box 1505, Kampala, Uganda. TEL 256-41-270324, FAX 256-41-242298, frontier@imul.com. Ed. Julia Lloyd.

577 GBR ISSN 0269-8463
QH540 CODEN: FECOE5
➤ **FUNCTIONAL ECOLOGY.** Text in English. 1987. bi-m. GBP 566 combined subscription in Europe to institutions print & online eds.; USD 1,046 combined subscription in the Americas to institutions & Caribbean (print & online eds.); GBP 622 combined subscription elsewhere to institutions print & online eds. (effective 2006). adv. back issues avail.; reprint service avail. from PSC. **Document type:** *Journal, Academic/Scholarly.* **Description:** Contains articles on ecological sciences for research workers and advanced students.
Related titles: Microform ed.: (from PQC); Online - full text ed.: ISSN 1365-2435. GBP 538 in Europe to institutions; USD 995 in the Americas to institutions & Caribbean; GBP 592 elsewhere to institutions (effective 2006) (from Blackwell Synergy, EBSCO Publishing, Gale Group, IngentaConnect, JSTOR (Web-based Journal Archive), O C L C Online Computer Library Center, Inc., Swets Information Services).
Indexed: AEA, ASCA, ASFA, AgBio, Agr, AgrForAb, AnBeAb, AnBrAb, ApEcolAb, ApicAb, B&BAb, BIOBASE, BIOSIS Prev, BibAg, BioCN&I, BiolAb, CPA, CurCont, DSA, EPB, ESPM, EntAb, FCA, FPA, ForAb, GEOBASE, GenetAb, HGA, HelmAb, HerbAb, HortAb, I&DA, IABS, ISR, IndVet, KWIWR, NemAb, NutrAb, OceAb, OrnHort, PBA, PGegResA, PGrRegA, PHN&I, PoultAb, ProtozoAb, RA&MP, RM&VM, RPP, RefZh, RevApplEntom, RiceAb, S&F, SCI, SFA, SIA, SWRA, SeedAb, SoyAb, TriticAb, VetBull, WeedAb, WildRev, ZooRec.
—BLDSC (4055.616000), CISTI, IDS, IE, Infotrieve, ingenta. **CCC.**
Published by: (British Ecological Society), Blackwell Publishing Ltd., 9600 Garsington Rd, Oxford, OX4 2ZG, United Kingdom. TEL 44-1865-776868, FAX 44-1865-714591, customerservices@oxon.blackwellpublishing.com, http://www.blackwellpublishing.com/journals/FEC. Eds. Charles W Fox, Steven Chown. Pub. Sue Hewitt. R&P Sophie Savage. Adv. contact Jenny Applin. Circ: 1,350.

636 USA
FUND FOR ANIMALS NEWSLETTER. Text in English. 1969. 3/yr. USD 20 to individuals; USD 10 to students. illus.
Formerly: Fund for Animals Quarterly
Published by: Fund for Animals Inc., 200 W 57th St, New York, NY 10019. TEL 212-246-2096. Pub. Michael Markarian. Circ: 180,000.

333.72 ARG
FUNDACION MIGUEL LILLO. SERIE CONSERVACION DE LA NATURALEZA. Text in Spanish; Summaries in English. 1979. irreg., latest vol.14, 1999. bk.rev. bibl.; charts; illus.; abstr. **Document type:** *Monographic series, Academic/Scholarly.*
Indexed: RefZh.
Published by: Fundacion Miguel Lillo, Miguel Lillo, 251, San Miguel de Tucuman, Tucuman 4000, Argentina. TEL 54-0381-4239960, FAX 54-0381-4330868, fmlinfonoa@tucbbs.com.ar, http://www.lillo.org.ar. Ed. Jose A Haedo Rossi.

639.9 ARG ISSN 0328-462X
HT395.A72
FUNDACION PATAGONIA NATURAL. INFORME TECNICO. Text in Spanish. 1995. m. **Document type:** *Journal, Academic/Scholarly.*
Indexed: ESPM.
Published by: Fundacion Patagonia Natural, Marcos A. Zar 760, Puerto Madryn, Argentina. informacion@patagonianatural.org, http://www.patagonianatural.org.

333.72 CHE
GAJAH. Text in English. 2/yr. **Document type:** *Newsletter.*
Formerly: International Union for Conservation of Nature and Natural Resources. Species Survival Commission - Asian Elephant Specialist Group. Newsletter
Indexed: ZooRec.
Published by: (Species Survival Commission - Asian Elephant Specialist Group), International Union for Conservation of Nature and Natural Resources, Rue Mauverney 28, Gland, 1196, Switzerland. TEL 41-22-9990001, FAX 41-22-9990002, mail@hq.iucn.org. **Subscr. to:** Dr. Charles Santiapillai, AESG, 110 Wattarantenne Rd., Kandy, Sri Lanka.

GAME AND WILDLIFE SCIENCE. see *BIOLOGY—Zoology*

GAMEWISE. see *BIOLOGY—Ornithology*

GAN NO SHINPOJUMU/SYMPOSIUM ON WILD GEESE. see *BIOLOGY—Zoology*

598.417 JPN
GAN NO TAYORI/GOOSE LETTER. Text in Japanese. 1971. s-a. JPY 1,000 (effective 1999 & 2000). bk.rev. **Document type:** *Newsletter.* **Description:** Covers the goose species in Japan and east Asia, their habitat, as well as conservation issues and activities of the Association.
Published by: Gan o Hogosurukai/Japanese Association for Wild Geese Protection, c/o Mr Kurechi, 16 Kawaminami Minamimachi, kurihara-gun, Wakayanagimachi, Miyagi-ken 989-5502, Japan. TEL 81-228-32-2004, FAX 81-228-32-3294, hgy02256@nifty.ne.jp. Ed. Yoshihiko Miyabayashi. Circ: 600.

GANKAMOKA NO CHORUI NO CHOSA HOKOKUSHO/ANNUAL CENSUS ON WILD GEESE, DUCKS AND SWANS IN JAPAN ADVOCATED BY THE MINISTRY OF THE ENVIRONMENT. see *BIOLOGY—Zoology*

333.72 USA
GARDEN STATE ENVIRONEWS. Text in English. d. free. back issues avail. **Document type:** *Newsletter.* **Description:** Covers environmental issues in the Garden State, New Jersey.
Media: Online - full text.
Published by: Garden State EnviroNet, 19 Boonton Ave., Boonton, NJ 07005-8902. TEL 973-586-4128, mailbox@gsenet.org, http://www.gsenet.org/. Ed., Pub., R&P Phil Reynolds. Circ: 350.

333.72 USA ISSN 0732-4715
SB482.A4
GEORGE WRIGHT FORUM. Text in English. 1981. q. USD 45 to individual members; USD 100 to institutional members; USD 25 to students membership (effective 2005). **Document type:** *Journal, Academic/Scholarly.* **Description:** Devoted to interdisciplinary inquiry about parks, protected areas, and cultural sites publishing critical thinking on all aspects of research, resource management, administration, and education relating to cultural and natural protected areas.
Related titles: Online - full content ed.
Indexed: ASFA, ESPM.
Published by: George Wright Society, PO Box 65, Hancock, MI 49930-0065 . TEL 906-487-9722, FAX 906-487-9405, info@georgewright.org, http://www.georgewright.org/forum.html.

333.72 340 USA
GEORGIA CONSERVATION LAW HANDBOOK. Text in English. 1995. a. looseleaf. USD 28 (effective 2000). **Document type:** *Government.* **Description:** Provides the full text of the complete Georgia Title 27 - Game and Fish; and related sections from Title 12 - Conservation and Natural Resources; Title 16 - Crimes and Offenses; Title 51 - Torts; and Title 52 - Waters of the State, Ports, and Watercraft.
Published by: Gould Publications, Inc. (Subsidiary of: LexisNexis), 1333 North US Hwy 17-92, Longwood, FL 32750-3724. TEL 800-717-7917, FAX 407-695-2906, info@gouldlaw.com, http://www.gouldlaw.com.

GEWAESSERGUETEBERICHT. see *WATER RESOURCES*

333.7845 DEU ISSN 0941-746X
P87
GEWAESSERGUTEBERICHT. Text in German. 1985. irreg. **Document type:** *Monographic series, Academic/Scholarly.*
Published by: Niedersaechsisches Landesamt fuer Oekologie, Postfach 101062, Hildesheim, 31110, Germany. TEL 49-5121-509-0, FAX 49-5121-509196, poststelle@nloe.niedersachsen.de, http://jupiter.nloe.de.

333.91 DEU ISSN 0947-5559
GEWAESSERUEBERWACHUNGSSYSTEM NIEDERSACHSEN. GRUNDWASSERBERICHT. Text in German. 1994. irreg. **Document type:** *Monographic series, Academic/Scholarly.*
Published by: Niedersaechsisches Landesamt fuer Oekologie, Postfach 101062, Hildesheim, 31110, Germany. TEL 49-5121-509-0, FAX 49-5121-509196, poststelle@nloe.niedersachsen.de, http://jupiter.nloe.de.

GLOBAL CHANGE; a review of climate change and ozone depletion. see *ENVIRONMENTAL STUDIES—Pollution*

GLOBAL ECOLOGY AND BIOGEOGRAPHY; a journal of macroecology. see *ENVIRONMENTAL STUDIES*

GLOBAL ENVIRONMENT OUTLOOK (YEAR). see *ENVIRONMENTAL STUDIES*

333.72 CHE ISSN 1017-2718
GNUSLETTER. Variant title: Antelope Specialist Group Gnusletter. Text in English. 1981. 3/yr. USD 10 (effective 2000). **Document type:** *Newsletter.*
Indexed: ZooRec.
Published by: (Species Survival Commission - Antelope Specialist Group), International Union for Conservation of Nature and Natural Resources, Rue Mauverney 28, Gland, 1196, Switzerland. TEL 41-22-9990001, FAX 41-22-9990002, mail@hq.iucn.org. **Subscr. to:** Dr. Richard D. Estes, 5 Granite St, USA, Peterborough, NH 03458.

333.7 MDA
GOLOS NARODA. Text in Russian. w. USD 249 in United States.
Address: Chishinau 45, Chisinau, Moldova. TEL 23-41-96, FAX 23-44-01. Ed. Georgiy Kopats. **US dist. addr.:** East View Information Services, 3020 Harbor Ln. N., Minneapolis, MN 55447. TEL 612-550-0961.

GOOSE STUDY. see *BIOLOGY—Zoology*

333.72 HRV ISSN 1330-1152
GOSPODARSTVO I OKOLIS. Text in Croatian. 1993. bi-m. adv. **Document type:** *Magazine, Trade.*
Published by: Privredni Marketing, Novakova 10, Zagreb, 10000, Croatia. TEL 385-1-391111.

GRANTS FOR ENVIRONMENTAL PROTECTION & ANIMAL WELFARE. see *EDUCATION—School Organization And Administration*

333.72 GBR ISSN 0956-6414
GRAPEVINE. Text in English. bi-m. free to members. adv. back issues avail. **Document type:** *Bulletin, Academic/Scholarly.* **Description:** Provides a calendar of events covering conferences, meetings, seminars and workshops, plus information for UKIC members. It also carries recruitment advertising for the Profession.
Related titles: Online - full text ed.
Published by: United Kingdom Institute for Conservation of Historic and Artistic Works, 3rd Fl, Downstream Building, 1 London Bridge, London, SE1 9BG, United Kingdom. TEL 44-20-77853805, FAX 44-20-77853806, ukic@ukic.org.uk, http://www.ukic.org.uk. Ed., Pub., Adv. contact Lyndsay Piper TEL 44-353-95-41073. B&W page GBP 275; 255 x 185. Circ: 2,000.

333.72 USA
GRASSROOTS (ST. LOUIS)✱. Text in English. q.
Published by: Grassroots Institute, PO Box 1866, E. St. Louis, IL 62208-0066. TEL 618-235-7775. Ed. Don Pierce.

346.044 GBR ISSN 0956-0769
GREAT BRITAIN. DEPARTMENT OF THE ENVIRONMENT. ENTERPRISE ZONE INFORMATION. Text in English. 1985. a.
—BLDSC (3776.633000).
Published by: (Great Britain. Department of Environment), Home Office, 50 Queen Anne's Gate, London, SW1 9AT, United Kingdom. http://www.open.gov.uk.

346.044 GBR ISSN 1369-930X
GREAT BRITAIN. DEPARTMENT OF THE ENVIRONMENT. ENVIRONMENTAL ACTION GUIDE ADVISORY NOTES. Text in English. 1993. irreg.
—BLDSC (3791.372300).
Published by: (Great Britain. Department of Environment), Home Office, 50 Queen Anne's Gate, London, SW1 9AT, United Kingdom. http://www.open.gov.uk.

GREAT BRITAIN. DEPARTMENT OF THE ENVIRONMENT, TRANSPORT AND THE REGIONS. ENVIRONMENTAL PROTECTION CONSULTATION PAPERS. see *ENVIRONMENTAL STUDIES*

333.76 363.7 GBR
GREAT BRITAIN. DEPARTMENT OF THE ENVIRONMENT, TRANSPORT AND THE REGIONS. WILDLIFE AND COUNTRYSIDE CONSULTATION PAPERS. Text in English. irreg., latest 2000. charts; stat. back issues avail. **Document type:** *Monographic series, Government.* **Description:** Examines in detail land-conservation issues in a public administration context.
Related titles: Online - full content ed.
Published by: Department for Transport, Local Government and the Regions, TSR5 Branch, Zone 2/18, Great Minster House, 76 Marsham St, London, SW1P 4DR, United Kingdom. TEL 44-20-7944-6642, publicity@detr.gov.uk, http://www.detr.gov.uk/consult.htm, http://www.dtlr.gov.uk/. **Subscr. to:** H.M.S.O., Publications Centre, PO Box 276, London SW8 5DT, United Kingdom. TEL 44-20-7873-9090, 44-870-600-5522, FAX 44-20-7873-8200, 44-870-600-5533.

363.70025 USA ISSN 1080-5664
GREAT LAKES ENVIRONMENTAL DIRECTORY. Text in English. 1995. biennial. USD 25 (effective 2001). index. **Document type:** *Directory.* **Description:** Annotated listings of citizen groups and government agencies in Illinois, Indiana, Michigan, Minnesota, Ohio, and Wisconsin.
Media: CD-ROM. **Related titles:** Diskette ed.; Online - full text ed.
Published by: Harbinger Communications, 616 Sumner St, Santa Cruz, CA 95062. TEL 406-721-0440, FAX 406-721-0440, ned@ism.net, http://eelink.net/gaindirectories.html.

333.7844 USA
GREAT LAKES NEWS; an international coalition to conserve and protect the Great Lakes - St. Lawrence River ecosystem. Text in English. 1986. q. USD 25 in US & Canada; USD 35 to libraries. adv. bk.rev. **Document type:** *Newsletter.* **Description:** Includes news and in-depth articles about the Great Lakes Basin.
Formerly (until 2000): Great Lakes United (1091-5605)
Related titles: Online - full text ed.
Indexed: EnvAb.
Published by: Great Lakes United, Buffalo State College, Cassety Hall, 1300 Elmwood Ave, Buffalo, NY 14222. TEL 716-886-0142, FAX 716-886-0303, glu@igc.org, http://www.great-lakes.net/glu. Ed. Reg Gilbert. adv.: page USD 400. Circ: 3,000.

GREEK COMMISSION ON IRRIGATION AND DRAINAGE. BULLETIN. see *WATER RESOURCES*

GREEN ANARCHIST; global anarcho-primitivist 'zine. see *POLITICAL SCIENCE*

333.72 USA
GREEN ANARCHY. Text in English. q. USD 11 domestic; USD 14 in Canada; USD 19 in the European Union; USD 2 newsstand/cover domestic; USD 3 newsstand/cover in Canada; USD 4 newsstand/cover in the European Union; free to prisoners (effective 2002). **Document type:** *Newspaper, Consumer.* **Description:** Dedicated to critiquing civilization, patriarchy and the techno-industrial nightmare in all its forms.
Address: PO Box 11331, Eugene, OR 97440. greenanarchy@tao.ca.

GREEN BOOK: THE DIRECTORY OF NATURAL HISTORY AND GENERAL STOCK PHOTOGRAPHY. see *PHOTOGRAPHY*

GREEN BUSINESS LETTER; the hands-on journal for environmentally conscious companies. see *BUSINESS AND ECONOMICS*

333.72 GBR ISSN 0263-0095
GREEN DRUM; the green paper for people who care. Text in English. 1974. q. GBP 3.50.
Formerly: Good Earth
Published by: Greenspur Enterprise, 18 Cofton Lake Rd, Birmingham, United Kingdom. Circ: 2,000.

333.72 333.79 363.7 GBR ISSN 1466-7959
GREEN LINES. Text in English. 1997. m. GBP 32 in British Isles (effective 1999). adv. bk.rev. charts; illus.; maps; tr.lit. back issues avail. **Document type:** *Magazine, Consumer.* **Description:** The promotion of greater protection for the environment. Highlighting environmental, Local Agenda 21, recycling, energy conservation, air/water quality and land regeneration issues within north east of England.
Related titles: E-mail ed.
Published by: The Publishing Centre, Polar House, Bowburn North Industrial Estate, Bowburn, County Durham DH6 5PF, United Kingdom. TEL 44-191-377-9805, FAX 44-191-377-3131, publishingcentre@btinternet.com. Ed. Rachel Townsend Green. R&P, Adv. contact Wayne Hughes. color page GBP 1,250; trim 18.6 x 26.1. Circ: 1,000 (paid); 19,000 (controlled).

333.72025 AUS ISSN 0727-0119
GREEN PAGES: DIRECTORY OF NON-GOVERNMENT ENVIRONMENTAL GROUPS IN AUSTRALIA. Text in English. 1970. irreg., latest 1998. AUD 15. **Document type:** *Directory.* **Description:** Addresses and telephone numbers of Australian conservation and environmental groups.
Formerly: Australian Conservation Foundation. Conservation Directory
Published by: Australian Conservation Foundation, 340 Gore St, Fitzroy, VIC 3065, Australia. TEL 61-3-94161166, FAX 61-3-94160767. Ed. Louise Ray.

GREEN POLITICS. see *POLITICAL SCIENCE*

333.72 AUS ISSN 1324-5740
GREENER TIMES✱. Text in English. 1990. m. (11/yr.). AUD 25 to non-members. **Document type:** *Newsletter.* **Description:** Highlights important environmental issues for conservation activists; provides a forum for debate about environmental issues.
Related titles: Online - full text ed.
Published by: Conservation Council of Western Australia (Inc.), City West Lotteries House, 2 Delhi St, Perth, W.A. 6005, Australia. TEL 61-8-94207266, FAX 61-8-94207273, conswa@conservationwa.asn.au, http://www.conservationwa.asn.au/.

C

GREENOTES. see *ENVIRONMENTAL STUDIES*

333.72 USA ISSN 0899-0190
QH75.A1
GREENPEACE QUARTERLY. Text in English. 1981. q. adv. illus. **Document type:** *Magazine, Consumer.* **Description:** Outlines the international group's protesting the destruction and abuse of the environment. Provides current news and articles on its worldwide activities.
Formerly: Greenpeace Examiner (0828-7988)
Related titles: Online - full text ed.
Indexed: AltPI, EPB, EnerRev, EnvAb.
—CCC.
Published by: Greenpeace, 702 H St NW, Ste 300, Washington, DC 20001. TEL 202-462-1177, 800-326-0959, FAX 202-462-4507, http://www.greenpeace.org/usa. Ed., Pub. David Barry. Circ: 240,000.

GREEN@WORK. see *BUSINESS AND ECONOMICS*

GROENWERK; praktijkboek voor bos, natuur en stedelijk groen. see *FORESTS AND FORESTRY*

333.72 AUS ISSN 1320-7849
THE GROWING IDEA. Text in English. 1992. q. free to members. **Document type:** *Newsletter.* **Description:** Covers activities of Greening Australia and issues in vegetation management.
Published by: Greening Australia Queensland Inc., 431 Montague Rd, West End, QLD 4101, Australia. TEL 61-7-3844-0211, FAX 61-7-3844-0727, lmorland@gld.greeningaustralia.org.au, http://www.gld.greeningaustralia.org.au. Ed., R&P Louise Morland.

333.72 DEU ISSN 0943-2949
GRUENER WEG 31A; Zeitschrift fuer die Ideen- und Sozialgeschichte der Umweltbewegnungen. Text in German. 1987. q. bk.rev. bibl.; illus. index. back issues avail. **Document type:** *Newsletter, Academic/Scholarly.* **Description:** Reports on social movements and the protection of natural resources.
Formerly (until 1992): Arbeiterkultur und Oekologie (0937-6798)
Published by: Institut und Studienarchiv Arbeiterkultur und Oekologie, Eco-Archiv, Bahnhofstr 26, Hofgeismar, 34369, Germany. TEL 49-5671-920885, FAX 49-5671-920887, eco-archiv@t-online.de. Ed. Klaus Peter Lorenz. Circ: 600 (paid).

333.95416 DEU ISSN 0178-1421
GRUENSTIFT (BERLIN); das regionale Umweltmagazin fuer Berlin und Brandenburg. Text in German. 1983. bi-m. adv. bk.rev. back issues avail. **Document type:** *Consumer.* **Description:** Promotes natural conservation and environmental protection in Berlin and the state of Brandenburg.

Published by: Stiftung Naturschutz Berlin, Potsdamer Str 68, Berlin, 10785, Germany. TEL 49-30-2626001, FAX 49-30-2615277, snb-gst@mail.blinx.de, http://www.snb.blinx.de. Ed. Juergen Herrmann. Pub. Holger Wonneberg. R&P Joerg Goetting Frosinski. Adv. contact Sabine Braun. Circ: 10,000.

GUILFOYLE REPORT. see *PHOTOGRAPHY*

333.72 363.7 CAN
GULF OF MAINE TIMES. Text in English. q. **Document type:** *Academic/Scholarly.*
Related titles: Online - full content ed.
Published by: Gulf of Maine Council on the Marine Environment, c/o Andi Rierden, PO Box 339, Annapolis Royal, NS BOS 1KO, Canada. TEL 902-532-0200, FAX 902-532-0250, editor@gulfofmaine.org, info@gulfofmaine.org, http://www.gulfofmaine.org/times.

H H S C HANDBOOK. see *ENVIRONMENTAL STUDIES*

333.73 AUS ISSN 0310-2939
QH77.A8 CODEN: HAAUE7
HABITAT AUSTRALIA. Text in English. 1973. bi-m. AUD 49. adv. illus. **Document type:** *Consumer.* **Description:** Concerned with environment, conservation, ecologically sustainable alternatives to current industry and consumer practices.
Formerly: Habitat
Related titles: Online - full text ed.: (from Florida Center for Library Automation, Gale Group, R M I T Publishing).
Indexed: ARI, AusPAIS, GdIns, SFA, WBA, WMB, WildRev, ZooRec.
—BLDSC (4237.370000), IE, ingenta.
Published by: Australian Conservation Foundation, 340 Gore St, Fitzroy, VIC 3065, Australia. TEL 61-3-94161166, FAX 61-3-94160767. Ed. Louise Ray. Adv. contact Ted Vining. Circ: 16,000.

333.95 AND
HABITATS; revista del Centre de Biodiversitat. Text in Catalan. 2000. s-a.
Published by: Institut D'Estudis Andorrans, Centre de Biodiversitat, C. La Valireta, 5 4t, Encamp, Andorra. TEL 376-731036, FAX 376-834-578, cbdiea@andorra.ad, http://www.iea.ad/.

333.72 JPN ISSN 0388-4732
HAKUSAN/HAKUSAN NATURE CONSERVATION CENTER. NEWS. Text in Japanese. 1973. q. **Document type:** *Newsletter.*
Published by: Ishikawa-ken Hakusan Shizen Hogo Senta/Hakusan Nature Conservation Center, Ishikawa Prefecture, Kinameri, Ishikawa-gun, Yoshinodanimura, Ishikawa-ken 920-2326, Japan. TEL 81-7619-5-5321, FAX 81-7619-5-5323.

HANA NO WA/HIROSHIMA CITY PARK ASSOCIATION. NEWS. see *BIOLOGY—Botany*

HANDBOOK OF NATURAL PRODUCTS DATA. see *CHEMISTRY*

HARAMATA - BULLETIN OF THE DRYLANDS. see *ENVIRONMENTAL STUDIES*

333.72 GBR ISSN 0141-3503
CODEN: HESNAW
THE HASTINGS & EAST SUSSEX NATURALIST. Text in English. 1906. a. GBP 5 to members. **Document type:** *Academic/Scholarly.*
Indexed: SFA, WildRev, ZooRec.
Published by: Hastings and East Sussex Natural History Society, c/o John A.B. Gale, Ed, Argosy, 11 Rockmead Rd, Fairlight, Hastings, E Sussex TN35 4DJ, United Kingdom. Circ: 150.

HAWK MIGRATION STUDIES. see *BIOLOGY—Ornithology*

HAWK MOUNTAIN NEWS. see *BIOLOGY—Ornithology*

333.72 CHE ISSN 0017-9817
HEIMATSCHUTZ/SAUVEGARDE. Text in French, German. 1906. q. CHF 20. bk.rev. charts; illus. **Document type:** *Bulletin.*
Published by: Schweizer Heimatschutz/Ligue Suisse du Patrimoine National, Merkurstr 45, Zuerich, 8032, Switzerland. TEL 41-1-2522660, FAX 41-1-2522870. Ed. Hans Gattiker. Pub. Marco Badilatti. Circ: 20,000.

HERITAGE LIVING. see *HISTORY—History Of Australasia And Other Areas*

333.72 USA
HERON CONSERVATION NEWSLETTER. Text in English. 1988. s-a. free. bk.rev. **Document type:** *Newsletter.*
Address: Patuxent Environmental Science Center, 12100 Beach Forest Rd, Laurel, MD 20708. TEL 601-232-7203. Ed. James Kushlan. Circ: 300.

333.72 USA
HI SIERRAN. Text in English. 1950. bi-m. USD 12 (effective 2005). adv. bk.rev. **Document type:** *Newsletter, Consumer.*
Related titles: Online - full text ed.
Published by: Sierra Club, San Diego Chapter, 3820 Ray St, San Diego, CA 92104-3623. TEL 619-299-1744, FAX 619-299-1742, http://sandiego.sierraclub.org/hi_sierran/index.html. Ed. Jimenez Pawlin. Circ: 16,000 (paid and controlled).

333.72 USA ISSN 0161-9896
HIGHLANDS VOICE. Text in English. 1967. m. free to members (effective 2005). bk.rev. charts; illus.; maps; stat. Index. 20 p./no.; back issues avail. **Document type:** *Newsletter, Academic/Scholarly.*
Related titles: E-mail ed.; Online - full text ed.
Published by: West Virginia Highlands Conservancy, Inc., PO Box 306, Charleston, WV 25321-0306. TEL 304-284-9548, http://www.wvhighlands.org. Ed. Bill Reed. Circ: 3,000.

333.72 JPN ISSN 0286-0627
HOKKAIDO NO SHIZEN/NATURE IN HOKKAIDO. Text in Japanese. a.
Published by: Hokkaido Shizen Hogo Kyokai/Nature Conservation Society of Hokkaido, 064 Kamori Bldg, Nishi (West) II, Kita (North) 3, Chuoh-ku (Central Ward), Sapporo, Japan.

333.72 USA ISSN 1098-8157
HOLISTIC MANAGEMENT IN PRACTICE. Text in English. 1983. bi-m. USD 30 domestic; USD 35 foreign (effective 2003). adv. bk.rev. charts; illus. back issues avail. **Document type:** *Newsletter.* **Description:** Examines issues related to community, family, economics and the environment using a holistic, regenerative approach.
Former titles (until 1998): Holistic Management Quarterly (1092-6623); (until 1996): Holistic Resource Management Quarterly (1069-2789); (until 1993): Holistic Resource Management Newsletter (1048-8472); (until 1989): Savory Letter
Published by: Center for Holistic Management, PO Box 7128, Albuquerque, NM 87194. TEL 505-842-5252, FAX 505-843-7900, anna@holisticmanagement.org, jodyb@holisticmanagement.org, http://www.holisticmanagement.org. Ed., Adv. contact Anne Adams TEL 505-842-5252. R&P Jody Butterfield. page USD 660; trim 10 x 7.25. Circ: 2,000.

333.72 USA ISSN 0073-3369
S900
HORACE M. ALBRIGHT CONSERVATION LECTURESHIP. Text in English. 1961. a. free. **Document type:** *Academic/Scholarly.*
Indexed: ForAb.
Published by: University of California at Berkeley, Department of Forestry and Resource Management, 145 Mulford Hall, Berkeley, CA 94720. TEL 415-642-0376.

333.72 JPN ISSN 0287-0606
N7350 CODEN: HKAGDY
HOZON KAGAKU/SCIENCE FOR CONSERVATION. Text in Japanese; Summaries in English, Japanese. 1964. a. **Document type:** *Bulletin.*
Indexed: A&ATA, ASFA, AgBio, ChemAb, ForAb, HerbAb, IndVet, PBA, PGegResA, RM&VM, RPP, RRTA, RefZh, RevApplEntom, SeedAb, WeedAb, ZooRec.
—BLDSC, CASDDS.
Published by: Agency for Cultural Affairs, Tokyo National Research Institute of Cultural Properties/Bunka-cho Tokyo Kokuritsu Bunkazai Kenkyujo Hozon Kagakubu, 13-27 Ueno Park, Taito-ku, Tokyo, 110, Japan. TEL 81-3-3823-2241, FAX 81-3-3828-2434, miura@tobunken.go.jp. Ed. Sadatoshi Miura.

HUMAN DIMENSIONS OF WILDLIFE. see *ENVIRONMENTAL STUDIES*

THE HUMAN ECOLOGIST. see *ENVIRONMENTAL STUDIES*

333.72 AUS ISSN 0085-1663
HUNTER VALLEY RESEARCH FOUNDATION. MONOGRAPHS. Text in English. 1959. irreg. price varies. **Document type:** *Monographic series.*
Indexed: ASI.
Published by: Hunter Valley Research Foundation, DC, PO Box 302, Hamilton, NSW 2303, Australia. TEL 61-49-69-4566, FAX 61-49-694566, oukhvrf@cc.newcastle.edu.au, http://www.hvrf.com.au.

333.72 AUS ISSN 0310-0111
HUNTER'S HILL TRUST JOURNAL. Text in English. 1971. 3/yr. AUD 15 to individuals (effective 2000). adv. bk.rev. back issues avail. **Document type:** *Newsletter.* **Description:** Covers environmental and architectural matters, especially regarding Hunters Hill, N.S.W., Australia.
Published by: Hunter's Hill Trust, PO Box 85, Hunters Hill, NSW 2110, Australia. TEL 61-2-98162627, FAX 61-2-98162627, http://www.interweb.com.au/hhti/. Ed., R&P Gil Wahlquist. Circ: 500 (paid).

333.73 USA ISSN 0018-8808
I C A S A L S NEWSLETTER. Text in English. 1968. s-a. free. bk.rev. illus. 12 p./no.; **Document type:** *Newsletter, Bibliography.*
—BLDSC (4360.280000), CISTI.
Published by: International Center for Arid and Semiarid Land Studies, Texas Tech Univ, Box 41036, Lubbock, TX 79409-1036. TEL 806-742-2218, FAX 806-742-1954. Ed. Idris R Traylor Jr. Circ: 3,000 (controlled).

333.72 USA
I P P L NEWS. Text in English. 1973. 3/yr. USD 20 (effective 2003). bk.rev. illus. 32 p./no. 3 cols./p.; back issues avail.; reprints avail. **Document type:** *Magazine.* **Description:** Deals with conservation and protection of primates.
Formerly (Until 1992): International Primate Protection League Newsletter (1040-3027)
Indexed: RefZh.
Published by: International Primate Protection League, PO Box 766, Summerville, SC 29484. TEL 843-871-2280, FAX 843-871-7988, info@ippl.org, http://www.ippl.org. Ed., R&P Shirley McGreal. Circ: 20,000.

333.73 USA
IDAHO BUREAU OF LAND MANAGEMENT TECHNICAL BULLETIN. Text in English. 1985. irreg., latest 1998. free. **Document type:** *Monographic series, Government.* **Description:** Contains information about natural resources.
Published by: U.S. Bureau of Land Management, Idaho State Office, 1387 S Vinnell Way, Boise, ID 83709. TEL 208-373-3827, FAX 208-373-3805, a1thom@id.blm,gov. Ed. Allan Thomas. Circ: 200 (controlled).

639 USA ISSN 0073-4527
IDAHO. DEPARTMENT OF FISH AND GAME. FEDERAL AID INVESTIGATION PROJECTS. PROGRESS REPORTS AND PUBLICATIONS. Text in English. 1948. irreg. (approx. a.). free. **Document type:** *Government.*
Related titles: Microfiche ed.
Published by: Department of Fish and Game, PO Box 25, Boise, ID 83707. TEL 208-334-3746, FAX 208-334-2148, dronayne@idfg.state.id.us, http://www.state.id.us/fishgame/fishgame.html. R&P Diane Ronayne. Circ: (controlled).

333.72 USA
IDAHO. DEPARTMENT OF FISH AND GAME. JOB COMPLETION REPORT. Text in English. irreg.
Published by: Department of Fish and Game, PO Box 25, Boise, ID 83707. TEL 208-334-3700, FAX 208-334-2148.

333.9 MLT
IL-KAMPANJA. Text in Maltese, English. q.
Published by: Nature Trust, P.O. Box 9, Valletta, CMR 01, Malta. info@naturetrustmalta.org, http://www.naturetrustmalta.org/.

333.95416 USA ISSN 1061-9801
ILLINOIS AUDUBON. Text in English. 1897. q. USD 25 (effective 2001). adv. bk.rev. stat. back issues avail. **Document type:** *Bulletin.*
Formerly: Illinois Audubon Bulletin
Indexed: SFA, WildRev.
Published by: Illinois Audubon Society, PO Box 2418, Danville, IL 61834-2418. TEL 217-446-5085, http://www.illinoisaudubon.org. Ed., R&P, Adv. contact Debbie Scott Newman. Circ: 3,000.

346.044 USA
ILLINOIS CONSERVATION LAW. Text in English. 1988. a. looseleaf. USD 21.95 (effective 2000). **Document type:** *Trade.* **Description:** Contains the complete, up-to-date Chapter 515 - Fish, and Chapter 520 - Wildlife, of the Illinois Compiled Statutes. Includes selected pertinent sections from other Chapters, which deal with laws related to conservation and wildlife.
Published by: Gould Publications, Inc. (Subsidiary of: LexisNexis), 1333 North US Hwy 17-92, Longwood, FL 32750-3724. TEL 407-695-9500, 800-717-7917, FAX 407-695-2906, info@gouldlaw.com, http://www.gouldlaw.com.

333.72 USA ISSN 0536-4132
ILLINOIS NATURAL HISTORY SURVEY REPORTS. Text in English. 1962. q. free. **Document type:** *Newsletter, Trade.* **Description:** Reports current research undertaken at the Illinois Natural History Survey, for a non-specialist audience.
Related titles: Online - full content ed.
Indexed: BiolDig, RefZh, SFA, WildRev.
Published by: Illinois Natural History Survey, Natural Resources Bldg, 607 E Peabody Dr, Champaign, IL 61820. TEL 217-244-2115, FAX 217-333-4949, rjohnson@inhs.uiuc.edu, http://www.inhs.uiuc.edu/chf/pub/surveyreports/sr-index.html. Ed. Charles Warwick. Circ: 2,200.

ILLINOIS PARKS & RECREATION. see *SPORTS AND GAMES—Outdoor Life*

333.72 USA ISSN 1058-9309
S932.I3
ILLINOIS STEWARD. Text in English. 1992. q. USD 10 domestic; USD 18 foreign (effective 2000). adv. illus. index. **Document type:** *Journal, Consumer.* **Description:** Articles pertaining to the understanding and care of Illinois' natural resources and heritage.
Published by: Illinois Stewardship Committee, W503 Turner Hall, 1102 S Goodwin Ave, Urbana, IL 61801. TEL 217-333-2778, FAX 217-244-3219, http://ilsteward.nres.uiuc.edu. Ed., R&P, Adv. contact Michael Bolin. Circ: 4,000.

C

333.95416 USA ISSN 0019-2317
ILLINOIS WILDLIFE∗ . Text in English. 1945. bi-m. USD 10
(effective 1999). adv. bk.rev. illus. **Document type:**
Newspaper.
Indexed: BiolDig.
Published by: Illinois Wildlife Federation, 2216 Troy Rd,
Edwardsville, IL 62025-2562. TEL 217-748-6365, FAX
217-748-6304, wildlife@htb.net, http://www.htb.net/~wildlife.
Ed., Pub. Tom Mills. R&P, Adv. contact Deborah Schuler. Circ:
12,500 (controlled).

333.72 BRA
IMAGENS DA AMAZONIA. Text in Portuguese. bi-m.
Published by: Editora Ecopress, Rua Jose Bonifacio 209, Sala
1009, Sao Paulo, SP 01003-902, Brazil. TEL 55-11-352221,
FAX 55-11-342059. Ed. Tania Nomura.

333.9 MLT
IN-NATURA. Text in English. irreg.
Published by: Nature Trust, P.O. Box 9, Valletta, CMR 01, Malta.
info@naturetrustmalta.org, http://www.naturetrustmalta.org/.

333.78 GBR ISSN 0966-2200
IN PRACTICE. Variant title: Ecology and Environmental
Management in Practice. Text in English. 1991. q. GBP 30
domestic to non-members; GBP 40 foreign to non-members
(effective 2003). adv. bk.rev. bibl.; illus. 24 p./no. 2 cols./p.;
back issues avail. **Document type:** *Bulletin,*
Academic/Scholarly. **Description:** Contains news and articles
of interest to professional ecologists. Offers vocational advice
and covers professional standards.
Published by: Institute of Ecology and Environmental
Management, 45 Southgate St, Winchester, Hants SO23 9EH,
United Kingdom. TEL 44-1962-868626, FAX 44-1962-868625,
enquiries@ieem.demon.co.uk, http://www.ieem.org.uk. Ed.,
Adv. contact Jim Thompson. page GBP 320; trim 184 x 260.
Circ: 1,100.

INDIAN FERN JOURNAL; an international journal of pteridology.
see *BIOLOGY—Botany*

INDIAN JOURNAL OF SOIL CONSERVATION. (Indian J. Soil.
Cons.) see *AGRICULTURE—Crop Production And Soil*

333.72 USA
THE INDIANA CONSERVANCY DISTRICT DIRECTORY. Text in
English. a. free. **Document type:** *Government.*
Published by: Indiana Department of Natural Resources, Division
of Water, 402 W Washington St, Rm W264, Indianapolis, IN
46204. TEL 317-232-4160, 877-928-3955,
http://www.state.in.us/dnr/water.

INDIANA. DEPARTMENT OF NATURAL RESOURCES.
DIVISION OF WATER. BULLETIN. see *WATER*
RESOURCES

333.72 USA
INDIANA. DEPARTMENT OF NATURAL RESOURCES.
DIVISION OF WATER. SHORELINES. Text in English. q. free.
Document type: *Government.*
Published by: Indiana Department of Natural Resources, Division
of Water, 402 W Washington St, Rm W264, Indianapolis, IN
46204. TEL 317-232-4160, 877-928-3955,
http://www.state.in.us/dnr/water.

363.70029 DEU
INFORMATION SOURCES IN ENVIRONMENTAL PROTECTION.
Text in English. 1996. irreg. USD 75 per vol. in North America
(effective 2001). bibl. **Document type:** *Directory, Bibliography.*
Description: Helps reference librarians identify key sources of
primary information in conservation issues and environmental
protection.
Related titles: ♦ Series: Information Sources for the Press and
Broadcast Media; ♦ Information Sources in Chemistry; ♦
Information Sources in Finance and Banking; ♦ Information
Sources in the Life Sciences; ♦ Information Sources in Grey
Literature; ♦ Information Sources in Physics; ♦ Guides to
Information Sources Series; ♦ Information Sources in
Architecture and Construction; ♦ Information Sources in
Development Studies; ♦ Information Sources in Engineering;
♦ Information Sources in Law; ♦ Information Sources in
Official Publications.
Published by: K.G. Saur Verlag GmbH (Subsidiary of: Gale
Group), Ortlerstr 8, Munchen, 81373, Germany. TEL
49-89-769020, FAX 49-89-76902150, info@saur.de,
http://www.saur.de. Eds. Judith Deschamps, Selwyn Eagle.

502.3 DEU ISSN 0934-7135
INFORMATIONSDIENST NATURSCHUTZ NIEDERSACHSEN.
Text in German. 1981. irreg. **Document type:** *Monographic*
series, Academic/Scholarly.
Formerly (until 1987): Informationsdienst Naturschutz (0724-2646)
Published by: Niedersaechsisches Landesamt fuer Oekologie,
Postfach 101062, Hildesheim, 31110, Germany. TEL
49-5121-509-0, FAX 49-5121-509196,
poststelle@nloe.niedersachsen.de, http://jupiter.nloe.de.

INSTITUTO ECUATORIANO DE CIENCIAS NATURALES.
CONTRIBUCIONES. see *SCIENCES: COMPREHENSIVE*
WORKS

333.95416 USA ISSN 0161-3332
SK352
INTERNATIONAL ASSOCIATION OF FISH AND WILDLIFE
AGENCIES. PROCEEDINGS OF THE CONVENTION. Text in
English. 1946. a. USD 20 (effective 2000). illus. back issues
avail. **Document type:** *Proceedings.*
Formerly: Convention of the International Association of Fish and
Wildlife Agencies (0163-8653)
—Linda Hall.
Published by: International Association of Fish and Wildlife
Agencies, 444 N. Capitol St NW, Ste. 725, Washington, DC
20001-1553. TEL 202-624-7890, FAX 202-624-7891,
iafwa@sso.org, http://www.sso.org/iafwa/. Ed. W Harold
Nesbitt. Circ: 600 (paid).

INTERNATIONAL BALTIC SEA FISHERY COMMISSION.
PROCEEDINGS. see *BIOLOGY*

INTERNATIONAL BEAR NEWS. see *BIOLOGY—Zoology*

INTERNATIONAL COMMISSION FOR THE CONSERVATION OF
ATLANTIC TUNAS. REPORT. see *BIOLOGY—Zoology*

333.72 USA
INTERNATIONAL EROSION CONTROL ASSOCIATION.
CONFERENCE PROCEEDINGS (CD-ROM). Text in English.
1974. a. USD 55 per issue (effective 2004). back issues avail.
Document type: *Proceedings, Academic/Scholarly.*
Former titles (until 2001): International Erosion Control
Association. Conference Proceedings (Print Edition)
(1092-2806); (until 1996): Erosion Control (1050-2106)
Media: CD-ROM.
—BLDSC (6842.980400).
Published by: International Erosion Control Association, PO Box
4904, Steamboat Springs, CO 80477-4904. TEL
970-879-3010, 800-455-4322, FAX 970-879-8563,
ecinfo@ieca.org, http://www.ieca.org. Ed. David Williams. Circ:
1,500.

333.72 USA
INTERNATIONAL EROSION CONTROL ASSOCIATION.
MID-ATLANTIC CHAPTER NEWSLETTER. Text in English.
adv. **Document type:** *Newsletter, Trade.*
Published by: International Erosion Control Association,
Mid-Atlantic Chapter, c/o Butch Wilson, 3912 Eaton Dr,
Jarrettsville, MD 21084-1314. TEL 410-316-0801,
scotsman@iximd.com, http://www.ieca.8m.com.

INTERNATIONAL EROSION CONTROL ASSOCIATION.
PRODUCTS & SERVICES DIRECTORY. see *BUSINESS AND*
ECONOMICS—Trade And Industrial Directories

INTERNATIONAL INSTITUTE FOR ENVIRONMENT AND
DEVELOPMENT. DISCUSSION PAPER. see *AGRICULTURE*

INTERNATIONAL INSTITUTE FOR ENVIRONMENT AND
DEVELOPMENT. DRYLANDS PAPER. see
ENVIRONMENTAL STUDIES

INTERNATIONAL INSTITUTE FOR ENVIRONMENT AND
DEVELOPMENT. PASTORAL LAND TENURE SERIES. see
ENVIRONMENTAL STUDIES

INTERNATIONAL INSTITUTE FOR ENVIRONMENT AND
DEVELOPMENT. SUSTAINABLE AGRICULTURE
PROGRAMME. HIDDEN HARVEST RESEARCH SERIES.
see *AGRICULTURE—Agricultural Economics*

639.9 GBR ISSN 1361-8628
INTERNATIONAL INSTITUTE FOR ENVIRONMENT AND
DEVELOPMENT. WILDLIFE AND DEVELOPMENT SERIES.
Text in English. 1995. irreg., latest vol.18, 2003. price varies.
Document type: *Monographic series.*
Indexed: RRTA, S&F, WAE&RSA.
Published by: (International Institute for Environment and
Development, Biodiversity and Livelihood Group), International
Institute for Environment and Development, 3 Endsleigh St,
London, WC1H 0DD, United Kingdom. TEL 44-20-73882117,
FAX 44-20-73882826, info@iied.org, http://www.iied.org/blg/
pubs/wilddev.html.

INTERNATIONAL JOURNAL OF ENVIRONMENT AND
POLLUTION; science - engineering - ecological economics -
policy. see *ENVIRONMENTAL STUDIES—Pollution*

INTERNATIONAL JOURNAL OF GLOBAL ENERGY ISSUES.
see *ENERGY*

INTERNATIONAL JOURNAL OF RURAL STUDIES. see
SOCIOLOGY

INTERNATIONAL JOURNAL OF SUSTAINABLE
DEVELOPMENT. see *ENVIRONMENTAL STUDIES*

333.95416 USA ISSN 1086-5519
QH75.A1
INTERNATIONAL JOURNAL OF WILDERNESS. Text in English.
1995. 3/yr. USD 35 to individuals; USD 55 to institutions; USD
25 to students (effective 2004). adv. back issues avail.
Document type: *Magazine, Consumer.* **Description:** Offers a
forum for reporting and discussing wilderness ideas and
events; planning, management and allocation strategies;
education; and research and policy aspects of wilderness
stewardship.
Indexed: ForAb, I&DA, PGegResA, RDA, RRTA, S&F,
WAE&RSA, WeedAb, WildRev, ZooRec.
—BLDSC (4542.701230). CCC.
Published by: (The Wild), Fulcrum Publishing, 16100 Table
Mountain Pkwy, 300, Golden, CO 80403. TEL 303-277-1623,
800-992-2908, FAX 303-279-7111, 800-726-7112,
fulcrum@fulcrum-books.com, http://ijw.wilderness.net/,
http://www.fulcrum-books.com. Ed. John C Hendee. R&P, Adv.
contact Vance Martin. B&W page USD 400; trim 8 x 10. Circ:
600 (paid); 900 (controlled).

333.72 USA ISSN 1046-8366
THE INTERNATIONAL PERMACULTURE SOLUTIONS
JOURNAL. Variant title: T I P S Journal. Text in English. irreg.
USD 25 (effective 2000). **Document type:** *Journal, Consumer.*
Description: Provides information, ideas, and tools for
solutions to the environmental crisis.
Supersedes in part (in 1990): T I P S Y: International
Permaculture Species Yearbook (0896-5781)
Indexed: WAE&RSA.
Published by: Yankee Permaculture, Hemenway Permaculture,
Box 52, Sparr, FL 32192-0052. permacultur@aol.com. Ed.,
R&P Dan Hemenway.

INTERNATIONAL PETROLEUM INDUSTRY ENVIRONMENTAL
CONSERVATION ASSOCIATION. REPORT SERIES. see
PETROLEUM AND GAS

333.95416 USA
INTERNATIONAL TOUR GUIDE. Text in English. a. **Document**
type: *Magazine, Consumer.*
Published by: (Texas Department of Economic Development),
Emmis Communications Custom Publishing, PO Box 1569,
Austin, TX 78767-1569. TEL 512-320-6901, FAX
512-476-9007. Circ: 30,000 (controlled).

333.9 CHE
INTERNATIONAL UNION FOR CONSERVATION OF NATURE
AND NATURAL RESOURCES. SPECIES SURVIVAL
COMMISSION - CROCODILE SPECIALIST GROUP
NEWSLETTER. Text in English. 4/yr. **Document type:**
Newsletter.
Published by: (Species Survival Commission - Crocodile
Specialist Group), International Union for Conservation of
Nature and Natural Resources, Rue Mauverney 28, Gland,
1196, Switzerland. TEL 41-22-9990001, FAX 41-22-9990002,
mail@hq.iucn.org, http://www.flmnh.ufl.edu/natsci/herpetology/
crocs. **Subscr. to:** Dr. J.P. Ross, Florida Museum of Natural
History, Box 117800, Gainesville, FL 32601. TEL
904-392-9367.

333.72 CHE
INTERNATIONAL UNION FOR CONSERVATION OF NATURE
AND NATURAL RESOURCES. SPECIES SURVIVAL
COMMISSION - DEER SPECIALIST GROUP. NEWSLETTER.
Text in English. 1975. a. **Document type:** *Newsletter.*
Published by: (Species Survival Commission - Deer Specialist
Group), International Union for Conservation of Nature and
Natural Resources, Rue Mauverney 28, Gland, 1196,
Switzerland. TEL 41-22-9990001, FAX 41-22-9990002,
mail@hq.iucn.org. **Subscr. to:** Dr. C.M. Wemmer, National
Zoological Park, Front Royal, VA 22630.

333.72 CHE
INTERNATIONAL UNION FOR CONSERVATION OF NATURE
AND NATURAL RESOURCES. SPECIES SURVIVAL
COMMISSION - HYAENA SPECIALIST GROUP BULLETIN.
Text in English. irreg., latest 1993. **Document type:** *Bulletin.*
Published by: (Species Survival Commission - Hyaena Specialist
Group), International Union for Conservation of Nature and
Natural Resources, Rue Mauverney 28, Gland, 1196,
Switzerland. TEL 41-22-9990001, FAX 41-22-9990002,
mail@hq.iucn.org. **Subscr. to:** Dr. M.G.L. Mills, Kruger
National Park, Private Bag X402, Skukuza 1350, South Africa.

333.72 CHE ISSN 1023-9030
INTERNATIONAL UNION FOR CONSERVATION OF NATURE
AND NATURAL RESOURCES. SPECIES SURVIVAL
COMMISSION - OTTER SPECIALIST GROUP BULLETIN.
Text in English. 1986. s-a. **Document type:** *Bulletin.*
Indexed: ZooRec.
Published by: (Species Survival Group - Otter Specialist Group),
International Union for Conservation of Nature and Natural
Resources, Rue Mauverney 28, Gland, 1196, Switzerland.
TEL 41-22-9990001, FAX 41-22-9990002, mail@hq.iucn.org.
Subscr. to: Dr. Arno Gutleb, Institute for Medical Chemistry,
University of Veterinary Medicine, Linke Bahngasse 11,
Vienna, W 1030, Austria.

C

▼ *new title* ➤ *refereed* ∗ *unverified* ♦ *full entry avail.*

333.9 USA
INTERNATIONAL UNION FOR CONSERVATION OF NATURE AND NATURAL RESOURCES. SPECIES SURVIVAL COMMISSION - SPECIALIST GROUP ON STORKS, IBISES, AND SPOONBILLS NEWSLETTER. Text in English. 1988. 2/yr. **Document type:** *Newsletter.*
Published by: (Species Survival Commission - Specialist Group on Storks, Ibises, and Spoonbills), International Union for Conservation of Nature and Natural Resources, c/o Malcolm Coulter, SREL, Drawer E, Aiken, SC 29802.

333.72 CHE
INTERNATIONAL UNION FOR CONSERVATION OF NATURE AND NATURAL RESOURCES. SPECIES SURVIVAL COMMISSION - VETERINARY SPECIALIST GROUP. NEWSLETTER. Text in English. a. USD 5 (effective 2000). **Document type:** *Newsletter.*
Published by: International Union for Conservation of Nature and Natural Resources, Rue Mauverney 28, Gland, 1196, Switzerland. TEL 41-22-9990001, FAX 41-22-9990002, mail@hq.iucn.org. **Subscr. to:** Dr. M. Woodford, 2440 Virginia Ave, N W, USA, Washington, DC 20037.

INTERNATIONAL WHALING COMMISSION. ANNUAL REPORT. see *BIOLOGY—Zoology*

333.95416 USA ISSN 0020-9112
QL81.5 CODEN: INWLAI
INTERNATIONAL WILDLIFE; dedicated to the conservation of the world's natural resources. Text in English. 1971. bi-m. incl. with membership. adv. charts; illus.; pat. index. reprint service avail. from PQC. **Document type:** *Magazine.* **Description:** Showcases the splendor of the natural world and its inhabitants. Discusses environmental issues and offers solutions to problems.
Related titles: Microfiche ed.: (from NBI); Microform ed.: (from PQC); Online - full text ed.: (from bigchalk, EBSCO Publishing, Florida Center for Library Automation, Gale Group, H.W. Wilson, Micromedia ProQuest, Northern Light Technology, Inc., O C L C Online Computer Library Center, Inc., ProQuest Information & Learning).
Indexed: APD, ASFA, Acal, BiolAb, BiolDig, CBCARef, CBPI, CPerl, EPB, ESPM, EnvAb, GSI, ICM, ISR, JHMA, MASUSE, MEA&I, MagInd, PMR, PollutAb, RGAb, RGPR, RGYP, RI-1, RI-2, SWRA, TOM, WBA, WMB, WildRev, ZooRec.
—BLDSC (4552.120000), IE, Infotrieve, Linda Hall.
Published by: National Wildlife Federation, 11100 Wildlife Center Dr., Reston, VA 20190-5362. TEL 703-790-4000, FAX 703-790-4544, pubs@nwf.org, http://www.nwf.org. Ed. Jon Fischer. Pub. Pub National Wildlife Federation. R&P Kelly Hartley TEL 703-790-4510. Adv. contact Thuy Senser. Circ: 200,000.

599.773 USA ISSN 1089-683X
INTERNATIONAL WOLF; the quarterly publication of the International Wolf Center. Text in English. 1990. q. USD 30; USD 6 newsstand/cover (effective 2002). adv. bk.rev. illus. reprints avail. **Document type:** *Magazine, Consumer.* **Description:** Covers international reintroduction plans and updates, human/wolf contact stories, wolf research updates, future wolf conferences and events, literature reviews and ongoing international Wolf Center and other wolf organizational activities.
Published by: International Wolf Center, 12615 County Road 9., # 200, Minneapolis, MN 55441-1248. TEL 763-560-7374, FAX 763-560-7368, mplspack@wolf.org, http://www.wolf.org. Ed., R&P Mary Ortiz. Adv. contact Carissa Knaack. B&W page USD 595, color page USD 695. Circ: 10,000.

333.7844 DEU ISSN 1011-1263
INTERNATIONALE GEWAESSERSCHUTZKOMMISSION FUER DEN BODENSEE. BERICHTE. Text in German. irreg., latest vol.52, 2000. **Document type:** *Monographic series, Academic/Scholarly.*
Published by: Internationale Gewaesserschutzkommission fuer den Bodensee, Argenweg 50/1, Langenargen, 88085, Germany. TEL 49-711-1261533, http://www.igkb.de.

333.7844 DEU ISSN 1011-1271
INTERNATIONALE GEWAESSERSCHUTZKOMMISSION FUER DEN BODENSEE. JAHRESBERICHT. Text in German. a. **Document type:** *Yearbook, Academic/Scholarly.*
Indexed: ESPM.
Published by: Internationale Gewaesserschutzkommission fuer den Bodensee, Argenweg 50/1, Langenargen, 88085, Germany. TEL 49-711-1261533, http://www.igkb.de. Ed. Bruno Blattner.

333.7845 DEU ISSN 1607-3657
INTERNATIONALE KOMMISSION ZUM SCHUTZE DES RHEINS. TAETIGKEITSBERICHT. Text in French. 1971. a. **Document type:** *Journal, Academic/Scholarly.* **Description:** Publishes research and papers on the problems and solutions of water protection for the Rhine river.
Supersedes in part: Internationale Kommission zum Schutze des Rheins gegen Verunreinigung. Taetigkeitsbericht (0173-6531)
Related titles: ◆ French ed.: Commission Internationale pour la Protection du Rhin. Rapport d'Activite. ISSN 1607-3649.
Published by: Internationale Kommission zum Schutze des Rheins/Commission Internationale pour la Protection du Rhin - Internationale Commissie ter Bescherming van de Rijn, Hohenzollernstr. 18, Koblenz, 56068, Germany. TEL 49-261-12495, FAX 49-261-36572, sekretariat@iksr.de, http://www.iksr.org.

INZHENERNAYA EKOLOGIYA. see *ENGINEERING*

333.7 USA ISSN 0021-0471
HC107.I7
IOWA CONSERVATIONIST. Text in English. 1942. bi-m. USD 12 (effective 2005). bk.rev. abstr.; charts; illus.; stat.; tr.mk. **Document type:** *Magazine.*
Indexed: BiolAb, SFA, WildRev, ZooRec.
—CISTI, Linda Hall.
Published by: Iowa Department of Natural Resources, Wallace State Office Bldg, 502 E Ninth St, Des Moines, IA 50319-0034. TEL 515-281-5918, FAX 515-281-8895, conservationist@dnr.state.ia.us, http://www.iowadnr.com/conservationist, http://www.state.ia.us/government/dnr/. Ed. Roger Sparks. Circ: 70,000.

333.72 639.2 USA
IOWA DEPARTMENT OF NATURAL RESOURCES. COMPLETION REPORT. Text in English. irreg.
Formerly: Iowa Conservation Commission. Completion Report
Published by: Iowa Department of Natural Resources, Wallace State Office Bldg, 502 E Ninth St, Des Moines, IA 50319-0034. TEL 515-281-5918, http://www.state.ia.us/government/dnr/.

363.7 USA
IOWA SIERRAN. Text in English. q. USD 5 to non-members. adv. **Description:** Provides information about club activities.
Published by: Sierra Club, Iowa Chapter, 3839 Merle Hay Rd, Ste 280, Des Moines, IA 53010. TEL 515-277-8868, iowa.chapter@sierraclub.org. Ed. Leigh Rigby Adcock.

333.95416 GBR ISSN 0260-986X
IRISH HARE. Text in English. 1978. 3/yr. membership. adv. bk.rev. illus. **Document type:** *Newsletter.*
Published by: Ulster Wildlife Trust, 3 New Line, Crossgar, Downpatrick, BT30 9EP, United Kingdom. Ed. William McNamara. Circ: 1,200.

333.72 JPN ISSN 0286-8660
ISHIKAWA-KEN HAKUSAN SHIZEN HOGO SENTA KENKYU HOKOKU/HAKUSAN NATURE CONSERVATION CENTER. ANNUAL REPORT. Text in Japanese; Summaries in English, Japanese. 1974. a. **Document type:** *Academic/Scholarly.*
Published by: Ishikawa-ken Hakusan Shizen Hogo Senta/Hakusan Nature Conservation Center, Ishikawa Prefecture, Kinameri, Yoshinodanimura, Ishikawa-gun, Ishikawa-ken 920-23, Japan. TEL 81-7619-5-5321, FAX 81-7619-5-5323.

ISLAND. see *LITERARY AND POLITICAL REVIEWS*

578.0942962 GBR ISSN 1367-6466
THE ISLAND NATURALIST. Text in English. 1981. 2/yr. GBP 10 (effective 2003). **Document type:** *Bulletin, Consumer.* **Description:** Contains annual bird reports and articles on natural history concerning the Pembrokeshire islands of Skokholm and Skomer.
Formerly (until 1995): Skomer and Skokholm Bulletin (0955-1735)
Indexed: ZooRec.
Published by: Wildlife Trust of South and West Wales, The Nature Centre, Tondu, Nr Brigend, CF32 0EH, United Kingdom. TEL 44-1656-724100, FAX 44-1656-726980, islandnaturalist@tesco.net, information@wtsww.cix.co.uk, http://www.wildlifetrust.org.uk/wtsww/. Ed. David Saunders. Circ: 400 (controlled).

ISTITUTO VENETO DI SCIENZE, LETTERE ED ARTI. SUMMER SCHOOL OF ENVIRONMENTAL DYNAMICS. ENVIRONMENTAL SERIES. see *ENVIRONMENTAL STUDIES*

639.9 GBR ISSN 0963-8091
J N C C REPORTS. Text in English. 1991. irreg., latest 2002. price varies. **Document type:** *Academic/Scholarly.*
Indexed: ForAb, S&F, ZooRec.
—BLDSC (7527.315500), IE.
Published by: Joint Nature Conservation Committee, Monkstone House, City Rd, Peterborough, Cambs PE1 1JY, United Kingdom. TEL 44-1803-865913, FAX 44-1803-865280, cherry-ann.vickery@jncc.gov.uk, http://www.jncc.gov.uk. **Dist. by:** Natural History Book Service Ltd., 2-3 Wills Rd, Totnes, Devon TQ9 5XN, United Kingdom. TEL 44-1803-865913, FAX 44-1803-865280, nhbs@nhbs.co.uk, http://www.nhbs.co.uk.

577 JAM ISSN 1018-1261
JAMAICA NATURALIST. Text in English. 1991. s-a. JMD 120, USD 15. adv. bk.rev. back issues avail.; reprints avail. **Description:** Covers fauna and flora of Jamaica, natural heritage, conservation of tropical biodiversity, and sustainable use of natural resources.
Indexed: ZooRec.
Published by: Natural History Society of Jamaica, c/o Peter Vogel Ed., Department of Zoology, University of the West Indies, W.I., Kingston, 7, Jamaica. TEL 809-927-1202, FAX 809-927-1640. Adv. contact Adam Hyde. Circ: 2,000.

333.72 USA
JERSEY SIERRAN. Text in English. bi-m. USD 7.50 to non-members. adv. bk.rev. **Description:** Covers conservation issues on a statewide and national basis, including information on the state legislative agenda. Also lists club hikes, meetings, and events statewide.
Published by: Sierra Club, New Jersey Chapter, 57 Mountain Ave, Princeton, NJ 08540. TEL 609-924-3141. Ed. Mary Penney. Circ: 15,000.

JOURNAL FOR NATURE CONSERVATION. see *ENVIRONMENTAL STUDIES*

JOURNAL OF ENVIRONMENTAL PROTECTION AND ECOLOGY. see *ENVIRONMENTAL STUDIES*

JOURNAL OF INDUSTRIAL POLLUTION CONTROL. see *ENVIRONMENTAL STUDIES*

JOURNAL OF INTERNATIONAL WILDLIFE LAW AND POLICY. see *ENVIRONMENTAL STUDIES*

JOURNAL OF MEDITERRANEAN ECOLOGY. see *ENVIRONMENTAL STUDIES*

333.72 IND ISSN 0970-5945
QH75.A1 CODEN: JNCOEA
JOURNAL OF NATURE CONSERVATION; an international journal devoted to nature, natural resource conservation and environment. Text in English. 1989. s-a. INR 200 domestic to individuals; USD 50 foreign to individuals; INR 300 domestic to institutions; USD 100 foreign to institutions. adv. bk.rev. **Document type:** *Academic/Scholarly.*
Indexed: ASFA, ESPM, EntAb, ZooRec.
—BLDSC (5021.302000).
Address: c/o G.R. Shukla Mng. Ed., 1351 South Civil Lines, Circular Rd., Charan Singh Colony, Muzaffarnagar, Uttar Pradesh 251 001, India. TEL 0131-401414. Ed. S R Verma. Adv. contact G R Shukla. page INR 500, page USD 175. Circ: 300.

JOURNAL OF PARK AND RECREATION ADMINISTRATION (ONLINE EDITION). see *SPORTS AND GAMES—Outdoor Life*

JOURNAL OF PRACTICAL ECOLOGY & CONSERVATION. see *BIOLOGY*

JOURNAL OF PRACTICAL ECOLOGY & CONSERVATION. SPECIAL PUBLICATION. see *BIOLOGY*

JOURNAL OF RURAL STUDIES. see *SOCIOLOGY*

333.72 IND ISSN 0022-457X
S954.I5 CODEN: JSWIAL
➤ **JOURNAL OF SOIL AND WATER CONSERVATION IN INDIA.** Text in English. 1952. 2/yr. INR 100 domestic to individuals; USD 70 foreign to individuals; INR 50 domestic to institutions; USD 500 foreign to institutions (effective 1999). adv. charts; illus. back issues avail. **Document type:** *Academic/Scholarly.* **Description:** Aimed at the scientific community, the developing agencies and policy managers. Includes assessments of natural resources, conservation, technical developments, socio-economic management strategies and such others.
Indexed: BiolAb, ChemAb, SSCI.
—CASDDS, CISTI, Linda Hall.
Published by: All India Soil & Land Use Survey, I.A.R.I Buildings, New Delhi, 110 012, India. TEL 91-11-5743811, aislus@vsnl.com. Ed. T K Sarkar. R&P S N Das TEL 91-11-5785263. Circ: 1,500 (controlled).

➤ **JOURNAL OF SUSTAINABLE AGRICULTURE**; innovations for the long-term and lasting maintenance and enhancement of agricultural resources, production and environmental quality. see *AGRICULTURE*

➤ **JOURNAL OF SUSTAINABLE DEVELOPMENT IN AFRICA.** see *ENVIRONMENTAL STUDIES*

➤ **JOURNAL OF WILDLIFE DISEASES.** see *VETERINARY SCIENCE*

333.95416 USA ISSN 0022-541X
SK351 CODEN: JWMAA9
➤ **THE JOURNAL OF WILDLIFE MANAGEMENT.** Text in English. 1937. q. USD 140 in North America to institutions; USD 155 elsewhere to institutions (effective 2004). bk.rev. bibl.; charts; illus.; stat.; abstr. index. 2 cols./p.; back issues avail.; reprint service avail. from PQC. **Document type:** *Journal, Academic/Scholarly.* **Description:** Disseminates scientific research and management information relating to all phases of wildlife science and management.
Related titles: Microform ed.: (from PQC); Online - full text ed.: (from ProQuest Information & Learning).

Indexed: AEA, ASCA, ASFA, AgBio, Agr, AgrForAb, AnBeAb, AnBrAb, ApEcolAb, B&AI, BIOBASE, BIOSIS Prev, BiolAb, CIS, CRFR, Cadscan, ChemAb, CurCont, DSA, EPB, ESPM, EnerRev, ExcerpMed, FCA, FPA, FoVS&M, ForAb, GEOBASE, GSI, HelmAb, HerbAb, HortAb, I&DA, IAA, IABS, IBR, INIS AtomInd, ISR, IndVet, KWIWR, LeadAb, MEA&I, MaizeAb, NutrAb, PGegResA, PN&I, PoultAb, ProtozoAb, RA&MP, RM&VM, RRTA, RevApplEntom, RiceAb, S&F, SCI, SFA, SWRA, SeedAb, SoyAb, TriticAb, VetBull, W&CBA, WAE&RSA, WLA, WeedAb, WildRev, Zincscan, ZooRec.
—BLDSC (5072.630000), CASDDS, CISTI, IE, Infotrieve, ingenta, Linda Hall.
Published by: The Wildlife Society, 5410 Grosvenor Ln, Ste 200, Bethesda, MD 20814. TEL 301-897-9770, FAX 301-530-2471, tws@wildlife.org, http://www.wildlife.org/publications/index.cfm?tname=journal. Ed. R Scott Lutz. R&P Yanin Walker. Circ: 7,000.

➤ **JUNGLE**; a journal for promotion of tourism and nature study. see *TRAVEL AND TOURISM*

333.95416 AUS
JUNIOR NATURALIST. Text in English. m.
Published by: Australian Wildlife Club, 2 Coolgardie Place, Sutherland, NSW 2232, Australia.

333.72 JPN ISSN 0914-8744
KANAGAWA-KENRITSU SHIZEN HOGO SENTA HOKOKU/KANAGAWA PREFECTURAL NATURE CONSERVATION CENTER. BULLETIN. Text in Japanese. 1984. a. **Description:** Presents research reports of the center.
Published by: Kanagawa-kenritsu Shizen Hogo Senta, 657 Nanasawa, Atsugi-shi, Kanagawa-ken 243-0121, Japan. TEL 81-462-48-0323, FAX 81-462-48-2560.

333.72 JPN
KANAGAWA SHIZEN HOZEN KENKYUKAI HOKOKUSHO/ KANAGAWA NATURAL PRESERVATION SOCIETY. JOURNAL. Text in Japanese; Summaries in English, Japanese. 1981. a.
Published by: Kanagawa Shizen Hozen Kenkyukai/Kanagawa Natural Preservation Society, c/o Mr Hidemaro Toshima, 27-5 Kamiyabe 5-chome, Sagamihara-shi, Kanagawa-ken 229-0001, Japan.

KANSAS SCHOOL NATURALIST. see *SCIENCES: COMPREHENSIVE WORKS*

333.783 USA ISSN 0898-6975
SK397 CODEN: KWPAE5
KANSAS WILDLIFE & PARKS. Text in English. 1938. bi-m. USD 10 (effective 2000). bk.rev. illus. **Description:** Main objective is to increase individual awareness of responsibility towards the land by examining the issue of conservation and the use of natural resources.
Former titles: Kansas Wildlife (0279-9030); Kansas Fish and Game (0022-8591)
Indexed: SFA, WildRev, ZooRec.
Published by: Department of Wildlife & Parks, Information - Education, 512 S E 25th Ave, Pratt, KS 67124-8174. TEL 316-672-5911, FAX 316-672-6020. Ed. Mike Miller. Circ: 46,000.

333.95416 USA ISSN 1059-9177
SK1
KENTUCKY AFIELD. Text in English. 1945. q. USD 5 (effective 2005). bk.rev. charts; illus. **Document type:** *Magazine, Consumer.* **Description:** Filled with tips and information about Kentucky's outdoors.
Formerly (until 1992): Kentucky Happy Hunting Ground (0023-0235)
Indexed: SFA, WildRev.
Published by: Kentucky Department of Fish and Wildlife Resources, Division of Information and Education, 1 Game Farm Rd, Frankfort, KY 40601. TEL 502-564-4336, 800-858-1549, FAX 502-564-6508, http://fw.ky.gov/navigation.asp?cid=120&NavPath=C105, http://www.state.ky.us/agencies/fw/kdfwr/htm. Ed. Dave Baker. Circ: 40,000 (paid and controlled).

346.044 USA
KENTUCKY FISH AND WILDLIFE STATUTES. Text in English. 1996. irreg., latest 2000. looseleaf. USD 35 (effective 2003). 114 p./no.; **Description:** Contains statutes covering fish and wildlife resources, boats and boating, and more.
Published by: Michie Company (Subsidiary of: LexisNexis North America), 701 E Water St, Charlottesville, VA 22902-5389. TEL 434-972-7600, 800-446-3410, FAX 434-972-7677, http://www.michie.com.

333.72 USA ISSN 1545-6102
KEYSTONE OUTDOORS. Text in English. q. (bi-m. until 2003).
Formerly (until 2000): Keystone Conservationist
Related titles: Online - full text ed.: (from EBSCO Publishing).
Indexed: MASUSE.
Published by: Penn-Wild Publications, Inc., 207 House Ave, Ste 103, Camp Hill, PA 17011-2308.

KIDSPOWER. see *CHILDREN AND YOUTH—For*

333.95416 ZMB ISSN 1015-5546
KOBUS. Text in English. 1987. bi-m. USD 20. **Document type:** *Newsletter.*
Published by: Wildlife Conservation Society of Zambia, PO Box 30255, Lusaka, Zambia. TEL 260-01-254226, FAX 260-01-222906. Ed. Mwape Sichilongo.

333.783 ZAF ISSN 0075-6458
QL337.S65 CODEN: KOEDB2
➤ **KOEDOE**; research journal for national parks in the Republic of South Africa. Text in English. 1958. a. ZAR 60 foreign (effective 2005); ZAR 45 - 60 domestic (effective 2000). bk.rev. abstr.; bibl.; charts. cum.index: vols.1-25 in vol.25, 1982; vols.26-35 in vol.35, 1992. Supplement avail. **Document type:** *Academic/Scholarly.* **Description:** Presents original papers concerned with the perpetuation of wildlife and the conservation of biological and associated natural resources.
Indexed: ASFA, AgrForAb, AnBeAb, ApEcolAb, BIOSIS Prev, BioCN&I, BiolAb, ESPM, EnvAb, FCA, FPA, ForAb, GEOBASE, HerbAb, HortAb, I&DA, IBR, IBZ, ISAP, IndVet, KWIWR, NemAb, NutrAb, OrnHort, PBA, PGegResA, RA&MP, RDA, RRTA, RefZh, RevApplEntom, S&F, SFA, SWRA, SeedAb, TDB, VetBull, WAE&RSA, WeedAb, WildRev, ZooRec.
—CIS.
Published by: South African National Parks/Suid-Afrikaanse Nasionale Parke, PO Box 787, Pretoria, 0001, South Africa. TEL 27-12-343-9770, FAX 27-12-343-2832, TELEX 321931 SA, kobier@parks-sa.ca.za, http://www.parks-sa.co.za. Ed. J C Rautenbach. Circ: 1,200.

333.72 ZAF ISSN 0075-6466
CODEN: KOEDAZ
KOEDOE. MONOGRAPHS. Text in English. 1966. irreg. ZAR 25. **Document type:** *Monographic series.*
Indexed: BiolAb, SFA, WildRev, ZooRec.
Published by: National Parks Board/Nasionale Parkeraad, PO Box 787, Pretoria, 0001, South Africa. TEL 27-12-343-9770, FAX 27-12-343-9958. Ed. J C Rautenbach. Circ: 2,000.

333.783 ISR
KOL ATAR; bulletin of the National Park Authority. Text in Hebrew. 1973. s-a. free.
Published by: National Park Authority, P O Box 7028, Tel Aviv, 61070, Israel. TEL 03-252281. Ed. S Raviv. Circ: 5,000.

333.95416 KEN
➤ **KOMBA.** Text in English. 1969. 3/yr. KES 2,000 domestic; USD 20 foreign (effective 1999). adv. bk.rev. **Document type:** *Academic/Scholarly.* **Description:** A wildlife and conservation magazine designed for the young wildlife club member.
Formerly (until 1978): Wildlife Clubs of Kenya Association. Newsletter
Published by: Wildlife Clubs of Kenya Association, PO Box 20184, Nairobi, Kenya. TEL 254-2-891904, FAX 254-2-891906. Ed., Adv. contact Rupi Mangat. B&W page USD 600, color page USD 650. Circ: 6,000.

333.72 PRK ISSN 0023-4036
KOREAN NATURE✶ . Text in Korean. 1967. q. charts; illus.
Published by: Korean Association for Conservation of Nature, Pyongyang, Korea, N.

333.95416 ZAF
QH195.A323
KWAZULU - NATAL WILDLIFE. Text in English. 1960. bi-m. ZAR 100 to members. adv. bk.rev. illus. **Description:** Includes news from all of the society's branches and from other organizations concerned with the environment.
Formerly: Natal Wildlife (0027-8343)
Published by: Wildlife and Environment Society of Southern Africa, Natal Branch/Natuurlewevereniging van Suidelike Afrika, 100 Brand Rd, Durban, KwaZulu-Natal 4001, South Africa. TEL 27-31-213126, FAX 27-31-219525. Ed. Els Van Asseltty. Circ: 5,000 (paid).

LAKES AND RESERVOIRS: RESEARCH AND MANAGEMENT. see *WATER RESOURCES*

333.72 ZAF ISSN 0075-7780
QH195.N3 CODEN: LMGYA3
➤ **LAMMERGEYER.** Text in English. 1960. irreg., latest vol.45, 1998. ZAR 20 domestic; USD 20 foreign (effective 2000). back issues avail. **Document type:** *Academic/Scholarly.* **Description:** Reports on nature conservation research in KwaZulu Natal, South Africa.
Indexed: ASFA, BiolAb, CurCont, ESPM, ISAP, IndVet, KWIWR, NutrAb, RRTA, RevApplEntom, S&F, SFA, VetBull, WLR, WildRev, ZooRec.
—BLDSC (5144.300000), CISTI, ingenta.
Published by: KwaZulu - Natal Nature Conservation Service, PO Box 13053, Cascades, 3202, South Africa. TEL 27-331-845-1422, FAX 27-331-845-1498, davejohn@kznncs.org.za. Ed. D.N. Johnson. R&P D N Johnson. Circ: 300 (paid); 200 (controlled).

333.72 USA ISSN 0192-9453
CODEN: LAWAEX
LAND & WATER; the magazine of natural resource management and restoration. Text in English. 1956. bi-m. USD 20 domestic; USD 32 foreign; USD 4 per issue (effective 2005). adv. bk.rev. illus.; stat. **Document type:** *Magazine.* **Description:** Edited for contractors, engineers, architects, government officials and those working in the field of natural resource management and restoration from idea stage through project completion and maintenance.
Former titles: Land and Water Development (0023-7590); Land and Water Contracting
Indexed: ASFA, BrCerAb, C&ISA, CerAb, CivEngAb, CorrAb, E&CAJ, EMA, ESPM, EnvEAb, ExcerpMed, HRIS, IAA, M&TEA, MBF, METADEX, PollutAb, SolStAb, WAA, WRCInf.
—BLDSC (5146.765000), CISTI, IE, ingenta, Linda Hall.
Published by: Land and Water, Inc., 320 A St, Fort Dodge, IA 50501. TEL 515-576-3191, FAX 515-576-2606, http://www.landandwater.com. Ed. Amy Dencklau. Pub. Ken Rasch. Adv. contact Gail Henry. B&W page USD 2,070, color page USD 2,900. Circ: 20,000 (paid and controlled).

333.77 USA
LAND AND WATER CONSERVATION FUND GRANTS MANUAL. Text in English. 1965. irreg. looseleaf. USD 45. **Document type:** *Government.*
Formerly: U.S. Bureau of Outdoor Recreation. Recreation Grants-in-Aid Manual
Published by: U.S. Department of the Interior, National Parks Service, 1849 C St NW, Washington, DC 20240. TEL 202-208-6843, http://www.nps.gov.

333.72 372.357 USA ISSN 0890-7625
LAND LETTER; the newsletter for natural resource professionals. Text in English. 1982. fortn. USD 795 (effective 2005). adv. index. **Document type:** *Newsletter.* **Description:** Reports on natural resources issues.
Related titles: Online - full text ed.: ISSN 1540-7888 (from LexisNexis).
—**CCC.**
Published by: (Conservation Fund), Environmental and Energy Publishing, LLC, 122 C St, N W, Ste 722, Washington, DC 20001. TEL 202-628-6500, FAX 202-737-5299, pubs@eenews.com, pubs@eenews.net, http://www.landletter.com, http://www.eenews.net. Ed. Kevin Braun. Pub. Michael Witt. Circ: 600 (paid).

C

LAND USE LAW REPORT. see *HOUSING AND URBAN PLANNING*

DE LANDEIGENAAR; maandblad voor beheer van het buitengebied. see *REAL ESTATE*

333.73 NLD ISSN 0169-2046
HT166 CODEN: LUPLEZ
➤ **LANDSCAPE AND URBAN PLANNING.** Text in English. 1974. 20/yr. EUR 1,523 in Europe to institutions; JPY 202,500 in Japan to institutions; USD 1,704 to institutions except Europe and Japan (effective 2006). adv. bk.rev. bibl.; charts; illus. Index. back issues avail.; reprints avail. **Document type:** *Journal, Academic/Scholarly.* **Description:** Concerned with conceptual, scientific, and design approaches to land use.
Incorporates (in 1988): Reclamation and Revegetation Research (0167-644X); (in 1986): Urban Ecology (0304-4009); Formerly: Landscape and Planning (0304-3924)
Related titles: Online - full text ed.: (from EBSCO Publishing, Gale Group, IngentaConnect, ScienceDirect, Swets Information Services).
Indexed: AEA, AESIS, AIAP, APD, ASCA, ASFA, AbHyg, AgrForAb, ApEcolAb, BIOBASE, BIOSIS Prev, BiolAb, CJA, CPA, CivEngAb, CurCont, EIA, EPB, ESPM, EnerInd, EnerRev, EngInd, EntAb, EnvAb, ExcerpMed, FCA, FPA, ForAb, GEOBASE, GardL, HerbAb, HortAb, I&DA, IABS, IMMAb, ISR, M&GPA, M&TEA, MaizeAb, OrnHort, PGegResA, PollutAb, RDA, RPP, RRTA, S&F, SFA, SPAA, SSCI, SUSA, SWRA, SoyAb, TDB, TriticAb, WAE&RSA, WeedAb, WildRev, ZooRec.
—BLDSC (5153.134000), CASDDS, CISTI, Ei, IDS, IE, Infotrieve, ingenta, Linda Hall. **CCC.**
Published by: Elsevier BV (Subsidiary of: Elsevier Science & Technology), Radarweg 29, Amsterdam, 1043 NX, Netherlands. TEL 31-20-4853911, FAX 31-20-4852457, nlinfo-f@elsevier.nl, http://www.elsevier.com/locate/landurbplan, http://www.elsevier.nl. Ed. J R Rodiek. **Subscr. to:** Elsevier, Subscription Customer Service, 6277 Sea Harbor Dr, Orlando, FL 32887-4800. TEL 407-345-4020, 877-839-7126, FAX 407-363-1354.

➤ **LANDSCAPE ARCHITECTURAL REVIEW/REVUE D'ARCHITECTURE DE PAYSAGE.** see *ARCHITECTURE*

➤ **LANDSCHAP**; tijdschrift voor landschapsecologie en milieukunde. see *ENVIRONMENTAL STUDIES*

➤ **LEBENSBAUM**; literarische Zeitschrift fuer Natur-Bewusstsein. see *LITERATURE*

333.72 DNK ISSN 0108-7991
LEVENDE NATUR; tidsskrift for international naturbevarelse. Text in Danish. 1983. q. DKK 195 (effective 2000). illus. **Document type:** *Bulletin.*
Formerly: Panda-Nyt (0105-7936)

▼ new title ➤ refereed ✶ unverified ♦ full entry avail.

Published by: Verdensnaturfonden/World Wide Fund for Nature, Denmark, Ryesgade 3F, Copenhagen N, 2200, Denmark. TEL 45-35-36-36-35, FAX 45-39-20-62. Ed. Nanet Poulsen. Circ: 28,000.

333.72   NLD   ISSN 0024-1520
LEVENDE NATUUR; tijdschrift voor natuurbehoud en natuurbeheer. Text in Dutch; Summaries in English. 1896. 6/yr. adv. bk.rev. charts; illus. Document type: Bulletin. Description: Journal of nature conservation and management.
Incorporates (1995-1996): Natuurontwikkelingen (1382-3906)
Indexed: BIOSIS Prev, BiolAb, ZooRec.
—BLDSC (5185.500000), IE, Infotrieve.
Published by: Stichting de Levende Natuur, Postbus 618, Wageningen, 6700 AP, Netherlands. TEL 31-317-427893, http://www.delevendenatuur.nl/. Eds. H L Schimmel-ten Kate, Bart van Tooren. adv.: B&W page EUR 575. Circ: 2,200.

LIBELLULA. see BIOLOGY—Entomology

333.75 634.9   USA
LIBRARY OF TREES. Text in English. 1998. bi-m. USD 25 (effective 2000). illus. back issues avail. Document type: Newsletter. Description: Each issue features a different tree species and information on how to plant and care for that species. Includes insight on the history, growth patterns, growing areas, and uses of the featured tree.
Published by: National Arbor Day Foundation, 100 Arbor Ave, Nebraska City, NE 68410. TEL 402-474-5655, FAX 402-474-0820. Ed. James R Fazio. Pub. John E Rosenow. R&P Gary Brienzo. Circ: 50,000.

LIDIA (AS). see AGRICULTURE

333.95416   GBR
LIFEWATCH. Text in English. 1989. 4/yr. GBP 22. adv. back issues avail. Document type: Newsletter.
Published by: London Zoo, London Zoo, Regents Park, London, NW1 4RY, United Kingdom. TEL 44-171-586-4443, FAX 44-171-586-6177. Ed., Adv. contact Gina Guarnieri. Circ: 28,000 (paid).

333.72   NLD   ISSN 1382-8088
LIMBURGS LANDSCHAP. Text in Dutch. 1973. q.
Indexed: RefZh.
Published by: Stichting het Limburgs Landschap, Boerderij Kloosterhof, Landgoed Arcen, Rijksstraatweg 1, Lomm, Postbus 4301, Arcen, 5944 ZG, Netherlands. TEL 31-77-4737575, FAX 31-77-4737576, info@Limburgs-Landschap.nl, http://www.limburgs-landschap.nl.

333.76 599   GBR
LINNEAN SOCIETY. OCCASIONAL PUBLICATIONS. Text in English. irreg., latest no.4.
—BLDSC (5221.492700).
Published by: (Linnean Society of London), Westbury Publishing, Ilkey Rd, Otley, W Yorks LS21 3JP, United Kingdom.

333.73   USA   ISSN 1444-4046
QH75.A1
LIVING PLANET. Text in English. 2000. q. USD 18 to institutions (effective until Jun. 2001). Document type: Magazine, Consumer. Description: For people who care about nature and the future of our planet. Features pictures by noted nature photographers around the world.
Published by: World Wildlife Fund, 1250 24th St, N W, Washington, DC 20037. TEL 202-293-4800, FAX 202-293-9211, membership@wwfus.org, http://www.worldwildlife.org/.

LIVING WITH THE SHORE. see ENVIRONMENTAL STUDIES

333.73   DNK   ISSN 1395-1270
LOES'NET. Variant title: Loesnet. Text in Danish. 1969. q. DKK 200 (effective 2005). adv. back issues avail. Document type: Magazine, Consumer.
Supersedes in part (in 1994): KoKoo (0907-1318)
Related titles: Online - full text ed.
Published by: Landsforeningen for OekoSamfund/Danish Association for Sustainable Communities, Landsbyvaenget 11, Galten, 8464, Denmark. TEL 45-87-546020, FAX 45-87-546021, los@pip.dknet.dk, http://www.losnet.dk.

LONG-TERM MONITORING OF THE GREAT BARRIER REEF: STATUS REPORT. see ENVIRONMENTAL STUDIES

333.95416   LKA   ISSN 0024-6514
SK1   CODEN: LRISAU
▶ LORIS; a journal on Sri Lankan wildlife. Text in English. 1936. s-a. USD 10. adv. bk.rev. illus. Document type: Academic/Scholarly. Description: Covers conservation of natural resources and environmental protection.
Indexed: BiolAb, SFA, SLSI, WildRev, ZooRec.
Published by: Wildlife & Nature Protection Society of Sri Lanka, No. 5, 19th Lane, Colombo, 3, Sri Lanka. TEL 941-325248, FAX 941-580721, TELEX 22933-METALIX-CE, metalixc@mail.slt.lk. Ed. Mrs. Sirancee Gunawardena. Circ: 2,300.

333.72   USA   ISSN 0024-6778
SK351
LOUISIANA CONSERVATIONIST. Text in English. 1923. bi-m. USD 10. charts; illus.; stat. Document type: Government. Description: Articles on hunting, fishing, and outdoor recreation in the state. Covers the laws and regulations that govern the management of the state's natural resources.
Indexed: ASFA, BiolDig, ChemAb, ESPM.
—Linda Hall.
Published by: Department of Wildlife and Fisheries, PO Box 98000, Baton Rouge, LA 70898-9000. TEL 504-765-2918, FAX 504-763-3568. Ed. Bob Dennie. Circ: 45,000 (paid).

LOV I RIBOLOV. see SPORTS AND GAMES—Outdoor Life

LUDWIG BOLTZMANN-INSTITUT FUER UMWELTWISSENSCHAFTEN UND NATURSCHUTZ. MITTEILUNGEN. see ENVIRONMENTAL STUDIES

333.72   USA   ISSN 0744-5288
MACKINAC∗. Text in English. 1966. q. USD 10 to non-members; USD 1 to members. adv. bk.rev. back issues avail. Document type: Newsletter. Description: Covers environmental issues and the chapter's educational and outdoor activities.
Indexed: MMI.
Published by: Sierra Club, Mackinac Chapter, 109 E Grand River Ave, Lansing, MI 48906-4348. TEL 517-484-2372, FAX 517-484-3108, mackinac.chapter@sierraclub.org, http://www.sierraclub.org/chapters/mi/. Ed., Adv. contact Gary Serner. R&P Alison Horton. Circ: 14,000.

MADAGASCAR PRIMATES. see BIOLOGY—Zoology

577   NAM   ISSN 1011-5498
QL84.6.S6   CODEN: MADOAL
MADOQUA; journal of arid zone biology and nature conservation research. Text in English. 1969. 2/yr. ZAR 25 (effective 1999). bk.rev. back issues avail. Document type: Academic/Scholarly. Description: Publishes papers on original and applied research concerning nature conservation in Namibia and adjacent countries, and on arid zone biology with a focus on the Namib desert.
Supersedes: Madoqua. Series 2 (1010-2302); (vol.9, 1975): Madoqua. Series 1; Namib Desert Research Station. Scientific Papers
Indexed: AnBrAb, BIOSIS Prev, BiolAb, CTO, CurCont, FCA, ForAb, HerbAb, ISAP, IndVet, KWIWR, RPP, RRTA, S&F, SFA, VetBull, WildRev, ZooRec.
—BLDSC (5330.969000).
Published by: Ministry of Environment and Tourism, Directorate of Resource Management and Research, Private Bag 13306, Windhoek, Namibia. TEL 061-63131, FAX 061-63195, TELEX 50-908-3180. Ed. C J Brown. Circ: 750.

333.72   USA   ISSN 0898-7742
MAINE ENVIRONMENT∗; news bulletin of Maine's leading conservation organization. Text in English. 1960. 6/yr. USD 28 (effective 2004). bk.rev. bibl.; illus. Document type: Newsletter, Consumer.
Published by: Natural Resources Council of Maine, 3 Wade St, Augusta, ME 04330-6351. TEL 207-622-3101, http://www.nrcm.org. Ed. Patty Renaud. Circ: 8,000 (paid and controlled).

333.95416   USA   ISSN 0360-005X
SH11   CODEN: MFWIDY
MAINE FISH AND WILDLIFE. Text in English. 1959. q. USD 9 (effective 1999). adv. illus. index, cum.index. Document type: Government. Description: Natural history, research and management programs.
Formerly: Maine Fish and Game Magazine (0025-0643)
Indexed: SFA, WildRev, ZooRec.
Published by: Department of Inland Fisheries and Wildlife, Station 41, 284 State St, Augusta, ME 04333. TEL 207-287-8000, http://www.state.me.us/ifw. Ed. V Paul Reynolds. Adv. contact V. Paul Reynolds. Circ: 12,000.

MALAWI. DEPARTMENT OF FORESTRY AND GAME. REPORT. see FORESTS AND FORESTRY

333.72   MYS   ISSN 0127-0206
QH185   CODEN: MLNTAR
MALAYAN NATURALIST. Text in English. 1978. q. membership. Document type: Magazine, Academic/Scholarly.
Related titles: ♦ Supplement to: Malayan Nature Journal. ISSN 0025-1291.
Indexed: SFA, WildRev, ZooRec.
—Linda Hall. CCC.
Published by: Malaysian Nature Society, JKR 641, Jalan Kelantan, Kuala Lumpur, Selangor 50480, Malaysia. TEL 60-3-22879422, FAX 60-3-22878773, natsoc@po.jaring.my, http://www.mns.org.my/publication.php.

333.72   CAN   ISSN 1497-9012
MANITOBA CONSERVATION. ANNUAL REPORT. Text in English. 1980. a.

Former titles (until 1999): Manitoba Natural Resources. Annual Report (0837-6786); (until 1983): Manitoba Department of Natural Resources. Annual Report (0711-8260); Which superseded in part (in 1980): Manitoba Department of Mines, Natural Resources and Environment. Annual Report (0711-8279)
Published by: Manitoba Conservation, 450 Broadway, Winnipeg, MB R3C 0V8, Canada. http://www.gov.mb.ca/conservation/annual-report/conservation/index.html.

333.72   DEU   ISSN 0934-5620
MANNHEIMER BEITRAEGE ZUR OEKONOMISCHEN OEKOLOGIE. Text in German. 1988. irreg. Document type: Monographic series, Academic/Scholarly.
Published by: Peter Lang GmbH Europaeischer Verlag der Wissenschaften, Eschborner Landstr 42-50, Frankfurt Am Main, 60489, Germany. TEL 49-69-7807050, FAX 49-69-78070543, zentrale.frankfurt@peterlang.com, http://www.peterlang.de. Ed. Gert von Kortzfleisch.

MARIN PABIRION/MARINE PAVILION. see EARTH SCIENCES—Oceanography

333.956   USA
MARINE BULLETIN. Text in English. 1973. q. USD 30 membership (effective 2000). Document type: Newsletter.
Formerly (until 1985): Right Rigger
Indexed: EnvAb.
Published by: National Coalition for Marine Conservation, 4 Royal St SE, Leesburg, VA 20175-3014. TEL 703-777-0037. Ed. Ken Hinman. Circ: 1,000.

MARINE CONSERVATION. see BIOLOGY

577   GBR
MARINE CONSERVATION AND DEVELOPMENT REPORT. Text in English. irreg.
Published by: I U C N - World Conservation Union, 219c Huntingdon Rd, Cambridge, CB3 0DL, United Kingdom. TEL 44-1223-277894, FAX 44-1223-277175, info@books.iucn.org, http://www.iucn.org.

333.9   USA
MARINE CONSERVATION NEWS; "for all at last returns to the sea - the beginning and the end." Rachel Carson. Text in English. 1976. 4/yr. membership. bk.rev. Description: News and articles on legislation, policy, and regulations pertaining to the conservation of marine species and their habitats.
Former titles: C E E Report; Whale Report
Indexed: WildRev.
Published by: Center for Marine Conservation, 1725 DeSales St, N W, Washington, DC 20036. TEL 202-429-5609, FAX 202-872-0619. Ed. Rose Bierce. Circ: 100,000.

MARINE FISHERIES REVIEW. see FISH AND FISHERIES

577   CAN
MARINE ISSUES COMMITTEE. SPECIAL PUBLICATION. Text in English. irreg.
Published by: Ecology Action Centre, 1568 Argyle St, Ste 31, Halifax, NS B3J 2B3, Canada. TEL 902-429-2202, FAX 902-422-6410, eac@ecologyaction.ca, http://www.ecologyaction.ca/EAC_WEB_1/HOME2/.

346.044   USA
MARINE MAMMAL COMMISSION. ANNUAL REPORT TO CONGRESS. Text in English. 2000. a. Description: Details marine mammal policies, conservation, and research activities carried out by various government organizations.
Related titles: Online - full content ed.
Published by: Marine Mammal Commission, 4340 East-West Hwy, Rm 905, Bethesda, MD 20814. TEL 301-504-0087, FAX 301-504-0099, http://www.mmc.gov/reports/annual/.

346.044   USA   ISSN 0196-4690
QL713.2
MARINE MAMMAL PROTECTION ACT OF 1972 ANNUAL REPORT. Text in English. a. Document type: Government.
Formerly: Administration of the Marine Mammal Protection Act of 1972 (0148-186X)
—Linda Hall.
Published by: U.S. National Marine Fisheries Service, National Oceanographic and Atmospheric Administration, 1335 East West Hwy, Silver Spring, MD 20910. TEL 301-713-2332.

MARINE TURTLE NEWSLETTER. see BIOLOGY—Zoology

333.9   GBR
MARPOL 73 - 78 AMENDMENTS. Text in English. 1991. irreg. GBP 8; GBP 10 overseas. illus. Description: Covers amendments enacted by the I.M.O. Marine Environment Protection Committee.
Related titles: Arabic ed.; Chinese ed.; French ed.; Russian ed.; Spanish ed.
Published by: International Maritime Organization/Organisation Maritime Internationale, 4 Albert Embankment, London, SE1 7SR, United Kingdom. TEL 44-20-7735-7611, FAX 44-20-7587-3210.

333.72 USA
MARYLAND. DEPARTMENT OF NATURAL RESOURCES. ANNUAL ACTIVITIES REPORT. Text in English. 1971. a. free. illus.
Published by: Maryland Department of Natural Resources, Tawes State Office Bldg D 4, 580 Taylor Ave, Annapolis, MD 21401. TEL 301-974-3990, FAX 301-974-5206. Ed. R L Gould. Circ: 1,500.

346.044 USA
MARYLAND DEPARTMENT OF NATURAL RESOURCES LAWS. Text in English. irreg. (w/ current supplement), latest 1999. USD 65 (effective 2003). index. 101 p./no.; **Description:** Contains selected titles from the Natural Resources Articles.
Published by: Michie Company (Subsidiary of: LexisNexis North America), 701 E Water St, Charlottesville, VA 22902-5389. TEL 434-972-7600, 800-446-3410, FAX 434-972-7677, http://www.michie.com. Ed. George Harley.

MASONRY INTERNATIONAL; journal of the British Masonry Society. see *ARCHITECTURE*

333.78 USA
MASSACHUSETTS. DIVISION OF FISHERIES AND WILDLIFE. ANNUAL REPORT. Text in English. 1866. a. USD 6.
Formerly: Massachusetts. Division of Fisheries and Game. Annual Report (0076-4957)
Published by: Division of Fisheries and Wildlife, One Rabbit Hill Rd., Westborough, MA 01581. TEL 508-792-7270, FAX 508-792-7275. Ed. Peter g Mirick. Circ: 18,700.

333.72 USA ISSN 1071-9229
MASSACHUSETTS SIERRAN✶. Text in English. 1970. 4/yr. membership. adv. **Document type:** *Newsletter.*
Formerly: New England Sierran (0164-4491)
Published by: Sierra Club, Boston Chapter, 100 Boylston St Ste 760, Boston, MA 02116-4610. TEL 617-423-5775. Ed. James B McCaffrey.

333.95416 USA ISSN 0025-4924
SK407
MASSACHUSETTS WILDLIFE. Text in English. 1949. q. USD 6 domestic; USD 25 foreign (effective 2000). bk.rev. charts; illus. back issues avail. **Document type:** *Government.*
Published by: Division of Fisheries and Wildlife, Field Headquarters, One Rabbit Hill Rd, Westborough, MA 01581. TEL 508-792-7270, FAX 508-792-7275, pmirick@state.ma.us. Ed., R&P Peter G Mirick. Circ: 20,000.

333.72 ITA ISSN 1121-2373
MATERIALI E STRUTTURE; problemi di conservazione. Text in Italian. 1991. 3/yr. price varies. **Document type:** *Monographic series, Trade.*
Published by: L'Erma di Bretschneider, Via Cassiodoro, 19, PO Box 6192, Rome, RM 00193, Italy. TEL 39-06-6874127, FAX 39-06-6874129, edizioni@lerma.it, http://www.lerma.it.

333.72 RUS
MATERYALY PRESSY PO PROBLEMAM MINERAL'NO-SYR'EVOGO KOMPLEKSA ROSSII. Text in Russian. 1996. 104/yr. USD 669 in North America.
Published by: Informatsionno-Izdatel'skii Tsentr po Geologii i Nedropol'zovaniu Geoinformmark, Goncharnaya 38, Moscow, 115172, Russian Federation. info@geoinform.ru. **Dist. by:** East View Information Services, 3020 Harbor Ln. N., Minneapolis, MN 55447. TEL 763-550-0961, FAX 763-559-2931.

069.4 SWE ISSN 0106-469X
MEDDELELSER OM KONSERVERING; tidsskrift for konservering og restaurering af kunst- og kulturhistoriske objekter. Text in Danish, Norwegian, Swedish. 1965. s-a. DKK 350; DKK 150 newsstand/cover (effective 2004). adv. cum.index: 1987-1994. **Document type:** *Journal, Academic/Scholarly.* **Description:** Promotes the preservation and conservation of antiquities, art, and architecture.
Indexed: A&ATA.
Published by: Nordisk Konservator Forbund, c/o Eva Ringberg, Oestergoetlands Laensmuseum, PO Box 232, Linkoeping, 88102, Sweden. TEL 46-13-230322, FAX 46-13-140562, redaktionen@nordiskkonservatorforbund.org, http://www.nordiskkonservatorforbund.org. Ed. Maj Stief. Circ: 1,500.

MEDICINAL PLANT CONSERVATION. see *BIOLOGY—Botany*

333.95 363.7 GBR ISSN 1352-674X
MEDINA VALLEY WILDLIFE. Text in English. 1994. a. GBP 1 domestic; USD 1 foreign; GBP 1 newsstand/cover (effective 2000 - 2001). back issues avail. **Description:** Contains information about the wildlife of the Medina Valley and the River Medina estuary from Cowes to Newport, Isle of Wight. Includes yearly weather report, bird report, butterfly report and other items of interest.
Published by: Medina Valley Centre, Dodnor Ln, Newport, Isle Of Wight P030 5TE, United Kingdom. TEL 44-1983-522195, FAX 44-1983-825962, info@medinavalleycentre.or.uk, fieldstudies@medinavalleycentre.org.uk, http://www.medinavalleycentre.org.uk. Ed. J R Ager. R&P Mr. P Savory. Circ: 140 (paid and controlled).

333.72 AUS ISSN 0725-8739
MERIGAL; a voice for the dingo. Text in English. 1977. q. AUD 20. back issues avail. **Document type:** *Newspaper.* **Description:** Promotes conservation of the Australian dingo.
Published by: Australian Native Dog Conservation Society Ltd., Dingo Sanctuary, 'Merigal', 590 Arina Rd., Bargo, NSW 2574, Australia. TEL 61-246-841156, FAX 61-246841156, merigal@zip.com.au, http://www.dingosanctuary.org. Ed. David Steward. R&P Berenice Walters. Circ: 300.

THE MESSAGE (NORTHBOROUGH). see *SPORTS AND GAMES—Outdoor Life*

333.72 FIN ISSN 0047-6986
METSASTAJA. Text in Finnish. 1954. bi-m. adv. bk.rev. back issues avail. **Document type:** *Magazine, Consumer.*
Related titles: Online - full text ed.; Swedish ed.: Jaegaren. ISSN 0355-2683.
Published by: Metsastajain Keskusjarjesto/Jaegarnas Centralorganisation - Hunters' Central Organisation, Fantsintie 13-14, Itaesalmi, 01100, Finland. TEL 358-9-8777677, FAX 358-9-8777617, klaus.ekman@riista.fi, mkj@riista.fi, http://www.riista.fi. Ed., R&P, Adv. contact Klaus Ekman. B&W page EUR 3,800, color page EUR 5,600; trim 185 x 271. Circ: 297,322 (controlled).

333.72 USA ISSN 0275-8180
SK351
MICHIGAN NATURAL RESOURCES MAGAZINE. Text in English. 1931. bi-m. USD 15; USD 23 foreign (effective 1999). adv. bk.rev. charts; illus. index every 2 yrs. **Document type:** *Consumer.* **Description:** Focuses on the natural resources of Michigan and outdoor recreation.
Former titles (until 1977): Michigan Natural Resources (0026-2358); Michigan Conservation
Indexed: MMI.
Published by: (Michigan. Michigan Department of Natural Resources), Kolka & Robb, Inc., PO Box 7355, Red Oak, IA 51591-0355. TEL 810-642-9580, 888-667-0015, FAX 810-642-5290, http://www.dnr.state.mi.us/www/mp/magazine.html. Ed. Richard Morscheck. Pub. Vicki Robb. Adv. contact Thomas Strong. Circ: 90,000.

333.72 USA ISSN 0026-2382
MICHIGAN OUT-OF-DOORS. Text in English. 1947. m. USD 25; USD 3.50 newsstand/cover (effective 2005). adv. bk.rev. illus. 72 p./no.; back issues avail. **Document type:** *Magazine, Consumer.* **Description:** Features, news, and departments on hunting, fishing and conservation activities in the state.
Related titles: Microfiche ed.
Indexed: MMI, PMR.
Published by: Michigan United Conservation Clubs Inc, 2101 Wood St, Lansing, MI 48912-3785. TEL 517-371-1041, FAX 517-371-1505, magazine@mucc.org, mucc@mucc.org, http://www.mucc.org. Pub. Sam Washington. Adv. contact Mark Klett. B&W page USD 2,850. Circ: 80,000 (paid).

MICROBIAL UTILIZATION OF RENEWABLE RESOURCES. see *BIOLOGY—Biotechnology*

MIGRANT; a quarterly journal devoted to Tennessee birds. see *BIOLOGY—Ornithology*

333.72 NLD ISSN 0165-9545
MILIEUDEFENSIE. Text in Dutch. 1972. m. adv. bk.rev. illus. **Document type:** *Magazine, Consumer.*
Indexed: ExcerpMed, KES.
—IE, Infotrieve.
Published by: Vereniging Milieudefensie, Postbus 19199, Amsterdam, 1000 GD, Netherlands. TEL 31-20-550-7300, FAX 31-20-550-7312, redactie@milieudefensie.nl. Ed. Koen Vink. R&P Helene Kleijburg. Circ: 18,000.

MILIEUMAGAZINE; vakblad voor milieumanagement. see *ENVIRONMENTAL STUDIES*

333.72 DNK ISSN 1395-489X
MILJOESK; tidsskrift om miljoe og samfund. Text in Danish. 1969. q. DKK 195 to individuals; DKK 355 to institutions (effective 2005). **Document type:** *Magazine, Consumer.*
Former titles (until 1995): N O A H - Bladet (0902-6657); (until 1986): N O A H (0105-4031)
Published by: Miljoebevaegelsen N O A H/Friends of the Earth Denmark, Noerrebrogade 39, Copenhagen N, 2200, Denmark. TEL 45-35-361212, FAX 45-35-361217, noah@noah.dk, http://www.noah.dk/miljosk/.

THE MINING RECORD. see *MINES AND MINING INDUSTRY*

333.72 USA ISSN 1523-6331
S916.M6
MINNESOTA CONSERVATION VOLUNTEER. Text in English. 1940. 6/yr. USD 15 out of state (effective 2000); free to Minnesota residents. bk.rev. illus. index. **Document type:** *Government.*
Former titles (until 1999): The Minnesota Volunteer (0196-593X); (until 1971): The Conservation Volunteer (0010-6496)
Indexed: WildRev.
—Linda Hall.
Published by: Minnesota Department of Natural Resources, 500 Lafayette Rd, St. Paul, MN 55155-4046. TEL 651-296-0888, FAX 651-296-0902, http://www.dnr.state.mn.us/information_and_education/publications/volunteer/. Ed. Kathleen Weflen. R&P Catherine Mix TEL 651-296-0894. Circ: 120,000.

333.72 USA
MINNESOTA OUT-OF-DOORS. Text in English. 1954. bi-m. USD 20 (effective 1999). **Document type:** *Newsletter.* **Description:** Provides the latest information on conservation issues in Minnesota and outdoor recreation opportunities.
Published by: Minnesota Conservation Federation, 551 S. Snelling Ave., St. Paul, MN 55116-1525. TEL 612-690-3077. Ed. Barb Prindle. R&P Shannon Long. Circ: 2,500.

MISSISSIPPI. DEPARTMENT OF WILDLIFE CONSERVATION. ANNUAL REPORT. see *FISH AND FISHERIES*

333.95416 USA ISSN 1041-9306
SH11.M7
MISSISSIPPI OUTDOORS. Text in English. 1935. bi-m. USD 6. bk.rev. charts; illus.
Former titles (until 1987): MS Outdoors (0732-6602); Mississippi Outdoors (0199-3240); (until 1981): Mississippi Game and Fish (0026-6256)
Indexed: SFA, WildRev.
—Linda Hall.
Published by: Department of Wildlife, Fisheries and Parks, PO Box 451, Jackson, MS 39205. TEL 601-364-2123, http://www.mdwfp.com/. Ed. David L Watts. Circ: 40,000.

333.72 USA ISSN 0026-6515
SK351
MISSOURI CONSERVATIONIST. Text in English. 1938. m. free in state; USD 7 out of state; USD 10 foreign (effective 2005). charts; illus. index. back issues avail. **Document type:** *Government.*
Related titles: Online - full text ed.
Indexed: BiolAb, SFA, WildRev, ZooRec.
—Linda Hall.
Published by: Missouri Department of Conservation, 2901 W Truman Blvd, PO Box 180, Jefferson City, MO 65109. TEL 573-751-4115, FAX 573-751-4467, internet@mail.conservation.state.mo.us, http://www.conservation.state.mo.us/. Ed. Tom Cwynar. Circ: 440,000; 15,000 (paid).

333.95416 USA ISSN 1082-8591
MISSOURI WILDLIFE. Text in English. 1939. bi-m. USD 20 (effective 2000). adv. bk.rev. 16 p./no. 4 cols./p.; **Document type:** *Newspaper.* **Description:** Editorials, news commentary, and informational articles on the environment and conservation in the state and on the preservation of land for hunting, fishing, and other outdoor recreational activities.
Published by: Conservation Federation of Missouri, 728 W Main, Jefferson City, MO 65101. TEL 573-634-2322, FAX 573-634-8205, cdfed@sockets.net. Ed., R&P Charles F Davidson TEL 800-575-2322. Adv. contacts Jennifer Mills, Laurie Coleman. page USD 475. Circ: 30,000 (paid).

333.72 NLD ISSN 0169-6459
MOLENS. Text in Dutch. 1954. q. adv. bk.rev.
Formerly (until 1986): Molennieuws - Windmill News (0026-8992)
Published by: Vereniging tot Behoud van Molens in Nederland/Association for the Preservation of Windmills in the Netherlands, Sarphatistraat 634, Amsterdam, 1018 AV, Netherlands. TEL 31-20-6238703. Ed. L M Endedijk. Circ: 13,000.

333.72 USA
MONTANA. DEPARTMENT OF FISH, WILDLIFE AND PARKS. JOB PROGRESS REPORT. Text in English. irreg.
Formerly: Montana. Department of Fish and Game. Job Progress Report
Published by: Department of Fish, Wildlife and Parks, 1420 E Sixth Ave, PO Box 200701, Helena, MT 59620-0701. TEL 406-444-2535, FAX 406-444-4952, fwpgen@state.mt.us, http://www.fwp.state.mt.us.

MOTHER EARTH. see *ENVIRONMENTAL STUDIES*

MOUNTAINEER (SEATTLE); to explore, study, preserve and enjoy the natural beauty of the Northwest and beyond. see *SPORTS AND GAMES—Outdoor Life*

MUELLERIA. see *BIOLOGY—Botany*

628.168 USA
MUSCONETCONG RIVER NEWS. Text in English. 1992. q. membership. charts; illus. **Document type:** *Newsletter.* **Description:** Reports on efforts to preserve the quality of the Musconetcong River, one of the most important waterways in the highlands of northern New Jersey.
Published by: Musconetcong Watershed Association, PO Box 87, Washington, NJ 07882. TEL 908-689-3260. Ed. Victoria Reiners.

N B I A NEWSLETTER. see *AGRICULTURE*

N E C N P NEWSLETTER. see *ENERGY*

333.78 USA
N F R A NEWSLETTER. Text in English. 1949. q. looseleaf. membership. back issues avail. **Document type:** *Newsletter.*
Published by: National Forest Recreation Association, PO Box 409, Mammoth Lakes, CA 93546. TEL 619-934-2887. Ed. Robert C Tanner. Circ: 2,000.

333.7 NOR ISSN 0805-469X
N I N A. FAGRAPPORT. (Norsk Institutt for Naturforskning) Text in English, Norwegian. 1995. a. **Document type:** *Monographic series, Academic/Scholarly.*
Formed by the merger of (1989-1995): N I N A Utredning (0802-3107); (1989-1995): N I N A Forskningsrapport (0802-3093)
Indexed: ASFA, ESPM, ZooRec.
Published by: Stiftelsen for Naturforskning og Kulturminneforskning/Foundation for Nature Research and Cultural Heritage Research, Tungasletta 2, Trondheim, 7485, Norway. TEL 47-73-801400, FAX 47-73-801401, firmapost@ninaniku.no, http://www.ninaniku.no.

333.72 NOR ISSN 1503-5204
▼ **N I N A FAKTA.** (Norsk Institutt for Naturforskning) Text in Norwegian. 2003. irreg. back issues avail.
Supersedes in part (in 2002): Fakta - N I N A N I K U (0809-1412)
Related titles: Online - full text ed.: ISSN 1503-5158.
Published by: Norsk Institutt for Naturforskning/Norwegian Institute for Nature Research, Tungasletta 2, Trondheim, 7485, Norway. TEL 47-73-801400, FAX 47-73-801401, nina@nina.no, http://www.nina.no. Ed. Tor B Gunneroed.

333.7 NOR ISSN 0802-4103
N I N A. OPPDRAGSMELDING. Text in Multiple languages. 1989. irreg. **Document type:** *Monographic series.*
Indexed: ASFA, ESPM.
Published by: Stiftelsen for Naturforskning og Kulturminneforskning/Foundation for Nature Research and Cultural Heritage Research, Tungasletta 2, Trondheim, 7485, Norway. TEL 47-73-801400, FAX 47-73-801401, firmapost@ninaniku.no, http://www.ninaniku.no.

N I W A TECHNICAL REPORT. see *FISH AND FISHERIES*

333.72 USA ISSN 0886-6619
CODEN: MTDEDP
N J AUDUBON. Text in English. 1940. q. USD 35 domestic to individuals; USD 40 foreign to individuals (effective 2004). adv. bk.rev. charts; illus. reprint service avail. from ISI. **Document type:** *Magazine, Consumer.* **Description:** Covers New Jersey's environment and the life, both wild and human, that it sustains. Emphasis is on conservation, education and research.
Formerly (until 1978): New Jersey Nature News (0028-5862)
Related titles: Microform ed.: (from PQC); ♦ Supplement(s): Records of New Jersey Birds.
Indexed: BiolDig, SFA, WildRev.
Published by: New Jersey Audubon Society, 9 Hardscrabble Rd, PO Box 126, Bernardsville, NJ 07924-0126. TEL 908-204-8998, hq@njaudubon.org, https://www.njaudubon.org. Ed. Peter Dunne. Circ: 9,500.

577.69 USA
N O A A COASTAL OCEAN PROGRAM PROJECT NEWS UPDATE. (National Oceanic and Atmospheric Administration) Text in English. 1997. irreg. back issues avail. **Document type:** *Newsletter.* **Description:** Provides scientific information to assist decision makers in meeting the challenges of managing US coastal resources.
Media: Online - full text.
Published by: (Coastal Ocean Program), U.S. National Climatic Data Center, National Coastal and Atmospheric Administration, 1315 East West Hwy, SSMC3, Rm 9608, Silver Spring, MD 20910. TEL 301-713-3338, coastalocean@cop.noaa.gov, http://www.cop.noaa.gov/pubs/newsletters.html.

333.71 GBR ISSN 1461-4154
N P O JOURNAL. (National Preservation Office) Text in English. 1983. biennial. GBP 20 in United Kingdom; GBP 24 overseas (effective 2000). bk.rev. bibl. back issues avail. **Document type:** *Trade.* **Description:** Promotes current preservation awareness for librarians, archivists and conservators with news, features, abstracts, announcements of forthcoming events, and periodical contents listings.
Formerly (until 1998): Library Conservation News (0265-041X)
Related titles: Online - full text ed.
—BLDSC (6180.522600). **CCC.**
Published by: (National Preservation Office), British Library, 96 Euston Rd, London, NW1 2DB, United Kingdom. TEL 44-20-7412-7612, FAX 44-20-7412-7796, npo@bl.uk, http://www.bl.uk/services/preservation. R&P Belinda Sanderson. Circ: 1,000 (paid and controlled). **Subscr. to:** Extenza - Turpin, Pegasus Dr, Stratton Business Park, Biggleswade, Beds SG18 8TQ, United Kingdom. TEL 44-1462-672555, FAX 44-1462-480-947.

333.72 DEU ISSN 0949-8265
NACHHALTIGES NIEDERSACHSEN. Text in German. 1995. irreg. **Document type:** *Monographic series, Academic/Scholarly.*
Published by: Niedersaechsisches Landesamt fuer Oekologie, Postfach 101062, Hildesheim, 31110, Germany. TEL 49-5121-509-0, FAX 49-5121-509196, poststelle@nloe.niedersachsen.de, http://jupiter.nloe.de.

333.72 578.77 LKA ISSN 1391-6246
NATIONAL AQUATIC RESOURCES RESEARCH AND DEVELOPMENT AGENCY. JOURNAL. Text in English. 1922. s-a. INR 250 domestic to individuals; INR 500 domestic to institutions; USD 10 foreign (effective 2003). **Description:** Publishes information on living and non-living aquatic resources and their management in the maritime zones of Sri Lanka.
Published by: National Aquatic Resources Research and Development Agency, Crow Island, Mattakkuliya, Colombo, 15, Sri Lanka. TEL 94-1-521633, FAX 94-1-521881, sumithra@nara.ac.lk, http://www.nara.ac.lk/nara_journal.htm. Ed. S. Thalakada.

333.72 USA ISSN 0047-8733
NATIONAL ASSOCIATION OF CONSERVATION DISTRICTS. TUESDAY LETTER. Text in English. 1952. q. USD 35. adv. bk.rev. illus. **Document type:** *Newsletter.* **Description:** Monitors issues, programs and activities of interest to the nation's 3000 soil and water conservation districts.
Formerly: National Association of Soil and Water Conservation Districts. Tuesday Letter (0027-8661)
Published by: National Association of Conservation Districts, PO Box 855, League City, TX 77574-0855. TEL 713-332-3402, FAX 713-332-5259. Ed., R&P Russell Slaton. Circ: 25,000.

333.785 USA
NATIONAL ASSOCIATION OF STATE PARK DIRECTORS. ANNUAL INFORMATION EXCHANGE. Text in English. 1978. a. membership only. **Document type:** *Trade.* **Description:** Provides information on state park systems throughout the United States.
Indexed: SRI.
Published by: National Association of State Park Directors, 5853 Steward Rd., Galena, OH 43021-9016. TEL 520-298-4924, FAX 520-298-6515, naspdglen@dakotacom.net, http://www.indiana.edu/~naspd. Ed., R&P Glen Alexander. Circ: 500 (controlled).

NATIONAL ENVIRONMENTAL SCORECARD. see *ENVIRONMENTAL STUDIES*

NATIONAL GEOGRAPHIC EXPLORER. see *GEOGRAPHY*

NATIONAL GEOGRAPHIC KIDS. see *GEOGRAPHY*

333.95416 AUS
NATIONAL PARK AND WILDLIFE JOURNAL. Text in English. q. AUD 19.80 domestic; AUD 27 foreign (effective 2003). **Description:** Provides informative articles about park management and wildlife conservation in South Australia.
Published by: National Parks and Wildlife South Australia, Public Communications, GPO Box 1047, Adelaide, SA 5001, Australia. http://www.environment.sa.gov.au/parks/pub.html#Parks_Journal.

NATIONAL PARKS. see *LEISURE AND RECREATION*

333.783 AUS ISSN 0047-9012
NATIONAL PARKS JOURNAL. Text in English. 1959. 6/yr. membership. adv. bk.rev. **Document type:** *Newsletter.* **Description:** Dedicated to preserving the natural heritage.
Indexed: CIJE, EPB, RefZh.
Published by: (National Parks Association of N.S.W.), N P A Publications Pty. Ltd., PO Box A 96, Sydney South, NSW 2000, Australia. TEL 61-2-2334660, FAX 61-2-2334880, editor@npansw.org.au, npansw@mbigpond.com. Ed., R&P Glyn Mather TEL 02-9-2990000. Circ: 5,000.

333.7845 USA
NATIONAL RIVERS HALL OF FAME NEWSLETTER. Text in English. 1985. q. USD 25. bk.rev. **Document type:** *Newsletter.* **Description:** For those interested in the people of the inland waters of America: explorers, inventors, steamboats and towboats, artists, and conservationists.
Formerly: River Yarns
Published by: National Rivers Hall of Fame, c/o Dubuque County Historical Society, Box 266, Dubuque, IA 52004-0266. TEL 319-583-1241. Ed. Jerome A Enzler. Circ: 900.

NATIONAL SOCIETY FOR THE PRESERVATION OF COVERED BRIDGES NEWSLETTER. see *HISTORY—History Of North And South America*

333.72 GBR
DA873
THE NATIONAL TRUST FOR SCOTLAND GUIDE (YEAR). Text in English. 1931. a., latest 1999. membership. adv. illus.; maps. back issues avail.; reprints avail. **Document type:** *Directory.* **Description:** Description and location of all properties owned or managed by the National Trust for Scotland, with details of facilities, opening times, admission prices etc.
Former titles (until 2000): Guide to Scotland's Best; (until 1997): Guide to Over 100 Properties (0269-0934); National Trust for Scotland Yearbook (0077-5916)
Related titles: E-mail ed.
Indexed: AIAP.
Published by: National Trust for Scotland, 28 Charlotte Sq, Edinburgh, Midlothian EH2 4ET, United Kingdom. TEL 44-131-243-9300, FAX 44-131-243-9501, information@nts.org.uk, http://www.nts.org.uk. Ed., R&P Hilary Horrocks TEL 44-131-243-9383. Circ: 250,000.

333.72 GBR
THE NATIONAL TRUST GUIDEBOOK. Text in English. 1968. 3/yr. free membership (effective 2005); includes National Trust Handbook. adv. bk.rev. **Document type:** *Newsletter, Consumer.* **Description:** Promotes the conservation of nature and history, with an emphasis on the countryside (gardens, uplands and country houses).
Former titles: National Trust (0266-8068); (until 1972): National Trust News
Indexed: AIAP, API.
—**CCC.**
Published by: National Trust for Places of Historic Interest or National Beauty, 36 Queen Annes Gate, London, SW1H 9AS, United Kingdom. TEL 44-870-6095380, FAX 44-20-72225097, enquiries@thenationaltrust.org.uk, http://www.nationaltrust.org.uk/. Ed. Gaynor Aaltonen. adv.: B&W page GBP 12,070, color page GBP 14,850. Circ: 1,800,000.

333.72 AUS ISSN 1036-9880
NATIONAL TRUST OF AUSTRALIA (NEW SOUTH WALES) NATIONAL TRUST QUARTERLY. Text in English. 1973 (no.58). q. AUD 49 (effective 2000). adv. bk.rev. bibl.; illus. 36 p./no.; **Document type:** *Magazine, Consumer.* **Description:** Covers heritage, environment, conservation issues, events & activities, special member events, house, gardens and news.
Former titles: National Trust of Australia (New South Wales) National Trust Magazine (0811-0964); National Trust of Australia (New South Wales) National Trust Bulletin (0047-9128)
—BLDSC (6033.191000).
Published by: National Trust of Australia (New South Wales), GPO Box 518, Sydney, NSW 2001, Australia. TEL 61-2-9258-0123, 61-2-92580143, FAX 61-2-9252-1264, alesueur@nsw.nationaltrust.org.au, http://www.nsw.nationaltrust.org.au. Ed. Angela Le Sueur. Adv. contact Peki Filray. page AUD 1,995. Circ: 25,000.

333.95416 USA ISSN 0028-0402
S964.U6
NATIONAL WILDLIFE; dedicated to the conservation of our nation's natural resources. Text in English. 1962. bi-m. USD 20 domestic membership; USD 26 foreign membership (effective 2005). adv. charts; illus.; pat.; tr.mk. index. reprint service avail. from PQC. **Document type:** *Magazine, Consumer.* **Description:** Features articles and photographs of the natural world and its inhabitants. Informs about issues affecting the environment, flora and fauna, and humans and suggests remedial actions.
Related titles: Microfiche ed.: (from NBI, PQC); Online - full text ed.: (from bigchalk, EBSCO Publishing, Florida Center for Library Automation, Gale Group, H.W. Wilson, Northern Light Technology, Inc., O C L C Online Computer Library Center, Inc., ProQuest Information & Learning); International ed.: National Wildlife World Edition. ISSN 1545-5157.
Indexed: APD, ARG, ASFA, AcaI, BiolAb, BiolDig, CIJE, CPerI, EPB, ESPM, EnvAb, EnvInd, GSI, GardL, ICM, ISR, JHMA, MASUSE, MEA&I, MagInd, PollutAb, RGAb, RGPR, RGYP, RI-1, RI-2, SSI, SWRA, TOM, WBA, WildRev.
—BLDSC (6033.350000), IE, Infotrieve, ingenta, Linda Hall.
Published by: National Wildlife Federation, 11100 Wildlife Center Dr., Reston, VA 20190-5362. TEL 703-438-6284, 800-822-9919, FAX 703-438-6349, pubs@nwf.org, http://www.nwf.org. Pub. Mark Wexler. R&P Kelly Senser TEL 703-790-4510. Adv. contact Thuy Senser. B&W page USD 12,852, color page USD 19,278. Circ: 500,000 (controlled).

333.783 DEU ISSN 0342-9806
NATIONALPARK; Wildnis - Mensch - Landschaft. Text in German. 1974. q. EUR 21 (effective 2002). **Document type:** *Magazine, Consumer.*
Published by: Morsak Verlag oHG, Wittelbacherstr 2-8, Grafenau, 94481, Germany. TEL 49-8552-4200, FAX 49-8552-42050, info@morsak.de, http://www.morsak.de. Eds. Anneliese Mueller, Eva Pongratz. Pub. Erich Stecher.

333.783 DEU ISSN 0937-0048
NATIONALPARK BAYERISCHER WALD. Text in German. 197?. irreg., latest vol.13, 1992. price varies. **Document type:** *Monographic series, Academic/Scholarly.*
Published by: Nationalparkverwaltung Bayerischer Wald, Freyunger Str. 2, Grafenau, 94481, Germany. TEL 49-8552-96000, FAX 49-8552-9600100, poststelle@fonpv-bay.bayern.de, http://www.forst.bayern.de/npv.

333.783 DEU ISSN 0172-0023
NATIONALPARK BERCHTESGADEN. FORSCHUNGSBERICHTE. Text in German. 1979. irreg., latest vol.46. price varies. **Document type:** *Monographic series, Academic/Scholarly.*
Indexed: ZooRec.
—BLDSC (4011.325000), IE, ingenta.

Published by: Nationalparkverwaltung Berchtesgaden, Doktorberg 6, Berchtesgaden, 83471, Germany. TEL 49-8652-96860, FAX 49-8652-968640, poststelle@nationalpark-berchtesgaden.de, http://www.nationalpark-berchtesgaden.de.

| 333.783 | DEU | ISSN 0946-7645 |

NATIONALPARK SCHLESWIG-HOLSTEINISCHES WATTENMEER. SCHRIFTENREIHE. Text in German. 1989. irreg., latest vol.13, 2000. Document type: Monographic series, Academic/Scholarly.

Indexed: ESPM.

Published by: Nationalpark Schleswig-Holsteinisches Wattenmeer, Schlossgarten 1, Toenning, 25832, Germany. TEL 49-4861-61670, FAX 49-4861-61679, service@wattenmeer-nationalpark.de, http://www.wattenmeer-nationalpark.de.

NATIVE FOREST NETWORK. EASTERN NORTH AMERICAN RESOURCE CENTER. BULLETIN. see FORESTS AND FORESTRY

NATUR OG MILJOE. see ENVIRONMENTAL STUDIES

| 333.72 | DEU |

NATUR-SPIEGEL. Text in German. q. adv. Document type: Newsletter.

Published by: (Naturschutzbund Deutschland e.V.), Stuenings Medien GmbH, Diessemer Bruch 167, Krefeld, 47805, Germany. medien@stuenings.de, http://www.stuenings.de. Ed., Adv. contact Ingrid Roesch. Co-sponsor: Bezirksverband Krefeld-Viersen e.V.

| 333.72 | DEU | ISSN 0028-0615 |
| QH77.G3 | | |

NATUR UND LANDSCHAFT; Zeitschrift fuer Naturschutz, Landschaftspflege und Umweltschutz. Text in German. 1925. m. EUR 60.90, CHF 119.20; CHF 79.80 to students; EUR 6.40, CHF 12.50 newsstand/cover (effective 2002). bk.rev. charts. index. Document type: Journal, Consumer.

Indexed: ASFA, BiolAb, DokStr, ESPM, ExcerpMed, ForAb, IBR, IBZ, KWIWR, RRTA, WAE&RSA.
—IE, Infotrieve. CCC.

Published by: (Germany. Bundesanstalt fuer Naturschutz und Landschaftsoekologie), W. Kohlhammer GmbH, Hessbruehlstr 69, Stuttgart, 70565, Germany. TEL 49-711-7863-1, FAX 49-711-7863263, info@kohlhammer-katalog.de, http://www.kohlhammer.de. Eds. Marlies Petzoldt, Dr. W Mrass.

NATURA & MONTAGNA; rivista semestrale di divulgazione naturalistica. see BIOLOGY

NATURAL AREAS JOURNAL. see ENVIRONMENTAL STUDIES

NATURAL AREAS NEWS. see ENVIRONMENTAL STUDIES

| 333.72 | AUS | ISSN 1440-7256 |
| S478.A1 | | |

NATURAL HERITAGE. Text in English. 1998. q.

Related titles: Online - full text ed.

Published by: Natural Heritage Trust, PO Box 144, Lyneham, ACT 2602, Australia. TEL 61-2-6207-5584, FAX 61-2-6207-2244, http://www.nht.gov.au/publications/index.html#journal. Ed. Sarah Mamalai.

| 333.72 | ZMB |

NATURAL HERITAGE. Text in English. 1993. irreg., latest vol.2. USD 2. adv.

Published by: National Heritage Conservation Commission, PO Box 60124, Livingstone, Zambia. TEL 260-320354, FAX 260-324509. Adv. contact Maxwell Zulu TEL 260-320481.

| 333.783 | HUN |

NATURAL HISTORY OF THE NATIONAL PARKS OF HUNGARY. Text in English. 1981. irreg. USD 60 foreign (effective 2000). back issues avail. Document type: Monographic series, Academic/Scholarly.

Published by: (Germany. Magyar Termeszettudomanyi Muzeum, Baross utca 13, Budapest, 1088, Hungary. TEL 36-1-2677100, FAX 36-1-3171669, perego@zoo.zoo.nhmus.hu, http://www.nhmus.hu. Ed. S Mahunka. R&P, Adv. contact I Matskasi TEL 36-1-2677100. Circ: 300.

NATURAL LIFE. see GENERAL INTEREST PERIODICALS—Canada

| 333.72 | USA | ISSN 1527-5736 |
| QH104.5.N4 | | |

NATURAL NEW ENGLAND. Text in English. 2000. 5/yr. USD 21; USD 3.95 newsstand/cover (effective 2001). Document type: Consumer.

Indexed: BiolDig.

Published by: Belfield Publishing, 11 Belfield Rd., Cape Elizabeth, ME 04107. TEL 207-767-7204, nne@maine.rr.com, http://www.naturalne.com. Ed., Pub. Gregory M Walsh.

| 333.72 363.73 | USA |

NATURAL OUTLOOK. Text in English. q. free to qualified personnel (effective 2005). back issues avail. Document type: Magazine, Government. Description: Covers environmental issues in Texas with a focus on air quality, water quality, drought and Sunset Advisory Commission Review.

Related titles: Online - full content ed.; Alternate Frequency ed(s).: Natural Outlook Monthly Update. m.

Published by: Texas Natural Resource Conservation Commission, Small Business and Environmental Assistance Division, Mail Code 106, P O Box 13087, Austin, TX 78711-3087. TEL 512-239-0010, FAX 512-239-5010, ac@tnrcc.state.tx.us, http://www.tnrcc.state.tx.us. Ed. Jorjanna Price TEL 512-239-0154.

NATURAL RESOURCE MANAGEMENT AND POLICY. see ENVIRONMENTAL STUDIES

NATURAL RESOURCE PERSPECTIVES. see BUSINESS AND ECONOMICS—International Development And Assistance

| 333.72 | USA | ISSN 1544-5429 |
| S900 | | |

NATURAL RESOURCE YEAR IN REVIEW. Text in English. 1996. a.

Related titles: Online - full text ed.: ISSN 1544-5437.

Published by: U.S. Department of the Interior, National Park Service, Natural Resource Information Division, Rm. 260, P. O. Box 260, Denver, CO 80225-0287. TEL 303-969-2147, http://www.nature.nps.gov/pubs/yir. Ed. Jeff Selleck.

NATURAL RESOURCES AND ENVIRONMENTAL ISSUES. see ENVIRONMENTAL STUDIES

NATURAL RESOURCES FORUM. see GEOGRAPHY

| 346.044 | USA | ISSN 0028-0739 |
| K14 | | CODEN: NRJOAB |

➤ THE NATURAL RESOURCES JOURNAL. Text in English. 1961. q. USD 40 domestic; USD 45 foreign; USD 15 newsstand/cover (effective 2005). adv. bk.rev. charts; illus.; abstr.; maps. index, cum.index every 10 yrs. 200 p./no.; back issues avail.; reprint service avail. from WSH. Document type: Journal, Academic/Scholarly.

Related titles: Microfiche ed.: (from PMC, WSH); Microfilm ed.: (from PMC, WSH); Microform ed.: (from WSH); Online - full text ed.: (from H.W. Wilson, LexisNexis, O C L C Online Computer Library Center, Inc.).

Indexed: ABCPolSci, AESIS, APD, ASCA, ASFA, Agr, BAS, BRI, CBRI, CLI, CPM, CurCont, DIP, EIA, EPB, ESPM, EnerRev, EnvAb, EnvEAb, EnvInd, ExcerpMed, FPA, ForAb, GEOBASE, I&DA, IBR, IBSS, IBZ, ILP, JEL, KES, LRI, LegCont, MAB, PAIS, PSA, PetrolAb, PollutAb, RASB, RDA, RRTA, RefZh, S&F, SFA, SSCI, SUSA, SWRA, WAE&RSA, WildRev.
—BLDSC (6040.750000), CIS, IDS, IE, Infotrieve, ingenta, PADDS.

Published by: University of New Mexico, School of Law, MSC11 6070, 1 University of New Mexico, Albuquerque, NM 87131-0001. TEL 505-277-8659, FAX 505-277-8342, nrj@law.unm.edu, lawrev@law.unm.edu, http://lawschool.unm.edu/nrj/index.htm, htttp://lawschool.unm.edu, Ed. G Emlen Hall TEL 505-277-2866. R&P, Adv. contact Susan Tackman. Circ: 2,000.

| 333.72 | CAN | ISSN 1713-8639 |
| | | CODEN: ALNAEC |

NATURE ALBERTA. Text in English. 1970. q. CND 20 to members (effective 2005). adv. bk.rev. cum.index: 1970-1980, 1981-1985, 1986-1990, 1991-1995. back issues avail. Document type: Newsletter. Description: Covers conservation, nature, rare plants, animals, birds, insects and environmental issues.

Formerly (until 2004): Alberta Naturalist (0318-5540)

Indexed: KWIWR, SFA, WildRev, ZooRec.
—CISTI. CCC.

Published by: Federation of Alberta Naturalists, 11759 Groat Rd, Edmonton, AB T5M 3K6, Canada. TEL 780-427-8124, FAX 780-422-2663, fan@fanweb.ca, http://www.fanweb.ca. Ed. Brian Parker. R&P, Adv. contact Karen Rimney. page CND 100. Circ: 500 (paid).

| 333.72 | FRA | ISSN 0252-0575 |

NATURE AND ENVIRONMENT SERIES. Text in English. 1967. irreg. price varies.

Formerly: Conservation of Nature and Natural Resources (0069-9144)

Related titles: French ed.: Collection Sauvegarde de la Nature. ISSN 0252-0567. 1968.

Indexed: KWIWR, REE&TA, ZooRec.
—BLDSC (6046.082500), IE.

Published by: Council of Europe/Conseil de l'Europe, Publications Section, Strasbourg, Cedex 67075, France. TEL 33-3-88412581, FAX 33-3-88413910, publishing@coe.fr, http://book.coe.fr. Dist. in U.S. by: Manhattan Publishing Co., 468 Albany Post Rd, Croton On Hudson, NY 10520.

| 333.72 | CAN | ISSN 0374-9894 |
| | | CODEN: NTCNBM |

NATURE CANADA; the national magazine on nature and the environment. Text in English. 1939. 4/yr. CND 37.45 domestic to individuals; CND 45 foreign to individuals; CND 30 domestic to institutions; CND 40 foreign to institutions; CND 3.50 newsstand/cover (effective 2000). adv. bk.rev. bibl.; charts; illus.; stat. Index. back issues avail.; reprints avail. Document type: Consumer. Description: Presents articles on Canadian nature, natural history and environment for members of the Canadian Nature Federation and the general population.

Former titles (until 1972): Canadian Audubon (0008-2929); (until 1958): Canadian Nature (0319-1451)

Related titles: Microform ed.: (from PQC); Online - full text ed.: (from Gale Group, Micromedia ProQuest).

Indexed: APD, BiolAb, BiolDig, CBPI, CPerl, EPB, ICM, KWIWR, MASUSE, MagInd, SFA.
—CISTI, Linda Hall.

Published by: Canadian Nature Federation, 1 Nicholas St, Ste 606, Ottawa, ON K1N 7B7, Canada. TEL 613-562-3447, 800-267-4080, FAX 613-562-3371, CNF@cnf.ca, naturecanada@cnf.ca, http://www.cnf.ca. Ed. Barbara Stevenson. R&P Cendrine Huemer. Adv. contact Carolyn Ford. B&W page USD 1,440, color page USD 2,010; trim 10.88 x 8.13. Circ: 13,350 (paid).

| 333.72 | USA | ISSN 1540-2428 |

NATURE CONSERVANCY. Text in English. 1951. q. USD 50 donation (effective 2005). adv. illus. reprints avail. Document type: Magazine, Consumer. Description: Membership magazine covering biological diversity and related conservation issues.

Former titles (until 1990): Nature Conservancy Magazine (1540-241X); (until 1987): Nature Conservancy News (0028-0852)

Related titles: Online - full text ed.

Indexed: BiolDig, EPB, EnvAb, GSI, GardL, WildRev.

Address: 4245 N Fairfax Dr, Ste 100, Arlington, VA 22203-1606. TEL 703-841-5300, 800-628-6860, FAX 703-841-1283, comment@tnc.org, http://www.nature.org, http://www.tnc.org/. Ed. Courtney Leatherman. Circ: 900,000 (controlled).

| 333.72 | POL |
| | | CODEN: OCPZAE |

➤ NATURE CONSERVATION. Text in English. 1920. a., latest vol.58, 2001. USD 15. bibl.; charts; illus. 120 p./no. 2 cols./p.; back issues avail. Document type: Journal, Academic/Scholarly.

Formerly (until 2001): Ochrona Przyrody (0078-3250)

Indexed: AgrLib, BiolAb, SFA, WildRev, ZooRec.

Published by: Polska Akademia Nauk, Instytut Ochrony Przyrody, al A Mickiewicza 33, Krakow, 31120, Poland. TEL 48-12-6320549, FAX 48-12-6322432, makomaska@iop.krakow.pl, http://www.iop.krakow.pl. Ed. Zbigniew Witkowski.

| 333.72 | AUS |

NATURE CONSERVATION NEWS✳. Text in English. 1972. 3/m. AUD 15. bk.rev. Description: Gives an update on environmental and conservation issues in NSW. It also serves as a notice of events, and as an agenda for council activities.

Former titles: Nature Conservation Council of N.S.W. Newsletter; Nature Conservation Council of N.S.W. Bulletin (0311-0745)

Published by: Nature Conservation Council of N.S.W., Level 5, 362 Kent St, Sydney, NSW 2000, Australia. TEL 61-2-92474206, FAX 61-2-92475945. Circ: 450.

| 333.72 | GHA |

NATURE ET FAUNE; international journal on nature conservation in Africa. Text in English, French. 1984. q. free. Description: Covers wildlife conservation and management in Africa.

Published by: Food and Agriculture Organization of the United Nations, Regional Office for Africa, PO Box 1628, Accra, Ghana. Ed. Pape D Kone. Circ: 1,500. Co-sponsor: United Nations Environment Programme.

NATURE ETHIQUE; la revue qui est dans le vent pour une meilleure qualite de vie. see SPORTS AND GAMES—Outdoor Life

| 333.72 639.9 | CAN | ISSN 1491-2139 |

NATURE MATTERS. Text in English. 1991. q. Description: Keeps members and donors informed about issues that the C N F is working on, such as conservation achievements and initiatives, and includes nature tips and calls to action.

Formerly (until 1999): Nature Alert (1185-8877)

Related titles: Online - full text ed.: (from bigchalk, EBSCO Publishing, Micromedia ProQuest).

Indexed: CPerl, MASUSE.
—CISTI.

Published by: Canadian Nature Federation, 1 Nicholas St, Ste 606, Ottawa, ON K1N 7B7, Canada. TEL 613-562-3447, FAX 613-562-3371, cnf@cnf.ca, http://www.cnf.ca/matters/index.html.

| 333.9516 | CAN |

NATURE NORTH ZINE. Text in English. 1998. q. Description: Aims to be a source for teachers and parents in helping them to understand nature and wildlife.

Media: Online - full text.

Address: 501 Craig St, Winnipeg, MB R3G 3C2, Canada. nnz@naturenorth.com, http://www.naturenorth.com/. Ed. Tom Keep.

333.72 USA
NATURE PAGES. Text in English. m. bk.rev. **Document type:** *Newsletter.* **Description:** For readers and authors of nature stories.
Media: Online - full text.
Address: hofferber@aol.com, mhoutrder@aol.com. Ed. Michael Hofferber.

NATURE STUDY. see *ENVIRONMENTAL STUDIES*

333.72 770 USA ISSN 1525-1837
NATURE'S BEST. Text in English. 199?. q. USD 20 domestic; USD 28 in Canada & Mexico; USD 46 elsewhere (effective 2002). adv. illus. **Document type:** *Magazine, Consumer.* **Description:** Offers a showcase presentation of the natural world recorded by the world's leading photographers, writers, and adventurers.
Published by: Image Hunter Publishing, PO Box 10070, McLea, VA 22102. TEL 703-759-6575, FAX 703-759-3193, editor@naturesbestmagazine.com, http://www.naturesbestmagazine.com. Ed., Pub. Stephen Freligh. R&P, Adv. contact Monica Ballenger.

333.7 CAN ISSN 1480-1167
NATURE'S RESOURCES. Variant title: Forestry, Minerals, Parks & Wildlife in Nova Scotia. Text in English. 1966. s-a. CND 5.75 domestic; CND 9 foreign (effective 2004). **Document type:** *Magazine, Consumer.* **Description:** Promotes the understanding and wise use of Nova Scotia's natural resources.
Former titles (until 1997): Conservation (0702-732X); (until 1977): Wildlife Newsletter (1191-4866)
Published by: Nova Scotia. Department of Natural Resources, PO Box 698, Halifax, NS B3J 2T9, Canada. TEL 902-424-5935, FAX 902-424-7735, emgratto@gov.ns.ca, http://www.gov.ns.ca/natr/publications/naturesresources/.

C

NATUREZA; revista dos amantes da natureza. see *GARDENING AND HORTICULTURE*

333.73 DNK ISSN 0908-8245
QH77.D4
NATURFORVALTNING; aarsberetning. Text in Danish. 2000. a., latest 1999. DKK 80 (effective 2003).
Related titles: Online - full content ed.: ISSN 1601-9083. free.
Published by: Miljoeministeriet, Skov- og Naturstyrelsen/Ministry of the Environment. Danish Forest & Nature Agency, Haraldsgade 53, Copenhagen OE, 2100, Denmark. TEL 45-39-472000, FAX 45-39-279899, sns@sns.dk, http://www.sns.dk/udgivelser, http://www.skovognatur.dk.

NATURFREUNDIN. see *SPORTS AND GAMES—Outdoor Life*

333.72 FRA ISSN 0250-7102
NATUROPA. Text in French. 1968. 3/yr. free. illus. **Document type:** *Monographic series.*
Formerly: Nature in Focus (0250-7064)
Related titles: German ed.: ISSN 0250-7099; English ed.: ISSN 0250-7072; Italian ed.: ISSN 0250-7080; Portuguese ed.: ISSN 1016-4979; Spanish ed.: ISSN 1011-6133; Russian ed.: ISSN 1560-7666.
Indexed: ASFA, BiolDig, EIP, EPB, EnvAb, ExcerpMed, KWIWR, RRTA, SFA, WAE&RSA, WildRev, ZooRec.
Published by: (Centre Naturopa), Council of Europe/Conseil de l'Europe, Publications Section, Strasbourg, Cedex 67075, France. TEL 33-3-88412581, FAX 33-3-88413910, publishing@coe.fr, http://book.coe.fr. Ed. Jean Pierre Ribaut. Circ: 25,000.

333.72 DEU ISSN 0934-8883
NATURSCHUTZ HEUTE. Text in German. 1969. q. EUR 48 membership (effective 2003). adv. bk.rev. **Document type:** *Magazine, Consumer.*
Indexed: DIP, IBR, IBZ, KWIWR.
Published by: Naturschutzbund Deutschland e.V., Herbert-Rabius-Str. 26, Bonn, 53225, Germany. TEL 49-228-40360, FAX 49-228-4036200, naturschutz.heute@nabu.de, nabu@nabu.de, http://www.nabu.de. Ed. Bernd Pieper. Adv. contact Anne Schoenhofer. B&W page EUR 3,680, color page EUR 5,280; trim 210 x 286. Circ: 253,615 (controlled).

333.72 DEU ISSN 0936-6954
NATURSCHUTZ, LANDSCHAFTSPFLEGE, JAGD- UND FORSTRECHT. Text in German. 1977. irreg. price varies. **Document type:** *Monographic series, Trade.*
Published by: Erich Schmidt Verlag GmbH & Co. (Berlin), Genthiner Str 30G, Berlin, 10785, Germany. TEL 49-30-250085-0, FAX 49-30-25008511, esv@esvmedien.de, http://www.erich-schmidt-verlag.de.

333.72 DEU ISSN 0933-1247
NATURSCHUTZ UND LANDSCHAFTSPFLEGE IN NIEDERSACHSEN. Text in German. 1961. irreg. **Document type:** *Monographic series, Academic/Scholarly.*
Indexed: ZooRec.
Published by: Niedersaechsisches Landesamt fuer Oekologie, Postfach 101062, Hildesheim, 31110, Germany. TEL 49-5121-509-0, FAX 49-5121-509196, poststelle@nloe.niedersachsen.de, http://jupiter.nloe.de.

333.72 SWE ISSN 1403-8234
NATURVAARDSVERKETS FOERFATTNINGSSAMLING. Text in Swedish. 1999. irreg. price varies. **Document type:** *Government.*
Formerly (until 1999): Statens Naturvaardsverks Foerfattningssamling (0347-5301); Which superseded in part (in 1999): Allmaenna Raad (0282-7271); Which was formerly (until 1984): Raad och Riktlinjer (0347-5506); Which superseded in part (in 1977): Statens Naturvaardsverk. Publikationer (0039-0259); Which was formed by the 1969 merger of: Information Fraan Statens Naturvaardsverk. L; Information Fraan Statens Naturvaardsverk. V; Meddelande Fraan Statens Naturvaardsverk. N; Meddelande Fraan Statens Naturvaardsverk. V
Related titles: Online - full text ed.
—CISTI.
Published by: Naturvaardsverket/Swedish Environmental Protection Agency, Blekholmsterrassen 36, Stockholm, 10648, Sweden. TEL 46-8-6981000, FAX 46-8-202925, natur@naturvardsverket.se, http://www.naturvardsverket.se.

333.72 DEU ISSN 1437-0093
QH77.G3
NATUSCHUTZ UND LANDSCHAFTESPFLEGE BADEN-WUERTTEMBERG. Text in German. 1925. a. price varies. bk.rev. **Document type:** *Journal, Government.*
Formerly: Veroeffentlichungen fuer Naturschutz und Landschaftspflege in Baden-Wuerttemberg (0342-684X)
Indexed: ZooRec.
Published by: Landesanstalt fuer Umweltschutz, Postfach 210752, Karlsruhe, 76157, Germany. TEL 49-721-9831428, FAX 49-721-9831456, bibliothek@lfuka.lfu.bwl.de, http://uvm.baden-wuerttemberg.de/lfu. Pub. Dr. Winfried Krahl. Circ: 2,000.

333.72 NLD ISSN 0166-2570
NATUUR EN MILIEU. Text in Dutch. 1977. 10/yr. EUR 25 (effective 2003). adv. bk.rev.; Website rev. charts; illus. index. **Document type:** *Journal, Academic/Scholarly.*
Formed by the merger of (1946-1976): Natuur en Landschap (0028-1077); Which incorporated (1910-1971): Water, Bodem, Lucht (0043-1176); And (1973-1976): Natuur Milieuzorg (0304-4890); Which superseded (1970-1973): Stichting Centrum Mileuzorg. Medelingen (1381-0448)
Indexed: BiolAb, ExcerpMed, KES.
—IE, Infotrieve.
Published by: Stichting Natuur en Milieu/Association for Nature and Environment, Donkerstraat 17, Utrecht, 3511 KB, Netherlands. TEL 31-30-233-1328, FAX 31-30-233-1311, snm@snm.nl, http://www.snm.nl. Ed. M Jehae. Adv. contact Adviesbwo Cadex TEL 0111-643307. Circ: 9,000.

333.72 USA ISSN 0047-9217
NEBRASKA RESOURCES. Text in English. q. illus. **Document type:** *Government.*
Published by: Natural Resources Commission, 301 Centennial Mall South, Box 94876, Lincoln, NE 68509. TEL 402-471-2081.

333.73 USA ISSN 0028-1964
GV54.N36
NEBRASKALAND. Text in English. 1926. 10/yr. USD 16 (effective 2005). adv. bk.rev. charts; illus.; tr.lit. **Document type:** *Magazine, Consumer.* **Description:** Covers outdoor recreation in the state. Includes history, wildlife and conservation.
Formerly (until 1964): Outdoor Nebraskaland (0091-6404)
Published by: Nebraska Game and Parks Commission, 2200 N 33rd St, PO Box 30370, Lincoln, NE 68503. TEL 402-471-0641, FAX 402-471-5528, twhite@ngpc.state.ne.us, ngpc@ngpc.state.ne.us, http://www.ngpc.state.ne.us. Ed. Tom White. Circ: 40,000 (paid and free).

DE NEDERLANDSE JAGER; tijdschrift over natuur, wildbeheer en jachthonden. see *SPORTS AND GAMES—Outdoor Life*

333.72 RUS
NEFT' I KAPITAL. Text in Russian. 1995. m. USD 295 in North America (effective 2000).
Indexed: RefZh.
Published by: Izdatel'skii Dom Neft' i Kapital, Ul Mikhailovskaya 38-3, Moscow, 125438, Russian Federation. TEL 7-095-7421872. Ed. E Druzenko. **Dist. by:** East View Information Services, 3020 Harbor Ln. N., Minneapolis, MN 55447. TEL 763-550-0961, FAX 763-559-2931.

333.72 RUS ISSN 1028-9976
NEFT' ROSSII. Text in Russian. 1994. m. USD 395 in North America (effective 2004). **Document type:** *Magazine, Trade.*
Indexed: RefZh.
Published by: Lukoil Inform, Sretenskii b-r 11, Moscow, 101000, Russian Federation. TEL 7-095-9271691, FAX 7-095-9271692, subscribe@oilru.com, http://www.oilru.com/nr. **Subscr. in US to:** East View Information Services, 3020 Harbor Ln. N., Minneapolis, MN 55447. TEL 800-477-1005, FAX 800-800-3839, eastview@eastview.com, http://www.eastview.com.

NEOTROPICAL PRIMATES. see *BIOLOGY—Zoology*

333.72 GBR
NETWORK 21. Text in English. 1993. 3/yr. adv.
Related titles: Online - full text ed.
Published by: The Conservation Foundation, 1 Kensington Gore, London, SW7 2AR, United Kingdom. TEL 44-20-75913111, FAX 44-20-75913110, conservef@gn.apc.org, http://www.cityoflondon.gov.uk/environment, http://www.conservationfoundation.co.uk. adv.: page GBP 2,000. Circ: 700.

THE NEW BOOKBINDER; journal of designer bookbinders. see *PUBLISHING AND BOOK TRADE*

NEW BRUNSWICK. TOURISM RECREATION & HERITAGE. TECHNICAL SERVICES BRANCH. PROVINCIAL PARK STATISTICS. see *CONSERVATION—Abstracting, Bibliographies, Statistics*

363.70025 USA ISSN 1078-4616
NEW ENGLAND ENVIRONMENTAL DIRECTORY. Text in English. 1995. biennial. USD 18.50 (effective 2001). index. **Document type:** *Directory.* **Description:** Annotated listings of citizen groups and government agencies in Connecticut, Massachusetts, Maine, Rhode Island, New Hampshire and Vermont.
Media: CD-ROM. **Related titles:** Diskette ed.; Online - full text ed.
Published by: Harbinger Communications, 616 Sumner St, Santa Cruz, CA 95062. TEL 406-721-0440, FAX 406-721-0440, ned@ism.net, http://eelink.net/gaindirectories.html.

NEW ENGLAND WILD FLOWER CONSERVATION NOTES. see *BIOLOGY—Botany*

NEW ENGLAND WILD FLOWER GARDEN, FARM, AND SANCTUARY NEWS. see *GARDENING AND HORTICULTURE*

333.72 USA ISSN 0162-5284
NEW HAMPSHIRE AUDUBON. Text in English. 1921. bi-m. USD 30 to individuals; USD 45 to institutions (effective 2000). bk.rev. charts; illus. **Document type:** *Newsletter.* **Description:** Focuses on conservation of wildlife and habitats in New Hampshire. Also includes articles on environmental policy and education.
Formerly: New Hampshire Audubon News (0028-520X)
Indexed: SFA, WildRev.
Published by: Audubon Society of New Hampshire, 3 Silk Farm Rd, Box 528 B, Concord, NH 03301. TEL 603-224-9909, FAX 603-226-0902, http://www.nhaudubon.org. Ed., Pub., R&P Miranda Levin. Circ: 7,000.

333.72 USA ISSN 0077-8362
NEW HAMPSHIRE. FISH AND GAME DEPARTMENT. BIENNIAL REPORT. Text in English. 1865. biennial. **Document type:** *Government.*
Published by: Fish and Game Department, 2 Hazen Dr, Concord, NH 03301. TEL 603-271-3211, 800-735-2964, FAX 603-271-1438, info@wildlife.state.n.h.us, http://www.wildlife.state.n.h.us. Ed., R&P Eric E Aldrich. Circ: 4,000.

NEW HAMPSHIRE WILDLIFE JOURNAL. see *SPORTS AND GAMES—Outdoor Life*

333.72 USA
NEW JERSEY CONSERVATION; magazine of the NJ Conservation Foundation. Text in English. 1997. q. USD 35 to members. bk.rev. illus.; maps. 16 p./no.; back issues avail. **Document type:** *Magazine, Consumer.* **Description:** Focuses on how to enjoy and protect New Jersey's farmland, landscapes, and outdoor recreation.
Formed by the merger of: Environmental Bulletin; Footprints (Far Hills); Land Forum
Indexed: AIAP.
Published by: New Jersey Conservation Foundation, 170 Longview Rd, Far Hills, NJ 07931. info@njconservation.org, http://www.njconservation.org. Ed. David Zuidema. Circ: 5,000.

333.72 USA
NEW JERSEY CONSERVATION FOUNDATION (YEAR) ANNUAL REPORT. Text in English. 1960. a. free or donation. back issues avail. **Document type:** *Yearbook, Corporate.* **Description:** Outlines the foundation's financial assets and liabilities and defines the organization's objectives. NJCF purchases the land or development rights of ecologically sensitive properties to conserve wildlife habitats.
Published by: New Jersey Conservation Foundation, 170 Longview Rd, Far Hills, NJ 07931. TEL 908-234-1225, FAX 908-234-1189, info@njconservation.or. Ed. David Zuidema. Pub. Michele S Byers. R&P Richard Ryan TEL 908-234-1225.

333.95416 USA ISSN 0028-6338
SK427 CODEN: NMWIAN
NEW MEXICO WILDLIFE. Text in English. 1961. bi-m. USD 10. bk.rev. charts; illus. index. reprint service avail. from PQC. **Document type:** *Government.*
Related titles: Microform ed.: (from PQC).
Indexed: BiolAb, SFA, WildRev, ZooRec.
—Linda Hall.

Published by: Department of Game and Fish, PO Box 25112, Sante Fe, NM 87504. TEL 505-827-7911, FAX 505-827-7915. Circ: 10,000.

333.78 CAN ISSN 1189-4512
NEW PARKS NORTH. Text in English. 1992. a. **Document type:** *Newsletter.* **Description:** Provides reports on projects concerning the establishment and development of new parks, related heritage areas, and other conservation initiatives in northern Canada.
Related titles: Online - full text ed.: ISSN 1495-5180.
Published by: Parks Canada, National Parks and National Historic Sites, Box 1166, Yellowknife, NT X1A 2N8, Canada. TEL 867-669-2820, FAX 867-669-2829, newparksnorth@pc.gc.ca, http://www.newparksnorth.org/index.htm, http://parkscanada.gc.ca. Ed. Judi Cozzetto.

▼ **NEW SOUTH WALES, AUSTRALIA. DEPARTMENT OF ENVIRONMENT AND CONSERVATION. ANNUAL REPORT.** see *PUBLIC ADMINISTRATION*

NEW YORK ENVIRONMENTAL CONSERVATION LAW. see *LAW*

333.72 USA
QH76.5.N7
THE NEW YORK STATE CONSERVATIONIST. Text in English. 1946. bi-m. USD 12 (effective 2001). bk.rev. charts; illus. 32 p./no. 3 cols./p.; back issues avail. **Document type:** *Magazine, Government.* **Description:** Aimed at people who like to fish, hike, hunt, camp, ski, bird watch, or just enjoy the outdoors.
Former titles (until vol.50, no.1, 1995): Conservationist (0010-650X); (until 1960): New York State Conservationist (0097-3319)
Related titles: Microform ed.: (from PQC); Online - full text ed.: (from EBSCO Publishing, Gale Group, H.W. Wilson, O C L C Online Computer Library Center, Inc., ProQuest Information & Learning).
Indexed: APD, BiolAb, BiolDig, CIJE, EPB, EnerRev, EnvAb, GSI, ISR, MASUSE, MagInd, PMR, RGAb, RGPR, SFA, WBA, WMB, WildRev, ZooRec.
—BLDSC (6089.726000), IE, ingenta, Linda Hall.
Published by: Department of Environmental Conservation, 625 Broadway 2nd Floor, Albany, NY 12233-4502. TEL 518-402-8031, FAX 518-402-9036, http://www.dec.state.ny.us/website/about/pubconl4.html. Eds. D. H. Nelson, R W Groneman. R&P Linda Kaska. Circ: 100,000. **Subscr. to:** PO Box 1500, Latham, NY 12110.

333.72 NZL ISSN 1175-6519
S934.N45
➤ **NEW ZEALAND DEPARTMENT OF CONSERVATION. SCIENCE INTERNAL SERIES.** Text in English. N.S. 2001. irreg. **Document type:** *Academic/Scholarly.*
Formed by the 2001 merger of: Science and Research Internal Report (0114-2798); (1993-2001): New Zealand Department of Conservation. Technical Series (1172-6873); (1992-2001): Conservation Advisory Science Notes (1171-9834)
Indexed: ASFA, ESPM, ForAb, HelmAb, IndVet, PBA, S&F, VetBull, WeedAb, ZooRec.
Published by: New Zealand Department of Conservation - Science Publications, PO Box 10-420, Wellington, New Zealand. http://www.doc.govt.nz/Publications/004—cience-and-Research/DOC-Science-Internal-Series.asp.

333.72 USA
NEWS TO USE. Text in English. q. membership.
Indexed: RefZh.
Published by: International Erosion Control Association, PO Box 4904, Steamboat Springs, CO 80477-4904. TEL 970-879-3010, 800-455-4322, FAX 970-879-8563, ecinfo@ieca.org, http://www.ieca.org.

333.783 CAN ISSN 0078-0502
NIAGARA PARKS COMMISSION. ANNUAL REPORT. Text in English. 1886. a. free.
—CISTI.
Published by: Niagara Parks Commission, P O Box 150, Niagara Falls, ON L2E 6T2, Canada. TEL 416-356-2241, FAX 416-354-6041. Ed. George Bailey. Circ: 500.

333.72 NLD ISSN 1386-4920
NIEUWE ZELFZWICHTER. Text in Dutch. 1974. q. EUR 14 to members (effective 2005). bk.rev. **Document type:** *Bulletin, Consumer.* **Description:** Publishes news and information on the history and restoration of mills in the Groningen area.
Formerly (until 1997): Zelfwichter (1383-3340)
Published by: Vereniging van Vrienden van de Groninger Molens, Lopende Diep 8, Groningen, 9712 NW, Netherlands. TEL 31-50-3121694, FAX 31-50-3142584, molens@museumhuisgroningen.nl, http://www.groningermolens.nl. Ed. H A Hachmer. Circ: 1,000. **Co-sponsor:** Stichting Groninger Molenvrienden.

NIHON SEITAI GAKKAI KANTO CHIKUKAI KAIHO/ ECOLOGICAL SOCIETY OF JAPAN. KANTO BRANCH. NEWS. see *BIOLOGY*

NIHON SEITAI GAKKAI KYUSHU CHIKUKAI KAIHO/ECOLOGICAL SOCIETY OF JAPAN. KYUSHU BRANCH. BULLETIN. see *BIOLOGY*

NIHON SEITAI GAKKAI TOHOKU CHIKUKAI KAIHO/ECOLOGICAL SOCIETY OF JAPAN. TOHOKU BRANCH. NEWS. see *BIOLOGY*

577.22 USA
EL NINO SOUTHERN OSCILLATION DIAGNOSTIC ADVISORY. Text in English. w. free. **Document type:** *Academic/Scholarly.* **Description:** Aims to maintain a continous watch on short-term climate fluctuations and to diagnose and predict them.
Media: Online - full text.
Published by: National Center for Environmental Prediction, W-NP52, Ste. 605, 5200 Auth Rd., Camp Springs, MD 20746-4304. wd52vk@hp31.wwb.noaa.gov, http://nic.fb4.noaa.gov/products/analysis_monitoring/enso-advisory. **Co-sponsor:** Climate Prediction Center.

333.95416 GBR
NORFOLK WILDLIFE TRUST. ANNUAL REVIEW. Text in English. a. GBP 16 to members (effective 2001). **Document type:** *Corporate.*
Formerly: Norfolk Naturalists Trust. Annual Review
Published by: Norfolk Naturalists Trust, 72 Cathedral Close, Norwich, Norfolk NR1 4DF, United Kingdom. TEL 441603-625540, FAX 441603-614430. Ed. Anne Bloomfield. Circ: 10,000.

333.7 NOR ISSN 0807-0946
NORGES NATURVERNFORBUND. RAPPORT. Text in Norwegian. 1988. a. **Document type:** *Monographic series.*
Formerly (until 1990): Norges Naturvernforbund. Miljoerapport (0803-1436)
Published by: Norges Naturvernforbund/Norwegian Society for the Conservation of Nature, PO Box 342, Oslo, 0101, Norway. TEL 47-23-109610, FAX 47-23-109611.

NORTH AMERICAN SWANS; bulletin of the Trumpeter Swan Society. see *BIOLOGY—Ornithology*

333.7 CAN ISSN 1098-1942
QH75.A1
NORTH AMERICAN WETLANDS CONSERVATION ACT PROGRESS REPORT. Text in English. a.
Published by: North American Wetlands Conservation Council, 1770 Pink Rd, Hull, PQ K1A 0S9, Canada. TEL 819-956-4802, FAX 819-994-1498.

333.95416 USA ISSN 0078-1355
SK351 CODEN: NAWTA6
NORTH AMERICAN WILDLIFE AND NATURAL RESOURCES CONFERENCE. TRANSACTIONS. Text in English. 1915. a. (vol.68, 2003 due approx. Dec. 2003), latest vol.67, 2002. USD 38 per vol. (effective 2004). cum.index. back issues avail.; reprint service avail. from ISI. **Document type:** *Proceedings, Trade.*
Former titles (until 1936): Transactions of the American Game Conference; North American Wildlife Conference. Transactions (0097-6830); North American Wildlife Conference. Proceedings
Indexed: ASFA, Agr, BIOSIS Prev, BiolAb, FPA, ForAb, IndVet, M&GPA, NAmW, ProtozoAb, SFA, W&CBA, WildRev, ZooRec.
—BLDSC (9020.551000), CISTI, IE, ingenta, Linda Hall.
Published by: Wildlife Management Institute, 1146 19th St NW, Ste. 700, Washington, DC 20036-3727. TEL 202-371-1808, FAX 202-408-5059, http://www.wildlifemanagementinstitute.org, Eds. Jennifer Rahm, Richard E McCabe. R&P Richard E McCabe. Circ: 1,000.

333.72 USA
NORTH CAL-NEVA RESOURCE CONSERVATION AND DEVELOPMENT AREA. ANNUAL WORK PLAN✶. Variant title: Plan of Action. Program of Action. Text in English. 1968. a. free. illus.
Formerly: North Cal-Neva Resource Conservation and Development Project. Annual Work Plan (0097-7268)
Published by: North Cal-Neva Resource Conservation and Development Area, 804 W 12th St, Alturas, CA 96101-3132. FAX 916-233-2709. Ed. Jan Dybdahl. Circ: 500.

333.72 USA ISSN 0029-2761
SK351 CODEN: NDODA7
NORTH DAKOTA OUTDOORS; official journal of the game and fish department. Text in English. 1933. 10/yr. USD 10 (effective 2005). bk.rev. charts; illus. index. **Document type:** *Magazine.* **Description:** Articles on North Dakota wildlife, hunting, fishing and boating.
Related titles: Online - full text ed.
Indexed: SFA, WildRev, ZooRec.
—Linda Hall.
Published by: North Dakota Game and Fish Department, 100 N Bismarck Expy, Bismarck, ND 58501-5095. TEL 701-328-6300, http://www.state.nd.us/gnf/ndoutdoors/ndoutdoorsmag.html. Ed. Ron Wilson. Circ: 19,000.

333.72 USA ISSN 0029-2958
NORTH WOODS CALL. Text in English. 1953. fortn. USD 25 (effective 2000). adv. bk.rev. **Document type:** *Newspaper.* **Description:** Advocates an environmentally sensitive response to all issues involving natural resources.
Indexed: MMI.
Published by: North Woods Call, Inc., Rt 1, 00509 Turkey Run, Charlevoix, MI 49720. TEL 231-547-9797, FAX 231-547-0367. Ed. Glen Sheppard. Circ: 10,000 (paid).

NORTHEAST MEMO. see *SPORTS AND GAMES—Outdoor Life*

NORTHERN LIGHTS (MISSOULA). see *ENVIRONMENTAL STUDIES*

333.95416 AUS
NORTHERN TERRITORY. PARKS AND WILDLIFE COMMISSION. ANNUAL REPORT. Text in English. 1978. a. free. **Document type:** *Government.*
Former titles: Northern Territory. Conservation Commission. Annual Report (0159-8821); Northern Territory. Territory Parks and Wildlife Commission. Annual Report
Published by: Parks and Wildlife Commission, PO Box 496, Palmerston, N.T. 0830, Australia. TEL 61-8-8999-5511, FAX 61-8-8932-3849, pwent@nt.gov.au, http://www.nt.gov.au/paw/. Ed. Kathy Williams. Circ: 575.

NORTHERN WOODLANDS. see *FORESTS AND FORESTRY*

NOTICIAS DE GALAPAGOS. see *SCIENCES: COMPREHENSIVE WORKS*

NOVA SCOTIA TRAPPERS NEWSLETTER. see *LEATHER AND FUR INDUSTRIES*

NOW & THEN; the Appalachian magazine. see *LITERATURE*

NYALA. see *BIOLOGY—Zoology*

333.72 USA
O F W I M NEWSLETTER. Text in English. irreg. USD 25 to individual members. **Document type:** *Newsletter.* **Description:** Promotes the management and conservation of natural resources by facilitating technology and information exchange among managers of fish and wildlife information.
Published by: Organization of Fish and Wildlife Information Managers, 26 Snow St., Penacook, NH 03303. amartin@dgif.state.va.us, http://fwie.fw.vt.edu/ofwim. Ed. Jeff Smith.

578.0913 USA
O T S LIANA. Text in English. 1967. s-a. USD 30 (effective 2000). bk.rev. back issues avail. **Document type:** *Newsletter.* **Description:** Includes details of the Organization for Tropical Studies' undergraduate, graduate and professional courses, research conducted at the biological stations in Costa Rica and conservation activities.
Related titles: Spanish ed.
Published by: Organization for Tropical Studies/Organizacion para Estudios Tropicales, PO Box 90632, Durham, NC 27708-0632. TEL 919-684-5774, FAX 919-684-5661. Eds. Christina Cheatham, Jonathan Giles. R&P Christina Cheatham. Circ: 3,500 (paid and controlled).

577 ITA ISSN 1591-2736
OASIS; natura, ecologia, fotografia e viaggi. Text in Italian. 1985. bi-m. EUR 17 (effective 2005). adv. **Document type:** *Magazine, Consumer.*
Published by: Industrie Grafiche Editoriali Musumeci SpA, Loc Amerique 99, Quart, AO 11020, Italy. TEL 39-0165-765853, FAX 39-0165-765106. Ed. Pietro Giglio. Circ: 65,000.

333.72 RUS
OBZORNAYA INFORMATSIYA. LABORATORNYE I TEKHNOLOGICHESKIE ISSLEDOVANIYA MINERAL'NOGO SYR'YA. Text in Russian. 1996. q. USD 69 in North America.
Published by: Informatsionno-Izdatel'skii Tsentr po Geologii i Nedropol'zovaniu Geoinformmark, Goncharnaya 38, Moscow, 115172, Russian Federation. info@geoinform.ru. **Dist. by:** East View Information Services, 3020 Harbor Ln. N., Minneapolis, MN 55447. TEL 763-550-0961, FAX 763-559-2931.

333.91 639.2 551.46 USA ISSN 0738-9833
GV840.S78
OCEAN REALM; international magazine of the sea. Text in English. 1988. q. USD 79.95 domestic (effective 2001); USD 99.95 foreign. adv. bk.rev. illus. back issues avail. **Document type:** *Consumer.* **Description:** Focuses on conservation and the protection of marine ecosystems by increasing awareness on issues of concern in the marine environment.
Indexed: BiolDig, SFA, WildRev.
Published by: Friends of the Sea, Inc., 4067 Broadway, PO Box 6768, San Antonio, TX 78209. TEL 210-824-8099, 800-746-2326, FAX 210-820-3522, oceanica@eden.com, http://www.oceanrealm.net. Ed. Charlene Dejori. Pub., R&P, Adv. contact Cheryl Schorp. color page USD 2,875; trim 10.88 x 8.88. Circ: 30,000; 27,457 (paid); 2,543 (controlled). **Subscr. to:** PO Box 99275, Collingswood, NJ 08108-9803.

OCEANS ILLUSTRATED; giving voice to the silent world. see *EARTH SCIENCES—Oceanography*

333.72 DEU ISSN 1430-6646
OEKOLOGIEPOLITIK. Text in German. 1984. bi-m. EUR 12; EUR 2.50 newsstand/cover (effective 2002). adv. bk.rev. **Document type:** *Magazine, Consumer.* **Description:** Contains political ecology and party-related information for party members and others interested in environmental politics.
Formerly: Oekologie und Politik
Published by: Oekologisch - Demokratische Partei, Bundesgeschaeftsstelle, Bohnesmuehlgasse 5, Wuerzburg, 97070, Germany. TEL 49-931-40486-0, FAX 49-931-4048629, geschaeftsstelle@oedp.de, http://www.oedp.de. Ed. Raphael Mankau. adv.: page EUR 739; trim 175 x 264. Circ: 6,700.

OF THE WORLD SERIES. see *BIOLOGY—Zoology*

OHIO ENVIRONMENTAL REPORT. see *ENVIRONMENTAL STUDIES*

OHIO FISH AND WILDLIFE REPORT. see *BIOLOGY—Zoology*

333.72 JPN ISSN 0912-4071
OKAYAMA NO SHIZEN/NATURE IN OKAYAMA. Text in Japanese. bi-m. JPY 300.
Published by: Okayama no Shizen o Mamoru Kai/Study Group of Nature Protection in Okayama, 1-21 Tsushima-Minami 1-chome, Okayama-shi, 700-0085, Japan.

333.72 RUS
OKHRANA DIKOI PRIRODY. Text in Russian. 1999. q. free. **Document type:** *Journal, Academic/Scholarly.*
—BLDSC (0128.668000).
Published by: Tsentr Okhrany Dikoi Prirody, Ul Vavilova 41, ofis 2, Moscow, 117312, Russian Federation. TEL 7-095-1245022, FAX 7-095-1247178, izdat@bcc.seu.ru, http://www.biodiversity.ru. Ed. E Pavlova. Circ: 1,500.

333.72 USA ISSN 0095-442X
S916.O5
OKLAHOMA. CONSERVATION COMMISSION. BIENNIAL REPORT. Text in English. 1941. biennial. free. stat. **Document type:** *Government.*
—CISTI.
Published by: Conservation Commission, 2800 Lincoln, Ste 160, Oklahoma City, OK 73105. TEL 405-521-2384. Ed. Mason Mungle. Circ: 175 (controlled).

333.72 HRV ISSN 1330-6154
OKOLIS. Text in Croatian. 1991. m. **Document type:** *Magazine, Consumer.*
Address: Ulica Grada Vukovara 78, Zagreb, 10000, Croatia. TEL 385-1-6106561, FAX 385-1-537203. Ed. Ante Kutle.

333.72 USA
ON THE EDGE (PHILADELPHIA)✶ . Text in English. 1976. 3/yr. USD 25 to members (effective 1999). **Document type:** *Newsletter.*
Published by: Wildlife Preservation Trust International, 1200 Lincoln Ave Apt 2, Prospect Park, PA 19076-2003. TEL 215-731-9770, 800-978-4275, FAX 215-731-9766, homeoffice@wpti.org, http://www.columbia.edu/cu/cerc/wpti.html. Ed. Mary C Pearl. Circ: 3,000.

ON THE WILD SIDE. see *ENVIRONMENTAL STUDIES*

ONE EARTH (HONG KONG). see *ENVIRONMENTAL STUDIES*

333.72 CAN
ONTARIO OUT OF DOORS HOTLINE; the angler & hunter hotline. Text in English. 1989. m. free to members. adv. back issues avail. **Document type:** *Newsletter.*
Published by: Ontario Federation of Anglers & Hunters, 4601 Guthrie Dr, P O Box 2800, Peterborough, ON K9J 8L5, Canada. TEL 705-748-6324, FAX 705-748-9577, ofah@ofah.org, http://www.ofah.org. Ed., R&P, Adv. contact Mark Holmes. Circ: 79,240 (paid).

333.78 GBR ISSN 0265-8445
OPEN SPACE. Text in English. 1927. 3/yr. GBP 7.50 domestic; GBP 10 in Europe; GBP 15 elsewhere (effective 2001). bk.rev. **Document type:** *Corporate.* **Description:** Journal of general interest to environmentalists concerned with land and public recreational access, especially commons, village greens and rights of way.
Formerly (until 1982): Commons, Open Spaces and Footpaths Preservation Society. Journal (0010-3322); Incorporates: Commons, Open Spaces and Footpaths Preservation Society. Annual Report
Indexed: RRTA, WAE&RSA.
Published by: Open Spaces Society, 25a Bell St, Henley-on-Thames, Oxon RG9 2BA, United Kingdom. TEL 44-1491-573535, osshq@aol.com, http://www.oss.org.uk. Ed., Adv. contact Kate Ashbrook. Circ: 2,300.

ORGANIC FARMING; Soil Association's journal for organic horticulture & agriculture. see *AGRICULTURE*

ORION (GREAT BARRINGTON); people and nature. see *ENVIRONMENTAL STUDIES*

ORNIS. see *BIOLOGY—Ornithology*

ORNIS JUNIOR. see *CHILDREN AND YOUTH—For*

DER ORNITHOLOGISCHE BEOBACHTER. see *BIOLOGY—Ornithology*

DER ORNITHOLOGISCHE BEOBACHTER. BEIHEFT. see *BIOLOGY—Ornithology*

ORNITHOLOGISCHER VEREIN ZU HILDESHEIM. NATURKUNDLICHE MITTEILUNGEN. see *BIOLOGY—Ornithology*

ORYX; journal of fauna and flora international. see *BIOLOGY—Zoology*

333.95416 USA
OTTER RAFT. Text in English. 1969. s-a. USD 15 to members. bk.rev. charts; illus. **Document type:** *Newsletter.* **Description:** Presents science and educational material on the sea otter and marine habitats. Focuses on protecting the species.
Published by: Friends of the Sea Otter, 2150 Garden Rd B 4, Monterey, CA 93940. TEL 408-373-2747, FAX 408-373-2749, fndseaottr@aol.com. Ed. Susan Brown. Circ: 4,500 (paid).

OUR PLANET (ONLINE EDITION). see *ENVIRONMENTAL STUDIES*

333.72 USA ISSN 1085-6153
SH11.A6 CODEN: ALCNAQ
OUTDOOR ALABAMA. Text in English. 1929. 5/yr. USD 8 (effective 2005). charts; illus. index, cum.index. 32 p./no. 3 cols./p.; back issues avail. **Document type:** *Magazine, Consumer.*
Formerly (until 1995): Alabama Conservation (0002-4171)
Indexed: BiolAb, SFA, WildRev.
Published by: Alabama Department of Conservation and Natural Resources, 64 N Union St, Montgomery, AL 36130. TEL 334-242-3151, FAX 334-242-1880, magazine@outdooralabama.com, http://www.outdooralabama.com. Ed. Kim G Nix. Circ: 8,000 (paid); 900 (free).

333.72 USA ISSN 0021-3314
SK1
OUTDOOR AMERICA. Text in English. 1922. q. USD 27 (effective 2005). adv. bk.rev. illus. reprints avail. **Document type:** *Magazine, Trade.* **Description:** Devoted to national environmental issues, recreation and conservation; covers current issues and membership news.
Formerly: Izaak Walton Magazine
Indexed: APD, EnvAb, EnvInd, SportS.
—IE.
Published by: Izaak Walton League of America, 707 Conservation Ln, Gaithersburg, MD 20878-2983. general@iwla.org; oa@iwla.org, http://www.iwla.org. Ed. Jason McGarvey. adv.: B&W page USD 1,150, color page USD 1,600; trim 7.5 x 10. Circ: 45,000 (paid).

OUTDOOR CANADA; the total outdoor experience. see *SPORTS AND GAMES—Outdoor Life*

333.72 USA ISSN 1068-3240
OUTDOOR DELAWARE. Text in English. 1956. q. USD 6 (effective 2000). adv. **Document type:** *Consumer.*
Formerly (until 1991): Delaware Conservationist (0045-9852)
Indexed: ESPM, EnvAb, PollutAb, SFA, SWRA, WildRev.
Published by: Delaware Department of Natural Resources and Environmental Control, 89 Kings Hwy, Dover, DE 19901. TEL 302-739-4506, FAX 302-739-6242, dnrec@state.de.us. Ed., Pub., R&P Kathleen M Jamison. Adv. contact Loreen E Burchett. Circ: 6,000 (paid); 9,000 (controlled).

333.72 USA ISSN 1072-7175
OUTDOOR ILLINOIS. Text in English. 1972. m. USD 10 (effective 2004). bk.rev. **Document type:** *Government.* **Description:** Provides information on hunting, fishing, camping, birding, hiking and other outdoor activities in Illinois. Includes profiles on conservation personalities, permit applications, and editorials.
Formerly (until vol.21, no.9, 1993): Illinois. Department of Conservation. Outdoor Highlights (0279-8700)
Published by: Illinois Department of Natural Resources, One Natural Resources Way, Springfield, IL 62702-1271. TEL 217-782-6302, editor@dnrmail.state.il.us, http://www.dnr.state.il.us/oi/index.htm. Ed. Gary Thomas. Circ: 25,000.

333.72 USA ISSN 0030-7068
HC107.I6
OUTDOOR INDIANA. Text in English. 1934. bi-m. USD 12 domestic; USD 20 foreign (effective 2003). bk.rev. charts; illus. cum.index: 1966-1981. **Document type:** *Government.* **Description:** Covers the natural resources and cultural history of the state. Reviews an Indiana trail each month.
Published by: Indiana Department of Natural Resources, 402 W Washington St, W 255B, Indianapolis, IN 46204-2748. TEL 317-232-4004, FAX 317-232-8036. Ed. Steve Sellers. Circ: 29,000.

333.72 USA ISSN 0279-9065
OUTDOOR NEWS. Text in English. 1951. 9/yr. USD 25 (effective 2000). adv. bk.rev. **Document type:** *Newspaper.* **Description:** Provides timely information on national, state and local conservation and environmental issues.
Published by: Oklahoma Wildlife Federation, PO Box 60126, Oklahoma City, OK 73146-0126. TEL 405-524-7009, FAX 405-521-9270, owf@nstar.net. Ed., R&P, Adv. contact Lance Meek. Pub. Margaret Ruff. Circ: 10,000 (paid).

333.72 USA ISSN 0030-7092
OUTDOOR NEWS BULLETIN. Text in English. 1947. m. free to members and qualified media representatives. bk.rev. reprint service avail. from ISI. **Document type:** *Bulletin.*
Media: Duplicated (not offset).
—CISTI.
Published by: Wildlife Management Institute, 1146 19th St NW, Ste. 700, Washington, DC 20036-3727. TEL 202-371-1808, FAX 202-408-5059, wmihq@aol.com, http://www.wildlifemgt.org/wmi, http://www.wildlifemanagementinstitute.org/. Ed. Richard E McCabe. Circ: 4,000.

333.72 USA ISSN 0030-7106
OUTDOOR OKLAHOMA. Text in English. 1945. bi-m. USD 10. bk.rev. illus. reprint service avail. from PQC. **Document type:** *Consumer.* **Description:** Covers hunting, fishing, the environment, and conservation.
Formerly: Oklahoma Wildlife
Related titles: Microform ed.: (from PQC).
Indexed: BiolAb, EnvAb, SFA, WildRev.
Published by: Department of Wildlife Conservation, 1801 N Lincoln, Oklahoma City, OK 73105. TEL 405-521-3855, FAX 405-521-6898. Ed., R&P Nels Rodefeld. Circ: 21,500 (controlled). **Co-sponsor:** Oklahoma Wildlife Conservation Commission.

OUTDOOR REPORT. see *LEISURE AND RECREATION*

333.72 USA ISSN 0030-7181
OUTDOORS UNLIMITED. Text in English. 1940. m. membership. bk.rev.; film rev. bibl.; illus. back issues avail. **Document type:** *Newsletter.*
Indexed: EnvAb, EnvInd, SportS.
Published by: Outdoor Writers Association of America, Inc., 121 Hickory St., Apt. 1, Missoula, MT 59801-1896. TEL 406-728-7434, FAX 406-728-7445. Circ: 2,600.

P I N. see *SPORTS AND GAMES*

P Q F NEWS. (Partridge, Quail and Francolin Specialist Group) see *BIOLOGY—Ornithology*

PACHYDERM. see *BIOLOGY—Zoology*

333.73 AUS ISSN 1038-2097
QH77.P3 CODEN: PCOBEK
➤ **PACIFIC CONSERVATION BIOLOGY.** Text in English. 1993. q. AUD 71.50 in Australia & New Zealand to individuals; AUD 90 elsewhere to individuals; AUD 204 in Australia & New Zealand to libraries; AUD 234 elsewhere to libraries (effective 2003). adv. bk.rev. bibl.; charts; illus.; abstr. index. 80 p./no. 2 cols./p.; back issues avail. **Document type:** *Journal, Academic/Scholarly.* **Description:** Publishes news and views, forum essays, research papers on conservation and land management in the Pacific region.
Indexed: BIOSIS Prev, BiolAb, EnvAb, GEOBASE, ZooRec.
—BLDSC (6329.075000), IE, ingenta.
Published by: Surrey Beatty & Sons, 43 Rickard Rd, Chipping Norton, NSW 2170, Australia. TEL 61-2-96023888, FAX 61-2-98211253, surreybeatty@iform.com.au, http://wwwscience.murdoch.edu.au/centres/others/pcb. Ed. Harry Recher. Pub., R&P, Adv. contact Ivor Beatty. page AUD 250; trim 210 x 897. Circ: 500.

363.70025 USA ISSN 1091-0301
GE300
PACIFIC NORTHWEST ENVIRONMENTAL DIRECTORY. Text in English. 1996. biennial. USD 18.50 (effective 2001). index. **Document type:** *Directory.* **Description:** Annotated listings of citizen groups and government agencies in Oregon, Washington and British Columbia.
Media: CD-ROM. **Related titles:** Diskette ed.; Online - full text ed.
Published by: Harbinger Communications, 616 Sumner St, Santa Cruz, CA 95062. TEL 406-721-0440, FAX 406-721-0440, ned@ism.net, http://eelink.net/gaindirectories.html.

333.95 FRA
PAN-EUROPEAN BIOLOGICAL AND DIVERSITY STRATEGY BULLETIN. Text in English. 1997. 6/yr. free. **Document type:** *Newsletter.*
Related titles: French ed.; Italian ed.; German ed.; Russian ed.
Published by: (Centre Naturopa), Council of Europe/Conseil de l'Europe, Publications Section, Strasbourg, Cedex 67075, France. TEL 33-3-88412581, FAX 33-3-88413910, publishing@coe.fr, http://book.coe.fr. Ed. Jean Pierre Ribaut. Circ: 20,000.

333.72 ITA ISSN 1122-732X
PANDA. Text in Italian. 1966. bi-m. adv. **Document type:** *Magazine, Consumer.*
Related titles: Online - full text ed.
Published by: Fondo Mondiale per la Natura/World Wildlife Fund, Via Po 25c, Rome, 00198, Italy. TEL 39-06-852492, FAX 39-06-8554410, wwf@wwf.it, http://www.wwf.it. Ed. Fulco Pratesi.

333.72 ESP ISSN 0212-6354
PANDA (MADRID). Text in Spanish. 1971. q. back issues avail.
Formerly (until 1983): Adena (0212-6311)
Related titles: Online - full text ed.; ♦ Supplement(s): Pandilla. ISSN 1134-3109.
—CINDOC.
Published by: W W F Adena, Gran Via de San Francisco, 8, Madrid, 28005, Spain. TEL 34-91-3540578, FAX 34-91-3656336, info@wwf.es, http://www.wwf.es/publicaciones_panda.php.

333.72 ITA
PANDA JUNIOR. Text in Italian. 1966. 5/yr. adv. **Document type:** *Magazine, Consumer.*
Published by: Fondo Mondiale per la Natura/World Wildlife Fund, Via Po 25c, Rome, 00198, Italy. TEL 39-06-852492, FAX 39-06-8554410, wwf@wwf.it, http://www.wwf.it. Ed. Fulco Pratesi.

333.95416 FRA ISSN 0248-8124
PANDA MAGAZINE - W W F FRANCE. Text in French. 1980. q. EUR 15 (effective 2004). bibl. **Description:** Includes research on the conservation of natural resources and wildlife as well as brief news items.
Published by: World Wide Fund for Nature - France, 188 Rue de la Roquette, Paris, 75011, France. TEL 33-1-55258484, FAX 33-1-55258474, sitivo@wwf.fr, http://www.wwf.fr. Ed. Corinne Brunois. Pub. Luc Hoffmann.

333.75 639.9 FRA ISSN 0241-8231
PARC NATIONAL DE PORT CROS. TRAVAUX SCIENTIFIQUES/PORT-CROS NATIONAL PARK. SCIENTIFIC REPORTS. Text in French. 1975. a.
Indexed: ESPM, ZooRec.
Published by: La Maison du Tourisme de la Provence d'Azur, Forum du Casino, 3, Avenue Ambroise Thomas, Hyeres, 83412, France.

PARC NATUREL REGIONAL DE CORSE. TRAVAUX SCIENTIFIQUES. see *ENVIRONMENTAL STUDIES*

333.783 BEL ISSN 1370-6322
PARCS ET RESERVES; revue trimestrielle d'Ardenne et Gaume. Text in French. 1946. q. EUR 4.85 per issue domestic (effective 2005). back issues avail. **Document type:** *Bulletin.* **Description:** Covers nature conservancy in Belgium, Europe, and Africa.
Formerly (until 1995): Parcs Nationaux (0770-206X)
Published by: Ardenne et Gaume, Rue des Croisiers 8, Namur, 5000, Belgium. charlesverstreeten@skynet.be, http://www.ardenneetgaume.be.tf.

PARK AND RECREATION OPPORTUNITIES JOB BULLETIN. see *OCCUPATIONS AND CAREERS*

PARK SCIENCE. see *ENVIRONMENTAL STUDIES*

333.783 GBR ISSN 0960-233X
SB481.A1 CODEN: PARKEE
PARKS; the international magazine dedicated to the protected areas of the world. Text in English; Summaries in English, French, Spanish. 1990. 3/yr. GBP 28.60 domestic; GBP 31.15 in Europe; GBP 35.65 elsewhere (effective 2005). adv. bk.rev. maps; stat. back issues avail. **Document type:** *Bulletin.* **Description:** Publishes papers and news items relating to national parks and other protected areas. Aimed at parks managers, policy-makers, administrators, and campaigners.
Indexed: EnvAb, ZooRec.
—BLDSC (6406.794000). **CCC.**
Published by: (I U C N - World Conservation Union, World Commission on Protected Areas), Nature Conservation Bureau Ltd., 36 Kingfisher Ct, Hambridge Rd, Newbury, Berks RG14 5SJ, United Kingdom. TEL 44-1635-550380, FAX 44-1635-550230, parks@naturebureau.co.uk, post@naturebureau.co.uk, http://www.naturebureau.co.uk/shop/books/parks.html. Ed., R&P Paul Goriup. Adv. contact Martin Harvey. page GBP 240; 135 x 210. Circ: 1,700.

PARKS AND GROUNDS; technical magazine for landscape design, construction and maintenance. see *GARDENING AND HORTICULTURE*

333.783 CAN ISSN 1497-2492
PARKS CANADA. STATE OF PROTECTED HERITAGE AREAS REPORT. Text in English. 1990. irreg.
Formerly (until 1999): Environment Canada. Parks Service. State of the Parks Report (1487-6329)
Related titles: Online - full text ed.: ISSN 1497-2514.
Published by: (Parks Canada), Parks Canada Agency, 25 Eddy St, Gatineau, PQ K1A 0M5, Canada. information@pc.gc.ca, http://www.pc.gc.ca/agen/.

333.783 AUS ISSN 1324-4361
PARKWATCH. Text in English. 1952. q. AUD 45 membership (effective 2004). adv. bk.rev. **Document type:** *Magazine, Consumer.* **Description:** Provides up-to-date information on current issues affecting the national parks in Victoria.
Published by: Victorian National Parks Association Inc., Level 3, 60 Leicester St, Carlton, VIC 3053, Australia. TEL 61-3-93475188, FAX 61-3-93475199, parkwatch@vnpa.org.au, vnpa@vnpa.org.au, http://www.vnpa.org.au/resources/parkwatch.htm. Ed. John Stirling. Circ: 3,400.

PASHOSH. see *CHILDREN AND YOUTH—For*

333.7845 USA
PASSAIC RIVER REVIEW. Text in English. 1981. s-a. looseleaf. free. bk.rev. **Document type:** *Newsletter.* **Description:** Publishes news and information on organization activities.
Formerly: Passaic River Restoration Newsletter
Published by: Passaic River Coalition, 246 Madisonville Rd, Basking Ridge, NJ 07920. TEL 908-766-7550, FAX 908-766-7550. Ed. Ella Filippone. Circ: 1,500.

371.38 333.72 CAN ISSN 0840-8114
PATHWAYS; the Ontario journal of outdoor education. Text in English. 1978. 5/yr. **Document type:** *Journal.*
Formerly (until 1989): Anee (0711-351X)
Indexed: CIJE.
—**CCC.**
Published by: Council of Outdoor Educators of Ontario, 1185 Eglinton Ave East, North York, ON M3C 3C6, Canada. http://webhome.idirect.com/~hesterkb/coeo/Pathways.html.

333.72 USA ISSN 1077-5110
PATHWAYS TO OUTDOOR COMMUNICATION. Key Title: New York State Outdoor Education Association's Pathways to Outdoor Communication. Text in English. 1991. 4/yr. membership. adv.
Formerly (until 1994): Pathways to Outdoor Communication (1077-5102); Supersedes: Outdoor Communicator
Indexed: CIJE.
Published by: New York State Outdoor Education Association, 418 Meery Rd, Amsterdam, NY 12010. TEL 518-842-0501, FAX 518-842-1646, nysoea@aol.com. Ed. Susan Amtower. Adv. contact Mary Lynne Malone.

346.044 USA
PEAK AND PRAIRIE. Text in English. 197?. q. USD 5 to non-members; free for 18 mos. to members (effective 2005). **Document type:** *Newsletter, Consumer.* **Description:** Covers environmental issues, legislative news, chapter activities, and events.
Related titles: Online - full text ed.
Published by: Sierra Club, Rocky Mountain Chapter, 1536 Wynkoop St, 4-C, Denver, CO 80202. TEL 303-861-8819, FAX 303-861-2436, editor@rmc.sierraclub.org, http://www.rmc.sierraclub.org/pandp/. Ed. Jason S Wells. Adv. contact Mr. Dan Disner. Circ: 18,000 (paid and controlled).

333.72 IRL ISSN 0791-2757
PEATLAND NEWS. Text in English. 1986. s-a. adv. bk.rev.; Website rev. back issues avail. **Document type:** *Newsletter.* **Description:** Botany, Conservation, Earth Sciences, Education.
Incorporates (1990-2002): Portach (0791-4490)
Published by: Irish Peatland Conservation Council, Bog of Allen Nature Centre, Lullymore, Rathangan, Co. Kildare 1, Ireland. TEL 353-45-860133, bogs@ipcc.ie, http://www.ipcc.ie. Ed., R&P, Adv. contact Catherine O'Connell. Circ: 1,500 (paid).

PEDAL UPDATE. see *SPORTS AND GAMES—Bicycles And Motorcycles*

333.72 USA
PEREGRINE FUND NEWSLETTER. Text in English. 1970. s-a. USD 25 (effective 1999). **Document type:** *Newsletter.* **Description:** Discusses programs of the organization for conservation of natural resources and wildlife.
Published by: Peregrine Fund, Inc., 5666 W Flying Hawk Ln, Boise, ID 83709. TEL 208-363-3716, FAX 208-362-2376, tpf@peregrinefund.org, http://www.peregrinefund.org. Ed. William Burnham. R&P Patricia Burnham.

333.72 GBR ISSN 0967-5663
PERMACULTURE MAGAZINE. Text in English. 1992. q. GBP 12.50 domestic; GBP 18 in Europe; GBP 22 elsewhere (effective 2005). 64 p./no.; **Document type:** *Magazine, Consumer.* **Description:** Covers organic gardening, sustainable agriculture, agroforestry, eco-villages, alternative technology, eco-architecture and building, community development and much more.
Indexed: GardL.
Published by: Permanent Publications, Hyden House Ltd, The Sustainability Centre, East Meon, Hampshire GU32 1HR, United Kingdom. TEL 44-1730-823311, FAX 44-1730-823322, info@permaculture.co.uk, http://www.permaculture.co.uk/mag/home.html.

333.72 USA
PERMACULTURE REVIEW, OVERVIEW AND DIGEST. Short title: P R O D. Text in English. irreg. USD 15 (effective 2000). **Document type:** *Newsletter.* **Description:** Includes digests of articles and other information sources.
Published by: Yankee Permaculture, Hemenway Permaculture, Box 52, Sparr, FL 32192-0052. permacultur@aol.com.

PETER T FLAWN SERIES IN NATURAL RESOURCE MANAGEMENT AND CONSERVATION. see *ENVIRONMENTAL STUDIES*

PHILIPPINES. BUREAU OF MINES. ANNUAL REPORT. see *MINES AND MINING INDUSTRY*

PHILIPPINES. MINISTRY OF NATURAL RESOURCES. ANNUAL REPORT. see *ENVIRONMENTAL STUDIES*

333.72 PHL
PHILIPPINES. MINISTRY OF NATURAL RESOURCES. PLANS AND PROGRAMS. Text in English. 1976. a. charts; stat.
Published by: Philippines. Ministry of Natural Resources, Diliman, Quezon City Mm, 1128, Philippines.

333.75 USA
THE PINES POST. Text in English. 1996. 2/yr. membership. **Document type:** *Newsletter.* **Description:** Covers news, activities, events funding, and legislative issues relating to efforts to preserve the New Jersey Pinelands.
Published by: Pinelands Preservation Alliance, 17 Pemberton Rd., Southampton, NJ 08088-8811. TEL 609-894-8000. Ed. Lisa Thibault.

PLANT TALK; news and views on plant conservation worldwide. see *BIOLOGY—Botany*

▼ **PLENTY.** see *ENVIRONMENTAL STUDIES*

POLISH JOURNAL OF ECOLOGY. see *ENVIRONMENTAL STUDIES*

POLLUTION RESEARCH. see *ENVIRONMENTAL STUDIES*

POTOMAC APPALACHIAN. see *SPORTS AND GAMES—Outdoor Life*

POWDER RIVER BREAKS. see *ENVIRONMENTAL STUDIES*

PRACTICAL QUEENSLAND LANDSCAPE DESIGN CONSTRUCTION AND MAINTENANCE; the newsmagazine for Queensland's landscaping industry. see *GARDENING AND HORTICULTURE*

333.72 DEU ISSN 0032-6542
AM1 CODEN: PPTRAA
DER PRAEPARATOR. Text in English, German. 1955. q. adv. bk.rev. charts; illus. index every 2 yrs. **Document type:** *Bulletin.*
Indexed: A&ATA, BHA, ChemAb, RASB, RefZh, ZooRec.
—GNLM.
Published by: Verband Deutscher Praeparatoren e.V., Middeweg 36, Bottrop, 46240, Germany. TEL 49-2041-96651, FAX 49-2041-29716. Ed. Siegfried Eckardt. Circ: 2,000.

796.522 USA ISSN 0032-6607
PRAIRIE CLUB BULLETIN; organized for the promotion of outdoor recreation in the form of walks, outings, camping and canoeing. Text in English. 1915 (no.45). bi-m. USD 15; free to qualified personnel (effective 2004). bk.rev. illus. **Document type:** *Bulletin.*
Published by: The Prairie Club, 110 E. Schiller St., Ste. 302, Elmhurst, IL 60126-2823. info@prairieclub.org, http://www.prairieclub.org. Ed. Susan Messer. R&P Loretta Davies. Circ: 1,000.

PRIMATE EYE. see *ANTHROPOLOGY*

PRIRODNYE RESURSY/NATURAL RESOURCES. see *ENVIRONMENTAL STUDIES*

PRIRODOPOL'ZOVANIYE/NATURE MANAGEMENT. see *ENVIRONMENTAL STUDIES*

PRZEGLAD PRZYRODNICZY. see *BIOLOGY*

333.76 USA ISSN 0270-8094
PUBLIC LANDS NEWS. Text in English. 1976. fortn. looseleaf. USD 227 (effective 2005). back issues avail. **Document type:** *Newsletter.*
Formerly: Public Lands Use
Related titles: E-mail ed.
Published by: Resources Publishing Co., P O Box 41320, Arlington, VA 22204-8320. TEL 703-553-0552, FAX 703-553-0558, coffinj@clark.net, http://www.plnfpr.com. Ed., Pub., R&P James B Coffin.

719.32 USA ISSN 0270-1308
E51
PUBLICATIONS IN ARCHAEOLOGY. Text in English. 1951. irreg.
Formerly: U.S. National Park Service. Archaeological Research Series (0083-2308)
Indexed: AIAP.

C

Published by: U.S. Department of the Interior, National Parks Service, 1849 C St NW, Washington, DC 20240. TEL 202-208-6843, http://www.nps.gov. **Orders to:** U.S. Government Printing Office, Superintendent of Documents, 732 N Capitol St, NW, Washington, DC 20401. orders@gpo.gov, http://www.gpoaccess.gov.

PUDDLER. see *CHILDREN AND YOUTH—For*

333.7 634.9   POL   ISSN 1232-4043
PUSZCZA KAMPINOSKA. Text in Polish. 1992. q. PLZ 3.50 (effective 2001). back issues avail. **Description:** Deals with forest conservation and preservation of wildlife.
Indexed: AgrLib.
Published by: Kampinoski Park Narodowy/Kampinos National Park, Ul Krasinskiego 49, Izabelin, 05080, Poland. TEL 48-22-7226021, FAX 48-22-7226560.

QUERCUS; revista de estudio y defensa de la naturaleza. see *ENVIRONMENTAL STUDIES*

R C O UPDATE. see *ENVIRONMENTAL STUDIES—Waste Management*

333.7   USA
R F F DISCUSSION PAPERS. Text in English. w.
Media: Online - full text.
Published by: Resources for the Future, Inc., 1616 P St, N W, Washington, DC 20036. TEL 202-328-5000, http://www.rff.org. Ed. Felicia Day.

333.7   USA
R F F NEWS. Text in English. w.
Media: Online - full text.
Published by: Resources for the Future, Inc., 1616 P St, N W, Washington, DC 20036. TEL 202-328-5000, http://www.rff.org. Ed. Felicia Day.

R G S MAGAZINE. see *SPORTS AND GAMES—Outdoor Life*

RAIN FOREST NEWS. see *FORESTS AND FORESTRY*

RANCHO SANTA ANA BOTANIC GARDEN OCCASIONAL PUBLICATIONS. see *BIOLOGY—Botany*

RANGELAND ECOLOGY & MANAGEMENT. see *BIOLOGY*

333.72   AUS   ISSN 1036-9872
RANGELAND JOURNAL. Text in English. 1976. s-a.
Formerly (until 1990): Australian Rangeland Journal (0313-4555)
Related titles: Online - full text ed.: (from EBSCO Publishing, Swets Information Services).
Indexed: AEA, Agr, AgrForAb, BioCN&I, CPA, CurCont, ForAb, HerbAb, I&DA, IndVet, NutrAb, PBA, PGegResA, PGrRegA, RRTA, S&F, SeedAb, WAE&RSA, WeedAb.
Published by: Australian Rangeland Society, c/o CSIRO, PO Box 2111, Alice Springs, N.T. 0871, Australia. TEL 61-8-89500137, FAX 61-8-89529587, http://www.austrangesoc.com.au/.

RANGER RICK. see *CHILDREN AND YOUTH—For*

THE RAPTOR REPORT. see *BIOLOGY—Ornithology*

333.95416   CHE
RE-INTRODUCTION NEWS. Text in English. 1990. 2/yr.
Document type: *Newsletter.*
Related titles: Online - full text ed.
Published by: (Species Survival Commission - Re-introduction Specialist Group), International Union for Conservation of Nature and Natural Resources, Rue Mauverney 28, Gland, 1196, Switzerland. TEL 41-22-9990001, FAX 41-22-9990002, mail@hq.iucn.org, http://www.africaonline.co.ke/AfricaOnline/rsg.html. Ed. Minoo Rahbar. **Subscr. to:** African Wildlife Foundation, PO Box 48177, Nairobi, Kenya. TEL 0254-2-332294.

333.72   CAN   ISSN 1180-5722
RECOVER; the environmental magazine. Text in English. 1990. q. CND 10.
Indexed: EnvAb.
Published by: Recover Enterprises, 114 Dollery Court, North York, ON M2R 3P1, Canada. Eds. Heather Sangster, Nancy Phillips.

333.95   CAN   ISSN 0847-0294
RECOVERY; an endangered species newsletter. Text in English. q. free. illus.; maps. back issues avail. **Document type:** *Newsletter, Academic/Scholarly.* **Description:** Publishes information and views on animal and plant species at risk.
Related titles: Online - full text ed.; French ed.: Sauvegarde. ISSN 0847-0308.
Published by: Canadian Wildlife Service/Service Canadien de la Faune, Environment Canada, Ottawa, ON K1A 0H3, Canada. TEL 819-997-1095, FAX 819-953-6283, http://www.ec.gc.ca/cws-scf/es/recovery/. Ed. Debbie Griff.

RECREATION AND PARKS LAW REPORTER. see *LAW*

REMEDIATION REVIEW; a newsletter of hazardous waste remediation. see *ENVIRONMENTAL STUDIES—Waste Management*

333.7   USA
RESOURCES. Text in English. q. 28 p./no.; back issues avail.; reprints avail. **Document type:** *Magazine, Academic/Scholarly.*
Media: Online - full text. **Related titles:** Print ed.
Published by: Resources for the Future, Inc., 1616 P St, N W, Washington, DC 20036. TEL 202-328-5000, http://www.rff.org. Ed. Felicia Day.

333.72   USA   ISSN 0048-7376
RESOURCES (WASHINGTON). Text in English. 1959. q. free. charts; illus. cum.index. reprint service avail. from PQC.
Document type: *Newsletter, Trade.* **Description:** Includes feature articles and briefer pieces on matters of the environment, natural resources, conservation, energy, etc. Reports on the activities and research performed at Resources for the Future.
Related titles: Microform ed.: (from PQC); Online - full text ed.
Indexed: ABIPC, ASFA, AgBio, EIA, EPB, ESPM, EnerRev, EnvAb, EnvEAb, ForAb, HortAb, I&DA, PAIS, PBA, PGegResA, PollutAb, RDA, RRTA, S&F, SWRA, ToxAb, WAE&RSA.
—BLDSC (7777.606500), CIS, CISTI, IE, ingenta, KNAW, Linda Hall. **CCC.**
Published by: Resources for the Future, Inc., 1616 P St, N W, Washington, DC 20036. TEL 202-328-5025, FAX 202-939-3460, info@rff.org, http://www.rff.org. Ed. Felicia Day. Circ: 14,000 (controlled).

RESOURCES, CONSERVATION AND RECYCLING. see *ENVIRONMENTAL STUDIES—Waste Management*

333.7   USA   ISSN 0486-5561
RESOURCES FOR THE FUTURE. ANNUAL REPORT. Text in English. a. free (effective 2005). **Document type:** *Consumer.*
—CISTI, Linda Hall. **CCC.**
Published by: Resources for the Future, Inc., 1616 P St, N W, Washington, DC 20036. TEL 202-328-5000, FAX 202-939-3460, http://www.rff.org. Ed. Felicia Day.

RESTORATION ECOLOGY. see *ENVIRONMENTAL STUDIES*

333.72   GBR   ISSN 1605-8410
                                      CODEN: RCEOAR
REVIEWS IN CONSERVATION. Text in English. 2000. a. GBP 12.50 per issue to non-members; free to members (effective 2005). back issues avail. **Document type:** *Journal, Academic/Scholarly.* **Description:** Aims to provide comprehensive coverage of literature in key areas of conservation and technical examination.
Indexed: A&ATA, IBR, IBZ.
—BLDSC (7789.077900).
Published by: International Institute for Conservation of Historic and Artistic Works, 6 Buckingham St, London, WC2N 6BA, United Kingdom. TEL 44-20-78395975, FAX 44-20-79761564, reviews@iiconservation.org, iic@iiconservation.org, http://www.iiconservation.org/publications/rcguide.php.

333.72   ESP   ISSN 1135-6316
REVISTA INTEGRAL. Text in Spanish. 1978. m. EUR 35.40 (effective 2005). bk.rev. **Document type:** *Magazine, Consumer.* **Description:** Covers ecology, personal development and alternative cultures.
Formerly (until 1995): Integral (0210-0134)
Published by: R B A Revistas S.A., Perez Galdos 36, Barcelona, 08012, Spain. TEL 34-93-4157374, FAX 34-93-2177378, http://www.larevistaintegral.com/index.jsp, http://www.rba.es/revistas. Ed. Jose Luis Cordoba. R&P Ila Matthiasdottir. Adv. contact Adriana Hernandez. Circ: 375,180.

RHEINGUTEBERICHT N R W. (Nordrhein-Westfalen) see *WATER RESOURCES*

333.72   UKR   ISSN 0131-6001
RIDNA PRYRODA. Text in Ukrainian. 1971. bi-m. USD 95 in United States (effective 2000).
Indexed: ASFA.
Address: Ul Anri Barbiusa 5-B, Kyiv, 252005, Ukraine. TEL 380-44-2207173. **Dist. by:** East View Information Services, 3020 Harbor Ln. N., Minneapolis, MN 55447. TEL 763-550-0961, FAX 763-559-2931.

RIVER; the journal of paddlesports and river adventure. see *SPORTS AND GAMES—Outdoor Life*

333.7845   AUS
RIVERLANDER NOTES. Text in English. 1946. q. AUD 30. adv. bk.rev. illus. index. **Document type:** *Newsletter.*
Formerly: Riverlander (0035-5682)
Published by: Murray Darling Association for Conservation and Sustainable Development, PO Box 359, Albury, NSW 2640, Australia. TEL 060-213655, FAX 060-212025. Ed., Adv. contact Adrian Wells. Circ: 3,500.

ROBIN WOOD MAGAZIN. see *ENVIRONMENTAL STUDIES*

363.70025   USA   ISSN 1067-4322
ROCKY MOUNTAIN ENVIRONMENTAL DIRECTORY. Text in English. 1992. biennial. USD 22.50 (effective 2001). index.
Document type: *Directory.* **Description:** Annotated listings of citizen groups and governement agencies in Colorado, Idaho, Montana, Utah and Wyoming.
Media: CD-ROM. **Related titles:** Diskette ed.; Online - full text ed.
Published by: Harbinger Communications, 616 Sumner St, Santa Cruz, CA 95062. TEL 406-721-0440, FAX 406-721-0440, ned@ism.net, http://eelink.net/gaindirectories.html.

333.72   NAM   ISSN 0257-2001
ROSSING MAGAZINE. Text in English. 1979. 2/yr. free. illus. **Document type:** *Consumer.* **Description:** Aims to contribute to a broader knowledge of Namibia, its people, and the environment. Each issue illustrates various aspects of the country.
Published by: Rossing Uranium Ltd., Corporate Affairs, PO Box 22391, Windhoek, 9000, Namibia. TEL 264-61-236760, FAX 264-61-228147. Eds. Anne Haarhoff, Dorian Haarhoff. R&P Gida Sekandi. Circ: 4,000 (controlled).

333.72   DEU
DIE ROTE MAPPE; Kritischer Jahresbericht zur Situation der Heimatpflege in unserem Land. Text in German. 1960. a. looseleaf. free. adv. back issues avail. **Document type:** *Yearbook, Trade.* **Description:** Critical report of nature and cultural matters of lower Saxony.
Published by: Niedersaechsischer Heimatbund e.V., Landschaftstr 6A, Hannover, 30159, Germany. TEL 49-511-3681251, FAX 49-511-3632780, nhbev@t-online.de, http://www.niedersaechsischer-heimatsbund.de. Ed., R&P, Adv. contact Rosawitha Sommer TEL 511-3681251. Circ: 7,000.

▼ **RURAL EUROPE**; agri-environment and rural development policy. see *ENVIRONMENTAL STUDIES*

333.72   GBR   ISSN 0267-4807
RURAL FORUM. Text in English. 1986. q. GBP 12.50 (effective 1999). adv. **Document type:** *Newspaper.* **Description:** Articles on rural development in Scotland.
Published by: Rural Forum Ltd., Highland House, St Catherines Rd, Perth, PH1 5RY, United Kingdom. TEL 44-1738-634565, FAX 44-1738-638699, rural@ruralforum.org.uk, http://www.ruralforum.org.uk. Ed. D Grimson. Circ: 1,800.

333.72   GBR
RURAL WALES - CYMRU WLEDIG. Text in English, Welsh. 3/yr. GBP 15 membership; GBP 20 overseas membership. adv. bk.rev. **Document type:** *Newsletter.* **Description:** Discusses actions that need to be taken to protect the Welsh countryside. For planners and decision-makers.
Former titles: Rural Wales (0142-0100); C P R W News; Council for the Protection of Rural Wales. Newsletter
Indexed: WAE&RSA.
Published by: Campaign for the Protection of Rural Wales, Campaign For The Protection Of Rural Wales, 31 High St, Welshpool, Powys SY21 7YD, United Kingdom. TEL 44-1938-552525, FAX 44-1938-552741, ydcw@aol.com. Ed. Merfyn Williams. Adv. contact Jenny Smith. Circ: 4,000.

RUSSELL REVIEW. see *HISTORY—History Of Australasia And Other Areas*

333.72   RUS   ISSN 0136-0027
QL401
RUTHENICA. Text in Russian. 1991. s-a. USD 175 in United States (effective 2000).
Indexed: ASFA, ESPM, ZooRec.
Published by: Bioinformservis, Ul Vavilova 40, Moscow, 117333, Russian Federation. Ed. N N Kir. **Dist. by:** East View Information Services, 3020 Harbor Ln. N., Minneapolis, MN 55447. TEL 763-550-0961, FAX 763-559-2931.

S A F E MAGAZINE; the voice for all animals. (Save Animals from Exploitation) see *ANIMAL WELFARE*

S.A. WILD & JAG/S.A. GAME & HUNT. see *SPORTS AND GAMES—Outdoor Life*

S C E N E S - SCOTTISH ENVIRONMENT NEWS. see *CONSERVATION—Abstracting, Bibliographies, Statistics*

333.72   NOR   ISSN 0803-7132
S M R RAPPORT. Text in English, Norwegian. 1992. irreg.
Document type: *Monographic series.*
Indexed: ASFA, ESPM.
Published by: Universitetet i Bergen, Senter for Miljoe- og Ressursstudier/University of Bergen, Centre for Studies of Environment and Resources, Postboks 7800, Bergen, 5020, Norway. TEL 47-55-584240, FAX 47-55-589687, http://www.uib.no/smr/SMR_rapportserie.htm.

S P R E P ENVIRONMENTAL CASE STUDIES. see *ENVIRONMENTAL STUDIES*

S P R E P FACT SHEET. see *ENVIRONMENTAL STUDIES*

S P R E P MEETING REPORTS. see *ENVIRONMENTAL STUDIES*

S P R E P OCCASIONAL PAPERS. see *ENVIRONMENTAL STUDIES*

S P R E P TOPIC REVIEW. see *ENVIRONMENTAL STUDIES*

S P R E P TRAINING REPORTS. see *ENVIRONMENTAL STUDIES*

SAGE NOTES. see *BIOLOGY—Botany*

333.78 CAN ISSN 1480-9745
SAGUENAY-ST. LAWRENCE MARINE PARK BULLETIN. Text in English. 1998. s-a.
Published by: Parka Canada. Saguenay-Saint Lawrence Marine Park, PO Box 220, Tadoussac, PQ G0T 2A0, Canada. TEL 418-235-4703, FAX 418-235-4686, parkscanada-que@pc.gc.ca, http://www.pc.gc.caamnc-nmca/qc/saguenay/index_e.asp.

333.95416 USA ISSN 0085-5898
SAN FRANCISCO BAY CONSERVATION AND DEVELOPMENT COMMISSION. ANNUAL REPORT. Text in English. 1971. a. free. illus.
Published by: San Francisco Bay Conservation and Development Commission, 50 California St, Ste 2600, San Francisco, CA 94111. TEL 415-352-3600, FAX 415-352-3606, info@bcdc.ca.gov, http://www.bcdc.ca.gov. Ed. R A Abramson. Circ: 10,000.

SAUMONS. see *BIOLOGY—Zoology*

577 CHE
SCHRIFTENREIHE UMWELT/CAHIERS DE L'ENVIRONNEMENT. Text in German, French. irreg. **Document type:** *Monographic series, Academic/Scholarly.*
Published by: Bundesamt fuer Umwelt, Wald und Landschaft, Gewaesserschutz und Fischerei, Worblentalstr 32, Ittigen, Bern, 3003, Switzerland. TEL 41-31-3226969, FAX 41-31-3230371, info@buwal.admin.ch, http://guf.unibe.ch, http://www.umwelt-schweiz.ch/buwal/de/index.html.

577.51 DEU ISSN 0943-9552
SCHUTZGEMEINSCHAFT DEUTSCHE NORDSEEKUESTE. SCHRIFTENREIHE. Text in German. 1992. irreg. **Document type:** *Monographic series, Academic/Scholarly.*
Indexed: ESPM.
Published by: Schutzgemeinschaft Deutsche Nordseekueste e.V., Marktstr. 6, Husum, 25813, Germany. TEL 49-4841-67640, FAX 49-4841-67657, rudolf-eugen.kelch@nordfriesland.de, http://www.sdn-web.de.

333.72099305 NZL ISSN 1173-2946
➤ **SCIENCE FOR CONSERVATION.** Text in English. 1995. irreg., latest no.183. price varies. back issues avail. **Document type:** *Monographic series, Academic/Scholarly.*
Indexed: AEA, ASFA, AgBio, AgrForAb, AnBrAb, BioCN&I, ESPM, EntAb, EnvEAb, ForAb, GEOBASE, H&SSA, HerbAb, HortAb, I&DA, IndVet, NemAb, NutrAb, PBA, PGegResA, PHN&I, RPP, RRTA, S&F, SeedAb, VetBull, WAE&RSA, WeedAb, ZooRec.
Published by: New Zealand Department of Conservation - Science Publications, PO Box 10-420, Wellington, New Zealand. http://www.doc.govt.nz/Publications/004—cience-and-Research/Science-for-Conservation.asp.

333.95416 GBR ISSN 0143-1234
CODEN: SCWIEC
SCOTTISH WILDLIFE; magazine of the Scottish wildlife trust. Text in English. 1964. 3/yr., latest vol.43, 2001. GBP 20 to individual members (effective 2001). adv. bk.rev. 35 p./no. 3 cols./p.; **Document type:** *Magazine, Consumer.* **Description:** Focuses on the flora and fauna of Scotland and work of the Scottish Wildlife Trust to protect it.
Formerly: Scottish Wildlife Trust. Newsletter
Indexed: SFA, WildRev, ZooRec.
Published by: Scottish Wildlife Trust, Cramond House, Kirk Cramond, Cramond Glebe Rd, Edinburgh, Scotland EH4 6NS, United Kingdom. TEL 44-131-312-7765, FAX 44-131-312-8705, http://www.swt.org.uk. Ed., Pub., R&P Nick Cheales TEL 44-131-312-7765. Adv. contact Kirstin Norrie TEL 44-131-663-6368. B&W page GBP 425, color page GBP 650. Circ: 20,000.

508 CAN ISSN 0227-793X
SEASONS; Ontario's nature and environment magazine. Text in English. q. CND 40 to individuals; CND 35 to institutions; CND 4.50 newsstand/cover (effective 2000). adv. bk.rev. bibl.; illus. reprint service avail. from PQC. **Document type:** *Consumer.*
Former titles (until 1980): Ontario Naturalist (0030-3046); (until 1963): Federation of Ontario Naturalists. Bulletin (0318-7268); Which superseded in part (in 1933): Federation of Ontario Naturalists. Circular; Incorporated (in 1975): Federation of Ontario Naturalists. Newsletter (0046-3574); Which was formerly (until 1965): F.O.N. News (0820-6732)
Related titles: Microfiche ed.: (from MML); Microform ed.: (from MML, PQC).
Indexed: BiolDig, CBCARef, CBPI, CPerl.
—CISTI.
Published by: Federation of Ontario Naturalists, 355 Lesmill Rd, Don Mills, ON M3B 2W8, Canada. TEL 416-444-8419, FAX 416-444-9866, seasons@ontarionature.org, http://www.ontarionature.org. Ed., R&P Nancy Clark. Adv. contact Carolyn Ford. Circ: 15,000.

333.72 USA
SEEDLING NEWS. Text in English. 1974. q. USD 25 to members. 8 p./no.; back issues avail. **Document type:** *Newsletter.*
Former titles: TreePeople News; Seedling News
Published by: TreePeople, 12601 Mulholland Dr, Beverly Hills, CA 90210. TEL 818-753-4600, FAX 818-753-4635, info@treepeople.org. Ed. Carol Oken TEL 818-623-4861. R&P Leslie Mylius TEL 818-623-4864. Circ: 21,000.

333.7844 DEU ISSN 1025-5044
SEESPIEGEL; Information rund um den Bodensee. Text in German. 1995. 2/yr. **Document type:** *Journal, Academic/Scholarly.*
Published by: Internationale Gewaesserschutzkommission fuer den Bodensee, Argenweg 50/1, Langenargen, 88085, Germany. TEL 49-711-1261533, http://www.seespiegel.de, http://www.igkb.de. Ed. Bruno Blattner.

SEINE. see *BIOLOGY—Zoology*

SENATE OF CANADA. STANDING COMMITTEE ON ENERGY, THE ENVIRONMENT AND NATURAL RESOURCES. PROCEEDINGS. see *ENVIRONMENTAL STUDIES*

639.9 CAN
SERVICE CANADIEN DE LA FAUNE. RESCAPE RAPPORT. Text in French. 1988. a. free. illus.; maps. back issues avail. **Document type:** *Bulletin, Government.*
Former titles (until 1997): Service Canadien de la Faune. Rescape Rapport Annuel; (until 1995): Service Canadien de la Faune. Rapport Annuel - Rescape (1484-1673); (until 1994): Service Canadien de la Faune. Rapport - Rescape (1190-9331); Which superseded in part (in 1990): Canadian Wildlife Service. Annual Report - Renew (1187-3876)
Related titles: Online - full text ed.; ♦ English ed.: Canadian Wildlife Service. R E N E W Report.
Published by: Canadian Wildlife Service/Service Canadien de la Faune, Environment Canada, Ottawa, ON K1A 0H3, Canada. TEL 819-997-1095, FAX 819-953-6283, http://www.ec.gc.ca/cws-scf/es/renew/RENEW98/FRE/indexf.html. Ed. Text In French.

SHENGTAI HUANJING YU BAOHU/ECOLOGICAL ENVIRONMENT AND PROTECTION. see *ENVIRONMENTAL STUDIES*

333.72 JPN
SHIZEN AIGO/NATURE OF KAGOSHIMA. Text in Japanese. 1975. a.
Published by: Kogoshimaken Shizen Aigo Kyokai/Society for the Preservation of Nature of Kagoshima, Kagoshima Daigaku Nogakubu, Kachiku Kaibogaku Kyoshitsu, 50-20 Shimoaratacho 4-chome, Kagoshima-shi, 890-0000, Japan.

SHIZEN KANSATSUKAI KAIHO. see *ENVIRONMENTAL STUDIES*

SHOKUCHU SHOKUBUTSU KENKYUKAI KAISHI/ INSECTIVOROUS PLANT SOCIETY. JOURNAL. see *BIOLOGY—Botany*

333.97 551.457 USA ISSN 0037-4237
TC330.A1 CODEN: SHBEAS
SHORE AND BEACH. Text in English. 1933. q. USD 75 to individuals; USD 50 to libraries; USD 25 to students (effective 2005). adv. bk.rev. cum.index: 1933-1965. back issues avail. **Document type:** *Journal, Trade.*
Indexed: ASFA, CivEngAb, EPB, ESPM, EngInd, EnvAb, FLUIDEX, M&TEA, OceAb, PollutAb, SWRA, WRCInf.
—BLDSC (8268.440000), CISTI, IE, ingenta, Linda Hall.
Published by: American Shore and Beach Preservation Association (Corvallis), 5460 Beaujolais Lane, Fort Myers, FL 33919. TEL 239-489-2616, editor@asbpa.org, http://www.asbpa.org/shore_beach.html. Ed. Ron Flick. Circ: 900.

627 CHN ISSN 1006-7175
♦ **SHUILI KEJI YU JINGJI/WATER CONSERVANCY SCIENCE AND TECHNOLOGY AND ECONOMY.** Text in Chinese. 1992. bi-m. CNY 6 newsstand/cover (effective 2004). **Document type:** *Journal, Academic/Scholarly.*
Related titles: Online - full text ed.: (from East View Information Services).
Indexed: ASFA, ESPM, RefZh, WRCInf.
Published by: Ha'erbin Shi Guihua Sheji Shuili Yanjiuyuan, Nangang-qu, 35, Xuanli Lu, Ha'erbin, 150001, China. TEL 86-451-82711207 ext 8404, 8405, FAX 86-451-82724300, ShuiLikeji@163.com, http://slkjyjj.periodicals.net.cn/default.html.

SHUITU BAOCHI TONGBAO/BULLETIN OF SOIL AND WATER CONSERVATION. see *AGRICULTURE—Crop Production And Soil*

SHUITU BAOCHI XUEBAO/JOURNAL OF SOIL AND WATER CONSERVATION. see *AGRICULTURE—Crop Production And Soil*

SHUITU BAOCHI YANJIU/RESEARCH OF SOIL AND WATER CONSERVATION. see *AGRICULTURE—Crop Production And Soil*

SHUTTERBUG'S OUTDOOR & NATURE PHOTOGRAPHY. see *PHOTOGRAPHY*

333.72 DEU
SIEBENSTERN; Vereinszeitschrift fuer Heimatpflege, Heimatkunde, Wandern und Naturschutz. Text in German. 1927. bi-m. adv. bk.rev. index. back issues avail.
Published by: Fichtelgebirgsverein e.V., Auguststr 6, Hof, 95028, Germany. TEL 09281-2531. Circ: 13,000.

333.72 USA ISSN 0161-7362
F868.S5
SIERRA; exploring, enjoying and protecting the planet. Text in English. 1893. bi-m. USD 39 membership; USD 12 to libraries (effective 2005). adv. bk.rev. illus.; tr.lit. cum.index (vols. 35-61, 1978). back issues avail.; reprint service avail. from PQC. **Document type:** *Magazine, Consumer.* **Description:** Provides commentary on environmental issues and articles on nature and the wilderness. Includes legislative developments, stories of outdoor adventures, and profiles of environmental activists.
Formerly: Sierra Club Bulletin (0037-4725)
Related titles: Microform ed.: (from PQC); Online - full text ed.: (from EBSCO Publishing, Florida Center for Library Automation, Gale Group, H.W. Wilson, Northern Light Technology, Inc., O C L C Online Computer Library Center, Inc., ProQuest Information & Learning).
Indexed: ASCA, Acal, AltPI, BAS, BRI, BiolAb, BiolDig, CBRI, CIJE, CalPI, EPB, EnerRev, EnvAb, EnvInd, GSI, LRI, M&GPA, MASUSE, MagInd, PMR, RGAb, RGPR, TOM.
—BLDSC (8274.050000), CIS, IE, Infotrieve, ingenta.
Published by: Sierra Club, 85 Second St, 2nd Fl, San Francisco, CA 94105-3441. TEL 415-977-5653, 415-977-5500, FAX 415-977-5799, sierra.magazine@sierraclub.org, http://www.sierraclub.org/sierra/. Ed. Joan Hamilton. Pub. Debbie Sorondo. R&P Bob Schildgen. Adv. contact Kristie Rummel. B&W page USD 25,165, color page USD 36,900; trim 8 x 10.5. Circ: 730,000 (controlled). **Subscr. to:** PO Box 52968, Boulder, CO 80328.

333.72 USA ISSN 0164-825X
SIERRA ATLANTIC. Text in English. 1974. q. USD 39 to members (effective 2005). adv. bk.rev.; film rev. **Document type:** *Newsletter, Consumer.* **Description:** Chapter newsletter on environmental issues of interest to club members in New York State.
Formerly: Subway Sierran
Published by: Sierra Club, Atlantic Chapter, 353 Hamilton St, Albany, NY 12210-1709. TEL 518-426-9144, FAX 518-427-0381, newyork@sierrablub.org, http://newyork.sierraclub.org. Ed. Hal Smith. adv.: B&W page USD 800; trim 10.88 x 8.25. Circ: 39,000 (paid and controlled). **Subscr. to:** Sierra Club, 730 Polk St, San Francisco, CA 94109.

333.72 CAN ISSN 1194-6148
SIERRA REPORT. Text in English. 197?. q. CND 15. adv. bk.rev. **Document type:** *Consumer.* **Description:** Covers environmental issues in the prairie provinces, Yukon, and British Columbia. Liaison with Alaska chapter on transboundary issues.
Formerly (until 1982): Sierra Club. Western Canada Chapter. Quarterly Newsletter
Published by: Sierra Club, Western Canada Chapter, 576 Johnson St, Victoria, BC V8W 1M3, Canada. TEL 604-873-5646, FAX 604-873-3549, sierrareport@yahoo.ca, http://www.sierraclub.ca/bc. Eds. Margaret Floyd, Morgan McDonald. Circ: 5,000.

333.72 CHE ISSN 1017-3439
SIRENEWS. Text in English. 1983. 2/yr. **Document type:** *Newsletter.*
Indexed: WildRev.
Published by: (Species Survival Commission - Sirenia Specialist Group), International Union for Conservation of Nature and Natural Resources, Rue Mauverney 28, Gland, 1196, Switzerland. TEL 41-22-9990001, FAX 41-22-9990002, mail@hq.iucn.org, http://pegasus.cc.ucf.edu/~smm/snews.htm. **Subscr. to:** Dr. Daryl P. Domning, Dept of Anatomy, Howard University, Washington, DC 20059.

SKOV OG NATUR; nyhedsbrev. see *SCIENCES: COMPREHENSIVE WORKS*

333.72 CHE ISSN 1019-5041
QL737.C2
SMALL CARNIVORE CONSERVATION. Text in English. s-a. USD 20 (effective 2000). **Document type:** *Newsletter.* **Description:** For those interested in mustelid, viverrid and procyonid conservation.
Formerly: Mustelid and Viverrid Conservation
Indexed: ZooRec.
—BLDSC (8309.980600).

C

▼ new title ➤ refereed ✶ unverified ♦ full entry avail.

Published by: (Species Survival Commission - Mustelid, Viverrid, and Procyonid Specialist Group), International Union for Conservation of Nature and Natural Resources, Rue Mauverney 28, Gland, 1196, Switzerland. TEL 41-22-9990001, FAX 41-22-9990002, mail@hq.iucn.org. **Subscr. to:** Harry von Rompaey, Jan Verbertlei 15, Edegem 2650, Belgium.

SOCIETY AND NATURAL RESOURCES. see *ENVIRONMENTAL STUDIES*

SOIL - PLANT ANALYST. see *AGRICULTURE—Crop Production And Soil*

SOIL SURVEY HORIZONS. see *AGRICULTURE—Crop Production And Soil*

SOSTOYANIYE PRIRODNOI SREDY BELARUSI/STATE OF NATURAL ENVIRONMENT OF BELARUS; ekologicheskii byulleten'. see *ENVIRONMENTAL STUDIES*

333.783 ZAF
SOUTH AFRICA. NATIONAL PARKS BOARD. ANNUAL REPORT. Text in English. a. free to qualified personnel. illus.; stat. **Document type:** *Government.*
Published by: National Parks Board/Nasionale Parkeraad, PO Box 787, Pretoria, 0001, South Africa. TEL 27-12-343-9770, FAX 27-12-343-9958, TELEX 321931 SA. Circ: (controlled).

333.95416 ZAF ISSN 0379-4369
SK575.S5 CODEN: SAJRDR
➤ **SOUTH AFRICAN JOURNAL OF WILDLIFE RESEARCH/SUID-AFRIKAANSE TYDSKRIF VIR NATUURNAVORSING.** Text and summaries in English. 1971. q. ZAR 300 domestic print & online eds.; USD 92 foreign print & online eds. (effective 2004). adv. bk.rev. charts; illus. **Document type:** *Journal, Academic/Scholarly.* **Description:** Publishes research papers and reviews on research and management in the field of renewable natural resources.
Former titles: South African Journal of Wildlife Management; (until vol.6, 1976): Southern African Wildlife Management Association. Journal
Related titles: Online - full text ed.: (from EBSCO Publishing, International Network for the Availability of Scientific Publications, African Journals Online).
Indexed: ASCA, ASFA, AbAn, AgBio, AgrForAb, AnBeAb, AnBrAb, ApEcolAb, BIOSIS Prev, BioCN&I, BiolAb, CurCont, DSA, EIA, ESPM, EnerInd, FCA, FPA, ForAb, GEOBASE, HelmAb, HerbAb, IBR, IBZ, ISAP, ISR, IndVet, KWIWR, NutrAb, PGegResA, PoultAb, ProtozoAb, RDA, RPP, RRTA, RevApplEntom, S&F, SCI, SFA, SeedAb, SoyAb, TriticAb, VetBull, WAE&RSA, WLR, WildRev, ZooRec.
—BLDSC (8340.330000), IDS, IE, ingenta, Linda Hall.
Published by: (Southern African Wildlife Management Association), South African Bureau for Scientific Publications, PO Box 11663, Pretoria, Hatfield 0028, South Africa. TEL 27-12-322-6404, FAX 27-12-320-7803, bspman@icon.co.za, http://www.safest.org.za/bsp. Ed., Adv. contact J H Koen. Circ: 600.

333.72 USA ISSN 0887-9249
SOUTH CAROLINA OUT-OF-DOORS✶. Text in English. 1974. m. USD 15 to members. adv. bk.rev. **Document type:** *Newsletter.*
Published by: South Carolina Wildlife Federation, 2711 Middleburg Dr, Ste 104, Columbia, SC 29204-2413. TEL 803-771-4417, FAX 803-771-6120. Ed., Adv. contact Juliet Fletcher. Circ: 7,000 (paid).

577.51 578.77 USA
SOUTH CAROLINA SEA GRANT CONSORTIUM. PROCEEDINGS. Text in English. irreg.
Published by: South Carolina Sea Grant Consortium, 287 Meeting St, Charleston, SC 29401. TEL 843-727-2078, FAX 843-727-2080, http://www.scseagrant.org.

333.95416 USA ISSN 0038-3198
SK1
SOUTH CAROLINA WILDLIFE. Text in English. 1954. bi-m. USD 10 (effective 2000). **Document type:** *Magazine, Government.*
Indexed: SFA, WildRev.
Published by: South Carolina Department of Natural Resources, PO Box 167, Columbia, SC 29202. TEL 803-734-3972, scwmed@scdnr.state.sc.us, http://www.scwildlife.com. Ed. Linda Renshaw. R&P Linda Renshaw TEL 803-734-3859. Circ: 60,000 (paid).

333.72 USA ISSN 0038-3279
SOUTH DAKOTA CONSERVATION DIGEST. Text in English. 1934. bi-m. USD 5 (effective 2000). bk.rev. illus. **Document type:** *Government.*
Indexed: BiolAb, WildRev.
Published by: Game, Fish and Parks Department, 523 E Capitol, Pierre, SD 57501-3182. TEL 605-773-3485. Ed., R&P Bruce Coonrod. Circ: 20,000.

363.70025 USA ISSN 1082-7196
SOUTHEAST ENVIRONMENTAL DIRECTORY. Text in English. 1995. biennial. USD 18.50 (effective 2001). index. **Document type:** *Directory.* **Description:** Annotated listings of citizen groups and government agencies in Alabama, Arkansas, Florida, Georgia, Kentucky, Louisiana, Mississippi, North Carolina, South Carolina and Tennessee.
Media: CD-ROM. **Related titles:** Diskette ed.; Online - full text ed.
Published by: Harbinger Communications, 616 Sumner St, Santa Cruz, CA 95062. TEL 406-721-0440, FAX 406-721-0440, ned@ism.net, http://eelink.net/gaindirectories.html.

SOUTHEASTERN ASSOCIATION OF FISH AND WILDLIFE AGENCIES. PROCEEDINGS. see *FISH AND FISHERIES*

333.95416 USA
SOUTHEASTERN COOPERATIVE WILDLIFE DISEASE STUDY BRIEFS. Text in English. q. back issues avail. **Document type:** *Newsletter, Academic/Scholarly.*
Related titles: Online - full text ed.
Published by: (Southeastern Cooperative Wildlife Disease Study), University of Georgia, College of Veterinary Medicine, Athens, GA 30602. TEL 706-542-1741, FAX 706-542-5865, http://www.vet.uga.edu/testbed/html/scwdswebpubs.html. Ed. Grary L Doster.

SOUTHERN BIRDS. see *BIOLOGY—Ornithology*

333.72 USA ISSN 1073-6875
SOUTHERN SIERRAN. Text in English. 1945. m. USD 5. adv. bk.rev. 12 p./no.; **Document type:** *Newsletter, Internal.*
Published by: Sierra Club, Los Angeles Chapter, 3435 Wilshire Blvd, Ste 320, Los Angeles, CA 90010-1904. TEL 213-387-4287 ext 212, FAX 213-387-5383, ssierrran@ix.netcom.com. Ed. Sharan Street. Circ: 54,000.

333.72 USA ISSN 1087-5026
SPECIAL PLACES. Text in English. 1967. q. **Document type:** *Newsletter, Consumer.* **Description:** Directed to members and donors to the Massachusetts non-profit conservation organization. Covers specific management practices, new land acquisitions, interpretation and events on the organization's 80 properties.
Formerly: Trustees of Reservations. Newsletter
Published by: The Trustees of Reservations, 572 Essex St, Beverly, MA 01915-1530. TEL 978-921-1944, FAX 978-921-1948, information@ttor.org, http://www.thetrustees.org. Ed. Dawn Sylvestor. Circ: 22,000 (controlled).

333.72 CHE ISSN 1016-927X
SPECIES. Text in English. 1983. s-a. CHF 25, USD 18 (effective 2000). **Document type:** *Newsletter.*
Indexed: KWIWR, SFA, WildRev, ZooRec.
Published by: International Union for Conservation of Nature and Natural Resources, Rue Mauverney 28, Gland, 1196, Switzerland. TEL 41-22-9990001, FAX 41-22-9990002, mail@hq.iucn.org. Eds. Diane Cavalieri, Timothy Sullivan. Circ: 3,000. **Subscr. to:** Species Survival Commission, c/o Chicago Zoological Society, 3300 S Golf Rd, Brookfield, IL 60513.

333.7 RUS
SPETSNAZ. Text in Russian. bi-m. USD 95 in United States.
Indexed: RASB.
Published by: Ozdorovitel'nyi i Nauchno-Informatsionnyi Tsentr Zdorov'e Naroda, Ul Nizhnyaya Pervomaiskaya 45, Moscow, 105203, Russian Federation. TEL 7-095-1657531, FAX 7-095-9652629. Ed. S V Yurkov. **US dist. addr.:** East View Information Services, 3020 Harbor Ln. N., Minneapolis, MN 55447. TEL 612-550-0961.

SPILL TECHNOLOGY NEWSLETTER/BULLETIN DE LA LUTTE CONTRE LES DEVERSEMENTS. see *SCIENCES: COMPREHENSIVE WORKS*

333.72 AUS
SPINIFEX. Text in English. 1973. q. AUD 45 (effective 1999). adv. bk.rev. **Document type:** *Newsletter.* **Description:** Covers all conservation issues relevant to Queensland, with reports on conservation groups' activities, environmental law battles and relevant work on government and industry committees.
Former titles: Ecosphere (1323-7594); Queensland Conservation Council Newsletter; Eco Info (0310-0294)
Published by: Queensland Conservation Council, Elizabeth St, PO Box 12046, Brisbane, QLD 4002, Australia. TEL 61-7-32210188, FAX 61-7-32297992, qccqld@powerup.com.au. Ed. Imogen Zethoven. R&P, Adv. contact Rose Kvlak. Circ: 2,000.

STACHLIGE ARGUMENTE. see *POLITICAL SCIENCE*

333.72 CAN ISSN 1185-5762
GE160.C2
STATE OF THE ENVIRONMENT REPORT FOR MANITOBA. Text in English. 1991. biennial. **Document type:** *Government.* **Description:** Contains a description of Manitoba's environmental quality and activities related to present environmental issues as well as future environmental issues, projected trends and environmental management activities.
Published by: Manitoba Environment, 123 Main St, Ste 160, Winnipeg, MB R3C 1A5, Canada. TEL 204-945-7093, FAX 204-948-2357, http://www.gov.mb.ca/environ. Circ: 5,000.

STEINI. see *CHILDREN AND YOUTH—For*

STIFTELSEN FOR NATURFORSKNING OG KULTURMINNEFORSKNING. PROJECT REPORT. see *ENVIRONMENTAL STUDIES*

THE STILT; the bulletin of the East Asian - Australasian flyway. see *BIOLOGY—Ornithology*

333.95416 POL
CODEN: SNPPD6
➤ **STUDIA NATURAE. WYDAWNICTWA NAUKOWE.** Text in English, Polish; Summaries in English. 1952. irreg., latest vol.48, 2001. USD 10 per vol. (effective 2003 - 2004). bibl.; charts. back issues avail. **Document type:** *Monographic series, Academic/Scholarly.*
Formerly: Studia Naturae. Seria A. Wydawnictwa Naukowe; Supersedes in part: Studia Naturae (0081-6760)
Published by: Polska Akademia Nauk, Instytut Ochrony Przyrody, al A Mickiewicza 33, Krakow, 31120, Poland. TEL 48-12-6320549, FAX 48-12-6322432, juchiewicz@iop.krakow.pl, http://www.iop.krakow.pl. Ed. Henryk Okarma. Circ: 320.

➤ **STUDIES IN VENETIAN ART AND CONSERVATION.** see *ART*

➤ **SUARA SAM**; Malaysia's leading environmental newspaper. see *ENVIRONMENTAL STUDIES*

➤ **SUIRI KAGAKU/WATER SCIENCE.** see *WATER RESOURCES*

333.72 AUS ISSN 1325-1554
SUPERVISING SCIENTIST REPORT. Text in English. 1995. irreg. AUD 25 domestic; AUD 40 foreign (effective 2003). **Document type:** *Journal, Academic/Scholarly.*
Formed by the merger of (1981-1995): Supervising Scientist for the Alligator Rivers Region. Technical Memorandum (0810-9532); (1982-1995): Supervising Scientist for the Alligator Rivers Region. Research Report (0810-9966); (1984-1995): Alligator Rivers Region Research Institute. Annual Research Summary (0815-9459); Which was formerly (until 1985): Alligator Rivers Region Research Institute. Research Report (0814-4311)
Indexed: ESPM.
Published by: Environment Australia, Supervising Scientist Division, GPO Box 461, Darwin, N.T. 0801, Australia. TEL 61-8-8920-1100, FAX 61-8-8920-1199, publications_ssd@ea.gov.au, http://ea.gov.au/ssd/publications/, http://www.ea.gov.au/ssd/.

333.72 SWE ISSN 1401-0054
SVENSKA NATURSKYDDSFOERENINGEN. AARSBOK. Text in Swedish. 1910. a., latest 2005. price varies. **Document type:** *Yearbook, Consumer.*
Formerly (until 1995): Naturskyddsfoereningen. Aarsbok: Sveriges Natur (0349-5264)
Published by: Svenska Naturskyddsfoereningen/Swedish Society for Nature Conservation, Aasoegatan 115, PO Box 4625, Stockholm, 11691, Sweden. TEL 46-8-7026500, FAX 46-8-7022702, info@snf.se, http://www.snf.se.

333.72 SWE ISSN 0039-6974
QH169 CODEN: SVNAA4
SVERIGES NATUR. Text in Swedish. 1910. 5/yr. SEK 280 to members (effective 2004). adv. bk.rev. index, cum.index: 1910-1959. back issues avail. **Document type:** *Magazine, Consumer.*
Incorporates (1999-2001): Haallbart (1404-0115)
Related titles: Audio cassette/tape ed.; Online - full text ed.
Indexed: BiolAb, RefZh, SFA, WildRev, ZooRec.
Published by: Svenska Naturskyddsfoereningen/Swedish Society for Nature Conservation, Aasoegatan 115, PO Box 4625, Stockholm, 11691, Sweden. TEL 46-8-7026500, FAX 46-8-7022702, sveriges.natur@snf.se, info@snf.se, http://www.snf.se/sveriges-natur/index.cfm. Eds. Carl-Axel Fall TEL 46-8-7026544, Mats Hellmark TEL 46-8-7026543. Adv. contact Kjell Dahlin. color page SEK 27,900, B&W page SEK 24,500; trim 194 x 237. Circ: 113,600 (controlled).

333.95416 KEN ISSN 1018-6174
➤ **SWARA**; the magazine of the East African Wildlife Society. Text in English. 1963. q. KES 3,000 domestic; USD 60 in Africa; CND 95 in Europe; USD 65 in the Americas (effective 2000 & 2001). adv. bk.rev. maps. 60 p./no.; back issues avail. **Document type:** *Journal, Academic/Scholarly.* **Description:** Publishes popular articles on wildlife and conservation in East Africa.
Formerly (until 1978): Africana (0002-0281)
Indexed: ASFA.
Published by: East African Wild Life Society, PO Box 20110, Nairobi, Kenya. TEL 254-2-574145, FAX 254-2-570335, eawls@kenyaweb.com, http://www.eawildlife.org. Ed., R&P Gordon Boy. Adv. contact Maggie Maina. B&W page KES 48,000, color page KES 60,000; 189 x 170. Circ: 20,000 (paid).

333.72 USA
SYLVANIAN✶. Text in English. 1983. bi-m. USD 10 to non-members. adv. **Document type:** *Newsletter.* **Description:** Discusses the activities of the Sierra Club Pennsylvania Chapter and state environmental highlights.
Published by: Sierra Club, Pennsylvania Chapter, 1009 River Oaks Dr, Pittsburgh, PA 15215-1618. TEL 717-232-0101. Ed. Chris De Cristopher. Circ: 19,000.

333.95416 GBR ISSN 0267-4297
T R A F F I C BULLETIN. (Trade Records Analysis of Flora and Fauna in Commerce) Text in English. 1980. irreg. (2-3/yr.), latest vol.18, no.3. free. bk.rev. 2 cols./p.; back issues avail. **Document type:** *Bulletin.* **Description:** Publishes recent information and original papers on the subject of international trade in wild animals and plants.
Formerly: Traffic Bulletin
Indexed: WildRev, ZooRec.
—BLDSC (8881.655000), IE, ingenta.
Published by: T R A F F I C International, 219c Huntingdon Rd, Cambridge, Cambs CB3 0DL, United Kingdom. TEL 44-1223-277427, FAX 44-1223-277237, traffic@trafficint.org, http://www.traffic.org. Ed., R&P Kim Lochen. Circ: 3,400.

TALL TIMBERS RESEARCH STATION. MISCELLANEOUS PUBLICATION. see *FORESTS AND FORESTRY*

333.72 CHE
TAPIR CONSERVATION. Text in English. 1990. a. USD 10 (effective 2000). **Document type:** *Newsletter.*
Formerly: International Union for Conservation of Nature and Natural Resources. Species Survival Commission - Tapir Specialist Group. Newsletter
Published by: (Species Survival Commission - Tapir Specialist Group), International Union for Conservation of Nature and Natural Resources, Rue Mauverney 28, Gland, 1196, Switzerland. TEL 41-22-9990001, FAX 41-22-9990002, mail@hq.iucn.org, http://www.tapirback.com. **Subscr. to:** Shery Todd, 40 W. Bond St., Apt. 101, Astoria, OR 97103-6017.

333.72 AUS ISSN 0725-0355
TASMANIAN CONSERVATIONIST. Text in English. 1969. 6/yr. AUD 27.50 to individuals; AUD 50 to institutions (effective 2001). adv. bk.rev. back issues avail. **Document type:** *Newsletter.* **Description:** Covers a broad range of local, national and global environmental issues affecting Tasmania.
Formerly (until 1981): Tasmania Conservation Trust Inc. Newsletter (0726-2442)
Published by: Tasmania Conservation Trust Inc., 102 Bathurst Street, Hobart, TAS 7000, Australia. TEL 61-02-343552, FAX 61-02-312491, tct@southcom.com.au, http://www.tct.org.au. Adv. contact Patricia McKeown. Circ: 500.

TECHNOLOGY TRANSFER. see *ENVIRONMENTAL STUDIES*

333.72 ARG
TEMA VERDE. Text in Spanish. 1994. q.?. free.
Published by: Fundacion para el Desarrollo Turistico y el Medio Ambiente, Calle 15, No. 568, La Plata, Buenos Aires 1900, Argentina. TEL 54-21-40714. Ed. Angel Merlo.

333.72 USA ISSN 0040-3202
THE TENNESSEE CONSERVATIONIST; nature, environmental issues. Text in English. 1937. bi-m. USD 15; USD 3.25 newsstand/cover (effective 2002). bk.rev. back issues avail. **Document type:** *Magazine, Government.* **Description:** Provides news items and nature, historical, environmental conservation and preservation articles and photo layouts.
Indexed: EnvAb.
—Linda Hall.
Published by: Department of Environment & Conservation, Nashville, TN 37243-0440. TEL 615-532-0060, FAX 615-532-8007, http://www.state.tn.us/environment/conserv/tn_consv/index.html. Ed., R&P Louise Zepp TEL 615-532-0063. Circ: 14,500 (paid).

333.72 USA ISSN 0363-101X
TK1425.M8
TENNESSEE VALLEY AUTHORITY. ANNUAL REPORT. Text in English. 1934. a. free. **Document type:** *Corporate.* **Description:** Includes chapters on the agency's work in energy, the environment, and economic development.
Indexed: ASFA, S&F.
—CISTI.
Published by: Tennessee Valley Authority, 400 W Summit Hill Dr, Knoxville, TN 37902-1499. TEL 423-632-8039, FAX 423-632-6783. Ed. Steve Bender. Circ: 75,000.

TENNESSEE WARBLER. see *BIOLOGY—Ornithology*

333.9 CHE ISSN 0958-5079
TENTACLE. Text in English. 1989. 2/yr. **Document type:** *Newsletter.*
Published by: (Species Survival Commission - Mollusc Specialist Group), International Union for Conservation of Nature and Natural Resources, Rue Mauverney 28, Gland, 1196, Switzerland. TEL 41-22-9990001, FAX 41-22-9990002, mail@hq.iucn.org. **Subscr. to:** Dr. Robert Cowie, Dept of Natural Sciences, Bishop Museum, 1525 Bernice St, P O Box 19000a, Honolulu, HI 96817-2704.

333.72 USA
TERRAIN (DENVER); a journal of the built and natural environments. Text in English. 1998. q. USD 15 (effective 2000). bk.rev. illus. back issues avail. **Document type:** *Academic/Scholarly.* **Description:** Publishes editorials, poetry, essays, fiction, articles, artwork, case studies, reviews, noteworthy news and more in each theme-based issue.
Media: Online - full text.
Published by: Terrain, PO Box 12478, Denver, CO 80212-0498. editors@terrain.org, buntin@bod.net, http://www.terrain.org, http://www.bod.net/terrain/. Ed. Simmons B Buntin.

333.72 910.91 FRA ISSN 0981-4140
TERRE SAUVAGE. Text in French. 1986. m. (11/yr.). EUR 45.80 domestic; EUR 61.80 in the European Union; EUR 74.80 elsewhere (effective 2005). **Description:** Reports on faraway places and offers itineraries to help travelers enjoy the Earth's natural beauties.
Indexed: EngInd.
Published by: Bayard Presse, 3 Rue Bayard, Paris, 75393 Cedex 08, France. TEL 33-1-44356060, FAX 33-1-44356161, redactions@bayard-presse.com, http://www.bayardpresse.com. Ed. Olivier Milhomme. Circ: 112,500.

TEXAS. NATURAL RESOURCES INFORMATION SYSTEM. NEWSLETTER. see *ENVIRONMENTAL STUDIES*

333.72 USA
TEXAS PARKS AND WILDLIFE DEPARTMENT. MANAGEMENT DATA SERIES. Text in English. irreg.
Published by: Texas Parks and Wildlife Department, 3000 S IH35, Ste 120, Austin, TX 78704. TEL 512-912-7000, FAX 512-707-1913, http://www.ptwd.state.tx.us.

333.95416 USA ISSN 0040-4586
SK1
TEXAS PARKS & WILDLIFE MAGAZINE; the outdoors magazine of Texas. Text in English. 1942. m. USD 19.95 domestic; USD 26.95 in Canada; USD 27.95 elsewhere; USD 3.95 per issue (effective 2005). bk.rev. charts; illus. index. 72 p./no.; back issues avail.; reprints avail. **Document type:** *Magazine, Consumer.*
Indexed: SFA, WildRev.
Published by: Texas Parks and Wildlife Department, 3000 S IH35, Ste 120, Austin, TX 78704. TEL 512-912-7000, FAX 512-707-1913, magazine@tpwd.state.tx.us, http://www.tpwmagazine.com, http://www.ptwd.state.tx.us. Ed., Pub. Randy Brudnicki. Circ: 156,000 (paid).

333.95416 USA
TEXAS TOUR GUIDE. Text in English. a. **Document type:** *Magazine, Consumer.*
Published by: (Texas Department of Economic Development), Emmis Communications Custom Publishing, PO Box 1569, Austin, TX 78767-1569. TEL 512-320-6901, FAX 512-476-9007. Circ: 65,000 (controlled).

THREATENED BIRDS OF AFRICA AND RELATED ISLANDS; the ICBP-IUCN Red Data Book. see *BIOLOGY—Ornithology*

THREATENED BIRDS OF THE AMERICAS; the ICBP-IUCN Red Data Book. see *BIOLOGY—Ornithology*

639.9 USA
TIDE. Text in English. 1977. bi-m. membership. adv. **Description:** Focuses on coastal and marine conservation issues and fishing activities from Texas to Maine. Includes information on programs in education, legislation, support for law enforcement and restocking.
Published by: Coastal Conservation Association, 6919 Portwest Dr., Ste. 100, Houston, TX 77024-8049. TEL 713-626-4234, 800-201-3474, FAX 713-961-3801, tide@joincca.org, http://www.joincca.org/html/tide.htm. Ed., R&P Doug Pike. Adv. contact Mike Haines. Circ: 60,000.

TIDINGS (BOSTON). see *ENVIRONMENTAL STUDIES*

333.72 DEU ISSN 0342-3018
TIERFREUND; Natur erleben, verstehen, schuetzen. Text in German. 1947. m. EUR 25.20 (effective 2003). **Document type:** *Magazine, Consumer.* **Description:** Information about nature, animals and environmental protection for children ages 9-15.
Published by: Johann Michael Sailer Verlag GmbH & Co. KG, Aeusserer Laufer Platz 17, Nuernberg, 90403, Germany. TEL 49-911-53960, FAX 49-911-5396912, sailer@sailer-verlag.de, http://www.sailer-verlag.de. Ed. Andrea Hoesel. Circ: 150,000.

TIERRA AMIGA. see *ENVIRONMENTAL STUDIES*

333.79 THA ISSN 1014-2789
QL84.5.A1 CODEN: TIGEE7
TIGER PAPER. Text in Thai. 1974. q. USD 12 (effective 1997). bk.rev. **Document type:** *Bulletin.* **Description:** Dedicated to the exchange of information relating to wildlife and national parks management for the Asia-Pacific Region.
Indexed: AgrForAb, CPA, FCA, FPA, ForAb, HelmAb, HerbAb, HortAb, I&DA, IndVet, KWIWR, MaizeAb, NutrAb, PGegResA, PN&I, PoultAb, RA&MP, RDA, RRTA, S&F, SFA, SeedAb, VetBull, WAE&RSA, WeedAb, WildRev, ZooRec.
—BLDSC (8835.040000), IE, ingenta.
Published by: Food and Agriculture Organization of the United Nations, Regional Office for Asia and the Pacific, Maliwan Mansion, 39 Phra Atit Rd, Bangkok, 10200, Thailand. TEL 662-281-7844, FAX 662-280-0445, TELEX 82815 FOODAG TH, fao-rap@field.fao.org. Ed. Mrs. J Naewboonnien. R&P Mrs. J. Naewboonnien. Circ: 2,000.

333.783 ZAF ISSN 1560-7143
SB484.S5
TIMBILA; rhythms of the earth. Text in Afrikaans, English. 1971. bi-m. ZAR 150; ZAR 15, USD 5 newsstand/cover. adv. bk.rev. illus. **Document type:** *Consumer.* **Description:** Profiles parks and wilderness preserves in southern Africa and the efforts to conserve these natural resources. Describes the native peoples inhabiting these areas.
Formed by the 1998 merger of: Custos (English Edition) (1022-5315); Custos (Afrikaans Edition) (1022-5307); Both of which superseded (in 1993): Custos (Bilingual Edition) (0379-9921)
Indexed: ISAP, SFA.
Published by: (South Africa. South African National Parks/Suid-Afrikaanse Nasionale Parke), Penta Publications, PO Box 781723, Sandton, Transvaal 2146, South Africa. TEL 27-11-482-8220, FAX 27-11-482-8208, subsl@pentapub.co.za, http://www.parks-sa.co.za. Ed., R&P Branco Brkic TEL 27-83-770-6266. Circ: 10,000.

333.72 JPN
TOKUSHIMA-KEN SHIZEN HOGO KYOKAI CHOSA HOKOKU. Text in Japanese. 1974. 3/yr. **Description:** Contains reports of the society.
Published by: Tokushima-ken Shizen Hogo Kyokai, Tokushima Daigaku Kyoikugakubu, 1-1 Minami-Josanjima-cho, Tokushima-shi, 770-0000, Japan.

TORONTO FIELD NATURALIST. see *BIOLOGY*

TORTOISE; the conservation magazine. see *ENVIRONMENTAL STUDIES*

333.95416 IND
TOURISM AND WILDLIFE. Text in English. 1972. q. INR 120, USD 20 (effective 2001). adv. bk.rev. charts; illus.; tr.lit. 60 p./no. 2 cols./p.; back issues avail.; reprints avail. **Document type:** *Trade.* **Description:** For the tourist industry as well as educational institutions. Covers various tourist and wildlife attractions, in addition to art and cultural events.
Media: Large Type (10 pt.).
Published by: G.C. Verma Ed. & Pub., Netaji Subash Marg, 24 Gola Market, New Delhi, 110 002, India. TEL 91-11-3272273, FAX 91-11-3711821, wildlife@grabmail.com. Ed., Pub. G C Verma. Adv. contact Deepa Bose. color page INR 18,000, B&W page INR 10,000; 22 x 18. Circ: 20,000.

333.72 USA
TRACES (JACKSON). Text in English. 5/yr. USD 8 to non-members. adv. **Description:** Provides information on club events, and on local legal developments related to the environment.
Published by: Sierra Club, Mississippi Chapter, 921 N Congress St, Jackson, MS 39202. TEL 601-352-1026. Ed. Harry Seeley. Circ: 550.

333.9522 USA ISSN 1540-8418
THE TRAFFIC REPORT. Text in English. 1979. q.
Formerly (until 2002): Traffic North America
Related titles: Spanish ed.: ISSN 1541-5139.
Published by: World Wildlife Fund, 1250 24th St, N W, Washington, DC 20037. TEL 202-293-4800, FAX 202-293-9211, http://www.worldwildlife.org/.

333.72 CAN ISSN 0041-0748
TRAIL AND LANDSCAPE. Text in English. 1967. 4/yr. CND 28 (effective 2000). charts; illus. index. back issues avail. **Document type:** *Journal.*
Indexed: SFA, WildRev.
—CISTI.
Published by: Ottawa Field-Naturalists' Club, Westgate, P O Box 35069, Ottawa, ON K1Z 1A2, Canada. TEL 613-722-3050. Ed. K Hamilton. Circ: 950.

TRAIL AND TIMBERLINE. see *SPORTS AND GAMES—Outdoor Life*

TRAIL WALKER; news of hiking and conservation. see *SPORTS AND GAMES—Outdoor Life*

333.72 NLD ISSN 0166-8358
TRIAS. Text in Dutch. 1973. q. bk.rev. illus.
Published by: Jeugdbond voor Natuur- en Milieustudie/Youth Federation for Nature and Environmental Study, Oude Gracht 42, Utrecht, 3511 AR, Netherlands. TEL 030-368925, FAX 030-343986. Circ: 2,500.

TROFEO CAZA; caza - naturaleza. see *SPORTS AND GAMES—Outdoor Life*

TROPICAL FOREST UPDATE. see *FORESTS AND FORESTRY*

333.72   USA
TROPINET. Text in English. q. free; USD 15 or more donation suggested. back issues avail. **Document type:** *Newsletter, Academic/Scholarly.*
Related titles: Online - full content ed.
Published by: Organization for Tropical Studies/Organizacion para Estudios Tropicales, PO Box 90632, Durham, NC 27708-0632. TEL 919-684-5774, FAX 919-684-5661, nao@duke.edu, http://www.atbio.org/tropinet.html, http://www.ots.duke.edu. Ed. Lyn Loveless TEL 330-263-2022.
Co-publisher: Association for Tropical Biology and Conservation.

333.95416   USA   ISSN 0041-3364
TROUT. Key Title: Trout Unlimited. Text in English. 1959. q. USD 35 (effective 2005). adv. bk.rev. illus. **Document type:** *Magazine, Consumer.* **Description:** Includes articles on trout, salmon, and steelhead angling, fish behavior and natural history, and environmental issues affecting fish and fishing.
Indexed: SFA, WildRev.
Published by: Trout Unlimited, 1300 N 17th St, Ste 500, Arlington, VA 22209. TEL 703-522-0200, FAX 703-284-9400, trout@tu.org, http://www.tu.org/trout/. Ed. Beth Duris. Circ: 125,000 (paid).

333.7   RUS
TRUBOPROVODY I EKOLOGIYA. Text in Russian. q. USD 79 in United States.
Indexed: RefZh.
Published by: Izdatel'stvo Stroipolimer, A-ya 1, Moscow, 109316, Russian Federation. TEL 7-095-2766591, FAX 7-095-2767491. Ed. V S Rameiko. **US dist. addr.:** East View Information Services, 3020 Harbor Ln. N., Minneapolis, MN 55447. TEL 612-550-0961.

333.7 320   RUS
TSENTR EKOLOGICHESKOI POLITIKI ROSSII. BYULLETEN'. Text in Russian. 1995. q. USD 275 in the Americas (effective 2000).
Published by: Tsentr Ekologicheskoi Politiki Rossii, Ul. Vavilova, 26, Moscow, 117334, Russian Federation. TEL 7-095-9522423, FAX 7-095-9523007. **Dist. by:** East View Information Services, 3020 Harbor Ln. N., Minneapolis, MN 55447. TEL 763-550-0961, FAX 763-559-2931.

333.72   DEU   ISSN 0722-494X
                                CODEN: TUEXDZ
➤ **TUEXENIA.** Text in German; Abstracts in English. 1928. a. EUR 60 (effective 2002). bk.rev. **Document type:** *Journal, Academic/Scholarly.* **Description:** Papers regarding floristic and vegetational topics of central Europe.
Formerly (until 1980): Floristisch - Soziologische Arbeitsgemeinschaft. Mitteilungen (0373-7632)
Indexed: AgrForAb, BIOSIS Prev, BiolAb, CPA, FCA, FaBeAb, ForAb, HerbAb, HortAb, I&DA, IBR, MaizeAb, OrnHort, PBA, PGegResA, RPP, RefZh, S&F, SeedAb, TriticAb, WAE&RSA, WeedAb.
—BLDSC (9068.584000), IE, ingenta.
Published by: Floristisch - Soziologische Arbeitsgemeinschaft, Wilhelm-Weber-Str 2, Goettingen, 37073, Germany. TEL 49-551-395700, FAX 49-551-392287, remy@biologie.uni-osnabrueck.de, http://www.biologie.uni-osnabrueck.de/oekologie/FSAG/fs_url.htm. Ed. Hartmut Dierschke. Circ: 1,600.

➤ **TURKEY CALL.** see *BIOLOGY—Ornithology*

333.72   AUS
TURNING THE TIDE. Text in English. 1978. s-a. AUD 35 (effective 2000). bk.rev. **Document type:** *Bulletin, Consumer.* **Description:** Contains commentary on Australian marine and coastal conservation issues, particularly the management of marine protected areas, including the Great Barrier Reef and Australian tidal wetlands.
Former titles: Australian Marine Conservation Society. Bulletin; Australian Littoral Society. Bulletin (0157-308X)
Published by: Australian Marine Conservation Society Inc., PO Box 3139, Yeronga, QLD 4104, Australia. FAX 61-7-38925814, ames@ozemail.com.au, http://www.ozemail.com.au/~amcs. Ed. Kris Plowman. R&P Anne Clarke TEL 61-7-38485235. Adv. contact Carol Deane. Circ: 2,000.

U K IRRIGATION. see *WATER RESOURCES*

333.72   GBR   ISSN 0963-8083
➤ **U K NATURE CONSERVATION.** Text in English. 1992. irreg., latest vol.9, 1994. price varies. **Document type:** *Academic/Scholarly.*
Indexed: ZooRec.
—BLDSC (9082.665175).
Published by: Joint Nature Conservation Committee, Monkstone House, City Rd, Peterborough, Cambs PE1 1JY, United Kingdom. TEL 44-1803-865913, FAX 44-1803-865280, nhbs@nhbs.co.uk, http://www.jncc.gov.uk. Ed., R&P John Bratton. **Dist. by:** Natural History Book Service Ltd., 2-3 Wills Rd, Totnes, Devon TQ9 5XN, United Kingdom. TEL 44-1803-865913, FAX 44-1803-865280, nhbs@nhbs.co.uk, http://www.nhbs.co.uk.

333.7845   USA
U R W A QUARTERLY NEWSLETTER. Text in English. q. USD 35 to members. illus.; maps. **Document type:** *Newsletter.*
Description: Educates environmentally conscientious persons about the association's efforts to encourage environmentally sound planning that minimizes impact on the many streams and tributaries feeding the Raritan River in northwestern New Jersey.
Published by: Upper Raritan Watershed Association, PO Box 273, Gladstone, NJ 07934. TEL 908-234-1852, FAX 908-234-0609.

333.72   USA   ISSN 0887-4980
TC423.6
U.S. BUREAU OF RECLAMATION. ANNUAL REPORT. Text in English. 1949. a. **Document type:** *Government.*
Former titles: U.S. Water and Power Resources Service. Annual Report; Federal Reclamation Projects: Water and Land Resource Accomplishments
Indexed: ASFA, ESPM.
Published by: U.S. Bureau of Reclamation (Denver), Reclamation Service Center, Denver Federal Center, Bldg 67, PO Box 25007, Denver, CO 80225-0007. TEL 303-236-7000. **Subscr. to:** National Technical Information Service, Government Research Center, 5285 Port Royal Rd, Springfield, VA 22161. TEL 703-605-6060, 800-363-2068, http://www.ntis.gov.

333.9   USA
U.S. DEPARTMENT OF AGRICULTURE. WETLANDS RESERVE PROGRAM. REPORT TO CONGRESS∗. Text in English. a. **Document type:** *Government.*
Published by: U.S. Department of Agriculture, Agricultural Stabilization and Conservation Service, c/o Conservation Communications Staff, PO Box 2890, Washington, DC 20013. TEL 202-720-7093. **Subscr. to:** U.S. Government Printing Office, Superintendent of Documents, PO Box 371954, Pittsburgh, PA 15250-7954. TEL 202-512-1800, FAX 202-512-2250, orders@gpo.gov, http://www.access.gpo.gov.

U.S. DEPARTMENT OF THE INTERIOR. MINERALS MANAGEMENT SERVICE. ALASKA OUTER CONTINENTAL SHELF REGION. REPORT. see *ENVIRONMENTAL STUDIES*

U.S. FISH AND WILDLIFE SERVICE. DIVISION OF FEDERAL AID. SPORT FISH AND WILDLIFE RESTORATION PROGRAM UPDATE. see *BIOLOGY—Zoology*

333.95   USA   ISSN 1078-6295
HC110.E5
U.S. NATIONAL COMMITTEE FOR MAN AND THE BIOSPHERE. BULLETIN. Key Title: U.S. M A B Bulletin. Text in English. 1976. irreg. (3-4/yr.). free. abstr. **Document type:** *Bulletin, Government.* **Description:** Reports on program directorates of the U.S. Man and the Biosphere Program, which include biosphere reserves, high-latitude research, human-dominated ecological systems research, marine and coastal research, temperate and tropical areas research, and other items of interest, including publications.
Related titles: Online - full text ed.
Published by: U.S. National Committee for the Man and the Biosphere, M A B Secretariat, U S Department of State, SA 44C, 1st Fl, Washington, DC 20522-4401. TEL 202-776-8318, FAX 202-776-8367, http://www.mabnet.org, http://www.state.gov. Ed., R&P Antoinette J Condo TEL 202-776-8316. Circ: 10,500.

333.783   USA   ISSN 0361-9737
SB482
U.S. NATIONAL PARK SERVICE. PUBLIC USE OF THE NATIONAL PARK SYSTEM: CALENDAR YEAR REPORT. Text in English. 1972. a. free.
Published by: U.S. Department of the Interior, National Parks Service, 1849 C St NW, Washington, DC 20240. TEL 202-208-6843, http://www.nps.gov. Circ: 2,000.

333.78   USA   ISSN 0093-3074
SB482
U.S. NATIONAL PARK SERVICE. PUBLIC USE OF THE NATIONAL PARK SYSTEM: FISCAL YEAR REPORT. Key Title: Public Use of the National Park System (Washington). Text in English. 1972. a. illus.; stat.
Published by: U.S. Department of the Interior, National Parks Service, 1849 C St NW, Washington, DC 20240. TEL 202-208-6843, http://www.nps.gov. Circ: 2,000.

333.783   USA
U.S. NATIONAL PARK SERVICE. RESEARCH REPORTS BY SERVICE PERSONNEL. Text in English. irreg. (5-10/yr.).
Published by: U.S. Department of the Interior, National Parks Service, 1849 C St NW, Washington, DC 20240. TEL 202-208-6843, http://www.nps.gov. **Orders to:** NTIS.

U T A INTERNATIONAL. (Umwelt Technologie Aktuell) see *ENVIRONMENTAL STUDIES*

333.72   DEU   ISSN 0948-5953
UMWELTBRIEF; Fakten, Hintergruende und Entscheidungshilfen fuer Wirtschaft und Verwaltung. Text in German. m. EUR 179.80 (effective 2005). bk.rev. back issues avail. **Document type:** *Journal, Trade.*
Formerly: I W L - Umweltbrief (0179-3462)
—IE.

Published by: (Industrie-Initiative fuer Umweltschutz), Deutscher Wirtschaftsdienst (Subsidiary of: Wolters Kluwer Deutschland GmbH), Schoenhauser Str 64, Cologne, 50968, Germany. TEL 49-221-937630, FAX 49-221-9376399, 49-221-9376399, box@dwd-verlag.de, http://www.dwd-verlag.de. Circ: 5,000.

614.7   DEU   ISSN 0343-1312
UMWELTBRIEF (BERLIN). Text in German. 1973. irreg. price varies. **Document type:** *Monographic series, Government.*
Published by: Bundesministerium des Innern, Alt-Moabit 101D, Berlin, 10559, Germany. TEL 49-1888-6810, FAX 49-1888-6812926, poststelle@bmi.bund.de, http://www.bmi.bund.de.

333.72   CAN
UNIT SCHEME AND CONSERVATION ORDER OUTLINES. Text in English. a. looseleaf. CND 4.50. **Document type:** *Government.* **Description:** Includes schemes such as approved water disposal, gas conservation orders, good engineering practice and unitization.
Published by: Ministry of Energy and Mines, c/o Communications Coordinator, Stn Prov Govt, PO Box 9324, Victoria, BC V8W 9N3, Canada. http://www.ogc.gov.bc.ca. **Subscr. to:** Crown Publications Inc., 521 Fort St, Victoria, BC BC V8W 1E7, Canada. TEL 250-386-4636, FAX 250-386-0221, crown@pinc.com, http://www.crownpub.bc.ca.

333.72   THA   ISSN 0255-9250
UNITED NATIONS. ECONOMIC AND SOCIAL COMMISSION FOR ASIA AND THE PACIFIC. DEVELOPMENT PAPERS. Text in Thai. 1981. irreg., latest no.22, 2003. price varies. index. back issues avail. **Document type:** *Monographic series.*
—CISTI.
Published by: United Nations Economic and Social Commission for Asia and the Pacific, United Nations Bldg., Rajadamnern Ave., Bangkok, 10200, Thailand. library-escap@un.org, http://www.unescap.org. **Subscr. to:** United Nations Publications, Distribution and Sales Section, Palais des Nations, Rm C-116, 8-14 av de la Paix, Geneva 1211, Switzerland; United Nations Publications, Rm DC2-853, United Nations Bldg, 2 United Nations Plaza, New York, NY 10017. **Dist. by:** United Nations Publications, Distribution and Sales Section, Palais des Nations, Rm C-116, 8-14 av de la Paix, Geneva 1211, Switzerland.; Conference Services Unit, Conference Services Unit, ESCAP, Bangkok 10200, Thailand.; United Nations Publications, Rm DC2-853, United Nations Bldg, 2 United Nations Plaza, New York, NY 10017.

333.95416   USA   ISSN 0073-4586
SD12
➤ **UNIVERSITY OF IDAHO. FOREST, WILDLIFE AND RANGE EXPERIMENT STATION, MOSCOW. STATION BULLETIN.** Text in English. 1965. irreg., latest vol.78, 2003. price varies. reprints avail. **Document type:** *Bulletin, Academic/Scholarly.* **Description:** Research results on forestry, forest products, fisheries, wildlife, and resource and tourism recreation management. Peer reviewed.
Indexed: BiolAb, ForAb.
—Linda Hall.
Published by: University of Idaho, College of Natural Resources, PO Box 441142, Moscow, ID 83844-1142. TEL 208-885-6673, FAX 208-885-5534, ortiz@uidaho.edu, suem@uidaho.edu, http://www.uidaho.edu/cfwr/public.html, http://www.cnr.uidaho.edu/cnr. R&P, Adv. contact Sue McMurray. Circ: 1,000.

➤ **UNIVERSITY OF MINNESOTA. CENTER FOR NATURAL RESOURCE POLICY AND MANAGEMENT. WORKING PAPERS.** see *WATER RESOURCES*

577.51 639.2   PRI
UNIVERSITY OF PUERTO RICO. SEA GRANT COLLEGE PROGRAM. REPORT. Text in English. irreg.
Published by: Puerto Rico Sea Grant College Program, PO Box 9011, Mayaguez, 00681, Puerto Rico. TEL 787-832-3585, FAX 787-265-2880, http://seagrant.uprm.edu/main.html.

333.72   AUS   ISSN 0811-580X
➤ **UNIVERSITY OF TASMANIA. CENTRE FOR ENVIRONMENTAL STUDIES. PROJECT REPORT.** Key Title: Environmental Studies Project Report. Text in English. 1975. irreg., latest 1992. price varies. back issues avail. **Document type:** *Academic/Scholarly.* **Description:** Records the results of short research projects.
Published by: University of Tasmania, Centre for Environmental Studies, GPO Box 252-78, Hobart, TAS 7001, Australia. TEL 61-3-62262384, FAX 61-3-62202989. Ed. John Todd. Circ: 50.

333.72   AUS   ISSN 0313-5780
UNIVERSITY OF TASMANIA. CENTRE FOR ENVIRONMENTAL STUDIES. WORKING PAPERS. Text in English. 1976. irreg., latest vol.24, 1993. price varies. back issues avail. **Document type:** *Academic/Scholarly.* **Description:** Results of long-term research projects.
Indexed: FPA.
—CISTI.
Published by: University of Tasmania, Centre for Environmental Studies, GPO Box 252-78, Hobart, TAS 7001, Australia. TEL 61-3-62202834, FAX 61-3-62202989. Ed. John Todd. Circ: 100.

UNIVERSITY OF WALES. WELSH INSTITUTE OF RURAL STUDIES. WORKING PAPER. see *SOCIOLOGY*

UNIVERSITY OF WATERLOO. DEPARTMENT OF GEOGRAPHY. PUBLICATION SERIES. see *GEOGRAPHY*

333.72 AUT ISSN 0042-0484
UNSER NEUSTADT. Text in German. 1957. q. USD 8 (effective 1999). bk.rev. **Document type:** *Bulletin.*
Published by: Wiener Neustaedter Denkmalschutzverein, Schneeberggasse 2, Wiener Neustadt, N 2700, Austria. Ed. Gerta Haring. Circ: 600.

UPWELLINGS. see *WATER RESOURCES*

URBAN ECOLOGY. see *HOUSING AND URBAN PLANNING*

333.95416 GBR ISSN 0268-2664
URBAN WILDLIFE NEWS. Text in English. 1984. q. free. bk.rev. **Document type:** *Newsletter, Government.* **Description:** Contains news items and informational articles on ecological conservation and management in architectural and landscape planning in and around urban areas with announcements of relevant seminars, publications, and events.
Published by: English Nature, Northminster House, Peterborough, Cambs PE1 1UA, United Kingdom. TEL 44-1733-455000, FAX 44-1733-568845, http://www.english-nature.org.uk. Ed., R&P George Barker TEL 44-1733-455215. Circ: 5,000.

V N R C BULLETIN. see *ENVIRONMENTAL STUDIES*

V N R C VERMONT ENVIRONMENTAL REPORT. see *ENVIRONMENTAL STUDIES*

333.73 DNK ISSN 0908-7761
➤ **VAND & JORD/WATER & SOIL**; tidsskrift for miljoe og natur. Text in Danish. 1983. q. DKK 287.50 to individuals; DKK 550 to institutions (effective 2004). adv. bk.rev. illus. **Document type:** *Journal, Academic/Scholarly.*
Related titles: Online - full text ed.
Indexed: INIS AtomInd.
Published by: Selskabet for Vand & Jord/Society for Water & Soil, c/o Kurt Jensen, Christiansdal 52, Roedovre, 2610, Denmark. http://www.vand-og-jord.dk/. Ed. Mogens Henze.

333.72 SVN ISSN 0506-4252
QH77.S57
VARSTVO NARAVE/NATURE CONSERVATION. Text in Slovenian; Summaries in English. 1962. a. adv. bk.rev. bibl.; illus.
Indexed: ZooRec.
—BLDSC (6046.438000).
Published by: Zavod Slovenije za Varstvo Naravne in Kulturne Dediscine, Plecnikov trg 2, Box 176, Ljubljana, 61001, Slovenia. FAX 38-61-213-120. Ed. Jelka Habjan. Circ: 800.

VATTEN/WATER; tidskrift foer vattenvaard/journal of water management and research. see *WATER RESOURCES*

333.72 USA
VELADOR. Variant title: Caribbean Conservation Corporation. Newsletter. Text in English. q. USD 25 domestic; USD 35 elsewhere (effective 2000). back issues avail. **Document type:** *Newsletter.* **Description:** Features articles on sea turtle conservation.
Related titles: Online - full text ed.
Published by: Caribbean Conservation Corporation, 4424 N W 13th St, Ste No A1, Gainesville, FL 32609. TEL 352-373-6441, 800-678-7853, ccc@ccturtle.org, http://ccturtle.org/velador.htm. Ed., Pub., R&P Dan Evans. Adv. contact Kim Allen.

DE VELUWENAAR. see *TRAVEL AND TOURISM*

VERDE OGGI; linea verde. see *GENERAL INTEREST PERIODICALS—Italy*

333.72 DEU ISSN 0300-8665
CODEN: SVWLAE
VEREIN FUER WASSER-, BODEN- UND LUFTHYGIENE. SCHRIFTENREIHE. Text in German. 1949. irreg., latest vol.113, 2004. price varies. **Document type:** *Monographic series, Academic/Scholarly.*
Indexed: ASFA, CIN, ChemAb, ChemTitl, FS&TA, IndMed, MEDLINE.
—BLDSC (8104.000000), CASDDS, CISTI, GNLM, IE, Infotrieve, ingenta, Linda Hall. **CCC.**
Published by: Verein fuer Wasser-, Boden- und Lufthygiene, Rotthauser Str 19, Gelsenkirchen, 45879, Germany. TEL 49-209-9242190, FAX 49-209-9242199, verein@wabolu.de, http://www.wabolu.de.

333.72 DEU ISSN 0171-4694
QH77.A46
➤ **VEREIN ZUM SCHUTZ DER BERGWELT. JAHRBUCH.** Text in German. 1900. a. EUR 25 (effective 2003). bibl. back issues avail. **Document type:** *Yearbook, Academic/Scholarly.* **Description:** Contains articles on the conservation of nature and landscapes in the Alps and other mountain ranges.
Formerly (until 1977): Verein zum Schutze der Alpenpflanzen und Tiere. Jahrbuch (0083-5625)
Indexed: BiolAb, DIP, IBR, IBZ, KWIWR, ZooRec.
—CISTI.
Published by: Verein zum Schutz der Bergwelt e.V., Praterinsel 5, Munich, 80538, Germany. TEL 49-8122-892466, FAX 49-8122-9599034, info@vzsb.de, http://www.vzsb.de. Ed. Hans Smettan. R&P Peter Juerging. Circ: 4,500 (controlled).

➤ **VERMONT FISH & WILDLIFE LAWS AND REGULATIONS.** see *SPORTS AND GAMES—Outdoor Life*

➤ **VERMONT NATURAL RESOURCES COUNCIL. BULLETIN.** see *ENVIRONMENTAL STUDIES*

500.9 AUS ISSN 0042-5184
QH1 CODEN: VICNAW
➤ **THE VICTORIAN NATURALIST.** Text in English. 1884. bi-m. free to members. bk.rev.; software rev. illus.; maps; stat. Index. 36 p./no.; back issues avail. **Document type:** *Journal, Academic/Scholarly.* **Description:** Publishes articles on all facets of natural history, primarily in Australia.
Formerly (until 1884): Southern Science Record
Indexed: BIOSIS Prev, BiolAb, FPA, ForAb, MLA, MLA-IB, SFA, WildRev, ZooRec.
—BLDSC (9232.650000), IE, ingenta, Linda Hall. **CCC.**
Published by: Field Naturalists Club of Victoria, 1 Gardenia St., Locked Bag 3, Blackburn, VIC 3130, Australia. vicnat@vicnet.net.au, fncv@vicnet.net.au, http://home.vicnet.net.au/~fncv/vicnat.htm. Ed. Anne Morton. Circ: 1,000 (paid).

639.9 SWE ISSN 1400-1667
VILTFORUM. Text in Swedish. 1994. irreg., latest 2001. price varies. back issues avail. **Document type:** *Monographic series.* **Description:** Research series from the Swedish Hunters' Association dealing with wildlife preservation in Sweden.
Published by: Svenska Jaegarefoerbundet/Swedish Hunters Association, Oester-Malma, Nykoeping, 61191, Sweden. TEL 46-155-246200, FAX 46-155-246250, http://www.jagareforbundet.se.

346.044 USA
VIRGINIA GAME, INLAND FISH AND BOAT LAWS. Text in English. irreg. (w/ current supplement), latest 2000. USD 34.50 base vol(s). (effective 2003). 382 p./no.; Supplement avail. **Description:** This fully annotated and indexed edition contains the general laws and regulations applicable to hunting, fishing and trapping, and boating safety.
Formerly: Virginia Game, Inland Fish and Boat Laws and Regulations
Published by: Michie Company (Subsidiary of: LexisNexis North America), 701 E Water St, Charlottesville, VA 22902-5389. TEL 434-972-7600, 800-446-3410, FAX 434-972-7677, http://www.michie.com.

VIRGINIA NATIVE PLANT SOCIETY. BULLETIN. see *BIOLOGY—Botany*

333.72 USA
VIRGINIA OUTDOORS PLAN (YEAR). Text in English. 1965. quinquennial. USD 20. illus.; tr.lit. **Document type:** *Government.* **Description:** Attempts to project future needs and to identify emerging trends and issues that may have an effect upon open space, natural resources and outdoor recreational resources, planning and management.
Formerly: Virginia's Common Wealth
Published by: Department of Conservation & Recreation, Division of Planning and Recreation Resources, 203 Governor St, Ste 326, Richmond, VA 23219. TEL 804-786-2556, FAX 804-371-7899. Ed., R&P John R Davy Jr.

333.95416 USA ISSN 0042-6792
SK137
VIRGINIA WILDLIFE. Text in English. 1947. m. USD 12.95 (effective 2004). bk.rev. illus. index. **Document type:** *Magazine, Government.* **Description:** Covers resource management, hunting and fishing.
Indexed: BiolAb, BiolDig, SFA, WildRev.
—Linda Hall.
Published by: Department of Game and Inland Fisheries, 4010 Broad St, Richmond, VA 23230. TEL 804-367-1000, dgifweb@dgif.state.va.us, https://estore.dgif.virginia.gov/proddetail.asp?prod=VWMag, http://www.dgif.state.va.us/. Ed., R&P Lee Walker. Circ: 40,000.

333.95416 USA
VIRGINIA WILDLIFE FEDERATION. FEDERATION RECORD. Text in English. 1938. m. USD 5. **Document type:** *Newspaper.*
Published by: Virginia Wildlife Federation, Inc., 1001 E Broad St, No LL5, Richmond, VA 23219-1928. TEL 804-648-3136. Ed. Nancy J Loveless. Circ: 15,000.

333.95416 ZAF ISSN 1022-1115
VISION OF WILDLIFE, ECOTOURISM AND THE ENVIRONMENT IN SOUTHERN AFRICA. Text in English. 1994. a. USD 30 (effective 2000). adv. illus.; maps. **Document type:** *Consumer.*
Indexed: ISAP, WildRev.
Published by: Endangered Wildlife Trust, Private Bag X11, Parkview, Johannesburg 2122, South Africa. TEL 27-11-486-1102, FAX 27-11-486-1506, ewtsa@global.co.za, http://ewt.org.za. Ed. David Holt Biddle. Adv. contact Lynn Ras.

333.72 630 DNK ISSN 1600-3888
VISMANDSRAPPORT. Text in Danish. 2000. irreg. price varies. back issues avail. **Document type:** *Monographic series, Academic/Scholarly.*
Related titles: Online - full text ed.: ISSN 1600-3934.
Published by: Naturraadet/Danish Nature Council, c/o Peder Agger, Roskilde Universitetscenter, PO Box 260, Roskilde, 4000, Denmark. TEL 45-46-742498, FAX 45-46-743041, pa@ruc.dk, http://www.naturraadet.com.

VITAL SIGNS (YEAR); the environmental trends that are shaping our future. see *ENVIRONMENTAL STUDIES*

VOGEL UND UMWELT; Zeitschrift fuer Vogelkunde und Naturschutz in Hessen. see *BIOLOGY—Ornithology*

VOGELKUNDLICHE NACHRICHTEN AUS OBEROESTERREICH; Naturschutz aktuell. see *BIOLOGY—Ornithology*

VOGELS. see *BIOLOGY—Ornithology*

333.783 USA ISSN 0898-6193
THE VOICE OF WALDEN ✶ . Text in English. 1981. q. membership. bk.rev. bibl.; illus. back issues avail. **Document type:** *Newsletter.* **Description:** Provides support for changing the status of Walden from a recreational park to a nature-preserve sanctuary.
Published by: Walden Forever Wild, Inc., 47 Graniteville Rd, Westford, MA 01886-2233. TEL 508-429-2839, FAX 860-487-1629. Ed. Mary P Sherwood. Circ: (controlled).

VULTURE NEWS; the journal of the vulture study group. see *BIOLOGY—Ornithology*

W A N D BULLETIN. see *WOMEN'S INTERESTS*

333.95416 USA ISSN 1062-0435
W E A LEGEND; developing outdoor leaders and educating wilderness users. Text in English. 1988. q. USD 30 to individuals; USD 100 to institutions. adv. bk.rev. **Document type:** *Newsletter, Academic/Scholarly.* **Description:** Promotes wilderness education and preservation through leadership training in the outdoor classroom.
Published by: Wilderness Education Association, Colorado State University, College of Natural Resources, Fort Collins, CO 80523. TEL 970-223-6252, FAX 970-223-6252, colostate.edu. Ed., Adv. contact Kent Clement. Circ: 2,000 (paid).

333.95416 JPN ISSN 0916-7846
W W F. (World Wide Fund) Text in Japanese. 1971. m. JPY 300 per issue (effective 2001). 24 p./no.
Published by: Sekai Shizen Hogo Kikin Japan/World Wide Fund for Nature Japan, 1-14 Shiba 3-chome, Minato-ku, Tokyo, 105-0014, Japan. TEL 81-3-3769-1771, FAX 81-3-3769-1717, communi@wwf.or.jp, http://www.wwf.or.jp. Ed. Junkichi Mima. Pub. Michio Hino. Circ: 20,000.

W W F INDIA QUARTERLY. (World Wide Fund) see *ENVIRONMENTAL STUDIES*

333.95416 DEU
W W F JOURNAL. (World Wildlife Fund) Text in German. q. adv. **Document type:** *Journal, Consumer.*
Published by: World Wildlife Fund Deutschland, Rebstoecker Str. 55, Frankfurt Am Main, 60326, Germany. TEL 49-69-791440, FAX 49-69-617221, info@wwf.de, http://www.wwf.de. Circ: 120,000 (controlled).

333.72 DEU ISSN 0922-7989
WADDEN SEA NEWSLETTER. Text in English. 1989. q. free. bk.rev. **Document type:** *Newsletter, Consumer.*
Indexed: SFA, ZooRec.
—BLDSC (9261.181000).
Published by: Common Wadden Sea Secretariat, Virchowstr 1, Wilhelmshaven, 26382, Germany. TEL 49-4421-9108-0, FAX 49-4421-910830, polanski@cwss.whv.net, http://cwss.www.de. Ed. Harald Marencic. Circ: 1,200.

333.72 NLD ISSN 1572-3453
WADDENMAGAZINE. Text in Dutch. 1965. q. EUR 1.95 newsstand/cover to non-members (effective 2005). adv. bk.rev. **Document type:** *Bulletin, Academic/Scholarly.* **Description:** Covers conservation and cultural history issues relating to the Waddensee and the North coast of Holland.
Formerly (until 2003): Waddenbulletin (0166-4824)
Indexed: RefZh.
—IE, Infotrieve.
Published by: Waddenvereniging, Postbus 90, Harlingen, 8860 AB, Netherlands. TEL 31-517-493696, FAX 31-517-493601, info@waddenvereniging.nl, http://www.waddenvereniging.nl/HTML/Publicaties/. Circ: 55,000.

WAKOU; pour les petits curieux de nature. see *CHILDREN AND YOUTH—For*

C

WALIA. see *ENVIRONMENTAL STUDIES*

333.72 GBR
WALK (LONDON). Text in English. 1949. q. free membership (effective 2005). adv. bk.rev. illus.; maps. 64 p./no. 3 cols./p.; **Document type:** *Magazine, Consumer.* **Description:** Covers walks in the countryside, long-distance trails and access to wild country. Focuses on the conservation of the countryside & access to the countryside.
Former titles (until Winter 2003): The Rambler; (until 2000): Rambling Today (0965-5727); (until 1991): Rambler (0951-5275); (until 1987): Rucksack Rambler (0951-4562); (until 1986): Rucksack (0006-7334); (until 1960): Rambler News
Related titles: Audio cassette/tape ed.
Published by: Ramblers' Association, Ramblers Association, 1-5 Wandsworth Rd, London, SW8 2XX, United Kingdom. TEL 44-20-7339-8500, FAX 44-20-7339-8501, ramblers@london.ramblers.org.uk, steveh@ppltd.co.uk, http://www.ramblers.org.uk/mag/. Ed. Christopher Sparrow TEL 44-20-7296-4245. R&P Denise Noble TEL 44-20-8339-8529. Circ: 130,000.

WAPITI; les sciences de la nature. see *CHILDREN AND YOUTH—For*

WASHINGTON (STATE). DEPARTMENT OF FISH AND WILDLIFE. ANNUAL REPORT. see *FISH AND FISHERIES*

WASHINGTON RECREATION AND PARK ASSOCIATION. SYLLABUS. see *PUBLIC ADMINISTRATION*

WATER RESOURCES JOURNAL. see *WATER RESOURCES*

WATER, WOODS & WILDLIFE. see *BIOLOGY—Botany*

333.9 USA
WATERSHED. Text in English. 1994. q. USD 15 to members. **Document type:** *Newsletter.*
Published by: Friends of the Santa Clara River, 660 Randy Dr, Newbury Park, CA 91320-3036. TEL 805-498-4323. Ed. Barbara Wampole.

WATERSHED FOCUS. see *ENVIRONMENTAL STUDIES—Pollution*

333.72 CAN ISSN 1188-360X
WATERSHED SENTINEL. Text in English. 1990. 6/yr. CND 12, USD 16; CND 3.50 newsstand/cover (effective 2000). adv. bk.rev. charts; illus. back issues avail. **Description:** Focus on forestry, toxics, pulp and paper and ozone.
Address: P O Box 39, Whaletown, BC V0P 1Z0, Canada. TEL 604-935-6992, wss@rfu.org. Ed., Pub. Delores Broten. adv.: B&W page CND 170; trim 10 x 8.5. Circ: 3,000.

333.72 DEU ISSN 0256-7059
WATTENMEER INTERNATIONAL. Text in German. 1983. q. free. **Document type:** *Newsletter, Consumer.*
Published by: Umweltstiftung W W F Deutschland, Norderstr 3, Husum, 25813, Germany. TEL 49-4841-62073, FAX 49-4841-4736, hofeditz@wwf.de, http://www.wwf.de. Ed. Hans Ulrich Roesner. R&P Sybille Mielke.

WEALTH ASIA. see *ENVIRONMENTAL STUDIES*

WEB ECOLOGY; the internet journal on ecology. see *ENVIRONMENTAL STUDIES*

THE WEEDPATCH GAZETTE; fine plant and garden quarterly. see *GARDENING AND HORTICULTURE*

WEIDWERK. see *SPORTS AND GAMES*

WENWU BAOHU YU KAOGU KEXUE/SCIENCES OF CONSERVATION AND ARCHAEOLOGY. see *ARCHAEOLOGY*

333.95416 USA ISSN 0198-6600
SK351 CODEN: WPAAED
WESTERN ASSOCIATION OF FISH AND WILDLIFE AGENCIES. PROCEEDINGS. Text in English. 1940. a. USD 10. cum.index: 1940-1969. **Document type:** *Proceedings.*
Formerly: Western Association of State Game and Fish Commissioners. Proceedings (0085-8102)
Media: Duplicated (not offset).
Indexed: FPA, ForAb, SFA, WildRev, ZooRec.
—BLDSC (6833.700000).
Published by: Western Association of Fish and Wildlife Agencies, c/o Larry L Kruckenberg, Game and Fish Dept, 5400 Bishop Blvd, Cheyenne, WY 82006. TEL 307-777-4569, FAX 307-777-4699. Circ: 400.

333.72 AUS ISSN 0815-4465
S934.A8
WESTERN AUSTRALIA. DEPARTMENT OF CONSERVATION AND LAND MANAGEMENT. LANDSCAPE. Text in English. 1970. 4/yr. AUD 27 domestic; AUD 47 foreign; AUD 6.95 newsstand/cover (effective 2003). 54 p./no.; back issues avail. **Document type:** *Magazine, Government.* **Description:** General information on conservation, wildlife, forests and national parks.
Formerly (until 1985): Western Australia. Forest Department. Forest Focus (0049-7320)
Indexed: ASFA, AgrForAb, ESPM, ForAb, RRTA, SFA, WAE&RSA, WildRev.
Published by: Department of Conservation and Land Management, Locked Bag 104, Bentley Delivery Centre, W.A. 6893, Australia. TEL 61-89334-0324, FAX 61-89334-0498, http://www.calm.wa.gov.au. Ed. David Gough. R&P Ronald Kawalilak TEL 61-89389-8644. Circ: 15,000.

363.7 AUS
WESTERN AUSTRALIA. DEPARTMENT OF ENVIRONMENTAL PROTECTION. ANNUAL REPORT. Text in English. 1994. a. free. **Document type:** *Government.*
—BLDSC (7429.190000).
Published by: Department of Environmental Protection, 8th Fl., Westralia Sq., 141 St. George's Terr., Perth, W.A. 6000, Australia. TEL 61-8-92227000, FAX 61-8-93221598, http://www.environ.wa.gov.au/. Ed. Jacqui Rovis Herman.

363.7 AUS
WESTERN AUSTRALIA. ENVIRONMENTAL PROTECTION AUTHORITY. ANNUAL REPORT. Text in English. 1972. a. free. **Document type:** *Government.*
Formerly: Western Australia. Department of Conservation and Environment. Annual Report; Which incorporated: Western Australia. Conservation and Environment Council. Annual Report; Formerly: Western Australia. Environmental Protection Council. Annual Report
Indexed: AESIS.
—BLDSC (1244.525000).
Published by: Environmental Protection Authority, Westralia Sq. Level 8, 141 St George Terr, Perth, W.A. 6000, Australia. TEL 61-8-92227000, FAX 61-8-93221598, http://www.environ.wa.gov.au/downloads/Annual_Reports/EPA/2000_01/Contents.pdf. Ed. Jacqui Rovis-Hermann. Circ: 1,000.

333.77 USA ISSN 0083-8934
WESTERN LANDS AND WATERS SERIES. Text in English. 1959. irreg. price varies. index. **Document type:** *Monographic series.*
Published by: Arthur H. Clark Co., PO Box 14707, Spokane, WA 99214. TEL 509-928-9540. Ed., R&P Robert A Clark.

333.72 363.7 AUS
WETLANDS ALIVE. Text in English. q. **Document type:** *Newsletter.*
Published by: Wetland Care Australia, P.O. Box 437, Berri, SA 5343, Australia. TEL 08-85823677, FAX 08-85825104, wca@riverland.net.au. Ed. He Shearer. Circ: 1,500.

WHALEWATCH. see *ANIMAL WELFARE*

333.9 USA ISSN 0273-4419
QL737.C4
WHALEWATCHER. Text in English. 1967. s-a. USD 35 domestic membership; USD 45 foreign membership (effective 2005). adv. bk.rev. charts; illus. index. back issues avail. **Document type:** *Journal, Academic/Scholarly.*
Indexed: ZooRec.
—BLDSC (9309.554500), IE, ingenta.
Published by: American Cetacean Society, PO Box 1391, San Pedro, CA 90733-1391. TEL 310-548-6279, FAX 310-548-6950, info@acsonline.org, http://www.acsonline.org/publications/whalewatcher/index.html. Ed., R&P Diane Alps. Circ: 1,000.

WHITESHELL ECHO. see *SPORTS AND GAMES—Outdoor Life*

WILD; canada's wildlife magazine for kids. see *CHILDREN AND YOUTH—For*

WILD ALABAMA; a guide for hikers, hunters, fishermen, backpackers, campers, and outdoor people. see *SPORTS AND GAMES—Outdoor Life*

333.72 USA ISSN 1526-047X
QL49
WILD ANIMAL BABY. Text in English. 2000. 10/yr. USD 19.95 domestic; USD 31.95 foreign (effective 2004). illus. **Document type:** *Magazine, Consumer.* **Description:** Offers fun and educational stories, articles, games, and activities featuring wild baby animals for children ages 1-3.
Published by: National Wildlife Federation, 11100 Wildlife Center Dr., Reston, VA 20190-5362. TEL 800-822-9919, http://www.nwf.org/wildanimalbaby/kzPage.cfm?siteId=1&CFID=1503634&CFTOKEN=61111810. Ed. Donna Johnson.
Subscr. to: PO Box 2038, Harlan, IA 51593-0017. TEL 800-611-1599.

333.95416 USA
THE WILD CANID CENTER REVIEW. Text in English. 1972. q. USD 30 domestic; USD 45 foreign (effective 2000). bk.rev. **Document type:** *Newsletter.* **Description:** As the offical publication of the WCSRC, summarizes captive breeding and reintroductions of federally sanctioned recovery programs (and WCSRC animals) as well as general (i.e. educational) activities of the organization.
Former titles: Wolf Sanctuary Review; Wolf Sanctuary Newsletter; (until 1985): Wolf Sanctuary's Bulletin; W C S R C News; W C S R C Bulletin
Published by: Wild Canid Survival & Research Center, PO Box 760, Eureka, MO 63025. TEL 636-938-5900, FAX 636-938-6490, http://www.wolfsanctuary.org. Ed. Sarah Newman. Pub. Debbie J Causevic. R&P Susan Lindsey. Circ: 3,000 (paid).

333.72 GBR ISSN 0260-7492
➤ **WILD CAT.** Text in English. 1977. s-a. GBP 5; GBP 7 foreign. adv. bk.rev. **Document type:** *Academic/Scholarly.*
Published by: Cat Survival Trust, The Centre, Codicote Rd, Welwyn, Herts AL6 9TU, United Kingdom. TEL 44-1438-71-6873, FAX 44-1438-71-7535. Ed. T Moore. Adv. contact P Watkiss. Circ: 1,800 (paid).

333.95416 USA ISSN 1055-1166
QH75.A1 CODEN: WIEAEI
WILD EARTH. Text in English. 1991. q. USD 25 domestic; USD 30 in Canada; USD 45 elsewhere (effective 2001). adv. bk.rev. illus. 90 p./no.; back issues avail.; reprints avail. **Document type:** *Academic/Scholarly.* **Description:** Serves academic and grassroots elements within the conservation movement: advocates the restoration and protection of natural biodiversity and wilderness.
Related titles: Microform ed.: (from PQC).
Indexed: AltPI, BiolDig, EPB, EnvAb, WildRev, ZooRec.
—BLDSC (9317.208000), IE, ingenta. CCC.
Address: PO Box 455, Richmond, VT 05477. TEL 802-434-4077, FAX 802-434-5980, info@wild-earth.org, http://www.wild-earth.org/. Ed. Tom Butler. Pub. Dave Foreman. Adv. contact Lina Miller. Circ: 6,500.

WILD HORSE AND BURRO DIARY. see *ANIMAL WELFARE*

508.415 IRL ISSN 1393-9491
WILD IRELAND; explore - inform - educate. Text in English. 2000. q. adv. **Document type:** *Magazine, Consumer.*
Related titles: Online - full text ed.
Published by: Wild Ireland Ltd., Leinster Mills, Osberstown, Naas, Co. Kildare, Ireland. TEL 353-45-894900, FAX 353-45-894905, editor@wildireland.ie, info@wildireland.ie, http://www.wildireland.ie. Ed. Juanita Browne. Adv. contact Helen Few. color page EUR 1,524; bleed 225 x 298. Circ: 8,500 (paid and controlled).

333.76 CAN ISSN 1192-6287
WILD LANDS ADVOCATE. Text in English. 1968. 10/yr. CND 25 to individuals; CND 100 to institutions (effective 1999). adv. bk.rev. illus.; stat. back issues avail. **Document type:** *Newsletter.* **Description:** Covers conservation issues of concern to Albertans, with the aim to protect wilderness areas.
Former titles: Wilderness Alberta (0830-8284); Alberta Wilderness Association. Newsletter (0380-562X)
Indexed: SportS.
Published by: Alberta Wilderness Association, P O Box 6398, Sta D, Calgary, AB T2P 2E1, Canada. TEL 403-283-2025, FAX 403-270-2743, awa@web.net, http://www.web.net/~awa/. Ed., R&P Wendy Adams. Circ: 4,000.

WILD OUTDOOR WORLD. see *CHILDREN AND YOUTH—For*

333.95416 USA
WILD RANCH REVIEW. Text in English. 1991. q. USD 15. **Document type:** *Newsletter.* **Description:** Offers in-depth profiles of grass-roots environmental groups.
Published by: Tim Haugh, Ed. & Pub., PO Box 91, Gulnare, CO 81042.

333.73 USA
WILDALERT. Text in English. w. free. **Document type:** *Bulletin.* **Description:** Alerts concerned people to pressing environmental issues and what they can do.
Media: E-mail.
Published by: Wilderness Society, 1516 M St, NW, Washington, DC 20036. TEL 202-833-2300, 800-843-9453, http://www.wilderness.org.

WILDBIOLOGIE. see *BIOLOGY—Zoology*

WILDERNESS NEWS. see *ENVIRONMENTAL STUDIES*

333.95416 USA ISSN 0194-3030
QH75.A1
➤ **WILDERNESS RECORD.** Text in English. 1976. q. free to members. adv. bk.rev. illus. **Document type:** *Newsletter, Academic/Scholarly.* **Description:** Covers California's existing and potential wilderness areas and biodiversity issues throughout California.
Related titles: Online - full text ed.

Published by: California Wilderness Coalition, 1212 Broadway, Ste. 1700, Oakland, CA 94612-1819. TEL 510-451-1450, FAX 510-451-1445, info@calwild.org, http://www.calwild.org. Ed. Michael Gelardi. Circ: 7,000 (controlled and free).

333.73 USA
THE WILDERNESS YEAR (YEAR). Text in English. a. USD 5 per vol. (effective 2000). charts; illus.; stat. back issues avail. **Document type:** *Corporate.* **Description:** Reports on the Wilderness Society's financial situation and outlines the organizatation's accomplishments for the year. Raises issues of environmental concern.
Formerly (until 1999): Wilderness
Related titles: Online - full content ed.: T W S Annual Report.
Published by: Wilderness Society, 1516 M St, NW, Washington, DC 20036. TEL 202-833-2300, 202-833-2300, http://www.wilderness.org/abouttws/annreport.

333.95416 PAK
WILDFIELDS✶. Text in English. m. PKR 2 per issue. adv.
Address: 15 Dayaram Gidumac Rd., Karachi 3, Pakistan. Ed. Mansoorul Hasan.

333.95416 CAN ISSN 0316-3350
WILDLAND NEWS. Text in English. 1968. q. CND 35. adv. bk.rev. illus. **Document type:** *Newsletter.* **Description:** News and views on current wilderness, forest management, forest policy and park issues in Ontario.
Published by: Wildlands League, 380 401 Richmond St W, Toronto, ON M5V 3A8, Canada. TEL 416-971-9453, FAX 416-979-3155, wildland@web.apc.org, http://web.idirect.can/~wildland. Ed. Sarah Ives. R&P Tim Gray. Circ: 4,000 (paid).

333.95416 USA
WILDLANDS NEWS. Text in English. 1973. q. free. **Document type:** *Newsletter.*
Published by: Plymouth County Wildlands Trust, PO Box 2282, Duxbury, MA 02331. TEL 617-934-9018. Ed. Lois Woods. Circ: 1,300 (controlled).

333.95416 USA
WILDLIFE AND BOATING SAFETY LAWS OF TENNESSEE. Text in English. irreg., latest 2001. USD 22 base vol(s). (effective 2003). 190 p./no.
Published by: (Tennessee Wildlife Resources Agency), Michie Company (Subsidiary of: LexisNexis North America), 701 E Water St, Charlottesville, VA 22902-5389. TEL 434-972-7600, 800-446-3410, FAX 434-972-7677, http://www.michie.com.

333.95416 AUS ISSN 0043-5481
QL338
WILDLIFE AUSTRALIA. Text in English. 1963. q. AUD 33 domestic; AUD 50 foreign (effective 2004). adv. bk.rev. illus. back issues avail. **Document type:** *Academic/Scholarly.* **Description:** Covers Australia wildlife and conservation issues aimed at increasing people's awareness of the precious Australian environment.
Related titles: Online - full text ed.
Indexed: ASFA, BiolAb, GdIns, KWIWR, WBA, WMB, WildRev.
Published by: Wildlife Preservation Society of Queensland, 1st Fl, 95 William St, Brisbane, QLD 4000, Australia. TEL 61-7-32210194, FAX 61-7-32210701, http://www.wildlife.org.au/magazine/magazine.html. Ed. Ron Hottenhaus. R&Ps Ewa Meyer, Ron Hottenhaus. Adv. contact Ewa Meyer. Circ: 6,500.

WILDLIFE BIOLOGY. see *BIOLOGY—Zoology*

333.95416 USA ISSN 1048-4949
QL1 CODEN: WICOEG
WILDLIFE CONSERVATION. Text in English. 1897. bi-m. USD 24.95 domestic; USD 26.95 foreign (effective 2005). adv. bk.rev. illus. index. back issues avail.; reprints avail. **Document type:** *Magazine, Consumer.* **Description:** Popular articles about wildlife conservation worldwide, for the general public.
Formerly (until 1990): Animal Kingdom (0003-3537); Which was formed by the 1942 merger of: New York Zoological Society. Journal; New York Zoological Society. Bulletin
Related titles: Microfiche ed.: (from PQC); Online - full text ed.
Indexed: BiolAb, BiolDig, EPB, GSI, KWIWR, RI-1, RI-2, SFA, WildRev, ZooRec.
—BLDSC (9317.330000), CISTI, IE, Infotrieve, ingenta, Linda Hall.
Published by: Wildlife Conservation Society, Wildlife Conservation Park, 2300 Southern Blvd, Bronx, NY 10460. TEL 718-220-5100, FAX 718-584-2625, feedback@wcs.org, http://www.wcs.org/news. Ed. Deborah Behler. Adv. contact Diana Warren. Circ: 150,000 (paid).

WILDLIFE DAMAGE REVIEW. see *ENVIRONMENTAL STUDIES*

WILDLIFE GUARDIAN. see *ANIMAL WELFARE*

333.95416 USA ISSN 0043-549X
SK351
WILDLIFE IN NORTH CAROLINA. Text in English. 1938. m. USD 7.50 (effective 1999). bk.rev. charts; illus. index. **Description:** Articles on wildlife, the outdoors, hunting, fishing and conservation.
Indexed: SFA, WildRev.
Published by: North Carolina Wildlife Resources Commission, Archdale Bldg, 512 N Salisbury St, Raleigh, NC 27604-1188. TEL 919-733-7123, FAX 919-715-2381, earley.larry@coned.wildlife.state.nc.us, http://www.sips.state.nc.us/Wildlife/ConservationEd/winc/. Ed. Lawrence S Earley. Circ: 70,000.

WILDLIFE MONOGRAPHS. see *BIOLOGY—Zoology*

WILDLIFE OF BRITAIN. see *BIOLOGY—Zoology*

333.95416 AUS
WILDLIFE PRESERVATION SOCIETY OF QUEENSLAND. NEWSLETTER. Text in English. 1968. q. AUD 25 domestic; AUD 40 foreign (effective 2000). **Document type:** *Newsletter.*
Published by: Wildlife Preservation Society of Queensland, 1st Fl, 95 William St, Brisbane, QLD 4000, Australia. TEL 61-7-32210194, FAX 61-7-32210701. R&P, Adv. contact Ewa Meyer.

333.95416 USA
WILDLIFE REHABILITATION. Text in English. 1996 (vol.14). a. USD 25 to members; USD 30 to non-members. **Document type:** *Proceedings.*
Indexed: ZooRec.
—BLDSC (9317.463000).
Published by: National Wildlife Rehabilitators Association, 2625 Clearwater Rd., Ste. 1, Saint Cloud, MN 56301-4539. TEL 320-259-4086, nwra@cloudnet.com, http://www.nwrawildlife.org.

639.9 USA ISSN 1535-2242
SF996.45
WILDLIFE REHABILITATION BULLETIN. Text in English. 1994. s-a. free to members NWRA (effective 2002).
Formerly (until 2001): N W R A Quarterly Journal (1522-6654)
Published by: National Wildlife Rehabilitators Association, 2625 Clearwater Rd., Ste. 1, Saint Cloud, MN 56301-4539. TEL 320-259-4086, nwra@nwrawildlife.org, http://www.nwrawildlife.org. Eds. Bea Orendorff, Sue Coulson.

WILDLIFE REHABILITATION TODAY. see *VETERINARY SCIENCE*

333.95416 CAN ISSN 1188-5106
WILDLIFE RESCUE. Text in English. 1979. q. looseleaf. CND 20 membership. adv. bk.rev. **Document type:** *Newsletter.* **Description:** Reviews the organization's activities in wildlife rehabilitation and education.
Published by: Wildlife Rescue Association of British Columbia, 5216 Glencarin Dr, Burnaby, BC V5B 3C1, Canada. TEL 604-526-7275, FAX 604-524-2890. Ed. Cinthia Picker. R&P, Adv. contact Maureen Roger. Circ: 2,000 (controlled).

WILDLIFE RESEARCH. see *BIOLOGY—Zoology*

WILDLIFE RESEARCH REPORT. see *BIOLOGY—Zoology*

WILDLIFE REVIEW ABSTRACTS; an indexing service for wildlife management. see *CONSERVATION—Abstracting, Bibliographies, Statistics*

WILDLIFE SOCIETY BULLETIN; perspectives on wildlife conservation and sustainable use. see *BIOLOGY—Zoology*

333.95416 USA
WILDLIFE WATCH. Text in English. q. USD 15 to members. back issues avail. **Description:** Describes IWC's wildlife rescue, rehabilitation and protection programs, and provides updates on critical issues facing wildlife around the world for IWC members.
Published by: International Wildlife Coalition, 70 E Falmouth Hwy, East Falmouth, MA 02536. TEL 508-548-8328. Ed. Stephen Best.

333.95416 CAN ISSN 1208-123X
WILDLIFE WATCHERS REPORT ON MONITORING. Text in English. 1995. a.
Published by: Environment Canada, 351 St Joseph Blvd, Hull, PQ K1A 0H3 , Canada. TEL 819-997-2800, FAX 819-953-2225, enviroinfo@ec.gc.ca, http://www.ec.gc.ca.

333.95416 USA ISSN 0163-6359
WILDLIFER. Text in English. 1939. bi-m. USD 59 to members (effective 2003). 2 cols./p.; **Document type:** *Newsletter, Internal.*
Formerly (until 1973): Wildlife Society News (0043-552X)
—Linda Hall.
Published by: The Wildlife Society, 5410 Grosvenor Ln, Ste 200, Bethesda, MD 20814. TEL 301-897-9770, FAX 301-530-2471, tws@wildlife.org, http://www.wildlife.org. Ed. Harry E Hodgdon. Circ: 9,000 (paid).

333.72 NLD
WINDMOLEN. Text in Dutch. 1975. 4/yr. bk.rev.
Published by: Vereniging tot Behoud van Molens in Zeeland, Ten Ankerweg 43, Tholen, 4691 GV, Netherlands. Ed. F D M Weemaes. Circ: 40.

333.95 USA
WINGS (PORTLAND); essays on invertebrate conservation. Text in English. 1987. 2/yr. USD 25 to members (effective 2000). bk.rev. **Description:** Dedicated to protecting invertebrates as the major component of biological diversity.
Published by: Xerces Society, 4828 S E Hawthorne Blvd, Portland, OR 97215-3252. TEL 503-232-6639, FAX 503-233-6794, xerces@teleport.com, http://www.xerces.org. Ed., R&P Mary Troychak. Circ: 5,000 (paid).

333.72 USA
WISCONSIN. DEPARTMENT OF NATURAL RESOURCES. RESEARCH - MANAGEMENT FINDINGS SERIES. Text in English. irreg. free.
Published by: Wisconsin Department of Natural Resources, PO Box 7191, Madison, WI 53707-7191. TEL 608-221-6356, FAX 608-221-6353, duvais@dnr.state.wi.us, http://www.dnr.state.wi.us, http://www.dnr.state.wi.us/.

333.72 USA
WISCONSIN. DEPARTMENT OF NATURAL RESOURCES. RESEARCH REPORT SERIES. Text in English. irreg. free.
Published by: Wisconsin Department of Natural Resources, PO Box 7191, Madison, WI 53707-7191. TEL 608-221-6356, FAX 608-221-6353, duvais@dnr.state.wi.su, http://www.dnr.state.wi.us/.

333.72 USA ISSN 0084-0564
SK463 CODEN: WDNTAD
WISCONSIN. DEPARTMENT OF NATURAL RESOURCES. TECHNICAL BULLETIN SERIES. Key Title: Technical Bulletin - Department of Natural Resources (Madison). Text in English. 1950. irreg., latest vol.191, 2000. free. **Document type:** *Government.*
Indexed: BIOSIS Prev, BiolAb, SFA, WildRev, ZooRec.
—BLDSC (8624.450000), CISTI, Linda Hall.
Published by: Wisconsin Department of Natural Resources, PO Box 7191, Madison, WI 53707-7191. TEL 608-221-6356, FAX 608-221-6353, duvais@dnr.state.wi.us, http://www.dnr.state.wi.us/. Ed., R&P Dreux J Watermolen. Circ: 3,000.

333.72 USA ISSN 0736-2277
HC107.W6
WISCONSIN NATURAL RESOURCES. Text in English. 1936. 6/yr., latest vol.25, 2001. USD 8.97; USD 3.50 newsstand/cover (effective 2005). bk.rev. illus. index. 48 p./no. 3 cols./p.; back issues avail. **Document type:** *Magazine, Consumer.*
Formerly (until 1977): Wisconsin Conservation Bulletin (0043-6410)
Related titles: Online - full text ed.
Indexed: BiolAb, SFA, WildRev.
—Linda Hall.
Published by: Wisconsin Department of Natural Resources, 101 S Webster St, Madison, WI 53702. TEL 608-266-1510, 800-678-9472, FAX 608-264-6293, sperld@dnr.state.wi.us, duvais@dnr.state.wi.us, http://www.wnrmag.com, http://www.dnr.state.wi.us/. Ed. David L. Sperling. Circ: 125,000 (paid).

WOMEN IN NATURAL RESOURCES; a journal of professional women in forestry, wildlife, fisheries, range, soils and the social sciences as they pertain to natural resources. see *WOMEN'S INTERESTS*

333.72 USA ISSN 0030-7157
SK461
WONDERFUL WEST VIRGINIA. Text in English. 1936. m. USD 17 domestic; USD 30 foreign (effective 2003). bk.rev. illus. 32 p./no.; back issues avail.; reprints avail. **Document type:** *Government.*
Formerly: Outdoor West Virginia
Related titles: Microfiche ed.: (from PQC).
Published by: West Virginia Division of Natural Resources, Capitol Complex, Building 3, Rm 662, 1900 Kanawha Blvd E, Charleston, WV 25305. TEL 304-558-9152, 800-225-5982, comments@wonderfulwv.com, hpuce@dnr.state.wv.us, http://www.wonderfulwv.com. Ed. Arnout Hyde Jr. Pub., R&P Harry Price TEL 304-558-3315. Adv. contact Robert J Wines TEL 304-269-0463. Circ: 49,500.

333.75 USA
▼ **WOODS, WATER & WILDLIFE.** Text in English. 2004. s-a. adv. **Document type:** *Magazine, Consumer.*
Published by: (International Paper), Grand View Media Group, Inc. (Subsidiary of: EBSCO Industries, Inc.), 200 Croft St., # 1, Birmingham, AL 35242-1824. TEL 888-431-2877, webmaster@grandviewmedia.com, http://www.gvmg.com/Publications/Custom/IP/Home.html, http://www.grandviewmedia.com. Pub. Derrick Nawrocki. Adv. contact David Farlow. color page USD 5,200; trim 7.75 x 10.625. Circ: 110,000 (controlled).

WORKING PAPERS IN COASTAL ZONE MANAGEMENT SERIES. see *WATER RESOURCES*

WORLD BIRDWATCH. see *BIOLOGY—Ornithology*

▼ new title ➤ refereed ✶ unverified ♦ full entry avail.

333.72 CHE ISSN 1027-0965
QH75.A1
WORLD CONSERVATION. Text in English. 1952. q. CHF 66, USD 45 (effective 2000). adv. bk.rev. illus. index. reprints avail. **Document type:** *Bulletin.*
Formerly (until 1996): I U C N Bulletin (0020-9058)
Related titles: French ed.: Planete Conservation. ISSN 1027-0973; Spanish ed.: Conservacion Mundial. ISSN 1027-099X.
Indexed: ASFA, BiolAb, ESPM, EnvAb, KWIWR, RefZh, SFA.
—CIS, CISTI, Linda Hall.
Published by: International Union for Conservation of Nature and Natural Resources, Rue Mauverney 28, Gland, 1196, Switzerland. TEL 41-22-9990001, FAX 41-22-9990002, mail@hq.iucn.org, http://www.iucn.org. Ed. Nikki Meith. Circ: 6,000.

333.72 CHE
WORLD CONSERVATION CONGRESS. PROCEEDINGS. Text in Multiple languages. 1948. triennial. **Document type:** *Proceedings.*
Formerly: International Union for Conservation of Nature and Natural Resources. Proceedings of the General Assembly (0074-929X)
Published by: International Union for Conservation of Nature and Natural Resources, Rue Mauverney 28, Gland, 1196, Switzerland. TEL 41-22-9990001, FAX 41-22-9990002, mail@hq.iucn.org.

333.72025 USA ISSN 0092-0908
S920
WORLD DIRECTORY OF ENVIRONMENTAL ORGANIZATIONS; a handbook of national and international organizations and programs, governmental and non-governmental, concerned with protecting the earth's resources. Text in English. 1973. irreg., latest vol.6, 2001. USD 60 domestic; USD 75 foreign (effective 2001). Index. 264 p./no.; **Document type:** *Directory.* **Description:** Provides a comprehensive global guide to organizations concerned with the environment and natural resources, covering more than 2,100 governmental and nongovernmental organizations in over 200 countries.
Published by: California Institute of Public Affairs, PO Box 189040, Sacramento, CA 95818. FAX 916-442-2478, cipa@cipahg.org, cipa@igc.org, www.cipahg.org, http://www.igc.org/cipa. Ed. Thaddeus C Trzyna. Circ: 3,000. **Co-sponsors:** International Union for Conservation of Nature and Natural Resources; IUCN - The World Conservation Union; Sierra Club.

WORLD GUIDE TO COVERED BRIDGES. see *HISTORY—History Of North And South America*

333.95416 ZAF
WORLD OF BIRDS WILDLIFE SANCTUARY CC, SOUTH AFRICA. NEWSLETTER. Text in English. 1978. bi-m. ZAR 175 (effective 2000). illus. **Document type:** *Newsletter, Academic/Scholarly.* **Description:** Covers the world of birds and the bird park and includes sanctuary updates and information. Supplies bird and animal breeding information, as well as commentary on birds and animal conservation and welfare.
Published by: World of Birds Wildlife Sanctuary CC, Valley Rd, Hout Bay, 7800, South Africa. TEL 27-21-790-2730, FAX 27-21-790-4839. Ed. Walter Mangold. Circ: 1,000.

WORLD RESOURCE REVIEW. see *ENVIRONMENTAL STUDIES*

333.72 USA ISSN 0887-0403
HC10 CODEN: WORSE9
WORLD RESOURCES (YEAR). Text in English. 1986. biennial, latest 2002-2004. USD 27 per vol. (effective 2005). **Document type:** *Academic/Scholarly.*
Related titles: Arabic ed.; French ed.; Chinese ed.; Japanese ed.
Indexed: BIOSIS Prev, RDA, SRI.
—BLDSC (9359.089000), CISTI.
Published by: World Resources Institute, 10 G St, N E, Ste 800, Washington, DC 20002. TEL 202-729-7600, FAX 202-729-7610, publications@wri.org, http://www.wristore.com/wristore/worresrep.html, http://www.wri.org/.

▼ **WORLD REVIEW OF ENTREPRENEURSHIP, MANAGEMENT AND SUSTAINABLE DEVELOPMENT.** see *BUSINESS AND ECONOMICS—Management*

333.78 USA
WORLD RIVERS REVIEW. Text in English. 1985. bi-m. USD 35 to individuals; USD 100 to institutions; USD 50 to non-profit organizations (effective 2001). bk.rev. back issues avail. **Document type:** *Newsletter.*
Formerly: International Rivers Network (0890-6211)
Indexed: AltPI.
Published by: International Rivers Network, 1847 Berkeley Way, Berkeley, CA 94703. TEL 510-848-1155, FAX 510-848-1008, irn@irn.org, http://www.irn.org. Ed., Adv. contact Lori Pottinger.

WORLD WATCH; working for a sustainable future. see *ENVIRONMENTAL STUDIES*

333.7 USA ISSN 1074-1283
WORLD WILDLIFE FUND. CONSERVATION ISSUES. Text in English. 1994. bi-m.
Indexed: PAIS.
Published by: World Wildlife Fund, 1250 24th St, N W, Washington, DC 20037.

WORLDWATCH PAPERS. see *ENVIRONMENTAL STUDIES*

333.95416 USA ISSN 0043-9819
SK465 CODEN: WYWLA
WYOMING WILDLIFE MAGAZINE. Text in English. 1936. m. USD 12.95 (effective 2004). bk.rev. charts; illus. index. back issues avail. **Document type:** *Magazine, Consumer.*
Formerly: Wyoming Game and Fish Commission. Bulletin
Related titles: Magnetic Tape ed.
Indexed: BiolAb, RefZh, SFA, WildRev, ZooRec.
—BLDSC (9365.550000), IE, ingenta.
Published by: Wyoming. Game and Fish Department, 5400 Bishop Blvd, Cheyenne, WY 82006. TEL 307-777-4600, 800-777-0015, http://gf.state.wy.us/services/publications/index.asp, http://gf.state.wy.us/admin/. Ed., R&P Chris Madson. Circ: 35,000.

799.1 799.2 333.95 USA
WYOMING WILDLIFE NEWS. Text in English. bi-m. USD 8 (effective 2002). **Document type:** *Newspaper.* **Description:** Provides information on Wyoming's hunting, fishing and trapping.
Published by: Wyoming. Game and Fish Department, 5400 Bishop Blvd, Cheyenne, WY 82006. FAX 307-777-4610, http://gf.state.wy.us/admin/.

XIANGJIAN XIAOLU/COUNTRY ROAD; if you eat, you are involved in agriculture. see *AGRICULTURE*

333.72 ISR ISSN 0334-0554
YEDI'ON; rashut shmurat hateva. Text in Hebrew. 1975. 3/yr. free. bk.rev. **Description:** Information on the Israeli nature reserves and the activities of the Authority.
Published by: Nature Reserves Authority, Rehov Yermeyahn 78, Jerusalem, 94467, Israel. TEL 972-2-5005444, FAX 972-2-5374887. Ed. Ms. Dina Winstaine. Circ: 500.

YEDI'OT KEREN KAYEMET LE-YISRA'EL. see *FORESTS AND FORESTRY*

333.9 NZL ISSN 1171-4131
YELLOW-EYED PENGUIN NEWS. Text in English. 1989. s-a. NZD 15 to individuals; NZD 8 to students (effective 2001). charts; illus.; maps. **Document type:** *Newsletter.* **Description:** Covers conservation of the yellow-eyed penguin in New Zealand.
Published by: Yellow-Eyed Penguin Trust, P.O. Box 5409, Dunedin, New Zealand. TEL 64-3-4790011, FAX 64-3-4790019, yept@clear.net.nz, http://www.yellow-eyedpenguin.org.nz. Ed. Sue Murrary. Circ: 2,000 (paid).

333.72 GBR ISSN 0265-6833
YORKSHIRE NATURALISTS' UNION. BULLETIN. Text in English. 1984. s-a. **Document type:** *Bulletin, Academic/Scholarly.*
Indexed: ZooRec.
—BLDSC (2822.480000), IE, ingenta.
Published by: Yorkshire Naturalists' Union, University of Bradford, Bradford, W Yorks BD7 1DP, United Kingdom. TEL 44-1274-234212, FAX 44-1274-234231, m.r.d.seaward@bradford.ac.uk, http://www.tka.co.uk/ynu.

354.689 ZMB ISSN 0084-4586
ZAMBIA. COMMISSION FOR THE PRESERVATION OF NATURAL AND HISTORICAL MONUMENTS AND RELICS. ANNUAL REPORT. Text in English. 1948. a. ZMK 3. **Document type:** *Government.*
Published by: National Heritage Conservation Commission525, National Heritage Conservation Commission, 525, PO Box 60124, Livingstone, Zambia. Ed., R&P Maxwell Zulu.

333.72 ZMB
ZAMBIA HERITAGE. Text in English. 1991. 2/yr. USD 4. adv.
Published by: National Heritage Conservation Commission, PO Box 60124, Livingstone, Zambia. TEL 260-320354, FAX 260-324509. Adv. contact Maxwell Zulu TEL 260-320481. Circ: 2,000 (paid).

333.72 ZMB
ZAMBIA. NATIONAL HERITAGE CONSERVATION COMMISSION. ANNUAL REPORT. Text in English. 1948. a. adv. **Document type:** *Government.*
Published by: National Heritage Conservation Commission, PO Box 60124, Livingstone, Zambia. TEL 260-320354, FAX 260-324509. Adv. contact Maxwell Zulu TEL 260-320481.

333.72 ZMB
ZAMBIA. NATURAL RESOURCES DEPARTMENT. ANNUAL REPORT. Text in English. 1964-1973; resumed 1976. a. ZMK 200. **Document type:** *Government.*
Former titles: Zambia. Natural Resources Advisory Board. Annual Report (0377-1709); Zambia. Office of the Conservateur of Natural Resources. Annual Report (0377-3906); Zambia. Natural Resources Board. Annual Report (0084-4993)
Published by: (Zambia. Natural Resources Department), Government Printing Department, PO Box 30136, Lusaka, Zambia.

333.72 RUS
ZELENYI KREST. Text in Russian. 1995. q. USD 85 in United States (effective 2000).
Indexed: RASB.
Published by: Redaktsiya Zelenyi Krest, Rostovskii per 2-14, Moscow, 119121, Russian Federation. TEL 7-095-2203633. **Dist. by:** East View Information Services, 3020 Harbor Ln. N., Minneapolis, MN 55447. TEL 763-550-0961, FAX 763-559-2931.

333.72 RUS
ZELENYI MIR. Text in Russian. 1990. 26/yr. USD 150 in United States (effective 2000).
Published by: Assotsyatsiya Rosekopress, Bogoyavlenskii pr-zd dom 3 str 3, Moscow, 103012, Russian Federation. TEL 7-095-9217331. Ed. M L Borozin. **Dist. by:** East View Information Services, 3020 Harbor Ln. N., Minneapolis, MN 55447. TEL 763-550-0961, FAX 763-559-2931.

333.72 CHN
ZHONGGUO GUOTUZIYUAN BAO/CHINA LAND AND RESOURCES NEWS. Text in Chinese. d. (Mon.-Fri.). CNY 240 (effective 2004). **Document type:** *Newspaper, Government.* **Description:** Covers wide range of issues related to land and resources management in China.
Published by: Zhonghua Renmin Gongheguo Guotuziyuanbu/Ministry of Land and Resources P.R.C, 64, Funei Dajie, Beijing, 100812, China. TEL 86-10-66558001, FAX 86-10-66558004, bzxx@mail.mlr.gov.cn, http://www.mlr.gov.cn/. **Dist. by:** China International Book Trading Corp, 35 Chegongzhuang Xilu, Haidian District, PO Box 399, Beijing 100044, China. TEL 86-10-68412045, FAX 86-10-68412023, cibtc@mail.cibtc.com.cn, http://www.cibtc.com.cn.

333.72 ZWE
ZIMBABWE. MINISTRY OF LANDS AND NATURAL RESOURCES. REPORT OF THE SECRETARY FOR LANDS AND NATURAL RESOURCES. Text in English. 1968. a. ZWD 1.05. stat. **Document type:** *Government.*
Supersedes in part: Rhodesia. Ministry of Mines and Lands. Report of the Secretary for Mines and Lands
Published by: Government Printer, Causeway, PO Box CY 341, Harare, Zimbabwe. Circ: 400.

333.95416 ZWE
➤ **ZIMBABWE WILDLIFE.** Text in English. 1973. q. ZWD 420 domestic; ZWD 50 overseas (effective 2003). adv. bk.rev. illus. **Document type:** *Journal, Academic/Scholarly.*
Formerly: Wild Rhodesia
Indexed: ZooRec.
Published by: Wildlife and Environment Zimbabwe, PO Box HG 996, Harare, Highlands, Zimbabwe. TEL 263-4-747500, FAX 263-4-747174, zimwild@ecoweb.co.zw, http://www.zimwild.org. Ed. Stephen Karindawaro. Circ: 5,500.

333.72 CHN ISSN 1000-0038
ZIRAN ZIYUAN/NATURAL RESOURCE. Text in Chinese. 1977. bi-m. adv. bk.rev. **Document type:** *Academic/Scholarly.* **Description:** Publishes articles on China's earth, water, biological, and atmospheric resources; results of research into their development, utilization, and protection; methods of investigations; and application of new technology in such investigations.
—Linda Hall.
Published by: (Zhongguo Kexueyuan, Dili Kexue yu Ziyuan Yanjiusuo/Chinese Academy of Sciences, Institute of Geographical Sciences and Natural Resources Research), Kexue Chubanshe/Science Press, 16 Donghuang Cheng Genbei Jie, Beijing, 100717, China. TEL 86-10-64000246, FAX 86-10-64030255, http://www.igsnrr.ac.cn/geo/zykx.jsp?objectid1=15. Circ: 11,000.

333.72 CHN ISSN 1005-8141
ZIYUAN KAIFA YU SHICHANG/RESOURCE DEVELOPMENT AND MARKET. Text in Chinese; Summaries in Chinese, English. 1985. bi-m. CNY 10 newsstand/cover (effective 2005). adv. bk.rev. **Document type:** *Journal, Academic/Scholarly.* **Description:** Covers development, protection and utilization of natural resources including water, soil, air, energy, living organisms, as well as tourism and land management.
Formerly: Ziyuan Kaifa yu Baohu (1001-3822)
Related titles: Online - full text ed.: (from East View Information Services, WanFang Data Corp.).
Published by: (Sichuansheng Ziran Ziyuan Yanjiusuo/Sichuan Institute of Natural Resource), Resource Development and Market Press, No24, Block 2 S. Yihuan Rd, Chengdu, Sichuan 610015, China. zzs@scppc.org, http://zykfysc.periodicals.net.cn/. Ed. Meng Aiguo. Pub. Lu Yongji. Adv. contact Fang Wang. Circ: 5,000 (paid).

ZNANSTVENO RAZISKOVALNO SREDISCE REPUBLIKE SLOVENIJE. ANNALES. SERIES HISTORIA NATURALIS. see *BIOLOGY*

ZOO (ANVERS). see *BIOLOGY—Zoology*

ZOONOOZ. see *BIOLOGY—Zoology*

333.72 CZE ISSN 1210-5538
N6
ZPRAVY PAMATKOVE PECE. Text in Czech; Summaries in German. 1937. 10/yr. CZK 300 domestic (effective 2000); CZK 35 newsstand/cover. adv. illus. **Document type:** *Newsletter, Academic/Scholarly.* **Description:** Contains articles and studies on research, conservation, and preservation of the historic buildings, monuments, conservation areas, etc. in the Czech republic.
Formerly (until 1992): Pamatky a Priroda (0139-9853); Formed by the merger of (1962-1976): Pamatkova Pece (0231-7966); (1946-1976): Ochrana Prirody (0029-8204)
Related titles: CD-ROM ed.
Indexed: A&ATA, BHA.
Published by: Statni Ustav Pamatkove Pece, Valdstejnske nam 3, Prague, 11801, Czech Republic. TEL 42-2-57010111, FAX 42-2-535496. Ed., Adv. contact Jan Sommer. R&P Josef Stulc. page CZK 10,000. Circ: 1,100. **Subscr. to:** Dupress, Podolska 110, Prague 4 147 00, Czech Republic. TEL 42-2-41433396. **Co-sponsor:** Ministertsvo Kultury Ceske Respubliky.

333.72 HRV ISSN 1330-1381
ZUBOR. Text in Croatian. 1992. q. **Document type:** *Magazine, Trade.*
Published by: Hrvatsko Drustvo za Zastitu Voda i Mora, Ul. Grada Vukovara 220, Zagreb, 10000, Croatia. TEL 385-1-6110522, FAX 385-1-6151749.

CONSERVATION—Abstracting, Bibliographies, Statistics

016.33372 USA ISSN 0140-5373
QH90.A1
AQUATIC SCIENCES & FISHERIES ABSTRACTS. PART 1: BIOLOGICAL SCIENCES AND LIVING RESOURCES. Text in English. 1971. m. USD 1,850 combined subscription print & online eds.; USD 2,915 combined subscription print, online & CD-ROM eds. of part.1, 2 & 3 (effective 2006). abstr.; bibl. index in Print & on CD-ROM. back issues avail. **Document type:** *Abstract/Index.* **Description:** International network of aquatic science centers' studies on marine, freshwater and brackish water organisms.
Supersedes in part: Aquatic Sciences and Fisheries Abstracts (0044-8516); Which was formed by the merger of: Aquatic Biology Abstracts (0003-7311); Current Bibliography for Aquatic Sciences and Fisheries (0011-3239)
Related titles: CD-ROM ed.; Online - full text ed.: ISSN 1555-6204. USD 1,385; USD 2,185 3 journals set (effective 2006).
—Linda Hall.
Published by: (Food and Agriculture Organization of the United Nations), C S A Journal Division (Subsidiary of: Cambridge Information Group), 7200 Wisconsin Ave, Ste 715, Bethesda, MD 20814. TEL 301-961-6798, 800-843-7751, FAX 301-961-6799, journals@csa.com, http://www.csa.com. Ed. Richard Pepe. Pub. Ted Caris. **Co-sponsors:** U.N. Division for Ocean Affairs and the Law of the Sea; U.N. Environment Programme; Intergovernmental Oceanographic Commission.

016.33372 USA
CONSERVATION BIOLOGY ABSTRACTS. Text in English. 1987. q. USD 100 to individuals; USD 175 to libraries; USD 325 universities; USD 475 region; USD 80 to students (effective 2005). **Document type:** *Abstract/Index.* **Description:** Contains 2400 + records including citations and abstracts from Conservation Biology (1987-2001).
Media: Online - full content. **Related titles:** CD-ROM ed.: USD 149 to individuals; USD 250 to libraries; USD 450 universities; USD 650 region; USD 129 to students (effective 2002).
Published by: ABSEARCH, Inc., 1204 Thatuna Ave, Moscow, ID 83843. TEL 208-883-5544, 800-867-1877, FAX 208-883-5554, custinfo@absearch.com, sales@absearch.com, http://www.absearch.com.

333.72021 CAN ISSN 1488-979X
ECONNECTIONS: LINKING THE ENVIRONMENT AND THE ECONOMY. INDICATORS AND DETAILED STATISTICS. Text in English. 1997. a. CND 80 (effective 2004).
Published by: Statistics Canada, Publications Sales and Services, Ottawa, ON K1A 0T6, Canada. TEL 613-951-8116, infostats@statcan.ca, http://www.statcan.ca/english/IPS/Data/16-200-XKE.htm.

016.33372 USA ISSN 0093-3287
GF1
ENVIRONMENT ABSTRACTS. Text in English. 1971. m. USD 1,835 domestic; USD 2,020 foreign (effective 2005). illus. Index. reprints avail. **Document type:** *Abstract/Index.* **Description:** Addresses the impact of humankind and technology on the environment with attention to air, water, and noise pollution; solid and toxic wastes; radiological contamination; toxicological effects; control technologies; resource management; population; endangered species; and geophysical and climatic change. Information is abstracted and indexed from scientific, technical, and business journals; conference and symposium proceedings; and academic and government reports.
Incorporates (1985-1991): Acid Rain Abstracts (0882-1402); Formerly (until 1974): Environment Information Access (0013-9181)
Related titles: CD-ROM ed.; Online - full text ed.: (from Data-Star, F I Z Technik, Questel Orbit Inc., The Dialog Corporation).
—BLDSC (3791.095010), Linda Hall.
Published by: Congressional Information Service, Inc. (Subsidiary of: LexisNexis), 7500 Old Georgetown Rd, Bethesda, MD 20814-6126. TEL 301-654-1550, 800-638-8380, FAX 301-657-3203, academicinfo@lexisnexis.com, http://www.lexisnexis.com/academic/3cis/cist/EnvironmentAbstracts.asp, http://www.lexisnexis.com/academic/3cis/cisMnu.asp.

333.75021 CAN
NEW BRUNSWICK. TOURISM RECREATION & HERITAGE. TECHNICAL SERVICES BRANCH. PROVINCIAL PARK STATISTICS. Text in English. 1971. a. free. illus.
Formerly: New Brunswick. Field Services Branch. Provincial Park Statistics
Published by: Tourism Recreation & Heritage, Technical Services Branch, P O Box 12345, Fredericton, NB E3B 5C3, Canada. TEL 506-453-2730, FAX 506-453-2416. Ed. Phillip Ossinger. Circ: 200.

NORTH AMERICAN WILDLIFE & NATURAL RESOURCES ABSTRACTS. see *BIOLOGY—Abstracting, Bibliographies, Statistics*

OBZORNAYA INFORMATSIYA. EKOLOGICHESKAYA EKSPERTIZA. see *ENVIRONMENTAL STUDIES—Abstracting, Bibliographies, Statistics*

333.7016 RUS
PRIRODA, PRIRODNYE RESURSY SIBIRI I DAL'NEGO VOSTOKA, IKH OKHRANA I RATSIONAL'NOE ISPOL'ZOVANIE; tekushchii ukazatel' literatury. Text in English, Russian, Multiple languages. 1995. 3/yr. USD 96 foreign. **Document type:** *Bibliography.* **Description:** Covers books, articles, summaries, and reports from conferences and symposia on natural resource protection and use.
Published by: Rossiiskaya Akademiya Nauk, Sibirskoe Otdelenie, Gosudarstvennaya Publichnaya Nauchno-Tekhnicheskaya Biblioteka/State Public Scientific and Technical Library of the Siberian Branch of the Russian Academy of Sciences, Ul Voskhod 15, Novosibirsk, 630200, Russian Federation. TEL 7-3832-661367, FAX 7-3832-663365, root@libr.nsk.su, onb@spsl.nsc.ru.

016.33372 GBR ISSN 0955-226X
S C E N E S - SCOTTISH ENVIRONMENT NEWS. Text in English. 1988. m. GBP 22 domestic to individuals; GBP 27 in Europe to individuals; GBP 40 domestic to institutions; GBP 46 in Europe to institutions (effective 2000). bk.rev. back issues avail. **Document type:** *Newsletter, Abstract/Index.* **Description:** Reports topical information on the Scottish environment.
Address: Strome House, North Strome, Lochcarron, Ross-shire IV54 8YJ, United Kingdom. TEL 44-1520-722901, FAX 44-1520-722902, scotennews@aol.com, enquiries@scenes.org.uk, http://www.scenes.org.uk. Eds. Michael Scott, Sue Scott. Circ: 580 (paid).

WILDLIFE ABSTRACTS. see *BIOLOGY—Abstracting, Bibliographies, Statistics*

016.33395 USA
SK351
WILDLIFE REVIEW ABSTRACTS; an indexing service for wildlife management. Text in English. 1935. q. bk.rev. cum.index: 1935-1951, 1952-1955, 1956-1960, 1961-1970, 1971-1975, 1976-1980. back issues avail. **Document type:** *Abstract/Index.* **Description:** Indexes articles from more than 1,300 journals and magazines and more than 500 books and symposia proceedings dealing with natural resources topics.
Formerly (until 1995): Wildlife Review (Fort Collins) (0043-5511)
Media: CD-ROM (from National Information Services Corp. (N I S C)). **Related titles:** Microform ed.: (from PQC); Online - full text ed.: (from National Information Services Corp. (N I S C)).
—CISTI, Linda Hall.
Published by: National Information Services Corp. (N I S C), Ste 6, Wyman Towers, 3100 St Paul St, Baltimore, MD 21218. TEL 410-243-0797, FAX 410-243-0982, sales@nisc.com, http://www.nisc.com.

CONSTITUTIONAL LAW

see LAW—Constitutional Law

CONSUMER EDUCATION AND PROTECTION

A B A CONSUMER BANKING DIGEST. see *BUSINESS AND ECONOMICS—Banking And Finance*

640.73 USA ISSN 1522-9688
A PENNY SAVED; dedicated to saving that penny earned. Text in English. 1994. bi-m. USD 14 domestic; USD 22 foreign (effective 2000 - 2001). bk.rev. **Document type:** *Newsletter, Consumer.* **Description:** Designed to help people save and spend money wisely. Includes all aspects of everyday life.
Published by: Penny Saved, PO Box 3471, Omaha, NE 68103-0471. TEL 402-556-5655, apennysvd@juno.com. Ed., Pub., R&P Diane M Rosener.

640.73 USA
AD SACK. Text in English. w.
Address: 3040 S Padre Island Dr, Corpus Christi, TX 78415. TEL 512-854-0137.

ADVANCES IN CONSUMER RESEARCH. see *BUSINESS AND ECONOMICS—Marketing And Purchasing*

640.73 USA ISSN 1047-031X
ALABAMA LIVING. Text in English. 1948. m. USD 6 to non-members; USD 3 to members (effective 2005). adv. bk.rev. 48 p./no. 3 cols./p.; **Document type:** *Magazine.* **Description:** Contains material of interest to members of rural electric cooperatives in Alabama.
Formerly (until 1989): A R E A Magazine (0883-7392)
Published by: Alabama Rural Electric Association of Cooperatives, PO Box 244014, Montgomery, AL 36124. FAX 334-215-2737, dgates@areapower.com, http://www.alabamaliving.com. Pub. Fred Braswell. R&P Darryl Gates. adv.: B&W page USD 4,232, color page USD 5,131. Circ: 371,000 (paid).

AMERICAN DEMOGRAPHICS; consumer trends for business leaders. see *POPULATION STUDIES*

AQUA BUYER'S GUIDE. see *PHYSICAL FITNESS AND HYGIENE*

640.73 USA
▼ **ARTHUR FROMMER'S SMART SHOPPING.** Text in English. 2005. q.
Published by: Arthur Frommer's Budget Travel, Inc. (Subsidiary of: John Wiley & Sons, Inc.), 251 W 57th St, New York, NY 10019. TEL 800-829-9161, FAX 212-445-5764, http://www.frommers.com.

ASHES TO DUST. see *PUBLIC HEALTH AND SAFETY*

640.73 USA
AUSTIN GREENSHEET. Text in English. w. free. **Document type:** *Consumer.*
Published by: Gordon Publications (Austin), PO Box 140721, Austin, TX 78714-0721. TEL 512-454-1003, FAX 512-454-2442. Pub. Kathleen Douglass. Circ: (controlled).

640.73 AUS
AUSTRALIAN CAPITAL TERRITORY ATTORNEY-GENERAL'S DEPARTMENT ANNUAL REPORT. Text in English. a. **Document type:** *Government.* **Description:** Provides information to the public on the operations and performance of the department, for the prior year ending 30 June.
Formerly: Consumer Affairs Council of the Australian Capital Territory. Annual Report
Published by: Attorney-General's Department, Consumer Affairs Bureau, GPO Box 158, Canberra, ACT 2601, Australia. TEL 61-6-2070400. Circ: 300.

AUSTRALIAN RECALLS AND CANCELLATIONS. see *PUBLIC HEALTH AND SAFETY*

THE AVIATION CONSUMER. see *AERONAUTICS AND SPACE FLIGHT*

BANKCARD BAROMETER. see *BUSINESS AND ECONOMICS—Banking And Finance*

BANKCARD UPDATE. see *BUSINESS AND ECONOMICS—Banking And Finance*

BARGAIN HUNTERS & BUDGETEERS OPPORTUNITY NEWSLETTER. see *HOME ECONOMICS*

640.73 381 AUS ISSN 0159-6861
BARGAIN SHOPPER'S GUIDE TO MELBOURNE. Text in English. biennial. AUD 9.90 (effective 2004).
—CCC.
Published by: Universal Magazines Pty. Ltd., Unite 5, 6-8 Byfield St, North Ryde, NSW 2113, Australia. TEL 61-2-98870399, FAX 61-2-98050714, info@universalmagazines.com.au, http://www.universalmagazines.com.au/.

640.73 381 AUS ISSN 0158-7358
BARGAIN SHOPPERS GUIDE TO SYDNEY. Text in English. 1985. biennial. AUD 9.90 (effective 2004).
Published by: Universal Magazines Pty. Ltd., Unite 5, 6-8 Byfield St, North Ryde, NSW 2113, Australia. TEL 61-2-98870399, FAX 61-2-98050714, info@universalmagazines.com.au, http://www.universalmagazines.com.au/.

C

640.73 USA ISSN 0730-9376
BAY AREA CONSUMERS' CHECKBOOK. Text in English. 1982. s-a. USD 30 for 2 yrs.; USD 6.95 newsstand/cover. adv. charts; illus.; mkt.; stat. cum.index. back issues avail.
Document type: *Consumer.* **Description:** Evaluates local Bay Area service firms, such as auto repair shops, medical services, home improvement firms, stores, insurance companies, etc.
Published by: Center for the Study of Services, 733 15th St, N W, Ste 820, Washington, DC 20005-2112. TEL 202-347-9612, 800-475-7283, editors@checkbook.org, http://www.checkbook.org. Ed. Robert Krugoff. Pub. Robert Krughoff. R&P Kevin Brassler. Adv. contact Tara Eberly. Circ: 35,000 (paid).

640.73 USA
▼ **BEST.** Text in English. 2003 (Nov.). q. USD 3.99 newsstand/cover (effective 2004). adv. **Document type:** *Magazine, Consumer.* **Description:** Covers shopping that is focused on the products and experiences of the upscale lifestyle.
Published by: (BestStuff, Inc.), Primedia Consumer Media & Magazine Group, 9036 Brittanyway, Tampa, FL 33619. TEL 813-679-3500, FAX 813-679-3999, http://www.primedia.com. Ed. John Kelley. Circ: 100,000 (controlled).

BLACK BOOK. NEW CAR COST GUIDE. see *TRANSPORTATION—Automobiles*

640.73 USA ISSN 1542-3522
▼ **BOSTON CONSUMERS' CHECKBOOK.** Text in English. 2003. s-a. USD 30 (effective 2003).
Related titles: Online - full text ed.: USD 25 (effective 2003).
Published by: Center for the Study of Services, 733 15th St, N W, Ste 820, Washington, DC 20005-2112. TEL 202-347-7283, FAX 202-347-4000, http://www.checkbook.org.

640.73 USA ISSN 0274-4805
HG179 CODEN: BLPEEB
BOTTOM LINE / PERSONAL. Text in English. 1979. s-m. USD 39 (effective 2004). bk.rev. 16 p./no. 4 cols./p.; back issues avail.; reprints avail. **Document type:** *Newsletter, Consumer.* **Description:** Provides valuable authoritative insider information to help people lead healthier, happier, and more productive lives.
Related titles: ♦ Special ed(s).: Bottom Line - Year Book.
Indexed: CCR.
Published by: Boardroom, Inc, 281 Tresser Blvd, 8th Fl., Stamford, CT 06901-3246. TEL 203-973-5900, FAX 203-967-3086, editors@boardroom.com, http://www.bottomlinesecrets.com, http://www.boardroom.com. Ed. Marjorie Abrams. Pub. Martin Edelston. R&P Bradley Velardo TEL 203-973-6204. Circ: 200,000. **Subscr. to:** PO Box 58446, Boulder, CO 80322-8446. TEL 800-274-5611, FAX 303-604-7455, bottomline@boardroom.com, http://www.blp.net/subscription.html.

640.73 USA
BOTTOM LINE - YEAR BOOK. Text in English. a. USD 19.95 newsstand/cover (effective 2003). **Document type:** *Yearbook, Consumer.* **Description:** Offers consumers little-known but valuable money-saving tips on enhancing one's life, health, and finances, covering such topics as medicine and health, legal issues, tax loopholes, insurance, real estate, banking, investments, and consumer savvy.
Related titles: ♦ Special ed. of: Bottom Line / Personal. ISSN 0274-4805.
Published by: Boardroom, Inc, 281 Tresser Blvd, 8th Fl., Stamford, CT 06901-3246. TEL 203-973-5900, FAX 203-967-3086, editors@boardroom.com, http://www.boardroom.com. Pub. Martin Edelston. R&P Bradley Velardo TEL 203-973-6204. **Subscr. to:** PO Box 11400, Des Moines, IA 50381-1400. TEL 800-678-5835, FAX 515-237-4752, classics@boardroom.com, http://ww2.blp.net/cust_service.

640.73 BEL ISSN 0772-9383
BUDGET ET DROITS. Text in French. bi-m. **Document type:** *Consumer.*
Formerly (until 1985): Test Achats Budget (0772-9766)
Related titles: Dutch ed.: Budget en Recht. ISSN 0772-9391.
Published by: Association des Consommateurs/Verbruikersunie, Rue de Hollande 13, Bruxelles, 1060, Belgium. TEL 32-2-542-3555, FAX 32-2-5423250, http://www.test-achats.be/map/show/70651/src/72101.htm.

640.73 BEL ISSN 0773-0748
BUDGET HEBDO. Text in French. m. (50/yr.). **Document type:** *Consumer.* **Description:** Aims at presenting economic facts, projections, activities and announcements concerning the European financial community.
Related titles: Dutch ed.: Budget Week.
Published by: Association des Consommateurs/Verbruikersunie, Rue de Hollande 13, Bruxelles, 1060, Belgium. TEL 32-2-542-3555, FAX 32-2-5423250, http://www.test-achats.be/map/show/70651/src/271971.htm.

BUSINESS & EMPLOYMENT LAW BULLETIN. see *LAW—Corporate Law*

640.73 JPN
BUYER'S GUIDE OF TOKYO (YEAR). Text in Japanese. a.
Published by: Tokyo Foreign Trade Association, Tokyo Trade Center, 1-7-8 Kaigan, Minato-ku, Tokyo, 105-0022, Japan. TEL 03-3438-2026, FAX 03-3433-7164.

640.73 USA
C E P REPORTS AND C E P BOOKS. Text in English. 1969. m. USD 100 to libraries. **Document type:** *Newsletter.* **Description:** In-depth, unbiased analysis of such vital issues as corporate social responsibility, military spending and the environment.
Former titles: C E P Reports and C E P Studies; Economic Priorities Report
Indexed: ABIn, PAIS.
Published by: Council on Economic Priorities, 30 Irving Pl, New York, NY 10003. TEL 212-420-1133, FAX 212-420-0988. Ed. Alice Tepper Marlin. R&P Thomas W Knowlton.

640.73 USA ISSN 0898-4328
C E P RESEARCH REPORT. Text in English. 1974. m. price varies. illus. back issues avail. **Description:** Concise, objective research on such vital issues as corporate social responsibility, military spending and the environment.
Former titles (until 1987): Council on Economic Priorities Newsletter (8755-3538); C E P Newsletter (0193-4066)
Published by: Council on Economic Priorities, 30 Irving Pl, New York, NY 10003. TEL 212-420-1133, FAX 212-420-0988. Ed. Alice Tepper Marlin. R&P Thomas W Knowlton.

640.73 USA ISSN 0732-8281
C F A NEWS (WASHINGTON). Text in English. 197?. 8/yr. USD 25. bk.rev. **Description:** News articles on legislative, regulatory, and policy issues pertaining to consumer issues.
Published by: Consumer Federation of America, 1424 16th St, N W, Washington, DC 20036. TEL 202-387-6121. Ed. Barbara Roper. Circ: 1,500.

MA CAISSE; revue d'information des caisses populaires et des caisses d'economie Desjardins. see *BUSINESS AND ECONOMICS—Banking And Finance*

640.73 USA
CALDRON ONLINE. Text in English. 1998. bi-m. back issues avail. **Description:** Explores the intersections between consumers, the products they consume, and the resulting culture.
Media: Online - full text.
Address: 36 Essex St, Wenham, MA 01984. TEL 978-468-1159, eschutz@mullen.com, http://www.mullen.com/cauldron/. Eds. E Schutz, J Field. Pub. Janet Mansfield.

640.73 658.7 USA
CALIFORNIA. DEPARTMENT OF CONSUMER AFFAIRS. ANNUAL REPORT. Text in English. 1975. a. free. **Document type:** *Government.*
Published by: Department of Consumer Affairs, 400 R St, Ste 3060, Sacramento, CA 95814-6213. TEL 916-324-1691, FAX 916-445-8796, http://www.dca.ca.gov. Ed. Susan Cowar-Scott. Circ: 1,000.

CALIFORNIA PRODUCTS LIABILITY ACTIONS. see *LAW*

CANADIAN BUSINESS LIFE. see *BUSINESS AND ECONOMICS*

CANADIAN MONEYSAVER; your personal finance guide. see *BUSINESS AND ECONOMICS—Investments*

CARDDIRECTORY. see *BUSINESS AND ECONOMICS—Banking And Finance*

CARDTRAK. see *BUSINESS AND ECONOMICS—Banking And Finance*

640.73 USA ISSN 0743-989X
CAVEAT EMPTOR CONSUMERS BULLETIN; the environmental and consumer protection monthly. Text in English. 1970. m. USD 10. bk.rev.
Formerly: Caveat Emptor (0045-6004)
Indexed: BRI.
Published by: Consumer Education Research Center, 439 Clark St, South Orange, NJ 07079. Ed. Robert Berko. Circ: 20,000.

640.73 USA ISSN 1083-897X
CHEAPSKATE MONTHLY. Text in English. 1992. m. looseleaf. USD 18; USD 24 in Canada; USD 30 elsewhere. bk.rev. index. **Document type:** *Newsletter.* **Description:** Helps those who are struggling to live within their means find practical and realistic methods and solutions to their financial problems.
Published by: Hunt Publishing Co., PO Box 2135, Paramount, CA 90703-8135. TEL 562-630-8845, FAX 562-630-3433, cheapsk8@ix.netcom.com, http://www.cheapskatemonthly.com. Ed. Mary Hunt. R&P Cathy Hollenbeck.

368.382 USA ISSN 0740-3925
JK794.H38
CHECKBOOK'S GUIDE TO HEALTH INSURANCE PLANS FOR FEDERAL EMPLOYEES. Text in English. 1979. a. USD 8.95 (effective 1999). adv. charts; illus.; stat. back issues avail. **Document type:** *Consumer.* **Description:** Compares health plans offered through the Federal Employee Health Benefits Program.
Published by: Center for the Study of Services, 733 15th St, N W, Ste 820, Washington, DC 20005-2112. TEL 202-347-9612, http://www.checkbook.org. Ed. Robert Krugoff. Pub. Robert Krughoff. R&P Kevin Brassler. Adv. contact Tara Eberly.

640.73 USA ISSN 1542-3530
▼ **CHICAGO CONSUMERS' CHECKBOOK.** Text in English. 2003. s-a. USD 30 (effective 2003).
Related titles: Online - full text ed.: USD 25 (effective 2003).
Published by: Center for the Study of Services, 733 15th St, N W, Ste 820, Washington, DC 20005-2112. TEL 202-347-7283, FAX 202-347-4000, http://www.checkbook.org.

917.1 028.5 CAN
CHILD AND FAMILY MAGAZINE. Text in English. 1984. q. CND 30. adv. **Document type:** *Consumer.* **Description:** For parents of children age 5 - 15.
Published by: Literati Publishing Corp., 50 Charles St E, Ste 966, Toronto, ON M4Y 2N9, Canada. TEL 416-963-5988. Ed. Joseph Holmes. **Co-publisher:** Ontario Child and Parent Publications Ltd.

640.73 AUS ISSN 0009-496X
CHOICE. Text in English. 1960. m. (Jan./Feb. comb. issue). AUD 66 to individuals; AUD 105 to institutions (effective 2005). bk.rev. cum.index. **Document type:** *Magazine, Consumer.* **Description:** Provides consumers with comparative product information.
Related titles: Online - full text ed.: (from Gale Group).
Indexed: ABIX, ARI, AusPAIS, BRD, GdIns, LibLit, Pinpoint, WBA, WMB.
Published by: Australian Consumers' Association, 57 Carrington Rd, Marrickville, NSW 2204, Australia. TEL 61-2-95773399, FAX 61-2-95773377, ausconsumer@choice.com.au, http://www.choice.com.au. Ed. Jane Mackenzie. Circ: 123,000.

CHOICE HEALTH READER. see *PHYSICAL FITNESS AND HYGIENE*

640 ESP ISSN 0212-4114
CIUDADANO; revista consumo y calidad de vida. Text in Spanish. 1973. m. adv. charts; illus.; stat. index. back issues avail.
Published by: Fundacion Ciudadano, Atocha, 26, Madrid, 28012, Spain. TEL 34-1-3691285, FAX 34-1-3690827. Ed. Carmen Martin Carrobles. Adv. contact Ana Quilez H. Circ: 70,000 (controlled).

051 USA ISSN 1053-6507
CLOTHING FOR LESS NEWSLETTER. Text in English. 1990. biennial. looseleaf. USD 5 (effective 2005). 4 p./no.; **Document type:** *Newsletter.* **Description:** Contains ideas on buying clothing for less.
—CCC.
Published by: Continnuus, c/o Prosperity & Profits Unlimited Distribution Services, P O Box 416, Denver, CO 80201-0416. TEL 303-575-5676, FAX 303-575-1187, starsuccess@excite.com, prosperity@breadpudding.net, http:/www.seyyesmarketing.com, http://www.curriculumresourceonline.com. Ed., R&P A C Doyle. Circ: 4,000 (paid and controlled).

640.73 USA
CO-OP AMERICA QUARTERLY. Text in English. 1985. q. USD 20 to non-members; USD 60 to members (effective 2004). adv. illus. back issues avail.; reprints avail. **Document type:** *Magazine, Consumer.* **Description:** Teaches consumers how to use their spending power to support socially and environmentally responsible businesses and promote social and economic justice.
Formerly (until 1991): Building Economic Alternatives (0885-9930)
Indexed: AltPI.
Published by: Co-op America Inc., 1612 K St, N W, Ste 600, Washington, DC 20006. TEL 202-872-5307, 800-584-7336, FAX 202-331-8166, info@coopamerica.org, http://www.coopamerica.org. Ed. Dennis Greenia. Pub., Adv. contact Denise Hamler. R&P Tracy Rysevy TEL 202-872-5328. B&W page USD 1,835; 10.75 x 8.25. Circ: 60,000 (paid).

640.73 USA
COMMONSENSE CONSUMER COLUMN. Text in English. 1996 (Nov.). m. **Document type:** *Consumer.* **Description:** Provides readers with reliable tips and information on how to be more self-reliant, savvy shoppers.
Media: Online - full text.
Published by: Consumer Alert, 3050 K St NW, Ste. 400, Washington, DC 20007-5100. info@consumeralert.org, http://www.consumeralert.org/pubs/commonsense/.

COMMUNITY RIGHT-TO-KNOW NEWS. see *SOCIAL SERVICES AND WELFARE*

COMPUTER CHOICE. see *COMPUTERS—Personal Computers*

C

640.73 USA
CONFIDENT CONSUMER MAGAZINE✶. Text in English. m.
Address: 113 Blue Bird Dr, Dothan, AL 36303-1389. TEL 205-671-4944. Ed. Jimmy Davis.

640.73 ITA
CONSUMATORI. Text in Italian. 1983. m. illus. **Document type:** *Magazine, Consumer.*
Published by: Editrice Consumatori, Viale Aldo Moro, 16, Bologna, BO 40127, Italy. TEL 39-51-6316911, FAX 39-51-6316908, redazione@consumatori.coop.it, edicons@interbusiness.it. Ed. Fabio Fogacci.

640.73 NLD ISSN 0165-6775
CONSUMENTENGIDS. Text in Dutch. 1953. m. EUR 39.60 (effective 2005). illus. **Document type:** *Magazine, Consumer.*
Related titles: Audio cassette/tape ed.
—IE, Infotrieve.
Published by: Consumentenbond, Enthovenplein 1, Postbus 1000, The Hague, 2500 BA, Netherlands. TEL 31-70-4454545, FAX 31-70-4454596, http://www.consumentenbond.nl. Circ: 650,000 (controlled).

640.73 NZL ISSN 0110-5949
CONSUMER. Text in English. m. (except Jan.). NZD 56.50 (effective 2000). **Document type:** *Consumer.* **Description:** Covers consumer testing and research: products, legislation, finance, food, health, safety, environment, welfare.
Indexed: INZP, Inpharma, PE&ON, Reac, WBA, WMB.
Published by: Consumers' Institute, Private Bag 6996, Wellington, 6035, New Zealand. TEL 64-4-384-7963, FAX 64-4-385-8752, chiefexec@consumer.org.nz, http://www.consumer.org.nz. Ed. Simon Wilson. Circ: 87,000 (paid).

640.73 AUS
CONSUMER AFFAIRS COUNCIL. ANNUAL REPORT. Text in English. 1971. a. free. stat. back issues avail.
Published by: Consumer Affairs Council, 99 Bathurst St, Hobart, TAS 7000, Australia. TEL 002-33-4567, FAX 002-33-4509. Circ: 1,000.

640.73 USA ISSN 0740-4964
CONSUMER ALERT COMMENTS. Text in English. 197?. irreg. (2-6 issues/yr.). **Document type:** *Journal, Consumer.*
Related titles: Online - full text ed.: (from bigchalk, EBSCO Publishing, Gale Group).
Indexed: MASUSE.
Published by: Consumer Alert, 3050 K St NW, Ste. 400, Washington, DC 20007-5100. info@consumeralert.org, http://www.consumeralert.org/pubs/comments/index.htm.

381.33 AUS ISSN 1441-0915
CONSUMER BULLETIN. Text in English. 1997. q. back issues avail. **Document type:** *Bulletin.* **Description:** Reports on consumer education issues within the communications industry,.
Media: Online - full text.
Published by: Australian Communications Authority, Box 78, Belconnen, ACT 2616, Australia. TEL 61-2-6219-5555, FAX 61-2-6219-5353, http://www.aca.gov.au/publications/index.htm#ConBull.

640.73 IRL ISSN 0790-486X
CONSUMER CHOICE. Text in English. 1968. m. EUR 78 to individuals; EUR 130.30 to institutions (effective 2005). **Document type:** *Consumer.* **Description:** Independent resource for information on products, services and issues of interest to Irish consumers.
Former titles (until 1985): Inform (0790-4894); (until 1971): News from C A I (0790-4886); (1970-1971): Inform (0790-4878); (until 1970): The Consumer (0332-155X)
Media: Duplicated (not offset).
Indexed: LibLit.
Published by: Consumers Association of Ireland Ltd., 44 Chelmsford Rd, Dublin, 6, Ireland. TEL 353-1-4978600, FAX 353-1-4978601, http://www.consumerassociation.ie. Ed., R&P Kieran Doherty. Circ: 11,000 (controlled).

640.73 USA ISSN 0735-7362
CONSUMER COMMENTS. Text in English. 1969. m. **Document type:** *Government.*
Related titles: Online - full text ed.
Published by: Department of Agriculture and Consumer Services, 1100 Bank St, Ste 805, Richmond, VA 23219-3638. TEL 804-786-2373, http://www.state.va.us/vdacs/vdacs.htm.

CONSUMER CREDIT DELINQUENCY BULLETIN. see *BUSINESS AND ECONOMICS—Banking And Finance*

CONSUMER CREDIT GUIDE. see *LAW*

640.73 USA ISSN 1536-6502
HC110.C6
CONSUMER DIMENSIONS. Text in English. 2000. a. USD 425 (effective 2001).
Published by: Media Dynamics, Inc., 570 7th Ave Rm 1906, New York, NY 10018-1619. TEL 212-704-0024, FAX 212-704-0023, info@mediadynamicsinc.com, http://www.mediadynamicsinc.com.

CONSUMER DRUG REFERENCE. see *PHARMACY AND PHARMACOLOGY*

CONSUMER FINANCE BULLETIN. see *BUSINESS AND ECONOMICS—Banking And Finance*

640.73 USA
CONSUMER GUIDE'S BEST BUYS ONLINE. Text in English. 2000. bi-m. USD 4.99 newsstand/cover (effective 2001). adv. **Document type:** *Consumer.*
Published by: Consumer Guide, 7373 N Cicero Ave, Lincolnwood, IL 60712. TEL 847-676-3470, http://www.consumerguide.com. Ed. Paul Kelly. Pub. Louis Weber.

640.73 USA
CONSUMER INFO NEWS. Text in English. w. USD 40; USD 2.95 per issue (effective 2004). **Document type:** *Magazine, Consumer.* **Description:** Reports on everything from electronics to autos and children's products as well as industry changes.
Published by: Kenneth Brown, Sr., 2446 E 65th St, Brooklyn, NY 11234. TEL 718-763-7034, FAX 718-763-7035. Ed. Phil Baron. Circ: 289,000 (paid).

CONSUMER INFORMATION CATALOG. see *BIBLIOGRAPHIES*

640.73 USA ISSN 1548-8705
HC110.C63
CONSUMER INTERESTS ANNUAL. Variant title: American Council on Consumer Interests. Conference. Text in English. 1957. a. USD 80 to non-members; USD 35 to members (effective 2002). **Document type:** *Consumer.*
Former titles (until 1994): American Council on Consumer Interests. Proceedings of the Annual Conference (0275-1356); Council on Consumer Information. Proceedings of Annual Conference
Related titles: Microfilm ed.; Online - full text ed.: ISSN 1548-8713 (from EBSCO Publishing).
Indexed: BPIA.
—BLDSC (3424.313630).
Published by: American Council on Consumer Interests, 61 Stanley Hall, University of Missouri, Columbia, MO 65211-0001. TEL 573-882-3817, FAX 573-884-6571, acci@missouri.edu, http://www.consumerinterests.org/public/articles/index.html?cat=16. Ed. Rosemary J Avery. Circ: 1,200.

CONSUMER LAW TODAY - THE FAIR TRADING MONITOR. see *LAW*

640.73 USA
HC110.C6
CONSUMER NEWS AND REVIEWS (ONLINE EDITION). Text in English. 1953. bi-m. USD 25 to individuals; USD 100 to institutions (effective 2003). bk.rev. illus. back issues avail.; reprints avail. **Document type:** *Newsletter, Trade.* **Description:** Offers information on the latest developments in the consumer field, and news of ACCI and other consumer organizations. Federal and state consumer activities, annotated listings of consumer resource materials, and special focus sections are included in each issue.
Former titles: Consumer News and Reviews (Print Edition) (1086-9107); (until 1989): A C C I Newsletter (0010-9975); (until 1969): Council on Consumer Information. Newsletter
Media: Online - full text. **Related titles:** Microfilm ed.
—BLDSC (3424.318605).
Published by: American Council on Consumer Interests, 61 Stanley Hall, University of Missouri, Columbia, MO 65211-0001. TEL 573-882-3817, FAX 573-884-6571, info@consumerinterests.org, http://www.consumerinterests.org/. Ed. Patricia Bonner. Circ: 1,200.

640.73 GBR ISSN 0961-1134
CONSUMER POLICY REVIEW. Text in English. 1991. bi-m. GBP 35, USD 52 to individuals; GBP 85, USD 145 to institutions.
Related titles: Online - full text ed.: (from bigchalk, EBSCO Publishing, Northern Light Technology, Inc., O C L C Online Computer Library Center, Inc.).
Indexed: ABIn, CPM, LJI, PAIS, SWA.
—BLDSC (3424.318680), IE, ingenta.
Published by: (Consumers' Association), Which? Ltd., 2 Marylebone Rd, London, NW1 4DF, United Kingdom. TEL 44-20-7830-6000, FAX 44-20-7830-6220, http://www.which.net. R&P Gill Rowley. **Subscr. to:** Consumers' Association, Castlemead, Gascoyne Way, Hertford, Herts SG14 1LH, United Kingdom. TEL 44-207-830-8500.

640.73 USA
CONSUMER PRODUCT SAFETY COMMISSION MONITOR. Variant title: C P S C Monitor. Text in English. 1996. m. **Document type:** *Newsletter, Consumer.*
Media: Online - full content.
Published by: Consumer Alert, 3050 K St NW, Ste. 400, Washington, DC 20007-5100. info@consumeralert.org, http://www.consumeralert.org/.

640.73 USA ISSN 0162-119X
CONSUMER PRODUCT SAFETY GUIDE. Text in English. 1972. 3 base vols. plus s-m. updates. looseleaf. USD 1,430 base vol(s). (effective 2004). **Description:** Covers Consumer Product Safety Commission (CPSC) and National Highway Traffic Safety Administration (NHTSA)'s latest regulations.
Related titles: CD-ROM ed.: USD 1,467 (effective 2004); Online - full content ed.: USD 1,600 (effective 2004).
—CCC.
Published by: C C H Inc., 2700 Lake Cook Rd, Riverwoods, IL 60015. TEL 847-267-7000, 800-449-6439, cust_serv@cch.com, http://www.cch.com. Pub. Stacey Caywood.

363.19 640.73 USA ISSN 1555-1172
TS175
CONSUMER PRODUCT SAFETY REVIEW. Text in English. 1976. q. USD 18 domestic; USD 25.20 foreign (effective 2005). **Document type:** *Magazine, Consumer.* **Description:** Informs consumers, public health and medical professionals, and industry about injuries and deaths associated with consumer products.
Former titles (until 1996): N E I S S Data Highlights; N E I S S News (0364-6475)
Related titles: Online - full content ed.: ISSN 1555-1180.
Indexed: AmStI.
Published by: U.S. Consumer Product Safety Commission, Washington, DC 20207. TEL 202-512-1800, info@cpsc.gov, http://www.cpsc.gov/cpscpub/pubs/cpsr.html. Ed. Nancy Sachs TEL 301-504-0554. Circ: 1,300 (paid). **Subscr. to:** U.S. Government Printing Office, Superintendent of Documents, 732 N Capitol St, NW, Washington, DC 20401. orders@gpo.gov, http://www.access.gpo.gov.

343.0721 346.07 640.73 USA
CONSUMER PROTECTION, ANTITRUST & UNFAIR BUSINESS PRACTICES NEWSLETTER. Text in English. 1974. q. looseleaf. USD 20 (effective 2000). back issues avail. **Document type:** *Newsletter.*
Formerly: Antitrust Law Section Newsletter
Published by: Washington State Bar Association, 2101 Fourth Ave, Ste 400, Seattle, WA 98121-2330. TEL 206-727-8239, FAX 206-727-8320. Circ: 330.

640.73 USA ISSN 0362-157X
KFW2630.A59
CONSUMER PROTECTION REPORT. Text in English. 1980. 10/yr. looseleaf. USD 145 (effective 1999). back issues avail. **Document type:** *Newsletter.*
Related titles: Online - full text ed.
Published by: National Association of Attorneys General, 12884 Harbor Dr., Woodbridge, VA 22192-2921. TEL 202-434-8000, FAX 202-434-8008. Ed. Sarah Reznek.

CONSUMER PSYCHOLOGY OF TOURISM, HOSPITALITY AND LEISURE. see *PSYCHOLOGY*

640.73 USA ISSN 0010-7174
CONSUMER REPORTS. Text in English. 1936. m. (except s-m. Dec.). USD 26; USD 4.95 newsstand/cover (effective 2005); includes Annual Buying Guide. charts; illus. index, cum.index. Supplement avail.; reprints avail. **Document type:** *Magazine, Consumer.* **Description:** Features objective comparative evaluations of consumer items, ranging from small household appliances to automobiles.
Related titles: Diskette ed.; Microfiche ed.: (from NBI); Online - full text ed.: Consumer Reports Online. USD 24 (effective 2000) (from America Online, Inc., EBSCO Publishing, Gale Group, LexisNexis, Micromedia ProQuest, ProQuest Information & Learning, The Dialog Corporation); ♦ Supplement(s): Consumer Reports Travel Letter. ISSN 0887-8439; ♦ Consumer Reports on Health. ISSN 1058-0832.
Indexed: ABIn, ARG, Acal, AgeL, Agr, BLI, CBCARef, CBPI, CHNI, CINAHL, CPerI, ConsI, CurPA, EnvAb, FLI, HRIS, HlthInd, IPA, IPARL, JHMA, KES, LRI, MASUSE, MEDLINE, MagInd, PAIS, PROMT, RASB, RGAb, RGPR, TOM, WBA, WMB.
—BLDSC (3424.500000), CASDDS, CISTI, IE, Infotrieve, ingenta, Linda Hall.
Published by: Consumers Union of the United States, Inc., 101 Truman Ave, Yonkers, NY 10703-1057. TEL 914-378-2000, 800-234-1645, FAX 914-378-2900, http://www.consumerreports.org, http://www.consumerreports.org. Ed. Julia Kagan. R&P Wendy Wintman. Circ: 4,100,000 (paid). **Subscr. to:** PO Box 53029, Boulder, CO 80322-3016.

640.73 388.3 USA ISSN 1556-2158
▼ **CONSUMER REPORTS BEST & WORST NEW CARS.** Variant title: Consumer Reports Cars: Best & Worst New Cars. Text in English. 2005. a. USD 5.99 newsstand/cover (effective 2006). **Document type:** *Magazine, Consumer.*
Published by: Consumers Union of the United States, Inc., 101 Truman Ave, Yonkers, NY 10703-1057. TEL 914-378-2000, FAX 914-378-2900, http://www.consumersunion.org.

640.73 USA ISSN 1528-4743
CONSUMER REPORTS BEST BUYS FOR YOUR HOME. Variant title: Best Buys For Your Home. Text in English. 199?. a. USD 9.95 newsstand/cover; USD 12.95 newsstand/cover in Canada (effective 2001). **Document type:** *Magazine, Consumer.*

C

Published by: Consumers Union of the United States, Inc., 101 Truman Ave, Yonkers, NY 10703-1057. TEL 914-378-2000, 800-234-1645, FAX 914-378-2900, http:// www.consumerreports.org.

640.73   USA   ISSN 1538-8581
HQ745
CONSUMER REPORTS BRIDES GUIDE. Text in English. 2002. irreg. USD 5.99 newsstand/cover (effective 2003).
Published by: Consumers Union of the United States, Inc., 101 Truman Ave, Yonkers, NY 10703-1057. TEL 914-378-2000, http://www.consumersunion.org. Ed. Andrea Scott.

640.73   USA   ISSN 1555-2357
TX335
CONSUMER REPORTS BUYING GUIDE. Text in English. a. USD 9.95 newsstand/cover; USD 12.95 newsstand/cover in Canada. **Document type:** Magazine, Consumer. **Description:** Rates and reviews various consumer goods, offering informed consumers practical, objective advice on such matters as value and reliability.
Formerly (until 1993): Consumer Reports Buying Guide Issue
Published by: Consumers Union of the United States, Inc., 101 Truman Ave, Yonkers, NY 10703-1057. TEL 914-378-2000, 800-234-1645, FAX 914-378-2900, http:// www.consumerreports.org.

640.73 388.3   USA   ISSN 1550-4301
▼ **CONSUMER REPORTS CARS: COMPLETE AUTO PRICING & RATINGS GUIDE.** Text in English. 2004. q. USD 9.99 newsstand/cover (effective 2004). **Document type:** Magazine, Consumer.
Published by: Consumers Union of the United States, Inc., 101 Truman Ave, Yonkers, NY 10703-1057. TEL 914-378-2000, http://www.consumersunion.org.

CONSUMER REPORTS FOR KIDS ONLINE. see CHILDREN AND YOUTH—For

640.73   USA   ISSN 1530-647X
HF5415.1265
CONSUMER REPORTS GUIDE TO ONLINE SHOPPING. Variant title: Guide to Online Shopping. Text in English. 2000. a. USD 5.95 newsstand/cover; USD 6.95 newsstand/cover in Canada (effective 2001). **Document type:** Magazine, Consumer. **Description:** Provides a variety of tips and strategies for shopping online.
Published by: Consumers Union of the United States, Inc., 101 Truman Ave, Yonkers, NY 10703-1057. TEL 914-378-2000, 800-234-1645, FAX 914-378-2900, http:// www.consumerreports.org/Services/Books/Reports/ book015.html.

640.73   USA   ISSN 1547-4534
HG179
▼ **CONSUMER REPORTS MONEY ADVISER.** Text in English. 2004. m. USD 24 (effective 2004). **Document type:** Newsletter, Consumer.
Published by: Consumers Union of the United States, Inc., 101 Truman Ave, Yonkers, NY 10703-1057. TEL 914-378-2000, http://www.consumersunion.org. Ed. Marlys Harris.

CONSUMER REPORTS NEW CAR BUYING GUIDE. see TRANSPORTATION—Automobiles

CONSUMER REPORTS NEW CAR PREVIEW. see TRANSPORTATION—Automobiles

CONSUMER REPORTS ON HEALTH. see PHYSICAL FITNESS AND HYGIENE

CONSUMER REPORTS S U V'S, WAGONS, MINIVANS, TRUCKS. see TRANSPORTATION—Automobiles

CONSUMER REPORTS TRAVEL LETTER. see TRAVEL AND TOURISM

CONSUMER REPORTS USED CAR BUYING GUIDE. see TRANSPORTATION—Automobiles

CONSUMER REPORTS USED CAR YEARBOOK. see TRANSPORTATION—Automobiles

640.73   USA
CONSUMER REPORTS YARD & GARDEN EQUIPMENT BUYING GUIDE. Text in English. a. USD 8.99.
Published by: Consumers Union of the United States, Inc., 101 Truman Ave, Yonkers, NY 10703-1057. TEL 914-378-2000, 800-234-1645, FAX 914-378-2900, http:// www.consumerreports.org.

640.73   USA   ISSN 0738-0518
HC110.C63
CONSUMER SOURCEBOOK. Text in English. 1974. irreg., latest vol.17, 2004. USD 345 (effective 2004). **Description:** Entries identify and describe more than 15000 programs and services available at little or no cost.

Published by: Gale Group (Subsidiary of: Thomson Corporation), 27500 Drake Rd, Farmington Hills, MI 48331-3535. TEL 248-699-8061, 800-877-4253, FAX 248-699-4253, galeord@gale.com, http://www.gale.com. Ed. Shawn Brennan.

640.73   BEL   ISSN 1560-263X
HC240.9.C63
CONSUMER VOICE. Text in English, French, German. 1991. q. free. bk.rev. charts; illus. back issues avail. **Document type:** Bulletin. **Description:** Covers issues of consumer policy within the EU, including consumer protection.
Formerly (until 1998): Info - C (English Edition) (1018-5755) —BLDSC (3424.732100).
Published by: European Commission, Directorate General - Health and Consumer Protection, Unit 3, rue de la Loi 200, Brussels, 1049, Belgium. TEL 32-2-2962154, FAX 32-2-2996302, sanco-consumer-voice@cec.eu.int, http://europa.eu.int/comm/dg24. Ed., R&P Brigitte Reichle. Circ: 10,000.

640.73   KEN
CONSUMER'S DIGEST. Text in English. m.
Published by: Nangina House, PO Box 50795, Nairobi, Kenya. TEL 21431. Ed. Eunice Mathu. Circ: 17,000.

640.73   USA   ISSN 0010-7182
TX335.A1
CONSUMERS DIGEST; best buys, best prices, best reports, for people who demand value. Text in English. 1959. bi-m. USD 4 newsstand/cover (effective 2005). adv. bk.rev. illus. cum.index. back issues avail.; reprints avail. **Document type:** Magazine, Consumer.
Indexed: ARG, AgeL, ConsI, HlthInd, LRI, MagInd, PMR, RGAb, RGPR, TOM.
Published by: Consumers Digest Communications LLC, 8001 N Lincoln Ave, 6th Fl, Skokie, IL 60077-3657. TEL 847-763-9200, FAX 847-763-0200, postmaster@consumersdigest.com, http:// www.consumersdigest.com. Ed. John Manos. Pub. Randy Weber. Adv. contact Howard Plissner. B&W page USD 24,840, color page USD 37,230. Circ: 1,250,000 (paid).

640.73   PHL
CONSUMERS FEDERATED GROUPS OF THE PHILIPPINES. NEWSLETTER. Text in English. q.
Published by: Consumers Federated Groups of the Philippines, 962 Josefa Llanes Escoda St, Ermita, Manila, 1000, Philippines.

640.73 362.11   USA   ISSN 1070-2644
RA981.A2
CONSUMERS' GUIDE TO HOSPITALS. Text in English. 1988. irreg. (approx. biennial). USD 19.95 (effective 2002). adv. charts; illus.; stat. back issues avail. **Document type:** Consumer. **Description:** Gives death rates at 5500 US hospitals as well as information on how to choose a hospital, how to get the best care wherever you go, and how to keep costs down.
Published by: Center for the Study of Services, 733 15th St, N W, Ste 820, Washington, DC 20005-2112. TEL 202-347-9612, 800-475-7283, http://www.checkbook.org. Pub. Robert Krughoff. R&P Kevin Brassler. Adv. contact Tara Eberly.

CONSUMERS SHOULD KNOW. see REAL ESTATE

640.73   AUS   ISSN 0728-3008
CONSUMING INTEREST. Text in English. 1981. q. AUD 29.70 to individuals; AUD 38.50 domestic to institutions (effective 2004). back issues avail. **Document type:** Magazine, Consumer.
Related titles: Online - full text ed.
Indexed: ABIX.
Published by: Australian Consumers' Association, 57 Carrington Rd, Marrickville, NSW 2204, Australia. TEL 61-2-95773399, FAX 61-2-95773377, ausconsumer@choice.com.au, http://www.choice.com.au. Ed. Peter Cerexre. Circ: 1,000.

028.7   USA
CONTENT INTELLIGENCE. Text in English. 2001 (May). m. **Description:** Probes content consumers' attitudes and behaviors with original primary research.
Related titles: Online - full text ed.
Published by: Lyra Research, Inc., 320 Nevada St., Newtonville, MA 02460-0143. TEL 617-454-2655, FAX 617-454-2601, http://www.contentintelligence.com.

640.73 340   USA   ISSN 1545-8075
▼ **CORPORATE ACCOUNTABILITY ALERT.** Text in English. 2003 (Jul.). 20/yr. USD 847 (effective 2003).
Published by: Strafford Publications, Inc., 590 Dutch Valley Rd, N E, Postal Drawer 13729, Atlanta, GA 30324-0729. TEL 404-881-1141, FAX 404-881-0074, editors@straffordpub.com, http://www.straffordpub.com.

▼ **CORPORATE ACCOUNTABILITY REPORT.** see LAW

381   USA
HC110.C63
COUNCIL OF BETTER BUSINESS BUREAUS. BUSINESS ADVISORY SERIES; tips on consumer information series. Text in English. 1972. irreg. USD 2 per issue (effective 2000). **Document type:** Consumer. **Description:** Over 30 titles on subjects of interest to consumers and businesses.
Formerly: Council of Better Business Bureaus. Annual Report (0094-8853)
Related titles: Online - full content ed.
Published by: Council of Better Business Bureaus, Publications Department, 4200 Wilson Blvd, Arlington, VA 22203-1804. TEL 703-276-0100. Ed. Saul David. R&P Steven B Davis.

640.73 658.8   USA   ISSN 1053-6523
COUPON TREASURE HUNT NEWSLETTER. Text in English. 1990. biennial. looseleaf. USD 3 (effective 2005). 4 p./no.; **Document type:** Newsletter. **Description:** Information on finding and redeeming coupons.
—CCC.
Published by: Continnuus, c/o Prosperity & Profits Unlimited Distribution Services, P O Box 416, Denver, CO 80201-0416. starsuccess@excite.com, http:// www.curriculumresourceonline.com. Ed., R&P A C Doyle. Circ: 1,500 (paid and controlled).

640.73   CAN   ISSN 1499-755X
CREDIT CARDS AND YOU. Text in English. 1987. q. **Document type:** Magazine, Consumer. **Description:** Provides a comparison of credit cards available in Canada and their service fees, as well as useful information on the terms and conditions of a credit card agreement.
Former titles (until 2001): Credit Card Costs Report (1493-860X); (until 1999): Credit Card Costs (1208-5715)
Related titles: Online - full text ed.; Online (1499-7576).
Published by: Financial Consumer Agency of Canada/Agence de la Consommation en Matiere Financiere du Canada, 427 Laurier Ave W, 6th Flr, Ottawa, ON K1R 1B9, Canada. TEL 613-996-5454, FAX 613-941-1436, http://www.fcac-acfc.gc.ca/ eng/publications/default.asp.

640.73 340   IND
CURRENT CONSUMER CASES. Text in English. 1994. m. USD 120 (effective 1998). **Description:** Contains judgments, whether reportable or nonreportable of the National Consumer Disputes Redressal Commission, Supreme Court of India, and more.
Published by: International Law Book Co., Nijhawan Bldg., Kashmere Gate, 1562 Church Rd., New Delhi, 110 006, India. TEL 91-11-296-7810, lakshmin@giasdla.vsnl.net.in.

640.73   USA
DALLAS GREENSHEET. Text in English. w. free.
Published by: Gordon Publications (Dallas), 7929 Brookriver Dr, Ste 700, Dallas, TX 75247-4900. TEL 214-905-8200, FAX 214-853-6007. Ed. Kathy Douglas.

DEALERNEWS BUYERS GUIDE. see SPORTS AND GAMES—Bicycles And Motorcycles

640.73   USA   ISSN 1542-3506
DELAWARE VALLEY CONSUMERS' CHECKBOOK. Text in English. 2002. s-a.
Published by: Center for the Study of Services, 733 15th St, N W, Ste 820, Washington, DC 20005-2112. TEL 202-347-7283, FAX 202-347-4000, http://www.checkbook.org.

DENKEN EN DOEN. see WOMEN'S INTERESTS

640.73   DNK   ISSN 1603-9742
DENMARK. FORBRUGERSTYRELSEN. FORBRUGERJURA. Text in Danish. 1989. a., latest 2003. free (effective 2005). back issues avail. **Document type:** Yearbook, Consumer.
Former titles (until 2004): Denmark. Forbrugerstyrelsen. Forbrugerredegoerelsen (Print) (1603-3523); (until 2003): Denmark. Forbrugerstyrelsen. Juridisk Aarbog (0905-2860); Which was formed by the merger of (1976-1989): Denmark. Forbrugerklagenaevnet. Aarsbeutning (0106-4932); (1977-1989): Denmark. Forbrugerombudsmanden. Beretning (0106-2328); (1936-1989): Denmark. Statens Husholdningsraad. Aarsberetning (0900-2170)
Media: Online - full content.
Published by: Forbrugerstyrelsen/National Consumer Agency of Denmark, Amagerfaelledvej 56, Copenhagen S, 2300, Denmark. TEL 45-32-669000, FAX 45-32-669100, forbrug@forbrug.dk, http://www.forbrug.dk/om/ forbrugerstyrelsen/juridiske-publikationer/aarbog-2003/.

640.73   DNK   ISSN 1399-2112
DENMARK. FORBRUGERSTYRELSEN. REN BESKED. Text in Danish. 1936. 6/yr. DKK 115; DKK 30 per issue (effective 2004). illus. **Document type:** Magazine, Consumer.
Former titles (until 1992): Denmark. Statens Husholdningsraad. Pjece (0908-9861); (until 1991): Denmark. Forbrugerstyrelsen. Pjece (0904-8529); (until 1989): Denmark. Statens Husholdningsraad. Pjece (0106-1887)
Published by: Forbrugerstyrelsen/National Consumer Agency of Denmark, Amagerfaelledvej 56, Copenhagen S, 2300, Denmark. forbrug@forbrug.dk, http://www.forbrug.dk. Circ: 65,000.

640.73 USA ISSN 0196-8203
DISCLOSURE (CHICAGO); the national newspaper of neighborhoods. Text in English. 1974. bi-m. USD 15 to individuals; USD 30 to institutions (effective 2000). bk.rev. charts; stat. back issues avail. **Document type:** *Newsletter.*
Related titles: Microform ed.: (from PQC); Online - full text ed.: (from ProQuest Information & Learning).
Indexed: AltPI.
Published by: National Training and Information Center, 810 N Milwaukee, Chicago, IL 60622. TEL 312-243-3035, FAX 312-243-7044. Ed., R&P Gordon Mayer. Circ: 6,000.

640.73 340 GBR
ENCYCLOPEDIA OF CONSUMER LAW. Text in English. 1980. base vol. plus updates 2/yr. looseleaf. GBP 420 base vol(s).; GBP 265, EUR 399 updates in Europe (effective 2005); GBP 275, USD 500 updates elsewhere; GBP 133, EUR 200 updates in Europe to students; GBP 138, USD 250 updates elsewhere to students (effective 2006). **Document type:** *Trade.*
Published by: Sweet & Maxwell Ltd., 100 Avenue Road, London, NW3 3PF, United Kingdom. TEL 44-20-74491111, FAX 44-20-74491144, customer.services@sweetandmaxwell.co.uk, http://www.sweetandmaxwell.co.uk. **Subscr. to:** Cheriton House, North Way, Andover, Hants SP10 5BE, United Kingdom.

640.73 340 GBR
ENCYCLOPEDIA OF DATA PROTECTION & PRIVACY. Text in English. 1988. 4 base vols. plus updates 3/yr. looseleaf. GBP 525 base vol(s).; GBP 525, EUR 790 updates in Europe; GBP 540, USD 981 updates elsewhere (effective 2006). **Document type:** *Trade.*
Formerly: Encyclopedia of Data Protection
Published by: Sweet & Maxwell Ltd., 100 Avenue Road, London, NW3 3PF, United Kingdom. TEL 44-20-74491111, FAX 44-20-74491144, customer.services@sweetandmaxwell.co.uk, http://www.sweetandmaxwell.co.uk. **Subscr. to:** Cheriton House, North Way, Andover, Hants SP10 5BE, United Kingdom.

ENERGIEDEPESCHE. see *ENERGY*

ENERGY & POWER MANAGEMENT; serving the commercial, industrial and institutional markets. see *ENERGY*

ENERGY USER NEWS DIGEST. see *ENERGY*

640.73 170.73 GBR ISSN 0955-8608
ETHICAL CONSUMER. Text in English. 1989. bi-m. GBP 19 in United Kingdom; GBP 23 in Europe; GBP 28 elsewhere (effective 2001). adv. bk.rev. abstr.; charts; stat. cum.index: 1994-1998. 38 p./no.; Supplement avail.; back issues avail. **Document type:** *Magazine, Consumer.* **Description:** Researches and disseminates information for consumers and how they can act to promote corporate ethics and responsibility for animal and human rights, the environment, and social well-being.
Published by: E C R A Publishing Ltd., 41 Old Birley St, Unit 21, The Workshop, Manchester, Lancs M15 5RF, United Kingdom. TEL 44-161-226-2929, FAX 44-161-226-6277, mail@ethicalconsumer.org, http://www.ethicalconsumer.org. Ed., R&P Rob Harrison. Adv. contact Simon Birch. B&W page GBP 500, color page GBP 760. Circ: 6,000.

640.73 USA
EXCHANGE (FAYETTEVILLE). Text in English. 1980. w. USD 15 (effective 2001). 28 p./no.; **Document type:** *Newspaper, Consumer.*
Published by: Exchange, Inc., 404 S Main St, PO Box 490, Fayetteville, TN 37334. TEL 931-433-9737, FAX 931-433-0053. Pub. Bill Thomas. Adv. contact Jim Bowers. Circ: 20,050 (controlled).

353.84 USA ISSN 0362-1332
HD9000.9.U5 CODEN: FDACBH
F D A CONSUMER. (Food and Drug Administration) Text in English. 1967. bi-m. USD 14 domestic; USD 19.60 foreign (effective 2005). illus. cum.index: vols. 1-22. back issues avail.; reprint service avail. from PQC. **Document type:** *Magazine, Consumer.* **Description:** Contains information for consumers about Food and Drug Administration regulatory and scientific decisions, and about the safe use of products regulated by FDA.
Formerly: F D A Papers (0014-5750)
Related titles: Microform ed.: (from PQC); Online - full text ed.: ISSN 1554-9852 (from bigchalk, EBSCO Publishing, Florida Center for Library Automation, Gale Group, H.W. Wilson, O C L C Online Computer Library Center, Inc., ProQuest Information & Learning, The Dialog Corporation).
Indexed: AbHyg, AcaI, AgBio, AgeL, Agr, BPIA, BibAg, BiolDig, CHNI, CINAHL, CLFP, ConsI, CurPA, DSA, ExcerpMed, FS&TA, GSI, HlthInd, IPA, IUSGP, IndVet, Inpharma, LRI, MASUSE, MEDLINE, MEDOC, MagInd, NRN, NutrAb, PAIS, PE&ON, PMR, RGAb, RGPR, Reac, RevApplEntom, SIA, TOM, Telegen, VetBull, WAE&RSA.
—BLDSC (3901.292000), CISTI, GNLM, IDS, IE, Infotrieve, ingenta, Linda Hall.
Published by: U.S. Department of Health and Human Services, Food and Drug Administration, 5600 Fishers Ln, Rockville, MD 20857. http://www.fda.gov/fdac/default.htm. Ed., R&P Dori Stehlin. Circ: 28,000 (paid). **Subscr. to:** U.S. Government Printing Office, Superintendent of Documents, PO Box 371954, Pittsburgh, PA 15250-7954. TEL 202-512-1800, FAX 202-512-2250, orders@gpo.gov, http://www.access.gpo.gov.

640.73 USA
F D A WEEK. (Food and Drug Administration) Text in English. w. USD 645 in US & Canada; USD 695 elsewhere (effective 2004). **Document type:** *Newsletter, Trade.*
Related titles: E-mail ed.
Published by: Inside Washington Publishers, PO Box 7176, Ben Franklin Sta, Washington, DC 20044-7176. TEL 703-416-8500, 800-424-9068, FAX 703-416-8543, custsvc@iwpnews.com, http://www.iwpnews.com. Ed. Donna Haseley.

F E B BULLETIN. see *BUSINESS AND ECONOMICS—Production Of Goods And Services*

F M O NEWS. see *REAL ESTATE*

640.73 USA
FACTORY OUTLET SHOPPING GUIDE FOR NEW ENGLAND✶ Text in English. 1973. a. USD 3.95. adv. bk.rev.
Published by: Factory Outlet Shopping Guide Publications, 11 Tory Ln, Rt 3, Newtown, CT 06470. Ed. Jean D Bird. Circ: 25,000.

FAMILY ECONOMICS AND NUTRITION REVIEW. see *HOME ECONOMICS*

FEDERATION DES ENTREPRISES DE BELGIQUE. RAPPORT ANNUEL. see *BUSINESS AND ECONOMICS—Production Of Goods And Services*

640.73 PHL
FILIPINO CONSUMER/MAMIMILING PINDY. Text in English. 1990. m. free. adv. **Document type:** *Newsletter, Government.* **Description:** Covers consumer laws, activities of consumer groups, government's action on consumer grievances, and other consumer-related news around the country.
Formerly (until Oct. 1996): Citizen Volunteer
Indexed: IPP.
Published by: Department of Trade and Industry, Trade & Industry Information Center, 385 Industry and Investments Bldg., Sen. Gil Puyat Ave., Makati City, 1200, Philippines. TEL 890-48-72, FAX 890-51-24. Ed. Minerva R Fajardo. R&P Alfonso M Valenzueia. Adv. contact Alfonso M Valenzuela. Circ: 5,000.

FINANCIAL AND ESTATE PLANNING FOR THE MATURE CLIENT IN ONTARIO. see *LAW—Estate Planning*

640 DEU ISSN 0939-1614
FINANZTEST. Text in German. 1991. m. **Document type:** *Consumer.* **Description:** Comparative analyses and other reports on financial services, private savings and investment, insurance, taxes and legal matters.
Published by: Stiftung Warentest, Luetzowplatz 11-13, Berlin, 10785, Germany. TEL 49-30-26312398, FAX 49-30-26312428, stiftung-warentest@stiftung-warentest.de, http://www.stiftung-warentest.de. Circ: 315,000.

FONDS ET SICAV. see *BUSINESS AND ECONOMICS—Banking And Finance*

FOOD FREE OR CHEAP NEWSLETTER. see *HOME ECONOMICS*

640.73 658.8 USA
FOODWATCH UPDATE✶. Text in English. 1992. q. USD 18 to non-members. back issues avail. **Document type:** *Newsletter.* **Description:** For those who are interested in food safety.
Published by: Agriculture Council of America, 11020 King St, Ste 205, Overland, Park, KS 66210-1201. TEL 202-682-9200, FAX 202-289-6648. Ed., R&P Mark Bennett. Circ: 10,000 (controlled).

640.73 DNK ISSN 0105-9122
FORBRUGERINDEKS. Text in Danish. 1978. a. DKK 1,425 (effective 2004). Supplement avail.; back issues avail. **Document type:** *Consumer.*
Related titles: Online - full text ed.: 1991. DKK 1,378.75 (effective 2001).
Published by: Dansk BiblioteksCenter AS, Tempovej 7-11, Ballerup, 2750, Denmark. TEL 45-44-867777, FAX 45-44-867892, dbc@dbc.dk, http://www.dbc.dk. Ed. Marja-Liisa Bindslev.

640.73 NOR ISSN 0046-449X
FORBRUKER-RAPPORTEN. Text in Norwegian; Summaries in English. 1958. 10/yr. NOK 195; NOK 29 newsstand/cover (effective 2000). illus. **Document type:** *Magazine, Consumer.*
—CCC.
Published by: Forbrukerraadet/Consumer Council, Postboks 123, Llysaker, 1325, Norway. TEL 47-67-59-96-00, FAX 47-67-53-14-50, fr-rapport@forbrukerradet.no, http://www.forbrukerradet.no. Ed. Barth Tholens. Circ: 60,000 (controlled).

640.73 USA
FOYER. Text in English. 2001. a. USD 9.95 newsstand/cover (effective 2001). adv. **Document type:** *Consumer.*
Published by: Foyer, Inc., 3551 Westview Dr., #C, Naples, FL 34104. TEL 941-263-9502, http://www.foyermag.com. Ed., Pub. Nancy Gordon.

640.73 USA ISSN 0148-2092
FREEBIES; the magazine with something for nothing. Text in English. 1977. 5/yr. USD 7.95; USD 3 newsstand/cover (effective 2004). adv. bk.rev. **Document type:** *Magazine, Consumer.*
Published by: Freebies Publishing Co., P O Box 21957, Santa Barbara, CA 93121. TEL 805-962-5014, FAX 805-962-6200, freebiespublishing@earthlink.com, freebiespublishing@earthlink.net, http://www.freebies.com. Ed. Megan Andreson. Pub. Gail Zannon. adv.: B&W page USD 4,000, color page USD 5,975. Circ: 360,000.

640.73 658.8 USA ISSN 1058-0271
FRONT LINES (PORTLAND). Text in English. 1977. bi-m. looseleaf. free. adv. bk.rev. back issues avail. **Document type:** *Newsletter.* **Description:** Consumer education regarding the natural foods industry, including product information, coverage of key issues and related environmental concerns.
Formerly: Food Front
Published by: Food Front Cooperative Grocery, 2375 N W Thurman, Portland, OR 97210-2572. TEL 503-222-5658, FAX 503-227-5140. Ed. Karen Foley. R&P Katelyn Lord. Adv. contact Judy Rose. Circ: 3,000.

C

FRUGAL CONSUMERS DOLLAR-STRETCHING POSSIBILITY NEWSLETTER. see *HOME ECONOMICS*

GALA NEWS. see *DRUG ABUSE AND ALCOHOLISM*

640.73 332 NLD
GELD. Text in Dutch. 1985. q. EUR 12.50 (effective 2005). adv. bk.rev. **Document type:** *Consumer.*
Published by: Service Pers BV, Spaarne 13, Haarlem, 2011 CC, Netherlands. TEL 31-23-5400223, FAX 31-23-5362545, info@serviceproductions.nl, http://www.geld.nl/, http://www.service-serie.nl/. Circ: 55,000.

658.8830941 GBR ISSN 1368-9320
GETTING PAID; your guide to consumer credit. Text in English. 1998. m. GBP 57.95 domestic; GBP 135 foreign (effective 2003). adv. 16 p./no.; **Document type:** *Journal, Consumer.* **Description:** Designed to provide readers with innovative strategies in the collection and recovery of consumer debt.
Related titles: Online - full text ed.
Published by: House of Words Ltd., 7 Greding Walk, Hutton, Brentwood, Essex CM13 2UF, United Kingdom. TEL 44-1277-225402, FAX 44-1277-201544, info@creditcontrol.co.uk, http://www.creditcontrol.co.uk. Ed., Adv. contact Carol Baker. Pub. Gareth Price. B&W page GBP 550, color page GBP 3,250. Circ: 1,000.

GOODE'S CONSUMER CREDIT LEGISLATION. see *LAW*

640.73 BEL
GUIDE DU CONTRIBUABLE. Text in French. a. BEF 495; included in subscr. to Budget et Droits.
Published by: Association des Consommateurs/Verbruikersunie, Rue de Hollande 13, Bruxelles, 1060, Belgium. TEL 32-2-5423211, FAX 32-2-5423250.

640.73 USA
GUIDE TO BAY AREA RESTAURANTS. Text in English. 1989. irreg. (approx. triennial). USD 7.95 (effective 1999). adv. charts; illus.; stat. back issues avail. **Document type:** *Consumer.* **Description:** Reports restaurant ratings from a local survey. Restaurants are rated for food, service, ambience, and value, and write-ups include remarks from professional restaurant critics.
Published by: Center for the Study of Services, 733 15th St, N W, Ste 820, Washington, DC 20005-2112. TEL 510-763-7979, http://www.checkbook.org. Ed. Robert Krugof. Pub. Robert M Krughoff. R&P Kevin Brassler. Adv. contact Tara Eberly.

640.73 USA
GUIDE TO WASHINGTON AREA RESTAURANTS. Text in English. 1988. irreg. (approx. triennial). USD 7.95 (effective 1999). adv. charts; illus.; stat. back issues avail. **Document type:** *Consumer.* **Description:** Reports restaurant ratings from a local survey. Restaurants are rated for food, service, ambience, and value, and write-ups include remarks from professional restaurant critics.
Published by: Center for the Study of Services, 733 15th St, N W, Ste 820, Washington, DC 20005-2112. TEL 202-347-9612, 800-475-7283, http://www.checkbook.org. Ed. Robert Krugoff. Pub. Robert M Krughoff. R&P Kevin Brassler. Adv. contact Tara Eberly.

640.73 BEL
GUIDES PRATIQUES. Text in French. q. **Document type:** *Consumer.*
Published by: Association des Consommateurs/Verbruikersunie, Rue de Hollande 13, Bruxelles, 1060, Belgium. TEL 32-2-5423211, FAX 32-2-5423250.

640.73 JPN
HANAKO. Text in Japanese. 1988. w. (49/yr.). JPY 16,660 (effective 2005). **Document type:** *Magazine, Consumer.* **Description:** Covers shopping, dining and travel.
Published by: Magazine House, Ltd., 3-13-10 Ginza, Chuo-ku, Tokyo, 104-8003, Japan. http://www.magazine.co.jp/subscribe/hanako/index.jsp, http//:www.magazine.co.jp. Circ: 301,000.

HARVEST TIMES. see *FOOD AND FOOD INDUSTRIES—Grocery Trade*

HEALTH LETTER (WASHINGTON). see *MEDICAL SCIENCES*

HOT TOPICS; burning legal issues in plain language. see *LAW*

051 USA
HOUSING CHEAP OR ON A BUDGET NEWSLETTER. Text in English. 1990. biennial. looseleaf. USD 6 (effective 2000). 4 p./no.; **Document type:** *Newsletter.* **Description:** Ideas on cheap housing.
Published by: Center for Self-Sufficiency, Publishing Division, c/o Prosperity & Profits Unlimited Distribution Services, Box 416, Denver, CO 80201-0416. TEL 303-575-5676, mail@breadpudding.net, http://www.centerforselfsufficiency.com. Ed. A Doyle. Circ: 4,500.

HUIS. see *REAL ESTATE*

THE HUMAN ECOLOGIST. see *ENVIRONMENTAL STUDIES*

C

640.73 FRA ISSN 1145-0673
I N C HEBDO CONSOMMATEURS ACTUALITES. Text in French. w. **Document type:** *Newsletter, Consumer.*
Formerly: Consommateurs Actualites (0339-154X)
Published by: Institut National de la Consommation, 80 rue Lecourbe, Paris, Cedex 15 75732, France. TEL 33-1-44907040, FAX 33-1-45662120, inc3@club-internet.fr, http://www.conso.net. Ed. Marie Jeanne Husset. Pub. Marc Deby.

917.1 CAN ISSN 0704-7428
IMAGE DE LA MAURICIE. Text in English. m. CND 15. adv.
Formerly (until 1977): Mauricie Touristique (0700-3188)
Published by: Publicite G.M. Inc., 564 Blvd des Prairies, Cap De La Madeleine, PQ G8T 1K9, Canada. TEL 819-378-2176. Ed. Gilles Mercier. Circ: 10,000 (controlled).

IMPACT (WASHINGTON, 1975). see *TRANSPORTATION—Automobiles*

640.73 USA ISSN 0162-1300
IMPACT JOURNAL. Text in English. 1972. irreg. USD 15. bk.rev. **Description:** Includes exposes on waste and mismanagement, fraud and rip-offs, and occasional travel articles.
Address: 301 Lynn Manor Dr, Rockville, MD 20850-4430. TEL 301-309-6790. Ed. A Louis Ripskis.

640.73 ITA ISSN 0020-1871
INSIEME (ROME). Text in Italian. 1959. bi-w. EUR 42 (effective 2004). charts; illus. index. **Document type:** *Consumer.*
Formerly: Rassegna dell'Economo Cattolico (0392-8381)
Published by: Editoriale Italiana, Via Vigliena 10, Rome, 00192, Italy. TEL 39-06-3230177, FAX 39-06-3211359, info@editoriale.it, http://www.editoriale.it. Ed. Giordano Treveri Gennari. Circ: 20,000.

640.73 387.7 CAN
INTER - CANADIAN. Text in English, French. 1989. 6/yr. **Description:** Covers consumer protection, education and general interest topics.
Formerly: Intair
Published by: R.E.P. Communications Inc., 1623 De Maricourt St, Montreal, PQ H4E 1V6, Canada. TEL 514-762-1667, FAX 514-769-9490. Ed. Andre Vigneau. adv.: B&W page CND 2,625, color page CND 3,500; trim 10.88 x 8. Circ: 25,000.

343.071 NLD
INTERNATIONAL CONSUMER PROTECTION. Text in English. 2 base vols. plus irreg. updates. looseleaf. EUR 488 (effective 2004). **Document type:** *Trade.* **Description:** Examines the area of consumer protection law in an international context.
Published by: (Center for International Legal Studies AUT), Brill Academic Publishers, PO Box 9000, Leiden, 2300 PA, Netherlands. TEL 31-71-53-53-500, FAX 31-71-53-17-532, cs@brill.nl, http://www.brill.nl. **Subscr. in N. America to:** PO Box 605, Herndon, VA 20172. TEL 703-661-1585, 800-337-9255, FAX 703-661-1501, cs@brillusa.com. **Distr. outside N. America by:** c/o Turpin Distribution, Stratton Business Park, Pegasus Drive, Biggleswade, BEDFORDSHIRE SG 18 8TQ, United Kingdom. TEL 44-1767-604-954, FAX 44-1767-601-640, brill@turpin-distribution.com.

640 GBR ISSN 1470-6423
TX1
➤ **INTERNATIONAL JOURNAL OF CONSUMER STUDIES.** Text in English. 1977. 5/yr. EUR 135, GBP 90 combined subscription in Europe to individuals print & online eds.; USD 166 combined subscription in the Americas to individuals & Caribbean (print & online eds.); GBP 99 combined subscription elsewhere to individuals print & online eds.; GBP 496 combined subscription in Europe to institutions print & online eds.; USD 916 combined subscription in the Americas to institutions & Caribbean (print & online eds.); GBP 545 combined subscription elsewhere to institutions print & online eds.; GBP 67, EUR 101 combined subscription in Europe to students print & online eds.; USD 124 combined subscription in the Americas to students & Caribbean (print & online eds.); GBP 74 combined subscription elsewhere to students print & online eds. (effective 2006). adv. abstr.; bibl.; illus. index. back issues avail.; reprint service avail. from ISI,PSC. **Document type:** *Journal, Academic/Scholarly.*
Formerly (until 2001): Journal of Consumer Studies & Home Economics (0309-3891)
Related titles: Microform ed.: (from PQC); Online - full text ed.: ISSN 1470-6431. 1999. GBP 432 in Europe to institutions; USD 798 in the Americas to institutions & Caribbean; GBP 475 elsewhere to institutions (effective 2005) (from Blackwell Synergy, EBSCO Publishing, Gale Group, IngentaConnect, O C L C Online Computer Library Center, Inc., Swets Information Services).
Indexed: ABIn, ASSIA, Agr, ERA, ETA, ExcerpMed, FS&TA, FamI, MEA, PAIS, PsycInfo, PsycholAb, SWA, TEA, WTA.
—BLDSC (4542.175930), CISTI, IE, Infotrieve, ingenta. **CCC.**
Published by: Blackwell Publishing Ltd., 9600 Garsington Rd, Oxford, OX4 2ZG, United Kingdom. TEL 44-1865-776868, FAX 44-1865-714591, customerservices@oxon.blackwellpublishing.com, http://www.blackwellpublishing.com/journals/IJC. Ed. Katherine Hughes. Pub. Elaine Stott. R&P Sophie Savage. Adv. contact Jenny Applin. Circ: 370.

640.73 614 NLD ISSN 1745-7300
CODEN: ICSPC3
➤ **INTERNATIONAL JOURNAL OF INJURY CONTROL AND SAFETY PROMOTION.** Text in English. 1994. q. GBP 320, USD 528 combined subscription to institutions print & online eds. (effective 2006). adv. bk.rev. back issues avail.; reprint service avail. from PSC. **Document type:** *Journal, Academic/Scholarly.* **Description:** Publishes original papers, review articles, short communications and news items relating to research in the etiology of accidents in everyday life, policy development and implementation of prevention strategies.
Former titles (until 2005): Injury Control and Safety Promotion (1566-0974); (until 2000): International Journal for Consumer and Product Safety (1387-3059); (until 1998): International Journal for Consumer Safety (0929-8347); Which superseded in part: E C O S A Newsletter
Related titles: Online - full text ed.: ISSN 1745-7319. GBP 304, USD 502 to institutions (effective 2006) (from EBSCO Publishing, Gale Group, IngentaConnect, O C L C Online Computer Library Center, Inc., Swets Information Services).
Indexed: ESPM, ErgAb, H&SSA, RiskAb.
—BLDSC (4514.410000), IE, Infotrieve, ingenta. **CCC.**
Published by: (European Consumer Safety Association), Taylor & Francis The Netherlands (Subsidiary of: Taylor & Francis Group), Schipolweg 107 C, PO Box 447, Leiden, 2316 XC, Netherlands. TEL 31-715-243080, FAX 31-715-234571, pub@swets.nl, infoho@swets.nl, http://www.tandf.co.uk/journals/titles/17457300.asp, http://www.tandf.co.uk/swets.asp. Ed. Wim Rogmans. R&Ps Chantal van Werkhoven, Martin D Scrivener. Adv. contact Miranda Mauritz. B&W page EUR 300; 17.5 x 22.8.

917.1 028.5 CAN ISSN 0838-5505
ISLAND PARENT MAGAZINE. Text in English. 1988. m. CND 28 domestic; CND 40 in United States (effective 2002). adv. bk.rev.; music rev.; Website rev. 64 p./no. 3 cols./p.; **Document type:** *Magazine, Consumer.* **Description:** Written for and by parents on Vancouver Island. Covers education, recreation, discipline, relationships, work, birth, grandparenting, family finance and other topics of interest to parents of children 0-18 months old.
Published by: Island Parent Group Enterprises Ltd., 526 Michigan St, Victoria, BC V8V 1S2, Canada. TEL 250-388-6905, FAX 250-388-6920, mail@islandparent.ca, http://www.islandparent.ca. Ed. Selinde Krayenhoff. R&P Mada Johnson. Adv. contact Michael Barnard. Circ: 25,000 (controlled).

640.73 CHE
J'ACHETE MIEUX. Text in French. 1959. 10/yr. CHF 60 (effective 2000). **Document type:** *Magazine, Consumer.*
Published by: Federation Romande des Consommateurs, Route de Geneve 7, Case Postale 2820, Lausanne, 1002, Switzerland. TEL 41-21-3128006, FAX 41-21-3128004, http://www.frc.ch. Circ: 43,000.

JOURNAL D'ECONOMIE MEDICALE. see *MEDICAL SCIENCES*

640.73 USA ISSN 0022-0078
HC110.C6
➤ **JOURNAL OF CONSUMER AFFAIRS.** Text in English. 1967. s-a. USD 100 domestic to individual members; USD 110 in Canada to individual members; USD 115 elsewhere to individual members; USD 50 to students (effective 2005); USD 295 combined subscription in the Americas to institutions print & online eds.; GBP 312 combined subscription elsewhere to institutions print & online eds. (effective 2006). bk.rev. abstr.; bibl.; charts; stat.; illus. reprint service avail. from PQC,PSC. **Document type:** *Academic/Scholarly.* **Description:** Fosters and disseminates professional thought and scholarly research having implications for government, household or business policy.
Related titles: Microform ed.: (from MIM, PQC); Online - full text ed.: ISSN 1745-6606. USD 280 in the Americas to institutional members; GBP 296 elsewhere to institutional members (effective 2006) (from bigchalk, Blackwell Synergy, EBSCO Publishing, Florida Center for Library Automation, Gale Group, H.W. Wilson, IngentaConnect, Northern Light Technology, Inc., O C L C Online Computer Library Center, Inc., ProQuest Information & Learning).
Indexed: ABIn, ASCA, AgBio, AgeL, Agr, ArtHuCI, BPI, BPIA, BRI, BusEdI, BusI, CBRI, CIJE, CommAb, ConsI, CurCont, CurPA, DIP, DSA, ESPM, Emerald, FamI, HortAb, IBR, IBSS, IBZ, IndVet, JEL, ManagCont, NutrAb, PAIS, PHN&I, PsycInfo, PsycholAb, RDA, RPFIA, RiskAb, SFA, SSCI, T&II, WAE&RSA.
—BLDSC (4965.210000), CISTI, IDS, IE, Infotrieve, ingenta. **CCC.**
Published by: American Council on Consumer Interests, 61 Stanley Hall, University of Missouri, Columbia, MO 65211-0001. TEL 573-882-3817, FAX 573-884-6571, acci@missouri.edu, http://www.consumerinterests.org/i4a/pages/Index.cfm?pageid=3311. Ed. Herbert Jack Rotfeld. Circ: 1,500. **Subscr. to:** Blackwell Publishing, Inc., subscrip@blackwellpub.com, http://www.blackwellpublishing.com.

640.73 GBR ISSN 1472-0817
➤ **JOURNAL OF CONSUMER BEHAVIOUR**; an international research review. Text in English. 2001. bi-m. USD 410 to institutions; USD 451 combined subscription to institutions print & online eds. (effective 2006). abstr.; bibl.; charts; stat. 96 p./no. 2 cols./p.; back issues avail.; reprint service avail. from PSC. **Document type:** *Journal, Academic/Scholarly.* **Description:** Aims to communicate the latest research and its application in a forum which will include case studies, research reports and forecasting trends as well as refereed articles on the latest empirical research and theoretical thinking in the field.
Related titles: Online - full content ed.: ISSN 1479-1838. USD 410 to institutions (effective 2006); Online - full text ed.: (from EBSCO Publishing, Gale Group, IngentaConnect, O C L C Online Computer Library Center, Inc., Swets Information Services, Wiley InterScience).
Indexed: PsycInfo, PsycholAb.
—BLDSC (4965.210140), IE, ingenta. **CCC.**
Published by: John Wiley & Sons Ltd. (Subsidiary of: John Wiley & Sons, Inc.), The Atrium, Southern Gate, Chichester, West Sussex PO19 8SQ, United Kingdom. TEL 44-1243-779777, FAX 44-1243-775878, cs-journals@wiley.co.uk, http://www.interscience.wiley.com/journal/cb, http://www.wiley.co.uk. Pub. Claire Plimmer. Circ: 500 (paid).

640 GBR ISSN 1469-5405
HC79.C6
➤ **JOURNAL OF CONSUMER CULTURE.** Text in English. 2001 (Jun.). 3/yr. GBP 257, USD 449 to institutions; GBP 267, USD 468 combined subscription to institutions print & online eds. (effective 2006). **Document type:** *Journal, Academic/Scholarly.* **Description:** Publishes debates and explorative articles focussing on modern consumer culture and its globalizing tendancies. The journal will be a central research forum for scholars across the social sciences and humanities.
Related titles: Online - full text ed.: ISSN 1741-2900. GBP 254, USD 444 to institutions (effective 2006) (from EBSCO Publishing, O C L C Online Computer Library Center, Inc., Sage Publications, Inc., Swets Information Services).
Indexed: CommAb, DIP, IBR, IBSS, IBZ, IPSA, PsycInfo, PsycholAb, RRTA, SociolAb, e-psyche.
—BLDSC (4965.210350), IE. **CCC.**
Published by: Sage Publications Ltd. (Subsidiary of: Sage Publications, Inc.), 1 Oliver's Yard, 55 City Rd, London, EC1 1SP, United Kingdom. TEL 44-20-73248500, FAX 44-20-73248600, info@sagepub.co.uk, http://www.sagepub.co.uk/journal.aspx?pid=105627. Ed. George Ritzer. **Subscr. in the Americas to:** Sage Publications, Inc., 2455 Teller Rd, Thousand Oaks, CA 91320. TEL 805-499-0721, FAX 805-499-0871, journals@sagepub.com.

640.73 USA ISSN 0168-7034
HF5415.3
➤ **JOURNAL OF CONSUMER POLICY**; consumer issues in law, economics and behavioral sciences. Text in English. 1977. q. EUR 418, USD 418, GBP 265 combined subscription to institutions print & online eds. (effective 2005). bk.rev. index. reprint service avail. from PSC. **Document type:** *Journal, Academic/Scholarly.* **Description:** Publishes research in a broad range of issues relating to consumer affairs, including discussion of social and economic structures influencing the consumer interest, and the impact of policies and actions of consumers, industry, organizations, government and educational institutions. Includes extensive systematic coverage of issues in consumer law and legislation in transnational communities such as the EC.
Formerly (until 1983): Zeitschrift fuer Verbraucherpolitik (0342-5843)
Related titles: Microform ed.: (from PQC); Online - full text ed.: ISSN 1573-0700 (from EBSCO Publishing, Gale Group, IngentaConnect, Kluwer Online, O C L C Online Computer Library Center, Inc., ProQuest Information & Learning, Springer LINK, Swets Information Services).
Indexed: ABIn, ASCA, Agr, BPIA, BibAg, BibLing, CurCont, DIP, ELJI, ELLIS, ESPM, FamI, H&SSA, IBR, IBSS, IBZ, JEL, LRI, PAIS, RefZh, RiskAb, SSCI, T&II, WAE&RSA.
—BLDSC (4965.212000), IE, Infotrieve, ingenta. **CCC.**
Published by: Springer-Verlag New York, Inc. (Subsidiary of: Springer Science+Business Media), 233 Spring St, New York, NY 10013. TEL 212-460-1500, FAX 212-460-1575, service@springer-ny.com, http://springerlink.metapress.com/openurl.asp?genre=journal&issn=0168-7034, http://www.springer-ny.com. Eds. Alan Mathios, Folke Olander, Geoffrey Woodroffe, Stephen Weatherill. **Subscr. to:** Journal Fulfillment, PO Box 2485, Secaucus, NJ 07096-2485. TEL 201-348-4033, FAX 201-348-4505, journals@springer-ny.com.

658.8830941 GBR ISSN 1464-4665
➤ **JOURNAL OF CREDIT CONTROL**✶. Text in English. 1998. quinquennial. GBP 259.95 domestic; GBP 455.35 foreign (effective 2005). adv. bk.rev. Index. 36 p./no.; back issues avail. **Document type:** *Journal, Academic/Scholarly.* **Description:** Incorporates practical illustrations as well as theoretical and empirical studies which address the key issues facing credit controllers, credit managers, credit analysts, accountants, and financial directors of multinational corporations.
Related titles: Online - full text ed.
Published by: House of Words Ltd., 7 Greding Walk, Hutton, Brentwood, Essex CM13 2UF, United Kingdom. TEL 44-1277-225402, FAX 44-1277-201544, info@creditcontrol.co.uk, http://www.creditcontrol.co.uk. Ed., Adv. contact Carol Baker. Pub. Gareth Price. B&W page GBP 550, color page GBP 1,950. Circ: 1,000 (paid).

➤ **JOURNAL OF FAMILY ECOLOGY AND CONSUMER SCIENCE (ONLINE EDITION)/TYDSKRIF VIR GESINEKOLOGIE EN VERBRUIKERSWETENSKAPPE.** see *HOME ECONOMICS*

➤ **JOURNAL OF INTERNATIONAL CONSUMER MARKETING.** see *BUSINESS AND ECONOMICS—Marketing And Purchasing*

640.73 AUS ISSN 1444-6359
➤ **JOURNAL OF RESEARCH FOR CONSUMERS.** Text in English. 2001. s-a. free (effective 2005). back issues avail. **Document type:** *Journal, Academic/Scholarly.* **Description:** Publishes consumer research that furthers the interests of consumers through information provision and theoretical advancements. Empirical, theoretical, and methodological articles are featured, along with commentaries and essays that seek to further consumers' understanding of the consumption process and its many implications.
Media: Online - full text.
Address: c/o Simone Pettigrew, Edith Cowan University, Pearson St, Churchlands, W.A. 6018, Australia. TEL 61-8-9273 8227, FAX 61-8-9273 8003, s.pettigrew@ecu.edu.au, http://www.jrconsumers.com/. Ed. Simone Pettigrew.

➤ **JURY INSTRUCTIONS ON PRODUCTS LIABILITY.** see *LAW—Judicial Systems*

➤ **K-SPEZIAL.** see *HOME ECONOMICS*

➤ **K-TIP.** see *HOME ECONOMICS*

640.73 IND
KARNATAKA CONSUMER VOICE. Text in English. m.
Published by: Karnataka Consumer Service Society, 877 Hal. 3rd Stage, Bangalore, Karnataka 560 075, India. TEL 576224.

640.73 IND
KEEMAT; consumer's voice. Text in English. 1972. m. INR 100 (effective 1999). bk.rev. **Document type:** *Magazine, Consumer.* **Description:** Contains articles of consumer interest, consumer issues, complaints and rights.
Published by: Consumer Guidance Society of India, Hutment J. Mahapalika Marg, Mumbai, Maharashtra 400 001, India. TEL 91-22-2621612, FAX 91-22-2659715, cgsibom@bom4.vsnl.net.in. Ed. N G Wagle. Circ: 2,000.

640.73 363.7 GBR
KEY NOTE MARKET ASSESSMENT. GREEN & ETHICAL CONSUMER. Text in English. 2000. irreg., latest 2000, Apr. GBP 730 per issue (effective 2002). **Description:** Provides an in-depth strategic analysis across a broad range of industries and contains an examination on the scope, dynamics and shape of key UK markets in the consumer, financial, lifestyle and business to business sectors.
Published by: Key Note Ltd., Field House, 72 Oldfield Rd, Hampton, Mddx TW12 2HQ, United Kingdom. TEL 44-20-8481-8750, FAX 44-20-8783-0049, info@keynote.co.uk, http://www.keynote.co.uk.

640.73 GBR
KEY NOTE MARKET ASSESSMENT. OVER-40S CONSUMER. Text in English. 2002. irreg., latest 2002, Jan. GBP 730 per academic year (effective 2002). **Description:** Provides an in-depth strategic analysis across a broad range of industries and contains an examination on the scope, dynamics and shape of key UK markets in the consumer, financial, lifestyle and business to business sectors.
Published by: Key Note Ltd., Field House, 72 Oldfield Rd, Hampton, Mddx TW12 2HQ, United Kingdom. TEL 44-20-8481-8750, FAX 44-20-8783-0049, info@keynote.co.uk, http://www.keynote.co.uk. Ed. Simon Taylor.

KOESTLICHKEITEN AUS ALLER WELT. see *FOOD AND FOOD INDUSTRIES*

640.73 AUT
KONSUMENT. Text in German. 1961. m. EUR 39.24 (effective 2005). bk.rev. **Document type:** *Magazine, Consumer.*
Published by: Verein fuer Konsumenteninformation, Mariahilfer Str 81, Vienna, W 1060, Austria. TEL 43-1-588770, FAX 43-1-5887771, konsument@vki.or.at, http://www.konsument.at. Ed. Gerhard Frueholz. Circ: 115,000.

640.73 LUX
DE KONSUMENT. Text in French, German. 1963. 18/yr. looseleaf.
Published by: Union Luxembourgeoise des Consommateurs, 55 rue des Bruyeres, Howald, 1274, Luxembourg. TEL 352-4960221, FAX 352-494957, http://www.ulc.lu. Circ: 35,000.

640.73 NLD ISSN 0929-0001
KRITISCH CONSUMEREN. Text in Dutch. 1982. 8/yr. adv. bk.rev. illus. a. back issues avail. **Document type:** *Magazine, Consumer.* **Description:** Provides information on issues relating to responsible consumerism, including the environment, Third World, animal welfare, and the working environment.
Former titles (until 1992): Voeding en Milieu (0926-0447); (until 1990): Alternatieve Konsumentengids (0168-0676)
Published by: Alternatieve Konsumenten Bond, Postbus 61236, Amsterdam, 1005 HE, Netherlands. TEL 31-20-6863338, FAX 31-20-6867361, akb@akb.a2000.nl, akb@xs4all.nl, http://www.pz.nl/akb, http://wwwpz.nl/akb. Ed. Morries Leeraert. Pub. Nienke Brouwer. Circ: 2,750 (paid).

640.73 FIN ISSN 0357-2854
KULUTTAJANSUOJA. Variant title: Consumer Protection. Konsumenskydd. Text in English, Finnish, Swedish. 1979. 5/yr. EUR 36 domestic; EUR 46 in Scandinavia and Baltic countries; EUR 49 in Europe; EUR 51 elsewhere (effective 2005). **Document type:** *Journal.* **Description:** Reports on decisions by the consumer Ombudsman and the Consumer Complaint Board in Finland. Monitors legislative decisions in Finland and the EU.
Published by: (Kauppa- ja Teollisuusministerio, Kuluttajavirasto - Asiamies/Ministry of Trade and Industry. Consumer Agnecy and Ombudsman), Stellatum Oy, Tyopajankatu 6 A, Helsinki, 00580, Finland. TEL 358-9-8689700, FAX 358-9-86897070, info@stellatum.fi, http://www.stellatum.fi. Ed. Anja Peltonen.

640.73 340 AUS ISSN 1031-8569
KUG6.5
➤ **THE LAW HANDBOOK**; your practical guide to the law in Victoria. Text in English. 1977. a., latest 2003, 26th ed. AUD 69 newsstand/cover domestic; AUD 78 newsstand/cover foreign (effective 2003). bibl.; illus. 850 p./no.; back issues avail. **Document type:** *Academic/Scholarly.* **Description:** Provides a plain english guide to the law in Victoria, Australia, for use by lawyers, students, and the average person.
Published by: Fitzroy Legal Service, PO Box 280, Fitzroy, VIC 3065, Australia. TEL 61-3-9411-1309, FAX 61-3-9416-1124, publications@fitzroy-legal.org.au, http://www.fitzroy-legal.org.au. Ed. Kath Harper. R&P, Adv. contact Ginny O'Loughlin. Circ: 3,200.

346.038 USA
LAW OF PRODUCTS LIABILITY. Text in English. 1990. latest 1994, 2 base vols. plus a. updates. USD 185. **Description:** Analyzes major issues that occur in product liability litigation, and summarizes the principal lines of development with up-to-date citations to case law.
Published by: LexisNexis (Subsidiary of: LexisNexis North America), PO Box 7587, Charlottesville, VA 22906-7587. TEL 804-972-7600, 800-562-1197, FAX 804-972-7666, llp.customer.support@lexis-nexis.com, http://www.lexislawpublishing.com. Ed. Marshall S Shapo.

LEADER'S PRODUCT LIABILITY LAW AND STRATEGY. see *BUSINESS AND ECONOMICS—Production Of Goods And Services*

LEMON AID MAGAZINE. see *TRANSPORTATION—Automobiles*

LEMON TIMES. see *TRANSPORTATION—Automobiles*

640.73 USA
LIVING CHEAP NEWS✶. Text in English. 1992. 10/yr. USD 12; USD 15 in Canada; USD 19 elsewhere (effective 2000). bk.rev. **Document type:** *Newsletter, Consumer.* **Description:** Eclectic frugality newsletter containing money-saving tips with emphasis on "doing without," smarter, cheaper ways to buy, travel, live.
Published by: Living Cheap Press, PO Box 8178, Kansas City, MO 64112-8178. FAX 816-523-0224, livcheap@aol.com. Ed. Larry Roth. Circ: 1,800 (paid).

LOOKOUT - FOODS. see *FOOD AND FOOD INDUSTRIES*

640.73 ISR
MA K'DAI. Text in Hebrew. 4/yr. ILS 10.
Published by: Israel Consumer Board, 28 Albert Mendeler St., Hakirya, Tel Aviv, Israel. TEL 03-266138. Circ: 10,000.

917.1 CAN ISSN 0832-557X
MAGAZINE LE CLAP. Text in English. 1986. bi-m. CND 23.95 (effective 2001). adv.
Published by: Cinema Le Clap, 2360 chemin Ste Foy, Ste Foy, PQ G1V 4H2, Canada. TEL 418-653-2470, FAX 418-653-6018, http://www.clap.qc.ca. Circ: 59,400.

THE MARKET GUIDE. see *BUSINESS AND ECONOMICS—Investments*

MASS CYCLIST. see *SPORTS AND GAMES—Bicycles And Motorcycles*

MASSCITIZEN. see *ENVIRONMENTAL STUDIES*

MEIO AMBIENTE. see *ENVIRONMENTAL STUDIES*

640.73 SWE ISSN 1102-2930
MERSMAK. Text in Swedish. 1953. 6/yr. membership. adv. 48 p./no. 3 cols./p.;
Formerly (until 1990): Storstaden (0491-113X)
Published by: Konsumentfoereningen Stockholm, Magnus Ladulasgatan 67, Stockholm, 11827, Sweden. TEL 46-8-743-50-00. Ed. Rune Struck. Pub. Laszlo Krisa. Adv. contact Ann Marie Sandstroem. B&W page SEK 40,800, color page SEK 51,100; trim 240 x 185. Circ: 372,000.

MILLER: PRODUCT LIABILITY AND SAFETY ENCYCLOPAEDIA. see *LAW*

640.73 USA
THE MILWAUKEE JOURNAL SENTINEL CONSUMER ANALYSIS. Text in English. 1923. a. USD 55 per issue (effective 2005). **Document type:** *Magazine, Trade.*
Formerly: Milwaukee Journal Consumer Analysis, The
Published by: Journal Sentinel, Inc., 333 W. State St., Milwaukee, WI 53201. TEL 414-224-2000, FAX 414-224-7690. Ed. Darrell Beneker. Circ: 1,500 (controlled and free).

MIR TSEN. see *BUSINESS AND ECONOMICS—Banking And Finance*

MONEY (NEW YORK). see *BUSINESS AND ECONOMICS—Banking And Finance*

640.73 381 USA
MONEY SAVER. Text in English. w.
Address: PO Box 152, Bolivar, TN 38008.

640.73 USA ISSN 0026-9646
TX335
MONEYSWORTH✶. Text in English. 1970. q. USD 10. adv. bk.rev.
Related titles: Microfilm ed.: (from PQC).
Indexed: HlthInd, LRI, MagInd.
—CCC.
Published by: Avant-Garde Media, Inc., 80 Central Park West, Ste 168, New York, NY 10023-5200. Ed., Pub. Ralph Ginzburg. Circ: 900,000.

640.73 USA ISSN 0739-392X
N A C A A NEWS. Text in English. 1978. 10/yr. USD 95; USD 75 to non-profit organizations. index. back issues avail. **Document type:** *Newsletter.* **Description:** What's happening in state, local and federal consumer protection agencies.
Published by: National Association of Consumer Agency Administrators, 750 Old Hickory Blvd., Ste. 150-2, Brentwood, TN 37027-4509. TEL 202-347-7395, http://www.nacaanet.org. Ed. Wendy J Weinberg. Circ: 300.

N A P O NEWS/ECHO DE L'O N A P. see *SOCIAL SERVICES AND WELFARE*

C

▼ *new title* ➤ *refereed* ✶ *unverified* ♦ *full entry avail.*

N C L C ENERGY & UTILITY UPDATE. see *LAW*

N C L C REPORTS: BANKRUPTCY & FORECLOSURES. see *LAW*

N C L C REPORTS: CONSUMER CREDIT & USURY. see *LAW*

N C L C REPORTS: DEBT COLLECTION & REPOSSESSIONS. see *LAW*

N C L C REPORTS: DECEPTIVE ACTS & WARRANTIES. see *LAW*

640.73 USA ISSN 1044-3134
N Y P I R G AGENDA. Text in English. 1978. q. USD 25 to members. bk.rev. **Document type:** *Newsletter.* **Description:** Provides updates on group's programs, including consumer protection, environmental preservation, energy conservation, food safety, government accountability, fairness in standardized testing, and citizen participation.
Formerly: Agenda for Citizen Involvement (0745-368X)
Indexed: AltPI.
Published by: New York Public Interest Research Group, Inc., 9 Murray St, 3rd Fl, New York, NY 10007-2272. TEL 212-349-6460, FAX 212-349-1366. Ed. Tracy Peel. Circ: 75,000.

640.73 USA ISSN 1055-923X
NATIONAL CONSUMERS LEAGUE BULLETIN. Text in English. 1937. bi-m. USD 20 to individuals; USD 100 to corporations (effective 2000). bk.rev. illus. reprints avail. **Document type:** *Newsletter.* **Description:** Investigates, educates and advocates consumer and worker rights on marketplace and workplace issues.
Published by: National Consumers League, Inc., 1701 K St, N W, Ste 1200, Washington, DC 20006. TEL 202-835-3323, FAX 202-835-0747, nclncl@aol.com, http://www.natlconsumersleague.org. Ed., R&P Holly Anderson. Circ: 5,000.

C

NATIONAL LIQUOR NEWS. see *BEVERAGES*

NEW JERSEY PRODUCT LIABILITY LAW. see *LAW*

NEW SOUTH WALES & AUSTRALIAN CAPITAL TERRITORY RETAIL DIRECTORY. see *BUSINESS AND ECONOMICS—Trade And Industrial Directories*

640.73 USA ISSN 0095-5590
HC107.N73
NEW YORK (STATE). CONSUMER PROTECTION BOARD. ANNUAL REPORT. Key Title: Annual Report - State Consumer Protection Board. Text in English. 1976. a. free to NY state residents. illus. **Document type:** *Government.*
Published by: Consumer Protection Board, 5 Empire State Plaza, Ste 2101, Albany, NY 12223-1556. TEL 518-474-8583, FAX 518-474-2474, http://www.consumer.state.ny.us. Circ: 500.

640.73 ISL ISSN 1021-7223
NEYTENDABLADID. Text in Icelandic. 1953. bi-m. ISK 2,600 to members (effective 1999). back issues avail. **Document type:** *Consumer.* **Description:** Contains tests, consumer information, legal aspects and more.
Published by: Neytendasamtoekin, Skulagata 26, Reykjavik, 101, Iceland. TEL 354-562-5000, FAX 354-562-4666, neytenda@itn.is. Ed. Johannes Gunnarsson. Circ: 17,000.

640.73 FRA ISSN 0184-9832
NOUS. Text in French. 1969. q. **Document type:** *Consumer.*
Published by: (Confederation Syndicale des Familles), Editions Garibaldi, 53 rue Riquet, Paris, 75019, France. TEL 33-1-44898680. Ed. Paul Emaer.

917.1 028.5 USA
O C FAMILY; the news magazine for parents. Text in English. 1999. m. USD 18 (effective 2004). adv. **Document type:** *Magazine, Consumer.* **Description:** Explores issues impacting today's families.
Published by: Churm Publishing, 1451 Quail St, Ste 201, Newport Beach, CA 92660. TEL 949-757-1404, FAX 949-757-1996, info@churmpublishing.com, http://www.churmpublishing.com. Ed. Craig Reem. Pub. Steve Churm.

640.73 CYP ISSN 0255-8408
O KATANALOTIS/CONSUMER. Text in Greek. 1977. q. free to members.
Address: PO Box 24874, Nicosia, 1304, Cyprus. TEL 357-25-16112-2-4, FAX 357-25-16118, cyconsas@spidernet.com.cy. Circ: 3,000.

640.73 DEU
OEKO-TEST JAHRBUCH. Text in German. 1985. a. EUR 8.90 newsstand/cover (effective 2003). adv. **Document type:** *Magazine, Consumer.*
Published by: Oeko-Test Verlag GmbH und Co. KG, Kasseler Str 1A, Frankfurt Am Main, 60486, Germany. TEL 49-69-97777-0, FAX 49-69-97777139, oet.verlag@oekotest.de, http://www.oekotest.de. adv.: B&W page EUR 4,400, color page EUR 7,150. Circ: 120,000 (paid).

640.73 DEU ISSN 0178-7608
OEKO-TEST MAGAZIN; oekologische Verbraucherzeitschrift. Text in German. 1985. m. EUR 39 domestic; EUR 46.67 foreign; EUR 3.50 newsstand/cover (effective 2005). adv. bk.rev. index. back issues avail. **Document type:** *Magazine, Consumer.* **Description:** Tests products for consumer health and environmental safety.
Incorporates (1997-2001): Oeko-Haus (1434-3851)
Related titles: CD-ROM ed.
—IE.
Published by: Oeko-Test Verlag GmbH und Co. KG, Kasseler Str 1A, Frankfurt Am Main, 60486, Germany. TEL 49-69-97777-0, FAX 49-69-97777139, oet.verlag@oekotest.de, http://www.oekotest.de. Ed. Juergen Stellpflug. Adv. contact Renate Zoerb. B&W page EUR 6,700, color page EUR 10,500; trim 183 x 253. Circ: 154,209 (paid).

640.73 DEU
OEKO-TEST RATGEBER. Text in German. 1985. 9/yr. EUR 52; EUR 7.50 newsstand/cover (effective 2003). adv. **Document type:** *Magazine, Consumer.*
Published by: Oeko-Test Verlag GmbH und Co. KG, Kasseler Str 1A, Frankfurt Am Main, 60486, Germany. TEL 49-69-97777-0, FAX 49-69-97777139, oet.verlag@oekotest.de, http://www.oekotest.de. adv.: B&W page EUR 4,250, color page EUR 6,900. Circ: 90,000 (paid and controlled).

OFF THE AIR. see *COMMUNICATIONS—Radio*

640.73 USA
OKLAHOMA. COMMISSION ON CONSUMER CREDIT. ANNUAL REPORT. Text in English. a.
Formerly: Oklahoma. Commission on Consumer Affairs. Annual Report
Published by: Commission on Consumer Credit, 4545 N Lincoln, 104, Oklahoma City, OK 73105. TEL 405-521-3653, 800-448-4904.

640.73 381 USA
PEDDLER. Text in English.
Address: PO Box 701, Cookville, TN 38503-0701. TEL 931-526-5910.

614 640.73 360 USA ISSN 0736-4873
PEOPLE'S MEDICAL SOCIETY NEWSLETTER. Text in English. 1983. bi-m. looseleaf. USD 24 membership (effective 2001). bk.rev. charts; stat.; illus. index. back issues avail.; reprints avail. **Document type:** *Newsletter.* **Description:** Provides medical consumers with previously unavailable medical information so that they can make informed decisions about their own health care.
Related titles: CD-ROM ed.; Online - full text ed.: (from bigchalk, EBSCO Publishing, Gale Group, Northern Light Technology, Inc., O C L C Online Computer Library Center, Inc., ProQuest Information & Learning).
Indexed: CHNI, CINAHL, HlthInd, MASUSE.
Published by: People's Medical Society, P.O. Box 868, Allentown, PA 18105-0868. TEL 610-770-1670, FAX 610-770-0607, info@peoplesmed.org, http://www.peoplesmed.org. Ed., R&P Karla Morales. Circ: 65,000.

640.73 USA
POCKET CHANGE INVESTOR. Text in English. 1990. q. looseleaf. USD 12.95 (effective 2000 - 2001). bk.rev. charts; stat. 8 p./no.; back issues avail. **Document type:** *Newsletter, Consumer.* **Description:** Teaches consumers how to save money on mortgages, credit cards, and other debts. Focuses on painless ways to save on other expenses, such as taxes, cars and insurance.
Formerly (until 1994): Banker's Secret Bulletin (1054-8920)
Published by: Good Advice Press, PO Box 78, Elizaville, NY 12523. TEL 845-758-1400, FAX 845-758-1475, goodadvice@ulster.net, http://www.goodadvicepress.com/. Ed. Marc Eisenson. Pub., R&P Nancy Castleman.

640.73 USA
▼ **J.D. POWER CAR GUIDE.** Text in English. 2003. s-a. (Mar. & Nov.). **Document type:** *Magazine, Consumer.*
Published by: Hearst Magazines (Subsidiary of: Hearst Corporation), 250 W 55th St, 5th Fl, New York, NY 10019. HearstMagazines@hearst.com, http://www.hearstcorp.com/magazines/. **Co-publisher:** J.D. Power and Associates.

658 USA ISSN 0748-4755
CODEN: PRADER
PRICING ADVISOR. Text in English. 1984. m. USD 195 in North America; USD 295 out of North America. bk.rev. **Document type:** *Newsletter.* **Description:** Delivers pricing solutions, principals, and practical answers. Informs readers of emerging competitive-pricing practices and new-product positioning strategies.
Address: 3277 Roswell Rd, Ste 620, Atlanta, GA 30305-1840. TEL 404-252-5708, 800-633-4931, FAX 404-252-0637. Ed. Eric G Mitchell. R&P Eric Mitchell.

PRIVACY JOURNAL; an independent monthly on privacy in a computer age. see *COMPUTERS—Computer Security*

640.73 SWE ISSN 0348-3312
PRIVATA AFFAERER. Text in Swedish. 1978. 11/yr. SEK 545 (effective 2004). adv. **Document type:** *Magazine, Consumer.*
Related titles: Online - full text ed.: Privata Affaerer (Online). ISSN 1402-4934.
Published by: Privata Affaerer Foerlag AB, Sveavaegen 53, Stockholm, 10544, Sweden. TEL 46-8-7365300, FAX 46-70-8251437, info@privataaffarer.se, http://www.privataaffarer.se. Ed. Hans Bolander TEL 46-8-7365780. Pub. Anders Andersson. Adv. contact Per Laredius TEL 46-8-7365637. color page SEK 61,400; trim 190 x 265. Circ: 106,300 (paid).

PRODUCT ALERT. see *FOOD AND FOOD INDUSTRIES*

PRODUCT LIABILITY AUSTRALIA. see *LAW*

PRODUCTS LIABILITY (CHARLOTTESVILLE). see *LAW*

PRODUCTS LIABILITY (NEWARK). see *LAW—Civil Law*

640.73 340 USA
PRODUCTS LIABILITY PRACTICE GUIDE. Text in English. 1988. 7 base vols. plus updates 2/yr. looseleaf. USD 959 base vol(s). (effective 2002). **Description:** Povides an unparalleled collection of winning strategies and tactics for an entire range of products. Each chapter written by an experienced plaintiff or defence attorney.
Published by: Matthew Bender & Co., Inc. (Subsidiary of: LexisNexis North America), 1275 Broadway, Albany, NY 12204. international@bender.com, http://bender.lexisnexis.com. Ed. John Vargo.

640.73 CAN ISSN 0701-8517
PROTEGEZ-VOUS. Text in French. 1973. m. CND 19.95. **Description:** Provides information on consumer rights and issues, comparative product tests, and product and service buying guides.
Indexed: CBCARef, CBPI, CPerI, PdeR, SportS.
—CISTI.
Published by: Office de la Protection du Consommateur, 5199 Sherbrooke St E, Ste 2580, Montreal, PQ H4N 1S2, Canada. TEL 514-873-7771, FAX 514-873-3429. Ed. Jacques Elliot. Circ: 150,000.

381.33 MEX
PROTEJA SU DINERO. Text in Spanish. 2000. m.
Published by: Comision Nacional para la Proteccion y Defensa de los Usuarios de Servicios Financieros, Insurgentes Sur 762, Col Del Valle, Del Benito Juarez, Mexico, D.F. 03810, Mexico. TEL 52-5-448-7000. Ed. Fernando Villarreal y Puga Colmenares.

640.73 CHE
PRUEF MIT. Text in German. 1969. 10/yr. CHF 42 domestic; CHF 52 foreign; CHF 5.70 newsstand/cover. **Document type:** *Consumer.*
Indexed: FS&TA.
Published by: Konsumentinnenforum Schweiz KF, Postfach, Zuerich, 8024, Switzerland. TEL 01-2523914, FAX 01-2611279. Eds. Christine Ruf Erne, Doris Huber. Circ: 44,000.

320 USA ISSN 0738-5927
HC79.C63
PUBLIC CITIZEN. Text in English. 1976. bi-m. adv. bk.rev. illus. back issues avail.; reprints avail. **Document type:** *Newspaper, Consumer.* **Description:** Articles for the politically active consumer.
Incorporates (1979-1987): Congress Watcher (0278-1093)
Related titles: Online - full text ed.
Indexed: AltPI, MCR.
Published by: Public Citizen, Inc., 1600 20th St, N W, Washington, DC 20009. TEL 202-588-1000, FAX 202-588-7799, public_citizen@citizen.org, http://www.citizen.org, http://www.citizen.org/pcnews. Ed., R&P Bob Mentzinger. Pub. Ralph Nader. Circ: 90,000 (controlled).

640.73 345.01 USA
THE PUBLIC EYE (MADISON). Text in English. 1975. s-a. USD 20 (effective 2000). **Document type:** *Newsletter.* **Description:** Reports on broad range of consumer and legal issues of interest to residents of Wisconsin.
Published by: Economic Justice Institute, Inc., 975 Bascom Mall, Madison, WI 53706. TEL 608-262-9143, eji@law.wisc.edu, http://www.law.wisc.edu/pal, http://www.law.wisc.edu/eji/. Circ: 1,200 (paid).

640.73 USA
PUBLIC HOUSING SPOTLIGHT ON N Y C H A. (New York City Housing Authority) Text in English. 1998. w. back issues avail. **Document type:** *Newsletter, Consumer.* **Description:** Covers the political, corruption and funding issues with the New York City Housing Authority.
Media: Online - full content.
Address: 250 Broadway, New York, NY 10007. TEL 212-306-3000, FAX 718-745-0170, spotlight@nycha-spotlight.com, http://nycha-spotlight.com/.

640.73 USA ISSN 1542-3514
PUGET SOUND CONSUMERS' CHECKBOOK. Text in English. 2002. s-a.
Published by: Center for the Study of Services, 733 15th St, N W, Ste 820, Washington, DC 20005-2112. TEL 202-347-7283, FAX 202-347-4000, http://www.checkbook.org.

640.73 FRA ISSN 0033-5932
QUE CHOISIR?. Text in French. 1961. m.
Published by: Union Federale des Consommateurs, 11 rue Guenot, Paris, Cedex 11 75555, France. TEL 33-1-43485548, FAX 33-1-43484435. Ed. Jean Paul Geai. Pub. Marie Jose Nicoli. **Subscr. to:** BP 400, Sainte Genevieve Cedex 60732, France.

REAL HEALTHCARE. see *HEALTH FACILITIES AND ADMINISTRATION*

640.73 USA ISSN 0736-1688
REFUNDING UPDATE. Text in English. 1983. s-a. looseleaf. USD 4 (effective 2001). adv. bibl. back issues avail. **Document type:** *Newsletter.*
Related titles: Microfiche ed.
Published by: Prosperity and Profits Unlimited, PO Box 416, Denver, CO 80201-0416. TEL 303-575-5676, mail@coursesmith.com, http://www.coursesmith.com. Ed., R&P A Doyle TEL 303-575-5676. Circ: 3,000.

640.73 USA ISSN 0194-0139
REFUNDLE BUNDLE; your bi-monthly guide to refund and coupon offers. Text in English. 1973. bi-m. USD 23.87 (effective 2004). adv. illus. 48 p./no.; back issues avail.; reprints avail. **Document type:** *Magazine, Consumer.* **Description:** Provides coupon and refund information on all current offers.
Address: PO Box 140, Centuck Sta, Yonkers, NY 10710. TEL 914-472-2227, info@refundlebundle.com, http://www.refundlebundle.com. Ed. Stephen M Samtur. Pub., R&P, Adv. contact Susan J Samtur. page USD 500. Circ: 70,000.

DE REISGIDS. see *TRAVEL AND TOURISM*

650 640 USA
REPORT TO BUSINESS. Text in English. 1975. q. free. stat.
Formerly: Report to Business and Consumer Information; Formed by the merger of: Better Business Bureau of Metropolitan New York. Report to Business (0045-1819); Consumer Information for Employees
Published by: Better Business Bureau of Metropolitan New York Inc., 257 Park Ave S, New York, NY 10010. TEL 212-533-7500. Ed. Carrie Getty. Circ: (controlled).

640.73 USA
RESOURCES (NASHVILLE); a consumer information source for customers of financial institutions. Text in English. 1983. q. looseleaf. free. **Document type:** *Newsletter.* **Description:** Consumer and lifestyle information for bank customers over 50. Provides practical solutions to the challenges of saving, spending and earning.
Published by: F I S I - Madison Financial (Subsidiary of: C U C International), PO Box 40726, Nashville, TN 37204. TEL 615-371-2658. Ed. Melany Klinck. Circ: 1,200,000 (controlled).

RIGHT-TO-KNOW PLANNING GUIDE (SERIES). see *SOCIAL SERVICES AND WELFARE*

640.73 RUS
S P R O S; spravochno-informatsionnoe izdanie dlya potrebitelei. (Sovety Potrebitelyam, Reitingi, Obzory, Situatsii) Text in Russian. 1992. m.?.
Address: Ul Varvarka 14, Moscow, 103690, Russian Federation. TEL 7-95-2984957. Ed. Larisa Leonova. Circ: 200,000.

640.73 ITA ISSN 1123-7236
IL SALVAGENTE; settimanale dei diritti dei consumi e delle scelte. Text in Italian. 1992. w. **Description:** Intends to provide a consumer advocacy service that exposes practices which may harm the public.
Published by: Societa Cooperativa Editoriale Il Salvagente a.r.l., Via Pinerolo, 43, Roma, 00182, Italy. TEL 39-06-7020265, FAX 39-06-7020026.

SAMARBETE. see *BUSINESS AND ECONOMICS—Cooperatives*

640.73 DNK ISSN 0036-3944
SAMVIRKE. Text in Danish. 1928. m. DKK 264 domestic to non-members; DKK 99 domestic to members; DKK 390 in Europe to non-members; DKK 558 elsewhere to non-members (effective 2005). adv. illus. index. back issues avail. **Document type:** *Newsletter, Consumer.* **Description:** Consumer news and articles reflecting latest news and trends.
Formerly (until 1945): Brugsforenings-Bladet
Published by: F D B - Faellesforeningen for Danmarks Brugsforeninger/Danish Consumers Cooperative Movement, Fanoegade 15, Copenhagen, 2100, Denmark. TEL 45-39-470000, FAX 45-39-470001, samvirke@fdb.dk, fdb@fdb.dk, http://www.fdb.dk/samvirke. Eds. Henrik Foehns TEL 45-39-470067, Soeren Berg. Circ: 470,000.

SCHOLASTIC CHOICES; personal development & living skills. see *EDUCATION—Teaching Methods And Curriculum*

SENIOR SUN. see *ENERGY*

640.73 NLD ISSN 0922-1646
SERVICESERIE. (Consists of: Auto; Geld; Huis; Lekker) Text in Dutch. 1978. 7/yr. adv. **Document type:** *Consumer.* **Description:** Publishes information for consumers on automobiles, housing, money and restaurants.
Published by: Premier Press B.V., Postbus 19217, Utrecht, 3501 DE, Netherlands. TEL 31-72-158084, FAX 31-72-157540. Ed. Peter Hooft.

SHEDDING LIGHT ON LEGISLATION. see *PUBLIC HEALTH AND SAFETY*

640.73 USA ISSN 1056-8832
TX356
SHOPPING FOR A BETTER WORLD; a quick and easy guide to socially responsible supermarket shopping. Text in English. a. USD 14.
Published by: Council on Economic Priorities, 30 Irving Pl, New York, NY 10003. TEL 800-729-4237, FAX 212-420-0988. Ed. Alice Tepper Marlin. R&P Karen Smith.

SPIELMITTEL; das Journal fuer Eltern. see *GIFTWARE AND TOYS*

640.73 RUS ISSN 1026-9444
SPROS. Text in Russian. 1992. m. RUR 816 domestic; USD 210 foreign (effective 2005). back issues avail. **Document type:** *Magazine, Consumer.* **Description:** Contains results of independent comparative tests of goods and services, legal advice.
Related titles: Online - full text ed.; ♦ Supplement(s): Denezhka.
Published by: Informatsionno-Izdatel'skii Fond Spros, ul Varvarka 14, magazin "Spros", Moscow, 109012, Russian Federation. TEL 7-095-2983583, info@spros.ru, http://www.spros.ru. Ed. Irina Vinogradova. Circ: 40,000. **US dist. addr.:** East View Information Services, 3020 Harbor Ln. N., Minneapolis, MN 55447. TEL 800-477-1005, FAX 800-800-3839, eastview@eastview.com, http://www.eastview.com.

SURVIVE & WIN. see *BUSINESS AND ECONOMICS—Computer Applications*

640.73 FIN ISSN 0355-4287
T M. TEKNIIKAN MAAILMA. Variant title: Tekniikan Maailma. Text in Finnish. 1953. 22/yr. EUR 103.90 (effective 2005). adv. **Document type:** *Magazine, Consumer.* **Description:** Covers automobiles, cameras, hi fi, television, aeroplanes, motorbikes, and telephones as well as the latest devices and ideas in technology.
Formerly (until 1974): Tekniikan Maailma (0789-3582)
Related titles: Online - full text ed.; ♦ Supplement(s): T M. Tekniikan Maailma. Automaailma. ISSN 0786-2016; ♦ T M Rakennusmaailma. ISSN 1459-1839.
Published by: Yhtyneet Kuvalehdet Oy/United Magazines Ltd., Maistraatinportti 1, Helsinki, 00015, Finland. TEL 358-9-15661, FAX 358-9-145650, http://www.tekniikanmaailma.fi/, http://www.kuvalehdet.fi/. Ed. Martti Merilinna. adv.: color page EUR 7,290; trim 280 x 217. Circ: 137,310.

T UE V AUTOREPORT. see *TRANSPORTATION—Automobiles*

T UE V JOURNAL. see *TECHNOLOGY: COMPREHENSIVE WORKS*

381.33 DNK ISSN 1604-6307
TAENK (2005)/THINK. Variant title: Taenk og test. Taenk plus Test. Text in Danish. 2000. 10/yr. DKK 298 (effective 2005). back issues avail. **Document type:** *Magazine, Consumer.*
Formerly (until 2005): Taenk + Test (1600-146X); Which was formed by the merger of (1964-2000): Taenk (0108-6243); (1961-2000): Raad og Resultater (0033-748X)
Published by: Forbrugerraadet/Danish Consumer Council, Fiolstraede 17, PO Box 2188, Copenhagen K, 1017, Denmark. TEL 45-77-417741, FAX 45-77-417742, red@taenk.dk, fbr@fbr.dk, http://www.taenk.dk, http://www.fbr.dk.

TAX HOTLINE; the inside report for people who need to be on top of every tax break the law allows. see *BUSINESS AND ECONOMICS—Public Finance, Taxation*

343.071 640.73 USA ISSN 1550-3658
KFT230.A29
TENNESSEE CONSUMER PROTECTION ACT. Variant title: Tennessee Consumer Protection Act and Related Laws. Text in English. 1987. irreg. (Annotated), latest 2000. USD 15 base vol(s). (effective 2003). 114 p./no.; Supplement avail.
Published by: Michie Company (Subsidiary of: LexisNexis North America), 701 E Water St, Charlottesville, VA 22902-5389. TEL 434-972-7600, 800-446-3410, FAX 434-972-7677, http://www.michie.com.

640 DEU ISSN 0040-3946
TEST. Text in German. 1966. m. EUR 41.40 domestic; EUR 47.40 foreign; EUR 3.90 newsstand/cover (effective 2005). bk.rev. charts; illus.; stat.; mkt. **Document type:** *Magazine, Consumer.* **Description:** Comparative analyses and reports on product quality.
Indexed: CIS, ChemAb, KES, RASB.
—BLDSC (8796.327000), IE, Infotrieve, ingenta.
Published by: (Bundesministerium fuer Verbraucherschutz), Stiftung Warentest, Luetzowplatz 11-13, Berlin, 10785, Germany. TEL 49-30-26312398, FAX 49-30-2611074, test@stiftung-warentest.de, stiftung-warentest@stiftung-warentest.de, http://www.stiftung-warentest.de/shop/alle/heftuebersicht_test.html. Ed. Hubertus Primus. Circ: 650,000.

640.73 BEL ISSN 0772-9413
TEST AANKOOP MAGAZINE. Text in Dutch. 1958. m.
Formerly (until 1984): Test Aankoop (0772-9758)
Related titles: Ed.: Test Achats Magazine. ISSN 0772-9405. 1958. BEF 2,856; in Belgium and Luxemburg (elsewhere 3208 BEF).
—IE.
Published by: Verbruikersunie/Association des Consommateurs, Rue de Hollande 13, Brussels, 1060, Belgium. TEL 32-2-5423211, FAX 32-2-5423250, TELEX 26771, http://www.test-aankoop.be.

640 DEU
TEST JAHRBUCH (YEAR). Text in German. a. **Document type:** *Consumer.*
Published by: Stiftung Warentest, Luetzowplatz 11-13, Berlin, 10785, Germany. TEL 49-30-26312398, FAX 49-30-26312428, stiftung-warentest@stiftung-warentest.de, http://www.stiftung-warentest.de. Circ: 420,000.

TEST SANTE. see *PUBLIC HEALTH AND SAFETY*

640.73 USA
TEXAS PRACTICE SERIES. CONSUMER RIGHTS AND REMEDIES. Text in English. 2 base vols. plus irreg. updates. USD 232 per vol. for 2 vol. set (effective 2004). **Document type:** *Monographic series, Academic/Scholarly.* **Description:** Covers consumer credit, debt collection, installment contracts, warranties, unconscionability, ownership and rental of real estate, and unfair or deceptive trade practices as regulated by the Consumer Protection Act.
Published by: Thomson West (Subsidiary of: Thomson Corporation, The), 610 Opperman Dr, Eagan, MN 55123-1396. TEL 651-687-7000, 800-328-4880, http://west.thomson.com/product/11839659/product.asp. Ed. Stephen G Cochran.

346.038 USA
TEXAS PRODUCTS LIABILITY LAW. Text in English. 1986 (2nd ed.). base vol. plus a. updates. USD 115. **Description:** Reference guide to the law of products liability in Texas.
Published by: LexisNexis (Subsidiary of: LexisNexis North America), PO Box 7587, Charlottesville, VA 22906-7587. TEL 804-972-7600, 800-562-1197, FAX 804-972-7666, llp.customer.support@lexis-nexis.com, http://www.lexislawpublishing.com. Ed. William Powers Jr.

TIGHTWAD LIVING. see *HOME ECONOMICS*

343.071 NLD ISSN 0169-1570
TIJDSCHRIFT VOOR CONSUMENTENRECHT. Text in Dutch. 1985. 5/yr. adv. back issues avail. **Document type:** *Academic/Scholarly.*
Indexed: ELLIS.
—IE, Infotrieve.
Published by: Kluwer B.V. (Subsidiary of: Wolters Kluwer N.V.), Postbus 23, Deventer, 7400 GA, Netherlands. TEL 31-570-673449, FAX 31-570-691555, juridisch@kluwer.nl, http://www.kluwer.nl. Circ: 550 (paid).

640.73 GBR ISSN 0269-2082
TIME OUT SHOPPING GUIDE. Text in English. 1986. a. GBP 7 (effective 2001). adv. maps. 244 p./no.; **Document type:** *Consumer.* **Description:** Unique directory of the best shops and services in London, carrying over 1,000 reviews and listings.
Published by: Time Out Group Ltd., Universal House, 251 Tottenham Court Rd, London, WIT 7AB, United Kingdom. FAX 44-20-7813-6001, net@timeout.co.uk, http://www.timeout.com. Ed. Sarah Guy. Pub. Tony Elliott. R&P Mike Hardwick. Adv. contact Mark Phillipps. B&W page GBP 2,110, color page GBP 2,505; 210 x 273. Circ: 45,000 (paid).

TIME OUT STUDENT GUIDE. see *EDUCATION*

TOPICS IN SAFETY, RISK, RELIABILITY AND QUALITY. see *OCCUPATIONAL HEALTH AND SAFETY*

TOUREN-FAHRER; Reportagen - Test - Technik. see *SPORTS AND GAMES—Bicycles And Motorcycles*

TOWN TRENDS. see *CHILDREN AND YOUTH—About*

C

▼ new title ➤ refereed ✶ unverified ♦ full entry avail.

640.73 USA ISSN 1542-3492
▼ **TWIN CITIES CONSUMERS' CHECKBOOK.** Text in English. 2003 (Winter). s-a.
Published by: Center for the Study of Services, 733 15th St, N W, Ste 820, Washington, DC 20005-2112. TEL 202-347-7283, FAX 202-347-4000, http://www.checkbook.org.

TYRES-ONLINE. see *TRANSPORTATION—Automobiles*

640.73 388.3 USA
TL162
ULTIMATE CAR BOOK (YEAR); an indispensable guide to the safest, most economical new cars. Key Title: The Ultimate Car Book (Year). Text in English. 1980. a. USD 25 (effective 2000). **Description:** Covers leasing versus buying, price comparisons, showroom strategies, insurance guide, and warranties.
Formerly: Car Book (Year) (0893-1208)
Published by: Center for Auto Safety, 1825 Connecticut Ave N W Ste 330, Washington, DC 20009. TEL 202-328-7700, http://www.essential.org/cas, http://www.autosafety.org.

UNABHAENGIGE BAUERNSTIMME; eine Zeitung von Baeuerinnen und Bauern. see *AGRICULTURE*

640.73 JAM
VALUE. Text in English. 1967. q. USD 100; free to members. bk.rev. **Description:** Includes a list of consumer rights and obligations, projects the League is involved in, and environmental education issues.
Published by: National Consumers' League, 29 Beechwood Ave, Kingston, 5, Jamaica. TEL 876-92-66388, FAX 876-92-65545. Ed. Tess Thomas. Circ: 1,000.

VEGETARIAN JOURNAL. see *NUTRITION AND DIETETICS*

640.73 DEU
VERBRAUCHER AKTUELL. Text in German. 1981. m. **Document type:** *Consumer.*
Published by: Verbraucher - Zentrale Nordrhein-Westfalen Landesarbeitsgemeinschaft der Verbraucherverbaende, Mintropstr 27, Duesseldorf, 40215, Germany. TEL 49-211-38090, FAX 49-211-3809172. Ed., R&P Bernd Huppertz.

640.73 DEU ISSN 1435-3547
VERBRAUCHER KONKRET. Text in German. 1987. bi-m. adv. bk.rev. **Document type:** *Magazine, Consumer.*
Formerly: Verbraucher Telegramm (0943-2116); Incorporates (1982-1989): Consum-Critik (0179-6704)
Published by: (Verbraucher Initiative e.V.), V I Verlags und Handels GmbH, Breite Str 51, Bonn, 53111, Germany. TEL 49-228-7263393, FAX 49-228-7263399, 100575.242@compuserve.com, mail@verbraucher-ini.de, http://www.verbraucher.com. R&P, Adv. contact Anne Schoenhofen.

640.73 DEU ISSN 0948-8464
VERBRAUCHERSCHUTZ, PRODUKTSICHERHEIT, UMWELTSCHUTZ. Text in German. 1990. irreg., latest vol.11, 2002. EUR 26 per vol. (effective 2003). **Document type:** *Monographic series, Trade.*
Published by: Verlag Versicherungswirtschaft GmbH, Klosestr. 22, Karlsruhe, 76137, Germany. TEL 49-721-3509-0, FAX 49-721-31833, kampf@vvw.de, http://www.vvw.de.

VERDICTSEARCH PRODUCTS LIABILITY. see *LAW*

VICTORIAN TASMANIAN RETAIL DIRECTORY. see *BUSINESS AND ECONOMICS—Trade And Industrial Directories*

640.73 IDN ISSN 0126-3455
WARTA KONSUMEN. Text in Indonesian. 1974. m. IDR 1,500. bk.rev.
Published by: Yayasan Lembaga Konsumen Indonesia/ Indonesian Consumer Organization, Duren Tiga, Jalan Pembangunan I 1, Jakarta, 12760, Indonesia. TEL 62-021-7971378, FAX 62-021-7981038. Circ: 300.

640.73 USA ISSN 0272-0469
TX335
WASHINGTON CONSUMERS' CHECKBOOK. Text in English. 1976. s-a. USD 30 for 2 yrs.; USD 6.95 newsstand/cover (effective 2005). adv. charts; illus.; mkt.; stat. cum.index. back issues avail. **Document type:** *Consumer.* **Description:** Evaluates local Washington, D.C. area service firms such as auto repair shops, medical services, home improvement firms, stores, insurance companies, etc.
Indexed: AgeL.
Published by: Center for the Study of Services, 733 15th St, N W, Ste 820, Washington, DC 20005-2112. TEL 202-347-7283, 800-475-7283, FAX 202-347-4000, editors@checkbook.org, http://www.checkbook.org. Ed. Robert Krugoff. Pub. Robert Krughoff. R&P Kevin Brassler. Adv. contact Tara Eberly. Circ: 55,000 (paid).

640.73 USA
WASHINGTON PUBLIC INTEREST RESEARCH GROUP REPORTS. Abbreviated title: Wash P I R G Reports. Text in English. 1981. q. USD 15. **Description:** Works to identify, research, analyze, and pursue solutions to consumer protection problems, environmental protection and preservation concerns, and corporate and governmental accountability.
Published by: Washington Public Interest Research Group, 3240 Eastlake Ave E, Ste 100, Seattle, WA 98102. TEL 206-322-9064. Ed. K Krushas. Circ: 30,000.

640.73 GBR ISSN 0043-4841
TX335.A1
WHICH?. Text in English. 1957. m. GBP 6.25 per month (effective 2005). charts; illus. index. **Document type:** *Magazine, Consumer.* **Description:** Deals with consumer education and protection based on testing of goods and services.
Related titles: Microfiche ed.; Online - full text ed.
Indexed: API, BrCerAb, FS&TA, KES, RICS, WSCA, WTA. —BLDSC (9310.800000), IE, Infotrieve, ingenta.
Published by: (Consumers' Association), Which? Ltd., 2 Marylebone Rd, London, NW1 4DF, United Kingdom. TEL 44-20-77707571, FAX 44-20-77707665, which@which.net, http://www.which.net. Ed. Helen Parker. Circ: 536,000.
Subscr. to: Consumers' Association, Castlemead, Gascoyne Way, Hertford, Herts SG14 1LH, United Kingdom. TEL 44-1992-822800, editor@which.net.

571.959 USA
WILD MATTERS. Text in English. 1992. 10/yr. USD 25 domestic; USD 40 in Canada; USD 45 elsewhere (effective 2003). bk.rev. charts; illus. back issues avail. **Document type:** *Magazine, Consumer.* **Description:** Aims to stimulate the necessary efforts to build local, safe, and sustainable alternatives in food production as well as provide the language, philosophy and strategic imperatives for lasting fundamental change.
Former titles (until 2003): Food & Water Journal (1524-010X); Safe Food News
Related titles: Online - full text ed.: (from SoftLine Information).
Indexed: AltPI.
Published by: Food and Water, Inc., P.O. Box 543, Montpelier, VT 05601. TEL 802-229-6222, 800-328-7233, FAX 802-229-6751, info@foodandwater.org, fwi@together.net, http://www.foodandwater.org/journal.asp. Ed. Michael Colby. Circ: 15,000.

640.73 CHE
WIRTSCHAFT UND ENERGIE. Text in German. irreg.
Published by: Schweizerischer Energie- Konsumentenverband von Industrie und Wirtschaft, Baumleingasse 22, Basel, 4001, Switzerland. TEL 233060.

640.73 CHN
ZHONGGUO XIAOFEIZHE BAO/CHINA CONSUMER NEWS. Text in Chinese. 6/w. USD 101, CNY 62.28. **Document type:** *Newspaper, Consumer.*
Contact Dist.: China Books & Periodicals Inc TEL 415-282-2994, FAX 415-282-0994. **Dist. by:** China International Book Trading Corp, 35 Chegongzhuang Xilu, Haidian District, PO Box 399, Beijing 100044, China. TEL 86-10-68412045, FAX 86-10-68412023, cibtc@mail.cibtc.com.cn, http://www.cibtc.com.cn.

640.73 FRA ISSN 1267-8066
60 MILLIONS DE CONSOMMATEURS. Variant title: Soixante Millions de Consommateurs. Text in French. 11/yr. **Document type:** *Newsletter, Consumer.*
Formerly: 50 Millions de Consommateurs (0339-1531)
Indexed: KES.
Published by: Institut National de la Consommation, 80 rue Lecourbe, Paris, Cedex 15 75732, France. TEL 33-1-44907040, FAX 33-1-45662120, inc1@club-internet.fr, http://www.conso.net. Ed. Marie Jeanne Husset. Pub. Marc Deby.

CONSUMER EDUCATION AND PROTECTION—Abstracting, Bibliographies, Statistics

338.528 GBR ISSN 1466-3554
BUSINESS MONITOR. MM23 CONSUMER PRICE INDICES. Text in English. 1999. m. GBP 185 (effective 2000).
Formerly (until 1999): Business Monitor. MM23 Retail Prices Index
—BLDSC (3424.355000).
Published by: Stationery Office, PO Box 276, London, SW8 5DT, United Kingdom. TEL 44-20-7873-0011, FAX 44-20-7873-8247, book.order.@theso.co.uk, http://www.tso.co.uk.

640.73 CAN ISSN 0703-9352
CANADA. STATISTICS CANADA. CONSUMER PRICE INDEX. Text in English. 1935. m. CND 93 domestic (effective 1999); USD 93 foreign. **Description:** Provides a descriptive capsule summary of retail price movements and the factors underlying them.
Indexed: RASB.
—CISTI.
Published by: Statistics Canada, Operations and Integration Division, Circulation Management, Jean Talon Bldg, 2 C12, Tunney's Pasture, Ottawa, ON K1A 0T6, Canada. TEL 613-951-7277, 800-267-6677, FAX 613-951-1584, http://www.statcan.ca.

640.73 CAN
CONSUMER PRICE INDEX (VICTORIA). Text in English. 12/yr. CND 60 (effective 1997). **Document type:** *Government.* **Description:** Price trends in British Columbia, Vancouver and Victoria for various categories of consumer spending. Includes historical summaries and comparisons with major Canadian cities.
Published by: Ministry of Finance and Corporate Relations, B C Stats, Sta Prov Govt, P O Box 9410, Victoria, BC V8W 9V1, Canada. TEL 250-387-0359, FAX 250-387-0380, bcstats@fincc04.fin.gov.bc.ca, http://www.bcstats.gov.bc.ca.

640.73 016 USA ISSN 0094-0534
TX335
CONSUMERS INDEX; to product evaluations and information sources. Text in English. 1973. q. (plus a. cumulation). USD 149; USD 275 with cumulation (effective 2005). illus. reprints avail. **Document type:** *Abstract/Index.* **Description:** Evaluations, descriptions and tests of a variety of products.
Related titles: ♦ CD-ROM ed.: Consumers Reference Disc. ISSN 1053-1424; Magnetic Tape ed.; ♦ Online - full text ed.: Consumers Index Database.
Published by: Pierian Press, PO Box 1808, Ann Arbor, MI 48106. TEL 734-434-5530, 800-678-2435, FAX 734-434-5582, pubinfo@pierianpress.com, http://www.pierianpress.com/index.php?section=databases&content=consumers.

640.73 USA
CONSUMERS INDEX DATABASE. Text in English. irreg.
Media: Online - full text. **Related titles:** ♦ CD-ROM ed.: Consumers Reference Disc. ISSN 1053-1424; Magnetic Tape ed.; ♦ Print ed.: Consumers Index. ISSN 0094-0534.
Published by: Pierian Press, PO Box 1808, Ann Arbor, MI 48106. TEL 734-434-5530, 800-678-2435, FAX 734-434-6409, pubinfo@pierianpress.com, http://www.pierianpress.com/index.php?section=databases&content=consumers.

016.64073 USA ISSN 1053-1424
CONSUMERS REFERENCE DISC. Text in English. 199?. q. USD 695 (effective 2000). **Document type:** *Abstract/Index.* **Description:** Provides access to abstracted articles from Consumers Index and Consumer Health & Nutrition Index from 1985 to the present.
Media: CD-ROM (from National Information Services Corp. (N I S C)). **Related titles:** Magnetic Tape ed.; ♦ Online - full text ed.: Consumers Index Database; ♦ Print ed.: Consumers Index. ISSN 0094-0534.
Published by: National Information Services Corp. (N I S C), Ste 6, Wyman Towers, 3100 St Paul St, Baltimore, MD 21218. TEL 410-243-0797, FAX 410-243-0982, sales@nisc.com, http://www.nisc.com. Pub. Fred Durr.

640.73 LUX ISSN 1013-3402
HB235.E82
EUROSTAT CONSUMER PRICE INDEX (MONTHLY EDITION); statistics in focus: economics and finance. Text in English. m. USD 105. Supplement avail.
Related titles: Microfiche ed.: (from CIS); French ed.: Indice des Prix a la Consommation. ISSN 1010-2787; German ed.: Eurostat Verbraucherpreisindex. ISSN 1021-5425; Alternate Frequency ed(s).: Eurostat Consumer Price Index (Quarterly Edition). ISSN 1011-7725. q.
Indexed: IIS.
Published by: European Commission, Office for Official Publications of the European Union, 2 Rue Mercier, Luxembourg, L-2985, Luxembourg. **Dist. in US by:** Bernan Associates, Bernan, 4611-F Assembly Dr., Lanham, MD 20706-4391. TEL 301-459-0056, 800-274-4447.

338.5 310 JPN ISSN 0289-1336
JAPAN. STATISTICS BUREAU. MANAGEMENT AND COORDINATION AGENCY. ANNUAL REPORT ON THE CONSUMER PRICE INDEX (YEAR)/NIHON TOKEI KYOKAI. SHOHISHA BUKKA SHISU NENPO. Text in Japanese. 1968. a. JPY 4,620 (effective 2000). **Document type:** *Government.*
Published by: Somucho. Tokeikyoko/Statistics Bureau. Management and Coordination Agency, 19-1 Wakamatsu-cho, Shinjyuku-ku, Tokyo, 162-8668, Japan. TEL 81-3-5273-1116, FAX 81-3-5273-1180, jsatokai@t3.rim.or.jp, http://www.jstat.or.jp. Ed., R&P, Adv. contact Akihiko Ito.

640.73 JPN ISSN 0288-920X
HB235.J3
JAPAN. STATISTICS BUREAU. MANAGEMENT AND COORDINATION AGENCY. MONTHLY REPORT ON THE CONSUMER PRICE INDEX/NIHON TOKEI KYOKAI. SHOHISHA BUKKA SHISU GEPPO. Text in English, Japanese. 1947. m. JPY 740 (effective 2000). **Document type:** *Government.*
Formerly (until 1983): Shohisha Bukka Shisu (0448-7222)
Published by: Somucho. Tokeikyoko/Statistics Bureau. Management and Coordination Agency, 19-1 Wakamatsu-cho, Shinjyuku-ku, Tokyo, 162-8668, Japan. TEL 81-3-5273-1116, FAX 81-3-5273-1180, jsatokai@t3.rim.or.jp, http://www.jstat.or.jp.

C

640.73   VUT
VANUATU. STATISTICS OFFICE. REPORTS ON CONSUMER PRICES INDEXES. Text in English, French. 1976. a. VUV 500, USD 5 (effective 1996). adv. stat. **Document type:** *Government.* **Description:** Provides information on movements in retail prices of goods and services commonly purchased by the wage and salary earner households living in the urban areas.
Former titles: Vanuatu. National Planning and Statistics Office. Consumer Prices Indexes; Vanuatu. Condominium Bureau of Statistics. Consumer Price Indexes
Published by: Statistics Office, PMB 19, Port Vila, Vanuatu. TEL 678-22110, FAX 678-24583. Ed. Jacob Isaiah. Adv. contact Tali Saurei. Circ: 300.

COOPERATIVES

see BUSINESS AND ECONOMICS—Cooperatives

CORPORATE LAW

see LAW—Corporate Law

CRIMINAL LAW

see LAW—Criminal Law

CRIMINOLOGY AND LAW ENFORCEMENT

see also CRIMINOLOGY AND LAW ENFORCEMENT—Security ; EDUCATION—Special Education And Rehabilitation ; MEDICAL SCIENCES—Forensic Sciences

A C J S PROGRAM BOOK. see EDUCATION—Higher Education

331.125   USA
A C J S TODAY. Text in English. q. membership only. adv. **Document type:** *Newsletter.* **Description:** Provides articles, news releases and information on events and job opportunities.
Formerly: Placement News
Published by: Academy of Criminal Justice Sciences, 7339 Hanover Pkwy., Ste. A, Greenbelt, MD 20770-3640. info@acjs.org, http://www.acjs.org. Ed. Laura Moriarty.

364   AUS
A I C NEWSLETTER. Text in English. q. **Document type:** *Academic/Scholarly.*
Published by: Australian Institute of Criminology, GPO Box 2944, Canberra, ACT 2601, Australia. TEL 61-2-6249-2479, FAX 61-2-6257-5088, aicpress@aic.gov.au, http://www.aic.gov.au.

364   USA   ISSN 0270-2991
A M S STUDIES IN CRIMINAL JUSTICE. Text in English. 1975. irreg., latest vol.3, 1980. price varies. back issues avail. **Document type:** *Monographic series.* **Description:** Series of monographs, reference works and bibliographies designed for the study of forensic science and law enforcement.
Published by: A M S Press, Inc., 63 Flushing Ave., # 417, Brooklyn, NY 11205-1005. TEL 212-777-4700, FAX 212-995-5413.

A N P I MAGAZINE (NEDERLANDSE EDITIE). (Association Nationale pour la Protection contre l'Incendie et l'Intrusion) see FIRE PREVENTION

364 340.6 614.19   JPN   ISSN 0302-0029
HV6005   CODEN: HAZAAY
ACTA CRIMINOLOGIAE ET MEDICINAE LEGALIS JAPONICA/HANZAIGAKU ZASSHI. Text in English, Japanese. 1928. bi-m. USD 55 (effective 1992). adv. bk.rev. **Document type:** *Academic/Scholarly.*
Indexed: AC&P, BiolAb, CIN, ChemAb, ChemTitl, ExcerpMed, JPI.
—CASDDS, GNLM.
Published by: Japanese Association of Criminology/Nihon Hanzai Gakkai, c/o Department of Criminal Psychiatry, Medical and Dental University, 2-3-10 Kanda-Surugadai, Chiyoda-ku, Tokyo, 101-0062, Japan. FAX 03-3291-5799, Ed. A Yamagami. Circ: 800.

364 345   ZAF   ISSN 1012-8093
➤ **ACTA CRIMINOLOGICA.** Text in English. 1988. s-a. ZAR 50 domestic to individual members; ZAR 250 domestic to institutional members; ZAR 50 domestic to students; USD 55 foreign (effective 2004). back issues avail. **Document type:** *Academic/Scholarly.* **Description:** Provides research findings, professional issues and statistical information in the field of criminal justice.
Related titles: Online - full text ed.: (from International Network for the Availability of Scientific Publications, African Journals Online).
Indexed: ISAP, SociolAb.

Published by: Criminological Society of Southern Africa, PO Box 28936, Sunnyside, Pretoria 0132, South Africa. TEL 27-12-4296808, FAX 27-12-4293221, neinajd@alpha.unisa.ac.za, http://www.journals.co.za/ej/ejour_crim.html. Ed. H J Prinsloo. Circ: 1,300.

364.4   USA   ISSN 1524-105X
ACTION LINE (SACRAMENTO); a crime and violence prevention newsjournal. Text in English. 1981. s-a. free. illus. **Document type:** *Newsletter.*
Former titles (until Fall 1994): Senior's Action Alert; Sentinel (Sacramento)
Published by: Attorney General's Office, Crime and Violence Prevention Center, PO Box 944255, Sacramento, CA 94244-2550. TEL 916-324-7863, FAX 916-327-2384, tullyw@hdcdojnet.state.ca.us, http://cagg.state.ca.us/cvpc. Ed., R&P Wendy Tully TEL 916-323-2166. Circ: 5,000 (paid).

ACTUALIDAD PENAL. see LAW—Criminal Law

363.2   FRA   ISSN 0339-7858
ACTUALITE POLICIERE. Text in French. 1948. bi-m. adv. **Description:** Discusses police administration.
Formerly (until 1975): Actualite Policiere. Police de Paris (0339-784X)
Address: Caserne de la Cite, 11 rue des Ursins, Paris, 75004, France. Ed. Serge Maciet. Circ: 20,000.

364   USA   ISSN 0894-2366
HV6001
➤ **ADVANCES IN CRIMINOLOGICAL THEORY.** Text in English. 1989. a. price varies. **Document type:** *Monographic series, Academic/Scholarly.* **Description:** Provides a forum for orginal work in criminological theory.
Related titles: CD-ROM ed.
—BLDSC (0704.195000). **CCC.**
Published by: (Rutgers University, School of Criminal Justice), Transaction Publishers, 390 Campus Dr, Somerset, NJ 07830. TEL 888-999-6778, FAX 732-748-9801, trans@transactionpub.com, http://www.newark.rutgers.edu/rscj/journals/advances.htm, http://www.transactionpub.com. Eds. Freda Adler, William S Laufer. **Subscr. to:** Transaction Distribution Center, 390 Campus Dr., Somerset, NJ 08873. TEL 732-445-1245, 888-999-6778, FAX 732-748-9801, orders@transactionpub.com.

365   OMN
AL-AIN ASSAHIRAH. Text in Arabic. 1976. q. free. **Document type:** *Government.* **Description:** Presents articles on security, police, cultural and social matters, and Royal Oman Police news.
Former titles: Majallat al-Shurtah; Al- Shurtah
Published by: Royal Oman Police, Directorate of Public Relations, P O Box 2, Muscat, 113, Oman. TEL 968-569216, FAX 968-567161, TELEX 5377 COMPOL MB. Ed. Brig. Mahmoud bin Amer Al-Kiyomi. R&P Lt.Col. Abdullah bin Amer Al-Kasbi. Circ: 12,000 (controlled).

ALARM/ALARME/ALLARME; modern fire protection and security systems bulletin. see FIRE PREVENTION

353.9   USA   ISSN 0095-3415
HV8691.U5
ALASKA. VIOLENT CRIMES COMPENSATION BOARD. ANNUAL REPORT. Key Title: Annual Report - State of Alaska. Violent Crimes Compensation Board. Text in English. 1973. a. illus.
Published by: Victims of Crimes Compensation Board, PO Box 111200, Juneau, AK 99811. TEL 907-465-3040.

364   NLD   ISSN 0002-5283
ALGEMEEN POLITIEBLAD VAN HET KONINKRIJK DER NEDERLANDEN. Text in Dutch. 1852. bi-w. free to qualified personnel. **Document type:** *Government.*
Indexed: AC&P, KES.
Published by: Ministerie van Justitie, Postbus 20301, The Hague, 2500 EH, Netherlands. TEL 31-70-370-7618, FAX 31-70-370-7948, kslabber@best-dep.minjus.nl. Ed. J van Schie. Circ: 40,000 (controlled).

ALIBI. see LAW—Criminal Law

365 616.8   USA
AMERICAN ASSOCIATION OF MENTAL HEALTH PROFESSIONALS IN CORRECTIONS. MONOGRAPH SERIES. Text in English. 1940. q. USD 60. **Document type:** *Monographic series, Academic/Scholarly.* **Description:** For professionals working in correctional settings.
Indexed: e-psyche.
Published by: (American Association of Mental Health Professionals in Corrections), Martin Psychiatric Research Foundation, PO Box 3365, Fairfield, CA 94533. TEL 707-864-0910, FAX 707-964-0910. Ed. Dr. Clyde Verne Martin. Circ: 4,000.

364   USA
▼ **AMERICAN COP.** Text in English. 2005. bi-m. USD 24.95 (effective 2005). adv. **Document type:** *Magazine, Trade.* **Description:** Covers police tactics, firearms, equipment, and other related topics.

Published by: Publishers Development Corp., 12345 World Trade Dr, San Diego, CA 92128. TEL 858-605-0253, FAX 858-605-0247, subs@americancopmagazine.com, http://www.americancopmagazine.com/. Eds. Adam Reiser, Julie Reiser. adv.: B&W page USD 2,995, color page USD 3,705; 7 x 10. Circ: 75,000.

343   USA   ISSN 0164-0364
K1
➤ **AMERICAN CRIMINAL LAW REVIEW.** Text in English. 1962. q. USD 30 domestic; USD 40 foreign; USD 10 newsstand/cover (effective 2005). adv. bk.rev. illus. Index. back issues avail.; reprint service avail. from WSH,PQC. **Document type:** *Journal, Academic/Scholarly.*
Former titles (until 1971): American Criminal Law Quarterly (0002-8118); (until 1963): Criminal Law Quarterly (0271-4574)
Related titles: Microfiche ed.: (from WSH); Microfilm ed.: (from PQC, WSH); Microform ed.: (from WSH); Online - full text ed.: (from Florida Center for Library Automation, Gale Group, H.W. Wilson, LexisNexis, Northern Light Technology, Inc., O C L C Online Computer Library Center, Inc., ProQuest Information & Learning, Thomson West).
Indexed: ABS&EES, AC&P, CJA, CJPI, CLI, CurCont, ESPM, FamI, ILP, LRI, LegCont, PCI, RASB, RiskAb, SSCI.
—BLDSC (0812.680000), IDS, IE, Infotrieve, ingenta.
Published by: Georgetown University Law Center, 600 New Jersey Ave, NW, Washington, DC 20001. TEL 202-662-9425, FAX 202-662-9492, aclr@law.georgetown.edu, http://www.ll.georgetown.edu/, http://www.law.gwu.edu/. Ed. Brian C Lewis. Circ: 2,153.

365   USA   ISSN 1056-0319
HV8745
AMERICAN JAILS; the magazine of the American Jail Association. Text in English. 1987. bi-m. USD 36 domestic membership; USD 42 in Canada membership; USD 54 elsewhere membership (effective 2005). adv. bk.rev. illus. Index. reprints avail. **Document type:** *Magazine, Trade.* **Description:** Covers jail programs, crowding, training, direct supervision, management, jail research, and standards.
Related titles: Online - full text ed.: (from EBSCO Publishing).
Indexed: CJA, CJPI.
Published by: American Jail Association, 1135 Professional Ct., Hagerstown, MD 21740-5853. TEL 301-790-3930, FAX 301-790-2941, jails@worldnet.att.net, http://www.corrections.com/aja, http://www.corrections.com/aja. Circ: 6,000.

364   USA   ISSN 1066-2316
                            CODEN: AJCJE4
➤ **AMERICAN JOURNAL OF CRIMINAL JUSTICE.** Text in English. s-a. **Document type:** *Journal, Academic/Scholarly.*
Related titles: Online - full text ed.: (from ProQuest Information & Learning).
Indexed: CJA, CJPI, IPSA, PAIS, PSA, PsycInfo, PsycholAb, SOPODA, SSA, SociolAb, e-psyche.
—BLDSC (0824.190000), IE, ingenta.
Published by: Southern Criminal Justice Association, c/o School of Criminology & Criminal Justice, Florida State University, Tallahassee, FL 32306-1127. http://www.criminology.fsu.edu/cj.html. Ed. Bill Doerner.

364   USA   ISSN 0092-2315
K1
AMERICAN JOURNAL OF CRIMINAL LAW. Text in English. 1972. 3/yr. USD 32.18 in state Austin & Texas; USD 30 domestic excluding Austin & Texas; USD 35 foreign (effective 2005). adv. bk.rev. cum.index. back issues avail.; reprint service avail. from WSH. **Document type:** *Journal, Academic/Scholarly.* **Description:** Features articles, essays, notes and reviews relevant to a national and international audience of legal scholars and practitioners.
Related titles: Online - full text ed.: (from EBSCO Publishing, H.W. Wilson, LexisNexis, O C L C Online Computer Library Center, Inc., ProQuest Information & Learning).
Indexed: AC&P, CJA, CJPI, CLI, CurCont, ESPM, FamI, ILP, LRI, LegCont, RiskAb, SSCI.
—BLDSC (0824.200000), IE, Infotrieve, ingenta.
Published by: University of Texas at Austin, School of Law Publications, 727 E 26th St., Ste 2.130, Austin, TX 78705-3299. TEL 512-232-1278, FAX 512-475-6988, ajcl@mail.law.utexas.edu, publications@mail.utexas.edu, http://www.utexas.edu/law/journals/ajcl, http://www.texaslawpublications.com/. Ed. Debra Innocenti. Circ: 600 (paid).

364.128   USA
AMERICAN POLYGRAPH ASSOCIATION NEWSLETTER. Text in English. 1966. bi-m. USD 80 domestic; USD 100 foreign (effective 2000). adv. bk.rev. back issues avail.; reprint service avail. from PQC. **Document type:** *Newsletter.* **Description:** Covers current cases, legal changes, news of technical interest, worldwide activities, and training.
Related titles: Microform ed.: (from PQC).
Indexed: e-psyche.
Published by: (American Polygraph Association), Seridan Press, PO Box 8037, Chattanooga, TN 37414-0037. TEL 423-892-3992, 800-272-8037. Ed. Donald Krapohl. R&P, Adv. contact Robbie Bennett. Circ: 3,500.

AMERICAN SERIES OF FOREIGN PENAL CODES. see LAW—Criminal Law

▼ *new title*   ➤ *refereed*   ✶ *unverified*   ◆ *full entry avail.*

C

AMNESTY. see *POLITICAL SCIENCE—International Relations*

AMNESTY INTERNATIONAL. see *POLITICAL SCIENCE—International Relations*

364.65 AUS ISSN 0256-0771
AMNESTY INTERNATIONAL AUSTRALIAN NEWSLETTER. Text in English. 1983. m. AUD 40. bk.rev. **Document type:** *Newsletter.*
Related titles: CD-ROM ed.
Published by: Amnesty International Australia, Private Bag 23, Broadway, NSW 2007, Australia. TEL 61-2-92113560, FAX 61-2-92113608, TELEX AA123206, hello@amnesty.org.au, http://www.amnesty.org.au. Ed. Tim Haydon. R&P Kelly Betts. Circ: 14,000.

AMNESTY INTERNATIONAL RAPPORT ANNUEL. see *POLITICAL SCIENCE—International Relations*

AMNESTY INTERNATIONAL REPORT. see *POLITICAL SCIENCE—International Relations*

364 USA ISSN 1557-0045
KF9350.A15
ANDREWS LITIGATION REPORTER: WHITE-COLLAR CRIME. Text in English. 1987. m. looseleaf. USD 743 (effective 2005). adv. bibl.; stat. back issues avail. **Document type:** *Newsletter, Trade.* **Description:** Each issue covers one topic in depth, with interviews and relevant news items involving white-collar crime.
Formerly (until 2004): White-Collar Crime Reporter (0891-6721)
Related titles: Online - full text ed.
Indexed: CJA.
—CCC.
Published by: Andrews Publications (Subsidiary of: Thomson West), 175 Strafford Ave, Ste 140, Wayne, PA 19087. TEL 610-225-0510, 800-345-1101, FAX 610-225-0501, west.customer.service@thomson.com, http://findlaw.west.thomson.com/product/40211194/product.asp, http://www.andrewsonline.com. Ed. Bob McSherry. Pub., R&P Robert Maroldo. Adv. contact Sofia Pables.

C

365.976317 USA ISSN 0402-4249
HV9475.L22
ANGOLITE; the prison newsmagazine. Text in English. 1952. bi-m. USD 20 domestic; USD 30 in Canada; USD 40 elsewhere (effective 1999). bk.rev. **Document type:** *Trade.* **Description:** Louisiana State Penitentiary's uncensored official prisoner publication.
Indexed: IPARL.
Published by: (Louisiana. Department of Corrections), Louisiana State Penitentiary, Angola, LA 70712. TEL 504-655-4411. Ed. Wilbert Rideau. R&P Cathy Jett. Circ: 2,000.

364 FRA ISSN 0003-4452
ANNALES INTERNATIONALES DE CRIMINOLOGIE/ANALES INTERNACIONALES DE CRIMINOLOGIA/INTERNATIONAL ANNALS OF CRIMINOLOGY. Text in English, French, Spanish. 1962. a. bk.rev. bibl. **Document type:** *Newsletter.*
Indexed: CJA, IBSS, PAIS.
—IE, Infotrieve. **CCC.**
Published by: International Society of Criminology/Societe Internationale de Criminologie, c/o Rachida Touahria, 4-14 rue Ferrus, Paris, 75014, France. TEL 33-1-45880023, FAX 33-1-45652722, crim.sic@wanadoo.fr.

634 USA
ANNUAL EDITIONS: CORRECTIONS. Text in English. 2000. a., latest 2000, 1st ed. USD 20.31 per vol. (effective 2004). **Document type:** *Academic/Scholarly.* **Description:** Contains a collection of current, carefully selected articles from some of the most respected magazine, newspapers, and journals published today. Features interesting, well-illustrated articles by authorities in the field, providing effective and useful perspectives on today's important topics in corrections.
Published by: McGraw-Hill - Dushkin (Subsidiary of: McGraw-Hill Higher Education), 2460 Kerper Blvd, Dubuque, IA 52001. TEL 800-243-6532, customer.service@mcgraw-hill.com, http://www.dushkin.com/text-data/catalog/0072404329.mhtml. Ed. Matthew Leone.

364 USA ISSN 0272-3816
HV8138
➤ **ANNUAL EDITIONS: CRIMINAL JUSTICE.** Text in English. 1976. a., latest 2004, 28th ed. USD 20.21 per vol. (effective 2004). illus. **Document type:** *Academic/Scholarly.*
Formerly: Annual Editions: Readings in Criminal Justice
Published by: McGraw-Hill - Dushkin (Subsidiary of: McGraw-Hill Higher Education), 2460 Kerper Blvd, Dubuque, IA 52001. TEL 800-243-6532, customer.service@mcgraw-hill.com, http://www.dushkin.com/text-data/catalog/007287435x.mhtml. Eds. Joanne Naughton, Joseph L Victor. Pub. Ian Nielsen. R&P Cheryl Greenleaf.

364 USA ISSN 1096-4207
HV6001
ANNUAL EDITIONS: CRIMINOLOGY. Text in English. 1997. a., latest 1999, 3rd ed. USD 20.21 per vol. (effective 2004). illus. **Document type:** *Academic/Scholarly.*
Published by: McGraw-Hill - Dushkin (Subsidiary of: McGraw-Hill Higher Education), 2460 Kerper Blvd, Dubuque, IA 52001. TEL 800-243-6532, customer.service@mcgraw-hill.com, http://www.dushkin.com. Ed. Mark Fisch.

▼ **ANNUAL EDITIONS: HOMELAND SECURITY.** see *PUBLIC HEALTH AND SAFETY*

ANNUAL EDITIONS: VIOLENCE AND TERRORISM. see *CIVIL DEFENSE*

364.1 12 CAN ISSN 1700-5531
ANNUAL REPORT ON ORGANIZED CRIME IN CANADA (ONLINE EDITION). Text in English. 1997. a. free. back issues avail. **Document type:** *Government.*
Media: Online - full content. **Related titles:** ♦ Print ed.: Annual Report on Organized Crime in Canada (Print Edition). ISSN 1208-3143; French ed.: Rapport Annuel sur le Crime Organise au Canada (En ligne). ISSN 1700-5558. 1997.
Published by: Criminal Intelligence Service Canada/Service Canadien de Renseignements Criminels, 1200 Vanier Pkwy, Ottawa, ON K1A OR2, Canada. TEL 877-660-4321, http://www.cisc.gc.ca/WebPage/index_b.htm.

364.1 CAN ISSN 1208-3143
ANNUAL REPORT ON ORGANIZED CRIME IN CANADA (PRINT EDITION). Text in English, French. 1995. a. stat. back issues avail. **Document type:** *Government.*
Formerly (until 1995): Annual Report on Eastern European Organized Crime (1204-8771)
Related titles: ♦ Online - full content ed.: Annual Report on Organized Crime in Canada (Online Edition). ISSN 1700-5531.
Published by: Criminal Intelligence Service Canada/Service Canadien de Renseignements Criminels, 1200 Vanier Pkwy, Ottawa, ON K1A OR2, Canada. TEL 877-660-4321, http://www.cisc.gc.ca/WebPage/index_b.htm.

353.39 KEN
ANNUAL REPORT ON THE ADMINISTRATION OF PRISONS IN KENYA. Text in English. a. **Document type:** *Government.*
Published by: (Kenya. Ministry of Home Affairs), Government Printing and Stationery Department, PO Box 30128, Nairobi, Kenya.

364 GBR
ANTI MONEY LAUNDERING GUIDE. Text in English. 1999. base vol. plus updates 8/yr. looseleaf. GBP 470 base vol(s).; GBP 449, EUR 675 updates in Europe; GBP 490, USD 890 updates elsewhere (effective 2006); 4 looseleaf releases, 4 CD updates plus 10 newsletters. **Document type:** *Journal, Trade.*
Related titles: CD-ROM ed.: ISSN 1466-4771.
Published by: Sweet & Maxwell Ltd., 100 Avenue Road, London, NW3 3PF, United Kingdom. TEL 44-20-74491111, FAX 44-20-74491144, customer.services@sweetandmaxwell.co.uk, http://www.sweetandmaxwell.co.uk. **Subscr. to:** Cheriton House, North Way, Andover, Hants SP10 5BE, United Kingdom.

364.4 ITA ISSN 0391-6227
ANTIFURTO; rivista mensile di studio dei problemi antifurto e antirapina. Text in Italian. 1974. m. EUR 80 domestic; EUR 90 in Europe; EUR 105 elsewhere (effective 2004). adv. bk.rev. illus. **Document type:** *Trade.*
Published by: Insic, Via dell' Acqua Traversa 189, Rome, 00135, Italy. TEL 39-06-3313000, FAX 39-06-33111043, info@insic.it, http://www.insic.it. Ed. Laura Lavarello. Pub. Pier Roberto Pais. Adv. contact Roberto Barberini. Circ: 7,500.

APPREHENDING AND PROSECUTING DRUNK DRIVERS. see *LAW—Criminal Law*

364 IND ISSN 0003-7540
ARAKSHA*. Text in Bengali, English. 1969. bi-m. INR 10, USD 12.
Published by: Criminalistics Research Institute, c/o Indian Law Institute, Opp. Supreme Court, Bhagwandas Rd., New Delhi, 110 001, India. Ed. S K Chatterjee. Circ: 2,000.

364 DEU ISSN 0003-9225
HV6003 CODEN: ARKRAI
ARCHIV FUER KRIMINOLOGIE; unter besonderer Beruecksichtigung der gerichtlichen Physik, Chemie und Medizin. Text in German. 1897. 6/yr. EUR 236; EUR 39.50 newsstand/cover (effective 2004). adv. bk.rev. bibl.; charts; illus. index. reprints avail. **Document type:** *Journal, Academic/Scholarly.*
Formerly (until 1916): Archiv fuer Kriminal-Anthropologie und Kriminalistik
Related titles: Microfiche ed.: (from BHP).
Indexed: AC&P, BIOSIS Prev, BiolAb, CJA, ChemAb, DIP, ExcerpMed, IBR, IBZ, INI, IndMed, MEDLINE, PCI, RASB.
—BLDSC (1615.650000), CASDDS, GNLM, IE, Infotrieve, ingenta. **CCC.**
Published by: Schmidt-Roemhild Verlag, Mengstr 16, Luebeck, 23552, Germany. TEL 49-451-7031-01, FAX 49-451-7031253, eickershoff@beleke.de, http://www.schmidt-roemhild.de. Eds. Dr. Harald Schulz, Dr. Stefan Pollak. Circ: 350 (paid and controlled).

ARCHIVOS DE CRIMINOLOGIA, NEURO-PSIQUIATRIA Y DISCIPLINAS CONEXAS. see *MEDICAL SCIENCES—Psychiatry And Neurology*

364 POL ISSN 0066-6890
ARCHIWUM KRYMINOLOGII. Text in Polish; Summaries in English. 1960. irreg., latest vol.18, 1992. price varies. bk.rev. **Document type:** *Academic/Scholarly.* **Description:** Research into problems of criminology in various spheres of life in Poland and in the world.
Indexed: AC&P, IBR, IBZ, RASB.
Published by: Polska Akademia Nauk, Instytut Nauk Prawnych/Polish Academy of Sciences, Institute of Law Studies, ul Nowy Swiat 72, Warszawa, 00330, Poland. TEL 48-22-268484, FAX 48-22-267853. Ed. J Jasinski. Circ: 500.

ARCHIWUM MEDYCYNY SADOWEJ I KRIMINOLOGII. see *MEDICAL SCIENCES—Forensic Sciences*

364 USA ISSN 8755-8300
KF9625.A59
ARREST LAW BULLETIN. Text in English. 1976. m. looseleaf. USD 147 (effective 2005). Index. back issues avail. **Document type:** *Newsletter, Trade.* **Description:** Provides summaries of current cases discussing arrest procedures. Written for non-lawyer law enforcement personnel.
Related titles: Microform ed.: (from PQC); Online - full text ed.: ISSN 1544-5038.
Indexed: CJPI.
—CCC.
Published by: Quinlan Publishing Group, Marine Industrial Park, 23 Drydock Ave, 6th Fl, Boston, MA 02210-2387. TEL 617-542-0048, 800-229-2084, FAX 617-507-1079, http://www.quinlan.com. Ed. Colin Thakkar. Pub. Dennis Hofmaier.

364 USA
ARRESTS OF YOUTH (YEAR). Text in English. a. stat. **Document type:** *Government.*
Published by: U.S. Department of Justice, Office of Juvenile Justice and Delinquency Prevention, 633 Indiana Ave, N W, Washington, DC 20531. TEL 202-307-5929. **Subscr. to:** U.S. Government Printing Office, Superintendent of Documents, PO Box 371954, Pittsburgh, PA 15250-7954. TEL 202-512-1800, FAX 202-512-2250, orders@gpo.gov, http://www.access.gpo.gov.

364 USA
▼ **ARSON INVESTIGATIONS LAW BULLETIN.** Text in English. 2005. m. USD 159 (effective 2005). **Document type:** *Newsletter, Trade.* **Description:** Reports on arson cases. Targets arson inverstigators who testify in depositions or in court on arson, conspiracy to commit arson, and insurance fraud cases.
Published by: E D M Publishers, 1528 Tremont St. - Unit 2B, Duxbury, MA 02332. TEL 781-934-6660, FAX 781-934-6644, info@edmpublishers.com, http://www.edmpublishers.com/.

ARSON REPORTER; arson cases and legislation. see *LAW*

ASHWORTH: SENTENCING AND CRIMINAL JUSTICE. see *LAW—Criminal Law*

364.36 GBR ISSN 0143-8387
ATTENDANCE CENTRE NEWS. Text in English. 1979. irreg. **Document type:** *Government.*
—CCC.
Published by: Home Office, 50 Queen Anne's Gate, London, SW1 9AT, United Kingdom. TEL 071-273-3877. Ed. John Race. Circ: 4,000.

364 AUS ISSN 0004-8658
HV6001
➤ **AUSTRALIAN AND NEW ZEALAND JOURNAL OF CRIMINOLOGY.** Text in English. 1968. 3/yr. (Apr., Aug. & Dec.). AUD 208 domestic to individuals; AUD 188 in New Zealand to individuals; AUD 209 elsewhere to individuals (effective 2005). adv. bk.rev. abstr.; charts; illus.; stat. Index. back issues avail.; reprint service avail. from WSH. **Document type:** *Journal, Academic/Scholarly.*
Related titles: Online - full text ed.: (from EBSCO Publishing, Gale Group, IngentaConnect, Swets Information Services).
Indexed: ABRCLP, AC&P, ASCA, AusPAIS, CBRI, CJA, CJPI, CLI, CurCont, FamI, HRIS, ILP, INZP, LRI, PSA, SSA, SSCI, SociolAb, V&AA, e-psyche.
—BLDSC (1796.885000), IDS, IE, Infotrieve, ingenta. **CCC.**
Published by: Australian Academic Press Pty. Ltd., 32 Jeays St, Bowen Hills, QLD 4006, Australia. TEL 61-7-32571176, FAX 61-7-32525908, info@australianacademicpress.com.au, http://www.australianacademicpress.com.au/Publications/Journals/Criminology/Criminology.htm. Ed. Dr. John Pratt. Adv. contact Jenny Mouzos.

340 AUS ISSN 0159-6667
AUSTRALIAN CRIMINAL REPORTS. Text in English. 1980. (in 7 vols., 4 nos./vol.), base vol. plus updates 7/yr. AUD 4,740 (effective 2004). cum.index: vols.1-50, vols.51-75, vols. 76-90. back issues avail. **Document type:** *Trade.* **Description:** Provides a comprehensive series of reports on the criminal decisions made by the High Court, Federal Court and the supreme courts of all Australian states and territories.

Related titles: CD-ROM ed.: AUD 2,470 for practices with up to 20 practitioners (effective 2003); Online - full content ed.: AUD 2,470 for practices with up to 20 practitioners (effective 2003).
Published by: Lawbook Co. (Subsidiary of: Thomson Legal & Regulatory Ltd.), PO Box 3502, Rozelle, NSW 2039, Australia. LRA.Service@thomson.com, http://onlineecom01.thomson.com.au/thomson/Catalog.asp?EES_CMD=SI&EES_ID=100450, http://www.lawbookco.com.au/. Ed. Fiori Rinaldi.

364 AUS ISSN 0311-449X
HV7171
AUSTRALIAN INSTITUTE OF CRIMINOLOGY. ANNUAL REPORT. Text in English. a. AUD 20. **Document type:** *Corporate.*
Incorporates (1972-1996): Criminology Research Council. Annual Report (0311-4481)
Related titles: Online - full text ed.
Published by: Australian Institute of Criminology, GPO Box 2944, Canberra, ACT 2601, Australia. TEL 61-262609256, FAX 61-262609260, aicpress@aic.gov.au. R&P Merril Thompson. **Dist. in US by:** Criminal Justice Press, PO Box 249, Monsey, NY 10952.

364 AUS
HV9873
AUSTRALIAN INSTITUTE OF CRIMINOLOGY. RESEARCH AND PUBLIC POLICY. Text in English. 1996. irreg. AUD 20. **Document type:** *Academic/Scholarly.*
Formed by the merger of (1992-1996): Deaths in Custody Australia (1038-667X); And part of (1990-1992): Homicides in Australia (1038-6912)
Published by: Australian Institute of Criminology, GPO Box 2944, Canberra, ACT 2601, Australia. TEL 61-262609256, FAX 61-262609256, aicpress@aic.gov.au. R&P Merril Thompson.

363.2 AUS ISSN 0005-0024
HV7551
AUSTRALIAN POLICE JOURNAL. Text in English. 1946. q. AUD 18 in Australia & New Zealand; AUD 28 elsewhere; AUD 7 newsstand/cover (effective 2001). adv. bk.rev. illus. back issues avail. **Document type:** *Academic/Scholarly.* **Description:** Covers all aspects of law enforcement: child abuse, narcotics control, homicide and firearms.
Indexed: AC&P, CJA, ExcerpMed, RASB.
Published by: New South Wales Police Service, GPO Box 45, Sydney, NSW 2001, Australia. TEL 61-2-9339-0277, FAX 61-2-9339-5564. Ed. Phil T Peters. Adv. contact P T Peters. Circ: 23,000.

364 AUS
AUSTRALIAN POLICE WORLD. Text in English. 1965. q. AUD 0.10 per issue.
Published by: (International Police Association, Australian Section), Percival Publishing Co. Pty. Ltd., 862-870 Elizabeth St, Waterloo Dc, NSW 2017, Australia.

345.73 USA ISSN 0098-8049
KF9219.3
B A R - B R I BAR REVIEW. CRIMINAL LAW. Text in English. a. price varies. **Document type:** *Trade.*
Indexed: CurCont.
Published by: B A R - B R I Bar Review, 3280 Motor Ave, Los Angeles, CA 90034-3710. TEL 213-477-2542, http://www.barbri.com.

346 USA ISSN 0098-7611
KF1250.Z9
B A R - B R I BAR REVIEW. TORTS. Text in English. a. USD 395.
Published by: B A R - B R I Bar Review, 3280 Motor Ave, Los Angeles, CA 90034-3710. TEL 213-477-2542.

363.2 USA
B J A BULLETIN. Text in English. irreg.
Indexed: CJA.
Published by: Bureau of Justice Assistance, 810 Seventh St NW, Washington, DC 20531. TEL 202-616-6500, FAX 202-305-1367, http://www.ojp.usdoj.gov/BJA. **Subscr. to:** Bureau of Justice Assistance Clearinghouse, PO Box 6000, Rockville, MD 20849-6000. TEL 800-688-4252, http://www.ncjrs.org.

364 USA ISSN 0742-7271
B J S BULLETIN. (Bureau of Justice Statistics) Text in English. 1981. irreg. stat. back issues avail. **Document type:** *Bulletin, Government.*
Related titles: Online - full content ed.
Indexed: CJA.
Published by: U.S. Department of Justice, Bureau of Justice Statistics, 810 Seventh St, N W, 2nd Fl, Washington, DC 20531. TEL 202-307-0765, FAX 202-307-0128, 202-307-5846, askbjs@ojp.usdoj.gov, http://www.ojp.usdoj.gov/bjs/pubalp2.htm. **Orders to:** Bureau of Justice Statistics Clearinghouse, Box 179, Dept BJS C 1, Annapolis, MD 20701-0179. FAX 410-792-4358.

364 USA
B J S CRIME DATA BRIEF. (Bureau of Justice Statistics) Text in English. irreg. looseleaf. stat. back issues avail. **Document type:** *Monographic series, Government.* **Description:** Presents data on topics of broad current interest in condensed form.
Published by: U.S. Department of Justice, Bureau of Justice Statistics, 810 Seventh St, N W, 2nd Fl, Washington, DC 20531. TEL 202-307-0765, FAX 202-307-5846, askbjs@ojp.usdoj.gov, http://www.ojp.usdoj.gov/bjs/pubalp2.htm. **Orders to:** Bureau of Justice Statistics Clearinghouse, Box 179, Dept BJS C 1, Annapolis, MD 20701-0179. FAX 410-792-4358.

364 USA
B J S DISCUSSION PAPER. (Bureau of Justice Statistics) Text in English. irreg. stat. back issues avail. **Document type:** *Monographic series, Government.*
Related titles: Online - full content ed.
Published by: U.S. Department of Justice, Bureau of Justice Statistics, 810 Seventh St, N W, 2nd Fl, Washington, DC 20531. TEL 202-307-0765, FAX 202-307-0128, 202-307-5846, askbjs@ojp.usdoj.gov, http://www.ojp.usdoj.gov/bjs/pubalp2.htm. **Orders to:** Bureau of Justice Statistics Clearinghouse, Box 179, Dept BJS C 1, Annapolis, MD 20701-0179. TEL 800-732-3277.

364 USA
B J S SELECTED FINDINGS. Text in English. irreg. stat. back issues avail. **Document type:** *Government.*
Related titles: Online - full content ed.
Published by: U.S. Department of Justice, Bureau of Justice Statistics, 810 Seventh St, N W, 2nd Fl, Washington, DC 20531. TEL 202-307-0765, FAX 202-307-0128, askbjs@ojp.usdoj.gov, http://www.ojp.usdoj.gov/bjs/pubalp2.htm. **Orders to:** Bureau of Justice Statistics Clearinghouse, Box 179, Dept BJS C 1, Annapolis, MD 20701-0179. FAX 410-792-4358.

364 USA
B J S SPECIAL REPORT. Text in English. irreg. stat. back issues avail. **Document type:** *Government.*
Related titles: Microfiche ed.; Online - full content ed.
Published by: U.S. Department of Justice, Bureau of Justice Statistics, 810 Seventh St, N W, 2nd Fl, Washington, DC 20531. TEL 202-307-0765, FAX 202-307-0128, 202-307-5846, askbjs@ojp.usdoj.gov, http://www.ojp.usdoj.gov/bjs. Circ: 17,000. **Orders to:** Bureau of Justice Statistics Clearinghouse, Box 179, Dept BJS C 1, Annapolis, MD 20701-0179. TEL 800-732-3277, FAX 410-792-4358.

364.4 NLD ISSN 0005-4259
BALANS; personeelsblad van de Directie Delinquentenzorg en Jeugdinrichtingen. Text in Dutch. 1970. m. adv. bk.rev. charts; illus.
Published by: Ministerie van Justitie, Redactie Balans, Terminal Noord Kamer 452, Postbus 20301, The Hague, 2500 EH, Netherlands. TEL 31-70-3702613. Circ: 5,400.

363.2 USA
BARS AND STRIPES. Text in English. 1965. m. USD 10. adv. **Document type:** *Newsletter.*
Published by: Detroit Police Lieutenants & Sergeants Association, 28 W. Adams Ave., # 700, Detroit, MI 48226-1609. Ed. Cynthia Falska. Circ: 2,900 (controlled).

365 CAN ISSN 1493-7662
BASIC FACTS ABOUT FEDERAL CORRECTIONS. Text in English. 1999. a.
Published by: Correctional Service of Canada/Service Correctionnel Canada, 340 Laurier Ave W, Ottawa, ON K1A 0P9, Canada. TEL 613-992-5891, FAX 613-943-1630, http://www.csc-scc.gc.ca.

364 345 USA
BASIC SECURITY INVESTIGATION. Text in English. 1997. irreg., latest 1997. USD 14.95 (effective 2000). **Description:** Presents an overview of security measures in the workplace. Includes sections on case initiation, the role of the undercover officer, surveillance, infiltration, interviewing techniques, evidence, internal controls, and document and report writing.
Published by: Gould Publications, Inc. (Subsidiary of: LexisNexis), 1333 North US Hwy 17-92, Longwood, FL 32750-3724. TEL 800-717-7917, info@gouldlaw.com, http://www.gouldlaw.com.

351.74 DEU ISSN 0723-3086
DIE BAYERISCHE POLIZEI. Text in German. 195?. q. adv. **Document type:** *Magazine, Trade.*
Published by: Helmut Preussler Verlag, Dagmarstr 8, Nuernberg, 90482, Germany. TEL 49-911-954780, FAX 49-911-542486, preussler-verlag@t-online.de, http://www.preussler-verlag.de. adv.: B&W page EUR 1,650, color page EUR 3,000; trim 185 x 265. Circ: 6,000 (controlled).

364 DEU
BAYERNS POLIZEI. Text in German. 1990. 5/yr. bk.rev. **Document type:** *Bulletin.*
Published by: Bayerisches Staatsministerium des Innern, Odeonsplatz 3, Munich, 80524, Germany. TEL 49-89-21922644, FAX 49-89-21922870, stmi.ic5@polizei.bayern.de. Ed. Wolfgang Schlee.

BEZBEDNOST. see *LAW—Criminal Law*

BIZNES I KRIMINAL. see *BUSINESS AND ECONOMICS*

364 305.896 USA
BLACKS IN LAW ENFORCEMENT; a living tribute to Black history. Text in English. 1986. irreg. USD 6.50 (effective 2005). adv. back issues avail. **Document type:** *Directory, Bibliography.* **Description:** Seeks to document, acknowledge, and publish the many important contributions Black officers have made to law enforcement.
Formerly: Top Blacks in Law Enforcement
Published by: Blacks in Law Enforcement, Inc, 256 E McLemore Ave, Memphis, TN 38106-2833. TEL 901-774-1118, 800-762-8676, FAX 901-774-1139. Ed. Samantha Macklin. Pub., R&P Clyde R Venson. Circ: 25,000.

363.2 CAN ISSN 0847-8538
BLUE LINE MAGAZINE. Text in English. 1988. m. CND 25 domestic; CND 50 foreign. adv. bk.rev. **Document type:** *Trade.* **Description:** Covers law enforcement throughout Canada, featuring case law, news, feature articles, and product information.
Address: 4981 Hwy 7 E, Unit 12A, 254, Markham, ON L3R 1N1, Canada. TEL 905-640-3048, FAX 905-640-7547, http://www.blueline.ca. Ed., Pub. Morley S Lymburner. Adv. contact Mary Lymburner. Circ: 10,000.

363.2 GBR
BLUEPRINT (WINFRITH). Text in English. 1974. 4/yr. free. bk.rev. **Document type:** *Government.*
Published by: Dorset Police, Force Headquarters, Dorset Police, Winfrith Newburgh, Dorchester, DT2 8DZ, United Kingdom. FAX 44-1929-463755. Ed., R&P Mike Maber. Circ: 4,000 (controlled).

BOLLETTINO PER LE FARMACODIPENDENZE E L'ALCOOLISMO. see *DRUG ABUSE AND ALCOHOLISM*

351.74 BWA ISSN 0068-046X
BOTSWANA. COMMISSIONER OF THE POLICE. ANNUAL REPORT. Text in English. 1885. a. BWP 10. **Document type:** *Government.*
Published by: Commissioner of the Police, c/o Assistant Commissioner, Police Headquarters, Gaborone, Botswana. Circ: 250.

364 GBR ISSN 1475-0279
➤ **BRITISH JOURNAL OF COMMUNITY JUSTICE.** Text in English. 2002 (Spring). 3/yr. **Document type:** *Journal, Academic/Scholarly.*
Indexed: CJA.
—BLDSC (2307.275000), IE, ingenta.
Published by: (De Montfort University, Sheffield Hallam University), Sheffield Hallam University Press, c/o Mrs. Monica Moseley, Pub., Sheffield Hallam University Press, Learning Centre, Sheffield, S Yorks S1 1WB, United Kingdom. TEL 44-114-2254702, FAX 44-114-2254478, bjcj@psc-uk.com, m.mosely@shu.ac.uk, http://www.shu.ac.uk/shupress/. Eds. Dr. Brian Williams, Paul Senior.

364 GBR ISSN 0007-0955
HV6001 CODEN: BJCDAR
➤ **THE BRITISH JOURNAL OF CRIMINOLOGY;** delinquency and deviant social behaviour. Text in English. 1950. bi-m. GBP 260, USD 455, EUR 390 to institutions; GBP 274, USD 480, EUR 411 combined subscription to institutions print & online eds. (effective 2006). adv. bk.rev. abstr.; bibl.; illus. index. 212 p./no.; back issues avail.; reprint service avail. from WSH,PSC. **Document type:** *Journal, Academic/Scholarly.* **Description:** Focuses on British and international criminology, including social deviance.
Formerly (until 1960): British Journal of Delinquency (0524-6369)
Related titles: Microform ed.; Online - full text ed.: ISSN 1464-3529. 1998. GBP 247, USD 432, EUR 371 to institutions (effective 2006) (from Chadwyck-Healey Inc., EBSCO Publishing, Florida Center for Library Automation, Gale Group, HighWire Press, IngentaConnect, Northern Light Technology, Inc., O C L C Online Computer Library Center, Inc., Oxford University Press Online Journals, ProQuest Information & Learning, R M I T Publishing, Swets Information Services).
Indexed: AC&P, AMHA, ASCA, ASSIA, AddicA, AgeL, BrEdI, BrHumI, CJA, CJPI, CLI, CurCont, ELJI, ERA, ESPM, FamI, IBR, IBSS, ILP, IMFL, LJI, LRI, MEA, MEA&I, PAIS, PCI, PSA, PsycInfo, PsycholAb, RASB, RiskAb, SOPODA, SSA, SSCI, SSI, SWA, SociolAb, V&AA, e-psyche.
—BLDSC (2307.300000), IDS, IE, Infotrieve, ingenta. **CCC.**
Published by: (Institute for the Study and Treatment of Delinquency), Oxford University Press, Great Clarendon St, Oxford, OX2 6DP, United Kingdom. TEL 44-1865-556767, FAX 44-1865-556646, jnl.orders@oup.co.uk, http://bjc.oxfordjournals.org/, http://www.oxfordjournals.org/. Ed. Geoffrey Pearson. Pub. Martin Green. R&P Fiona Bennett. Adv. contact Helen Pearson. B&W page GBP 335, B&W page USD 545; 140 x 210. Circ: 2,000.

C

▼ new title ➤ refereed ✶ unverified ♦ full entry avail.

365 364.4 SWE ISSN 0283-3352
BROTTSFOEREBYGGANDE RAADETS TIDSKRIFT APROPAA.
Variant title: Apropaa. Text in Swedish. 1975. 5/yr. free.
(until 1986): B R Aa - Apropaa (0346-9360)
Related titles: Online - full text ed.
Published by: Brottsfoerebyggande Raadet/National Council for Crime Prevention, Tegnergatan 23, PO Box 1386, Stockholm, 11193, Sweden. TEL 46-08-401 87 00, http://www.bra.se/extra/apropa/. Ed. Magnus Vaesterbo TEL 46-08-401 87 62. Pub. Gunilla Wiklund.

343.8 SWE ISSN 1101-2331
BROTTSFOEREBYGGANDE RAADET. B R AA-REPORT. Text in English. 1975. irreg.
Former titles (until 1986): National Council for Crime Prevention. Report (0282-6585); (until 1984): National Swedish Council for Crime Prevention. Report (0346-8224)
Published by: Brottsfoerebyggande Raadet/National Council for Crime Prevention, Tegnergatan 23, PO Box 1386, Stockholm, 11193, Sweden.

363.2 DEU ISSN 0932-5409
BUERGERRECHTE & POLIZEI. Text in German; Summaries in English. 1978. 3/yr. EUR 18.50 to individuals; EUR 32.50 to institutions; EUR 7.20 newsstand/cover (effective 2005). adv. bk.rev. index. 110 p./no. 1 cols./p.; back issues avail. **Document type:** *Journal, Academic/Scholarly.* **Description:** Review of the structure, function and daily work of Germany's police and intelligence agencies.
Formerly (until 1983): C I L I P. Deutsche Ausgabe (0172-1895)
Related titles: Microfiche ed.; Online - full text ed.
Indexed: AC&P, CJA, IBR, IBZ.
Published by: Verlag C I L I P, c/o FU Berlin, Malteserstr 74-100, Berlin, 12249, Germany. TEL 49-30-83870462, FAX 49-30-7751073, info@cilip.de, http://www.cilip.de/infos/cilip.htm. Ed., Adv. contact Heiner Busch. Circ: 1,000.

364 DEU ISSN 1439-3662
BUNDESPOLIZEI. Text in German. 1979. 10/yr. EUR 0.80 newsstand/cover (effective 2005). adv. **Document type:** *Magazine, Trade.*
Published by: (Bundesgrenzschutz-Verband e.V.), D P U Verlag und Sozialwerk GmbH, Seelower Str 17, Berlin, 10439, Germany. TEL 49-30-44678721, FAX 49-30-44714320, bundespolizei@dorias.de, http://www.bundespolizeigewerkschaft.de. Ed., Adv. contact Baerbel Dorias. B&W page EUR 4,830, color page EUR 5,350; trim 280 x 440. Circ: 15,000.

BUSINESS ESPIONAGE REPORT; controls and countermeasures training for managers. see *BUSINESS AND ECONOMICS—International Commerce*

332.1 GBR
BUTTERWORTHS MONEY LAUNDERING LAW. Text in English. 1998. s-a. looseleaf. GBP 195 (effective 2000). back issues avail. **Document type:** *Trade.* **Description:** Contains everything practitioners need on suspicious transactions, analysis of the law, guidance as to procedure of relevant materials. Includes a compliance manual.
Published by: Butterworths Tolley (Subsidiary of: LexisNexis UK (Scottish Office)), Halsbury House, 35 Chancery Ln, London, Mddx WC2A 1EL, United Kingdom. TEL 44-20-74002500, FAX 44-20-74002583, http://www.butterworths.co.uk/. Ed. Chris Howard.

364 ITA ISSN 0223-582X
CAHIERS DE DEFENSE SOCIALE. Text in French. 1955. a. EUR 23 membership (effective 2003).
Formerly (until 1973): Societe Internationale de Defense Sociale. Bulletin (1250-8810)
Indexed: CJA.
Published by: Societe Internationale de Defense Sociale pour une Politique Criminelle Humaniste/International Society of Social Defence and Humane Criminal Policy, c/o Centro Nazionale di Prevenzione e Difesa Sociale, Palazzo Comunale delle Scienze Sociali, e, Piazza Castello, Milan, 20121, Italy. TEL 39-02-86460714, FAX 39-02-72008431, http://www.defensesociale.org/home_f.htm.

364 USA ISSN 0194-1682
CALIFORNIA CORRECTIONAL NEWS. Text in English. 1946. 6/yr. USD 18 to non-members; USD 15 to libraries. adv. bk.rev. **Document type:** *Newsletter.* **Description:** Examines issues relating to the penal system in California.
Indexed: CalPI.
Published by: California Probation, Parole and Correctional Association, 1455 Response Rd., Ste. 190, Sacramento, CA 95815-5266. http://www.cppca.org/cn.html, cppca@ns.net, http://www.cppca.org. Ed., R&P Romel White. Adv. contact Renee Bitton. Circ: 2,900.

CALIFORNIA CRIMINAL DEFENSE PRACTICE. see *LAW—Criminal Law*

CALIFORNIA CRIMINAL DEFENSE PRACTICE REPORTER. see *LAW—Criminal Law*

364 USA ISSN 0890-8400
CALIFORNIA DISTRICT ATTORNEYS ASSOCIATION. CASE DIGEST. Text in English. s-m. USD 150 (effective 2000). index. back issues avail. **Description:** Summarizes California case decisions.
Published by: California District Attorneys Association, 731 K St, Third Fl, Sacramento, CA 95814-3402. TEL 916-443-2017, FAX 916-443-0540, cdaa@ix.netcom.com, general@cdaa.org. Ed. Sarah N Saria. R&P Cat Karnezis. Circ: 2,600.

THE CALIFORNIA PRISONER. see *LAW—Constitutional Law*

364.4 USA ISSN 0739-0394
HV8290
CAMPUS LAW ENFORCEMENT JOURNAL; professional publication for campus law enforcement administrators, campus safety, security adm. Text in English. 1970. bi-m. USD 30 in North America; USD 35 foreign (effective 2003). adv. bk.rev. illus. 40 p./no.; back issues avail.; reprint service avail. from PQC. **Document type:** *Journal, Trade.*
Related titles: Microform ed.: (from PQC).
Indexed: CJPI.
Published by: International Association of Campus Law Enforcement Administrators, 342 N Main St, West Hartford, CT 06117-2507. TEL 860-586-7517, FAX 860-586-7550, kbreseman@iaclea.org, http://www.iaclea.org/pubs/index.htm#subscription. Ed. Peter J Berry. R&Ps, Adv. contacts Karen E Breseman TEL 860-586-7517, Lisa Johnson. Circ: 1,700.

354.71 CAN ISSN 0383-4379
HV7315
CANADA. CORRECTIONAL INVESTIGATOR. ANNUAL REPORT. Text in English, French. 1974. a. illus.
Published by: (Canada. Correctional Investigator), Supply and Services Canada, Printing and Publishing, 270 Albert St, Ottawa, ON K1A 0S9, Canada. TEL 613-993-6425. Circ: 2,500.

364 365 CAN ISSN 1707-7753
HV6001
➤ **CANADIAN JOURNAL OF CRIMINOLOGY AND CRIMINAL JUSTICE/REVUE CANADIENNE DE CRIMINOLOGIE A JUSTICE PENALE.** Text in English, French. 1958. q. CND 55 domestic to individuals; CND 70 foreign to individuals; CND 107 domestic to institutions; CND 122 foreign to institutions (effective 2005). adv. bk.rev. charts; illus. index, cum.index. reprint service avail. from PQC. **Document type:** *Journal, Academic/Scholarly.*
Former titles (until 2003, vol.45): Canadian Journal of Criminology (0704-9722); (until vol.19): Canadian Journal of Criminology and Corrections (0315-5390); (until vol.13): Canadian Journal of Corrections (0008-4069)
Related titles: Microform ed.: (from PQC); Online - full text ed.: (from EBSCO Publishing, Florida Center for Library Automation, Gale Group, Northern Light Technology, Inc., O C L C Online Computer Library Center, Inc., ProQuest Information & Learning).
Indexed: AC&P, ASCA, ASSIA, AmH&L, CBCARef, CBPI, CJA, CJPI, CLI, CPerI, CurCont, EAA, ESPM, HRA, HistAb, IBSS, ICLPL, LRI, PRA, PdeR, PsycInfo, PsycholAb, RASB, RiskAb, SFSA, SPAA, SRRA, SSCI, SSI, SUSA, SWR&A, SociolAb, V&AA, e-psyche.
—BLDSC (3031.131000), IDS, IE, Infotrieve, ingenta. **CCC.**
Published by: Canadian Criminal Justice Association/Association Canadienne de Justice Penale, 1750, Courtwood Crescent, Ste 308, Ottawa, ON K2C 2B5, Canada. TEL 613-725-3715, FAX 613-725-3720, ccja@bellnet.ca, http://www.ccja-acjp.ca/en/cjc.html. Ed. M Peter Carrington. adv.: page USD 325. Circ: 1,300. **Subscr. to:** University of Toronto Press, Journals Division, 5201 Dufferin St, Toronto, ON M3H 5T8, Canada. TEL 416-667-7810, FAX 416-667-7881, journals@utpress.utoronto.ca, http://www.utpjournals.com.

363.2 CAN ISSN 1709-8769
▼ ➤ **CANADIAN JOURNAL OF POLICE AND SECURITY SERVICES.** Text in English. 2003. q. CND 65 domestic to individuals; CND 90 foreign to individuals; CND 200 domestic to institutions; CND 250 foreign to institutions (effective 2005). **Document type:** *Journal, Academic/Scholarly.* **Description:** Presents reports of original empirical research, theoretical contributions, development and testing of innovative programs and practices, and critical reviews of literature or theory on central topics related to policing and security services.
—BLDSC (3034.530000).
Published by: Meritus Solutions, 2341 McIntyre St, Regina, SK S4P 2S3, Canada. TEL 306-721-0620, FAX 306-721-1569, cjpss@meritussolutions.ca, info@meritussolutions.ca, http://www.police-securityjournal.ca.

364 CAN ISSN 0713-4517
CANADIAN POLICE CHIEF NEWSLETTER. Text in English; Text occasionally in French. 1930. q. CND 53.50 domestic; CND 60 in United States; CND 70 elsewhere (effective 1999). adv. bk.rev. back issues avail. **Document type:** *Newsletter.*
Formerly (until 1982): Canadian Police Chief (0315-2464)
Indexed: CJA.
Published by: Canadian Association of Chiefs of Police, 130 Albert St, Ste 1710, Ottawa, ON K1P 5G4, Canada. TEL 613-233-1106, FAX 613-233-6960. Ed. Bryan McConnell. adv.: B&W page CND 500; trim 11 x 8.5. Circ: 1,300.

363.2 CAN ISSN 1181-6244
CANADIAN POLICE RESEARCH CENTRE. ANNUAL REPORT. Text in English, French. 197?. a. back issues avail.
Former titles (until 1989): Canadian Program of Science and Technology in Support of Law Enforcement, Annual Report (0828-3842); (until 1984): Program of Science and Technology in Support of Law Enforcement in Canada (0839-6183)
Related titles: Online - full text ed.: ISSN 1700-6929.
Published by: Canadian Police Research Centre, PO Box 8885, Ottawa, ON K1G 3M8, Canada. TEL 613-998-6343, FAX 613-952-0156, http://www.cprc.org/annualreport/, htttp://www.cprc.org/.

CANADIAN SOCIETY OF FORENSIC SCIENCE JOURNAL/SOCIETE CANADIENNE DES SCIENCES JUDICIAIRES JOURNAL. see *LAW*

CANINE COURIER. see *PETS*

365 USA ISSN 0198-9693
K3 CODEN: CULRDZ
CAPITAL UNIVERSITY LAW REVIEW. Text in English. 1972. q. USD 36; USD 12 newsstand/cover (effective 2005). adv. bk.rev. reprint service avail. from WSH. **Document type:** *Journal, Academic/Scholarly.* **Description:** A scholarly compilation of legal articles written by jurists, distinguished scholars and prominent members of the law profession.
Related titles: Microfiche ed.: (from WSH); Microform ed.: (from WSH); Online - full text ed.: (from H.W. Wilson, LexisNexis, O C L C Online Computer Library Center, Inc., Thomson West).
Indexed: CJA, CLI, FamI, ILP, LRI, LegCont, MAB.
—BLDSC (3050.669500), IE, ingenta. **CCC.**
Published by: Capital University, Law School, 303 E Broad St, Columbus, OH 43215. TEL 614-236-6500, FAX 614-236-6972, https://culsnet.law.capital.edu/LawReview/, http://www.law.capital.edu/. R&P Matthew T Schaeffer. Adv. contact Bill Nicolozakes. Circ: 1,200.

364 343 VEN ISSN 0798-9598
➤ **CAPITULO CRIMINOLOGICO.** Text in Spanish; Abstracts in English, Spanish. 1973. 4/yr. VEB 18,000 domestic; USD 70 in Latin America; USD 80 elsewhere (effective 2001). adv. bk.rev. **Document type:** *Academic/Scholarly.* **Description:** Covers criminology, criminal policy, social control, law enforcement, juridical sociology, social reaction, violence, human rights, and criminal psychology.
Published by: Universidad del Zulia, Instituto de Criminologia, Apdo 526, Maracaibo, Venezuela. TEL 58-61-596663, FAX 58-61-596666, jparraga@luz.ve. Ed. Jesus Parraga. Circ: 1,000.

364 302 TTO ISSN 1025-5591
HV6001
➤ **CARIBBEAN JOURNAL OF CRIMINOLOGY & SOCIAL PSYCHOLOGY.** Text in English. 1996. s-a. (Jan., July). TTD 130 domestic to individuals; USD 25 foreign to individuals; TTD 170 domestic to institutions; USD 30 foreign to institutions; TTD 70 newsstand/cover domestic to individuals; USD 15 newsstand/cover foreign to individuals; TTD 90 newsstand/cover domestic to institutions; USD 20 newsstand/cover foreign to institutions (effective 2000). adv. bk.rev. **Document type:** *Academic/Scholarly.* **Description:** Encourages cross-cultural, multidisciplinary research in this area of criminology. Makes policy recommendations both within the Caribbean and worldwide.
Indexed: CJA, PAIS, PsycInfo, PsycholAb, SSA, SociolAb, e-psyche.
—BLDSC (3053.029500).
Published by: University of the West Indies, Centre for Criminology & Criminal Justice, St. Augustine Campus, St. Augustine, Trinidad & Tobago. TEL 868-662-2002 ext 3352, FAX 868-645-1020, crimrd@trinidad.net, http://web.carib-link.net/soc-sci/centres/journal.htm. Ed. Ramesh Deosaran. Circ: 121 (paid). **Dist. by:** William W Gaunt & Sons Inc, Gaunt Bldg.m 3011 Gulf Dr, Holmes Beach, FL 34217-2199. TEL 800-942-8683, 941-778-5211, 941-778-5252.

➤ **CASE COMMENTARIES AND BRIEFS.** see *LAW*

365 USA
CATALYST (WASHINGTON); for community crime and drug prevention. Text in English. 1980. 10/yr. free. **Document type:** *Newsletter.* **Description:** News and resources for community anti-crime initiatives.
Related titles: Online - full text ed.
Published by: National Crime Prevention Council, 1000 Connecticut Ave N W, 13th Fl, Washington, DC 20036. TEL 202-466-6272, FAX 202-296-1356, http://www.ncpc.org. Ed. Judy Kirby. R&P Jean O'Neil. Circ: 16,000 (controlled).

THE CHAMPION. see *LAW—Criminal Law*

CHARTERED INSTITUTE OF PUBLIC FINANCE AND ACCOUNTANCY. ADMINISTRATION OF JUSTICE. ESTIMATES & ACTUALS. see *CRIMINOLOGY AND LAW ENFORCEMENT—Abstracting, Bibliographies, Statistics*

363.2 USA ISSN 0889-9207
CHIEF OF POLICE. Text in English. 1986. bi-m. USD 18 (effective 2000). adv. **Document type:** *Trade.*
Formerly: Police Command

C

Published by: National Association of Chiefs of Police, 6350 Horizon Dr., Titusville, FL 32780-8002. TEL 305-573-0070, FAX 305-573-9819, policeinfo@aphf.org. Ed., R&P Jim Gordon. Adv. contact Joe Kirby. Circ: 22,500.

364   362.7   GBR

CHILD ABUSE. Text in English. a., latest 2003, 3rd Ed. GBP 45 per issue (effective Mar. 2003). **Document type:** *Academic/Scholarly.* **Description:** Sets out the procedures for using the range of civil and criminal proceedings available for protecting children and prosecuting their abusers.
  Published by: Jordan Publishing Ltd., 21 St Thomas St, Bristol, BS1 6JS, United Kingdom. TEL 44-117-9230600, FAX 44-117-9250486, andy_delderfield@jordanpublishing.co.uk, http://www.jordanpublishing.co.uk. Eds. Christina Lyon, Peter de Cruz.

CHILDREN'S COURT OF NEW SOUTH WALES INFORMATION BULLETIN. see *LAW—Criminal Law*

LA CHRONIQUE D'AMNESTY INTERNATIONAL. see *POLITICAL SCIENCE—International Relations*

364.6   CRI

CIENCIAS PENALES. Text in Spanish. 1989. m.?.
  Published by: Asociacion de Ciencias Penales de Costa Rica, c/o Corte Suprema de Justicia, San Jose, 4-1003, Costa Rica.

363.2   USA   ISSN 0091-8806
HV7586

CINCINNATI. DIVISION OF POLICE. ANNUAL REPORT. Key Title: Annual Report of the Division of Police (Cincinnati). Text in English. 1929. a. free. stat. **Description:** Reports of the division's organizational structure, budget, crime statistics and brief historical information.
  Published by: (Cincinnati. Records Section), Division of Police, Department of Safety, 310 Ezzard Charles Dr, Cincinnati, OH 45214. TEL 513-352-3519, FAX 513-352-1422. Circ: 2,000.

CIVIL R I C O LITIGATION REPORTER; the national journal of record of litigation brought under the Federal Racketeer Influenced Corrupt Organizations Act. see *LAW—Civil Law*

CLEARWAY; traffic magazine of the metropolitan police. see *TRANSPORTATION—Roads And Traffic*

365.6   USA

COALITION FOR PRISONERS' RIGHTS NEWSLETTER. Text in English. 1976. m. USD 12 to individuals; USD 25 to institutions; free to prisoners (effective 2002). stat. back issues avail. **Document type:** *Newsletter, Consumer.* **Description:** Discusses politics and prison conditions, including prison and death penalty abolition issues, resources for prisoners, and commentary and analysis from prisoners.
  Published by: Coalition for Prisoners' Rights, PO Box 1911, Santa Fe, NM 87504-1911. TEL 505-982-9520, FAX 505-982-9520. Ed., Pub., R&P Mara Taub. Circ: 7,000 (paid and controlled).

364.1   314   GBR   ISSN 0958-8973

COMMENTARY ON NORTHERN IRELAND CRIME STATISTICS. Text in English. 1986. irreg.
—BLDSC (3334.360000).
  Published by: H.M.S.O. (N. Ireland), 80 Chichester St, Belfast, Co Antrim BT1 4JY, United Kingdom.

364.4   GBR   ISSN 1012-2710
HV6652

COMMERCIAL CRIME INTERNATIONAL. Text in English. 1983. m. GBP 95, USD 160 (effective 2001). bk.rev. back issues avail. **Document type:** *Newsletter, Trade.* **Description:** Directed to senior executives, risk managers, insurance managers, security directors and all who are concerned with commercial crime and fraud prevention.
  Former titles: International Cargo Crime Prevention (0266-3988); Business and Crime: Cargoes
  Related titles: Online - full content ed.
—CCC.
  Published by: Commercial Crime Services, Maritime House, 1 Linton Rd, Barking, Essex IG11 8HG, United Kingdom. TEL 44-208-591-3000, FAX 44-208-594-2833, TELEX 8956492 IMBLDN G, ccs@icc-ccs.org, http://www.icc-ccs.org. Ed. Andy Holder. Circ: 1,100 (paid and controlled).

363.2   IRL   ISSN 1393-0974

COMMUNIQUE (DUBLIN). Variant title: An Garda Siochana Management Journal. Text in English. 1994. q.
  Related titles: Online - full text ed.
  Published by: An Garda Siochana/Ireland's National Police Service, Garda Headquarters, Phoenix Park, Dublin, Ireland. http://www.irlgov.ie/garda/angarda/pub/communiquedec2001.pdf.

364.4   USA   ISSN 1072-5415
KF9728.A15

COMMUNITY CORRECTIONS REPORT; on law and corrections practice. Text in English. 1993. bi-m. USD 169.95 (effective 2004). **Document type:** *Newsletter.* **Description:** Provides practical guidance to innovative alternatives to incarceration; also includes latest legal developments in probation, parole, and community-based treatment of offenders.
  Indexed: CJPI.
  Published by: Civic Research Insitute, 4490 US Route 27, PO Box 585, Kingston, NJ 08528. TEL 609-683-4450, FAX 609-683-7291, order@civicresearchinstitute.com, http://www.civicresearchinstitute.com. Ed. Todd Clear.

COMMUNITY MENTAL HEALTH REPORT. see *SOCIAL SERVICES AND WELFARE*

364   USA   ISSN 1059-6569

COMPILER. Text in English. 1979. q. free. bk.rev. stat. back issues avail. **Document type:** *Newsletter.* **Description:** Presents criminal justice research and information issues.
  Published by: Illinois Criminal Justice Information Authority, 120 S Riverside Plaza, Rm 1016, Chicago, IL 60606-3997. TEL 312-793-8550, FAX 312-793-8422, ddighton@icjia.state.il.us, http://www.cjia.state.il.us. Ed., R&P Daniel Dighton. Circ: 6,000 (controlled).

COMPOSITE ART MANUAL. see *MEDICAL SCIENCES—Forensic Sciences*

364.143   USA   ISSN 1550-7866

▼ **CONCEALED CARRY MAGAZINE;** information & support for those who carry concealed weapons. Text in English. 2004. 6/yr. USD 39.97 (effective 2004). **Document type:** *Monographic series, Consumer.*
  Published by: Delta Media LLC, 4466 Hwy P Ste 204, Jackson, WI 53037. TEL 262-677-8877, http://www.concealedcarrymag.com. Ed. Timothy J. Schmidt.

364   USA   ISSN 1065-9455

➤ **CONFIDENTIAL A-I-R LETTER.** Text in English. 1993. irreg. (approx 7/yr.). USD 108 (effective 1996). bk.rev. **Document type:** *Newsletter, Academic/Scholarly.* **Description:** Presents specialist research analysis and comment on terrorism and untoward events in aviation.
  Published by: Air Incident Research, PO Box 4745, East Lansing, MI 48826. TEL 517-336-9375, FAX 517-336-9375. Ed. Michael Morris. Pub. Maureen MacLaughlin. Circ: 120 (paid).

364   USA   ISSN 0090-2756
HV7256

CONNECTICUT. DEPARTMENT OF CORRECTION. PUBLICATIONS✱. Text in English. 1970. irreg. stat.
  Media: Duplicated (not offset).
  Published by: Department of Corrections, Research Section, 24 Wolcott Hill Rd, Wethersfield, CT 06109-1152. TEL 203-566-5710. Ed. James Harris. Circ: 200 (controlled).

364   USA

CONNECTICUT LAW ENFORCEMENT HANDBOOK. Text in English. 1988. a. USD 7.95 (effective 2000). **Document type:** *Trade.* **Description:** Contains US. cases and Constitutional Crim. Pro. subjects. Also contains statutes condensed into a series of elements covering Title 14 - Motor Vehicles; Title 15 - Navigations and Aeronautics; Title 16 - Public Service Companies; Title 16a - Planning and Energy Policy; Title 21a - Consumer Protection; Title 22a - Environmental Protection; Title 29 - Public Safety and State Police; Title 46a - Human rights; Title 53 - Crimes; and Title 53a - Penal Code. Also includes Connecticut Motor Vehicles and Traffic Stop Guidelines, a Glossary and a Directory.
  Published by: Gould Publications, Inc. (Subsidiary of: LexisNexis), 1333 North US Hwy 17-92, Longwood, FL 32750-3724. TEL 407-695-9500, 800-717-7917, FAX 407-695-2906, info@gouldlaw.com, http://www.gouldlaw.com.

363.2   GBR   ISSN 0010-6607
HV7551

CONSTABULARY GAZETTE; Ulster police magazine. Text in English. 1933. m. GBP 6. adv. bk.rev.; film rev. illus. **Document type:** *Consumer.*
  Published by: Howard Publications, 39 Boucher Rd, Belfast, Co Antrim, N Ireland BT12 6UT, United Kingdom. Ed. R Catterson. Circ: (controlled).

364   GBR

CONSTABULARY MAGAZINE. Text in English. 1979. m. GBP 29.95 worldwide (effective 2001). adv. bk.rev.; play rev.; film rev.; software rev.; video rev.; Website rev. **Document type:** *Magazine, Trade.* **Description:** Covers police news, political interviews, police technology, training, motoring (police and domestic), travel, leisure sport, celebrity interviews, and recruitment.
  Published by: National Press Publishers, Peel House, 5 Balfour Rd, Weybridge, Surrey KT13 8HE, United Kingdom. TEL 44-1932-859155, FAX 44-1932-859661, constabmag@aol.com. Eds. Chris Locke, Maureene Morgan. Pub. Chris Locke. Adv. contact Gaynor Garton. Circ: 76,000.

363.2   DEU

CONTACT; Gewerkschaft der Polizei. Text in German. q. EUR 1.30 newsstand/cover (effective 2004). adv. **Document type:** *Magazine, Trade.*
  Published by: Verlag Deutsche Polizeiliteratur GmbH, Forststr 3A, Hilden, 40721, Germany. TEL 49-211-71040, FAX 49-211-7104174, vdp.buchvertrieb@vdpolizei.de, http://www.vdpolizei.de. Ed. Sascha Goeritz. Adv. contact Michael Schwarz.

CONTEMPORARY CRIMINAL PROCEDURE; court decisions for law enforcement officers. see *LAW—Criminal Law*

364   USA

CONTEMPORARY ISSUES IN CRIME AND JUSTICE. Text in English. irreg., latest 2004. price varies. **Document type:** *Monographic series.* **Description:** Provides perspectives on crime and justice, controversies in the operation of the criminal justice system, and analysis of important questions in criminal justice.
  Indexed: CJA.
  Published by: Wadsworth Publishing Co., 10 Davis Dr, Belmont, CA 94002. TEL 650-595-2350, FAX 650-637-7544, http://www.wadsworth.com. Ed. Todd Clear.

364   USA   ISSN 0732-4464

CONTRIBUTIONS IN CRIMINOLOGY AND PENOLOGY. Text in English. 1983. irreg., latest vol.55, 2003. price varies. **Document type:** *Monographic series, Academic/Scholarly.* —BLDSC (3458.295500), IE, ingenta.
  Published by: Greenwood Publishing Group Inc. (Subsidiary of: Harcourt International), 88 Post Rd W, PO Box 5007, Westport, CT 06881. TEL 203-226-3571, FAX 203-226-1502, webmaster@greenwood.com, http://www.greenwood.com.

CONTROLLED SUBSTANCES REGULATION. see *DRUG ABUSE AND ALCOHOLISM*

COPSNKIDS CHRONICLES. see *CHILDREN AND YOUTH—For*

CORHEALTH. see *MEDICAL SCIENCES*

▼ **CORHEALTH JOURNAL.** see *MEDICAL SCIENCES*

CORPORATE COUNSEL'S GUIDE TO WHITE-COLLAR CRIME. see *LAW—Corporate Law*

365   USA

CORRECTIONAL & OSBORNE ASSOCIATIONS NEWSLETTER. Text in English. 1966-197?; resumed 1984. q. free. bk.rev. bibl.; illus. **Document type:** *Newsletter.*
  Supersedes: Gateway Alliance Newsletter; Which was formerly (until Mar. 1993): Correctional Association of New York. News Bulletin; Correctional Association of New York. Newsletter
  Published by: Correctional Association of New York, 135 E 15th St, New York, NY 10003. TEL 212-254-5700, FAX 212-473-2807. Ed., R&P Ilene S Wittner TEL 212-673-6633. Circ: 5,500. **Co-sponsor:** Osborne Association.

CORRECTIONAL FOODSERVICE MAGAZINE. see *FOOD AND FOOD INDUSTRIES*

(YEAR) CORRECTIONAL FOODSERVICE WHO'S WHO. see *FOOD AND FOOD INDUSTRIES*

364.6   610   USA   ISSN 1526-9450
HV8843

CORRECTIONAL HEALTH CARE REPORT. Text in English. bi-m. USD 182.95 domestic; USD 212.95 foreign (effective 2004). **Document type:** *Newsletter.* **Description:** A guide to the special challenges of providing health care services in a correctional setting.
  Published by: Civic Research Insitute, 4490 US Route 27, PO Box 585, Kingston, NJ 08528. TEL 609-683-4450, FAX 609-683-7291, order@civicresearchinstitute.com, http://www.civicresearchinstitute.com/co2.html. Ed. Jacqueline Moore.

364.6   365.068   USA   ISSN 1043-6766

CORRECTIONAL LAW REPORTER. Text in English. 1989. bi-m. USD 169.95 domestic; USD 199.95 foreign (effective 2005). **Document type:** *Newsletter.* **Description:** Helps prison and jail managers and their legal counsel operate programs more effectively and stay in full compliance with the law.
  Indexed: CJPI.
—CCC.
  Published by: Civic Research Insitute, 4490 US Route 27, PO Box 585, Kingston, NJ 08528. TEL 609-683-4450, FAX 609-683-7291, order@civicresearchinstitute.com, http://www.civicresearchinstitute.com. Ed. William Collins.

364.6   616.858   USA   ISSN 1526-9515

CORRECTIONAL MENTAL HEALTH REPORT. Text in English. 1999. bi-m. USD 169.95 domestic; USD 199.95 foreign (effective 2004). **Document type:** *Newsletter.* **Description:** Devoted to the legal, administrative and treatment issues faced by professionals who manage and treat mentally disordered offenders.

C

▼ *new title*   ➤ *refereed*   ✱ *unverified*   ◆ *full entry avail.*

Published by: Civic Research Insitute, 4490 US Route 27, PO Box 585, Kingston, NJ 08528. TEL 609-683-4450, FAX 609-683-7291, order@civicresearchinstitute.com, http://www.civicresearchinstitute.com. Ed. Fred Cohen.

365 CAN
CORRECTIONAL SERVICE OF CANADA. OUTLOOK. Text in English. 1996. a.
Published by: Correctional Service of Canada/Service Correctionnel Canada, 340 Laurier Ave W, Ottawa, ON K1A 0P9, Canada. TEL 613-992-5891, FAX 613-943-1630, http://www.csc-scc.gc.ca.

364 USA ISSN 1075-203X
CORRECTIONS ALERT. Text in English. 1994. bi-w. USD 227 domestic; USD 272 foreign (effective 2000). **Document type:** *Newsletter, Trade.* **Description:** Provides current correction news, trends, and professional resource information from around the nation and the world.
Related titles: Online - full text ed.: (from ProQuest Information & Learning).
Indexed: CJPI.
Published by: Aspen Publishers, Inc. (Subsidiary of: Wolters Kluwer N.V.), 5301 Buckeystown Pike, Ste. 400, Frederick, MD 21704-8319. TEL 800-638-8437, customer.service@aspenpubl.com, http://www.aspenpub.com. Ed. Shartel Stratton. **Dist. by:** Distribution Center, 7201 McKinney Circle, Frederick, MD 21701. TEL 301-698-7100, FAX 301-417-7550.

364 345 USA ISSN 1094-9518
CORRECTIONS CASELAW QUARTERLY. Text in English. 1997. q. looseleaf. USD 60; USD 90 foreign (effective 1999). back issues avail. **Document type:** *Bulletin.* **Description:** Offers concise summaries of court decisions that address jails and prisons.
Related titles: Online - full text ed.: (from Florida Center for Library Automation, Gale Group).
Published by: C R S, Inc., PO Box 555, Poolesville, MD 20837-0555. TEL 301-349-5701, FAX 301-349-5702, rcmiller@erols.com, http://www.correction.org. Ed., R&P Rod Miller. Circ: 300 (paid).

364 USA ISSN 0738-8144
CORRECTIONS COMPENDIUM; the national journal for corrections. Text in English. 1976. bi-m. USD 60 (effective 2005). adv. bk.rev. charts; illus.; stat.; tr.lit. back issues avail.; reprints avail. **Document type:** *Newsletter, Trade.* **Description:** Covers news, research and statistics dealing with criminal justice, emphasis on corrections.
Related titles: Microfilm ed.; Online - full text ed.: (from Florida Center for Library Automation, Gale Group, ProQuest Information & Learning).
Indexed: CJA, CJPI.
Published by: American Correctional Association, 4380 Forbes Blvd, Lanham, MD 20706-4322. TEL 301-918-1898, FAX 301-918-1886, gdaley@aca.org, http://www.aca.org, http://www.corrections.com/aca/. R&P Gabriella M Daley. Adv. contact Laura Tucker. page USD 500. Circ: 1,000 (paid and controlled).

365 USA ISSN 0010-9045
CORRECTIONS DIGEST; the only independent news service for the corrections professional. Text in English. 1970. w. (51/yr.). looseleaf. USD 345 (effective 2005). bk.rev. reprint service avail. from PQC. **Document type:** *Newsletter, Trade.* **Description:** Discusses US and foreign legal and corrections topics. Includes job listings.
Related titles: Microform ed.: (from PQC); Online - full text ed.: (from ProQuest Information & Learning).
Indexed: CJPI.
Published by: Washington Crime News Services, 1209 National Press Bldg, 529 14th St, N W, Ste 9, Washington, DC 22045-0001. TEL 202-662-7035, editor@washingtoncrime.com, nvanwyen@washingtoncrime.com, http://www.crimepolicyreports.com. Ed. Leonard Curry. Pub. Sonja Weisel. Circ: 800 (paid).

365 USA ISSN 1072-9275
CORRECTIONS FORUM. Text in English. 1992. bi-m. free to qualified personnel (effective 2005). adv. bk.rev. **Document type:** *Magazine, Government.* **Description:** Presents and promotes the latest developments in corrections.
Related titles: Online - full text ed.: (from Northern Light Technology, Inc., ProQuest Information & Learning).
Indexed: AC&P, CJPI.
Address: 19 Hanover Pl, PMB 221, Hicksville, NY 11801-5103. TEL 516-579-5063, FAX 516-579-5479, publihser@correctionsforum.com, http://www.correctionsforum.com. Ed., Pub., R&P, Adv. contact Tom Kapinos. B&W page USD 1,800; trim 8.125 x 10.875. Circ: 12,206 (controlled).

364 USA
CORRECTIONS JOURNAL✶. Text in English. 1996. s-m. USD 249. **Document type:** *Newsletter.*
Published by: Pace Publications, 527 Third Ave, Ste 300, New York, NY 10016-4168. TEL 212-685-5450, FAX 212-679-4701. Ed. Vincent Taylor.

364 USA ISSN 1096-8490
HV9469
➤ **CORRECTIONS MANAGEMENT QUARTERLY.** Abbreviated title: C M Q. Text in English. 1997. q. USD 125 to individuals; USD 38 newsstand/cover (effective 2002). **Document type:** *Journal, Academic/Scholarly.* **Description:** Offers practical and strategic guidance for the corrections administrator.
Incorporates: Journal of Rehabilitation Outcomes Measurement (1086-9654)
Related titles: Online - full text ed.: (from EBSCO Publishing, Florida Center for Library Automation, ProQuest Information & Learning).
Indexed: CJA, CJPI, PAIS, SSA.
—BLDSC (3472.164000).
Published by: Aspen Publishers, Inc. (Subsidiary of: Wolters Kluwer N.V.), 5301 Buckeystown Pike, Ste. 400, Frederick, MD 21704-8319. TEL 800-638-8437, customer.service@aspenpubl.com, http://www.aspenpublishers.com. Ed. Richard P Seiter. **Dist. by:** Distribution Center, 7201 McKinney Circle, Frederick, MD 21701. TEL 301-698-7100, FAX 301-695-7931.

365.068 USA ISSN 1083-3382
CORRECTIONS MANAGERS' REPORT. Text in English. 1995. bi-m. USD 169.85 domestic; USD 199.85 foreign (effective 2004). **Document type:** *Newsletter.* **Description:** Presents proven solutions to manage correctional facilities, staff, and inmate populations.
—CCC.
Published by: Civic Research Insitute, 4490 US Route 27, PO Box 585, Kingston, NJ 08528. TEL 609-683-4450, FAX 609-683-7291, order@civicresearchinstitute.com, http://www.civicresearchinstitute.com. Ed. Gary W DeLand.

365.068 USA ISSN 1086-1351
THE CORRECTIONS PROFESSIONAL. Text in English. 1995. bi-w. (21/yr.). USD 215 (effective 2006). **Document type:** *Newsletter, Trade.* **Description:** Gives strategies and techniques to help you with employee training and retention, security, health services, inmate education programs, etc.
Related titles: Online - full text ed.: (from LexisNexis).
—CCC.
Published by: L R P Publications, 747 Dresher Rd, PO Box 980, Horsham, PA 19044. TEL 215-784-0860, 800-341-7874, FAX 215-784-9639, custserve@lrp.com, http://www.shoplrp.com/product/p-7500.CP.html, http://www.lrp.com.

365.068 USA ISSN 1094-7027
CORRECTIONS TECHNOLOGY & MANAGEMENT. Text in English. 1997. bi-m. USD 18 domestic; USD 78 foreign (effective 2001). adv. bk.rev.; software rev. maps; tr.lit. back issues avail. **Document type:** *Journal, Trade.* **Description:** Covers the professional management and maintenance of correctional facilities at all levels.
Related titles: Microfilm ed.; Online - full text ed.
Published by: Hendon Publishing Company, 130 Waukegan Rd, Deerfield, IL 60015. TEL 847-444-3300, FAX 847-444-3333, info@hendonpub.com, http://www.ctmmag.com. Ed., R&P Tim Burke. Pub. H Scott Kingwill. Adv. contact Pete Kingwill. B&W page USD 1,800, color page USD 2,550; trim 10.88 x 8.13. Circ: 1,000 (paid); 20,000 (controlled). **Subscr. to:** PO Box 15788, North Hollywood, CA 91615. TEL 888-329-0770.

365 USA ISSN 0190-2563
HV7231
CORRECTIONS TODAY. Text in English. 1939. 7/yr. USD 25 to libraries; free to members (effective 2004). adv. bk.rev. illus. index. back issues avail.; reprints avail. **Document type:** *Magazine, Trade.* **Description:** Covers adult, juvenile and community corrections and criminal justice.
Former titles (until 1979): American Journal of Correction (0002-9203); (until 1954): Prison World; (until 1941): Jail Association Journal
Related titles: Microfilm ed.: (from MIM, PQC); Online - full text ed.: (from EBSCO Publishing, Florida Center for Library Automation, Gale Group, H.W. Wilson, Northern Light Technology, Inc., O C L C Online Computer Library Center, Inc., ProQuest Information & Learning).
Indexed: ABRCLP, ABS&EES, CJA, CJPI, IPARL, PAIS, PCI, RASB, SSI.
—BLDSC (3472.166000), IE, ingenta.
Published by: American Correctional Association, 4380 Forbes Blvd, Lanham, MD 20706-4322. TEL 301-918-1800, FAX 301-918-1886, gdaley@aca.org, http://www.aca.org/publications/ctmagazine.asp, http://www.corrections.com/aca/pubs.html. Ed. Gabrielle Degoot. R&P Gabriella M Daley. Adv. contact Marge Restivo. B&W page USD 1,778, color page USD 3,259. Circ: 20,000 (controlled).

CRACKDOWN!. see *INSURANCE*

364 USA ISSN 0011-1287
HV6001 CODEN: CRDLAL
➤ **CRIME & DELINQUENCY.** Text in English. 1955. q. USD 708, GBP 457 to institutions; USD 737, GBP 476 combined subscription to institutions print & online eds. (effective 2006). adv. bk.rev. charts; illus. index. back issues avail.; reprint service avail. from WSH. **Document type:** *Journal, Academic/Scholarly.* **Description:** Addresses specific policy or program implications or issues (social, political, and economic) of great topical interest to professionals in the criminal justice system.
Formerly (until 1960): National Probation and Parole Association Journal
Related titles: Microfiche ed.: (from WSH); Microfilm ed.: (from PMC, WSH); Microform ed.: (from WSH); Online - full text ed.: ISSN 1552-387X. USD 701, GBP 452 to institutions (effective 2006) (from C S A, EBSCO Publishing, Florida Center for Library Automation, Gale Group, O C L C Online Computer Library Center, Inc., Sage Publications, Inc., Swets Information Services).
Indexed: ABS&EES, AC&P, ASCA, ASSIA, AgeL, CIJE, CJA, CJPI, CLI, CurCont, ESPM, ExcerpMed, FamI, IBSS, ILP, IMFL, LRI, PAIS, PRA, PsycInfo, PsycholAb, RASB, RI-1, RI-2, RILM, RiskAb, SFSA, SOPODA, SPAA, SRRA, SSA, SSCI, SSI, SUSA, SociolAb, V&AA, e-psyche.
—BLDSC (3487.337000), IDS, IE, Infotrieve, ingenta. **CCC.**
Published by: (National Council on Crime and Delinquency), Sage Publications, Inc., 2455 Teller Rd, Thousand Oaks, CA 91320. TEL 805-499-0721, FAX 805-499-8096, info@sagepub.com, http://www.sagepub.com/journal.aspx?pid=209. Ed. Elizabeth Piper Deschenes. Pub. Sara Miller McCune. R&P Tanya Udin TEL 805-499-0721 ext 7716. Adv. contact Kirsten Beaulieu TEL 805-499-0721 ext 7160. page USD 350. Circ: 1,400 (paid). **Subscr. overseas to:** Sage Publications Ltd., 1 Oliver's Yard, 55 City Rd, London EC1 1SP, United Kingdom. TEL 44-20-73740645, FAX 44-20-73748741, subscription@sagepub.co.uk.

364 USA ISSN 0192-3234
HV6001 CODEN: CMJTFB
➤ **CRIME AND JUSTICE**; a review of research. Text in English. 1979. irreg. (1-3/yr.), latest vol.31, 2004. price varies. bk.rev. back issues avail.; reprint service avail. from PQC,WSH,ISI. **Document type:** *Journal, Academic/Scholarly.* **Description:** Treats important developments in the criminal justice system. Covers legal, psychological, biological, sociological, historical and ethical considerations.
Formerly: Studies in Crime and Justice
Related titles: Online - full text ed.: (from JSTOR (Web-based Journal Archive)).
Indexed: ASCA, CJA, CLI, IBSS, PSA, RI-1, RI-2, SOPODA, SSA, SSCI, SSI, SociolAb.
—BLDSC (3487.340300), IE, ingenta. **CCC.**
Published by: University of Chicago Press, Journals Division, Journals Division, PO Box 37005, Chicago, IL 60637. TEL 773-702-7600, FAX 773-702-0172, mr@press.uchicago.edu, http://www.journals.uchicago.edu/CJ/home.html. Ed. Michael Tonry.

364 AUS ISSN 1030-1046
CRIME AND JUSTICE BULLETIN. Text in English. 1987. irreg., latest vol.76, 2003. **Document type:** *Monographic series.*
Indexed: CJA.
Published by: Attorney General's Department, Bureau of Crime Statistics and Research, GPO Box 6, Sydney, NSW 2000, Australia. TEL 61-2-92319190, FAX 61-2-92319187, bcsr@agd.nsw.gov.au, http://www.lawlink.nsw.gov.au/bocsar.

364 USA ISSN 1096-8733
CRIME & JUSTICE INTERNATIONAL; worldwide news and trends. Text in English. 1985. m. USD 29 domestic to individuals; USD 44 foreign to individuals; USD 59 domestic to institutions; USD 89 foreign to institutions (effective 2004). adv. index. **Document type:** *Newsletter, Trade.* **Description:** Focuses on criminal justice issues around the world.
Formerly: C J International (0882-0244)
Indexed: AC&P, CJA, CJPI, PAIS.
—BLDSC (3487.340570), IE, ingenta.
Published by: (Sam Houston State University, College of Criminal Justice), Office of International Criminal Justice, PO Box 1819, Huntsville, TX 77342-1819. TEL 936-436-9454, FAX 936-436-9483. Ed. Richard Ward. R&P Russell Schlotfeldt. Adv. contact Harriet Brewster.

364 USA ISSN 1555-2888
HV6787
CRIME AND THE NATION'S HOUSEHOLDS (YEAR). (Subseries of: National Crime Victimization Survey Report) Text in English. 1973. a. free. stat. **Document type:** *Government.*
Related titles: Online - full text ed.: ISSN 1555-287X.
Published by: U.S. Department of Justice, Bureau of Justice Statistics, 633 Indiana Ave, N W, Washington, DC 20531. Circ: 17,000. **Orders to:** U.S. Government Printing Office, Superintendent of Documents.

364 USA ISSN 0011-1295
CRIME CONTROL DIGEST; a comprehensive and independent news summary for the law enforcement professional. Text in English. 1967. w. (51/yr.). looseleaf. USD 345 domestic (effective 2004); includes q. Calendar of Events. bk.rev. tr.lit.; illus. reprint service avail. from PQC. **Document type:** *Newsletter, Trade.* **Description:** Reviews current criminal laws and criminal-justice issues.
Related titles: Microform ed.: (from PQC); Online - full text ed.: (from ProQuest Information & Learning).
Indexed: CJPI, ChPerl, RASB.
Published by: Washington Crime News Services, 529 14th St, NW, Ste 9600, Washington, DC 20045. TEL 202-662-7035, 800-422-9267, FAX 703-352-2323, nvanwyen@washingtoncrime.com, http://www.crimepolicyreports.com. Ed. Leonard Curry. Circ: 800 (paid and free).

C

364 900 CHE ISSN 1422-0857
HV7231
CRIME, HISTOIRE ET SOCIETES/CRIME, HISTORY AND SOCIETIES. Text and summaries in French, English. 1997. 2/yr. EUR 40.30 to individuals; EUR 61.70 to institutions; EUR 32.50 to students (effective 2001). **Document type:** *Journal, Academic/Scholarly.* **Description:** Review about the history of crime.
Indexed: AmH&L, CJA, HistAb, IBR, IBZ.
—BLDSC (3487.342757), IE, ingenta.
Published by: Librairie Droz S.A., 11 rue Massot, Geneva 12, 1211, Switzerland. TEL 41-22-3466666, FAX 41-22-3472391, droz@droz.org, http://www.droz.org. Ed. Rene Levy.

364 USA ISSN 0146-5759
HV7296
CRIME IN VIRGINIA ✶. Text in English. a.
Related titles: Microfiche ed.: (from CIS).
Indexed: SRI.
Published by: Department of State Police, Uniform Crime Reporting Section, PO Box 27472, Richmond, VA 23261-7472. TEL 804-323-2031.

364 USA
CRIME INVESTIGATION QUIZER. Text in English. 1993. irreg. USD 21.95 (effective 2000). **Document type:** *Trade.* **Description:** Covers crime investigation using questions and answers and true - false exercises.
Published by: Gould Publications, Inc. (Subsidiary of: LexisNexis), 1333 North US Hwy 17-92, Longwood, FL 32750-3724. TEL 407-695-9500, 800-717-7917, FAX 407-695-2906, info@gouldlaw.com, http://www.gouldlaw.com.

364 343 360 NLD ISSN 0925-4994
HV6001 CODEN: CSCJEL
➤ **CRIME, LAW AND SOCIAL CHANGE**; an interdisciplinary journal. Text in English. 1977. 10/yr. EUR 968, USD 988, GBP 615 combined subscription to institutions print & online eds. (effective 2005). adv. bk.rev. illus. index. reprint service avail. from PSC. **Document type:** *Journal, Academic/Scholarly.* **Description:** Seeks essays and reviews in several areas, most particularly ones dealing with the political economy of organized crime whether at the transnational, international, national regional or local levels.
Formerly: Contemporary Crises (0378-1100); Incorporates (1986-1992): Corruption and Reform (0169-7528)
Related titles: Microform ed.: (from PQC); Online - full text ed.: ISSN 1573-0751 (from EBSCO Publishing, Gale Group, IngentaConnect, Kluwer Online, O C L C Online Computer Library Center, Inc., Ovid Technologies, Inc., ProQuest Information & Learning, Springer LINK, Swets Information Services).
Indexed: ABCPolSci, ABIn, AC&P, ASCA, AmH&L, ArtHuCI, BAS, BibLing, CJA, CJPI, CurCont, DIP, HistAb, IBR, IBSS, IBZ, IPSA, LeftInd, PAIS, PSA, RASB, SOPODA, SSA, SSCI, SSI, SociolAb.
—BLDSC (3487.342795), IDS, IE, Infotrieve, ingenta. **CCC.**
Published by: Springer-Verlag Dordrecht (Subsidiary of: Springer Science+Business Media), Van Godewijckstraat 30, Dordrecht, 3311 GX, Netherlands. TEL 31-78-6576050, FAX 31-78-6576474, http://springerlink.metapress.com/openurl.asp?genre=journal&issn=0925-4994, http://www.springeronline.com. Eds. Nikos Passas, Peter K Manning.

364 USA ISSN 1549-196X
▼ **CRIME, MEDIA, AND POPULAR CULTURE.** Text in English. 2003. irreg. **Document type:** *Monographic series, Academic/Scholarly.*
Published by: Praeger Publishers (Subsidiary of: Greenwood Publishing Group Inc.), 88 Post Rd W, Box 5007, Westport, CT 06881-5007. TEL 203-226-3571, info@greenwood.com, http://www.greenwood.com.

364 GBR ISSN 1741-6590
▼ ➤ **CRIME, MEDIA, CULTURE**; an international journal. Text in English. 2005 (Apr.). 3/yr. GBP 236, USD 412 to institutions; GBP 245, USD 429 combined subscription to institutions print & online eds. (effective 2006). adv. **Document type:** *Journal, Academic/Scholarly.* **Description:** Aims to promote a broad cross-disciplinary understanding of the relationship between crime, criminal justice, media and culture.
Related titles: Online - full text ed.: ISSN 1741-6604. GBP 233, USD 408 to institutions (effective 2006) (from EBSCO Publishing, HighWire Press, Sage Publications, Inc.).
—**CCC.**
Published by: Sage Publications Ltd. (Subsidiary of: Sage Publications, Inc.), 1 Oliver's Yard, 55 City Rd, London, EC1 1SP, United Kingdom. TEL 44-20-73248500, FAX 44-20-73248600, info@sagepub.co.uk, http://www.sagepub.co.uk/journal.aspx?pid=105850. Eds. Chris Greer, Jeff Ferrell, Yvonne Jewkes. **Subscr. in the Americas to:** Sage Publications, Inc., 2455 Teller Rd, Thousand Oaks, CA 91320. TEL 805-499-0721, FAX 805-499-0871, journals@sagepub.com.

364 GBR ISSN 1460-3780
CRIME PREVENTION AND COMMUNITY SAFETY; an international journal. Text in English. 1999. q. GBP 195 domestic; GBP 215, USD 295 foreign (effective 2004). adv. bk.rev. back issues avail. **Document type:** *Journal, Academic/Scholarly.* **Description:** Examines all aspects of crime prevention, order maintenance, community safety, criminal justice and policing.
Indexed: CJA, PSA, SSA, SociolAb.
—BLDSC (3487.342970), IE, ingenta.
Published by: Perpetuity Press, PO Box 376, Leicester, LE2 1UP, United Kingdom. TEL 44-116-2217778, FAX 44-116-2217171, orders@perpetuitypress.com, info@perpetuitypress.com, http://www.perpetuitypress.com. Ed., R&P Karen Gill. Adv. contact Sara Millington.

364 AUS ISSN 1031-5330
CRIME PREVENTION SERIES. Text in English. irreg. price varies. **Document type:** *Monographic series.*
Published by: Australian Institute of Criminology, GPO Box 2944, Canberra, ACT 2601, Australia. TEL 61-262609256, FAX 61-262609260, aicpress@aic.gov.au. R&P Merril Thompson. **Dist. in US by:** Criminal Justice Press, PO Box 249, Monsey, NY 10952.

364 USA ISSN 1065-7029
CRIME PREVENTION STUDIES. Text in English. 1993. s-a. USD 47.50 per issue (effective 2005). **Document type:** *Monographic series, Academic/Scholarly.* **Description:** Covers international research and practice on situational crime prevention and other measures to limit opportunities for crime. Papers include prevention-oriented analyses of specific crime problems, evaluations of crime prevention programs, and theoretical discussions of the philosophy and methods of situational crime prevention.
Indexed: ChemAb.
—BLDSC (3487.343650), IE, ingenta. **CCC.**
Published by: (Rutgers University, School of Criminal Justice), Criminal Justice Press, PO Box 249, Monsey, NY 10952. TEL 845-362-8376, FAX 845-354-9139, cjpress@ucs.net, http://www.criminaljusticepress.com/sub_cps.html. Ed. Ronald V Clarke. Pub. Richard Allinson TEL 845-354-9.39.

364.4 GBR
CRIME REDUCTION NEWS. Text in English. 1969. q. **Document type:** *Government.*
Formerly (until 2003): Crime Prevention News
—BLDSC (3487.344020).
Published by: (Great Britain. Home Office), Communications Team, Exmouth House, 3-11 Pine St, London, EC1R 0JH, United Kingdom. TEL 44-20-79235400, FAX 44-20-78373966, info@communicationsteam.com, http://www.communicationsteam.com. Ed. Emma Bower. Pub. Mike Lamond. Circ: 65,000.

364 GBR ISSN 1468-5205
CRIME REDUCTION RESEARCH SERIES. Text in English. 1999. irreg. **Document type:** *Monographic series.*
Related titles: Online - full text ed.
—BLDSC (3487.344070). **CCC.**
Published by: Home Office, Policing and Reducing Crime Unit, Clive House, Petty France, London, SW1H 9HD, United Kingdom. TEL 44-20-7271-8568, FAX 44-20-7271-8344, http://www.homeoffice.gov.uk/dob/prcu.htm.

362.88 USA ISSN 1092-6372
CRIME VICTIMS REPORT. Text in English. 1997. bi-m. USD 169.95 domestic; USD 199.95 foreign (effective 2004). **Document type:** *Newsletter.* **Description:** Dedicated to programs and legal developments affecting and assisting victims of crime.
—**CCC.**
Published by: Civic Research Insitute, 4490 US Route 27, PO Box 585, Kingston, NJ 08528. TEL 609-683-4450, FAX 609-683-7291, order@civicresearchinstitute.com, http://www.civicresearchinstitute.com. Ed. Ellen J. Halbert.

364 FRA ISSN 1244-5770
LES CRIMES DE L'ANNEE. Text in French. 1986. irreg. price varies. bibl. **Document type:** *Monographic series, Consumer.*
Formerly (until 1990): Les Crimes du Trimestre (0767-3973)
Published by: (Bibliotheque des Litteratures Policieres), Paris Bibliotheques, 6 rue Francois Miron, Paris, 75004, France. TEL 33-1-44788050, FAX 33-1-44788055, http://www.paris-bibliotheques.org.

364 GBR ISSN 0070-1521
KD7865.A2
CRIMINAL APPEAL REPORTS. Text in English. 1908. 10/yr. GBP 545, EUR 820 in Europe; GBP 575, USD 1,045 elsewhere; GBP 273, EUR 410 in Europe to students; GBP 288, USD 523 elsewhere to students (effective 2006). adv. index. **Document type:** *Bulletin, Trade.* **Description:** Reports on cases decided in the House of Lords, the Privy Council, the Court of Appeal (Criminal Division) and Divisional Court.
Related titles: CD-ROM ed.: Justis Criminal Appeal Reports and Sentencing. ISSN 1461-8753. GBP 700; GBP 400 renewals (from Context Ltd.); Online - full text ed.
—BLDSC (3487.346000), IE. **CCC.**
Published by: Sweet & Maxwell Ltd., 100 Avenue Road, London, NW3 3PF, United Kingdom. TEL 44-20-74491111, FAX 44-20-74491144, customer.services@sweetandmaxwell.co.uk, http://www.sweetandmaxwell.co.uk. Ed. Rebecca Hough. Adv. contact Jackie Wood. **Subscr. outside the UK to:** Cheriton House, North Way, Andover, Hants SP10 5BE, United Kingdom. TEL 44-1264-342706, sminfo@itps.co.uk.

CRIMINAL BEHAVIOUR AND MENTAL HEALTH. see *MEDICAL SCIENCES—Psychiatry And Neurology*

364 USA
CRIMINAL EVIDENCE FOR LAW ENFORCEMENT OFFICERS (2ND EDITION). Text in English. 1992. biennial. USD 29.95 (effective 2000). **Document type:** *Trade.* **Description:** Acts as guide to the basic principles, rules and constitutional provisions regulating the admission of evidence in criminal courts. Includes: Evidence and the Adversary System; Basic Principles and Definitions; Forms of Evidence; Preservation of/Access to Evidence; The Hearsay Evidence Rules and Its Exemptions and Executions; Direct vs. Circumstantial Evidence; Competence, Materiality & Relevance; Judicial Notice; Stipulations, and Privileges. Includes complete and unannotated Federal Rules of Evidence.
Published by: Gould Publications, Inc. (Subsidiary of: LexisNexis), 1333 North US Hwy 17-92, Longwood, FL 32750-3724. TEL 407-695-9500, 800-717-7917, FAX 407-695-2906, info@gouldlaw.com, http://www.gouldlaw.com.

363.25 345.052 USA
CRIMINAL INVESTIGATION HANDBOOK. Text in English. 1990. base vol. plus irreg. updates. looseleaf. USD 178 base vol(s). (effective 2005). **Description:** contains critical information you need to know of the internet in perpetrating a computer crime.
Formerly: Police Investigation Handbook
Published by: Matthew Bender & Co., Inc. (Subsidiary of: LexisNexis North America), 1275 Broadway, Albany, NY 12204. TEL 518-487-3575, 800-252-9257, FAX 518-462-3788, international@bender.com, http://bender.lexisnexis.com. Ed. Thomas Mauriello.

C

364 GBR ISSN 1466-8025
HV7231
➤ **CRIMINAL JUSTICE**; the international journal of policy and practice. Text in English. 2001 (Feb.). q. GBP 301, USD 526 to institutions; GBP 313, USD 548 combined subscription to institutions print & online eds. (effective 2006). **Document type:** *Journal, Academic/Scholarly.* **Description:** Focuses on the general field of criminal justice policy and practice. Covers all areas of crime and criminal justice: from policing to sentencing, community penalties; and from crime prevention to victims of crime.
Related titles: Online - full text ed.: ISSN 1741-3230. GBP 298, USD 521 to institutions (effective 2006) (from C S A, EBSCO Publishing, O C L C Online Computer Library Center, Inc., Sage Publications, Inc., Swets Information Services).
Indexed: CJA, CLI, DIP, ESPM, FamI, IBR, IBSS, IBZ, PSA, PsycInfo, PsycholAb, RiskAb, SociolAb, V&AA.
—BLDSC (3487.346810), IE. **CCC.**
Published by: Sage Publications Ltd. (Subsidiary of: Sage Publications, Inc.), 1 Oliver's Yard, 55 City Rd, London, EC1 1SP, United Kingdom. TEL 44-20-73248500, FAX 44-20-73248600, info@sagepub.co.uk, http://www.sagepub.co.uk/journal.aspx?pid=105505. Eds. George Mair, Tim Newburn. **Subscr. in the Americas to:** Sage Publications, Inc., 2455 Teller Rd, Thousand Oaks, CA 91320. TEL 805-499-0721, FAX 805-499-0871, journals@sagepub.com.

345 USA
KFI1762.A15I55
CRIMINAL JUSTICE (SPRINGFIELD). Text in English. 1957. q. looseleaf. USD 68; USD 38 to non-profit organizations (effective 2006). back issues avail. **Document type:** *Newsletter, Trade.*
Published by: (Section on Criminal Justice), Illinois State Bar Association, Illinois Bar Center, 424 S Second St, Springfield, IL 62701. TEL 217-525-1760, 800-252-8908, sanderson@isba.org, http://www.isba.org. Ed. Donald Parkinson. Circ: 2,350.

364 150 USA ISSN 0093-8548
HV9261 CODEN: CJBHAB
➤ **CRIMINAL JUSTICE & BEHAVIOR.** Text in English. 1973. bi-m. USD 613, GBP 396 to institutions; USD 638, GBP 412 combined subscription to institutions print & online eds. (effective 2006). adv. bk.rev. illus. index. back issues avail.; reprint service avail. from PQC,WSH. **Document type:** *Journal, Academic/Scholarly.* **Description:** Covers criminal justice relating to mental health, personality assessment, and changes. Advances the knowledge and expertise of professionals and academics involved in forensic psychology, with a concentration in correctional psychology.
Supersedes: Correctional Psychologist (0589-8218)
Related titles: Microfiche ed.: (from WSH); Microfilm ed.: (from PMC, PQC, WSH); Online - full text ed.: ISSN 1552-3594. USD 607, GBP 392 to institutions (effective 2006) (from C S A, EBSCO Publishing, Florida Center for Library Automation, Gale Group, O C L C Online Computer Library Center, Inc., Sage Publications, Inc., Swets Information Services).

Indexed: ABRCLP, AC&P, ASCA, ASSIA, AgeL, BRI, CBRI, CIJE, CJA, CJPI, CLI, CurCont, ESPM, ExcerpMed, FamI, HRA, IPARL, LRI, LegCont, MEA, MEA&I, PAIS, PRA, PsycInfo, PsycholAb, PsycholRG, RASB, RiskAb, SENA, SFSA, SPAA, SSA, SSCI, SSI, SUSA, SociolAb, V&AA, e-psyche.
—BLDSC (3487.348000), IDS, IE, Infotrieve, ingenta. **CCC.**
Published by: (American Association of Correctional Psychologists), Sage Publications, Inc., 2455 Teller Rd, Thousand Oaks, CA 91320. TEL 805-499-0721, FAX 805-499-0871, info@sagepub.com, http://www.sagepub.com/journal.aspx?pid=210. Ed. Dr. Curt R Bartol. Pub. Sara Miller McCune. R&P Tanya Udin TEL 805-499-0721 ext 7716. Adv. contact Kirsten Beaulieu TEL 805-499-0721 ext 7160. B&W page USD 385, color page USD 775; trim 5.5 x 8.5. Circ: 1,150 (paid). **Subscr. overseas to:** Sage Publications Ltd., 1 Oliver's Yard, 55 City Rd, London EC1 1SP, United Kingdom. TEL 44-20-73740645, FAX 44-20-73748741, subscription@sagepub.co.uk. **Affiliate:** American Correctional Association.

➤ **CRIMINAL JUSTICE ETHICS.** see *PHILOSOPHY*

364 361.73 USA ISSN 1092-5163
CRIMINAL JUSTICE FUNDING REPORT. Text in English. 1997. bi-w. USD 278 (effective Aug. 2001). back issues avail. **Document type:** *Newsletter.* **Description:** Covers new and proposed federal grant programs, federal budget news, key legislation, funding trends and priorities, and appropriations for law enforcement and criminal justice grants. Also highlights relevant grant application deadlines and includes a conference calendar and profiles of private funding sources.
Supersedes in part (in 1997): Drug and Crime Prevention Funding News (1076-1519); Which was formerly (1992-1994): Anti-Drug Funding Alert (1060-4707)
—**CCC.**
Published by: Capitol City Publishers, 3485 S. Wakefield St., Arlington, VA 22206-1719. TEL 703-525-3080, FAX 703-525-3044, inquiry@capitolcitypublishers.com, http://capitolcitypublishers.com. Ed. Erika Fitzpatrick. Pub., R&P Joel Drucker.

C

364.9 USA ISSN 0194-0953
HV7921
CRIMINAL JUSTICE HISTORY; an international annual. Text in English. 1980. irreg., latest vol.18, 2003. price varies. **Document type:** *Journal, Academic/Scholarly.*
Indexed: AmH&L, HistAb.
—BLDSC (3487.350200), Infotrieve.
Published by: Greenwood Publishing Group Inc. (Subsidiary of: Harcourt International), 88 Post Rd W, PO Box 5007, Westport, CT 06881. TEL 203-226-3571, FAX 203-226-1502, webmaster@greenwood.com, http://www.greenwood.com. Ed. Louis Knafla.

364 GBR ISSN 0962-7251
CRIMINAL JUSTICE MATTERS. Abbreviated title: C J M. Text in English. 1988. q. GBP 20 in United Kingdom to non-members; GBP 26 in Europe to non-members; GBP 32 elsewhere to non-members; GBP 6 newsstand/cover (effective 2001). adv. bk.rev. 44 p./no.; back issues avail. **Document type:** *Magazine, Academic/Scholarly.* **Description:** Provides information and informed opinion on all aspects of criminal justice, including the policy, the magistracy, crime prevention, forensic psychiatry, prisons, victims, and women and crime, both in the UK and abroad.
Incorporates: I S T D Bulletin
—BLDSC (3274.273400), IE, ingenta.
Published by: Center for Crime and Justice Studies, King's College London, 75-79 York Rd, London, SEI 7AW, United Kingdom. TEL 44-20-7401-2625, FAX 44-20-7401-2436, ccjs.enq@kcl.ac.uk, http://www.kcl.ac.uk/ccjs. Ed. Valerie Schloredt. R&P Una Padel. Adv. contact Julie Grogan. Circ: 1,600.

364 USA ISSN 0045-9038
K3
CRIMINAL JUSTICE NEWSLETTER. Text in English. 1970. s-m. USD 248 (effective 2005). bk.rev. index. **Document type:** *Newsletter, Trade.* **Description:** Systemwide perspective on the criminal justice system, covering law enforcement, courts, and corrections.
Indexed: CJPI, CLI, LRI.
Published by: Pace Publications, 2100 M St NW, Washington, DC 20037-1207. craigfischer@compuserve.com, http://www.csub.edu/criminaljustice/. Ed. Craig Fischer. Pub. Sid Goldstein.

364 USA ISSN 1526-9507
CRIMINAL JUSTICE RESEARCH REPORTS. Text in English. 1999. bi-m. USD 169.95 domestic; USD 199.95 foreign (effective 2004). **Document type:** *Newsletter.*
Published by: Civic Research Insitute, 4490 US Route 27, PO Box 585, Kingston, NJ 08528. TEL 609-683-4450, FAX 609-683-7291, order@civicresearchinstitute.com, http://www.civicresearchinstitute.com. Ed. Henry G. Sontheimer.

CRIMINAL LAW FORUM; official journal of the Society for the Reform of Criminal Law. see *LAW—Criminal Law*

364 USA ISSN 1073-8290
CRIMINAL ORGANIZATIONS. Text in English. 1985. q. USD 25 to members. adv. bk.rev. back issues avail. **Document type:** *Newsletter.* **Description:** Includes articles, book reviews, news and notes, member network and summaries on organized crime issues.
Formerly: International Association for the Study of Organized Crime. Update
Indexed: CJA.
Published by: International Association of the Study of Organized Crime (IASOC), Sam Houston State University, College of Criminal Justice, PO Box 2296, Huntsville, TX 77341. TEL 812-855-0889, stdrly@shsu.edu, http://www.shsu.edu/cjcenter/iasoc/home.htm. Ed. Kip Schlegel. Adv. contact Jeff Builta. Circ: 600.

CRIMINAL PROCEDURE ACT. see *LAW—Criminal Law*

364 USA ISSN 1549-5213
THE CRIMINALIST. Text in English. 1986. q. USD 20 membership (effective 2004). adv. **Document type:** *Journal, Trade.* **Description:** Contains articles dealing with crime scene investigation and related forensic issues.
Published by: International Association for Identification, New Jersey Division, PO Box 2413, Edison, NJ 08818. TEL 732-548-8431, editor@njiai.org, http://www.njiai.org. adv.: page USD 200. Circ: 260 (paid and controlled).

364 CAN ISSN 0316-0041
CRIMINOLOGIE. Text in French; Abstracts in English. 1968. 2/yr. CND 32 to individuals; CND 53 to institutions. reprint service avail. from PQC. **Document type:** *Academic/Scholarly.*
Formerly: Acta Criminologica (0065-1168)
Indexed: AC&P, CJA, DIP, IBR, IBSS, IBZ, ICLPL, PAIS, PdeR, SOPODA, SSA, SociolAb.
—BLDSC (3487.369000), IE, Infotrieve.
Published by: Presses de l'Universite de Montreal, 3535, chemin Queen-Mary, Bureau 206, Montreal, PQ H3V 1H8, Canada. TEL 514-343-6933, FAX 514-343-2232, pum@umontreal.ca, http://www.erudit.org/revue/crimino, http://www.pum.umontreal.ca. Ed. Pierre Landreville. Circ: 900.

364 USA ISSN 0164-0240
CRIMINOLOGIST. Text in English. 1976. bi-m. USD 25 domestic; USD 30 foreign (effective 2005). adv. back issues avail. **Document type:** *Newsletter.*
Published by: American Society of Criminology, 1314 Kinnear Rd, Columbus, OH 43212. TEL 614-292-9207, FAX 614-292-6767. Ed. Miriam A Delone. Circ: 2,800.

364 USA ISSN 0011-1384
HV6001 CODEN: CRINYA
➤ **CRIMINOLOGY**; an interdisciplinary journal. Text in English. 1963. q. USD 130 to individuals; USD 145 to institutions (effective 2005). illus. index. back issues avail.; reprint service avail. from WSH,PQC. **Document type:** *Journal, Academic/Scholarly.*
Formerly: Criminologica
Related titles: Microfilm ed.: (from PQC); Online - full text ed.: ISSN 1745-9125 (from bigchalk, Blackwell Synergy, EBSCO Publishing, Northern Light Technology, Inc., O C L C Online Computer Library Center, Inc., ProQuest Information & Learning).
Indexed: ABRCLP, AC&P, ASCA, AgeL, CJA, CJPI, CLI, ChPerI, CurCont, DIP, ESPM, ExcerpMed, FamI, H&SSA, IBR, IBSS, IBZ, ILP, LRI, MEA&I, PAIS, PCI, PsycholAb, RASB, RiskAb, SOPODA, SSA, SSCI, SSI, SWR&A, SociolAb, e-psyche.
—BLDSC (3487.374000), IE, Infotrieve, ingenta. **CCC.**
Published by: (American Society of Criminology), Blackwell Publishing, Inc. (Subsidiary of: Blackwell Publishing Ltd.), Commerce Place, 350 Main St, Malden, MA 02148. TEL 781-388-8206, FAX 781-388-8232, http://www.blackwellpublishing.com/journal.asp?ref=0011-1384&site=1. Ed. Ray Paternoster. R&P Sarah Hall. Circ: 4,000.

364 USA
CRIMINOLOGY AND CRIME CONTROL POLICY. Text in English. 1992. irreg. price varies. **Document type:** *Monographic series.*
Published by: Praeger Publishers (Subsidiary of: Greenwood Publishing Group Inc.), 88 Post Rd W, Box 5007, Westport, CT 06881-5007. TEL 203-226-3571, FAX 203-222-1502.

364 351 USA ISSN 1538-6473
HV6001
CRIMINOLOGY AND PUBLIC POLICY. Text in English. 2001. q. USD 234 in the Americas to institutions; GBP 127 elsewhere to institutions (effective 2006). **Document type:** *Journal, Academic/Scholarly.*
Related titles: Online - full text ed.: ISSN 1745-9133. USD 191 in the Americas to institutions; GBP 121 elsewhere to institutions (effective 2006) (from Blackwell Synergy, EBSCO Publishing, IngentaConnect, O C L C Online Computer Library Center, Inc.).
Indexed: CJA.
—BLDSC (3487.375150). **CCC.**
Published by: (American Society of Criminology), Blackwell Publishing, Inc. (Subsidiary of: Blackwell Publishing Ltd.), Commerce Place, 350 Main St, Malden, MA 02148. TEL 781-388-8206, FAX 781-388-8232, asc41@infinet.com, http://www.blackwellpublishing.com/cpp. Ed. Todd R Clear.

364 USA
CRIMINOLOGY STUDIES. Text in English. 1997. irreg. (3-4/y.), latest vol.18, 2002. price varies. **Document type:** *Monographic series, Academic/Scholarly.*
Published by: Edwin Mellen Press, 415 Ridge St, P.O. Box 450, Lewiston, NY 14092. TEL 716-754-2266, FAX 716-754-4056, cservice@mellenpress.com, http://www.mellenpress.com/.

364 GBR
CROPWOOD ROUND-TABLE CONFERENCE PAPERS. Text in English. 1968. irreg., latest vol.23, 1997. GBP 6. back issues avail. **Document type:** *Monographic series, Academic/Scholarly.*
Published by: University of Cambridge, Institute of Criminology, 7 West Rd, Cambridge, CB3 9DT, United Kingdom. TEL 44-1223-335362, FAX 44-1223-335356.

364 AUS ISSN 1034-5329
HV7231
➤ **CURRENT ISSUES IN CRIMINAL JUSTICE.** Text in English. 1967. 3/yr. AUD 110 domestic; AUD 115 foreign (effective 2005). adv. bk.rev. cum.index. back issues avail.; reprint service avail. from WSH. **Document type:** *Journal, Academic/Scholarly.* **Description:** New and upcoming events and issues in the field of criminology.
Supersedes (in 1989): University of Sydney. Institute of Criminology. Proceedings (0085-7033)
Related titles: Online - full text ed.: (from R M I T Publishing).
Indexed: AusPAIS, CJA, CLI, FamI, LRI.
—BLDSC (3499.061000), IE, ingenta. **CCC.**
Published by: University of Sydney, Law School. Institute of Criminology, 173-175 Phillip St, Sydney, NSW 2000, Australia. TEL 61-2-93510239, FAX 61-2-93510200, criminology@law.usyd.edu.au, http://www.criminology.law.usyd.edu.au/publicat/journal/journal.htm. adv.: B&W page AUD 550; trim 240 x 155. Circ: 300. **Dist. in US by:** Wm. W. Gaunt & Sons Inc., Gaunt Bldg, 3011 Gulf Dr, Holmes Beach, FL 34217-2199. TEL 941-778-5211, 941-778-5252.

➤ **D P I C REPORTS.** (Death Penalty Information Center) see *POLITICAL SCIENCE—Civil Rights*

363.2 CHN ISSN 1003-9325
DANGDAI JINGCHA/POLICE TODAY. Text in Chinese. 1990. m. CNY 60 (effective 2004). **Document type:** *Journal, Government.*
Contact Dist.: China International Book Trading Corp/Zhongguo Guoji Tushu Maoyi Zonggongsi, 35 Chegongzhuang Xilu, Haidian District, PO Box 399, Beijing, 100044, China. TEL 86-10-68412045, FAX 86-10-68412023, 3374004499@163.com, cibtc@mail.cibtc.com.cn, http://www.police-today.com/, http://www.cibtc.com.cn.

363.2 DNK ISSN 0905-7498
DANSK POLITI. Text in Danish. 1971. 11/yr. adv. back issues avail. **Document type:** *Magazine, Trade.*
Formerly (until 1988): Tidsskrift for Dansk Politi (0900-0879); Which was formed by the merger of (1938-1971): Politiet (0908-5726); (1969-1971): Dansk Politi (0908-5734)
Related titles: Online - full text ed.
Published by: Dansk Politiforbund/Police Union in Denmark, H. C. Andersens Boulevard 38, Copenhagen V, 1553, Denmark. TEL 47-33-455900, FAX 47-33-455901, dp@politiforbund.dk, http://www.politiforbund.dk. Eds. Mette Jensen TEL 45-33-455924, Tommy Agerskov Thomsen. Circ: 15,000. **Co-sponsors:** Dansk Kriminalpolitiforening; Rigspolitichefen; Foreningen af Politimestre i Danmark.

DEATH PENALTY IN (YEAR): YEAR END REPORT. see *POLITICAL SCIENCE—Civil Rights*

364.66 USA
DEATH PENALTY NEWS. Text in English. irreg. (approx. bi-w.). **Document type:** *Newsletter.* **Description:** Dedicated to the U.S. death penalty and its uses.
Media: Online - full text.
—BLDSC (3535.960440).
Address: rhalperi@mail.smu.edu, http://www.smu.edu/~deathpen/. Ed. Rick Halperin.

364.66 USA
KF9725.D432
DEATH ROW U.S.A. REPORTER. Text in English. 1975. irreg. looseleaf. USD 70 per issue (effective 2005). back issues avail.; reprint service avail. from WSH. **Document type:** *Newsletter.*
Published by: (N A A C P Legal Defense Educational Fund), William S. Hein & Company, Incorporated, 1285 Main St, Buffalo, NY 14209-1987. TEL 716-882-2600, 800-828-7571, FAX 716-883-8100.

DEFENSIVE TACTICS FOR LAW ENFORCEMENT, PUBLIC SAFETY & CORRECTION OFFICERS. see *LAW—Criminal Law*

364 ITA ISSN 1590-5837
DEI DELITTI E DELLE PENE. Text in Italian. 1975. 3/yr.
Formerly (until 1983): La Questione Criminale (0390-0401)
Indexed: PCI.

Published by: (Universitaet des Saarlandes DEU, Institut fuer Rechts-und Sozialphilosophie DEU), Edizioni Scientifiche Italiane SpA, Via Chiatamone 7, Naples, NA 80121, Italy. TEL 39-081-7645443, FAX 39-081-7646477, info@esispa.com, http://www.esispa.com. Ed. Alessandro Baratta.

DELIKT EN DELINKWENT; tijdschrift voor strafrecht. see *LAW—Criminal Law*

345 DNK ISSN 0904-1990
HV8437
DENMARK. DIREKTORATET FOR KRIMINALFORSORGEN. AARSBERETNING. Text in Danish. 1974. a., latest 2003. free. bk.rev. illus. back issues avail. **Document type:** *Government.*
Formerly (until 1988): Denmark. Direktoratet for Kriminalforsorgen. Kriminalforsorgen (1974) (0107-511X)
Related titles: Online - full text ed.
Published by: Direktoratet for Kriminalforsorgen/Danish Prison and Probation Service, Strandgade 100, Copenhagen K, 1401, Denmark. TEL 45-32-684000, FAX 45-32-684050, dfk@kriminalforsorgen.dk, http://www.kriminalforsorgen.dk.

364 MEX ISSN 0045-9992
DERECHO PENAL CONTEMPORANEO✶. Text in Spanish. bi-m. MXP 60, USD 6. bk.rev.
Published by: Universidad Nacional Autonoma de Mexico, Facultad de Derecho, Ciudad Universitaria, Mexico City, DF 04510, Mexico.

364 BGD
DETECTIVE. Text in English. 1960. w. adv. charts; illus.
Related titles: Bengali ed.
Indexed: CJPI.
Published by: East Pakistan Police Co-Operative Society, Polwell Bhaban, Naya Paltan, Dhaka 2, Bangladesh. TEL 2-402757. Ed. Syed Amjad Hossain. Circ: 3,000.

364 340 USA ISSN 0742-552X
KF9730.A15
DETENTION REPORTER; a monthly resource for detention & corrections. Text in English. 1983. m. USD 48 (effective 2000). adv. bk.rev. back issues avail. **Document type:** *Newsletter.*
Description: Summaries of news, special issues and court decisions for detention and corrections.
Published by: C R S, Inc., PO Box 555, Poolesville, MD 20837-0555. TEL 301-349-5701, FAX 301-349-5702, rcmiller@erols.com, http://www.correction.org. Ed., R&P, Adv. contact Rod Miller. Circ: 700 (paid).

363.2 DEU ISSN 0012-057X
DEUTSCHE POLIZEI. Text in German. 1951. m. EUR 2.90 newsstand/cover (effective 2004). adv. bk.rev. bibl.; charts; illus. **Document type:** *Magazine, Trade.*
—CCC.
Published by: (Gewerkschaft der Polizei), Verlag Deutsche Polizeiliteratur GmbH, Forststr 3A, Hilden, 40721, Germany. TEL 49-211-71040, FAX 49-211-7104174, vdp.buchvertrieb@vdpolizei.de, http://www.vdpolizei.de. adv.: B&W page EUR 8,375, color page EUR 12,150. Circ: 190,911 (paid and controlled).

363.2 DEU ISSN 0175-4815
DEUTSCHES POLIZEIBLATT; Fachzeitschrift fuer die Aus- und Fortbildung in Bund und Laendern. Short title: D Pol Bl. Text in German. 1983. bi-m. EUR 40.50; EUR 10.50 newsstand/cover (effective 2005). adv. back issues avail. **Document type:** *Magazine, Trade.*
Indexed: RASB.
—CCC.
Published by: Richard Boorberg Verlag GmbH und Co. KG, Scharrstr 2, Stuttgart, 70563, Germany. TEL 49-711-73850, FAX 49-711-7385100, mail@boorberg.de, http://www.boorberg.de. Ed. Gert Taures. adv.: B&W page EUR 1,590, color page EUR 2,520. Circ: 3,570 (paid).

DEVIANT BEHAVIOR; an interdisciplinary journal. see *SOCIOLOGY*

364 USA
DICTIONARY OF CRIMINAL JUSTICE. Text in English. irreg., latest 2004, 6th ed. USD 24.37 per vol. (effective 2004). illus. **Document type:** *Academic/Scholarly.* **Description:** Brings together, in one, easy-to-use guide, more than 3,600 definitions from the many disciplines that compose the field of criminal justice—including U.S. and English common law, penology, psychology, law enforcement, political science, and business administration. Also features summaries of nearly 1,000 key U.S. Supreme Court rulings affecting criminal justice.
Indexed: IBSS.
Published by: McGraw-Hill - Dushkin (Subsidiary of: McGraw-Hill Higher Education), 2460 Kerper Blvd, Dubuque, IA 52001. TEL 800-243-6532, customer.service@mcgraw-hill.com, http://www.dushkin.com/catalog/0072951125.mhtml. Ed. George E Rush. Pub. Jeffrey Hahn. R&P Cheryl Greenleaf.

364 USA ISSN 1071-3530
HV9463
DIRECTORY - JUVENILE AND ADULT CORRECTIONAL DEPARTMENTS, INSTITUTIONS, AGENCIES, AND PAROLING AUTHORITIES. Text in English. 1939. a. USD 80 to non-members; USD 64 to members. adv. **Document type:** *Directory.*
Former titles (until 1992): Juvenile and Adult Correctional Departments, Institutions, Agencies, and Paroling Authorities of the United States and Canada (0190-2555); (until 1979): Directory - Juvenile and Adult Correctional Departments, Institutions, Agencies, and Paroling Authorities of the United States and Canada (0362-9287); (until 1976): Directory - Juvenile Adult Correctional Institutions and Agencies of the United States of America, Canada, and Great Britain (0090-4872); (until 1972): Directory of Correctional Institutions and Agencies of the United States of America, Canada, and Great Britain (0070-5373); American Correctional Association Directory: State and Federal Correctional Institutions (0065-7956)
Related titles: Microfiche ed.: 1939 (from CIS).
Indexed: SRI.
Published by: American Correctional Association, 4380 Forbes Blvd, Lanham, MD 20706-4322. TEL 301-918-1800. Ed. Gabriella M Daley. Adv. contact Marge Restivo. Circ: 5,000.

364 USA ISSN 1081-6933
HV9955.C2
DIRECTORY OF CALIFORNIA JUSTICE AGENCIES. Text in English. 1993. a. USD 14.95 per vol. (effective 1999 & 2000). **Document type:** *Directory.* **Description:** Compiles the addresses and phone numbers for California county jails, probation departments, district attorneys, and municipal and university police departments, along with the California Highway Patrol.
Related titles: Diskette ed.: USD 29.95.
Published by: California Probation, Parole and Correctional Association, 1455 Response Rd., Ste. 190, Sacramento, CA 95815-5266. cppca@ns.net, http://www.cppca.org/Justice_dir.htm, http://www.cppca.org.

344 343 USA
DIRECTORY OF JUSTICE ISSUES IN THE STATES. Text in English. 1984. a. USD 30 (effective 2002). **Document type:** *Directory.*
Formerly (until 199?): Directory of Criminal Justice Issues in the States
Published by: Justice Research and Statistics Association, Inc., 777 N Capitol St, N E, Ste 801, Washington, DC 20002. TEL 202-842-9330, FAX 202-842-9329, cjinfo@jrsa.org, http://www.jrsa.org. Ed., R&P Karen F Maline. Circ: 1,000.

DIRECTORY OF SERVICES FOR VICTIMS OF CRIME/REPERTOIRE DES SERVICES AUX VICTIMES D'ACTES CRIMINELS. see *SOCIAL SERVICES AND WELFARE*

327.174 GBR ISSN 1362-6450
DISARMAMENT DIPLOMACY. Text in English. 1994. 10/yr. free (effective 2001). bk.rev. 2 cols./p.; back issues avail. **Document type:** *Journal, Academic/Scholarly.* **Description:** Aims to stimulate debate on topical disarmament and arms control issues.
Formerly (until 1996): Nuclear Proliferation News (1355-2295)
Related titles: Online - full text ed.
Published by: Acronym Institute, 288 St Paul's Rd, London, N1 2LH, United Kingdom. TEL 44-20-7688-0450, FAX 44-20-7688-0451, acronym@gn.apc.org, http://www.acronym.org.uk/dd/index.htm. Ed. Sean Howard.

364 NIC
DOCUMENTOS PENALES Y CRIMINOLOGICOS. Text in Spanish. 1993. 3/yr. **Description:** Promotes scientific discussion of penal and criminological sciences.
Address: APDO POSTAL A, 113, Managua, Nicaragua. Eds. Diego-Manuel Luzon Pena, Sergio J. Cuarezma Teran.

364.15553 USA ISSN 1086-1270
KF9320.A15
DOMESTIC VIOLENCE REPORT. Text in English. 1995 (Oct./Nov.). bi-m. USD 169.95 domestic; USD 199.95 foreign (effective 2005). **Document type:** *Newsletter.* **Description:** Devoted to innovative programs, legal developments, and current services and research in domestic violence law and prevention.
—CCC.
Published by: Civic Research Insitute, 4490 US Route 27, PO Box 585, Kingston, NJ 08528. TEL 609-683-4450, FAX 609-683-7291, order@civicresearchinstitute.com, http://www.civicresearchinstitute.com. Ed. Joan Zorza.

364 301 150 USA
DOMESTIC VIOLENCE SOURCEBOOK. Text in English. 1999 (May). irreg., latest 2004, 2nd edition. USD 78 per issue (effective 2004). charts; bibl. master index master index.
Description: Contains basic information about spousal/partner, child, and elder physical, emotional, and sexual abuse, teen dating violence, and stalking. Includes information about hotlines, safe houses, safety plans, and other resources for support and assistance, community initiative, and reports on current directions in research and treatment, along with a glossary, sources for further reading, and governmental and non-governmental organizations contact information.
Formerly (until 2004): Domestic Violence and Child Abuse Sourcebook
Published by: Omnigraphics, Inc., 615 Griswold St, Detroit, MI 48226. TEL 313-961-1340, 800-234-1340, FAX 313-961-1383, 800-875-1340, http://www.omnigraphics.com. Ed. Helene Henderson.

DRUG DETECTION REPORT; the newsletter on drug testing in the workplace. see *BUSINESS AND ECONOMICS—Personnel Management*

DRUG ENFORCEMENT ADMINISTRATION REGISTRATION FILE - ACTIVE. see *MEDICAL SCIENCES*

365 USA ISSN 0894-1300
HV5825
DRUG ENFORCEMENT REPORT. Text in English. 1984. s-m. USD 257 (effective 2004). back issues avail. **Document type:** *Newsletter.* **Description:** Reports on federal developments in drug enforcement policy.
Indexed: HlthInd.
Published by: Pace Publications, 2100 M St NW, Washington, DC 20037-1207. Ed. Dean Boyd. Pub. Sid Goldstein.

DRUG TRAFFICKING IN THE UNITED STATES. see *DRUG ABUSE AND ALCOHOLISM*

C

364 FRA ISSN 1811-9123
▼ **E R C E S QUARTERLY REVIEW.** (European and International Resarch Group on Crime, Ethics and Social Philosophy) Text in English. 2004. q. free (effective 2005). **Document type:** *Journal, Academic/Scholarly.*
Media: Online - full content.
Published by: European and International Resarch Group on Crime, Ethics and Social Philosophy http://ercesinternational.tripod.com/journal/Journal.htm.

363.2 345 NLD ISSN 1386-4726
K5
EAST AND CENTRAL EUROPEAN JOURNAL ON CRIME AND CRIMINAL LAW. Text in English. 1998. s-a. bibl. reprint service avail. from WSH. **Document type:** *Academic/Scholarly.* **Description:** Reports on recent developments in criminal law in the region.
Indexed: CJA.
Published by: Global Law Association, PO Box 9001, Tilburg, 5000 HA, Netherlands. TEL 31-13-544-3135, FAX 31-24-355-4827, globallaw@writeme.com, http://web.inter.nl.net/hcc/global.wolf/cri.htm, http://www.globallaw.org. Ed. J Oblovski. **Dist. in N. America by:** Wm. W. Gaunt & Sons Inc., Gaunt Bldg, 3011 Gulf Dr, Holmes Beach, FL 34217-2199. TEL 941-778-5211, 941-778-5252.

365 USA ISSN 0046-1059
THE ECHO (HUNTSVILLE); Texas prison news. Text in English. 1929. m. USD 8 (effective 1999 - 2000). bk.rev. charts; illus.; stat. back issues avail. **Document type:** *Newspaper.*
Description: Prison newspaper with news and information for and about the Texas criminal justice system. Includes current events, criminal justice issues, legal issues, prison activities, and official notices for Texas prisoners and families.
Published by: Department of of Criminal Justice, Institutional Division, PO Box 99, Huntsville, TX 77342. TEL 409-295-1302. Ed. David M Hargrove. R&P Larry Fitzgerald TEL 409-294-1302. Circ: 150,000.

364 USA
EIGHTEEN-ELEVEN. Text in English. 1978. m. membership.
Description: Covers subjects of interest to federal law enforcement officers and criminal investigators.
Published by: Federal Law Enforcement Officers Association, PO Box 326, Lewisberry, PA 17339. TEL 717-938-2300, FAX 717-932-2262, fleoaservice@aol.com, http://www.fleoa.org. Ed. Kathleen A Desch. Circ: 5,000.

EMPLOYEE TESTING & THE LAW; reporting legal, technical, and business developments in employee testing. see *BUSINESS AND ECONOMICS—Personnel Management*

364 BRA
ESCOLA DO SERVICO PENITENCIARIO DO RIO GRANDE DO SUL. REVISTA. Text in Portuguese. 1990. q.
Published by: Escola do Servico Penitenciario do Rio Grande do Sul, Av Borges de Medeiros, 1501 Ala N Andar 9, Pr Belas, Porto Alegre, RGS 90110-150, Brazil. TEL 0512-26-7563.

▼ *new title* ➤ *refereed* ✶ *unverified* ♦ *full entry avail.*

363.2 FRA ISSN 0338-1595
ESSOR DE LA GENDARMERIE NATIONALE. Text in French. 4/yr.
Formerly (until 1971): Essor de la Gendarmerie et de la Garde (0338-1587)
Address: 132 rue du Faubourg Saint Denis, Paris, Cedex 10 75481, France. TEL 40-36-44-64, FAX 40-36-90-20. Ed. Jacques Revise. Circ: 40,000.

ETHICS AND JUSTICE; an interdisciplinary public affairs journal. see *LAW*

364 POL ISSN 0860-3723
EUROCRIMINOLOGY. Text in English. 1987. a. bibl.; stat. **Document type:** *Academic/Scholarly.* **Description:** Eurocriminology explores and analyses the most current trends in the fields of criminolofy, victimology, and criminal justice system. It deals with the practical and theoretical aspects of crime control, its combating, symptoms and the genesis of crime.
Indexed: AC&P, CJA, CJPI.
Published by: University of Lodz, Department of Criminal Procedure and Criminalistics, Ul Narutowicza 65, Lodz, 90236, Poland. TEL 48-6-784148, FAX 48-6-784533. Ed. Brunon Holyst. Circ: 200. **Dist by:** Wasmuth Buchhandlung & Antiquariat, Pfalzburger Str 43-44, Berlin 10717, Germany. TEL 49-30-863099-0, FAX 49-30-863099; **Dist. in U.S. by:** Criminal Justice Press, 124 Willow Tree Rd, Monsey, NY 10952. TEL 914-354-9139, 914-362-8376.

364 USA ISSN 1237-4741
EUROPEAN INSTITUTE FOR CRIME PREVENTION AND CONTROL. PUBLICATION SERIES. Text in English. 1983. irreg.
Formerly (until 1994): H E U N I Publication Series (0780-3656)
Indexed: SSA, SociolAb.
—BLDSC (7141.390000), IE, ingenta.
Published by: (European Institute for Crime Prevention and Control FIN), Criminal Justice Press, PO Box 249, Monsey, NY 10952. cjpress@ucs.net, http://www.heuni.fi/12541.htm, http://www.criminaljusticepress.com.

C

EUROPEAN JOURNAL OF CRIME, CRIMINAL LAW AND CRIMINAL JUSTICE. see *LAW—Criminal Law*

364 GBR ISSN 1477-3708
HV6001
▼ **EUROPEAN JOURNAL OF CRIMINOLOGY.** Text in English. 2004 (Jan.). q. GBP 286, USD 499 to institutions; GBP 297, USD 520 combined subscription to institutions print & online eds. (effective 2006). **Document type:** *Journal, Academic/Scholarly.* **Description:** Brings together broad theoretical accounts of crime, analyses of quantitative data, comparative studies, systematic evaluations of interventions and discussions of criminal justice institutions.
Related titles: Online - full text ed.: ISSN 1741-2609. GBP 283, USD 494 to institutions (effective 2006) (from EBSCO Publishing, O C L C Online Computer Library Center, Inc., Sage Publications, Inc., Swets Information Services).
Indexed: CJA, ESPM, PRA, RiskAb, SociolAb, V&AA.
—BLDSC (3829.728243), IE. **CCC.**
Published by: (University of Edinburgh, Centre for Law and Society), Sage Publications Ltd. (Subsidiary of: Sage Publications, Inc.), 1 Oliver's Yard, 55 City Rd, London, EC1 1SP, United Kingdom. TEL 44-20-73248500, FAX 44-20-73248600, info@sagepub.co.uk, http://www.sagepub.co.uk/journal.aspx?pid=105537. Ed. David J Smith. **Subscr. in the Americas to:** Sage Publications, Inc., 2455 Teller Rd, Thousand Oaks, CA 91320. TEL 805-499-0721, FAX 805-499-0871, journals@sagepub.com.

364 345 NLD ISSN 0928-1371
CODEN: EJCRF5
EUROPEAN JOURNAL ON CRIMINAL POLICY AND RESEARCH. Text in English. 1993. q. EUR 203, USD 295, GBP 183 combined subscription to institutions print & online eds. (effective 2005). adv. abstr. index, cum.index (1991-1997). back issues avail.; reprint service avail. from PSC. **Document type:** *Journal, Academic/Scholarly.* **Description:** Provides a platform for discussion and information exchange on the crime problem in Europe.
Related titles: Online - full text ed.: ISSN 1572-9869 (from EBSCO Publishing, Gale Group, IngentaConnect, Kluwer Online, O C L C Online Computer Library Center, Inc., ProQuest Information & Learning, Springer LINK, Swets Information Services).
Indexed: ABIn, BibLing, CJA, CJPI, IBSS, PSA, SSA, SociolAb.
—BLDSC (3829.728240), IE, Infotrieve, ingenta. **CCC.**
Published by: (Netherlands. Ministrie van Justitie, Netherlands. Research and Documentation Centre), Springer-Verlag Dordrecht (Subsidiary of: Springer Science+Business Media), Van Godewijckstraat 30, Dordrecht, 3311 GX, Netherlands. TEL 31-78-6576050, FAX 31-78-6576474, http://springerlink.metapress.com/openurl.asp?genre=journal&issn=0928-1371, http://www.springeronline.com. Ed. Ernesto U Savona.

364 USA ISSN 0014-5688
F B I LAW ENFORCEMENT BULLETIN. (Federal Bureau of Investigation) Text in English. 1932. m. USD 36 domestic; USD 45 foreign (effective 2004). bk.rev. illus. Index. 32 p./no.; back issues avail.; reprint service avail. from PQC. **Document type:** *Magazine, Government.* **Description:** Discusses current issues in law enforcement.
Related titles: Microform ed.: (from MIM, PQC); Online - full text ed.: (from bigchalk, EBSCO Publishing, Florida Center for Library Automation, Gale Group, H.W. Wilson, O C L C Online Computer Library Center, Inc., ProQuest Information & Learning).
Indexed: AC&P, AgeL, CJA, CJPI, ExcerpMed, IUSGP, PAIS, SSI.
—BLDSC (3901.007000), IE, ingenta.
Published by: U.S. Federal Bureau of Investigation (Subsidiary of: U.S. Department of Justice), 935 Pennsylvania Ave NW, Ste 7350, Washington, DC 20535. TEL 202-324-3000, leb@fbiacademy.edu, http://www.fbi.gov/publications/leb/leb.htm. Ed. John E Ott. Circ: 43,000. **Subscr. to:** U.S. Government Printing Office, Superintendent of Documents, PO Box 371954, Pittsburgh, PA 15250-7954. TEL 202-512-1800, FAX 202-512-2250, orders@gpo.gov, http://www.access.gpo.gov.

364 USA ISSN 1057-9397
F D A ENFORCEMENT REPORT. (Food and Drug Administration) Text in English. w. USD 97; USD 121.25 foreign (effective 1998). **Document type:** *Government.* **Description:** Lists actions taken in connection with agency regulatory activities.
Related titles: Online - full text ed.: (from Factiva).
Published by: U.S. Department of Health and Human Services, Food and Drug Administration, 5600 Fishers Ln, Rockville, MD 20857. TEL 301-443-3285. **Subscr. to:** U.S. Government Printing Office, Superintendent of Documents.

363.2 USA
F T C REVIEW. Text in English. 1997. m. **Document type:** *Newsletter.*
Media: Online - full text.
Published by: Arent Fox Kintner Plotkin & Kahn PLLC, 1050 Connecticut Ave, NW, Washington, DC 20036-5339. TEL 202-827-6000, FAX 202-857-6395, infolaw@arentfox.com, http://www.arentfox.com/.

FAMILY VIOLENCE & SEXUAL ASSAULT BULLETIN. see *SOCIAL SERVICES AND WELFARE*

364.4 CHN
FAZHI LIAOWANG/LEGAL OUTLOOK. Text in Chinese. bi-m. CNY 6. **Description:** Publishes results of criminological research and discussions of legal issues in special economic zones and focuses on special laws covering Taiwan and Hong Kong.
Formerly: Fujian Cifa
Published by: Fazhi Liaowang Zazhishe, Xihu Jingbianting, Fuzhou, Fujian 350003, China. **Dist. overseas by:** Jiangsu Publications Import & Export Corp., 56 Gao Yun Ling, Nanjing, Jiangsu, China.

364 USA ISSN 1094-723X
THE FEDERAL INVESTIGATOR. Text in English. 1996. m. USD 25 (effective 2000). adv. **Document type:** *Newsletter.*
Formerly: Pro-Gram
Published by: (Federal Criminal Investigators Association), Financial Programs, Inc., PO Box 23400, Washington, DC 20026. TEL 800-403-3347. Ed., R&P Dennis Boyd TEL 703-455-5947. Adv. contact Nick Cordovana.

364 AUS
FEDERAL OFFENCES. Text in English. 1985. 3 base vols. plus m. updates. AUD 1,393 for 3 base vols. & 1 yr updates (effective 2004); AUD 1,015 for 2 base vols. & 1 yr updates (effective 2003). **Document type:** *Trade.* **Description:** Offers a definitive treatment of all offenses created by commonwealth laws, both Acts of Parliament and by Regulations.
Formerly: Australian Criminal Law : Federal Offences
Related titles: CD-ROM ed.: AUD 1,115 for practices with up to 20 practitioners (effective 2003); Online - full content ed.: AUD 1,115 for practices with up to 20 practitioners.
Published by: Lawbook Co. (Subsidiary of: Thomson Legal & Regulatory Ltd.), PO Box 3502, Rozelle, NSW 2039, Australia. TEL 61-2-85877000, FAX 61-2-85877100, LRA.Service@thomson.com, http://onlineecom01.thomson.com.au/thomson/Catalog.asp?EES_CMD=SI&EES_ID=100445, http://www.lawbookco.com.au/. Eds. Michael G Walton, R S Watson.

365 USA ISSN 0014-9128
FEDERAL PROBATION; a journal of correctional philosophy and practice. Variant title: Federal Probation Newsletter. Text in English. 1937. 3/yr. USD 16.50 domestic; USD 22.40 foreign (effective 2004). bk.rev. abstr.; bibl.; illus.; charts; stat. index; cum.index every 5 yrs. back issues avail.; reprint service avail. from PQC,WSH. **Document type:** *Journal, Academic/Scholarly.* **Description:** Contains articles relating to preventive and correctional activities in delinquency and crime.
Formerly (until 1937): U.S. Probation System. News Letter
Related titles: Microform ed.: (from MIM, PQC); Online - full text ed.: ISSN 1555-0303 (from EBSCO Publishing, H.W. Wilson, Northern Light Technology, Inc., O C L C Online Computer Library Center, Inc., ProQuest Information & Learning).
Indexed: AC&P, AMHA, ASCA, AgeL, BRI, CBRI, CJA, CJPI, CLI, CurCont, EIA, EnerInd, ExcerpMed, FamI, IBR, ILP, IUSGP, LRI, MEA&I, PAIS, PCI, PsycInfo, PsycholAb, SPAA, SSCI, SSI, V&AA, e-psyche.
—BLDSC (3901.932000), IDS, IE, Infotrieve, ingenta.
Published by: Administrative Office of the United States Courts, Federal Corrections and Supervision Division, 1 Columbus Circle, NE, Washington, DC 20544. TEL 202-502-1600, FAX 202-502-1677, http://www.uscourts.gov/library/fpcontents.html. Ed. Ellen Wilson Fielding. R&P Karen S Henkel. Circ: 6,500. **Subscr. to:** U.S. Government Printing Office, Superintendent of Documents, PO Box 371954, Pittsburgh, PA 15250-7954. TEL 202-512-1800, FAX 202-512-2250, orders@gpo.gov, http://www.access.gpo.gov.

340 USA ISSN 1059-180X
KF9685
FEDERAL SENTENCING GUIDELINES HANDBOOK: TEXT, ANALYSIS, CASE DIGEST. Text in English. 1990. a. USD 80. **Document type:** *Trade.*
Published by: Shepard's (Subsidiary of: LexisNexis North America), 555 Middle Creek Pkwy, Colorado Springs, CO 80921. TEL 800-743-7393, customer_service@shepards.com, http://www.shepards.com, http://www.lexisnexis.com/shepards/.

340 USA ISSN 1053-9867
KF9685.A59
➤ **FEDERAL SENTENCING REPORTER.** Text in English. 1988. 5/yr. USD 225 in North America to individuals; USD 241 combined subscription in North America to institutions print & online eds.; USD 261 combined subscription foreign to institutions print & online eds.; USD 116 combined subscription to students print & online eds. (effective 2005). 60 p./no.; back issues avail.; reprint service avail. from PQC,WSH. **Document type:** *Journal, Academic/Scholarly.* **Description:** Provides up-to-date information on and thorough analysis of contemporary federal sentencing issues.
Related titles: Microform ed.: (from PQC); Online - full text ed.: USD 217 to institutions (effective 2005) (from EBSCO Publishing, Gale Group, O C L C Online Computer Library Center, Inc., ProQuest Information & Learning, Swets Information Services, Thomson West).
Indexed: CJPI, CLI, FamI, ILP, LRI, PAIS.
—IE.
Published by: (Vera Institute of Justice), University of California Press, Journals Division, 2000 Center St, Ste 303, Berkeley, CA 94704-1223. TEL 510-643-7154, FAX 510-642-9917, journals@ucpress.edu, http://www.ucpress.edu/journals/fsr. Eds. Douglas J Berman, Nora Demleitner. R&Ps Darcy Dapra, Marge Dean TEL 510-642-6188. Circ: 2,450.

364 USA
FELONY DEFENDANTS IN LARGE URBAN COUNTIES. Text in English. 1988. biennial. free. stat. back issues avail. **Document type:** *Government.* **Description:** Contains data collected from a representative sample of felony cases filed in the Nation's 75 largest counties.
Formerly: National Pretrial Reporting Program (Year)
Related titles: Online - full content ed.
Published by: U.S. Department of Justice, Bureau of Justice Statistics, 810 Seventh St, N W, 2nd Fl, Washington, DC 20531. TEL 202-307-0765, FAX 202-307-0128, askbjs@ojp.usdoj.gov, http://www.ojp.usdoj.gov/bjs/pubalp2.htm#F. Circ: 17,000. **Orders to:** BJS Clearinghouse, Box 179, Annapolis Junction, MD 20701-0179. TEL 800-732-3277, FAX 410-792-4358.

364 USA ISSN 1557-0851
▼ **FEMINIST CRIMINOLOGY.** Text in English. 2006. q. USD 423, GBP 273 to institutions; USD 440, GBP 284 combined subscription to institutions print & online eds. (effective 2006). **Document type:** *Journal, Academic/Scholarly.*
Related titles: Online - full text ed.: ISSN 1557-086X. 2006. USD 418, GBP 270 to institutions (effective 2006).
Published by: Sage Publications, Inc., 2455 Teller Rd, Thousand Oaks, CA 91320. TEL 805-499-0721, 800-818-7243, FAX 805-499-8096, 800-583-2665, info@sagepub.com, http://www.sagepub.com/journal.aspx?pid=11595. Ed. Susan F Sharp. **Subscr. to:** Sage Publications Ltd., 1 Oliver's Yard, 55 City Rd, London EC1 1SP, United Kingdom. TEL 44-20-73740645, FAX 44-20-73748741, subscription@sagepub.co.uk.

363.2 ITA
FIAMME D'ARGENTO. Text in Italian. m.
Published by: Associazione Nazionale Carabinieri, Via Legnano, 1-a, Rome, RM 00040, Italy. Ed. Efisio Anedda.

363.2 UAE ISSN 1681-5297
AL FIKR AL-SURTI/POLICE THOUGHT. Text in Arabic. 1992. q. **Document type:** *Journal.* **Description:** Concerned with publication of scientific research and studies in the field of security in its broader context (the criminal, economic, social, cultural, environmental, nutrition, industrial, administration, crisis management etc.).
Published by: Al-Fikr Al-Shurti, c/o Abdullah Bin Nassar, Director, Sharjah Police Research Center, P O Box 29, Sharjah, United Arab Emirates. TEL 97150-4886967, 936-662-4091, FAX 97160-5551095, drmamdooh@hotmail.com. Ed. Abdullah Bin Nassar.

363.24 614.19   GBR   ISSN 0951-1288
FINGERPRINT WORLD. Text in English. 1975. q. GBP 17 in the European Union to individuals; USD 40 elsewhere to individuals; GBP 20 in the European Union to institutions; USD 60 elsewhere to institutions. adv. bk.rev. **Document type:** *Academic/Scholarly.*
Published by: Fingerprint Society, Merseyside Police, Fingerprint Bureau, Canning Pl., Liverpool, Merseyside L1 8JX, United Kingdom. Ed., R&P Graham Hughes. Adv. contact Steve Mewett. Circ: 1,200. **Subscr. to:** Vivienne Galloway, The Fingerprint Society, 5 Slate Close, Glenfield, Leics LE3 8QQ, United Kingdom.

364 343   USA   ISSN 1059-7298
HV8079.A7
FIRE AND ARSON INVESTIGATOR∗ . Text in English. 1949. q. subscr. incld. with membership. adv. bk.rev. back issues avail. **Document type:** *Journal, Academic/Scholarly.* **Description:** Covers all fields related to arson investigation.
Indexed: AC&P, CJA.
—BLDSC (3930.140000).
—**Published by:** International Association of Arson Investigators, Inc., 12770 Boenker Rd, St Louis, MO 63044. TEL 314-739-4224, FAX 314-739-4219, http://www.firearson.com/. Circ: 7,500.

FIRE AND POLICE PERSONNEL REPORTER. see *BUSINESS AND ECONOMICS—Personnel Management*

364   USA
FLORIDA CRIMINAL LAWS. Text in English. 1992. a. looseleaf. USD 16.95 (effective 2000). **Document type:** *Trade.* **Description:** Selected chapters of the Criminal Laws of the State of Florida, including Rules of Criminal Procedure.
Related titles: CD-ROM ed.: USD 49.95 (effective 2000).
Published by: Gould Publications, Inc. (Subsidiary of: LexisNexis), 1333 North US Hwy 17-92, Longwood, FL 32750-3724. TEL 407-695-9500, 800-717-7917, FAX 407-695-2906, info@gouldlaw.com, http://www.gouldlaw.com.

363.2   USA
THE FLORIDA POLICE CHIEF∗ . Text in English. 1961. m. USD 20 (effective 1999). back issues avail. **Document type:** *Trade.* **Description:** Informs and educates on law enforcement trends in the state.
Published by: Florida Police Chiefs Association, 924 N Gadsen St, Tallahassee, FL 32303-6316. TEL 904-385-9046, FAX 904-386-3272. adv.: B&W page USD 600, color page USD 1,200; trim 11 x 8.25. Circ: 1,000. **Subscr. to:** PO Box 14038, Tallahassee, FL 32317-4038.

364 345   USA
FLORIDA SECURITY OFFICER'S HANDBOOK. Text in English. 1995. irreg. USD 15.95 (effective 2000). **Document type:** *Monographic series.* **Description:** Includes extensive information about the laws, procedures, measures, and terminology essential to a security officer.
Published by: Gould Publications, Inc. (Subsidiary of: LexisNexis), 1333 North US Hwy 17-92, Longwood, FL 32750-3724. TEL 407-695-9500, 800-717-7917, FAX 407-695-2906, info@gouldlaw.com, http://www.gouldlaw.com.

363.2   CAN   ISSN 0703-4725
FLUTE. Text in French. 1945. m. free. illus.
Formerly: Revue des Agents de Police (0035-1903)
Published by: Montreal Urban Community Policemen's Brotherhood Inc./Fraternite des Policiers de la Communaute Urbaine de Montreal, 480 Gilford St, Montreal, PQ H2J 1N3, Canada. TEL 514-527-4161, FAX 514-527-7830. Ed. Gerald Deslandes. Circ: 9,000.

364.163 558.473   USA
FOCUS ON FRAUD; alliance against fraud in telemarketing and electronic commerce. Text in English. 1991. q. USD 9 domestic; USD 12 foreign (effective 2000). back issues avail. **Document type:** *Newsletter.* **Description:** Contains articles about law-enforcement, legislation, other initiatives to address telemarketing and internet fraud. Also lists educational materials.
Formerly: Quarterly - Alliance Against Fraud in Telemarketing (1055-4491)
Published by: National Consumers League, Inc., 1701 K St, N W, Ste 1200, Washington, DC 20006. TEL 202-835-3323, FAX 202-835-0747, http://www.fraud.org/aaft/aaftset.htm. Ed. Susan Grant. Circ: 1,500.

FORENSIC ACCOUNTING REVIEW. see *BUSINESS AND ECONOMICS*

FORENSIC SCIENCE COMMUNICATIONS. see *MEDICAL SCIENCES—Forensic Sciences*

365   USA   ISSN 0015-8275
FORTUNE NEWS. Text in English. 1967. q. USD 25 to non-members; free to qualified personnel (effective 2005). adv. bk.rev. back issues avail. **Document type:** *Newsletter.* **Description:** Reports on prison facilities, criminal justice issues, and root causes of crime.
Related titles: Online - full content ed.

Published by: Fortune Society, 39 W 19th St, New York, NY 10011. TEL 212-206-7070, FAX 212-633-6845, http://www.fortunesociety.org/news.htm. Ed. Erica Eaton. Adv. contact Joanne Page. Circ: 40,000.

363.2   DEU   ISSN 1618-4912
FORUM KRIMINALPRAEVENTION. Text in German. 2001. q. EUR 19; EUR 5 newsstand/cover (effective 2004). **Document type:** *Magazine, Trade.*
Published by: (Stiftung Deutsches Forum fuer Kriminalpraevention), Verlag Deutsche Polizeiliteratur GmbH, Forststr 3A, Hilden, 40721, Germany. TEL 49-211-71040, FAX 49-211-7104174, vdp.buchvertrieb@vdpolizei.de, http://forum-kriminalpraevention.de, http://www.vdpolizei.de. Ed. Edwin Kube. Adv. contact Michael Schwarz.

365   CAN   ISSN 0847-0464
HV7231
FORUM ON CORRECTIONS RESEARCH. Text in English. 1989. 3/yr. free (effective 2005). **Document type:** *Government.*
Related titles: French ed.: Forum, Recherche sur l'Actualite Correctionnelle. ISSN 0847-0472.
Indexed: CJA.
—BLDSC (4024.085160), IE, ingenta. **CCC.**
Published by: Correctional Service of Canada/Service Correctionnel Canada, 340 Laurier Ave W, Ottawa, ON K1A 0P9, Canada. TEL 613-992-5891, FAX 613-943-1630, http://www.csc-scc.gc.ca/text/pblct/forum/index_e.shtml. Ed., R&P Larry Motiuk TEL 613-995-4694. Circ: 6,000.

364   USA   ISSN 1020-9212
JX1977
FORUM ON CRIME AND SOCIETY. Text in English. 1946. a. USD 25 (effective 1997). reprint service avail. from PQC,PSC.
Formerly (until 1996): International Review of Criminal Policy (0074-7688)
Related titles: Microform ed.: (from PQC); French ed.: Forum sur le Crime et la Societe. ISSN 1020-9255; Russian ed.: Forum po Problemam Prestupnosti i Obsestva. ISSN 1020-9247; Spanish ed.: Foro Sobre el Delito y la Sociedad. ISSN 1020-9263; Arabic ed.: Muntada Hawla al-Garimat wa-al-Mugtama'. ISSN 1020-9271; Chinese ed.: Fanzui yu Shehui Wenti Luntan. ISSN 1020-928X.
Indexed: AC&P, CJA, CLI, ExcerpMed, FLP, ILP, MEA&I, PAIS, RASB.
Published by: (United Nations, Department of Economic and Social Affairs), United Nations Publications, 2 UN Plaza, DC2 Room 856, New York, NY 10017. TEL 212-963 3489, 800-253-9646, FAX 212-963 3489, publications@un.org, http://www.un.org/Pubs.

FRAUD REPORT. see *BUSINESS AND ECONOMICS—Banking And Finance*

FRAUD WATCH. see *BUSINESS AND ECONOMICS—Banking And Finance*

364.4 658   USA
FRESNO DAILY LEGAL REPORT∗ . Text in English. 1886. d. USD 130. adv. **Description:** Covers court and commercial interests.
Published by: G.M. Webster Jr., P O Box 126, Fresno, CA 93707. TEL 209-237-0114. Ed. G M Webster Jr. Circ: 1,125.

363.2   CHN
FUJIAN GONG'AN/FUJIAN PUBLIC SECURITY. Text in Chinese. 1949. m. CNY 15.60. **Document type:** *Consumer.*
Published by: (Fujian Sheng Gong'an Ting/Fujian Provincial Bureau of Public Security), Fujian Gong'an Publishing House, 12 Hualin Rd, Fuzhou, Fujian 350003, China. TEL 8093063. Ed. Li Jiaju. Circ: 65,000. **Dist. overseas by:** Jiangsu Publications Import & Export Corp., 56 Gao Yun Ling, Nanjing, Jiangsu, China.

G C D: LA REVISTA DE LA SEGURIDAD. see *PUBLIC ADMINISTRATION*

362.2   IRL   ISSN 0332-463X
GARDA NEWS. Text in English. 10/yr.
Formerly (until 1982): Horizon (0332-4621)
Published by: Association of Garda Sergeants & Inspectors, Phibsboro Tower, 6th Fl., Dublin, 7, Ireland. TEL 303752, FAX 303465. Ed. Austin Kenny. Circ: 5,000.

363.2   IRL
GARDA REVIEW. Text in English. 1924. m. EUR 16.64 (effective 2005). adv. bk.rev. charts; illus.; tr.lit. **Document type:** *Journal, Trade.* **Description:** Monthly publication of the Irish police force, or Garda.
Formerly: Iris an Gharda (0021-101X)
Published by: Dyflin Publications Ltd., 99 S Circular Rd., Dublin, 8, Ireland. TEL 353-1-4167900, FAX 353-1-4167901, gardareview@dyflin.ie. adv.: B&W page EUR 1,900, color page EUR 2,700; 210 x 297. Circ: 12,000.

363.2   IRL
AN GARDA SIOCHANA. ANNUAL POLICING PLAN. Text in English. a.
Related titles: Online - full text ed.
—BLDSC (1089.725350).

Published by: An Garda Siochana/Ireland's National Police Service, Garda Headquarters, Phoenix Park, Dublin, Ireland. http://www.irlgov.ie/garda/angarda/othdocs.html. **Subscr. to:** Government Publications Office, Sun Alliance House, Molesworth St, Dublin 2, Ireland. TEL 353-1-6613111.

363.2   IRL   ISSN 0791-0584
AN GARDA SIOCHANA. ANNUAL REPORT. Text in English. 1935. a.
Formerly (until 1980): Garda Directory (0791-0576)
Related titles: Online - full text ed.
Published by: An Garda Siochana/Ireland's National Police Service, Garda Headquarters, Phoenix Park, Dublin, Ireland. http://www.irlgov.ie/garda/angarda/annreport.html. **Subscr. to:** Government Publications Office, Sun Alliance House, Molesworth St, Dublin 2, Ireland. TEL 353-1-6613111.

363.2   IRL
GARDA TIMES. Text in English. q. adv. **Document type:** *Magazine, Trade.*
Published by: (Association of Garda Superintendents), Ashville Media Group, Apollo House, Tara St., Dublin, 2, Ireland. TEL 353-1-4322200, FAX 353-1-6727100, info@ashville.com. Ed. John Grant. Adv. contact Brian O'Neill.

365   GBR
GATELODGE. Text in English. 1939. bi-m. GBP 6, GBP 8 to non-members; GBP 16 foreign to non-members; GBP 6 to senior citizens. adv. bk.rev. **Document type:** *Trade.*
Formerly (until 1986): Prison Officers Magazine (0032-8863)
Indexed: AC&P.
Published by: Prison Officers' Association, Cronin House, 245 Church St, London, N9 9HW, United Kingdom. TEL 0181-803-0255, FAX 0181-803-1761. Ed. David Evans. Circ: 17,500.

364   USA
GEORGIA SECURITY OFFICER'S HANDBOOK. Text in English. 1997. irreg. USD 15.95 (effective 2000). **Description:** Includes information on the following subjects: chain of command, general orders, disciplinary action charges, uniform and equipment issues, termination of employment, code of ethics, regulations, personal conduct and appearance, vehicle safety checks, vehicle escort procedures, self-defense, courtroom testimony, Georgia State traffic laws, arrests, search and seizure, and firearms and deadly force.
Published by: Gould Publications, Inc. (Subsidiary of: LexisNexis), 1333 North US Hwy 17-92, Longwood, FL 32750-3724. TEL 800-717-7917, FAX 407-695-2906, info@gouldlaw.com, http://www.gouldlaw.com.

GLOBAL CRIME. see *POLITICAL SCIENCE—International Relations*

GLOBAL JOURNAL ON CRIME AND CRIMINAL LAW. see *LAW—Criminal Law*

327.117   NLD   ISSN 1386-4637
GLOBAL TERRORISM COLLECTION. Text in English. 1998. 6 base vols. plus irreg. updates. reprint service avail. from WSH. **Document type:** *Journal, Academic/Scholarly.* **Description:** Publishes important documents on efforts by nations to prevent acts of terrorism. Includes texts of relevent resolutions of the UN General Assembly.
Published by: Global Law Association, PO Box 9001, Tilburg, 5000 HA, Netherlands. TEL 31-13-544-3135, FAX 31-24-355-4827, globallaw@writeme.com, http://www.globallaw.org. Ed. J Graham. **Subscr. to:** PO Box 30151, Nijmegen 6503 CB, Netherlands. **Dist. in N. America by:** Wm. W. Gaunt & Sons Inc., Gaunt Bldg, 3011 Gulf Dr, Holmes Beach, FL 34217-2199. TEL 941-778-5211, 941-778-5252.

GLOBAL WAR CRIMES TRIBUNAL COLLECTION. see *LAW—International Law*

364   DEU   ISSN 0017-1956
K1
GOLTDAMMER'S ARCHIV FUER STRAFRECHT. Text in German. 1853. m. EUR 258 domestic; EUR 264 foreign; EUR 20 newsstand/cover (effective 2003). adv. bk.rev. bibl.; charts; illus.; stat. index. reprints avail. **Document type:** *Magazine, Academic/Scholarly.*
Indexed: DIP, FLP, IBR, IBZ.
—IE, Infotrieve.
Published by: R. v. Decker's Verlag Huethig GmbH, Im Weiher 10, Heidelberg, 69121, Germany. TEL 49-6221-489454, FAX 49-6221-489624, hsv_zeitschrift@huethig.de, http://www.huethig.de. Ed. P G Poetz. adv.: page EUR 450. Circ: 650.

GOVERNMENT COMPUTER NEWS. STATE & LOCAL. see *PUBLIC ADMINISTRATION—Computer Applications*

363.2   GBR
GREAT BRITAIN. HOME OFFICE. CRIME REDUCTION PROGRAMME GUIDANCE NOTE. Text in English. 1999. irreg.
—BLDSC (3487.344050).

C

▼ *new title*   ➤ *refereed*   ∗ *unverified*   ◆ *full entry avail.*

Published by: Home Office, 50 Queen Anne's Gate, London, SW1 9AT, United Kingdom. TEL 44-171-273-3072, http://www.open.gov.uk.

364.1 GBR ISSN 0959-597X
GREAT BRITAIN. HOME OFFICE. POLICE RESEARCH GROUP. CRIME PREVENTION UNIT. PAPERS. Text in English. 1992 (no.32). irreg. price varies. **Document type:** *Monographic series, Government.*
Published by: (Great Britain. Home Office), Home Office, Police Research Group (Subsidiary of: Home Office), Crime Prevention Unit, 50 Queen Anne's Gate, London, SW1H 9AT, United Kingdom.

365 GBR ISSN 0265-573X
HV9649.E5
GREAT BRITAIN. HOME OFFICE. PROBATION STATISTICS ENGLAND & WALES (YEAR). Key Title: Probation Statistics England & Wales (Year). Text in English. a. **Document type:** *Government.*
—BLDSC (6617.256500). **CCC.**
Published by: (Great Britain. Publications Office), Home Office, 50 Queen Anne's Gate, London, SW1 9AT, United Kingdom. **Subscr. to:** Research and Statistics Department, Lunar House, Croydon, Surrey CR0 9YD, United Kingdom. TEL 081-760-2850.

GREAT BRITAIN. HOME OFFICE. RESEARCH AND PLANNING UNIT. PROGRAMME (YEAR). see *PUBLIC ADMINISTRATION*

GREAT BRITAIN. HOME OFFICE. RESEARCH AND STATISTICS DEPARTMENT. RESEARCH BULLETIN. see *PUBLIC ADMINISTRATION*

GREAT BRITAIN. HOME OFFICE. RESEARCH, DEVELOPMENT AND STATISTICS DIRECTORATE. FINDINGS. see *PUBLIC ADMINISTRATION*

364 GBR ISSN 0072-6435
GREAT BRITAIN. HOME OFFICE. RESEARCH STUDIES. Text in English. 1969. irreg. reprint service avail. from PQC. **Document type:** *Monographic series, Government.* **Description:** Publishes results of studies on social and operational research on the criminal justice system and community relations.
—BLDSC (4326.110000), IE, ingenta. **CCC.**
Published by: (Great Britain. Research and Planning Unit), Home Office, Research and Statistics Department, 50 Queen Anne's Gate, London, SW1 9AT, United Kingdom. **Orders to:** H.M.S.O., PO Box 276, London SW8 5DT, United Kingdom. TEL 44-207-873-0011, FAX 44-20-7873-8200.

363.2 GBR
GREAT BRITAIN. NATIONAL CRIME SQUAD. INSPECTION. Text in English. biennial.
—BLDSC (4518.464450).
Published by: National Crime Squad, P.O. Box 2500, London, SW1V 2WF, United Kingdom. http://www.nationalcrimesquad.police.uk.

363.2 799.3 USA ISSN 1058-2975
GUNS & WEAPONS FOR LAW ENFORCEMENT. Text in English. 1990. 8/yr. USD 23.97 domestic; USD 31.16 in Canada; USD 47.97 elsewhere (effective 2005). adv. **Document type:** *Magazine, Trade.* **Description:** Provides information and features on the weapons and tools used by law enforcement organizations and personnel.
Published by: Harris Publications, Inc., 800 Kennesaw Ave, Ste 220, Marietta, GA 30060. TEL 770-421-8160, 888-456-6247, 800-866-2886, harrismags@aol.com, http://www.guns-weapons.com. adv.: B&W page USD 3,080, color page USD 4,150; trim 8 x 10.875. Circ: 82,000 (paid).

364 GBR
H M INSPECTORATE OF PROBATION. QUALITY & EFFECTIVENESS INSPECTION REPORTS. Text in English. irreg.
Published by: (H M Inspectorate of Probation), Home Office, 50 Queen Anne's Gate, London, SW1 9AT, United Kingdom. TEL 44-171-273-3072.

364 325.1 GBR
H M P REVIEW. Text in English. 1994. 3/yr. GBP 35 (effective 1999). adv. tr.lit. back issues avail. **Document type:** *Journal, Trade.* **Description:** Contains interviews and articles relevant to police, prisons, immigration, and customs.
Published by: Harrison Belmont, Broadway House, Bedford, United Kingdom. TEL 44-1234-348878, hbellmont@atlas.co.uk. Ed. Jan Goode. Pub. S Mitchell. R&P S. Mitchell. adv.: B&W page GBP 995, color page GBP 1,095.

HANDBOOK OF FORENSIC SERVICES. see *MEDICAL SCIENCES—Forensic Sciences*

353.9 USA ISSN 0098-5708
HV8688
HAWAII. CRIMINAL INJURIES COMPENSATION COMMISSION. ANNUAL REPORT. Key Title: Annual Report - Criminal Injuries Compensation Commission. Text in English. 1967. a.
Published by: Criminal Injuries Compensation Commission, 333 Queen St, Rm 404, Honolulu, HI 96813. TEL 808-587-1143, FAX 808-548-8102.

351.74 DEU ISSN 0343-3757
HESSISCHE POLIZEIRUNDSCHAU. Text in German. m. **Document type:** *Magazine, Trade.*
Published by: A. Bernecker Verlag, Unter dem Schoeneberg 1, Melsungen, 34212, Germany. TEL 49-5661-7310, FAX 49-5661-731111, http://www.bernecke.de.

353.9 364.4 USA ISSN 1543-4427
▼ **HOMELAND SECURITY BRIEFING.** Text in English. 2003. d. (Mon.-Fri.). USD 1,010 domestic (effective 2005 - 2006).
Media: Online - full content. **Related titles:** Online - full text ed.: (from The Bureau of National Affairs, Inc.).
—**CCC.**
Published by: The Bureau of National Affairs, Inc., 1231 25th St., NW, Washington, DC 20037. TEL 202-452-4200, 800-372-1033, FAX 202-452-4644, http://www.bna.com/products/corplaw/hsdm.htm. Ed., Pub. Greg C McCaffery.

▼ **THE HOMELAND SECURITY REVIEW.** see *PUBLIC ADMINISTRATION*

364.021 USA ISSN 0098-8537
HV6533.C2
HOMICIDE IN CALIFORNIA. Text in English. 1963. irreg. free. illus.; stat.
Related titles: Online - full text ed.
Published by: Department of Justice, Criminal Justice Statistics Center, PO Box 903427, Sacramento, CA 95820. TEL 916-227-3509.

364.1 USA ISSN 1088-7679
HV6515
➤ **HOMICIDE STUDIES**; an interdisciplinary & international journal. Text in English. 1997. q. USD 501, GBP 323 to institutions; USD 521, GBP 337 combined subscription to institutions print & online eds. (effective 2006). adv. illus. reprints avail. **Document type:** *Journal, Academic/Scholarly.* **Description:** Devoted to the dissemination of information concerning research, public policy and applied knowledge relating to the study of homicide.
Related titles: Online - full text ed.: ISSN 1552-6720. USD 495, GBP 320 to institutions (effective 2006) (from C S A, EBSCO Publishing, O C L C Online Computer Library Center, Inc., Sage Publications, Inc., Swets Information Services).
Indexed: ASG, CJA, CJPI, DIP, ESPM, H&SSA, IBR, IBZ, PRA, PSA, PsycInfo, PsycholAb, RiskAb, SFSA, SPAA, SSA, SUSA, SociolAb, V&AA.
—BLDSC (4326.177900), IE, Infotrieve, ingenta. **CCC.**
Published by: Sage Publications, Inc., 2455 Teller Rd, Thousand Oaks, CA 91320. TEL 805-499-0721, FAX 805-499-8096, info@sagepub.com, http://www.sagepub.com/journal.aspx?pid=74. Eds. Jay Corzine, Thomas Petee. R&P Tanya Udin TEL 805-499-0721 ext 7716. Adv. contact Kirsten Beaulieu TEL 805-499-0721 ext 7160. B&W page USD 350, color page USD 1,150. **Subscr. overseas to:** Sage Publications Ltd., 1 Oliver's Yard, 55 City Rd, London EC1 1SP, United Kingdom. TEL 44-20-73740645, FAX 44-20-73748741, subscription@sagepub.co.uk.

364 340 USA ISSN 0895-3171
HOTLINE (STONY BROOK); news service on the missing children field. Text in English. 1980. q. looseleaf. free. bk.rev. back issues avail.
Published by: Children's Rights of New York, Inc., 15 Arbutus Lane, Stony Brook, NY 11790-1408. TEL 516-751-7840. Ed. John E Gill. Circ: 1,700.

364 USA
HOW TO FIND ANYONE ANYWHERE; secret sources & techniques for locating missing persons. Text in English. 1981. a. USD 35 (effective 2000). **Description:** Contains how-to tips for investigators.
Published by: (National Association of Investigative Specialists), Thomas Publishing (Austin), PO Box 33244, Austin, TX 78764. TEL 512-719-3595. Ed. Ralph Thomas. Circ: 2,500.

365 GBR ISSN 0265-5527
HV8995.A1
➤ **THE HOWARD JOURNAL OF CRIMINAL JUSTICE.** Text in English. 1941. 5/yr. GBP 54, EUR 81 combined subscription in Europe to individuals print & online eds.; USD 144 combined subscription in the Americas to individuals & Caribbean, print & online eds.; GBP 86 combined subscription elsewhere to individuals print & online eds.; GBP 331 combined subscription in Europe to institutions print & online eds.; USD 675 combined subscription in the Americas to institutions & Caribbean, print & online eds.; GBP 402 combined subscription elsewhere to institutions print & online eds.; EUR 32 combined subscription in Europe to students print & online eds.; USD 35 combined subscription in the Americas to students & Caribbean, print & online eds.; GBP 21 combined subscription elsewhere to students print & online eds. (effective 2006). bk.rev. illus. cum.index 1941-1975. reprint service avail. from PQC,PSC. **Document type:** *Journal, Academic/Scholarly.* **Description:** Offers commentary and reviews on both the theory and the practice of criminal justice and the study of criminals. Reports academic research and makes complex material accessible to criminal-justice professionals.
Formerly (until Feb. 1984): Howard Journal of Penology and Crime Prevention (0073-3741)
Related titles: Microform ed.: (from PQC); Online - full text ed.: ISSN 1468-2311. GBP 314 in Europe to institutions; USD 642 in the Americas to institutions & Caribbean; GBP 382 elsewhere to institutions (effective 2006) (from Blackwell Synergy, EBSCO Publishing, Gale Group, IngentaConnect, O C L C Online Computer Library Center, Inc., Swets Information Services).
Indexed: AC&P, ASSIA, AddicA, BrHumI, CJA, CJPI, CLI, DIP, ELJI, FamI, IBR, IBSS, IBZ, LJI, LRI, PAIS, PSA, PsycInfo, PsycholAb, SOPODA, SSA, SociolAb.
—BLDSC (4335.244300), IE, Infotrieve, ingenta. **CCC.**
Published by: (Howard League for Penal Reform), Blackwell Publishing Ltd., 9600 Garsington Rd, Oxford, OX4 2ZG, United Kingdom. TEL 44-1865-776868, FAX 44-1865-714591, customerservices@oxon.blackwellpublishing.com, http://www.blackwellpublishing.com/journals/HOJO. Eds. David Wilson, Tony Fowles. Circ: 1,700.

365 GBR ISSN 1463-435X
HOWARD LEAGUE MAGAZINE. Text in English. 1970. 4/yr. GBP 12 to members; GBP 3.50 newsstand/cover. adv. bk.rev. illus. **Document type:** *Newsletter.* **Description:** Reports on prison facilities and administration.
Former titles (until Jan. 1998): Criminal Justice (0264-987X); (until 1983): Howard League for Penal Reform Newsletter
Related titles: Microform ed.: (from PQC).
Indexed: CJPI, CLI.
—BLDSC (4319.240000), IE, ingenta.
Published by: Howard League, 708 Holloway Rd, London, N19 3NL, United Kingdom. TEL 44-171-281-7722, FAX 44-171-281-5506, howard.league@ukonline.co.uk, http://web.ukonline.co.uk/howard.league. Ed. Frances Crook. Adv. contact Euginia Lolomari. Circ: 3,000.

▼ **HSTODAY**; insight & analysis for homeland security policy makers. (Homeland Security) see *PUBLIC ADMINISTRATION*

HUMAN KINDNESS FOUNDATION NEWSLETTER; a little good news. see *RELIGIONS AND THEOLOGY*

363.2 USA
I A C P MODEL POLICY ISSUES. Text in English. bi-m. USD 30 to institutions under 50 officers; USD 50 to institutions over 50 officers (effective 1999). **Document type:** *Trade.*
Formerly: I A C P - B J A Policy Issues
Published by: International Association of Chiefs of Police, Inc., 515 N Washington St, Alexandria, VA 22314-2340. TEL 703-836-6767, FAX 703-836-4543, information@theiacp.org, http://www.theiacp.org/. Ed. Philip Lynn. Circ: (controlled).

363.2 USA
I A C P TRAINING KEY. Text in English. m. USD 6 (effective 1999).
Indexed: CJA, CJPI.
Published by: International Association of Chiefs of Police, Inc., 515 N Washington St, Alexandria, VA 22314-2340. TEL 703-836-6767, FAX 703-836-4543, information@theiacp.org, http://www.theiacp.org/. Circ: (controlled).

364 USA
I A I MEMBERSHIP DIRECTORY. Text in English. a. members only. **Document type:** *Directory, Trade.*
Published by: International Association for Identification, 2535 Pilot Knob Rd, Ste 117, Mendota Heights, MN 55120-1120. TEL 651-681-8566, FAX 651-681-8443, iaisecty@theiai.org, http://www.theiai.org/.

364 USA ISSN 1546-7627
I C C A JOURNAL ON COMMUNITY CORRECTIONS. Variant title: Journal of Community Corrections. Text in English. 1967. 4/yr. USD 50 (effective 2000). adv. bk.rev. bibl.; stat. **Document type:** *Trade.* **Description:** Seeks to promote and enhance community-based criminal justice and alternative services.

Former titles: International Association of Residential and Community Alternatives. Journal; International Halfway House Association. Newsletter
Indexed: CJA.
Published by: International Community Corrections Association, PO Box 1987, La Crosse, WI 54602-1987. TEL 608-785-0200, FAX 608-784-5335, icca@execpc.com, http://www.iccaweb.org. R&P Peter Kinziger. Circ: 3,000.

364 USA
I D CHECKING GUIDE (INTERNATIONAL). Text in English. 1993. s-a. USD 32.95 domestic; USD 34.95 foreign (effective 2000). **Description:** Features full-color coverage of driver's licenses for countries outside of the U.S. and Canada.
Published by: Drivers License Guide Company, 1492 Oddstad Dr, Redwood City, CA 94063. TEL 650-369-4849.

343 364.4 USA ISSN 1041-5793
HV8074
I D CHECKING GUIDE (YEAR); U.S. & Canadian edition. Text in English. 1971. a. USD 24.95 domestic; USD 27 foreign (effective 2000). **Description:** Full color coverage of all driver's licenses valid-in-use in U.S. and Canada.
Formerly: Drivers License Guide (0276-1696)
Published by: Drivers License Guide Company, 1492 Oddstad Dr, Redwood City, CA 94063. TEL 650-369-4849. Ed. Keith Doerge. Circ: 50,000.

I F A R JOURNAL. see *ART*

363.2 DEU ISSN 1435-6422
I P A AKTUELL. (International Police Association) Text in German. 1955. 4/yr. EUR 25 membership (effective 2005). adv. bk.rev. **Document type:** *Journal, Trade.*
Published by: International Police Association, Deutsche Sektion e.V., Schulze-Delitzsch-Str 4, Bexbach, 66450, Germany. TEL 49-6826-510990, FAX 49-6826-510991, webmaster@ipa-deutschland.de, http://www.ipa-deutschland.de. Ed. Hubert Vitt. adv.: page EUR 3,250; trim 181 x 271. Circ: 60,500 (controlled).

364.4 346.01 GBR ISSN 0284-9887
I P A - JOURNAL✶. Text in Swedish. 1964. bi-m. SEK 75 to members (effective 1990).
Formerly (until vol.3, 1988): International Police Association
Published by: International Police Association, Svenska Sektionen, c/o I P A- International Administration, 1 Fox Rd, West Bridgford, Nottingham, Notts NG2 6AJ, United Kingdom.

363.2 USA ISSN 0019-2171
HV7551
ILLINOIS POLICE ASSOCIATION. OFFICIAL JOURNAL✶. Text in English. 1945. bi-m. USD 10. adv. bk.rev.
Published by: Illinois Police Association, 220 Yosemite Cir N, Minneapolis, MN 55422-5032. Ed. E B Hoffman. Circ: 17,000 (controlled).

364 IND ISSN 0376-9844
HV6201 CODEN: IJOCDS
➤ **INDIAN JOURNAL OF CRIMINOLOGY.** Text in English. 1973. s-a. USD 30 (effective 2000). bk.rev. bibl. **Document type:** *Academic/Scholarly.*
Indexed: CJA, DIP, IBR, IPsyAb.
—BLDSC (4410.900000).
Published by: Indian Society of Criminology, c/o Department of Psychology, University of Madras, Chennai, Tamil Nadu 600 005, India. TEL 91-44-25366988, FAX 91-44-26181751, thilagaraj@hotmail.com. Ed., R&P K V Kaliappan. Circ: 1,200.

363.2 IND ISSN 0537-2429
HV7551
INDIAN POLICE JOURNAL. Text in English. 1954. q. INR 7. bk.rev. illus. **Document type:** *Government.*
Indexed: BAS, PAA&I.
Published by: Ministry of Home Affairs, Intelligence Bureau, 25 Akbar Rd., New Delhi, 110 011, India.

365 ITA ISSN 0019-7084
K9
INDICE PENALE. Text in Italian. 1967. 4/yr. EUR 100 domestic; EUR 125 foreign (effective 2004). **Document type:** *Journal, Academic/Scholarly.* **Description:** Review of law, criminal procedure and criminology.
—IE.
Published by: C E D A M, Via Giuseppe Jappelli 5-6, Padua, PD 35121, Italy. TEL 39-049-8239111, FAX 39-049-8752900, info@cedam.com, http://www.cedam.com. Ed. Alesso Lanzi. Circ: 700.

364 DEU
INFO INTERN. Text in German. 1951. bi-m. EUR 24 (effective 2005). 20 p./no.; **Document type:** *Bulletin, Trade.* **Description:** Provides press reviews on judgement decisions, investigation reports, and general information for members.
Published by: Bundesverband Deutscher Detektive e.V., Koehlstr 16, Bonn, 53125, Germany. TEL 49-228-298085, FAX 49-228-298091, bddev@bdd.de, http://www.bdd.de. Ed., Adv. contact Josef Riehl. Circ: 250 (paid).

364.660973 USA ISSN 1538-6678
INFORMATION PLUS REFERENCE SERIES. CAPITAL PUNISHMENT; cruel and unusual?. Text in English. 1978. biennial. USD 40 per vol. (effective 2005). **Document type:** *Monographic series, Academic/Scholarly.*
Related titles: Online - full content ed.; ♦ Series of: Information Plus Reference Series.
Published by: Gale Group (Subsidiary of: Thomson Corporation), 27500 Drake Rd, Farmington Hills, MI 48331-3535. TEL 248-699-4253, 800-877-4253, FAX 248-699-8035, 800-414-5043, galeord@gale.com, http://www.galegroup.com.

364 USA ISSN 1532-2696
HV6201
INFORMATION PLUS REFERENCE SERIES. CRIME; a serious American problem. Text in English. 1980. biennial. USD 40 per vol. (effective 2005). **Document type:** *Monographic series, Academic/Scholarly.*
Related titles: Online - full content ed.; ♦ Series of: Information Plus Reference Series.
Published by: Gale Group (Subsidiary of: Thomson Corporation), 27500 Drake Rd, Farmington Hills, MI 48331-3535. TEL 248-699-4253, 800-877-4253, FAX 248-699-8035, 800-414-5043, galeord@gale.com, http://www.galegroup.com.

363.330973 USA ISSN 1534-1909
INFORMATION PLUS REFERENCE SERIES. GUN CONTROL; restricting rights or protecting people?. Text in English. 1985. biennial. USD 40 per vol. (effective 2005). **Document type:** *Monographic series, Academic/Scholarly.*
Related titles: Online - full content ed.; ♦ Series: Information Plus Reference Series.
Published by: Gale Group (Subsidiary of: Thomson Corporation), 27500 Drake Rd, Farmington Hills, MI 48331-3535. TEL 248-699-4253, 800-877-4253, FAX 248-699-8035, 800-414-5043, galeord@gale.com, http://www.galegroup.com.

365 USA ISSN 1536-5190
INFORMATION PLUS REFERENCE SERIES. PRISONS AND JAILS; a deterrent to crime?. Text in English. 1995. biennial, latest 2003. USD 40 per issue (effective 2005). **Document type:** *Monographic series, Academic/Scholarly.*
Related titles: Online - full content ed.; ♦ Series of: Information Plus Reference Series.
Published by: Gale Group (Subsidiary of: Thomson Corporation), 27500 Drake Rd, Farmington Hills, MI 48331-3535. TEL 248-699-4253, 800-877-4253, FAX 248-699-8035, 800-414-5043, galeord@gale.com, http://www.galegroup.com.

INFORMATION PLUS REFERENCE SERIES. VIOLENT RELATIONSHIPS; battering and abuse among adults. see *SOCIOLOGY*

INFORMATION PLUS REFERENCE SERIES. YOUTH VIOLENCE CRIME & GANGS; children at risk. see *CHILDREN AND YOUTH—About*

364 GBR
INSTITUTE OF CRIMINAL STUDIES. OCCASIONAL PAPERS. Text in English. irreg., latest no.9. **Document type:** *Monographic series, Academic/Scholarly.*
—BLDSC (6224.129700).
Published by: University of Portsmouth, Institute of Criminal Studies, Ravelin House, Revelin Park, Museum Rd, Portsmouth, Hants PO1 2QQ, United Kingdom. TEL 44-23-92843933, FAX 44-23-92843939, a.smith@port.ac.uk, http://www.hum.port.ac.uk/icjs/.

364 AUS
INSTITUTE OF CRIMINOLOGY. OCCASIONAL PAPERS. Text in English. irreg. AUD 12 newsstand/cover (effective 2001). **Document type:** *Journal, Academic/Scholarly.* **Description:** Addresses significant issues in the area of criminology.
Published by: University of Sydney, Law School. Institute of Criminology, 173-175 Phillip St, Sydney, NSW 2000, Australia. FAX 61-2-93510200, criminology@law.usyd.edu.au, http://www.law.usyd.edu.au/~criminology/.

364 AUS
INSTITUTE OF CRIMINOLOGY. PROCEEDINGS. Text in English. 1967. irreg. AUD 8 newsstand/cover (effective 2001). **Document type:** *Proceedings, Academic/Scholarly.*
Published by: University of Sydney, Law School. Institute of Criminology, 173-175 Phillip St, Sydney, NSW 2000, Australia. FAX 61-2-93510200, criminology@law.usyd.edu.au, http://www.law.usyd.edu.au/~criminology/.

364 USA ISSN 1538-7909
HV7231
INSTITUTE OF JUSTICE AND INTERNATIONAL STUDIES. JOURNAL. Text in English. 2002. irreg. **Document type:** *Journal, Academic/Scholarly.*
Related titles: Online - full text ed.: ISSN 1538-7917.
Published by: Central Missouri State University, Institute of Justice and International Studies, Dept. of Criminal Justice, Humphreys Bldg. Rm. 300, Warrensburg, MO 64093. TEL 660-543-4950, FAX 660-543-8306, holden@cmsu1.cmsu.edu, http://www.cmsu.edu/cj/journal.

INSTITUTO NACIONAL DE MEDICINA LEGAL DE COLOMBIA. REVISTA. see *MEDICAL SCIENCES—Forensic Sciences*

364 NER ISSN 0534-4816
INTER-AFRICAN CONFERENCE ON THE TREATMENT OF OFFENDERS. MEETINGS. REUNION✶. Text in English, French. 1953. irreg. **Document type:** *Proceedings.*
Published by: (Commission for Technical Co-Operation in Africa South of the Sahara), Maison de l'Afrique, BP 878, Niamey, Niger.

364 DEU ISSN 0937-0773
➤ **INTERDISZIPLINAERE BEITRAEGE ZUR KRIMINOLOGISCHEN FORSCHUNG.** Text in German. 1989. irreg., latest vol.25, 2003. price varies. reprint service avail. from IRC. **Document type:** *Monographic series, Academic/Scholarly.*
Published by: (Kriminologisches Forschungsinstitut Niedersachsen), Nomos Verlagsgesellschaft mbH und Co. KG, Waldseestr 3-5, Baden-Baden, 76530, Germany. TEL 49-7221-2104-0, FAX 49-7221-210427, nomos@nomos.de, http://www.nomos.de.

➤ **INTERFACE (SACRAMENTO).** see *COMPUTERS*

364 USA ISSN 0538-7191
INTERNATIONAL DIRECTORY OF PRISONERS AID AGENCIES✶. Text in English. irreg.
Published by: International Prisoners Aid Association, U of Louisville, Dept of Sociology, Louisville, KY 40292.

INTERNATIONAL DIRECTORY OF SAFETY, SECURITY AND FIRE FIGHTING EQUIPMENT IMPORTERS. see *BUSINESS AND ECONOMICS—Trade And Industrial Directories*

364.4 USA ISSN 0148-4648
HV5800
INTERNATIONAL DRUG REPORT. Text in English. 1960. q. USD 35 domestic; USD 50 foreign (effective 2001). bk.rev.; film rev. charts; stat. index. **Document type:** *Newsletter.*
Supersedes: International Narcotic Conference. Report: Proceedings of Annual Conference (0074-7114); Former titles: International Narcotic Report (0020-806X); International Drug Reporter
Published by: International Narcotic Enforcement Officers Association, 112 State St, Ste 1200, Albany, NY 12207. TEL 518-463-6232. Ed., R&P Celeste Morga. Circ: 10,000.

364 USA ISSN 0192-4036
HV6001
➤ **INTERNATIONAL JOURNAL OF COMPARATIVE AND APPLIED CRIMINAL JUSTICE.** Text in English. 1977. s-a. USD 75 to institutions; USD 40 to qualified personnel; USD 30 to students (effective 2004). adv. bk.rev. bibl.; charts; stat.; illus. back issues avail.; reprint service avail. from PQC. **Document type:** *Journal, Academic/Scholarly.*
Related titles: Microform ed.: (from PQC).
Indexed: AC&P, BAS, CJA, CJPI, CLI, ESPM, IBSS, LRI, RiskAb.
—BLDSC (4542.172700), IE, ingenta.
Published by: Wichita State University, Department of Criminal Justice, PO Box 135, Wichita, KS 67260-0135. TEL 316-978-6517, FAX 316-978-3626, dchang@twsuvm.uc.twsu.edu, http://www.cj.msu.edu/~international/, http://www.twsu-edu/. Ed., Pub., R&P, Adv. contact Dae H Chang. Circ: 500.

364 CAN ISSN 1201-9607
INTERNATIONAL JOURNAL OF COMPARATIVE CRIMINOLOGY. Text in English. 2001. s-a. CND 54.75 to individuals print & online eds.; CND 72.25 to institutions print & online eds. (effective 2001).
Related titles: Online - full content ed.: ISSN 1496-8266. CND 40 to institutions; CND 30 to individual members (effective 2001); Online - full text ed.: (from Gale Group, IngentaConnect, Swets Information Services).
Indexed: CJA.
—BLDSC (4542.172830), IE.
Published by: de Sitter Publications, 374 Woodsworth Rd, Willowdale, ON M2L 2T6, Canada. TEL 416-483-5656, FAX 416-441-3035, sales@desitterpublications.com, http://www.desitterpublications.com. Ed. Shivu Ishwaran. Circ: 250 (paid).

364 USA
▼ **INTERNATIONAL JOURNAL OF DIGITAL EVIDENCE.** Text in English. 2003. irreg. free (effective 2004). back issues avail. **Document type:** *Journal, Academic/Scholarly.* **Description:** Aims to be a forum for discussion of theory, research, policy, and practice in the rapidly field of digital evidence.
Media: Online - full content.
Published by: (Utica College, Economic Crime Institute), International Journal of Digital Evidence, c/o Dr. Gary R. Gordon, IJDE Ed, Utica College, 1600 Burrstone Rd, Utica, NY 13502. http://www.ijde.org/. Ed. Gary R Gordon.
Co-sponsor: Computer Forensics Research and Development Center.

C

616.8 364.3 USA ISSN 0306-624X
HV9261 CODEN: IOTCAH
➤ **INTERNATIONAL JOURNAL OF OFFENDER THERAPY AND COMPARATIVE CRIMINOLOGY.** Text in English. 1957. bi-m. USD 586, GBP 378 to institutions; USD 610, GBP 394 combined subscription to institutions print & online eds. (effective 2006). adv. bk.rev. bibl.; stat.; illus. index, cum.index: 1957-1975. back issues avail.; reprint service avail. from WSH. **Document type:** *Journal, Academic/Scholarly.* **Description:** International forum for research, discussion, and treatment of variables associated with crime and delinquency, with an emphasis on the theoretical and clinical treatment of the offender.
Former titles (until 1972): International Journal of Offender Therapy (0020-7497); (until 1966): Journal of Offender Therapy; (until 1961): Association for Psychiatric Treatment of Offenders. Journal
Related titles: Microfilm ed.: (from PQC); Online - full text ed.: ISSN 1552-6933. USD 580, GBP 374 to institutions (effective 2006) (from C S A, EBSCO Publishing, O C L C Online Computer Library Center, Inc., Sage Publications, Inc., Swets Information Services).
Indexed: ABRCLP, ABS&EES, AC&P, ASCA, ASSIA, AgeL, CJA, CJPI, CLI, CurCont, DIP, ESPM, ExcerpMed, FamI, H&SSA, IBR, IBSS, IBZ, ILP, IMFL, IPARL, LRI, MEA&I, PSA, PsycInfo, PsycholAb, RefZh, RiskAb, SFSA, SOPODA, SSA, SSCI, SSI, SUSA, SociolAb, V&AA, e-psyche.
—BLDSC (4542.424000), GNLM, IDS, IE, Infotrieve, ingenta. **CCC.**
Published by: Sage Publications, Inc., 2455 Teller Rd, Thousand Oaks, CA 91320. TEL 805-499-0721, FAX 805-499-8096, info@sagepub.com, http://www.sagepub.com/journal.aspx?pid=180. Eds. George Palermo, Susan Hanscom. Pub. Sara Miller McCune. R&P Tanya Udin TEL 805-499-0721 ext 7716. Adv. contact Kirsten Beaulieu TEL 805-499-0721 ext 7160. page USD 350. Circ: 650 (paid and free). **Subscr. overseas to:** Sage Publications Ltd., 1 Oliver's Yard, 55 City Rd, London EC1 1SP, United Kingdom. TEL 44-20-73740645, FAX 44-20-73748741, subscription@sagepub.co.uk.

C

363.2 GBR ISSN 1461-3557
INTERNATIONAL JOURNAL OF POLICE SCIENCE AND MANAGEMENT. Text in English. 1998. q. GBP 178, USD 303; GBP 231.74, USD 364 combined subscription print & online (effective 2005). adv. bk.rev. back issues avail. **Document type:** *Journal, Academic/Scholarly.* **Description:** Publishes original empirical work, conceptual articles and theoretical overviews or reviews, as well as articles on good practice or practice evaluation.
Related titles: Online - full content ed.: ISSN 1478-1603. GBP 188, USD 272 to institutions (effective 2005); Online - full text ed.: (from EBSCO Publishing, Swets Information Services).
Indexed: CJA.
—BLDSC (4542.470300), IE, ingenta. **CCC.**
Published by: Vathek Publishing, Bridge House, Dolby, Isle of Man, IM5 3BP, United Kingdom. TEL 44-1624-844056, FAX 44-1624-845043, mlw@vathek.com, http://www.vathek.com/ijpsm/index.shtml. Pub., Adv. contact Mairwen Lloyd-Williams. Circ: 500 (paid). **Dist. by:** Portland Press Ltd., Commerce Way, Colchester CO2 8HP, United Kingdom. TEL 44-1206-796351, FAX 44-1206-799331, sales@portland-services.com.

▼ **INTERNATIONAL JOURNAL OF PRISONER HEALTH.** see *PUBLIC HEALTH AND SAFETY*

364.4 USA
INTERNATIONAL NARCOTIC ENFORCEMENT OFFICERS ASSOCIATION DIRECTORY. Text in English. a. membership only. **Document type:** *Directory.*
Published by: International Narcotic Enforcement Officers Association, 112 State St, Ste 1200, Albany, NY 12207. TEL 518-463-6232. Ed. Celeste Morga. Circ: 10,000.

340 USA
INTERNATIONAL NARCOTICS CONTROL STRATEGY REPORT. Text in English. a. **Document type:** *Government.*
Related titles: Online - full text ed.
Published by: U.S. Department of State, Bureau for International Narcotics and Law Enforcement Affairs, 2201 C St, N W, Washington, DC 20520. TEL 202-647-6575, usdosweb@uic.edu, http://www.state.gov.

INTERNATIONAL PRISONERS AID ASSOCIATION. NEWSLETTER. see *SOCIAL SERVICES AND WELFARE*

364 360 GBR ISSN 0269-7580
HV6250 CODEN: IRVIE2
➤ **INTERNATIONAL REVIEW OF VICTIMOLOGY.** Text in English. 1990. 3/yr. GBP 169, USD 279 to institutions (effective 2005). abstr.; bibl.; charts; illus. back issues avail. **Document type:** *Journal, Academic/Scholarly.* **Description:** Covers all aspects of victimological research, victimization surveys, broader theoretical issues and philosophy of victimology, criminal justice, compensation, and more.
Related titles: Online - full text ed.
Indexed: AC&P, ASSIA, CJA, CLI, DIP, ERA, FamI, IBR, IBZ, IPsyAb, LRI, MEA, PerIslam, PsycInfo, PsycholAb, SFSA, SOPODA, SSA, SUSA, SWA, SociolAb, V&AA, e-psyche.
—BLDSC (4547.980000), IE, ingenta. **CCC.**
Published by: A B Academic Publishers, PO Box 42, Bicester, Oxon OX26 6NW, United Kingdom. jrnls@abapubl.demon.co.uk. Eds. David Miers, Edna Erez.

364 FRA ISSN 0539-032X
INTERNATIONAL SOCIETY OF CRIMINOLOGY. BULLETIN. Text in French. irreg.
Published by: International Society of Criminology/Societe Internationale de Criminologie, c/o Rachida Touahria, 4-14 rue Ferrus, Paris, 75014, France. TEL 33-1-45880023, FAX 33-1-45894076.

364 FRA
INTERNATIONAL SOCIETY OF CRIMINOLOGY. RAPPORTS ANNUELS. Text in English, French. a.
Formerly: International Society of Criminology. Rapport Quinquennaux
Published by: International Society of Criminology/Societe Internationale de Criminologie, c/o Rachida Touahria, 4-14 rue Ferrus, Paris, 75014, France. TEL 33-1-45880023, FAX 33-1-45894076.

364
INTERNATIONAL SYMPOSIUM ON FINGERPRINT DETECTION AND IDENTIFICATION. PROCEEDINGS. Text in English. irreg. USD 75 (effective 2003). 435 p./no.; **Document type:** *Proceedings, Academic/Scholarly.*
Published by: International Association for Identification, 2535 Pilot Knob Rd, Ste 117, Mendota Heights, MN 55120-1120. TEL 651-681-8566, FAX 651-681-8443, iaisecty@theiai.org, http://www.theiai.org/. Eds. Eliot Springer, Joseph Almog.

INTERPOL - MOSKVA. see *LITERATURE—Mystery And Detective*

364 USA ISSN 1544-6409
INVESTIGATIVE STOPS LAW BULLETIN. Text in English. 2002 (Nov.). m. USD 147 (effective 2005). **Document type:** *Newsletter, Trade.*
Related titles: Online - full text ed.: ISSN 1544-6417.
Published by: Quinlan Publishing Group, Marine Industrial Park, 23 Drydock Ave, 6th Fl, Boston, MA 02210-2387. TEL 800-229-2084, FAX 617-345-9646, 617-507-1079, info@quinlan.com, http://www.quinlan.com. Ed. Colin Thakkar. Pub. Dennis Hofmaier.

364.029 USA
INVESTIGATOR'S INTERNATIONAL ALL-IN-ONE DIRECTORY OF THE INVESTIGATIVE INDUSTRY. Text in English. 1981. a. USD 30 (effective 2000).
Published by: (National Association of Investigative Specialists), Thomas Publishing (Austin), PO Box 33244, Austin, TX 78764. TEL 512-719-3595. Ed. Ralph D Thomas. Circ: 2,000.

363.2 USA ISSN 0021-0633
IOWA POLICE JOURNAL✶ . Text in English. 1969. q. USD 4. adv. bk.rev. stat.
Published by: Iowa State Policeman's Association, PO Box 1615, Des Moines, IA 50306-1615. Ed. Michael R Hoffman. Circ: 5,000.

364 CAN ISSN 0075-1391
HV7131.I8
ISRAEL STUDIES IN CRIMINOLOGY. Text in English. 1970. irreg., latest vol.8, 2003, Winter. **Document type:** *Journal, Academic/Scholarly.*
Published by: (Tel Aviv University ISR, Institute of Criminology and Criminal Law GBR), de Sitter Publications, 374 Woodsworth Rd, Willowdale, ON M2L 2T6, Canada. info@desitterpublications.com, http://www.desitterpublications.com/Journals/isc.asp. Eds. Paul Knepper, Shlomo G Shoham.

ISSUES IN CHILD ABUSE ACCUSATIONS (ONLINE). see *CHILDREN AND YOUTH—About*

364 USA
J R S A FORUM. Text in English. q. free to members (effective 2002). **Document type:** *Newsletter.* **Description:** Addresses the concerns and interests of state-level criminal justice researchers and analysts, and UCR managers.
Formerly: C J S A Forum
Published by: Justice Research and Statistics Association, Inc., 777 N Capitol St, N E, Ste 801, Washington, DC 20002. TEL 202-842-9330, FAX 202-842-9329, cjinfo@jrsa.org, http://www.jrsa.org. Ed. Karen F Maline. Circ: 750.

JAIL AND PRISONER LAW BULLETIN. see *LAW—Criminal Law*

365.07 USA
JAIL OPERATIONS BULLETIN. Text in English. 1988. a. USD 63 to non-members; USD 39 to members (effective 2000). **Document type:** *Bulletin.* **Description:** Used for in-service training, formal classroom study, and individual study by jail officers.
Published by: American Jail Association, 1135 Professional Ct., Hagerstown, MD 21740-5853. TEL 301-790-3930, FAX 301-790-2941, jails@worldnet.att.net. Ed. Debra Goldentyer.

363.2 355.343 GBR
JANE'S POLICE AND SECURITY LIBRARY. Text in English. q. GBP 4,950, USD 7,950 (effective 2001). **Document type:** *Trade.* **Description:** Includes all titles from Jane's Police and Security libraries and special reports.
Media: CD-ROM. **Related titles:** Online - full text ed.: GBP 5,450, USD 8,750 (effective 2001).
Published by: Jane's Information Group, Sentinel House, 163 Brighton Rd, Coulsdon, Surrey CR5 2YH, United Kingdom. TEL 44-20-87003700, FAX 44-20-87631006, info@janes.co.uk, http://catalogue.janes.com/jpsl.shtml, http://www.janes.com. **Dist. in Asia by:** Jane's Information Group Asia, 60 Albert St, #15-01 Albert Complex, Singapore 189969, Singapore. TEL 65-331-6280, FAX 65-336-9921, info@janes.com.sg; **Dist. in Australia by:** Jane's Information Group Australia, PO Box 3502, Rozelle, NSW 2039, Australia. TEL 61-2-8587-7900, FAX 61-2-8587-7901, info@janes.thomson.com.au; **Dist. in the Americas by:** 1340 Braddock Pl, Ste 300, Alexandria, VA 22314-1651. TEL 703-683-3700, 800-824-0768, FAX 703-836-0297, 800-836-0297, info@janes.com.

363.2 GBR ISSN 0309-1414
JANE'S POLICE REVIEW. Variant title: Police Review. Text in English. 1893. w. GBP 79 in United Kingdom; GBP 99 in Europe; USD 126.40 in the Americas; AUD 205.40 in Australia & New Zealand; GBP 150 rest of world (effective 2005). adv. bk.rev. charts; illus.; tr.lit. Index. reprints avail. **Document type:** *Magazine, Trade.* **Description:** Provides expert briefings on the latest news affecting British police forces and their operational officers.
Related titles: CD-ROM ed.: GBP 160, USD 260, AUD 415 (effective 2004); Online - full text ed.: GBP 165, USD 265, AUD 430 (effective 2004).
Indexed: AC&P, ASSIA, CLI, HRIS, ILP, RASB, SSI.
—BLDSC (6543.262000), IE, ingenta.
Published by: Jane's Information Group, Sentinel House, 163 Brighton Rd, Coulsdon, Surrey CR5 2YH, United Kingdom. TEL 44-20-87003700, FAX 44-20-87631006, customerservices.uk@janes.com, info@janes.co.uk, http://pr.janes.com/, http://www.janes.com. Ed. Catriona Marchant. R&P Sergio Deoliveira. Adv. contact Janine Boxall TEL 44-20-87003852. Circ: 25,000 (paid). **Dist. by:** 1340 Braddock Pl, Ste 300, Alexandria, VA 22314-1651. TEL 703-683-3700, 800-824-0768, FAX 703-836-0297, 800-836-0297, info@janes.com; Jane's Information Group Asia, 60 Albert St, #15-01 Albert Complex, Singapore 189969, Singapore. TEL 65-331-6280, FAX 65-336-9921, info@janes.com.sg; Jane's Information Group Australia, PO Box 3502, Rozelle, NSW 2039, Australia. TEL 61-2-8587-7900, FAX 61-2-8587-7901, info@janes.thomson.com.au.

363.2 CHN ISSN 1005-6556
JING FANG/CHINA POLICE. Text in Chinese. 1994. m. CNY 60; USD 47 foreign. 64 p./no.; **Document type:** *Journal, Consumer.* **Description:** Covers public security issues, police and policemen, and the relationship between the police and the people.
Published by: (Jiangsu Sheng Gongan Ting), Jing Fang Zazhishe, 1 Yangzhou Lu, Nanjing, Jiangsu 210024, China. TEL 86-25-3329130, FAX 86-25-3735454, cnpolice@public1.ptt.js.cn, http://www.chinapolice.com. Ed. Wang Qi. R&P Yang Wang. Adv. contact Jingyu Qu. Circ: 260,000. **Dist. overseas by:** China International Book Trading Corp, 35 Chegongzhuang Xilu, Haidian District, PO Box 399, Beijing 100044, China.

▼ **JOURNAL FOR CRIME, CONFLICT AND MEDIA CULTURE.** see *LAW*

364.3 USA ISSN 1083-9267
HV9104
➤ **JOURNAL FOR JUVENILE JUSTICE AND DETENTION SERVICES.** Text in English. 1990. s-a. USD 45 to non-members (effective 2005). **Description:** Focuses on effective strategies, programs, trends, legal and ethical issues, and leadership and training in juvenile justice.
Indexed: CJA, SWR&A, SociolAb.
Published by: National Juvenile Detention Association, EKU/301 Perkins Bldg, 521 Lancaster Ave, Richmond, KY 40475-3102. FAX 859-622-2333, http://www.njda.com/learn-materials-journal.html.

➤ **JOURNAL OF ADDICTIONS & OFFENDER COUNSELING.** see *PSYCHOLOGY*

363.2 USA ISSN 0449-5063
JOURNAL OF CALIFORNIA LAW ENFORCEMENT. Text in English. 1966. q. USD 35; USD 50 foreign (effective 1999). **Document type:** *Journal, Trade.*
Related titles: Online - full text ed.: (from Northern Light Technology, Inc., ProQuest Information & Learning).
Indexed: AC&P, CJA, CJPI.
—BLDSC (4954.742000), ingenta.
Published by: California Peace Officers Association, 1455 Response Rd, Ste 190, Sacramento, CA 95815-4501. TEL 916-923-1825, FAX 916-263-6090. Ed. Leslie McGill. Circ: 1,100 (paid).

JOURNAL OF CLINICAL FORENSIC MEDICINE. see *MEDICAL SCIENCES—Forensic Sciences*

JOURNAL OF CONTEMPORARY CRIMINAL JUSTICE. see *LAW—Criminal Law*

364.07 USA ISSN 0740-2708
HV8875
➤ **JOURNAL OF CORRECTIONAL EDUCATION.** Text in English. 1949-1972; resumed 1974. q. USD 50 membership; USD 85 to libraries; USD 30 to students (effective 2004). adv. bk.rev. bibl.; charts; illus.; tr.lit. index, cum.index: 1959-1966. reprint service avail. from PQC. **Document type:** *Journal, Academic/Scholarly.* **Description:** Covers topics in the field of correctional education.
Related titles: Microform ed.: (from PQC); Online - full text ed.: (from EBSCO Publishing, H.W. Wilson, O C L C Online Computer Library Center, Inc., ProQuest Information & Learning).
Indexed: AC&P, CIJE, CJA, CJPI, CPE, EduInd.
—BLDSC (4965.350000), IE, ingenta.
Published by: (Correctional Educational Association), Ashland University, 401 College Ave, Ashland, OH 44805. TEL 800-882-1548, FAX 419-289-5999, steurer1@aol.com, http://www.ashland.edu/correctionaled. Eds. John J Dowdell, Rusell Craig. Pub. Carolyn Eggleston. Adv. contact Karen Kowmas. Circ: 3,300.

➤ **JOURNAL OF CORRECTIONAL HEALTH CARE.** see *MEDICAL SCIENCES*

364 USA ISSN 1064-508X
HV9470
JOURNAL OF CORRECTIONAL TRAINING✶. Text in English. 1986. q.
Published by: American Association of Correctional Training Personnel, Eastern Kentucky University, 217 Perkins Bldg, 521 Lancaster Ave, Richmond, KY 40475-3101.

364 USA ISSN 0735-648X
HV6201
➤ **JOURNAL OF CRIME & JUSTICE.** Text in English. 1981. s-a. USD 70 to libraries (effective 2005). adv. illus. reprints avail. **Document type:** *Journal, Academic/Scholarly.*
Indexed: AC&P, CJA, CJPI, CurCont, FamI.
—BLDSC (4965.526000), IE, ingenta.
Published by: (Rochester Institute of Technology, Department of Criminal Justice, Midwestern Criminal Justice Association), Anderson Publishing Co (Subsidiary of: LexisNexis North America), 9443 Springboro Pike, Miamisburg, OH 45342-4425. TEL 513-421-4142, 800-582-7295, FAX 513-562-8116, mail@andersonpublishing.com, http://www.ilstu.edu/~cjschre/JCJ.htm, http://www.andersonpublishing.com. Ed. Dr. Christopher J Schreck TEL 585-475-2462.

➤ **JOURNAL OF CRIMINAL JUSTICE.** see *LAW—Criminal Law*

364 USA ISSN 1070-8286
➤ **JOURNAL OF CRIMINAL JUSTICE AND POPULAR CULTURE.** Text in English. 1993. bi-w. free (effective 2005). bk.rev.; film rev.; play rev. back issues avail. **Document type:** *Journal, Academic/Scholarly.* **Description:** Publishes research and opinion on the intersection of crime, criminal justice and popular culture.
Media: Online - full text.
Indexed: CJA, CommAb, ESPM, H&SSA, RiskAb.
Published by: State University of New York at Albany, School of Criminal Justice, 135 Western Ave, Albany, NY 12222. TEL 518-442-5609, FAX 518-442-5716, sunycrj@cnsunix.albany.edu, sunycrj@csc.albany.edu, http://www.albany.edu/scj/jcjpc/. Ed., R&P Sean E Anderson.

364.07 GBR ISSN 1051-1253
HV7419.5
➤ **JOURNAL OF CRIMINAL JUSTICE EDUCATION.** Text in English. 1990. s-a. GBP 172, USD 283 combined subscription to institutions print & online eds. (effective 2006). adv. illus. Index. reprint service avail. from PSC. **Document type:** *Journal, Academic/Scholarly.* **Description:** Provides a forum for the examination, discussion and debate of a broad range of issues concerning post-secondary education in criminal justice, criminology and related areas.
Related titles: Online - full text ed.: GBP 163, USD 269 to institutions (effective 2006) (from EBSCO Publishing, ProQuest Information & Learning).
Indexed: CJA, CJPI.
—BLDSC (4965.535000), IE, ingenta.
Published by: (Academy of Criminal Justice Sciences USA), Routledge (Subsidiary of: Taylor & Francis Group), 4 Park Sq, Milton Park, Abingdon, Oxon OX14 4RN, United Kingdom. TEL 44-1235-828600, FAX 44-1235-829000, journals@routledge.com, http://www.tandf.co.uk/journals/titles/10511253.asp, http://www.routledge.com. Ed. Dr. Craig Hemmens. Circ: 3,000.

➤ **JOURNAL OF CRIMINAL LAW/KEIHO ZASSHI.** see *LAW—Criminal Law*

343 USA ISSN 0091-4169
CODEN: JCLCFB
➤ **JOURNAL OF CRIMINAL LAW & CRIMINOLOGY.** Short title: J C L C. Text in English. 1910. q. USD 45 domestic; USD 50 foreign; USD 13 newsstand/cover domestic; USD 15 newsstand/cover foreign (effective 2005). bk.rev. abstr.; bibl.; illus. index, cum.index: vols.1-24 (1910-1934). reprint service avail. from WSH. **Document type:** *Journal, Academic/Scholarly.*
Supersedes in part (in 1972): Journal of Criminal Law, Criminology and Police Science (0022-0205); Which had former titles (until 1951): Journal of Criminal Law & Criminology (Chicago, 1931) (0885-2731); (until 1940): American Institute of Criminal Law and Criminology. Journal (0885-4173)
Related titles: Microfiche ed.: (from WSH); Microfilm ed.: (from WSH); Microform ed.: (from PQC); Online - full text ed.: (from EBSCO Publishing, Florida Center for Library Automation, Gale Group, H.W. Wilson, JSTOR (Web-based Journal Archive), Northern Light Technology, Inc., O C L C Online Computer Library Center, Inc., ProQuest Information & Learning, Thomson West).
Indexed: ABCPolSci, AC&P, ASCA, CJA, CJPI, CLI, CurCont, DIP, ExcerpMed, FamI, IBR, IBSS, IBZ, ILP, IndIslam, LRI, LegCont, MEA&I, PAIS, PCI, PSA, PsycholAb, RASB, SSA, SSCI, SSI, SociolAb.
—BLDSC (4965.590000), IE, Infotrieve, ingenta.
Published by: (Northwestern University, School of Law), University of Illinois Press, 1325 S Oak St, Champaign, IL 61820-6903. TEL 866-244-0626, FAX 217-244-9910, jclclaw@nwu.edu, journals@uillinois.edu, http://www.law.northwestern.edu/jclc/, http://www.press.uillinois.edu. Ed. Matthew Burke. Circ: 2,700.

364 USA ISSN 1537-7938
HV9950
▼ **JOURNAL OF ETHNICITY IN CRIMINAL JUSTICE.** Text in English. 2003 (Spr.). q. USD 245 combined subscription domestic to institutions print & online eds.; USD 330.75 combined subscription in Canada to institutions print & online eds.; USD 355.25 combined subscription elsewhere to institutions print & online eds. (effective 2006). adv. reprint service avail. from HAW. **Document type:** *Journal, Academic/Scholarly.*
Related titles: Online - full text ed.: ISSN 1537-7946. 2003 (Spr.) (from EBSCO Publishing, O C L C Online Computer Library Center, Inc., Swets Information Services).
Indexed: CJA, CJPI, DIP, ESPM, FamI, IBR, IBZ, PAIS, RefZh, RiskAb, SWR&A, SociolAb, e-psyche.
—Haworth. **CCC.**
Published by: Haworth Press, Inc., 10 Alice St, Binghamton, NY 13904-1580. TEL 607-722-5857, 800-429-6784, FAX 607-722-1424, 800-895-0582, getinfo@haworthpress.com, http://www.haworthpress.com/web/JECJ. Ed. Janice Joseph. Pub. William Cohen. R&P Ruth Ann Heath TEL 607-722-5857 ext 316. Adv. contact Rebecca Miller-Baum TEL 607-722-5857 ext 337. B&W page USD 315, color page USD 550; trim 4.375 x 7.125.

364 NLD ISSN 1573-3750
▼ **JOURNAL OF EXPERIMENTAL CRIMINOLOGY.** Text in English. 2005. q. EUR 318, USD 398, GBP 255 combined subscription to institutions print & online eds. (effective 2005). bk.rev. **Document type:** *Journal, Academic/Scholarly.* **Description:** Focuses on experimental and quasi-experimental research in the development of evidence-based crime and justice policy and is commited to the advancement of the science of systematic reviews and experimental methods in criminology and criminal justice.
Related titles: Online - full text ed.: (from EBSCO Publishing, Springer LINK); Print ed.: ISSN 1572-8315.
—**CCC.**
Published by: Springer-Verlag Dordrecht (Subsidiary of: Springer Science+Business Media), Van Godewijckstraat 30, Dordrecht, 3311 GX, Netherlands. TEL 31-78-6576050, FAX 31-78-6576474, http://springerlink.metapress.com/openurl.asp?genre=journal&issn=1573-3750, http://www.springeronline.com. Ed. David Weisburd.

306.85 USA ISSN 0885-7482
HQ809 CODEN: JFVIEV
➤ **JOURNAL OF FAMILY VIOLENCE.** Text in English. 1986. bi-m. EUR 658, USD 678, GBP 368 combined subscription to institutions print & online eds. (effective 2005). adv. bk.rev. illus. Index. back issues avail.; reprint service avail. from PSC. **Document type:** *Journal, Academic/Scholarly.* **Description:** Examines clinical and investigative efforts concerning all forms of family violence; includes case studies and reviews.
Related titles: Microfilm ed.: (from PQC); Online - full text ed.: ISSN 1573-2851 (from EBSCO Publishing, Gale Group, IngentaConnect, Kluwer Online, O C L C Online Computer Library Center, Inc., Springer LINK, Swets Information Services).
Indexed: ASCA, ASG, ASSIA, AgeL, BibLing, CINAHL, CJA, CJPI, CurCont, DIP, ESPM, FamI, H&SSA, IBR, IBSS, IBZ, IMFL, IPARL, PRA, PsycInfo, PsycholAb, RASB, RI-1, RI-2, RiskAb, SFSA, SOPODA, SSA, SSCI, SSI, SUSA, SociolAb, V&AA, e-psyche.
—BLDSC (4983.746000), IDS, IE, Infotrieve, ingenta. **CCC.**
Published by: Plenum US (Subsidiary of: Springer Science+Business Media), 233 Spring St, New York, NY 10013. TEL 212-460-1500, FAX 212-460-1575, service@springer-ny.com, http://springerlink.metapress.com/openurl.asp?genre=journal&issn=0885-7482, http://www.springeronline.com. Eds. Michel Hersen, Vincent B Van Hasselt.

➤ **JOURNAL OF FORENSIC ACCOUNTING**; auditing, fraud, and taxation. see *BUSINESS AND ECONOMICS—Accounting*

364 USA ISSN 1079-3062
HV6439.U5
➤ **JOURNAL OF GANG RESEARCH.** Text in English. 1992. q. USD 85 domestic to individuals; USD 120 domestic to institutions; USD 195 foreign (effective 2004). bk.rev. **Document type:** *Journal, Academic/Scholarly.* **Description:** Deals with gangs and related problems through papers, book reviews, and interviews.
Formerly (until 1994): Gang Journal (1061-5326)
Indexed: CJA, PsycInfo, PsycholAb, SSA, SociolAb.
—BLDSC (4987.230000), IE, ingenta.
Published by: National Gang Crime Research Center, PO Box 990, Peotone, IL 60468-0990. TEL 773-258-9111, FAX 708-258-9546, gangcrime@aol.com, http://www.ngcrc.com.

364 GBR ISSN 1478-1387
K10
▼ **JOURNAL OF INTERNATIONAL CRIMINAL JUSTICE.** Text in English. 2003 (Spring). 5/yr. GBP 265, USD 451, EUR 398 to institutions; GBP 279, USD 474, EUR 419 combined subscription to institutions print & online eds. (effective 2006). adv. **Document type:** *Journal, Academic/Scholarly.* **Description:** Aims to promote a profound collective reflection on the new problems facing international law.
Related titles: Online - full text ed.: ISSN 1478-1395. GBP 251, USD 427, EUR 377 to institutions (effective 2006) (from EBSCO Publishing, Gale Group, HighWire Press, IngentaConnect, O C L C Online Computer Library Center, Inc., Oxford University Press Online Journals, Swets Information Services).
Indexed: CJA.
—BLDSC (5007.634000), IE. **CCC.**
Published by: Oxford University Press, Great Clarendon St, Oxford, OX2 6DP, United Kingdom. TEL 44-1865-556767, FAX 44-1865-556646, jnl.orders@oup.co.uk, http://jicj.oxfordjournals.org/, http://www.oxfordjournals.org/. Ed. Antonio Cassese. adv.: B&W page GBP 250, B&W page USD 420; 115 x 190.

364 USA ISSN 0886-2605
➤ **JOURNAL OF INTERPERSONAL VIOLENCE**; concerned with the study and treatment of victims and perpetrators of physical and sexual violence. Text in English. 1986. m. USD 915, GBP 591 to institutions; USD 953, GBP 615 combined subscription to institutions print & online eds. (effective 2006). adv. illus. Index. back issues avail.; reprints avail. **Document type:** *Journal, Academic/Scholarly.* **Description:** Provides a forum for the discussion of the concerns and activities of professionals and researchers working in domestic violence, child sexual abuse, rape and sexual assault, physical child abuse, and other violent crimes.
Related titles: Online - full text ed.: ISSN 1552-6518. USD 906, GBP 585 to institutions (effective 2006) (from C S A, EBSCO Publishing, Florida Center for Library Automation, Gale Group, O C L C Online Computer Library Center, Inc., Sage Publications, Inc., Swets Information Services).
Indexed: AC&P, ASCA, ASG, ASSIA, AddicA, AgeL, CIJE, CINAHL, CJA, CJPI, CurCont, DIP, ESPM, FamI, IBR, IBZ, IMFL, INI, MEA, PsycInfo, PsycholAb, RASB, RiskAb, SENA, SFSA, SOPODA, SRRA, SSA, SSCI, SSI, SWA, SWR&A, SociolAb, V&AA, e-psyche.
—BLDSC (5007.693500), IDS, IE, Infotrieve, ingenta. **CCC.**
Published by: Sage Publications, Inc., 2455 Teller Rd, Thousand Oaks, CA 91320. TEL 805-499-0721, 800-818-7243, FAX 805-499-8096, 800-583-2665, info@sagepub.com, http://www.sagepub.com/journal.aspx?pid=108. Ed. Jon R Conte. Pub. Sara Miller McCune. R&P Tanya Udin TEL 805-499-0721 ext 7716. Adv. contact Kirsten Beaulieu TEL 805-499-0721 ext 7160. page USD 350. Circ: 1,000 (paid and free). **Subscr. overseas to:** Sage Publications Ltd., 1 Oliver's Yard, 55 City Rd, London EC1 1SP, United Kingdom. TEL 44-20-73740645, FAX 44-20-73748741.

▼ ➤ **JOURNAL OF INVESTIGATIVE PSYCHOLOGY AND OFFENDER PROFILING.** see *PSYCHOLOGY*

364 USA ISSN 1043-500X
HV9304
JOURNAL OF OFFENDER MONITORING. Text in English. 1988. s-a. USD 92.95 to individuals; USD 132.95 to libraries (effective 2004). **Document type:** *Journal, Trade.* **Description:** Focused exclusively on monitoring technology and its use in enhancing public safety.
Formerly (until 1988): Offender Monitor (0894-4644)
Indexed: CJA.
—**CCC.**
Published by: Civic Research Insitute, 4490 US Route 27, PO Box 585, Kingston, NJ 08528. TEL 609-683-4450, FAX 609-683-7291, order@civicresearchinstitute.com, http://www.civicresearchinstitute.com/co16.html. Ed. Peggy Conway.

C

364 362.8 USA ISSN 1050-9674
HV9261 CODEN: JOFHEB
➤ **JOURNAL OF OFFENDER REHABILITATION**; a multidisciplinary journal of innovation in research, services, and programs in corrections and criminal justice. Abbreviated title: J O R. Text in English. 1976. q. USD 425 combined subscription domestic to institutions print & online eds.; USD 573.75 combined subscription in Canada to institutions print & online eds.; USD 616.25 combined subscription elsewhere to institutions print & online eds. (effective academic year 2005 - 2006). adv. bk.rev. illus. index. 120 p./no. 1 cols./p.; back issues avail.; reprint service avail. from HAW. **Document type:** *Journal, Academic/Scholarly.* **Description:** Publishes research and concepts on the rehabilitation of criminal offenders, both in custodial and community settings.
Former titles (until 1990): Journal of Offender Counseling, Services and Rehabilitation (0195-6116); (until 1980): Offender Rehabilitation (0364-3093)
Related titles: Microfiche ed.: (from PQC); Microform ed.; Online - full text ed.: ISSN 1540-8558. free to institutions (effective 2003); free with print subs. (from EBSCO Publishing, O C L C Online Computer Library Center, Inc., Swets Information Services).
Indexed: AC&P, AMHA, AltPI, BehAb, CERDIC, CIJE, CJA, CJPI, CPLI, ChPerI, CurCont, DIP, ESPM, FamI, H&SSA, HRA, IBR, IBZ, IMFL, PC&CA, PRA, PsycInfo, PsycholAb, RefZh, RiskAb, SFSA, SOPODA, SPAA, SSA, SSI, SUSA, SWA, SWR&A, SociolAb, V&AA, e-psyche.
—BLDSC (5026.218000), Haworth, IE, Infotrieve, ingenta. **CCC.**
Published by: Haworth Press, Inc., 10 Alice St, Binghamton, NY 13904-1580. TEL 607-722-5857, 800-429-6784, FAX 607-722-1424, getinfo@haworthpress.com, http://www.haworthpress.com/web/JOR. Ed. Nancy Wolff. Pub. William Cohen. R&P Ruth Ann Heath TEL 607-722-5857 ext 316. Adv. contact Rebecca Miller-Baum TEL 607-722-5857 ext 337. B&W page USD 315, color page USD 550; trim 4.375 x 7.125. Circ: 328 (paid).

C

364 USA ISSN 0882-0783
➤ **JOURNAL OF POLICE AND CRIMINAL PSYCHOLOGY.** Text in English. 1985. s-a. USD 50 to members; USD 100 to institutions (effective 2004). **Document type:** *Journal, Academic/Scholarly.*
Related titles: Microfilm ed.: (from PQC).
Indexed: CJA, CJPI, CLT&T, HRIS, e-psyche.
Published by: Society of Police and Criminal Psychology, c/o Dr Wayman Mullins, Southwest Texas State University, Hines Academic Center, Rm 120, San Marcos, TX 78666. TEL 512-245-2174, FAX 512-245-8063, http://cep.jmu.edu/spcp/journal.htm. R&P Wayman C Mullins. Circ: 350.

365 CAN ISSN 0838-164X
HV8301
JOURNAL OF PRISONERS ON PRISONS. Text in English. 1988. s-a. USD 10 to individuals; USD 20 to institutions. back issues avail.
Related titles: Online - full text ed.
Indexed: AltPI.
Published by: University of Manitoba, University Centre, P O Box 54, Winnipeg, MB R3T 2N2, Canada. arrakis@synapse.net, http://www.synapse.net/~arrakis/jpp/jpp.html.

364 USA ISSN 0748-4518
CODEN: JQCRE6
➤ **JOURNAL OF QUANTITATIVE CRIMINOLOGY.** Text in English. 1984. q. EUR 698, USD 728, GBP 438 combined subscription to institutions print & online eds. (effective 2005). adv. illus. Index. back issues avail.; reprint service avail. from PSC. **Document type:** *Journal, Academic/Scholarly.*
Related titles: Microfilm ed.: (from PQC); Online - full text ed.: ISSN 1573-7799 (from EBSCO Publishing, Gale Group, IngentaConnect, Kluwer Online, O C L C Online Computer Library Center, Inc., Ovid Technologies, Inc., Springer LINK, Swets Information Services).
Indexed: AC&P, ASCA, BibLing, CJA, CJPI, CurCont, FamI, IPARL, PsycInfo, PsycholAb, RefZh, SOPODA, SSA, SSCI, SociolAb, e-psyche.
—BLDSC (5043.696000), IDS, IE, Infotrieve, ingenta. **CCC.**
Published by: Plenum US (Subsidiary of: Springer Science+Business Media), 233 Spring St, New York, NY 10013. TEL 212-460-1500, FAX 212-460-1575, service@springer-ny.com, http://springerlink.metapress.com/openurl.asp?genre=journal&issn=0748-4518, http://www.springeronline.com. Ed. David McDowall.

364 USA ISSN 1061-3455
HV8074
➤ **JOURNAL OF QUESTIONED DOCUMENT EXAMINATION.** Text in English. 1988. a. USD 40 (effective 2003). bk.rev. **Document type:** *Journal, Academic/Scholarly.* **Description:** Contains papers and information on document examination and handwriting identification.
Formerly (until 1992): Independent Association of Questioned Document Examiners. Journal (1056-8972)
Published by: Independent Association of Questioned Document Examiners, Inc., 115 N. Arlington Heights Rd., Arlington Heights, IL 60004. TEL 847-726-6904, FAX 847-255-6692, ebiestek@biestek.com. Ed., R&P Elizabeth M. Biestek. Circ: 75.

364 USA ISSN 0022-4278
HV6001
➤ **JOURNAL OF RESEARCH IN CRIME AND DELINQUENCY.** Text in English. 1964. q. USD 508, GBP 328 to institutions; USD 529, GBP 342 combined subscription to institutions print & online eds. (effective 2006). adv. charts; illus.; stat. Index. back issues avail.; reprint service avail. from WSH. **Document type:** *Journal, Academic/Scholarly.* **Description:** Reports on original research in crime and deliquency, new theory, and the critical analyses of theories and concepts pertinent to research development in the field.
Related titles: Microfiche ed.: (from WSH); Microfilm ed.: (from WSH); Microform ed.: (from PMC, WSH); Online - full text ed.: ISSN 1552-731X. USD 503, GBP 325 to institutions (effective 2006) (from C S A, EBSCO Publishing, Florida Center for Library Automation, Gale Group, O C L C Online Computer Library Center, Inc., Sage Publications, Inc., Swets Information Services).
Indexed: AC&P, AMHA, ASCA, ASSIA, AddicA, AgeL, CIJE, CIS, CJA, CJPI, CLI, CurCont, DIP, ESPM, ExcerpMed, FamI, IBR, IBSS, IBZ, ILP, IMFL, MEA&I, PRA, PsycInfo, PsycholAb, RASB, RILM, RiskAb, SFSA, SOPODA, SPAA, SRRA, SSA, SSCI, SSI, SUSA, SWA, SWR&A, SociolAb, V&AA, e-psyche.
—BLDSC (5052.005000), IDS, IE, Infotrieve, ingenta. **CCC.**
Published by: (National Council on Crime and Delinquency, Rutgers University, School of Criminal Justice), Sage Publications, Inc., 2455 Teller Rd, Thousand Oaks, CA 91320. TEL 805-499-0721, 800-818-7243, FAX 805-499-8096, 800-583-2665, info@sagepub.com, http://www.sagepub.com/journal.aspx?pid=145. Ed. Clayton Hartjen. Pub. Sara Miller McCune. R&P Tanya Udin TEL 805-499-0721 ext 7716. Adv. contact Kirsten Beaulieu TEL 805-499-0721 ext 7160. B&W page USD 350. Circ: 1,100 (paid). **Subscr. overseas to:** Sage Publications Ltd., 1 Oliver's Yard, 55 City Rd, London EC1 1SP, United Kingdom. TEL 44-20-73740645, FAX 44-20-73748741, subscription@sagepub.co.uk.

➤ **THE JOURNAL OF SAFE MANAGEMENT OF DISRUPTIVE AND ASSAULTIVE BEHAVIOR.** see *BUSINESS AND ECONOMICS—Management*

364.4 345.85 NOR ISSN 1404-3858
➤ **JOURNAL OF SCANDINAVIAN STUDIES IN CRIMINOLOGY AND CRIME PREVENTION.** Text in English. 2000. s-a. GBP 82, USD 135 combined subscription to institutions print & online eds. (effective 2006). adv. reprint service avail. from PSC. **Document type:** *Journal, Academic/Scholarly.* **Description:** Aims to combine criminological and crime prevention oriented scientific works.
Formed by the merger of (1965-2000): Scandinavian Studies in Criminology (0085-5936); (1992-2000): Studies on Crime and Crime Prevention (1102-3937); (until 1992): National Council for Crime Prevention. Information Bulletin (0281-336X)
Related titles: Online - full text ed.: ISSN 1651-2340. GBP 78, USD 128 to institutions (effective 2006) (from EBSCO Publishing, Gale Group, IngentaConnect, O C L C Online Computer Library Center, Inc., Swets Information Services).
Indexed: CJA, CJPI, ESPM, PsycInfo, PsycholAb, RiskAb.
—BLDSC (5052.400000), IE, Infotrieve, ingenta. **CCC.**
Published by: (Brottsfoerebyggande Raadet), Taylor & Francis A S (Subsidiary of: Taylor & Francis Group), Biskop Gunnerusgate 14A, PO Box 12 Posthuset, Oslo, 0051, Norway. TEL 47-23-103460, FAX 47-23-103461, journals@tandf.no, http://www.tandf.co.uk/journals/titles/14043858.asp. Ed. Filepe Estrada TEL 46-8-6747055. **Subscr. to:** Taylor & Francis Ltd, Journals Customer Service, Rankine Rd, Basingstoke, Hants RG24 8PR, United Kingdom. TEL 44-1256-813000, FAX 44-1256-330245, enquiry@tandf.co.uk.

➤ **JOURNAL OF SEXUAL AGGRESSION.** see *PSYCHOLOGY*

➤ **JUBILEE**; the monthly newsletter of Prison Fellowship. see *RELIGIONS AND THEOLOGY—Protestant*

➤ **JUDICIAL INTERIM RELEASE: BAIL MANUAL.** see *LAW—Criminal Law*

364 USA
▼ **JUSTICE.** Text in English. 2005. 10/yr. USD 17.97 (effective 2005). **Document type:** *Magazine, Consumer.*
Published by: Doubledown Media, LLC, 36 W. 44th St., 4th Fl., New York, NY 10036. TEL 212-719-9500, http://www.justicemag.com/. Ed. Randall Lane TEL 212-672-5173. Pub., Adv. contact Alan Stiles TEL 212-672-5178. Circ: 250,000.

364 AUS ISSN 0814-0278
JUSTICE AND THE J.P. Text in English. 1983. bi-m. AUD 50. adv. bk.rev. **Document type:** *Newsletter.*
Published by: State Council of the Queensland Justices' and Community Legal Officers' Association Inc. (QJA), Level 2, 349 Queen St, Brisbane, QLD 4000, Australia. TEL 61-7-32297061, FAX 61-7-32297048. Ed. Peter H MacDonald. Adv. contact Carlo Marchese. Circ: 10,000. **Subscr. to:** GPO Box 653, Brisbane, QLD 4001, Australia.

JUSTICE - DIRECTORY OF SERVICES/JUSTICE - REPERTOIRE DES SERVICES. see *SOCIAL SERVICES AND WELFARE*

364 USA ISSN 1541-6038
THE JUSTICE EXPRESS. Text in English. 1992. q. USD 20 to individuals; USD 45 to institutions (effective 2002).
Formerly (until 2002): North Coast Xpress
Published by: Xpress Collective, P. O. Box 1226, Occidental, CA 95465. TEL 707-874-1453, FAX 707-874-3104. Ed. Doret Kollerer.

JUSTICE IN AMERICA SERIES. see *LAW*

364 340 GBR ISSN 0741-8825
HV7231
➤ **JUSTICE QUARTERLY.** Text in English. 1984. q. GBP 253, USD 419 combined subscription to institutions print & online eds. (effective 2006). adv. bk.rev. illus. back issues avail.; reprint service avail. from PSC. **Document type:** *Journal, Academic/Scholarly.* **Description:** Features scholarly articles on issues of criminal justice, criminology and justice studies.
Related titles: Microform ed.: 1984; Online - full text ed.: ISSN 1745-9109. GBP 240, USD 398 to institutions (effective 2006) (from EBSCO Publishing, Gale Group, IngentaConnect, ProQuest Information & Learning).
Indexed: AC&P, CJA, CJPI, CurCont, ESPM, PRA, RiskAb, SFSA, SRRA, SSA, SSCI, SSI, SUSA, SociolAb, V&AA.
—BLDSC (5075.673700), IE, ingenta.
Published by: (Academy of Criminal Justice Sciences USA), Routledge (Subsidiary of: Taylor & Francis Group), 4 Park Sq, Milton Park, Abingdon, Oxon OX14 4RN, United Kingdom. TEL 44-1235-828600, FAX 44-1235-829000, journals@routledge.com, http://www.tandf.co.uk/journals/titles/07418825.asp, http://www.routledge.com. Ed. Chester Britt TEL 602-543-6676. Circ: 3,000.

365 CAN ISSN 0823-9436
HV9960.C2
JUSTICE REPORT/ACTUALITES JUSTICE. Text in English, French. 1957. q. CND 45 (effective 2005). bk.rev. bibl. **Document type:** *Magazine, Trade.* **Description:** Contains information and opinions for members of the association written by professional journalists.
Incorporates (1989-2004): Canadian Criminal Justice Association. Bulletin (0843-8439); Former titles (until 1984): Canadian Association for the Prevention of Crime. Bulletin - Societe Canadienne pour la Prevention du Crime. Bulletin (0705-9094); (until 1977): Canadian Criminology and Corrections Association. Bulletin (0045-463X); (until 1971): Correctional Process (0045-8635); (until 1970): Readaption (0034-0367)
Indexed: ICLPL.
Published by: Canadian Criminal Justice Association/Association Canadienne de Justice Penale, 1750, Courtwood Crescent, Ste 308, Ottawa, ON K2C 2B5, Canada. TEL 613-725-3715, FAX 613-725-3720, ccja@bellnet.ca, http://www.ccja-acjp.ca. Circ: 1,000.

364 USA ISSN 1525-1071
HV9950
➤ **JUSTICE RESEARCH AND POLICY.** Text in English. 1999. s-a. free to members; USD 45 to individuals; USD 85 to institutions; USD 25 per issue (effective 2002). adv. abstr.; illus. **Document type:** *Journal, Academic/Scholarly.* **Description:** Publishes articles that relate to some aspect of applied criminal justice research, program evaluation, or data analysis. The journal's mission is to disseminate policy-oriented research and analysis and help bridge the gap between researchers and policymakers.
Indexed: BrCerAb, C&ISA, CJA, CerAb, CorrAb, E&CAJ, EMA, IAA, M&TEA, MBF, METADEX, PSA, SSA, SociolAb, WAA.
—BLDSC (5075.675200).
Published by: Justice Research and Statistics Association, Inc., 777 N Capitol St, N E, Ste 801, Washington, DC 20002. TEL 202-842-9330, FAX 202-842-9329, cjinfo@jrsa.org, http://www.jrsa.org. Eds. Robert F McManus, Timothy Bynum. adv.: page USD 250;. Circ: 300.

365 CAN ISSN 1181-9243
JUSTICE RESEARCH NOTES. Text in English. 1990. irreg.
Published by: Canada Department of Justice, Research and Statistics Division, 284 Wellington St, Ottawa, ON K1A 0H8, Canada. TEL 613-946-0460, FAX 613-941-1845, rsd.drs@justice.gc.ca, http://canada.justice.gc.ca.

364.4 USA ISSN 1521-9569
JUSTICE TECHNOLOGY MONITOR. Text in English. 1998. m. USD 277 (effective 2001). back issues avail. **Document type:** *Newsletter, Trade.* **Description:** Reports on the latest news, model programs, and developments in new and emerging technologies. Includes new and federal grant programs, key legislation, funding trends, and appropriations and application deadlines for law enforcement and criminal justice grants. Technologies covered include computer analysis, wireless communications, DNA analysis, highway safety enforcement, crime mapping, video taping and conferencing, weapons, drug & alcohol detection, prisoner control and data collection and sharing.
—**CCC.**
Published by: Capitol City Publishers, 3485 S. Wakefield St., Arlington, VA 22206-1719. TEL 703-525-3080, FAX 703-525-3044, inquiry@capitolcitypublishers.com, http://capitolcitypublishers.com. Eds. Jeanne Williams, Jessica Gowen. Pub. Joel M Drucker. R&P Joel Drucker.

JUSTNOTES. see *COLLEGE AND ALUMNI*

JUVENILE AND FAMILY COURT JOURNAL. see *LAW—Family And Matrimonial Law*

JUVENILE AND FAMILY JUSTICE TODAY. see *LAW—Family And Matrimonial Law*

364.6 616.891 155.5 USA ISSN 1531-7285
RJ506.J88
JUVENILE CORRECTIONAL MENTAL HEALTH REPORT. Text in English. bi-m. USD 169.95 domestic; USD 199.95 foreign (effective 2004). **Document type:** *Newsletter, Trade.* **Description:** Essential guidance for clinicians, counselors, administrators, law enforcement and legal personnel.
Published by: Civic Research Insitute, 4490 US Route 27, PO Box 585, Kingston, NJ 08528. TEL 609-683-4450, FAX 609-683-7291, order@civicresearchinstitute.com, http://www.civicresearchinstitute.com/ch4.html. Ed. Fred Cohen.

364 USA ISSN 1524-3230
HV9103
JUVENILE JUSTICE. Text in English. 1993. s-a. free. **Document type:** *Journal, Government.*
Indexed: CJA, PAIS.
Published by: (Information Dissemination Unit), U.S. Department of Justice, Office of Juvenile Justice and Delinquency Prevention, 633 Indiana Ave, N W, Washington, DC 20531. TEL 202-512-1800, FAX 202-512-2250, askncjrs@ncjrs.org, http://www.ncjrs.org/ojjdp/. Circ: 60,000. **Subscr. to:** Juvenile Justice Clearinghouse, PO Box 6000, Rockville, MD 20849-6000.

364.36 USA ISSN 0094-2413
K10
JUVENILE JUSTICE DIGEST; an independent summary of significant events in the field of juvenile delinquency prevention. Text in English. 1973. s-m. looseleaf. USD 225 domestic (effective 2005). bk.rev. reprint service avail. from PQC. **Document type:** *Newsletter, Trade.* **Description:** Focuses on deliquency issues. Includes job listings.
Related titles: Microform ed.: (from PQC); Online - full text ed.: (from bigchalk, ProQuest Information & Learning).
Indexed: AMHA, CJA, CJPI.
Published by: Washington Crime News Services, 1209 National Press Bldg, 529 14th St, N W, Ste 9, Washington, DC 22045-0001. TEL 202-662-7035, nvanwyen@washingtoncrime.com, http://www.crimepolicyreports.com. Ed. Leonard Curry. Pub. Sonja Weisel. Circ: 500 (paid).

364.36 USA ISSN 1080-0360
KF9772
JUVENILE JUSTICE UPDATE. Text in English. 1995. bi-m. USD 169.95 domestic; USD 199.95 foreign (effective 2005). **Document type:** *Newsletter.* **Description:** Helping courts, law enforcement and corrections officials, prosecutors and defenders, aftercare and social service professionals deal with the critical problems of juvenile crime.
Indexed: CJPI.
—CCC.
Published by: Civic Research Insitute, 4490 US Route 27, PO Box 585, Kingston, NJ 08528. TEL 609-683-4450, FAX 609-683-7291, order@civicresearchinstitute.com, http://www.civicresearchinstitute.com/ch2.html. Ed. Henry G. Sontheimer.

364.4 JPN ISSN 0451-1999
HV6005
KAGAKU KEISATSU KENKYUJO HOKOKU BOHAN SHONEN HEN/NATIONAL RESEARCH INSTITUTE OF POLICE SCIENCE. REPORT. RESEARCH ON PREVENTION OF CRIME AND DELINQUENCY. Text in Japanese; Summaries in English. 1960. s-a. **Document type:** *Academic/Scholarly.*
Indexed: CJA, PsycInfo, PsycholAb.
—BLDSC (7570.222800), ingenta.
Published by: Kagaku Keisatsu Kenkyujo/National Research Institute of Police Science, 6-3-1, Kashiwanoha, Kashiwa-shi, Chiba 277-0882, Japan. TEL 81-3-32619986, FAX 81-3-32211245, http://www.nrips.go.jp. Ed. Taizo Nagano. Circ: 900.

364 JPN ISSN 0453-0667
KAGAKU KEISATSU KENKYUJO NENPO/NATIONAL RESEARCH INSTITUTE OF POLICE SCIENCE. ANNUAL REPORT. Text in Japanese. 1948. a. **Document type:** *Bulletin.*
Published by: Kagaku Keisatsu Kenkyujo/National Research Institute of Police Science, 6-3-1, Kashiwanoha, Kashiwa-shi, Chiba 277-0882, Japan. TEL 81-3-32619986, FAX 81-3-32211245, http://www.nrips.go.jp. Circ: 1,000.

KENTUCKY PENAL CODE, VEHICLES, RULES & RELATED STATUTES. see *LAW—Criminal Law*

363.2 KEN ISSN 0023-0448
KENYA POLICE REVIEW. Text in English. 1956. q. KES 180, USD 4 (effective 1995). adv. bk.rev. **Document type:** *Newsletter.* **Description:** Seeks to advocate for the officers of the Kenya Police Force.
Published by: Kenya Police Force, Force Headquarters, PO Box 30083 NBI, Nairobi, Kenya. TEL 254-2-335124, FAX 254-2-330495, TELEX 22720 COMPOL KE. Ed. M N Kabetu. Circ: 30,000 (paid).

364 RUS
KRIMINAL-EKSPRESS. Text in Russian. w.
Address: Pr Marksa 39, Omsk, 644056, Russian Federation. TEL 7-3812-314432, 7-3832-310590, krim@dionis.omskelecom.ru. Ed. E V Nazarenko. Circ: 18,468.

364 DEU ISSN 0722-3501
DER KRIMINALIST. Text in German. 1969. m. adv. bk.rev. illus. reprints avail. **Document type:** *Journal, Trade.*
Indexed: AC&P.
Published by: (Bund Deutscher Kriminalbeamter), Schmidt-Roemhild Verlag, Mengstr 16, Luebeck, 23552, Germany. TEL 49-451-7031-01, FAX 49-451-7031253, eickershoff@beleke.de, http://www.schmidt-roemhild.de. Ed. G Rudnick. Circ: 20,000.

364 DEU ISSN 0023-4699
➤ **KRIMINALISTIK**; Zeitschrift fuer die gesamte kriminalistische Wissenschaft und Praxis. Text in German. 1946. 11/yr. EUR 145 domestic; EUR 151 foreign; EUR 12 newsstand/cover (effective 2005). adv. bk.rev. bibl.; charts; illus. index. reprint service avail. from SCH. **Document type:** *Journal, Academic/Scholarly.*
Indexed: AC&P, ASCA, CJA, DIP, ExcerpMed, IBR, IBZ, PAIS, RASB, SSCI.
—BLDSC (5118.235000), IDS, IE, Infotrieve, ingenta. **CCC.**
Published by: Kriminalistik Verlag Huethig GmbH & Co. KG, Im Weiher 10, Heidelberg, 69121, Germany. TEL 49-6221-489416, FAX 49-6221-489624, aboservice@huethig.de, http://www.kriminalistik.de, http://www.huethig.de. Ed. Klaus Juergen Timm. Adv. contact Judith Hamm. B&W page EUR 1,200, color page EUR 2,280; trim 178 x 257. Circ: 2,508 (paid and controlled).

364 RUS
KRIMINAL'NAYA KHRONIKA. Text in Russian. w.
Published by: Novyi Vek, Tsvetnoi Bul'var, 21, bld. 2, Moscow, 103051, Russian Federation. TEL 7-095-9210349. Ed. L K Sharov. Circ: 300,000 (paid).

363.2 DEU ISSN 0938-9636
DIE KRIMINALPOLIZEI. Text in German. 1983. q. EUR 12; EUR 3.50 newsstand/cover (effective 2004). adv. **Document type:** *Magazine, Trade.*
Published by: Verlag Deutsche Polizeiliteratur GmbH, Forststr 3A, Hilden, 40721, Germany. TEL 49-211-71040, FAX 49-211-7104174, info@die-kriminalpolizei.de, vdp.buchvertrieb@vdpolizei.de, http://www.die-kriminalpolizei.de, http://www.vdpolizei.de. Ed. Manfred Teufel. Adv. contact Michael Schwarz.

364 DEU
DIE KRIMINALPRAEVENTION; europaeische beitraege zu kriminalitaet und praevention. Text in German. 1997. 5/yr. EUR 30 (effective 2003).
Formerly (until 1999): Europaeische Beitraege zu Kriminalitaet und Praevention (1434-0585)
Indexed: CJA.
Published by: Europaeisches Zentrum fuer Kriminalpraevention eV, Kautenstege 10, Steinfurt, 48565, Germany. TEL 49-2551-836400, FAX 49-2551-8364011, home@ezkev.de, http://www.ezkev.de/zeitschrift/Page1.html. Eds. Andreas Kohl, Dr. Peter Krevert.

364.4 346 SWE ISSN 0347-2612
KRIMINALVAARDSVERKETS FOERFATTNINGSSAMLING. Text in Swedish. 1976. irreg. free.
Published by: Kriminalvaardsstyrelsen, Norrkoeping, 60180, Sweden. TEL 46-11-193000, FAX 46-11-19-36-72.

364 DEU
KRIMINALWISSENSCHAFTLICHE STUDIEN. Text in German. irreg., latest vol.23, 1997. **Document type:** *Monographic series.*
Published by: N.G. Elwert Verlag, Reitgasse 7-9, Marburg, 35037, Germany. TEL 49-6421-17090, FAX 49-6421-13760, elwert@ibm.net, elwertmail@elwert.de.

364 HRV ISSN 1330-2604
KRIMINOLOGIJA & SOCIJALNA INTEGRACIJA. Text in Serbo-Croatian. 1993. s-a. **Document type:** *Academic/Scholarly.*
Indexed: PsycInfo, PsycholAb, SSA, SociolAb.
Published by: Fakultet za Defektologiju, Odsjek Za Socijalnu Pedagogiju, Kuslanova 59a, Zagreb, 10000, Croatia. TEL 385-1-2338022, FAX 385-1-229950.

364 DEU ISSN 0341-1966
HV6003
KRIMINOLOGISCHES JOURNAL. Text in German. 1969. q. EUR 48.20 domestic; EUR 54.50 foreign (effective 2003). adv. bk.rev. index. 80 p./no.; reprint service avail. from SCH. **Document type:** *Journal, Academic/Scholarly.*
Indexed: AC&P, CJA, DIP, IBR, IBZ.
—IE, Infotrieve. **CCC.**
Published by: (Arbeitskreis Junger Kriminologen), Juventa Verlag GmbH, Ehretstr 3, Weinheim, 69469, Germany. TEL 49-6201-90200, FAX 49-6201-902013, juventa@juventa.de, http://www.juventa.de. Adv. contact Silke Schweim. page EUR 250; trim 113 x 193. Circ: 700 (paid and controlled).

KRONIEK VAN HET STRAFRECHT. see *LAW—Criminal Law*

363.2 GBR
LANCASHIRE CONSTABULARY JOURNAL. Text in English. 1936. 4/yr. free. adv. bk.rev. **Document type:** *Newsletter.* **Description:** News, views and features from Lancashire Constabulary.
Published by: Lancashire Constabulary, County Police Headquarters, Lancashire Constabulary, PO Box 77, Hutton, Preston PR4 5SB, United Kingdom. TEL 44-1772-618444, FAX 44-1772-618356. Ed., R&P Roger Blaxall. Circ: 4,000 (controlled).

352 363.2 USA ISSN 0023-9194
HV7551
LAW AND ORDER MAGAZINE; the magazine for police management. Text in English. 1953. m. USD 25 domestic; USD 85 foreign (effective 2005). adv. bk.rev.; software rev.; video rev. illus.; maps; tr.lit. index. back issues avail.; reprint service avail. from PQC. **Document type:** *Magazine, Trade.* **Description:** Covers all issues relating to managing and the daily operations of a police department.
Related titles: Microfilm ed.: (from PQC); Online - full text ed.: (from CompuServe Inc., ProQuest Information & Learning).
Indexed: AC&P, CJA, CJPI, RASB.
—BLDSC (5161.360000), IE, ingenta.
Published by: Hendon Publishing Company, 130 Waukegan Rd, Deerfield, IL 60015. TEL 847-444-3300, FAX 847-444-3333, info@hendonpub.com. Ed. Ed Sanow. Pub. H Scott Kingwill. Adv. contact Pete Kingwill. B&W page USD 2,650, color page USD 3,400; trim 10.88 x 8.13. Circ: 35,000 (controlled).
Subscr. to: PO Box 15788, North Hollywood, CA 91615. TEL 888-329-0770.

345 346 USA ISSN 1070-9967
KF9614
LAW ENFORCEMENT LEGAL REVIEW. Text in English. 1970. bi-m. USD 98 (effective 2002). bibl. index. **Document type:** *Newsletter.* **Description:** Covers criminal law and procedure.
Formerly (until 1990): I A C P Law Enforcement Legal Review
Indexed: CJPI.
Published by: Law Enforcement Legal Publications, 421 Ridgewood Ave, Ste 100, Glen Ellyn, IL 60137-4900. TEL 630-858-6392, FAX 630-858-6392, lelp@xnet.com, http://home.xnet.com/~lelp, http://www.xnet.com/~lelp. Ed., Pub., Adv. contact James P Manak. Circ: 500.

LAW ENFORCEMENT LIABILITY REPORTER. see *LAW—Civil Law*

363.2 USA ISSN 1551-8752
▼ **LAW ENFORCEMENT MANAGEMENT BULLETIN.** Text in English. 2004 (Jun). m. USD 187 (effective 2004).
Related titles: Online - full text ed.: ISSN 1551-8760.
Published by: Quinlan Publishing Group, Marine Industrial Park, 23 Drydock Ave, 6th Fl, Boston, MA 02210-2387. TEL 617-542-0048, 800-229-2084, FAX 617-507-1079, info@quinlan.com, http://www.quinlan.com. Ed. Patricia J. Lloyd. Pub. Dennis Hofmaier.

363.2 USA ISSN 0364-1724
LAW ENFORCEMENT NEWS. Text in English. 1975. 15/yr. USD 28 domestic; USD 45 foreign (effective 2005). adv. bk.rev. charts; illus. back issues avail.; reprint service avail. from PQC. **Document type:** *Journal, Academic/Scholarly.*
Formerly: John Jay College of Criminal Justice. Criminal Justice Center. Monographs
Related titles: Microform ed.: (from PQC).
Indexed: CJPI, ChPerI.
Published by: John Jay College of Criminal Justice, 555 W 57th St, New York, NY 10019. TEL 212-237-8442, FAX 212-237-8486, len@jjay.cuny.edu, http://www.lib.jjay.cuny.edu/len/, http://www.jjay.cuny.edu/. Ed. Peter C Dodenhoff. Pub. Marie Simonetti Rosen. Circ: 4,000.

363.2 USA ISSN 0747-7961
HV8143
LAW ENFORCEMENT OFFICERS KILLED AND ASSAULTED. Text in English. 1982. a. **Document type:** *Government.*
Formed by the 1981 merger of: Assaults on Federal Officers (0148-4257); (1977-1981): Law Enforcement Officers Killed (0191-2712); Which was formerly (until 1976): Law Enforcement Officers Killed: Summary (0364-3743)
Published by: U.S. Federal Bureau of Investigation, Uniform Crime Reporting Program, Criminal Justice Information Services Division, 1000 Custer Hollow Rd, Clarksburg, WV 26306. TEL 304-625-4995, FAX 304-625-5394, cjis_comm@leo.gov, http://www.fbi.gov/ucr/ucr.htm.

C

▼ *new title* ➤ *refereed* ✶ *unverified* ♦ *full entry avail.*

364.6 USA ISSN 1060-5126
LAW ENFORCEMENT PRODUCT NEWS. Text in English. 1990. bi-m. free; USD 48 domestic; USD 70 in Canada; USD 199 elsewhere (effective 2005). adv. bk.rev.; software rev.; video rev. abstr.; bibl.; charts; illus.; maps; stat. back issues avail. **Document type:** *Magazine, Trade.* **Description:** Covers new products, equipment and services for the law enforcement and corrections markets.
Incorporates (1990-1991): Inside Product News
Related titles: Online - full text ed.: (from Gale Group, ProQuest Information & Learning).
—CCC.
Published by: Cygnus Business Media, Inc., 1233 Janesville Ave, Fort Atkinson, WI 53538-0803. TEL 920-563-1698, FAX 920-568-2244, jeannine.heinecke@cygnus626.com, http://www.officer.com. Ed. Jeannine Heinecke. Pub. Michael George. Adv. contact Charles Cummings. B&W page USD 4,210, color page USD 5,085; trim 10.75 x 14.5. Circ: 30,000 (controlled).

364 USA ISSN 0747-3680
LAW ENFORCEMENT TECHNOLOGY. Text in English. 1974. m. free to qualified personnel; USD 66 domestic; USD 88 in Canada; USD 129 elsewhere (effective 2005). adv. bk.rev. illus.; stat.; tr.lit. back issues avail.; reprints avail. **Document type:** *Magazine, Trade.* **Description:** Management, operations and technical information for senior law enforcement personnel.
Formerly (until 1984): Law Enforcement Communications (0193-0540)
Related titles: Online - full text ed.: (from Gale Group, ProQuest Information & Learning).
—CCC.
Published by: Cygnus Business Media, Inc., 1233 Janesville Ave, Fort Atkinson, WI 53538-0803. TEL 920-568-8307, FAX 920-563-1699, http://www.enforcement.com. Pub. Patrick Bernardo. adv.: B&W page USD 3,175, color page USD 4,050; trim 7.875 x 10.75. Circ: 30,000.

346.013 USA
LAW ENFORCEMENT VOLUNTEERS. Text in English. q. **Description:** For, about, and by volunteers who work with law enforcement agencies and officials.
Published by: (Criminal Justice Services), American Association of Retired Persons, 601 E St, NW, Washington, DC 20049. TEL 202-662-4842.

THE LAW OF PROBATION AND PAROLE. see *LAW—Criminal Law*

364 USA
▼ **LAW OFFICER.** Text in English. 2005. bi-m. (9/yr. in 2006). free domestic to qualified personnel; USD 47.90 in Canada; USD 49.90 elsewhere (effective 2005). adv. **Document type:** *Magazine, Trade.* **Description:** Provides information on tactics, technology and training information to police officers from entry level through middle management.
Published by: J E M S Communications (Subsidiary of: Elsevier Inc.), 525 B St, Ste 1900, San Diego, CA 92101. TEL 619-687-3272, FAX 619-699-6396, jemspub@jems.com, http://www.jems.com/lawofficermagazine/. Ed. Dale Stockton. Pub. Jeff Berend TEL 619-699-6566. adv.: color page USD 4,000, B&W page USD 3,005. Circ: 41,000 (controlled).

363.2 USA ISSN 0145-6571
KF9202
LAW OFFICERS' BULLETIN. Text in English. 1976. bi-w. looseleaf. USD 169 (effective 2003). illus. back issues avail.; reprints avail. **Document type:** *Newsletter.* **Description:** Provides an update of court decisions, Justice Department proposals and congressional actions involving law enforcement officers, describing the legal reasoning and explaining the impact on the law enforcement community.
Related titles: Online - full content ed.
Indexed: CJPI.
—CCC.
Published by: Pike & Fischer, Inc. (Subsidiary of: The Bureau of National Affairs, Inc.), 1010 Wayne Ave, Ste 1400, Silver Spring, MD 20910. TEL 301-562-1530, 800-255-8131, FAX 301-562-1521, pike@pf.com, http://www.pf.com/pdf/lob.pdf. Ed. Mary B Murphy.

363.2 USA ISSN 1553-9555
▼ **LAW OFFICER'S MAGAZINE.** Text in English. 2005. 9/yr. USD 49.90 to individuals; USD 47.90 in Canada to individuals; USD 29.90 in United States to individuals; USD 49.90 to institutions; USD 29.90 in United States to institutions; USD 47.90 in Canada to institutions; USD 49.90 to students; USD 29.90 in United States to students (effective 2006).
Published by: Elsevier Inc. (Subsidiary of: Elsevier Science & Technology), 360 Park Ave. S, New York, NY 10010-1710. TEL 212-989-5800, 888-437-4636, FAX 212-633-3990, usinfo-f@elsevier.com, http://www.jems.com/lawofficermagazine/index.html, http://www.elsevier.com.

363.2 USA ISSN 0271-7182
HV8141
LAW OFFICER'S POCKET MANUAL. Text in English. 1972. a., latest 2003. USD 15.95 per vol. plus tax, shipping & handling (effective Nov. 2003). **Document type:** *Trade.* **Description:** Gives police officers reliable advice on the latest rules regarding searches, arrests, and interrogation. Helps officers make swift, enforceable decisions in everyday situations on the basis of the latest US Supreme Court rulings.
Published by: B N A Inc. (Subsidiary of: The Bureau of National Affairs, Inc.), 1231 25th St, NW, Washington, DC 20037. TEL 202-452-4343, FAX 202-452-4997, info@bna.org, http://www.bnabooks.com. Ed. Hugh B Kaplan. **Subscr. to:** PO Box 7814, Edison, NJ 08818-7814. TEL 800-960-1220, FAX 732-346-1624.

364 MUS
LAZOL; the prison magazine. Text in English. irreg.
Indexed: PLESA.
Address: c/o T. Printers Co Ltd, Residence de 5 Palmiers, 198 rte Royale, Beau Bassin, Mauritius.

LEGAL AND CRIMINOLOGICAL PSYCHOLOGY. see *PSYCHOLOGY*

LEX. see *COLLEGE AND ALUMNI*

LEX REVIEW. see *COLLEGE AND ALUMNI*

LOKALES; Stadtzeitung fuer Babenhausen. see *POLITICAL SCIENCE*

LOUISIANA CRIMINAL LAW AND MOTOR VEHICLE HANDBOOK. see *LAW—Criminal Law*

363.2 DEU ISSN 0944-8764
MAGAZIN FUER DIE POLIZEI; internationales unabhaengiges Fachmagazin. Text in German. 1970. bi-m. EUR 18 (effective 2005). adv. bk.rev. charts; illus. 40 p./no.; **Document type:** *Magazine, Trade.*
Formerly (until 1987): Polizeimagazin (0032-3543)
Indexed: RASB.
Published by: Almanach Verlags Joering e.K., Postfach 100135, Aschaffenburg, 63701, Germany. TEL 49-6028-997321, FAX 49-6028-996191, info@magazin-fuer-die-polizei.de, http://www.magazin-fuer-die-polizei.de. Ed., Pub., Adv. contact Hans Elmar Joering. page EUR 1,230; trim 180 x 265. Circ: 3,000.

364 MWI ISSN 0076-308X
MALAWI. POLICE FORCE. ANNUAL REPORT. Text in English. a. **Document type:** *Government.*
Published by: (Malawi. Police Force), Government Printer, PO Box 37, Zomba, Malawi.

364 DEU ISSN 0172-8563
MANNHEIMER HEFTE FUER SCHRIFTVERGLEICHUNG. Text in German. 1975. q. **Document type:** *Journal, Academic/Scholarly.*
Indexed: DIP, IBR, IBZ.
Published by: Schmidt-Roemhild Verlag, Mengstr 16, Luebeck, 23552, Germany. TEL 49-451-7031-01, FAX 49-451-7031253, eickershoff@beleke.de, http://www.schmidt-roemhild.de. Ed. Lothar Michel.

364 ISR
MAROTE HAMISHTARAH. Text in Hebrew. q. free. adv. bk.rev.
Published by: Israel National Police, c/o Chief Education Officer, Central Police Headquarters, Jerusalem, Israel. Ed. Oded Neev. Circ: 22,000.

MARTIN'S RELATED CRIMINAL STATUTES. see *LAW—Criminal Law*

MARYLAND CRIMINAL LAW AND MOTOR VEHICLE HANDBOOK. see *LAW—Criminal Law*

353.9 USA ISSN 0362-9198
HV7270
MARYLAND. DIVISION OF CORRECTION. REPORT✶. Key Title: Report - Maryland Division of Correction. Text in English. a.
Published by: Division of Correction, 6776 Reisterstown Rd, Ste 309, Baltimore, MD 21215-2306.

MASSACHUSETTS CRIMINAL DEFENSE MANUAL. see *LAW—Criminal Law*

364 GBR ISSN 0262-4141
MASTER DETECTIVE. Text in English. m. GBP 15; GBP 1.80 newsstand/cover (effective 1999). **Document type:** *Consumer.*
Published by: Magazine Design & Publishing Ltd., PO Box 735, London, SE26 5NQ, United Kingdom. TEL 44-181-778-0514, http://www.magazineshop.co.uk. **Dist. by:** Comag Specialist Division, Tavistock Works, Tavistock Rd, W Drayton, Mddx UB7 7QX, United Kingdom. TEL 44-1895-433800, FAX 44-1895-433801.

363.2 MUS
MAURITIUS POLICE FORCE. ANNUAL REPORT. Text in English. a.
Published by: Police Force, Police Headquarters, Line Barracks, Port Louis, Mauritius.

363.2 MUS
MAURITIUS POLICE MAGAZINE. Text in English, French. 1953. a. MUR 35. adv.
Published by: Police Force, Police Headquarters, Line Barracks, Port Louis, Mauritius. Circ: 6,000.

364.4 345 USA ISSN 1074-8083
THE MCGRUFFLETTER (NATIONAL EDITION); the nation's crime prevention newsletter. Text in English. 1987. q. USD 12 domestic; USD 20 foreign (effective 2002). adv. illus. 8 p./no.; **Document type:** *Newsletter, Consumer.* **Description:** Provides crime-prevention (includes drugs, tabacco, guns, cyber, back to school gangs, home alone etc.) information for children and families.
Supersedes: McGruffletter (1063-2999)
Published by: (U.S. National Crime Prevention Council), Jam Communications, 200 Hudson St, 3rd fl, New York, NY 10013. TEL 800-966-2478, FAX 212-624-4167, jamcommunications@earthlink.net. Ed., Adv. contact Ken Sanes. Pub., R&P Joseph Mangini. Circ: 160,000 (paid).

MENAI PAPERS. see *SOCIAL SCIENCES: COMPREHENSIVE WORKS*

353.9 USA
MICHIGAN. DEPARTMENT OF STATE POLICE. ANNUAL REPORT. Text in English. 1919. a. illus.
Formerly: Michigan. State Police. Annual Report
Related titles: Online - full text ed.
Published by: Department of State Police, 714 S Harrison Rd, East Lansing, MI 48823. TEL 517-332-2521, http://www.msp.sate.mi.us. Circ: (controlled).

MICHIGAN JOURNAL OF INTERNATIONAL LAW. see *LAW—International Law*

364 USA
MICHIGAN POLICE CHIEFS NEWSLETTER. Text in English. 1979. m. USD 30 (effective 2000). adv. **Document type:** *Newsletter.*
Formerly: Michigan Police Journal (0085-3380)
Published by: Michigan Association of Chiefs of Police, 2133 University Dr, 200, Okemos, MI 48864. TEL 517-349-9420. Ed. Thomas A Hendrickson. Circ: 1,600.

363.2 USA
MINNESOTA POLICE CHIEF✶. Text in English. 1981. q. USD 20; avail. only to qualified personnel and libraries. adv. bk.rev.
Published by: (Minnesota Chiefs of Police Association), Callan Publishing, Inc., 13120 County Road 6, Minneapolis, MN 55441-3830. TEL 612-920-4848, FAX 612-541-0435. Ed. Toni Johnson. Circ: 2,500.

363.2 USA ISSN 0026-5624
MINNESOTA POLICE JOURNAL. Text in English. 1928. bi-m. USD 13; subscr. avail. only to qualified personnel and libraries. adv. bk.rev. **Description:** Law enforcement and police administration.
Published by: Minnesota Police & Peace Officers Association, 327 York Ave, St. Paul, MN 55101-4090. TEL 651-291-1119, mppoa@hotmail.com, http://www.mppoa.com. Ed. Dennis J Flaherty. Adv. contact Stan Burzynski. Circ: 6,500.

364 649 ITA ISSN 1121-2845
MINORI GIUSTIZIA. Text in Italian. 1992. q. EUR 46 domestic; EUR 73 foreign (effective 2003). **Document type:** *Journal, Academic/Scholarly.* **Description:** Juridical, pedagogical, psychological and social studies on the relationship between minors and the justice system.
Indexed: DIP, IBR, IBZ.
Published by: Franco Angeli Edizioni, Viale Monza 106, Milan, 20127, Italy. TEL 39-02-2837141, FAX 39-02-26144793, redazioni@francoangeli.it, http://www.francoangeli.it.

364.4 RUS
MIR BEZOPASNOSTI. Text in Russian; Summaries in English. 1992. 6/yr. USD 85 in United States. adv. bibl.; illus. index. back issues avail. **Description:** Provides information about security: industry, equipment, techniques, law, and detective agencies.
Formerly: Chastnyi Sysk, Okhrana, Bezopasnost'
Indexed: RefZh.
Published by: Aktsionernoe Obshchestvo Vitiaz, Tikhvinskaya ul 39, str 2, Moscow, 103055, Russian Federation. TEL 7-095-9724450, FAX 7-095-9724450. Ed. V V Yunak. Adv. contact Alexander Vlasov. page USD 2,400. Circ: 27,000. **US dist. addr.:** East View Information Services, 3020 Harbor Ln. N., Minneapolis, MN 55447. TEL 612-550-0961.

364   DEU   ISSN 0026-9301
K13
MONATSSCHRIFT FUER KRIMINOLOGIE UND STRAFRECHTSREFORM. Text in German. 1917. bi-m. EUR 92; EUR 17 newsstand/cover (effective 2004). adv. bk.rev. charts. index. reprint service avail. from SCH. **Document type:** *Journal, Trade.*
Formerly: Aschaffenburg'she Monatsschrift
Indexed: AC&P, CJA, DIP, IBR, IBZ, PAIS, RASB.
—IE, Infotrieve. **CCC.**
Published by: (Gesellschaft fuer die Gesamte Kriminologie), Carl Heymanns Verlag KG, Luxemburger Str 449, Cologne, 50939, Germany. TEL 49-221-943730, FAX 49-221-94373901, marketing@heymanns.com, http://www.heymanns.com. adv.: B&W page EUR 667. Circ: 950 (paid and controlled).

364   USA   ISSN 1046-3070
KF1030.R3
MONEY LAUNDERING ALERT. Text in English. 1989. m. looseleaf. USD 395 domestic; USD 475 foreign (effective 2000). adv. back issues avail.; reprints avail. **Document type:** *Newsletter.* **Description:** Covers all pertinent enforcement actions, regulatory changes, statutory amendments, criminal and civil cases, and international developments in the field of money laundering, asset forfeiture and related fields.
Related titles: Online - full text ed.: (from Factiva, LexisNexis).
—IE. **CCC.**
Published by: Alert Global Media, Inc., PO Box 310037, Miami, FL 33231. TEL 305-530-0500, 800-232-3652, FAX 305-530-9434, http://www.moneylaundering.com. Ed. Nikolas Korba. Pub. Charles A Intriago. R&P Deborah Pelland. Adv. contact John Voss. Circ: 1,475 (paid).

MONOGRAFIEEN STRAFRECHT. see *LAW—Criminal Law*

363.2   ARG   ISSN 0030-7955
MUNDO POLICIAL✳. Variant title: P F A Revista. Text in Spanish. 1969. bi-m. ARS 18,188, USD 90. adv. bk.rev. abstr.; bibl.; charts; illus. **Description:** Deals with law enforcement and administration.
Published by: (Argentina. Policia Federal Argentina), Editorial Policial, Lavalle, 1280, Capital Federal, Buenos Aires 1048, Argentina. Eds. Juana Maissonave, Miguel A Pinella.

364.1   GBR   ISSN 1364-5803
MURDER IN MIND. Text in English. 1996. bi-w. GBP 1.99 newsstand/cover. **Document type:** *Consumer.* **Description:** Presents dossiers of real-life criminals and the crimes they committed.
Published by: Marshall Cavendish Partworks Ltd., 119 Wardour St, London, W1V 3TD, United Kingdom. **Subscr. to:** PO Box 1, Hastings, E Sussex TN35 4TJ, United Kingdom.

364.6   USA
N A A W S GRAPEVINE NEWSLETTER. Text in English. q. USD 25. bk.rev. charts; stat.; tr.lit. **Description:** Covers issues of current interest to wardens and superintendents of prisons.
Published by: (North American Association of Wardens and Superintendents), Central Michigan Printers, 221 W Main St, Ionia, MI 48846. TEL 616-527-2500. Ed. Pam Whitman. Circ: 4,500.

364.3 361.6   GBR
N A C R O ANNUAL REPORT. Text in English. a. free. **Document type:** *Corporate.*
Published by: National Association for the Care and Resettlement of Offenders, 169 Clapham Rd, London, SW9 0PU, United Kingdom. TEL 44-20-7582-6500, FAX 44-20-7735-4666.

364.3 361.6   GBR
N A C R O NEWS✳. Text in English. q. **Document type:** *Newsletter.*
Published by: National Association for the Care and Resettlement of Offenders, 169 Clapham Rd, London, SW9 0PU, United Kingdom. TEL 44-20-7582-6500, FAX 44-20-7735-4666.

364.3   GBR
N A C R O RACE UNIT NEWSLETTER. Text in English. q. free. **Document type:** *Newsletter.*
Published by: National Association for the Care and Resettlement of Offenders, 169 Clapham Rd, London, SW9 0PU, United Kingdom. TEL 44-20-7582-6500, FAX 44-20-7735-4666.

N A C R O YOUTH CRIME SECTION. see *CHILDREN AND YOUTH—About*

364.6   USA
N A J C A NEWS. Text in English. 1987. q. **Document type:** *Newsletter.* **Description:** Highlights changes and innovations in juvenile corrections in various states. Includes training opportunities of interest to members.
Published by: National Association of Juvenile Correction Agencies, 55 Albin Rd, Bow, NH 03304-3703. TEL 603-224-9749, FAX 603-226-4020, najcajohn@aol.com. Ed. John J Sheridan. Circ: 400.

363.2   GBR
N A P O NEWS. Text in English. 1965. m. membership. adv. bk.rev. **Document type:** *Newsletter.* **Description:** For law enforcement and probation administration, prison, and criminal justice personnel.
Formerly: N A P O Newsletter
Published by: National Association of Probation Officers, 3 Chivalry Rd, London, SW11 1HT, United Kingdom. FAX 44-171-223-3503. Ed. Harry Fletcher. Circ: 7,500.

363.2   GBR   ISSN 0142-1328
HV9345
N A P O PROBATION DIRECTORY. Text in English. 1974. a. GBP 9.50 (effective 2001). **Document type:** *Directory.*
Published by: (National Association of Probation Officers), Shaw & Sons Ltd., Shaway House, 21 Bourne Park, Bourne Rd, Crayford, Kent DA1 4BZ, United Kingdom. TEL 44-1322-621100, FAX 44-1322-550553, sales@shaws.co.uk, http://www.shaws.co.uk. Ed. Owen Wells. Pub., R&P Crispin Williams. Circ: 12,000 (controlled).

365   GBR   ISSN 0306-3313
N A P V NEWSLETTER. Text in English. 196?. s-a. GBP 1.50. bk.rev. back issues avail. **Document type:** *Newsletter.*
Published by: National Association of Prison Visitors, Fleur Field, Kingsdale Rd, Berkhamsted, Herts HP4 3BS, United Kingdom. FAX 01442-875785. Ed. Carol Green. Circ: 1,500 (controlled).

364.6   USA
N C J R S CATALOG. (National Criminal Justice Reference Service) Text in English. bi-m. **Document type:** *Catalog, Government.*
Published by: National Criminal Justice Reference Service, PO Box 6000, Rockville, MD 20849-6000. TEL 800-851-3420, FAX 301-251-5212, http://www.ncjrs.org/, http://tellncjrs.ncjrs.org. Circ: 80,000.

N R F PUBLIKATIES. see *LAW—Criminal Law*

364 345   USA
N.Y. DEFENSE OF JUSTIFICATION; penal law - article 35 review. Text in English. 1988. irreg. (1995-1996). USD 4.95 (effective 2000). **Document type:** *Monographic series.* **Description:** Presents a review of the use of physical force and deadly physical force, including definitions and questions and answers on the subject, as an aid in the training of law enforcement officers.
Published by: Gould Publications, Inc. (Subsidiary of: LexisNexis), 1333 North US Hwy 17-92, Longwood, FL 32750-3724. TEL 407-695-9500, 800-717-7917, FAX 407-695-2906, info@gouldlaw.com, http://www.gouldlaw.com.

NARC OFFICER. see *LAW*

364   ITA   ISSN 1127-9117
HV5800
NARCOMAFIE; mensile d'informazione, analisi e documentazione. Text in Italian; Abstracts in English. 1993. m. EUR 30 domestic; EUR 49 foreign (effective 2005). **Document type:** *Magazine, Trade.* **Description:** Contains recent news and reports on drug and mafia activity in various countries.
Published by: Edizioni Gruppo Abele, Corso Trapani 95, Turin, TO 10141, Italy. TEL 39-011-3841011, FAX 39-011-3841031, redazione@narcomafie.it, segreteria@gruppoabele.org, http://www.narcomafie.it, http://www.gruppoabele.org. Ed. Luigi Ciotti.

340   USA   ISSN 1079-1582
NARCOTICS ENFORCEMENT & PREVENTION DIGEST. Text in English. 1971. s-m. looseleaf. USD 225 domestic; USD 231 in Canada (effective 2005). bk.rev. reprint service avail. from PQC. **Document type:** *Newsletter, Consumer.* **Description:** Covers various law-enforcement topics and news in the U.S. and throughout the world. Includes job listings.
Former titles (until 1995): Narcotics Demand Reduction Digest (1043-8572); (until 1989): Narcotics Control Digest (0889-5708)
Related titles: Microform ed.: (from PQC); Online - full text ed.: (from ProQuest Information & Learning).
Indexed: CJPI.
Published by: Washington Crime News Services, 1209 National Press Bldg, 529 14th St, N W, Ste 9, Washington, DC 22045-0001. nvanwyen@washingtoncrime.com. Ed. Robert H Feldkamp. Circ: 1,000 (controlled and free).

350.765   USA   ISSN 8755-8289
KF3890.A59
NARCOTICS LAW BULLETIN. Text in English. 1974. m. looseleaf. USD 147 (effective 2004). index. reprint service avail. from PQC. **Document type:** *Newsletter.* **Description:** Contains summaries of current cases concerning narcotics, for non-lawyer law enforcement personnel.
Related titles: Microform ed.: (from PQC); Online - full text ed.: ISSN 1544-5151.
Indexed: CJPI.
—CCC.
Published by: Quinlan Publishing Group, Marine Industrial Park, 23 Drydock Ave, 6th Fl, Boston, MA 02210-2387. info@quinlan.com, http://www.policecenter.com.

364   USA
NATIONAL ASSOCIATION OF DOCUMENT EXAMINERS. COMMUNIQUE. Text in English. bi-m. USD 15. bk.rev. back issues avail. **Document type:** *Newsletter, Trade.*
Published by: National Association of Document Examiners, Inc., PO Box 324, Joppa, MD 21085. TEL 410-679-8257. Ed. Katherine M Koppenhaver TEL 919-556-7414.

340   USA   ISSN 8755-1020
NATIONAL ASSOCIATION OF DOCUMENT EXAMINERS. JOURNAL. Text in English. 1980. 3/yr. USD 50. bk.rev. charts; illus. back issues avail.
Published by: National Association of Document Examiners, Inc., PO Box 324, Joppa, MD 21085. TEL 410-679-8257, Presidentnade@aol.com, http://www.documentexaminers.org. Ed. Emily Will. Circ: 130.

371.93   USA
NATIONAL ASSOCIATION OF JUVENILE CORRECTION AGENCIES. PROCEEDINGS. Text in English. 1904. a. USD 20 to non-members; USD 5 to libraries. adv. **Document type:** *Proceedings.*
Formerly (until 1980): National Association of Training Schools and Juvenile Agencies. Proceedings (0077-3476)
Published by: National Association of Juvenile Correction Agencies, 55 Albin Rd, Bow, NH 03304-3703. TEL 603-224-9749, najcajohn@aol.com. Ed., R&P, Adv. contact John J Sheridan. Circ: 1,000.

363.2 305.896073   USA
NATIONAL BLACK - POLICE ASSOCIATION. NEWSLETTER. Text in English. 1985. q. USD 20 (effective 2000). adv. index. **Document type:** *Newsletter.*
Published by: National Black - Police Association, 3251 Mt Pleasant St, N W, Washington, DC 20010-2103. TEL 202-986-2070, FAX 202-987-0410. Ed., R&P, Adv. contact Fran Lassiter. Pub. Ronald E Hampton. Circ: 2,500.

NATIONAL BULLETIN ON DOMESTIC VIOLENCE PREVENTION. see *PUBLIC HEALTH AND SAFETY*

364.36   USA   ISSN 0163-2973
KF9772.3
NATIONAL CENTER FOR JUVENILE JUSTICE. ANNUAL REPORT. Text in English. 1974. a. illus.; stat. **Document type:** *Corporate.* **Description:** Presents an overview of the research activities and projects of the center.
Published by: National Center for Juvenile Justice, 710 Fifth Ave, Pittsburgh, PA 15219. TEL 412-227-6950, FAX 412-227-6955. Ed. E Hunter Hurst III.

364   USA
NATIONAL CENTER FOR STATE COURTS. CASELOAD HIGHLIGHTS. Text in English. irreg.
Indexed: CJA.
Published by: National Center for State Courts, 300 Newport Ave, Williamsburg, VA 23187-8798. TEL 757-253-2000, 800-616-6164, FAX 757-564-2022, http://www.ncsconline.org.

364   USA
NATIONAL COUNCIL ON CRIME AND DELINQUENCY. JUVENILE CUSTODY TRENDS. Cover title: Juvenile Court Trends. Text in English. irreg. stat. **Document type:** *Government.*
Published by: U.S. Department of Justice, National Council on Crime and Delinquency, Constitution Ave & 10th St, N W, Washington, DC 20530. TEL 202-739-0411. **Subscr. to:** U.S. Government Printing Office, Superintendent of Documents, PO Box 371954, Pittsburgh, PA 15250-7954. TEL 202-512-1800, FAX 202-512-2250, orders@gpo.gov, http://www.access.gpo.gov.

364   USA
NATIONAL COUNCIL ON CRIME AND DELINQUENCY. JUVENILES TAKEN INTO CUSTODY: FISCAL YEAR REPORT. Cover title: Juveniles Taken into Custody: Fiscal Year Report. Text in English. irreg. **Document type:** *Government.*
Published by: U.S. Department of Justice, National Council on Crime and Delinquency, 633 Indiana Ave, N W, Washington, DC 20531. TEL 202-739-0411. **Subscr. to:** U.S. Government Printing Office, Superintendent of Documents, PO Box 371954, Pittsburgh, PA 15250-7954. TEL 202-512-1800, FAX 202-512-2250, orders@gpo.gov, http://www.access.gpo.gov.

025.49364   USA
Z695.1.C84
NATIONAL CRIMINAL JUSTICE THESAURUS (ONLINE). Text in English. a. USD 35. **Document type:** *Government.*
Formerly: National Criminal Justice Thesaurus (Print) (0198-6546)
Media: Online - full content.
Published by: National Criminal Justice Reference Service, PO Box 6000, Rockville, MD 20849-6000. TEL 800-851-3420, FAX 301-251-5212, http://www.ncjrs.org/, http://tellncjrs.ncjrs.org.

C

365 USA ISSN 1066-5595
HV8130
NATIONAL DIRECTORY OF LAW ENFORCEMENT ADMINISTRATORS AND CORRECTIONAL INSTITUTIONS. Text in English. 1964. a., latest vol.38, 2003. USD 129 (effective 2003). adv. **Document type:** *Directory, Trade.*
Formerly (until 198?): National Directory of Law Enforcement Administrators, Prosecutors, Correctional Institutions, and Related Agencies (0733-3811)
Related titles: Online - full text ed.
Published by: National Public Safety Information Bureau, 3273 Church St, PO Box 365, Stevens Point, WI 54481. TEL 800-647-7579, FAX 715-345-7288, info@safetysource.com, http://www.safetysource.com. Ed. Steve Cywinski. Circ: 10,000.

NATIONAL DISTRICT ATTORNEYS ASSOCIATION. DIRECTORY OF PROSECUTING ATTORNEYS. see *LAW—Criminal Law*

364 USA
NATIONAL F O P JOURNAL. Text in English. 1915. q. USD 10. adv. **Document type:** *Trade.*
Published by: National Fraternal Order of Police, c/o Grand Lodge F O P, 1410 Donelson Pke A17, Nashville, TN 37217-2933. TEL 615-399-0900, FAX 615-399-0400. Ed. Jerry Atnip. Adv. contact Lynne S Martin.

364.1 306.4 USA ISSN 1553-2909
NATIONAL INDIAN GAMING DIGEST. Text in English. m. USD 129 (effective 2005). **Document type:** *Newsletter.*
Formerly (until 2004): Casino Crime Digest (1531-2178)
Published by: Falmouth Institute, Inc., 3702 Pender Dr, Ste 300, Fairfax, VA 22030-6066. TEL 703-352-2250, FAX 703-352-2323, information@falmouthinstitute.com, http://www.falmouthinstitute.com. Ed. Randi H Rowe.

364 USA
NATIONAL INSTITUTE OF JUSTICE. SPONSORED RESEARCH PROGRAMS. Text in English. a.
Published by: U.S. Department of Justice, National Institute of Justice, 633 Indiana Ave, N W, 11th Fl, Washington, DC 20531.

363.23 USA
NATIONAL LAW ENFORCEMENT AND CORRECTIONS TECHNOLOGY NEWS SUMMARY. Text in English. 1998. w. back issues avail. **Document type:** *Government.* **Description:** Provides a service to law enforcement, corrections, and forensic science practitioners.
Media: Online - full text.
Published by: National Law Enforcement and Corrections Technology Center, PO Box 1160, Rockville, MD 20849-1160. TEL 800-148-2742, dengler@nlectc.org, http://www.nlectc.org/inthenews/NewsSummary/weeklynews.html. Ed. Donna Engler.

364 USA ISSN 1041-3022
NATIONAL MISSING PERSONS REPORT. Text in English. 1980. 3/yr. free to qualified personnel. bk.rev. **Document type:** *Newsletter.* **Description:** Provides information to law enforcement personnel about missing persons of all ages, including unidentified bodies.
Published by: Search Reports, Inc., 345 Boulevard, Hasbrouck Heights, NJ 07604. TEL 201-288-4445, FAX 201-288-8055. Ed. Charles A Sutherland. Pub. Henry Moore. Circ: 45,000 (controlled).

NATIONAL ORGANIZATION FOR VICTIM ASSISTANCE NEWSLETTER. see *SOCIAL SERVICES AND WELFARE*

363.2 USA ISSN 1072-6551
HV7551
NATIONAL POLICE REVIEW. Text in English. 1962. q. membership only. adv. bk.rev. charts; illus. **Description:** Reports on policing methods and administration.
Former titles (until 1991): Enforcement Journal (0042-2347); (until 1971): Valor Magazine
Indexed: AC&P, CJPI.
Published by: National Police Officers Association, 7811 Old Tree Run, Louisville, KY 40222-4694. TEL 502-425-9215. Ed. John R Moore.

365 USA ISSN 1076-769X
NATIONAL PRISON PROJECT JOURNAL. Text in English. 1984. s-a. USD 30 (effective 2000 - 2001). bk.rev. back issues avail. **Document type:** *Newsletter.* **Description:** Publishes information on prison issues, prisoner rights, litigation, and women in prison.
Formerly (until 1990): American Civil Liberties Union Foundation. National Prison Project. Journal (0748-2655)
Indexed: CJPI.
Published by: American Civil Liberties Union Foundation, Inc., National Prison Project, 733 15th St, N W, Ste 620, Washington, DC 20005. TEL 202-393-4930, FAX 202-393-4931, kgotsch@npp-aclu.org, http://www.aclu.org/issues/prisons/npp_mission.html. Ed., R&P Kara Gotsch. Circ: 2,000.

364 EGY ISSN 0028-0054
NATIONAL REVIEW OF CRIMINAL SCIENCES. Text in Arabic, English. 1957. 3/yr. USD 30 (effective 1998). adv. bk.rev. charts; illus. **Document type:** *Academic/Scholarly.*
Published by: National Center for Social and Criminological Research, Zamalek P.O., Cairo, Egypt. TEL 20-2-3472484, FAX 20-2-3036069. Ed. Dr. Ahmed M Khalifa. Adv. contact Sohier Ali.

NATIONAL REVIEW OF SOCIAL SCIENCES/AL-MAGALLAT AL-IGTIMA'IYYAT AL-QAWMIYYAT. see *SOCIAL SCIENCES: COMPREHENSIVE WORKS*

NETWORKS. see *SOCIAL SERVICES AND WELFARE*

364 DEU
NEUE KRIMINOLOGISCHE SCHRIFTENREIHE. Text in German. 1961. irreg. price varies. adv. **Document type:** *Monographic series, Academic/Scholarly.*
Formerly: Kriminologische Schriftenreihe
Indexed: IBZ.
Published by: (Neue Kriminologische Gesellschaft), Kriminalistik Verlag Huethig GmbH & Co. KG, Im Weiher 10, Heidelberg, 69121, Germany. TEL 49-6221-489416, FAX 49-6221-489624, aboservice@huethig.de, http://www.huethig.de. Eds. Christoph Mayerhofer, Joerg Martin Jehle.

363.2 DEU ISSN 0028-3681
NEUES POLIZEIARCHIV; ein Nachschlagewerk in Monatsheften. Text in German. 1952. m. adv. bk.rev. **Document type:** *Bulletin.*
—CCC.
Published by: Richard Boorberg Verlag GmbH und Co. KG, Scharrstr 2, Stuttgart, 70563, Germany. TEL 49-711-7385-0. Ed. Hans Joern Bury.

NEW ENGLAND JOURNAL ON CRIMINAL AND CIVIL CONFINEMENT. see *LAW*

364 USA
NEW JERSEY LAW ENFORCEMENT HANDBOOK. Text in English. 1988. a. (in 2 vols.). looseleaf. USD 79.95; USD 129.95 CD-ROM (effective 2000). adv. bk.rev. **Description:** Dissects and analyzes court decisions for NJ, with question and answer format covering many topics.
Related titles: CD-ROM ed.: USD 90.
Published by: Gould Publications, Inc. (Subsidiary of: LexisNexis), 1333 North US Hwy 17-92, Longwood, FL 32750-3724. TEL 407-695-9500, 800-717-7917, FAX 407-695-2906, info@gouldlaw.com, http://www.gouldlaw.com. Ed. Larry E Holtz.

NEW LIFE (LONDON, 1971); prison service chaplaincy review. see *RELIGIONS AND THEOLOGY*

364 USA ISSN 1555-3418
▼ **NEW PERSPECTIVES IN CRIMINOLOGY AND CRIMINAL JUSTICE.** Text in English. forthcoming 2006 (Jan.). irreg. **Document type:** *Monographic series.*
Published by: Peter Lang Publishing, Inc., 275 Seventh Ave, 28th Fl, New York, NY 10001. TEL 212-647-7700, 800-770-5264, FAX 212-647-7707, customerservice@plang.com, http://www.peterlangusa.com.

364.4 USA
NEW SPIRIT. Text in English. 1981. q. USD 25 (effective 2001). adv. bk.rev. **Document type:** *Newsletter.*
Published by: National Association of Town Watch, Inc., 1 Wynnewood Rd, Ste 102, Box 303, Wynnewood, PA 19096. TEL 610-649-7055, 800-648-3688, FAX 610-649-5456, info@natw.org, http://www.natw.org. Ed. Matt Peskin. Circ: 8,000. **Co-sponsor:** America's Night Out Against Crime.

NEW YORK (CITY). DEPARTMENT OF JUVENILE JUSTICE. ANNUAL REPORT. see *LAW—Family And Matrimonial Law*

364 USA
NEW YORK (CITY). OFFICE OF MIDTOWN ENFORCEMENT. ANNUAL REPORT. Text in English. a. **Document type:** *Government.*
Published by: Office of Midtown Enforcement, 330 W 42nd St, 26th Fl, New York, NY 10036. TEL 212-971-6865.

364 USA
NEW YORK (STATE). CRIME VICTIMS BOARD. REPORT. Text in English. 1967. irreg. free. **Document type:** *Government.*
Formerly (until 1982): New York (State) Crime Victims Compensation Board. Report (0077-9148)
Published by: (New York (State). Counsel's Office), Crime Victims Board, 845 Central Ave, Rm 107, Albany, NY 12206-1588. TEL 578-457-8066, FAX 578-457-8658. R&P Everett A Mayhew. Circ: 2,000 (controlled).

353.9 USA ISSN 0095-4047
HV7282
NEW YORK (STATE). DIVISION OF CRIMINAL JUSTICE SERVICES. ANNUAL REPORT. Text in English. 1973. a.
Published by: Division of Criminal Justice Services, Office of Justice Systems Analysis, 4 Tower Pl, Albany, NY 12203. TEL 581-457-3724. Circ: 200.

NEW YORK (STATE). DIVISION OF CRIMINAL JUSTICE SERVICES. FELONY PROCESSING QUARTERLY REPORT. see *LAW—Criminal Law*

NEW YORK (STATE). DIVISION OF CRIMINAL SERVICES. OFFICE OF JUSTICE SYSTEMS ANALYSIS. STATISTICAL INDICATOR BULLETIN. see *CRIMINOLOGY AND LAW ENFORCEMENT—Abstracting, Bibliographies, Statistics*

363.2 USA
HV7551
THE NEW YORK STATE TROOPER. Text in English. 1963. q. free to qualified personnel. illus. **Document type:** *Government.*
Formerly: Trooper (0564-3287)
Published by: State Police, Public Security Bldg, State Campus, Albany, NY 12226. FAX 518-485-7818. Ed. Jon A Lupo. Circ: 14,000 (controlled).

363.2 USA
NEW YORK'S FINEST. Text in English. 1980. bi-m. membership only. illus.
Published by: Patrolmen's Benevolent Association of the City of New York, Inc., 40 Fulton St, New York, NY 10038. TEL 212-233-5531, FAX 212-233-3952. Ed. Joe Mancini. Circ: 32,000.

364 NLD ISSN 0925-2711
NIEUWSBRIEF POLITIE. Text in Dutch. 1990. bi-w. **Document type:** *Newsletter.*
Published by: Samsom H.D. Tjeenk Willink B.V. (Subsidiary of: Wolters Kluwer N.V.), Postbus 316, Alphen aan den Rijn, 2400 AH, Netherlands. TEL 31-1720-66822, FAX 31-1720-66639.

364.072 345.48 SWE ISSN 0805-5033
NORDISK KRIMINOLOGI; nyhetsbrev. Text in Multiple languages. 1975. 3/yr. free. adv. **Document type:** *Newsletter.* **Description:** News from the fields of criminology and criminal policy in the Nordic countries.
Formerly (until 1992): Nordisk Kriminologi. Nyhetsbrev (0349-1730)
Related titles: Online - full text ed.
Published by: Nordiska Samarbetsraadet foer Kriminologi/Scandinavian Research Council for Criminology, c/o Dept of Criminology, Stockholm University, Stockholm, 106 91, Sweden. TEL 46- 8-164674, FAX 46-8-157881, http://www.nsfk.org/publications/newsletter.shtml. Ed. Mia Soderbarj. Circ: 1,200.

364 ITA ISSN 0392-0100
HV7748
NUOVA POLIZIA E RIFORMA DELLO STATO✶. Text in Italian. 1977. m. USD 77. adv.
Published by: Editoriale Nuova Polizia Srl., Via Antonio Chinotto, 16, Rome, RM 00195, Italy. TEL 06-388910, FAX 06-3728091. Ed. Franco Fedeli. Circ: 60,000.

364.6 USA ISSN 1093-7439
OFFENDER PROGRAMS REPORT. Text in English. 1997. bi-m. USD 169.95 domestic; USD 199.95 foreign (effective 2005). **Document type:** *Newsletter.* **Description:** Devoted to innovative programs, management strategies, and legal developments in offender rehabilitation.
—CCC.
Published by: Civic Research Insitute, 4490 US Route 27, PO Box 585, Kingston, NJ 08528. TEL 609-683-4450, FAX 609-683-7291, order@civicresearchinstitute.com, http://www.civicresearchinstitute.com/co8.html. Ed. Russ Immarigeon.

OFFENDER SUBSTANCE ABUSE REPORT. see *DRUG ABUSE AND ALCOHOLISM*

364 343 USA
KFO561.A29
OHIO CRIMINAL LAW HANDBOOK. Text in English. a., latest 16th ed. USD 45 (effective 2005). **Document type:** *Consumer.* **Description:** Collects in a compact format statutes, rules, and special features for the use of judges, attorneys, law enforcement officers and others involved in the Ohio criminal justice process from before July 1, 1996.
Related titles: CD-ROM ed.: ISSN 1552-1907.
Published by: Anderson Publishing Co (Subsidiary of: LexisNexis North America), 9443 Springboro Pike, Miamisburg, OH 45342-4425. TEL 513-421-4142, 800-833-9844, FAX 513-562-8116, mail@andersonpublishing.com, http://bookstore.lexis.com/bookstore/catalog?action=product&prod_id=45129, http://www.andersonpublishing.com.

364 USA ISSN 1096-8504
HV9955.O5
OKLAHOMA CRIMINAL JUSTICE RESEARCH CONSORTIUM. JOURNAL. Text in English. 1994. a. **Document type:** *Journal.*
Indexed: CJA.
Published by: (Oklahoma Department of Corrections), Oklahoma Criminal Justice Research Consortium, c/o Oklahoma Department of Corrections, PO Box 11400, Oklahoma City, OK 73136-0400. TEL 405-425-2627, FAX 405-425-2741, http://www.doc.state.ok.us/DOCS/OCJRC/OCJRC_Journals.htm, http://www.doc.state.ok.us/DOCS/OCJRC/index.htm. Ed. Dan Lawrence.

ONDERZOEK EN BELEID. see *LAW—Criminal Law*

C

ONTARIO BOARD OF PAROLE. ANNUAL REPORT. see *PUBLIC ADMINISTRATION—Municipal Government*

364 USA
OREGON CRIMES AND PUNISHMENTS, VEHICLES & RELATED STATUTES. Text in English. 1996. a. USD 49.95 (effective 2000).
Related titles: CD-ROM ed.
Published by: Gould Publications, Inc. (Subsidiary of: LexisNexis), 1333 North US Hwy 17-92, Longwood, FL 32750-3724. TEL 407-695-9500, 800-717-7917, FAX 407-695-2906, info@gouldlaw.com, http://www.gouldlaw.com.

364 USA ISSN 1521-7310
HV6446
ORGANIZED CRIME DIGEST; an independent news summary of organized crime activities. Text in English. 1980. s-m. looseleaf. USD 225 domestic; USD 331 in Canada (effective 2005). reprint service avail. from PQC. **Document type:** *Newsletter, Trade.* **Description:** Covers issues in organized crime in the US and throughout the world.
Formerly (until 1998): Washington Crime News Services' Organized Crime Digest (0889-5716)
Related titles: Microform ed.: (from PQC); Online - full text ed.: (from ProQuest Information & Learning).
Indexed: CJPI.
Published by: Washington Crime News Services, 1209 National Press Bldg, 529 14th St, N W, Ste 9, Washington, DC 22045-0001. TEL 202-662-7035, nvanwyen@washingtoncrime.com. Eds. Leonard Curry, Robert H Feldkamp. Circ: 700 (paid and free).

OUNCE OF PREVENTION; survey of security & loss prevention in the retail industry. see *BUSINESS AND ECONOMICS—Marketing And Purchasing*

363.2 ZWE ISSN 0030-7289
HV8272.A2
OUTPOST. Text in English. 1911. m. ZWD 120; ZWD 30 in South Africa; GBP 15 elsewhere (effective 1999). adv. bk.rev. illus. **Document type:** *Trade.* **Description:** Covers law enforcement and administration.
Published by: Zimbabwe Republic Police, Highlands, PO Box HG 106, Harare, Zimbabwe. FAX 263-4-728768. Ed. Elvis Chipuka. R&P, Adv. contact Robson Mantoro TEL 263-4-724571. B&W page ZWD 3,500, color page ZWD 6,500. Circ: 23,000.

365 USA ISSN 1077-8209
HV7231 CODEN: OVTIFJ
OVERCROWDED TIMES; solving the prison problem. Text in English. 1990. bi-m. USD 39 to individuals; USD 75 to institutions.
Indexed: CJPI, SOPODA.
Published by: Castine Research Corporation, PO Box 110, Castine, ME 04421. TEL 207-326-9521, FAX 207-326-9528. Ed. Michael Tonry.

363.5 USA
P C N Y STATE REPORT. Text in English. 4/yr. USD 20. illus. **Document type:** *Corporate.*
Published by: Police Conference of New York, Inc., 112 State St, Ste 1120, Albany, NY 12207. Ed. Edward W Guzdek. Circ: 24,000.

364 DEU ISSN 0720-6283
HV7551
P F A SCHRIFTENREIHE. Text in German. irreg. (3-4/yr.). **Document type:** *Monographic series, Trade.*
Published by: (Polizei-Fuehrungsakademie), Schmidt-Roemhild Verlag, Mengstr 16, Luebeck, 23552, Germany. TEL 49-451-7031-01, FAX 49-451-7031253, eickershoff@beleke.de, http://www.schmidt-roemhild.de.

P F I WORLD REPORT. see *RELIGIONS AND THEOLOGY*

364 USA
P I MAGAZINE; America's private investigation journal. (Private Investigator) Text in English. 1988. q. USD 24 (effective 1999). adv. bk.rev. illus. back issues avail. **Document type:** *Trade.* **Description:** Source of information for the latest trends and investigative techniques for the professional private investigator.
Published by: Bob Mackowiak, Ed. & Pub., 755 Bronx Dr, Toledo, OH 43609. TEL 419-382-0967, FAX 419-382-0967, pimag1@aol.com, http://www.pimall.com. Adv. contact Bob Mackowiak. page USD 700; trim 9.75 x 7.5. Circ: 5,200.

PANOPTICON; tijdschrift voor strafrecht, criminologie en forensisch welzijnswerk. see *LAW—Criminal Law*

PARKER'S CALIFORNIA PENAL & VEHICLE CODE. see *LAW—Criminal Law*

363 GBR
PATROL. Text in English. m. **Document type:** *Bulletin.*
Published by: Sussex Police HQ, Public Relations Office, Mailing House, Lewes, E Sussex BN7 2DZ, United Kingdom. TEL 44-1273-475432, FAX 44-1273-404280. Ed. Jill Pedersen. Circ: 10,000.

363.2 USA ISSN 0031-4404
PENNSYLVANIA CHIEFS OF POLICE ASSOCIATION BULLETIN✶. Text in English. 1931. q. USD 50. adv. bk.rev. bibl.; charts; illus.; stat. **Document type:** *Bulletin.* **Description:** News and features of interest to members of the association.
Indexed: PAIS.
Published by: Pennsylvania Chiefs of Police Association, Public Relations Committee, 3905 N Front St, Harrisburg, PA 17110-1536. TEL 717-236-1059. Ed. Amy Corl. Circ: 1,300.

364 USA ISSN 0091-4118
HV7288
PENNSYLVANIA. CRIME COMMISSION. REPORT✶. Text in English. 1970. a. free. **Document type:** *Government.*
Published by: Crime Commission, 1800 Elmerton Ave, 3rd Fl, Harrisburg, PA 17110-9718. TEL 215-834-1164, FAX 215-834-0737. Circ: 40,000 (controlled).

345.748 USA ISSN 0098-7174
KFP575.A59
PENNSYLVANIA POLICE CRIMINAL LAW BULLETIN. Text in English. 1972. m. looseleaf. USD 36 (effective 1999). adv. index. back issues avail. **Document type:** *Bulletin.*
Published by: Stanley Cohen, Ed. & Pub., 125 E North St, Newcastle, PA 16101. R&P, Adv. contact Stanley Cohen. Circ: 650 (paid).

365 FRA ISSN 1028-625X
HV9638
PENOLOGICAL INFORMATION BULLETIN. Text in English, French. 1983. 2/yr. USD 4. charts.
Formerly (until 1992): Prison Information Bulletin (0254-5233)
Related titles: French ed.: Bulletin d'Information Penologique. ISSN 1023-2990.
Indexed: AC&P.
Published by: (Directorate of Legal Affairs), Council of Europe/Conseil de l'Europe, Publications Section, Strasbourg, Cedex 67075, France. TEL 33-3-88412581, FAX 33-3-88413910, publishing@coe.fr, http://book.coe.fr. Ed. Marguerite Sophie Eckert. **Dist. in U.S. by:** Manhattan Publishing Co., 468 Albany Post Rd, Croton On Hudson, NY 10520.

352 ROM ISSN 1220-6792
PENTRU PATRIE. Text in Romanian. 1949. m. ROL 1,000. illus. **Document type:** *Government.* **Description:** Presents the activities of the Ministry: police, fire brigades, boundary police, passport services, frontier guards, national archives. Publishes criminal laws and defends human rights.
Published by: Ministerul Interior, Str. Mihai Voda 17, Sector 5, Bucharest, 70622, Romania. TEL 40-16138202, FAX 40-12121390, TELEX 88810 ZZRPP R. Ed. Nicolae Rotaru. Pub. Jon Anghel Manastire. Circ: 200,000.

PERSONAL IDENTIFICATION NEWS. see *BUSINESS AND ECONOMICS—Banking And Finance*

364.6 USA ISSN 0821-1507
➤ **PERSPECTIVES (LEXINGTON).** Text in English. q. USD 50 to individual members; USD 60 to libraries; USD 12 per issue to libraries (effective 2005). adv. back issues avail. **Document type:** *Journal, Academic/Scholarly.* **Description:** Presents research, evaluations of innovative programs, and supervision strategies for criminal justice professionals.
Indexed: CJA.
Published by: American Probation and Parole Association, PO Box 11910, Lexington, KY 40578. TEL 859-244-8203, FAX 859-244-8001, dkincaid@csg.org, appa@csg.org, http://www.appa-net.org/publications%20and%20resources/perspect.htm. adv.: B&W page USD 920. Circ: 4,500.

364 USA ISSN 1099-971X
HV9950
PERSPECTIVES ON CRIME AND JUSTICE. Text in English. 1997. a. **Document type:** *Government.*
Published by: U.S. Department of Justice, National Institute of Justice, 810 Seventh St, NW, Washington, DC 20531. TEL 202-307-2942, askncjrs@ncjrs.org, http://www.ojp.usdoj.gov/nij.

364 USA
PHYSICAL SURVEILLANCE TRAINING MANUAL. Text in English. 1981. a. USD 20 (effective 2000).
Published by: (National Association of Investigative Specialists), Thomas Publishing (Austin), PO Box 33244, Austin, TX 78764. TEL 512-719-3595. Circ: 2,500.

363.2 USA ISSN 0893-8989
HV7936.E7
POLICE; the law enforcement magazine. Text in English. 1976. m. USD 25 domestic; USD 40 in Canada; USD 60 elsewhere (effective 2004). adv. illus. reprints avail. **Document type:** *Magazine, Trade.* **Description:** Trade journal for police officers.
Formerly: Police Product News (0164-5196)
Related titles: Online - full text ed.: (from Northern Light Technology, Inc., ProQuest Information & Learning).
Indexed: CJPI.
Published by: Bobit Business Media, 3520 Challenger St, Torrance, CA 90503. TEL 310-533-2400, FAX 310-533-2500, info@policemag.com, http://policemag.com, http://www.bobit.com. Ed. David Griffith. Pub. Leslie Maris. adv.: B&W page USD 2,825, color page USD 3,620. Circ: 52,484 (paid).

363.2 GBR ISSN 0032-2555
POLICE. Text in English. 1968. m. GBP 15 (effective 2000). adv. bk.rev. charts; illus. **Document type:** *Trade.* **Description:** Gives officers the latest information on current developments in professional matters and on changes to their pay and conditions of service.
Related titles: Online - full text ed.: (from Northern Light Technology, Inc.).
Indexed: AC&P, RefZh.
—BLDSC (6543.202000).
Published by: Police Federation of England and Wales, The Police Federation, 15 Langley Rd, Surbiton, Surrey KT6 6LP, United Kingdom. TEL 44-20-8335-1000, FAX 44-20-8335-1018. Ed., R&P Stewart Goodwin. Adv. contact David Pughe. Circ: 41,000. **Subscr. to:** Avon Direct Mail, Unit 12-14, Old Mill Rd, Portishead, Bristol, Avon BS20 9EG, United Kingdom.

363.2 GBR ISSN 0477-2008
POLICE & CONSTABULARY ALMANAC; official register. Text in English. 1861. a. GBP 28, USD 48.50 (effective 2002). adv. index. 390 p./no. 1 cols./p.; **Document type:** *Directory.* **Description:** Lists all U.K. police forces and organizations, along with their senior personnel.
—CCC.
Published by: Court & Judicial Publishing Co. Ltd., Box 39, Henley-on-Thames, Oxon RG9 5UA, United Kingdom. TEL 44-1491-641018. Ed. C G A Parker. Adv. contact C George. Circ: 20,000 (paid). **Co-publisher:** R. Hazell & Co.

C

345 USA ISSN 0092-8933
HV8138
POLICE AND LAW ENFORCEMENT. Text in English. 1973. a. USD 57.50. bibl.; stat. index. back issues avail. **Description:** Annual collection of articles covering major facets of police work and law enforcement in the United States.
Published by: A M S Press, Inc., 63 Flushing Ave., # 417, Brooklyn, NY 11205-1005. TEL 212-777-4700, FAX 212-995-5413. Eds. Daniel B Kennedy, Robert J Homant.

363.2 USA ISSN 1070-8111
CODEN: JNEOEK
POLICE AND SECURITY NEWS. Text in English. 1984. bi-m. USD 15 domestic; USD 29 foreign (effective 2000). adv. back issues avail. **Document type:** *Trade.* **Description:** Information, products and training directed to middle- and upper-administration personnel in the law enforcement and security fields.
Published by: Days Communications Inc., 1690 Quarry Rd, Box 330, Kulpsville, PA 19443. TEL 215-362-2233, FAX 215-368-9955. Ed. James Devery. Pub. David Yaw. R&P, Adv. contact Al Menear. Circ: 22,500 (controlled).

363 GBR
POLICE BEAT. Text in English. 11/yr. **Document type:** *Trade.*
Published by: Royal Ulster Constabulary Police Federation for Northern Ireland, Garnerville, Belfast, Co Antrim BT4 2NX, United Kingdom. TEL 0232-760831. Ed. D Rogers. Circ: 5,000.

364 USA ISSN 0032-2571
HV7551
POLICE CHIEF; professional voice of law enforcement. Text in English. 1934. m. USD 25 (effective 2005). adv. film rev. illus. index. back issues avail.; reprint service avail. from PQC. **Document type:** *Magazine.*
Related titles: Microfilm ed.: (from PQC); Online - full text ed.
Indexed: AC&P, CJA, CJPI, CurCont, HRIS, PAIS, RASB, SPAA, SSCI, SSI.
—BLDSC (6543.220000), IE, Infotrieve, ingenta.
Published by: International Association of Chiefs of Police, Inc., 515 N Washington St, Alexandria, VA 22314-2340. TEL 703-836-6767, FAX 703-836-4543, higginboth@theiacp.org, information@theiacp.org, http://www.theiacp.org, http://www.theiacp.org/. Eds. Charles E Higginbotham, Dan Rosenblatt. Adv. contact B.J. Hendrickson. Circ: 22,000.

345.052 363.2 USA
POLICE CIVIL LIABILITY. Text in English. 1986. 2 base vols. plus updates 2/yr. looseleaf. USD 273 base vol(s). (effective 2002). **Description:** A comprehensive guide to the personal injury and civil rights aspects of police misconduct. Includes an extensive array of forms, which are now on a 3.5" disk product that accompanies the print version. An essential resource for personal injury lawyers—plaintiff and defense, civil rights attorneys, government counsel, and for law enforcement officers at all levels, this handy work provides numerous practice aids and forms throughout.
Related titles: CD-ROM ed.
Published by: Matthew Bender & Co., Inc. (Subsidiary of: LexisNexis North America), 1275 Broadway, Albany, NY 12204. international@bender.com, http://bender.lexisnexis.com. Ed. Isidore Silver.

POLICE, CRIMES AND OFFENSES AND MOTOR VEHICLE LAWS OF VIRGINIA. see *LAW—Criminal Law*

331 364   USA   ISSN 1075-900X
POLICE DEPARTMENT DISCIPLINARY BULLETIN. Text in English. 1992. m. looseleaf. USD 147 (effective 2004). index. back issues avail. **Document type:** *Newsletter, Trade.* **Description:** Discusses all aspects of disciplinary issues facing U.S. police departments, including off-duty misconduct, insubordination, sexual harassment, falsification of reports, drug testing and more.
Formerly (until 1993): Police Department Disciplinary Law Bulletin
Related titles: Online - full text ed.: ISSN 1544-6425 (from ProQuest Information & Learning).
Indexed: CJPI.
—CCC.
Published by: Quinlan Publishing Group, Marine Industrial Park, 23 Drydock Ave, 6th Fl, Boston, MA 02210-2387. TEL 617-542-0048, 800-229-2084, FAX 617-345-9646, info@quinlan.com, http://www.quinlan.com. Ed. Leslie Rosenbloom. Pub. Dennis Hofmaier.

363.2   USA   ISSN 1544-0524
POLICE FLEET MANAGER. Text in English. 2002. m. adv.
Related titles: Online - full text ed.: (from ProQuest Information & Learning).
Published by: Hendon Publishing Company, 130 Waukegan Rd, Deerfield, IL 60015. TEL 847-444-3300, FAX 847-444-3333, info@hendonpub.com. Ed. Ed Sanow. Pub. H Scott Kingwill. Adv. contact Pete Kingwill.

363.2   USA   ISSN 1061-1517
POLICE FORUM. Text in English. 1991. q. free to qualified personnel (effective 2005). **Document type:** *Newsletter, Trade.*
Indexed: ABIn, CJA, CJPI.
Published by: Academy of Criminal Justice Sciences, 7339 Hanover Pkwy., Ste. A, Greenbelt, MD 20770-3640. TEL 800-757-2257, info@acjs.org, http://www.acjs.org.

364   USA
KF5399.A59
POLICE IMMUNITY LAW BULLETIN. Text in English. 1982. m. looseleaf. USD 79 (effective 1999). index. back issues avail. **Document type:** *Newsletter.* **Description:** Covers legal aspects of police misconduct and challenges to law enforcement personnel on such issues as wrongful death, civil rights, immunity, confessions, false arrest, brutality, use of force, and entrapment.
Former titles: Quinlan Law Bulletin on Police Immunity (1095-8118); (until 1997): National Bulletin on Police Misconduct (1042-5810); (until 1988): Law Enforcement Misconduct Bulletin (8755-8238)
Indexed: CJPI.
—CCC.
Published by: Quinlan Publishing Group, Marine Industrial Park, 23 Drydock Ave, 6th Fl, Boston, MA 02210-2387. TEL 617-542-0048, 800-229-2084, FAX 617-345-9646.

363.2   GBR   ISSN 0032-258X
HV7551
➤ **POLICE JOURNAL;** a quarterly review for the police forces of the Commonwealth and English-speaking world. Text in English. 1927. q. GBP 102, USD 173 to institutions; GBP 133.20, USD 209 combined subscription to institutions print & online (effective 2005). adv. bk.rev. illus.; abstr. index, cum.index. 96 p./no. 1 cols./p.; back issues avail.; reprints avail. **Document type:** *Journal, Academic/Scholarly.* **Description:** Contains articles on judicial decisions, home office statistics and advise.
Related titles: Online - full content ed.: ISSN 1740-5599. GBP 108.10, USD 156 to institutions (effective 2005); Online - full text ed.: (from EBSCO Publishing, Swets Information Services).
Indexed: AC&P, ASSIA, BAS, CJA, CJPI, ELJI, ExcerpMed, HRIS, LJI, PAA&I, RASB.
—BLDSC (6543.250000), IE, ingenta.
Published by: Vathek Publishing, Bridge House, Dolby, Isle of Man, IM5 3BP, United Kingdom. TEL 44-1624-844056, FAX 44-1624-845043, mlw@vathek.com, http://www.vathek.com/pj/index.shtml. Ed. John Jones. Pub., Adv. contact Mairwen Lloyd-Williams. **Circ:** 400. **Dist. by:** Portland Press Ltd., Commerce Way, Colchester CO2 8HP, United Kingdom. TEL 44-1206-796351, FAX 44-1206-799331, sales@portland-services.com, sales@rscdistribution.org.

363.2   AUS   ISSN 0032-2598
POLICE LIFE. Text in English. 1955. q. free. bk.rev. illus. index. **Document type:** *Government.*
Indexed: RASB.
Published by: Victoria Police, 637 Flinders St., Melbourne, VIC 3005, Australia. TEL 61-3-92475979, FAX 61-3-92475982. Ed. Marilyn Miller. Circ: 13,000.

364   USA   ISSN 0164-8365
POLICE MARKSMAN. Text in English. bi-m. USD 18.95.
Document type: *Trade.*
Published by: Police Marksman Association, 6000 E Shirley Ln, Montgomery, AL 36117-6201. TEL 334-271-2010, FAX 334-279-9267. Ed. Connie Dees. Pub. Charles Dees.

363.2 796.8   CAN   ISSN 1198-8398
POLICE MARTIAL ARTS ASSOCIATION NEWS. Text in English. 1994. bi-m. looseleaf. CND 20, USD 15. adv. back issues avail. **Document type:** *Newsletter.* **Description:** Covers police and martial arts issues for a law enforcement readership base. Studies use of force research, specialized training and procedures, confrontational analysis, officer safety and protection.
Published by: Police Martial Arts Association, P O Box 7303, Sub 12, Riverview, NB E1B 4T9, Canada. TEL 506-387-5126, FAX 506-387-5126. Eds. Doug Devlin, Foster MacLeod. Circ: 1,000 (controlled).

323.4   USA   ISSN 0738-0623
KF4742
POLICE MISCONDUCT AND CIVIL RIGHTS LAW REPORT. Text in English. 1983. bi-m. looseleaf. USD 297 (effective 2004). index. back issues avail. **Document type:** *Trade.* **Description:** Contains articles on the most current issues in police misconduct and civil rights litigation.
Published by: (National Lawyers Guild, Civil Liberties Committee), Thomson West (Subsidiary of: Thomson Corporation, The), 610 Opperman Dr, Eagan, MN 55123-1396. TEL 651-687-8000, 800-328-4880, FAX 651-687-7302, http://west.thomson.com/product/14048156/product.asp.

363.2   GHA
POLICE NEWS. Text in English. m.
Published by: Police Headquarters, Accra, Ghana. Ed. S S Appiah. Circ: 20,000.

344.01   USA   ISSN 0887-8285
KF5398.P6
POLICE OFFICER GRIEVANCES BULLETIN. Text in English. 1982. m. looseleaf. USD 147 (effective 2004). index. back issues avail. **Document type:** *Newsletter.* **Description:** Discusses decisions and legal issues relating to grievances and police labor issues such as hiring, firing, arbitration, notice and hearing procedures, for police and police-related employees.
Related titles: Online - full text ed.: ISSN 1544-502X.
Indexed: CJPI.
—CCC.
Published by: Quinlan Publishing Group, Marine Industrial Park, 23 Drydock Ave, 6th Fl, Boston, MA 02210-2387. TEL 800-229-2084, info@quinlan.com, http://www.policecenter.com/bulletins.

363.2   USA   ISSN 1062-5216
POLICE OFFICERS JOURNAL★. Text in English. 1957. 4/yr. membership only. adv. bk.rev. charts; illus. **Document type:** *Newsletter.* **Description:** Covers issues of labor, crime and safety.
Formerly (until 1992): Peace Officer (0031-3556)
Published by: (Police Officers Labor Council), Dale Corporation, 27301 Dequindre Rd, Ste 302, Madison Heights, MI 48071-3459. TEL 248-945-1600, FAX 248-945-1811, dalecorp@yahoo.com. Ed. Barbara Logan. R&P Dale Jablonski. adv.: B&W page USD 925, color page USD 1,425; trim 8.5 x 11. Circ: 5,000.

364   GBR   ISSN 1561-4263
HV7935
➤ **POLICE PRACTICE AND RESEARCH;** an international journal. Text in English. 2000. 5/yr. GBP 241, USD 397 combined subscription to institutions print & online eds. (effective 2006). reprint service avail. from PSC. **Document type:** *Journal, Academic/Scholarly.* **Description:** Presents current and innovative police research as well as operational and administrative practices from around the world.
Related titles: Online - full text ed.: ISSN 1477-271X. GBP 229, USD 377 to institutions (effective 2006) (from EBSCO Publishing, Gale Group, IngentaConnect, O C L C Online Computer Library Center, Inc., Swets Information Services).
Indexed: CJA, ESPM, H&SSA, PAIS, PSA, RiskAb, SociolAb.
—BLDSC (6543.256700), IE, Infotrieve, ingenta. **CCC.**
Published by: Routledge (Subsidiary of: Taylor & Francis Group), 4 Park Sq, Milton Park, Abingdon, Oxon OX14 4RN, United Kingdom. TEL 44-1235-828600, FAX 44-1235-829000, info@routledge.co.uk, http://www.tandf.co.uk/journals/titles/15614263.asp, http://www.routledge.co.uk. Ed. Dilip Das. **Subscr. to:** Taylor & Francis Ltd. enquiry@tandf.co.uk.

➤ **POLICE QUARTERLY.** see *LAW—Criminal Law*

364   GBR
POLICE RESEARCH SERIES. Text in English. 1985. irreg.
Document type: *Monographic series.*
Former titles: Police Research Group Crime Detection and Prevention Series Papers; Police Research Group Crime Prevention Unit Series Papers
Related titles: Online - full text ed.
—BLDSC (6543.261700).
Published by: Home Office, Policing and Reducing Crime Unit, Clive House, Petty France, London, SW1H 9HD, United Kingdom. TEL 44-20-7271-8568, FAX 44-20-7271-8344, http://www.homeoffice.gov.uk/dob/prcu.htm.

364   USA
POLICE SCIENCE FUNDAMENTALS. Text in English. 1973. irreg. USD 11.95 (effective 2000). **Description:** Approximately 800 questions and answers on the basic law enforcement operations. Used for studying for the law enforcement promotion exam.
Published by: Gould Publications, Inc. (Subsidiary of: LexisNexis), 1333 North US Hwy 17-92, Longwood, FL 32750-3724. TEL 407-695-9500, 800-717-7917, FAX 407-693-2906, info@gouldlaw.com, http://www.gouldlaw.com.

363.2   USA
POLICE TIMES. Text in English. 1964. q. free membership (effective 2003). adv. bk.rev. charts; illus. reprints avail.
Document type: *Trade.*
Former titles: Police Times and Police Command; Police Times (0032-2601)
Published by: American Federation of Police & Concerned Citizens, 6250 Horizon Dr, Titusville, FL 32780. TEL 321-264-0911, FAX 321-264-0033, policeinfo@aphf.org, http://www.aphf.org. Ed. Jim Gordon. Circ: 50,000.

363.2   ESP   ISSN 0213-4012
POLICIA. Text in Spanish. 1984. m. adv. bk.rev. charts; illus.
Formed by the merger of (1962-1984): Policia Espanola (0048-4709); (1961-1984): Policia Nacional (0210-5896); Which was formerly (until 1978): Policia Armada (0210-590X)
Published by: (Spain. Seccion de Documentacion y Publicaciones), Direccion General de Policia, Instituto de Estudios de Policia, Rafael Calvo, 33 3a pl, Madrid, 28010, Spain. TEL 34-1-4351720. Circ: 19,000.

363.2   GBR   ISSN 1363-951X
HV7551
➤ **POLICING;** an international journal of police strategies and management. Text in English. 1978. q. EUR 2,043.41 in Europe; USD 1,909 in North America; AUD 3,079 in Australasia; GBP 1,434.41 in UK & elsewhere (effective 2006). bk.rev. illus. index. back issues avail.; reprint service avail. from PSC. **Document type:** *Journal, Academic/Scholarly.* **Description:** Devoted to the craft, science and practice of police work for senior police officers, government officials, university teachers, instructors, students and research workers.
Formerly (until 1997): Police Studies (0141-2949); Incorporates (1981-1997): American Journal of Police (0735-8547)
Related titles: Microfilm ed.: (from PQC); Online - full text ed.: (from EBSCO Publishing, Emerald Group Publishing Limited, Gale Group, IngentaConnect, O C L C Online Computer Library Center, Inc., ProQuest Information & Learning, Swets Information Services).
Indexed: ABS&EES, AC&P, CJA, CJPI, CurCont, ESPM, EmerIntel, IBSS, PAIS, PCI, PRA, PSA, RASB, SOPODA, SSA, SSCI, SUSA, SociolAb, V&AA.
—BLDSC (6543.283900), IE, Infotrieve, ingenta. **CCC.**
Published by: Emerald Group Publishing Limited, 60-62 Toller Ln, Bradford, W Yorks BD8 9BY, United Kingdom. TEL 44-1274-777700, FAX 44-1274-785200, infomation@emeraldinsight.com, http://www.emeraldinsight.com/pijpsm.htm. Ed. Lawrence F Travis III.

364   GBR
POLICING AND REDUCING CRIME UNIT. BRIEFING NOTES. Text in English. 1999. m.
Media: Online - full text.
—BLDSC (2283.958073).
Published by: Home Office, Policing and Reducing Crime Unit, Clive House, Petty France, London, SW1H 9HD, United Kingdom. TEL 44-20-7271-8568, FAX 44-20-7271-8344, http://www.homeoffice.gov.uk/prgpubs.htm, http://www.homeoffice.gov.uk/dob/prcu.htm.

363.2   GBR   ISSN 1355-4557
POLICING TODAY. Variant title: Jane's Policing Today. Text in English. 1984. m. GBP 45 in United Kingdom; GBP 50 rest of Europe; USD 108 in the Americas; GBP 65 rest of world (effective 2001). adv. **Document type:** *Trade.* **Description:** Provides all the news, information and analysis that helps key decision makers implement law enforcement policies at the highest level.
Indexed: AC&P, CJA, ELJI, LJI.
—BLDSC (6543.287000), IE, Infotrieve, ingenta. **CCC.**
Published by: Jane's Information Group, Sentinel House, 163 Brighton Rd, Coulsdon, Surrey CR5 2YH, United Kingdom. TEL 44-20-87003700, FAX 44-20-87631006, info@janes.co.uk, http://catalogue.janes.com/pt.shtml, http://www.janes.com. Ed. Sean Howe. Pub. Fabiana Angelini. R&P Sergio Deoliveira. Adv. contact Alice Codrington. Circ: 1,300 (paid). **Dist. in Asia by:** Jane's Information Group Asia, 60 Albert St, #15-01 Albert Complex, Singapore 189969, Singapore. TEL 65-331-6280, FAX 65-336-9921, info@janes.com.sg; **Dist. in Australia by:** Jane's Information Group Australia, PO Box 3502, Rozelle, NSW 2039, Australia. TEL 61-2-8587-7900, FAX 61-2-8587-7901, info@janes.thomson.com.au; **Dist. in the Americas by:** 1340 Braddock Pl, Ste 300, Alexandria, VA 22314-1651. TEL 703-683-3700, 800-824-0768, FAX 703-836-0297, 800-836-0297, info@janes.com.

364.0711 POL ISSN 1640-9280
POLICJA. Text in Polish. 1993. q. charts; illus.; bibl. **Document type:** *Journal, Academic/Scholarly.* **Description:** Covers police education and law.
Formerly (until 2000): Policyjny Biuletyn Szkoleniowy (1230-9273)
Related titles: Online - full content ed.
Published by: Wydawnictwo Wyzszej Szkoly Policyjnej, ul Marsz J Pilsudskiego 111, Szczytno, 12101, Poland. TEL 48-89-6215385, FAX 48-89-6242610, wspol@wspol.edu.pl, http://www.wspol.edu.pl/wspol. R&P Wieslaw Piywaczewski TEL 48-89-6215100. Circ: 600 (controlled).

363.2 FIN ISSN 1238-5387
POLIISI & OIKEUS. Text in Finnish. 1929. 10/yr. adv. bk.rev. charts; illus.; stat. **Document type:** *Magazine, Trade.*
Formerly (until 1995): Poliisimies (0048-4725)
Published by: Suomen Poliisijarjestojen Liitto ry, Asemamiehenkatu 2, Helsinki, 00520, Finland. TEL 358-9-1551, FAX 358-9-1481132, http://www.spjl.fi. Ed. Seppo Yrjoenen TEL 358-9-1552498. adv.: B&W page EUR 858, color page EUR 1,497; 185 x 240.

363.2 SWE ISSN 0345-9454
POLISTIDNINGEN. Text in Swedish. 1904. 8/yr. SEK 220 (effective 2004). **Document type:** *Magazine, Trade.*
Formerly (until 1941): Svensk Polistidning
Published by: Svenska Polisfoerbundet, PO Box 5583, Stockholm, 11485, Sweden. TEL 46-8-6769726, FAX 46-8-232410, polistidningen@polisforbundet.se, http://www.polistidningen.org, http://www.polisforbundet.se. Ed. Ylva Norberg. Adv. contact Joakim Lind TEL 46-8-55696015.

364 USA
HV6431
POLITICAL VIOLENCE AGAINST AMERICANS. Text in English. a. **Document type:** *Government.*
Formerly: Significant Incidents of Political Violence Against Americans
Related titles: Online - full content ed.
Published by: U.S. Department of State, Office of Intelligence and Threat Analysis, c/o Andrew Corsun, 2201 C St. NW, Washington, DC 20520. http://www.state.gov/m/ds/rls/rpt/19691.htm, http://www.state.gov/m/ds/terrorism/c8584.htm.

363.209489 DNK ISSN 0108-3376
HV7766
POLITIETS AARSBERETNING. Text in Danish, English. 1948. a. free. **Document type:** *Government.* **Description:** Presents the annual report of the Chief of State Police.
Published by: Rigspolitichefen, Afdeling E/National Police Commissioner, Polititorvet 14, Copenhagen V, 1588, Denmark. TEL 45-33-14-88-88, FAX 45-33-91-22-78, http://www.politi.dk. Ed., R&P Jens Bang. Circ: 6,100.

363.2 331.88 NOR ISSN 1500-6921
POLITIFORUM. Text in Norwegian. 1975. m. free membership. adv. bk.rev. bibl.
Formerly (until 1998): Politi- og Lensmannsetaten (0803-4087); Which was formed by the merger of (1975-1991): Politibladet (0332-7655); (1985-1991): Lensmannsetaten (0801-5325)
Published by: Politiets Fellesforbund, Storgatan 32, Oslo, 0184, Norway. TEL 47-23-16-31-00, FAX 47-23-16-31-40, redaktion@pf.no. Ed. Ole Martin Mortvedt TEL 47-62-53-90-00.

363.2 DNK ISSN 0107-3893
POLITIHISTORISK SELSKAB. AARSSKRIFT. Text in Danish. 1981. a. DKK 80. illus.
Published by: Polithistorisk Selskab/Danish Police Historical Society, Polititorvet 14, Copenhagen V, 1780, Denmark. FAX 45-31-39-69-36. Ed. Flemming Steen Munch. Circ: 3,500.

363.2 DEU ISSN 0032-3519
DIE POLIZEI; Zentralorgan fuer das Sicherheits- und Ordnungswesen. Text in German. 1908. m. EUR 88; EUR 9 newsstand/cover (effective 2004). adv. bk.rev. illus.; stat. index. **Document type:** *Journal, Trade.*
Indexed: AC&P, CJA, DIP, IBR, IBZ, RASB.
Published by: Carl Heymanns Verlag KG, Luxemburger Str 449, Cologne, 50939, Germany. TEL 49-221-943730, FAX 49-221-94373901, marketing@heymanns.com, http://www.heymanns.com. Ed. O Wenzky. adv.: B&W page EUR 953, color page EUR 1,772. Circ: 1,200 (paid and controlled).

364 AUT
POLIZEI AKTUELL. Text in German. q. **Document type:** *Magazine, Trade.*
Published by: Klub der Exekutive, Sektion Sicherheitswache im Bund Oeffentlicher Angestellter, Salztorgasse 5-III, Vienna, W 1010, Austria. TEL 43-1-531262802, FAX 43-1-531262810, info@polizei-aktuell.at, info@polizeigewerkschaft-fsg.at, http://www.polizei-aktuell.at/poa/index.asp, http://www.polizeigewerkschaft-fsg.at. Ed. Herbert Leisser. Circ: 20,000.

363.2 DEU ISSN 0947-4021
POLIZEI-HEUTE; Fuehrung - Technik - Ausbildung - Recht. Text in German. 1982. bi-m. EUR 35; EUR 8 newsstand/cover (effective 2004). adv. bk.rev. index. back issues avail. **Document type:** *Journal, Trade.*
Formerly (until 1994): Bereitschaftspolizei Heute (0723-6123); Which was formed by the merger of (1971-1982): Bereitschaftspolizei Heute. Baden-Wuerttemberg (0720-8340); (1971-1982): Bereitschaftspolizei Heute. Bayern (0720-8359); (1971-1982): Bereitschaftspolizei Heute. Berlin (0720-8367); (1971-1982): Bereitschaftspolizei Heute. Bremen (0720-8375); (1971-1982): Bereitschaftspolizei Heute. Hamburg (0720-8383); (1971-1982): Bereitschaftspolizei Heute. Hessen (0171-287X); (1971-1982): Bereitschaftspolizei Heute. Niedersachsen (0720-8391); (1971-1982): Bereitschaftspolizei Heute. Nordrhein-Westfalen (0720-8405); (1971-1982): Bereitschaftspolizei Heute. Rheinland-Pfalz (0720-8413); (1971-1982): Bereitschaftspolizei Heute. Saarland (0720-8421)
Published by: Richard Boorberg Verlag GmbH und Co. KG, Scharrstr 2, Stuttgart, 70563, Germany. TEL 49-711-73850, FAX 49-711-7385100, mail@boorberg.de, http://www.boorberg.de. Ed., Adv. contact Helmut Brueckmann. Pub. Erhard Denninger. B&W page EUR 1,310, color page EUR 2,240; trim 171 x 262. Circ: 3,400 (paid).

363.2 DEU ISSN 0943-9463
POLIZEISPIEGEL. Text in German. 1964. m. EUR 38 domestic; EUR 46 foreign; EUR 3.90 newsstand/cover (effective 2005). adv. bk.rev. charts; illus.; tr.lit. **Document type:** *Magazine, Trade.*
Indexed: PAIS, RASB.
Published by: (Polizeigewerkschaft im Deutschen Beamtenbund), D B B Verlag GmbH, Reinhardtstr 29, Berlin, 10117, Germany. TEL 49-30-72619170, FAX 49-30-726191740, kontakt@dbbverlag.de, http://www.dpolg.de/Polizeispiegel.htm, http://www.dbbverlag.de. adv.: B&W page EUR 3,600, color page EUR 4,950. Circ: 57,000 (paid and controlled).

363.2 DEU ISSN 0722-5962
POLIZEIVERKEHR UND TECHNIK; Fachzeitschriften fuer Verkehrs- und Polizeitechnik. Text in German. 1956. bi-m. adv. bk.rev. illus. index. **Document type:** *Journal, Trade.*
Formerly: Polizei Technik Verkehr (0032-3535)
Indexed: RefZh.
Published by: Schmidt-Roemhild Verlag, Mengstr 16, Luebeck, 23552, Germany. TEL 49-451-7031-01, FAX 49-451-7031253, eickershoff@beleke.de, http://www.schmidt-roemhild.de. Ed. Eugen Sauer. Circ: 2,000.

080 362.127 USA ISSN 0197-7024
HV8078.A1
POLYGRAPH. Text in English. 1972. q. USD 80 domestic; USD 100 foreign (effective 2005). adv. bk.rev. charts. index. reprint service avail. from PQC. **Document type:** *Academic/Scholarly.* **Description:** Discusses forensic psychophysiology, polygraph operations, research, history, psychology, physiology, instrumentation, law notes, abstracts, and training.
Supersedes: American Polygraph Association. Journal (0003-0562)
Related titles: Microfilm ed.: (from PQC).
Indexed: A&ATA, AC&P, CJA, CJPI, P&BA, e-psyche.
Published by: (American Polygraph Association), Sheridan Press, PO Box 8037, Chattanooga, TN 37414-0037. TEL 423-892-3992, FAX 423-894-5435. R&P, Adv. contact Robbie Bennett. Circ: 3,500.

POMPE REEKS. see *LAW—Criminal Law*

364 USA
PRACTICAL TIPS FOR NEW YORK LAW ENFORCEMENT. Text in English. 1994. irreg. USD 5.95 (effective 2000). **Document type:** *Trade.* **Description:** Invaluable information for the law enforcement officer who faces a multitude of court-made rules before an arrest can be made. Valuable tips assist the officer in making arrests which will lead to convictions. Whether the arrest is on the street, in a car, or in a home, the officer can be confident the evidence will not be suppressed.
Published by: Gould Publications, Inc. (Subsidiary of: LexisNexis), 1333 North US Hwy 17-92, Longwood, FL 32750-3724. TEL 407-695-9500, 800-717-7917, FAX 407-695-2906, info@gouldlaw.com, http://www.gouldlaw.com.

364 364.4 USA ISSN 0193-4015
KF9632.A15
THE PRETRIAL REPORTER. Text in English. 1977. bi-m. USD 48 (effective 2005). bk.rev. back issues avail. **Document type:** *Newsletter, Trade.* **Description:** Examines pretrial issues and jail crowding on a national basis, including legislation, program practices, research and case law. Serves as a resource for jobs, conferences and publications.
Published by: Pretrial Services Resource Center, 1325 G St, N W, Ste 770, Washington, DC 20005. TEL 202-638-3080, FAX 202-347-0493, psrc@pretrial.org, pretrial@gslink.com, http://www.pretrial.org, http://www.gslink.com/~pretrial. Ed., R&P John Clark. Circ: 300 (paid).

306.95 362.82 CAN ISSN 1485-0176
PREVENTING FAMILY VIOLENCE; a catalogue of Canadian videos on family violence for the general public and for professionals working in the field. Text in English. a.
Media: Video.
Published by: Health Canada, A.L. 0900C2, Ottawa, ON K1A OK9, Canada. TEL 613-954-8842, FAX 613-990-7097.

365 USA ISSN 0032-8855
HV7231
➤ **THE PRISON JOURNAL.** Text in English. 1845. q. USD 406, GBP 262 to institutions; USD 422, GBP 273 combined subscription to institutions print & online eds. (effective 2006). adv. bk.rev. illus.; abstr. index. back issues avail.; reprints avail. **Document type:** *Journal, Academic/Scholarly.* **Description:** Devoted to the advancement of theory, research, policy, and practice in the areas of adult and juvenile incarceration and all related aspects of the more broadly defined field of correctional alternatives and penal sanctions.
Related titles: Microform ed.: (from PQC); Online - full text ed.: ISSN 1552-7522. USD 401, GBP 259 to institutions (effective 2006) (from C S A, EBSCO Publishing, Florida Center for Library Automation, Gale Group, O C L C Online Computer Library Center, Inc., Sage Publications, Inc., Swets Information Services).
Indexed: AC&P, ASG, AltPI, CJA, CJPI, ChPerI, CurCont, ESPM, FamI, H&SSA, PAIS, PRA, PsycInfo, PsycholAb, RASB, RiskAb, SOPODA, SPAA, SSA, SSCI, SSI, SUSA, SociolAb, V&AA.
—BLDSC (6617.058000), IE, Infotrieve, ingenta. **CCC.**
Published by: (Pennsylvania Prison Society), Sage Publications, Inc., 2455 Teller Rd, Thousand Oaks, CA 91320. TEL 805-499-0721, FAX 805-499-0871, info@sagepub.com, http://www.sagepub.com/journal.aspx?pid=49. Ed. Rosemary L Gido. R&P Tanya Udin TEL 805-499-0721 ext 7716. Adv. contact DeAnna Vega Hammersley. Circ: 1,000. **Subscr. overseas to:** Sage Publications Ltd., 1 Oliver's Yard, 55 City Rd, London EC1 1SP, United Kingdom. TEL 44-20-73740645, FAX 44-20-73748741, subscription@sagepub.co.uk.

➤ **PRISON LEGAL NEWS;** working to extend democracy to all. see *LAW*

C

364 USA ISSN 1072-1037
PRISON MIRROR✶; The Prison Mirror. Text in English. 1887. m. USD 5 to prison inmates; USD 15 domestic to individuals; USD 27 foreign to individuals. bk.rev. reprint service avail. from PQC. **Document type:** *Newspaper.* **Description:** Oldest continuously published prison newspaper in the United States.
Published by: Minnesota Correctional Facility, 970 Pickett St, N, Bayport, MN 55003-1490. TEL 612-779-2809, FAX 612-779-2788. Ed., R&P Jeff Anderson. Circ: 3,400.

365 GBR
PRISON REFORM TRUST. ANNUAL LECTURE. Text in English. a. **Document type:** *Monographic series.*
—BLDSC (6617.058870).
Published by: Prison Reform Trust, 15 Northburgh St, London, EC1V 0AY, United Kingdom. TEL 44-20-7251-5070, FAX 44-20-7251-5076.

365 GBR ISSN 0953-4377
PRISON REPORT. Text in English. 1988. q. GBP 20 in United Kingdom to individuals; GBP 25 to individuals rest of Europe; GBP 30 rest of world to individuals; GBP 30 in United Kingdom to institutions; GBP 35 to institutions rest of world; GBP 40 rest of world to institutions (effective 2000). adv. bk.rev. **Document type:** *Newsletter.*
Published by: Prison Reform Trust, 15 Northburgh St, London, EC1V 0AY, United Kingdom. TEL 44-20-7251-5070, FAX 44-20-7251-5076, prt@prisonreform.demon.co.uk. Ed. Stephen Shaw. R&P, Adv. contact Diana Ruthven. Circ: 2,000.

365 GBR ISSN 0300-3558
HV7231
➤ **PRISON SERVICE JOURNAL.** Text in English. 1960; N.S. 1971. bi-m. GBP 16.50 domestic to individuals; GBP 21.50 foreign to individuals; GBP 25 domestic to institutions; GBP 30 foreign to institutions (effective 2005). adv. bk.rev. illus. 70 p./no. 2 cols./p.; back issues avail. **Document type:** *Journal, Academic/Scholarly.* **Description:** Purpose is to raise and discuss issues related to the work of the prison service, the wider criminal justice system and associated fields. It aims to present reliable information and a range of views about these issues.
Related titles: Microform ed.: N.S. (from PQC).
Indexed: AC&P, ASSIA, CJPI, ELJI, LJI.
—BLDSC (6617.059000), IE, ingenta. **CCC.**
Published by: H M Prison Service, The Secretariat, HM Prison Service Headquarters, Cleland House, Page St, London, SW1P 4LN, United Kingdom. prisons.dg@homeoffice.gsi.gov.uk, http://www.hmprisonservice.gov.uk/resourcecentre/prisonservicejournal/. Ed. Mr. Jamies Bennett. adv.: page GBP 220. Circ: 6,300 (controlled). **Subscr. requests to:** c/o Print Shop Manager, HMP Leyhill, Wotton-under-Edge, Glou GL12 8HL, United Kingdom.

364 GBR ISSN 0264-1461
PRISON SERVICE NEWS. Text in English. 1982. m. GBP 12. adv. bk.rev. 24 p./no.; back issues avail. **Document type:** *Government.* **Description:** Contains news and features of interest to staff of Her Majesty's Prison Service personnel and their families.
Published by: H.M. Prison Service, Cleland House, Rm 302, Page St, London, SW1P 4LN, United Kingdom. TEL 44-171-217-6575, FAX 44-171-828-8692. Ed., R&P Philip Wisdom. Adv. contact T G Scott. Circ: 30,000 (controlled).

▼ new title ➤ refereed ✶ unverified ♦ full entry avail.

PRISON WRITING. see *LITERATURE*

365 USA
PRISONERS AND THE LAW. Text in English. 1985. 5 base vols. plus s-a. updates. USD 610 base vol(s). (effective 2004). **Document type:** *Trade.* **Description:** Covers critical issues involving prisoners' rights.
Published by: Thomson West (Subsidiary of: Thomson Corporation, The), 610 Opperman Dr, Eagan, MN 55123-1396. TEL 651-687-8000, 800-328-4880, FAX 651-687-7302, http://west.thomson.com/product/13516385/product.asp. Ed. Ira P Robbins.

365 USA
PRISONERS' ASSISTANCE DIRECTORY. Text in English. 1977. biennial. USD 30 (effective 2000 - 2001). **Document type:** *Directory.* **Description:** Identifies and describes national, state and local organizations and agencies that provide legal, library, AIDS, family support, and ex-offender aid and assistance to prisoners.
Published by: American Civil Liberties Union Foundation, Inc., National Prison Project, 733 15th St, N W, Ste 620, Washington, DC 20005. TEL 202-393-4930, FAX 202-393-4931, tmiller@npp-aclu.org, kgotsch@npp-aclu.org, http://www.aclu.org/issues/prisons/npp_mission.html. Ed. Kara Gotsch.

364 USA
PRISONERS IN (YEAR). Text in English. 1971. a. free. stat.; charts. back issues avail. **Document type:** *Bulletin, Government.* **Description:** Contains census of persons in State and Federal prisons at year-end.
Published by: U.S. Department of Justice, Bureau of Justice Statistics, 810 Seventh St, N W, 2nd Fl, Washington, DC 20531. TEL 202-307-0765, FAX 202-307-5846, askbjs@ojp.usdoj.gov, www.ojp.usdoj.gov/bjs/pubalp2.htm#p, http://www.ojp.usdoj.gov/bjs. Circ: 15,000. **Orders to:** BJS Clearinghouse, Box 179, Annapolis Junction, MD 20701-0179. TEL 800-732-3277, FAX 410-792-4358.

PROBATION AND PAROLE LAW REPORTS. see *LAW—Judicial Systems*

365 GBR ISSN 0264-5505
HV9345.A5
PROBATION JOURNAL. Text in English. 1913. q. GBP 230, USD 402 to institutions; GBP 239, USD 419 combined subscription to institutions print & online eds. (effective 2006). adv. bk.rev. **Document type:** *Journal, Academic/Scholarly.* **Description:** Provides a national and international forum for sharing good practice, disseminating criminal justice research and developing debate about the theory and practice of work with offenders.
Formerly: Probation (0048-539X)
Related titles: Online - full text ed.: ISSN 1741-3079. GBP 228, USD 398 to institutions (effective 2006) (from C S A, EBSCO Publishing, O C L C Online Computer Library Center, Inc., Sage Publications, Inc., Swets Information Services).
Indexed: AC&P, AMHA, ASSIA, CJA, DIP, ELJI, ESPM, FamI, IBR, IBZ, LJI, RASB, RiskAb.
—BLDSC (6617.243000), IE, Infotrieve, ingenta. **CCC.**
Published by: (National Association of Probation Officers), Sage Publications Ltd. (Subsidiary of: Sage Publications, Inc.), 1 Oliver's Yard, 55 City Rd, London, EC1 1SP, United Kingdom. TEL 44-20-73248500, FAX 44-20-73248600, info@sagepub.co.uk, http://www.sagepub.co.uk/journal.aspx?pid=105742. Ed. Hindpal Singh Bhui. adv.: page GBP 200. Circ: 7,200. **Subscr. in the Americas to:** Sage Publications, Inc., 2455 Teller Rd, Thousand Oaks, CA 91320. TEL 805-499-0721, FAX 805-499-0871, journals@sagepub.com.

364 AUS
PROBATION OFFICER. Text in English. 1960. q. AUD 10. bk.rev. **Description:** Support magazine for volunteers in Community Corrections.
Indexed: AC&P.
Published by: Probation Officers and Volunteers in Corrections Inc., GPO Box 634 E, Melbourne, VIC 3001, Australia. TEL 61-394160408, FAX 61-394162362. Ed. Cleone Sandford. Circ: 1,000.

364 NLD ISSN 0165-0076
PROCES; maandblad voor berechting en reclassering. Text in Dutch. m. adv. **Description:** Penal law enforcement and probation.
Indexed: AC&P, IPSA.
—IE, Infotrieve, KNAW.
Published by: Barneveldse Drukkerij en Uitgeverij B.V., PO Box 67, Barneveld, 3770 AB, Netherlands. TEL 31-3420-94911, FAX 31-3420-13141. Ed. K de Graaf. Circ: 500.

364.4 GBR
PROFESSIONAL SECURITY MAGAZINE. Text in English. 1990. m. GBP 30; GBP 40 foreign. adv. bk.rev. illus.; stat.; tr.lit. **Document type:** *Trade.* **Description:** Covers all aspects of business to business end-user security.
Published by: J T C Association Ltd., 4 Elms Ln, Shareshill, Wolverhampton, W Mids WV10 7JS, United Kingdom. TEL 44-1922-415233, FAX 44-1922-415208, info@jtc.u-net.com, http://www.professionalsecurity.co.uk. Ed., Pub. John Cully. adv.: B&W page GBP 1,050, color page GBP 1,520. Circ: 8,500 (paid).

PROFESSIONAL TRAINING SERIES. see *POLITICAL SCIENCE—Civil Rights*

363.2 USA
PROMOTIONAL TEST QUESTIONS. Text in English. 1991. irreg., latest 1991. USD 21.95 (effective 2000). **Document type:** *Trade.* **Description:** Consists of approximately 2,000 multiple-choice questions and answers. Looks to increase the efficiency and effectiveness of the law enforcement professional and aid preparation for promotional examinations.
Published by: Gould Publications, Inc. (Subsidiary of: LexisNexis), 1333 North US Hwy 17-92, Longwood, FL 32750-3724. TEL 800-717-7917, FAX 407-695-2906, info@gouldlaw.com, http://www.gouldlaw.com.

364 GBR
PROSECUTIONS REVIEW. Text in English. 1996. a. GBP 65; GBP 75 foreign. back issues avail. **Description:** Reports on prosecutions heard during the year.
Published by: Monitor Press Ltd. (Subsidiary of: T & F Informa plc), Suffolk House, Church Field Rd, Sudbury, Suffolk CO10 2YA, United Kingdom. TEL 44-1787-378607, FAX 44-1787-881147. **Orders in the US to:** IBC (USA), 290 Eliot St, Box 91004, Ashland, MA 01721-9104. TEL 508-881-2800, FAX 508-881-0982.

PROSECUTOR. see *LAW—Criminal Law*

364 USA
PROSECUTOR'S BRIEF. Text in English. 1975. q. USD 25 (effective 2000). adv. bk.rev. cum.index every 10 yrs. back issues avail. **Description:** Covers issues that affect California prosecutors.
Published by: California District Attorneys Association, 731 K St, Third Fl, Sacramento, CA 95814-3402. TEL 916-443-2017, FAX 916-443-0540, cdaa@ix.netcom.com, general@cdaa.org. R&P Cat Karnezis. Circ: 5,000.

PROTECTING CHILDREN. see *SOCIAL SERVICES AND WELFARE*

364 DEU ISSN 0256-4319
PROTECTOR; die europaeische Zeitschrift fuer Sicherheit. Text in German. 1973. 14/yr. EUR 115.50 domestic; EUR 124.50 foreign; EUR 15 newsstand/cover (effective 2005). adv. bk.rev. illus.; tr.lit. **Document type:** *Magazine, Trade.*
Published by: I G T Informationsgesellschaft Technik GmbH, Albert-Schweitzer-Str 64, Munich, 81735, Germany. TEL 49-89-67369711, FAX 49-89-6376708, info@protector-online.com, info@igt-verlag.de, http://www.protector-online.com. Ed. Hagen Zumpe. Pub., R&P Lothar Zobel. Adv. contact Gabi Strixner. B&W page EUR 2,150, color page EUR 3,440; trim 175 x 265. Circ: 10,218 (controlled).

364.0711 POL ISSN 0867-5708
PRZEGLAD POLICYJNY. Text in Polish; Summaries in English, German. 1991. q. abstr. back issues avail. **Document type:** *Academic/Scholarly.* **Description:** Covers police education, police history, police law, and criminology.
Published by: Wydawnictwo Wyzszej Szkoly Policyjnej, ul Marsz J Pilsudskiego 111, Szczytno, 12101, Poland. TEL 48-89-6215102, FAX 48-89-6242610, wydwspol@sprint.com.pl, http://www.wspol.edu.pl/per/pp/index.htm. Circ: 200 (paid).

PSYCHOLOGY, CRIME AND LAW. see *PSYCHOLOGY*

PUBLIC SAFETY AND JUSTICE POLICIES - STATE CAPITALS. see *LAW*

PUNGOLO; periodico dei giovani. see *CHILDREN AND YOUTH—For*

364.6 GBR ISSN 1462-4745
HV8665
➤ **PUNISHMENT & SOCIETY**; the international journal of penology. Text in English. 1999. q. GBP 353, USD 617 to institutions; GBP 367, USD 643 combined subscription to institutions print & online eds. (effective 2006). adv. bk.rev. **Document type:** *Journal, Academic/Scholarly.* **Description:** Provides an interdisciplinary forum for research and scholarship dealing with punishment, penal institutions, and penal control.
Related titles: Online - full text ed.: ISSN 1741-3095. GBP 349, USD 611 to institutions (effective 2006) (from C S A, EBSCO Publishing, O C L C Online Computer Library Center, Inc., Sage Publications, Inc., Swets Information Services).
Indexed: ASSIA, CJA, CurCont, DIP, ESPM, IBR, IBSS, IBZ, PRA, PSA, RiskAb, SRRA, SSA, SSCI, SUSA, SociolAb, V&AA, e-psyche.
—BLDSC (7160.237260), IE, Infotrieve, ingenta. **CCC.**
Published by: Sage Publications Ltd. (Subsidiary of: Sage Publications, Inc.), 1 Oliver's Yard, 55 City Rd, London, EC1 1SP, United Kingdom. TEL 44-20-73248500, FAX 44-20-73248600, info@sagepub.co.uk, http://www.sagepub.co.uk/journal.aspx?pid=105749. Eds. Jonathan Simon, Malcolm M Feeley. adv.: page GBP 195; trim 185 x 114. Circ: 1,200. **Subscr. in the Americas to:** Sage Publications, Inc., 2455 Teller Rd, Thousand Oaks, CA 91320. TEL 805-499-0721, FAX 805-499-0871, journals@sagepub.com.

365 USA
QUESTION MARK. Text in English. 1973. m. USD 8. adv. bk.rev.
Formerly: Colony (0045-740X)
Published by: (Massachusetts Correctional Institution, Norfolk Resident Council), Norfolk Inmate Council Publishing, PO Box 43, Norfolk, MA 02056-0043. TEL 617-668-0800, FAX 617-727-1480. Ed. Ralph Carey. Circ: 1,500.

R P U PAPERS. see *PUBLIC ADMINISTRATION*

362.7 GBR
RAINER FOUNDATION. ANNUAL REPORT. Text in English. 1876. a. free. **Document type:** *Corporate.*
Formerly: London Police Court Mission. Annual Report
Published by: Rainer Foundation, 89 Blackheath Hill, London, SE10 8TJ, United Kingdom. Ed. J Longley. Circ: 5,000.

364 ITA ISSN 1121-1717
HV6004
RASSEGNA ITALIANA DI CRIMINOLOGIA. Text in Italian. 1970. q. EUR 61.97 in the European Union; EUR 92.96 elsewhere (effective 2002). **Description:** Covers issues in the ever changing sector of criminology and law-psychiatry. Gives special attention to activities of the Italian Society of Criminology as well as relevant national and international conventions.
Formerly (until 1990): Rassegna di Criminologia (0390-8976)
Indexed: CJA.
Published by: (Societa Italiana di Criminologia), Casa Editrice Dott. A. Giuffre (Subsidiary of: LexisNexis Europe and Africa), Via Busto Arsizio, 40, Milan, MI 20151, Italy. TEL 39-02-28089200, FAX 39-02-38009582, giuffre@giuffre.it, http://www.giuffre.it. Ed. Giacomo Canepa.

365 ITA ISSN 0392-7156
RASSEGNA PENITENZIARIA E CRIMINOLOGICA. Text in Italian; Summaries in English, French, German. 1931. 3/yr. EUR 39 domestic; EUR 57 foreign (effective 2004). adv. bk.rev. abstr.; bibl.; charts. index. **Document type:** *Journal, Government.* **Description:** Collection of juridical, penitentiary, psychological and pedagogical writings with regard to life of the prisioner, his treatment and insertion in society.
Formed by the 1978 merger of: Quaderni di Criminologia Clinica (0033-4928); Rassegna di Studi Penitenziari (0033-9628); Which was formerly (until 1951): Rivista di Diritto Penitenziario
Indexed: MEDLINE.
—GNLM.
Published by: (Italy. Ministero di Grazia e Giustizia, Dipartimento dell'Amministrazione Penitenziaria), Istituto Poligrafico e Zecca dello Stato, Piazza Verdi 10, Rome, 00198, Italy. TEL 39-06-85082147, editoriale@ipzs.it, http://www.ipzs.it. Ed. Marcello Marinari. Circ: 2,500.

364 DEU ISSN 0931-6183
RECHTSPRECHUNG; Materialen und Studien. Text in German, Multiple languages. 1986. irreg., latest vol.16, 2000. price varies. back issues avail. **Document type:** *Monographic series, Academic/Scholarly.* **Description:** Covers various topics in the administration of justice.
Published by: (Max-Planck-Institut fuer Europaeische Rechtsgeschichte), Vittorio Klostermann, Frauenlobstr 22, Frankfurt Am Main, 60487, Germany. TEL 49-69-9708160, FAX 49-69-708038, verlag@klostermann.de, http://www.klostermann.de.

364 CHE ISSN 0034-138X
RECHTSPRECHUNG IN STRAFSACHEN. Text in French, German. q. CHF 44 domestic; CHF 48 foreign (effective 2003). **Document type:** *Journal, Trade.*
—CCC.
Published by: (Schweizerische Kriminalistische Gesellschaft), Staempfli Verlag AG (Subsidiary of: LexisNexis Europe and Africa), Woelflistr 1, Bern, 3001, Switzerland. TEL 41-31-3006666, FAX 41-31-3006699, verlag@staempfli.com, http://www.staempfli.com. Circ: 2,400.

RED FEMINISTA LATINOAMERICANA Y DEL CARIBE CONTRA LA VIOLENCIA DOMESTICA Y SEXUAL. BOLETIN. see *WOMEN'S STUDIES*

REGENCY INTERNATIONAL DIRECTORY; of private investigators, process servers, private detectives & debt collecting agencies. see *BUSINESS AND ECONOMICS—Trade And Industrial Directories*

364 365 AUS ISSN 0157-3470
RELEASE. Text in English. 1969. q. AUD 10; AUD 25 foreign. adv. bk.rev. illus. **Document type:** *Newsletter.*

Published by: Offenders Aid & Rehabilitation Services of South Australia Inc., 234 Sturt St, Adelaide, SA 5000, Australia. TEL 61-8-82100828, FAX 61-8-82125515. Ed. Leigh Garrett. Circ: 3,500.

363.2 CHN
RENMIN JINGCHA/PEOPLE'S POLICE. Text in Chinese. m. USD 30; USD 1.90 newsstand/cover (effective 2001).
Published by: Shanghai Shi Gong'an Ju, 21 Shaoxing Lu, Shanghai, 200020, China. TEL 86-21-4373247. Ed. Zhou Guangwen. **Dist. by:** China International Book Trading Corp, 35 Chegongzhuang Xilu, Haidian District, PO Box 399, Beijing 100044, China. TEL 86-10-68412045, FAX 86-10-68412023, cibtc@mail.cibtc.com.cn, http://www.cibtc.com.cn.

365 MUS
REPORT ON THE TREATMENT OF OFFENDERS IN MAURITIUS: PART 1: PRISONS. Text in English. irreg., latest 1992. price varies. **Document type:** *Government.*
Published by: Government Printing Office, Elizabeth II Ave, Port Louis, Mauritius. TEL 230-2345330, FAX 230-2345322. **Subscr. to:** La Tour Koenig, Pointe-aux-sables, Mauritius.

364 MUS
REPORT ON THE TREATMENT OF OFFENDERS IN MAURITIUS: PART 2: PROBATION SERVICE. Text in English. irreg., latest 1986. price varies. **Document type:** *Government.*
Published by: Government Printing Office, Elizabeth II Ave, Port Louis, Mauritius. TEL 230-2345330, FAX 230-2345322. **Subscr. to:** La Tour Koenig, Pointe-aux-sables, Mauritius.

REPORTE POLITICO POLICIACO. see *BUSINESS AND ECONOMICS—Economic Situation And Conditions*

364 USA ISSN 1042-4636
RESEARCH AND BIBLIOGRAPHICAL GUIDES IN CRIMINAL JUSTICE. Text in English. 1989. irreg. price varies. **Document type:** *Monographic series, Academic/Scholarly.*
Published by: Greenwood Publishing Group Inc. (Subsidiary of: Harcourt International), 88 Post Rd W, PO Box 5007, Westport, CT 06881. TEL 203-226-3571, FAX 203-226-1502, webmaster@greenwood.com, http://www.greenwood.com.

RESEARCH DEVELOPMENT AND STATISTICS DIRECTORATE. OCCASIONAL PAPERS. see *SOCIOLOGY*

364 SVN ISSN 0034-690X
REVIJA ZA KRIMINALISTIKO IN KRIMINOLOGIJO. Text in Slovenian; Summaries in English. 1950. q. USD 30 to individuals; USD 50 to institutions (effective 2001). adv. bk.rev. abstr.; bibl.; charts; stat. index. 80 p./no. 2 cols./p.; back issues avail. **Document type:** *Journal, Government.* **Description:** Examines juvenile delinquency, criminal justice, juvenile justice, social work, crime and deviance, and forensic sciences.
Indexed: AC&P, CJA, PSA, SociolAb.
Published by: Ministrstvo za Notranje Zadeve Republiki Slovenije/Ministry of the Interiror of the Republic of Slovenia, Stefanova 2, Ljubljana, 1000, Slovenia. TEL 386-1-4725111, FAX 386-1-2514330, http://www.mnz.si. Eds. Darko Maver, Dusan Mohorko. Adv. contact Anton Vozelj. Circ: 600.

365 ARG ISSN 0325-9501
K19
REVISTA ARGENTINA DE CIENCIAS PENALES. Text in Spanish. 1975. q.
Published by: Editorial Plus Ultra, Avda. Callao, 575, Capital Federal, Buenos Aires 1022, Argentina. Ed. Ricardo Levene.

364 VEN ISSN 0798-9202
➤ **REVISTA C E N I P E C.** Variant title: Centro de Investigaciones Penales y Criminologicas. Revista. Text in Spanish. 1976 (June). a. USD 9 per issue (effective 2004). bk.rev. **Document type:** *Journal, Academic/Scholarly.*
Related titles: Online - full text ed.: 2001. free (effective 2005).
Published by: Universidad de los Andes, Centro de Investigaciones Penales y Criminologicas, Apdo 730, Merida, Tachira 5101, Venezuela. FAX 58-74-402050, cenipec@ula.ve, http://www.saber.ula.ve/revistacenipec. Ed. Mireya Bolanos. Circ: 500.

363.2 ESP
REVISTA CIENCIA POLICIAL. Text in Spanish. bi-m. **Document type:** *Government.* **Description:** Provides technical information on police subjects.
—CINDOC.
Published by: (Spain. Seccion de Documentacion y Publicaciones), Direccion General de Policia, Instituto de Estudios de Policia, Rafael Calvo, 33 3a pl, Madrid, 28010, Spain. TEL 34-1-4351720.

364 CHL ISSN 0716-792X
REVISTA DE CIENCIAS PENALES✶. Text in Spanish. 1971 (vol.30). s-a. bk.rev. bibl.
Published by: Instituto de Ciencias Penales, Of 546, Huerfanos, 1147, Santiago, Chile. Ed. Juan Bustos.

REVISTA DE DERECHO PENAL Y CRIMINOLOGIA. see *LAW—Criminal Law*

REVISTA ESPANOLA DE PSIQUIATRIA FORENSE, PSICOLOGIA FORENSE Y CRIMINOLOGIA. see *MEDICAL SCIENCES—Forensic Sciences*

363.2 345 ESP ISSN 0255-4321
REVISTA INTERNACIONAL DE POLICIA CRIMINAL. Text in Spanish. 1954. bi-m. **Document type:** *Government.*
Related titles: Arabic ed.: Al Magalla ad-Duwaliyya li-s-surta al-Gina'iyya. ISSN 0255-2752; English ed.: International Criminal Police Review. ISSN 0367-729X.
Published by: Direccion General de Policia, Instituto de Estudios de Policia, Rafael Calvo, 33 3a pl, Madrid, 28010, Spain. TEL 34-1-3223329.

REVUE DE DROIT PENAL ET DE CRIMINOLOGIE. see *LAW—Criminal Law*

364 365 FRA ISSN 0035-1733
K21
REVUE DE SCIENCE CRIMINELLE ET DE DROIT PENAL COMPARE. Text in French. 1936. q. EUR 140 domestic; EUR 156 foreign (effective 2005). bk.rev. abstr.; bibl.; tr.lit. index. reprint service avail. from SCH. **Document type:** *Academic/Scholarly.*
Indexed: AC&P, CJA, ELLIS, FLP, IBR, IBSS, IBZ, PAIS, RASB.
—BLDSC (7947.600000), IE, Infotrieve, ingenta. **CCC.**
Published by: (Universite de Paris II (Pantheon-Assas), Institut de Droit Compare), Editions Dalloz Sirey, 31-35 rue Froidevaux, Paris, Cedex 14 75685, France. TEL 33-1-40645353, FAX 33-1-40645471. Eds. Genevieve Giudicelli-Delage, Mireille Delma-Marty.

364 CHE
REVUE I P A. Text in German. 6/yr.
Published by: International Police Association, Chemin de l Epine, Froideville, 1055, Switzerland. TEL 021-8812627. Ed. Maurice Gehri. Circ: 8,000.

364 CHE ISSN 1424-4683
HV6002
REVUE INTERNATIONALE DE CRIMINOLOGIE ET DE POLICE TECHNIQUE ET SCIENTIFIQUE. Text in French. 1947. q. CHF 140; CHF 126 to libraries; CHF 100 to students; CHF 30 newsstand/cover (effective 2005). adv. bk.rev. bibl.; charts; illus. index, cum.index: 1947-1961. reprints avail. **Document type:** *Journal, Trade.*
Former titles (until 1998): Revue Internationale de Criminologie et de Police Technique (0035-3329); (until 1953): Revue de Criminologie et de Police Technique (1423-4300)
Indexed: AC&P, CJA, ChemAb, PAIS, PsycInfo, PsycholAb, RASB, e-psyche.
—BLDSC (7924.580000), Infotrieve, ingenta. **CCC.**
Published by: Polymedia Meichtry SA, Chemin de la Caroline 26, Petit-Lancy, 1213, Switzerland. TEL 41-22-8798820, FAX 41-22-8798825, info@polymedia.ch, http://www.polymedia.ch. Ed. Pierre-Henri Bolle. R&P Michel Giannoni. Adv. contact Jean-Marc Fermaud. Circ: 1,500 (controlled).

REVUE PENITENTIAIRE ET DE DROIT PENAL. see *LAW*

363.24 614.19 GBR ISSN 0951-645X
RIDGE DETAIL IN NATURE. Text in English. 1979. a. USD 5. **Document type:** *Trade.*
Published by: Fingerprint Society, Merseyside Police, Fingerprint Bureau, Canning Pl., Liverpool, Merseyside L1 8JX, United Kingdom. Ed. John Berry. Circ: 100. **Subscr. to:** The Fingerprint Society, Vivienne Galloway, 5 Slate Close, Glenfield, Leicester LE3 8QQ, United Kingdom.

363.2 ITA ISSN 0035-6476
RIVISTA DI POLIZIA; rassegna di dottrina tecnica e legislazione. Text in Italian. 1947. m. bk.rev. abstr.
Address: Via Mazzocchi, 175, Santa Maria Capua Vetere, CE 81055, Italy.

363.2 ITA ISSN 0394-834X
RIVISTA GIURIDICA DI POLIZIA LOCALE; bimestrale di dottrina, giurisprudenza e legislazione. Key Title: Rivista Giuridica di Polizia. Text in Italian. 1984. bi-m. EUR 70 to individuals; EUR 138 to institutions (effective 2005). **Document type:** *Magazine, Trade.* **Description:** Addresses various issues which affect the municipal police. Includes legal decisions, legislation and various "real life" problems faced by the force.
Published by: Maggioli Editore, Via del Carpino 8/10, Santarcangelo di Romagna, RN 47822, Italy. TEL 39-0541-628111, FAX 39-0541-622020, editore@maggioli.it, http://www.maggioli.it.

365 USA
ROCKETEER. Text in English. 1976. m. free.
Former titles: Inmate Free Press; Rocketeer (0035-7502)
Published by: Missouri Training Center for Men, PO Box 7, Moberly, MO 65270. TEL 660-236-3778, FAX 660-263-1730. Ed. Bill Caudel. Circ: 2,700 (controlled).

363.2 CAN ISSN 1196-6513
ROYAL CANADIAN MOUNTED POLICE. GAZETTE. Variant title: Gendarmerie Royale du Canada. Gazette. Text in English, French. 1994. q. **Document type:** *Journal, Trade.*
Formed by the merger of (1935-1994): Gazette de la Gendarmerie Royale du Canada (0826-9564); (1935-1994): Royal Canadian Mounted Police Gazette (0826-9556)
Indexed: CJA.
Published by: Royal Canadian Mounted Police, 1200 Vanier Parkway, Ottawa, ON K1A 0R2, Canada. TEL 613-993-7267, FAX 613-993-3098, http://www.rcmp-grc.gc.ca/gazette/index_e.htm, http://www.rcmp.ca. Ed. Anna Nicolle. Pub. Renee Couturier. Circ: 7,500.

363.2 CAN ISSN 0824-9415
ROYAL CANADIAN MOUNTED POLICE. QUARTERLY/G R C REVUE TRIMESTRIELLE. Text in English. 1933. q. CND 22 domestic; CND 28 in United States; CND 44 elsewhere (effective 2003). adv. bk.rev. illus. back issues avail.
Former titles (until 1979): R C M P Quarterly (0033-6858); (until 1966): Royal Canadian Mounted Police Quarterly (0317-8250)
Related titles: French ed.
Indexed: AC&P.
Published by: Royal Canadian Mounted Police Veterans' Association, 1200 Vanier Parkway, Ottawa, ON K1A 0R2, Canada. TEL 613-993-3738, FAX 613-993-4353, quarterly@rcmp-grc.gc.ca, http://www.rcmp-grc.gc.ca/quarterly/quarterly_e.htm. Ed. Natalie Egan. Circ: 12,000.

351 RUS
RUSSKII POLIS. Text in Russian. 1999. m. **Document type:** *Journal, Consumer.*
Address: Ul Tverskaya 18, korp 1, Moscow, 103791, Russian Federation. TEL 7-095-2003618, 7-095-2003184, ruspolis@alpha-ag.ru. Ed. Vadim Demchenko. Circ: 7,000.

364 ZAF
S A CRIME QUARTERLY. Text in English. 2002. q. ZAR 190 domestic; USD 38 in Africa; USD 54 elsewhere (effective 2005). **Document type:** *Journal, Academic/Scholarly.*
Supersedes: Nedbank Crime Index
Published by: Institute for Security Studies, Brooklyn Sq, P.O. Box 1787, Pretoria, 0075, South Africa. TEL 27-12-3469500, FAX 27-12-4600998, iss@iss.co.za, http://www.iss.co.za/Publications/CrimeQuarterlyIndex.html.

C

364 NLD ISSN 0920-5128
S E C; tijdschrift over samenleving en criminaliteitspreventie. Text in Dutch. 1986. bi-m. free. bk.rev. bibl.; illus. index. back issues avail. **Document type:** *Government.* **Description:** Contains articles about crime prevention, including residential burglary, designed to inform about and stimulate crime prevention projects.
—KNAW.
Published by: Ministerie van Justitie, Postbus 20301, The Hague, 2500 EH, Netherlands. TEL 31-70-370-6542, FAX 31-70-370-7916, kslabber@best-dep.minjus.nl, http://www.minjust.nl. Ed. I L van Erpecum. **Dist. by:** Sdu Uitgevers bv, Postbus 20014, The Hague 2500 EA, Netherlands. TEL 31-70-378-9538, FAX 31-70-383-8151.

364.4 USA ISSN 1062-2365
TS532
S.W.A.T. MAGAZINE; the magazine for prepared Americans. (Special Weapons and Tactics) Text in English. 1982. 9/yr. USD 26.95 domestic; USD 36.95 foreign (effective 2000). adv. bk.rev. **Description:** Covers weapons and police equipment for special tactical duty use.
Published by: Larry Flynt Publications, Inc., 8484 Wilshire Blvd, Ste 900, Beverly Hills, CA 90211. TEL 310-858-7100, FAX 310-274-7985. Ed. Denny Hansen. Circ: 80,500.

364.6 GBR ISSN 1464-8415
SAFER SOCIETY. Text in English. 1998. q. GBP 20; GBP 30 foreign. **Document type:** *Bulletin.* **Description:** Reports on the gamut of measures to prevent and respond to crime, to help offenders conduct law-abiding lives.
Formerly (until 1998): N A C R O Criminal Justice Digest
Published by: National Association for the Care and Resettlement of Offenders, 169 Clapham Rd, London, SW9 0PU, United Kingdom. TEL 44-20-7582-6500, FAX 44-20-7735-4666.

365 USA
SAFETY SOURCER NATIONAL PUBLIC SAFETY YELLOW PAGES. Text in English. 1995. a. USD 19 (effective 2003). **Document type:** *Directory, Trade.*
Published by: National Public Safety Information Bureau, 3273 Church St, PO Box 365, Stevens Point, WI 54481. TEL 800-647-7579, FAX 715-345-7288, info@safetysource.com, http://www.safetysource.com. Pub. Steve Cywinski.

364 AUS ISSN 1326-4672
SAFETYLINE. Text in English. q.
Media: Online - full text. **Related titles:** Print ed.: ISSN 1031-301X. 1988.
Published by: WorkSafe Western Australia, PO Box 294, West Perth, W.A. 6872, Australia. TEL 61-8-9327-8777, FAX 61-8-9321-8973, dohswa@yarrow.wt.com.au, http://www1.safetyline.wa.gov.au/sub12.htm. Eds. Gail McDowan, Janette Gerreyn.

▼ *new title* ➤ *refereed* ✶ *unverified* ♦ *full entry avail.*

343 USA
SAGE CRIMINAL JUSTICE SYSTEMS SERIES. Text in English. 1972. irreg. (Jul. 1993). USD 21.95; USD 46 hardcover ed.. back issues avail. **Document type:** *Monographic series, Academic/Scholarly.*
Published by: Sage Publications, Inc., Books, 2455 Teller Rd, Thousand Oaks, CA 91320. TEL 805-499-0721, FAX 805-499-0871, libraries@sagepub.com, journals@sagepub.com, http://www.sagepub.com. **Subscr. Europe to:** Sage Publications Ltd., 1 Oliver's Yard, 55 City Rd, London EC1 1SP, United Kingdom; **Subscr. in Asia to:** Sage Publications India Pvt. Ltd., M-32 Market, Greater Kailash-I, PO Box 4215, New Delhi 110 048, India.

364 NLD ISSN 0925-0530
SANCTIES; tijdschrift over straffen en maatregelen. Text in Dutch. 1980. bi-m. EUR 94.50 (effective 2003). **Document type:** *Academic/Scholarly.* **Description:** Publishes scholarly studies on issues and developments in criminal law, and documentary information on penal law enforcement, including case law and circulars.
Formerly (until 1990): Penitentiaire Informatie (0166-610X)
Published by: Kluwer B.V. (Subsidiary of: Wolters Kluwer N.V.), Postbus 23, Deventer, 7400 GA, Netherlands. TEL 31-570-673449, FAX 31-570-691555, juridisch@kluwer.nl, http://www.kluwer.nl.

364 CAN ISSN 0316-4209
SCARLET & GOLD. Text in English. 1919. a. CND 10. adv. bk.rev. back issues avail. **Document type:** *Bulletin.* **Description:** Articles about the mounted police, written mainly by veterans.
Published by: (Veterans of Royal Canadian Mounted Police, Vancouver Division), Scarlet & Gold Enterprises, 1215 Alder Bay Walk, Vancouver, BC V6H 3T6, Canada. TEL 604-738-4423. Ed. J Murphy. Circ: 2,500.

364 GBR
SCARMAN CENTRE. OCCASIONAL PAPER SERIES. Text in English.
Formerly: Studies in Crime Order and Policing Occasional Papers —BLDSC (6224.065000).
Published by: University of Leicester, Scarman Centre, 154 Upper New Walk, Leicester, LE1 7QA, United Kingdom. TEL 44-116-252-3946, FAX 44-116-252-5788, scarman.centre@le.ac.uk, http://www.le.ac.uk/scarman.

364 DEU ISSN 0558-9126
SCHRIFTEN ZUM STRAFRECHT. Text in German. 1961. irreg., latest vol.141, 2003. price varies. **Document type:** *Monographic series, Academic/Scholarly.*
Published by: Duncker und Humblot GmbH, Carl-Heinrich-Becker-Weg 9, Berlin, 12165, Germany. TEL 49-30-7900060, FAX 49-30-79000631, info@duncker-humblot.de, http://www.duncker-humblot.de.

365 CHE ISSN 0036-7893
K23
SCHWEIZERISCHE ZEITSCHRIFT FUER STRAFRECHT/REVUE PENALE SUISSE/RIVISTA PENALE SVIZZERA. Text in French, German, Italian. 1888. q. CHF 118 domestic; CHF 127.50 foreign (effective 2003). adv. bk.rev. bibl. index. **Document type:** *Journal, Trade.*
Indexed: AC&P, DIP, FLP, IBR, IBZ, RASB.
—IE, Infotrieve. **CCC.**
Published by: Staempfli Verlag AG (Subsidiary of: LexisNexis Europe and Africa), Woelflistr 1, Bern, 3001, Switzerland. TEL 41-31-3006666, FAX 41-31-3006688, verlag@staempfli.com, http://www.staempfli.com. Eds. Andreas Donatsch, Robert Roth. Circ: 1,300.

364 GBR ISSN 0950-2254
SCOTTISH OFFICE. CENTRAL RESEARCH UNIT PAPERS. Text in English. 1977. irreg. **Document type:** *Monographic series, Academic/Scholarly.* **Description:** Aims to inform the Translation, Interpreting and Communications Support Services Group in it's work to develop a national cross-sectional framework of standards for these services.
—BLDSC (8211.089000).
Published by: Scottish Executive, Central Research Unit, St Andrew's House, Regent Rd, Edinburgh, EH1 3DG, United Kingdom. TEL 44-131-244-2118, FAX 44-131-244-5393, Joe.Curran@scotland.gsi.gov.uk, http://www.scotland.gov.uk.

343 USA ISSN 0037-0193
KF9630.A59
SEARCH AND SEIZURE BULLETIN. Text in English. 1964. m. looseleaf. USD 147 (effective 2005). cum.index. back issues avail.; reprint service avail. from PQC. **Document type:** *Newsletter, Trade.* **Description:** Summarizes current cases involving search and seizure. For non-lawyer law enforcement personnel.
Related titles: Microform ed.: (from PQC); Online - full text ed.: ISSN 1544-5003.
Indexed: CJPI.
—**CCC.**
Published by: Quinlan Publishing Group, Marine Industrial Park, 23 Drydock Ave, 6th Fl, Boston, MA 02210-2387. Ed. Colin Thakkar. Pub. Dennis Hofmaier.

SECURE SIGNALS. see *COMMUNICATIONS—Television And Cable*

364.4029 GBR
SECURITECH; the international guide to security equipment. Text in English, French, Italian, Spanish. 1972. a. GBP 77.50 domestic; GBP 85.75 foreign (effective 1999). **Document type:** *Directory.* **Description:** Lists equipment and services for the security industry.
Former titles: Securitech Europe; Securitech (0307-7780)
Published by: D M G World Media Ltd. (Subsidiary of: Daily Mail and General Trust PLC), Queensway House, 2 Queensway, Redhill, Surrey RH1 1QS, United Kingdom. TEL 44-1737-768611, FAX 44-1737-855475, http://www.dmg.co.uk, http://www.dmgworldmedia.com. Circ: 8,000.

365 BRA
SERIE ESTUDOS PENITENCIARIOS. Text in Portuguese. irreg. bibl.
Published by: Cortez e Moraes Ltda., Rua Ministro Godoy, 1002, Perdizes, Sao Paulo, SP 05015-001, Brazil.

363.2 ZAF ISSN 1015-2385
SERVAMUS; policing magazine. Text in Afrikaans, English. 1913. m. ZAR 131.88 domestic; ZAR 115.68 foreign (effective 2001). adv. bk.rev. illus. 106 p./no.; back issues avail. **Document type:** *Magazine, Government.* **Description:** Contains police information and educational news.
Former titles (until Apr. 1979): S A P Magazine; S A R P (0036-4819); (until 1964): Justitie; (until 1961): Nongqai
Related titles: E-mail ed.; Online - full text ed.
Published by: (South African Police Service), S A R P Publishers, PO Box 828, Pretoria, 0001, South Africa. TEL 27-12-3215282, 27-11-469-0220, FAX 27-12-3285104, 27-11-469-4365, johan@servamus.co.za, isak@servamus.co.za, bonshell@mweb.co.za, http://www.servamus.co.za. Ed., R&P Johan Heuer TEL 27-12-666-1076. Circ: 37,000.

SEX OFFENDER LAW REPORT. see *LAW—Criminal Law*

SEXUAL ABUSE; a journal of research and treatment. see *PSYCHOLOGY*

364.153 USA ISSN 1096-0155
HV6592
SEXUAL ASSAULT REPORT. Text in English. 1997. bi-m. USD 169.95 domestic; USD 199.95 foreign (effective 2005). **Document type:** *Newsletter.* **Description:** Brings together ideas from experts in criminal and civil law, nursing and emergency medicine, law enforcement, counseling and social services.
—**CCC.**
Published by: Civic Research Insitute, 4490 US Route 27, PO Box 585, Kingston, NJ 08528. TEL 609-683-4450, FAX 609-683-7291, order@civicresearchinstitute.com, http://www.civicresearchinstitute.com/vi4.html. Ed. Joan Zorza.

SHARING TIMES. see *SOCIOLOGY*

363.25 USA ISSN 1072-0383
SHEPARD'S EXPERT AND SCIENTIFIC EVIDENCE QUARTERLY. (Part of the Evidence Series) Text in English. 1994. q. back issues avail. **Document type:** *Magazine, Trade.*
Published by: Shepard's (Subsidiary of: LexisNexis North America), 555 Middle Creek Pkwy, Colorado Springs, CO 80921. TEL 800-743-7393, customer_service@shepards.com, http://www.shepards.com, http://www.lexisnexis.com/shepards/.

▼ **SHEPHARD'S PUBLIC SERVICE AVIATION HANDBOOK.** see *TRANSPORTATION—Air Transport*

363.2 USA ISSN 1070-8170
HV7551
SHERIFF MAGAZINE. Text in English. 1948. bi-m. USD 30 (effective 2005). adv. charts; illus.; stat. index. 72 p./no.; reprints avail. **Document type:** *Magazine, Trade.* **Description:** Features practices, procedures, and research in law enforcement, corrections, and court security in order to make the criminal justice system more efficient and effective. Covers law enforcement programs, NSA activities, news, legislative updates, and a calendar of industry events. Reaches law enforcement officials on the federal, state and local levels.
Formerly (until 1991): National Sheriff (0028-016X)
Related titles: Online - full text ed.: (from ProQuest Information & Learning).
Indexed: CJA, CJPI.
Published by: National Sheriffs' Association, 1450 Duke St, Alexandria, VA 22314-3490. TEL 703-836-7827, FAX 703-683-6541, mterault@sheriffs.org, nsamail@sherrifs.org, http://www.sheriffs.org, http://www.sheriffs.org/. Ed., R&P Mike Terault. Adv. contact Kim Bright. B&W page USD 1,650, color page USD 2,275; trim 8.25 x 10.875. Circ: 21,300 (paid and free).

363.2 UAE
AL-SHURTI/POLICEMAN. Text in Arabic. 1989. m. per issue exchange basis. **Description:** Covers local police affairs.
Related titles: Supplement(s): Al- Shurti al-Saghir.
Published by: General Administration for Sharjah Police, Public Relations Department, PO Box 29, Sharjah, United Arab Emirates. TEL 541664, FAX 541595, TELEX 69611 SHURTAH EM. Circ: 2,000.

364 DEU ISSN 0933-6648
SICHERHEITSTECHNIK. Text in German. 1969. irreg. price varies. **Document type:** *Monographic series, Trade.*
Published by: Erich Schmidt Verlag GmbH & Co. (Berlin), Genthiner Str 30G, Berlin, 10785, Germany. TEL 49-30-250085-0, FAX 49-30-25008511, esv@esvmedien.de, http://www.erich-schmidt-verlag.de.

363.2 USA ISSN 0037-5012
SIGNAL 8-2. Text in English. 1958. s-a. illus.; stat.
Published by: Port Authority of New York and New Jersey, Police Division, J S T C, One Path Plaza, Jersey City, NJ 07306. TEL 201-963-7111. Ed. Sgt. Paul Magda.

364 USA
▼ **SNITCH (LEXINGTON).** Text in English. 2003 (Oct.). w. free. **Document type:** *Newsletter, Consumer.*
Related titles: ♦ Regional ed(s).: Snitch (Louisville).
Published by: Central Kentucky Crime LLC, 4390 Clearwater Way, Ste 1108, Lexington, KY 40515 . TEL 859-272-9246. Pub. Tim Woodburn.

364 USA
SNITCH (LOUISVILLE). Text in English. 2001. w. free (effective 2003). **Document type:** *Newspaper, Consumer.*
Related titles: Online - full content ed.; ♦ Regional ed(s).: Snitch (Lexington).
Published by: Snitch LLC, 161 Chenoweth Ln, Louisville, KY 40207. TEL 502-893-3005, FAX 502-896-4824, tsanford@snitch.com, http://www.snitch.com/. Ed. Richard Des Ruisseaux.

364 IND ISSN 0037-7716
HV9398 CODEN: SDEFDL
SOCIAL DEFENCE; a quarterly review of policies and practices in the field of prevention of crime and treatment of offenders. Text in English. 1961. q. INR 60, USD 31.60. adv. bk.rev. bibl.; stat. **Document type:** *Government.*
Indexed: BAS, CJA, PsycholAb.
Published by: Government of India, Department of Publications, Civil Lines, New Delhi, 110 054, India. Ed. Hira Singh. Circ: 500.

SOCIAL JUSTICE; a journal of crime, conflict and world order. see *POLITICAL SCIENCE—International Relations*

364.12 USA ISSN 0038-0008
SOCIETY OF PROFESSIONAL INVESTIGATORS. BULLETIN✶ . Text in English. 1956. a. free to qualified personnel. bk.rev.
Media: Duplicated (not offset).
Indexed: AC&P.
Published by: Society of Professional Investigators, 85-04 Queens Midtown Expy., Elmhurst, NY 11373. TEL 718-335-3257. Circ: 1,000.

364 340.115 USA ISSN 1521-6136
HM210
SOCIOLOGY OF CRIME, LAW AND DEVIANCE. Text in English. 1998. a., latest vol.5, 2005. price varies. back issues avail. **Document type:** *Monographic series, Academic/Scholarly.*
Indexed: SSA, SociolAb.
—BLDSC (8319.677500).
Published by: J A I Press Inc. (Subsidiary of: Elsevier Science & Technology), 360 Park Ave S, New York, NY 10010-1710. TEL 212-989-5800, FAX 212-633-3990, usinfo-f@elsevier.com, http://www.elsevier.com/wps/find/bookseriesdescription.cws_home/BS_SCLD/description. Ed. M Deflem.

363.2 CAN ISSN 1707-7702
SOLICITOR GENERAL ON THE ADMINISTRATION OF THE FIREARMS ACT. REGISTRAR'S REPORT. Text in English. 197?. a.
Former titles (until 2000): Report on the Administration of the Firearms Act to the Solicitor General by the Registrar (1495-8945); (until 1998): Firearms Report to the Solicitor General by the Canadian Firearms Registry (1491-9311); (until 1997): Firearms Report to the Solicitor General by the Commissioner of the R C M P (1497-8253); (until 1993): Solicitor General of Canada by the Commissioner of the R C M P, Section 117 Criminal Code. Annual Firearms Report (1497-8245)
Published by: Royal Canadian Mounted Police, 1200 Vanier Parkway, Ottawa, ON K1A 0R2, Canada. TEL 613-993-7267, FAX 613-993-3098, http://www.rcmp.ca.

363.2 USA
SPECIAL OPERATIONS REPORT. Text in English. 4/yr. USD 40 domestic; USD 56 in Canada; USD 70 elsewhere (effective 2005). **Document type:** *Magazine, Trade.* **Description:** Contains news and articles on counter terrorism, intelligence, global low-intensity conflicts, and law enforcement and military special operations.

Published by: Wizard Entertainment, 151 Wells Ave, Congers, NY 10920. TEL 914-268-2000, FAX 914-268-2392, customerservice@WizardUniverse.com, http://www.wizarduniverse.com. Eds. Samuel Katz, Steven Hartov.

SPECIAL WEAPONS FOR MILITARY & POLICE. see *SPORTS AND GAMES—Outdoor Life*

363.2   RUS   ISSN 1608-5353
SPETSSLUZHBY. Text in Russian. 1997. w. USD 756 (effective 2004).
Published by: W P S Agentstvo Obzora Sredstv Massovoi Informatsii/WPS, Russian Media Monitoring Agency, a/ya 90, Moscow, 115191, Russian Federation. TEL 7-095-9552708, FAX 7-095-9552927, wpsinfo@wps.ru, http://www.wps.ru/e_index.html.

363.2   USA   ISSN 0038-8572
HV7551
SPRING 3100; the magazine for the department by the department. Text in English. 1930-1981; resumed 198?. bi-m. bk.rev. illus. **Document type:** *Newsletter.* **Description:** Contains feature articles about law enforcement, human interest stories about active and retired police officers, informative news regarding employee assistance, and news from each of the commands citywide.
Published by: New York City Police Department, One Police Plaza, 7th Fl, New York, NY 10038. http://www.ci.nyc.ny.us/nyclink/html/nypd/html/3100. Ed. Edelle James.

363.2   USA
ST. LOUIS METRO EVENING WHIRL. Text in English. 1938. w. (Tue.). USD 50; USD 40 for 6 mos.; USD 0.50 newsstand/cover (effective 2004). adv. **Document type:** *Newspaper, Consumer.* **Description:** Crime-fighting publication.
Published by: Thomas Publishing Co., Inc., PO Box 5088, St. Louis, MO 63115. TEL 314-535-4033, FAX 314-535-4280, tpcwhirl@aol.com, onewhirl@aol.com, http://www.stlwhirl.com. Pub., Adv. contact Barry R Thomas. col. inch USD 18. Circ: 40,000 (paid). Wire service: AP.

▼ **STATE AND LOCAL GOVERNMENT HOMELAND SECURITY UPDATE.** see *PUBLIC ADMINISTRATION*

364   USA   ISSN 0090-3221
HV7277
STATE OF NEBRASKA UNIFORM CRIME REPORT. Cover title: Crime in Nebraska. Text in English. 1972. a. free. charts; stat. **Document type:** *Government.*
Published by: Commission on Law Enforcement and Criminal Justice, PO Box 94946, Lincoln, NE 68509. Ed. Marilyn Keelan. Circ: 1,500.

364   DEU   ISSN 0720-6860
STRAFRECHT UND KRIMINOLOGIE. Text in German. 1976. irreg., latest vol.16, 2002. price varies. **Document type:** *Monographic series, Academic/Scholarly.*
Published by: Duncker und Humblot GmbH, Carl-Heinrich-Becker-Weg 9, Berlin, 12165, Germany. TEL 49-30-7900060, FAX 49-30-79000631, info@duncker-humblot.de, http://www.duncker-humblot.de.

343   DEU   ISSN 0720-7271
STRAFRECHTLICHE ABHANDLUNGEN. Text in German. 1896. irreg., latest vol.150, 2003. price varies. **Document type:** *Monographic series, Academic/Scholarly.*
Published by: Duncker und Humblot GmbH, Carl-Heinrich-Becker-Weg 9, Berlin, 12165, Germany. TEL 49-30-7900060, FAX 49-30-79000631, info@duncker-humblot.de, http://www.duncker-humblot.de.

DER STRAFVERTEIDIGER. see *LAW—Criminal Law*

363.2   DEU   ISSN 0585-4202
STREIFE. Text in German. m. **Document type:** *Bulletin.*
Published by: (Innenministerium fuer Beschaeftige der Polizei in N R W), Vereinigte Verlagsanstalten GmbH, Hoeherweg 278, Duesseldorf, 40231, Germany. TEL 49-211-7357589, FAX 49-211-7357507, am@vva.de, info@vva.de, http://www.vva.de. Circ: 24,000 (controlled).

364 158.7   USA
STRESS MANAGEMENT FOR LAW ENFORCEMENT; behind the shield: combating trauma. Text in English. 199?. irreg., latest 1999. USD 19.95 (effective 2000). **Document type:** *Trade.* **Description:** Handbook covering stress and trauma associated with the law enforcement and criminal justice professional. Includes related topics dealing with this growing problem.
Indexed: e-psyche.
Published by: Gould Publications, Inc. (Subsidiary of: LexisNexis), 1333 North US Hwy 17-92, Longwood, FL 32750-3724. TEL 800-717-7917, FAX 407-695-2906, info@gouldlaw.com, http://www.gouldlaw.com. Ed. Peter Pranzo.

364   USA   ISSN 1529-2444
STUDIES IN CRIME AND PUNISHMENT. Text in English. 2002. irreg., latest 2004. price varies. back issues avail. **Document type:** *Monographic series, Academic/Scholarly.* **Description:** Publishes scholarly and teaching materials from a wide range of methodological perspectives and explores sentencing and criminology issues from a single nation or comparative perspective.
Published by: Peter Lang Publishing, Inc., 275 Seventh Ave, 28th Fl, New York, NY 10001. TEL 212-647-7700, 800-770-5264, FAX 212-647-7707, customerservice@plang.com, http://www.peterlangusa.com. Eds. Christina DeJong, David Schultz.

364.4   HRV   ISSN 1330-6456
STUDIJSKI CENTAR SOCIJALNOG RADA. LJETOPIS. Text in Serbo-Croatian. 1994. a. HRK 80 (effective 2005).
Indexed: SSA, SociolAb.
Published by: Sveuciliste u Zagrebu, Pravni Fakultet/University of Zagreb, Faculty of Law, Trg Marsala Tita 14, Zagreb, Croatia. TEL 385-1-4564-332, FAX 385-1-4564-030, http://zakon.pravo.hr/7_izdavanje/ljetopis/ljetopis.htm.

363.2   USA   ISSN 1084-7316
SUBJECT TO DEBATE. Text in English. 1987. m. USD 35 (effective 1999). adv. bk.rev. back issues avail. **Document type:** *Newsletter.* **Description:** Informs police chiefs, municipal officials, criminal justice experts, community groups, and legislators about advances and issues in policing, public safety, and crime prevention.
Published by: Police Executive Research Forum, 1120 Connecticut Ave, N W, Ste 930, Washington, DC 20036. TEL 202-466-7820, 888-202-4563, FAX 202-466-7826, egratto@policeforum.org, http://www.policeforum.org. Ed., R&P, Adv. contact Ellen Dollar. Circ: 1,400.

363.2   PAN
SUCESOS. Text in Spanish. w. USD 0.25 newsstand/cover. **Document type:** *Newspaper.* **Description:** Sensationalist paper of police cases.
Published by: Geo-Media S.A., Urb. Obarrio Calle 58, Edificio El Siglo Apto. W, Zona 4, Panama, 4, Panama. TEL 507-269-3311, FAX 507-2696954. Ed. Roberto Rodriguez. Circ: 18,000 (paid).

364   AUS
SUMMARY JUSTICE SOUTH AUSTRALIA. Text in English. 1983; N.S. 1993. bi-m. looseleaf. AUD 2,195 (effective 2004). **Document type:** *Trade.* **Description:** Provides South Australia practitioners with a comprehensive guide to the practice and procedure of the criminal jurisdiction of the Magistrates Courts.
Published by: Lawbook Co. (Subsidiary of: Thomson Legal & Regulatory Ltd.), PO Box 3502, Rozelle, NSW 2039, Australia. LRA.Service@thomson.com, http://onlineecom01.thomson.com.au/thomson/Catalog.asp?EES_CMD=SI&EES_ID=100367, http://www.lawbookco.com.au/. Ed. P M St L Kelly.

351.74   SWE   ISSN 0562-7370
SVENSK POLIS. Text in Swedish. 1962. 10/yr. adv. **Document type:** *Magazine, Trade.*
Published by: Rikspolisstyrelsen, Box 12256, Stockholm, 10226, Sweden. TEL 46-8-401-90-00, FAX 46-8-401-90-65. Ed. Mattias Wising.

363.2 340   SWE   ISSN 1101-6817
SVENSKA NARKOTIKAPOLISFOERENINGEN. PUBLIKATION.
Key Title: Publikation foer Svenska Narkotikapolisfoereningen. Variant title: Svenska Narkotikapolisfoereningens Tidning. Text in Swedish. 1988. q. adv.
Published by: Svenska Narkotikapolisfoereningen (SNPF)/Swedish Narcotic Officers' Association, PO Box 429, Goeteborg, 40126, Sweden. TEL 46-31-7392467, FAX 46-31-7392417, supf@supf.se, http://www.snpf.org/, http://www.supf.se. Ed. Jim Bjoerk.

364.4   USA   ISSN 1041-8474
HV6431
T V I REPORT✳ ; comprehensively reporting terrorism, violence, insurgency worldwide. (Terrorism Violence Insurgency) Text in English. 1979. q. USD 85; USD 110 foreign. bk.rev. bibl.; charts; stat. index.
Formerly (until vol.6): T V I Journal
Indexed: PAIS.
Published by: T V I, Inc., PO Box 1055, Beverly Hills, CA 90213-1055. TEL 213-276-3378. Ed. Brian Michael Jenkins. Circ: 900.

363.2   USA   ISSN 1543-8856
TACTICAL RESPONSE; the magazine for special enforcement. Text in English. 2002. m.
Related titles: Online - full text ed.: (from ProQuest Information & Learning).
Published by: Hendon Publishing Company, 130 Waukegan Rd, Deerfield, IL 60015. TEL 847-444-3300, FAX 847-444-3333, info@hendonpub.com, http://www.trmagonline.com. Ed. Ed Sanow.

364   USA   ISSN 1557-6361
▼ **TAKING SIDES: CLASHING VIEWS IN CRIMINAL JUSTICE.** Text in English. forthcoming 2006. biennial. **Document type:** *Monographic series.*
Published by: McGraw-Hill - Dushkin (Subsidiary of: McGraw-Hill Higher Education), 2460 Kerper Blvd, Dubuque, IA 52001. TEL 800-243-6532, customer.service@mcgraw-hill.com, http://www.dushkin.com.

364   USA   ISSN 1098-5379
HV6001
TAKING SIDES: CLASHING VIEWS ON CONTROVERSIAL ISSUES IN CRIME AND CRIMINOLOGY. Text in English. 1989. irreg., latest 2000. 6th ed. USD 20.50 per vol. (effective 2004). illus. **Document type:** *Academic/Scholarly.*
Published by: McGraw-Hill - Dushkin (Subsidiary of: McGraw-Hill Higher Education), 2460 Kerper Blvd, Dubuque, IA 52001. TEL 800-243-6532, customer.service@mcgraw-hill.com, http://www.dushkin.com/text-data/catalog/007237151x.mhtml. Ed. Richard C Monk. Pub. David Dean. R&P Cheryl Greenleaf.

363.2   IND   ISSN 0039-9329
TAMIL NADU POLICE JOURNAL. Text in English. 1969 (vol.30). q. INR 24. adv. bk.rev. charts; illus.; stat.
Published by: North Arcot Police Department, Police Training College, North Arcot District, Vellore, Tamil Nadu, India. Ed. J Vasudeva Bhat. Circ: 2,500.

363.2   USA   ISSN 0040-327X
TENNESSEE LAW ENFORCEMENT JOURNAL. Text in English. 1955. q. USD 10 (effective 1999). adv. bk.rev. charts; illus.; stat. **Document type:** *Trade.*
Published by: Tennessee Law Enforcement Officers Association, c/o Lt J P Ruff, Box 139, Ellendale, TN 38029-0139. FAX 612-541-0435. Ed. Mike Callan. Circ: 3,000 (controlled).

TERRORISM AND POLITICAL VIOLENCE. see *POLITICAL SCIENCE—International Relations*

364   USA
TERRORISM IN THE UNITED STATES. Text in English. a. **Document type:** *Government.*
Related titles: Online - full content ed.
Published by: U.S. Federal Bureau of Investigation (Subsidiary of: U.S. Department of Justice), 935 Pennsylvania Ave NW, Ste 7350, Washington, DC 20535. http://www.fbi.gov/publications/terror/terroris.htm.

364.6   USA   ISSN 0095-1900
HV9274
TEXAS. DEPARTMENT OF CRIMINAL JUSTICE. INSTITUTIONAL DIVISION. RESEARCH REPORT. Text in English. 1971. irreg.
Formerly: Texas. Department of Corrections. Research and Development Division. Research Report
Published by: Department of Criminal Justice, Institutional Division, PO Box 99, Huntsville, TX 77342-0099. TEL 713-295-6371.

365   USA
TEXAS JOURNAL OF CORRECTIONS. Text in English. 1991. bi-m. USD 50 to non-members; free to members (effective 2003). adv. charts; illus.; stat.; tr.lit. **Document type:** *Newsletter, Trade.* **Description:** Focuses on association news and subjects relating to the Texas correction system for both juveniles and adults, and studies options regarding rehabilitation and correction methods.
Related titles: Online - full text ed.
Published by: Texas Corrections Association, PO Box 140647, Austin, TX 78714-0647. TEL 512-454-8626, FAX 512-454-3036, tca@assnmgmt.com, http://www.txcorrections.org/. Ed. Dan Richard Beto. R&P, Adv. contact Tracie Harris. B&W page USD 300, color page USD 800; trim 9.5 x 7.13. Circ: 1,300.

363.2   USA   ISSN 0040-442X
TEXAS LAWMAN; dedicated to all Texas peace officers. Text in English. 1930. q. membership. adv. bk.rev. illus.
Published by: Sheriffs' Association of Texas, 1601 S. I H 35., Austin, TX 78741-2503. TEL 512-445-5888, FAX 512-445-0228. Ed. Dolores Shirley. Circ: 30,000.

363.2   GBR   ISSN 1369-2070
THAMES VALLEY POLICE AUTHORITY. ANNUAL POLICING PLAN. Text in English. a.
Related titles: Online - full text ed.
—BLDSC (1089.725400).
Published by: Thames Valley Police Authority, c/o Mr Springthorpe, Clerk and Treasurer, The Farmhouse, Oxford Rd, Kidlington, Oxon OX5 2NX, United Kingdom. tvpa@dial.pipex.com, http://dspace.dial.pipex.com/town/terrace/hw34/home.html.

▼ *new title* ➤ *refereed* ✳ *unverified* ◆ *full entry avail.*

364 GBR ISSN 1362-4806
HV6001 CODEN: TRCNFA
➤ **THEORETICAL CRIMINOLOGY**; an international journal. Text in English. 1997. q. GBP 346, USD 605 to institutions; GBP 360, USD 630 combined subscription to institutions print & online eds. (effective 2006). adv. bk.rev. illus. reprints avail. **Document type:** *Journal, Academic/Scholarly.* **Description:** Concerned with theories, concepts, narratives and myths of crime, criminal behavior, social deviance, criminal law, morality, justice and social regulation.
Related titles: Online - full text ed.: ISSN 1461-7439. GBP 342, USD 599 to institutions (effective 2006) (from C S A, EBSCO Publishing, O C L C Online Computer Library Center, Inc., Sage Publications, Inc., Swets Information Services).
Indexed: CJA, CJPI, CurCont, DIP, ERA, ESPM, IBR, IBZ, PsycInfo, PsycholAb, RiskAb, SFSA, SOPODA, SPAA, SSA, SSCI, SUSA, SWA, SociolAb, V&AA.
—BLDSC (8814.556500), IE, Infotrieve, ingenta. **CCC.**
Published by: Sage Publications Ltd. (Subsidiary of: Sage Publications, Inc.), 1 Oliver's Yard, 55 City Rd, London, EC1 1SP, United Kingdom. TEL 44-20-73248500, FAX 44-20-73248600, info@sagepub.co.uk, http://www.sagepub.co.uk/journal.aspx?pid=105792. Eds. Eugene McLaughlin, Lynn Chancer. Adv. contact Jenny Kirby. page GBP 220. **Subscr. in the Americas to:** Sage Publications, Inc., 2455 Teller Rd, Thousand Oaks, CA 91320. TEL 805-499-0721, FAX 805-499-0871, journals@sagepub.com.

364 SWE ISSN 0040-6821
TIDSKRIFT FOER KRIMINALVAARD. Text in Swedish. 1946. q. SEK 100 (effective 2004). bk.rev. bibl. **Document type:** *Trade.*
Published by: Svenska Faangvaardssaellskapet, Slottsgatan 78, Norrkoeping, 60180, Sweden. TEL 46-11-4963000, FAX 46-11-4963037, http://www.algonet.se/~schlyter/tfk.html. Eds. Frans Schlyter, Jan E Gustavsson.

364 NLD ISSN 0165-182X
HV6005
TIJDSCHRIFT VOOR CRIMINOLOGIE. Text in Dutch. 1959. q. adv. bk.rev. abstr.; charts; illus. index. **Document type:** *Academic/Scholarly.* **Description:** Studies and abstracts on criminology.
Formerly: Nederlands Tijdschrift voor Criminologie (0028-2154)
Indexed: AC&P, ExcerpMed.
—IE, Infotrieve, KNAW.
Published by: Kluwer B.V. (Subsidiary of: Wolters Kluwer N.V.), Postbus 23, Deventer, 7400 GA, Netherlands. TEL 31-570-673449, FAX 31-570-691555, juridisch@kluwer.nl, http://www.kluwer.nl. Circ: 600 (controlled).

C

363.2 NLD ISSN 0165-0122
HET TIJDSCHRIFT VOOR DE POLITIE. Text in Dutch. 1934. 10/yr. EUR 90 (effective 2005). adv. bk.rev. charts; illus.; abstr. **Document type:** *Trade.* **Description:** Information on police science.
Indexed: AC&P.
—IE, Infotrieve.
Published by: Reed Business Information bv (Subsidiary of: Reed Business), Postbus 16500, Den Haag, 2500 BM, Netherlands. TEL 31-70-4415000, FAX 31-70-4415917, info@reedbusiness.nl, http://www.tijdschriftvoordepolitie.nl/, http://www.reedbusiness.nl. Ed. P Eringa. adv.: B&W page EUR 827, color page EUR 1,986; trim 210 x 297. Circ: 1,127.

364.4 USA
TODAY'S POLICEMAN✶. Text in English. 1960. q. USD 9 (effective 1999). adv. **Document type:** *Trade.* **Description:** Covers police work, crime prevention, the public and law enforcement.
Published by: Towerhigh Publications Inc., PO Box 1982, Long Beach, CA 90801-1982. TEL 310-795-4010. Ed. Jayney Mack. Circ: 15,400.

363.2 CAN ISSN 1480-655X
TORONTO POLICE ASSOCIATION. TOUR OF DUTY. Text in English. 1962. m. CND 44.94 domestic; CND 53.50 in United States; CND 64.20 elsewhere. adv. bk.rev. **Document type:** *Newsletter, Trade.*
Formerly: Metropolitan Toronto Police Association. News & Views (1201-5318)
Published by: Toronto Police Association, 180 Yorkland Blvd, North York, ON M2J 1R5, Canada. TEL 416-491-4301, FAX 416-491-7421, info@tpassn.com. Ed., R&P Elizabeth Alexander. Adv. contact Brian Shugar. B&W page CND 900, color page CND 1,650; trim 10.88 x 8.13. Circ: 9,400.

364 AUS ISSN 0817-8542
TRENDS AND ISSUES IN CRIME AND CRIMINAL JUSTICE. Text in English. 1986. 20/yr. AUD 5.50 per issue (effective 2003). **Document type:** *Monographic series.* **Description:** Presents papers promoting justice and the prevention of crime, which provide quality information to assist in governmental decisions.
Incorporates in part (1990-1992): Homicides in Australia (1038-6912)
Indexed: CJA.
Published by: Australian Institute of Criminology, GPO Box 2944, Canberra, ACT 2601, Australia. TEL 61-2-6260-9200, 61-2-6260-9255, FAX 61-2-6260-9201, aicpress@aic.gov.au, http://www.aic.gov.au/publications/tandi/. Ed. Adam Graycar. R&P Merril Thompson.

364 USA ISSN 1056-4160
HV6771.U6
TRENDS IN MONEY LAUNDERING✶. Text in English. irreg.
Published by: Financial Crimes Enforcement Network, 207 Chain Bridge Rd, Vienna, VA 22182. TEL 703-516-0591.

364 USA ISSN 1084-4791
HV6441
TRENDS IN ORGANIZED CRIME. Text in English. 1995. q. USD 72 to individuals; USD 224 to institutions (effective 2003). adv. back issues avail.; reprint service avail. from PSC. **Document type:** *Academic/Scholarly.* **Description:** Provides information and analysis about international efforts to anticipate the development of organized crime activities and to devise strategies to counter them.
Related titles: Online - full text ed.: (from EBSCO Publishing, Gale Group, O C L C Online Computer Library Center, Inc., Swets Information Services).
Indexed: CJA.
—BLDSC (9049.668900). **CCC.**
Published by: Transaction Publishers, 390 Campus Dr, Somerset, NJ 07830. TEL 888-999-6778, FAX 732-748-9801, trans@transactionpub.com, http://www.transactionpub.com. Ed. James Finckenauer. Pub. Mary Curtis. R&P Marlena Davidian TEL 732-445-2280 ext 100. Adv. contact Alicja Garbie. page USD 200; 5 x 8.25. Circ: 400. **Subscr. to:** Transaction Distribution Center, 390 Campus Dr., Somerset, NJ 08873. TEL 732-445-1245, 888-999-6778, FAX 732-748-9801, orders@transactionpub.com.

363.2 USA
TRUE POLICE CASES. Text in English. bi-m. USD 19.22 (effective 1999); USD 25 foreign; USD 2.50 newsstand/cover; GBP 1.50 newsstand/cover in United Kingdom; CND 2.75 newsstand/cover in Canada. **Document type:** *Consumer.*
Published by: American Media, Inc., 1000 American Media Way, Boca Raton, FL 33464-1000. TEL 800-724-6411. Ed. Dominick A Merle.

364 JPN ISSN 0256-5471
U N A F E I. RESOURCE MATERIAL SERIES. Text in English. 1971. s-a.
Indexed: CJA.
Published by: United Nations, Asia and Far East Institute for the Prevention of Crime and the Treatment of Offenders, 1-26, Harumi-cho, Fuchu-shi, Tokyo, 183-0057, Japan. TEL 81-42-3337021, FAX 81-42-3337024, unafei@moj.go.jp, http://www.unafei.or.jp/english/publications/resource.html.

364.164 USA ISSN 0273-5032
HV6635
U.S. BUREAU OF ALCOHOL, TOBACCO AND FIREARMS. EXPLOSIVES INCIDENTS; annual report. Text in English. 1977. a.
Published by: U.S. Bureau of Alcohol, Tobacco & Firearms, 12th & Pennsylvania Ave, N W, Washington, DC 20224. TEL 202-566-7777.

363.2 USA ISSN 1057-9958
KF3902
U.S. BUREAU OF ALCOHOL, TOBACCO AND FIREARMS. QUARTERLY BULLETIN. Text in English. 1983. q. USD 18 (effective 2001). **Document type:** *Government.* **Description:** Announces all new laws, regulations, codes and rulings or changes relating to alcohol, tobacco and firearms.
Related titles: Online - full text ed.: (from EBSCO Publishing).
Published by: U.S. Bureau of Alcohol, Tobacco & Firearms, 650 Massachusetts Ave, N W, Washington, DC 20226. **Subscr. to:** U.S. Government Printing Office, Superintendent of Documents, PO Box 371954, Pittsburgh, PA 15250-7954. TEL 202-512-1800, FAX 202-512-2250, orders@gpo.gov, http://www.access.gpo.gov.

364 USA
U.S. DEPARTMENT OF JUSTICE. OFFICE OF JUVENILE JUSTICE AND DELINQUENCY PREVENTION. ANNUAL REPORT. Text in English. a. **Document type:** *Government.*
Published by: U.S. Department of Justice, Office of Juvenile Justice and Delinquency Prevention, 633 Indiana Ave, N W, Washington, DC 20531. TEL 202-307-5911. **Subscr. to:** U.S. Government Printing Office, Superintendent of Documents, PO Box 371954, Pittsburgh, PA 15250-7954. TEL 202-512-1800, FAX 202-512-2250, orders@gpo.gov, http://www.access.gpo.gov.

364.1 USA
HV8059
U.S. FEDERAL BUREAU OF INVESTIGATION. (YEAR) BOMBING INCIDENTS. Text in English. 1970. a. **Document type:** *Government.* **Description:** Compiles bombings in the U.S. over the past year.
Supersedes (in 1994): U.S. Federal Bureau of Investigation. Bomb Summary (0360-3245)
Published by: U.S. Federal Bureau of Investigation, Explosives Unit, Bomb Data Center, 935 Pennsylvania Ave, N W, Washington, DC 20535-0001. TEL 202-324-3000.

364 USA ISSN 0732-6688
HV8074
U S IDENTIFICATION MANUAL. Text in English. 1976. base vol. plus q. updates. USD 149 for base vol.; USD 72.50 updates (effective 2000). **Description:** Covers all classes of licenses and special licenses. Contains full front and back description, expiration, restrictions and license number coding.
Published by: Drivers License Guide Company, 1492 Oddstad Dr, Redwood City, CA 94063. TEL 650-369-4849.

353 USA ISSN 0272-8974
HV7245
U.S. URBAN INITIATIVES ANTI-CRIME PROGRAM. ANNUAL REPORT TO CONGRESS. Key Title: Annual Report to Congress - Urban Initiatives Anti-Crime Program. Text in English. 1980. a. **Document type:** *Government.*
Published by: (Urban Initiatives Anti-Crime Program), U.S. Department of Housing and Urban Development, 451 Seventh St, S W, Washington, DC 20410. TEL 202-655-4000. **Subscr. to:** HUD User, PO Box 280, Germantown, MD 20874-0280. TEL 800-245-2691.

364 USA ISSN 0082-7592
HV6787
UNIFORM CRIME REPORTS FOR THE UNITED STATES. Cover title: Crime in the United States. Variant title: Uniform Crime Reports. Text in English. 1929. a. (plus s-a. updates). price varies. charts; stat. 450 p./no.; back issues avail. **Document type:** *Government.*
Published by: U.S. Federal Bureau of Investigation, Uniform Crime Reporting Program, Criminal Justice Information Services Division, 1000 Custer Hollow Rd, Clarksburg, WV 26306. TEL 304-625-4995, FAX 304-625-5394, cjis_comm@leo.gov, http://www.fbi.gov/ucr/ucr.htm. Ed., R&P Communications Unit. **Dist. by:** U.S. Government Printing Office, Superintendent of Documents, PO Box 371954, Pittsburgh, PA 15250-7954. TEL 202-512-1800, FAX 202-512-2250, orders@gpo.gov, http://www.access.gpo.gov.

364 USA ISSN 0082-8025
UNITED NATIONS CONGRESS ON THE PREVENTION OF CRIME AND THE TREATMENT OF OFFENDERS. REPORT. Text in English. 1956. irreg. price varies.
Related titles: Microfiche ed.
Published by: United Nations Publications, Rm DC2-853, United Nations Bldg, 2 United Nations Plaza, New York, NY 10017. TEL 212-963-8302, 800-253-9646, FAX 212-963-3489, publications@un.org, http://www.un.org/publications, http://www.un.org/Pubs.

364 ITA ISSN 1020-1548
HV6024.5 CODEN: ISREFC
UNITED NATIONS INTERREGIONAL CRIME AND JUSTICE RESEARCH INSTITUTE. ISSUES AND REPORTS SERIES/INSTITUTE INTERREGIONAL DE RECHERCHE DES NATIONS UNIES SUR LA CRIMINALITE ET LA JUSTICE. THEMES ET RAPPORTS SERIE. Text in English, French. 1994. irreg., latest vol.12. free. **Document type:** *Monographic series, Academic/Scholarly.* **Description:** Explores criminal justice issues throughout the world.
Indexed: SOPODA, SSA, SociolAb.
Published by: United Nations Interregional Crime and Justice Research Institute/Institut Interregional de Recherche des Nations Unies sur la Criminalite et la Justice, Via Giulia, 52, Rome, RM 00186, Italy. TEL 06-6877437, FAX 06-6892638, unicri@unicri.it.

364 ITA
UNITED NATIONS INTERREGIONAL CRIME AND JUSTICE RESEARCH INSTITUTE. PUBLICATION. Text in Italian. 1969. irreg. **Document type:** *Monographic series.*
Formerly: United Nations Social Defence Research Institute. Publication
Indexed: SOPODA.
Published by: United Nations Interregional Crime and Justice Research Institute/Institut Interregional de Recherche des Nations Unies sur la Criminalite et la Justice, Via Giulia, 52, Rome, RM 00186, Italy. TEL 06-6877437, FAX 06-6892638, unicri@unicri.it. Circ: 2,000.

364 VEN ISSN 0507-570X
UNIVERSIDAD CENTRAL DE VENEZUELA. INSTITUTO DE CIENCIAS PENALES Y CRIMINOLOGICAS. ANUARIO. Text in Spanish. 1967. irreg., latest vol.5, 1977. price varies. bk.rev. bibl.; charts.
Published by: (Instituto de Ciencias Penales y Criminologicas), Universidad Central de Venezuela, Facultad de Ciencias Juridicas y Politicas, Caracas, Venezuela. Ed. Tulio Chiossone.

364 CAN ISSN 0824-5134
UNIVERSITY OF ALBERTA. CENTRE FOR CRIMINOLOGICAL RESEARCH. DISCUSSION PAPERS. Text in English. 1983. irreg. free. **Description:** Monographs by scholars in criminology and related fields.
Related titles: Microfiche ed.: (from MML).
Published by: University of Alberta, Department of Sociology, Centre for Criminological Research, 5-21 Tory Building, Edmonton, AB T6G 2H4, Canada. TEL 403-492-3322, FAX 403-492-7196. Circ: 150 (controlled).

364 GBR
UNIVERSITY OF CAMBRIDGE. INSTITUTE OF CRIMINOLOGY. CROPWOOD OCCASIONAL PAPERS. Variant title: Cropwood Occasional Papers. Text in English. 1974. irreg., latest vol.23, 1998. GBP 5. back issues avail. **Document type:** *Academic/Scholarly.* **Description:** Previous topics have included: working with racially motivated crime and probation practice, a guide for those working in the English legal system with non-English speakers, etc.
Formerly (until 1995): University of Cambridge. Institute of Criminology. Occasional Papers
—BLDSC (3488.743000).
Published by: University of Cambridge, Institute of Criminology, 7 West Rd, Cambridge, CB3 9DT, United Kingdom. TEL 44-1223-335362, FAX 44-1223-335356, http://www.law.ac.cam/crim/lochpg.htm.

363.2 GBR
UNIVERSITY OF OXFORD. CENTRE FOR CRIMINOLOGICAL RESEARCH. OCCASIONAL PAPER. Text in English. irreg., latest vol.19, 1999. price varies. back issues avail. **Document type:** *Monographic series, Academic/Scholarly.* **Description:** Examines issues in criminal policy and practice in the UK and rest of Europe.
—BLDSC (6224.128000).
Published by: University of Oxford, Centre for Criminological Research, 12 Bevington Rd, Oxford, OX2 6LH, United Kingdom. TEL 44-1865-274448, FAX 44-1865-274445, CCR@crim.ox.ac.uk, http://www.crim.ox.ac.uk.

363.2 GBR
UNIVERSITY OF OXFORD. CENTRE FOR CRIMINOLOGICAL RESEARCH. PROBATION STUDIES UNIT REPORT. Text in English. 1996. irreg., latest vol.7, 1998. price varies. back issues avail. **Document type:** *Academic/Scholarly.* **Description:** Examines the role and effectiveness of probation.
Published by: University of Oxford, Centre for Criminological Research, 12 Bevington Rd, Oxford, OX2 6LH, United Kingdom. TEL 44-1865-274448, FAX 44-1865-274445, CCR@crim.ox.ac.uk, http://www.crim.ox.ac.uk.

365 360 AUS ISSN 1039-9216
V A C R O REPORTER. Text in English. 1977. 3/yr. AUD 20. adv. bk.rev. back issues avail. **Document type:** *Academic/Scholarly.*
Formerly (until Aug. 1992): Bridge
Published by: Victorian Association for the Care and Resettlement of Offenders, PO Box 14093, Melbourne Mail Centre, VIC 8001, Australia. TEL 61-3-93298865, FAX 61-3-93298852. Ed. Judith Lazarus. Circ: 2,000.

VANDALISME, CRIMINALITEIT EN VOLKSHUISVESTING. see *HOUSING AND URBAN PLANNING*

365.6 USA
VAR HAMARR✶ /OUR HAMMER. Text in English. 1994. irreg. free. **Document type:** *Newsletter.* **Description:** Discusses the organization's projects with prison inmates in several U.S. states.
Formerly: Odonist Prison Project and Second Mountain Kindred. Joint Publication
Published by: (Odinist Prison Project), White House Press, PO Box 6088, Harrisburg, PA 17112-0088. Ed., Pub., R&P Eric Lowe. Circ: 700. **Co-sponsor:** Second Mountain Kindred.

363.2 GBR ISSN 1464-6870
VARSITY DIRECTORY OF INVESTIGATORS & PROCESS SERVERS. Text in English. 1984. a. GBP 30 (effective 2001). adv. index. **Document type:** *Directory.* **Description:** Lists private investigators, certified bailiffs, process servers, and security consultants throughout the UK.
Former titles (until 1999): British Directory of Investigators and Process Servers (0267-8047); (until 1985): British Directory of Enquiry Agents and Process Servers (0267-6842)
Published by: Shaw & Sons Ltd., Shaway House, 21 Bourne Park, Bourne Rd, Crayford, Kent DA1 4BZ, United Kingdom. TEL 44-1322-621100, FAX 44-1322-550553, sales@shaws.co.uk, http://www.varsityinvestigators.co.uk, http://www.shaws.co.uk. Ed., Pub., R&P, Adv. contact Crispin Williams. B&W page GBP 375; trim 148 x 210. Circ: 2,000 (paid).

363.2 SVN ISSN 1580-0253
VARSTVOSLOVJE. Text in Slovenian. 198?. q.
Formerly (until 1999): Visja Sola za Notranje Zadeve. Zbornik Strokovno Znanstvenih Razprav (1318-0916)
Indexed: PSA.
Published by: Ministrstvo za Notranje Zadeve, Visoka Policijsko-Varnostna Sola, Kotnikova ulica 8, Ljubljana, 1000, Slovenia. TEL 386-1-3008308, FAX 386-1-2302687, revijaVS@vpvs.uni-lj.si, http://www.vpvs.uni-lj.si/varstvoslovje. Ed. Anton Dvorsek.

364.155 362.6 362.4 USA ISSN 1098-5131
HV6250.4.A34
VICTIMIZATION OF THE ELDERLY AND DISABLED. Text in English. 1998 (May/Jun.). bi-m. USD 169.95 domestic; USD 199.95 foreign (effective 2004). **Document type:** *Newsletter.* **Description:** Devoted to protecting, assisting, counseling and treating elderly and disabled adults.
Indexed: CINAHL.
—CCC.
Published by: Civic Research Insitute, 4490 US Route 27, PO Box 585, Kingston, NJ 08528. TEL 609-683-4450, FAX 609-683-7291, order@civicresearchinstitute.com, http://www.civicresearchinstitute.com/vi3.html. Ed. Joanne B. Otto.

364 USA ISSN 1556-4886
▼ ➤ **VICTIMS & OFFENDERS.** Text in English. forthcoming 2006 (Jan.). q. USD 350, GBP 212 combined subscription to institutions print & online eds. (effective 2006). **Document type:** *Journal, Academic/Scholarly.*
Related titles: Online - full text ed.: ISSN 1556-4991. forthcoming 2006 (Jan.). USD 333, GBP 201 to institutions (effective 2006).
Published by: Taylor & Francis Inc. (Subsidiary of: Taylor & Francis Group), 325 Chestnut St, Ste 800, Philadelphia, PA 19016. TEL 215-625-8900, FAX 215-625-8914, info@taylorandfrancis.com, http://www.tandf.co.uk/journals/titles/15564886.asp, http://www.taylorandfrancis.com. Ed. Dr. Alan R Roberts.

➤ **VICTIMS OF VIOLENCE NEWSLETTER.** see *LAW—Criminal Law*

363.2 ITA ISSN 0394-8285
IL VIGILE URBANO; rivista mensile di polizia municipale. Text in Italian. 1974. m. (11/yr.). EUR 54 to individuals; EUR 136 to institutions (effective 2005). bk.rev. **Document type:** *Magazine, Trade.* **Description:** Directed to personnel at all levels of the corps of municipal police, the journal offers a panorama of relevant material including doctrinal, legislative or legal decisions as well as personal experiences. All information is analyzed with regards to procedural application.
Related titles: CD-ROM ed.
Published by: Maggioli Editore, Via del Carpino 8/10, Santarcangelo di Romagna, RN 47822, Italy. TEL 39-0541-628111, FAX 39-0541-622020, editore@maggioli.it, http://www.maggioli.it. Circ: 6,726.

VIOLENCE AND VICTIMS. see *SOCIOLOGY*

364 929 973 398.21 USA ISSN 1064-5071
F596
VIOLENT KIN. Text in English. 1989. q. USD 11.95 (effective 1999). bk.rev.; video rev. illus.; maps. back issues avail. **Document type:** *Newsletter, Academic/Scholarly.* **Description:** Features violent people and events of American history, with genealogical notes on famous outlaws and law men for the fearless family historian.
Published by: Paul W. Meredith, Ed. & Pub., 5065 Westwood Lake Dr, Miami, FL 33165.

VOICE FOR THE DEFENSE. see *LAW*

364 USA
W A D E JOURNAL. Text in English. 1970. q. **Document type:** *Trade.* **Description:** Presents scientific studies in the field of questioned document examination.
Published by: World Association of Document Examiners, 111 N Canal St, Chicago, IL 60606. TEL 312-930-9446, wade4@earthlink.net. Ed. Lew Osborne.

364 DEU ISSN 1612-3360
HV8290
W & S; Sicherheitsmagazin fuer Trends, Technik und Dienstleistung. Text in German. 1980. 9/yr. EUR 169 domestic; EUR 176.50 foreign; EUR 19 newsstand/cover (effective 2004). adv. index. **Document type:** *Magazine, Trade.*
Former titles (until 2002): W & S - Wirtschaftsschutz und Sicherheitstechnik (0179-0927); (until 1985): Wirtschaftsschutz und Sicherheitstechnik (0173-3303); Which was formed by the merger of (1977-1980): Sicherheitstechnik (0342-3034); (1979-1980): Wirtschaftsschutz (0171-9262)
Indexed: PROMT, RASB.
—CCC.
Published by: Verlagsgruppe Huethig Jehle Rehm GmbH (Subsidiary of: Sueddeutscher Verlag GmbH), Emmy-Noether-Str 2, Munich, 80992, Germany. TEL 49-89-5485206, FAX 49-89-548528230, info@hjr-verlag.de, http://www.huethig-jehle-rehm.de. adv.: B&W page EUR 2,190; trim 210 x 297. Circ: 6,614 (controlled).

364 332.1 DEU ISSN 1615-455X
W I K - ZEITSCHRIFT FUER DIE SICHERHEIT DER WIRTSCHAFT. Variant title: Zeitschrift fuer die Sicherheit der Wirtschaft. Text in German. 1979. bi-m. EUR 101 domestic; EUR 114.50 foreign; EUR 21 newsstand/cover (effective 2004). adv. bk.rev. index. back issues avail. **Document type:** *Journal, Trade.*
Incorporates (1993-2003): Sicherheits Markt (0944-7520); Former titles (until 2001): W I K - Zeitschrift fuer Wirtschaft, Kriminalitaet und Sicherheit (0935-5758); (until 1986): W I K - Wirtschafts - Kriminalitaet (0177-5251); (until 1984): Wirtschaftskriminalitaet (0171-7774)
—CCC.
Published by: SecuMedia Verlags GmbH, Lise-Meitner-Str 4, Gau-Algesheim, 55435, Germany. TEL 49-6725-93040, FAX 49-6725-5994, redaktion.wik@secumedia.de, info@secumedia.de, http://www.wik.info, http://www.secumedia.de. Ed. Horst Schaerges. Adv. contact Andreas Hey. B&W page EUR 1,900, color page EUR 2,850. Circ: 7,867 (paid and controlled).

363.2 614.86 USA
WASHINGTON (STATE) PATROL. ANNUAL REPORT. Text in English. a. free. **Document type:** *Government.*
Published by: State Patrol, Research & Development, General Administration Bldg, Box 42607, Olympia, WA 98504-2607. TEL 206-753-4453, FAX 206-753-2492.

364 345 USA
WASHINGTON CRIMES, PUNISHMENTS, VEHICLES AND RELATED STATUTES. Text in English. 1996. a. USD 49.95 (effective 2000). **Document type:** *Government.* **Description:** Covers the complete, up-to-date Crimes and Punishment (Title 9), Criminal Code (9A), Procedure (Title 10), Motor Vehicles (Title 46), plus related statutes with all legislative changes in text.
Related titles: CD-ROM ed.
Published by: Gould Publications, Inc. (Subsidiary of: LexisNexis), 1333 North US Hwy 17-92, Longwood, FL 32750-3724. TEL 407-695-9500, 800-717-7917, FAX 407-695-2906, info@gouldlaw.com, http://www.gouldlaw.com.

363.2 614.86 USA ISSN 0883-5799
WASHINGTON TROOPER. Text in English. 1981. q. USD 9.97. adv. bk.rev. back issues avail.
Published by: (Washington State Patrol Troopers Association), Mercury Services Inc., PO Box 1523, Longview, WA 98632-0144. TEL 206-577-8598. Ed. Bruce D Grimm. Circ: 5,000. **Subscr. to:** Bob Wheeler, WSPTA, Box 916, Kelso, WA 98626.

C

WAYNE STATE UNIVERSITY LAW SCHOOL. COMPARATIVE CRIMINAL LAW PROJECT. PUBLICATIONS SERIES. see *LAW—Criminal Law*

364 USA ISSN 1096-4886
HV6001
➤ **WESTERN CRIMINOLOGY REVIEW.** Text in English. 1998. 3/yr. free (effective 2005). **Document type:** *Journal, Academic/Scholarly.* **Description:** Serves as a forum for the publication and discussion of theory, research, policy and practice in the rapidly changing and interdisciplinary fields of criminology and criminal justice.
Media: Online - full text.
Indexed: CJA.
Published by: Western Society of Criminology, 2084 Stevenson Hall, Sonoma State University, Rohnert Park, CA 94928. TEL 707-664-2126, FAX 707-664-3920, wcr@sonoma.edu, http://wcr.sonoma.edu. Ed., Pub., R&P Patrick Jackson.

364.16 USA ISSN 1071-4464
WHITE-COLLAR CRIME FIGHTER. Text in English. 1999. m. USD 275 (effective 2003).
Published by: White-Collar Crime 101, LLC, 213 Ramapoo Rd., Ridgefield, CT 06877. TEL 800-440-2261, FAX 203-431-6054, http://www.wccfighter.com. Ed. Peter Goldmann.

363.2 JPN
WHITE PAPER ON POLICE (YEAR). Text in English. a. JPY 2,000. **Document type:** *Government.* **Description:** Covers international safety, the general crime situation and investigative activities, police activities for residents in regional communities, prevention of juvenile delinquency, environmental safety and cleanliness, traffic safety, public security, disasters and accidents, and support for police activities.
Published by: (Japan. National Police Agency), The Japan Times Ltd., 5-4, Shibaura 4-chome, Minato-ku, Tokyo, 108-0023, Japan. TEL 81-3-453-2013, FAX 81-3-3453-8023, http://www.bookclub.jpantimes.co.jp/.

364 808.83872 USA ISSN 1091-3602
WHITECHAPEL JOURNAL. Text in English. 1996. s-a. USD 30 for 2 yrs. domestic; GBP 20 for 2 yrs. in United Kingdom (effective 2000). bk.rev. back issues avail. **Document type:** *Newsletter.* **Description:** Focuses mainly on Jack the Ripper. Also concerned with "true crime" in general, and especially with the phenomenon of serial killers, and also review selective mystery fiction and biographies.
Address: PO Box 1341, F D R Sta, New York, NY 10150-1341. Ed. Stephen Wright.

363.2 GBR
THE WIRE (GLASGOW). Text in English. 1996. q. free. adv. **Document type:** *Newsletter.* **Description:** Contains topical policing issues and news from around the Force.
Published by: Strathclyde Police, 173 Pitt St, Glasgow, Lanarkshire G2 4JS, United Kingdom. TEL 44-141-532-2659, FAX 44-141-532-2562. R&P Valerie Chisholm White. Adv. contact Gina Ireland.

THE WIRE (LONDON, 1963). see *POLITICAL SCIENCE—International Relations*

365 USA
WISCONSIN ADULT JAIL POPULATION (YEAR). Text in English. a. **Document type:** *Government.*
Published by: Office of Justice Assistance, Statistical Analysis Center, 131 West Wilson, Ste 202, Madison, WI 53702. TEL 608-266-3323, FAX 608-266-6676.

364 USA
WISCONSIN SHERIFF AND DEPUTY. Text in English. 1949. q. USD 5. adv. bk.rev. charts; illus.
Published by: Wisconsin Sheriffs and Deputy Sheriffs Association, PO Box 145, Chippewa Falls, WI 54724. TEL 715-723-7173. Ed. James I Cardinal. Circ: 3,000.

323.34 364.1 AUS ISSN 1327-5550
WOMEN AGAINST VIOLENCE; an Australian feminist journal. Text in English. 1996. a. **Document type:** *Journal.*
—BLDSC (9343.224300), IE, ingenta.
Published by: C A S A HOUSE, 270 Cardigan St, Carlton, VIC 3053, Australia. casa@cryptic.rch.unimel.edu.au, http://casa.org.au/.

364.3 305.4 USA ISSN 1529-0689
WOMEN, GIRLS & CRIMINAL JUSTICE. Text in English. 2000. bi-m. USD 169.95 domestic; USD 199.95 foreign (effective 2004). **Document type:** *Newsletter.* **Description:** Designed for professionals in all disciplines working with women and girls who have been accused or convicted of criminal offenses.
Published by: Civic Research Insitute, 4490 US Route 27, PO Box 585, Kingston, NJ 08528. TEL 609-683-4450, FAX 609-683-7291, order@civicresearchinstitute.com, http://www.civicresearchinstitute.com/co9.html. Ed. Russ Immarigeon.

363.2 USA
WOMENPOLICE; the official publication of the International Association of Women Police. Text in English. 1987. q. USD 25 domestic; USD 35 foreign (effective 2003). adv. bk.rev. tr.lit.; illus. back issues avail.; reprints avail. **Document type:** *Magazine, Government.* **Description:** Promotes the professional development of women police officers and the utilization of women police officers internationally.
Formerly (until 1990): I A W P Bulletin (0890-5894)
Related titles: Microfiche ed.; Microfilm ed.; Online - full text ed.: (from Northern Light Technology, Inc., ProQuest Information & Learning).
Indexed: CJPI.
Published by: International Association of Women Police, 690418, Tulsa, OK 74169-0418. JVanLand@aol.com, http://www.iawp.org/wom_pol.htm. Ed. Jean VanLandingham. R&P Jeanette Taylor. adv.: B&W page USD 823, color page USD 1,071; trim 8.5 x 11. Circ: 3,500 (controlled).

364 USA ISSN 1064-8585
WORKING TOGETHER (SEATTLE). Text in English. s-a. **Document type:** *Newsletter, Academic/Scholarly.* **Description:** Includes articles, editorials, book reviews, resources and information about local, national and international prevention efforts addressing domestic violence, sexual violence, child abuse and sexual abuse by clergy.
Published by: FaithTrust Institute, 2400 N 45th St. #10, Seattle, WA 98103. TEL 206-634-1903, FAX 206-634-0115, info@faithtrustinstitute.org, http://www.faithtrustinstitute.org/Newsletter/index.htm.

WORLDWIDE MILITARY AND POLICE AWARD. see *MILITARY*

WOUND BALLISTICS REVIEW. see *MEDICAL SCIENCES—Forensic Sciences*

365 302.224 USA
WRITE IT RIGHT; quarterly for corrections personnel. Text in English. q. USD 32 to members; USD 48 to non-members (effective 2001). **Description:** Aims to assist jail personnel at all levels to become more effective communicators. Each issue concentrates on a specific topic or topics and includes exercises designed to reinforce the subject matter.
Published by: American Jail Association, 1135 Professional Ct., Hagerstown, MD 21740-5853. TEL 301-790-3930, FAX 301-790-2941, http://www.corrections.com/aja., http://www.corrections.com/aja/mags/publications.html.

WUJING YIXUE/MEDICAL JOURNAL OF THE CHINESE PEOPLE'S ARMED POLICE FORCES. see *MEDICAL SCIENCES*

YOUTH AND POLICY; the journal of critical analysis. see *CHILDREN AND YOUTH—About*

364 GBR ISSN 1473-2254
➤ **YOUTH JUSTICE.** Text in English. 2001. 3/yr. GBP 240, USD 420 to institutions; GBP 250 combined subscription to institutions print & online eds.; USD 438 to institutions print & online eds. (effective 2006). bk.rev. 64 p./no.; back issues avail. **Document type:** *Journal, Academic/Scholarly.* **Description:** Covers youth justice theory, law, policy & practice; and provides a major forum for discussion, dissemination and analysis across the UK and the international community.
Related titles: Online - full text ed.: ISSN 1747-6283. GBP 238, USD 416 to institutions (effective 2006).
Indexed: SociolAb.
—CCC.
Published by: (National Association For Youth Justice), Sage Publications Ltd. (Subsidiary of: Sage Publications, Inc.), 1 Oliver's Yard, 55 City Rd, London, EC1 1SP, United Kingdom. TEL 44-20-73248500, FAX 44-20-73248600, info@sagepub.co.uk, http://www.sagepub.co.uk/journal.aspx?pid=107370. Eds. Barry Goldson, John Muncie. **Subscr. to:** Sage Publications, Inc., 2455 Teller Rd, Thousand Oaks, CA 91320. TEL 805-499-0721, FAX 805-499-0871, journals@sagepub.com.

364 USA ISSN 1541-2040
HV9069
▼ **YOUTH VIOLENCE AND JUVENILE JUSTICE.** Text in English. 2003. q. USD 240, GBP 155 to institutions; USD 250, GBP 162 combined subscription to institutions print & online eds. (effective 2006). **Document type:** *Journal, Academic/Scholarly.* **Description:** Provides academics and practitioners in juvenile justice and related fields with a resource for publishing current empirical research, discussing theoretical issues, and reviewing promising interventions and programs in the areas of youth violence, juvenile justice, and school safety.
Related titles: Online - full text ed.: ISSN 1556-9330. USD 238, GBP 154 to institutions (effective 2006) (from EBSCO Publishing, O C L C Online Computer Library Center, Inc., Sage Publications, Inc., Swets Information Services).
Indexed: CJA, SFSA, SSA, SociolAb, V&AA.
—BLDSC (9421.583460), IE. **CCC.**
Published by: Sage Publications, Inc., 2455 Teller Rd, Thousand Oaks, CA 91320. TEL 800-818-7243, FAX 800-583-2665, info@sagepub.com, http://www.sagepub.com/journal.aspx?pid=342. Eds. Eric J Fritsch, Tory J Caeti. **Subscr. to:** Sage Publications Ltd., 1 Oliver's Yard, 55 City Rd, London EC1 1SP, United Kingdom. TEL 44-20-73740645, FAX 44-20-73748741, subscription@sagepub.co.uk.

364.36 USA ISSN 1548-8020
RJ506.V56
▼ **YOUTH VIOLENCE, CRIME, AND GANGS**; children at risk. Text in English. 2004. biennial. USD 38 per issue (effective 2004).
Published by: Gale Group (Subsidiary of: Thomson Corporation), 27500 Drake Rd, Farmington Hills, MI 48331-3535. TEL 248-699-4253, 800-347-4253, FAX 248-699-8035, http://www.gale.com.

ZAKBOEK STRAFVORDERING VOOR DE HULPOFFIZIER VAN JUSTITIE. see *LAW—Criminal Law*

364 RUS ISSN 0869-4486
ZAKONNOST'. Text in Russian. 1934. m. USD 160. adv. bk.rev. index. **Document type:** *Magazine, Academic/Scholarly.* **Description:** Covers the theory and practice of the Directorate of Public Prosecutions, along with legislative news.
Formerly (until 1992): Sotsialisticheskaya Zakonnost' (0038-1691)
Related titles: Diskette ed.; Fax ed.
Indexed: CDSP, FLP, RASB, WBSS.
—East View.
Published by: General'naya Prokuratura Rossiiskoi Federacii, B Dmitrovka 9, str 6, Moscow, 103868, Russian Federation. TEL 7-095-2290106, FAX 7-095-2924515. Eds. Nikolai Zaikin, Sergei V Pyktin. Adv. contact Lyubov' N Lozovskaya. Circ: 10,000. **US dist. addr.:** East View Information Services, 3020 Harbor Ln. N., Minneapolis, MN 55447. TEL 612-550-0961. **Co-sponsor:** Goskomitet po Pechati.

365 ZMB ISSN 0084-4659
ZAMBIA. PRISONS DEPARTMENT. REPORT. Text in English. 1964. a. ZMK 250. **Document type:** *Government.*
Published by: (Zambia. Prisons Department ZAF), Government Printing Department, PO Box 30136, Lusaka, Zambia.

364 DEU ISSN 0342-3514
ZEITSCHRIFT FUER STRAFVOLLZUG UND STRAFFAELLIGENHILFE. Text in German. 1954. 6/yr. EUR 21; EUR 6 newsstand/cover. adv. bk.rev. index. back issues avail. **Document type:** *Journal, Academic/Scholarly.*
Formerly (until 1975): Zeitschrift fuer Strafvollzug (0513-9139)
Indexed: AC&P, CJA, DIP, IBR, IBZ.
Published by: Gesellschaft fuer Fortbildung der Strafvollzugsbediensteten e.V., Mittelberg 1, Heimsheim, 71296, Germany. TEL 49-511-1209231. Ed., Adv. contact Heinz Mueller-Dietz. R&P Heinz Mueller Dietz. Circ: 2,550.

ZERO HOUR; where culture meets crime. see *LITERARY AND POLITICAL REVIEWS*

364 CHN ISSN 1007-9017
ZHONGGUO XINGSHIFA ZAZHI/CHINESE CRIMINAL SCIENCE. Text in Chinese. 1991. bi-m. **Document type:** *Journal, Academic/Scholarly.*
Related titles: Online - full content ed.; Online - full text ed.: (from East View Information Services).
Address: Shijingshan-qu, 5, Lugu Xilu, Beijing, 100040, China. TEL 86-10-68630197, FAX 86-10-68630141, http://zgxsfzz.periodicals.net.cn/.

CRIMINOLOGY AND LAW ENFORCEMENT—Abstracting, Bibliographies, Statistics

365.021 AUS ISSN 0813-2364
HV9872
AUSTRALIA. BUREAU OF STATISTICS. AUSTRALIAN PRISONERS. Text in English. a. price varies. **Document type:** *Government.* **Description:** For all working in the fields of criminology, corrections, probation and parole.
Published by: Australian Bureau of Statistics, PO Box 10, Belconnen, ACT 2616, Australia. TEL 61-2-6252-5249, FAX 61-2-6252-6778, http://www.abs.gov.au.

364.021 AUS
AUSTRALIA. BUREAU OF STATISTICS. AUSTRALIAN STANDARD OFFENCE CLASSIFICATION. Text in English. 1985. irreg., latest 1997. AUD 37 (effective 2003). **Document type:** *Government.* **Description:** Publishes crime statistics for government bodies and the community in general.
Published by: Australian Bureau of Statistics, PO Box 10, Belconnen, ACT 2616, Australia. TEL 61-2-6252-5249, FAX 61-2-6252-6778, http://www.abs.gov.au.

364.021 AUS
AUSTRALIA. BUREAU OF STATISTICS. COMMUNITY ATTITUDES TO CRIME AND POLICING, AUSTRALIA. Text in English. 1998. irreg. AUD 25 (effective 1998). **Document type:** *Government.*
Published by: Australian Bureau of Statistics, PO Box 10, Belconnen, ACT 2616, Australia. TEL 61-2-6252-5249, FAX 61-2-6252-6778, http://www.abs.gov.au.

364.021 AUS
AUSTRALIA. BUREAU OF STATISTICS. CRIME AND SAFETY, AUSTRALIA. Text in English. 1993. irreg., latest 2003. AUD 23 (effective 2003). **Document type:** *Government.* **Description:** Includes household break-ins, attempted break-ins and motor vehicle theft, personal robberies, assaults and some data on sexual assaults.
Published by: Australian Bureau of Statistics, PO Box 10, Belconnen, ACT 2616, Australia. TEL 61-2-6252-5249, FAX 61-2-6252-6778, http://www.abs.gov.au.

364.4021 AUS
AUSTRALIA. BUREAU OF STATISTICS. NEW SOUTH WALES OFFICE. HOME SECURITY PRECAUTIONS, NEW SOUTH WALES. Text in English. 1999. irreg. AUD 16 (effective 2003). **Document type:** *Government.*
Published by: Australian Bureau of Statistics, New South Wales Office, St. Andrews House, 5th Fl., Sydney Square George St., Sydney, NSW 2000, Australia. TEL 61-2-9268-4620, FAX 61-2-9268-4668, http://www.abs.gov.au.

365.34021 AUS
AUSTRALIA. BUREAU OF STATISTICS. SECURITY SERVICES, AUSTRALIA. Text in English. 2000. irreg. AUD 16 (effective 2003). **Document type:** *Government.*
Published by: Australian Bureau of Statistics, PO Box 10, Belconnen, ACT 2616, Australia. TEL 61-2-6252-5249, FAX 61-2-6252-6778, http://www.abs.gov.au.

364.021 AUS
AUSTRALIA. BUREAU OF STATISTICS. SOUTH AUSTRALIAN OFFICE. CRIME AND SAFETY, SOUTH AUSTRALIA. Text in English. 1991. irreg., latest 2000. AUD 18.50 (effective 2003). **Document type:** *Government.*
Published by: Australian Bureau of Statistics, South Australian Office, GPO Box 2272, Adelaide, SA 5001, Australia. TEL 61-8-82377582, FAX 61-8-8237-7566, http://www.abs.gov.au.

364.021 AUS
AUSTRALIA. BUREAU OF STATISTICS. TASMANIAN OFFICE. COMMUNITY SAFETY, TASMANIA. Text in English. 1998. irreg. AUD 16 (effective 2003).
Published by: Australian Bureau of Statistics, Tasmanian Office, GPO Box 66 A, Hobart, TAS 7001, Australia. TEL 61-3-6222-5800, FAX 61-3-6222-5995, http://www.abs.gov.au.

364.021 AUS
AUSTRALIA. BUREAU OF STATISTICS. VICTORIAN OFFICE. CRIME AND SAFETY, VICTORIA. Text in English. 1994. irreg. AUD 13 (effective 1998). **Document type:** *Government.*
Published by: Australian Bureau of Statistics, Victorian Office, GPO Box 2796 Y, Melbourne, VIC 3001, Australia. TEL 61-3-9615-7929, FAX 61-3-9615-7798, http://www.abs.gov.au.

364.021 AUS
AUSTRALIA. BUREAU OF STATISTICS. WESTERN AUSTRALIAN OFFICE. CRIME AND SAFETY, WESTERN AUSTRALIA. Text in English. 1995. irreg., latest 1999. AUD 16 (effective 2003). **Document type:** *Government.*
Published by: Australian Bureau of Statistics, Western Australian Office, PO Box K 881, Perth, W.A. 6001, Australia. TEL 61-8-9360-5307, FAX 61-8-9360-5955.

614.599392 USA
BUREAU OF JUSTICE STATISTICS. BULLETIN. HIV IN PRISONS AND JAILS. Variant title: Bureau of Justice Statistics. Bulletin. HIV in Prisons. Text in English. a.
Document type: *Bulletin, Government.*
Related titles: Online - full content ed.
Published by: U.S. Department of Justice, Bureau of Justice Statistics, 810 Seventh St, N W, 2nd Fl, Washington, DC 20531. http://www.ojp.usdoj.gov/bjs.

362.8 USA
BUREAU OF JUSTICE STATISTICS REPORTS. JUSTICE EXPENDITURE AND EMPLOYMENT. Text in English. 1969. irreg. free. back issues avail. **Document type:** *Government.*
Former titles: Justice Expenditure and Employment Data in the U.S.; Expenditure and Employment Data for the Criminal Justice Systems (0149-0478)
Related titles: Online - full content ed.
Published by: U.S. Department of Justice, Bureau of Justice Statistics, 810 Seventh St, N W, 2nd Fl, Washington, DC 20531. TEL 202-307-0765, FAX 202-307-0128, 202-307-5846, askbjs@ojp.usdoj.gov, http://www.ojp.usdoj.gov/bjs/pubalp2.htm#j. Circ: 8,800. **Orders to:** Bureau of Justice Statistics Clearinghouse, Box 179, Dept BJS C 1, Annapolis, MD 20701-0179. TEL 800-732-3277.

364.9 USA
CALIFORNIA. BUREAU OF CRIMINAL INFORMATION AND ANALYSIS. CRIMINAL JUSTICE PROFILE: STATEWIDE. Text in English. a.
Formerly: California. Bureau of Criminal Statistics and Special Services. Criminal Justice Profile: Statewide
Indexed: SRI.
Published by: (California. Bureau of Criminal Information and Analysis), Department of Justice, Division of Law Enforcement, PO Box 903427, Sacramento, CA 94203-4270. TEL 916-227-3481.

364.021 CAN ISSN 0715-2973
CANADA. STATISTICS CANADA. ADULT CORRECTIONAL SERVICES IN CANADA. Text in English, French. 1982. a.
Document type: *Government.*
Formed by the merger of (1876-1982): Canada. Statistics Canada. Correctional Services in Canada (0711-6802); (1876-1982): Canada. Statistique Canada. Services Correctionnels au Canada (0711-6810); Both of which superseded in part (in 1979): Canada. Statistics Canada. Correctional Institutions Statistics (0708-6326); Which was formerly (until 1976): Canada. Statistics Canada. Penitentiary Statistics (0706-4055); (until 1975): Canada. Statistics Canada. Correctional Institution Statistics (0575-8270); (until 1959): Canada. Statistics Canada. Annual Report of Statistics of Criminal and Other Offenses (0319-8227); (until 1926): Canada. Dominion Bureau of Statistics. Annual Report of Criminal Statistics (0828-3613); (until 1919): Canada. Dominion Bureau of Statistics. Criminal Statistics (0825-1150)
Published by: Statistics Canada, Canadian Centre for Justice Statistics, Rm 1500 Main Bldg, Holland Ave, Ottawa, ON K1A 0T6, Canada. TEL 613-951-8116, infostats@statcan.ca, http://www.statcan.ca.

364.021 CAN ISSN 1201-3501
CANADA. STATISTICS CANADA. ADULT CRIMINAL COURT STATISTICS. Text in English. a. CND 11 (effective 2004).
Published by: (Statistics Canada, Canadian Centre for Justice Statistics), Statistics Canada, Publications Sales and Services, Ottawa, ON K1A 0T6, Canada. TEL 613-951-8116, infostats@statcan.ca, http://www.statcan.ca/english/IPS/Data/85-002-XPE2003010.htm.

CANADA. STATISTICS CANADA. FAMILY VIOLENCE IN CANADA, A STATISTICAL PROFILE. see *SOCIAL SERVICES AND WELFARE—Abstracting, Bibliographies, Statistics*

363.22021 CAN ISSN 1488-867X
CANADA. STATISTICS CANADA. POLICE RESOURCES IN CANADA (ONLINE EDITION). Text in English. 1999. a. CND 28 (effective 2004).
Formed by the merger of (1998-1999): Canada. Statistics Canada. Police Personnel and Expenditures in Canada (Online Edition) (1481-5389); (1997-1999): Canada. Statistics Canada. Crime and Police Resources in Canadian Municipalities (Online Edition) (1481-5400)
Media: Online - full content.
Published by: (Statistics Canada, Canadian Centre for Justice Statistics), Statistics Canada, Publications Sales and Services, Ottawa, ON K1A 0T6, Canada. TEL 613-951-8116, infostats@statcan.ca, http://www.statcan.ca/english/IPS/Data/85-225-XIE.htm.

364.36021 CAN ISSN 1488-4887
CANADA. STATISTICS CANADA. YOUTH COURT DATA TABLES (ONLINE EDITION). Text in English. 1987. a. CND 26 (effective 2004). **Description:** Presents summary data on cases and charges dealt with in youth courts across Canada.
Incorporates (1987-200?): Canada. Statistics Canada. Youth Court Data Tables (Print Edition) (1497-2085); Which was formerly (until 1999): Canada. Statistics Canada. Youth Court Statistics (1200-4804)
Media: Online - full content.
Published by: (Statistics Canada, Canadian Centre for Justice Statistics), Statistics Canada, Publications Sales and Services, Ottawa, ON K1A 0T6, Canada. TEL 613-951-8116, infostats@statcan.ca, http://www.statcan.ca/english/IPS/Data/85F0030XIE.htm.

362.8 USA ISSN 0191-3220
HV8699.U5
CAPITAL PUNISHMENT (YEAR). Text in English. 1971. a. free. charts; stat. back issues avail. **Document type:** *Bulletin, Government.* **Description:** Describes capital punishment court cases throughout the nation for year; also studies state statutory provisions relating to the death penalty and provides demographic statistics of death row inmates.
Related titles: Online - full content ed.; Series of: U.S. Department of Justice. Bureau of Justice Statistics Reports. Corrections.
Published by: U.S. Department of Justice, Bureau of Justice Statistics, 810 Seventh St, N W, 2nd Fl, Washington, DC 20531. FAX 202-307-0128, askbjs@ojp.usdoj.gov, http://www.ojp.usdoj.gov/bjs/pubalp2.htm#C. Circ: 15,000. **Subscr. to:** Bureau of Justice Statistics Clearinghouse, Box 179, Dept BJS C 1, Annapolis, MD 20701-0179. TEL 800-732-3277, FAX 410-792-4358.

364 GBR ISSN 0967-5159
KD327
CHARTERED INSTITUTE OF PUBLIC FINANCE AND ACCOUNTANCY. ADMINISTRATION OF JUSTICE. ESTIMATES & ACTUALS. Text in English. 1983. a. GBP 55. back issues avail.
Formerly (until 1992): Chartered Institute of Public Finance and Accountancy. Administration of Justice. Estimates (0264-6552)
—CCC.
Published by: (Statistical Information Service), Chartered Institute of Public Finance and Accountancy, 3 Robert St, London, WC2N 6RL, United Kingdom. TEL 44-20-7543-5800, FAX 44-20-7543-5700, http://www.cipfa.org.uk.

363.2 GBR
CHARTERED INSTITUTE OF PUBLIC FINANCE AND ACCOUNTANCY. POLICE STATISTICS. ACTUALS. Text in English. 1949-1989; resumed 199?. a. GBP 80. back issues avail.
Supersedes in part: Chartered Institute of Public Finance and Accountancy. Police Statistics. Actuals and Estimates; Which was formed by the merger of: Chartered Institute of Public Finance and Accountancy. Police Statistics. Actuals (0144-9915); Chartered Institute of Public Finance and Accountancy. Police Statistics. Estimates (0144-9885)
—BLDSC (6543.263000).
Published by: (Statistical Information Service), Chartered Institute of Public Finance and Accountancy, 3 Robert St, London, WC2N 6RL, United Kingdom. TEL 44-20-7543-5800, FAX 44-20-7543-5700, http://www.cipfa.org.uk.

364 310 GBR
CHARTERED INSTITUTE OF PUBLIC FINANCE AND ACCOUNTANCY. POLICE STATISTICS. ESTIMATES. Text in English. a. GBP 80.
Supersedes in part: Chartered Institute of Public Finance and Accountancy. Police Statistics. Actuals and Estimates; Which was formed by the merger of: Chartered Institute of Public Finance and Accountancy. Police Statistics. Actuals (0144-9915); Chartered Institute of Public Finance and Accountancy. Police Statistics. Estimates (0144-9885)
—BLDSC (6543.263000).
Published by: (Statistical Information Service), Chartered Institute of Public Finance and Accountancy, 3 Robert St, London, WC2N 6RL, United Kingdom. TEL 44-20-7543-5800, FAX 44-20-7543-5700, http://www.cipfa.org.uk.

CHARTERED INSTITUTE OF PUBLIC FINANCE AND ACCOUNTANCY. PROBATION. ESTIMATES & ACTUALS. see *SOCIAL SERVICES AND WELFARE—Abstracting, Bibliographies, Statistics*

364 317 USA ISSN 1081-6453
HV6787
CITY CRIME RANKINGS; crime in metropolitan America. Text in English. 1995. a. USD 42.95 (effective 2002). 408 p./no.; **Document type:** *Bulletin.* **Description:** Provides detailed comparative crime statistics on cities with more than 75,000 inhabitants and all metro areas.
Related titles: Diskette ed.
Published by: Morgan Quitno Corporation, PO Box 1656, Lawrence, KS 66044. TEL 785-841-3534, 800-457-0742, FAX 913-841-3568, http://www.morganquitno.com. Eds. Scott Morgan, Kathleen O'Leary Morgan. R&P Scott Morgan.

364.021 USA
CORRECTIONAL POPULATIONS IN THE U S (YEAR). Text in English. 1985. a. free. stat. **Document type:** *Government.*
Related titles: Microfiche ed.; Series of: National Crime Victimization Survey Report.
Published by: U.S. Department of Justice, Bureau of Justice Statistics, 810 Seventh St, N W, 2nd Fl, Washington, DC 20531. TEL 800-732-3200, FAX 410-792-4358, http://www.ojp.usdoj.gov/bjs. Circ: 17,000.

364.36 USA
CRIME IN CALIFORNIA. Text in English. 1965. a. free. charts. **Document type:** *Government.*
Former titles (until 2002): Crime and Delinquency in California (0590-0832); California. Bureau of Criminal Statistics. Crime and Delinquency; Incorporates: Adult Criminal Detention Reference Tables (0092-2080); Adult Probation Program Report; Which was formerly: Adult Probation Reference Report; Adult Prosecution; Crimes and Arrests; Juvenile Probation; (until 1972): Reference Tables Adult and Juvenile Probation (0094-7717)
Indexed: SRI.
Published by: Department of Justice, Criminal Justice Statistics Center, PO Box 903427, Sacramento, CA 95820. TEL 916-227-3509.

364.973021 USA ISSN 1077-4408
HV6787
CRIME STATE RANKINGS; crime in the 50 United States. Text in English. 1994. a. USD 54.95 (effective 2002). stat. 540 p./no.; **Description:** Provides detailed, comparative statistical information on crime and law enforcement in more than 512 categories, for each of the 50 states.
Media: Diskette.
Published by: Morgan Quitno Corporation, PO Box 1656, Lawrence, KS 66044. TEL 785-841-3534, 800-457-0742, FAX 785-841-3568, http://www.morganquitno.com. Ed. Kathleen O'Leary Morgan. R&P Scott Morgan.

364 016 USA ISSN 0146-9177
HV6001
CRIMINAL JUSTICE ABSTRACTS. Text in English. 1968. q. USD 816, GBP 526 to institutions (effective 2006). adv. abstr.; bibl.; illus. index, cum.index. reprint service avail. from WSH. **Document type:** *Journal, Abstract/Index.* **Description:** Contains hundreds of in-depth abstracts of current books, journal articles, government reports, and dissertations published worldwide.
Former titles: Abstracts on Crime and Juvenile Delinquency; Crime and Delinquency Literature (0037-1327); Formed by the merger of: Information Review on Crime and Delinquency; Selected Highlights of Crime and Delinquency
Related titles: CD-ROM ed.: (from SilverPlatter Information, Inc.); Microfiche ed.: (from WSH); Microfilm ed.: (from PMC, WSH); Microform ed.: (from PQC, WSH); Online - full text ed.: ISSN 1551-1685 (from SilverPlatter Information, Inc.).
Indexed: CJPI, RASB.
—BLDSC (3487.347500). **CCC.**
Published by: Sage Publications, Inc., 2455 Teller Rd, Thousand Oaks, CA 91320. TEL 805-499-0721, 800-818-7243, FAX 805-499-8096, 800-583-2665, info@sagepub.com, http://www.sagepub.com/journal.aspx?pid=253. Ed. Judith Anne Ryder. Adv. contact Kirsten Beaulieu TEL 805-499-0721 ext 7160. page USD 350. Circ: 1,000. **Subscr. outside N America to:** Sage Publications Ltd., 1 Oliver's Yard, 55 City Rd, London EC1 1SP, United Kingdom. TEL 44-20-73740645, FAX 44-20-73748741, subscription@sagepub.co.uk.

C

016.364 USA ISSN 0145-5818
Z5118.C9
CRIMINAL JUSTICE PERIODICAL INDEX. Text in English. 1975. 3/yr. bk.rev. illus. Index. back issues avail.; reprints avail. **Document type:** *Abstract/Index.*
Media: Online - full text.
Published by: ProQuest Information & Learning, 300 N Zeeb Rd., PO Box 1346, Ann Arbor, MI 48106-1346. TEL 734-761-4700, 800-521-0600, info@il.proquest.com, http://www.proquest.com/products/pt-product-Criminal.shtml.

364 614.19 USA
CRIMINALIST'S SOURCE BOOK. Text in English. a. USD 25.
Published by: International Reference Organization in Forensic Medicine & Sciences, PO Box 8282, Wichita, KS 67208. TEL 316-685-7612.

364 NLD ISSN 1205-8629
JC578 CODEN: CCRRA4
➤ **CRITICAL CRIMINOLOGY**; international journal. Text in English. 1989. 3/yr. EUR 293, USD 295, GBP 185 combined subscription to institutions print & online eds. (effective 2005). adv. bk.rev. reprint service avail. from PSC. **Document type:** *Journal, Academic/Scholarly.* **Description:** Offers a forum for progressive analyses of economic, gender, legal and political relations as they pertain to studies of social justice worldwide.
Formerly: Journal of Human Justice (0847-2971)
Related titles: Online - full text ed.: ISSN 1572-9877 (from EBSCO Publishing, Gale Group, IngentaConnect, Kluwer Online, O C L C Online Computer Library Center, Inc., Springer LINK, Swets Information Services).
Indexed: BibLing, CJA.
—BLDSC (3487.451740), IE, Infotrieve, ingenta. **CCC.**
Published by: (American Society of Criminology USA, Division of Critical Criminology CAN), Springer-Verlag Dordrecht (Subsidiary of: Springer Science+Business Media), Van Godewijckstraat 30, Dordrecht, 3311 GX, Netherlands. TEL 31-78-6576050, FAX 31-78-6576474, http://springerlink.metapress.com/openurl.asp?genre=journal&issn=1205-8629, http://www.springeronline.com. Ed. Barbara Sims. Circ: 300.

364 314   CYP   ISSN 0253-8695
HV8485.C93
CYPRUS. DEPARTMENT OF STATISTICS AND RESEARCH. CRIMINAL STATISTICS. Text in English, Greek. 1974. a. CYP 6 (effective 1999). **Document type:** *Government.*
Description: Gives police, judicial, and prison statistics.
Published by: Ministry of Finance, Department of Statistics and Research, 13 Andreas Araouzos St, Nicosia, 1444, Cyprus. TEL 357-2-309318, FAX 357-2-374830, cydsr@cytanet.com.cy, http://www.pio.gov.cy/dsr.

364.9489   DNK   ISSN 0070-3540
HV7023
DENMARK. DANMARKS STATISTIK. KRIMINALSTATISTIK (YEAR)/CRIMINAL STATISTICS. Text in Danish. 1933. a. DKK 164.80 (effective 2000). **Document type:** *Government.*
Indexed: RASB.
Published by: Danmarks Statistik, Sejroegade 11, Copenhagen Oe, 2100, Denmark. TEL 45-39-17-39-17, FAX 45-31-18-48-01.

364 318   COL
ESTADISTICA DE CRIMINALIDAD. Text in Spanish. 1963. a. illus.; stat.
Formerly (until 1973): Criminalidad
Published by: Policia Nacional, Carrera 15 No. 10-41, Bogota, CUND, Colombia.

363.2   CHL
ESTADISTICAS POLICIALES. CARABINEROS DE CHILE. Text in Spanish. 1977. a. CLP 2,000; USD 13.50 in United States; USD 14.20 elsewhere.
Published by: Instituto Nacional de Estadisticas, Casilla 498, Correo 3, Ave. Bulnes, 418, Santiago, Chile. TEL 56-2-6991441, FAX 56-2-6712169.

363.2   CHL
ESTADISTICAS POLICIALES. POLICIA DE INVESTIGACIONES DE CHILE. Text in Spanish. 1983. a. CLP 2,000; USD 13.50 in United States; USD 15.90 elsewhere.
Published by: Instituto Nacional de Estadisticas, Casilla 498, Correo 3, Ave. Bulnes, 418, Santiago, Chile. TEL 56-2-6991441, FAX 56-2-6712169.

364   USA
HV9278
FELONY SENTENCES IN STATE COURTS. Text in English. 1989. biennial. free. stat.; charts. back issues avail. **Document type:** *Bulletin, Government.* **Description:** Provides statistics on felony arrests in the U.S. and data on outcomes of arrests.
Published by: U.S. Department of Justice, Bureau of Justice Statistics, 810 Seventh St, N W, 2nd Fl, Washington, DC 20531. TEL 202-307-0765, FAX 202-307-0128, askbjs@ojp.usdoj.gov, http://www.ojp.usdoj.gov/bjs/pubalp2.htm#F. Circ: 13,300. **Orders to:** BJS Clearinghouse, PO Box 179, Annapolis, MD 20701-0179. TEL 800-732-3277, FAX 410-792-4358.

364.021   FIN   ISSN 1236-2638
KJT31
FINLAND. TILASTOKESKUS. OIKEUSTILASTOLLINEN VUOSIKIRJA/FINLAND. STATISTICS FINLAND. YEARBOOK OF JUSTICE STATISTICS. Text in Finnish, English, Swedish. 1993. a., latest 2005. EUR 47 (effective 2005). **Document type:** *Yearbook, Government.*
Formed by the merger of (1988-1993): Poliisin Tietoon Tullut Rikollisuus: Vuositilasto (0784-8838); (1988-1993): Tuomioistuinten Toiminta (0784-8854); (1988-1993): Tuomioistuinten Tutkimat Rikokset (0784-8862)
Related titles: ◆ Series of: Finland. Tilastokeskus. Oikeus. ISSN 0784-8366.
Published by: Tilastokeskus/Statistics Finland, Tyopajakatu 13, Statistics Finland, Helsinki, 00022, Finland. TEL 358-9-17341, FAX 358-9-17342750, http://www.stat.fi/.

364   FIN   ISSN 0784-882X
HA1448
FINLAND. TILASTOKESKUS. POLIISIN TIETOON TULLUT RIKOLLISUUS/FINLAND. CENTRAL STATISTICAL OFFICE. CRIMINALITY KNOWN TO THE POLICE/FINLAND. STATISTIKCENTRALEN. BROTTSLIGHET SOM KOMMIT TILL POLISENS KAENNEDOM. Text in English, Finnish, Swedish. 1928. a., latest 2004. EUR 20 (effective 2005). **Document type:** *Government.*
Formerly: Finland. Tilastokeskus. Rikollisuus. Poliisin Tietoon Tullut Rikollisuus (0355-2160)
Published by: Tilastokeskus/Statistics Finland, Tyopajakatu 13, Statistics Finland, Helsinki, 00022, Finland. TEL 358-9-17341, FAX 358-9-17342750, http://www.stat.fi/.

363.2021   GBR   ISSN 0950-5237
HV8485.G7
GREAT BRITAIN. HOME OFFICE. CRIMINAL STATISTICS. ENGLAND AND WALES. SUPPLEMENTARY TABLES. Text in English. 1981. a.
—BLDSC (3487.361000). **CCC.**
Published by: Home Office, 50 Queen Anne's Gate, London, SW1 9AT, United Kingdom. TEL 44-171-273-3072, http://www.open.gov.uk.

364   GRC   ISSN 0256-3665
GREECE. NATIONAL STATISTICAL SERVICE. STATISTICS ON CIVIL, CRIMINAL AND REFORMATORY JUSTICE. Text in Greek. 1962. a., latest 1995. back issues avail. **Document type:** *Government.*
Formerly (until 1961): Greece. National Statistical Service. Criminal Justice Statistics
Published by: National Statistical Service of Greece, Statistical Information and Publications Division/Ethniki Statistiki Yperesia tes Ellados, 14-16 Lykourgou St, Athens, 101 66, Greece. TEL 30-1-3289-397, FAX 30-1-3241-102, http://www.statistics.gr, http://www.statistics.gr/Main_eng.asp.

364.021   USA
HATE CRIME STATISTICS. Text in English. a., latest 2003. stat. **Document type:** *Government.* **Description:** Presents data regarding incidents, offenses, victims, and offenders in reported crimes that were motivated in whole or in part by a bias against the victim's perceived race, religion, ethnicity, sexual orientation, or disability.
Related titles: Online - full content ed.
Published by: U.S. Federal Bureau of Investigation, Uniform Crime Reporting Program, Criminal Justice Information Services Division, 1000 Custer Hollow Rd, Clarksburg, WV 26306. TEL 304-625-4995, FAX 304-625-5394, cjis_comm@leo.gov, http://www.fbi.gov/ucr/ucr.htm#hate.

HOMICIDE IN CALIFORNIA. see *CRIMINOLOGY AND LAW ENFORCEMENT*

364.021 302.045195   HKG
HONG KONG SPECIAL ADMINISTRATIVE REGION OF CHINA. CENSUS AND STATISTICS DEPARTMENT. CRIME AND ITS VICTIMS IN HONG KONG. Text in Chinese, English. 1979. irreg., latest 1999. HKD 16.40 newsstand/cover (effective 2001). stat. **Document type:** *Government.* **Description:** Shows the number and characteristics of crime and crime victims in the survey period.
Published by: Census and Statistics Department/Zhengfu Tongjichu, Social Statistics Branch, 5/F Fortress Tower, 250 King's Rd, North Point, Hong Kong. TEL 852-2887-5508, FAX 852-2508-1501, ghs2_1@censtatd.gov.hk, http://www.info.gov.hk/censtatd/eng/public/pub_list/GHS2/cvs_index.html, http://www.statisticalbookstore.gov.hk. **Subscr. to:** Information Services Department, Publications Sales Section, 4/F, Murray Bldg, Garden Rd, Hong Kong, Hong Kong. TEL 852-2842-8844, FAX 852-2598-7482, puborder@isd.gcn.gov.hk, http://www.info.gov.hk/isd/book_e.htm. **Dist. by:** Government Publications Centre, Low Block, Ground Fl, Queensway Government Offices, 66 Queensway, Hong Kong, Hong Kong. TEL 852-2537-1910, FAX 852-2523-7195.

364.021   USA
INDICATORS OF SCHOOL CRIME AND SAFETY. Text in English. a. stat. **Document type:** *Government.* **Description:** Presents data on crime at school from the perspectives of students, teachers, principals, and the general population.
Related titles: Online - full content ed.
Published by: U.S. Department of Justice, Bureau of Justice Statistics, 810 Seventh St, N W, 2nd Fl, Washington, DC 20531. http://www.ojp.usdoj.gov/bjs.

INFORMATSIONNYI BYULLETEN'. BOR'BA S PRESTUPNOSTYU ZA RUBEZHOM. see *CRIMINOLOGY AND LAW ENFORCEMENT—Security*

016.36534   RUS
INFORMATSIONNYI BYULLETEN'. INOSTRANNAYA PECHAT' O TEKHNICHESKOM OSNASHCHENII POLITSII ZARUBEZHNYKH GOSUDARSTV. Text in Russian. 1996. m. USD 90 foreign (effective 2006). **Document type:** *Journal, Abstract/Index.*
Indexed: RASB.
Published by: Vserossiiskii Institut Nauchnoi I Tekhnicheskoi Informatsii (VINITI), Ul Usievicha 20, Moscow, 125190, Russian Federation. TEL 7-095-1526441, FAX 7-095-9430060, dir@viniti.ru, http://www.viniti.ru. **Dist. by:** Informnauka Ltd., Ul Usievicha 20, Moscow 125190, Russian Federation. alfimov@viniti.ru.

364   ISR   ISSN 0075-1006
ISRAEL. CENTRAL BUREAU OF STATISTICS. CRIMINAL STATISTICS. Text in English, Hebrew. 1948. irreg., latest 1992. ILS 18.50. **Document type:** *Government.*
Published by: Central Bureau of Statistics, PO Box 13015, Jerusalem, 91130, Israel. TEL 972-2-6553364, FAX 972-2-6521340.

362.8   ISR   ISSN 0333-7634
HV6665.I8
ISRAEL. CENTRAL BUREAU OF STATISTICS. VICTIMIZATION SURVEY. Text in English, Hebrew. 1981. irreg., latest 1990. **Document type:** *Government.*
Published by: Central Bureau of Statistics, PO Box 13015, Jerusalem, 91130, Israel. TEL 972-2-6553364, FAX 972-2-6521340.

364.021   USA
JAILS IN INDIAN COUNTRY. Text in English. a., latest 2002. stat. **Document type:** *Government.*

Related titles: Online - full content ed.
Published by: U.S. Department of Justice, Bureau of Justice Statistics, 810 Seventh St, N W, 2nd Fl, Washington, DC 20531. http://www.ojp.usdoj.gov/bjs.

340 364 016   NLD   ISSN 0167-5850
JUSTITIELE VERKENNINGEN. Text in Dutch; Summaries in Dutch, English. 1956. 9/yr. EUR 65 (effective 2003). abstr. index. **Document type:** *Academic/Scholarly.* **Description:** Short studies on criminology and abstracts of books and journals in the field.
Formerly (until 1974): Documentatieblad (0012-4532)
Indexed: AC&P, CJA, KES.
—IE, Infotrieve, KNAW.
Published by: (Netherlands. Ministerie van Justitie, Wetenschappelijk Onderzoek- en Documentatiecentrum), Kluwer B.V. (Subsidiary of: Wolters Kluwer N.V.), Postbus 23, Deventer, 7400 GA, Netherlands. TEL 31-570-673449, FAX 31-570-691555, bstokkom@best-dep.minijust.nl, juridisch@kluwer.nl, http://www.minijust.nl/wodc, http://www.kluwer.nl. Ed. B van Stokkom. Circ: 3,500.

364   USA
LAW ENFORCEMENT MANAGEMENT AND ADMINISTRATIVE STATISTICS (YEAR). Text in English. 1987. triennial. free. stat.; charts. back issues avail. **Document type:** *Government.* **Description:** Contains data on over 3,000 state and local law enforcement agencies, including all who employ 100 or more sworn officers, and a national representation of smaller agencies.
Related titles: Microfiche ed.; Online - full content ed.
Published by: U.S. Department of Justice, Bureau of Justice Statistics, 810 Seventh St, N W, 2nd Fl, Washington, DC 20531. TEL 202-307-0765, FAX 202-307-0128, askbjs@ojp.usdoj.gov, http://www.ojp.usdoj.gov/bjs/pubalp2.htm#L. Circ: 17,000. **Orders to:** BJS Clearinghouse, PO Box 179, Annapolis, MD 20701-0179. TEL 800-732-3277, FAX 410-729-4358.

364   USA
NATIONAL JUDICIAL REPORTING PROGRAM. Text in English. 1983. biennial. free. charts. back issues avail. **Document type:** *Government.* **Description:** Provides statistics on felony arrests in large urban counties with qualitative data on arrest decisions.
Formerly (until 1992): Prosecution of Felony Arrests (Year)
Related titles: Microfiche ed.
Published by: U.S. Department of Justice, Bureau of Justice Statistics, 810 Seventh St, N W, 2nd Fl, Washington, DC 20531. TEL 202-307-0765, FAX 202-307-0128, askbjs@ojp.usdoj.gov, http://www.ojp.usdoj.gov/bjs. Ed. Patrick Langan. Circ: 13,000. **Orders to:** BJS Clearinghouse, Box 179, Annapolis Junction, MD 20701-0179. TEL 800-732-3277, FAX 410-729-4358.

353.9   USA   ISSN 0094-1247
HV7571.N25
NEBRASKA. STATE PATROL. ANNUAL REPORT. Key Title: Annual Report - Nebraska State Patrol. Text in English. 197?. a. free. **Document type:** *Government.*
Published by: State Patrol, State House, Box 94907, Lincoln, NE 68509. TEL 402-471-4545. Circ: 75.

364   DEU
NEUE KRIMINOLOGISCHE LITERATUR/NEW CRIMINOLOGICAL LITERATURE/NOUVELLE LITTERATURE CRIMINOLOGIQUE/NUEVA LITERATURA CRIMINOLOGICA. Text in German. irreg. free. **Document type:** *Bibliography.*
Media: Online - full content. **Related titles:** CD-ROM ed.; Krimdok.
Published by: Universitaetsbibliothek Tuebingen, Schwerpunkt Kriminologie, Postfach 2620, Tuebingen, 72016, Germany. TEL 49-7071-2977844, FAX 49-7071-293123, kriminologie@ub.uni-tuebingen.de, http://www.ifk.jura.uni-tuebingen.de/krimdok/kd3query.html, http://www.uni-tuebingen.de/ub. Circ: 406.

364.021   AUS
NEW SOUTH WALES. ATTORNEY GENERAL'S DEPARTMENT. BUREAU OF CRIME STATISTICS AND RESEARCH. RESEARCH STUDIES. Text in English. 1982. irreg. **Document type:** *Academic/Scholarly.*
Formerly: New South Wales. Attorney-General Justice Department. Bureau of Crime Statistics and Research. Research Report
Published by: Attorney General's Department, Bureau of Crime Statistics and Research, GPO Box 6, Sydney, NSW 2000, Australia.

364   USA
NEW YORK (STATE). DIVISION OF CRIMINAL SERVICES. OFFICE OF JUSTICE SYSTEMS ANALYSIS. STATISTICAL INDICATOR BULLETIN. Text in English. 1987. irreg., latest vol.3, 1997. free. **Document type:** *Bulletin, Government.*
Former titles: New York (State). Division of Criminal Services. Office of Justice Systems Analysis. Criminal Justice Indicators Bulletin; New York (State). Division of Criminal Services. Office of Justice Systems Analysis. Bulletin

Published by: Division of Criminal Justice Services, Office of Justice Systems Analysis, Bureau of Statistical Services, Executive Park Tower, Stuyvesant Plaza, Albany, NY 12203. TEL 518-457-3724.

345 NOR ISSN 0809-0742
HA1501
NORWAY. STATISTISK SENTRALBYRAA. KRIMINALSTATISTIKK/STATISTICS NORWAY. CRIME STATISTICS. Text in English, Norwegian. 1997. a., latest 2000. **Document type:** *Government.*
Formed by the merger of (1980-1997): Norway. Statistisk Sentralbyraa. Kriminalstatistikk. Anmeldte og Etterforskede Lovbrudd (0807-5840); (1980-1997): Norway. Statistisk Sentralbyraa. Kriminalstatistikk. Straffereaksjoner og Fengslinger (0807-5832); Both of which superseded in part (in 1996): Norway. Statistisk Sentralbyraa. Kriminalstatistikk (0333-3914)
Related titles: Online - full text ed.; ♦ Series of: Norges Offisielle Statistikk. ISSN 0300-5585.
Published by: Statistisk Sentralbyraa/Statistics Norway, Kongensgate 6, Postboks 8131, Dep, Oslo, 0033, Norway. TEL 47-21-090000, FAX 47-21-094973, ssb@ssb.no, http://www.ssb.no/emner/03/05/nos_kriminal/.

365 310 USA ISSN 0031-4366
PENNSYLVANIA. BOARD OF PROBATION AND PAROLE. MONTHLY STATISTICAL REPORT. Text in English. 1942. m. free. stat. **Document type:** *Government.*
Incorporates: Pennsylvania. Board of Probation and Parole. Quarterly Statistical Report (0031-4374)
Media: Duplicated (not offset).
Published by: Pennsylvania Board of Probation and Parole, 1101 S Front St, Ste 5000, Harrisburg, PA 17104-2515. TEL 717-787-5699, http://www.pbpp.state.us. Circ: 205.

364 DEU ISSN 0943-4674
HV7349
POLIZEILICHE KRIMINALSTATISTIK BUNDESREPUBLIK DEUTSCHLAND (YEAR). Text in German; Summaries in English. 1953. a. **Document type:** *Government.* **Description:** Crime statistics of the police in Germany.
Formerly (until 1992): Germany. Bundeskriminalamt. Polizeiliche Kriminalstatistik (Year) (0431-5480)
Published by: Bundeskriminalamt, KI-12, Thaerstr 11, Wiesbaden, 65173, Germany. TEL 49-611-5516834, FAX 49-611-5516804, TELEX 4186867-BKA-D, uwe.doermann@bka.bund.de, http://www.bka.de/pks. Ed. Uwe Doermann. Circ: 3,200.

364 DEU ISSN 0171-2721
HV7349.S38
POLIZEILICHE KRIMINALSTATISTIK NIEDERSACHSEN MIT INFORMATIONEN AUS DEM LANDESKRIMINALAMT. Text in German. 1971. a. free. back issues avail. **Document type:** *Government.*
Published by: Landeskriminalamt Niedersachsen, Schuetzenstr 25, Hannover, 30161, Germany. TEL 49-511-330-0, FAX 49-511-3301250. Circ: 300.

364 DEU ISSN 0171-2802
POLIZEILICHE KRIMINALSTATISTIK NORDRHEIN-WESTFALEN. Text in German. 1958. a. free. **Document type:** *Government.* **Description:** Information and statistics on crime in the Nordrhein-Westphalia district of Germany.
Published by: Landeskriminalamt Nordrhein-Westfalen, Voelklingerstr 49, Duesseldorf, 40221, Germany. TEL 49-211-9396038, FAX 49-211-9396941.

PRESTUPLENIA I OSUDENI LITSA. see *STATISTICS*

362.8 USA
PROBATION AND PAROLE (YEAR). Text in English. 1976. a. free. back issues avail. **Document type:** *Bulletin, Government.* **Description:** Compiles statistics on the number of entries and exits of adults under probation or parole supervision for each state, including the District of Columbia. Also describes programs of adult and juvenile agencies nationwide and provides a demographic summary.
Formerly: Parole in the United States
Related titles: Online - full content ed.; Series of: U.S. Department of Justice. Bureau of Justice Statistics Reports. Corrections.
Published by: U.S. Department of Justice, Bureau of Justice Statistics, 810 Seventh St, N W, 2nd Fl, Washington, DC 20531. TEL 202-307-0765, FAX 202-307-0128, askbjs@ojp.usdoj.gov, http://www.ojp.usdoj.gov/bjs/pubalp2.htm#p. Circ: 25,000. **Subscr. to:** Bureau of Justice Statistics Clearinghouse, Box 179, Dept BJS C 1, Annapolis, MD 20701-0179. TEL 800-732-3277, FAX 410-792-4358.

364.1021 GBR ISSN 1350-441X
SCOTTISH OFFICE. STATISTICAL BULLETIN. CRIMINAL JUSTICE SERIES. Text in English. 1990. irreg. GBP 2. **Document type:** *Government.*
—BLDSC (8447.679402).
Published by: Scottish Office, New St Andrew's House, Rm 1-44, Edinburgh, Midlothian EH1 3TG, United Kingdom. TEL 0131-244-4806.

362.8 USA ISSN 0360-3431
HV7245
SOURCEBOOK OF CRIMINAL JUSTICE STATISTICS. Text in English. 1973. a. price varies. bibl.; charts. back issues avail. **Document type:** *Government.* **Description:** Presents a wide variety of criminal justice data on characteristics of the criminal justice system, public attitudes toward crime and enforcement, the nature and distribution of known offenses, demographics of persons arrested. Judicial processing of defendants, and persons under correctional supervision.
Related titles: CD-ROM ed.: 1998. USD 8.25 newsstand/cover domestic; USD 15 newsstand/cover elsewhere (effective 2001); Online - full content ed.
Indexed: CWI, RASB.
Published by: U.S. Department of Justice, Bureau of Justice Statistics, 810 Seventh St, N W, 2nd Fl, Washington, DC 20531. FAX 202-307-0128, askbjs@ojp.usdoj.gov, http://www.albany.edu/sourcebook/. Circ: 22,000. **Subscr. to:** Bernan Associates. TEL 800-274-4447, FAX 301-459-0056.

364.021 ZAF
SOUTH AFRICA. STATISTICS SOUTH AFRICA. VICTIMS OF CRIME SURVEY (YEAR). Text in English. irreg., latest 1998. Free. **Document type:** *Government.*
Published by: Statistics South Africa/Statistieke Suid-Afrika, Private Bag X44, Pretoria, 0001, South Africa. TEL 27-12-310-8911, FAX 27-12-310-8500, info@statssa.pwv.gov.za, http://www.statssa.gov.za.

364.021 USA ISSN 1075-3702
T E L E M A S P BULLETIN. (Texas Law Enforcement Management and Administrative Statistics Program) Text in English. 1994. m. USD 24 (effective 2002). **Document type:** *Trade.* **Description:** Distributes information about comparative administrative practices of law enforcement agencies throughout the state of Texas.
Related titles: Online - full text ed.: (from ProQuest Information & Learning).
Indexed: CJPI.
Published by: Law Enforcement Management Institute of Texas (Subsidiary of: Sam Houston State University), Sam Houston State University, Huntsville, TX 77341-2417. TEL 936-294-4600, FAX 936-294-3926, http://www.shsu.edu/~lemit.

362.8 USA
U.S. DEPARTMENT OF JUSTICE. BUREAU OF JUSTICE STATISTICS. CRIME AND JUSTICE DATA. Text in English. a. **Description:** Provides a statistical overview of criminal law enforcement and prison populations.
Media: CD-ROM.
Published by: (U.S. Bureau of Justice Statistics), Inter-University Consortium for Political and Social Research, PO Box 1248, Ann Arbor, MI 48106-1248. TEL 313-764-2570, 800-999-0960, FAX 313-764-8041, netmail@icpsr.umich.edu. **Orders to:** Justice Statistics Clearinghouse, National Criminal Justice Reference Service, Box 6000, Rockville, MD 20850. TEL 800-732-3277.

362.8 USA
HV7245
U.S. DEPARTMENT OF JUSTICE. BUREAU OF JUSTICE STATISTICS. CRIMINAL VICTIMIZATION. Text in English. 1973. a. free. stat.; charts. back issues avail. **Document type:** *Government.* **Description:** Contains detailed data on major variables measured by the National Crime Victimization Survey (NCVS).
Formerly (until 1995): Criminal Victimization in the United States (0095-5833)
Related titles: Microfiche ed.; Online - full content ed.: 1996; Supplement(s): National Crime Victimization Survey Report.
Published by: U.S. Department of Justice, Bureau of Justice Statistics, 810 Seventh St, N W, 2nd Fl, Washington, DC 20531. TEL 202-307-0765, askbjs@usdoj.gov, http://www.ojp.usdoj.gov/bjs/pubalp2.htm#C. Circ: 17,000. **Dist. by:** National Criminal Justice Reference Service, PO Box 6000, Rockville, MD 20849-6000.

364 USA ISSN 0360-9146
HV6793.M5
UNIFORM CRIME REPORT FOR THE STATE OF MICHIGAN. Text in English. 1973. a. illus.
Formerly: Michigan Law Enforcement Officials Report on Crime
Related titles: Microfiche ed.: (from CIS); Online - full text ed.
Indexed: SRI.
Published by: Department of State Police, 714 S Harrison Rd, East Lansing, MI 48823. TEL 517-332-2521, http://www.msp.state.mi.us.

364 USA
WISCONSIN CRIME AND ARRESTS (YEAR). Text in English. 1969. a. free. adv. index. **Document type:** *Government.* **Description:** Provides crime and arrest statistics for Wisconsin and each law enforcement agency in the state. Contains current statistics and depicts five- and ten-year trends.
Indexed: SRI.
Published by: Office of Justice Assistance, Statistical Analysis Center, 131 West Wilson, Ste 202, Madison, WI 53702. TEL 608-266-7644, FAX 608-266-6676, http://oja.state.wi.us. Ed. Thomas G Eversen. Pub., R&P, Adv. contact Thomas G Everson. Circ: 800.

365 USA
WISCONSIN. DIVISION OF CORRECTIONS. OFFICE OF INFORMATION MANAGEMENT. ADMISSIONS TO JUVENILE INSTITUTIONS. Text in English. 1972. a. stat.
Media: Duplicated (not offset).
Published by: Division of Corrections, Office of Information Management, PO Box 7925, Madison, WI 53707. TEL 608-266-2471.

365 USA
WISCONSIN. DIVISION OF CORRECTIONS. OFFICE OF INFORMATION MANAGEMENT. RELEASES FROM JUVENILE INSTITUTIONS. Text in English. 1972. a. stat.
Formerly: Wisconsin. Division of Corrections. Bureau of Planning, Development and Research. Releases from Juvenile Institutions (0362-7470)
Media: Duplicated (not offset).
Published by: Division of Corrections, Office of Information Management, PO Box 7925, Madison, WI 53707. TEL 608-266-2471.

CRIMINOLOGY AND LAW ENFORCEMENT—Computer Applications

345.052 USA
TECH BEAT; law enforcement technology news. Text in English. 1995. q.
Media: Online - full text.
Published by: National Law Enforcement and Corrections Technology Center, PO Box 1160, Rockville, MD 20849-1160. dengler@nlectc.org, http://www.nlectc.org. Ed. Donna Engler.

345.052 USA
TECH CONNECTION. Text in English. 1997. irreg.
Related titles: Online - full text ed.
Published by: National Law Enforcement and Corrections Technology Center, PO Box 1160, Rockville, MD 20849-1160. dengler@nlectc.org, http://www.nlectc.org. Ed. Donna Engler.

C

CRIMINOLOGY AND LAW ENFORCEMENT—Security

see also COMPUTERS—Computer Security

A C M WORKSHOP ON PRIVACY IN THE ELECTRONIC SOCIETY. PROCEEDINGS. see *LAW—Constitutional Law*

A S I S SECURITY INDUSTRY BUYERS GUIDE. see *BUSINESS AND ECONOMICS—Trade And Industrial Directories*

363.22 690 USA
ACCESS CONTROL & SECURITY SYSTEMS. Text in English. 1957. m. (plus a. Buyer's Guide). USD 60 domestic; USD 180 foreign (effective 2005). adv. charts; illus.; tr.lit. index. reprint service avail. from PQC. **Document type:** *Magazine, Trade.* **Description:** Provides information to access control dealers and installers, security managers, architects and specifiers. Includes installation case histories, product overviews, consultants' articles and trade literature covering access control and fencing equipment, and alarm and sensor systems.
Former titles: Access Control & Security Systems Integration (1084-6425); (until 1995): Access Control (1042-2617); (until 1988): Access Control - Fence Industry (0894-6639); (until 1987): Fence Industry - Access Control (0885-8411); Fence Industry Trade News (0014-9977)
Related titles: Microform ed.; Online - full text ed.: (from Gale Group, H.W. Wilson, LexisNexis, O C L C Online Computer Library Center, Inc.).
Indexed: BPI.
—CCC.
Published by: Primedia Business Magazines & Media, Inc. (Subsidiary of: Primedia, Inc.), 6151 Powers Ferry Rd Ste 200, Atlanta, GA 30339. TEL 770-955-2500, FAX 770-618-0204, landerson@primediabusiness.com, inquiries@primediabusiness.com, http://www.securitysolutions.com/, http://www.primediabusiness.com. Ed. Larry Anderson. adv.: B&W page USD 5,525, color page USD 6,890. Circ: 39,000 (paid).

365.64 BHR
AFAQ AMNIYA/SECURITY OUTLOOK. Text in Arabic. 1983. m.
Published by: Ministry of the Interior, Police Fort Compound, PO Box 13, Manama, Bahrain. TEL 254021, TELEX 8333.

AIRPORT SAFETY - SECURITY - SERVICE. see *TRANSPORTATION—Air Transport*

365.34 NOR ISSN 0808-6567
AKTUELL SIKKERHET. Text in Norwegian. 1997. 6/yr. NOK 390 domestic; NOK 420 foreign (effective 2005). adv. **Document type:** *Magazine, Trade.*
Published by: Vanebo Fagpresse AS, PO Box 130, Kirkenaer, 2260, Norway. TEL 47-62-941000, FAX 47-62-941010, firmapost@vanebo.no, http://www.vanebo.no. Ed. Jan Tveita TEL 47-62-829101. Adv. contact Rolf Goplen. B&W page NOK 12,500, color page NOK 16,500; 190 x 265. Circ: 8,416.

▼ new title ➤ refereed ✶ unverified ♦ full entry avail.

621.389 FRA ISSN 0290-0106
ALARMES - PROTECTION - SECURITE. Text in French. bi-m. adv. **Document type:** *Trade.*
Formerly: Alarmes Protection Vol (0240-8155)
Address: 70 rue Rivay, Levallois-Perret, Cedex 92532, France. TEL 33-1-47565089, FAX 33-1-47565227, TELEX 250 303. Ed. Jean Francois Sol Dourdin. Pub. Delphine Caillot. Adv. contact Caroline Debrito. Circ: 6,000.

365.64 UAE
AL-AMN/SECURITY. Text in Arabic. 1975. m.
Published by: General Directorate of Police, Public Relations, P O Box 1493, Dubai, United Arab Emirates. TEL 291279, FAX 662219. Circ: 1,000.

365.34 GBR ISSN 1479-9855
▼ **ASIAN SECURITY.** Text in English. 2005 (Jan.). 3/yr. GBP 190, USD 282 combined subscription to institutions print & online eds. (effective 2006). **Document type:** *Journal, Academic/Scholarly.* **Description:** Covers all aspects of national and international security in Asia like interstate warfare, the regional balance of power, alliances and other multilateral security institutions, national defense policies, strategic culture, civil-military relations, nuclear proliferation, conventional arms racing, arms control, conflict-prone areas, the stability of democratic transitions, globalization and its backlash, ethnic conflict, insurgency and counterinsurgency, failing states, and transnational terrorism.
Related titles: Online - full text ed.: ISSN 1555-2764. GBP 181, USD 268 to institutions (effective 2006) (from EBSCO Publishing).
Published by: Routledge (Subsidiary of: Taylor & Francis Group), 4 Park Sq, Milton Park, Abingdon, Oxon OX14 4RN, United Kingdom. TEL 44-1235-828600, FAX 44-1235-829000, info@routledge.co.uk, http://www.tandf.co.uk/journals/titles/14799855.asp, http://www.routledge.com. Ed. Sumit Ganguly.

365.64 HKG ISSN 0259-059X
ASIAN SECURITY & SAFETY JOURNAL. Text in Chinese. 1984. 6/yr. USD 28 domestic; USD 35 foreign. bk.rev. **Description:** Introduces new security, fire protection and industrial safety products and services and provides professional advice to installers, practitioners, and endusers.
Published by: Elgin Consultants Ltd., Crawford Tower 18th Fl Ste. B, 99 Jervois St, Sheung Wan, Hong Kong, Hong Kong. TEL 852-815-1680, FAX 852-815-1706, security@netrigator.com. Ed., Pub., R&P, Adv. contact David Slough. Circ: 12,000.

365.34 338.025 HKG
ASIAN SOURCES SECURITY PRODUCTS. Text in English. 1995. m. USD 60. **Document type:** *Trade.* **Description:** Covers home, auto and personal security products.
Indexed: HongKongiana.
Published by: Asian Sources Media Group, GPO Box 12367, Hong Kong, Hong Kong. TEL 852-2555-4777, asmgroup@singnet.com.sg. Ed. Spenser Au. **Subscr. to:** Wordright Enterprises Inc., PO Box 3062, Evanston, IL 60204-3062. TEL 708-475-1900.

AUERBACH DATA SECURITY MANAGEMENT. see *COMPUTERS—Computer Security*

AUSTRALIA. BUREAU OF STATISTICS. NEW SOUTH WALES OFFICE. HOME SECURITY PRECAUTIONS, NEW SOUTH WALES. see *CRIMINOLOGY AND LAW ENFORCEMENT—Abstracting, Bibliographies, Statistics*

AUSTRALIA. BUREAU OF STATISTICS. SECURITY SERVICES, AUSTRALIA. see *CRIMINOLOGY AND LAW ENFORCEMENT—Abstracting, Bibliographies, Statistics*

BAILRIGG MEMORANDA. see *POLITICAL SCIENCE—International Relations*

BAILRIGG PAPERS ON INTERNATIONAL SECURITY. see *POLITICAL SCIENCE—International Relations*

363 NLD ISSN 0926-7859
BEVEILIGING; onafhankelijk vakblad voor de beveiligingsector. Text in Dutch. 1988. m. EUR 99.50 domestic; EUR 124.50 foreign; EUR 37.50 to students; EUR 10.50 newsstand/cover (effective 2005). adv. **Document type:** *Journal, Trade.*
—IE, Infotrieve.
Published by: Prosper Business Media, Postbus 12936, Amsterdam, 1100 AX, Netherlands. TEL 31-20-3122070, FAX 31-20-3122080, info@beveiliging.nl, http://www.beveiliging.nl. Ed. Vincent Vreeken. Circ: 5,500.

365.34 NLD ISSN 0923-053X
BEVEILIGINGS JAARBOEK. Text in Dutch. 1983. a.
—IE, Infotrieve.
Published by: Uitgeverij Noorduijn bv, Postbus 23, Deventer, 7400 GA, Netherlands. TEL 31-570-647111, FAX 31-570-634740. Ed. T Boot.

BIOMETRIC TECHNOLOGY TODAY. see *ELECTRONICS*

364.4 CAN
C A N A S A NEWSLETTER✶. (Canadian Alarm & Security Association) Text in English. q. free to members. adv. **Document type:** *Newsletter.* **Description:** Provides information on the latest technologies, products and legislation in the electronic security industry and chapter news.
Formerly: C A N A S A British Columbia Chapter Bulletin
Published by: Canadian Alarm & Security Association, B.C. Chapter, 700555 West Hastings St, Vancouver, BC V6B 4NJ, Canada. TEL 604-986-1829, FAX 604-9861448. Ed. Norm Cheesman. R&P, Adv. contact Shayla Gunter.

365.34 330 DEU ISSN 0947-871X
C D SICHERHEITS-MANAGEMENT. (Criminal Digest) Text in German. 1976. bi-m. EUR 54 domestic; EUR 57 foreign; EUR 11.50 newsstand/cover (effective 2004). adv. bk.rev. back issues avail. **Document type:** *Magazine, Trade.*
Former titles (until 1994): Criminal Digest (0933-0186); (until 1987): Polizei-Digest (0720-8332)
Published by: Richard Boorberg Verlag GmbH und Co. KG, Scharrstr 2, Stuttgart, 70563, Germany. TEL 49-711-73850, FAX 49-711-7385100, mail@boorberg.de, http://www.boorberg.de. Ed., Adv. contact Helmut Brueckmann. B&W page EUR 1,915, color page EUR 3,145; trim 125 x 180. Circ: 9,777 (controlled).

352.379 USA ISSN 1540-904X
HV8290
C S O. (Chief Security Officer) Text in English. 2002 (Sep.). m. USD 70 in US & Canada; USD 95 elsewhere; free to qualified personnel (effective 2005). **Document type:** *Magazine, Trade.*
Related titles: Online - full text ed.
Published by: C X O Media Inc. (Subsidiary of: I D G Communications Inc.), 492 Old Connecticut Path, PO Box 9208, Framingham, MA 01701-9208. http://www.csoonline.com/, http://www.cxo.com/. Ed. Lew McCreary.

352.379 FRA ISSN 1765-1336
▼ **C S O (FRANCE).** (Chief Security Officer) Text in French. 2003. bi-m. **Document type:** *Magazine, Trade.*
Published by: I D G Communications France, 5 rue Chantecoq, Puteaux, 92808, France. TEL 33-1-4197-6161, FAX 33-1-4197-6160, http://www.idg.fr.

327.12 FRA ISSN 1150-1634
CAHIERS DE LA SECURITE INTERIEURE. Text in French. 4/yr. EUR 57.50 domestic; EUR 59 in the European Union; EUR 63 DOM-TOM; EUR 66 elsewhere (effective 2003). **Document type:** *Government.* **Description:** Seeks a better understanding of security problems.
Related titles: Microfiche ed.
Indexed: AC&P, CJA.
Published by: (Institut des Hautes Etudes de la Securite Interieure), Documentation Francaise, 29-31 quai Voltaire, Paris, Cedex 7 75344, France. FAX 33-1-40157230.

CAMPUS CRIME. see *EDUCATION—Higher Education*

363.119378 USA ISSN 1055-4319
LB2866
CAMPUS SECURITY REPORT. Text in English. 1990. m. looseleaf. USD 185 (effective 2006). 16 p./no.; back issues avail.; reprints avail. **Document type:** *Newsletter, Trade.*
Related titles: Online - full content ed.
—CCC.
Published by: L R P Publications, 747 Dresher Rd, PO Box 980, Horsham, PA 19044. TEL 215-784-0860, 800-341-7874, FAX 215-784-9639, custserve@lrp.com, http://www.shoplrp.com/product/p-31100.html, http://www.lrp.com. Circ: 680 (paid and controlled).

364.4 CAN ISSN 0709-3403
CANADIAN SECURITY; journal of protection and communications. Text in English. 1979. 9/yr. CND 40 domestic; USD 60 in United States; USD 75 elsewhere (effective 2005). adv. bk.rev. **Document type:** *Magazine, Trade.* **Description:** For Canadian protection and communications professionals.
Published by: C L B Media, Inc. (Subsidiary of: Canada Law Book Inc.), 240 Edward St, Aurora, ON L4G 3S9, Canada. TEL 905-727-0077, FAX 905-727-0017, mneeb@clbmedia.ca, fshoniker@clbmedia.ca, http://www.canadiansecuritymag.com, http://www.clbmedia.ca. Circ: 14,000.

CARD TECHNOLOGY TODAY. see *ELECTRONICS*

CHIEFS OF STATE AND CABINET MEMBERS OF FOREIGN GOVERNMENTS. see *POLITICAL SCIENCE—International Relations*

COMPUTER FRAUD & SECURITY. see *COMPUTERS—Computer Security*

COMPUTER SECURITY, DEPENDABILITY AND ASSURANCE. see *COMPUTERS—Computer Security*

COMPUTER SECURITY JOURNAL. see *COMPUTERS—Computer Security*

COMPUTERS & SECURITY. see *COMPUTERS—Computer Security*

COMPUTING & COMMUNICATIONS: LAW & PROTECTION REPORT. see *COMPUTERS—Computer Security*

636.22 346 USA ISSN 0897-4101
KF9351.A15
CORPORATE CRIME REPORTER. Text in English. 1987. 48/yr. looseleaf. USD 795 to institutions; USD 595 to non-profit organizations (effective 2005). index. back issues avail. **Document type:** *Newsletter, Trade.*
Published by: Washington Crime News Services, 1209 National Press Bldg, 529 14th St, N W, Ste 9, Washington, DC 22045-0001. TEL 202-737-1680, russell@corporatecrimereporter.com, nvanwyen@washingtoncrime.com, http://www.corporatecrimereporter.com.

364.4 USA ISSN 1040-4201
HV8290
CORPORATE SECURITY. Text in English. 1975. bi-w. looseleaf. USD 330 (effective 2005). index. reprints avail. **Document type:** *Newsletter, Corporate.* **Description:** Updates on security law without all the legal jargon.
Incorporates (in 1995): Security Technology News (1068-8374); Incorporates: Corporate Security's Technology Alert; Formerly (until 1981): Protection Management (0048-5624)
Related titles: Microform ed.: 1975 (from PQC); Online - full text ed.: 1975 (from LexisNexis).
Indexed: CJPI.
—CCC.
Published by: Strafford Publications, Inc., 590 Dutch Valley Rd, N E, Postal Drawer 13729, Atlanta, GA 30324-0729. TEL 404-881-1141, FAX 404-881-0074, editors@straffordpub.com, http://www.straffordpub.com. Ed. Jon McKenna.

365.34 GBR ISSN 1361-875X
CROSS BORDER CONTROL INTERNATIONAL. Text in English. 1996. bi-m. GBP 32; GBP 8 newsstand/cover (effective 1999). adv. **Document type:** *Magazine, Consumer.*
Published by: Archant Specialist Ltd. (Subsidiary of: Archant), The Mill, Bearwalden Business Park, Royston Rd, Wendens Ambo, Essex CB11 4GB, United Kingdom. TEL 44-1799-544200, subscribe@marketlink.co.uk, farine.clarke@archant.co.uk, http://www.archant.co.uk/. Ed. Bernadette Faurie.

364.4 ESP ISSN 1698-4269
CUADERNOS DE SEGURIDAD. Text in Spanish. 1988. 11/yr. adv. bk.rev. **Document type:** *Monographic series.*
Published by: Estudios Tecnicos S.A., Antonio Lopez, 249 - 1(UNKNOWN CHARACTER) planta, Madrid, 28041, Spain. TEL 34-91-500-1724, FAX 34-91-500-2281, cuadernos@getseguridad.com, http://www.cuadernosdeseguridad.com. Ed., R&P Manuel Sanchez Gomez-Merelo. Adv. contact Adolfo Castano Megia. color page EUR 1,520; trim 210 x 280. Circ: 4,000 (controlled).

DATA SECURITY LETTER. see *COMPUTERS—Computer Security*

621.3 ZAF
ELECTRONIC SECURITY SOLUTIONS BUYER'S GUIDE. Text in English. 1997. a. adv. **Document type:** *Trade.* **Description:** Offers advice on purchasing security systems.
Formerly: Electronic Security Systems Buyer's Guide
Published by: Technews (Pty.) Ltd., PO Box 626, Kloof, 3640, South Africa. TEL 27-31-764-0593, FAX 27-31-764-0386, technews@iafrica.com, technews@iafrica.com.za. Pub. Kevin Beaumont. Adv. contact Vivian Dorrington TEL 27-11-886-3640.

365.34 USA ISSN 0894-2080
EMPLOYEE SECURITY CONNECTION. Text in English. 1987. q. USD 695 (effective 2001). **Document type:** *Newsletter, Trade.* **Description:** Publishes security awareness information for corporate employees.
Related titles: Online - full content ed.
Published by: National Security Institute, 116 Main St, Ste 200, Medway, MA 02053. TEL 508-533-9099, FAX 508-533-3761, infoctr@nsi.org, http://nsi.org/.

365 FRA
ERGONOMIE, HYGIENE ET SECURITE. Text in French. 4/yr.
Published by: Editions d' Ergonomie, 48 rue Raphael, BP 138, Marseille, Cedex 8 13267, France. TEL 91-22-17-25, FAX 91-71-00-10. Ed. Charles P Bernard. Circ: 9,500.

364.4 ITA ISSN 0394-8625
ESSECOME. Text in Italian. 1981. m. (11/yr.). USD 75 (effective 1998). adv. bk.rev. **Document type:** *Magazine, Trade.* **Description:** Deals with security technology, applications and problems.
Formerly: Selezione Sicurezze
Published by: E D I S Edizioni Specializzate Srl, Via Pietro Miliani 7, Bologna, BO 40132, Italy. TEL 39-051-6419611, FAX 39-051-6419620, redazione.edis@securindex.com, http://www.securindex.com. Ed. Andrea Sandrolini. Adv. contact Carolina Pattuelli. Circ: 10,800.

364.4 ITA
ESSECOME INTERNATIONAL. Text in English. 1990. 6/yr. USD 145 (effective 1998). adv. **Document type:** *Magazine, Trade.*
Published by: E D I S Edizioni Specializzate Srl, Via Pietro Miliani 7, Bologna, BO 40132, Italy. TEL 39-051-6419611, FAX 39-051-6419620, redazione.edis@securindex.com, http://www.securindex.com. Ed. Andrea Sandrolini. Adv. contact Carolina Pattuelli. Circ: 6,800.

365.34 USA ISSN 1081-2717
FAXNEWZ. Text in English. 1992. w. free. tr.lit. back issues avail. **Document type:** *Trade.* **Description:** Covers human resources, security and risk issues; provides information for managers concerned with all aspects of negligent hiring.
Media: Online - full text. **Related titles:** Fax ed.
Published by: Integrity Center, Inc., 2828 Forest Ln, Ste 1008, Dallas, TX 75234. TEL 972-484-6140, FAX 972-484-6381, service@integctr.com, http://www.integctr.com. Pub. Dr. John J Allan III. R&P John Allan.

363.2 020 069 USA ISSN 1071-9997
Z679.6
FOCUS ON SECURITY; the magazine of library, archive and museum security. Text and summaries in English. 1993. q. USD 70 (effective 2004). bk.rev.; video rev.; Website rev. illus.; stat.; bibl. back issues avail. **Document type:** *Journal.* **Description:** Features articles on emergency planning, policies and procedures, personnel hiring and training, personal security, and theft notices. Written for directors, security managers, and staff.
Published by: The Triad Company, 401 Pintail Ln, Moscow, ID 83843-8200. TEL 208-883-0817, FAX 208-883-5353, focus@turbonet.com. Ed., Pub., R&P Eileen E Brady. Circ: 102.

365.64 ITA
FORCESICUREZZA. Text in Italian. 1986. m. USD 107 (effective 1995). adv. **Document type:** *Trade.* **Description:** Covers the security industry and technology and operational aspects of crime fighting.
Formerly: Force (1120-1673)
Related titles: Special ed(s).: La Sicurezza in Italia.
Published by: Publi & Consult SpA, Via Tagliamento, 29, Rome, RM 00198, Italy. TEL 39-6-8543267, FAX 39-6-85350021. Adv. contact Claudia Severini. B&W page USD 2,040, color page USD 3,250; trim 275 x 185.

364.4 ESP ISSN 1130-9148
FORMACION DE SEGURIDAD. Text in Spanish. 1988. 4/yr.
Address: D. Ramon de la Cruz 68, 6o, Madrid, 28001, Spain. TEL 1-40-296-19, FAX 1-401-88-74. Ed. Francisco J B Marti. Circ: 12,000.

364.1 USA ISSN 1553-6645
HV6769
FRAUD MAGAZINE. Text in English. 1987. bi-m. USD 55 domestic to non-members; USD 75 foreign to non-members; free to members (effective 2005). adv. **Document type:** *Magazine, Trade.* **Description:** Presents technical articles on a variety of issues related to the detection and deterrence of white-collar crime. Includes case studies of actual fraud schemes, columns, departments, and news articles on fraud to increase the knowledge of auditing and security practitioners.
Formerly (until 2004): The White Paper (1097-8216)
Published by: Association of Certified Fraud Examiners, 716 West Ave, Austin, TX 78701. TEL 512-478-9070, 800-245-3321, FAX 512-478-9297, FraudMagazine@CFEnet.com, dick@cfenet.com, http://marketplace.cfenet.com/products/ProductDetail.asp?CatID=100089, http://www.cfenet.com. Ed. Dick Carozza. Pub. Kathie Green. Adv. contact Glenn Garrett. B&W page USD 1,210, color page USD 1,525; trim 8.375 x 10.875. Circ: 30,000 (paid).

FRONTERA NORTE SUR. see *POLITICAL SCIENCE—International Relations*

364 GBR ISSN 1475-9330
G S R - GLOBAL SECURITY REVIEW/INTERNATIONALE ZEITSCHRIFT FUR SCHUTZ UND SICHERHEIT/REVISTA INTERNACIONAL DE LA SEGURIDAD/REVUE INTERNATIONALE DE LA SURETE ET DE LA SECURITE. Text in English, French, German, Spanish. 1978. bi-m. GBP 110 foreign; GBP 80 domestic; GBP 25 per issue (effective 2002). **Document type:** *Trade.* **Description:** Serves the commercial and industrial security market.
Formerly (until 2001): International Security Review (0141-8017); Incorporates (in 1991): Security Times (0265-6442)
Related titles: Online - full text ed.: (from EBSCO Publishing).
Indexed: ABS&EES, DM&T, RefZh.
—BLDSC (4223.831500), IE, ingenta.
Published by: Pro-Activ Publications Ltd., 3 High St, Chislehurst, Kent BR7 5AB, United Kingdom. TEL 44-20-8295-1414, FAX 44-20-8295-1401, editorial@globalsecurityreview.com, http://www.globalsecurityreview.com. Ed. Pete Conway TEL 44-20-8295-8370. Adv. contact Graeme Tucker TEL 44-20-8295-8360.

638.5 669 ITA
GIORNALE DEL FABBRO E DEL SERRAMENTISTA. Text in Italian. 12/yr.
Address: Via Toce, 4, Varese, VA 21100, Italy. TEL 332-224-068, FAX 332-212-312. Ed. Franco Diari. Circ: 8,000.

365.34 GBR
▼ **GLOBAL FACILITATION NETWORK FOR SECURITY SECTOR REFORM. NEWSLETTER.** Text in English. 2003. bi-m. **Document type:** *Newsletter, Academic/Scholarly.*
Media: E-mail. **Related titles:** Online - full content ed.; French ed.; Spanish ed.; Portuguese ed.
Published by: Global Facilitation Network for Security Sector Reform, Rm 247, Wellington Hall, Cranfield University, Shrivenham, SN6 8LA, United Kingdom. TEL 44-1793-785020, FAX 44-1793-782179, gfn-enquiries@gfn-ssr.org, http://www.gfn-ssr.org/newsletter.cfm, http://www.gfn-ssr.org/home.cfm.

365.34 USA ISSN 1544-1687
UA927
GOVERNMENT SECURITY; technology solutions in defense of the homeland. Text in English. 2002. m. free to qualified personnel. **Document type:** *Magazine, Trade.*
Related titles: Online - full text ed.: (from bigchalk, Gale Group).
—**CCC.**
Published by: Primedia Business Magazines & Media, Inc. (Subsidiary of: Primedia, Inc.), 6151 Powers Ferry Rd Ste 200, Atlanta, GA 30339. TEL 770-955-2500, FAX 770-618-0204, inquiries@primediabusiness.com, http://govtsecurity.securitysolutions.com/, http://www.primediabusiness.com.

364.4 658.3 USA ISSN 0897-3156
JK2445.P82
THE GUIDE TO BACKGROUND INVESTIGATIONS; a comprehensive source directory for employee screening and background investigations. Text in English. 1987. irreg., latest 2000, 9th ed. USD 187 (effective 1999 & 2000). adv. **Document type:** *Directory.* **Description:** Lists sources for obtaining public records to use in background searches.
Related titles: CD-ROM ed.
Published by: Total Information Services Inc. (T I S I), 4500 S 129th E Ave, Ste 200, Tulsa, OK 74134. TEL 918-664-8799, 800-247-8713, FAX 918-664-8313, comments@usetheguide.com, http://www.usetheguide.com. R&P Toni Barton. Adv. contact Victoria Burge.

GUIDE TO HEALTH DATA SECURITY. see *MEDICAL SCIENCES—Computer Applications*

HEALTHCARE DATA SECURITY MANUAL. see *HEALTH FACILITIES AND ADMINISTRATION*

621.3 ZAF
HI-TECH SECURITY SOLUTIONS SOUTH AFRICA. Text in English. 1995. m. ZAR 90 (effective 2001). adv. bk.rev. illus. back issues avail. **Document type:** *Magazine, Trade.* **Description:** Addresses professional and business personnel concerned with the design, installation, operation and end use of advanced-technology electronic security devices.
Former titles: Hi-Tech Security Systems South Africa (1562-9511); Electronic Security Systems South Africa
Related titles: Online - full text ed.
Indexed: ISAP.
Published by: Technews (Pty.) Ltd., PO Box 626, Kloof, 3640, South Africa. TEL 27-31-764-0593, FAX 27-31-764-0386, technews@iafrica.com.za, http://www.technews.co.za. Pub. Kevin Beaumont. Adv. contact Vivian Dorrington TEL 27-11-886-3640. B&W page ZAR 4,515, color page ZAR 6,125; 180 x 260. Circ: 4,400.

HOME TECHNOLOGY PRODUCTS. see *ELECTRONICS*

365.34 USA ISSN 1556-0031
HOMELAND PROTECTION PROFESSIONAL; coordinating domestic preparedness. Text in English. 2002 (Jul.). 10/yr. adv. **Document type:** *Magazine, Trade.* **Description:** Created to assist the American emergency response community in preparing for and responding to acts of domestic terrorism.
Address: 4057 Forest Ave., Western Springs, IL 60558. TEL 708-246-2525, FAX 708-246-4152, editor@hppmag.com, tony@hppmag.com, http://www.hppmag.com. Ed. Scott Baltic TEL 773-275-7898. Pub., Adv. contact Anthony J. Parrino. B&W page USD 3,200, color page USD 4,050; trim 8.125 x 10.875.

▼ **HOMELAND SECURITY BUYERS GUIDE.** see *BUSINESS AND ECONOMICS—Trade And Industrial Directories*

▼ **HOMELAND SECURITY FUNDING WEEK.** see *PUBLIC ADMINISTRATION*

353.9 364.4 USA ISSN 1551-3327
HV6432
▼ **HOMELAND SECURITY SOLUTIONS.** Text in English. 2003. bi-m. free to qualified personnel (effective 2004). **Document type:** *Magazine, Trade.*
Published by: PennWell Corp., 98 Spit Brook Rd, Nashua, NH 03062-5737. TEL 603-891-0123, 800-331-4463, FAX 603-891-9177, 603-891-9146, http://www.homelandsecuritysolutions.com/, http://www.pennwell.com. Ed. John McHale TEL 603-891-9119. Pub. Ron Mastro TEL 603-891-9323.

364.34 USA
HOMELAND SECURITY WEEKLY. Text in English. 2000. w. free (effective 2003).
Media: Online - full text.
Published by: Two Tigers Radiological, PO Box 1333, Carolina Beach, NC 28428. TEL 910-458-0690, info@twotigersonline.com, http://www.twotigersonline.com/lastissue.html. Ed. Steven Aukstakalnis. Circ: 140,000.

364.4 USA ISSN 0745-1148
HOSPITAL SECURITY AND SAFETY MANAGEMENT. Text in English. 1980. m. USD 249 domestic; USD 274 foreign (effective 2005). tr.lit. back issues avail.; reprints avail. **Document type:** *Newsletter, Trade.* **Description:** Newsletter on hospital security and safety management for security directors at hospitals and medical centers.
Indexed: INI, MEDLINE.
—**CCC.**
Published by: Rusting Publications, PO Box 604550, Bayside, NY 11360-4550. TEL 718-423-5111, 800-341-7874, custserv@rustingpubs.com, rustingpubs@aol.com, http://www.rustingpubs.com. Eds. Robert R Rusting, Susan Krivin. Circ: 1,200.

365.34 USA
HOTEL/CASINO/RESORT SECURITY. Text in English. 1982. m. USD 249 domestic; USD 274 elsewhere (effective 2004). **Document type:** *Newsletter, Trade.*
Published by: Rusting Publications, PO Box 604550, Bayside, NY 11360-4550. TEL 718-423-5111, FAX 718-423-5112, rustingpubs@aol.com, http://www.rustingpubs.com. Ed. Robert R. Rusting. Circ: 550 (paid).

I E E E SYMPOSIUM ON SECURITY AND PRIVACY. PROCEEDINGS. see *COMPUTERS—Computer Security*

I O M A'S SECURITY DIRECTOR'S REPORT. see *COMMUNICATIONS—Television And Cable*

365.34 020 CHE
➤ **INFORMATION & SECURITY/INFORMATSIYA I BEZOPASNOST'/INFORMATSIYA I SIGURNOST**; an international journal. Text in English. q. USD 68 (effective 2004). **Document type:** *Journal, Academic/Scholarly.* **Description:** Publishes articles on scientific and technical issues related to national and international security in the Information Age, information operations, information warfare, command and control warfare, critical information technologies, computer aided exercises, simulators, and information security.
Related titles: Online - full content ed.
—BLDSC (4481.862000).
Published by: (Information & Security BGR), International Relations and Security Network, c/o Center for Security Studies, ETH Zentrum LEH, Zurich, 8092, Switzerland. TEL 41-1-6320757, FAX 41-1-6321413, infosec@mbox.digsys.bg, isn@sipo.gess.ethz.ch, http://www.isn.ethz.ch/researchpub/publihouse/infosecurity. Ed. Dr. Todor Tagarev.

352.379 USA ISSN 1543-5407
▼ **INFORMATION PLUS REFERENCE SERIES. NATIONAL SECURITY.** Variant title: National Security (Farmington Hills). Text in English. 2003. biennial, latest 2003. USD 40 per issue (effective 2005). **Document type:** *Monographic series, Academic/Scholarly.*
Related titles: Online - full content ed.; ♦ Series of: Information Plus Reference Series.
Published by: Gale Group (Subsidiary of: Thomson Corporation), 27500 Drake Rd, Farmington Hills, MI 48331-3535. TEL 248-699-4253, 800-877-4253, FAX 248-699-8035, 800-414-5043, galeord@gale.com.

016.36534 RUS
INFORMATSIONNYI BYULLETEN'. BOR'BA S PRESTUPNOSTYU ZA RUBEZHOM. Text in Russian. 1996. 12/yr. USD 88 foreign (effective 2005). **Document type:** *Journal, Abstract/Index.*
Published by: Vserossiiskii Institut Nauchnoi i Tekhnicheskoi Informatsii (VINITI), Ul Usievicha 20, Moscow, 125190, Russian Federation. TEL 7-095-1526441, FAX 7-095-9430060, dir@viniti.ru, http://www.viniti.ru. **Dist. by:** Informnauka Ltd., Ul Usievicha 20, Moscow 125190, Russian Federation. alfimov@viniti.ru.

INFORMATSIONNYI BYULLETEN'. INOSTRANNAYA PECHAT' O TEKHNICHESKOM OSNASHCHENII POLITSII ZARUBEZHNYKH GOSUDARSTV. see *CRIMINOLOGY AND LAW ENFORCEMENT—Abstracting, Bibliographies, Statistics*

364.4 USA
INTELLIGENCE PROFESSION SERIES. Text in English. irreg. USD 11.95 per issue. **Document type:** *Monographic series.*

C

▼ new title ➤ refereed ✶ unverified ♦ full entry avail.

Published by: Association of Former Intelligence Officers, 6723 Whittier Ave, Ste, 303A, Mclean, VA 22101. TEL 707-790-0320.

621.389   USA   ISSN 1071-6572
INTERNATIONAL CARNAHAN CONFERENCE OF SECURITY TECHNOLOGY. PROCEEDINGS. Text in English. 1983. a. **Document type:** *Proceedings.* **Description:** Conference sponsored by a number of international organizations that have a sincere interest in creating an open forum for the exchange of information related to security technology.
Published by: (Institute of Electrical and Electronics Engineers, Lexington Section), O E S Publications, Office of Engineering Services, University of Kentucky, Lexington, KY 40506-0046. TEL 606-257-3343, FAX 606-257-3342. **Co-sponsors:** Institute of Electrical and Electronics Engineers, Lexington Section; I E E E Aerospace and Electronic Systems Society.

364.4   GBR   ISSN 1470-6784
INTERNATIONAL POLICING TECHNOLOGY. Text in English. 1994. q. **Document type:** *Trade.*
Former titles (until 1999): European Police and Government Security Technology (1460-8820); (until 1998): Police and Government Security Technology (1355-6479)
—BLDSC (4544.956850), ingenta.
Published by: Redmund Russell Partnership Ltd, 11 Bryanston Mews E, London, W1H 7FH, United Kingdom. TEL 44-20-7724-0085, FAX 44-20-7258-1646, info@redruss.com, http://www.redruss.com.

INTERNATIONALES WAFFEN-MAGAZIN. see *SPORTS AND GAMES*

364.4   GBR   ISSN 0963-0058
INTERSEC; the journal of international security. Text in English. 1991. 10/yr., latest vol.12, 2001. EUR 78 in Europe; USD 145 in US & Canada; GBP 97, USD 160 rest of world (effective 2001). adv. bk.rev. back issues avail. **Document type:** *Trade.* **Description:** Covers risk assessment, drug detection, international policing issues, fraud, computer and communications security.
—CCC.
Published by: Intersec Publishing Ltd., Bridge House, Aviary Rd, Pyrford, Woking, Surrey GU22 8TH, United Kingdom. TEL 44-1932-340418, FAX 44-1932-340419, sales@intersec.co.uk, subs@intersec.co.uk, http://www.intersec.co.uk. Ed. Kathleen Williams. Pub. Susan Ayre. Adv. contact Kym Ridge. Circ: 10,429.

365.64   USA   ISSN 0743-3077
INTRIGUE. Text in English. 1983. s-m. USD 290. adv.
Published by: Ted Michaels, Ed. & Pub., PO Box 68, Woodbridge, NJ 07095-0068.

364.4 613   IRL
IRISH SECURITY NEWS. Text in English. 3/yr.
Published by: Security Media, Baldoyle, PO Box 1822, Dublin, 13, Ireland. TEL 391115, FAX 735934. Ed. Fionnuala Tattersall. Circ: 3,000.

JANE'S GEOPOLITICAL LIBRARY. see *MILITARY*

355.0335   GBR   ISSN 1366-0012
JANE'S POLICE AND SECURITY EQUIPMENT. Text in English. 1988. a. USD 525 per issue in the Americas; GBP 335 per issue elsewhere (effective 2002 - 2003). **Document type:** *Yearbook, Trade.* **Description:** Over 2,000 items of security equipment for police, military, and security organizations.
Former titles (1995): Jane's Security and Co-In Equipment (0966-3681); (until 1991): Jane's Security and Co-In (0954-3783)
Related titles: CD-ROM ed.: USD 1,305 in the Americas; GBP 815 elsewhere (effective 2002); Online - full text ed.: USD 1,435 in the Americas; GBP 895 elsewhere (effective 2002).
—BLDSC (4647.093000).
Published by: Jane's Information Group, Sentinel House, 163 Brighton Rd, Coulsdon, Surrey CR5 2YH, United Kingdom. TEL 44-20-87003700, FAX 44-20-87631006, info@janes.co.uk, http://catalogue.janes.com/pol_sec_equip.shtml, http://www.janes.com. Ed. Charles Heyman. **Dist. in Asia by:** Jane's Information Group Asia, 60 Albert St, #15-01 Albert Complex, Singapore 189969, Singapore. TEL 65-331-6280, FAX 65-336-9921, info@janes.com.sg; **Dist. in Australia by:** Jane's Information Group Australia, PO Box 3502, Rozelle, NSW 2039, Australia. TEL 61-2-8587-7900, FAX 61-2-8587-7901, info@janes.thomson.com.au; **Dist. in the Americas by:** 1340 Braddock Pl, Ste 300, Alexandria, VA 22314-1651. TEL 703-683-3700, 800-824-0768, FAX 703-836-0297, 800-836-0297, info@janes.com.

JANE'S POLICE AND SECURITY LIBRARY. see *CRIMINOLOGY AND LAW ENFORCEMENT*

365.34   GBR
JANE'S SENTINEL SECURITY ASSESSMENTS. Text in English. m. GBP 590, USD 945, AUD 1,535 (effective 2004). **Document type:** *Trade.* **Description:** Covers the latest events and trends in political, security and military affairs with a detailed breakdown of global military and political structures on a regional basis.

Related titles: CD-ROM ed.: GBP 950, GBP 1,520, AUD 2,470 (effective 2004); Online - full content ed.: GBP 1,030, USD 1,650, USD 26,800 (effective 2004); Series: Jane's Sentinel Security Assessments. Central Africa; Jane's Sentinel Security Assessments. Central America and the Caribbean; Jane's Sentinel Security Assessments. Central Europe and the Baltic States; Jane's Sentinel Security Assessments. China and Northeast Asia; Jane's Sentinel Security Assessments. Eastern Mediterranean; Jane's Sentinel Security Assessments. North Africa; Jane's Sentinel Security Assessments. North America; Jane's Sentinel Security Assessments. Oceania; Jane's Sentinel Security Assessments. Russia and the C I S; Jane's Sentinel Security Assessments. South America; Jane's Sentinel Security Assessments. South Asia; Jane's Sentinel Security Assessments. Southeast Asia; Jane's Sentinel Security Assessments. Southern Africa; Jane's Sentinel Security Assessments. The Balkans; Jane's Sentinel Security Assessments. The Gulf States; Jane's Sentinel Security Assessments. West Africa; Jane's Sentinel Security Assessments. Western Europe.
Published by: Jane's Information Group, Sentinel House, 163 Brighton Rd, Coulsdon, Surrey CR5 2YH, United Kingdom. TEL 44-20-87003700, FAX 44-20-87631006, info@janes.co.uk, http://sentinel.janes.com/, http://www.janes.com. **Dist. by:** Jane's Information Group Australia, PO Box 3502, Rozelle, NSW 2039, Australia. TEL 61-2-8587-7900, FAX 61-2-8587-7901, info@janes.thomson.com.au; 1340 Braddock Pl, Ste 300, Alexandria, VA 22314-1651. TEL 703-683-3700, 800-824-0768, FAX 703-836-0297, 800-836-0297; Jane's Information Group Asia, 60 Albert St, #15-01 Albert Complex, Singapore 189969, Singapore. TEL 65-331-6280, FAX 65-336-9921, info@janes.com.sg.

JANE'S TERRORISM & SECURITY MONITOR. see *POLITICAL SCIENCE—International Relations*

303.625   GBR
JANE'S WORLD INSURGENCY AND TERRORISM. Text in English. s-a. GBP 795, USD 1,265, AUD 2,070 (effective 2004). **Document type:** *Trade.* **Description:** Profiles every significant terrorist, guerrilla and insurgency movement around the world. This intelligence source analyses terrorist tactics and methodology, assesses a group's capability to impact upon state security and details their internal command structures and inventories.
Related titles: CD-ROM ed.: GBP 1,165, USD 1,865, AUD 3,030 (effective 2004); Online - full content ed.: GBP 1,250, USD 1,999, AUD 3,250 (effective 2004).
Published by: Jane's Information Group, Sentinel House, 163 Brighton Rd, Coulsdon, Surrey CR5 2YH, United Kingdom. TEL 44-20-87003700, FAX 44-20-87631006, info@janes.co.uk, http://jwit.janes.com/, http://www.janes.com. **Dist. by:** 1340 Braddock Pl, Ste 300, Alexandria, VA 22314-1651. TEL 703-683-3700, 800-824-0768, FAX 703-836-0297, 800-836-0297; Jane's Information Group Asia, 60 Albert St, #15-01 Albert Complex, Singapore 189969, Singapore. TEL 65-331-6280, FAX 65-336-9921, info@janes.com.sg; Jane's Information Group Australia. info@janes.thomson.com.au.

327.117   USA   ISSN 1552-5155
HV6431
JOURNAL OF COUNTERTERRORISM & HOMELAND SECURITY INTERNATIONAL. Text in English. 1989. q. USD 65 membership (effective 2005). adv. bk.rev. **Document type:** *Journal, Consumer.* **Description:** Provides analysis, interviews, reports, and information in the world of terrorism.
Former titles (until 2002): Journal of Counterterrorism & Security International (1520-6254); (until 1997): Counterterrorism & Security; (until 1994): Counterterrorism & Security Report (1064-9093); (until 1992): International Counterterrorism & Security; (until 1991): Counterterrorism & Security (1047-8779)
Related titles: Online - full text ed.
Indexed: PAIS.
Published by: International Association for Counterterrorism and Security Professionals (IACSP), PO Box 10265, Arlington, VA 22210. TEL 703-243-0993, FAX 703-243-1197, iacsp@erols.com, http://www.securitynet.net. Ed., Pub., R&P Steven J Fustero. Adv. contact Phil Friedman. Circ: 20,000 (paid and controlled).

365.94 004   USA   ISSN 1556-7281
▼ **JOURNAL OF DIGITAL FORENSIC PRACTICE.** Text in English. forthcoming 2006. q. USD 295, GBP 179 combined subscription to institutions print & online eds. (effective 2006). **Document type:** *Journal, Academic/Scholarly.* **Description:** Knowledge resource for practitioners of digital investigation, digital forensic science, electronic fraud investigation, and cyber crime and cyber terror investigation and analysis.
Related titles: Online - full text ed.: ISSN 1556-7346. forthcoming 2006. GBP 170, USD 280 to institutions (effective 2006).
Published by: Taylor & Francis Inc. (Subsidiary of: Taylor & Francis Group), 325 Chestnut St, Ste 800, Philadelphia, PA 19016. TEL 215-625-8900, 800-354-1420, FAX 215-625-2940, info@taylorandfrancis.com, http://www.tandf.co.uk/journals/titles/15567281.asp, http://www.taylorandfrancis.com. Ed. Peter R Stephenson.

JOURNAL OF HEALTHCARE PROTECTION MANAGEMENT. see *HEALTH FACILITIES AND ADMINISTRATION*

364.34   USA
JOURNAL OF HOMELAND SECURITY. Text in English. 2001.

Published by: A N S E R Homeland Security, 2900 South Quincy Street, Ste 800, Arlington, VA 22206. TEL 703-416-3597, homelandsecurity@anser.org, http://www.homelandsecurity.org.

365.34   USA   ISSN 1547-7355
▼ **JOURNAL OF HOMELAND SECURITY AND EMERGENCY MANAGEMENT.** Text in English. 2004. m. USD 35 to individuals; USD 225 to institutions (effective 2006). back issues avail. **Document type:** *Journal, Academic/Scholarly.* **Description:** Contains research papers, comments and reports from the field, and summaries/abstracts of related research appearing in other journals.
Media: Online - full content (from O C L C Online Computer Library Center, Inc.).
Indexed: ESPM, H&SSA, PAIS, RiskAb, SociolAb.
Published by: Berkeley Electronic Press, 2809 Telegraph Ave., Ste 202, Berkeley, CA 94705. TEL 510-665-1200, FAX 510-665-1201, info@bepress.com, http://www.bepress.com/jhsem/.

363.2   USA   ISSN 0195-9425
HV8290
▶ **JOURNAL OF SECURITY ADMINISTRATION.** Text in English. 1977. s-a. USD 25 domestic to individuals; USD 45 foreign to individuals; USD 40 domestic to institutions; USD 60 foreign to institutions (effective 2003). bk.rev.; video rev. 125 p./no. 1 cols./p.; back issues avail.; reprint service avail. from PQC. **Document type:** *Journal, Academic/Scholarly.* **Description:** Covers business administration, criminal justice, law, psychology, public administration, and sociology topics related to the field of security administration.
Formerly (until 1978): Journal of Security Administration and Private Police (0195-9433)
Related titles: Online - full text ed.: (from ProQuest Information & Learning).
Indexed: ABIn, C&CSA, CJA, CJPI.
Published by: (Western Illinois University), B L S S, Inc., PO Box 164509, Miami, FL 33116-4509. TEL 305-254-7006, FAX 305-254-9662, normanr@infi.net. Ed., R&P, Adv. contact Norman R Bottom, Ph.D. Circ: 2,500. **Co-sponsor:** Academy of Criminal Justice Sciences.

▼ ▶ **JOURNAL OF SECURITY EDUCATION;** new directions in education, training, and accreditation. see *EDUCATION*

365.34   GBR   ISSN 1740-2425
JZ5588
▼ **JOURNAL OF SECURITY SECTOR MANAGEMENT.** Text in English. 2003. q. free (effective 2005). **Document type:** *Journal, Academic/Scholarly.*
Media: Online - full content.
Published by: Global Facilitation Network for Security Sector Reform, Rm 247, Wellington Hall, Cranfield University, Shrivenham, SN6 8LA, United Kingdom. TEL 44-1793-785020, FAX 44-1793-782179, editors@gfn-ssr.org, gfn-enquiries@gfn-ssr.org, http://www.jofssm.org/, http://www.gfn-ssr.org/home.cfm. Eds. Anicia Lala, Ann Fitz-Gerald, Nick Luft.

365.34   GBR   ISSN 1464-567X
KEY NOTE MARKET REPORT: ACCESS CONTROL. Text in English. 1998. irreg., latest 2002, Jan. GBP 340 per issue (effective 2002). **Document type:** *Trade.* **Description:** Provides an overview of a specific UK market segment and includes executive summary, market definition, market size, industry background, competitor analysis, current issues, forecasts, company profiles, and more.
Published by: Key Note Ltd., Field House, 72 Oldfield Rd, Hampton, Mddx TW12 2HQ, United Kingdom. TEL 44-20-8481-8750, FAX 44-20-8783-0049, info@keynote.co.uk, http://www.keynote.co.uk. Ed. Emily Pattullo.

365   GBR
KEY NOTE MARKET REPORT: PRISON SERVICES. Variant title: Prison Services. Text in English. 1994. irreg., latest 1994, May. GBP 340 per issue (effective 2002). **Document type:** *Trade.* **Description:** Provides an overview of a specific UK market segment and includes executive summary, market definition, market size, industry background, competitor analysis, current issues, forecasts, company profiles, and more.
Formerly: Key Note Report: Prison Services (1355-0063)
Related titles: CD-ROM ed.; Online - full text ed.
Published by: Key Note Ltd., Field House, 72 Oldfield Rd, Hampton, Mddx TW12 2HQ, United Kingdom. TEL 44-20-8481-8750, FAX 44-20-8783-0049, info@keynote.co.uk, http://www.keynote.co.uk.

KEY NOTE MARKET REPORT: VEHICLE SECURITY. see *TRANSPORTATION—Automobiles*

365.64   GBR   ISSN 1356-613X
KEY NOTE MARKET REVIEW: U K SECURITY. Variant title: U K Security Market Review. Text in English. 1992. irreg., latest 2000, Dec. GBP 565 per issue (effective 2002). **Document type:** *Trade.* **Description:** Designed to keep you up to date with the developments and opportunities across entire industry sectors. They provide a comprehensive analysis of the industry by drawing together key related market segments under one cover.
Related titles: CD-ROM ed.; Online - full text ed.

C

Published by: Key Note Ltd., Field House, 72 Oldfield Rd, Hampton, Mddx TW12 2HQ, United Kingdom. TEL 44-20-8481-8750, FAX 44-20-8783-0049, info@keynote.co.uk, http://www.keynote.co.uk. Ed. Dominic Fenn.

365.64 USA ISSN 0277-0792
TS519
KEYNOTES (DALLAS). Text in English. 1957. m. USD 15 to members. tr.lit. 98 p./no.; reprints avail. **Document type:** *Magazine, Trade.* **Description:** Covers locks, safes, lock devices, lock opening techniques, and related trade tips.
Published by: Associated Locksmiths of America, Inc., 3500 Easy St., Dallas, TX 75247-6416. TEL 214-827-1701, FAX 214-827-1810, keynotes@aloa.org, aloa@aloa.org, http://www.aloa.org. Ed. Jim DeSimone. Adv. contact Susan Haverkamp. Circ: 17,000.

KOKUSAI ANZEN HOSHO/JOURNAL OF INTERNATIONAL SECURITY. see *POLITICAL SCIENCE*

LIBRARY & ARCHIVAL SECURITY. see *LIBRARY AND INFORMATION SCIENCES*

364.4 USA
LIPMAN REPORT. Text in English. m. USD 60 (effective 2000). **Document type:** *Newsletter, Trade.*
Published by: Guardsmark, Inc., PO Box 444, Memphis, TN 38101. TEL 901-522-6092, FAX 901-522-7905, lipmanreport@guardsmark.com, httw://www.guardsmark.com. Ed. Ira A Lipman.

683.3029 USA
TS519
LOCKSMITH LEDGER - INTERNATIONAL DIRECTORY. Text in English. 1939. a. USD 28 (effective 1999). adv. reprint service avail. from PQC. **Document type:** *Directory.*
Former titles: Locksmith Ledger - International Directory; Locksmith Ledger - Security Guide and Directory
Published by: Locksmith Publishing Corp., Rumpf Publishing Division, 100 Colony Park Dr., Ste. 203, Cumming, GA 30040-2774. FAX 847-692-4604. Ed. Gale Johnson. R&P Perrin Davis. Adv. contact Nancy L Levenson. Circ: 25,000.

LOSS PREVENTION LETTER FOR SUPERMARKET EXECUTIVES. see *FOOD AND FOOD INDUSTRIES—Grocery Trade*

MERCADO PREVISOR. see *INSURANCE*

363.22 USA ISSN 0882-9667
N S I ADVISORY. Text in English. 1985. m. (includes w. updates via e-mail). USD 345. adv. **Document type:** *Newsletter.* **Description:** Provides news, analysis, and commentary on national security issues of concern to government and industry security directors.
Published by: National Security Institute, 116 Main St, Ste 200, Medway, MA 02053. TEL 508-533-9099, FAX 508-533-3761, infoctr@nsi.org, http://nsi.org/. Ed., Pub. David A Marston. R&P, Adv. contact Stephen S Burns.

365.64 USA ISSN 0364-3719
TS519.N3
NATIONAL LOCKSMITH. Text in English. 1929. m. USD 46 domestic (effective 2005). adv. **Document type:** *Magazine, Trade.* **Description:** Focuses on security and locksmithing.
Published by: National Publishing Co., 1533 Burgundy Pkwy, Streamwood, IL 60107. TEL 630-837-2044, FAX 630-837-1210, http://beta.thenationallocksmith.com/index.asp. Ed. Gregory Mango. Pub. Marc Goldberg. Adv. contact Jeff Adair. Circ: 17,500 (paid).

365.34 340 USA
NEW YORK SECURITY OFFICER TRAINING MANUAL. Text in English. 1995. irreg., latest 1995. USD 12.95 (effective 2000). **Document type:** *Trade.* **Description:** Looks at the eight hour pre-assignment course and the laws that apply for certification and registration. Offers a guideline for the sixteen hour on-the-job training course. Organizes the D.C.J.S. course outlines.
Published by: Gould Publications, Inc. (Subsidiary of: LexisNexis), 1333 North US Hwy 17-92, Longwood, FL 32750-3724. TEL 800-717-7917, FAX 407-675-2906, info@gouldlaw.com, http://www.gouldlaw.com.

365.34 614.85 USA
OMNIGRAPHICS' SECURITY OFFICER REFERENCE SERIES. Text in English. 2002. irreg. 500 p./no.; **Description:** Provides general readers seeking ways to guard against danger from crimes and accidents with information on a wide range of security and safety issues.
Published by: Omnigraphics, Inc., 615 Griswold St, Detroit, MI 48226. TEL 313-961-1340, 800-234-1340, FAX 313-961-1383, 800-875-1340, info@omnigraphics.com, http://www.omnigraphics.com.

364.4 USA ISSN 1044-3819
JK468.I6
PERISCOPE (MCLEAN). Text in English. 1975. q. membership. **Document type:** *Newsletter.*
Published by: Association of Former Intelligence Officers, 6723 Whittier Ave, Ste, 303A, Mclean, VA 22101. TEL 703-790-0320.

364.4 GBR ISSN 1359-7523
POLICE SCIENCE & TECHNOLOGY REVIEW. Text in English. 1995. q. GBP 45; GBP 49 in Europe; GBP 57 elsewhere. adv. **Document type:** *Trade.*
Published by: Police Review Publishing Co. Ltd., 100 Avenue Rd, Swiss Cottage, London, NW3 3PG, United Kingdom. TEL 44-171-393-7600, FAX 44-171-393-7471. Ed. Gary Mason. Pub. Fabiana Angelini. Adv. contact Melvyn Broad.

364 USA
PRATT'S BANK SECURITY REPORT. Text in English. 1972. m. looseleaf. USD 375 (effective 2004). **Document type:** *Newsletter.* **Description:** Informs security operations officers of the latest developments and newest strategies in both physical and computer security.
Former titles: Bank Security Report (0162-7457); (until 1993): Bank Technology Report
Related titles: Microform ed.: (from PQC); Online - full text ed.
Indexed: BLI, CJPI.
—CCC.
Published by: A.S. Pratt & Sons, Inc., 1911 Fort Myer Dr, Arlington, VA 22209. TEL 703-528-0145, 800-572-2797, FAX 703-528-1736, pratt.info@thomsonmedia.com, http://www.sheshunoff.com/store/860.html, http://www.aspratt.com/. Ed. Richard Cross. Circ: 2,000 (paid).

365.64 FRA ISSN 1262-4055
T55.A1 CODEN: RTFEAJ
PREVENTIQUE SECURITE. Text in French. 1992. 9/yr. adv. bk.rev. bibl.; charts; illus.; stat.; tr.lit. index. **Document type:** *Magazine, Trade.* **Description:** Information on present-day and future security systems and how to obtain them.
Incorporates (1995-1996): Preventique Securite. Supplement Sciences & Techniques (1281-8135); Formerly (until 1994): Securite (1244-5053); Which was formed by the merger of (19??-1992): Preventique (0766-5687); Which was formerly (until 1985): Revue de la Securite (0035-1261); (until 1965): Protection, Securite, Hygiene du Travail; (1981-1992): Revue Generale de Securite (0242-6277); Which was formed by the merger of (1969-1981): Revue Technique du Feu (0048-8194); (1958-1981): Revue de la Protection des Hommes et des Biens (0240-9747); Which was formerly (until 1980): Revue de la Protection (0035-1253)
Indexed: CISA, INIS AtomInd.
—CASDDS, CISTI, IE, Infotrieve.
Published by: Societe Alpine de Publications, 7 chemin de Gordes, Grenoble, 38100, France. Circ: 6,500.

365 GBR
PRISON REVIEW. Text in English. 1992. q. GBP 10 domestic; GBP 15 foreign (effective 2001). bk.rev.; film rev.; software rev.; tel.rev.; video rev.; Website rev. **Document type:** *Magazine, Trade.* **Description:** Covers prison news, political interviews, prison profiles, travel, leisure, training, recruitment, and motoring.
Formerly: Prison Service Review
Published by: National Press Publishers, Peel House, 5 Balfour Rd, Weybridge, Surrey KT13 8HE, United Kingdom. TEL 44-1932-859155, FAX 44-1932-859661, PrisonReview@aol.com. Ed. Chris Locke. Adv. contact Robin Packman. Circ: 33,000.

PRIVACY AND SECURITY 2001. see *LAW*

364 343 USA ISSN 0738-6958
KF5399.5.P7
PRIVATE SECURITY CASE LAW REPORTER; the security professional's digest of state & federal court decisions. Text in English. 1982. 10/yr., latest vol.39. looseleaf. USD 347 (effective 2005). index, cum.index: 1982-1991. back issues avail. **Document type:** *Newsletter.* **Description:** Covers a wide range of judicial decisions on all areas of interest to private security managers in all industries.
Related titles: Online - full text ed.: (from LexisNexis).
Published by: Strafford Publications, Inc., 590 Dutch Valley Rd, N E, Postal Drawer 13729, Atlanta, GA 30324-0729. TEL 404-881-1141, FAX 404-881-0074, editors@straffordpub.com, custserv@straffordpub.com, http://www.straffordpub.com. Ed. Jennifer F Vaughan. Pub. Richard M Ossoff.

▼ **PRODUCT ID**; the journal of automatic prodict id technolgy. see *BUSINESS AND ECONOMICS—Production Of Goods And Services*

364.4 USA
PROTECTION NEWS✶. Text in English. 1980. q. USD 18 (effective 2000 - 2001). adv. **Document type:** *Newsletter, Trade.*
Former titles: Protection Officer News (0823-9304); (until 1984): Professional Protection Magazine; (until 1981): Protection Canada
Published by: International Foundation for Protection Officers, PO Box 771329, Naples, FL 34107-1329. TEL 941-430-0534, FAX 941-430-0533, sandi@ifpo.com, http://www.ifpo.com. Ed. Sandi J Davies. Circ: 10,000.

364.4 USA ISSN 0740-137X
CODEN: PABUEW
PROTECTION OF ASSETS BULLETIN. Text in English. 1974. m. looseleaf. USD 397; to qualified personnel. bk.rev. index. **Document type:** *Newsletter.*
—CASDDS.
Published by: Merritt Publishing, 1661 Ninth St, P O Box 955, Santa Monica, CA 90406. TEL 310-845-7234, FAX 310-396-4563. Ed. Timothy J Walsh. Circ: 3,500.

363.1 GBR
PUBLIC SECURITY. Text in English. 1998. q. **Document type:** *Trade.*
Published by: (Association of Police and Public Security Supplies), P M H Publications Ltd., PO Box 100, Chichester, W Sussex PO18 8HD, United Kingdom. TEL 44-1243-576444, FAX 44-1243-576456, admin@pmh.uk.com, http://www.pmh.uk.com. Ed. Ray Fox. Pub. Peter Harkness. Adv. contact Paul Russell. Circ: 5,000 (controlled).

365.34 USA
▼ **PUBLIC VENUE SECURITY**; the magazine for security professionals of stadiums, arenas and entertainment venues. Text in English. 2003 (Sept.). bi-m. adv. **Document type:** *Magazine, Trade.*
Published by: Virgo Publishing, Inc., 3300 N. Central Ave., Ste 300, Phoenix, AZ 85012. TEL 480-990-1101, FAX 480-990-0819, cs@vpico.com, http://www.publicvenuesecurity.com/, http://www.vpico.com. Pub. Marla Ellerman. adv.: B&W page USD 2,800; trim 8.125 x 10.875. Circ: 10,000.

Q C J J NEWSLETTER; quaker committee on jails and justice. see *LAW—Judicial Systems*

365.34 GBR
R U S I / JANE'S HOMELAND SECURITY & RESILIENCE MONITOR. (Royal United Services Institute) Text in English. 10/yr. GBP 180, USD 288, AUD 468 (effective 2004). **Document type:** *Magazine, Trade.* **Description:** Provides analysis and assessment for the security and disaster response communities in both the public and commercial sectors, covering strategic, operational and tactical issues with man-made, man-assisted and natural emergencies and disasters.
Related titles: CD-ROM ed.: GBP 340, USD 545, AUD 885 (effective 2004); Online - full content ed.: GBP 400, USD 640, AUD 1,040 (effective 2004).
Published by: (Royal United Services Institute for Defence and Security), Jane's Information Group, Sentinel House, 163 Brighton Rd, Coulsdon, Surrey CR5 2YH, United Kingdom. TEL 44-20-87003700, FAX 44-20-87631006, info@janes.co.uk, http://rjhm.janes.com/, http://www.janes.com. **Dist. by:** 1340 Braddock Pl, Ste 300, Alexandria, VA 22314-1651. TEL 703-683-3700, 800-824-0768, FAX 703-836-0297, 800-836-0297; Jane's Information Group Australia, PO Box 3502, Rozelle, NSW 2039, Australia. TEL 61-2-8587-7900, FAX 61-2-8587-7901, info@janes.thomson.com.au; Jane's Information Group Asia, 60 Albert St, #15-01 Albert Complex, Singapore 189969, Singapore. TEL 65-331-6280, FAX 65-336-9921, info@janes.com.sg.

365.34 IRL
RISK MANAGER. Text in English. q. adv. **Document type:** *Magazine, Trade.*
Published by: Millennium Publications, 625 N. Circular Rd., Dublin, 1, Ireland. TEL 353-1-8552900, FAX 353-1-8552964, millennium.publications@indigo.ie. adv.: page EUR 1,143; bleed 210 x 297. Circ: 9,000 (controlled).

365.34 GBR
▼ **ROYAL UNITED SERVICES INSTITUTE FOR DEFENCE STUDIES / JANE'S HOMELAND SECURITY & RESILIENCE MONITOR.** Text in English. 2003. 10/yr. GBP 180, USD 270, AUD 509.40 (effective 2003). **Document type:** *Journal, Academic/Scholarly.*
Related titles: CD-ROM ed.: GBP 340, USD 493, AUD 884 (effective 2003); Online - full content ed.: GBP 400, USD 580, AUD 1,040 (effective 2003).
Published by: (Royal United Services Institute for Defence Studies), Jane's Information Group, Sentinel House, 163 Brighton Rd, Coulsdon, Surrey CR5 2YH, United Kingdom. TEL 44-20-87003700, FAX 44-20-87631006, info@janes.co.uk, http://catalog.janes.com/catalog/public/index.cfm?fuseaction=home.ProductInfoDetailed&product_id=37529, http://www.janes.com.

S C MAGAZINE (UK / EUROPE EDITION); the international journal of computer security. see *COMPUTERS—Computer Security*

S C MAGAZINE (US EDITION). see *COMPUTERS—Computer Security*

S D M DEALER - INSTALLER MARKETPLACE. (Security Distributing and Marketing) see *BUSINESS AND ECONOMICS—Marketing And Purchasing*

S D M MUNDO MERCANTIL. (Security Distributing and Marketing) see *BUSINESS AND ECONOMICS—Marketing And Purchasing*

365.34   CAN
S P&T NEWS. Variant title: Security Products & Technology News. Text in English. 1996. bi-m. **Document type:** *Magazine, Trade.* **Description:** Provides information for Canadian installers, dealers, specifiers and resellers in the security and alarm industry. Covers the news, technology, installation tips and techniques.
Published by: C L B Media, Inc. (Subsidiary of: Canada Law Book Inc.), 240 Edward St, Aurora, ON L4G 3S9, Canada. TEL 905-727-0077, FAX 905-727-0017, http://www.clbmedia.ca.

683   USA   ISSN 0889-9010
CODEN: REICET
SAFE & VAULT TECHNOLOGY. Text in English. 1983. m. USD 96 domestic; USD 109 in Canada; USD 136 overseas. adv. bk.rev. tr.lit. **Document type:** *Trade.* **Description:** Directed exclusively to the safe, vault and physical security fields.
Formerly (until 1986): Professional Locksmithing
Published by: Safe & Vault Technicians Association, 3500 Easy St., Dallas, TX 75247-6416. TEL 214-827-7233, FAX 214-827-1810, tech@aloa.org, http://www.savta.org/. Ed. Amy Gallagher. R&P Charles Gibson. Adv. contact Marvin Diamond. Circ: 2,500 (paid).

SAFETY REMINDER. see *OCCUPATIONAL HEALTH AND SAFETY*

363.22   DEU   ISSN 0937-2555
SCHUTZ AKTUELL; magazin fuer sicherheit. Text in German. 1986. q. adv. bk.rev. back issues avail. **Document type:** *Consumer.*
Formerly: Katastrophenschutz Aktuell (0930-1240)
Published by: Thome Verlag GmbH, Goethestr 21, Munich, 80336, Germany. TEL 089-591964, FAX 089-553079. Ed. Angela Christiane Grond. Adv. contact Doris Tegethoff. Circ: 6,500.

SCIENCE AND GLOBAL SECURITY; the technical basis for arms control and environmental policy initiatives. see *SCIENCES: COMPREHENSIVE WORKS*

658.478   JPN
SECOM ANNUAL REPORT (YEAR). Text in English. a. free. charts; stat.; illus. **Document type:** *Corporate.*
Published by: Secom Co., Ltd., Management Control Division, Shinjuku Nomura Bldg, 26-2 Nishi Shinjuku 1-chome, Shinjuku-ku, Tokyo, 163-05, Japan. TEL 03-3348-7511, FAX 03-3348-1799, TELEX 0232-4982-3.

621.389   FRA   ISSN 1151-4787
SECURITE ECHOS. Text in French. 21/yr.
Published by: Editions du Gaillard, 5 av. de la Republique, Paris, Cedex 75130, France. TEL 33-1-53364035, FAX 33-1-53364061, courrier@editions-du-gaillard.fr, http://www.editions-du-gaillard.fr/automatisation. Circ: 5,000.

365   USA   ISSN 0890-8826
HV8290   CODEN: SECUEU
SECURITY; the magazine for buyers of security products, systems and service. Text in English. 1964. m. USD 82.90 domestic; USD 113.90 in Canada; USD 102.90 in Mexico; USD 154.90 elsewhere; USD 10 per issue domestic; USD 15 per issue foreign; free to qualified personnel (effective 2005). adv. charts; illus.; tr.lit. index. reprint service avail. from PQC. **Document type:** *Magazine, Trade.* **Description:** For buyers and specifiers of security products, systems and services in corporate, institutional, financial, retail, and government settings. Finely focused articles update readers on the latest technology available in categories including access control, CCTV, fire protection, identification, integrated systems, monitoring, and hardware.
Formerly (until 1986): Security World (0037-0703)
Related titles: Microfiche ed.: (from CIS); Microform ed.: (from PQC); Online - full text ed.: (from EBSCO Publishing, Gale Group, O C L C Online Computer Library Center, Inc., ProQuest Information & Learning).
Indexed: ABIn, C&ISA, CJA, CJPI, E&CAJ, IAA, Inspec, RASB, SRI.
—BLDSC (8217.143000), AskIEEE, IE, Infotrieve. **CCC.**
Published by: B N P Media, 2401 W Big Beaver Rd, 7th Fl., Troy, MI 48084. TEL 248-362-3700, FAX 248-362-0317, http://www.securitymagazine.com, http://www.bnpmedia.com/. Ed. Bill Zalud TEL 630-694-4029. adv.: B&W page USD 5,280, color page USD 6,805; trim 8.38 x 10.88. Circ: 35,000.

364.5 614.84   AUS   ISSN 0728-3725
SECURITY AUSTRALIA. Text in English. 198?. m. AUD 114.35 (effective 2001). adv. **Document type:** *Trade.* **Description:** Provides news and information on commercial, industrial and domestic security.
Published by: Reed Business Information Pty Ltd (Subsidiary of: Reed Business Information International), Locked Bag 2999, Chatswood, NSW 2067, Australia. customerservice@reedbusiness.com.au, http://www.reedbusiness.com.au. Ed. Adrian Dolahenty. Pub. David Strong. Adv. contact Jonathan Sismey. Circ: 6,716.

SECURITY DEALER. see *BUSINESS AND ECONOMICS—Office Equipment And Services*

365.34 330   USA
▼ **SECURITY DIRECTOR NEWS.** Text in English. 2004. m. USD 65 in US & Canada; USD 150 elsewhere; free in US & Canada to qualified personnel (effective 2005). adv. **Document type:** *Magazine, Trade.* **Description:** Business newspaper for corporate and public security directors, offering breaking news coverage of industry events.
Published by: United Publications, Inc., 106 Lafayette St, PO Box 995, Yarmouth, ME 04096. TEL 207-846-0600, FAX 207-846-0657, http://www.securitydirectornews.com/, http://www.unitedpublications.com/. Pub. Carol Enman. Adv. contact Kris Cornish. B&W page USD 4,065, color page USD 5,265; trim 10.625 x 13.625. Circ: 30,100 (controlled).

SECURITY DIRECTOR'S REPORT YEARBOOK. see *COMMUNICATIONS—Television And Cable*

SECURITY DISTRIBUTING & MARKETING. see *BUSINESS AND ECONOMICS—Marketing And Purchasing*

364.4   GBR   ISSN 0049-0024
SECURITY GAZETTE. Text in English. 1958. m. GBP 48. adv. bk.rev. illus.; tr.lit. index. reprint service avail. from PQC.
Document type: *Trade.* **Description:** Provides information for security executives in industry and commerce.
Incorporates: Crime and Fire Prevention (0071-5387)
Related titles: Microform ed.: (from PQC).
Indexed: AC&P, CJPI, RASB.
—**CCC.**
Published by: Security Publishing Ltd., Berwick House 8-10, Knoll Rise, Orpington, Kent BR6 0PS, United Kingdom. TEL 44-171-565-4200. Ed. Nigel Blackman. Circ: 3,764.

SECURITY INVESTING. see *BUSINESS AND ECONOMICS—Investments*

364 658   GBR   ISSN 0955-1662
HV8290   CODEN: SJOUEN
➤ **SECURITY JOURNAL.** Text in English. 1989. q. GBP 295 domestic; GBP 320, USD 480 foreign (effective 2004). adv. bk.rev. back issues avail.; reprints avail. **Document type:** *Journal, Academic/Scholarly.* **Description:** Provides a forum for research and findings in industrial, commercial, institutional and governmental security. Covers such topics as management, operations, crime prevention and technology as they relate to security.
Incorporates (1996-1998): International Journal of Risk, Security and Crime Prevention (1359-1886)
Related titles: Microform ed.: (from PQC); Online - full text ed.: (from EBSCO Publishing).
Indexed: AC&P, CJA, CJPI, Inspec, RASB, SOPODA.
—BLDSC (8217.206500), AskIEEE, IE, ingenta. **CCC.**
Published by: American Society for Industrial Security USA), Perpetuity Press, PO Box 376, Leicester, LE2 1UP, United Kingdom. TEL 44-116-2217778, FAX 44-116-2217171, info@perpetuitypress.com, http://www.perpetuitypress.com/acatalog/Security_Journal.html. Eds. Bonnie Fisher, Martin Gill. Pub., R&P, Adv. contact Karen Gill.

364.4   USA   ISSN 0889-0625
SECURITY LAW NEWSLETTER. Text in English. 1981. m. USD 297 (effective 2005). **Document type:** *Newsletter.* **Description:** Monthly updates on security law without all the legal jargon.
Related titles: Online - full text ed.: (from LexisNexis).
Indexed: CJPI.
Published by: Strafford Publications, Inc., 590 Dutch Valley Rd, N E, Postal Drawer 13729, Atlanta, GA 30324-0729. TEL 404-881-1141, 800-926-7926, FAX 404-881-0074, custserv@straffordpub.com, http://www.straffordpub.com. Pub. Richard C Ossoff.

381   USA   ISSN 0363-4922
CODEN: SECLD2
SECURITY LETTER. Text in English. 1970. 22/yr. USD 187 in US & Canada; USD 217 elsewhere (effective 2000). bk.rev. stat. index. reprint service avail. from PQC. **Document type:** *Newsletter.* **Description:** Covers all aspects of corporate, institutional, and governmental security.
Media: Duplicated (not offset). **Related titles:** Microform ed.: (from PQC).
Indexed: CJPI.
—**CASDDS.**
Published by: Robert D. McCrie, Ed. & Pub., 166 E 96th St, New York, NY 10128. TEL 212-348-1553, FAX 212-534-2957, rmccrie@mindspring.com.

364   USA   ISSN 0736-0401
HD9999.S453
SECURITY LETTER SOURCE BOOK. Text in English. 1983. biennial. USD 75 (effective 2000). adv. **Document type:** *Directory.* **Description:** Directory of leading security consultants, services, systems, and products. Provides information on training, standards, reference materials and industry compensation.
Published by: (Security Letter), Robert D. McCrie, Ed. & Pub., 166 E 96th St, New York, NY 10128. TEL 212-348-1553, FAX 212-534-2957, rmccrie@mindspring.com. Circ: 3,000.

363.35   GBR   ISSN 1471-3578
THE SECURITY MAGAZINE. Abbreviated title: T S M. Text in English. 1970. bi-m. GBP 34 domestic; GBP 38 foreign (effective 2000). adv. bk.rev. charts; illus. index. **Document type:** *Magazine, Trade.*
Formerly (until 2000): Security Surveyor (0306-6118)
Indexed: IBuildSA.
—BLDSC (9067.700000), IE.
Published by: (Association of Burglary Insurance Surveyors), C M P Information Ltd. (Subsidiary of: United Business Media), 630 Chiswick High Rd, London, W4 5BG, United Kingdom. enquiries@cmpinformation.com, http://www.securitymags.com/, http://www.cmpinformation.com. Ed., R&P Ian Drury. Pub. Paul Thandi. Adv. contact John McDowell. Circ: 7,100.

SECURITY MANAGEMENT. see *BUSINESS AND ECONOMICS—Management*

363.22   GBR   ISSN 1472-2534
SECURITY MANAGEMENT TODAY. Abbreviated title: S M T. Text in English. 1997. m. GBP 70 domestic; GBP 57 in Europe; GBP 84 rest of world (effective 2003). adv. bk.rev. tr.lit. back issues avail. **Document type:** *Journal, Trade.* **Description:** Deals with all aspects of security affecting business. Aimed primarily at chiefs of security in all sectors of business and commerce.
Formerly (until 2000): Security Management & Industry Today (1368-5325); Which was formed by the merger of (1990-1997): Security Management Today (0960-2895); (1989-1997): Security Industry (0955-3592)
—BLDSC (8313.595000). **CCC.**
Published by: Builder Group plc., 7th Floor, Anchorage House, 2 Clove Crescent, London, London E14 2BE, United Kingdom. TEL 44-20-75604000, FAX 44-20-75604026, http://www.smtdirect.co.uk/. Ed. Tom Reeve. adv.: B&W page GBP 1,610, color page GBP 2,260; trim 224 x 297. Circ: 9,674.

365.34   AUS
SECURITY OZ MAGAZINE. Text in English. m. AUD 59.95 membership (effective 2001). **Document type:** *Trade.* **Description:** Aims to provide readers in Australia's security industry a window to "Total Security Solutions".
Address: PO BOX 1100G, Greythorn, VIC 3104, Australia. TEL 61-1300-300552, FAX 61-3-9857-7499, http://www.safecity.com.au/securityoz.htm. Ed. John Bigelow. Adv. contact Sam Grillo.

365.4   DEU   ISSN 1617-1748
SECURITY POINT. Text in German. 1988. bi-m. EUR 30 (effective 2004). adv. **Document type:** *Journal, Trade.*
Published by: Richard Boorberg Verlag GmbH und Co. KG, Scharrstr 2, Stuttgart, 70563, Germany. TEL 49-711-73850, FAX 49-711-7385100, mail@boorberg.de, http://www.boorberg.de. adv.: B&W page EUR 2,065, color page EUR 3,145. Circ: 10,774 (paid and controlled).

365.34 628.92   USA   ISSN 1520-376X
SECURITY PRODUCTS. Text in English. 1997. m. USD 75 domestic; USD 105 in Canada; USD 115 elsewhere (effective 2001); Free to qualified subscribers. adv. **Document type:** *Magazine, Trade.* **Description:** Publishes information on products and services in the security, safety and fire protection industries.
Related titles: Online - full content ed.
Published by: Stevens Publishing Corporation, 5151 Beltline Rd, 10th Fl, Dallas, TX 75240. http://www.secprodonline.com/, http://www.stevenspublishing.com/. Ed. Jeff Wilson.

364.4 338.4768   GBR   ISSN 0266-318X
SECURITY RETAILER. Text in English. 1984. bi-m. GBP 15; GBP 18.60 foreign. adv. back issues avail. **Document type:** *Trade.*
Published by: (Builder Group Ltd.), S P L (Subsidiary of: Highbury House Communications PLC), Berwick House, 8-10 Knoll Rise, Orpington, Kent BR6 0PS, United Kingdom. TEL 44-1689-874025, FAX 44-1689-896847. Ed. Tom Reeve. Pub., R&P John Beese. Adv. contact Jane Morris. page GBP 1,850; trim 210 x 297. Circ: 5,000.

SECURITY SALES; technology for security installation and service. see *BUILDING AND CONSTRUCTION—Hardware*

364.4   GBR
SECURITY SPECIFIER. Text in English. 1984. 6/yr. GBP 24 (effective 2000). **Document type:** *Trade.*
Published by: Specifiers Journals Ltd, 32 Portland St, Cheltenham, Glos GL52 2PB, United Kingdom. TEL 44-1242-583222, FAX 44-1242-222331. Ed. D G Constantine. Adv. contact Christopher Musk. Circ: 14,803.

365.34   USA   ISSN 1528-0519
SECURITY SYSTEMS NEWS. Text in English. m. USD 65 in US & Canada; USD 150 elsewhere; free in US & Canada to qualified personnel (effective 2005). **Document type:** *Newspaper, Trade.* **Description:** Covers news and trends of the alarm and security industry.
Related titles: Online - full text ed.: (from ProQuest Information & Learning).
Indexed: ABIn, CJPI.

Published by: United Publications, Inc., 106 Lafayette St, PO Box 995, Yarmouth, ME 04096. TEL 207-846-0600, FAX 207-846-0657, info@securitysystemsnews.com, http://www.securitysystemsnews.com/, http://www.unitedpublications.com/. Ed. Chelsie Woods. Pub. Carol Enman.

363.22   USA   ISSN 1069-1804
SECURITY TECHNOLOGY & DESIGN. Text in English. 1991. m. free to qualified personnel. adv. **Document type:** *Magazine, Trade.* **Description:** Devoted to sophisticated integrated systems, including their applications and technical aspects.
Related titles: Online - full text ed.: (from Gale Group, ProQuest Information & Learning).
Indexed: C&ISA, E&CAJ, ESPM, IAA, RiskAb.
—CCC.
Published by: Cygnus Business Media, Inc., 100 Colony Park Dr, Suite 230, Cumming, GA 30040. TEL 770-886-0800, FAX 770-889-7703, http://www.securityinfowatch.com/magazine/std.jsp, http://www.cygnusb2b.com/. Ed. Marleah Blades. Pub. Steven Lasky. adv.: B&W page USD 3,065, color page USD 4,060; trim 10.88 x 8.13. Circ: 34,004 (controlled).

365.34   IRL
SECURITY WORLD. Text in English. q. adv. **Document type:** *Magazine, Trade.*
Address: Brookfield House, Brookfield Terrace, Blackrock, Co. Dublin, Ireland. TEL 353-1-2833500, FAX 353-1-2833592. adv.: B&W page EUR 825, color page EUR 952. Circ: 5,000 (paid and controlled).

364.4   BRA
SEGURIDAD∗ /SECURITY. Text in English, Spanish. bi-m.
Published by: International Security Association, Rua Almirante Baltazar no. 349, Sao Cristovao, RJ 20941, Brazil.

364.4   ESP   ISSN 0210-8747
SEGURITECNICA. Text in Spanish. 198?. m. **Document type:** *Trade.*
Address: Muntaner, 117, Barcelona, 08036, Spain. TEL 3-253-60-90, FAX 3-401-88-74. Ed. Jose A Loren. Circ: 25,000.

364.4   ITA
SICUREZZA; componenti, sistemi, tecnologie, normative, mercato, gestione. Text in Italian. 1978. m. (11/yr.). EUR 51 (effective 2005). **Document type:** *Magazine, Trade.* **Description:** Provides information on systems and equipment to crime prevention.

Formerly: Sicurezza e Prevenzione (0392-9000)
Published by: Gruppo Editoriale J C E, Via Patecchio 2, Milan, MI 20141, Italy. TEL 39-02-57316011, FAX 39-02-57316291, info@jce.it, http://www.jce.it. Ed. Bruno Carlucci. Pub. Jacopo Castelfranchi. Circ: 7,000.

▼ **SICUREZZA DIGITALE.** see *COMMUNICATIONS*

643.16 368.8   SWE   ISSN 0283-5452
SKYDD & SAEKERHET/SAFETY AND SECURITY. Abbreviated title: S O S. Text in Swedish. 1964. 9/yr. SEK 325 (effective 2004). adv. **Document type:** *Newspaper, Trade.*
Incorporates: Stoeldskydd; Supersedes in part (in 1986): Brandfoersvar (0006-9051)
—CISTI.
Published by: Svenska Stoeldskyddsfoereningen/Swedish Theft Prevention Association, Tegeluddsvaegen 100, Stockholm, 11587, Sweden. TEL 46-8-7837450, FAX 46-8-6639652, info@ssf.nu, http://www.stoldskydd.se/SOS/index.htm, http://www.ssf.nu. Ed. Georg Hahne TEL 46-8-7837425. Pub. Staffan Groendahl. Adv. contact Jonas From TEL 46-8-55667750. B&W page SEK 16,400, color page SEK 21,700; trim 185 x 265. Circ: 23,000.

658.47 365.34   USA   ISSN 0039-1867
STORES. Text in English. 1912. m. free to qualified personnel; USD 120 (effective 2005). adv. bk.rev. illus.; tr.lit. back issues avail.; reprints avail. **Document type:** *Magazine, Trade.* **Description:** Reports on the full spectrum of retail operations and merchandising. For senior retail headquarters executives in chain store retailing, including specialty stores, general merchandise chains, department stores, home furnishings stores, drug stores, wholesale clubs, hardware stores, grocery chains and convenience stores; restaurants; and direct mail and marketing firms.
Related titles: Online - full text ed.: (from O C L C Online Computer Library Center, Inc.).
Indexed: ABIn, B&I, BPI, DPD, PAIS, T&II.
—BLDSC (8466.380000), IE, Infotrieve, ingenta.
Published by: (National Retail Federation), N R F Enterprises, Inc., 325 7th St, N W, Ste 1000, Washington, DC 20004-2802. TEL 202-626-8101, FAX 202-626-8191, http://www.stores.org, http://www.stores.com/. Ed. Susan Reda. Pub. Rick Gallagher. adv.: B&W page USD 3,990. Circ: 35,000 (paid).

365.34 387.7   USA
HE9797.4.S4
TRANSPORTATION SECURITY. Text in English. 2002 (Nov.). m. **Document type:** *Magazine, Trade.* **Description:** Provide news and information about the airport security industry.

Published by: Primedia Business Magazines & Media, Inc. (Subsidiary of: Primedia, Inc.), 6151 Powers Ferry Rd Ste 200, Atlanta, GA 30339. TEL 770-955-2500, FAX 770-618-0204, inquiries@primediabusiness.com, http://www.primediabusiness.com. Circ: 50,000.

270   FIN   ISSN 0782-7571
TURVALLISUUS. Text in Finnish. 1984. 6/yr. adv. **Document type:** *Magazine, Trade.* **Description:** Covers a broad range of safety issues, from data security to risk management.
Published by: Sanoma Magazines Finland Corporation, Hoylaamotie 1 D, P.O. Box 100, Helsinki, 00040, Finland. TEL 358-9-1201, FAX 358-9-1205171, info@sanomamagazines.fi, http://www.sanomamagazines.fi. adv.: B&W page EUR 1,750, color page EUR 2,235.

364.4 363   COL
VENTAS DE SEGURIDAD; la revista para la industria de la seguridad en America Latina. Text in Spanish. bi-m. adv.
Published by: Latin Press Inc., Apartado Postal 67 252, Medellin, ANT, Colombia. TEL 57-4-4140169, FAX 57-4-2506990, http://www.latinpressinc.com. Circ: 10,000.

VYZOV. see *POLITICAL SCIENCE—Civil Rights*

CROP PRODUCTION AND SOIL

see *AGRICULTURE—Crop Production And Soil*

CRYSTALLOGRAPHY

see *CHEMISTRY—Crystallography*

CYBERNETICS

see *COMPUTERS—Cybernetics*

CYTOLOGY AND HISTOLOGY

see *BIOLOGY—Cytology And Histology*

C

DAIRYING AND DAIRY PRODUCTS

see AGRICULTURE—Dairying And Dairy Products

DANCE

see also MUSIC ; THEATER

A D T A NEWSLETTER. see *MEDICAL SCIENCES—Physical Medicine And Rehabilitation*

A I C F NEWSLETTER. see *ART*

793.33 USA
ABILITY BALLROOM DANCE JOURNAL✶ . Text in English. q. USD 25. **Description:** Covers news, interviews, sports medicine and health products.
Published by: World Dance and Dance Sport Council, 301 W 55th St, Ste 4, New York, NY 10019-4532. Ed. Richard Diaz.

AEROBIC BEAT. see *PHYSICAL FITNESS AND HYGIENE*

AFRICAN JOURNAL FOR PHYSICAL, HEALTH EDUCATION, RECREATION AND DANCE. see *PHYSICAL FITNESS AND HYGIENE*

793.3 USA ISSN 1061-8155
AMATEUR DANCERS. Text in English. 1979. bi-m. USD 25; USD 4.50 newsstand/cover (effective 2003). adv. bk.rev.; dance rev.; music rev.; software rev. charts; illus.; stat. back issues avail. **Document type:** *Newsletter.* **Description:** Covers national and international news on ballroom dancing, competition calendar and results, professional pointers, articles, opinions and reports.
Published by: United States Amateur Ballroom Dancers Association, Inc., 152988, Cape Coral, FL 33915-2988. TEL 800-447-9047, FAX 717-235-4183, ad-editor@usabda.org, amdanmeyer@aol.com, http://www.usabda.org. Ed., Pub., R&P Robert Jacob Meyer. Adv. contact Robert J Meyer. B&W page USD 840, color page USD 1,300; trim 11 x 8.5. Circ: 20,000.

AMERICAN CHEERLEADER JUNIOR. see *SPORTS AND GAMES*

793.31 USA
AMERICAN DANCE CIRCLE. Text in English. 1979. q. USD 25 to members (effective 2000). adv. bk.rev. **Document type:** *Newsletter.* **Description:** Presents articles on American folk dance and dance events, and dance descriptions.
Published by: Lloyd Shaw Foundation, 2924 Hickory Ct, Manhattan, KS 66503. TEL 785-539-6306, ecocke@ksu.edu, http://www.lloydshaw.org. Ed. Enid Cocke. R&P, Adv. contact Diane Ortner. Circ: 450.

793 USA
AMERICAN DANCE GUILD QUARTERLY✶ . Text in English. 1955. q. membership. adv. bk.rev. bibl. back issues avail. **Document type:** *Newsletter.* **Description:** Covers issues of concern in the field, reviews and member news.
Formerly: American Dance Guild Newsletter (0300-7448)
Media: Duplicated (not offset).
Published by: American Dance Guild, PO Box 2006, New York, NY 10021-0051. TEL 212-932-2789. Ed., Adv. contact Marilynn Danitz. Circ: 400.

AMERICAN DANCE THERAPY ASSOCIATION. (NO.) ANNUAL CONFERENCE PROCEEDINGS. see *MEDICAL SCIENCES—Physical Medicine And Rehabilitation*

792.8 USA ISSN 0146-3721
RC489.D3
➤ **AMERICAN JOURNAL OF DANCE THERAPY.** Text in English. 1968. s-a. EUR 338, USD 345, GBP 215 combined subscription to institutions print & online eds. (effective 2005). adv. bk.rev. abstr.; bibl.; illus. Index. back issues avail.; reprint service avail. from PSC. **Document type:** *Journal, Academic/Scholarly.* **Description:** Covers clinical use of dance therapy, theoretical considerations which provide a framework for dance therapy intervention, and research in dance therapy.
Supersedes (in 1977): American Dance Therapy Association. Monograph
Related titles: Online - full text ed.: ISSN 1573-3262. USD 345 to institutions (effective 2005) (from EBSCO Publishing, Gale Group, IngentaConnect, Kluwer Online, O C L C Online Computer Library Center, Inc., Springer LINK, Swets Information Services).
Indexed: ASCA, AgeL, ArtHuCI, BibLing, CurCont, ExcerpMed, FamI, IDP, IIPA, PEI, PsycInfo, PsycholAb, RILM, RefZh, SSCI, e-psyche.
—BLDSC (0824.220000), GNLM, IDS, IE, Infotrieve, ingenta. **CCC.**
Published by: (American Dance Therapy Association), Plenum US (Subsidiary of: Springer Science+Business Media), 233 Spring St, New York, NY 10013. TEL 212-460-1500, FAX 212-460-1575, service@springer-ny.com, http://springerlink.metapress.com/openurl.asp?genre=journal&issn=0146-3721, http://www.springeronline.com. Eds. Cathy Appel, Danielle L Fraenkel.

793.31 USA
AMERICAN MORRIS NEWSLETTER✶ . Text in English. 1976. 3/yr. USD 14 in US & Canada; USD 18 elsewhere (effective 2000); (includes Annual Directory of Morris Sides in North America). adv. bk.rev. **Description:** Current issues and historical background of English ritual dances known as Morris Dancing.
Indexed: IDP, IIPA, RILM.
Address: c/o Jocelyn Reynolds, 2586 36th Ave., San Francisco, CA 94116. TEL 415-731-7104, AMN@periodpieces.com, http://web.syr.edu/~hytelnet/amn/. Circ: 400.

793.34 USA ISSN 0091-3383
GV1763
AMERICAN SQUAREDANCE; the international magazine of square dancing. Text in English. 1945. m. USD 27.50 domestic; USD 35 in Canada; USD 92 elsewhere; USD 3 newsstand/cover (effective 2005). adv. bk.rev. bibl.; illus. index. **Document type:** *Magazine, Consumer.* **Description:** Covers all aspects of square dancing worldwide.
Former titles (until 1972): New Square Dance (0091-3359); (until 1968): Square Dance (0038-8734)
Related titles: Microform ed.: (from PQC).
Published by: American Squaredance, 34 E Main St, Apopka, FL 32703. TEL 888-588-2362, FAX 407-886-8464, americansquaredance@earthlink.net, http://www.americansquaredance.com/index.htm. Ed. William Boyd. Pubs. Randy Boyd, William Boyd. adv.: page USD 351. Circ: 12,000 (paid).

793.3 DEU ISSN 1433-6146
ANDA; Zeitschrift fuer Flamenco. Text in German. 1994. bi-m. EUR 30 domestic; EUR 40 foreign; EUR 5 newsstand/cover (effective 2005). adv. **Document type:** *Magazine, Consumer.* **Description:** Covers all aspects of the flamenco dance for practitioners and enthusiasts.
Published by: Anda Verlag GmbH, Rothenburg 41, Muenster, 48143, Germany. TEL 49-251-48278-0, FAX 49-251-4827829, contact@anda.de, http://www.anda.de. Ed., Adv. contact Oliver Farke.

ANNUAIRE MUSIQUE ET DANSE. see *MUSIC*

ANY SWING GOES; swing music magazine. see *MUSIC*

793.31 781.7 USA
ARKANSAS COUNTRY DANCER. Text in English. 1980. q. USD 7.50 (effective 1999). adv. **Document type:** *Newsletter.* **Description:** Provides news about the society, including information about traditional Arkansas, American, English, Irish dance and music.
Published by: Arkansas Country Dance Society, 52 Ridge Dr, Greenbrier, AR 72058-9646. TEL 501-679-2935. Ed., Pub., R&P, Adv. contact Cyndie Conn TEL 501-868-7820. Circ: 175.

ARTS COUNCIL. ANNUAL REPORT/AN CHOMHAIRLE EALAION. TUARASCAIL BHILANTUIL. see *ART*

ARTS MANAGEMENT. see *THEATER*

ARTSWEST; supporting & promoting the arts in Western Sydney. see *ART*

793 USA ISSN 0882-3472
GV1580
ATTITUDE; the dancers' magazine. Text in English. 1982. q. USD 20 domestic; USD 50 foreign (effective 2005). adv. bk.rev. illus. reprints avail. **Document type:** *Magazine, Consumer.* **Description:** Artist initiated trade journal and audience development tool that fosters cultural pluralism by documenting the diverse artists of New York State. Includes features, reviews and research news.
Related titles: Online - full text ed.: (from Chadwyck-Healey Inc.).
Indexed: IDP, IIPA.
Published by: Dance Giant Steps, Inc., 8743 Fannette St., Houston, TX 77029-3324. http://pawi.org/AffiliateArtists/Attitude/indexDanceGiantSteps.html. Ed. Arthur T Wilson. Pub., R&P, Adv. contact Bernadine Jennings. Circ: 2,500.
Dist. by: Ubiquity Distributors, 607 Degraw St, Brooklyn, NY 11217. TEL 718-875-5491.

792.8 AUS
AUSDANCE GUIDE TO AUSTRALIAN DANCE COMPANIES. Text in English. 1994. irreg. AUD 25; AUD 45 foreign (effective 2000). **Document type:** *Directory.*
Published by: (Ausdance National Secretariat), Australian Dance Council - Ausdance National Secretariat, 40 Mort St. 1st Fl, PO Box 45, Braddon, ACT 2612, Australia. TEL 61-2-6248-8992, FAX 61-2-6247-4701, ausdance.national@anu.edu.au, national@ausdance.org.au, http://ausdance.anu.edu.au. Ed. Clare Dyson.

792.8 AUS ISSN 1033-6605
AUSDANCE N S W. Text in English. 1990. m. AUD 50 (effective 2000). adv. dance rev. **Document type:** *Newspaper, Consumer.* **Description:** Contains information on dance workshops and classes, performances, events, auditions, resources, and news for the dance community of New South Wales, Australia.
Published by: Australian Dance Council - N S W, Peir 4, The Wharf, Hickson Rd., Walsh Bay, NSW 2000, Australia. TEL 61-2-9241-4022, FAX 61-2-9241-1331, ausdance@pip.com.au, ausdancensw@dance.net.au. Ed. Paul Tibbles. Adv. contact Malcolm McCormick. B&W page AUD 400, color page AUD 1,000; trim 395 x 272. Circ: 1,500 (paid).

792.8 AUS ISSN 0818-6022
AUSTRALIAN BALLET NEWS. Text in English. 1986. 3/yr. bk.rev. **Document type:** *Newsletter.* **Description:** Contains articles and news of the company's members and events.
Related titles: Online - full text ed.
Published by: Australian Ballet, Level 5, 2 Kavanagh St, Southbank, VIC 3006, Australia. TEL 61-3-9684-8600, FAX 61-3-9686-7081, debrah@austballet.telstra.com.au, http://www.australianballet.com.au, http://www.austballet.telstra.com.au. Ed., R&P Debra Howlett. Circ: 35,000 (controlled).

792.8 RUS ISSN 0869-5199
GV1663
BALET. Text in Russian. bi-m. USD 95 in United States.
Indexed: RASB.
—East View.
Address: Tverskaya ul 18, korp 1, Moscow, 103050, Russian Federation. TEL 7-095-2003815, FAX 7-095-2000784. Ed. V I Ural'skaya. **US dist. addr.:** East View Information Services, 3020 Harbor Ln. N., Minneapolis, MN 55447. TEL 612-550-0961.

792.8 JPN
BALLET. Text in Japanese. q. JPY 1,600. adv. **Document type:** *Trade.* **Description:** Covers ballet scenes in Japan and abroad.
Formerly: Ballet no Hon - Book on Ballet
Published by: Ongaku No Tomo Sha Corp., c/o KakuyukiNabeshima, 6-30 Kagura-Zaka, Shinjuku-ku, Tokyo, 162-0825, Japan. FAX 81-3-3235-2129. Ed. Kaneyoshi Umekawa. Pub. Jun Meguro. R&P Tetsuo Morita TEL 81-3-3235-2111. Adv. contact Takao Oya. B&W page JPY 288,000, color page JPY 552,000; trim 210 x 277. Circ: 100,000.

792.8 FRA ISSN 1166-5025
BALLET 2000. Text in French. bi-m. adv. **Document type:** *Newspaper.*
Published by: Editions Ballet 2000, 37 Boulevard Dubouchage, Nice, 06000, France. TEL 33-2-58111192, FAX 33-2-58111238. Ed. Alfio Agostini. Adv. contact Antoms Defreitas.

792.8 USA
BALLET ALERT ONLINE; a place for people who love ballet. Text in English. 1997. bi-m. USD 25; USD 30 foreign (effective 1999). bk.rev. **Document type:** *Newsletter.*
Media: Online - full text.
Address: PO Box 34435, Washington, DC 20043. tomalonis@balletalert.com, http://www.balletalert.com. Ed. Alexandra Tomalonis.

792.8 CAN ISSN 0045-1347
BALLET-HOO. Text in English. 1969. q. USD 10 to members (effective 1999). adv. **Description:** Contains news about the Royal Winnipeg Ballet, its various activities, artists and performances.
Published by: Royal Winnipeg Ballet, Communications Department, 380 Graham Ave, Winnipeg, MB R3C 4K2, Canada. TEL 204-956-0183, FAX 204-943-1994, ballet@rwb.org, ballet@rub.org, http://www.rwb.org. Ed., Adv. contact Arlette Anderson. Circ: 53,000 (controlled).

792.8 USA ISSN 0522-0653
GV1787
BALLET REVIEW. Text in English. 1965. q. USD 25 domestic; USD 33 foreign (effective 2005). adv. bk.rev.; dance rev.; video rev.; music rev. charts; illus. 100 p./no. 2 cols./p.; back issues avail.; reprints avail. **Document type:** *Journal, Academic/Scholarly.* **Description:** Explores modern dance, ballet, world dance, broadway, ballroom, and avant-garde. Includes unusual contemporary and historic photographs.
Related titles: E-mail ed.; Fax ed.; Microform ed.: (from PQC); Online - full text ed.
Indexed: ABS&EES, ASCA, AmHI, ArtHuCI, CurCont, HumInd, IDP, IIPA, MEA&I, PCI, RASB, RILM.
—BLDSC (1861.029000), IDS, IE, ingenta. **CCC.**
Published by: Dance Research Foundation, Inc., 37 W 12th St 7J, New York, NY 10011. TEL 212-924-5183, FAX 212-924-2176, info@balletreview.com, http://www.balletreview.com. Ed. Francis Mason. R&P Roberta Hellman TEL 212-924-5183. Adv. contact Marvin Hoshino TEL 212-431-7967. page USD 375; trim 9.25 x 6. Circ: 2,000 (paid); 4,000 (controlled). **Dist. by:** Ubiquity Distributors Inc., 607 DeGraw St, Brooklyn, NY 11217. TEL 718-875-5491, FAX 718-875-8047.

792.8 DEU ISSN 1612-6890
GV1787
BALLETTANZ; Europe's leading dance magazine. Text in German, English. 1994. m. (11/yr.). EUR 96 domestic; EUR 110 in Europe; EUR 115 elsewhere; EUR 8 newsstand/cover (effective 2005). adv. bk.rev. illus. back issues avail.; reprints avail. **Document type:** *Magazine, Consumer.* **Description:** Covers all aspects and developments of the international dance scene.
Formerly (until 2002): Ballett International - Tanz Aktuell (0947-0484); Which was formed by the merger of (1986-1994): Tanz Aktuell (0933-0585); (1982-1994): Ballett International (0722-6268); Which incorporated (1990-1991): Tanz International (0937-8286); (1958-1989): Tanz (0138-1482)
Related titles: English ed.
Indexed: ASCA, ArtHuCI, CurCont, DIP, IBR, IBZ, IDP, IIPA, RASB, RILM, SSCI.
—BLDSC (1861.029330), IDS. **CCC.**
Published by: Friedrich Berlin Verlagsgesellschaft mbH, Reinhardtstr 29, Berlin, 10117, Germany. TEL 49-30-25449520, FAX 49-30-25449524, redaktion@ballet-tanz.de, verlag@friedrichberlin.de, http://www.ballet-tanz.de, http://www.friedrichberlin.de. Eds. Arnd Wesemann, Hartmut Regitz. Adv. contact Heike Drisch TEL 49-30-25449521. B&W page EUR 1,600, color page EUR 2,300; trim 240 x 300. Circ: 15,000 (paid).

792.8 ITA ISSN 1123-7813
GV1787
BALLETTO OGGI; attualita e cultura di danza. Text in Italian. 1980. bi-m. adv. bk.rev. back issues avail. **Document type:** *Newspaper.* **Description:** Covers national and international dance and dance culture.
Related titles: English ed.; French ed.
Indexed: IDP, RASB.
Published by: Editions Ballet 2000, Alzaia Naviglio Grande 46, Milan, MI 20144, Italy. TEL 2-58-111192, FAX 2-58-111238. Ed. Alfio Agostini. Circ: 20,000.

793.33 USA ISSN 1057-4042
THE BALLROOM DANCER'S RAG. Text in English. 1977. 10/yr. USD 15 domestic; USD 25 foreign; USD 1.75 newsstand/cover domestic; USD 2.50 newsstand/cover foreign (effective 1999). adv. **Document type:** *Newsletter.* **Description:** Covers dance scene in San Francisco, Monterey, and Sacramento areas. Includes calendar of monthly events, competition results, and articles of general dance interest.
Published by: Cottage Industry, 332 Silberhorn Dr, Folsom, CA 95630-6806. TEL 916-983-3098, FAX 916-983-3089, maluca@worldnet.att.net. Ed. Rosmary Wilson. Pub. Dick Wilson. adv.: page USD 65. Circ: 1,500.

BETRIFFT SPORT. see *PHYSICAL FITNESS AND HYGIENE*

615.85155 615.82 616.891 GBR ISSN 1743-2979
▼ ➤ **BODY, MOVEMENT AND DANCE IN PSYCHOTHERAPY**; an international journal for theory, research and practice. Text in English. forthcoming 2006. s-a. GBP 92, USD 161 combined subscription to institutions print & online eds. (effective 2006). **Document type:** *Journal, Academic/Scholarly.* **Description:** Explores the relationship between body and mind and focusing on the significance of the body and movement in the therapeutic setting.
Related titles: Online - full content ed.: Body, Movement and Dance in Psychotherapy Online. ISSN 1743-2987. forthcoming. GBP 87, USD 153 to institutions (effective 2006).
Published by: Routledge (Subsidiary of: Taylor & Francis Group), 4 Park Sq, Milton Park, Abingdon, Oxon OX14 4RN, United Kingdom. TEL 44-1235-828600, FAX 44-1235-829000, info@routledge.co.uk, http://www.tandf.co.uk/journals/titles/17432979.asp, http://www.routledge.com. Eds. Gill Westland, Roz Carrol, Dr. Vicky Karkou, Dr. Helen L Payne.

➤ **BOLETIN DE MUSICA Y DANZA.** see *MUSIC*

793.31 USA ISSN 0274-6034
BOW & SWING. Text in English. 1951. m. USD 15 (effective 2005). adv. **Document type:** *Magazine, Trade.* **Description:** Contains information and news on square and round dancing.
Published by: (Florida Callers Association, Inc.), Atek - Gramac, Inc., 34 E Main St, Apopka, FL 32703. TEL 407-886-7151, FAX 407-886-8464, rgboyd@earthlink.net, http://www.bow-n-swing.com. Ed. Randy Boyd. Circ: 1,100 (paid).

BRITISH PERFORMING ARTS YEARBOOK. see *THEATER*

792.8 AUS ISSN 1322-7645
GV1580
BROLGA; an Australian journal about dance. Text in English. 1994. s-a. AUD 40 domestic to individuals; AUD 60 foreign to individuals; AUD 80 domestic to institutions; AUD 100 foreign to institutions (effective 2000). **Document type:** *Journal, Academic/Scholarly.* **Description:** Provides a forum for current research and critical thinking. Documents creative activities relating to, and impinging on, dance in a cultural context in Australia and elsewhere.
Published by: Australian Dance Council - Ausdance National Secretariat, 40 Mort St. 1st Fl, PO Box 45, Braddon, ACT 2612, Australia. TEL 61-2-6248-8992, FAX 61-2-6247-4701, ausdance.national@anu.edu.au, national@ausdance.org.au, http://www.ausdance.anu.edu.au.

C A NEWS. see *ART*

793.3 USA ISSN 1069-7241
C C D R NEWSLETTER. Text in English. 1983. s-a. looseleaf. USD 50 membership (effective 2003). back issues avail. **Document type:** *Newsletter.* **Description:** To learn about culture through studying movement - dance.
Related titles: Online - full content ed.
Published by: Cross-Cultural Dance Resources, Inc., 518 S Agassiz, Flagstaff, AZ 86001-5711. TEL 928-774-8108, FAX 928-774-8108, jwk3@ccdr.org, http://www.ccdr.org. Circ: 1,000.

793.3 USA
C C T NEWSLETTER. (Choreographers Theatre) Text in English. irreg. USD 10.
Address: 94 Chambers St, 3rd Fl, New York, NY 10007. TEL 212-925-3721.

792.8 USA ISSN 1078-9561
C O R D MEMBERSHIP DIRECTORY. (Congress on Research in Dance Membership Directory) Text in English. 1994. a.
Published by: Congress on Research in Dance, Department of Dance, SUNY, College at Brockport, 350 New Campus Drive, Brockport, NY 14420. TEL 585-395-2590, FAX 585-395-5413, gcarlson@brockport.edu, http://www.cordance.org.

792.8 USA ISSN 0734-4856
C O R D NEWSLETTER. Text in English. 1981. s-a. USD 65 in North America to individuals; USD 77 elsewhere to individuals; USD 115 in North America to institutions; USD 127 elsewhere to institutions; USD 30 in North America to students; USD 42 elsewhere to students (effective 2005). adv. bk.rev.; dance rev.; film rev. 10 p./no.; reprint service avail. from ISI. **Document type:** *Newsletter.* **Description:** Features news, activities, inquiries, and brief articles on dance and related areas.
Indexed: IDP.
—**CCC.**
Published by: Congress on Research in Dance, Department of Dance, SUNY, College at Brockport, 350 New Campus Drive, Brockport, NY 14420. TEL 585-395-2590, FAX 585-395-5413, gcarlson@brockport.edu, http://www.cordance.org. Ed. Katherine Thomas. R&P Ginger Carlson. adv.: page USD 350; 7 x 9.75. Circ: 850.

793.33 USA
C T A B D A NEWSLETTER. Text in English. m. **Document type:** *Newsletter.*
Published by: Connecticut American Ballroom Dance Association, 3 Bright Hill Dr, Clinton, CT 06413. Ed. Sandra Trahan.

793 ESP ISSN 1135-9137
CAIRON. Text in Multiple languages. 1995. a.
Indexed: RILM.
Published by: (Universidad de Alcala de Henares, Aula de Danza), Universidad de Alcala de Henares, Servicio de Publicaciones, Colegio Mayor de San Ildefonso, Plaza San Diego, Alcala de Henares, Madrid, Spain. TEL 34-918-854468, FAX 34-918-855161, suscripcion.public@uah.es, http://www.uah.es/servi/publicaciones.

792.8 USA
CAJUN NEWS. Text in English. every 5 wks.
Address: 19 Purcell Dr, Danbury, CT 06810. Ed. Nancy Weston.

LA CANA DE FLAMENCO. see *MUSIC*

CHELSEA SCHOOL RESEARCH CENTRE EDITION. see *EDUCATION*

793.3 ITA ISSN 1125-6230
CHOREGRAPHIE; studi e ricerche sulla danza. Text in Italian; Abstracts in English. 1993. s-a. EUR 20.65 (effective 2005). bk.rev. **Document type:** *Journal, Academic/Scholarly.* **Description:** Dedicated to updating information on technical-cultural developments and new research in the various specializations within the art of dance.
Indexed: IDP, RILM.
Published by: (National Research Council USA), DiGiacomo Editore, Via Assisi 37, Rome, 00181, Italy. TEL 39-06-7804838, FAX 39-06-7800011, digiacomoeditore@tiscalinet.it, http://www.digiacomoeditore.com. Ed. Flavia Pappacena. Circ: 1,000.

793.31 USA
CINCINNATI FOLK LIFE. Text in English. m. USD 20 (effective 1999). **Document type:** *Newsletter.*
Address: PO Box 9008, Cincinnati, OH 45209-9998. TEL 513-533-4822, cfl@fuse.net, http://home.fuse.net/cfl. Ed. Joann Buck. Circ: 300.

793.33 ARG ISSN 0328-0403
GV1796.T3
CLUB DE TANGO. Text in Spanish. 1993. bi-m.
Address: Of. 114, Parana, 123 Piso 5, Capital Federal, Buenos Aires 1017, Argentina. TEL 54-114-3727251, FAX 54-114-3727251. Ed. Oscar B Himschoot.

793 IRL ISSN 1649-1513
CLUBBING.COM. Text in English. 2001. m. EUR 49.99 in Ireland & the U.K.; EUR 69.99 in Europe; EUR 79.99 elsewhere (effective 2002). adv. **Document type:** *Magazine, Consumer.* **Description:** Contains the latest news and reviews on the clubbing scene.
Related titles: Online - full text ed.
Published by: H & H Publishing Ltd., 19 Eglington St., Galway, Ireland. TEL 353-91-563585, FAX 353-91-565376, http://www.clubbing.com. Ed. Conor Montague. Adv. contact Paul Cotter. color page EUR 2,793; 210 x 297. Circ: 15,000 (paid and controlled).

790 USA ISSN 0198-9634
GV1580
CONTACT QUARTERLY; a vehicle for moving ideas. Text in English. 1975. 2/yr. USD 20 in US & Canada to individuals; USD 32 elsewhere to individuals; USD 25 in US & Canada to institutions; USD 29 elsewhere to institutions (effective 2004). adv. bk.rev. charts; illus. cum.index. back issues avail.; reprints avail. **Document type:** *Newsletter, Academic/Scholarly.* **Description:** Journal of contemporary dance, improvisation and performance. Offers views on the craft of movement expression through articles, interviews, poetry, photos and graphics.
Indexed: IDP, IIPA.
Published by: Contact Collaborations, Inc., PO Box 603, Northampton, MA 01060. TEL 413-586-1181. Eds. Lisa Nelson, Nancy Stark Smith. Circ: 2,400.

CONTRIBUTIONS TO THE STUDY OF MUSIC AND DANCE. see *MUSIC*

CORADDI. see *ART*

793.31 USA ISSN 1070-8251
GV1763
COUNTRY DANCE & SONG SOCIETY NEWS. Abbreviated title: C D S S News. Text in English. 1966. bi-m. USD 22 (effective 2001). adv. bk.rev. 32 p./no. 2 cols./p.; **Document type:** *Newsletter.*
Indexed: IIMP, MusicInd.
Published by: Country Dance & Song Society, Inc., PO Box 338, Hadenville, MA 01039-0338. TEL 413-268-7426, FAX 413-268-7471, news@cdss.org. Ed. Caroline Batson. Circ: 3,500.

793 USA ISSN 1083-3307
CODEN: CSPNFV
COUNTRY DANCE LINES. Text in English. 1984. m. USD 35 domestic; USD 55 in Canada & Mexico; USD 75 elsewhere (effective 2003). adv. bk.rev. **Document type:** *Magazine, Consumer.* **Description:** Provides dance news, views and information written by, for and about country/western dancers, choreographers, teachers and students.
Address: PO Box 243, Reynoldsburg, OH 43068. TEL 614-470-3101, editor@countrydancelines.com, kenlasky@prodigy.net. Ed., Pub., R&P, Adv. contact Ken Laskey. Circ: 10,000 (paid).

793.34 CAN ISSN 0319-8561
CROSS TRAIL NEWS. Text in English. 1977 (vol.25). 5/yr. adv.
Published by: Vancouver Island Western Square Dance Association, 244 Fenton Rd, Victoria, BC V9B 1C1, Canada.

792.8 CUB ISSN 0864-1307
CUBA EN EL BALLET. Text in Spanish. 4/yr. USD 10 in North America; USD 12 in South America; USD 17 elsewhere. illus. **Description:** Presents articles and commentaries on the national and international activities of the National Ballet of Cuba, including theoretical papers on ballet and related topics, plus news and information.
Indexed: IBR.
Published by: (Cuba. Ministerio de Cultura), Ediciones Cubanas, Obispo No. 527, Apdo. 605, Havana, Cuba.

792.8 NZL ISSN 1173-7972
D A N Z. (Dance Aotearoa New Zealand) Variant title: Dance Aotearoa New Zealand. Text in English. s-a.
Formerly (until 1996): D A N Z Bulletin (1173-2083)
Published by: Danz, P.O. Box 9885, Wellington, New Zealand. TEL 64-4-801-9885, FAX 64-4-801-9883, danz@danz.org.nz, http://www.danz.org.nz.

793.33 USA
DANCE ACTION INTERNATIONAL✶. Text in English. 8/yr. USD 40. **Description:** Contains color action photos and specialty columns with emphasis on California.
Address: 21544 Wesley Dr, Apt 9, Laguna Beach, CA 92651-8102. Ed. Cay Cannon.

793.3 780 USA ISSN 1062-4066
DANCE AND MUSIC SERIES. Text in English. 1987. irreg., latest vol.10, 1997. **Document type:** *Monographic series.*
Published by: Pendragon Press, PO Box 190, Hillsdale, NY 12529-0190. TEL 518-325-6100, FAX 518-325-6102, info@taconic.net, penpress@taconic.net, http://www.pendragonpress.com/. Ed. Wendy Hilton.

D

792.8 USA
DANCE AND THE ARTS. Text in English. 1983. bi-m. USD 18 domestic; USD 30 in Canada; USD 36 in Europe; USD 48 in Asia. adv. **Document type:** *Consumer.* **Description:** Provides articles on all aspects of dance, with a dual emphasis on teaching and performance. Features include profiles of dancers and dance companies, reviews of musicals, and a calendar of events for both New York and the rest of the dance world. Includes information on dance schools and instructors.
Former titles (until 1995): Dance Pages Magazine (1064-6183); (until 1989): Dance Pages (0882-5211)
Indexed: IDP.
—CCC.
Published by: Dance Pages, Inc., 1818 20 Amsterdam Ave, New York, NY 10031. FAX 212-362-8118, http://www.arts-online.com/danceart.htm. Ed., Pub. Donna Gianell. R&P, Adv. contact Kenneth Romo.

793.3 780 USA
GV1580
DANCE ANNUAL DIRECTORY. Text in English. 1967. a. USD 65 (effective 2000). adv. index. **Document type:** *Directory, Trade.*
Former titles (until 2004): Stern's Directory (1529-9570); (until 2000): Stern's Performing Arts Directory (1529-9589); (until 1989): Performing Arts Directory (0896-3193); (until 1986): Dance Magazine Annnual Performing Arts Directory (1044-5226); Dance Magazine Annual (0070-2684)
Indexed: MagInd.
Published by: Dance Magazine, Inc., 111 Myrtle St, Ste 203, Oakland, CA 94607. TEL 510-839-6060, FAX 510-839-6066, dancemag@dancemagazine.com, http://www.dancemagazine.com. Ed. Stephanie Forster. Pub., R&P Karla Johnson. Adv. contact Howard Bronstone. Circ: 6,000.

793.3 AUS ISSN 0159-6330
DANCE AUSTRALIA. Text in English. 1980. bi-m. AUD 37 domestic; AUD 50 in New Zealand; AUD 55 in Asia; AUD 75 elsewhere (effective 2005). adv. bk.rev. **Document type:** *Magazine, Consumer.* **Description:** Devoted to dance both as artistic expression and recreational activity.
Indexed: GdIns, IDP, IIPA, PCI, RASB.
—BLDSC (3518.223200), IE, ingenta.
Published by: Yaffa Publishing Group Pty Ltd., 17-21 Bellevue St, Surry Hills, NSW 2010, Australia. TEL 61-2-92812333, FAX 61-2-92812750, yaffa@yaffa.com.au, http://www.yaffa.com.au. Ed. Karen Van Ulzen. Pub. Michael Merrick. Adv. contact Ann Nelson. B&W page AUD 1,805, color page AUD 2,730; trim 210 x 273. Circ: 5,217.

D

792.8 USA
DANCE BEAT. Text in English. 12/yr. USD 30. **Description:** Covers news from the governing bodies, both here and world-wide, plus informative articles on all aspects of dancesport.
Address: 12265 S Dixie Hwy, Ste 909, Miami, FL 33156. TEL 305-251-6477, FAX 305-665-0828. Ed. Keith Todd.

793.3 USA ISSN 0271-9940
DANCE BOOK FORUM✶. Text in English. 1980. q. USD 6. bk.rev. bibl.; illus.; tr.lit.
Published by: Dance Institute International, c/o Zuck, Box 105, New York, NY 10024-0105. Ed. Maria Ann Bryant. Circ: 15,000.

792.8 USA ISSN 0147-2526
GV1580 CODEN: DCHRD2
DANCE CHRONICLE; studies in dance & the related arts. Text in English. 1978. 3/yr. GBP 499, USD 824 combined subscription to institutions print & online eds. (effective 2006). adv. illus. Index. reprint service avail. from PSC. **Document type:** *Journal, Academic/Scholarly.* **Description:** Covers dance and music, theater, film, literature, painting and aesthetics.
Related titles: Microform ed.: (from RPI); Online - full text ed.: ISSN 1532-4257. GBP 474, USD 783 to institutions (effective 2006) (from Chadwyck-Healey Inc., EBSCO Publishing, O C L C Online Computer Library Center, Inc., Swets Information Services).
Indexed: ABS&EES, ASCA, ArtHuCI, CurCont, HumInd, IDP, IIPA, MusicInd, PEI, RASB, RILM.
—BLDSC (3518.224000), IDS, IE, Infotrieve, ingenta. **CCC.**
Published by: Taylor & Francis Inc. (Subsidiary of: Taylor & Francis Group), 325 Chestnut St, Ste 800, Philadelphia, PA 19016. TEL 215-625-8900, 800-354-1420, FAX 215-625-2940, info@taylorandfrancis.com, http://www.tandf.co.uk/journals/titles/01472526.asp, http://www.taylorandfrancis.com. Eds. George Dorris, Jack Anderson. adv.: B&W page USD 800. Circ: 450.

792.8 USA
DANCE CORRAL. Text in English. m. USD 12; USD 25 in Canada; USD 30 elsewhere. **Description:** Covers country dancers and dances.
Address: PO Box 27, Berrien Springs, MI 49103. TEL 616-473-3261. Ed. Dennis Waite.

793.3 USA
DANCE CRITICS ASSOCIATION. NEWSLETTER. Text in English. 1978. q. looseleaf. USD 40 membership; USD 47 foreign membership. bk.rev. illus.; tr.lit. **Document type:** *Newsletter.* **Description:** Contains articles on the writing of dance criticism. Also covers job opportunities, and news of conventions and seminars.
Published by: Dance Critics Association, PO BOX 1882, OLD CHELSEA STA, New York, NY 10011. TEL 212-343-3584. Ed. Rita Felciano.

792.8 GBR
DANCE CURRENT AWARENESS BULLETIN. Text in English. 1982. 3/yr. **Document type:** *Magazine, Consumer.*
Related titles: CD-ROM ed.
Published by: National Resource Centre for Dance, University of Surrey, Guilford, Surrey GU2 7Xh, United Kingdom. TEL 44-1483-689316, FAX 44-1483-689500, nrcd@surrey.ac.uk, http://www.surrey.ac.uk.

792.8 USA ISSN 0894-4849
GV1580
➤ **DANCE: CURRENT SELECTED RESEARCH.** Text in English. 1988. a. USD 62.50 (effective 2002). bk.rev. illus.; bibl. index. 300 p./no.; back issues avail. **Document type:** *Academic/Scholarly.* **Description:** Review articles and essays on experimental, historical, philosophical and anthropological aspects of dance.
Indexed: RILM.
Published by: (National Dance Foundation), A M S Press, Inc., 63 Flushing Ave., # 417, Brooklyn, NY 11205-1005. TEL 212-777-4700, FAX 212-995-5413, amserve@earthlink.net. Eds. James H Humphrey, Lynette Y Overby.

792.8 USA
DANCE DIRECTORY OF BALLET COMPANIES. AMERICAN EDITION. Text in English. 1994. a. USD 39.95 (effective 2000). **Document type:** *Directory.*
Published by: Dance Directory, PO Box 230904, New York, NY 10023. TEL 212-873-3433, FAX 212-873-3433, danceprofessionals@worldnet.att.net, http://www.dancepro.com.

792.8 USA
DANCE DIRECTORY OF BALLET COMPANIES. EUROPEAN EDITION. Text in English. 1995. a. USD 39.95 (effective 2000).
Published by: Dance Directory, PO Box 230904, New York, NY 10023. TEL 212-873-3433, FAX 212-873-3433, danceprofessionals@worldnet.att.net, http://www.dancepro.com. Pub. Faith Shaw Petrides.

792.8 GBR
DANCE EUROPE. Text in English. 1995. m. GBP 33.50 domestic; GBP 43 in Europe; GBP 80 elsewhere (effective 2004). dance rev. **Document type:** *Magazine, Trade.* **Description:** Contains interviews with dancers, ex-dancers & choreographers, including features, comments, news and information on performances.
Address: PO Box 12661, London, E5 9TZ, United Kingdom. TEL 44-20-89857767, FAX 44-20-85250462, edit@danceeurope.net, http://www.danceeurope.net/. Ed. Emma Manning TEL 44-20-85337815. Adv. contact Naresh Kaul TEL 44-20-89857767.

792.8 GBR ISSN 1468-5809
DANCE EXPRESSION. Text in English. 1998. m. GBP 21.50 domestic; GBP 27 foreign (effective 2005). adv. dance rev. 4 cols./p.; back issues avail.; reprints avail. **Document type:** *Magazine, Consumer.*
—CCC.
Published by: A.E. Morgan Publications Ltd., Stanley House, 9 West St, Epsom, Surrey KT18 7RL, United Kingdom. TEL 44-1372-741411, FAX 44-1372-744493, valerie@aemorgan.co.uk. Adv. contact Gavin Roebuck TEL 44-20-7370-7324. B&W page GBP 620; 180 x 262.

793.33 JPN
DANCE FAN; monthly ballroom dancing magazine. Text in Japanese. m. JPY 700 per issue.
Published by: Byakuya Shobou, 3-29-3 Takada, Toshima-ku, Tokyo, 171-0033, Japan. TEL 81-3-5950-3561, FAX 81-3-5950-4905.

792.8 AUS ISSN 1328-3308
DANCE FORUM. Text in English. 1987. q. AUD 35 (effective 2000). **Document type:** *Newsletter.*
Former titles: Ausdance Forum (1039-8783); (until 1992): A A D E Dance Forum (1036-3815); (until 1990): Dance Action National (1034-5906)
Indexed: RILM.
Published by: Australian Dance Council - Ausdance National Secretariat, 40 Mort St. 1st Fl, PO Box 45, Braddon, ACT 2612, Australia. TEL 61-2-6248-8992, FAX 61-2-6247-4701, ausdance.national@anu.edu.au, national@ausdance.org.au, http://ausdance.anu.edu.au.

792.8 GBR ISSN 0306-0128
DANCE GAZETTE; membership magazine for the Royal Academy of Dance. Text in English. 1930. 3/yr. GBP 2.50 newsstand/cover to members. adv. bk.rev.; dance rev.; film rev.; music rev.; play rev.; video rev.; Website rev. 60 p./no.; back issues avail. **Document type:** *Magazine.* **Description:** Provides a membership magazine for members of the Royal Academy of Dancing, including teaching technique for classical ballet training, and coverage of events and activities.
Related titles: Microform ed.: (from PQC).
Indexed: IDP, IIPA, RASB.
Published by: Royal Academy of Dance, 36 Battersea Sq, London, SW11 3RA, United Kingdom. TEL 44-207-3268-8000, FAX 44-207-924-2311, gazette@rad.org.uk, http://www.rad.org.uk. Ed., R&P Raechel Boden. Pub. Luke Rittner. Adv. contact Pagricia Bartholomeou TEL 20-7326-8002. B&W page USD 495, color page USD 695. Circ: 18,000. **Subscr. to:** 1412 17th St., Ste. 259, Bakersfield, CA 93301-5219.

792.8 USA
DANCE GYPSY. Text in English. 1990. 12/yr. USD 12 (effective 1996). bk.rev.; rec.rev. **Document type:** *Newsletter.* **Description:** Covers contra, square, swing, ballroom and international folk dances in Vermont, Massachusetts, New Hampshire, and New York area.
Address: 2518 Sunset Lake Rd., Brattleboro, VT 05301-9293. TEL 802-899-2378, FAX 802-899-1394. Ed. Valerie Medve. Circ: 600 (paid).

792.8 CAN ISSN 1189-9816
GV1580
DANCE INTERNATIONAL. Text in English. 1984. q. CND 25.68 domestic to individuals; USD 36 in United States to individuals; CND 44 elsewhere to individuals; CND 44 domestic to institutions; USD 54 in United States to institutions; CND 62 elsewhere to institutions; CND 6 newsstand/cover (effective 2002). adv. bk.rev.; dance rev. illus. 56 p./no.; back issues avail. **Document type:** *Magazine, Consumer.* **Description:** Covers all facets of dance in Canada and abroad with critical and analytical writing, featuring regular and special reports from correspondents in all corners of the world.
Former titles (until 1993): Vandance International (1189-9808); (until 1992): Vandance (0705-8063); (until 1977): Vancouver Ballet Society. Newsletter (0703-1335); Ballet - Who (0005-4348)
Related titles: Microfiche ed.
Indexed: CBCARef, CBPI, IDP, IIPA.
Published by: Vancouver Ballet Society, Level 6, 677 Davie St, Vancouver, BC V6B 2G6, Canada. TEL 604-681-1525, FAX 604-681-7732, danceint@direct.ca, http://www.danceinternational.org. R&P, Adv. contact Maureen Riches. B&W page CND 900, color page CND 1,325; trim 11.75 x 8.25. Circ: 4,000.

793.3 USA ISSN 0011-6009
GV1580
DANCE MAGAZINE. Text in English. 1927. m. USD 34.95 domestic; USD 46.95 in Canada; USD 66.95 foreign; USD 4.95 newsstand/cover (effective 2005). adv. bk.rev.; film rev.; play rev. illus. index. reprints avail. **Document type:** *Magazine, Consumer.* **Description:** Articles on International listing of dance performances, workshops, courses, festivals, and tours.
Former titles (until 1948): Dance (0270-2215); (until 1945): Dance Magazine (0270-2207); (until 1943): Dance (0270-2193); (until 1942): The American Dancer (0270-2185)
Related titles: Microform ed.: (from PQC); Online - full text ed.: (from bigchalk, EBSCO Publishing, Florida Center for Library Automation, Gale Group, Northern Light Technology, Inc., O C L C Online Computer Library Center, Inc.).
Indexed: ABS&EES, ASCA, AcaI, AmHI, ArtHuCI, BRI, CBRI, CurCont, FLI, HumInd, IBRH, IDP, IIPA, MASUSE, MEA&I, MRD, MagInd, PEI, RASB, RGAb, RGPR, RILM, SPI, TOM.
—BLDSC (3518.227500), IDS, IE, Infotrieve. **CCC.**
Published by: McFadden Communication Group, 333 Seventh Ave, New York, NY 10001. TEL 212-979-4803, FAX 646-674-0102, dancemag@dancemagazine.com, http://www.dancemagazine.com. Ed. Wendy Perron. Pub. Karia Johnson. adv.: B&W page USD 3,295, color page USD 5,115; trim 8.25 x 10.75. Circ: 52,000 (paid).

792.8071 USA ISSN 0193-1202
GV1623
DANCE MAGAZINE COLLEGE GUIDE; a directory to dance in North American colleges and universities. Text in English. biennial. USD 19.95 (effective 2004). adv. illus. **Document type:** *Directory, Consumer.*
Formerly: Dance Magazine Directory of College and University Dance
Published by: Dance Magazine, Inc., 111 Myrtle St, Ste 203, Oakland, CA 94607. TEL 510-839-6060, FAX 510-839-6066, dancemag@dancemagazine.com, http://www.dancemagazine.com. Ed. Stephanie Forster. Pub. Karla Johnson. Adv. contact Howard Bronstone.

DANCE MEDICINE - HEALTH NEWSLETTER. see *MEDICAL SCIENCES—Physical Medicine And Rehabilitation*

DANCE MUSIC AUTHORITY. see *MUSIC*

793.3 NZL ISSN 0112-4951
DANCE NEWS. Text in English. 1977. 3/yr. free. adv. bk.rev. illus. back issues avail. **Document type:** *Newsletter.* **Description:** A newsletter detailing ballet and dance tours and productions in New Zealand including profiles on dancers and information of interest to dancers, teachers and patrons.
Formerly (until 1988): Pointe
—CCC.
Published by: Royal New Zealand Ballet, Private Box 27 050, Wellington, 6036, New Zealand. TEL 64-4-3819000, FAX 64-4-3819003, jane.wenzballet.org.nz, jane.w@nzballet.org.nz, http://www.nzballet.org.nz. Ed., R&P, Adv. contact Jane Wynyard TEL 64-4-3819018. Circ: 3,000.

793.3 GBR ISSN 0966-6346
GV1580
DANCE NOW. Text in English. 1992. q. GBP 15 domestic; GBP 17.50 foreign (effective 2005). adv. bk.rev.; dance rev.; music rev.; rec.rev.; video rev. illus. 96 p./no. 2 cols./p.; reprints avail. **Document type:** *Magazine, Consumer.* **Description:** Contains reviews and articles on all forms of theatrical dance.
Indexed: IDP, IIPA, RILM.
—CCC.
Published by: Dance Books Ltd., The Old Bakery, 4 Lenten St, Alton, Hamps GU34 1HG, United Kingdom. TEL 44-1420-86138, FAX 44-1420-86142, now@dancebooks.co.uk, dl@dancebooks.co.uk, http://www.dancebooks.co.uk/now.asp. Ed. Allen Robertson. Pub. John O'Brien. Adv. contact Susan Philo TEL 44-1367-820367. page GBP 350; 134 x 250. Circ: 5,000 (paid).

793.3 USA ISSN 1098-8084
GV1779
DANCE ON CAMERA JOURNAL. Text in English. 1967. bi-m. USD 35 to members; USD 65 to institutions; USD 20 to students; USD 45 foreign (effective 2000). bk.rev. **Document type:** *Newsletter.*
Former titles: Dance on Camera News (0270-8981); Dance Films Association. Bulletin; Dance Films Association Newsletter; Dance Films Association and Dance Society. Newsletter (0011-5991); Dance Films Newsletter
Published by: Dance Films Association, Inc., 48 W 21st St, 9th Fl, New York, NY 10010. TEL 212-727-0764, FAX 212-727-0764, dfa5@juno.com, http://www.dancefilmsassn.org. Ed. Deirdre Towers. Circ: 500.

792.8 USA
DANCE ONLINE; new dance from around the world. Text in English. 1995. w.
Media: Online - full content.
Address: information@danceonline.com, http://www.danceonline.com. Ed. Jane Buchanan.

793 GBR ISSN 0264-2875
GV1580
DANCE RESEARCH. Text in English. 1984. s-a. GBP 72 in Europe; USD 147 in North America; GBP 82 elsewhere (effective 2005). adv. bk.rev. back issues avail. **Document type:** *Journal, Academic/Scholarly.* **Description:** Contains academic and scholarly articles on all forms of dance ranging from the history of European theatre to dance anthropology and Renaissance spectacle.
Related titles: Online - full text ed.: (from EBSCO Publishing, JSTOR (Web-based Journal Archive)).
Indexed: BrHumI, IDP, IIPA, PCI, RILM.
—BLDSC (3518.233800), IE, ingenta. **CCC.**
Published by: (Dance Research Society), Edinburgh University Press, 22 George Sq, Edinburgh, Midlothian EH8 9LF, United Kingdom. TEL 44-131-650-6207, FAX 44-131-662-0053, journals@eup.ed.ac.uk, http://www.eup.ed.ac.uk/journals/content.aspx?pageId=1&journalId=12150. Ed. Richard Ralph. Pub. Nina Curtis. R&P Joolz Longley. Adv. contact Douglas McNaughton TEL 44-131-6504420. page GBP 250. Circ: 650 (controlled).

793.3 USA ISSN 0149-7677
GV1580
➤ **DANCE RESEARCH JOURNAL.** Text in English. 1969. s-a. USD 65 in North America to individuals; USD 77 elsewhere to individuals; USD 30 in North America to students; USD 42 elsewhere to students; USD 30 in North America to senior citizens; USD 42 elsewhere to senior citizens; USD 115 in North America to institutions; USD 127 elsewhere to institutions (effective 2004). adv. bk.rev.; film rev.; dance rev. abstr.; bibl.; charts; illus. 160 p./no.; back issues avail.; reprint service avail. from ISI. **Document type:** *Journal, Academic/Scholarly.* **Description:** Includes a newsletter with activities, inquiries, and articles on dance and related areas as well as a journal of recent doctorial dissertations and general information related to dance.
Formerly: C O R D News (0588-7356)
Related titles: Online - full text ed.: (from Chadwyck-Healey Inc., ProQuest Information & Learning).
Indexed: ABS&EES, ASCA, AmHI, ArtHuCI, BRI, CBRI, CurCont, HumInd, IDP, IIPA, PCI, RASB, RILM, SRRA.
—CCC.
Published by: Congress on Research in Dance, Department of Dance, SUNY, College at Brockport, 350 New Campus Drive, Brockport, NY 14420. TEL 585-395-2590, FAX 585-395-5413, gcarlson@brockport.edu, http://www.cordance.org. Eds., Adv. contacts Ann Dils TEL 336-334-3047, Jill Green TEL 336-334-3047. R&P Ginger Carlson. Circ: 850.

792.8 USA ISSN 1541-0307
DANCE RETAILER NEWS; the news magazine for the retail community. Text in English. 2002. m. USD 108; USD 9 per issue; free to qualified personnel (effective 2003). adv. **Document type:** *Magazine, Trade.*
Published by: Lifestyle Media Inc., 110 William St, 23rd Fl, New York, NY 10038-3900. http://danceretailernews.com/, http://www.lifestyleventures.com/. Pub. Carrie Molay. adv.: B&W page USD 2,585, color page USD 3,275; trim 10.75 x 14.5. Circ: 6,000.

792.8 USA ISSN 1094-0588
DANCE SPIRIT. Text in English. 1997. 10/yr. USD 16.95 domestic; USD 28 foreign; USD 4.99 newsstand/cover domestic (effective 2005). adv. 120 p./no. 3 cols./p.; back issues avail.; reprints avail. **Document type:** *Magazine, Consumer.* **Description:** Provides young dancers and dance instructors with essential dance information. Includes topics from dance fashions to health and fitness.
Related titles: Online - full text ed.: (from bigchalk, EBSCO Publishing, ProQuest Information & Learning); Supplement(s): Dance Spirit's in Motion. ISSN 1528-0306.
Indexed: MASUSE.
—CCC.
Published by: Lifestyle Media Inc., 110 William St, 23rd Fl, New York, NY 10038-3900. editors@dancespirit.com, http://www.dancespirit.com, http://www.lifestyleventures.com/. Ed. Sarah Jarrett. Pub., R&P Carrie Molay. adv.: color page USD 5,200. Circ: 100,000 (paid and controlled).

792.807 USA ISSN 1524-4474
GV1580
DANCE TEACHER; the magazine for dance professionals. Text in English. 1979. 10/yr. USD 24.95 domestic; USD 38 in Canada & Mexico; USD 48 elsewhere; USD 4.99 per issue domestic (effective 2005). adv. bk.rev. tr.lit.; illus. Index. reprints avail. **Document type:** *Magazine, Consumer.* **Description:** Dance journal for educators and serious students.
Formerly (until 1999): Dance Teacher Now (0199-1795)
Related titles: Online - full text ed.: (from bigchalk, Chadwyck-Healey Inc., ProQuest Information & Learning).
Indexed: IDP, IIPA.
—BLDSC (3518.244800). **CCC.**
Published by: Lifestyle Media Inc., 110 William St, 23rd Fl, New York, NY 10038-3900. editor@dance-teacher.com, http://www.dance-teacher.com/, http://www.lifestyleventures.com/. Ed. Susan Amoruso. Pub. Carrie Molay. Circ: 25,000 (paid).

792.8071 GBR
DANCE TEACHER✶. Text in English. 1951. m. adv. bk.rev.; dance rev.; film rev.; video rev. illus. back issues avail. **Document type:** *Magazine, Trade.* **Description:** Contains information on area meetings and dance, with reviews, letters and photographs.
Indexed: IIPA, RASB.
Published by: International Dance Teachers' Association, International House, 76 Bennett Rd, Brighton, BN2 5JL, United Kingdom. TEL 44-1273-685652, FAX 44-1273-674388, info@idta.co.uk, http://www.idta.co.uk. Ed., R&P Jay Dearling TEL 44-1273-685682. Adv. contact Elaine Bailey. page GBP 170; 130 x 185. Circ: 6,000.

792.8 GBR ISSN 0264-9160
GV1645
DANCE THEATRE JOURNAL. Text in English. 1982. q. GBP 15 domestic to individuals; EUR 32 in Europe to individuals; USD 45 elsewhere to individuals; GBP 25 domestic to institutions; EUR 50 in Europe to institutions; USD 65 elsewhere to institutions (effective 2005). adv. bk.rev.; dance rev.; tel.rev.; video rev.; film rev. illus. Index. 48 p./no. 2 cols./p.; back issues avail.; reprints avail. **Document type:** *Magazine, Consumer.* **Description:** For dance professionals, students and those who take an informed interest in dance. Covers ballet, contemporary, new and non-Western dance and national dance listings.
Formerly (until 1983): Labanews
Indexed: ASCA, ArtHuCI, CurCont, IDP, IIPA, RASB, RILM.
—BLDSC (3518.248000), IDS, IE, ingenta.
Published by: Laban, Creekside, London, SE8 3DZ, United Kingdom. TEL 44-20-86918600, FAX 44-20-86918400, dtj@laban.org, info@laban.org, http://www.laban.org/laban/publications/dance_theatre_journal.phtml. Ed., R&P Ian Bramley. Adv. contact Brian Shilling. B&W page GBP 890, color page GBP 1,180; trim 185 x 272. Circ: 2,000.

793.33 GBR ISSN 1475-2336
DANCE TODAY!. Text in English. 1956. m. GBP 16 domestic; GBP 18 foreign; GBP 1.10 newsstand/cover (effective 2003). adv. dance rev.; rec.rev. illus. back issues avail.; reprints avail. **Document type:** *Consumer.*
Formerly (until 2001): Ballroom Dancing Times (0005-4380)
Indexed: IDP, IIPA, RASB.
Published by: Dancing Times Ltd., Clerkenwell House, 45-47 Clerkenwell Green, London, EC1R 0EB, United Kingdom. TEL 44-20-7250-3006, FAX 44-20-7253-6679, http://www.dt-ltd.dircon.co.uk. Ed. Sylvia Boerner. Adv. contact Anne Mottram.

793.3 USA ISSN 1064-6515
GV1623
DANCE / U S A JOURNAL. Text in English. 1983. q. USD 40 (effective 2001).
Indexed: IIPA.
Published by: Dance/U S A, 1156 15th St., N.W., Ste. 820, Washington, DC 20005-1704. Ed. Libby Smigel. Pub. Andrea E Snyder.

792.8 USA
DANCE VIEW. Text in English. 1979. q. USD 30; USD 35 foreign (effective 1999).
Related titles: Online - full text ed.
Address: PO Box 34435, Washington, DC 20043. tomalonis@balletalert.com, http://www.balletalert.com. Ed. Alexandra Tomalonis.

793.33 USA
DANCE VISION U S A IN THE NEWS; most comprehensive dance video library in the world. Text in English. 1995. q. free (effective 2005). adv. dance rev.; rec.rev. illus. **Document type:** *Consumer.*
Published by: Dance Vision U S A, 9081 W. Sahara Ave., Ste 100, Las Vegas, NV 89117-4803. TEL 800-851-2813, FAX 702-256-4227, http://www.dancevision.com. Ed. Wayne Eng. Circ: 7,000.

792.8 USA
DANCE WEEK. Text in English. 1976. 52/yr. USD 33; USD 40 in Canada. adv. music rev. **Document type:** *Newsletter.* **Description:** Provides up-to-date information on ballroom dance events, people, and competitions.
Published by: Charles Zwerling, Ed. & Pub., 2709 Medical Office Plc, Goldsboro, NC 27534. TEL 919-736-3937, FAX 919-735-3701, telemarit96@aol.com. Pub., R&P, Adv. contact Charles Zwerling. Circ: 600 (paid).

792.8 DNK ISSN 0904-5813
DANCELETTER. Text in Danish. 1981. m. DKK 150. illus.
Formerly (until 1987): Dansens Blad (0108-8343)
Published by: Foreningen Ny Dans, c/o Erik Agergaard, Graabroedre Torv 14, Copenhagen K, 1154, Denmark.

793.33 USA
DANCERS' DATELINE. Text in English. 1992. m. USD 16 (effective 2001). adv. bk.rev. 4 p./no.; **Document type:** *Newsletter.* **Description:** Contains information about ballroom dances, showcases and competitions in Southern Wisconsin.
Address: PO Box 346, Random Lake, WI 53075-0346. TEL 920-994-9244, FAX 920-994-4817, sounder@execpc.com. Ed., R&P, Adv. contact Gary Feider. Circ: 1,000 (paid).

793.33 USA
DANCESPORT AMERICA. Text in English. 1998. m. USD 39.95 to members (effective 1998). **Document type:** *Consumer.* **Description:** Sporting the new term for competitive ballroom dancing, the magazine is devoted to virtually every issue of interest to professional and amateur dancers. Includes a special section devoted to children.
Address: PO Box 2816, Westfield, NJ 07090. info@dancesportamerica.com, http://www.dancesportamerica.com. Eds. Dennis Rogers, Jackie Rogers.

793.3 USA ISSN 1077-0577
DANCEVIEW; a quarterly review of dance. Text in English. ceased 1988; resumed 1992. q. USD 20. bk.rev. illus. reprints avail. **Description:** Covers companies and dance events across the country.
Formerly (until 1992): Washington Danceview (0739-4527)
Related titles: Online - full text ed.: (from Chadwyck-Healey Inc.).
Indexed: IDP, IIPA.
Address: PO Box 34435, Martin Luther King Sta, Washington, DC 20043. Ed. Alexandra Tomalonis.

793.3 GBR ISSN 0011-605X
DANCING TIMES. Text in English. 1910. m. GBP 30 domestic; GBP 35 foreign (effective 2004). adv. bk.rev. illus. back issues avail.; reprints avail. **Document type:** *Consumer.* **Description:** Provides international coverage of theater dance with special reference to dance medicine and teaching.
Indexed: ASCA, ArtHuCI, CurCont, IDP, IIPA, RASB, RILM.
—BLDSC (3518.300000), IE, ingenta. **CCC.**
Published by: Dancing Times Ltd., Clerkenwell House, 45-47 Clerkenwell Green, London, EC1R 0EB, United Kingdom. TEL 44-20-7250-3006, FAX 44-20-7253-6679, dt@dancing-times.co.uk, http://www.dancing-times.co.uk/html.pages/dtltd_frameset.html, http://www.dt-ltd.dircon.co.uk. Ed. Mary Clarke. Adv. contact Anne Mottram. Circ: 12,000.

793.33 780 USA ISSN 1053-5454
DANCING U S A. Text in English. 1983. bi-m. USD 24.97 domestic (effective 2001); USD 41.97 in Canada & Mexico; USD 55 elsewhere; USD 4.50 newsstand/cover. adv. bk.rev.; music rev. **Document type:** *Magazine, Consumer.* **Description:** Contains ballroom Latin and swing dance techniques and tips, inspiring stories, history of dance and big bands, as well as source for how-to videos, music, dancing shoes, big bands and dance styles.
Formerly (until 1989): Ballroom Dancing Across the U S A

D

▼ new title ➤ refereed ✶ unverified ♦ full entry avail.

Published by: Dancing U S A, LLC, 188 W. Industrial Dr., Ste. 215, Elmhurst, IL 60126-1684. TEL 630-782-1260, 800-290-1307, FAX 630-617-9950, ballroom@dancingusa.com, http://www.dancingusa.com. Ed., Pub. Michael Fitzmaurice. adv.: B&W page USD 1,360, color page USD 1,789; trim 10.5 x 8.38. Circ: 20,000. **Dist. by:** International Publishers Direct, 27500 Riverview Center Blvd, Bonita Springs, FL 34134. TEL 858-320-4563, FAX 858-677-3220.

793.33 GBR ISSN 1368-9126
DANCING YEAR BOOK✶. Text in English. 1958. a. GBP 15.50 to non-members (effective 2001). adv. bibl. index, cum.index. 168 p./no.; **Document type:** *Yearbook, Trade.* **Description:** Reference to dance organizations, dancing press, ballroom, and theater festivals.
Formerly: Ballroom Dancing Year Book (0404-6919)
Published by: International Dance Teachers' Association, International House, 76 Bennett Rd, Brighton, BN2 5JL, United Kingdom. TEL 44-1273-685652, FAX 44-1273-674388, info@idta.co.uk, http://www.idta.co.uk. Ed. Jay Dearling TEL 44-1273-685682. Adv. contact Elaine Bailey. B&W page EUR 178; 13 x 18.5. Circ: 4,000.

792.8 USA ISSN 0745-3949
DANCSCENE✶. Text in English. 6/yr.
Published by: Koine Publishing Co., c/o Suzanna Penn, P O Box 4422, New York, NY 10163-4422. TEL 214-750-0275.

792.8 NLD ISSN 0168-0137
DANS. Text in Dutch. 1982. bi-m. EUR 30 domestic; EUR 40 foreign; EUR 5 newsstand/cover (effective 2005). adv. bk.rev. **Document type:** *Magazine, Consumer.*
—IE, Infotrieve.
Published by: Landelijk Centrum voor Amateurdans, Postbus 452, Utrecht, 3500 AL, Netherlands. TEL 31-30-2334255, FAX 31-30-2332721, lca@dansweb.nl, http://www.dansweb.nl. Ed. Sietske de Haan. Circ: 1,500 (paid).

793.319489 DNK ISSN 0107-685X
DANSK DANSEHISTORISK ARKIV. MEDDELELSER; dansearkivets aarsskrift. Text in Danish; Summaries in English. 1981. a. DKK 100 domestic (effective 2000). illus. **Document type:** *Academic/Scholarly.*
Published by: Dansk Dansehistorisk Arkiv, Musikvidenskabeligt Institut, Klerkegade 2, Copenhagen K, 1308, Denmark. Ed. Henning Urup.

792.8 793.3 SWE ISSN 1102-0814
DANSTIDNINGEN. Text in Swedish. 1991. bi-m. SEK 150 domestic; SEK 250 in Scandinavia; SEK 400 elsewhere (effective 2003). adv. bk.rev.; dance rev.; film rev.; music rev.; play rev.; software rev.; tel.rev.; video rev.; Website rev. 48 p./no.; back issues avail. **Document type:** *Magazine, Trade.* **Description:** Contains articles and news about all forms of dance; training, competitions and performances in Denmark, Finland, Iceland, Norway and Sweden.
Indexed: IDP.
Published by: Danstidningen i Stockholm Ekonomisk Foerening, P O Box 2133, Stockholm, 10314, Sweden. TEL 46-70-3346998, FAX 46-8-6690111, kalendarium@danstidningen.se, http://www.danstidningen.se. Ed. Ann Marie Wrange. adv.: color page SEK 8,000; 185 x 272. Circ: 3,000. **Subscr. to:** Naetverkstan Ekonomitjaenst, PO Box 31120, Goeteborg 40032, Sweden. TEL 46-31-7439905.

D

792.8 MEX
DANZARIA; danza viva de Iberoamerica. Text in Spanish. 1986 (Oct.). q. MXP 120 (effective 2001). **Description:** Documents, presents and supports national and Latin American dance movements.
Address: VISTA HERMOSA 65, Col Portales, Mexico City, DF 03300, Mexico. TEL 525-5490282, FAX 525-5490282, danzaria@mexico.com, http://www.planet-interkom.de/ruhrland2/index.htm. Ed. Roberto Aguilar.

DENVER ARTS CENTER PROGRAMS. see *THEATER*

793.3 USA ISSN 0363-972X
GV1623
DIRECTORY OF DANCE COMPANIES✶. Text in English. a.
Published by: (National Endowment for the Arts), Charles Reinhart Management, Inc., 1697 Broadway, Ste 1201, New York, NY 10019-5904.

793.3 ARG ISSN 0329-093X
DOCUMENTOS E INVESTIGACIONES SOBRE LA HISTORIA DEL TANGO✶. Text in Spanish. 1994. irreg. price varies. adv. bk.rev.; dance rev. illus. back issues avail. **Document type:** *Monographic series.* **Description:** Covers all aspects of tango and related fields. Instruments, singers and old tango orchestras in Buenos Aires.
Published by: Instituto de Investigaciones del Tango, Yatay No. 296, Piso 1 C, Buenos Aires, 1184, Argentina. TEL 54-11-49828399, FAX 54-11-43285521, gomezq@mbox.servicenet.com.ar. Ed., Pub., R&P, Adv. contact Marisa Donadio. Circ: 1,000 (paid).

793 IRL
DUBFLY; youth urban culture guide. Text in English. m. free. adv. **Document type:** *Magazine, Consumer.* **Description:** Contains news and reviews of the clubbing scene in Ireland.
Address: Space 28, North Lotts, Dublin, 1, Ireland. TEL 353-1-8786875, FAX 353-1-8726827, info@dubfly.com, http://www.dubfly.com. adv.: page EUR 2,285; 105 x 148. Circ: 15,000 (controlled).

DUE SOUTH; the biggest guide to what's on in the South. see *ARTS AND HANDICRAFTS*

792.8 USA ISSN 1048-9894
EMERALD CITY DANCE NEWS✶. Text in English. 1984. m. USD 15; USD 35 foreign (effective 1997). **Document type:** *Newsletter.*
Address: 17408 44th Ave W, Unit 2, Lynnwood, WA 98037-7407. TEL 206-542-1639, FAX 206-542-1639, ecdnj@aol.com. Ed. Joan Adams. Circ: 350.

ENERGY MAGAZINE. see *MUSIC*

ENGLISH DANCE AND SONG. see *MUSIC*

793.3 CHE
FESTIVALMAGAZIN. Text in German. 1988. a. free. adv. back issues avail. **Document type:** *Magazine, Consumer.*
Published by: Verein Berner Tanztage, Postfach 317, Bern 14, 3000, Switzerland. TEL 41-31-3760303, FAX 41-31-3710333, info@tanztage.ch, http://www.tanztage.ch. Eds. Anne Jaeggi, Claudia Rosiny. Adv. contact Reto Clavadetscher. Circ: 25,000 (controlled).

781.626 793.319 SWE
FLAMENCOTIDNINGEN DUENDE. Text in Swedish. 1996. q. SEK 120 to members. **Description:** Deals with flamenco as dance, music, culture and living art form.
Published by: Goeteborgs Flamencofoerening, c/o Arbaeus, Lovskogsgatan 2 C, Goeteborg, 41320, Sweden. TEL 46-31-16-04-88, elli.arbaeus@mailbox.swipnet.se.

793.31 USA ISSN 0163-528X
FOLK DANCE DIRECTORY. Text in English. a. USD 0.60.
Published by: Folk Dance Association, PO Box 500, Midwood Sta, Brooklyn, NY 11230. TEL 718-434-2304.

793.31 398.2 USA ISSN 1081-2695
GV1587.5
FOLK DANCE PHONE BOOK AND GROUP DIRECTORY (YEAR); a demographic study of recreational international folk dancing. Text in English. 1993. a. USD 25 per issue (effective 2005). adv. **Document type:** *Directory.*
Published by: Society of Folk Dance Historians, 2100 Rio Grande St, Austin, TX 78705-5578. TEL 512-478-9676, fdhist@yahoo.com, http://www.recfd.com/sofdhfly.htm. Ed., Pub., R&P Ron Houston. adv.: page USD 150. Circ: 700.

793.31 398.2 USA ISSN 1081-7654
GV1743
FOLK DANCE PROBLEM SOLVER (YEAR). Text in English. 1987. a. USD 20 (effective 2003). **Document type:** *Monographic series, Academic/Scholarly.* **Description:** Descriptions, histories, backgrounds, lyrics, anecdotes, essays, poetry, scores, and illustrations about international folk dances.
Published by: Society of Folk Dance Historians, 2100 Rio Grande St, Austin, TX 78705-5578. sofdh@juno.com, fdhist@yahoo.com, http://www.recfd.com/sofdhfly.htm. Ed. Ron Houston. Circ: 700 (controlled).

793.31 CAN
GV1743
FOLK DANCER. Text in English. 1969. m. (7/yr.). CND 20. adv. bk.rev. illus. **Document type:** *Newsletter.* **Description:** Listings, articles and reviews concerning international folk dance and folklore.
Formerly: Ontario Folkdancer (0384-5052)
Published by: Ontario Folk Dance Association, 30 Chichester Place, Unit 27, Scarborough, ON M1T 3S5, Canada. TEL 416-489-1621, kbudd@interlog.com, http://www.web.net/~ofda. Ed., R&P Kevin Budd. Adv. contact Margaret Whelan. page CND 45. Circ: 500.

793.31 GBR
FOLK DIRECTORY. Text in English. 197?. a. GBP 5.50 to non-members; GBP 4.50 to members (effective 1999). **Document type:** *Directory.*
Published by: English Folk Dance and Song Society, Cecil Sharp House, 2 Regents Park Rd, London, NW1 7AY, United Kingdom. TEL 44-20-7425-2206, FAX 44-20-7284-0534, efdss@efdss.org, http://www.efdss.org.

FOLK MUSIC JOURNAL. see *MUSIC*

FOLK NORTH-WEST. see *MUSIC*

THE FOLKFIRE; St. Louis dance & music. see *MUSIC*

793.33 USA
FOOTNOTES (HUDSON)✶. Text in English. bi-m.?. **Document type:** *Newsletter.*
Published by: New Hampshire American Ballroom Dance Association, 8 Kimball Hill Rd, Hudson, NH 03051-3915. Ed. Bill Cahill.

793.31 USA
FORWARD AND BACK. Text in English. 1979. irreg. USD 1 per issue.
Published by: Jacob Bloom, Ed. & Pub., 34 Andrew St, Newton, MA 02161. Circ: 100.

FOTNOTEN. see *MUSIC*

793.3 USA
FRIENDS LINE. Text in English. s-a. membership. **Document type:** *Newsletter.*
Published by: Paul Taylor Dance Company, 552 Broadway, New York, NY 10012. TEL 212-431-5562, FAX 212-966-5673.

793.33 USA
FRIENDS OF BALLROOM DANCING NEWSLETTER. Text in English. bi-m.?. **Document type:** *Newsletter.*
Address: 253 E Main Rd, Portsmouth, RI 02871. Ed. Skip Jones.

792.8 AUS ISSN 0819-9833
FURTHER STUDIES IN DANCE; a guide for Australian dance students. Text in English. 1990. a. AUD 5 domestic; AUD 15 foreign (effective 2000). **Document type:** *Bulletin.*
Published by: Australian Dance Council - Ausdance National Secretariat, 40 Mort St. 1st Fl, PO Box 45, Braddon, ACT 2612, Australia. TEL 61-2-6248-8992, FAX 61-2-6247-4701, ausdance.national@anu.edu.au, national@ausdance.org.au, http://www.ausdance.anu.edu.au.

792.8 780.904 ITA ISSN 0017-0232
GIORNALE DELLO SPETTACOLO. Text in Italian. 1945. w. looseleaf. adv. film rev. charts; stat. **Document type:** *Newspaper.*
Formerly (until 1957): Bollettino dello Spettacolo (1122-3286)
Indexed: RASB, RILM.
Published by: Gestioni Editoriali A G I S, Via Di Villa Patrizi, 10, Rome, RM 00161, Italy. TEL 39-06-884731, FAX 39-06-88473213. Ed. Luigi Filippi. Circ: 14,000 (controlled).

DER HEIMATPFLEGER; Zeitschrift fuer Volkstanz, Volksmusik, Brauchtum und Heimatpflege. see *FOLKLORE*

793.31 781.7 SWE ISSN 0346-9018
HEMBYGDEN. Text in Swedish. 1921. q. adv. bk.rev. illus. **Document type:** *Consumer.* **Description:** Folkdance and folk music.
Formerly (until 1923): Folkdansringen; Incorporates (1959-1962): Spelmansbladet
Indexed: NAA.
Published by: Svenska Ungdomsringen foer Bygdekultur, PO Box 34056, Stockholm, 10026, Sweden. TEL 46-8-6950015, FAX 46-8-6950022, rikskansliet@ungdomsringen.se, http://www.ungdomsringen.se/riks/default.htm. Circ: 35,000.

INDIAN MUSICOLOGICAL SOCIETY. JOURNAL. see *MUSIC*

INSIDE ARTS. see *THEATER*

INTER - ART ACTUEL. see *ARCHITECTURE*

792.8 IRL ISSN 1649-1122
IRELAND IN LINE. Text in English. 2001. bi-m. adv. **Document type:** *Magazine, Consumer.* **Description:** Covers all aspects of line dancing.
Published by: Vine Publications Ltd., 29 Dublin Rd., Bray, Co. Wicklow, Ireland. TEL 353-1-2765288, FAX 353-1-2765289. adv.: B&W page EUR 311, color page EUR 381.

IRISH MUSIC AND DANCE ASSOCIATION NEWSLETTER. see *MUSIC*

793.31 ISR
ISRAEL DANCE QUARTERLY. Text in English, Hebrew. 1993. q. USD 37 (effective 1998). adv. bk.rev. illus. index. **Document type:** *Newspaper.* **Description:** News of dance activities in Israel.
Supersedes (1975-1989): Israel Dance (Annual) (0334-2301)
Indexed: IDP, IHP, RILM.
Published by: Zoom Hafakot, 39 Shoham St., Haifa, 34679, Israel. TEL 972-4-8344051, FAX 972-4-8344051. Ed. Giora Manor. Circ: 2,000.

792.8 USA
JITTERBUG✶; the premiere swing dance publication. Text in English. 4/yr. USD 25. **Description:** Covers star biographies, swing history, competition reviews, coming events, and music and video listings.
Published by: Jitterbug Press, 21544 Wesley Dr., Apt. 9, Laguana Beach, CA 92651-8102. TEL 714-494-5086. Ed. Catherine E Cannon.

792.8 USA ISSN 1529-0824
JOURNAL OF DANCE EDUCATION. Text in English. q. USD 57 domestic to individuals; USD 69 foreign to individuals; USD 72 domestic to institutions; USD 84 foreign to institutions (effective 2005); free to members. **Document type:** *Journal, Academic/Scholarly.*

—BLDSC (4967.355000), IE. **CCC.**
Published by: (National Dance Education Organization), Ryan J. Michael Publishing, Inc., 24 Crescent Dr N, Andover, NJ 07821. TEL 973-786-7777, FAX 973-786-7776, http://www.ndeo.org/publications.asp.

JUILLIARD JOURNAL; monthly newspaper. see *MUSIC*

793 IND ISSN 0047-3103
PN1582.I4
KALAKALPAM. Text in English. 1966. s-a. INR 2. adv. illus.
Published by: Karyalaya Natya Kala Kendram Institute, 30-A Paddapukur Rd., Kolkata, West Bengal 700 020, India. Ed. Ammini S Menon.

793.3 052 CAN ISSN 1495-8503
KLUBLIFE. Text in English. 1997. m. CND 20 domestic; USD 20 in United States; CND 40 elsewhere; CND 1 newsstand/cover (effective 2000). **Document type:** *Magazine.*
Former titles (until 1999): Klublife Magazine (1490-2907); (until 1998): Klublife (1481-4021)
Related titles: Online - full text ed.
Published by: Klublife Publications, 439 King St W, 4th Fl, Toronto, ON M5V 1K4, Canada. TEL 416-644-8680, editor@klublife.com, http://www.klublife.com.

792.8 ESP
KOS. Text in Spanish. 6/yr. adv.
Published by: Associacio de Ballarins i Coreografs Professionals de Catalunya, Via Laietana, 52, Barcelona, 08003, Spain. TEL 34-3-2682473, FAX 34-3-2680680. Adv. contact Elisa Huertas.

LEAPING; magazine of Christian dance fellowship of Australia. see *RELIGIONS AND THEOLOGY—Other Denominations And Sects*

792.8 USA ISSN 0024-1253
GV1580
LET'S DANCE✶ . Text in English. 1949. m. (10/yr.). USD 15; USD 20 foreign (effective 2000). adv. **Description:** Covers the where, when, how and who of international folk dance.
Published by: Folk Dance Federation of California, South, P O Box 789, Kenwood, CA 95452-0789. FAX 510-814-9282, bbrux@wco.com. Ed. Genevieve Pereira. adv.: B&W page USD 80; 10 x 7.5. Circ: 500.

793.34 GBR ISSN 0301-8881
GV1763
LET'S SQUARE DANCE. Text in English. 1953. m. GBP 2.70. adv.
Published by: British Association of American Square Dance Clubs, 32 Great Whyte, Ramsey, Huntingdon, Cambs PE17 1HA, United Kingdom. Ed. D White. Circ: 1,000. **Subscr. to:** Mr. S. Nye, 4 Devonshire Gardens, London N21 2AL, United Kingdom.

792.8 GBR ISSN 1366-6509
LINEDANCER. Text in English. 1996. m. GBP 27 domestic; GBP 38 in Europe; GBP 54 elsewhere; GBP 2.80 newsstand/cover (effective 2001). illus. back issues avail. **Document type:** *Consumer.* **Description:** Covers all aspects of linedancing.
Published by: Champion Publications, Clare House, 166 Lord St, Southport, Merseyside PR9 0QA, United Kingdom. TEL 44-1704-501235, FAX 44-1704-501678, dancers@linedancermagazine.com, http://www.linedancermagazine.com. Ed. Tim Matthews. Pub. Betty Drummond. Adv. contact Sam Fraser. **Dist. by:** Warners Group Publications Plc, The Maltings, West St, Bourne, Lincs PE10 9PH, United Kingdom. TEL 44-1778-393652, FAX 44-1778-393668, tomb@warnersgroup.co.uk.

M O D - MUSIC, OPERA, DANCE & DRAMA IN ASIA, THE PACIFIC AND NORTH AMERICA. see *THEATER*

M6 DANCE. see *MUSIC*

MAILOUT; arts work with people. see *ART*

MARCAN HANDBOOK OF ARTS ORGANISATIONS. see *ART*

793.33 USA
MASSACHUSETTS AMERICAN BALLROOM DANCE ASSOCIATION NEWSLETTER. Short title: Mass A B D A Newsletter. Text in English. bi-m. **Document type:** *Newsletter.*
Published by: Massachusetts American Ballroom Dance Association, 9 Isabelle Cir, Rowley, MA 01969-2517.

MEDICAL PROBLEMS OF PERFORMING ARTISTS. see *MEDICAL SCIENCES*

792.8 USA ISSN 1041-7591
MIDDLE EASTERN DANCER MAGAZINE. Text in English. 1979. m. USD 24 domestic; USD 34 in Canada & Mexico; USD 44 elsewhere. adv. bk.rev.; film rev.; play rev. illus.; tr.lit. back issues avail. **Description:** Covers dance and culture of the Middle East for performers and enthusiasts; news and reviews.
Formerly: Southern Dancer
Published by: Mideastern Connection, Inc., 5097 Ernst Ct., Orlando, FL 32819-7549. TEL 407-831-3402, FAX 407-869-0830. Ed. Karen Kuzsel. adv.: B&W page USD 195. Circ: 2,500.

792.8 USA
MINNESOTA DANCE NEWSLETTER. Text in English. 1979. bi-m. USD 15 (effective 2000). adv. bk.rev. **Document type:** *Newsletter.*
Formerly: M I C A Newsletter
Published by: Minnesota Dance Alliance, 528 Hennepin Ave., Ste. 510, Minneapolis, MN 55403-1810. TEL 612-340-1900, FAX 612-340-9919. Ed., Adv. contact Nancy Mason Hauser. R&P June Wilson. Circ: 1,600.

MISSOURI JOURNAL OF HEALTH, PHYSICAL EDUCATION, RECREATION AND DANCE. see *PHYSICAL FITNESS AND HYGIENE*

792.8 GBR
➤ **MOVEMENT AND DANCE QUARTERLY.** Text in English. 1948. q. GBP 20 domestic; GBP 25 foreign (effective 2000). adv. bk.rev. **Document type:** *Newsletter, Academic/Scholarly.* **Description:** Explores dance and movement based upon Laban's principles and analysis of human movement as applied to theatre, therapy, recreational dance, management consultancy, education, and choreography.
Former titles (until 1992): Movement and Dance; (until Jan. 1982): Laban Art of Movement Guild Magazine
Published by: Laban Guild, 3 Layton Ln, Shaftesbury, Dorset SP7 8EY, United Kingdom. TEL 44-1747-54634. Ed., R&P Lydia Everitt. Adv. contact Ann Ward. Circ: 1,000.

792.8 USA ISSN 1077-0933
NX456.5.P38
MOVEMENT RESEARCH PERFORMANCE JOURNAL. Text in English. 1990. s-a. USD 5 domestic; USD 15 foreign (effective 2001). adv. **Document type:** *Consumer.*
Published by: Movement Research Inc., Dance Theater Workshop, 219 W 19th St, New York, NY 10011. info@movementresearch.org, http://www.movementresearch.org/performancejournal/index.html. Ed. Sarah Michelson.

793.33 780 USA ISSN 1072-8481
MUSIC & DANCE NEWS. Text in English. 1972. bi-m. USD 15 domestic; USD 24 foreign (effective 2002). adv. rec.rev. **Document type:** *Newspaper.* **Description:** News, articles, announcements, and reviews on ballroom, polka, country and swing dancing in the Midwest. Includes features on different ballrooms. Audience is generally 50 and over.
Formerly (until 1992): Entertainment Bits (0192-8430)
Published by: (Minnesota Ballroom Operators Association), Von Meyer Publishing, PO Box 324, St. Joseph, MN 56374-0324. TEL 320-363-7741, 800-386-2261, FAX 320-363-4195, newsleader@mn.astound.net. Ed., R&P, Adv. contact Janelle Von Pinnon. page USD 784. Circ: 16,000.

MUSIK & THEATER; die aktuelle Kulturzeitschrift. see *MUSIC*

N C A NEWS. see *ART*

793.34 790.1 USA ISSN 0195-0150
N S D C A TIMES. Text in English. 1969. q. USD 15 to members. adv. bk.rev. **Document type:** *Newsletter, Consumer.*
Published by: National Square Dance Campers Association, PO Box 18, Lower Waterford, VT 05848-0018. TEL 802-748-9478, FAX 802-748-4742, nsdcatimes@juno.com. Ed. Barbara Connelly. Pub. Troll Press. R&P, Adv. contact Peg Tirrell TEL 802-748-8538. page USD 100; 6.88 x 9.5. Circ: 3,500 (controlled).

N Y C - ON STAGE. (New York City) see *THEATER*

NATIONAL FOUNDATION FOR ADVANCEMENT IN THE ARTS. ANNUAL REPORT. see *ART*

793.34 USA ISSN 0746-3685
NATIONAL SQUARES✶ ; a national square dance magazine. Text in English. 1977. q. USD 6. adv. **Description:** Covers past and future conventions and other activities of the Convention.
Published by: National Square Dance Convention, 8805 Madison Ave, Apt 309D, Indianapolis, IN 46227-6458. TEL 317-787-7864. Ed. Clare Lively. Circ: 3,000.

792.8 USA
NEW YORK CITY BALLET NEWS. Text in English. 1977. 3/yr. membership. **Document type:** *Newsletter.* **Description:** Features articles, news and updates on the company, its dancers, and people and events which influence the world of ballet. Includes dancer profiles and notices of events.
Published by: New York City Ballet Guild, New York City Ballet, Inc., New York State Theater, 20 Lincoln Center, New York, NY 10023. TEL 212-870-5677, FAX 212-870-4244. Ed. Carol Landers. Circ: 6,000 (controlled).

793.33 USA
NEXT GENERATION NEWSLETTER. Text in English. 1989. q. USD 25 to members. adv. **Document type:** *Newsletter.*
Published by: Next Generation Swing Dance Club, 236 W Portal Ave, Ste 329, San Francisco, CA 94127-0901. TEL 415-979-4456.

793.34 USA ISSN 1044-2928
THE NORTHEAST SQUARE DANCER MAGAZINE. Text in English. 1951. m. USD 27.50 domestic; USD 30 in Canada (effective 2005). adv. bk.rev. **Document type:** *Magazine, Consumer.*
Formerly: New England Square Dance Caller (0028-4920)
Published by: E & P J Enterprises, 145 Stone Dam Rd, N Scituate, RI 02857. TEL 401-647-9688, 800-333-6236, nsd@squaredance.ws, http://www.squaredance.ws/. Ed., Pub. Ed Juaire. adv.: page USD 351. Circ: 5,000.

792.8 BEL ISSN 0778-9580
GV1580
NOUVELLES DE DANSE. Text in French. 1990. q. EUR 38 to individuals; EUR 70 to institutions (effective 2002). adv. bk.rev. bibl.; illus. back issues avail. **Description:** Covers dance as a performing art. Publishes articles on specific topics in dance.
Indexed: IDP.
Published by: Contredanse, Rue de Flandres 46, Brussels, 1000, Belgium. TEL 32-2-5020327, FAX 32-2-5138739, contredanse@skynet.be, http://users.skynet.be/contredanse. Ed. Patricia Kuypers.

OBITUARIES IN THE PERFORMING ARTS. see *THEATER*

792.8 USA ISSN 1060-3972
ON POINTE; the magazine for young dance enthusiasts. Text in English. 1992. bi-m. USD 25; USD 4.50 newsstand/cover. **Document type:** *Consumer.*
Published by: Solebury Press, PO Box 512, Solebury, PA 18963.

ON TOUR; drama and dance newsletter. see *THEATER*

792.8 USA
PARTY PLATTER. Text in English. 1988. q. **Document type:** *Newsletter.* **Description:** Covers news and information on ballroom dancing in New England.
Address: 229 Coolidge Ave, Apt 304, Watertown, MA 02172-1554. TEL 617-923-8211, atheling@earthlink.net. Ed., R&P Anne Atheling.

PARTY-TIME. see *MUSIC*

PERFORMANCE RESEARCH; a journal of the performing arts. see *THEATER*

PERFORMING ARTS AND ENTERTAINMENT IN CANADA. see *THEATER*

791.43 USA
PERFORMING ARTS BUYERS GUIDE. Text in English. 1974. q. free (effective 2005). adv. bk.rev. tr.lit. back issues avail. **Document type:** *Catalog.*
Formerly: Performing Arts Buyers Guide: Footnotes; Incorporates: Buyers Guide: Footnotes; Footnotes (Philadelphia)
Indexed: RASB.
Published by: Stagestep, 4701 Bath St., # 46, Philadelphia, PA 19137-2229. TEL 215-636-9000, FAX 800-877-3342, stagestep@stagestep.com, http://www.stagestep.com. Ed. Virginia Villion. Pub. Randy Swartz. Adv. contact Barbara Solot. Circ: 300,000 (controlled).

PERFORMING ARTS YEARBOOK FOR EUROPE. see *THEATER*

PLACE DES ARTS. MAGAZINE. see *THEATER*

792.8 USA ISSN 1529-6741
GV1787
POINTE; ballet at its best. Text in English. 2000. bi-m. USD 13.98; USD 4.99 (effective 2005). adv. illus. **Document type:** *Magazine, Trade.* **Description:** Covers all aspects of ballet from training ot performance.
Formerly: Points
Related titles: Online - full text ed.: (from EBSCO Publishing, O C L C Online Computer Library Center, Inc., ProQuest Information & Learning).
Indexed: MASUSE.
Published by: Lifestyle Media Inc., 110 William St, 23rd Fl, New York, NY 10038-3900. vjohnson@lifestyleventures.com, http://www.pointemagazine.com. Ed. Virginia Johnson. Pub. Carrie Molay. Adv. contact Joanna Harp. Circ: 30,000 (paid).

792.8 ESP ISSN 1134-6612
POR LA DANZA. Text in Spanish. 1990. q. EUR 21.04 domestic; EUR 28.85 foreign (effective 2003). 54 p./no.; **Document type:** *Magazine, Consumer.* **Description:** Provides in-depth reviews of the world of Spanish dance and its leading figures, promoting knowledge of its manifestations, whether Flamenco, ballet or contemporary dance.
Published by: Asociacion Cultural por la Danza, C Atocha 105, 1o. A, Madrid, 28012, Spain. TEL 34-91-4203032, FAX 34-91-4203963, danza@wanadoo.es. Ed. Ana V Cabo. **Dist. by:** Asociacion de Revistas Culturales de Espana, Hortaleza, 75, Madrid 28004, Spain. TEL 34-91-3086066, FAX 34-91-3199267, info@arce.es, http://www.arce.es.

D

793.3 FRA ISSN 0183-3189
POUR LA DANSE✱; chaussons et petits rats. Text in French. 1975 (no.31). bi-m. adv. bk.rev. charts; illus.
Published by: Societe Rivanova, 51 rue de Belleville, Paris, 75019, France. Ed. Annie Bozzini.

PRATT INSTITUTE CREATIVE ARTS THERAPY REVIEW. see *MEDICAL SCIENCES—Physical Medicine And Rehabilitation*

793 780 792 CAN
PRELUDE (OTTAWA)✱. Text in English, French. 1969. 5/yr. free. adv. **Document type:** *Bulletin.*
Former titles: N A C Calendar of Events; Ovation; National Arts Centre. Calendar of Events (0033-1023); Supersedes: Prologue
Indexed: CMPI.
Published by: National Arts Centre, Marketing Department, 53 Elgin St, P O Box 1534, Stn B, Ottawa, ON K1P 5W1, Canada. TEL 613-996-5051, FAX 613-996-9578. Ed. Jennifer Millar. Adv. contact Dianne Wing. Circ: 56,000.

PRESENS. see *THEATER*

793.33 USA
R I A B D A NEWSLETTER. Text in English. bi-m. **Document type:** *Newsletter.*
Published by: Rhode Island American Ballroom Dance Association, 25 Zipporah St, North Providence, RI 02911. Ed. Gall Stone.

REALTIME; + OnScreen. see *THEATER*

792.8 GBR ISSN 1464-7893
GV1589
RESEARCH IN DANCE EDUCATION. Text in English. 2000. s-a. GBP 152, USD 245 combined subscription to institutions print & online eds. (effective 2006). bk.rev. reprint service avail. from PSC. **Document type:** *Journal.* **Description:** Aims to inform, stimulate and promote the development of research in dance education and is relevant to both learners and teachers.
Related titles: Online - full text ed.: ISSN 1470-1111. GBP 144, USD 245 to institutions (effective 2006) (from EBSCO Publishing, Gale Group, IngentaConnect, O C L C Online Computer Library Center, Inc., Swets Information Services).
Indexed: BrEdI, ERA, ETA, MEA, PEI, RHEA, SEA, SENA, SOMA, SWA, TEA.
—Infotrieve. **CCC.**
Published by: Routledge (Subsidiary of: Taylor & Francis Group), 4 Park Sq, Milton Park, Abingdon, Oxon OX14 4RN, United Kingdom. TEL 44-1235-828600, FAX 44-1235-829000, info@routledge.co.uk, http://www.tandf.co.uk/journals/titles/14647893.asp, http://www.routledge.co.uk. Ed. Linda M Rolfe. **Subscr. to:** Taylor & Francis Ltd, Journals Customer Service, Rankine Rd, Basingstoke, Hants RG24 8PR, United Kingdom. TEL 44-1256-813000, FAX 44-1256-330245.

D

792.8 GBR
ROYAL ACADEMY OF DANCING. ANNUAL REPORT. Text in English. a. membership. **Document type:** *Corporate.*
Published by: Royal Academy of Dance, 36 Battersea Sq, London, SW11 3RA, United Kingdom. TEL 44-171-223-0091, FAX 44-171-924-3129. Ed. Antonia Price. Pub. David Watchman.

793.31 GBR
ROYAL SCOTTISH COUNTRY DANCE SOCIETY BULLETIN. Text in English. 1924. a. membership. adv. **Document type:** *Newsletter.*
Published by: Royal Scottish Country Dance Society, 12 Coates Crescent, Edinburgh, EH3 7AF, United Kingdom. TEL 44-131-225-3854, FAX 44-131-225-7783. Circ: 24,500.

793.3 USA
S O S CAREFREE TIMES. (Society of Stranders) Text in English. 2/yr. USD 12. **Description:** Covers about 90 Shag clubs in Southeast U.S.
Published by: Association of Carolina Shag Clubs, PO Box 4688, Columbia, SC 29204. Ed. Phil Sawyer.

793.31 200 USA ISSN 1043-5328
SACRED DANCE GUILD JOURNAL. Text in English. 1958. 3/yr. USD 28 domestic membership; USD 31 in Canada membership; USD 37 elsewhere membership (effective 2000). adv. bk.rev. **Document type:** *Academic/Scholarly.* **Description:** Contains chapter and membership news to network information. Also shares insights in the field of sacred dance.
Published by: Sacred Dance Guild, 201 Hewitt, Carbondale, IL 62901. TEL 618-457-8603. Ed., Pub., R&P, Adv. contact Toni Intravaia. Circ: 600.

SAN FRANCISCO ARTS MONTHLY. see *MUSEUMS AND ART GALLERIES*

SANGEET NATAK; journal of Indian music, dance, theatre and drama. see *MUSIC*

SCREEN & STAGE DIRECTORY; national casting guide. see *THEATER*

793.3 DEU
SENIOREN TANZEN. Text in German. 1980. q. EUR 34; EUR 8.50 newsstand/cover (effective 2005). adv. **Document type:** *Magazine, Consumer.* **Description:** Dancing for senior citizens and handicapped people.
Formerly: Bundesverband Seniorentanz. Informationsblatt
Published by: Bundesverband Seniorentanz e.V., Insterburger Str 25, Bremen, 28207, Germany. TEL 49-421-441180, FAX 49-421-4986217, verband@seniorentanz.de, http://www.seniorentanz.de.

793.31 398.2 USA
SOCIETY OF FOLK DANCE HISTORIANS. REPORT TO MEMBERS. Text in English. 1990. q. USD 20 (effective 2000 - 2001). bk.rev. **Document type:** *Newsletter, Corporate.*
Published by: Society of Folk Dance Historians, 2100 Rio Grande St, Austin, TX 78705-5578. sofdh@juno.com, fdhist@yahoo.com, http://www.recfd.com/sofdhfly.htm. Ed. Ron Houston. Circ: 700.

SPILLEROM; tidsskrift for scenekunst. see *THEATER*

SRUTI; India's premier music and dance magazine. see *MUSIC*

STAGE STEPS. see *THEATER*

STATE OF THE ARTS. see *MUSEUMS AND ART GALLERIES*

781.6 973.34 DNK ISSN 0906-1061
STRINGS AND SQUARES; bladet for traditionel amerikansk dans og musik i Danmark. Text in Danish. 1984. bi-m. DKK 50 domestic; DKK 100 foreign (effective 2001). adv. bk.rev.; rec.rev. illus. back issues avail. **Document type:** *Newsletter.* **Description:** Covers square and contra dancing and bluegrass and old-time music events in Denmark.
Former titles: Lydhullet (0109-2480); Broken Strings (0107-4172)
Related titles: Online - full text ed.
Published by: Traditional Square & Contra Dance in Denmark, c/o Margot Gunzenhauser, Hasselvej 18, Virum, 2830, Denmark. TEL 45-45-83-99-83, mgunz@worldonline.dk, http://hjem.get2net.dk/squaredancepartners. Ed. Joern Borggreen. Pub., R&P, Adv. contact Margot Gunzenhauser TEL 45-45-83-99-83. B&W page DKK 500; trim 210 x 150. Circ: 1,300. **Subscr. to:** Line Bach Nielsen, Byagervej 63 C, Beder 8330, Denmark.

793.3 USA ISSN 1043-7592
GV1601
➤ **STUDIES IN DANCE HISTORY.** Text in English. 1989. irreg. price varies. adv. illus. back issues avail. **Document type:** *Monographic series, Academic/Scholarly.* **Description:** Covers the history of dance and related disciplines.
Related titles: Microform ed.: (from RPI).
Indexed: ABS&EES, AmH&L, BibInd, HistAb, IDP, IIPA, RILM.
Published by: (Society of Dance History Scholars), University of Wisconsin Press, Books Division, 1930 Monroe St, 3rd Fl, Madison, WI 53711-2059. TEL 608-263-1110, FAX 608-263-1120, uwiscpress@uwpress.wisc.edu, http://www.sdhs.org/studies.html, http://www.wisc.edu/wisconsinpress/books.html. adv.: page USD 300. Circ: 650.

➤ **SWING TIME.** see *MUSIC*

792.8 CHE
TANZ DER DINGE. Text in German. 1988. 6/yr. CHF 48 domestic; CHF 58 foreign (effective 2001). adv. music rev.; Website rev.; dance rev. illus. back issues avail. **Document type:** *Magazine, Consumer.* **Description:** Contains information on contemporary dance, including dance history, coming events, reviews, and national and international news.
Published by: Tanzding Verlag, Postfach, Zuerich, 8025, Switzerland. TEL 41-1-2622660, FAX 41-1-2622660, tanzding@hotmail.com, http://www.tanzding.ch. Eds. Marianne Forster, Wolfgang Brunner. adv.: page CHF 1,100; trim 205 x 270. Circ: 3,000.

793 796.41 CHE
TANZ UND GYMNASTIK. Text in German, French. 1944. q. CHF 35; CHF 40 foreign. adv. bk.rev. illus. **Document type:** *Bulletin.* **Description:** Focuses on ballet and modern dance. Includes coming events, courses, workshops, auditions, book information and reviews.
Indexed: IDP, IIPA.
Published by: Schweizerischer Berufsverband fuer Tanz und Gymnastik/Association of Swiss Professionals in Dance and Movement, c/o Marianne Forster, Ed., Mittlere Str 4, Basel, 4056, Switzerland. TEL 41-61-2611662, FAX 41-61-2611604. Adv. contact Hans Ritmeyer. Circ: 1,100.

793.3 DEU ISSN 0724-1062
TANZEN. Text in German. 1983. q. EUR 36 domestic; EUR 40 foreign; EUR 9.80 newsstand/cover (effective 2004). adv. back issues avail.; reprints avail. **Document type:** *Magazine, Trade.*
Indexed: DIP, IBR, IBZ, IDP, IIPA.
Published by: (Deutscher Bundesverband Tanz e.V.), Mediengruppe Koenig, Aeussere Zeulenrodaer Str 11, Greiz, 07973 , Germany. TEL 49-3661-674213, FAX 49-3661-674214, verlag-koenig@t-online.de, http://www.die-tanzen.de, http://www.mediengruppe-koenig.de. Adv. contact Uwe Hilke. B&W page EUR 1,170, color page EUR 1,555; trim 185 x 265. Circ: 2,200.

793.3 DEU ISSN 0940-1008
TANZFORSCHUNG. Text in German. 1991. a. **Document type:** *Academic/Scholarly.*
Published by: (Gesellschaft fuer Tanzforschung e.V.), Florian Noetzel Verlag, Heinrichshofen Buecher, Valoisstr 11, Wilhelmshaven, 26382, Germany.

793.3 DEU ISSN 0931-5640
TANZSPIEGEL. Text in German. 1987. m. EUR 30.70 domestic; EUR 49.50 in Europe; EUR 61.50 elsewhere; EUR 2.56 newsstand/cover (effective 2002). adv. **Document type:** *Magazine, Consumer.*
Superseded in part (1986-1987): Tanzen (0930-536X)
Published by: (Deutscher Tanzsportverband e.V.), Tanzwelt Verlag GmbH, Haus des Sports II, Otto-Fleck-Schneise 12, Frankfurt Am Main, 60528, Germany. TEL 49-69-677285-0, FAX 49-69-67728530, tanzwelt@tanzsport.de, http://www.tanzsport.de/templates/i_tanzspiegel.html. adv.: B&W page EUR 920, color page EUR 1,280; trim 210 x 297. Circ: 19,000 (paid and controlled).

792.8 DEU ISSN 1434-0771
TERPSICHORE; Tanzhistorische Studien. Text in German. 1997. irreg., latest vol.3, 1999. price varies. **Document type:** *Monographic series, Academic/Scholarly.* **Description:** Studies the history of dance.
Published by: Georg Olms Verlag, Hagentorwall 7, Hildesheim, 31134, Germany. TEL 49-5121-1501-0, FAX 49-5121-150150, info@olms.de, http://www.olms.de. R&P Christiane Busch.

THEATER HEUTE. see *THEATER*

UP MAGAZINE. see *MUSIC*

UPDATE (LONDON); the essential dance music weekly. see *MUSIC*

792.8 USA
VAIL INTERNATIONAL DANCE FESTIVAL. Text in English. a.
Published by: Mac Media LLC, The Media Center, 2955 Village Dr, PO Box 774328, Steamboat Springs, CO 80477. TEL 970-879-5250, FAX 970-879-4650, http://www.macmediaweb.com.

VICE; art and entertainment newsmagazine. see *ART*

VISSLINGAR & ROP. see *THEATER*

VOLKSDANS. see *FOLKLORE*

W P A S MUSELETTER; Membership Newsletter of Washington Performing Arts Society. see *MUSIC*

793.31 USA
WOODS HOLE FOLK MUSIC SOCIETY NEWSLETTER. Text in English. 1975. irreg., latest vol.2, 1991. free to qualified personnel. illus. back issues avail. **Document type:** *Newsletter.* **Description:** Presents folk performers of the society, local folk festivals, club business, and local folk radio.
Published by: Woods Hole Folk Music Society, 174 Lakeshore Dr, East Falmouth, MA 02536. TEL 508-540-0320. Circ: 600.

793.3 CHN ISSN 0512-4204
GV1580
WUDAO/DANCING. Text in Chinese. 1958. bi-m. USD 30; USD 5 newsstand/cover (effective 2001).
Related titles: Online - full text ed.: (from East View Information Services).
Published by: Zhongguo Wudaojia Xiehui/China Dancers' Association, Wenlian Dalou 16th Fl, 10 Nongzhanguan Nanli, Beijing, 100026, China. TEL 86-1-5003414. **Dist. in US by:** China Books & Periodicals Inc, 360 Swift Ave., Ste. 48, S San Fran, CA 94080-6220. TEL 415-282-2994; **Dist. by:** China International Book Trading Corp, 35 Chegongzhuang Xilu, Haidian District, PO Box 399, Beijing 100044, China. TEL 86-10-68412045, FAX 86-10-68412023, cibtc@mail.cibtc.com.cn, http://www.cibtc.com.cn.

793.3 CHN
WUDAO LUNCONG/FORUM OF DANCING. Text in Chinese. s-a. USD 12.
Contact Dist.: China Books & Periodicals Inc, 360 Swift Ave., Ste. 48, S San Fran, CA 94080-6220. info@chinabooks.com, http://www.chinabooks.com/. **Dist. by:** China International Book Trading Corp, 35 Chegongzhuang Xilu, Haidian District, PO Box 399, Beijing 100044, China. TEL 86-10-68412045, FAX 86-10-68412023, cibtc@mail.cibtc.com.cn, http://www.cibtc.com.cn.

793.3 CHN ISSN 1003-3777
WUDAO YISHU/ART OF DANCING. Text in Chinese. q.
Indexed: RILM.
Published by: Zhongguo Yishu Yanjiuyuan/Chinese Academy of Arts, 17 Qianhai Xijie, Beijing, 100009, China. TEL 651128. Ed. Zi Huajun.

WUTAI YISHU/STAGECRAFT. see *MUSIC*

792.8 USA
▼ **YOUNG DANCER.** Text in English. 2005. 5/yr. USD 15.80 (effective 2005). adv. **Document type:** *Magazine, Consumer.*

Published by: Macfadden Publishing, 333 Seventh Ave, 11th Fl, New York, NY 10001. TEL 212-979-4800, FAX 646-674-0102. Pub. Karla Johnson TEL 212-979-4859. adv.: B&W page USD 5,000, color page USD 7,100; trim 7.875 x 10.8125. Circ: 125,000.

DANCE—Abstracting, Bibliographies, Statistics

016.7928 USA ISSN 0889-8847
GV1580
ATTITUDES AND ARABESQUES. Text in English. 1980. m. USD 25 domestic to individuals; USD 35 in Canada & Mexico to individuals; USD 35 in North America to institutions; USD 40 elsewhere to institutions. bk.rev. illus. Index. reprints avail. **Document type:** *Bibliography.* **Description:** Bibliographic guide to English language dance periodicals and publications.
Indexed: SportS.
Published by: Mid-Peninsula Dance Guild, Cultural Center, 1313 Newell Rd, Palo Alto, CA 94303. TEL 415-962-1642, jogil415@aol.com. Ed., R&P Leslie Getz. Circ: 248.

016.7928 USA ISSN 0360-2737
Z7514.D2
BIBLIOGRAPHIC GUIDE TO DANCE. Text in English. 1975. a. USD 699 (effective 2005). **Document type:** *Bibliography.* **Description:** Covers all aspects of dance and every type of dance.
Published by: G.K. Hall & Co. (Subsidiary of: Gale Group), 12 Lunar Dr, Woodbridge, CT 06525. TEL 203-397-2600, FAX 203-397-8296, remmel.nunn@gale.com. **Subscr. to:** Simon & Schuster, PO Box 7500, Riverside, NJ 08075-8075. TEL 800-223-2336.

BIBLIOGRAPHIES AND INDEXES IN THE PERFORMING ARTS. see *THEATER—Abstracting, Bibliographies, Statistics*

BIO-BIBLIOGRAPHIES IN THE PERFORMING ARTS. see *THEATER—Abstracting, Bibliographies, Statistics*

016.7928 USA ISSN 1059-0382
Z7514.D2
DANCE RESEARCH. Text in English. 1989. biennial. USD 15. **Document type:** *Bibliography.*
Published by: International Council for Traditional Music Study Group on Ethnochoreology, Dept of Dance, Dance Bldg, University of California, Los Angeles, CA 90095-1608. TEL 310-825-3951, FAX 310-825-7507. Ed. Elsie Ivancich Dunin. **Co-sponsor:** Study Group on Ethnochoreology.

016.7928 USA ISSN 1058-6350
Z7514.D2
INDEX TO DANCE PERIODICALS. Text in English. 1991. a. USD 360 (effective 2005). illus. reprints avail. **Document type:** *Abstract/Index.* **Description:** Indexes articles, reviews, essays, biographical articles, and obituaries from approximately 30 periodicals published in the US, Canada, England, France, Germany, Italy, Spain and other countries.
Published by: G.K. Hall & Co. (Subsidiary of: Gale Group), PO Box 95501, Chicago, IL 60694-5501. TEL 800-877-4253, FAX 800-414-5043, gale.galeord@thomson.com, http://www.galegroup.com/gkhall.

MUSIC AND DANCE PERIODICALS; an international directory and guide book. see *MUSIC—Abstracting, Bibliographies, Statistics*

DATA BASE MANAGEMENT

see COMPUTERS—Data Base Management

DATA COMMUNICATIONS AND DATA TRANSMISSION SYSTEMS

see COMPUTERS—Data Communications And Data Transmission Systems

DENTISTRY

see MEDICAL SCIENCES—Dentistry

DERMATOLOGY AND VENEREOLOGY

see MEDICAL SCIENCES—Dermatology And Venereology

DOMESTIC COMMERCE

see BUSINESS AND ECONOMICS—Domestic Commerce

DRUG ABUSE AND ALCOHOLISM

see also PHARMACY AND PHARMACOLOGY

362.29 FIN ISSN 1457-7704
A JOUR. Text in Swedish. 2000. s-a. **Document type:** *Newsletter, Consumer.*
Related titles: Online - full text ed.: ISSN 1457-7690.
Published by: Kristliga Blabandsfoerbundet foer Rehabiliteringsarbete bland Alkohol- och Narkotikamissbrukare i Svenskfinland, Kraemertsvaegen 2, Helsingfors, 00620, Finland. TEL 358-9-72061532, FAX 358-9-72061531, kran@sininauhallito.fi, http://www.kran.fi.

616.86 USA
➤ **A S A M NEWS.** Text in English. 1985. bi-m. USD 50 to non-members. adv. bk.rev. **Document type:** *Newsletter, Academic/Scholarly.* **Description:** Covers health care reform; current information related to alcohol, tobacco, and other addicting drugs; association news.
Formerly: American Medical Society on Alcoholism and Other Drug Dependencies. Newsletter (0889-9215)
Related titles: Online - full text ed.
Published by: American Society of Addiction Medicine, 4601 N Park Ave, Ste U101, Chevy Chase, MD 20815-4519. TEL 703-538-2285, FAX 703-536-6186, bbwilford@aol.com, http://www.asam.org. Ed., R&P Bonnie B Wilford. Adv. contact Dennis Matos. Circ: 3,200.

616.86 CHE ISSN 1420-2999
ABHAENGIGKEITEN. Text in German. 1995. 3/yr. CHF 45 domestic to individuals; CHF 50 elsewhere to individuals; CHF 63 domestic to institutions; CHF 68 elsewhere to institutions; CHF 20 newsstand/cover domestic; CHF 25 newsstand/cover elsewhere (effective 2001). adv. bk.rev. abstr.; bibl. **Document type:** *Bulletin, Consumer.* **Description:** Provides experts and other interested people with results of the latest research and information on the prevention and treatment of alcoholism and other addictions.
Formed by the merger of (1977-1995): Drogalkohol (0250-6815); (1932-1995): Suchtprobleme und Sozialarbeit (1420-3065); Which was formerly (until 1980): Fuersorger (0016-3139)
Indexed: RefZh.
—GNLM.
Published by: Schweizerische Fachstelle fuer Alkohol- und Andere Drogenprobleme, Postfach 870, Lausanne, 1010, Switzerland. TEL 41-21-3212976, FAX 41-21-3212940, hfahrenkrug@sfa-ispa.ch, http://www-sfa-ispa.ch. Ed. Hermann Fahrenkrug. Adv. contact Madelene Gentil. Circ: 1,100.

616.86 SWE ISSN 0345-0406
ACCENT. Text in Swedish. 1879. 8/yr. SEK 175 (effective 2003). adv. bk.rev. **Document type:** *Magazine, Consumer.*
Formerly (until 1974): Accent, Unga Tankar; Incorporates (1905-1972): Unga Tankar; (1969-1981): Friscus (0345-3715)
Related titles: ♦ Includes: Motdrag. ISSN 0280-3348.
Published by: I O G T - N T O/International Organization of Good Templars, Gammelgaerdsvaegen 38-42, Store Essingen, PO Box 12825, Stockholm, 11297, Sweden. TEL 46-8-6726000, FAX 46-8-6726001, accent@iogt.se, info@iogt.se, http://www.iogt.se/templates/template_263.asp?. Ed. Eva Aahlstroem. adv.: B&W page SEK 10,500, color page SEK 12,000; 190 x 255. Circ: 40,000 (controlled).

616.861 GBR ISSN 0969-899X
ACQUIRE. Text in English. 1992. q. GBP 30 (effective 2002). **Document type:** *Bulletin.* **Description:** Contains updates on the current research in the field of alcohol abuse.
Published by: Alcohol Concern, Waterbridge House, 32-36 Loman St, London, SE1 0EE, United Kingdom. TEL 44-20-79287377, FAX 44-20-79284644, contact@alcoholconcern.org.uk, http://www.alcoholconcern.org.uk.

616.86 GBR ISSN 0965-2140
HV5800 CODEN: ADICE5
➤ **ADDICTION.** Text in English. 1884. m. GBP 295, EUR 443 combined subscription in Europe to individuals print & online eds.; USD 548 combined subscription in the Americas to individuals & the Caribbean (print & online eds.); GBP 326 combined subscription elsewhere to individuals print & online eds.; GBP 1,006 combined subscription in Europe to institutions print & online eds.; USD 1,860 combined subscription in the Americas to institutions & the Caribbean (print & online eds.); GBP 1,107 combined subscription elsewhere to institutions print & online eds. (effective 2006). adv. bk.rev. charts; illus.; stat. index. back issues avail.; reprint service avail. from PSC. **Document type:** *Journal, Academic/Scholarly.* **Description:** Contains research reports on alcohol, illicit drugs and tobacco bringing together research conducted within many different disciplines. Also features editorials, commentaries, reviews, historical articles, interviews with leading figures in addiction, letters, news and a comprehensive book review section, with listings in collaboration with SALIS.
Former titles (until 1993): British Journal of Addiction (0952-0481); (until 1980): British Journal of Addiction to Alcohol and Other Drugs (0007-0890); (until 1947): British Journal of Inebriety (0366-0796)
Related titles: Microfiche ed.; Online - full text ed.: ISSN 1360-0443. GBP 956 in Europe to institutions; USD 1,767 in the Americas to institutions & Caribbean; GBP 1,052 elsewhere to institutions (effective 2006) (from bigchalk, Blackwell Synergy, EBSCO Publishing, Gale Group, IngentaConnect, Northern Light Technology, Inc., O C L C Online Computer Library Center, Inc., Ovid Technologies, Inc., ProQuest Information & Learning, Swets Information Services); Supplement(s): Addiction Supplement. ISSN 1359-6357.
Indexed: AC&P, AMHA, ASCA, ASSIA, AbHyg, AddicA, AgeL, ArtHuCI, BIOSIS Prev, BibInd, BiolAb, BrHumI, BrNI, CINAHL, CJA, ChemAb, CurCont, DSA, ERA, ESPM, ETA, ExcerpMed, FamI, H&SSA, IBSS, IMFL, IPA, IPsyAb, ISR, IndMed, Inpharma, MEA, MEA&I, MEDLINE, NRN, NutrAb, PE&ON, PHN&I, PSA, ProtozoAb, PsycInfo, PsycholAb, RDA, RHEA, RRTA, Reac, RefZh, SCI, SEA, SENA, SOMA, SOPODA, SSA, SSCI, SWA, SociolAb, TDB, TEA, THA, WAE&RSA, e-psyche.
—BLDSC (0678.548000), GNLM, IDS, IE, Infotrieve, ingenta, KNAW. **CCC.**
Published by: (Society for the Study of Addiction), Blackwell Publishing Ltd., 9600 Garsington Rd, Oxford, OX4 2ZG, United Kingdom. TEL 44-1865-776868, FAX 44-1865-714591, customerservices@oxon.blackwellpublishing.com, http://www.blackwellpublishing.com/journals/ADD. Ed. Robert West.

616.86 GBR ISSN 0968-7610
ADDICTION ABSTRACTS. Text in English. 1994. q. GBP 456, USD 753 combined subscription to institutions print & online eds. (effective 2006). adv. index. reprint service avail. from PSC. **Document type:** *Abstract/Index.* **Description:** A focused, unbiased, and international abstracting service, spanning all addictive substances as well as other compulsive behaviours.
Related titles: Microfiche ed.; Online - full text ed.: ISSN 1469-2856. GBP 433, USD 715 to institutions (effective 2006).
—**CCC.**
Published by: Taylor & Francis Ltd (Subsidiary of: Taylor & Francis Group), 4 Park Sq, Milton Park, Abingdon, OX14 4RN, United Kingdom. TEL 44-1235-828600, FAX 44-1235-829000, info@tandf.co.uk, http://www.tandf.co.uk/addiction-abs/, http://www.tandf.co.uk/journals. Ed. Michael Gossop. **Subscr. to:** Journals Customer Service, Rankine Rd, Basingstoke, Hants RG24 8PR, United Kingdom. TEL 44-1256-813000, FAX 44-1256-330245, enquiry@tandf.co.uk.

616.86 GBR ISSN 1355-6215
RC563 CODEN: ADBIFN
➤ **ADDICTION BIOLOGY.** Text in English. 1996. q. GBP 481, USD 795 combined subscription to institutions print & online eds. (effective 2006). reprint service avail. from PSC. **Document type:** *Journal, Academic/Scholarly.*
Related titles: Online - full text ed.: ISSN 1369-1600. GBP 457, USD 755 to institutions (effective 2006) (from EBSCO Publishing, Gale Group, IngentaConnect, Northern Light Technology, Inc., O C L C Online Computer Library Center, Inc., Swets Information Services).
Indexed: AbHyg, AddicA, AgrForAb, AnBrAb, CJA, CurCont, ESPM, ExcerpMed, FoP, H&SSA, HortAb, Inpharma, MEDLINE, NSCI, NutrAb, PE&ON, PHN&I, RA&MP, RDA, RRTA, Reac, RefZh, SIA, SWA, TDB, ToxAb, WAE&RSA.
—BLDSC (0678.557000), CASDDS, CISTI, GNLM, IDS, IE, Infotrieve, ingenta, KNAW. **CCC.**
Published by: Taylor & Francis Ltd (Subsidiary of: Taylor & Francis Group), 4 Park Sq, Milton Park, Abingdon, OX14 4RN, United Kingdom. TEL 44-1235-828600, FAX 44-1235-829000, info@tandf.co.uk, http://www.tandf.co.uk/journals/titles/13556215.asp. Ed. Dr. Kim Wolff. **Subscr. to:** Journals Customer Service, Rankine Rd, Basingstoke, Hants RG24 8PR, United Kingdom. TEL 44-1256-813000, FAX 44-1256-330245, enquiry@tandf.co.uk.

616.86 USA ISSN 1542-8435
▼ **ADDICTION PROFESSIONAL.** Text in English. 2003 (Jan.). bi-m. USD 67 (effective 2003). back issues avail.; reprints avail. **Document type:** *Magazine, Trade.* **Description:** Covers clinical issues for front-line professionals dealings with addiction treatment and prevention.
Related titles: Online - full text ed.: (from Gale Group).
Published by: Manisses Communications Group, Inc., PO Box 9758, Providence, RI 02906-9758. TEL 401-831-6020, FAX 401-861-6370, manissescs@manisses.com, http://www.manisses.com. Ed. Karienne Stovell. Pub. Fraser A Lang. R&P Steven Marchesi. Adv. contact Paul Newman. Circ: 15,000 (paid); 6,000 (controlled).

616.86 GBR ISSN 1606-6359
HV4997 CODEN: AREREQ
➤ **ADDICTION RESEARCH AND THEORY.** Text in English. 1993. bi-m. GBP 357, USD 470 combined subscription to institutions (effective 2006). reprint service avail. from PSC. **Document type:** *Journal, Academic/Scholarly.* **Description:** Cross-disciplinary journal examining the effects of context on the use and misuse of substances, and on the nature of intoxications of all kinds.
Formerly: Addiction Research (1058-6989)
Related titles: Microform ed.; Online - full text ed.: ISSN 1476-7392. GBP 339, USD 447 to institutions (effective 2006) (from EBSCO Publishing, Gale Group, IngentaConnect, O C L C Online Computer Library Center, Inc., Swets Information Services).

D

Indexed: AddicA, AgeL, CJA, CurCont, ERA, ETA, Faml, MEA, PsycInfo, PsycholAb, RHEA, SEA, SENA, SOMA, SOPODA, SSA, SSCI, SWA, SociolAb, TEA, e-psyche.
—BLDSC (0678.595000), GNLM, IE, Infotrieve, ingenta. **CCC.**
Published by: Routledge (Subsidiary of: Taylor & Francis Group), 4 Park Sq, Milton Park, Abingdon, Oxon OX14 4RN, United Kingdom. TEL 44-1235-828600, FAX 44-1235-829000, info@routledge.co.uk, http://www.tandf.co.uk/journals/titles/16066359.asp, http://www.routledge.com. Eds. Ernest Drucker, John B Davies. **Subscr. to:** Taylor & Francis Ltd, Journals Customer Service, Rankine Rd, Basingstoke, Hants RG24 8PR, United Kingdom. TEL 44-1256-813000, FAX 44-1256-330245, enquiry@tandf.co.uk.

616.863 GBR
ADDICTION TODAY. Text in English. 1989. bi-m. GBP 30; GBP 45 in United States. adv. bk.rev. **Document type:** *Trade.*
Description: Reports on approaches to treatment, controversial issues, news and developments in drug and alcohol rehabilitation, and addictive behavior and related issues.
Formerly (until vol.9, no.52): Addiction Counselling World (1351-8151)
—BLDSC (0678.660000).
Published by: Addiction Recovery Foundation, 122A Wilton Rd, London, SW1V 1JZ, United Kingdom. TEL 44-171-233-5333, FAX 44-171-233-8123, ACW@easynet.co.uk, http://easyweb.easynet.co.uk/~acw. Ed. Lynda Pritchard. Adv. contact David Leonard. Circ: 8,000.

616.86 USA
ADDICTION TREATMENT FORUM. Text in English. 1994. q. **Document type:** *Newsletter.* **Description:** For addiction treatment community - both professionals and patients. Focuses on opiate addiction and the benefits of methadone treatment.
Media: Online - full text.
Address: 1759 E Golf Rd, Ste 320, Schaumburg, IL 60173. http://www.atforum.com/.

616.86 GBR ISSN 0306-4603
RC565
➤ **ADDICTIVE BEHAVIORS.** Text in English. 1976. 12/yr. EUR 177 in Europe to individuals; JPY 23,500 in Japan to individuals; USD 199 to individuals except Europe and Japan; EUR 1,242 in Europe to institutions; JPY 164,900 in Japan to institutions; USD 1,390 to institutions except Europe and Japan (effective 2006). adv. bk.rev. charts; illus. index. reprints avail. **Document type:** *Journal, Academic/Scholarly.*
Description: Publishes original research and theoretical papers in the area of substance abuse, with particular emphasis on alcohol and drug abuse, smoking and problems associated with eating.
Incorporates (1990-1994): Annual Review of Addictions Research and Treatment (0955-663X)
Related titles: Microform ed.: (from PQC); Online - full text ed.: (from EBSCO Publishing, Gale Group, IngentaConnect, ScienceDirect, Swets Information Services).
Indexed: AC&P, AMHA, ASCA, AbAn, AbHyg, AddicA, AgeL, BIOSIS Prev, BMAb, BiolAb, CJA, ChPerI, CurCont, DSA, ERA, ESPM, ETA, ExcerpMed, Faml, H&SSA, HEA, HRIS, INI, IndMed, MEA, MEA&I, MEDLINE, NutrAb, PsycInfo, PsycholAb, RHEA, RRTA, RiskAb, SEA, SENA, SOMA, SSCI, SSI, SWA, TEA, e-psyche.
—BLDSC (0678.750000), CISTI, GNLM, IDS, IE, Infotrieve, ingenta, KNAW. **CCC.**
Published by: Pergamon (Subsidiary of: Elsevier Science & Technology), The Boulevard, Langford Ln, East Park, Kidlington, Oxford OX5 1GB, United Kingdom. TEL 44-1865-843000, FAX 44-1865-843010, http://www.elsevier.com/locate/addictbeh. Ed. Dr. Peter M Miller. Circ: 1,200. **Subscr. to:** Elsevier BV, PO Box 211, Amsterdam 1000 AE, Netherlands. TEL 31-20-485-3757, FAX 31-20-485-3432, nlinfo-f@elsevier.nl, http://www.elsevier.nl.

362.29 USA ISSN 1531-5754
RC563 CODEN: ADTTA5
➤ **ADDICTIVE DISORDERS & THEIR TREATMENT.** Text in English. 2002. q., latest vol.2. USD 91 to individuals; USD 206 to institutions (effective 2006). adv. bk.rev. 65 p./no.; back issues avail.; reprints avail. **Document type:** *Journal, Academic/Scholarly.* **Description:** Devoted to practical clinical research and treatment issues related to the misuse of alcohol and licit and illicit drugs and the study and treatment of addictive disorders and their behaviors.
Related titles: Online - full text ed.: USD 195 academic site license; USD 217.50 corporate site license (effective 2002) (from EBSCO Publishing, Ovid Technologies, Inc., Swets Information Services).
Indexed: CINAHL, ExcerpMed, PsycInfo, PsycholAb, RefZh.
—BLDSC (0678.810000), CISTI, IE. **CCC.**
Published by: Lippincott Williams & Wilkins (Subsidiary of: Wolters Kluwer N.V.), 530 Walnut St, Philadelphia, PA 19106-3621. TEL 215-521-8300, FAX 215-521-8902, mmcmicha@lww.com, custserv@lww.com, http://www.addictiondisorders.com, http://www.lww.com. Ed. Dr. Pedro Ruiz. Pub. Maria McMichael. Adv. contact Ray Thibodeau. B&W page USD 970; trim 8.25 x 11. Circ: 497 (paid). **Subscr. to:** PO Box 1620, Hagerstown, MD 21741. TEL 301-223-2300, 800-638-3030, FAX 301-223-2365.

616.8 ESP ISSN 0214-4840
➤ **ADICCIONES.** Text in Spanish. 1989. q. EUR 36 domestic to individuals; EUR 55 foreign to individuals; EUR 55 domestic to institutions; EUR 125 foreign to institutions (effective 2005). adv. bk.rev. **Document type:** *Academic/Scholarly.*
Description: Journal on drug issues for Spanish-speaking audience.
Related titles: Online - full text ed.
Indexed: AddicA, ExcerpMed, PsycInfo, PsycholAb.
—BLDSC (0681.401000), CINDOC, IE, ingenta. **CCC.**
Published by: Socidrogalcohol, La Rambla, 15, 2a 3a, Palma De Mallorca, Baleares 07003, Spain. TEL 34-971-727434, FAX 34-971-213306, secretaria@adic.e.telefonica.net, http://socidrogalcohol.psiquiatria.com/adicciones/index.es.html. Ed., R&P, Adv. contact Amador Calafat. Circ: 2,000.

➤ **AKTION JUGENDSCHUTZ. INFORMATIONEN.** see *CHILDREN AND YOUTH—About*

616.86 SWE
AKTUELLT. Text in Swedish. 1922. 4/yr. SEK 95 (effective 2001). adv. bk.rev. illus. **Document type:** *Newspaper.* **Description:** Presents articles on social work from a Christian perspective.
Former titles (until 1996): Drogfritt Liv (1101-7015); (until vol.5, 1989): Folkets Vael (0015-5861)
Published by: Hela Manniskan, Sundbyberg, 17299, Sweden. TEL 46-8-453-68-50, FAX 46-8-453-68-60. Ed. Carl Johan Friman. Pub. Karin Israelsson. Circ: 7,000.

616.861 USA ISSN 1054-1446
AL-ANON SPEAKS OUT; a community resource for professionals. Text in English, Spanish, French. 1978. s-a. free. **Document type:** *Newsletter.* **Description:** Informs members of the helping professions about the help available to the families and friends of alcoholics through Al-Anon - Alateen program.
Published by: (Al-Anon Family Group Headquarters, Inc.), A F G, Inc., 1600 Corporate Landing Pkwy, Virginia Beach, VA 23454-5617. TEL 757-563-1600, FAX 757-563-1655, http://www.al-anon.alateen.org. Ed., R&P Claire Ricewasser. Circ: 9,000.

353.9 USA
HV5297.A4
ALASKA. DEPARTMENT OF HEALTH AND SOCIAL SERVICES. DIVISION OF ALCOHOLISM AND DRUG ABUSE. REPORT. Text in English. a. free. illus.
Formerly: Alaska. Department of Health and Social Services. Office of Alcoholism. Report (0095-3318)
Published by: Department of Health and Social Services, Division of Alcoholism and Drug Abuse, PO Box 110607, Juneau, AK 99811-0607. TEL 907-465-2071, FAX 907-465-2185.

ALATEEN TALK. see *CHILDREN AND YOUTH—For*

616.861 362.292 CAN ISSN 0840-7819
HV5305
ALBERTA ALCOHOL AND DRUG ABUSE COMMISSION. ANNUAL REPORT. Text in English. 1970. a. adv. **Document type:** *Government.* **Description:** Provides a concise program, financial and statistical summary of AADAC's activities.
Formerly: Alberta. Alcoholism and Drug Abuse Commission. Annual Report (0319-423X)
Published by: Alcohol and Drug Abuse Commission, Production & Distribution, Pacific Plaza Bldg, 2nd Fl, 10909 Jasper Ave, Edmonton, AB T5J 3M9, Canada. TEL 403-427-7319, FAX 403-422-5237. Ed., R&P Lisa Austin. Adv. contact Grace Whitehouse. Circ: 1,200.

616.861 USA ISSN 0741-8329
QP801 CODEN: ALCOEX
➤ **ALCOHOL (NEW YORK).** Text in English. 1984. 9/yr. USD 263 domestic to individuals; USD 281 foreign to individuals; USD 1,635 domestic to institutions; USD 1,766 foreign to institutions (effective 2006). adv. illus.; abstr. Index. back issues avail.; reprints avail. **Document type:** *Journal, Academic/Scholarly.* **Description:** Publishes original research articles and reviews on biomedical aspects of alcohol abuse and alcoholism.
Incorporates (1980-1987): Alcohol and Drug Research (0883-1386); Which was formerly (until 1985): Substance and Alcohol Actions - Misuse (0191-8877); Substance and Alcohol Misuse
Related titles: Microform ed.: (from PQC); Online - full text ed.: (from EBSCO Publishing, Gale Group, IngentaConnect, ScienceDirect, Swets Information Services).
Indexed: AbHyg, BIOBASE, BIOSIS Prev, BiolAb, CIN, ChemAb, ChemTitl, CurCont, DSA, ESPM, ExcerpMed, FoP, H&SSA, HortAb, IABS, IPsyAb, ISR, IndMed, MEDLINE, NRN, NSCI, NutrAb, PN&I, PsycInfo, PsycholAb, RA&MP, SCI, ToxAb, VITIS, e-psyche.
—BLDSC (0786.754600), CASDDS, CISTI, GNLM, IDS, IE, Infotrieve, ingenta, KNAW. **CCC.**
Published by: Elsevier Inc. (Subsidiary of: Elsevier Science & Technology), 360 Park Ave. S, New York, NY 10010-1710. TEL 212-633-3730, 888-437-4636, FAX 212-633-3680, usinfo-f@elsevier.com, http://www.elsevier.com/locate/alcohol. Ed. Charles R. Goodlett. adv.: B&W page USD 1,065, color page USD 1,270. Circ: 260 (paid and free).

178.1 GBR ISSN 1460-7174
HV5441
ALCOHOL ALERT. Text in English. 1854. q. GBP 15 domestic; GBP 18 foreign (effective 2001). adv. bk.rev. abstr.; charts; illus.; stat. **Document type:** *Newsletter.* **Description:** Presents news articles, briefs, and commentary on government policies and social activities directed against drug, alcohol, and tobacco use and abuse.
Former titles (until 1997): U K Alcohol Alert (0969-2029); (until 1991): United Kingdom Temperance Alliance. Alliance News (0309-3115)
Related titles: Online - full text ed.
—BLDSC (0786.754640).
Published by: United Kingdom Temperance Alliance Ltd. (Subsidiary of: Institute of Alcohol Studies), Alliance House, 12 Caxton St, London, SW1H 0QS, United Kingdom. TEL 44-20-7222-5880, 44-20-7222-4001, FAX 44-20-7799-2510, info@ias.org.uk, http://www.ias.org.uk/alert/default.htm. Ed. A McNeill. Circ: 5,000.

616.861 GBR ISSN 0735-0414
HV5441 CODEN: ALALDD
➤ **ALCOHOL & ALCOHOLISM.** Text in English. 1963. bi-m. GBP 464, USD 845, EUR 696 to institutions; GBP 488, USD 878, EUR 732 combined subscription to institutions print & online eds. (effective 2006). adv. bk.rev. charts; stat. index. 112 p./no.; Supplement avail.; back issues avail.; reprint service avail. from PQC,PSC. **Document type:** *Journal, Academic/Scholarly.* **Description:** Publishes research from all clinical disciplines of medicine, the basic medical sciences, psychology, sociology, and epidemiology.
Former titles (until 1983): British Journal on Alcohol and Alcoholism (0309-1635); (until 1976): Journal of Alcoholism: Bulletin of Alcoholism (0021-8685); Medical Bulletin on Alcoholism
Related titles: Microfilm ed.: (from PQC); Online - full text ed.: ISSN 1464-3502. 199?. GBP 439, USD 790, EUR 659 to institutions (effective 2006) (from EBSCO Publishing, Gale Group, HighWire Press, IngentaConnect, O C L C Online Computer Library Center, Inc., Ovid Technologies, Inc., Oxford University Press Online Journals, ProQuest Information & Learning, Swets Information Services); Supplement(s): Alcohol & Alcoholism. Supplement. ISSN 1358-6173.
Indexed: AC&P, ASCA, ASSIA, AbHyg, AddicA, AnBeAb, BIOBASE, BIOSIS Prev, BiolAb, CIN, ChemAb, ChemTitl, CurCont, ERA, ESPM, ETA, ExcerpMed, Faml, FoP, H&SSA, HortAb, IABS, ISR, IndMed, Inpharma, MEA, MEDLINE, NRN, NSCI, NutrAb, PE&ON, PsycInfo, PsycholAb, RA&MP, RHEA, Reac, SCI, SEA, SENA, SIA, SOMA, SOPODA, SSA, SSCI, SWA, SociolAb, TDB, TEA, THA, ToxAb, VITIS, e-psyche.
—BLDSC (0786.754800), CASDDS, CISTI, GNLM, IDS, IE, Infotrieve, ingenta, KNAW. **CCC.**
Published by: (Medical Council on Alcoholism), Oxford University Press, Great Clarendon St, Oxford, OX2 6DP, United Kingdom. TEL 44-1865-556767, FAX 44-1865-556646, jnl.orders@oup.co.uk, http://alcalc.oxfordjournals.org/, http://www.oxfordjournals.org/. Eds. Jonathan D Chick, P De Witte. Pub. Mandy Sketch. R&P Fiona Bennett. adv.: B&W page GBP 270, B&W page USD 485; trim 216 x 280. Circ: 540. **Co-sponsor:** European Society for Biomedical Research on Alcoholism.

616.861 GBR
ALCOHOL CONCERN ANNUAL REPORT. Text in English. a. **Description:** Includes information about Alcohol Concern's work over the year, updates on the work of the various departments and plans for the future.
Related titles: Online - full content ed.: 2001.
Published by: Alcohol Concern, Waterbridge House, 32-36 Loman St, London, SE1 0EE, United Kingdom. TEL 44-20-79287377, FAX 44-20-79284644, contact@alcoholconcern.org.uk, http://www.alcoholconcern.org.uk.

ALCOHOL ISSUES INSIGHTS. see *BEVERAGES*

616.861 USA ISSN 1535-7414
HV5285 CODEN: AHRWDZ
➤ **ALCOHOL RESEARCH & HEALTH.** Text in English. 1975. q. USD 25 domestic (effective 2005). bibl.; charts; illus.; abstr. Index. back issues avail.; reprints avail. **Document type:** *Journal, Academic/Scholarly.* **Description:** Presents current research findings and contains articles on the effects, prevention and treatment of alcohol abuse and alcoholism.
Formerly (until 1999): Alcohol Health & Research World (0090-838X)
Related titles: Online - full text ed.: free (effective 2005) (from EBSCO Publishing, Florida Center for Library Automation, Gale Group, H.W. Wilson, O C L C Online Computer Library Center, Inc., ProQuest Information & Learning).
Indexed: AMHA, ASCA, AgeL, Agr, AmStI, CINAHL, CJA, ChemAb, CurCont, Faml, HRIS, HlthInd, IPsyAb, IUSGP, IndMed, MASUSE, MEA&I, MEDLINE, MEDOC, MagInd, NRN, PAIS, PsycInfo, PsycholAb, RefZh, SSCI, SSI, SWR&A, e-psyche.
—BLDSC (0786.781400), CASDDS, GNLM, IDS, IE, ingenta.

D

Published by: U.S. National Institute on Alcohol Abuse and Alcoholism, 6000 Executive Blvd, Bethesda, MD 20892-7003. TEL 301-443-3860, FAX 301-480-1726, http://www.niaaa.nih.gov. Ed. Dianne M Welsh. R&P Barbara Vann TEL 202-842-7600. Circ: 3,700 (paid). **Subscr. to:** U.S. Government Printing Office, Superintendent of Documents, PO Box 371954, Pittsburgh, PA 15250-7954. TEL 202-512-1800, FAX 202-512-2250, orders@gpo.gov, http://www.access.gpo.gov; National Technical Information Service, Government Research Center, 5285 Port Royal Rd, Springfield, VA 22161. TEL 703-605-6060, 800-363-2068, http://www.ntis.gov.

616.86 HRV ISSN 0002-502X
CODEN: ALCMAN

➤ **ALCOHOLISM**; journal on alcoholism and related addictions. Text in English; Summaries in Croatian, English. 1965. s-a. USD 30 (effective 2005). adv. bk.rev.; Website rev. charts; illus.; stat. index. 96 p./no.; reprint service avail. from PQC. **Document type:** *Journal, Academic/Scholarly.* **Description:** Publishes original scientific papers, short communications, professional papers concerning man's use and misuse of ethyl alcohol and other substance dependency.
Related titles: CD-ROM ed.; E-mail ed.; Fax ed.; Microfilm ed.; Online - full text ed.: USD 30 (effective 2003) (from Northern Light Technology, Inc.); ♦ Supplement(s): Alcoholism. Supplement. ISSN 1330-6170.
Indexed: ASCA, AddicA, BIOSIS Prev, BiolAb, CHNI, ExcerpMed, FamI, NRN, PAIS, PsycInfo, PsycholAb, RILM, SociolAb, TDB, e-psyche.
—GNLM, IE, KNAW.
Published by: Centar za Proucavanje i Suzbijanje Alkoholizma i Drugih Ovisnosti/Centre for Study and Control of Alcoholism and Other Addictions, Vinogradska 29, Zagreb, 10000, Croatia. alcoholism@kbsm.hr, vlatko.thaller@zg.tel.hr, http://www.alcoholism.kbsm.hr. Ed., R&P, Adv. contact Vlatko Thaller. Circ: 1,000. **Co-sponsor:** International Council on Alcoholism and Addictions.

616.863 USA ISSN 1042-1394

ALCOHOLISM & DRUG ABUSE WEEKLY; news for policy and program decision-makers in the addiction field. Text in English. 1986. 48/yr., latest vol.13, 2001. USD 3,435 domestic to institutions; USD 3,579 in Canada & Mexico to institutions; USD 3,627 elsewhere to institutions; USD 3,779 combined subscription domestic to institutions print & online eds.; USD 3,923 combined subscription in Canada & Mexico to institutions print & online eds.; USD 3,971 combined subscription elsewhere to institutions print & online eds. (effective 2006). 8 p./no.; back issues avail.; reprints avail. **Document type:** *Newsletter, Trade.* **Description:** Includes news and anlysis of federal and state public policy development funding, cutting-edge programs and legislation in the addiction field.
Incorporates (in 1991): Addictions Program Management; Formerly (until 1988): Drug Abuse Report (0889-7050)
Related titles: Online - full text ed.: ISSN 1556-7591. USD 3,435 to institutions (effective 2006) (from Data-Star, EBSCO Publishing, Florida Center for Library Automation, Gale Group, Northern Light Technology, Inc., O C L C Online Computer Library Center, Inc., The Dialog Corporation).
Indexed: CINAHL, MASUSE, e-psyche.
Published by: John Wiley & Sons, Inc., 111 River St, Hoboken, NJ 07030-5774. TEL 201-748-6000, 800-825-7550, FAX 201-748-5915, bmcalarney@manisses.com, uscs-wis@wiley.com, http://www.manisses.com, http://www.wiley.com.

616.861 USA ISSN 0145-6008
RC565 CODEN: ACRSDM

➤ **ALCOHOLISM: CLINICAL AND EXPERIMENTAL RESEARCH.** Text in English. 1977. m. USD 402 domestic to individuals; USD 482 foreign to individuals; USD 798 domestic to institutions; USD 895 foreign to institutions (effective 2006). adv. back issues avail. **Document type:** *Journal, Academic/Scholarly.* **Description:** Presents original clinical and research studies on alcoholism, alcohol-induced syndromes and resultant organ damage.
Related titles: Microfilm ed.: (from WWS); Online - full text ed.: ISSN 1530-0277 (from EBSCO Publishing, Ovid Technologies, Inc., Swets Information Services).
Indexed: AMHA, AbHyg, AddicA, BIOBASE, BIOSIS Prev, BMAb, BiolAb, CIN, CINAHL, CJA, ChPerI, ChemTitl, CurCont, ERA, ETA, ExcerpMed, FamI, FoP, IABS, IDIS, INI, ISR, IndMed, Inpharma, JW-P, MEA, MEDLINE, NSCI, NemAb, NutrAb, PE&ON, PN&I, PsycInfo, PsycholAb, RA&MP, RHEA, Reac, SCI, SEA, SENA, SIA, SOMA, SSCI, SWA, TEA, THA, VITIS, WAE&RSA, e-psyche.
—BLDSC (0786.789300), CASDDS, CISTI, GNLM, IDS, IE, Infotrieve, ingenta, KNAW. **CCC.**
Published by: (Research Society on Alcoholism), Lippincott Williams & Wilkins (Subsidiary of: Wolters Kluwer N.V.), 530 Walnut St, Philadelphia, PA 19106-3621. TEL 215-521-8300, 800-638-3030, FAX 215-521-8902, http://www.alcoholism-cer.com, http://www.lww.com. Ed. Ivan Diamond. Pubs. John Ewers, Katey Millet TEL 410-528-4456. adv.: B&W page USD 480, color page USD 1,450; trim 8.13 x 10.88. Circ: 1,705 (paid and controlled). **Co-sponsor:** International Society for Biomedical Research on Alcoholism.

362.2 616.8 USA ISSN 0093-3279
HV5001

ALCOHOLISM DIGEST ANNUAL✶. Text in English. 1973. a. illus.
Published by: Information Planning Associates Inc., 5203 Leesburg Pike Ste 505, Falls Church, VA 22041-3404. TEL 202-820-6100.

616.86 HRV ISSN 1330-6170

ALCOHOLISM. SUPPLEMENT. Text in English; Summaries in Croatian, English. 1967. irreg., latest vol.39, 2003. USD 30 (effective 2003). bk.rev.; Website rev. charts; illus.; stat. index. 96 p./no.; **Document type:** *Proceedings, Academic/Scholarly.*
Related titles: CD-ROM ed.; E-mail ed.; Fax ed.; Microfilm ed.; Online - full content ed.; ♦ Supplement to: Alcoholism. ISSN 0002-502X.
Published by: Centar za Proucavanje i Suzbijanje Alkoholizma i Drugih Ovisnosti/Centre for Study and Control of Alcoholism and Other Addictions, Vinogradska 29, Zagreb, 10000, Croatia. vlatko.thaller@zg.tel.hr. Ed. Vlatko Thaller. **Co-publisher:** International Council on Alcohol and Addictions.

616.861 USA ISSN 0734-7324

ALCOHOLISM TREATMENT QUARTERLY; the practitioner's quarterly for individual, group, and family therapy. Abbreviated title: A T Q. Text in English. 1984. q. USD 585 combined subscription domestic to institutions print & online eds.; USD 789.75 combined subscription in Canada to institutions print & online eds.; USD 848.25 combined subscription elsewhere to institutions print & online eds. (effective 2006). adv. bk.rev. abstr.; bibl. 120 p./no. 1 cols./p.; back issues avail.; reprint service avail. from HAW. **Document type:** *Journal, Trade.* **Description:** Geared toward the needs of clinicians who work with alcoholic clients and their families.
Formerly: Alcoholism Counseling and Treatment
Related titles: Microfiche ed.: (from PQC); Microform ed.; Online - full text ed.: ISSN 1544-4538 (from EBSCO Publishing, O C L C Online Computer Library Center, Inc., Swets Information Services).
Indexed: AC&P, AD&D, AbAn, CJA, ESPM, ExcerpMed, FamI, H&SSA, IMFL, IPARL, PC&CA, PsycInfo, PsycholAb, RefZh, RehabLit, RiskAb, SFSA, SOPODA, SSA, SWA, SWR&A, SociolAb, THA, e-psyche.
—BLDSC (0786.797000), GNLM, Haworth, IE, Infotrieve, ingenta, KNAW. **CCC.**
Published by: Haworth Press, Inc., 10 Alice St, Binghamton, NY 13904-1580. TEL 607-722-5857, 800-429-6784, FAX 607-722-1424, 800-895-0582, getinfo@haworthpress.com, http://www.haworthpress.com/web/ATQ. Ed. Thomas McGovern. Pub. William Cohen. R&P Ruth Ann Heath TEL 607-722-5857 ext 316. adv.: B&W page USD 315, color page USD 550; trim 4.375 x 7.125. Circ: 364 (paid).

616.861 362.29 344 ITA ISSN 0394-9826

ALCOLOGIA; European journal of alcohol studies. Text in English. 1989. 3/yr. EUR 46.50 (effective 2005). adv. **Document type:** *Journal, Academic/Scholarly.* **Description:** Published under the auspices of Societa Italiana di Alcologia, it means to promote the exchange of opinions and information on alcohol and drug related pathologies and problems, behavior and lifestyles.
Indexed: AddicA, ExcerpMed.
—BLDSC (0786.797300), IE, ingenta.
Published by: Eurohealth Editors srl, Via Castiglione 28, Bologna, 40124, Italy. TEL 39-051-263703, FAX 39-051-238564, mcccongress@tin.it, http://www.alcologia.it. Circ: 1,100.

616.8 FRA ISSN 0002-5054

ALCOOL OU SANTE. Text in French. 1951. q. adv. bk.rev. abstr.; bibl.; charts; illus. index. **Document type:** *Consumer.* **Description:** Covers the different aspects of alcoholism such as prevention, trafficking, public health, foreign countries, general news.
Indexed: RefZh.
—**CCC.**
Published by: Association Nationale de Prevention de l'Alcoolisme, 20 rue St. Fiacre, Paris, 75002, France. TEL 33-1-42335104, FAX 33-1-45081702, contact@anpa.asso.fr, http://www.anpa.asso.fr. Ed. Patrick Elineau. R&P Elisabeth Francois. Circ: 7,000.

616.86 FRA ISSN 1620-4522

➤ **ALCOOLOGIE ET ADDICTOLOGIE.** Text in French; Summaries in English, French. 1978. q. EUR 69 in Europe to individuals; EUR 89 elsewhere to individuals; EUR 97 in Europe to institutions; EUR 115 elsewhere to institutions; EUR 50 in Europe to students; EUR 24.50 newsstand/cover (effective 2003). bk.rev. back issues avail.; reprints avail. **Document type:** *Journal, Academic/Scholarly.* **Description:** Transdisciplinary approach of alcoholism and other addictions.
Former titles (until 2000): Alcoologie (1142-1983); (until 1989): Societe Francaise d'Alcoologie. Bulletin (0245-6664)
Indexed: AddicA.
—BLDSC (0786.802000), IE, ingenta.
Published by: (Societe Francaise d'Alcoologie), Princeps Editions, 64 av. du General de Gaulle, Issy-les-Moulineaux, 92130, France. TEL 33-1-46382414, FAX 33-1-40957215, princeps.gdumas@wanadoo.fr. Ed. M Lejoyeux. Adv. contact G Gilkes-Duras.

617.8 USA

ALERT (EWING); news on alcoholism and drug addiction services for persons who are hard of hearing. Text in English. 1989. s-a. free. adv. back issues avail. **Document type:** *Newsletter.* **Description:** Disseminates local and national news on alcohol and drug use among persons who are deaf or hard of hearing. Contains information on service providers.
Published by: Sings of Sobriety, Inc., 865 Lower Ferry Rd., Ste. B-12, Ewing, NJ 08628. TEL 609-882-7177, 800-332-7677, FAX 609-882-6808, sosnj@juno.com, http://www.members.aol.com/sosnj. Ed. Steven Shevlin. R&P Lisetle Ortiz. Adv. contact Heather Bird. Circ: 2,000.

616.86 SWE ISSN 0345-0732

ALKOHOL & NARKOTIKA/ALCOHOL AND OTHER DRUGS. Text in Swedish; Summaries in English. 1956. 6/yr. SEK 250; SEK 48 newsstand/cover (effective 2003). adv. bk.rev. bibl.; illus.; stat. index, cum.index. **Document type:** *Magazine, Consumer.* **Description:** Monitors drug trends in Sweden.
Incorporates (1979-1987): Forskningsnytt (0349-1781); Formerly (until 1973): Alkoholfraagen (0002-5518); Which was formed by the 1956 merger of: Tidskrift foer Systembolagen; Tirfing
—GNLM.
Published by: Centralfoerbundet foer Alkohol- och Narkotikaupplysning/Swedish Council on Information on Alcohol and Other Drugs, Olof Palmes Gata 17, PO Box 70412, Stockholm, 10133, Sweden. TEL 46-8-4124600, FAX 46-8-4124641, staffan.hasselgren@can.se, http://www.can.se. Ed. Staffan Hasselgren. Circ: 6,000.

616.861 616.863 POL ISSN 0867-4361

ALKOHOLIZM I NARKOMANIA. Text in Polish. 1988. q. EUR 30 foreign (effective 2005). **Document type:** *Journal.*
Published by: Instytut Psychiatrii i Neurologii w Warszawie, Zespol Profilaktyki i Leczenia Uzaleznien, Al Sobieskiego 9, Warszawa, 02957, Poland. habratb@ipin.edu.pl, http://www.ipin.edu.pl/ain. Ed. Boguslaw Habrat. **Dist. by:** Ars Polona, Krakowskie Przedmiescie 7, Warsaw, Poland. TEL 48-22-9263914, FAX 48-22-9265334, arspolona@arspolona.com.pl, http://www.arspolona.com.pl.

616.863 USA ISSN 0095-2990
HV5800 CODEN: AJDABD

➤ **AMERICAN JOURNAL OF DRUG AND ALCOHOL ABUSE.** Text in English. 1975. q. USD 1,170, GBP 710 combined subscription to institutions print & online eds. (effective 2006). adv. bibl.; charts; illus. back issues avail.; reprint service avail. from PSC. **Document type:** *Journal, Academic/Scholarly.* **Description:** Dedicated to the presentation of essential aspects of drug and alcohol abuse.
Related titles: Microform ed.: (from RPI); Online - full text ed.: ISSN 1097-9891. USD 1,112, GBP 675 to institutions (effective 2006) (from EBSCO Publishing, Gale Group, O C L C Online Computer Library Center, Inc., Swets Information Services).
Indexed: ABS&EES, AMHA, ASCA, AddicA, AgeL, BIOSIS Prev, BMAb, BiolAb, CJA, CLFP, CurCont, ESPM, ExcerpMed, FamI, GSI, H&SSA, HRIS, INI, IPA, IndMed, MEA&I, MEDLINE, NRN, PsycInfo, PsycholAb, RASB, RefZh, SOPODA, SSA, SSCI, SSI, SWA, SWR&A, SociolAb, THA, ToxAb, e-psyche.
—BLDSC (0824.320000), CASDDS, CISTI, GNLM, IDS, IE, Infotrieve, ingenta, KNAW. **CCC.**
Published by: Taylor & Francis Inc. (Subsidiary of: Taylor & Francis Group), 325 Chestnut St, Ste 800, Philadelphia, PA 19016. TEL 215-625-8900, FAX 215-625-2940, customerservice@taylorandfrancis.com, info@taylorandfrancis.com, http://www.tandf.co.uk/journals/titles/00952990.ASP. Ed. Edward Kaufman. R&P Jill Milland. Adv. contact Robin Castorina. B&W page USD 890, color page USD 1,945; trim 8.25 x 10.875. Circ: 825.

616.8 USA ISSN 1055-0496
RC563 CODEN: AJADEA

➤ **AMERICAN JOURNAL ON ADDICTIONS.** Text in English. 1992. 6/yr. USD 580, GBP 352 combined subscription to institutions print & online eds. (effective 2006). adv. bk.rev. abstr.; bibl.; charts; illus.; stat. index. reprint service avail. from PSC. **Document type:** *Journal, Academic/Scholarly.* **Description:** Presents original research related to the assessment and treatment of addictive disorders.
Related titles: Microform ed.: (from PQC); Online - full text ed.: ISSN 1521-0391. USD 551, GBP 334 to institutions (effective 2006) (from EBSCO Publishing, Gale Group, IngentaConnect, O C L C Online Computer Library Center, Inc., Swets Information Services).
Indexed: ASCA, AddicA, CJA, CurCont, ERA, ETA, ExcerpMed, FamI, IndMed, JW-P, MEA, MEDLINE, PsycInfo, PsycholAb, RHEA, SEA, SENA, SOMA, SSCI, SWA, TEA, e-psyche.
—BLDSC (0820.947000), GNLM, IDS, IE, Infotrieve, ingenta, KNAW. **CCC.**
Published by: (American Academy of Psychiatrists in Alcoholism and Addictions), Taylor & Francis Inc. (Subsidiary of: Taylor & Francis Group), 325 Chestnut St, Ste 800, Philadelphia, PA 19016. TEL 215-625-8900, 800-354-1420, FAX 215-625-2940, info@taylorandfrancis.com, http://www.tandf.co.uk/journals/titles/10550496.asp, http://www.taylorandfrancis.com. Ed. Sheldon Miller. Circ: 1,300. **Subsc. addr. in Europe:** Taylor & Francis Ltd, Journals Customer Service, Rankine Rd, Basingstoke, Hants RG24 8PR, United Kingdom. TEL 44-1256-813000, FAX 44-1256-330245, enquiry@tandf.co.uk.

D

▼ new title ➤ refereed ✶ unverified ♦ full entry avail.

➤ **ANABOLIC INSIDER.** see *BIOLOGY—Biochemistry*

362.29 616.863 SWE ISSN 0280-512X
ANHOERIG. Text in Swedish. 1981. irreg.
Published by: Riksfoerbundet Foeraeldrafoereningen mot Narkotika, Friluftsvaegen 29, Sundbyberg, 17240, Sweden. TEL 46-08-642 06 50, FAX 46-08-640 00 65.

616.861 USA ISSN 1091-9945
HV5825
ANNUAL EDITIONS: DRUGS, SOCIETY & BEHAVIOR. Text in English. 1986. a., latest 2003, 19th ed. USD 20.31 per vol. (effective 2004). illus. **Document type:** *Academic/Scholarly.*
Published by: McGraw-Hill - Dushkin (Subsidiary of: McGraw-Hill Higher Education), 2460 Kerper Blvd, Dubuque, IA 52001. TEL 800-243-6532, customer.service@mcgraw-hill.com, http://www.dushkin.com/text-data/catalog/0072860731.mhtml. Ed. Hugh Wilson. Pub. Ian Nielsen. R&P Cheryl Greenleaf.

362.29 LUX ISSN 1609-6150
HV5840.E8
ANNUAL REPORT ON THE STATE OF THE DRUGS PROBLEM IN THE EUROPEAN UNION. Text in English. 1996. a. **Document type:** *Government.*
Related titles: Spanish ed.: Informe Anual Sobre el Problema de la Drogodependencia en la Union Europea. ISSN 1609-607X; German ed.: Jahresbericht uber den Stand der Drogenproblematik in der Europaischen Union. ISSN 1609-6088; Danish ed.: Aarsberetning om Narkotikasituationen i Den Europaeiske Union. ISSN 1609-6096; French ed.: Rapport Annuel sur l'Etat du Phenomene de la Drogue dans l'Union Europeenne. ISSN 1609-6142; Greek ed.: Etesia Ekthese Shetika me ten Katastase tou Problematos ton Narkotikon sten Europaike Enose. ISSN 1609-610X; Italian ed.: Relazione Annuale Sull'evoluzione del Fenomeno della Droga nell'Unione Europea. ISSN 1609-6169; Ed.: Jaarverslag over de Stand van de Drugsproblematiek in de Europese Unie. ISSN 1609-6177; Portuguese ed.: Relatorio Anual Sobre a Evolucao do Fenomeno da Droga na Uniao Europeia. ISSN 1609-6185; Finnish ed.: Vuosiraportti Euroopan Unionin Huumeongelmasta. ISSN 1609-6193; Swedish ed.: Aarsrapport over Situationen paa Narkotikaomraadet i Europeiska Unionen. ISSN 1609-6207; Norwegian ed.: Aarsrapport om Narkotikasituasjonen i Den Europeiske Union. ISSN 1682-2773.
Published by: European Commission, Office for Official Publications of the European Union, 2 Rue Mercier, Luxembourg, L-2985, Luxembourg. info-info-opoce@cec.eu.int, http://publications.eu.int.

362.29 616.863 SWE ISSN 0281-577X
ANONYMA ALKOHOLISTER. BULLETIN. Text in Swedish. 1965-1980; resumed 1982. bi-m. SEK 120 (effective 1994). **Document type:** *Bulletin.*
Published by: Anonyma Alkoholister, Fack 16387, Stockholm, 10327, Sweden. TEL 47-8-642-26-09, FAX 47-8-714-82-24. Circ: 1,500.

615.1 VEN ISSN 0798-0264
ARCHIVOS VENEZOLANOS DE FARMACOLOGIA Y TERAPEUTICA. Text in Spanish. 1982. 3/yr.
Related titles: Online - full text ed.: free (effective 2005).
Published by: Sociedad Venezolana de Farmacologia Clinica y Terapeutica, Catedra de Farmacologia, Piso 3, Esq. de San Jacinto, San Jose, Caracas, Venezuela. TEL 58-212-5619871, FAX 58-212-3214385. Ed. Manuel Velasco.

616.861 JPN ISSN 0910-495X
ARUKORU IRYO KENKYU/JAPANESE STUDIES ON ALCOHOLISM TREATMENT. Text in Japanese. 1984. q. JPY 1,880.
Published by: (Shiheki Mondai Rinsho Kenkyujo), Seiwa Shoten Co. Ltd., 2-5 Kami-Takai-Do 1-chome, Suginami-ku, Tokyo, 168-0074, Japan.

ASHES TO DUST. see *PUBLIC HEALTH AND SAFETY*

ASSOCIATION OF NURSES IN SUBSTANCE ABUSE. JOURNAL BULLETIN. see *MEDICAL SCIENCES—Nurses And Nursing*

616.861 AUS ISSN 0726-4607
AUSTRA-LINK. Text in English. 1981. m. AUD 12 domestic; AUD 25 foreign (effective 2003). 12 p./no.; **Document type:** *Magazine, Consumer.* **Description:** Recovering from effects of living with someone else's alcoholism, using the Al-Anon 12-step program.
Published by: Al-Anon Family Groups (Australia) Pty. Ltd., GPO Box 1002 H, Melbourne, VIC 3001, Australia. TEL 61-3-9654-8838, FAX 61-3-9654-8865, agso@alphalink.com.au, http://www.al-anon.alateen.org/australia. Ed., R&P Mary Richards. Circ: 1,350.

AUSTRALIAN COUNCIL ON SMOKING AND HEALTH NEWSLETTER. see *PHYSICAL FITNESS AND HYGIENE*

178 AUS
AUTUMN SCHOOL OF STUDIES ON ALCOHOL & DRUGS. PROCEEDINGS OF SEMINARS. Text in English. 1966. a. AUD 18. back issues avail. **Document type:** *Proceedings.*
Published by: St. Vincent Hospital, Department of Drug and Alcohol Studies, Victoria Parade, Fitzroy, VIC 3065, Australia. TEL 61-3-288-2627, FAX 61-3-288-2642, TELEX SVHOSM AA 32229. Circ: 250.

B I M S. (Blaukreuz Information - Meinungen - Szene) see *RELIGIONS AND THEOLOGY—Protestant*

BACK STREET HEROES. see *TRANSPORTATION—Automobiles*

BEHAVIORAL HEALTH BUSINESS NEWS. see *INSURANCE*

616.86 USA ISSN 1075-6701
HV5285
BEHAVIORAL HEALTH MANAGEMENT. Text in English. 1980. bi-m. USD 94 domestic; USD 105 foreign (effective 2005). adv. bk.rev. **Document type:** *Magazine, Trade.* **Description:** Addresses the problems of providing cost-effective mental health and substance abuse treatment in an environment of managed care.
Former titles (until 1994): Addiction and Recovery (1052-4614); (until 1989): Alcoholism and Addiction and Recovery Life (1053-3923); (until 1988): Alcoholism and Addiction (0899-8043); (until 1987): Alcoholism and Addiction Magazine (0884-1403); (until 1985): Alcoholism (0275-9519)
Related titles: Online - full text ed.: (from bigchalk, EBSCO Publishing, Florida Center for Library Automation, Gale Group, Northern Light Technology, Inc., O C L C Online Computer Library Center, Inc., ProQuest Information & Learning).
Indexed: HlthInd, SSI.
Published by: Medquest Communications, LLC, 3800 Lakeside Ave, Ste 201, Cleveland, OH 44114. TEL 216-391-9100, FAX 216-391-9200, http://www.behavioral.net, http://primarycare.medscape.com. Ed. Monica Oss. Pub. Mark Goodman. Circ: 21,056.

362.29 616.863 SWE ISSN 0345-1577
BLAA BANDET; Blaabandsroerelsens tidning. Text in Swedish. 1883. 9/yr. SEK 75 (effective 1999). **Document type:** *Newsletter.*
Address: Fack 1233, Orebro, 70112, Sweden. TEL 46-19-130575, FAX 46-19-121136. Ed. Per Olof Svensson.

362.29 616.863 SWE ISSN 0345-1585
BLAA KORSET; informationsblad. Text in Swedish. 1969. q. SEK 30 (effective 1990).
Address: Soergaarden, Koeping, 73192, Sweden.

616.86 344 DEU ISSN 0006-5250
K2 CODEN: BLALAL
BLUTALKOHOL; wissenschaftliche Zeitschrift fuer die medizinische und juristische Praxis. Text in English, German. 1961. bi-m. EUR 49.40 domestic; EUR 53.15 in Europe; EUR 53.65 elsewhere; EUR 8.70 newsstand/cover (effective 2004). adv. bk.rev. bibl.; charts. s-a. index, cum.index: 1961-62. back issues avail. **Document type:** *Journal, Academic/Scholarly.*
Indexed: AC&P, BIOSIS Prev, BiolAb, CIN, ChemAb, ChemTitl, DIP, ExcerpMed, MEDLINE, MSB.
—CASDDS, GNLM, KNAW. **CCC.**
Published by: (Bund gegen Alkohol im Strassenverkehr e.V.), Steintor Verlag GmbH, Graphengiesserstr 30, Luebeck, 23566, Germany. TEL 49-451-8798849, FAX 49-451-8798837, info@steintor-verlag.de. Eds. Klaus Pueschel, Uwe Scheffler. R&P R Jacobson. Circ: 3,200.

178 364 ITA ISSN 0392-3126
BOLLETTINO PER LE FARMACODIPENDENZE E L'ALCOOLISMO. Text in Italian. 1991. q. free. bk.rev. **Document type:** *Bulletin, Government.*
—BLDSC (2236.530000), IE, ingenta.
Published by: (Italy. Ministero della Sanita, Settore Tossicodipendenze e Patologie), United Nations Interregional Crime and Justice Research Institute/Institut Interregional de Recherche des Nations Unies sur la Criminalite et la Justice, Via Giulia, 52, Rome, RM 00186, Italy. TEL 39-6-6877437, FAX 39-6-6892638, unicri@unicri.it. Ed. Dr. Carlo Vetere. Circ: 7,000.

616.863 USA ISSN 1040-6328
RC563
BROWN UNIVERSITY DIGEST OF ADDICTION THEORY & APPLICATION; monthly synopsis of critical research developments in the treatment and prevention of alcoholism and drug abuse. Variant title: D A T A. Text in English. 1981. m. USD 995 domestic to institutions; USD 1,043 in Canada & Mexico to institutions; USD 1,061 elsewhere to institutions; USD 1,095 combined subscription domestic to institutions print & online eds.; USD 1,143 combined subscription in Canada & Mexico to institutions print & online eds.; USD 1,161 combined subscription elsewhere to institutions print & online eds. (effective 2006). 8 p./no.; back issues avail.; reprints avail. **Document type:** *Newsletter, Abstract/Index.* **Description:** News-style synopsis of critical research developments in the treatment and prevention of addiction.
Incorporates (in 1991): Addictions Alert (0887-8145)
Related titles: Online - full text ed.: ISSN 1556-7559. USD 995 (effective 2006) (from EBSCO Publishing, Gale Group, O C L C Online Computer Library Center, Inc.).
Indexed: CINAHL, RefZh, e-psyche.
Published by: John Wiley & Sons, Inc., 111 River St, Hoboken, NJ 07030-5774. TEL 201-748-6000, 800-825-7550, FAX 201-748-5915, uscs-wis@wiley.com, http://www.wiley.com.

616.86 USA
C S A P PREVENTION MONOGRAPH. (Center for Substance Abuse Prevention) Text in English. irreg., latest vol.14, 1993. **Document type:** *Monographic series, Government.*
Published by: National Clearinghouse for Alcohol and Drug Information, Center for Substance Abuse Prevention, PO Box 2345, Rockville, MD 20847-2345. TEL 800-729-6686, FAX 301-468-6433, info@prevline.health.org, http://www.health.org.

616.86 HRV ISSN 0033-8567
CENTAR ZA PROUCANANJE I SUZBIJANJE ALKOHOLIZMA I DRUGIH OVISNOSTI. RADOVI. Text in Croatian; Summaries in English. 1966. irreg. price varies. adv. illus.; stat.
Published by: Centar za Proucavanje i Suzbijanje Alkoholizma i Drugih Ovisnosti/Centre for Study and Control of Alcoholism and Other Addictions, Vinogradska 29, Zagreb, 10000, Croatia. vlatko.thaller@zg.tel.hr. Ed. Dr. Vladimir Hudolin. Circ: 1,000.

362.29 614 SWE ISSN 1400-5360
CENTRALFOERBUNDET FOER ALKOHOL- OCH NARKOTIKAUPPLYSNING. RAPPORT. Text in Swedish. 1995. irreg. back issues avail.
Related titles: English ed.: ISSN 1402-7429.
Published by: (Statens Folkhaelsoinstitut/National Institute of Public Health in Sweden), Centralfoerbundet foer Alkohol- och Narkotikaupplysning/Swedish Council on Information on Alcohol and Other Drugs, Olof Palmes Gata 17, PO Box 70412, Stockholm, 10133, Sweden. TEL 46-8-4124600, FAX 46-8-4124641, http://www.can.se. **Co-publisher:** Statens Folkhaelsoinstitut/National Institute of Public Health in Sweden.

616.86 157.63 CAN
CENTRE FOR ADDICTION AND MENTAL HEALTH. ANNUAL REPORT. Text in English. 1951. a. free (2000). **Document type:** *Government.*
Former titles: Addiction Research Foundation of Ontario. Annual Report; Alcoholism and Drug Addiction Research Foundation. Annual Report (0065-6119)
—CISTI.
Published by: Centre for Addiction and Mental Health, 33 Russell St, Toronto, ON M5S 2S1, Canada. TEL 416-595-6059, FAX 416-593-4694, mkt@arf.org, http://www.arf.org. Circ: 2,000 (controlled).

CLINICAL TOXICOLOGY. see *PHARMACY AND PHARMACOLOGY*

616.86 USA
COMMUNITY OF RECOVERY. Text in English. 1998. q. free to qualified personnel. **Document type:** *Newsletter, Trade.* **Description:** Provides mostly current information regarding the treatment of the disease of chemical dependency.
Published by: Sundown M. Ranch, 2280 State Rte 821, Yakima, WA 98284-0735. TEL 360-757-1606, 800-326-7444. Ed., R&P Len Baltzer. **Subscr. to:** Sundown M Ranch, PO Box 735, Sedro Wooley, WA 98284-9913.

616.861 CAN ISSN 0045-799X
CONCERNS. Text in English. 1902. q. CND 25 to members. bk.rev. illus. **Document type:** *Newsletter.* **Description:** Informs members of issues and programs involving the organization, its Board and staff.
Formerly: Advocate (Scarborough)
Indexed: ABRCLP.
—**CCC.**
Published by: Concerns Canada, 4500 Sheppard Ave., E., Ste. 112H, Agincourt, ON M1S 3R6, Canada. TEL 416-293-3400, FAX 416-293-1142. Ed. Karl N Burden. Circ: 16,000.

616.863 USA
CONTROLLED SUBSTANCES REGULATION. Text in English. 1972. q. looseleaf. USD 287. **Description:** Comprehensive guide to current Drug Enforcement Administration requirements for manufacturing, storing, securing, shipping and distributing controlled substances.
Formerly: Controlled Substances Handbook
Published by: Government Information Services (Subsidiary of: Thompson Publishing Group), 1725 K St, N W, 7th Fl, Washington, DC 20006. TEL 800-876-0226, FAX 202-759-9657. Ed. Ken Baumgartner.

COUNSELOR; the magazine for addiction professionals. see *PSYCHOLOGY*

616.86 CAN ISSN 1706-9548
RC563
CROSSCURRENTS (TORONTO). Text in English, French. 1998. bi-m. CND 16 domestic in Ontario; CND 28.69 domestic in Nova Scotia, New Brunswick, Newfoundland; CND 36.95 foreign (effective 2005). adv. bk.rev. abstr. index. back issues avail. **Document type:** *Newsletter, Trade.* **Description:** Covers the latest developments in the mental health and addictions fields for professionals and consumers.
Formerly (until 2002): The Journal of Addiction and Mental Health (1481-3122); Which was formed by the merger of (1972-1998): Addiction and Mental Health Services Corporation. Journal (0044-6203); (1994-1998): Fondation de la Recherche sur la Toxicomanie. Journal (1201-2572)

D

Related titles: CD-ROM ed.; Online - full text ed.: (from Gale Group, Micromedia ProQuest); French ed.: Le Journal de Toxicomanie et de Sante Mentale. ISSN 1481-3254.
Indexed: CBCARef, CBPI, CPerl, e-psyche.
—CCC.
Published by: Centre for Addiction and Mental Health, 33 Russell St, Toronto, ON M5S 2S1, Canada. TEL 416-595-6111, 800-463-6273, public_affairs@camh.net, http://www.camh.net/publications/crosscurrents.html. Ed., R&P Anita Dubey. Adv. contact Doreen Grbic. B&W page CND 1,300. Circ: 8,000; 1,000 (paid); 1,500 (controlled).

616.863   ITA   ISSN 1121-0311
IL DELFINO. Text in Italian. 1976. bi-m. EUR 21 (effective 2004). adv. bk.rev.; film rev. index. **Document type:** *Magazine, Consumer.* **Description:** Focuses its attention on the drug addict, includes interviews, looks at personal experiences of the drug addict, family and friends. Also looks at other addictions such as alcoholism, smoking and other forms of drugs.
Published by: Centro Italiano di Solidarieta, Via Attilio Ambrosini 129, Rome, 00147, Italy. TEL 39-06-541951, FAX 39-06-5407304, ceis@inroma.roma.it, http://www.ceis.it. Ed. Enzo Caffarelli. Adv. contact Simona Cordeschi.

DEPARTMENT OF ALCOHOLIC BEVERAGE CONTROL. ANNUAL REPORT. see *BEVERAGES*

362   CAN   ISSN 1498-6477
DIRECTORY OF ADDICTIONS ORGANIZATIONS IN CANADA. Text in English. 1992. biennial. CND 49.95 for 2 yrs. (effective 2004 - 2005).
Formerly (until 2000): Directory of Substance Abuse Organizations in Canada (1188-4886)
Published by: Canadian Centre on Substance Abuse/Centre Canadien de Lutte Contre l'Alcoholisme et les Toxicomanies, 75 Albert St., Ste 300, Ottawa, ON K1P 5E7, Canada. TEL 613-235-4048, FAX 613-235-8101, http://www.ccsa.ca/index.asp?menu=Publications&ID=154.

616.8   AUS
DIRECTORY OF AL-ANON AND ALATEEN MEETINGS IN AUSTRALIA. Text in English. 1991. s-a. AUD 1 domestic; AUD 2 foreign (effective 2001). back issues avail. **Document type:** *Directory.*
Published by: Al-Anon Family Groups (Australia) Pty. Ltd., GPO Box 1002 H, Melbourne, VIC 3001, Australia. TEL 61-3-9654-8838, FAX 61-3-9654-8865, http://www.al-anon.alateen.org/australia. Ed. Beryl Stone. Circ: 50.

394.12   CAN
DRINK SMART. Text in English. 1998. irreg. **Document type:** *Bulletin.* **Description:** Explores issues relating to the consumption of alcohol and promotes responsible drinking.
Media: Online - full text.
Published by: Young People's Press, 110 Eglinton Ave W, Ste 200, Toronto, ON M4R 1A3, Canada. TEL 416-484-4570, FAX 416-484-8173, yppto@planeteer.com, http://www.drinksmart.org. Ed. Michael Hoechsmann.

616.8   USA   ISSN 0882-7826
HV5822.M3
DRUG ABUSE AND DRUG ABUSE RESEARCH. Text in English. 1971. biennial.
Formerly (until 1984): Marijuana and Health: Annual Report to the U.S. Congress from the Secretary of Health, Education and Welfare (0272-2046)
Published by: U.S. Department of Health and Human Services, National Institute on Drug Abuse, 6001 Executive Blvd., Rm. 5213, Bethesda, MD 20892-9561. TEL 301-443-6500.

616.86   USA   ISSN 1067-814X
RC564.73
DRUG, ALCOHOL, AND OTHER ADDICTIONS. Text in English. 1989. irreg. **Document type:** *Directory.*
Related titles: Magnetic Tape ed.
Published by: Oryx Press (Subsidiary of: Greenwood Publishing Group Inc.), 4041 N Central Ave, Phoenix, AZ 85012-3397. TEL 602-265-2651, FAX 602-265-6250, info@oryxpress.com, http://www.oryxpress.com. Eds. Jennifer Ashley, Anne Thompson. Pub. Phyllis Steckler.

616.86   IRL   ISSN 0376-8716
                                        CODEN: DADEDV
➤ **DRUG AND ALCOHOL DEPENDENCE.** Text in English. 1975. 15/yr. EUR 213 in Europe to individuals; JPY 28,300 in Japan to individuals; USD 239 elsewhere to individuals; EUR 1,763 in Europe to institutions; JPY 234,000 in Japan to institutions; USD 1,972 elsewhere to institutions (effective 2006). bk.rev. abstr. back issues avail. **Document type:** *Academic/Scholarly.* **Description:** For workers in the fields of biomedical, as well as clinical, epidemiological, psychosocial, socio-cultural, educational and medico-legal research.
Related titles: Microform ed.: (from PQC); Online - full text ed.: (from EBSCO Publishing, Gale Group, IngentaConnect, ScienceDirect, Swets Information Services).

Indexed: AC&P, AMHA, ASCA, ASSIA, AbHyg, AddicA, AnBrAb, BIOBASE, BIOSIS Prev, BiolAb, CIN, CINAHL, CJA, CMHR, ChPerl, ChemAb, ChemTitl, CurCont, DSA, ERA, ESPM, ExcerpMed, FamI, FoP, H&SSA, HRIS, IABS, INI, IPA, ISR, IndMed, Inpharma, MEA&I, MEDLINE, NSCI, NutrAb, PE&ON, PsycInfo, PsycholAb, RM&VM, Reac, SCI, SOPODA, SSA, SSCI, SWA, SociolAb, TDB, THA, VetBull, e-psyche.
—BLDSC (3627.890000), CASDDS, CISTI, GNLM, IDS, IE, Infotrieve, ingenta, KNAW. **CCC.**
Published by: (International Council on Alcohol and Addictions), Elsevier Ireland Ltd (Subsidiary of: Elsevier Science & Technology), Elsevier House, Brookvale Plaza, E. Park, Shannon, Co. Clare, Ireland. TEL 353-61-709600, FAX 353-61-709100, http://www.elsevier.com/locate/drugalcdep. **Subscr. to:** Elsevier BV, PO Box 211, Amsterdam 1000 AE, Netherlands. TEL 31-20-485-3757, FAX 31-20-485-3432, nlinfo-f@elsevier.nl, http://www.elsevier.nl. **Co-sponsor:** College on Problems of Drug Dependence.

616.86   GBR
DRUG AND ALCOHOL FINDINGS. Text in English. q. GBP 60 (effective 2000).
—BLDSC (3627.891000).
Published by: The Findings Partnership, c/o DrugScope, 32-36 Loman St, London, SE1 0EE, United Kingdom. FAX 44-20-8888-6277, findings@mashton.cix.co.uk. Ed. Mike Ashton.

178   GBR   ISSN 0959-5236
➤ **DRUG AND ALCOHOL REVIEW.** Text in English. 1982. bi-m. GBP 929, USD 1,532, AUD 1,800 combined subscription to institutions print & online eds. (effective 2006). bk.rev. index. back issues avail.; reprint service avail. from PSC. **Document type:** *Journal, Academic/Scholarly.* **Description:** Reviews the clinical, biomedical, psychological and sociological aspects of alcohol, tobacco, and drug use.
Former titles (until Jan. 1990): Australian Drug and Alcohol Review; Australian Alcohol - Drug Review (0726-4550)
Related titles: Online - full text ed.: ISSN 1465-3362. GBP 883, USD 1,455, AUD 1,710 to institutions (effective 2006) (from EBSCO Publishing, Gale Group, IngentaConnect, O C L C Online Computer Library Center, Inc., ProQuest Information & Learning, R M I T Publishing, Swets Information Services).
Indexed: ASCA, ASSIA, AddicA, CJA, CurCont, ERA, ESPM, ETA, FamI, H&SSA, MEA, PsycInfo, PsycholAb, RHEA, RiskAb, SEA, SENA, SFSA, SOMA, SSA, SSCI, SWA, SociolAb, TEA, ToxAb, V&AA, e-psyche.
—BLDSC (3627.895000), IDS, IE, Infotrieve, ingenta, KNAW. **CCC.**
Published by: (Australian Medical and Professional Society on Alcohol and Drug Related Problems AUS), Taylor & Francis Ltd (Subsidiary of: Taylor & Francis Group), 4 Park Sq, Milton Park, Abingdon, OX14 4RN, United Kingdom. TEL 44-1235-828600, FAX 44-1235-829000, info@tandf.co.uk, http://www.tandf.co.uk/journals/titles/09595236.asp. Ed. John B Saunders. **Subscr. in N. America to:** Taylor & Francis Inc., Customer Services Dept, 325 Chestnut St, 8th Fl, Philadelphia, PA 19106. TEL 215-625-8900, 800-354-1420, FAX 215-625-8914, customerservice@taylorandfrancis.com; **Subscr. to:** Journals Customer Service, Rankine Rd, Basingstoke, Hants RG24 8PR, United Kingdom. TEL 44-1256-813000, FAX 44-1256-330245, enquiry@tandf.co.uk.

➤ **DRUG DETECTION REPORT;** the newsletter on drug testing in the workplace. see *BUSINESS AND ECONOMICS— Personnel Management*

362.29 371.7   GBR   ISSN 1461-8842
DRUG EDUCATION MATTERS. Text in English. 1998. 3/yr. bk.rev. **Document type:** *Newsletter.* **Description:** Covers the recent developments in drug education and contains features on drug education in practice.
Indexed: e-psyche.
—CCC.
Published by: National Children's Bureau, 8 Wakley St, London, EC1V 7QE, United Kingdom. TEL 44-20-78436000, FAX 44-20-72789512, http://www.ncb.org.uk. Circ: 2,000.

DRUG INDUCED DISORDERS. see *PHARMACY AND PHARMACOLOGY*

362.29   GBR   ISSN 1356-9961
DRUG MISUSE IN BRITAIN. Text in English. 1990. a.
—BLDSC (3629.334000).
Published by: Institute for the Study of Drug Dependence, Waterbridge House, Institute For The Study Of Drug Dependence (I S D), 32-36 Loman St, London, SE1 0EE, United Kingdom. TEL 44-207-928-1211, FAX 44-207-928-1771, http://www.isdd.co.uk.

362.29   GBR   ISSN 0962-3582
DRUG TARIFF. Text in English. 1990. irreg.
—BLDSC (3629.420000). **CCC.**
Published by: Home Office, 50 Queen Anne's Gate, London, SW1 9AT, United Kingdom. http://www.open.gov.uk.

616.863 364   USA
DRUG TRAFFICKING IN THE UNITED STATES. Text in English. irreg. **Document type:** *Government.*
Media: Online - full content.

Published by: U.S. Drug Enforcement Administration, Office of Domestic Intelligence, Domestic Strategic Intelligence Unit, Mailstop: AXS, 2401 Jefferson Davis Hwy, Alexandria, VA 22301. TEL 202-307-8726, http://www.dea.gov/pubs/intel/01020/.

616.863   GBR   ISSN 0957-3100
DRUGLINK. Text in English. 1976. bi-m. GBP 51; GBP 64 foreign (effective 1999). adv. bk.rev. bibl. back issues avail. **Document type:** *Newsletter.* **Description:** Examines the abuse and misuse of drugs.
Formerly (until 1986): Druglink Information Letter (0305-4349)
Related titles: Supplement(s): Drugs Prevention News. ISSN 1353-0003.
Indexed: ASSIA.
—BLDSC (3629.520000), IE, ingenta. **CCC.**
Published by: Institute for the Study of Drug Dependence, Waterbridge House, Institute For The Study Of Drug Dependence (I S D, 32-36 Loman St, London, SE1 0EE, United Kingdom. TEL 44-207-928-1211, FAX 44-207-928-1771, services@isdd.co.uk, http://www.isdd.co.uk. Ed. Neil Bell. R&P Harry Shapiro. Adv. contact Jan Hodgman. page GBP 220; 181 x 264. Circ: 2,300.

362.29   LUX   ISSN 0873-5379
DRUGNET EUROPE. Text in English. 1996. bi-m.
Related titles: Online - full text ed.: ISSN 1683-3252; French ed.: ISSN 0873-5387; German ed.: ISSN 0873-5395; Portuguese ed.: ISSN 0873-5409; Spanish ed.: ISSN 1683-3236.
—BLDSC (3629.565000).
Published by: European Commission, Office for Official Publications of the European Union, 2 Rue Mercier, Luxembourg, L-2985, Luxembourg. FAX 352-2929-1, http://publications.eu.int.

616.86   GBR   ISSN 0968-7637
                                        CODEN: DEPPEH
➤ **DRUGS;** education, prevention & policy. Text in English. 1994. bi-m. GBP 631, USD 1,040 combined subscription to institutions print & online eds. (effective 2006). adv. bk.rev. index. reprint service avail. from PSC. **Document type:** *Journal, Academic/Scholarly.* **Description:** Publishes multidisciplinary papers on the prevention of substance abuse and related problems. Provides a forum for those concerned with education and prevention policy and its application in the community, and promotes dialogue with those affected by such applications and community practice.
Related titles: Microfiche ed.; Online - full text ed.: ISSN 1465-3370. GBP 599, USD 988 to institutions (effective 2006) (from EBSCO Publishing, Gale Group, IngentaConnect, O C L C Online Computer Library Center, Inc., ProQuest Information & Learning, Swets Information Services).
Indexed: ASCA, ASSIA, AddicA, BrEdI, CJA, CurCont, ERA, ESPM, ETA, FamI, H&SSA, MEA, PSA, PsycInfo, PsycholAb, RHEA, RiskAb, SEA, SENA, SOMA, SOPODA, SRRA, SSA, SSCI, SWA, SociolAb, TEA, e-psyche.
—BLDSC (3629.818000), IDS, IE, Infotrieve, ingenta. **CCC.**
Published by: Taylor & Francis Ltd (Subsidiary of: Taylor & Francis Group), 4 Park Sq, Milton Park, Abingdon, OX14 4RN, United Kingdom. TEL 44-1235-828600, FAX 44-1235-829000, info@tandf.co.uk, http://www.tandf.co.uk/journals/titles/09687637.asp. Ed. Dr. Betsy Thom. **Subscr. in N. America to:** Taylor & Francis Inc., Customer Services Dept, 325 Chestnut St, 8th Fl, Philadelphia, PA 19106. TEL 215-625-8900, 800-354-1420, FAX 215-625-8914, customerservice@taylorandfrancis.com; **Subscr. to:** Journals Customer Service, Rankine Rd, Basingstoke, Hants RG24 8PR, United Kingdom. TEL 44-1256-813000, FAX 44-1256-330245, enquiry@tandf.co.uk.

362.29   GBR
DRUGS AND ALCOHOL TODAY. Text in English. 2001. q. GBP 40 domestic to individuals; GBP 45 in Europe to individuals; GBP 55 elsewhere to individuals; GBP 140 domestic to institutions; GBP 150 in Europe to institutions; GBP 160 elsewhere to institutions (effective 2004). adv. back issues avail. **Document type:** *Journal, Academic/Scholarly.* **Description:** Aims to be a first contact reference point for those professionals having face to face contact with the individual experiencing harmful consequences of their substance abuse.
Formerly (until July 2004): The Drug and Alcohol Professional (1475-0384)
Related titles: Online - full content ed.
Indexed: BrNI, CINAHL, e-psyche.
—BLDSC (3629.612500), IE, ingenta.
Published by: Pavilion Publishing Ltd., The Ironworks, Cheapside, Brighton, E Sussex BN1 4GD, United Kingdom. TEL 44-1273-623222, FAX 44-1273-625526, The_DrugandAlcohol_Professional@btinternet.com, info@pavpub.com, http://www.pavpub.com. Ed. Gary Hayes. Adv. contact Vicki Smith. B&W page GBP 350.

616.863   USA   ISSN 0744-2823
HV5825
DRUGS & DRUG ABUSE EDUCATION. NEWSLETTER✱. Text in English. 1969. m. USD 79. bk.rev. charts. **Description:** Covers treatment, prevention education, congressional and agency developments, and state and local programs.
Incorporates: Alcoholism and Alcohol Education (0044-7226); Formerly: Washington Drug Review (0146-728X)

D

Published by: Editorial Resources, Inc., PO Box 20754, Scattle, WA 98102-1754. TEL 206-322-8387. Ed. David L Howell.

345.027 340 USA
DRUGS AND THE LAW; detection, recognition & investigation. Text in English. 1992. irreg. USD 44.95 (effective 2000). **Document type:** *Government.* **Description:** A publication for anyone involved with the problem of drug abuse. Covers topics such as current patterns in drug abuse. Drugs, crime and violence, addiction and behavior, drug law enforcement, drug treatment, rehabilitation, prevention, education and more.
Published by: Gould Publications, Inc. (Subsidiary of: LexisNexis), 1333 North US Hwy 17-92, Longwood, FL 32750-3724. TEL 407-695-9500, 800-717-7917, FAX 407-695-2906, info@gouldlaw.com, http://www.gouldlaw.com.

362.29 LUX ISSN 1681-5157
HV5840.E85
DRUGS IN FOCUS. Text in English. 2001. bi-m.
Related titles: Spanish ed.: Las Drogas en el Punto de Mira. ISSN 1681-6307; German ed.: Drogen im Blickpunkt. ISSN 1681-6323; Danish ed.: Fokus paa Narkotika (Dansk Udg.). ISSN 1681-6315; French ed.: Objectif Drogues. ISSN 1681-634X; Italian ed.: Focus sulle Droghe. ISSN 1681-6358; Dutch ed.: Drugs in Beeld. ISSN 1681-6366; Portuguese ed.: As Drogas em Destaque. ISSN 1681-6374; Norwegian ed.: Fokus paa Narkotika (Norsk Utg.). ISSN 1681-6382; Finnish ed.: Teemana Huumeet. ISSN 1681-6390; Swedish ed.: Fokus paa Narkotika (Svensk Utg.). ISSN 1681-6404; Greek ed.: Ta Narkotika sto Proskenio. ISSN 1681-6331.
—BLDSC (3629.830000).
Published by: European Commission, Office for Official Publications of the European Union, 2 Rue Mercier, Luxembourg, L-2985, Luxembourg. info-info-opoce@cec.eu.int, http://www.emcdda.eu.int/index.cfm?fuseaction=public.Content&nNodeID=439&sLanguageISO=EN, http://publications.eu.int. **Co-publisher:** European Monitoring Centre for Drugs and Drug Addiction.

362.29 AUS ISSN 1036-9864
DRUGS IN SOCIETY. Text in English. 1986. q. back issues avail.
Formerly (1986-1991): Channel A D F Q (1030-8342)
Related titles: Online - full text ed.
Published by: Alcohol and Drug Foundation, PO Box 332, Spring Hill, QLD 4004, Australia. TEL 61-7-38323798, FAX 61-7-38322527, dinie@ats.com.au, http://www.adfq.org. Ed. Craig Ashdown.

616.86 USA ISSN 0273-8910
HF5549.5.E42 CODEN: EAPDEW
E A P DIGEST. (Employee Assistance Programs) Text in English. 1980. q. USD 36 domestic; USD 45 in Canada; USD 55 elsewhere (effective 2005). adv. bk.rev. **Document type:** *Magazine, Trade.*
Indexed: SWR&A, e-psyche.
Published by: Performance Resource Press, Inc., 1270 Rankin Dr, Ste F, Troy, MI 48083-2843. TEL 800-453-7733, http://www.prponline.net. Ed. Erin Brown Bell. Circ: 5,000 (paid and controlled).

D

362.29 USA
EPIDEMIOLOGIC TRENDS IN DRUG ABUSE; proceedings of the Community Epidemiology Work Group. Text in English. s-a. **Document type:** *Proceedings, Government.*
Related titles: Online - full content ed.
Published by: Community Epidemiology Work Group, Division of Epidemiology, Services & Prevention Research, 6001 Executvie Blvd, Rm 5153 MSC 9589, Bethesda, MD 20892-9589. http://www.nida.nih.gov/about/organization/cewg/Reports.html, http://www.nida.nih.gov/about/organization/CEWG/CEWGHome.html. **Dist. by:** National Clearinghouse for Alcohol and Drug Information, PO Box 2345, Rockville, MD 20852-2345. TEL 301-468-2600, 800-729-6686, FAX 301-468-6433.

362.29 616.86 CHE ISSN 1022-6877
CODEN: EADREE
➤ **EUROPEAN ADDICTION RESEARCH.** Text in English. 1995. q. CHF 781 in Europe to institutions; CHF 794.60 elsewhere to institutions; CHF 841 combined subscription in Europe to institutions print & online eds.; CHF 854.60 combined subscription elsewhere to institutions print & online eds. (effective 2006). adv. back issues avail. **Document type:** *Journal, Academic/Scholarly.* **Description:** International forum for the exchange of interdisciplinary information and expert opinions on all aspects of addiction research. Coverage ranges from clinical and research advances in the fields of psychiatry, biology, pharmacology and epidemiology to the social, and legal implications of political decisions.
Related titles: Online - full text ed.: ISSN 1421-9891. CHF 753 to institutions (effective 2006) (from EBSCO Publishing, O C L C Online Computer Library Center, Inc., Swets Information Services).
Indexed: AbHyg, AddicA, CJA, CurCont, ExcerpMed, FamI, IndMed, MEDLINE, SSCI, SWA, TDB, e-psyche.
—BLDSC (3829.482945), CISTI, GNLM, IDS, IE, Infotrieve, ingenta, KNAW. **CCC.**
Published by: S. Karger AG, Allschwilerstr 10, Basel, 4009, Switzerland. TEL 41-61-3061111, FAX 41-61-3061234, karger@karger.ch, http://www.karger.com/EAR, http://www.karger.ch. Eds. A Uchtenhagen, C Haasen, M Krausz. adv.: page USD 1,195.

616.863 DEU
FAMILIEN-KALENDER. Text in German. 1902. a. EUR 4.80 (effective 2005). bk.rev. back issues avail. **Document type:** *Bulletin, Consumer.*
Published by: Blaukreuz Verlag, Freiligrathstr 27, Wuppertal, 42289, Germany. TEL 49-202-6200370, versand@blaukreuz.de, http://www.blaukreuz.de. Ed. Claudius Schillinger. Circ: 16,000.

FAMILY RESEARCH REPORT. see *HOMOSEXUALITY*

THE FARNATCHI SERIES. see *EDUCATION—Teaching Methods And Curriculum*

616.861 GBR
FINDINGS. Text in English. q. GBP 48 to members; GBP 60 to non-members (effective 2002). **Document type:** *Bulletin.* **Description:** Publishes the latest research in the drug field: treatment, education and prevention.
Published by: Alcohol Concern, Waterbridge House, 32-36 Loman St, London, SE1 0EE, United Kingdom. TEL 44-20-79287377, FAX 44-20-79284644, contact@alcoholconcern.org.uk, http://www.alcoholconcern.org.uk.

345.0277 340 345 614.19 USA ISSN 1048-8731
FORENSIC DRUG ABUSE ADVISOR; a monthly digest of information on the forensic aspects of drug abuse. Text in English. 1989. m. USD 197 (effective 2005). bk.rev. stat. 8 p./no. 2 cols./p.; back issues avail. **Document type:** *Newsletter, Academic/Scholarly.* **Description:** An information source for medical, legal, and substance abuse professionals and libraries. Emphasizes latest scientific discoveries in drug abuse, work place testing, federal regulations, and the law.
Published by: Forensic Drug Abuse Advisor, Inc., PO Box 5139, Berkeley, CA 94705-0139. TEL 510-849-0923, FAX 510-849-0958, fdaa@fdaa.com, http://www.fdaa.com. Ed. Steven B Karch. Pub., R&P Donna Leonti. Circ: 800 (paid).

362.29 DEU ISSN 1610-921X
▼ **FORSCHUNGSERGEBNISSE ZUR SUCHTPRAEVENTION.** Text in German. 2003. irreg., latest vol.3, 2005. price varies. **Document type:** *Monographic series, Academic/Scholarly.*
Published by: Verlag Dr. Kovac, Arnoldstr 49, Hamburg, 22763, Germany. TEL 49-40-3988800, FAX 49-40-39888055, info@verlagdrkovac.de, http://www.verlagdrkovac.de/17-2.htm.

616.86 USA ISSN 0194-8121
THE FORUM (VIRGINIA BEACH). Text in English. 1952. m. USD 10 domestic; USD 11 foreign (effective 2004). index. back issues avail. **Document type:** *Magazine, Consumer.* **Description:** Family members and friends of alcoholics relate personal experiences regarding Twelve Step program of recovery.
Published by: (Al-Anon Family Group Headquarters, Inc.), A F G, Inc., 1600 Corporate Landing Pkwy, Virginia Beach, VA 23454-5617. TEL 757-563-1600, FAX 757-563-1655, wso@al-anon.org, http://www.al-anon.org/forum.html, http://www.al-anon.alateen.org. Ed. Patrick Quiggle. R&P Caryn Johnson. Circ: 40,000.

178 CAN
FORWARD. Text in English. 1894. m. CND 2, USD 2.25. adv. illus.
Published by: (Grand Division Sons of Temperance of Nova Scotia), David Allbon & Co. Ltd., P O Box 1090, Windsor, NS B0N 2T0, Canada. TEL 902-798-2456. Ed. Annie L Bird. Circ: 600.

FREIE FAHRT/ROUTE LIBRE. see *PUBLIC HEALTH AND SAFETY*

616.861 DEU ISSN 0342-4685
FUEREINANDER. Text in German. 1971. s-m. reprints avail. **Document type:** *Bulletin, Consumer.*
Incorporated (1906-1999): Rettung (0048-7430)
—CCC.
Published by: (Blaues Kreuz in Deutschland e.V.), Blaukreuz Verlag, Freiligrathstr 27, Wuppertal, 42289, Germany. TEL 49-202-6200370, versand@blaukreuz.de, http://www.blaukreuz.de. Ed. Claudius Schillinger. Circ: 14,000.

616.861 640.73 NZL
GALA NEWS. Text in English. 1972. q. **Document type:** *Newsletter.*
Formerly: Celebration News
Published by: Group Against Liquor Advertising, Mt Eden, P.O. Box 67 023, Auckland, New Zealand. TEL 64-4-2982952, FAX 64-4-2982953. Ed. Viola Palmer. Circ: 400 (paid).

616.86 362.1 NLD ISSN 0166-2880
➤ **DE GEHEEL-ONTHOUDER**; feiten en commentaren over alcohol en drugs. Text in Dutch. 1901. bi-m. EUR 8 domestic; EUR 12 foreign (effective 2005). bk.rev. illus.; stat. back issues avail. **Document type:** *Journal, Academic/Scholarly.* **Description:** Reports new facts on the medical, criminological, and sociological aspects of drug and alcohol abuse to increase public awareness of this problem.
Related titles: Fax ed.
Published by: Algemeen Nederlandse Geheel-Onthouders Bond (ANGOB), Stationsweg 11, Maarssen, 3603 ED, Netherlands. TEL 31-346-562563, redactie@angob.nl, secretaris@angob.nl, http://www.angob.nl. Ed. D Korf. **Dist. by:** Drukkerij Banda, PO Box 14, Kollum 9290, Netherlands. TEL 31-511-451341, FAX 31-511-451312.

362.29 USA
GET SMART ABOUT DRUGS (GRADE LEVELS 2-3). Text in English. w. **Document type:** *Magazine, Academic/Scholarly.*
Published by: Weekly Reader Corp. (Subsidiary of: W R C Media Inc.), 200 First Stamford Pl, PO Box 120023, Stamford, CT 06912-0023. TEL 203-705-3500, FAX 203-705-1662, http://www.weeklyreader.com/store/wrgetsmart.asp.

362.29 USA
GET SMART ABOUT DRUGS (GRADE LEVELS 4-6). Text in English. w. **Document type:** *Magazine, Academic/Scholarly.*
Published by: Weekly Reader Corp. (Subsidiary of: W R C Media Inc.), 200 First Stamford Pl, PO Box 120023, Stamford, CT 06912-0023. TEL 203-705-3500, FAX 203-705-1662, http://www.weeklyreader.com/store/wrgetsmart.asp.

362.29 USA
GET SMART ABOUT DRUGS (GRADE LEVELS 7-9). Text in English. w. **Document type:** *Magazine, Academic/Scholarly.* **Description:** Provides materials and methods to enlighten children about drugs, the various types of drugs, what constitutes a 'drug', and why drugs are so dangerous.
Published by: Weekly Reader Corp. (Subsidiary of: W R C Media Inc.), 200 First Stamford Pl, PO Box 120023, Stamford, CT 06912-0023. TEL 203-705-3500, FAX 203-705-1662, http://www.weeklyreader.com/store/wrgetsmart.asp.

362.29 GBR ISSN 0801-2547
THE GLOBE. Text in English. 1853. q. GBP 10 (effective 2001). bk.rev. charts; illus. index. **Description:** Covers alcohol and other drug problems.
Formerly (until 1974): International Organization of Good Templars Journal (0020-8175)
Indexed: RefZh.
Published by: Institute of Alcohol Studies, Alliance House, 12 Caxton St, London, SW1H 0QS, United Kingdom. TEL 44-20-7976-7785, theglobe@ias.org.uk, info@ias.org.uk, http://www.ias.org.uk/theglobe. Eds. Andrew McNeill TEL 44-1480-466766, Derek Rutherford. R&P Andrew McNeill TEL 44-1480-466766. Circ: 5,000. **Co-sponsor:** Global Alcohol Policy Alliance.

GRANTS FOR MENTAL HEALTH, ADDICTIONS & CRISIS SERVICES. see *EDUCATION—School Organization And Administration*

616.861 USA ISSN 0362-2584
HV5275
GRAPEVINE; the international monthly journal of Alcoholics Anonymous. Text in English. 1944. m. USD 15 domestic; USD 23 foreign (effective 2000). **Document type:** *Consumer.*
Published by: Alcoholics Anonymous Grapevine, Inc., PO Box 1980, Grand Central Sta, New York, NY 10163-1980. TEL 212-870-3400, FAX 212-870-3301, gveditorial@aagrapevine.org, http://www.aagrapevine/@org. Ed. Ames Sweet. R&P Maggie Keough TEL 212-870-3390.

616.86 USA
GUILFORD SUBSTANCE ABUSE SERIES. Text in English. irreg. price varies. **Document type:** *Monographic series, Academic/Scholarly.* **Description:** Provides therapies and theories that can be used to treat and understand people with alcohol and drug problems and their families.
Indexed: e-psyche.
Published by: Guilford Publications, Inc., 72 Spring St, 4th Fl, New York, NY 10012. TEL 212-431-9800, 800-365-7006, FAX 212-966-6708, info@guilford.com. Ed. Seymour Weingarten. Pub. Robert Matloff. R&P David Mitchell. Adv. contact Christine Luberto.

362.29 SWE ISSN 1100-4312
HASSELA SOLIDARITET. Text in Swedish. 1985. q. SEK 100 (effective 2001).
Published by: Foerbundet Hassela Solidaritet, Fatburgsgatan 15A, Stockholm, 11828, Sweden. TEL 46-8-7208600, FAX 46-8-7208609, info@hasselasolidaritet.se, http://www.hasselasolidaritet.se.

616.86 USA
HAZELDEN VOICE; news and opinion for recovering people and professionals. Text in English. 1990. 2/yr. free. bk.rev. 16 p./no.; **Document type:** *Newsletter, Consumer.* **Description:** Covers a broad range of issues for professionals in the chemical health field and for those in recovery from chemical dependency and other related addictive behaviors.
Formerly (until 1996): Hazelden News and Professional Update
Published by: Hazelden Foundation, PO Box 11, Center City, MN 55012-0011. TEL 651-213-4455, FAX 651-213-4344, mduda@hazelden.org, info@hazelden.org, http://www.hazelden.org/servlet/hazelden/cms/ptt/hazl_7030_shade.html?sf=t&sh=t&page_id=28169. Ed., R&P Marty Duda. Circ: 100,000 (free).

616.863 610   USA   ISSN 0098-311X
RA1242.T6
THE HEALTH CONSEQUENCES OF SMOKING. (Includes sub-series: Health Benefits of Smoking Cessation; Health Consequences of Involuntary Smoking; Health Consequences of Smoking; Health Consequences of Smoking for Women; Preventing Tobacco Use Among Young People; Reducing the Health Consequences of Smoking; Smoking and Health in the Americas) Text in English. 1964. a. free. bibl.; charts; illus.; stat. index, cum.index: 1964-1982. **Document type:** *Consumer.* **Description:** Addresses the prevention and cessation of tobacco use and the protection of nonsmokers. —CISTI.
Published by: (Office on Smoking and Health), U.S. Centers for Disease Control and Prevention, National Center for Chronic Disease Prevention and Health Promotion, 4770 Buford Hwy, NE, MS K 50, Atlanta, GA 30341-3724. TEL 404-488-5705, 800-CDC-1311, FAX 404-488-5939. Circ: (controlled). **Subscr. to:** U.S. Government Printing Office, Superintendent of Documents, PO Box 371954, Pittsburgh, PA 15250-7954. TEL 202-512-1800, FAX 202-512-2250, orders@gpo.gov, http://www.access.gpo.gov.

178   GBR
THE HERALD (BRISTOL). Text in English. 1836. 2/yr. free. **Document type:** *Bulletin.* **Description:** Facts, views, comments from Christian viewpoint, on the alcohol-drug scene.
Formerly: Western Temperance Herald (0049-7517)
Published by: Western Alcohol and Drugs Education Society, Upper, 6 Gloucester St, Eastville, Bristol, BS5 6QE, United Kingdom. TEL 0272-512187. Ed. Raymond Foster. Circ: 3,500.

HIGHLIFE; tijdschrift voor levensgenieters. see *LITERARY AND POLITICAL REVIEWS*

362.2   HKG
HONG KONG NARCOTICS REPORT. Text in Chinese. 1965. a. free to qualified personnel. illus.
Former titles: Action Committee Against Narcotics. Annual Report; Narcotics Progress Report
Published by: Action Committee Against Narcotics, c/o Narcotics Division Government Secretariat, Queensway Government Offices, High Block, 66 Queensway, Hong Kong, Hong Kong. FAX 852-2521-7761. Circ: 10,000.

613.81   CHE   ISSN 1012-8360
I C A A NEWS. Text in English. 1973. q. CHF 45, USD 40 (effective 2000). **Document type:** *Newsletter, Consumer.*
Published by: International Council on Alcohol and Addictions, Case Postale 189, Lausanne, 1001, Switzerland. TEL 41-21-3209865, FAX 41-21-3209817, infoconf@icaa.ch, http://www.icaa.ch. Ed. R&P Archer Tongue.

178   CHE
I C A A PUBLICATIONS. Text in English. 1982. irreg. price varies. **Document type:** *Monographic series, Academic/Scholarly.* **Description:** Discusses innovations in treatment, education and control of substance abuse.
Published by: International Council on Alcohol and Addictions, Case Postale 189, Lausanne, 1001, Switzerland. TEL 41-21-3209865, FAX 41-21-3209817, infoconf@icaa.ch, http://www.icaa.ch. Ed. R&P Christian Pellet.

613.8   USA   ISSN 1016-0477
I C A D T S REPORTER. (International Council on Alcohol, Drugs and Traffic Safety) Text in English. 1990. q. free (effective 2003). bk.rev. 4 p./no. 2 cols./p.; back issues avail.; reprints avail. **Document type:** *Newsletter, Academic/Scholarly.* **Description:** Aims to reduce mortality and morbidity brought about by misuse of alcohol and drugs by operators of vehicles in all modes of transportation.
Published by: International Council on Alcohol, Drugs and Traffic Safety, 3798 Mosswood Dr, Lafayette, CA 94549. TEL 925-962-1810, FAX 925-962-1810, sweedlb@hotmail.com, http://www.icadts.org/reporter. Eds. Barry Sweedler, Kathryn Stewart.

616.863   ESP   ISSN 1130-474X
IDEA PREVENCION. Text in Spanish. 1990. s-a. back issues avail.
Related titles: Online - full text ed.
—CINDOC.
Published by: Idea-Prevencion, Apdo. de Correos 57067, Pozuelo de Alarcon, Madrid, 28223, Spain. TEL 34-91-3515361, FAX 34-91-5515337, jgarcia@idea-prevencion.com, http://www.idea-prevencion.com/. Ed. Teresa Salvador Llivina.

IMPAIRED DRIVING & BREATHALYZER LAW; recent case law. see *LAW*

362.29   USA   ISSN 1536-5239
HV5285
INFORMATION PLUS REFERENCE SERIES. ALCOHOL AND TOBACCO; America's drug of choice. Text in English. 1997. biennial. USD 40 per vol. (effective 2005). **Document type:** *Monographic series, Academic/Scholarly.*
Related titles: Online - full content ed.; ◆ Series of: Information Plus Reference Series.

Published by: Gale Group (Subsidiary of: Thomson Corporation), 27500 Drake Rd, Farmington Hills, MI 48331-3535. TEL 248-699-4253, 800-877-4253, FAX 248-699-8035, 800-414-5043, galeord@gale.com, http://www.galegroup.com.

362.29   USA   ISSN 1536-5220
HV5825
INFORMATION PLUS REFERENCE SERIES. ILLEGAL DRUGS; America's anguish. Text in English. 1997. biennial, latest 2003. USD 40 per issue (effective 2005). **Document type:** *Monographic series, Academic/Scholarly.*
Related titles: Online - full content ed.; ◆ Series of: Information Plus Reference Series.
Published by: Gale Group (Subsidiary of: Thomson Corporation), 27500 Drake Rd, Farmington Hills, MI 48331-3535. TEL 248-699-4253, 800-877-4253, FAX 248-699-8035, 800-414-5043, galeord@gale.com, http://www.galegroup.com.

616.863   CAN   ISSN 1681-696X
INTERNATIONAL ADDICTION. Text in English. 2000. a. free. **Document type:** *Consumer.*
Media: Online - full text.
Published by: (International Society of Addiction Medicine), University of Calgary Press, University of Calgary, Faculty of Education ETD 722, 2500 University Dr N W, Calgary, AB T2N 1N4, Canada. TEL 403-220-7736, FAX 403-282-0085, ucpmail@ucalgary.ca, http://ahdp.lib.ucalgary.ca/ia/, http://www.uofcpress.com. Ed. N el-Guebaly.

613.81   CHE
INTERNATIONAL CONGRESS ON ALCOHOLISM AND DRUG DEPENDENCE. PROCEEDINGS. Text in Multiple languages. triennial. CHF 175. **Document type:** *Proceedings, Academic/Scholarly.*
Former titles: International Congress on Alcoholism and Addictions. Proceedings; International Congress on Alcohol and Alcoholism. Proceedings
Published by: International Council on Alcohol and Addictions, Case Postale 189, Lausanne, 1001, Switzerland. TEL 41-21-3209865, FAX 41-21-3209817, infoconf@icaa.ch, http://www.icaa.ch. Ed., R&P Dr. Joerg Spieldenner.

INTERNATIONAL DRUG REPORT. see *CRIMINOLOGY AND LAW ENFORCEMENT*

613.81   CHE
HV5801   CODEN: PIIDD3
INTERNATIONAL INSTITUTE ON THE PREVENTION AND TREATMENT OF DEPENDENCIES. SELECTED PAPERS. Text in English. 1970. irreg. **Document type:** *Monographic series, Academic/Scholarly.*
Former titles (until 1996): International Institutes on the Prevention and Treatment of Addictions. Selected Papers (0254-2536); International Institute on the Prevention and Treatment of Drug Dependence. Selected Papers
Indexed: ChemAb.
—CASDDS.
Published by: International Council on Alcohol and Addictions, Case Postale 189, Lausanne, 1001, Switzerland. TEL 41-21-3209865, FAX 41-21-3209817, infoconf@icaa.ch, http://www.icaa.ch. Ed., R&P Dr. Joerg Spieldenner. Circ: 1,000.

616.86   NLD   ISSN 0955-3959
HV5800   CODEN: IJDPED
➤ **INTERNATIONAL JOURNAL OF DRUG POLICY.** Text in English. 1989. 6/yr. EUR 181 in Europe to individuals; JPY 24,100 in Japan to individuals; USD 202 elsewhere to individuals; EUR 459 in Europe to institutions; JPY 60,900 in Japan to institutions; USD 513 elsewhere to institutions (effective 2006). adv. bk.rev. **Document type:** *Journal, Academic/Scholarly.* **Description:** Presents current research, reliable information and in-depth policy analyses of the global drugs debate.
Related titles: Online - full text ed.: (from EBSCO Publishing, Gale Group, IngentaConnect, ScienceDirect, Swets Information Services).
Indexed: AC&P, ASSIA, AbHyg, AddicA, CINAHL, CJA, ESPM, ExcerpMed, H&SSA, IBSS, IPA, MEDLINE, NutrAb, PsycInfo, PsycholAb, RDA, RefZh, SSA, SociolAb, TDB, ToxAb, VirolAbstr, WAE&RSA, e-psyche.
—BLDSC (4542.188500), IE, Infotrieve, ingenta, KNAW. **CCC.**
Published by: Elsevier BV (Subsidiary of: Elsevier Science & Technology), Radarweg 29, Amsterdam, 1043 NX, Netherlands. TEL 31-20-4853911, FAX 31-20-4852457, nlinfo-f@elsevier.nl, http://www.elsevier.com/locate/drugpo, http://www.elsevier.nl. Eds. S. Panda, T Rhodes. adv.: page GBP 225. Circ: 400. **Subscr. to:** PO Box 211, Amsterdam 1000 AE, Netherlands. TEL 31-20-485-3757, FAX 31-20-485-3432.

▼ ➤ **INTERNATIONAL JOURNAL OF MENTAL HEALTH AND ADDICTION.** see *PSYCHOLOGY*

➤ **INTERNATIONAL JOURNAL OF PSYCHOSOCIAL REHABILITATION.** see *PSYCHOLOGY*

➤ **INTERNATIONAL NARCOTIC ENFORCEMENT OFFICERS ASSOCIATION DIRECTORY.** see *CRIMINOLOGY AND LAW ENFORCEMENT*

➤ **INTERNATIONAL NARCOTICS CONTROL BOARD. REPORT FOR (YEAR).** see *PHARMACY AND PHARMACOLOGY*

616.86   CHE
INTERNATIONALES SYMPOSIUM GEGEN DROGEN IN DER SCHWEIZ. Text in German. 1991. irreg. **Document type:** *Proceedings.*
Indexed: e-psyche.
Published by: Verein zur Foerderung der Psychologischen Menschenkenntnis, Susenbergstr 53, Zuerich, 8044, Switzerland.

362.2   USA
IOWA SUBSTANCE ABUSE REPORT (YEAR). Text in English. 1973. a. free. **Document type:** *Government.*
Former titles: Iowa Comprehensive State Plan for Substance Abuse (Year); Iowa Comprehensive State Plan for Substance Abuse Prevention: Annual Performance Report; (until 1980): Iowa Comprehensive State Plan for Drug Abuse Prevention: Annual Performance Report (0363-4507)
Published by: Department of Public Health, Division of Substance Abuse, Lucas State Office Bldg, 321 E 12th St, Des Moines, IA 50319. TEL 515-281-3641, FAX 515-281-4535. Circ: 1,000.

616.8   DEU   ISSN 0940-4910
JAHRBUCH SUCHT. Text in German. 1958. a. EUR 13.90 (effective 2003). adv. 256 p./no.; **Document type:** *Yearbook, Academic/Scholarly.*
Former titles (1990): Jahrbuch zur Frage der Suchtgefahren (0170-7337); (until 1972): Jahrbuch zur Alkohol- und Tabakfrage (0075-2827)
Indexed: DIP, IBR, IBZ.
—GNLM.
Published by: (Deutsche Hauptstelle gegen die Suchtgefahren), Neuland Verlagsgesellschaft mbH, Markt 24-26, Geesthacht, 21502, Germany. TEL 49-4152-81342, FAX 49-4152-81343, vertrieb@neuland.com, http://www.neuland.com. Circ: 7,000.

362.29   SWE   ISSN 0348-1565
JEPPE. Text in Swedish. 1974. bi-m. SEK 75 to members (effective 1990).
Published by: Alkoholproblematikers Riksorganisation (ALRO), Fack 17009, Stockholm, 10462, Sweden.

JOURNAL OF ADDICTIONS NURSING. see *MEDICAL SCIENCES—Nurses And Nursing*

616.86   USA   ISSN 1055-0887
HV5800   CODEN: JADDER
➤ **JOURNAL OF ADDICTIVE DISEASES;** the official journal of the American Society of Addictive Medicine. Abbreviated title: J A D. Text in English. 1978. q. USD 625 combined subscription domestic to institutions print & online eds.; USD 843.75 combined subscription in Canada to institutions print & online eds.; USD 906.25 combined subscription elsewhere to institutions print & online eds. (effective academic year 2005 - 2006). adv. bk.rev. bibl. 120 p./no.; back issues avail.; reprint service avail. from HAW. **Document type:** *Journal, Academic/Scholarly.* **Description:** Covers current topics in alcoholism and substance abuse field and devotes an entire issue to each topic.
Former titles (until 1991): Advances in Alcohol and Substance Abuse (0270-3106); (until 1981): Drug Abuse and Alcoholism Review (0149-5968)
Related titles: Microfiche ed.: (from PQC); Microform ed.; Online - full content ed.: ISSN 1545-0848. free to institutions (effective 2003); free with print subs.; Online - full text ed.: (from EBSCO Publishing, O C L C Online Computer Library Center, Inc., Swets Information Services).
Indexed: AC&P, AMHA, ASCA, AbAn, AddicA, BIOSIS Prev, BiolAb, CDA, CINAHL, CJA, CJPI, ChemAb, CurCont, ERA, ESPM, ETA, ExcerpMed, Faml, H&SSA, IMFL, INI, IPA, IndMed, MEA, MEDLINE, PC&CA, PsycInfo, PsycholAb, RHEA, RiskAb, SEA, SENA, SFSA, SOMA, SOPODA, SRRA, SSA, SSCI, SWA, SWR&A, SociolAb, TEA, THA, ToxAb; V&AA, e-psyche.
—BLDSC (4918.934050), CASDDS, GNLM, Haworth, IDS, IE, Infotrieve, ingenta, KNAW. **CCC.**
Published by: (American Society of Addiction Medicine), The Haworth Medical Press (Subsidiary of: Haworth Press, Inc.), 10 Alice St, Binghamton, NY 13904. TEL 607-722-5857, 800-429-6784, FAX 607-771-0012, 800-895-0582, getinfo@haworthpress.com, http://www.haworthpress.com/web/ JAD. Ed. Barry Stimmel TEL 212-241-6694. Pub. William Cohen. R&P Ruth Ann Heath TEL 607-722-5857 ext 316. Adv. contact Rebecca Miller-Baum TEL 607-722-5857 ext 337. B&W page USD 375, color page USD 650; trim 4.375 x 7.125. Circ: 420 (paid).

616.86   USA   ISSN 0090-1482
HV5128.U5   CODEN: JADEDT
➤ **JOURNAL OF ALCOHOL AND DRUG EDUCATION.** Short title: J.A.D.E. Text in English. 1955. 3/yr. USD 45 domestic; USD 55 foreign (effective 2004). back issues avail.; reprint service avail. from PQC. **Document type:** *Academic/Scholarly.* **Description:** Serves as a forum for various educational philosophies and differing points of view in regard to alcohol and drugs. Reports teacher experience and experiments and provides a reference for actual teaching materials, factual guide for prevention, techniques and procedures.
Formerly: Journal of Alcohol Education (0021-8677)

D

Related titles: Microform ed.: (from PQC); Online - full text ed.: (from bigchalk, EBSCO Publishing, Gale Group, H.W. Wilson, O C L C Online Computer Library Center, Inc., ProQuest Information & Learning).
Indexed: ABIn, AMHA, ASCA, AddicA, AgeL, CIJE, CINAHL, CJA, CPE, CurCont, ERA, ESPM, ETA, EduInd, FamI, H&SSA, HEA, HRIS, MEA, PsycInfo, PsycholAb, RASB, RHEA, RILM, RiskAb, SEA, SENA, SOMA, SSCI, SWA, TEA, e-psyche. —BLDSC (4926.720000), GNLM, IDS, IE, Infotrieve, ingenta. **CCC.**
Published by: American Alcohol and Drug Information Foundation (Lansing), 1120 East Oakland, P O Box 10212, Lansing, MI 48901-0212. TEL 517-484-2636, FAX 517-484-0444, dcorbin@coe.unomaha.edu, http://www.unomaha.edu/~healthed/JADE.html. Eds. David E Corbin, Manoj Sharma, Allen B Rice II. R&P Kenton L Owens.

➤ **JOURNAL OF BEHAVIORAL HEALTH SERVICES AND RESEARCH.** see *PUBLIC HEALTH AND SAFETY*

616.863 USA ISSN 1067-828X
RJ506.D78 CODEN: JCAAFI
➤ **JOURNAL OF CHILD & ADOLESCENT SUBSTANCE ABUSE.** Abbreviated title: J C A S A. Text in English. 1989. q. USD 335 combined subscription domestic to institutions print & online eds.; USD 452.25 combined subscription in Canada to institutions print & online eds.; USD 485.75 combined subscription elsewhere to institutions print & online eds. (effective academic year 2005 - 2006). adv. bk.rev. 120 p./no. 1 cols./p.; back issues avail.; reprint service avail. from HAW. **Document type:** *Journal, Academic/Scholarly.* **Description:** Provides realistic and usable strategies in a clear and concise manner for the chemically dependent adolescent and his or her family.
Formerly (until 1994): Journal of Adolescent Chemical Dependency (0896-7768)
Related titles: Microfiche ed.: (from PQC); Microform ed.; Online - full text ed.: ISSN 1547-0652. free to institutions (effective 2003); free with print subs. (from EBSCO Publishing, O C L C Online Computer Library Center, Inc., Swets Information Services).
Indexed: ASCA, BibInd, BiolDig, CDA, CIJE, CINAHL, CJA, ChemAb, CurCont, ECER, ERA, ESPM, ETA, FamI, H&SSA, IMFL, IndMed, MEA, PsycInfo, PsycholAb, RHEA, RiskAb, SEA, SENA, SFSA, SOMA, SOPODA, SSA, SSCI, SWA, SWR&A, SociolAb, TEA, THA, V&AA, e-psyche. —BLDSC (4957.425300), GNLM, Haworth, IDS, IE, ingenta, KNAW. **CCC.**
Published by: Haworth Press, Inc., 10 Alice St, Binghamton, NY 13904-1580. TEL 607-722-5857, 800-429-6784, FAX 607-722-1424, 800-895-0582, getinfo@haworthpress.com, http://www.haworthpress.com/web/JCASA. Eds. Brad Donohue, Vincent B Van Hasselt. Pub. William Cohen. R&P Ruth Ann Heath TEL 607-722-5857 ext 316. Adv. contact Rebecca Miller-Baum TEL 607-722-5857 ext 337. B&W page USD 315, color page USD 550; trim 4.375 x 7.125. Circ: 285 (paid).

362.293 USA ISSN 0047-2379
HV5808 CODEN: JDGEBT
➤ **JOURNAL OF DRUG EDUCATION.** Text in English. 1970. q. USD 67 to individuals; USD 274 domestic to institutions; USD 282 foreign to institutions (effective 2005). adv. bk.rev. abstr.; charts; illus. back issues avail.; reprints avail. **Document type:** *Journal, Academic/Scholarly.* **Description:** Contains current, authoritative and practical articles on the latest developments in preventive practices, and issues and trends in drug education and addiction management.
Related titles: Online - full text ed.: ISSN 1541-4159 (from EBSCO Publishing).
Indexed: ABIn, AMHA, ASCA, ASSIA, AbAn, AgeL, Agr, BiolAb, CIJE, CINAHL, CJA, CPE, ChPerI, CurCont, DIP, ERA, ESPM, ETA, EduInd, ExcerpMed, FamI, H&SSA, IBR, IBZ, IPA, IndMed, MEA, MEA&I, MEDLINE, PsycInfo, PsycholAb, RefZh, RiskAb, SENA, SOPODA, SSA, SSCI, SWA, SociolAb, TEA, e-psyche. —BLDSC (4970.550000), GNLM, IDS, IE, Infotrieve, ingenta, KNAW. **CCC.**
Published by: Baywood Publishing Co., Inc., 26 Austin Ave, PO Box 337, Amityville, NY 11701-0337. TEL 631-691-1270, FAX 631-691-1770, info@baywood.com, http://www.baywood.com/Journals/PreviewJournal.asp?Id=0047-2379. R&P Julie Krempa. Adv. contact Rochelle Grant.

616.863 371.9 USA ISSN 1546-6965
HV5800
▼ ➤ **JOURNAL OF DRUG EDUCATION AND AWARENESS.** Text in English. 2003. q. USD 175 (effective 2005). **Document type:** *Journal, Academic/Scholarly.* **Description:** Devoted to the study of various misused and , in particular, abused drugs and their effects on global society.
Published by: Nova Science Publishers, Inc., 400 Oser Ave, Ste 1600, Hauppauge, NY 11788-3619. TEL 631-231-7269, FAX 631-231-8175, novascience@earthlink.net, http://www.novapublishers.com/journals/drugawareness.html.

616.86 USA ISSN 0022-0426
HV5800 CODEN: JDGIA6
➤ **JOURNAL OF DRUG ISSUES.** Text in English. 1971. q. USD 95 domestic to individuals; USD 105 foreign to individuals; USD 120 domestic to institutions; USD 130 foreign to institutions (effective 2004). bk.rev. bibl.; charts. index, cum.index. 300 p./no. 1 cols./p.; back issues avail.; reprint service avail. from WSH,PQC. **Document type:** *Journal, Academic/Scholarly.* **Description:** Critical commentary on a wide range of drug policy issues.
Related titles: Microfilm ed.: (from PQC); Online - full text ed.: (from bigchalk, EBSCO Publishing, H.W. Wilson, Northern Light Technology, Inc., O C L C Online Computer Library Center, Inc., ProQuest Information & Learning).
Indexed: AC&P, AMHA, ASCA, ASSIA, AddicA, AgeL, BehAb, BiolAb, CJA, CLI, CurCont, DIP, ERA, ESPM, ETA, ExcerpMed, FamI, H&SSA, IBR, IBZ, ILP, IMFL, IPA, IPARL, MEA, MEA&I, PCI, PSA, PsycInfo, PsycholAb, RHEA, RI-1, RI-2, RefZh, RiskAb, SEA, SENA, SOMA, SOPODA, SSA, SSCI, SSI, SWA, SWR&A, SociolAb, TEA, THA, e-psyche. —BLDSC (4970.570000), GNLM, IDS, IE, Infotrieve, ingenta, KNAW. **CCC.**
Published by: Florida State University, School of Criminology & Criminal Justice, PO Box 66696, Tallahassee, FL 32313-6696. TEL 850-664-7368, FAX 850-644-9614, jdi@garnet.fsu.edu, http://www2.criminology.fsu.edu/~jdi/, http://wwwz.criminology.fsu.edu. Ed. Bruce Bullington. R&P Claire Knox TEL 850-644-6157. Circ: 1,000.

616.863 USA ISSN 1550-4263
RC563
➤ **JOURNAL OF DUAL DIAGNOSIS.** Abbreviated title: J C D T. Text in English. 1987. q. USD 300 combined subscription domestic to institutions print & online eds.; USD 405 combined subscription in Canada to institutions print & online eds.; USD 435 combined subscription elsewhere to institutions print & online eds. (effective academic year 2005 - 2006). adv. 120 p./no. 1 cols./p.; back issues avail.; reprint service avail. from HAW. **Document type:** *Journal, Academic/Scholarly.* **Description:** Provides direct clinical services. Each issue examines a specific chemical dependency problem. Stresses clinical techniques and methods while integrating theory and research.
Formerly (until Fall 2004): Journal of Chemical Dependency Treatment (0885-4734)
Related titles: Microfiche ed.: (from PQC); Online - full text ed.: ISSN 1550-4271 (from EBSCO Publishing, Swets Information Services).
Indexed: CJA, ESPM, ExcerpMed, FamI, H&SSA, IMFL, PsycholAb, RefZh, SWR&A, THA, e-psyche. —BLDSC (4970.587000), GNLM, Haworth, IE, Infotrieve, ingenta. **CCC.**
Published by: Haworth Press, Inc., 10 Alice St, Binghamton, NY 13904-1580. TEL 607-722-5857, 800-429-6784, FAX 607-722-1424, 800-895-0582, getinfo@haworthpress.com, http://www.haworthpress.com/web/JDD. Eds. David Powell, Gerald Shulman. Pub. William Cohen. R&P Ruth Ann Heath TEL 607-722-5857 ext 316. Adv. contact Rebecca Miller-Baum TEL 607-722-5857 ext 337. B&W page USD 315, color page USD 550; trim 4.375 x 7.125. Circ: 190 (paid).

➤ **JOURNAL OF EMPLOYEE ASSISTANCE & WORKPLACE BEHAVIORAL HEALTH.** see *BUSINESS AND ECONOMICS—Personnel Management*

616.863 USA ISSN 1533-2640
HV4997 CODEN: JESACH
➤ **JOURNAL OF ETHNICITY IN SUBSTANCE ABUSE.** Abbreviated title: J E S A. Text in English. 1986. q. USD 420 combined subscription domestic to institutions print & online eds.; USD 567 combined subscription in Canada to institutions print & online eds.; USD 609 combined subscription elsewhere to institutions print & online eds. (effective 2006). adv. bk.rev. 120 p./no. 1 cols./p.; back issues avail.; reprint service avail. from HAW. **Document type:** *Journal, Academic/Scholarly.* **Description:** Provides current information pertaining to the field of substance abuse. Directed toward researchers, professionals, and practitioners in substance abuse related fields and to students seeking to enter the field.
Supersedes (in 2002, vol.16, 1&2): Drugs & Society (8756-8233)
Related titles: Microfiche ed.: (from PQC); Microform ed.; Online - full text ed.: ISSN 1533-2659 (from EBSCO Publishing, O C L C Online Computer Library Center, Inc., Swets Information Services).
Indexed: ASSIA, AbAn, CDA, CINAHL, CJA, CJPI, DIP, ERA, ESPM, ETA, ExcerpMed, FamI, H&SSA, IBR, IBZ, IMFL, IPA, IPSA, MEA, PAIS, PsycInfo, PsycholAb, RHEA, RefZh, RiskAb, SEA, SENA, SOMA, SOPODA, SSA, SSI, SWA, SWR&A, SociolAb, TEA, ToxAb, V&AA, e-psyche. —BLDSC (4979.602100), GNLM, Haworth, IE, ingenta. **CCC.**
Published by: Haworth Press, Inc., 10 Alice St, Binghamton, NY 13904-1580. TEL 607-722-5857, 800-429-6784, FAX 607-722-1424, 800-895-0582, getinfo@haworthpress.com, http://www.haworthpress.com/web/JESA. Ed. Peter Myers. Pub. William Cohen. R&P Ruth Ann Heath TEL 607-722-5857 ext 316. Adv. contact Rebecca Miller-Baum TEL 607-722-5857 ext 337. B&W page USD 315, color page USD 550; trim 4.375 x 7.125. Circ: 214 (paid).

➤ **JOURNAL OF F A S INTERNATIONAL.** (Fetal Alcohol Syndrome) see *MEDICAL SCIENCES—Pediatrics*

362.29286 USA ISSN 1556-035X
▼ ➤ **JOURNAL OF GROUPS IN ADDICTION & RECOVERY.** Text in English. forthcoming 2006 (Spr.). q. USD 400 combined subscription domestic to institutions print & online eds.; USD 540 combined subscription in Canada to institutions print & online eds.; USD 580 combined subscription elsewhere to institutions print & online eds. (effective 2006). reprint service avail. from HAW. **Document type:** *Journal, Academic/Scholarly.* **Description:** Provides a forum for group therapists and addictions treatment professionals to learn about the latest developments in addictions treatment.
Related titles: Online - full text ed.: ISSN 1556-0368. forthcoming 2006 (Spr.).
Published by: Haworth Press, Inc., 10 Alice St, Binghamton, NY 13904-1580. TEL 607-722-5857, 800-429-6784, FAX 607-722-1424, 800-895-0582, getinfo@haworthpress.com, http://www.haworthpress.com/store/product.asp?sku=J384. Ed. Dr. Jeffrey Roth. Adv. contact Christine Miner.

616.863 USA ISSN 1091-1332
RC568.M4
➤ **JOURNAL OF MAINTENANCE IN THE ADDICTIONS;** innovations in research, theory, & practice. Abbreviated title: J M A. Text in English. 1996. q. USD 125 combined subscription domestic to institutions print & online eds.; USD 168.75 combined subscription in Canada to institutions print & online eds.; USD 181.25 combined subscription elsewhere to institutions print & online eds. (effective 2006). adv. 120 p./no.; back issues avail.; reprint service avail. from HAW. **Document type:** *Journal, Academic/Scholarly.* **Description:** Provides cutting-edge articles that assist in the understanding of clinical management at the most practical level.
Related titles: Microfiche ed.: (from PQC); Microform ed.; Online - full text ed.: ISSN 1540-7624. free to institutions (effective 2003); free with print subs. (from EBSCO Publishing, Swets Information Services).
Indexed: RefZh, SWR&A, e-psyche. —BLDSC (5010.797500), Haworth, IE, ingenta. **CCC.**
Published by: The Haworth Medical Press (Subsidiary of: Haworth Press, Inc.), 10 Alice St, Binghamton, NY 13904. TEL 607-722-5857, 800-429-6784, FAX 607-771-0012, 800-895-0582, getinfo@haworthpress.com, http://www.haworthpress.com/web/JMA. Eds. Ira J Marion, Joan Zweben, Karol Kaltenbach. Pub. William Cohen. R&P Ruth Ann Heath TEL 607-722-5857 ext 316. Adv. contact Rebecca Miller-Baum TEL 607-722-5857 ext 337. B&W page USD 315, color page USD 550; trim 4.375 x 7.125. Circ: 523 (paid).

301 616.8 615 USA ISSN 0279-1072
RM315 CODEN: JPDRD3
➤ **JOURNAL OF PSYCHOACTIVE DRUGS;** a multidisciplinary forum. Text in English. 1967. q. USD 90 to individuals; USD 160 to institutions (effective 2004). adv. bk.rev. charts; illus.; stat.; abstr. 110 p./no. 2 cols./p.; reprint service avail. from PQC,ISI. **Document type:** *Journal, Academic/Scholarly.* **Description:** Focuses on human use and abuse of alcohol and other drugs, as well as related issues, such as treatment modalities, AIDS, and dual diagnosis.
Formerly (until vol.13, 1981): Journal of Psychedelic Drugs (0022-393X)
Related titles: Microform ed.: (from PQC); Online - full text ed.: (from bigchalk, Northern Light Technology, Inc., ProQuest Information & Learning).
Indexed: AMHA, ASCA, AddicA, AgeL, BIOSIS Prev, BiolAb, CJA, ChPerI, ChemAb, CurCont, EPB, ERA, ETA, ExcerpMed, FamI, HRIS, IMFL, INI, IndMed, MEA, MEDLINE, PsycInfo, PsycholAb, RHEA, RefZh, SEA, SENA, SFSA, SOMA, SRRA, SSCI, SSI, SWA, TEA, THA, V&AA, e-psyche. —BLDSC (5043.263000), CASDDS, CISTI, GNLM, IDS, IE, Infotrieve, ingenta, KNAW. **CCC.**
Published by: Haight-Ashbury Publications, 612 Clayton St, San Francisco, CA 94117. TEL 415-565-1904, FAX 415-864-6162, journal@hafci.org, http://www.hafci.org/journal. Eds. Richard B Seymour, Terry Chambers. Circ: 800.

➤ **JOURNAL OF PUBLIC HEALTH POLICY.** see *PUBLIC HEALTH AND SAFETY*

362.29 USA ISSN 1065-2019
JOURNAL OF RATIONAL RECOVERY. Text in English. 1988. bi-m. USD 32 domestic; USD 50 foreign; USD 11 base vol(s). per issue (effective 2001). **Document type:** *Journal, Academic/Scholarly.*
Indexed: NTA.
Published by: Rational Recovery Systems, Inc., Box 800, Lotus, CA 95651. TEL 530-621-4374, 530-621-2667, http://www.rational.org/.

JOURNAL OF SOCIAL WORK PRACTICE. see *SOCIAL SERVICES AND WELFARE*

JOURNAL OF SOCIAL WORK PRACTICE IN THE ADDICTIONS. see *SOCIAL SERVICES AND WELFARE*

JOURNAL OF SPIRITUALITY IN ADDICTION & RECOVERY. see *RELIGIONS AND THEOLOGY*

D

616.861 016 USA ISSN 0096-882X
CODEN: JSALDP
➤ **JOURNAL OF STUDIES ON ALCOHOL.** Text in English. 1940. bi-m. USD 140 domestic to individuals; USD 155 foreign to individuals; USD 175 domestic to institutions; USD 190 foreign to institutions (effective 2005). adv. bk.rev. abstr.; bibl.; charts; illus. index. 144 p./no. 2 cols./p.; back issues avail.; reprints avail. **Document type:** *Journal, Academic/Scholarly.* **Description:** Contributes to knowledge about alcohol, its use, misuse and its biomedical, behavioral and sociocultural effects.
Formerly (until 1974): Quarterly Journal of Studies on Alcohol (0033-5649)
Related titles: Microform ed.: (from PQC); Online - full text ed.: (from Florida Center for Library Automation, Gale Group, H.W. Wilson, Northern Light Technology, Inc., O C L C Online Computer Library Center, Inc.).
Indexed: AC&P, AMHA, ASCA, ASFA, ASSIA, AbHyg, AddicA, AgeL, AmH&L, BAS, BIOBASE, BIOSIS Prev, BMAb, BiolAb, CISA, CJA, ChemAb, CurCont, DentInd, DokArb, ERA, ESPM, ETA, ExcerpMed, Faml, H&SSA, HEA, HRIS, HistAb, IABS, INI, ISR, IndMed, Inpharma, JW-P, MEA, MEA&I, MEDLINE, NSCI, NutrAb, PAIS, PCI, PE&ON, PEI, PsycInfo, PsycholAb, PsychopharAb, RASB, RHEA, RRTA, Reac, RefZh, RiskAb, SCI, SEA, SENA, SOMA, SRRA, SSA, SSCI, SSI, SWA, SWR&A, SociolAb, TDB, TEA, THA, ToxAb, VITIS, e-psyche.
—BLDSC (5066.895000), CASDDS, GNLM, IDS, IE, Infotrieve, ingenta, KNAW, Linda Hall. **CCC.**
Published by: (Rutgers Center of Alcohol Studies), Alcohol Research Documentation, Inc., c/o Paul Candon, Man Ed, Rutgers Center of Alcohol Studies, 607 Allison Rd, Piscataway, NJ 08854-8001. TEL 732-445-3510, FAX 732-445-3500, d, http://www.rci.rutgers.edu/~cas2/journal/. Ed. Marc A Schuckit TEL 858-642-3885. R&P Pat Castellano TEL 908-445-3510. Adv. contact Charles B Rouse. page USD 300. Circ: 1,900 (paid).

363 USA ISSN 0740-5472
RC563 CODEN: JSATEG
➤ **JOURNAL OF SUBSTANCE ABUSE TREATMENT.** Text in English. 1984. 8/yr. USD 236 to individuals; USD 218 in United States to individuals; USD 767 to institutions; USD 710 in United States to institutions (effective 2006). adv. bk.rev. index. back issues avail. **Document type:** *Journal, Academic/Scholarly.* **Description:** Features original contributions and articles on the clinical treatment of substance abuse and alcoholism.
Related titles: Microfilm ed.: (from PQC); Online - full text ed.: (from EBSCO Publishing, Gale Group, IngentaConnect, ScienceDirect, Swets Information Services).
Indexed: ASCA, AbAn, AddicA, BIOBASE, BIOSIS Prev, BiolAb, CJA, CurCont, ESPM, ExcerpMed, Faml, H&SSA, IDIS, INI, IndMed, MEDLINE, PsycInfo, PsycholAb, RiskAb, SOPODA, SSA, SSCI, SWA, SociolAb, THA, e-psyche.
—BLDSC (5066.932000), GNLM, IDS, IE, Infotrieve, ingenta, KNAW. **CCC.**
Published by: (North Shore University Hospital), Elsevier Inc. (Subsidiary of: Elsevier Science & Technology), 360 Park Ave. S, New York, NY 10010-1710. TEL 212-989-5800, 888-437-4636, FAX 212-633-3990, agaskin@elsevier.com, usinfo-f@elsevier.com, http://www.elsevier.com/locate/jsat. Ed. A. Thomas McLellan. adv.: B&W page USD 1,065, color page USD 2,335. Circ: 773 (paid and free).

616.8 610.73 GBR ISSN 1465-9891
CODEN: JSUSFC
➤ **JOURNAL OF SUBSTANCE USE;** for nursing, health and social care. Text in English. 1996. bi-m. GBP 321, USD 529 combined subscription to institutions print & online eds. (effective 2006). adv. back issues avail.; reprint service avail. from PSC. **Document type:** *Journal, Academic/Scholarly.* **Description:** Aims to educate, inform, update and act as a forum for standard setting for health and social care professionals working with individuals and families with substance use problems.
Formerly (until 1999): Journal of Substance Misuse (1357-5007)
Related titles: Online - full text ed.: ISSN 1475-9942. 2001. GBP 305, USD 503 to institutions (effective 2006) (from EBSCO Publishing, Gale Group, IngentaConnect, O C L C Online Computer Library Center, Inc., Swets Information Services).
Indexed: ASSIA, AddicA, BrNI, CINAHL, CJA, ERA, ESPM, ETA, ExcerpMed, H&SSA, MEA, PsycInfo, PsycholAb, RHEA, RefZh, RiskAb, SEA, SENA, SOMA, TEA, ToxAb.
—BLDSC (5066.932700), GNLM, IE, Infotrieve, ingenta. **CCC.**
Published by: Taylor & Francis Ltd (Subsidiary of: Taylor & Francis Group), 4 Park Sq, Milton Park, Abingdon, OX14 4RN, United Kingdom. TEL 44-1235-828600, FAX 44-1235-829000, info@tandf.co.uk, http://www.tandf.co.uk/journals/titles/14659891.asp. Ed. Richard Pates TEL 44-29-2046-0362. **Subscr. to:** Journals Customer Service, Rankine Rd, Basingstoke, Hants RG24 8PR, United Kingdom. TEL 44-1256-813000, FAX 44-1256-330245, enquiry@tandf.co.uk.

➤ **JOURNAL OF TEACHING IN THE ADDICTIONS.** see *EDUCATION—Teaching Methods And Curriculum*

616.861 DEU ISSN 0935-6223
KRANKENTRANSPORT UND RETTUNGSWESEN. Text in German. 1978. irreg. price varies. **Document type:** *Monographic series, Trade.*
Published by: Erich Schmidt Verlag GmbH & Co. (Berlin), Genthiner Str 30G, Berlin, 10785, Germany. TEL 49-30-250085-0, FAX 49-30-25008511, esv@esvmedien.de, http://www.erich-schmidt-verlag.de.

362.29 SWE ISSN 0345-7478
LAENK-NYTT. Text in Swedish. 1951. m. SEK 70 (effective 1990).
Published by: Fria Saellskapen Laenkerna, Laenk-nytt, Fack 6056, Goeteborg, 40060, Sweden.

616.863 USA ISSN 0024-435X
HV5285
LISTEN; journal of drug-free living for teens. Text in English. 1947. m. USD 24.97 (effective 1999). adv. illus. index.
Related titles: Microform ed.: (from PQC); Online - full text ed.: (from bigchalk, Northern Light Technology, Inc., ProQuest Information & Learning); Supplement(s): Teaching Guide.
Indexed: CCR.
Published by: Health Connection, 55 W Oak Ridge Dr, Hagerstown, MD 21740. TEL 800-548-8700, FAX 1-888-294-8405. Ed. Lincoln Steed. Adv. contact Melanie Tooley. Circ: 40,000.

616.863 331 USA
MAINE. DEPARTMENT OF LABOR. BUREAU OF LABOR STANDARDS. SUBSTANCE ABUSE TESTING REPORT. Text in English. 1990. a. free. **Document type:** *Government.* **Description:** Contains results of the annual substance abuse testing survey.
Published by: Department of Labor, Bureau of Labor Standards, 45 State House Station, Augusta, ME 04333-0045. TEL 207-624-6440, FAX 207-624-6449, webmaster_bls@state.me.us. Ed., R&P Ruth A Ladd. Circ: 251.

616.8 340 USA ISSN 1010-9595
HD9665.3
MANUFACTURE OF NARCOTIC DRUGS AND PSYCHOTROPIC SUBSTANCES UNDER INTERNATIONAL CONTROL. Text in English, French, Spanish. 1948. a.
Formed by the 1987 merger of: Manufacture of Narcotic Drugs and Psychotropic Substances (0251-6713); Fabrication de Stupefiants et de Substances Psychotropes (0251-673X); Fabricacion de Estupefacientes y Sustancias Sicotropicas (0251-6721)
Published by: (United Nations, Commission on Narcotic Drugs), United Nations Publications, Rm DC2-853, United Nations Bldg, 2 United Nations Plaza, New York, NY 10017. TEL 212-963-8302, 800-253-9646, FAX 212-963-3489, publications@un.org, http://www.un.org/publications, http://www.un.org/Pubs.

MEDITSINSKI PREGLED. NEVROLOGIIA I PSICHIATRIIA. see *MEDICAL SCIENCES—Psychiatry And Neurology*

362.29 NLD ISSN 1384-0606
MEELEVEN; kwartaalblad over verslaving en kerk. Text in Dutch. 1975. q. free. 4 p./no.; **Document type:** *Newsletter, Corporate.* **Description:** Includes information on drug assistance work and parent training programs for various types of addiction in society.
Formerly (until 1995): Mee - Leven met de Regenboog (1384-0592)
Published by: Stichting de Regenboog, Postbus 10887, Amsterdam, 1001 EW, Netherlands. TEL 31-20-531-7600, FAX 31-20-420-3528, meeleven@deregenboog.org, http://www.deregenboog.org. Ed. Merlyn van Hasselt. Circ: 10,000.

616.861 USA ISSN 0891-8651
HV5282
MONDAY MORNING REPORT. Text in English. 1977. s-m. USD 100 (effective 2003). **Document type:** *Newsletter.* **Description:** Covers significant issues, events, and opinions in the alcohol problems field.
Incorporates (in 2001): The Bottom Line on Alcohol in Society (0891-6950); Which was formerly (until 1977): The Bottom Line (0161-1267); Formed by the 1977 merger of: Alcohol Abstracts; Report on Alcohol (0002-7774); Viewpoint
Address: 430 Lathrope St, Lansing, MI 48912. TEL 517-485-9900, FAX 517-485-1928. Ed. Robert Hammond. Circ: 1,000.

362.29 USA
MONITORING THE FUTURE: NATIONAL SURVEY RESULTS ON DRUG USE. Text in English. a. **Document type:** *Government.*
Published by: U.S. Department of Health and Human Services, National Institute on Drug Abuse, 6001 Executive Blvd., Rm. 5213, Bethesda, MD 20892-9561. TEL 301-443-1124, Information@lists.nida.nih.gov, http://www.nida.nih.gov/.

362.2 USA
MONTANA COMPREHENSIVE CHEMICAL DEPENDENCY PLAN. Text in English. 1972. a. free. **Document type:** *Government.*
Formerly: Montana State Plan for Alcohol Abuse and Alcoholism Prevention, Treatment and Rehabilitation (0090-3809)
Published by: Department of Corrections and Human Services, 1539 11th Ave, Helena, MT 59620. TEL 406-449-3930. Circ: 100.

306 362.29 616.89 SWE ISSN 0280-3348
MOTDRAG; Accent. Text in Swedish. 1980. 8/yr. SEK 60 (effective 2003).
Incorporates (in 1988): Accent Ung; Former titles (until 1982): Motdrag foer Drogfrihet; (until 1981): Klartext om Droger (0349-408X)
Related titles: ♦ Issued with: Accent. ISSN 0345-0406.
Published by: U N F - Ungdomens Nykterhetsfoerbund, PO Box 12825, Stockholm, 11297, Sweden. TEL 46-8-6726066, FAX 46-8-6726001, motdrag@unf.se, info@unf.se, http://epi.unf.se/UNFTemplates/PaperList____1969.asp.

362.29 FIN ISSN 0359-7024
N A D - PUBLIKATION. (Nordiska Naemnden foer Alkohol- och Drogforskning) Text in Multiple languages. 1980. irreg. free (effective 2005). back issues avail. **Document type:** *Monographic series, Academic/Scholarly.*
Published by: Nordiska Naemnaden foer Alkohol- och Drogforskning/Nordic Council for alcohol and Drug Research, Annegatan 29 A 23, Helsinki, 00100, Finland. TEL 358-9-6948082, FAX 358-9-6949081, nads@nad.fi, http://www.nad.fi/index.php?lang=se&id=pub.

362 USA ISSN 1046-5421
THE N A WAY MAGAZINE. (Narcotics Anonymous) Text in English. 1982. m. USD 15 domestic; USD 20 in Canada. illus. back issues avail. **Description:** Covers drug addiction, the N A recovery fellowship and more.
Formerly (until 1988): N.A. Way (0896-9116)
Published by: Narcotics Anonymous, World Service Office, PO Box 9999, Van Nuys, CA 91409. TEL 818-773-9999, FAX 818-700-0700. Ed. Cynthia Tooredman. Circ: 10,000.

N C A A DRUG TESTING PROGRAM. (National Collegiate Athletic Association) see *SPORTS AND GAMES*

616.863 USA ISSN 0048-0673
N C I CATALYST✶ ; interfaith action on alcohol and other drug problems. Text in English. 1967. s-a. USD 15. bk.rev. bibl.; illus. **Document type:** *Newsletter.*
Published by: North Conway Institute, Inc., 168 Mount Vernon St, West, Newton, MA 02165-2517. TEL 617-742-0424. Ed. Priscilla Martin. Circ: 2,500.

616.861 USA ISSN 0147-0515
N I A A A - R U C A S ALCOHOLISM TREATMENT SERIES. (National Institute on Alcohol Abuse and Alcoholism - Rutgers University Center of Alcohol Studies) Text in English. 1978. irreg. price varies. index. **Document type:** *Monographic series, Academic/Scholarly.*
Formerly: N.I.A.A.A. - R.U.C.A.S. Alcoholism Treatment Monographs
Indexed: PsycholAb.
Published by: Rutgers Center of Alcohol Studies, Publications Division, c/o Charles Rouse, Bus Admin, 607 Allison Rd, Piscataway, NJ 08854-8001. TEL 732-445-2190. Ed. Marc Schuckit.

362.29 USA ISSN 1535-7325
N I D A NOTES. Text in English. 1979. bi-m. free (effective 2005).
Former titles (until 1985): Treatment Research Notes (0278-9205); (until 1981): Services Research Notes (0731-6771)
Related titles: Online - full text ed.: ISSN 1535-7716. free (effective 2005).
Published by: Masimax Resources, Inc, 1375 Piccard Dr Ste 175, Rockeville, MD 20850. TEL 240-632-5614, FAX 240-632-0519, nidanotes@masimax.com, http://www.drugabuse.gov/NIDA_Notes/NNIndex.html. Ed. David Anderson.

616.863 USA ISSN 1046-9516
CODEN: MIDAD
N I D A RESEARCH MONOGRAPH. Text in English. 1975. irreg., latest vol.121, 1992. free. bibl.; charts. back issues avail. **Document type:** *Monographic series, Government.*
Formerly (until 1976): U.S. National Institute on Drug Abuse. Research Monograph Series (0361-8595)
Related titles: Microfiche ed.
Indexed: BIOSIS Prev, CIN, ChemAb, ChemTitl, CurCont, ExcerpMed, Faml, IndMed, MEDLINE, PsycholAb, PsychopharAb.
—BLDSC (6110.170000), CASDDS, CISTI, GNLM, Infotrieve, ingenta, KNAW.
Published by: U.S. Department of Health and Human Services, National Institute on Drug Abuse, 6001 Executive Blvd., Rm. 5213, Bethesda, MD 20892-9561. TEL 301-443-1124, Information@lists.nida.nih.gov, http://165.112.78.65/pubs/rmpubs2.taf?function=form. Circ: 3,000.

NARC OFFICER. see *LAW*

362.29 616.863 SWE ISSN 0281-3629
NARCONON-NYTT. Text in Swedish. 1977-1978; resumed 1982. q. SEK 100 (effective 1990). **Document type:** *Newspaper.*
Published by: Riksorganisationen Narconon i Sverige (RONS), Fack 3081, Varby, 14303, Sweden. Ed. Haakan Larsson.

D

▼ *new title* ➤ *refereed* ✶ *unverified* ♦ *full entry avail.*

616.86 USA ISSN 0094-3991
HV5800
NARCOTICS AND DRUG ABUSE A TO Z. Text in English. 1971. base vol. plus q. updates. looseleaf. USD 329.95 base vol(s). (effective 2005). bibl. **Document type:** *Directory.* **Description:** Lists narcotics and drugs and treatment centers arranged by state.
Published by: Croner Publications, Inc., 10951 Sorrento Valley Rd, Ste 1D, San Diego, CA 92121-1613. TEL 800-441-4033, 800-441-4033, FAX 800-809-0334, paul@croner.com, http://www.croner.com.

NARCOTICS LAW BULLETIN. see *CRIMINOLOGY AND LAW ENFORCEMENT*

362.29 SWE ISSN 0347-4836
NARKOTIKAFRAAGAN. Text in Swedish. 1971-1972; resumed 1976. bi-m. SEK 125 (effective 1997). adv. bk.rev.
Description: Focuses on drug problem and the drug policy in Sweden as well as international drug problems and treatment.
Published by: R N S - Riksfoerbundet Narkotikafritt Samhaelle/National Association for a Drug Free Society, Ragvaldsgatan 14, 2 tr, Stockholm, 11846, Sweden. TEL 46-8-643-04-67, FAX 46-8-643-04-98. Ed. Pelle Olsson. Adv. contact Ulla Soederberg. Circ: 19,000 (paid).

616.861 616.863 USA
NATIONAL DIRECTORY OF DRUG ABUSE AND ALCOHOLISM TREATMENT AND PREVENTION PROGRAMS. Text in English. 1979. a. free. **Document type:** *Directory, Government.*
Published by: U.S. Substance Abuse and Mental Health Services Administration, Office of Applied Studies, 5600 Fishers Ln, Rm 16 105, Rockville, MD 20857. TEL 301-443-7934, FAX 301-443-9847. Circ: 12,500.

NATIONAL LAWS AND REGULATIONS RELATING TO THE CONTROL OF NARCOTIC DRUGS. CUMULATIVE INDEX (YEARS). see *LAW—Criminal Law*

178 DEU
NEUES VON SYNANON; der nuechterne Weg. Text in German. q. free. back issues avail. **Document type:** *Bulletin.*
Description: News and information from Synanon, a self-help group of former drug addicts and alcoholics.
Published by: Stiftung Synanon, Bernburger Str 10, Berlin, 10963, Germany. TEL 49-30-55000-0, FAX 49-30-55000220. Ed., R&P, Adv. contact Michael Frommhold. Circ: 50,000.

362.29 USA
NEW MEDICAL THERAPIES BRIEFS. ADDICTION. Text in English. irreg. free. **Document type:** *Newsletter, Trade.*
Media: Online - full content.
Published by: Thomson CenterWatch, Inc., 22 Thomson Pl, Bldg 36 TI, Boston, MA 02210. TEL 617-856-5900, FAX 617-247-2535, http://www.centerwatch.com/bookstore/pubs_cons_nmtbriefs.html.

NICOTINE & TOBACCO RESEARCH. see *TOBACCO*

616.861 JPN ISSN 1341-8963
CODEN: NAYZF5
NIHON ARUKORU, YAKUBUTSU IGAKKAI ZASSHI/JAPANESE JOURNAL OF ALCOHOL STUDIES AND DRUG DEPENDENCE (KYOTO, 1996). Text in English, Japanese. 1966. q. adv. bk.rev. abstr.; bibl.; charts; illus. index. **Document type:** *Academic/Scholarly.*
Former titles (until 1995): Arukoru Kenkyu to Yakubutsu Izon/Japanese Journal of Alcohol Studies and Drug Dependence (Kyoto, 1981) (0389-4118); (until 1981): Arukoru Kenkyu/Japanese Journal of Studies on Alcohol (0021-5244)
Indexed: AddicA, BIOSIS Prev, BiolAb, ChemAb, ExcerpMed, INI, IndMed, MEDLINE.
—BLDSC (4650.783000), CASDDS, GNLM, IE, Infotrieve, ingenta.
Published by: Nihon Arukoru Igakkai/Japanese Medical Society of Alcohol Studies, c/o Kyoto Furitsu Ika Daigaku Hoigaku Kyoshitsu, 465 Kajiicho, Hirokoji Agaru, Kawaramachi Dori, Kamigyo-ku, Kyoto-shi, 602, Japan. Circ: 1,000.

362.29 616.8632 FIN ISSN 1455-0725
HV5516 CODEN: NANTFY
➤ **NORDISK ALKOHOL- & NARKOTIKATIDSKRIFT/NORDIC STUDIES ON ALCOHOL AND DRUGS.** Variant title: N A T. Text in Swedish, Danish, Norwegian; Summaries in English. 1984. 6/yr. EUR 26; EUR 13 to students (effective 2005). adv. bk.rev. stat. back issues avail. **Document type:** *Journal, Academic/Scholarly.* **Description:** Presents articles in the social science of drug and alcohol abuse in Nordic society.
Former titles (until 1997): Nordisk Alkoholtidskrift (0789-6069); (until 1991): Alkoholpolitik (0782-9671)
Related titles: Online - full content ed.: ISSN 1458-6126; Supplement(s):.
Indexed: AddicA, SOPODA, SSA, SociolAb.
—BLDSC (6117.945300), IE, ingenta.
Published by: Stakes Forsknings-och Utvecklingscentralen foer Social- och Haelsovaarden/National Research and Development Centre for Welfare and Health, PL 220, Helsinki, 00531, Finland. TEL 358-9-3967-2198, FAX 358-9-39672191, nat@stakes.fi, http://www.stakes.fi/nat. Ed., Pub., R&P Kerstin Stenius TEL 358-9-3967-2197. Circ: 1,500. **Co-publisher:** Nordiska Naemnaden foer Alkohol- och Drogforskning/Nordic Council for alcohol and Drug Research.

362.29 616.86 344 SWE ISSN 1102-9021
OBEROENDE. Text in Swedish. 1969. q. SEK 145 (effective 2003).
Former titles (until 1992): Slaa Tillbaka (0349-2958); (until 1980): RFHL Kontakt (0345-9993)
Published by: R F H L - Riksfoerbundet foer Hjaelp aat Narkotiska- och Laekemedelsberoeende/National Association for Aid to People Addictive to Drugs and Pharmaceuticals, Norrtullsgatan 45, Stockholm, 11345, Sweden. TEL 46-8-54556060, FAX 46-8-335866, info@rfhl.se, http://www.rfhl.se/.

362.29 ESP
OBSERVATORIO VASCO DE DROGODEPENDENCIA. INFORME. Text in Spanish; Summaries in Spanish. 1997. a. **Document type:** *Magazine, Corporate.*
Published by: Eusko Jaurlaritzaren Argitalpen-Zerbitzu Nagusia/Servicio Central de Publicaciones del Gobierno Vasco, Donostia-San Sebastian, 1, Vitoria-gasteiz, Alava 01010, Spain. TEL 34-945-018561, FAX 34-945-018709, hac-sabd@ej-gv.es, http://www.ej-gv.net/publicaciones.

616.86 364.3 USA ISSN 1533-0133
OFFENDER SUBSTANCE ABUSE REPORT. Text in English. 2001 (Jan./Feb.). bi-m. USD 169.95 domestic; USD 199.95 foreign (effective 2004). **Document type:** *Newsletter.*
Description: Helps professionals to manage and treat substance abusing offenders, promote rehabilitation, and reduce recidivism.
Published by: Civic Research Insitute, 4490 US Route 27, PO Box 585, Kingston, NJ 08528. TEL 609-683-4450, FAX 609-683-7291, order@civicresearchinstitute.com, http://www.civicresearchinstitute.com/co17.html. Eds. David Farabee, Kevin Knight.

THE OFFICIAL INTERNATIONAL PHARMACY DIRECTORY. see *PHARMACY AND PHARMACOLOGY*

616.863 USA
P R I D E QUARTERLY NEWSLETTER. Text in English. q. bk.rev. **Description:** Covers activities of PRIDE and information concerning drug education and prevention.
Published by: (National Parents' Resource Institute for Drug Education, Inc.), Standard Press, 1210 Menlo Dr, Atlanta, GA 30318. TEL 404-351-6780. Ed. Doug Hall. **Subscr. to:** PRIDE, The Hurt Bldg, Ste 210, 50 Hurt Plaza, Atlanta, GA 30303.

178 IRL
PIONEER. Text in English. 1948. m. EUR 19 in Ireland; GBP 16 in United Kingdom; EUR 40 in United States; EUR 30 elsewhere (effective 2005). adv. bk.rev. charts; illus. **Document type:** *Newsletter, Consumer.*
Former titles: New Pioneer (0332-1827); (until vol.33, Sep. 1980): Pioneer (0031-997X)
Published by: Pioneer Total Abstinence Association, 27 Upper Sherrard St., Dublin, 1, Ireland. TEL 353-1-8749464, FAX 353-1-8748485, pioneer@jesuit.ie, http://www.pioneertotal.ie. Ed. Maureen Manning. Circ: 16,000.

362.29 SWE ISSN 0347-1322
POCKETTIDNINGEN R. Text in Swedish. 1970. 5/yr. SEK 280; SEK 70 per issue (effective 2002). **Document type:** *Magazine, Consumer.*
Related titles: Audio cassette/tape ed.
Published by: (R F H L - Riksfoerbundet foer Hjaelp aat Narkotiska- och Laekemedelsberoeende/National Association for Aid to People Addictive to Drugs and Pharmaceuticals), Stiftelsen Pockettidningen R, Sjoebjoernsvaegen 15 A, Stockholm, 11767, Sweden. pocket.r@telia.se, pocket.r@telia.com. Circ: 5,000 (paid). **Co-sponsors:** R S M H - Riksfoerbundet foer Social och Mental Haelsa; Verdandi Arbetarnas Socialpolitiska Organisation.

616.86 USA ISSN 1040-9882
HV5285
PREVENTION PIPELINE; an alcohol and drug awareness service. Variant title: C S A P Prevention Pipeline. Text in English. 1982. bi-m. USD 28; USD 32 foreign (effective 1999). **Document type:** *Government.* **Description:** Intended to stimulate an exchange of information and experiences among specialists in the field of drug and alcohol abuse prevention, focusing on the announcement of programmatic resources and selected scientific and technical literature, upcoming conferences, and news from the field.
Formerly (until 1987): Alcohol Awareness Service
Indexed: HRIS.
Published by: National Clearinghouse for Alcohol and Drug Information, Center for Substance Abuse Prevention, PO Box 2345, Rockville, MD 20847-2345. TEL 800-729-6686, FAX 301-468-6433, info@prevline.health.org, http://www.health.org. Ed. Barbara Ryan. R&P Craig Steinberg TEL 301-468-2600. Circ: 3,200 (paid).

362.292 POL ISSN 0032-9495
PROBLEMY ALKOHOLIZMU. Text in Polish; Summaries in English. 1975. m. PLZ 60,000. bk.rev. abstr. back issues avail.
Supersedes in part (in 1976): Problemy Alkoholizmu, Zdrowie i Trzezwosc (0137-3889); Which was formed by the merger of (1957-1975): Zdrowie i Trzezwosc (0867-3632); (1966-1975): Problemy Alkoholizmu (0239-4308); Which was formerly (1953-1965): Walka z Alkoholizmem (0509-5948)
Indexed: RASB, RefZh.
Published by: Spoleczny Komitet Przeciwalkoholowy, Ul Lwowska 5, Warsaw, 00660, Poland. TEL 48-22-256626. Ed. Jan Brodzki. Circ: 6,000.

616.86 NLD ISSN 0921-8742
PROGRESS IN ALCOHOL RESEARCH. Text in English. 1985. irreg., latest vol.2, 1990. price varies. back issues avail. **Document type:** *Monographic series, Academic/Scholarly.* **Description:** Reports on the effects of alcoholism on ultrastructural and neurochemical levels.
—KNAW.
Published by: V S P (Subsidiary of: Brill Academic Publishers), Brill Academic Publishers, PO Box 9000, Leiden, 2300 PA, Netherlands. TEL 31-71-5353500, FAX 31-71-5317532, vsppub@brill.nl, http://www.vsppub.com/books/bs14.html. Ed. H Ollat. **Dist. in US & Canada by:** Books International, PO Box 605, Herndon, VA 20172. TEL 703-661-1500, FAX 703-661-1501.

616.86 CAN ISSN 0229-2947
PROJECTION (TORONTO)✶; an audio-visual review service. Text in English. 1971. bi-m. looseleaf. CND 18; CND 23 foreign. film rev.
Published by: (Addiction Research Foundation of Ontario, Subscription - Marketing Department), Canadian Centre on Substance Abuse/Centre Canadien de Lutte Contre l'Alcoholisme et les Toxicomanies, 75 Albert St., Ste 300, Ottawa, ON K1P 5E7, Canada. TEL 613-235-4048, FAX 613-235-8101. Ed. Debbie Monkman. Circ: 750.

616.86 USA ISSN 0893-164X
RC563 CODEN: PABEEI
➤ **PSYCHOLOGY OF ADDICTIVE BEHAVIORS.** Text in English. 1983. q. USD 73 domestic to individuals; USD 91 foreign to individuals; USD 250 domestic to institutions; USD 285 foreign to institutions; USD 64 domestic to members; USD 77 foreign to members (effective 2005). adv. bk.rev. back issues avail.; reprint service avail. from PSC. **Document type:** *Journal, Academic/Scholarly.* **Description:** Covers alcoholism, drug abuse, eating disorders, smoking and nicotine addiction, and other compulsive behaviors such as gambling.
Former titles (until 1987): Society of Psychologists in Addictive Behaviors. Bulletin (0883-9646); Society of Psychologists in Substance Abuse. Bulletin
Related titles: Online - full text ed.: (from C S A, EBSCO Publishing, O C L C Online Computer Library Center, Inc., Ovid Technologies, Inc., ScienceDirect).
Indexed: ASCA, ASSIA, AddicA, CJA, CurCont, ERA, ETA, ExcerpMed, FamI, IndMed, MEA, MEDLINE, PsycInfo, PsycholAb, RHEA, SEA, SENA, SOMA, SSCI, SWR&A, TEA, e-psyche.
—BLDSC (6946.535315), IDS, IE, Infotrieve, ingenta. **CCC.**
Published by: American Psychological Association, 12884 Harbor Dr., Woodbridge, VA 22192-2921. TEL 800-374-2721, journals@apa.org, http://www.apa.org/journals/adb.html. Ed. Howard J Shaffer. R&P Karen Thomas. Adv. contact Jodi Ashcraft TEL 202-336-5500. B&W page USD 225. Circ: 1,760 (paid).

➤ **PSYCHOTHERAPY NETWORKER;** the magazine for today's helping professional. see *PSYCHOLOGY*

➤ **PUBLIC HEALTH REVIEWS;** an international quarterly. see *PUBLIC HEALTH AND SAFETY*

616.8 SWE ISSN 1404-224X
R F M A DEBATT. (Riksfoerbundet mot Alkohol- och Narkotikamissbruk) Text in Swedish. 1954. q. adv. bk.rev. illus.
Formerly (until 1997): Alkoholdebatt (0002-550X)
Related titles: Microfilm ed.: 1954 (from PQC).
Published by: Riksfoerbundet Mot Alkohol- och Narkotikamissbruk, PO Box 23201, Stockholm, 10435, Sweden. TEL 46-8-30-25-07.

616.863 USA ISSN 0738-422X
HV5001 CODEN: RDALE9
➤ **RECENT DEVELOPMENTS IN ALCOHOLISM.** Text in English. irreg., latest vol.17, 2005. price varies. **Document type:** *Monographic series, Academic/Scholarly.*
Indexed: CIN, ChemAb, ChemTitl, DentInd, IndMed, MEDLINE, PsycholAb.
—BLDSC (7304.104500), CASDDS, GNLM, IE, Infotrieve, ingenta, KNAW. **CCC.**
Published by: (American Medical Society on Alcoholism), Springer-Verlag New York, Inc. (Subsidiary of: Springer Science+Business Media), 233 Spring St, New York, NY 10013. TEL 212-460-1500, FAX 212-460-1575, service@springer-ny.com, http://www.springer-ny.com. Ed. M Galanter. **Co-sponsor:** Research Society on Alcoholism.

D

616.86 USA ISSN 1061-7191
RECOVERY TODAY; the newsmagazine for today's recovering community. Text in English. 1990. m. USD 15. **Description:** Focuses on recovery from alcoholism, drug addiction and eating disorders. Promotes personal growth.
Indexed: e-psyche.
Address: 1313 S Military Tr, Ste 314, Deerfield Beach, FL 33442. TEL 407-488-6362. Ed. Kathleen Low. Circ: 30,000.

616.861 USA
REPORT ON ALCOHOL, DRUGS, AND DISABILITY. Text in English. 1992. q. free. bk.rev. **Document type:** *Newsletter.* **Description:** Includes a calendar of events and activities, legislative updates, successful program descriptions, editorial opinion, leadership profiles, and networking opportunities.
Related titles: Audio cassette/tape ed.
Published by: National Association on Alcohol, Drugs, and Disability, 2165 Bunker Hill Dr, San Mateo, CA 94402-3801. TEL 650-578-8047. Ed. John De Miranda. Circ: 1,500.

RESEARCH COMMUNICATIONS IN ALCOHOL & SUBSTANCES OF ABUSE. see *PHARMACY AND PHARMACOLOGY*

RESEARCH DEVELOPMENT AND STATISTICS DIRECTORATE. OCCASIONAL PAPERS. see *SOCIOLOGY*

615 ESP ISSN 0213-7615
REVISTA ESPANOLA DE DROGODEPENDENCIAS. Text in Spanish. 1976. q.
Formerly (until 1987): Drogalcohol (0210-6140)
Indexed: BIOSIS Prev, BiolAb.
—CINDOC.
Published by: Asociacion Cientifica Drogalcohol, Apartado de Correo 477, Valencia, 46080, Spain. TEL 34-96-1600151, FAX 34-96-3601506. Ed. Francesc Freixa i Sanfeliu.

616.861 AUS
REVIVER. Text in English. 1954. m. AUD 24. **Document type:** *Directory, Consumer.*
Published by: Alcoholics Anonymous Central Service Office, 127 Edwin St, Croydon, NSW 2132, Australia. TEL 61-2-97991199, FAX 61-2-9716754. Circ: 2,500 (paid).

362.29 FRA ISSN 1629-9655
REVUE - TOXIBASE. Text in French. 1989. q. EUR 40 domestic; EUR 50 foreign; EUR 30 to students; EUR 11 per issue (effective 2005). **Document type:** *Journal, Academic/Scholarly.*
Former titles (until 2001): Revue Documentaire - Toxibase (1240-2494); (until 1992): Revue Bibliographique - Toxibase (0996-8393)
Related titles: Online - full text ed.
Published by: Reseau National d'Information et de Documentation, 76 r. Pierre Delore, Lyon, 69008, France. TEL 33-4-7872-4745, FAX 33-4-7272-9344, toxibase@toxibase.org, http://www.toxibase.org/Revue/Default.asp. Ed. Thomas Rouault.

616.86 NOR ISSN 0809-2834
RUS & AVHENGIGHET. Text in Norwegian. 1980. 6/yr. NOK 325 to individuals; NOK 650 to institutions; NOK 200 to students; NOK 75 per issue (effective 2004). adv. bk.rev. back issues avail. **Document type:** *Journal, Academic/Scholarly.* **Description:** Presents information and debate on drug problems in Norway and internationally.
Formerly (until 1998): Stoffmisbruk (0333-144X)
Related titles: Online - full text ed.
—CCC.
Published by: Universitetsforlaget AS/Scandinavian University Press (Subsidiary of: Aschehoug & Co.), Sehesteds Gate 3, Postboks 508, Oslo, 0105, Norway. TEL 47-24-147500, FAX 47-24-147501, post@universitetsforlaget.no, http://www.rus.no, http://www.universitetsforlaget.no. Ed. Martin Blindheim. Adv. contact Vidar Roeggen. B&W page NOK 6,000, color page NOK 9,000; 184 x 240. Circ: 3,000.

616.8 USA
RUTGERS CENTER OF ALCOHOL STUDIES. MONOGRAPH. Text in English. 1958. irreg., latest vol.14, 1981. price varies. index. **Document type:** *Monographic series, Academic/Scholarly.*
Formerly: Rutgers University. Center of Alcohol Studies. Monograph (0080-4983)
Indexed: BiolAb.
Published by: Rutgers Center of Alcohol Studies, Publications Division, c/o Charles Rouse, Bus Admin, 607 Allison Rd, Piscataway, NJ 08854-8001. TEL 732-445-2190. Ed. Marc Schuckit.

S A L I S DIRECTORY. see *LIBRARY AND INFORMATION SCIENCES*

S A L I S NEWS. see *LIBRARY AND INFORMATION SCIENCES*

616.861 USA
S A M H S A NEWS. Text in English. bi-m. USD 9.50; USD 11.90 foreign (effective 1995). back issues avail. **Document type:** *Newsletter, Government.* **Description:** Publishes articles on agency-related issues, such as AIDS, alcoholism, drug abuse, and general mental health. Publicizes agency events.
Published by: U.S. Substance Abuse and Mental Health Services Administration, Office of Applied Studies, 5600 Fishers Ln, Rm 16 105, Rockville, MD 20857. TEL 301-443-7934, FAX 301-443-9847. **Subscr. to:** U.S. Government Printing Office, Superintendent of Documents.

SALUTE E PREVENZIONE. see *PSYCHOLOGY*

SCHOOL INTERVENTION REPORT. see *CHILDREN AND YOUTH—About*

362.29 GBR
SCOTTISH SCHOOLS DRUGS SURVEY. Text in English. a. **Document type:** *Bulletin.*
Published by: Scotland Against Drugs, 40 Anderston Quay, Glasgow, G3 8BX, United Kingdom. TEL 44-141-204-3380, FAX 44-141-226-5724, 106004.1166@compuserve.com.

SMOKER'S CLUB. see *TOBACCO*

SMOKING AND HEALTH NEWSLETTER. see *PHYSICAL FITNESS AND HYGIENE*

616.86 USA ISSN 1059-6259
SOBER TIMES✶ ; the recovery magazine. Text in English. 1987. bi-m. USD 16.50; USD 39 foreign. adv. bk.rev. **Document type:** *Consumer.* **Description:** Focuses on ways to maintain happy, healthy lives, free of substance abuse and compulsive behavior.
Address: PO Box 13013, Mill Creek, WA 98082-1013. Ed. Cliff Creager. Pub. Jerauld D Miller. Adv. contact Joe Wooley. Circ: 80,000 (controlled).

362.292 USA ISSN 1071-4111
SOBERING THOUGHTS. Text in English. 1976. m. USD 14.95 domestic; CND 21.95 in Canada; USD 26.95 elsewhere (effective 2001). bk.rev. index. 16 p./no.; back issues avail. **Document type:** *Newsletter.* **Description:** For women who are recovering alcoholics. Contains personal reminiscences, inspirational articles, and news of self-help groups worldwide.
Formerly: Women for Sobriety. Newsletter
Published by: Women for Sobriety, Inc., PO Box 618, Quakertown, PA 18951. TEL 215-536-8026, FAX 215-538-9026, newlife@nni.com, http://www.womenforsobriety.org. Ed., R&P Rebecca M Fenner. Circ: 2,000 (paid).

616.86 CAN ISSN 0845-924X
SOCIETE DES ALCOOLS DU QUEBEC. RAPPORT ANNUEL. Text in English. 1971. a. free. **Document type:** *Corporate.*
Former titles (until 1985): Societe des Alcools du Quebec. Rapport d'Activite (0715-8254); (until 1982): Societe des Alcools du Quebec. Rapport Annuel (0715-884X); Which has English editions (1972-1974): Quebec Liquor Corporation. Annual Report (0715-8858); (1962-1971): Quebec. Liquor Board. Annual Report (0481-2875)
Published by: Societe des Alcools du Quebec, 905 DeLorimier, Montreal, PQ H2K 3V9, Canada. TEL 514-873-2020, info@saq.com, http://www.saq.com. Ed. Lyne Bellavance. R&P Nicole Creamer.

362.29 616.861 USA ISSN 0278-713X
HV5285
SPECIAL REPORT TO THE U S CONGRESS ON ALCOHOL AND HEALTH FROM THE SECRETARY OF HEALTH AND HUMAN SERVICES. Text in English. 1971. irreg. **Document type:** *Government.*
Published by: U.S. National Institute on Alcohol Abuse and Alcoholism, 5635 Fishers Ln MSC 9304, Bethesda, MD 20892-9304. TEL 301-443-3860, FAX 301-480-1726, http://www.niaaa.nih.gov.

362.29 LUX
THE STATE OF THE DRUGS PROBLEM IN THE ACCEDING AND CANDIDATE COUNTRIES TO THE EUROPEAN UNION. Text in English. a.
Related titles: Online - full text ed.
Published by: (European Monitoring Centre for Drugs and Drug Addiction PRT), European Commission, Office for Official Publications of the European Union, 2 Rue Mercier, Luxembourg, L-2985, Luxembourg. info-info-opoce@cec.eu.int, http://candidates.emcdda.eu.int, http://www.eurunion.org/publicat/index.htm.

616.861 GBR ISSN 0267-3282
STRAIGHT TALK; the alcohol concern quaterly magazine. Text in English. 1985. q. GBP 35 (effective 2002). **Description:** Contain information on development in alcohol field, news, updates and contributions from agencies.
—BLDSC (0786.772000), IE, ingenta.
Published by: Alcohol Concern, Waterbridge House, 32-36 Loman St, London, SE1 0EE, United Kingdom. TEL 44-20-79287377, FAX 44-20-79284644, contact@alcoholconcern.org.uk, http://www.alcoholconcern.org.uk.

STRAIGHT TALK (PLEASANTVILLE); a magazine for youth. see *CHILDREN AND YOUTH—For*

616.863 USA ISSN 0735-6544
RM301.15
STREET PHARMACOLOGIST. Text in English. 1978. 4/yr. USD 25. bk.rev.; film rev. bibl.; charts; illus.; stat. index, cum.index: 1978-1983. back issues avail. **Description:** Discusses substance abuse trends and other drug-related issues.
Published by: Up Front, Inc., 5701 Biscayne Blvd, Ste 602, Miami, FL 33137. TEL 305-757-2566, FAX 305-758-4676. Ed. James N Hall. Circ: 1,500.

STREETWIZE COMMUNICATIONS; youth rights comics. see *CHILDREN AND YOUTH—For*

616.86 USA ISSN 1042-6388
STUDENT ASSISTANCE JOURNAL. Text in English. 1988. 5/yr. USD 34 (effective 2004). film rev. tr.lit. back issues avail. **Document type:** *Magazine, Consumer.* **Description:** Looks at the various personal problems of students and how they affect their behavior at school. Emphasis is on drug abuse and alcoholism.
Indexed: SWR&A, e-psyche.
Published by: Performance Resource Press, Inc., 1270 Rankin Dr, Ste F, Troy, MI 48083-2843. TEL 810-588-7733, FAX 810-588-6633. Ed. Gerri Andrews. Circ: 10,000.

616.863 USA ISSN 0889-7077
RC563 CODEN: SUABE7
➤ **SUBSTANCE ABUSE.** Text in English. 1984. q. USD 400 combined subscription domestic to institutions print & online eds.; USD 540 combined subscription in Canada to institutions print & online eds.; USD 580 combined subscription elsewhere to institutions print & online eds. (effective 2006). bk.rev. back issues avail.; reprint service avail. from HAW. **Document type:** *Journal, Academic/Scholarly.* **Description:** Publishes international, interdisciplinary forum for the publication of original empirical research papers and reviews in the field of addiction and substance abuse. Topics covered include clinical and preclinical research, education, health-service delivery, and policy.
Related titles: Online - full text ed.: ISSN 1547-0164 (from EBSCO Publishing, Gale Group, IngentaConnect, Kluwer Online, O C L C Online Computer Library Center, Inc., Springer LINK, Swets Information Services).
Indexed: AddicA, BibLing, CINAHL, ERA, ETA, ExcerpMed, FamI, HRA, IBR, IBZ, MEA, PsycInfo, PsycholAb, RHEA, RefZh, SEA, SENA, SFSA, SOMA, SWA, SWR&A, SociolAb, TEA, e-psyche.
—BLDSC (8503.481000), Haworth, IE, Infotrieve, ingenta. **CCC.**
Published by: (Association for Medical Education and Research in Substance Abuse), The Haworth Medical Press (Subsidiary of: Haworth Press, Inc.), 10 Alice St, Binghamton, NY 13904. TEL 607-722-5857, 800-429-6784, FAX 607-771-0012, 800-895-0582, getinfo@haworthpress.com, http://www.haworthpress.com/web/SUBA. Ed. Marc Galanter. Pub. William Cohen. R&P Ruth Ann Heath TEL 607-722-5857 ext 316. Adv. contact Rebecca Miller-Baum TEL 607-722-5857 ext 337. Circ: 600.

D

362.293 USA ISSN 1076-979X
SUBSTANCE ABUSE LETTER✶ ; an independent report on prevention and treatment issues. Text in English. s-m. looseleaf. USD 195. **Document type:** *Newsletter.*
Indexed: e-psyche.
Published by: Pace Publications, 527 Third Ave, Ste 300, New York, NY 10016-4168. TEL 212-685-5450, FAX 212-679-4701. Ed. Molly Parrish.

616.863 USA ISSN 1040-4163
SUBSTANCE ABUSE REPORT✶ ; twice-monthly newsletter covering all aspects of drug abuse: its prevention, detection and treatment. Text in English. 1970. s-m. USD 275. bk.rev. **Document type:** *Magazine, Trade.* **Description:** Analyzes developments in the field of substance abuse treatment. Contains news and information on treatment programs, medical research and laboratory breakthroughs written for a professional audience.
Former titles: Addiction and Substance Abuse Report (0160-967X); Addiction and Drug Abuse Report (0001-8074)
Related titles: Online - full text ed.
Indexed: CJPI.
—CCC.
Published by: Business Research Publications, Inc., 210 E 39th St, New York, NY 10016-2754. Ed. Alison Knopf.

616.86 USA ISSN 1082-6084
RC566.A1 CODEN: SUMIFL
➤ **SUBSTANCE USE AND MISUSE.** Text in English. 1966. 14/yr. USD 2,886, GBP 1,737 combined subscription to institutions print & online eds. (effective 2006). adv. charts. reprint service avail. from PSC. **Document type:** *Journal, Academic/Scholarly.* **Description:** Disseminates facts, theories, points of view, and highlighting of critical unresolved issues in related areas of substance use, misuse and dependency, eating disorders, and gambling.
Formerly (until vol.31, 1996): International Journal of the Addictions (0020-773X)
Related titles: Microform ed.; Online - full text ed.: ISSN 1532-2491. USD 2,723, GBP 1,650 to institutions (effective 2006) (from EBSCO Publishing, O C L C Online Computer Library Center, Inc., Swets Information Services).

▼ new title ➤ refereed ✶ unverified ♦ full entry avail.

Indexed: AC&P, AMHA, ASCA, ASSIA, AddicA, AgeL, BiolAb, CINAHL, CJA, ChPerl, ChemAb, CurCont, DIP, ESPM, ExcerpMed, FamI, H&SSA, IBR, IBZ, INI, IPA, IPsyAb, ISR, IndMed, Inpharma, MEA&I, MEDLINE, NRN, PE&ON, PsycInfo, PsycholAb, RILM, Reac, RefZh, RiskAb, SCI, SOPODA, SSA, SSCI, SWR&A, SociolAb, ToxAb, e-psyche.
—BLDSC (8503.493000), CISTI, GNLM, IDS, IE, Infotrieve, ingenta, KNAW. **CCC.**
Published by: Taylor & Francis Inc. (Subsidiary of: Taylor & Francis Group), 325 Chestnut St, Ste 800, Philadelphia, PA 19016. TEL 215-625-8900, FAX 215-625-2940, info@taylorandfrancis.com, http://www.tandf.co.uk/journals/titles/10826084.asp, http://www.taylorandfrancis.com. Ed. Stanley Einstein. R&P Jill Milland. Adv. contact Robin Castorina. page USD 800. Circ: 650 (paid and free).

616.861 DEU ISSN 0939-5911
➤ **SUCHT.** Text in German; Abstracts in English. 1955. bi-m. EUR 110 domestic; EUR 148 foreign (effective 2005). adv. bk.rev. index. 48 p./no.; back issues avail. **Document type:** *Journal, Academic/Scholarly.*
Formerly (until 1991): Suchtgefahren (0491-421X)
Indexed: AddicA, DIP, ExcerpMed, IBR, IBZ, PsycInfo, PsycholAb.
—BLDSC (8505.640000), GNLM, IE, Infotrieve, ingenta, KNAW. **CCC.**
Published by: (Deutsche Hauptstelle gegen die Suchtgefahren), Neuland Verlagsgesellschaft mbH, Markt 24-26, Geesthacht, 21502, Germany. TEL 49-4152-81342, FAX 49-4152-81343, vertrieb@neuland.com, http://www.neuland.com/sucht/index.php. Ed. Gerhard Buehringer. R&P, Adv. contact Jens Burmester. Circ: 3,000.

362.29 DEU ISSN 1437-5567
➤ **SUCHTMEDIZIN IN FORSCHUNG UND PRAXIS.** Text in German. 1999. q. EUR 135; EUR 148.50 combined subscription print & online eds.; EUR 33 newsstand/cover (effective 2005). adv. **Document type:** *Journal, Academic/Scholarly.* **Description:** Provides a forum for research on all aspects of addiction.
Related titles: Online - full text ed.: EUR 108 (effective 2002) (from EBSCO Publishing).
Indexed: ExcerpMed.
—BLDSC (8505.675000). **CCC.**
Published by: Ecomed Verlagsgesellschaft AG & Co. KG, Justus-von-Liebig-Str 1, Landsberg, 86899, Germany. TEL 49-8191-1250, FAX 49-8191-125492, info@ecomed.de, http://www.ecomed.de/journals/sfp/welcome.htm. Ed. Dr. Michael Soyka. Adv. contact Gerhard Heinzmann. B&W page EUR 1,780; trim 176 x 252. Circ: 1,000 (paid and controlled).

178 DEU ISSN 0930-8350
SUCHTREPORT. Text in German. 6/yr. **Document type:** *Bulletin.*
Indexed: DIP, IBR, IBZ.
—GNLM.
Published by: Stiftung Synanon, Bernburger Str 10, Berlin, 10963, Germany. TEL 49-30-55000255, FAX 49-30-55000282. Ed., R&P, Adv. contact Michael Frommhold.

178 DEU ISSN 1439-9903
➤ **SUCHTTHERAPIE.** Text in German. 2000. q. EUR 115.80 domestic to institutions; EUR 119.80 in Europe to institutions; EUR 124.80 elsewhere to institutions; EUR 34 newsstand/cover (effective 2006). adv. **Document type:** *Journal, Academic/Scholarly.*
Related titles: Online - full text ed.: (from EBSCO Publishing, Swets Information Services).
—IE, Infotrieve. **CCC.**
Published by: Georg Thieme Verlag, Ruedigerstr 14, Stuttgart, 70469, Germany. TEL 49-711-89310, FAX 49-711-8931298, sucht@thieme.de, kunden.service@thieme.de, http://www.thieme.de/suchttherapie/index.html. Eds. Dr. Joachim Koerkel, Dr. Michael Krausz. adv.: B&W page EUR 1,370, color page EUR 2,435. Circ: 2,200 (paid).

➤ **T H S LA REVUE DES ADDICTIONS.** (Toxicomanies, Hepatites, Sida) see *MEDICAL SCIENCES—Communicable Diseases*

616.863 USA ISSN 1094-7566
TAKING SIDES: CLASHING VIEWS ON CONTROVERSIAL ISSUES IN DRUGS AND SOCIETY. Text in English. 1993. irreg., latest 2003, 6th ed. USD 22.50 per vol. (effective 2004). illus. **Document type:** *Academic/Scholarly.*
Published by: McGraw-Hill - Dushkin (Subsidiary of: McGraw-Hill Higher Education), 2460 Kerper Blvd, Dubuque, IA 52001. TEL 800-243-6532, customer.service@mcgraw-hill.com, http://www.dushkin.com/text-data/catalog/0072873043.mhtml. Ed. Raymond Goldberg. Pub. David Dean. R&P Cheryl Greenleaf.

616.86 NLD ISSN 0378-2778
RC566.A1
TIJDSCHRIFT VOOR ALCOHOL, DRUGS EN ANDERE PSYCHOTROPE STOFFEN. Text in Dutch; Summaries in Dutch, English. 1975. 4/yr. adv. bk.rev. back issues avail. **Document type:** *Academic/Scholarly.*
Indexed: AC&P, AddicA, PsycInfo, PsycholAb, e-psyche.
—BLDSC (8837.860000), GNLM, IE, Infotrieve, ingenta, KNAW. **CCC.**
Published by: Stichting T A D P, PO Box 725, Utrecht, 3500 AS, Netherlands. Circ: 1,500.

TOBACCO INDUCED DISEASES. see *TOBACCO*

613.84 SWE ISSN 1651-7725
TOBAK ELLER HAELSA. Text in Swedish. 1955. q. **Description:** Information about tobacco misuse and health damages created by smoking.
Former titles (until 2002): Tobaksfronten (1104-5639); (until 1991): Nytt fraan NTS (0283-1392); (until 1985): Tobaken och Vi (0346-3257)
Published by: (Statens Folkhaelsoinstitut/National Institute of Public Health in Sweden), Yrkesfoereningar mot Tobak, Stockholm, 10125, Sweden. TEL 46-8-6771090, FAX 46-8-6771093, http://www.tobaksfakta.org. Ed., Pub. Carl-Olof Ryden TEL 46-8-6698158.

615.9 ARG ISSN 0325-3961
TOXICOMANIAS. Text in Spanish. 1974. 3/yr.
Address: Paraguay, 2155, Capital Federal, Buenos Aires 1121, Argentina.

616.86 ESP ISSN 1575-0973
TRASTORNOS ADICTIVOS. Text in Spanish; Summaries in English. 1999. q. EUR 68.05 domestic to individuals print & online eds.; EUR 113.41 domestic to institutions print & online eds.; EUR 130.43 in the European Union print & online eds.; EUR 112.44 elsewhere print & online eds. (effective 2004); includes Trastornos Adictivos. Monografico. back issues avail. **Document type:** *Academic/Scholarly.*
Related titles: Online - full text ed.: ISSN 1578-2638. 1999 (from EBSCO Publishing); ♦ Supplement(s): Trastornos Adictivos. Monografico. ISSN 1578-262X.
Published by: Ediciones Doyma S.A. (Subsidiary of: Groupe Medimedia France), Traversa de Gracia 17-21, Barcelona, 08021, Spain. TEL 34-93-2000711, FAX 34-93-2091136, doyma@doyma.es, http://www.doyma.es/ta/.

616.86 ESP ISSN 1578-262X
TRASTORNOS ADICTIVOS. MONOGRAFICO. Text in Spanish. 2001. irreg. included in subscrip.of Trastornos Adictivos.
Related titles: Online - full text ed.: ISSN 1578-2646. 2001; ♦ Supplement to: Trastornos Adictivos. ISSN 1575-0973.
Published by: Ediciones Doyma S.A. (Subsidiary of: Groupe Medimedia France), Traversa de Gracia 17-21, Barcelona, 08021, Spain. TEL 34-93-2000711, FAX 34-93-2091136, doyma@doyma.es, http://www.doyma.es/.

616.86 USA ISSN 1530-6402
TREATING TOBACCO USE AND DEPENDENCE; clinical practice guideline. Text in English. 2000. a. **Document type:** *Government.*
Published by: U.S. Public Health Service, Department of Health and Human Services, 2101 East Jefferson St., Ste. 501/5E80, Rockville, MD 20852.

616.863 USA
TWELVE STEP RAG. Variant title: The Rag. Text in English. 1972. bi-m. USD 4.50 domestic; USD 10.50 foreign (effective 2003). 8 p./no.; back issues avail. **Document type:** *Newsletter.* **Description:** Provides an information source for families and friends affected by someone else's use of drugs, alcohol or related behavioral problems.
Published by: Families Anonymous, Inc., PO Box 3475, Culver City, CA 90231-3475. TEL 310-815-8010, 800-736-9805, FAX 310-815-9682, famanon@familiesanonymous.org, http://www.familiesanonymous.org. Circ: 2,500.

178.8 USA ISSN 0041-7033
UNION SIGNAL. Text in English. 1875. q. USD 8; USD 8.75 in Canada; USD 8.90 elsewhere (effective 1999). illus. back issues avail. **Document type:** *Bulletin.* **Description:** Contains material on the dangers of alcohol, tobacco, drugs, and gambling, and related historical articles.
Related titles: Microform ed.: (from PQC).
Published by: National Woman's Christian Temperance Union, 1730 Chicago Ave, Evanston, IL 60201-4585. TEL 847-864-1396, FAX 847-864-9497, sarah@wctu.org, http://www.wctu.org. Ed. Sarah F Ward. Circ: 2,500 (paid).
Subscr. to: PO Box 69, Hutchinson, KS 67504-0069.

615.1 USA ISSN 0007-523X
HV5800 CODEN: BNUNA5
UNITED NATIONS. BULLETIN ON NARCOTICS. Text in English. 1949. q. USD 10 per issue. bibl.; charts; illus. index. reprint service avail. from PQC. **Document type:** *Journal.* **Description:** Provides current information on all aspects of national and international drug control.
Formerly: Bulletin of Narcotic Drugs
Related titles: Microform ed.: (from PMC, PQC); Online - full text ed.: ISSN 1564-8680. 199?; Arabic ed.: Nashrat al-Mukhaddirat. ISSN 0256-9000. 1985; Chinese ed.: Mazuipin Gongbao. ISSN 0251-8694; French ed.: Bulletin des Stupefiant. ISSN 0251-3706; Russian ed.: Byulleten' po Narkoticheskim Sredstvam. ISSN 0251-7094; Spanish ed.: Boletin de Estupefacientes. ISSN 0251-7086. 1952.
Indexed: AC&P, AMHA, AbHyg, AddicA, BIOSIS Prev, BiolAb, CIN, CJA, ChemAb, ChemTitl, CurCont, DBA, ExcerpMed, HRIS, IIS, IPA, ISR, IndMed, MEDLINE, PAIS, PsycholAb, RASB, SSCI, SSI, TDB.
—BLDSC (2881.430000), CASDDS, GNLM, IE, Infotrieve, Linda Hall. **CCC.**
Published by: United Nations Publications, Rm DC2-853, United Nations Bldg, 2 United Nations Plaza, New York, NY 10017. TEL 212-963-8302, 800-253-9646, FAX 212-963-3489, publications@un.org, http://www.un.org/publications, http://www.un.org/Pubs. **Dist. by:** Distribution and Sales Section, Palais des Nations, Geneva CH-1211, Switzerland.

616.863 AUT
UNITED NATIONS. OFFICE ON DRUGS AND CRIME. GLOBAL ILLICIT DRUG TRENDS. Text in English, Spanish, French. 1999. a.
Related titles: Online - full text ed.
Published by: United Nations, Office on Drugs and Crime, International Drug Control Programme Research Section, Vienna International Centre, P.O. Box 500, Vienna, A-1400, Austria. FAX 43-1-26060-5866, undcp_hq@undcp.org, http://www.undcp.org/odccp/global_illicit_drug_trends.html.

178 SWE ISSN 0346-3869
VERDANDISTEN; spraakroer foer socialpolitik och medmaensklighet. Text in Swedish. 1897. irreg. (4-6/yr.). adv.
Published by: Verdandi Arbetarnas Socialpolitiska Organisation, Peter Myndes Backe 12, Stockholm, 11846, Sweden. TEL 46-8-642-28-80, FAX 46-8-642-28-20.

616.86 362.29 SWE ISSN 0346-427X
VI LAENKAR. Text in Swedish. 1957. 9/yr. SEK 100 (effective 1998). 56 p./no. 3 cols./p.
Published by: Laenkarnas Riksfoerbund, Blommensbergsvaegen 178, Haegersten, 12652, Sweden. TEL 46-8-18-96-880, FAX 46-8-18-29-89. Ed. Sven Erik Johansson. Pub. Ingemar Rosen. adv.: B&W page SEK 6,000; trim 248 x 171. Circ: 2,300.

616.863 RUS
VOPROSY NARKOLOGII. Text in Russian. bi-m. **Document type:** *Journal, Academic/Scholarly.*
Published by: Izdatel'stvo Anakharsis, M Mogil'tsevskii per, dom 4A, kv 2, ofis 1, Moscow, 119002, Russian Federation. TEL 7-095-2415925, http://www.narko.ru, http://www.anakharsis.ru.

362.295 GBR ISSN 1358-6912
CODEN: WWEPFQ
WEED WORLD. Text in English. bi-m. GBP 18 domestic; GBP 22 in Europe; USD 32.35 in United States; CND 43.15 in Canada (effective 2001). back issues avail. **Document type:** *Magazine, Consumer.* **Description:** Covers cannabis smokin, growing, legal news, political change, travel info, competitions, new products, medical breakthroughs and more.
Address: PO Box 1332, Coventry, CV8 3YA, United Kingdom. editor@weedworld.co.uk, http://www.weedworld.co.uk/.
Subscr. to: DirectMag, PO Box 2165, Williamsville, NY 14231. TEL 877-474-3321, FAX 905-619-2903.

178.8 GBR ISSN 0043-4973
THE WHITE RIBBON. Text in English. 1896. q. GBP 2. adv. bk.rev. illus. **Document type:** *Newsletter.*
Published by: The White Ribbon Association, Rosalind Carlisle House, 23 Dawson Pl, London, W2 4TH, United Kingdom. TEL 44-171-229-0804. Ed., R&P Maureen Long. Circ: 1,000.

178 USA ISSN 0043-4965
WHITE RIBBON BULLETIN. Text in English. 1883. q. USD 7 (effective 1998). bk.rev. **Document type:** *Newsletter.*
Published by: (World's Woman's Christian Temperance Union), M & D Printing Co., R I Box 43, Lowpoint, IL 61545. TEL 309-443-5275, FAX 309-364-3355. Ed. Mrs. Melvin Christ. Circ: 4,250.

616.8 USA ISSN 0043-5937
WINNER. Text in English. 1957. m. (during school term). USD 11.70; USD 20.65 includes Teaching Guide (effective 2003). charts; illus. **Description:** Alerts pre-teens and grade-schoolers to the dangers of drug use, and teaches them to live happy, healthy lives.
Related titles: Online - full text ed.: (from EBSCO Publishing).
Published by: Review and Herald Publishing Association, 55 W Oak Ridge Dr, Hagerstown, MD 21740-3790. TEL 301-393-4019, editor@listenmagazine.org, info@rhpa.org, http://www.listenmagazine.org/, http://www.rhpa.org/. Ed. Anita Jacobs TEL 301-393-4010. Circ: 35,000.

616.863 362.29 USA ISSN 1091-823X
HV4997
WORKPLACE SUBSTANCE ABUSE ADVISOR. Text in English. 1986. 22/yr. USD 377 (effective 2006). Index. back issues avail. **Document type:** *Newsletter, Trade.* **Description:** Reviews federal, state, local laws and regulations involving alcohol and drug use, testing policies, EAP's, court decisions, and drug enforcement budgets.
Formerly (until 1996): National Report on Substance Abuse (0891-5709)
Related titles: E-mail ed.; Online - full text ed.: (from LexisNexis).
—**CCC.**
Published by: L R P Publications, 747 Dresher Rd, PO Box 980, Horsham, PA 19044. TEL 215-784-0941, 800-341-7874, FAX 215-784-9639, custserve@lrp.com, http://www.shoplrp.com/product/p-5047.SA.html, http://www.lrp.com. Ed. Larry Graff.

D

178 360 USA
WORLD'S WOMAN'S CHRISTIAN TEMPERANCE UNION. TRIENNIAL REPORT. Text in English. 1891. triennial. USD 5. bk.rev. index. **Document type:** *Proceedings.*
Formerly: World's Woman's Christian Temperance Union. Convention Report (0084-2540)
Published by: World's Woman's Christian Temperance Union, HCR 3, Box 155, Wannaska, MN 56761. Ed. Pearl Loe. Circ: 600.

362.29 FIN ISSN 1455-6901
YHTEISKUNTAPOLITIIKKA. Text in Finnish. 1936. bi-m. EUR 26 (effective 2004).
Former titles (until 1998): Alkoholipolitiikka (0355-9750); (until 1953): Alkoholiliikkeen Aikakauskirja (0782-856X)
Related titles: Online - full text ed.: ISSN 1458-6118. 2001.
Indexed: AddicA, SSA, SociolAb.
Published by: Stakes Forsknings-och Utvecklingscentralen foer Social- och Haelsovaarden/National Research and Development Centre for Welfare and Health, PL 220, Helsinki, 00531, Finland. TEL 358-9-39671, FAX 358-9-39672191, bengt.jansson@stakes.fi, http://www.stakes.fi/yp/.

616.86 POL ISSN 0513-8809
ZDROWIE I TRZEZWOSC∗ . Text in Polish. 1976. m. PLZ 180,000. back issues avail.
Supersedes in part (in 1976): Problemy Alkoholizmu, Zdrowie i Trzezwosc (0137-3889); Which was formed by the merger of (1957-1975): Zdrowie i Trzezwosc (0867-3632); (1966-1975): Problemy Alkoholizmu (0239-4308); Which was formerly (1953-1965): Walka z Alkoholizmem (0509-5948)
Published by: Polska Liga "Trzezwosc", Ul Kopernika 36-40, Warsaw, 00924, Poland. TEL 48-22-6358620. Ed. Henryk Babendich. Circ: 70,000.

616.863 CHN ISSN 1007-9718
ZHONGGUO YAOWU YILAIXING ZAZHI/CHINESE JOURNAL OF DRUG DEPENDENCE. Text in Chinese. 1992. q. CNY 40 domestic; USD 20.80 foreign; CNY 10 newsstand/cover domestic; USD 5.20 newsstand/cover foreign (effective 2001). back issues avail. **Document type:** *Journal, Academic/Scholarly.* **Description:** Publishes scientific research on drug dependence, the social issue of addiction, prevention and treatment of drug abuse.
Formerly (until 1998): Zhongguo Yaowu Yilaixing Tongbao/Chinese Bulletin on Drug Dependence (1004-6445)
Related titles: Online - full content ed.: (from WanFang Data Corp.); Online - full text ed.: (from East View Information Services).
—BLDSC (3180.317120), IE, ingenta.

Published by: Zhongguo Yaowu Yilaixing Yanjiusuo/National Institute on Drug Dependence, Peking Xueyuan Lu 38 Hao, 280 Xinxiang, Beijing, 100083, China. TEL 86-10-62032625, FAX 68-10-62032624, niddbmu@public3.bta.net.cn, lyh509@21cn.com, http://www.periodicals.com.cn/gyjs.asp?ID= 297699, http://www.nidd.ac.cn/. **Dist. by:** China International Book Trading Corp, 35 Chegongzhuang Xilu, Haidian District, PO Box 399, Beijing 100044, China. TEL 86-10-68412045, FAX 86-10-68412023, cibtc@mail.cibtc.com.cn, http://www.cibtc.com.cn.

12; life in recovery. see *RELIGIONS AND THEOLOGY*

DRUG ABUSE AND ALCOHOLISM—
Abstracting, Bibliographies, Statistics

616.863021 AUS
AUSTRALIA. BUREAU OF STATISTICS. AUSTRALIAN STANDARD CLASSIFICATION OF DRUGS OF CONCERN. Text in English. 2000. irreg. AUD 27 (effective 2003).
Published by: Australian Bureau of Statistics, PO Box 10, Belconnen, ACT 2616, Australia. TEL 61-2-6252-5249, FAX 61-2-6252-6778, http://www.abs.gov.au.

DRUG FILE UPDATE; a current awareness index to publications on drugs and doping in sport. see *SPORTS AND GAMES—Abstracting, Bibliographies, Statistics*

016.61383 NLD ISSN 0925-5958
CODEN: DRDPA
EXCERPTA MEDICA. SECTION 40: DRUG DEPENDENCE, ALCOHOL ABUSE AND ALCOHOLISM. Text in English. 1973. 6/yr. EUR 1,486 in Europe to institutions; JPY 196,900 in Japan to institutions; USD 1,661 elsewhere to institutions (effective 2006). adv. index, cum.index. **Document type:** *Abstract/Index.* **Description:** Provides a comprehensive current-awareness service for trade and scholarly articles covering all aspects of the abuse of drugs, alcohol and organic solvents and includes material relating to the experimental pharmacology of addiction.
Formerly: Excerpta Medica. Section 40: Drug Dependence (0304-4041)
Related titles: CD-ROM ed.: (from SilverPlatter Information, Inc.); Online - full text ed.: (from Data-Star, DIMDI, JICST, The Dialog Corporation).
—GNLM, Linda Hall. CCC.
Published by: Excerpta Medica Medical Communications BV (Subsidiary of: Elsevier Health Sciences), Rooseveltweg 15, Almere, 1314 SJ, Netherlands. TEL 31-36-5385600, FAX 31-36-5385650, info@excerptamedica.com, http://www.elsevier.com/locate/drug, http://www.excerptamedica.com. **Subscr. to:** Elsevier BV, PO Box 211, Amsterdam 1000 AE, Netherlands. TEL 31-20-485-3757, FAX 31-20-485-3432, nlinfo-f@elsevier.nl, http://www.elsevier.nl.

616.863 310 GBR ISSN 0143-1463
HV5840.G7
GREAT BRITAIN. HOME OFFICE. STATISTICS OF THE MISUSE OF DRUGS: SEIZURES AND OFFENDERS DEALT WITH, UNITED KINGDOM (YEAR). Text in English. 1978. a.
Former titles (until 1992): Great Britain. Home Office. Statistics of the Misuse of Drugs in the United Kingdom: Seizures and Offenders Dealt with; (until 1986): Great Britain. Home Office. Statistics of the Misuse of Drugs in the United Kingdom, Supplementary Tables.
Published by: Home Office, 50 Queen Anne's Gate, London, SW1 9AT, United Kingdom.

616.861 016 USA ISSN 0074-204X
INTERNATIONAL BIBLIOGRAPHY OF STUDIES ON ALCOHOL. Text in English. 1966. irreg. price varies. bibl. index. **Document type:** *Monographic series, Bibliography.*
—CCC.
Published by: Rutgers Center of Alcohol Studies, Publications Division, c/o Charles Rouse, Bus Admin, 607 Allison Rd, Piscataway, NJ 08854-8001. TEL 732-445-2190. Ed. Marc Schuckit.

INTERNATIONAL NARCOTICS CONTROL BOARD. PSYCHOTROPIC SUBSTANCES; assessments of medical and scientific requirements for substances in schedules II, III and IV. Requirements of import authorization for substances in schedules III and IV. see *PHARMACY AND PHARMACOLOGY—Abstracting, Bibliographies, Statistics*

616 SWE
NORDRUG 2000 (ONLINE EDITION); Nordic research on alcohol and other drugs. Text in English. 2001. irreg. **Document type:** *Abstract/Index.*
Media: Online - full text.
Published by: Centralfoerbundet foer Alkohol- och Narkotikaupplysning/Swedish Council on Information on Alcohol and Other Drugs, Olof Palmes Gata 17, PO Box 70412, Stockholm, 10133, Sweden. TEL 46-8-4124600, FAX 46-8-4124641, biblioteket@can.se, http://www.can.se. Ed. Staffan Hasselgren.

016.616863 RUS
REFERATIVNYI ZHURNAL. NARKOLOGICHESKAYA TOKSIKOLOGIYA. Text in Russian. m. USD 254 foreign (effective 2006). **Document type:** *Journal, Abstract/Index.*
Related titles: CD-ROM ed.; Online - full text ed.
Published by: Vserossiiskii Institut Nauchnoi i Tekhnicheskoi Informatsii (VINITI), Ul Usievicha 20, Moscow, 125190, Russian Federation. TEL 7-095-1526441, FAX 7-095-9430060, dir@viniti.ru, http://www.viniti.ru. **Dist. by:** Informnauka Ltd., Ul Usievicha 20, Moscow 125190, Russian Federation. alfimov@viniti.ru.

D

EARTH SCIENCES

see also EARTH SCIENCES—Computer Applications ; EARTH SCIENCES—Geology ; EARTH SCIENCES—Geophysics ; EARTH SCIENCES—Hydrology ; EARTH SCIENCES—Oceanography

A N A R E REPORTS. (Australian National Antarctic Research Expeditions) see *SCIENCES: COMPREHENSIVE WORKS*

AARDKUNDIGE MEDEDELINGEN. see *GEOGRAPHY*

550 570 DEU ISSN 0515-2712
CODEN: AARAAJ
ACTA ALBERTINA RATISBONENSIA. Text in German. 1951. irreg. back issues avail. **Document type:** *Academic/Scholarly.*
Indexed: ZooRec.
—CASDDS, Linda Hall.
Published by: Naturwissenschaftlicher Verein Regensburg e.V., Herzogspalais, Am Prebrunntor 4, Regensburg, 93047, Germany. TEL 49-941-5073443, FAX 49-941-5073445. Circ: 1,000.

550 577 SVN ISSN 0583-6050
GB608.67 CODEN: ACLOBC
➤ **ACTA CARSOLOGICA/KARSTOLOGICAL REVIEW/KRASOSLOVNI ZBORNIK.** Text mainly in English, Slovenian; Abstracts in English; Summaries in English. 1955. s-a. SIT 5,000, EUR 20, USD 20 (effective 2004). bk.rev. 239 p./no.; back issues avail. **Document type:** *Proceedings, Academic/Scholarly.* **Description:** Publishes research articles and treatises on karst and caves from multiple scientific perspectives, as well as proceedings of related conferences, and reports on international scientific meetings. Emphasizes geology, geography, hydrology, sedimentology, biology and history of karst and cave science.
Related titles: Diskette ed.; Online - full text ed.: ISSN 1580-2612.
Indexed: RefZh, ZooRec.
—CISTI, KNAW, Linda Hall.
Published by: (Slovenska Akademija Znanosti in Umetnosti, Znanstvenoraziskovalni Center, Institut za Raziskovanje Krasa/Slovenian Academy of Sciences and Arts, Scientific Research Centre, Karst Research Institute), Zalozba Z R C/Scientific Research Centre Publishing, Novi trg 2, P.O. Box 306, Ljubljana, 1001, Slovenia. TEL 386-1-4706474, FAX 386-1-4257794, zalozba@zrc-sazu.si, http://www.zrc-sazu.si/izrk/carsologica, http://www.zrc-sazu.si/zalozba. Ed. Andrej Kranjc. Circ: 700.

550 DEU ISSN 1680-7340
▼ ➤ **ADVANCES IN GEOSCIENCES.** Text in English. 2003. irreg. EUR 30 per issue to members; EUR 60 per issue in Europe to non-members; EUR 70 per issue elsewhere to non-members (effective 2004). **Document type:** *Journal, Academic/Scholarly.*
Related titles: Online - full text ed.: ISSN 1680-7359. free (effective 2005).
Published by: (European Geosciences Union), Copernicus GmbH, Max-Planck Str 13, Katlenburg-Lindau, 37191, Germany. TEL 49-5556-91099, info@copernicus.org, http://www.copernicus.org/EGU/adgeo/adgeo.htm.

➤ **ADVANCES IN GEOTECHNICAL ENGINEERING AND TUNNELLING.** see *ENGINEERING—Civil Engineering*

550 NLD
➤ **ADVANCES IN POROUS MEDIA.** Text in English. 1991. irreg., latest vol.3, 1996. price varies. illus. back issues avail. **Document type:** *Monographic series, Academic/Scholarly.* **Description:** Examines research and developments in the subspecialty of porous media.
Published by: Elsevier BV (Subsidiary of: Elsevier Science & Technology), Radarweg 29, Amsterdam, 1043 NX, Netherlands. TEL 31-20-4853911, FAX 31-20-4852457, nlinfo-f@elsevier.nl, http://www.elsevier.nl. Ed. Dr. M Y Corapcioglu.

550 EGY
ADVANCES IN SOIL AND WATER RESEARCH IN ALEXANDRIA. Text in English. 1981. a. USD 15. **Document type:** *Monographic series.* **Description:** Reviews research work and developments in the field of soil and water sciences at the University of Alexandria.
Published by: A.M. Balba Group for Soil and Water Research, College of Agriculture, University of Alexandria, El-Shatby, Alexandria, 21545, Egypt. TEL 03-575405, FAX 03-5904684. Ed. A. Monem Balba.

551.9 RUS
AKADEMIYA NAUK C.S.S.R. VOSTOCHNO-SIBIRSKII FILIAL, IRKUTSK. INSTITUT GEOKHIMII. GEOKHIMICHESKIE METODY POISKOV, METODY ANALIZA. Text in Russian. 1977. irreg.
Published by: Institut Geokhimii, Ul Favorskogo 1, Irkutsk, 664033, Russian Federation. Ed. L Tauson. Circ: 700.

551.9 RUS
AKADEMIYA NAUK C.S.S.R. VOSTOCHNO-SIBIRSKII FILIAL, IRKUTSK. INSTITUT GEOKHIMII. GEOKHIMYA ENDOGENNYCH PROTSESSOV. Text in Russian. 1977. irreg.
Published by: Institut Geokhimii, Ul Favorskogo 1, Irkutsk, 664033, Russian Federation. Ed. L Tauson. Circ: 700.

AKADEMIYA NAUK RESPUBLIKI UZBEKISTAN. DOKLADY: MATEMATIKA, TEKHNICHESKIE NAUKI, ESTESTVOZNANIE. see *MATHEMATICS*

550 CAN
ALBERTA GEOLOGICAL SURVEY. EARTH SCIENCE REPORTS. Text in English. 1955. irreg. price varies.
Formerly: Alberta Research Council. Earth Science Reports
Published by: Alberta Geological Survey, 4999 - 98th Ave, 4th Fl, Twin Atria, Edmonton T6B 2X3, AB T6B 2X3, Canada. TEL 780-422-3767, FAX 780-422-1918, EUB.AGS-Infosales@gov.ab.ca, http://www.ags.gov.ab.ca.

550 CAN ISSN 0383-5359
ALBERTA RESEARCH COUNCIL. BULLETIN. Text in English. 1958. irreg. price varies. bibl.; charts; illus.; stat.
Former titles (until 1975): Research Council of Alberta. Bulletin (0034-5172); (until 1960): Research Council of Alberta. Geological Division. Bulletin (0370-3282)
—BLDSC, CISTI, Linda Hall.
Published by: Alberta Geological Survey, Alberta Energy and Utilities Board, Twin Atria 4th fl, 4999 98 Avenue, Edmonton, AB T6B 2X3, Canada. TEL 780-422-3767, FAX 780-422-1918, http://www.ags.gov.ab.ca.

550 USA ISSN 0002-9599
CODEN: AJSCAP
➤ **AMERICAN JOURNAL OF SCIENCE;** devoted to the geological sciences and to related fields. Text in English. 1818. 10/yr. USD 75 domestic to individuals; USD 100 foreign to individuals; USD 175 domestic to institutions; USD 200 foreign to institutions; USD 35 to students (effective 2005). bk.rev. bibl.; illus. index. back issues avail.; reprints avail. **Document type:** *Journal, Academic/Scholarly.*
Former titles (until 1880): American Journal of Science and Arts (0099-5363); (until 1820): American Journal of Science (1818) (0271-681X)
Related titles: Microform ed.: (from PMC, PQC); Online - full text ed.
Indexed: AESIS, AS&TI, ASCA, ASFA, AmH&L, BiolAb, BrCerAb, BrGeoL, BullT&T, CCI, CIN, Cadscan, ChemAb, ChemTitl, CurCont, E&PHSE, EEA, ESPM, EngInd, EnvAb, ExcerpMed, ForAb, GEOBASE, GP&P, GSI, GeotechAb, IBR, ISR, Inspec, LeadAb, MinerAb, OceAb, OffTech, PetrolAb, RASB, RefZh, S&F, SCI, SSCI, SWRA, WildRev, Zincscan.
—BLDSC (0838.000000), AskIEEE, CASDDS, CISTI, Ei, IDS, IE, Infotrieve, ingenta, KNAW, Linda Hall, PADDS. **CCC.**
Published by: (Yale University, Kline Geology Laboratory), American Journal of Science, 217 Kline Geology Laboratory, Yale University, PO Box 208109, New Haven, CT 06520-8109. TEL 203-432-3174, FAX 203-432-5668, ajs@hess.geology.yale.edu, http://love.geology.yale.edu/. Eds. Danny M Rye, Jay J Ague. Circ: 1,727 (paid).

➤ **ANNALS OF ARID ZONE.** see *AGRICULTURE—Crop Production And Soil*

➤ **ANNALS OF BANGLADESH AGRICULTURE.** see *AGRICULTURE*

550 USA ISSN 0084-6597
QE1 CODEN: AREPCI
➤ **ANNUAL REVIEW OF EARTH AND PLANETARY SCIENCES.** Text in English. 1973. a., latest vol.32, 2004. USD 205 to institutions print or online ed.; USD 246 combined subscription to institutions print & online eds. (effective 2006). bibl.; charts; abstr. index, cum.index. back issues avail.; reprint service avail. from PSC. **Document type:** *Academic/Scholarly.* **Description:** Original critical reviews of the significant primary literature and current developments in the earth and planetary sciences.
Related titles: Microfilm ed.: (from PQC); Online - full content ed.: ISSN 1545-4495. USD 200 (effective 2005) (from HighWire Press); Online - full text ed.: (from bigchalk, EBSCO Publishing, H.W. Wilson, ProQuest Information & Learning, Swets Information Services).
Indexed: AESIS, ASCA, ASFA, BrCerAb, C&ISA, CerAb, ChemAb, CorrAb, CurCont, E&CAJ, EMA, ESPM, EngInd, FLUIDEX, GEOBASE, GSI, IAA, ISR, Inspec, M&GPA, M&TEA, MBF, METADEX, MRD, OceAb, SCI, SWRA, WAA, ZooRec.
—BLDSC (1522.350000), CASDDS, CISTI, Ei, IDS, IE, Infotrieve, ingenta, Linda Hall. **CCC.**
Published by: Annual Reviews, 4139 El Camino Way, Palo Alto, CA 94303-0139. TEL 650-493-4400, 800-523-8635, FAX 650-424-0910, service@annualreviews.org, http://arjournals.annualreviews.org/loi/earth, http://www.annualreviews.org. Ed. Raymond Jeanloz. R&P Laura Folkner.

➤ **ANTARCTIC SCIENCE.** see *BIOLOGY*

551.9 NLD ISSN 1380-6165
GB855 CODEN: AQGEFP
➤ **AQUATIC GEOCHEMISTRY.** Text in English. 1995. q. EUR 374, USD 374, GBP 246 combined subscription to institutions print & online eds. (effective 2005). illus. reprint service avail. from PSC. **Document type:** *Journal, Academic/Scholarly.* **Description:** Publishes original studies relating to the geochemistry of natural waters and their interactions with rocks and minerals.
Related titles: Online - full text ed.: ISSN 1573-1421. USD 374 to institutions (effective 2005) (from EBSCO Publishing, Gale Group, IngentaConnect, Kluwer Online, O C L C Online Computer Library Center, Inc., Springer LINK, Swets Information Services).
Indexed: ASFA, BibLing, CIN, ChemAb, ChemTitl, CurCont, ESPM, EnvEAb, FLUIDEX, ForAb, GEOBASE, I&DA, M&GPA, MSB, OceAb, PollutAb, RefZh, S&F, SWRA.
—BLDSC (1582.380000), CASDDS, CISTI, IE, Infotrieve, ingenta, Linda Hall. **CCC.**
Published by: Springer-Verlag Dordrecht (Subsidiary of: Springer Science+Business Media), Van Godewijckstraat 30, Dordrecht, 3311 GX, Netherlands. TEL 31-78-6576050, FAX 31-78-6576474, http://springerlink.metapress.com/openurl.asp?genre=journal&issn=1380-6165, http://www.springeronline.com. Ed. George W Luther III.

➤ **ARCTIC AND MARINE OILSPILL PROGRAM REPORT.** see *ENVIRONMENTAL STUDIES*

➤ **ARCTIC AND MARINE OILSPILL PROGRAM TECHNICAL SEMINAR. PROCEEDINGS.** see *ENVIRONMENTAL STUDIES*

➤ **ARCTIC, ANTARCTIC, AND ALPINE RESEARCH.** see *SCIENCES: COMPREHENSIVE WORKS*

550 GBR ISSN 0066-8044
ARTHUR HOLMES SOCIETY. JOURNAL. Text in English. 1959-1981; resumed 1985. a. GBP 17 (effective 1996 & 1997). adv. **Document type:** *Academic/Scholarly.*
Formerly (until 1966): Durham University Geological Society. Journal
Published by: Arthur Holmes Society, University of Durham, Department of Geological Sciences, South Rd, Durham, DH1 3LE, United Kingdom. TEL 44-191-3742520, FAX 44-191-3742510, TELEX 537351 DURLIB G. Ed., Adv. contact David Wigham. Circ: 100.

550 ARG ISSN 0325-0253
CODEN: RAASE9
ASOCIACION ARGENTINA DE MINERALOGIA, PETROLOGIA Y SEDIMENTOLOGIA. REVISTA. Text in English, Spanish; Abstracts in English. 1970. s-a. ARS 10; USD 35 foreign. bk.rev. charts; illus. back issues avail.
Indexed: MinerAb.
—CASDDS, Linda Hall.
Published by: Asociacion Argentina de Mineralogia, Petrologia y Sedimentologia, Ciudad Universitaria, Pabellon, 2 piso 1 Nunez, Buenos Aires, 1428, Argentina. Ed. Hugo Corbella. Circ: 300.

550 551.46 NLD ISSN 1383-8601
➤ **ATMOSPHERIC AND OCEANOGRAPHIC SCIENCES LIBRARY.** Text in Dutch. 1982. irreg., latest vol.30, 2004. price varies. back issues avail. **Document type:** *Monographic series, Academic/Scholarly.*
Incorporates (1984-1995): Oceanographic Sciences Library (0924-4565); Formerly (until 1995): Atmospheric Science Library (0926-4701)
—BLDSC (1767.118500).
Published by: Springer-Verlag Dordrecht (Subsidiary of: Springer Science+Business Media), Van Godewijckstraat 30, Dordrecht, 3311 GX, Netherlands. TEL 31-78-6576050, FAX 31-78-6576474, http://www.springeronline.com. Eds. Kevin Hamilton, Lawrence A Mysak.

550 560 ITA ISSN 0394-0691
QE1 CODEN: ATSTEE
➤ **ATTI TICINENSI DI SCIENZE DELLA TERRA.** Text mainly in Italian. 1943. a. price varies. maps. back issues avail. **Document type:** *Journal, Academic/Scholarly.* **Description:** Presents articles in paleontology and the earth sciences.
Formerly (until 1985): Universita di Pavia. Istituto Geologico. Atti (0365-317X)
Indexed: BIOSIS Prev, BiolAb, RefZh, ZooRec.
Published by: Universita degli Studi di Pavia, Dipartimento di Scienze della Terra, Strada Nuova 65, Pavia, 27100, Italy. TEL 39-0382-981, FAX 39-0382-984529, http://www.unipv.it. Ed. Mario Vanossi. Pub. M Botta.

550 AUS ISSN 1035-9338
QE48.A8
AUSGEO NEWS. Key Title: Aus Geo News. Text in English. 1990. bi-m. free. **Document type:** *Newsletter, Government.* **Description:** Designed to keep AGSO clients informed of research results, program changes, staff movements, new publications and data releases.
Indexed: AESIS, RefZh.

Published by: Australian Geological Survey Organisation, GPO Box 378, Canberra, ACT 2601, Australia. TEL 61-6-2499249, FAX 61-6-2499984, julie.wissmann@agso.gov.au, http://www.agso.gov.au/information/ausgeonews/. Ed., R&P Julie Wissmann.

AUSTRALIA. BUREAU OF RESOURCE SCIENCES. AUSTRALIAN PETROLEUM ACCUMULATIONS REPORT. see *PETROLEUM AND GAS*

AUSTRALIA. GEOSCIENCE AUSTRALIA. MINERAL RESOURCE REPORT. see *MINES AND MINING INDUSTRY*

553 AUS ISSN 1444-0865
AUSTRALIAN GEODYNAMIC COOPERATIVE RESEARCH CENTRE. ANNUAL REPORT. Text in English. a.
Related titles: ♦ Online - full text ed.: Australian Geodynamic Cooperative Research Centre. Annual Report (Online Edition). ISSN 1444-0873.
Published by: Australian Geodynamics Cooperative Research Centre, C S I R O Exploration & Mining, 39 Fairway, PO Box 437, Nedlands, W.A. 6009, Australia. TEL 61-8-9389-8421, FAX 61-8-9389-1906, geomgc@pop.latrobe.edu.au.

553 AUS ISSN 1444-0873
AUSTRALIAN GEODYNAMIC COOPERATIVE RESEARCH CENTRE. ANNUAL REPORT (ONLINE EDITION). Text in English. a.
Media: Online - full text. **Related titles:** ♦ Print ed.: Australian Geodynamic Cooperative Research Centre. Annual Report. ISSN 1444-0865.
Published by: Australian Geodynamics Cooperative Research Centre, C S I R O Exploration & Mining, 39 Fairway, PO Box 437, Nedlands, W.A. 6009, Australia. TEL 61-8-9389-8421, FAX 61-8-9389-1906, geomgc@pop.latrobe.edu.au, http://www.agcrc.csiro.au/publications/#newsletters.

550 AUS ISSN 1039-2645
QE340 CODEN: ABULEA
AUSTRALIAN GEOLOGICAL SURVEY ORGANISATION. BULLETIN. Text in English. 1932. irreg. price varies. **Document type:** *Academic/Scholarly.*
Formerly: Australia. Bureau of Mineral Resources, Geology and Geophysics. Bulletin (0084-7089)
Indexed: AESIS, ASI, BiolAb, IMMAb, Inspec, ZooRec.
—BLDSC (2409.316500), AskIEEE, CASDDS, CISTI, Linda Hall. **CCC.**
Published by: Australian Geological Survey Organisation, GPO Box 378, Canberra, ACT 2601, Australia. TEL 61-6-2499249, FAX 61-6-2499984, julie.wissmann@agso.gov.au, http://www.agso.gov.au. Ed., R&P Julie Wissmann.

550 AUS ISSN 1443-1017
QE340
AUSTRALIAN INSTITUTE OF GEOSCIENTISTS JOURNAL; applied geoscientific research and practice in Australia. Abbreviated title: A I G Journal. Text in English. 1999. irreg. free (effective 2005). **Document type:** *Journal, Academic/Scholarly.* **Description:** Contains papers, reviews and short notes dealing with any aspect of applied geoscientific research and practice.
Media: Online - full content.
Published by: Australian Institute of Geoscientists, Perth Business Centre, PO Box 8463, Perth, W.A. 6849, Australia. TEL 61-8-94270820, FAX 61-8-94270821, aigjournal@aig.asn.au, aig@aig.asn.au, http://www.aig.asn.au/aigjournal/.

550 551.6 USA
AVALANCHE REVIEW. Text in English. 1982. 6/yr. (Nov.-Apr.). USD 20 (effective 1999). adv. bk.rev. bibl.; charts; illus.; stat. cum.index. back issues avail. **Document type:** *Newsletter.* **Description:** Current snow and avalanche information.
Published by: American Association of Avalanche Professionals, PO Box 1032, Bozeman, MT 58771. TEL 406-587-3830, FAX 406-586-4307, wwan@avalanche.org, http://www.avalanche.org. Ed. Steve Conger. R&P, Adv. contact Don Bachman. Circ: 1,000.

550 GBR ISSN 0950-091X
QE571 CODEN: BSNREL
➤ **BASIN RESEARCH.** Text in English. 1988. q. GBP 105, EUR 158 combined subscription in Europe to individuals print & online eds.; USD 192 combined subscription in the Americas to individuals & Caribbean, print & online eds.; GBP 114 combined subscription elsewhere to individuals print & online eds.; GBP 600 combined subscription in Europe to institutions print & online eds.; USD 1,109 combined subscription in the Americas to institutions & Caribbean, print & online eds.; GBP 660 combined subscription elsewhere to institutions print & online eds. (effective 2006). adv. bk.rev. abstr.; bibl.; illus. Index. back issues avail.; reprint service avail. from PSC. **Document type:** *Journal, Academic/Scholarly.* **Description:** Presents original research papers on sedimentary basins, of interest to earth scientists in all specializations.
Related titles: Microform ed.: (from PQC); ♦ Online - full text ed.: Basin Research Online. ISSN 1365-2117.
Indexed: AESIS, ASCA, ASFA, BrGeoL, CurCont, E&PHSE, ESPM, EngInd, GEOBASE, GP&P, ISR, OffTech, PetrolAb, RefZh, SCI, SWRA.
—BLDSC (1864.520000), CISTI, Ei, IDS, IE, Infotrieve, ingenta, Linda Hall, PADDS. **CCC.**
Published by: (European Association of Geoscientists and Engineers), Blackwell Publishing Ltd., 9600 Garsington Rd, Oxford, OX4 2ZG, United Kingdom. TEL 44-1865-776868, FAX 44-1865-714591, customerservices@oxon.blackwellpublishing.com, http://www.blackwellpublishing.com/journals/BRE. Eds. Hugh D Sinclair TEL 44-131-6505931, Joe Cartwright, Peter DeCelles. Circ: 700. **Co-sponsor:** International Association of Sedimentologists.

550 GBR ISSN 1365-2117
➤ **BASIN RESEARCH ONLINE.** Text in English. q. GBP 570 in Europe to institutions; USD 1,053 in the Americas to institutions & Caribbean; GBP 627 elsewhere to institutions (effective 2006). **Document type:** *Academic/Scholarly.*
Media: Online - full text (from Blackwell Synergy, EBSCO Publishing, Gale Group, IngentaConnect, O C L C Online Computer Library Center, Inc., Swets Information Services).
Related titles: Microform ed.: (from PQC); ♦ Print ed.: Basin Research. ISSN 0950-091X.
Published by: Blackwell Publishing Ltd., 9600 Garsington Rd, Oxford, OX4 2ZG, United Kingdom. TEL 44-1865-776868, FAX 44-1865-714591, customerservices@oxon.blackwellpublishing.com, http://www.blackwellpublishing.com.

▼ ➤ **BIOGEOSCIENCES.** see *BIOLOGY*

▼ ➤ **BIOGEOSCIENCES DISCUSSIONS.** see *BIOLOGY*

550 USA
BLUELINE (COLLEGE STATION). Text in English. 1967. q. USD 30 (effective 1998). bk.rev. back issues avail. **Document type:** *Newsletter.* **Description:** Keeps members informed of association activities and educates about editing anomalies in the earth sciences.
Published by: Association of Earth Science Editors, c/o Ocean Drilling Program, 1000 Discovery Program, College Station, TX 77845-9547. TEL 409-845-2729, FAX 409-845-1160, Ann_Klaus@odp.tamu.edu, http://www-odp.tamu.edu/publications/AESE/. Ed. Patrick Edwards. R&P, Adv. contact Ann Klaus. Circ: 400. **Subscr. to:** Katherine B. Lessing, 781 Northwest Dr, Morgantown, WV 26505.

550 520 BRA ISSN 0102-6275
BOLETIM I G - U S P. PUBLICACAO ESPECIAL. Text in Portuguese. 1984. irreg. USD 20 per issue (effective 2000). **Document type:** *Academic/Scholarly.* **Description:** Covers all aspects of earth science.
Supersedes in part (1970-1985): Boletim I G
Published by: Universidade de Sao Paulo, Instituto de Geociencias, Attn: Editorial Committee President, Cidade Universitaria, Pinheiros, Caixa Postal 11348, Sao Paulo, SP 05422-970, Brazil. TEL 55-11-818-3973, rosimone@usp.br. Ed. Vincente Antonio Vitorio Girardi. Pub., Adv. contact Rosane Simone. Circ: 450.

550 520 BRA ISSN 0102-6283
CODEN: BICIE5
BOLETIM I G - U S P. SERIE CIENTIFICA. Text in Portuguese. 1984. a., latest vol.29, 1999. USD 20 per issue (effective 2000). bk.rev. bibl.; illus. back issues avail. **Document type:** *Bulletin.* **Description:** Presents scientific papers on earth science.
Supersedes in part (1970-1985): Boletim I G
Related titles: Diskette ed.
Indexed: ZooRec.
—CASDDS.
Published by: Universidade de Sao Paulo, Instituto de Geociencias, Attn: Editorial Committee President, Cidade Universitaria, Pinheiros, Caixa Postal 11348, Sao Paulo, SP 05422-970, Brazil. TEL 55-11-818-3973, FAX 55-11-818-4861, rosimone@usp.br. Ed. Vicente Antonio Vitorio Girardi. Pub., Adv. contact Rosane Simone. Circ: 500.

550 520 BRA ISSN 0102-6291
BOLETIM I G - U S P. SERIE DIDATICA. Text in Portuguese. 1985. irreg. USD 20 per issue (effective 2000). **Document type:** *Monographic series.* **Description:** Monographs on the earth sciences.
Supersedes in part (1970-1985): Boletim I G
Published by: Universidade de Sao Paulo, Instituto de Geociencias, Attn: Editorial Committee President, Cidade Universitaria, Pinheiros, Caixa Postal 11348, Sao Paulo, SP 05422-970, Brazil. TEL 55-11-818-3973, rosimone@usp.br. Ed. Vincente Antonio Vitorio Girardi. Pub., Adv. contact Rosane Simone. Circ: 450.

549.0972 MEX
BOLETIN DE MINERALOGIA. Text in Spanish. a. free. **Description:** Publishes articles on mineralogy in Mexico.
Published by: Universidad Nacional Autonoma de Mexico, Facultad de Ingenieria, Palacio de Mineria, Tacuba No. 5, Centro Historico, Mexico City, 06000, Mexico. TEL 52-5-6220851, FAX 52-5-5500040. Ed. Carlos Garza Gonzalez Velez. **Co-sponsor:** Sociedad Mexicana de Mineralogia.

550 BOL ISSN 1023-7674
CODEN: GBBLAB
BOLIVIA. SERVICIO NACIONAL DE GEOLOGIA Y MINERIA. BOLETIN. Text in Spanish, English. 1961. irreg., latest vol.15, 1998. price varies. **Document type:** *Bulletin, Government.* **Description:** Comprises information relative to the ground water resources.
Formerly: Bolivia. Servicio Geologico. Boletin; Supersedes (in 1993): Bolivia. Servicio Geologico. Boletin Serie A (0255-707X); Which was formerly: Bolivia. Servicio Geologico. Boletin (0067-9828); (until 1965): Bolivia. Departamento Nacional de Geologia. Boletin (0366-1199)
Published by: Servicio Nacional de Geologia y Mineria, Casilla 2729, La Paz, Bolivia. FAX 591-2-391725, sergeomi@caoba.entelnet.bo. Ed. Carlos Riera Kilibarda. R&P Marcelo Claure-Zapata TEL 591-2-330895.

550 ITA ISSN 0006-6710
QB275 CODEN: BGSAA9
BOLLETTINO DI GEODESIA E SCIENZE AFFINI. Text in Italian, English; Summaries in English, French, German, Italian, Spanish. 1921. q. EUR 22 domestic; EUR 30 foreign (effective 2004). adv. bk.rev. charts; illus. index. back issues avail. **Document type:** *Bulletin, Academic/Scholarly.* **Description:** Covers geodesy, cartography, remote sensing, and photogrammetry.
Former titles (until 1950): Istituto Geografico Militare. Bollettino Geodetico (1124-5158); (until 1941): Consiglio Nazionale delle Ricerche. Comitato per la Geodesia e la Geofisica. Bollettino (1124-514X); (until 1933): Comitato Nazionale Italiano per la Geodesia e la Geofisica. Bollettino (1124-5131); (until 1930): Comitato Nazionale Italiano Geodetico - Geofisico. Bollettino (1124-481X)
Indexed: BibCart, IBR, RefZh.
—CISTI.
Published by: Istituto Geografico Militare, Via Cesare Battisti 10, Florence, FI 50100, Italy. TEL 39-055-27321, FAX 39-055-282172, http://www.igmi.org. Ed. Alberto Coticchia. Adv. contact Andrea Manetti. Circ: 800.

550 ITA ISSN 0393-0742
BOLLETTINO GEOFISICO. Text in Italian. 1978. q. bk.rev. **Document type:** *Magazine, Academic/Scholarly.* **Description:** Explores the Earth's systems: the lithosphere, atmosphere, hydrosphere and biosphere.
Published by: Associazione Geofisica Italiana, c/o CNR - Viale dell'Universita 11, Rome, 00185, Italy. http://www.ifa.rm.cnr.it/AGI/associaz.html.

614.8 624.15 JPN ISSN 0916-6564
TA495
BOSAI KAGAKU GIJUTSU KENKYUJO KENKYU HOKOKU. Text in Japanese. 1968. s-a. **Document type:** *Journal, Academic/Scholarly.*
Formerly (until 1990): Kokuritsu Bosai Kagaku Gijutsu Senta Kenkyu Hokoku (0386-3360)
Indexed: EEA, RefZh.
—BLDSC (7570.220500), CISTI.
Published by: Kagaku Gijutsucho Bosai Kagaku Gijutsu Kenkyujo/National Research Institute for Earth Science and Disaster Prevention, 3-1,Tennodai, Tsukuba-shi, Ibaraki-ken 305, Japan. TEL 81-298-51-1611, FAX 81-298-51-1622, http://www.bosai.go.jp/ad/Jpn/kankou.htm.

614.8 JPN ISSN 0917-057X
BOSAI KAGAKU GIJUTSU KENKYUJO KENKYU SHIRYO/NATIONAL RESEARCH INSTITUTE FOR EARTH SCIENCE AND DISASTER PREVENTION. TECHNICAL NOTE. Text in Japanese. irreg. **Document type:** *Journal, Academic/Scholarly.*
Formerly (until 1989): Bosai Kagaku Gijutsu Kenkyu Shiryo
Indexed: RefZh.
Published by: Kagaku Gijutsucho Bosai Kagaku Gijutsu Kenkyujo/National Research Institute for Earth Science and Disaster Prevention, 3-1,Tennodai, Tsukuba-shi, Ibaraki-ken 305, Japan. TEL 81-298-51-1611, FAX 81-298-51-1622, http://www.bosai.go.jp/ad/Jpn/kankou.htm.

550 362.1 624 JPN ISSN 0918-6441
BOSAI KAGAKU GIJUTSU KENKYUJO NENPO/NATIONAL RESEARCH INSTITUTE FOR EARTH SCIENCE AND DISASTER PREVENTION. ANNUAL REPORT. Text in Japanese. irreg. **Document type:** *Government.*
Formerly (until 1989): Kokuritsu Bosai Kagaku Gijutsu Senta Nenpo
Published by: Kagaku Gijutsucho Bosai Kagaku Gijutsu Kenkyujo/National Research Institute for Earth Science and Disaster Prevention, 3-1,Tennodai, Tsukuba-shi, Ibaraki-ken 305, Japan. TEL 81-298-51-1611, FAX 81-298-51-1622, http://www.bosai.go.jp/ad/Jpn/kankou.htm.

550 GBR ISSN 0144-9761
BRITISH NATURALIST. Text in English. 1980. 2/yr. membership. **Document type:** *Newsletter.*
Published by: British Naturalists' Association, c/o Mrs. Y. Griffiths, 1 Bracken Mews, Chingford, London, E4 7UT, United Kingdom. FAX 44-1933-314672. Ed. David Applin. R&P J F Pearton. **Subscr. to:** Mrs. Y. Griffiths, 1 Bracken Mews, Chingford, London E1X 74T, United Kingdom.

E

▼ *new title* ➤ *refereed* ✶ *unverified* ♦ *full entry avail.*

550 ALB
BULETINI I SHKENCAVE NATYRES/BULLETIN DES SCIENCES NATURELLES. Text in Albanian; Summaries in French. 1957. q. USD 7.20.
Published by: Enver Hoxha Universitet, Tirana, Albania. Ed. Muharrem Frasheri.

551.469 BGR
BULGARIAN ANTARCTIC RESEARCH LIFE SCIENCES. Text in English. irreg., latest vol.3, 2002. **Document type:** *Monographic series, Academic/Scholarly.*
Indexed: BIOSIS Prev, BiolAb.
Published by: Pensoft Publishers, Akad G Bonchev 6, Sofia, 1113, Bulgaria. TEL 359-2-716451, FAX 359-2-8704508, pensoft@mbox.infotel.bg, http://www.pensoft.net. Ed. V Golemansky.

550 CHE ISSN 0374-6402
➤ **BULLETIN DE LA MURITHIENNE.** Text in French, German; Summaries in English, German. 1869. a. CHF 30 to members; CHF 35 to non-members (effective 2003). bk.rev. abstr.; bibl.; charts; illus.; maps. back issues avail. **Document type:** *Bulletin, Academic/Scholarly.*
Indexed: BiolAb, ZooRec.
Published by: La Murithienne, Societe Valaisanne des Sciences Naturelles, Secretariat, Musee Cantonale d'Histoire Naturelle, Av de la Gare 42, CP 2251, Sion, 1950, Switzerland. TEL 41-27-6064732, FAX 41-27-6064734, lamurithienne@admin.ch, lamurithienne@vs.ch, http://www.murithienne.unibe.ch. Circ: 850.

550.5 IND
BULLETIN OF EARTH SCIENCES. Text in English. 1972. a. INR 15, USD 3. adv. illus.
Published by: Indian Society of Earth Scientists, c/o Dept. of Geology, Poona University, Pune, Maharashtra 411 007, India. Ed. V G Phansalkar. Circ: 300.

550 333.79 346.066 GBR
C E P M L P INTERNET JOURNAL. (Centre for Energy, Petroleum and Mineral Law and Policy) Text in English. 1997. irreg.
Media: Online - full text.
Published by: University of Dundee, Centre for Energy, Petroleum and Mineral Law and Policy, Dundee, DD1 4HN, United Kingdom. TEL 44-1382-344302, FAX 44-1382-322578, http://www.cepmlp.org/journal/, http://www.dundee.ac.uk/cepmlp/main/welcome.htm. Ed. Thomas Waelde.

550 BRA ISSN 0103-1597
QE1
CADERNOS DE GEOCIENCIAS. Text in Portuguese; Abstracts in English, Portuguese. 1988. q. bk.rev. charts; illus.; maps. **Document type:** *Government.*
Published by: Fundacao Instituto Brasileiro de Geografia e Estatistica, Diretoria de Geociencias, Av Brasil, 15671, Bloco IIIB, Terreo Prada de Lucas, Rio De Janeiro, RJ 21241-051, Brazil. TEL 55-21-3911420, cbge@cbge.gov.br.

CANADA DEPARTMENT OF ENERGY, MINES AND RESOURCES. PUBLICATIONS OF THE EARTH PHYSICS BRANCH. see *ENERGY*

550.5 CAN ISSN 1709-5727
QE48.C2
CANADA. EARTH SCIENCES SECTOR. ANNUAL REVIEW. Text in English. a.
Incorporates (1989-2001): Geomatics Canada (1491-5480); Which was formerly (until 1996): Geomatics Canada - Annual Review (1190-965X); (until 1994): Canada. Surveys, Mapping and Remote Sensing Sector. Annual Review (0846-8370)
Published by: Natural Resources Canada, Earth Sciences Sector, 350-601 Booth St, Ottawa, ON K1A 0E8, Canada. TEL 613-996-3919, FAX 613-943-8742.

550 CAN ISSN 0008-3674
CODEN: CGJOAH
➤ **CANADIAN GEOTECHNICAL JOURNAL/REVUE CANADIENNE DE GEOTECHNIQUE.** Text mainly in English; Text occasionally in French. 1963. bi-m. CND 122 domestic to individuals; USD 122 foreign to individuals; CND 342 domestic to institutions; USD 342 foreign to institutions (effective 1999). adv. bk.rev. bibl.; illus. index. back issues avail.; reprint service avail. from PQC. **Document type:** *Academic/Scholarly.*
Related titles: Microfiche ed.: (from MML); Microform ed.: (from MML, PQC); Online - full text ed.: ISSN 1208-6010 (from bigchalk, EBSCO Publishing, Gale Group, IngentaConnect, Micromedia ProQuest, O C L C Online Computer Library Center, Inc., ProQuest Information & Learning, Swets Information Services).
Indexed: AESIS, AJEE, AS&TI, ASCA, ASFA, BrCerAb, BrGeoL, C&ISA, CBCARef, CIN, CurCont, CerAb, ChemAb, ChemTitl, CivEngAb, CorrAb, CurCont, E&CAJ, E&PHSE, EEA, EMA, ESPM, EngInd, EnvEAb, ExcerpMed, F&EA, FLUIDEX, GEOBASE, GP&P, GeotechAb, IAA, IBR, ICEA, ISR, M&TEA, MBF, METADEX, MSCI, OceAb, OffTech, PetrolAb, PollutAb, SCI, SWRA, SoftAbEng, SolStAb, WAA, WTA.
—BLDSC (3027.005000), CASDDS, CISTI, Ei, IDS, IE, Infotrieve, ingenta, Linda Hall, PADDS. **CCC.**
Published by: (Canadian Geotechnical Society), N R C Research Press, Building M 55, Ottawa, ON K1A 0R6, Canada. TEL 613-993-0362, 800-668-1222, FAX 613-952-7656, pubs@nrc-cnrc.gc.ca, http://pubs.nrc-cnrc.gc.ca/cgi-bin/rp/rp2_desc_e?cgj. Ed. Bruce P Dancik. Adv. contact Judy Heyman. B&W page CND 675; trim 11 x 8.5. Circ: 2,491.

550 CAN ISSN 0008-4077
QE1 CODEN: CJESAP
➤ **CANADIAN JOURNAL OF EARTH SCIENCES/JOURNAL CANADIEN DES SCIENCES DE LA TERRE.** Text mainly in English; Text occasionally in French. 1963. m. CND 229 domestic to individuals print ed.; USD 229 foreign to individuals print ed.; CND 701 domestic to institutions print ed.; CND 701 foreign to institutions print ed.; CND 206.10 domestic to individuals online ed.; USD 206.10 foreign to individuals online ed.; CND 630.90 domestic to institutions online ed.; CND 630.90 foreign to institutions online ed. (effective 2001). adv. bibl.; charts; illus. index. back issues avail.; reprint service avail. from PQC. **Document type:** *Journal, Academic/Scholarly.*
Related titles: Microfiche ed.: (from MML); Microform ed.: (from MML, PMC, PQC); Online - full text ed.: ISSN 1480-3313 (from bigchalk, EBSCO Publishing, Gale Group, IngentaConnect, Micromedia ProQuest, O C L C Online Computer Library Center, Inc., ProQuest Information & Learning, Swets Information Services).
Indexed: AESIS, AJEE, ASCA, ASFA, BiolAb, BrCerAb, BrGeoL, C&ISA, CBCARef, CIN, CIS, CTO, CerAb, ChemAb, ChemTitl, CorrAb, CurCont, E&CAJ, E&PHSE, EEA, EIA, EMA, EPB, ESPM, EngInd, EnvAb, GEOBASE, GP&P, GeophysAb, GeotechAb, HRIS, IAA, IBR, INIS AtomInd, ISR, Inspec, M&GPA, M&TEA, MBF, METADEX, MSB, MinerAb, OffTech, PetrolAb, PollutAb, RefZh, S&F, SCI, SWRA, SolStAb, WAA, ZooRec.
—BLDSC (3031.150000), AskIEEE, CASDDS, CIS, CISTI, Ei, IDS, IE, Infotrieve, ingenta, Linda Hall, PADDS. **CCC.**
Published by: (Geological Association of Canada), N R C Research Press, Building M 55, Ottawa, ON K1A 0R6, Canada. TEL 613-993-0362, 800-668-1222, FAX 613-952-7656, pubs@nrc-cnrc.gc.ca, http://www.nrc.ca/cgi-bin/cisti/journals/rp/rp2_desc_e?cjes, http://pubs.nrc-cnrc.gc.ca. Ed. Bruce P Dancik. Adv. contact Judy Heyman. B&W page CND 675; trim 11 x 8.5. Circ: 1,572.

➤ **CARTA GEOLOGICA DE CHILE. SERIE GEOFISICA.** see *PHYSICS*

550 LUX ISSN 1026-1907
CENTRE EUROPEEN DE GEODYNAMIQUE ET DE SEISMOLOGIE. CAHIERS. Text in English. 1989. irreg., latest 2003.
Published by: Centre Europeen de Geodynamique et de Seismologie/European Center for Geodynamics and Seismology, Rue Josy Welter, 19, Walferdange, L-7256, Luxembourg. TEL 352-331487-1, FAX 352-331487-88, http://www.ecgs.lu/index.php?option=displaypage&Itemid=48&op=page&SubMenu=.

CEYLON GEOGRAPHER. see *GEOGRAPHY*

550 CHN ISSN 0253-6072
CHANGCHUN DIZHI XUEYUAN XUEBAO/CHANGCHUN UNIVERSITY OF SCIENCE AND TECHNOLOGY. JOURNAL. Text in Chinese. 1959. q. **Document type:** *Academic/Scholarly.*
Indexed: ZooRec.
—Linda Hall.
Published by: Changchun University of Science and Technology, No 6. Xi Minzhu St., Changchun, China. TEL 86-431-8502424, http://www.cust.jl.cn/.

551.9 NLD ISSN 0009-2541
QE515 CODEN: CHGEAD
➤ **CHEMICAL GEOLOGY.** Text in English, French, German. 1966. 44/yr. EUR 3,586 in Europe to institutions; JPY 475,600 in Japan to institutions; USD 4,017 elsewhere to institutions (effective 2006). adv. bk.rev. bibl.; charts; illus. index. reprints avail. **Document type:** *Journal, Academic/Scholarly.* **Description:** Publishes original articles in the field of organic and inorganic geochemistry.
Incorporates (in 1993): Chemical Geology. Isotope Geoscience Section (0168-9622); Which was formerly (1983-1985): Isotope Geoscience (0167-6695)
Related titles: Microform ed.: (from PQC); Online - full text ed.: (from EBSCO Publishing, Gale Group, IngentaConnect, ScienceDirect, Swets Information Services).
Indexed: AESIS, ASCA, ASFA, AnalAb, BrGeoL, CCI, CIN, ChemAb, ChemTitl, CurCont, E&PHSE, ESPM, F&EA, FLUIDEX, GEOBASE, GP&P, ISR, Inspec, MSB, MinerAb, OceAb, OffTech, PetrolAb, PollutAb, RefZh, S&F, SCI, SFA, SPPI, SWRA.
—BLDSC (3146.550000), AskIEEE, CASDDS, CISTI, IDS, IE, Infotrieve, ingenta, Linda Hall, PADDS. **CCC.**
Published by: (European Association for Geochemistry), Elsevier BV (Subsidiary of: Elsevier Science & Technology), Radarweg 29, Amsterdam, 1043 NX, Netherlands. TEL 31-20-4853911, FAX 31-20-4852457, nlinfo-f@elsevier.nl, http://www.elsevier.com/locate/chemgeo, http://www.elsevier.nl. Eds. Christa Gopel, Dr. Peter Deines, Dr. Steven L. Goldstein.

550 910 JPN ISSN 0022-135X
G1 CODEN: CGZAAL
CHIGAKU ZASSHI/JOURNAL OF GEOGRAPHY. Text in Japanese; Abstracts and contents page in English. 1889. bi-m. JPY 16,800; JPY 2,500 newsstand/cover (effective 2005). adv. bk.rev. Index. reprints avail. **Document type:** *Journal, Academic/Scholarly.* **Description:** Covers the broad field of earth science, including geography, geology and geophysics.
Indexed: ASCA, ChemAb, INIS AtomInd.
—BLDSC (4992.001000), CASDDS, IE, ingenta. **CCC.**
Published by: Tokyo Chigaku Kyokai/Tokyo Geographical Society, 12-2 Nibancho, Chiyoda, Tokyo, 102-0084, Japan. TEL 81-3-32610809, FAX 81-3-32630257, tokyogeo@geog.or.jp, tyo-geog@ka2.so-net.ne.jp, http://www.geog.or.jp/journal/, http://wwwsoc.nii.ac.jp/tokyogeo/. Ed. Tokihiko Matsuda. Circ: 1,100.

500 USA
CHIHUAHUAN DESERT DISCOVERY. Text in English. 1975. s-a. membership. **Document type:** *Newsletter.* **Description:** Presents articles on the natural sciences in the Chihuahan Desert region of the United States and Mexico.
Published by: Chihuahuan Desert Research Institute, PO Box 905, Ft. Davis, TX 79734. TEL 915-364-2499, manager@cdri.org. Circ: 1,000.

550 570 USA
CHIHUAHUAN DESERT NEWSBRIEFS. Text in English. 1983. s-a. free. **Document type:** *Newsletter.*
Published by: Chihuahuan Desert Research Institute, PO Box 905, Ft. Davis, TX 79734. TEL 915-364-2499, manager@cdri.org. R&P Dennis J Miller. Circ: 5,000.

550 JPN
CHIJIKI SEKAI SHIRYO KAISEKI SENTA NYUSU/DATA ANALYSIS CENTER FOR GEOMAGNETISM AND SPACE MAGNETISM. OPERATING WORLD DATA CENTER C2 FOR GEOMAGNETISM. Text in Japanese. bi-m.
Published by: (Fuzoku Chijiki Sekai Shiryo Kaiseki Senta), Kyoto Dagaku, Rigakubu/Kyoto University, Faculty of Science, Data Analysis Center for Geomagnetism and Space Magnetism, Kita-Shirakawaoiwake-cho, Sakyo-ku, Kyoto-shi, 606-8224, Japan.

550 JPN ISSN 0366-6611
QE1 CODEN: CKKAA8
CHIKYU KAGAKU/EARTH SCIENCE. Text in English, Japanese. 1949. bi-m. membership. **Document type:** *Journal, Academic/Scholarly.*
Indexed: BiolAb, CIN, ChemAb, ChemTitl, INIS AtomInd, JPI, RefZh, ZooRec.
—CASDDS, CISTI. **CCC.**
Published by: Chigaku Dantai Kenkyukai/Association for the Geological Collaboration in Japan, Rm 507 Kawai Building, 1-24-1,Minami Ikebukuro, Toshima-ku, Tokyo, 171, Japan. TEL 81-3-39833378, FAX 81-3-39837525, chidanken@tokyo.email.ne.jp, http://wwwsoc.nii.ac.jp/agcj/ES/chikyu_e.html.

551.9 JPN ISSN 0386-4073
QE514 CODEN: CKNKDM
➤ **CHIKYU KAGAKU/GEOCHEMISTRY.** Text in Japanese; Summaries in English. 1967. q. 60 p./no.; back issues avail. **Document type:** *Journal, Academic/Scholarly.*
Indexed: ChemAb, INIS AtomInd, JPI, RefZh.
—CASDDS, CISTI.
Published by: Nihon Chikyu Kagakkai/Geochemical Society of Japan, Nihon Gakkai Jimu Senta, 16-19 Honkomagome 5-chome, Bunkyo-ku, Tokyo, 113-0021, Japan.

➤ **CHIKYU KANKYO.** see *ENVIRONMENTAL STUDIES*

550 CHN ISSN 1002-0705
CODEN: JCUGEX
➤ **CHINA UNIVERSITY OF GEOSCIENCES. JOURNAL.** Text in English. 1990. bi-m. USD 80 foreign to individuals; USD 120 foreign to institutions; CNY 30 newsstand/cover domestic; USD 36 newsstand/cover foreign (effective 2005). back issues avail. **Document type:** *Journal, Academic/Scholarly.* **Description:** Covers all branches of geology and associated technology in the exploration and utilization of earth resources. Also reports on the essential research findings and original academic thoughts for persistent development in the field.
Related titles: Online - full content ed.: (from WanFang Data Corp.); Online - full text ed.: (from East View Information Services); ♦ Chinese ed.: Diqiu Kexue. ISSN 1000-2383.
Indexed: ASFA, BrCerAb, C&ISA, CerAb, CorrAb, E&CAJ, EMA, ESPM, IAA, M&TEA, MBF, METADEX, RefZh, SWRA, WAA, ZooRec.
—Linda Hall.
Published by: Zhongguo Dizhi Daxue/China University of Geosciences, Editorial Office of Journal China University of Geosciences, Yujiashan, Wuhan, Hubei 430074, China. ejournal@cug.edu.cn, http://www.earth-science.net/ev/ev.htm, http://www.cugb.edu.cn. Ed. Hengjun Wang TEL 86-27-87436361. **Subscr. outside China to:** Maney Publishing, China Journal Distribution Services, Hudson Rd, Leeds LS9 7DI, United Kingdom. TEL 44-113-2497481, FAX 44-113-2486983, subscriptions@maney.co.uk.

E

550 CHN ISSN 1007-7065
CHINESE JOURNAL OF POLAR SCIENCE. Text in Chinese. 1990. s-a. USD 210 foreign; CNY 30 newsstand/cover (effective 2005). 80 p./no.; **Document type:** *Journal, Academic/Scholarly.*
Formerly (until 1997): Antarctic Research (1004-4078)
Related titles: Online - full text ed.: (from East View Information Services); ♦ Chinese ed.: Nanji Yanjiu. ISSN 1000-4947.
Published by: Zhongguo Jidi Yanjiusuo/Polar Research Institute of China, Pudongxin-qu, 451, Jinqiao Lu, Shanghai, 200129, China. TEL 86-21-58713650, FAX 86-21-58711663, pricsh@online.sh.cn, http://jdkx-e.periodicals.net.cn/. **Dist. by:** Haiyang Chubanshe, International Department, 8 Dahuisi Rd, Haidian District, Beijing 100081, China. TEL 86-01-62179976, FAX 86-01-62173569, oceanpress@china.com, http://www.oceanpress.cn/.

550 CUB ISSN 0253-5637
QE222 CODEN: CTESEV
CIENCIAS DE LA TIERRA Y EL ESPACIO. Text in Spanish. s-a. USD 15 in the Americas; USD 16 in Europe.
Indexed: ASFA, EIP, Inspec.
—AskIEEE, CASDDS.
Published by: (Academia de Ciencias de Cuba), Ediciones Cubanas, Obispo No. 527, Apdo. 605, Havana, Cuba.

549 553 GBR ISSN 0009-8558
QE389.625 CODEN: CLMIAF
➤ **CLAY MINERALS;** journal of the European Clay Groups . Text in English. 1947. q. (issue numbers 1-4 last issue includes index). GBP 189, USD 346; GBP 47 per issue (effective 2005). bk.rev. abstr.; bibl.; charts; illus. index. back issues avail.; reprints avail. **Document type:** *Monographic series, Academic/Scholarly.*
Formerly (until 1964): Clay Minerals Bulletin (0412-7528)
Related titles: Online - full text ed.: ISSN 1471-8030 (from EBSCO Publishing, Gale Group, HighWire Press, IngentaConnect, O C L C Online Computer Library Center, Inc., Swets Information Services).
Indexed: ABIPC, AESIS, ASCA, BrCerAb, BrGeoL, C&ISA, CIN, CISA, CRIA, CerAb, ChemAb, ChemTitl, CorrAb, CurCont, E&CAJ, EMA, EngInd, F&EA, GEOBASE, GSW, GeotechAb, IAA, ISR, MSCI, MinerAb, RefZh, S&F, SCI, SolStAb, WAA.
—BLDSC (3276.900000), CASDDS, CISTI, IDS, IE, Infotrieve, ingenta, Linda Hall. **CCC.**
Published by: Mineralogical Society, 41 Queens Gate, London, SW7 5HR, United Kingdom. TEL 44-20-75847516, FAX 44-20-78238021, info@minersoc.org, http://www.minersoc.org. Ed. J M Adams. Circ: 1,500.

549 IND ISSN 0255-7193
CODEN: CLRSD5
CLAY RESEARCH. Text in English. s-a.
Indexed: CIN, ChemAb, ChemTitl, FCA, HortAb, PotatoAb, RPP, RevApplEntom, S&F.
—CASDDS, CISTI, Linda Hall.
Published by: Clay Minerals Society of India, Division of Agricultural Physics, New Delhi, 110 012, India.

550 NLD ISSN 1469-3062
QC981.8.C5
CLIMATE POLICY. Text in English. 2001. q. EUR 128 in Europe to individuals; JPY 17,100 in Japan to individuals; USD 144 elsewhere to individuals; EUR 387 in Europe to institutions; JPY 51,400 in Japan to institutions; USD 432 elsewhere to institutions; EUR 112 in Europe to qualified personnel; JPY 14,900 in Japan to qualified personnel; USD 126 elsewhere to qualified personnel (effective 2004). **Document type:** *Journal, Academic/Scholarly.* **Description:** Aims to address the broad spectrum of policy issues raised by the prospect of changes in the global climate and climate change.
Related titles: Online - full text ed.: (from EBSCO Publishing, Gale Group, IngentaConnect, ScienceDirect, Swets Information Services).
Indexed: ASFA, CurCont, ESPM, EnvEAb, GEOBASE, M&GPA, PollutAb, RefZh, SSCI.
—BLDSC (3279.170000), CISTI, IE, ingenta. **CCC.**
Published by: (Imperial College of Science, Technology and Medicine GBR), Elsevier BV (Subsidiary of: Elsevier Science & Technology), Radarweg 29, Amsterdam, 1043 NX, Netherlands. TEL 31-20-4853911, FAX 31-20-4852457, climatepolicy@ic.ac.uk, nlinfo-f@elsevier.nl, http://www.elsevier.com/locate/clipol, http://www.elsevier.nl. Ed. M Grubb.

551.6 USA ISSN 0364-5851
QC983
CLIMATOLOGICAL DATA. OREGON. Text in English. 1896. m.
—Linda Hall.
Published by: U.S. National Climatic Data Center (Subsidiary of: National Oceanic and Atmospheric Administration), 14th St and Constitution Ave, N W, Washington, DC 20230. TEL 202-482-6090, FAX 202-482-3154, webmaster@ncdc.noaa.gov, http://www.ncdc.noaa.gov.

550 GTM
COLECCION EDITORIAL UNIVERSITARIA. Text in Spanish. irreg., latest vol.63, 1983.
Published by: Universidad de San Carlos de Guatemala, Ciudad Universitaria, zona 12, Edificio de Rectoria, Of. 307, Guatemala, Guatemala.

628 550 JPN ISSN 0547-1435
COLLECTED PAPERS ON SCIENCES OF ATMOSPHERE AND HYDROSPHERE. Text in English, Japanese. 1964. a. per issue exchange basis.
Published by: Nagoya Daigaku, Suiken Kagaku Kenkyujo/Nagoya University, Water Research Institute, Furo-cho, Chikusa-ku, Nagoya-shi, Aichi-ken 464-0814, Japan.

550 363.7 USA
➤ **COLUMBIA EARTHSCAPE.** Text in English. 1999. irreg. USD 295 to individuals; USD 495 to institutions with 2500 or fewer FTEs; USD 495 to corporations with 250 or fewer FTEs (effective 2005). bk.rev. charts; illus.; maps. **Document type:** *Magazine, Academic/Scholarly.* **Description:** Connects research, education, public interest and resources. Includes information on research, education, and resources.
Media: Online - full content.
Published by: Columbia University Press, 61 W 62nd St, New York, NY 10023. TEL 212-854-0423, FAX 212-854-6309, ml1047@columbia.edu, http://www.earthscape.org. Eds. John Haber, Michael Luby. Pub. William Strachan. R&P John Haber.

550 USA ISSN 0894-802X
QE1 CODEN: CSGEAM
➤ **THE COMPASS (NORMAN);** an honorary scientific society magazine devoted to the earth sciences. Text in English. 1920. q. charts; illus. Index. back issues avail.; reprints avail. **Document type:** *Journal, Academic/Scholarly.*
Formerly: Compass of Sigma Gamma Epsilon (0010-4213)
Indexed: GEOBASE, PetrolAb.
—BLDSC (3363.920000), Linda Hall, PADDS. **CCC.**
Published by: Society of Sigma Gamma Epsilon, c/o Charles J Mankin, University of Oklahoma, 100 E Boyd St, Rm N 131, Norman, OK 73019. TEL 405-325-3031, FAX 405-325-7069, cjmankin@ou.edu, bbellis-sge@ou.edu. Ed. R Nowell Donovan. R&P Don C Steinker TEL 419-372-7200. Circ: 1,800.

➤ **COMPUTERS & GEOSCIENCES.** see *EARTH SCIENCES—Computer Applications*

➤ **CONSTRUCTION ENGINEERING RESEARCH INSTITUTE. MEMOIRS.** see *ENGINEERING—Engineering Mechanics And Materials*

550 CHN ISSN 1006-7825
QE500 CODEN: CODYFA
CONTINENTAL DYNAMICS. Text and summaries in English. 1996. s-a. CNY 90; USD 24 foreign (effective 2000). charts; illus.; maps. back issues avail. **Description:** Covers the study of the dynamic mechanism of the continental formation and evolution; involving such geoscientific branches as tectonics, geophysics, geochemistry and so on.
Related titles: Online - full text ed.: (from East View Information Services).
Published by: Chinese Academy of Geological Sciences, Institute of Geology, 26 Baiwanzhuang Rd, Xicheng District, Beijing, 100037, China. TEL 86-10-6831-1293, FAX 86-10-6831-1293. Ed. Liu Zhigang. Pub. Xu Zhigin. R&P Zhigang Liu TEL 86-1-6831-1133. Circ: 500 (controlled).

CONTRIBUTIONS IN MARINE SCIENCE. see *BIOLOGY*

CORSONAT. see *CONSERVATION*

550 GBR ISSN 0195-6671
QE685 CODEN: CRRSDD
➤ **CRETACEOUS RESEARCH.** Text in English. 1980. 6/yr. EUR 343 in Europe to individuals; JPY 37,100 in Japan to individuals; USD 305 to individuals except Europe and Japan; EUR 1,095 in Europe to institutions; JPY 118,300 in Japan to institutions; USD 974 to institutions except Europe and Japan (effective 2006). adv. bk.rev. illus. Index. reprints avail. **Document type:** *Academic/Scholarly.* **Description:** Provides a forum for the rapid publication of research on all aspects of the Cretaceous Period, including its boundaries with the Jurassic and Tertiary.
Related titles: Online - full text ed.: ISSN 1095-998X. USD 1,027 (effective 2002) (from EBSCO Publishing, Gale Group, IngentaConnect, O C L C Online Computer Library Center, Inc., ScienceDirect, Swets Information Services).
Indexed: AESIS, ASCA, ASFA, BIOSIS Prev, BiolAb, ChemAb, CurCont, E&PHSE, ESPM, GEOBASE, GP&P, ISR, OffTech, PetrolAb, SCI, ZooRec.
—BLDSC (3487.324000), CASDDS, IDS, IE, Infotrieve, ingenta, Linda Hall, PADDS. **CCC.**
Published by: Academic Press (Subsidiary of: Elsevier Science & Technology), Harcourt Pl, 32 Jamestown Rd, London, NW1 7BY, United Kingdom. TEL 44-20-7424-4200, FAX 44-20-7483-2293, apsubs@acad.com, http://www.elsevier.com/locate/cretres. Eds. Douglas J. Nichols, D. J. Batten. R&P Catherine John. Adv. contact Nik Screen. **Subscr. to:** Harcourt Publishers Ltd., Foots Cray High St, Sidcup, Kent DA14 5HP, United Kingdom. TEL 44-208-3085700, FAX 44-20-83090807.

550 USA
➤ **CURRENT RESEARCH IN EARTH SCIENCES.** Text in English. 1993. irreg. (3-4/yr). free (effective 2005). back issues avail. **Document type:** *Journal, Academic/Scholarly.* **Description:** Contains short articles on a wide range of topics, with special emphasis on topics relating to Kansas geosciences.
Formerly (until 1995): Current Research on Kansas Geology
Media: Online - full content.
Published by: Kansas Geological Survey, 1930 Constant Ave, The University of Kansas, Lawrence, KS 66047-3726. TEL 785-864-3965, FAX 785-864-5317, lbrosius@kgs.ukans.edu, marla@kgs.ku.edu, http://www.kgs.ku.edu/Current, http://www.kgs.ku.edu/kgs.html. Ed. Liz Brosius.

550 CYP
CYPRUS. GEOLOGICAL SURVEY DEPARTMENT. BULLETIN. Text in English. 1963. irreg., latest vol.10, 1997. price varies. **Description:** Papers on hydrogeology, economic and engineering geology and seismology of Cyprus.
Published by: Geological Survey Department, 1415, Nicosia, Cyprus. R&P George Petrides.

550 CYP ISSN 0574-8259
QE316
CYPRUS. GEOLOGICAL SURVEY DEPARTMENT. MEMOIRS. Text and summaries in English. 1959. irreg., latest vol.9. CYP 0.35 (effective 2000). charts; illus. **Description:** Detailed description of the geology and mineral resources of a specific area of Cyprus.
Indexed: IMMAb.
—Linda Hall.
Published by: Geological Survey Department, 1415, Nicosia, Cyprus.

DECHENIANA. see *BIOLOGY*

DECHENIANA-BEIHEFTE (BONN). see *BIOLOGY*

DENVER MUSEUM OF NATURAL HISTORY. PROCEEDINGS. see *BIOLOGY—Zoology*

DEVELOPMENTS IN APPLIED EARTH SCIENCES. see *ENGINEERING*

550 570 NLD ISSN 0924-5286
➤ **DEVELOPMENTS IN BIOGEOCHEMISTRY.** Text in English. 1984. irreg., latest vol.4, 1998. price varies. **Document type:** *Monographic series, Academic/Scholarly.*
—CISTI.
Published by: Springer-Verlag Dordrecht (Subsidiary of: Springer Science+Business Media), Van Godewijckstraat 30, Dordrecht, 3311 GX, Netherlands. TEL 31-78-6576050, FAX 31-78-6576474, http://www.springeronline.com.

550 CHN ISSN 1000-2383
QE1 CODEN: DIKEEL
➤ **DIQIU KEXUE/EARTH SCIENCE.** Text in Chinese; Abstracts and contents page in English. 1957. bi-m. CNY 60; CNY 10 newsstand/cover (effective 2005). back issues avail. **Document type:** *Journal, Academic/Scholarly.* **Description:** Covers all aspects of Earth science, including geology, geochemistry, tectonics, urban engineering, various computer models and more.
Related titles: Online - full content ed.: (from WanFang Data Corp.); Online - full text ed.: (from East View Information Services); ♦ English ed.: China University of Geosciences. Journal. ISSN 1002-0705.
Indexed: ASFA, BrCerAb, C&ISA, CerAb, CorrAb, E&CAJ, EEA, EMA, ESPM, EngInd, IAA, M&TEA, MBF, METADEX, RefZh, SWRA, WAA, ZooRec.
—Linda Hall.
Published by: Zhongguo Dizhi Daxue/China University of Geosciences, Hongshan-qu, 388, Lumo Lu, Wuhan, Hubei 430074, China. xbb@cug.edu.cn; cjournal@cug.edu.cn, http://dqkx.periodicals.net.cn/default.html, http://www.cugb.edu.cn. Ed. Hengjun Wang TEL 86-27- 87436361. **Dist. by:** China International Book Trading Corp, 35 Chegongzhuang Xilu, Haidian District, PO Box 399, Beijing 100044, China. TEL 86-10-68412045, FAX 86-10-68412023, cibtc@mail.cibtc.com.cn, http://www.cibtc.com.cn.

550 CHN ISSN 1001-8166
QE26.2 CODEN: DKJIE8
DIQIU KEXUE JINZHAN/ADVANCE IN EARTH SCIENCES. Text in Chinese; Abstracts in English. 1986. bi-m. CNY 120 domestic; USD 120 foreign (effective 2003). 160 p./no.; **Document type:** *Journal, Academic/Scholarly.* **Description:** Reviews developments in earth sciences, especially global change research, and sustainable development.
Related titles: CD-ROM ed.; Online - full content ed.: (from WanFang Data Corp.); Online - full text ed.: (from East View Information Services).
Indexed: RefZh.
Published by: Zhongguo Kexueyuan, Ziyuan Huanjing Kexue Xinxi Zhongxin/Chinese Academy of Sciences, Scientific Information Center for Resources and Environment, 342 Tianshui Rd, Lanzhou, Gansu 730000, China. TEL 86-931-8271245, FAX 86-931-8275743, adearth@ns.lzb.ac.cn, sicre@ns.lzb.ac.cn, http://159.226.136.229/adearth/

E

ADEARTH.htm. Ed. Xiuji Zhou. Adv. contact Ming Li. **Co-sponsors:** Guojia Ziran Kexue Jijin Weiyuanhui, Diqiu Kexuebu/National Science Foundation of China, Earth Science Department; Zhongguo Kexueyuan, Ziyuan Huangjing Kexue Xingxi Zhongxin/Chinese Academy of Sciences, Bureau of Science and Technology for Resources and Environment.

550 CHN ISSN 1004-2903
DIQIU WULIXUE JINZHAN/PROGRESS IN GEOPHYSICS. Text in Chinese. 1986. q. CNY 20 (effective 2004). **Document type:** *Journal, Academic/Scholarly.*
Related titles: Online - full content ed.: (from WanFang Data Corp.); Online - full text ed.: (from East View Information Services).
Published by: Zhongguo Kexueyuan, Dizhi yu Diqiu Wuli Yanjiusuo/Chinese Academy of Sciences, Institute of Geology and Geophysics, PO BOX 9825, Beijing, 100029, China. TEL 86-10-64889035, 86-10-64889036, shliu@cgs.org.cn; dqwj@cgs.org.cn; shliu@mail.igcas.ac.cn, http://dqwlxjz.periodicals.net.cn/default.html, http://www.igcas.ac.cn/. Ed. Guang-ding Liu. **Dist. by:** China International Book Trading Corp, 35 Chegongzhuang Xilu, Haidian District, PO Box 399, Beijing 100044, China. TEL 86-10-68412045, FAX 86-10-68412023, cibtc@mail.cibtc.com.cn, http://www.cibtc.com.cn.

550.71025 USA
QE47.A1
DIRECTORY OF GEOSCIENCE DEPARTMENTS. Text in English. 1952. a. USD 40 to libraries (effective 2003). adv. index. back issues avail. **Document type:** *Directory.* **Description:** Identifies more than 10,000 geoscientists in US, Canada, and Mexico by institution, rank, and specialty. Includes colleges, universities, selected national laboratories, natural history museums, and field courses and camps.
Former titles: Directory of Geoscience Departments, North America; Directory of Geoscience Departments, United States and Canada (0364-7811)
—Linda Hall. **CCC.**
Published by: American Geological Institute, 4220 King St, Alexandria, VA 22302-1502. TEL 703-379-2480, FAX 703-379-7563, pubs@agiweb.org, http://www.agiweb.org/pubs. Ed. Nicholas H Claudy. Pub. Marcus Milling. R&P Julie Jackson. Circ: 1,500.

550 CHN ISSN 1005-2321
➤ **DIXUE QIANYUAN/EARTH SCIENCE FRONTIERS.** Text in Chinese, English. 1994. q. CNY 150 domestic; USD 150 foreign (effective 2003). bibl.; abstr. 240 p./no.; reprints avail. **Document type:** *Journal, Academic/Scholarly.* **Description:** Covers original research and recent advances in the field of Earth sciences.
Related titles: Online - full content ed.: (from WanFang Data Corp.); Online - full text ed.: (from East View Information Services).
Indexed: ASFA, BrCerAb, C&ISA, CerAb, CorrAb, E&CAJ, EMA, ESPM, IAA, M&TEA, MBF, METADEX, RefZh, SWRA, WAA.
—BLDSC (3643.511000), IE, ingenta.
Published by: Zhongguo Dizhi Daxue/China University of Geosciences, Editorial Office of Earth Science Frontiers, 29 Xueyuan Lu, Beijing, 100083, China. frontier@cugb.edu.cn, http://dxqy.periodicals.net.cn/default.html, http://www.cugb.edu.cn. Ed. Hong-zhen Wang. Circ: 500 (paid); 1,000 (controlled).

➤ **DIZHI JISHU JINGJI GUANLI/GEOLOGICAL TECHNOECONOMIC MANAGEMENT.** see *BUSINESS AND ECONOMICS*

550 RUS ISSN 1028-334X
QE1 CODEN: DESOAP
DOKLADY EARTH SCIENCES. Text in English. 1933. 9/yr. USD 4,048 in North America; USD 4,652 elsewhere (effective 2004). adv. bibl.; charts; illus. index. reprint service avail. from PQC. **Document type:** *Journal, Academic/Scholarly.* **Description:** Covers geology, geophysics, oceanography, mineralogy, and geochemistry.
Former titles (until 1998): Russian Academy of Sciences. Transactions (Doklady). Earth Science Section (1083-3552); (until 1992): U S S R Academy of Sciences. Transactions (Doklady). Earth Science Sections (0891-5571); (until 1985): Academy of Sciences of the U S S R. Doklady. Earth Science Sections (0012-494X)
Related titles: Microfiche ed.: (from BHP); Microform ed.: (from BHP, PQC); ♦ Partial translation of: Rossiiskaya Akademiya Nauk. Doklady. ISSN 0869-5652.
Indexed: AESIS, ASFA, ChemAb, CivEngAb, CurCont, ESPM, ExcerpMed, GEOBASE, ISR, PetrolAb, PotatoAb, SCI.
—BLDSC (0411.335000), CISTI, Ei, IE, Infotrieve, ingenta, Linda Hall, PADDS. **CCC.**
Published by: (Rossiiskaya Akademiya Nauk/Russian Academy of Sciences), M A I K Nauka - Interperiodica, Profsoyuznaya ul 90, Moscow, 117997, Russian Federation. TEL 7-095-3347420, FAX 7-095-3360666, compmg@maik.ru, http://www.maik.rssi.ru/journals/earthsci.htm, http://www.maik.ru. Ed. Dibya R Sakya. Circ: 500. **Subscr. to:** Interperiodica, PO Box 1831, Birmingham, AL 35201-1831. TEL 205-995-1567, 800-633-4931, FAX 205-995-1588. **Co-sponsor:** American Geological Institute.

DORTMUNDER BEITRAEGE ZUR LANDESKUNDE. see *BIOLOGY*

550 530 363.7 551 FRA ISSN 1729-3782
➤ **E A R SE L EPROCEEDINGS.** Text in English. 2001. irreg. free (effective 2005). **Document type:** *Journal, Academic/Scholarly.* **Description:** Devoted to refereed scientific publications in all fields of Earth observation and remote sensing.
Media: Online - full text.
Published by: European Association of Remote Sensing Laboratories/Association Europeenne de Laboratoires de Teledetection, 2 Av Rapp, Paris, Cedex 7 75340, France. TEL 33-1-45567360, FAX 33-1-45567361, earsel@meteo.fr, http://las.physik.uni-oldenburg.de/eProceedings/, http://www.earsel.org.

550 FRA ISSN 0257-0521
E A R SE L NEWSLETTER. Text in English. 1977. q. adv. bk.rev. back issues avail. **Document type:** *Newsletter.* **Description:** Gives an overview on the latest news concerning remote sensing research in Europe and throughout the world.
Formerly (until 1990): E A R Se L News
Indexed: RefZh.
Published by: European Association of Remote Sensing Laboratories/Association Europeenne de Laboratoires de Teledetection, 2 Av Rapp, Paris, Cedex 7 75340, France. TEL 33-1-45567360, FAX 33-1-45567361, earsel@meteo.fr, http://www.earsel.org. Ed. Niall McCormick. Circ: 750.

550 620 USA ISSN 0270-8337
TH1095
E E R I NEWSLETTER. Text in English. 1966. m. free to members. bk.rev. **Document type:** *Newsletter.* **Description:** Provides news of the institute and other related professions in earthquake hazard reduction.
Indexed: CurCont, EEA, RefZh.
—CISTI, Linda Hall.
Published by: Earthquake Engineering Research Institute, 499 14th St., Ste 320, Oakland, CA 94612-1934. TEL 510-451-0905, FAX 510-451-5411. Ed. Stephanie King. Circ: 2,800.

550 NLD ISSN 1385-013X
➤ **E P S L ONLINE.** (Earth and Planetary Science Letters) Text in English. 1996. q. **Document type:** *Academic/Scholarly.*
Media: Online - full text (from EBSCO Publishing, Gale Group, IngentaConnect, ScienceDirect, Swets Information Services).
Related titles: Microform ed.: (from PQC); ♦ Print ed.: Earth and Planetary Science Letters. ISSN 0012-821X.
Published by: Elsevier BV (Subsidiary of: Elsevier Science & Technology), Radarweg 29, Amsterdam, 1043 NX, Netherlands. TEL 31-20-4853911, FAX 31-20-4852457, nlinfo-f@elsevier.nl, http://www.elsevier.nl/locate/epsl.

550 USA ISSN 0026-4539
TN210 CODEN: EMISAK
EARTH AND MINERAL SCIENCES. Text in English. 1931. s-a. free. bibl.; charts; illus.; stat. **Document type:** *Bulletin.*
Formerly: Mineral Industries
Indexed: AESIS, BrCerAb, C&ISA, CerAb, ChemAb, CorrAb, E&CAJ, EMA, IMMAb, RefZh, SolStAb, WAA.
—BLDSC (3643.050000), CISTI, Infotrieve, ingenta, Linda Hall.
Published by: Pennsylvania State University, College of Earth & Mineral Sciences, 116 Deike Bldg, University Park, PA 16802. TEL 814-863-4667, FAX 814-863-7708. Ed. Judy Kiusalaas. Circ: 18,000 (controlled).

550 NLD ISSN 0012-821X
QE1 CODEN: EPSLA2
➤ **EARTH AND PLANETARY SCIENCE LETTERS.** Text and summaries in English, French, German. 1966. 48/yr. EUR 3,551 in Europe to institutions; JPY 471,100 in Japan to institutions; USD 3,972 elsewhere to institutions; EUR 202 in Europe to qualified personnel; JPY 26,500 in Japan to qualified personnel; USD 225 elsewhere to qualified personnel (effective 2006). abstr.; illus.; stat. Index. reprints avail. **Document type:** *Journal, Academic/Scholarly.* **Description:** Covers research into all aspects of solid and non-solid earth sciences, including lunar studies, plate tectonics, ocean floor spreading, and continental drift, as well as basic studies of the physical, chemical and mechanical properties of the Earth's crust and mantle, the atmosphere and the hydrosphere.
Related titles: Microform ed.: (from PQC); ♦ Online - full text ed.: E P S L Online. ISSN 1385-013X.
Indexed: AESIS, ASCA, ASFA, BrArAb, BrCerAb, BrGeoL, C&ISA, CIN, Cadscan, CerAb, ChemAb, ChemTitl, CorrAb, CurCont, E&CAJ, E&PHSE, EMA, ESPM, EngInd, EnvEAb, ExcerpMed, GEOBASE, GP&P, IAA, ISR, Inspec, LeadAb, M&GPA, M&TEA, MBF, METADEX, MSB, MinerAb, OceAb, OffTech, PetrolAb, PhysBer, PollutAb, RefZh, SCI, SWRA, WAA, Zincscan, ZooRec.
—BLDSC (3643.100000), AskIEEE, CASDDS, CISTI, Ei, IDS, IE, Infotrieve, ingenta, Linda Hall, PADDS. **CCC.**
Published by: Elsevier BV (Subsidiary of: Elsevier Science & Technology), Radarweg 29, Amsterdam, 1043 NX, Netherlands. TEL 31-20-4853911, FAX 31-20-4852457, nlinfo-f@elsevier.nl, http://www.elsevier.com/locate/epsl, http://www.elsevier.nl. Eds. H Elderfield, V Courtillot.

550 USA ISSN 1087-3562
QE1 CODEN: EINTFP
➤ **EARTH INTERACTIONS.** Text in English. 1996. d. USD 115 to institutions 1-100 workstations (effective 2005 - 2006). illus. reprints avail. **Document type:** *Academic/Scholarly.* **Description:** Electronic journal dealing with the interactions between the lithosphere, hydrosphere, atmosphere, and biosphere in the context of global issues or change.
Media: Online - full text (from O C L C Online Computer Library Center, Inc.).
Indexed: ASFA, ESPM, M&GPA, SWRA.
—Infotrieve.
Published by: American Geophysical Union, 2000 Florida Ave, NW, Washington, DC 20009-1277. TEL 202-462-6900, 800-966-2481, FAX 202-328-0566, institutions@agu.org, http://earthinteractions.org/, http://www.agu.org. Ed. Jon Foley. **Co-sponsors:** Association of American Geographers; American Meteorological Society.

550 USA ISSN 1076-3430
G70.2
EARTH OBSERVATION MAGAZINE; the magazine for geographic mapping, earth information. Short title: E O M. Text in English. 1992. m. USD 67 in US & Canada; USD 107 elsewhere (effective 2004). bk.rev. illus. back issues avail.; reprints avail. **Document type:** *Magazine, Consumer.* **Description:** Deals with geographic mapping, and all sorts of earth related information.
—BLDSC (3792.852000), IE, Infotrieve.
Published by: Professional Surveyors Publishing Co., Inc., 100 Tuscanney Dr, Ste B-1, Frederick, MD 21702. TEL 301-682-6101, FAX 301-682-6105, eomaged@aol.com, http://www.eomonline.com/. Ed. Roland Mangold TEL 303-713-9500. Circ: 30,000.

550 JPN ISSN 1343-8832
QB630 CODEN: EPSPFJ
➤ **EARTH, PLANETS AND SPACE.** Text in English. 1997. bi-m. USD 42 to individuals; USD 490 to institutions (effective 2004). adv. illus.; mkt. cum.index every 13 yrs. **Document type:** *Journal, Academic/Scholarly.* **Description:** Contains original papers reflecting new and interdisciplinary subjects in Earth, planetary and space sciences.
Formed by the merger of (1953-1997): Journal of Physics of the Earth (0022-3743); (1949-1997): Journal of Geomagnetism and Geoelectricity (0022-1392)
Related titles: Online - full text ed.: (from EBSCO Publishing).
Indexed: AESIS, AJEE, ASCA, ASFA, ApMecR, BrCerAb, C&ISA, CerAb, ChemAb, CorrAb, CurCont, E&CAJ, EEA, EMA, ESPM, GEOBASE, IAA, ISR, Inspec, M&GPA, M&TEA, MBF, METADEX, MSB, PhysBer, RefZh, SCI, WAA.
—BLDSC (3643.240000), AskIEEE, CASDDS, CISTI, Ei, IDS, IE, Infotrieve, ingenta, Linda Hall, PADDS. **CCC.**
Published by: (Society of Geomagnetism and Earth, Planetary and Space Science), Terra Scientific Publishing Company, 5-27-19 Okusawa, Setagaya-ku, Tokyo, 158-0083, Japan. TEL 81-3-3718-7500, FAX 81-3-3718-4406, eps@terrapub.co.jp, terrapub@terrapub.co.jp, http://www.terrapub.co.jp/journals/EPS/index.html. Ed. Yoshimori Honkura. Circ: 800.

550 NLD ISSN 0012-8252
QE1 CODEN: ESREAV
➤ **EARTH - SCIENCE REVIEWS.** Text in Dutch. 1966. 24/yr. EUR 1,322 in Europe to institutions; JPY 175,500 in Japan to institutions; USD 1,478 elsewhere to institutions; EUR 127 in Europe to qualified personnel; JPY 16,800 in Japan to qualified personnel; USD 141 elsewhere to qualified personnel (effective 2006). adv. abstr.; charts; illus. Index. back issues avail.; reprints avail. **Document type:** *Journal, Academic/Scholarly.* **Description:** Provides information for instructors, students, research scientists, and government agencies involved in program support management and in environmental assessment and control, private industries concerned with planetary resources, and the independent consultant.
Related titles: Microform ed.: (from PQC); Online - full text ed.: (from EBSCO Publishing, Gale Group, IngentaConnect, ScienceDirect, Swets Information Services).
Indexed: AESIS, ASCA, ASFA, BiolAb, CIN, Cadscan, ChemAb, ChemTitl, CurCont, EPB, ESPM, EngInd, GEOBASE, GSI, IBR, ISR, Inspec, LeadAb, M&GPA, MinerAb, OceAb, PhysBer, PollutAb, SCI, SWRA, Zincscan.
—BLDSC (3643.540000), AskIEEE, CASDDS, CISTI, Ei, IDS, IE, Infotrieve, ingenta, Linda Hall, PADDS. **CCC.**
Published by: Elsevier BV (Subsidiary of: Elsevier Science & Technology), Radarweg 29, Amsterdam, 1043 NX, Netherlands. TEL 31-20-4853911, FAX 31-20-4852457, nlinfo-f@elsevier.nl, http://www.elsevier.com/locate/earscirev, http://www.elsevier.nl. **Subscr. to:** Elsevier, Subscription Customer Service, 6277 Sea Harbor Dr, Orlando, FL 32887-4800. TEL 407-345-4020, 877-839-7126, FAX 407-363-1354.

E

550 USA ISSN 0736-623X
QE11 CODEN: ESHIEV
➤ **EARTH SCIENCES HISTORY.** Text in English. 1982. s-a. USD 42 domestic to individuals; USD 47 foreign to individuals; USD 72 domestic to institutions; USD 77 foreign to institutions (effective 2004). bk.rev. illus.; abstr.; bibl. index. back issues avail. **Document type:** *Journal, Academic/Scholarly.*
Description: Publishes papers dealing with the history of earth sciences for historians of the earth sciences and for earth scientists. Includes articles on geography, geology, oceanograph and atmospheric and space sciences.
Related titles: Online - full text ed.
Indexed: AESIS, AmH&L, HistAb, ZooRec.
—BLDSC (3643.555000), IE, Infotrieve, ingenta, Linda Hall.
Published by: History of Earth Sciences Society, West Virginia University, Department of History, 202 Woodburn Hall, Box 6303, Morgantown, WV 26506-6303. TEL 304-293-2421, FAX 304-293-6858, greg.good@mail.wvu.edu, http://www.historyearthscience.org. Ed. Gregory A Good. Circ: 450 (paid). **Subscr. to:** Ed Rogers, PO Box 455, Poncha Springs, CO 81242. FAX 719-539-4542, erogers@geology-books.com.

550 FRA ISSN 0070-7910
AS4.U8
EARTH SCIENCES SERIES. Text in English, French. 1969. irreg., latest vol.19. price varies.
—Linda Hall.
Published by: UNESCO Publishing, 7 place de Fontenoy, Paris, 75352, France. TEL 33-1-45684300, FAX 33-1-45685737, http://www.unesco.org/publications. **Dist. in U.S. by:** Bernan Associates, Bernan, 4611-F Assembly Dr., Lanham, MD 20706-4391. TEL 800-274-4447, FAX 800-865-3450.

550 FRA ISSN 0750-6066
CODEN: MLBGBV
ECOLE PRATIQUE DES HAUTES ETUDES. LABORATOIRE DE GEOMORPHOLOGIE. MEMOIRES. Text in French. 1971. irreg. **Document type:** *Monographic series.*
Indexed: ESPM.
Published by: Ecole Pratique des Hautes Etudes, Laboratoire de Geomorphologie, UMR 8586 - PRODIG, 191 Rue Saint-Jacques, Paris, 75005, France. TEL 33-1-44321481, FAX 33-1-43296383, prodig@univ-paris1.fr, http://www.ephe.sorbonne.fr/Portail Geomorphologie.htm.

ECOLOGIA EN BOLIVIA. see *BIOLOGY*

550 JPN ISSN 0009-3831
QE48.J3
EDUCATION OF EARTH SCIENCE/CHIGAKU KYOIKU. Text in Japanese; Summaries in English. 1948. bi-m. USD 10. bk.rev.; film rev. abstr.
—CCC.
Published by: Japan Society of Earth Science Education/Nihon Chigaku Kyoiku Gakkai, c/o Tokyo Gakugei Daigaku Chigaku Kyoshitsu, 4-1 Nukui-Kita-Machi, Koganei-shi, Tokyo-to 184-0015, Japan. Ed. Dr. H Hirayama. Circ: 1,500.

550 363.7 EGY ISSN 1110-2004
EGYPTIAN JOURNAL FOR REMOTE SENSING. Text in English. 1991. irreg. EGP 20 (effective 2003). **Document type:** *Journal, Academic/Scholarly.*
Published by: National Information and Documentation Centre (NIDOC), Tahrir St., Dokki, Awqaf P.O., Giza, Egypt. TEL 20-2-3371696, FAX 20-2-3371746, http://derp.sti.sci.eg/data/0221.htm. Ed. Dr. Muhammad Ezz-El-Din El-Raei.

ELECTRICITE DE FRANCE. DIRECTION DES ETUDES ET RECHERCHES. COLLECTION DE NOTES INTERNES. BIOLOGIE, SCIENCES DE LA TERRE ET ENVIRONNEMENT. see *BIOLOGY*

ELECTRONIC JOURNAL OF GEOTECHNICAL ENGINEERING. see *ENGINEERING—Civil Engineering*

550 NLD ISSN 0924-5405
ENVIRONMENTAL FLUID MECHANICS (DORDRECHT, 1982). Text in English. 1982. irreg., latest 1990. price varies. **Document type:** *Monographic series.*
Indexed: Inspec.
Published by: Springer-Verlag Dordrecht (Subsidiary of: Springer Science+Business Media), Van Godewijckstraat 30, Dordrecht, 3311 GX, Netherlands. TEL 31-78-6576050, FAX 31-78-6576474, http://www.springeronline.com. **Dist. by:** Springer-Verlag New York, Inc., Journal Fulfillment, PO Box 2485, Secaucus, NJ 07096-2485.

550 NLD ISSN 1567-7419
QC150
ENVIRONMENTAL FLUID MECHANICS (DORDRECHT, 2001). Variant title: E F M. Text in English. 2001. 6/yr. EUR 198, USD 198, GBP 130 combined subscription to institutions print & online eds. (effective 2005). reprint service avail. from PSC. **Document type:** *Journal, Academic/Scholarly.* **Description:** Devoted to the publication of basic and applied studies broadly relating to natural fluid systems, particularly as agents for the transport and dispersion of environmental contamination.
Related titles: Online - full text ed.: ISSN 1573-1510 (from EBSCO Publishing, Gale Group, IngentaConnect, Kluwer Online, O C L C Online Computer Library Center, Inc., Springer LINK, Swets Information Services).
Indexed: ASFA, ApMecR, BibLing, CurCont, EPB, ESPM, EnvEAb, FLUIDEX, GEOBASE, Inspec, M&GPA, OceAb, PollutAb, SWRA.
—BLDSC (3791.465540), CISTI, IE, ingenta. **CCC.**
Published by: Springer-Verlag Dordrecht (Subsidiary of: Springer Science+Business Media), Van Godewijckstraat 30, Dordrecht, 3311 GX, Netherlands. TEL 31-78-6576050, FAX 31-78-6576474, http://springerlink.metapress.com/openurl.asp?genre=journal&issn=1567-7419, http://www.springeronline.com. Ed. Benoit Cushman-Roisin.

ENVIRONMENTAL GEOSCIENCES. see *ENVIRONMENTAL STUDIES*

ENVIRONMENTAL NEWS DIGEST. see *ENVIRONMENTAL STUDIES*

550 DEU ISSN 0170-3188
CODEN: ERFODV
ERDWISSENSCHAFTLICHE FORSCHUNG. Text in English, German. irreg., latest vol.41, 2002. price varies. **Document type:** *Monographic series, Academic/Scholarly.*
—CCC.
Published by: (Akademie der Wissenschaften und der Literatur, Mainz, Kommission fuer Erdwissenschaftliche Forschung), Franz Steiner Verlag Stuttgart GmbH, Birkenwaldstr 44, Stuttgart, 70191, Germany. TEL 49-711-25820, FAX 49-711-2582390, franz.steiner.verlag@t-online.de, http://www.steiner-verlag.de. Ed. Wilhelm Lauer. R&P Sabine Koerner.

550 ESP ISSN 0367-0449
QE283 CODEN: EGLMA9
➤ **ESTUDIOS GEOLOGICOS.** Text and summaries in English, French, Spanish. 1945. bi-m. EUR 32.50 (effective 2005). bk.rev. back issues avail. **Document type:** *Journal, Academic/Scholarly.* **Description:** Publishes research papers concerned with mineralogy, petrology, geochemistry, geomorphology, stratigraphy and related topics.
Indexed: BIOSIS Prev, BiolAb, CIN, ChemAb, ChemTitl, GEOBASE, IBR, IECT, MinerAb, RefZh, ZooRec.
—BLDSC (3812.750000), CASDDS, CINDOC, IE, ingenta, Linda Hall. **CCC.**
Published by: (Museo Nacional de Ciencias Naturales), Consejo Superior de Investigaciones Cientificas, Departamento de Publicaciones, Vitruvio 8, Madrid, 28006, Spain. TEL 34-91-561-2833, FAX 34-91-562-9634, publ@orgc.csic.es, http://www.csic.es/publica. Ed. Jose Lopez Ruiz. Circ: 625.

550 DEU ISSN 0932-2205
EXCELLENCE IN ECOLOGY. Text in English. 1987. irreg., latest vol.19, 2005. price varies. **Document type:** *Monographic series, Academic/Scholarly.* **Description:** Addresses researchers, teachers, students and interested laymen, as well as administrators and politicians engaged in ecology-related decision making.
Indexed: ASFA, BIOBASE, BIOSIS Prev, ESPM, IABS, ZooRec.
—BLDSC (3835.146000), CISTI, IE, ingenta. **CCC.**
Published by: Ecology Institute, Nordbuente 23, Oldendorf, 21385, Germany. TEL 49-4132-7127, FAX 49-4132-8883, books@int-res.com, http://www.int-res.com/eebooks/. Ed. Otto Kinne. R&P H Witt.

551.9 CAN
EXPLORE (NEPEAN). Text in English. q. USD 70 membership; USD 40 to students. **Document type:** *Newsletter.*
Published by: Association of Exploration Geochemists, 72 Robertson Rd, P O Box 26099, Nepean, ON K2H 9R0, Canada. TEL 613-828-0199, FAX 613-828-9288, aeg@synapse.net, http://aeg.org/aeg/aeghome.html, http://www.aeg.org/. Ed. Sherman P Marsh. R&P Owen P Lavin TEL 303-708-4140.

550 551 560 DEU ISSN 0172-9179
QE640 CODEN: FACSEN
➤ **FACIES;** international journal of paleontology, sedimentology and geology. Text in English. 1979. q. EUR 348 combined subscription to institutions print & online eds. (effective 2005). **Document type:** *Journal, Academic/Scholarly.*
Related titles: Online - full text ed.: ISSN 1612-4820 (from EBSCO Publishing, Springer LINK, Swets Information Services).
Indexed: ASCA, ASFA, BIOSIS Prev, BiolAb, CurCont, E&PHSE, GEOBASE, GP&P, OffTech, PetrolAb, ZooRec.
—BLDSC (3863.425000), IDS, IE, ingenta, PADDS. **CCC.**
Published by: (Universitaet Erlangen - Nuernberg, Institut fuer Palaeontologie), Springer-Verlag (Subsidiary of: Springer Science+Business Media), Tiergartenstr 17, Heidelberg, 69121, Germany. TEL 49-6221-3450, FAX 49-6221-345229, efluegel@pal.pal.uni-erlangen.de, orders@springer.de, http://www.geol.uni-erlangen.de/pal/facies.htm, http://www.springer.de. Ed. Andre Freiwald. Adv. contact Stephan Kroeck TEL 49-30-827875739. Circ: 300.

➤ **FLORIDA MUSEUM OF NATURAL HISTORY. BULLETIN.** see *BIOLOGY*

➤ **FOUNDATION FOR SCIENTIFIC RESEARCH IN THE CARIBBEAN REGION. PUBLICATION.** see *BIOLOGY*

550 THA
G E - I R C CURRENT AWARENESS SERVICE. (Geotechnical Engineering International Resources Center) Text in Thai. 1976. q. USD 65 in Asia to individuals; USD 86 elsewhere to individuals; USD 118 in Asia to institutions; USD 128 elsewhere to institutions. adv. bk.rev. abstr.; charts. **Document type:** *Academic/Scholarly.*
Formerly: A G E Current Awareness Service (0301-4150)
Published by: Asian Institute of Technology, Geotechnical Engineering International Resources Center, Klong Luang, PO Box 4, Pathum Thani, 12120, Thailand. TEL 66-2-524-5862, FAX 66-2-524-5870, TELEX 84276 TH, geoferro@ait.ac.th, http://www.ait.ac.th/clair/centers/geirc. Circ: 200.

G I M INTERNATIONAL; the worldwide magazine for geomatics. (Geomatics Info Magazine) see *GEOGRAPHY*

550 USA ISSN 1062-791X
G I S NEWSLETTER. Text in English. 1966. bi-m. USD 40; USD 45 foreign (effective 1998). adv. bibl. back issues avail. **Document type:** *Newsletter.*
Formerly (until no.27, 1973): Geoscience Information Society. Newsletter (0046-5801)
Media: Duplicated (not offset).
Indexed: AESIS.
Published by: Geoscience Information Society, c/o Jim O'Donnell, Geology Library 100-23, Caltech, Pasadena, CA 91125. Ed., Adv. contact Mary Frances Lembo. R&P Connie Manson TEL 504-286-7280. Circ: 300 (controlled).

G L A FACHBERICHTE. see *ENVIRONMENTAL STUDIES*

550 USA ISSN 1525-2027
QE514 CODEN: GGGGFR
G3: GEOCHEMISTRY, GEOPHYSICS, GEOSYSTEMS; an electronic journal of the earth sciences. Text in English. bi-m. USD 350 to institutions (effective 2006). **Description:** Publishes papers of broad interests in the earth sciences. Includes contributions that report on observational, experimental, and theoretical investigations pertinent to the understanding of that system.
Media: Online - full text.
Indexed: CurCont.
Published by: American Geophysical Union, 2000 Florida Ave, NW, Washington, DC 20009-1277. TEL 202-462-6900, 800-966-2481, FAX 202-328-0566, institutions@agu.org, http://www.agu.org/journals/gc/.

GACETA INFORMATIVA I N E G I. see *BUSINESS AND ECONOMICS—Economic Situation And Conditions*

550 USA ISSN 1099-1999
➤ **GAEA.** Text in English. 1977. q. USD 50 (effective 2004). adv. bk.rev. back issues avail. **Document type:** *Newsletter, Academic/Scholarly.* **Description:** Provides technical and career information to geoscientists.
Related titles: Diskette ed.
Published by: Association for Women Geoscientists, P O Box 30645, Lincoln, NE 68503-0645. TEL 651-426-3316, FAX 651-426-5449, gaea@awg.org, http://www.awg.org. Ed. Margnesite Toscaro. R&P Jeanette Leete. Adv. contact Sarah Stoll. Circ: 1,100 (paid).

550 JPN ISSN 0387-3498
GEKKAN CHIKYU/CHIKYU MONTHLY. Text in Japanese. 1979. m. JPY 2,000 per issue.
Published by: Kaiyo Shuppan Co. Ltd., 675-5 Misawa, Hino-shi, Tokyo-to 191-0032, Japan.

550 ITA ISSN 1721-8039
GEOACTA; an international journal of earth sciences. Text in English. 2002. s-a. **Document type:** *Journal, Academic/Scholarly.* **Description:** Covers all sectors of the Earth Sciences ranging from Geology-Paleontology to Mineralogy-Petrography-Geochemistry-Vulcanology to Applied and Environmental Geology.
Formed by the Merger of (1926-2000): Giornale di Geologia (0017-0291); Which was formerly (1903-1925): Giornale di Geologia Pratica (1125-291X); (1963-2000): Mineralogica et Petrographica Acta (0540-1437); Which was formerly (1948-1964): Acta Geologica Alpina (0365-253X)
Indexed: GEOBASE, RefZh.
Published by: Universita degli Studi di Bologna, Dipartimento di Scienze della Terra e Geologico - Ambientali, c/o Gianni Cortecci, Piazza Porta San Donato 1, Bologna, I-40126, Italy. TEL 39-051-209-4944, FAX 39-051-209-4904, http://www.geomin.unibo.it/riviste/riviste.htm.

550 ARG ISSN 0326-7237
GEOACTA. Text in Spanish. 1960. a. **Document type:** *Monographic series.*
Indexed: ESPM.
Published by: Asociacion Argentina de Geofisicos y Geodestas, Observatorio Astronomico de la Plata, Paseo del Bosque s/n, La Plata, 1900, Argentina. FAX 54-21-211761, jero@aagg.org.ar.

GEOBIOS; an international journal of life sciences on earth. see *BIOLOGY*

GEOBIOS NEW REPORTS; biannual journal of life sciences. see *BIOLOGY*

E

GEOBIT; das Magazin fuer raumbezogene Informationstechnologie. see *EARTH SCIENCES—Computer Applications*

551.9 JPN ISSN 0016-7002
QE514 CODEN: GEJOBE
➤ **GEOCHEMICAL JOURNAL.** Text in English. 1966. bi-m. USD 160. adv. charts; stat. **Document type:** *Academic/Scholarly.*
Related titles: Online - full text ed.: (from EBSCO Publishing).
Indexed: AESIS, ASCA, ASFA, BiolAb, CIN, ChemAb, ChemTitl, CurCont, E&PHSE, ESPM, ExcerpMed, GEOBASE, GP&P, INIS AtomInd, ISR, JTA, MSB, MinerAb, OffTech, PetrolAb, PollutAb, RefZh, SCI, SWRA.
—BLDSC (4116.920000), CASDDS, CISTI, IDS, IE, Infotrieve, ingenta, Linda Hall, PADDS.
Published by: (Geochemical Society of Japan), Business Center for Academic Societies Japan/Nihon Gakkai Jimu Senta, 5-16-19 Honkomagome, Bunkyo-ku, Tokyo, 113-0021, Japan. TEL 81-3-5814-5811, FAX 81-3-5814-5822. Circ: 1,300.

551.9 RUS ISSN 0016-7029
QE515 CODEN: GCINAP
➤ **GEOCHEMISTRY INTERNATIONAL.** Text in English. 1956. m. USD 3,485 in North America; USD 3,994 elsewhere (effective 2004). adv. bk.rev. bibl.; illus. index. back issues avail.; reprints avail. **Document type:** *Journal, Academic/Scholarly.* **Description:** Covers terrestrial and planetary rocks and atmospheres, rock evolution, parageneses and alteration, geochemical ore-prospecting techniques, ore-zone compositions and distribution, hydrocarbon generation and migration.
Formerly (until 1963): Geochemistry (0435-3269)
Related titles: Microform ed.: (from PQC); ♦ Russian ed.: Geokhimiya. ISSN 0016-7525; ♦ Translation of: Geokhimiya. ISSN 0016-7525.
Indexed: AESIS, ASFA, CIS, CurCont, E&PHSE, ESPM, ExcerpMed, GEOBASE, GP&P, MinerAb, OceAb, OffTech, PetrolAb, PollutAb, SCI, SWRA.
—BLDSC (0411.775000), CISTI, IE, Infotrieve, ingenta, Linda Hall, PADDS. **CCC.**
Published by: (Rossiiskaya Akademiya Nauk/Russian Academy of Sciences), M A I K Nauka - Interperiodica, Profsoyuznaya ul 90, Moscow, 117997, Russian Federation. TEL 7-095-3347420, FAX 7-095-3360666, compmg@maik.ru, http://www.maik.rssi.ru/journals/geochem.htm, http://www.maik.ru. Ed. Igor' D Ryabchikov. R&P Vladimir I Vasil'ev. Circ: 675. **Subscr. to:** Interperiodica, PO Box 1831, Birmingham, AL 35201-1831. TEL 205-995-1567, 800-633-4931, FAX 205-995-1588. **Co-sponsors:** American Geological Institute; American Geophysical Union.

550 BRA ISSN 0101-9082
QE235 CODEN: GESPDU
➤ **GEOCIENCIAS.** Text in Portuguese; Summaries in English, Portuguese. 1982. s-a. free (effective 2005). bibl.; charts; illus.; abstr. back issues avail. **Document type:** *Journal, Academic/Scholarly.* **Description:** Covers all areas of geology, mineralogy, paleontology and applied geophysics.
Incorporates: Noticia Geomorfologica
Indexed: EIP, PetrolAb, RefZh, ZooRec.
—BLDSC (4117.300000), CISTI, PADDS.
Published by: Fundacao Editora U N E S P, Praca da Se 108, Sao Paulo, SP 01001-900, Brazil. TEL 55-11-32427171, cgb@marilia.unesp.br, http://www.unesp.br. Ed. Dr. Antenor Zanardo. Circ: 1,000.

526.8 HRV ISSN 0016-710X
➤ **GEODETSKI LIST.** Contents page in English, French, German, Russian. 1947. q. HRK 120 domestic; EUR 30 foreign (effective 2002). adv. bk.rev.; software rev. abstr.; bibl.; charts; illus.; maps. index. 80 p./no.; **Document type:** *Academic/Scholarly.*
Indexed: BibCart, RefZh.
Published by: Hrvatsko Geodetsko Drustvo, Berislaviceva 6, Zagreb, 10000, Croatia. TEL 385-1-4872495, FAX 385-1-4872495, hgd@geof.hr, http://www.geof.hr. Ed. Stanislav Franges.

550 DEU ISSN 0170-3250
GEOECOLOGICAL RESEARCH. Text in English. irreg., latest vol.8, 1999. price varies. **Document type:** *Monographic series, Academic/Scholarly.*
Published by: Franz Steiner Verlag Stuttgart GmbH, Birkenwaldstr 44, Stuttgart, 70191, Germany. TEL 49-711-25820, FAX 49-711-2582390, franz.steiner.verlag@t-online.de, http://www.steiner-verlag.de. Ed. Ulrich Schweinfurth. R&P Sabine Koerner.

GEOFORUM. see *GEOGRAPHY*

GEOGRAFISKA ANNALER. SERIES A. PHYSICAL GEOGRAPHY. see *GEOGRAPHY*

GEOGRAPHIE - ECOLOGIE - ENVIRONNEMENT; organisation de l'espace. see *GEOGRAPHY*

GEOGRAPHIE ET TELEDETECTION. BULLETIN DE RECHERCHE. see *GEOGRAPHY*

GEOJOURNAL; an international journal on human geography and environmental sciences. see *GEOGRAPHY*

551.9 552 549 BGR ISSN 0324-1718
QE381.B8 CODEN: GMPED4
GEOKHIMIIA, MINERALOGIIA I PETROLOGIIA. Text in Multiple languages; Summaries in English. 1975. 3/yr. price varies. illus. reprint service avail. from IRC.
Indexed: BSLGeo, ChemAb, IAA, IMMAb, RefZh.
—CASDDS, KNAW, Linda Hall.
Published by: (Bulgarska Akademiya na Naukite/Bulgarian Academy of Sciences), Universitetsko Izdatelstvo Sv. Kliment Okhridski/Publishing House of the Sofia University St. Kliment Ohridski, Akad G Bonchev 6, Sofia, 1113, Bulgaria. Ed. I Kostov. Circ: 420.

551.9 BEL ISSN 1374-8505
QE1 CODEN: GEBEFG
➤ **GEOLOGICA BELGICA.** Text mainly in English; Text occasionally in Dutch, French, German. 1998. s-a. EUR 62 domestic; EUR 70 in Europe; EUR 80 elsewhere (effective 2004). adv. bk.rev. bibl.; charts; illus. index. 150 p./no.; back issues avail. **Document type:** *Journal, Academic/Scholarly.* **Description:** Publishes papers on the regional geology of Belgium and neighboring areas, with reports of current research in earth science institutes in Belgium, and discussions of applied geology, including hydrogeology, building materials, remote sensing, and conservation issues.
Formed by the merger of (1879-1998): Societe Geologique de Belgique. Annales (0037-9395); (1974-1998): Societe Belge de Geologie. Bulletin (0379-1807); Which was formerly (1887-1974): Societe Belge de Geologie, de Paleontologie et d'Hydrologie. Bulletin (0037-8909)
Indexed: BIOSIS Prev, BiolAb, ChemAb, EngInd, IBR, IMMAb, INIS AtomInd, MinerAb, PetrolAb, RefZh, ZooRec.
—BLDSC (4131.020000), CASDDS, CISTI, Linda Hall, PADDS.
Address: Rue Jenner 13, Brussels, 1000, Belgium. TEL 32-2-6270350, FAX 32-2-6477359, www.ulg.ac.be/geolsed/gb. Ed., Pub. J.C. Duchesne. Adv. contact Michiel Dusar. Circ: 650 (paid); 450 (controlled).

550 CAN ISSN 1706-936X
GEOLOGICAL ASSOCIATION OF CANADA. MISCELLANEOUS PUBLICATION. Text in English. 2002. irreg. CND 30 per issue (effective 2004). **Document type:** *Academic/Scholarly.*
Related titles: CD-ROM ed.
Published by: Geological Association of Canada, c/o Dept. of Earth Sciences, Memorial Univ. of Newfoundland, St. John's, NF A1B 3X5, Canada. TEL 709-737-7660, FAX 709-737-2532, http://www.gac.ca. Pub., R&P Ms. K Dawe TEL 709-737-7660.

GEOLOGICAL SOCIETY OF CHINA. JOURNAL. see *EARTH SCIENCES—Geology*

550 CAN ISSN 1195-1036
➤ **GEOMATICA.** Text in English, French. 1922. q. CND 275 (effective 2005). adv. bk.rev. abstr.; charts; illus. index. 126 p./no.; back issues avail. **Document type:** *Journal, Academic/Scholarly.* **Description:** Dedicated to the dissemination of information on technical advances in the geomatic sciences.
Former titles: C I S M Journal A C S G (0841-8233); Canadian Surveyor - Geometre Canadien (0008-5103)
Related titles: Microfiche ed.
Indexed: BibCart, EngInd, FPA, ForAb, GEOBASE, RefZh.
—BLDSC (4147.253000), CISTI, IE, Infotrieve, ingenta, Linda Hall. **CCC.**
Published by: Canadian Institute of Geomatics/Association Canadienne des Sciences Geomatiques, 1390 Prince of Wales Dr, Ste 400, Ottawa, ON K2C 3N6, Canada. TEL 613-224-9851, FAX 613-224-9577, admincig@magma.ca, editgeo@magma.com, http://www.cig-acsg.ca/page.asp?intNodeID=15. Ed. Mike Pinch. R&P, Adv. contact Carol E Railer. B&W page CND 600; trim 11 x 8.5. Circ: 1,070.

550 VEN ISSN 0016-7975
CODEN: GMNSAX
GEOMINAS. Text in Spanish. 1964. irreg. per issue exchange basis. bk.rev. bibl.; charts. **Document type:** *Bulletin.*
—CASDDS.
Published by: Universidad de Oriente, Escuela de Ciencias de la Tierra, c/o Comision de Publicaciones, La Sabaneta, 8001, Bolivar, 8001, Venezuela. FAX 58-85-26678. Ed. Jose Herrero Noguerol. Circ: (controlled).

550 RUS ISSN 0435-4281
CODEN: GMFLA6
GEOMORFOLOGIYA. Text in English, Russian. 1970. q. USD 144 foreign (effective 2005). **Document type:** *Journal, Academic/Scholarly.*
Indexed: GEOBASE, RefZh.
—CISTI, East View, KNAW, Linda Hall. **CCC.**
Published by: Izdatel'stvo Nauka, Profsoyuznaya ul 90, Moscow, 117864, Russian Federation. TEL 7-095-3347151, FAX 7-095-4202220, secret@naukaran.ru, http://www.naukaran.ru. **US dist. addr.:** East View Information Services; **Dist. by:** M K - Periodica, ul Gilyarovskogo 39, Moscow 129110, Russian Federation. TEL 7-095-2845008, FAX 7-095-2813798, info@periodicals.ru, http://www.mkniga.ru.

550 CAN ISSN 0821-381X
➤ **GEOSCIENCE CANADA REPRINT SERIES.** Text in English. 1979. irreg. CND 80 per issue (effective 2004). **Document type:** *Academic/Scholarly.*
—**CCC.**
Published by: Geological Association of Canada, c/o Dept. of Earth Sciences, Memorial Univ. of Newfoundland, St. John's, NF A1B 3X5, Canada. TEL 709-737-7660, FAX 709-737-2532, http://www.gac.ca. Pub., R&P Ms. K Dawe TEL 709-737-7660.

550 GBR
GEOSCIENCE IN SOUTH-WEST ENGLAND. Text in English. irreg.
Indexed: ZooRec.
Address: Dept. of Geology, University of Plymouth, Plymouth, Devon PL4 8AA, United Kingdom. TEL 01752-233100, manderson@plymouth.ac.uk.

550 USA ISSN 0072-1409
QE48.85 CODEN: GISPAL
➤ **GEOSCIENCE INFORMATION SOCIETY. PROCEEDINGS.** Text in English. 1969. a., latest vol.33, 2003. USD 45 to non-members (effective 2004). **Document type:** *Proceedings, Academic/Scholarly.* **Description:** Contains papers presented at symposium, technical and poster sessions held at annual meeting.
Indexed: AESIS, IMMAb.
—BLDSC (6704.350000), Linda Hall.
Published by: Geoscience Information Society, c/o Jim O'Donnell, Geology Library 100-23, Caltech, Pasadena, CA 91125. TEL 626-395-2199, FAX 626-568-0935, http://www.geoinfo.org/pubslist.html#procs. Circ: 250.

550 KOR ISSN 1226-4806
GEOSCIENCES JOURNAL. Text in English. q. **Description:** Covers the all aspects of geoscience, including geology, geophysics, geochemistry, paleontology, mineralogy, petrology, sedimentology, hydrology, and others.
Indexed: CurCont.
—BLDSC (4158.892200), IE.
Published by: (Association of Korean Geoscience Societies), Han Rim Won Publishing Company, 206-3 Ohjang-Dong, Choong Gu, Seoul, 100-310, Korea, S. TEL 82-2-2273-4201, FAX 82-2-2266-9083, hanrim@chollian.dacom.co.kr, http://gj.gskorea.or.kr. Ed. Wooil M Moon.

GEOTECHNICAL ENGINEERING. see *ENGINEERING—Civil Engineering*

550 THA ISSN 0858-4869
TA703
GEOTECHNICAL ENGINEERING BULLETIN. Text in Thai. 4/yr. USD 65 in Asia to individuals; USD 97 elsewhere to individuals; USD 86 in Asia to institutions; USD 118 elsewhere to institutions. bk.rev. **Document type:** *Bulletin, Academic/Scholarly.*
Formerly (until 1992): A G E News (0125-1767)
Indexed: EEA.
Published by: Asian Institute of Technology, Geotechnical Engineering International Resources Center, Klong Luang, PO Box 4, Pathum Thani, 12120, Thailand. TEL 66-2-524-5862, FAX 66-2-524-5870, geoferro@ait.ac.th, http://www.ait.ac.th/clair/centers/geirc. Circ: 200.

550 CAN ISSN 1208-2260
➤ **GEOTEXT.** Text in English; Abstracts in English, French. 1992. irreg. CND 80 per issue worldwide (effective 2005). **Document type:** *Monographic series, Academic/Scholarly.*
Published by: Geological Association of Canada, c/o Dept. of Earth Sciences, Memorial Univ. of Newfoundland, St. John's, NF A1B 3X5, Canada. TEL 709-737-7660, FAX 709-737-2532, http://www.gac.ca. Pub. Ms. K Dawe TEL 709-737-7660.

550 GBR ISSN 0375-6505
GB1001 CODEN: GTMCAT
➤ **GEOTHERMICS.** Text and summaries in English, French. 1972. 6/yr. EUR 1,112 in Europe to institutions; JPY 147,700 in Japan to institutions; USD 1,245 elsewhere to institutions (effective 2006). adv. bk.rev. charts; illus. index. back issues avail.; reprint service avail. from PQC. **Document type:** *Journal, Academic/Scholarly.* **Description:** Publishes papers addressing all aspects of the utilization of geothermal resources, including theory and new exploration techniques.
Related titles: Microfilm ed.: (from PQC); Online - full text ed.: (from EBSCO Publishing, Gale Group, IngentaConnect, ScienceDirect, Swets Information Services).
Indexed: AEA, AJEE, ASCA, ASFA, BrCerAb, C&ISA, CIN, CerAb, ChemAb, ChemTitl, CivEngAb, CorrAb, CurCont, E&CAJ, E&PHSE, EEA, EIA, EMA, EPB, ESPM, EngInd, EnvAb, FLUIDEX, GEOBASE, GP&P, HerbAb, HortAb, I&DA, IAA, ISMEC, Inspec, M&TEA, MBF, METADEX, OffTech, OrnHort, PetrolAb, PollutAb, RefZh, S&F, SWRA, SolStAb, WAA, WAE&RSA.
—BLDSC (4161.040000), AskIEEE, CASDDS, CISTI, Ei, IDS, IE, Infotrieve, ingenta, Linda Hall, PADDS. **CCC.**
Published by: (International Institute for Geothermal Research, Pisa ITA), Pergamon (Subsidiary of: Elsevier Science & Technology), The Boulevard, Langford Ln, East Park, Kidlington, Oxford OX5 1GB, United Kingdom. TEL 44-1865-843000, FAX 44-1865-843010, http://www.elsevier.com/locate/geothermics. Ed. M J Lippmann. Circ: 1,075. **Subscr. to:** Elsevier BV, PO Box 211, Amsterdam 1000 AE, Netherlands. TEL 31-20-485-3757, FAX 31-20-485-3432, nlinfo-f@elsevier.nl, http://www.elsevier.nl.

E

550 USA ISSN 0016-8556
QE1 CODEN: GEOTAJ
GEOTIMES; newsmagazine of the earth sciences. Text in English. 1956. m. USD 42.95 domestic to individuals; USD 53.95 in Canada to individuals; USD 72.95 elsewhere to individuals; USD 85 domestic to institutions; USD 96 in Canada to institutions; USD 115 elsewhere to institutions; USD 24.95 domestic to members; USD 34.45 in Canada to members; USD 52.95 elsewhere to members; USD 14.95 domestic to students; USD 24.45 in Canada to students; USD 42.95 elsewhere to students (effective 2005). adv. bk.rev.; software rev.; Website rev. illus.; stat. index. back issues avail.; reprints avail. **Document type:** *Magazine.*
Related titles: Microform ed.: (from PQC); Online - full text ed.
Indexed: AESIS, ASCA, ASFA, BiolAb, BiolDig, CIJE, CTO, CurCont, EEA, ESPM, GEOBASE, GSI, OceAb, PetrolAb, SPPI, SSCI, SWRA.
—BLDSC (4161.050000), CASDDS, CISTI, IDS, IE, Infotrieve, ingenta, Linda Hall, PADDS. **CCC.**
Published by: American Geological Institute, 4220 King St, Alexandria, VA 22302-1502. TEL 703-379-2480, FAX 703-379-7563, geotimes@agiweb.org, agi@agiweb.org, http://www.geotimes.org/, http://www.agiweb.org/pubs. Ed., R&P Liza Pinsker. Pub. Marcus Milling. Adv. contact John Rasanen. B&W page USD 1,390, color page USD 1,668. Circ: 15,000.

550 JPN ISSN 1342-937X
QE511.5 CODEN: GROEBW
➤ **GONDWANA RESEARCH.** Text in English. 1997. 8/yr. EUR 755 in Europe to institutions; JPY 102,800 in Japan to institutions; USD 950 to institutions except Europe and Japan; EUR 159 in Europe to qualified personnel; JPY 21,600 in Japan to qualified personnel; USD 200 to qualified personnel except Europe and Japan (effective 2006). abstr.; bibl.; charts; illus.; maps. 200 p./no.; back issues avail. **Document type:** *Journal, Academic/Scholarly.*
Indexed: CurCont.
—BLDSC (4201.283500), IE, ingenta.
Published by: Internationl Association for Godwana Research, Faculty of Science, Kochi University, Akebono-cho, Kochi, 780-8520, Japan. gondwana@cc.kochi-u.ac.jp, gondwana@cc.koch-u.ac.jp, http://www.elsevier.com/locate/jcr, http://www.indstate.eud/gga/gy. Eds. M Santosh, M Yoshida.

550 GTM
GUATEMALA. INSTITUTO NACIONAL DE SISMOLOGIA, VULCANOLOGIA, METEOROLOGIA E HIDROLOGIA. BOLETIN. Text in Spanish. 1974 (vol.7). m. USD 20. bk.rev. charts; stat.
Former titles: I N S I V U M E H Boletin; Observatorio Nacional de Guatemala. Boletin
Published by: Instituto Nacional de Sismologia, Vulcanologia, Meteorologia e Hidrologia (INSIVUMEH), Ministerio de Comunicaciones y Obras Publicas, 7 Avenida 14-57, Guatemala City Zona, Guatemala. FAX 502-2-315005. Circ: 100.

550 665.5 531.64 USA
Z6026.G3
GUIDE TO U S G S PUBLICATIONS★. (U.S. Geological Survey) Text in English. 1986. biennial. USD 215. **Document type:** *Abstract/Index.*
Formerly (until 1994): Guide to U S G S Geologic and Hydrologic Maps (0891-4915)
Published by: Documents Index, Inc., 6121 Kellys Gln, Mineral, VA 23117-5022. TEL 703-257-4844. Ed. Laurie Andriot.

621.3678 CHN ISSN 1001-070X
GUOTU ZIYUAN YAOGAN/REMOTE SENSING FOR LAND & RESOURCES. Text in Chinese. 1989. q. CNY 5 newsstand/cover domestic (effective 2000). **Document type:** *Academic/Scholarly.*
Related titles: Online - full content ed.: (from WanFang Data Corp.); Online - full text ed.: (from East View Information Services).
Indexed: RefZh.
Published by: (Dikuang Bu, Hangtian Wutangan Zhongxin), Dizhi Chubanshe, Beijing Xueyuan Lu 29-Hao, Beijing, 100083, China. TEL 86-1-82329054. Ed. Tong-bing Ji.

550 620 NLD
➤ **HANDBOOK OF SOIL MECHANICS.** Text in English. 1974, irreg., latest vol.4, 1990. price varies. illus. **Document type:** *Monographic series, Academic/Scholarly.* **Description:** Offers a reference in the geological specialty of soil mechanics.
Published by: Elsevier BV (Subsidiary of: Elsevier Science & Technology), Radarweg 29, Amsterdam, 1043 NX, Netherlands. TEL 31-20-4853911, FAX 31-20-4852457, nlinfo-f@elsevier.nl, http://www.elsevier.nl. Ed. A Kezdi.

550 AND ISSN 1681-5602
HORITZO; revista del Centre de Recerva en Ciencies de la Terra. Text in Catalan. 2002. s-a. **Description:** Includes research papers on earth sciences.
Media: Online - full text.
Published by: Institut D'Estudis Andorrans, Centre de Recerca en Ciencies de la Terra, C. La Valireta, 5 4t, Encamp, Andorra. TEL 376-731036, FAX 376-834578, crecit@andorra.ad, http://www.iea.ad/crecit/revistahoritzo.html.

HUMBOLDT SOCIETY NEWSLETTER; lesbian and gay naturalists of philadelphia. see *HOMOSEXUALITY*

550 CHN ISSN 1003-5427
GB1737
➤ **HUPO KEXUE/JOURNAL OF LAKE SCIENCES.** Text in Chinese. 1989. q. CNY 40 (effective 2004). bk.rev. abstr.; bibl.; charts; illus. back issues avail. **Document type:** *Journal, Academic/Scholarly.* **Description:** Focuses on the recent achievements in environmental evolution, utilization of lakes, reservoirs and their catchments.
Related titles: Online - full text ed.: (from East View Information Services, WanFang Data Corp.).
Indexed: AESIS, ASFA, BiolAb, ESPM, EnvEAb, M&GPA, M&TEA, PollutAb, SWRA.
—BLDSC (5010.060000).
Published by: (Zhongguo Kexueyuan, Nanjing Deli yu Hubei Yanjiusuo, Zhongguo Haiyang Huzhao Xuehui), Kexue Chubanshe/Science Press, 16 Donghuang Cheng Genbei Jie, Beijing, 100717, China. TEL 86-10-64000246, FAX 86-10-64030255, jlakes@niglas.ac.cn, http://hpkx.periodicals.net.cn/default.html, http://www.sciencep.com/. Ed. Ya-feng Shi. Circ: 1,000. **Dist. by:** China International Book Trading Corp, 35 Chegongzhuang Xilu, Haidian District, PO Box 399, Beijing 100044, China. TEL 86-10-68412045, FAX 86-10-68412023, cibtc@mail.cibtc.com.cn, http://www.cibtc.com.cn.

551.46 GBR ISSN 0309-7846
VK588
HYDROGRAPHIC JOURNAL. Text in English. 1972. q. GBP 60 to non-members; GBP 15 per issue (effective 2005). adv. bk.rev. index. back issues avail. **Document type:** *Journal, Academic/Scholarly.* **Description:** Contains authoritative articles and papers dealing with all aspects of hydrographic surveying and related sciences authored by acknowledged experts.
Incorporates (1973-1996): Hydrographic Society. International Headquarters. Information Bulletin (0309-7838)
Indexed: ASFA, ESPM, FLUIDEX, GEOBASE, PollutAb, RICS, RefZh.
—BLDSC (4346.100000), CISTI, IE, Infotrieve, ingenta.
Published by: Hydrographic Society, International Headquarters, University of East London, Longbridge Rd, Dagenham, Essex RM8 2AS, United Kingdom. TEL 44-20-85971946, FAX 44-20-85909730, hydrosoc@compuserve.com, info@hydrographicsociety.org, http://www.hydrographicsociety.org/Publications/Journal/welcome.htm. Ed., Adv. contact Helen L Atkinson. Circ: 1,500.

I E E E TRANSACTIONS ON GEOSCIENCE AND REMOTE SENSING. see *ENGINEERING—Electrical Engineering*

I G B P SCIENCE. (International Geosphere - Biosphere Programme) see *SOCIAL SCIENCES: COMPREHENSIVE WORKS*

550 JPN ISSN 0910-9900
CODEN: TRISEK
I S E I TECHNICAL REPORT. SERIES A. Text in English. 1985. irreg.
Published by: Okayama University, Institute for Study of the Earth's Interior/Okayama Daigaku Chikyu Naibu Kenkyu Senta, 827 Yamada, Tohaku-gun, Misasa-cho, Tottori-ken 682-0122, Japan.

550 JPN ISSN 0911-4114
CODEN: TRIBE3
I S E I TECHNICAL REPORT. SERIES B. Text in English. 1985. s-a.
Indexed: CIN, ChemAb, ChemTitl, INIS AtomInd.
—CASDDS.
Published by: Okayama University, Institute for Study of the Earth's Interior/Okayama Daigaku Chikyu Naibu Kenkyu Senta, 827 Yamada, Tohaku-gun, Misasa-cho, Tottori-ken 682-0122, Japan.

550 JPN ISSN 0911-4122
CODEN: TRICE6
I S E I TECHNICAL REPORT. SERIES C. (Institute for Study of the Earth's Interior) Text in Japanese. 1985. irreg.
—CASDDS.
Published by: Okayama University, Institute for Study of the Earth's Interior/Okayama Daigaku Chikyu Naibu Kenkyu Senta, 827 Yamada, Tohaku-gun, Misasa-cho, Tottori-ken 682-0122, Japan.

550 NLD ISSN 1389-9368
I T C NEWS. Text in English. 1999. q. **Document type:** *Newsletter.*
—CISTI, Linda Hall.
Published by: International Institute for Geo-Information Science and Earth Observation, Hengelosestraat 99, PO Box 6, Enschede, 7500 AA, Netherlands. TEL 31-53-487-4444, FAX 31-53-487-4400, itcnews@itc.nl, http://www.itc.nl/alumni/itcnews/default.asp.

555.4 IND ISSN 0379-5160
QE295 CODEN: JIGSB4
➤ **INDIAN ACADEMY OF GEOSCIENCE. JOURNAL.** Text in English. 1959. s-a. INR 200 domestic; USD 24 in United States; GBP 10 in United Kingdom (effective 1999). adv. bk.rev. illus.; maps. back issues avail. **Document type:** *Academic/Scholarly.* **Description:** Publishes research articles pertaining to all branches of earth sciences. May include review articles as well as information pertaining to its subject.
Formerly: Indian Geoscience Association. Journal
Indexed: ZooRec.
—CISTI, Linda Hall.
Published by: Indian Academy of Geoscience, Osmania University, Department of Geology, Hyderabad, Andhra Pradesh 500 007, India. TEL 91-40-7018951, FAX 91-40-7019020. Ed., Adv. contact Sudarsana Raju. Circ: 300. **Subscr. to:** Prints India, 11 Darya Ganj, New Delhi 110 002, India.

550 NLD ISSN 0168-6402
CODEN: INESEL
INDIAN EDITION SERIES. Text in Dutch. 1982. irreg. price varies. **Document type:** *Monographic series.*
Indexed: ZooRec.
Published by: A A Balkema (Subsidiary of: Taylor & Francis The Netherlands), PO Box 1675, Rotterdam, 3000 BR, Netherlands.

550 IND ISSN 0046-8983
TA710 CODEN: IGTJAG
INDIAN GEOTECHNICAL JOURNAL. Text in English. 1962. q. INR 100, USD 30. adv. bk.rev. bibl.; charts; illus. **Document type:** *Academic/Scholarly.*
Formerly (until 1971): Indian National Society for Soil Mechanics and Foundation Engineering. Journal
Indexed: AJEE, ApMecR, CRIA, EEA, GeotechAb.
—Linda Hall.
Published by: Indian Geotechnical Society, Department of Civil Engineering, Indian Institute of Technology Bombay, Powai, Mumbai, 400 076, India. Ed. R Kuberan. Circ: 1,200.

560.5 IND ISSN 0379-5128
QE295 CODEN: IJEAB4
➤ **INDIAN JOURNAL OF EARTH SCIENCES.** Abbreviated title: I J E S. Text in English. 1974. q. INR 75 domestic to individuals; INR 200 domestic to institutions; USD 60 foreign (effective 2005). adv. bk.rev. charts; stat. **Document type:** *Academic/Scholarly.*
Indexed: ASFA, BiolAb, CIN, CRIA, ChemAb, ChemTitl, ESPM, GEOBASE, HerbAb, MinerAb, PetrolAb, ZooRec.
—CASDDS, CISTI, Linda Hall, PADDS.
Published by: Indian Society of Earth Sciences, Department of Geology, Presidency College, Kolkata, West Bengal 700 073, India. TEL 91-33-2192636. Ed. G S Ghatak. Pub. A K Ray. adv.: page INR 500, page USD 180; trim 18.5 x 24.5. Circ: 500. **Dist. overseas by:** H P C Publishers Distributors Pvt. Ltd., 4805 Bharat Ram Rd, 24 Darya Ganj, New Delhi 110 002, India. TEL 91-11-325-4401, FAX 91-11-686-3511.

550 910.02 IND
➤ **INDIAN JOURNAL OF GEOMORPHOLOGY.** Text in English. 1996. s-a. INR 550 domestic; USD 120 foreign (effective 2003). adv. bk.rev. illus.; maps. 90 p./no.; back issues avail.; reprints avail. **Document type:** *Journal, Academic/Scholarly.*
Published by: Academic & Law Serials, F-22B/3, Laxmi Nagar, Delhi, 110 092, India. TEL 91-11-23282663, FAX 91-11-22422664, alsindia@hclinfinet.com. Ed. Victor Rajamanickam. Pub. S K Puri. adv.: B&W page USD 200; 14 x 20. Circ: 330.

550 USA
INDIANA STUDIES. PROFESSIONAL PAPER. Text in English. irreg. **Document type:** *Academic/Scholarly.* **Description:** Provides information on natural and human landscapes of Indiana.
Published by: (Indiana State University, Department of Anthropology, Indiana State University, Department of Geology, Indiana State University, Department of Geography), Indiana State University, 200 N Seventh St, Terre Haute, IN 47809.

INSTITUT FRANCAIS D'ETUDES ANDINES. BULLETIN/ INSTITUTO FRANCES DE ESTUDIOS ANDINOS. BOLETIN. see *SOCIAL SCIENCES: COMPREHENSIVE WORKS*

INSTITUT FRANCAIS D'ETUDES ANDINES. TRAVAUX. see *SOCIAL SCIENCES: COMPREHENSIVE WORKS*

550 MAR
INSTITUT SCIENTIFIQUE. BULLETIN. SECTION SCIENCES DE LA TERRE. Text in French. a.
Indexed: ZooRec.
Published by: Universite Mohammed V, Institut Scientifique, Ave Ibn Batouta, BP 703, Rabat-Agdal, Rabat, 10106, Morocco. TEL 212-37-774548, FAX 212-37-774540.

INSTITUTION OF MINING AND METALLURGY. TRANSACTIONS. SECTION B: APPLIED EARTH SCIENCE. see *MINES AND MINING INDUSTRY*

E

▼ new title ➤ refereed ★ unverified ♦ full entry avail.

550 ARG ISSN 0524-9376
G845
INSTITUTO ANTARTICO ARGENTINO. CONTRIBUCIONES. Text in Spanish. 1961. irreg. **Document type:** *Monographic series.*
Indexed: ESPM, ZooRec.
Published by: Direccion Nacional del Antartico, Instituto Antartico Argentino, Cerrito, 1248, Buenos Aires, 1010, Argentina. TEL 54-11-4812 0071, FAX 54-11-4813-7807, diriaa@dna.gov.ar, http://www.dna.gov.ar.

550 CHL ISSN 0073-9871
G845 CODEN: IACSCK
INSTITUTO ANTARTICO CHILENO. CONTRIBUTION. SERIE CIENTIFICA. Text in Spanish; Summaries in English. 1964; N.S. 1969. a. per issue exchange basis. **Document type:** *Academic/Scholarly.*
Supersedes: Instituto Antartico Chileno. Publicacion
Indexed: ASFA, ESPM, SFA, ZooRec.
Published by: Instituto Antartico Chileno, Casilla 16521, Correo 9, Luis Thayer Ojeda, 814, Santiago, Chile. FAX 56-2-2320440, inach@inach.cl. Ed. Daniel Torres N. Circ: 600.

550 PRT ISSN 0871-1798
INSTITUTO DE INVESTIGACAO CIENTIFICA TROPICAL. COMUNICACOES. SERIE DE CIENCIAS DA TERRA. Text in Portuguese. 1989. irreg., latest vol.8. price varies. back issues avail. **Document type:** *Monographic series.*
Published by: Instituto de Investigacao Cientifica Tropical, Rua da Junqueira, 30, Lisbon, 1349-007, Portugal. TEL 351-21-3622621, FAX 351-21-3631460, iict@iict.pt. Circ: 1,000. **Subscr. to:** Centro de Documentacao e Informacao, Rua de Jau, 47, Lisbon 1300, Portugal. TEL 351-21-3644846, FAX 351-21-3628218.

550 PRT ISSN 0873-9498
INSTITUTO GEOLOGICO E MINEIRO. MEMORIAS. Text in English, French, Portuguese, Spanish. 1865. irreg., latest vol.33, 1997. EUR 12.50 (effective 2001). bibl.; charts; illus.; maps. back issues avail. **Document type:** *Monographic series, Academic/Scholarly.*
Formerly (until 1995): Servicios Geologicos de Portugal. Memorias (0370-0623)
Indexed: IMMAb, ZooRec.
Published by: Ministerio da Economia, Instituto Geologico e Mineiro, Apartado 7586, Zambujal, Alfragide, 2721-866, Portugal. TEL 351-21-4705400, FAX 351-21-4720203, web.nbp@igm.pt, http://www.igm.pt. R&P Miguel Magalhaes Ramalho.

550 560 ROM
QE287 CODEN: MIGRAX
INSTITUTUL GEOLOGIC AL ROMANIEI. MEMOIRE. Cover title: Memoriile Institutului Geologic al Romaniei. Text in English, French. 1924. irreg., latest vol.36, 1996. USD 35 (effective 1999). bk.rev. abstr.; charts; illus. **Document type:** *Academic/Scholarly.*
Formerly: Institutul de Geologie si Geofizica. Memoire (0254-7112)
Indexed: ZooRec.
—Linda Hall.
Published by: Institutul Geologic al Romaniei, Str. Caransebes 1, Bucharest, 78344, Romania. FAX 40-1-3128444, udubasa@igr.ro. Ed. A Rusu. R&P Serban Veliciu TEL 40-1-2242093. Circ: 550.

550 RUS
INTELLEKTUAL'NYE RESURSY ROSSII. Text in Russian. 1994. 24/yr. USD 245 in North America (effective 2000).
Published by: Izdatel'stvo Ekotass, Filevskii bul 1, Moscow, 121601, Russian Federation. TEL 7-095-2906351. **Dist. by:** East View Information Services, 3020 Harbor Ln. N., Minneapolis, MN 55447. TEL 763-550-0961, FAX 763-559-2931.

550 FRA ISSN 0074-1035
INTER - NORD. Text in French, English. 1961. irreg., latest vol.20, 2003. EUR 100 per vol. (effective 2005). **Description:** An interdisciplinary and international French arctic journal.
Published by: (Museum National d'Histoire Naturelle, Ecole des Hautes Etudes en Sciences Sociales, France. Centre National de la Recherche Scientifique), Editions Economica, 49 rue Hericart, Paris, 75015, France. TEL 33-1-45781292, FAX 33-1-45750567, http://www.economica.fr.

INTERNATIONAL GEOSCIENCE AND REMOTE SENSING SYMPOSIUM DIGEST. see *GEOGRAPHY*

INTERNATIONAL JOURNAL FOR NUMERICAL AND ANALYTICAL METHODS IN GEOMECHANICS. see *ENGINEERING—Civil Engineering*

INTERNATIONAL JOURNAL OF APPLIED EARTH OBSERVATION AND GEOINFORMATION. see *GEOGRAPHY*

550 681 GBR ISSN 0143-1161
G70.4 CODEN: IJSEDK
➤ **INTERNATIONAL JOURNAL OF REMOTE SENSING.** Text in English. 1980. s-m. GBP 3,355, USD 5,532 combined subscription to institutions print & online eds. (effective 2006). adv. bk.rev. bibl.; illus. Index. reprint service avail. from PSC. **Document type:** *Journal, Academic/Scholarly.* **Description:** Concerned with the science and technology of remote sensing and the applications of remotely sensed data in all major disciplines.
Related titles: Online - full text ed.: ISSN 1366-5901. GBP 3,187, USD 5,255 to institutions (effective 2006) (from EBSCO Publishing, Gale Group, IngentaConnect, O C L C Online Computer Library Center, Inc., Swets Information Services).
Indexed: AEA, AESIS, ASCA, ASFA, AgBio, AgrForAb, BIOSIS Prev, BiolAb, BrCerAb, C&ISA, CPA, CTO, CerAb, CivEngAb, CorrAb, CurCont, E&CAJ, EMA, ESPM, EngInd, EnvEAb, ExcerpMed, FCA, FLUIDEX, FPA, ForAb, GEOBASE, HerbAb, HortAb, I&DA, IAA, IMMAb, ISMEC, ISR, Inspec, M&GPA, M&TEA, MBF, METADEX, MaizeAb, OceAb, OrnHort, PBA, PGegResA, PhotoAb, PollutAb, PotatoAb, RA&MP, RASB, RDA, RPP, RRTA, RevApplEntom, RiceAb, S&F, SCI, SFA, SIA, SSCI, SWRA, SolStAb, SoyAb, TriticAb, VITIS, WAA, WAE&RSA, WRCInf, WTA, WeedAb, WildRev.
—BLDSC (4542.528000), AskIEEE, CISTI, Ei, IDS, IE, Infotrieve, ingenta, Linda Hall. **CCC.**
Published by: Taylor & Francis Ltd (Subsidiary of: Taylor & Francis Group), 4 Park Sq, Milton Park, Abingdon, OX14 4RN, United Kingdom. TEL 44-1235-828600, FAX 44-1235-829000, info@tandf.co.uk, http://www.tandf.co.uk/journals/titles/01431161.asp. Ed. Arthur P Cracknell. Circ: 800. **Subscr. in N. America to:** Taylor & Francis Inc., Customer Services Dept, 325 Chestnut St, 8th Fl, Philadelphia, PA 19106. TEL 215-625-8900, 800-354-1420, FAX 215-625-8914, customerservice@taylorandfrancis.com; **Subscr. to:** Journals Customer Service, Rankine Rd, Basingstoke, Hants RG24 8PR, United Kingdom. TEL 44-1256-813000, FAX 44-1256-330245, enquiry@tandf.co.uk.

500 USA
THE INTERNATIONAL TSUNAMI INFORMATION CENTER (YEAR) ANNUAL. Text in English. 1968. a. free. bk.rev. bibl. back issues avail. **Document type:** *Newsletter.* **Description:** Providing news and information for scientists, engineers, educators, community protection agencies and government throughout the world.
Former titles (until 19??): Tsunami Newsletter (0259-3637); (until 1978): International Tsunami Information Center. Newsletter (1016-2755)
Related titles: Online - full text ed.
Indexed: EEA.
Published by: International Tsunami Information Center, 737 Bishop St, Ste 2200, Honolulu, HI 96813-3213. TEL 808-532-6442, FAX 808-532-5576, itic@itic.noaa.gov, http://www.shoa.cl/oceano/itic/itic.html. Ed. Michael Blackford. Circ: 1,000.

551.9 USA ISSN 1528-588X
INTUITIVE FLASH; forecasting environmental, economic, and societal trends. Text in English. 1991. 10/yr. USD 49 in United States; USD 59 elsewhere (effective 2001). bk.rev. stat. back issues avail. **Document type:** *Newsletter, Consumer.* **Description:** Includes the forecasts of intuitive Gordon-Michael Scallion and the insights of visionary Cynthia Keyes as they relate to personal and planetary transformation.
Formerly (until 2000): Earth Changes Report (1058-8981)
Published by: Matrix Institute, Inc., PO Box 367, W Chesterfld, NH 03466-0367. TEL 603-363-4164, 800-628-7493, FAX 603-363-4168, mail@matrixinstitute.com, http://www.matrixinstitute.com, http://www.earthchanges.com. Eds. Cynthia Keyes, Gordon Michael Scallion. R&P Cynthia Keyes.

551.9 BGR ISSN 0204-7934
TA705 CODEN: IGKHD2
INZENERNA GEOLOGIIA I KHIDROGEOLOGIIA. Text in Multiple languages. 1975. 3/yr. BGL 0.75 per issue. illus. reprint service avail. from IRC.
Supersedes in part: Bulgarska Akademiia na Naukite. Geologicheski Institut. Izvestiia
Indexed: BSLGeo.
—KNAW, Linda Hall.
Published by: (Bulgarska Akademiya na Naukite/Bulgarian Academy of Sciences, Geologicheski Institut), Universitetsko Izdatelstvo Sv. Kliment Okhridski/Publishing House of the Sofia University St. Kliment Ohridski, Akad G Bonchev 6, Sofia, 1113, Bulgaria. Ed. M Minkov. Circ: 450.

550 UKR
IONOSFERA. Text in Ukrainian. 1990. irreg. USD 12 newsstand/cover.
Published by: Kharkivs'kyi Politekhnichnyi Instytut, Ul Frunze 21, Kharkov, 310002, Ukraine.

550 551 IRL ISSN 0790-1763
QE1 CODEN: IJESER
IRISH JOURNAL OF EARTH SCIENCES. Text in English. 1978. a. EUR 19 to individuals; EUR 38 to institutions (effective 2005). back issues avail. **Document type:** *Academic/Scholarly.*
Formerly (until 1984): Journal of Earth Sciences (0332-1851)
Indexed: BiolAb, BrGeoL, GEOBASE, MinerAb, S&F, ZooRec.
—BLDSC (4571.930000), CASDDS, CISTI, IE, ingenta, Linda Hall. **CCC.**
Published by: Royal Irish Academy, 19 Dawson St., Dublin, 2, Ireland. TEL 353-1-6762570, FAX 353-1-6762346, h.shiels@ria.ie, publications@ria.ie, http://www.ria.ie/publications/journals/ijes/ijes.html. **Dist. by:** International Specialized Book Services Inc., 5804 N E Hassalo St, Portland, OR 97213-3644. TEL 503-287-3093, 800-944-6190, FAX 503-280-8832, sales@isbs.com.

550 ISR ISSN 0021-2164
QE318 CODEN: IJERAK
➤ **ISRAEL JOURNAL OF EARTH SCIENCES.** Text in English. 1951. q. USD 260 (effective 2002). adv. bk.rev. charts; illus. index. 64 p./no. 2 cols./p.; back issues avail. **Document type:** *Journal, Academic/Scholarly.*
Related titles: Online - full content ed.; Online - full text ed.: (from EBSCO Publishing).
Indexed: AESIS, ASFA, AgrForAb, BIOSIS Prev, BiolAb, CIN, ChemAb, ChemTitl, CurCont, E&PHSE, EEA, ESPM, ExcerpMed, ForAb, GEOBASE, GP&P, HerbAb, I&DA, IHP, IMMAb, ISR, Inspec, MinerAb, OffTech, PGegResA, PetrolAb, RefZh, S&F, SCI, SWRA, ZooRec.
—AskIEEE, CASDDS, CISTI, Linda Hall, PADDS. **CCC.**
Published by: Laser Pages Publishing Ltd., P O Box 35409, Jerusalem, 91352, Israel. laserpages@netmedia.net.il, http://www.sciencefromisrael.com. Eds. A Almogi, Alan Mathews. R&P R Lichtensztajn. Adv. contact Elcya Weiss. Circ: 750.

550 540 RUS
ISSLEDOVANIYA V OBLASTI KHIMII REDKOZEMEL'NYKH ELEMENTOV. Text in Russian. 1969. irreg.
Published by: Saratovskii Universitet, Saratov, Russian Federation.

ISSUES (CAMBERWELL). see *EDUCATION—Teaching Methods And Curriculum*

ISTITUTO UNIVERSITARIO NAVALE. FACOLTA DI SCIENZE NAUTICHE, NAPLES. ANNALI. see *MILITARY*

IZVESTIYA VYSSHIKH UCHEBNYKH ZAVEDENII. SEVERO-KAVKAZSKII REGION. ESTESTVENNYE NAUKI/NORTH-CAUCASUS SCIENTIFIC CENTER OF HIGH SCHOOL. NATURAL SCIENCES. NEWS. see *MATHEMATICS*

550 JPN ISSN 0373-3602
JAPAN. MARITIME SAFETY AGENCY. HYDROGRAPHIC DEPARTMENT. REPORT OF HYDROGRAPHIC RESEARCH. Text in English, Japanese. 1966. a. per issue exchange basis. **Document type:** *Government.*
Indexed: ASFA, RefZh.
Published by: Kaijo Hoancho, Suirobu/Maritime Safety Agency, Hydrographic Department, 3-1 Tsuki-Ji 5-chome, Chuo-ku, Tokyo, 104-0045, Japan. TEL 81-3-3541-4296, FAX 81-3-3545-2885, consult@cue.jhd.go.jp, http://www.jhd.go.jp/.

550 JPN ISSN 0075-3343
Q115 CODEN: JADRDY
JAPANESE ANTARCTIC RESEARCH EXPEDITION DATA REPORTS. Text in English. 1966. irreg., latest vol.273, 2003. per issue exchange basis. **Document type:** *Academic/Scholarly.* **Description:** Discusses upper atmosphere physics, ionosphere, meteorology, earth science, glaciology, seismology, geochemistry, oceanography, marine biology and terrestrial biology.
Indexed: ASFA, BIOSIS Prev, BiolAb, M&GPA, RefZh, SFA.
—CISTI, KNAW, Linda Hall.
Published by: National Institute of Polar Research/Kokuritsu Kyokuchi Kenkyujo, Publications, 9-10, Kiga 1-chome, Itabashi-ku, Tokyo, 173, Japan. TEL 81-3-3962-2214, FAX 81-3-3962-2225, TELEX 272-3515 POLRSCJ, publication@nipr.ac.jp. Ed. Okitsugu Watanabe. Circ: 600.

551.9 JPN
JAPANESE ANTARCTIC RESEARCH REPORT TO S C A R. (Scientific Committee on Antarctic Research) Text in English. 1985. a.
Published by: National Institute of Polar Research/Kokuritsu Kyokuchi Kenkyujo, Publications, 9-10, Kiga 1-chome, Itabashi-ku, Tokyo, 173, Japan. TEL 81-3-3962-2214, FAX 81-3-3962-2225, publication@nipr.ac.jp. Ed. Okitsugu Watanabe.

550 CHN ISSN 1007-7073
JIDI YANJIU/CHINESE JOURNAL OF POLAR RESEARCH. Text in Chinese. 1988. q. CNY 24 (effective 2004). **Document type:** *Journal, Academic/Scholarly.*
Related titles: Online - full content ed.: (from WanFang Data Corp.); Online - full text ed.: (from East View Information Services).
Indexed: ASFA, ESPM.

E

Published by: (Zhongguo Jidi Yanjiusuo/Polar Research Institute of China), Kexue Chubanshe/Science Press, 16 Donghuang Cheng Genbei Jie, Beijing, 100717, China. TEL 86-10-64000246, FAX 86-10-64030255, http://jdyj.periodicals.net.cn/default.html. **Dist. by:** China International Book Trading Corp, 35 Chegongzhuang Xilu, Haidian District, PO Box 399, Beijing 100044, China. TEL 86-10-68412045, FAX 86-10-68412023, cibtc@mail.cibtc.com.cn, http://www.cibtc.com.cn.

550 USA
JOURNAL E; real stories from planet earth. Text in English. irreg. free.
Media: Online - full text.
Address: 10201 Meredith Ave., Silver Spring, MD 20910-1061. http://www.journale.com.

550 JPN ISSN 0022-0442
QE304 CODEN: JEASAD
JOURNAL OF EARTH SCIENCES. Text in Japanese. 1953. a. per issue exchange basis.
Indexed: AESIS, BiolAb, BrGeoL, ChemAb, NutrAb.
—CASDDS, CISTI, Linda Hall.
Published by: (Chikyu Kagaku Kyoshitsu/Institute of Geosciences), Nagoya Daigaku, Rigakubu/Nagoya University, Faculty of Science, Department of Earth Sciences, Furo-cho, Chikusa-ku, Nagoya-shi, Aichi-ken 464-0814, Japan. FAX 052-782-7091. Circ: 376.

550 IND
QE1 CODEN: PIESDS
➤ **JOURNAL OF EARTH SYSTEM SCIENCE.** Text in English. 1934. bi-m. INR 125 domestic to individuals; USD 30 foreign to individuals; INR 200 domestic to institutions; USD 100 foreign to institutions (effective 2003). bibl.; illus.; charts; maps. index. 100 p./no. 2 cols./p.; back issues avail.; reprint service avail. from PQC,ISI. **Document type:** *Journal, Academic/Scholarly.* **Description:** New results and ideas defining structure evloutionary processes, and sensitivities of earth septem elements. Also papers on solid earth, ocean and atmosphere.
Formerly (until 2005): Indian Academy of Sciences. Proceedings. Earth and Planetary Sciences (0253-4126); Supersedes in part (in 1978): Indian Academy of Sciences. Proceedings. Part A. Physical Sciences (0370-0089)
Related titles: Microfilm ed.: (from PQC); Online - full text ed.: free (effective 2005).
Indexed: AESIS, ASCA, ASFA, CIN, ChemAb, ChemTitl, CurCont, ESPM, EnvAb, FCA, ForAb, GEOBASE, I&DA, Inspec, M&GPA, MSB, MinerAb, RefZh, RiceAb, S&F, SCI, SSCI.
—BLDSC (4971.220000), AskIEEE, CASDDS, CISTI, IDS, IE, ingenta, KNAW, Linda Hall.
Published by: Indian Academy of Sciences, C.V. Raman Ave., Sadashivanagar, P O Box 8005, Bangalore, Karnataka 560 080, India. TEL 91-80-23612546, FAX 91-80-23616094, jessci@ias.ernet.in, http://www.ias.ac.in/jessci. Ed. S R Shetye. R&P G Madhavan. Circ: 1,000.

➤ **JOURNAL OF ELECTROTOPOGRAPHY.** see *PHYSICS*

551.9 NLD ISSN 0375-6742
TN270.A1 CODEN: JGCEAT
➤ **JOURNAL OF GEOCHEMICAL EXPLORATION.** Text in English. 1972. 12/yr. EUR 197 in Europe to individuals; JPY 26,100 in Japan to individuals; USD 220 to individuals except Europe and Japan; EUR 1,284 in Europe to institutions; JPY 170,600 in Japan to institutions; USD 1,436 to institutions except Europe and Japan (effective 2006). bk.rev. illus. Index. back issues avail.; reprint service avail. from ISI. **Document type:** *Journal, Academic/Scholarly.* **Description:** Covers all aspects of the application of geochemistry to the exploration and study of mineral resources and related fields.
Related titles: Microform ed.: (from PQC); Online - full text ed.: (from EBSCO Publishing, Gale Group, IngentaConnect, ScienceDirect, Swets Information Services).
Indexed: AESIS, ASCA, ASFA, BrGeoL, CIN, CIS, ChemAb, ChemTitl, CivEngAb, CurCont, E&PHSE, EngInd, EnvAb, ExcerpMed, FLUIDEX, GEOBASE, GP&P, IMMAb, ISR, MinerAb, OffTech, PetrolAb, RefZh, S&F, SCI, WRCInf.
—BLDSC (4991.900000), CASDDS, CISTI, Ei, IDS, IE, Infotrieve, ingenta, Linda Hall, PADDS. **CCC.**
Published by: Elsevier BV (Subsidiary of: Elsevier Science & Technology), Radarweg 29, Amsterdam, 1043 NX, Netherlands. TEL 31-20-4853911, FAX 31-20-4852457, nlinfo-f@elsevier.nl, http://www.elsevier.com/locate/gexplo, http://www.elsevier.nl. Ed. R Swennen. **Subscr. in the Americas to:** Elsevier, Subscription Customer Service, 6277 Sea Harbor Dr, Orlando, FL 32887-4800. TEL 407-345-4020, 877-839-7126, FAX 407-363-1354.

550 JPN ISSN 0449-2560
QE1 CODEN: JOGSAB
➤ **JOURNAL OF GEOSCIENCES/OSAKA-SHIRITSU DAIGAKU RIGAKUBU CHIKYUGAKU KIYO.** Text in English. 1954. a. per issue exchange basis. **Document type:** *Academic/Scholarly.*
Indexed: ASFA, BIOSIS Prev, BiolAb, ESPM, FLUIDEX, GEOBASE, RefZh, SWRA, ZooRec.
—BLDSC (4995.060000), IE, ingenta, Linda Hall.
Published by: Osaka City University, Department of Geosciences/Osaka-shiritsu Daigaku Rigakubu Chikyugaku Kyoshitsu, Faculty of Science, 3-3-138 Sugimoto, Sumiyoshi-ku, Osaka-shi, 558-8585, Japan. TEL 81-6-6605-2587, FAX 81-6-6605-2522. Circ: 1,000.

550 IND ISSN 0970-7050
JOURNAL OF HILL RESEARCH. Text in English. 1987. s-a. INR 500 domestic to universities and libraries; USD 50 foreign (effective 2000). bk.rev. **Description:** Publishes original research papers covering all aspects of natural and physical sciences relevant to hills.
Indexed: AEA, AgBio, AgrForAb, AnBrAb, B&BAb, BIOSIS Prev, BioCN&I, BiolAb, CPA, EPB, EntAb, FCA, FPA, ForAb, HerbAb, HortAb, I&DA, MaizeAb, NemAb, NutrAb, OrnHort, PBA, PGegResA, PGrRegA, PHN&I, PN&I, PotatoAb, PoultAb, RA&MP, RDA, RM&VM, RPP, RiceAb, S&F, SIA, SeedAb, SoyAb, TDB, TriticAb, WAE&RSA, WeedAb.
—BLDSC (4998.680000).
Published by: Sikkim Science Society, c/o Sikkim Government College, Department of Botany, Gangtok, Sikkim 737 102, India. Ed. Jyoti Prakash Tamang.

550 GBR ISSN 1747-4248
▼ **JOURNAL OF LAND USE SCIENCE.** Text in English. forthcoming 2006. q. GBP 45, USD 72 to individuals; GBP 175, USD 280 to institutions (effective 2006). **Document type:** *Journal, Academic/Scholarly.*
Media: Online - full text. **Related titles:** Print ed.: ISSN 1747-423X. forthcoming 2006. GBP 166, USD 266 (effective 2006).
Published by: Taylor & Francis Ltd (Subsidiary of: Taylor & Francis Group), 4 Park Sq, Milton Park, Abingdon, OX14 4RN, United Kingdom. TEL 44-1235-828600, FAX 44-1235-829000, info@tandf.co.uk, http://www.tandf.co.uk/journals/titles/1747423X.asp. Ed. Richard Aspinall.

551.9 USA ISSN 1527-1404
QE471 CODEN: JSRAEA
➤ **JOURNAL OF SEDIMENTARY RESEARCH.** Text in English. 1996. bi-m. USD 210 to non-members; USD 70 to members; USD 35 to students (effective 2005); includes Section B. adv. bk.rev. illus. index. 2 cols./p.; back issues avail. **Document type:** *Journal, Academic/Scholarly.* **Description:** Emphasizes the physical and chemical aspects of sedimentology and sedimentary petrology with increased emphasis on stratigraphy and global studies.
Formed by the merger of (1994-1996): Journal of Sedimentary Research. Section A: Sedimentary Petrology and Processes (1073-130X); (1994-1996): Journal of Sedimentary Research. Section B: Stratigraphy and Global Studies (1073-1318); Both superseded in part (1931-1994): Journal of Sedimentary Petrology (0022-4472)
Related titles: Microform ed.: (from PMC, PQC); Online - full text ed.: (from HighWire Press).
Indexed: AESIS, ASCA, ASFA, BiolAb, BrGeoL, CIS, CRIA, ChemAb, CurCont, E&PHSE, ESPM, ExcerpMed, FLUIDEX, GEOBASE, GP&P, GSW, ISR, M&GPA, OceAb, OffTech, PetrolAb, PollutAb, RefZh, S&F, SCI, SWRA.
—BLDSC (5063.000050), CASDDS, CISTI, IDS, IE, ingenta, Linda Hall, PADDS. **CCC.**
Published by: S E P M - Society for Sedimentary Geology, 6128 E. 38th St., Ste. 308, Tulsa, OK 74135-5814. TEL 918-610-3361, FAX 918-610-1685, http://www.sepm.org. Eds. Colin P North, Kitty L Milliken. Circ: 5,000.

558 GBR ISSN 0895-9811
QE200 CODEN: JAESE9
➤ **JOURNAL OF SOUTH AMERICAN EARTH SCIENCES.** Text in English. 1988. 8/yr. EUR 135 in Europe to individuals; JPY 17,800 in Japan to individuals; USD 151 to individuals except Europe and Japan; EUR 904 in Europe to institutions; JPY 120,100 in Japan to institutions; USD 1,013 to institutions except Europe and Japan (effective 2006). abstr. back issues avail. **Document type:** *Journal, Academic/Scholarly.* **Description:** Covers all aspects of earth sciences in the South American continent and surrounding oceans.
Related titles: Microfilm ed.: (from PQC); Online - full text ed.: (from EBSCO Publishing, Gale Group, IngentaConnect, ScienceDirect, Swets Information Services).
Indexed: AESIS, ASCA, CurCont, E&PHSE, EngInd, ForAb, GEOBASE, GP&P, HerbAb, I&DA, MaizeAb, OffTech, PetrolAb, RefZh, S&F, SCI, WeedAb, ZooRec.
—BLDSC (5066.002400), CISTI, Ei, IDS, IE, Infotrieve, ingenta, Linda Hall, PADDS. **CCC.**
Published by: Pergamon (Subsidiary of: Elsevier Science & Technology), The Boulevard, Langford Ln, East Park, Kidlington, Oxford OX5 1GB, United Kingdom. TEL 44-1865-843000, FAX 44-1865-843010, http://www.elsevier.com/locate/jsames. Ed. James N. Kellogg. Circ: 350. **Subscr. to:** Elsevier BV, PO Box 211, Amsterdam 1000 AE, Netherlands. TEL 31-20-485-3757, FAX 31-20-485-3432, nlinfo-f@elsevier.nl, http://www.elsevier.nl.

550 USA ISSN 1530-4736
GB651
➤ **JOURNAL OF SPATIAL HYDROLOGY.** Text in English. 2001. s-a. free (effective 2005). back issues avail. **Document type:** *Journal, Academic/Scholarly.* **Description:** Dedicated to on-going research in earth sciences.
Media: Online - full content. **Related titles:** CD-ROM ed.: ISSN 1550-0896.
Published by: Spatial Hydrology josh@spatialhydrology.com, http://www.spatialhydrology.com/journal/.

➤ **KAZE NI KANSURU SHINPOJUMU KOEN YOSHISHU/PROCEEDINGS OF THE WIND SYMPOSIUM.** see *METEOROLOGY*

550 GBR ISSN 0140-9565
KENT FIELD CLUB. BULLETIN. Text in English. 1956. a.
Indexed: ZooRec.
Published by: Kent Field Club, Ecology Group, Christ Church College, Stodmarsh Rd, Kent, Canterbury CT3 4AQ, United Kingdom. TEL 44-1227-767700, FAX 44-1227-786501.

550 GBR
KENT FIELD CLUB. NEWSLETTER. Text in English. q.
Published by: Kent Field Club, Ecology Group, Christ Church College, Stodmarsh Rd, Kent, Canterbury CT3 4AQ, United Kingdom. TEL 44-1227-767700, FAX 44-1227-786501.

550 GBR ISSN 0141-1225
KENT FIELD CLUB. TRANSACTIONS. Text in English. 1957. a.
—BLDSC (8976.900000).
Published by: Kent Field Club, Ecology Group, Christ Church College, Stodmarsh Rd, Kent, Canterbury CT3 4AQ, United Kingdom. TEL 44-1227-767700, FAX 44-1227-786501.

KEVO SUBARCTIC RESEARCH INSTITUTE. REPORTS. see *BIOLOGY*

550 SAU
KING ABDUL AZIZ UNIVERSITY. FACULTY OF EARTH SCIENCES. BULLETIN. Text in Arabic. 1981 (no.4). a.
Published by: King Abdul Aziz University, Faculty of Earth Sciences, P O Box 1540, Jeddah, 21441, Saudi Arabia. TEL 6952386, FAX 6952381, TELEX 601141 KAUNI SJ.

KOBLENZER GEOGRAPHISCHES KOLLOQUIUM. see *GEOGRAPHY*

550 JPN
KOKURITSU KYOKUCHI KENKYUJO KYODO KENKYU HOKOKUSHO/NATIONAL INSTITUTE OF POLAR RESEARCH. JOINT RESEARCH REPORT. Text in Japanese. 1977. irreg., latest vol.13, 2002.
Published by: National Institute of Polar Research/Kokuritsu Kyokuchi Kenkyujo, Publications, 9-10, Kiga 1-chome, Itabashi-ku, Tokyo, 173, Japan. TEL 81-3-3962-2214, FAX 81-3-3962-2225, xkawa@nipr.ac.jp. Ed. Okitsugu Watanabe.

550 JPN
KOKURITSU KYOKUCHI KENKYUJO NENPO/NATIONAL INSTITUTE OF POLAR RESEARCH. ANNUAL REPORT. Text in Japanese. 1974. a. **Document type:** *Yearbook.*
Published by: National Institute of Polar Research/Kokuritsu Kyokuchi Kenkyujo, Publications, 9-10, Kiga 1-chome, Itabashi-ku, Tokyo, 173, Japan. TEL 81-3962-2214, FAX 81-3-3962-2225, publication@nipr.ac.jp. Ed. Okitsugu Watanabe.

551.22 JPN ISSN 0910-6324
KOKUSAI JISHINGAKU OYOBI JISHIN KOGAKU KENSHU NENPO/INTERNATIONAL STUDY REPORT ON THE EARTHQUAKE AND EARTHQUAKE ENGINEERING. Variant title: Kokusai Jishin Oyobi Jishin Kogaku Kenshu Nenpo. Text in Japanese. 1972. a. per issue exchange basis. **Document type:** *Bulletin.* **Description:** Reviews the history and current activities of the IISEE.
Published by: Kokusai Jishin Kogakubu, Kensetsusho Kenchiku Kenkyujo/International Institute of Seismology and Earthquake Engineering, Building Research Institute, 1, Tachihara, Tsukuba-shi, Ibaraki-ken 305-0802, Japan. TEL 81-298-79-0680, FAX 81-298-64-6777, iisee@kenken.go.jp, http://iisee.kenken.go.jp. Ed. Mitsumasa Midorikawa. Circ: 350.

KONGELIGE DANSKE VIDENSKABERNES SELSKAB. BIOLOGISKE SKRIFTER. see *BIOLOGY*

550 RUS ISSN 1560-7496
KRIOSFERA ZEMLI. Text in Russian. 1997. q. RUR 290 for 6 mos. domestic; USD 60 foreign (effective 2005). **Document type:** *Journal, Academic/Scholarly.*
Indexed: GEOBASE, RefZh.
Published by: (Kriosfera Zemli), Izdatel'stvo Sibirskogo Otdeleniya Rossiiskoi Akademii Nauk/Publishing House of the Russian Academy of Sciences, Siberian Branch, Morskoi pr 2, a/ya 187, Novosibirsk, 630090, Russian Federation. TEL 7-3832-300570, FAX 7-3832-333755, psb@ad-sbras.nsc.ru, http://www-psb.ad-sbras.nsc.ru/kriosw.htm. Ed. V P Melnikov. **Dist. by:** Informnauka Ltd., Ul Usievicha 20, Moscow 125190, Russian Federation. alfimov@viniti.ru.

KUANGWU XUEBAO/ACTA MINERALOGICA SINICA. see *MINES AND MINING INDUSTRY*

550 JPN ISSN 0911-0410
KYOKUCHIKEN NYUSU/NATIONAL INSTITUTE OF POLAR RESEARCH. NEWS. Text in Japanese. 1974. bi-m. **Document type:** *Newsletter.*

E

▼ new title ➤ refereed ✶ unverified ♦ full entry avail.

Published by: National Institute of Polar Research/Kokuritsu Kyokuchi Kenkyujo, Publications, 9-10, Kiga 1-chome, Itabashi-ku, Tokyo, 173, Japan. TEL 81-3-3962-2214, FAX 81-3-3962-2225, publication@nipr.ac.jp. Ed. Okitsugu Watanabe.

550   JPN   ISSN 0453-0276
QE1   CODEN: KDKCAJ
KYUSHU DAIGAKU KYOYOBU CHIGAKU KENKYU HOKOKU/KYUSHU UNIVERSITY. COLLEGE OF GENERAL EDUCATION. REPORTS ON EARTH SCIENCE. Text in English, Japanese. 1955. irreg.
Indexed: ChemAb, JPI.
Published by: Kyushu Daigaku, Kyoyobu, Chigaku Kyoshitsu/Kyushu University, College of General Education, Department of Earth Science, 2-1 Ropponmatsu 4-chome, Chuo-ku, Fukuoka-shi, 810-0044, Japan.

550   GBR   ISSN 1085-3278
S622   CODEN: LDDEF6
➤ **LAND DEGRADATION AND DEVELOPMENT.** Text in English. 1989. bi-m. USD 1,025 to institutions; USD 1,128 combined subscription to institutions print & online eds. (effective 2006). adv. back issues avail.; reprint service avail. from PSC.
Document type: Journal, Academic/Scholarly. **Description:** Seeks to promote rational study of the recognition, monitoring, control, and rehabilitation of degradation in terrestrial environments.
Formerly: Land Degradation and Rehabilitation (0898-5812)
Related titles: Microform ed.: (from PQC); Online - full text ed.: ISSN 1099-145X. 1997. USD 1,025 to institutions (effective 2006) (from EBSCO Publishing, Swets Information Services, Wiley InterScience).
Indexed: ASCA, ASFA, Agr, AgrForAb, AnBrAb, BIOSIS Prev, BiolAb, CPA, CivEngAb, CurCont, EPB, ESPM, EngInd, EnvEAb, FCA, FLUIDEX, FPA, ForAb, GEOBASE, HerbAb, HortAb, I&DA, M&TEA, MaizeAb, PGegResA, PollutAb, RA&MP, RDA, RPP, RRTA, RiceAb, S&F, SIA, SSCI, SWRA, SeedAb, SoyAb, TDB, TriticAb, WAE&RSA, WeedAb.
—BLDSC (5146.796790), Ei, IDS, IE, Infotrieve, ingenta, Linda Hall. **CCC.**
Published by: John Wiley & Sons Ltd. (Subsidiary of: John Wiley & Sons, Inc.), The Atrium, Southern Gate, Chichester, West Sussex PO19 8SQ, United Kingdom. TEL 44-1243-779777, FAX 44-1243-775878, customer@wiley.co.uk, http://www.interscience.wiley.com/journal/ldr, http://www.wiley.co.uk. Ed. Dr. Chris Barrow. adv.: B&W page GBP 650, color page GBP 1,550; trim 200 x 260. **Subscr. in the Americas to:** John Wiley & Sons, Inc., 111 River St, Hoboken, NJ 07030-5774. TEL 201-748-6645, FAX 201-748-6088, subinfo@wiley.com.

➤ **LANDCARE RESEARCH SCIENCE SERIES.** see BIOLOGY

550   DEU
                                              CODEN: AGLWAT
➤ **LANDESAMT FUER GEOLOGIE, ROHSTOFFE UND BERGBAU BADEN-WUERTTEMBERG. ABHANDLUNGEN.** Text in German; Summaries in English, French, German. 1953. irreg., latest vol.14, 1997. price varies. back issues avail. **Document type:** Monographic series, Academic/Scholarly.
Formerly: Geologisches Landesamt Baden-Wuerttemberg. Abhandlungen (0408-1552)
—CASDDS.
Published by: Landesamt fuer Geologie Rohstoffe und Bergbau Baden-Wuerttemberg, Albertstr 5, Freiburg Im Breisgau, 79104, Germany. TEL 49-761-204-4375, FAX 49-761-204-4438, poststelle@lgrb.uni-freiburg.de.

550   DEU   ISSN 1617-1330
QE269.A19   CODEN: JGLBAV
LANDESAMT FUER GEOLOGIE, ROHSTOFFE UND BERGBAU BADEN-WUERTTEMBERG. JAHRESHEFTE. Text and summaries in English, French, German. 1955. a., latest vol.38, 1999. cum.index. back issues avail. **Document type:** Bulletin, Academic/Scholarly.
Formerly: (until 1999): Geologisches Landesamt Baden-Wuerttemberg. Jahreshefte (0408-1560)
Indexed: IBR, ZooRec.
—CASDDS.
Published by: Landesamt fuer Geologie Rohstoffe und Bergbau Baden-Wuerttemberg, Albertstr 5, Freiburg Im Breisgau, 79104, Germany. TEL 49-761-204-4375, FAX 49-761-204-4438, poststelle@lgrb.uni-freiburg.de.

LANDSCAPES. see ARCHAEOLOGY

550   DEU   ISSN 0930-0317
                                              CODEN: LNESEK
LECTURE NOTES IN EARTH SCIENCES. Text in English. 1985. irreg., latest vol.107, 2006. price varies. **Document type:** Monographic series, Academic/Scholarly.
Indexed: Inspec, ZentMath, ZooRec.
—BLDSC (5180.193000), CASDDS, CISTI, IE, ingenta, Linda Hall. **CCC.**
Published by: Springer-Verlag (Subsidiary of: Springer Science+Business Media), Haber Str 7, Heidelberg, 69126, Germany. TEL 49-6221-3450, FAX 49-6221-229, subscriptions@springer.de, http://www.springer.de. Adv. contact Stephan Kroeck TEL 49-30-827875739.

LINNEAN SOCIETY OF NEW SOUTH WALES. PROCEEDINGS. see BIOLOGY—Zoology

550   RUS   ISSN 0131-1719
QE420   CODEN: LIPADJ
LITOLOGIYA I PALEOGEOGRAFIYA. Text in Russian. 1972. triennial. RUR 10 (effective 1999). bibl.; illus. **Document type:** Academic/Scholarly. **Description:** Deals with the sedimentary deposition and paleogeographia within various regions in Russia and other countries.
—Linda Hall.
Published by: Izdatelstvo Sankt-Peterburgskogo Universiteta, Universitetskaya nab 7-9, St Petersburg, 199034, Russian Federation. TEL 7-812-2189671, FAX 7-812-1141470. Ed. V N Shvanov. Circ: 600.

LUNAR AND PLANETARY INFORMATION BULLETIN. see ASTRONOMY

M E S A JOURNAL. (Mines and Energy South Australia) see MINES AND MINING INDUSTRY

550   FIN   ISSN 0781-9625
MAGNETIC RESULTS SODANKYLA. Text in Multiple languages. 1972. a. **Document type:** Academic/Scholarly.
Related titles: ◆ Series of: Oulun Ylipiston.Sodankylan Geofysiikan Observatorio. Publications. ISSN 1456-3673.
Published by: Oulun Ylipiston, Sodankylan Geofysiikan Observatorio/University of Oulu. Sodankyla Geophysical Observatory, Taehtelaentie 62, Sodankyla, 99600, Finland. TEL 358-16-619811, FAX 358-16-619875, http://www.sgo.fi.

538   USA   ISSN 1535-1998
MAGNETICS BUSINESS & TECHNOLOGY. Text in English. 2002 (Mar.). q. free domestic to qualified personnel; USD 44 domestic; USD 60 foreign (effective 2005). adv. **Document type:** Magazine, Trade.
—CCC.
Published by: Webcom Communications Corp., 7355 E Orchard Rd, Ste 100, Greenwood Village, CO 80111. TEL 720-528-3770, 800-803-9488, FAX 720-528-3771, johncg@infowebcom.com, http://www.magneticsmagazine.com, http://www.infowebcom.com. Ed., Pub. David Webster.

MALAYSIAN JOURNAL OF SCIENCE. SERIES B: PHYSICAL & EARTH SCIENCES. see PHYSICS

550   ESP   ISSN 1131-9100
MAPPING; la revista tematica interactiva de ciencias de la tierra. Text in Spanish. 1991. bi-m. USD 120 foreign (effective 2002).
Related titles: Online - full text ed.
Indexed: IECT.
—CINDOC.
Published by: Carsigma Cartografica, Sta. Maria de la Cabeza, 42-1, Ofic. 3, Madrid, 28045, Spain. TEL 34-91-5471116, FAX 34-91-5477469, http://www.mappinginteractivo.com/.

551.46   NLD   ISSN 0304-4203
GC109   CODEN: MRCHBD
➤ **MARINE CHEMISTRY.** Text in Dutch. 1972. 20/yr. EUR 2,017 in Europe to institutions; JPY 267,500 in Japan to institutions; USD 2,256 to institutions except Europe and Japan; EUR 318 in Europe to qualified personnel; JPY 42,300 in Japan to qualified personnel; USD 357 to qualified personnel except Europe and Japan (effective 2006). adv. bk.rev. bibl.; charts; illus. cum.index. reprints avail. **Document type:** Journal, Academic/Scholarly. **Description:** Publishes original studies and occasional reviews in the field of chemistry in the marine environment, from chemical processes to theoretical and experimental work, with emphasis on the dynamic approach. Provides a central channel of communication to speed the flow of information in this relatively new and rapidly expanding discipline.
Related titles: Microform ed.: (from PQC); Online - full text ed.: (from EBSCO Publishing, Gale Group, IngentaConnect, ScienceDirect, Swets Information Services).
Indexed: ASCA, ASFA, AnalAb, BIOBASE, BIOSIS Prev, BiolAb, CCI, CIN, Cadscan, ChemAb, ChemTitl, CurCont, E&PHSE, EIA, EPB, ESPM, EnerInd, ExcerpMed, FLUIDEX, GEOBASE, GP&P, IABS, ISR, LeadAb, M&GPA, M&TEA, MBA, MSB, MSCT, NutrAb, OceAb, OffTech, PetrolAb, PollutAb, RefZh, SCI, SFA, SWRA, WRCInf, Zincscan.
—BLDSC (5373.760000), CASDDS, CISTI, IDS, IE, Infotrieve, ingenta, Linda Hall, PADDS. **CCC.**
Published by: Elsevier BV (Subsidiary of: Elsevier Science & Technology), Radarweg 29, Amsterdam, 1043 NX, Netherlands. TEL 31-20-4853911, FAX 31-20-4852457, nlinfo-f@elsevier.nl, http://www.elsevier.com/locate/marchem, http://www.elsevier.nl. Ed. Frank J Millero. **Subscr. to:** Elsevier, Subscription Customer Service, 6277 Sea Harbor Dr, Orlando, FL 32887-4800. TEL 407-345-4020, 877-839-7126, FAX 407-363-1354.

550   USA
MASSACHUSETTS INSTITUTE OF TECHNOLOGY. DEPARTMENT OF EARTH, ATMOSPHERIC AND PLANETARY SCIENCES. REPORT. Text in English. irreg.
Published by: Massachusetts Institute of Technology, Department of Earth, Atmospheric and Planetary Sciences, 77 Massachusetts Ave, Cambridge, MA 02139. http://www-eaps.mit.edu.

MEDITERRANEE (AIX-EN-PROVENCE); revue geographique des pays mediterraneens. see GEOGRAPHY

LA MER/UMI. see BIOLOGY

550   JPN
METEORITES NEWS. Text in English. 1982. irreg., latest vol.11, 2002.
Published by: National Institute of Polar Research/Kokuritsu Kyokuchi Kenkyujo, Publications, 9-10, Kiga 1-chome, Itabashi-ku, Tokyo, 173, Japan. TEL 81-3-3962-2214, FAX 81-3-3962-2225, publication@nipr.ac.jp. Ed. Okitsugu Watanabe.

METEORITICS AND PLANETARY SCIENCE. see ASTRONOMY

551.9   NLD   ISSN 0076-6895
                                              CODEN: MGEGAA
➤ **METHODS IN GEOCHEMISTRY AND GEOPHYSICS.** Text in English. 1964. irreg., latest vol.37, 2002. price varies. back issues avail. **Document type:** Monographic series, Academic/Scholarly. **Description:** Describes research and applications in geochemistry and geophysics.
Indexed: ChemAb, ChemTitl, IMMAb, Inspec.
—BLDSC (5748.080000), CASDDS, CISTI, IE, ingenta. **CCC.**
Published by: Elsevier BV (Subsidiary of: Elsevier Science & Technology), Radarweg 29, Amsterdam, 1043 NX, Netherlands. TEL 31-20-4853911, FAX 31-20-4852457, nlinfo-f@elsevier.nl, http://www.elsevier.nl.

➤ **MINERALOGIA POLONICA.** see MINES AND MINING INDUSTRY

➤ **THE MINERALOGICAL RECORD.** see HOBBIES

➤ **MINERALOGICHESKII ZHURNAL/MINERALOGICAL JOURNAL;** nauchno-teoreticheskii zhurnal. see MINES AND MINING INDUSTRY

550   DEU   ISSN 1435-1943
QE701
➤ **MITTEILUNGEN AUS DEM MUSEUM FUER NATURKUNDE IN BERLIN - GEOWISSENSCHAFTLICHE REIHE;** an international journal of geoscience. Text in German. a., latest vol.9, 2006. EUR 258 in Europe; CHF 388 in Switzerland & Liechtenstein; USD 344 elsewhere (effective 2006). **Document type:** Journal, Academic/Scholarly.
Related titles: Online - full text ed.: (from Wiley InterScience).
Indexed: ZooRec.
—CCC.
Published by: Wiley - V C H Verlag GmbH & Co. KGaA (Subsidiary of: John Wiley & Sons, Inc.), Boschstr 12, Weinheim, 69469, Germany. TEL 49-6201-6060, FAX 49-6201-606328, adsales@wiley-vch.de, subservice@wiley-vch.de, info@wiley-vch.de, http://www.wiley-vch.de. Ed. H P Schulze. R&P Claudia Rutz. Adv. contact Aenne Anders TEL 49-6201-606552.

550   USA   ISSN 0276-4741
GB500
➤ **MOUNTAIN RESEARCH AND DEVELOPMENT.** Text in English; Summaries in French, German; Text occasionally in Spanish. 1981. q. USD 70 in US & Canada to individuals; USD 90 elsewhere to individuals; USD 150 in US & Canada to institutions; USD 170 elsewhere to institutions (effective 2005). adv.bk.rev. index. back issues avail. **Document type:** Journal, Academic/Scholarly. **Description:** Takes an interdisciplinary approach to the study of mountain regions and the exploitation of their resources, as well as the well-being of mountain people.
Related titles: Microfilm ed.: (from PQC); Online - full text ed.: (from BioOne, C S A, O C L C Online Computer Library Center, Inc.).
Indexed: AEA, ASCA, AgBio, Agr, AgrForAb, AnthLit, BIOSIS Prev, BiolAb, CPA, CurCont, DSA, EnvEAb, FCA, FPA, ForAb, GEOBASE, HerbAb, HortAb, I&DA, ISR, IndVet, M&GPA, MaizeAb, NutrAb, OrnHort, PBA, PGegResA, PHN&I, PotatoAb, PoultAb, RA&MP, RDA, RM&VM, RPP, RRTA, RevApplEntom, RiceAb, S&F, SCI, SFA, SSCI, SeedAb, TDB, TriticAb, WAE&RSA, WeedAb, WildRev, ZooRec.
—BLDSC (5978.990000), CISTI, IDS, IE, Infotrieve, ingenta, Linda Hall. **CCC.**
Contact Dist.: Allen Press Inc., PO Box 1897, Lawrence, KS 66044. TEL 785-843-1235, FAX 785-843-1274, mrd@allenpress.com, orders@allenpress.com, http://www.mrd-journal.org, http://www.allenpress.com. Ed. Jack D Ives. adv.: B&W page USD 275. Circ: 900 (paid).

➤ **MUSEO CIVICO DI STORIA NATURALE DI VENEZIA. BOLLETTINO.** see BIOLOGY

➤ **MUSEO CIVICO DI STORIA NATURALE DI VENEZIA. QUADERNI.** see BIOLOGY

550   ITA
MUSEO CIVICO DI STORIA NATURALE DI VERONA. MEMORIE. SERIE 2, SEZIONE B: SCIENZE DELLA TERRA. Text in Italian. 1977. irreg., latest vol.5, 1993. price varies.
Formerly: Museo Civico di Storia Naturale di Verona. Memorie. Serie 2, Part 2: Abiologica.
Indexed: ZooRec.

Published by: Museo Civico di Storia Naturale di Verona, Lungadige Porta Vittoria 9, Verona, VR 37129, Italy. TEL 39-045-8079400, FAX 39-045-8035639, mcsnat@comune.verona.it, http://www.museostorianaturaleverona.it.

550 BRA
QE235 CODEN: BMPTET
MUSEU PARAENSE EMILIO GOELDI. BOLETIM. NOVA SERIE GEOLOGIA. Text in Portuguese; Abstracts in English. 1957; N.S. 1989. s-a. BRL 18 per issue domestic; USD 25 per issue foreign (effective 2000). bibl.; charts; illus.; stat. **Description:** Publishes original papers in earth sciences.
Former titles (until 1999, no. 11): Museu Paraense Emilio Goeldi. Boletim. Serie Ciencias da Terra (0103-4278); (until 1988): Museu Paraense Emilio Goeldi. Boletim. Nova Serie: Geologia (0077-2224)
Indexed: BIOSIS Prev, BiolAb, I&DA, RefZh, S&F, ZooRec.
—CASDDS.
Published by: Conselho Nacional de Desenvolvimento Cientifico e Tecnologico, Museu Paraense Emilio Goeldi, Comercio, Caixa Postal 399, Belem, PA 66017-970, Brazil. TEL 091-274-2195, FAX 091-274-1811, mgdoc@musu-goeldi.br. Circ: 1,000.

550 363.7 USA ISSN 1568-1238
N A T O SCIENCE SERIES. SERIES IV: EARTH AND ENVIRONMENTAL SCIENCES. Text in English. 2000. irreg., latest vol.57, 2005. price varies. **Document type:** *Monographic series, Academic/Scholarly.*
Formed by the merger of (1995-2000): N A T O Science Partnership Sub-Series 2: Environmental Security (1389-1839); Which was formerly (until 1998): N A T O Advances Science Institute Series. Partnership Sub-Series 2: Environment (1431-7141); (1994-2000): N A T O Science Partnership Sub-Series 1: Disarmament Technologies (1389-1820); Which was formerly (until 1998): N A T O Advances Science Institute Series. Partnership Sub-Series 1: Disarmament Technologies (1383-715X)
Indexed: BIOSIS Prev.
—BLDSC (6033.693330), CISTI, IE, ingenta. **CCC.**
Published by: (North Atlantic Treaty Organization, Scientific Affairs Division BEL), Springer-Verlag New York, Inc. (Subsidiary of: Springer Science+Business Media), 233 Spring St, New York, NY 10013. TEL 212-460-1500, FAX 212-460-1575, service@springer-ny.com, http://www.springer-ny.com.

550 JPN ISSN 1342-4033
QC994.8
N I P R ARCTIC DATA REPORTS. Text in Japanese. 1996. irreg., latest vol.5, 2002. per issue exchange basis. **Document type:** *Academic/Scholarly.* **Description:** Contains field data acquired in the Arctic region. Research in the Arctic is in wide variety of areas, including atmosphere, cryosphere, hydrosphere, lithosphere, biosphere and other natural environments.
Indexed: M&GPA.
—CISTI, Linda Hall.
Published by: National Institute of Polar Research/Kokuritsu Kyokuchi Kenkyujo, Publications, 9-10, Kiga 1-chome, Itabashi-ku, Tokyo, 173, Japan. TEL 81-3-3962-2214, FAX 81-3-3962-2225, TELEX 272-3515 POLRSCJ, publication@nipr.ac.jp. Ed. Okitsugu Watanabe. Circ: 1,000.

N I W A. ANNUAL REPORT. (National Institute of Water and Atmospheric) see *ENVIRONMENTAL STUDIES*

333.1 USA
N R R I NOW. Text in English. 1987. 3/yr. free. back issues avail. **Document type:** *Newsletter.* **Description:** Reports the institute's activities in promoting the economic development of Minnesota's natural resources in an environmentally sound manner.
Published by: University of Minnesota, Duluth, Natural Resources Research Institute, 5013 Miller Trunk Hwy, Duluth, MN 55811. TEL 218-720-4280, FAX 218-720-4219. Ed. Nora Kubazewski. Circ: 2,500 (controlled).

550 JPN ISSN 0386-8559
NAGASAKIKEN CHIGAKKAISHI/NAGASAKI EARTH SCIENCE ASSOCIATION. JOURNAL. Text in Japanese. 1962. s-a. JPY 3,000 (effective 1996). **Document type:** *Academic/Scholarly.*
Published by: Nagasakiken Chigakkai, Nagasaki Daigaku Kyoikugakubu Chigaku Kyoshitsu, 1-14 Bunkyo-Machi, Nagasaki-shi, 852-8131, Japan. TEL 0958-47-1111, FAX 0958-44-0401. Ed. Yasuhiko Kamad.

550 CHN ISSN 1000-4947
G845
NANJI YANJIU/SOUTH POLE RESEARCH. Text in Chinese. q. **Document type:** *Academic/Scholarly.*
Related titles: ♦ Chinese ed.: Chinese Journal of Polar Science. ISSN 1007-7065.
Published by: (Zhongguo Jidi Yanjiusuo/Polar Research Institute of China), Kexue Chubanshe/Science Press, 16 Donghuang Cheng Genbei Jie, Beijing, 100717, China. TEL 86-10-64000246, FAX 86-10-64030255, http://www.sciencep.com/.

NANKYOKU SHIRYO/ANTARCTIC RECORD. see *GEOGRAPHY*

550 NOR ISSN 0802-9601
NANSEN REMOTE SENSING CENTER. TECHNICAL REPORT/NANSEN SENTER FOR MILJOE OG FJERNMAALING. TEKNISK RAPPORT. Text in English, Norwegian. 1987. 3/yr. **Document type:** *Monographic series.*
Indexed: ASFA, ESPM.
Published by: Nanser Senter for Miljoe og Fjernmaaling/Nansen Environmental and Remote Sensing Center, Edv Griegsvei 3a, Bergen, 5059, Norway. TEL 47-55-297288, FAX 47-55-200050, http://www.nersc.no.

550 559 JPN ISSN 0386-5533
CODEN: MNISDG
➤ **NATIONAL INSTITUTE OF POLAR RESEARCH. MEMOIRS. SERIES C: EARTH SCIENCES.** Text and summaries in English. 1964. irreg., latest vol.16, 1984. per issue exchange basis. **Document type:** *Monographic series, Academic/Scholarly.*
Supersedes: Japanese Antarctic Research Expedition, 1956-1962. Scientific Reports. Series C: Earth Sciences (0075-3378)
Indexed: ASFA, ESPM.
—Linda Hall.
Published by: National Institute of Polar Research/Kokuritsu Kyokuchi Kenkyujo, Publications, 9-10, Kiga 1-chome, Itabashi-ku, Tokyo, 173, Japan. TEL 81-3-3962-2214, FAX 81-3-3962-2225, publication@nipr.ac.jp. Ed. Okitsugu Watanabe. Circ: 1,000.

550 JPN ISSN 0386-0744
QB755.5.A6 CODEN: MNIRDD
➤ **NATIONAL INSTITUTE OF POLAR RESEARCH. MEMOIRS. SPECIAL ISSUE.** Text and summaries in English. 1967. irreg., latest vol.57, 2003. per issue exchange basis. **Document type:** *Proceedings, Academic/Scholarly.*
Formerly (until 1972): Japanese Antarctic Research Expedition Scientific Reports. Special Issue (0386-5452)
Indexed: RefZh, ZooRec.
—BLDSC (5626.800000), CASDDS, CISTI, KNAW.
Published by: National Institute of Polar Research/Kokuritsu Kyokuchi Kenkyujo, Publications, 9-10, Kiga 1-chome, Itabashi-ku, Tokyo, 173, Japan. TEL 81-3-3962-2214, FAX 81-3-3962-2225, publication@nipr.ac.jp. Ed. Okitsugu Watanabe. Circ: 1,000.

➤ **NATUR UND MENSCH.** see *BIOLOGY*

550 ITA ISSN 0392-4149
NATURA ALPINA. Text in Italian. 1950. q. EUR 16 to members (effective 2005). **Document type:** *Magazine, Consumer.*
Indexed: RefZh, ZooRec.
Published by: (Societa di Scienze Naturali del Trentino), Museo Tridentino di Scienze Naturali, Via Calepina 14, Trento, TN 38100, Italy. TEL 39-0461-270311, FAX 39-0461.233830, info@mtsn.tn.it, http://www.mtsn.tn.it. Ed. Gino Tomasi.

550 NLD ISSN 0921-030X
GB5000 CODEN: NAHZEL
➤ **NATURAL HAZARDS.** Text in Dutch. 1988. 9/yr. EUR 1,078, USD 1,125, GBP 715 combined subscription to institutions print & online eds. (effective 2005). back issues avail.; reprint service avail. from PSC. **Document type:** *Journal, Academic/Scholarly.* **Description:** Publishes original research work on the physical aspects of natural hazards, the statistics of forecasting catastrophic events, risk assessment, and the nature of precursors of natural and/or technological hazards.
Related titles: Microform ed.: (from PQC); Online - full text ed.: ISSN 1573-0840 (from EBSCO Publishing, Gale Group, IngentaConnect, Kluwer Online, O C L C Online Computer Library Center, Inc., Springer LINK, Swets Information Services).
Indexed: AJEE, ASCA, ASFA, BibLing, BrCerAb, C&ISA, CerAb, CivEngAb, CorrAb, CurCont, E&CAJ, EEA, EMA, EPB, ESPM, FLUIDEX, GEOBASE, H&SSA, IAA, IBR, ICEA, Inspec, M&GPA, M&TEA, MBF, METADEX, RefZh, RiskAb, SOPODA, WAA.
—BLDSC (6037.780000), AskIEEE, CISTI, IDS, IE, Infotrieve, ingenta, Linda Hall. **CCC.**
Published by: (International Society for the Prevention and Mitigation of Natural Hazards), Springer-Verlag Dordrecht (Subsidiary of: Springer Science+Business Media), Van Godewijckstraat 30, Dordrecht, 3311 GX, Netherlands. TEL 31-78-6576050, FAX 31-78-6576474, http://springerlink.metapress.com/openurl.asp?genre=journal&issn=0921-030x, http://www.springeronline.com. Eds. Tad S Murty, Tom Beer, Vladimir Schenk.

➤ **NATURAL HISTORY MUSEUM AND INSTITUTE, CHIBA. JOURNAL. SPECIAL ISSUE.** see *BIOLOGY*

➤ **NATURAL HISTORY RESEARCH. SPECIAL ISSUE.** see *BIOLOGY*

550 001.3 FRA ISSN 1240-1307
CODEN: NSCSEX
➤ **NATURES - SCIENCES - SOCIETES.** Text in French; Text occasionally in English. 1993. q. EUR 82 combined subscription domestic to individuals print & online eds.; EUR 91 combined subscription in the European Union to individuals print & online eds.; EUR 98 combined subscription elsewhere to individuals print & online eds.; EUR 148 combined subscription domestic to institutions print & online eds.; EUR 169 combined subscription in the European Union to institutions print & online eds.; EUR 179 combined subscription elsewhere to institutions print & online eds. (effective 2006). adv. back issues avail. **Document type:** *Academic/Scholarly.* **Description:** Examines the relationship of man to the physical and living world, which is responsible for environmental problems.
Related titles: Online - full text ed.: ISSN 1765-2979. EUR 123 (effective 2006) (from EBSCO Publishing, Gale Group, IngentaConnect, ScienceDirect, Swets Information Services).
Indexed: ASFA, DIP, ESPM, GEOBASE, IBR, IBZ, INIS AtomInd.
—BLDSC (6048.018000), CISTI, IE, Infotrieve, ingenta. **CCC.**
Published by: (Association Natures Sciences Societes-Dialogues), E D P Sciences, 17 Ave du Hoggar, Parc d'Activites de Courtaboeuf, BP 112, Cedex A, Les Ulis, F-91944, France. TEL 33-1-69187575, FAX 33-1-69860678, subscribers@edpsciences.org, http://www.elsevier.com/locate/natsci, http://www.edpsciences.org.

➤ **NATURHISTORISCHE GESELLSCHAFT HANNOVER. BEIHEFTE ZU DEN BERICHTEN.** see *BIOLOGY*

550 DEU ISSN 0365-9844
QH5 CODEN: BENHAP
NATURHISTORISCHE GESELLSCHAFT HANNOVER. BERICHTE. Summaries in English, German. 1800. a. **Document type:** *Proceedings.*
Indexed: BiolAb, IBR, ZooRec.
—**CCC.**
Published by: Naturhistorische Gesellschaft Hannover, Willy-Brandt-Allee 5, Hannover, 30169, Germany. TEL 49-511-9807-860, FAX 49-511-9807-880. Circ: 900.

NATURHISTORISCHE GESELLSCHAFT NUERNBERG. ABHANDLUNGEN. see *ARCHAEOLOGY*

NATURHISTORISCHES MUSEUM IN WIEN. ANNALEN. SERIE A, MINERALOGIE UND PETROGRAPHIE, GEOLOGIE UND PALAEONTOLOGIE, ANTHROPOLOGIE UND PRAEHISTORIE. see *SCIENCES: COMPREHENSIVE WORKS*

NATURWISSENSCHAFTLICHE ZEITSCHRIFT FUER NIEDERBAYERN. see *BIOLOGY*

NATURWISSENSCHAFTLICHER VEREIN WUERZBURG. ABHANDLUNGEN. see *BIOLOGY*

NATURWISSENSCHAFTLICHER VEREIN ZU BREMEN. ABHANDLUNGEN. see *BIOLOGY*

550 NLD ISSN 0166-2627
NATUURBEHOUD. Text in Dutch. 1970. q. EUR 18.50 (effective 2003).
Incorporated: Natuurspoor (1388-7734)
—BLDSC (6049.950000), IE, Infotrieve.
Published by: Vereniging tot Behoud van Natuurmonumenten in Nederland, Postbus 9955, 's-Graveland, 1243 ZS, Netherlands. TEL 31-35-655-9933, http://www.natuurmonumenten.nl/nieuws/p_natuurbehoud.asp?cc=6, http://www.natuurmonumenten.nl/index_ho.asp.

526 551 NLD
CODEN: NRGPBY
NEDERLANDSE COMMISSIE VOOR GEODESIE. PUBLICATIONS ON GEODESY. Text mainly in English. 1961. irreg., latest vol.49, 2000. price varies. charts; illus. back issues avail. **Document type:** *Monographic series, Academic/Scholarly.* **Description:** Publishes geodetic research.
Former titles: Nederlandse Commissie voor Geodesie. Publications on Geodesy. New Series (0165-1706); Netherlands. Rijkscommissie voor Geodesie. Publications on Geodesy. New Series (0077-7625)
Indexed: RefZh.
—BLDSC (7129.850000), KNAW.
Published by: Nederlandse Commissie voor Geodesie/Netherlands Geodetic Commission, PO Box 5030, Delft, 2600 GA, Netherlands. TEL 31-15-278-2819, FAX 31-15-278-1775, ncg@geo.tudelft.nl, http://www.ncg.knaw.nl/. Pub. F H Schroder. Circ: 700.

550 JPN
NIHON CHIKYU KAGAKKAI NYUSU/GEOCHEMICAL SOCIETY OF JAPAN. NEWS. Text in Japanese. 1954. 4/yr., latest no.165. **Document type:** *Newsletter, Academic/Scholarly.*
Published by: Nihon Chikyu Kagakkai/Geochemical Society of Japan, Nihon Gakkai Jimu Senta, 16-19 Honkomagome 5-chome, Bunkyo-ku, Tokyo, 113-0021, Japan. Ed. S Nakai.

E

551.9 JPN ISSN 1343-2745
NIHON DAIGAKU BUNRIGAKUBU SHIZEN KAGAKU KENKYUJO KENKYU KIYO. CHIKYU SYSTEM KAGAKU/NIHON UNIVERSITY. INSTITUTE OF NATURAL SCIENCES. PROCEEDINGS. GEOSYSTEM SCIENCES. Text in English, Japanese. a. **Document type:** *Proceedings, Academic/Scholarly.*
Formerly: Nihon Daigaku Bunrigakubu Shizen Kagaku Kenkyujo Kenkyu Kiyo. Oyo Chigaku - Nihon University. Institute of Natural Sciences. Proceedings. Applied Earth Sciences (0911-4971)
Published by: (Shizen Kagaku Kenkyujo), Nihon Daigaku, Bunrigakubu Shizen Kagaku Kenkyujo/Nihon University, College of Humanities and Sciences, Institute of Natural Sciences, 25-40 Sakurajosui 3-chome, Setagaya-ku, Tokyo, 156-0045, Japan. TEL 81-3-5317-9724, FAX 81-3-5317-9430.

552.5 627 CHN ISSN 0468-155X
NISHA YANJIU/JOURNAL OF SEDIMENT RESEARCH. Text in Chinese; Abstracts in English. 1956. bi-m. CNY 10 per issue domestic (effective 2003). back issues avail. **Document type:** *Academic/Scholarly.*
Related titles: Online - full content ed.: (from WanFang Data Corp.); Online - full text ed.: (from East View Information Services).
Indexed: EngInd.
Published by: Zhongguo Shuili Xuehui, Nisha Zhuanyewei Yuanhui/Sedimentation Committee, Chinese Society of Hydraulic Engineering, 20 Chegongzhuang Xi Lu, Beijing, 100044, China. TEL 86-10-68415522 ext 6628, FAX 86-10-68416371. Ed. Guo-Han Du.

526 550 NOR ISSN 0803-0421
NORSK POLARINSTITUTT. RAPPORTSERIE. Text in English, Norwegian. 1979. irreg., latest vol.122, 2003. price varies. back issues avail. **Document type:** *Monographic series, Academic/Scholarly.*
Formed by the merger of (1926-2000): Norsk Polarinstitutt. Meddelelser (0373-5605); (1922-2000): Norsk Polarinstitutt. Skrifter (0369-5417)
Indexed: ASFA, BiolAb, ESPM, M&GPA.
Published by: Norsk Polarinstitutt/Norwegian Polar Institut, Polar Environmental Centre, Tromsoe, 9296, Norway. TEL 47-77-750500, FAX 47-77-750501, http://www.npolar.no.

NORWEGIAN PETROLEUM SOCIETY. SPECIAL PUBLICATION. see *PETROLEUM AND GAS*

ODYSSEY (PERU); adventures in science. see *CHILDREN AND YOUTH—For*

OESTERREICHISCHE AKADEMIE DER WISSENSCHAFTEN. ABTEILUNG 1: BIOLOGISCHE WISSENSCHAFTEN UND ERDWISSENSCHAFTEN. SITZUNGSBERICHTE UND ANZEIGER. see *BIOLOGY*

OESTERREICHISCHE GEOGRAPHISCHE GESELLSCHAFT. MITTEILUNGEN. see *GEOGRAPHY*

550 ITA ISSN 0391-2612
CODEN: OFIOD4
OFIOLITI; an international journal on ophiolites and related topics. Text in English. 1976. s-a. EUR 31 in the European Union to individuals; EUR 40 elsewhere to individuals; EUR 40 in the European Union to institutions; EUR 70 elsewhere to institutions (effective 2004). **Document type:** *Bulletin, Academic/Scholarly.*
Indexed: CurCont, GEOBASE, RefZh, ZooRec.
Published by: Edizioni E T S, Piazza Carrara 16-19, Pisa, Italy. TEL 39-050-29544, FAX 39-050-20158, info@edizioniets.it, http://www.edizioniets.it. Circ: 210 (controlled); 150 (paid).

550 JPN ISSN 1340-7414
OKAYAMA UNIVERSITY EARTH SCIENCE REPORT/OKAYAMA DAIGAKU CHIKYU KAGAKU KENKYU HOKOKU. Text in English, Japanese. 1994. a.
—BLDSC (3643.530000), IE, ingenta.
Published by: Okayama University, Department of Earth Sciences, 1-1, Tsushima-Naka 3chome, Okayama, 700-8530, Japan. TEL 81-86-251-7891, FAX 81-86-251-7895, http://www.desc.okayama-u.ac.jp/index.html.

550 570 JPN ISSN 0289-7857
➤ **OKINAWA TOSHO KENKYU/ISLAND STUDIES IN OKINAWA.** Text in English, Japanese. 1983. a. per issue exchange basis. **Document type:** *Academic/Scholarly.*
Indexed: ZooRec.
Published by: (Iriomote Yamaneko Seitai Jikken Kenkyushitsu), Ryukyu Daigaku, Rigakubu Seibutsugakka/University of Ryukyus, College of Science, Department of Biology, Iriomote Cat Research Laboratory, 1 Senbaru, Nakagami-gun, Nishihara-cho, Okinawa-ken 903-0129, Japan. TEL 81-98-895-8541, FAX 81-98-895-5376. Eds. Hidetoshi Ota, Masako Izawa.

➤ **ORNITHOLOGISCHER VEREIN ZU HILDESHEIM. NATURKUNDLICHE MITTEILUNGEN.** see *BIOLOGY—Ornithology*

➤ **PALAEOGEOGRAPHY, PALAEOCLIMATOLOGY, PALAEOECOLOGY.** see *PALEONTOLOGY*

551.3 CHN ISSN 1002-0160
CODEN: PDOSEA
➤ **PEDOSPHERE/TURANG QUAN.** Text in English. 1991. q. CNY 144 (effective 2004). 96 p./no.; **Document type:** *Journal, Academic/Scholarly.* **Description:** Covers the fields of protection of soil resources, promotion of soil fertility and improvement of ecological environment.
Related titles: Online - full text ed.: (from East View Information Services, WanFang Data Corp.).
Indexed: ASFA, AgrForAb, BiolAb, CPA, ChemAb, ChemTitl, CurCont, ESPM, EnvEAb, FCA, FLUIDEX, FPA, ForAb, GEOBASE, HerbAb, HortAb, I&DA, M&GPA, MaizeAb, NemAb, NutrAb, PBA, PGrRegA, PN&I, PollutAb, PotatoAb, RA&MP, RDA, RPP, RefZh, RevApplEntom, RiceAb, RiskAb, S&F, SIA, SWRA, SeedAb, SoyAb, TriticAb, WAE&RSA, WeedAb.
—BLDSC (6417.798000), CASDDS, CISTI.
Published by: (Zhongguo Kexueyuan, Nanjing Turang Yanjiusuo/Chinese Academy of Sciences, Institution of Soil Science), Kexue Chubanshe/Science Press, 16 Donghuang Cheng Genbei Jie, Beijing, 100717, China. TEL 86-10-64000246, FAX 86-10-64030255, rmdu@mail.issas.ac.cn, http://trq-e.periodicals.net.cn/default.html, http://www.sciencep.com/. Ed. Du Rongmin. **Dist. by:** China International Book Trading Corp, 35 Chegongzhuang Xilu, Haidian District, PO Box 399, Beijing 100044, China. TEL 86-10-68412045, FAX 86-10-68412023, cibtc@mail.cibtc.com.cn, http://www.cibtc.com.cn.

➤ **PERIODICO DI MINERALOGIA.** see *MINES AND MINING INDUSTRY*

➤ **PHELSUMA.** see *BIOLOGY*

614.7 USA ISSN 0272-3646
G1
➤ **PHYSICAL GEOGRAPHY.** Text in English. 1980. 6/yr. USD 58 in North America to individuals; USD 385 in North America to institutions; USD 397 elsewhere to institutions (effective 2005). abstr.; bibl.; charts; illus.; stat. index. back issues avail.; reprints avail. **Document type:** *Journal, Academic/Scholarly.*
Related titles: Online - full text ed.: (from Gale Group, IngentaConnect).
Indexed: AESIS, ASCA, CTO, CurCont, ESPM, FLUIDEX, GEOBASE, M&GPA, M&TEA, SWRA, WildRev.
—BLDSC (6475.615000), CISTI, IDS, IE, Infotrieve, ingenta, Linda Hall. **CCC.**
Published by: Bellwether Publishing, Ltd., 8640 Guilford Rd, Ste 200, Columbia, MD 21046. TEL 410-290-3870, FAX 410-290-8726, bellpub@bellpub.com, http://www.bellpub.com. Ed. Antony R Orme. Circ: 400.

550 GBR ISSN 1474-7065
QE501 CODEN: PCEHAI
➤ **PHYSICS AND CHEMISTRY OF THE EARTH.** Text in English. 1956. 18/yr. EUR 2,267 in Europe to institutions; JPY 301,200 in Japan to institutions; USD 2,537 to institutions except Europe and Japan (effective 2006). abstr. index. back issues avail.; reprints avail. **Document type:** *Journal, Academic/Scholarly.* **Description:** Covers significant developments in the physics and chemistry of the earth and planets, including geophysics and geochemistry, physical and chemical oceanography and atmospheric physics and chemistry.
Incorporates (in 2002): Physics and Chemistry of the Earth Part A: Solid Earth & Geodesy (1464-1895); Physics and Chemistry of the Earth Part B: Hydrology, Oceans & Atmosphere (1464-1909); Physics and Chemistry of the Earth Part C: Solar, Terrestrial & Planetary Science (1464-1917); Supersedes in part: Physics and Chemistry of the Earth (0079-1946)
Related titles: Microfilm ed.: (from PQC); Online - full text ed.: (from EBSCO Publishing, Gale Group, IngentaConnect, ScienceDirect, Swets Information Services).
Indexed: ASFA, BrCerAb, C&ISA, CerAb, ChemAb, CorrAb, CurCont, E&CAJ, EMA, ESPM, EngInd, EnvEAb, GEOBASE, IAA, Inspec, M&GPA, M&TEA, MBF, METADEX, OceAb, PollutAb, SWRA, WAA.
—BLDSC (6478.040000), CASDDS, CISTI, IE, ingenta, Linda Hall. **CCC.**
Published by: Pergamon (Subsidiary of: Elsevier Science & Technology), The Boulevard, Langford Ln, East Park, Kidlington, Oxford OX5 1GB, United Kingdom. TEL 44-1865-843000, FAX 44-1865-843010, http://www.elsevier.com/locate/pce. Eds. G M Ganssen, H-P Plag, N Balling. **Subscr. to:** Elsevier BV, PO Box 211, Amsterdam 1000 AE, Netherlands. TEL 31-20-485-3757, FAX 31-20-485-3432, nlinfo-f@elsevier.nl, http://www.elsevier.nl.

➤ **PLANETARY AND SPACE SCIENCE.** see *ASTRONOMY*

➤ **POLAR RECORD.** see *GEOGRAPHY*

919 DEU ISSN 0032-2490
CODEN: POLFAT
➤ **POLARFORSCHUNG.** Text in English, German. 1931. 3/yr. EUR 30 membership (effective 2005). adv. bk.rev. bibl.; charts; illus.; stat. **Document type:** *Journal, Academic/Scholarly.*
Indexed: ASFA, ChemAb, ESPM, GEOBASE, IBR, ZooRec.
—CISTI, Linda Hall. **CCC.**
Published by: Deutsche Gesellschaft fuer Polarforschung e.V./German Society of Polar Research, Am Alten Hafen 26, Bremerhaven, 27568, Germany. kleinschmidt@em.uni-frankfurt.de, http://www.awi-bremerhaven.de/GEO/DGfP/Impressum/. Eds. D K Fuetterer, E Treude. Circ: 650.

011.4309982 DNK ISSN 0907-2322
QH84.1
POLARFRONTEN. Text in Danish. 1992. q. free (effective 2003). bk.rev. illus. cum.index. back issues avail. **Document type:** *Journal, Academic/Scholarly.* **Description:** Polar research.
—Linda Hall.
Published by: Dansk Polarcenter/Danish Polar Center, Strandgade 100 H, Copenhagen K, 1401, Denmark. TEL 45-32-880100, FAX 45-32-880101, polarfronten@dpc.dk, dpc@dpc.dk, http://www.dpc.dk. Eds. Hanne K.e Petersen, Poul-Erik Philbert, Henning Thing. Circ: 5,000.

550 POL ISSN 0138-0338
G575
POLISH POLAR RESEARCH. Text in English; Summaries in Polish. 1980. q. USD 80 foreign (effective 2003). charts; illus.; maps. 200 p./no.; **Document type:** *Journal, Academic/Scholarly.* **Description:** Presents original scientific papers containing the results of investigations carried out in polar regions, expedition reports, reminiscences.
Indexed: ASFA, AgrAg, AgrLib, BIOSIS Prev, BiolAb, ESPM, GEOBASE, M&GPA, ZooRec.
Published by: (Polska Akademia Nauk, Komitet Badan Polarnych), Wydawnictwo Naukowe P W N SA/Polish Scientific Publishers P W N, ul Miodowa 10, Warsaw, 00251, Poland. TEL 48-22-6954181, FAX 48-22-6954288, ksiegarnia@pwn.pl, http://en.pwn.pl. Ed. Andrzej Gazdzicki TEL 48-22-6978796.

550 570 DEU ISSN 0341-9665
CODEN: MIPOD4
POLLICHIA. MITTEILUNGEN. Summaries in English, French, German. 1888. a. back issues avail. **Document type:** *Academic/Scholarly.*
Indexed: BiolAb, IBR, ZooRec.
—CISTI, Linda Hall. **CCC.**
Published by: Pollichia Verein fuer Naturforschung und Landespflege, Hermann Schaefer Str 17, Bad Duerkheim, 67098, Germany. stapf@mail.uni-mainz.de. Ed. Karl Stapf. Circ: 3,000.

PRIRODNYE RESURSY/NATURAL RESOURCES. see *ENVIRONMENTAL STUDIES*

PROBLEMY ARKTIKI I ANTARKTIKI. see *METEOROLOGY*

550 560 DEU ISSN 0941-0414
QE1
PROFIL (STUTTGART). Text in English, German; Summaries in English, French, German, Spanish. 1992. 2/yr. **Document type:** *Academic/Scholarly.*
Indexed: RefZh.
—Linda Hall. **CCC.**
Published by: Universitaet Stuttgart, Institut fuer Geologie und Palaeontologie, Herdweg 51, Stuttgart, 70174, Germany. TEL 49-711-1211344, FAX 49-711-1211341, http://www.uni-stuttgart.de/uniuser/igps/literature/profilcont.html. Ed. Dr. Manfred Krautter.

QUARTERNARY AUSTRALASIA. see *GEOGRAPHY*

551.79 ITA ISSN 0394-3356
➤ **QUATERNARIO.** Text in English, Italian; Summaries in English. 1988. s-a. abstr.; bibl.; charts; illus.; maps. index. back issues avail. **Document type:** *Journal, Academic/Scholarly.* **Description:** Presents research on quaternary sciences.
Indexed: ASFA, ForAb, OceAb.
Published by: Associazione Italiana per lo Studio del Quaternario, c/oc/o Museo Civico di Storia Naturale, Lungadige Porta Vittoria 9, Verona, 37129, Italy. quaternario@irtr.rm.cnr.it, http://www.aiqua.irtr.rm.cnr.it. Ed. C Carrara. Circ: 800 (paid).

550 535 GBR
REMOTE IMAGING GROUP JOURNAL. Text in English. 1985. q. GBP 11 in United Kingdom; GBP 13 in Europe; USD 20 in United States; GBP 15 elsewhere (effective 2001). adv. software rev. illus. back issues avail. **Document type:** *Journal, Academic/Scholarly.*
Formerly (until 1993): Remote Imaging Group Newsletter
—BLDSC (4846.420000).
Published by: Remote Imaging Group, 34 Ellerton Rd, Surbiton, KT6 7TX, United Kingdom. editor@rig.org.uk, help@rig,org.uk, http://www.rig.org.uk. Eds. Kevin Chown, Les Hamilton. R&P Les Hamilton. Adv. contact John Tellick. Circ: 2,500 (paid).

550 CAN ISSN 0226-479X
REMOTE SENSING IN CANADA. Text in Multiple languages. 1972. s-a. back issues avail. **Document type:** *Newsletter, Academic/Scholarly.* **Description:** Provides a comprehensive view of remote sensing research, programmes, products, and activities happening at the Canada Centre for Remote Sensing.
Related titles: Online - full text ed.: ISSN 1494-0329. 1995.
—BLDSC (7356.815500).

E

Published by: Canada Centre for Remote Sensing, 588 Boot St, Ottawa, ON K1A OY7, Canada. TEL 613-947-1216, FAX 613-947-1382, contak@ccrs.nrcan.gc.ca, info@ccrs.nrcan.gc.ca, http://www.ccrs.nrcan.gc.ca/ccrs/com/rsnewsltr/rsicintro_e.html, http://www.ccrs.nrcan.gc.ca/ccrs/homepg.pl?e.

550	NLD	ISSN 0924-6010
		CODEN: RSEEEB

➤ **REMOTE SENSING OF EARTH RESOURCES AND ENVIRONMENT.** Text in English. 1984. irreg., latest vol.3, 1985. price varies. **Document type:** *Monographic series, Academic/Scholarly.*
—CCC.
Published by: Springer-Verlag Dordrecht (Subsidiary of: Springer Science+Business Media), Van Godewijckstraat 30, Dordrecht, 3311 GX, Netherlands. TEL 31-78-6576050, FAX 31-78-6576474, http://www.springeronline.com.

➤ **REMOTE SENSING OF ENVIRONMENT.** see *GEOGRAPHY*

550	CHN	ISSN 1004-0323

REMOTE SENSING TECHNOLOGY AND APPLICATION. Text in Chinese; Summaries in Chinese, English. 1986. bi-m. CNY 60, USD 40 (effective 2004). adv. 60 p./no.; reprints avail. **Document type:** *Journal, Academic/Scholarly.* **Description:** Introduces the latest developments and trends in remote-sensing technology, and its applications in China.
Related titles: ◆ CD-ROM ed.: Chinese Academic Journals Full-Text Database. Electronic Technology & Information Science. ISSN 1008-6293; Online - full content ed.: (from WanFang Data Corp.); Online - full text ed.: (from East View Information Services).
Published by: Zhongguo Kexueyuan, Ziyuan Huanjing Kexue Xinxi Zhongxin/Chinese Academy of Sciences, Scientific Information Center for Resources and Environment, 342 Tianshui Rd, Lanzhou, Gansu 730000, China. TEL 86-931-8272180, FAX 86-931-8275743, rsta@ns.lzb.ac.cn, sicre@ns.lzb.ac.cn, http://159.226.136.229/. Adv. contact Yun Feng. page USD 500; 170 x 250.

RENEWABLE RESOURCES JOURNAL. see *ENVIRONMENTAL STUDIES*

550	DEU	ISSN 0935-7238

RESEARCH & DEVELOPMENT. Text in German. 1989. s-m. **Document type:** *Trade.*
Published by: T N V GmbH, An den Eichen, Hennef, 53773, Germany. TEL 49-2248-1881. Ed. Stephen Wright.

RESEARCH INSTITUTE NEDRI-AS. BULLETIN. see *BIOLOGY—Botany*

550	BRA	ISSN 0375-7536
		CODEN: RBGCAS

REVISTA BRASILEIRA DE GEOCIENCIAS. Text in English, French, Portuguese, Spanish. 1952. q. membership. index. back issues avail.
Formerly (until 1971): Sociadade Brasileira de Geologia. Boletim (0583-7804)
Related titles: Online - full text ed.: (from SciELO).
Indexed: AESIS, ChemAb, ChemTitl, IMMAb, INIS AtomInd, ZooRec.
—CASDDS.
Published by: Sociedade Brasileira de Geologia, Pinheiros, Caixa Postal 11348, Sao Paulo, SP 05422-970, Brazil. TEL 55-11-2126166, hjost@tba.com.br, http://www.scielo.br/. Ed. Hardy Jost. Circ: 4,000.

REVISTA DE GEOGRAFIA CANARIA. see *GEOGRAPHY*

REVISTA MINELOR. see *MINES AND MINING INDUSTRY*

REVUE D'AUVERGNE. see *HISTORY—History Of Europe*

RIKAGAKKAISHI/JOURNAL OF PHYSICS, CHEMISTRY AND EARTH SCIENCE. see *SCIENCES: COMPREHENSIVE WORKS*

ROMANIAN ACADEMY. PROCEEDINGS. SERIES B: CHEMISTRY, LIFE SCIENCES AND GEOSCIENCES. see *CHEMISTRY*

549	ROM	ISSN 1220-5648
QE390		

ROMANIAN JOURNAL OF MINERAL DEPOSITS. Text in English. a. USD 35 (effective 1999). **Document type:** *Academic/Scholarly.*
Former titles (until 1992): Institutul de Geologie si Geofizica. Dari de Seama ale Sedintelor. 2. Zacaminte, Geochimie (1221-468X); Institutul de Geologie si Geofizica. Dari de Seama ale Sedintelor. 2. Zacaminte (0254-7287); Institutul Geologic. Dari de Seama ale Sedintelor. Zacaminte (0379-3605)
Indexed: MinerAb.
Published by: Institutul Geologic al Romaniei, Str. Caransebes 1, Bucharest, 78344, Romania. TEL 40-1-2242091, FAX 40-1-2240404, udubasa@igr.ro. Ed. Gheorghe Udubasa. R&P Serban Veliciu TEL 40-1-2242093. Circ: 550.

550	RUS	ISSN 1681-1178

ROSSIJSKIJ ZURNAL NAUK O ZEMLE. Text in Russian. 1998. bi-m. **Document type:** *Journal, Academic/Scholarly.*
Related titles: ◆ Online - full content ed.: Rossijskij Zurnal Nauk o Zemle (Online). ISSN 1681-1194.
Address: c/o V. Nechitailenko, Geophysical Center, RAS, Molodezhnaya 3, Moscow, 117296 , Russian Federation. TEL 7-95-9305649, FAX 7-95-9305509. Ed. A F Grachev.

550	RUS	ISSN 1681-1194

ROSSIJSKIJ ZURNAL NAUK O ZEMLE (ONLINE). Text in Russian. 2001. bi-m. **Document type:** *Journal, Academic/Scholarly.*
Media: Online - full content. **Related titles:** ◆ Print ed.: Rossijskij Zurnal Nauk o Zemle. ISSN 1681-1178; English ed.: Russian Journal of Earth Sciences. ISSN 1681-1208. 2001. USD 196 to institutions (effective 2006).
Published by: Rossijskij Zurnal Nauk o Zemle, c/o V. Nechitailenko, Geophysical Center, RAS, Molodezhnaya 3, Moscow, 117296 , Russian Federation. TEL 7-95-9305649, FAX 7-95-9305509. Ed. A F Grachev.

ROTUNDA. see *ART*

550	GBR	ISSN 0263-5933
		CODEN: TRSSDZ

➤ **ROYAL SOCIETY OF EDINBURGH. TRANSACTIONS. EARTH SCIENCES.** Text in English. 1783. 4/yr. GBP 168, USD 294 (effective 2005); includes free online access. 96 p./no. 2 cols./p.; back issues avail. **Document type:** *Journal, Academic/Scholarly.* **Description:** Covers all aspects of earth and related planetary sciences and contains contributions that emphasize principles and represent a worldwide authorship rather than locally orientated topics.
Formerly (until 1980): Royal Society of Edinburgh. Transactions (0080-4568)
Related titles: Microform ed.: (from PMC); Online - full text ed.: ISSN 1473-7116 (from EBSCO Publishing, Gale Group, IngentaConnect).
Indexed: AESIS, ASCA, BIOSIS Prev, BiolAb, BrGeoL, ChemAb, ChemTitl, CurCont, ESPM, EngInd, GEOBASE, IBR, IndMed, Inspec, MathR, MinerAb, RefZh, SCI, SFA, ZooRec.
—BLDSC (9000.000000), CASDDS, CISTI, IE, ingenta, Linda Hall. CCC.
Published by: The R S E Scotland Foundation (Subsidiary of: Royal Society of Edinburgh), 22 George St, Edinburgh, EH2 2PQ, United Kingdom. TEL 44-131-2405000, FAX 44-131-2405024, publications@royalsoced.org.uk, http://www.royalsoced.org.uk/publications/volumes/trans.htm. Ed. E N K Clarkson. R&P Vicki Ingpen. Circ: 450. **Subscr. to:** CABI Publishing, CAB International, Wallingford, Oxon OX10 8DE, United Kingdom. TEL 44-1491-832111, FAX 44-1491-829292, orders@cabi.org, http://www.cabi-publishing.org/.

➤ **RUDOLSTAEDTER NATURHISTORISCHE SCHRIFTEN.** see *BIOLOGY*

550 620	NLD	ISSN 0168-6453

RUSSIAN TRANSLATIONS SERIES. Text in English. 1983. irreg., latest vol.115, 1996. price varies. **Document type:** *Monographic series.* **Description:** Publishes translations of Russian scholarly works in the earth sciences and their applications, and related fields.
—CISTI. CCC.
Published by: A A Balkema (Subsidiary of: Taylor & Francis The Netherlands), PO Box 1675, Rotterdam, 3000 BR, Netherlands. FAX 31-10-413-5947, sales@balkema.nl, http://www.balkema.nl. **Dist. in U.S. by:** Ashgate Publishing Co, Old Post Rd, Brookfield, VT 05036. TEL 800-535-9544.

551.9	JPN	

RYOKKA NI KANSURU CHOSA HOKOKU/RESEARCH REPORT OF REVEGETATION IN TOKYO PREFECTURE. Text in Japanese. 1973. a.
Published by: Tokyoto Kensetsukyoku/Tokyo Metropolitan Government, Bureau of Construction, 8-1 Nishi-Shinjuku 2-chome, Shinjuku-ku, Tokyo, 160-0023, Japan.

550	ITA	ISSN 1592-792X

S L M. (Sopra il Livello del Mare) Text in Italian. 2001. q. **Document type:** *Journal, Academic/Scholarly.* **Description:** This is the official review of Istituto Nazionale della Montagna and it covers scientific and technological subjects related to mountains.
Incorporates (1988-2001): Montagna Oggi (1124-1462); Which was formerly (1982-1987): Il Montanaro d'Italia (1124-1446)
Published by: (Istituto Nazionale della Montagna), Editrice Compositori Srl, Via Stalingrado 97-2, Bologna, 40128, Italy. TEL 39-051-3540111, FAX 39-051-327877, 1865@compositori.it, http://www.compositori.it. Ed. Antonio Ciaschi.

333.79	EGY	ISSN 1110-077X

SAHARA REVIEW; an annual periodical for reviews of research work on deserts and arid lands. Text in English. 1989. a. USD 5 (effective 2003). **Document type:** *Monographic series.*
Published by: A.M. Balba Group for Soil and Water Research, College of Agriculture, University of Alexandria, El-Shatby, Alexandria, 21545, Egypt. TEL 20-3-5975405, FAX 20-3-5904684. Ed. A. Monem Balba.

550	JPN	ISSN 1343-828X

SAITAMA DAIGAKU KYOIKUGAKUBU CHIKYU KAGAKU KANSOKU JIKKENSHITSU KENKYU HOKOKU/SAITAMA UNIVERSITY. FACULTY OF EDUCATION. EARTH SCIENCE LABORATORY. BULLETIN. Text in English, Japanese. 1979. biennial. free. **Document type:** *Bulletin.*
Published by: (Chikyu Kagaku Kansoku Jikkenshitsu), Saitama Daigaku, Kyoikugakubu/Saitama University, Faculty of Education, 255 Shimo-Okubo, Urawa shi, Saitama ken 3380825, Japan. TEL 81-48-858-3228, FAX 81-48-858-3228, chuji@post.saitama-u.ac.jp. Ed. Chuji Takahashi. Circ: 200 (paid).

550	CHN	ISSN 1006-9313
QE1		CODEN: SCDEF8

➤ **SCIENCE IN CHINA. SERIES D: EARTH SCIENCES.** Text in English. 1952. m. USD 627 to individuals; USD 1,195 to institutions; USD 1,607 to individuals for full set, series A-G; USD 2,990 to institutions for full set, series A-G (effective 2004). **Document type:** *Journal, Academic/Scholarly.* **Description:** Contains academic papers on scientific work in the field of earth sciences.
Supersedes in part (in 1996): Science in China. Series B: Chemistry, Life Sciences and Earth Sciences (1001-652X); Which was formerly (until 1989): Scientia Sinica. Series B: Chemistry, Life Sciences and Earth Sciences (0253-5823); Which superseded in part: Scientia Sinica
Related titles: Online - full text ed.: USD 50 (effective 2004) (from East View Information Services, WanFang Data Corp.); ◆ Chinese ed.: Zhongguo Kexue. D Ji: Diqiu Kexue. ISSN 1006-9267.
Indexed: ASFA, CurCont, ESPM, EngInd, FLUIDEX, GEOBASE, IAA, ISR, M&GPA, RefZh, SCI, SWRA, ZooRec.
—BLDSC (8141.670230), CASDDS, CISTI, GNLM, IDS, IE, ingenta, Linda Hall. CCC.
Published by: (Chinese Academy of Sciences/Zhongguo Kexueyuan), Zhongguo Kexue Zazhishe/Science in China Press, 16 Donghuangchenggen North Street, Beijing, 100717, China. TEL 86-10-64019820, FAX 86-10-64031816, sale@scichina.com, http://www.scienceinchina.com/ scienceinchina_d_en.htm, http://www.scichina.com/. **Subscr. to:** Maney Publishing, China Journal Distribution Services, Hudson Rd, Leeds LS9 7DI, United Kingdom. TEL 44-113-2497481, FAX 44-113-2486983, subscriptions@maney.co.uk.

➤ **SCIENCES DE LA TERRE: SERIE INFORMATIQUE GEOLOGIQUE.** see *EARTH SCIENCES—Geology*

550	DEU	ISSN 1430-5267
QE269		

SCRIPTUM; Arbeitsergebnisse aus dem Geologischen Dienst Nordrhein-Westfalen. Text in German; Summaries in English. 1996. irreg., latest 2001. EUR 7 (effective 2001). bibl.; charts; illus.; maps. back issues avail. **Document type:** *Bulletin, Government.* **Description:** Publishes the results of the research done by the geological survey of North Rhine and West Phalia.
Related titles: Online - full text ed.
Published by: Geologischer Dienst Nordrhein-Westfalen, De-Greiff-Str 195, Krefeld, 47803, Germany. TEL 49-2151-8971, FAX 49-2151-897505, poststelle@gd.nrw.de, http://www.gd.nrw.de. Ed., R&P Rainer Wolf TEL 49-2151-897332. Circ: 400.

553.2	NLD	

➤ **SEDIMENTARY BASINS OF THE WORLD.** Text in English. 1989. irreg., latest vol.4, 1999. price varies. illus. **Document type:** *Monographic series, Academic/Scholarly.* **Description:** Examines the geology of sedimentary basins worldwide.
—BLDSC (8217.318000).
Published by: Elsevier BV (Subsidiary of: Elsevier Science & Technology), Radarweg 29, Amsterdam, 1043 NX, Netherlands. TEL 31-20-4853911, FAX 31-20-4852457, nlinfo-f@elsevier.nl, http://www.elsevier.nl.

➤ **SENATE OF CANADA. STANDING COMMITTEE ON ENERGY, THE ENVIRONMENT AND NATURAL RESOURCES. PROCEEDINGS.** see *ENVIRONMENTAL STUDIES*

550 551	JPN	ISSN 0373-1006
TD839.J3		

➤ **SEPPYO/JAPANESE SOCIETY OF SNOW AND ICE. JOURNAL.** Text in Japanese; Summaries in English. 1939. 6/yr. JPY 8,000 membership (effective 2005). **Document type:** *Journal, Academic/Scholarly.*
Indexed: JPI, RefZh.
—CISTI, Linda Hall. CCC.
Published by: Nihon Seppyo Gakkai/Japanese Society of Snow and Ice, Kagaku-Kaikan 3F, 1-5 Kanda-Surugadai, Chiyoda, Tokyo, 101-0062, Japan. TEL 81-3-52595245, FAX 81-3-52595246, jimu@seppyo.org, http://wwwsoc.nii.ac.jp/jssi/. Ed., R&P Atsushi Sato TEL 81-233-22-7550. Circ: 1,500.

550	ESP	

SERIE NOVATERRA. Text in Spanish. 1990. irreg. price varies. **Document type:** *Monographic series.*
Published by: (Laboratorio Xeoloxico de Laxe), Seminario de Estudos Galegos, El Castro, Sada, (La Coruna) 15168, Spain.

E

▼ *new title* ➤ *refereed* ✶ *unverified* ◆ *full entry avail.*

620 550 CHE ISSN 0080-9004
CODEN: SRSMC
SERIES ON ROCK AND SOIL MECHANICS. Text in English. 1971. irreg. (4-6/yr.). price varies. **Document type:** *Monographic series, Academic/Scholarly.*
Indexed: GeotechAb, IMMAb.
—BLDSC (8250.202000), CISTI, ingenta. **CCC.**
Published by: Trans Tech Publications Ltd., Brandrain 6, Uetikon-Zurich, CH-8707, Switzerland. TEL 41-1-9221022, FAX 41-1-9221033, ttp@ttp.ch, http://www.ttp.ch. Ed. R H Wohlbier.

550 JPN ISSN 0389-9128
SHIGA SHIZEN KYOIKU KENKYU SHISETSU KENKYU GYOSEKI/INSTITUTE OF NATURE EDUCATION IN SHIGA HEIGHTS. BULLETIN. Text in Japanese, English; Summaries in English, Japanese. 1962. a. back issues avail. **Document type:** *Bulletin, Academic/Scholarly.*
Formerly (until 1965): Shiga Kogen Seibutsu Kenkyujo Kenkyu Gyoseki (0583-0095)
Indexed: BIOSIS Prev, BiolAb, JPI, ZooRec.
—BLDSC (2581.802000).
Published by: Shinshu Daigaku, Kyoikugakubu Fuzoku Shiga Shizen Kyoiku Kenkyu Shisetsu/Shinshu University, Faculty of Education, Institute of Nature Education in Shiga Heights, 1-Ha 7148 Shiga Kogen, Hirao, Shimotakai-gun, Yamanouchi-machi, Nagano-ken 381-0401, Japan. TEL 81-269-34-2607, FAX 81-269-34-3229, shigasu@gipnc.shinshu-u.ac.jp. Eds. Hideyuki Ida, Hiroshi Nakamura, Katsura Beppu, Sadayuki Akahane.

550 JPN ISSN 0388-6298
➤ **SHIZUOKA DAIGAKU CHIKYU KAGAKU KENKYU HOKOKU/SHIZUOKA UNIVERSITY. GEOSCIENCE REPORTS.** Text in English, Japanese. 1975. a. 100 p./no.; back issues avail.; reprints avail. **Document type:** *Academic/Scholarly.*
Indexed: GEOBASE, ZooRec.
Published by: (Chikyu Kagaku Kyoshitsu/Institute of Geosciences), Shizuoka Daigaku, Rigakubu/Shizuoka University, Faculty of Science, 836 Oya, Shizuoka, 422-8529, Japan. TEL 81-54-238-4795, FAX 81-54-238-0491, http://www.sci.shizuoka.ac.jp/~geo/temp-g.html.

➤ **SHUILI FADIAN/HYDROELECTRIC POWER.** see *WATER RESOURCES*

550 CZE ISSN 0323-0627
QH7 CODEN: CASNAH
SLEZSKE ZEMSKE MUZEUM. CASOPIS. SERIE A. VEDY PRIRODNI. Text in Czech. 1952. q.
Indexed: ASFA, EntAb, ZooRec.
—CISTI.
Published by: Slezske Zemske Muzeum, Masarykova tr 35, Opava, 74646, Czech Republic. Ed. Jaromir Kalus.

550 SVK ISSN 1335-096X
CODEN: ZKSMDY
➤ **SLOVAK GEOLOGICAL MAGAZINE.** Text in English. 1995. q. USD 48 (effective 2002). adv. bk.rev. illus.; maps; abstr. index. 90 p./no. 2 cols./p.; back issues avail. **Document type:** *Magazine, Academic/Scholarly.* **Description:** Covers mineralogy, engineering geology, regional geology, stratigraphy, petrology, tectonics, geothermal energy, hydrogeology, geochemistry, metallogeny, environmental studies, petroarcheology and more.
Formed by the merger of (1974-1995): Geologicky Ustav Dionyza Stura. Zapadne Karpaty. Seria Geologia (0139-8288); (1974-1995): Geologicky Ustav Dionyza Stura. Zapadne Karpaty. Seria Paleontologia (0139-7435); (1978-1995): Geologicky Ustav Dionyza Stura. Zapadne Karpaty. Mineralogia, Petrografia, Geochemia, Metalogeneza (0139-8946); Which was formerly (1947-1978): Geologicky Ustav Dionyza Stura. Zapadne Karpaty. Seria Mineralogia, Petrografia, Geochemia, Loziska (0139-7389); (1994-1995): Geologicky Ustav Dionyza Stura. Zapadne Karpaty. Seria Hydrogeologia, Inzinierska Geologia a Geotermalna Energia; Which was formerly (1974-1994): Geologicky Ustav Dionyza Stura. Zapadne Karpaty. Seria Hydrogeologia a Inzinierska Geologia (0139-7583); All Series superseded (in 1974): Geologicky Ustav Dionyza Stura. Zbornik Geologickych Vied. Zapadne Karpaty (0036-5262); Which was formerly (until 1964): Geologicky Ustav Dionyza Stura. Geologicke Prace (0431-218X); (1941-1952): Statny Geologicky Ustav. Prace (0370-1891)
Related titles: E-mail ed.
Indexed: ChemAb, RefZh, ZooRec.
—CASDDS, CISTI, Linda Hall.
Published by: Dionyz Stur Publishers, Mlynska dolina 1, Bratislava, 81704, Slovakia. TEL 421-2-59375351, FAX 421-2-54771940, hok@gssr.sk, http://www.gssr.sk. Ed., Adv. contact Jozef Hok. B&W page USD 75, color page USD 100; trim 29.7 x 21. Circ: 400.

550 USA ISSN 0081-0274
QE1 CODEN: SCESBH
SMITHSONIAN CONTRIBUTIONS TO THE EARTH SCIENCES. Text in English. 1969. irreg., latest vol.32, 2000. free. reprint service avail. from PQC. **Document type:** *Monographic series.*
Indexed: AESIS, ASFA, BiolAb, ESPM, OceAb, ZooRec.
—CASDDS, CISTI, Linda Hall.
Published by: Smithsonian Institution Press, 750 Ninth St., N. W., Suite 4300, Washington, DC 20560-0950. TEL 202-275-2233, FAX 202-275-2274. Ed. Diane Tyler. Circ: 2,000.

550 MEX ISSN 0370-7415
QH7 CODEN: RSMNA6
SOCIEDAD MEXICANA DE HISTORIA NATURAL. REVISTA. Text in Spanish; Summaries in English. 1940. a. MXP 250, USD 25. bk.rev. back issues avail.
Indexed: ASFA, BiolAb, ESPM.
Published by: Sociedad Mexicana de Historia Natural, Ave Dr Vertiz 724, Mexico City 12, DF, Mexico. Ed. Raul Goldriguez. Circ: 1,000.

SOCIETA VENEZIANA DI SCIENZE NATURALI. LAVORI. see *SCIENCES: COMPREHENSIVE WORKS*

SOCIETE DES NATURALISTES LUXEMBOURGEOIS. BULLETIN. see *BIOLOGY*

SOCIETE D'HISTOIRE NATURELLE DE TOULOUSE. BULLETIN. see *BIOLOGY*

SOCIETE D'HISTOIRE NATURELLE DES ARDENNES. BULLETIN. see *BIOLOGY*

550 USA ISSN 0037-9913
SOCIETY OF INDEPENDENT PROFESSIONAL EARTH SCIENTISTS. NEWSLETTER. Text in English. 1964. q. USD 15 (effective 1999). adv. **Document type:** *Newsletter.*
Published by: Society of Independent Professional Earth Scientists, 4925 Greenville, Ste 1106, Dallas, TX 75206-4008. Ed., R&P Diane M Finstrom TEL 214-363-1780. Circ: 1,500.

550 NLD ISSN 0924-462X
CODEN: SESLFG
➤ **SOLID EARTH SCIENCES LIBRARY.** Text in English. 1984. irreg., latest vol.11, 2004. price varies. **Document type:** *Monographic series, Academic/Scholarly.*
—BLDSC (8327.290000), CASDDS.
Published by: Springer-Verlag Dordrecht (Subsidiary of: Springer Science+Business Media), Van Godewijckstraat 30, Dordrecht, 3311 GX, Netherlands. TEL 31-78-6576050, FAX 31-78-6576474, http://www.springeronline.com.

736 ZAF ISSN 0038-237X
SOUTH AFRICAN LAPIDARY MAGAZINE. Text in English. 1967. 3/yr. USD 22. adv. bk.rev. **Document type:** *Consumer.* **Description:** Amateur publication for those interested in collecting minerals, lapidary, geology and related fields.
Indexed: ISAP.
Published by: Federation of South African Gem & Mineralogical Societies, PO Box 28744, Sunnyside, Pretoria 0132, South Africa. TEL 27-12-44-4620. Ed. L Dreyer. Circ: 600 (controlled).

550 622 AUS ISSN 0726-1527
CODEN: SPSEE3
SOUTH AUSTRALIA. DEPARTMENT OF MINES AND ENERGY. SPECIAL PUBLICATIONS. Text in English. 1982. irreg. price varies. back issues avail. **Document type:** *Government.* **Description:** Historical, scientific or general interest publications dealing with special subjects, particularly those not accomodated by other departmental titles.
Indexed: AESIS, IMMAb.
Published by: (South Australia. Department of Mines and Energy CAN), Mines and Energy South Australia, PO Box 151, Eastwood, SA 5063, Australia. TEL 61-8-2747500, FAX 61-8-2727597. Circ: 300.

551.9 ESP
SPAIN. INSTITUTO TECNOLOGICO GEOMINERO DE ESPANA. COLECCION TEMAS GEOLOGICOS - MINEROS. Text in Spanish. 1977. irreg., latest vol.23, 1998. price varies. **Document type:** *Monographic series, Academic/Scholarly.* **Description:** Covers diverse themes of geology and mining. Many volumes cover congresses, symposiums or courses.
Formerly: Spain. Instituto Geologico y Minero. Coleccion Temas Geologicos - Mineros
Published by: El Instituto Geologico y Minero de Espana, Rios Rosas 23, Madrid, 28003, Spain. TEL 34-91-3495819, FAX 34-91-3495830, http://www.igme.es/internet/principal.asp.

550 398 910 ITA ISSN 0394-5057
SPELEO. Text in Italian. 1978. q. adv. bk.rev. bibl. back issues avail. **Document type:** *Academic/Scholarly.*
Related titles: Fax ed.
Published by: Speleo Club Firenze, Via Torre del Gallo, 30, Florence, FI 50125, Italy. TEL 39-55-8448155, FAX 39-55-470642. Ed., R&P Franco Utili. Adv. contact Ennio Bazzoni. Circ: 10,000.

550 910 JPN ISSN 0386-233X
GB601.A1
SPELEOLOGICAL SOCIETY OF JAPAN. JOURNAL. Text in English, Japanese. 1976. a. JPY 3,000, USD 25. back issues avail.
Indexed: RefZh, ZooRec.
Published by: Speleological Society of Japan/Nihon Kokutsu Gakkai, Akiyoshidai Kagaku Hakubutsukan, Akiyoshi, Mine-gun, Shuho-cho, Yamaguchi-ken 754-0511, Japan. Eds. K Yoshimura, T Kuramoto. Circ: 250.

STUDIES IN THE HISTORY AND PHILOSOPHY OF THE EARTH SCIENCES. see *HISTORY*

SYMBIOSES. see *BIOLOGY*

550 TWN ISSN 1017-0839
QC801 CODEN: TAOSEX
T A O: TERRESTRIAL, ATMOSPHERIC AND OCEANIC SCIENCES/DIQIU KEXUE JIKAN. Text in Chinese, English. 1990. q. USD 40. **Document type:** *Academic/Scholarly.* **Description:** Serves as a medium for the publication of research papers on the atmosphere, the ocean and the solid earth.
Incorporates (in 1990): Papers in Meteorological Research; Bulletin of Geophysics
Indexed: ASFA, CurCont, EEA, ESPM, GEOBASE, I&DA, ISR, M&GPA, S&F, SCI.
—BLDSC (8796.065000), CISTI, Ei, IDS, IE, ingenta, Linda Hall.
Published by: Academia Sinica, Institute of Earth Sciences, P.O. Box 23-59, Taipei, Taiwan. FAX 886-2-3632583.

551.41 553.21 DEU ISSN 0340-4927
CODEN: TELMDR
TELMA. Text in German. 1971. a. EUR 40 (effective 2003). bk.rev. **Document type:** *Journal, Academic/Scholarly.*
Indexed: CIN, ChemAb, ChemTitl, GEOBASE, IBR, RefZh, ZooRec.
—BLDSC (8789.100000), CASDDS, CISTI, IE, ingenta.
Published by: Deutsche Gesellschaft fuer Moor- und Torfkunde e.V., Stilleweg 2, Hannover, 30655, Germany. TEL 49-643-2241, FAX 49-643-2304, TELEX 923730-BGR-HA-D. Ed. Gerfried Caspers.

559.89 ITA ISSN 1122-8628
➤ **TERRA ANTARTICA.** Text in Italian. 1994. s-a. EUR 30 in the European Union to individuals; EUR 35 elsewhere to individuals; EUR 90 in the European Union to institutions; EUR 95 elsewhere to institutions; EUR 15 in the European Union to students; EUR 20 elsewhere to students (effective 2002). adv. Supplement avail.; back issues avail. **Document type:** *Journal, Academic/Scholarly.* **Description:** Presents the exchange of ideas and results in the field of Antarctic Earth Sciences.
Indexed: GEOBASE.
—BLDSC (8794.530000), CISTI, IE, ingenta.
Published by: (Universita degli Studi di Siena, Departimento di Scienze della Terra), Universita degli Studi di Siena, Museo Nazionale dell'Antartide Felice Ippolito, Via del Laterino 8, Siena, 53100, Italy. http://www.mna.unisi.it/MNA/terranta.html.
Subscr. to: Allen Press Inc., PO Box 1897, Lawrence, KS 66044.

550 GBR ISSN 0954-4879
QE1 CODEN: TENOEA
➤ **TERRA NOVA**; the European journal of geosciences. Text in English. 1989. bi-m. GBP 85, EUR 128 combined subscription in Europe to individuals print & online eds.; USD 155 combined subscription in the Americas to individuals & Caribbean, print & online eds.; GBP 92 combined subscription elsewhere to individuals print & online eds.; GBP 488 combined subscription in Europe to institutions print & online eds.; USD 900 combined subscription in the Americas to institutions & Caribbean, print & online eds.; GBP 536 combined subscription elsewhere to institutions print & online eds. (effective 2006); includes Terra Abstracts. adv. bk.rev. bibl.; illus. index. back issues avail.; reprint service avail. from PSC. **Document type:** *Journal, Academic/Scholarly.* **Description:** Contains papers on all aspects of significant earth and planetary sciences research.
Related titles: Microform ed.: (from PQC); ♦ Online - full text ed.: Terra Nova Online. ISSN 1365-3121.
Indexed: ArtHuCI, CurCont, EPB, GEOBASE, ISR, PetrolAb, SCI, ZooRec.
—BLDSC (8794.761100), CISTI, Ei, IDS, IE, Infotrieve, ingenta, PADDS. **CCC.**
Published by: (European Union of Geosciences), Blackwell Publishing Ltd., 9600 Garsington Rd, Oxford, OX4 2ZG, United Kingdom. TEL 44-1865-776868, FAX 44-1865-714591, customerservices@oxon.blackwellpublishing.com, http://www.blackwellpublishing.com/journals/TER. Eds. Adolphe Nicolas TEL 33-1-67143602, Alfred Kroener TEL 49-6131-3922163, Georges Calas TEL 33-1-44276872, Max Coleman TEL 44-118-9316627. Pub. Sue Hewitt. R&P Sophie Savage. Adv. contact Martine Cariou Keen. Circ: 1,765.

550 GBR ISSN 1365-3121
➤ **TERRA NOVA ONLINE.** Text in English. 1999. bi-m. GBP 464 in Europe to institutions; USD 855 in the Americas to institutions & Caribbean; GBP 509 elsewhere to institutions (effective 2006). **Document type:** *Academic/Scholarly.*
Media: Online - full text (from Blackwell Synergy, EBSCO Publishing, Gale Group, IngentaConnect, O C L C Online Computer Library Center, Inc., Swets Information Services).
Related titles: Microform ed.: (from PQC); ♦ Print ed.: Terra Nova. ISSN 0954-4879.

E

Published by: Blackwell Publishing Ltd., 9600 Garsington Rd, Oxford, OX4 2ZG, United Kingdom. TEL 44-1865-776868, FAX 44-1865-714591, customerservices@oxon.blackwellpublishing.com, http://www.blackwellpublishing.com.

550 AUS
TERRADAILY. Text in English. d. **Document type:** *Academic/Scholarly.* **Description:** Contains articles and information on the study of Earth, including technology, science, and orbital spacecrafts.
Media: Online - full content.
Published by: Space Daily, PO Box A447, Sydney South, NSW 2000, Australia. TEL 61-2-9360-2257, simon@spacer.com, http://www.terradaily.com/, http://www.spacedaily.com/.

TERRITORIS. see *GEOGRAPHY*

TEXAS. NATURAL RESOURCES INFORMATION SYSTEM. NEWSLETTER. see *ENVIRONMENTAL STUDIES*

526.3 USA ISSN 0098-6488
TIDE TABLES, HIGH AND LOW WATER PREDICTIONS, EAST COAST OF NORTH AND SOUTH AMERICA, INCLUDING GREENLAND. Text in English. 1958. a.
Published by: U.S. Department of Commerce, National Geodetic Survey, SSMC-3 # 9202, 1315 E W Highway, Silver Spring, MD 20910-3282. TEL 301-713-3242, FAX 301-713-4172, http://www.ngs.noaa.gov/.

551.9 JPN ISSN 0910-688X
TOKYO DAIGAKU RIGAKUBU CHIKAKU KAGAKU JIKKEN SHISETSU IHO/LABORATORY FOR EARTHQUAKE CHEMISTRY. BULLETIN. Text in Japanese; Summaries in English. 1979. irreg.
Published by: (Chikaku Kagaku Jikken Shiesetsu), Tokyo Daigaku, Rigakubu, 3-1 Hongo 7-chome, Bunkyo-ku, Tokyo, 113-0033, Japan. TEL 81-3-3813-9270, FAX 81-3-3816-1784.

549 GBR ISSN 1354-1528
TREASURES OF THE EARTH; the minerals and gemstones collection. Text in English. 1994. bi-w. illus. **Document type:** *Consumer.* **Description:** Examines the fascinating world of minerology and the insights this study gives us into all the other sciences and human history.
Published by: Orbis Publishing Ltd., Griffin House, 161 Hammersmith Rd, London, W6 8SD, United Kingdom. http://www.treasures-of-the-earth.com.

550 ESP ISSN 1130-4995
TREBALLS DEL MUSEU DE GEOLOGIA DE BARCELONA. Text in Catalan, English, French, Spanish. 1990. a. USD 25 foreign (effective 2001). bibl.; illus.; maps. back issues avail. **Document type:** *Monographic series, Academic/Scholarly.* **Description:** Diffuses and promotes research in the Earth sciences, mainly of Catalonia and Spain, and encourages the study of the museum's collection.
Indexed: ZooRec.
—CINDOC.
Published by: Museu de Geologia de Barcelona, Parc de la Ciutadella, S/N, Barcelona, 08003, Spain. TEL 34-93-319-6895, FAX 34-93-319-9312, museugeologia@mail.bcn.es, http://www.bcn.es. Ed. A Masriera. Circ: 700.

550 JPN ISSN 0913-6800
QH188 CODEN: TSJHEX
TSUKUBA DAIGAKU SUGADAIRA KOGEN JIKKEN SENTA KENKYU HOKOKU/UNIVERSITY OF TSUKUBA. SUGADAIRA MONTANE RESEARCH CENTER. BULLETIN. Text in English, Japanese. 1967. a.
Indexed: ZooRec.
Published by: Tsukubu Daigaku, Sugadaira Kogen Jikken Senta/University of Tsukuba, Sugadaira Montane Research Center, Sugadaira, Chiisagata-gun, Sanadamachi, Nagano-ken 386-22, Japan.

549 631.4 CHN ISSN 0253-9829
TURANG/SOIL. Text in Chinese. 1958. bi-m. CNY 60 (effective 2004). **Document type:** *Journal, Academic/Scholarly.*
Related titles: Online - full text ed.: (from East View Information Services).
Indexed: CIN, ChemAb, ChemTitl.
Published by: Zhongguo Kexueyuan, Nanjing Turang Yanjiusuo/Chinese Academy of Sciences, Institution of Soil Science, 71 Beijing Donglu, Nanjing, Jiangsu 210008, China. tr@mail.periodicals.net.cn, iss@issas.ac.cn, http://www.issas.ac.cn/. **Dist. by:** China International Book Trading Corp, 35 Chegongzhuang Xilu, Haidian District, PO Box 399, Beijing 100044, China. TEL 86-10-68412045, FAX 86-10-68412023, cibtc@mail.cibtc.com.cn, http://www.cibtc.com.cn.

549 CHN ISSN 0564-3929
S590 CODEN: TJHPAE
➤ **TURANG XUEBAO/ACTA PEDOLOGICA SINICA.** Text in Chinese; Summaries in English. 1948. q. CNY 112 (effective 2004). adv. **Document type:** *Academic/Scholarly.* **Description:** Reports on improvement and utilization of soil, provides original theses on this subject. Contains news and information on technology and devices, as well as reviews and discussions of the subject.
Related titles: Online - full text ed.: (from East View Information Services, WanFang Data Corp.).
Indexed: AEA, AgBio, AgrForAb, BiolAb, CPA, CTFA, ChemAb, ExcerpMed, FCA, FPA, ForAb, HerbAb, HortAb, I&DA, MaizeAb, MinerAb, OrnHort, PBA, PGrRegA, PN&I, PoultAb, RA&MP, RDA, RPP, RevApplEntom, RiceAb, S&F, SIA, SeedAb, SoyAb, TriticAb, WAE&RSA, WeedAb.
—BLDSC (0644.400000), CASDDS, CISTI, IE, Infotrieve, ingenta, Linda Hall.
Published by: (Zhongguo Kexueyuan, Nanjing Turang Yanjiusuo/Chinese Academy of Sciences, Institution of Soil Science), Kexue Chubanshe/Science Press, 16 Donghuang Cheng Genbei Jie, Beijing, 100717, China. TEL 86-10-64000246, FAX 86-10-64030255, actapedo@issas.ac.cn, http://www.issas.ac.cn/xuebao/new_page_xuebao_home.htm, http://www.sciencep.com/. Circ: 11,000. **Dist. by:** China International Book Trading Corp, 35 Chegongzhuang Xilu, Haidian District, PO Box 399, Beijing 100044, China. TEL 86-10-68412045, FAX 86-10-68412023, cibtc@mail.cibtc.com.cn, http://www.cibtc.com.cn.

549 631.4 CHN ISSN 0254-010X
S590 CODEN: TUJIDF
TURANGXUE JINZHAN/PROGRESS IN SOIL SCIENCE. Text in Chinese. 1979. bi-m.
Indexed: CIN, ChemAb, ChemTitl.
—CASDDS.
Published by: Zhongguo Kexueyuan, Nanjing Turang Yanjiusuo/Chinese Academy of Sciences, Institution of Soil Science, 71 Beijing Donglu, Nanjing, Jiangsu 210008, China. iss@issas.ac.cn, http://trxjz.periodicals.net.cn/default.html, http://www.issas.ac.cn/. Ed. Shi Hua. **Dist. by:** China International Book Trading Corp, 35 Chegongzhuang Xilu, Haidian District, PO Box 399, Beijing 100044, China. TEL 86-10-68412045, FAX 86-10-68412023, cibtc@mail.cibtc.com.cn, http://www.cibtc.com.cn.

550 TUR ISSN 1300-0985
QE316 CODEN: TEASEP
➤ **TURKISH JOURNAL OF EARTH SCIENCES.** Text in English. 1992. 3/yr. USD 90 (effective 2005). **Document type:** *Journal, Academic/Scholarly.*
Incorporates (in 1995): Turk Yerbilimleri Dergisi (1300-0136); Supersedes in part (in 1994): Doga Turkish Journal of Earth Sciences - Doga Turk Yerbilimleri Dergisi
Related titles: Online - full text ed.: ISSN 1303-619X. free (effective 2005) (from EBSCO Publishing).
Indexed: ChemAb, CurCont, GEOBASE, ZooRec.
—CASDDS.
Published by: Scientific and Technical Research Council of Turkey - TUBITAK/Turkiye Bilimsel ve Teknik Arastirma Kurumu, Ataturk Bulvari No. 221, Kavaklidere, Ankara, 06100, Turkey. TEL 90-312-468-5300, FAX 90-312-426-8073, bdym@tubitak.gov.tr, http://journals.tubitak.gov.tr/earth/index.php, http://www.tubitak.gov.tr. Ed. Erdin Bozkurt.

➤ **UNIVERSIDAD CENTRAL DE VENEZUELA. FACULTAD DE INGENIERIA. REVISTA.** see *ENGINEERING*

550 CHL ISSN 0069-357X
UNIVERSIDAD DE CHILE. DEPARTAMENTO DE GEOLOGIA. SERIE COMUNICACIONES. Text in Spanish; Summaries in English. 1960. a. USD 10. bk.rev. **Description:** Original papers on Andean geology, including economic and structural geology and geochronology, petrology, and volcanology.
Published by: Universidad de Chile, Departamento de Geologia, Casilla 13518, Correo, 21, Santiago, Chile. FAX 69630509, TELEX 240523 CENET GL. Ed. Estanislao Godoy. Circ: 400.

550 URY ISSN 0250-6521
UNIVERSIDAD DE LA REPUBLICA. FACULTAD DE HUMANIDADES Y CIENCIAS. REVISTA. SERIE CIENCIAS DE LA TIERRA. Text in Spanish. N.S. 1979. irreg. per issue exchange basis.
Supersedes in part: Universidad de la Republica. Facultad de Humanidades y Ciencias. Revista
—Linda Hall.
Published by: Universidad de la Republica, Facultad de Humanidades y Ciencias, c/o Seccion Revista, Dr. Tristan Narvaja, 1674, Montevideo, 11205, Uruguay. Ed. Beatriz Martinez Osorio.

550 BRA
UNIVERSIDADE FEDERAL DE PERNAMBUCO. DEPARTAMENTO DE GEOLOGIA. SERIE B. ESTUDOS E PESQUISAS. Text in Portuguese; Summaries in English, French, German. 1971. irreg. per issue exchange basis.
Formerly: Universidade Federal de Pernambuco. Instituto de Geociencias. Serie B: Estudos e Pesquisas (0080-0244)
Published by: Universidade Federal de Pernambuco, Centro de Tecnologia, Recife, PE, Brazil. Ed. J M Mabesoone. Circ: 1,000.

550 BRA
QE235 CODEN: PUFGDD
UNIVERSIDADE FEDERAL DO RIO GRANDE DO SUL. INSTITUTO DE GEOCIENCIAS. PESQUISAS EM GEOCIENCIAS. Text in English, French, Portuguese, Spanish; Summaries in English. 1972. s-a. exchange basis. adv. bibl. 100 p./no.; **Document type:** *Journal, Academic/Scholarly.*
Formerly (until vol. 26, 1999): Universidade Federal do Rio Grande do Sul. Instituto de Geociencias. Pesquisas (0100-5375)
Indexed: GeosDoc, ZooRec.
—Linda Hall.
Published by: Universidade Federal do Rio Grande do Sul, Instituto de Geociencias, Av Bento Goncalves, 9500, Predio 43113, Porto Alegre, RGS 91540000, Brazil. TEL 55-51-33166402, FAX 55-51-33167302, bibgeo@vortex.ufrgs.br, http://www.bibgeo.ufrgs.br/. Ed. Yvonne T Sanginetti.

550 USA ISSN 0068-645X
QE1 CODEN: UCGSAE
➤ **UNIVERSITY OF CALIFORNIA PUBLICATIONS IN GEOLOGICAL SCIENCES.** Text in English. 1893. irreg., latest vol.146, 2004. price varies. back issues avail. **Document type:** *Monographic series, Academic/Scholarly.*
Indexed: BiolAb, ZooRec.
—BLDSC (9105.150000), CISTI, Linda Hall. **CCC.**
Published by: University of California Press, Book Series, 2120 Berkeley Way, Berkeley, CA 94720. TEL 510-642-4247, FAX 510-643-7127, askucp@ucpress.edu, http://www.ucpress.edu/books/UCGS.ser.html, http://www.ucpress.edu/books/series.html. **Orders to:** California - Princeton Fulfillment Services, 1445 Lower Ferry Rd, Ewing, NJ 08618. TEL 800-777-4726, FAX 800-999-1958, orders@cpfs.pupress.princeton.edu.

➤ **UNIVERSITY OF COLORADO. INSTITUTE OF ARCTIC AND ALPINE RESEARCH. OCCASIONAL PAPERS.** see *SCIENCES: COMPREHENSIVE WORKS*

➤ **UNIVERSITY OF WISCONSIN-MILWAUKEE. FIELD STATION BULLETIN.** see *BIOLOGY*

550 JPN ISSN 0288-3155
CODEN: ABKUDK
URBAN KUBOTA. Text in Japanese. 1969. a.
—CASDDS.
Published by: Kubota Corp., 2-47 Shikitsu-Higashi 1-chome, Naniwa-ku, Osaka-shi, 556-0012, Japan.

551 USA
UTAH GEOLOGICAL SURVEY. MISCELLANEOUS PUBLICATIONS. Text in English. irreg. price varies. back issues avail. **Document type:** *Government.*
Published by: Utah Geological Survey, 1594 W North Temple, Ste 3110, Box 146100, Salt Lake City, UT 84114-6100. TEL 801-537-3320, FAX 801-537-3395, http://geology.utah.gov/.

VADOSE ZONE JOURNAL. see *ENVIRONMENTAL STUDIES*

VEGETATION HISTORY AND ARCHAEOBOTANY. see *BIOLOGY—Botany*

WASEDA DAIGAKU KYOIKUGAKUBU GAKUJUTSU KENKYU. SEIBUTSUGAKU, CHIGAKU HEN/WASEDA UNIVERSITY. SCHOOL OF EDUCATION. SCIENTIFIC RESEARCHES: BIOLOGY, GEOLOGY. see *BIOLOGY*

WAY NORTH; our natural and cultural heritage. see *ANTHROPOLOGY*

WEBSURFERS BIWEEKLY EARTH SCIENCE REVIEW. see *COMPUTERS—Internet*

WHO'S DRILLING. see *PETROLEUM AND GAS*

550 CHN ISSN 1001-1749
WUTAN HUATAN JISUAN JISHU. Text in Chinese. 1979. q. **Document type:** *Journal, Academic/Scholarly.*
Related titles: Online - full text ed.: (from East View Information Services, WanFang Data Corp.).
Published by: Chengdu Ligong Daxue/Chengdu University of Technology, No.1 3rd East Road, Chengdu, Sichuan 610059, China. wtht@cdut.edu.cn, http://wthtjsjs.periodicals.net.cn/.

550 CHN
WUTAN HUATAN YICONG. Text in Chinese. bi-m.
Published by: Dizhi Kuangchan Bu, Diqiu Wuli Diqiu Huaxue Kanca Yanjiusuo/Ministry of Geology and Mineral Products, Institute of Geophysics and Geochemistry Prospecting, Baiwanzhuang, Fuchengmenwai, Beijing, 100037, China. TEL 8311133. Ed. Li Xingyi.

WYOMING GEOLOGICAL ASSOCIATION. GUIDEBOOK. see *PETROLEUM AND GAS*

550 JPN ISSN 0289-9787
YAMAGUCHI CHIGAKKAISHI/GEOLOGICAL SOCIETY OF YAMAGUCHI. REPORTS. Text in Japanese. s-a. **Document type:** *Newsletter.*
Published by: Yamaguchi Chigakkai/Geological Society of Yamaguchi, Yamaguchi Hakubutsukan, 8-2 Kasuga-cho, Yamaguchi-shi, Yamaguchi-ken 753-0073, Japan. TEL 81-83-922-0294, FAX 81-83-922-0353.

E

550 CZE ISSN 0232-0916
Z DEJIN GEODEZIE A KARTOGRAFIE. Text in Czech. 1981. irreg. per issue exchange basis. bibl.; illus.
Published by: Narodni Technicke Muzeum, Kostelni 42, Prague 7, 170 78, Czech Republic.

550 ZMB ISSN 1010-5913
CODEN: ZJASEO
ZAMBIA JOURNAL OF APPLIED EARTH SCIENCES. Text in English. 1987. s-a.
Indexed: INIS AtomInd.
Published by: Geological Society of Zambia, PO Box 32379, Lusaka, Zambia. bdewaele@mines.unza.zm.

550 RUS
ZEMLYA I TRUD. Text in Russian. w.
Indexed: RASB.
Published by: Profsoyuz Rabotnikov Agropromyshlennogo Kompleksa, Leninskii pr-t 42, korp 1, Moscow, 117119, Russian Federation. TEL 7-095-9388463, FAX 7-095-9388684. Ed. V A Krest'yaninov. **US dist. addr.:** East View Information Services, 3020 Harbor Ln. N., Minneapolis, MN 55447. TEL 612-550-0961.

550 RUS
ZEMLYA SIBIRSKAYA, DAL'NEVOSTOCHNAYA. Text in Russian. m.
Indexed: RASB.
Published by: Zemlya Sibirskaya Dal'nevostochnaya, Ul Lenina 20, Omsk, 644024, Russian Federation. **US dist. addr.:** East View Information Services, 3020 Harbor Ln. N., Minneapolis, MN 55447. TEL 612-550-0961.

551.46 CHN ISSN 1007-7995
GC29.2.C6
ZHANJIANG HAIYANG DAXUE XUEBAO/ZHANJIANG OCEAN UNIVERSITY. JOURNAL. (Zhanjiang Haiyang Daxue/Zhanjiang Ocean University incorporates in 1998: Zhejiang Shuichan Xueyuan/Zhejiang College of Fisheries and Zhoushan Shifanzhuan Kexueyuan) Text in Chinese. 1975. q. CNY 4 newsstand/cover (effective 2005). **Document type:** *Journal, Academic/Scholarly.*
Incorporates (1982-1998): Zhejiang Shuichan Xueyuan Xuebao/Zhejiang College of Fisheries. Journal (1000-212X)
Related titles: Online - full content ed.: (from WanFang Data Corp.); Online - full text ed.: (from East View Information Services).
Indexed: ESPM.
—BLDSC (9512.661370).
Published by: Zhanjiang Haiyang Daxue/Zhanjiang Ocean University, 40 Jiefang Road, Xiashan District, Zhanjiang City, Guangdong Province 524025, China. TEL 86-759-2382396, xbbjb@zjou.edu.cn, http://zjhydxxb.periodicals.com.cn/default.html, http://www.zjou.edu.cn. Ed. Chuwu Liu. **Dist. by:** China International Book Trading Corp, 35 Chegongzhuang Xilu, Haidian District, PO Box 399, Beijing 100044, China. TEL 86-10-68412045, FAX 86-10-68412023, cibtc@mail.cibtc.com.cn, http://www.cibtc.com.cn.

550 CHN ISSN 1000-694X
ZHONGGUO SHAMO/JOURNAL OF CHINA DESERT RESEARCH. Text in Chinese; Summaries in Chinese, English. 1981. q. CNY 48 (effective 2004). **Document type:** *Journal, Academic/Scholarly.* **Description:** Contains papers reflecting every aspect of desert discipline and being of creativeness; new theories, new techniques and new views on desert development-utilization and land desertification control; research bulletin, academic discussions, views, and summaries.
Related titles: CD-ROM ed.; Online - full text ed.: (from WanFang Data Corp.); (from East View Information Services).
Indexed: ESPM, EnvEAb, M&GPA, PollutAb, SWRA.
Published by: (Lanzhou Shamo Yanjiusuo/Lanzhou Institute of Desert Research), Kexue Chubanshe/Science Press, 16 Donghuang Cheng Genbei Jie, Beijing, 100717, China. TEL 86-10-64000246, FAX 86-10-64030255, cibidr@ns.lzb.ac.cn, http://zgsm.periodicals.net.cn/default.html, http://www.sciencep.com/. Ed. Xin Min Liu. Circ: 800. **Dist. overseas by:** China International Book Trading Corp, 35 Chegongzhuang Xilu, Haidian District, PO Box 399, Beijing 100044, China. TEL 86-10-68412045, FAX 86-10-68412023, cibtc@mail.cibtc.com.cn, http://www.cibtc.com.cn.

550 CHN ISSN 1000-3037
➤ **ZIRAN ZIYUAN XUEBAO/JOURNAL OF NATURAL RESOURCES.** Text in Chinese. 1986. bi-m. CNY 132 (effective 2004). **Document type:** *Academic/Scholarly.*
Related titles: Online - full text ed.: (from East View Information Services).
Published by: (Zhongguo Kexueyuan, Dili Kexue yu Ziyuan Yanjiusuo/Chinese Academy of Sciences, Institute of Geographical Sciences and Natural Resources Research, Zhongguo Ziran Ziyuan Xuehui), Kexue Chubanshe/Science Press, 16 Donghuang Cheng Genbei Jie, Beijing, 100717, China. TEL 86-10-64000246, FAX 86-10-64030255, zrzyxb@igsnrr.ac.cn, http://www.igsnrr.ac.cn/geo/zrzyxb.jsp?objectid1=13, http://www.sciencep.com/. Ed. Wen-hua Li. **Dist. by:** China International Book Trading Corp, 35 Chegongzhuang Xilu, Haidian District, PO Box 399, Beijing 100044, China. TEL 86-10-68412045, FAX 86-10-68412023, cibtc@mail.cibtc.com.cn, http://www.cibtc.com.cn.

➤ **ZIYUAN KEXUE/RESOURCES SCIENCE.** see *ENVIRONMENTAL STUDIES*

550 RUS
ZOLOTO ROSSII. Text in Russian. 1994. s-a. USD 85 in United States (effective 2000).
Indexed: RASB.
Address: Ul B Nikitskaya 50-5, Moscow, 121069, Russian Federation. TEL 7-095-2039367. **Dist. by:** East View Information Services, 3020 Harbor Ln. N., Minneapolis, MN 55447. TEL 763-550-0961, FAX 763-559-2931.

EARTH SCIENCES—Abstracting, Bibliographies, Statistics

551 USA ISSN 0741-059X
QE696
A M Q U A PROGRAM AND ABSTRACTS. Text in English. 1970. s-a. free to members. **Document type:** *Abstract/Index.* **Description:** Contains abstracts of a topical nature with different themes in each issue related to the interdisciplinary fields in the Quaternary.
—Linda Hall.
Published by: American Quaternary Association, c/o Bonnie Whatley Styles, Illinois State Museum, 1011 E Ash St, Springfield, IL 62703. TEL 217-782-7475, FAX 217-785-2857, styles@museum.state.il.us, http://www4.nau.edu/amqua/, http://www.usu.edu/~amqua/. Circ: 1,000.

A S F A MARINE BIOTECHNOLOGY ABSTRACTS (ONLINE EDITION). see *BIOLOGY—Abstracting, Bibliographies, Statistics*

550 CAN ISSN 0225-5170
A S T I S OCCASIONAL PUBLICATIONS. Text in English. 1979. irreg. price varies. back issues avail. **Document type:** *Bibliography.*
Related titles: CD-ROM ed.: (from National Information Services Corp. (N I S C)); Online - full text ed.: (from QuickLaw Inc.).
Indexed: AnthLit.
—CISTI.
Published by: Arctic Science & Technology Information System, Arctic Institute of North America, University of Calgary, 2500 University Dr N W, Calgary, AB T2N 1N4, Canada. TEL 403-220-4036, FAX 403-282-4609, rgoodwin@ucalgary.ca. Ed. C Ross Goodwin.

551 CHN ISSN 0258-6746
ABSTRACTS OF CHINESE GEOLOGICAL LITERATURE✶. Text in English. 1985. q. USD 100. reprints avail. **Document type:** *Abstract/Index.* **Description:** Provides bibliographic information on Chinese geological literature.
Published by: National Geological Library, PO Box 8324, Beijing, 100083, China. TEL 86-1-8327337, FAX 86-1-8323270. Ed. Chen Minghui. Circ: 100. **Dist. by:** China National Publications Import and Export Corporation, PO Box 88, Beijing 100020, China. TEL 86-1-5063069.

AFRICA GEOSCIENCE REVIEW. see *EARTH SCIENCES—Geology*

016.651 USA ISSN 1043-7479
GB398.5
ARCTIC & ANTARCTIC REGIONS. Text in English. 1989. s-a. USD 895 (effective 2000). adv. **Document type:** *Academic/Scholarly.* **Description:** Provides a reference information resource for polar literature citations and abstracts from 1800 and earlier to the present.
Media: CD-ROM (from National Information Services Corp. (N I S C)).
Published by: National Information Services Corp. (N I S C), Ste 6, Wyman Towers, 3100 St Paul St, Baltimore, MD 21218. TEL 410-243-0797, FAX 410-243-0982, sales@nisc.com, http://www.nisc.com. Ed., Pub. Fred Durr. Adv. contact Debbie Durr.

551.021 AUS
AUSTRALIA. BUREAU OF STATISTICS. MINERAL ACCOUNT, AUSTRALIA. Text in English. 1998. irreg. AUD 28 (effective 2002). **Document type:** *Government.*
Published by: Australian Bureau of Statistics, PO Box 10, Belconnen, ACT 2616, Australia. TEL 61-2-6252-5249, FAX 61-2-6252-6778, http://www.abs.gov.au.

016.550 016.551 ROM ISSN 1221-4779
BIBLIOGRAFIA GEOLOGICA SI GEOFIZICA A ROMANIEI/GEOLOGICAL AND GEOPHYSICAL BIBLIOGRAPHY OF ROMANIA. Text in English. 1926. irreg., latest vol.8, 1994. USD 15 (effective 1999). **Document type:** *Proceedings, Academic/Scholarly.*
Formerly: Bibliografia Geologica si Geofizica a Republicii Socialiste Romania (1013-2104)
Published by: Institutul Geologic al Romaniei, Str. Caransebes 1, Bucharest, 78344, Romania. TEL 40-1-2242091, udubasa@igr.ro. Ed. Gheorghe Udubasa. R&P Serban Veliciu TEL 40-1-2242093. Circ: 550.

551 POL ISSN 0373-1987
BIBLIOGRAFIA GEOLOGICZNA POLSKI. Text in Polish. 1922. a. price varies. index. back issues avail. **Document type:** *Bibliography.* **Description:** Focuses on the fields of geophysics, geomorphology, stratigraphy, paleontology, mineralogy, petrography, hydrogeology, drilling and ecology.
—Linda Hall.
Published by: Panstwowy Instytut Geologiczny/Polish Geological Institute, ul Rakowiecka 4, Warsaw, 00975, Poland. TEL 48-22-8495351, FAX 48-22-8495342, zapolski@pgi.waw.pl, dystryb@pgi.wa.pl, http://www.pgi.waw.pl. Circ: 400.

016.551 USA ISSN 0098-2784
Z6031 CODEN: BBIGB
BIBLIOGRAPHY AND INDEX OF GEOLOGY. Text in English. 1969. 13/yr. USD 1,295 domestic; USD 1,420 foreign (effective 2005). index. 600 p./no.; **Document type:** *Bibliography.* **Description:** Scans articles related to geology from more than 3,000 periodicals in 40 languages; provides bibliographic information on journals, newsletters, government documents, geologic survey maps, and other documents.
Formed by the merger of (1907-1969): Bibliography of North American Geology (0740-6347); (1933-1969): Bibliography and Index of Geology Exclusive of North America (0376-1673)
Related titles: ♦ CD-ROM ed.: GeoRef. ISSN 0197-7482.
Indexed: ZooRec.
—BLDSC (2001.800000), Linda Hall. **CCC.**
Published by: American Geological Institute, 4220 King St, Alexandria, VA 22302-1502. TEL 703-379-2480, FAX 703-379-7563, kyost@agiweb.org, http://www.agiweb.org/, http://www.agiweb.org/pubs. Ed. Sharon Tahirkheli. R&P Kay Yost TEL 703-379-2480 ext 230. Circ: 170.

016.551 ZAF ISSN 0584-2360
Z6034.S57 CODEN: BSIGDW
BIBLIOGRAPHY AND SUBJECT INDEX OF SOUTH AFRICAN GEOLOGY. Text in English. 1957. irreg., latest 1994. price varies. **Document type:** *Bibliography.* **Description:** Lists geological articles appearing in South African publications for a particular year with an abstract of each.
—CISTI.
Published by: Council for Geoscience, Private Bag X112, Pretoria, 0001, South Africa. TEL 27-12-841-1911, FAX 27-12-841-1203, rprice@geoscience.org.za. R&P R R M Price TEL 27-12-8411018. Circ: 2,000.

016.33379 016.3382 GBR ISSN 0264-4126
BIBLIOGRAPHY OF ECONOMIC GEOLOGY. Text in English. 1968. bi-m. GBP 90, USD 180 (effective 1999). adv. bk.rev. index. **Document type:** *Bibliography.* **Description:** Bibliography of economic geology including minerals, petroleum, exploration, production and mining.
Formerly (until 1982): Geocom Bulletin (0016-7053)
Related titles: CD-ROM ed.: (from National Information Services Corp. (N I S C)); Online - full text ed.
—Linda Hall.
Published by: Geosystems, Geosystems, PO Box 40, Didcot, Oxon OX11 9BX, United Kingdom. TEL 44-1235-813913, FAX 44-1235-813913, geoarchive@aol.com. Ed. Rosalind Templeman.

016.559 559 FJI ISSN 0252-8398
BIBLIOGRAPHY OF THE GEOLOGY OF FIJI. Text in English. 1969. irreg. price varies. **Document type:** *Bibliography.* **Description:** Works on geology, geophysics, and mining on the islands and ocean areas of Fiji.
Published by: Mineral Resources Department, P.M. Bag, Suva, Fiji. TEL 679-381611, FAX 679-370039, http://www.mrd.gov.fj/. Ed. Peter Rodda. Circ: 500.

016.557 USA ISSN 0067-7272
BIBLIOGRAPHY OF THE GEOLOGY OF MISSOURI. Text in English. 1956. a. price varies. **Document type:** *Government.*
Published by: Missouri Department of Natural Resources, Division of Geology and Land Survey, PO Box 250, Rolla, MO 65401. TEL 573-368-2125. Ed. Dwight Weaver.

BIBLIOGRAPHY ON COLD REGIONS SCIENCE & TECHNOLOGY. see *ENGINEERING—Abstracting, Bibliographies, Statistics*

016.354 BWA ISSN 1011-9906
BOTSWANA. GEOLOGICAL SURVEY DEPARTMENT. ANNOTATED BIBLIOGRAPHY AND INDEX OF THE GEOLOGY OF BOTSWANA. Text in English. 1968. irreg. **Document type:** *Bibliography.*
Published by: Geological Survey Department, Lobatse, Botswana. TEL 267-330327, FAX 267-332013. Ed. B G Aboneng. Circ: 400.

557 016 CAN ISSN 1184-6941
Z6034.C19 CODEN: INCIEF
CANADA. GEOLOGICAL SURVEY. INFORMATION CIRCULAR/CANADA. COMMISSION GEOLOGIQUE. BULLETIN D'INFORMATION. Text in English, French. 1973. m. bibl. **Document type:** *Newsletter, Government.* **Description:** Announces the publication of new reports and maps (and reprints), and the release of open files.
Formerly (until 1990): Canada. Geological Survey. Monthly Information Circular (0837-256X)
Media: Online - full text.

Published by: Natural Resources Canada, 601 Booth St, Ottawa, ON K1A 0E8, Canada. TEL 613-995-4342, http://www.nrcan.gc.ca/gsc/gicd/pubs/circu_e.html. Ed., R&P M F Dufour TEL 613-995-7648. Circ: 5,100.

016.55146   AUS   ISSN 1327-5232
COASTAL BIBLIOGRAPHY SERIES. Text in English. irreg. **Document type:** *Government.*
Media: Online - full text.
Published by: Australian Heritage Commission, Education and Communication Section, GPO Box 787, Canberra, ACT 2601, Australia. TEL 61-2-6274-2111, FAX 61-2-6274-2095, ahc.library@ahc.gov.au, http://www.environment.gov.au/heritage/infores/HERA/coastal_bibliographies/coast.html.

622 669 550 016   JPN   ISSN 0011-3301
CURRENT BIBLIOGRAPHY ON SCIENCE AND TECHNOLOGY: EARTH SCIENCE, MINING AND METALLURGY/KAGAKU GIJUTSU BUNKEN SOKUHO. KINZOKU KOGAKU, KOZAN KOGAKU, CHIKYU NO KAGAKU-HEN. Text in Japanese. 1958. s-m. USD 1,760. index.
Related titles: CD-ROM ed.; Online - full text ed.: (from JICST).
Published by: Japan Science and Technology Corporation, Information Center for Science and Technology/Kagaku Gijutsu Shinko Jigyodan, 5-3 Yonban-cho, Chiyoda-ku, Tokyo, 102-0081, Japan. TEL 81-3-5214-8413, FAX 81-3-5214-8410. Circ: 600.

CURRENT CONTENTS: PHYSICAL, CHEMICAL & EARTH SCIENCES. see *CHEMISTRY—Abstracting, Bibliographies, Statistics*

551.22   CHN   ISSN 1003-2894
DIZHEN WENZHAI/SEISMOLOGICAL ABSTRACTS. Text in Chinese. 1982. bi-m. **Document type:** *Abstract/Index.*
Published by: (Keji Qingbao Zhongxin), Guojia Dizhen-ju/State Seismological Bureau, Editorial Office of Chinese Seismology, 63 Fuxing Lu, Beijing, 100036, China. TEL 8115331. Ed. Cheng Ronglian.

EARTHQUAKE ENGINEERING ABSTRACTS DATABASE. see *ENGINEERING—Abstracting, Bibliographies, Statistics*

EARTHQUAKES AND THE BUILT ENVIRONMENT INDEX. see *ENGINEERING—Abstracting, Bibliographies, Statistics*

GEOGRAPHICAL ABSTRACTS: PHYSICAL GEOGRAPHY. see *GEOGRAPHY—Abstracting, Bibliographies, Statistics*

551   HUN   ISSN 0230-7065
GEOLOGIAI ES GEOFIZIKAI SZAKIRODALMI TAJEKOZTATO/GEOLOGY AND GEOPHYSICS ABSTRACTS. Text in Hungarian. 1983. m. HUF 6,000. abstr. index.
Published by: Orszagos Muszaki Informacios Kozpont es Konyvtar/National Technical Information Centre and Library, Muzeum utca 17, PO Box 12, Budapest, 1428, Hungary. Ed. Otto Tomschey. Circ: 270. **Subscr. to:** Kultura, PO Box 149, Budapest 1389, Hungary.

016.551   GBR   ISSN 0954-0512
QE1   CODEN: GEABF2
GEOLOGICAL ABSTRACTS. Text in English. 1977. 12/yr. EUR 2,559 in Europe to institutions; JPY 339,300 in Japan to institutions; USD 2,863 to institutions except Europe and Japan (effective 2006). abstr. index. back issues avail.; reprints avail. **Document type:** *Journal, Abstract/Index.* **Description:** International abstracting service for geologists.
Formed by the 1989 merger of: Geological Abstracts: Geophysics and Tectonics (0268-7941); Geological Abstracts: Economic Geology (0268-800X); Geological Abstracts: Palaeontology and Stratigraphy (0268-8018); Geological Abstracts: Sedimentary Geology; Geological Abstracts: Geophysics and Tectonics was formerly:: Geophysics and Tectonics Abstracts (0262-0847); Geological Abstracts: Sedimentary Geology was formerly: Sedimentology (0268-8026)
Related titles: Online - full content ed.: GEOBASE (from The Dialog Corporation).
—BLDSC (4131.230000), PADDS. **CCC.**
Published by: Elsevier - Geo Abstracts (Subsidiary of: Elsevier Science & Technology), Duke St., 34, Norwich, NR3 3AP, United Kingdom. TEL 44-1603-626327, FAX 44-1603-667934, geoabs@elsevier.co.uk, http://www.elsevier.com/locate/geolab. Circ: 600. **Subscr. to:** Elsevier BV, PO Box 211, Amsterdam 1000 AE, Netherlands. TEL 31-20-485-3757, FAX 31-20-485-3432, nlinfo-f@elsevier.nl, http://www.elsevier.nl.

551 016   USA   ISSN 0016-7592
QE1   CODEN: GAAPBC
GEOLOGICAL SOCIETY OF AMERICA. ABSTRACTS WITH PROGRAMS. Text in English. 1961. 7/yr. USD 132 domestic to non-members; USD 142 foreign to non-members (effective 2005). **Document type:** *Abstract/Index.* **Description:** Abstracts of scientific papers to be presented at the Society's sections and annual meetings, and program of events.
Formerly (until 1969): Geological Society of America. Abstracts (0435-3986)
Indexed: AESIS, ASFA, ESPM, Inspec, M&GPA, PetrolAb, SFA, SWRA.
—CISTI, Linda Hall, PADDS. **CCC.**

Published by: Geological Society of America, 3300 Penrose Pl, Boulder, CO 80301-1806. TEL 303-447-2020, FAX 303-447-1133, pubs@geosociety.org, http://www.geosociety.org. Circ: 7,000.

016.559   AUS   ISSN 0729-011X
GEOLOGICAL SOCIETY OF AUSTRALIA. ABSTRACTS SERIES. Text in English. 1980. irreg. price varies. abstr. back issues avail. **Document type:** *Monographic series, Abstract/Index.* **Description:** Contains Abstracts papers presented at all G.S.A. meetings.
Indexed: AESIS.
—BLDSC (4136.810000), CISTI, IE, ingenta. **CCC.**
Published by: Geological Society of Australia Inc., Ste 706, 301 George St, Sydney, NSW 2000, Australia. TEL 61-2-92902194, FAX 61-2-92902198, info@gsa.org.au, http://www.gsa.org.au.

016.551   EGY   ISSN 0446-4648
GEOLOGICAL SOCIETY OF EGYPT. ANNUAL MEETING. ABSTRACTS OF PAPERS. Summaries in English. 1963. a. free. reprint service avail. from IRC. **Document type:** *Proceedings.*
Published by: (Research Department), Geological Society of Egypt, Osiris St. 1, Garden City, Cairo, Egypt. Ed. E M El Shazly.

016.55   GBR   ISSN 1365-1617
TA703   CODEN: GMABFO
➤ **GEOMECHANICS ABSTRACTS.** Text in English. 1964; N.S. 1997. 6/yr. EUR 750 in Europe to institutions; JPY 99,300 in Japan to institutions; USD 837 to institutions except Europe and Japan (effective 2006). back issues avail. **Document type:** *Journal, Abstract/Index.* **Description:** Provides comprehensive coverage of papers published on rock and soil mechanics and geotechnics.
Supersedes in part (in 1997): International Journal of Rock Mechanics and Mining Sciences and Geomechanics Abstracts (0148-9062); Which was formed by the merger of: International Journal of Rock Mechanics and Mining Sciences (0020-7624); Rock Mechanics Abstracts (0035-7456)
Related titles: Online - full content ed.: GEOBASE (from The Dialog Corporation); Online - full text ed.: (from Gale Group, IngentaConnect, ScienceDirect).
Indexed: AESIS, SCI.
—BLDSC (4147.258000), CISTI, IDS, Linda Hall. **CCC.**
Published by: Elsevier - Geo Abstracts (Subsidiary of: Elsevier Science & Technology), Duke St., 34, Norwich, NR3 3AP, United Kingdom. TEL 44-1603-626327, FAX 44-1603-667934, http://www.elsevier.com/locate/geomech. Ed. S. E. Long. **Subscr. to:** Elsevier BV, PO Box 211, Amsterdam 1000 AE, Netherlands. TEL 31-20-485-3757, FAX 31-20-485-3432, nlinfo-f@elsevier.nl, http://www.elsevier.nl.

016.551   USA   ISSN 0197-7482
QE1
GEOREF. Text in English. 1990. m. **Document type:** *Abstract/Index.* **Description:** Contains bibliographic references for more than 3,000 journals (spanning 40 languages), maps, and other documents covering geology worldwide. All references are indexed by key words and some include abstracts.
Media: CD-ROM (from SilverPlatter Information, Inc.). **Related titles:** ◆ Print ed.: Bibliography and Index of Geology. ISSN 0098-2784.
—Linda Hall.
Published by: American Geological Institute, 4220 King St, Alexandria, VA 22302-1502. TEL 703-379-2480, FAX 703-379-7563, kyost@agiweb.org, http://www.agiweb.org/, http://www.agiweb.org/pubs. Ed. Sharon Tahirkheli. R&P Kay Yost TEL 703-379-2480 ext 230.

016.551   USA   ISSN 1069-1022
                                      CODEN: PCETEO
GEOREF SERIALS LIST. Text in English. 1981. a. looseleaf. USD 118.75 (effective 2002). 550 p./no.; **Description:** Provides an electronic online database of bibliographic references for more than 3,000 journals (spanning 40 languages), maps, and other documents covering geology worldwide. All references are indexed by keyword and some include abstracts.
Media: Online - full text.
—**CCC.**
Published by: American Geological Institute, 4220 King St, Alexandria, VA 22302-1502. TEL 703-379-2480, FAX 703-379-2480, kyost@agiweb.org, http://www.agiweb.org/, http://www.agiweb.org/pubs. Ed. Sharon Tahirkheli. R&P Kay Yost TEL 703-379-2480 ext 230.

557 016   USA
GEORGIA GEOLOGIC SURVEY. CIRCULAR 1. LIST OF PUBLICATIONS. Text in English. 1973 (14th ed.). irreg., latest vol.21, 1990. free. **Description:** Listing and charges for all geologic survey publications.
Formerly: Georgia Geological Survey. Circular 1. List of Publications
Related titles: ◆ Series of: Georgia Geologic Survey. Circular.
Published by: Georgia Department of Natural Resources, Georgia Geologic Survey, 19 Martin Luther King Jr Dr, S W, Rm 400, Atlanta, GA 30334. TEL 404-656-3214.

016 550   GBR   ISSN 0016-8483
QE1
GEOSCIENCE DOCUMENTATION; a bi-monthly journal for the study of geoscience literature. Text in English. 1969. bi-m. bk.rev. pat.; stat. index. **Document type:** *Abstract/Index.* **Description:** Bibliography of interest to earth science librarians giving information on serials, monographs, reviews, history and overviews.
Related titles: CD-ROM ed.: (from National Information Services Corp. (N I S C)); Online - full text ed.
—Linda Hall.
Published by: Geosystems, Geosystems, PO Box 40, Didcot, Oxon OX11 9BX, United Kingdom. geoarchive@aol.com. Ed. Rosalind Templeman.

016.551   USA
GEOSCIENCEWORLD. Abbreviated title: G S W. Text in English. base vol. plus d. updates. **Document type:** *Abstract/Index.*
Media: Online - full text.
Address: http://www.geoscienceworld.org.

550   GBR
GEOSOURCES. Text in English. 1969. irreg. GBP 50, USD 100 (effective 1999). adv. **Document type:** *Bibliography.* **Description:** Lists serials Geosystems uses to compile its earth sciences bibliographies.
Formerly: Geoserials (0072-1417)
Related titles: CD-ROM ed.: (from National Information Services Corp. (N I S C)).
Published by: Geosystems, Geosystems, PO Box 40, Didcot, Oxon OX11 9BX, United Kingdom. TEL 44-1385-813913, FAX 44-1385-813913, geoarchive@aol.com.

016.3637   CAN   ISSN 0831-5000
GEOTECHNICAL SCIENCE LABORATORIES. PUBLICATIONS, REPORTS, AND THESES. Text in English. 1972. a. free. index, cum.index: 1976-1984. **Document type:** *Academic/Scholarly.* **Description:** Lists scientific reports, papers in journals, theses and other items available.
Published by: Geotechnical Science Laboratories, Carleton University, 1125 Colonel By Dr, Ottawa, ON K1S 5B6, Canada. TEL 613-520-2852, FAX 613-520-3640, gsl@carleton.ca, http://www.carleton.ca/GSL. Circ: 550.

016 550   GBR   ISSN 0952-2700
Z6032
GEOTITLES; geoscience bibliography. Text in English. 1969. m. GBP 425, USD 800 (effective 1999). adv. **Document type:** *Bibliography.* **Description:** Lists and indexes articles, books, and monographs in geology, petroleum, minerals, hydrology, oceanography, paleontology, geophysics, and environment.
Formerly (until 1985): Geotitles Weekly (0016-8564)
Related titles: CD-ROM ed.: (from National Information Services Corp. (N I S C)); Online - full text ed.
—BLDSC (4161.090000).
Published by: Geosystems, Geosystems, PO Box 40, Didcot, Oxon OX11 9BX, United Kingdom. TEL 44-1235-813913, FAX 44-1235-813913, geoarchive@aol.com, http://www.nisc.com.

551   CHN   ISSN 1003-2924
GUOWAI KEJI ZILIAO MULU (DIZHIXUE)/FOREIGN SCIENCE AND TECHNOLOGY CATALOGUE (GEOLOGY). Text in Chinese. q.
Published by: Zhongguo Dizhi Kuangchan Xinxi Yanjiuyuan/Chinese Institute of Geology and Mineral Products Information, 277 Fuchengmenwai Beijie, Beijing, 100037, China. TEL 892243. Ed. Bao Yongquan. **Affiliate:** 1977.

016.551   GBR   ISSN 0953-7589
HYDROTITLES; hydroscience bibliography. Text in English. 1989. bi-m. USD 170; GBP 85 in Europe. **Document type:** *Abstract/Index.* **Description:** Covers hydrology, hydroelectric power, climate change, glaciology, geomorphology, hydrogeology, meteorology, water resources, hydraulics, and soil science.
Related titles: CD-ROM ed.: (from National Information Services Corp. (N I S C)); Online - full text ed.
Published by: Geosystems, Geosystems, PO Box 40, Didcot, Oxon OX11 9BX, United Kingdom. TEL 44-1235-813913, FAX 44-1235-813913, cd2rom@aol.com, http://www.nisc.com. Ed. Roger F Templeman.

016.551   ISR
ISRAEL GEOLOGICAL SOCIETY ABSTRACTS. Text in English. a.
—BLDSC (0553.170000), ingenta.
Published by: Israel Geological Society, 30 Malkhe Israel St, Jerusalem, 95501, Israel. TEL 972-2-5314271, FAX 972-2-5380688, http://www.igs.org.il/siteFrame.asp.

550   ISR
ISRAEL. GEOLOGICAL SURVEY. BIBLIOGRAPHY SERIES. Text in English, French, German, Hebrew. irreg. USD 15 per issue. **Document type:** *Bibliography.*
Published by: Geological Survey Library, 30 Malkhe Israel St, Jerusalem, 95501, Israel. TEL 972-2-314266.

551.22   JPN
JISHIN KOGAKU BUNKEN MOKUROKU/BIBLIOGRAPHY OF EARTHQUAKE ENGINEERING. Text in English, Japanese. 1968. biennial. JPY 700 per issue. **Document type:** *Bibliography.*

E

▼ *new title*   ➤ *refereed*   ✳ *unverified*   ◆ *full entry avail.*

Published by: (Taishin Kogaku Iinkai), Doboku Gakkai/Japan Society of Civil Engineers, Mu-banchi, Yotsuya 1-chome, Shinjuku-ku, Tokyo, 160-0004, Japan.

550 JPN
MINERALOGICAL SOCIETY OF JAPAN. ANNUAL MEETING ABSTRACTS/NIHON KOBUTSU GAKKAI NENKAI KOEN YOSHISHU. Text in English, Japanese. a. JPY 3,000 (effective 2001).
Published by: Mineralogical Society of Japan, Nogizaka Bldg, 6-41, Akasaka 9-chome, Minato-ku, Tokyo, 107-0052, Japan. TEL 81-3-3475-0824, FAX 81-3-3475-5287.

016.55146 RUS
MIROVOI OKEAN. INFORMATSIONNO-ANALITICHESKII SBORNIK. Text in Russian. 2000. irreg. subscr. price on request. **Document type:** *Journal, Abstract/Index.*
Published by: Vserossiiskii Institut Nauchnoi i Tekhnicheskoi Informatsii (VINITI), Ul Usievicha 20, Moscow, 125190, Russian Federation. TEL 7-095-1526441, FAX 7-095-9430060, dir@viniti.ru, http://www.viniti.ru. **Dist. by:** Informnauka Ltd., Ul Usievicha 20, Moscow 125190, Russian Federation. alfimov@viniti.ru.

621.4 016 USA
N T I S ALERTS: OCEAN SCIENCES & ENGINEERING. Text in English. s-m. USD 241.50 in North America; USD 316.25 elsewhere (effective 2005). index. back issues avail. **Document type:** *Newsletter, Bibliography.* **Description:** Provides summaries of titles received by NTIS - results of research and studies sponsored by the U.S. government and international sources. Covers biological and dynamic oceanography, hydrography, marine engineering, geophysics, etc.
Former titles: N T I S Alerts: Ocean Technology and Engineering; Abstract Newsletter: Ocean Technology and Engineering; Weekly Abstract Newsletter: Ocean Technology and Engineering; Weekly Government Abstracts. Ocean Technology and Engineering (0364-6424)
Related titles: Microform ed.: (from NTI).
Published by: U.S. Department of Commerce, National Technical Information Service, 5285 Port Royal Rd, Springfield, VA 22161. TEL 703-605-6000, info@ntis.gov, http://www.ntis.gov.

550 JPN
NIHON CHIKYU KAGAKKAI NENKAI KOEN YOSHISHU/ GEOCHEMICAL SOCIETY OF JAPAN. ABSTRACTS OF REPORTS ON ANNUAL MEETING. Text in English, Japanese. a. **Document type:** *Abstract/Index.*
Published by: Nihon Chikyu Kagakkai/Geochemical Society of Japan, Nihon Gakkai Jimu Senta, 16-19 Honkomagome 5-chome, Bunkyo-ku, Tokyo, 113-0021, Japan.

551 JPN ISSN 0917-3404
NIHON CHISHITSU GAKKAI KANTO SHIBU SHINPOJUMU KOEN YOSHISHU/GEOLOGICAL SOCIETY OF JAPAN. ABSTRACTS OF KANTO BRANCH SYMPOSIUM. Text in Japanese. s-a. price varies. **Document type:** *Abstract/Index.*
Published by: (Kanto Shibu), Nihon Chishitsu Gakkai/Geological Society of Japan, 10-4 Kaji-cho 1-chome, Chiyoda-ku, Tokyo, 101-0044, Japan. TEL 03-3252-7242, FAX 03-5256-5676.

551.48 JPN
NIHON RIKUSUI GAKKAI KOEN YOSHISHU/JAPANESE SOCIETY OF LIMNOLOGY. ABSTRACTS OF MEETING. Text in Japanese. a. **Document type:** *Abstract/Index.*
Published by: Nihon Rikusui Gakkai, c/o Shiga University, 2-5-1 Hiratsu, Otsu, Shiga-ken 520-0862, Japan. TEL 81-775-37-7735, endoh@sue.shiga-u.ac.jp. Ed. O Mitamura.

551.46 016 USA ISSN 0748-1489
GC1 CODEN: OABTAE
OCEANIC ABSTRACTS. Text in English. 1964. m. (except Dec.). USD 1,830 combined subscription print & online eds. (effective 2006). bibl.; illus. a. index on CD-ROM. back issues avail.; reprints avail. **Document type:** *Abstract/Index.* **Description:** Covers marine biology, oceanography, ships and shipping, marine pollution, and offshore engineering.
Former titles (until 1984): Oceanic Abstracts with Indexes (0093-6901); (until 1972): Oceanic Index (0029-8093); Oceanic Citation Index (0029-8085)
Related titles: CD-ROM ed.: (from National Information Services Corp. (N I S C)); Online - full text ed.: ISSN 1555-452X. USD 1,375 (effective 2006).
—BLDSC (6231.430000).
Published by: C S A Journal Division (Subsidiary of: Cambridge Information Group), 7200 Wisconsin Ave, Ste 715, Bethesda, MD 20814. TEL 301-961-6798, 800-843-7751, FAX 301-961-6799, journals@csa.com, http://www.csa.com/factsheets/oceanic-set-c.php. Eds. Catherine E Deckard, Katina Bucher Norris, Laura Griesbauer. Pub. Ted Caris.

016.55146 GBR ISSN 0967-0653
Z6004.P6
➤ **OCEANOGRAPHIC LITERATURE REVIEW.** Text in English. 1967. 12/yr. EUR 2,429 in Europe to institutions; JPY 322,600 in Japan to institutions; USD 2,718 to institutions except Europe and Japan; EUR 125 in Europe to qualified personnel; JPY 16,600 in Japan to qualified personnel; USD 139 to qualified personnel except Europe and Japan (effective 2006). adv. bk.rev. bibl.; charts; illus.; pat. index. back issues avail.; reprints avail. **Document type:** *Journal, Bibliography.* **Description:** Provides an annotated bibliography to international research literature in all disciplines pertaining to oceanography.
Former titles (until 1993): Deep-Sea Research. Part B: Oceanographic Literature Review (0198-0254); (until 1979): Oceanographic Abstracts and Bibliography (0146-6305); (until 1977): Deep-Sea Research. Oceanographic Abstracts and Oceanographic Bibliography Section (0418-4890)
Related titles: CD-ROM ed.: Marine Literature Review. ISSN 1362-2196. EUR 2,351 in Europe to institutions; JPY 312,400 in Japan to institutions; USD 2,631 elsewhere to institutions (effective 2006) (from National Information Services Corp. (N I S C)); Microfilm ed.: (from PQC); Online - full content ed.: GEOBASE (from The Dialog Corporation); Online - full text ed.: (from EBSCO Publishing, Gale Group, ScienceDirect).
—BLDSC (6232.130000), IE, Infotrieve, Linda Hall. **CCC.**
Published by: Pergamon (Subsidiary of: Elsevier Science & Technology), The Boulevard, Langford Ln, East Park, Kidlington, Oxford OX5 1GB, United Kingdom. TEL 44-1865-843000, FAX 44-1865-843010, http://www.elsevier.com/locate/olr. Eds. F K Cooper, N T Davey. **Subscr. to:** Elsevier BV, PO Box 211, Amsterdam 1000 AE, Netherlands. TEL 31-20-485-3757, FAX 31-20-485-3432, nlinfo-f@elsevier.nl, http://www.elsevier.nl.

551.46 JPN
OCEANOGRAPHICAL SOCIETY OF JAPAN. ABSTRACTS ON THE CONFERENCE/NIHON KAIYO GAKKAI TAIKAI KOEN YOSHISHU. Text in English, Japanese. s-a. JPY 3,500 per issue. adv. **Document type:** *Abstract/Index.*
Published by: Oceanographical Society of Japan/Nippon Kaiyo Gakkai, 6-14 Minami-Dai 1-chome, Nakano-ku, Tokyo, 164-0014, Japan. TEL 81-3-3377-3951, FAX 81-3-3378-9419. Ed. Nobuyuki Shikama. Adv. contact Keisuke Taira.

016.9198 GBR ISSN 0957-5073
Z6005.P7
POLAR AND GLACIOLOGICAL ABSTRACTS. Text in English. 1931. 3/yr. GBP 140 to institutions; USD 219 in North America to institutions (effective 2006). adv. Index. back issues avail. **Document type:** *Journal, Abstract/Index.* **Description:** Covers literature relating to both polar regions and adjacent areas.
Supersedes (in 1990): Recent Polar and Glaciological Literature (0263-547X); Which was formerly (until 1981): Recent Polar Literature (0267-0283)
Related titles: CD-ROM ed.; Online - full text ed.: (from QuickLaw Inc.).
—Linda Hall. **CCC.**
Published by: (Scott Polar Research Institute), Cambridge University Press, The Edinburgh Bldg, Shaftesbury Rd, Cambridge, CB2 2RU, United Kingdom. TEL 44-1223-312393, FAX 44-1223-315052, journals@cambridge.org, http://uk.cambridge.org/journals/pga, http://www.cup.cam.ac.uk/. Ed. William Mills. R&P Linda Nicol TEL 44-1223-325757. Adv. contact Rebecca Curtis TEL 44-1223-325757. **Subscr. to:** Cambridge University Press, 100 Brook Hill Dr, West Nyack, NY 10994. TEL 845-353-7500, FAX 845-353-4141, journals_subscriptions@cup.org

016.5503 RUS ISSN 0202-9340
REFERATIVNYI ZHURNAL. ANTROPOGENOVYI PERIOD. GEOMORFOLOGIYA SUSHI I MORSKOGO DNA. Text in Russian. 1954. m. USD 243 foreign (effective 2006). **Document type:** *Abstract/Index.*
Related titles: CD-ROM ed.; Online - full text ed.
—East View.
Published by: Vserossiiskii Institut Nauchnoi i Tekhnicheskoi Informatsii (VINITI), Ul Usievicha 20, Moscow, 125190, Russian Federation. TEL 7-095-1526441, FAX 7-095-9430060, dir@viniti.ru, http://www.viniti.ru. Ed. Yurii Arskii. **Dist. by:** Informnauka Ltd., Ul Usievicha 20, Moscow 125190, Russian Federation. alfimov@viniti.ru.

016.551 RUS ISSN 0202-9456
REFERATIVNYI ZHURNAL. FIZIKA ZEMLI. Text in Russian. 1957. m. USD 217 foreign (effective 2006). **Document type:** *Journal, Abstract/Index.*
Related titles: CD-ROM ed.; Online - full text ed.
—East View.
Published by: Vserossiiskii Institut Nauchnoi i Tekhnicheskoi Informatsii (VINITI), Ul Usievicha 20, Moscow, 125190, Russian Federation. TEL 7-095-1526441, FAX 7-095-9430060, dir@viniti.ru, http://www.viniti.ru. **Dist. by:** Informnauka Ltd., Ul Usievicha 20, Moscow 125190, Russian Federation. alfimov@viniti.ru.

016.526 RUS ISSN 0375-9717
REFERATIVNYI ZHURNAL. GEODEZIYA I AEROS'EMKA. Text in Russian. 1953. m. USD 256 foreign (effective 2006). **Document type:** *Abstract/Index.*
Formerly: Referativnyi Zhurnal. Geodeziya (0034-2351)
Related titles: CD-ROM ed.; Online - full text ed.
Indexed: ChemAb.
—Linda Hall.
Published by: Vserossiiskii Institut Nauchnoi i Tekhnicheskoi Informatsii (VINITI), Ul Usievicha 20, Moscow, 125190, Russian Federation. TEL 7-095-1526441, FAX 7-095-9430060, dir@viniti.ru, http://www.viniti.ru. Ed. Yurii Arskii. **Dist. by:** Informnauka Ltd., Ul Usievicha 20, Moscow 125190, Russian Federation. alfimov@viniti.ru.

016.551 RUS ISSN 0034-236X
CODEN: RZGFAZ
REFERATIVNYI ZHURNAL. GEOFIZIKA. Text in Russian. 1957. m. USD 888 foreign (effective 2006). **Document type:** *Journal, Abstract/Index.*
Related titles: CD-ROM ed.; Online - full text ed.
Indexed: ChemAb.
—East View, Linda Hall.
Published by: Vserossiiskii Institut Nauchnoi i Tekhnicheskoi Informatsii (VINITI), Ul Usievicha 20, Moscow, 125190, Russian Federation. TEL 7-095-1526441, FAX 7-095-9430060, dir@viniti.ru, http://www.viniti.ru. Ed. Andrei Kapitsa. **Dist. by:** Informnauka Ltd., Ul Usievicha 20, Moscow 125190, Russian Federation. alfimov@viniti.ru.

016.5519 016.549 RUS ISSN 0202-9367
REFERATIVNYI ZHURNAL. GEOKHIMIYA, MINERALOGIYA, PETROGRAFIYA. Text in Russian. 1954. m. USD 624 foreign (effective 2006). **Document type:** *Abstract/Index.*
Related titles: CD-ROM ed.; Online - full text ed.
—East View.
Published by: Vserossiiskii Institut Nauchnoi i Tekhnicheskoi Informatsii (VINITI), Ul Usievicha 20, Moscow, 125190, Russian Federation. TEL 7-095-1526441, FAX 7-095-9430060, dir@viniti.ru, http://www.viniti.ru. **Dist. by:** Informnauka Ltd., Ul Usievicha 20, Moscow 125190, Russian Federation. alfimov@viniti.ru.

016.5519 RUS ISSN 0202-9359
REFERATIVNYI ZHURNAL. GEOLOGICHESKIE I GEOKHIMICHESKIE METODY POISKOV POLEZNYKH ISKOPAEMYKH. Text in Russian. m. USD 260 foreign (effective 2006). **Document type:** *Abstract/Index.*
Related titles: CD-ROM ed.; Online - full text ed.
—East View.
Published by: Vserossiiskii Institut Nauchnoi i Tekhnicheskoi Informatsii (VINITI), Ul Usievicha 20, Moscow, 125190, Russian Federation. TEL 7-095-1526441, FAX 7-095-9430060, dir@viniti.ru, http://www.viniti.ru. **Dist. by:** Informnauka Ltd., Ul Usievicha 20, Moscow 125190, Russian Federation. alfimov@viniti.ru.

016.551 RUS ISSN 0486-2309
CODEN: RZGLAJ
REFERATIVNYI ZHURNAL. GEOLOGIYA. Text in Russian. 1954. m. USD 2,087 foreign (effective 2006). **Document type:** *Abstract/Index.*
Related titles: CD-ROM ed.; Online - full text ed.
Indexed: ChemAb.
—CASDDS, East View, Linda Hall.
Published by: Vserossiiskii Institut Nauchnoi i Tekhnicheskoi Informatsii (VINITI), Ul Usievicha 20, Moscow, 125190, Russian Federation. TEL 7-095-1526441, FAX 7-095-9430060, dir@viniti.ru, http://www.viniti.ru. Ed. Viktor E Khain. **Dist. by:** Informnauka Ltd., Ul Usievicha 20, Moscow 125190, Russian Federation. alfimov@viniti.ru.

016.551 RUS ISSN 0202-9448
REFERATIVNYI ZHURNAL. GEOMAGNETIZM I VYSOKIE SLOI ATMOSFERY. Text in Russian. 1957. m. USD 203 foreign (effective 2006). **Document type:** *Journal, Abstract/Index.*
Related titles: CD-ROM ed.; Online - full text ed.
—East View.
Published by: Vserossiiskii Institut Nauchnoi i Tekhnicheskoi Informatsii (VINITI), Ul Usievicha 20, Moscow, 125190, Russian Federation. TEL 7-095-1526441, FAX 7-095-9430060, dir@viniti.ru, http://www.viniti.ru. Ed. Yurii Arskii. **Dist. by:** Informnauka Ltd., Ul Usievicha 20, Moscow 125190, Russian Federation. alfimov@viniti.ru.

016.5514 RUS ISSN 0202-9375
REFERATIVNYI ZHURNAL. GIDROGEOLOGIYA, INZHENERNAYA GEOLOGIYA, MERZLOTOVEDENIE. Text in Russian. 1954. m. USD 348 foreign (effective 2006). **Document type:** *Abstract/Index.*
Related titles: CD-ROM ed.; Online - full text ed.
—East View.
Published by: Vserossiiskii Institut Nauchnoi i Tekhnicheskoi Informatsii (VINITI), Ul Usievicha 20, Moscow, 125190, Russian Federation. TEL 7-095-1526441, FAX 7-095-9430060, dir@viniti.ru, http://www.viniti.ru. **Dist. by:** Informnauka Ltd., Ul Usievicha 20, Moscow 125190, Russian Federation. alfimov@viniti.ru.

REFERATIVNYI ZHURNAL. ISSLEDOVANIE ZEMLI IZ KOSMOSA. see *ASTRONOMY—Abstracting, Bibliographies, Statistics*

016.551 RUS ISSN 0202-9391
REFERATIVNYI ZHURNAL. NEMETALLICHESKIE POLEZNYE ISKOPAEMYE. Text in Russian. 1954. m. USD 74 foreign (effective 2006). **Document type:** *Abstract/Index.*
Related titles: CD-ROM ed.; Online - full text ed.

E

—East View.
Published by: Vserossiiskii Institut Nauchnoi i Tekhnicheskoi Informatsii (VINITI), Ul Usievicha 20, Moscow, 125190, Russian Federation. TEL 7-095-1526441, FAX 7-095-9430060, dir@viniti.ru, http://www.viniti.ru. **Dist. by:** Informnauka Ltd., Ul Usievicha 20, Moscow 125190, Russian Federation. alfimov@viniti.ru.

016.551   RUS   ISSN 0202-9405
REFERATIVNYI ZHURNAL. OBSHCHAYA GEOLOGIYA. Text in Russian. 1954. m. USD 465 foreign (effective 2006). **Document type:** *Abstract/Index.*
Related titles: CD-ROM ed.; Online - full text ed.
Published by: Vserossiiskii Institut Nauchnoi i Tekhnicheskoi Informatsii (VINITI), Ul Usievicha 20, Moscow, 125190, Russian Federation. TEL 7-095-1526441, FAX 7-095-9430060, dir@viniti.ru, http://www.viniti.ru. **Dist. by:** Informnauka Ltd., Ul Usievicha 20, Moscow 125190, Russian Federation. alfimov@viniti.ru.

016.55146   RUS   ISSN 0202-9316
REFERATIVNYI ZHURNAL. OKEANOLOGIYA. GIDROLOGIYA SUSHI. GLYATSIOLOGIYA. Text in Russian. 1956. m. USD 213 foreign (effective 2006). **Document type:** *Abstract/Index.*
Related titles: CD-ROM ed.; Online - full text ed.
—East View.
Published by: Vserossiiskii Institut Nauchnoi i Tekhnicheskoi Informatsii (VINITI), Ul Usievicha 20, Moscow, 125190, Russian Federation. TEL 7-095-1526441, FAX 7-095-9430060, dir@viniti.ru, http://www.viniti.ru. Ed. Yurii Arskii. **Dist. by:** Informnauka Ltd., Ul Usievicha 20, Moscow 125190, Russian Federation. alfimov@viniti.ru.

REFERATIVNYI ZHURNAL. RUDNYE MESTOROZHDENIYA. see *MINES AND MINING INDUSTRY*

016.551   RUS   ISSN 0202-943X
REFERATIVNYI ZHURNAL. TEKHNIKA GEOLOGO-RAZVEDOCHNYKH RABOT. Text in Russian. 1954. m. USD 112 foreign (effective 2006). **Document type:** *Abstract/Index.*
Related titles: CD-ROM ed.; Online - full text ed.
—East View.
Published by: Vserossiiskii Institut Nauchnoi i Tekhnicheskoi Informatsii (VINITI), Ul Usievicha 20, Moscow, 125190, Russian Federation. TEL 7-095-1526441, FAX 7-095-9430060, dir@viniti.ru, http://www.viniti.ru. **Dist. by:** Informnauka Ltd., Ul Usievicha 20, Moscow 125190, Russian Federation. alfimov@viniti.ru.

551   AUS   ISSN 1326-6969
REGIONAL BIBLIOGRAPHY SERIES. Text in English. 1989. irreg. price varies. **Document type:** *Bibliography.*
Published by: Sydney Speleological Society, PO Box 198, Broadway, NSW 2007, Australia. FAX 61-2-96601217. Ed. Gregory Middleton. R&P Ross A Ellis. Circ: 50.

550   FRA
▶ **REUNION DES SCIENCES DE LA TERRE**; resumes des communications. Text in English, French. 1973. biennial. price varies. illus. back issues avail. **Document type:** *Proceedings, Academic/Scholarly.* **Description:** Abstracts articles on the geological sciences.
Formerly: Reunion Annuelle des Sciences de la Terre (0249-7557).
Published by: Societe Geologique de France, 77 rue Claude Bernard, Paris, 75005, France. TEL 33-01-43317735, FAX 33-01-45357910, accueil@sgfr.org, http://www.sgfr.org. Ed. Dominique Frizon de LaMotte. R&P Francoise Peiffer Rangin.

551   USA
SCARECROW AREA BIBLIOGRAPHY SERIES. Text in English. 1992. irreg. latest vol.20, 2001. **Document type:** *Bibliography.*
Published by: Scarecrow Press, Inc. (Subsidiary of: Rowman & Littlefield Publishers, Inc.), 4501 Forbes Blvd., Suite 200, Lanham, MD 20706. TEL 301-459-3366, FAX 301-429-5748, custserv@rowman.com, http://www.scarecrowpress.com. Ed. Jon W Woronoff.

551.22   JPN
SEISMOLOGICAL SOCIETY OF JAPAN. PROGRAMME AND ABSTRACTS. Text in English, Japanese. 1980. s-a.
Published by: Jishin Gakkai/Seismological Society of Japan, Daigaku Jishin Kenkyujo, 1-1 Yayoi 1-chome, Bunkyo-ku, Tokyo, 113-0032, Japan.

016.55 551   NLD   ISSN 1380-7838
SOIL SCIENCE ALERT; an alerting service covering current articles in Elsevier soil science journals. Text in English. 1994. 6/yr. free to qualified personnel. **Document type:** *Bulletin, Abstract/Index.* **Description:** Provides abstracts of current and forthcoming articles from 6 journals: Applied Soil Ecology; Catena; Geoderma; Soil Biology and Biochemistry; Soil & Tillage Research; Soil Technology.
Published by: Elsevier BV (Subsidiary of: Elsevier Science & Technology), Radarweg 29, Amsterdam, 1043 NX, Netherlands. TEL 31-20-4853911, FAX 31-20-4852457, nlinfo-f@elsevier.nl, http://www.elsevier.nl. Circ: (controlled).

016.55144   CHE   ISSN 0253-8296
Z6033.C3
SPELEOLOGICAL ABSTRACTS/BULLETIN BIBLIOGRAPHIQUE SPELEOLOGIQUE. Text in English, French. 1969. a. CHF 25 print or CD; CHF 45 combined subscription print & CD (effective 2005). adv. bk.rev. **Document type:** *Abstract/Index.*
Related titles: CD-ROM ed.
Published by: (British Cave Research Association GBR), International Union of Speleology, Bibliotheque de la Societe Suisse de Speleologie, Ch. des Invuex, Granges, 1614, Switzerland. FAX 41-21-9475378, ssslib@vtx.ch, http://www.ssslib.ch. **Dist. by:** British Cave Research Association, The Old Methodist Chapel, Great Hucklow, Buxton, Derbys SK17 8RG, United Kingdom.

526.9   JPN
SUIJUN KIHYO SOKURYO SEIKAHYO/REPORTS ON THE SURVEY OF LEVEL REFERENCE POINTS. Text in Japanese. a. stat. **Document type:** *Academic/Scholarly.* **Description:** Contains statistical reports on the survey of level reference points.
Published by: Tokyo Doboku Gijutsu Kenkyujo/Tokyo Metropolitan Government, Institute of Civil Engineering, 9-15 Shinsuna 1-chome, Koto-ku, Tokyo, 136-0075, Japan. Ed. Yoshiaki Kaneko.

551 011   GBR   ISSN 0954-4887
TERRA ABSTRACTS. Text in English. 1989. irreg. included with subscr. to Terra Nova. **Document type:** *Abstract/Index.* **Description:** Abstracts meetings and conferences on earth sciences.
Supersedes in part: Terra Cognita
Indexed: IMMAb, PetrolAb.
—PADDS. **CCC.**
Published by: (European Union of Geosciences), Blackwell Publishing Ltd., 9600 Garsington Rd, Oxford, OX4 2ZG, United Kingdom. TEL 44-1865-776868, FAX 44-1865-714591, customerservices@oxon.blackwellpublishing.com, http://www.blackwellpublishing.com. Ed. R Muir Wood. Pub. Amanda McLean Inglis. R&P Sophie Savage. Adv. contact Jenny Applin.

551.46   USA
UNDERWATER AND HYPERBARIC MEDICINE: ABSTRACTS FROM THE LITERATURE. Text in English. bi-m. USD 100; USD 50 diskette (effective 2000). **Document type:** *Abstract/Index.*
Former titles: Underwater Medicine: Abstracts from the Literature (0886-3474); Underwater Physiology Abstracts
Related titles: Diskette ed.
Published by: Undersea and Hyperbaric Medical Society, Inc., 1020, Dunkirk, MD 20754-1020. TEL 301-942-2980, FAX 301-942-7804, uhms@uhms.org, http://www.uhms.org. Ed. Leon J Greenbaum Jr. Circ: 250.

551.46 016   VEN   ISSN 0590-3343
                                         CODEN: OUIBAX
UNIVERSIDAD DE ORIENTE. INSTITUTO OCEANOGRAFICO BIBLIOTECA. BOLETIN BIBLIOGRAFICO. Text in Spanish. 1964. a. USD 1.50. bibl. **Document type:** *Bulletin, Bibliography.* **Description:** Journal of research in oceanography.
Published by: Universidad de Oriente, Instituto Oceanografico, Biblioteca, Apartado Postal 94, Cumana, Sucre 6101, Venezuela. Ed. Francisco V Pinto C. Circ: 1,000 (controlled).

WATER RESOURCES ABSTRACTS (BETHESDA, ONLINE EDITION). see *WATER RESOURCES—Abstracting, Bibliographies, Statistics*

WATER RESOURCES ABSTRACTS. VOLUME 1. see *WATER RESOURCES—Abstracting, Bibliographies, Statistics*

WATER RESOURCES WORLDWIDE. see *WATER RESOURCES—Abstracting, Bibliographies, Statistics*

551.31   USA
WORLD DATA CENTER A FOR GLACIOLOGY (SNOW AND ICE). NEW ACCESSIONS LIST. Text in English. 1990 (no.46). irreg. (3-4/yr). free. **Document type:** *Bibliography.*
Related titles: Online - full text ed.
Published by: National Snow and Ice Data Center, NSIDC User Services, CIRES, Campus Box 449, University of Colorado, Boulder, CO 80309-0449. TEL 303-492-8028, FAX 303-492-2468, nsidc@kryos.colorado.edu, nsidc@nsidc.org, http://www-nsidc.colorado.edu, http://nsidc.org. Ed. Ann Brennan.

WYOMING GEOLOGICAL ASSOCIATION. OIL & GAS FIELDS SYMPOSIUM. see *PETROLEUM AND GAS*

551 016   DEU   ISSN 0340-5109
QE1   CODEN: ZGPAAK
ZENTRALBLATT FUER GEOLOGIE UND PALAEONTOLOGIE. TEIL I: ALLGEMEINE, ANGEWANDTE, REGIONALE UND HISTORISCHE GEOLOGIE. Text in English, German. 1950. irreg. EUR 86 per issue domestic; EUR 89.70 per issue foreign (effective 2005). adv. bk.rev. **Document type:** *Journal, Academic/Scholarly.*

Formed by the merger of (1900-1950): Zentralblatt fuer Mineralogie, Geologie und Palaeontologie. Teil 1: Kristallographie und Mineralogie (0372-9362); (1900-1950): Zentralblatt fuer Mineralogie, Geologie und Palaeontologie. Teil 2: Gesteinskunde, Lagerstaettenkunde, Allgemeine und Angewandte Geologie (0372-932X); (1900-1950): Zentralblatt fuer Mineralogie, Geologie und Palaeontologie. Teil 3: Historische und Regionale Geologie, Palaeontologie (0372-9346); All of which superseded in part (in 1943): Zentralblatt fuer Mineralogie, Geologie und Palaeontologie (0372-9338)
Indexed: BibCart, ChemAb, I&DA, IBR, IMMAb, S&F.
—IE, Infotrieve, Linda Hall. **CCC.**
Published by: E. Schweizerbart'sche Verlagsbuchhandlung, Johannesstr 3A, Stuttgart, 70176, Germany. TEL 49-711-3514560, FAX 49-711-35145699, mail@schweizerbart.de, http://www.schweizerbart.de.

551 549   CHN
ZHONGGUO DIZHI WENZHAI. Text in Chinese. m.
Related titles: English ed.: Chinese Geology Abstracts.
Published by: Zhongguo Dizhi Kuangchan Xinxi Yanjiuyuan/Chinese Institute of Geology and Mineral Products Information, 277 Fuchengmenwai Beijie, Beijing, 100037, China. TEL 892243. Eds. Bao Yongquan, Li Meiqiu.

EARTH SCIENCES—Computer Applications

▼ **APPLIED G I S.** (Geographic Information Systems) see *GEOGRAPHY—Computer Applications*

550.285   NLD   ISSN 1420-0597
QE33.2.M3   CODEN: CGOEBD
▶ **COMPUTATIONAL GEOSCIENCES**; modeling, simulation and data analysis. Text in English. 1997. q. EUR 353, USD 354, GBP 232 combined subscription to institutions print & online eds. (effective 2005). back issues avail.; reprint service avail. from PSC. **Document type:** *Journal, Academic/Scholarly.* **Description:** Publishes hith-quality papers on mathematical modeling, simulation, data analysis, imaging, inversion, and interpretation, with applications in the geosciences. Focuses mainly on the quantitative aspects of models describing transport processes in permeable media.
Related titles: Online - full text ed.: ISSN 1573-1499 (from EBSCO Publishing, Gale Group, IngentaConnect, Kluwer Online, O C L C Online Computer Library Center, Inc., Ovid Technologies, Inc., Springer LINK, Swets Information Services).
Indexed: ApMecR, BibLing, CCMJ, CMCI, CurCont, FLUIDEX, GEOBASE, MathR, MathSciNet, RefZh.
—BLDSC (3390.592500), CISTI, IE, Infotrieve, ingenta. **CCC.**
Published by: Springer-Verlag Dordrecht (Subsidiary of: Springer Science+Business Media), Van Godewijckstraat 30, Dordrecht, 3311 GX, Netherlands. TEL 31-78-6576050, FAX 31-78-6576474, http://springerlink.metapress.com/openurl.asp?genre=journal&issn=1420-0597, http://www.springeronline.com. Eds. Jerome Jaffre, Mary F Wheeler.

620 550   GBR   ISSN 0098-3004
QE48.8   CODEN: CGEODT
▶ **COMPUTERS & GEOSCIENCES.** Text in English. 1975. 10/yr. EUR 2,013 in Europe to institutions; JPY 267,400 in Japan to institutions; USD 2,253 to institutions except Europe and Japan; EUR 218 in Europe to qualified personnel; JPY 29,000 in Japan to qualified personnel; USD 244 to qualified personnel except Europe and Japan (effective 2006). adv. bk.rev. charts; illus. index. reprints avail. **Document type:** *Academic/Scholarly.* **Description:** Covers all aspects of the application of computers to the geosciences, including algorithms, programming, computational problem-solving techniques, as well as data processing and file maintenance concerns.
Incorporates: Geocom Programs (0305-0017)
Related titles: Microfilm ed.: (from PQC); Online - full text ed.: (from EBSCO Publishing, Gale Group, IngentaConnect, ScienceDirect, Swets Information Services).
Indexed: AEA, AESIS, AS&TI, ASCA, ASFA, AgrForAb, BrCerAb, C&ISA, CIN, CIS, CMCI, CPA, CerAb, ChemAb, ChemTitl, CivEngAb, CompAb, CompC, CompLI, CompR, CorrAb, CurCont, CybAb, E&CAJ, E&PHSE, EMA, ESPM, EngInd, FCA, FLUIDEX, ForAb, GEOBASE, GP&P, HerbAb, HortAb, I&DA, IAA, ICEA, IMMAb, ISMEC, ISR, InfoSAb, Inspec, M&GPA, M&TEA, MBF, METADEX, OffTech, PGegResA, PetrolAb, PollutAb, RefZh, S&F, SCI, SIA, SSCI, ST&MA, SWRA, SoftAbEng, SolStAb, SoyAb, WAA.
—BLDSC (3394.695000), AskIEEE, CASDDS, CISTI, Ei, IDS, IE, Infotrieve, ingenta, Linda Hall, PADDS. **CCC.**
Published by: (International Association for Mathematical Geology USA), Pergamon (Subsidiary of: Elsevier Science & Technology), The Boulevard, Langford Ln, East Park, Kidlington, Oxford OX5 1GB, United Kingdom. TEL 44-1865-843000, FAX 44-1865-843010, http://www.elsevier.com/locate/cageo. Ed. Graeme Bonham-Carter. Circ: 1,100. **Subscr. to:** Elsevier BV, PO Box 211, Amsterdam 1000 AE, Netherlands. TEL 31-20-485-3757, FAX 31-20-485-3432, nlinfo-f@elsevier.nl, http://www.elsevier.nl.

E

550 551 SVK
CZECHOSLOVAK NATIONAL WORKSHOP ON SEISMIC DATA ACQUISITION AND COMPUTER PROCESSING. PROCEEDINGS. Text in English. 1984. a. free. **Description:** Contains papers presented at the annual Czechoslovak workshop on seismic data acquisition and computer processing.
Published by: (Slovenska Akademia Vied, Geofyzikalny Ustav), Vydavatel'stvo Slovenskej Akademie Vied Veda/Veda, Publishing House of the Slovak Academy of Sciences, Dubravska cesta 9, Bratislava, 84234, Slovakia. markova@centrum.sk. Eds. Klara Mrazova, Libuse Ruprechtova. Circ: 250.

551 622 USA
EARTH SCIENCE COMPUTER APPLICATIONS. Text in English. 1985. m. looseleaf. USD 90 domestic; USD 115 foreign (effective 2000). adv. bk.rev. back issues avail. **Document type:** *Newsletter.* **Description:** Computer applications for earth sciences, mining and geology.
Formerly: Computers and Mining (1068-4425)
Indexed: AESIS, IMMAb.
Published by: Gibbs Associates, PO Box 706, Boulder, CO 80306. TEL 303-444-6032, FAX 303-444-6032, bgibbs@csn.org. Ed. Betty L Gibbs. Circ: 200.

EDUCATION TECHNOLOGY LITERATURE REVIEW. see *EDUCATION—School Organization And Administration*

ESCHOOL NEWS. see *EDUCATION—School Organization And Administration*

G I S EUROPEAN YEARBOOK. (Geographic Information Systems) see *GEOGRAPHY—Computer Applications*

550 DEU ISSN 1430-3663
GEOBIT; das Magazin fuer raumbezogene Informationstechnologie. Text in German. 1996. 12/yr. EUR 152.40 domestic; EUR 162 foreign; EUR 15 newsstand/cover (effective 2003). adv. **Document type:** *Magazine, Trade.*
Related titles: Supplement(s): Geo - Informations - Systeme. ISSN 0935-1523. 1987.
Indexed: RefZh.
Published by: Herbert Wichmann Verlag Huethig GmbH, Im Weiher 10, Heidelberg, 69121, Germany. TEL 49-6221-489-0, FAX 49-6221-489450, hvs_zeitschrift@huethig.de, http://www.huethig.de. adv.: B&W page EUR 2,100, color page EUR 3,050. Circ: 5,519 (paid and controlled).

550 USA ISSN 1384-6175
G70.212 CODEN: GEOIFP
➤ **GEOINFORMATICA**; an international journal on advances of computer science for geographic information systems. Text in English. 1997. q. EUR 568, USD 578, GBP 358 combined subscription to institutions print & online eds. (effective 2005). adv. reprint service avail. from PSC. **Document type:** *Journal, Academic/Scholarly.* **Description:** Aims to promote the most innovative results coming from the research in the field of computer science applied to geographic information systems.
Related titles: Online - full text ed.: ISSN 1573-7624 (from EBSCO Publishing, Gale Group, IngentaConnect, Kluwer Online, O C L C Online Computer Library Center, Inc., Ovid Technologies, Inc., Springer LINK, Swets Information Services).
Indexed: ASFA, BibLing, CMCI, CompAb, CompLI, CurCont, ESPM, EngInd, GEOBASE, Inspec, RefZh, SWRA.
—BLDSC (4129.857000), IE, Infotrieve, ingenta. **CCC.**
Published by: Springer-Verlag New York, Inc. (Subsidiary of: Springer Science+Business Media), 233 Spring St, New York, NY 10013. TEL 212-460-1500, FAX 212-460-1575, service@springer-ny.com, http://springerlink.metapress.com/openurl.asp?genre=journal&issn=1384-6175, http://www.springer-ny.com. Eds. John R Herring, Shashi Shekhar. **Subscr. to:** Journal Fulfillment, PO Box 2485, Secaucus, NJ 07096-2485. TEL 201-348-4033, FAX 201-348-4505, journals@springer-ny.com.

551.46 GBR ISSN 1476-6027
VM480
MARITIME I T & ELECTRONICS. Text in English. 2002. bi-m. GBP 12 to members; GBP 40 to non-members (effective 2005). software rev.; Website rev. 4 cols./p.; back issues avail. **Document type:** *Journal, Trade.* **Description:** Offers the latest IT developments and application of new techniques directed at the utilization of modern technology in analysis, design and practice across all disciplines of marine engineering, science and technology.
Indexed: BrCerAb, C&ISA, CerAb, CorrAb, E&CAJ, EEA, EMA, IAA, M&TEA, MBF, METADEX, SolStAb, WAA.
—Linda Hall.
Published by: Institute of Marine Engineering, Science and Technology, 80 Coleman St, London, EC2R 5BJ, United Kingdom. TEL 44-20-73822600, FAX 44-20-73822669, info@imarest.org, http://www.imarest.org/marite/. Ed. Christopher James Brown. Adv. contact Ian Glen TEL 44-20-73822649. Circ: 250 (paid); 13,933 (controlled).

NUMERICAL MODELS IN GEOMECHANICS. see *EARTH SCIENCES—Geophysics*

POSITION MAGAZINE. see *GEOGRAPHY—Computer Applications*

SAFE SCHOOLS TODAY. see *EDUCATION—School Organization And Administration*

SCHOOL TECHNOLOGY FUNDING BULLETIN. see *EDUCATION—School Organization And Administration*

EARTH SCIENCES—Geology

see also MINES AND MINING INDUSTRY

A A P G BULLETIN. see *PETROLEUM AND GAS*

552 USA ISSN 0270-8043
A A P G CONTINUING EDUCATION COURSE NOTE SERIES. Text in English. 1975. irreg. price varies. **Document type:** *Monographic series.*
—BLDSC (0537.502200). **CCC.**
Published by: American Association of Petroleum Geologists, 1444 S Boulder, Tulsa, OK 74119. TEL 918-584-2555, FAX 918-560-2652, http://www.aapg.org.

A A P G EXPLORER. see *PETROLEUM AND GAS*

551 665.5 USA ISSN 0271-8529
CODEN: MAPGAN
➤ **A A P G MEMOIR.** Text in English. 1962. irreg., latest vol.72, 2000. price varies. cum.index. **Document type:** *Monographic series, Academic/Scholarly.* **Description:** Series of reference titles of current and future value.
Formerly (until 1979): American Association of Petroleum Geologists. Memoir (0065-731X)
Related titles: Online - full text ed.
Indexed: AESIS, BiolAb, GEOBASE.
—BLDSC (5576.300000), CASDDS, CISTI, IE, ingenta. **CCC.**
Published by: American Association of Petroleum Geologists, PO Box 979, Tulsa, OK 74101-0979. bulletin@aapg.org, http://www.aapg.org.

➤ **A A P G STUDIES IN GEOLOGY SERIES.** see *PETROLEUM AND GAS*

551 USA ISSN 0899-5788
A E G NEWS. Text in English. 1958. q. USD 135 in North America; USD 145 elsewhere (effective 1999). adv. bibl.; tr.lit. 40 p./no. 3 cols./p.; **Document type:** *Newsletter, Academic/Scholarly.* **Description:** Contains reports, news, technical news articles, and annual meeting announcements and information.
Former titles (until 1988): Association of Engineering Geologists. Newsletter (0888-305X); (until 1984): A E G Newsletter (0514-9142)
Indexed: BrCerAb, C&ISA, CerAb, CorrAb, E&CAJ, EEA, EMA, IAA, M&TEA, MBF, METADEX, WAA.
—BLDSC (0719.701800), Linda Hall.
Published by: Association of Engineering Geologists, Dept of Geology & Geophysics, Texas A&M University MS-3115, College Station, TX 77843-3115. TEL 979-845-0142, FAX 979-862-7959, aeghq@aol.com. Ed. Jeff Neathery. Circ: 3,600.

551 AUS ISSN 1039-0073
QE48.A8
A G S O RECORD. Text in English. 1942. irreg. price varies. **Document type:** *Government.*
Formerly: B M R Record (0811-062X)
Indexed: AESIS, IMMAb.
Published by: Australian Geological Survey Organisation, GPO Box 378, Canberra, ACT 2601, Australia. TEL 61-6-2499249, FAX 61-6-2499984, julie.wissmann@agso.gov.au, http://www.agso.gov.au. Ed., R&P Julie Wissmann.

550 HUN ISSN 0368-9751
A MAGYAR ALLAMI FOLDTANI INTEZET EVI JELENTESE. Text in Hungarian. irreg.
Published by: Magyar Geologiai Szolgalat, Stefania ut 14, Budapest, 1143, Hungary. TEL 36-1-267-1421, http://www.mgsz.hu/.

A P P E A JOURNAL. see *PETROLEUM AND GAS*

551 910.02 DNK ISSN 0909-3486
AARHUS GEOSCIENCE. Text in English. 1978. irreg., latest vol.8, 1999. illus. **Document type:** *Monographic series, Academic/Scholarly.*
Former titles (until 1994): Aarhus Universitet. Geologisk Institut. Geoskrifter (0105-824X); Skrifter i Fysisk Geografi
Indexed: ZooRec.
—BLDSC (0537.537664).
Published by: Aarhus Universitet, Department of Earth Science, C F Mollers Alle, Aarhus C, 8000, Denmark. TEL 45-89-28-99, FAX 45-86-13-92-48. Circ: 300.

ABSTRACTS OF CHINESE GEOLOGICAL LITERATURE. see *EARTH SCIENCES—Abstracting, Bibliographies, Statistics*

551 USA ISSN 1050-8309
CODEN: APGSEP
➤ **ACADEMIC PRESS GEOLOGY SERIES.** Text in English. 1981. irreg., latest vol.10, 1991. reprint service avail. from ISI. **Document type:** *Academic/Scholarly.*
Indexed: IMMAb, Inspec.
—**CCC.**
Published by: Academic Press (Subsidiary of: Elsevier Science & Technology), 525 B St, Ste 1900, San Diego, CA 92101-4495. apsubs@acad.com, http://www.academicpress.com.

➤ **ACTA ALBERTINA RATISBONENSIA.** see *EARTH SCIENCES*

551 CZE ISSN 1214-9705
▼ **ACTA GEODYNAMICA ET GEOMATERIALIA.** Text in English. 2004. q. EUR 12 per issue (effective 2005). **Description:** Devoted to geodynamics of the upper part of Earth's crust and relations between natural factors and human activity (local natural and induced seismic activities, an earthquake hazard, natural slope stability, physical properties of rocks), geophysical and geological investigations of lithosphere, especially tectonics, engineering and geomechanical aspects.
Formed by the merger of (1967-2004): Acta Montana - Rada A (Geodynamics) (1211-1910); (1967-2004): Acta Montana - Rada B (Fuel, Carbon, Mineral Processing) (1211-1929); Both of which superseded in part (in 1991): Acta Montana (0365-1398); Which was formerly (until 1970): Zpravy Hornickeho Ustavu C S A V (0372-8986)
—BLDSC (0618.600000), IE.
Published by: Akademie Ved Ceske Republiky, Ustav Struktury a Mechaniky Hornin/Academy of Sciences of Czech Republic, Institute of Rock Structures and Mechanics, V Holesovickach 41, Prague, 18209, Czech Republic. TEL 420-2-66009111, FAX 420-2-84680105, irsm@irsm.cas.cz, http://www.irsm.cas.cz. Ed. Vladamir Rudajev.

ACTA GEOGRAPHICA AC GEOLOGICA ET METEOROLOGICA DEBRECINA. see *GEOGRAPHY*

551 551.4 HRV ISSN 0448-0155
QH178.Y8 CODEN: AGJAAL
ACTA GEOLOGICA. Text and summaries in Croatian, English, French, German. 1913. s-a. USD 10. back issues avail. **Document type:** *Academic/Scholarly.*
Indexed: BiolAb.
—KNAW, Linda Hall.
Published by: Hrvatska Akademija Znanosti i Umjetnosti/Croatian Academy of Sciences and Arts, A Hebranga 1, Zagreb, 10000, Croatia. TEL 385-1-4569079, FAX 385-1-4819979. Ed. Ivan Gusic. Circ: 800. **Co-sponsor:** Ministry of Sciences and Technology.

550 HUN ISSN 0236-5278
QE1 CODEN: AGHUE7
ACTA GEOLOGICA HUNGARICA. Text in English. 1952. q. USD 300 (effective 2006). adv. bk.rev. bibl.; charts; illus.; abstr.; maps. index. 120 p./no.; back issues avail. **Document type:** *Journal, Academic/Scholarly.* **Description:** Covers all fields of geology, including crystallography, mineralogy, petrography, geochemistry and paleontology.
Formerly (until 1982): Academiae Scientiarum Hungaricae. Acta Geologica (0001-5695)
Related titles: Online - full text ed.: ISSN 1588-2594 (from EBSCO Publishing, Swets Information Services).
Indexed: BiolAb, CIN, ChemAb, ChemTitl, GEOBASE, IBR, INIS AtomInd, MinerAb, ZooRec.
—CASDDS, CISTI, KNAW, Linda Hall. **CCC.**
Published by: (Magyar Tudomanyos Akademia/Hungarian Academy of Sciences), Akademiai Kiado Rt. (Subsidiary of: Wolters Kluwer N.V.), Prielle Kornelia U. 19, Budapest, 1117, Hungary. TEL 36-1-4648282, FAX 36-1-4648221, journals@akkrt.hu, http://www.akkrt.hu.

ACTA GEOLOGICA LEOPOLDENSIA. see *SCIENCES: COMPREHENSIVE WORKS*

550 ARG ISSN 0567-7513
QE231 CODEN: AGELAT
ACTA GEOLOGICA LILLOANA. Text in Spanish; Summaries in English, French, German, Italian. 1957. irreg., latest vol.18, no.1, 1998. bk.rev. bibl.; charts; illus.; stat. index. back issues avail. **Document type:** *Monographic series, Academic/Scholarly.*
Indexed: ASFA, BIOSIS Prev, BiolAb, ESPM, RefZh, ZooRec.
—CASDDS, CISTI, Linda Hall.
Published by: Fundacion Miguel Lillo, Miguel Lillo, 251, San Miguel de Tucuman, Tucuman 4000, Argentina. TEL 54-0381-4239960, FAX 54-0381-4330868, fmlinfonoa@tucbbs.com.ar, http://www.lillo.org.ar. Ed. Jose A Haedo Rossi.

550 POL ISSN 0001-5709
QE1 CODEN: AGLPA8
ACTA GEOLOGICA POLONICA. Text in English; Summaries in Polish. 1950. q. EUR 70 foreign (effective 2005). charts; illus.; maps. index. **Document type:** *Journal, Academic/Scholarly.*
Indexed: ASFA, BiolAb, ChemAb, ESPM, GEOBASE, IBR, PetrolAb, ZooRec.
—CASDDS, CISTI, Linda Hall, PADDS.

E

Published by: (Polska Akademia Nauk, Komitet Nauk Geologicznych, Uniwersytet Warszawski, Instytut Geologii), Wydawnictwo Naukowe INVIT, ul Bema 65, Warsaw, 01244, Poland. agp@geo.uw.edu.pl, invit@seges.pl, http://www.geo.uw.edu.pl/agp/index.htm. Ed. Ryszard Marcinowski. Circ: 680. **Dist. by:** Ars Polona, Krakowskie Przedmiescie 7, Warsaw, Poland. TEL 48-22-9263914, FAX 48-22-9265334, arspolona@arspolona.com.pl, http://www.arspolona.com.pl.

551   CHN   ISSN 1000-9515
QE1
➤ **ACTA GEOLOGICA SINICA.** Text in English. 1988. 4/yr. index. back issues avail. **Document type:** *Academic/Scholarly.*
Related titles: Microform ed.; Online - full content ed.: (from WanFang Data Corp.); ◆ Chinese ed.: Dizhi Xuebao. ISSN 0001-5717.
Indexed: CurCont, IAA, IMMAb, MinerAb, ZooRec.
—BLDSC (0621.500500), IDS, IE, ingenta.
Published by: Geological Society of China, 26 Baiwanzhuang Rd, Fuwai, Beijing, 100037, China, geoacta@public.fhnet.cn.net. Ed. Yuqi Chen.

550.1   TWN   ISSN 0065-1265
QE1   CODEN: SRTUAW
➤ **ACTA GEOLOGICA TAIWANICA.** Key Title: Yanjiu Baogao - Guoli Taiwan Daxue Lixueyuan Dizhixue Xi. Text in English. 1947. a. exchange basis. bk.rev. **Document type:** *Academic/Scholarly.*
Indexed: BIOSIS Prev, BiolAb, CIN, ChemAb, ChemTitl, IBR, MinerAb, ZooRec.
—BLDSC (8156.000000), CASDDS.
Published by: National Taiwan University, Department of Geosciences, Taipei, 10764, Taiwan. TEL 886-2-2363-5924, FAX 886-2-2363-6095, loch@ccms.ntu.edu.tw. Ed. Tsung Kwei Liu. Circ: 600.

551 363.7   SVK   ISSN 1335-2830
QE1   CODEN: AGUCFJ
➤ **ACTA GEOLOGICA UNIVERSITATIS COMENIANAE.** Text in Slovak, English. 1958. a., latest vol.57, 2002. price varies. back issues avail. **Document type:** *Journal, Academic/Scholarly.* **Description:** Presents the results of a wide range of geological research.
Formerly (until I992): Acta Geologica et Geographica Universita tis Comenianae. Geologica (0567-7491)
Related titles: Diskette ed.
Indexed: ZooRec.
—CASDDS, Linda Hall.
Published by: Univerzita Komenskeho, Matematicko-Fizikalna Fakulta, Mlynska Dolina, Bratislava, 84248, Slovakia. TEL 421-7-65428981, FAX 421-7-65428981, inzgeologia@fns.uniba.sk. Ed. Lidia Turanova. Pub. Sergej Troscak.

▼ ➤ **ACTA GEOTECHNICA SLOVENICA.** see *EARTH SCIENCES—Geophysics*

551 622   SVK   ISSN 1335-1788
➤ **ACTA MONTANISTICA SLOVACA.** Text in Multiple languages. 1996. q. **Document type:** *Journal, Academic/Scholarly.* **Description:** Publishes articles on basic and applied research in such fields as geology and geological survey, mining, earth resources, underground engineering and geotechnics, mining mechanization, mining transport, deep hole drilling, surveying and engineering geodesy, ecotechnology and mineralurgy, process control, automation and applied informatics in raw materials extraction, utilization and processing.
Related titles: Online - full text ed.: free (effective 2005).
Published by: Technicka Univerzita v Kosiciach, Fakulta BERG/Technical University of Kosice, Faculty of Mining, Geology, Process Control and Geotechnology, c/o Prof Tibor Sasvari EIC, Acta Montanistica Slovaca, Letna 9, Kosice, 04200, Slovakia. TEL 421-55-6022945, FAX 421-55-6023128, http://actamont.tuke.sk/.

554   CZE   ISSN 1211-8796
ACTA MUSEI MORAVIAE. SCIENTIAE GEOLOGICAE/ MORAVSKE ZEMSKE MUZEUM. CASOPIS. VEDY GEOLOGICKE. Text in Czech, English, German, French; Summaries in English, German. 1901. a. USD 16 (effective 2000). **Document type:** *Academic/Scholarly.*
Supersedes in part (in 1998): Moravske Zemske Muzeum. Casopis. Vedy Prirodni (Acta Musei Moraviae. Scientiae Naturales) (0521-2359); Which superseded in part (in 1950): Moravskeho Musea v Brne. Casopis (1212-1967); Which was formerly (until 1949): Zemskeho Musea v Brne. Casopis (1212-1959); (until 1947): Moravskeho Musea Zemskeho. Casopis (1212-1940)
Related titles: ◆ Supplement to: Acta Musei Moraviae. Scientiae Biologicae. ISSN 1211-8788.
Indexed: ZooRec.
Published by: Moravske Zemske Muzeum, Zelny trh 6, Brno, 65937, Czech Republic. TEL 420-5-42321205, FAX 420-5-42212792, mzm@mzm.cz, http://www.mzm.cz. Eds. M Novak, S Houzar.

550   CZE   ISSN 0001-7132
QE1   CODEN: AUCGAY
ACTA UNIVERSITATIS CAROLINAE: GEOLOGICA. Text in Czech, English, German, Russian. 1954. q. USD 60 (effective 1999). illus.; maps. **Document type:** *Academic/Scholarly.*

Indexed: BIOSIS Prev, BiolAb, CIN, ChemAb, ChemTitl, FLUIDEX, GEOBASE, IBR, MinerAb, ZooRec.
—BLDSC (0584.510000), CASDDS, CISTI, IE, ingenta, Linda Hall.
Published by: (Univerzita Karlova, Prirodovedecka Fakulta), Vydavatelstvi Karolinum, Celetna 18, Prague 1, 116 36, Czech Republic. TEL 42-2-24491270, FAX 42-2-24212041, edice@cuni.cz. Ed. Oldrich Fatka. Circ: 500. **Dist. by:** Geological Library, Faculty of Science, Albertov 6, Prague 12843, Czech Republic. TEL 42-2-2152156, FAX 42-2-291425.

551   CZE   ISSN 1212-2025
ACTA UNIVERSITATIS PALACKIANAE OLOMUCENSIS. FACULTAS RERUM NATURALIUM. GEOLOGICA. Text in Multiple languages. 1962. biennial.
Supersedes in part (1962-1994): Acta Universitatis Palackianae Olomucensis. Facultas Rerum Naturalium. Geographica-Geologica (0231-9365); Which was formerly (until 1982): Univerzita Palackeho v Olomouci. Prirodovedecka Fakulta. Sbornik Praci. Geografie-Geologie (0474-1129)
Indexed: RefZh.
—Linda Hall.
Published by: Univerzita Palackeho v Olomouci, Prirodovedecka Fakulta, tr Svobody 26, c.p.686, Olomouc, 77146, Czech Republic. TEL 420-68-5634060, FAX 420-68-5225737, dekanprf@risc.upd.cz, http://www.upd.cz.

550 551   POL   ISSN 0525-4132
QE1   CODEN: PGEMBS
ACTA UNIVERSITATIS WRATISLAVIENSIS. PRACE GEOLOGICZNO - MINERALOGICZNE. Text in Polish; Summaries in English. 1969. irreg. price varies. charts; illus.; maps. **Document type:** *Academic/Scholarly.*
Indexed: ZooRec.
—KNAW, Linda Hall.
Published by: (Uniwersytet Wroclawski), Wydawnictwo Uniwersytetu Wroclawskiego Spolka z o.o., Pl Uniwersytecki 9-13, Wroclaw, 50-137, Poland. TEL 48-71-441006, FAX 48-71-402735. Ed. Irena Wojciechowska. Circ: 250.

551   NLD
ADVANCES IN GEOECOLOGY. Text and summaries in English. 1982. 2/yr. price varies. index. back issues avail. **Document type:** *Proceedings.*
Formerly (until no.27): Catena Supplement (0722-0723)
Related titles: ◆ Supplement to: CATENA. ISSN 0341-8162.
Indexed: AEA, AESIS, AgrForAb, AnBrAb, BIOSIS Prev, CPA, ChemAb, CurCont, DSA, FCA, FPA, ForAb, HerbAb, HortAb, I&DA, MaizeAb, NutrAb, OrnHort, PGegResA, PotatoAb, RA&MP, RDA, RRTA, RiceAb, S&F, SCI, SIA, SoyAb, TriticAb, WAE&RSA, WeedAb, ZooRec.
—BLDSC (0708.050000), CISTI, ingenta. **CCC.**
Published by: (International Society of Soil Science), Elsevier BV (Subsidiary of: Elsevier Science & Technology), Radarweg 29, Amsterdam, 1043 NX, Netherlands. TEL 31-20-4853911, FAX 31-20-4852457, nlinfo-f@elsevier.nl, http://www.elsevier.nl. Ed. Rorke B Bryan. Circ: 1,000.

ADVANCES IN PETROLEUM GEOCHEMISTRY. see *PETROLEUM AND GAS*

016.556   FRA   ISSN 1117-370X
QE320
➤ **AFRICA GEOSCIENCE REVIEW.** Text in English, French. 1994. 4/yr. EUR 430 in the European Union; EUR 454 elsewhere (effective 2003). adv. bibl. back issues avail. **Document type:** *Academic/Scholarly.* **Description:** Devoted to the geology of the African continent and neighbouring countries.
Incorporates (1972-1995): Current Bibliography of Middle East Geology (0334-3510); Which was formerly: Selected Bibliography of Middle East Geology
Indexed: ZooRec.
—BLDSC (0732.157395), IE, ingenta. **CCC.**
Published by: Rock View International, Tour Onyx, 10 rue Vandrezanne, Paris, 75013, France. TEL 33-1-45805161, FAX 33-1-45809209, geoscafr@wanadoo.fr, http://www.geoscafr.com. Ed. C A Kogbe. R&P, Adv. contact C.A. Kogbe.

551   POL   ISSN 0138-0974
QE1   CODEN: GEOLDW
➤ **AKADEMIA GORNICZO-HUTNICZA IM. STANISLAWA STASZICA. GEOLOGIA. KWARTALNIK.** Text in English, Polish; Summaries in English, Polish. 1975. q. EUR 37 foreign (effective 2005). illus.; abstr.; bibl. 130 p./no. 1 cols./p.; **Document type:** *Journal, Academic/Scholarly.* **Description:** Covers regional geology, mineralogy and applied mineralogy, petrography, environmental protection, paleontology, stratigraphy, geophysics, physical geology, sedimentology, tectonics and structural geology, palaeoecology and ecology, geology of ore deposits, environmental geology, hydrogeology, engineering geology and geotechnics.
Related titles: ◆ Series of: Zeszyty Naukowe Akademii Gorniczo-Hutniczej im. Stanislawa Staszica. ISSN 0373-8558.
Indexed: RefZh.
—CASDDS, Linda Hall.

Published by: (Akademia Gorniczo-Hutnicza im. Stanislawa Staszica/University of Mining and Metallurgy), Wydawnictwo A G H, al Mickiewicza 30, Krakow, 30059, Poland. TEL 48-12-6173228, FAX 48-12-6364038, wydagh@uci.agh.edu.pl, http://www.wydawnictwoagh.pl. Ed. A J Wichur. Circ: 150 (paid). **Dist. by:** Ars Polona, Krakowskie Przedmiescie 7, Warsaw, Poland. TEL 48-22-9263914, FAX 48-22-9265334, arspolona@arspolona.com.pl, http://www.arspolona.com.pl.

➤ **AKADEMIYA NAUK TURKMENISTANA. IZVESTIYA. SERIYA FIZIKO-TEKHNICHESKIKH, KHIMICHESKIKH I GEOLOGICHESKIKH NAUK.** see *PHYSICS*

557   USA   ISSN 0065-5635
QE81   CODEN: AGAFAP
➤ **ALABAMA GEOLOGICAL SOCIETY. GUIDEBOOK FOR THE ANNUAL FIELD TRIP.** Text in English. 1964. a. USD 10 per issue (effective 2003). **Document type:** *Academic/Scholarly.*
Published by: Alabama Geological Society, PO Box 866184, Tuscaloosa, AL 35486-0055. TEL 205-349-2852. Circ: 150.

551   USA
ALASKA. DIVISION OF GEOLOGICAL AND GEOPHYSICAL SURVEYS. ADMINISTRATIVE REPORTS. Text in English. irreg. **Document type:** *Academic/Scholarly.*
Published by: Alaska Department of Natural Resources, Division of Geological and Geophysical Surveys, 794 University Ave, Ste 200, Fairbanks, AK 99709-3645. TEL 907-451-5000, FAX 907-451-5050, http://www.dggs.dnr.state.ak.us.

ALASKA. DIVISION OF GEOLOGICAL AND GEOPHYSICAL SURVEYS. ALASKA TERRITORIAL DEPARTMENT OF MINES REPORTS. see *MINES AND MINING INDUSTRY*

551   USA   ISSN 0741-5168
HD9506.U63
ALASKA. DIVISION OF GEOLOGICAL AND GEOPHYSICAL SURVEYS. ALASKA'S MINERAL INDUSTRY. Text in English. 1982. a.
Related titles: ◆ Series: Alaska. Division of Geological and Geophysical Surveys. Special Report. ISSN 0360-3881.
—Linda Hall.
Published by: Alaska Department of Natural Resources, Division of Geological and Geophysical Surveys, 794 University Ave, Ste 200, Fairbanks, AK 99709-3645. TEL 907-451-5000, FAX 907-451-5050, http://www.dggs.dnr.state.ak.us.

ALASKA. DIVISION OF GEOLOGICAL AND GEOPHYSICAL SURVEYS. GEOPHYSICAL REPORTS. see *EARTH SCIENCES—Geophysics*

551   USA
ALASKA. DIVISION OF GEOLOGICAL AND GEOPHYSICAL SURVEYS. GUIDEBOOK OF PERMAFROST AND RELATED FEATURES OF THE DALTON HIGHWAY, YUKON RIVER TO PRUDHOE BAY, ALASKA. VOLUME 2. Text in English. 1985. irreg.
Published by: Alaska Department of Natural Resources, Division of Geological and Geophysical Surveys, 794 University Ave, Ste 200, Fairbanks, AK 99709-3645. TEL 907-451-5000, FAX 907-451-5050, http://www.dggs.dnr.state.ak.us. Eds. Charles G Mull, Karen E Adams.

551   USA
ALASKA. DIVISION OF GEOLOGICAL AND GEOPHYSICAL SURVEYS. GUIDEBOOK TO PERMAFROST AND QUATERNARY GEOLOGY ALONG THE RICHARDSON AND GLENN HIGHWAYS BETWEEN FAIRBANKS AND ANCHORAGE, ALASKA. Text in English. 1983. irreg.
Published by: Alaska Department of Natural Resources, Division of Geological and Geophysical Surveys, 794 University Ave, Ste 200, Fairbanks, AK 99709-3645. TEL 907-451-5000, FAX 907-451-5050, http://www.dggs.dnr.state.ak.us.

551   USA
ALASKA. DIVISION OF GEOLOGICAL AND GEOPHYSICAL SURVEYS. GUIDEBOOK TO PERMAFROST AND RELATED FEATURES ALONG THE ELLIOTT AND DALTON HIGHWAYS, FOX TO PRUDHOE BAY. Text in English. 1983. irreg.
Published by: Alaska Department of Natural Resources, Division of Geological and Geophysical Surveys, 794 University Ave, Ste 200, Fairbanks, AK 99709-3645. TEL 907-451-5000, FAX 907-451-5050, http://www.dggs.dnr.state.ak.us. Eds. Jerry Brown, R A Kreig.

551   USA
ALASKA. DIVISION OF GEOLOGICAL AND GEOPHYSICAL SURVEYS. GUIDEBOOK TO PERMAFROST AND RELATED FEATURES AT PRUDHOE BAY. Text in English. 1983. irreg.
Published by: Alaska Department of Natural Resources, Division of Geological and Geophysical Surveys, 794 University Ave, Ste 200, Fairbanks, AK 99709-3645. TEL 907-451-5000, FAX 907-451-5050, http://www.dggs.dnr.state.ak.us. Ed. S E Rawlinson.

551   USA
ALASKA. DIVISION OF GEOLOGICAL AND GEOPHYSICAL SURVEYS. GUIDEBOOK TO PERMAFROST AND RELATED FEATURES OF THE COLVILLE RIVER DELTA, ALASKA. Text in English. 1983. irreg.

E

Published by: Alaska Department of Natural Resources, Division of Geological and Geophysical Surveys, 794 University Ave, Ste 200, Fairbanks, AK 99709-3645. TEL 907-451-5000, FAX 907-451-5050, http://www.dggs.dnr.state.ak.us. Ed. H J Walker.

551 USA
ALASKA. DIVISION OF GEOLOGICAL AND GEOPHYSICAL SURVEYS. GUIDEBOOK TO PERMAFROST AND RELATED FEATURES OF THE DALTON HIGHWAY, YUKON RIVER TO PRUDHOE BAY, ALASKA. VOLUME 1. Text in English. 1985. irreg.
Published by: Alaska Department of Natural Resources, Division of Geological and Geophysical Surveys, 794 University Ave, Ste 200, Fairbanks, AK 99709-3645. TEL 907-451-5000, FAX 907-451-5050, http://www.dggs.dnr.state.ak.us. Eds. Charles G Mull, Karen E Adams.

551 USA
ALASKA. DIVISION OF GEOLOGICAL AND GEOPHYSICAL SURVEYS. GUIDEBOOK TO PERMAFROST AND RELATED FEATURES OF THE NORTHERN YUKON TERRITORY AND MACKENZIE DELTA, ALASKA. Text in English. 1983. irreg.
Published by: Alaska Department of Natural Resources, Division of Geological and Geophysical Surveys, 794 University Ave, Ste 200, Fairbanks, AK 99709-3645. TEL 907-451-5000, FAX 907-451-5050, http://www.dggs.dnr.state.ak.us. Eds. H M French, J A Heginbottom.

551 USA
ALASKA. DIVISION OF GEOLOGICAL AND GEOPHYSICAL SURVEYS. GUIDEBOOKS. Text in English. 1983. irreg.
Published by: Alaska Department of Natural Resources, Division of Geological and Geophysical Surveys, 794 University Ave, Ste 200, Fairbanks, AK 99709-3645. TEL 907-451-5000, FAX 907-451-5050, http://www.dggs.dnr.state.ak.us.

557 USA ISSN 0065-5759
CODEN: AGICCO
➤ **ALASKA. DIVISION OF GEOLOGICAL AND GEOPHYSICAL SURVEYS. INFORMATION CIRCULAR.** Text in English. irreg. free. **Document type:** *Academic/Scholarly.*
—Linda Hall.
Published by: Alaska Department of Natural Resources, Division of Geological and Geophysical Surveys, 794 University Ave, Ste 200, Fairbanks, AK 99709-3645. FAX 907-479-4779, dggs@dnr.state.ak.us.

551 USA ISSN 0065-5783
ALASKA. DIVISION OF GEOLOGICAL AND GEOPHYSICAL SURVEYS. MISCELLANEOUS PAPERS. Text in English. 1964. irreg.
Formerly: Alaska. Division of Geological Survey. Miscellaneous Paper (0095-7437)
Published by: Alaska Department of Natural Resources, Division of Geological and Geophysical Surveys, 794 University Ave, Ste 200, Fairbanks, AK 99709-3645. TEL 907-451-5000, FAX 907-451-5050, dggs@dnr.state.ak.us, http://www.dggs.dnr.state.ak.us.

551 USA
ALASKA. DIVISION OF GEOLOGICAL AND GEOPHYSICAL SURVEYS. PRELIMINARY INVESTIGATIVE REPORTS. Text in English. irreg.
Published by: Alaska Department of Natural Resources, Division of Geological and Geophysical Surveys, 794 University Ave, Ste 200, Fairbanks, AK 99709-3645. TEL 907-451-5000, FAX 907-451-5050, http://www.dggs.dnr.state.ak.us.

551 USA ISSN 0737-6022
➤ **ALASKA. DIVISION OF GEOLOGICAL AND GEOPHYSICAL SURVEYS. PROFESSIONAL REPORTS.** Text in English. 1962. irreg. price varies. **Document type:** *Academic/Scholarly.*
Formerly (until 1982): Alaska. Division of Geological and Geophysical Surveys. Geologic Reports (0065-5740)
Related titles: ♦ Series: Alaska. Division of Geological and Geophysical Surveys. Short Notes on Alaskan Geology.
—Linda Hall.
Published by: Alaska Department of Natural Resources, Division of Geological and Geophysical Surveys, 794 University Ave, Ste 200, Fairbanks, AK 99709-3645. FAX 907-479-4779, dggs@dnr.state.ak.us.

551 USA
ALASKA. DIVISION OF GEOLOGICAL AND GEOPHYSICAL SURVEYS. RAW DATA FILES. Text in English. irreg.
Formerly (until 1999): Alaska. Division of Geological and Geophysical Surveys. Public Data Files
Published by: Alaska Department of Natural Resources, Division of Geological and Geophysical Surveys, 794 University Ave, Ste 200, Fairbanks, AK 99709-3645. TEL 907-451-5000, FAX 907-451-5050, http://www.dggs.dnr.state.ak.us.

551 USA
➤ **ALASKA. DIVISION OF GEOLOGICAL AND GEOPHYSICAL SURVEYS. REPORT OF INVESTIGATIONS.** Text in English. irreg. price varies.
Former titles: Alaska. Division of Geological and Geophysical Surveys. Open-File Report; Alaska. Division of Geological and Geophysical Surveys. Laboratory Notes (0065-5767)

Published by: Alaska Department of Natural Resources, Division of Geological and Geophysical Surveys, 794 University Ave, Ste 200, Fairbanks, AK 99709-3645. FAX 907-479-4779, dggs@dnr.state.ak.us.

551 USA
ALASKA. DIVISION OF GEOLOGICAL AND GEOPHYSICAL SURVEYS. SHORT NOTES ON ALASKAN GEOLOGY. Text in English. 1976. irreg.
Related titles: ♦ Series: Alaska. Division of Geological and Geophysical Surveys. Professional Reports. ISSN 0737-6022.
Published by: Alaska Department of Natural Resources, Division of Geological and Geophysical Surveys, 794 University Ave, Ste 200, Fairbanks, AK 99709-3645. TEL 907-451-5000, FAX 907-451-5050, http://www.dggs.dnr.state.ak.us.

551 USA ISSN 0360-3881
CODEN: SRASD2
➤ **ALASKA. DIVISION OF GEOLOGICAL AND GEOPHYSICAL SURVEYS. SPECIAL REPORT.** Text in English. 1967. irreg. price varies. **Document type:** *Academic/Scholarly.*
Related titles: ♦ Series: Alaska. Division of Geological and Geophysical Surveys. Alaska's Mineral Industry. ISSN 0741-5168.
Indexed: ChemAb.
—CASDDS, Linda Hall.
Published by: Alaska Department of Natural Resources, Division of Geological and Geophysical Surveys, 794 University Ave, Ste 200, Fairbanks, AK 99709-3645. FAX 907-479-4779, dggs@dnr.state.ak.us.

551 USA
ALASKA. DIVISION OF GEOLOGICAL AND GEOPHYSICAL SURVEYS. THE ALASKA RAILROAD BETWEEN ANCHORAGE AND FAIRBANKS; guidebook to permafrost and engineering problems. Text in English. 1983. irreg.
Published by: Alaska Department of Natural Resources, Division of Geological and Geophysical Surveys, 794 University Ave, Ste 200, Fairbanks, AK 99709-3645. TEL 907-451-5000, FAX 907-451-5050, http://www.dggs.dnr.state.ak.us. Ed. T C Fuglestad.

556 DZA
QE329 CODEN: ASMBBM
ALGERIA. OFFICE NATIONALE DE LA GEOLOGIE. BULLETIN. Text in French. irreg. (approx. 2/yr.). price varies. **Document type:** *Bulletin.*
Formerly: Algeria. Service Geologique. Bulletin (0401-345X)
Published by: Office Nationale de la Geologie, 18A Ave. Mustapha el-Ouali, Algiers, Algeria. TEL 213-74-08-64. Ed. Mahwoud Amokrane.

ALTENBURGER NATURWISSENSCHAFTLICHE FORSCHUNGEN. see *BIOLOGY*

AMERICAN ASSOCIATION OF STRATIGRAPHIC PALYNOLOGISTS. CONTRIBUTIONS SERIES. see *PALEONTOLOGY*

551.7 560 USA ISSN 0192-7299
CODEN: NASPDB
AMERICAN ASSOCIATION OF STRATIGRAPHIC PALYNOLOGISTS. NEWSLETTER. Text in English. 1968. q. USD 45 to members (effective 2003). bk.rev. back issues avail. **Document type:** *Newsletter.* **Description:** News of the organization's activities and information of interest to palynologists.
Related titles: Online - full text ed.
Indexed: AESIS.
Published by: American Association of Stratigraphic Palynologists Foundation, c/o Vaughn M Bryant, Jr, Palynology Laboratory, Texas A & M Univ, College Station, TX 77843-4352. TEL 979-845-5255, FAX 979-845-4070, vbryant@tamu.edu, http://www.palynology.org. Ed. James B Riding. R&P Vaughn M Bryant. Circ: 1,100 (paid).

AMERICAN MINERALOGIST; an international journal of earth and planetary materials. see *MINES AND MINING INDUSTRY*

AMERICAN MUSEUM NOVITATES. see *BIOLOGY—Zoology*

ANCIENT T L. see *ARCHAEOLOGY*

ANDRIAS. see *BIOLOGY—Botany*

550 AGO ISSN 0003-3456
QE337 CODEN: AGMBA5
ANGOLA. DIRECCAO PROVINCIAL DOS SERVICOS DE GEOLOGIA E MINAS. BOLETIM. Text in English, French, Portuguese. 1960. irreg. charts; illus.; maps; stat.
Published by: Direccao Provincial dos Servicos de Geologia e Minas, C.P. 1260-C, Luanda, Angola. **Co-sponsor:** Instituto Nacional de Geologia.

550.1 FIN ISSN 1239-632X
Q60 CODEN: AAFGAB
➤ **ANNALES ACADEMIAE SCIENTIARUM FENNICAE. GEOLOGICA-GEOGRAPHICA.** Text in English, French, German. 1941. irreg. price varies. back issues avail. **Document type:** *Academic/Scholarly.*

Formerly (until 1995): Annales Academiae Scientiarum Fennicae. Geologica-Geographica (0066-197X)
Related titles: Microform ed.
Indexed: BiolAb, GEOBASE, IBR, INIS AtomInd, PsycholAb, RefZh, ZooRec.
—CISTI, Linda Hall.
Published by: Suomalainen Tiedeakatemia/Academia Scientiarum Fennica, Mariankatu 5, Helsinki, 00170, Finland. TEL 358-9-636800, FAX 358-9-660117, acadsci@acadsci.fi, http://www.acadsci.fi. Ed. Matti Saarnisto. Circ: 540. **Dist. by:** Bookstore Tiedekirja, Kirkkokatu 14, Helsinki 00170, Finland. TEL 358-9-635177, FAX 358-9-635017, tiedekirja@pp.kolumbus.fi, http://www.tsv.fi/tkirja/tiekirj.html.

551 556 TUN ISSN 0365-4397
ANNALES DES MINES ET DE LA GEOLOGIE. Text in French. 1947. a. TND 15 (effective 1999). back issues avail. **Document type:** *Academic/Scholarly.*
Indexed: IMMAb, ZooRec.
Published by: Service Geologique de Tunisie, Office National des Mines, 24 rue 8601-2035 La Charquia, Tunis, Tunisia. TEL 216-1-788842-787-366, FAX 216-1-788842-794-016. Circ: 500.

550 GRC ISSN 1105-0004
ANNALES GEOLOGIQUES DES PAYS HELLENIQUES. Text in French. 1942. a.
Indexed: ZooRec.
Published by: National & Kapodistrian University of Athens, Faculty of Geology, Dept. of Historical Geology and Paleontology, Athens, 10561, Greece. TEL 00300107247322.

ANNALES UNIVERSITATIS MARIAE CURIE-SKLODOWSKA. SECTIO B. GEOGRAPHIA, GEOLOGIA, MINERALOGIA ET PETROGRAPHIA. see *GEOGRAPHY*

551.31 GBR ISSN 0260-3055
CODEN: ANGLDN
➤ **ANNALS OF GLACIOLOGY.** Text in English. 1980. irreg. (1-2/yr.), latest vols. 34 & 35. price varies. illus. **Document type:** *Proceedings, Academic/Scholarly.* **Description:** Contains selected papers from IGS sponsored or co-sponsored symposia.
Related titles: Online - full text ed.: ISSN 1727-5644 (from Gale Group, IngentaConnect).
Indexed: ASFA, CIN, ChemAb, ChemTitl, FLUIDEX, ForAb, GEOBASE, I&DA, ISR, Inspec, M&GPA, S&F, SCI.
—BLDSC (1040.830000), AskIEEE, CASDDS, CISTI, IE, Infotrieve, ingenta. **CCC.**
Published by: International Glaciological Society, Lensfield Rd, Cambridge, CB2 1ER, United Kingdom. TEL 44-1223-355974, FAX 44-1223-336543, http://www.igsoc.org/annals/. Circ: 700.

➤ **ANTARCTIC METEORITE NEWSLETTER.** see *ASTRONOMY*

551 JPN ISSN 1343-4284
QB755.5.A6 CODEN: AMERFQ
➤ **ANTARCTIC METEORITE RESEARCH.** Text and summaries in English. 1967. a., latest vol.16, 2003. per issue exchange basis. **Document type:** *Academic/Scholarly.*
Formerly (until 1997): N I P R Symposium on Antarctic Meteorites. Proceedings (0914-5621); Which superseded in part (in 1987): National Institute of Polar Research. Memoirs. Special Issue (0386-0744); Which was formerly (until 1972): Japanese Antarctic Research Expedition Scientific Reports. Special Issue (0386-5452)
Indexed: CIN, ChemAb, ChemTitl, M&GPA, MinerAb, RefZh.
—BLDSC (1542.108600), CASDDS, CISTI, KNAW.
Published by: National Institute of Polar Research/Kokuritsu Kyokuchi Kenkyujo, Publications, 9-10, Kiga 1-chome, Itabashi-ku, Tokyo, 173, Japan. TEL 81-3-3962-2214, FAX 81-3-3962-2225, publication@nipr.ac.jp. Ed. Okitsugu Watanabe. Circ: 1,000.

➤ **ANUARIO DE LA MINERIA DE CHILE.** see *MINES AND MINING INDUSTRY*

551 NLD ISSN 0169-1317
CODEN: ACLSER
➤ **APPLIED CLAY SCIENCE.** Text in Dutch. 1985. 20/yr. EUR 976 in Europe to institutions; JPY 129,700 in Japan to institutions; USD 1,092 to institutions except Europe and Japan; EUR 97 in Europe to qualified personnel; JPY 12,800 in Japan to qualified personnel; USD 106 to qualified personnel except Europe and Japan (effective 2006). adv. bk.rev. abstr. back issues avail. **Document type:** *Journal, Academic/Scholarly.* **Description:** Publishes research papers, reviews and short communications in the field of applied clay science and clay technology in a broad sense.
Related titles: Microform ed.: (from PQC); Online - full text ed.: (from EBSCO Publishing, Gale Group, IngentaConnect, ScienceDirect, Swets Information Services).
Indexed: ASCA, BrCerAb, C&ISA, CCI, CIN, CerAb, ChemAb, ChemTitl, CorrAb, CurCont, E&CAJ, EMA, EngInd, ExcerpMed, GEOBASE, ISR, Inspec, MSCI, MinerAb, S&F, SCI, SIA, SolStAb, WAA, WTA, WeedAb.
—BLDSC (1571.936000), CASDDS, CISTI, Ei, IDS, IE, Infotrieve, ingenta, Linda Hall. **CCC.**

Published by: Elsevier BV (Subsidiary of: Elsevier Science & Technology), Radarweg 29, Amsterdam, 1043 NX, Netherlands. TEL 31-20-4853911, FAX 31-20-4852457, nlinfo-f@elsevier.nl, http://www.elsevier.com/locate/clay, http://www.elsevier.nl. Eds. F J Eckhardt, Colin C. Harvey, G. Legaly.

551.9 GBR ISSN 0883-2927
QE514 CODEN: APPGEY
➤ **APPLIED GEOCHEMISTRY.** Text in English. 1986. 12/yr. EUR 1,074 in Europe to institutions; JPY 142,600 in Japan to institutions; USD 1,200 to institutions except Europe and Japan (effective 2006). bk.rev. abstr.; illus. index. back issues avail.; reprints avail. **Document type:** *Journal, Academic/Scholarly.* **Description:** International journal devoted to original research papers in geochemistry and cosmochemistry.
Related titles: Microfilm ed.: (from PQC); Online - full text ed.: (from EBSCO Publishing, Gale Group, IngentaConnect, ScienceDirect, Swets Information Services).
Indexed: AESIS, ASCA, ASFA, BIOBASE, ChemAb, CivEngAb, CurCont, E&PHSE, ESPM, EngInd, EnvAb, EnvEAb, FCA, ForAb, GEOBASE, GP&P, HortAb, IABS, IMMAb, ISR, M&GPA, MinerAb, OffTech, PetrolAb, PollutAb, S&F, SCI, SWRA, SoyAb, WRCInf.
—BLDSC (1572.585000), CASDDS, CISTI, Ei, IDS, IE, Infotrieve, ingenta, Linda Hall, PADDS. **CCC.**
Published by: (International Association of Geochemistry and Cosmochemistry), Pergamon (Subsidiary of: Elsevier Science & Technology), The Boulevard, Langford Ln, East Park, Kidlington, Oxford OX5 1GB, United Kingdom. TEL 44-1865-843000, FAX 44-1865-843010, http://www.elsevier.com/locate/apgeochem. **Subscr. to:** Elsevier BV, PO Box 211, Amsterdam 1000 AE, Netherlands. TEL 31-20-485-3757, FAX 31-20-485-3432, nlinfo-f@elsevier.nl, http://www.elsevier.nl.

➤ **AQUA**; mensile di acqua, natura, vita. see *EARTH SCIENCES—Hydrology*

550 DEU ISSN 0949-152X
ARBEITSHEFTE BAUGRUND. Text in German. irreg. EUR 18 per issue domestic (effective 2005). **Document type:** *Monographic series, Academic/Scholarly.*
Published by: E. Schweizerbart'sche Verlagsbuchhandlung, Johannesstr 3A, Stuttgart, 70176, Germany. TEL 49-711-3514560, FAX 49-711-35145699, mail@schweizerbart.de, http://www.schweizerbart.de/j/arbeitshefte.

550 DEU ISSN 0949-1538
ARBEITSHEFTE BODEN. Text in German. irreg., latest vol.5, 2004. EUR 18 per issue domestic (effective 2005). **Document type:** *Monographic series, Academic/Scholarly.*
Published by: E. Schweizerbart'sche Verlagsbuchhandlung, Johannesstr 3A, Stuttgart, 70176, Germany. TEL 49-711-3514560, FAX 49-711-35145699, mail@schweizerbart.de, http://www.schweizerbart.de/j/arbeitshefte.

550 DEU ISSN 0949-1546
ARBEITSHEFTE DEPONIEN. Text in German. 1995. irreg. EUR 18 per issue domestic (effective 2005). **Document type:** *Monographic series, Academic/Scholarly.*
Published by: E. Schweizerbart'sche Verlagsbuchhandlung, Johannesstr 3A, Stuttgart, 70176, Germany. TEL 49-711-3514560, FAX 49-711-35145699, mail@schweizerbart.de, http://www.schweizerbart.de.

550 DEU ISSN 0949-1554
ARBEITSHEFTE GEOLOGIE. Text in German. 1995. irreg. EUR 18 per issue domestic (effective 2005). **Document type:** *Monographic series, Academic/Scholarly.*
Published by: E. Schweizerbart'sche Verlagsbuchhandlung, Johannesstr 3A, Stuttgart, 70176, Germany. TEL 49-711-3514560, FAX 49-711-35145699, mail@schweizerbart.de, http://www.schweizerbart.de/j/arbeitshefte.

551 AUT ISSN 0253-097X
TN3 CODEN: ALGBDD
ARCHIV FUER LAGERSTAETTENFORSCHUNG. Text in German. 1963. irreg. adv. **Document type:** *Bulletin, Academic/Scholarly.*
Formerly (until 1980): Archiv fuer Lagerstaettenforschung in den Ostalpen (0570-6750)
Indexed: IBR, RefZh.
—CASDDS.
Published by: Geologische Bundesanstalt, Rasumofskygasse 23, Vienna, W 1031, Austria. TEL 43-1-71256740, FAX 43-1-712567456, sekretariat@geolba.ac.at, http://www.geolba.ac.at. Ed. Albert Daurer. R&P Tillfried Cernajsek TEL 43-1-7125674500. Adv. contact Melanie Reinberger.

550 POL ISSN 0066-6912
QE351 CODEN: ARWMAT
➤ **ARCHIWUM MINERALOGICZNE**; a journal of geochemistry, mineralogy and petrology. Text and summaries in English. 1925. s-a. PLZ 25 domestic; USD 40 foreign (effective 2003). **Document type:** *Journal, Academic/Scholarly.* **Description:** Covers a large spectrum of mineralogical sciences: petrology, geochemistry, systematic mineralogy, crystallography, crystal chemistry, experimental and applied mineralogy, as well as some aspects of environmental geology.
Indexed: CIN, ChemAb, ChemTitl, MinerAb.
—CASDDS, CISTI, Linda Hall.
Published by: (Komitet Nauk Mineralogicznych/Committee on Mineralogical Sciences USA, Polska Akademia Nauk/Polish Academy of Sciences), Polska Akademia Nauk, Instytut Nauk Mineralogicznych/Polish Academy of Sciences, Institute of Mineralogical Sciences, Ul Twarda 51-55, Warsaw, 00818, Poland. TEL 48-22-6978742, FAX 48-22-6206223, nbakun@twarda.pan.pl, http://www.geo.uw.edu.pl/AM/index_arch.htm. Ed. Maria Borkowska. R&P Andrzej Manecki. Circ: 500. **Dist. by:** Ars Polona, Krakowskie Przedmiescie 7, Warsaw, Poland. TEL 48-22-9263914, FAX 48-22-9265334, arspolona@arspolona.com.pl, http://www.arspolona.com.pl.

998 NOR ISSN 0803-0634
ARCTIC NEWS-RECORD & POLAR BULLETIN. Text in English. 1983. irreg. NOK 910; USD 137 in Europe; USD 140 elsewhere. **Document type:** *Newsletter.*
Formerly (until 1987): Arctic News-Record (0800-093X)
Published by: Scanews, Postboks 124, Sentrum, Oslo, 0102, Norway. TEL 47-22-385-539, FAX 47-22-38-55-39. Ed. Nicholas Wade.

550 TUR ISSN 1434-5641
➤ **ARI**; an interdisciplinary journal of physical and engineering sciences. Text in English. 1934. s-a. **Document type:** *Journal, Academic/Scholarly.* **Description:** Focuses on applied research that combines approaches from continuum physics, materials science, system science, and the geosciences.
Former titles (until 1997): Technical University of Istanbul. Bulletin (0254-4121); (until 1982): Istanbul Teknik Universitesi. Bulteni (0368-0355)
Related titles: Online - full text ed.: ISSN 1434-565X (from EBSCO Publishing, Springer LINK, Swets Information Services).
Indexed: Inspec.
—BLDSC (1668.180000), CISTI, IE, Infotrieve, Linda Hall. **CCC.**
Published by: (Technical University of Istanbul DEU), Technical University of Istanbul, Department of Physics, Maslak, Istanbul, 80626, Turkey. bulletin@itu.edu.tr, http://www.ari.itu.edu.tr/. Ed. A Nihat Berker.

557 USA ISSN 0066-7412
QE85 CODEN: AGSDA7
➤ **ARIZONA GEOLOGICAL SOCIETY DIGEST.** Text in English. 1958. irreg., latest vol.21, 2002. price varies. adv. **Document type:** *Journal, Academic/Scholarly.*
Indexed: IMMAb.
—Linda Hall, PADDS.
Published by: Arizona Geological Society, PO Box 40952, Tucson, AZ 85717. TEL 520-670-5544, secretary@arizonageologicalsoc.org, http://www.arizonageologicalsoc.org. Circ: 1,000. **Subscr. to:** Arizona Geological Survey, 416 W Congress, Ste 100, Tucson, AZ 85701.

➤ **ARIZONA GEOLOGICAL SURVEY. OPEN-FILE REPORT.** see *PETROLEUM AND GAS*

531.64 551 USA ISSN 1045-4802
TN24.A6
ARIZONA GEOLOGY; investigation, service, information. Text in English. 1971. q. bk.rev. bibl.; charts; illus. cum.index: 1971-1989. back issues avail. **Document type:** *Newsletter, Consumer.* **Description:** Semitechnical articles on Arizona's geology, summaries of survey research and activities, and announcements of new publications.
Formerly (until vol.18, no.3, 1988): Fieldnotes
Indexed: EEA.
—Linda Hall.
Published by: Arizona Geological Survey, 416 W Congress, Ste 100, Tucson, AZ 85701. TEL 520-770-3500, FAX 520-770-3505. Ed. Larry D Fellows. R&P Rose Ellen Cdonnell. Circ: 3,000.

557 USA
ARKANSAS. GEOLOGICAL COMMISSION. BULLETIN. Text in English. 1930 (no.5). irreg., latest vol.23, 1987. price varies. back issues avail. **Document type:** *Bulletin.*
Published by: Geological Commission, Vardelle Parham Geology Center, 3815 W Roosevelt Rd, Little Rock, AR 72204. TEL 501-296-1877, FAX 501-663-7360, AGC@mail.state.ar.us, http://www.state.ar.us/agc/agc.htm.

557 USA
ARKANSAS. GEOLOGICAL COMMISSION. INFORMATION CIRCULARS. Text in English. 1936 (no.8). irreg., latest vol.32, 1995. price varies. illus. back issues avail.
Published by: Geological Commission, Vardelle Parham Geology Center, 3815 W Roosevelt Rd, Little Rock, AR 72204. TEL 501-296-1877, FAX 501-663-7360, AGC@mail.state.ar.us.

557 USA
ARKANSAS. GEOLOGICAL COMMISSION. MISCELLANEOUS PUBLICATIONS. Text in English. 1940. irreg., latest vol.21, 1988. price varies. illus. back issues avail. **Document type:** *Monographic series.*
Published by: Geological Commission, Vardelle Parham Geology Center, 3815 W Roosevelt Rd, Little Rock, AR 72204. TEL 501-296-1877, FAX 501-663-7360, AGC@mail.state.ar.us. Circ: 1,000.

ASIAN GEOGRAPHER; a geographical journal on Asia and the Pacific Rim. see *GEOGRAPHY*

551 THA ISSN 1513-6728
ASIAN JOURNAL OF GEOINFORMATICS. Text in English. 2000. q. USD 60 for membership to individuals (effective 2004). **Document type:** *Journal, Academic/Scholarly.* **Description:** Publishes scientific and technical developments in the diverse field of Geoinformatics encompassing remote sensing, photogrammetry, geographic information system, and global positioning systems.
—BLDSC (1742.493000), IE.
Published by: (Asian Association on Remote Sensing JPN), Asian Remote Sensing Research Information Network, c/o Nitin Kumar Tripathi, Space Technology Application & Research Program, Asian Institute of Technology, PO Box # 4, Klong Luang, Pathumthani, Thailand. TEL 66-2-5246392, FAX 66-2-5245597, http://www.arsrin.net/. Ed. Nitin Kumar Tripathi.

550 ARG ISSN 0328-2724
ASOCIACION GEOLOGICA ARGENTINA. BOLETIN INFORMATIVO. Text in Spanish. 1994. s-a.
Published by: Asociacion Geologica Argentina, Maipu 645, Piso 1, Buenos Aires, C1006ACG, Argentina. TEL 54-11-4322-2820, FAX 54-11-4325-3104, postmaster@aga.inv.org.ar, http://157.92.20.1135/aga/raga/htm.

550 ARG ISSN 0004-4822
CODEN: RAGAAF
➤ **ASOCIACION GEOLOGICA ARGENTINA. REVISTA.** Text in Spanish, English. 1946. q. USD 90 (effective 2000). bk.rev. charts; illus.; maps; abstr. back issues avail. **Document type:** *Magazine, Academic/Scholarly.* **Description:** Includes works on all aspects of geology.
Formerly (until 1948): Sociedad Geologica Argentina. Revista (0370-7288)
Indexed: BiolAb, ChemAb, GEOBASE, ZooRec.
—BLDSC (7804.200000), CASDDS, CISTI, Linda Hall. **CCC.**
Published by: Asociacion Geologica Argentina, Maipu 645, Piso 1, Buenos Aires, C1006ACG, Argentina. TEL 54-11-4322-2820, FAX 54-11-4325-3104, postmaster@aga.inu.org.ar, postmaster@aga.inv.org.ar, http://157.92.20.1135/aga/raga/htm. Ed. Milka Brodtkorb. Circ: 700.

551 EGY
ASSIUT UNIVERSITY. FACULTY OF SCIENCE. BULLETIN: F. GEOLOGY. Text in English. irreg.
Indexed: ZooRec.
Published by: Assiut University, Faculty of Science, c/o Dr. Muhammad Bahey, Assiut, Egypt. TEL 20-88-411376, FAX 20-88-342708, http://www.aun.eun.eg.

551 EGY ISSN 1110-7367
ASSIUT UNIVERSITY. FACULTY OF SCIENCE. BULLETIN. SECTION F. GEOLOGY. Text in English. 1988. s-a. free (effective 2004). **Document type:** *Bulletin, Academic/Scholarly.*
Supersedes in part (in 1988): Assiut University. Faculty of Science. Bulletin. Section C. Biology and Geology (1010-2698); Which was formerly (until 1982): Assiut University. Faculty of Science. Bulletin. Section B. Biological and Geological Studies (0254-6256); Which superseded in part (in 1979): Assiut University. Science and Technology. Bulletin (0379-3389)
Published by: Assiut University, Faculty of Science, c/o Dr. Muhammad Bahey, Assiut, Egypt. TEL 20-88-411376, FAX 20-88-342708, science@aun.edu.eg, sup@aun.eun.eg, http://derp.sti.sci.eg/data/0300.htm, http://www.aun.eun.eg.

550 FRA ISSN 0374-1346
CODEN: BGBPA3
ASSOCIATION DES GEOLOGUES DU BASSIN DE PARIS. BULLETIN D'INFORMATION. Key Title: Bulletin d'Information des Geologues du Bassin de Paris. Text in French. 1964. q.
Indexed: ZooRec.
Published by: Association des Geologues du Bassin de Paris, 4 Place de Jussieu, Paris Cedex 05, 75252, France.

551.3 FRA ISSN 0990-3925
ASSOCIATION DES SEDIMENTOLOGISTES FRANCAIS. Text in French. 1987. irreg. **Document type:** *Monographic series, Academic/Scholarly.*
Address: c/o Sebastien Zaragosi, Secretaire, Universite de Bordeaux I, Bordeaux, France. http://www.epoc.u-bordeaux.fr/ASF/ash.html.

550 FRA ISSN 0249-0102
ASSOCIATION GEOLOGIQUE AUBOISE. BULLETIN ANNUEL. Text in French. 1977. a.
Indexed: ZooRec.

E

Published by: Association Geologique Auboise, 11 rue du 11 Novembre, Sainte Sauvine, 10300, France. Ed. Claude Collete.

551 USA
ASSOCIATION OF ENGINEERING GEOLOGISTS. SPECIAL PUBLICATIONS. Text in English. irreg. price varies.
Document type: *Monographic series.*
Indexed: AESIS.
—BLDSC (8372.374500).
Published by: Association of Engineering Geologists, Dept of Geology & Geophysics, Texas A&M University MS-3115, College Station, TX 77843-3115. TEL 979-845-0142, FAX 979-862-7959, aeg@aeg.tamu.edu, http://www.aegweb.org/.

ASSOCIATION OF MARINE LABORATORIES OF THE CARIBBEAN. NEWSLETTER. see *EARTH SCIENCES—Oceanography*

ASSOCIATION OF MARINE LABORATORIES OF THE CARIBBEAN. PROCEEDINGS. see *EARTH SCIENCES—Oceanography*

551.3 CAN ISSN 0843-5561
GC380 CODEN: ATGEEB
➤ **ATLANTIC GEOLOGY.** Text in English; Abstracts in English, French. 1965. 3/yr. CND 45 domestic to individuals; USD 45 foreign to individuals; CND 70 domestic to institutions; USD 70 foreign to institutions; CND 35 to members (effective 2005). bk.rev. abstr.; illus. index, cum.index. 2 cols./p.; back issues avail.; reprints avail. **Document type:** *Journal, Academic/Scholarly.* **Description:** Publishes papers, notes and discussions on original research and review papers on all aspects of the geology of Atlantic Canada and related areas.
Former titles (until 1990): Maritime Sediments and Atlantic Geology (0711-1150); (until 1982): Maritime Sediments (0025-3456)
Related titles: Online - full text ed.: (from Gale Group).
Indexed: ASCA, ASFA, BiolAb, CPerI, CurCont, E&PHSE, ESPM, FLUIDEX, GEOBASE, GP&P, OceAb, OffTech, PetrolAb, RefZh, ZooRec.
—BLDSC (1765.903000), CISTI, IDS, IE, Infotrieve, ingenta, Linda Hall, PADDS. **CCC.**
Published by: Atlantic Geoscience Society, Dept of Geology, Acadia University, PO Box 116, Wolfville, NS B4P 2R6, Canada. TEL 902-585-1340, FAX 902-585-1816, sandra.barr@acadiau.ca, http://www.atlanticgeology.ca. Ed. Sandra M Barr. Adv. contact Sandra Barr. Circ: 350.

551 DEU ISSN 0004-7856
QE1 CODEN: AFSLAO
DER AUFSCHLUSS. Text in German. 1950. bi-m. EUR 62 domestic to non-members; EUR 72 foreign to non-members; EUR 44 domestic to members; EUR 54 foreign to members (effective 2005). **Document type:** *Journal, Academic/Scholarly.*
Indexed: CIN, ChemAb, ChemTitl, IBR, MinerAb, RefZh, SFA, ZooRec.
—CASDDS. **CCC.**
Published by: Vereinigung der Freunde der Mineralogie und Geologie e.V., Blumenthalstr 40, Heidelberg, 69120, Germany. TEL 49-6221-413411, FAX 49-6221-472660, aktuell@vfmg.de, http://www.vfmg.de/vfmg/aufschlu.htm. Ed. H Poellmann. Circ: 4,500.

AUSTRALIA. BUREAU OF STATISTICS. MINERAL ACCOUNT, AUSTRALIA. see *EARTH SCIENCES—Abstracting, Bibliographies, Statistics*

559.4 AUS ISSN 0312-4711
THE AUSTRALIAN GEOLOGIST. Text in English. 1974. q. AUD 51 (effective 2005). adv. bk.rev. illus. 80 p./no.; **Document type:** *Newsletter, Academic/Scholarly.* **Description:** Covers items of interest to geoscientists. Reports on forthcoming meetings.
Indexed: AESIS.
Published by: Geological Society of Australia Inc., Ste 706, 301 George St, Sydney, NSW 2000, Australia. TEL 61-2-92902194, FAX 61-2-92902198, info@gsa.org.au, http://www.gsa.org.au. adv.: B&W page AUD 665, color page AUD 1,200; trim 182 x 250. Circ: 2,800.

AUSTRALIAN INSTITUTE OF PETROLEUM. ANNUAL REPORT. see *PETROLEUM AND GAS*

551 GBR ISSN 0812-0099
QE340 CODEN: AJESE7
➤ **AUSTRALIAN JOURNAL OF EARTH SCIENCES.** Text in English. 1953. bi-m. GBP 625, USD 1,032, AUD 814 combined subscription to institutions print & online eds. (effective 2006). adv. bibl.; illus. index. back issues avail.; reprint service avail. from PQC. **Document type:** *Journal, Academic/Scholarly.* **Description:** Publishes theoretical and experimental research papers as well as significant review articles of more general interest to geoscientists. Covers the whole field of earth science including basin studies, regional geophysical studies and metallogeny.
Incorporates (1993-1997): A G S O Journal of Australian Geology and Geophysics (1320-1271); Which was formerly (1976-1992): B M R Journal of Australian Geology and Geophysics (0312-9608); Supersedes: Geological Society of Australia. Journal (0016-7614)
Related titles: Microform ed.: (from PQC); Online - full text ed.: ISSN 1440-0952. GBP 594, USD 980, AUD 773 to institutions (effective 2006) (from Blackwell Synergy, EBSCO Publishing, Gale Group, IngentaConnect, O C L C Online Computer Library Center, Inc., Swets Information Services).
Indexed: AEA, AESIS, ASCA, ASFA, BioCN&I, C&ISA, CIN, ChemAb, ChemTitl, CurCont, E&CAJ, E&PHSE, EEA, EPB, ESPM, EngInd, FLUIDEX, GEOBASE, GP&P, GeotechAb, I&DA, IAA, IABS, ICEA, IMMAb, INIS AtomInd, ISR, Inspec, MinerAb, NutrAb, OffTech, PetrolAb, PollutAb, RefZh, RevApplEntom, S&F, SCI, SPPI, SWRA, ZooRec.
—BLDSC (1807.555000), AskIEEE, CASDDS, CISTI, Ei, IDS, IE, Infotrieve, ingenta, Linda Hall, PADDS. **CCC.**
Published by: (Geological Society of Australia Inc. AUS), Taylor & Francis Ltd (Subsidiary of: Taylor & Francis Group), 4 Park Sq, Milton Park, Abingdon, OX14 4RN, United Kingdom. TEL 44-1235-828600, FAX 44-1235-829000, info@tandf.co.uk, http://www.tandf.co.uk/journals/titles/08120099.asp. Ed. A E Cockbain. adv.: B&W page USD 1,175, color page USD 2,460; trim 210 x 275. Circ: 3,250.

551.44 GBR
B C R A CAVE STUDIES SERIES. Text in English. 1987. irreg., latest vol.9, 2001. **Document type:** *Monographic series.*
Published by: British Cave Research Association, c/o E Shield, Village Farm, Mill Lane, Great Thirkleby, N Yorks YO7 2AT, United Kingdom. enquiries@bcra.org.uk, publications-sales@bcra.org.uk, http://www.bcra.org.uk/. Ed. Bryan Ellis.

BADANIA FIZJOGRAFICZNE NAD POLSKA ZACHODNIA. SERIA A. GEOGRAFIA FIZYCZNA. see *GEOGRAPHY*

BADISCHER LANDESVEREIN FUER NATURKUNDE UND NATURSCHUTZ, FREIBURG. MITTEILUNGEN. NEUE FOLGE. see *BIOLOGY*

BASE LINE. see *GEOGRAPHY*

551 USA ISSN 0005-7266
CODEN: BGOBAQ
BAYLOR GEOLOGICAL STUDIES BULLETIN. Text in English. 1961. s-a. USD 5. bibl.; charts; illus. index. **Document type:** *Bulletin, Academic/Scholarly.*
Related titles: Microfilm ed.
Indexed: ANAG, ChemAb.
—Linda Hall.
Published by: Baylor University, Geology Department, PO Box 97354, Waco, TX 76798-7354. TEL 817-755-2361, FAX 817-755-2673. Ed. Joe Yelderman Jr. Circ: 700.

BEITRAEGE ZUR NATURKUNDE IN OSTHESSEN. see *BIOLOGY*

550 DEU ISSN 0522-7038
CODEN: BRGEA4
BEITRAEGE ZUR REGIONALEN GEOLOGIE DER ERDE. Text in German, English. 1961. irreg., latest vol.31, 2003. price varies. Website rev. back issues avail. **Document type:** *Monographic series, Academic/Scholarly.*
—BLDSC (1887.300000). **CCC.**
Published by: Gebrueder Borntraeger Verlagsbuchhandlung, Johannesstr. 3A, Stuttgart, 70176, Germany. TEL 49-711-3514560, FAX 49-711-35145699, mail@schweizerbart.de, http://www.schweizerbart.de/j/beitraege-zur-regionalen-geologie-der-erde.

BEITRAEGE ZUR RHEINKUNDE. see *HISTORY—History Of Europe*

554 BEL ISSN 0408-9510
QE274 CODEN: BSGMB2
BELGIUM. GEOLOGICAL SURVEY OF BELGIUM. MEMOIRS/BELGISHE GEOLOGISCHE DIENST. VERHANDELING. Key Title: Service Geologique de Belgique. Text in Dutch, English, French, German. 1955. irreg., latest vol.47, 2001. price varies. charts; illus.; maps. 125 p./no.; back issues avail. **Document type:** *Monographic series, Government.*
Formerly: Memoires pour Servir a l'Explication des Cartes Geologiques et Minieres de la Belgique (0408-9529)
Indexed: RefZh, ZooRec.
Published by: (Belgium. Ministere des Affaires Economiques, Direction Generale des Etudes et de la Documentation/ Ministerie van Economische Zaken, Algemene Directie voor Studien en Documentatie), Service Geologique de Belgique/Geological Survey of Belgium, Rue Jenner 13, Brussels, 1000, Belgium. TEL 32-2-6270350, FAX 32-2-6477359, bgd.sgb@pophost.eunet.be. Ed. L Dejonghe. Pub. M Mainjot. R&P M Dusar. Circ: 1,000.

554 BEL ISSN 0378-0902
QE274 CODEN: BGPPB6
BELGIUM. GEOLOGICAL SURVEY OF BELGIUM. PROFESSIONAL PAPERS. Text in French, Dutch, English, German. 1966. irreg., latest vol.293, 2001. Price varies. illus.; maps; charts. 60 p./no.; back issues avail. **Document type:** *Monographic series, Academic/Scholarly.*
Indexed: RefZh, ZooRec.
Published by: (Belgium. Ministere des Affaires Economiques, Direction Generale des Etudes et de la Documentation/ Ministerie van Economische Zaken, Algemene Directie voor Studien en Documentatie), Service Geologique de Belgique/Geological Survey of Belgium, Rue Jenner 13, Brussels, 1000, Belgium. TEL 32-2-6270350, FAX 32-2-6477359, bgd.sgb@pophost.eunet.be. Ed. L Dejonghe. Pub. M Mainjot. R&P M Dusar. Circ: 1,000.

BERICHTE DER DEUTSCHEN MINERALOGISCHEN GESELLSCHAFT; Beihefte zum European Journal of Mineralogy. see *MINES AND MINING INDUSTRY*

BERINGERIA; Wuerzburger geowissenschaftliche Mitteilungen. see *PALEONTOLOGY*

BIBLIOGRAFIA GEOLOGICA SI GEOFIZICA A ROMANIEI/GEOLOGICAL AND GEOPHYSICAL BIBLIOGRAPHY OF ROMANIA. see *EARTH SCIENCES—Abstracting, Bibliographies, Statistics*

BIBLIOGRAFIA GEOLOGICZNA POLSKI. see *EARTH SCIENCES—Abstracting, Bibliographies, Statistics*

BIBLIOGRAPHY AND INDEX OF GEOLOGY. see *EARTH SCIENCES—Abstracting, Bibliographies, Statistics*

BIBLIOGRAPHY OF THE GEOLOGY OF FIJI. see *EARTH SCIENCES—Abstracting, Bibliographies, Statistics*

BIOLOGY AND ENVIRONMENT; proceedings of the Royal Irish Academy. see *BIOLOGY*

551 GBR ISSN 0260-714X
BLACK COUNTRY GEOLOGIST. Text in English. 1981. a. illus.
Published by: Black Country Geological Society, c/o HoN Sec., 16 St Nicolas Gardens, Kings Norton, Birmingham, Worcs B38 8TW, United Kingdom.

558 COL ISSN 0120-1425
QE239 CODEN: BGINBX
BOLETIN GEOLOGICO. Text in Spanish. 1953. irreg., latest vol.35, 1995, no.2-3. price varies. **Document type:** *Bulletin.*
Indexed: ChemAb, IBR.
—CASDDS, Linda Hall.
Published by: Instituto de Investigacion e Informacion Geocientifica, Minero-Ambiental y Nuclear Ingeominas, Diagonal 53, 34-53, Apartado Aereo 4865, Bogota, CUND, Colombia. TEL 57-1-2221811, FAX 57-1-2220797, cliente@ingeomin.gov.co, http://www.ingeomin.gov.co.

551 622 ESP ISSN 0366-0176
QE283 CODEN: BGMIA3
BOLETIN GEOLOGICO Y MINERO. Text in Spanish. 1874. q. EUR 36 (effective 2005). bibl.; charts. index. **Document type:** *Bulletin, Academic/Scholarly.*
Formed by the merger of (1928-1967): Notas y Comunicaciones del Instituto y Minero de Espana (0369-5050); (1927-1967): Instituto Geologico y Minero de Espana. Boletin (0366-0168); Which was formerly (until 1927): Instituto Geologico de Espana. Boletin (0211-0253); Superseded (in 1910): Comision del Mapa Geologico de Espana. boletin (0211-0245)
Indexed: FLUIDEX, GEOBASE, IBR, IECT, INIS AtomInd, MinerAb, RefZh, ZooRec.
—CASDDS, CINDOC, CISTI, Linda Hall. **CCC.**
Published by: El Instituto Geologico y Minero de Espana, Rios Rosas 23, Madrid, 28003, Spain. TEL 34-91-3495819, FAX 34-91-3495830, publicaciones@igme.es, http://www.igme.es/internet/principal.asp.

551 622 ESP
BOLETIN GEOLOGICO Y MINERO. PUBLICACIONES ESPECIALES. Text in Spanish. 1980. irreg., latest vol.14, 1992. price varies. **Document type:** *Monographic series, Academic/Scholarly.* **Description:** Selected articles from the Boletin Geologico y Minero on specific topics.
Published by: El Instituto Geologico y Minero de Espana, Rios Rosas 23, Madrid, 28003, Spain. TEL 34-91-3495819, FAX 34-91-3495830, http://www.igme.es/internet/principal.asp.

551 560 NOR ISSN 0300-9483
CODEN: BRESB3
➤ **BOREAS**; an international journal of quaternary research. Text in English. 1972. q. GBP 167, USD 275 combined subscription to institutions print & online eds. (effective 2006). adv. bk.rev. illus. Index. back issues avail.; reprint service avail. from ISI,PSC. **Document type:** *Journal, Academic/Scholarly.*
Related titles: Microform ed.: (from PQC); Online - full text ed.: ISSN 1502-3885. GBP 159, USD 261 to institutions (effective 2006) (from EBSCO Publishing, Gale Group, IngentaConnect, O C L C Online Computer Library Center, Inc., Swets Information Services).
Indexed: AESIS, ASFA, ASTIS, AbAn, ApEcolAb, BIOSIS Prev, BiolAb, BrArAb, BrGeoL, CTO, ChemAb, CurCont, ESPM, EntAb, GEOBASE, IBR, ISR, M&GPA, NumL, PBA, RASB, RefZh, S&F, SCI, SWRA, ZooRec.
—BLDSC (2251.385000), CISTI, IDS, IE, Infotrieve, ingenta, Linda Hall. **CCC.**

E

Published by: Taylor & Francis A S (Subsidiary of: Taylor & Francis Group), Biskop Gunnerusgate 14A, PO Box 12 Posthuset, Oslo, 0051, Norway. TEL 47-23-103460, FAX 47-23-103461, journals@tandf.no, http://www.tandf.co.uk/journals/titles/03009483.asp. Ed. Jan A Piotrowski. Circ: 700.

➤ **BOTSWANA. GEOLOGICAL SURVEY DEPARTMENT. ANNOTATED BIBLIOGRAPHY AND INDEX OF THE GEOLOGY OF BOTSWANA.** see *EARTH SCIENCES—Abstracting, Bibliographies, Statistics*

354 BWA ISSN 0524-1502
QE48.B53
BOTSWANA. GEOLOGICAL SURVEY DEPARTMENT. ANNUAL REPORTS. Text in English. 1953. a. USD 3. illus. **Document type:** *Government.*
Formerly (until 1966): Botswana. Geological Survey and Mines Department. Annual Reports (0250-3506)
Published by: Geological Survey Department, Lobatse, Botswana. TEL 267-330327, FAX 267-31-332013. Ed. B G Aboneng. Circ: 300.

354 BWA ISSN 0522-5612
CODEN: BBGDDS
BOTSWANA. GEOLOGICAL SURVEY DEPARTMENT. BULLETINS. Text in English. 1966. irreg. USD 3. **Document type:** *Bulletin, Government.*
Indexed: IMMAb.
—CASDDS, Linda Hall.
Published by: Geological Survey Department, Lobatse, Botswana. TEL 267-330327, FAX 267-332013. Ed. B G Aboneng. Circ: 300.

354 BWA ISSN 0379-119X
CODEN: DMGBDJ
BOTSWANA. GEOLOGICAL SURVEY DEPARTMENT. DISTRICT MEMOIRS. Text in English. 1973. irreg. USD 4. **Document type:** *Government.*
Indexed: IMMAb.
Published by: Geological Survey Department, Lobatse, Botswana. TEL 267-330327, FAX 267-332013. Ed. B G Aboneng. Circ: 450.

354 BWA
BOTSWANA. GEOLOGICAL SURVEY DEPARTMENT. MINERAL RESOURCES REPORTS. Text in English. 1959. irreg. USD 3. **Document type:** *Monographic series, Government.*
Indexed: IMMAb.
Published by: Geological Survey Department, Lobatse, Botswana. FAX 267-332013. Ed. Clement M Siyumbwa. Circ: 300.

354 BWA ISSN 0522-5620
CODEN: RGLSA
BOTSWANA. GEOLOGICAL SURVEY DEPARTMENT. RECORDS OF THE GEOLOGICAL SURVEY. Text in English. 1958. irreg. USD 2. **Document type:** *Monographic series, Government.*
Published by: Geological Survey Department, Lobatse, Botswana. TEL 267-330327, FAX 267-332013. Ed. B G Aboneng. Circ: 300.

BRAGANTIA. see *AGRICULTURE*

558 BRA ISSN 0103-8966
BRAZIL. DEPARTAMENTO NACIONAL DA PRODUCAO MINERAL. SERIE GEOLOGIA. Text in Portuguese. 1976. irreg., latest vol.27, 1985. price varies. **Document type:** *Bulletin, Government.*
Published by: Departamento Nacional da Producao Mineral, Setor Autarquia Norte, Quadra 1, Bloco B, Brasilia, DF 70040, Brazil. TEL 55-61-224-2670. Ed. Frederico L M Barboza.

557 USA ISSN 1041-7184
BRIGHAM YOUNG UNIVERSITY GEOLOGY STUDIES. Text in English. 1954. a. USD 25 (effective 1999). adv. cum.index (1954-1992). back issues avail. **Document type:** *Academic/Scholarly.*
Former titles (until 1969): Brigham Young University. Department of Geology. Geology Studies (0068-1016); (until 1960): Brigham Young University Research Studies. Geology Series
Related titles: Microfilm ed.
Indexed: E&PHSE, EngInd, GP&P, OffTech, PetrolAb, ZooRec.
—BLDSC (2283.970000), Ei, IE, ingenta, Linda Hall, PADDS.
Published by: Brigham Young University, Department of Geology, PO Box 24606, S 389 A ESC, Provo, UT 84602-4606. TEL 801-378-2578, FAX 801-378-8143, mhm@geology.byu.edu. Ed. Scott Ritter. R&P, Adv. contact Marge Morgan. Circ: 600.

622 557 CAN ISSN 0068-144X
TN27
BRITISH COLUMBIA. DEPARTMENT OF MINES AND PETROLEUM RESOURCES. BULLETIN. Text in English. irreg. price varies. **Document type:** *Bulletin, Government.*
Former titles (until 1960): British Columbia. Department of Mines. Bulletin (0365-9364); (1917-1959): British Columbia. Bureau of Mines. Bulletin (0848-2276)
Indexed: EngInd, IMMAb.
—CISTI, Linda Hall.
Published by: (British Columbia. Ministry of Energy, Mines and Petroleum Resources, British Columbia. Publications Distribution Section), Queen's Printer, Victoria, 563 Superior St, Victoria, BC V8V 1X4, Canada. **Subscr. to:** Crown Publications Inc., 521 Fort St, Victoria, BC BC V8W 1E7, Canada. TEL 250-386-4636, FAX 250-386-0221, crown@pinc.com, http://www.crownpub.bc.ca.

551 560 POL
BUDOWA GEOLOGICZNA POLSKI. Text in Polish. 1968. irreg. price varies. bibl. **Document type:** *Academic/Scholarly.*
Description: Explores the areas of paleontology, stratigraphy, tectonics, hydrogeology, and economic geology.
Published by: Panstwowy Instytut Geologiczny/Polish Geological Institute, ul Rakowiecka 4, Warsaw, 00975, Poland. TEL 48-22-8495351, FAX 48-22-8495342, dystryb@pgi.wa.pl. Circ: 1,000.

551 622 ALB ISSN 0254-5276
QE1 CODEN: BSGJDT
BULETINI I SHKENCAVE GJEOLOGJIKE. Text in Albanian; Summaries in English. 1965-1991; resumed 1994. s-a. USD 30 to individuals; USD 60 to institutions. adv. **Document type:** *Bulletin.*
Formerly (until 1982): Instituti i Studimeve dhe Kerkimeve Industriale e Minerale. Permbledhje Studimesh (0370-1638)
Indexed: IMMAb.
—CASDDS.
Published by: Instituti i Studimeve dhe i Projektimeve te Gjeologjise, Blloku Vasil Shanto, Tirana, Albania. TEL 355-42-26597, FAX 355-42-26597, ispgj@ingeol.tirana.al. Ed., Adv. contact Afat Serjani. R&P A Kodra. Circ: 200.

550 BGR ISSN 0007-3938
QE1 CODEN: SBGDA8
BULGARSKO GEOLOGICHESKO DRUZHESTVO. SPISANIE. Summaries in English, French, German, Russian. 1927. 3/yr. BGL 1.65 per issue; USD 78 foreign (effective 2002). bk.rev. abstr.; illus. index. reprint service avail. from IRC. **Document type:** *Journal.* **Description:** Publishes articles with the results of the researches in all fields of geology, geophysics, geomorphology.
Indexed: BSLGeo, BiolAb, CIN, ChemAb, ChemTitl, IAA, ZooRec.
—CASDDS, CISTI, Linda Hall.
Published by: (Bulgarska Akademiya na Naukite/Bulgarian Academy of Sciences), Universitetsko Izdatelstvo Sv. Kliment Okhridski/Publishing House of the Sofia University St. Kliment Ohridski, Akad G Bonchev 6, Sofia, 1113, Bulgaria. Ed. Khr Spasov. Circ: 1,090. **Dist. by:** Hemus, 6 Rouski Blvd., Sofia 1000, Bulgaria; **Dist. by:** Sofia Books, ul Silivria 16, Sofia 1404, Bulgaria. TEL 359-2-9586257, info@sofiabooks-bg.com, http://www.sofiabooks-bg.com.

BULLETIN DES CENTRES DE RECHERCHES EXPLORATION-PRODUCTION ELF-AQUITAINE. MEMOIRE. see *PETROLEUM AND GAS*

BULLETIN FUER ANGEWANDTE GEOLOGIE/BULLETIN POUR LA GEOLOGIE APPLIQUEE. see *PETROLEUM AND GAS*

551 IND ISSN 0970-4639
QE1 CODEN: BPASF7
➤ **BULLETIN OF PURE & APPLIED SCIENCES. SECTION F: GEOLOGY.** Text in English. 1982. s-a. INR 300, USD 50 (effective 2005). adv. bk.rev. 75 p./no.; back issues avail. **Document type:** *Journal, Academic/Scholarly.*
Supersedes in part (in 1983): Bulletin of Pure & Applied Sciences (0970-4604)
Media: Large Type (11 pt.). **Related titles:** E-mail ed.
Indexed: GEOBASE.
—CISTI, Linda Hall. **CCC.**
Published by: A.K. Sharma, Ed. & Pub., 19-A, D D A Flats, Mansarover Park, Shahdara, New Delhi, 110 032, India. TEL 91-11-2117408, bulletin@mantraonline.com, ajaykumarsharma1955@yahoo.com. Ed., Pub., R&P, Adv. contact A K Sharma. B&W page INR 1,000, B&W page USD 50, color page INR 2,000, color page USD 100. Circ: 600.

➤ **C M S WORKSHOP LECTURES.** see *MINES AND MINING INDUSTRY*

551 FRA ISSN 0246-5582
CAHIERS DU QUATERNAIRE. Text in French. 1979. irreg. price varies. **Document type:** *Monographic series, Academic/Scholarly.*
Published by: C N R S Editions, 15 Rue Malebranche, Paris, 75005, France. TEL 33-1-53102700, FAX 33-1-53102727, http://www.cnrseditions.fr.

551 FRA ISSN 0008-0241
CAHIERS GEOLOGIQUES. Text and summaries in English, French. 1950. s-a. adv. bk.rev. abstr.; bibl.; illus.; stat. index. **Document type:** *Newsletter, Academic/Scholarly.*
Indexed: BiolAb, ChemAb.
—CISTI, Linda Hall. **CCC.**
Published by: Association des Amis et Anciens Eleves du Laboratoire de Geologie, I, Universite Paris VI Tour 14-15-16, 4 place Jussieu, 4e Etage, Paris, 75005, France. Ed. Jean Pierre Michel. Circ: 1,000.

551 560 NLD ISSN 1570-0399
QE735
➤ **CAINOZOIC RESEARCH.** Text in English. 2002. s-a. EUR 64 (effective 2004). back issues avail. **Document type:** *Journal, Academic/Scholarly.*
Formed by the merger of (1964-2001): Contributions to Tertiary and Quaternary Geology (0165-280X); (1976-2001): Tertiary Research (0308-9649)
Published by: Backhuys Publishers BV, Postbus 321, Leiden, 2300 AH, Netherlands. TEL 31-71-517-0208, FAX 31-71-517-1856, backhuys@backhuys.com, http://www.backhuys.com. Circ: 600 (paid).

551 622 USA ISSN 0527-0014
TN24.C2 CODEN: CCGRA
CALIFORNIA. DIVISION OF MINES AND GEOLOGY. SPECIAL REPORT. Text in English. irreg. price varies. **Document type:** *Monographic series, Government.*
Indexed: IMMAb.
—Linda Hall.
Published by: Resources Agency, Division of Mines and Geology, 801 K St MSC14 30, Sacramento, CA 95814-3531. TEL 916-445-5716.

CAMBRIDGE PLANETARY SCIENCE SERIES. see *ASTRONOMY*

557 CAN ISSN 0068-7626
QE185 CODEN: CMGEAE
CANADA. GEOLOGICAL SURVEY. BULLETIN. Text in English, French. 1945. irreg. price varies. index, cum.index: 1945-1969. **Document type:** *Bulletin, Government.*
Incorporates: Canada. Geological Survey. Memoir (0068-7634); Canada. Geological Survey. Economic Geology Reports
Related titles: Microfilm ed.: (from BHP).
Indexed: AESIS, BiolAb, GEOBASE, IBR, IMMAb, PetrolAb, ZooRec.
—BLDSC (2528.300000), CASDDS, CISTI, IE, ingenta, Linda Hall, PADDS. **CCC.**
Published by: Natural Resources Canada, 601 Booth St, Ottawa, ON K1A 0E8, Canada. TEL 613-996-3919, FAX 613-943-8742, info-ottawa@gsc.nrcan.gc.ca, http://www.nrcan.gc.ca/gsc. R&P M F Dufour TEL 613-995-7648. Circ: 800.

557 CAN ISSN 0704-2884
QE48 CODEN: CRGCED
CANADA. GEOLOGICAL SURVEY. CURRENT RESEARCH. Text in English, French. 1935. irreg. price varies. bibl. index, cum.index. **Document type:** *Monographic series, Government.*
Supersedes: Canada. Geological Survey. Paper (0068-7650); Canada. Earth Physics Branch. Seismological Series (0084-8387); Canada. Earth Physics Branch. Gravity Map Series; Canada. Earth Physics Branch. Geothermal Series (0704-3066); Canada. Earth Physics Branch. Geomagnetic Series (0704-3015); Canadian Earthquakes - Tremblements de Terre Canadiens (0225-6002); Canada. Earth Physics Branch. Geodynamic Series
Indexed: AESIS, BiolAb, CIN, ChemAb, ChemTitl, E&PHSE, GP&P, IMMAb, Inspec, OffTech, PetrolAb,
—AskIEEE, CASDDS, CISTI, Linda Hall, PADDS. **CCC.**
Published by: Natural Resources Canada, 601 Booth St, Ottawa, ON K1A 0E8, Canada. TEL 613-996-3919, FAX 613-943-8742, info-ottawa@gsc.nrcan.gc.ca, http://www.nrcan.gc.ca/gsc. R&P M F Dufour TEL 613-995-7648. Circ: 800.

557 CAN ISSN 0068-7642
QE185 CODEN: CGSRA3
CANADA. GEOLOGICAL SURVEY. MISCELLANEOUS REPORT. Text in English. 1960. irreg. price varies. **Document type:** *Monographic series, Government.*
Indexed: AESIS, IMMAb.
—CISTI, Linda Hall.
Published by: Natural Resources Canada, 601 Booth St, Ottawa, ON K1A 0E8, Canada. TEL 613-995-4342. R&P M F Dufour TEL 613-995-7648. Circ: 800.

549 CAN ISSN 0008-4476
QE376 CODEN: CAMIA6
➤ **CANADIAN MINERALOGIST;** crystallography, geochemistry, mineralogy, petrology, mineral deposits. Text in English, French; Summaries in English, French. 1921. q. CND 80 domestic to individuals; USD 80 foreign to individuals; CND 295 domestic to institutions; USD 295 foreign to institutions (effective 1999). bk.rev. charts; illus. index. reprints avail. **Document type:** *Academic/Scholarly.* **Description:** Reports the results of original research in crystallography, geochemistry, mineralogy, petrology and mineral deposits.
Formerly (until 1957): Contributions to Canadian Mineralogy (0701-3876)
Related titles: Online - full text ed.: (from EBSCO Publishing, Swets Information Services).
Indexed: AESIS, APD, ASCA, BrCerAb, C&ISA, CCI, CIN, CerAb, ChemAb, ChemTitl, CivEngAb, CorrAb, CurCont, E&CAJ, EMA, EngInd, GEOBASE, IAA, IBR, IMMAb, ISMEC, ISR, M&TEA, MBF, METADEX, MSCI, MinerAb, PetrolAb, RefZh, SCI, SolStAb, WAA.
—BLDSC (3040.300000), CASDDS, CISTI, Ei, IDS, IE, Infotrieve, ingenta, Linda Hall, PADDS. **CCC.**

E

Published by: Mineralogical Association of Canada/Association Mineralogique du Canada, 1460 Merivale Rd, PO Box 78087, Meriline Postal Outlet, Ottawa, ON K2E 1B1, Canada. canmin.mac.ottawa@sympatico.ca, http://pubs.nrc-cnrc.gc.ca/mineral/mineralogist.html, http://www.mineralogicalassociation.ca. Ed. R F Martin. R&P Robert Martin. Circ: 2,000.

➤ **CANADIAN MINING JOURNAL.** see *MINES AND MINING INDUSTRY*

➤ **CANADIAN PETROLEUM GEOLOGY. BULLETIN.** see *PETROLEUM AND GAS*

➤ **CANADIAN SOCIETY OF PETROLEUM GEOLOGISTS. MEMOIR.** see *PETROLEUM AND GAS*

551 USA ISSN 0891-2556
QE471 CODEN: CAEVE9
➤ **CARBONATES AND EVAPORITES.** Text in English. 1986. 2/yr. USD 48 domestic to individuals; USD 63 foreign to individuals; USD 68 domestic to institutions; USD 88 foreign to institutions (effective 2005). adv. bk.rev. charts; illus.; maps. index. back issues avail. **Document type:** *Journal, Academic/Scholarly.* **Description:** Professional reports on all aspects of carbonates and evaporites.
Indexed: AESIS, ASCA, CIN, ChemAb, ChemTitl, CurCont, GEOBASE, GP&P, ISR, OffTech, PetrolAb, RefZh, SCI.
—BLDSC (3050.996800), CASDDS, IDS, IE, Infotrieve, ingenta, Linda Hall, PADDS. **CCC.**
Published by: Northeastern Science Foundation, Inc., PO Box 746, Troy, NY 12181-0746. TEL 518-273-3247, FAX 518-273-3249, gmfriedman@juno.com. Ed. Gerald M Friedman.

551 JAM
CODEN: JGSJBN
➤ **CARIBBEAN JOURNAL OF EARTH SCIENCE.** Text in English. 1958. a. (plus special issues), latest vol.36. USD 31 membership (effective 2003). adv. bk.rev. charts; illus. back issues avail. **Document type:** *Journal, Academic/Scholarly.*
Former titles (until 1999): Geological Society of Jamaica. Journal (0435-401X); (until 1965): Geonotes (0376-0642)
Indexed: BiolAb, IMMAb.
Published by: Geological Society of Jamaica, c/o Dept. of Geology, University of the West Indies, Mona Campus, W.I., Kingston, 7, Jamaica. Ed. Dr. Simon F Mitchell. Circ: 500.

551 FRA ISSN 1634-0744
➤ **CARNETS DE GEOLOGIE/NOTEBOOKS ON GEOLOGY;** notebooks on geology. Text mainly in English, French; Text occasionally in German, Italian, Spanish. 2001 (Oct.). irreg. free (effective 2005). back issues avail. **Document type:** *Journal, Academic/Scholarly.* **Description:** An open-access geoscience journal published electronically, which concentrates on stratigraphy, sedimentology and paleontology.
Media: Online - full content. **Related titles:** CD-ROM ed.: Carnets de Geologie (Cederom). ISSN 1765-2553.
Address: Department des Sciences de la Terre, Universite de Bretagne Occidentale, 6 avenue Le Gorgeu, Brest Cedex 3, 29238, France. TEL 33-298016289, carnetsdegeologie@hotmail.com, http://paleopolis.rediris.es/cg/.Ed., R&P, Adv. contact Dr. Bruno R C Granier.

558 CHL ISSN 0717-7283
CARTA GEOLOGICA DE CHILE. SERIE GEOLOGICA BASICA. Text in Spanish; Summaries in English. 1959. irreg. USD 35 (effective 2003). bk.rev. abstr.; bibl.; charts; illus.; maps. **Document type:** *Monographic series, Government.*
Formerly (until 2001): Carta Geologica de Chile (0716-0194)
Indexed: ABIPC, EngInd, IMMAb.
Published by: Servicio Nacional de Geologia y Mineria, Ave. Santa Maria, 104, Providencia, Santiago, Chile. TEL 56-2-737-5050, FAX 56-2-735-6960, mcortes@sernageomin.cl. Ed. Constantino Mpodozis. Circ: 1,000.

558 CHL ISSN 0717-7267
CARTA GEOLOGICA DE CHILE. SERIE HIDROGEOLOGIA. Text in Spanish; Summaries in English. 1990. irreg. USD 35 (effective 2003). **Document type:** *Government.*
Formerly (until 2001): Carta Hidrogeologica de Chile (0716-7555)
Published by: Servicio Nacional de Geologia y Mineria, Ave. Santa Maria, 104, Providencia, Santiago, Chile. TEL 56-2-737-5050, FAX 56-2-735-6960, mcortes@sernageomin.cl, bigem@reuna.cl. Ed. Constantino Mpodozis. Circ: 1,000.

558 BRA ISSN 0101-1642
CARTA GEOLOGICA DO BRASIL AO MILIONESIMO. Text in Portuguese. 1974. irreg., latest vol.19, 1979. USD 15 (effective 1997). charts. **Document type:** *Bulletin, Government.*
Published by: Departamento Nacional da Producao Mineral, Setor Autarquia Norte, Quadra 1, Bloco B, Brasilia, DF 70040, Brazil. TEL 55-61-224-2670. Ed. Frederico L M Barboza.

551 NLD ISSN 0341-8162
CODEN: CIJPD3
➤ **CATENA.** Text and summaries in English. 1973. 12/yr. EUR 1,276 in Europe to institutions; JPY 169,300 in Japan to institutions; USD 1,428 elsewhere to institutions (effective 2006). abstr. index. back issues avail. **Document type:** *Journal, Academic/Scholarly.* **Description:** Publishes original research contributions in geoecology and landscape evolution.
Related titles: Microform ed.: (from PQC); Online - full text ed.: (from EBSCO Publishing, Gale Group, IngentaConnect, ScienceDirect, Swets Information Services); ♦ Supplement(s): Advances in Geoecology.
Indexed: AEA, AESIS, ASCA, ASFA, AgrForAb, AnBrAb, BIOBASE, BIOSIS Prev, BiolAb, CIN, ChemAb, ChemTitl, CivEngAb, CurCont, ESPM, FCA, FPA, ForAb, GEOBASE, HerbAb, HortAb, I&DA, IABS, IBR, ISR, M&GPA, M&TEA, PBA, PGegResA, RefZh, RevApplEntom, S&F, SCI, SIA, SWRA, SeedAb, TriticAb, VITIS, WAE&RSA.
—BLDSC (3092.590000), CASDDS, CISTI, IDS, IE, Infotrieve, ingenta, Linda Hall. **CCC.**
Published by: Elsevier BV (Subsidiary of: Elsevier Science & Technology), Radarweg 29, Amsterdam, 1043 NX, Netherlands. TEL 31-20-4853911, FAX 31-20-4852457, nlinfo-f@elsevier.nl, http://www.elsevier.com/locate/catena, http://www.elsevier.nl. Eds. H. A. Viles, J. Poesen, K. Auerswald. Circ: 1,000.

551.44 GBR ISSN 1356-191X
➤ **CAVE AND KARST SCIENCE.** Text in English. 1974. 3/yr. GBP 16 domestic; GBP 18 foreign (effective 2001). adv. index. **Document type:** *Academic/Scholarly.* **Description:** Covers all aspects of science, technology and exploration associated with caves and limestones.
Former titles (until 1994): Cave Science (0263-760X); (until 1982): British Cave Research Association. Transactions (0305-859X); Which was formed by the 1974 merger of: British Speleological Association. Journal (0008-8617); Cave Research Group of Great Britain. Transactions (0069-1305); Which incorporated: British Hypogean Fauna and Biological Records
Indexed: BrArAb, GEOBASE, ZooRec.
—BLDSC (3093.780000), IE, ingenta, Linda Hall. **CCC.**
Published by: British Cave Research Association, The Old Methodist Chapel, Great Hucklow, Buxton, Derbys SK17 8RG, United Kingdom. enquiries@bcra.org.uk, http://www.bcra.org.uk/. Eds. D J Lowe, J Gunn. Circ: 1,400.

551.447 USA ISSN 0749-8969
CODEN: CAGEDZ
CAVE GEOLOGY. Text in English. 1976. irreg., latest vol.2, no.5, 2002. price varies. bk.rev. back issues avail. **Document type:** *Academic/Scholarly.* **Description:** Covers geology with emphasis on caves and karst systems.
Published by: National Speleological Society, Section of Cave Geology and Geography, c/o Elisabeth L. White, Miller Rd. RR1, PO Box 527, Petersburg, PA 16669-9211. TEL 814-667-2709, wbw2@psu.edu, http://www.caves.org/section/geogeo/. Eds. Elizabeth L White, William B White. R&P Elizabeth L White. Circ: 200.

CAVES AND CAVERNS; national caves association directory. see *TRAVEL AND TOURISM*

551.44 GBR ISSN 0142-1832
CAVES & CAVING. Text in English. 1973. q. GBP 10 domestic; GBP 13 foreign (effective 2001). adv. bk.rev. **Document type:** *Bulletin.*
Supersedes: British Speleological Association. Bulletin (0045-3153); And: Cave Research Group of Great Britain Newsletter
—BLDSC (3094.019000). **CCC.**
Published by: British Cave Research Association, The Old Methodist Chapel, Great Hucklow, Buxton, Derbys SK17 8RG, United Kingdom. enquiries@bcra.org.uk, http://www.bcra.org.uk/. Ed. H St Lawrence. Adv. contact Wendy Barr TEL 44-1524-841010. Circ: 1,500.

556 FRA ISSN 0769-0541
CENTRE INTERNATIONAL POUR LA FORMATION ET LES ECHANGES GEOLOGIQUES. PUBLICATION OCCASIONNELLE/INTERNATIONAL CENTER FOR TRAINING AND EXCHANGES IN THE GEOSCIENCES. OCCASIONAL PUBLICATION. Text and summaries in English, French. 1983. irreg., latest vol.37, 2001. price varies. **Document type:** *Monographic series.* **Description:** Scientific papers on geosciences, mainly extended abstracts of conferences on African geology.
Indexed: IMMAb.
Published by: Centre International pour la Formation et les Echanges Geologiques/International Center for Training and Exchanges in the Geosciences, 3 avenue Claude Guillemin, BP 6517, Orleans, Cedex 2 45065, France. TEL 33-2-38643367, FAX 33-2-38643472, m.laval@brgm.fr. Ed. Michel Laval. R&P Sylvie Orlyk. Circ: 200.

796.525 GBR ISSN 0045-6381
CHELSEA SPELAEOLOGICAL SOCIETY. NEWSLETTER. Text in English. 1959. m. GBP 10 (effective 2001). charts. index. back issues avail.; reprints avail. **Document type:** *Newsletter.*
Media: Duplicated (not offset).
Published by: Chelsea Spelaeological Society, The Chelsea Centre, World's End Estate, King's Rd, Chelsea, London, SW10 0DR, United Kingdom. TEL 44-1749-670568, newsletter@chelseaspelaeo.org.uk, secretary@chelseaspelaeo.org.uk, http://www.chelseaspelaeo.org.uk. Ed., R&P John Cooper. Circ: 150.

796.525 GBR ISSN 0309-409X
CHELSEA SPELAEOLOGICAL SOCIETY. RECORDS. Text in English. irreg. back issues avail.; reprints avail. **Document type:** *Directory.*
Media: Duplicated (not offset).
Published by: Chelsea Spelaeological Society, The Chelsea Centre, World's End Estate, King's Rd, Chelsea, London, SW10 0DR, United Kingdom. TEL 44-20-7265-0514, secretary@chelseaspelaeo.org.uk, http://www.chelseaspelaeo.org.uk. R&P Harry Pearman. Circ: 250.

550 DEU ISSN 0009-2819
QE1 CODEN: CERDAA
➤ **CHEMIE DER ERDE / GEOCHEMISTRY/GEOCHEMISTRY.** Text in English. 1914. 4/yr. EUR 100 in Europe to individuals; JPY 12,500 in Japan to individuals; USD 99 to individuals except Europe and Japan; EUR 286 to institutions; EUR 338 in Europe to institutions; JPY 44,900 in Japan to institutions; USD 372 to institutions except Europe and Japan (effective 2006). adv. bk.rev. bibl.; charts; illus. index, cum.index: vols.1-45. back issues avail.; reprint service avail. from ISI. **Document type:** *Journal, Academic/Scholarly.* **Description:** Covers broad interdisciplinary discussions on chemical problems in the geosciences, geoecology, and environmental sciences.
Related titles: Online - full text ed.: (from EBSCO Publishing, Gale Group, IngentaConnect, O C L C Online Computer Library Center, Inc., ScienceDirect, Swets Information Services).
Indexed: ASCA, ASFA, CIN, ChemAb, ChemTitl, CurCont, ESPM, ExcerpMed, ForAb, GEOBASE, MinerAb, RefZh, S&F, SWRA.
—BLDSC (3156.000000), CASDDS, CISTI, IDS, IE, Infotrieve, ingenta, Linda Hall. **CCC.**
Published by: Elsevier GmbH, Urban & Fischer Verlag (Subsidiary of: Elsevier Science & Technology), Loebdergraben 14a, Jena, 07743, Germany. TEL 49-3641-626462, FAX 49-3641-626417, marketing.journals@urbanfischer.de, http://www.elsevier.com/locate/chemerd, http://www.urbanfischer.de/journals. Ed. Klaus Heide TEL 49-3641-948700. R&P Frances Rothwell. Adv. contact Cora Grotzke. B&W page EUR 320, color page EUR 1,265; trim 165 x 240. Circ: 350 (paid and controlled).
Subscr. to: Nature Publishing Group, Brunel Rd, Houndmills, Basingstoke, Hamps RG21 6XS, United Kingdom. TEL 44-1256-302629, FAX 44-1256-476117, subscriptions@nature.com.

➤ **CHENGSHI FANGZHEN JIANZAI/CITY EARTHQUAKE REDUCTION AND DISASTERS PREVENTION.** see *ENGINEERING—Civil Engineering*

551.3 CHN ISSN 1000-0550
QE571 CODEN: CHXUEE
➤ **CHENJI XUEBAO/ACTA SEDIMENTOLOGICA SINICA.** Text in Chinese; Summaries in English. 1983. q. CNY 60 (effective 2004). adv. **Document type:** *Journal, Academic/Scholarly.*
Related titles: Online - full content ed.: (from WanFang Data Corp.); Online - full text ed.: (from East View Information Services).
Indexed: ASFA, ESPM, RefZh, ZooRec.
—BLDSC (0663.259000), CASDDS, IE, ingenta.
Published by: (Zhongguo Kexueyuan, Lanzhou Dizhi Yanjiusuo), Kexue Chubanshe/Science Press, 16 Donghuang Cheng Genbei Jie, Beijing, 100717, China. TEL 86-10-64000246, FAX 86-10-64030255, cjxb@ns.lzb.ac.cn, http://cjxb.periodicals.net.cn/default.html, http://www.sciencep.com/. Ed. Xi Lian Jun. Circ: 4,000. **Dist. by:** China International Book Trading Corp, 35 Chegongzhuang Xilu, Haidian District, PO Box 399, Beijing 100044, China. TEL 86-10-68412045, FAX 86-10-68412023, cibtc@mail.cibtc.com.cn, http://www.cibtc.com.cn.

550 JPN
CHIBAKEN KOGAI KENKYUJO CHIKA SHIGEN JIBAN SAIGAI KENKYU SHIRYO/RESEARCH REPORT OF GEOLOGICAL SURVEY AND LANDSUBSIDENCE IN CHIBA PREFECTURE. Text in Japanese. a. stat. **Document type:** *Academic/Scholarly.*
Published by: Chibaken Kogai Kenkyujo/Chiba Prefectural Research Institute for Environmental Pollution, 8-8 Iwasaki-Nishi 1-chome, Ichihara-shi, Chiba-ken 290-0046, Japan.

551 JPN ISSN 0912-5760
CHIDANKEN SENPO✶ /ASSOCIATION FOR GEOLOGICAL COLLABORATION IN JAPAN. BULLETIN. Text in Japanese; Summaries in English. 1972. irreg. **Document type:** *Bulletin.*
Published by: Chigaku Dantai Kenkyukai/Association for the Geological Collaboration in Japan, Rm 507 Kawai Building, 1-24-1,Minami Ikebukuro, Toshima-ku, Tokyo, 171, Japan.

551 JPN ISSN 0388-5208
CHIGAKU DANTAI KENKYUKAI SOKUHO✶ /ASSOCIATION FOR THE GEOLOGICAL COLLABORATION IN JAPAN. NEWS. Text in Japanese. m.

E

—CCC.
Published by: Chigaku Dantai Kenkyukai/Association for the Geological Collaboration in Japan, Rm 507 Kawai Building, 1-24-1,Minami Ikebukuro, Toshima-ku, Tokyo, 171, Japan.

---

551   JPN   ISSN 0366-5933
CODEN: CGKUA6
CHIGAKU KENKYU/GEOSCIENCE MAGAZINE. Text in Japanese. 1946. q. JPY 1,500 per issue.
Indexed: CIN, ChemAb, ChemTitl, INIS AtomInd, JPI, MinerAb.
—CASDDS.
Published by: Nippon Chigaku Kenkyukai, Karasuma Demizu Nishi Iru, Kamigyo-ku, Kyoto-shi, 602, Japan.

---

550 624   JPN
CHIKA KUKAN RIYO SHINPOJUMU/SYMPOSIUM ON UTILITY OF UNDERGROUND SPACE. Text in Japanese; Summaries in English. 1988. a. JPY 5,000.
Published by: Doboku Gakkai/Japan Society of Civil Engineers, Mu-banchi, Yotsuya 1-chome, Shinjuku-ku, Tokyo, 160-0004, Japan.

---

551   JPN   ISSN 0389-1755
➤ **CHIKEI/JAPANESE GEOMORPHOLOGICAL UNION. TRANSACTIONS.** Text in English, Japanese; Abstracts in English. 1980. q. JPY 3,000 per issue membership (effective 2005). bk.rev. **Document type:** *Journal, Academic/Scholarly.* **Description:** Contains academic articles on pure and applied geomorphology as well as announcements, proceedings, and other news useful for geomorphologists.
Indexed: GEOBASE.
—CCC.
Published by: Japanese Geomorphological Union, c/o Kyoto University, Disaster Prevention Research Institute, Division of Geo-Disaster, Gokasho, Uji, Kyoto 611-0011, Japan. TEL 81-774-384097, FAX 81-774-384105, jgu@slope.dpri.kyoto-u.ac.jp, http://wwwsoc.nii.ac.jp/jgu/, http://wwwsoc.nacsis.ac.jp/jgu/. Ed. Yukinori Matsukura. Circ: 777. **Subscr. to:** Maruzen Co., Ltd., Export Dept., PO Box 5050, Tokyo International 100-3191, Japan. FAX 81-3-3278-9256, journal@maruzen.co.jp, http://www.maruzen.co.jp.

---

550   CHL   ISSN 0020-3939
QE237   CODEN: BIGCA3
CHILE. SERVICIO NACIONAL DE GEOLOGIA Y MINERIA. BOLETIN. Text in Spanish; Summaries in English. 1958. irreg. USD 30 (effective 2003). bk.rev. bibl.; charts; illus.; maps. **Document type:** *Bulletin, Trade.*
Indexed: IMMAb, ZooRec.
—BLDSC (2188.475000), CASDDS.
Published by: Servicio Nacional de Geologia y Mineria, Ave. Santa Maria, 104, Providencia, Santiago, Chile. TEL 56-2-737-5050, FAX 56-2-735-6960, mcortes@sernageomin.cl. Ed. Constantino Mpodozis. Circ: 1,000.

---

551   CHL   ISSN 0717-277X
CHILE. SERVICIO NACIONAL DE GEOLOGIA Y MINERIA. DOCUMENTOS DE TRABAJO. Text in Spanish. 1991. irreg. USD 25. bk.rev. bibl.; illus.; maps. **Document type:** *Monographic series, Government.*
Related titles: CD-ROM ed.
Published by: Servicio Nacional de Geologia y Mineria, Ave. Santa Maria, 104, Providencia, Santiago, Chile. TEL 56-2-737-5050, FAX 56-2-735-6960, mcortes@sernageomin.cl. Ed. Constantino Mpodozis. Circ: 1,000.

---

558 622   CHL   ISSN 0717-3407
CHILE. SERVICIO NACIONAL DE GEOLOGIA Y MINERIA. MISCELANEA. Text in Spanish. 1982. irreg. price varies. bk.rev. bibl.; charts; illus. **Document type:** *Monographic series, Government.*
Published by: Servicio Nacional de Geologia y Mineria, Ave. Santa Maria, 104, Providencia, Santiago, Chile. TEL 56-2-737-5050, FAX 56-2-735-6960, mcortes@sernageomin.cl. Ed. Constantino Mpodozis. Circ: 300.

---

555   CHN   ISSN 1002-0063
GB316
➤ **CHINESE GEOGRAPHICAL SCIENCE/ZHONGGUO DILI KEXUE.** Text in English. 1991. q. CNY 100, USD 36.40 (effective 2003). 96 p./no.; **Document type:** *Journal, Academic/Scholarly.*
Related titles: Online - full text ed.: (from East View Information Services, WanFang Data Corp.); ♦ Chinese ed.: Dili Kexue. ISSN 1000-0690.
Indexed: GEOBASE, RefZh.
—BLDSC (3180.278900), IE, Infotrieve, ingenta.
Published by: Kexue Chubanshe/Science Press, 16 Donghuang Cheng Genbei Jie, Beijing, 100717, China. TEL 86-10-64000246, FAX 86-10-64030255, egeoscien@mail.neigae.ac.cn, http://zgdl.e.periodicals.net.cn/default.html, http://www.sciencep.com/. Ed. Huang Xichou.
Dist. by: China International Book Trading Corp, 35 Chegongzhuang Xilu, Haidian District, PO Box 399, Beijing 100044, China. TEL 86-10-68412045, FAX 86-10-68412023, cibtc@mail.cibtc.com.cn, http://www.cibtc.com.cn.

551.9 552   CHN   ISSN 1000-9426
CODEN: CJGEEV
➤ **CHINESE JOURNAL OF GEOCHEMISTRY.** Text in English. 1982. q. USD 1,000 in the Americas to institutions; EUR 800 elsewhere to institutions (effective 2006). adv. back issues avail.; reprint service avail. from PSC. **Document type:** *Academic/Scholarly.* **Description:** Includes research on petrology, mineralogy and economic geology, as well as isotopic geology, cosmochemistry, and quaternary geology.
Formerly: Geochemistry (0253-486X)
Related titles: Online - full text ed.: (from East View Information Services, EBSCO Publishing); ♦ Chinese ed.: Diqiu Huaxue. ISSN 0379-1726.
Indexed: ASFA, CIN, ChemAb, ChemTitl, E&PHSE, ESPM, EngInd, GEOBASE, GP&P, IAA, IMMAb, MinerAb, OffTech, PetrolAb, RefZh.
—BLDSC (3180.335000), CASDDS, CISTI, Ei, IE, Infotrieve, ingenta, Linda Hall, PADDS.
Published by: Kexue Chubanshe/Science Press, 16 Donghuang Cheng Genbei Jie, Beijing, 100717, China. TEL 86-10-64000246, FAX 86-10-64030255, http://www.brill.nl/m_catalogue_sub6_id9717.htm. Ed. Tu Guangzhi. Circ: 6,000.
Dist. outside China by: V S P, Brill Academic Publishers, PO Box 9000, Leiden 2300 PA, Netherlands. TEL 31-30-6925790, FAX 31-30-6932081, http://www.vsppub.com.

---

555   JPN   ISSN 0016-7665
GC821
CHISHITSU CHOSAJO GEPPO/GEOLOGICAL SURVEY OF JAPAN. BULLETIN. Text in English, Japanese. 1950. m. charts; illus. index, cum.index every 5 yrs. **Document type:** *Bulletin, Government.*
Indexed: BiolAb, ChemAb, EngInd, IMMAb, JPI, MinerAb, PetrolAb, RefZh, ZooRec.
—BLDSC (2533.000000), CASDDS, IE, ingenta, Linda Hall, PADDS.
Published by: Kogyo Gijutsuin, Chishitsu Chosajo/National Institute of Advanced Industrial Science & Technology, Geological Survey of Japan, AIST Tsukuba Central 7, 1-1, Higashi 1-Chome, Tsukuba, Ibaraki 305-0046, Japan. TEL 81-29-8619122, FAX 81-29-8613672, http://www.aist.go.jp, http://www.gsj.jp/. Ed. Kisaburo Kodama. Circ: 1,650.

---

551   JPN   ISSN 0366-5542
CODEN: CCHHAQ
CHISHITSU CHOSAJO HOKOKU/GEOLOGICAL SURVEY OF JAPAN. REPORT. Text in English, Japanese; Summaries in English, Japanese. 1907. irreg.
Indexed: AESIS, BiolAb, IMMAb, JPI, RefZh.
—BLDSC (7484.910000), Linda Hall.
Published by: Kogyo Gijutsuin, Chishitsu Chosajo/National Institute of Advanced Industrial Science & Technology, Geological Survey of Japan, AIST Tsukuba Central 7, 1-1, Higashi 1-Chome, Tsukuba, Ibaraki 305-0046, Japan. TEL 81-29-8619122, FAX 81-29-8613672, http://www.aist.go.jp, http://www.gsj.jp/.

---

551   JPN
CHISHITSU CHOSAJO NENPO/GEOLOGICAL SURVEY OF JAPAN. ANNUAL REPORT. Text in Japanese. 1882. a.
Published by: Kogyo Gijutsuin, Chishitsu Chosajo/National Institute of Advanced Industrial Science & Technology, Geological Survey of Japan, AIST Tsukuba Central 7, 1-1, Higashi 1-Chome, Tsukuba, Ibaraki 305-0046, Japan. TEL 81-29-8619122, FAX 81-29-8613672, http://www.aist.go.jp, http://www.gsj.jp/.

---

555   JPN   ISSN 0009-4854
QE1   CODEN: CHNYB7
CHISHITSU NYUSU/GEOLOGY NEWS. Text in Japanese. 1953. m. JPY 785 per issue. bk.rev. back issues avail. **Document type:** *Bulletin.* **Description:** Contains information designed to propagate the knowledge on geoscience to general Japanese people, as well as teachers, students, consulting geologists and engineers.
Indexed: A&ATA, CIN, ChemAb, ChemTitl, MSB, RefZh.
—CASDDS, CISTI.
Published by: (Japan. Geological Survey of Japan), Jitsugyo Kohosha Co., 1-7-8 Kudan-Kita, Chiyoda-ku, Tokyo, 102-0073, Japan. TEL 81-3-3265-0951, FAX 31-3-3265-0952, gsjnews@gsj.go.jp. Ed. Masafumi Arita. Circ: 4,000.

---

552 551.3   JPN   ISSN 0385-8545
QE304   CODEN: CSGRBS
CHISHITSUGAKU RONSHU/GEOLOGICAL SOCIETY OF JAPAN. MEMOIRS. Text in Japanese. 1968. irreg. JPY 5,000. back issues avail. **Description:** Original papers on geoscientific topics.
Indexed: JPI.
—BLDSC (5606.090000), CASDDS, CISTI, Linda Hall. CCC.
Published by: Nihon Chishitsu Gakkai/Geological Society of Japan, 10-4 Kaji-cho 1-chome, Chiyoda-ku, Tokyo, 101-0044, Japan. Circ: 1,500.

---

555   JPN   ISSN 0016-7630
QE1   CODEN: CHTZA5
CHISHITSUGAKU ZASSHI/GEOLOGICAL SOCIETY OF JAPAN. JOURNAL. Text in English, Japanese. 1893. m. JPY 12,000. adv. bk.rev. index. **Description:** Original papers on earth sciences.
Related titles: Online - full text ed.: ISSN 1349-9963 (from J-Stage).

Indexed: ASFA, BiolAb, ChemAb, ESPM, INIS AtomInd, JPI, MinerAb, ZooRec.
—BLDSC (4757.000000), CISTI, IE, ingenta, Linda Hall.
Published by: Nihon Chishitsu Gakkai/Geological Society of Japan, 10-4 Kaji-cho 1-chome, Chiyoda-ku, Tokyo, 101-0044, Japan. Ed. Yasumoto Suzuki. Circ: 5,500.

796.525   ITA   ISSN 0009-7268
CODEN: CSPNAQ
CIRCOLO SPELEOLOGICO ROMANO. NOTIZIARIO. Text in Italian; Summaries in English, Italian. 1947. a. USD 12. adv. bk.rev. bibl.; charts; illus. **Document type:** *Bulletin.* **Description:** Covers speleology, subterranean hydrology, geology, speleogenesis, and biospeleology.
Indexed: ApMecR, MathR.
Published by: Circolo Speleologico Romano, Via Ulisse Aldrovandi, 18, Rome, RM 00197, Italy. TEL 39-6-3216223. Ed., Pub. Circollo Speleollogico Romana. R&P, Adv. contact Giorgio Marzolla. Circ: 1,000.

---

550   DEU   ISSN 0069-4584
CODEN: CLTHBE
CLAUSTHALER TEKTONISCHE HEFTE. Text in German. 1959. irreg., latest vol.29, 1997. price varies. **Document type:** *Monographic series, Academic/Scholarly.*
—Linda Hall.
Published by: Springer-Verlag (Subsidiary of: Springer Science+Business Media), Haber Str 7, Heidelberg, 69126, Germany. TEL 49-6221-3450, FAX 49-6221-229, orders@springer.de, http://www.springer.de.

---

557   USA   ISSN 1046-0136
COASTAL GEOLOGY TECHNICAL REPORT. Text in English. 1985. irreg., latest vol.9, 1995. price varies. **Document type:** *Government.*
—Linda Hall.
Published by: Louisiana Geological Survey, 208 Howe-Russell, Louisiana State University, Baton Rouge, LA 70803. TEL 225-578-5320, FAX 225-578-3662, pat@lgs.bri.lsu.edu, http://www.lgs.lsu.edu.

---

550   NLD   ISSN 1384-6434
COASTAL SYSTEMS AND CONTINENTAL MARGINS. Text in English. 1995. irreg., latest vol.8, 2005. price varies. **Document type:** *Monographic series, Academic/Scholarly.*
—BLDSC (3292.421500), IE, ingenta.
Published by: Springer-Verlag Dordrecht (Subsidiary of: Springer Science+Business Media), Van Godewijckstraat 30, Dordrecht, 3311 GX, Netherlands. TEL 31-78-6576050, FAX 31-78-6576474, http://www.springeronline.com. Ed. Bilal U Haq.

---

557   USA   ISSN 0375-6157
QE91   CODEN: CGBLB3
COLORADO GEOLOGICAL SURVEY. BULLETIN. Text in English. 1910. irreg.
—Linda Hall.
Published by: Colorado Geological Survey, 1313 Sherman St., Rm 715, Denver, CO 80203. TEL 303-866-2611, FAX 303-866-2461, cgspubs@state.co.us, http://geosurvey.state.co.us.

---

557   USA   ISSN 0271-0285
COLORADO GEOLOGICAL SURVEY. INFORMATION SERIES. Text in English. 1976. irreg. **Document type:** *Government.*
—Linda Hall.
Published by: Colorado Geological Survey, 1313 Sherman St., Rm 715, Denver, CO 80203.

---

557   USA   ISSN 0099-6459
COLORADO GEOLOGICAL SURVEY. SPECIAL PUBLICATION. Text in English. irreg. price varies.
—Linda Hall.
Published by: Colorado Geological Survey, 1313 Sherman St., Rm 715, Denver, CO 80203. TEL 303-866-2611, FAX 303-866-2461, cgspubs@state.co.us, http://geosurvey.state.co.us.

---

551   FRA   ISSN 0074-9427
COMMISSION FOR THE GEOLOGICAL MAP OF THE WORLD. BULLETIN. Text in English, French. 1962. a. adv. bk.rev. illus. **Document type:** *Bulletin.* **Description:** Details CGMW's activities in the preceding year.
Published by: Commission for the Geological Map of the World (CGMW), Maison de la Geologie, 77 rue Claude Bernard, Paris, 75005, France. TEL 33-1-47072284, FAX 33-1-43369518, TELEX 206 411 F. Ed. P Bouysse. R&P Philippe Bouysse. Circ: 300.

526.9 622   JPN
COMMITTEE FOR COORDINATION OF JOINT PROSPECTING FOR MINERAL RESOURCES IN ASIAN OFFSHORE AREAS. TECHNICAL BULLETIN. Text in English. 1968. irreg., latest vol.26, 1997. **Document type:** *Bulletin.*
Indexed: AESIS, IMMAb.

E

Published by: Kogyo Gijutsuin, Chishitsu Chosajo/National Institute of Advanced Industrial Science & Technology, Geological Survey of Japan, AIST Tsukuba Central 7, 1-1, Higashi 1-Chome, Tsukuba, Ibaraki 305-0046, Japan. TEL 81-29-8619122, FAX 81-29-8613672, http://www.aist.go.jp, http://www.gsj.jp/. Eds. Hideo Takeda, Kisaburo Kodama, Masakatsu Sasada. Adv. contact Masakatsu Sasada. Circ: 1,550. **Co-sponsor:** Committee for Coordination of Joint Prospecting for Mineral Resources in Asian Offshore Areas (CCOP).

551 NLD ISSN 0169-6548
COMMUNICATIONS ON HYDRAULIC AND GEOTECHNICAL ENGINEERING. Text in English. 1986. triennial. **Document type:** *Academic/Scholarly.*
Indexed: FLUIDEX, GEOBASE.
—BLDSC (7414.552700).
Published by: Technische Universiteit Delft/Delft University of Technology, PO Box 5, Delft, 2600 AA, Netherlands. TEL 31-15-2785860, FAX 31-15-2781855. Ed. Philip Broos.

COMPUTATIONAL GEOSCIENCES; modeling, simulation and data analysis. see *EARTH SCIENCES—Computer Applications*

551 USA ISSN 1059-8618
CONCEPTS IN SEDIMENTOLOGY AND PALEONTOLOGY. Text in English. 1987. irreg.
Indexed: ZooRec.
—BLDSC (3399.413900), Linda Hall. **CCC.**
Published by: Society of Economic Paleontologists and Mineralogists, PO Box 4756, Tulsa, OK 74159-0756.

551.44 CHE ISSN 0069-8911
CONGRES NATIONAL DE SPELEOLOGIE. ACTES∗. Text in French, German. 1963. irreg. price varies.
Published by: Societe Suisse de Speleologie, Bibliotheque Centrale, Chemin des Invuex, Granges (Veveyse), 1614, Switzerland. Ed. J C Lalou.

551 ARG ISSN 0325-2620
CONGRESO GEOLOGICO ARGENTINO. ACTAS. Text in Spanish. 1960. triennial. USD 100 (effective 2005).
Formerly (until 1972): Actas de las Jornadas Geologicas Argentinas (0449-1653)
—CCC.
Published by: Asociacion Geologica Argentina, CP 1900, La Plata, Argentina. congreso@congresogeologico.org.ar, http://www.congresogeologico.org.ar.

550 500 USA
CONNECTICUT GEOLOGIC AND NATURAL HISTORY BULLETINS. Text in English. irreg., latest vol.9, 2001. illus.
Published by: (Connecticut. Natural Resources Center, Department of Environmental Protection), Environmental and Geographic Information Center, 79 Elm St., Hartford, CT 06106. TEL 860-424-3540, allan.williams@po.state.ct.us, http://dep.state.ct.us. R&P Allan Williams.

551 USA ISSN 1049-5231
CONTRIBUTION TO PRECAMBRIAN GEOLOGY. Text in English. 1969. irreg. price varies. bibl.; charts; illus. **Document type:** *Government.*
Indexed: IMMAb.
Published by: Missouri Department of Natural Resources, Division of Geology and Land Survey, PO Box 250, Rolla, MO 65401. TEL 573-368-2125. Ed. Dwight Weaver. Circ: 1,500.

CONTRIBUTIONS IN BIOLOGY AND GEOLOGY. see *BIOLOGY*

551 IND ISSN 0970-5325
CODEN: CMRPD3
CONTRIBUTIONS TO HIMALAYAN GEOLOGY. Text in English. 1979. irreg., latest vol.4, no.4, 1989. price varies. back issues avail. **Document type:** *Monographic series.*
Published by: Hindustan Publishing Corporation (India), 4805-24, Bharat Ram Rd., 1st Fl., Flats 1 & 2, Darya Ganj, New Delhi, 110 002, India. TEL 91-11-325-4401, FAX 91-11-6193511, hpcpd@hpc.cc, http://www.hpc.cc, http://www.bizdelhi.com/publisher/hpc. Ed. V J Gupta.

552 549 DEU ISSN 0010-7999
CODEN: CMPEAP
➤ **CONTRIBUTIONS TO MINERALOGY AND PETROLOGY.** Text in English. 1947. m. EUR 3,298 combined subscription to institutions print & online eds. (effective 2005). adv. bibl.; charts; illus. index. reprint service avail. from ISI. **Document type:** *Journal, Academic/Scholarly.* **Description:** Original articles presenting essentially new scientific findings on geochemistry. Includes isotope geology; the petrology and genesis of igneous, metamorphic, and sedimentary rocks; experimental petrology and mineralogy; and distribution and significance of elements and their isotopes in the rocks.
Related titles: Microform ed.: (from PQC); Online - full text ed.: ISSN 1432-0967 (from EBSCO Publishing, Springer LINK, Swets Information Services).
Indexed: AESIS, ASCA, ASFA, BrGeoL, CCI, CIN, ChemAb, ChemTitl, CurCont, EPB, ESPM, GEOBASE, IBR, ISR, MSCI, MinerAb, PetrolAb, RefZh, SCI, SPPI.
—BLDSC (3461.020000), CASDDS, CISTI, IDS, IE, Infotrieve, ingenta, Linda Hall, PADDS. **CCC.**
Published by: Springer-Verlag (Subsidiary of: Springer Science+Business Media), Tiergartenstr 17, Heidelberg, 69121, Germany. TEL 49-6221-3450, FAX 49-6221-345229, http://link.springer.de/link/service/journals/00410/index.htm. Adv. contact Stephan Kroeck TEL 49-30-827875739. **Subscr. in the Americas to:** Springer-Verlag New York, Inc., Journal Fulfillment, PO Box 2485, Secaucus, NJ 07096-2485. TEL 800-777-4643, 201-348-4033, FAX 201-348-4505, journals@springer-ny.com, http://www.springer-ny.com; **Subscr. to:** Springer GmbH Auslieferungsgesellschaft, Haberstr 7, Heidelberg 69126, Germany. TEL 49-6221-345-0, FAX 49-6221-345-4229, subscriptions@springer.de.

551.3 DEU ISSN 1436-3542
QE471 CODEN: CBSDAS
CONTRIBUTIONS TO SEDIMENTARY GEOLOGY. Text in English, German. 1973. irreg., latest vol.22, 2002. price varies. **Document type:** *Monographic series, Academic/Scholarly.*
Formerly (until 1997): Contributions to Sedimentology (0343-4125)
Indexed: ASFA, ESPM, GEOBASE, OceAb, PetrolAb, PollutAb.
—Linda Hall. **CCC.**
Published by: E. Schweizerbart'sche Verlagsbuchhandlung, Johannesstr 3A, Stuttgart, 70176, Germany. TEL 49-711-3514560, FAX 49-711-35145699, mail@schweizerbart.de, http://www.schweizerbart.de.

550 ESP ISSN 0214-4328
CORPUS GEOLOGICUM GALLAECIAE. Text in Spanish. N.S. 1981. irreg. price varies. **Document type:** *Monographic series.*
Published by: Fundacion Pedro Barrie de la Maza, Canton Grande, 9, La Coruna, 15003, Spain. TEL 981223830, FAX 981225105.

551 ZAF ISSN 1680-0370
QE325 CODEN: RAMBAE
COUNCIL FOR GEOSCIENCE OF SOUTH AFRICA. BULLETIN. Text in English. 1934. irreg., latest vol.136, 2003. price varies. **Document type:** *Bulletin, Government.* **Description:** Presents the results of geological investigations of localized scope.
Former titles (until 1999): South Africa. Department of Mineral and Energy Affairs. Geological Survey. Bulletin (1015-8049); (until 1957): Republiek van Suid-Afrika. Geologiese Opname. Bulletin (0370-3371)
Indexed: AESIS, GEOBASE, IMMAb, ZooRec.
—CISTI.
Published by: Council for Geoscience, Private Bag X112, Pretoria, 0001, South Africa. TEL 27-12-841-1911, FAX 27-12-841-1203, TELEX 350286-SAGEO, rprice@geoscience.org.za, http://www.geoscience.org.za/publications/index.htm. R&P R R M Price TEL 27-12-8411018.

551 ESP ISSN 0214-1744
CUATERNARIO Y GEOMORFOLOGIA. Text in Spanish, English. 1987. s-a.
Related titles: Online - full text ed.
Indexed: IECT.
—CINDOC.
Published by: Geoforma Ediciones, Apdo. de Correos 1293, Logrono, 26080, Spain. geoforma@arrakis.es, http://www.geoforma.net/. Ed. Pablo Silva Barroso.

551 USA ISSN 1076-4674
QH541.5.M3
CURRENT TOPICS IN WETLAND BIOGEOCHEMISTRY. Text in English. 1994. a. USD 25 to individuals; USD 35 to libraries (effective 2002).
Indexed: ASFA, ESPM, SWRA.
Published by: Louisiana State University, Wetland Biogeochemistry Institute, Baton Rouge, LA 70803-7511. TEL 225-578-8810, cowgro@lsu.edu, http://www.wetlandbiogeochemistry.lsu.edu/. Ed. K. R. Reddy.

550 549 CZE ISSN 1210-8197
QE351 CODEN: JCZSEQ
➤ **CZECH GEOLOGICAL SOCIETY. JOURNAL/CESKA GEOLOGICKA SPOLECNOST. CASOPIS.** Text in English; Text occasionally in Czech, French, German. 1956. s-a. adv. bk.rev. charts; illus. index. **Document type:** *Academic/Scholarly.* **Description:** Covers all fields of geology, mineralogy, paleontology and applied geophysics.
Formerly (until 1993): Casopis pro Mineralogii a Geologii (0008-7378)
Indexed: CIN, ChemAb, ChemTitl, E&PHSE, GEOBASE, GP&P, MinerAb, OffTech, PetrolAb, ZooRec.
—CASDDS, CISTI, Linda Hall, PADDS.
Published by: Akademie Ved Ceske Republiky, Geologicky Ustav/Academy of Sciences of Czech Republic, Geological Institute, Klarov 3, Prague, 11821, Czech Republic. TEL 42-2-24002523, FAX 42-2-24510, http://www.natur.cuni.cz/~cgs/jcgs.htm, http://www.lib.cas.cz/knav/journals/eng/Journal_of_Czech_Geological_Society. Ed. Stanislav Vrana. Circ: 900. **Dist. in Western countries by:** Kubon & Sagner Buchexport - Import GmbH, Postfach 24, Munich 34 8000, Germany.

551 CZE ISSN 1210-8960
CZECH GEOLOGICAL SURVEY. SPECIAL PAPERS. Text in English. 1993. irreg.
Indexed: GEOBASE, ZooRec.
Published by: Ceska Geologicka Sluzba/Czech Geological Survey, Klarov 3, Prague, 11821, Czech Republic. TEL 42-02-24002658, FAX 42-02-57320438, http://www.geology.cz.

551 CHN ISSN 1001-1552
QE601 CODEN: DGYXEW
➤ **DADI GOUZAO YU CHENGKUANGXUE.** Text in Chinese. 1977. q. CNY 40 (effective 2004). adv. **Document type:** *Journal, Academic/Scholarly.* **Description:** Covers the structure of the earth and the formation of mineral deposits.
Related titles: Online - full content ed.: (from WanFang Data Corp.); Online - full text ed.: (from East View Information Services); English ed.: Geotectonica et Metallogenia. ISSN 1006-513X. 1990.
Indexed: CIN, ChemAb, ChemTitl.
—CASDDS.
Published by: Zhongguo Kexueyuan, Guangzhou Diqiu Huaxue Yanjiusuo/Chinese Academy of Sciences, Guangzhou Institute of Geochemistry, PO Box 1131, Guangzhou, 510640, China. ddgz@gig.ac.cn; ddgz02@163.com; geotec@gig.ac.cn, http://ddgzyckx.periodicals.net.cn/default.html, http://www.gig.ac.cn/. Circ: 5,500. **Dist. by:** China International Book Trading Corp, 35 Chegongzhuang Xilu, Haidian District, PO Box 399, Beijing 100044, China. TEL 86-10-68412045, FAX 86-10-68412023, cibtc@mail.cibtc.com.cn, http://www.cibtc.com.cn.

560 JPN ISSN 0418-2642
QE696
DAIYONKI KENKYU/QUATERNARY RESEARCH. Text in Japanese; Summaries in English. 1957. bi-m. free to members. bk.rev. Index. back issues avail. **Document type:** *Journal, Academic/Scholarly.*
Indexed: AESIS, BIOSIS Prev, BiolAb, CIN, ChemAb, ChemTitl, ZooRec.
—CCC.
Published by: Nihon Daiyonki Gakkai/Japan Association for Quaternary Research, Rakuyo Bldg. 3F, 519 Waseda Tsurumaki-cho, Shinjuku-ku, Tokyo, 162-0041, Japan. TEL 86-3-52916231, FAX 86-3-52912176, daiyonki@shunkosha.com, http://wwwsoc.nii.ac.jp/qr/QR2home.htm. Circ: 1,900.

557 USA ISSN 0070-3273
QE95 CODEN: DGSBAY
DELAWARE GEOLOGICAL SURVEY. BULLETIN. Text in English. 1953. irreg., latest vol.20, 1996. **Document type:** *Bulletin, Academic/Scholarly.*
Indexed: ANAG.
—Linda Hall.
Published by: Delaware Geological Survey, University of Delaware, Newark, DE 19716. TEL 302-831-2833, FAX 302-831-3579, delgeosurvey@udel.edu, http://www.udel.edu/dgs/dgs.htm/. Ed. Richard Benson.

551 USA ISSN 0895-0717
QE95.5
DELAWARE GEOLOGICAL SURVEY. INFORMATION SERIES. Text in English. 1986. irreg., latest vol.7, 1992. **Document type:** *Academic/Scholarly.*
Published by: Delaware Geological Survey, University of Delaware, Newark, DE 19716. TEL 302-831-2833, FAX 302-831-3579, delgeosurvey@udel.edu, http://www.udel.edu/dgs/dgs.htm/. Ed. Richard N Benson.

557 USA ISSN 0011-7749
QE95 CODEN: DGRIAG
DELAWARE GEOLOGICAL SURVEY. REPORTS OF INVESTIGATIONS. Text in English. 1957. irreg., latest vol.58, 1999. **Document type:** *Academic/Scholarly.*
Indexed: ANAG, ChemAb, RefZh.
—Linda Hall.
Published by: Delaware Geological Survey, University of Delaware, Newark, DE 19716. TEL 302-831-2833, FAX 302-831-3579, delgeosurvey@udel.edu, http://www.udel.edu/dgs/dgs.htm/. Ed. Richard Benson.

557 USA ISSN 8755-1969
DELAWARE GEOLOGICAL SURVEY. SPECIAL PUBLICATION. Text in English. irreg. **Document type:** *Monographic series, Government.*
—Linda Hall.
Published by: Delaware Geological Survey, University of Delaware, Newark, DE 19716. TEL 302-831-2833, FAX 302-831-3579, delgeosurvey@udel.edu, http://www.udel.edu/dgs/dgs.htm/.

551 DEU ISSN 0375-6262
DEUTSCHE GEOLOGISCHE GESELLSCHAFT. NACHRICHTEN. Text in German. 1969. a. back issues avail.; reprint service avail. from IRC. **Document type:** *Journal, Academic/Scholarly.*
Published by: Deutsche Gesellschaft fuer Geowissenschaften, Stilleweg 2, Hannover, 30655, Germany. webmaster@dgg.de, http://www.dgg.de. Circ: 3,300.

551 DEU ISSN 1860-1804
CODEN: ZDGGA6
DEUTSCHE GESELLSCHAFT FUER GEOWISSENSCHAFTEN. ZEITSCHRIFT. Text and summaries in English, French, German. q. EUR 178 domestic; EUR 192.70 foreign (effective 2005). index. reprint service avail. from IRC. **Document type:** *Journal, Academic/Scholarly.* **Description:** Scientific publication covering historical and regional geology, stratigraphy, petrography, deposits, and hydrogeology, mainly in central Europe.
Formerly (until 2004): Deutsche Geologische Gesellschaft. Zeitschrift (0012-0189)
Related titles: Online - full text ed.: (from EBSCO Publishing, Gale Group, IngentaConnect).
Indexed: GeotechAb, IMMAb, PetrolAb, RefZh.
—BLDSC (9442.000000), CASDDS, CISTI, IE, ingenta, Linda Hall, PADDS. **CCC.**
Published by: (Deutsche Gesellschaft fuer Geowissenschaften), E. Schweizerbart'sche Verlagsbuchhandlung, Johannesstr 3A, Stuttgart, 70176, Germany. TEL 49-711-3514560, FAX 49-711-35145699, mail@schweizerbart.de, http://www.schweizerbart.de/pubs/books/es/zeitschrif-171015601-desc.html. Ed. H Vossmerbaeumer.

550 NLD ISSN 0928-2025
➤ **DEVELOPMENTS IN EARTH SURFACE PROCESSES.** Text in English. 1990. irreg., latest vol.6, 1998. price varies. back issues avail. **Document type:** *Monographic series, Academic/Scholarly.* **Description:** Discusses new geological research in earth-surface processes.
—BLDSC (3579.070850).
Published by: Elsevier BV (Subsidiary of: Elsevier Science & Technology), Radarweg 29, Amsterdam, 1043 NX, Netherlands. TEL 31-20-4853911, FAX 31-20-4852457, nlinfo-f@elsevier.nl, http://www.elsevier.nl.

551 NLD ISSN 0168-6178
CODEN: DGEOD6
➤ **DEVELOPMENTS IN ECONOMIC GEOLOGY.** Text in English. 1975. irreg., latest vol.30, 1997. price varies. back issues avail. **Document type:** *Monographic series, Academic/Scholarly.* **Description:** Discusses geologic developments from an economics perspective.
Indexed: IMMAb, Inspec.
—BLDSC (3579.071000), CASDDS. **CCC.**
Published by: Elsevier BV (Subsidiary of: Elsevier Science & Technology), Radarweg 29, Amsterdam, 1043 NX, Netherlands. TEL 31-20-4853911, FAX 31-20-4852457, nlinfo-f@elsevier.nl, http://www.elsevier.nl.

551.8 NLD ISSN 0419-0254
CODEN: DEVGAG
➤ **DEVELOPMENTS IN GEOTECTONICS.** Text in Dutch. 1965. irreg., latest vol.24, 1999. price varies. back issues avail. **Document type:** *Monographic series, Academic/Scholarly.* **Description:** Reports on developments in the field of geotectonics.
Indexed: Inspec.
—BLDSC (3579.074000), CISTI. **CCC.**
Published by: Elsevier BV (Subsidiary of: Elsevier Science & Technology), Radarweg 29, Amsterdam, 1043 NX, Netherlands. TEL 31-20-4853911, FAX 31-20-4852457, nlinfo-f@elsevier.nl, http://www.elsevier.nl.

549 NLD ISSN 0167-4528
CODEN: DMPRDA
➤ **DEVELOPMENTS IN MINERAL PROCESSING.** Text in Dutch. 1977. irreg., latest vol.14, 2001. price varies. back issues avail. **Document type:** *Monographic series, Academic/Scholarly.* **Description:** Examines issues and developments in all areas of mineral processing.
Indexed: CIN, ChemAb, ChemTitl, IMMAb.
—BLDSC (3579.085300), CASDDS, CISTI. **CCC.**
Published by: Elsevier BV (Subsidiary of: Elsevier Science & Technology), Radarweg 29, Amsterdam, 1043 NX, Netherlands. TEL 31-20-4853911, FAX 31-20-4852457, nlinfo-f@elsevier.nl, http://www.elsevier.nl.

552 NLD ISSN 0167-2894
CODEN: DEPEDH
➤ **DEVELOPMENTS IN PETROLOGY.** Text in English. 1971. irreg., latest vol.15, 1996. price varies. back issues avail. **Document type:** *Monographic series, Academic/Scholarly.* **Description:** Disseminates research and other developments in the field of petrology.
Indexed: CIN, ChemAb, ChemTitl.
—BLDSC (3579.086000), CASDDS.
Published by: Elsevier BV (Subsidiary of: Elsevier Science & Technology), Radarweg 29, Amsterdam, 1043 NX, Netherlands. TEL 31-20-4853911, FAX 31-20-4852457, nlinfo-f@elsevier.nl, http://www.elsevier.nl.

551 NLD ISSN 0166-2635
CODEN: DPGEDF
DEVELOPMENTS IN PRECAMBRIAN GEOLOGY. Text in English. 1978. irreg., latest vol.11, 1994. price varies. back issues avail. **Document type:** *Monographic series, Academic/Scholarly.* **Description:** Disseminates paleontological research in the geology of the Precambrian era.
Indexed: ChemAb, IMMAb.
—BLDSC (3579.087400), CASDDS.
Published by: Elsevier BV (Subsidiary of: Elsevier Science & Technology), Radarweg 29, Amsterdam, 1043 NX, Netherlands. TEL 31-20-4853911, FAX 31-20-4852457, nlinfo-f@elsevier.nl, http://www.elsevier.nl.

551.3 NLD ISSN 0070-4571
CODEN: DVSDA9
➤ **DEVELOPMENTS IN SEDIMENTOLOGY.** Text in English. 1964. irreg., latest vol.55, 2001. price varies. back issues avail. **Document type:** *Monographic series, Academic/Scholarly.* **Description:** Publishes research in the earth sciences field of sedimentology.
Indexed: CIN, ChemAb, ChemTitl, IMMAb, Inspec.
—BLDSC (3579.087900), CASDDS, CISTI, IE, ingenta. **CCC.**
Published by: Elsevier BV (Subsidiary of: Elsevier Science & Technology), Radarweg 29, Amsterdam, 1043 NX, Netherlands. TEL 31-20-4853911, FAX 31-20-4852457, nlinfo-f@elsevier.nl, http://www.elsevier.nl.

550 NLD
➤ **DEVELOPMENTS IN STRUCTURAL GEOLOGY.** Text in Dutch. 1988. irreg., latest vol.1, 1988. price varies. **Document type:** *Monographic series, Academic/Scholarly.* **Description:** Reports on new research in the subfield of structural geology.
Published by: Elsevier BV (Subsidiary of: Elsevier Science & Technology), Radarweg 29, Amsterdam, 1043 NX, Netherlands. TEL 31-20-4853911, FAX 31-20-4852457, nlinfo-f@elsevier.nl, http://www.elsevier.nl.

551 CHN ISSN 0253-4959
QE640 CODEN: DICZEA
➤ **DICENGXUE ZAZHI/JOURNAL OF STRATIGRAPHY.** Text in Chinese. 1966. q. CNY 48 (effective 2004). adv. **Document type:** *Journal, Academic/Scholarly.* **Description:** Contains treatises and articles on biostratigraphy, petrostratigraphy, chronostratigraphy, tectonic stratigraphy, paleogeography, paleoclimatology, and paleomagnetism. Introduces and discusses new techniques, methods, and achievements in stratigraphic research.
Formerly: Acta Stratigraphica Sinica
Related titles: Online - full content ed.: (from WanFang Data Corp.); Online - full text ed.: (from East View Information Services).
Indexed: IMMAb, ZooRec.
—BLDSC (5066.873500), CISTI, Linda Hall.
Published by: (Zhongguo Kexueyuan, Nanjing Dizhi Gushengwu Yanjiusuo/Chinese Academy of Sciences, Nanjing Institute of Geology and Palaeontology), Kexue Chubanshe/Science Press, 16 Donghuang Cheng Genbei Jie, Beijing, 100717, China. TEL 86-1-64034205, FAX 86-1-64010642, http://www.nigpas.ac.cn/pub/Jour-str.htm, http://www.sciencep.com/. Circ: 7,000. **Dist. by:** China International Book Trading Corp, 35 Chegongzhuang Xilu, Haidian District, PO Box 399, Beijing 100044, China. TEL 86-10-68412045, FAX 86-10-68412023, cibtc@mail.cibtc.com.cn, http://www.cibtc.com.cn.

551 CHN ISSN 1001-8107
DILIXUE YU GUOTU YANJIU. Text in Chinese. q.
Related titles: Online - full text ed.: (from East View Information Services).
Published by: Hebei Sheng Kexueyuan, Dili Yanjiusuo/Hebei Provincial Academy of Sciences, Institute of Geology, 24 Fanxi Lu, Shijiazhuang, Hebei 050011, China. TEL 49375. Ed. Si Youyuan.

555 540 CHN ISSN 0379-1726
QE514 CODEN: TCHHCB
➤ **DIQIU HUAXUE/GEOCHEMICA.** Text in Chinese; Summaries in English. 1973. q. CNY 192, USD 69.60 (effective 2003). adv. bk.rev. **Document type:** *Journal, Academic/Scholarly.* **Description:** Covers research on isotopic geology, cosmochemistry, organic, structural, environmental and experimental geochemistry, quaternary geology, petrology, and applied geochemistry.
Related titles: Online - full content ed.: (from WanFang Data Corp.); Online - full text ed.: (from East View Information Services); ♦ English ed.: Chinese Journal of Geochemistry. ISSN 1000-9426.
Indexed: CIN, ChemAb, ChemTitl, IAA, IMMAb, ISR, MSB.
—BLDSC (4116.990000), CASDDS, CISTI, Linda Hall.
Published by: (Zhongguo Kexueyuan, Guangzhou Diqiu Huaxue Yanjiusuo/Chinese Academy of Sciences, Guangzhou Institute of Geochemistry), Kexue Chubanshe/Science Press, 16 Donghuang Cheng Genbei Jie, Beijing, 100717, China. TEL 86-10-64000246, FAX 86-10-64030255, dqhx@gig.ac.cn; dqhx@163.net; geochem@sti.gd.cn, http://dqhx.periodicals.net.cn/default.html, http://www.sciencep.com/. Circ: 11,000. **Dist. by:** China International Book Trading Corp, 35 Chegongzhuang Xilu, Haidian District, PO Box 399, Beijing 100044, China. TEL 86-10-68412045, FAX 86-10-68412023, cibtc@mail.cibtc.com.cn, http://www.cibtc.com.cn.

550 CHN ISSN 1006-3021
QE294 CODEN: DIXUFX
DIQIU XUEBAO/ACTA GEOSCIENTIA SINICA. Text in Chinese. 1979. q. CNY 10 domestic (effective 2000).
Formerly (until 1994): Zhongguo Dizhi Kexueyuan Yuanbao - Chinese Academy of Geological Sciences. Bulletin (0254-3176)
Related titles: Online - full content ed.: (from WanFang Data Corp.); Online - full text ed.: (from East View Information Services).
Indexed: C&ISA, CIN, ChemAb, ChemTitl, E&CAJ, IAA, IMMAb, RefZh, ZooRec.
—BLDSC (0622.508000), CASDDS, CISTI, IE, ingenta.
Published by: Zhongguo Dizhi Kexueyuan, Fuchengmen Wai, Baiwan-Zhuang, Beijing, 100037, China. **Dist. overseas by:** China International Book Trading Corp, 35 Chegongzhuang Xilu, Haidian District, PO Box 399, Beijing 100044, China.

551 IRL
DIRECTORY OF GEOSERVICES IN IRELAND. Text in English. 1996. a. EUR 13 per issue (effective 2005). **Document type:** *Directory, Government.* **Description:** Includes information on 119 organizations and individuals in Ireland providing geological or geo-related services.
Published by: Geological Survey of Ireland/Suirbheireacht Gheolaiochta Eireann, Beggars Bush, Haddington Rd, Dublin, 4, Ireland. TEL 353-1-6782868, FAX 353-1-6681782, gsisales@gsi.ie, http://www.gsi.ie/. Ed. Kate Claringbold.

557.1128 AUS ISSN 1328-2409
DISCOVERY; Victoria's earth resources journal. Text in English. 1997. q. free. **Document type:** *Government.*
Indexed: AESIS.
Published by: Minerals and Petroleum Victoria, PO Box 500, East Melbourne, VIC 3002, Australia. TEL 61-3-9637-8532, FAX 61-3-9637-8118.

551 CHN ISSN 1001-7410
QE696
➤ **DISIJI YANJIU/QUATERNARY SCIENCES.** Text in Chinese; Summaries in English. 1958. bi-m. CNY 120 (effective 2004). adv. **Document type:** *Journal, Academic/Scholarly.*
Related titles: Online - full content ed.: (from WanFang Data Corp.); Online - full text ed.: (from East View Information Services).
—BLDSC (7210.221500).
Published by: (China Quaternaria Research Committee), Kexue Chubanshe/Science Press, 16 Donghuang Cheng Genbei Jie, Beijing, 100717, China. TEL 86-10-64000246, FAX 86-10-64030255, dsjb009@sohu.com, http://dsjyj.periodicals.net.cn/default.html, http://www.sciencep.com/. Ed. Dong-Sheng Liu. Circ: 4,000. **Dist. by:** China International Book Trading Corp, 35 Chegongzhuang Xilu, Haidian District, PO Box 399, Beijing 100044, China. TEL 86-10-68412045, FAX 86-10-68412023, cibtc@mail.cibtc.com.cn, http://www.cibtc.com.cn.

➤ **DIZHEN DIZHI/SEISMOLOGY AND GEOLOGY.** see *EARTH SCIENCES—Geophysics*

➤ **DIZHEN WENZHAI/SEISMOLOGICAL ABSTRACTS.** see *EARTH SCIENCES—Abstracting, Bibliographies, Statistics*

551.22 CHN ISSN 1000-0666
DIZHEN YANJIU/JOURNAL OF SEISMOLOGICAL RESEARCH. Text in Chinese. 1979. q. **Document type:** *Academic/Scholarly.*
Related titles: Online - full content ed.: (from WanFang Data Corp.); Online - full text ed.: (from East View Information Services).
—Linda Hall.
Published by: Yunnan-Sheng Dizhenju, 43 ZhiChun Jie, Kunming, Yunnan 650041, China. seisr@netease.con. Ed. Feng-Tong Yan. **Dist. by:** China International Book Trading Corp, 35 Chegongzhuang Xilu, Haidian District, PO Box 399, Beijing 100044, China. TEL 86-10-68412045, FAX 86-10-68412023, cibtc@mail.cibtc.com.cn, http://www.cibtc.com.cn.

551.9 CHN ISSN 1008-0244
DIZHI DIQIU HUAXUE/GEOLOGY - GEOCHEMISTRY. Text in Chinese. 1973. q. **Document type:** *Academic/Scholarly.*
Related titles: Online - full content ed.: (from WanFang Data Corp.); Online - full text ed.: (from East View Information Services).
Published by: Zhongguo Kexueyuan, Diqiu Huaxue Yanjiusuo, 73 Guanshui Lu, Guiyan, 550002, China. Ed. Yang Zi Yuan Ou.

551 CHN ISSN 1003-2932
DIZHI KEJI DONGTAI/GEOLOGY SCIENCE AND TECHNOLOGY DEVELOPMENT. Text in Chinese. 1977. s-m.
Published by: Zhongguo Dizhi Kuangchan Xinxi Yanjiuyuan/Chinese Institute of Geology and Mineral Products Information, 277 Fuchengmenwai Beijie, Beijing, 100037, China. TEL 892243. Ed. Qin Guoxing.

DIZHI KEJI GUANLI/SCIENTIFIC AND TECHNOLOGICAL MANAGEMENT IN GEOLOGICAL EXPLORATION. see *BUSINESS AND ECONOMICS—Management*

551.22 CHN ISSN 1000-7849
QE1 CODEN: DKQIFA
DIZHI KEJI QINGBAO/GEOLOGICAL SCIENCE AND TECHNOLOGY INFORMATION. Text in Chinese. 1982. q. CNY 10 domestic (effective 2000). **Document type:** *Journal, Academic/Scholarly.*
Related titles: Online - full content ed.: (from WanFang Data Corp.); Online - full text ed.: (from East View Information Services).

Indexed: Englnd, MSB, RefZh.
Published by: Zhongguo Dizhi Daxue/China University of Geosciences, Editorial Department of Geological Science & Technology Information, Wuhan, Hubei 430074, China. TEL 86-27-87436860, kjqb@cug.edu.cn, http://dzkjqb.wanfangdata.com.cn/default.html. Ed. Shu-Zhen Yao.

551 CHN ISSN 0563-5020
QE1 CODEN: TCKHAO
➤ **DIZHI KEXUE/SCIENTIA GEOLOGICA SINICA.** Text in Chinese; Summaries in English. 1958. q. CNY 120 (effective 2004). adv. **Document type:** *Journal, Academic/Scholarly.*
Description: Contains representative theses on geology, reports of achievements, and comments.
Related titles: Online - full text ed.: (from East View Information Services); ♦ English ed.: Scientia Geologica Sinica. ISSN 1004-3543.
Indexed: BiolAb, C&ISA, CIN, ChemAb, ChemTitl, E&CAJ, GEOBASE, IAA, ZooRec.
—CASDDS, CISTI, Linda Hall.
Published by: Kexue Chubanshe/Science Press, 16 Donghuang Cheng Genbei Jie, Beijing, 100717, China. TEL 86-10-64000246, FAX 86-10-64030255, dzkx@mail.igcas.ac.cn, http://dzkx.periodicals.net.cn/default.html, http://www.sciencep.com/. Circ: 12,000. **Dist. by:** China International Book Trading Corp, 35 Chegongzhuang Xilu, Haidian District, PO Box 399, Beijing 100044, China. TEL 86-10-68412045, FAX 86-10-68412023, cibtc@mail.cibtc.com.cn, http://www.cibtc.com.cn.

551 CHN ISSN 0371-5736
QE294 CODEN: TCLPAJ
DIZHI LUN-PING/GEOLOGICAL REVIEW. Text in Chinese. 1936. bi-m. CNY 50 per issue (effective 2004). **Document type:** *Journal, Academic/Scholarly.*
Related titles: Online - full text ed.: (from WanFang Data Corp.).
Indexed: C&ISA, E&CAJ, IAA, RefZh, ZooRec.
—CISTI, Linda Hall.
Published by: Zhongguo Dizhi Xuehui/Geological Society of China, Fuchengmen Wai, 26, Baimozhuang Lu, Beijing, 100037, China. TEL 86-10-68312410, geoview@public.bta.net.cn, http://dzlp.periodicals.net.cn/default.html, http://www.geosociety.org.cn/. **Dist. by:** China International Book Trading Corp, 35 Chegongzhuang Xilu, Haidian District, PO Box 399, Beijing 100044, China. TEL 86-10-68412045, FAX 86-10-68412023, cibtc@mail.cibtc.com.cn, http://www.cibtc.com.cn.

550 CHN ISSN 0001-5717
QE1 CODEN: TCHPAX
➤ **DIZHI XUEBAO/ACTA GEOLOGICA SINICA.** Text in Chinese; Summaries in English. 1922. q. CNY 200 (effective 2004). adv. charts; illus.; maps. **Document type:** *Journal, Academic/Scholarly.* **Description:** Contains theses relating to stratigraphy, geological history, paleontology, rocks and minerals, geochemistry, structural geology, ore-deposit geology, hydrogeology, engineering geology, regional geology, and other multidisciplinary topics.
Formerly (until 1952): Zhongguo Dizhi Xuehui Zhi
Related titles: Online - full content ed.: (from WanFang Data Corp.); ♦ English ed.: Acta Geologica Sinica. ISSN 1000-9515.
Indexed: BIOSIS Prev, BiolAb, CIN, ChemAb, ChemTitl, CurCont, GEOBASE, IAA, ISR, PetrolAb, SCI, ZooRec.
—BLDSC (0621.500000), CASDDS, CISTI, IE, ingenta, Linda Hall, PADDS.
Published by: (Zhongguo Dizhi Xuehui/Geological Society of China), Kexue Chubanshe/Science Press, 16 Donghuang Cheng Genbei Jie, Beijing, 100717, China. TEL 86-10-64000246, FAX 86-10-64030255, geoacta@public.fhnet.cn.net, http://dizhixb.periodicals.net.cn/default.html. Ed. Yu-qu Cheng. Circ: 12,000. **Dist. by:** China International Book Trading Corp, 35 Chegongzhuang Xilu, Haidian District, PO Box 399, Beijing 100044, China. TEL 86-10-68412045, FAX 86-10-68412023, cibtc@mail.cibtc.com.cn, http://www.cibtc.com.cn.

E

551 CHN ISSN 0495-5331
DIZHI YU KANTAN/GEOLOGY AND PROSPECTING. Text in Chinese. 1957. bi-m. CNY 5 domestic (effective 2000). **Document type:** *Academic/Scholarly.*
Related titles: Online - full content ed.: (from WanFang Data Corp.); Online - full text ed.: (from East View Information Services).
Indexed: IMMAb, RefZh.
Published by: Guojia Yejin Gongyeju, Dizhi Kancha Zhongju, Anchenli 2-qu 11 Lou 1 Ceng, Beijing, 100029, China. TEL 86-1-64435074, FAX 86-1-64435075.

DIZHI ZAIHAI YU HUANJING BAOHU/GEOLOGICAL HAZARDS AND ENVIRONMENT PRESERVATION. see *ENVIRONMENTAL STUDIES*

551 CHN ISSN 1001-1412
CODEN: DJLUEN
DIZHI ZHAOKUANG LUNCONG/CONTRIBUTIONS TO GEOLOGY AND MINEREL RESOURCES RESEARCH. Text in Chinese; Summaries in English. 1986. q. CNY 5 domestic (effective 2000). **Document type:** *Academic/Scholarly.*
Description: Covers geology and mineral resource researches.
Related titles: Online - full content ed.: (from WanFang Data Corp.); Online - full text ed.: (from East View Information Services).
Indexed: CIN, ChemAb, ChemTitl, RefZh.
—CASDDS.
Published by: Tianjin Dizhi Yanjiusuo/Tianjin Geological Academy, 42 Youyi Lu, Hexi-qu, Tianjin 300061, China. TEL 86-22-2836-7243, FAX 86-22-2835-7460. Ed. Yu Heyong.

DOJIN/ASSOCIATION OF JAPANESE CAVERS. JOURNAL. see *PALEONTOLOGY*

550 665.5 GBR
E A G E SPECIAL PUBLICATION. Text in English. irreg., latest vol.5, 1996. **Document type:** *Monographic series.*
Formerly (until 1995): European Association of Petroleum Geoscientists. Special Publication
Published by: (European Association of Geoscientists and Engineers), Geological Society Publishing House, Unit 7, Brassmill Enterprise Centre, Brassmill Ln, Bath, Avon BA1 3JN, United Kingdom. TEL 44-1225-445046, FAX 44-1225-442836, dawn.angel@geolsoc.org.uk, http://www.geolsoc.org.uk, http://www.bookshop.geolsoc.org.uk. **Dist. in US by:** A A P G Bookstore, PO Box 979, Tulsa, OK 74101-0979. TEL 918-584-2555, 918-560-2652.

E A N H S BULLETIN. see *BIOLOGY*

E A R SE L EPROCEEDINGS. see *EARTH SCIENCES*

551 GBR
THE EARTH IN OUR HANDS; how geoscientists serve and protect the public. Text in English. irreg. free.
Published by: Geological Society of London, Burlington House, Piccadilly, London, W1J 0BG, United Kingdom. TEL 44-20-7434-9944, FAX 44-20-7439-8975, enquiries@geolsoc.org.uk, http://www.geolsoc.org.uk.

EARTH SCIENCE COMPUTER APPLICATIONS. see *EARTH SCIENCES—Computer Applications*

551.3 GBR ISSN 0197-9337
GB400 CODEN: ESPLDB
➤ **EARTH SURFACE PROCESSES AND LANDFORMS.** Text in English. 1976. 14/yr. USD 2,965 to institutions; USD 3,262 combined subscription to institutions print & online eds. (effective 2006). adv. illus. Index. back issues avail.; reprint service avail. from PSC,PQC,ISI. **Document type:** *Journal, Academic/Scholarly.* **Description:** Contains important research papers on all aspects of geomorphology interpreted in its widest sense, including both pure and applied.
Formerly (until Jan. 1981): Earth Surface Processes (0360-1269)
Related titles: Microform ed.: (from PQC); Online - full content ed.: ISSN 1096-9837. USD 2,965 to institutions (effective 2006); Online - full text ed.: (from EBSCO Publishing, Swets Information Services, Wiley InterScience).
Indexed: AEA, AESIS, ASCA, ASFA, AgrForAb, BrGeoL, CIN, CTO, ChemAb, ChemTitl, CivEngAb, CurCont, EPB, ESPM, Englnd, FCA, FLUIDEX, FPA, ForAb, GEOBASE, GeotechAb, HerbAb, HortAb, I&DA, ICEA, ISR, Inspec, M&GPA, M&TEA, MaizeAb, NemAb, OrnHort, PBA, PollutAb, RA&MP, RDA, S&F, SCI, SFA, SWRA, TriticAb, WAE&RSA, WeedAb, WildRev.
—BLDSC (3643.564030), AskIEEE, CASDDS, CISTI, Ei, IDS, IE, Infotrieve, ingenta, Linda Hall. **CCC.**
Published by: (British Geomorphological Research Group), John Wiley & Sons Ltd. (Subsidiary of: John Wiley & Sons, Inc.), The Atrium, Southern Gate, Chichester, West Sussex PO19 8SQ, United Kingdom. TEL 44-1243-779777, FAX 44-1243-775878, customer@wiley.co.uk, http://www3.interscience.wiley.com/cgi-bin/jhome/2388, http://www.wiley.co.uk. Ed. Michael J Kirkby. adv.: B&W page GBP 650, color page GBP 1,550; trim 200 x 260. Circ: 1,050. **Subscr. in the Americas to:** John Wiley & Sons, Inc., 111 River St, Hoboken, NJ 07030-5774. TEL 201-748-6645, 800-225-5945, subinfo@wiley.com.

550.34 TWN ISSN 1562-7969
EARTHQUAKE ENGINEERING AND ENGINEERING SEISMOLOGY. Text in English. 1999. s-a. back issues avail. **Document type:** *Journal, Academic/Scholarly.*
Related titles: Online - full content ed.
Indexed: EEA.
Published by: Chinese Taiwan Society for Earthquake Engineering, National Center for Research on Earthquake Engineering, 200 Section 3, Hsin-Hai Road, Taipei, 106, Taiwan. TEL 886-2-3782466 ext 504, http://www.ctsee.org.tw/publication.html, http://www.ctsee.org.tw/main.html.

554 CHE ISSN 0012-9402
QE1 CODEN: EGHVAG
➤ **ECLOGAE GEOLOGICAE HELVETIAE.** Text in English, French, German, Italian. 1888. 3/yr. EUR 728 to institutions (effective 2005). charts; illus. index, cum.index. back issues avail. **Document type:** *Journal, Academic/Scholarly.*
Related titles: Online - full text ed.: ISSN 1420-9128 (from Springer LINK).
Indexed: AESIS, ASCA, BIOSIS Prev, BiolAb, ChemAb, CurCont, DIP, E&PHSE, GEOBASE, GP&P, IBR, ISR, OffTech, PetrolAb, SCI, ZooRec.
—BLDSC (3648.000000), CASDDS, CISTI, IDS, IE, Infotrieve, ingenta, Linda Hall, PADDS. **CCC.**
Published by: (Schweizerische Geologische Gesellschaft), Birkhaeuser Verlag AG (Subsidiary of: Springer Science+Business Media), Viaduktstr 42, Postfach 133, Basel, 4051, Switzerland. TEL 41-61-2050707, FAX 41-61-2050799, eclogae@birkhauser.ch, info@birkhauser.ch, http://www.birkhauser.ch/journals/1500/1500_tit.htm. Ed. Jurgen Remane TEL 41-32-718-2826. **Dist. in N. America by:** Springer-Verlag New York, Inc., Journal Fulfillment, PO Box 2485, Secaucus, NJ 07096-2485. TEL 800-777-4643, 201-348-4033, FAX 201-348-4505, journals@birkhauser.com; **Subscr. in the Americas to:** Springer GmbH Auslieferungsgesellschaft, Haberstr 7, Heidelberg 69126, Germany. TEL 49-6221-345-0, FAX 49-6221-345-4229, birkhauser@springer.de.

553 USA ISSN 0361-0128
QE1 CODEN: ECGLAL
➤ **ECONOMIC GEOLOGY AND THE BULLETIN OF THE SOCIETY OF ECONOMIC GEOLOGISTS.** Text in English. 1905. irreg. free to members (effective 2005). adv. bk.rev. bibl.; charts; illus.; maps. index. back issues avail.; reprints avail. **Document type:** *Journal, Academic/Scholarly.*
Formerly (until 1930): Economic Geology (0013-0109); Which superseded in part (in 1906): American Geologist (0190-518X)
Related titles: Microfilm ed.: (from PMC, PQC); Online - full text ed.: ISSN 1554-0774 (from EBSCO Publishing, HighWire Press).
Indexed: AESIS, AS&TI, ASCA, ASFA, BrGeoL, CIN, ChemAb, ChemTitl, CivEngAb, CurCont, DIP, EIA, ESPM, EnerInd, Englnd, F&EA, GEOBASE, GSW, IBR, IBZ, IMMAb, ISR, PetrolAb, RefZh, SCI, SPPI, SWRA.
—BLDSC (3653.120000), CASDDS, CISTI, Ei, IDS, IE, Infotrieve, ingenta, Linda Hall, PADDS. **CCC.**
Published by: (Society of Economic Geologists), Economic Geology Publishing Co., 7811 Shaffer Pkwy, Littleton, CO 80127. TEL 720-981-7882, FAX 720-981-7874, seg@segweb.org, http://www.segweb.org/journal.htm. Ed. Mark D Hannington. R&P John Thoms. Adv. contact Lisa Laird. Circ: 5,000 (paid).

551 GBR ISSN 0265-7244
EDINBURGH GEOLOGIST. Text in English. 1977. irreg.
—BLDSC (3660.968000).
Published by: Edinburgh Geological Society, c/o Caroline Paterson, Editor, 4 South Sq, Fittie, Aberdeen, AB11 5DT, United Kingdom. http://www.edinburghgeolsoc.org.

551 USA ISSN 0553-5700
QE157
EDUCATIONAL SERIES - PENNSYLVANIA GEOLOGIC SURVEY. Text in English. 1962. irreg. **Document type:** *Monographic series.*
—BLDSC (3662.200000).
Published by: Pennsylvania Department of Conservation and Natural Resources, Bureau of Topographic and Geologic Survey, 3240 Schoolhouse Rd, Middletown, PA 17057. TEL 717-702-2017, FAX 717-702-2065.

550 EGY ISSN 0258-3704
QE328 CODEN: EGJGAF
EGYPTIAN JOURNAL OF GEOLOGY/AL-MAGALLA AL-MISRIYYA LI-ILM AL-GIYULUGIYA. Text in English; Summaries in Arabic, English. 1957. s-a. USD 30. charts; illus. **Document type:** *Journal, Academic/Scholarly.*
Former titles (until 1972): United Arab Republic Journal of Geology (0022-1384); (until 1959): Egyptian Journal of Geology (0367-0430)
Indexed: BiolAb, ChemAb, IBR, IMMAb, ZooRec.
—CISTI, IE, Linda Hall.
Published by: Egyptian Geological Society, Tager Bldg., 1 Osiris St., Garden City, Cairo, Egypt. TEL 20-2-3541857, http://http://derp.sti.sci.eg/data/0277.htm. Ed. A M Husain.

EGYPTIAN MINERALOGIST/AL-MAGALLAT AL-MISRIYYAT LI-'LM AL-MA'ADIN. see *MINES AND MINING INDUSTRY*

551.34 DEU ISSN 0013-2705
EISBERICHT. Text in German. 1903. d. (Mon.-Fri.) (during Winter & Spring). EUR 200 domestic; EUR 240 foreign (effective 2005). charts. **Document type:** *Newsletter, Trade.*
Published by: Bundesamt fuer Seeschiffahrt und Hydrographie, Bernhard-Nocht-Str 78, Hamburg, 20359, Germany. TEL 49-40-31900, FAX 49-40-31905000, posteingang@bsh.de, http://www.bsh.de. Ed. Klaus Struebing.

551 RUS
EKSPRESS-INFORMATSIYA. GEOLOGICHESKOE IZUCHENIE NEDR. Text in Russian. m. USD 125 in United States.
Published by: Informatsionno-Izdatel'skii Tsentr po Geologii i Nedropol'zovaniu Geoinformmark, Goncharnaya 38, Moscow, 115172, Russian Federation. TEL 7-095-9156724. **US dist. addr.:** East View Information Services, 3020 Harbor Ln. N., Minneapolis, MN 55447. TEL 612-550-0961.

551 RUS ISSN 0236-3674
EKSPRESS-INFORMATSIYA. GEOLOGIYA, METODY POISKOV, RAZVEDKI I OTSENKI MESTOROZHDENII TVERDYKH POLEZNYKH ISKOPAEMYKH. Text in Russian. 1990. m. USD 129.95 in United States.
—East View.

Published by: Vserossiiskii Institut Ekonomiki Mineral'nogo Syr'ya i Nedropol'zopvaniya, 3-ya Magistral'naya ul 38, Moscow, 123007, Russian Federation. TEL 7-095-2596988, FAX 7-095-2599125, admin@viems.ru, http://www.viems.ru. **US dist. addr.:** East View Information Services, 3020 Harbor Ln. N., Minneapolis, MN 55447. TEL 612-550-0961.

ELF EXPLORATION PRODUCTION. CENTRES DE RECHERCHES. BULLETIN. see *PETROLEUM AND GAS*

557 USA ISSN 0013-676X
CODEN: ESGGAG

EMPIRE STATE GEOGRAM. Text in English. 1962. a. free. bibl.; charts; illus.; stat. **Document type:** *Government.* **Description:** Reports on current research in geology in New York State and lists geologic publications available from the New York State Museum.
Published by: (North Dakota. North Dakota Geological Survey), New York State Museum, Publication Sales, Rm 3140, Cultural Education Center, Albany, NY 12230. Eds. John B Skiba, William B Rogers. Circ: 1,300.

ENERGY EXPLORATION & EXPLOITATION. see *ENERGY*

ENGINEERING GEOLOGY SPECIAL PUBLICATION. see *ENGINEERING—Civil Engineering*

ENTWICKLUNGSLAENDER-STUDIEN; Bibliographie entwicklungslaenderbezogener Forschungsarbeiten. see *BUSINESS AND ECONOMICS—Abstracting, Bibliographies, Statistics*

551 USA ISSN 1078-7275
TA705 CODEN: EEGEFJ

➤ **ENVIRONMENTAL AND ENGINEERING GEOSCIENCE**; serving professionals in engineering, environmental, and ground-water geology. Text in English. 1963. q. USD 175 to non-members (effective 2005). adv. bk.rev. abstr.; charts; illus. Index. back issues avail.; reprints avail. **Document type:** *Journal, Academic/Scholarly.* **Description:** Publishes selected technical papers in the field of engineering geology.
Former titles (until 1995): Association of Engineering Geologists. Bulletin (0004-5691); (until 1968): Engineering Geology (0094-923X)
Related titles: Online - full text ed.: (from HighWire Press).
Indexed: AESIS, ASFA, BrCerAb, C&ISA, CerAb, ChemAb, CorrAb, CurCont, E&CAJ, EEA, EMA, ESPM, ExcerpMed, F&EA, FLUIDEX, GEOBASE, GSW, GeotechAb, HRIS, IAA, M&TEA, MBF, METADEX, OceAb, SWRA, SolStAb, WAA.
—BLDSC (3791.382000), CASDDS, CISTI, IDS, IE, ingenta, Linda Hall. **CCC.**
Published by: Geological Society of America, 3300 Penrose Pl, Boulder, CO 80301-1806. TEL 303-447-2020, FAX 303-447-1133, http://www.geosociety.org. Ed. Normetan R Tilford. Circ: 3,500. **Co-publisher:** Association of Engineering Geologists.

551 DEU ISSN 0943-0105
QE1 CODEN: ENGOE9

➤ **ENVIRONMENTAL GEOLOGY**; international journal of geosciences. Text in English. 1975. 16/yr. EUR 1,748 combined subscription to institutions print & online eds. (effective 2005). adv. bk.rev. charts; illus. Index. back issues avail.; reprint service avail. from ISI,PSC. **Document type:** *Journal, Academic/Scholarly.* **Description:** Concerned with all aspects of interactions between humans, ecosystems and the earth.
Former titles (until 1993): Environmental Geology and Water Sciences (0177-5146); (until 1984): Environmental Geology (0099-0094)
Related titles: Microform ed.: (from PQC); Online - full text ed.: ISSN 1432-0495 (from EBSCO Publishing, Springer LINK, Swets Information Services).
Indexed: AEA, AESIS, APD, AS&TI, ASCA, ASFA, AbHyg, Agr, AgrForAb, AnBrAb, BIOBASE, BIOSIS Prev, BibAg, BiolAb, CIN, CPA, CTO, ChemAb, ChemTitl, CivEngAb, CurCont, EIA, EPB, ESPM, EnerRev, EngInd, EnvAb, EnvEAb, EnvInd, ExcerpMed, FCA, FLUIDEX, FPA, ForAb, GEOBASE, HRIS, HelmAb, HerbAb, HortAb, I&DA, IABS, ICEA, ISR, M&GPA, M&TEA, MinerAb, OceAb, OrnHort, PBA, PGegResA, PHN&I, PetrolAb, PollutAb, PotatoAb, ProtozoAb, RA&MP, RDA, RRTA, RiceAb, S&F, SCI, SFA, SIA, SSCI, SWRA, TDB, WAE&RSA, WeedAb, WildRev, ZooRec.
—BLDSC (3791.466930), CASDDS, CISTI, Ei, IDS, IE, Infotrieve, ingenta, Linda Hall. **CCC.**
Published by: Springer-Verlag (Subsidiary of: Springer Science+Business Media), Tiergartenstr 17, Heidelberg, 69121, Germany. TEL 49-6221-3450, FAX 49-6221-345229, http://link.springer.de/link/service/journals/00254/index.htm. Ed. Gunter Doerhoefer. Adv. contact Stephan Kroeck TEL 49-30-827875739. **Subscr. in the Americas to:** Springer-Verlag New York, Inc., Journal Fulfillment, PO Box 2485, Secaucus, NJ 07096-2485. TEL 800-777-4643, 201-348-4033, FAX 201-348-4505, journals@springer-ny.com, http://www.springer-ny.com; **Subscr. to:** Springer GmbH Auslieferungsgesellschaft, Haberstr 7, Heidelberg 69126, Germany. TEL 49-6221-345-0, FAX 49-6221-345-4229, subscriptions@springer.de.

551 CHN ISSN 0705-3797
QE1 CODEN: EPSDDF

➤ **EPISODES**; journal of international geoscience. Text in English. 1978. q. USD 24 (effective 2004). adv. bk.rev. illus. Index. 80 p./no.; back issues avail.; reprints avail. **Document type:** *Journal, Academic/Scholarly.* **Description:** Covers developments of regional and global importance in the earth sciences.
Supersedes: International Union of Geological Sciences. Geological Newsletter (0047-1267)
Indexed: AESIS, ChemAb, CurCont, ESPM, ExcerpMed, GEOBASE, IMMAb, ISR, M&GPA, PetrolAb, RefZh, SCI, SWRA.
—BLDSC (3793.838000), CASDDS, CISTI, IDS, IE, Infotrieve, ingenta, Linda Hall, PADDS. **CCC.**
Published by: International Union of Geological Sciences, 26 Baiwanzhuang Road, PO Box 82, Beijing, 100037, China. TEL 80-10-68329084, FAX 86-10-68328928, episodes@public2.bta.net.cn, http://www.episodes.org/. Ed. Hongren Zhang. Circ: 3,000.

550 560 DEU

ERDGESCHICHTE MITTELEUROPAEISCHER REGIONEN. Text in German. 1994. irreg. **Document type:** *Monographic series.*
Published by: Verlag Dr. Friedrich Pfeil, Wolfratshauser Str 27, Munich, 81379, Germany. info@pfeil-verlag.de, http://www.pfeil-verlag.de. Eds. Wighart Koenigswald, Wilhelm Meyer.

554 DEU ISSN 0071-1160
QE1 CODEN: EGABAN

ERLANGER GEOLOGISCHE ABHANDLUNGEN. Text in German. 1952. 2/yr. **Document type:** *Journal, Academic/Scholarly.*
Indexed: RefZh, ZooRec.
—Linda Hall. **CCC.**
Published by: Universitaet Erlangen - Nuernberg, Institut fuer Geologie und Mineralogie, Schlossgarten 5, Erlangen, 91054, Germany. TEL 49-9131-8522615, FAX 49-9131-8522995, geologie@geol.uni-erlangen.de, http://www.geol.uni-erlangen.de. Ed. W Buggisch.

550 DEU ISSN 1430-3469

➤ **ERRATICA**; Monographien zur Geschiebekunde. Text in German. 1996. irreg. (1-2/yr.). price varies. **Document type:** *Monographic series, Academic/Scholarly.*
Address: Wohldtor 12, Wankendorf, 24601, Germany. TEL 49-4326-2205, FAX 49-4326-2205, fossilbuch@t-online.de, http://www.fossilbuch.de. Ed., Pub. Frank Rudolph.

551 EST ISSN 1406-0132
QE1 CODEN: ENTGDF

➤ **ESTONIAN ACADEMY OF SCIENCES. PROCEEDINGS. GEOLOGY/AKADEMIYA NAUK ESTONII. IZVESTIYA. GEOLOGIYA/EESTI TEADUSTE AKADEEMIA TOIMETISED. GEOLOOGIA.** Text in English; Summaries in English, Estonian. 1956. q. EUR 85 foreign (effective 2005). adv. charts; illus.; maps; abstr. 64 p./no.; back issues avail. **Document type:** *Journal, Academic/Scholarly.*
Formerly (until 1990): Akademiya Nauk Estonskoi S.S.R. Izvestiya. Geologiya (0201-8136); Which superseded in part (in 1978): Akademiya Nauk Estonskoi S.S.R. Izvestiya. Khimiya. Geologiya
Related titles: Online - full text ed.: (from EBSCO Publishing).
Indexed: ASFA, ESPM, FLUIDEX, GEOBASE, INIS AtomInd, ZooRec.
—CASDDS, CISTI, KNAW, Linda Hall. **CCC.**
Published by: (Eesti Teaduste Akadeemia), Teaduste Akadeemia Kirjastus/Estonian Academy Publishers, Kohtu 6, Tallinn, 10130, Estonia. TEL 372-6-454504, FAX 372-6-466026, niine@kirj.ee, http://www.kirj.ee. Eds. Anto Raukas, Hillar Aben. Pub. Ylo Niine. R&P Asta Tikerpae TEL 373-6-454504. Adv. contact Asta Tikerpae TEL 373-6-454106.

➤ **ESTUDOS TECNOLOGICOS.** see *SCIENCES: COMPREHENSIVE WORKS*

550 NLD ISSN 1028-3668

EUROPEAN ASSOCIATION OF GEOSCIENTISTS AND ENGINEERS. CONFERENCE AND TECHNICAL EXHIBITION. Text in English. 1995. a.
—BLDSC (3408.947400).
Published by: European Association of Geoscientists and Engineers, PO Box 59, Houten, 3990, Netherlands. TEL 31-30-6354055, FAX 31-30-6343524, eage@eage.nl, http://www.eage.org.

EUROPEAN JOURNAL OF MINERALOGY. see *MINES AND MINING INDUSTRY*

551 622 CAN ISSN 0964-1823
TN260 CODEN: EMGEE6

➤ **EXPLORATION & MINING GEOLOGY**; journal of the Geological Society of C I M. (Canadian Institute of Metallurgy) Text in English. 1992. q. CND 325 domestic to institutions; USD 235 foreign to institutions; CND 140 domestic to non-members; USD 105 foreign to non-members; CND 35 to members CIM; CND 20 to students CIM (effective 2003). illus. index. back issues avail.; reprints avail. **Document type:** *Journal, Academic/Scholarly.* **Description:** Deals with mineral deposits, mining geology, geomathematics, and directly related environmental and earth science studies.
Related titles: Microfilm ed.: (from PQC); Online - full text ed.: (from HighWire Press).
Indexed: AESIS, ASCA, CIN, ChemAb, ChemTitl, CurCont, GEOBASE, GSW, IMMAb, MinerAb.
—BLDSC (3842.155280), CASDDS, CISTI, IDS, IE, ingenta. **CCC.**
Published by: Canadian Institute of Metallurgy, 3400 de Maisonneuve Blvd, W, Ste 1210, Montreal, PQ H3Z 3B8, Canada. TEL 514-939-2710, FAX 514-939-2714, cim@cim.org, http://www.cim.org/geosoc/indexEmg.cfm.

559 AUS ISSN 1321-9952
CODEN: EMRNFL

EXPLORATION AND MINING RESEARCH NEWS. Text in English. 1989. s-a.
Formerly (until 1994): Exploration Research News (1032-2930)
Indexed: INIS AtomInd.
Published by: Commonwealth Scientific and Industrial Research Organisation, Division of Exploration and Mining, Limestone Ave, Canberra, ACT 2612, Australia. http://www.dem.csiro.au/em/newsandinformation/publications/emrn.htm, http://www.dem.csiro.au/em/.

557 622 CAN ISSN 0823-2059
TN270

EXPLORATION IN BRITISH COLUMBIA. Text in English. 1969. a. price varies. **Document type:** *Government.* **Description:** Records the results of mineral exploration and development in British Columbia.
Supersedes in part: Geology, Exploration and Mining in British Columbia (0085-1027); Which was formerly: Lode Metals in British Columbia
—CISTI, Linda Hall.
Published by: Ministry of Energy, Mines and Petroleum Resources, 5th Fl, 1810 Blanshard St, Victoria, BC V8V 1X4, Canada. Ed. Dorothe Jakobsen. **Subscr. to:** Crown Publications Inc., 521 Fort St, Victoria, BC BC V8W 1E7, Canada. TEL 604-386-4636.

551 USA ISSN 0937-9738

EXPLORATION OF THE DEEP CONTINENTAL CRUST. Text in English. 1986. irreg., latest vol.4, 1999. price varies. reprint service avail. from ISI. **Document type:** *Monographic series, Academic/Scholarly.*
Published by: Springer-Verlag New York, Inc. (Subsidiary of: Springer Science+Business Media), 233 Spring St, New York, NY 10013. TEL 212-460-1500, 800-777-4643, FAX 212-473-6272, http://www.springer-ny.com.

550 DEU ISSN 0945-8492

EXTRALAPIS. Text in German. 1991. irreg., latest vol.25, 2003. EUR 17.80 per vol. (effective 2004). charts; illus.; maps. 100 p./no.; back issues avail. **Document type:** *Monographic series, Academic/Scholarly.*
Related titles: ♦ English Translation: ExtraLapis English.
Published by: Christian Weise Verlag GmbH, Orleansstr 69, Munich, 81667, Germany. TEL 49-89-4802933, FAX 49-89-6886160, lapis.mineralienmagazin@t-online.de, lapis@lapis.de, http://www.lapis.de. Ed. Max Glas. Pub. Christian Weise. Circ: 6,500 (paid).

FACIES; international journal of paleontology, sedimentology and geology. see *EARTH SCIENCES*

624.12 DEU ISSN 0174-6979
TA740

➤ **FELSBAU**; journal for engineering geology, geomechanics and tunnelling. Text in German, English. 1983. 6/yr. EUR 62.80 domestic; EUR 113.80 foreign (effective 2003). adv. bk.rev. abstr.; bibl.; illus.; maps. 64 p./no. 3 cols./p.; back issues avail.; reprints avail. **Document type:** *Journal, Academic/Scholarly.*
Related titles: CD-ROM ed.
Indexed: BrCerAb, C&ISA, CEABA, CerAb, CorrAb, E&CAJ, EMA, FLUIDEX, GEOBASE, GeotechAb, IAA, M&TEA, MBF, METADEX, RefZh, WAA.
—Linda Hall.
Published by: (Oesterreichische Gesellschaft fuer Geomechanik AUT), Verlag Glueckauf GmbH, Postfach 185620, Essen, 45206, Germany. TEL 49-2054-9240, FAX 49-2054-924139, helmut.richter@vge.de, vertrieb@vge.de, http://www.vge.de. Ed. Helmut Richter. R&P Eckart Pasche TEL 49-2054-924120. Adv. contact Ute Perkovic TEL 49-2054-924130. B&W page EUR 2,100, color page EUR 3,150; trim 182 x 269. Circ: 3,000.

551 USA ISSN 0096-2651
QE1 CODEN: FLDGAV

FIELDIANA: GEOLOGY. Text in English. 1895. irreg. price varies. bibl.; charts; illus. back issues avail.; reprint service avail. from PQC. **Document type:** *Monographic series, Academic/Scholarly.* **Description:** Contains primarily paleontological studies involving Field Museum collections and field research.
Former titles (until 1945): Field Museum of Natural History. Geological Series. Publication (0376-1711); (until 1908): Field Columbian Museum. Geological Series. Publication (0097-3637)
Indexed: AESIS, BIOSIS Prev, BiolAb, ChemAb, IBR, RefZh, ZooRec.
—BLDSC (3923.000000), CISTI, Linda Hall.

E

▼ new title ➤ refereed ✶ unverified ♦ full entry avail.

Published by: Field Museum, Roosevelt Rd at Lake Shore Dr, Chicago, IL 60605-2496. TEL 312-922-9410, FAX 312-427-7269. Circ: 475.

559 FJI ISSN 0379-1580
FIJI. MINERAL RESOURCES DEPARTMENT. BULLETIN. Text in English. 1958. irreg. price varies. **Document type:** *Bulletin.* **Description:** Description and map of geology of parts of Fiji.
Formerly (until 1972): Fiji. Geological Survey. Bulletin (0250-7242)
Indexed: IMMAb.
Published by: Mineral Resources Department, P.M. Bag, Suva, Fiji. TEL 679-381611, FAX 679-370039, http://www.mrd.gov.fj/. Ed. Peter Rodda. Circ: 300.

559 FJI ISSN 0250-7277
FIJI. MINERAL RESOURCES DEPARTMENT. GEOTHERMAL REPORT. Text in English. 1980. irreg. price varies. **Document type:** *Monographic series.* **Description:** Results of investigations of geothermal areas.
Published by: Mineral Resources Department, P.M. Bag, Suva, Fiji. TEL 679-381611, FAX 679-370039, http://www.mrd.gov.fj/. Ed. Peter Rodda. Circ: 300.

551 FJI ISSN 1011-7512
FIJI. MINERAL RESOURCES DEPARTMENT. HYDROGEOLOGICAL REPORT. Text in English. 1988. irreg. price varies. **Document type:** *Monographic series.* **Description:** Results of hydrogeological investigations in Fiji.
Published by: Mineral Resources Department, P.M. Bag, Suva, Fiji. TEL 679-381611, FAX 679-370039, http://www.mrd.gov.fj/. Ed. Peter Rodda. Circ: 300.

551 FJI ISSN 1016-2135
FIJI. MINERAL RESOURCES DEPARTMENT. INFORMATION NOTES. Text in English, Fijian, Hindi. 1986. irreg. free. **Document type:** *Monographic series.*
Published by: Mineral Resources Department, P.M. Bag, Suva, Fiji. TEL 679-381611, FAX 679-370039, http://www.mrd.gov.fj/. Circ: 10,000.

551 FJI ISSN 0252-2497
FIJI. MINERAL RESOURCES DEPARTMENT. MEMOIR. Text in English. 1964. irreg. price varies. **Document type:** *Monographic series.* **Description:** Results of investigations into earth sciences in Fiji.
Formerly (until 1976): Fiji. Geological Survey. Memoir (0250-7269)
Indexed: AESIS, IMMAb.
Published by: Mineral Resources Department, P.M. Bag, Suva, Fiji. TEL 679-381611, FAX 679-370039, http://www.mrd.gov.fj/. Ed. Peter Rodda. Circ: 300.

551 FJI ISSN 0250-7234
FIJI. MINERAL RESOURCES DEPARTMENT. REPORT. Text in English. 1952. irreg. price varies. **Document type:** *Monographic series.*
Former titles (until 1980): Fiji. Geological Survey Department. Report (0250-720X); (until 1961): Fiji. Geological Survey Department. Long Report
Indexed: IMMAb.
Published by: Mineral Resources Department, P.M. Bag, Suva, Fiji. TEL 679-381611, FAX 679-370039, http://www.mrd.gov.fj/. Ed. Peter Rodda. Circ: 300.

FINER POINTS MAGAZINE. see *BUSINESS AND ECONOMICS*

551 USA ISSN 1052-6536
QE99
FLORIDA GEOLOGICAL SURVEY. BIENNIAL REPORT. Text in English. 1985. biennial, latest vol.21, 2001. free. **Document type:** *Government.* **Description:** Presents a summary of the extended services and activities of the FGS.
—Linda Hall.
Published by: Florida Geological Survey, Publications Office, 903 W Tennessee St, Tallahassee, FL 32304-7700. TEL 850-488-9380, http://www.dep.state.fl.us/geology. Circ: 1,000.

557 USA ISSN 0271-7832
QE99 CODEN: FCGBA2
FLORIDA GEOLOGICAL SURVEY. BULLETIN. Text in English. 1908. irreg., latest vol.65, 2002. price varies.
Formerly: Florida. Bureau of Geology. Geological Bulletins (0085-0608)
Indexed: BIOSIS Prev, BiolAb.
—Linda Hall.
Published by: Florida Geological Survey, Publications Office, 903 W Tennessee St, Tallahassee, FL 32304-7700. TEL 850-488-9380, http://www.dep.state.fl.us/geology. Circ: 1,000.

557 USA
QE99
FLORIDA GEOLOGICAL SURVEY. INFORMATION CIRCULAR. Text in English. 1948. irreg., latest vol.112, 1999. price varies.
Formerly: Florida. Bureau of Geology. Information Circulars (0085-0616)
—Linda Hall.
Published by: Florida Geological Survey, Publications Office, 903 W Tennessee St, Tallahassee, FL 32304-7700. TEL 850-488-9380, http://www.dep.state.fl.us/geology. Circ: 1,000.

557 USA
FLORIDA GEOLOGICAL SURVEY. MAP SERIES. Text in English. 1952. irreg., latest vol.147, 2000. price varies.
Formerly: Florida. Bureau of Geology. Map Series (0085-0624)
Published by: Florida Geological Survey, Publications Office, 903 W Tennessee St, Tallahassee, FL 32304-7700. TEL 850-488-9380, http://www.dep.state.fl.us/geology. Circ: 1,000.

557 USA ISSN 1053-0533
QE99
FLORIDA GEOLOGICAL SURVEY. REPORT OF INVESTIGATIONS. Text in English. 1934. irreg., latest vol.101, 2002. price varies.
Former titles (until 1986): Florida. Bureau of Geology. Report of Investigations (0096-0489); (until 1970): Florida. Division of Geology. Report of Investigations (0160-1016); (until 1967): Florida Geological Survey. Report of Investigations (0160-0982); (until 1942): Florida. Geological Department. Report of Investigations (0160-1024)
—Linda Hall.
Published by: Florida Geological Survey, Publications Office, 903 W Tennessee St, Tallahassee, FL 32304-7700. TEL 850-488-9380, http://www.dep.state.fl.us/geology. Circ: 1,000.

551.44 USA ISSN 0071-6006
FLORIDA SPELEOLOGICAL SOCIETY. SPECIAL PAPERS. Text in English. 1961. irreg. membership.
Published by: Florida Speleological Society, PO Box 12581, University Sta, Gainesville, FL 32604. TEL 904-372-0521, FAX 904-392-2831. Ed. Lisa Sandlin. Circ: 150.

551.44 USA
FLORIDA SPELEOLOGIST. Text in English. 1961. q. per issue exchange basis. bk.rev.
Published by: Florida Speleological Society, PO Box 12581, University Sta, Gainesville, FL 32604. TEL 904-372-0521, FAX 904-332-2276. Ed. Mardi Krause. Circ: 100.

554 560 333.91 HUN ISSN 0015-542X
QE1 CODEN: FOKOA9
➤ **FOLDTANI KOZLONY**; bulletin of the Hungarian geological society. Text in Hungarian; Summaries in English, French, German, Hungarian. 1871. q. USD 30; USD 50 foreign (effective 1999). adv. bk.rev. charts; illus. cum.index: 1901-1960. back issues avail. **Document type:** *Bulletin, Academic/Scholarly.* **Description:** Papers dedicated to any branches of geology are welcome, including pure scientific subjects and applied as well.
Indexed: BiolAb, CIN, ChemAb, ChemTitl, PetrolAb, ZooRec.
—CASDDS, CISTI, Linda Hall, PADDS.
Published by: Hungarian Geological Society, Fo utca 68, Budapest, 1027, Hungary. TEL 36-1-201-2011, FAX 36-1-156-1215, mail.mft@mtesz.hu. Ed., Adv. contact Geza Csaszar. Pub., R&P Jstvan Berczi. B&W page USD 60, color page USD 30; trim 196 x 126. Circ: 1,300 (paid). **Subscr. addr.:** PO Box 433, Budapest 1371, Hungary. TEL 36-1-201-9129, FAX 36-1-201-9129.

550 CZE
FOLIA FACULTATIS SCIENTIARUM NATURALIUM UNIVERSITATIS MASARYKIANAE BRUNENSIS: GEOLOGIA. Text in Czech. a. price varies. **Document type:** *Monographic series, Academic/Scholarly.*
Formerly: Folia Facultatis Scientiarum Naturalium Universitatis Purkynianae Brunensis: Geologia (0323-0139)
—CISTI, Linda Hall.
Published by: Masarykova Universita, Prirodovedecka Fakulta/Masaryk University, Faculty of Sciences, Kotlarska 2, Brno, 61137, Czech Republic. Ed. Rostislav Brzobohaty.

FOLIA GEOGRAPHICA. GEOGRAPHICA-PHYSICA. see *GEOGRAPHY*

550 CZE ISSN 0139-9764
QE267 CODEN: FMBOAI
FOLIA MUSEI RERUM NATURALIUM BOHEMIAE OCCIDENTALIS. GEOLOGICA. Text in Czech. 1971. irreg. **Document type:** *Academic/Scholarly.*
Indexed: HerbAb, SFA, WildRev, ZooRec.
Published by: Zapadoceske Muzeum, Kopeckeho sady 2, Plzen, 30135, Czech Republic. TEL 42-19-7236541, FAX 42-19-7236541, zpcm@pm.cesnet.cz.

554 DEU ISSN 0071-8009
CODEN: FGRWAC
➤ **FORTSCHRITTE IN DER GEOLOGIE VON RHEINLAND UND WESTFALEN.** Text in German; Summaries in English, French. 1958. irreg., latest vol.39, 1999. EUR 19 (effective 2002). back issues avail. **Document type:** *Monographic series, Academic/Scholarly.* **Description:** Studies earth sciences, mainly in the area of North Rhine-Westphalia.
Related titles: Online - full text ed.
Indexed: BiolAb, F&EA, PetrolAb, ZooRec.
—CISTI, Linda Hall. **CCC.**
Published by: Geologischer Dienst Nordrhein-Westfalen, De-Greiff-Str 195, Krefeld, 47803, Germany. TEL 49-2151-8971, FAX 49-2151-897505, poststelle@gd.nrw.de, http://www.gd.nrw.de. Ed., R&P Rainer Wolf TEL 49-2151-897332. Circ: 900. **Dist. by:** Postfach 1080, Krefeld 47710, Germany.

➤ **FOSSILIEN**; Zeitschrift fuer Sammler und Hobbypalaeontologen. see *PALEONTOLOGY*

551 FRA ISSN 0221-2536
CODEN: DOBRDM
FRANCE. BUREAU DE RECHERCHES GEOLOGIQUES ET MINIERES. DOCUMENTS. Text and summaries in English, French. 1973; N.S. 1979. irreg. (15-20/yr.). price varies. adv. **Document type:** *Government.*
Indexed: ChemAb.
—CASDDS, CISTI, Linda Hall. **CCC.**
Published by: (France. Bureau de Recherches Geologiques et Minieres), Editions B R G M, B.P. 6009, Orleans, Cedex 2 45060, France. TEL 33-2-38643321, FAX 33-2-38643990, g.sustrac@brgm.fr. Ed. Gerard Sustrac. Adv. contact Florence Jaudin.

551 622 FRA ISSN 0245-9345
FRANCE. BUREAU DE RECHERCHES GEOLOGIQUES ET MINIERES. MANUELS ET METHODES. Text in French. 1980. irreg. (2-3/yr.). price varies. adv. **Document type:** *Government.*
Indexed: ChemAb, IMMAb.
—CISTI.
Published by: (France. Bureau de Recherches Geologiques et Minieres), Editions B R G M, B.P. 6009, Orleans, Cedex 2 45060, France. TEL 33-2-38643321, FAX 33-2-38643990, g.sustrac@brgm.fr. Ed. Gerard Sustrac. Adv. contact Florence Jaudin.

557 560 DEU ISSN 0173-1742
FRANKFURTER GEOWISSENSCHAFTEN ARBEITEN. SERIE A. GEOLOGIE PALAEONTOLOGIE. Text in English. 1982. irreg.
Indexed: ZooRec.
—Linda Hall.
Published by: Johann Wolfgang Goethe Universitaet Frankfurt, Fachbereich Geowissenschaften, Bockenheimer Landstr. 133, 6, OG, Frankfurt am Main, 60054, Germany. TEL 49-69-798-28128, FAX 49-69-798-28416, dekanat-geowiss@em.uni-frankfurt.de.

551.34 USA ISSN 1021-8610
FROZEN GROUND. Text in English. 198?. a. **Document type:** *Bulletin.*
Published by: International Permafrost Association, c/o Dr Jerry Brown, PO Box 7, Woods Hole, MA 02345. TEL 508-457-4982, jerrybrown@igc.org, http://www.geo.uio.no/IPA/.

551 CHN ISSN 1001-3970
FUJIAN DIZHI/FUJIAN GEOLOGY. Text in Chinese. q. CNY 12. **Document type:** *Academic/Scholarly.* **Description:** Covers stratigraphy, palaeontology, petrology, mineralogy, geophysics and other fields associated with geology.
Related titles: Online - full text ed.: (from East View Information Services).
Published by: Fujiansheng Dizhi Kuangchan Ju, Fujian Dizhi Bianjibu/Fujian Provincial Bureau of Geology and Mineralogy, Editorial Department of Fujian Geology, 285 Wusi St, Fuzhou, Fujian 350003, China. TEL 0591-845388, FAX 0591-845666. Ed. Gao Tianjun. **Dist. overseas by:** China National Publishing Industry Trading Corporation, PO Box 782, Beijing 100011, China.

551 SWE ISSN 1103-5897
QE1 CODEN: GFFGEE
➤ **G F F.** (Geografiska Foereningens i Stockholm Foerhandlingar) Text in English. 1872. q. SEK 510 domestic; SEK 550 in Europe; SEK 580 elsewhere (effective 2005). adv. bk.rev. abstr.; bibl.; charts; illus. index, cum.index (every 10 vols.). back issues avail. **Document type:** *Journal, Academic/Scholarly.* **Description:** Covers the whole field of geology and palaeonology; issues in geochemistry and geophysics are discussed within the context of geology.
Formerly (until 1994): Geologiska Foereningen i Stockholm. Foerhandlingar (0016-786X)
Indexed: A&ATA, AESIS, ASCA, BiolAb, CIN, ChemAb, ChemTitl, CurCont, E&PHSE, GEOBASE, GP&P, GeotechAb, INIS AtomInd, MinerAb, OffTech, PetrolAb, RefZh, ZooRec.
—BLDSC (4166.000000), CASDDS, CISTI, IDS, IE, ingenta, Linda Hall, PADDS.
Published by: Swedish Science Press, P O Box 118, Uppsala, 75104, Sweden. TEL 46-18-365566, FAX 46-18-365277, info@ssp.nu, http://www.geologiskaforeningen.nu, http://www.ssp.nu. Ed. Joakim Mansfeld TEL 46-8-6747727. **Co-sponsor:** Geologiska Foereningen/Geological Society of Sweden.

553.2809982 DNK ISSN 0909-0630
TN271.P4
➤ **G H E X I S NEWSLETTER.** (Greenland Hydrocarbon Exploration Information Service) Key Title: Ghexis Newsletter. Text in English. 1990. irreg. (1-2/yr). free. illus. **Document type:** *Newsletter, Government.* **Description:** Contains a wide range of information pertaining to the oil and gas industry in Greenland including expedition news, geological-geophysical data and assessments, new publications, and licence and regulatory conditions.
Related titles: Online - full content ed.

E

Published by: (Greenland. Bureau of Minerals and Petroleum GRL), Miljoeministeriet, Danmarks og Groenlands Geologiske Undersoegelse (GEUS)/Danish Ministry of the Environment. Geological Survey of Denmark and Greenland, Oester Voldgade 10, Copenhagen K, 1350, Denmark. TEL 45-38-142000, FAX 45-38-142050, ghexis@geus.dk, http://www.geus.dk/ghexis/index.htm. Ed. Jens Christian Olsen. Circ: 400.

| 551 | USA | ISSN 1052-5173 |
| QE1 | | |

G S A TODAY. Text in English. 1978. m. USD 75 (effective 2005). adv. back issues avail. **Document type:** *Journal, Trade.* **Description:** For professional geologists in academia, government, industry, and business. News items about the Society's activities and the geologic community at large.
Former titles (until 1990): Geological Society of America. News and Information (8755-4976); (until 1983) G S A News and Information (0164-5854)
Related titles: CD-ROM ed.; Online - full text ed.: (from EBSCO Publishing).
Indexed: AESIS, GEOBASE, PetrolAb.
—BLDSC (4223.692500), IE, Infotrieve, ingenta, Linda Hall, PADDS. **CCC.**
Published by: Geological Society of America, 3300 Penrose Pl, Boulder, CO 80301-1806. TEL 303-447-2020, 800-472-1988, FAX 303-447-1133, pubs@geosociety.org, http://www.geosociety.org. Ed. Faith Rogers. Circ: 17,500.

| 555 | PAK | |
| QE295 | | CODEN: GGSPB8 |

G S P NEWS. Text in English. 1968. irreg., latest vol.2, 1972.
Formerly (until Jul. 1994): Geonews (0435-4311)
—CASDDS.
Published by: Geological Survey of Pakistan, c/o Chief Librarian, P O Box 15, Quetta, 87550, Pakistan. TEL 92-81-9211038. Ed. Asif Nazeer Rana TEL 92-81-442540.

GAKEKUZURE SAIGAI NO JITTAI/RESEARCH DATA OF LANDSLIDE DISASTERS. see *CIVIL DEFENSE*

GANBAN RIKIGAKU NI KANSURU SHINPOJUMU RONBUNSHU/SYMPOSIUM ON ROCK MECHANICS. PROCEEDINGS. see *ENGINEERING—Civil Engineering*

| 551 | JPN | ISSN 1345-630X |
| QE351 | | CODEN: GKKABJ |

➤ **GANSEKI KOBUTSU KAGAKU/JAPANESE MAGAZINE OF MINERALOGICAL AND PETROLOGICAL SCIENCES.** Text in Japanese. 2000. bi-m. JPY 7,500 (effective 2001). **Document type:** *Academic/Scholarly.*
Formed by the merger of part of (1953-2000): Mineralogical Journal (0544-2540); part of (1952-2000): Kobutsugaku Zasshi (0454-1146); part of (1988-2000): Ganko (0914-9783); Which was formerly (1941-1987): Ganseki Kobutsu Kosho Gakkaishi (0021-4825); (1929- 1940): Ganseki Kobutsu Koshogaku
Related titles: Online - full text ed.: ISSN 1349-7979 (from J-Stage).
Indexed: RefZh.
—BLDSC (4659.341500), CISTI, Linda Hall.
Published by: Japanese Association of Mineralogists Petrologists and Economic Geologists, c/o Graduate School of Science, Tohoku University, Aoba, Sendai, 981-0945, Japan. TEL 81-22-224-3852, FAX 81-22-224-3852, kyl04223@nifty.ne.jp, http://wwwsoc.nacsis.ac.jp/jampeg/index.html. Circ: 1,600.

| 555 | CHN | ISSN 1006-7493 |
| QE1 | | |

➤ **GAOXIAO DIZHI XUEBAO/GEOLOGICAL JOURNAL OF CHINA UNIVERSITIES.** Text in Chinese. 1995. q. USD 100 foreign (effective 2000). bk.rev. index. back issues avail. **Document type:** *Journal, Academic/Scholarly.* **Description:** Covers comprehensive geological sciences organized by the geological colleges and departments of the universities in China.
Related titles: ◆ CD-ROM ed.: Chinese Academic Journals Full-Text Database. Science & Engineering, Series A. ISSN 1007-8010; E-mail ed.; Fax ed.; Online - full text ed.: (from East View Information Services).
Indexed: RefZh.
—BLDSC (4133.605000).
Published by: Nanjing Daxue, Diqiu Kexuexi/Nanjing University, Department of Earth Sciences, 22 Hankou Rd, Nanjing, 210093, China. TEL 86-25-3592342, FAX 86-25-3302728, editors@public1.ptt.js.cn, http://gxdzxb.periodicals.net.cn/default.html, http://es.nju.edu.cn/. Ed. WangDezi Dezi. Adv. contact Guijun Shi. Circ: 1,500 (paid and controlled).

| 581 | PRT | ISSN 0378-1240 |
| QE337 | | CODEN: GOGLAP |

GARCIA DE ORTA: SERIE DE GEOLOGIA. Text in Portuguese. 1953. irreg., latest vol.17, 1998. price varies. back issues avail. **Document type:** *Academic/Scholarly.*
Supersedes in part (in 1973): Garcia de Orta (0016-4569)
Indexed: S&F.
Published by: Instituto de Investigacao Cientifica Tropical, Rua da Junqueira, 30, Lisbon, 1349-007, Portugal. TEL 351-21-3622621, FAX 351-21-3631460, iict@iict.pt. Circ: 1,000. **Subscr. to:** Centro de Documentacao e Informacao, Rua de Jau, 47, Lisbon 1300, Portugal. TEL 351-21-3644846, FAX 351-21-3628218.

| 551 551.46 | DEU | ISSN 0276-0460 |
| QE39 | | CODEN: GMLEDI |

➤ **GEO-MARINE LETTERS**; an international journal of marine geology. Text in English. 1980. bi-m. EUR 778 combined subscription to institutions print & online eds. (effective 2005). adv. bk.rev. illus. Index. reprint service avail. from ISI,PSC. **Document type:** *Journal, Academic/Scholarly.* **Description:** Publishes short articles in such fields as marine geology, marine chemistry, marine geophysics, and marine environment.
Related titles: Microform ed.: (from PQC); Online - full text ed.: ISSN 1432-1157 (from EBSCO Publishing, Springer LINK, Swets Information Services).
Indexed: AESIS, ASCA, ASFA, CIN, CTO, ChemAb, ChemTitl, CurCont, E&PHSE, ESPM, EngInd, GEOBASE, GP&P, IBR, ISR, M&TEA, OceAb, OffTech, PetrolAb, PollutAb, RefZh, SCI, SPPI, SWRA.
—BLDSC (4147.230000), CASDDS, CISTI, Ei, IDS, IE, Infotrieve, ingenta, PADDS. **CCC.**
Published by: Springer-Verlag (Subsidiary of: Springer Science+Business Media), Tiergartenstr 17, Heidelberg, 69121, Germany. TEL 49-6221-3450, FAX 49-6221-345229, http://link.springer.de/link/service/journals/00367/index.htm. Ed. Burg W Flemming. Adv. contact Stephan Kroeck TEL 49-30-827875739. **Subscr. in the Americas to:** Springer-Verlag New York, Inc., Journal Fulfillment, PO Box 2485, Secaucus, NJ 07096-2485. TEL 800-777-4643, 201-348-4033, FAX 201-348-4505, journals@springer-ny.com, http://www.springer-ny.com; **Subscr. to:** Springer GmbH Auslieferungsgesellschaft, Haberstr 7, Heidelberg 69126, Germany. TEL 49-6221-345-0, FAX 49-6221-345-4229, subscriptions@springer.de.

➤ **GEO-OEKO.** see *GEOGRAPHY*

| 551 570 | GBR | ISSN 1472-4677 |
| QH343.4 | | CODEN: GEOBCZ |

GEOBIOLOGY. Text in English. q. GBP 90, EUR 135 combined subscription in Europe to individuals print & online eds.; USD 168 combined subscription in the Americas to individuals & Caribbean (print & online eds.); GBP 100 combined subscription elsewhere to individuals print & online eds.; GBP 295 combined subscription in Europe to institutions print & online eds.; USD 544 combined subscription in the Americas to institutions & Caribbean (print & online eds.); GBP 324 combined subscription elsewhere to institutions print & online eds. (effective 2006). reprint service avail. from PSC.
Description: Publishes papers crossing disciplines and containing both geological and biological elements, including microbiology, microbial ecology, plant physiology, molecular biology, paleontology, early evolutionary biology, mineralogy, geochemistry, sedimentology, envirnomental geology, oceanography, atmospheric sciences, and astrobiology. .
Related titles: Online - full text ed.: ISSN 1472-4669. GBP 280 in Europe to institutions; USD 517 in the Americas to institutions & Caribbean; GBP 308 elsewhere to institutions (effective 2006) (from Blackwell Synergy, EBSCO Publishing, Gale Group, IngentaConnect, O C L C Online Computer Library Center, Inc., Swets Information Services).
—BLDSC (4116.900700), IE. **CCC.**
Published by: Blackwell Publishing Ltd., 9600 Garsington Rd, Oxford, OX4 2ZG, United Kingdom. TEL 44-1865-776868, FAX 44-1865-714591, customerservices@oxon.blackwellpublishing.com, http://www.blackwellpublishing.com/journals/GBI. Ed. Kurt Konhauser.

| 550 580 | NLD | ISSN 0169-3174 |
| | | CODEN: GEOBD2 |

➤ **GEOBOTANY.** Text in English. 1981. irreg., latest vol.29, 2004. price varies. **Document type:** *Monographic series, Academic/Scholarly.*
Indexed: BIOSIS Prev.
—BLDSC (4116.916000), CISTI, IE, ingenta. **CCC.**
Published by: Springer-Verlag Dordrecht (Subsidiary of: Springer Science+Business Media), Van Godewijckstraat 30, Dordrecht, 3311 GX, Netherlands. TEL 31-78-6576050, FAX 31-78-6576474, http://www.springeronline.com. Ed. M J A Werger.

➤ **GEOCARTO INTERNATIONAL**; multi-disciplinary journal of remote sensing and GIS. see *GEOGRAPHY*

| 551 | USA | |

THE GEOCHEMICAL NEWS. Text in English. q. membership. **Document type:** *Academic/Scholarly.*
Related titles: Online - full text ed.
Published by: The Geochemical Society, Department of Earth & Planetary Sciences, Washington University, One Brookings Dr, St Louis, MO 63130-4899. TEL 314-935-4131, FAX 314-935-4121, gsoffice@gs.wustl.edu, http://gs.wustl.edu.

| 551 | IND | ISSN 0368-2323 |
| QE514 | | CODEN: JGSIBK |

GEOCHEMICAL SOCIETY OF INDIA. JOURNAL. Text in English. 1965. a. INR 35, USD 8. bk.rev. bibl.; charts; illus.
Indexed: ChemAb.
Published by: Geochemical Society of India, Patna, Bihar 5, India. Ed. R C Sinha.

| 551.9 540 | USA | |

GEOCHEMICAL SOCIETY. SPECIAL PUBLICATION. Text in English. 1987. irreg., latest vol.7, 2000. **Document type:** *Monographic series, Academic/Scholarly.*
Indexed: CIN, ChemAb, ChemTitl.
—BLDSC (8378.618000).
Published by: The Geochemical Society, Department of Earth & Planetary Sciences, Washington University, One Brookings Dr, St Louis, MO 63130-4899. TEL 314-935-4131, FAX 314-935-4121, gsoffice@gs.wustl.edu, http://gs.wustl.edu.

| 551.9 | GBR | ISSN 1467-7873 |
| QE514 | | CODEN: GEEAAE |

➤ **GEOCHEMISTRY: EXPLORATION, ENVIRONMENT, ANALYSIS.** Text in English. 2001 (Mar.). q. GBP 110 in Europe; USD 180 in North America; GBP 125, USD 210 elsewhere (effective 2003). bk.rev. abstr.; illus.; maps. 96 p./no. 2 cols./p.; back issues avail. **Document type:** *Journal, Academic/Scholarly.* **Description:** Covers all aspects of the application of geochemistry to the exploration and study of mineral resources, and related fields, including the geochemistry of the environment.
Related titles: Online - full text ed.: (from EBSCO Publishing, Gale Group, HighWire Press, IngentaConnect, Swets Information Services).
Indexed: CurCont, FLUIDEX, GEOBASE.
—BLDSC (4116.947500), CISTI, IE, ingenta, Linda Hall.
Published by: (Geological Society, Association of Exploration Geochemists CAN), Geological Society Publishing House, Unit 7, Brassmill Enterprise Centre, Brassmill Ln, Bath, Avon BA1 3JN, United Kingdom. TEL 44-1225-445046, FAX 44-1225-442836, dawn.angel@geolsoc.org.uk, rebecca.toop@geolsoc.org.uk, enquiries@geolsoc.org.uk, http://www.geolsoc.org.uk. Eds. Diana Swan, Gwendy Hall. Adv. contact Sean Kehoe TEL 44-117-904-1283. Circ: 1,000 (paid).

| 551 | GBR | ISSN 0016-7037 |
| QE351 | | CODEN: GCACAK |

➤ **GEOCHIMICA ET COSMOCHIMICA ACTA.** Text in English, French, German. 1950. 24/yr. EUR 2,448 in Europe to institutions; JPY 325,100 in Japan to institutions; USD 2,738 to institutions except Europe and Japan (effective 2006). adv. bk.rev. abstr.; bibl.; charts; illus. index. back issues avail.; reprint service avail. from PQC. **Document type:** *Journal, Academic/Scholarly.* **Description:** Publishes original research covering the spectrum of geochemistry and cosmochemistry, incorporating chemistry, geology, physics and astronomy.
Related titles: Microfilm ed.: (from PQC); Online - full text ed.: (from EBSCO Publishing, Gale Group, IngentaConnect, ScienceDirect, Swets Information Services). ◆ Supplement(s): Geochimica et Cosmochimica Acta. Supplement. ISSN 0046-564X.
Indexed: AESIS, ASCA, ASFA, AnalAb, BiolAb, BrCerAb, BrGeoL, C&ISA, CCI, CIN, CIS, CTA, CerAb, ChemAb, ChemTitl, CivEngAb, CorrAb, CurCont, E&CAJ, E&PHSE, EMA, ESPM, EngInd, EnvEAb, ExcerpMed, F&EA, FLUIDEX, ForAb, GEOBASE, GP&P, IAA, IBR, INIS AtomInd, ISR, Inspec, M&GPA, M&TEA, MBF, METADEX, MSB, MSCI, MinerAb, OceAb, OffTech, PetrolAb, PollutAb, RefZh, S&F, SCI, SFA, SPPI, SWRA, WAA, WRCInf.
—BLDSC (4117.000000), AskIEEE, CASDDS, CISTI, Ei, IDS, IE, Infotrieve, ingenta, Linda Hall, PADDS. **CCC.**
Published by: (Geochemical Society), Pergamon (Subsidiary of: Elsevier Science & Technology), The Boulevard, Langford Ln, East Park, Kidlington, Oxford OX5 1GB, United Kingdom. TEL 44-1865-843000, FAX 44-1865-843010, office@gca.wustl.edu, http://www.elsevier.com/locate/gca. Ed. L Trower. Circ: 3,800. **Subscr. to:** Elsevier BV, PO Box 211, Amsterdam 1000 AE, Netherlands. TEL 31-20-485-3757, FAX 31-20-485-3432, nlinfo-f@elsevier.nl, http://www.elsevier.nl. **Co-sponsor:** Meteoritical Society.

| 551 | GBR | ISSN 0046-564X |
| | | CODEN: GCASD3 |

GEOCHIMICA ET COSMOCHIMICA ACTA. SUPPLEMENT. Text in English, French, German. 1970. irreg. EUR 2,210 in Europe; JPY 293,500 in Japan; USD 2,471 elsewhere (effective 2004). included with subscr. to Geochimica et Cosmochimica Acta.
Related titles: ◆ Supplement to: Geochimica et Cosmochimica Acta. ISSN 0016-7037.
—CISTI. **CCC.**
Published by: Pergamon (Subsidiary of: Elsevier Science & Technology), The Boulevard, Langford Ln, East Park, Kidlington, Oxford OX5 1GB, United Kingdom. TEL 44-1865-843000, FAX 44-1865-843010.

| 551 | FRA | ISSN 0292-8477 |
| QE1 | | CODEN: GECHDS |

GEOCHRONIQUE; le magazine des sciences de la Terre. Text in French. 1982. q. EUR 44 domestic to non-members; EUR 22 domestic to members (effective 2005). bk.rev. abstr.; charts; illus. index. back issues avail. **Document type:** *Newsletter.* **Description:** Earth science magazine featuring geological news, synoptic articles, news of organizations, society activities and calendar.
Formed by the 1982 merger of: France. Bureau de Recherches Geologiques et Minieres. Section 4: Geologie Generale. Bulletin. (0153-8446); Which was formerly (until 1971): France. Bureau de Recherches Geologiques et Minieres. Section 4: Geologie Generale et Divers. Bulletin (0007-6112); Which superseded in part (in 1968): France. Bureau de

E

Recherches Geologiques et Minieres. Bulletin (0532-3460); Which was formerly (1953-1961): France. Bureau de Recherches Geologiques, Geophysiques et Minieres. Publications (0367-2638); Societe Geologique de France. Bulletin. Supplement (0750-7461); Which was formerly (1910-1971): Societe Geologique de France. Compte Rendu Sommaire des Seances (0037-9417)
Indexed: ChemAb, IMMAb, INIS AtomInd, PetrolAb, RefZh.
—CASDDS, CISTI, IE, Infotrieve, Linda Hall. **CCC.**
Published by: Societe Geologique de France, 77 rue Claude Bernard, Paris, 75005, France. TEL 33-01-43317735, FAX 33-01-45357910, accueil@sgfr.org, http://sgfr.free.fr/publier/coeditions/Geochronique/SommGeochr.html, http://www.sgfr.org. Adv. contact J Lorenz. Circ: 3,300.
Co-sponsor: Bureau de Recherches Geologiques et Minieres.

551 NLD
GEODE. Text in Dutch. 1974. 10/yr. adv. **Description:** Covers news and information of interest to mineral collectors, including meetings and excursions.
Published by: Association of Collectors of Minerals - Fossils, c/o A.J. Zantvoort-van Bossum, Prinsessenpark 28, Zwijndrecht, 3331 GZ, Netherlands. Ed. D M A Houtman. Circ: 500.

551.9 RUS
GEOEKOLOGICHESKIE ISSLEDOVANIYA I OKHRANA NEDR. Text in Russian. 3/yr. USD 85 in United States.
Indexed: RefZh.
Published by: Informatsionno-Izdatel'skii Tsentr po Geologii i Nedropol'zovaniu Geoinformmark, Goncharnaya 38, Moscow, 115172, Russian Federation. TEL 7-095-9156724. **US dist. addr.:** East View Information Services, 3020 Harbor Ln. N., Minneapolis, MN 55447. TEL 612-550-0961.

551.9 RUS ISSN 0869-7809
GEOEKOLOGIYA, INZHENERNAYA GEOLOGIYA, GIDROGEOLOGIYA, GEOKRIOLOGIYA. Text in Russian. bi-m. RUR 990 for 6 mos. domestic (effective 2004). **Document type:** *Journal, Academic/Scholarly.* **Description:** Deals with the conservation of the environment, development of its potential and the improvement of human living conditions.
Related titles: Online - full text ed.
Indexed: RefZh.
—East View.
Published by: Izdatel'stvo Nauka, Profsoyuznaya ul 90, Moscow, 117864, Russian Federation. TEL 7-095-3347151, FAX 7-095-4202220, secret@naukaran.ru, http://www.maik.ru/cgi-bin/list.pl?page=geoekol, http://www.naukaran.ru.

551 GBR ISSN 1468-8115
QC809.F5 CODEN: GEOFBC
GEOFLUIDS. Text in English. 2001. q. GBP 66, EUR 99 combined subscription in Europe to individuals print & online eds.; USD 121 combined subscription in the Americas to individuals & Caribbean, print & online eds.; GBP 72 combined subscription in the Americas to individuals print & online eds.; GBP 333 combined subscription in Europe to institutions print & online eds.; USD 615 combined subscription in the Americas to institutions & Caribbean, print & online eds.; GBP 366 combined subscription elsewhere to institutions print & online eds. (effective 2006). adv. **Document type:** *Journal, Academic/Scholarly.* **Description:** Provides an international forum for original research into the role of fluids in mineralogical, chemical, and structural evolution of the Earth's crust.
Related titles: ♦ Online - full text ed.: Geofluids Online. ISSN 1468-8123.
Indexed: CurCont, FLUIDEX, GEOBASE.
—BLDSC (4121.445000), IE, Infotrieve. **CCC.**
Published by: Blackwell Publishing Ltd., 9600 Garsington Rd, Oxford, OX4 2ZG, United Kingdom. TEL 44-1865-776868, FAX 44-1865-714591, customerservices@oxon.blackwellpublishing.com, http://www.blackwellpublishing.com/journals/GFL. Eds. Bruce Yardley, Grant Garven, John Parnell.

551 GBR ISSN 1468-8123
➤ **GEOFLUIDS ONLINE.** Text in English. 2001. q. GBP 316 in Europe to institutions; USD 585 in the Americas to institutions & Caribbean; GBP 348 elsewhere to institutions (effective 2006). **Document type:** *Journal, Academic/Scholarly.* **Description:** Provides an international forum for original research into the role of fluids in mineralogical, chemical, and structural evolution of the Earth's crust.
Media: Online - full text (from Blackwell Synergy, EBSCO Publishing, Gale Group, IngentaConnect, O C L C Online Computer Library Center, Inc., Swets Information Services).
Related titles: ♦ Print ed.: Geofluids. ISSN 1468-8115.
—CCC.
Published by: Blackwell Publishing Ltd., 9600 Garsington Rd, Oxford, OX4 2ZG, United Kingdom. TEL 44-1865-776868, FAX 44-1865-714591, customerservices@oxon.blackwellpublishing.com, http://www.blackwellpublishing.com/journal.asp?ref=1468-8115&site=1. Ed. Grant Garven.

554 ESP ISSN 0213-683X
GEOGACETA. Text in Spanish. 1986. s-a. EUR 12 membership (effective 2005).
Indexed: IECT, ZooRec.
—CINDOC. **CCC.**
Published by: Sociedad Geologica de Espana, Plaza de la Mercedes, s-n, Salamanca, 37008, Spain. TEL 34-923-294752, info@geologicas.es, http://www.sociedadgeologica.es/. Ed. Jose Manuel Gonzalez Casado.

551.31 ITA ISSN 0391-9838
QE696 CODEN: GFDQDX
➤ **GEOGRAFIA FISICA E DINAMICA QUATERNARIA.** Text mainly in English, Italian; Text occasionally in French. 1914. s-a. price varies. bk.rev. charts; illus. Supplement avail. **Document type:** *Monographic series, Academic/Scholarly.* **Description:** Publishes original papers, short communications, and news of physical geography, geomorphology and quaternary geology.
Former titles (until 1977): Comitato Glaciologico Italiano. Bollettino (0084-8948); (until 1947): Comitato Glaciologico Italiano e Commissione Glaciologica. Bollettino (1120-3692)
Indexed: GEOBASE, RefZh.
—CASDDS.
Published by: Comitato Glaciologico Italiano, Via Accademia delle Scienze, 5, Turin, TO 10123, Italy. TEL 39-011-658813, FAX 39-011-6707155, http://users.unimi.it/glaciol/cgi.html. Ed. Paolo Roberto Federici. R&P Biancotti Augusto TEL 39-11-658813. Circ: 375; 375 (controlled).

551 JPN
GEOINFORMATICS. Text in Japanese. 1975. q. JPY 5,000 membership (effective 2002). **Document type:** *Bulletin, Academic/Scholarly.*
Formerly (until 1989): Joho Chishitsu (Geological Data Processing) (0388-502X)
Related titles: Online - full content ed.; Online - full text ed.: ISSN 1347-541X (from J-Stage); English ed.
—BLDSC (4129.860000), IE, ingenta. **CCC.**
Published by: Japan Society of Geoinformatics, Dept. Geosci., Fac. Sci., Osaka City University, 3-3-138, Sugimoto, Sumiyoshi-ku, Osaka, 558, Japan. TEL 81-6-605-2593, FAX 81-6-605-3071, http://geoinformatics.jstage.jst.go.jp/, http://wwwsoc.nii.ac.jp/jsgi/index.html.

551 RUS
GEOINFORMATIKA. Text in Russian. 1995. q. USD 95 in North America (effective 2000).
Indexed: RefZh.
Address: Varshavskoe shosse 8, Moscow, 113105, Russian Federation. TEL 7-095-9520324, FAX 7-095-9543711. Ed. N P Lavrov. **Dist. by:** East View Information Services, 3020 Harbor Ln. N., Minneapolis, MN 55447. TEL 763-550-0961, FAX 763-559-2931.

550 NLD ISSN 0924-5499
CODEN: GELIE9
➤ **GEOJOURNAL LIBRARY.** Text in English. 1984. irreg., latest vol.81, 2005. price varies. **Document type:** *Monographic series, Academic/Scholarly.*
Indexed: BIOSIS Prev.
—BLDSC (4129.920000), IE, ingenta. **CCC.**
Published by: Springer-Verlag Dordrecht (Subsidiary of: Springer Science+Business Media), Van Godewijckstraat 30, Dordrecht, 3311 GX, Netherlands. TEL 31-78-6576050, FAX 31-78-6576474, http://www.springeronline.com. Ed. I Max Barlow.

➤ **GEOKATALOG 2 - GEOSCIENCES.** see *GEOGRAPHY*

551 RUS ISSN 0016-7525
QE515 CODEN: GEOKAQ
➤ **GEOKHIMIYA.** Text in Russian; Abstracts and contents page in English. 1956. m. RUR 850 for 6 mos. domestic; USD 396 foreign (effective 2004). charts; illus. index. **Document type:** *Journal, Academic/Scholarly.* **Description:** Covers terrestrial and planetary rocks and atmospheres, rock evolution, parageneses and alteration, geochemical ore-prospecting techniques, ore-zone compositions and distribution, hydrocarbon generation and migration.
Related titles: Online - full text ed.; ♦ English ed.: Geochemistry International. ISSN 0016-7029; ♦ English Translation: Geochemistry International. ISSN 0016-7029.
Indexed: ASCA, ASFA, BiolAb, CIN, ChemAb, ChemTitl, CurCont, ESPM, EngInd, ISR, PetrolAb, RefZh, S&F, SCI.
—BLDSC (0047.980000), CASDDS, CISTI, East View, Ei, IDS, Linda Hall. **CCC.**
Published by: (Rossiiskaya Akademiya Nauk/Russian Academy of Sciences, Institut Geokhimii i Analiticheskoi Khimii im. V.I. Vernadskogo), Izdatel'stvo Nauka, Profsoyuznaya ul 90, Moscow, 117864, Russian Federation. TEL 7-095-3347151, FAX 7-095-4202220, secret@naukaran.ru, http://www.maik.rssi.ru/cgi-bin/list.pl?page=geokhim, http://www.naukaran.ru. **Subscr. to:** Interperiodica, PO Box 1831, Birmingham, AL 35201-1831. TEL 205-995-1567, 800-633-4931, FAX 205-995-1588. **Dist. by:** M K - Periodica, ul Gilyarovskogo 39, Moscow 129110, Russian Federation.

551.9 UKR ISSN 0130-1128
CODEN: GKROAR
GEOKHIMIYA I RUDOOBRAZOVANIE; respublikanskii mezhvedomstvennyi sbornik nauchnykh trudov. Text in Russian. 1972. a.
Indexed: CIN, ChemAb, ChemTitl.
—CASDDS, CISTI, Linda Hall. **CCC.**
Published by: (Institut Geokhimii i Fiziki Mineralov), Natsional'na Akademiya Nauk Ukrainy, vul Volodymyrs'ka 54, Kyiv, 01601, Ukraine. TEL 380-44-2352239, FAX 380-44-2343243, prez@nas.gov.ua, http://www.nas.gov.ua. **Dist. by:** M K - Periodica, ul Gilyarovskogo 39, Moscow 129110, Russian Federation.

551 CZE ISSN 1210-9606
GEOLINES. Text in English. 1994. a. **Document type:** *Monographic series, Academic/Scholarly.* **Description:** Includes monographs on and abstracts of geological research.
Published by: Akademie Ved Ceske Republiky, Geologicky Ustav/Academy of Sciences of Czech Republic, Geological Institute, Rozvojova 135, Lysolaje, Prague 6, 16502, Czech Republic. TEL 42-2-24311421, FAX 42-2-24311578, inst@gli.cas.cz, http://www.lib.cas.cz/knav/journals/eng/Geolines.htm.

551 CAN ISSN 0227-3713
CODEN: GACNBG
GEOLOG. Text in English. 1970. 4/yr. CND 15. adv. bk.rev. **Document type:** *Newsletter.* **Description:** Reports on current happenings in the Canadian geological community.
—CCC.
Published by: (Geological Association of Canada), G A C Publications, Department of Earth Sciences, Memorial University of Newfoundland, St. John's, NF A1B 3X5, Canada. TEL 709-737-7660, FAX 709-737-2532. Ed., R&P Paul Metcalfe.

551 FIN ISSN 0046-5720
CODEN: GEOHAH
GEOLOGI. Text in English, Finnish, Swedish; Summaries in English. 1949. 8/yr. EUR 18 domestic; EUR 23 foreign (effective 2003). adv. bk.rev. cum.index. back issues avail. **Document type:** *Newsletter, Academic/Scholarly.* **Description:** Contains scientific articles on geology, mainly about Finland, as well as news, book reveiws etc.. Targets members of the Finnish Geological Society.
Indexed: BiolAb, CIN, ChemAb, ChemTitl, NAA, RefZh, S&F.
—CASDDS.
Published by: Suomen Geologinen Seura/Geological Society of Finland, Betonimiehenkuja 4, PO Box 96, Espoo, 02150, Finland. TEL 358-20-5502565, FAX 358-20-55016, http://www.pro.tsv.fi/sgs, http://www.gsf.fi. Ed. Anu Karanka. Adv. contact Pasi Eilu. B&W page EUR 270, color page EUR 540; 148 x 205. Circ: 710 (paid); 740 (controlled).

554 DNK ISSN 1600-6356
GEOLOGI - GEUS-IMIT NUTAARIASSAT; immikkut saqqummersitaq. Text in Eskimo. 1999. irreg. free. **Document type:** *Monographic series, Academic/Scholarly.*
Related titles: ♦ Danish ed.: Geoviden. ISSN 1604-6935.
Published by: Miljoeministeriet, Danmarks og Groenlands Geologiske Undersoegelse (GEUS)/Danish Ministry of the Environment. Geological Survey of Denmark and Greenland, Oester Voldgade 10, Copenhagen K, 1350, Denmark. TEL 45-38-142000, FAX 45-38-142050.

551 624 ITA ISSN 0435-3870
QE272 CODEN: GAIDBG
GEOLOGIA APPLICATA E IDROGEOLOGIA. Text and summaries in English, Italian. 1986. a. charts; illus. back issues avail.
—CASDDS, Linda Hall.
Published by: Istituto di Geologia Applicata e Geotecnica, Universita di Bari, Facolta di Ingegneria, Via Re David 200, Bari, BA 70125, Italy. TEL 080 242362. Circ: 1,000.
Co-sponsor: Italian National Research Council (C.N.R.).

558 COL ISSN 0072-0992
CODEN: GECBA7
➤ **GEOLOGIA COLOMBIANA.** Text in Spanish; Summaries in English, French, German, Italian. 1962. a. USD 12 domestic; USD 75 foreign; COP 1,500 newsstand/cover (effective 2001). bk.rev. bibl. back issues avail. **Document type:** *Bulletin, Academic/Scholarly.* **Description:** Contains articles on Earth Science relating to Colombia, the Caribbean and South America.
Related titles: Fax ed.
Indexed: RefZh, ZooRec.
—Linda Hall.
Published by: Universidad Nacional de Colombia, Departamento de Geociencias, Ciudad Universitaria, Apdo Aereo 14490, Bogota, Colombia. TEL 57-1-316-5207, FAX 57-1-3165390, dgeologia@ciencias.unal.edu.co. Ed. Jairo Mojica. Pub. Carlos Macia. R&P Javier Guerrero TEL 57-1-3165390. Circ: 1,000 (controlled).

550 HRV ISSN 1330-030X
QE1 CODEN: GCROE9
➤ **GEOLOGIA CROATICA.** Text in English. 1947. s-a. HRK 400, USD 60 (effective 2004); or exchange basis. adv. **Document type:** *Journal, Academic/Scholarly.*
Formerly (until 1992): Geoloski Vjesnik (0016-7924)
Related titles: Online - full text ed.: ISSN 1333-4875. free (effective 2005).
Indexed: BiolAb, CIN, ChemAb, ChemTitl, IMMAb, MinerAb, PetrolAb, ZooRec.
—CASDDS, PADDS.

Published by: Institut za Geoloska Istrazivanja/Institute of Geology, Sachsova 2, PO Box 268, Zagreb, 10000, Croatia. TEL 385-1-6160786, FAX 385-1-6144718, geologia-croatica@zg.htnet.hr, amartek@igi.hr, http://www.geologia-croatica.hr. Eds. Igor Vlahovie, Ivo Velic TEL 385-1-6160811. Pub. Dubravko Maticee. R&P, Adv. contact Alisa Martek TEL 385-1-6160786. Circ: 600.

550 POL ISSN 0072-100X
QE276.5 CODEN: GLSDA6
➤ **GEOLOGIA SUDETICA.** Text in English, Polish. 1964. a., latest vol.33. price varies. **Document type:** *Monographic series, Academic/Scholarly.* **Description:** Covers regional geology, mineralogy and petrology of the Sudetes and their surroundings.
Indexed: AgrAg, AgrLib, ChemAb, GEOBASE, MinerAb.
—CASDDS, Linda Hall.
Published by: Polska Akademia Nauk, Instytut Nauk Mineralogicznych/Polish Academy of Sciences, Institute of Mineralogical Sciences, Ul Twarda 51-55, Warsaw, 00818, Poland. TEL 48-22-6978701, FAX 48-22-6206223, andrzejz@twarda.pan.pl, inglib@twarda.pan.pl, http://www.ing.twarda.pan.pl. Ed. Jerzy Don. R&P Andrzej Zelazniewicz. Circ: 500. **Dist. by:** Ars Polona, Krakowskie Przedmiescie 7, Warsaw, Poland. **Co-sponsor:** Uniwersytet Wroclawski, Instytut Nauk Geologicznych/Wroclaw University, Institute of Geological Sciences.

551 ITA
GEOLOGIA TECNICA & AMBIENTALE; journal of technical and environmental geology. Text in Italian. 1993. q. EUR 51.65 domestic; EUR 61.97 foreign (effective 2002).
—BLDSC (4130.470000).
Published by: Ordine Nazionale dei Geologi, Via Vittoria Colonna 40, Rome, 00193, Italy. TEL 39-06-68807736, FAX 39-06-68807742, cng.stampa@geologi.it, http://www.geologi.it/cng.

554.897 FIN ISSN 0781-643X
➤ **GEOLOGIAN TUTKIMUSKESKUS. OPAS/GEOLOGICAL SURVEY OF FINLAND. GUIDE.** Text in English, Finnish, Swedish. 1964. irreg. price varies. maps. back issues avail. **Document type:** *Monographic series, Academic/Scholarly.*
Formerly (until 1984): Geologinen Tutkimuslaitos - Opas (0430-5116)
Published by: Geological Survey of Finland, Betonimiehenkuja 4, PO Box 96, Espoo, 02151, Finland. TEL 358-205-550-11, FAX 358-205-550-12, info@gsf.fi, http://www.gsf.fi/info/og.html.

554.897 FIN
GEOLOGIAN TUTKIMUSKESKUS. TOIMINTAKERTOMUS/ GEOLOGICAL SURVEY OF FINLAND. ANNUAL REPORT. Text in English, Finnish. 1995. a. free. **Document type:** *Corporate.*
—BLDSC (1279.250000).
Published by: Geological Survey of Finland, Betonimiehenkuja 4, PO Box 96, Espoo, 02151, Finland. TEL 358-205-550-11, FAX 358-205-550-12, info@gsf.fi.

554.897 FIN ISSN 0781-4240
CODEN: TGTUE4
➤ **GEOLOGIAN TUTKIMUSKESKUS. TUTKIMUSRAPORTTI/ GEOLOGICAL SURVEY OF FINLAND. REPORT OF INVESTIGATION.** Text in English, Finnish. 1967. irreg. price varies. maps. back issues avail. **Document type:** *Monographic series, Academic/Scholarly.*
Formerly (until 1984): Geologinen Tutkimuslaitos - Tutkimusraportti (0430-5124)
Indexed: AESIS, CIN, ChemAb, ChemTitl, GEOBASE, IMMAb, RefZh.
—BLDSC (7654.860000), CASDDS, CISTI, Linda Hall.
Published by: Geological Survey of Finland, Betonimiehenkuja 4, PO Box 96, Espoo, 02151, Finland. TEL 358-205-550-11, FAX 358-205-550-12, info@gsf.fi, http://www.gsf.fi/info/tr.html.

551 ESP ISSN 1695-6133
QE1 CODEN: GAECBR
➤ **GEOLOGICA ACTA.** Text in Catalan, English, French, Spanish; Summaries in English, French, Spanish. 1966. q. EUR 29 domestic; EUR 34 foreign (effective 2005). bibl.; charts; illus. index. **Document type:** *Journal, Academic/Scholarly.* **Description:** Publishes articles in the broad field of the Earth Sciences. Its scope includes relevant conceptual developments in any area of the geological sciences and the geology of the whole world with special emphasis on Europe, the Mediterranean, South America and the Caribbean.
Formerly (until 2003): Acta Geologica Hispanica (0567-7505)
Related titles: Online - full text ed.: ISSN 1696-5728. free (effective 2005).
Indexed: BIOSIS Prev, BiolAb, ChemAb, GEOBASE, IECT, MinerAb, RefZh, ZooRec.
—BLDSC (4130.860000), CASDDS, CINDOC, IE, ingenta. **CCC.**
Published by: (Institut de Ciencies de la Terra Jaume Almera/Institute of Earth Sciences Jaume Almera, Universitat de Barcelona, Facultat de Geologia), Universitat de Barcelona, Servei de Publicacions, Gran Via Corts Catalanes 585, Barcelona, 08007, Spain. TEL 34-93-4021100, geologica-acta@ija.csic.es, http://www.geologica-acta.com:8080/geoacta/HomeAC.do, http://www.publicacions.ub.es. Ed. Lluis Cabrera. Circ: 1,100 (controlled).

550 BGR ISSN 0324-0894
QE287 CODEN: GEBAD2
GEOLOGICA BALCANICA. Text in English. 1975. 4/yr. USD 76 foreign to institutions (effective 2002). bk.rev. reprint service avail. from IRC. **Document type:** *Journal, Academic/Scholarly.* **Description:** Covers all aspects of geology of the Balkan Peninsula, regional geology, geoktonics, paleontology, mineralogy, hydrogeology, etc.
Indexed: BIOSIS Prev, BSLGeo, BiolAb, CIN, ChemAb, ChemTitl, IBR, MinerAb, RefZh, ZooRec.
—BLDSC (4130.900000), CASDDS, CINDOC, CISTI, IE, ingenta, KNAW, Linda Hall.
Published by: (Bulgarska Akademiya na Naukite/Bulgarian Academy of Sciences, Geologicheski Institut), Akademichno Izdatelstvo Prof. Marin Drinov/Prof. Marin Drinov Academic Publishing House, Akad G Bonchev 6, Sofia, 1113, Bulgaria. Ed. I. Zagorchev. Pub. I Zagorchev. **Dist. by:** Pensoft Publishers, Akad G Bonchev 6, Sofia 1113, Bulgaria. TEL 359-2-716451, FAX 359-2-704508.

554 DEU ISSN 0016-755X
QE269 CODEN: GEBAAX
GEOLOGICA BAVARICA. Text in German. 1949. irreg., latest vol.104, 1999. price varies. charts; illus.; maps. **Document type:** *Academic/Scholarly.* **Description:** Covers the regional geology of Bavaria, including mineral deposits.
Indexed: BIOSIS Prev, BiolAb, ChemAb, IBR.
Published by: Bayerisches Geologisches Landesamt, Hess-Str 128, Munich, 80797, Germany. poststelle@gla.bayern.de, http://www.geologie2.bayern.de. Ed. Hans Risch. Circ: 800.

550 SVK ISSN 1335-0552
QE1 CODEN: GECAE8
GEOLOGICA CARPATHICA; international geological journal. Text and summaries in English. 1950. 6/yr. USD 140 foreign (effective 2005). adv. bk.rev. charts; illus.; maps. cum.index: 1950-1959 in 1 vol. reprints avail. **Document type:** *Journal, Academic/Scholarly.* **Description:** Publishes original scientific works from all geological disciplines, including stratigraphic geology, depositary geology, geochemistry, paleontology, petrography, tectonics, and engineering geology. Focuses chiefly on the Carpathian and Balkan mountain ranges with occasional contributions concerning adjacent European mountain ranges.
Formerly (until 1991): Geologicky Zbornik Geologica Carpathica (0016-7738)
Indexed: ASCA, BIOSIS Prev, BiolAb, CIN, ChemAb, ChemTitl, CurCont, GEOBASE, IBR, INIS AtomInd, MinerAb, PetrolAb, RefZh, ZooRec.
—BLDSC (4131.050000), CASDDS, CISTI, IDS, IE, ingenta, Linda Hall, PADDS.
Published by: (Slovenska Akademia Vied, Geologicky Ustav/Slovak Academy of Sciences, Geological Institute), Vydavatel'stvo Slovenskej Akademie Vied Veda/Veda, Publishing House of the Slovak Academy of Sciences, Dubravska cesta 9, Bratislava, 84234, Slovakia. TEL 421-2-54774253, FAX 421-2-54772682, geolchor@savba.sk, markova@centrum.sk, http://www.geologicacarpathica.sk, http://www.veda-sav.sk. Ed. Jozef Vozar. Circ: 1,100. **Dist. by:** Slovak Academic Press Ltd., Nam Slobody 6, PO Box 57, Bratislava 81005, Slovakia. sap@sappress.sk, http://www.sappress.sk.

551 560 DEU ISSN 0072-1018
QE1 CODEN: GPALA2
➤ **GEOLOGICA ET PALAEONTOLOGICA.** Text in English, German, French, Spanish. 1967. a. EUR 90 (effective 2005). **Document type:** *Journal, Academic/Scholarly.* **Description:** Publishes original articles on all fields of paleontology, earth history, stratigraphy, and sedimentology.
Indexed: AESIS, ASFA, ESPM, IBR, RefZh, ZooRec.
—Linda Hall. **CCC.**
Published by: N.G. Elwert Verlag, Reitgasse 7-9, Marburg, 35037, Germany. TEL 49-6421-17090, FAX 49-6421-15487, elwertmail@elwert.de, http://www.elwert.de. Eds. G Hahn, M R W Amler. Circ: 500.

551 MKD ISSN 0352-1206
CODEN: GEOME2
GEOLOGICA MACEDONICA. Text in English, Macedonian. 1983. irreg., latest vol.16, 2002.
Indexed: INIS AtomInd.
Published by: Univerzitet "Kiril i Metodij" Skopje, Rudarsko-Geoloski Fakultet Stip/University St. Cyril and Methodius Skopje. Faculty of Mining and Geology-Stip, Goce Delcev 89, Stip, 2000, Macedonia. TEL 389-32-223410, FAX 389-32-223411, http://www.rgf.edu.mk/.

551 ITA ISSN 0435-3927
CODEN: GROMAL
GEOLOGICA ROMANA. Text in Italian, English. 1962. a., latest vol.36. EUR 90 per vol. (effective 2004). **Document type:** *Journal, Academic/Scholarly.* **Description:** Presents original research papers pertaining to the earth sciences, and in particular, general geology, applied geology, geomorphology, paleontology, sedimentology, geochemistry and petrography.
Indexed: BIOSIS Prev, BiolAb, GEOBASE, RefZh.
—Linda Hall.
Published by: Universita degli Studi di Roma "La Sapienza", Dipartimento di Scienze della Terra, Piazzale Aldo Moro 5, Rome, 00185, Italy. TEL 39-06-49914917, caputo@uniroma1.it, http://tetide.geo.uniroma1.it/riviste/georom/georom.html. Ed. Claudio Caputo.

554 NLD ISSN 0072-1026
QE1 CODEN: GEULAP
➤ **GEOLOGICA ULTRAIECTINA**; medelingen van de Faculteit Aardwetenschappen, Universiteit Utrecht. Text in English. 1957. irreg. EUR 29.50 per vol. (effective 2003). **Document type:** *Journal, Academic/Scholarly.* **Description:** Devoted to scientific research in the earth sciences.
Indexed: ZooRec.
—CASDDS, KNAW.
Published by: Universiteit Utrecht, Faculteit Aardwetenschappen, Library Geowetenschappen, Princetonlaan 6, Utrecht, 3584 CB, Netherlands. TEL 31-30-2534994, bibliotheek@geo.uu.nl, geo@library.uu.nl, http://www.geo.uu.nl/index.html. Circ: 200.

550 CAN ISSN 1189-6094
GEOLOGICAL ASSOCIATION OF CANADA. SHORT COURSE NOTES. Text in English. irreg. CND 80 per issue. bibl.
Indexed: IMMAb.
—**CCC.**
Published by: Geological Association of Canada, c/o Dept. of Earth Sciences, Memorial Univ. of Newfoundland, St. John's, NF A1B 3X5, Canada. TEL 709-737-7660, FAX 709-737-2532. Ed. G V Middleton. Pub., R&P Ms. K Dawe TEL 709-737-7660.

557 CAN ISSN 0072-1042
CODEN: GASPBY
GEOLOGICAL ASSOCIATION OF CANADA. SPECIAL PAPER. Text in English. 1956. irreg. CND 60 domestic; USD 60 foreign (effective 2005). back issues avail. **Document type:** *Monographic series, Academic/Scholarly.*
Indexed: AESIS, BiolAb, CIN, ChemAb, ChemTitl, IMMAb.
—CASDDS, CISTI, Linda Hall. **CCC.**
Published by: Geological Association of Canada, c/o Dept. of Earth Sciences, Memorial Univ. of Newfoundland, St. John's, NF A1B 3X5, Canada. TEL 709-737-7660, FAX 709-737-2532.

551 TUR ISSN 1300-6827
➤ **GEOLOGICAL BULLETIN OF TURKEY.** Text in English. 1947. 4/yr. USD 60 (effective 1999). adv. index. back issues avail.; reprints avail. **Document type:** *Bulletin, Academic/Scholarly.* **Description:** Includes original research papers in any subjects of geology of Turkey and surroundings.
Related titles: Turkish ed.
Indexed: ASFA, ESPM, OceAb, SWRA, ZooRec.
—CISTI.
Published by: Chamber of Geological Engineers of Turkey/TMMOB Jeoloji Muhendisleri Odasi, Yenisehir, P O Box 464, Ankara, 06444, Turkey. TEL 90-312-4342388, FAX 90-312-4342388, tmmobj-o@tr-net.net.tr, http://www.jmo.org.tr. Ed. Cem Sarac. Pub. Tmmob Jeologi Muhendisleri Odasi. R&P, Adv. contact Tmmob Jmo. Circ: 1,700 (paid); 300 (controlled).

551 GBR ISSN 0965-9994
GEOLOGICAL CONSERVATION REVIEW SERIES. Text in English. 1992. irreg. **Document type:** *Monographic series.*
—BLDSC (4133.230000), IE, ingenta.
Published by: Chapman & Hall, Journals Department (Subsidiary of: International Thomson Publishing Group), Chapman & Hall, 2-6 Boundary Row, London, SE1 8HN, United Kingdom. TEL 44-20-7865-0066, FAX 44-20-7522-9323, jhelp@chall.co.uk, http://www.chaphall.com/chaphall/journals.html.

551 FRA ISSN 0302-069X
GEOLOGICAL CORRELATION; progress report of the international geological correlation programme. Text in English, French. 1973. a., latest vol.27, 1999. free to qualified personnel. Website rev. back issues avail. **Document type:** *Monographic series.* **Description:** Contains information on National Committees, reports on sessions, lists of accepted projects, annual reports of the Scientific Committee and the Board, composition, work plans and progress reports of project working groups, current bibliographies of IGCP publications, secretariat news.
Related titles: French ed.: Correlation Geologique. ISSN 0302-0703.
Indexed: AESIS.
—Linda Hall.
Published by: UNESCO, International Geological Correlation Programme, 1 rue Miollis, Paris, Cedex 15 75732, France. TEL 33-1-45684115, FAX 33-1-45685822, TELEX 204461 PARIS, igcp@unesco.org, http://www.unesco.org/science. Ed. Wolfgang Eder. Circ: 5,500.

E

GEOLOGICAL CURATOR. see *MUSEUMS AND ART GALLERIES*

GEOLOGICAL CURATOR. SUPPLEMENT. see *MUSEUMS AND ART GALLERIES*

557 CAN ISSN 0381-243X
QE187
GEOLOGICAL FIELDWORK. Text in English. a. price varies. back issues avail. **Document type:** *Government.* **Description:** Summarizes field activity and current research of the geological survey branch of the division.
—**CCC.**
Published by: Ministry of Energy, Mines and Petroleum Resources, 5th Fl, 1810 Blanshard St, Victoria, BC V8V 1X4, Canada. Ed. Dorothe Jakobsen. **Subscr. to:** Crown Publications Inc., 521 Fort St, Victoria, BC BC V8W 1E7, Canada. TEL 604-386-4636.

554 GBR ISSN 0072-1050
QE1 CODEN: GELJA8
➤ **GEOLOGICAL JOURNAL.** Text in English. 1966. 5/yr. USD 1,260 to institutions; USD 1,386 combined subscription to institutions print & online eds. (effective 2006). adv. bk.rev. illus. Index. reprint service avail. from PQC,ISI. **Document type:** *Journal, Academic/Scholarly.*
Formerly (until 1964): Liverpool and Manchester Geological Journal
Related titles: Online - full content ed.: ISSN 1099-1034. USD 1,260 to institutions (effective 2006); Online - full text ed.: (from EBSCO Publishing, Swets Information Services, Wiley InterScience).
Indexed: ASCA, ASFA, BrGeoL, CIN, ChemAb, ChemTitl, CurCont, E&PHSE, ESPM, EngInd, GEOBASE, GP&P, IBR, ISR, Inspec, MinerAb, OffTech, PetrolAb, PollutAb, RefZh, SCI, SWRA, ZooRec.
—BLDSC (4133.600000), AskIEEE, CASDDS, Ei, IDS, IE, Infotrieve, ingenta, Linda Hall, PADDS. **CCC.**
Published by: (Liverpool Geological Society), John Wiley & Sons Ltd. (Subsidiary of: John Wiley & Sons, Inc.), The Atrium, Southern Gate, Chichester, West Sussex PO19 8SQ, United Kingdom. TEL 44-1243-779777, FAX 44-1243-775878, customer@wiley.co.uk, http://www3.interscience.wiley.com/cgi-bin/jhome/1903, http://www.wiley.co.uk. Ed. Ian D. Somerville. adv.: B&W page GBP 650, color page GBP 1,550; trim 200 x 260. Circ: 700. **Subscr. to:** John Wiley & Sons, Inc., 111 River St, Hoboken, NJ 07030-5774. TEL 201-748-6645, 800-225-5945, subinfo@wiley.com. **Co-sponsor:** Manchester Geological Society.

551 GBR ISSN 0435-3951
CODEN: GEJLA4
GEOLOGICAL JOURNAL - SPECIAL ISSUES. Text in English. 1965. irreg., latest 2001. price varies. bk.rev. reprint service avail. from PQC,ISI. **Document type:** *Academic/Scholarly.*
—CISTI.
Published by: John Wiley & Sons Ltd. (Subsidiary of: John Wiley & Sons, Inc.), The Atrium, Southern Gate, Chichester, West Sussex PO19 8SQ, United Kingdom. TEL 44-1243-779777, FAX 44-1243-775878, customer@wiley.co.uk, http://www.wiley.co.uk. Ed. P J Brenchley. Circ: 850.

551 GBR ISSN 0016-7568
QE1 CODEN: GEMGA4
➤ **GEOLOGICAL MAGAZINE.** Text in English. 1864. bi-m. GBP 339 to institutions; USD 564 in North America to institutions; GBP 378 combined subscription to institutions print & online eds.; USD 630 combined subscription in North America to institutions print & online eds. (effective 2006). adv. bk.rev. abstr.; bibl.; charts; illus.; maps. index, cum.index: 1904-1963. back issues avail.; reprint service avail. from PQC,PSC. **Document type:** *Journal, Academic/Scholarly.*
Related titles: Microfilm ed.: (from BHP); Online - full text ed.: ISSN 1469-5081. GBP 325 to institutions; USD 540 in North America to institutions (effective 2006) (from EBSCO Publishing, HighWire Press, O C L C Online Computer Library Center, Inc., Swets Information Services).
Indexed: AESIS, ASCA, ASFA, BiolAb, BrCerAb, BrGeoL, ChemAb, ChemTitl, CurCont, E&PHSE, ESPM, EngInd, ForAb, GEOBASE, GP&P, GSI, GSW, IBR, ICEA, IMMAb, ISR, MASUSE, MinerAb, OffTech, PetrolAb, PollutAb, RefZh, SCI, SPPI, SWRA, ZooRec.
—BLDSC (4134.000000), CASDDS, Ei, IDS, IE, Infotrieve, ingenta, Linda Hall, PADDS. **CCC.**
Published by: Cambridge University Press, The Edinburgh Bldg, Shaftesbury Rd, Cambridge, CB2 2RU, United Kingdom. TEL 44-1223-312393, FAX 44-1223-315052, geolmag@esc.cam.ac.uk, journals@cambridge.org, http://uk.cambridge.org/journals/geo. Eds. D M Pyle, Graham E Budd, I. N. McCave, M B Allen. R&P Linda Nicol TEL 44-1223-325757. Adv. contact Rebecca Curtis TEL 44-1223-325757. **Subscr. to:** Cambridge University Press, 100 Brook Hill Dr, West Nyack, NY 10994. TEL 845-353-7500, FAX 845-353-4141, journals_subscriptions@cup.org

550 553 IND ISSN 0016-7576
QE1 CODEN: BGMSAX
GEOLOGICAL, MINING AND METALLURGICAL SOCIETY OF INDIA. BULLETIN. Text in English. 1936. irreg. price varies. charts; illus.; maps. **Document type:** *Bulletin, Academic/Scholarly.*
—CISTI, Linda Hall.
Published by: Geological Mining and Metallurgical Society of India, Geology Department, University of Calcutta, 35 Ballygunge Circular Rd., Kolkata, West Bengal 700 019, India. TEL 91-33-475-3681. Eds. Dhruba Mukhopadhyay, Sanjib C Sarkar. Circ: 300.

750 POL ISSN 1641-7291
QE1 CODEN: KWGEA2
➤ **GEOLOGICAL QUARTERLY.** Text in English. 1957. q. EUR 34 foreign (effective 2005). charts. **Document type:** *Journal, Academic/Scholarly.* **Description:** Covers all aspects of Earth and related sciences, particularly important geological topics of Central Europe.
Formerly (until 1996): Kwartalnik Geologiczny (0023-5873)
Related titles: Online - full content ed.: 2003 (May).
Indexed: ApMecR, ChemAb, CurCont, GEOBASE, IBR, MinerAb, PetrolAb, RefZh, ZooRec.
—BLDSC (4134.750000), CASDDS, CISTI, Linda Hall, PADDS.
Published by: Panstwowy Instytut Geologiczny/Polish Geological Institute, ul Rakowiecka 4, Warsaw, 00975, Poland. TEL 48-22-8495351, FAX 48-22-8495342, GQ@pgi.waw.pl, dystryb@pgi.wa.pl, http://www.pgi.waw.pl. Eds. Dr. Andrzej Ber, Dr. Marek Narkiewicz. Circ: 750. **Dist. by:** Ars Polona, Krakowskie Przedmiescie 7, Warsaw, Poland. TEL 48-22-9263914, FAX 48-22-9265334, arspolona@arspolona.com.pl, http://www.arspolona.com.pl.

551 CAN
GEOLOGICAL REFERENCE BOOK. Text in English. a. looseleaf. CND 112. back issues avail. **Document type:** *Government.* **Description:** Indicates the Division's interpretation of the various pools in the province with interpretative net pay maps.
Published by: Ministry of Energy and Mines, c/o Communications Coordinator, Stn Prov Govt, PO Box 9324, Victoria, BC V8W 9N3, Canada. TEL 250-952-0525, http://www.ogc.gov.bc.ca. **Subscr. to:** Crown Publications Inc., 521 Fort St, Victoria, BC BC V8W 1E7, Canada. TEL 250-386-4636, FAX 250-386-0221, crown@pinc.com, http://www.crownpub.bc.ca.

551 GBR ISSN 0016-7649
QE1 CODEN: JGSLAS
➤ **GEOLOGICAL SOCIETY. JOURNAL.** Text in English. 1826. bi-m. GBP 530 domestic; GBP 605, USD 1,089 foreign (effective 2005). adv. bibl.; illus.; maps. index, cum.index approx. every 50 vols. back issues avail.; reprints avail. **Document type:** *Journal, Academic/Scholarly.* **Description:** It is among the world's leading references for significant research in geology. Edited for geologists in academia, government, industry, and business, and it includes a special paper section for rapid publication.
Former titles (until 1971): Geological Society of London. Quarterly Journal (0370-291X); (until 1845): Geological Society of London. Proceedings
Related titles: Online - full text ed.: (from bigchalk, EBSCO Publishing, Gale Group, HighWire Press, IngentaConnect, O C L C Online Computer Library Center, Inc., ProQuest Information & Learning, Swets Information Services).
Indexed: AESIS, ASCA, ASFA, BiolAb, BrArAb, BrGeoL, CIN, ChemAb, ChemTitl, CurCont, E&PHSE, ESPM, EngInd, GEOBASE, GP&P, GSW, IMMAb, ISR, Inspec, MinerAb, OffTech, PetrolAb, RefZh, SCI, ZooRec.
—BLDSC (4755.900000), AskIEEE, CASDDS, CISTI, Ei, IDS, IE, Infotrieve, ingenta, Linda Hall, PADDS. **CCC.**
Published by: (Geological Society of London), Geological Society Publishing House, Unit 7, Brassmill Enterprise Centre, Brassmill Ln, Bath, Avon BA1 3JN, United Kingdom. TEL 44-1225-445046, FAX 44-1225-442836, dawn.angel@geolsoc.org.uk, rebecca.toop@geolsoc.org.uk, http://www.geolsoc.org.uk/template.cfm?name=Journals_JGS_home_page. Ed. Nick Rogers. Pub. M Collins. Circ: 5,200.

551 USA ISSN 0016-7606
QE1 CODEN: BUGMAF
➤ **GEOLOGICAL SOCIETY OF AMERICA. BULLETIN.** Text in English. 1890. m. USD 560 domestic; USD 575 foreign; USD 710 combined subscription domestic print & online ed.; USD 725 combined subscription foreign print & online ed. (effective 2005). adv. bibl.; illus.; maps; abstr. index. back issues avail.; reprint service avail. from PQC. **Document type:** *Journal, Academic/Scholarly.* **Description:** Presents papers on the results of international research on all earth science disciplines.
Formerly (until 1961): Bulletin of the Geological Society of America (1050-9747)
Related titles: CD-ROM ed.; Microform ed.: (from PMC, PQC); Online - full text ed.: (from EBSCO Publishing, HighWire Press).
Indexed: AESIS, AJEE, AS&TI, ASCA, ASFA, BibAg, BiolAb, BrCerAb, BrGeoL, C&ISA, CIN, CTO, CerAb, ChemAb, ChemTitl, CivEngAb, CorrAb, CurCont, E&CAJ, E&PHSE, EEA, EIA, EMA, ESPM, EngInd, EnvAb, GEOBASE, GP&P, GSI, GSW, GeotechAb, HRIS, IAA, ICEA, INIS AtomInd, ISR, M&GPA, M&TEA, MBF, METADEX, MinerAb, OceAb, OffTech, PetrolAb, RefZh, S&F, SCI, SPPI, SWRA, SolStAb, WAA, ZooRec.
—BLDSC (4136.800000), CASDDS, CISTI, IDS, IE, Infotrieve, ingenta, Linda Hall, PADDS. **CCC.**
Published by: Geological Society of America, 3300 Penrose Pl, Boulder, CO 80301-1806. TEL 303-447-2020, 800-472-1988, FAX 303-447-1133, pubs@geosociety.org, http://www.geosociety.org/pubs/. Adv. contact Ann Crawford. Circ: 7,500. **Subscr. to:** Allen Press Inc., PO Box 1897, Lawrence, KS 66044. TEL 785-843-1235, FAX 785-843-1274.

551 USA ISSN 0096-4271
QE1
GEOLOGICAL SOCIETY OF AMERICA, INC. PROCEEDINGS VOLUME. Text in English. 1933. a.
Formerly (until 1941): Geological Society of America. Proceedings (0160-2381)
—CISTI.
Published by: Geological Society of America, 3300 Penrose Pl, Boulder, CO 80301-1806. TEL 303-447-2020, FAX 303-447-1133, pubs@geosociety.org, http://www.geosociety.org.

551 USA ISSN 0272-0795
CODEN: MSGADL
➤ **GEOLOGICAL SOCIETY OF AMERICA. MAP AND CHART SERIES.** Text in English. irreg. price varies. **Document type:** *Monographic series, Academic/Scholarly.*
—**CCC.**
Published by: Geological Society of America, 3300 Penrose Pl, Boulder, CO 80301-1806. TEL 303-447-2020, 888-443-4472, FAX 303-447-1133, pubs@geosociety.org, http://www.geosociety.org.

551 560 USA ISSN 0072-1069
CODEN: GSAMAQ
➤ **GEOLOGICAL SOCIETY OF AMERICA. MEMOIRS.** Text in English. 1888. irreg., latest vol.197, 2004. price varies. index. **Document type:** *Monographic series, Academic/Scholarly.* **Description:** Presents results of long-term geological studies and projects.
Indexed: AESIS, BiolAb, ChemAb, E&PHSE, EEA, GP&P, IMMAb, OffTech, PetrolAb, ZooRec.
—BLDSC (5606.000000), CASDDS, IE, ingenta, Linda Hall, PADDS. **CCC.**
Published by: Geological Society of America, 3300 Penrose Pl, Boulder, CO 80301-1806. TEL 303-447-2020, FAX 303-447-1133, pubs@geosociety.org, http://www.geosociety.org.

551 USA ISSN 0091-5041
QE21 CODEN: GSCMB3
GEOLOGICAL SOCIETY OF AMERICA. MEMORIALS. Key Title: Memorials - Geological Society of America. Text in English. 1973. a. price varies. bibl.; illus. **Document type:** *Journal, Academic/Scholarly.* **Description:** Contains memorials to deceased fellows and society members. Most include bibliographies of their work.
Indexed: IMMAb.
—Linda Hall. **CCC.**
Published by: Geological Society of America, 3300 Penrose Pl, Boulder, CO 80301-1806. TEL 303-447-2020, FAX 303-447-1133, pubs@geosociety.org, http://www.geosociety.org.

551 560 USA ISSN 0072-1077
CODEN: GSAPAZ
➤ **GEOLOGICAL SOCIETY OF AMERICA. SPECIAL PAPERS.** Text in English. 1934. irreg., latest vol.380, 2004. price varies. charts; illus.; maps. index. **Document type:** *Monographic series, Academic/Scholarly.* **Description:** State of the art research in the earth sciences.
Indexed: AESIS, BIOSIS Prev, BiolAb, ChemAb, E&PHSE, GP&P, IMMAb, OffTech, PetrolAb, ZooRec.
—BLDSC (8368.000000), CASDDS, IE, ingenta, Linda Hall, PADDS. **CCC.**
Published by: Geological Society of America, 3300 Penrose Pl, Boulder, CO 80301-1806. TEL 303-447-2020, FAX 303-447-1133, pubs@geosociety.org, http://www.geosociety.org.

551 USA ISSN 1556-4800
▼ **GEOLOGICAL SOCIETY OF AMERICA. SPECIALTY MEETINGS, ABSTRACTS WITH PROGRAMS.** Text in English. 2005. irreg.
Published by: Geological Society of America, 3300 Penrose Pl, Boulder, CO 80301-1806. TEL 303-447-2020, 888-443-4472, FAX 303-447-1133, pubs@geosociety.org, http://www.geosociety.org.

GEOLOGICAL SOCIETY OF AUSTRALIA. ABSTRACTS SERIES. see *EARTH SCIENCES—Abstracting, Bibliographies, Statistics*

559.4 AUS ISSN 0072-1085
CODEN: GSASBB
GEOLOGICAL SOCIETY OF AUSTRALIA. SPECIAL PUBLICATION. Text in English. 1967. irreg. price varies. back issues avail. **Document type:** *Academic/Scholarly.*
Indexed: AESIS, IMMAb.
—CISTI. **CCC.**
Published by: Geological Society of Australia Inc., Ste 706, 301 George St, Sydney, NSW 2000, Australia. TEL 61-2-92902194, FAX 61-2-92902198, info@gsa.org.au, http://www.gsa.org.au.

E

551.9 TWN ISSN 1018-7057
QE1 CODEN: JGSCE5
➤ **GEOLOGICAL SOCIETY OF CHINA. JOURNAL.** Text in English. 1958. q. USD 30 (effective 1999). back issues avail. **Document type:** *Academic/Scholarly.*
Formerly (until 1992): Zhongguo Dizhi Xuehui Huikan - Geological Society of China. Proceedings (0431-2155)
Indexed: AESIS, BiolAb, CIN, ChemAb, ChemTitl, GEOBASE, MinerAb, PetrolAb, RefZh, ZooRec.
—BLDSC (4756.250000), CASDDS, Ei, ingenta, PADDS.
Published by: Geological Society of China, 245 Choushan Rd, Taipei, Taiwan. TEL 886-2-23622629, FAX 886-2-23621843, geolsoc@w2.ohya.com.tw. Ed. Yuan Wang. **Co-sponsor:** Academia Sinica, Institute of Earth Sciences.

554 DNK ISSN 0011-6297
CODEN: MDGFAU
➤ **GEOLOGICAL SOCIETY OF DENMARK. BULLETIN.** Text in English; Summaries in Danish. 1894. 2/yr. DKK 480 to individual members; DKK 900 to institutional members; DKK 240 to students; DKK 75 per issue (effective 2004). adv. bk.rev. bibl.; charts; illus. cum.index. back issues avail. **Document type:** *Journal, Academic/Scholarly.* **Description:** Emphasis on geology in Denmark, the Faroe Islands, and Greenland.
Formerly (until 1970): Dansk Geologisk Forening. Meddelelser (0105-1040)
Related titles: Online - full text ed.
Indexed: BIOSIS Prev, BiolAb, BrGeoL, CIN, ChemAb, ChemTitl, CurCont, PetrolAb, ZooRec.
—CASDDS, Linda Hall, PADDS. **CCC.**
Published by: Dansk Geologisk Forening/Geological Society of Denmark, Oester Voldgade 5-7, Copenhagen K, 1350, Denmark. TEL 46-35-322354, FAX 46-35-322325, dgf@geologi.com, http://www.2dgf.dk/Publikationer/ramme-publikat.htm. Eds. Michael Houmark-Nielsen, Svend Stouge. Circ: 1,100.

➤ **GEOLOGICAL SOCIETY OF EGYPT. ANNUAL MEETING. ABSTRACTS OF PAPERS.** see *EARTH SCIENCES—Abstracting, Bibliographies, Statistics*

550 FIN ISSN 0367-5211
QE276.3 CODEN: GSFBBJ
➤ **GEOLOGICAL SOCIETY OF FINLAND. BULLETIN.** Text in English. 1929. s-a. EUR 32 (effective 2003). 2 cols./p.; back issues avail. **Document type:** *Bulletin, Academic/Scholarly.*
Formerly (until 1968): Suomen Geologisen Seuran Julkaisuja (0355-4716)
Indexed: BIOSIS Prev, BiolAb, GEOBASE, INIS AtomInd, RefZh.
—BLDSC (2525.550000), CISTI, IE, ingenta, Linda Hall.
Published by: Suomen Geologinen Seura/Geological Society of Finland, Betonimiehenkuja 4, PO Box 96, Espoo, 02150, Finland. TEL 358-20-5502565, FAX 358-20-55016, http://www.pro.tsv.fi/sgs, http://www.gsf.fi. Ed. Petri Peltonen. Circ: 165 (paid); 175 (controlled).

551 GRC ISSN 0438-9557
GEOLOGICAL SOCIETY OF GREECE. BULLETIN/DELTIO TES ELLENIKES GEOLOGIKES ETAIREIAS. Text and summaries in English, Greek. 1951. a. USD 30 foreign. back issues avail. **Document type:** *Bulletin.*
Indexed: ASFA, ESPM, ZooRec.
Published by: Geological Society of Greece, 50 Konstantilieri, PO Box 71539, Vyronas, Athens 162 31, Greece. TEL 30-1-7644677, FAX 30-1-7644677, skarpelis@geol.uoa.gr. Circ: 1,200.

550 IND ISSN 0016-7622
QE1 CODEN: JGSIAJ
➤ **GEOLOGICAL SOCIETY OF INDIA. JOURNAL.** Text in English. 1959. m. USD 400 to institutions (effective 2006). bk.rev. charts; illus. index. back issues avail. **Document type:** *Journal, Academic/Scholarly.* **Description:** Research articles promoting the cause of investigation, discovery and inventions in the field of earth sciences.
Related titles: Microform ed.: (from PQC).
Indexed: AESIS, ASCA, ASFA, BiolAb, CIN, CRIA, CRICC, ChemAb, ChemTitl, CurCont, E&PHSE, ESPM, EngInd, GEOBASE, GP&P, INIS AtomInd, MSB, MinerAb, OffTech, PetrolAb, ZooRec.
—BLDSC (4756.800000), CASDDS, CISTI, Ei, IDS, IE, ingenta, Linda Hall, PADDS. **CCC.**
Published by: (Geological Society of India), Scientific Publishers, 5-A New Pali Rd., Near Hotel Taj Hari Mahal, PO Box 91, Jodhpur, Rajasthan 342 003, India. TEL 91-291-2433323, FAX 91-291-2512580, info@scientificpub.com, http://www.scientificpub.com/bookdetails.php?booktransid=483&bookid=479. Circ: 2,000 (controlled).

550 IND ISSN 0435-4001
GEOLOGICAL SOCIETY OF INDIA. MEMOIR. Text in English. 1963. irreg. **Document type:** *Government.*
Indexed: ZooRec.
—BLDSC (5606.080000), IE, ingenta, Linda Hall.
Published by: (Geological Society of India), Scientific Publishers, 5-A New Pali Rd., Near Hotel Taj Hari Mahal, PO Box 91, Jodhpur, Rajasthan 342 003, India.

550 GBR ISSN 0435-4052
GEOLOGICAL SOCIETY OF LONDON. MEMOIRS. Text in English. 1958. irreg. **Document type:** *Government.*
—ingenta, Linda Hall. **CCC.**
Published by: (Geological Society of London), Geological Society Publishing House, Unit 7, Brassmill Enterprise Centre, Brassmill Ln, Bath, Avon BA1 3JN, United Kingdom.

550 GBR ISSN 0305-0394
GEOLOGICAL SOCIETY OF LONDON. MISCELLANEOUS PAPER. Text in English. 1974. irreg. **Document type:** *Government.*
—BLDSC (5814.450000), CISTI, Linda Hall. **CCC.**
Published by: (Geological Society of London), Geological Society Publishing House, Unit 7, Brassmill Enterprise Centre, Brassmill Ln, Bath, Avon BA1 3JN, United Kingdom.

550 GBR
GEOLOGICAL SOCIETY OF LONDON. PROFESSIONAL HANDBOOK SERIES. Text in English. irreg. **Document type:** *Government.*
Published by: (Geological Society of London), Geological Society Publishing House, Unit 7, Brassmill Enterprise Centre, Brassmill Ln, Bath, Avon BA1 3JN, United Kingdom.

555 MYS ISSN 0126-6187
QE299.5 CODEN: BPMAEC
➤ **GEOLOGICAL SOCIETY OF MALAYSIA. BULLETIN.** Text in English. 1968. irreg. price varies. back issues avail. **Document type:** *Bulletin, Academic/Scholarly.* **Description:** Studies the geology of the South-East Asian region and surrounding marine areas.
Indexed: BiolAb, IMMAb, PetrolAb.
—Linda Hall, PADDS.
Published by: Geological Society of Malaysia/Persatuan Geologi Malaysia, d/a Jabatan Geologi, Universiti Malaya, Kuala Lumpur, 50603, Malaysia. TEL 60-3-79577036, FAX 60-3-79563900, geologi@po.jaring.my, http://www.angelfire.com.la/gsm. Circ: 600.

550 GBR ISSN 0143-9286
CODEN: BGSNDH
GEOLOGICAL SOCIETY OF NORFOLK. BULLETIN. Text in English. 1968. irreg.
Indexed: ZooRec.
—BLDSC (2525.820000).
Published by: Geological Society of Norfolk, 8 Eaton Old Hall, Hurd Rd, Eaton, Norfolk, Norwich NR4 7BE, United Kingdom. TEL 44-1603-708098, http://www.norfolkgeology.co.uk/.

550 GBR
GEOLOGICAL SOCIETY OF NORFOLK. NEWSLETTER. Text in English. q.
Published by: Geological Society of Norfolk, 8 Eaton Old Hall, Hurd Rd, Eaton, Norfolk, Norwich NR4 7BE, United Kingdom. TEL 44-1603-708098, http://www.norfolkgeology.co.uk/.

556 ZAF ISSN 0256-3029
GEOLOGICAL SOCIETY OF SOUTH AFRICA. GEOBULLETIN/GEOLOGIESE VERENIGING VAN SUID-AFRICA. GEOBULLETIN. Key Title: Geobulletin. Text in English; Text occasionally in Afrikaans. 1958. q. ZAR 48. bk.rev. charts; illus. **Document type:** *Bulletin.* **Description:** Provides news and information in the field of geology, including technical articles, reports, society and branch news, and announcements of events of interest to geologists.
Formerly (until 1984): Geological Society of South Africa. Quarterly News Bulletin - Geologiese Vereniging van Suid-Afrika. Kwartaalikse Nuusbulletin (0016-7657)
Indexed: AESIS, IMMAb.
Published by: Geological Society of South Africa/Geologiese Vereniging van Suid-Afrika, PO Box 44283, Linden, Gauteng 2104, South Africa. TEL 27-11-888-2288, FAX 27-11-888-1632. Circ: 800.

556 ZAF
GEOLOGICAL SOCIETY OF SOUTH AFRICA. SPECIAL PUBLICATION. Text in English. 1970. irreg. (SP13), latest 1986. price varies.
Indexed: IMMAb.
Published by: Geological Society of South Africa/Geologiese Vereniging van Suid-Afrika, PO Box 44283, Linden, Gauteng 2104, South Africa. TEL 27-11-888-2288, FAX 27-11-888-1632. Circ: 2,000.

557 USA ISSN 0270-5451
➤ **GEOLOGICAL SOCIETY OF THE OREGON COUNTRY. GEOLOGICAL NEWSLETTER.** Text in English. 1935. m. USD 15 (effective 2002); for libraries and organizations. bk.rev. abstr.; charts; illus.; maps. index. 6 p./no.; back issues avail.; reprints avail. **Document type:** *Newsletter, Academic/Scholarly.* **Description:** News items and announcements pertaining to the members and activities of the society.
Published by: Geological Society of the Oregon Country, PO Box 907, Portland, OR 97207. TEL 360-574-9650. Ed., R&P Marlene Adams. Circ: 300 (paid).

550 NLD ISSN 0921-4054
CODEN: GSZPES
GEOLOGICAL SOCIETY OF ZIMBABWE. Text in English. 1984. irreg. **Document type:** *Monographic series.*
—CASDDS.
Published by: (Geological Society of Zimbabwe), A A Balkema (Subsidiary of: Taylor & Francis The Netherlands), PO Box 1675, Rotterdam, 3000 BR, Netherlands. FAX 31-10-413-5947, sales@balkema.nl, http://www.balkema.nl. **Dist. in U.S. by:** Ashgate Publishing Co, Old Post Rd, Brookfield, VT 05036. TEL 800-535-9544.

551 GBR ISSN 0305-8719
CODEN: GSSPDQ
GEOLOGICAL SOCIETY SPECIAL PUBLICATION. Text in English. irreg., latest vol.170. price varies. illus.; maps. **Document type:** *Monographic series.*
Indexed: BrArAb, FLUIDEX, GEOBASE, IMMAb, MSB, ZooRec.
—BLDSC (8378.660000), CASDDS, CISTI, IE, ingenta. **CCC.**
Published by: (Geological Society of London), Geological Society Publishing House, Unit 7, Brassmill Enterprise Centre, Brassmill Ln, Bath, Avon BA1 3JN, United Kingdom. TEL 44-1225-445046, FAX 44-1225-442836, collinsm@geolsoc.org.uk, rebecca.toop@geolsoc.org.uk, http://www.geolsoc.org.uk, http://www.bookshop.geolsoc.org.uk. **Dist. by:** A A P G Bookstore, PO Box 979, Tulsa, OK 74101-0979. TEL 918-584-2555, 918-560-2652.

557 USA ISSN 0097-3262
QE81 CODEN: AGBLAE
GEOLOGICAL SURVEY OF ALABAMA. BULLETIN. Text in English. 1886. q. **Document type:** *Bulletin, Government.*
Indexed: ZooRec.
—CISTI, Linda Hall.
Published by: Geological Survey of Alabama, 420 Hackberry Lane, Tuscaloosa, AL 35486. TEL 205-349-2852, FAX 205-349-2861, info@state.al.us, http://www.gsa.state.al.us.

557 USA ISSN 0097-3149
GEOLOGICAL SURVEY OF ALABAMA. CIRCULAR. Text in English. 1895. irreg. **Document type:** *Government.*
—CISTI, Linda Hall.
Published by: Geological Survey of Alabama, 420 Hackberry Lane, Tuscaloosa, AL 35486. TEL 205-349-2852, FAX 205-349-2861, info@state.al.us, http://www.gsa.state.al.us.

557 353.9 USA
GEOLOGICAL SURVEY OF ALABAMA. GEOLOGY AND GROUND WATER RESOURCES REPORT. Text in English. irreg. **Document type:** *Government.*
Published by: Geological Survey of Alabama, 420 Hackberry Lane, Tuscaloosa, AL 35486. TEL 205-349-2852, FAX 205-349-2861, info@state.al.us, http://www.gsa.state.al.us.

557 USA ISSN 0886-7526
GEOLOGICAL SURVEY OF ALABAMA. MONOGRAPH. Text in English. 1883. irreg. **Document type:** *Monographic series, Government.*
Indexed: ZooRec.
—CISTI, Linda Hall.
Published by: Geological Survey of Alabama, 420 Hackberry Lane, Tuscaloosa, AL 35486. TEL 205-349-2852, FAX 205-349-2861, info@state.al.us, http://www.gsa.state.al.us.

GEOLOGICAL SURVEY OF ALABAMA. OIL AND GAS REPORT. see *PETROLEUM AND GAS*

551 DNK
▼ ➤ **GEOLOGICAL SURVEY OF DENMARK AND GREENLAND BULLETIN.** Text in English. 2003. irreg. **Document type:** *Monographic series, Academic/Scholarly.*
Formed by the merger of (1948-2003): Geology of Greenland Survey Bulletin (1397-1905); (1995-2003): Geology of Denmark Survey Bulletin (1397-1891)
Published by: Miljoeministeriet, Danmarks og Groenlands Geologiske Undersoegelse (GEUS)/Danish Ministry of the Environment. Geological Survey of Denmark and Greenland, Oester Voldgade 10, Copenhagen K, 1350, Denmark. TEL 45-38-142000, FAX 45-38-142050, geus@geus.dk, htpp://www.geus.dk. Ed. Peter R Dawes TEL 45-38-14-22-01.

554.897 FIN ISSN 0367-522X
CODEN: GSFNAK
➤ **GEOLOGICAL SURVEY OF FINLAND. BULLETIN.** Text in English. 1895. irreg. maps. Supplement avail.; back issues avail. **Document type:** *Bulletin, Academic/Scholarly.*
Formerly (until 1971): Bulletin de la Commission Geologique de Finlande (0365-9283)
Indexed: AESIS, GEOBASE, IMMAb, INIS AtomInd, Inspec, RefZh.
—CASDDS, CISTI, Linda Hall.
Published by: Geological Survey of Finland, Betonimiehenkuja 4, PO Box 96, Espoo, 02151, Finland. TEL 358-205-550-11, FAX 358-205-550-12, info@gsf.fi, http://www.gsf.fi/info/bt.html.

554.897 FIN ISSN 0782-8535
CODEN: GSFPEU
➤ **GEOLOGICAL SURVEY OF FINLAND. SPECIAL PAPER.** Text in English. 1987. irreg. price varies. maps. back issues avail. **Document type:** *Proceedings, Academic/Scholarly.*
Indexed: GEOBASE, IMMAb.
—BLDSC (8368.008000), CISTI, IE, ingenta, Linda Hall.
Published by: Geological Survey of Finland, Betonimiehenkuja 4, PO Box 96, Espoo, 02151, Finland. TEL 358-205-550-11, FAX 358-205-550-12, info@gsf.fi, http://www.gsf.fi/info/sp.html.

555.2 JPN
TN270.A1 CODEN: CHCHB3
GEOLOGICAL SURVEY OF HOKKAIDO. REPORT. Text in Japanese; Abstracts in English. 1950. a. per issue exchange basis. back issues avail. **Document type:** *Academic/Scholarly.*
Former titles (until Mar. 2001): Hokkaidoritsu Chishitsu Kenkyusho Hokoku (1345-3815); (until 1999): Chika Shigen Chosajo Hokoku (0441-0785); (until 1958): Hokkaido Chika Shigen Chosa Hokoku (0286-7583)
Indexed: ChemAb, JPI.
Published by: Hokkaidoritsu Chishitsu Kenkyusyo/Geological Survey of Hokkaido, N19 W12, Kita-ku, Sapporo, Hokkaido 060-0819, Japan. TEL 81-11-747-2211, FAX 81-11-737-9071, gsh@gsh.pref.hokkaido.jp, http://www.gsh.pref.hokkaido.jp. Ed., Pub. Toru Wake. R&P Kunihiko Kurosawa. Circ: 900 (controlled).

551 IND ISSN 0378-4029
QE295 CODEN: GSINB2
GEOLOGICAL SURVEY OF INDIA. NEWS. Text in English. 1970. m. free. adv. charts; illus.
Indexed: CRIA, CRICC, RefZh.
Published by: Geological Survey of India, 29 Jawaharlal Nehru Rd., Kolkata, West Bengal 700 016, India. Ed. T K Kurien. Circ: 2,500.

554 IRL ISSN 0085-0985
QE265 CODEN: GSVIBI
GEOLOGICAL SURVEY OF IRELAND. BULLETIN. Text in English. 1970. irreg., latest vol.4, 1991, part 3. free (effective 2005). adv. cum.index. **Document type:** *Bulletin.*
Indexed: BrGeoL, IMMAb.
—CISTI.
Published by: Geological Survey of Ireland/Suirbheireacht Gheolaiochta Eireann, Beggars Bush, Haddington Rd, Dublin, 4, Ireland. TEL 353-1-6782868, FAX 353-1-6681782, gsisales@gsi.ie, http://www.gsi.ie/. Circ: 650.

551 IRL ISSN 0790-7753
GEOLOGICAL SURVEY OF IRELAND. GROUNDWATER NEWSLETTER. Variant title: G S I Groundwater Newsletter. Text in English. 1986. q.
—BLDSC (4223.779000).
Published by: Geological Survey of Ireland/Suirbheireacht Gheolaiochta Eireann, Beggars Bush, Haddington Rd, Dublin, 4, Ireland. TEL 353-1-6782868, FAX 353-1-6681782.

554 IRL ISSN 0790-0260
GEOLOGICAL SURVEY OF IRELAND. GUIDE SERIES. Text in English. 1976. irreg., latest 1983. price varies. **Document type:** *Monographic series.*
Published by: Geological Survey of Ireland/Suirbheireacht Gheolaiochta Eireann, Beggars Bush, Haddington Rd, Dublin, 4, Ireland. TEL 353-1-6782868, FAX 353-1-6681782.

554 IRL ISSN 0085-0993
GEOLOGICAL SURVEY OF IRELAND. INFORMATION CIRCULARS. Text in English. 1970. irreg., latest 1989. price varies. adv. **Document type:** *Monographic series.*
Indexed: IMMAb.
Published by: Geological Survey of Ireland/Suirbheireacht Gheolaiochta Eireann, Beggars Bush, Haddington Rd, Dublin, 4, Ireland. TEL 353-1-6782868, FAX 353-1-6681782. Circ: 500.

554 IRL ISSN 0790-0279
GEOLOGICAL SURVEY OF IRELAND. REPORT SERIES. Text in English. irreg., latest 1994. price varies. **Document type:** *Monographic series.*
Indexed: IMMAb.
—BLDSC (7671.928000).
Published by: Geological Survey of Ireland/Suirbheireacht Gheolaiochta Eireann, Beggars Bush, Haddington Rd, Dublin, 4, Ireland. TEL 353-1-6782868, FAX 353-1-6681782.

554 IRL ISSN 0085-1019
GEOLOGICAL SURVEY OF IRELAND. SPECIAL PAPERS. Text in English. 1971. irreg. price varies. **Document type:** *Monographic series.*
Indexed: IMMAb.
Published by: Geological Survey of Ireland/Suirbheireacht Gheolaiochta Eireann, Beggars Bush, Haddington Rd, Dublin, 4, Ireland. TEL 353-1-6782868, FAX 353-1-6681782. Circ: 600.

551 JPN ISSN 0288-5980
CODEN: CRGJDX
GEOLOGICAL SURVEY OF JAPAN. CRUISE REPORT. Text in English. 1974. irreg. charts; illus.
Indexed: ASFA, BiolAb.
Published by: Kogyo Gijutsuin, Chishitsu Chosajo/National Institute of Advanced Industrial Science & Technology, Geological Survey of Japan, AIST Tsukuba Central 7, 1-1, Higashi 1-Chome, Tsukuba, Ibaraki 305-0046, Japan. TEL 81-29-8619122, FAX 81-29-8613672, http://www.aist.go.jp, http://www.gsj.jp/. Ed. Hideo Takeda.

556 NAM ISSN 1026-2954
QE339.N34
GEOLOGICAL SURVEY OF NAMIBIA. COMMUNICATIONS. Text in English. 1985. a. price varies. **Document type:** *Government.*
Formerly (until vol.5, 1989): Geological Survey of South West Africa - Namibia. Communications (0256-1697)
Indexed: AESIS, IMMAb.
—BLDSC (3351.591000), Linda Hall.
Published by: Ministry of Mines and Energy, Geological Survey of Namibia, Aviation Rd 1, PO Box 2168, Windhoek, Namibia. TEL 264-61-249150, FAX 264-61-249144. Circ: 800.

556 NAM
GEOLOGICAL SURVEY OF NAMIBIA. MEMOIRS. Text in English. 1965. irreg., latest vol.17, 1993. price varies. **Document type:** *Monographic series.*
Former titles (until 1990): Geological Survey of South West Africa - Namibia. Memoirs; (until 1981): South West Africa Series. Memoirs
Indexed: AESIS, IMMAb.
Published by: Ministry of Mines and Energy, Geological Survey of Namibia, Aviation Rd 1, PO Box 2168, Windhoek, Namibia. TEL 264-61-249150, FAX 264-61-249144. Circ: 800.

556 NAM
GEOLOGICAL SURVEY OF NAMIBIA. REPORTS ON OPEN FILE. C D M MINERAL SURVEYS. Text in English. irreg., latest vol.12, 1996. price varies. **Document type:** *Government.*
Published by: Ministry of Mines and Energy, Geological Survey of Namibia, Aviation Rd 1, PO Box 2168, Windhoek, Namibia. TEL 264-61-249150, FAX 264-61-249144.

553 NAM
GEOLOGICAL SURVEY OF NAMIBIA. REPORTS ON OPEN FILE. ECONOMIC GEOLOGY. Text in English; Text occasionally in Afrikaans. 1921. irreg., latest vol.101, 1998. price varies. **Document type:** *Government.* **Description:** Series of preliminary reports on topics in economic geology.
Published by: Ministry of Mines and Energy, Geological Survey of Namibia, Aviation Rd 1, PO Box 2168, Windhoek, Namibia. TEL 264-61-249150, FAX 264-61-249144.

556 620 NAM
GEOLOGICAL SURVEY OF NAMIBIA. REPORTS ON OPEN FILE. ENGINEERING GEOLOGY. Text in English. 1983. irreg. price varies. **Document type:** *Government.* **Description:** Series of preliminary reports on topics in engineering geology.
Published by: Ministry of Mines and Energy, Geological Survey of Namibia, Aviation Rd 1, PO Box 2168, Windhoek, Namibia. TEL 264-61-249150, FAX 264-61-249144.

556 NAM
GEOLOGICAL SURVEY OF NAMIBIA. REPORTS ON OPEN FILE. MINERAL RESOURCE SERIES. Text in English. irreg., latest vol.51, 1992. price varies. **Document type:** *Government.* **Description:** Series of preliminary reports from mineral resource studies.
Published by: Ministry of Mines and Energy, Geological Survey of Namibia, Aviation Rd 1, PO Box 2168, Windhoek, Namibia. TEL 264-61-249150, FAX 264-61-249144.

556 NAM
GEOLOGICAL SURVEY OF NAMIBIA. REPORTS ON OPEN FILE. REGIONAL GEOLOGY. Text in English; Text occasionally in Afrikaans. 1970. irreg., latest vol.8, 1984. price varies. **Document type:** *Government.* **Description:** Series of preliminary reports on topics in regional geology.
Published by: Ministry of Mines and Energy, Geological Survey of Namibia, Aviation Rd 1, PO Box 2168, Windhoek, Namibia. TEL 264-61-249150, FAX 264-61-249144.

559.4 AUS ISSN 0365-4400
GEOLOGICAL SURVEY OF SOUTH AUSTRALIA. BULLETIN. Text in English. 1912. irreg., latest vol.54, 1995. price varies. back issues avail. **Document type:** *Bulletin, Government.* **Description:** Regional geological research studies. Includes information on groundwater and mineral resources.
Related titles: Microfiche ed.
Indexed: AESIS, IMMAb.
Published by: Primary Industries and Resources South Australia, GPO Box 1671, Adelaide, SA 5001, Australia. TEL 61-8-84633000, FAX 61-8-82041880. Ed. John F Drexel. Circ: 1,000.

551 AUS ISSN 0572-0125
GEOLOGICAL SURVEY OF SOUTH AUSTRALIA. EXPLANATORY NOTES. Text in English. 1972. irreg. AUD 20 including map (effective 2000). back issues avail. **Document type:** *Government.* **Description:** Explanatory notes to the standard 1:250000 geological map sheets, containing summaries of geology, stratigraphy, tectonics and mineral occurrences.
Indexed: AESIS, EngInd, IMMAb.
Published by: Primary Industries and Resources South Australia, GPO Box 1671, Adelaide, SA 5001, Australia. TEL 61-8-84633000, FAX 61-8-84041880.

551 AUS ISSN 0016-7681
QE345 CODEN: AMGNAJ
GEOLOGICAL SURVEY OF SOUTH AUSTRALIA. REPORT OF INVESTIGATIONS. Text in English. 1954. irreg. price varies. back issues avail. **Document type:** *Government.* **Description:** Technical accounts of investigations in applied geology.
Indexed: AESIS, EngInd, IMMAb.
Published by: Primary Industries and Resources South Australia, GPO Box 1671, Adelaide, SA 5001, Australia. TEL 61-8-84633000, FAX 61-8-82041880.

550 ARM ISSN 0016-769X
GEOLOGICHESKII ZHURNAL ARMENII/GITUTSUNNER ERKRY MASSIN. Text and summaries in Armenian, English, Russian. 1948. 3/yr. AMD 300. charts; illus. index. **Document type:** *Academic/Scholarly.*
Published by: Hayastany Guitoutyunnery Azgayin Academia/National Academy of Sciences of the Republic of Armenia, Marshal Bagramyan Ave 24b, Erevan, 375019, Armenia. Ed. R T Jrbashian.

551 RUS
GEOLOGICHESKOE IZUCHENIE I ISPOL'ZOVANIE NEDR. Text in Russian. m. USD 249.95 in United States.
Published by: Informatsionno-Izdatel'skii Tsentr po Geologii i Nedropol'zovaniu Geoinformmark, Goncharnaya 38, Moscow, 115172, Russian Federation. TEL 7-095-9156724. **US dist. addr.:** East View Information Services, 3020 Harbor Ln. N., Minneapolis, MN 55447. TEL 612-550-0961.

550 UKR ISSN 1025-6814
QP1 CODEN: GEZHA4
GEOLOGICHNYI ZHURNAL. Text in Ukrainian; Summaries in English, Russian. 1934. bi-m. USD 130. charts; illus. **Document type:** *Academic/Scholarly.*
Former titles (until 1995): Geologicheskii Zhurnal (0367-4290); (until 1968): Geologichnyi Zhurnal (0016-7703)
Indexed: ASFA, ChemAb, Djerelo, ESPM, INIS AtomInd, RefZh, ZooRec.
—CASDDS, CISTI, East View, Linda Hall. **CCC.**
Published by: Natsional'na Akademiya Nauk Ukrainy, Instytut Heologichnykh Nauk, Vul O Gonchara 55-b, Kiev, Ukraine. TEL 380-44-2163096. Ed. Ya N Belevtsev. **US dist. addr.:** East View Information Services, 3020 Harbor Ln. N., Minneapolis, MN 55447. TEL 612-550-0961.

551 DEU
GEOLOGIE. Text in German. 1973. q. USD 20. back issues avail. **Document type:** *Academic/Scholarly.* **Description:** Covers geology: caves, minerals, fossils.
Published by: Motivgruppe Mineralogie - Palaeontologie - Spelaeologie e.V., Steinknoeck 3, Erlangen, 91054, Germany. TEL 09131-51815. Ed. Johan C van Soeren.

554 FRA ISSN 1638-5977
QE268 CODEN: GEFRE6
GEOLOGIE DE LA FRANCE/GEOLOGY OF FRANCE AND SURROUNDING AREAS. Text in French. 1889. q. abstr.; charts; illus. index. **Document type:** *Bulletin.* **Description:** Covers essentially the notes and works of collaborators and organizations responsible for the geological mapping of France.
Former titles (until 2001): Geologie de la France (Print) (0246-0874); (until 1983): France. Bureau de Recherches Geologiques et Minieres. Bulletin. Section 1: Geologie de la France (0007-6104); Service de la Carte Geologique de la France. Bulletin
Media: Online - full content.
Indexed: CIN, ChemAb, ChemTitl, EngInd, ZooRec.
—CASDDS, CISTI, Ei, Linda Hall.
Published by: (France. Bureau de Recherches Geologiques et Minieres), Editions B R G M, B.P. 6009, Orleans, Cedex 2 45060, France. TEL 33-2-38643161, FAX 33-2-38643333, p.rossi@brgm.fr. Ed. Philipe Rossi. Pub. Gerard Sustrac. Circ: 1,500.

554 FRA ISSN 0397-2844
QE350.2 CODEN: AUPGDY
GEOLOGIE MEDITERRANEENNE. Text in French. 1974. q. **Document type:** *Proceedings.* **Description:** Articles on the geology of the Mediterranean countries.
Indexed: ASFA, ChemAb, ESPM, GEOBASE, ZooRec.
—CASDDS, CISTI, Linda Hall.
Published by: Universite de Provence, U.F.R. Sciences de la Vie, de la Terre et de l'Environnement, Centre Saint-Charles Place Victor Hugo, Marseille, Cedex 3 13331, France.

551 DEU ISSN 0176-148X
GEOLOGIE UND PALAEONTOLOGIE IN WESTFALEN. Text in German. 1983. irreg. (2-4/yr.). price varies. charts; illus.; maps. 32 p./no. 1 cols./p.; **Document type:** *Monographic series, Academic/Scholarly.*
Indexed: GEOBASE, ZooRec.
Published by: Westfaelisches Museum fuer Naturkunde, Sentruper Str 285, Muenster, 48161, Germany. TEL 49-251-59105, FAX 49-251-5916098, naturkundemuseum@lwl.org, http://www.naturkundemuseum-muenster.e.

550 SVN ISSN 0016-7789
QE287 CODEN: GERPAM
GEOLOGIJA; razprave in porocila. Text in English, French, German, Serbo-Croatian, Slovenian. 1953. biennial. SIT 400, USD 14. bk.rev. charts; illus. index.
Indexed: ChemAb, ZooRec.
—CASDDS, Linda Hall.
Published by: Geoloski Zavod/Geological Survey, Parmova ul 33, Ljubljana, 1000, Slovenia. Ed. Stefan Kolenko. Circ: 1,000.
Co-sponsor: Slovensko Geolosko Drustvo.

551 560 DEU ISSN 0341-4043
GEOLOGISCHE ABHANDLUNGEN HESSEN. Text in German. 1950. a. price varies. back issues avail. **Document type:** *Proceedings, Academic/Scholarly.*
Formerly (until 1976): Hessisches Landesamt fuer Bodenforschung. Abhandlungen (0440-7423)
Indexed: RefZh, ZooRec.
—Linda Hall. **CCC.**
Published by: Hessisches Landesamt fuer Umwelt und Geologie, Postfach 3209, Wiesbaden, 65022, Germany. TEL 49-611-701034, FAX 49-611-9740813, vertrieb@hlug.de, http://www.hlug.de. Ed. Roland Becker. **Subscr. to:** Vertriebsstelle, Hasengartenstr 26, Wiesbaden 65189, Germany.

554 DEU ISSN 0016-7797
CODEN: GBNBA7
GEOLOGISCHE BLAETTER FUER NORDOST-BAYERN UND ANGRENZENDE GEBIETE. Text in German. 1951. irreg. (1-4/yr.). adv. bk.rev. charts; illus. **Document type:** *Academic/Scholarly.* **Description:** Studies geological and paleontological topics relating to Northern Bavaria.
Indexed: BiolAb, ChemAb, IBR, RefZh, ZooRec.
—CASDDS.
Published by: Universitaet Erlangen - Nuernberg, Institut fuer Geologie und Mineralogie, Schlossgarten 5, Erlangen, 91054, Germany. geologie@geol.uni-erlangen.de. Ed. R Rossner.

551 AUT ISSN 0378-0864
QE266 CODEN: AGBDAO
GEOLOGISCHE BUNDESANSTALT. ABHANDLUNGEN. Text mainly in German. 1852. irreg. price varies. **Document type:** *Monographic series, Academic/Scholarly.*
Related titles: Microfilm ed.
Indexed: IBR, RefZh, ZooRec.
—BLDSC (0540.749800), CASDDS, CISTI, ingenta, Linda Hall.
Published by: Geologische Bundesanstalt, Rasumofskygasse 23, Vienna, W 1031, Austria. TEL 43-1-71256740, FAX 43-1-712567456, sekretariat@geolba.ac.at, http://www.geolba.ac.at. Ed. Albert Daurer. R&P Tillfried Cernajsek TEL 43-1-7125674500. Circ: 800.

551 AUT ISSN 1017-8880
CODEN: BEBUN
GEOLOGISCHE BUNDESANSTALT. BERICHTE. Text in German. 1986. irreg. **Document type:** *Monographic series, Academic/Scholarly.*
Indexed: RefZh.
Published by: Geologische Bundesanstalt, Rasumofskygasse 23, Vienna, W 1031, Austria. TEL 43-1-71256740, FAX 43-1-712567456, sekretariat@geolba.ac.at, http://www.geolba.ac.at. R&P Tillfried Cernajsek TEL 43-1-7125674500.

551 AUT
GEOLOGISCHE BUNDESANSTALT. BUNDESLAENDERSERIE. Text in German. irreg. **Document type:** *Monographic series, Academic/Scholarly.*
Published by: Geologische Bundesanstalt, Rasumofskygasse 23, Vienna, W 1031, Austria. TEL 43-1-71256740, FAX 43-1-712567456, sekretariat@geolba.ac.at, http://www.geolba.ac.at. Ed. Albert Daurer. R&P Tillfried Cernajsek TEL 43-1-7125674500.

551 AUT ISSN 1015-6208
QE266 CODEN: ATBUN
GEOLOGISCHE BUNDESANSTALT. FUEHRER ZU DEN ARBEITSTAGUNGEN. Text in German. irreg. **Document type:** *Monographic series, Academic/Scholarly.*
Published by: Geologische Bundesanstalt, Rasumofskygasse 23, Vienna, W 1031, Austria. TEL 43-1-71256740, FAX 43-1-712567456, sekretariat@geolba.ac.at, http://www.geolba.ac.at. Ed. Albert Daurer. R&P Tillfried Cernajsek TEL 43-1-7125674500.

551 560 AUT ISSN 0016-7800
CODEN: JAGBAW
GEOLOGISCHE BUNDESANSTALT. JAHRBUCH. Text and summaries in English, German. 1850. q. price varies. **Document type:** *Bulletin, Academic/Scholarly.*
Related titles: Microfilm ed.; Online - full text ed.
Indexed: BiolAb, IBR, RefZh, ZooRec.
—CASDDS, Linda Hall.
Published by: Geologische Bundesanstalt, Rasumofskygasse 23, Vienna, W 1031, Austria. TEL 43-1-7125674, FAX 43-1-712567456, sekretariat@geolba.ac.at, http://www.geolba.ac.at. Ed. Albert Daurer. R&P Tillfried Cernajsek TEL 43-1-7125674500.

551 AUT ISSN 1013-0349
QE266
GEOLOGISCHE BUNDESANSTALT. JAHRESBERICHT. Text in German. 1982. a. **Document type:** *Academic/Scholarly.*
—Linda Hall.
Published by: Geologische Bundesanstalt, Rasumofskygasse 23, Vienna, W 1031, Austria. TEL 43-1-71256740, FAX 43-1-712567456, sekretariat@geolba.ac.at, http://www.geolba.ac.at. Ed. Albert Daurer. R&P Tillfried Cernajsek TEL 43-1-7125674500.

551 AUT
GEOLOGISCHE BUNDESANSTALT. POPULAERWISSENSCHAFTLICHE VEROEFFENTLICHUNGEN. Text in German. 1984. irreg. **Document type:** *Monographic series, Academic/Scholarly.*
Published by: Geologische Bundesanstalt, Rasumofskygasse 23, Vienna, W 1031, Austria. TEL 43-1-71256740, FAX 43-1-712567456, verlag@cc.geolba.ac.at, sekretariat@geolba.ac.at. Ed. Albert Daurer. R&P Tillfried Cernajsek TEL 43-1-7125674500.

551 560 DEU ISSN 0341-4027
QE269.A19 CODEN: GJHEDB
GEOLOGISCHES JAHRBUCH HESSEN. Text in German. 1976. a. price varies. back issues avail. **Document type:** *Yearbook, Academic/Scholarly.*
Indexed: BIOSIS Prev, BiolAb, CIN, ChemAb, ChemTitl, E&PHSE, GP&P, IBR, OffTech, PetrolAb, ZooRec.
—CASDDS, Linda Hall, PADDS.
Published by: Hessisches Landesamt fuer Umwelt und Geologie, Postfach 3209, Wiesbaden, 65022, Germany. TEL 49-611-701034, FAX 49-611-9740813, vertrieb@hlug.de, http://www.hlug.de. Ed. Roland Becker. **Subscr. to:** Vertriebsstelle, Hasengartenstr 26, Wiesbaden 65189, Germany.

554 560 DEU ISSN 0341-6399
QE269 CODEN: GJRABD
GEOLOGISCHES JAHRBUCH. REIHE A: ALLGEMEINE UND REGIONALE GEOLOGIE B.R. DEUTSCHLAND UND NACHBARGEBIETE, TEKTONIK, STRATIGRAPHIE, PALAEONTOLOGIE. Text in German; Summaries in English, French, Italian, Russian, Spanish. irreg., latest vol.157, 2004. EUR 45 per issue domestic; EUR 49.10 per issue foreign (effective 2005). illus. **Document type:** *Monographic series, Academic/Scholarly.*
Supersedes in part (in 1972): Geologisches Jahrbuch (0016-7851); Which was formerly (until 1943): Jahrbuch der Reichsstelle fuer Bodenforschung (0368-1270); (until 1939): Jahrbuch der Preussischen Geologischen Landesanstalt (0368-1262); (until 1906): Jahrbuch der Koeniglich Preussischen Landesanstalt und Bergakademie zu Berlin
Indexed: AESIS, ChemAb, E&PHSE, GP&P, OffTech, PetrolAb, RefZh, ZooRec.
—BLDSC (4145.320000), CASDDS, CISTI, ingenta, Linda Hall, PADDS. **CCC.**
Published by: (Germany. Bundesanstalt fuer Geowissenschaften und Rohstoffe), E. Schweizerbart'sche Verlagsbuchhandlung, Johannesstr 3A, Stuttgart, 70176, Germany. TEL 49-711-3514560, FAX 49-711-35145699, mail@schweizerbart.de, http://www.schweizerbart.de.

554 DEU ISSN 0341-6402
QE1 CODEN: GJRBAF
GEOLOGISCHES JAHRBUCH. REIHE B: REGIONALE GEOLOGIE AUSLAND. Text in German; Summaries in English, French, German, Russian. 1906. irreg., latest vol.96, 2004. EUR 45 per issue domestic; EUR 49.10 per issue foreign (effective 2005). illus. **Document type:** *Monographic series, Academic/Scholarly.*
Supersedes in part (in 1972): Geologisches Jahrbuch (0016-7851); Which was formerly (until 1943): Jahrbuch der Reichsstelle fuer Bodenforschung (0368-1270); (until 1939): Jahrbuch der Preussischen Geologischen Landesanstalt (0368-1262); Beihefte zum Geologischen Jahrbuch (0005-8017)
Indexed: AESIS, ChemAb, IMMAb, PetrolAb, RefZh, ZooRec.
—BLDSC (4145.330000), CASDDS, CISTI, IE, ingenta, Linda Hall. **CCC.**
Published by: (Germany. Bundesanstalt fuer Geowissenschaften und Rohstoffe), E. Schweizerbart'sche Verlagsbuchhandlung, Johannesstr 3A, Stuttgart, 70176, Germany. TEL 49-711-3514560, FAX 49-711-35145699, mail@schweizerbart.de, http://www.schweizerbart.de.

551 DEU ISSN 0341-6410
GB651 CODEN: GJRCAI
GEOLOGISCHES JAHRBUCH. REIHE C: HYDROGEOLOGIE. INGENIEURGEOLOGIE. Text in German; Summaries in English, French, German, Russian. 1972. irreg., latest vol.69, 2004. EUR 30 per issue domestic; EUR 32.90 per issue foreign (effective 2005). illus. **Document type:** *Monographic series, Academic/Scholarly.*
Supersedes in part: Geologisches Jahrbuch (0016-7851); Which was formerly: Beihefte zum Geologischen Jahrbuch (0005-8017)
Indexed: ChemAb, PetrolAb, RefZh.
—CASDDS, CISTI, Linda Hall. **CCC.**
Published by: (Germany. Bundesanstalt fuer Geowissenschaften und Rohstoffe), E. Schweizerbart'sche Verlagsbuchhandlung, Johannesstr 3A, Stuttgart, 70176, Germany. TEL 49-711-3514560, FAX 49-711-35145699, mail@schweizerbart.de, http://www.schweizerbart.de.

551 549 DEU ISSN 0341-6429
QE351 CODEN: GJRDAL
GEOLOGISCHES JAHRBUCH. REIHE D: MINERALOGIE. PETROGRAPHIE, GEOCHEMIE, LAGERSTAETTENKUNDE. Text in German; Summaries in English, French, German, Russian. 1972. irreg., latest vol.111, 2004. EUR 45 per issue domestic; EUR 47.90 per issue foreign (effective 2005). illus. **Document type:** *Monographic series, Academic/Scholarly.*
Supersedes in part: Geologisches Jahrbuch (0016-7851); Which was formerly: Beihefte zum Geologischen Jahrbuch (0005-8017)
Indexed: AESIS, CIN, ChemAb, ChemTitl, E&PHSE, GP&P, IMMAb, MinerAb, OffTech, PetrolAb, RefZh, ZooRec.
—CASDDS, CISTI, Linda Hall, PADDS. **CCC.**
Published by: (Germany. Bundesanstalt fuer Geowissenschaften und Rohstoffe), E. Schweizerbart'sche Verlagsbuchhandlung, Johannesstr 3A, Stuttgart, 70176, Germany. TEL 49-711-3514560, FAX 49-711-35145699, mail@schweizerbart.de, http://www.schweizerbart.de/j/geologische-jahrbuecher.

551 DEU ISSN 0341-6437
QE500 CODEN: GJREAO
GEOLOGISCHES JAHRBUCH. REIHE E: GEOPHYSIK. Text in English, German; Summaries in English, French, German, Russian. 1972. irreg., latest vol.58, 2001. EUR 19 per issue domestic; EUR 21.90 per issue foreign (effective 2005). illus. **Document type:** *Monographic series, Academic/Scholarly.*
Indexed: AESIS, BiolAb, PetrolAb, RefZh.
—CISTI, Linda Hall. **CCC.**
Published by: (Germany. Bundesanstalt fuer Geowissenschaften und Rohstoffe), E. Schweizerbart'sche Verlagsbuchhandlung, Johannesstr 3A, Stuttgart, 70176, Germany. TEL 49-711-3514560, FAX 49-711-35145699, mail@schweizerbart.de, http://www.schweizerbart.de/j/geologische-jahrbuecher.

551 DEU ISSN 0341-6445
S599.4.G3 CODEN: GJRFAR
GEOLOGISCHES JAHRBUCH. REIHE F: BODENKUNDE. Text in English, German; Summaries in English, French, German, Russian. 1973. irreg., latest vol.33, 1997. EUR 19 per issue domestic; EUR 21.90 per issue foreign (effective 2005). **Document type:** *Monographic series, Academic/Scholarly.*
Indexed: ChemAb, S&F.
—CASDDS, Linda Hall. **CCC.**
Published by: (Germany. Bundesanstalt fuer Geowissenschaften und Rohstoffe), E. Schweizerbart'sche Verlagsbuchhandlung, Johannesstr 3A, Stuttgart, 70176, Germany. TEL 49-711-3514560, FAX 49-711-35145699, mail@schweizerbart.de, http://www.schweizerbart.de/j/geologische-jahrbuecher/.

554 560 DEU ISSN 1431-5084
GEOLOGISCHES JAHRBUCH. REIHE G: INFORMATIONEN AUS DEN BUND - LAENDER-ARBEITSGRUPPEN DER GEOLOGISCHEN DIENSTE. Text in German. irreg., latest vol.12, 2004. EUR 26 per issue domestic; EUR 28.90 per issue foreign (effective 2005). **Document type:** *Monographic series, Academic/Scholarly.*
Indexed: RefZh.
Published by: E. Schweizerbart'sche Verlagsbuchhandlung, Johannesstr 3A, Stuttgart, 70176, Germany. TEL 49-711-3514560, FAX 49-711-35145699, mail@schweizerbart.de, http://www.schweizerbart.de/j/geologische-jahrbuecher/.

554 560 DEU ISSN 1431-5092
GEOLOGISCHES JAHRBUCH. REIHE H: WIRTSCHAFTSGEOLOGIE, BERICHTE ZUR ROHSTOFFWIRTSCHAFT. Text in German. irreg., latest vol.10, 2004. EUR 30 per issue domestic; EUR 32.90 per issue foreign (effective 2005). **Document type:** *Monographic series, Academic/Scholarly.*
Indexed: RefZh.
Published by: E. Schweizerbart'sche Verlagsbuchhandlung, Johannesstr 3A, Stuttgart, 70176, Germany. TEL 49-711-3514560, FAX 49-711-35145699, mail@schweizerbart.de, http://www.schweizerbart.de/j/geologische-jahrbuecher.

550 DNK ISSN 1395-0150
GEOLOGISK TIDSSKRIFT. Text in Danish. 1995. irreg. price varies. back issues avail. **Document type:** *Monographic series, Academic/Scholarly.*
Formerly (1990-1991): DGFnyt (0906-3625)
Indexed: ZooRec.
Published by: Dansk Geologisk Forening/Geological Society of Denmark, Oester Voldgade 5-7, Copenhagen K, 1350, Denmark. TEL 46-35-322354, FAX 46-35-322325, dgf@geologi.com, http://www.2dgf.dk. Ed. Martin Soenderholm.

551 SWE ISSN 1104-4721
GEOLOGISKT FORUM. Text in Swedish. 1994. q. SEK 160; SEK 40 per issue (effective 2005). adv.
Published by: Geologiska Foereningen/Geological Society of Sweden, c/o Joakim Mansfeld, Dept. of Geology and Geochemistry, Stockholm University, Stockholm, 10691, Sweden. TEL 46-8-6747727, FAX 46-8-164424, gff@geo.su.se, http://www.geologiskaforeningen.nu, http://www.geografiskaforeningen.nu. Ed. Joakim Mansfeld. adv.: page SEK 5,000; 154 x 210. Circ: 1,800. **Dist. by:** Swedish Science Press.

E

▼ new title ➤ refereed ✶ unverified ♦ full entry avail.

551 GBR ISSN 0016-7878
CODEN: PGAEAH

➤ **GEOLOGISTS' ASSOCIATION. PROCEEDINGS.** Text in English. 1859. q. GBP 168 domestic; GBP 168, USD 303 foreign (effective 2005). adv. bk.rev. charts; illus. index covering 10 yrs. back issues avail. **Document type:** *Proceedings, Academic/Scholarly.* **Description:** Contains articles on the spectrum of the geological sciences, including results of current research and reviews of progress in rapidly advancing areas of the science.
Related titles: Online - full text ed.: (from EBSCO Publishing, Gale Group, IngentaConnect, Swets Information Services).
Indexed: AESIS, ASCA, ASFA, BiolAb, BrGeoL, ChemAb, CurCont, ESPM, GEOBASE, MinerAb, PetrolAb, PollutAb, RefZh, SWRA, ZooRec.
—BLDSC (6704.000000), IDS, IE, Infotrieve, ingenta, Linda Hall, PADDS. **CCC.**
Published by: (Geologists' Association), Geological Society Publishing House, Unit 7, Brassmill Enterprise Centre, Brassmill Ln, Bath, Avon BA1 3JN, United Kingdom. TEL 44-1225-445046, FAX 44-1225-442836, dawn.angel@geolsoc.org.uk, http://www.geolsoc.org.uk/template.cfm?name=journals_pga_home_page_. Ed. R J Howarth. Circ: 2,500.

551 GBR ISSN 0260-0463
GEOLOGIST'S DIRECTORY. Text in English. 1980. a. GBP 80 (effective 2000). adv. **Document type:** *Directory.* **Description:** Directory of U.K. geological activities in government, academia and industry.
—BLDSC (4146.412000).
Published by: Geological Society Publishing House, Unit 7, Brassmill Enterprise Centre, Brassmill Ln, Bath, Avon BA1 3JN, United Kingdom. TEL 44-1225-445046, FAX 44-1225-442836, dawn.angel@geolsoc.org.uk. Ed. G M Reeves. Pub. M Collins. Adv. contact Glen Wilders. Circ: 2,000.

551 RUS ISSN 0234-1581
GEOLOGIYA, GEOFIZIKA I RAZRABOTKA NEFTYANYKH MESTOROZHDENII. Text in Russian. 1988. m. USD 270 in United States (effective 2004). **Document type:** *Journal.*
Indexed: PetrolAb, RefZh.
—East View, Linda Hall, PADDS.
Published by: Vserossiiskii Nauchno-Issledovatel'skii Institut Organizatsii Upravleniya i Ekonomiki Neftegazovoi Promyshlennosti (VNIIOENG), Nametkina 14, korp B, Moscow, 117420, Russian Federation. TEL 7-095-3320022, FAX 7-095-3316877, vniioeng@mcn.ru, http://vniioeng.mcn.ru. **US dist. addr.:** East View Information Services, 3020 Harbor Ln. N., Minneapolis, MN 55447. TEL 800-477-1005, FAX 800-800-3839, eastview@eastview.com, http://www.eastview.com.

551 RUS ISSN 0016-7886
CODEN: GGASAS

➤ **GEOLOGIYA I GEOFIZIKA.** Text in Russian; Summaries in English. 1960. m. RUR 750 for 6 mos. domestic; USD 392 foreign (effective 2005). illus. index. **Document type:** *Journal, Academic/Scholarly.* **Description:** Presents theoretical and methodological papers on all problems of geology and geophysics. Some issues publish proceedings of international meetings held in Novosibirsk and other Siberian cities.
Formerly: Geofizicheskii Byulleten' (0072-1182)
Related titles: ♦ English ed.: Russian Geology and Geophysics. ISSN 1068-7971.
Indexed: CIN, ChemAb, ChemTitl, CurCont, E&PHSE, GEOBASE, GP&P, Inspec, OffTech, PetrolAb, RefZh, ZooRec.
—AskIEEE, CASDDS, CISTI, East View, IDS, Linda Hall, PADDS. **CCC.**
Published by: (Rossiiskaya Akademiya Nauk, Sibirskoe Otdelenie, Ob'edinennyi Institut Geologii, Geofiziki, i Mineralogii im A. A. Trofimuka/Russian Academy of Sciences, Siberian Branch, Trofimuk United Institute of Geology, Geophysics and Mineralogy), Izdatel'stvo Sibirskogo Otdeleniya Rossiiskoi Akademii Nauk/Publishing House of the Russian Academy of Sciences, Siberian Branch, Morskoi pr 2, a/ya 187, Novosibirsk, 630090, Russian Federation. TEL 7-3832-300570, FAX 7-3832-333755, psb@ad-sbras.nsc.ru, http://www-psb.ad-sbras.nsc.ru/geolw.htm. Ed. Nikolai V Sobolev. Circ: 680. **Dist. by:** Informnauka Ltd., Ul Usievicha 20, Moscow 125190, Russian Federation. alfimov@viniti.ru.

551 FRA ISSN 0016-7916
CODEN: GEOLBU

GEOLOGUES. Text in French. 1966. q.
—BLDSC (4146.430000), IE, ingenta.
Published by: Union Francaise des Geologues, Maison de la Geologie, 77 Rue Claude Bernard, Paris, 75005, France. jean-claude.vidal@ufg.asso.fr, http://www.ufg.asso.fr.

551 USA ISSN 0091-7613
QE1 CODEN: GLGYBA

➤ **GEOLOGY (BOULDER).** Text in English. 1973. m. USD 560 domestic to non-members; USD 575 foreign to non-members; USD 710 combined subscription domestic to non-members print & online ed.; USD 725 combined subscription foreign to non-members print & online ed. (effective 2005). adv. abstr.; illus.; charts. back issues avail. reprint service avail. from PQC. **Document type:** *Journal, Academic/Scholarly.* **Description:** Topical scientific papers on all earth science disciplines worldwide.
Related titles: CD-ROM ed.; Microform ed.: (from PQC); Online - full text ed.: (from EBSCO Publishing, HighWire Press).
Indexed: A&ATA, AESIS, AS&TI, ASCA, ASFA, BiolAb, BrGeoL, CIN, CTO, ChemAb, CivEngAb, CurCont, E&PHSE, EEA, EPB, ESPM, EngInd, ExcerpMed, F&EA, FLUIDEX, GEOBASE, GP&P, GSI, GSW, IAA, ICEA, INIS AtomInd, ISR, Inspec, M&GPA, OceAb, OffTech, PetrolAb, PollutAb, RefZh, SCI, SFA, SWRA, ZooRec.
—BLDSC (4146.432000), AskIEEE, CASDDS, CISTI, IDS, IE, Infotrieve, ingenta, Linda Hall, PADDS. **CCC.**
Published by: Geological Society of America, 3300 Penrose Pl, Boulder, CO 80301-1806. TEL 303-447-2020, FAX 303-447-1133, pubs@geosociety.org, http://www.geosociety.org/pubs/. Circ: 9,500. **Subscr. to:** Allen Press Inc., PO Box 1897, Lawrence, KS 66044. TEL 785-843-1234, FAX 785-843-1274, http://www.allenpress.com.

555 JPN
GEOLOGY AND MINERAL RESOURCES OF JAPAN/NIHON CHISHITSU KOSANSHI. Text in English. 1956. irreg. per issue exchange basis.
Published by: Kogyo Gijutsuin, Chishitsu Chosajo/National Institute of Advanced Industrial Science & Technology, Geological Survey of Japan, AIST Tsukuba Central 7, 1-1, Higashi 1-Chome, Tsukuba, Ibaraki 305-0046, Japan. TEL 81-29-8619122, FAX 81-29-8613672, http://www.aist.go.jp, http://www.gsj.jp/.

551 POL ISSN 0138-0389
QE276.5
GEOLOGY OF POLAND. Text in English. 1979. irreg. (approx. a.). price varies. **Document type:** *Academic/Scholarly.*
Indexed: ChemAb.
Published by: Panstwowy Instytut Geologiczny/Polish Geological Institute, ul Rakowiecka 4, Warsaw, 00975, Poland. TEL 48-22-8495351, FAX 48-22-8495342, dystryb@pgi.wa.pl. Circ: 400.

551 GBR ISSN 0266-6979
QE1
➤ **GEOLOGY TODAY.** Text in English. 1985. bi-m. GBP 46, EUR 69 combined subscription in Europe to individuals print & online eds.; USD 84 combined subscription in the Americas to individuals & Caribbean (print & online eds.); GBP 50 combined subscription elsewhere to individuals print & online eds.; GBP 373 combined subscription in Europe to institutions print & online eds.; USD 690 combined subscription in the Americas to institutions & Caribbean (print & online eds.); GBP 411 combined subscription elsewhere to institutions print & online eds.; GBP 28, EUR 42 combined subscription in Europe to students print & online eds.; USD 54 combined subscription in the Americas to students & Caribbean (print & online eds.); GBP 32 combined subscription elsewhere to students print & online eds. (effective 2006). adv. bk.rev. illus.; charts; maps. Index. back issues avail.; reprints avail. **Document type:** *Journal, Academic/Scholarly.*
Related titles: Microform ed.: (from PQC); ♦ Online - full text ed.: Geology Today Online. ISSN 1365-2451.
Indexed: AESIS, GEOBASE, GSI, IMMAb, MASUSE, RefZh, ZooRec.
—BLDSC (4146.640000), IE, Infotrieve, ingenta, Linda Hall. **CCC.**
Published by: (Geological Society of London), Blackwell Publishing Ltd., 9600 Garsington Rd, Oxford, OX4 2ZG, United Kingdom. TEL 44-1865-776868, FAX 44-1865-714591, customerservices@oxon.blackwellpublishing.com, http://www.blackwellpublishing.com/journals/GTO. Ed. Peter Doyle. Pub. Amanda McLean Inglis. R&P Sophie Savage. Adv. contact Jenny Applin. Circ: 2,550. **Co-sponsor:** Geologists' Association.

551 GBR ISSN 1365-2451
➤ **GEOLOGY TODAY ONLINE.** Text in English. 1998. bi-m. GBP 354 in Europe to institutions; USD 655 in the Americas to institutions & Caribbean; GBP 390 elsewhere to institutions (effective 2006). **Document type:** *Academic/Scholarly.* **Description:** Reviews topics of current interest in the Earth Sciences - written for the general reader by experts in the field.
Media: Online - full text (from Blackwell Synergy, EBSCO Publishing, Gale Group, IngentaConnect, O C L C Online Computer Library Center, Inc., Swets Information Services). **Related titles:** Microform ed.: (from PQC); ♦ Print ed.: Geology Today. ISSN 0266-6979.
Published by: Blackwell Publishing Ltd., 9600 Garsington Rd, Oxford, OX4 2ZG, United Kingdom. TEL 44-1865-776868, FAX 44-1865-714591, customerservices@oxon.blackwellpublishing.com, http://www.blackwellpublishing.com.

➤ **GEOMAGNETISM AND AERONOMY.** see *EARTH SCIENCES—Geophysics*

551 DEU
GEOMAX; Neugierig auf Wissenschaft. Text in German. 2000. 2/yr. free. **Document type:** *Newsletter, Academic/Scholarly.*
Published by: Max-Planck-Gesellschaft zur Foerderung der Wissenschaften, Hofgartenstr 8, Munich, 80539, Germany. TEL 49-89-21081232, FAX 49-89-21081405, presse@mpg-gv.mpg.de, http://www.mpg.de/bilderBerichteDokumente/multimedial/geomax/index.html, http://www.maxplanck.de. Ed., R&P Christina Beck.

550 620 NLD
GEOMECHANICS RESEARCH SERIES. Text in English. 1993. irreg. **Document type:** *Monographic series.*
—BLDSC (4147.267500).
Published by: A A Balkema (Subsidiary of: Taylor & Francis The Netherlands), PO Box 1675, Rotterdam, 3000 BR, Netherlands. TEL 31-10-10-4145822, FAX 31-10-413-5947, sales@balkema.nl, http://www.balkema.nl. **Dist. in U.S. by:** Ashgate Publishing Co, Old Post Rd, Brookfield, VT 05036. TEL 800-535-9544.

GEOMIMET. see *MINES AND MINING INDUSTRY*

551 FRA ISSN 1266-5304
GB400
➤ **GEOMORPHOLOGIE;** relief, processus, environnement. Text in French. 1995. q. EUR 40 to members; EUR 68 to non-members; EUR 98 to institutions; EUR 30 per issue (effective 2005). bk.rev. 72 p./no.; back issues avail. **Document type:** *Journal, Academic/Scholarly.* **Description:** Features papers about geomorphology, relationships between geomorphology and other sciences, IAG newsletters, and book reviews.
—BLDSC (4147.660000), IE, ingenta.
Published by: Institut de Geographie, Groupe Francais de Geomorphologie, 191 rue Saint-Jacques, Paris, 75005, France. FAX 33-01-46658923, raffy.geo@wanadoo.fr, http://www.univ-st-etienne.fr/gfg. Ed. Jean-Claude Thouret. Circ: 375 (paid and controlled).

551 NLD ISSN 0169-555X
GB400 CODEN: GEMPEZ
➤ **GEOMORPHOLOGY.** Text in Dutch. 1987. 40/yr. EUR 1,891 in Europe to institutions; JPY 251,200 in Japan to institutions; USD 2,112 to institutions except Europe and Japan (effective 2006). adv. bk.rev. illus. back issues avail.; reprints avail. **Document type:** *Journal, Academic/Scholarly.* **Description:** Publishes review articles, research papers and letters related to pure and applied geomorphology, including modeling of landforms, extraterrestrial landforms, tectonic and climatological geomorphology.
Related titles: Microform ed.: (from PQC); Online - full text ed.: (from EBSCO Publishing, Gale Group, IngentaConnect, ScienceDirect, Swets Information Services).
Indexed: AESIS, ASCA, ASFA, CivEngAb, CurCont, ESPM, FLUIDEX, ForAb, GEOBASE, I&DA, ISR, M&GPA, M&TEA, OceAb, S&F, SCI, SWRA.
—BLDSC (4147.680000), CISTI, IDS, IE, Infotrieve, ingenta, Linda Hall. **CCC.**
Published by: Elsevier BV (Subsidiary of: Elsevier Science & Technology), Radarweg 29, Amsterdam, 1043 NX, Netherlands. TEL 31-20-4853911, FAX 31-20-4852457, nlinfo-f@elsevier.nl, http://www.elsevier.com/locate/geomorph, http://www.elsevier.nl. Eds. A. M. Harvey, R. A. Marston.

➤ **GEOREF.** see *EARTH SCIENCES—Abstracting, Bibliographies, Statistics*

➤ **GEOREF SERIALS LIST.** see *EARTH SCIENCES—Abstracting, Bibliographies, Statistics*

551 CHE
GEORESEARCH FORUM. Text in English. 1996. irreg. **Document type:** *Academic/Scholarly.*
Formerly: GeoScience and Technology Forum (1421-0282)
Indexed: ZooRec.
—BLDSC (4158.200910).
Published by: Trans Tech Publications Ltd., Brandrain 6, Uetikon-Zurich, CH-8707, Switzerland. TEL 41-1-9221022, FAX 41-1-9221033, ttp@ttp.ch, http://www.ttp.net.

551 523.1 RUS ISSN 1608-5043
GEORESURSY. Text in Russian. 1999. q. USD 10 domestic; USD 25 foreign; USD 2.50 newsstand/cover domestic; USD 7 newsstand/cover foreign (effective 2002). **Description:** Publishes papers on the study of the physical processes occuring within the Earth, and in the space surrounding it, including its interaction with other bodies in the Galaxy.
Related titles: Online - full text ed.: ISSN 1608-5078; English ed.: Georesources. ISSN 1608-5035. 2000.
Indexed: RefZh.
Published by: Kazanskii Gosudarstvennyi Universitet/Kazan State University, 18 Kremlyovskaya St, Kazan, 420008, Russian Federation. TEL 7-8432-388800, FAX 7-8432-387418, georesources@mail.ru, public.mail@ksu.ru, http://www.kcn.ru/tat_en/science/georesources/index.htm, http://www.kcn.ru/tat_en/university/index.php3. Ed. N Khristoforova. **Co-publisher:** Gosudarstvennyi Komitet Respubliki Tatarstan po Geologii i Ispol'zovaniyu Nedr/Geological State Committee for the Use of Natural Resources of the Republic of Tatarstan.

557 USA
GEORGIA GEOLOGIC SURVEY. BULLETIN. Text in English. 1894. irreg., latest vol.124, 1990. price varies. **Document type:** *Bulletin.* **Description:** Discusses geologic and mineral resources on a multi-region and statewide basis.
Published by: Georgia Department of Natural Resources, Georgia Geologic Survey, 19 Martin Luther King Jr Dr, S W, Rm 400, Atlanta, GA 30334. TEL 404-656-3214.

E

550 USA
GEORGIA GEOLOGIC SURVEY. CIRCULAR. Text in English. 1981. irreg., latest vol.14, 1991. price varies. **Description:** Provides information on the Survey and its facilities and data.
Related titles: ♦ Series: Georgia Geologic Survey. Circular 2. Mining Directory of Georgia; ♦ Georgia Geologic Survey. Circular 1. List of Publications; ♦ Georgia Geologic Survey. Circular 3. The Mineral Industry of Georgia.
Published by: Georgia Department of Natural Resources, Georgia Geologic Survey, 19 Martin Luther King Jr Dr, S W, Rm 400, Atlanta, GA 30334. TEL 404-656-3214.

557 USA
GEORGIA GEOLOGIC SURVEY. GEOLOGIC GUIDE. Text in English. 1977. irreg., latest vol.9, 1985. price varies. **Description:** Brief reports detailing the geology of some of Georgia's parks.
Published by: Georgia Department of Natural Resources, Georgia Geologic Survey, 19 Martin Luther King Jr Dr, S W, Rm 400, Atlanta, GA 30334. TEL 404-656-3214.

551 USA
GEORGIA GEOLOGIC SURVEY. GEOLOGIC REPORT. Text in English. 1971. irreg., latest vol.7, 1992. price varies. **Description:** Brief reports discussing specific commodities and geologic topics in specific areas of the State.
Published by: Georgia Department of Natural Resources, Georgia Geologic Survey, 19 Martin Luther King Jr Dr, S W, Rm 400, Atlanta, GA 30334. TEL 404-656-3214.

557 USA
GEORGIA GEOLOGIC SURVEY. GUIDEBOOK. Text in English. 1962. irreg., latest vol.22, 1980. price varies. **Description:** Detailed field trips conducted by the Georgia Geological Society.
Published by: Georgia Department of Natural Resources, Georgia Geologic Survey, 19 Martin Luther King Jr Dr, S W, Rm 400, Atlanta, GA 30334. TEL 404-656-3214.

557 USA
GEORGIA GEOLOGIC SURVEY. MISCELLANEOUS PUBLICATION. Text in English. 1963. irreg., latest vol.7, 1984. price varies. **Description:** Hydrologic topics of special time-limited interest.
Formerly: Georgia Geologic Survey. Special Publication
Published by: Georgia Department of Natural Resources, Georgia Geologic Survey, 19 Martin Luther King Jr Dr, S W, Rm 400, Atlanta, GA 30334. TEL 404-656-3214.

557 USA
GEORGIA GEOLOGIC SURVEY. OPEN FILE REPORT. Text in English. 1979. irreg., latest 1992, no.92-4. price varies.
Published by: Georgia Department of Natural Resources, Georgia Geologic Survey, 19 Martin Luther King Jr Dr, S W, Rm 400, Atlanta, GA 30334. TEL 404-656-3214.

557 USA
GEORGIA GEOLOGIC SURVEY. PROJECT REPORT. Text in English. 1966. irreg., latest vol.17, 1992. price varies. **Description:** Concerned with the potential for mineral resources in the coastal zone of the Georgia Coastal Plain.
Published by: Georgia Department of Natural Resources, Georgia Geologic Survey, 19 Martin Luther King Jr Dr, S W, Rm 400, Atlanta, GA 30334. TEL 404-656-3214.

557 USA ISSN 0277-9420
GEORGIA GEOLOGICAL SURVEY. BULLETIN. Text in English. 1978. irreg. **Document type:** *Monographic series.*
—Linda Hall.
Published by: Georgia Geological Survey, 3039 Amwiler Rd, Ste 130, Atlanta, GA 30360-2824. TEL 770-903-9100, FAX 770-903-9199.

557 USA ISSN 0278-3398
GEORGIA GEOLOGICAL SURVEY. INFORMATION CIRCULAR. Text in English. 1978. irreg. **Document type:** *Government.*
—Linda Hall.
Published by: Georgia Geological Survey, 3039 Amwiler Rd, Ste 130, Atlanta, GA 30360-2824.

GEORGIAN GEOPHYSICAL SOCIETY. JOURNAL. see *EARTH SCIENCES—Geophysics*

551 VEN ISSN 0435-5601
CODEN: GEOSAG
GEOS. Text in Spanish; Summaries in English. 1959. a. USD 15. back issues avail. **Document type:** *Bulletin.* **Description:** Publishes developments and research in earth sciences from Venezuela and related areas.
—CASDDS.
Published by: (Escuela de Geologia), Universidad Central de Venezuela, Facultad de Ingenieria, Apdo 54008, Caracas, DF 1053-A, Venezuela. TEL 58-212-6053249, FAX 58-2-6053195. Ed. Franco Urbani. Circ: 1,000.

550 CAN ISSN 0315-0941
CODEN: GSCNA5
➤ **GEOSCIENCE CANADA.** Text in English. 1948. q. USD 110, CND 117.70 (effective 2005). adv. bk.rev. illus. reprint service avail. from PQC. **Document type:** *Journal, Academic/Scholarly.* **Description:** Contains state-of-the-art reviews, summaries of recent developments, and conference reports.
Formerly (until 1974): Geological Association of Canada. Proceedings (0072-1034)
Related titles: Microform ed.: (from PQC); Online - full text ed.: (from Gale Group).
Indexed: AESIS, AJEE, ASCA, ASFA, CurCont, E&PHSE, EEA, ESPM, Englnd, FLUIDEX, GEOBASE, GP&P, HortAb, IMMAb, ISR, OffTech, PetrolAb, S&F, SCI, SRRA, SWRA, VITIS.
—BLDSC (4158.838000), CISTI, Ei, IDS, IE, Infotrieve, ingenta, Linda Hall, PADDS. **CCC.**
Published by: Geological Association of Canada, c/o Dept. of Earth Sciences, Memorial Univ. of Newfoundland, St. John's, NF A1B 3X5, Canada. TEL 709-737-7660, FAX 709-737-2532, http://www.gac.ca/JOURNALS/geocan.html. Ed. G Nowlan. Pub., R&P, Adv. contact Ms. K Dawe TEL 709-737-7660. Circ: 3,300.

557 USA
CODEN: IGSEAU
GEOSCIENCE EDUCATION. Text in English. 1931. irreg., latest vol.14, 1998. price varies. charts; illus.; stat.
Formerly (until 1998): Illinois. State Geological Survey. Educational Series. (0073-5078)
—Linda Hall.
Published by: State Geological Survey, Natural Resources Bldg, 615 E Peabody Dr, Champaign, IL 61820. TEL 217-333-4747, isgs@isgs.uiuc.edu, http://www.isgs.uiuc.edu. R&P Marie-France DuFour TEL 217-333-5115. Circ: 5,000.

557 IND ISSN 0252-1970
CODEN: GEJLD7
GEOSCIENCE JOURNAL. Text in English. 1980. s-a. **Document type:** *Journal, Academic/Scholarly.*
Indexed: PetrolAb.
—CISTI, Linda Hall, PADDS.
Published by: Nav Jyoti Scientific Publications, c/o D.S.N. Raju, Lucknow, India.

557 USA ISSN 0164-2049
QE179 CODEN: GEWIDT
GEOSCIENCE WISCONSIN. Text in English. 1977. irreg., latest vol.18, 2001. price varies. **Document type:** *Government.*
Related titles: Online - full content ed.
Indexed: IBR.
—CASDDS, Linda Hall.
Published by: Wisconsin Geological and Natural History Survey, University of Wisconsin Extension, 3817 Mineral Point Rd, Madison, WI 53705-4096. TEL 608-262-1705, FAX 608-262-8086, http://www.uwex.edu/wgnhs/. Ed. Mindy James.

550 CZE ISSN 1214-1119
QE267.C8 CODEN: VCGUEZ
➤ **GEOSCIENCES. BULLETIN/CESKY GEOLOGICKY USTAV. VESTNIK.** Text in English, French, German; Summaries in English, German, Czech. 1925. q. EUR 95 (effective 2002). bk.rev. bibl.; charts; illus.; maps. back issues avail. **Document type:** *Bulletin, Academic/Scholarly.* **Description:** Reports of geological studies and investigations made by Czech specialists at home and abroad; information about recent foreign research relevant to Czech geology.
Former titles (until 2002): Czech Geological Survey. Bulletin (1210-3527); (until 1992): Ustredni Ustav Geologicky. Vestnik (0042-4730); (until 1951): Statni Ustav Geologicky. Vestnik (0042-1359)
Indexed: BiolAb, ChemAb, GEOBASE, IBR, ZooRec.
—BLDSC (9221.200000), CASDDS, CISTI, Linda Hall.
Published by: Ceska Geologicka Sluzba/Czech Geological Survey, Klarov 3, Prague, 11821, Czech Republic. TEL 42-02-57320438, pasava@cgu.cz, http://www.geology.cz. Ed. Jan Pasava. Circ: 950. **Dist. in Western countries by:** Kubon & Sagner Buchexport - Import GmbH, Postfach 24, Munich 34 8000, Germany.

➤ **GEOSCIENCEWORLD.** see *EARTH SCIENCES—Abstracting, Bibliographies, Statistics*

551 GBR ISSN 0961-5628
QE1
GEOSCIENTIST. Text in English. 1991. m. GBP 80 domestic; GBP 88, USD 158 foreign (effective 2005). adv. bk.rev. back issues avail. **Document type:** *Magazine.* **Description:** It informs new developments in the earth sciences by the inclusion of timely stories as well as feature articles covering the entire span of earth sciences.
Incorporates: British Geologist (0144-0063)
Indexed: AESIS, IMMAb, RefZh.
—BLDSC (4158.892500). **CCC.**
Published by: Geological Society Publishing House, Unit 7, Brassmill Enterprise Centre, Brassmill Ln, Bath, Avon BA1 3JN, United Kingdom. TEL 44-1225-445046, FAX 44-1225-442836, sales@geolsoc.org.uk, enquiries@geolsoc.org.uk, http://www.geolsoc.org.uk/template.cfm?name=journals_geoscientist_home_page. Ed. Tony Harris. adv.: B&W page GBP 1,200, color page GBP 1,800; 190 x 270. Circ: 8,000.

091 FRA ISSN 0150-5505
QE516.3 CODEN: GENEE7
➤ **GEOSTANDARDS NEWSLETTER**; the journal of geostandards and geoanalysis. Text in French. 1977. 3/yr. EUR 153 in Europe to institutions; EUR 162, USD 210 elsewhere to institutions (effective 2005). bk.rev. bibl. index. 100 p./no.; back issues avail. **Document type:** *Journal, Academic/Scholarly.* **Description:** Publishes articles dedicated to advancing the science of reference materials, analytical techniques and data quality relevant to the chemical analysis of geological and environmental samples.
Indexed: ASCA, ASFA, AnalAb, BrCerAb, CIN, ChemAb, ChemTitl, CurCont, ISR, M&GPA, MSB, SCI.
—BLDSC (4158.896800), CASDDS, CISTI, IDS, IE, Infotrieve, ingenta. **CCC.**
Published by: (Geostandards), Association Scientifique pour la Geologie et ses Applications, Rue du Doyen Roubault, BP 40, Vandoeuvre, Cedex 54501, France. TEL 33-3-83594218, FAX 33-3-83511798, geostan@crpg.cnrs-nancy.fr, http://www.crpg.cnrs-nancy.fr/Geostandards/. Eds. Mireille Polve, Philip J Potts. R&P, Adv. contact Edward A Williams. Circ: 650; 500 (controlled).

551 CAN ISSN 0823-650X
CODEN: GENWER
GEOTECHNICAL NEWS. Text in English. 1982. q. CND 51 domestic; USD 51 in United States; USD 75 elsewhere (effective 2005). adv. bk.rev. **Document type:** *Newsletter, Trade.* **Description:** Contains news on geotechnical activities in Canada, the US, Mexico and Europe, including special sections on waste geotechnics and geosynthetics, calendar of geotechnical events and instrumentation.
Formerly: C G S News (0710-0477)
Indexed: BrCerAb, C&ISA, CerAb, CivEngAb, CorrAb, E&CAJ, EEA, EMA, Englnd, GeotechAb, IAA, IMMAb, M&TEA, MBF, METADEX, RefZh, SolStAb, WAA.
—BLDSC (4158.945000), Ei, IE, Infotrieve, ingenta, Linda Hall. **CCC.**
Published by: BiTech Publishers Ltd., 173 11860 Hammersmith Way, Richmond, BC V7A 5G1, Canada. TEL 604-277-4250, FAX 604-277-8125, books@bitech.ca, http://www.bitech.ca. Ed., Pub. John Gadsby. R&P, Adv. contact Lynn Pugh. Circ: 6,500 (paid).

551 624.176 USA ISSN 0895-0563
CODEN: GSPUER
GEOTECHNICAL SPECIAL PUBLICATIONS. Text in English. irreg., latest vol.93, 2000. price varies. illus. **Document type:** *Monographic series, Academic/Scholarly.*
Related titles: Microform ed.: (from PQC).
Indexed: CivEngAb, Englnd.
—BLDSC (4158.955000), CASDDS, CISTI, Ei, IE, ingenta. **CCC.**
Published by: American Society of Civil Engineers, 1801 Alexander Bell Dr, Reston, VA 20191-4400. TEL 703-295-6300, 800-548-2723, FAX 703-295-6222, http://www.pubs.asce.org, http://www.asce.org. R&P Karen Ryan TEL 703-295-6212.

GEOTECHNIK; Zeitschrift fuer Bodenmechanik, Erd- und Grundbau, Felsmechanik, Ingenieurgeologie, Geokunststoffe, Deponien und Altlasten. see *ENGINEERING*

550 NLD ISSN 0926-5074
GEOTECHNIKA; selected translations of Russian geotechnical literature. Text in English. 1991. irreg., latest vol.13, 1995. price varies. **Document type:** *Monographic series.* **Description:** Monographs on specific geotechnical topics, including soil mechanics and electromagnetic phenomena, and their applications in the design and construction of buildings.
—BLDSC (4158.978000), CISTI.
Published by: A A Balkema (Subsidiary of: Taylor & Francis The Netherlands), PO Box 1675, Rotterdam, 3000 BR, Netherlands. FAX 31-10-413-5947, sales@balkema.nl, http://www.balkema.nl. **Dist. in U.S. by:** Ashgate Publishing Co, Old Post Rd, Brookfield, VT 05036. TEL 800-535-9544.

551 HRV
GEOTEHNIKA; informativno glasilo radne zajednice Geotehnika. Text in Croatian. 1965. irreg.
Indexed: ChemAb.
Address: Kupska 2, Zagreb, Croatia. Ed. Zvonko Jelic.

551 RUS ISSN 0016-853X
CODEN: GTKTA2
GEOTEKTONIKA. Text in Russian. 1965. bi-m. RUR 930 for 6 mos. domestic (effective 2004). bk.rev. charts; illus. index. **Document type:** *Journal, Academic/Scholarly.* **Description:** Publishes articles on general and regional techtonics, structural geology, geodynamics, and experimental tectonics, considers the relation of tectonics to the deep structure of the earth, magmatism, metamorphism, and mineral resources.
Related titles: Online - full text ed.; ♦ English Translation: Geotectonics. ISSN 0016-8521.
Indexed: CIN, ChemAb, ChemTitl, E&PHSE, GP&P, Inspec, OffTech, PetrolAb, RefZh.
—AskIEEE, CASDDS, CISTI, East View, KNAW, Linda Hall, PADDS. **CCC.**

E

▼ new title ➤ refereed ✶ unverified ♦ full entry avail.

Published by: (Rossiiskaya Akademiya Nauk, Geologicheskii Institut), Izdatel'stvo Nauka, Profsoyuznaya ul 90, Moscow, 117864, Russian Federation. TEL 7-095-3347151, FAX 7-095-4202220, secret@naukaran.ru, http://www.maik.ru/cgi-bin/list.pl?page=geotekt, http://www.naukaran.ru.

551.8 BGR ISSN 0324-1661
QE601 CODEN: GTGED8
GEOTEKTONIKA, TEKTONOFIZIKA I GEODINAMIKA. Text in Bulgarian; Summaries in English, French. 1975. 3/yr. reprint service avail. from IRC.
—KNAW, Linda Hall.
Published by: (Bulgarska Akademiya na Naukite/Bulgarian Academy of Sciences), Universitetsko Izdatelstvo Sv. Kliment Okhridski/Publishing House of the Sofia University St. Kliment Ohridski, Akad G Bonchev 6, Sofia, 1113, Bulgaria. Ed. J Karagiuleva. Circ: 450.

550 ESP ISSN 1576-5172
GEOTEMAS. Text in Spanish. 2000. irreg. **Document type:** *Journal, Academic/Scholarly.*
Published by: Sociedad Geologica de Espana, Plaza de la Mercedes, s-n, Salamanca, 37008, Spain. TEL 34-923-294752, info@geologicas.es, http://www.sociedadgeologica.es/.

GEOTHERMAL HOTLINE. see *ENERGY—Geothermal Energy*

551 DNK ISSN 1604-6935
➤ **GEOVIDEN;** geologi og geografi. Text in Danish. 1984. q. free. illus. back issues avail. **Document type:** *Newsletter, Academic/Scholarly.*
ormer titles (until 2005): Geologi - Nyt fra GEUS (1396-2353); (until 1995): D G U Information (0109-2367)
Related titles: CD-ROM ed.; Online - full text ed.: ISSN 1604-8172; ♦ Eskimo ed.: Geologi - GEUS-imit Nutaariassat. ISSN 1600-6356.
Indexed: NAA.
Published by: (Denmark. Miljoeministeriet, Danmarks og Groenlands Geologiske Undersoegelse (GEUS)/Danish Ministry of the Environment. Geological Survey of Denmark and Greenland, Koebenhavns Universitet, Geologisk Institut), Miljoeministeriet, Geocenter Koebenhavn, Oester Voldgade 10, Copenhagen K, 1350, Denmark. TEL 45-38-142000, geus@geus.dk, http://geocenter.dk/publikationer/geoviden/index.html. Ed. Ole Bennike. Circ: 3,000.

551 363.7 DEU ISSN 1435-8956
➤ **GEOWISSENSCHAFTEN ONLINE.** Short title: G.O. Text in German, English. d. free (effective 2005). **Document type:** *Journal, Academic/Scholarly.*
Media: Online - full text (from EBSCO Publishing).
—IE. **CCC.**
Published by: Springer-Verlag (Subsidiary of: Springer Science+Business Media), Tiergartenstr 17, Heidelberg, 69121, Germany. TEL 49-6221-3450, FAX 49-6221-345229, http://www.g-o.de/. **Subscr. in the Americas to:** Springer-Verlag New York, Inc., Journal Fulfillment, PO Box 2485, Secaucus, NJ 07096-2485. TEL 800-777-4643, 201-348-4033, FAX 201-348-4505, journals@springer-ny.com, http://www.springer-ny.com; **Subscr. to:** Springer GmbH Auslieferungsgesellschaft, Haberstr 7, Heidelberg 69126, Germany. TEL 49-6221-345-0, FAX 49-6221-345-4229, subscriptions@springer.de.

550 DEU ISSN 0340-4056
QE269
➤ **DER GESCHIEBESAMMLER.** Text in German. 1966. q. EUR 26.50 (effective 2005). adv. bk.rev. **Document type:** *Journal, Academic/Scholarly.*
Indexed: ZooRec.
Published by: Geschiebesammler, Wohldtor 12, Wankendorf, 24601, Germany. TEL 49-4326-2205, FAX 49-4326-980523, info@geschiebesammler.de, http://www.geschiebesammler.de. Ed., Pub. Frank Rudolph.

551 551.4 560 AUT
QE1
GESELLSCHAFT DER GEOLOGIE- UND BERGBAUSTUDENTEN. MITTEILUNGEN. Text in German. 1949. a. adv. bk.rev. back issues avail. **Document type:** *Journal, Academic/Scholarly.*
Published by: Gesellschaft der Geologie- und Bergbaustudenten, Althanstr 14, Vienna, W 1090, Austria. TEL 43-1-427753401, FAX 43-1-42779534, geologie@univie.ac.at. Eds. Marion Jarnik, Richard Lein. Circ: 450.

551.31 USA ISSN 0149-1776
GB2401
GLACIOLOGICAL DATA. Text in English. 1977. irreg. per issue exchange basis. bk.rev. index. back issues avail. **Document type:** *Monographic series.*
Supersedes the quarterly issued from 1960-1976: Glaciological Notes (0017-0712)
—CISTI, Linda Hall.
Published by: National Snow and Ice Data Center, NSIDC User Services, CIRES, Campus Box 449, University of Colorado, Boulder, CO 80309-0449. TEL 303-492-8028, FAX 303-492-2468, nsidc@kryos.colorado.edu, nsidc@nsidc.org, www-nsidc.colorado.edu/WDC/GD. Ed. R G Barry. Circ: 1,100.

551 560 NLD ISSN 0924-5006
➤ **GLACIOLOGY AND QUATERNARY GEOLOGY.** Text in Dutch. 1985. irreg., latest vol.7, 1991. price varies. **Document type:** *Monographic series, Academic/Scholarly.*
Published by: Springer-Verlag Dordrecht (Subsidiary of: Springer Science+Business Media), Van Godewijckstraat 30, Dordrecht, 3311 GX, Netherlands. TEL 31-78-6576050, FAX 31-78-6576474, http://www.springeronline.com. Ed. C R Bentley.

551 NLD ISSN 0921-8181
QE1 CODEN: GPCHE4
➤ **GLOBAL AND PLANETARY CHANGE.** Text in English. 1988. 20/yr. EUR 1,452 in Europe to institutions; JPY 192,700 in Japan to institutions; USD 1,623 to institutions except Europe and Japan (effective 2006). adv. bk.rev. abstr.; illus. Index. back issues avail.; reprints avail. **Document type:** *Journal, Academic/Scholarly.* **Description:** Focuses on the causes, processes and limits of variability in planetary change, the record of change in earth history, and the analysis and prediction of recent and future changes. Includes discussions of ocean, climate and atmosphere, geophysics, human geography and global ecology.
Related titles: Microform ed.: (from PQC); Online - full text ed.: (from EBSCO Publishing, Gale Group, IngentaConnect, ScienceDirect, Swets Information Services); ♦ Supplement to: Palaeogeography, Palaeoclimatology, Palaeoecology. ISSN 0031-0182.
Indexed: AESIS, ASCA, ASFA, AgrForAb, BIOBASE, CivEngAb, CurCont, EPB, ESPM, EnvAb, ForAb, GEOBASE, HerbAb, I&DA, IABS, ISR, Inspec, M&GPA, M&TEA, OceAb, PollutAb, RASB, RefZh, S&F, SCI, SSCI, SWRA, WAE&RSA, ZooRec.
—BLDSC (4195.345000), AskIEEE, CISTI, IDS, IE, Infotrieve, ingenta, Linda Hall, PADDS. **CCC.**
Published by: Elsevier BV (Subsidiary of: Elsevier Science & Technology), Radarweg 29, Amsterdam, 1043 NX, Netherlands. TEL 31-20-4853911, FAX 31-20-4852457, nlinfo-f@elsevier.nl, http://www.elsevier.com/locate/gloplacha, http://www.elsevier.nl. Eds. C. Covey, S. Cloetingh.

551 SWE ISSN 0284-5865
QC903
GLOBAL CHANGE NEWSLETTER. Text in English. 1989. q. free. bk.rev. charts; illus. back issues avail. **Document type:** *Newsletter.* **Description:** Reports news of the IGBP, its conferences, and the staff. Covers IGBP-sponsored research and reports on forthcoming events.
—CISTI.
Published by: Royal Swedish Academy of Science, International Geosphere-Biosphere Programme, IGBP Secretariat, Box 50005, Stockholm, 10405, Sweden. TEL 46-8-166448, FAX 46-8-166405, sec@igbp.kva.se, http://www.igbp.kva.se/. Ed. Clare Bradshaw. R&P Sheila M Lunter. Circ: 10,000 (controlled). **Co-sponsor:** International Council of Scientific Unions.

551 NGA ISSN 1596-6798
➤ **GLOBAL JOURNAL OF GEOLOGICAL SCIENCES.** Text in English. 2002. s-a. NGN 1,500 domestic; USD 50 foreign (effective 2004). bk.rev. back issues avail.; reprints avail. **Document type:** *Journal, Academic/Scholarly.*
Related titles: Online - full text ed.: (from International Network for the Availability of Scientific Publications, African Journals Online).
Published by: Global Journal of Pure and Applied Sciences, c/o Prof. Barth N. Ekwueme,, University of Calabar, Department of Geology, PO Box 3651, Calabar, Nigeria. ekwueme@unical.anpa.net.ng, http://www.inasp.info/ajol/journals/gjgs/about.html. Ed. Barth N Ekwueme.

551 DEU ISSN 0163-3171
GLOBAL TECTONICS AND METALLOGENY. Text in English. 1978. irreg. EUR 126 per vol. domestic; EUR 131.45 per vol. foreign (effective 2005). **Document type:** *Monographic series, Academic/Scholarly.*
Indexed: AESIS, IBR, IMMAb.
—CISTI, Linda Hall. **CCC.**
Published by: E. Schweizerbart'sche Verlagsbuchhandlung, Johannesstr 3A, Stuttgart, 70176, Germany. TEL 49-711-3514560, FAX 49-711-35145699, mail@schweizerbart.de, http://www.schweizerbart.de. Ed. Jan Kutina.

550 USA ISSN 1050-4818
QE1
GLOBAL VOLCANISM NETWORK. BULLETIN. Text in English. 1978. m. looseleaf. USD 22 domestic; USD 39 foreign (effective 2000). illus.; stat. back issues avail. **Document type:** *Bulletin, Academic/Scholarly.* **Description:** Reports on active volcanoes, their behavior, earthquakes and other seismic activity, forecasting, atmospheric hazards, and health impacts.
Formerly (until 1989): Scientific Event Alert Network. Bulletin (0731-7573)
Indexed: EnvAb.
—Linda Hall.
Published by: (Smithsonian Institution), Global Volcanism Network, National Museum of Natural History, MRC 129, Washington, DC 20560. TEL 202-357-1511, FAX 202-357-2476, mnhms017@SIVM.SI.EDU, http://www.volcano.si.edu/GVP/. Eds. Edward Venzke, Richard L Wunderman. Circ: 1,300. **Subscr. to:** American Geophysical Union, 2000 Florida Ave, NW, Washington, DC 20009-1277.

551 CHN ISSN 1004-9665
GONGCHENG DIZHI XUEBAO/JOURNAL OF ENGINEERING GEOLOGY. Text in Chinese. 1993. q. CNY 100 (effective 2004). **Document type:** *Journal, Academic/Scholarly.*
Related titles: Online - full content ed.; Online - full text ed.: (from East View Information Services).
Indexed: C&ISA, E&CAJ, IAA.
Published by: (Zhongguo Kexueyuan, Dizhi yu Diqiu Wuli Yanjiusuo/Chinese Academy of Sciences, Institute of Geology and Geophysics), Kexue Chubanshe/Science Press, 16 Donghuang Cheng Genbei Jie, Beijing, 100717, China. TEL 86-10-64000246, FAX 86-10-64030255, gcdz@mail.igcas.ac.cn, http://gcdzxb.periodicals.net.cn/default.html, http://www.sciencep.com/. **Dist. by:** China International Book Trading Corp, 35 Chegongzhuang Xilu, Haidian District, PO Box 399, Beijing 100044, China. TEL 86-10-68412045, FAX 86-10-68412023, cibtc@mail.cibtc.com.cn, http://www.cibtc.com.cn.

554.81 NOR ISSN 0807-4801
QE281 CODEN: NGUSB2
GRAASTEINEN. Text in Norwegian; Summaries in English. 1972. irreg. price varies. **Document type:** *Monographic series, Academic/Scholarly.* **Description:** Consists of descriptions of geological map sheets, either bedrock or Quaternary geology.
Formerly (until 1996): N G U Skrifter (0377-8894); Which superseded in part (1890-1972: Norges Geologiske Undersoekelse. Aarbok (0801-6755)
Indexed: BrGeoL.
—CASDDS, Linda Hall.
Published by: Norges Geologiske Undersoekelse/Geological Survey of Norway, Leiv Erikssons Vei 39, Trondheim, 7491, Norway. TEL 47-73-90-40-11, FAX 47-92-16-20. Eds. Anne Birkeland, Morten Thoresen.

551 GBR ISSN 0958-6148
GREAT BRITAIN. NATIONAL ENVIRONMENT RESEARCH COUNCIL. BRITISH GEOLOGICAL SURVEY. REPORT. Text in English. 1953. a. price varies. illus. **Document type:** *Government.*
Former titles (until 1988): Great Britain. British Geological Survey. Annual Report (0957-7750); (until Jan. 1984): Great Britain. Institute of Geological Sciences. Annual Report (0073-9308); (until 1965): Great Britain. Geological Survey. Summary of Progress (0309-6467)
Indexed: IMMAb.
—CISTI, Linda Hall. **CCC.**
Published by: British Geological Survey, British Geological Survey, Kingsley Dunham Centre, Nicker Hill, Keyworth, Nottingham, NG12 5GG, United Kingdom. TEL 44-115-936-3100, FAX 44-115-936-3200, TELEX 378173 BGSKEY G, sales@bgs.ac.uk, http://www.nkw.ac.uk/bgs/. Circ: 2,000. **Subscr. to:** The Stationery Office, c/o Liason Officer, Atlantic House, Holborn Viaduct, London EC1P 1BW, United Kingdom.

554 GBR ISSN 0367-3928
GREAT BRITAIN. NATURAL ENVIRONMENT RESEARCH COUNCIL. BRITISH GEOLOGICAL SURVEY. BRITISH REGIONAL GEOLOGY. Text in English. 1935. irreg. price varies. illus. **Document type:** *Government.* **Description:** Describes the various geological regions in the U.K.
Indexed: IMMAb.
Published by: Natural Environment Research Council, British Geological Survey, British Geological Survey, Kingsley Dunham Centre, Nicker Hill, Keyworth, Nottingham, NG12 5GG, United Kingdom. TEL 44-115-936-3100, FAX 44-115-936-3200, sales@bgs.ac.uk, Enquiries@bgs.ac.uk, http://www.nkw.ac.uk/bgs/, http://www.bgs.ac.uk/. Circ: 15,000. **Subscr. to:** The Stationery Office, c/o Liason Officer, Atlantic House, Holborn Viaduct, London EC1P 1BW, United Kingdom.

551 557 GBR
GREAT BRITAIN. NATURAL ENVIRONMENT RESEARCH COUNCIL. BRITISH GEOLOGICAL SURVEY. CLASSICAL AREAS OF BRITISH GEOLOGY. Text in English. 1968. irreg. **Document type:** *Government.* **Description:** Acts as a guide to the geology of various areas in the U.K.
Formerly (until Jan. 1984): Great Britain. Institute of Geological Sciences. Classical Areas of British Geology
Published by: Natural Environment Research Council, British Geological Survey, British Geological Survey, Kingsley Dunham Centre, Nicker Hill, Keyworth, Nottingham, NG12 5GG, United Kingdom. TEL 44-115-936-3100, FAX 44-115-936-3200, sales@bgs.ac.uk, Enquiries@bgs.ac.uk, http://www.nkw.ac.uk/bgs/., http://www.bgs.ac.uk/. Circ: 2,500. **Subscr. to:** The Stationery Office, c/o Liason Officer, Atlantic House, Holborn Viaduct, London EC1P 1BW, United Kingdom.

E

554 560 GBR
GREAT BRITAIN. NATURAL ENVIRONMENT RESEARCH COUNCIL. BRITISH GEOLOGICAL SURVEY. MEMOIRS. Text in English. 1846. irreg. price varies. illus. **Document type:** *Monographic series, Government.* **Description:** Presents geological studies of Great Britain, including Northern Ireland.
Formerly (until Jan. 1984): Great Britain. Institute of Geological Sciences. Memoirs of the Geological Survey of Great Britain (0072-6494)
Indexed: IMMAb.
Published by: Natural Environment Research Council, British Geological Survey, British Geological Survey, Kingsley Dunham Centre, Nicker Hill, Keyworth, Nottingham, NG12 5GG, United Kingdom. TEL 44-115-936-3100, FAX 44-115-936-3200, TELEX 9378173 BGSKEY G, sales@bgs.ac.uk, Enquiries@bgs.ac.uk, http://www.nkw.ac.uk/bgs/, http://www.bgs.ac.uk/. Circ: 2,000. **Subscr. to:** The Stationery Office, Kingsley Dunham Centre, Nine Elms Ln, London SW8 5DR, United Kingdom.

551 GBR ISSN 0030-7467
TN57 CODEN: OGMRA3
GREAT BRITAIN. NATURAL ENVIRONMENT RESEARCH COUNCIL. BRITISH GEOLOGICAL SURVEY. OVERSEAS GEOLOGY AND MINERAL RESOURCES. Text in English. 1950. irreg. price varies. illus. **Document type:** *Monographic series, Government.* **Description:** Examines papers on geological aspects of the developing areas of the world.
Formerly (until Jan. 1984): Great Britain. Institute of Geological Sciences. Overseas Geology and Mineral Resources (0073-9332)
Indexed: IMMAb.
—CASDDS, CISTI, Linda Hall. **CCC.**
Published by: Natural Environment Research Council, British Geological Survey, British Geological Survey, Kingsley Dunham Centre, Nicker Hill, Keyworth, Nottingham, NG12 5GG, United Kingdom. sales@bgs.ac.uk, Enquiries@bgs.ac.uk, http://www.bgs.ac.uk/. Circ: 1,500.

551 GBR ISSN 0951-6646
CODEN: OMISDV
GREAT BRITAIN. NATURAL ENVIRONMENT RESEARCH COUNCIL. BRITISH GEOLOGICAL SURVEY. OVERSEAS MEMOIRS. Text in English. 1976. irreg. price varies. illus.; maps. **Document type:** *Monographic series, Government.* **Description:** Studies the geology of various countries.
Formerly (until Jan. 1984): Great Britain. Institute of Geological Sciences. Overseas Memoirs (0308-5325)
Indexed: IMMAb.
—BLDSC (6316.690000), CASDDS, CISTI, Linda Hall. **CCC.**
Published by: Natural Environment Research Council, British Geological Survey, British Geological Survey, Kingsley Dunham Centre, Nicker Hill, Keyworth, Nottingham, NG12 5GG, United Kingdom. TEL 44-115-936-3100, FAX 44-115-936-3200, sales@bgs.ac.uk, Enquiries@bgs.ac.uk, http://www.nkw.ac.uk/bgs/, http://www.bgs.ac.uk/. Circ: 1,250. **Subscr. to:** The Stationery Office, c/o Liason Officer, Atlantic House, Holborn Viaduct, London EC1P 1BW, United Kingdom.

550 GBR
GREAT BRITAIN. NATURAL ENVIRONMENT RESEARCH COUNCIL. BRITISH GEOLOGICAL SURVEY. UNITED KINGDOM OFFSHORE REGIONAL REPORTS. Text in English. 1995. irreg. price varies. illus. **Document type:** *Government.*
Published by: Natural Environment Research Council, British Geological Survey, British Geological Survey, Kingsley Dunham Centre, Nicker Hill, Keyworth, Nottingham, NG12 5GG, United Kingdom. TEL 44-115-936-3100, FAX 44-115-936-3200, sales@bgs.ac.uk, Enquiries@bgs.ac.uk, http://www.nkw.ac.uk/bgs/., http://www.bgs.ac.uk/. Circ: 1,000 (controlled). **Subscr. to:** The Stationery Office, c/o Liason Officer, Atlantic House, Holborn Viaduct, London EC1P 1BW, United Kingdom.

551.447 GRC ISSN 0374-0390
GREEK SPELEOLOGICAL SOCIETY. DELTION (OR HELLENIC SPELEOLOGICAL SOCIETY)/SOCIETE SPELEOLOGIQUE DE GRECE. BULLETIN TRIMESTRIEL; Bulletin of Hellenic Speleological Society. Text in Greek; Summaries in French, English. 1952. biennial. membership or on exchange basis. bibl. index. **Document type:** *Bulletin.* **Description:** Articles about missions to explore caves and specialized scientific research.
Published by: Hellenic Speleological Society, 32, Sina St., Athens, 106 72, Greece. TEL 30-1-3617824, FAX 30-1-3643476, ellspe@otenet.gr, http://www.otenet.gr/ellspe. Circ: 1,000.

551 NLD ISSN 0017-4505
➤ **GRONDBOOR EN HAMER.** Text in Dutch; Summaries in English. 1955. 5/yr. EUR 14 domestic; EUR 23.50 foreign (effective 2005). adv. bk.rev. bibl.; charts; illus. index, cum.index. **Document type:** *Bulletin, Academic/Scholarly.*
Indexed: ZooRec.
—CISTI.
Published by: Nederlandse Geologische Vereniging, c/o W Felder, Oude Trichterweg 26, Vijlen, 6294 AL, Netherlands. TEL 31-43-3061919, http://www.geo.uu.nl/ngv/publicaties/publicaties.htm. Ed. Irene M Groenendijk. Circ: 1,600.

551.910 ITA ISSN 0373-7500
GROTTE D'ITALIA. Text in Italian. 1927. a.
Published by: Societa Speleologica Italiana, Via Zamboni, 67, Bologna, BO 40126, Italy. FAX 3951-354522. Ed. Paolo Forti. Circ: 1,000.

796.525 VEN ISSN 1011-7407
CODEN: GUACDD
EL GUACHARO; Boletin de divulgacion espeleologica. Text in Spanish; Summaries in English. 1967. 6/yr. VEB 15,000, USD 10 (effective 2003). 60 p./no.; back issues avail. **Document type:** *Newsletter, Academic/Scholarly.*
Formerly (until 1969): Sociedad Venezolana de Espeleologia. Biblioteca. Boletin
Related titles: CD-ROM ed.
Indexed: SpeleolAb.
Published by: Sociedad Venezolana de Espeleologia, Apdo 47334, Caracas, DF 1041-A, Venezuela. TEL 58-212-2720724, svespeleo@cantv.net. Ed. Franco Urbani. Circ: 500.

555 CHN ISSN 1001-8670
GUANGDONG DIZHI/GUANGDONG GEOLOGY. Text in Chinese; Abstracts in English. 1986. q. CNY 5 newsstand/cover domestic (effective 2000). adv. **Document type:** *Academic/Scholarly.* **Description:** Carries academic articles on geological sciences, and latest developments in science and technology.
Related titles: Online - full content ed.: (from WanFang Data Corp.).
Indexed: ZooRec.
Published by: Guangdong-sheng Dizhi Kuangchan Ju/Bureau of Geology and Mineral Resources of Guangdong Province, No 739, Dongfeng Rd East, Guangzhou, Guangdong 510080, China. TEL 778992. Ed. Shao-mei Peng. Circ: 1,000.

551 CHN ISSN 1003-7861
GUANGXI DIZHI/GUANGXI GEOLOGY. Text in Chinese. 1984. q. CNY 5 newsstand/cover domestic (effective 2000). **Document type:** *Academic/Scholarly.*
Related titles: Online - full content ed.: (from WanFang Data Corp.).
Indexed: ZooRec.
Address: Jianzheng-Lu 1-Hao, Nanning, 530023, China. Ed. Kai-li Chen.

551 USA ISSN 0533-6562
QE1 CODEN: TGCGA9
GULF ASSOCIATION OF GEOLOGICAL SOCIETIES. TRANSACTIONS. Text in English. 1953. a. USD 40 (effective 2004). **Document type:** *Abstract/Index.*
—BLDSC (8933.450000), IE, Linda Hall, PADDS. **CCC.**
Published by: Gulf Coast Association of Geological Societies, University Station Box X, University of Texas at Austin, Austin, TX 78713-8924. TEL 512-471-1543, FAX 512-471-0140, gcags@beg.utexas.edu, http://www.gcags.org.

551 CHN
GUOWAI DIZHI/GEOLOGY ABROAD. Text in Chinese. bi-m.
Published by: Zhongguo Kexueyuan, Dizhi Yanjiusuo/Chinese Academy of Sciences, Institute of Geology, Qijia Huozi, Deshengmenwai, Beijing, 100029, China. TEL 4016611. Ed. Yi Shanfeng.

551 CHN ISSN 1003-2959
GUOWAI DIZHI KEJI/FOREIGN GEOLOGY SCIENCE AND TECHNOLOGY. Text in Chinese. 1978. 8/yr.
Published by: Zhongguo Dizhi Kuangchan Xinxi Yanjiuyuan/Chinese Institute of Geology and Mineral Products Information, 277 Fuchengmenwai Beijie, Beijing, 100037, China. TEL 892243. Ed. Wang Liwen.

GUOWAI KEJI ZILIAO MULU (DIZHIXUE)/FOREIGN SCIENCE AND TECHNOLOGY CATALOGUE (GEOLOGY). see *EARTH SCIENCES—Abstracting, Bibliographies, Statistics*

551 CHN ISSN 1001-5825
GUOWAI YOUQI KANTAN. Text in Chinese. bi-m.
Published by: Nengyuan Bu, Dili Wuli Kantan Ju, P.O. Box 11-1, Zuozhou, Hebei 072751, China.

551.4608 CHN ISSN 0256-1492
QE39 CODEN: HDYDDS
HAIYANG DIZHI YU DISIJI DIZHI/MARINE GEOLOGY & QUATERNARY GEOLOGY. Text in Chinese. 1981. q. CNY 18 newsstand/cover domestic; USD 6 newsstand/cover foreign (effective 2004). **Document type:** *Journal, Academic/Scholarly.*
Related titles: Online - full content ed.: (from WanFang Data Corp.).
Indexed: ASFA, ESPM, RefZh, ZooRec.
—BLDSC (5375.450000), IE, ingenta, Linda Hall.
Published by: Kexue Chubanshe/Science Press, 16 Donghuang Cheng Genbei Jie, Beijing, 100717, China. TEL 86-10-64000246, FAX 86-10-64030255, gwzhang@qd-public.sd.cninfo.net, http://hydzydsjdz.wanfangdata.com.cn/default.html, http://www.sciencep.com/. Ed. Guang-Wei Zhang. **Dist. by:** China International Book Trading Corp, 35 Chegongzhuang Xilu, Haidian District, PO Box 399, Beijing 100044, China. TEL 86-10-68412045, FAX 86-10-68412023, cibtc@mail.cibtc.com.cn, http://www.cibtc.com.cn.

550 DEU ISSN 1432-3699
HALLESCHES JAHRBUCH FUER GEOWISSENSCHAFTEN. REIHE A: GEOGRAPHIE UND GEOOEKOLOGIE. Text in German. 1949. a. **Document type:** *Journal, Academic/Scholarly.*
Supersedes in part (in 1995): Hallesches Jahrbuch Geowissenschaften (0138-3647); Which was formerly (until 1977): Hallesches Jahrbuch fuer Mitteldeutsche Erdgeschichte (0367-5602)
—CISTI.
Published by: Martin-Luther-Universitaet Halle-Wittenberg, Institut fuer Geologische Wissenschaften und Geiseltalmuseum, Domstr. 5, Halle, 06108, Germany. TEL 49-345-5526111, FAX 49-345-5527180, institut@geologie.uni-halle.de, http://www.geologie.uni-halle.de.

550 DEU ISSN 1432-3702
QE269 CODEN: HJGEDH
HALLESCHES JAHRBUCH FUER GEOWISSENSCHAFTEN. REIHE B: GEOLOGIE, PALAEONTOLOGIE, MINERALOGIE. Text in German. 1949. a. **Document type:** *Journal, Academic/Scholarly.*
Supersedes in part (in 1995): Hallesches Jahrbuch fuer Geowissenschaften (0138-3647); Which was formerly (until 1977): Hallesches Jahrbuch fuer Mitteldeutsche Erdgeschichte (0367-5602)
Indexed: IBR, RefZh, ZooRec.
—CASDDS, CISTI, Linda Hall.
Published by: Martin-Luther-Universitaet Halle-Wittenberg, Institut fuer Geologische Wissenschaften und Geiseltalmuseum, Domstr. 5, Halle, 06108, Germany. Ed. K H Krause.

550 DEU ISSN 0943-4658
HAMBURGER MINERALISCHEN MUSEUM. SCHRIFTEN. Text in German. 1992. irreg. **Document type:** *Monographic series.*
Published by: (Hamburger Mineralischen Museum), Verlag Sven von Loga, Koenigsforststr 29, Cologne, 51109, Germany. TEL 49-180-5671231, FAX 49-221-386737. Ed. W Liessmann.

551 NLD ISSN 0168-6275
➤ **HANDBOOK OF EXPLORATION GEOCHEMISTRY.** Text in English. 1981. irreg., latest vol.7, 2000. price varies. illus. **Document type:** *Monographic series, Academic/Scholarly.* **Description:** Highlights research and developments in the field of exploration geochemistry.
Indexed: CIN, ChemAb, ChemTitl, IMMAb, Inspec.
—BLDSC (4250.464000), CISTI.
Published by: Elsevier BV (Subsidiary of: Elsevier Science & Technology), Radarweg 29, Amsterdam, 1043 NX, Netherlands. TEL 31-20-4853911, FAX 31-20-4852457, nlinfo-f@elsevier.nl, http://www.elsevier.nl. Ed. G J S Govett.

➤ **HAN'GUG HAEYANG HAGHOEJI/KOREAN SOCIETY OF OCEANOGRAPHY. JOURNAL.** see *EARTH SCIENCES—Oceanography*

551 CHN ISSN 1002-2325
HEILONGJIANG DIZHI/HEILONGJIANG GEOLOGY. Text in Chinese. 1990. q. CNY 5 newsstand/cover domestic (effective 2000). **Document type:** *Academic/Scholarly.*
Related titles: Online - full content ed.: (from WanFang Data Corp.).
Published by: Heilongjiang-sheng Dizhi Kuangchanju/Bureau of Geology and Mineral Resources of Heilongjiang Province, 65 Zhongshan Lu, Ha'erbin, 150036, China. Ed. Yan-qiang Xu.

551.447 AUS ISSN 0017-9973
CODEN: HELIBH
➤ **HELICTITE**; journal of Australasian speleological research. Text in English. 1962. s-a. AUD 27 per vol. in Australia & New Zealand; AUD 30 per vol. elsewhere (effective until 2004). bk.rev. abstr.; charts; illus. cum.index: 1962-1984. back issues avail.; reprints avail. **Document type:** *Journal, Academic/Scholarly.*
Indexed: AESIS, ZooRec.
Published by: Australian Speleological Federation Inc., PO Box 2277, Mount Waverley, VIC 3149, Australia. TEL 61-3-9808-7248, gnbaddeley@pacific.net.au, gnb@mira.net, s.white@latrobe.edu.au, http://www.home.pacific.net.au/~gnb/helictite/, http://www.caves.org.au. Eds. Ken G Grimes, Stefan Eberhard, Susan White. Pub. Mr. Glenn N Baddeley. R&P Susan White. Circ: 180.

550 ESP ISSN 0214-6088
HENARES: REVISTA DE GEOLOGIA. Text in Spanish. 1987. a. price varies.
Published by: Universidad de Alcala de Henares, Facultad de Ciencias, Apdo. 20, Alcala De Henares, (Madrid) 28880, Spain.

551 UKR ISSN 1727-835X
HEOLOH UKRAINY. Text in Ukrainian. 2001. q. USD 89 foreign (effective 2005).
—BLDSC (0047.675000).
Published by: Spilka Heolohiv Ukrainy, vul O Honchara 55b, Kyiev, 01054, Ukraine. TEL 380-44-2210711, FAX 380-44-2468008, journal@geolog.org.ua. Ed. P O Zagorodnyuk. **Dist. by:** East View Information Services, 3020 Harbor Ln. N., Minneapolis, MN 55447. TEL 800-477-1005, FAX 800-800-3839, eastview@eastview.com, http://www.eastview.com.

E

551 UKR ISSN 0869-0774
TN260 CODEN: GGGKF5
➤ **HEOLOHIYA I HEOKHIMIYA HORIUCHYKH KOPALYN/GEOLOGY AND GEOCHEMISTRY OF COMBUSTIBLE MINERALS.** Text in Ukrainian, Russian, English. 1965. q. UAK 12 domestic; USD 30 foreign (effective 2003). adv. bk.rev. **Document type:** *Journal, Academic/Scholarly.* **Description:** Focuses on questions of theory and method in geology, geochemistry, hydrogeology, geotechnology, conditions of extraction and complex employment of combustible minerals, and history of geology and science.
Former titles: Geologiya i Geokhimiya Goryuchikh Iskopaemykh (0135-2164); (until 1974): Geologiya i Geokhimiya Goryuchikh Kopalin (0435-4117)
Indexed: CIN, ChemAb, ChemTitl, RefZh.
—CASDDS, Linda Hall. **CCC.**
Published by: Natsional'na Akademiya Nauk Ukrainy, Instytut Heologii i Heokhimii Horiuchykh Kopalyn/National Academy of Sciences of Ukraine, Institute of Geology & Geochemistry of Combustible Minerals, vul Naukova 3-a, Lviv, 290053, Ukraine. TEL 380-322-632541, FAX 380-322-632209, igggk@ah.ipm.lviv.ua, http://www.geofuel.lviv.net. Ed. S.O. Lyzoon. R&P S O Lyzoon TEL 38-322-632541. Circ: 250.

555 JPN ISSN 0073-2303
QE304 CODEN: HIRDAP
HIROSHIMA DAIGAKU CHIGAKU KENKYU HOKOKU/ HIROSHIMA UNIVERSITY. GEOLOGICAL REPORT. Text in Japanese; Summaries in English. 1951. a.
Indexed: BiolAb, JPI.
Published by: Hiroshima University, Faculty of Science, Department of Earth and Planetary Systems Science/Hiroshima Daigaku Rigakubu Chishitsugaku Kobutsugaku Kyoshitsu, Kagami-yama 1-3-1, Higashi-Hiroshima, Hiroshima, 739, Japan. TEL 81-824-24-7469, FAX 81-824-24-0735, http://www.geol.sci.hiroshima-u.ac.jp/~info/index_e.html, http://www.geol.sci.hiroshima-u.ac.jp/~info/index.html.

551 549 JPN
HIROSHIMA UNIVERSITY. JOURNAL OF SCIENCE. SERIES C. EARTH AND PLANETARY SCIENCES. Text in English. 1951. irreg., latest vol.10, no.3, 1995. index. **Document type:** *Bulletin.*
Formerly (until 1995): Hiroshima University. Journal of Science. Series C. Geology and Mineralogy (0075-4374)
Indexed: BiolAb, JTA, RefZh.
—BLDSC (5054.000000), CISTI, ingenta.
Published by: Hiroshima University, Faculty of Science/Hiroshima Daigaku Rigakubu Chikyu Wakuseisisutemugaku, Kagamiyama, Higashihiroshima-shi, Hiroshima-ken 739-0046, Japan. TEL 0824-24-7459, FAX 0824-24-0735.

551 558 VEN ISSN 0258-3135
QE48.V4
➤ **HISTORIA DE LAS GEOCIENCIAS EN VENEZUELA. BOLETIN.** Text in Spanish. 1984. bi-m. VEB 50,000, USD 25 (effective 2005). bk.rev. index. 50 p./no.; back issues avail. **Document type:** *Bulletin, Academic/Scholarly.* **Description:** Publishes works on historical aspects of geology, geophysics and the mining and petroleum industry in Venezuela. Includes biographical and bibliographical works.
Related titles: CD-ROM ed.; E-mail ed.
Published by: Sociedad Venezolana de Historia de las Geociencias, Apdo 47334, Caracas, DF 1041-A, Venezuela. TEL 58-212-2720724, svhgc@yahoo.com. Ed. Dr. Franco Urbani. Circ: 300.

E

➤ **HOBETSU-CHORITSU HAKUBUTSUKAN KENKYU HOKOKU/HOBETSU MUSEUM. BULLETIN.** see *PALEONTOLOGY*

551.447 AUT ISSN 0018-3091
GB601.A1 CODEN: HOHLA7
DIE HOEHLE; Zeitschrift fuer Karst- und Hoehlenkunde. Text in German. 1950. q. EUR 10.20 (effective 2003). bk.rev. index. 32 p./no. 2 cols./p.; **Document type:** *Journal, Academic/Scholarly.* **Description:** Information and new research on karstology and speleology.
Indexed: BiolAb, IBR, RefZh, ZooRec.
—CISTI.
Published by: Verband Oesterreichischer Hoehlenforscher, Obere Donaustr 97-1-61, Vienna, 1020, Austria. webmaster@hoehle.org, http://www.hoehle.org. Ed. Hubert Trimmel. Circ: 2,000.

551.44 CHE ISSN 0018-3105
HOEHLENPOST. Text in German. 1963. 3/yr. CHF 25 domestic; CHF 28 foreign (effective 2003). adv. bk.rev. **Document type:** *Bulletin, Academic/Scholarly.*
Published by: Ostschweizerische Gesellschaft fuer Hoehlenforschung, Bruggwiesenstr 6, Hettlingen, 8442, Switzerland. TEL 41-52-3161737. Ed., R&P Rene Scherrer. Circ: 200.

HOKKAIDO KYOIKU DAIGAKU KIYO. DAI-2-BU, B. SEIBUTSUGAKU, CHIGAKU, NOGAKU-HEN/HOKKAIDO UNIVERSITY OF EDUCATION. JOURNAL. SECTION 2 B. BIOLOGY, GEOLOGY, AND AGRICULTURE. see *BIOLOGY*

551.22 JPN
HOKKAIDO UNIVERSITY. URAKAWA SEISMOLOGICAL OBSERVATORY. BULLETIN✶. Text in English. s-a. per issue exchange basis. **Document type:** *Bulletin.*
Published by: Hokkaido University, Urakawa Seismological Observatory, c/o Hokkaido University, Nishi 5, Kita 8, Kita-ku, Sapporo, 060, Japan.

555 HKG ISSN 1024-669X
HONG KONG GEOLOGIST. Text in English; Abstracts in Chinese. 1982. s-a. HKD 200 to members; HKD 250 to institutions; HKD 50 to students (effective 2004).
Formerly (until 1993): Geological Society of Hong Kong. Newsletter (1010-335X)
Published by: Geological Society of Hong Kong, Tsim Sha Tsui Post Office, P O Box 92341, Kowloon, Hong Kong. http://www.geolsoc.org.hk. Ed. Bernie Owen.

557 USA ISSN 0018-6686
CODEN: BHGLA
➤ **HOUSTON GEOLOGICAL SOCIETY. BULLETIN.** Text in English. 1958. m. (Sep.-Jun.). USD 20 membership (effective 2005). adv. bk.rev. abstr.; charts; illus. **Document type:** *Bulletin, Academic/Scholarly.*
Indexed: PetrolAb.
—BLDSC (4335.153195), IE, ingenta, PADDS.
Published by: Houston Geological Society, 10575 Katy Freeway, Ste 290, Houston, TX 77024. TEL 713-463-9476, FAX 713-463-9160, lilly@hgs.org, http://www.hgs.org. Ed. Lynne Feldkamp. Adv. contact John King. B&W page USD 780. Circ: 5,400.

551 CHN ISSN 1000-2251
HUADONG DIZHI XUEYUAN XUEBAO/EAST CHINA GEOLOGICAL INSTITUTE. JOURNAL. Text in Chinese. 1978. q. CNY 5 newsstand/cover domestic (effective 2000). **Document type:** *Academic/Scholarly.*
Related titles: Online - full content ed.: (from WanFang Data Corp.); Online - full text ed.: (from East View Information Services).
Indexed: INIS AtomInd.
Published by: Huadong Dizhi Xueyuan/East China Geological Institute, 14 Huancheng Xi Lu, Fuzhou, Jiangxi 344000, China.

HYDROCARBON AND BYPRODUCT RESERVES IN BRITISH COLUMBIA. see *PETROLEUM AND GAS*

577.276 SWE ISSN 1368-8766
I G B P BOOK SERIES. (International Geosphere-Biosphere Programme) Text in English. 1997. irreg., latest vol.5, 1999. price varies. **Document type:** *Monographic series, Academic/Scholarly.*
Indexed: BIOSIS Prev.
—BLDSC (4540.610550).
Published by: Royal Swedish Academy of Science, International Geosphere-Biosphere Programme, IGBP Secretariat, Box 50005, Stockholm, 10405, Sweden. TEL 46-8-166448, FAX 46-8-166405, sec@igbp.kva.se, http://www.igbp.kva.se/.

577.276 SWE
I G B P DIRECTORY. (International Geosphere-Biosphere Programme) Text in English. 1994. a. **Document type:** *Directory, Academic/Scholarly.*
Related titles: ♦ Issued with: I G B P Global Change Report. ISSN 0284-8015.
Published by: Royal Swedish Academy of Science, International Geosphere-Biosphere Programme, IGBP Secretariat, Box 50005, Stockholm, 10405, Sweden. TEL 46-8-166448, FAX 46-8-166405, sec@igbp.kva.se, http://www.igbp.kva.se/.

577.276 SWE ISSN 0284-8015
GE149
➤ **I G B P GLOBAL CHANGE REPORT.** (International Geosphere-Biosphere Programme) Key Title: Global Change - IGBP. Variant title: Global Change Report. Text in English. 1986. irreg. (4-5/yr.). free. **Document type:** *Monographic series, Academic/Scholarly.* **Description:** Publishes science plans and research of the core projects and framework activities of the International Geosphere-Biosphere Programme.
Related titles: ♦ Includes: I G B P Directory.
—BLDSC (4363.390500), CISTI. **CCC.**
Published by: Royal Swedish Academy of Science, International Geosphere-Biosphere Programme, IGBP Secretariat, Box 50005, Stockholm, 10405, Sweden. TEL 46-8-166448, FAX 46-8-166405, sec@igbp.kva.se, http://www.igbp.kva.se/igbpint.html/. Circ: 5,000 (controlled).

➤ **I S E T JOURNAL OF EARTHQUAKE TECHNOLOGY.** see *ENGINEERING—Civil Engineering*

551.31 GBR ISSN 0019-1043
GB2401 CODEN: ICEXAN
ICE. Text in English. 1958. 3/yr. GBP 26 (effective 2002). adv. bk.rev. back issues avail. **Document type:** *Bulletin.*
Indexed: RefZh.
—CISTI, Linda Hall.
Published by: International Glaciological Society, Lensfield Rd, Cambridge, CB2 1ER, United Kingdom. TEL 44-1223-355974, FAX 44-1223-336543, http://www.igsoc.org/. Ed. C S L Ommanney. R&P C.S.L. Ommanney. Circ: 1,100.

557 622 USA ISSN 0734-3825
IDAHO. GEOLOGICAL SURVEY. BULLETIN. Text in English. 1920. irreg., latest vol.26, 1982. price varies. **Document type:** *Bulletin, Government.*
Formerly (until 1984): Idaho. Bureau of Mines and Geology. Bulletin (0073-442X)
Indexed: IMMAb.
—Linda Hall.
Published by: Idaho Geological Survey, Morrill Hall, Rm 332, University of Idaho, Moscow, ID 83843. TEL 208-885-7991.

557 USA
IDAHO. GEOLOGICAL SURVEY. INFORMATION CIRCULAR. Text in English. 1957. irreg., latest vol.40, 1986. price varies.
Formerly (until 1984): Idaho. Bureau of Mines and Geology. Information Circular (0073-4446)
Indexed: CIN, ChemAb, ChemTitl, IMMAb.
—Linda Hall.
Published by: Idaho Geological Survey, Morrill Hall, Rm 332, University of Idaho, Moscow, ID 83843. TEL 208-885-7991.

551 USA
IDAHO. GEOLOGICAL SURVEY. TECHNICAL REPORT. Text in English. 1978. irreg. (6-10/yr.).
Formerly (until 1984): Idaho. Geological Survey. Open-File Report
Published by: Idaho Geological Survey, Morrill Hall, Rm 332, University of Idaho, Moscow, ID 83843. TEL 208-885-7991.

IDRIJSKI RAZGLEDI. see *HISTORY*

ILLINOIS MINERALS. see *MINES AND MINING INDUSTRY*

ILLINOIS PETROLEUM. see *PETROLEUM AND GAS*

557 USA ISSN 0073-5051
ILLINOIS. STATE GEOLOGICAL SURVEY. BULLETIN. Text in English. 1906. irreg., latest vol.105, 2001. price varies. abstr.; bibl.; charts; illus.; maps. **Document type:** *Bulletin.*
Indexed: BiolAb.
—Linda Hall.
Published by: State Geological Survey, Natural Resources Bldg, 615 E Peabody Dr, Champaign, IL 61820. TEL 217-333-4747. R&P Marie-France DuFour TEL 217-333-5115. Circ: 1,200.

557 USA ISSN 0073-506X
CODEN: ILGCAX
ILLINOIS. STATE GEOLOGICAL SURVEY. CIRCULAR. Text in English. 1932. irreg., latest vol.565, 2005. price varies. abstr.; bibl.; charts; illus.; maps; stat. **Document type:** *Government.*
Indexed: BiolAb, RefZh.
—CASDDS, Linda Hall.
Published by: State Geological Survey, Natural Resources Bldg, 615 E Peabody Dr, Champaign, IL 61820. TEL 217-333-4747. R&P Marie-France DuFour TEL 217-333-5115.

ILLINOIS. STATE GEOLOGICAL SURVEY. COOPERATIVE GROUNDWATER REPORT. see *WATER RESOURCES*

557 USA ISSN 1060-1988
QE105 CODEN: IEGNAH
ILLINOIS. STATE GEOLOGICAL SURVEY. ENVIRONMENTAL GEOLOGY. Text in English. 1965. irreg., latest vol.152, 1999. price varies. abstr.; bibl.; charts; illus.; stat.
Formerly: Illinois. State Geological Survey. Environmental Geology Notes (0073-5086)
Indexed: ASFA, BiolAb, ESPM, SWRA.
—Linda Hall.
Published by: State Geological Survey, Natural Resources Bldg, 615 E Peabody Dr, Champaign, IL 61820. TEL 217-333-4747. R&P Marie-France DuFour TEL 217-333-5115.

557 USA ISSN 0073-5094
QE105 CODEN: IGSSA4
ILLINOIS. STATE GEOLOGICAL SURVEY. GUIDEBOOK SERIES. Text in English. 1950. irreg., latest vol.33, 2001. price varies. abstr.; bibl.; charts; illus.; stat.
Indexed: BiolAb, RefZh.
—Linda Hall.
Published by: State Geological Survey, Natural Resources Bldg, 615 E Peabody Dr, Champaign, IL 61820. TEL 217-333-4747, FAX 217-244-7004. Circ: 1,000.

551.3 IND ISSN 0970-3268
QE471
INDIAN ASSOCIATION OF SEDIMENTOLOGISTS. JOURNAL. Text in English. 1981. s-a. USD 60 (effective 2001). bk.rev. charts. back issues avail. **Document type:** *Academic/Scholarly.*
Published by: (Indian Association of Sedimentologists), Hindustan Publishing Corporation (India), 4805-24, Bharat Ram Rd., 1st Fl., Flats 1 & 2, Darya Ganj, New Delhi, 110 002, India. TEL 91-11-325-4401, FAX 91-11-6193511, hpcpd@nda.vsnl.net.in, hpcpd@hpc.cc, http://www.hpc.cc, http://www.bizdelhi.com/publisher/hpc. Ed. S M Mathur.

551 IND ISSN 0379-5098
QE295 CODEN: BIGABW
➤ **INDIAN GEOLOGISTS' ASSOCIATION. BI-ANNUAL BULLETIN.** Text in English. 1968. s-a. INR 75, USD 40. adv. bk.rev. charts; illus. back issues avail. **Document type:** *Bulletin, Academic/Scholarly.*

Indexed: ZooRec.
—CISTI, Linda Hall.
Published by: Indian Geologists' Association, c/o N. Kochhar, Secretary, Department of Geology, Panjab University, Chandigarh, Haryana 160 014, India. TEL 91-172-541-740, FAX 91-172-541-409, TELEX 3957464 RSIC IN. Ed. L N . Gupta. R&P Naresh Kochhar. Circ: 250 (paid).

551.9 IND ISSN 0970-9088
QE514 CODEN: IJGEET
INDIAN JOURNAL OF GEOCHEMISTRY. Text in English. 1983. s-a. USD 200 (effective 2000). **Document type:** *Academic/Scholarly.*
Published by: (Indian Association of Geochemists), H P C Publishers Distributors Pvt. Ltd., 4805 Bharat Ram Rd, 24 Darya Ganj, New Delhi, 110 002, India. TEL 91-11-3254401, FAX 91-11-619-3511, hpcpd@nda.vsnl.net.in, hpcpd@hpc.cc, http://www.hpc.cc, http://www.bizdelhi.com/publisher/hpc, http://www.indianindustry.com.

550 553 IND ISSN 0970-1354
QE1 CODEN: IJOGE7
INDIAN JOURNAL OF GEOLOGY. Text in English. 1926. q. USD 55. adv. bk.rev. charts; illus. index. **Document type:** *Bulletin, Academic/Scholarly.*
Formerly: Geological, Mining and Metallurgical Society of India. Quarterly Journal (0016-7584)
Indexed: CRIA, CRICC, ChemAb, IMMAb, ZooRec.
—BLDSC (4413.300000), CASDDS, CISTI, IE, ingenta, Linda Hall.
Published by: Geological Mining and Metallurgical Society of India, Geology Department, University of Calcutta, 35 Ballygunge Circular Rd., Kolkata, West Bengal 700 019, India. TEL 91-33-475-3681. Eds. Dhruba Mukhopadhyay, Sanjib C Sarkar. Circ: 500.

INDIAN MINERALOGIST. see *MINES AND MINING INDUSTRY*

551.3 IND ISSN 0970-3918
CODEN: TISTEA
INDIAN SOCIETY OF DESERT TECHNOLOGY. TRANSACTIONS. Text in English. 1976. a. USD 20. adv. bk.rev.
Formerly (until 1987): Indian Society of Desert Technology and University Centre of Desert Studies. Transactions (0379-0568)
Indexed: AgrForAb, ChemAb, EngInd, ExcerpMed, FCA, I&DA, MaizeAb, PGrRegA, S&F, S&MA.
—CASDDS, CISTI, Ei, Linda Hall. **CCC.**
Published by: Indian Society of Desert Technology, A-42 Shastri Nagar, Jodhpur, Rajasthan 342 003, India. Ed. Alam Singh. Circ: 1,000.

557 USA ISSN 0160-3051
INDIANA. GEOLOGICAL SURVEY BULLETIN. Text in English. 1964. irreg. **Document type:** *Bulletin, Government.*
—Linda Hall.
Published by: South Carolina Geological Survey, Department of Natural Resources, Indianapolis, IN 46204. TEL 803-896-7700, FAX 803-896-7695.

557 USA ISSN 0149-2470
INDIANA. GEOLOGICAL SURVEY OCCASIONAL PAPER. Text in English. 1974. irreg. **Document type:** *Monographic series, Government.*
—Linda Hall.
Published by: South Carolina Geological Survey, Department of Natural Resources, Indianapolis, IN 46204. TEL 803-896-7700, FAX 803-896-7695.

557 USA ISSN 0537-2933
QE109 CODEN: IGSSB5
INDIANA. GEOLOGICAL SURVEY SPECIAL REPORT. Text in English. 1963. irreg. **Document type:** *Government.*
Formerly (until 1964): Indiana. Geological Survey. Special Report (0886-0734)
—Linda Hall.
Published by: South Carolina Geological Survey, Department of Natural Resources, Indianapolis, IN 46204. TEL 803-896-7700, FAX 803-896-7695.

551 GBR
TN799.5
INDUSTRIAL MINERALS: A GLOBAL GEOLOGY. Text in English. 1984. irreg. **Document type:** *Trade.* **Description:** Covers geology and uses of 50 industrial rocks and minerals.
Former titles (until 1998): Industrial Minerals: Geology and World Deposits (0957-4433); Geology of Nonmetallics (0266-1411)
Published by: Industrial Minerals Information Ltd. (Subsidiary of: Metal Bulletin plc), 1 Park House, Park Terr, Worcester Park, Surrey KT4 7HY, United Kingdom. TEL 44-2078-279977, FAX 44-2083-378943, books@metalbulletin.plc.uk, http://www.mineralnet.co.uk. Eds. P W Harben, R L Bates.
Orders in the US to: Metal Bulletin Inc., 1250 Broadway, 26th fl., New York, NY 10001-7708. TEL 212-213-6202.

▼ **INSIGHT (MILWAUKEE).** see *BIOLOGY*

551 FRA ISSN 0335-8178
INSTITUT DE MONTPELLIER. MEMOIRES ET TRAVAUX. Key Title: Memoires et Travaux de l'Institut de Montpellier. Text in English. 1973. irreg.
Published by: Ecole Practique des Hautes Edutes, Institut de Montpellier, 45-47 rue des Ecoles, Paris, 75005, France.

551.3 BEL ISSN 0374-6291
QE755.B4 CODEN: BISTCE
➤ **INSTITUT ROYAL DES SCIENCES NATURELLES DE BELGIQUE. BULLETIN. SERIE SCIENCES DE LA TERRE.** Text in English, French, German. 1930. a., latest vol.73, 2003. EUR 40.90 (effective 2003). abstr.; bibl.; charts; illus. cum.index. back issues avail. **Document type:** *Bulletin, Academic/Scholarly.*
Indexed: BIOSIS Prev, BiolAb, GEOBASE, RefZh, ZooRec.
—CISTI, Linda Hall.
Published by: Koninklijk Belgisch Instituut voor Natuurwetenschappen/Institut Royal des Sciences Naturelles de Belgique, Vautierstraat 29, Brussels, 1000, Belgium. TEL 32-2-6274211, FAX 32-2-6274113, annie.dhondt@naturalsciences.be, bib@naturalsciences.be. Ed. Annie Dhondt.

538.7 BEL ISSN 0770-4569
INSTITUT ROYAL METEOROLOGIQUE DE BELGIQUE. ANNUAIRE: MAGNETISME TERRESTRE/KONINKLIJK METEOROLOGISCH INSTITUUT VAN BELGIE. JAARBOEK: AARDMAGNETISME. Text in Dutch, French. 1964. a. **Document type:** *Bulletin, Trade.* **Description:** Discusses research into Earth's magnetic fields.
Published by: Institut Royal Meteorologique de Belgique/Koninklijk Meteorologisch Instituut van Belgie, Av Circulaire 3, Brussels, 1180, Belgium. TEL 32-2-373-0502, FAX 32-2-375-1259, http://www.meteo.oma.be. Ed. H Malcorps. Circ: 150.

INSTITUTE FOR THE STUDY OF EARTH AND MAN NEWSLETTER. see *ARCHAEOLOGY*

559 NZL ISSN 1171-9168
INSTITUTE OF GEOLOGICAL AND NUCLEAR SCIENCES. GEOLOGICAL MAP. Text in English. irreg. price varies. **Document type:** *Academic/Scholarly.* **Description:** Includes geological maps mostly about New Zealand regional geology, usually at scale 1-50 thousand.
Supersedes: New Zealand Geological Survey Map Series
Indexed: IMMAb.
Published by: Institute of Geological and Nuclear Sciences Ltd., PO Box 30-368, Lower Hutt, New Zealand. TEL 64-4-5701444, FAX 64-4-5704600, webmaster@gns.cri.nz, http://www.gns.cri.nz. R&P D Kelly. Circ: 450.

559 NZL ISSN 1172-028X
INSTITUTE OF GEOLOGICAL AND NUCLEAR SCIENCES. MONOGRAPH. Text in English. 1993. irreg. price varies. bibl.; charts; illus. back issues avail. **Document type:** *Monographic series.* **Description:** Monographs about New Zealand regional geology, paleontology, basin studies, petrology, minerals, and volcanoes.
Formed by the merger of: New Zealand Geological Survey Basin Studies; New Zealand Geological Survey Bulletin; Which was formerly: New Zealand. Department of Scientific and Industrial Research. Geological Survey. Bulletin (0077-9628); New Zealand Geological Survey Paleontological Bulletin (0114-2283); Which was formerly: New Zealand. Department of Scientific and Industrial Research. Paleontological Bulletin (0078-8589)
Indexed: AESIS, GEOBASE, IMMAb, ZooRec.
—CISTI, Linda Hall. **CCC.**
Published by: Institute of Geological and Nuclear Sciences Ltd., PO Box 30-368, Lower Hutt, New Zealand. TEL 64-4-5701444, FAX 64-4-5704600, webmaster@gns.cri.nz, http://www.gns.cri.nz. R&P D Kelly. Circ: 450.

559 NZL ISSN 1171-9184
INSTITUTE OF GEOLOGICAL AND NUCLEAR SCIENCES. SCIENCE REPORTS. Text in English. 1992. irreg. price varies. **Document type:** *Academic/Scholarly.* **Description:** Covers specific topics in earth and isotope sciences.
Indexed: IMMAb.
Published by: Institute of Geological and Nuclear Sciences Ltd., PO Box 30-368, Lower Hutt, New Zealand. TEL 64-4-5701444, FAX 64-4-5704600, webmaster@gns.cri.nz, http://www.gns.cri.nz. R&P D Kelly.

558 COL
INSTITUTO DE INVESTIGACION E INFORMACION GEOCIENTIFICA, MINERO-AMBIENTAL Y NUCLEAR INGEOMINAS. INFORME ANUAL DE ACTIVIDADES. Text in Spanish. a., latest 1998. **Document type:** *Corporate.*
Former titles: Instituto Nacional de Investigaciones en Geociencias, Mineria y Quimica. Informe Anual de Actividades; Instituto Nacional de Investigaciones Geologico Mineras. Informe Anual de Actividades
Published by: Instituto de Investigacion e Informacion Geocientifica, Minero-Ambiental y Nuclear Ingeominas, Diagonal 53, 34-53, Apartado Aereo 4865, Bogota, CUND, Colombia. TEL 57-1-2221811, FAX 57-1-2220797, cliente@ingeomin.gov.co.

558 COL ISSN 0120-078X
CODEN: PGEIDI
INSTITUTO DE INVESTIGACION E INFORMATION GEOCIENTIFICA, MINERO-AMBIENTAL Y NUCLEAR INGEOMINAS. PUBLICACIONES GEOLOGICAS ESPECIALES DEL INGEOMINAS. Text in Spanish. 1978. irreg., latest vol.22, 1999. **Document type:** *Monographic series.*
Former titles: Instituto Nacional de Investigaciones en Geociencias, Mineria y Quimica. Publicaciones Geologicas Especiales del Ingeominas; Instituto Nacional de Investigaciones Geologico Mineras. Publicaciones Geologicas Especiales del Ingeominas
—CASDDS, Linda Hall.
Published by: Instituto de Investigacion e Informacion Geocientifica, Minero-Ambiental y Nuclear Ingeominas, Diagonal 53, 34-53, Apartado Aereo 4865, Bogota, CUND, Colombia. TEL 57-1-2221811, FAX 57-1-2220797, cliente@ingeomin.gov.co.

551 ARG ISSN 1514-4186
➤ **INSTITUTO SUPERIOR DE CORRELACION GEOLOGICA. SERIE CORRELACION GEOLOGICA.** Text in English, Spanish. 1986. biennial, latest vol.15, 2001. USD 20 domestic; USD 30 foreign (effective 2003). illus.; maps. **Document type:** *Magazine, Bibliography.* **Description:** Contains articles on paleontology, hydrogeology, stratigraphy and regional geology.
Related titles: Online - full text ed.
Indexed: ZooRec.
Published by: Instituto Superior de Correlacion Geologica, Miguel Lillo 205, San Miguel de Tucuman, Tucuman 4000, Argentina. insugeo@unt.edu.ar. Ed. F G Acenolaza. Circ: 500.

551 ARG ISSN 1514-4836
➤ **INSTITUTO SUPERIOR DE CORRELACION GEOLOGICA. SERIE MISCELANEA.** Text in Spanish, English; Summaries in English. 1995. a., latest vol.7, 2001. illus.; maps. **Document type:** *Monographic series, Academic/Scholarly.*
Related titles: Online - full text ed.
Indexed: ZooRec.
Published by: Instituto Superior de Correlacion Geologica, Miguel Lillo 205, San Miguel de Tucuman, Tucuman 4000, Argentina. insugeo@unt.edu.ar. Circ: 500.

550 ROM
QE287.6 CODEN: AIGGD7
INSTITUTUL GEOLOGIC AL ROMANIEI. ANUARUL. Cover title: Anuarul Institutului Geologic al Romaneiei. Text in English, French, Romanian. 1908. a., latest vol.69, 1996. USD 35 (effective 1997). **Document type:** *Journal, Academic/Scholarly.*
Former titles: Institutul de Geologie si Geofizica. Anuarul (0250-2933); (until 1975): Institutului Geologic. Anuarul (1017-866X); (until 1970): Comitetului de Stat al Geologiei. Anuarul (0365-1223); (unitl 1966): Comitetului Geologic. Anuarul (1010-9498); (until 1950): Institutului Geologic al Romaniei. Anuarul (0365-3188)
Indexed: RefZh, ZooRec.
—Linda Hall.
Published by: Institutul Geologic al Romaniei, Str. Caransebes 1, Bucharest, 78344, Romania. TEL 40-1-2242091, FAX 40-1-2240404, udubasa@igr.ro. Ed. Gheorghe Udubasa. R&P Serbau Veliciu TEL 40-1-2242093. Circ: 550.

552.5 GBR ISSN 0141-3600
INTERNATIONAL ASSOCIATION OF SEDIMENTOLOGISTS. SPECIAL PUBLICATION. Text in English. 1974. irreg. price varies. **Document type:** *Academic/Scholarly.*
—BLDSC (8379.250000), CISTI, IE, ingenta. **CCC.**
Published by: (International Association of Sedimentologists ESP), Blackwell Publishing Ltd., 9600 Garsington Rd, Oxford, OX4 2ZG, United Kingdom. TEL 44-1865-776868, FAX 44-1865-714591, customerservices@oxon.blackwellpublishing.com, http://www.blackwellpublishing.com. Ed. Dr. Ian Jarvis.

INTERNATIONAL CONTRIBUTIONS TO HYDROGEOLOGY. see *EARTH SCIENCES—Hydrology*

551 USA ISSN 0020-6814
QE1 CODEN: IGREAP
INTERNATIONAL GEOLOGY REVIEW. Text in English. 1958. m. USD 1,285 in North America; USD 1,310 elsewhere (effective 2005). adv. bibl.; charts; illus.; stat. index. back issues avail.; reprints avail. **Document type:** *Journal, Academic/Scholarly.* **Description:** Presents original papers in English on the tectonic framework of the earth and the location of mineral deposits within that framework.
Related titles: Online - full text ed.: (from EBSCO Publishing, Gale Group, IngentaConnect).
Indexed: AESIS, ASFA, ChemAb, CurCont, E&PHSE, ESPM, EngInd, GEOBASE, GP&P, INIS AtomInd, OceAb, OffTech, PetrolAb, PollutAb, SWRA.
—BLDSC (4540.600000), CISTI, Ei, IDS, IE, Infotrieve, ingenta, Linda Hall, PADDS. **CCC.**
Published by: (International Union of Geological Sciences NOR), Bellwether Publishing, Ltd., 8640 Guilford Rd, Ste 200, Columbia, MD 21046. TEL 410-290-3870, FAX 410-290-8726, bellpub@bellpub.com, http://www.bellpub.com. Eds. Brian J Skinner, W G Ernst. Circ: 500.

E

551 622.33 NLD ISSN 0166-5162
TN799.9 CODEN: IJCGDE
➤ **INTERNATIONAL JOURNAL OF COAL GEOLOGY.** Text in English. 1981. 16/yr. EUR 1,868 in Europe to institutions; JPY 248,200 in Japan to institutions; USD 2,089 to institutions except Europe and Japan; EUR 126 in Europe to qualified personnel; JPY 16,900 in Japan to qualified personnel; USD 139 to qualified personnel except Europe and Japan (effective 2006). adv. bk.rev. charts; illus. back issues avail.; reprints avail. **Document type:** *Journal, Academic/Scholarly.* **Description:** Covers basic and applied aspects of the geology and petrology of coal.
Related titles: Microform ed.: (from PQC); Online - full text ed.: (from EBSCO Publishing, Gale Group, IngentaConnect, ScienceDirect, Swets Information Services).
Indexed: AESIS, ASCA, C&ISA, CIN, ChemAb, ChemTitl, CurCont, E&CAJ, E&PHSE, EIA, EngInd, EnvAb, FLUIDEX, GEOBASE, GP&P, ISMEC, ISR, MSB, MinerAb, OffTech, PetrolAb, RefZh, SCI, SolStAb.
—BLDSC (4542.172200), CASDDS, CISTI, Ei, IDS, IE, Infotrieve, ingenta, Linda Hall, PADDS. **CCC.**
Published by: Elsevier BV (Subsidiary of: Elsevier Science & Technology), Radarweg 29, Amsterdam, 1043 NX, Netherlands. TEL 31-20-4853911, FAX 31-20-4852457, nlinfo-f@elsevier.nl, http://www.elsevier.com/locate/coal, http://www.elsevier.nl. Ed. J C Hower.

551 DEU ISSN 1437-3254
QE1 CODEN: IJESFS
➤ **INTERNATIONAL JOURNAL OF EARTH SCIENCES.** Text in English, French, German. 1910. bi-m. (in 1 vol., 6 nos./vol.). EUR 848 combined subscription to institutions print & online eds. (effective 2005). adv. illus. Index. reprint service avail. from IRC. **Document type:** *Journal, Academic/Scholarly.* **Description:** Contains original contributions and reviews of the entire field of geology and related sciences. Covers regional geology, stratigraphy, structural geology, tectonics, geodynamics and more.
Formerly (until 1998): Geologische Rundschau (0016-7835)
Related titles: Microfiche ed.: (from BHP); Online - full text ed.: ISSN 1437-3262 (from EBSCO Publishing, Springer LINK, Swets Information Services).
Indexed: AESIS, ASCA, ASFA, BibCart, BibInd, BrGeoL, CIN, ChemAb, ChemTitl, CurCont, E&PHSE, ESPM, EngInd, GEOBASE, GP&P, IBR, ISR, MinerAb, OffTech, PetrolAb, PollutAb, RefZh, SCI, SWRA, ZooRec.
—BLDSC (4542.194000), CASDDS, CISTI, Ei, IDS, IE, Infotrieve, ingenta, Linda Hall, PADDS. **CCC.**
Published by: (Geologische Vereinigung), Springer-Verlag (Subsidiary of: Springer Science+Business Media), Tiergartenstr 17, Heidelberg, 69121, Germany. TEL 49-6221-3450, FAX 49-6221-345229, http://link.springer.de/link/service/journals/00531/index.htm. Ed. Wolf-Christian Dullo TEL 49-431-600-2215. Adv. contact Stephan Kroeck TEL 49-30-827875739. **Subscr. in the Americas to:** Springer-Verlag New York, Inc., Journal Fulfillment, PO Box 2485, Secaucus, NJ 07096-2485. TEL 800-777-4643, 201-348-4033, FAX 201-348-4505, journals@springer-ny.com, http://www.springer-ny.com; **Subscr. to:** Springer GmbH Auslieferungsgesellschaft, Haberstr 7, Heidelberg 69126, Germany. TEL 49-6221-345-0, FAX 49-6221-345-4229, subscriptions@springer.de.

➤ **INTERNATIONAL JOURNAL OF GEOMAGNETISM AND AERONOMY.** see *EARTH SCIENCES—Geophysics*

550 USA ISSN 1532-3641
INTERNATIONAL JOURNAL OF GEOMECHANICS. Text in English. 2001. q. **Document type:** *Journal, Academic/Scholarly.* **Description:** Contains articles on the theory, formulations, and applications of geomechanics, including constitutive laws and recent developments.
Related titles: Online - full text ed.: (from EBSCO Publishing, O C L C Online Computer Library Center, Inc., Swets Information Services).
Indexed: ASFA, BrCerAb, C&ISA, CerAb, CorrAb, E&CAJ, EMA, H&SSA, HRIS, IAA, ICEA, M&TEA, MBF, METADEX, PollutAb, SWRA, WAA, WRCInf.
—BLDSC (4542.266500), CISTI, IE, Infotrieve, Linda Hall.
Published by: C R C Press, LLC (Subsidiary of: Taylor & Francis Group), 2000 N W Corporate Blvd, Boca Raton, FL 33431. TEL 800-272-7737, journals@crcpress.com, http://www.crcpress.com/. Ed. Chandra Desai.

551.447 ITA ISSN 0392-6672
GB601.A1 CODEN: ISPEAV
INTERNATIONAL JOURNAL OF SPELEOLOGY. Text in English, French, German. 1964. q. adv. bk.rev. charts; illus. **Document type:** *Academic/Scholarly.*
Indexed: BIOSIS Prev, BiolAb, ChemAb, SFA, ZooRec.
—Linda Hall.
Published by: (International Union of Speleology), International Journal of Speleology, c/o Dept. Biologia Animale Dell Uomo, Viale Dell' Universita', 32, Rome, RM 00185, Italy. Circ: 600.

INTERNATIONAL OIL SCOUTS ASSOCIATION DIRECTORY. see *BUSINESS AND ECONOMICS—Trade And Industrial Directories*

INTERNATIONAL PEAT JOURNAL. see *BIOLOGY—Botany*

INTERNATIONAL SCHOOL OF HYDROCARBON MEASUREMENT. PROCEEDINGS. see *PETROLEUM AND GAS*

551.3 ESP ISSN 0074-7904
INTERNATIONAL SEDIMENTOLOGICAL CONGRESS. GUIDEBOOK. Text in German. 1946. quadrennial. price varies. **Document type:** *Proceedings, Academic/Scholarly.*
Published by: International Association of Sedimentologists, c/o Jose-Pedro Calvo, Dpto Petrologia y Geoquimica, Universidad Complutense, Madrid, 28040, Spain. TEL 34-91-3944905, FAX 34-91-5442535, info@iasnet.org, http://www.iasnet.org.

INTERNATIONAL SOCIETY FOR ROCK MECHANICS. CONGRESS. PROCEEDINGS. see *ENGINEERING—Civil Engineering*

551.7 CAN ISSN 0254-2897
INTERNATIONAL UNION OF GEOLOGICAL SCIENCES. PUBLICATION. Text in English. 1980. irreg.
—ingenta. **CCC.**
Published by: International Committee on Stratigraphy, 601 Booth St, Ottawa, ON K1A 0E8, Canada. TEL 613-995-7277, FAX 613-995-9273.

557 USA
IOWA GEOLOGICAL SURVEY BUREAU. AEROMAGNETIC SURVEY SERIES. Text in English. irreg. **Document type:** *Government.*
Published by: Geological Survey Bureau, 109 Trowbridge Hall, Iowa City, IA 52242-1319.

557 USA
IOWA GEOLOGICAL SURVEY BUREAU. ANNUAL REPORT. Text in English. a. **Document type:** *Government.*
Published by: Geological Survey Bureau, 109 Trowbridge Hall, Iowa City, IA 52242-1319.

557 USA
IOWA GEOLOGICAL SURVEY BUREAU. EDUCATIONAL SERIES. Text in English. irreg. **Document type:** *Government.*
Published by: Geological Survey Bureau, 109 Trowbridge Hall, Iowa City, IA 52242-1319.

557 USA
IOWA GEOLOGICAL SURVEY BUREAU. GUIDEBOOK SERIES. Text in English. irreg. **Document type:** *Government.*
Published by: Geological Survey Bureau, 109 Trowbridge Hall, Iowa City, IA 52242-1319.

557 USA
IOWA GEOLOGICAL SURVEY BUREAU. MISCELLANEOUS PUBLICATIONS. Text in English. irreg. **Document type:** *Government.*
Published by: Geological Survey Bureau, 109 Trowbridge Hall, Iowa City, IA 52242-1319.

557 USA
IOWA GEOLOGICAL SURVEY BUREAU. OPEN-FILE REPORT SERIES. Text in English. irreg. **Document type:** *Government.*
Published by: Geological Survey Bureau, 109 Trowbridge Hall, Iowa City, IA 52242-1319.

557 USA
IOWA GEOLOGICAL SURVEY BUREAU. PUBLIC INFORMATION CIRCULAR. Text in English. irreg. **Document type:** *Government.*
Published by: Geological Survey Bureau, 109 Trowbridge Hall, Iowa City, IA 52242-1319.

557 USA
IOWA GEOLOGICAL SURVEY BUREAU. SPECIAL REPORT. Text in English. irreg. **Document type:** *Government.*
Published by: Geological Survey Bureau, 109 Trowbridge Hall, Iowa City, IA 52242-1319.

557 USA
IOWA GEOLOGICAL SURVEY BUREAU. TECHNICAL INFORMATION SERIES. Text in English. irreg. **Document type:** *Government.*
Published by: Geological Survey Bureau, 109 Trowbridge Hall, Iowa City, IA 52242-1319.

557 USA
IOWA GEOLOGICAL SURVEY BUREAU. TECHNICAL PAPERS; coal resources. Text in English. irreg. **Document type:** *Government.*
Published by: Geological Survey Bureau, 109 Trowbridge Hall, Iowa City, IA 52242-1319.

557 USA ISSN 0193-4856
QE111
IOWA GEOLOGY. Text in English. 1979. irreg. **Document type:** *Journal, Government.*
—BLDSC (4566.260000), IE, ingenta, Linda Hall.
Published by: Geological Survey Bureau, 109 Trowbridge Hall, Iowa City, IA 52242-1319.

IRISH JOURNAL OF EARTH SCIENCES. see *EARTH SCIENCES*

550 AUS ISSN 1038-4871
QE511.4 CODEN: ISARFY
➤ **THE ISLAND ARC.** Text in English. 1992. q. USD 211 combined subscription in the Americas to individuals & Caribbean, print & online eds.; EUR 195 combined subscription in Europe to individuals print & online eds.; GBP 130 combined subscription elsewhere to individuals print & online eds.; USD 863 combined subscription in the Americas to institutions & Caribbean, print & online eds.; GBP 533 combined subscription elsewhere to institutions print & online eds. (effective 2006). adv. bk.rev. abstr.; charts; illus.; maps; stat. back issues avail. **Document type:** *Journal, Academic/Scholarly.* **Description:** Focuses on the geological, geochemical and geophysical problems related to modern and ancient plate convergent processes, of the western Pacific Rim in particular.
Related titles: Online - full text ed.: ISSN 1440-1738. USD 820 in the Americas to institutions & Caribbean; GBP 506 elsewhere to institutions (effective 2006) (from Blackwell Synergy, EBSCO Publishing, Gale Group, IngentaConnect, O C L C Online Computer Library Center, Inc., Swets Information Services).
Indexed: AESIS, ASCA, ASFA, CIN, ChemAb, ChemTitl, CurCont, ESPM, GEOBASE, ISR, PetrolAb, PollutAb, SCI, SWRA, ZooRec.
—BLDSC (4583.097700), CASDDS, CISTI, IDS, IE, Infotrieve, PADDS. **CCC.**
Published by: (Geological Society of Japan JPN), Blackwell Publishing Asia (Subsidiary of: Blackwell Publishing Ltd.), 550 Swanston St, Carlton South, VIC 3053, Australia. TEL 61-383591011, FAX 61-383591120, subs@blackwellpublishingasia.com, http://www.blackwellpublishing.com/journals/IAR. Eds. Akira Ishiwatari, Simon R Wallis. Adv. contact Kathryn O'Brien. B&W page AUD 935, color page AUD 1,950; trim 210 x 275. Circ: 1,000. **Subscr. to:** PO Box 378, Carlton South, VIC 3053, Australia. **Co-sponsors:** Japan Association for Quatenary Research; Japanese Association of Mineralogists, Peterologists and Economic Geologists; Paleontological Society of Japan; Society of Resources Geology.

➤ **ISRAEL GEOLOGICAL SOCIETY ABSTRACTS.** see *EARTH SCIENCES—Abstracting, Bibliographies, Statistics*

551 ISR ISSN 0334-0694
ISRAEL GEOLOGICAL SOCIETY. ANNUAL MEETING PROCEEDINGS. Text in Multiple languages. 1963. a.
—BLDSC (1087.833800).
Published by: Israel Geological Society, 30 Malkhe Israel St, Jerusalem, 95501, Israel. TEL 972-2-5314271, FAX 972-2-5380688, http://www.igs.org.il/siteFrame.asp.

555 ISR ISSN 0075-1200
QE319.I8 CODEN: ISGBBC
ISRAEL. GEOLOGICAL SURVEY. BULLETIN. Key Title: Bulletin - Geological Survey of Israel. Text in English; Summaries in Hebrew. 1956. irreg., latest vol.83, 1992. price varies. **Document type:** *Bulletin, Government.*
Indexed: BIOSIS Prev, BiolAb, IMMAb, ZooRec.
—Linda Hall.
Published by: Geological Survey Library, 30 Malkhe Israel St, Jerusalem, 95501, Israel. TEL 972-2-314266. Circ: 1,200.

555 ISR ISSN 0333-6425
QE48.I75
ISRAEL. GEOLOGICAL SURVEY. CURRENT RESEARCH. Text in English. 1975. a. USD 10.
Indexed: IMMAb, ZooRec.
—BLDSC (4137.350000), Linda Hall.
Published by: Geological Survey Library, 30 Malkhe Israel St, Jerusalem, 95501, Israel.

ISRAEL JOURNAL OF EARTH SCIENCES. see *EARTH SCIENCES*

IVORY COAST. DIRECTION DES MINES ET DE LA GEOLOGIE. RAPPORT PROVISOIRE SUR LES ACTIVITIES DU SECTEUR. see *MINES AND MINING INDUSTRY*

550 RUS ISSN 0016-7762
QE1 CODEN: IVUGAF
➤ **IZVESTIYA VYSSHIKH UCHEBNYKH ZAVEDENII. GEOLOGIYA I RAZVEDKA.** Text in Russian. 1958. bi-m. USD 425 foreign (effective 2005). bk.rev. charts; illus.; maps. **Document type:** *Journal, Academic/Scholarly.* **Description:** Publishes papers on various subjects in Earth sciences: geology, mineralogy, lithology, methods of minerals searching and investigation, geophysical methods of investigation, investigation technology, geoecology, legal foundations of entrails use, etc.
Indexed: AESIS, CIN, ChemAb, ChemTitl, PetrolAb, RefZh.
—BLDSC (0077.430000), CASDDS, CISTI, East View, Linda Hall, PADDS. **CCC.**
Published by: Moskovskaya Gosudarstvennaya Geologorazvedochnaya Akademiya, Ul Miklukho Maklaya 23, Moscow, 117873, Russian Federation. Ed. L G Grabchak. Circ: 2,500. **US dist. addr.:** East View Information Services, 3020 Harbor Ln. N., Minneapolis, MN 55447. TEL 800-477-1005, FAX 800-800-3839, eastview@eastview.com, http://www.eastview.com.

E

551 549 RUS ISSN 0536-1028
CODEN: IVUOA5
IZVESTIYA VYSSHIKH UCHEBNYKH ZAVEDENII. GORNYI ZHURNAL. Text in Russian. 1958. m. USD 162 foreign (effective 2005). **Document type:** *Journal, Academic/Scholarly.* **Description:** Covers aspects of physical processes of mining production, exploitation of useful mineral deposits, construction of mines and underground structures, etc. Generalizes experience in applications of advanced technologies and modern equipment.
Indexed: Inspec, RefZh.
—BLDSC (0077.460000), CISTI, Linda Hall. **CCC.**
Published by: Ural'skaya Gosudarstvennaya Gorno-Geologicheskaya Akademiya/Ural State Academy of Mining and Geology, ul Kuibisheva 30, Yekaterinburg, 620144, Russian Federation. TEL 7-3432-2574407, http://www2.usmga.ru/english. Ed. A. Trop. **Dist. by:** East View Information Services, 3020 Harbor Ln. N., Minneapolis, MN 55447. TEL 800-477-1005, FAX 800-800-3839, eastview@eastview.com, http://www.eastview.com.

J A M S T E C JOURNAL OF DEEP SEA RESEARCH (II) GEOLOGY, GEOCHEMISTRY, GEOPHYSICS AND DIVE SURVEY. see *EARTH SCIENCES—Oceanography*

551 CHN ISSN 1001-7356
JIANGXI DIZHI/JIANGXI GEOLOGY. Text in English. 1987. q. **Document type:** *Academic/Scholarly.*
Related titles: Online - full content ed.: (from WanFang Data Corp.); Online - full text ed.: (from East View Information Services).
Published by: Jiangxi-sheng Dizhi Kuangchan Ting, Nanjing, 330201, China. TEL 86-791-5735027. Ed. Jian-quo Yang.

551 CHN ISSN 1003-6474
JIANSU DIZHI/JIANSU GEOLOGY. Text in Chinese. 1977. q. CNY 6 newsstand/cover domestic (effective 2000). **Document type:** *Abstract/Index.*
Related titles: Online - full content ed.: (from WanFang Data Corp.); Online - full text ed.: (from East View Information Services).
—BLDSC (4668.490000), IE.
Published by: (Jiangsu-sheng Dizhi Kuangchan Ting), Jiangsu-sheng Dizhi Xuehui, Zhujiang Lu 700-Hao, Nanjing, 210018, China. TEL 86-25-4806183, JSGeoinf@publicl.ptt.js.cn. Ed. Yong-kang Zhang.

550 JPN ISSN 0911-0143
JIBAN KOGAKU KENKYUJO HOKOKU/GEOTECHNICAL RESEARCH INSTITUTE. TECHNICAL REPORTS. Text in Japanese; Summaries in English, Japanese. 1985. a. **Document type:** *Academic/Scholarly.*
Published by: (Jiban Kogaku Kenkyujo), Nishinippon Kogyo Daigaku/Nishinippon Institute of Technology, 1633 Aratsu, Miyako-gun, Kanda-machi, Fukuoka-ken 800-0344, Japan. TEL 81-9302-3-1491, FAX 81-9302-4-7900. Ed. Bungo Tamada.

550 JPN
JIBAN SHINDO SHINPOJUMU/SYMPOSIUM ON GROUND VIBRATIONS. Text in Japanese; Summaries in English. a.
Published by: Nihon Kenchiku Gakkai/Architectural Institute of Japan, 26-20 Shiba 5-chome, Minato-ku, Tokyo, 108-0014, Japan.

550 JPN
➤ **JIOSINSETIKKUSU SHINPOJUMU HAPPYO RONBUNSHU/INTERNATIONAL GEOSYNTHETICS SOCIETY. SYMPOSIUM PROCEEDINGS.** Text and summaries in English, Japanese. 1986. a. JPY 4,000 to non-members; JPY 3,000 to members. **Document type:** *Proceedings, Academic/Scholarly.*
Formerly: Jiotekisutairu Shinpojumu Happyo Ronbunshu (0913-7882)
Published by: Kokusai Jiosinsetikkusu Gakkai, Nihon Shibu/International Geosynthetics Society, Japan Chapter, Doshitsu Kogakkai, 2-23 Kanda-Awaji-cho, Chiyoda-ku, Tokyo, 101-0063, Japan. TEL 81-3-3251-7661, FAX 81-3-3251-6688. Circ: 500.

551 560 AUT ISSN 1562-9449
JOANNEA GEOLOGIE UND PALAEONTOLOGIE. Text in German. 1937. a. **Document type:** *Journal, Academic/Scholarly.* **Description:** Publishes papers involving geological research and phenomena from the Steiermark region of Austria.
Former titles (until 1998): Mitteilungen Geologie und Palaeontologie am Landesmuseum Joanneum (1562-0875); (until 1996): Mitteilungen der Abteilung fuer Geologie und Palaeontologie am Landesmuseum Joanneum (1562-0867); (until 1986): Mitteilungen der Abteilung fuer Geologie, und Palaeontologie und Bergbau am Landesmuseum Joanneum (0379-1432); (until 1970): Mitteilungen des Museums fuer Bergbau, Geologie und Technik am Landesmuseum Joanneum (0369-0857)
Related titles: Online - full text ed.: 1999. free (effective 2005).
Published by: Landesmuseum Joanneum, Abteilung fuer Geologie und Palaeontologie, Raubergasse 10, Graz, St 8010, Austria. TEL 43-316-80179730, FAX 43-316-80179842, http://www.museum-joanneum.steiermark.at/cms/beitrag/10148082/3446627.

551 551.31 551.4 ISL ISSN 0449-0576
GB2496.I3 CODEN: JOKUA3
➤ **JOKULL;** journal of the glaciological and geological societies of Iceland. Text in English, Icelandic; Summaries in English. 1951. a., latest vol.50, 2001. ISK 3,100, USD 40 to members (effective 2001). bk.rev. abstr.; bibl.; illus.; maps. 100 p./no.; back issues avail. **Document type:** *Academic/Scholarly.*
Published by: Joklarannsoknafelag Islands/Glaciological and Geological Societies of Iceland, Science Institute, University of Iceland, Dunhaga 3, Reykjavik, 107, Iceland. TEL 354-525-4800, FAX 354-525-4499, TELEX 2307 ISINFO IS, bryndis@raunvis.hi.is. Eds. Aslaug Geirsdottir, Bryndis Brandsdottir TEL 354-525-4774. R&P Bryndis Brandsdottir TEL 354-525-4774. Circ: 1,000. **Subscr. to:** PO Box 5128, Reykjavik 125, Iceland. **Co-sponsor:** Jardfraedafelag Islands - Geoscience Society of Iceland.

556 GBR ISSN 1464-343X
QE320 CODEN: JOASEJ
➤ **JOURNAL OF AFRICAN EARTH SCIENCES.** Text in English. 1983. 15/yr. EUR 2,183 in Europe to institutions; JPY 289,900 in Japan to institutions; USD 2,443 elsewhere to institutions; EUR 135 in Europe to qualified personnel; JPY 17,800 in Japan to qualified personnel; USD 151 elsewhere to qualified personnel (effective 2006). back issues avail. **Document type:** *Journal, Academic/Scholarly.* **Description:** Explores all aspects of geological investigations, especially the search for natural resources, on the African continent and its once surrounding Gondwana fragments.
Former titles (until 1994): Journal of African Earth Sciences (and the Middle East) (0899-5362); (until 1987): Journal of African Earth Sciences (0731-7247)
Related titles: Microfilm ed.: (from PQC); Online - full text ed.: (from EBSCO Publishing, Gale Group, IngentaConnect, ScienceDirect, Swets Information Services).
Indexed: ASCA, ASFA, CIN, ChemAb, ChemTitl, CurCont, E&PHSE, ESPM, Englnd, ForAb, GEOBASE, GP&P, HerbAb, I&DA, Inspec, M&GPA, MinerAb, OffTech, PetrolAb, RefZh, S&F, SWRA, ZooRec.
—BLDSC (4919.989000), AskIEEE, CASDDS, Ei, IDS, IE, ingenta, Linda Hall, PADDS. **CCC.**
Published by: Pergamon (Subsidiary of: Elsevier Science & Technology), The Boulevard, Langford Ln, East Park, Kidlington, Oxford OX5 1GB, United Kingdom. TEL 44-1865-843000, FAX 44-1865-843010, http://www.elsevier.com/locate/jafrearsci. Eds. P. Eriksson, S. Muhongo. **Subscr. to:** Elsevier BV, PO Box 211, Amsterdam 1000 AE, Netherlands. TEL 31-20-485-3757, FAX 31-20-485-3432, nlinfo-f@elsevier.nl, http://www.elsevier.nl.

555.95 GBR ISSN 1367-9120
CODEN: JSASED
➤ **JOURNAL OF ASIAN EARTH SCIENCES.** Text in English. 1987. 12/yr. EUR 1,085 in Europe to institutions; JPY 144,000 in Japan to institutions; USD 1,212 elsewhere to institutions; EUR 62 in Europe to qualified personnel; JPY 8,400 in Japan to qualified personnel; USD 71 elsewhere to qualified personnel (effective 2006). abstr. back issues avail. **Document type:** *Journal, Academic/Scholarly.* **Description:** Publishes research results on regional geology, economic geology, geochemistry, petroleum geology and petrology, palaeontology, geophysics, tectonics, geomorphology, Quaternary geology and analysis of sedimentary basins.
Formerly (until 1997): Journal of Southeast Asian Earth Sciences (0743-9547)
Related titles: Microfilm ed.: (from PQC); Online - full text ed.: (from EBSCO Publishing, Gale Group, IngentaConnect, ScienceDirect, Swets Information Services).
Indexed: AESIS, ASCA, CurCont, E&PHSE, ForAb, GEOBASE, GP&P, HerbAb, I&DA, OffTech, PetrolAb, RefZh, S&F, ZooRec.
—BLDSC (4947.234500), CISTI, Ei, IDS, IE, Infotrieve, ingenta, Linda Hall, PADDS. **CCC.**
Published by: Pergamon (Subsidiary of: Elsevier Science & Technology), The Boulevard, Langford Ln, East Park, Kidlington, Oxford OX5 1GB, United Kingdom. TEL 44-1865-843000, FAX 44-1865-843010, http://www.elsevier.com/locate/jseaes. Ed. Dr. K Burke. **Subscr. to:** Elsevier BV, PO Box 211, Amsterdam 1000 AE, Netherlands. TEL 31-20-485-3757, FAX 31-20-485-3432, nlinfo-f@elsevier.nl, http://www.elsevier.nl.

551.44 USA ISSN 1090-6924
GB601 CODEN: JCKSFK
➤ **JOURNAL OF CAVE AND KARST STUDIES.** Text in English. 1940. 3/yr. USD 36 domestic to individual members; USD 45 in Canada & Mexico to individual members; USD 51 elsewhere to individual members; USD 75 domestic to institutional members; USD 84 in Canada & Mexico to institutional members; USD 90 elsewhere to institutional members (effective 2005). bibl.; charts; illus. index, cum.index every 5 yrs. back issues avail. **Document type:** *Journal, Academic/Scholarly.* **Description:** Discusses cave science.
Former titles (until 1996): N S S Bulletin (0146-9517); (until 1974): National Speleological Society. Bulletin (0028-0216); (until 1955): American Caver
Related titles: Online - full content ed.
Indexed: ASFA, BIOSIS Prev, BiolAb, BiolDig, BrCerAb, C&ISA, CIN, CerAb, ChemAb, ChemTitl, CivEngAb, CorrAb, CurCont, E&CAJ, EMA, ESPM, EntAb, GEOBASE, IAA, M&TEA, MBF, METADEX, SFA, SWRA, SolStAb, WAA, ZooRec.
—CASDDS, Linda Hall.
Published by: National Speleological Society, Inc., 2813 Cave Ave, Huntsville, AL 35810-4431. TEL 256-852-1300, FAX 256-851-9241, nss@caves.org, http://www.caves.org/pub/journal. Ed. Louise Hose. Circ: 8,000.

➤ **JOURNAL OF COASTAL RESEARCH;** an international forum for the littoral sciences. see *EARTH SCIENCES—Oceanography*

➤ **JOURNAL OF COASTAL RESEARCH. SPECIAL ISSUE.** see *EARTH SCIENCES—Oceanography*

551 IND
JOURNAL OF ECONOMIC GEOLOGY. Text in English. 1997. a. USD 75 (effective 2000). **Document type:** *Academic/Scholarly.*
Published by: (Indian Association of Economic Geology), Hindustan Publishing Corporation (India), 4805-24, Bharat Ram Rd., 1st Fl., Flats 1 & 2, Darya Ganj, New Delhi, 110 002, India. TEL 91-11-325-4401, FAX 91-11-6193511, hpcpd@nda.vsnl.net.in, hpcpd@hpc.cc, http://www.hpc.cc, http://www.bizdelhi.com/publisher/hpc. Ed. K L Rai.

JOURNAL OF GEODYNAMICS. see *EARTH SCIENCES—Geophysics*

551 USA ISSN 0022-1376
QE1 CODEN: JGEOAZ
➤ **THE JOURNAL OF GEOLOGY.** Text in English. 1893. bi-m. USD 52 combined subscription to individuals print & online eds.; USD 182 combined subscription to institutions print & online eds.; USD 13 per issue to individuals; USD 38 per issue to institutions (effective 2006). adv. bk.rev. illus. cum.index. 225 p./no.; reprint service avail. from PQC,ISI. **Document type:** *Journal, Academic/Scholarly.*
Related titles: Microform ed.: (from PMC, PQC); Online - full text ed.: ISSN 1537-5269. USD 164 to institutions (effective 2006) (from EBSCO Publishing, Gale Group, ProQuest Information & Learning).
Indexed: AESIS, AS&TI, ASCA, ASFA, BiolAb, BrGeoL, CIN, CIS, CTO, ChemAb, ChemTitl, CurCont, E&PHSE, EEA, EPB, ESPM, FLUIDEX, GEOBASE, GP&P, GSI, GeotechAb, IAA, IBR, ICEA, ISR, Inspec, M&GPA, MEDLINE, MinerAb, OceAb, OffTech, PetrolAb, PhysBer, PollutAb, RefZh, S&F, SCI, SPPI, SSCI, SWRA, ZooRec.
—BLDSC (4993.000000), AskIEEE, CASDDS, CISTI, IDS, IE, Infotrieve, ingenta, Linda Hall, PADDS. **CCC.**
Published by: University of Chicago Press, Journals Division, Journals Division, PO Box 37005, Chicago, IL 60637. TEL 773-753-3347, 877-705-1878, FAX 773-753-0811, 877-705-1879, subscriptions@press.uchicago.edu, http://www.journals.uchicago.edu/JG. Ed. Alfred T Anderson Jr. Adv. contact Cheryl Jones. page USD 475; trim 8.5 x 11. Circ: 1,600 (paid).

551.0711 USA ISSN 1089-9995
QE40
➤ **JOURNAL OF GEOSCIENCE EDUCATION.** Text in English. 1951. 5/yr. USD 55 domestic individuals & libraries; USD 67 foreign individuals & libraries (effective 2005). adv. bk.rev. abstr.; illus. index, cum.index: 1951-1979. back issues avail.; reprint service avail. from PQC. **Document type:** *Journal, Academic/Scholarly.* **Description:** Fosters improvement in teaching of earth sciences at all levels of instruction, emphasizes the cultural and environmental significance of the field, and disseminates information on related topics of interest.
Formerly (until vol.44, 1996): Journal of Geological Education (0022-1368)
Related titles: Microform ed.: (from PQC).
Indexed: ABIn, CIJE, CIS, CPE, ChemAb, EEA, ERA, EduInd, EngInd, ExcerpMed, GEOBASE, ISR.
—BLDSC (4995.055000), Ei, IE, Infotrieve, ingenta, Linda Hall.
Published by: National Association of Geoscience Teachers, c/o Carl Drummond , Editor, Dept of Geosciences, Indiana University Purdue University, Fort Wayne, IN 46805-1499. TEL 219-481-6253, jge@ipfw.edu, http://www.nagt.org/jge.html. Ed. Carl N Drummond TEL 360-481-6253. Circ: 2,800 (paid).

557 USA ISSN 1523-1771
JOURNAL OF GEOSCIENCES OF CHINA. Text in English. 1999.
Media: Online - full text.
Published by: Scripps Institution of Oceanography, 8602 La Jolla Shores Dr, La Jolla, CA 92037. http://www.sio.ucsd.edu.

JOURNAL OF GEOTECHNICAL AND GEOENVIRONMENTAL ENGINEERING. see *ENGINEERING—Civil Engineering*

551.31 GBR ISSN 0022-1430
GB2401 CODEN: JOGLAO
➤ **JOURNAL OF GLACIOLOGY.** Text in English. 1947. q. free membership (effective 2005). bk.rev. abstr.; illus. Index. back issues avail.; reprints avail. **Document type:** *Journal, Academic/Scholarly.*
Related titles: Online - full text ed.: ISSN 1727-5652 (from EBSCO Publishing, Gale Group, IngentaConnect).
Indexed: AESIS, ASCA, ASFA, BibInd, CIN, ChemAb, ChemTitl, CurCont, ESPM, FLUIDEX, GEOBASE, IBR, ISR, Inspec, M&GPA, RefZh, SCI, SSCI, SWRA.
—BLDSC (4996.000000), CASDDS, CISTI, IDS, IE, Infotrieve, ingenta, Linda Hall. **CCC.**

E

▼ new title ➤ refereed ✶ unverified ♦ full entry avail.

Published by: International Glaciological Society, Lensfield Rd, Cambridge, CB2 1ER, United Kingdom. TEL 44-1223-355974, FAX 44-1223-336543, http://www.igsoc.org/journal/. Ed. T H Jacka. Circ: 1,300.

555 IND ISSN 0970-0951
QE319.H5 CODEN: HMLGBX
JOURNAL OF HIMALAYAN GEOLOGY. Text in English. 1971. s-a. USD 50 (effective 2000); price varies. back issues avail.
Document type: *Monographic series, Academic/Scholarly.*
Formerly (until 1988): Indian Journal of Management & Systems; (until 1982): Himalayan Geology (0379-5101)
Indexed: ChemAb.
—CASDDS, Linda Hall.
Published by: (Wadia Institute of Himalayan Geology), Hindustan Publishing Corporation (India), 4805-24, Bharat Ram Rd., 1st Fl., Flats 1 & 2, Darya Ganj, New Delhi, 110 002, India. TEL 91-11-325-4401, FAX 91-11-6193511, hpcpd@nda.vsnl.net.in, hpcpd@hpc.cc, http://www.hpc.cc, http://www.bizdelhi.com/publisher/hpc.

554 ESP
QE283 CODEN: CUGIAE
➤ **JOURNAL OF IBERIAN GEOLOGY.** Text in English, French, Spanish; Summaries in English, French, German, Spanish. 1970. a., latest vol.27, 2001. EUR 21 in the European Union; EUR 30 elsewhere (effective 2005). charts; illus.; maps. 350 p./no.; **Document type:** *Monographic series, Academic/Scholarly.* **Description:** Covers stratigraphy, tectonics, sedimentology, paleontology and more.
Formerly (until 2001): Cuadernos de Geologia Iberica (0378-102X)
Indexed: IECT, ZooRec.
—CASDDS, CINDOC.
Published by: (Universidad Complutense de Madrid, Facultad de Ciencias Geologicas), Universidad Complutense de Madrid, Servicio de Publicaciones, C Isaac Peral s/n, Ciudad Universitaria, Madrid, 28040, Spain. TEL 34-91-3946934, FAX 34-91-3946978, cuadernos@geo.ucm.es, servicio@publicaciones.ucm.es, http://www.ucm.es/publicaciones. Eds. Javier Martin Chivelet, Jose Lopez Gomez. Circ: 800.

551 GBR ISSN 0263-4929
QE475.A2 CODEN: JMGEER
➤ **JOURNAL OF METAMORPHIC GEOLOGY.** Text in English. 1982. 9/yr. GBP 84, EUR 126 combined subscription in Europe to individuals print & online eds.; USD 155 combined subscription in the Americas to individuals & Caribbean, print & online eds.; GBP 92 combined subscription elsewhere to individuals print & online eds.; GBP 979 combined subscription in Europe to institutions print & online eds.; USD 1,076 combined subscription in the Americas to institutions & Caribbean, print & online eds.; GBP 979 combined subscription elsewhere to institutions print & online eds. (effective 2006). adv. bk.rev. bibl.; charts; illus. reprint service avail. from PSC. **Document type:** *Journal, Academic/Scholarly.* **Description:** Covers entire range of metamorphic studies from the scale of the individual crystal to that of the lithospheric plate; includes geochemistry.
Related titles: Online - full text ed.: ISSN 1525-1314. GBP 930 in Europe to institutions; USD 1,717 in the Americas to institutions & Caribbean; GBP 1,022 elsewhere to institutions (effective 2006) (from Blackwell Synergy, EBSCO Publishing, Gale Group, IngentaConnect, O C L C Online Computer Library Center, Inc., Swets Information Services).
Indexed: AESIS, ASCA, CIN, ChemAb, ChemTitl, CurCont, EngInd, GEOBASE, ISR, MinerAb, RefZh, SCI, SPPI.
—BLDSC (5018.500000), CASDDS, Ei, IDS, IE, Infotrieve, ingenta, Linda Hall. **CCC.**
Published by: Blackwell Publishing Ltd., Blackwell Publishing, Inc., 9600 Garsington Rd, Oxford, OX4 2ZG, United Kingdom. TEL 44-1865-776868, FAX 44-1865-714591, customerservices@oxon.blackwellpublishing.com, http://www.blackwellpublishing.com/journals/JMG. Eds. Doug Robinson TEL 44-117-9545400, Jean Morrison TEL 213-740-3551, Michael Brown TEL 301-405-4365, Roger Powell TEL 61-3-3446520. R&P Sophie Savage. Adv. contact Jenny Applin. Circ: 364.

551 JPN ISSN 1345-6296
QE351 CODEN: JMPSCA
➤ **JOURNAL OF MINERALOGICAL AND PETROLOGICAL SCIENCES.** Text in English. 2000. bi-m. JPY 8,400 domestic; USD 40 foreign; JPY 1,400 newsstand/cover domestic; USD 7 newsstand/cover foreign (effective 2001). bk.rev. abstr. Index. back issues avail. **Document type:** *Academic/Scholarly.* **Description:** Publishes original scientific papers for researchers and professionals in mineralogy, petrology and economic geology.
Formed by the merger of part of (1953-2000): Mineralogical Journal (0544-2540); part of (1952-2000): Kobutsugaku Zasshi (0454-1146); part of (1988-2000): Ganko (0914-9783); Which was formerly (1941-1987): Ganseki Kobutsu Kosho Gakkaishi (0021-4825); (1929-1940): Ganseki Kobutsu Koshogaku
Related titles: Online - full text ed.: ISSN 1349-3825 (from J-Stage).
Indexed: RefZh.
—BLDSC (5020.143700), CISTI, IE, ingenta, Linda Hall.
Published by: Japanese Association of Mineralogists Petrologists and Economic Geologists, c/o Graduate School of Science, Tohoku University, Aoba, Sendai, 981-0945, Japan. TEL 81-22-224-3852, FAX 81-22-224-3852, kyl04223@nifty.ne.jp, http://wwwsoc.nacsis.ac.jp/jampeg/index.html. Ed., Pub. Kiyoshi Fujino. Circ: 1,600.

➤ **JOURNAL OF MINING AND GEOLOGY.** see *MINES AND MINING INDUSTRY*

➤ **JOURNAL OF MINING RESEARCH.** see *MINES AND MINING INDUSTRY*

➤ **JOURNAL OF MINING SCIENCE.** see *MINES AND MINING INDUSTRY*

➤ **JOURNAL OF PETROLEUM SCIENCE AND ENGINEERING.** see *PETROLEUM AND GAS*

552 GBR ISSN 0022-3530
QE420 CODEN: JPTGAD
➤ **JOURNAL OF PETROLOGY.** Text in English. 1960. m. GBP 730, USD 1,278, EUR 1,095 to institutions; GBP 768, USD 1,344, EUR 1,152 combined subscription to institutions print & online eds. (effective 2006). adv. bk.rev. bibl.; charts; illus. index, cum.index every 4 yrs. reprint service avail. from PSC. **Document type:** *Journal, Academic/Scholarly.* **Description:** Presents papers on the physics and chemistry of rocks, experimental petrology and mineralogy, rock-forming minerals and their paragenesis, microstructure of rocks, and isotope geochemistry and geochronology as applied to problems of petrogenesis.
Related titles: Microform ed.: (from PQC); Online - full text ed.: ISSN 1460-2415. 1997. GBP 691, USD 1,209, EUR 1,037 to institutions (effective 2006) (from EBSCO Publishing, Gale Group, HighWire Press, IngentaConnect, O C L C Online Computer Library Center, Inc., Oxford University Press Online Journals, ProQuest Information & Learning, Swets Information Services).
Indexed: AESIS, ASCA, ASFA, BAS, BrCerAb, BrGeoL, CIN, Cadscan, ChemAb, ChemTitl, CurCont, EngInd, GEOBASE, IBR, IMMAb, ISR, Inspec, LeadAb, MSB, MinerAb, RefZh, SCI, Zincscan.
—BLDSC (5031.200000), CASDDS, CISTI, Ei, IDS, IE, Infotrieve, ingenta, Linda Hall. **CCC.**
Published by: Oxford University Press, Great Clarendon St, Oxford, OX2 6DP, United Kingdom. TEL 44-1865-556767, FAX 44-1865-556646, jnl.orders@oup.co.uk, http://petrology.oxfordjournals.org/, http://www.oxfordjournals.org/. Ed. Marjorie Wilson. Pub. David Prosser. R&P Fiona Bennett. adv.: B&W page GBP 300, B&W page USD 570; trim 178 x 255. Circ: 930.

551 560 570 GBR ISSN 0267-8179
QE696
➤ **JOURNAL OF QUATERNARY SCIENCE.** Abbreviated title: J Q S. Text in English. 1986. 8/yr. USD 1,525 to institutions; USD 1,678 combined subscription to institutions print & online eds. (effective 2006). adv. bk.rev. illus. Index. back issues avail.; reprint service avail. from PSC. **Document type:** *Journal, Academic/Scholarly.* **Description:** Acts as a forum for the exchange and integration of information and ideas from studies of the quaternary stratigraphic record, recent geological processes, the development and modification of natural ecosystems, the evolution and effects of man, and the nature and causes of climatic change.
Related titles: Microform ed.: (from PQC); Online - full text ed.: ISSN 1099-1417. USD 1,525 to institutions (effective 2006) (from EBSCO Publishing, Florida Center for Library Automation, Swets Information Services, Wiley InterScience).
Indexed: ASCA, ASFA, CurCont, EPB, ESPM, EngInd, GEOBASE, IBR, ISR, M&GPA, RASB, RefZh, S&F, SCI, SWRA, ZooRec.
—BLDSC (5043.752000), CISTI, Ei, IDS, IE, Infotrieve, ingenta, Linda Hall. **CCC.**
Published by: (Quaternary Research Association), John Wiley & Sons Ltd. (Subsidiary of: John Wiley & Sons, Inc.), The Atrium, Southern Gate, Chichester, West Sussex PO19 8SQ, United Kingdom. TEL 44-1243-779777, FAX 44-1243-775878, customer@wiley.co.uk, http://www3.interscience.wiley.com/cgi-bin/jhome/2507, http://www.wiley.co.uk. Ed. C J Caseldine. adv.: B&W page GBP 650, color page GBP 1,550; trim 210 x 297. Circ: 700. **Subscr. in the Americas to:** John Wiley & Sons, Inc., 111 River St, Hoboken, NJ 07030-5774. TEL 201-748-6645, 800-225-5945, subinfo@wiley.com.

➤ **JOURNAL OF SALT HISTORY/JAHRBUCH FUER SALZGESCHICHTE;** Annales d'Histoire du Sel. see *ARCHAEOLOGY*

551.44 USA ISSN 0022-4693
JOURNAL OF SPELEAN HISTORY. Text in English. 1968. q. USD 8 to individuals; USD 7 to libraries (effective 2000). adv. bk.rev. bibl.; charts; illus. reprints avail. **Document type:** *Bulletin.* **Description:** Exploration of caves.
Related titles: Microfiche ed.
Published by: American Spelean History Association, c/o Jack H Speece, 711 E Atlantic Ave, Altoona, PA 16602. TEL 814-946-3155. Ed. Jack Speece. Circ: 150.

551 GBR ISSN 0191-8141
QE601 CODEN: JSGEDY
➤ **JOURNAL OF STRUCTURAL GEOLOGY.** Text in English. 1979. 12/yr. EUR 1,436 in Europe to institutions; JPY 190,600 in Japan to institutions; USD 1,605 to institutions except Europe and Japan; EUR 181 in Europe to qualified personnel; JPY 24,100 in Japan to qualified personnel; USD 202 to qualified personnel except Europe and Japan (effective 2006). adv. bk.rev. abstr.; illus. back issues avail.; reprints avail. **Document type:** *Journal, Academic/Scholarly.* **Description:** Covers all aspects and processes of deformation in rocks, including folds, fracture and fabrics, structural associations in orogenic rocks, strike slip zones, and related phenomena.
Related titles: Microfilm ed.: (from PQC); Online - full text ed.: (from EBSCO Publishing, Gale Group, IngentaConnect, ScienceDirect, Swets Information Services).
Indexed: AESIS, ASCA, ASFA, ApMecR, BrCerAb, C&ISA, CerAb, ChemAb, CivEngAb, CorrAb, CurCont, E&CAJ, E&PHSE, EEA, EMA, ESPM, EngInd, FLUIDEX, GEOBASE, GP&P, IAA, ISMEC, ISR, Inspec, M&TEA, MBF, METADEX, MSCI, MinerAb, OffTech, PetrolAb, RefZh, SCI, SWRA, SolStAb, WAA.
—BLDSC (5066.878000), CASDDS, CISTI, IDS, IE, Infotrieve, ingenta, Linda Hall, PADDS. **CCC.**
Published by: Pergamon (Subsidiary of: Elsevier Science & Technology), The Boulevard, Langford Ln, East Park, Kidlington, Oxford OX5 1GB, United Kingdom. TEL 44-1865-843000, FAX 44-1865-843010, http://www.elsevier.com/locate/jsg. Ed. C W Passchier. Circ: 2,000. **Subscr. to:** Elsevier BV, PO Box 211, Amsterdam 1000 AE, Netherlands. TEL 31-20-485-3757, FAX 31-20-485-3432, nlinfo-f@elsevier.nl, http://www.elsevier.nl.

551 GBR ISSN 1477-2019
QE1
▼ ➤ **JOURNAL OF SYSTEMATIC PALAEONTOLOGY.** Text in English. 2003. q. GBP 144 to institutions; USD 240 in North America to institutions; GBP 158 combined subscription to institutions print & online eds.; USD 260 combined subscription in North America to institutions print & online eds. (effective 2006). bibl.; illus.; stat. index. **Document type:** *Journal, Academic/Scholarly.* **Description:** Contains papers regarding the research carried out on the museum's collection.
Former titles (until 2003): Natural History Museum. Bulletin. Geology (0968-0462); (until 1994): British Museum (Natural History). Bulletin. Geology (0007-1471); Which incorporated (1950-1974): British Museum (Natural History). Bulletin. Mineralogy (0007-148X)
Related titles: Online - full text ed.: ISSN 1478-0941. GBP 140 to institutions; USD 230 in North America to institutions (effective 2006) (from EBSCO Publishing, O C L C Online Computer Library Center, Inc., Swets Information Services).
Indexed: BiolAb, BrGeoL, ChemAb, E&PHSE, GP&P, OffTech, PetrolAb, RefZh, SFA, ZooRec.
—BLDSC (5068.061000), CISTI, IE, ingenta, Linda Hall, PADDS. **CCC.**
Published by: (Natural History Museum), Cambridge University Press, The Edinburgh Bldg, Shaftesbury Rd, Cambridge, CB2 2RU, United Kingdom. TEL 44-1223-312393, FAX 44-1223-315052, journals@cambridge.org, http://uk.cambridge.org, http://uk.cambridge.org/journals. Ed. Dr. Andrew B Smith. Circ: 750. **Subscr. to:** Cambridge University Press, 100 Brook Hill Dr, West Nyack, NY 10994. TEL 845-353-7500, FAX 845-353-4141, journals_subscriptions@cup.org

551 AUS ISSN 1441-8142
➤ **THE JOURNAL OF THE VIRTUAL EXPLORER.** Text in English. 1999. 4/yr. AUD 60 to individuals; AUD 250 to institutions; AUD 80 combined subscription to individuals online & CD eds.; AUD 750 combined subscription to individuals online, print & CD eds.; AUD 300 combined subscription to institutions online & CD eds.; AUD 950 combined subscription to institutions online, print & CD eds. (effective 2003). illus.; maps. back issues avail. **Document type:** *Journal, Academic/Scholarly.* **Description:** Dedicated to the rapid publication of world class geological research, using a dynamic review process that places articles in the public arena.
Media: Online - full text. **Related titles:** CD-ROM ed.: ISSN 1441-8134. AUD 250 combined subscription to individuals CD & hardcover eds.; AUD 500 combined subscription to institutions CD & hardcover eds. (effective 2003); Print ed.: ISSN 1441-8126. 1999.
Published by: Monash University, Australian Crustal Research Centre, PO Box 28E, VIC 3800, Australia. TEL 61-3-9905-5760, FAX 61-3-9905-5062, gordon@mail.earth.monash.edu.au, mail@virtualexplorer.com.au, http://virtualexplorer.com.au. Ed. Gordon Lister. Adv. contact Megan Hough TEL 61-3-9905-5774.

➤ **JOURNAL OF VOLCANOLOGY AND GEOTHERMAL RESEARCH.** see *EARTH SCIENCES—Geophysics*

551 NLD ISSN 0165-7720
K.N.G.M.G. NIEUWSBRIEF. Text in Dutch. 1975. 10/yr. membership. adv. bk.rev. bibl. **Document type:** *Newsletter.*
Published by: Koninklijk Nederlands Geologisch Mijnbouwkundig Genootschap/Royal Geological and Mining Society of the Netherlands, PO Box 6012, Delft, 2600, Netherlands. TEL 31-30-2697006, FAX 31-30-152564800. Eds. C W Dubelaar, J C Blom. Circ: 2,000.

557 USA ISSN 0097-4471
QE113 CODEN: KSGBAX
KANSAS GEOLOGICAL SURVEY. BULLETIN. Text in English. 1913. irreg., latest vol.244, pt.3. price varies. illus.; maps.
Document type: *Bulletin, Trade.*
Media: Online - full text.
Indexed: ZooRec.
—BLDSC (2598.060000), CASDDS, CISTI, Linda Hall.
Published by: Kansas Geological Survey, 1930 Constant Ave, The University of Kansas, Lawrence, KS 66047-3726. TEL 785-864-3965, FAX 785-864-5317, marla@kgs.ku.edu, http://www.kgs.ku.edu/kgs.html.

557 USA ISSN 0731-616X
CODEN: ESKSD7
KANSAS GEOLOGICAL SURVEY. EDUCATIONAL SERIES. Text in English. 1973. irreg., latest vol.15. price varies. **Document type:** *Monographic series, Academic/Scholarly.*
Published by: Kansas Geological Survey, 1930 Constant Ave, The University of Kansas, Lawrence, KS 66047-3726. TEL 785-864-3965, FAX 785-864-5317, marla@kgs.ku.edu, http://www.kgs.ku.edu/kgs.html.

551 551.4 USA
KARST WATERS INSTITUTE. SPECIAL PUBLICATIONS. Text in English. 1994. irreg., latest vol.7, 2002. price varies. bk.rev. bibl.; illus.; maps. back issues avail. **Document type:** *Monographic series, Academic/Scholarly.* **Description:** Covers proceedings from professional meetings.
Related titles: CD-ROM ed.
Published by: Karst Waters Institute, PO Box 490, Charles Town, WV 25414. TEL 304-725-1211, publications@karstwaters.org, http://www.karstwaters.org/publications/curpubslist.htm. R&P Elizabeth L White TEL 814-667-2709. **Subscr. to:** c/o E.L. White, Miller Rd, R R 1, Box 527, 1669 9211, Petersburg, PA. TEL 814-725-1211.

796.525 FRA ISSN 0751-7688
➤ **KARSTOLOGIA.** Text in French. 1983. s-a. bk.rev. abstr.; bibl.; charts; illus.; maps; stat. 64 p./no.; back issues avail.
Document type: *Journal, Academic/Scholarly.* **Description:** Describes the world of speleology and karst geosciences through explorations, descriptions of geological conditions encountered, awareness of the underground environment, and karst evolution.
Indexed: RefZh.
Published by: Federation Francaise de Speleologie, 130 rue Saint-Maur, Paris, 75011, France. TEL 33-1-43575654, FAX 33-1-49230095, ffs-paris@wanadoo.fr, http://www.ffspeleo.fr. Eds. Jean-Jacques Delannoy, Noel Salomon, Richard Maire.

➤ **KAUPIA**; Darmstaedter Beitraege zur Naturgeschichte. see *SCIENCES: COMPREHENSIVE WORKS*

550 KAZ ISSN 1810-8776
QE1 CODEN: IKAGA8
KAZAKSTAN RESPUBLIKASYNYN ULTTYK GYLYM AKADEMIASYNYN HABARLARY. GEOLOGIALYK SERIASY/NATIONAL ACADEMY OF SCIENCES OF THE REPUBLIC OF KAZAKHSTAN. GEOLOGY SERIES. Text in Russian. 1940. bi-m. USD 382 foreign (effective 2005). charts; illus.; maps. **Document type:** *Journal, Academic/Scholarly.*
Former titles (until 2003): Kazakstan Geologiasy/Geology of Kazakhstan (1025-4617); (until 1994): Akademiya Nauk Respubliki Kazakhstan. Izvestiya. Seriya Geologicheskaya (1025-4595); (until 1992): Akademiya Nauk Kazakhskoi S.S.R. Izvestiya. Seriya Geologicheskaya (0002-3175)
Indexed: ChemAb, IMMAb, INIS AtomInd.
—CASDDS, CISTI, Linda Hall. **CCC.**
Published by: (Kazakstan Respublikasy Ulttyk Gylym Akademiasy/National Academy of Sciences of the Republic of Kazakhstan), Gylym, Pushkina 111-113, Almaty, 480100, Kazakstan. TEL 3272-611877. **Dist. by:** East View Information Services, 3020 Harbor Ln. N., Minneapolis, MN 55447. TEL 800-477-1005, FAX 800-800-3839, eastview@eastview.com, http://www.eastview.com.

557 USA ISSN 0075-5559
QE115
KENTUCKY GEOLOGICAL SURVEY. BULLETIN. Text in English. 1879; N.S. 1999. irreg., latest no.5, 1999. price varies.
Document type: *Monographic series.* **Description:** Detailed treatment of a subject and extensive interpretation of geologic data.
—Linda Hall.
Published by: Kentucky Geological Survey, 228 Mining and Mineral Resources Bldg, University of Kentucky, Lexington, KY 40506-0107. TEL 606-257-5500. R&P Carol L Ruthven.

557 USA ISSN 0075-5567
CODEN: KGUCBN
KENTUCKY GEOLOGICAL SURVEY. COUNTY REPORT. Text in English. 1912. irreg., latest no.2, 1982. price varies.
Document type: *Monographic series.* **Description:** Summary of the geology and mineral resources of individual counties.
—Linda Hall.
Published by: Kentucky Geological Survey, 228 Mining and Mineral Resources Bldg, University of Kentucky, Lexington, KY 40506-0107. TEL 606-257-5500. R&P Carol L Ruthven.

557 USA ISSN 0075-5575
KENTUCKY GEOLOGICAL SURVEY. GUIDEBOOK TO GEOLOGICAL FIELD TRIPS. Text in English. 1952. irreg., latest 1994. price varies. **Document type:** *Monographic series.* **Description:** Guidebooks for the annual Field Conference of the Geological Society of Kentucky.
Published by: Kentucky Geological Survey, 228 Mining and Mineral Resources Bldg, University of Kentucky, Lexington, KY 40506-0107. TEL 606-257-5500. R&P Carol L Ruthven.

557 USA ISSN 0075-5583
KENTUCKY GEOLOGICAL SURVEY. INFORMATION CIRCULAR. Text in English. 1951; N.S. 1999. irreg., latest no.1, 1999. price varies. **Document type:** *Monographic series.* **Description:** Mainly data compilations, with some interpretation provided.
Published by: Kentucky Geological Survey, 228 Mining and Mineral Resources Bldg, University of Kentucky, Lexington, KY 40506-0107. TEL 606-257-5500. R&P Carol L Ruthven.

551 USA ISSN 1522-0834
KENTUCKY GEOLOGICAL SURVEY. MAP AND CHART SERIES. Text in English. 1989; N.S. 1999. irreg., latest no.1, 1999. price varies. **Document type:** *Monographic series.* **Description:** Includes maps, cross sections, and charts that are larger than 8.5 by 11 inches.
Published by: Kentucky Geological Survey, 228 Mining and Mineral Resources Bldg, University of Kentucky, Lexington, KY 40506-0107. TEL 606-257-5500. R&P Carol L Ruthven.

557 USA ISSN 0075-5591
CODEN: KUSRAJ
KENTUCKY GEOLOGICAL SURVEY. REPORT OF INVESTIGATIONS. Text in English. 1949; N.S. 1999. irreg., latest no.1, 1999. price varies. **Document type:** *Monographic series.* **Description:** Reports current research findings.
—Linda Hall.
Published by: Kentucky Geological Survey, 228 Mining and Mineral Resources Bldg, University of Kentucky, Lexington, KY 40506-0107. TEL 606-257-5500. R&P Carol L Ruthven.

557 USA ISSN 0075-5605
CODEN: KGRSAL
KENTUCKY GEOLOGICAL SURVEY. REPRINTS. Text in English. 1925; N.S. 1999. irreg., latest no.1, 1999. price varies.
Document type: *Monographic series.* **Description:** Reprints of articles dealing with the geology or mineral resources of Kentucky.
Published by: Kentucky Geological Survey, 228 Mining and Mineral Resources Bldg, University of Kentucky, Lexington, KY 40506-0107. TEL 606-257-5500. R&P Carol L Ruthven.

557 USA ISSN 0075-5613
QE115 CODEN: KUSSBN
KENTUCKY GEOLOGICAL SURVEY. SPECIAL PUBLICATION. Text in English. 1953. irreg., latest no.22, 1996. price varies.
Document type: *Monographic series.* **Description:** Covers the geology of Kentucky parks and scenic areas and other reports.
—Linda Hall.
Published by: Kentucky Geological Survey, 228 Mining and Mineral Resources Bldg, University of Kentucky, Lexington, KY 40506-0107. TEL 606-257-5500. R&P Carol L Ruthven.

557 USA ISSN 0075-5621
QE115 CODEN: KGTSAV
KENTUCKY GEOLOGICAL SURVEY. THESIS SERIES. Text in English. 1966; N.S. 1999. irreg., latest no.1, 1999. price varies. **Document type:** *Monographic series.* **Description:** Masters and doctoral theses about Kentucky geology.
—Linda Hall.
Published by: Kentucky Geological Survey, 228 Mining and Mineral Resources Bldg, University of Kentucky, Lexington, KY 40506-0107. TEL 606-257-5500. R&P Carol L Ruthven.

551 JPN ISSN 0389-0295
CODEN: MFSGE9
KOCHI UNIVERSITY. FACULTY OF SCIENCE. MEMOIRS. SERIES E, GEOLOGY. Text in English. 1980. a.
Indexed: ZooRec.
—BLDSC (5597.838000), CISTI.
Published by: Kochi University, Faculty of Science/Kochi Daigaku Rigakubu, 5-1 Akebono-cho 2-chome, Kochi-shi, 780-8072, Japan.

551 DNK ISSN 0906-0294
KOEBENHAVNS UNIVERSITET. GEOLOGISK CENTRALINSTITUT. AARSBERETNING. Text in Danish. 1970. a. free.
Published by: Koebenhavns Universitet, Geologisk Institut, Oester Voldgade 10, Copenhagen K, 1350, Denmark. TEL 33-11-22-32. Circ: 525 (controlled).

554 DEU ISSN 1437-3246
CODEN: SVGKB
KOELNER FORUM FUER GEOLOGIE UND PALAEONTOLOGIE. Text and summaries in English, German. 1956. irreg., latest vol.13, 2003. price varies. back issues avail. **Document type:** *Monographic series, Academic/Scholarly.*
Formerly (until 1998): Universitaet zu Koeln. Geologisches Institut. Sonderveroeffentlichungen (0069-5874)
Indexed: ZooRec.
—**CCC.**
Published by: Universitaet zu Koeln, Geologisches Institut, Zuelpicher Str 49, Cologne, 50674, Germany. TEL 49-221-4702533, FAX 49-221-4705080, geobibliothek@uni-koeln.de, http://www.uni-koeln.de/math-nat-fak/geomin/publikationen/forum/forum.html, http://www.uni-koeln.de/math-nat-fak/geologie. Ed., R&P, Adv. contact Hans-Georg Herbig. Circ: 250.

551 622 NLD ISSN 0075-6741
QE1 CODEN: VGMGAD
➤ **KONINKLIJK NEDERLANDS GEOLOGISCH MIJNBOUWKUNDIG GENOOTSCHAP. VERHANDELINGEN.** Text in English. 1912. irreg., latest vol.32, 1980. price varies.
Document type: *Monographic series, Academic/Scholarly.*
—Linda Hall. **CCC.**
Published by: Koninklijk Nederlands Geologisch Mijnbouwkundig Genootschap/Royal Geological and Mining Society of the Netherlands, PO Box 6012, Delft, 2600, Netherlands. TEL 31-30-2697006, FAX 31-30-152564800, kngmg@kngmg.nl, http://www.kngmg.nl/.

552 CZE ISSN 0454-5524
QE475 CODEN: KRYSAV
KRYSTALINIKUM; studies in geology, mineralogy, petrography. Variant title: Contributions to the Geology and Petrology of Crystalline Complexes. Text in English. 1962. a. USD 35 (effective 2000). bibl.; charts; illus. **Document type:** *Academic/Scholarly.*
Indexed: BrGeoL, CIN, ChemAb, ChemTitl.
—CASDDS, CISTI, Linda Hall.
Published by: Moravske Zemske Muzeum, Zelny trh 6, Brno, 65937, Czech Republic. TEL 420-5-42321205, FAX 420-5-42212792, mzm@mzm.cz, http://www.mzm.cz. Ed. M Suk.

KUANGCHAN YU DIZHI/MINERALS AND GEOLOGY. see *METALLURGY*

KUANGSHAN DIZHI. see *MINES AND MINING INDUSTRY*

551 CHN ISSN 1001-6872
KUANGWU YANSHI/JOURNAL OF MINERALOGY AND PETROLOGY. Text in Chinese. 1980. q. CNY 5 newsstand/cover (effective 2005). **Document type:** *Journal, Academic/Scholarly.*
Related titles: Online - full text ed.: (from East View Information Services, WanFang Data Corp.).
Published by: Chengdu Ligong Daxue/Chengdu University of Technology, No.1 3rd East Road, Chengdu, Sichuan 610059, China. TEL 86-28-84078994, Ljh@cdut.edu.cn, http://kwys.periodicals.net.cn/.

551 CHN ISSN 1007-2802
KUANGWU YANSHI DIQIU HUAXUE TONGBAO/BULLETIN OF MINERALOGY, PETROLOGY AND GEOCHEMISTRY. Text in Chinese. 1982. q. CNY 20 newsstand/cover (effective 2005).
Document type: *Journal, Academic/Scholarly.*
Related titles: Online - full text ed.: (from East View Information Services, WanFang Data Corp.).
Published by: Zhongguo Kuangwu Yanshi Diqiu Huaxue Xuehui/Chinese Society for Mineralogy, Petrology and Geochemistry, 73, Guanshui Lu, Guiyang, 550002, China. TEL 86-851-5895823, FAX 86-851-5895574, kydhthb@263.sina.net, http://kwysdqhxtb.periodicals.net.cn/.

555 JPN
KUMAMOTO UNIVERSITY. DEPARTMENT OF GEOLOGY. JOURNAL. Text in English. 1952. irreg. on exchange basis.
Published by: Kumamoto Daigaku, Rigakubu Sugaku Kyoshitsu/Kumamoto University, Faculty of Science, Department of Mathematics, 39-1 Kurokami 2-chome, Kumamoto-shi, 860-0862, Japan.

555 549 JPN ISSN 0454-7810
QE304 CODEN: KFMGAL
KYOTO UNIVERSITY. FACULTY OF SCIENCE. MEMOIRS. SERIES OF GEOLOGY AND MINERALOGY. Text in English. 1924. a. per issue exchange basis.
Indexed: BiolAb, IMMAb, INIS AtomInd, ZooRec.
—BLDSC (5597.870000), CASDDS, CISTI, KNAW, Linda Hall.
Published by: (Department of Geology and Mineralogy), Kyoto University, Faculty of Science/Kyoto Daigaku Rigakubu, Kita-Shirakawaoiwake-cho, Sakyo-ku, Kyoto-shi, 606-8224, Japan.

550 JPN ISSN 0916-7390
QE1 CODEN: MFSCEV
➤ **KYUSHU UNIVERSITY. FACULTY OF SCIENCES. MEMOIRS. SERIES D: EARTH AND PLANETARY SCIENCES/KYUSHU DAIGAKU RIGAKUBU KIYO D. CHIKYUWAKUSEI KAGAKU.** Text in English. 1940. irreg. exchange basis.
Document type: *Academic/Scholarly.*
Formerly (until 1989): Kyushu University. Faculty of Science. Memoirs. Series D: Geology (0023-6179)
Indexed: BIOSIS Prev, BiolAb, ChemAb, RefZh, ZooRec.
—CASDDS, CISTI, Linda Hall.
Published by: Kyushu University, Faculty of Science, Department of Earth & Planetary Sciences, 6-10-1 Hakozaki, Higashi-ku, Fukuoks City, 812-8581, Japan. TEL 81-92-6422521, FAX 81-92-6422522, http://www.geo.kyushu-u.ac.jp/. Ed. Shimada Nobutaka. Circ: 1,100.

E

551 560 665.5 JPN ISSN 1348-0545
QE304 CODEN: KDRKEE
➤ **KYUUSHUU DAIGAKU. DAIGAKUIN RIGAKU KENKYUUIN KENKYUU HOUKOKU. CHIKYUU WAKUSEI KAGAKU/KYUSHU UNIVERSITY. DEPARTMENT OF EARTH AND PLANETARY SCIENCES. SCIENCE REPORTS.** Text in Japanese; Summaries in English. 1941. irreg. exchange basis only. **Document type:** *Academic/Scholarly.*
Former titles (until 1999): Kyushu Daigaku. Rigakubu Kenkyu Hokoku. Chikyu-Wakusei-Kagaku (0916-7315); (until 1991): Kyushu Daigaku. Rigakubu Kenkyu Hokoku. Chishitsugaku (0385-8278); Kyushu Teikoku Daigaku. Rigakubu Kenkyu Hokoku. Chishitsugaku no Bu
Indexed: ChemAb, GEOBASE, RefZh, ZooRec.
—CASDDS, Linda Hall.
Published by: Kyushu University, Faculty of Science, Department of Earth & Planetary Sciences, 6-10-1 Hakozaki, Higashi-ku, Fukuoks City, 812-8581, Japan. TEL 81-92-6422521, FAX 81-92-6422522, http://www.geo.kyushu-u.ac.jp/. Ed. Shimada Nobutaka. Circ: 700.

551 FRA ISSN 0750-6635
LABORATOIRES DE GEOLOGIE LYON. DOCUMENTS. Text in French. irreg.
Indexed: ZooRec.
Published by: Universite Claude-Bernard Lyon 1, U.F.R. des Sciences de la Terre, 2 rue Raphael Dubois, Villeurbanne Cedex, 69622, France. TEL 33-4-72448103, http://dlgl.univ-lyon1.fr/.

551 FRA ISSN 0245-9825
LABORATOIRES DE GEOLOGIE LYON. DOCUMENTS. HORS SERIE. Text in French. irreg.
Published by: Universite Claude-Bernard Lyon 1, U.F.R. des Sciences de la Terre, 2 rue Raphael Dubois, Villeurbanne Cedex, 69622, France. TEL 33-4-72448103, http://dlgl.univ-lyon1.fr/.

550 ESP ISSN 0213-4497
QE283
LABORATORIO XEOLOXICO DE LAXE. CADERNOS. Text in Spanish. 1980. a. **Document type:** *Academic/Scholarly.*
Indexed: GEOBASE, IECT, ZooRec.
—CINDOC.
Published by: (Universidade da Coruna, Servicio de Publicacions), Seminario de Estudos Galegos, El Castro, Sada, (La Coruna) 15168, Spain. Ed. J R Vidal Romani.

551 USA ISSN 0572-8258
LAMONT-DOHERTY GEOLOGICAL OBSERVATORY. TECHNICAL REPORT. Text in English. irreg. **Document type:** *Monographic series.*
Published by: Columbia University, Lamont-Doherty Earth Observatory, 61 Route 9W, PO Box 1000, Palisades, NY 10964-1000. TEL 914-365-8474, FAX 845-359-2931, publ@ldeo.columbia.edu, http://doherty.ldeo.columbia.edu.

554 DEU
LANDESAMT FUER GEOLOGIE, ROHSTOFFE UND BERGBAU BADEN-WUERTTEMBERG. INFORMATIONEN. Text in German. 1990. irreg., latest vol.13, 2000. back issues avail. **Document type:** *Monographic series, Academic/Scholarly.*
Formerly: Geologisches Landesamt Baden-Wuerttemberg. Informationen (0940-0834)
Published by: Landesamt fuer Geologie Rohstoffe und Bergbau Baden-Wuerttemberg, Albertstr 5, Freiburg Im Breisgau, 79104, Germany. TEL 49-761-204-4375, FAX 49-761-204-4438, poststelle@lgrb.uni-freiburg.de.

LANDESMUSEUM JOANNEUM. REFERAT FUER GEOLOGIE UND PALAEONTOLOGIE. MITTEILUNGEN. see *PALEONTOLOGY*

551 CHN ISSN 1000-6273
LIAONING DIZHI/LIAONING GEOLOGY. Text in Chinese. 1984. q. CNY 2. **Document type:** *Academic/Scholarly.* **Description:** Publishes geology research results and progress in and around Liaoning Province.
Indexed: ZooRec.
Published by: (Liaoning Dizhi Kuangchan-ju/Liaoning Bureau of Geology and Mineral Resources), Liaoning Dizhi Bianjibu, No. 29, Beiling Dajie, Shenyang, Liaoning 110032, China. TEL 646573, FAX 024-662688. Ed. Chen Shichi. Circ: 2,000.

LIETUVOS AUKSTUJU MOKYKLU MOKSLO DARBAI. GEOGRAFIJA. see *GEOGRAPHY*

550 LTU ISSN 1392-110X
CODEN: LAMGDY
LIETUVOS AUKSTUJU MOKYKLU MOKSLO DARBAI. GEOLOGIJA. Text in Lithuanian. 1961. a. USD 80 foreign. adv. **Document type:** *Academic/Scholarly.*
Formerly (until 1990): Lietuvos T.S.R Aukstuju Mokyklu Mokslo Darbai. Geologija (0202-327X); Supersedes in part (in 1980): Lietuvos T S R Aukstuju Mokslo Darbai. Geografija ir Geologija (0459-3448)
Indexed: RefZh, ZooRec.
—CASDDS, CISTI, Linda Hall. **CCC.**
Published by: (Vilniaus Universitetas/University of Vilnius), Leidykla Academia, A Gostauto 12, Vilnius, 2000, Lithuania. TEL 370-2-626851. R&P A Garliauskas. Adv. contact A. Garliauskas.

551 BLR ISSN 1680-2373
LITASFERA/LITHOSPHERE. Text in Belorussian, Russian, English. 1994. s-a. **Document type:** *Journal, Academic/Scholarly.*
Indexed: RefZh.
Published by: (Natsiyanal'naya Akademiya Navuk Belarusi, Instytut Gealagichnykh Navuk/National Academy of Sciences of Belarus, Institute of Geological Sciences), Vydavetstvo Belaruskaya Navuka/Publishing House Belaruskaya Navuka, 18 Academician V F Kuprevich St, Minsk, 220141, Belarus. TEL 375-17-2632327, FAX 375-17-2637618, belnauka@infonet.by, http://www.ac.by/publications/litho/index.html. Ed. Radim Garetskii.

552 553 RUS ISSN 0024-4902
TN1 CODEN: LTMRAR
➤ **LITHOLOGY AND MINERAL RESOURCES.** Text in English. 1963. bi-m. EUR 3,428, USD 3,098, GBP 2,138 combined subscription to institutions print & online eds. (effective 2005). back issues avail. **Document type:** *Journal, Academic/Scholarly.* **Description:** Reviews a wide range of problems related to the formation of sedimentary rocks and ores.
Related titles: Microfilm ed.: (from PQC); Online - full text ed.: ISSN 1608-3229 (from EBSCO Publishing, Gale Group, IngentaConnect, Kluwer Online, O C L C Online Computer Library Center, Inc., Springer LINK, Swets Information Services); ♦ Translation of: Litologiya i Poleznye Iskopaemye. ISSN 0024-497X.
Indexed: AESIS, BibLing, CurCont, EngInd.
—BLDSC (0415.580000), CISTI, IE, Infotrieve, ingenta, Linda Hall. **CCC.**
Published by: (Rossiiskaya Akademiya Nauk/Russian Academy of Sciences), M A I K Nauka - Interperiodica, Profsoyuznaya ul 90, Moscow, 117997, Russian Federation. TEL 7-095-3347420, FAX 7-095-3360666, compmg@maik.ru, http://www.maik.ru/cgi-bin/journal.pl?name=litmin&page=main. Ed. Vladimir N Kholodov. **Subscr. to:** Springer-Verlag Dordrecht, Journals Department, PO Box 322, Dordrecht, Netherlands. TEL 31-78-6576392, FAX 31-78-6576474.

549 552 551.9 NLD ISSN 0024-4937
QE1 CODEN: LITHAN
➤ **LITHOS.** Text in English. 1968. 28/yr. EUR 1,398 in Europe to institutions; JPY 185,800 in Japan to institutions; USD 1,569 to institutions except Europe and Japan; EUR 286 in Europe to qualified personnel; JPY 37,600 in Japan to qualified personnel; USD 319 to qualified personnel except Europe and Japan (effective 2006). adv. bk.rev. bibl.; charts; illus. index. back issues avail.; reprints avail. **Document type:** *Academic/Scholarly.* **Description:** Publishes original research papers on mineralogy, petrology and geochemistry, emphasizing the application of mineralogy and geochemistry to petrogenetic problems.
Related titles: Microform ed.: (from PQC); Online - full text ed.: (from EBSCO Publishing, Gale Group, IngentaConnect, ScienceDirect, Swets Information Services).
Indexed: AESIS, ASCA, ASFA, CIN, ChemAb, ChemTitl, CurCont, ESPM, GEOBASE, ISR, MSB, MinerAb, PollutAb, RefZh, SCI, SSCI.
—BLDSC (5277.300000), CASDDS, CISTI, IDS, IE, Infotrieve, ingenta, Linda Hall. **CCC.**
Published by: Elsevier BV (Subsidiary of: Elsevier Science & Technology), Radarweg 29, Amsterdam, 1043 NX, Netherlands. TEL 31-20-4853911, FAX 31-20-4852457, nlinfo-f@elsevier.nl, http://www.elsevier.com/locate/lithos, http://www.elsevier.nl. Eds. I Buick, S Foley. Circ: 1,000.

➤ **LOUISIANA GEOLOGICAL SURVEY. ANTHROPOLOGICAL STUDIES SERIES.** see *ANTHROPOLOGY*

557 USA
LOUISIANA GEOLOGICAL SURVEY. EDUCATIONAL SERIES. Text in English. 1999. irreg., latest vol.3, 2001. price varies. **Document type:** *Monographic series, Academic/Scholarly.*
Published by: Louisiana Geological Survey, 208 Howe-Russell, Louisiana State University, Baton Rouge, LA 70803. TEL 225-578-5320, FAX 225-578-3662, pat@lgs.bri.lsu.edu, http://www.lgs.lsu.edu.

557 USA ISSN 0458-3329
LOUISIANA GEOLOGICAL SURVEY. FOLIO SERIES. Text in English. 1960. irreg., latest vol.7, 1984. price varies. **Document type:** *Monographic series, Government.*
—Linda Hall.
Published by: Louisiana Geological Survey, 208 Howe-Russell, Louisiana State University, Baton Rouge, LA 70803. TEL 225-578-5320, FAX 225-578-3662, pat@lgs.bri.lsu.edu, http://www.lgs.lsu.edu.

557 USA ISSN 0096-3720
QE117 CODEN: LCGBAY
LOUISIANA GEOLOGICAL SURVEY. GEOLOGICAL BULLETIN. Text in English. 1931. irreg., latest vol.45, 1993. price varies. **Document type:** *Bulletin, Government.*
—Linda Hall.
Published by: Louisiana Geological Survey, 208 Howe-Russell, Louisiana State University, Baton Rouge, LA 70803. TEL 225-578-5320, FAX 225-578-3662, pat@lgs.bri.lsu.edu, http://www.lgs.lsu.edu.

557 USA
LOUISIANA GEOLOGICAL SURVEY. GEOLOGICAL PAMPHLETS. Text in English. 1939. irreg., latest vol.11, 1998. price varies. **Document type:** *Monographic series, Government.*
Published by: Louisiana Geological Survey, 208 Howe-Russell, Louisiana State University, Baton Rouge, LA 70803. TEL 225-578-5320, FAX 225-578-3662, pat@lgs.bri.lsu.edu, http://www.lgs.lsu.edu.

557 USA ISSN 1047-739X
LOUISIANA GEOLOGICAL SURVEY. GUIDEBOOK SERIES. Text in English. 1982. irreg., latest vol.5, 1989. price varies. **Document type:** *Monographic series, Government.*
Published by: Louisiana Geological Survey, 208 Howe-Russell, Louisiana State University, Baton Rouge, LA 70803. TEL 225-578-5320, FAX 225-578-3662, pat@lgs.bri.lsu.edu, http://www.lgs.lsu.edu.

557 USA ISSN 0160-8517
CODEN: LMRBAN
LOUISIANA GEOLOGICAL SURVEY. MINERAL RESOURCES BULLETIN. Text in English. 1969. irreg., latest vol.3, 1978. price varies. **Document type:** *Monographic series, Government.*
Published by: Louisiana Geological Survey, 208 Howe-Russell, Louisiana State University, Baton Rouge, LA 70803. TEL 225-578-5320, FAX 225-578-3662, pat@lgs.bri.lsu.edu, http://www.lgs.lsu.edu.

557 USA
LOUISIANA GEOLOGICAL SURVEY. PUBLIC INFORMATION SERIES. Text in English. 1998. irreg., latest vol.8, 2001. free (effective 2004). **Document type:** *Monographic series, Government.*
Published by: Louisiana Geological Survey, 208 Howe-Russell, Louisiana State University, Baton Rouge, LA 70803. TEL 225-578-5320, FAX 225-578-3662, pat@lgs.bri.lsu.edu, http://www.lgs.lsu.edu.

557 USA ISSN 0278-4777
LOUISIANA GEOLOGICAL SURVEY. RESOURCES INFORMATION SERIES. Text in English. 1980. irreg., latest vol.8, 1992. price varies. **Document type:** *Monographic series, Government.*
Published by: Louisiana Geological Survey, 208 Howe-Russell, Louisiana State University, Baton Rouge, LA 70803. TEL 225-578-5320, FAX 225-578-3662, pat@lgs.bri.lsu.edu, http://www.lgs.lsu.edu.

557 USA ISSN 0459-8474
GB705.L8 CODEN: LGWBA6
LOUISIANA GEOLOGICAL SURVEY. WATER RESOURCES BULLETIN. Text in English. 1960. irreg., latest vol.20, 1975. illus. back issues avail. **Document type:** *Bulletin, Government.*
—Linda Hall.
Published by: Louisiana Geological Survey, 208 Howe-Russell, Louisiana State University, Baton Rouge, LA 70803. TEL 225-578-5320, FAX 225-578-3662, pat@lgs.bri.lsu.edu, http://www.lgs.lsu.edu.

551 JPN ISSN 1344-9656
LOWLAND TECHNOLOGY INTERNATIONAL. Text in English. 1999. s-a. free to members (effective 2004). **Description:** Publishes research papers, technical notes, and technical reports covering all aspects of lowland technology, particularly geotechnical engineering, water management, environment, and development.
Indexed: FLUIDEX, GEOBASE.
Published by: International Association of Lowland Technology, Institute of Lowland Technology, Saga University, 1 Honjo, Saga, 840-0027, Japan. TEL 81-952-288571, FAX 81-952-288189, ilt@saga-u.ac.jp, http://www.ilt.saga-u.ac.jp/ialt/lti/index.html, http://www.ilt.saga-u.ac.jp/ialt/index.html. Ed. Hiroyuki Araki.

551 SWE ISSN 0281-3033
LUNDQUA THESIS. Text in Multiple languages. 1973. irreg., latest vol.51, 2003. **Document type:** *Monographic series.*
Formerly (until 1983): University of Lund. Department of Quaternary Geology. Thesis (0346-8976)
Indexed: GEOBASE.
Published by: Lunds Universitet, Kvartaergeologiska Avdelningen/University of Lund, Department of Geology, Quaternary Sciences, Soelvegatan 12, Lund, 223 62, Sweden. TEL 46-46-2227880, FAX 46-46-2224830, http://www.geol.lu.se/kvg/ediss.htm, http://www.geol.lu.se/kvg/shome.htm.

796.525 AUS ISSN 1035-4697
M U C G - RAKER. Text in English. 1977. a. free to members. bk.rev. **Document type:** *Newsletter.* **Description:** Presents caving as a sport and science, as well as discussing canyoning, bushwalking, conservation and related club activities.
Formerly (until no.10, 1989): Quaver (0155-2880)
Published by: Macquarie University, Caving Group, c/o Macquarie University Sports Association, Macquarie University, NSW 2109, Australia. TEL 61-2-98507635, FAX 61-2-98885179, http://www.mq.edu.au/~musa/mucg/. Ed., R&P Lucinda Coates. Circ: 100.

E

553 COD ISSN 0250-538X
TN119.Z3 CODEN: MAADDA
MAADINI; bulletin d'information de la GECAMINES. Text in French. 1974. q. illus.
Indexed: ChemAb.
—CASDDS.
Published by: (Generale des Carrieres et des Mines, Division des Relations Publiques COG), Generale des Carrieres et des Mines, BP 450, Lubumbashi, Congo, Dem. Republic. Ed. Kamuanga Tshiayembela. Circ: 5,000.

556 MDG
MADAGASCAR. SERVICE GEOLOGIQUE. RAPPORT D'ACTIVITE: GEOLOGIE. Text in French. 1975. a. MGF 7,000 (effective 2001). charts; maps. **Document type:** *Bulletin.* **Description:** Features articles on geological research findings.
Published by: Service Geologique de Madagascar, BP 322, Antananarivo, Madagascar. TEL 261-20-2240048, FAX 261-20-2241873, mdonna@dts.mg, http://www.cite.mg/mine.

557 USA ISSN 0097-0204
QE119 CODEN: MEGBAP
MAINE GEOLOGICAL SURVEY. BULLETIN. Text in English. 1944. irreg. **Document type:** *Monographic series.*
—Linda Hall.
Published by: Maine Geological Survey, 22 State House Station, Augusta, ME 04333. TEL 207-287-2801, mgs@state.me.us, http://www.state.me.us/doc/nrimc/pubedinf/pubs/pubs.htm.

557 USA
MAINE GEOLOGICAL SURVEY. GLACIAL GEOLOGY REPORT. Text in English. irreg. **Document type:** *Bulletin, Government.*
Published by: Maine Geological Survey, 22 State House Station, Augusta, ME 04333.

557 USA
MAINE GEOLOGICAL SURVEY. LANDSLIDES. Text in English. irreg. **Document type:** *Bulletin, Government.*
Published by: Maine Geological Survey, 22 State House Station, Augusta, ME 04333.

557 USA
MAINE GEOLOGICAL SURVEY. MAINE GEOLOGY REPORT. Text in English. irreg. **Document type:** *Bulletin, Government.*
Published by: Maine Geological Survey, 22 State House Station, Augusta, ME 04333.

557 USA
MAINE GEOLOGICAL SURVEY. PEAT REPORT. Text in English. irreg. **Document type:** *Bulletin, Government.*
Published by: Maine Geological Survey, 22 State House Station, Augusta, ME 04333.

557 USA
MAINE GEOLOGICAL SURVEY. SEA-LEVEL RISE REPORT. Text in English. irreg. **Document type:** *Government.*
Published by: Maine Geological Survey, 22 State House Station, Augusta, ME 04333.

557 USA
MAINE GEOLOGICAL SURVEY. STUDIES IN MAINE GEOLOGY. Text in English. irreg. **Document type:** *Government.*
Published by: Maine Geological Survey, 22 State House Station, Augusta, ME 04333.

557 USA
MAINE GEOLOGICAL SURVEY. TOPICAL REPORT ON MAINE BEDROCK GEOLOGY. Text in English. irreg. **Document type:** *Bulletin, Government.*
Published by: Maine Geological Survey, 22 State House Station, Augusta, ME 04333.

557 333.9 USA
MAINE GEOLOGICAL SURVEY. U S G S STREAM SEDIMENT STUDIES. Text in English. irreg. **Document type:** *Bulletin, Government.*
Published by: Maine Geological Survey, 22 State House Station, Augusta, ME 04333.

551 USA ISSN 0270-8345
THE MAINE GEOLOGIST. Text in English. 1973. irreg. (approx. 3/yr.). USD 7 (effective 1999). **Document type:** *Newsletter.*
Published by: Geological Society of Maine, Inc., 111 Edward T Bryant Global Center, University of Maine, Orono, ME 04469. TEL 207-848-5714. Ed. Daniel Belknap. Circ: 300 (paid).

554 DEU ISSN 0340-4404
QE269 CODEN: MZGMAZ
MAINZER GEOWISSENSCHAFTLICHE MITTEILUNGEN. Text in English, German; Summaries in English, French, German. 1972. a. price varies. charts; illus. back issues avail. **Document type:** *Academic/Scholarly.* **Description:** Studies earth sciences and paleontology of the Rhineland-Palatinate area.
Indexed: GEOBASE, RefZh, ZooRec.
—CISTI. **CCC.**
Published by: Geologisches Landesamt, Emy-Roeder-Str 5, Mainz, 55129, Germany. TEL 49-6131-9254-0, FAX 49-6131-9254123, office@gla-rlp.de, vertrieb@gla-rlp.de, http://www.gla-rlp.de/schriften.html. Ed. Klaus Steingoetter. Circ: 800.

556 MWI ISSN 0076-311X
MALAWI. GEOLOGICAL SURVEY DEPARTMENT. ANNUAL REPORT. Text in English. 1923. a. price varies. **Document type:** *Government.* **Description:** Reports on activities of the survey: mineral exploration and staff matters.
Published by: Geological Survey Department, PO Box 27, Zomba, Malawi. TEL 265-50-524166, TELEX 44382.

559 MYS ISSN 0127-0559
QE299.5 CODEN: AGSMD3
MALAYSIA. GEOLOGICAL SURVEY. ANNUAL REPORT ✶ . Text in English. 1949. a. MYR 20.
Indexed: BiolAb, IMMAb.
—Linda Hall.
Published by: Geological Survey, c/o Ministry of Information, Angkasapuri Bukit Putra, Kuala Lumpur, 50610, Malaysia. FAX 082-415290. Ed. Yin Ee Heng. Circ: 500.

526.9 MYS
➤ **THE MALAYSIAN SURVEYOR.** Text in English, Malay. 1963. q. MYR 40 domestic; USD 40 in Asia; USD 55 in Europe; USD 80 in North America (effective 2002). adv. bk.rev. charts; illus. 86 p./no.; back issues avail. **Document type:** *Journal, Academic/Scholarly.* **Description:** Touches upon the development of the surveying profession, innovations in surveying technology and surveyors' contribution towards the property market and building industry.
Formerly (until 1999): Surveyor (0126-6268)
Indexed: RICS.
Published by: Institution of Surveyors, Malaysia, 3rd fl. Bongunan Juruukur, 64-66 Jalan 52-4, Petaling, Selangor Darul Ehsan 46200, Malaysia. TEL 60-3-756-9728, FAX 60-3-755-0253, ism@po.jaring.my, http://www.ismy.org. Ed. Hj Iskandar Ismail. R&P, Adv. contact Katherine Thiang TEL 60-3-7955-1773. B&W page USD 650, color page USD 900; 11.75 x 8.25. Circ: 3,000.

557 622 CAN
MANITOBA INDUSTRY, TRADE AND MINES. AGGRAGATE REPORT SERIES. Text in English. irreg. **Document type:** *Monographic series, Government.*
Published by: Manitoba Industry, Trade and Mines, 360 1395 Ellice Ave, Winnipeg, MB R3G 3P2, Canada. TEL 204-945-4154, FAX 204-945-8427, publications@gov.mb.ca.

557 CAN
MANITOBA INDUSTRY, TRADE AND MINES. CANADIAN GEOSCIENCE PUBLICATIONS DIRECTORY. Text in English. a. **Document type:** *Directory, Government.*
Published by: Manitoba Industry, Trade and Mines, 360 1395 Ellice Ave, Winnipeg, MB R3G 3P2, Canada. TEL 204-945-4154, FAX 204-945-8427, publications@gov.mb.ca.

557 CAN ISSN 0826-8916
MANITOBA INDUSTRY, TRADE AND MINES. ECONOMIC GEOLOGY PAPER SERIES. Text in English. 1979. irreg. price varies. **Document type:** *Government.* **Description:** Contains overviews on specific economic geology topics relating to Manitoba.
Former titles: Manitoba Energy and Mines. Economic Geology Paper Series; Manitoba. Mineral Resources Division. Economic Geology Paper Series
Published by: Manitoba Industry, Trade and Mines, 360 1395 Ellice Ave, Winnipeg, MB R3G 3P2, Canada. TEL 204-945-4154, FAX 204-945-8427, publications@gov.mb.ca, http://www.infomine.com/index/suppliers/Manitoba_Industry,_Trade_and_Mines.html.

557 CAN ISSN 0228-8311
MANITOBA INDUSTRY, TRADE AND MINES. ECONOMIC GEOLOGY REPORT SERIES. Text in English. irreg. **Document type:** *Monographic series, Government.*
—Linda Hall.
Published by: Manitoba Industry, Trade and Mines, 360 1395 Ellice Ave, Winnipeg, MB R3G 3P2, Canada. TEL 204-945-4154, FAX 204-945-8427, publications@gov.mb.ca.

557 CAN
MANITOBA INDUSTRY, TRADE AND MINES. EDUCATIONAL SERIES. Text in English. 1976. irreg. price varies. **Document type:** *Government.* **Description:** General information about geology and mineral resources of Manitoba.
Former titles: Manitoba Energy and Mines. Educational Series; Manitoba. Mineral Resources Division. Educational Series
Published by: Manitoba Industry, Trade and Mines, 360 1395 Ellice Ave, Winnipeg, MB R3G 3P2, Canada. TEL 204-945-4154, FAX 204-945-8427, publications@gov.mb.ca, http://www.infomine.com/index/suppliers/Manitoba_Industry,_Trade_and_Mines.html.

MANITOBA INDUSTRY, TRADE AND MINES. FEDERAL - PROVINCIAL ANNUAL PROGRESS REPORTS. see *MINES AND MINING INDUSTRY*

551 CAN
MANITOBA INDUSTRY, TRADE AND MINES. GEOLOGICAL PAPER SERIES. Text in English. 1968. irreg. price varies. **Document type:** *Government.* **Description:** Deals with specific geological topic or introduces new data or concepts.
Former titles: Manitoba Energy and Mines. Geological Paper; Manitoba. Mineral Resources Division. Geological Paper (0076-387X)
—Linda Hall.
Published by: Manitoba Industry, Trade and Mines, 360 1395 Ellice Ave, Winnipeg, MB R3G 3P2, Canada. TEL 204-945-4154, FAX 204-945-8427, publications@gov.mb.ca, http://www.infomine.com/index/suppliers/Manitoba_Industry,_Trade_and_Mines.html.

557 CAN
MANITOBA INDUSTRY, TRADE AND MINES. GEOLOGICAL REPORT SERIES. Text in English. 1937. irreg. price varies. **Document type:** *Government.* **Description:** Results of comprehensive geological studies of specific projects.
Former titles: Manitoba Energy and Mines. Geological Report; Manitoba. Mineral Resources Division. Geological Report; Manitoba. Mines Branch. Publication (0085-3070)
—CISTI, Linda Hall.
Published by: Manitoba Industry, Trade and Mines, 360 1395 Ellice Ave, Winnipeg, MB R3G 3P2, Canada. TEL 204-945-4154, FAX 204-945-8427, publications@gov.mb.ca, http://www.infomine.com/index/suppliers/Manitoba_Industry,_Trade_and_Mines.html.

557 622 CAN
MANITOBA INDUSTRY, TRADE AND MINES. MINERAL DEPOSIT REPORT SERIES. Text in English. irreg. **Document type:** *Monographic series, Government.*
Published by: Manitoba Industry, Trade and Mines, 360 1395 Ellice Ave, Winnipeg, MB R3G 3P2, Canada. TEL 204-945-4154, FAX 204-945-8427, publications@gov.mb.ca.

MANITOBA INDUSTRY, TRADE AND MINES. MINERAL EDUCATION SERIES. see *MINES AND MINING INDUSTRY*

MANITOBA INDUSTRY, TRADE AND MINES. MISCELLANEOUS PUBLICATION SERIES. see *MINES AND MINING INDUSTRY*

557 CAN
MANITOBA INDUSTRY, TRADE AND MINES. OPEN FILE REPORT SERIES. Text in English. 1976. irreg. price varies. **Document type:** *Government.* **Description:** Information on specific geological topics or results of other activities which may be of immediate interest to the public.
Former titles: Manitoba Energy and Mines. Open File Report Series; Manitoba. Mineral Resources Division. Open File Report Series
Published by: Manitoba Industry, Trade and Mines, 360 1395 Ellice Ave, Winnipeg, MB R3G 3P2, Canada. TEL 204-945-4154, FAX 204-945-8427, publications@gov.mb.ca, http://www.infomine.com/index/suppliers/Manitoba_Industry,_Trade_and_Mines.html.

557 622 CAN
MANITOBA INDUSTRY, TRADE AND MINES. PUBLICATIONS SERIES. Text in English. irreg. **Document type:** *Monographic series, Government.*
Published by: Manitoba Industry, Trade and Mines, 360 1395 Ellice Ave, Winnipeg, MB R3G 3P2, Canada. TEL 204-945-4154, FAX 204-945-8427, publications@gov.mb.ca.

557 CAN
MANITOBA INDUSTRY, TRADE AND MINES. REPORT OF ACTIVITIES SERIES. Text in English. 1968. a. price varies. **Document type:** *Government.* **Description:** Summarizes field activities carried out by the Minerals Division of the Department.
Former titles: Manitoba Energy and Mines. Report of Field Activities; Manitoba. Mineral Resources Division. Report of Field Activities; Manitoba. Mines Branch. Summary of Geological Field Work
Published by: Manitoba Industry, Trade and Mines, 360 1395 Ellice Ave, Winnipeg, MB R3G 3P2, Canada. TEL 204-945-4154, FAX 204-945-8427, publications@gov.mb.ca, http://www.infomine.com/index/suppliers/Manitoba_Industry,_Trade_and_Mines.html.

551 CHL ISSN 0717-2532
MAPAS GEOLOGICOS. Text in Spanish. 1996. irreg. USD 25. bk.rev. bibl.; illus.; maps. **Document type:** *Monographic series, Government.*
Related titles: CD-ROM ed.
Indexed: IMMAb.
Published by: Servicio Nacional de Geologia y Mineria, Ave. Santa Maria, 104, Providencia, Santiago, Chile. TEL 56-2-737-5050, FAX 56-2-735-6960, mcortes@sernageomin.cl. Circ: 1,000.

E

551 GBR ISSN 0264-8172
QE39 CODEN: MPEGD8
➤ **MARINE AND PETROLEUM GEOLOGY.** Text in English. 1971. 10/yr. EUR 1,827 in Europe to institutions; JPY 242,600 in Japan to institutions; USD 2,044 to institutions except Europe and Japan; EUR 234 in Europe to qualified personnel; JPY 31,000 in Japan to qualified personnel; USD 262 to qualified personnel except Europe and Japan (effective 2006). adv. bk.rev. illus. index. back issues avail.; reprints avail. **Document type:** *Academic/Scholarly.* **Description:** Aimed at explorationists in industry, government and academia. Presents multidisciplinary concepts and technologies of direct relevance to all concerned with marine and petroleum geology.
Former titles (until 1983): Underwater Information Bulletin (0302-3478); (until 1973): Underwater Journal Information Bulletin (0306-3887); Which was formed by the merger of: Underwater Science and Technology Journal (0503-1745); Underwater Science and Technology Information Bulletin (0503-1737); Underwater Journal and Information Bulletin (0041-6614)
Related titles: Microform ed.: (from PQC); Online - full text ed.: (from EBSCO Publishing, Gale Group, IngentaConnect, ScienceDirect, Swets Information Services).
Indexed: AESIS, ASCA, ASFA, CIN, ChemAb, ChemTitl, CurCont, E&PHSE, EIA, ESPM, EngInd, EnvAb, FLUIDEX, GEOBASE, GP&P, ISR, Inspec, OceAb, OffTech, PetrolAb, RefZh, SCI.
—BLDSC (5373.632100), AskIEEE, CASDDS, CISTI, Ei, IDS, IE, Infotrieve, ingenta, Linda Hall, PADDS. **CCC.**
Published by: (Geological Society), Elsevier Ltd. (Subsidiary of: Elsevier Science & Technology), The Boulevard, Langford Ln, Kidlington, Oxford, OX5 1GB, United Kingdom. TEL 44-1865-843000, FAX 44-1865-843010, http://www.elsevier.com/locate/marpetgeo. Ed. D. G. Roberts. **Subscr. to:** Elsevier BV, PO Box 211, Amsterdam 1000 AE, Netherlands. TEL 31-20-485-3757, FAX 31-20-485-3432, nlinfo-f@elsevier.nl, http://www.elsevier.nl.

➤ **MARSCHENRAT ZUR FOERDERUNG DER FORSCHUNG IM KUESTENGEBIET DER NORDSEE. NACHRICHTEN.** see *SCIENCES: COMPREHENSIVE WORKS*

557 USA ISSN 0076-4779
QE121 CODEN: MGSBBW
MARYLAND. GEOLOGICAL SURVEY. BULLETIN. Text in English. 1944. irreg., latest vol.37, 1990. price varies. index. **Document type:** *Bulletin.*
Indexed: ChemAb.
—Linda Hall.
Published by: Maryland Geological Survey, 2300 St Paul St, Baltimore, MD 21218. TEL 301-554-5500, FAX 301-554-5502.

557 USA ISSN 0076-4787
QE121 CODEN: MGSVBO
MARYLAND. GEOLOGICAL SURVEY. EDUCATIONAL SERIES. Text in English. 1964. irreg., latest vol.6, 1989. price varies.
—Linda Hall.
Published by: Maryland Geological Survey, 2300 St Paul St, Baltimore, MD 21218. TEL 301-554-5500, FAX 301-554-5502.

557 USA ISSN 0076-4795
CODEN: MGICAI
MARYLAND. GEOLOGICAL SURVEY. INFORMATION CIRCULAR. Text in English. 1963. irreg., latest vol.50. price varies.
—Linda Hall.
Published by: Maryland Geological Survey, 2300 St Paul St, Baltimore, MD 21218. TEL 301-554-5500, FAX 301-554-5502.

557 USA ISSN 0076-4809
QE121 CODEN: MGRIAD
MARYLAND. GEOLOGICAL SURVEY. REPORT OF INVESTIGATIONS. Text in English. 1965. irreg., latest vol.53. price varies.
—Ei, Linda Hall.
Published by: Maryland Geological Survey, 2300 St Paul St, Baltimore, MD 21218. TEL 301-554-5500, FAX 301-554-5502.

550 CZE
MASARYK UNIVERSITY. FACULTY OF SCIENCES. SCRIPTA GEOLOGIA/SCRIPTA FACULTATIS SCIENTIARUM NATURALIUM UNIVERSITATIS MASARYKIANAE BRUNENSIS. GEOLOGIA. Text in English, French, German, Russian. 1971. a. price varies. illus. **Document type:** *Academic/Scholarly.* **Description:** Compiles original articles written by geologists on the staff of the Masaryk University Faculty of Science.
Formerly: Scripta Facultatis Scientiarum Naturalium Universitatis Purkynianae Brunensis. Geologia (0322-824X)
—CISTI, Linda Hall.
Published by: Masarykova Universita, Prirodovedecka Fakulta/Masaryk University, Faculty of Sciences, Kotlarska 2, Brno, 61137, Czech Republic. Ed. Milos Suk.

551 NLD ISSN 0924-4972
➤ **MATERIALS SCIENCE OF MINERALS AND ROCKS.** Text in Dutch. 1983. irreg., latest 1995. price varies. **Document type:** *Monographic series, Academic/Scholarly.*
Published by: Springer-Verlag Dordrecht (Subsidiary of: Springer Science+Business Media), Van Godewijckstraat 30, Dordrecht, 3311 GX, Netherlands. TEL 31-78-6576050, FAX 31-78-6576474, http://www.springeronline.com.

551 526 NLD ISSN 0882-8121
QE1 CODEN: MATGED
➤ **MATHEMATICAL GEOLOGY.** Text in English. 1969. 8/yr. EUR 1,038, USD 968, GBP 685 combined subscription to institutions print & online eds. (effective 2005). adv. bk.rev. illus. back issues avail.; reprint service avail. from PSC. **Document type:** *Journal, Academic/Scholarly.* **Description:** Investigates the use of new and improved applications of mathematics to geological data.
Formerly (until 1986): International Association for Mathematical Geology. Journal (0020-5958)
Related titles: Microfilm ed.: (from PQC); Online - full text ed.: ISSN 1573-8868 (from EBSCO Publishing, Gale Group, IngentaConnect, Kluwer Online, O C L C Online Computer Library Center, Inc., Ovid Technologies, Inc., Springer LINK, Swets Information Services).
Indexed: AESIS, ASCA, ASFA, ApMecR, BibLing, BrCerAb, C&ISA, CCMJ, CIN, CIS, CMCI, CerAb, ChemAb, ChemTitl, CorrAb, CurCont, E&CAJ, EEA, EMA, ESPM, EngInd, FLUIDEX, GEOBASE, I&DA, IAA, ISR, M&TEA, MBF, METADEX, MathR, MathSciNet, PetrolAb, RefZh, SCI, SWRA, SolStAb, WAA.
—BLDSC (5402.200000), CASDDS, CISTI, Ei, IDS, IE, Infotrieve, ingenta, Linda Hall, PADDS. **CCC.**
Published by: (International Association for Mathematical Geology USA), Springer-Verlag Dordrecht (Subsidiary of: Springer Science+Business Media), Van Godewijckstraat 30, Dordrecht, 3311 GX, Netherlands. TEL 31-78-6576050, FAX 31-78-6576474, http://springerlink.metapress.com/openurl.asp?genre=journal&issn=0882-8121, http://www.springeronline.com. Ed. W E Sharp.

551 DEU
MATHEMATISCHE GEOLOGIE. Text in German, English. irreg.
Published by: CPress Verlag, PF 19 2409, Dresden, D-01282, Germany. FAX 49-0-351-3100951, info@cp-v.de. Ed. Thomas Steuber.

559.82 DNK ISSN 0106-1046
QE70 CODEN: GRGEDS
MEDDELELSER OM GROENLAND, GEOSCIENCE. Variant title: Greenland Geoscience. Text mainly in English; Text occasionally in Danish, French, German. 1878. irreg., latest vol.41, 2002. price varies. maps; illus.; charts. **Document type:** *Monographic series, Academic/Scholarly.*
Supersedes in part (in 1979): Meddelelser om Groenland (0025-6676)
Indexed: BiolAb, ChemAb, ZooRec.
—CASDDS, CISTI, Linda Hall.
Published by: Dansk Polarcenter/Danish Polar Center, Strandgade 100 H, Copenhagen K, 1401, Denmark. TEL 45-32-880100, FAX 45-32-880101, dpc@dpc.dk, http://www.dpc.dk/polarpubs/. Ed. S Funder.

550 ESP ISSN 0212-4300
QE283
MEDITERRANEA. SERIE DE ESTUDIOS GEOLOGICOS. Text in Spanish. 1983. a.
Indexed: IECT.
—**CCC.**
Published by: (Departamento de Investigaciones Geologicas), Universidad de Alicante, Facultad de Ciencias, Apartado 99, Alicante, 03080, Spain. TEL 96-590-3400, FAX 96-590-3464.

622.1824 CHN ISSN 1001-1986
MEITIAN DIZHI YU KANTAN/COAL GEOLOGY AND PROSPECTING. Text in Chinese. 1973. bi-m. CNY 5, USD 2.40 newsstand/cover (effective 2004).
Related titles: Online - full text ed.: (from East View Information Services, WanFang Data Corp.).
—BLDSC (3289.860000).
Published by: Meitan Kexue Yanjiuyuan Dizhi Kantan Fenyuan/China Coal Research Institute, Xian Branch, 52, Yanta Beilu, Xi'an, 710054, China. TEL 86-29-87857567, FAX 86-29-87850504, mtdzykt@pub.xaonline.com, xian_jyc@xianccri.com, http://mtdzykt.periodicals.net.cn/default.html, http://www.xianccri.com/. **Dist. by:** China International Book Trading Corp, 35 Chegongzhuang Xilu, Haidian District, PO Box 399, Beijing 100044, China. TEL 86-10-68412045, FAX 86-10-68412023, cibtc@mail.cibtc.com.cn, http://www.cibtc.com.cn.

551 ITA ISSN 0536-0242
QE272 CODEN: SGIMAC
MEMORIE DESCRITTIVE DELLA CARTA GEOLOGICA D'ITALIA. Text in Italian. 1886. 3/w. **Document type:** *Monographic series.*
Indexed: RefZh, ZooRec.
—Linda Hall.
Published by: Servizio Geologico d'Italia, Largo di Santa Susanna 13, Rome, Italy. TEL 39-06-4743081.

551 ITA ISSN 0391-8602
QE272 CODEN: MSGEDX
➤ **MEMORIE DI SCIENZE GEOLOGICHE.** Text mainly in English; Text occasionally in French, German, Italian; Summaries in English, Italian. 1912. a. **Document type:** *Academic/Scholarly.*
Indexed: BiolAb, ZooRec.
Published by: (Universita degli Studi di Padova, Dipartimento di Geologia Paleontologia e Geofisica), Societa Cooperativa Tipografica, Via Fra Paolo Sarpi 38, Padua, 35138, Italy. TEL 39-049-8750575, FAX 39-049-657464, cooptip@tin.it, http://www.geol.unipd.it/01_dipartimento/memorie.htm. Ed. Giampietro Braga. Circ: 400.

554 GBR ISSN 0025-990X
QE262.M6 CODEN: MGEOAY
➤ **MERCIAN GEOLOGIST.** Text in English. 1964. a., latest vol.15, 2003, part 4. GBP 6 per vol. (effective 2003). bk.rev. bibl.; charts; illus.; maps. cum.index. 60 p./no. 2 cols./p.; back issues avail. **Document type:** *Journal, Academic/Scholarly.*
Indexed: AESIS, BrGeoL, ChemAb, F&EA, GEOBASE, ZooRec.
—BLDSC (5679.100000), IE, ingenta.
Published by: East Midlands Geological Society, 11 Selby Rd, Nottingham, NG2 7BP, United Kingdom. TEL 44-115-9813833, alan.filmer@which.net. Ed., R&P Tony Waltham. Circ: 500.

551 FRA ISSN 0222-5123
MET MAR. Text in French. 1960. q. **Description:** Publishes research papers on marine meteorology and geographical and historical chronicles.
Indexed: ASFA, ESPM, RefZh.
—**CCC.**
Published by: Meteo France, 1 quai Branly, Paris, Cedex 7 75340, France. TEL 33-1-45567461, FAX 33-1-45567459, metmar@meteo.fr, http://www.meteo.fr. Ed. Michel Hontarrede. Pub. Jean Pierre Beysson.

551 DEU ISSN 0076-7689
QE269 CODEN: MEYNAF
➤ **MEYNIANA;** Veroeffentlichungen aus dem Institut fuer Geowissenschaften. Text in German, English; Abstracts in English, German. 1952. a., latest vol.56, 2004. EUR 10 (effective 2005). back issues avail. **Document type:** *Bulletin, Academic/Scholarly.*
Indexed: ASFA, BIOSIS Prev, BiolAb, ESPM, IBR, RefZh, ZooRec.
Published by: Universitaet Kiel, Institut fuer Geowissenschaften, Olshausenstr 40, Kiel, 24118, Germany. TEL 49-431-8803254, FAX 49-431-8804376, kw@gpi.uni-kiel.de, http://www.ifg.uni-kiel.de/zentral/veroeffent.html. Ed., R&P Kyaw Winn. Circ: 400.

557 USA
QE125 CODEN: MGDRA4
MICHIGAN. GEOLOGICAL SURVEY DIVISION. BULLETIN. Text in English. 1964. irreg., latest vol.6, 1976. price varies. illus.; maps. **Document type:** *Government.*
Published by: Department of Environmental Quality, Geological Survey Division, Information Services Center, Box 30256 7756, Lansing, MI 48909. TEL 517-334-6907. Ed. S E Wilson.

557 USA ISSN 0543-8497
QE125 CODEN: MGDRA4
MICHIGAN. GEOLOGICAL SURVEY DIVISION. REPORT OF INVESTIGATION. Text in English. 1963. irreg., latest vol.28. price varies. illus.; maps. **Document type:** *Government.*
Formerly: Michigan. Department of Conservation. Geological Survey Division. Progress Report (0096-5022)
Indexed: IMMAb.
—Linda Hall.
Published by: Department of Environmental Quality, Geological Survey Division, Information Services Center, Box 30256 7756, Lansing, MI 48909. TEL 517-334-6907. Ed. S E Wilson.

551 CAN ISSN 1189-6000
MINERAL MATTERS/PARLONS MINERAUX. Text in English. 1992. irreg. free. **Document type:** *Newsletter.*
Indexed: IMMAb.
Published by: Canada Department of Natural Resources and Energy/Ministere des Ressources Naturelles et de l'Energie, Rm. 150, Hugh John Flemming Forestry Centre, P O Box 6000, Fredericton, NB E3B 5H1, Canada. TEL 506-453-3837, FAX 506-453-3671.

363.7 GBR ISSN 0267-1409
MINERAL PLANNING. Text in English. 1979. q. GBP 60 domestic; GBP 65 in Europe; GBP 68 elsewhere (effective 2000). adv. bk.rev.; software rev. illus.; stat. index. **Document type:** *Academic/Scholarly.* **Description:** Covers development planning relating to minerals industries.
Indexed: IMMAb, WasteInfo.
—BLDSC (5779.590000), CISTI, IE, ingenta.
Address: 2 The Greenways, Little Fencote, Northallerton, N Yorks DL7 0TS, United Kingdom. TEL 44-1609-748709, FAX 44-1609-748709. Eds. M C Harrison, Steven Machin. Adv. contact E A Harrison. Circ: 1,000 (paid).

550 GBR ISSN 0969-6547
MINERAL PLANNING APPEALS IN GREAT BRITAIN. Text in English. 1988. a. GBP 98 (effective 2000). adv. illus.; stat. index. back issues avail. **Document type:** *Academic/Scholarly.*
—BLDSC (5779.595000).
Published by: Mineral Planning, 2 The Greenways, Little Fencote, Northallerton, N Yorks DL7 0TS, United Kingdom. TEL 44-1609-748709, FAX 44-1609-748709. Eds. M C Harrison, Steven Machin. Adv. contact E A Harrison. Circ: 350 (paid).

MINERAL RESOURCES DATA SYSTEM. see *MINES AND MINING INDUSTRY*

555 549 PAK
MINERAL REVIEW. Text in English, Urdu. q. free.
Published by: Pakistan Mineral Development Corporation, P I D C House, Dr. Ziauddin Ahmed Rd., Karachi 4, Pakistan. Ed. Sajid Hussain. Circ: 1,000.

MINERALES. see *MINES AND MINING INDUSTRY*

550 DEU ISSN 0176-1285
MINERALIEN-MAGAZIN LAPIS. Text in German. 1976. m. EUR 44 (effective 2005). adv. bk.rev. charts; illus.; maps. index. back issues avail. **Document type:** *Magazine, Trade.*
Description: Covers mineralogy, gemology and mining for collectors and dealers of minerals and gems.
Formed by the 1984 merger of: Lapis (0342-2933); Mineralien-Magazin (0341-907X)
—BLDSC (5786.145000), IE, ingenta. **CCC.**
Published by: Christian Weise Verlag GmbH, Orleansstr 69, Munich, 81667, Germany. TEL 49-89-4802933, FAX 49-89-6886160, lapis.mineralienmagazin@t-online.de, lapis@lapis.de, http://www.lapis.de. Ed. Stefan Weiss. Pub., R&P Christian Weise. Adv. contact Viola Moenius. Circ: 12,000.

551 549 551.9 DEU ISSN 0026-4598
QE351 CODEN: MIDEBE
➤ **MINERALIUM DEPOSITA**; international journal of geology, mineralogy, and geochemistry of mineral deposits. Text in English. 1966. 8/yr. EUR 1,298 combined subscription to institutions print & online eds. (effective 2005). adv. bk.rev. charts; illus. index. back issues avail.; reprint service avail. from ISI. **Document type:** *Journal, Academic/Scholarly.*
Description: Introduces new observations, principles, and interpretations from the fields of economic geology and applied geochemistry, with emphasis on mineral deposits.
Related titles: Microform ed.: (from PQC); Online - full text ed.: ISSN 1432-1866 (from EBSCO Publishing, Springer LINK, Swets Information Services).
Indexed: AESIS, ASCA, ASFA, BrGeoL, CIN, Cadscan, ChemAb, ChemTitl, CurCont, ESPM, EngInd, GEOBASE, IBR, IMMAb, ISR, LeadAb, MinerAb, PollutAb, RefZh, SCI, Zincscan.
—BLDSC (5786.200000), CASDDS, CISTI, Ei, IDS, IE, Infotrieve, ingenta, Linda Hall. **CCC.**
Published by: (Society for Geology Applied to Mineral Deposits), Springer-Verlag (Subsidiary of: Springer Science+Business Media), Tiergartenstr 17, Heidelberg, 69121, Germany. TEL 49-6221-3450, FAX 49-6221-345229, http://link.springer.de/link/service/journals/00126/index.htm. Eds. Bernd Lehmann TEL 49-5323-722511, Lawrence D Meinert. Adv. contact Stephan Kroeck TEL 49-30-827875739. **Subscr. in the Americas to:** Springer-Verlag New York, Inc., Journal Fulfillment, PO Box 2485, Secaucus, NJ 07096-2485. TEL 800-777-4643, 201-348-4033, FAX 201-348-4505, journals@springer-ny.com, http://www.springer-ny.com; **Subscr. to:** Springer GmbH Auslieferungsgesellschaft, Haberstr 7, Heidelberg 69126, Germany. TEL 49-6221-345-0, FAX 49-6221-345-4229, subscriptions@springer.de.

551 RUS ISSN 0869-3188
TN85
MINERAL'NYE RESURSY ROSSII. EKONOMIKA I UPRAVLENIE. Text in Russian. bi-m. USD 99.95 in United States.
Indexed: RefZh.
—East View.
Published by: Informatsionno-Izdatel'skii Tsentr po Geologii i Nedropol'zovaniu Geoinformmark, Goncharnaya 38, Moscow, 115172, Russian Federation. TEL 7-095-9156724. **US dist. addr.:** East View Information Services, 3020 Harbor Ln. N., Minneapolis, MN 55447. TEL 612-550-0961.

551 549 USA ISSN 0343-2181
MINERALS AND ROCKS; monograph series of theoretical and experimental studies. Text in English. 1968. irreg., latest vol.22, 1996. price varies. back issues avail.; reprint service avail. from ISI. **Document type:** *Monographic series.*
Description: Publishes research in geology and inorganic chemistry.
Former titles: Mineralogie und Petrographie in Einzel Darstellungen; Minerals, Rocks and Inorganic Materials (0076-8944)
Indexed: IMMAb, Inspec.
—CISTI.
Published by: Springer-Verlag New York, Inc. (Subsidiary of: Springer Science+Business Media), 233 Spring St, New York, NY 10013. TEL 212-460-1500, FAX 212-473-6272, journals@springer-ny.com, http://www.springer-ny.com. Ed. P J Wyllie. **Subscr. to:** Journal Fulfillment, PO Box 2485, Secaucus, NJ 07096-2485. TEL 800-777-4643, 201-348-4033, FAX 201-348-4505, journals@springer-ny.com.

MINFO; New South Wales mining and exploration quarterly. see *MINES AND MINING INDUSTRY*

MINING AND GEOLOGY. see *MINES AND MINING INDUSTRY*

557 USA ISSN 0076-9169
QE127 CODEN: MGSBAV
MINNESOTA GEOLOGICAL SURVEY. BULLETIN. Text in English. 1889. irreg., latest vol.48, 2000. price varies. **Document type:** *Bulletin, Academic/Scholarly.*
—CISTI, Linda Hall.
Published by: Minnesota Geological Survey, 2642 University Ave. W., St. Paul, MN 55114-1057. TEL 612-627-4780, FAX 612-627-4778, mgs@tc.umn.edu, http://www.geo.umn.edu/mgs.

551.07 USA ISSN 0544-3083
CODEN: MGSEB7
MINNESOTA GEOLOGICAL SURVEY. EDUCATIONAL SERIES. Text in English. 1979 (no.2). irreg., latest vol.10, 1999. price varies. **Document type:** *Monographic series, Academic/Scholarly.*
—Linda Hall.
Published by: Minnesota Geological Survey, 2642 University Ave. W., St. Paul, MN 55114-1057. TEL 612-627-4780, FAX 612-627-4778, mgs@tc.umn.edu, http://www.geo.umn.edu/mgs.

551 USA ISSN 0192-6268
CODEN: MGLGAB
MINNESOTA GEOLOGICAL SURVEY. GUIDEBOOK SERIES. Text in English. 1982 (no.14). irreg., latest vol.18, 1992. price varies. **Document type:** *Monographic series, Academic/Scholarly.*
Published by: Minnesota Geological Survey, 2642 University Ave. W., St. Paul, MN 55114-1057. TEL 612-627-4780, FAX 612-627-4778, mgs@tc.umn.edu, http://www.geo.umn.edu/mgs.

557 USA ISSN 0544-3105
QE127 CODEN: MGSIBJ
MINNESOTA GEOLOGICAL SURVEY. INFORMATION CIRCULAR. Text in English. 1962. irreg., latest vol.47, 2001. price varies. back issues avail. **Document type:** *Monographic series, Academic/Scholarly.* **Description:** Presents results of scientific test drilling for minerals in southwestern Minnesota.
—Linda Hall.
Published by: Minnesota Geological Survey, 2642 University Ave. W., St. Paul, MN 55114-1057. TEL 612-627-4780, FAX 612-627-4778, mgs@tc.umn.edu, http://www.geo.umn.edu/mgs.

557.76 USA ISSN 0544-3113
G4141.C5 svar CODEN: MMSSDP
MINNESOTA GEOLOGICAL SURVEY. MISCELLANEOUS MAP SERIES. Text in English. 1965. irreg., latest vol.130, 2002. price varies. **Document type:** *Monographic series, Academic/Scholarly.*
Published by: Minnesota Geological Survey, 2642 University Ave. W., St. Paul, MN 55114-1057. TEL 612-627-4780, FAX 612-627-4778, mgs@tc.umn.edu, http://www.geo.umn.edu/mgs.

557 USA ISSN 0076-9177
QE127
MINNESOTA GEOLOGICAL SURVEY. REPORT OF INVESTIGATIONS. Text in English. 1963. irreg., latest vol.58, 2002. price varies. back issues avail. **Document type:** *Monographic series, Academic/Scholarly.*
Indexed: RefZh.
—Linda Hall.
Published by: Minnesota Geological Survey, 2642 University Ave. W., St. Paul, MN 55114-1057. TEL 612-627-4780, FAX 612-627-4778, mgs@tc.umn.edu, http://www.geo.umn.edu/mgs. Circ: 400.

557 USA ISSN 0275-8555
QE129
MISSISSIPPI GEOLOGY. Text in English. 1980. q. free (effective 2005). bk.rev. bibl.; charts; illus.; stat.; maps. back issues avail. **Document type:** *Journal, Government.* **Description:** Articles and abstracts on geological research in the state, with news items, reviews, and lists of relevant publications.
Indexed: PetrolAb, ZooRec.
—BLDSC (5828.926500), ingenta, Linda Hall, PADDS.
Published by: Department of Environmental Quality, Office of Geology, PO Box 20307, Jackson, MS 39289. TEL 601-961-5500, FAX 601-961-5521, Michael_Bograd@deq.state.ms.us, http://www.deq.state.ms.us/newweb. Eds. David Dockery, Michael B E Bograd. R&P Michael B E Bograd. Circ: 1,100.

557 USA ISSN 1046-0594
MISSOURI. DIVISION OF GEOLOGY AND LAND SURVEY. SPECIAL PUBLICATION. Text in English. irreg. **Document type:** *Monographic series, Government.*
—Linda Hall.
Published by: Missouri Department of Natural Resources, Division of Geology and Land Survey, PO Box 250, Rolla, MO 65401. TEL 573-368-2125.

551 NLD ISSN 0168-6151
QE696
MODERN QUATERNARY RESEARCH IN SOUTHEAST ASIA. Text in Dutch. 1975. a. USD 70 (effective 1999). **Document type:** *Academic/Scholarly.*
Indexed: AnthLit, BAS.
—Linda Hall. **CCC.**
Published by: A A Balkema (Subsidiary of: Taylor & Francis The Netherlands), PO Box 1675, Rotterdam, 3000 BR, Netherlands. FAX 31-10-413-5947, sales@balkema.nl, http://www.balkema.nl. Eds. G J Bartstra, W A Casparie. **Dist. in U.S. by:** Ashgate Publishing Co, Old Post Rd, Brookfield, VT 05036. TEL 800-535-9544.

MONTANA. BUREAU OF MINES AND GEOLOGY. BIENNIAL REPORT. see *MINES AND MINING INDUSTRY*

557 USA ISSN 0077-1090
CODEN: MBGBA4
MONTANA. BUREAU OF MINES AND GEOLOGY. BULLETIN. Text in English. 1919. irreg., latest vol.131, 1993. price varies. **Document type:** *Directory, Government.* **Description:** Series includes data sources, catalogs, bibliographies, indexes, categorized studies and information.
Incorporates (in 1960): Montana. Bureau of Mines and Geology. Ground Water Reports (0077-1112)
Indexed: IMMAb.
—CASDDS, CISTI, Linda Hall.
Published by: Nevada Bureau of Mines and Geology, University of Montana, Montana Tech, 1300 West Park St, Butte, MT 59701-8997. TEL 406-496-4167, FAX 406-496-4451, http://mbmgsun.mtech.edu. Ed. M A Coffey. R&P M.A. Coffey.

557 622 USA ISSN 0077-1120
CODEN: MBGMA3
MONTANA. BUREAU OF MINES AND GEOLOGY. MEMOIR. Text in English. 1928. irreg., latest vol.68, 1995. **Document type:** *Government.* **Description:** Presents detailed, scientific studies of specific subjects in earth science.
Indexed: IMMAb.
—Linda Hall.
Published by: Nevada Bureau of Mines and Geology, University of Montana, Montana Tech, 1300 West Park St, Butte, MT 59701-8997. TEL 406-496-4167, FAX 406-496-4451, http://mbmgsun.mtech.edu. Ed. M A Coffey.

557 USA ISSN 0077-1139
CODEN: MBGSAL
MONTANA. BUREAU OF MINES AND GEOLOGY. SPECIAL PUBLICATIONS. Text in English. 1957. irreg., latest vol.111, 1995. price varies. **Document type:** *Directory, Government.*
Description: Features a compilation of various works, guidebooks, proceedings, multiple authorships. May include treatments suitable for laypersons.
Indexed: IMMAb.
—CASDDS, CISTI, Linda Hall.
Published by: Nevada Bureau of Mines and Geology, University of Montana, Montana Tech, 1300 West Park St, Butte, MT 59701-8997. TEL 406-496-4167, FAX 406-496-4451, http://mbmgsun.mtech.edu. Ed. M A Coffey.

551 USA ISSN 0145-8752
QE1 CODEN: MUGBD4
➤ **MOSCOW STATE UNIVERSITY GEOLOGY BULLETIN.** Text in English. 1974. bi-m. USD 2,130 per vol. in US & Canada; USD 2,430 per vol. elsewhere (effective 2006). charts; illus.; abstr.; maps. index. back issues avail. **Document type:** *Journal, Academic/Scholarly.* **Description:** Covers petrology and exploration methods, sedimentory processes, fault tectonics, and paleogeography.
Related titles: ♦ Translation of: Moskovskii Gosudarstvennyi Universitet. Vestnik. Seriya 4: Geologiya. ISSN 0579-9406.
Indexed: ExcerpMed.
—BLDSC (0416.238500), CISTI, IE, ingenta. **CCC.**
Published by: (Moskovskii Gosudarstvennyi Universitet im. M.V. Lomonosova/M.V. Lomonosov Moscow State University RUS), Allerton Press, Inc., 18 W 27th St, New York, NY 10001. TEL 646-424-9686, FAX 646-424-9695, journals@allertonpress.com, http://www.allertonpress.com/journals/mug.htm. Ed. Boris A Sokolov.

551 RUS ISSN 0579-9406
QE1 CODEN: VMUGAR
MOSKOVSKII GOSUDARSTVENNYI UNIVERSITET. VESTNIK. SERIYA 4: GEOLOGIYA. Text in Russian; Contents page in English. 1950. bi-m. USD 66 foreign (effective 2004). bk.rev. bibl. index. **Document type:** *Journal, Academic/Scholarly.*
Supersedes in part (in 1960): Moskovskii Universitet. Vestnik. Seriya Biologii Pocvovedeniya, Geologii, Geografii (0541-0770); Which superseded in part (in 1956): Moskovskogo Universiteta. Vestnik. Seria Fiziko-Matematiceskih i Estestvennyh Nauk (0463-5434)
Related titles: ♦ English Translation: Moscow State University Geology Bulletin. ISSN 0145-8752.
Indexed: BibCart, CIN, ChemAb, ChemTitl, RASB, RefZh.
—BLDSC (0032.510000), CASDDS, CISTI, East View, Linda Hall. **CCC.**
Published by: (Moskovskii Gosudarstvennyi Universitet im. M.V. Lomonosova, Geologicheskii Fakul'tet/M.V. Lomonosov Moscow State University, Department of Geology), Izdatel'stvo Moskovskogo Gosudarstvennogo Universiteta im. M. V. Lomonosova/Publishing House of Moscow State University, B Nikitskaya 5/7, Moscow, 103009, Russian Federation. TEL 7-095-2295091, FAX 7-095-2036671, kd_mgu@rambler.ru, http://www.msu.ru/depts/MSUPubl. **Dist. by:** M K - Periodica, ul Gilyarovskogo 39, Moscow 129110, Russian Federation. TEL 7-095-2845008, FAX 7-095-2813798, info@periodicals.ru, http://www.mkniga.ru.

E

550 RUS ISSN 0366-1318
Q60 CODEN: BMPGAK
MOSKOVSKOE OBSHCHESTVO ISPYTATELEI PRIRODY. GEOLOGICHESKII OTDEL. BYULLETEN/MOSCOW SOCIETY OF NATURALISTS. GEOLOGICAL SERIES. BULLETIN/SOCIETE IMPERIALE DES NATURALISTES DE MOSCOU. SECTION GEOLOGIQUE. BULLETIN. Text in Russian; Summaries in English. 1922. q. USD 84 foreign (effective 2004). bk.rev. abstr.; bibl.; charts; illus. **Document type:** *Journal, Academic/Scholarly.*
Indexed: BiolAb, CIN, ChemAb, ChemTitl, IBR, RefZh, ZooRec.
—CASDDS, CISTI, East View, Linda Hall. **CCC.**
Published by: (Moskovskoe Obshchestvo Ispytatelei Prirody, Geologicheskii Otdel/Moscow Society of Naturalists, Geological Section), Izdatel'stvo Moskovskogo Gosudarstvennogo Universiteta im. M. V. Lomonosova/ Publishing House of Moscow State University, B Nikitskaya 5/7, Moscow, 103009, Russian Federation. TEL 7-095-2295091, FAX 7-095-2036671, kd_mgu@rambler.ru, http://www.msu.ru/depts/MSUPubl. Ed. D P Naidin. R&P Tamara A Ivanova. Circ: 460. **Dist. by:** M K - Periodica, ul Gilyarovskogo 39, Moscow 129110, Russian Federation. TEL 7-095-2845008, FAX 7-095-2813798, info@periodicals.ru, http://www.mkniga.ru.

551 USA ISSN 0027-254X
QE79 CODEN: MOGEA2
➤ **MOUNTAIN GEOLOGIST.** Text in English. 1964. q., latest vol.39. free to members (effective 2004). adv. charts; illus. index, cum.index. back issues avail. **Document type:** *Journal, Academic/Scholarly.* **Description:** Contains scientific papers dealing with the geology of the Rocky Mountain region. Covers topics ranging from plate tectonics and structured geology to sedimentology and paleontology.
Indexed: ChemAb, GEOBASE, PetrolAb.
—BLDSC (5978.900000), IE, ingenta, Linda Hall, PADDS. **CCC.**
Published by: Rocky Mountain Association of Geologists, 820 16th St, 505, Denver, CO 80202-3218. TEL 303-573-8621, FAX 303-628-0546, rmagdenver@aol.com, http://www.rmag.org/mtngeologist/index.asp. Ed. Michele Bishop. R&P, Adv. contact Sandi Pellissier TEL 303-573-862. Circ: 2,400 (controlled).

➤ **MUENCHNER GEOWISSENSCHAFTLICHE ABHANDLUNGEN. REIHE A: GEOLOGIE UND PALAEONTOLOGIE.** see *PALEONTOLOGY*

551 DEU ISSN 0931-8739
MUENCHNER GEOWISSENSCHAFTLICHE ABHANDLUNGEN. REIHE B: ALLGEMEINE UND ANGEWANDTE GEOLOGIE. Text in English, French, German. 1988. irreg., latest vol.9. back issues avail. **Document type:** *Monographic series.* **Description:** Covers all areas of geology and applied geology.
—CISTI.
Published by: Verlag Dr. Friedrich Pfeil, Wolfratshauser Str 27, Munich, 81379, Germany. info@pfeil-verlag.de, http://www.pfeil-verlag.de. Ed. Friedrich H Pfeil. Circ: 500.

551 DEU ISSN 0368-9654
CODEN: MFGPB7
MUENSTERSCHE FORSCHUNGEN ZUR GEOLOGIE UND PALAEONTOLOGIE. Text in German, English, Spanish; Abstracts in English. 1965. irreg., latest vol.96, 2003. price varies. bk.rev. abstr.; bibl.; illus.; maps; stat. back issues avail. **Document type:** *Monographic series, Academic/Scholarly.* **Description:** Publishes papers involving all aspects of geology and palaeontology.
Indexed: ZooRec.
—CCC.
Published by: Westfaelische Wilhelms-Universitaet Muenster, Geologisch-Palaeontologisches Institut, Corrensstr 24, Muenster, 48149, Germany. TEL 49-251-8333979, FAX 49-251-8333968, muefogeo@uni-muenster.de, http://www.uni-muenster.de/GeoPalaeontologie/Muefo/ Muefo.html. Ed. Judith J Nagel. Pub. Wolfgang H Peters-Kottig. Circ: 300.

551 BEL ISSN 0368-489X
QE1 CODEN: KBGWAB
MUSEE ROYAL DE L'AFRIQUE CENTRALE. ANNALES - SCIENCES GEOLOGIQUES. SERIE IN 8/KONINKLIJK MUSEUM VOOR MIDDEN-AFRIKA. ANNALEN - GEOLOGISCHE WETENSCHAPPEN. REEKS IN 8. Text in French. 1948. irreg., latest no.101 1995. price varies. charts; illus. **Document type:** *Monographic series.*
Indexed: BiolAb, RefZh, ZooRec.
—Linda Hall.
Published by: Musee Royal de l'Afrique Centrale/Koninklijk Museum voor Midden-Afrika, Steenweg op Leuven 13, Tervuren, 3080, Belgium. TEL 32-2-7695299, FAX 32-7670242.

551 BEL ISSN 0378-0953
QE48.A43 CODEN: MRGRAS
MUSEE ROYAL DE L'AFRIQUE CENTRALE. DEPARTEMENT DE GEOLOGIE ET DE MINERALOGIE. RAPPORT ANNUEL. Text in French. 1957. biennial. price varies. charts.
Indexed: BiolAb, ChemAb, ZooRec.
Published by: Musee Royal de l'Afrique Centrale/Koninklijk Museum voor Midden-Afrika, Steenweg op Leuven 13, Tervuren, 3080, Belgium. TEL 32-2-7695299, FAX 32-2-767-0242. Ed. J Klerkx. Circ: 1,000.

551 580 ITA ISSN 1127-4476
➤ **MUSEO CIVICO DI STORIA NATURALE DI FERRARA. ANNALI.** Text in English, Italian. 1998. a., latest vol.4. 130 p./no.; back issues avail. **Document type:** *Journal, Academic/Scholarly.*
Indexed: ZooRec.
Published by: Museo Civico di Storia Naturale di Ferrara, Via Filippo de Pisis, 24, Ferrara, FE 44100, Italy. TEL 39-0532-203381, FAX 39-0532-210508, museo.storianaturale@comune.fe.it, http://www.comune.fe.it/ storianaturale. Ed. Stefano Mazzotti. Pub. Fausto Pesarini.

551 300 ITA ISSN 1590-8402
MUSEO CIVICO DI STORIA NATURALE DI VERONA. BOLLETTINO. GEOLOGIA PALEONTOLOGIA PREISTORIA. Text in Multiple languages. 2000. a.
Supersedes in part (in 2000): Museo Civico di Storia Naturale di Verona. Bollettino (0392-0062)
Indexed: RefZh, ZooRec.
—Linda Hall.
Published by: Museo Civico di Storia Naturale di Verona, Lungadige Porta Vittoria 9, Verona, VR 37129, Italy. TEL 39-045-8079400, FAX 39-045-8035639, mcsnat@comune.verona.it, http:// www.museostorianaturaleverona.it.

551 ESP ISSN 1134-0207
MUSEO DE GEOLOGIA DE EXTREMADURA. PUBLICACIONES. Text in Spanish. 1992. a.
—CINDOC.
Published by: Museo de Geologia de Extramdura, C. Almendralejo, s-n Edif. El Costurero, Merida, Extremadura 06800, Spain.

551 ARG ISSN 0372-462X
QE1
MUSEO DE LA PLATA. REVISTA. SECCION GEOLOGIA. Text in Spanish. 1890. irreg.
Supersedes in part (in 1936): Museo de La Plata. Revista (0375-1147)
Indexed: ESPM.
—CISTI, Infotrieve.
Published by: Universidad Nacional de La Plata, Facultad de Ciencias Naturales y Museo, Avenidas 60 y 122, La Plata, Buenos Aires, Argentina. TEL 54-221-4258252, facultad@museo.fcnym.unlp.edu.ar.

550 BRA ISSN 0080-3200
QE235 CODEN: BOJAAK
MUSEU NACIONAL. BOLETIM. GEOLOGIA. Text in Portuguese, English. 1943. irreg., latest vol.67, 2003. exchange only.
Supersedes in part (1923-1943): Museu Nacional. Boletim (0100-1507)
Indexed: BiolAb, ZooRec.
—CISTI, Linda Hall.
Published by: Museu Nacional, Quinta da Boa Vista, Sao Cristovao, Rio de Janeiro, RJ 20940-040, Brazil. TEL 55-21-25688262, FAX 55-21-25681352, museu@mn.ufrj.br, http://www.acd.ufjr.br/~museuhp/homep.htm.

551 FRA ISSN 1280-9659
QE1 CODEN: BMNMDV
➤ **MUSEUM NATIONAL D'HISTOIRE NATURELLE. GEODIVERSITAS.** Text and summaries in English, French. 1895. q. EUR 75 to individuals; EUR 150 to institutions (effective 2004). 150 p./no.; back issues avail. **Document type:** *Journal, Academic/Scholarly.* **Description:** Publishes papers on earth sciences with an emphasis on the history of sedimentary basins, paleobiodiversity and paleoenvironments.
Former titles (until 1997): Museum National d'Histoire Naturelle. Bulletin - Section C (Sciences de la Terre: Paleontologie, Geologie, Mineralogie) (0181-0642); (until 1979): Museum National d'Histoire Naturelle. Bulletin (Sciences de la Terre) (0376-446X); Which superseded in part (in 1972): Museum National d'Histoire Naturelle. Bulletin (1148-8425); Which was formerly (until 1907): Museum d'Histoire Naturelle. Bulletin (0027-4070)
Related titles: Online - full text ed.: ISSN 1638-9395. 2000. free (effective 2005).
Indexed: ASFA, BIOSIS Prev, BiolAb, CurCont, ESPM, RefZh, SFA, ZooRec.
—BLDSC (4119.752150), CISTI, Linda Hall.
Published by: Museum National d'Histoire Naturelle, 57 Rue Cuvier, Paris, 75231 Cedex 05, France. TEL 33-1-40793777, geodiv@mnhn.fr, http://www.mnhn.fr/publication/geodiv/ ageodiv.html.

➤ **MUSEUM VICTORIA. MEMOIRS.** see *BIOLOGY—Zoology*

550 POL ISSN 0032-6275
CODEN: PMUZAI
➤ **MUZEUM ZIEMI. PRACE.** Text in English, Polish. 1958. irreg. (approx. 1-2/yr.). **Document type:** *Proceedings, Academic/Scholarly.*
Indexed: ChemAb, ZooRec.
Published by: Polska Akademia Nauk, Muzeum Ziemi, Al Na Skarpie 20-26, Warsaw, 00488, Poland. TEL 48-22-6298061, FAX 48-22-6297497. Ed. Krzysztof Jakubowski.

557 USA ISSN 0749-937X
N B M G. OPEN-FILE REPORT. Text in English. 1971. irreg. price varies. back issues avail. **Document type:** *Government.* **Description:** Publishes preliminary data in photocopy form.
Published by: Nevada Bureau of Mines and Geology, Publications Sales, Mail Stop 178, University of Nevada at Reno, Reno, NV 89557-0088. TEL 775-784-6691, FAX 775-784-1709, info@nbmg.unr.edu, http://www.nbmg.unr.edu/ sales/pbs.php?ser=o. Ed. Richard Meewig.

N C A CAVE TALK. see *TRAVEL AND TOURISM*

551 USA
N C G S OPEN-FILE REPORT. Text in English. 1966. irreg., latest 1998. price varies. **Document type:** *Bulletin, Government.*
Published by: (North Carolina. Department of Environment, Health and Natural Resources, North Carolina. Division of Land Resources), North Carolina Geological Survey, PO Box 27687, Raleigh, NC 27611. TEL 919-733-2423, FAX 919-733-0900.

554.81 NOR ISSN 0801-5961
N G U SPECIAL PUBLICATION. Text in English. 1987. irreg. price varies. back issues avail. **Document type:** *Proceedings, Academic/Scholarly.* **Description:** Presents papers and proceedings from national and international symposia or meetings dealing with Norwegian and international geology, geophysics and geochemistry; features some thematic articles.
—Linda Hall.
Published by: Norges Geologiske Undersoekelse/Geological Survey of Norway, Leiv Eriksson Vei 39, Trondheim, 7491, Norway. TEL 47-73-904000, FAX 47-73-921620, ngu@ngu.no, http://www.ngu.no. Ed. David Roberts. Circ: 1,000.

551 USA ISSN 1085-5386
N O R M REPORT. (Naturally Occurring Radioactive Material) Variant title: Norm Report. Text in English. q. **Document type:** *Journal, Academic/Scholarly.* **Description:** Contains articles and results from tests and studies on concentrations of naturally occurring radionuclides found in the earth's crust.
Published by: Peter Gray & Associates, PO Box 470932, Tulsa, OK 74147-0932.

551.31 USA
N S I D C ANNUAL REPORT. Text in English. irreg.
Related titles: Online - full content ed.
Published by: National Snow and Ice Data Center, NSIDC User Services, CIRES, Campus Box 449, University of Colorado, Boulder, CO 80309-0449. TEL 303-492-6199, FAX 303-492-2468, nsidc@nsidc.org, http://nsidc.org/pubs/ NSIDC_Annual_Report_2001.pdf.

551.31 USA
N S I D C NOTES. (National Snow and Ice Data Center) Text in English. 1991. q. free. **Document type:** *Newsletter, Academic/Scholarly.* **Description:** Provides news and information of interest to users of the National Snow and Ice Data Center data, including relevant meetings, products and services, and publications. Also contains short items from readers of interest to the cryospheric community.
Formerly (until 1992): C D M S Notes
Related titles: Online - full content ed.
Published by: National Snow and Ice Data Center, NSIDC User Services, CIRES, Campus Box 449, University of Colorado, Boulder, CO 80309-0449. TEL 303-492-6199, FAX 303-492-2468, nsidc@nsidc.org, http://nsidc.org/pubs/notes/. Ed. Laura Cheshire.

551.31 USA
N S I D C SPECIAL REPORTS. Text in English. irreg.
Related titles: Online - full content ed.
Published by: National Snow and Ice Data Center, NSIDC User Services, CIRES, Campus Box 449, University of Colorado, Boulder, CO 80309-0449. TEL 303-492-6199, FAX 303-492-2468, nsidc@nsidc.org, http://nsidc.org/pubs/special/ index.html.

551.44 USA ISSN 0027-7010
GV200.6
N S S NEWS. Text in English. 1943. m. USD 36 domestic to individual members; USD 45 in Canada & Mexico to individual members; USD 51 elsewhere to individual members; USD 75 domestic to institutional members; USD 84 in Canada & Mexico to institutional members; USD 90 elsewhere to institutional members (effective 2005). adv. bk.rev. bibl.; charts; illus.; stat. index. 32 p./no.; back issues avail. **Document type:** *Newsletter, Academic/Scholarly.* **Description:** Discusses cave exploration.
Indexed: BiolAb, METADEX.
—Linda Hall.
Published by: National Speleological Society, Inc., 2813 Cave Ave, Huntsville, AL 35810-4431. TEL 256-852-1300, FAX 256-851-9241, nssnews@caves.org, nss@caves.org, http://www.caves.org/pub/nssnews. Ed. Dave Bunnell. R&P Ray Keeler. Adv. contact Bert Ashbrook. B&W page USD 672, color page USD 1,352; trim 8.5 x 11. Circ: 10,500.

551.44 AUS ISSN 1037-4361
NARGUN. Text in English. 1967. 10/yr. AUD 50 (effective 1999). adv. bk.rev. **Document type:** *Newsletter.*
Indexed: ASA.

E

Published by: Victorian Speleological Association Inc., GPO Box 5425 CC, Melbourne, VIC 3001, Australia. vsa@werple.net.au, http://www.werple.net.au/~vsa. Ed. P.J. Ackroyd. Adv. contact P J Ackroyd. Circ: 150.

551 GBR ISSN 0962-0575
NATIONAL MUSEUMS & GALLERIES OF WALES. GEOLOGICAL SERIES. Text in English. 1982. irreg. **Document type:** *Monographic series.*
Indexed: ZooRec.
—BLDSC (4136.675000).
Published by: National Museums & Galleries of Wales/Amgueddfa Genedlaethol Cymru, Cathays Park, Cardiff, CF10 3NP, United Kingdom. TEL 44-029-20397951, FAX 44-029-20373219, http://www.nmgw.ac.uk.

551 JPN ISSN 0385-244X
QE304 CODEN: BNSPD4
NATIONAL SCIENCE MUSEUM. BULLETIN. SERIES C: GEOLOGY & PALEONTOLOGY. Text in English. 1939. q. illus. **Document type:** *Bulletin, Academic/Scholarly.*
Formerly: National Science Museum. Bulletin. Series C: Geology; Which superseded in part (in 1975): National Science Museum. Bulletin (0028-0119)
Indexed: ASFA, BIOSIS Prev, BiolAb, ESPM, MinerAb, SFA, ZooRec.
—CISTI.
Published by: Monbusho, Kokuritsu Kagaku Hakubutsukan/ Ministry of Education, Science and Culture, National Science Museum, 7-20 Ueno-Koen, Taito-ku, Tokyo, 110-0007, Japan.

NATUR UND MENSCH. see *BIOLOGY*

NATURAL HAZARDS REVIEW. see *ENVIRONMENTAL STUDIES*

NATURAL RESOURCES RESEARCH. see *MINES AND MINING INDUSTRY*

551 ARG ISSN 0327-5272
➤ **NATURALIA PATAGONICA. SERIE CIENCIAS DE LA TIERRA.** Text in Spanish; Summaries in English. 1992. a., latest vol.4. ARS 10 (effective 2001). back issues avail. **Document type:** *Academic/Scholarly.* **Description:** Contains articles on geology, geomorphology, vulcanism, and paleontology from the region of Patagonia.
Published by: Universidad Nacional de la Patagonia San Juan Bosco, Facultad de Ciencias Naturales, Ciudad Universitaria Km 4, Comodoro Rivadavia, Chubut 9005, Argentina. uvin@unpata.edu.ar, http://www.unp.edu.ar. Ed. Hector E Zaixso. Circ: 300.

➤ **IL NATURALISTA VALTELLINESE**; atti del Museo Civico di Storia Naturale di Morbegno. see *BIOLOGY*

➤ **NATURFORSCHENDE GESELLSCHAFT DER OBERLAUSITZ. BERICHTE.** see *BIOLOGY—Botany*

➤ **NATURHISTORISCHES MUSEUM BASEL. VEROEFFENTLICHUNGEN.** see *SCIENCES: COMPREHENSIVE WORKS*

➤ **NATURKUNDEMUSEUMS GOERLITZ. ABHANDLUNGEN UND BERICHTE.** see *BIOLOGY—Botany*

➤ **NATURWISSENSCHAFTLICHER VEREIN WUPPERTAL. JAHRESBERICHTE**; Heft 52. see *BIOLOGY—Botany*

526 RUS
NAUCHNO-ISSLEDOVATEL'SKII INSTITUT PRIKLADNOI GEODEZII. TRUDY. Text in Russian. 1976. irreg. abstr.; charts.
Published by: (Nauchno-Issledovatel'skii Institut Prikladnoi Geodezii), Izdatel'stvo Tsniigaik, Onezhskaya ul 26, Moscow AY13, Russian Federation. Ed. V Chernikov. Circ: 500.

551 JPN ISSN 0470-6455
QE389.625 CODEN: NEKAAJ
NENDO KAGAKU. Text in Japanese. 1961. 3/yr. back issues avail. **Document type:** *Journal, Academic/Scholarly.*
Related titles: Online - full content ed.; ♦ English ed.: Clay Science. ISSN 0009-8574.
Indexed: I&DA, S&F, SIA.
—BLDSC (4729.690000). **CCC.**
Published by: Nippon Nendo Gakkai/Clay Science Society of Japan, c/o Takabumi Sakamoto, Okayama University of Science, Dept of Applied Science, 1-1, Ridai-cho, Okayama, 700-0005, Japan. nendo@das.ous.ac.jp, http://wwwsoc.nii.ac.jp/cssj2. Ed. Ryuji Kitagawa.

554 NLD
NETHERLANDS INSTITUTE OF APPLIED GEOSCIENCE T N O. ANNUAL REPORT. Text in Dutch, English. 1941. a. free. **Document type:** *Government.*
Former titles (until 1970): Netherlands. Rijks Geologische Dienst. Jaarverslag (0165-1455); Netherlands. Geologische Stichting. Jaarverslag (0924-8773)
Published by: Netherlands Institute of Applied Geoscience T N O/Nederlands Instituut voor Toegepaste Geowetenschappen T N O, Postbus 6012, Delft, 2600 JA, Netherlands. TEL 31-15-2696900, FAX 31-15-2564800, TELEX 71105 GEOLD NL, info@nitg.tno.nl, http://www.nitg.tno.nl.

551 622 NLD
QE1 CODEN: GEMIAA
➤ **NETHERLANDS JOURNAL OF GEOSCIENCES/GEOLOGY AND MINING.** Text in English; Text occasionally in German, French, Spanish, Dutch; Summaries in English. 1921. q. EUR 278, USD 272 to institutions (effective 2004). adv. bk.rev. abstr.; charts; illus. index, cum.index. reprints avail. **Document type:** *Academic/Scholarly.* **Description:** Publishes articles from the entire area of geoscience with frequent thematic issues and covers aspects of coastal and deltaic lowlands, both ancient and modern.
Former titles: Geologie en Mijnbouw (0016-7746); (until 1931): Mijnwezen (0923-1129); (until 1928): Mijnwezen en Metallurgie (0923-1110); (until 1925): Mijnwezen (0923-1102); Incorporates (1946-1999): Nederlands Instituut voor Toegepaste Geowetenschappen T N O. Mededelingen (1388-3453); Which was formerly (until 1997): Rijks Geologische Dienst. Mededelingen (0921-5646); (until 1977): Rijks Geologische Dienst. Mededelingen. Nieuwe Serie (0165-1951); (until 1968): Geologische Stichting. Mededelingen. Nieuwe Serie (0921-5638)
Related titles: Microform ed.: (from PQC, SWZ); Online - full text ed.: (from EBSCO Publishing, Gale Group, IngentaConnect, O C L C Online Computer Library Center, Inc., Swets Information Services).
Indexed: AESIS, ASCA, ASFA, BIOSIS Prev, BiolAb, BrGeoL, ChemAb, CurCont, E&PHSE, ESPM, EngInd, GEOBASE, GP&P, IBR, IMMAb, Inspec, OceAb, OffTech, PetrolAb, RefZh, SWRA, ZooRec.
—BLDSC (4143.000000), AskIEEE, CASDDS, Ei, IDS, IE, ingenta, Linda Hall, PADDS. **CCC.**
Published by: (Nederlands Instituut voor Toegepaste Geowetenschappen, Koninklijk Nederlands Geologisch Mijnbouwkundig Genootschap/Royal Geological and Mining Society of the Netherlands), Netherlands Journal of Geosciences Foundation, PO Box 80015, Utrecht, 3508 TA, Netherlands. TEL 31-30-2564600, FAX 31-30-2564605, njg@geo.vu.nl, http://www.nitg.tno.nl/eng/products/pub/njg. Ed. Theo Wong. Circ: 2,250.

551 560 DEU ISSN 0077-7749
CODEN: NEJPAP
NEUES JAHRBUCH FUER GEOLOGIE UND PALAEONTOLOGIE. ABHANDLUNGEN. Text in German, English. 1807. m. EUR 91 per issue domestic; EUR 94.70 per issue foreign (effective 2005). adv. index. **Document type:** *Monographic series, Academic/Scholarly.*
Formerly (until 1950): Neues Jahrbuch fuer Mineralogie, Geologie und Palaeontologie. Abteilung B (0369-4496); Which superseded in part (in 1925): Neues Jahrbuch fuer Mineralogie, Geologie und Palaeontologie. Beilageband
Related titles: Microfiche ed.: (from BHP).
Indexed: ASFA, BiolAb, CIN, ChemAb, ChemTitl, CurCont, ESPM, IBR, PetrolAb, SFA, ZooRec.
—BLDSC (6078.000000), CISTI, IE, Infotrieve, ingenta, Linda Hall, PADDS. **CCC.**
Published by: E. Schweizerbart'sche Verlagsbuchhandlung, Johannesstr 3A, Stuttgart, 70176, Germany. TEL 49-711-3514560, FAX 49-711-35145699, mail@schweizerbart.de, http://www.schweizerbart.de/j/n-jb-geol-pal.

551 560 DEU ISSN 0028-3630
QE1 CODEN: NJGMA2
NEUES JAHRBUCH FUER GEOLOGIE UND PALAEONTOLOGIE. MONATSHEFTE. Text in English, German. 1900. m. EUR 286 for 6 mos. domestic; EUR 305 for 6 mos. foreign (effective 2005). adv. bk.rev. bibl.; charts; illus. **Document type:** *Journal, Academic/Scholarly.*
Indexed: BiolAb, ChemAb, CurCont, EngInd, IBR, PetrolAb, ZooRec.
—BLDSC (6078.100000), CASDDS, CISTI, Ei, IE, Infotrieve, ingenta, Linda Hall, PADDS. **CCC.**
Published by: E. Schweizerbart'sche Verlagsbuchhandlung, Johannesstr 3A, Stuttgart, 70176, Germany. TEL 49-711-3514560, FAX 49-711-35145699, mail@schweizerbart.de, http://www.schweizerbart.de/j/n-jb-geol-pal. Ed. Guenter Schweigert.

NEUES JAHRBUCH FUER MINERALOGIE. ABHANDLUNGEN; merged with Neues Jahrbuch fuer Mineralogie, Monatshefte. see *MINES AND MINING INDUSTRY*

557 622 USA ISSN 0097-191X
CODEN: NBMGBR
NEVADA. BUREAU OF MINES AND GEOLOGY. BULLETIN. Text in English. 1904. irreg., latest vol.110, 1995. price varies. back issues avail. **Document type:** *Government.*
Former titles (until 1971): Nevada. Bureau of Mines. Bulletin (0097-5281); (1939-1957): University of Nevada. Mackay School of Mines. Bulletin. Geology and Mining Series. Bulletin (0097-2401)
Indexed: AESIS, IMMAb.
—CASDDS, Linda Hall.
Published by: Nevada Bureau of Mines and Geology, Publications Sales, Mail Stop 178, University of Nevada at Reno, Reno, NV 89557-0088. TEL 775-784-6691, FAX 775-784-1709, info@nbmg.unr.edu, http://www.nbmg.unr.edu. Ed. Richard Meewig.

557 USA
NEVADA. BUREAU OF MINES AND GEOLOGY. EDUCATIONAL SERIES. Text in English. 1986. irreg., latest vol.40. price varies. back issues avail. **Document type:** *Government.* **Description:** Provides educational materials for all levels.
Published by: Nevada Bureau of Mines and Geology, Publications Sales, Mail Stop 178, University of Nevada at Reno, Reno, NV 89557-0088. TEL 775-784-6691, FAX 775-784-1709, info@nbmg.unr.edu, http://www.nbmg.unr.edu. Ed. Richard Meewig.

227 622 USA
NEVADA. BUREAU OF MINES AND GEOLOGY. LISTS. Text in English. 1978. irreg. price varies. back issues avail. **Document type:** *Government.*
Published by: Nevada Bureau of Mines and Geology, Publications Sales, Mail Stop 178, University of Nevada at Reno, Reno, NV 89557-0088. TEL 775-784-6691, FAX 775-184-1709, info@nbmg.unr.edu, http://www.nbmg.unr.edu. Ed. Richard Meewig.

557 662 USA
NEVADA. BUREAU OF MINES AND GEOLOGY. PAMPHLET. Text in English. 1980. a. price varies. back issues avail. **Document type:** *Government.*
Published by: Nevada Bureau of Mines and Geology, Publications Sales, Mail Stop 178, University of Nevada at Reno, Reno, NV 89557-0088. TEL 775-784-6691, FAX 775-784-1709, info@nbmg.unr.edu, http://www.nbmg.unr.edu. Ed. Richard Meewig.

557 622 USA ISSN 0095-5264
TN24.N3 CODEN: RNMGDL
NEVADA. BUREAU OF MINES AND GEOLOGY. REPORT. Key Title: Report - Nevada Bureau of Mines and Geology. Text in English. 1962. irreg., latest vol.50, 2003. illus. back issues avail. **Document type:** *Government.*
Supersedes: Nevada. Bureau of Mines. Report
Indexed: IMMAb.
—CASDDS, Linda Hall.
Published by: Nevada Bureau of Mines and Geology, Publications Sales, Mail Stop 178, University of Nevada at Reno, Reno, NV 89557-0088. TEL 775-784-6691, FAX 775-784-1709, info@nbmg.unr.edu, http://www.nbmg.unr.edu. Ed. Richard Meewig.

557 USA ISSN 0275-6285
NEVADA. BUREAU OF MINES AND GEOLOGY. SPECIAL PUBLICATIONS. Text in English. 1975. irreg. price varies. back issues avail. **Document type:** *Government.*
Indexed: IMMAb.
Published by: Nevada Bureau of Mines and Geology, Publications Sales, Mail Stop 178, University of Nevada at Reno, Reno, NV 89557-0088. TEL 775-784-6691, FAX 775-784-1709, info@nbmg.unr.edu, http://www.nbmg.unr.edu. Ed. Richard Meewig.

557 USA ISSN 1045-473X
NEVADA GEOLOGY. Text in English. 1988. q. free. bk.rev. charts; maps; stat. **Document type:** *Government.* **Description:** News of projects and publications sponsored by the Nevada Bureau of Mines and Geology, and other items of geological interest.
Published by: Nevada Bureau of Mines and Geology, Publications Sales, Mail Stop 178, University of Nevada at Reno, Reno, NV 89557-0088. TEL 775-784-6691, FAX 775-784-1709, info@nbmg.unr.edu, http://www.nbmg.unr.edu. Ed. Richard Meewig.

557 USA
NEVADA MINERAL INDUSTRY (YEAR). Text in English. 1979. a., latest 2000. price varies. back issues avail. **Document type:** *Government.* **Description:** Includes listing of active mines.
Published by: Nevada Bureau of Mines and Geology, Publications Sales, Mail Stop 178, University of Nevada at Reno, Reno, NV 89557-0088. TEL 775-784-6691, FAX 775-784-1709, info@nbmg.unr.edu, http://www.nbmg.unr.edu. Ed. Richard Meewig.

NEW CALEDONIA. SERVICE DES MINES ET DE L'ENERGIE. RAPPORT ANNUEL. see *MINES AND MINING INDUSTRY*

557 USA
NEW HAMPSHIRE GEOLOGICAL SURVEY. 15-MINUTE QUADRANGLE REPORT. Text in English. irreg. **Document type:** *Government.*
Published by: New Hampshire Geological Survey, Public Information Center, 6 Hazen Drive, Concord, NH 03301.

557 USA
NEW HAMPSHIRE GEOLOGICAL SURVEY. BULLETIN. Text in English. irreg. **Document type:** *Bulletin, Government.*
Published by: New Hampshire Geological Survey, Public Information Center, 6 Hazen Drive, Concord, NH 03301.

557 USA
NEW HAMPSHIRE GEOLOGICAL SURVEY. GEOLOGY OF NEW HAMPSHIRE SERIES. Text in English. irreg. **Document type:** *Government.*
Published by: New Hampshire Geological Survey, Public Information Center, 6 Hazen Drive, Concord, NH 03301.

E

NEW HAMPSHIRE GEOLOGICAL SURVEY. MINERAL RESOURCE SURVEY. see *MINES AND MINING INDUSTRY*

557 USA
NEW HAMPSHIRE GEOLOGICAL SURVEY. OPEN-FILE REPORT. Text in English. irreg. **Document type:** *Government.*
Published by: New Hampshire Geological Survey, Public Information Center, 6 Hazen Drive, Concord, NH 03301.

557 USA
NEW JERSEY. GEOLOGICAL SURVEY. BULLETIN. Text in English. 1910. irreg., latest vol.76, 1982. price varies. **Document type:** *Bulletin, Government.*
Formerly: New Jersey Bureau of Geology and Topography. Bulletin
Published by: New Jersey Geological Survey, PO Box 427, Trenton, NJ 08625. TEL 609-292-2576, http://www.state.nj.us/dep/nigs/index.html. Ed., R&P Thomas Seckler. Circ: 500.

557 USA ISSN 1048-6275
Z6034.U5
NEW JERSEY. GEOLOGICAL SURVEY. REPORT. Text in English. 1959. irreg., latest vol.36, 1994. price varies. **Document type:** *Government.*
Former titles (until 1987): New Jersey. Geological Survey. Geological Report (1048-6267); (until 198?): New Jersey. Geological Survey. Geologic Report Series (0741-7357); New Jersey. Bureau of Geology and Topography. Geologic Report Series
—Linda Hall.
Published by: New Jersey Geological Survey, PO Box 427, Trenton, NJ 08625. http://www.state.nj.us/dep/nigs/index.html. R&P Thomas Seckler. Circ: 500.

NEW MEXICO. BUREAU OF GEOLOGY AND MINERAL RESOURCES. CIRCULAR. see *MINES AND MINING INDUSTRY*

501 911 910.02 USA
NEW MEXICO. BUREAU OF GEOLOGY AND MINERAL RESOURCES. SCENIC TRIPS TO THE GEOLOGIC PAST. Text in English. 1968. irreg., latest vol.17, 1998. price varies. **Document type:** *Government.* **Description:** Explores New Mexico's roadside geology, varied landscapes and climates, and cultural and economic histories.
Published by: Bureau of Geology and Mineral Resources, New Mexico Tech, 801 Leroy Pl, Socorro, NM 87801-4796. TEL 505-835-5410, http://geoinfo.nmt.edu/publications/scenictrips/home.html. Ed. Nancy S Gilson.

557 USA ISSN 0077-8567
QE1 CODEN: NMGGA5
➤ **NEW MEXICO GEOLOGICAL SOCIETY. GUIDEBOOK, FIELD CONFERENCE.** Text in English. 1950. a., latest 2004. USD 45 per vol. (effective 2005). adv. **Document type:** *Academic/Scholarly.*
Indexed: ZooRec.
—BLDSC (3919.800000). **CCC.**
Published by: New Mexico Geological Society, Inc., c/o New Mexico Bureau of Geology, 801 Leroy Place, Socorro, NM 87801. TEL 505-835-5490, FAX 505-835-6333, amato@nmsu.edu, http://geoinfo.nmt.edu/nmgs/pubs.html. Eds. Frank J. Pazzaglia, Spencer G. Lucas. R&P G S Austin TEL 505-835-5230.

557 USA ISSN 0548-6327
NEW MEXICO GEOLOGICAL SURVEY. SPECIAL PUBLICATION. Text in English. 1964. irreg. **Document type:** *Monographic series, Government.*
—Linda Hall.
Published by: New Mexico Geological Society, Inc., c/o New Mexico Bureau of Geology, 801 Leroy Place, Socorro, NM 87801. http://geoinfo.nmt.edu/nmgs.

551 USA ISSN 0196-948X
QE143 CODEN: NMGED2
➤ **NEW MEXICO GEOLOGY.** Text in English. 1979. q. USD 12; USD 20 for 2 yrs.; USD 3.50 newsstand/cover (effective 2005). bk.rev. abstr.; illus.; maps. index. 32 p./no. 3 cols./p.; back issues avail. **Document type:** *Journal, Government.* **Description:** New Mexico Geology is a quarterly peer-reviewed journal for regional research and services directed to the geoscience community.
Indexed: GEOBASE, IMMAb, PetrolAb, RefZh, ZooRec.
—CASDDS, Linda Hall, PADDS.
Published by: Bureau of Geology and Mineral Resources, New Mexico Tech, 801 Leroy Pl, Socorro, NM 87801-4796. TEL 505-835-5490, FAX 505-835-6333, jane@gis.nmt.edu, pubsofc@geo.nmt.edu, geoinfo.nmt.edu/publications/nmg/home.htm, http://geoinfo.nmt.edu. Eds. Jane C Love, Nancy S Gilson. Circ: 1,200.

559.4 AUS ISSN 0155-5561
CODEN: NSWGAP
NEW SOUTH WALES. GEOLOGICAL SURVEY. BULLETIN. Text in English. 1922. irreg., latest vol.33, 1993. price varies. index. **Document type:** *Bulletin, Government.*
Indexed: AESIS, IMMAb.
—BLDSC (2534.800000), Linda Hall.
Published by: Department of Mineral Resources, PO Box 536, St Leonards, NSW 2065, Australia. TEL 61-2-9901-8269, FAX 61-2-9901-8247. Ed. H Basden. Circ: 400.

559.4 AUS ISSN 0077-8710
QE341 CODEN: NGMGAR
NEW SOUTH WALES. GEOLOGICAL SURVEY. MEMOIRS: GEOLOGY. Text in English. 1887. irreg., latest vol.12, 1993. AUD 105. index. **Description:** Contains information ranging from basic data to interpretation and application of modern basin analysis techniques to the evaluation of the fossil fuel resources.
Indexed: AESIS.
—CISTI, Linda Hall.
Published by: Department of Mineral Resources, PO Box 536, St Leonards, NSW 2065, Australia. TEL 61-2-9901-8269, FAX 61-2-9901-8247. Ed. H Basden. Circ: 400.

551 549 AUS
NEW SOUTH WALES. GEOLOGICAL SURVEY. METALLOGENIC STUDY AND MINERAL DEPOSIT DATA SHEETS. Text in English. 1972. irreg. price varies. **Document type:** *Government.* **Description:** Contains mineral deposit inventory with geological and metallogenic discussion.
Former titles: New South Wales. Geological Survey. Mineral Deposit Data Sheets and Metallogenic Study; New South Wales. Geological Survey. Mine Data Sheets and Metallogenic Study (0727-9418)
Published by: Department of Mineral Resources, PO Box 536, St Leonards, NSW 2065, Australia. TEL 61-2-9901-8269, FAX 61-2-9908247. Circ: 400.

NEW SOUTH WALES. GEOLOGICAL SURVEY. MINERAL INDUSTRY SERIES. see *MINES AND MINING INDUSTRY*

NEW SOUTH WALES. GEOLOGICAL SURVEY. MINERAL RESOURCES SERIES. see *MINES AND MINING INDUSTRY*

551 AUS ISSN 0155-3410
QE341 CODEN: QNGSDG
NEW SOUTH WALES. GEOLOGICAL SURVEY. QUARTERLY NOTES. Text in English. 1970. q. free. **Document type:** *Government.* **Description:** Directed to academic and minerals-industry geologists.
Indexed: AESIS.
—BLDSC (7196.750000).
Published by: Department of Mineral Resources, PO Box 536, St Leonards, NSW 2065, Australia. TEL 61-2-9901-8269, FAX 61-2-9901-8247. Ed. H Basden. Circ: 700.

559.4 AUS ISSN 0155-3372
NEW SOUTH WALES. GEOLOGICAL SURVEY. RECORDS. Text in English. 1889. irreg., latest vol.104, 1997. price varies. **Document type:** *Government.* **Description:** Papers on geology and mineral deposits.
Indexed: AESIS, IMMAb.
—CISTI.
Published by: Department of Mineral Resources, PO Box 536, St Leonards, NSW 2065, Australia. TEL 61-2-9901-8269, FAX 61-2-9901-8247. Ed. H Basden. Circ: 400.

557 USA ISSN 1061-8724
NEW YORK STATE GEOLOGICAL ASSOCIACTION. GUIDEBOOK MEETING. Text in English. 19??. a.
Published by: New York State Geological Association, c/o William Kelly, NY State Geological Survey, Room 3140 CEC, Albany, NY 12230. wkely@mail.nysed.gov, http://www.nysgaonline.org/.

551 USA ISSN 0097-3793
CODEN: NYMCC7
NEW YORK STATE MUSEUM. MAP AND CHART SERIES. Text in English. 1960. irreg., latest vol.43, 1993. price varies. **Document type:** *Government.* **Description:** Geologic maps and charts of New York State, with annotation and commentary.
—Linda Hall.
Published by: New York State Museum, Publication Sales, Rm 3140, Cultural Education Center, Albany, NY 12230.

526.9 NZL ISSN 1173-5651
NEW ZEALAND INSTITUTE OF SURVEYORS. SURVEY QUARTERLY. Text in English. q. NZD 50; NZD 67.50 with N Z Surveyor. **Document type:** *Academic/Scholarly.*
Published by: New Zealand Institute of Surveyors, PO Box 831, Wellington, New Zealand. TEL 64-4-4711774, FAX 64-4-4711907. Ed. Judith van Eeden.

551 559.3 NZL ISSN 0028-8306
QE1 CODEN: NEZOAY
➤ **NEW ZEALAND JOURNAL OF GEOLOGY AND GEOPHYSICS**; an international journal of Pacific Rim geosciences. Text in English. 1958. q. NZD 210, USD 140 combined subscription to individuals print & online eds.; NZD 445, USD 320 combined subscription to institutions print & online eds. (effective 2006). adv. abstr.; bibl.; charts; illus. Index. back issues avail. **Document type:** *Journal, Academic/Scholarly.* **Description:** Publishes papers on all aspects of earth sciences with particular interest in papers of the circum-Pacific region.
Related titles: Online - full text ed.: NZD 180, USD 120 to individuals; NZD 380, NZD 275 to institutions (effective 2006) (from EBSCO Publishing).
Indexed: AESIS, AJEE, ASCA, ASFA, BiolAb, CIN, ChemAb, ChemTitl, CurCont, EEA, ESPM, GEOBASE, IBR, INIS AtomInd, ISR, M&GPA, MinerAb, OceAb, PetrolAb, S&F, SCI, SFA, SWRA, ZooRec.
—BLDSC (6094.500000), CASDDS, CISTI, IDS, IE, ingenta, Linda Hall, PADDS. **CCC.**
Published by: R S N Z Publishing, PO Box 598, Wellington, New Zealand. TEL 64-4-4727421, FAX 64-4-4731841, sales@rsnz.org, http://www.rsnz.govt.nz/publish/nzjgg/. Ed. R Lynch. Circ: 600. **Subscr. to:** R S N Z Publishing, PO Box 7075, Lawrence, KS 66044-7075. TEL 785-843-1235, FAX 785-843-1274, sir@allenpress.com.

526.9 NZL ISSN 0048-0150
NEW ZEALAND SURVEYOR. Text in English. 1889. a. NZD 25; NZD 67.50 with Survey Quarterly (effective 1999). adv. bk.rev. stat. index, cum.index every 3 yrs. **Document type:** *Academic/Scholarly.*
Indexed: INZP, SPPI.
—**CCC.**
Published by: New Zealand Institute of Surveyors, PO Box 831, Wellington, New Zealand. TEL 64-4-4711774, FAX 64-4-4711907. Ed. John Baldwin. Circ: 1,340.

551 AUS ISSN 0727-0097
NEWCASTLE SYMPOSIUM ON "ADVANCES IN THE STUDY OF THE SYDNEY BASIN.". Text in English. a.
Published by: University of Newcastle, School Environmental and Life Sciences, University Drive, Callaghan, NSW 2308, Australia. TEL 61-2-4921-5411, FAX 61-2-4921-6925, geology-admin@newcastle.edu.au.

557 CAN
CODEN: NEWRAS
NEWFOUNDLAND. DEPARTMENT OF MINES AND ENERGY. GEOLOGICAL SURVEY BRANCH. MINERAL RESOURCE REPORT SERIES. Text in English. 1959. irreg. price varies. adv. **Document type:** *Monographic series, Government.*
Formerly (until 1988): Newfoundland. Department of Mines. Mineral Development Division. Mineral Resources Report Series (0078-0359)
—Linda Hall.
Published by: Department of Mines and Energy, Geological Survey, P O Box 8700, St. John's, NF A1B 4J6, Canada. TEL 709-729-3159, FAX 709-729-3493, pub@zeppo.geosurv.gov.nf.ca. Ed., Adv. contact B. Kean.

NEWFOUNDLAND. DEPARTMENT OF MINES AND ENERGY. GEOLOGICAL SURVEY BRANCH. ORE HORIZONS. see *MINES AND MINING INDUSTRY*

551 AUS ISSN 1328-8369
NEWS VEIN. Text in English. 1995. q. **Document type:** *Newsletter.*
Formerly (until June 1997): A G C R C Newsletter (1326-1487)
Media: Online - full text.
Published by: Australian Geodynamics Cooperative Research Centre, C S I R O Exploration & Mining, 39 Fairway, PO Box 437, Nedlands, W.A. 6009, Australia. TEL 61-8-9389-8421, FAX 61-8-9389-1906, geomgc@pop.latrobe.edu.au, http://www.agcrc.csiro.au/publications/#newsletters. Ed. Meg Cooper.

551.7 DEU ISSN 0078-0421
QE640 CODEN: NLSGAO
➤ **NEWSLETTERS ON STRATIGRAPHY.** Text in English, German. 1970. 3/yr. EUR 220 (effective 2005). adv. abstr.; charts; illus. **Document type:** *Journal, Academic/Scholarly.* **Description:** Publishes articles of international interest dealing with stratigraphical matters, including descriptions of new stratotypes, redefinitions of existing stratotypes, new approaches to the subdivision of stratigraphic units, and the discussion of problems associated with particular boundaries.
Related titles: Online - full text ed.: (from EBSCO Publishing, Gale Group, IngentaConnect, Swets Information Services).
Indexed: ASCA, BIOSIS Prev, BiolAb, BrGeoL, GEOBASE, IBR, PetrolAb, ZooRec.
—BLDSC (6108.740000), IDS, IE, ingenta, Linda Hall, PADDS. **CCC.**
Published by: Gebrueder Borntraeger Verlagsbuchhandlung, Johannesstr. 3A, Stuttgart, 70176, Germany. TEL 49-711-3514560, FAX 49-711-35145699, mail@schweizerbart.de, http://www.schweizerbart.de/j/newsletters-on-stratigraphy. Ed. Gerd Luettig.

551 JPN ISSN 0912-6627
NIHON CHISHITSU GAKKAI KANSAI SHIBU KAIHO/GEOLOGICAL SOCIETY OF JAPAN. KANSAI BRANCH. PROCEEDINGS. Text in Japanese. irreg. **Document type:** *Proceedings.*
Published by: Nihon Chishitsu Gakkai, Jansai Shibu/Geological Society of Japan, Kansai Branch, Shiritsu Daigaku Rigakubu Chigaku Kyoshitsu, 3-138 Sugimo-To 3-chome, Sumiyoshi-ku, Osaka-shi, 558-0022, Japan.

NIHON DOKETSUGAKU KENKYUJO HOKOKU/SPELEOLOGICAL RESEARCH INSTITUTE OF JAPAN. ANNUAL. see *PALEONTOLOGY*

551   JPN
NIHON OYO CHISHITSU GAKKAI KENKYU HAPPYOKAI KOEN RONBUNSHU∗/JAPAN SOCIETY OF ENGINEERING GEOLOGY. PROCEEDINGS OF MEETING. Text in Japanese. a. **Document type:** *Proceedings.*
Published by: Nihon Oyo Chishitsu Gakkai/Japan Society of Engineering Geology, Ochanomizu Sakurai Bldg, 2-3-14 Kanda surugadai, Chiyoda-ku, Tokyo, 101-0062, Japan.

551   JPN   ISSN 0917-2289
NIHON OYO CHISHITSU GAKKAI KYUSHU SHIBU KAIHO/JAPAN SOCIETY OF ENGINEERING GEOLOGY. KYUSHU BRANCH REPORT. Text in Japanese. a.
Published by: Nihon Oyo Chishitsu Gakkai, Kyushu Shibu/Japan Society of Engineering Geology, Kyushu Branch, Nihon Chiken K.K., 25-25 Moroka 5-chome, Hakata-ku, Fukuoka-shi, 816-0094, Japan.

555 549   JPN   ISSN 0369-5638
QE1 .N64   CODEN: NSEGB4
NIIGATA UNIVERSITY. FACULTY OF SCIENCE. SCIENCE REPORTS. SERIES E: GEOLOGY AND MINERALOGY/ NIIGATA DAIGAKU RIGAKUBU KENKYU HOKOKU. E-RUI, CHISHITSU KOBUTSUGAKU. Text in English. 1952. a. per issue exchange basis.
Supersedes in part (in 1964): Niigata University. Faculty of Science. Journal. Series 2: Biology, Geology, and Mineralogy (0549-4842)
Indexed: BiolAb.
—CISTI.
Published by: Niigata Daigaku, Rigakubu/Niigata University, Faculty of Science, 8050 Igarashi Nino-cho, Niigata-shi, Niigata-ken 950-21, Japan.

NISHINIHON GANBAN KOGAKU SHINPOJUMU RONBUNSHU/PROCEEDINGS OF WEST JAPAN SYMPOSIUM ON ROCK ENGINEERING. see *ENGINEERING—Civil Engineering*

554.81   NOR   ISSN 0807-8297
QE281
NORGES GEOLOGISKE UNDERSOEKELSE. AARSRAPPORT. Text in Norwegian. 1922. a. free. illus. **Document type:** *Academic/Scholarly.*
Former titles (until 1994): Norges Geologiske Undersoekelse. Aarsmelding (0333-4112); (until 1973): Norges Geologiske Undersoekelse. Aarsberetning for (Year) (0807-8289)
Indexed: CIN, ChemAb, ChemTitl.
Published by: Norges Geologiske Undersoekelse/Geological Survey of Norway, Leiv Erikssons Vei 39, Trondheim, 7491, Norway. FAX 7-92-16-20, TELEX 55417-NGU-N. Ed. Anne Katharine Dahl. Circ: 5,000.

554.81   NOR   ISSN 0332-5768
QE281   CODEN: NGUBBJ
NORGES GEOLOGISKE UNDERSOEKELSE. BULLETIN. Text in English. 1972. irreg. (1-2/yr). price varies. bibl.; charts; illus. back issues avail. **Document type:** *Bulletin, Academic/Scholarly.* **Description:** Comprises scientific contributions to the earth sciences of regional Norwegian, general or specialist interest.
Supersedes in part (in 1972): Norges Geologiske Undersoegelse. Aarbok (0801-6755)
Indexed: ASFA, BiolAb, BrGeoL, ChemAb, ESPM, MinerAb, PollutAb, RefZh, SWRA.
—BLDSC (6129.000000), CASDDS, CISTI, IE, ingenta, Linda Hall. **CCC.**
Published by: Norges Geologiske Undersoekelse/Geological Survey of Norway, Leiv Erikssons Vei 39, Trondheim, 7491, Norway. TEL 47-73-904000, FAX 47-73-921620, ngu@ngu.no. http://www.ngu.no. Ed. David Roberts.

554.81   NOR   ISSN 0806-4555
NORGES GEOLOGISKE UNDERSOEKELSE. KARTKATALOG (YEAR). Text in Norwegian. a. charts; illus. **Document type:** *Catalog.*
Formerly (until 1991): Norges Geologiske Undersoekelse - Publikasjoner og Kart (0800-3424)
Published by: Norges Geologiske Undersoekelse/Geological Survey of Norway, Leiv Erikssons Vei 39, Trondheim, 7491, Norway. TEL 47-73-90-40-11, FAX 47-73-92-16-20.

550   NOR   ISSN 0029-196X
QE1   CODEN: NOGTAO
➤ **NORSK GEOLOGISK TIDSSKRIFT.** Variant title: Journal of the Norwegian Geological Society. Text in English. 1905. q. NOK 1,500 in Scandinavia; NOK 2,000, EUR 250 elsewhere (effective 2004). adv. bk.rev. charts; illus. index. back issues avail.; reprint service avail. from ISI. **Document type:** *Journal, Academic/Scholarly.* **Description:** Main journal for Norwegian geological research, distributed to all members of the Norwegian Geological Society and internationally.
Related titles: Microform ed.: (from PQC); Online - full text ed.: (from EBSCO Publishing, Gale Group, IngentaConnect, O C L C Online Computer Library Center, Inc., Swets Information Services); Supplement(s): Norsk Geologisk Tidsskrift. Supplement. ISSN 0801-4736. 1986.
Indexed: ASCA, ASFA, BiolAb, BrGeoL, CIN, ChemAb, ChemTitl, CurCont, EnerRA, GEOBASE, IBR, ISR, M&GPA, NAA, PetrolAb, RefZh, SCI, ZooRec.
—BLDSC (6140.000000), CASDDS, CISTI, IDS, IE, Infotrieve, ingenta, Linda Hall, PADDS. **CCC.**

Published by: Norsk Geologisk Forening/Norwegian Geological Society, Leiv Erikssons Vei 39, Trondheim, 7491, Norway. TEL 47-73-904468, FAX 47-73-921620, ngf@geologi.no, http://www.geologi.no/njg/. Eds. Christine Fischler, Morten Smelror. adv.: color page NOK 9,500; 174 x 244. Circ: 1,400.

508.982   NOR   ISSN 0804-9505
G575   CODEN: NPOAAE
NORSK POLARINSTITUTT. AARSMELDING. Text in Norwegian; Summaries in English. 1960. a. free. **Document type:** *Academic/Scholarly.* **Description:** Annual report of the Norwegian Polar Institute.
Formerly (until 1990): Norsk Polarinstitutt. Aarbok (0085-4271)
—Linda Hall. **CCC.**
Published by: Norsk Polarinstitutt/Norwegian Polar Institut, Polar Environmental Centre, Tromsoe, 9296, Norway. TEL 47-77-750500, FAX 47-77-750501, rydmark@npolar.no, http://www.npolar.no. Ed., R&P Dag Rydmark.

998.1   NOR   ISSN 0474-8042
NORSK POLARINSTITUTT. POLARHAANDBOK. Short title: Polarhaandbok. Text in Norwegian; Text occasionally in English. 1964. irreg., latest vol.12, 1998. price varies. back issues avail. **Document type:** *Monographic series, Academic/Scholarly.* **Description:** Each handbook on a separate subject concerning the polar regions.
Related titles: English ed.
Indexed: BIOSIS Prev.
Published by: Norsk Polarinstitutt/Norwegian Polar Institut, Polar Environmental Centre, Tromsoe, 9296, Norway. TEL 47-77-750500, FAX 47-77-750501, http://www.npolar.no. Ed., R&P Dag Rydmark.

551   NOR   ISSN 0801-8588
NORSK POLARINSTITUTT. TEMAKART. Text in English, Norwegian. 1986. irreg., latest vol.31, 2002. price varies. back issues avail. **Document type:** *Monographic series, Academic/Scholarly.*
Indexed: Inspec.
Published by: Norsk Polarinstitutt/Norwegian Polar Institut, Polar Environmental Centre, Tromsoe, 9296, Norway. TEL 47-77-750500, FAX 47-77-750501, http://www.npolar.no.

551   USA
NORTH CAROLINA. DEPARTMENT OF ENVIRONMENT, HEALTH, AND NATURAL RESOURCES. DIVISION OF LAND RESOURCES. BULLETIN. Text in English. 1893. irreg., latest vol.97, 1996. price varies. **Document type:** *Bulletin, Government.*
Former titles: North Carolina. Department of Natural Resources and Community Development. Division of Land Resources. Bulletin; North Carolina. Division of Mineral Resources. Bulletin
Published by: (North Carolina. Department of Environment, Health and Natural Resources, North Carolina. Division of Land Resources), North Carolina Geological Survey, PO Box 27687, Raleigh, NC 27611. TEL 919-733-2423, FAX 919-733-0900.

551   USA
NORTH CAROLINA. DEPARTMENT OF ENVIRONMENT, HEALTH, AND NATURAL RESOURCES. DIVISION OF LAND RESOURCES. INFORMATION CIRCULAR. Text in English. 1940. irreg., latest vol.30, 1995. price varies. **Document type:** *Bulletin, Government.*
Former titles: North Carolina. Department of Natural Resources and Community Development. Division of Land Resources. Information Circular; North Carolina. Division of Mineral Resources. Information Circular
Published by: (North Carolina. Department of Environment, Health and Natural Resources, North Carolina. Division of Land Resources), North Carolina Geological Survey, PO Box 27687, Raleigh, NC 27611. TEL 919-733-2423, FAX 919-733-0900.

557   USA   ISSN 0091-9004
QE149   CODEN: NDGSBD
NORTH DAKOTA. GEOLOGICAL SURVEY. EDUCATIONAL SERIES. Key Title: Educational Series - North Dakota Geological Survey. Text in English. 1972. irreg., latest vol.27, 2001. price varies. illus. back issues avail. **Document type:** *Monographic series, Academic/Scholarly.*
—BLDSC (3662.506000), Linda Hall.
Published by: North Dakota Geological Survey, 600 E Boulevard Ave, Bismarck, ND 58505-0840. TEL 701-328-8000, FAX 701-328-8010, http://www.state.nd.us/ndgs.

557   USA   ISSN 1070-2873
NORTH DAKOTA. GEOLOGICAL SURVEY. FIELD STUDY. Text in English. 1993. irreg. USD 3 per vol.. **Document type:** *Bulletin.*
—Linda Hall.
Published by: North Dakota Geological Survey, 600 E Boulevard Ave, Bismarck, ND 58505-0840. TEL 701-328-8000, FAX 701-328-8010, http://www.state.nd.us/ndgs/Publication_List/ fieldstd_h.htm. Ed. John P Bluemle.

557   USA   ISSN 0078-1576
QE149   CODEN: NDGXAR
NORTH DAKOTA. GEOLOGICAL SURVEY. MISCELLANEOUS SERIES. Text in English. 1957. irreg., latest vol.89, 2001. price varies. back issues avail.

—BLDSC (5827.200000), Linda Hall.
Published by: North Dakota Geological Survey, 600 E Boulevard Ave, Bismarck, ND 58505-0840. TEL 701-328-8000, FAX 701-328-8010, http://www.state.nd.us/ndgs.

552   USA   ISSN 0889-3594
QE149
NORTH DAKOTA. GEOLOGICAL SURVEY. NEWSLETTER. Key Title: N D G S Newsletter. Text in English. 1973. s-a. free. back issues avail. **Document type:** *Newsletter.*
—Linda Hall.
Published by: North Dakota Geological Survey, 600 E Boulevard Ave, Bismarck, ND 58505-0840. TEL 701-328-8000, FAX 701-328-8010, http://www.state.nd.us/ndgs. Circ: 2,000.

551   USA   ISSN 0099-4227
TN24.N9
NORTH DAKOTA. GEOLOGICAL SURVEY. REPORT OF INVESTIGATIONS. Text in English. 1955. irreg., latest vol.101, 2001. price varies. illus. back issues avail.
—BLDSC (7658.000000), Linda Hall.
Published by: North Dakota Geological Survey, 600 E Boulevard Ave, Bismarck, ND 58505-0840. TEL 701-328-8000, FAX 701-328-8010, http://www.state.nd.us/ndgs. Circ: 1,500.

557   USA
QE78.3   CODEN: NOESDE
➤ **NORTHEASTERN GEOLOGY AND ENVIRONMENTAL SCIENCES;** a journal of the northeast for earth and environmental sciences. Text in English. 1979. q. USD 52 domestic to individuals; USD 69 foreign to individuals; USD 84 domestic to institutions; USD 99 foreign to institutions (effective 2004). adv. bk.rev. charts; illus. index. back issues avail. **Document type:** *Academic/Scholarly.* **Description:** Research papers on the geology of northeastern North America.
Formerly (until vol.17, 1995): Northeastern Geology (0194-1453); Incorporates (1982-1990): Northeastern Environmental Science (0730-630X)
Indexed: FLUIDEX, GEOBASE, PetrolAb, ZooRec.
—BLDSC (6150.297200), CASDDS, CISTI, IE, ingenta, Linda Hall, PADDS. **CCC.**
Published by: (Northeastern Science Foundation, Inc.), Allen Press Inc., PO Box 7075, Lawrence, KS 66044-7075. TEL 785-843-1235, FAX 785-843-1274, orders@allenpress.com, http://www.allenpress.com. Ed. Gerald M Friedman.

➤ **NOTES DU SERVICE GEOLOGIQUE DE TUNISIE.** see *GENERAL INTEREST PERIODICALS—Tunisia*

➤ **O.R.S.T.O.M. RESUMES DES TRAVAUX. OCEANOGRAPHIE.** see *EARTH SCIENCES—Oceanography*

551   DEU   ISSN 0078-2947
                                    CODEN: JMOGAZ
OBERRHEINISCHER GEOLOGISCHER VEREIN. JAHRESBERICHTE UND MITTEILUNGEN. Text in German. 1911. a. EUR 42 domestic; EUR 47.20 foreign (effective 2005). **Document type:** *Journal, Academic/Scholarly.*
Indexed: IBR, ZooRec.
—CISTI. **CCC.**
Published by: (Oberrheinischer Geologischer Verein), E. Schweizerbart'sche Verlagsbuchhandlung, Johannesstr 3A, Stuttgart, 70176, Germany. TEL 49-711-3514560, FAX 49-711-35145699, mail@schweizerbart.de, http://www.schweizerbart.de/j/ogv. Ed. P Rothe.

538.7   ESP   ISSN 1139-5745
QC830.O24
OBSERVATORIO DEL EBRO. MAGNETISMO. BOLETIN. Text in Spanish. 1943-1966; resumed 1995. irreg. **Document type:** *Academic/Scholarly.* **Description:** Publishes articles on geomagnetic data.
Formerly: Boletin Mensual del Observatorio del Ebro. Serie B. Magnetismo y Electricidad Terrestre (1139-126X)
—Linda Hall.
Published by: Observatorio del Ebro, Roquetes, Tarragona 43520, Spain. TEL 34-977-500511, FAX 34-977-504660, http://www.readysoft.es/home/observebre/.

551   RUS
OBSHCHAYA I REGIONAL'NAYA GEOLOGIYA, GEOLOGIYA MOREI I OKEANOV, GEOLOGICHESKOE KARTOROVANIE. Text in Russian. bi-m. USD 79.95 in United States.
Published by: Informatsionno-Izdatel'skii Tsentr po Geologii i Nedropol'zovaniu Geoinformmark, Goncharnaya 38, Moscow, 115172, Russian Federation. TEL 7-095-9156724. **US dist.** **addr.:** East View Information Services, 3020 Harbor Ln. N., Minneapolis, MN 55447. TEL 612-550-0961.

551   RUS   ISSN 0235-554X
OBZORNAYA INFORMATSIYA. GEOLOGIYA, METODY POISKOV, RAZVEDKI I OTSENKI MESTOROZHDENII TOPLIVNOENERGETICHESKOGO SYR'IA. Text in Russian. bi-m. USD 159.95 in United States.
—East View.
Published by: Informatsionno-Izdatel'skii Tsentr po Geologii i Nedropol'zovaniu Geoinformmark, Goncharnaya 38, Moscow, 115172, Russian Federation. TEL 7-095-9156724. **US dist.** **addr.:** East View Information Services, 3020 Harbor Ln. N., Minneapolis, MN 55447. TEL 612-550-0961.

E

551 RUS ISSN 0235-5531
OBZORNAYA INFORMATSIYA. GEOLOGIYA, METODY POISKOV, RAZVEDKI I OTSENKI MESTOROZHDENII TVERDYKH POLEZNYKH ISKOPAEMYKH. Text in Russian. 7/yr. USD 199.95 in United States.
—East View.
Published by: Informatsionno-Izdatel'skii Tsentr po Geologii i Nedropol'zovaniu Geoinformmark, Goncharnaya 38, Moscow, 115172, Russian Federation. TEL 7-095-9156086, info@geoinform.ru, http://www.geoinform.ru. **US dist. addr.:** East View Information Services, 3020 Harbor Ln. N., Minneapolis, MN 55447. eastview@eastview.com, http://www.eastview.com.

551 560 AUT ISSN 0251-7493
QE1
➤ **OESTERREICHISCHE GEOLOGISCHE GESELLSCHAFT. MITTEILUNGEN.** Text in German; Summaries in English. 1908. a. adv. bk.rev. **Document type:** *Journal, Academic/Scholarly.*
Former titles (until 1974): Geologische Gesellschaft in Wien. Mitteilungen (1812-8327); (until 1943): Alpenlaendischer Geologischer Verein. Mitteilungen (0368-8399); (until 1939): Geologische Gesellschaft in Wien. Mitteilungen (0072-1123)
Indexed: BiolAb, INIS AtomInd, RefZh, ZooRec.
—Linda Hall.
Published by: Oesterreichische Geologische Gesellschaft, c/o Geological Survey of Austria, Rasumofskygasse 23, Postfach 127, Vienna, W 1031, Austria. TEL 43-1-712567443, FAX 43-1-712567456, oegg@cc.geolba.ac.at, http://www.geol-ges.at/index.htm. Ed., Adv. contact Volker Hoeck. Circ: 1,300.

557 USA ISSN 0097-5478
CODEN: ODGBA6
OHIO. DIVISION OF GEOLOGICAL SURVEY. BULLETIN. Text in English. 1903. irreg., latest vol.73, 1998. price varies. illus. back issues avail. **Document type:** *Bulletin, Government.*
Indexed: ZooRec.
Published by: Ohio Department of Natural Resources, Division of Geological Survey, 4383 Fountain Square Dr, Columbus, OH 43224-1362. TEL 614-265-6576, FAX 614-447-1918, geo.survey@dnr.state.oh.us, http://www.dnr.state.oh.us/odnr/geo_survey/. R&P Merrianne Hackathorn TEL 614-265-6590.

557 USA ISSN 0472-6685
OHIO. DIVISION OF GEOLOGICAL SURVEY. EDUCATIONAL LEAFLET. Text in English. 1956. irreg., latest vol.15, 1989. free. back issues avail. **Document type:** *Government.*
Indexed: RefZh.
Published by: Ohio Department of Natural Resources, Division of Geological Survey, 4383 Fountain Square Dr, Columbus, OH 43224-1362. TEL 614-265-6576, FAX 614-447-1918, geo.survey@dnr.state.oh.us, http://www.dnr.state.oh.us/odnr/geo_survey/. R&P Merrianne Hackathorn TEL 614-265-6590.

557 USA
OHIO. DIVISION OF GEOLOGICAL SURVEY. GEOLOGICAL NOTE. Text in English. 1975. irreg., latest vol.6, 1979. price varies. illus. back issues avail. **Document type:** *Government.*
Published by: Ohio Department of Natural Resources, Division of Geological Survey, 4383 Fountain Square Dr, Columbus, OH 43224-1362. TEL 614-265-6576, FAX 614-447-1918, geo.survey@dnr.state.oh.us, http://www.dnr.state.oh.us/odnr/geo_survey/. R&P Merrianne Hackathorn TEL 614-265-6590.

557 USA ISSN 0097-9473
QE151 CODEN: OGSGA
OHIO. DIVISION OF GEOLOGICAL SURVEY. GUIDEBOOK. Key Title: Guidebook - State of Ohio, Department of Natural Resources, Division of Geological Survey. Text in English. 1973. irreg., latest vol.16, 1998. price varies. illus. back issues avail. **Document type:** *Monographic series, Government.*
—Linda Hall.
Published by: Ohio Department of Natural Resources, Division of Geological Survey, 4383 Fountain Square Dr, Columbus, OH 43224-1362. TEL 614-265-6576, FAX 614-447-1918, geo.survey@dnr.state.oh.us, http://www.dnr.state.oh.us/odnr/geo_survey/. R&P Merrianne Hackathorn TEL 614-265-6590.

557 USA ISSN 0097-5605
QE151 CODEN: ODGCA9
OHIO. DIVISION OF GEOLOGICAL SURVEY. INFORMATION CIRCULAR. Text in English. 1946. irreg., latest vol.60, 1997. price varies. illus. back issues avail. **Document type:** *Government.*
—Linda Hall.
Published by: Ohio Department of Natural Resources, Division of Geological Survey, 4383 Fountain Square Dr, Columbus, OH 43224-1362. TEL 614-265-6576, FAX 614-447-1918, geo.survey@dnr.state.oh.us, http://www.dnr.state.oh.us/odnr/geo_survey/. R&P Merrianne Hackathorn TEL 614-265-6590.

557 USA ISSN 0361-0519
CODEN: MOGSDD
OHIO. DIVISION OF GEOLOGICAL SURVEY. MISCELLANEOUS REPORT. Key Title: Miscellaneous Report - State of Ohio, Department of Natural Resources, Division of Geological Survey. Text in English. 1974. irreg., latest vol.6, 1992. back issues avail. **Document type:** *Government.*
Indexed: ChemAb.
Published by: Ohio Department of Natural Resources, Division of Geological Survey, 4383 Fountain Square Dr, Columbus, OH 43224-1362. TEL 614-265-6576, FAX 614-447-1918, geo.survey@dnr.state.oh.us, http://www.dnr.state.oh.us/odnr/geo_survey/. R&P Merrianne Hackathorn TEL 614-265-6590.

557 USA
OHIO. DIVISION OF GEOLOGICAL SURVEY. REPORT OF INVESTIGATIONS. Text in English. 1947. irreg., latest vol.145, 1996. price varies. illus. back issues avail. **Document type:** *Government.*
Published by: Ohio Department of Natural Resources, Division of Geological Survey, 4383 Fountain Square Dr, Columbus, OH 43224-1362. TEL 614-265-6576, FAX 614-447-1918, geo.survey@dnr.state.oh.us, http://www.dnr.state.oh.us/odnr/geo_survey/. R&P Merrianne Hackathorn TEL 614-265-6590.

551 USA
OHIO GEOLOGICAL SOCIETY. PUBLICATIONS✶ . Text in English. 1970. irreg., latest vol.12, 1995. price varies. **Document type:** *Monographic series.* **Description:** Publishes papers on topics in Ohio geology.
Published by: Ohio Geological Society, PO Box 14304, Columbus, OH 43214-0304.

550 USA
OHIO GEOLOGY. Text in English. 1981. q. free. 8 p./no.; **Document type:** *Newsletter, Government.*
Formerly (until 1990): Ohio Geology Newsletter
Published by: Ohio Department of Natural Resources, Division of Geological Survey, 4383 Fountain Square Dr, Columbus, OH 43224-1362. TEL 614-265-6576, FAX 614-447-1918, geo.survey@dnr.state.oh.us, http://www.dnr.state.oh.us/odnr/geo_survey/. Ed. Michael C. Hansen. R&P Merrianne Hackathorn TEL 614-265-6590.

OIL AND GAS; monthly report on drilling in Illinois. see *PETROLEUM AND GAS*

552 CAN
OIL AND GAS FIELD DESIGNATIONS. Text in English. q. CND 45. back issues avail. **Document type:** *Government.* **Description:** Field descriptions consisting of the lands contained within each field.
Media: Duplicated (not offset).
Published by: Ministry of Energy and Mines, c/o Communications Coordinator, Stn Prov Govt, PO Box 9324, Victoria, BC V8W 9N3, Canada. TEL 250-952-0525, http://www.ogc.gov.bc.ca. **Subscr. to:** Crown Publications Inc.

552 665.5 CAN
OIL AND GAS POOL DESCRIPTIONS. Text in English. q. CND 65. **Document type:** *Government.* **Description:** Descriptions of oil and gas pools as designated or amended.
Published by: Ministry of Energy and Mines, c/o Communications Coordinator, Stn Prov Govt, PO Box 9324, Victoria, BC V8W 9N3, Canada. TEL 250-952-0525, http://www.ogc.gov.bc.ca. **Subscr. to:** Crown Publications Inc.

553.28 665.5 AUS ISSN 1038-118X
TN878.A1
OIL AND GAS RESOURCES OF AUSTRALIA. Text in English. 1991. a. **Description:** Covers exploration, reserves, undiscovered resources, development, coalbed methane resources, production, crude and shale oil, and supporting information and statistics.
Published by: Geoscience Australia, GPO Box 378, Canberra, ACT 2601, Australia. http://www.ga.gov.au/oceans/projects/ogra.jsp.

OIL SHALE/GORYUCHIE SLANTSY. see *MINES AND MINING INDUSTRY*

OILFIELD REVIEW. see *PETROLEUM AND GAS*

551.23 JPN ISSN 0289-3134
OITAKEN ONSEN CHOSA HOKOKU/OITA PREFECTURE. ANNUAL DATA OF HOT SPRING RESEARCH. Text in Japanese. 1959. a. **Document type:** *Government.*
Published by: Oitaken Hoken Kankyobu/Oita Prefectural Government, Health and Environment Division, 1-1 Ote-Machi 3-chome, Oita-shi, 870-0022, Japan.

551.23 JPN ISSN 0289-2413
OITAKEN ONSEN CHOSA KENKYUKAI HOKOKU/HOT SPRING RESEARCH ASSOCIATION OF OITA PREFECTURE. ANNUAL BULLETIN. Text in Japanese. 1949. a.
Indexed: INIS AtomInd.
Published by: Oitaken Onsen Chosa Kenkyukai, Oitaken Kankyo Hokenbu, 1-1 Ote-Machi 3-chome, Oita-shi, 870-0022, Japan.

550 624 JPN ISSN 0917-5687
OKINAWA DOSHITSU KOGAKU KENKYU HAPPYOKAI KOEN GAIYOSHU/OKINAWA GEOTECHNICAL SOCIETY. PAPERS OF ANNUAL MEETING. Text in Japanese. 1988. a.
Published by: Okinawa Doshitsu Kogaku Kenkyukai, Ryukyu Daigaku Kogakubu Doboku Kogakka, 1 Senbaru, Nakagami-gun, Nishihara-cho, Okinawa-ken 903-0129, Japan.

557 USA ISSN 0078-4389
QE153 CODEN: OKGBAL
OKLAHOMA GEOLOGICAL SURVEY. BULLETIN. Text in English. 1908. irreg., latest vol.147, 2000. price varies. bibl.; charts; illus. index. back issues avail. **Document type:** *Bulletin.*
Related titles: Microfilm ed.
Indexed: ChemAb, PetrolAb, RefZh, ZooRec.
—CISTI, Linda Hall.
Published by: Oklahoma Geological Survey, 100 E Boyd, Rm N 131, Norman, OK 73019. TEL 405-325-3031, 800-330-3996, FAX 405-325-7689, ogs-web@gcn.ou.edu, http://www.ogs.ou.edu. Ed. Christie Cooper. R&P Charles Mankin. Circ: 500.

557 USA ISSN 0078-4397
QE153 CODEN: OKGCAO
OKLAHOMA GEOLOGICAL SURVEY. CIRCULAR. Text in English. 1908. irreg., latest vol.108, 2003. price varies. bibl.; charts; illus.; stat. index. back issues avail. **Document type:** *Bulletin, Government.*
Related titles: Microfilm ed.
Indexed: BiolAb, ChemAb, PetrolAb, RefZh, ZooRec.
—CASDDS, Linda Hall.
Published by: Oklahoma Geological Survey, 100 E Boyd, Rm N 131, Norman, OK 73019. TEL 405-325-3031, 800-330-3996, FAX 405-325-7689, ogs-web@gcn.ou.edu, http://www.ogs.ou.edu. Ed. Christie Cooper. R&P Charles Mankin. Circ: 500.

557 USA ISSN 0160-8746
CODEN: OGSEBT
OKLAHOMA GEOLOGICAL SURVEY. EDUCATIONAL PUBLICATION. Text in English. 1971. irreg., latest vol.7, 2001. price varies. reprint service avail. from PQC. **Document type:** *Monographic series.*
Published by: Oklahoma Geological Survey, 100 E Boyd, Rm N 131, Norman, OK 73019. TEL 405-325-3031, 800-330-3996, FAX 405-325-7689, ogs-web@gcn.ou.edu, http://www.ogs.ou.edu. Ed. Christie Cooper. R&P Charles Mankin. Circ: 1,200.

557 USA ISSN 0078-4400
QE153 CODEN: OGGBAR
OKLAHOMA GEOLOGICAL SURVEY. GUIDEBOOK. Text in English. 1953. irreg., latest vol.33, 2001. price varies. reprint service avail. from PQC. **Document type:** *Monographic series.*
—Linda Hall.
Published by: Oklahoma Geological Survey, 100 E Boyd, Rm N 131, Norman, OK 73019. TEL 405-325-3031, 800-330-3996, FAX 405-325-7689, ogs-web@gcn.ou.edu, http://www.ogs.ou.edu. Ed. Christie Cooper. R&P Charles Mankin. Circ: 500.

557 USA ISSN 0275-0929
➤ **OKLAHOMA GEOLOGICAL SURVEY. SPECIAL PUBLICATION SERIES.** Text in English. irreg., latest 2002. price varies. reprint service avail. from PQC. **Document type:** *Monographic series, Academic/Scholarly.*
Indexed: IMMAb, ZooRec.
—BLDSC (8379.655000), IE, ingenta, Linda Hall.
Published by: Oklahoma Geological Survey, 100 E Boyd, Rm N 131, Norman, OK 73019. TEL 405-325-3031, 800-330-3996, FAX 405-325-7689, ogs-web@gcn.ou.edu, http://www.ogs.ou.edu. Ed. Christie Cooper. R&P Charles Mankin.

557 USA ISSN 0030-1736
TN1 CODEN: OKGNAN
OKLAHOMA GEOLOGY NOTES. Text in English. 1941. bi-m. USD 6 (effective 2003 - 2004). bk.rev. bibl.; charts; illus.; abstr.; maps; stat.; tr.lit. index. back issues avail.; reprint service avail. from PQC. **Document type:** *Government.*
Formerly (until 1956): Hopper
Related titles: Microfilm ed.: (from PQC).
Indexed: BiolAb, ChemAb, PetrolAb, RefZh.
—Linda Hall, PADDS.
Published by: Oklahoma Geological Survey, 100 E Boyd, Rm N 131, Norman, OK 73019. TEL 405-325-3031, 800-330-3996, FAX 405-325-7689, ogs-web@gcn.ou.edu, http://www.ogs.ou.edu. Ed. Christie Cooper. R&P Charles Mankin. Circ: 1,500.

551.23 JPN ISSN 0369-7665
CODEN: ONKOBY
ONSEN KOGAKKAISHI/SOCIETY OF ENGINEERS FOR MINERAL SPRINGS. JOURNAL. Text in Japanese; Summaries in English, Japanese. 1963. 2/yr. JPY 1,500 per issue.
Indexed: INIS AtomInd, JPI.
—CASDDS.
Published by: Onsen Kogakkai, Chuo Onsen Kenkyujo, 42-10 Takada 3-chome, Toshima-ku, Tokyo, 171-0033, Japan.

557 622 CAN
ONTARIO GEOLOGICAL SURVEY. GUIDE BOOKS. Text in English. 1968. irreg. (1-2/yr.). price varies. back issues avail. **Document type:** *Government.*
Formerly: Ontario. Division of Mines. Guide Books

Published by: Ontario Geological Survey, 933 Ramsey Lake Rd, Sudbury, ON P3E 6B5, Canada. TEL 705-670-5691, FAX 705-670-5770, pubsales@ndm.gov.on.ca, http://www.gov.on.ca/mndm.

ONTARIO GEOLOGICAL SURVEY. REPORT. see *MINES AND MINING INDUSTRY*

ONTARIO GEOLOGICAL SURVEY. REPORT OF ACTIVITIES, RESIDENT GEOLOGISTS. see *MINES AND MINING INDUSTRY*

551 CAN ISSN 0835-3530
OPEN FILE. BRITISH COLUMBIA, GEOLOGICAL SURVEY BRANCH. Text in English. 1986. irreg. price varies.
—CCC.
Published by: (Geological Survey of Canada, Pacific Division), Crown Publications Inc., 521 Fort St, Victoria, BC BC V8W 1E7, Canada. TEL 250-386-4636, FAX 250-386-0221, http://www.em.gov.bc.ca/Mining/Geolsurv/Publications/catalog/cat_of.htm, http://www.crownpub.bc.ca.

551 NLD ISSN 0169-1368
CODEN: OGREER
➤ **ORE GEOLOGY REVIEWS.** Text in English. 1986. 8/yr. EUR 870 in Europe to institutions; JPY 115,700 in Japan to institutions; USD 975 elsewhere to institutions (effective 2006). **Document type:** *Journal, Academic/Scholarly.* **Description:** Focuses on recent advances in a number of interconnected disciplines related to the study of, and search for, ore deposits.
Related titles: Microform ed.: (from PQC); Online - full text ed.: (from EBSCO Publishing, Gale Group, IngentaConnect, ScienceDirect, Swets Information Services).
Indexed: AESIS, ASCA, CurCont, EngInd, GEOBASE, IMMAb, ISR, MinerAb, RefZh, SCI.
—BLDSC (6280.830000), CASDDS, CISTI, Ei, IDS, IE, Infotrieve, ingenta, Linda Hall. **CCC.**
Published by: Elsevier BV (Subsidiary of: Elsevier Science & Technology), Radarweg 29, Amsterdam, 1043 NX, Netherlands. TEL 31-20-4853911, FAX 31-20-4852457, nlinfo-f@elsevier.nl, http://www.elsevier.com/locate/oregeorev, http://www.elsevier.nl. Eds. H. Foerster, N J Cook.

557 622 USA ISSN 0078-5709
QE155 CODEN: OGMBAN
OREGON. DEPARTMENT OF GEOLOGY AND MINERAL INDUSTRIES. BULLETIN. Text in English. 1937. irreg., latest vol.103, 1987. price varies. **Document type:** *Monographic series.*
—Linda Hall.
Published by: Department of Geology and Mineral Industries, 800 N E Oregon St, 28, Ste 965, Portland, OR 97232-2109. TEL 503-731-4100, FAX 503-731-4066, http://www.sarvis.dogami.state.or.us. Ed. Klaus Neuendorf.

557 333.9 USA
OREGON. DEPARTMENT OF GEOLOGY AND MINERAL INDUSTRIES. COASTAL HAZARD PUBLICATION. Text in English. irreg. **Document type:** *Government.*
Published by: Department of Geology and Mineral Industries, 800 N E Oregon St, 28, Ste 965, Portland, OR 97232-2109.

557 USA
OREGON. DEPARTMENT OF GEOLOGY AND MINERAL INDUSTRIES. EARTHQUAKE HAZARD PUBLICATION. Text in English. irreg. **Document type:** *Government.*
Published by: Department of Geology and Mineral Industries, 800 N E Oregon St, 28, Ste 965, Portland, OR 97232-2109.

OREGON. DEPARTMENT OF GEOLOGY AND MINERAL INDUSTRIES. OIL AND GAS INVESTIGATIONS. see *PETROLEUM AND GAS*

550 USA
OREGON. DEPARTMENT OF GEOLOGY AND MINERAL INDUSTRIES. OPEN FILE REPORTS. Text in English. 1966. irreg., latest 1999. price varies. stat. **Document type:** *Monographic series.*
Published by: Department of Geology and Mineral Industries, 800 N E Oregon St, 28, Ste 965, Portland, OR 97232-2109. TEL 503-731-4100, FAX 503-731-4066, http://www.sarvis.dogami.state.or.us. R&P Klaus Neuendorf.

551 USA ISSN 0278-3703
QE155 CODEN: SSOIDF
OREGON. DEPARTMENT OF GEOLOGY AND MINERAL INDUSTRIES. SPECIAL PAPERS. Text in English. 1978. irreg., latest vol.29, 1999. price varies. back issues avail. **Document type:** *Monographic series.*
—BLDSC (8372.374500), CASDDS, Linda Hall.
Published by: Department of Geology and Mineral Industries, 800 N E Oregon St, 28, Ste 965, Portland, OR 97232-2109. TEL 503-731-4100, FAX 503-731-4066, http://www.sarvis.dogami.state.or.us. R&P Klaus Neuendorf.

553 USA ISSN 0164-3304
TN1 CODEN: ORGEEF
➤ **OREGON GEOLOGY.** Text in English. 1939. bi-m. USD 10 (effective 2000). bk.rev. bibl.; charts; illus. back issues avail. **Document type:** *Academic/Scholarly.*
Formerly (until vol.40, no.12, 1978): Ore Bin (0148-1827)
Indexed: EEA, PetrolAb.
—Linda Hall, PADDS.
Published by: Department of Geology and Mineral Industries, 800 N E Oregon St, 28, Ste 965, Portland, OR 97232-2109. TEL 503-731-4100, FAX 503-731-4066, http://www.sarvis.dogami.state.or.us. Ed., R&P Klaus Neuendorf. Circ: 2,000.

➤ **ORGANIC GEOCHEMISTRY.** see *CHEMISTRY—Organic Chemistry*

➤ **OSNOVANIYA, FUNDAMENTY I MEKHANIKA GRUNTOV.** see *ENGINEERING—Civil Engineering*

550 RUS ISSN 0869-7175
QE1 CODEN: SVGLA2
➤ **OTECHESTVENNAYA GEOLOGIYA.** Text in Russian; Summaries in English. 1933. bi-m. USD 180 (effective 2005). bk.rev. charts; illus. index. **Document type:** *Journal, Academic/Scholarly.* **Description:** Contains articles concerning methodology of forecasting and evaluation of mineral deposits, the development of priority trends of geological science and practice.
Formerly (until 1992): Sovetskaya Geologiya (0038-5069)
Indexed: CIN, ChemAb, ChemTitl, EngInd, IBR, IMMAb, PetrolAb, RefZh.
—BLDSC (0128.433005), CASDDS, CISTI, Linda Hall, PADDS. **CCC.**
Published by: (Tsentral'nyi Nauchno-Issledovatel'skii Institut Tsvetnykh i Blagorodnykh Metallov/Central Research Institute of Geological Prospecting for Base and Precious Metals), Informatsionno-Izdatel'skii Tsentr po Geologii i Nedropol'zovaniu Geoinformmark, Goncharnaya 38, Moscow, 115172, Russian Federation. info@geoinform.ru, http://www.geoinform.ru. Ed., R&P Anatoly I Krivtsov TEL 7-095-3152638. Circ: 1,500 (controlled). **US dist. addr.:** East View Information Services, 3020 Harbor Ln. N., Minneapolis, MN 55447. TEL 612-550-0961.

550 GBR ISSN 0952-7028
CODEN: OMGGEK
➤ **OXFORD MONOGRAPHS ON GEOLOGY AND GEOPHYSICS.** Text in English. irreg., latest vol.40, 2000. price varies. **Document type:** *Monographic series, Academic/Scholarly.*
Formerly (until 1985): Oxford Geological Sciences Series
Indexed: IMMAb, ZooRec.
—BLDSC (6321.007400), ingenta.
Published by: Oxford University Press, Great Clarendon St, Oxford, OX2 6DP, United Kingdom. TEL 44-1865-556767, FAX 44-1865-556646, enquiry@oup.co.uk, http://www.oup-usa.org/catalogs/general/series/Oxford_Monographs_on_Geology_and_Geophysics.html, http://www.oup.co.uk/. **Subscr. to:** Oxford University Press, 2001 Evans Rd, Cary, NC 27513. jnlorders@oup-usa.org.

551 JPN ISSN 0286-7737
OYO CHISHITSU✶ /APPLIED GEOLOGY. Variant title: Japan Society of Engineering Geology. Journal. Text in Japanese; Summaries in English. 1960. bi-m. JPY 7,000 membership (effective 2005). **Document type:** *Journal, Academic/Scholarly.*
Indexed: JPI.
—CISTI. **CCC.**
Published by: Nihon Oyo Chishitsu Gakkai/Japan Society of Engineering Geology, Ochanomizu Sakurai Bldg, 2-3-14 Kanda surugadai, Chiyoda-ku, Tokyo, 101-0062, Japan. TEL 81-3-32598232, FAX 81-3-32598233, kyw04560@nifty.com, http://wwwsoc.nii.ac.jp/jseg/.

551 JPN ISSN 0912-6325
OYO CHISHITSU NENPO/OYO TECHNICAL REPORT. Text in English, Japanese; Summaries in English. 1979. a. **Document type:** *Academic/Scholarly.*
Published by: Oyo Chishitsu/Oyo Corp., c/o Motoo Nagura, Gen. Mgr. Int'l. Div., 2-6 kudan-Kita 4-chome, Chiyoda-ku, Tokyo, 102-0073, Japan. TEL 81-3-3234-0811, FAX 81-3-3262-5169.

THE P E G G. (Professional Engineer, Geologist, Geophysicist) see *ENGINEERING*

555 PAK ISSN 0078-8163
QE295 CODEN: RGPAAY
PAKISTAN. GEOLOGICAL SURVEY. RECORDS. Text in English. 1949. irreg. price varies. **Document type:** *Newsletter, Government.*
Published by: Geological Survey of Pakistan, c/o Chief Librarian, P O Box 15, Quetta, 87550, Pakistan. TEL 92-81-9211038. Circ: 1,500.

557 CAN ISSN 0821-7556
PALAEONTOGRAPHICA CANADIANA. Text in English. 1983. irreg. **Document type:** *Government.*
Indexed: GEOBASE, ZooRec.
—BLDSC (6343.620000), CISTI, Linda Hall. **CCC.**
Published by: Geological Association of Canada, c/o Dept. of Earth Sciences, Memorial Univ. of Newfoundland, St. John's, NF A1B 3X5, Canada.

554 560 GBR ISSN 0269-3445
➤ **PALAEONTOGRAPHICAL SOCIETY. MONOGRAPHS (LONDON).** Text in English; Summaries in French, German, Russian. 1848. a., latest vol.155, 2001. GBP 33 to individuals; GBP 90 to institutions (effective 2003). illus. Index. back issues avail.; reprints avail. **Document type:** *Monographic series, Academic/Scholarly.*
Formerly: Monographs of the Palaeontological Society (0376-2734)
Related titles: Microfiche ed.
Indexed: BIOSIS Prev, BiolAb, ZooRec.
—BLDSC (6343.640000), Linda Hall.
Published by: Palaeontographical Society, Department of Paleontology, Natural History Museum, Cromwell Rd, London, SW7 5BD, United Kingdom. TEL 44-20-79425195, FAX 44-20-79425546, P.Ensom@nhm.ac.uk, http://www.nhm.ac.uk/hosted_sites/palsoc/. Eds. A W A Rushton, M Williams. Circ: 368.

➤ **PALEOBIOS.** see *PALEONTOLOGY*

➤ **PALYNOLOGY.** see *PALEONTOLOGY*

551 POL ISSN 0867-6143
➤ **PANSTWOWY INSTYTUT GEOLOGICZNY. BIULETYN.** Text in Polish; Summaries in English. 1938. irreg. PLZ 10 per issue (effective 2003). **Document type:** *Bulletin, Academic/Scholarly.* **Description:** Contains research on the regional geology of Poland.
Formerly (until 1989): Instytut Geologiczny. Biuletyn (0208-6603)
Related titles: Online - full text ed.
Indexed: GEOBASE, RefZh.
—BLDSC (2103.480000), CISTI, Linda Hall.
Published by: Panstwowy Instytut Geologiczny/Polish Geological Institute, ul Rakowiecka 4, Warsaw, 00975, Poland. TEL 48-22-8495351, FAX 48-22-8495342, dystryb@pgi.wa.pl, http://www.pgi.waw.pl. Circ: 400.

551 560 POL ISSN 0866-9465
CODEN: IGEPAR
➤ **PANSTWOWY INSTYTUT GEOLOGICZNY. PRACE.** Text in Polish; Summaries in English. 1921. irreg., latest vol.177, 2003. price varies. abstr.; bibl.; charts; illus. back issues avail. **Document type:** *Monographic series, Academic/Scholarly.* **Description:** Contains research on the regional geology of Poland.
Formerly (until 1988): Instytut Geologiczny. Prace (0208-645X)
Indexed: GEOBASE, IMMAb, RefZh, ZooRec.
—CISTI, Linda Hall.
Published by: Panstwowy Instytut Geologiczny/Polish Geological Institute, ul Rakowiecka 4, Warsaw, 00975, Poland. TEL 48-22-8495351, FAX 48-22-8495342, dystryb@pgi.wa.pl, http://www.pgi.waw.pl. Circ: 400.

➤ **PEATLANDS INTERNATIONAL.** see *MINES AND MINING INDUSTRY*

557 USA ISSN 0146-6666
PENNSYLVANIA. BUREAU OF TOPOGRAPHIC AND GEOLOGIC SURVEY. ENVIRONMENTAL GEOLOGY REPORT. Text in English. 1972. irreg., latest vol.9, 1999. price varies.
Formerly (until 1982): Pennsylvania. Bureau of Topographic and Geologic Survey. Bulletin EG (0890-8516)
—Linda Hall.
Published by: Pennsylvania Department of Conservation and Natural Resources, Bureau of Topographic and Geologic Survey, 3240 Schoolhouse Rd, Middletown, PA 17057. TEL 717-702-2017, http://www.dcnr.state.pa.us/topogeo/. **Subscr. to:** Pennsylvania State Bookstore, Commonwealth Keystone Bldg., 400 North St, Harrisburg, PA 17120-0053. TEL 717-787-5109.

557 USA ISSN 0160-824X
PENNSYLVANIA. BUREAU OF TOPOGRAPHIC AND GEOLOGIC SURVEY. MINERAL RESOURCE REPORT. Text in English. 1922. irreg., latest vol.99, 2004. price varies. **Document type:** *Monographic series.*
Formerly (until 1973): Pennsylvania. Bureau of Topographic and Geologic Survey. Bulletin M (0097-5117)
Published by: Pennsylvania Department of Conservation and Natural Resources, Bureau of Topographic and Geologic Survey, 3240 Schoolhouse Rd, Middletown, PA 17057. TEL 717-702-2017. **Subscr. to:** Pennsylvania State Bookstore, Commonwealth Keystone Bldg., 400 North St, Harrisburg, PA 17120-0053. TEL 717-787-5109.

557 USA ISSN 0048-3214
QE157 CODEN: PAGYBW
PENNSYLVANIA GEOLOGY. Text in English. 1969. bi-m. free. bk.rev. bibl.; charts; illus. **Document type:** *Academic/Scholarly.*
—Linda Hall.
Published by: Department of Environmental Resources, Bureau of Topographic and Geologic Survey, PO Box 8453, Harrisburg, PA 17105-8453. TEL 717-787-2169, FAX 717-783-7267. Eds. Christine Dodge, Donald M Hoskins. Circ: 3,000.

E

551 GBR ISSN 1045-6740
GB641 CODEN: PEPPED
➤ **PERMAFROST AND PERIGLACIAL PROCESSES.** Text in English. 1990. q. USD 995 to institutions; USD 1,095 combined subscription to institutions print & online eds. (effective 2006). adv. back issues avail.; reprints avail. **Document type:** *Journal, Academic/Scholarly.* **Description:** Presents papers on earth surface cryogenic processes, landforms, and sediments present in arctic, antarctic, and high-mountain environments.
Related titles: Microform ed.: (from PQC); Online - full text ed.: ISSN 1099-1530. USD 995 to institutions (effective 2006) (from EBSCO Publishing, Swets Information Services, Wiley InterScience).
Indexed: AEA, ASCA, ASFA, CurCont, ESPM, ForAb, GEOBASE, HerbAb, I&DA, ISR, M&GPA, M&TEA, S&F, SCI, SWRA.
—BLDSC (6426.685000), CISTI, Ei, IDS, IE, Infotrieve, ingenta, Linda Hall. **CCC.**
Published by: John Wiley & Sons Ltd. (Subsidiary of: John Wiley & Sons, Inc.), The Atrium, Southern Gate, Chichester, West Sussex PO19 8SQ, United Kingdom. TEL 44-1243-779777, FAX 44-1243-775878, customer@wiley.co.uk, http://www3.interscience.wiley.com/cgi-bin/jhome/14053, http://www.wiley.co.uk. Ed. H M French. adv.: B&W page GBP 650, color page GBP 1,550; trim 200 x 260. Circ: 500. **Subscr. in the Americas to:** John Wiley & Sons, Inc., 111 River St, Hoboken, NJ 07030-5774. TEL 201-748-6645, 800-225-5945, subinfo@wiley.com.

➤ **PETROLEUM GEOLOGY OF TAIWAN/T'AIWAN SHIH-YU TI-CHIH.** see *PETROLEUM AND GAS*

➤ **PETROLEUM GEOLOGY SPECIAL PAPER SERIES.** see *PETROLEUM AND GAS*

552 GBR ISSN 1354-0793
TN870.5 CODEN: PEGEF4
➤ **PETROLEUM GEOSCIENCE.** Text in English. 1995. q. GBP 195 in Europe; USD 351 in United States; GBP 225, USD 405 elsewhere (effective 2005). adv. bk.rev. illus. index. reprints avail. **Document type:** *Journal, Academic/Scholarly.* **Description:** It publishes balanced mix of articles from the geoscience disciplines involved in the exploration, appraisal and development of hydrocarbon resources.
Related titles: Online - full text ed.: (from EBSCO Publishing, Gale Group, IngentaConnect, Swets Information Services).
Indexed: AESIS, BrCerAb, C&ISA, CerAb, CivEngAb, CorrAb, CurCont, E&CAJ, EMA, FLUIDEX, GEOBASE, IAA, ISR, M&TEA, MBF, METADEX, PetrolAb, SCI, SolStAb, WAA.
—BLDSC (6433.520000), CISTI, IDS, IE, Infotrieve, ingenta, Linda Hall, PADDS. **CCC.**
Published by: (European Association of Geoscientists and Engineers), Geological Society Publishing House, Unit 7, Brassmill Enterprise Centre, Brassmill Ln, Bath, Avon BA1 3JN, United Kingdom. TEL 44-1225-445046, FAX 44-1225-442836, enquiries@geolsoc.org.uk, http://www.geolsoc.org.uk. Circ: 3,500.

552 RUS ISSN 0869-5903
PETROLOGIYA. Text in Russian. 1993. m. USD 208 foreign (effective 2005). **Document type:** *Journal, Academic/Scholarly.* **Description:** Publishes comprehensive information on all multidisciplinary aspects of theoretical, experimental , and applied petrology.
Related titles: Online - full text ed.; ♦ Russian Translation: Petrology. ISSN 0869-5911.
Indexed: ChemAb, ChemTitl, RefZh.
—Linda Hall. **CCC.**
Published by: (Rossiiskaya Akademiya Nauk/Russian Academy of Sciences), Izdatel'stvo Nauka, Profsoyuznaya ul 90, Moscow, 117864, Russian Federation. TEL 7-095-3347151, FAX 7-095-4202220, secret@naukaran.ru, http://www.maik.rssi.ru/cgi-bin/list.pl?page=petrus, http://www.naukaran.ru. **Dist. by:** M K - Periodica, ul Gilyarovskogo 39, Moscow 129110, Russian Federation. TEL 7-095-2845008, FAX 7-095-2813798, info@periodicals.ru, http://www.mkniga.ru.

E

552 RUS ISSN 0869-5911
QE420 CODEN: PROLEJ
➤ **PETROLOGY.** Text in Russian. 1993. m. USD 1,365 in North America; USD 1,564 elsewhere (effective 2004). **Document type:** *Journal, Academic/Scholarly.* **Description:** Publishes comprehensive information on all multidisciplinary aspects of theoretical, experimental, and applied petrology.
Related titles: ♦ Translation of: Petrologiya. ISSN 0869-5903.
Indexed: ASCA, CurCont, ISR, SCI.
—BLDSC (0416.760000), CISTI, East View, IDS, IE, ingenta. **CCC.**
Published by: M A I K Nauka - Interperiodica, Profsoyuznaya ul 90, Moscow, 117997, Russian Federation. TEL 7-095-3347420, FAX 7-095-3360666, compmg@maik.ru, http://www.maik.rssi.ru/journals/petreng.htm, http://www.maik.ru. Ed. Vilen A Zharikov. **Subscr. to:** Interperiodica, PO Box 1831, Birmingham, AL 35201-1831. TEL 205-995-1567, 800-633-4931, FAX 205-995-1588.

550 NLD ISSN 0924-1957
PETROLOGY AND STRUCTURAL GEOLOGY. Text in English. 1986. irreg., latest vol.12, 2002. price varies. **Document type:** *Monographic series, Academic/Scholarly.*
—BLDSC (6436.460000).

Published by: Springer-Verlag Dordrecht (Subsidiary of: Springer Science+Business Media), Van Godewijckstraat 30, Dordrecht, 3311 GX, Netherlands. TEL 31-78-6576050, FAX 31-78-6576474, http://www.springeronline.com. Ed. Adolphe Nicolas.

551 USA ISSN 1059-860X
THE PHYTOLITHARIEN. Text in English. 1981. 3/yr.
Formerly (until 1989): Phytolitharien Newsletter (1043-5301)
Published by: Society for Phytolith Research, c/o Irwin Rouner, Box 8107, Raleigh, NC 27695-8107. TEL 919-515-2491, FAX 919-515-2610, irv@server.sasw.ncsu.edu.

551 BEL ISSN 1373-7007
PIERRE ET MARBRE/STEEN EN MARMER. Text in French. 1955. q.
Published by: Federation Royale des Maitres Tailleurs de Pierres de Belgique, Galerie du Centre, Bureau 220, Rue des Fripiers 15-17, Bruxelles, 1000, Belgium. TEL 32-2-223-0647, FAX 32-2-223-0538.

PIRINEOS; a journal on mountain ecology. see *BIOLOGY*

PLINIUS; Supplemento italiano all'European Journal of Mineralogy. see *MINES AND MINING INDUSTRY*

POLAR GEOGRAPHY. see *GEOGRAPHY*

551 JPN ISSN 1344-3194
QE350
➤ **POLAR GEOSCIENCE.** Text in English. 1967. a., latest vol.15, 2002. per issue exchange basis. **Document type:** *Academic/Scholarly.*
Former titles (until 1997): N I P R Symposium on Antarctic Geosciences. Proceedings. (0914-2029); Supersedes in part (in 1987): National Institute of Polar Research. Memoirs. Special Issue (0386-0744); Which was formerly (until 1972): Japanese Antarctic Research Expedition Scientific Reports. Special Issue (0386-5452)
Indexed: M&GPA, RefZh.
—BLDSC (6541.939200), CASDDS, CISTI, KNAW.
Published by: National Institute of Polar Research/Kokuritsu Kyokuchi Kenkyujo, Publications, 9-10, Kiga 1-chome, Itabashi-ku, Tokyo, 173, Japan. TEL 81-3-3962-2214, FAX 81-3-3962-2225, publication@nipr.ac.jp. Ed. Okitsugu Watanabe. Circ: 1,000.

551 JPN ISSN 1344-3437
QC994.75 CODEN: MNIRDD
➤ **POLAR METEOROLOGY AND GLACIOLOGY.** Text in English. 1967. a., latest vol.16, 2002. exchange basis. **Document type:** *Academic/Scholarly.*
Former titles (until 1997): N I P R Symposium on Polar Meteorology and Glaciology. Proceedings. (0914-2037); Supersedes in part (in 1987): National Institute of Polar Research. Memoirs. Special Issue (0386-0744); Which was formerly (until 1972): Japanese Antarctic Research Expedition Scientific Reports. Special Issue (0386-5452)
Indexed: M&GPA, RefZh.
—BLDSC (6541.939590), CASDDS, CISTI, KNAW.
Published by: National Institute of Polar Research/Kokuritsu Kyokuchi Kenkyujo, Publications, 9-10, Kiga 1-chome, Itabashi-ku, Tokyo, 173, Japan. TEL 81-3-3962-2214, FAX 81-3-3962-2225, publication@nipr.ac.jp. Ed. Yoshiyuki Fujii. Circ: 1,000.

551 POL ISSN 1507-9791
QE1
➤ **POLISH GEOLOGICAL INSTITUTE. SPECIAL PAPERS.** Text in English. 1999. irreg., latest vol.7, 2002. price varies. **Document type:** *Monographic series, Academic/Scholarly.*
Indexed: GEOBASE.
Published by: Panstwowy Instytut Geologiczny/Polish Geological Institute, ul Rakowiecka 4, Warsaw, 00975, Poland. TEL 48-22-8495351, FAX 48-22-8495342, dystryb@pgi.waw.pl, http://www.pgi.waw.pl. Circ: 450.

550 POL ISSN 0079-3361
QE276.5 CODEN: PRGLA9
POLSKA AKADEMIA NAUK. ODDZIAL W KRAKOWIE. KOMISJA NAUK GEOLOGICZNYCH. PRACE GEOLOGICZNE. Text in Polish; Summaries in English, Russian. 1960. irreg., latest vol.137, 1992. price varies. index. **Document type:** *Monographic series.* **Description:** Monographs in regional and applied geology, geochemistry and petrography of mineral products, works in geophysics and hydrogeology.
—CISTI.
Published by: (Komisja Nauk Geologicznych), Polska Akademia Nauk, Oddzial w Krakowie, ul sw Jana 28, Krakow, 31018, Poland. TEL 48-12-224853, FAX 48-12-222791. Ed. Roman Ney.

550 POL ISSN 0079-3396
QE351 CODEN: PAPMB7
POLSKA AKADEMIA NAUK. ODDZIAL W KRAKOWIE. KOMISJA NAUK MINERALOGICZNYCH. PRACE MINERALOGICZNE. Text in English, Polish; Summaries in English, Russian. 1965. irreg., latest vol.82, 1992. price varies. **Document type:** *Monographic series.*
Indexed: ChemAb.
—CASDDS, CISTI.

Published by: (Komisja Nauk Mineralogicznych), Polska Akademia Nauk, Oddzial w Krakowie, ul sw Jana 28, Krakow, 31018, Poland. TEL 48-12-224853, FAX 48-12-222791. Ed. Andrzej Bolewski.

551 BRA ISSN 0104-9364
PONTIFICIA UNIVERSIDADE CATOLICA DO RIO GRANDE DO SUL. MUSEU DE CIENCIAS E TECNOLOGIA. COMUNICACOES. SERIE CIENCIAS DA TERRA. Variant title: Museu de Ciencias e Tecnologia da P U C R G S. Comunicacoes. Serie Ciencias da Terra. Text in Portuguese. 1995. irreg.
Indexed: ASFA, ESPM.
—CISTI.
Published by: Pontificia Universidade Catolica do Rio Grande do Sul, Museu de Ciencias e Tecnologia, Av Ipiranga 6681, Predio 40, Porto Alegre, RS 90619-900, Brazil. TEL 55-512-3203597, http://www.mct.pucrs.br/. **Subscr. to:** Av Ipiranga 6681, Predio 33, Caixa Postal 1429, Porto Alegre, RS 90619-900, Brazil. edipucrs@pucrs.br, http://www.pucrs.br/edipucrs.

551 PRT ISSN 0873-948X
QE284 CODEN: CGEPAT
➤ **PORTUGAL. INSTITUTO GEOLOGICO E MINEIRO. COMUNICACOES.** Text and summaries in English, French, Portuguese, Spanish. 1887. a., latest vol.89, 2002. EUR 9.50 (effective 2002). bibl.; charts; illus.; maps. back issues avail. **Document type:** *Academic/Scholarly.*
Formerly: Portugal. Servicos Geologicos. Comunicacoes (0037-2730)
Indexed: BiolAb, RefZh, ZooRec.
—BLDSC (3396.550000), CASDDS, CISTI.
Published by: Ministerio da Economia, Instituto Geologico e Mineiro, Apartado 7586, Zambujal, Alfragide, 2721-866, Portugal. TEL 351-21-4705400, FAX 351-21-4720203, web.nbp@igm.pt, http://www.igm.pt. Ed., R&P Miguel Magalhaes Ramalho.

550 910 POL ISSN 0137-9771
➤ **POZNANSKIE TOWARZYSTWO PRZYJACIOL NAUK. KOMISJA GEOGRAFICZNO-GEOLOGICZNA. PRACE.** Text in Polish; Summaries in English. 1936. irreg., latest vol.33, 2002. price varies. bibl. **Document type:** *Monographic series, Academic/Scholarly.*
Published by: (Poznanskie Towarzystwo Przyjaciol Nauk, Komisja Geograficzno-Geologiczna), Poznanskie Towarzystwo Przyjaciol Nauk/Poznan Society for the Advancement of the Arts and Sciences, ul Sew Mielzynskiego 27-29, Poznan, 61725, Poland. TEL 48-61-8527441, FAX 48-61-8522205, sekretariat@ptpn.poznan.pl, wydawnictwo@ptpn.poznan.pl, http://www.ptpn.poznan.pl. Ed. Henryk Rogacki. Circ: 400. **Dist. by:** Ars Polona, Krakowskie Przedmiescie 7, Warsaw, Poland. TEL 48-22-9263914, FAX 48-22-9265334, arspolona@arspolona.com.pl, http://www.arspolona.com.pl.

551 NLD ISSN 0301-9268
CODEN: PCBRBY
➤ **PRECAMBRIAN RESEARCH.** Text in English. 1974. 32/yr. EUR 2,453 in Europe to institutions; JPY 325,600 in Japan to institutions; USD 2,745 to institutions except Europe and Japan; EUR 322 in Europe to qualified personnel; JPY 43,300 in Japan to qualified personnel; USD 361 to qualified personnel except Europe and Japan (effective 2006). adv. bk.rev. illus. Index. reprints avail. **Document type:** *Journal, Academic/Scholarly.* **Description:** Publishes studies on all aspects of the early stages of the history and evolution of the Earth and its planetary neighbors.
Related titles: Microform ed.: (from PQC); Online - full text ed.: (from EBSCO Publishing, Gale Group, IngentaConnect, ScienceDirect, Swets Information Services).
Indexed: AESIS, ASCA, ASFA, BiolAb, BrGeoL, CIN, ChemAb, ChemTitl, CurCont, EngInd, GEOBASE, ISR, Inspec, MinerAb, PetrolAb, RefZh, SCI, ZooRec.
—BLDSC (6603.860000), AskIEEE, CASDDS, IDS, IE, Infotrieve, ingenta, Linda Hall, PADDS. **CCC.**
Published by: (International Union of Geological Sciences NOR, Subcommission on Precambrian Stratigraphy), Elsevier BV (Subsidiary of: Elsevier Science & Technology), Radarweg 29, Amsterdam, 1043 NX, Netherlands. TEL 31-20-4853911, FAX 31-20-4852457, nlinfo-f@elsevier.nl, http://www.elsevier.com/locate/precamres, http://www.elsevier.nl. Eds. A Kroener, K A Eriksson. **Subscr. to:** PO Box 211, Amsterdam 1000 AE, Netherlands. TEL 31-20-485-3757, FAX 31-20-485-3432; Elsevier, Subscription Customer Service, 6277 Sea Harbor Dr, Orlando, FL 32887-4800. TEL 407-345-4020, 877-839-7126, FAX 407-363-1354.

551.9 USA
➤ **PRINCETON SERIES IN GEOCHEMISTRY.** Text in English. 1980. irreg., latest vol.3, 1998. price varies. illus. **Document type:** *Monographic series, Academic/Scholarly.* **Description:** Explores noteworthy new findings in the field of geochemistry.

Published by: Princeton University Press, 41 William St, Princeton, NJ 08540-5237. TEL 609-258-4900, 800-777-4726, FAX 609-258-6305, http://www.pupress.princeton.edu/catalogs/series/psg.html. **Subscr. addr. in US:** California - Princeton Fulfillment Services, 1445 Lower Ferry Rd, Ewing, NJ 08618. TEL 800-777-4726, FAX 800-999-1958, orders@cpfs.pupress.princeton.edu. **Dist. addr. in Canada:** University Press Group, 164 Hillsdale Ave E, Toronto, ON M4S 1T5, Canada.; **Dist. addr. in UK:** John Wiley & Sons Ltd., The Atrium, Southern Gate, Chichester, West Sussex PO19 8SQ, United Kingdom.

550 551.4 USA ISSN 0279-0521
PROFESSIONAL GEOLOGIST. Text in English. 1964. m. USD 30 domestic to non-members; USD 40 in Canada to non-members; USD 48 elsewhere to non-members; USD 20 to members. adv. back issues avail. **Document type:** *Newsletter.* **Description:** Covers proposed legislation and regulations of concern to geologists, business news, public attitudes and trends, on-the-job techniques, current research and recent publications of interest.
Published by: American Institute of Professional Geologists, 7828 Vance Dr, Arvada, CO 80003-2125. TEL 303-412-6205, FAX 303-431-1332, aipg@aipg.com. Ed. Dale Nations. R&P Myrna Killey TEL 217-244-2409. Adv. contact Wendy Davidson. Circ: 6,000.

551 CAN
PROVINCIAL GEOLOGISTS JOURNAL. Text in English. 1983. irreg., latest vol.15, 1997. price varies. back issues avail. **Document type:** *Journal, Government.*
Published by: Ministry of Energy and Mines, c/o Communications Coordinator, Stn Prov Govt, PO Box 9324, Victoria, BC V8W 9N3, Canada. TEL 250-952-0525, http://www.ogc.gov.bc.ca. **Subscr. to:** Crown Publications Inc., 521 Fort St, Victoria, BC BC V8W 1E7, Canada. TEL 250-386-4636, FAX 250-386-0221, crown@pinc.com, http://www.crownpub.bc.ca.

551 POL ISSN 0033-2151
QE1 CODEN: PRZGAL
PRZEGLAD GEOLOGICZNY/GEOLOGICAL REVIEW. Text in Polish; Summaries in English. 1953. m. PLZ 16.50 per quarter domestic; PLZ 33 per quarter foreign (effective 2003). adv. bk.rev. bibl.; charts; illus. index. **Document type:** *Newsletter, Academic/Scholarly.* **Description:** Focuses on geology, hydrogeology, engineering geology, geophysics and environmental protection.
Indexed: AgrLib, BibCart, ChemAb, GEOBASE, GeotechAb, IBR, MinerAb, ZooRec.
—BLDSC (6942.000000), CASDDS, Linda Hall.
Published by: Panstwowy Instytut Geologiczny/Polish Geological Institute, ul Rakowiecka 4, Warsaw, 00975, Poland. TEL 48-22-8495351, FAX 48-22-8495342, prz.geol@pgi.waw.pl, http://www.pgi.waw.pl. Ed. Wladzimierz Mizerski. Circ: 900.

550 ITA ISSN 1593-8433
QUADERNI DI GEOLOGIA APPLICATA. Text in Italian. 1994. s-a. EUR 36 in the European Union; USD 60 elsewhere (effective 2003).
Published by: Pitagora Editrice, Via del Legatore 3, Bologna, BO 40138, Italy. TEL 39-051-530003, FAX 39-051-535301, pited@pitagoragroup.it, http://www.pitagoragroup.it/editrice.html.

551 NLD ISSN 0924-1973
➤ **QUANTITATIVE GEOLOGY AND GEOSTATISTICS.** Text in Dutch. 1985. irreg., latest vol.14, 2005. price varies. **Document type:** *Monographic series, Academic/Scholarly.*
—BLDSC (7168.333500).
Published by: Springer-Verlag Dordrecht (Subsidiary of: Springer Science+Business Media), Van Godewijckstraat 30, Dordrecht, 3311 GX, Netherlands. TEL 31-78-6576050, FAX 31-78-6576474, http://www.springeronline.com.

➤ **QUARTERLY JOURNAL OF ENGINEERING GEOLOGY AND HYDROGEOLOGY.** see *ENGINEERING—Civil Engineering*

551 FRA ISSN 1142-2904
QE696 CODEN: QUATE5
QUATERNAIRE. Text and summaries in English, French, German. 1964. q. adv. bk.rev. charts; illus. index. **Document type:** *Academic/Scholarly.* **Description:** International journal dealing with all aspects related to the Quaternary.
Formerly: Association Francaise pour l'Etude du Quaternaire. Bulletin (0004-5500)
Indexed: GEOBASE, ZooRec.
—BLDSC (7209.960000), IE, Infotrieve, ingenta, Linda Hall.
Published by: Maison de la Geology, 79 Claude Bernard, Paris, 75005, France. TEL 33-2-31565718, FAX 33-1-31565757. Ed. J C Miskovsky. Adv. contact Jean Pierre Coutard. Circ: 450.

QUATERNARIA NOVA. see *PALEONTOLOGY*

551 NLD ISSN 1871-1014
▼ ➤ **QUATERNARY GEOCHRONOLOGY.** Text in English. 2006. 4/yr. EUR 350 in Europe to institutions; JPY 41,400 in Japan to institutions; USD 370 to institutions except Europe and Japan (effective 2006). **Document type:** *Journal, Academic/Scholarly.* **Description:** Devoted to the publication of the highest-quality, peer-reviewed articles on all aspects of dating methods applicable to the Quaternary Period - the last 2.6 million years of Earth history.
Published by: Elsevier BV (Subsidiary of: Elsevier Science & Technology), Radarweg 29, Amsterdam, 1043 NX, Netherlands. TEL 31-20-4853911, FAX 31-20-4852457, nlinfo-f@elsevier.nl, http://www.elsevier.com/wps/find/journaldescription.cws_home/706731/description?navopenmenu=1. Ed. R Gruen.

551 GBR ISSN 1040-6182
QE696 CODEN: QUINER
➤ **QUATERNARY INTERNATIONAL.** Text in English. 1989. 17/yr. EUR 90 in Europe to individuals; JPY 11,900 in Japan to individuals; USD 102 to individuals except Europe and Japan; EUR 960 in Europe to institutions; JPY 126,700 in Japan to institutions; USD 1,071 to institutions except Europe and Japan (effective 2006). illus.; abstr. back issues avail.; reprints avail. **Document type:** *Journal, Academic/Scholarly.* **Description:** Publishes original research from the full spectrum of physical and natural sciences addressing problems in quaternary science.
Related titles: Microfilm ed.: (from PQC); Online - full text ed.: (from EBSCO Publishing, Gale Group, IngentaConnect, ScienceDirect, Swets Information Services).
Indexed: ASCA, CurCont, EngInd, GEOBASE, ISR, RefZh, SCI, ZooRec.
—BLDSC (7210.043000), CISTI, Ei, IDS, IE, Infotrieve, ingenta, Linda Hall. **CCC.**
Published by: (International Union for Quaternary Research), Pergamon (Subsidiary of: Elsevier Science & Technology), The Boulevard, Langford Ln, East Park, Kidlington, Oxford OX5 1GB, United Kingdom. TEL 44-1865-843000, FAX 44-1865-843010, http://www.elsevier.com/locate/quaint. Ed. N R Catto. **Subscr. to:** Elsevier BV, PO Box 211, Amsterdam 1000 AE, Netherlands. TEL 31-20-485-3757, FAX 31-20-485-3432, nlinfo-f@elsevier.nl, http://www.elsevier.nl.

551 560 GBR ISSN 0143-2826
➤ **QUATERNARY NEWSLETTER.** Text in English. 1970. 3/yr. **Document type:** *Academic/Scholarly.*
Indexed: ZooRec.
—BLDSC (7210.047000), IE, ingenta.
Published by: University of Sussex, School of Chemistry, Physics and Environmental Science, Quaternary Research Association, Brighton, BN1 9QJ, United Kingdom. J.B.Murton@sussex.ac.uk. Ed. Dr. J Murton.

551 570 GBR ISSN 0168-6305
QE696 CODEN: QSAPED
➤ **QUATERNARY OF SOUTH AMERICA AND ANTARCTIC PENINSULA.** Text in Dutch. 1983. irreg. price varies. illus.; maps. **Document type:** *Journal, Academic/Scholarly.* **Description:** Emphasis is on the paleoenvironmental and paleoclimatic approach. Helps to correlate South American environmental events and endogenous episodes with equivalents in other parts of the world.
Indexed: ZooRec.
—CISTI. **CCC.**
Published by: Taylor & Francis Ltd (Subsidiary of: Taylor & Francis Group), 4 Park Sq, Milton Park, Abingdon, OX14 4RN, United Kingdom. TEL 44-1235-828600, FAX 44-1235-829000, info@tandf.co.uk, http://www.balkema.nl/series_list.asp?series=20, http://www.tandf.co.uk/books/. Ed. Jorge Rabassa. **Dist. in US by:** Ashgate Publishing Co, Old Post Rd, Brookfield, VT 05036. TEL 802-276-3126.

551 GBR ISSN 0965-1357
QE696
QUATERNARY PERSPECTIVE. Variant title: I N Q U A Newsletter. Text in English. 1990. irreg. free to members and subscribers of Quaternary International. **Document type:** *Newsletter.* **Description:** Covers news, meetings, publications and other issues of interest to quaternarists.
Related titles: Online - full text ed.: (from Swets Information Services).
Indexed: BrArAb, NumL.
—BLDSC (7210.080000).
Published by: (International Union for Quaternary Research), Pergamon (Subsidiary of: Elsevier Science & Technology), The Boulevard, Langford Ln, East Park, Kidlington, Oxford OX5 1GB, United Kingdom. TEL 44-1865-843000, FAX 44-1865-843010. **Subscr. to:** Elsevier BV, PO Box 211, Amsterdam 1000 AE, Netherlands. TEL 31-20-485-3757, FAX 31-20-485-3432, nlinfo-f@elsevier.nl, http://www.elsevier.nl.

551 560 USA ISSN 0033-5894
QE696 CODEN: QRESAV
➤ **QUATERNARY RESEARCH.** Text mainly in English; Text occasionally in French, German, Russian. 1970. 6/yr. EUR 440 in Europe to individuals; JPY 45,900 in Japan to individuals; USD 383 to individuals except Europe and Japan; EUR 931 in Europe to institutions; JPY 97,300 in Japan to institutions; USD 739 to institutions except Europe and Japan; EUR 112 in Europe to students; JPY 11,600 in Japan to students; USD 98 to students except Europe and Japan (effective 2006). bk.rev. illus. index. back issues avail.; reprints avail. **Document type:** *Journal, Academic/Scholarly.* **Description:** Focuses on studies in the earth and biological sciences. Features papers on previously unpublished research results that will be of interest to a diverse interdisciplinary audience.
Related titles: Online - full text ed.: ISSN 1096-0287. USD 762 (effective 2002) (from EBSCO Publishing, Gale Group, IngentaConnect, O C L C Online Computer Library Center, Inc., ScienceDirect, Swets Information Services).
Indexed: AESIS, ASFA, AbAn, Agr, AgrForAb, AnBrAb, AnthLit, ApEcolAb, ArtHuCI, BIOSIS Prev, BiolAb, BrArAb, BrGeoL, CCA, CPA, CTO, ChemAb, CivEngAb, CurCont, ESPM, FPA, ForAb, GEOBASE, HerbAb, I&DA, ISR, Inspec, M&GPA, NutrAb, OceAb, PGegResA, RASB, RRTA, RiceAb, S&F, SCI, SPPI, SWRA, TriticAb, WAE&RSA, ZooRec.
—BLDSC (7210.100000), AskIEEE, CASDDS, CISTI, Ei, IDS, IE, Infotrieve, ingenta, Linda Hall. **CCC.**
Published by: Academic Press (Subsidiary of: Elsevier Science & Technology), 525 B St, Ste 1900, San Diego, CA 92101-4495. TEL 619-231-6616, 800-894-3434, FAX 619-699-6422, apsubs@acad.com, http://www.elsevier.com/locate/yqres, http://www.academicpress.com. Eds. A. R. Gillespie, E Steig.

551 560 GBR ISSN 0261-3611
QUATERNARY RESEARCH ASSOCIATION. FIELD GUIDE SERIES. Text in English. irreg.
Published by: University of Sussex, School of Chemistry, Physics and Environmental Science, Quaternary Research Association, Brighton, BN1 9QJ, United Kingdom. J.B.Murton@sussex.ac.uk.

551 560 GBR
QUATERNARY RESEARCH ASSOCIATION. TECHNICAL GUIDE SERIES. Text in English. irreg.
Published by: University of Sussex, School of Chemistry, Physics and Environmental Science, Quaternary Research Association, Brighton, BN1 9QJ, United Kingdom. J.B.Murton@sussex.ac.uk.

551 GBR ISSN 0277-3791
QE696 CODEN: QSREDU
➤ **QUATERNARY SCIENCE REVIEWS.** Text in English. 1982. 24/yr. EUR 1,707 in Europe to institutions; JPY 226,600 in Japan to institutions; USD 1,908 to institutions except Europe and Japan; EUR 238 in Europe to qualified personnel; JPY 31,700 in Japan to qualified personnel; USD 266 to qualified personnel except Europe and Japan (effective 2006). bk.rev. abstr. back issues avail. **Document type:** *Journal, Academic/Scholarly.* **Description:** Publishes research in all aspects of quaternary science, including geology, geomorphology, geography, archaeology, soil science, palaeontology, palaeoclimatology and the full range of applicable dating methods.
Related titles: Microfilm ed.: (from PQC); Online - full text ed.: (from EBSCO Publishing, Gale Group, IngentaConnect, ScienceDirect, Swets Information Services).
Indexed: AESIS, ASCA, ASFA, AbAn, AnthLit, BIOBASE, BrArAb, ChemAb, CurCont, ESPM, EngInd, GEOBASE, ISR, Inspec, M&GPA, NumL, OceAb, PlantSci, RefZh, SCI, SWRA, ZooRec.
—BLDSC (7210.220000), AskIEEE, CASDDS, CISTI, Ei, IDS, IE, Infotrieve, ingenta, Linda Hall. **CCC.**
Published by: Pergamon (Subsidiary of: Elsevier Science & Technology), The Boulevard, Langford Ln, East Park, Kidlington, Oxford OX5 1GB, United Kingdom. TEL 44-1865-843000, FAX 44-1865-843010, http://www.elsevier.com/locate/quascirev. Eds. D H Keen, P. U. Clark, Jim Rose. **Subscr. to:** Elsevier BV, PO Box 211, Amsterdam 1000 AE, Netherlands. TEL 31-20-485-3757, FAX 31-20-485-3432, nlinfo-f@elsevier.nl, http://www.elsevier.nl.

557 CAN
CODEN: RGRNAF
QUEBEC (PROVINCE). DEPARTMENT OF ENERGY AND RESOURCES. GEOLOGICAL REPORTS. Text mainly in French. 1886. irreg. price varies. **Document type:** *Government.*
Formerly: Quebec (Province). Department of Natural Resources. Geological Reports (0079-8738)
Related titles: Microfiche ed.
Indexed: IMMAb.
—CASDDS, Linda Hall.
Published by: Department of Energy and Resources, Centre de Diffusion des Donnees Geoscientifiques/Ministere de l'Energie et des Ressources, 5700 4e Ave Ouest, Local A 209, Charlesbourg, PQ G1H 6R1, Canada. TEL 418-643-4601, FAX 418-644-3814. Circ: 1,200.

557 CAN
QUEBEC (PROVINCE). MINISTERE DES RESSOURCES NATURELLES. RAPPORT DES GEOLOGUES RESIDENTS SUR L'ACTIVITE MINIERE REGIONALE. Text in English, French. 1927. a. CND 4. **Document type:** *Government.*
Former titles: Quebec (Province). Ministere de l'Energie et des Resources. Rapport des Geologues Residents sur l'Activite Miniere Regionale; Quebec (Province). Department d'Energie et Resources. Rapport des Representants Regionaux; (until 1985): Quebec (Province). Ministere des Richesses Naturelles. Travaux sur le Terrain (0079-8746)
Indexed: IMMAb.
Published by: Ministere des Ressources Naturelles, Centre de Diffusion, 5700 4e Av Ouest, Local A 209, Charlesbourg, PQ G1H 6R1, Canada. TEL 418-643-4601, FAX 418-644-3814.

E

R M Z - MATERIALS AND GEOENVIRONMENT/MATERIALS AND GEOENVIRONMENT; periodical for mining, metallurgy and geology. (Rudarsko Metalurski Zbornik) see *MINES AND MINING INDUSTRY*

622.362 DNK ISSN 1603-8665
HF1054.D4
RAASTOFPRODUKTION I DANMARK, HAVOMRAADET (ONLINE); produktionsmaengden fra samtlige optagningslokaliteter samt udlosningssteder og maengder. Text in Danish. 1976. a.
Former titles (until 2002): Raastofproduktion i Danmark, Havomraadet (Print edition) (0109-7466); (until 1984): Raastofproduktionsopgoerelse fra Havbunden (0109-5048)
Media: Online - full content.
Published by: Miljoeministeriet, Skov- og Naturstyrelsen/Ministry of the Environment. Danish Forest & Nature Agency, Haraldsgade 53, Copenhagen OE, 2100, Denmark. TEL 45-39-472000, FAX 45-39-279899, sns@sns.dk, http://www.sns.dk/raastof/rastofhv.htm, http://www.skovognatur.dk.

RAZVEDKA I OKHRANA NEDR/EXPLORATION AND PROTECTION OF MINERAL RESOURCES. see *MINES AND MINING INDUSTRY*

REAL SOCIEDAD ESPANOLA DE HISTORIA NATURAL. BOLETIN. ACTAS. see *BIOLOGY*

554 ESP ISSN 0583-7510
QE1 CODEN: BRSGA2
REAL SOCIEDAD ESPANOLA DE HISTORIA NATURAL. BOLETIN. SECCION GEOLOGICA. Text in Spanish; Summaries in English, French. 1901. a., latest vol.96, 2001. reprints avail. **Document type:** *Bulletin.*
Supersedes in part (in 1950): Real Sociedad Espanola de Historia Natural. Boletin (0365-9755)
Indexed: ASFA, BIOSIS Prev, BiolAb, ESPM, FPA, ForAb, HerbAb, I&DA, IECT, S&F, WAE&RSA, ZooRec.
—CASDDS, CINDOC, CISTI, Linda Hall. **CCC.**
Published by: Real Sociedad Espanola de Historia Natural, Facultades de Biologia y Geologia, Universidad Complutense, Madrid, 28040, Spain. rsehno@eucmax.sim.ucm.es, http://www.ucm.es/info/rsehn/. Ed. Antonio Perejon Rincon.

551 IND
RECENT RESEARCHES IN ECONOMIC GEOLOGY. Text in English. irreg., latest vol.18, 1996. price varies. **Document type:** *Monographic series, Academic/Scholarly.*
Published by: (Indian Association of Economic Geology), Hindustan Publishing Corporation (India), 4805-24, Bharat Ram Rd., 1st Fl., Flats 1 & 2, Darya Ganj, New Delhi, 110 002, India. TEL 91-11-325-4401, FAX 91-11-6193511, hpcpd@nda.vsnl.net.in, hpcpd@hpc.cc, http://www.hpc.cc, http://www.bizdelhi.com/publisher/hpc. Ed. K L Rai.

551 IND ISSN 0970-9606
RECENT RESEARCHES IN GEOLOGY. Text in English. 1973. irreg., latest vol.19, 1997. price varies. back issues avail. **Document type:** *Monographic series, Academic/Scholarly.*
Published by: Hindustan Publishing Corporation (India), 4805-24, Bharat Ram Rd., 1st Fl., Flats 1 & 2, Darya Ganj, New Delhi, 110 002, India. TEL 91-11-325-4401, FAX 91-11-6193511, hpcpd@nda.vsnl.net.in, hpcpd@hpc.cc, http://www.hpc.cc, http://www.bizdelhi.com/publisher/hpc.

550 IND
RECENT RESEARCHES IN SEDIMENTOLOGY. Text in English. 1993. irreg. price varies. back issues avail. **Document type:** *Monographic series, Academic/Scholarly.*
Published by: Hindustan Publishing Corporation (India), 4805-24, Bharat Ram Rd., 1st Fl., Flats 1 & 2, Darya Ganj, New Delhi, 110 002, India. TEL 91-11-325-4401, FAX 91-11-6193511, hpcpd@nda.vsnl.net.in, hpcpd@hpc.cc, http://www.hpc.cc. Ed. Vinay Jhingran.

REFERATIVNYI ZHURNAL. GEOKHIMIYA, MINERALOGIYA, PETROGRAFIYA. see *EARTH SCIENCES—Abstracting, Bibliographies, Statistics*

REFERATIVNYI ZHURNAL. GEOLOGICHESKIE I GEOKHIMICHESKIE METODY POISKOV POLEZNYKH ISKOPAEMYKH. see *EARTH SCIENCES—Abstracting, Bibliographies, Statistics*

REFERATIVNYI ZHURNAL. GEOLOGIYA. see *EARTH SCIENCES—Abstracting, Bibliographies, Statistics*

REFERATIVNYI ZHURNAL. GIDROGEOLOGIYA, INZHENERNAYA GEOLOGIYA, MERZLOTOVEDENIE. see *EARTH SCIENCES—Abstracting, Bibliographies, Statistics*

REFERATIVNYI ZHURNAL. NEMETALLICHESKIE POLEZNYE ISKOPAEMYE. see *EARTH SCIENCES—Abstracting, Bibliographies, Statistics*

REFERATIVNYI ZHURNAL. OBSHCHAYA GEOLOGIYA. see *EARTH SCIENCES—Abstracting, Bibliographies, Statistics*

REFERATIVNYI ZHURNAL. TEKHNIKA GEOLOGO-RAZVEDOCHNYKH RABOT. see *EARTH SCIENCES—Abstracting, Bibliographies, Statistics*

796.525 BEL ISSN 1379-8413
REGARDS - SPELEO INFO. Text in French. 2000. bi-m. adv. back issues avail. **Document type:** *Newsletter, Academic/Scholarly.*
Former titles (until 2002): Speleo Info Regards (1376-649X); (until 2000): U B S Info Regards (1377-7149); Which was formed by the merger of (1967-2000): Regards (0774-4617); Which was formerly (until 1987): Speleo Flash (0771-3754); (1988-2000): U B S Info (0776-4065)
Published by: La Societe de Speleologique de Wallonie, Avenue Arthur Proces, 5, Namur, 5000, Belgium. TEL 32-81-230009, FAX 32-81-225798, administration@speleo.be, http://www.speleo.be/ssw/index.htm.

REGIONAL BIBLIOGRAPHY SERIES. see *EARTH SCIENCES—Abstracting, Bibliographies, Statistics*

551 FRA ISSN 1259-4415
LE REGNE MINERAL; mineralogie, geologie. Text in French. 1995. 6/yr. adv. bk.rev. **Description:** Offers practical information for amateurs and mineral collectors.
Published by: Editions du Piat, 1 bis rue Piat, Monistrol-sur-Loire, 43120, France. TEL 33-4-71665467, FAX 33-4-71665467, baylerm@club-internet.fr. Ed., Pub., Adv. contact Louis Dominique Bayle. R&P Loius Dominique Bayle.

551 DEU ISSN 0720-4876
RELIEF, BODEN, PALAEOKLIMA. Text in German, English. 1981. irreg., latest vol.20, 2004. EUR 78 per issue foreign (effective 2005). **Document type:** *Monographic series, Academic/Scholarly.*
—**CCC.**
Published by: (Kommission fuer Geomorphologie der Bayerischen Akademie der Wissenschaften), Gebrueder Borntraeger Verlagsbuchhandlung, Johannesstr. 3A, Stuttgart, 70176, Germany. TEL 49-711-3514560, FAX 49-711-35145699, mail@schweizerbart.de, http://www.schweizerbart.de/j/relief-boden-palaeoklima. Ed. H Hagedorn.

RESERVOIR. see *PETROLEUM AND GAS*

551 JPN ISSN 1344-1698
TN260 CODEN: SHCHEC
➤ **RESOURCE GEOLOGY.** Text in English. 1951. q. JPY 3,000 per issue (effective 2002). bk.rev. 100 p./no.; back issues avail.; reprints avail. **Document type:** *Journal, Academic/Scholarly.*
Related titles: ♦ Japanese ed.: Shigen Chishitsu. ISSN 0918-2454.
Indexed: CurCont, INIS AtomInd.
—BLDSC (7777.602560), IE, ingenta, Linda Hall.
Published by: Shigen Chishitsu Gakkai/Society of Resource Geology, Nogizaka Bldg, 9-6-41 Akasaka, Minato-ku, Tokyo, 107-0052, Japan. TEL 81-3-34755287, FAX 81-3-34750824, srg@kt.rim.or.jp, http://www.kt.rim.or.jp/~srg/. Ed. H Shimazaki. Circ: 1,400.

551 USA ISSN 0741-0123
REVIEWS IN ECONOMIC GEOLOGY. Text in English. 1984. a., latest vol.14, 2001. price varies.
—BLDSC (7790.193500), CISTI, Linda Hall. **CCC.**
Published by: Society of Economic Geologists, 7811 Shaffer Pkwy., Littleton, CO 80127-3732. TEL 720-981-7882, FAX 720-981-7874, seg@segweb.org, https://store.agiweb.org/seg/pubindex.html?Catagory=Reviews, http://www.segweb.org.

557 CRI ISSN 0256-7024
QE210
REVISTA GEOLOGICA DE AMERICA CENTRAL. Text in Spanish. 1984. s-a. USD 30 (effective 2000). adv. **Document type:** *Academic/Scholarly.*
Related titles: Online - full text ed.: (from Gale Group).
Indexed: IBR.
Published by: Editorial de la Universidad de Costa Rica, Apdo. 75-2060, Ciudad Universitaria Rodrigo Facio Brenes, San Pedro de Montes de Oca, San Jose, 2050, Costa Rica. TEL 506-207-4000, FAX 506-207-5535, cmmoreno@cariari.ucr.ac.cr, http://www.egeol.ucr.ac.cr/revista/, http://www.ucr.ac.cr/. Ed. Siegfried Kussmaul. R&P Mario Murillo TEL 506-2075003. Adv. contact Cristina Moreno Murillo.

558 CHL ISSN 0716-0208
CODEN: RGCHDR
➤ **REVISTA GEOLOGICA DE CHILE.** Text in Spanish, English; Summaries in English, Spanish. 1974. s-a. USD 50 (effective 2005). bk.rev. abstr.; bibl.; charts; illus.; maps. **Document type:** *Journal, Academic/Scholarly.* **Description:** Publishes original papers on geology, earth sciences and similar topics.
Related titles: Online - full text ed.: ISSN 0717-618X. 1998. free (effective 2005) (from SciELO).
Indexed: ASCA, CIN, ChemAb, ChemTitl, CurCont, FLUIDEX, GEOBASE, IBR, IMMAb, ZooRec.
—BLDSC (7858.230000), CASDDS, IDS, IE, ingenta.
Published by: Servicio Nacional de Geologia y Mineria, Ave. Santa Maria, 104, Providencia, Santiago, Chile. TEL 56-2-737-5050, FAX 56-2-735-6960, mcortes@sernageomin.cl, http://www.scielo.cl/scielo.php?script=sci_serial&pid=0716-0208&lng=en&nrm=iso. Ed. Manuel Suarez. Circ: 1,000.

558 COL ISSN 0121-6007
REVISTA INGEOMINAS. Text in Spanish. 1992. irreg., latest vol.5. price varies. **Document type:** *Corporate.*
Published by: Instituto de Investigacion e Informacion Geocientifica, Minero-Ambiental y Nuclear Ingeominas, Diagonal 53, 34-53, Apartado Aereo 4865, Bogota, CUND, Colombia. TEL 57-1-2221811, FAX 57-1-2220797, cliente@ingeomin.gov.co.

557 MEX ISSN 1026-8774
QE201 CODEN: RUNGD7
REVISTA MEXICANA DE CIENCIAS GEOLOGICAS. Text mainly in English; Text occasionally in French, Spanish. 1977. s-a. MXP 160 domestic; USD 45 foreign (effective 2003). adv. bk.rev. charts. reprints avail. **Document type:** *Academic/Scholarly.* **Description:** Publishes the results of research work in geologic sciences.
Formerly (until 1994): Universidad Nacional Autonoma de Mexico. Instituto de Geologia. Revista (0185-0962)
Indexed: BiolAb, ChemAb, CurCont, IMMAb, ZooRec.
—CASDDS, Linda Hall.
Published by: Universidad Nacional Autonoma de Mexico, Instituto de Geologia, Circuito de la Investigacion Cientifica s-n, Ciudad Universitaria, Del. Coyoacan, Mexico City, DF 04510, Mexico. TEL 52-5-6224314, FAX 52-5-5508432, publigl@geologia.unam.mx, http://satori.unicit.unam.mx/RMCG.htm. Ed. Luca Ferrari. Circ: 1,200. **Subscr. to:** Departamento de Publicaciones, Apdo. Postal 70-296, Ciudad Universitaria, Del. Coyoacan, 04510, Mexico City, DF 04510, Mexico.

551 CUB
REVISTA TECNOLOGIA: GEOLOGIA. Text in Spanish. s-a. USD 12.
Published by: (Cuba. Ministerio de la Industria Basica), Ediciones Cubanas, Obispo No. 527, Apdo. 605, Havana, Cuba. TEL 32-5556.

551 560 CHE ISSN 0253-6730
➤ **REVUE DE PALEOBIOLOGIE.** Text in English, French, German, Spanish. 1982. s-a. CHF 30 per issue (effective 2003). adv. bk.rev. index. back issues avail. **Document type:** *Journal, Academic/Scholarly.* **Description:** Presents the results of international research in paleobiology, palaeontology, stratigraphy, palaeogeography, palaeoecology and archeozoology.
Indexed: BIOSIS Prev, BiolAb, GEOBASE, RefZh, ZooRec.
—BLDSC (7940.800000), IE, ingenta.
Address: 1 Route de Malagnou, Case Postale 6434, Geneva 6, 1211, Switzerland. TEL 41-22-4186300, FAX 41-22-4186301, christian.meister@mhn.ville-ge.ch, http://www.ville-ge.ch/musinfo/mhng/page/paleo.htm. Ed. Christian Meister. Circ: 400 (paid and controlled).

➤ **REVUE DES REGIONS ARIDES.** see *GEOGRAPHY*

➤ **REVUE DES SCIENCES NATURELLES D'AUVERGNE.** see *BIOLOGY*

➤ **REVUE FRANCAISE DE GEOTECHNIQUE.** see *TECHNOLOGY: COMPREHENSIVE WORKS*

551 ROM ISSN 1220-529X
QE287 CODEN: RRGGBH
REVUE ROUMAINE DE GEOLOGIE. Text in English, French, German, Russian. 1957. a. bk.rev. charts; illus. index.
Formerly (until 1991): Revue Roumaine de Geologie, Geophysique et Geographie (0556-8102); Which supersedes in part (in 1963): Revue de Geologie et de Geographie (1220-1855)
Indexed: ChemAb, EIP, MinerAb, S&F, ZooRec.
—CASDDS, CISTI, KNAW.
Published by: (Academia Romana), Editura Academiei Romane/Publishing House of the Romanian Academy, Calea 13 Septembrie 13, Sector 5, Bucharest, 76117, Romania. TEL 40-21-4119008, FAX 40-21-4103983, edacad@ear.ro. Ed. Dan Radulescu. **Dist. by:** Rodipet S.A., Piata Presei Libere 1, sector 1, PO Box 33-57, Bucharest 3, Romania. TEL 40-21-2224126, 40-21-2226407, rodipet@rodipet.ro.

557 USA
RHODE ISLAND GEOLOGICAL SURVEY. BULLETIN. Text in English. irreg. **Document type:** *Government.*
Published by: Rhode Island Geological Survey, Office of the State Geologist, Dept of Geology, University of Rhode Island, Kingston, RI 02881.

551 ITA ISSN 0557-1405
CODEN: RITGAI
RIVISTA ITALIANA DI GEOTECNICA/ITALIAN GEOTECHNICAL JOURNAL. Text in English, Italian. 1967. q. EUR 70 domestic to individuals; EUR 120 foreign to individuals; EUR 90 domestic to institutions; EUR 120 foreign to institutions (effective 2005). **Document type:** *Journal, Academic/Scholarly.* **Description:** Publishes technical and scientific articles in the field of pure and applied geotechnics.

E

Indexed: ICEA, SoftAbEng.
—CISTI, Linda Hall.
Published by: (Associazione Geotecnica Italiana), Patron Editore, Via Badini 12, Quarto Inferiore, BO 40050, Italy. TEL 39-051-767003, FAX 39-051-768252, info@patroneditore.com, http://www.patroneditore.com. Ed. Roberto Nova.

551 570   ITA   ISSN 1121-1423
➤ RIVISTA PIEMONTESE DI STORIA NATURALE. Text in English, French, Spanish, Italian; Summaries in English, French. 1980. a., latest vol.23, 2002. EUR 100 (effective 2003). bk.rev. bibl.; illus. 350 p./no.; back issues avail. Document type: Bulletin, Academic/Scholarly.
Indexed: ZooRec.
Published by: Associazione Naturalistica Piemontese, c/o Museo Civico di Storia Naturale, Parco Cascina Vigna, Casella Postale 89, Carmagnola, TO 10022, Italy. TEL 39-011-9724390, FAX 39-011-9713040, musnat@comune.carmagnola.to.it, http://www.storianaturale.org/anp. Ed. Achille Casale. Circ: 450.

552 624.151   AUT   ISSN 0723-2632
TA710.A1   CODEN: RMREDX
➤ ROCK MECHANICS AND ROCK ENGINEERING. Text in English. 1929. 5/yr. EUR 415 combined subscription to institutions print & online eds. (effective 2005). adv. bk.rev. charts; illus.; abstr. index. back issues avail. Document type: Journal, Academic/Scholarly. Description: Covers the experimental and theoretical aspects of rock mechanics, including laboratory and field testing, methods of computation and field observation of structural behavior.
Former titles (until 1983): Rock Mechanics (0035-7448); Felsmechanik und Ingenieur Geologie
Related titles: Microform ed.: (from PQC); Online - full text ed.: ISSN 1434-453X (from EBSCO Publishing, Springer LINK, Swets Information Services).
Indexed: ASCA, ApMecR, ChemAb, CivEngAb, CurCont, EngInd, F&EA, GEOBASE, GeotechAb, IBR, ICEA, IMMAb, ISR, Inspec, PetrolAb, RefZh, SCI, SoftAbEng.
—BLDSC (8001.806000), CISTI, Ei, IDS, IE, Infotrieve, ingenta, Linda Hall, PADDS. CCC.
Published by: Springer-Verlag Wien (Subsidiary of: Springer Science+Business Media) journals@springer.at, http://www.springer.at/rock_mechanics. Ed. G Barla. R&P Angela Foessl TEL 43-1-3302415517. Adv. contact Michael Katzenberger TEL 43-1-3302415220. B&W 1/2 page EUR 1,000; 120 x 190. Subscr. in the Americas to: Springer-Verlag New York, Inc., Journal Fulfillment, PO Box 2485, Secaucus, NJ 07096-2485. TEL 800-777-4643, 201-348-4033, FAX 201-348-4505, journals@springer-ny.com, http://www.springer-ny.com.

➤ ROCKS AND MINERALS; mineralogy, geology, lapidary. see MINES AND MINING INDUSTRY

551   USA   ISSN 1555-7332
QE1   CODEN: WUGGAO
➤ ROCKY MOUNTAIN GEOLOGY. Text in English. 1962. s-a. USD 20. bk.rev. bibl.; charts; illus. cum.index: 1962-1986. back issues avail. Document type: Academic/Scholarly. Description: Items dealing with geological problems especially pertinent to the Rocky Mountain region.
Formerly: Contributions to Geology (0010-7980)
Related titles: Online - full text ed.: ISSN 1555-7340 (from HighWire Press).
Indexed: AESIS, BiolAb, ChemAb, EngInd, GSW, IBR, MinerAb, ZooRec.
—BLDSC (8002.627800), CASDDS, Linda Hall, PADDS.
Published by: University of Wyoming, Department of Geology and Geophysics, PO Box 3006, University Sta, Laramie, WY 82071. TEL 307-766-3386, FAX 307-766-6679, TELEX 9109494949. Ed. Ms. Buff Moore. Circ: 680.

➤ ROMANIAN JOURNAL OF MINERAL DEPOSITS. see EARTH SCIENCES

549   ROM   ISSN 1220-5621
   CODEN: DSSGDY
ROMANIAN JOURNAL OF MINERALOGY. Text in English, French, Romanian; Summaries in English, French; Contents page in English. 1910. a. USD 35 (effective 1999). bk.rev. Supplement avail. Document type: Academic/Scholarly.
Supersedes in part (in 1992): Institutul de Geologie si Geofizica. Dari de Seama ale Sedintelor. 1. Mineralogie, Petrologie (1221-4671); Which was formerly: Institutul de Geologie si Geofizica. Dari de Seama ale Sedintelor. 1. Mineralogie, Petrologie, Geochimie (0378-0589); (until 1974): Institutul Geologic. Dari de Seama ale Sedintelor. 1. Mineralogie, Petrologie, Geochimie (1010-9420); Supersedes in part (in 1970): Comitetul de Stat al Geologiei. Dari de Seama ale Sedintelor (0366-9726)
—CASDDS.
Published by: Institutul Geologic al Romaniei, Str. Caransebes 1, Bucharest, 78344, Romania. TEL 40-1-2242091, FAX 40-1-2240404, udubasa@igr.ro. Ed. Gheorghe Udubasa. R&P Serban Veliciu TEL 40-1-2242093.

552   ROM   ISSN 1220-563X
QE451.R6   CODEN: DSSGDY
➤ ROMANIAN JOURNAL OF PETROLOGY. Text in English. 1910. a. USD 35 (effective 1999). Document type: Academic/Scholarly.

Supersedes in part (in 1992): Institutul de Geologie si Geofizica. Dari de Seama ale Sedintelor. 1. Mineralogie, Petrologie (1221-4671); Which was formerly: Institutul de Geologie si Geofizica. Dari de Seama ale Sedintelor. 1. Mineralogie, Petrologie, Geochimie (0378-0589); (until 1974): Institutul Geologic. Dari de Seama ale Sedintelor. 1. Mineralogie, Petrologie, Geochimie (1010-9420); Supersedes in part (in 1970): Comitetul de Stat al Geologiei. Dari de Seama ale Sedintelor (0366-9726)
—CASDDS.
Published by: Institutul Geologic al Romaniei, Str. Caransebes 1, Bucharest, 78344, Romania. TEL 40-1-2242091, FAX 40-1-2240404. Ed. Gheorghe Udubasa. R&P Serban Veliciu TEL 40-1-2242093. Circ: 550.

551.7   ROM   ISSN 1220-5664
QE640
ROMANIAN JOURNAL OF STRATIGRAPHY. Text in English. 1910. a. USD 35 (effective 1999). Document type: ♦ Academic/Scholarly.
Former titles (until 1992): Institutul de Geologie si Geofizica. Dari de Seama ale Sedintelor. 4. Stratigrafie (0254-7309); (until 1974): Institutul Geologic. Dari de Seama ale Sedintelor. 4. Stratigrafie (1010-9412); Supersedes in part (in 1967): Comitetul de Stat al Geologiei. Dari de Seama ale Sedintelor (0366-9726)
Published by: Institutul Geologic al Romaniei, Str. Caransebes 1, Bucharest, 78344, Romania. TEL 40-1-2242091, FAX 40-1-2240404, udubasa@igr.ro. Ed. Gheorghe Udubasa. R&P Serban Veliciu TEL 40-1-2242093. Circ: 550 (paid).

551.8   ROM   ISSN 1221-4663
QE287.6
ROMANIAN JOURNAL OF TECTONICS AND REGIONAL GEOLOGY. Text in English. 1910. a. USD 35 (effective 1999). Supplement avail. Document type: Academic/Scholarly.
Formerly (until 1992): Institutul de Geologie si Geofizica. Dari de Seama ale Sedintelor. 5. Tectonica si Geologie Regionala (0253-1798)
—Linda Hall.
Published by: Institutul Geologic al Romaniei, Str. Caransebes 1, Bucharest, 78344, Romania. TEL 40-1-2242091, FAX 40-1-2240404, udubasa@igr.ro. Ed. Gheorghe Udubasa. R&P Serban Veliciu TEL 40-1-2242093. Circ: 550.

550   RUS
   CODEN: IANGA3
ROSSIISKAYA AKADEMIYA NAUK. IZVESTIYA. SERIYA GEOLOGICHESKAYA. Text in Russian; Contents page in English. 1936. m. bk.rev. bibl.; charts; illus.; maps. index. reprints avail.
Formerly (until no.2, 1992): Akademiya Nauk S.S.S.R. Izvestiya. Seriya Geologicheskaya (0321-1703)
Indexed: BiolAb, ChemAb, EngInd, IBR.
—CASDDS, CISTI, Linda Hall, PADDS. CCC.
Published by: (Rossiiskaya Akademiya Nauk/Russian Academy of Sciences), Izdatel'stvo Nauka, Profsoyuznaya ul 90, Moscow, 117864, Russian Federation. TEL 7-095-3347151, FAX 7-095-4202220, secret@naukaran.ru, http://www.naukaran.ru. Circ: 2,550. Dist. by: M K - Periodica, ul Gilyarovskogo 39, Moscow 129110, Russian Federation. TEL 7-095-2845008, FAX 7-095-2813798, info@periodicals.ru, http://www.mkniga.ru.

551   RUS   ISSN 1027-3603
ROSSIISKAYA AKADEMIYA NAUK. SIBIRSKOE OTDELENIE. OB'EDINENNYI INSTITUT GEOLOGII, GEOFIZIKI, I MINERALOGII. TRUDY. Text in Russian. 1960. irreg. Document type: Academic/Scholarly.
Formerly (until 1993): Institut Geologii i Geofiziki. Trudy (0568-658X)
—Linda Hall. CCC.
Published by: Rossiiskaya Akademiya Nauk, Sibirskoe Otdelenie, Ob'edinennyi Institut Geologii, Geofiziki, i Mineralogii im A. A. Trofimuka/Russian Academy of Sciences, Siberian Branch, Trofimuk United Institute of Geology, Geophysics and Mineralogy, Pr-t Akad Koptyuga 3, Novosibirsk, 630090, Russian Federation. TEL 7-3832-343127, geolgeof@uiggm.nsc.ru, http://www.uiggm.nsc.ru.

551 622   HRV   ISSN 0353-4529
RUDARSKO-GEOLOSKO-NAFTNI ZBORNIK/MINING-GEOLOGICAL-PETROLEUM ENGINEERING BULLETIN. Text in English. 1989. a.
Indexed: FLUIDEX, GEOBASE, RefZh.
—CISTI, Linda Hall.
Published by: Sveuciliste u Zagrebu, Rudarsko Geologsko Naftni Fakultet/University of Zagreb, Faculty of Mining, Geology and Petroleum Engineering, Pierottijeva 6, Zagreb, 10000, Croatia. TEL 385-1-4605103, FAX 385-1-4836051, library@rudar.rgn.hr, http://www.rudar.rgn.hr.

RUDARSTVO. see MINES AND MINING INDUSTRY

RUDARSTVO - GEOLOGIJA - METALURGIJA. see METALLURGY

551   BGR   ISSN 0204-5311
TN95.B8   CODEN: RPMNDM
RUDOOBRAZUVATELNI PROTSESI I MINERALNI NAKHODISHTA. Text in Multiple languages. 1975. 3/yr. price varies. reprint service avail. from IRC.

Indexed: CIN, ChemAb, ChemTitl.
—CASDDS, Linda Hall.
Published by: (Bulgarska Akademiya na Naukite/Bulgarian Academy of Sciences), Universitetsko Izdatelstvo Sv. Kliment Okhridski/Publishing House of the Sofia University St. Kliment Ohridski, Akad G Bonchev 6, Sofia, 1113, Bulgaria. Circ: 420.

551 554   RUS   ISSN 1068-7971
QE1   CODEN: RGEGEZ
➤ RUSSIAN GEOLOGY AND GEOPHYSICS. Text in English. 1974. m. USD 654 foreign to institutions (effective 2006). Document type: Journal, Academic/Scholarly. Description: Contains papers and reviews of geology and geophysics with attention to Siberia and Asia as a whole.
Formerly (until 1992): Soviet Geology and Geophysics (0361-7149); Which was formed by the 1974 merger of: Soviet Geology; Soviet Geophysics
Related titles: ♦ Russian ed.: Geologiya i Geofizika. ISSN 0016-7886.
Indexed: AESIS, ASFA, CurCont, IMMAb, Inspec.
—BLDSC (0420.760600), AskIEEE, CISTI, IE, ingenta. CCC.
Published by: (Rossiiskaya Akademiya Nauk/Russian Academy of Sciences), Izdatel'stvo Sibirskogo Otdeleniya Rossiiskoi Akademii Nauk/Publishing House of the Russian Academy of Sciences, Siberian Branch, Morskoi pr 2, a/ya 187, Novosibirsk, 630090, Russian Federation. TEL 7-3832-300570, FAX 7-3832-333755, institutions@agu.org, psb@ad-sbras.nsc.ru, http://www.agu.org/wps/rgg, http://www-psb.ad-sbras.nsc.ru. Ed. N V Sobolev. Subscr. to: American Geophysical Union, 2000 Florida Ave, NW, Washington, DC 20009-1277. TEL 800-966-2481, service@agu.org, http://www.agu.org.

551.44   AUS
S U S S BULL. Text in English. 1950. 4/yr. AUD 30 to members. bk.rev. Document type: Bulletin. Description: Exploration and study of caves and karst.
Formerly: S U S S Bulletin
Indexed: ASA.
Published by: University of Sydney, Speleological Society, Holme Bldg., University of Sydney, PO Box 35, Sydney, NSW 2006, Australia. TEL 61-2-99593613, keir@es.su.oz.au, http://www.es.su.oz.au/staffprofiles/keir/caves/SUSS/SUSS_Home_Page. Ed. Christopher Norton. Circ: 180 (paid).

THE SAND PAPER. see HOBBIES

550   RUS
AS262   CODEN: VELUA2
SANKT-PETERBURGSKII UNIVERSITET. SERIYA GEOLOGIYA I GEOGRAFIYA. Text in Russian; Abstracts and contents page in English. 1946. q. bk.rev. abstr.; charts; illus. index.
Formerly (until 1992): Leningradskii Universitet. Vestnik. Seriya Geologiya i Geografiya (0024-0834)
Related titles: Microform ed.: (from EVP).
Indexed: ASFA, BibCart, CIN, ChemAb, ChemTitl, GEOBASE, RASB, RefZh.
—CASDDS, CISTI, Linda Hall. CCC.
Published by: Izdatelstvo Sankt-Peterburgskogo Universiteta, Universitetskaya nab 7-9, St Petersburg, 199034, Russian Federation. TEL 7-812-2189784. Ed. S P Merkur'ev. Circ: 1,225. US dist. addr.: East View Information Services, 3020 Harbor Ln. N., Minneapolis, MN 55447. TEL 612-550-0961.

554   RUS
AS262
SANKT-PETERBURGSKII UNIVERSITET. UCHENYE ZAPISKI. SERIYA GEOLOGICHESKIKH NAUK. Text in Russian. 1950. irreg. illus. Description: Provides articles on research in geology, geochemistry and geophysics.
Formerly: Leningradskii Universitet. Uchenye Zapiski. Seriya Geologicheskikh Nauk (0459-0805)
—CISTI, Linda Hall.
Published by: (Geologicheskii Fakultet), Izdatelstvo Sankt-Peterburgskogo Universiteta, Universitetskaya nab 7-9, St Petersburg, 199034, Russian Federation.

557 553   CAN   ISSN 0228-5657
QE194
SASKATCHEWAN GEOLOGICAL SURVEY. SUMMARY OF INVESTIGATIONS. Text in English. a.
Published by: Government of Saskatchewan, Department of Mineral Resources, 1310 La Ronge Ave, Box 5000, La Ronge, SK S0J 1L0, Canada. TEL 306-425-4498, FAX 306-425-4471.

550   CZE   ISSN 0036-5270
QE697   CODEN: SGANA9
➤ SBORNIK GEOLOGICKYCH VED: ANTROPOZOIKUM/JOURNAL OF GEOLOGICAL SCIENCES: ANTHROPOZOIC. Text and summaries in Czech, English, French, German. 1951. irreg., latest vol.24, 2000. price varies. charts; illus.; abstr.; maps. 180 p./no. 2 cols./p.; back issues avail. Document type: Journal, Academic/Scholarly. Description: Papers by Czech and foreign specialists on Quaternary research.
Indexed: ChemAb, GEOBASE.
—CASDDS, Linda Hall.

E

Published by: Ceska Geologicka Sluzba/Czech Geological Survey, Klarov 3, Prague, 11821, Czech Republic. TEL 42-02-57320438, tyracek@cgu.cz, http://www.geology.cz. Ed. Jaroslav Tyracek. Circ: 600. **Subscr. to:** Myris Trade, V Stihlach 1311, PO Box 2, Prague 4 14201, Czech Republic.

551 CZE ISSN 0581-9172
QE267.C8 CODEN: SGVGAP
➤ **SBORNIK GEOLOGICKYCH VED: GEOLOGIE/JOURNAL OF GEOLOGICAL SCIENCES: GEOLOGY.** Text in Czech, English, German; Abstracts occasionally in French, Russian. 1921. irreg., latest vol.49, 1999. price varies. charts; illus.; maps. 120 p./no. 2 cols./p.; back issues avail. **Document type:** *Journal, Academic/Scholarly.* **Description:** Papers by Czech and foreign specialists on general geology, mostly related to the Czech republic (i.e. Bohemian Massif, Carpathian system). Also examines monothematic issues.
Indexed: ChemAb, IBR.
—CASDDS, Linda Hall.
Published by: Ceska Geologicka Sluzba/Czech Geological Survey, Klarov 3, Prague, 11821, Czech Republic. TEL 42-02-57320438, kukal@cgu.cz, http://www.geology.cz. Ed. Zdenek Kukal. Circ: 850. **Subscr. to:** Myris Trade, V Stihlach 1311, PO Box 2, Prague 4 14201, Czech Republic. TEL 420-2-34035200, FAX 420-2-34035207.

551 CZE ISSN 0581-9180
QE267.C8 CODEN: SVLMDX
➤ **SBORNIK GEOLOGICKYCH VED: LOZISKOVA GEOLOGIE, MINERALOGIE/JOURNAL OF GEOLOGICAL SCIENCES: ECONOMIC GEOLOGY, MINERALOGY.** Text in Czech, English, German; Abstracts occasionally in French, Russian. 1963. irreg., latest vol.31, 1997. price varies. charts; illus.; maps. 180 p./no. 2 cols./p.; back issues avail. **Document type:** *Journal, Academic/Scholarly.* **Description:** Papers of Czech and foreign specialists on economic geology and minerology.
Indexed: ChemAb, GEOBASE, IMMAb.
—CASDDS, Linda Hall.
Published by: Ceska Geologicka Sluzba/Czech Geological Survey, Klarov 3, Prague, 11821, Czech Republic. TEL 42-02-57320438, zak@cgu.cz, http://www.geology.cz. Ed. Karel Zak. Circ: 600. **Subscr. to:** Myris Trade, V Stihlach 1311, PO Box 2, Prague 4 14201, Czech Republic. TEL 420-2-34035200, FAX 420-2-34035207.

➤ **SCARECROW AREA BIBLIOGRAPHY SERIES.** see *EARTH SCIENCES—Abstracting, Bibliographies, Statistics*

➤ **SCHWEIZERISCHE MINERALOGISCHE UND PETROGRAPHISCHE MITTEILUNGEN/BOLLETTINO SVIZZERO DI MINERALOGIA E PETROGRAFIA/BULLETIN SUISSE DE MINERALOGIE ET PETROGRAPHIE/SWISS BULLETIN OF MINERALOGY AND PETROLOGY;** eine europaeische Zeitschrift fuer Mineralogie, Geochemie und Petrographie. see *MINES AND MINING INDUSTRY*

551.23 JPN ISSN 0030-2821
SCIENCE OF HOT SPRINGS✶ /ONSEN KAGAKU. Text in Japanese; Summaries in English. 1933. 4/yr. JPY 6,000.
Indexed: INIS AtomInd.
Published by: Balneological Society of Japan/Nippon Onsen Kagakukai, c/o Kazuhisa Miyashita, Secretary Balneological Society of Japan, Wakayama Kenritsu Ika Daigaku, Kimiidera 811-1, Wakayama, 641-8509, Japan. miyaka@wakayama-med.ac.jp, http://wwwsoc.nii.ac.jp/bsj3/. Ed. Susumu Nishimura. Circ: 500.

551.9 FRA ISSN 0335-9255
CODEN: STIGDK
SCIENCES DE LA TERRE: SERIE INFORMATIQUE GEOLOGIQUE. Cover title: Sciences de la Terre: Informatique Geologique. Text in English, French. 1973. irreg., latest vol.32, 1995. price varies. play rev. back issues avail. **Document type:** *Proceedings.*
Indexed: ChemAb, ChemTitl, IMMAb.
—CASDDS, Linda Hall.
Published by: Association Scientifique pour la Geologie et ses Applications, Rue du Doyen Roubault, BP 40, Vandoeuvre, Cedex 54501, France. TEL 33-3-83596306, FAX 33-3-83510599. Ed. J J Royer. Circ: 400.

551 FRA ISSN 0582-2300
QE1 CODEN: SCTMA5
SCIENCES DE LA TERRE: SERIE MEMOIRES. Text in French. 1955. irreg., latest vol.51, 1990. price varies. back issues avail. **Document type:** *Monographic series.*
Indexed: IMMAb.
—CASDDS, Linda Hall.
Published by: Association Scientifique pour la Geologie et ses Applications, Rue du Doyen Roubault, BP 40, Vandoeuvre, Cedex 54501, France. TEL 33-3-83596306, FAX 33-3-83510599.

551 FRA ISSN 0302-2692
QE269 CODEN: BIGPA8
SCIENCES GEOLOGIQUES. BULLETIN. Text in English, French; Summaries in English. 1920. q. price varies. charts; illus. index, cum.index.
Formerly: Service de la Carte Geologique d'Alsace et de Lorraine. Bulletin (0037-2560)
Indexed: CIN, ChemAb, ChemTitl.
—CASDDS, CISTI, Linda Hall.
Published by: Universite de Strasbourg I (Louis Pasteur), Institut de Geologie, 1 rue Blessig, Strasbourg, Cedex 67084, France. TEL 88-35-85-31, FAX 88-36-72-35. Ed. Bertrand Fritz. Circ: 775.

554 FRA ISSN 0302-2684
QE269 CODEN: SGQMAI
SCIENCES GEOLOGIQUES - MEMOIRES. Text in French. 1929. irreg. (1-2/yr.). price varies. adv. bk.rev.
Formerly: Service de la Carte Geologique d'Alsace et de Lorraine. Memoires (0080-9020)
Indexed: AESIS, ChemAb, IMMAb, RefZh.
—Linda Hall. **CCC.**
Published by: Universite de Strasbourg I (Louis Pasteur), Institut de Geologie, 1 rue Blessig, Strasbourg, Cedex 67084, France. TEL 88-35-85-31, FAX 88-36-72-35. Ed. Bertrand Fritz. Circ: 1,000.

551 CHN ISSN 1004-3543
➤ **SCIENTIA GEOLOGICA SINICA.** Text in English. 1992. q. CNY 160 (effective 2004). 128 p./no.; **Document type:** *Journal, Academic/Scholarly.* **Description:** Covers geology and its broader branches, including mineralogy, petrology and palaeontology, structural geology and regional tectonics, sedimentology and stratigraphy, geochemistry and geophysics, and more.
Related titles: Online - full text ed.: (from East View Information Services, WanFang Data Corp.); ♦ Chinese ed.: Dizhi Kexue. ISSN 0563-5020.
Indexed: IMMAb, MinerAb, ZooRec.
Published by: (Zhongguo Kexueyuan, Dizhi yu Diqiu Wuli Yanjiusuo/Chinese Academy of Sciences, Institute of Geology and Geophysics), Kexue Chubanshe/Science Press, 16 Donghuang Cheng Genbei Jie, Beijing, 100717, China. TEL 86-10-64000246, FAX 86-10-64030255, sgs@igcas.ac.cn, http://dzkx-e.periodicals.net.cn/default.html, http://www.sciencep.com/. Ed. Wang Sijing. **Dist. by:** China International Book Trading Corp, 35 Chegongzhuang Xilu, Haidian District, PO Box 399, Beijing 100044, China. TEL 86-10-68412045, FAX 86-10-68412023, cibtc@mail.cibtc.com.cn, http://www.cibtc.com.cn.

➤ **SCOPOLIA.** see *BIOLOGY*

➤ **SCOPOLIA. SUPPLEMENTUM.** see *BIOLOGY*

554 GBR ISSN 0036-9276
QE1 CODEN: SJGEAX
➤ **SCOTTISH JOURNAL OF GEOLOGY.** Text in English. 1965. s-a. GBP 132 domestic; GBP 132, USD 237 foreign (effective 2005). adv. index. back issues avail. **Document type:** *Journal, Academic/Scholarly.* **Description:** Contains original papers on all aspects of the geology of Scotland and neighboring areas including Europe, the North Sea and the margins of the North Atlantic.
Related titles: Online - full text ed.: (from EBSCO Publishing, Gale Group, IngentaConnect, Swets Information Services).
Indexed: AESIS, ASCA, ASFA, BiolAb, BrGeoL, ChemAb, CurCont, ESPM, EngInd, F&EA, GEOBASE, IBR, ISR, MinerAb, PetrolAb, RefZh, SCI, ZooRec.
—BLDSC (8210.500000), CASDDS, CISTI, Ei, IDS, IE, ingenta, Linda Hall, PADDS. **CCC.**
Published by: Geological Society Publishing House, Unit 7, Brassmill Enterprise Centre, Brassmill Ln, Bath, Avon BA1 3JN, United Kingdom. TEL 44-1225-445046, FAX 44-1225-442836, sally.oberst@geolsoc.org.uk, enquiries@geolsoc.org.uk, http://www.geolsoc.org.uk/template.cfm?name=Journal_SJG_home_page. Circ: 1,800. **Co-sponsor:** Geological Societies of Edinburgh & Glasgow.

551 NLD ISSN 0375-7587
QE1 CODEN: SCGLA5
SCRIPTA GEOLOGICA. Text in English; Text occasionally in French, German, Spanish. 1971. irreg., latest vol.115, 1997. price varies. bibl.; charts; illus. **Document type:** *Academic/Scholarly.*
Indexed: AESIS, GEOBASE, MinerAb, RefZh, ZooRec.
—Linda Hall.
Published by: Nationaal Natuurhistorisch Museum, Postbus 9517, Leiden, 2300 RA, Netherlands. R&P C Vanachterberg. Circ: 575 (controlled). **Dist. by:** Backhuys Publishers - Universal Book Services, PO Box 321, Leiden 2300 AH, Netherlands. TEL 31-71-517-0208, FAX 31-71-517-1856.

551.3 NLD ISSN 0037-0738
QE471 CODEN: SEGEBX
➤ **SEDIMENTARY GEOLOGY.** Text in English, French, German. 1967. 40/yr. EUR 2,833 in Europe to institutions; JPY 376,400 in Japan to institutions; USD 3,171 to institutions except Europe and Japan; EUR 177 in Europe to qualified personnel; JPY 23,100 in Japan to qualified personnel; USD 197 to qualified personnel except Europe and Japan (effective 2006). adv. bk.rev. abstr.; charts; illus. index. reprints avail. **Document type:** *Academic/Scholarly.* **Description:** Provides a forum for the publication of research papers across the entire subject, from analytical techniques to regional or geodynamical aspects of sedimentary systems and basin analysis.
Related titles: Microform ed.: (from PQC); Online - full text ed.: (from EBSCO Publishing, Gale Group, IngentaConnect, ScienceDirect, Swets Information Services).
Indexed: AESIS, ASCA, ASFA, BiolAb, BrGeoL, CIS, ChemAb, ChemTitl, CurCont, ESPM, EngInd, F&EA, GEOBASE, IBR, ISR, M&GPA, OceAb, PetrolAb, PollutAb, SCI, SWRA, ZooRec.
—BLDSC (8217.320000), CASDDS, CISTI, Ei, IDS, IE, Infotrieve, ingenta, Linda Hall, PADDS. **CCC.**
Published by: Elsevier BV (Subsidiary of: Elsevier Science & Technology), Radarweg 29, Amsterdam, 1043 NX, Netherlands. TEL 31-20-4853911, FAX 31-20-4852457, nlinfo-f@elsevier.nl, http://www.elsevier.com/locate/sedgeo, http://www.elsevier.nl. Eds. A D Miall, B W Sellwood, K A W Crook.

552.5 GBR ISSN 0037-0746
QE471 CODEN: SEDIAT
➤ **SEDIMENTOLOGY.** Text in English, French, German. 1952. bi-m. GBP 719 combined subscription in Europe to institutions print & online eds.; USD 1,329 combined subscription in the Americas to institutions & Carribean, print & online eds.; GBP 791 combined subscription elsewhere to institutions print & online eds. (effective 2006). adv. bk.rev. abstr.; charts; illus. index, cum.index: vols. 1-10. back issues avail.; reprint service avail. from ISI. **Document type:** *Journal, Academic/Scholarly.* **Description:** Publishes papers in many areas of sedimentology, sedimentary geology and sedimentary geochemistry.
Related titles: Microform ed.: (from PQC); ♦ Online - full text ed.: Sedimentology Online. ISSN 1365-3091.
Indexed: AESIS, ASCA, ASFA, BiolAb, BrGeoL, CIN, CTO, ChemAb, ChemTitl, CurCont, ESPM, EngInd, F&EA, FLUIDEX, GEOBASE, ISR, M&GPA, M&TEA, OceAb, PetrolAb, PollutAb, RefZh, SCI, SFA, SWRA, WildRev, ZooRec.
—BLDSC (8217.400000), CASDDS, CISTI, Ei, IDS, IE, Infotrieve, ingenta, Linda Hall, PADDS. **CCC.**
Published by: (International Association of Sedimentologists ESP), Blackwell Publishing Ltd., 9600 Garsington Rd, Oxford, OX4 2ZG, United Kingdom. TEL 44-1865-776868, FAX 44-1865-714591, customerservices@oxon.blackwellpublishing.com, http://www.blackwellpublishing.com/journals/SED. Eds. Adrian Immenhauser, Isabel Montanez TEL 530-754-7823, Paul A Carling TEL 44-2380-592214, Peter Haughton TEL 353-1-7062244. Pub. Sue Hewitt. R&P Sophie Savage. Adv. contact Martine Cariou Keen. Circ: 2,870.

➤ **SEDIMENTOLOGY AND PETROLEUM GEOLOGY.** see *PETROLEUM AND GAS*

551 EGY ISSN 1110-2527
SEDIMENTOLOGY OF EGYPT/AL-MAGALLAT AL-MISRIYYAT LI-'ILM AL-RUSUBIYYAAT. Text in English. 1993. a. **Document type:** *Journal, Academic/Scholarly.*
Published by: The Sedemintological Society of Egypt, Faculty of Science, Ain Shams University, PO Box 11566, Cairo, Egypt. TEL 20-2-4821096, http://derp.sti.sci.eg/data/0237.htm. Ed. Dr. Sulayman M Sulayman.

552.5 GBR ISSN 1365-3091
➤ **SEDIMENTOLOGY ONLINE.** Text in English. 1998. bi-m. GBP 683 in Europe to institutions; USD 1,262 in the Americas to institutions & Caribbean; GBP 751 elsewhere to institutions (effective 2006). **Document type:** *Academic/Scholarly.*
Media: Online - full text (from Blackwell Synergy, EBSCO Publishing, Gale Group, IngentaConnect, O C L C Online Computer Library Center, Inc., Swets Information Services).
Related titles: Microform ed.: (from PQC); ♦ Print ed.: Sedimentology. ISSN 0037-0746.
Published by: Blackwell Publishing Ltd., 9600 Garsington Rd, Oxford, OX4 2ZG, United Kingdom. TEL 44-1865-776868, FAX 44-1865-714591, customerservices@oxon.blackwellpublishing.com, http://www.blackwellpublishing.com.

552.5 GBR ISSN 0967-8883
SEDIMENTOLOGY REVIEW. Text in English. 1993. irreg., latest vol.1, 1993. USD 99.50 in US & Canada; GBP 37.50 elsewhere (effective 2004). **Document type:** *Monographic series.* **Description:** Covers the most recent developments in sedimentology.
Published by: Blackwell Publishing Ltd., 9600 Garsington Rd, Oxford, OX4 2ZG, United Kingdom. TEL 44-1865-776868, FAX 44-1865-714591, customerservices@oxon.blackwellpublishing.com, http://www.blackwellpublishing.com/book.asp?ref=0632031026&site=1. Ed. V P Wright.

SEMINAR ON PETROLIFEROUS BASINS OF INDIA. PROCEEDINGS. see *PETROLEUM AND GAS*

551.7 ESP ISSN 0211-2256
CODEN: SMEGAG
SEMINARIOS DE ESTRATIGRAFIA. SERIE MONOGRAFIAS. Text in Spanish; Summaries in English, French, Spanish. 1968. irreg. price varies. charts; illus. **Document type:** *Monographic series, Academic/Scholarly.*
Supersedes (in 1976): Seminarios de Estratigrafia (0375-7609)
Indexed: IECT.
Published by: Universidad Complutense de Madrid, Instituto de Geologica Economica, Donoso Cortes, 65, Madrid, 28015, Spain. TEL 34-1-3946372. Ed. Alfredo Arche. Circ: 1,000.

E

SENCKENBERGIANA LETHAEA. see *PALEONTOLOGY*

SENCKENBERGISCHE NATURFORSCHENDE GESELLSCHAFT. ABHANDLUNGEN. see *BIOLOGY*

551 ITA ISSN 0366-2241
SERVIZIO GEOLOGICO D'ITALIA. BOLLETTINO. Text in Italian. 1870. a.
Former titles (until 1947): Ufficio Geologico d'Italia. Bollettino (0366-2314); (until 1921): R. Comitato Geologico d'Italia. Bollettino (1122-2115)
Indexed: RefZh, ZooRec.
Published by: Servizio Geologico d'Italia, Largo di Santa Susanna 13, Rome, Italy. TEL 39-06-4743081.

557 USA ISSN 0037-3257
QE153 CODEN: SHSKAT
SHALE SHAKER. Text in English. 1950. bi-m. USD 30 domestic; USD 35 foreign (effective 2005). adv. bibl.; charts. **Document type:** *Newsletter.*
Indexed: PetrolAb.
—BLDSC (8254.588000), IE, ingenta.
Published by: Oklahoma City Geological Society, Inc., 120 North Robinson, Ste 900 Center, Oklahoma City, OK 73102. TEL 405-236-8086, FAX 405-236-8085, ocgs@oklahoma.net, http://www.ocgs.org/shaleshaker.asp. Ed. Ron Krakowski. Adv. contact Carol Jones. Circ: 1,250 (controlled).

555 CHN ISSN 1008-2786
➤ **SHANDI XUEBAO/JOURNAL OF MOUNTAIN SCIENCE.** Text in Chinese. 1983. bi-m. CNY 60 (effective 2004). adv. **Document type:** *Journal, Academic/Scholarly.*
Formerly: Shandi Yanjiu (1000-002X)
Related titles: Online - full text ed.: (from East View Information Services, WanFang Data Corp.).
—BLDSC (5021.052500).
Published by: (Chengdu Shandi Zaihai yu Huanjing Yanjiusuo/Chinese Academy of Sciences, Institute of Mountain Hazards and Environment), Kexue Chubanshe/Science Press, 16 Donghuang Cheng Genbei Jie, Beijing, 100717, China. TEL 86-10-64000246, FAX 86-10-64030255, hyfeng@imde.ac.cn, http://sdxb.periodicals.net.cn/default.html, http://www.sciencep.com/. Circ: 5,500. **Dist. by:** China International Book Trading Corp, 35 Chegongzhuang Xilu, Haidian District, PO Box 399, Beijing 100044, China. TEL 86-10-68412045, FAX 86-10-68412023, cibtc@mail.cibtc.com.cn, http://www.cibtc.com.cn.

551 JPN ISSN 0918-2454
TN260 CODEN: SHCHEC
➤ **SHIGEN CHISHITSU.** Text in Japanese; Abstracts in English. 1951. s-a. JPY 8,500 membership (effective 2005). bk.rev. back issues avail.; reprints avail. **Document type:** *Journal, Academic/Scholarly.*
Formerly (until 1992): Kozan Chishitsu/Mining Geology (0026-5209)
Related titles: ♦ English ed.: Resource Geology. ISSN 1344-1698.
Indexed: AESIS, CIN, ChemAb, ChemTitl, INIS AtomInd.
—CASDDS, Linda Hall. **CCC.**
Published by: Shigen Chishitsu Gakkai/Society of Resource Geology, Nogizaka Bldg, 9-6-41 Akasaka, Minato-ku, Tokyo, 107-0052, Japan. TEL 81-3-34755287, FAX 81-3-34750824, khayashi@mail.cc.tohoku.ac.jp, srg@kt.rim.or.jp, http://www.kt.rim.or.jp/~srg/. Ed. Shigen Chishitsu. Circ: 1,400.

551 JPN ISSN 0287-816X
SHIMANE DAIGAKU CHISHITSUGAKU KENKYU HOKOKU/SHIMANE UNIVERSITY. GEOLOGICAL REPORTS. Text in English, Japanese; Summaries in English. 1982. a.
Published by: (Chishitsugaku Kyoshitsu), Shimane Daigaku, Rigakubu/Shimane University, Faculty of Science, Department of Geology, 1060 Nishikawa-Tsu-cho, Matsue-shi, Shimane-ken 690-0823, Japan.

551 CHN ISSN 1000-7210
TN270.A1
SHIYOU DILI WULI KANTAN/OIL GEOPHYSICAL PROSPECTING. Text in Chinese, English. 1966. bi-m. USD 60. adv. **Document type:** *Academic/Scholarly.* **Description:** Provides information on the new technical developments in geophysical exploration.
Related titles: Online - full text ed.: (from East View Information Services).
Indexed: C&ISA, E&CAJ, EngInd, IAA, PetrolAb, RefZh.
—BLDSC (6252.026000), IE, ingenta, Linda Hall, PADDS.
Published by: Nengyuan Bu, Dili Wuli Kantan Ju, P.O. Box 11-1, Zuozhou, Hebei 072751, China. TEL 3234-332901, TELEX 222998 BGPPC CN. Ed. Yu Shoupeng. Adv. contact Huang Xiangxiu. B&W page USD 1,000, color page USD 2,000; trim 260 x 188. Circ: 10,000. **Dist. outside China by:** China International Book Trading Corp, 35 Chegongzhuang Xilu, Haidian District, PO Box 399, Beijing 100044, China.

552 CHN ISSN 0253-9985
➤ **SHIYOU YU TIANRANQI DIZHI/OIL AND GAS GEOLOGY.** Text in Chinese. 1980. q. CNY 27.20, USD 12. adv. 85 p./no.; **Document type:** *Journal, Academic/Scholarly.* **Description:** Publishes the latest achievements in petroleum exploration, production, and scientific research in China.
Related titles: Online - full text ed.: (from East View Information Services).
Indexed: CIN, ChemAb, ChemTitl, PetrolAb, RefZh, ZooRec.
—BLDSC (6249.847000), Linda Hall, PADDS.
Published by: Zhongguo Dizhi Xuehui, Shiyou Dizhi Zhuanye Weiyuanhui, No 31 Xueyuan Rd, Haidian District, Beijing, 100083, China. TEL 86-10-82312982, FAX 86-10-82312089, oil-gasgeology@pepris.com. Ed. Wang Tingbin. Adv. contact Peng Yueh. page USD 1,600. Circ: 2,000. **Dist. by:** China International Book Trading Corp, 35 Chegongzhuang Xilu, Haidian District, PO Box 399, Beijing 100044, China.

551 JPN ISSN 0285-0753
SHIZUOKA CHIGAKU/SHIZUOKA GEOSCIENCE LETTERS. Text in Japanese. 1964. s-a.
Published by: Shizuokaken Chigakkai/Shizuoka Geoscience Association, Shizuoka Daigaku Kyoikugakubu Chigaku Kyoshitsu, 836 Oya, Shizuoka-shi, Shizuoka-ken 422-8017, Japan.

551 CHN ISSN 1001-6112
➤ **SHUYOU SHIYAN DIZHI/PETROLEUM GEOLOGY & EXPERIMENT.** Text in Chinese, English. 1963. bi-m. USD 60 (effective 2003). adv. illus. 96 p./no.; back issues avail. **Document type:** *Journal, Academic/Scholarly.* **Description:** Studies the formation and evolution of petroliferous sedimentary basins, petroleum experimental technology, as well as the formation and distribution patterns of oil, gas fields.
Related titles: ♦ CD-ROM ed.: Chinese Academic Journals Full-Text Database. Science & Engineering, Series B. ISSN 1007-8029; Online - full text ed.: (from East View Information Services, WanFang Data Corp.).
Indexed: RefZh, ZooRec.
—BLDSC (3840.035000), IE.
Published by: (China National Star Petroleum Corp.), Shiyan Dizhi Yanjiusuo/Research Institute of Experimental Geology, P.O. Box 916, Wuxi, Jiangsu 214151, China. TEL 86-510-320-1044, FAX 86-510-320-2742, mailto:sysydz@pub.wx.jsinfo.net, http://sysydz.wanfangdata.com.cn/default.html. Ed., R&P Deliao Ye TEL 86-510-3203146. Adv. contact Ms. Li Jun TEL 86-510-3209032. **Dist. by:** China Publications International Trading Corporation, P.O. Box 782, Beijing, China.

551 CHN ISSN 1006-0995
SICHUAN DIZHI XUEBAO/ACTA GEOLOGICA SICHUAN. Text in Chinese. 1980. q. **Document type:** *Journal, Academic/Scholarly.*
Related titles: Online - full text ed.: (from East View Information Services, WanFang Data Corp.).
Address: 25, Renmin Beilu, 1-duan, Chengdu, 610081, China. TEL 86-28-83224539, scdzxb@yahoo.com.cn, http://scdzxb.periodicals.net.cn/.

550 ESP ISSN 0214-2708
SOCIEDAD GEOLOGICA DE ESPANA. REVISTA. Text in Spanish. 1988. s-a. EUR 12 membership (effective 2005).
Indexed: IECT, MinerAb, ZooRec.
—CINDOC. **CCC.**
Published by: Sociedad Geologica de Espana, Plaza de la Mercedes, s-n, Salamanca, 37008, Spain. TEL 34-923-294752, info@geologicas.es, http://www.sociedadgeologica.es/. Ed. Jose Manuel Gonzalez Casado.

558 PER ISSN 0079-1091
QE1 CODEN: BOGPAG
➤ **SOCIEDAD GEOLOGICA DEL PERU. BOLETIN.** Text in Spanish; Summaries in English, French, Spanish. 1925. 3/yr. PEN 1,500 domestic; USD 20 foreign (effective 2005). adv. bk.rev. cum.index: vols.1-18 (1925-45), vols.19-27 (1946-55), vols.20-50 (1947-75), vols.51-81 (1976-1990). **Document type:** *Bulletin, Academic/Scholarly.*
Indexed: BiolAb, ZooRec.
—CISTI, Linda Hall.
Published by: Sociedad Geologica del Peru, Arnaldo Marquez 2277 Jesus Maria, Lima, 11, Peru. TEL 51-1-4616897, FAX 51-1-4615272, public@sgp.prg.pe, http://www.sgp.org.pe/boletines.htm. Ed. O Orrego. Circ: 800.

551 URY ISSN 0797-2997
SOCIEDAD URUGUAYA DE GEOLOGIA. REVISTA. Text in Spanish. 1985. a.
Indexed: INIS AtomInd.
Published by: Sociedad Uruguaya de Geologia, Colonia 922, Oficina 507, Montevideo, 11200, Uruguay. secretaria@sugeologia.org, http://www.sugeologia.org/publicaciones/revista/revista.htm.

796.525 VEN ISSN 0583-7731
GB608 CODEN: SVEBAU
SOCIEDAD VENEZOLANA DE ESPELEOLOGIA. BOLETIN. Text in Spanish; Summaries in English. 1967. a. VEB 6,000, USD 15 (effective 2003). 80 p./no.; back issues avail. **Document type:** *Bulletin.*
Related titles: Online - full text ed.: free (effective 2005).
Indexed: BiolAb, GEOBASE, SpeleolAb, ZooRec.
—Linda Hall.
Published by: Sociedad Venezolana de Espeleologia, Apdo 47334, Caracas, DF 1041-A, Venezuela. TEL 58-212-2720724, svespeleo@cantv.net. Ed. Francisco Herrera. Circ: 1,000.

551 VEN ISSN 0583-774X
SOCIEDAD VENEZOLANA DE GEOLOGOS. BOLETIN. Text in Spanish. 1965. 3/yr. USD 90. adv. **Document type:** *Bulletin, Academic/Scholarly.*
Indexed: GEOBASE, IMMAb.
—PADDS.
Published by: Sociedad Venezolana de Geologos, Apdo 2006, Caracas, DF 1010-A, Venezuela. FAX 58-2-573-3968, TELEX 21470 CIVFC VE. Circ: 1,000.

554 ITA ISSN 0037-8763
QE1 CODEN: BOGIAT
SOCIETA GEOLOGICA ITALIANA. BOLLETTINO. Text in Italian; Summaries in English, French, German. 1882. 3/yr. price varies. bibl.; charts; illus.; mkt. index, cum.index. **Document type:** *Bulletin.*
Indexed: BiolAb, ChemAb, CurCont, IBR, RefZh, ZooRec.
—BLDSC (2230.500000), CASDDS, IE, ingenta, Linda Hall.
Published by: Universita degli Studi di Roma "La Sapienza", Societa Geologica Italiana, Piazzale Aldo Moro, 5, Rome, RM 00185, Italy. Ed. Dr. Achille Zuccari. Circ: 2,200.

551 ITA ISSN 0375-9857
QE272 CODEN: MSGLAH
SOCIETA GEOLOGICA ITALIANA. MEMORIE. Text in Italian. irreg. **Document type:** *Monographic series.*
Indexed: RefZh, ZooRec.
—Linda Hall.
Published by: Universita degli Studi di Roma "La Sapienza", Societa Geologica Italiana, Piazzale Aldo Moro, 5, Rome, RM 00185, Italy.

SOCIETAT D'HISTORIA NATURAL DE LES BALEARS. MONOGRAFIE. see *BIOLOGY*

551 POL ISSN 0208-9068
QE1 CODEN: ASGPD2
➤ **SOCIETATIS GEOLOGORUM POLONIAE. ANNALES/POLSKIE TOWARZYSTWO GEOLOGICZNE. ROCZNIK.** Key Title: Annales Societatis Geologorum Poloniae. Text in English. 1921. q. PLZ 30, USD 10 (effective 2002). adv. bk.rev. bibl.; charts; illus. index. **Document type:** *Academic/Scholarly.* **Description:** Publishes scientific contributions from all fields of geological science.
Formerly (until 1981): Polskie Towarzystwo Geologiczne. Rocznik (0079-3663)
Indexed: RefZh, ZooRec.
—BLDSC (0946.420000), CASDDS, CISTI, Linda Hall.
Published by: Polskie Towarzystwo Geologiczne/Geological Society of Poland, Ul Oleandry 2 A, Krakow, 30063, Poland. FAX 48-12-221609. Ed. Zbigniew Wilk. R&P, Adv. contact Andrzej Slaczka. page USD 250. Circ: 900. **Dist. in UK by:** UCL Press, University College of, Gower St, London WC1E 6BT, United Kingdom. **Co-sponsor:** Polska Akademia Nauk, Komitet Badan Naukowych.

➤ **SOCIETE D'HISTOIRE NATURELLE DE COLMAR. BULLETIN.** see *BIOLOGY—Botany*

554 FRA ISSN 0037-9409
QE1 CODEN: BSGFAE
➤ **SOCIETE GEOLOGIQUE DE FRANCE. BULLETIN.** Text and summaries in English, French. 1830. bi-m. EUR 106.72 domestic; EUR 125 foreign (effective 2003). charts; illus. index, cum.index: 1830-1958 (in 6 vols.). 120 p./no.; back issues avail. **Document type:** *Bulletin, Academic/Scholarly.* **Description:** Publishes papers in the geological sciences.
Related titles: Microfilm ed.: (from BHP); Online - full text ed.: (from HighWire Press).
Indexed: ASCA, ASFA, BiolAb, BrGeoL, CIN, ChemAb, ChemTitl, CurCont, DIP, E&PHSE, ESPM, EngInd, FLUIDEX, GEOBASE, GP&P, GSW, IAA, IBR, INIS AtomInd, ISR, OffTech, PetrolAb, PollutAb, RefZh, SCI, SFA, SWRA, ZooRec.
—BLDSC (2742.000000), CASDDS, CISTI, Ei, IDS, IE, Infotrieve, ingenta, Linda Hall, PADDS. **CCC.**
Published by: Societe Geologique de France, 77 rue Claude Bernard, Paris, 75005, France. TEL 33-01-43317735, FAX 33-01-45357910, accueil@sgfr.org, http://www.sgfr.org. Ed. Dominique Frizon de LaMotte. R&P Francoise Peiffer Rangin. Circ: 1,500.

554 FRA ISSN 0249-7549
➤ **SOCIETE GEOLOGIQUE DE FRANCE. MEMOIRES.** Text in English, French. 1962. irreg., latest 2002. EUR 50. **Document type:** *Monographic series, Academic/Scholarly.* **Description:** Scientific papers on geological subjects; each volume studies a particular theme.
Indexed: BiolAb, BrGeoL, RefZh, ZooRec.
—BLDSC (5569.000000), IE, ingenta, Linda Hall. **CCC.**
Published by: Societe Geologique de France, 77 rue Claude Bernard, Paris, 75005, France. TEL 33-01-43317735, FAX 33-01-45357910, accueil@sgfr.org, http://www.sgfr.org. Ed. Dominique Frizon de LaMotte. R&P Francoise Peiffer Rangin.

E

554 930.1 FRA ISSN 0336-9994
➤ **SOCIETE GEOLOGIQUE DE NORMANDIE ET DES AMIS DU MUSEUM DU HAVRE. BULLETIN TRIMESTRIEL.** Text in French. 1871. q. EUR 39 domestic to non-members; EUR 54 foreign to non-members; EUR 23 to members (effective 2003). bk.rev. illus.; abstr.; bibl.; maps. back issues avail. **Document type:** *Bulletin, Academic/Scholarly.*
Supersedes: Societe Geologique de Normandie, Le Havre. Bulletin
Indexed: BiolAb, GEOBASE, ZooRec.
Published by: (Societe Geologique de Normandie et des Amis du Museum du Havre), Editions du Museum du Havre, Place du Vieux Marche, Le Havre, 76600, France. TEL 33-2-35413728, FAX 33-2-35421240. Ed., R&P, Adv. contact Gerard Breton. Circ: 1,000. **Co-sponsor:** Museum d'Histoire Naturelle du Havre.

551 FRA ISSN 0767-7367
QE1 CODEN: ASGNAR
SOCIETE GEOLOGIQUE DU NORD. ANNALES. Text in English, French; Summaries in English, French, Spanish. 1870. q. adv. bk.rev. **Document type:** *Bulletin.*
Indexed: BiolAb, BrGeoL, IBR, PetrolAb, RefZh, ZooRec.
—BLDSC (0949.100000), CISTI, IE, ingenta, PADDS.
Published by: Societe Geologique du Nord, B.P. 36, Villeneuve d'Ascq, F-59655, France. TEL 33-3-20434145. Ed. Paule Corsin. Adv. contact Olivier Averbuch.

SOCIETE LINNEENNE DE BORDEAUX. BULLETIN. see *BIOLOGY—Zoology*

552.5 USA ISSN 1060-071X
CODEN: SSGPEV
SOCIETY FOR SEDIMENTARY GEOLOGY. SPECIAL PUBLICATION. Text in English. 1951. irreg. price varies. **Document type:** *Monographic series, Academic/Scholarly.*
Formerly (until 1991): Society of Economic Paleontologists and Mineralogists. Special Publication (0097-3270)
—BLDSC (8380.790000), CISTI, IE, ingenta. **CCC.**
Published by: Society for Sedimentary Geology, 6128 E 38th St, Ste 308, Tulsa, OK 74135-5814. TEL 918-493-2093.

551 USA
SOCIETY OF ECONOMIC GEOLOGIST. SPECIAL PUBLICATIONS SERIES. Text in English.
—BLDSC (8380.790000), ingenta.
Published by: Society of Economic Geologists, 7811 Shaffer Pkwy., Littleton, CO 80127-3732. socecongeol@csn.net.

551 BGR ISSN 0324-0479
QE287 CODEN: GSUFE7
➤ **SOFIISKI UNIVERSITET SV. KLIMENT OHRIDSKI. GEOLOGO-GEOGRAFSKI FAKULTET. GODISHNIK. KNIGA 1. GEOLOGIYA.** Text in Bulgarian, English, Russian; Summaries in English, French. 1905. a. USD 50 per issue (effective 2000). adv. bk.rev. charts; maps. 250 p./no.; reprints avail. **Document type:** *Yearbook, Academic/Scholarly.*
Formerly (until 1981): Sofiiski Universitet. Geologo-Geografski Fakultet. Godishnik. Kniga 1. Geologiya (1310-537X)
Indexed: RefZh.
—CASDDS, CISTI, Linda Hall.
Published by: (Sofiiski Universitet Sv. Kliment Ohridski, Geologo-Geografski Fakultet), Universitetsko Izdatelstvo Sv. Kliment Okhridski/Publishing House of the Sofia University St. Kliment Ohridski, Akad G Bonchev 6, Sofia, 1113, Bulgaria. TEL 359-2-9792914. Ed. Dimiter Tashev. Circ: 350.

▼ ➤ **SOIL EROSION & HYDROSEEDING.** see *ENVIRONMENTAL STUDIES—Waste Management*

➤ **SOIL SCIENCE ALERT;** an alerting service covering current articles in Elsevier soil science journals. see *EARTH SCIENCES—Abstracting, Bibliographies, Statistics*

➤ **SOLOS E ROCHAS/SOILS AND ROCKS/SUELOS Y ROCAS;** revista latino-americano de geotecnia - Latin-American geotechnical journal. see *ENGINEERING*

796.525 551.44 CAN ISSN 0827-9772
SOUS TERRE. Text in English. 1983. q. USD 30 to individuals; USD 50 to institutions (effective 2000). **Document type:** *Bulletin.* **Description:** Covers the activities of cavers and cave research.
Formerly: Societe Quebecoise de Speleologie. Bulletin
Published by: Societe Quebecoise de Speleologie, 4545 Av Pierre de Coubertin, C P 1000, Succ M, Montreal, PQ H1V 3R2, Canada. TEL 514-252-3006, FAX 514-252-3201. Ed. Jacques Kirouac. Circ: 1,250.

551 ZAF ISSN 1016-5991
QE325
SOUTH AFRICA. COUNCIL FOR GEOSCIENCE. ANNUAL TECHNICAL REPORT. Text in Afrikaans, English. 1962. irreg., latest 1995. price varies. **Document type:** *Corporate.* **Description:** Summary of research papers by staff members on various aspects of southern African geology, geophysics, geochemistry, and engineering geology. Includes annual report of the Chief Director, and progress reports on Geological Survey projects.
Former titles: South Africa. Geological Survey. Annual Technical Report; (until 1988): South Africa. Geological Survey. Annals (0584-2352)
Indexed: AESIS, IMMAb, INIS AtomInd, ISAP.
—CISTI, Linda Hall.
Published by: Council for Geoscience, Private Bag X112, Pretoria, 0001, South Africa. TEL 27-12-841-1911, FAX 27-12-841-1203, rprice@geoscience.org.za. R&P R R M Price TEL 27-12-8411018.

551 ZAF
SOUTH AFRICA. COUNCIL FOR GEOSCIENCE. GEOLOGICAL MAPS. Text in Afrikaans, English. 1911. irreg. price varies. **Document type:** *Government.* **Description:** Includes maps of South Africa at scales 1:1,000,000; 1:250,000; or 1:50,000. Maps of other countries produced on an irregular basis.
Formerly: South Africa. Geological Survey. Geological Maps; South Africa. Geological Survey. Special Publications
Published by: Council for Geoscience, Private Bag X112, Pretoria, 0001, South Africa. TEL 27-12-841-1911, FAX 27-12-841-1203, rprice@geoscience.org.za. Ed. M Roos. R&P R R M Price TEL 27-12-8411018.

556 ZAF ISSN 1010-545X
CODEN: RMOSAN
SOUTH AFRICA. COUNCIL FOR GEOSCIENCE. GEOLOGICAL MAPS. EXPLANATIONS. Text in Afrikaans, English. 1907. irreg., latest 1993. price varies. **Document type:** *Government.* **Description:** Geological explanatory notes to accompany published geological maps.
Formerly (until 1911): South Africa. Geological Survey. Geological Maps. Explanations (0254-1920)
Indexed: IMMAb.
Published by: Council for Geoscience, Private Bag X112, Pretoria, 0001, South Africa. TEL 27-12-841-1911, FAX 27-12-841-1203, rprice@geoscience.org.za.

550 ZAF
CODEN: RMGHAI
SOUTH AFRICA. COUNCIL FOR GEOSCIENCE. HANDBOOK. Text in Afrikaans, English. 1959. irreg., latest vol.15. price varies. **Document type:** *Monographic series, Academic/Scholarly.* **Description:** Deals with investigations having a countrywide scope.
Formerly: South Africa. Geological Survey. Handbook (0560-9208)
Indexed: AESIS, IMMAb.
Published by: Council for Geoscience, Private Bag X112, Pretoria, 0001, South Africa. TEL 27-12-841-1911, FAX 27-12-841-1203, rprice@geoscience.org.za.

551 ZAF ISSN 1681-6099
SOUTH AFRICA. COUNCIL FOR GEOSCIENCE. MEMOIR. Text in English. 1905. irreg., latest vol.83. price varies. **Document type:** *Monographic series, Academic/Scholarly.* **Description:** Presents the results of comprehensive research in a specified field, or on a geological subject or entity.
Formerly (until 1999): South Africa. Geological Survey. Memoir (0370-3401)
Indexed: AESIS, IMMAb, ZooRec.
—CISTI.
Published by: Council for Geoscience, Private Bag X112, Pretoria, 0001, South Africa. TEL 27-12-841-1911, FAX 27-12-841-1203, rprice@geoscience.org.za.

551 ZAF
SOUTH AFRICA. COUNCIL FOR GEOSCIENCE. SOUTH AFRICAN COMMITTEE FOR STRATIGRAPHY. BIOSTRATIGRAPHIC SERIES. Text in English. 1996. irreg. price varies. **Document type:** *Academic/Scholarly.* **Description:** Provides details of formal rock units according to international principles.
Published by: (South Africa. South African Committee for Stratigraphy), Council for Geoscience, Private Bag X112, Pretoria, 0001, South Africa. TEL 27-12-841-1911, FAX 27-12-841-1203, rprice@geoscience.org.za.

551.7 ZAF ISSN 1019-1879
QE325
SOUTH AFRICA. COUNCIL FOR GEOSCIENCE. SOUTH AFRICAN COMMITTEE FOR STRATIGRAPHY. CATALOGUE OF SOUTH AFRICAN LITHOSTRATIGRAPHIC UNITS. Text in English. 1989. irreg., latest vol.5. price varies. **Document type:** *Catalog, Academic/Scholarly.* **Description:** Comprehensive descriptions in brief of rock units.
Formerly: South Africa. Geological Survey. South African Committee for Stratigraphy. Catalogue of South African Lithostratigraphic Units
—CISTI.
Published by: (South Africa. South African Committee for Stratigraphy), Council for Geoscience, Private Bag X112, Pretoria, 0001, South Africa. TEL 27-12-841-1911, FAX 27-12-841-1203, rprice@geoscience.org.za.

551.7 ZAF ISSN 1018-0206
SOUTH AFRICA. COUNCIL FOR GEOSCIENCE. SOUTH AFRICAN COMMITTEE FOR STRATIGRAPHY. CHRONOSTRATIGRAPHIC SERIES. Text in English. 1989. irreg. price varies. **Document type:** *Academic/Scholarly.* **Description:** Provides detailed descriptions of formal chronostratigraphic rock units according to international principles.
Formerly: South Africa. Geological Survey. South African Committee for Stratigraphy. Chronostratigraphic Series
Published by: (South Africa. South African Committee for Stratigraphy), Council for Geoscience, Private Bag X112, Pretoria, 0001, South Africa. TEL 27-12-841-1911, FAX 27-12-841-1203, rprice@geoscience.org.za.

551.7 ZAF ISSN 1017-5571
SOUTH AFRICA. COUNCIL FOR GEOSCIENCE. SOUTH AFRICAN COMMITTEE FOR STRATIGRAPHY. CIRCULAR. Text in English. 1987. irreg. price varies. **Document type:** *Academic/Scholarly.* **Description:** Guidelines for standardized lithostratigraphic descriptions.
Formerly: South Africa. Geological Survey. South African Committee for Stratigraphy. Circular
Published by: (South Africa. South African Committee for Stratigraphy), Council for Geoscience, Private Bag X112, Pretoria, 0001, South Africa. TEL 27-12-841-1911, FAX 27-12-841-1203, rprice@geoscience.org.za.

551 ZAF ISSN 1017-1436
QE640
SOUTH AFRICA. COUNCIL FOR GEOSCIENCE. SOUTH AFRICAN COMMITTEE FOR STRATIGRAPHY. LITHOSTRATIGRAPHIC SERIES. Text in English. 1987. irreg., latest vol.31, 1995. **Document type:** *Academic/Scholarly.* **Description:** Provides detailed descriptions of formal rock units according to international principles.
Formerly: South Africa. Geological Survey. South African Committee for Stratigraphy. Lithostratigraphic Series
—CISTI.
Published by: (South Africa. South African Committee for Stratigraphy), Council for Geoscience, Private Bag X112, Pretoria, 0001, South Africa. TEL 27-12-841-1911, FAX 27-12-841-1221, rprice@geoscience.org.za. Circ: 2,000.

SOUTH AFRICA. DEPARTMENT OF MINERALS AND ENERGY. ANNUAL REPORT. see *MINES AND MINING INDUSTRY*

556 ZAF
SOUTH AFRICA. GEOLOGICAL SURVEY. OPEN FILE REPORTS. Text in English. ceased 199?; resumed. irreg. price varies. stat. **Document type:** *Academic/Scholarly.*
Published by: Council for Geoscience, Private Bag X112, Pretoria, 0001, South Africa. TEL 27-12-841-1911, FAX 27-12-841-1203, TELEX 350286 SAGEO, rprice@geoscience.org.z.

556 ZAF ISSN 1012-0750
QE1 CODEN: TGSAA3
➤ **SOUTH AFRICAN JOURNAL OF GEOLOGY.** Text and summaries in English. 1896. q. adv. bibl.; illus. cum.index every 10 yrs. **Document type:** *Journal, Academic/Scholarly.* **Description:** Publishes articles, notes, discussions and short commentaries on a wide variety of geological topics.
Former titles (until 1987): Geological Society of South Africa. Transactions (0371-7208); Geological Society of South Africa. Transactions and Proceedings.
Related titles: Microfiche ed.: (from BHP); Online - full text ed.: (from EBSCO Publishing, HighWire Press).
Indexed: AESIS, ASFA, BiolAb, CIN, ChemAb, ChemTitl, CurCont, ESPM, ForAb, GEOBASE, GSW, IMMAb, INIS AtomInd, ISAP, MinerAb, OceAb, PetrolAb, PollutAb, RefZh, S&F, SWRA, ZooRec.
—BLDSC (8338.868000), CASDDS, CISTI, IDS, IE, Infotrieve, ingenta, Linda Hall, PADDS.
Published by: (Geological Society of South Africa/Geologiese Vereniging van Suid-Afrika), South African Bureau for Scientific Publications, PO Box 11663, Pretoria, Hatfield 0028, South Africa. TEL 27-12-322-6404, FAX 27-12-320-7803, bspman@icon.co.za, http://www.safest.org.za/bsp. Ed., Adv. contact J Barton. Circ: 1,800.

557 USA ISSN 0271-8812
SOUTH CAROLINA GEOLOGICAL SURVEY. BULLETIN. Text in English. irreg. **Document type:** *Monographic series.*
—Linda Hall.
Published by: South Carolina Geological Survey, 5 Geology Rd, Columbia, SC 29212. TEL 803-896-7708, FAX 803-8967695, dc_sc@usgs.gov.

557 USA
SOUTH CAROLINA GEOLOGICAL SURVEY. CIRCULAR. Text in English. irreg. **Document type:** *Government.*
Published by: South Carolina Geological Survey, 5 Geology Rd, Columbia, SC 29212.

557 USA
SOUTH CAROLINA GEOLOGICAL SURVEY. FIELD TRIP GUIDEBOOK. Text in English. irreg. **Document type:** *Government.*
Published by: South Carolina Geological Survey, 5 Geology Rd, Columbia, SC 29212.

557 622 USA
SOUTH CAROLINA GEOLOGICAL SURVEY. MINERAL RESOURCES SERIES. Text in English. irreg. **Document type:** *Government.*
Published by: South Carolina Geological Survey, 5 Geology Rd, Columbia, SC 29212.

E

557 USA
SOUTH CAROLINA GEOLOGICAL SURVEY. OPEN-FILE REPORT. Text in English. irreg. **Document type:** *Government.*
Published by: South Carolina Geological Survey, 5 Geology Rd, Columbia, SC 29212.

557 USA
SOUTH CAROLINA GEOLOGICAL SURVEY. PROCEEDINGS. Text in English. irreg. **Document type:** *Government.*
Published by: South Carolina Geological Survey, 5 Geology Rd, Columbia, SC 29212.

557 622 USA
SOUTH CAROLINA GEOLOGICAL SURVEY. SOUTH CAROLINA MINERALS AND ROCKS. Text in English. irreg. **Document type:** *Government.*
Published by: South Carolina Geological Survey, 5 Geology Rd, Columbia, SC 29212.

557 USA ISSN 0085-6479
QE163 CODEN: SDGBB
SOUTH DAKOTA GEOLOGICAL SURVEY. BULLETIN. Text in English. 1894. irreg., latest vol.38, 1997. price varies. **Document type:** *Government.* **Description:** Publishes detailed reports to inform those persons in the geological sciences of the results and conclusions of field and laboratory studies which have been completed by the survey.
—Linda Hall.
Published by: South Dakota Geological Survey, Akeley-Lawrence Science Center, USD, 414 East Clark St, Vermillion, SD 57069-2390. TEL 605-677-5227, FAX 605-677-5895, diles@usd.edu, http://www.sdgs.usd.edu. Circ: (controlled).

557 USA ISSN 0085-6495
CODEN: SDGRAU
SOUTH DAKOTA GEOLOGICAL SURVEY. REPORTS OF INVESTIGATION. Text in English. 1930. irreg., latest vol.114, 2002. price varies. **Document type:** *Government.*
Indexed: BiolAb.
—Linda Hall.
Published by: South Dakota Geological Survey, Akeley-Lawrence Science Center, USD, 414 East Clark St, Vermillion, SD 57069-2390. TEL 605-677-5227, FAX 605-677-5895, diles@usd.edu, http://www.sdgs.usd.edu. Circ: (controlled).

557 551.9 USA ISSN 0038-3678
CODEN: SOGEAY
➤ **SOUTHEASTERN GEOLOGY.** Text in English. 1959 (Apr.). irreg., latest vol.42, 2003. USD 23 per vol. domestic to individuals; USD 30 per vol. foreign to individuals; USD 33 per vol. domestic to institutions; USD 40 per vol. foreign to institutions (effective 2004). charts; illus. 2 cols./p.; back issues avail.; reprint service avail. from PQC. **Document type:** *Journal, Academic/Scholarly.*
Related titles: Microform ed.: (from PQC).
Indexed: ANAG, ASFA, BiolAb, ChemAb, ESPM, GEOBASE, MinerAb, PetrolAb, PollutAb, SWRA.
—Linda Hall, PADDS. **CCC.**
Published by: Duke University, Division of Earth & Ocean Sciences, 103 Old Chemistry, PO Box 90233, Durham, NC 27708. TEL 919-684-5321, FAX 919-684-5833, duncan.heron@duke.edu, http://www.southeasterngeology.org. Ed., R&P Dr. S Duncan Heron. Circ: 500 (paid).

551 ZAF
SOUTHERN AFRICAN ASSOCIATION OF GEOMORPHOLOGISTS. NEWSLETTER. Text in English. s-a. membership. **Document type:** *Newsletter, Academic/Scholarly.* **Description:** Alerts members of the South African Association of Geomorphologists to important developments, issues, and forthcoming conferences and symposia.
Published by: South African Association of Geomorphologists, Zama Simamane, Treas, c/o Dept of Geography and Environmental Studies, University of the North West, Pvt Bag X2046, Mafeking, 2735, South Africa. FAX 27-18-389-2325, NZSGEO@unibo.uniwest.ac.za, ZASGEO@unibo.uniwest.ac.za, http://www.up.ac.za/science/geog/saag.html.

551 622 ESP
SPAIN. INSTITUTO TECNOLOGICO GEOMINERO DE ESPANA. COLECCION MEMORIAS. Text in Spanish. 1854. irreg., latest vol.104, 1998. price varies. **Document type:** *Monographic series, Academic/Scholarly.*
Formerly: Spain. Instituto Geologico y Minero. Coleccion Memorias
Published by: El Instituto Geologico y Minero de Espana, Rios Rosas 23, Madrid, 28003, Spain. TEL 34-91-3495819, FAX 34-91-3495830, http://www.igme.es/internet/principal.asp.

551 622 ESP
SPAIN. INSTITUTO TECNOLOGICO GEOMINERO DE ESPANA. INFORMES. (In 4 subseries: 1. Geologia; 2. Mineria; 3. Monografias; 4. Aguas Subterraneas) Text in Spanish. 1972. irreg. price varies. **Document type:** *Monographic series, Academic/Scholarly.*
Formerly: Spain. Instituto Geologico y Minero. Informes
Published by: El Instituto Geologico y Minero de Espana, Rios Rosas 23, Madrid, 28003, Spain. TEL 34-91-3495819, FAX 34-91-3495830, http://www.igme.es/internet/principal.asp.

SPATIAL BUSINESS NEWSLETTER. see *GEOGRAPHY—Computer Applications*

551.447 USA ISSN 0584-8717
SPELEO DIGEST. Text in English. 1988. a. free to members. **Document type:** *Trade.*
Related titles: Online - full content ed.
Published by: National Speleological Society, Inc., 2813 Cave Ave, Huntsville, AL 35810-4431. TEL 256-852-1300, nss@caves.org, http://www.caves.org/pub/speleodigest/. Ed. Scott Fee.

796.525 BEL ISSN 0778-8916
SPELEOCHRONOS. Text in French. 1989. a.
Published by: Faculte Polytechnique de Mons, Centre d'Etudes et de Recherches Appliquees au Karst, 9, rue de Houdain, Mons, B-7000, Belgium. quinif@fpms.ac.be.

796.525 ITA ISSN 1123-9875
SPELEOLOGIA IBLEA. Text in English, Italian. 1990. a., latest vol.9. EUR 30 (effective 2003). video rev. back issues avail. **Document type:** *Monographic series, Academic/Scholarly.* **Description:** Presents speleological research performed in Italy and abroad.
Published by: Centro Ibleo di Ricerche Speleo-Idrogeologiche, Via Carducci, 165, Ragusa, RG 97100, Italy. TEL 39-0932-669062, FAX 39-0932-621699, cirsggr@inwind.it, http://www.avvenimentiiblei.it/cirs.

796.525 FRA ISSN 0242-1771
SPELUNCA. Text in French. 1895. q. adv. bk.rev. illus.; bibl.; maps. 60 p./no.; back issues avail. **Document type:** *Bulletin, Academic/Scholarly.* **Description:** Describes the world of speleology through explorations, descriptions of geological and biological conditions encountered, awareness of the underground environment.
Indexed: RefZh.
Published by: Federation Francaise de Speleologie, 130 rue Saint-Maur, Paris, 75011, France. TEL 33-1-43575654, FAX 33-1-49230095, ffs-paris@wanadoo.fr, http://www.ffspeleo.fr. Ed. Philippe Drouin. Pub. Pascal Vautier.

551.44 CHE ISSN 0038-9226
STALACTITE. Text in French, German. 1950. 2/yr. CHF 30. bk.rev. charts. **Document type:** *Bulletin.*
Indexed: SportS, ZooRec.
Published by: Societe Suisse de Speleologie, Bibliotheque, Ch. des Invuex, Granges, 1614, Switzerland. FAX 021-9475378. Circ: 1,400.

557 USA ISSN 0095-8638
QH105.C8 CODEN: CNGBAC
STATE GEOLOGICAL AND NATURAL HISTORY SURVEY OF CONNECTICUT. BULLETIN. Text in English. 1904. irreg. **Document type:** *Monographic series.*
Indexed: ZooRec.
—CISTI, Linda Hall.
Published by: State Geological and Natural History Survey of Connecticut, 79 Elm St, Hartford, CT 06106-5127. TEL 860-424-3540.

551 USA ISSN 0039-0089
QE1 CODEN: SGJOAN
STATE GEOLOGISTS JOURNAL. Text in English. 1949. a. USD 10 (effective 2000 - 2001). back issues avail. **Document type:** *Trade.* **Description:** Summary of activities for state geological surveys.
Published by: Association of American State Geologists, c/o North Dakota Geological Survey, 600 E Boulevard Ave, Bismarck, ND 58505-0840. TEL 701-328-8000, FAX 701-328-8010. Ed., R&P John P Bluemle. Circ: 200 (controlled).

557 USA ISSN 0096-7866
QE165 CODEN: TCGBAK
STATE OF TENNESSEE. DEPARTMENT OF CONSERVATION. DIVISION OF GEOLOGY. BULLETIN. Text in English. 1923. irreg. **Document type:** *Monographic series.*
Indexed: ZooRec.
—Linda Hall.
Published by: Department of Conservation, Division of Geology, 401 Church St, 13th Fl, L&C Tower, Nashville, TN 37243-0445. TEL 615-532-1516, FAX 615-532-1517, geologysales@mail.state.tn.us.

500 SVK ISSN 0433-4795
QE1 b .G491455 CODEN: GEPZA8
➤ **STATNY GEOLOGICKY USTAV DIONYZA STURA. GEOLOGICKE PRACE. SPRAVY.** Text in Slovak. 1954. irreg., latest vol.105, 2001. SKK 45 (effective 2002). adv. bk.rev. illus.; maps. back issues avail. **Document type:** *Academic/Scholarly.* **Description:** Covers regional geology, geological maps, lithology, stratigraphy, petrology, mineralogy, paleontology, geochemistry etc.
Former titles (until 2001): Geologicka Sluzba Slovenskej Republiky. Geologicke Prace. Spravy; (until 1995): Statny Geologicky Ustav Dionyza Stura. Geologicke Prace. Spravy
Related titles: Diskette ed.; E-mail ed.; Fax ed.
Indexed: RefZh, ZooRec.
—BLDSC (4140.000000), CASDDS, CISTI, Linda Hall.
Published by: (Statny Geologicky Ustav Dionyza Stura), Dionyz Stur Publishers, Mlynska dolina 1, Bratislava, 81704, Slovakia. TEL 421-2-59375119, FAX 421-2-54771940, simon@gssr.sk, http://www.gssr.sk. Ed. Ladislav Simon. Circ: 350.

551 RUS ISSN 0869-592X
STRATIGRAFIYA, GEOLOGICHESKAYA KORRELYATSIYA. Text in Russian. 1993. 6/yr. RUR 850 for 6 mos. domestic (effective 2004). **Document type:** *Journal, Academic/Scholarly.*
Related titles: Online - full text ed.; ♦ English Translation: Stratigraphy and Geological Correlation. ISSN 0869-5938.
Indexed: RefZh, ZooRec.
—KNAW, Linda Hall. **CCC.**
Published by: (Rossiiskaya Akademiya Nauk, Geologicheskii Institut), Izdatel'stvo Nauka, Profsoyuznaya ul 90, Moscow, 117864, Russian Federation. TEL 7-095-3347151, FAX 7-095-4202220, secret@naukaran.ru, http://www.maik.rssi.ru/cgi-bin/list.pl?page=stratrus, http://www.naukaran.ru.

551.7 USA ISSN 1547-139X
QE701
▼ ➤ **STRATIGRAPHY.** Text in English. 2004 (Fall). q. USD 140 to individuals; USD 280 to institutions; USD 320 combined subscription to individuals print & online eds.; USD 640 combined subscription to institutions print & online eds. (effective 2006). **Document type:** *Journal, Academic/Scholarly.*
Related titles: Online - full text ed.
Published by: (American Museum of Natural History), Micropaleontology Press, 256 Fifth Ave, New York, NY 10001. TEL 212-481-2997, FAX 212-481-3268, http://www.micropress.org/stratigraphy, http://micropress.org/. Ed. John A Van Couvering.

551.7 CAN
STRATIGRAPHY. Text in English. 4/yr. USD 140 to individuals; USD 280 to institutions (effective 2004). **Document type:** *Monographic series.*
Related titles: Online - full text ed.
Published by: International Committee on Stratigraphy, 601 Booth St, Ottawa, ON K1A 0E8, Canada. TEL 613-995-7277, FAX 613-995-9273.

551 RUS ISSN 0869-5938
QE640
➤ **STRATIGRAPHY AND GEOLOGICAL CORRELATION.** Text in English. 1993. 6/yr. USD 1,365 in North America; USD 1,564 elsewhere (effective 2004). **Document type:** *Journal, Academic/Scholarly.* **Description:** Discusses the fundamental and applied aspects of stratigraphy and the correlation of geologic events and processes in time and space.
Related titles: ♦ Translation of: Stratigrafiya, Geologicheskaya Korrelyatsiya. ISSN 0869-592X.
Indexed: ASCA, CurCont, GEOBASE, PetrolAb.
—BLDSC (0425.890200), CISTI, IDS, Infotrieve, PADDS.
Published by: (Rossiiskaya Akademiya Nauk/Russian Academy of Sciences), M A I K Nauka - Interperiodica, Profsoyuznaya ul 90, Moscow, 117997, Russian Federation. TEL 7-095-3347420, FAX 7-095-3360666, compmg@maik.ru, http://www.maik.rssi.ru/journals/strteng.htm, http://www.maik.ru. Ed. Boris S Sokolov. **Subscr. to:** Interperiodica, PO Box 1831, Birmingham, AL 35201-1831. TEL 205-995-1567, 800-633-4931, FAX 205-995-1588.

551 SWE ISSN 0345-0074
CODEN: STREDP
➤ **STRIAE;** a monograph series for quaternary studies. Text in English, French, German. 1975. irreg., latest vol.38. price varies. **Document type:** *Monographic series, Academic/Scholarly.* **Description:** Monographs on geology in the form of doctoral dissertations or other major research reports.
Indexed: ZooRec.
Published by: (Societas Upsaliensis Pro Geologia Quaternaria), Uppsala Universitet, Kvartaergeologiska Avdeling/Department of Quaternary Geology, c/o Uppsala University, PO Box 256, Uppsala, 75105, Sweden. TEL 46-18-471-00-00, tgups@heby.mail.telia.com. Circ: 400.

550 ITA ISSN 0392-0534
CODEN: STSGD2
STUDI TRENTINI DI SCIENZE NATURALI. ACTA GEOLOGICA. Text in Italian. 1965. q. **Document type:** *Journal, Academic/Scholarly.*
Formerly (until 1976): Studi Trentini di Scienze Naturali. Sezione A. Abiologica (0585-5608)
Indexed: MLA-IB, RefZh, ZooRec.
—CASDDS.
Published by: Museo Tridentino di Scienze Naturali, Via Calepina 14, Trento, TN 38100, Italy. TEL 39-0461-270311, FAX 39-0461.233830, info@mtsn.tn.it, http://www.mtsn.tn.it. Ed. Gino Tomasi.

550 POL ISSN 0081-6426
QE1 CODEN: SGPOAJ
➤ **STUDIA GEOLOGICA POLONICA.** Text in English, Polish; Summaries in English. 1958. irreg., latest vol.119, 2002. price varies. **Document type:** *Monographic series, Academic/Scholarly.* **Description:** Covers stratigraphy, sedimentology, tectonics, regional geology of Poland, Arctic and Antarctic.

E

▼ *new title* ➤ *refereed* ✶ *unverified* ♦ *full entry avail.*

Indexed: BiolAb, PetrolAb.
—Linda Hall, PADDS.
Published by: Polska Akademia Nauk, Instytut Nauk Mineralogicznych/Polish Academy of Sciences, Institute of Mineralogical Sciences, Ul Twarda 51-55, Warsaw, 00818, Poland. TEL 48-22-6978742, FAX 48-22-6206223, inglib@twarda.pan.pl, http://www.ing.twarda.pan.pl. Ed. Krzysztof Birkenmajer. Circ: 500.

551 ESP ISSN 0211-8327
STUDIA GEOLOGICA SALMANTICENSIA. Text in Spanish. 1970. a., latest vol.35, 1999. **Document type:** *Academic/Scholarly.*
Formerly (until 1979): Universidad de Salamanca. Studia Geologica (0370-9957)
Indexed: IECT, IMMAb, ZooRec.
—CINDOC.
Published by: Ediciones Universidad de Salamanca, Apartado 325, Salamanca, 37080, Spain. TEL 34-923-294598, FAX 34-923-262579, http://www3.usal.es/~eus/indexsp.htm. Ed. Emiliano Jimenez Fuentes.

STUDIA GEOTECHNICA ET MECHANICA. see *ENGINEERING*

STUDIA I MATERIALY DO DZIEJOW ZUP SOLNYCH W POLSCE. see *ARCHAEOLOGY*

551 POL ISSN 1641-5558
STUDIA QUATERNARIA; an interdisciplinary journal on the quaternary. Text in English. 1979. a., latest vol.19, 2002. PLZ 20 domestic (effective 2003). **Document type:** *Journal, Academic/Scholarly.* **Description:** Covers stratigraphy and reconstruction of the past environments, including palaeogeography, palaeoclimatology, palaeohydrology.
Formerly (until 2000): Quaternary Studies in Poland (0137-9798)
—BLDSC (8483.203050).
Published by: Polska Akademia Nauk, Instytut Nauk Geologicznych, Komitet Badan Czwartorzedu/Polish Academy of Sciences, Institute of Geological Sciences, Committee on Quaternary Research, Twarda 51/55, Warsaw, 00818, Poland. TEL 48-22-6978701, FAX 48-22-6206223, inglib@twarda.pan.pl, http://www.studia.quaternaria.pan.pl, http://www.ing.twarda.pan.pl. Eds. H Hercman, T Goslar. Pub. Anna Morawska.

STUDIA SOCIETATIS SCIENTIARUM TORUNENSIS. SECTIO C. GEOGRAFIA ET GEOLOGIA. see *GEOGRAPHY*

550 ROM ISSN 1221-0803
QE287.6 CODEN: SBBGAQ
STUDIA UNIVERSITATIS "BABES-BOLYAI". GEOLOGIA. Text in English, French, German, Romanian. 1958. s-a. per issue exchange basis. bk.rev. charts; illus.; maps; abstr.; bibl.; stat. index. **Document type:** *Academic/Scholarly.*
Supersedes in part (in 1990): Studia Universitatis "Babes-Bolyai". Geologia - Geographia (0039-341X)
Indexed: BiolAb, ChemAb, RefZh, ZooRec.
Published by: Universitatea "Babes-Bolyai", Biblioteca Centrala Universitara/Babes-Bolyai University, Central University Library in Cluj-Napoca, Mihail Kogalniceanu 1B, Cluj-Napoca, 3400, Romania. TEL 40-64-194315, FAX 40-64-191906, staff@staff.ubbcluj.ro, http://www.ubbcluj.ro. Ed. Alina Vesa.

557 USA ISSN 0081-8747
QE171 CODEN: SVTGB
STUDIES IN VERMONT GEOLOGY. Text in English. 1970. irreg., latest vol.4, 1988. USD 4 per issue. illus. **Document type:** *Academic/Scholarly.* **Description:** Presents topical geologic studies of a specific site or area in Vermont.
Indexed: BiolAb.
—Linda Hall.
Published by: Vermont Geological Survey, Agency of Natural Resources, 103 S Main St, Center Bldg, Waterbury, VT 05676. TEL 802-241-3608. Ed. Charles A Ratte. R&P Marjorie Gale.

551 ROM ISSN 1220-4994
CODEN: SCGGAO
STUDII SI CERCETARI DE GEOLOGIE/STUDIES AND RESEARCH IN GEOLOGY. Text in Romanian. 1958. a. **Document type:** *Academic/Scholarly.*
Former titles (until 1990): Studii si Cercetari de Geologie, Geofizica si Geographie. Geologie (0567-6096); (until 1964): Studii si Cercetari de Geologie (1010-688X)
Indexed: ZooRec.
—CASDDS, CISTI.
Published by: (Academia Romana), Editura Academiei Romane/Publishing House of the Romanian Academy, Calea 13 Septembrie 13, Sector 5, Bucharest, 76117, Romania. TEL 40-21-4119008, FAX 40-21-4103983, edacad@ear.ro, http://www.ear.ro. Ed. Dan Radulescu. **Dist. by:** Rodipet S.A., Piata Presei Libere 1, sector 1, PO Box 33-57, Bucharest 3, Romania. TEL 40-21-2224126, 40-21-2226407, rodipet@rodipet.ro.

557 DEU ISSN 0341-0153
QE1 CODEN: SBNBA3
➤ **STUTTGARTER BEITRAEGE ZUR NATURKUNDE. SERIE B. GEOLOGIE UND PALAEONTOLOGIE.** Text in German. 1957. irreg., latest vol.351, 2004. price varies. **Document type:** *Monographic series, Academic/Scholarly.*
Supersedes in part (in 197?): Stuttgarter Beitraege zur Naturkunde aus dem Staatlichen Museum fuer Naturkunde in Stuttgart (0562-4452)
Indexed: BIOSIS Prev, BiolAb, ESPM, EntAb, RefZh, ZooRec.
—BLDSC (8501.510000), CISTI, Linda Hall. **CCC.**
Published by: Staatliches Museum fuer Naturkunde Stuttgart, Rosenstein 1, Stuttgart, 70191, Germany. TEL 49-711-89360, FAX 49-711-8936200, museum.SMNS@naturkundemuseum-bw.de, http://www.naturkundemuseum-bw.de/stuttgart/. Ed. R Boettcher.

551.4 796.5 ISL ISSN 1017-2742
P87
SURTUR. Text in Icelandic; Summaries in English. 1990. a. **Description:** Caves and their exploration in Iceland.
Published by: Hellarannsoknafelag Islands/Icelandic Speleological Society, PO Box 342, Reykjavik, 121, Iceland.

SURVEY REVIEW. see *ENGINEERING—Civil Engineering*

554 SWE ISSN 1103-3371
QE282
SVERIGES GEOLOGISKA UNDERSOEKNING. SERIE C. FORSKNINGSRAPPORTER/GEOLOGICAL SURVEY OF SWEDEN. SERIES C. RESEARCH PAPERS. Text in English, German, Swedish; Summaries in English. 1868. irreg., latest vol.819, 1988. price varies. cum.index: 1858-1958. **Document type:** *Government.*
Formerly (until 1992): Sveriges Geologiska Undersoekning. Serie C. Avhandlingar och Uppsatser (0082-0024)
Indexed: RefZh, ZooRec.
—CISTI, Linda Hall.
Published by: Sveriges Geologiska Undersoekning/Geological Survey of Sweden, Fack 670, Uppsala, 75128, Sweden.

554 SWE ISSN 1103-3363
CODEN: SGUAA2
SVERIGES GEOLOGISKA UNDERSOEKNING. SERIE CA. AVHANDLINGAR OCH UPPSATSER I KVARTO/ GEOLOGICAL SURVEY OF SWEDEN. SERIES CA. NOTICES IN FOLIO AND QUARTO. Text in Swedish. 1900. irreg., latest vol.89, 1999. price varies. **Document type:** *Government.*
Formerly (until 1991): Sveriges Geologiska Undersokning. Ser. Ca, Avhandlingar Och Uppsatser (0348-1352)
Indexed: RefZh, ZooRec.
—CISTI, Linda Hall.
Published by: Sveriges Geologiska Undersoekning/Geological Survey of Sweden, Fack 670, Uppsala, 75128, Sweden.

538.7 SWE ISSN 0281-1049
SVERIGES GEOLOGISKA UNDERSOEKNING. SERIE CB. JORDMAGNETISKA PUBLIKATIONER/GEOLOGICAL SURVEY OF SWEDEN. GEOMAGNETIC PUBLICATIONS. Text in English. 1922. irreg. SEK 50 per issue (effective 2000). **Document type:** *Government.*
Formerly (until 1976): Jordmagnetiska Publikationer (0075-403X)
Published by: Sveriges Geologiska Undersoekning/Geological Survey of Sweden, Fack 670, Uppsala, 75128, Sweden.

556 622 SWZ ISSN 0081-9999
QE327.S8 CODEN: SGMDA5
SWAZILAND. GEOLOGICAL SURVEY AND MINES DEPARTMENT. ANNUAL REPORT. Text in English. 1947. a. price varies. **Document type:** *Government.* **Description:** Provides a brief description of current work and progress on mining geology, research, chemical analysis and statistics.
Indexed: RASB.
—Linda Hall.
Published by: Geological Survey and Mines Department, PO Box 9, Mbabane, Swaziland. FAX 268-45215. Ed. Ettie Ngubonde. Circ: 500.

556 622 SWZ ISSN 0082-0008
UNC CODEN: SGMBAX
SWAZILAND. GEOLOGICAL SURVEY AND MINES DEPARTMENT. BULLETIN. Text in English. 1961. a. price varies. **Document type:** *Bulletin, Government.* **Description:** Covers special topics related to mineral-bearing regions in mining geology, geochemistry and geophysics in Swaziland.
Indexed: IMMAb.
—Linda Hall.
Published by: Geological Survey and Mines Department, PO Box 9, Mbabane, Swaziland. FAX 268-45215. Ed. Ettie Ngubonde. Circ: 500.

796.525 AUS ISSN 1036-6784
SYDNEY SPELEOLOGICAL SOCIETY. JOURNAL. Text in English. 1957. m. AUD 45; AUD 45 foreign (effective 1999). bk.rev. illus. index. **Document type:** *Newsletter.*
Former titles (until 1970): Stop Press; Communications; S S S Newsletter
Indexed: ASA.
Published by: Sydney Speleological Society, PO Box 198, Broadway, NSW 2007, Australia. FAX 61-2-96920908, el-bsnurse@real.net.au. Ed. Ross A Ellis. Circ: 200.

551.44 AUS
SYDNEY SPELEOLOGICAL SOCIETY. OCCASIONAL PAPER. Text in English. 1965. irreg. price varies.
Formerly: Sydney Speleological Society. Communications (0085-7017)
Indexed: ASA.
Published by: Sydney Speleological Society, PO Box 198, Broadway, NSW 2007, Australia. FAX 61-2-96601217. R&P Ross A Ellis.

796.525 AUS
SYDNEY SPELEOLOGICAL SOCIETY. REPRINT SERIES. Text in English. 1993. irreg. price varies. **Document type:** *Monographic series.*
Published by: Sydney Speleological Society, PO Box 198, Broadway, NSW 2007, Australia. FAX 61-2-96601217. Ed. Ross A Ellis. Circ: 2,000.

551 JPN ISSN 1342-310X
➤ **TAISEKIGAKU KENKYU/SEDIMENTOLOGICAL SOCIETY OF JAPAN. JOURNAL.** Text in English, Japanese. 1969. s-a. JPY 3,000 per issue (effective 2001). bk.rev. 100 p./no.; **Document type:** *Academic/Scholarly.* **Description:** Contains scientific papers on the sedimentological researches in and around Japan, includes news of the society activities.
Formerly (until 1994): Taisekigaku Kenkyukaiho (0285-1555)
—BLDSC (8598.534500).
Published by: Taisekigaku Kenkyukai/Sedimentological Society of Japan, c/o Dept. of Environmental Sciences, Fac. of Science, Shinshu University, Asahi 3-1-1, Matsumoto, 390-8621, Japan. TEL 81-263-37-2479, FAX 81-263-37-2506, taisekiken@ripms.shinshu-u.ac.jp, http://geogate.shinshu-u.ac.jp/SSJ/SSJ-E/SSJ.html. Ed. Osam Takano. R&P M Tateishi. Circ: 520 (paid); 10 (controlled).

551 TWN ISSN 1012-6821
TAIWAN, REPUBLIC OF CHINA. CENTRAL GEOLOGICAL SURVEY. BULLETIN. Text in Chinese, English. 1981. irreg. USD 30 (effective 1991). **Document type:** *Academic/Scholarly.*
Supersedes: China, Republic. Geological Survey of Taiwan. Bulletin
Indexed: ZooRec.
—BLDSC (2435.950000).
Published by: Ministry of Economic Affairs, Central Geological Survey, 2 Ln 109, Huahsin St, Chungho, Taiwan. FAX 886-2-9429291. Ed. F C Chien. Pub. F C Chen. Circ: 750. **Subscr. to:** Central Geological Survey, Ministry of Economic Affairs, P.O. Box 968, Taipei, Taiwan.

559.4 AUS
TASMANIA. MINERAL RESOURCES. GEOLOGICAL SURVEY BULLETINS. Text in English. 1907. irreg., latest vol.71, 2000. price varies. **Document type:** *Academic/Scholarly.* **Description:** Publishes articles in the field of geology, mining, mineral resources, water resources, and palaeontology.
Former titles: Tasmania. Department of Resources and Energy. Division of Mines and Mineral Resources. Geological Survey Bulletins; Tasmania. Department of Mines. Geological Survey Bulletins (0082-2043)
Indexed: AESIS, IMMAb.
—CISTI, Linda Hall.
Published by: (Tasmania. Mineral Resources), Mineral Resources Tasmania, PO Box 56, Rosny Park, TAS 7018, Australia. FAX 61-3-6233-8338. Circ: 300.

559.4 AUS
TASMANIA. MINERAL RESOURCES. REPORT. Text in English. irreg. **Document type:** *Government.*
Formerly: Tasmania. Department of Resources and Energy. Division of Mines and Mineral Resources. Report (Years)
Indexed: AESIS.
Published by: (Tasmania. Mineral Resources), Mineral Resources Tasmania, PO Box 56, Rosny Park, TAS 7018, Australia. FAX 61-3-62339339. Ed. Michael Dix.

551.0711 GBR ISSN 0957-8005
➤ **TEACHING EARTH SCIENCES.** Text in English. 1976. q. GBP 25 (effective 2003). adv. bk.rev.; film rev.; software rev.; Website rev. bibl.; charts; illus.; stat.; maps. 48 p./no. 2 cols./p.; back issues avail. **Document type:** *Journal, Academic/Scholarly.*
Formerly (until 1989): Geology Teaching (0308-1567)
Indexed: BrEdI, CPE, ERA, ETA, MEA, RHEA, SEA, SENA, SOMA, TEA.
—BLDSC (8614.090000), IE, ingenta.
Published by: Earth Science Teacher's Association, School of Education, University of Exeter, Exeter, EX1 2LU, United Kingdom. TEL 44-1392-264768, r.d.trend@exeter.ac.uk, http://www.esta-uk.org/. Ed., Pub., R&P Roger Trend. Adv. contact Ian Ray. Circ: 800 (paid). **Subscr. to:** Owain/Thomas, PO Box 10, Narberth, Pembrokeshire SA67 7YE, United Kingdom. thomas@owain.plus.com. **Dist. by:** Chartacter Design, High Ridge, Wrigglebrook Ln, Kingsthorne, Hereford HR2 8AW, United Kingdom. info@characterdesign.co.uk.

550 POL
CODEN: TGEODC
➤ **TECHNIKA POSZUKIWAN GEOLOGICZNYCH, GEOSYNOPTYKA I GEOTERMIA/EXPLORATION TECHNOLOGY, GEOSYNOPTICS AND GEOTHERMAL ENERGY.** Text in Polish; Summaries in English. 1962. bi-m. EUR 35 foreign (effective 2005). adv. bk.rev. charts; illus.; pat.; tr.lit.; tr.mk. index. **Document type:** *Journal, Academic/Scholarly.* **Description:** Addresses drilling, hydrogeological engineering and geophysical techniques and geothermal problems.

Former titles: Technika Poszukiwan Geologicznych (0304-520X); (until 1974): Technika Poszukiwan (0040-1161)
Indexed: AgrLib, CIN, ChemAb, ChemTitl, RefZh.
—CASDDS, Linda Hall.
Published by: Polska Akademia Nauk, Instytut Gospodarki Surowcami Mineralnymi i Energia, ul J Wybickiego 7, Krakow, 31261, Poland. TEL 48-12-6323835, FAX 48-12-6323524, centrum@min-pan.krakow.pl, http://www.min-pan.krakow.pl. Ed. Wieslaw Bujakowski. Circ: 500. **Dist. by:** Ars Polona, Krakowskie Przedmiescie 7, Warsaw, Poland. TEL 48-22-9263914, FAX 48-22-9265334, arspolona@arspolona.com.pl, http://www.arspolona.com.pl.
Co-sponsor: Osrodek Badawczo-Rozwojowy Techniki Geologicznej.

551 RUS
TEKHNIKA, TEKHNOLOGIYA I ORGANIZATSIYA GEOLOGO-RAZVEDOCHNYKH RABOT; obzornaya informatsiya. Text in Russian. q. USD 69.95 in United States.
Published by: Informatsionno-Izdatel'skii Tsentr po Geologii i Nedropol'zovaniu Geoinformmark, Goncharnaya 38, Moscow, 115172, Russian Federation. TEL 7-095-9156724. **US dist. addr.:** East View Information Services, 3020 Harbor Ln. N., Minneapolis, MN 55447. TEL 612-550-0961.

551 USA ISSN 0497-2074
TENNESSEE. DIVISION OF GEOLOGY. REPORT OF INVESTIGATIONS. Text in English. 1955. irreg.
—Linda Hall.
Published by: Tennessee, Department of Environment & Conservation, The Geology Division, 401 Church St, 13th Floor, L & C Tower, Nashville, TN 37243-0445. TEL 615-532-1500, http://www.state.tn.us/environment/tdg.

556.3 ITA ISSN 1592-8594
TEVERE. Text in Italian. 1996. 4/yr. EUR 18.60 (effective 2004).
Document type: *Journal, Academic/Scholarly.*
Published by: Gangemi Editore, Piazza San Pantaleo 4, Rome, Italy. TEL 39-06-6872774, FAX 39-06-68806189, gangemieditorerc@tin.it, http://www.gangemieditore.it.

551.44 USA
TEXAS MEMORIAL MUSEUM. SPELEOLOGICAL MONOGRAPHS. Text in English. 1966. irreg., latest vol.3, 1992. price varies. **Document type:** *Academic/Scholarly.*
Published by: Texas Memorial Museum, University of Texas at Austin, 2400 Trinity, Austin, TX 78705. TEL 512-471-1604.

TIANRANQI GONGYE/NATURAL GAS INDUSTRY. see *PETROLEUM AND GAS*

551 ESP ISSN 1131-5016
TIERRA Y TECNOLOGIA. Text in Spanish. 1991. q.
Indexed: IECT.
—CINDOC.
Published by: Colegio Oficial de Geologos de Espana, Ave. Reina Victoria, 8 4o. B, Madrid, 28003, Spain. FAX 34-91-5330343, icog@icog.es, http://www.icog.es/tt/. Ed. Oswaldo Garcia-Hernan.

551.46 RUS ISSN 0207-4028
QE350.4
TIKHOOKEANSKAYA GEOLOGIYA/GEOLOGY OF THE PACIFIC OCEAN. Text in Russian. 1982. bi-m. USD 326 foreign (effective 2005). **Document type:** *Journal, Academic/Scholarly.*
Indexed: RefZh.
—CISTI, East View, Linda Hall. **CCC.**
Published by: Redaktsiya Zhurnala Tikhookeanskaya Geologiya, ul Kim Yu Chena 65, Khabarovsk, 680000, Russian Federation. TEL 7-4212-210859, FAX 7-4212-227684, kirillova@itig.as.khb.ru, http://www.itig.khv.ru/POG/indexE.htm. Ed. V G Moiseenko. **US dist. addr.:** East View Information Services, 3020 Harbor Ln. N., Minneapolis, MN 55447. TEL 800-477-1005, FAX 800-800-3839, eastview@eastview.com, http://www.eastview.com.

551 560 JPN ISSN 0082-4658
CODEN: TDRCAH
TOHOKU DAIGAKU RIGAKUBU CHISHITSUGAKU KOSEIBUTSUGAKU KYOSHITSU KENKYU HOBUN HOKOKU/TOHOKU UNIVERSITY. FACULTY OF SCIENCE. INSTITUTE OF GEOLOGY AND PALEONTOLOGY. CONTRIBUTIONS. Text in Japanese; Summaries in English. 1921. irreg., latest vol.91, 1988. per issue exchange basis.
Document type: *Academic/Scholarly.*
Indexed: BiolAb, JPI.
—Linda Hall.
Published by: (Chishitsugaku Koseibutsugaku Kyoshitsu), Tohoku Daigaku, Rigakubu Chishitsugaku Koseibutsugaku Kyoshitsu/Tohoku University, Faculty of Science, Institute of Geology and Paleontology, Aoba, Aramaki, Aoba-ku, Sendai-shi, Miyagi-ken, 980, Japan. Circ: 750.

551 560 JPN ISSN 0082-464X
Q77.T55 CODEN: STUGA9
TOHOKU UNIVERSITY. SCIENCE REPORTS. SERIES 2: GEOLOGY/TOHOKU DAIGAKU RIKA HOKOKU. DAI 2-SHU, CHISHITSUGAKU. Text and summaries in English. 1912. s-a. per issue exchange basis. **Document type:** *Academic/Scholarly.*
Indexed: BIOSIS Prev, BiolAb, ZooRec.
—BLDSC (8157.000000), CISTI, Linda Hall.
Published by: (Chishitsugaku Koseibutsugaku Kyoshitsu), Tohoku Daigaku, Rigakubu/Tohoku University, Faculty of Science, Laboratory of Nuclear Science, Aramaki, Aoba-ku, Sendai-shi, Miyagi-ken 981-0945, Japan. Circ: 750.

TOHOKU UNIVERSITY. SCIENCE REPORTS. SERIES 3: MINERALOGY, PETROLOGY AND ECONOMIC GEOLOGY/TOHOKU DAIGAKU RIKA HOKOKU. DAI 3-SHU, GANSEKIGAKU KOBUTSUGAKU KOSHOGAKU. see *MINES AND MINING INDUSTRY*

551 570 USA ISSN 0275-0120
CODEN: TBGBDG
➤ **TOPICS IN GEOBIOLOGY.** Text in English. 1980. irreg., latest vol.23, 2005. price varies. **Document type:** *Monographic series, Academic/Scholarly.* **Description:** Covers the history of life on Earth. The series aims for high quality, scholarly volumes of original research as well as broad reviews. Recent volumes have showcased a variety of organisms including cephalopods, corals, and rodents. They discuss the biology of these organisms - their ecology, phylogeny, and mode of life and in addition, their fossil record - their distribution in time and space.
Indexed: Agr, BIOSIS Prev, ZooRec.
—BLDSC (8867.441000), CASDDS, CISTI, IE, ingenta. **CCC.**
Published by: Springer-Verlag New York, Inc. (Subsidiary of: Springer Science+Business Media), 233 Spring St, New York, NY 10013. TEL 212-460-1500, FAX 212-460-1575, service@springer-ny.com, http://www.springer-ny.com. Eds. Douglas S Jones, Neil H Landman. **Dist. by:** Journal Fulfillment, PO Box 2485, Secaucus, NJ 07096-2485.

551 ESP ISSN 0474-9588
CODEN: TBGLA9
TRABAJOS DE GEOLOGIA. Text in Spanish. 1954. a. price varies. abstr.; illus. **Document type:** *Academic/Scholarly.*
Supersedes (1954-1960): Monografias Geologicas (0473-6311)
Indexed: BiolAb, IECT, ZooRec.
—CASDDS, CINDOC. **CCC.**
Published by: Universidad de Oviedo, Servicio de Publicaciones, Campus de Humanidades, Oviedo, Asturias 33001, Spain. TEL 34-985-104941, FAX 34-985-104940, servipub@uniovi.es, http://www.geol.uniovi.es/TDG/, http://www.uniovi.es/publicaciones/. Ed. Alberto Marcos Valaure. Circ: 1,000.

550 MAR
TRAVAUX DE L'INSTITUT SCIENTIFIQUE. SERIE GEOLOGIE ET GEOGRAPHIE PHYSIQUE. Text in French. irreg.
Published by: Universite Mohammed V, Institut Scientifique, Ave Ibn Batouta, BP 703, Rabat-Agdal, Rabat, 10106, Morocco. TEL 212-37-774548, FAX 212-37-774540.

TURUN YLIOPISTO. JULKAISUJA. SARJA A. II. BIOLOGICA - GEOGRAPHICA - GEOLOGICA/ANNALES UNIVERSITATIS TURKUENSIS. see *BIOLOGY*

551.44 CZE ISSN 0254-9824
U I S BULLETIN. Text in English, French, German, Spanish. 1970. s-a. USD 5 (effective 1996 & 1997). bk.rev.
Published by: Union Internationale de Speleologie, c/o Dr. Pavel Bosak, Secretary General, Czech Speleological Society, Kalisnicka 4-6, Prague 3, Czech Republic. TEL 42-2-7651444, FAX 42-2-272460. Circ: 2,200.

557 USA ISSN 0083-1093
CODEN: XDIGAS
U.S. GEOLOGICAL SURVEY. BULLETIN. Text in English. 1883. irreg. **Document type:** *Bulletin, Government.* **Description:** Focuses on resource studies and on geologic and topographic investigations; the bulletins are "more limited" in scope than professional papers.
Related titles: Microform ed.: 1883 (from PMC).
Indexed: AESIS, ASFA, ESPM, GEOBASE, IMMAb, MinerAb, RefZh, S&F, ZooRec.
—CASDDS.
Published by: U.S. Department of the Interior, Geological Survey, 12201 Sunrise Valley Dr, Reston, VA 20192. TEL 888-275-8747, ask@usgs.gov, http://water.usgs.gov/pubs/.
Subscr. to: USGS Information Services, Denver Federal Center, Box 25286, Denver, CO 80225-0046. FAX 303-202-4693, infoservices@usgs.gov.

750 USA ISSN 8755-531X
U.S. GEOLOGICAL SURVEY BULLETIN. Text in English. 1949. irreg.
Formerly (until 1983): Geological Survey Bulletin (0364-4510)
—BLDSC (9124.744830), CISTI.
Published by: U.S. Geological Survey, 12201 Sunrise Valley Dr, Reston, VA 20192. TEL 703-648-7346.

557 USA ISSN 1067-084X
QE75 CODEN: XICIA5
U. S. GEOLOGICAL SURVEY CIRCULAR. Text in English. 1933. irreg. free. **Document type:** *Government.*
Former titles (until 1984): Geological Survey Circular (0364-6017); (until 1949): U.S. Geological Survey. Circular (0083-1107)
Indexed: AESIS, FLUIDEX, GEOBASE, IMMAb, S&F.
—CASDDS, CISTI.
Published by: U.S. Department of the Interior, Geological Survey, 12201 Sunrise Valley Dr, Reston, VA 20192. TEL 888-275-8747, ask@usgs.gov, http://water.usgs.gov/pubs/.
Subscr. to: USGS Information Services, Denver Federal Center, Box 25286, Denver, CO 80225-0046. FAX 303-202-4693, infoservices@usgs.gov.

551 USA
U.S. GEOLOGICAL SURVEY. COMPLETION REPORT. Text in English. irreg.
Published by: U.S. Department of the Interior, Geological Survey, 12201 Sunrise Valley Dr, Reston, VA 20192. TEL 888-275-8747, ask@usgs.gov.

551 USA ISSN 0196-1497
U.S. GEOLOGICAL SURVEY. OPEN-FILE REPORT. Text in English. 1978. irreg. price varies. **Document type:** *Monographic series.*
Formerly (until 1978): Geological Survey Open-File Report (0163-0393)
Related titles: CD-ROM ed.
Indexed: EEA, S&F.
—CISTI.
Published by: U.S. Department of the Interior, Geological Survey, 12201 Sunrise Valley Dr, Reston, VA 20192. TEL 888-275-8747, ask@usgs.gov, http://pubs.usgs.gov/products/books/openfile/. **Subscr. to:** USGS Information Services, Denver Federal Center, Box 25286, Denver, CO 80225-0046. TEL 303-202-4210, FAX 303-202-4693, infoservices@usgs.gov, http://mapping.usgs.gov/esic/.

557 USA ISSN 1044-9612
U.S. GEOLOGICAL SURVEY. PROFESSIONAL PAPERS. Text in English. 1902. irreg. back issues avail. **Document type:** *Monographic series, Government.* **Description:** Reports on the results of resource studies and on topographic, hydrologic and geologic investigations.
Former titles (until 1984): Geological Survey Professional Paper (0096-0446); (until 1949): U.S. Geological Survey. Professional Paper (1044-9620)
Related titles: Microform ed.: 1902 (from PMC).
Indexed: AESIS, ASFA, BibCart, FLUIDEX, GEOBASE, IMMAb, RefZh, S&F, ZooRec.
—CISTI.
Published by: U.S. Department of the Interior, Geological Survey, 12201 Sunrise Valley Dr, Reston, VA 20192. TEL 703-648-4000, 888-275-8747, FAX 703-648-4888, ask@usgs.gov, http://water.usgs.gov/pubs/. **Subscr. to:** USGS Information Services, Denver Federal Center, Box 25286, Denver, CO 80225-0046. FAX 303-202-4693, infoservices@usgs.gov.

U.S. NATIONAL COMMITTEE FOR MAN AND THE BIOSPHERE. BULLETIN. see *CONSERVATION*

510 USA
U.S. NATIONAL GEOPHYSICAL DATA CENTER. DATA ANNOUNCEMENT. Text in English. irreg. free. **Document type:** *Bulletin, Government.* **Description:** Outlines new studies available from N.O.A.A.
Published by: (National Oceanic and Atmospheric Administration), U.S. National Geophysical Data Center, 325 Broadway, E CG4, Boulder, CO 80303-3328. TEL 303-497-6338, FAX 303-497-6513, info@ngdc.noaa.gov, http://www.ngdc.noaa.gov.

551 669 MEX ISSN 0581-5207
QE1 CODEN: UAIFA5
UNIVERSIDAD AUTONOMA DE SAN LUIS POTOSI. INSTITUTO DE GEOLOGIA. FOLLETO TECNICO. Text in Spanish. 1962. irreg., latest vol.123, 1997. per issue exchange basis.
Document type: *Monographic series, Academic/Scholarly.*
Formerly: Universidad Autonoma de San Luis Potosi. Instituto de Geologia y Metalurgia. Folleto Tecnico
Indexed: ChemAb.
—CASDDS.
Published by: Universidad Autonoma de San Luis Potosi, Instituto de Geologia, Av. Dr. Manuel Nava 5, San Luis Potosi, Mexico. TEL 444-817-1039, FAX 444-811-1741, labarthe@uaslp.mx. Ed. Guillermo Labarthe.

550 COL ISSN 0120-0283
➤ **UNIVERSIDAD INDUSTRIAL DE SANTANDER. BOLETIN DE GEOLOGIA.** Text in Spanish; Text occasionally in English, French. 1958. a. USD 8 (effective 2003). abstr.; charts; illus.; bibl.; maps. 100 p./no.; **Document type:** *Bulletin, Academic/Scholarly.*
Indexed: BiolAb, ChemAb.
Published by: Universidad Industrial de Santander, Apartado Aereo 678, Bucaramanga, SANT, Colombia. TEL 57-976-6345106, FAX 57-976-6321931, escgeo@uis.edu.co, http://www.uis.edu.co. Circ: 1,200.

550 MEX ISSN 0185-5530
UNIVERSIDAD NACIONAL AUTONOMA DE MEXICO. INSTITUTO DE GEOLOGIA. BOLETIN. Text in Spanish. 1895. irreg., latest vol.109, 1996. USD 25 (effective 1998 & 1999). **Document type:** *Academic/Scholarly.*
—Linda Hall.

E

Published by: Universidad Nacional Autonoma de Mexico, Instituto de Geologia, Del Coyoacan, Mexico City, DF 04510, Mexico. TEL 52-5-622-4304, FAX 52-5-622-4318, publigl@geologia.unam.mx. **Orders to:** Departamento de Publicaciones, Apdo. Postal 70-296, Ciudad Universitaria, Del. Coyoacan, 04510, Mexico City, DF 04510, Mexico. TEL 52-5-622-4297.

551 BRA ISSN 0101-5400
CODEN: BCDGDT
UNIVERSIDADE FEDERAL DO RIO GRANDE DO NORTE. DEPARTAMENTO DE GEOLOGIA. BOLETIM. Text in Portuguese; Abstracts in English. 1981. q. adv. abstr.; bibl.; illus.; charts. **Document type:** *Bulletin, Academic/Scholarly.*
Indexed: ChemAb.
—CASDDS.
Published by: Universidade Federal do Rio Grande do Norte, Departamento de Geologia, Campus Universitario, Lga Nova, Caixa Postal 1639, Natal, RN 59072-970, Brazil. Ed. Peter Christian Hackspacher. Circ: 1,000.

554 560 ITA
UNIVERSITA DEGLI STUDI DI FERRARA. ISTITUTO DI GEOLOGIA. PUBBLICAZIONI. Text in English, French, Italian. 1950. a. exchange basis. index. **Document type:** *Academic/Scholarly.*
Formerly: Universita degli Studi di Ferrara. Istituto di Geologia, Paleontologia e Paleontologia Umana. Pubblicazioni (0071-4577)
Published by: Universita degli Studi di Ferrara, Istituto di Geologia, C.So Ercole 1 d'Este 32, Ferrara, Italy. Circ: 450.

551 ITA ISSN 0041-8978
QE272 CODEN: AGUGAQ
UNIVERSITA DEGLI STUDI DI GENOVA. ISTITUTO DI GEOLOGIA. ATTI✶. Text in Italian. 1963. 2/yr. **Document type:** *Academic/Scholarly.*
Published by: Universita degli Studi di Genova, Istituto di Geologia, Via Balbi 5, Genoa, GE, Italy.

551 560 ITA ISSN 0071-4550
UNIVERSITA DI FERRARA. ANNALI. SEZIONE 9: SCIENZE GEOLOGICHE E MINERALOGICHE. Text in English, French, Italian. 1951. a., latest vol.3, no.2, 1981. price varies. index. **Document type:** *Academic/Scholarly.*
Formerly: Universita di Ferrara. Annali. Sezione 9: Scienze geologiche e paleontologiche (0374-518X)
—Linda Hall.
Published by: (Universita degli Studi di Ferrara), Casa Editrice Leo S. Olschki, Viuzzo del Pozzetto 8, Florence, 50126, Italy. TEL 39-055-6530684, FAX 39-055-6530214, celso@olschki.it, http://www.olschki.it. Circ: 450.

554 560 DEU ISSN 0072-1115
QE1 CODEN: MGPHBZ
UNIVERSITAET HAMBURG. GEOLOGISCH-PALAEONTOLOGISCHES INSTITUT. MITTEILUNGEN. Text in English, German. 1948. a. price varies. **Document type:** *Journal, Academic/Scholarly.*
Formerly (until 1969): Geologisches Staatsinstitut in Hamburg. Mitteilungen (0369-0016)
Indexed: BiolAb, IBR, RefZh, ZooRec.
—CCC.
Published by: Universitaet Hamburg, Geologisch-Palaeontologisches Institut, Bundesstr 55, Hamburg, 20146, Germany. TEL 49-40-428384999, FAX 49-40-428385007, geologie@geowiss.uni-hamburg.de, http://www.geowiss.uni-hamburg.de/i-geolo/. Ed. Wolfgang Weitschat.

554 AUT
UNIVERSITAET INNSBRUCK. ALPENKUNDLICHE STUDIEN✶. Text in German. 1968. irreg., latest vol.10, 1972. price varies. **Document type:** *Academic/Scholarly.*
Related titles: Series of: Universitaet Innsbruck. Veroeffentlichungen.
Published by: (Universitaet Innsbruck), Oesterreichische Kommissionsbuchhandlung, Glasmalereistr 6, Innsbruck, T 6020, Austria. TEL 43-512-587039, FAX 43-512-5870394, oekobuch@aon.at, http://www.oekobuch.com. Ed. Franz Fliri.

551 DEU
UNIVERSITAET KIEL. INSTITUT FUER GEOWISSENSCHAFTEN. BERICHTE - REPORTS. Text in German, English; Abstracts in English, German. 1983. irreg., latest vol.21, 2004. price varies. back issues avail. **Document type:** *Monographic series, Academic/Scholarly.*
Formerly (until 1999): Universitaet Kiel. Geologisch-Palaeontologisches Institut. Berichte - Reports (0175-9302)
Published by: Universitaet Kiel, Institut fuer Geowissenschaften, Olshausenstr 40, Kiel, 24118, Germany. TEL 49-431-8803254, FAX 49-431-8804376, kw@gpi.uni-kiel.de, http://www.ifg.uni-kiel.de/zentral/veroeffent.html. Ed. Kyaw Winn.

551 HUN ISSN 0365-0634
UNIVERSITATIS SCIENTIARUM BUDAPESTINENSIS DE ROLANDO EOTVOS NOMINATAE. ANNALES. SECTIO GEOLOGICA. Text in Hungarian. 1957. irreg.
Indexed: GEOBASE, RefZh, ZooRec.
—CISTI, Linda Hall.
Published by: Eotvos Lorand Tudomanyegyetem, Allam- es Jogtudomanyi Kara/Eotvos Lorand University, Egyetem ter 1-3, Budapest, 1364, Hungary. TEL 1-174-930.

551 FRA ISSN 1162-9584
QE1 CODEN: ASBGEJ
UNIVERSITE DE FRANCHE-COMTE. ANNALES SCIENTIFIQUES. GEOLOGIE. Text in French. 1946. irreg.
Former titles (until 1989): Universite de Besancon. Annales Scientifiques. Geologie (0523-056X); (until 1950): Annales Scientifiques de Franche-Comte. Geologie (0150-679X); Which superseded in part (in 1949): Annales Scientifiques de Franche-Comte (0365-6764)
Indexed: ESPM, ZooRec.
—CISTI, Linda Hall.
Published by: (Universite de Franche-Comte, U F R des Sciences et Techniques), Presses Universitaires Franche-Comte, Place St Jacques, Besancon, 25030, France. TEL 03-81-66-59-70, FAX 03-81-66-59-80, pufc@univ-fcomte.fr, http://pufc.univ-fcomte.fr.

551 TUR ISSN 1303-6025
CODEN: CFSGDY
UNIVERSITY OF ANKARA. FACULTY OF SCIENCE. COMMUNICATIONS. SERIES C: BIOLOGY, GEOLOGICAL ENGINEERING AND GEOPHYSICAL ENGINEERING. Text in English, French, German. 1947. a. per issue exchange basis. back issues avail. **Document type:** *Academic/Scholarly.*
Formed by the merger of (1975-1985): Universite d'Ankara. Faculte des Sciences. Communications. Serie C1. Geologie (0253-1216); (1983-1985): Universite d'Ankara. Faculte des Sciences. Communications. Serie C. Biologie (0256-7865); Which was formed by the merger of (1975-1983): Communications de la Faculte des Sciences de l'Universite d'Ankara. Serie C 2, Botanique (0253-2190); (1975-1983): Communications de la Faculte des Sciences de l'Universite d'Ankara. Serie C 3, Zoologie (0253-2204); Both of which superseded in part (in 1975): Communications de la Faculte des Sciences de l'Universite d'Ankara. Serie C: Sciences Naturelles (0570-1422); Which superseded in part (in 1950): Communications de la Faculte des Sciences de l'Universite d'Ankara (0366-6956)
Related titles: Online - full text ed.: (from EBSCO Publishing).
Indexed: BiolAb.
—CISTI.
Published by: Ankara Universitesi, Fen Fakultesi, Dogol Caddesi, Ankara, 06100, Turkey. Circ: 250.

557 CAN ISSN 0705-3207
UNIVERSITY OF BRITISH COLUMBIA. DEPARTMENT OF GEOLOGICAL SCIENCES. REPORT. Text in English. 1962. irreg., latest vol.19, 1990. CND 3. **Document type:** *Academic/Scholarly.*
Formerly: University of British Columbia. Department of Geology. Report (0068-1733)
Published by: University of British Columbia, Department of Geological Sciences, Vancouver, BC V6T 2B4, Canada. TEL 604-228-2211, FAX 604-822-6088. Ed. W R Danner. Circ: 400.

556 ZAF
UNIVERSITY OF CAPE TOWN. DEPARTMENT OF GEOLOGICAL SCIENCES. PRECAMBRIAN RESEARCH UNIT. BULLETIN. Text in English. 1965. irreg., latest vol.38, 1993. ZAR 200, USD 60; or exchange basis. bibl.; charts. **Document type:** *Bulletin, Academic/Scholarly.*
Formerly: University of Cape Town. Department of Geology. Precambrian Research Unit. Bulletin (0041-9478)
Indexed: AESIS.
Published by: University of Cape Town, Department of Geological Sciences Precambrian Research Unit, Rondebosch, Cape Town 7700, South Africa. TEL 27-21-6502917. Ed. C W Stowe. Circ: 375.

553 557 USA ISSN 0082-3287
QE167 CODEN: TGARBX
➤ **UNIVERSITY OF TEXAS AT AUSTIN. BUREAU OF ECONOMIC GEOLOGY. ANNUAL REPORT.** Text in English. 1960. a., latest 2000. free (effective 2003). adv. reprint service avail. from PQC. **Document type:** *Academic/Scholarly.*
Description: Provides advisory, technical, and informational services relating to the resources and geology of Texas and selected other areas.
Indexed: AESIS.
—BLDSC (1132.600000), Linda Hall. **CCC.**
Published by: University of Texas at Austin, Bureau of Economic Geology, c/o A Masterson, Pub Sales, Box X, University Sta, Austin, TX 78713-8924. TEL 512-471-7144, 888-839-4365, FAX 512-471-0140, pubsales@beg.utexas.edu, http://www.beg.utexas.edu/. Ed. S Doenges. R&P S. Doenges. Adv. contact Doug Ratcliff.

557 USA ISSN 0082-3309
CODEN: GCUGDX
➤ **UNIVERSITY OF TEXAS AT AUSTIN. BUREAU OF ECONOMIC GEOLOGY. GEOLOGICAL CIRCULAR.** Text in English. 1965-1967; resumed 1969. irreg., latest 2001. price varies. adv. back issues avail.; reprint service avail. from PQC. **Document type:** *Monographic series, Academic/Scholarly.*
Indexed: AESIS, IMMAb.
—Linda Hall. **CCC.**
Published by: University of Texas at Austin, Bureau of Economic Geology, c/o A Masterson, Pub Sales, Box X, University Sta, Austin, TX 78713-8924. TEL 512-471-7144, 888-839-4365, FAX 512-471-0140, pubsales@beg.utexas.edu, http://www.beg.utexas.edu/. Ed. S Doenges. R&P A Masterson. Adv. contact Doug Ratcliff.

557 USA ISSN 0363-4132
CODEN: TEGGAF
➤ **UNIVERSITY OF TEXAS AT AUSTIN. BUREAU OF ECONOMIC GEOLOGY. GUIDEBOOK.** Text in English. 1958. irreg., latest vol.28, 2001. price varies. adv. reprint service avail. from PQC. **Document type:** *Academic/Scholarly.*
Formerly: University of Texas. Bureau of Economic Geology. Guidebook (0082-3295)
Indexed: AESIS.
—Linda Hall. **CCC.**
Published by: University of Texas at Austin, Bureau of Economic Geology, c/o A Masterson, Pub Sales, Box X, University Sta, Austin, TX 78713-8924. TEL 512-471-7144, 888-839-4365, FAX 512-471-0140, pubsales@beg.utexas.edu, http://www.beg.utexas.edu/. Ed. S Doenges. Adv. contact Doug Ratcliff.

553 USA ISSN 0082-3333
➤ **UNIVERSITY OF TEXAS AT AUSTIN. BUREAU OF ECONOMIC GEOLOGY. MINERAL RESOURCE CIRCULARS.** Variant title: Mineral Resource Circulars. Text in English. 1930. irreg., latest vol.85, 1994. price varies. adv. back issues avail.; reprint service avail. from PQC. **Document type:** *Monographic series, Academic/Scholarly.*
Indexed: IMMAb.
—CCC.
Published by: University of Texas at Austin, Bureau of Economic Geology, c/o A Masterson, Pub Sales, Box X, University Sta, Austin, TX 78713-8924. TEL 512-471-7144, 888-839-4365, FAX 512-471-0140, pubsales@beg.utexas.edu, http://www.beg.utexas.edu/. Ed. S Doenges. R&P A Masterson. Adv. contact Doug Ratcliff.

551 USA
➤ **UNIVERSITY OF TEXAS AT AUSTIN. BUREAU OF ECONOMIC GEOLOGY. OTHER PUBLICATIONS.** Text in English. irreg. price varies. adv. back issues avail. **Document type:** *Monographic series, Academic/Scholarly.*
Formerly: University of Texas at Austin. Bureau of Economic Geology. Special Publications
Published by: University of Texas at Austin, Bureau of Economic Geology, c/o A Masterson, Pub Sales, Box X, University Sta, Austin, TX 78713-8924. TEL 512-471-7144, 888-839-4365, FAX 512-471-0140, pubsales@beg.utexas.edu, http://www.beg.utexas.edu/. Ed. S Doenges. R&P A Masterson. Adv. contact Doug Ratcliff.

557 USA ISSN 0888-6725
QE167.T42 CODEN: TUGRAO
➤ **UNIVERSITY OF TEXAS AT AUSTIN. BUREAU OF ECONOMIC GEOLOGY. REPORT OF INVESTIGATIONS.** Text in English. 1946. irreg., latest vol.261, 2000. price varies. adv. back issues avail.; reprint service avail. from PQC. **Document type:** *Monographic series, Academic/Scholarly.*
Indexed: AESIS, IMMAb.
—BLDSC (7659.200000), Linda Hall. **CCC.**
Published by: University of Texas at Austin, Bureau of Economic Geology, c/o A Masterson, Pub Sales, Box X, University Sta, Austin, TX 78713-8924. TEL 512-471-7144, 888-839-4365, FAX 512-471-0140, pubsales@beg.utexas.edu, http://www.beg.utexas.edu/. Ed. S Doenges. R&P A Masterson. Adv. contact Doug Ratcliff.

550 PAK ISSN 0079-8037
QE1 CODEN: GBPUA6
UNIVERSITY OF THE PUNJAB. INSTITUTE OF GEOLOGY. GEOLOGICAL BULLETIN. Text in English. 1961. a. PKR 100. bk.rev. back issues avail. **Document type:** *Bulletin, Academic/Scholarly.*
Indexed: BiolAb, MinerAb.
Published by: University of the Punjab, Institute of Geology, Qaid-E-Azam Campus, Lahore, Pakistan. TEL 92-42-5866809. Circ: (controlled).

551 JPN ISSN 0388-6182
QE1
UNIVERSITY OF TSUKUBA. INSTITUTE OF GEOSCIENCE. SCIENCE REPORTS. SECTION B: GEOLOGICAL SCIENCES. Text in English. 1980. a.
Indexed: GEOBASE, RefZh, ZooRec.
—BLDSC (8153.820000), CISTI, Linda Hall.
Published by: University of Tsukuba, Institute of Geoscience/Tsukuba Daigaku Chikyu Kagakukei, 1-1 Tenno-Dai 1-chome, Tsukuba-shi, Ibaraki-ken 305-0006, Japan.

559.8 597 551.9 NZL ISSN 0110-2192
QE350 CODEN: RUWADY
UNIVERSITY OF WAIKATO. ANTARCTIC RESEARCH UNIT. REPORT. Text in English. 1972. a. free. **Document type:** *Academic/Scholarly.*
Indexed: ChemAb.
Published by: University of Waikato, Antarctic Research Unit, Private Bag 3105, Hamilton, New Zealand. Circ: 350.

E

550 POL ISSN 0239-7560
UNIWERSYTET IM. ADAMA MICKIEWICZA. GEOLOGIA. Text in Polish. 1961. irreg., latest vol.15, 1993. price varies. **Document type:** *Academic/Scholarly.* **Description:** Every volume contains current research results of one author in the field of earth sciences, including Ph.D. papers and monographs.
Formerly (until 1979): Uniwersytet im. Adama Mickiewicza w Poznaniu. Wydzial Biologii i Nauk o Ziemi. Prace. Seria Geologia (0083-4238)
Published by: Wydawnictwo Naukowe Uniwersytetu im. Adama Mickiewicza/Adam Mickiewicz University Press, Nowowiejskiego 55, Poznan, 61-734, Poland. TEL 48-61-527380, FAX 48-61-527701. Pub. Maria Jankowska. R&P Malgorzata Bis. Circ: 350.

796.525 POL ISSN 0208-5534
QE1
➤ **UNIWERSYTET SLASKI W KATOWICACH. PRACE NAUKOWE. GEOLOGIA.** Text in Polish; Summaries in English, Russian. 1977. irreg., latest vol.15, 2002. price varies. **Document type:** *Monographic series, Academic/Scholarly.* **Description:** Covers basic geology, palaeontology, stratigraphy, geochemistry, mineralogy, petrography, hydrogeology, engineering geology, geology of deposits.
Indexed: RefZh.
Published by: (Uniwersytet Slaski w Katowicach), Wydawnictwo Uniwersytetu Slaskiego w Katowicach, Ul Bankowa 12B, Katowice, 40007, Poland. TEL 48-32-2596915, FAX 48-32-2582735, TELEX 0315584 uskpl, wydawus@us.edu.pl, http://www.us.edu.pl/uniwersytet/jednostki/ogolne/wydawnictwo. **Dist. by:** CHZ Ars Polona, Biblioteka PAN w Warszawie, PO Box 1001, Warsaw 00950, Poland.

796.525 POL ISSN 0137-5482
GB601.A1
➤ **UNIWERSYTET SLASKI W KATOWICACH. PRACE NAUKOWE. KRAS I SPELEOLOGIA.** Text in English, Polish; Summaries in English, French, Polish. 1977. irreg., latest vol.10, 2000. price varies. **Document type:** *Monographic series, Academic/Scholarly.* **Description:** Covers karst in Poland and Europe, with thermokarst and pseudokarst, and cave explorations.
Indexed: RefZh.
Published by: (Uniwersytet Slaski w Katowicach), Wydawnictwo Uniwersytetu Slaskiego w Katowicach, Ul Bankowa 12B, Katowice, 40007, Poland. TEL 48-32-2596915, FAX 48-32-2582735, TELEX 0315584 uskpl, wydawus@us.edu.pl, http://www.us.edu.pl/uniwersytet/jednostki/ogolne/wydawnictwo. **Dist. by:** CHZ Ars Polona, Biblioteka PAN w Warszawie, PO Box 1001, Warsaw 00950, Poland.

551 GBR ISSN 0566-3954
USSHER SOCIETY. PROCEEDINGS. Text in English. 1962. a. **Document type:** *Proceedings, Academic/Scholarly.*
—IE.
Published by: (Ussher Society), Kyrtonia ExPress, 115 High St, Crediton, Devon, EX17 3LG, United Kingdom. TEL 44-136-377-2060, FAX 44-136-377-4030, phillco@gobalnet.co.uk. Ed. B J Williams.

557 USA ISSN 0083-484X
➤ **UTAH GEOLOGICAL ASSOCIATION. ANNUAL GUIDEBOOK.** Text in English. 1971. a. price varies. **Document type:** *Academic/Scholarly.* **Description:** Presents papers on a specific area's geology and related topics, with emphasis on field trips.
Indexed: ZooRec.
—BLDSC (9135.175000).
Published by: Utah Geological Association, PO Box 520100, Salt Lake City, UT 84152-0100. TEL 801-364-6613, FAX 801-741-8097. Ed. Paul B Anderson. Circ: 850. **Subscr. to:** Utah Geological Survey, 1594 W North Temple, Ste 3110, Box 146100, Salt Lake City, UT 84114-6100. TEL 801-537-3320, FAX 801-537-3395.

557 553 USA
QE169
UTAH GEOLOGICAL SURVEY. BULLETIN. Text in English. 1948 (no.35). irreg., latest vol.131, 2000. price varies. illus.; maps. back issues avail. **Document type:** *Bulletin, Government.*
Former titles (until 1990): Utah. Geological and Mineral Survey. Bulletin (0098-4825); (until 1973): Utah. Geological Mineralogical Survey. Bulletin (0096-9605)
Indexed: AESIS, ChemAb, RefZh, ZooRec.
—Linda Hall.
Published by: Utah Geological Survey, 1594 W North Temple, Ste 3110, Box 146100, Salt Lake City, UT 84114-6100. TEL 801-537-3320, FAX 801-537-3395, http://geology.utah.gov/. Ed. Jim Stringfellow.

551 USA
UTAH GEOLOGICAL SURVEY. OPEN-FILE REPORTS. Text in English. irreg. price varies. back issues avail. **Document type:** *Government.*
Formerly: Utah Geological and Mineral Survey. Open-File Report (0741-0840)
Published by: Utah Geological Survey, 1594 W North Temple, Ste 3110, Box 146100, Salt Lake City, UT 84114-6100. TEL 801-537-3320, FAX 801-537-3395, http://geology.utah.gov/.

551 USA
UTAH GEOLOGICAL SURVEY. PUBLIC INFORMATION SERIES. Text in English. irreg. price varies. **Document type:** *Government.*
Published by: Utah Geological Survey, 1594 W North Temple, Ste 3110, Box 146100, Salt Lake City, UT 84114-6100. TEL 801-537-3320, FAX 801-537-3395, http://geology.utah.gov/.

551 USA
UTAH GEOLOGICAL SURVEY. REPORTS OF INVESTIGATION. Text in English. irreg. price varies. back issues avail. **Document type:** *Government.*
Published by: Utah Geological Survey, 1594 W North Temple, Ste 3110, Box 146100, Salt Lake City, UT 84114-6100. TEL 801-537-3320, FAX 801-537-3395, http://geology.utah.gov/.

557 553 USA ISSN 1063-4916
TN24.U8 CODEN: UGMSA4
UTAH GEOLOGICAL SURVEY. SPECIAL STUDY. Text in English. 1962. irreg., latest no.99, 2000. price varies. illus.; maps. back issues avail. **Document type:** *Government.*
Former titles (until 1991): Utah. Geological and Mineral Survey. Special Studies (0098-115X); (until 1973): Utah Geological and Mineralogical Survey. Special Studies (0566-4128)
Indexed: RefZh.
—CASDDS, Linda Hall.
Published by: Utah Geological Survey, 1594 W North Temple, Ste 3110, Box 146100, Salt Lake City, UT 84114-6100. TEL 801-537-3320, FAX 801-537-3395, http://geology.utah.gov/. R&P J. Stringfellow.

557 553 USA ISSN 1061-7930
QE169
UTAH GEOLOGICAL SURVEY. SURVEY NOTES. Text in English. 1964. 3/yr. free in the U.S.. bk.rev. charts; illus.; stat. back issues avail. **Document type:** *Newsletter, Government.*
Former titles: Utah. Geological and Mineral Survey. Survey Notes (0362-6288); Utah. Geological and Mineral Survey. Quarterly Review (0042-1421)
Related titles: Online - full content ed.
Indexed: AESIS, EEA, RefZh.
—BLDSC (8550.712000), Linda Hall.
Published by: Utah Geological Survey, 1594 W North Temple, Ste 3110, Box 146100, Salt Lake City, UT 84114-6100. TEL 801-537-3320, FAX 801-537-3395, http://geology.utah.gov/. Ed. J Stringfellow. R&P J. Stringfellow. Circ: 3,600.

559.4 665.5 AUS ISSN 1323-4536
V I M P REPORT. Text in English. 1994. irreg. price varies. **Document type:** *Government.*
Indexed: AESIS.
Published by: Geological Survey of Victoria, Minerals and Petroleum, Victoria, PO Box 500, East Melbourne, VIC 3002, Australia. TEL 61-3-9412-5020, FAX 61-3-9412-5157.

559 VUT
QE349.N43 CODEN: NHGRA3
VANUATU. GEOLOGICAL SURVEY. REPORTS. Text in English. 1966. irreg. price varies. **Document type:** *Government.* **Description:** Descriptive reports of geology of island groups within Vanuatu. Reports published separately from geological maps.
Formerly: New Hebrides Condominium. Geological Survey. Report (0077-8443)
Published by: Geological Survey, GPO, Port Vila, Vanuatu. FAX 22213, TELEX 1040 NH VANGOV.

550 VEN ISSN 0006-6281
QE251 CODEN: VMMGAL
VENEZUELA. MINISTERIO DE ENERGIA Y MINAS. BOLETIN DE GEOLOGIA. Text in Spanish; Summaries in English, Spanish. 1951. irreg. price varies. **Document type:** *Government.*
Indexed: BiolAb, IBR.
—Linda Hall.
Published by: Ministerio de Energia y Minas, Torre Oeste Piso 8, Parque Central, Caracas, DF 1010, Venezuela. Ed. Nelly Pimentel de Bellizia.

551.44 DEU ISSN 0505-2211
GB599
VERBAND DER DEUTSCHEN HOEHLEN- UND KARSTFORSCHER. MITTEILUNGEN. Text in Multiple languages. 1960. q. EUR 15 (effective 2004).
Indexed: GEOBASE, RefZh.
Published by: Verband der Deutschen Hoehlen- und Karstforscher e.V., c/o Michael Laumanns, Unter den Eichen 4 C, Rangsdorf, 15834, Germany. http://www.hfc-hersfled.de/vdhk/. **Subscr. to:** c/o Thomas Matthalm, Schellingstr 88, Muenchen 80798, Germany. TEL 49-89-52310578, Thomas.Matthalm@gmx.de.

557 USA
QE171 CODEN: VGSBAS
VERMONT DIVISION OF GEOLOGY AND MINERAL RESOURCES. BULLETIN. Text in English. 1950. irreg., latest vol.32, 1984. price varies. **Document type:** *Bulletin, Government.* **Description:** Covers the geology of 15-minute quadrangles in Vermont.
Formerly: Vermont Geological Survey. Bulletin (0083-5757)
Indexed: BiolAb.
—Linda Hall.
Published by: Vermont Division of Geology and Mineral Resources, 103 S Main St, Laundry Bldg, Waterbury, VT 05671-0301. TEL 802-241-3608.

557 551 USA
QE171
VERMONT DIVISION OF GEOLOGY AND MINERAL RESOURCES. ECONOMIC GEOLOGY REPORT. Text in English. 1966. irreg., latest vol.8, 1972. USD 1 per issue (effective 2000). illus. **Document type:** *Academic/Scholarly.* **Description:** Contains information on magnetic, geochemical, resistivity surveys and geology of economic mineral deposits in Vermont.
Formerly: Vermont Geological Survey. Economic Geology (0531-8262)
—Linda Hall.
Published by: Vermont Division of Geology and Mineral Resources, 103 S Main St, Laundry Bldg, Waterbury, VT 05671-0301. TEL 802-241-3608. R&P Marjorie Gale.

557 USA
VERMONT DIVISION OF GEOLOGY AND MINERAL RESOURCES. GEOLOGY OF STATE PARKS. Text in English. irreg. **Document type:** *Government.*
Published by: Vermont Division of Geology and Mineral Resources, 103 S Main St, Laundry Bldg, Waterbury, VT 05671-0301.

557 USA
VERMONT DIVISION OF GEOLOGY AND MINERAL RESOURCES. OPEN-FILE REPORT. Text in English. irreg. **Document type:** *Government.*
Published by: Vermont Division of Geology and Mineral Resources, 103 S Main St, Laundry Bldg, Waterbury, VT 05671-0301.

557 USA
VERMONT DIVISION OF GEOLOGY AND MINERAL RESOURCES. SPECIAL BULLETIN. Text in English. 1968. irreg., latest vol.14, 1995. price varies. illus. **Document type:** *Bulletin, Government.* **Description:** Covers the geology of Vermont.
Formerly: Vermont Geological Survey. Special Bulletin (0506-7553)
—Linda Hall.
Published by: Vermont Division of Geology and Mineral Resources, 103 S Main St, Laundry Bldg, Waterbury, VT 05671-0301. TEL 802-241-3608.

557 551.4 USA
QE747.V4 CODEN: VGSPA2
VERMONT DIVISION OF GEOLOGY AND MINERAL RESOURCES. SPECIAL PUBLICATION. Text in English. 1962. irreg., latest vol.3, 1982. price varies. illus. **Document type:** *Government.* **Description:** Covers general-interest topics on Vermont geology.
Formerly: Vermont Geological Survey. Special Publication (0083-5765)
—Linda Hall.
Published by: Vermont Division of Geology and Mineral Resources, 103 S Main St, Laundry Bldg, Waterbury, VT 05671-0301. TEL 802-241-3608.

557 USA
VERMONT DIVISION OF GEOLOGY AND MINERAL RESOURCES. STUDIES IN VERMONT GEOLOGY. Text in English. irreg. **Document type:** *Government.*
Published by: Vermont Division of Geology and Mineral Resources, 103 S Main St, Laundry Bldg, Waterbury, VT 05671-0301.

559.4 AUS ISSN 0810-6959
VICTORIA, AUSTRALIA. GEOLOGICAL SURVEY. REPORT. Text in English. 1968. irreg. price varies. **Document type:** *Monographic series, Government.*
Indexed: AESIS, IMMAb.
Published by: Geological Survey of Victoria, Minerals and Petroleum, Victoria, PO Box 500, East Melbourne, VIC 3002, Australia. TEL 61-3-9412-5020, FAX 61-3-9412-5157. R&P Tom Dickson.

559.4 AUS ISSN 1324-0307
VICTORIA, AUSTRALIA. GEOLOGICAL SURVEY. TECHNICAL RECORD. Text in English. 1995. irreg. price varies. **Document type:** *Government.*
Published by: Geological Survey of Victoria, Minerals and Petroleum, Victoria, PO Box 500, East Melbourne, VIC 3002, Australia. TEL 61-3-9412-5020, FAX 61-3-9412-5157. R&P Tom Dickson.

VIRGINIA. DIVISION OF MINERAL RESOURCES. PUBLICATIONS. see *MINES AND MINING INDUSTRY*

557 USA ISSN 0507-1259
VIRGINIA POLYTECHNIC INSTITUTE AND STATE UNIVERSITY. DEPARTMENT OF GEOLOGICAL SCIENCES. GEOLOGICAL GUIDEBOOKS. Text in English. 1961. irreg., latest vol.10, 1994. price varies. back issues avail. **Document type:** *Monographic series.*
Formerly: Virginia Polytechnic Institute, Blacksburg. Engineering Extension Division. Geological Guidebook

E

Published by: Virginia Polytechnic Institute and State University, Department of Geological Sciences, 4044 Derring Hall, Blacksburg, VA 24061. TEL 540-231-6521. Circ: (controlled).

526 BGR ISSN 0324-1114
QB275 CODEN: VGEOEZ
VISSHA GEODEZIIA. Text in Multiple languages. 1975. irreg. BGL 1.10 per issue. reprint service avail. from IRC. **Document type:** *Academic/Scholarly.*
Indexed: BSLGeo, RefZh.
—Linda Hall.
Published by: (Bulgarska Akademiya na Naukite/Bulgarian Academy of Sciences), Universitetsko Izdatelstvo Sv. Kliment Okhridski/Publishing House of the Sofia University St. Kliment Ohridski, Akad G Bonchev 6, Sofia, 1113, Bulgaria. Circ: 480.

551 DEU ISSN 1610-2924
➤ **VISUAL GEOSCIENCES.** Text in English. a. EUR 420 (effective 2005). **Document type:** *Journal, Academic/Scholarly.* **Description:** Covers the entire spectrum of earth sciences.
Former titles (until 2002): Electronic Geosciences (1436-2511); (until 1998): Electronic Geology
Media: Online - full content (from Springer LINK). **Related titles:** CD-ROM ed.
Indexed: GEOBASE.
—IE. **CCC.**
Published by: Springer-Verlag (Subsidiary of: Springer Science+Business Media), Tiergartenstr 17, Heidelberg, 69121, Germany. TEL 49-6221-3450, FAX 49-6221-345229, subscriptions@springer.de, http://link.springer.de/link/service/journals/10069/index.htm, http://www.springer.de. Ed. John D Clemens. Adv. contact Stephan Kroeck TEL 49-30-827875739.

551 RUS
VORONEZHSKII GOSUDARSTVENNYI UNIVERSITET. VESTI. GEOLOGIYA. Text in Russian. 2000. irreg.
Related titles: Online - full text ed.
Published by: Voronezhskii Gosudarstvennyi Universitet, Universitetskaya pl 1, Voronezh, 394693, Russian Federation. TEL 7-0732-789657, FAX 7-0732-554308, office@main.vsu.ru, http://www.vsu.ru/dept/science/public/vest_vsu/geol.html. Ed. A. D. Savko.

549 RUS ISSN 0869-6055
QE351 CODEN: ZVMOAG
➤ **VSEROSSIISKOE MINERALOGICHESKOE OBSHCHESTVO. ZAPISKI/RUSSIAN MINERALOGICAL SOCIETY. PROCEEDINGS.** Text in English, Russian; Abstracts and contents page in English, Russian. 1830. bi-m. USD 238 foreign (effective 2005). adv. bk.rev. abstr.; charts; illus. index. reprints avail. **Document type:** *Journal, Academic/Scholarly.* **Description:** Informs readers about the main achievements of Russian scientists in the fields of mineralogy, petrology, crystallography, geochemistry and the science of mineral deposits, as well as the scientific-public activities of the society. Analyzes in detail questions of genesis, constitution of materials and their properties, crystallomorphology, physical and chemical parameters of the mineral forming processes, typical parageneses, and mineral associations of rocks and ores. Contains information on the discovery of new minerals within Russia and other countries and papers on new techniques and methods of investigation for minerals, rocks, and ores.
Formerly (until 1992): Vsesoyuznoe Mineralogicheskoe Obshchestvo. Zapiski (0044-1805)
Related titles: Microform ed.; Online - full text ed.
Indexed: AESIS, EngInd, MinerAb, RefZh.
—BLDSC (0069.930000), CASDDS, CISTI, East View, KNAW, Linda Hall. **CCC.**
Published by: (Vserossiiskoe Mineralogicheskoe Obshchestvo/Russian Mineralogical Society), Izdatel'stvo Nauka, Sankt-Peterburgskoe Otdelenie, Mendeleevskaya liniya 1, St Petersburg, 199034, Russian Federation. TEL 7-812-3286291, marin@mineral.ras.spb.ru, http://www.mineral.ras.spb.ru/proc/proc_e.html. Ed. Yuri B Marin. Adv. contact Larisa I Korchemkina. Circ: 400. **Dist. by:** East View Information Services, 3020 Harbor Ln. N., Minneapolis, MN 55447. TEL 800-477-1005, FAX 800-800-3839, eastview@eastview.com, http://www.eastview.com.
Co-sponsor: Rossiiskaya Akademiya Nauk, Otdelenie Geologii, Geofiziki, Geokhimii i Gornykh Nauk/Russian Academy of Sciences, Department of Geology, Geophysics, Geochemistry and Mining.

551 CZE ISSN 0474-8476
TN5 CODEN: SRHSAY
VYSOKA SKOLA BANSKA. SBORNIK VEDECKYCH PRACI: RADA HORNICKA-GEOLOGICKA. Text in Czech; Summaries in English, German, Russian. 1955. irreg.
Indexed: ChemAb, ChemTitl, IMMAb, ZentMath.
—CASDDS, Linda Hall.
Published by: Vysoka Skola Banska/Technical University of Mining and Metallurgy, Trida 17 Listopadu 15, Ostrava, 708 33, Czech Republic. Ed. Alena Bichlerova. **Subscr. to:** Ustredni Knihovna, Studijni Informacni Centrum, Studentska ul 1770, Ostrava-poruba 708 33, Czech Republic.

550 DEU
WANDERUNGEN IN DIE ERDGESCHICHTE. Text in German. irreg., latest vol.9, 1996. **Document type:** *Monographic series.*
Published by: Verlag Dr. Friedrich Pfeil, Wolfratshauser Str 27, Munich, 81379, Germany. info@pfeil-verlag.de, http://www.pfeil-verlag.de.

551 MYS ISSN 0126-5539
QE299.5 CODEN: WAGEDH
WARTA GEOLOGI/GEOLOGICAL SOCIETY OF MALAYSIA NEWSLETTER. Text in English. 1967. bi-m. MYR 30 (effective 2004). back issues avail. **Document type:** *Newsletter, Academic/Scholarly.* **Description:** Contains articles, progress reports, and general information for members.
Indexed: AESIS, BiolAb, IMMAb.
Published by: Geological Society of Malaysia/Persatuan Geologi Malaysia, d/a Jabatan Geologi, Universiti Malaya, Kuala Lumpur, 50603, Malaysia. TEL 60-3-79577036, FAX 60-3-79563900, geologi@po.jaring.my, http://www.angelfire.com.la/gsm. Circ: 700.

557 622 USA ISSN 1045-2982
QE175
WASHINGTON (STATE). DEPARTMENT OF NATURAL RESOURCES. DIVISION OF GEOLOGY AND EARTH RESOURCES. BULLETIN. Text in English. 1945. irreg., latest vol.81, 1996. price varies. back issues avail. **Document type:** *Bulletin, Government.* **Description:** Provides technical information on various aspects of the geology of the state of Washington.
Former titles (until 1973): Washington (State). Geology and Earth Resources Division. Bulletin (0363-3101); (until 1972): Washinton. Department of Natural Resources. Division of Mines and Geology. Bulletin (0096-6045)
Indexed: IMMAb.
—Linda Hall.
Published by: Washington State Department of Natural Resources, Division of Geology and Earth Resources, Natural Resources Bldg, Rm 148, 1111 Washington St S E, Olympia, WA 98501 . TEL 360-902-1450, FAX 360-902-1785, geology@wadnr.gov. Ed. Jari Roloff.

557.97 USA ISSN 0147-1783
TN24.W2 CODEN: ICDRD3
WASHINGTON (STATE). DEPARTMENT OF NATURAL RESOURCES. DIVISION OF GEOLOGY AND EARTH RESOURCES. INFORMATION CIRCULAR. Key Title: Information Circular - State of Washington, Department of Natural Resources, Division of Geology and Earth Resources. Text in English. 1939. irreg., latest vol.90, 1996. price varies. **Document type:** *Newsletter, Academic/Scholarly.* **Description:** Provides technical geological information on the state of Washington.
Indexed: IMMAb.
—BLDSC (4489.055000), Linda Hall.
Published by: Division of Geology and Earth Resources, 1111 Washington St, S E, Box 47007, Olympia, WA 98504-7007. TEL 360-902-1450, FAX 360-902-1785, geology@wadnr.gov, http://www.wa.gov/dnr/ger/ger.html. Ed. Jari Roloff.

551 USA
WASHINGTON (STATE). DEPARTMENT OF NATURAL RESOURCES. DIVISION OF GEOLOGY AND EARTH RESOURCES. REPORT OF INVESTIGATIONS. Text in English. 1926. irreg., latest vol.32, 1995. price varies. **Document type:** *Government.* **Description:** Information on a single topic of the geology of the state of Washington.
Indexed: IMMAb.
Published by: Washington State Department of Natural Resources, Division of Geology and Earth Resources, Natural Resources Bldg, Rm 148, 1111 Washington St S E, Olympia, WA 98501 . TEL 360-902-1450, FAX 360-902-1785, geology@wadnr.gov. Ed. Jari Roloff. Circ: 1,000.

557 622 USA
WASHINGTON. DIVISION OF MINES AND GEOLOGY. BULLETIN. Text in English. irreg. **Document type:** *Government.*
Published by: Washington State Department of Natural Resources, PO Box 47003, Olympia, WA 98504-7003. TEL 360-902-1016, http://www.dnr.wa.gov.

557 USA
WASHINGTON GEOLOGICAL SURVEY. ANNUAL REPORT. Text in English. a. **Document type:** *Government.*
Published by: Washington State Department of Natural Resources, Division of Geology and Earth Resources, Natural Resources Bldg, Rm 148, 1111 Washington St S E, Olympia, WA 98501.

557 USA
WASHINGTON GEOLOGICAL SURVEY. BULLETIN. Text in English. irreg. **Document type:** *Government.*
Published by: Washington State Department of Natural Resources, Division of Geology and Earth Resources, Natural Resources Bldg, Rm 148, 1111 Washington St S E, Olympia, WA 98501.

551.44 GBR
WESSEX CAVE CLUB JOURNAL. Text in English. 1934. irreg. (approx. 6/yr.). GBP 12.50 (effective 2001). bk.rev. illus.; maps. index. 20 p./no.; back issues avail. **Document type:** *Journal, Internal.* **Description:** Features articles by members of the club on earth science, speleology, sport caving and exploration.
Formerly: Wessex Cave Club Occasional Publication (0083-811X)
Published by: Wessex Cave Club, Upper Pitts, Priddy, Somers BA5 3AX, United Kingdom. TEL 44-1749-672310, vern@libertus.demon.co.uk, editor@wessex-cave-club.org. Eds. Maurice Hewins, Vern Freeman. R&P Maurice Hewins. Circ: 300.

557 USA ISSN 0739-5957
WEST TEXAS GEOLOGICAL SOCIETY. BULLETIN. Text in English. m. adv. **Document type:** *Bulletin.*
Formerly (until 1983): West Texas Geological Society. Newsletter (0510-1395)
Indexed: PetrolAb.
—PADDS.
Published by: West Texas Geological Society, PO Box 1595, Midland, TX 79702. TEL 432-683-1573, FAX 432-686-7827, wtgs@basinlink.com, http://www.wtgs.org. adv.: B&W page USD 1,010; 7.5 x 10.

557 USA
WEST TEXAS GEOLOGICAL SOCIETY. FIELDTRIP GUIDEBOOKS. Text in English. a. price varies. **Document type:** *Bulletin, Trade.*
Published by: West Texas Geological Society, PO Box 1595, Midland, TX 79702. TEL 432-683-1573, FAX 432-686-7827, wtgs@basinlink.com, http://www.wtgs.org.

557 USA
WEST TEXAS GEOLOGICAL SOCIETY. SPECIAL PUBLICATIONS. Text in English. 1939. irreg., latest 1996. price varies. adv. **Document type:** *Bulletin, Trade.*
—BLDSC (7116.980000), ingenta.
Published by: West Texas Geological Society, PO Box 1595, Midland, TX 79702. TEL 432-683-1573, FAX 432-686-7827, wtgs@basinlink.com, http://www.wtgs.org.

551 USA ISSN 0161-1011
QE177 CODEN: WVGAAD
WEST VIRGINIA. GEOLOGICAL AND ECONOMIC SURVEY. ANNUAL REPORT. Text in English. 1897. a. free. **Document type:** *Government.* **Description:** Covers activities, research, personnel and finances of the survey.
—BLDSC (1495.380000), Linda Hall.
Published by: Geological and Economic Survey, PO Box 879, Morgantown, WV 26507-0879. TEL 304-594-2331. Circ: 3,000.

557 USA ISSN 0363-1052
QE177 CODEN: WVGBAG
WEST VIRGINIA GEOLOGICAL AND ECONOMIC SURVEY. BULLETIN. Text in English. 1955. irreg. **Document type:** *Monographic series.*
—Linda Hall.
Published by: West Virginia Geological and Economic Survey, Box 879, Morgantown, WV 26507-0879. TEL 304-594-2331, 800-984-3656, FAX 304-594-2575, info@geosrv.wvnet.edu, http://www.wvgs.wvnet.edu.

551 910 AUS ISSN 0729-3720
WESTERN AUSTRALIA. GEOLOGICAL SURVEY. 1: 250,000 GEOLOGICAL SERIES. EXPLANATORY NOTES. Text in English. 1966. irreg. price varies. back issues avail. **Document type:** *Government.* **Description:** Provides geological maps of the state of Western Australia.
Indexed: IMMAb.
Published by: Geological Survey of Western Australia, Mineral House, 100 Plain St, East Perth, W.A. 6004, Australia. TEL 61-8-9222-3333, FAX 61-8-9222-3633, b.knyn@dme.wa.gov.au, http://www.dme.wa.gov.au, http://www.doir.wa.gov.au/GSWA/.

559 AUS ISSN 1324-504X
QE348
WESTERN AUSTRALIA. GEOLOGICAL SURVEY. ANNUAL REVIEW. Text in English. 1995. a. free.
Indexed: AESIS.
Published by: Geological Survey of Western Australia, Mineral House, 100 Plain St, East Perth, W.A. 6004, Australia. TEL 61-8-9222-3333, FAX 61-8-9222-3633.

559.4 AUS ISSN 0085-8137
QE348 CODEN: AWGBAJ
WESTERN AUSTRALIA. GEOLOGICAL SURVEY. BULLETIN. Text in English. 1896. irreg., latest vol.144, 2001. price varies. back issues avail. **Document type:** *Monographic series, Government.* **Description:** Provides technical reports on geology of Western Australia.
Related titles: Microfiche ed.
Indexed: AESIS, IMMAb, RefZh, ZooRec.
—BLDSC (2541.000000), CISTI, Linda Hall.
Published by: Geological Survey of Western Australia, Mineral House, 100 Plain St, East Perth, W.A. 6004, Australia. TEL 61-8-9222-3333, FAX 61-8-9222-3633, b.knyn@dme.wa.gov.au, http://www.dme.wa.gov.au, http://www.doir.wa.gov.au/GSWA/.

559 AUS ISSN 0728-2311
WESTERN AUSTRALIA. GEOLOGICAL SURVEY. RECORDS. Text in English. 1964. irreg. price varies.
Indexed: AESIS.
Published by: Geological Survey of Western Australia, Mineral House, 100 Plain St, East Perth, W.A. 6004, Australia. TEL 61-8-9222-3333, FAX 61-8-9222-3633.

559.4 AUS ISSN 0508-4741
WESTERN AUSTRALIA. GEOLOGICAL SURVEY. REPORT. Text in English. 1969. irreg., latest vol.95, 2004. price varies.
Document type: *Monographic series, Government.*
Description: Presents specific reports on aspects of Western Australian geology.
Indexed: AESIS, IMMAb, RefZh.
—BLDSC (7490.430000), CISTI.
Published by: Geological Survey of Western Australia, Mineral House, 100 Plain St, East Perth, W.A. 6004, Australia. TEL 61-8-92223222, FAX 61-8-92223369, publications@doir.wa.gov.au, http://www.doir.wa.gov.au/GSWA.

551.44 AUS
WESTERN CAVER. Text in English. 1960. a. AUD 10. adv. bk.rev.
Document type: *Newsletter.*
Published by: Western Australian Speleological Group, PO Box 67, Nedlands, W.A. 6909, Australia. TEL 61-9-3465550, rauleigh@techpkwa.curtin.edu.au, http://techpkwa.curtin.edu.au/Speleology/. Ed., R&P Steve Wright. Circ: 200 (controlled).

551.41 NLD
WETLANDS INTERNATIONAL✶. Text in Dutch. 1989. s-a. GBP 12, USD 24. bk.rev. maps. **Document type:** *Newsletter.*
Description: Reports on Wetlands International activities and global wetlands news. Also alerts members of important conferences and symposia.
Formerly (until 1996): I W R B News (1016-1317)
Address: PO Box 471, AL Wageningen, 6700, Netherlands. TEL 31-317-478854, FAX 31-317-478850, simon.nash@wetlands.org, http://www.wetlands.org/pubs&/newsletter.htm. Ed. Simon Nash. Circ: 300 (paid); 1,700 (controlled). **Dist. by:** Natural History Book Service Ltd., 2-3 Wills Rd, Totnes, Devon TQ9 5XN, United Kingdom. TEL 44-1803-865913, FAX 44-1803-865280, nhbs@nhbs.co.uk, http://www.nhbs.co.uk.

557 USA ISSN 0375-8265
QE179
WISCONSIN GEOLOGICAL AND NATURAL HISTORY SURVEY. BULLETIN. Text in English. 1898. irreg., latest vol.99, 2001. price varies. **Document type:** *Bulletin, Government.*
Indexed: BiolAb.
—Linda Hall.
Published by: Wisconsin Geological and Natural History Survey, University of Wisconsin Extension, 3817 Mineral Point Rd, Madison, WI 53705-4096. TEL 608-262-1705, FAX 608-262-8086, http://www.uwex.edu/wgnhs/.

557 USA
WISCONSIN GEOLOGICAL AND NATURAL HISTORY SURVEY. EDUCATIONAL SERIES. Variant title: Educational Series. Text in English. 1953. irreg., latest vol.42, 2000. price varies.
Document type: *Government.*
Formerly: Wisconsin Geological and Natural History Survey. Geoscience Educational Series; Which superseded: Wisconsin. Geological and Natural History Survey. Geoscience Information Series
Published by: Wisconsin Geological and Natural History Survey, University of Wisconsin Extension, 3817 Mineral Point Rd, Madison, WI 53705-4096. TEL 608-262-1705, FAX 608-262-8086, http://www.uwex.edu/wgnhs/. Ed. Mindy James.

551 USA ISSN 0271-8502
WISCONSIN GEOLOGICAL AND NATURAL HISTORY SURVEY. FIELD TRIP GUIDE BOOKS. Text in English. 1978. irreg., latest vol.13, 1986. price varies. **Document type:** *Government.*
Published by: Wisconsin Geological and Natural History Survey, University of Wisconsin Extension, 3817 Mineral Point Rd, Madison, WI 53705-4096. TEL 608-262-1705, FAX 608-262-8086, http://www.uwex.edu/wgnhs/. Ed. Mindy James.

557 USA ISSN 0512-0640
QE179 CODEN: WGICA
WISCONSIN GEOLOGICAL AND NATURAL HISTORY SURVEY. INFORMATION CIRCULARS. Text in English. 1955. irreg., latest vol.75, 1992. price varies. **Document type:** *Government.*
Indexed: IBR.
—Linda Hall.
Published by: Wisconsin Geological and Natural History Survey, University of Wisconsin Extension, 3817 Mineral Point Rd, Madison, WI 53705-4096. TEL 608-262-1705, FAX 608-262-8086, http://www.uwex.edu/wgnhs/. Ed. Mindy James.

557 USA ISSN 0512-0659
CODEN: SUWSDV
WISCONSIN. GEOLOGICAL AND NATURAL HISTORY SURVEY. SPECIAL REPORT. Text in English. 1967. irreg., latest vol.13, 1996. price varies. **Document type:** *Government.*
—Linda Hall.
Published by: Wisconsin Geological and Natural History Survey, University of Wisconsin Extension, 3817 Mineral Point Rd, Madison, WI 53705-4096. TEL 608-262-1705, FAX 608-262-8086, http://www.uwex.edu/wgnhs/, mcjames@facstaff.wisc.edu. Ed. Mindy James.

551 USA ISSN 8756-0348
TN24.W8
WYOMING GEO-NOTES. Text in English. 1977. q. USD 15 (effective 2001). bk.rev. stat.; illus.; maps. back issues avail.
Document type: *Newsletter, Government.* **Description:** Describes the state's geology and mineral resources, and activities. Includes minerals exploration and production information.
Related titles: Online - full content ed.
Published by: Wyoming State Geological Survey, PO Box 3008, Laramie, WY 82071. TEL 307-766-2286, FAX 307-766-2605, sales@wsgs.uwyo.edu, http://www.wsgsweb.uwyo.edu. Ed. Richard W Jones. Pub. Lance Cook. R&P Richard Jones. Circ: 500.

551 USA ISSN 0096-9842
HD9506.U63
WYOMING MINERAL YEARBOOK. Text in English. 1971. a.
Document type: *Government.*
Indexed: SRI.
Published by: Wyoming Business Council, Minerals Energy & Transfer Tation Div., Herschler Bldg, 1st Fl, E Wing, Cheyenne, WY 82002. TEL 307-777-7284, FAX 307-777-5840. Ed., R&P Dale S Hoffman. Circ: 1,000 (controlled).

557 USA
QE181 CODEN: GSWBAZ
WYOMING STATE GEOLOGICAL SURVEY. BULLETIN. Text in English. 1911. irreg., latest vol.71, 2001. price varies. illus.; maps. Index. 250 p./no.; **Document type:** *Bulletin, Academic/Scholarly.* **Description:** Covers extensive treatment of variable topics for public and technical readers.
Formerly: Geological Survey of Wyoming. Bulletin (0096-6053)
—Linda Hall.
Published by: Wyoming State Geological Survey, PO Box 3008, Laramie, WY 82071. TEL 307-766-2286, FAX 307-766-2605, sales@wsgs.uwyo.edu, http://www.wsgsweb.uwyo.edu. Ed., R&P Richard W Jones. Pub. Lance Cook.

551 USA
WYOMING STATE GEOLOGICAL SURVEY. EDUCATIONAL SERIES; Wyoming geo-maps. Text in English. 1989. irreg. price varies. maps. **Document type:** *Journal, Government.*
Description: Covers a broad range of geological topics for the general public and public school audiences. Classroom activity suggestions and other teaching materials upon request.
Formerly: Geological Survey of Wyoming. Educational Series
Published by: Wyoming State Geological Survey, PO Box 3008, Laramie, WY 82071. TEL 307-766-2286, FAX 307-766-2605, sales@wsgs.uwyo.edu, http://www.wsgsweb.uwyo.edu. Pub. Lance Cook. R&P Richard W Jones.

550 USA ISSN 0512-493X
CODEN: WGSMB5
WYOMING STATE GEOLOGICAL SURVEY. MEMOIR. Text in English. 1968. irreg., latest vol.5, 1993. price varies.
Document type: *Monographic series, Academic/Scholarly.*
Description: Comprehensive coverage of selected earth science topic or topics.
—CASDDS, Linda Hall.
Published by: Wyoming State Geological Survey, PO Box 3008, Laramie, WY 82071. TEL 307-766-2286, FAX 307-766-2605, sales@wsgs.uwyo.edu, http://www.wsgsweb.uwyo.edu. Pub. Lance Cook. R&P Richard Jones.

557 USA
WYOMING STATE GEOLOGICAL SURVEY. PUBLIC INFORMATION CIRCULAR. Text in English. 1976. irreg., latest vol.41, 2001. price varies. **Document type:** *Monographic series, Consumer.* **Description:** Covers geologic hazards, and earth resources for a semi-technical to nontechnical audience.
Formerly (until 199?): Geological Survey of Wyoming. Public Information Circular (0160-3655)
—Linda Hall.
Published by: Wyoming State Geological Survey, PO Box 3008, Laramie, WY 82071. TEL 307-766-2286, FAX 307-766-2605, sales@wsgs.uwyo.edu, http://www.wsgsweb.uwyo.edu. Ed. Richard W Jones. Pub. Lance Cook.

557 USA
WYOMING STATE GEOLOGICAL SURVEY. REPORT OF INVESTIGATIONS. Text in English. 1934. irreg., latest vol.53, 1998. price varies. **Document type:** *Monographic series, Consumer.* **Description:** For technical and mineral industry personnel.
Formerly: Geological Survey of Wyoming. Report of Investigations
Published by: Wyoming State Geological Survey, PO Box 3008, Laramie, WY 82071. TEL 307-766-2286, FAX 307-766-2605, sales@wsgs.uwyo.edu, http://www.wsgsweb.uwyo.edu. Pub. Lance Cook. R&P Richard W Jones.

551 CHN ISSN 1000-8527
QE1 CODEN: XIDZEV
➤ **XIANDAI DIZHI/GEOSCIENCE.** Text in Chinese, English. 1987. q. CNY 40 domestic; USD 50 foreign (effective 2003). bibl.; abstr. 120 p./no.; reprints avail. **Document type:** *Academic/Scholarly.* **Description:** Covers all the fields of Earth sciences.
Related titles: Online - full text ed.: (from East View Information Services, WanFang Data Corp.).
Indexed: RefZh, ZooRec.
—BLDSC (4158.770000).
Published by: Zhongguo Dizhi Daxue/China University of Geosciences, 29 Xueyuan Lu, Beijing, 100083, China. TEL 86-10-82322463, xddz@cugb.edu.cn, http://xddz.periodicals.net.cn/default.html, http://www.cugb.edu.cn. Ed. Jun Deng. Circ: 800.

555 CHN ISSN 1004-7786
QE294
➤ **XIBEI DIXHI KEXUE/NORTHWEST GEOSCIENCES.** Text in Chinese; Summaries in English. 1980. biennial. CNY 5 per vol.; USD 40 per vol. foreign. adv. bk.rev. abstr.; illus.; mkt. Index. back issues avail. **Document type:** *Academic/Scholarly.* **Description:** Covers geology and mineral resources, oil and gas, water resources, present conditions and progress of metallurgy in Northwestern China.
Media: E-mail. **Related titles:** Magnetic Tape ed.; Online - full text ed.
Indexed: ZooRec.
Published by: (Xian Institute of Geology and Mineral Resources. CAGS), China National Publishing Industry Trading Co., 166 East Youyi Rd, Xian, Shaanxi 710054, China. TEL 86-29-7802045, FAX 86-29-7802701, xigmrx@pub.xa-online.sn.cn, http://www.chinainfo.gov.cn/periodical. Ed. Li Xiling. adv.: B&W page USD 500, color page USD 1,000; trim 260 x 185.

551 CHN ISSN 1000-8845
XINJIANG DIZHI/XINJIANG GEOLOGY. Text in Chinese. 1983. quadrennial. CNY 5 domestic (effective 2000). **Document type:** *Academic/Scholarly.*
Related titles: Online - full content ed.: (from WanFang Data Corp.); Online - full text ed.: (from East View Information Services).
Indexed: RefZh.
Address: 16 Youhao Bei Lu, Urumqi, 830000, China. TEL 86-991-4841511, FAX 86-911-4816435, xjdi@chinajournal.net.cn. Ed. Xiang Dong Li.

551 JPN ISSN 0911-8179
YAMAGATA OYO CHISHITSU/APPLIED GEOLOGY OF YAMAGATA. Text in Japanese. 1981. a. membership.
Published by: Yamagata Oyo Chishitsu Kenkyukai/Association of Applied Geology of Yamagata, Department of Earth and Environmental Sciences, Faculty of Science, Yamagata University, Kojirakawa-machi 1-4-12, Yamagata-shi, Yamagata-ken 990-8560, Japan. TEL 81-23-628-4776, FAX 81-23-628-4665, www@sci.kj.yamagata-u.ac.jp, http://www-sci.yamagata-u.ac.jp.

YAMAGUCHI GANBAN KENKYU/YAMAGUCHI ROCK ENGINEERING SOCIETY. SELECTED RESEARCH. see *ENGINEERING*

YAMAGUCHI KEIBINGU KURABU KAIHO/YAMAGUCHI CAVING CLUB. REPORT. see *PALEONTOLOGY*

526.9 CHN ISSN 0254-5357
QE438 CODEN: YACEDJ
YANKUANG CESHI/ACTA PETROLOGICA MINERALOGICA ET ANALYTICA. Text in Chinese. q. USD 32.
Related titles: CD-ROM ed.; Online - full text ed.: (from East View Information Services).
Indexed: CIN, ChemAb, MSB, RefZh.
—BLDSC (8001.433000), CASDDS.
Published by: (Dizhi Kuangchan Bu/Ministry of Geology and Mineral Products, Yankuang Ceshi Yanjiusuo/Institute of Rock and Mineral), Dizhi Chubanshe, 29 Xueyuan Lu, Haidian-qu, Beijing, 100083, China. TEL 86-10-6238-3322. Ed. Shao Jixin.
Dist. outside China by: China International Book Trading Corp, 35 Chegongzhuang Xilu, Haidian District, PO Box 399, Beijing 100044, China.

YANSHI KUANGWUXUE ZAZHI/ACTA PETROLOGICA ET MINERALOGICA. see *PETROLEUM AND GAS*

552 CHN ISSN 1000-0569
➤ **YANSHI XUEBAO/ACTA PETROLOGICA SINICA.** Text in Chinese; Summaries in English. 1985. q. CNY 600 (effective 2004). adv. **Document type:** *Academic/Scholarly.*
Description: Publishes research papers on petrological, petrogeochemical, petrogenetic, and petrotectonic studies of igneous, metamorphic, and sedimentary rocks. Also includes some papers on related topics, such as mineralogy and metallogeny.
Related titles: Online - full text ed.: (from East View Information Services, WanFang Data Corp.).
Indexed: ASFA, BrCerAb, C&ISA, CerAb, CorrAb, CurCont, E&CAJ, EMA, GEOBASE, IAA, M&TEA, MBF, METADEX, OceAb, RefZh, SolStAb, WAA.
—BLDSC (0644.540000), Linda Hall.

Published by: (Zhongguo Kexueyuan, Dizhi yu Diqiu Wuli Yanjiusuo/Chinese Academy of Sciences, Institute of Geology and Geophysics), Kexue Chubanshe/Science Press, 16 Donghuang Cheng Genbei Jie, Beijing, 100717, China. TEL 86-10-64000246, FAX 86-10-64030255, ysxb@china.com, http://ysxb.periodicals.net.cn/default.html, http://www.sciencep.com/. Circ: 6,000. **Dist. by:** China International Book Trading Corp, 35 Chegongzhuang Xilu, Haidian District, PO Box 399, Beijing 100044, China. TEL 86-10-68412045, FAX 86-10-68412023, cibtc@mail.cibtc.com.cn, http://www.cibtc.com.cn.

551 GBR ISSN 0044-0604
CODEN: PYGSAB
➤ **YORKSHIRE GEOLOGICAL SOCIETY. PROCEEDINGS.** Text in English. 1871. s-a. GBP 108 domestic; GBP 108, USD 194 foreign (effective 2005). adv. bibl.; illus.; maps. index. back issues avail. **Document type:** *Proceedings, Academic/Scholarly.* **Description:** Contains original research papers on the geology of northern England.
Indexed: ASFA, CurCont, ESPM, GEOBASE, IBR, MinerAb, PetrolAb, ZooRec.
—BLDSC (6834.750000), IDS, IE, ingenta, PADDS. **CCC.**
Published by: (Yorkshire Geological Society), Geological Society Publishing House, Unit 7, Brassmill Enterprise Centre, Brassmill Ln, Bath, Avon BA1 3JN, United Kingdom. TEL 44-1225-445046, FAX 44-1225-442836, enquiries@geolsoc.org.uk, http://www.geolsoc.org.uk/template.cfm?name=journals_pygs_home_page. Ed. Stewart Molyneux. Circ: 1,400.

553.4932 CHN ISSN 1000-0658
CODEN: YODIEX
YOUKUANG DIZHI/URANIUM GEOLOGY. Text in Chinese. 1985. bi-m. CNY 48 (effective 2004). **Document type:** *Journal, Academic/Scholarly.*
Related titles: Online - full text ed.: (from East View Information Services, WanFang Data Corp.).
Indexed: INIS AtomInd.
—BLDSC (9123.140620), IE.
Address: PO Box 9818, Beijing, 100029, China. TEL 86-10-64965404, FAX 86-10-64917143, ykdz@chinajournal.net.cn, http://ykdz.periodicals.net.cn/default.html. **Dist. by:** China International Book Trading Corp, 35 Chegongzhuang Xilu, Haidian District, PO Box 399, Beijing 100044, China. TEL 86-10-68412045, FAX 86-10-68412023, cibtc@mail.cibtc.com.cn, http://www.cibtc.com.cn.

556 ZMB ISSN 0084-473X
QE327.R55 CODEN: ARGZDP
ZAMBIA. GEOLOGICAL SURVEY. ANNUAL REPORTS. Text in English. 1951. a., latest 1986. price varies. **Document type:** *Government.*
—Linda Hall.
Published by: Geological Survey, PO Box R W 50135, Lusaka, Zambia.

556 ZMB ISSN 0084-4748
TN119.R38 CODEN: ZGSEAD
ZAMBIA. GEOLOGICAL SURVEY. ECONOMIC REPORTS. Text in English. 1964. irreg., latest 1979. price varies. **Document type:** *Government.*
Indexed: IMMAb.
—Linda Hall.
Published by: Geological Survey, PO Box R W 50135, Lusaka, Zambia.

556 ZMB ISSN 0084-4756
ZAMBIA. GEOLOGICAL SURVEY. OCCASIONAL PAPERS. Text in English. irreg., latest vol.146. price varies. **Document type:** *Government.*
Published by: Geological Survey, PO Box R W 50135, Lusaka, Zambia.

556 ZMB ISSN 0084-4764
ZAMBIA. GEOLOGICAL SURVEY. REPORTS. Text in English. 1954. irreg., latest vol.68. price varies. **Document type:** *Government.*
Indexed: IMMAb.
—Linda Hall.
Published by: Geological Survey, PO Box R W 50135, Lusaka, Zambia.

556 ZMB
ZAMBIA. GEOLOGICAL SURVEY. TECHNICAL REPORTS. Text in English. irreg., latest vol.99. price varies. **Document type:** *Government.*
Published by: Geological Survey, PO Box R W 50135, Lusaka, Zambia.

550 DEU ISSN 0044-2259
QE1 CODEN: ZANGAK
ZEITSCHRIFT FUER ANGEWANDTE GEOLOGIE. Text in German; Summaries in English, German. 1955. 2/yr. EUR 26 domestic; EUR 33.40 foreign (effective 2005). adv. bk.rev. abstr.; bibl.; charts; illus.; stat. index, cum.index. **Document type:** *Journal, Academic/Scholarly.*
Indexed: ASFA, BibCart, BrGeoL, CIN, ChemAb, ChemTitl, CurCont, ESPM, GEOBASE, GeotechAb, IBR, IMMAb, MinerAb, PetrolAb, ZooRec.
—BLDSC (9448.700000), CASDDS, CISTI, IE, ingenta, Linda Hall, PADDS. **CCC.**
Published by: (Germany. Bundesanstalt fuer Geowissenschaften und Rohstoffe), E. Schweizerbart'sche Verlagsbuchhandlung, Johannesstr 3A, Stuttgart, 70176, Germany. TEL 49-711-3514560, FAX 49-711-35145699, mail@schweizerbart.de, http://www.schweizerbart.de/zeitschrift-fuer-angewandte-geologie. Ed. Deddo Hagen.

551.4 DEU ISSN 0372-8854
G1 CODEN: ZGMPAG
➤ **ZEITSCHRIFT FUER GEOMORPHOLOGIE/ANNALES DE GEOMORPHOLOGIE/ANNALS OF GEOMORPHOLOGY;** annals of geomorphology - annales de Geomorphologie (a journal recognized by the Int. Assoc. of Geomorphologists (IAG)). Text in English, French, German. N.S. 1957. q. USD 263 (effective 2005). adv. bk.rev. abstr.; bibl.; charts; illus.; pat. index. back issues avail. **Document type:** *Journal, Academic/Scholarly.*
Related titles: ♦ Supplement(s): Zeitschrift fuer Geomorphologie, Supplementbaende. ISSN 0044-2798.
Indexed: AESIS, ASCA, BibCart, BrGeoL, CCA, ChemAb, CurCont, GEOBASE, IBR, ISR, RefZh, S&F, SCI, SPPI, SSCI.
—BLDSC (9462.600000), CISTI, IDS, IE, Infotrieve, ingenta, Linda Hall. **CCC.**
Published by: Gebrueder Borntraeger Verlagsbuchhandlung, Johannesstr. 3A, Stuttgart, 70176, Germany. TEL 49-711-3514560, FAX 49-711-35145699, mail@borntraeger-cramer.de, mail@schweizerbart.de, http://www.schweizerbart.de/j/zeitschrift-fuer-geomorphologie. Ed. K H Pfeffer.

➤ **ZEITSCHRIFT FUER GEOMORPHOLOGIE, SUPPLEMENTBAENDE/ANNALES DE GEOMORPHOLOGIE, SUPPLEMENTS/ANNALS OF GEOMORPHOLOGY, SUPPLEMENT VOLUMES.** see *GEOGRAPHY*

551.31 AUT ISSN 0044-2836
QE575 CODEN: ZGGGAR
ZEITSCHRIFT FUER GLETSCHERKUNDE UND GLAZIALGEOLOGIE. Text in English, French, German, Italian, Spanish; Summaries in English, German, Multiple languages. 1949. s-a. bk.rev. bibl.; charts; illus.; maps. index. back issues avail. **Document type:** *Journal, Academic/Scholarly.* **Description:** Dedicated to publications on snow and ice in all forms of their appearance.
Indexed: BibCart, ChemAb, IBR.
—CISTI, IE, Linda Hall. **CCC.**
Published by: Universitaetsverlag Wagner, Andreas Hofer Str 13, Innsbruck, T 6020, Austria. TEL 43-512-587721, FAX 43-512-582209, mail@uvw.at, http://www.uvw.at. Eds. Gernot Patzelt, Michael Kuhn. Pub., R&P Gottfried Grasl.

551.9 DEU ISSN 0947-7152
ZENTRUM FUER MEERES- UND KLIMAFORSCHUNG. BERICHTE. REIHE D: BIOGEOCHEMIE UND MEERESCHEMIE. Text in German. irreg.
Supersedes in part (in 1992): Universitaet Hamburg. Zentrum fuer Meeres- und Klimaforschung. Berichte (0936-949X); Which was formerly (until 1988): Universitaet Hamburg. Institut fuer Meereskunde. Mitteilungen (0017-6907)
Published by: Universitaet Hamburg, Zentrum fuer Meeres- und Klimaforschung/University of Hamburg, Center for Marine and Climate Research, Bundesstr. 55, Hamburg, 20146, Germany. TEL 49-40-42838-4523, FAX 49-40-42838-5235, http://www.uni-hamburg.de/Wiss/SE/ZMK.

016 549.68 RUS ISSN 0134-5559
ZEOLITY, IKH SVOISTVA I PRIMENENIE; tekushchii ukazatel' literatury. Text in Russian, English, Multiple languages. 1987. 3/yr. USD 55 foreign. **Description:** Covers books, articles, summaries of reports at conferences and symposia on antural and synthetic zeolites and their use in industry, agriculture, ecology, medicine, and biology.
Published by: Rossiiskaya Akademiya Nauk, Sibirskoe Otdelenie, Gosudarstvennaya Publichnaya Nauchno-Tekhnicheskaya Biblioteka/State Public Scientific and Technical Library of the Siberian Branch of the Russian Academy of Sciences, Ul Voskhod 15, Novosibirsk, 630200, Russian Federation. TEL 7-3832-661367, FAX 7-3832-660308, TELEX 133220, root@libr.nsk.su, onb@spsl.nsc.ru. Ed. B A Fursenko.

551 CHN ISSN 1000-3657
ZHONGGUO DIZHI/GEOLOGY IN CHINA. Text in Chinese. m.
Related titles: Online - full text ed.: (from East View Information Services).
Indexed: ASFA, C&ISA, E&CAJ, ESPM, IAA, RefZh, SWRA, ZooRec.
—BLDSC (4146.442700).
Published by: Zhongguo Dizhi Diaochaju/China Geological Survey, 31 Xueyuan Road, Haidian District, Beijing, 100083, China. TEL 86-10-82327346, 86-10-82332415, FAX 86-10-82329008, zhgdzh@chinaren.com, http://www.cgs.gov.cn/. Ed. Tingdong Li. **Dist. by:** China International Book Trading Corp, 35 Chegongzhuang Xilu, Haidian District, PO Box 399, Beijing 100044, China. TEL 86-10-68412045, FAX 86-10-68412023, cibtc@mail.cibtc.com.cn, http://www.cibtc.com.cn.

551 CHN ISSN 1001-4810
GB600.4.C6 CODEN: ZHOYEU
➤ **ZHONGGUO YANRONG/CARSOLOGICA SINICA.** Text in Chinese; Abstracts in English. 1982. q. USD 40 (effective 2002). adv. abstr.; charts. 80 p./no.; **Document type:** *Journal, Academic/Scholarly.* **Description:** Covers regional karst geology, karst hydrogeology, karst engineering geology, karst environment geology, conservation of karst ecology, karst dynamics and carbon cycle, development and utilization of karst resources, karst geomorphology, karst detection and test technology.
Related titles: CD-ROM ed.; Online - full text ed.: (from East View Information Services).
—BLDSC (3055.810000).
Published by: Chinese Academy of Geological Sciences, Institute of Karst Geology, 50 Qixing Lu, Guilin, Guangxi 541004, China. TEL 86-773-5817314, FAX 86-773-5813708, carso@163.net. Ed. Yuan Daoxian. Circ: 1,000. **Co-sponsor:** Geological Society of China.

557 ZWE ISSN 0253-0503
ZIMBABWE GEOLOGICAL SURVEY. BULLETIN. Text in English. irreg. **Document type:** *Monographic series.*
—BLDSC (2822.560000), Linda Hall.
Published by: Zimbabwe Geological Survey, Causeway, Box CY210, Harare, Zimbabwe. TEL 263-4-726342, FAX 263-4-739601, zgs@samara.co.zw, http://www.geosurvey.co.zw.

ZIMBABWE. MINISTRY OF ENERGY AND WATER RESOURCES AND DEVELOPMENT. HYDROLOGICAL SUMMARIES. see *ENGINEERING—Hydraulic Engineering*

ZITTELIANA; Abhandlungen der Bayerischen Staatssammlung fuer Palaeontologie und historische Geologie. see *PALEONTOLOGY*

ZITTELIANA. REIHE A. MITTEILUNGEN DER BAYERISCHEN STAATSSAMMLUNG FUR PALAONTOLOGIE UND GEOLOGIE. see *PALEONTOLOGY*

551 739.27 CHN ISSN 1671-1947
ZIZHI YU ZIYUAN/GEOLOGY AND RESOURCES. Text in Chinese. 1982. q. CNY 8.50 newsstand/cover (effective 2004). **Document type:** *Journal, Academic/Scholarly.*
Former titles (until 1992): Guijinshu Dizhi/Journal of Precious Metallic Geology (1002-4182); (until 1991): Zhongguo Dizhi Kexueyuan Shenyang Dizhi Kuangchan Yanjiusuo Suokan (1004-1907)
Related titles: Online - full text ed.: (from East View Information Services).
Indexed: BrCerAb, C&ISA, CerAb, CorrAb, E&CAJ, EMA, IAA, M&TEA, MBF, METADEX, RefZh, WAA.
—Linda Hall.
Published by: Zhongguo Dizhi Diaochaju, Shenyang Dizhi Diaocha Zhongxin/Chinese Geographical Survey, Shenyang Center, 25 Beiling Dajie, Shenyang, 110033, China. TEL 86-24-86846212, FAX 86-24-86843124, gjsd@chinajournal.net.cn, http://gjsdz.periodicals.net.cn/default.html, http://www.shenyang.cgs.gov.cn. **Dist. by:** China International Book Trading Corp, 35 Chegongzhuang Xilu, Haidian District, PO Box 399, Beijing 100044, China. TEL 86-10-68412045, FAX 86-10-68412023, cibtc@mail.cibtc.com.cn, http://www.cibtc.com.cn.

EARTH SCIENCES—Geophysics

A G S O RECORD. see *EARTH SCIENCES—Geology*

551 USA ISSN 1080-305X
➤ **A G U REFERENCE SHELF SERIES.** Text in English. 1994. irreg., latest vol.4, 1999. price varies. back issues avail. **Document type:** *Monographic series, Academic/Scholarly.* **Description:** Covers general references for work in many different disciplines of the geophysical sciences. Provides selected critical information for students and researches.
—**CCC.**
Published by: American Geophysical Union, 2000 Florida Ave, NW, Washington, DC 20009-1277. TEL 202-462-6900, 800-966-2481, FAX 202-328-0566, http://www.agu.org.

551 HUN ISSN 1217-8977
QB275 CODEN: AGGHFW
ACTA GEODAETICA ET GEOPHYSICA HUNGARICA. Text in English. 1966. q. USD 332 (effective 2006). adv. bk.rev. bibl.; charts; illus.; abstr. 120 p./no.; back issues avail. **Document type:** *Journal, Academic/Scholarly.* **Description:** Publishes original research papers in the field of geodesy and geophysics.
Former titles (until 1993): Acta Geodaetica, Geophysica et Montanistica Hungarica (0236-5758); (until 1982): Academiae Scientiarum Hungaricae. Acta Geodaetica, Geophysica et Montanistica (0374-1842); Supersedes (in 1966): Acta Technica. Series Geodaetica et Geophysica (0567-8145); Which supersedes in part (in 1959): Academiae Scientiarum Hungaricae. Acta Technica (0001-7035)
Related titles: Online - full text ed.: ISSN 1587-1037 (from EBSCO Publishing, Swets Information Services).
Indexed: EngInd, FLUIDEX, GEOBASE, Inspec.
—AskIEEE, CISTI, Ei, Linda Hall. **CCC.**

E

Published by: (Magyar Tudomanyos Akademia/Hungarian Academy of Sciences), Akademiai Kiado Rt. (Subsidiary of: Wolters Kluwer N.V.), Prielle Kornelia U. 19, Budapest, 1117, Hungary. TEL 36-1-4648282, FAX 36-1-4648221, journals@akkrt.hu, http://www.akkrt.hu. Ed. Jozsef Vero.

▼ **ACTA GEODYNAMICA ET GEOMATERIALIA.** see *EARTH SCIENCES—Geology*

551 POL ISSN 0001-5725
QC801 CODEN: AGPOAP
ACTA GEOPHYSICA POLONICA. Text in English. 1953. q. EUR 97 foreign (effective 2005). charts. index. **Document type:** *Journal, Academic/Scholarly.*
Indexed: ApMecR, ChemAb, E&PHSE, Englnd, FLUIDEX, GEOBASE, GP&P, IBR, Inspec, M&GPA, OffTech, PetrolAb, RefZh.
—BLDSC (0622.000000), AskIEEE, CASDDS, CISTI, IE, ingenta, Linda Hall, PADDS.
Published by: Polska Akademia Nauk, Instytut Geofizyki/Polish Academy of Sciences, Institute of Geophysics, Ul Ksiecia Janusza 64, Warsaw, 01452, Poland. http://www.igf.edu.pl/acta. Ed. Roman Teisseyre. Circ: 700. **Dist. by:** Ars Polona, Krakowskie Przedmiescie 7, Warsaw, Poland. TEL 48-22-9263914, FAX 48-22-9265334, arspolona@arspolona.com.pl, http://www.arspolona.com.pl.

551 624 SVN ISSN 1854-0171
▼ **ACTA GEOTECHNICA SLOVENICA.** Abbreviated title: A G S. Text in English; Summaries in English, Slovenian. 2004. s-a. EUR 42 domestic to institutions; EUR 50 foreign to institutions (effective 2005). adv. charts; illus. back issues avail. **Document type:** *Journal, Academic/Scholarly.* **Description:** Aims to play an important role in publishing high-quality, theoretical papers from important and emerging areas that will have a lasting impact on fundamental and practical aspects of geomechanics and geotechnical engineering.
Published by: Univerza v Mariboru, Fakulteta za Gradbenistvo/University of Maribor, Faculty of Civil Engineering, Smetanova ul 17, Maribor, 2000, Slovenia. TEL 386-2-2294300, FAX 386-2-2524179, ags@uni-mb.si, http://fg.uni-mb.si/journal-ags. Ed. Ludvik Trauner. adv.: B&W page EUR 100, color page EUR 200. Circ: 500 (paid).

550 SWE ISSN 0072-4815
QC801
ACTA REGIAE SOCIETATIS SCIENTIARUM ET LITTERARUM GOTHOBURGENSIS. GEOPHYSICA. Text in Multiple languages. 1968. irreg., latest vol.3, 1990. price varies. **Document type:** *Monographic series.*
Supersedes in part: Goeteborgs Kungliga Vetenskaps- och Vitterhets-Samhaelle. Handlingar
—CISTI, Linda Hall.
Published by: Kungliga Vetenskaps- och Vitterhets-Samhaelle, c/o Goeteborgs Universitetsbibliotek, PO Box 222, Goeteborg, 40530, Sweden. TEL 46-31-7731733, FAX 46-31-163797.

551 622 CZE
➤ **ACTA RESEARCH REPORT.** Text in Czech, English. 1967. irreg., latest vol.13, 2004. EUR 12 per vol. (effective 2005). back issues avail. **Document type:** *Academic/Scholarly.* **Description:** Contains essays, dissertations, and results of grant projects.
Formerly: Acta Montana - Rada AB (Miscellanea) (1212-1576); Which superseded in part (in 1990): Acta Montana (0365-1398); Which was formerly (until 1970): Ceskoslovenska Akademie Ved. Hornicky Ustav. Zpravy (0372-8986)
—BLDSC (0638.900000), IE, ingenta, Linda Hall.
Published by: Akademie Ved Ceske Republiky, Ustav Struktury a Mechaniky Hornin/Academy of Sciences of Czech Republic, Institute of Rock Structures and Mechanics, V Holesovickach 41, Prague, 18209, Czech Republic. TEL 420-2-66009111, FAX 420-2-84680105, irsm@irsm.cas.cz, http://www.irsm.cas.cz. Ed. Vladimir Rudajev.

551.22 CHN ISSN 1000-9116
QE531 CODEN: ASSNEN
➤ **ACTA SEISMOLOGICA SINICA.** Text in English. 1988. 4/yr. CNY 300, USD 108.60 (effective 2004). adv. bk.rev. back issues avail. **Document type:** *Academic/Scholarly.* **Description:** A comprehensive academic journal on seismological science.
Related titles: Microform ed.; Online - full content ed.: (from WanFang Data Corp.); Online - full text ed.: (from East View Information Services); ◆ Chinese ed.: Dizhen Xuebao. ISSN 0253-3782.
Indexed: C&ISA, E&CAJ, EEA, Englnd, IAA, RefZh.
—BLDSC (0663.271000), CISTI, Ei, IE, ingenta.
Published by: (Seismological Society of China), Kexue Chubanshe/Science Press, 16 Donghuang Cheng Genbei Jie, Beijing, 100717, China. TEL 86-10-64000246, FAX 86-10-64030255, dzxb@ns.cdsn.org.cn, http://dizhen-e.periodicals.net.cn/default.html, http://www.sciencep.com/. Ed. Yuntai Chen. R&P, Adv. contact Yiqin Zhang. **Dist. by:** China International Book Trading Corp, 35 Chegongzhuang Xilu, Haidian District, PO Box 399, Beijing 100044, China. TEL 86-10-68412045, FAX 86-10-68412023, cibtc@mail.cibtc.com.cn, http://www.cibtc.com.cn.

➤ **ACTA UNIVERSITATIS WRATISLAVIENSIS. PRACE GEOLOGICZNO - MINERALOGICZNE.** see *EARTH SCIENCES—Geology*

551 ITA ISSN 1121-9114
QE527
ACTA VULCANOLOGICA. Text in Italian. 1991. s-a. EUR 50 domestic to individuals; EUR 80 foreign to individuals; EUR 140 domestic to institutions; EUR 195 foreign to institutions (effective 2004). **Document type:** *Monographic series, Academic/Scholarly.* **Description:** Covers all research aspects of volcanology. Devotes a section to the activity of Italian volcanoes recorded during the year.
—BLDSC (0672.100000), CISTI, IE, ingenta.
Published by: (National Volcanic Group of Italy), Istituti Editoriali e Poligrafici Internazionali (Subsidiary of: Libra Web), Via Giosue' Carducci, 60, Ghezzano - La Fontina, PI 56010, Italy. TEL 39-050-878066, FAX 39-050-878732, iepi@iepi.it, http://www.iepi.it.

ADVANCES IN EARTHQUAKE ENGINEERING. see *ENGINEERING—Civil Engineering*

551 USA ISSN 0065-2687
QC801 CODEN: ADGOAR
➤ **ADVANCES IN GEOPHYSICS.** Text in English. 1952. irreg., latest vol.45, 2002. USD 140 per vol. vol.46 (effective 2004). index. reprint service avail. from ISI. **Document type:** *Academic/Scholarly.* **Description:** Contains much material still relevant today an essential publication for researchers in all fields of geophysics.
Related titles: ◆ Supplement(s): Advances in Geophysics. Supplement. ISSN 0065-2695.
Indexed: ASCA, F&EA, ISR, Inspec, PetrolAb, SCI.
—BLDSC (0709.000000), CASDDS, CISTI, IE, ingenta, Linda Hall. **CCC.**
Published by: Academic Press (Subsidiary of: Elsevier Science & Technology), 525 B St, Ste 1900, San Diego, CA 92101-4495. TEL 619-231-6616, 800-894-3434, FAX 619-699-6422, apsubs@acad.com, http://www.academicpress.com. Ed. Barry Saltzman.

551 USA ISSN 0065-2695
QC801
ADVANCES IN GEOPHYSICS. SUPPLEMENT. Text in English. 1966. irreg., latest vol.2, 1981. price varies.
Related titles: ◆ Supplement to: Advances in Geophysics. ISSN 0065-2687.
—Linda Hall.
Published by: Academic Press (Subsidiary of: Elsevier Science & Technology), 525 B St, Ste 1900, San Diego, CA 92101-4495. TEL 619-231-6616, FAX 619-699-6422. Ed. H E Landsberg.

ALASKA. DIVISION OF GEOLOGICAL AND GEOPHYSICAL SURVEYS. ADMINISTRATIVE REPORTS. see *EARTH SCIENCES—Geology*

ALASKA. DIVISION OF GEOLOGICAL AND GEOPHYSICAL SURVEYS. ALASKA TERRITORIAL DEPARTMENT OF MINES REPORTS. see *MINES AND MINING INDUSTRY*

ALASKA. DIVISION OF GEOLOGICAL AND GEOPHYSICAL SURVEYS. ALASKA'S MINERAL INDUSTRY. see *EARTH SCIENCES—Geology*

551.22 USA
ALASKA. DIVISION OF GEOLOGICAL AND GEOPHYSICAL SURVEYS. CATALOG OF ALASKAN EARTHQUAKES. Text in English. a.
Published by: Alaska Department of Natural Resources, Division of Geological and Geophysical Surveys, 794 University Ave, Ste 200, Fairbanks, AK 99709-3645. TEL 907-451-5000, FAX 907-451-5050, http://www.dggs.dnr.state.ak.us.

551 USA
ALASKA. DIVISION OF GEOLOGICAL AND GEOPHYSICAL SURVEYS. GEOPHYSICAL REPORTS. Text in English. irreg.
Published by: Alaska Department of Natural Resources, Division of Geological and Geophysical Surveys, 794 University Ave, Ste 200, Fairbanks, AK 99709-3645. TEL 907-451-5000, FAX 907-451-5050, http://www.dggs.dnr.state.ak.us.

ALASKA. DIVISION OF GEOLOGICAL AND GEOPHYSICAL SURVEYS. GUIDEBOOK OF PERMAFROST AND RELATED FEATURES OF THE DALTON HIGHWAY, YUKON RIVER TO PRUDHOE BAY, ALASKA. VOLUME 2. see *EARTH SCIENCES—Geology*

ALASKA. DIVISION OF GEOLOGICAL AND GEOPHYSICAL SURVEYS. GUIDEBOOK TO PERMAFROST AND QUATERNARY GEOLOGY ALONG THE RICHARDSON AND GLENN HIGHWAYS BETWEEN FAIRBANKS AND ANCHORAGE, ALASKA. see *EARTH SCIENCES—Geology*

ALASKA. DIVISION OF GEOLOGICAL AND GEOPHYSICAL SURVEYS. GUIDEBOOK TO PERMAFROST AND RELATED FEATURES ALONG THE ELLIOTT AND DALTON HIGHWAYS, FOX TO PRUDHOE BAY. see *EARTH SCIENCES—Geology*

ALASKA. DIVISION OF GEOLOGICAL AND GEOPHYSICAL SURVEYS. GUIDEBOOK TO PERMAFROST AND RELATED FEATURES AT PRUDHOE BAY. see *EARTH SCIENCES—Geology*

ALASKA. DIVISION OF GEOLOGICAL AND GEOPHYSICAL SURVEYS. GUIDEBOOK TO PERMAFROST AND RELATED FEATURES OF THE COLVILLE RIVER DELTA, ALASKA. see *EARTH SCIENCES—Geology*

ALASKA. DIVISION OF GEOLOGICAL AND GEOPHYSICAL SURVEYS. GUIDEBOOK TO PERMAFROST AND RELATED FEATURES OF THE DALTON HIGHWAY, YUKON RIVER TO PRUDHOE BAY, ALASKA. VOLUME 1. see *EARTH SCIENCES—Geology*

ALASKA. DIVISION OF GEOLOGICAL AND GEOPHYSICAL SURVEYS. GUIDEBOOK TO PERMAFROST AND RELATED FEATURES OF THE NORTHERN YUKON TERRITORY AND MACKENZIE DELTA, ALASKA. see *EARTH SCIENCES—Geology*

ALASKA. DIVISION OF GEOLOGICAL AND GEOPHYSICAL SURVEYS. GUIDEBOOKS. see *EARTH SCIENCES—Geology*

ALASKA. DIVISION OF GEOLOGICAL AND GEOPHYSICAL SURVEYS. INFORMATION CIRCULAR. see *EARTH SCIENCES—Geology*

ALASKA. DIVISION OF GEOLOGICAL AND GEOPHYSICAL SURVEYS. MISCELLANEOUS PAPERS. see *EARTH SCIENCES—Geology*

ALASKA. DIVISION OF GEOLOGICAL AND GEOPHYSICAL SURVEYS. PRELIMINARY INVESTIGATIVE REPORTS. see *EARTH SCIENCES—Geology*

ALASKA. DIVISION OF GEOLOGICAL AND GEOPHYSICAL SURVEYS. PROFESSIONAL REPORTS. see *EARTH SCIENCES—Geology*

ALASKA. DIVISION OF GEOLOGICAL AND GEOPHYSICAL SURVEYS. RAW DATA FILES. see *EARTH SCIENCES—Geology*

ALASKA. DIVISION OF GEOLOGICAL AND GEOPHYSICAL SURVEYS. REPORT OF INVESTIGATIONS. see *EARTH SCIENCES—Geology*

ALASKA. DIVISION OF GEOLOGICAL AND GEOPHYSICAL SURVEYS. SPECIAL REPORT. see *EARTH SCIENCES—Geology*

ALASKA. DIVISION OF GEOLOGICAL AND GEOPHYSICAL SURVEYS. THE ALASKA RAILROAD BETWEEN ANCHORAGE AND FAIRBANKS; guidebook to permafrost and engineering problems. see *EARTH SCIENCES—Geology*

551 DEU ISSN 0992-7689
QC801 CODEN: ANNGEA
➤ **ANNALES GEOPHYSICAE**; atmospheres, hydrospheres and space sciences. Text in English. 1983. m. EUR 1,950 combined subscription print & online eds.; EUR 160 newsstand/cover (effective 2005). adv. abstr.; bibl.; illus. index. reprints avail. **Document type:** *Journal, Academic/Scholarly.* **Description:** Information on interplanetary medium, magnetosphere and upper atmosphere of the earth and planets, terrestrial and planetary boundary layers.
Formed by the merger of (1983-1988): Annales de Geophysicae. Serie A: Upper Atmosphere and Space Sciences (0980-8752); (1983-1988): Annales Geophysicae. Serie B: Terrestrial and Planetary Physics (0980-8760); Both of which superseded in part (in 1985): Annales Geophysicae (0755-0685); Which was formed by the merger of (1944-1983): Annales de Geophysique (0003-4029); (1948-1983): Annali di Geofisica (0365-2556)
Related titles: Online - full text ed.: ISSN 1432-0576. free (effective 2005) (from EBSCO Publishing, Springer LINK, Swets Information Services).
Indexed: AESIS, ASCA, ASFA, CIN, ChemAb, ChemTitl, CivEngAb, CurCont, ESPM, Englnd, GEOBASE, INIS Atomlnd, ISR, Inspec, M&GPA, PhysBer, SCI, WRCInf.
—BLDSC (0977.900000), AskIEEE, CASDDS, CISTI, Ei, IDS, IE, ingenta, Linda Hall, PADDS. **CCC.**
Published by: (European Geosciences Union, European Geophysical Society USA), Copernicus GmbH, Max-Planck Str 13, Katlenburg-Lindau, 37191, Germany. TEL 49-5556-91099, info@copernicus.org, http://www.cesr.fr/~anngeo, http://www.copernicus.org. Ed. Denis Alcayde. Circ: 600.

551.22 ITA ISSN 0394-5596
ANNALES TECTONICAE. Text in Italian. s-a.
—BLDSC (1001.900000), IE, ingenta.
Published by: Editrice Il Sedicesimo, Via Mannelli, 29, Florence, FI 50136, Italy. TEL 39-055-2476781, FAX 39-055-2478568.

551 ITA ISSN 1593-5213
CODEN: AGFRAI
ANNALS OF GEOPHYSICS/ANNALI DI GEOFISICA. Text in Italian. 1983. bi-m. USD 40 foreign to individuals; USD 100 foreign to institutions (effective 2005). **Document type:** *Journal, Academic/Scholarly.*

E

▼ new title ➤ refereed ✱ unverified ◆ full entry avail.

Former titles (until 2003): Annali di Geofisica (1590-1815); (until 1993): Annales Geophysicae (0755-0685); Which was formed by the merger of (1944-1983): Annales de Geophysique (0003-4029); (1948-1983): Annali de Geofisica (0365-2556)
Indexed: ASFA, ESPM, GEOBASE, Inspec, M&GPA, OceAb, RefZh, SWRA.
—BLDSC (1040.810000), AskIEEE, CISTI, IDS, Linda Hall.
Published by: (Istituto Nazionale di Geofisica e Vulcanologia), Editrice Compositori Srl, Via Stalingrado 97-2, Bologna, 40128, Italy. TEL 39-051-3540111, FAX 39-051-327877, 1865@compositori.it, http://www.ingv.it/~wwwannali/, http://www.compositori.it. Ed. Enzo Boschi. Circ: 1,500 (paid).

551 USA
ANTARCTIC RESEARCH BOOK SERIES. Text in English. 1964. irreg., latest vol.77. price varies. back issues avail.; reprint service avail. from ISI. **Document type:** *Monographic series, Academic/Scholarly.*
Formerly: Antarctic Research Series (0066-4634)
Indexed: ASFA, BiolAb, ESPM, ZooRec.
—BLDSC (1542.130000), CISTI, Linda Hall. **CCC.**
Published by: American Geophysical Union, 2000 Florida Ave, NW, Washington, DC 20009-1277. TEL 202-462-6900, 800-966-2481, FAX 202-328-0566, http://www.agu.org. Ed. A F Spilhaus Jr.

551 CHN ISSN 1672-7975
▼ **APPLIED GEOPHYSICS.** Variant title: Chinese Geophysical Scoiety. Journal. Text in English. 2004. q. CNY 30 newsstand/cover (effective 2005). **Document type:** *Journal, Academic/Scholarly.*
Related titles: Online - full text ed.: (from WanFang Data Corp.).
Published by: Zhongguo Diqiu Wuli Xuehui/Chinese Geophysical Society, No. 19, West Road, Hepingli, Beijing, 100013, China. TEL 86-10-84288401, FAX 86-10-84274066, yydqwl@periodicals.net.cn; cgsag@sina.com, http://yydqwl.periodicals.net.cn/, http://www.cgs.org.cn. Ed. Weicui Fan. **Dist. by:** China International Book Trading Corp, 35 Chegongzhuang Xilu, Haidian District, PO Box 399, Beijing 100044, China. TEL 86-10-68412045, FAX 86-10-68412023, cibtc@mail.cibtc.com.cn, http://www.cibtc.com.cn.

AQUA; mensile di acqua, natura, vita. see *EARTH SCIENCES—Hydrology*

ARCTIC. see *SCIENCES: COMPREHENSIVE WORKS*

ARI; an interdisciplinary journal of physical and engineering sciences. see *EARTH SCIENCES—Geology*

551 POL
Z5064.A7
➤ **ARTIFICIAL SATELLITES**; journal of planetary geodesy. Text and summaries in English. 1960. q. PLZ 160 domestic; USD 60 foreign (effective 2003). bibl.; charts; illus.; abstr. **Document type:** *Journal, Academic/Scholarly.* **Description:** Offers a forum for scientific publications on different aspects of geodesy and geodynamics.
Formerly (until vol.32, no.1, 1997): Artificial Satellites. Planetary Geodesy (0208-841X); Which supersedes in part: Artificial Satellites (0571-205X)
Indexed: IAA, Inspec, RefZh.
—AskIEEE, CISTI, Linda Hall.
Published by: Polska Akademia Nauk, Centrum Badan Kosmicznych/Polish Academy of Sciences, Space Research Center, Ul Bartycka 18 a, Warsaw, 00716, Poland. TEL 48-22-8403766, FAX 48-22-8403131, artsat@cbk.waw.pl, wp@cbk.waw.pl, http://www.artsat.cbk.waw.pl. Ed. Wojciech Pachelski. Circ: 350 (paid and controlled).

526 551 BEL ISSN 0542-6766
QC809.E2 CODEN: MTBIBP
➤ **ASSOCIATION INTERNATIONALE DE GEODESIE. COMMISSION DES MAREES TERRESTRES. MAREES TERRESTRES BULLETIN D'INFORMATION.** Key Title: Marees Terrestres. Text in French. 1957. 3/yr. adv. **Document type:** *Bulletin, Academic/Scholarly.* **Description:** Covers earth tides, geophysics, and geodynamics.
Formerly: Association Internationale de Geodesie. Commission Permanaete des Marees Terrestres. Marees Terrestres Bulletin d'Information
Published by: Association Internationale de Geodesie, Commission des Marees Terrestres, c/o Observatoire Royal de Belgique, Av Circulaire 3, Brussels, 1180, Belgium. TEL 32-2-3730248, FAX 32-2-3749822, ducarme@oma.be, http://www.oma.be. Ed., Adv. contact B. Ducarme. Pub. B Ducarme.

550.3 IND ISSN 0257-1412
ASSOCIATION OF EXPLORATION GEOPHYSICISTS. JOURNAL. Text in English. q. USD 250 (effective 2000). **Document type:** *Academic/Scholarly.*
Indexed: AESIS, Inspec, PetrolAb.
—AskIEEE, CISTI, Linda Hall, PADDS.
Published by: (Association of Exploration Geophysicists), H P C Publishers Distributors Pvt. Ltd., 4805 Bharat Ram Rd, 24 Darya Ganj, New Delhi, 110 002, India. TEL 91-11-3254401, FAX 91-11-619-3511, hpcpd@nda.vsnl.net.in, hpcpd@hpc.cc, http://www.hpc.cc, http://www.bizdelhi.com/publisher/hpc, http://www.indianindustry.com.

ASTRONOMICHESKII VESTNIK. see *ASTRONOMY*

AUSTRIA. ZENTRALANSTALT FUER METEOROLOGIE UND GEODYNAMIK. JAHRBUCH. see *METEOROLOGY*

551 DEU ISSN 0340-7691
BAYERISCHE KOMMISSION FUER DIE INTERNATIONALE ERDMESSUNG. VEROEFFENTLICHUNGEN. Text in German. 1896. irreg., latest vol.61, 2000. price varies. **Document type:** *Monographic series, Academic/Scholarly.* **Description:** Includes scientific research studies. Each volume is devoted to a single subject.
Indexed: RefZh.
—CISTI.
Published by: Bayerische Kommission fuer die Internationale Erdmessung, Marstallplatz 8, Munich, 80539, Germany. TEL 49-89-23031270, FAX 49-89-23031100, post@bek.badw-muenchen.de.

551 DEU ISSN 0722-687X
BERLINER GEOWISSENSCHAFTLICHE ABHANDLUNGEN. REIHE B, GEOPHYSIK. Text in German. 1965. irreg. **Document type:** *Monographic series, Academic/Scholarly.*
Formerly (until 1978): Geophysikalische Abhandlungen (0522-9901)
—Linda Hall.
Published by: Dietrich Reimer Verlag GmbH, Neue Gruenstr 17, Berlin, 10179, Germany. TEL 49-30-2790760, FAX 49-30-27907655, vertrieb-kunstverlage@reimer-verlag.de, http://www.dietrichreimerverlag.de.

BIBLIOGRAFIA GEOLOGICA SI GEOFIZICA A ROMANIEI/GEOLOGICAL AND GEOPHYSICAL BIBLIOGRAPHY OF ROMANIA. see *EARTH SCIENCES—Abstracting, Bibliographies, Statistics*

551.22 CHN ISSN 1000-0240
QE575 CODEN: BDONEB
BINGCHUAN DONGTU/JOURNAL OF GLACIOLOGY AND GEOCRYOLOGY. Text in Chinese; Summaries in English. 1978. bi-m. CNY 60 (effective 2004). adv. **Document type:** *Journal, Academic/Scholarly.* **Description:** Covers the physical and chemical properties of ice and frozen ground, glaciers, glaciation, and environment in quaternary, permafrost, seasonally frozen ground, glacial deposits and geomorphology, periglacial landforms, glacial debris flow, avalanches, snow-drifts, sea ice, river ice, and lake ice. Also includes reviews, short communications, and news of scientific activities.
Former English title: Journal of Glaciology and Cryopedology
Related titles: Online - full text ed.: (from East View Information Services, WanFang Data Corp.).
Indexed: ASFA, ESPM, M&GPA, PollutAb, RefZh, SWRA.
—BLDSC (4996.060000).
Published by: Zhongguo Kexueyuan, Hanquhanqu Huanjing yu Gongcheng Yanjiusuo, 260, Donggang Xilu, Lanzhou, 730000, China. edjgg@ns.lzb.ac.cn; shenyp@ns.lzb.ac.cn, http://bcdt.wanfangdata.com.cn/default.html. Circ: 6,000. **Dist. by:** China International Book Trading Corp, 35 Chegongzhuang Xilu, Haidian District, PO Box 399, Beijing 100044, China. TEL 86-10-68412045, FAX 86-10-68412023, cibtc@mail.cibtc.com.cn, http://www.cibtc.com.cn.

551 POL ISSN 0067-9038
QE1 CODEN: BIPEAK
BIULETYN PERYGLACJALNY. Text in English. 1954. irreg., latest vol.39, 2001. USD 59 (effective 2000). **Document type:** *Government.* **Description:** Contains articles by Polish and foreign authors on periglacial structures, continental glaciation, laboratory experiments documented with line-drawings, photographs and tables.
Indexed: AgrAg, AgrLib, BrGeoL, S&F.
—BLDSC (2105.450000), CISTI, Linda Hall.
Published by: Lodzkie Towarzystwo Naukowe/Lodz Scientific Society, ul. M. Sklodowskiej-Curie 11, Lodz, 90-505, Poland. TEL 48-42-6361026, FAX 48-42-6361995. **Co-sponsor:** Komitet Badan Naukowych/Committee of Scientific Research.

551.22 ITA ISSN 0006-6729
QC801 CODEN: BGTAAE
BOLLETTINO DI GEOFISICA TEORICA ED APPLICATA. Text in English. 1959. q. EUR 60 domestic; EUR 120 in Europe; EUR 140 elsewhere (effective 2002). adv. bk.rev. abstr.; charts; illus. index. **Document type:** *Academic/Scholarly.* **Description:** Covers theoretical and applied geophysics.
Incorporates: Bollettino di Oceanologia, Teorica ed Applicata (0393-196X)
Indexed: AJEE, BHA, E&PHSE, EEA, GP&P, Inspec, OffTech, PetrolAb.
—AskIEEE, CISTI, Linda Hall, PADDS.
Published by: Istituto Nazionale di Oceanografia e di Geofisica Sperimentale - O G S, Borgo Grotta Gigante 42c, Sgonico (Trieste), 34010, Italy. TEL 39-040-21401, FAX 39-040-327307, http://www.ogs.trieste.it. Ed. Emile Klingele. R&P Dario Slejko. Adv. contact Paolo Giurco. Circ: 500.

551 BGR ISSN 1311-753X
QC801 CODEN: BGSPDN
BULGARIAN GEOPHYSICAL JOURNAL. Text in English; Abstracts in Bulgarian. q. USD 86 foreign (effective 2003). 140 p./no. 1 cols./p.; **Document type:** *Journal, Academic/Scholarly.* **Description:** Publishes original research and theoretical and experimental papers dealing with geophysics: physics and dynamics of the atmosphere, geospace, theoretical and applied seismology, dynamics of structures and soils, earth magnetism and gravimetry, and applied geophysics.
Former titles (until 1998): Bulgarsko Geofizichno Spisanie (0323-9918); (until 1975): Geofizichniyat Institut. Izvestiya (0068-3736)
Indexed: M&GPA.
—CISTI, Linda Hall.
Published by: Bulgarska Akademiya na Naukite, Geofizichniyat Institut/Bulgarian Academy of Sciences, Institute of Geophysics, Acad G Bonchev Blvd 3, Sofia, 1113, Bulgaria. TEL 359-2-9712677, FAX 359-2-917005, bgj@geophys.bas.bg, office@geophys.bas.bg, http://www.geophys.bas.bg. Ed. Nikolai Miloshev. **Dist. by:** Sofia Books, ul Silivria 16, Sofia 1404, Bulgaria. TEL 359-2-9586257, info@sofiabooks-bg.com, http://www.sofiabooks-bg.com.

551.2 NLD ISSN 1570-761X
▼ ➤ **BULLETIN OF EARTHQUAKE ENGINEERING.** Text in English. 2003. 3/yr. EUR 161, USD 160, GBP 109 combined subscription to institutions print & online eds. (effective 2005). reprint service avail. from PSC. **Document type:** *Journal, Academic/Scholarly.* **Description:** Provides a forum for the European Earthquake Engineering Community to present and discuss matters of major interest e.g. important European damaging earthquakes, new developments in earthquake regulations, national policies applied after the occurrence of major seismic events (for example strengthening of existing buildings, etc.).
Related titles: Online - full text ed.: ISSN 1573-1456 (from EBSCO Publishing, Gale Group, IngentaConnect, Kluwer Online, O C L C Online Computer Library Center, Inc., Springer LINK, Swets Information Services).
Indexed: ASFA, BibLing, ESPM, H&SSA, OceAb, RiskAb.
—BLDSC (2849.613520), IE. **CCC.**
Published by: (European Association for Earthquake Engineering TUR), Springer-Verlag Dordrecht (Subsidiary of: Springer Science+Business Media), Van Godewijckstraat 30, Dordrecht, 3311 GX, Netherlands. TEL 31-78-6576050, FAX 31-78-6576474, http://springerlink.metapress.com/openurl.asp?genre=journal&issn=1570-761X, http://www.springeronline.com. Ed. Atilla Ansal.

551.31 JPN ISSN 1345-3807
GB2401 CODEN: BGREFL
➤ **BULLETIN OF GLACIOLOGICAL RESEARCH.** Text in English. 1987. a. subscr. incld. with membership. adv. **Document type:** *Bulletin, Academic/Scholarly.* **Description:** Contains scientific papers which highlight the recent progress in the fields of snow and ice studies.
Formerly (until 2000): Bulletin of Glacier Research (0913-4190)
—BLDSC (2855.672500), CISTI, IE, ingenta.
Published by: Nihon Seppyo Gakkai/Japanese Society of Snow and Ice, Kagaku-Kaikan 3F, 1-5 Kanda-Surugadai, Chiyoda, Tokyo, 101-0062, Japan. TEL 81-3-52595245, FAX 81-3-52595246, jimu@seppyo.org, http://wwwsoc.nii.ac.jp/jssi/hyoga/bgr/bgr.html. Ed. Renji Naruse TEL 81-11-7065486.

551.21 DEU ISSN 0258-8900
CODEN: BUVOEW
➤ **BULLETIN OF VOLCANOLOGY.** Text in English. 1924. 8/yr. (in 1 vol., 8 nos./vol.). EUR 1,058 combined subscription to institutions print & online eds. (effective 2005). adv. illus. Index. reprints avail. **Document type:** *Journal, Academic/Scholarly.* **Description:** Covers articles relating to the understanding of volcanic phenomena.
Formerly (until 1984): Bulletin Volcanologique (0366-483X)
Related titles: Online - full text ed.: ISSN 1432-0819 (from EBSCO Publishing, Springer LINK, Swets Information Services).
Indexed: AESIS, ASCA, ChemAb, CurCont, FLUIDEX, GEOBASE, ISR, MinerAb, RefZh, SCI, SPPI.
—BLDSC (2925.020000), CASDDS, IDS, IE, Infotrieve, ingenta, Linda Hall. **CCC.**
Published by: (International Association of Volcanology and Chemistry of the Earth's Interior JPN), Springer-Verlag (Subsidiary of: Springer Science+Business Media), Tiergartenstr 17, Heidelberg, 69121, Germany. TEL 49-6221-3450, FAX 49-6221-345229, http://link.springer.de/link/service/journals/00445/index.htm. Ed. J Stix. Adv. contact Stephan Kroeck TEL 49-30-827875739. **Subscr. in the Americas to:** Springer-Verlag New York, Inc., Journal Fulfillment, PO Box 2485, Secaucus, NJ 07096-2485. TEL 800-777-4643, 201-348-4033, FAX 201-348-4505, journals@springer-ny.com, http://www.springer-ny.com; **Subscr. to:** Springer GmbH Auslieferungsgesellschaft, Haberstr 7, Heidelberg 69126, Germany.

551 JPN ISSN 0912-7984
TN269
BUTSURI TANSA/GEOPHYSICAL EXPLORATION. Text in English, Japanese. 1948. bi-m. free to members. **Document type:** *Journal, Academic/Scholarly.*

E

Formerly (until 1986): Butsuri Tanko/Geophysical Exploration (0521-9191)
Indexed: AESIS, INIS AtomInd, Inspec, JPI, PetrolAb.
—AskIEEE, CISTI, Linda Hall, PADDS. **CCC.**
Published by: Butsuri Tansa Gakkai/Society of Exploration Geophysicists of Japan, San-esu Bldg, 2-2-18 Nakamagome, Ota-ku, Tokyo, 143-0027, Japan. http://www.segj.org/committee/hensyu/journal/index_e.html.

551 JPN
BUTSURI TANSA CHOSA KENKYU ICHIRAN/GEOPHYSICAL ACTIVITY IN JAPAN. Text in Japanese. 1956. a.
Published by: Kogyo Gijutsuin, Chishitsu Chosajo/National Institute of Advanced Industrial Science & Technology, Geological Survey of Japan, AIST Tsukuba Central 7, 1-1, Higashi 1-Chome, Tsukuba, Ibaraki 305-0046, Japan. TEL 81-29-8619122, FAX 81-29-8613672, http://www.aist.go.jp, http://www.gsj.jp/.

551 JPN
BUTSURI TANSA GAKKAI GAKUJUTSU KOENKAI KOEN RONBUNSHU/SOCIETY OF EXPLORATION GEOPHYSICISTS OF JAPAN. CONFERENCE. PROCEEDINGS. Text in English, Japanese; Summaries in English. 1984. s-a.
Published by: Butsuri Tansa Gakkai/Society of Exploration Geophysicists of Japan, San-esu Bldg, 2-2-18 Nakamagome, Ota-ku, Tokyo, 143-0027, Japan.

551.22 USA
C U S E C JOURNAL. Text in English. irreg. free. **Document type:** *Newsletter.*
Formerly (until vol.4, 1992): Fault Line
—BLDSC (3506.095800).
Published by: Central United States Earthquake Consortium, 2630 Holmes Rd E, Memphis, TN 38118-8001. TEL 901-345-0932, FAX 901-345-0998. Circ: 3,000.

550 CHN ISSN 1001-1595
CEHUI XUEBAO/ACTA GEODAETICA ET CARTOGRAPHICA SINICA. Text in Chinese; Abstracts in English. 1957. q. CNY 6 newsstand/cover (effective 2003). bk.rev. **Document type:** *Journal, Academic/Scholarly.*
Related titles: Online - full content ed.: (from WanFang Data Corp.); Online - full text ed.: (from East View Information Services).
Indexed: BrCerAb, C&ISA, CerAb, CorrAb, E&CAJ, EMA, IAA, M&TEA, MBF, METADEX, RefZh, SolStAb, WAA.
—Linda Hall.
Published by: Cehui Chubanshe, Fuxingmen Wai, 50 Sanlihe Lu, Beijing, 100045, China. xhxb@periodicals.net.cn, http://chxb.wanfangdata.com.cn/default.html. Ed. Junyong Chen.

551 PRT ISSN 0870-4716
CENTRO DE FISICA DA ATMOSFERA DE LISBOA. BOLETIM. Text in Portuguese. 1955. m. charts; stat. **Document type:** *Bulletin.* **Description:** Observations of the electric field of the atmosphere.
Formerly (until 1977): Boletim Geoelectrico (0006-5994)
Media: Duplicated (not offset).
Indexed: M&GPA.
Published by: (Portugal. Centro de Fisica da Atmosfera de Lisboa), Instituto de Meteorologia, Rua C do Aeroporto, Lisbon, 1749-077, Portugal. TEL 351-21-8447000, FAX 351-21-8402370, informacoes@meteo.pt, http://www.meteo.pt/.

551 JPN ISSN 0913-9214
G70.4
CHIBA DAIGAKU EIZO KAKUSOKU KENKYU SENTA. SENTA NENPO/CHIBA UNIVERSITY. REMOTE SENSING AND IMAGE RESEARCH CENTER. ANNUAL REPORT. Text in Japanese. 1987. a.
Published by: Chiba Daigaku, Eizo Kakusoku Kenkyu Senta/Chiba University, Remote Sensing and Image Research Center, 1-33 Yayoi-cho, Inage-ku, Chiba-shi, Chiba-ken 263-0022, Japan.

551 JPN
CHIJIKI KANSOKUJO GIJUTSU HOKOKU/KAKIOKA MAGNETIC OBSERVATORY. TECHNICAL REPORT. Text in Japanese. s-a.
Published by: Kishocho, Chijiki Kansokujo/Japan Meteorological Agency, Kakioka Magnetic Observatory, 595 Kakioka, Niihari-gun, Yasato-machi, Ibaraki-ken 315-0116, Japan.

551 JPN
CHIJIKI KANSOKUJO YOHO/KAKIOKA MAGNETIC OBSERVATORY. MEMOIRS. Text in English, Japanese. 1938. s-a.
Published by: Kishocho, Chijiki Kansokujo/Japan Meteorological Agency, Kakioka Magnetic Observatory, 594 Yasato-cho, Niihari-gun, Kakioka, Ibaraki-ken 315-0116, Japan.

551 JPN
CHIKYU DENJIKI CHIKYU WAKUSEIKEN GAKKAI KAIHO/SOCIETY OF GEOMAGNETISM AND EARTH, PLANETARY AND SPACE SCIENCES. NEWS. Text in Japanese. 4/yr.
Published by: Chikyu Denjiki Chikyu Wakuseiken Gakkai/Society of Geomagnetism and Earth, Planetary and Space Sciences, Nihon Gakkai Jimu Senta, 16-9 Honkomagome 5-chome, Bunkyo-ku, Tokyo, 113-0021, Japan.

551 JPN
CHIKYU DENJIKI CHIKYU WAKUSEIKEN GAKKAI KOENKAI KOEN YOKOSHU/SOCIETY OF GEOMAGNETISM AND EARTH, PLANETARY AND SPACE SCIENCES. PREPRINTS OF THE MEETING. Text in Japanese; Summaries in English. s-a. JPY 3,500 per issue.
Published by: Chikyu Denjiki Chikyu Wakuseiken Gakkai/Society of Geomagnetism and Earth, Planetary and Space Sciences, Nihon Gakkai Jimu Senta, 16-9 Honkomagome 5-chome, Bunkyo-ku, Tokyo, 113-0021, Japan.

551 JPN
CHIKYU JIKI KANSOKU HOKOKU/GEOMAGNETIC OBSERVATIONS AT MIZUSAWA AND KANOZAN. Text in English. 1982. a.
Published by: Kokudo Chiriin/Geographical Survey Institute, Ministry of Construction, 1 Kita-Sato, Tsukuba-shi, Ibaraki-ken 305-0811, Japan.

551 CHN
➤ **CHINESE JOURNAL OF GEOPHYSICS (ONLINE EDITION).** Text in English. s-m. USD 100 to institutions (effective 2006). back issues avail. **Document type:** *Journal, Academic/Scholarly.*
Media: Online - full content. **Related titles:** Ed.: (from WanFang Data Corp.).
Published by: Zhongguo Diqiu Wuli Xuehui/Chinese Geophysical Society, 5, Minzuxueyuan Nanlu, Beijing, Haidian District 100081, China. TEL 86-10-68729347, FAX 86-10-68460283, actageop@mail.c-geos.ac.cn, http://www.agu.org/wps/ChineseJGeo, http://www.cgs.org.cn. Ed. Li Guang-Ding. **Subscr. to:** American Geophysical Union, 2000 Florida Ave, NW, Washington, DC 20009-1277. TEL 800-344-6902, 516-576-2270.

➤ **CHINETSU/JAPAN GEOTHERMAL ENERGY ASSOCIATION. JOURNAL.** see *ENERGY—Geothermal Energy*

➤ **CHINETSU GIJUTSU/GEOTHERMAL ENERGY RESEARCH AND DEVELOPMENT CO., LTD. JOURNAL.** see *ENERGY—Geothermal Energy*

➤ **CIEL ET TERRE.** see *ASTRONOMY*

551.22 500 USA ISSN 0733-5792
QE531 CODEN: CEPEE7
COMPUTATIONAL SEISMOLOGY. Text in English. 1979-1992; resumed 1994. irreg. USD 62 per issue to institutions (effective 2005 - 2006). **Document type:** *Academic/Scholarly.* **Description:** Devoted to the applications of modern mathematics and computer science to seismology and related studies of the solid Earth.
Related titles: Translation of: Vychislitel'naya.
Indexed: EEA, Inspec.
—AskIEEE, CISTI. **CCC.**
Published by: American Geophysical Union, 2000 Florida Ave, NW, Washington, DC 20009-1277. TEL 202-462-6900, 800-966-2481, FAX 202-328-0566, institutions@agu.org, http://www.agu.org. Ed. A F Spilhaus Jr.

624.151 CZE ISSN 0139-9292
CZECH SEISMOLOGICAL STATIONS: PRUHONICE, PRAHA, KASPERSKE HORY. BULLETIN. Text in English. 1965. a. free. **Document type:** *Bulletin.*
Supersedes in part (in 1966): Czechoslovak Seismological Stations: Pryhonice, Praha, Kaspersk Hory, Cheb, Bratislava, Srobarova, Hurbanovo and Skalnate Pleso. Bulletin (0139-9209)
Published by: Akademie Ved Ceske Republiky, Geofyzikalni Ustav, Bocni II/1401, Prague, 14131, Czech Republic. TEL 420-2-67103383, FAX 420-2-72761549, gfu@ig.cas.cz, http://www.ig.cas.cz. Ed. Jan Zednik. Circ: 250.

CZECHOSLOVAK NATIONAL WORKSHOP ON SEISMIC DATA ACQUISITION AND COMPUTER PROCESSING. PROCEEDINGS. see *EARTH SCIENCES—Computer Applications*

551.22 CHN ISSN 1671-5942
DADI CELIANG YU DIQIU DONGLIXUE/JOURNAL OF GEODESY AND GEODYNAMICS. Text in Chinese. 1981. q. CNY 7.50 domestic; USD 15 foreign (effective 2004). 128 p./no.; back issues avail. **Document type:** *Journal, Academic/Scholarly.*
Formerly (until Jan. 2002): Dike Xingbian yu Dizhen / Crustal Deformation and Earthquake (1003-4137)
Related titles: ♦ CD-ROM ed.: Chinese Academic Journals Full-Text Database. Science & Engineering, Series A. ISSN 1007-8010; Online - full content ed.: (from WanFang Data Corp.); Online - full text ed.: (from East View Information Services).
Published by: Guojia Dizhen-ju, Dizhen Yanjiusuo, Xiaohong-shan, Wuchang, 430071, China. TEL 86-27-87864009, FAX 86-27-87874426. Ed. Hongjiao Xue. Pub. Qiang Li. **Dist. by:** China International Book Trading Corp, 35 Chegongzhuang Xilu, Haidian District, PO Box 399, Beijing 100044, China. TEL 86-10-68412045, FAX 86-10-68412023, cibtc@mail.cibtc.com.cn, http://www.cibtc.com.cn.

DADI GOUZAO YU CHENGKUANGXUE. see *EARTH SCIENCES—Geology*

383 JPN ISSN 0389-8229
QC879.59.A1
DATA IN WORLD DATA CENTER C2 FOR IONOSPHERE. CATALOGUE. Text in English. 1958. a. **Document type:** *Catalog.*
Published by: Yuseisho, Tsushin Sogo Kenkyujo/Ministry of Posts and Telecommunications, Communications Research Laboratory, 2-1 Nukui-Kita-Machi 4-chome, Koganei-shi, Tokyo-to 184-0015, Japan.

551 DNK
DENMARK. DANMARKS METEOROLOGISKE INSTITUT. MAGNETIC RESULTS - BRORFELDE, QEQERTARSUAQ, QAANAAQ AND NARSARSUAQ OBSERVATORIES (ONLINE EDITION). Text in Danish, English. 1992. a. free. illus. **Document type:** *Government.* **Description:** Publishes the results of geomagnetic data gathered at the Danish Meteorological Institute's permanent observatories.
Former titles (until 2003): Danish Meteorological Institute. Magnetic Results - Brorfelde, Qeqertarsuaq, Qaanaaq and Narsarsuaq Observatories (Print edition) (1397-8365); (until 1997): Danish Meteorological Institute. Magnetic Results - Brorfelde, Godhavn, Thule and Narsarsuaq Observatories (0908-2883); Which was formed by the merger of (1965-1992): Magnetic Results - Thule Geophysical Observatory (0901-8107); Which was formerly (until 1985): Thule Magnetic Results (0109-2723); (until 1983): Thule Geophysical Observatory. Magnetic Results (0564-636X); (until 1982): Magnetisk Aarbog. Del. 2. Groenland. B; (1965-1992): Godhavn Geophysical Observatory. Magnetic Results (0904-7719); Which was formerly (until 1983): Godhavn Magnetic Results (0109-4300); (until 1982): Godhavn Geophysical Observatory. Magnetic Results (0107-7341); (1972-1992): Narsarsuaq Geophysical Observatory. Magnetic Results (0903-2746); Which was formerly (until 1987): Narssarssuaq Magnetic Results (0901-1935); (until 1982): Narssarssuaq Geophysical Observatory (0105-2470); (1983-1992): Brorfelde Geophysical Observatory. Magnetic Results (0901-9413); Which was formerly (until 1985): Brorfelde Magnetic Results (0109-2170)
Media: Online - full content.
Published by: Danmarks Meteorologiske Institut/Danish Meteorological Institute, Lyngbyvej 100, Copenhagen Oe, 2100, Denmark. TEL 45-39-157500, FAX 45-39-271080, http://www.dmi.dk. Circ: 250.

551.22 TUR
DEPREM ARASTIRMA BULTENI/EARTHQUAKE RESEARCH DEPARTMENT. BULLETIN. Text in Turkish; Summaries in English, Turkish. 1973. q. free. adv. abstr.; bibl.; stat. **Document type:** *Bulletin, Government.*
Formerly: Deprem Arastirma Enstitusu Bulteni
Indexed: AJEE.
—BLDSC (3554.588000).
Published by: Ministry of Public Works and Settlement, Earthquake Research Department/Afet Isleri Genel Mudurlugu - Deprem Arastirma Enstitusu, Kizilay, P K 763, Ankara, Turkey. Ed. Erol Aytac. Pub. Oktay Ergunay. Circ: 1,250.

551 510 NLD ISSN 0167-5982
➤ **DEVELOPMENTS IN GEOMATHEMATICS.** Text in Dutch. 1974. irreg., latest vol.6, 1988. price varies. **Document type:** *Monographic series, Academic/Scholarly.* **Description:** Discusses topics in geostatistics.
Indexed: IMMAb.
Published by: Elsevier BV (Subsidiary of: Elsevier Science & Technology), Radarweg 29, Amsterdam, 1043 NX, Netherlands. TEL 31-20-4853911, FAX 31-20-4852457, nlinfo-f@elsevier.nl, http://www.elsevier.nl.

551 NLD ISSN 0419-0297
CODEN: DSEGAT
➤ **DEVELOPMENTS IN SOLID EARTH GEOPHYSICS.** Text in English. 1964. irreg., latest vol.18, 1990. price varies. back issues avail. **Document type:** *Monographic series, Academic/Scholarly.*
Indexed: Inspec.
—CISTI. **CCC.**
Published by: Elsevier BV (Subsidiary of: Elsevier Science & Technology), Radarweg 29, Amsterdam, 1043 NX, Netherlands. TEL 31-20-4853911, FAX 31-20-4852457, nlinfo-f@elsevier.nl, http://www.elsevier.nl.

551.21 NLD
➤ **DEVELOPMENTS IN VOLCANOLOGY.** Text in Dutch. 1983. irreg., latest vol.6, 2003. price varies. illus. **Document type:** *Monographic series, Academic/Scholarly.* **Description:** Presents news of geological research into the study of volcanos.
Indexed: Inspec.

E

▼ *new title* ➤ *refereed* ✶ *unverified* ♦ *full entry avail.*

Published by: Elsevier BV (Subsidiary of: Elsevier Science & Technology), Radarweg 29, Amsterdam, 1043 NX, Netherlands. TEL 31-20-4853911, FAX 31-20-4852457, nlinfo-f@elsevier.nl, http://www.elsevier.nl.

➤ **DICENGXUE ZAZHI/JOURNAL OF STRATIGRAPHY.** see *EARTH SCIENCES—Geology*

551 CHN ISSN 0001-5733
QC801 CODEN: TCWHAG
➤ **DIQIU WULI XUEBAO/CHINESE JOURNAL OF GEOPHYSICS.** Text in Chinese; Summaries in English. 1948. bi-m. CNY 25 newsstand/cover (effective 2005). adv. **Document type:** *Journal, Academic/Scholarly.* **Description:** Covers geophysical research in China, including seismology, physics of the earth's interior, and geodesy.
Related titles: Online - full content ed.: (from WanFang Data Corp.); Online - full text ed.: (from East View Information Services).
Indexed: AESIS, C&ISA, ChemAb, CurCont, E&CAJ, FLUIDEX, GEOBASE, IAA, IBR, IMMAb, ISR, Inspec, PetrolAb, RefZh, SCI.
—AskIEEE, CISTI, Linda Hall, PADDS. **CCC.**
Published by: (Zhongguo Kexueyuan, Diqiu Wuli Yanjiusuo), Kexue Chubanshe/Science Press, 16 Donghuang Cheng Genbei Jie, Beijing, 100717, China. TEL 86-10-64000246, FAX 86-10-64030255, actageop@mail.igcas.ac.cn, http://www.sciencep.com/gb/content/2001-05/14/content_675.htm. Ed. Guang-ding Liu. Circ: 12,000. **Dist. by:** China International Book Trading Corp, 35 Chegongzhuang Xilu, Haidian District, PO Box 399, Beijing 100044, China. TEL 86-10-68412045, FAX 86-10-68412023, cibtc@mail.cibtc.com.cn, http://www.cibtc.com.cn.

551.22 CHN ISSN 1000-3274
DIZHEN/EARTHQUAKE. Text in Chinese. 1980. q. CNY 80 (effective 2004). adv. **Document type:** *Journal, Academic/Scholarly.* **Description:** Aims to publicize the study of seismic precursors and earthquake prediction. Covers theories and methods of earthquake prediction, application of observation techniques, and analysis of available data.
Formerly (until 1981): Zhongguo Dizhi Kexueyuan Yuanbaokuangchuang Dizhi Yanjiusuo Fenkan (1002-0004)
Related titles: Online - full content ed.: (from WanFang Data Corp.); Online - full text ed.: (from East View Information Services).
Indexed: GEOBASE.
—BLDSC (3643.571000), IE, ingenta.
Published by: (Zhongguo Dizhen Xuehui), Kexue Chubanshe/Science Press, 16 Donghuang Cheng Genbei Jie, Beijing, 100717, China. TEL 86-1-64034205, FAX 86-1-64010642, http://www.sciencep.com/. Ed. Guo-ming Zhang. Circ: 31,000. **Dist. by:** China International Book Trading Corp, 35 Chegongzhuang Xilu, Haidian District, PO Box 399, Beijing 100044, China. TEL 86-10-68412045, FAX 86-10-68412023, cibtc@mail.cibtc.com.cn, http://www.cibtc.com.cn.

551.22 CHN ISSN 1003-3246
QE538.8 CODEN: DDGYEQ
➤ **DIZHEN DICI GUANCE YU YANJIU/SEISMOLOGICAL AND GEOMAGNETIC OBSERVATION AND RESEARCH.** Text in Chinese. 1980. bi-m. CNY 11 domestic (effective 2000). adv. back issues avail. **Document type:** *Academic/Scholarly.*
Related titles: CD-ROM ed.; Online - full content ed.: (from WanFang Data Corp.); Online - full text ed.: (from East View Information Services).
Published by: Guojia Dizhenju Diqiu Wuli Yanjiusuo, Haidian-qu, 5 Minzuxueyuan Nan Lu, Beijing, 100081, China. TEL 86-10-8417744, FAX 86-10-8415372. Eds. Peishan Chen, Ruifen Li. R&P, Adv. contact Ruifen Li.

E

551.22 551 CHN ISSN 0253-4967
QE531 CODEN: DDIZD4
➤ **DIZHEN DIZHI/SEISMOLOGY AND GEOLOGY.** Text in Chinese. 1979. q. CNY 12 (effective 2000). bk.rev. abstr. index. **Document type:** *Academic/Scholarly.* **Description:** Academic publication covers the latest development in earth sciences, especially in the fields of seismology and geology.
Related titles: Online - full content ed.: (from WanFang Data Corp.); Online - full text ed.: (from East View Information Services).
Indexed: AJEE, C&ISA, E&CAJ, GEOBASE, IAA, Inspec, RefZh.
—BLDSC (8227.750000), Linda Hall.
Published by: Guojia Dizhen-ju, Dizhi Yanjiusuo/China Seismological Bureau, Institute of Geology, Deshengmen Wai, Qijia Huozi, Beijing, 100029, China. TEL 86-1-2023377, FAX 86-1-2028617. Ed. Ma Xingyuan. Circ: 1,200.

551.22 CHN
DIZHEN DIZHI YICONG/TRANSLATED LITERATURE ON SEISMOLOGY AND GEOLOGY. Text in Chinese, bi-m.
Published by: Guojia Dizhen-ju, Dizhi Yanjiusuo/China Seismological Bureau, Institute of Geology, Deshengmen Wai, Qijia Huozi, Beijing, 100029, China. TEL 4016611. Ed. Ma Xingheng.

551.22 CHN ISSN 1000-1301
➤ **DIZHEN GONGCHENG YU GONGCHENG ZHENDONG/EARTHQUAKE ENGINEERING AND ENGINEERING VIBRATION.** Text in Chinese. 1981. q. CNY 60 (effective 2004). adv. **Document type:** *Academic/Scholarly.* **Description:** Contains research papers on both theory and applications.
Related titles: Online - full content ed.: (from WanFang Data Corp.); Online - full text ed.: (from East View Information Services).
Indexed: C&ISA, E&CAJ, EEA, FLUIDEX, GEOBASE, IAA.
—BLDSC (3643.574000), IE, ingenta, Linda Hall.
Published by: (Zhongguo Dizhenju Gongcheng Lixue Yanjiusuo), Kexue Chubanshe/Science Press, 16 Donghuang Cheng Genbei Jie, Beijing, 100717, China. TEL 86-1-64034205, FAX 86-1-64010642, eeev@0451.com, http://dzgcygczd.periodicals.net.cn/default.html, http://www.sciencep.com/. Ed. Li-Li Xie. Circ: 6,000. **Dist. by:** China International Book Trading Corp, 35 Chegongzhuang Xilu, Haidian District, PO Box 399, Beijing 100044, China. TEL 86-10-68412045, FAX 86-10-68412023, cibtc@mail.cibtc.com.cn, http://www.cibtc.com.cn.

551.22 CHN ISSN 0253-3782
QE531 CODEN: ASSID7
➤ **DIZHEN XUEBAO/ACTA SEISMOLOGICA SINICA.** Text in Chinese; Summaries in English. 1979. q. CNY 120 (effective 2004). adv. **Document type:** *Journal, Academic/Scholarly.* **Description:** Publishes articles on research work in seismology, and papers on basic geophysical studies of seismology, seismotectonics, seismic precursor, earthquake engineering, and related technology. Contains reviews and information on activities.
Related titles: Online - full content ed.: (from WanFang Data Corp.); Online - full text ed.: (from East View Information Services); ♦ English ed.: Acta Seismologica Sinica. ISSN 1000-9116.
Indexed: GEOBASE, Inspec.
—AskIEEE, CISTI, Linda Hall.
Published by: (Zhongguo Dizhen Xuehui), Kexue Chubanshe/Science Press, 16 Donghuang Cheng Genbei Jie, Beijing, 100717, China. TEL 86-10-64000246, FAX 86-10-64030255, dzxb@ns.cdsn.org.cn, http://dizhen.periodicals.net.cn/default.html, http://www.sciencep.com/. Ed. Yun-tai Chen. Circ: 12,000. **Dist. by:** China International Book Trading Corp, 35 Chegongzhuang Xilu, Haidian District, PO Box 399, Beijing 100044, China. TEL 86-10-68412045, FAX 86-10-68412023, cibtc@mail.cibtc.com.cn, http://www.cibtc.com.cn.

551 CHN
DIZHI LIXUE XUEBAO/JOURNAL OF GEOMECHANICS. Text in English. 1995. q. CNY 6 domestic (effective 2000). **Document type:** *Academic/Scholarly.*
Related titles: Online - full content ed.: (from WanFang Data Corp.).
Indexed: RefZh.
—BLDSC (4994.150000), ingenta.
Published by: Zhongguo Dizhi Kexueyuan, Dizhilixue Yanjiusuo, Haidian-qu, Minzhu Xueyuan Nan Lu 11 Hao, Beijing, 100081, China. http://www.cajcd.edu.cn. Ed. Qing-xuan Chen.

551 IRL ISSN 0070-7422
CODEN: CDDBDW
DUBLIN INSTITUTE FOR ADVANCED STUDIES. SCHOOL OF COSMIC PHYSICS. GEOPHYSICAL BULLETIN. Variant title: Dublin Institute for Advanced Studies. Communications. Series D. Text in English. 1950. irreg., latest vol.46. price varies. **Document type:** *Academic/Scholarly.*
Formerly (until 1964): Dublin Institute for Advanced Studies. Geophysical Bulletin (1393-0230)
—BLDSC (4149.000000), CISTI, Linda Hall.
Published by: Dublin Institute for Advanced Studies, 10 Burlington Rd., Dublin, 4, Ireland. TEL 353-1-6680748, FAX 353-1-6680561.

551 USA ISSN 0096-3941
QE500 CODEN: EOSTA
➤ **E O S;** transactions, American Geophysical Union . Text in English. 1919. w. USD 465 to institutions; free to members (effective 2006). adv. bk.rev. abstr.; bibl.; charts; illus. index. reprint service avail. from ISI. **Document type:** *Newspaper, Academic/Scholarly.* **Description:** For geophysicists; carries articles on recent research; news; employment opportunities; meeting programs and reports; announcements of grants and fellowships; and AGU activities.
Formerly (until 1969): American Geophysical Union. Transactions (0002-8606)
Related titles: Microfiche ed.: (from AGU, AIP); Microform ed.: (from AGU).
Indexed: A&ATA, ASFA, ApicAb, BiolAb, C&ISA, E&CAJ, EEA, Englnd, EnvAb, HRIS, IAA, Inspec, M&GPA, PetrolAb, RevApplEntom.
—AskIEEE, CISTI, IE, Linda Hall, PADDS. **CCC.**
Published by: American Geophysical Union, 2000 Florida Ave, NW, Washington, DC 20009-1277. TEL 202-462-6900, 800-966-2481, FAX 202-328-0566, institutions@agu.org, http://www.agu.org. Eds. Keith Alverson, A F Spilhaus Jr. Pub. Stephen Cole. Adv. contact Carla Childres TEL 202-777-7536. Circ: 35,000 (paid).

551 USA ISSN 1533-0605
EARTH ALMANAC; an annual geophysical review of the state of the planet. Text in English. 2000. a. **Document type:** *Journal.*
—BLDSC (3643.016500).
Published by: Oryx Press (Subsidiary of: Greenwood Publishing Group Inc.), 88 Post Rd W, Westport, CT 06881. info@oryxpress.com, http://www.oryxpress.com.

551.2 USA ISSN 1671-3664
➤ **EARTHQUAKE ENGINEERING AND ENGINEERING VIBRATION.** Text in English. 2002 (June). s-a. USD 80, CNY 80 to institutions (effective 2005). **Document type:** *Journal, Academic/Scholarly.* **Description:** Promotes scientific exchange between Chinese and international scientists by introducing pertinent results of research and practice in China to the international earthquake engineering community; and informing researchers and practitioners in China about recent international developments in earthquake engineering and engineering vibration.
Indexed: C&ISA, E&CAJ, ESPM, H&SSA, IAA.
—BLDSC (3643.574100).
Published by: (Institute of Engineering Mechanics, China Seismological Bureau CHN), Multidisciplinary Center for Earthquake Engineering Research, University of Buffalo, Red Jacket Quad, Buffalo, NY 14261. TEL 716-645-3377, FAX 716-645-3391, jestoyle@buffalo.edu, mceer@mceermail.buffalo.edu, http://mceer.buffalo.edu/eeev. Eds. Dr. George C Lee, Dr. Xiaozhai Qi. **Subscr. outside N. America to:** Institute of Engineering Mechanics, China Seismological Bureau, 9 Xuefu Rd, Harbin 150080, China.

551.22 USA
EARTHQUAKE HISTORY OF THE UNITED STATES. Text in English. 1928. irreg. (approx. every 5 yrs.). price varies. stat. **Document type:** *Government.* **Description:** Tells the location and effects of U.S. earthquakes from earliest recorded history to present.
Related titles: CD-ROM ed.; Microfiche ed.: (from NTI).
Published by: (National Oceanic and Atmospheric Administration), U.S. National Geophysical Data Center, 325 Broadway, E CG4, Boulder, CO 80303-3328. TEL 303-497-6826, FAX 303-497-6513, info@ngdc.noaa.gov, http://www.ngds.noaa.gov, http://www.ngdc.noaa.gov.

551 USA ISSN 8755-2930
TA654.6
EARTHQUAKE SPECTRA. Text in English. 1984. q. bk.rev. back issues avail. **Document type:** *Journal, Academic/Scholarly.* **Description:** Aimed at professions involved in earthquake hazards reduction.
Related titles: Online - full text ed.: (from EBSCO Publishing).
Indexed: AJEE, ApMecR, B&BAb, BrCerAb, C&ISA, CerAb, CorrAb, CurCont, E&CAJ, EEA, EMA, Englnd, IAA, Inspec, M&TEA, MBF, METADEX, RefZh, SUSA, SolStAb, WAA.
—BLDSC (3643.595800), CISTI, Ei, IE, Infotrieve, ingenta, Linda Hall.
Published by: Earthquake Engineering Research Institute, 499 14th St., Ste 320, Oakland, CA 94612-1934. TEL 510-451-0905, FAX 510-451-5411, spectra@eeri.org, eeri@eeri.org, http://scitation.aip.org/EarthquakeSpectra/, http://www.eeri.org. Ed. Roger D Borcherdt. R&P Nancy Sutherland. Circ: 2,800.

528.7 CHE ISSN 0252-9335
EIDGENOESSISCHE TECHNISCHE HOCHSCHULE ZUERICH. INSTITUT FUER GEODAESIE UND PHOTOGRAMMETRIE. MITTEILUNGEN. Text in German. 1945. irreg., latest vol.82, 2003. price varies.
Formerly (until 1969): Eidgenoessische Technische Hochschule Zuerich. Geodatischen Institut. Mitteilungen (1423-372X)
Indexed: RefZh.
—CISTI.
Published by: Eidgenoessische Technische Hochschule Zuerich, Institut fuer Geodaesie und Photogrammetrie, Schafmattstr 34, Zuerich, 8093, Switzerland. TEL 41-1-6332661, FAX 41-1-6331066, jrene.mueller@geod.baug.ethz.ch, http://www.igp.ethz.ch.

ELECTROMAGNETICS. see *ENGINEERING—Electrical Engineering*

ENGINEERING GEOLOGY & GEOTECHNICAL ENGINEERING SYMPOSIUM. PROCEEDINGS. see *ENGINEERING—Civil Engineering*

EUROPEAN EARTHQUAKE ENGINEERING; international journal of earthquake engineering and engineering seismology. see *ENGINEERING*

EUROPEAN GEOPHYSICAL SOCIETY SERIES ON HYDROLOGICAL SCIENCES. see *EARTH SCIENCES—Hydrology*

551 AUS ISSN 0812-3985
TN269 CODEN: EXGEEF
EXPLORATION GEOPHYSICS✶. Text in English. 1970. q. AUD 135 in Australasia; AUD 235 elsewhere (effective 2003). adv. cum.index: 1970-1987. Supplement avail.; back issues avail.
Formerly: Australian Society of Exploration Geophysicists. Bulletin (0314-2876)
Related titles: Microfiche ed.: 1970.
Indexed: AESIS, E&PHSE, GP&P, Inspec, OffTech, PetrolAb.

—BLDSC (3842.155750), AskIEEE, CASDDS, Ei, IE, Infotrieve, ingenta, PADDS. **CCC.**
Published by: Australian Society of Exploration Geophysicists, PO Box 42, Everton Park, QLD 4053, Australia. TEL 61-3-98221399, FAX 61-3-98221711. Ed. John Denham. Adv. contact Brian Wickins. page AUD 450. Circ: 1,300.

551.1 FIN ISSN 0782-6117
QC989.F3
FINNISH METEOROLOGICAL INSTITUTE. CONTRIBUTIONS. Text in English. 1925. irreg. price varies. back issues avail. **Document type:** *Monographic series, Academic/Scholarly.*
Former titles (until 1988): Ilmatieteen Laitoksen Toimituksia - Finnish Meteorological Institute Contributions (0071-5190); (until 1969): Ilmatieteellisen Keskuslaitoksen Toimituksia
Indexed: M&GPA.
Published by: Ilmatieteen Laitos/Finnish Meteorological Institute, Vuorikatu 24, PO Box 503, Helsinki, 00101, Finland. TEL 358-9-19291, FAX 358-9-179581, http://www.fmi.fi/view/kirjasto/julkaisut_2.html.

551 FIN ISSN 0782-6087
FINNISH METEOROLOGICAL INSTITUTE. GEOPHYSICAL PUBLICATIONS/ILMATIETEEN LAITOS. GEOFYSIKAALISIA JULKAISUJA. Text in English, Finnish. 1986. irreg., latest vol.56, 2002. price varies. back issues avail. **Document type:** *Monographic series, Government.*
Indexed: M&GPA.
—BLDSC (4156.400000).
Published by: Ilmatieteen Laitos/Finnish Meteorological Institute, Vuorikatu 24, PO Box 503, Helsinki, 00101, Finland. TEL 358-9-19291, FAX 358-9-179581, http://www.fmi.fi/view/kirjasto/julkaisut_12.html.

538.78 FIN ISSN 1235-4732
FINNISH METEOROLOGICAL INSTITUTE. MAGNETIC RESULTS. Text in English, Finnish. 1992. a., latest 2002. price varies. **Document type:** *Government.*
Published by: Ilmatieteen Laitos/Finnish Meteorological Institute, Vuorikatu 24, PO Box 503, Helsinki, 00101, Finland. TEL 358-9-19291, FAX 358-9-179581, http://www.fmi.fi.

551 NLD ISSN 0263-5046
TA404.5 CODEN: XNBSAV
➤ **FIRST BREAK.** Text in English. 1983. m. EUR 50 membership print & online eds.; EUR 25 membership student, print & online eds. (effective 2004). adv. bk.rev. bibl.; charts; illus. index. **Document type:** *Journal, Academic/Scholarly.* **Description:** Designed for practitioners and researchers within the oil industry, providing a rich mixture of short, authoritative articles covering applied geophysics, petroleum geology and reservoir engineering.
Related titles: ♦ Online - full text ed.: First Break Online. ISSN 1365-2397.
Indexed: AESIS, ASFA, E&PHSE, EPB, ESPM, FLUIDEX, GEOBASE, GP&P, OceAb, OffTech, PetrolAb, PollutAb, WRCInf.
—BLDSC (3934,438000), IE, Infotrieve, ingenta, Linda Hall, PADDS.
Published by: European Association of Geoscientists and Engineers, PO Box 59, Houten, 3990, Netherlands. TEL 31-30-6354055, FAX 31-30-6343524, firstbreak@eage.nl, eage@eage.nl, http://www.firstbreak.nl/, http://www.eage.org. Circ: 6,150.

551 NLD ISSN 1365-2397
TN269
➤ **FIRST BREAK ONLINE.** Text in English. m. EUR 50 membership; EUR 25 membership student (effective 2004). **Document type:** *Journal, Academic/Scholarly.*
Media: Online - full text (from Blackwell Synergy, EBSCO Publishing, Gale Group, IngentaConnect, O C L C Online Computer Library Center, Inc., Swets Information Services).
Related titles: ♦ Print ed.: First Break. ISSN 0263-5046.
Published by: European Association of Geoscientists and Engineers, PO Box 59, Houten, 3990, Netherlands. TEL 31-30-6354055, FAX 31-30-6343524, firstbreak@eage.nl, eage@eage.nl, http://www.firstbreak.nl/, http://www.eage.org.

551 ESP ISSN 0214-4557
QC801
➤ **FISICA DE LA TIERRA.** Text in English, Spanish. 1989. a., latest vol.13, 2001. EUR 18 in the European Union; EUR 30 elsewhere (effective 2005). bk.rev. charts; illus.; maps. 300 p./no.; back issues avail. **Document type:** *Monographic series, Academic/Scholarly.* **Description:** Devoted to earth sciences, with articles on geophysics, geodesy and atmospheric sciences.
Indexed: IECT.
—CINDOC.
Published by: (Universidad Complutense de Madrid, Facultad de Ciencias Fisicas), Universidad Complutense de Madrid, Servicio de Publicaciones, C Isaac Peral s/n, Ciudad Universitaria, Madrid, 28040, Spain. TEL 34-91-3946934, FAX 34-91-3946978, secreta@fis.ucm.es, servicio@publicaciones.ucm.es, http://www.ucm.es/publicaciones. Ed. Agustin Udias. Circ: 300.

➤ **FIZIKO-TEKHNICHESKIE PROBLEMY RAZRABOTKI POLEZNYKH ISKOPAEMYKH.** see *MINES AND MINING INDUSTRY*

551 SVN ISSN 0351-0271
GEODETSKI VESTNIK. Text in Slovenian. 1957. q. **Document type:** *Journal, Academic/Scholarly.*
Related titles: Online - full text ed.: ISSN 1581-1328.
Indexed: ASFA, BrCerAb, C&ISA, CerAb, CorrAb, DIP, E&CAJ, EMA, ESPM, GEOBASE, IAA, M&TEA, MBF, METADEX, RefZh, SolStAb, WAA.
Published by: Sveza Geodetov Slovenije, Opekarska 11, Ljubljana, 1000, Slovenia. TEL 386-1-4292670, FAX 386-1-2839208, Bojan.Stanonik@gov.si, http://www.geodetski-vestnik.com.

526 RUS ISSN 0201-5137
GEODEZIYA, AEROS'EMKA, KARTOGRAFIYA: SOSTOYANIE I PERSPEKTIVY RAZVITIYA TSIFROVOGO KARTOGRAFII. Text in Russian. 3/yr. USD 129.95 in United States.
—East View.
Published by: T.S.N.I.I. Geodezii Aeros'emki i Kartografii im. F.N. Krasovskogo, Onezhskaya ul 26, Moscow, 125413, Russian Federation. TEL 7-095-4569531, FAX 7-095-4569531. **US dist. addr.:** East View Information Services, 3020 Harbor Ln. N., Minneapolis, MN 55447. TEL 612-550-0961.

526 RUS ISSN 0016-7126
CODEN: GZKGA5
GEODEZIYA I KARTOGRAFIYA. Text in Russian. 1956. m. USD 129.95. bibl. index.
Indexed: BibCart, RefZh.
—BLDSC (0047.320000), CISTI, East View, Linda Hall.
Published by: Kartgeotsentr-Geodezizdat, Onezhskaya ul 26, Moscow, 125413, Russian Federation. TEL 7-095-4569301, FAX 7-095-4569538. Ed. V I Berk. **US dist. addr.:** East View Information Services, 3020 Harbor Ln. N., Minneapolis, MN 55447. TEL 612-550-0961, FAX 612-559-2931.

526 RUS ISSN 0201-890X
GEODEZIYA, TOPOGRAFIYA, KARTOGRAFIYA. SERIYA: DISTANTSIONNOE ZONDIROVANIE ZEMLI DLYA EKOLOGII I PRIRODOPOL'ZOVANIYA. Text in Russian. q. USD 99.95 in United States.
—East View.
Published by: T.S.N.I.I. Geodezii Aeros'emki i Kartografii im. F.N. Krasovskogo, Onezhskaya ul 26, Moscow, 125413, Russian Federation. TEL 7-095-4569531. **US dist. addr.:** East View Information Services, 3020 Harbor Ln. N., Minneapolis, MN 55447. TEL 612-550-0961.

526 RUS
GEODEZIYA, TOPOGRAFIYA, KARTOGRAFIYA. SERIYA: DISTANTSIONNOE ZONDIROVANIE ZEMLI V RAIONAKH SLOZHNYKH EKOLOGICHESKIKH SITUATSII. Text in Russian. 3/yr. USD 129.95 in United States.
Published by: T.S.N.I.I. Geodezii Aeros'emki i Kartografii im. F.N. Krasovskogo, Onezhskaya ul 26, Moscow, 125413, Russian Federation. TEL 7-095-4569531. **US dist. addr.:** East View Information Services, 3020 Harbor Ln. N., Minneapolis, MN 55447. TEL 612-550-0961.

526 RUS ISSN 0869-6802
GEODEZIYA, TOPOGRAFIYA, KARTOGRAFIYA. SERIYA: GEODEZIYA, TOPOGRAFIYA, FOTOTOPOGRAFIYA. Text in Russian. q. USD 99.95 in United States.
—East View.
Published by: T.S.N.I.I. Geodezii Aeros'emki i Kartografii im. F.N. Krasovskogo, Onezhskaya ul 26, Moscow, 125413, Russian Federation. TEL 7-095-4569531. **US dist. addr.:** East View Information Services, 3020 Harbor Ln. N., Minneapolis, MN 55447. TEL 612-550-0961.

526 RUS ISSN 0202-6619
GEODEZIYA, TOPOGRAFIYA, KARTOGRAFIYA. SERIYA: KARTOGRAFIYA I GEOGRAFICHESKIE INFORMATSIONNYE SISTEMY. Text in Russian. q. USD 99.95 in United States.
—East View.
Published by: T.S.N.I.I. Geodezii Aeros'emki i Kartografii im. F.N. Krasovskogo, Onezhskaya ul 26, Moscow, 125413, Russian Federation. TEL 7-095-4569531. **US dist. addr.:** East View Information Services, 3020 Harbor Ln. N., Minneapolis, MN 55447. TEL 612-550-0961.

526 RUS
GEODEZIYA, TOPOGRAFIYA, KARTOGRAFIYA. SERIYA: PRIKLADNAYA GEODEZIYA. Text in Russian. q. USD 99.95 in United States.
Published by: T.S.N.I.I. Geodezii Aeros'emki i Kartografii im. F.N. Krasovskogo, Onezhskaya ul 26, Moscow, 125413, Russian Federation. TEL 7-095-4569531. **US dist. addr.:** East View Information Services, 3020 Harbor Ln. N., Minneapolis, MN 55447. TEL 612-550-0961.

526 POL ISSN 0016-7134
CODEN: GEJKAZ
GEODEZJA I KARTOGRAFIA/GEODESY AND CARTHOGRAPHY. Text in Polish; Summaries in English, Russian. 1952. q. EUR 65 foreign (effective 2005). bibl.; illus. index. **Document type:** *Journal, Academic/Scholarly.* **Description:** Covers geodesy, geodetic astronomy and gravimetry, geodetic surveying of deformations of buildings, structures, topography and mining surveys.
Indexed: BibCart.
—CISTI, Linda Hall.
Published by: (Polska Akademia Nauk, Komitet Geodezji), Wydawnictwo Naukowe P W N SA/Polish Scientific Publishers P W N, ul Miodowa 10, Warsaw, 00251, Poland. TEL 48-22-6954181, FAX 48-22-6954288, ksiegarnia@pwn.pl, http://en.pwn.pl. Circ: 1,040. **Dist. by:** Ars Polona, Krakowskie Przedmiescie 7, Warsaw, Poland. TEL 48-22-9263914, FAX 48-22-9265334, arspolona@arspolona.com.pl, http://www.arspolona.com.pl.

551 USA ISSN 0277-6669
➤ **GEODYNAMICS SERIES.** Text in English. 1980. irreg., latest vol.28, 1998. price varies. back issues avail. **Document type:** *Monographic series, Academic/Scholarly.* **Description:** Devoted to the understanding of the kinematics of major plate movements and the dynamics of the processes that caused these movements. Aimed at geologists, geophysicists, and geochemists.
Related titles: CD-ROM ed.; Online - full text ed.
Indexed: Inspec.
—BLDSC (4119.753000), CISTI. **CCC.**
Published by: American Geophysical Union, 2000 Florida Ave, NW, Washington, DC 20009-1277. TEL 202-462-6900, 800-966-2481, FAX 202-328-0566, orders@agu.org, http://www.agu.org.

551 COL ISSN 0121-2974
➤ **GEOFISICA COLOMBIANA.** Text in Spanish. 1992. a. USD 3 (effective 2004). adv. **Document type:** *Journal, Academic/Scholarly.* **Description:** Aims to divulge technical and scientific results of researches including seismology, volcanology, geophysical instrumentation, geology, oil and ore prospecting and environmental hazards.
Published by: Universidad Nacional de Colombia, Departamento de Geociencias, Ciudad Universitaria, Apdo Aereo 14490, Bogota, Colombia. TEL 57-1-316-5207, FAX 57-1-3165390, lamontesv@unal.edu.co, dgeologia@ciencias.unal.edu.co, http://www.unal.edu.co/geociencias/GeofisicaColombiana.htm, http://www.geogencias.unal.edu.co. Ed., Adv. contact Luis Alfredo Montes Vides. B&W page USD 50. Circ: 1,000 (paid and controlled).

551 ITA
GEOFISICA DELL'AMBIENTE E DEL TERRITORIO. Text in Italian. 1992. irreg., latest vol.3, 1997. price varies. adv. **Document type:** *Monographic series.*
Published by: Liguori Editore srl, Via Posillipo 394, Naples, 80123, Italy. TEL 39-81-7206111, FAX 39-81-7206244, http://www.liguori.it. Ed. Antonio Rapolla. Pub. Guido Liguori. Adv. contact Maria Liguori.

551 MEX ISSN 0016-7169
QC801 CODEN: GFINAC
➤ **GEOFISICA INTERNACIONAL.** Text in English, French, Spanish. 1961. q. USD 70. adv. bibl.; charts. index. **Document type:** *Academic/Scholarly.* **Description:** Prints original unpublished material on earth sciences: atmospheric science, geochemistry, hydrology, exploration geophysics, physical oceanography, paleomagnetism, tectonics, seismology, vulcanology and space physics.
Indexed: ASFA, CIN, ChemAb, ChemTitl, ESPM, FLUIDEX, GEOBASE, IBR, M&GPA, MinerAb.
—BLDSC (4120.300000), CASDDS, CISTI, IE, ingenta, Linda Hall.
Published by: Universidad Nacional Autonoma de Mexico, Instituto de Geofisica, Circuito Exterior, Ciudad Universitaria, Mexico, DF 20, Mexico. TEL 52-5-622-4113, FAX 52-5-550-2486, geofint@tonatiuh.igeofcu.unam.mx. Ed. Cinna Lomnitz. Adv. contact Jorge Arturo Arzate. Circ: 1,200 (controlled).

551 UKR ISSN 0203-3100
QC801 CODEN: GEZHD7
GEOFIZICHESKII ZHURNAL/JOURNAL OF GEOPHYSICS; nauchno-teoretichskii zhurnal. Text in Russian; Summaries in English. 1979. bi-m. USD 110. **Document type:** *Academic/Scholarly.*
Formerly: Geofizicheskii Sbornik (0568-6989)
Indexed: ChemAb, Djerelo, INIS AtomInd, Inspec, PhysBer, RefZh.
—AskIEEE, CASDDS, CISTI, East View, KNAW, Linda Hall. **CCC.**
Published by: Natsional'na Akademiya Nauk Ukrainy, Instytut Heofizyky im. S.I. Subbotina, Pr Palladina 32, Kiev, 252142, Ukraine. TEL 38-44-4441165. Ed. A V Chekunov. **Dist. by:** M K - Periodica, ul Gilyarovskogo 39, Moscow 129110, Russian Federation; **US dist. addr.:** East View Information Services, 3020 Harbor Ln. N., Minneapolis, MN 55447. TEL 612-550-0961.

551 HRV ISSN 0352-3659
QC801
➤ **GEOFIZIKA.** Text in Croatian. 1923. a. per issue exchange basis only. adv. bk.rev. **Document type:** *Journal, Academic/Scholarly.* **Description:** Publishes contributions dealing with physics of the atmosphere, the sea and the Earth's interior.
Formerly: Sveuciliste u Zagrebu. Prirodoslovno-Matematicki Fakultet. Radovi
Related titles: Online - full text ed.: 2003. free (effective 2005).
Indexed: GEOBASE, HistAb, M&GPA, RefZh.
—BLDSC (4121.260000), Linda Hall.

▼ *new title* ➤ *refereed* ✶ *unverified* ♦ *full entry avail.*

Published by: Sveuciliste U Zagrebu, Prirodoslovno-Matematicki Fakultet, Geofizicki Zavod, Andrija Mohorovicic Geophysical Institute, Horvatovac bb, Zagreb, 10000, Croatia. http://geofizika-journal.gfz.hr/, http://www.gfz.hr. Circ: 350.

538.7 DEU ISSN 0948-1761
➤ **GEOFORSCHUNGSZENTRUM POTSDAM. ADOLF-SCHMIDT-OBSERVATORIUM FUER GEOMAGNETISMUS. JAHRBUCH.** Text in German, English. 1890. a. 100 p./no.; back issues avail. **Document type:** *Bulletin, Academic/Scholarly.*
Former titles (until 1993): GeoForschungsZentrum Potsdam. Adolf-Schmidt-Observatorium fuer Erdmagnetismus. Jahrbuch (0065-2016); (until 1957): Erdmagnetisches Jahrbuch mit Wissenschaftlichen Mitteilungen (0232-461X)
Published by: GeoForschungsZentrum Potsdam, Adolf-Schmidt-Observatorium fuer Geomagnetismus, Lindenstr 7, Niemegk, 14823, Germany. TEL 49-33843-62414, FAX 49-33843-62423, linthe@gfz-potsdam.de, http://www.gfz-potsdam.de. Ed. Hans-Joachim Linthe. R&P Hans Joachim Linthe.

551 CUB ISSN 1028-8961
GEOINFO. Text in Spanish. 1997. biennial.
Media: Online - full text.
Published by: Instituto de Geofisica y Astronomia, Calle 212 No. 2906 entre 29 y 31, La Coronela, La Lisa, Havana, Cuba. oscaralv@geoastro.pco.cu, raone@infomed.sld.cu.

GEOLOGICAL SOCIETY OF CHINA. JOURNAL. see *EARTH SCIENCES—Geology*

GEOLOGICAL SURVEY OF NAMIBIA. REPORTS ON OPEN FILE. C D M MINERAL SURVEYS. see *EARTH SCIENCES—Geology*

556 NAM
GEOLOGICAL SURVEY OF NAMIBIA. REPORTS ON OPEN FILE. GEOPHYSICS. Text in English; Text occasionally in Afrikaans. 1971. irreg., latest vol.65, 1985. price varies. **Document type:** *Government.* **Description:** Series of preliminary reports on topics in geophysics.
Published by: Ministry of Mines and Energy, Geological Survey of Namibia, Aviation Rd 1, PO Box 2168, Windhoek, Namibia. TEL 264-61-249150, FAX 264-61-249144.

GEOLOGISCHE ABHANDLUNGEN HESSEN. see *EARTH SCIENCES—Geology*

GEOLOGISCHES JAHRBUCH HESSEN. see *EARTH SCIENCES—Geology*

GEOLOGIYA I GEOFIZIKA. see *EARTH SCIENCES—Geology*

551 USA
GEOMAGNETIC INDICES BULLETIN. Text in English. m. looseleaf. USD 17 (effective 1998). back issues avail. **Document type:** *Bulletin, Government.*
Published by: (National Oceanic and Atmospheric Administration), U.S. National Geophysical Data Center, 325 Broadway, E CG4, Boulder, CO 80303-3328. TEL 303-497-6836, FAX 303-497-6513, info@ngdc.noaa.gov, http://www.ngdc.noaa.gov.

551.5 FIN ISSN 1455-867X
GEOMAGNETIC, IONOSPHERIC AND AURORAL DATA FROM FINLAND. Text in English. 1995. m.
Published by: (Finland. Ilmatieteen Laitos/Finnish Meteorological Institute), Oulun Yliopiston, Sodankylan Geofysiikan Observatorio/University of Oulu. Sodankyla Geophysical Observatory, Taehtelaentie 62, Sodankyla, 99600, Finland. TEL 358-16-619811, FAX 358-16-619875, http://www.sgo.fi.

538.7 551 RUS ISSN 0016-7932
QC811 CODEN: GMARAX
➤ **GEOMAGNETISM AND AERONOMY.** Text in English. 1961. bi-m. USD 1,056 in North America; USD 1,213 elsewhere (effective 2004). charts; illus. index. reprint service avail. from ISI. **Document type:** *Journal, Academic/Scholarly.* **Description:** Covers fields of interplanetary space, geoeffective solar events, the magnetosphere, the ionosphere, the upper and middle atmosphere, the action of solar variability and activity on atmospheric parameters and climate.
Related titles: ♦ Translation of: Geomagnetizm i Aeronomiya. ISSN 0016-7940.
Indexed: CurCont, Inspec.
—BLDSC (0411.800000), AskIEEE, CISTI, IE, ingenta, Linda Hall. **CCC.**
Published by: (Rossiiskaya Akademya Nauk), M A I K Nauka - Interperiodica, Profsoyuznaya ul 90, Moscow, 117997, Russian Federation. TEL 7-095-3347420, FAX 7-095-3360666, compmg@maik.ru, http://www.maik.ru/journals/geomag.htm. Ed. Oleg M Raspopov. R&P Vladimir I Vasil'ev. **Subscr. in US to:** Interperiodica, PO Box 1831, Birmingham, AL 35201-1831. TEL 205-995-1567, 800-633-4931, FAX 205-995-1588.

538 RUS ISSN 0016-7940
CODEN: GEAEA6
➤ **GEOMAGNETIZM I AERONOMIYA.** Text in Russian. 1961. bi-m. RUR 1,050 for 6 mos. domestic (effective 2004). bk.rev. charts; illus. index. **Document type:** *Journal, Academic/Scholarly.* **Description:** Covers fields of interplanetary space, geoeffective solar events, the magnetosphere, the ionosphere, the upper and middle atmosphere, the action of solar variability and activity on atmospheric parameters and climate.
Related titles: Online - full text ed.; ♦ English Translation: Geomagnetism and Aeronomy. ISSN 0016-7932.
Indexed: ASCA, CIN, ChemAb, ChemTitl, CurCont, GEOBASE, IAA, ISR, Inspec, PhysBer, RefZh, SCI.
—AskIEEE, CASDDS, CISTI, East View, IDS, KNAW, Linda Hall. **CCC.**
Published by: (Rossiiskaya Akademiya Nauk/Russian Academy of Sciences), Izdatel'stvo Nauka, Profsoyuznaya ul 90, Moscow, 117864, Russian Federation. TEL 7-095-3347151, FAX 7-095-4202220, secret@naukaran.ru, http://www.maik.rssi.ru/cgi-bin/list.pl?page=geoaer, http://www.naukaran.ru.

551 FIN ISSN 0367-4231
QC801 CODEN: GEPHAM
➤ **GEOPHYSICA.** Text in English. 1935. biennial. USD 25 per issue (effective 2005). **Document type:** *Journal, Academic/Scholarly.*
Indexed: ESPM, GEOBASE, M&GPA, RefZh.
—Linda Hall.
Published by: Geofysiikan Seura/Geophysical Society of Finland, c/o Pertti Seuna, Finnish Environmental Institute, Mechelinimkatu 34, PO Box 140, Helsinki, 00251, Finland. http://pro.tsv.fi/geofysiikanseura/geophy.htm. Ed. Matti Lepparanda. **Dist. by:** Tiedekirja OY - Vetenskapsbokhandeln.

551 GBR ISSN 0309-1929
QC809.F5 CODEN: GAFDD3
➤ **GEOPHYSICAL AND ASTROPHYSICAL FLUID DYNAMICS.** Text in English. 1970. bi-m. GBP 1,793, USD 2,681 combined subscription to institutions print & online eds. (effective 2006). adv. bk.rev. charts; illus. cum.index. reprint service avail. from PSC. **Document type:** *Journal, Academic/Scholarly.* **Description:** Publishes original research papers and short communications, occasional survey articles and conference reports on the fluid mechanics of the earth and planets, including oceans, atmospheres and interiors, and the fluid mechanics of the sun, stars and other astrophysical objects.
Formerly (until 1976): Geophysical Fluid Dynamics (0016-7991)
Related titles: CD-ROM ed.: ISSN 1026-7506; Microform ed.; Online - full text ed.: ISSN 1029-0419. 1996. GBP 1,703, USD 2,547 to institutions (effective 2006) (from EBSCO Publishing, Gale Group, IngentaConnect, O C L C Online Computer Library Center, Inc., Swets Information Services).
Indexed: A&AAb, AESIS, ASCA, ASFA, ApMecR, BrCerAb, C&ISA, CCMJ, CerAb, CivEngAb, CorrAb, CurCont, E&CAJ, EMA, ESPM, Englnd, FLUIDEX, GEOBASE, IAA, ISMEC, ISR, Inspec, M&GPA, M&TEA, MBF, METADEX, MathR, MathSciNet, OceAb, PhysBer, SCI, SolStAb, WAA.
—BLDSC (4148.600000), AskIEEE, CISTI, IE, Infotrieve, ingenta, Linda Hall. **CCC.**
Published by: Taylor & Francis Ltd (Subsidiary of: Taylor & Francis Group), 4 Park Sq, Milton Park, Abingdon, OX14 4RN, United Kingdom. TEL 44-1235-828600, FAX 44-1235-829000, info@tandf.co.uk, http://www.tandf.co.uk/journals/titles/03091929.asp. Ed. Andrew M Soward. **Subscr. in N. America to:** Taylor & Francis Inc., Customer Services Dept, 325 Chestnut St, 8th Fl, Philadelphia, PA 19106. TEL 215-625-8900, 800-354-1420, FAX 215-625-8914, customerservice@taylorandfrancis.com; **Subscr. to:** Journals Customer Service, Rankine Rd, Basingstoke, Hants RG24 8PR, United Kingdom. TEL 44-1256-813000, FAX 44-1256-330245, enquiry@tandf.co.uk.

551 USA
GEOPHYSICAL DIRECTORY. Text in English. 1946. a. USD 75 domestic; USD 90 foreign (effective 2000). adv. **Document type:** *Directory.* **Description:** Lists oil companies and key personnel that use geophysical techniques as well as supply and service companies in the petroleum and mineral exploration industry worldwide.
Related titles: Diskette ed.
Published by: Geophysical Directory, Inc., 2200 Welch Ave, Box 130508, Houston, TX 77219. TEL 713-529-8789, FAX 713-529-3646. Ed. Claudia La Calli. Pub. Sidney Schafer. R&P Stuart Schafer. Adv. contact Claudia LaCalli. Circ: 5,000.

551 GBR ISSN 0956-540X
QC801 CODEN: GJINEA
➤ **GEOPHYSICAL JOURNAL INTERNATIONAL.** Text in English. 1958. m. EUR 291 combined subscription in Europe to individuals print & online eds.; USD 360 combined subscription in the Americas to individuals & Caribbean (print & online eds.); GBP 214 combined subscription elsewhere to individuals print & online eds.; GBP 1,099 combined subscription in Europe to institutions print & online eds.; USD 2,033 combined subscription in the Americas to institutions & Caribbean (print & online eds.); GBP 1,210 combined subscription elsewhere to institutions print & online eds. (effective 2006). adv. abstr.; bibl.; charts; illus. index. back issues avail.; reprint service avail. from PSC. **Document type:** *Journal, Academic/Scholarly.*
Formerly (until 1989): Geophysical Journal (0952-4592); Which was formed by the 1987 merger of part of: Annales Geophysicae. Series B: Terrestrial and Planetary Physics (0980-8760); Royal Astronomical Society Geophysical Journal (0016-8009); Which was formerly (until 1958): Royal Astronomical Society. Monthly Notices. Geophysical Supplement
Related titles: Microform ed.: (from PQC); Online - full text ed.: ISSN 1365-246X. GBP 1,044 in Europe to institutions; USD 1,932 in the Americas to institutions & Caribbean; GBP 1,150 elsewhere to institutions (effective 2006) (from Blackwell Synergy, EBSCO Publishing, Gale Group, IngentaConnect, O C L C Online Computer Library Center, Inc., Swets Information Services).
Indexed: AESIS, ASCA, ASFA, BrCerAb, BrGeoL, C&ISA, CMCI, CerAb, ChemAb, CivEngAb, CorrAb, CurCont, E&CAJ, E&PHSE, EMA, FLUIDEX, GEOBASE, GP&P, IAA, ISR, Inspec, M&GPA, M&TEA, MBF, METADEX, MathSciNet, OffTech, PetrolAb, RefZh, SCI, WAA.
—BLDSC (4150.800000), AskIEEE, CASDDS, CISTI, Ei, IDS, IE, Infotrieve, ingenta, Linda Hall, PADDS. **CCC.**
Published by: (Royal Astronomical Society), Blackwell Publishing Ltd., 9600 Garsington Rd, Oxford, OX4 2ZG, United Kingdom. TEL 44-1865-776868, FAX 44-1865-714591, customerservices@oxon.blackwellpublishing.com, http://www.blackwellpublishing.com/journals/GJI. Pub. Sue Hewitt. R&P Sophie Savage. Adv. contact Jenny Applin. Circ: 1,585. **Co-sponsor:** Deutsche Geophysikalische Gesellschaft, European Geophysical Society.

551 JPN ISSN 0016-8017
QC801 CODEN: GEOMAW
GEOPHYSICAL MAGAZINE✶ /KISHOCHO OBUN IHO. Text in English. 1926. a. JPY 2,100.
Indexed: ASFA, ApMecR, ChemAb, Inspec, JTA, M&GPA.
—AskIEEE, CISTI, Linda Hall.
Published by: Japan Meteorological Agency/Kishocho, Otemachi 1-3-4, Chiyoda-ku, Tokyo, 100-8122, Japan. http://www.jma.go.jp/JMA_HP/jma/index.html. Circ: 849.

551 USA
CODEN: GPMGAD
➤ **GEOPHYSICAL MONOGRAPHS BOOK SERIES.** Text in English. 1956. irreg., latest vol.125. price varies. reprint service avail. from ISI. **Document type:** *Monographic series, Academic/Scholarly.*
Former titles (until 199?): American Geophysical Union. Geophysical Monographs; American Geophysical Union. Geophysical Monograph (0065-8448)
Indexed: AESIS, IMMAb, Inspec, M&GPA.
—BLDSC (4154.500000), CASDDS, CISTI, IE, ingenta. **CCC.**
Published by: American Geophysical Union, 2000 Florida Ave, NW, Washington, DC 20009-1277. TEL 202-462-6900, 800-966-2481, FAX 202-328-0566, http://www.agu.org.

622.15 GBR ISSN 0016-8025
TN269 CODEN: GPPRAR
➤ **GEOPHYSICAL PROSPECTING.** Text in English, French, German; Summaries in English. 1953. bi-m. GBP 585 combined subscription in Europe to institutions print & online eds.; USD 1,080 combined subscription in the Americas to institutions & Caribbean (print & online eds.); GBP 643 combined subscription elsewhere to institutions print & online eds. (effective 2006). adv. bk.rev. abstr.; bibl.; charts; illus. index, cum.index. back issues avail.; reprint service avail. from PSC. **Document type:** *Journal, Academic/Scholarly.*
Related titles: Microform ed.: (from PQC); Online - full text ed.: Geophysical Prospecting Online. ISSN 1365-2478. 1998. GBP 556 in Europe to institutions; USD 1,026 in the Americas to institutions & Caribbean; GBP 611 elsewhere to institutions (effective 2006) (from Blackwell Synergy, EBSCO Publishing, Gale Group, IngentaConnect, O C L C Online Computer Library Center, Inc., Swets Information Services).
Indexed: AESIS, ASCA, ASFA, BrGeoL, C&ISA, ChemAb, CurCont, E&CAJ, E&PHSE, Englnd, F&EA, FLUIDEX, GEOBASE, GP&P, GeotechAb, IMMAb, ISMEC, ISR, Inspec, OffTech, PetrolAb, RefZh, SCI, SolStAb.
—BLDSC (4156.000000), AskIEEE, CISTI, Ei, IDS, IE, Infotrieve, ingenta, Linda Hall, PADDS. **CCC.**
Published by: (European Association of Geoscientists and Engineers), Blackwell Publishing Ltd., 9600 Garsington Rd, Oxford, OX4 2ZG, United Kingdom. TEL 44-1865-776868, FAX 44-1865-714591, customerservices@oxon.blackwellpublishing.com, http://www.blackwellpublishing.com/journal.asp?ref=0016-8025&site=1. Ed. R E White. Circ: 4,750.

551 USA ISSN 0094-8276
QE500 CODEN: GPRLAJ
➤ **GEOPHYSICAL RESEARCH LETTERS.** Text in English. 1974. s-m. USD 1,750 to institutions (effective 2006). bibl.; illus. index. reprint service avail. from ISI. **Document type:** *Journal, Academic/Scholarly.* **Description:** Provides a forum for the rapid dissemination of current research of broad geophysical interest.
Related titles: Microfiche ed.: (from AGU, AIP); Microform ed.: (from AGU); Online - full content ed.; Online - full text ed.: (from EBSCO Publishing).

E

Indexed: AESIS, ASCA, ASFA, AbHyg, CCI, CIN, CIS, CPA, ChemAb, ChemTitl, CivEngAb, CurCont, E&PHSE, EEA, EMA, ESPM, EngInd, ExcerpMed, FCA, FLUIDEX, ForAb, GEOBASE, GP&P, HerbAb, I&DA, IAA, INIS AtomInd, ISR, Inspec, M&GPA, M&TEA, MBF, MSB, MinerAb, OceAb, OffTech, PetrolAb, PhysBer, PollutAb, RefZh, S&F, SCI, SPINweb, SWRA, VITIS, WAA, WAE&RSA.
—BLDSC (4156.900000), AskIEEE, CASDDS, CISTI, Ei, IDS, IE, Infotrieve, ingenta, Linda Hall, PADDS. **CCC.**
Published by: American Geophysical Union, 2000 Florida Ave, NW, Washington, DC 20009-1277. TEL 202-462-6900, 800-966-2481, FAX 202-328-0566, institutions@agu.org, http://www.agu.org/journals/gl/. Ed. Judy C Holoviak.

551 HUN ISSN 0016-7177
QC801.M3 CODEN: GEKOAI
➤ **GEOPHYSICAL TRANSACTIONS/GEOFIZICHESKII BYULLETEN'/GEOFIZIKAI KOZLEMENYEK.** Text in English; Abstracts in Hungarian. 1952. q. USD 90 foreign (effective 2001). charts; illus.; maps. back issues avail. **Document type:** *Journal, Academic/Scholarly.* **Description:** Contains methodological and instrumental research and occasional studies on regional problems of central Europe.
Indexed: AESIS, ApMecR, ChemAb, GEOBASE, Inspec, PetrolAb.
—BLDSC (4157.700500), AskIEEE, CASDDS, CISTI, IE, Linda Hall.
Published by: Eotvos Lorand Geophysical Institute of Hungary, Columbus utca 17-23, Budapest, 1145, Hungary. TEL 36-1-3632835, 36-1-2524999, FAX 36-1-3637256. Ed., R&P Zsuzsanna Hegybiro. Pub. Tamas Bodoky. Circ: 1,250.

551 USA ISSN 0016-8033
QE500 CODEN: GPYSA7
➤ **GEOPHYSICS.** Text in English. 1936. bi-m. USD 435 domestic; USD 470 in Canada, Mexico, Central and South America and Caribbean; USD 495 in Europe, Asia, Middle East, Africa and Oceania (effective 2005). adv. bk.rev. abstr.; illus.; pat. index. 2 cols./p.; reprint service avail. from PQC. **Document type:** *Journal, Academic/Scholarly.*
Related titles: Microform ed.: (from PQC); Online - full text ed.: USD 395 worldwide (effective 2005) (from EBSCO Publishing).
Indexed: AESIS, AS&TI, ASCA, ASFA, ApMecR, BiolAb, C&ISA, CMCI, ChemAb, CivEngAb, CurCont, E&CAJ, E&PHSE, EIA, ESPM, EnerInd, EngInd, FLUIDEX, GEOBASE, GP&P, GeotechAb, IMMAb, INIS AtomInd, ISMEC, ISR, Inspec, OffTech, PetrolAb, PhysBer, PollutAb, RefZh, SCI, SWRA, SolStAb, WRCInf.
—BLDSC (4158.000000), AskIEEE, CASDDS, CISTI, Ei, IDS, IE, Infotrieve, ingenta, Linda Hall, PADDS. **CCC.**
Published by: Society of Exploration Geophysicists, PO Box 702740, Tulsa, OK 74170-2740. TEL 918-497-5500, FAX 918-497-5557, books@seg.org, http://scitation.aip.org/geophysics, http://www.seg.org. Ed. Gerard Herman. adv.: B&W page USD 2,000, color page USD 2,900. Circ: 3,000 (paid). **Subscr. to:** American Institute of Physics, PO Box 503284, St Louis, MO 63150-3284. TEL 800-344-6902, subs@aip.org, http://librarians.aip.org.

➤ **GEOPHYSICS AND ASTROPHYSICS MONOGRAPHS**; a series of graduate-level textbooks and monographs on plasma astrophysics and geophysics, including magnetospheric, solar, and stellar physics. see *ASTRONOMY*

➤ **GEORESURSY.** see *EARTH SCIENCES—Geology*

551 372.357 GEO ISSN 1512-1127
➤ **GEORGIAN GEOPHYSICAL SOCIETY. JOURNAL.** (In 2 parts: A: Physics of Solid Earth; B: Physics of Atmosphere, Ocean and Cosmic Rays) Text in English. s-a. looseleaf. GEL 10 domestic; USD 50 foreign (effective 2004). adv. bk.rev. abstr.; bibl.; illus.; maps. back issues avail. **Document type:** *Journal, Academic/Scholarly.* **Description:** Covers all branches of geophysics. Includes research papers, reviews, short communications, discussions, announcements.
Indexed: RefZh.
Published by: Georgian Geophysical Society, I Alexidze St, Tbilisi, 0193, Georgia. TEL 995-32-335703, FAX 995-32-332867, z.javakh@ig.acnet.ge. Eds. A Kordzadze, K Kartvelishvili. Pub. Z Javakhishvili. Circ: 200.

551 GBR ISSN 0278-7091
GEOSCIENCE TEXTS. Text in English. 1980. irreg., latest 2002, Sept. price varies. **Document type:** *Monographic series.*
Indexed: Inspec.
Published by: Blackwell Publishing Ltd., 9600 Garsington Rd, Oxford, OX4 2ZG, United Kingdom. TEL 44-1865-776868, FAX 44-1865-714591, customerservices@oxon.blackwellpublishing.com, http://www.blackwellpublishing.com.

551.8 DEU
GEOTECTONIC RESEARCH. Text in English, German; Summaries in English, French, German, Italian, Spanish. 1937. irreg. EUR 98.30 per issue domestic; EUR 100 per issue foreign (effective 2005). charts; illus. **Document type:** *Journal, Academic/Scholarly.*
Formerly (until 2003): Geotektonische Forschungen (0016-8548)
Indexed: ChemAb.
—Linda Hall. **CCC.**
Published by: E. Schweizerbart'sche Verlagsbuchhandlung, Johannesstr 3A, Stuttgart, 70176, Germany. TEL 49-711-3514560, FAX 49-711-35145699, mail@schweizerbart.de, http://www.schweizerbart.de/j/geotectonic-research. Ed. K Weber.

551.8 RUS ISSN 0016-8521
QE500 CODEN: GEOTBK
GEOTECTONICS. Text in English. 1965. bi-m. USD 824 in North America; USD 893 elsewhere (effective 2004). bibl.; charts; maps; illus. index. reprint service avail. from ISI. **Document type:** *Journal, Academic/Scholarly.* **Description:** Publishes articles on general and regional techtonics, structural geology, geodynamics, and experimental tectonics, considers the relation of tectonics to the deep structure of the earth, magmatism, metamorphism, and mineral resources.
Related titles: ♦ Translation of: Geotektonika. ISSN 0016-853X.
Indexed: AESIS, AJEE, ASFA, CurCont, EEA, ESPM, ISR, Inspec, OceAb, PetrolAb, PhysBer, PollutAb, SCI, SWRA.
—BLDSC (0411.950000), AskIEEE, CISTI, IE, Infotrieve, ingenta, Linda Hall, PADDS. **CCC.**
Published by: (Rossiiskaya Akademiya Nauk/Russian Academy of Sciences), M A I K Nauka - Interperiodica, Profsoyuznaya ul 90, Moscow, 117997, Russian Federation. TEL 7-095-3347420, FAX 7-095-3360666, compmg@maik.ru, http://www.maik.rssi.ru/journals/geoteng.htm, http://www.maik.ru. Ed. Yurii M Pushcharovskii. R&P Vladimir I Vasil'ev. Circ: 245. **Dist. by:** Interperiodica, PO Box 1831, Birmingham, AL 35201-1831. TEL 205-995-1567, 800-633-4931, FAX 205-995-1588.

551 USA ISSN 0149-8991
CODEN: RGRCDJ
GEOTHERMAL RESOURCES COUNCIL. SPECIAL REPORT. Text in English. 1972 (no.2). irreg., latest vol.19, 1999. price varies. **Document type:** *Monographic series.*
—CISTI, Linda Hall.
Published by: Geothermal Resources Council, PO Box 1350, Davis, CA 95617-1350. TEL 530-758-2360, FAX 530-758-2839, grc@geothermal.org, http://www.geothermal.org/pubs.html.

551 USA ISSN 0193-5933
GB1199.5 CODEN: TGRCD7
GEOTHERMAL RESOURCES COUNCIL. TRANSACTIONS. Text in English. 1977. a. USD 65 (effective 2004). **Document type:** *Proceedings, Academic/Scholarly.* **Description:** Provides educational awareness of existing technology and how we benefit from it. Updates members of the geothermal field.
Indexed: CIN, ChemAb, ChemTitl, CivEngAb, EngInd.
—BLDSC (8933.220000), CASDDS, CISTI, Ei, IE, ingenta, Linda Hall.
Published by: Geothermal Resources Council, PO Box 1350, Davis, CA 95617-1350. TEL 530-758-2360, FAX 530-758-2839, tclutter@geothermal.org, http://www.geothermal.org. Ed. Ted Clutter.

GEOTITLES; geoscience bibliography. see *EARTH SCIENCES—Abstracting, Bibliographies, Statistics*

GLOBAL BIOGEOCHEMICAL CYCLES; an international journal of global change. see *SCIENCES: COMPREHENSIVE WORKS*

551.2 USA
GRAVITY (YEAR) (BOULDER). Text in English. a. USD 245; USD 185 to non-profit organizations. **Document type:** *Government.* **Description:** Includes station data, gravity networks, regional surveys, gravity-anomaly grids, and satellite measurements.
Media: CD-ROM.
Published by: (National Oceanic and Atmospheric Administration), U.S. National Geophysical Data Center, 325 Broadway, E CG4, Boulder, CO 80303-3328. TEL 303-497-6836, FAX 303-497-6513, info@.ngdc.noaa.gov, info@ngdc.noaa.gov, http://www.ngdc.noaa.gov.

538.7 GBR ISSN 0073-9316
GREAT BRITAIN. NATURAL ENVIRONMENT RESEARCH COUNCIL. BRITISH GEOLOGICAL SURVEY. GEOMAGNETIC BULLETIN. Key Title: Geomagnetic Bulletin. Text in English. 1969. irreg. price varies. **Document type:** *Bulletin, Government.*
Formerly (until Jan. 1984): Great Britain. Institute of Geological Sciences. Geomagnetic Bulletin
—BLDSC (4147.070000).
Published by: Natural Environment Research Council, British Geological Survey, British Geological Survey, Kingsley Dunham Centre, Nicker Hill, Keyworth, Nottingham, NG12 5GG, United Kingdom. TEL 44-115-936-3100, FAX 44-115-936-3200, TELEX 9378173 BGSEKY G, sales@bgs.ac.uk, Enquiries@bgs.ac.uk, http://www.nkw.ac.uk/bgs/., http://www.bgs.ac.uk/. Circ: 600. **Subscr. to:** The Stationery Office, c/o Liason Officer, Atlantic House, Holborn Viaduct, London EC1P 1BW, United Kingdom.

551.2 CHN ISSN 0253-4975
QE531
GUOJI DIZHEN DONGTAI/RECENT DEVELOPMENTS OF WORLD SEISMOLOGY. Text in Chinese. 1971. m. CNY 4.50 newsstand/cover domestic (effective 2000).
Related titles: Online - full content ed.: (from WanFang Data Corp.); Online - full text ed.: (from East View Information Services).
Indexed: EEA, RPP.
—Linda Hall.
Published by: Zhongguo Dizhenju, Diqiu Wuli Yanjiusuo, Haidian-qu, Minzu Daxue Nan-Lu 5-Hao, Beijing, 100081, China. Ed. Chuan-zhen Zhu.

551 GBR ISSN 0950-1401
HANDBOOK OF GEOPHYSICAL EXPLORATION. Text in English. 1983. irreg., latest vol.21, 1988. price varies. index. back issues avail. **Document type:** *Academic/Scholarly.* **Description:** Encyclopedia of current information for geophysicists, geologists, seismologists and engineers.
Indexed: Inspec.
—BLDSC (4250.475000), IE.
Published by: Elsevier Ltd., Books Division (Subsidiary of: Elsevier Science & Technology), Kidlington, PO Box 800, Oxford, OX2 1DX, United Kingdom. TEL 44-1865-843000, FAX 44-1865-843410. Eds. K Helbig, S Treitel. Circ: 2,000. **Subscr. to:** Elsevier BV, PO Box 211, Amsterdam 1000 AE, Netherlands. TEL 31-20-485-3757, FAX 31-20-485-3432, nlinfo-f@elsevier.nl, http://www.elsevier.nl.

551 USA ISSN 8755-1217
QC804
HISTORY OF GEOPHYSICS SERIES. Text in English. 1984. irreg., latest vol.7, 1997. back issues avail. **Document type:** *Monographic series, Academic/Scholarly.* **Description:** Includes original papers on the history of an area of research or assignment event or organization of interest to researchers and students in the geophysical sciences and to historians of science.
—CCC.
Published by: American Geophysical Union, 2000 Florida Ave, NW, Washington, DC 20009-1277. TEL 202-462-6900, 800-966-2481, FAX 202-328-0566, http://www.agu.org.

551 JPN ISSN 0439-3503
QC801
HOKKAIDO DAIGAKU CHIKYU BUTSURIGAKU KENKYU HOKOKU/HOKKAIDO UNIVERSITY. GEOPHYSICAL BULLETIN. Text in Japanese; Summaries in English. 1951. s-a.
Indexed: ASFA, ESPM, JPI, RefZh.
—Linda Hall.
Published by: (Chikyu Butsurigaku Kyoshitsu), Hokkaido Daigaku, Rigakubu Sugaku Kyoshitsu/Hokkaido University, Faculty of Science, Department of Mathematics, Nishi-8-chome, Kita-10-jo, Kita-ku, Sapporo, 060-0810, Japan.

551.22 JPN
HOKKAIDO JISHIN KAZAN GEPPO/SEISMOLOGICAL AND VOLCANOLOGICAL MONTHLY REPORT IN HOKKAIDO. Text in Japanese. 1984. m.
Published by: Kishocho, Sapporo Kanku Kishodai/Japan Meteorological Agency, Sapporo District Meteorological Observatory, 2, Nishi 18-chome, Kita 2-jo, Chuo-ku, Sapporo-shi, Hokkaido 060, Japan.

551.2 JPN
HOKKAIDO JISHIN KAZAN NENPO/SEISMOLOGICAL AND VOLCANOLOGICAL ANNUAL REPORT IN HOKKAIDO. Text in Japanese. a.
Published by: Kishocho, Sapporo Kanku Kishodai/Japan Meteorological Agency, Sapporo District Meteorological Observatory, 2, Nishi 18-chome, Kita 2-jo, Chuo-ku, Sapporo-shi, Hokkaido 060, Japan.

551 JPN ISSN 0441-067X
➤ **HOKKAIDO UNIVERSITY. FACULTY OF SCIENCE. JOURNAL. SERIES 7: GEOPHYSICS.** Text in English. 1957. a. per issue exchange basis. back issues avail. **Document type:** *Academic/Scholarly.*
Indexed: FLUIDEX, GEOBASE, M&GPA, RefZh.
—BLDSC (4749.010000), CISTI, Linda Hall.
Published by: Hokkaido University, Faculty of Science/Hokkaido Daigaku Rigakubu, Nishi-8-chome, Kita-10-jo, Kita-ku, Sapporo, 060-0810, Japan. FAX 81-11-746-0394. Ed. Yasunori Nishida. Circ: 400.

551 CHN ISSN 1003-1375
HUABEI DIZHEN KEXUE/NORTH CHINA EARTHQUAKE SCIENCES. Text in Chinese. 1983. q. CNY 5 newsstand/cover domestic (effective 2000). adv. bk.rev. **Document type:** *Academic/Scholarly.*
Related titles: Online - full content ed.: (from WanFang Data Corp.); Online - full text ed.: (from East View Information Services).
Published by: Hebei Dizhen-ju/Hebei Seismology Bureau, 262 Huaizhong Lu, Shijiazhuang, Hebei 050021, China. TEL 86-311-60159566. Ed. Lan-ge Luo.

551.22 CHN ISSN 1001-8662
HUANAN DIZHEN/SOUTH CHINA SEISMOLOGICAL JOURNAL. Text in Chinese. 1981. q. CNY 6 newsstand/cover domestic (effective 2000). **Document type:** *Academic/Scholarly.*
Related titles: Online - full content ed.: (from WanFang Data Corp.); Online - full text ed.: (from East View Information Services).

E

Published by: Guangzhou-sheng Dizhen Ju, Xianliezhong Lu 81 Hao, Dayuan 1 Hao, Guangzhou, 510070, China. Ed. Ke-sen Zhou.

HVAR OBSERVATORY BULLETIN. see *ASTRONOMY*

HYDROLOGY AND EARTH SYSTEM SCIENCES. see *EARTH SCIENCES—Hydrology*

▼ **HYDROLOGY AND EARTH SYSTEM SCIENCES DISCUSSIONS.** see *EARTH SCIENCES—Hydrology*

538.7 SWE ISSN 0534-6967
CODEN: IAGABJ
I A G A BULLETIN. Text in English. irreg. bk.rev. **Document type:** *Bulletin, Academic/Scholarly.*
—BLDSC (4359.515000), Linda Hall.
Published by: International Association of Geomagnetism and Aeronomy/Association Internationale de Geomagnetisme et d'Aeronomie, c/o Bengt Hultqvist, The Swedish Institute of Space Physics, Box 812, 325 Broadway, Kiruna, S-98128, Sweden. hultqv@irf.se, http://www.iugg.org/IAGA/. Circ: (controlled).

538.7 SWE ISSN 0536-1095
I A G A NEWS. Text in English. 1963. a. free to members. bk.rev. **Document type:** *Newsletter, Academic/Scholarly.*
Description: Informs members of association news, along with forthcoming events and publications.
Published by: International Association of Geomagnetism and Aeronomy/Association Internationale de Geomagnetisme et d'Aeronomie, c/o Bengt Hultqvist, The Swedish Institute of Space Physics, Box 812, 325 Broadway, Kiruna, S-98128, Sweden. jjoselyn@sec.noaa.gov, hultqv@irf.se, http://www.ngdc.noaa.gov/IAGA, http://www.iugg.org/IAGA/. Circ: 2,400 (controlled).

551 526 USA
QC801
I U G G YEAR BOOK/ANNUAIRE U G G I. Text in English, French. 1957. a. USD 30 (effective 2000). **Document type:** *Directory, Academic/Scholarly.*
Formerly: I U G G Chronicle (0047-1259)
Indexed: ASFA, ESPM.
—Linda Hall.
Published by: International Union of Geodesy and Geophysics, c/o CIRES, CB 216, University of Colorado, Boulder, CO 80309-0216. TEL 303-497-5147, FAX 303-497-3645, jjoselyn@cires.colorado.edu, http://www.iugg.org. Ed. JoAnn Joselyn. Circ: 1,200.

551.22 NOR ISSN 1013-5189
I U G S. UNESCO. I C G P. PROJECT 133. BULLETIN DE LIAISON ET INFORMATION. (International Union of Geological Sciences. United Nations Educational, Scientific and Cultural Orga) Text in French. 1976. irreg.
Indexed: PAIS.
Published by: International Union of Geological Sciences, IUGS Secretariat, Geological Survey of Norway, Trondheim, 7491, Norway. TEL 47-73-904040, FAX 47-73-502230.

551 SWE ISSN 0281-7578
INFORMATION. Text in English, Swedish. 1982. irreg. price varies. back issues avail. **Document type:** *Monographic series, Academic/Scholarly.*
Published by: Statens Geotekniska Institut/Swedish Geotechnical Institute, Olaus Magnus Vaeg 35, Linkoeping, 58193, Sweden. TEL 46-13-201800, sgi@swedgeo.se, http://www.swedgeo.se.

INGEGNERIA SISMICA. see *ENGINEERING*

551.44 ROM ISSN 0301-9187
QH89 CODEN: TISPBT
INSTITUT DE SPEOLOGIE EMIL RACOVITZA. TRAVAUX. Text in English, French, German. 1962. a. bk.rev.
Indexed: BiolAb, RefZh, ZooRec.
—KNAW, Linda Hall.
Published by: (Institutul de Speologie "Emil Racovita"), Editura Academiei Romane/Publishing House of the Romanian Academy, Calea 13 Septembrie 13, Sector 5, Bucharest, 76117, Romania. Circ: 450. **Dist. by:** Rodipet S.A., Piata Presei Libere 1, sector 1, PO Box 33-57, Bucharest 3, Romania. TEL 40-21-2224126, 40-21-2226407, rodipet@rodipet.ro.

551 BEL ISSN 0020-2525
INSTITUT ROYAL METEOROLOGIQUE DE BELGIQUE. BULLETIN MENSUEL: OBSERVATIONS GEOPHYSIQUES/ KONINKLIJK METEOROLOGISCH INSTITUUT VAN BELGIE. MAANDBULLETIN. GEOFYSICHE WAARNEMINGEN. Key Title: Bulletin Mensuel: Observations Geophysiques - Maandbulletin: Geofysische Waarnemingen. Text in Dutch, French. 1961. m. charts; stat. **Document type:** *Bulletin, Trade.* **Description:** Discusses observations in the field of geophysics.
Related titles: Magnetic Tape ed.
Published by: Institut Royal Meteorologique de Belgique/Koninklijk Meteorologisch Instituut van Belgie, Av Circulaire 3, Brussels, 1180, Belgium. TEL 32-2-373-0502, FAX 32-2-375-1259, http://www.meteo.oma.be. Ed. H Malcorps. Circ: 220.

INSTITUTE FOR PETROLEUM RESEARCH AND GEOPHYSICS, HOLON, ISRAEL. REPORT. see *PETROLEUM AND GAS*

551 DEU ISSN 0939-9585
INTERNATIONAL ASSOCIATION OF GEODESY SYMPOSIA. Text in German. 19??. irreg., latest vol.126, 2004. price varies. **Document type:** *Monographic series, Academic/Scholarly.*
—BLDSC (4536.227000).
Published by: (International Association of Geodesy), Springer-Verlag (Subsidiary of: Springer Science+Business Media), Haber Str 7, Heidelberg, 69126, Germany. TEL 49-6221-3450, FAX 49-6221-229, subscriptions@springer.de, http://www.springer.de. Ed. Wolfgang Torge. **Subscr. in N. America to:** Springer-Verlag New York, Inc., Journal Fulfillment, PO Box 2485, Secaucus, NJ 07096-2485. TEL 212-460-1500, FAX 212-473-6272.

551 USA ISSN 0074-6142
CODEN: IGPSAN
INTERNATIONAL GEOPHYSICS SERIES. Text in English. 1959. irreg., latest vol.47, 1991. reprint service avail. from ISI. **Document type:** *Monographic series, Academic/Scholarly.*
Indexed: Inspec.
—BLDSC (4540.610000), CISTI, IE, ingenta. **CCC.**
Published by: Academic Press (Subsidiary of: Elsevier Science & Technology), 525 B St, Ste 1900, San Diego, CA 92101-4495. apsubs@acad.com, http://www.academicpress.com. Ed. William L Donn.

531.14 FRA
INTERNATIONAL GRAVIMETRIQUE BUREAU. BULLETIN D'INFORMATION. Text in English, French. 1960. s-a. adv. **Document type:** *Bulletin.* **Description:** Presents technical results achieved by individuals, as well as internal matters and the status of the Bureau's database.
Indexed: RefZh.
Published by: Bureau Gravimetric International, 18 av. Edouard Belin, Toulouse, Cedex 4 31401, France. TEL 33-5-61332980, FAX 33-5-61253098. Pub. J.P. Barriot. Circ: 350 (controlled).

551.22 624.151 JPN ISSN 0074-655X
QE531
INTERNATIONAL INSTITUTE OF SEISMOLOGY AND EARTHQUAKE ENGINEERING. BULLETIN. Text in English. 1964. a. **Document type:** *Bulletin.* **Description:** Covers interdisciplinary study of seismology and earthquake engineering.
Indexed: AJEE, EEA, GEOBASE, RefZh.
—BLDSC (2588.100000), CISTI, Linda Hall.
Published by: International Institute of Seismology and Earthquake Engineering, Building Research Institute-Ministry of Construction, 1 Tatehara, Oho-machi, Tsukuba-gun, Ibaraki 305, Japan. TEL 81-298-79-0680, FAX 81-298-64-6777, iisee@kenken.go.jp. Ed., R&P Mitsumasa Midorikawa. Circ: 820.

551.22 JPN
INTERNATIONAL INSTITUTE OF SEISMOLOGY AND EARTHQUAKE ENGINEERING. INDIVIDUAL STUDIES BY PARTICIPANTS AT I I S E E. Text in Japanese. 1965. a.
Formerly: International Institute of Seismology and Earthquake Engineering. Report of Individual Study by Participants to I S E E (0074-6606)
Indexed: AJEE, EEA, RefZh.
—BLDSC (4437.530000), CISTI, Linda Hall.
Published by: International Institute of Seismology and Earthquake Engineering, Building Research Institute-Ministry of Construction, 1 Tatehara, Oho-machi, Tsukuba-gun, Ibaraki 305, Japan. TEL 81-298-79-0680, FAX 81-298-64-6777, iisee@kenken.go.jp. R&P Mitsumasa Midorikawa. Circ: 560.

551.22 JPN ISSN 0074-6614
INTERNATIONAL INSTITUTE OF SEISMOLOGY AND EARTHQUAKE ENGINEERING. YEAR BOOK. Text in Japanese. 1964. biennial. **Document type:** *Directory.* **Description:** Provides the exchange of information between the Institute and developing countries.
Published by: International Institute of Seismology and Earthquake Engineering, Building Research Institute-Ministry of Construction, 1 Tatehara, Oho-machi, Tsukuba-gun, Ibaraki 305, Japan. TEL 81-298-79-0679, FAX 81-298-64-6777, iisee@kenken.go.jp. Ed., R&P Mitsumasa Midorikawa. Circ: (controlled).

538.7 551 USA ISSN 1524-4423
QC811 CODEN: IGAEFD
➤ **INTERNATIONAL JOURNAL OF GEOMAGNETISM AND AERONOMY.** Text in English. 1998. irreg., latest vol.2. USD 160 to institutions (effective 2005 - 2006). Website rev. bibl.; illus. back issues avail. **Document type:** *Journal, Academic/Scholarly.* **Description:** Provides a window on research in Russia and elsewhere in the fields of geomagnetism, terrestrial magnetism, aeronomy, solar terrestrial relationships and more.
Related titles: Online - full content ed.; Online - full text ed.: (from EBSCO Publishing).
Indexed: M&GPA.
—BLDSC (4542.266400), CISTI, IE, ingenta.
Published by: American Geophysical Union, 2000 Florida Ave, NW, Washington, DC 20009-1277. TEL 202-462-6900, 800-966-2481, FAX 202-328-0566, institutions@agu.org, http://www.agu.org/journals/ijga/.

551.22 GBR ISSN 0020-8671
QE532.I56 CODEN: ISCBBQ
INTERNATIONAL SEISMOLOGICAL CENTRE. BULLETIN. Text in English. 1964. bi-m. GBP 200 (effective 2001). back issues avail. **Document type:** *Bulletin.* **Description:** Covers seismology.
Related titles: CD-ROM ed.
Published by: International Seismological Centre, Pipers Ln, Thatcham, Newbury, Berks RG13 4NS, United Kingdom. TEL 44-1635-861022, FAX 44-1635-872351, admin@isc.ac.uk, http://www.isc.ac.uk.

551.22 GBR ISSN 0034-334X
QE532 CODEN: RCEABK
INTERNATIONAL SEISMOLOGICAL CENTRE. REGIONAL CATALOGUE OF EARTHQUAKES. Text in English. 1964. s-a. GBP 85 (effective 2001). back issues avail.
Related titles: CD-ROM ed.
—BLDSC (7336.573000), Linda Hall.
Published by: International Seismological Centre, Pipers Ln, Thatcham, Newbury, Berks RG13 4NS, United Kingdom. TEL 44-1635-861022, FAX 44-1635-872351, admin@isc.ac.uk, http://www.isc.ac.uk.

551 CAN
QC808.5
INTERNATIONAL SYMPOSIUM ON REMOTE SENSING OF THE ENVIRONMENT. PROCEEDINGS. Text in English. 1962. irreg.
Former titles (until 1996): International Symposium on Remote Sensing and Environmental Change. Proceedings (1068-9281); (until 1993): International Symposium on Remote Sensing of the Environment (0275-5505); (until 1969): Symposium on Remote Sensing of Environment. Proceedings (0586-3015)
—BLDSC (6846.840000).
Published by: Canadian Remote Sensing Society, 130 Slater St Ste 618, Ottawa, ON K1P 6E2, Canada. TEL 613-234-0191, FAX 613-234-9039, http://www.casi.ca/remote.htm.

551 910 USA ISSN 0074-9419
INTERNATIONAL UNION OF GEODESY AND GEOPHYSICS. PROCEEDINGS OF THE GENERAL ASSEMBLY. Text in English, French. 1921. quadrennial. price varies. **Document type:** *Proceedings.*
—Linda Hall.
Published by: International Union of Geodesy and Geophysics, c/o CIRES, CB 216, University of Colorado, Boulder, CO 80309-0216. TEL 202-462-6900. Circ: 3,500.

IZVESTIYA VYSSHIKH UCHEBNYKH ZAVEDENII. GEOLOGIYA I RAZVEDKA. see *EARTH SCIENCES—Geology*

551 USA ISSN 0148-0227
➤ **J G R: JOURNAL OF GEOPHYSICAL RESEARCH.** Text in English. 1896. 5/m. USD 5,680 to institutions (effective 2006). **Document type:** *Journal, Academic/Scholarly.* **Description:** Integrated Earth and space science journal in seven disciplines. Topics cover space physics, atmospheres, oceans, biogeosciences, solid earth, planets and earth surface.
Former titles (until 1949): Terrestrial Magnetism and Atmospheric Electricity (0096-8013); (until 1899): Terrestrial Magnetism (0272-7528)
Related titles: Online - full content ed.; Online - full text ed.: (from EBSCO Publishing).
Indexed: ASFA, BrCerAb, C&ISA, CerAb, CorrAb, CurCont, E&CAJ, EMA, ESPM, FCA, IAA, Inspec, M&GPA, M&TEA, MBF, METADEX, OceAb, PollutAb, SWRA, WAA.
—BLDSC (4995.000000), CISTI, IE, Infotrieve, ingenta, Linda Hall, PADDS. **CCC.**
Published by: American Geophysical Union, 2000 Florida Ave, NW, Washington, DC 20009-1277. TEL 202-462-6900, 800-966-2481, FAX 202-328-0566, institutions@agu.org, service@agu.org, http://www.agu.org. Eds. Janet Luhmann, Judy C Holoviak, Mary Anne Carroll, Roni Avissar.

551 JPN ISSN 1342-3800
JAPAN METEOROLOGICAL AGENCY. REPORT OF MAGNETIC PULSATIONS. Text in English. 1976. a.
—Linda Hall.
Published by: Japan Meteorological Agency, Kakioka Magnetic Observatory/Kishocho Chijiki Kansokujo, 595 Kakioka, Niihari-gun, Yasato-machi, Ibaraki-ken 315-0116, Japan. FAX 02994-3-1154.

511.22 JPN
JAPAN UNIVERSITY NETWORK EARTHQUAKE CATALOG/KOKURITSU DAIGAKU KANSOKUMO JISHIN KATAROGU. Text in English, Japanese. s-a. **Document type:** *Catalog.*
Published by: Tokyo Daigaku, Jishin Kenkyujo/University of Tokyo, Earthquake Research Institute, 1-1 Yayoi 1-chome, Bunkyo-ku, Tokyo, 113-0032, Japan.

551.22 JPN ISSN 0037-1114
QE531 CODEN: ZIZIA6
JISHIN/SEISMOLOGICAL SOCIETY OF JAPAN. JOURNAL. Text in English, Japanese; Summaries in English. 1948. q. USD 20. abstr. index.
Indexed: AESIS, AJEE, EEA, Inspec, JTA, RefZh.
—AskIEEE, Linda Hall.

E

Published by: Jishin Gakkai/Seismological Society of Japan, Daigaku Jishin Kenkyujo, 1-1 Yayoi 1-chome, Bunkyo-ku, Tokyo, 113-0032, Japan.

551.22 JPN ISSN 0289-2723
QE537.2.J3
JISHIN KANSOKU HOKOKU/MATSUSHIRO SEISMOLOGICAL OBSERVATORY. SEISMOLOGICAL BULLETIN. Text in English. 1973. s-a.
Indexed: RefZh.
Published by: Kishocho, Jishiu-kazahbu Jishin-tsunami-kanshika Seimitsu-jishin-kansokushitsu/Japan Meteorological Agency, Matsushiro Seismological Observatory, 3511, Nishijo, Matsushiro-cho, Nagano-shi, Nagano-ken 381-12, Japan.

551.22 JPN
JISHIN KOGAKU KENKYU HAPPYOKAI KOEN GAIYO/JAPAN SOCIETY OF CIVIL ENGINEERS. EARTHQUAKE ENGINEERING SYMPOSIUM. PROCEEDINGS. Text in Japanese. 1968. biennial. **Document type:** *Proceedings.*
Published by: (Taishin Kogaku linkai), Doboku Gakkai/Japan Society of Civil Engineers, Mu-banchi, Yotsuya 1-chome, Shinjuku-ku, Tokyo, 160-0004, Japan.

551.22 JPN
JISHIN KOGAKU SHINKOKAI NYUSU/JAPAN SOCIETY FOR EARTHQUAKE ENGINEERING PROMOTION NEWS. Text in Japanese. 1962. bi-m. JPY 2,000 per issue. adv. **Document type:** *Academic/Scholarly.*
Published by: Shinsai Yobo Kyokai/Association for Earthquake Disaster Prevention, Kenchiku Kaikan, 26-20 Shiba 5-chome, Minato-ku, Tokyo, 108-0014, Japan. Ed. K. Kawashima. Adv. contact T Hosobuchi.

551.22 JPN
JISHIN SAIGAI YOSOKU NO KENKYU/SEISMICITY AND SEISMIC HAZARD. Text in Japanese; Summaries in English. 1984. a.
Published by: Songai Hoken Ryoritsu Santeikai/Fire and Marine Insurance Rating Association of Japan, Tokyo Yamca Building; 9 Kanda Awajicho 2chome, Chiyoda-ku, Tokyo, 101, Japan. TEL 86-3-5259-0811.

551.22 JPN ISSN 0386-0086
JISHIN TO YOCHI✶ /EARTHQUAKE AND PREDICTION. Text in Japanese. 1974. m. JPY 200 per issue. **Document type:** *Academic/Scholarly.*
Published by: Nihon Jishin Yochi Kurabu/Japan Earthquake Prediction Club, c/o Nihon Jishin Sha, 13-13-202 Tabata 5-chome, Kita-ku, Tokyo, 114-0014, Japan.

551.2 JPN
JISUBERI KYUKEISHACHI NO CHOSA TO TAISAKU KOZA/INVESTIGATION OF LANDSLIDES AND THEIR CONTROL. Text in Japanese. s-a.
Published by: Zenkoku Jisuberi Gake Kuzure Taisaku Kyogikai/National Conference of Landslide and Slope Fall Control, Niigataken Dobokubu Saboka, 4-1 Shinko-cho, Niigata-shi, 950-0965, Japan.

JOKULL; journal of the glaciological and geological societies of Iceland. see *EARTH SCIENCES—Geology*

622.15 NLD ISSN 0926-9851
CODEN: JAGPEA
➤ **JOURNAL OF APPLIED GEOPHYSICS.** Text in English, French, German. 1963. 12/yr. EUR 1,022 in Europe to institutions; JPY 135,600 in Japan to institutions; USD 1,143 to institutions except Europe and Japan (effective 2006). adv. bk.rev. bibl.; charts; illus. index. back issues avail.; reprints avail. **Document type:** *Journal, Academic/Scholarly.* **Description:** Publishes papers on a wide variety of applied geophysical topics such as environmental, geotechnical engineering and hydrological geophysics, mining and petroleum geophysics and petrophysics.
Formerly (until 1992): Geoexploration (0016-7142)
Related titles: Microform ed.: (from PQC); Online - full text ed.: (from EBSCO Publishing, Gale Group, IngentaConnect, ScienceDirect, Swets Information Services).
Indexed: AESIS, ASCA, ASFA, BrGeoL, CIS, ChemAb, CivEngAb, CurCont, E&PHSE, ESPM, Englnd, ExcerpMed, FLUIDEX, GEOBASE, GP&P, GeotechAb, IMMAb, ISMEC, ISR, Inspec, OceAb, OffTech, PetrolAb, PollutAb, RefZh, SCI, SWRA.
—BLDSC (4942.614000), AskIEEE, CASDDS, CISTI, Ei, IDS, IE, Infotrieve, ingenta, Linda Hall, PADDS. **CCC.**
Published by: Elsevier BV (Subsidiary of: Elsevier Science & Technology), Radarweg 29, Amsterdam, 1043 NX, Netherlands. TEL 31-20-4853911, FAX 31-20-4852457, nlinfo-f@elsevier.nl, http://www.elsevier.com/locate/jappgeo, http://www.elsevier.nl. Eds. A. Hoerdt, J. W. Rector III.

➤ **JOURNAL OF ASTRONOMY AND ASTROPHYSICS.** see *ASTRONOMY*

551.5 523.01 GBR ISSN 1364-6826
QC801 CODEN: JASPF3
➤ **JOURNAL OF ATMOSPHERIC AND SOLAR - TERRESTRIAL PHYSICS.** Text in English. 1950. 18/yr. EUR 3,138 in Europe to institutions; JPY 416,600 in Japan to institutions; USD 3,509 elsewhere to institutions; EUR 174 in Europe to qualified personnel; JPY 23,100 in Japan to qualified personnel; USD 194 elsewhere to qualified personnel (effective 2006). adv. bk.rev. back issues avail.; reprint service avail. from PQC. **Document type:** *Journal, Academic/Scholarly.* **Description:** International journal concerned with the interdiciplinary science of the earth's atmospheric and space environment.
Formerly (until Jan. 1997): Journal of Atmospheric and Terrestrial Physics (0021-9169)
Related titles: Microfilm ed.: (from PQC); Online - full text ed.: (from EBSCO Publishing, Gale Group, IngentaConnect, ScienceDirect, Swets Information Services).
Indexed: ASCA, ASFA, BrCerAb, C&ISA, CIN, CerAb, ChemAb, ChemTitl, CivEngAb, CorrAb, CurCont, E&CAJ, EMA, ESPM, Englnd, FLUIDEX, GEOBASE, IAA, ISR, Inspec, M&GPA, M&TEA, MBF, METADEX, PhysBer, PollutAb, RefZh, SCI, SPPI, WAA.
—BLDSC (4947.950000), AskIEEE, CASDDS, CISTI, Ei, IDS, IE, Infotrieve, ingenta, Linda Hall. **CCC.**
Published by: Pergamon (Subsidiary of: Elsevier Science & Technology), The Boulevard, Langford Ln, East Park, Kidlington, Oxford OX5 1GB, United Kingdom. TEL 44-1865-843000, FAX 44-1865-843010, http:// www.elsevier.com/locate/jastp. Ed. J. M. C. Plane. Circ: 1,350. **Subscr. to:** Elsevier BV, PO Box 211, Amsterdam 1000 AE, Netherlands. TEL 31-20-485-3757, FAX 31-20-485-3432, nlinfo-f@elsevier.nl, http://www.elsevier.nl.

551.2 CHN ISSN 1002-1604
JOURNAL OF EARTHQUAKE PREDICTION RESEARCH. Text in English. 1992. q. **Document type:** *Journal, Academic/Scholarly.* **Description:** Covers the advances in earthquake prediction research in China, Russia and other countries. Also covers geophysics, earthquake engineering and countermeasurements for disaster reduction.
Indexed: EEA.
—BLDSC (4971.305000), CISTI.
Published by: Kexue Chubanshe/Science Press, 16 Donghuang Cheng Genbei Jie, Beijing, 100717, China. TEL 86-10-64000246, FAX 86-10-64030255. Eds. Guoming Zhang, V N Strakhov. Circ: 190. **Dist. by:** China International Book Trading Corp, 35 Chegongzhuang Xilu, Haidian District, PO Box 399, Beijing 100044, China. TEL 86-10-68412045, FAX 86-10-68412023, cibtc@mail.cibtc.com.cn, http://www.cibtc.com.cn.

550 333.7 USA ISSN 1083-1363
QC808.5
➤ **JOURNAL OF ENVIRONMENTAL & ENGINEERING GEOPHYSICS.** Text in English. 1995. q. USD 125 in US & Canada; USD 200 elsewhere (effective 2004). adv. back issues avail. **Document type:** *Journal, Academic/Scholarly.* **Description:** Designed to foster and encourage the application of geophysics techniques for environmental, engineering and mining applications.
Indexed: ASFA, CurCont, ESPM, PollutAb, SWRA.
—BLDSC (4979.358500), IE, ingenta.
Address: 1720 S Bellaire, Ste 110, Denver, CO 80222-4303. TEL 303-531-7517, FAX 303-820-3844, eegs@neha.org, http://www.eegs.org/jeeg/index.html. Ed. Jonathan E Nyquist. Adv. contact Michael Thompson. page USD 770; 7 x 10.

628 FRA ISSN 1359-8155
TA703
➤ **JOURNAL OF ENVIRONMENTAL AND ENGINEERING GEOPHYSICS.** Key Title: European Journal of Environmental and Engineering Geophysics. Text in French. 1996. q. GBP 160. adv. **Document type:** *Journal, Academic/Scholarly.* **Description:** Provides a means of communication between geophysicists and those who use geophysical data. Places particular emphasis on environmental, engineering and hydrological aspects.
Indexed: GEOBASE.
—CISTI, Linda Hall.
Published by: (Environmental and Engineering Society (EEGS), European Section), Geophysical Press, 24 Domaine des Aigueilleres, Montferrier-sur-Lez, 34980, France. TEL 33-467-598963, geopress@worldonline.fr, http://www.eegs-es.org/e-02.htm. Ed. Ugur Yaramanci. adv.: B&W page USD 900, color page USD 1,500.

551 DEU ISSN 0949-7714
QB275 CODEN: JOGEF8
➤ **JOURNAL OF GEODESY.** Text in English. 1995. m. EUR 898 combined subscription to institutions print & online eds. (effective 2005). adv. bk.rev. charts. back issues avail. **Document type:** *Journal, Academic/Scholarly.* **Description:** Concerned with the study of scientific problems of geodesy and related interdisciplinary sciences.
Formed by the merger of (1924-1995): Bulletin Geodesique (0007-4632); (1978-1995): Manuscripta Geodaetica (0340-8825)
Related titles: Microfiche ed.; Online - full text ed.: ISSN 1432-1394 (from EBSCO Publishing, Springer LINK, Swets Information Services).
Indexed: ASCA, ASFA, CIS, CMCI, CurCont, ESPM, FLUIDEX, GEOBASE, GeophysAb, HistAb, IAA, IBR, ISR, Inspec, M&GPA, MathR, OceAb, PollutAb, RefZh, SCI.
—BLDSC (4991.940000), AskIEEE, CISTI, IDS, IE, Infotrieve, ingenta, Linda Hall. **CCC.**
Published by: (International Union of Geodesy and Geophysics GBR), Springer-Verlag (Subsidiary of: Springer Science+Business Media), Tiergartenstr 17, Heidelberg, 69121, Germany. TEL 49-6221-3450, FAX 49-6221-345229, http://link.springer.de/link/service/journals/00190/index.htm. Ed. W E Featherstone. Adv. contact Stephan Kroeck TEL 49-30-827875739. Circ: 1,200. **Subscr. in the Americas to:** Springer-Verlag New York, Inc., Journal Fulfillment, PO Box 2485, Secaucus, NJ 07096-2485. TEL 800-777-4643, 201-348-4033, FAX 201-348-4505, journals@springer-ny.com, http://www.springer-ny.com; **Subscr. to:** Springer GmbH Auslieferungsgesellschaft, Haberstr 7, Heidelberg 69126, Germany. TEL 49-6221-345-0, FAX 49-6221-345-4229, subscriptions@springer.de.

551 GBR ISSN 0264-3707
QE500 CODEN: JOGEE7
➤ **JOURNAL OF GEODYNAMICS.** Text and summaries in English. 1984. 10/yr. EUR 1,504 in Europe to institutions; JPY 199,700 in Japan to institutions; USD 1,683 to institutions except Europe and Japan (effective 2006). adv. index. back issues avail. **Document type:** *Journal, Academic/Scholarly.* **Description:** Publishes research on the dynamics and the dynamic history of the earth, with emphasis on deep-seated foundations of geological phenomena, including investigations of movements and deformations, past and present, and of the lithosphere and all relevant properties of the earth's interior.
Related titles: Microform ed.: (from PQC); Online - full text ed.: (from EBSCO Publishing, Gale Group, IngentaConnect, ScienceDirect, Swets Information Services).
Indexed: AESIS, ASCA, CurCont, GEOBASE, GeosDoc, IAA, ISR, Inspec, M&GPA, RefZh, SCI, SSCI.
—BLDSC (4991.950000), AskIEEE, CISTI, IDS, IE, Infotrieve, ingenta, Linda Hall, PADDS. **CCC.**
Published by: Pergamon (Subsidiary of: Elsevier Science & Technology), The Boulevard, Langford Ln, East Park, Kidlington, Oxford OX5 1GB, United Kingdom. TEL 44-1865-843000, FAX 44-1865-843010, http:// www.elsevier.com/locate/jog. Eds. Wolf R. Jacoby, G. Ranalli. Circ: 900. **Subscr. to:** Elsevier BV, PO Box 211, Amsterdam 1000 AE, Netherlands. TEL 31-20-485-3757, FAX 31-20-485-3432, nlinfo-f@elsevier.nl, http://www.elsevier.nl.

551 EGY ISSN 1687-0999
JOURNAL OF GEOPHYSICS. Text in English. 1930. s-a. **Document type:** *Journal, Academic/Scholarly.*
Supersedes in part (in 2002): National Research Institute of Astronomy and Geophysics. Section B. Geophysics (1110-6417); Which superseded in part (in 1981): Helwan Institute of Astronomy and Geophysics; Which was formerly (until 1970): Helwan Observatory Bulletin
Published by: National Research Institute of Astronomy and Geophysics, Egyptian Economic Center, Haroun Tower, 18 El Mansoura St, Heliopolis, Cairo, Egypt. TEL 20-2-2437710.

551 620 GBR ISSN 1742-2132
QE500
▼ ➤ **JOURNAL OF GEOPHYSICS AND ENGINEERING.** Text in English. 2004. q. USD 1,255 combined subscription in the Americas to institutions print & online eds.; GBP 650 combined subscription rest of world to institutions print & online eds. (effective 2005). **Document type:** *Journal, Academic/Scholarly.* **Description:** Published articles on research and developments in geophysics and related areas of engineering. It has predominantly and applied science and engineering focus, but solicits and accepts high-quality contributions in all earth-physics disciplines from global geophysics to applied and engineering geophysics, including geodynamics, natural and controlled-source seismology, oil, gas and mineral exploration, petrophysics and reservoir geophysics.
Related titles: Microfiche ed.: USD 941 in North America; GBP 488 elsewhere (effective 2004); Online - full content ed.: ISSN 1742-2140; Online - full text ed.: (from EBSCO Publishing, Swets Information Services).
Indexed: Inspec.
—BLDSC, IE.
Published by: Institute of Physics Publishing, Dirac House, Temple Back, Bristol, BS1 6BE, United Kingdom. TEL 44-117-9297481, FAX 44-117-9294318, jge@iop.org, custserv@iop.org, http://www.iop.org/EJ/journal/jge. Eds. Jian Guo, Mike Warner. **Subscr. to:** American Institute of Physics, PO Box 503284, St Louis, MO 63150-3284. FAX 516-349-9704. **Dist. by:** Maruzen Co., Ltd., 3-10 Nihonbashi 2-chome, Chuo-ku, Tokyo 103-0027, Japan. TEL 81-3-32758591, FAX 81-3-32750657, journal@maruzen.co.jp.; China National Publications Import & Export Corp., 16 Gongti Dong Lu, Chaoyang-qu, PO Box 88, Beijing 100020, China. TEL 86-10-65086953, FAX 86-10-65866970, orderuk.p@cnpiec.com.cn.

E

551.22 NLD ISSN 0963-0651
TN269.8
➤ **JOURNAL OF SEISMIC EXPLORATION.** Text in English. 1992. quadrennial. **Document type:** *Journal, Academic/Scholarly.* **Description:** Contains research in seismic modeling, processing, inversion, interpretation, field techniques, borehole techniques, tomography, instrumentation and software.
Indexed: CurCont, GEOBASE, PetrolAb.
—BLDSC (5063.350000), CISTI, IE, Infotrieve, ingenta, Linda Hall, PADDS.
Published by: Geophysical Press, Kruislaan 12, Bilthoven AM, 3721, Netherlands. TEL 33-5-67794151, FAX 33-5-67794151.

551 NLD ISSN 1383-4649
QE531 CODEN: DXUEF7
➤ **JOURNAL OF SEISMOLOGY.** Text in English. 1997. q. EUR 385, USD 386, GBP 253 combined subscription to institutions print & online eds. (effective 2005). back issues avail.; reprint service avail. from PSC. **Document type:** *Journal, Academic/Scholarly.* **Description:** Provides a medium for rapid publication of scientific papers on observational and theoretical aspects of seismological research. Among topics included are: local, regional and global seismicity and seismotectonics, seismic harzard and risk, earthquake engineering and earthquake prediction.
Related titles: Microform ed.: (from PQC); Online - full text ed.: ISSN 1573-157X (from EBSCO Publishing, Gale Group, IngentaConnect, Kluwer Online, O C L C Online Computer Library Center, Inc., Ovid Technologies, Inc., Springer LINK, Swets Information Services).
Indexed: ASFA, BibLing, BrCerAb, C&ISA, CerAb, CorrAb, CurCont, E&CAJ, EEA, EMA, ESPM, GEOBASE, H&SSA, IAA, ISR, Inspec, M&TEA, MBF, METADEX, RefZh, RiskAb, SCI, SWRA, WAA.
—BLDSC (5063.376000), IDS, IE, Infotrieve, ingenta, Linda Hall. **CCC.**
Published by: Springer-Verlag Dordrecht (Subsidiary of: Springer Science+Business Media), Van Godewijckstraat 30, Dordrecht, 3311 GX, Netherlands. TEL 31-78-6576050, FAX 31-78-6576474, http://springerlink.metapress.com/openurl.asp?genre=journal&issn=1383-4649, http://www.springeronline.com. Ed. Augustin Udías.

551 IRN
JOURNAL OF SEISMOLOGY AND EARTHQUAKE ENGINEERING. Text in English. 1997. q. **Document type:** *Journal, Academic/Scholarly.*
Published by: International Institute of Earthquake Engineering & Seismology, Tehran, Iran. parsi@dena.iiees.ac.ir, http://www.iiees.ac.ir/.

551.2 NLD ISSN 0377-0273
QE521.5 CODEN: JVGRDQ
➤ **JOURNAL OF VOLCANOLOGY AND GEOTHERMAL RESEARCH.** Text in English. 1976. 40/yr. EUR 2,715 in Europe to institutions; JPY 360,200 in Japan to institutions; USD 3,044 to institutions except Europe and Japan; EUR 193 in Europe to qualified personnel; JPY 25,300 in Japan to qualified personnel; USD 217 to qualified personnel except Europe and Japan (effective 2006). adv. bk.rev. abstr.; illus. Index. back issues avail.; reprint service avail. from ISI. **Document type:** *Journal, Academic/Scholarly.* **Description:** Provides volcanologists, petrologists and geochemists with a source of information and an outlet for rapid publication of papers in the field.
Related titles: Microform ed.: (from PQC); Online - full text ed.: (from EBSCO Publishing, Gale Group, IngentaConnect, ScienceDirect, Swets Information Services).
Indexed: AESIS, ASCA, ASFA, CIN, ChemAb, ChemTitl, CurCont, E&PHSE, ESPM, EngInd, EnvAb, GEOBASE, GP&P, IAA, IMMAb, ISR, MinerAb, OffTech, PetrolAb, PhysBer, PollutAb, RefZh, SCI, SWRA.
—BLDSC (5072.513000), CASDDS, CISTI, Ei, IDS, IE, Infotrieve, ingenta, Linda Hall, PADDS. **CCC.**
Published by: Elsevier BV (Subsidiary of: Elsevier Science & Technology), Radarweg 29, Amsterdam, 1043 NX, Netherlands. TEL 31-20-4853911, FAX 31-20-4852457, nlinfo-f@elsevier.nl, http://www.elsevier.com/locate/jvolgeores, http://www.elsevier.nl. Eds. B D Marsh, G Chiodini, L Wilson, M. T. Mangan, S. D. Weaver.

551 JPN ISSN 0914-5753
QB275
KAIJO HOANCHO. SUIROBU KANSOKU HOKOKU. EISEI SOKUCHI HEN/DATA REPORT OF HYDROGRAPHIC OBSERVATIONS. SERIES OF SATELLITE GEODESY. Text in English, Japanese; Summaries in English. 1988. a. **Document type:** *Government.* **Description:** Provides annual reports of satellite geodesy observations by the JHD.
Media: Online - full text.
Published by: Kaijo Hoancho, Suirobu/Maritime Safety Agency, Hydrographic Department, 3-1 Tsuki-Ji 5-chome, Chuo-ku, Tokyo, 104-0045, Japan. TEL 81-3-3541-3816, FAX 81-3-3541-3816, rekisan@cue.jhd.go.jp, http://www.jhd.go.jp/cue/KOHO/astro/htm. Circ: 220.

551.4 JPN ISSN 0287-2633
KAIJO HOANCHO. SUIROBU KANSOKU HOKOKU. TENMON SOKUCHI HEN/DATA REPORT OF HYDROGRAPHIC OBSERVATIONS. SERIES OF ASTRONOMY AND GEODESY. Text in English, Japanese; Summaries in English. 1966. a. stat. **Document type:** *Government.* **Description:** Annual report of astronomical and geodetic observations by the JHD.
Media: Online - full text.
Published by: Kaijo Hoancho, Suirobu/Maritime Safety Agency, Hydrographic Department, 3-1 Tsuki-Ji 5-chome, Chuo-ku, Tokyo, 104-0045, Japan. TEL 81-3-3541-3816, FAX 81-3-3541-3816, rekisan@cue.jhd.go.jp, http://www.jhd.go.jp/cue/KOHO/report, http://www.jhd.go.jp/cue/KOHO/astro.htm.

551 JPN
KAKIOKA MAGNETIC OBSERVATORY. REPORT. GEOELECTRICITY/KISHOCHO CHIJIKI KANSOKUJO HOKOKU. CHIKYU DENKI. Text in English. a.
Published by: Kishocho, Chijiki Kansokujo/Japan Meteorological Agency, Kakioka Magnetic Observatory, 595 Kakioka, Niihari-gun, Yasato-machi, Ibaraki-ken 315-0116, Japan.

551 JPN
KAKIOKA MAGNETIC OBSERVATORY. REPORT. GEOMAGNETISM/KISHOCHO CHIJIKI KANSOKUJO HOKOKU. CHIKYU JIKI. Text in English. a.
Published by: Kishocho, Chijiki Kansokujo/Japan Meteorological Agency, Kakioka Magnetic Observatory, 595 Kakioka, Niihari-gun, Yasato-machi, Ibaraki-ken 315-0116, Japan.

KANKYO CHISHITSUGAKU SHINPOJUMU KOEN RONBUNSHU/SYMPOSIUM ON GEO-ENVIRONMENTS. PROCEEDINGS. see *ENVIRONMENTAL STUDIES*

KATASTAR I GEOINFORMACIJE. see *GEOGRAPHY*

551.2 JPN ISSN 0389-9713
QE521.5
KAZAN FUNKA YOCHI RENRAKUKAI KAIHO/COORDINATING COMMITTEE FOR PREDICTION OF VOLCANIC ERUPTION. REPORT. Text in Japanese. 1974. 3/yr.
Published by: Kishocho/Japan Meteorological Agency, 3-4 Ote-Machi 1-chome, Chiyoda-ku, Tokyo, 100-0004, Japan.

551.21 JPN ISSN 0447-3892
QE537.2.J3
KAZAN HOKOKU/JAPAN METEOROLOGICAL AGENCY. Text in English, Japanese. 1962. q. USD 284.
Indexed: RefZh.
Published by: Kishocho/Japan Meteorological Agency, 3-4 Ote-Machi 1-chome, Chiyoda-ku, Tokyo, 100-0004, Japan.

551.22 JPN
KENSHIN JIHO✶ /QUARTERLY JOURNAL OF SEISMOLOGY. Text in Japanese; Summaries in English. 1925. q. JPY 3,811.
Indexed: Inspec, JPI.
Published by: Japan Meteorological Agency/Kishocho, Otemachi 1-3-4, Chiyoda-ku, Tokyo, 100-8122, Japan. http://www.jma.go.jp/JMA_HP/jma/index.html. Circ: 535.

550 SWE ISSN 0453-9478
KIRUNA GEOPHYSICAL DATA; data summary. Text in English. 1959. q. free to qualified personnel. charts. Supplement avail.; back issues avail. **Document type:** *Bulletin, Academic/Scholarly.*
Related titles: Online - full text ed.
—BLDSC (5097.640000).
Published by: Institutet foer Rymdfysik/Swedish Institute of Space Physics, PO Box 812, Kiruna, 98128, Sweden. TEL 46-980-79000, FAX 46-980-79050, victoria.barabash@irf.se, irf@irf.se, http://www.irf.se/publications/. Ed. Victoria Barabash.

551 JPN
KISHO YORAN/GEOPHYSICAL REVIEW. Text in Japanese. 1890. m.
Published by: Kishocho/Japan Meteorological Agency, 3-4 Ote-Machi 1-chome, Chiyoda-ku, Tokyo, 100-0004, Japan.

551 JPN ISSN 0447-3868
KISHOCHO GIJUTSU HOKOKU/JAPAN METEOROLOGICAL AGENCY. TECHNICAL REPORT. Text in Japanese. 1960. irreg. price varies.
Published by: Kishocho/Japan Meteorological Agency, 3-4 Ote-Machi 1-chome, Chiyoda-ku, Tokyo, 100-0004, Japan. Circ: 575.

551.22 JPN ISSN 0388-7359
KISHOCHO JISHIN KANSOKUJO GIJUTSU HOKOKU/ MATSUSHIRO SEISMOLOGICAL OBSERVATORY. TECHNICAL REPORTS. Text in Japanese; Summaries in English. 1980. a.
Published by: Kishocho, Jishiu-kazahbu Jishin-tsunami-kanshika Seimitsu-jishin-kansokushitsu/Japan Meteorological Agency, Matsushiro Seismological Observatory, 3511, Nishijo, Matsushiro-cho, Nagano-shi, Nagano-ken 381-12, Japan.

551.22 JPN
KOCHI UNIVERSITY. EARTHQUAKE OBSERVATORY. SEISMOLOGICAL BULLETIN. Text in English. 1973. q. stat.
Published by: Kochi University, Earthquake Observatory, Asakura, Kochi, 780, Japan.

551.2 JPN
KOKUSAI JISUBERI NYUSU RETA/LANDSLIDE NEWS. Text in Japanese. 1987. a. JPY 1,000.
Related titles: English ed.
Published by: Jisuberi Gakkai/Japan Landslide Society, 30-7 Shinbashi 5-chome, Minato-ku, Tokyo, 105-0004, Japan.

KVANT; tidsskrift for fysik og astronomi. see *PHYSICS*

551.22 JPN ISSN 0454-7659
KYOTO UNIVERSITY. ABUYAMA SEISMOLOGICAL OBSERVATORY. SEISMOLOGICAL BULLETIN/KYOTO DAIGAKU ABUYAMA JISHIN KANSOKU HOKOKU. Text in English. 1952. s-a. free.
Published by: Kyoto University, Abuyama Seismological Observatory/Kyoto Daigaku Abuyama Jishin Kansokujo, Nasahara, Takatsuki-shi, Osaka-fu 569-1041, Japan. Circ: 300.

551.2 JPN ISSN 0285-0958
KYUSHU CHIIKI KAZAN KIDO KANSOKU JISSHI HOKOKU/REPORT OF VOLCANO OBSERVATION IN KYUSHU DISTRICT. Text in Japanese. 1981. a.
Published by: Kishocho, Fukuoka Kanku Kishodai/Japan Meteorological Agency, Fukuoka District Meteorological Observatory, 1-2-36 Ohori, Chuo-ku, Fukuoka-shi, 810-0052, Japan.

551 JPN ISSN 0916-2259
KYUSHU DAIGAKU RIGAKUBU SHIMABARA JISHIN KAZAN KANSOKUJO KENKYU HOKOKU/KYUSHU UNIVERSITY. FACULTY OF SCIENCE. SHIMABARA EARTHQUAKE AND VOLCANO OBSERVATORY. SCIENCES REPORTS. Text in Japanese; Summaries in English. 1965. a. per issue exchange basis. **Document type:** *Academic/Scholarly.* **Description:** Contains seismological and volcanological reports, especially concerning Unzen volcano, Kyushu, Japan.
Former titles (until 1985): Kyushu Daigaku Rigakubu Shimabara Kazan Kansokujo Kenkyu Hokoku (0385-8286); (until 1971): Kyushu Daigaku Rigakubu Shimabara Kazan Onsen Kenkyujo Kenkyu Hokoku (0454-8205)
Published by: (Shimabara Jishin Kazan Kansokujo), Kyushu Daigaku, Rigakubu/Kyushu University, Faculty of Science, Shimabara Earthquake and Volcano Observatory, 5643-29 Shinyama 2-chome, shimabara-shi, Nagasaki-ken 855-0843, Japan. TEL 0957-62-6621, FAX 0957-63-0225. Ed. Kazuya Ohta. Circ: 500.

KYUSHU UNIVERSITY. FACULTY OF SCIENCES. MEMOIRS. SERIES D: EARTH AND PLANETARY SCIENCES/KYUSHU DAIGAKU RIGAKUBU KIYO D. CHIKYUWAKUSEI KAGAKU. see *EARTH SCIENCES—Geology*

KYUUSHUU DAIGAKU. DAIGAKUIN RIGAKU KENKYUUIN KENKYUU HOUKOKU. CHIKYUU WAKUSEI KAGAKU/KYUSHU UNIVERSITY. DEPARTMENT OF EARTH AND PLANETARY SCIENCES. SCIENCE REPORTS. see *EARTH SCIENCES—Geology*

551.2 FRA ISSN 0982-9601
L A V E. LIASON DES AMATEURS DE VOLCANOLOGIE EUROPEENNE. Text in French. 1986. irreg. **Document type:** *Journal, Academic/Scholarly.*
Published by: Association Volcanique Europeenne, 7 Rue de la Guadeloupe, Paris, 75018, France. TEL 31-1-42057257, FAX 31-1-42053080.

551 NLD ISSN 0928-2122
L G R - SERIES. (Laboratorium voor Geodetische Rekentechniek - Series) Text in English. 1991. irreg. **Document type:** *Academic/Scholarly.*
Published by: Technische Universiteit Delft, Department of Mathematical Geodesy and Positioning/Delft University of Technology, Thijsseweg 11, JADelft, 2629, Netherlands. TEL 31-15-2783546, FAX 31-15-2783711, mgp@geo.tudelft.nl.

LAND CONTAMINATION & RECLAMATION. see *ENVIRONMENTAL STUDIES—Pollution*

551.22 DEU ISSN 1612-510X
▼ ➤ **LANDSLIDES.** Text in English. 2004. q. (in 1 vol., 4 nos./vol.). EUR 248 combined subscription to institutions print & online eds. (effective 2005). **Document type:** *Journal, Academic/Scholarly.* **Description:** Contains integrated research on landslide risk mitigation and the protection of cultural and natural heritage.
Related titles: Online - full text ed.: ISSN 1612-5118 (from EBSCO Publishing, Springer LINK, Swets Information Services).
Indexed: ASFA, ESPM, H&SSA, RiskAb.
—BLDSC (5153.175300). **CCC.**

Published by: Springer-Verlag (Subsidiary of: Springer Science+Business Media), Tiergartenstr 17, Heidelberg, 69121, Germany. TEL 49-6221-3450, FAX 49-6221-345229, orders@springer.de, http://www.springer.de. Ed. Kyoji Sassa. Adv. contact Stephan Kroeck TEL 49-30-827875739. **Subscr. to:** Springer-Verlag New York, Inc., Journal Fulfillment, PO Box 2485, Secaucus, NJ 07096-2485. TEL 800-777-4643, 201-348-4033, FAX 201-348-4505, journals@springer-ny.com; Springer GmbH Auslieferungsgesellschaft, Haberstr 7, Heidelberg 69126, Germany. TEL 49-6221-345-0, FAX 49-6221-345-4229, subscriptions@springer.de.

551 USA ISSN 1070-485X
TN269 CODEN: LEEDFF
THE LEADING EDGE (TULSA). Abbreviated title: T L E. Text in English. 1982. m. USD 95 domestic; USD 115 foreign (effective 2004). adv. charts; illus.; stat. index. back issues avail.; reprints avail. **Document type:** *Journal, Academic/Scholarly.*
Formerly: Geophysics: The Leading Edge of Exploration (0732-989X)
Related titles: CD-ROM ed.; Online - full text ed.: (from EBSCO Publishing, HighWire Press).
Indexed: AESIS, ASFA, CivEngAb, E&PHSE, EngInd, GP&P, GSW, Inspec, M&GPA, OffTech, PetrolAb, RefZh.
—BLDSC (5162.872500), CISTI, Ei, IE, Infotrieve, ingenta, Linda Hall, PADDS. **CCC.**
Published by: Society of Exploration Geophysicists, PO Box 702740, Tulsa, OK 74170-2740. TEL 918-497-5500, dclark@seg.org, books@seg.org, http://sepwww.stanford.edu/seg/tle.html, http://www.seg.org. Ed. Dean Clark. Circ: 20,000 (paid). **Subscr. to:** American Institute of Physics, PO Box 503284, St Louis, MO 63150-3284. TEL 800-344-6902, subs@aip.org, http://librarians.aip.org.

624.1762 551.22 USA ISSN 1520-2933
M C E E R BULLETIN. Variant title: Multidisciplinary Center for Earthquake Engineering Research Bulletin. Text in English. 1987. q. free (effective 2004). back issues avail. **Document type:** *Academic/Scholarly.* **Description:** Features detailed technical articles describing center-sponsored research, news announcements concerning center activities, and news of general interest to earthquake engineering scientists.
Formerly (until 1998): N C E E R Bulletin (1088-3789)
Related titles: Online - full text ed.: ISSN 1520-4960.
Published by: Multidisciplinary Center for Earthquake Engineering Research, University of Buffalo, Red Jacket Quad, Buffalo, NY 14261. TEL 716-645-3377, FAX 716-645-3391, mceer@buffalo.edu, mceer@mceermail.buffalo.edu, http://mceer.buffalo.edu, http://mceer.eng.buffalo.edu/bulletin.

M C E E R INFORMATION SERVICE NEWS. see *ENGINEERING*

551.2 USA ISSN 1520-295X
➤ **M C E E R TECHNICAL REPORT SERIES.** Text in English. 1987 (Jan.). a. USD 300 domestic; USD 400 foreign; USD 150 domestic to non-profit organizations; USD 250 foreign to non-profit organizations (effective 2005). **Document type:** *Academic/Scholarly.* **Description:** Presents detailed accounts of current research work.
Published by: Multidisciplinary Center for Earthquake Engineering Research, University of Buffalo, Red Jacket Quad, Buffalo, NY 14261. TEL 716-645-3377, FAX 716-645-3391, mceer@mceermail.buffalo.edu, http://mceer.buffalo.edu. R&P Ms. Jane E Stoyle.

551.22 USA
MAINE GEOLOGICAL SURVEY. GENERAL GEOPHYSICS REPORT. Text in English. irreg. **Document type:** *Government.*
Published by: Maine Geological Survey, 22 State House Station, Augusta, ME 04333.

551.22 USA
MAINE GEOLOGICAL SURVEY. GRAVITY REPORT. Text in English. irreg. **Document type:** *Government.*
Published by: Maine Geological Survey, 22 State House Station, Augusta, ME 04333.

551.22 USA
MAINE GEOLOGICAL SURVEY. NEOTECTONICS IN MAINE. Text in English. irreg. **Document type:** *Government.*
Published by: Maine Geological Survey, 22 State House Station, Augusta, ME 04333.

551.22 USA
MAINE GEOLOGICAL SURVEY. POST-GLACIAL FAULTING REPORT. Text in English. irreg. **Document type:** *Government.*
Published by: Maine Geological Survey, 22 State House Station, Augusta, ME 04333.

MARINE GEOPHYSICAL RESEARCHES; an international journal for the study of the earth beneath the sea. see *EARTH SCIENCES—Oceanography*

551.4 RUS ISSN 0130-3686
GB2401
➤ **MATERIALY GLYATSIOLOGICHESKIKH ISSLEDOVANII/ DATA OF GLACIOLOGICAL STUDIES.** Text mainly in Russian; Text occasionally in English; Abstracts in English. 1961. irreg. (2-3/yr.). USD 20 domestic to individuals; USD 40 foreign to individuals; USD 80 domestic to institutions; USD 100 foreign to institutions (effective 2003). adv. bk.rev. bibl. **Document type:** *Journal, Academic/Scholarly.* **Description:** Snow cover and snow avalanches; atmospheric ice, mudflows, sea, lake and river ice; ground ice; mountain glaciers, and ice sheets; paleoglaciology.
Indexed: RefZh.
—CISTI, Linda Hall.
Published by: Rossiiskaya Akademiya Nauk, Institut Geografii/Russian Academy of Science, Institute of Geography, Staromonetnyi ul 29, Moscow, 109017, Russian Federation. TEL 7-095-1259011, FAX 7-095-9590033, geography@glas.apc.org. Ed. V.M. Kotlyakov. Pub. V M Kotlyakov. Adv. contact Vladimir Mikhalenko. Circ: 500. **Co-sponsor:** Glaciological Association.

551 JPN ISSN 0385-2016
MATSUSHIRO GUNPATSU JISHIN SHIRYO HOKOKU/ BULLETIN OF DATA AND INFORMATION ON THE MATSUSHIRO EARTHQUAKE SWARM. Text in Japanese. 1972. a. **Document type:** *Bulletin.*
Published by: Matsushiro Jishin Senta/Research Center of Matsushiro Earthquake Swarm, Kishocho Jishin Kansokujo, 3511, Nishijo, Matsushiro-machi, Nagano-shi, Nagano-ken 381-12, Japan.

551 USA ISSN 0197-6346
MAURICE EWING SERIES. Text in English. 1977. irreg. **Document type:** *Monographic series.*
Indexed: Inspec.
Published by: American Geophysical Union, 2000 Florida Ave, NW, Washington, DC 20009-1277. TEL 202-462-6900, 800-966-2481, FAX 202-328-0566, http://www.agu.org.

MAUSAM. see *METEOROLOGY*

MEMORIE DI SCIENZE GEOLOGICHE. see *EARTH SCIENCES—Geology*

METEOROLOGISCHE ZEITSCHRIFT. see *METEOROLOGY*

METHODS IN GEOCHEMISTRY AND GEOPHYSICS. see *EARTH SCIENCES*

MIZUSAWA ASTROGEODYNAMICS OBSERVATORY. ANNUAL REPORT. see *ASTRONOMY*

551 NLD ISSN 0924-6096
➤ **MODERN APPROACHES IN GEOPHYSICS.** Text in Dutch. 1985. irreg., latest vol.22, 2004. price varies. back issues avail. **Document type:** *Monographic series, Academic/Scholarly.*
Formerly (until 1988): Seismology and Exploration Geophysics (0924-6088)
—BLDSC (5883.640500), IE, ingenta.
Published by: Springer-Verlag Dordrecht (Subsidiary of: Springer Science+Business Media), Van Godewijckstraat 30, Dordrecht, 3311 GX, Netherlands. TEL 31-78-6576050, FAX 31-78-6576474, http://www.springeronline.com. Ed. Guust Nolet.

551 MOZ
MOZAMBIQUE. DIRECCAO NACIONAL DE GEOLOGIA. BOLETIM GEOMAGNETICO PRELIMINAR. Text in Portuguese. 1957. m. free. stat. **Document type:** *Bulletin.*
Former titles: Mozambique. Instituto Nacional de Geologia. Departamento Geofisica Global. Boletim Geomagnetico Preliminar; Mozambique. Servico Meteorologico. Boletim Geomagnetico Preliminar (0006-6001)
Media: Duplicated (not offset).
Published by: Direccao Nacional de Geologia, C.P. 217, Maputo, Mozambique. TEL 258-1-420797, TELEX 6-584 GEOMI MO, geologia@zebra.uem.mz. Ed. Elias Daudi.

551.22 MOZ
MOZAMBIQUE. DIRRECAO NACIONAL DE GEOLOGIA. BOLETIM SEISMIQUE. Text in Portuguese. 1957. m. free. stat. **Document type:** *Bulletin.* **Description:** Concentrates on seismology.
Formerly: Mozambique. Servico Meteorologico. Boletim Seismique (0006-6095)
Media: Duplicated (not offset).
Published by: Direccao Nacional de Geologia, C.P. 217, Maputo, Mozambique. TEL 258-1-420797, TELEX 6-584 GEOMI MO, geologia@zebra.uem.mz. Ed. Elias Daudi.

MOZAMBIQUE. INSTITUTO NACIONAL DE METEOROLOGIA. BOLETIM METEOROLOGICO PARA AGRICULTURA. see *METEOROLOGY*

551.5 520 MOZ
MOZAMBIQUE. INSTITUTO NACIONAL DE METEOROLOGIA. INFORMACOES DE CARACTER ASTRONOMICO (ASTRONOMICAL INFORMATION). Text in Portuguese. 1955. a. MZM 1,200,000 domestic; USD 100 foreign (effective 2000). stat. 90 p./no.; **Document type:** *Yearbook, Government.*
Formerly: Mozambique. Servico Meteorologico. Informacoes de Caracter Astronomico
Published by: Instituto Nacional de Meteorologia, C.P. 256, Maputo, Mozambique. mozmet@zebra.uem.mz, mozmet@inam.gov.mz. Ed. Filipe Freires Domingos Lucio.

551 DEU ISSN 0931-2145
MUENCHNER GEOPHYSIKALISCHE MITTEILUNGEN. Text in German. 1960. irreg., latest vol.8, 1999. EUR 25 per issue (effective 2003). **Document type:** *Academic/Scholarly.*
Formerly (until 1986): Universitaet Muenchen. Geophysikalisches Observatorium, Fuerstenfeldbruck. Veroeffentlichungen. Serie B (0077-2100)
—CISTI.
Published by: Universitaet Muenchen, Geophysikalisches Observatorium, Ludwigshoehe 8, Fuerstenfeldbruck, 82256, Germany. TEL 49-8141-5346760, FAX 49-8141-5346770, obs@geophysik.uni-muenchen.de, http://obsfur.geophysik.uni-muenchen.de/.

NATIONAL ASTRONOMICAL OBSERVATORY. MIZUSAWA ASTROGEODYNAMICS OBSERVATORY. MIZUSAWA KANSOKU CENTER. TECHNICAL REPORT. see *ASTRONOMY*

551 DEU ISSN 1561-8633
GB5000
➤ **NATURAL HAZARDS AND EARTH SYSTEM SCIENCES.** Text in English. bi-m. free. **Document type:** *Journal, Academic/Scholarly.* **Description:** Publishes original research concerning natural hazards.
Related titles: Online - full text ed.: ISSN 1684-9981. free (effective 2005).
Indexed: ASFA, CurCont, ESPM, GEOBASE, RiskAb, SWRA.
—BLDSC (6037.835000).
Published by: (European Geosciences Union), Copernicus GmbH, Max-Planck Str 13, Katlenburg-Lindau, 37191, Germany. http://www.copernicus.org/EGU/nhess/nhess.htm.

551 NLD ISSN 1569-4445
NEAR SURFACE GEOPHYSICS. Text in English. 4/yr. EUR 190 to non-members individuals; EUR 470 to non-members institutions; EUR 50 membership (effective 2005). **Document type:** *Journal, Academic/Scholarly.* **Description:** International journal for the publication of research and development in geophysics applied to near surface. It places emphasis on geological, hydrogeological, geotechnical, environmental, engineering, mining, archaeological, agricultural and other applications of geophysics as well as on physical soil and rock properties.
—BLDSC (6067.946400).
Published by: E A G E Publications BV, P O Box 59, Houten, 3990 DB, Netherlands. TEL 31-30-6354059, FAX 31-30-6343524, nearsurfacegeophysics@eage.org, http://www.nearsurfacegeophysics.org. Ed. Ugur Yaramanci.

NEW MEXICO. BUREAU OF GEOLOGY AND MINERAL RESOURCES. CIRCULAR. see *MINES AND MINING INDUSTRY*

NEW MEXICO GEOLOGY. see *EARTH SCIENCES—Geology*

NEW ZEALAND JOURNAL OF GEOLOGY AND GEOPHYSICS; an international journal of Pacific Rim geosciences. see *EARTH SCIENCES—Geology*

551.22 JPN ISSN 0919-5319
QE5311
NIHON JISHIN GAKKAI NYUSU RETA/SEISMOLOGICAL SOCIETY OF JAPAN. NEWSLETTER. Text in Japanese. 1989. bi-m. **Document type:** *Newsletter.*
Formerly (until 1993): Jishin Gakkai Nyusu Reta (0916-2720)
Indexed: RefZh.
—Linda Hall.
Published by: Nihon Jishin Gakkai, Daigaku Jishin Kenkyujo, 1-1 Yayoi 1-chome, Bunkyo-ku, Tokyo, 113-0032, Japan.

551.22 JPN
NIHON JISHIN KOGAKU SHINPOJUMU KOENSHU/JAPAN EARTHQUAKE ENGINEERING SYMPOSIUM. PROCEEDINGS. Text in English, Japanese; Summaries in English. 4/yr. membership. **Document type:** *Proceedings.*
Published by: Jishin Gakkai/Seismological Society of Japan, Daigaku Jishin Kenkyujo, 1-1 Yayoi 1-chome, Bunkyo-ku, Tokyo, 113-0032, Japan.

551 JPN ISSN 1348-3986
QE599.A1 CODEN: JISUD4
NIHON JISUBERI GAKKAISHI/LANDSLIDES. Text in Japanese, English. 1963. q. back issues avail. **Document type:** *Journal, Academic/Scholarly.*
Formerly (until 2003): Jisuberi (0285-2926)
—CASDDS. **CCC.**

E

▼ new title ➤ refereed ✶ unverified ♦ full entry avail.

Published by: Jisuberi Gakkai/Japan Landslide Society, 30-7 Shinbashi 5-chome, Minato-ku, Tokyo, 105-0004, Japan. Ed. Shinichi Yamaguchi. Circ: 2,300.

551 USA ISSN 1023-5809
QC801
NONLINEAR PROCESSES IN GEOPHYSICS. Text in English. 1994. 4/yr., latest vol.8. USD 520 to institutions (effective 2006). back issues avail. **Document type:** *Journal.* **Description:** Publishes original contributions from both dynamical system theorists and researchers applying non-linear methods to fundamental problems in geoscience.
Related titles: Online - full text ed.: ISSN 1607-7946. 2000. free (effective 2005) (from EBSCO Publishing).
Indexed: ASFA, CurCont, FLUIDEX, GEOBASE, M&GPA, OceAb, RefZh.
—BLDSC (6117.316950), IE, ingenta.
Published by: American Geophysical Union, 2000 Florida Ave, NW, Washington, DC 20009-1277. TEL 202-462-6900, 800-966-2481, FAX 202-328-0566, institutions@agu.org, http://www.copernicus.org/EGU/npg/prices.html, http://www.agu.org. Ed. A F Spilhaus Jr. **Co-sponsor:** European Geophysical Society.

551.2 NLD
NUMERICAL MODELS IN GEOMECHANICS. Short title: N U M O G. Text in English. irreg., latest vol.7, 1999. price varies. charts. back issues avail. **Document type:** *Monographic series, Academic/Scholarly.*
—BLDSC (6184.696760).
Published by: A A Balkema (Subsidiary of: Taylor & Francis The Netherlands), PO Box 1675, Rotterdam, 3000 BR, Netherlands. TEL 31-10-414-5822, FAX 31-10-413-5947, balkema@balkema.nl, http://www.balkema.nl.

551 ESP ISSN 0211-5166
QC881.2.I6
OBSERVATORIO DEL EBRO. BOLETIN, IONSOFERA. Text in Spanish. 1948. irreg. per issue exchange basis. **Description:** Presents ionospheric data.
—BLDSC (4564.850000), Linda Hall.
Published by: Observatorio Fisica Cosmica del Ebro, Roquetes, Tarragona 43520, Spain. TEL 34-77-500511, FAX 34-77-504660.

551 520 ESP ISSN 0212-9760
OBSERVATORIO DEL EBRO. PUBLICACIONES. MEMORIA. Text in Spanish. 1906. irreg. free. **Document type:** *Monographic series.*
Indexed: IECT.
Published by: Observatorio Fisica Cosmica del Ebro, Roquetes, Tarragona 43520, Spain. TEL 34-977-500511, FAX 34-977-504660. Ed. L F Alberca.

551 ESP ISSN 0211-4534
OBSERVATORIO DEL EBRO. PUBLICACIONES. MISCELANEA. Text in Spanish. 1947. irreg. **Document type:** *Monographic series.*
Indexed: IECT.
—BLDSC (6987.000000), CINDOC.
Published by: Observatorio Fisica Cosmica del Ebro, Roquetes, Tarragona 43520, Spain. TEL 34-77-500511, FAX 34-77-504660. Ed. L F Alberca.

OBSERVATORIO NACIONAL RIO DE JANEIRO. PUBLICACOES. see *ASTRONOMY*

551.2 CRI
OBSERVATORIO SISMOLOGICO Y VULCANOLOGICO DE ARENAL Y MIRAVALLES. BOLETIN. Text in English, Spanish; Abstracts in English, Spanish. 1988. irreg. (approx. 2/yr.). free. **Document type:** *Bulletin, Government.* **Description:** Provides the latest results of research and collaborations on vulcanology and seismology from the observatory.
Formerly: Observatorio Vulcanologico del Arenal. Boletin (1015-4396)
Published by: Instituto Costarricense de Electricidad (ICE), Apdo 10032, San Jose, 1000, Costa Rica. TEL 506-2-207441, FAX 506-2-208217. Ed. Guillermo E Alvarado. Circ: 250.

551 RUS
OBZORNAYA INFORMATSIYA. RAZVEDOCHNAYA GEOFIZIKA. Text in Russian. q. USD 59.95 in United States.
Published by: Informatsionno-Izdatel'skii Tsentr po Geologii i Nedropol'zovaniu Geoinformmark, Goncharnaya 38, Moscow, 115172, Russian Federation. TEL 7-095-9156724. **US dist. addr.:** East View Information Services, 3020 Harbor Ln. N., Minneapolis, MN 55447. TEL 612-550-0961.

OESTERREICHISCHE BEITRAEGE ZU METEOROLOGIE UND GEOPHYSIK. see *METEOROLOGY*

551 SEN
OFFICE DE LA RECHERCHE SCIENTIFIQUE ET TECHNIQUE OUTRE-MER DE M'BOUR. CENTRE DE GEOPHYSIQUE. BULLETIN SEISMIQUE✶. Text in French. 1974. m. charts; stat.
Published by: Office de la Recherche Scientifique et Technique Outre-Mer de M'Bour, Centre de Geophysique, BP 50, M'bour, Senegal.

OHIO STATE UNIVERSITY. BYRD POLAR RESEARCH CENTER. MISCELLANEOUS SERIES. see *SCIENCES: COMPREHENSIVE WORKS*

OHIO STATE UNIVERSITY. BYRD POLAR RESEARCH CENTER. REPORT SERIES. see *SCIENCES: COMPREHENSIVE WORKS*

OILFIELD REVIEW. see *PETROLEUM AND GAS*

551 NLD
ORIENTATIE OP PLANOLOGISCHE EN JURIDISCHE GEODESIE. Text in Dutch. 1993. irreg., latest vol.12, 1997. price varies. **Document type:** *Monographic series.*
Published by: Delft University Press (Subsidiary of: Technische Universiteit Delft/Delft University of Technology), PO Box 98, Delft, 2600 MG, Netherlands. TEL 31-15-278-3254, FAX 31-15-2781661, dup@dup.tudelft.nl.

551 FIN ISSN 1456-3673
OULUN YLIPISTON.SODANKYLAN GEOFYSIIKAN OBSERVATORIO. PUBLICATIONS. Text in Finnish. 1921. irreg. **Document type:** *Monographic series, Academic/Scholarly.*
Former titles (until 1998): Veroeffentlichungen des Geophysikalischen Observatoriums der Finnischen Akademie der Wissenschaften (0355-0826); (until 1937): Veroeffentlichungen des Magnetischen Observatoriums der Finnischen Akademie der Wissenschaften zu Sodankyla (1236-3804)
Related titles: ♦ Series: Magnetic Results Sodankyla. ISSN 0781-9625.
Indexed: RefZh.
—CISTI.
Published by: Oulun Ylipiston, Sodankylan Geofysiikan Observatorio/University of Oulu. Sodankyla Geophysical Observatory, Taehtelaentie 62, Sodankyla, 99600, Finland. TEL 358-16-619811, FAX 358-16-619875, http://www.sgo.fi.

OXFORD MONOGRAPHS ON GEOLOGY AND GEOPHYSICS. see *EARTH SCIENCES—Geology*

551.2 USA
TA654.6
THE P E E R REVIEW. (Pacific Earthquake Engineering Center) Text in English. 1983. a. free (effective 2005). back issues avail. **Document type:** *Newsletter, Trade.* **Description:** Highlights selected research, education, and information resources of interest to earthquake engineering researchers and professionals.
Former titles (until Winter 2001): P E E R Center News (1521-3714); (until 1998): University of California. Earthquake Engineering Research Center. News (0739-7704)
—Linda Hall.
Published by: University of California at Berkeley, Pacific Earthquake Engineering Research Center, 1301 S 46th St, Richmond, CA 94804-4698. TEL 510-231-9554, FAX 510-231-9461, eerclib@nisee.ce.berkeley.edu, http://peer.berkeley.edu. Ed. Janine Hannel. Circ: 4,400 (paid and controlled).

PAPERS IN METEOROLOGY AND GEOPHYSICS. see *METEOROLOGY*

551 NLD ISSN 0031-9201
QE500 CODEN: PEPIAM
➤ **PHYSICS OF THE EARTH AND PLANETARY INTERIORS.** Text in Dutch. 1967. 24/yr. EUR 2,472 in Europe to institutions; JPY 328,700 in Japan to institutions; USD 2,766 to institutions except Europe and Japan; EUR 147 in Europe to qualified personnel; JPY 19,500 in Japan to qualified personnel; USD 164 to qualified personnel except Europe and Japan (effective 2006). bk.rev. illus. Index. back issues avail.; reprints avail. **Document type:** *Journal, Academic/Scholarly.* **Description:** Devoted to observational and experimental studies of the earth and planetary interiors and their theoretical interpretation by the physical sciences.
Related titles: Microform ed.: (from PQC); Online - full text ed.: (from EBSCO Publishing, Gale Group, IngentaConnect, ScienceDirect, Swets Information Services).
Indexed: AESIS, ASCA, ASFA, ChemAb, ChemTitl, CurCont, EEA, EngInd, GEOBASE, IAA, ISR, Inspec, M&GPA, MSCI, PetrolAb, PhysBer, RefZh, SCI, SPPI.
—BLDSC (6478.525000), AskIEEE, CASDDS, CISTI, Ei, IDS, IE, Infotrieve, ingenta, Linda Hall, PADDS. **CCC.**
Published by: Elsevier BV (Subsidiary of: Elsevier Science & Technology), Radarweg 29, Amsterdam, 1043 NX, Netherlands. TEL 31-20-4853911, FAX 31-20-4852457, nlinfo-f@elsevier.nl, http://www.elsevier.com/locate/pepi, http://www.elsevier.nl. Eds. B L N Kennett, D Rubie, G Schubert. **Subscr. to:** PO Box 211, Amsterdam 1000 AE, Netherlands. TEL 31-20-485-3757, FAX 31-20-485-3432.

551 POL ISSN 0137-2440
POLISH ACADEMY OF SCIENCES. INSTITUTE OF GEOPHYSICS. PUBLICATIONS. SERIES A: PHYSICS OF THE EARTH'S INTERIOR. Key Title: Publications of the Institute of Geophysics. A: Physics of the Earth's Interior. Text and summaries in English. 1963. irreg. price varies. **Document type:** *Academic/Scholarly.*
Supersedes in part (in 1975): Polska Akademia Nauk. Instytut Geofizyki. Materialy i Prace (0079-3574)
Indexed: RefZh.
—CISTI, Linda Hall.
Published by: Polska Akademia Nauk, Instytut Geofizyki/Polish Academy of Sciences, Institute of Geophysics, Ul Ksiecia Janusza 64, Warsaw, 01452, Poland. Ed. Roman Teisseyre.

551 POL ISSN 0138-0109
QE531 CODEN: PIGSD4
POLISH ACADEMY OF SCIENCES. INSTITUTE OF GEOPHYSICS. PUBLICATIONS. SERIES B: SEISMOLOGY. Key Title: Publications of the Institute of Geophysics. B: Seismology. Text in English; Summaries in English, Polish. 1963. irreg. price varies. **Document type:** *Academic/Scholarly.*
Supersedes in part (in 1975): Polska Akademia Nauk. Instytut Geofizyki. Materialy i Prace (0079-3574)
Indexed: RefZh.
—CISTI, Linda Hall.
Published by: Polska Akademia Nauk, Instytut Geofizyki/Polish Academy of Sciences, Institute of Geophysics, Ul Ksiecia Janusza 64, Warsaw, 01452, Poland. Ed. Roman Teisseyre.

551 POL ISSN 0138-0117
QC830.A3
POLISH ACADEMY OF SCIENCES. INSTITUTE OF GEOPHYSICS. PUBLICATIONS. SERIES C: GEOMAGNETISM. Key Title: Publications of the Institute of Geophysics. C: Geomagnetism. Text and summaries in English. 1963. irreg. price varies. **Document type:** *Academic/Scholarly.*
Supersedes in part (in 1975): Polska Akademia Nauk. Instytut Geofizyki. Materialy i Prace (0079-3574)
Indexed: RefZh.
—CISTI, Linda Hall.
Published by: Polska Akademia Nauk, Instytut Geofizyki/Polish Academy of Sciences, Institute of Geophysics, Ul Ksiecia Janusza 64, Warsaw, 01452, Poland. Ed. Roman Teisseyre.

551 POL ISSN 0138-0125
CODEN: PIGPDT
POLISH ACADEMY OF SCIENCES. INSTITUTE OF GEOPHYSICS. PUBLICATIONS. SERIES D: PHYSICS OF THE ATMOSPHERE. Key Title: Publications of the Institute of Geophysics. D: Physics of the Atmosphere. Text in English; Summaries in English, Polish. 1963. irreg. price varies. **Document type:** *Academic/Scholarly.*
Supersedes in part (in 1975): Polska Akademia Nauk. Instytut Geofizyki. Materialy i Prace (0079-3574)
Indexed: M&GPA, RefZh.
—CASDDS, CISTI, Linda Hall.
Published by: Polska Akademia Nauk, Instytut Geofizyki/Polish Academy of Sciences, Institute of Geophysics, Ul Ksiecia Janusza 64, Warsaw, 01452, Poland. Ed. Roman Teisseyre.

551 POL ISSN 0138-0133
POLISH ACADEMY OF SCIENCES. INSTITUTE OF GEOPHYSICS. PUBLICATIONS. SERIES E: WATER RESOURCES. Key Title: Publications of the Institute of Geophysics. E: Water Resources. Text and summaries in English. 1963. irreg. price varies. **Document type:** *Academic/Scholarly.*
Supersedes in part (in 1975): Polska Akademia Nauk. Instytut Geofizyki. Materialy i Prace (0079-3574)
—BLDSC (7081.820000), CISTI, Linda Hall.
Published by: Polska Akademia Nauk, Instytut Geofizyki/Polish Academy of Sciences, Institute of Geophysics, Ul Ksiecia Janusza 64, Warsaw, 01452, Poland. Ed. Roman Teisseyre.

551 POL ISSN 0138-0141
POLISH ACADEMY OF SCIENCES. INSTITUTE OF GEOPHYSICS. PUBLICATIONS. SERIES F: PLANETARY GEODESY. Key Title: Publications of the Institute of Geophysics. F: Planetary Geodesy. Text in English; Summaries in English, Polish. 1963. irreg. price varies. **Document type:** *Academic/Scholarly.*
Supersedes in part (in 1975): Polska Akademia Nauk. Instytut Geofizyki. Materialy i Prace (0079-3574)
Indexed: RefZh.
—CISTI, Linda Hall.
Published by: Polska Akademia Nauk, Instytut Geofizyki/Polish Academy of Sciences, Institute of Geophysics, Ul Ksiecia Janusza 64, Warsaw, 01452, Poland. Ed. Roman Teisseyre.

551 POL ISSN 0138-015X
CODEN: PGPMEI
POLISH ACADEMY OF SCIENCES. INSTITUTE OF GEOPHYSICS. PUBLICATIONS. SERIES M: MISCELLANEA. Key Title: Publications of the Institute of Geophysics. M: Miscellanea. Text and summaries in English, Polish. 1963. irreg. price varies. **Document type:** *Academic/Scholarly.*
Supersedes in part (in 1975): Polska Akademia Nauk. Instytut Geofizyki. Materialy i Prace (0079-3574)
Indexed: GEOBASE, RefZh.
—CISTI, Linda Hall.
Published by: Polska Akademia Nauk, Instytut Geofizyki/Polish Academy of Sciences, Institute of Geophysics, Ul Ksiecia Janusza 64, Warsaw, 01452, Poland. Ed. Roman Teisseyre.

E

551.993 USA
POWER PLACES OF CALIFORNIA. Text in English. 1988. irreg. USD 10 (effective 2001). bk.rev. abstr.; bibl.; illus. back issues avail. **Document type:** *Newsletter.* **Description:** Locates specific geomagnetic anomalies producing physical and perceptual responses, and speculates on their implications.
Published by: Louise Lacey, Ed. & Pub., PO Box 489, Berkeley, CA 94701. TEL 510-232-9865. Circ: 250.

551 RUS ISSN 0478-2003
CODEN: PGVGAQ
PRIKLADNAYA GEOFIZIKA. Text in Russian. 1977 (vol.85). irreg. abstr.
Indexed: ChemAb, Inspec.
—CASDDS, Linda Hall.
Published by: (Vsesoyuznyi Nauchno-Issledovatel'skii Institut Geofizicheskikh Metodov Razvedki), Izdatel'stvo Nedra, Tverskaya Zastava pl 3, Moscow, 125047, Russian Federation. TEL 7-095-2505255, FAX 7-095-2502772. Ed. M Polshkov. Circ: 25,000.

551.2 USA ISSN 1549-201X
➤ **PRINCETON SERIES IN GEOPHYSICS.** Text in English. 1994. irreg., latest vol.2, 2000. price varies. back issues avail. **Document type:** *Monographic series, Academic/Scholarly.* **Description:** Explores and disseminates findings in the field of geophysics.
Published by: Princeton University Press, 41 William St, Princeton, NJ 08540-5237. TEL 609-258-4900, FAX 609-258-6305, http://pup.princeton.edu/catalogs/series/psgs.html. **Subscr. addr. in US:** California - Princeton Fulfillment Services, 1445 Lower Ferry Rd, Ewing, NJ 08618. TEL 800-777-4726, FAX 800-999-1958, orders@cpfs.pupress.princeton.edu. **Dist. addr. in Canada:** University Press Group, 164 Hillsdale Ave E, Toronto, ON M4S 1T5, Canada.; **Dist. addr. in UK:** John Wiley & Sons Ltd., The Atrium, Southern Gate, Chichester, West Sussex PO19 8SQ, United Kingdom.

526 POL ISSN 0033-2127
PRZEGLAD GEODEZYJNY. Text in Polish. 1924. m. PLZ 168; PLZ 14 per issue (effective 2004). adv. bk.rev. index. 36 p./no.; **Document type:** *Trade.*
Indexed: AgrLib, ApMecR, BibCart.
—CISTI, Linda Hall.
Published by: (Stowarzyszenie Geodetow Polskich), Wydawnictwo SIGMA - N O T Sp. z o.o., ul Ratuszowa 11, PO Box 1004, Warsaw, 00950, Poland. TEL 48-22-8180918, FAX 48-22-6192187, http://www.sigma-not.pl. Ed. Wojciech Wilkowski TEL 48-22-6191995. adv.: B&W page PLZ 900, color page PLZ 1,850. Circ: 1,800.

551 POL ISSN 0033-2135
QC851 CODEN: PRGEAM
PRZEGLAD GEOFIZYCZNY/REVIEW OF GEOPHYSICS. Text in Polish; Summaries in English. 1948. q. USD 60 foreign (effective 2003). bk.rev. charts; illus.; maps. index. 100 p./no.; **Document type:** *Journal, Academic/Scholarly.* **Description:** Covers hydrology, oceanology, meteorology with climatology, biometeorology with agrometeorology, etc.
Formerly (until 1956): Przeglad Meteorologiczny i Hydrologiczny
Indexed: BibCart, GEOBASE.
—CISTI, Linda Hall.
Published by: (Polskie Towarzystwo Geofizyczne/Polish Society of Geophysics), Wydawnictwo Naukowe P W N SA/Polish Scientific Publishers P W N, ul Miodowa 10, Warsaw, 00251, Poland. TEL 48-22-6954181, FAX 48-22-6954288, ksiegarnia@pwn.pl, http://en.pwn.pl. Ed. Z Mikulski. Circ: 860.

PRZEGLAD GEOLOGICZNY/GEOLOGICAL REVIEW. see *EARTH SCIENCES—Geology*

551.22 FIN ISSN 0079-774X
PUBLICATIONS IN SEISMOLOGY✶ . Text in English; Text occasionally in Finnish. 1960. irreg. per issue exchange basis.
Published by: Helsingin Yliopisto, Seismologian Laitos/University of Helsinki, Institute of Seismology, Et Hesperiankatu 4, Helsinki 10, Finland. Ed. Ekjo Vesanen.

551 CHE ISSN 0033-4553
QC801 CODEN: PAGYAV
➤ **PURE AND APPLIED GEOPHYSICS.** Variant title: PAGEOPH. Text in English, French, German. 1939. m. EUR 2,598 combined subscription to institutions print & online eds. (effective 2005). bk.rev. illus. index. back issues avail.; reprints avail. **Document type:** *Journal, Academic/Scholarly.* **Description:** Publishes original scientific contributions in the fields of solid earth and atmospheric sciences as well as oceanic sciences.
Formerly: Geofisica
Related titles: Online - full text ed.: ISSN 1420-9136. 1997 (from EBSCO Publishing, Springer LINK, Swets Information Services).
Indexed: AESIS, ASCA, ASFA, ApMecR, BAS, CIS, ChemAb, CurCont, ESPM, EngInd, ExcerpMed, FLUIDEX, GEOBASE, IAA, INIS AtomInd, ISR, Inspec, M&GPA, PetrolAb, PhysBer, RefZh, SCI, SWRA.
—BLDSC (7161.400000), AskIEEE, CASDDS, CISTI, Ei, IDS, IE, Infotrieve, ingenta, Linda Hall, PADDS. **CCC.**
Published by: Birkhaeuser Verlag AG (Subsidiary of: Springer Science+Business Media), Viaduktstr 42, Postfach 133, Basel, 4051, Switzerland. TEL 41-61-2050707, FAX 41-61-2050799, pageoph@birkhauser.ch, info@birkhauser.ch, http://link.springer.de/link/service/journals/00024/index.htm, http://www.birkhauser.ch/journals. Eds. Brian J Mitchell TEL 314-977-3131, Renata Dmowska. **Subscr. in the Americas to:** Springer-Verlag New York, Inc., Journal Fulfillment, PO Box 2485, Secaucus, NJ 07096-2485. TEL 201-348-4033, FAX 201-348-4505, journals@birkhauser.com. **Dist. by:** Springer GmbH Auslieferungsgesellschaft.

551 537.534 USA ISSN 0048-6604
QC851 CODEN: RASCAD
➤ **RADIO SCIENCE.** Text in English. 1928. bi-m. USD 450 to institutions (effective 2006). charts; illus. index. back issues avail.; reprint service avail. from PQC,ISI. **Document type:** *Journal, Academic/Scholarly.* **Description:** Contains original articles on all aspects of electromagnetic phenomena related to physical problems.
Former titles (until 1965): National Bureau of Standards. Journal of Research. D, Radio Science (0502-2568); (until 1963): National Bureau of Standards. Journal of Research. D, Radio Propagation (1060-1783); Supersedes in part (in 1959): National Bureau of Standards. Journal of Research (0091-0635); Which was formerly (until 1934): Bureau of Standards. Journal of Research (0091-1801)
Related titles: Microfiche ed.: (from AGU, AIP); Microform ed.: (from AGU, PQC); Online - full text ed.: (from EBSCO Publishing).
Indexed: ASCA, AcoustA, BrCerAb, C&ISA, CMCI, CerAb, ChemAb, CorrAb, CurCont, E&CAJ, EMA, EngInd, ExcerpMed, IAA, ISMEC, ISR, Inspec, M&GPA, M&TEA, MBF, METADEX, PetrolAb, PhysBer, RefZh, SCI, SPINweb, SolStAb, TelAb, WAA.
—BLDSC (7232.999500), AskIEEE, CASDDS, CISTI, Ei, IDS, IE, Infotrieve, ingenta, Linda Hall, PADDS. **CCC.**
Published by: American Geophysical Union, 2000 Florida Ave, NW, Washington, DC 20009-1277. TEL 202-462-6900, 800-966-2481, FAX 202-328-0566, institutions@agu.org, http://www.agu.org/journals/rs/. Ed. A F Spilhaus Jr.

➤ **REFERATIVNYI ZHURNAL. FIZIKA ZEMLI.** see *EARTH SCIENCES—Abstracting, Bibliographies, Statistics*

➤ **REFERATIVNYI ZHURNAL. GEOFIZIKA.** see *EARTH SCIENCES—Abstracting, Bibliographies, Statistics*

➤ **REFERATIVNYI ZHURNAL. GEOMAGNETIZM I VYSOKIE SLOI ATMOSFERY.** see *EARTH SCIENCES—Abstracting, Bibliographies, Statistics*

551 CZE
RESULTS OF GEOMAGNETIC MEASUREMENTS MADE AT THE BUDKOV OBSERVATORY. Text in English. a. **Document type:** *Journal, Academic/Scholarly.* **Description:** Contains all processed values of the Earth's magnetic field for the given year, as measured at the Budkov observatory.
Published by: Akademie Ved Ceske Republiky, Geofyzikalni Ustav, Bocni II/1401, Prague, 14131, Czech Republic. TEL 420-2-67103383, FAX 420-2-72761549, jstr@ig.cas.cz, gfu@ig.cas.cz, http://www.ig.cas.cz. Ed. Jaroslav Strestik.

551 523.01 USA ISSN 8755-1209
QC801 CODEN: REGEEP
➤ **REVIEWS OF GEOPHYSICS.** Text in English. 1963. q. USD 230 to institutions (effective 2006). abstr.; bibl.; charts; illus. index. back issues avail.; reprint service avail. from ISI. **Document type:** *Journal, Academic/Scholarly.* **Description:** Covers all areas of earth and space science. Examines recent research and explains the current level of understanding within a field.
Former titles: Reviews of Geophysics and Space Physics (0034-6853); (until 1969): Reviews of Modern Physics (0096-1043); Reviews of Geophysics
Related titles: Microfiche ed.: (from AGU, AIP); Microform ed.: (from AGU); Online - full content ed.
Indexed: AESIS, ASCA, ASFA, Cadscan, ChemAb, CurCont, ESPM, EngInd, EnvAb, ExcerpMed, GEOBASE, IAA, IBR, ISR, Inspec, LeadAb, M&GPA, MathR, PhysBer, PollutAb, RefZh, SCI, SPINweb, SWRA, Zincscan.
—BLDSC (7790.760000), AskIEEE, CASDDS, CISTI, Ei, IDS, IE, Infotrieve, ingenta, Linda Hall. **CCC.**
Published by: American Geophysical Union, 2000 Florida Ave, NW, Washington, DC 20009-1277. TEL 202-462-6900, 800-966-2481, FAX 202-328-0566, institutions@agu.org, service@agu.org, http://www.agu.org/journals/rg/. Ed. Judy C Holoviak. Circ: 3,000.

550 BRA ISSN 0102-261X
REVISTA BRASILEIRA DE GEOFISICA/BRAZILIAN JOURNAL OF GEOPHYSICS. Text in Portuguese; Abstracts in English. 1982. s-a. USD 50 to individuals; USD 70 to institutions (effective 2003). back issues avail. **Description:** Publishes technical and original articles in the areas of solid earth geophysics, spatial science and applied geophysics.
Related titles: Online - full text ed.: free (effective 2005) (from SciELO).
Indexed: AESIS, GEOBASE, INIS AtomInd, PetrolAb.
—PADDS.
Published by: Sociedade Brasileira de Geofisica, Ave Rio Branco 156, Sala 2510, Rio de Janeiro, 20043-900, Brazil. TEL 55-21-533-0064, http://www.scielo.br/rbg. Ed. Vitorello Icaro.

551 MEX ISSN 0252-9769
QC801
REVISTA GEOFISICA. Text in Spanish. 1974. s-a. MXP 75 domestic; USD 21 in North America; USD 24.50 in South America; USD 28 in Asia & the Pacific (effective 2005). illus. reprint service avail. from PQC. **Document type:** *Academic/Scholarly.*
Supersedes (in 1975): Geofisica Panamericana
Related titles: Online - full text ed.: (from Gale Group).
Indexed: ASFA, GEOBASE.
—CISTI, Linda Hall.
Published by: Instituto Panamericano de Geografia e Historia, Ex-Arzobispado 29, Col Observatorio, Del Miguel Hidalgo, Mexico City, DF 11860, Mexico. TEL 52-55-52775791, FAX 52-55-52716172, ipgh@laneta.apc.org, info@ipgh.org.mx, http://www.ipgh.org.mx/. Ed. Ana Lilliam Martin del Pozo. **Subscr. to:** IPGH-Depto. de Distribucion y Ventas, Apdo. 18879, Mexico City, DF 11870, Mexico.

551 ROM ISSN 1220-5303
CODEN: RRGPA9
REVUE ROUMAINE DE GEOPHYSIQUE. Text in English, French, German, Russian. 1957. a. bk.rev. charts; illus. index.
Formerly (until 1990): Revue Roumaine de Geologie, Geophysique et Geographie. Geophysique (0556-8110); Which supersedes in part (in 1963): Revue de Geologie et de Geographie (1220-1855)
—CISTI, KNAW, Linda Hall.
Published by: (Academia Romana, Institutul de Geodinamica), Editura Academiei Romane/Publishing House of the Romanian Academy, Calea 13 Septembrie 13, Sector 5, Bucharest, 76117, Romania. TEL 40-21-4119008, FAX 40-21-4103983, edacad@ear.ro. Ed. Liviu Constantinescu. **Dist. by:** Rodipet S.A., Piata Presei Libere 1, sector 1, PO Box 33-57, Bucharest 3, Romania. TEL 40-21-2224126, 40-21-2226407, rodipet@rodipet.ro.

551 ROM ISSN 1220-5680
TN95.R8 CODEN: IGGFA7
ROMANIAN JOURNAL OF GEOPHYSICS. Text in English. 1947. a. USD 35 (effective 1999). **Document type:** *Academic/Scholarly.*
Former titles (until 1992): Institutul de Geologie si Geofizica. Studii Tehnice si Economice. Geofizica (1018-0494); (until 1984): Institutul de Geologie si Geofizica. Studii Tehnice si Economice. Seria D, Prospectiuni Geofizice (0376-4834); (until 1974): Institutul Geologic. Studii Tehnice si Economice. Seria D, Prospectiuni Geofizice (0374-1494)
Indexed: RefZh.
—CASDDS.
Published by: Institutul Geologic al Romaniei, Str. Caransebes 1, Bucharest, 78344, Romania. TEL 40-1-2442091, FAX 40-1-2240404, udubasa@igr.ro. Ed. Gheorghe Udubasa. R&P Serban Veliciu TEL 40-1-2242093. Circ: 550.

551 RUS ISSN 1026-3527
QC801 CODEN: IAFZAK
ROSSIISKAYA AKADEMIYA NAUK. IZVESTIYA. FIZIKA ZEMLI. Text in Russian. 1965. m. RUR 850 for 6 mos. domestic (effective 2004). bk.rev. charts; illus. index. **Document type:** *Journal, Academic/Scholarly.* **Description:** Publishes results of original theoretical and experimental research in relevant areas of the physics of the earth's interior and applied geophysics.
Formerly (until 1992): Akademiya Nauk S.S.S.R. Izvestiya. Fizika Zemli (0002-3337); Supersedes: Akademiya Nauk S.S.S.R. Izvestiya. Seriya Geofizicheskaya
Related titles: Online - full text ed.; ♦ English Translation: Russian Academy of Sciences. Izvestiya. Physics of the Solid Earth. ISSN 1069-3513.
Indexed: CCMJ, CIN, ChemAb, ChemTitl, CurCont, Inspec, MathR, MathSciNet, PetrolAb, RefZh.
—BLDSC (0389.743000), AskIEEE, CASDDS, CISTI, East View, IDS, KNAW, Linda Hall, PADDS. **CCC.**
Published by: (Rossiiskaya Akademiya Nauk/Russian Academy of Sciences), Izdatel'stvo Nauka, Profsoyuznaya ul 90, Moscow, 117864, Russian Federation. TEL 7-095-3347151, FAX 7-095-4202220, journal@uipe-ras.scgis.ru, secret@naukaran.ru, http://www.maik.rssi.ru/cgi-bin/list.pl?page=fizzemli, http://www.naukaran.ru. **US dist. addr.:** Interperiodica, PO Box 1831, Birmingham, AL 35201-1831. TEL 205-995-1567, 800-633-4931, FAX 205-995-1588.

ROSSIISKAYA AKADEMIYA NAUK. SIBIRSKOE OTDELENIE. OB'EDINENNYI INSTITUT GEOLOGII, GEOFIZIKI, I MINERALOGII. TRUDY. see *EARTH SCIENCES—Geology*

551 RUS ISSN 1069-3513
QC801 CODEN: IASEEQ
RUSSIAN ACADEMY OF SCIENCES. IZVESTIYA. PHYSICS OF THE SOLID EARTH. Text in English. 1957. m. USD 1,202 in North America; USD 1,329 elsewhere (effective 2004). bibl.; charts; illus. index. reprint service avail. from ISI. **Document type:** *Journal, Academic/Scholarly.* **Description:** Publishes results of original theoretical and experimental research in relevant areas of the physics of the earth's interior and applied geophysics.

E

Formerly (until 1992): Academy of Sciences of the U S S R. Izvestiya. Physics of the Solid Earth (0001-4354); Which superseded in part (in 1965): Academy of Sciences of the U S S R. Bulletin. Geophysics Series (0568-5249)
Related titles: ♦ Translation of: Rossiiskaya Akademiya Nauk. Izvestiya. Fizika Zemli. ISSN 1026-3527.
Indexed: ASFA, ApMecR, CurCont, EEA, ESPM, Inspec, MathR, PetrolAb, PhysBer.
—BLDSC (0412.740595), AskIEEE, CISTI, IE, Infotrieve, ingenta, Linda Hall, PADDS. **CCC.**
Published by: (Rossiiskaya Akademiya Nauk/Russian Academy of Sciences), M A I K Nauka - Interperiodica, Profsoyuznaya ul 90, Moscow, 117997, Russian Federation. TEL 7-095-3347420, FAX 7-095-3360666, compmg@maik.ru, http://www.maik.rssi.ru/journals/physeth.htm, http://www.maik.ru. Ed. Aleksandr A Kalachnikov. **Dist by:** Interperiodica, PO Box 1831, Birmingham, AL 35201-1831, TEL 205-995-1567, 800-633-4931, FAX 205-995-1588.

RUSSIAN GEOLOGY AND GEOPHYSICS. see *EARTH SCIENCES—Geology*

622.15   USA   ISSN 0737-0164
S E G ABSTRACTS. (Society of Exploration Geophysicists) Text in English. irreg.
Formerly (until 1981): Society of Exploration Geophysicists. International Meeting. Abstracts (0740-543X)
—**CCC.**
Published by: Society of Exploration Geophysicists, PO Box 702740, Tulsa, OK 74170-2740. TEL 918-497-5500, FAX 918-497-5558, http://www.seg.org.

551   SWE   ISSN 0283-0175
S G I - NU. Text in Swedish. 1985. biennial.
Related titles: Online - full text ed.
Published by: Statens Geotekniska Institut/Swedish Geotechnical Institute, Olaus Magnus Vaeg 35, Linkoeping, 58193, Sweden. TEL 46-13-201800, sgi@swedgeo.se, http://www.swedgeo.se. Ed. Goeran Karlsson. Circ: 3,000.

551   USA
SCHOOL OF OCEAN AND EARTH SCIENCE AND TECHNOLOGY. BIENNIAL REPORT. Text in English. biennial. free to qualified personnel.
Former titles: Hawaii Institute of Geophysics. Technical Reports and Special Publications; S O E S T Special Publications
Indexed: ASFA.
Published by: School of Ocean and Earth Science and Technology, 2525 Correa Rd, Honolulu, HI 96822. TEL 808-956-7059.

SCRIPTUM; Arbeitsergebnisse aus dem Geologischen Dienst Nordrhein-Westfalen. see *EARTH SCIENCES*

551.22   USA   ISSN 0747-9239
QE541   CODEN: SIEEEK
➤ **SEISMIC INSTRUMENTS.** Text in English. 1979. irreg., latest vol.33. USD 600 per vol. worldwide (effective 2006). abstr.; charts; maps. back issues avail. **Document type:** *Journal, Academic/Scholarly.* **Description:** Covers instrument design, monitoring seismic data interpretation, and computerized seismic stations.
Related titles: Translation of: Seismicheskie Pribory. ISSN 0131-6230. 1969.
Indexed: Inspec.
—AskIEEE, CISTI, Linda Hall. **CCC.**
Published by: (Rossiiskaya Akademiya Nauk, Institut Fiziki Zemli RUS), Allerton Press, Inc., 18 W 27th St, New York, NY 10001. TEL 646-424-9686, FAX 646-424-9695, journals@allertonpress.com, http://www.allertonpress.com/journals/shi.htm. Ed. Anatolii V Rykov.

551   USA   ISSN 1043-2175
SEISMIC INTERPRETATION SERIES. Text in English. 1989. a.
Document type: *Academic/Scholarly.*
—**CCC.**
Published by: Society of Exploration Geophysicists, PO Box 702740, Tulsa, OK 74170-2740. TEL 918-497-5546, FAX 918-497-5558.

551.22   PRT
SEISMOLOGICAL BULLETIN. Text in English. 1946. 6/yr. free to scientific institutions. back issues avail. **Document type:** *Bulletin.*
Formerly (until 2001): Station Seismographique de Lisboa. Bulletin Seismique (0039-0356)
Related titles: E-mail ed.; Online - full text ed.
Published by: Instituto Geofisico do Infante D. Luis, Rua da Escola Politecnica, 58, Lisbon, 1250, Portugal. FAX 351-1-3953327, TELEX 404-65869 FCULIS-P, sisgidl@fc.ul.pt, http://www.iigidl.ul.pt/boletimsismico.htm. Ed. Luis Alberto Mendes Victor. Circ: 230.

551.22   USA   ISSN 0895-0695
QE531   CODEN: SRLEEG
➤ **SEISMOLOGICAL RESEARCH LETTERS.** Text in English. 1929. bi-m. USD 140 in North America; USD 150 elsewhere; USD 565 combined subscription in North America includes Seismological Sociaty of America. Bulletin; USD 585 combined subscription elsewhere includes Seismological Sociaty of America. Bulletin (effective 2006). bk.rev.; software rev. charts; illus.; stat.; maps. 80 p./no.; back issues avail.; reprint service avail. from PQC. **Document type:** *Journal, Academic/Scholarly.* **Description:** Dedicated to general issues that affect seismology, earthquake engineering, seismologists, earthquake engineers, and the public at large.
Formerly (until vol.57, 1986): Earthquake Notes (0012-8287)
Related titles: Microform ed.: (from PQC.)
Indexed: AJEE, ASFA, C&ISA, CurCont, E&CAJ, EEA, ESPM, EngInd, H&SSA, IAA, Inspec, SWRA.
—BLDSC (8227.200000), AskIEEE, CISTI, IE, Infotrieve, ingenta, Linda Hall. **CCC.**
Published by: Seismological Society of America, 201 Plaza Professional Bldg, El Cerrito, CA 94530-4003. TEL 510-525-5474, FAX 510-525-7204, info@seismosoc.org, publications@seismosoc.org, http://www.seismosoc.org/ssa/. Ed. susan Hough. R&P Janice Sellers TEL 510-559-1780. Circ: 2,200 (paid).

551.22   USA   ISSN 0037-1106
QE531   CODEN: BSSAAP
➤ **SEISMOLOGICAL SOCIETY OF AMERICA. BULLETIN.** Key Title: Bulletin of the Seismological Society of America - B S S A. Text in English. 1911. bi-m. USD 450 in North America to institutions; USD 460 elsewhere to institutions; USD 565 combined subscription in North America to institutions includes Seismological Research Letters; USD 585 combined subscription elsewhere to institutions includes Seismological Research Letters (effective 2006). bibl.; charts; illus.; maps. index, cum.index. 275 p./no.; back issues avail.; reprints avail. **Document type:** *Journal, Academic/Scholarly.* **Description:** Publishes scientific papers on the various aspects of seismology, including investigation of specific earthquakes, theoretical and observational studies of seismic waves and earthquake hazard and risk estimation.
Related titles: Microfiche ed.; Microfilm ed.; Online - full text ed.: (from HighWire Press, O C L C Online Computer Library Center, Inc.)
Indexed: AESIS, AJEE, AS&TI, ASCA, ASFA, AcoustA, ApMecR, CCMJ, CIS, CurCont, EEA, ESPM, EngInd, GEOBASE, GSW, GeotechAb, IAA, INIS AtomInd, ISR, Inspec, MathR, MathSciNet, PetrolAb, RefZh, S&F, SCI, SPPI.
—BLDSC (2711.000000), AskIEEE, CISTI, Ei, IDS, IE, Infotrieve, ingenta, Linda Hall, PADDS. **CCC.**
Published by: Seismological Society of America, 201 Plaza Professional Bldg, El Cerrito, CA 94530-4003. TEL 510-525-5474, FAX 510-525-7204, info@seismosoc.org, publications@seismosoc.org, http://www.seismosoc.org/ssa/. Ed. Michael Fehler. R&P Janice Sellers TEL 510-559-1780. Circ: 2,500 (paid).

551.22   RUS
SEISMOSTOIKOE STROITEL'STVO. BEZOPASNOST' SOORUZHENII/EARTHQUAKE ENGINEERING. Text in Russian; Abstracts and contents page in English, Russian. 1974. bi-m. RUR 420, USD 60 (effective 2000). bibl.; illus. **Description:** Covers research on earthquake engineering, earthquake-resistant building design, seismology, seismoisolation, and seismic observations on buildings and structures.
Formerly (until 2000): Seismostoikoe Stroitel'stvo (1562-2487)
Indexed: RefZh.
Published by: Vserossiiskii Gosudarstvennyi Nauchno-Issledovatel'skii Institut Problem Nauchno-Tekhnicheskogo Progressa i Informatsii v Stroitel'stve, 1-ya Tverskaya-Yamskaya 6, Moscow, 125147, Russian Federation. TEL 7-095-251-1795, FAX 7-095-133-5130, director@vniintpi.net.ru, eisenberg@glasnet.ru, http://www.vniintpi.net.ru. Ed. J M Eisenberg TEL 7-095-174-7064. Pub., R&P Gennady Vorontsov. **Dist. by:** Rospechat', Pr-t Marshala Zhukova 4, Moscow 123995, Russian Federation; **US dist. addr.:** East View Information Services, 3020 Harbor Ln. N., Minneapolis, MN 55447. TEL 612-550-0961.

551.22   CHN   ISSN 1000-6265
SHANXI DIZHEN/EARTHQUAKE RESEARCH IN SHANXI. Text in Chinese. 1973. q. CNY 1.50 per issue.
Related titles: Online - full text ed.: (from East View Information Services)
Published by: Shanxi Dizhen-ju/Shanxi Seismology Bureau, 10 Xinjian Lu, Taiyuan, Shanxi 030002, China. TEL 222090. Ed. Sun Guoxue. Circ: 2,000.

551.22   CHN   ISSN 1003-3238
SHIJIE DIZHEN YICONG/TRANSLATED WORLD SEISMOLOGY. Text in Chinese. 1982. bi-m. **Document type:** *Journal, Academic/Scholarly.*
Published by: Guojia Dizhen-ju, Diqiu Wuli Yanjiusuo/National Bureau of Seismology, Institute of Geophysics, 5, Minzuxueyuan Nanlu, Haidian District, Beijing, 100081, China. TEL 86-10-68417744, FAX 86-10-68415372, snowyang@263.net, http://www.eq-igp.ac.cn/. Ed. Chen Yuntai.

551   SVK   ISSN 1335-2806
QC801   CODEN: CGISAO
➤ **SLOVAK ACADEMY OF SCIENCES. GEOPHYSICAL INSTITUTE. CONTRIBUTIONS TO GEOPHYSICS AND GEODESY.** Text and summaries in English, Russian. 1971. q. USD 60 foreign (effective 2001). adv. bk.rev. **Document type:** *Academic/Scholarly.* **Description:** Contains scientific papers concerning the theory of geophysical potential fields, applied and environmental geophysics, geodesy, meteorology and climatology.
Formerly (until 1998): Slovak Academy of Sciences. Geophysical Institute. Contributions (0586-4607)
Indexed: GEOBASE, INIS AtomInd, Inspec, M&GPA.
—AskIEEE, CISTI.
Published by: Slovenska Akademia Vied, Geofyzikalny Ustav, Dubravska cesta 9, Bratislava, 842 28, Slovakia. TEL 421-7-59410603, FAX 421-7-59410626, geoflabi@savba.sk, http://gpi.savba.sk. Ed. Milan Hvozdara. adv.: page USD 700. Circ: 300.

551   SVK   ISSN 0139-9349
SLOVAK SEISMOGRAPHIC STATIONS: BRATISLAVA, SROBAROVA, HURBANOVO AND SKALNATE PLESO. BULLETIN. Text and summaries in English. 1965. a. USD 2.85. abstr.
Supersedes in part (in 1966): Czechoslovak Seismological Stations: Pryhonice, Praha, Kaspersk Hory, Cheb, Bratislava, Srobarova, Hurbanovo and Skalnate Pleso. Bulletin (0139-9209)
Published by: (Slovenska Akademia Vied/Slovak Academy of Sciences, Geofyzikalny Ustav), Vydavatel'stvo Slovenskej Akademie Vied Veda/Veda, Publishing House of the Slovak Academy of Sciences, Dubravska cesta 9, Bratislava, 84234, Slovakia. Ed. Klara Mrazova. Circ: 500. **Dist. by:** Slovart G.T.G. s.r.o., Krupinska 4, PO Box 152, Bratislava 85299, Slovakia. TEL 421-2-63839472, FAX 421-2-63839485, http://www.slovart-gtg.sk.

SOCIETA ITALIANA DI FISICA. NUOVO CIMENTO C. GEOPHYSICS AND SPACE PHYSICS. see *PHYSICS*

551   USA   ISSN 1052-3812
SOCIETY OF EXPLORATION GEOPHYSICISTS. EXPANDED ABSTRACTS WITH BIOGRAPHIES. Text in English. 19??. a. **Document type:** *Monographic series, Academic/Scholarly.*
Former titles (until 1983): Technical Program, Abstracts and Biographies (1059-0811); (until 1981): Society of Exploration Geophysicists. International Meeting and Exposition. Technical Papers (0733-6063)
—**CCC.**
Published by: Society of Exploration Geophysicists, PO Box 702740, Tulsa, OK 74170-2740. TEL 918-497-5500, FAX 918-497-5557, books@seg.org, http://www.seg.org.

551   USA   ISSN 1046-0586
SOCIETY OF EXPLORATION GEOPHYSICISTS. GEOPHYSICAL DEVELOPMENT SERIES. Text in English. 1987. irreg., latest vol.131, 2003. price varies. **Document type:** *Monographic series.*
—BLDSC (4149.600000). **CCC.**
Published by: Society of Exploration Geophysicists, PO Box 702740, Tulsa, OK 74170-2740. TEL 918-497-5500, FAX 918-497-5557, http://www.seg.org.

551   USA   ISSN 0734-5631
SOCIETY OF EXPLORATION GEOPHYSICISTS. GEOPHYSICS REPRINT SERIES. Text in English. 1978. irreg., latest vol.198, 2001. price varies.
—BLDSC (4158.127000), CISTI. **CCC.**
Published by: Society of Exploration Geophysicists, PO Box 702740, Tulsa, OK 74170-2740. TEL 918-497-5500, FAX 918-497-5557, http://www.seg.org.

622.15   USA
SOCIETY OF EXPLORATION GEOPHYSICISTS. INTERNATIONAL MEETING. PROCEEDINGS. Text in English. a.
—BLDSC (1086.700000), ingenta.
Published by: Society of Exploration Geophysicists, PO Box 702740, Tulsa, OK 74170-2740. TEL 918-497-5500, FAX 918-497-5557, books@seg.org, http://www.seg.org.

622.15   USA
➤ **SOCIETY OF EXPLORATION GEOPHYSICISTS. SPECIAL PUBLICATIONS (SYMPOSIA) SERIES.** Text in English. 1947. irreg. price varies. **Document type:** *Monographic series, Academic/Scholarly.*
Related titles: Microform ed.
Published by: Society of Exploration Geophysicists, PO Box 702740, Tulsa, OK 74170-2740. TEL 918-497-5500.

551 624.176   GBR   ISSN 0267-7261
TA710.A1
➤ **SOIL DYNAMICS AND EARTHQUAKE ENGINEERING.** Text in English. 1982. 12/yr. EUR 2,017 in Europe to institutions; JPY 267,700 in Japan to institutions; USD 2,254 elsewhere to institutions (effective 2006). adv. reprints avail. **Document type:** *Academic/Scholarly.* **Description:** Covers applications of mechanics, mathematics, engineering and other applied sciences to problems in the field of earthquake and geotechnical engineering.

Formerly (until 1984): International Journal of Soil Dynamics and Earthquake Engineering (0261-7277)
Related titles: Microform ed.: (from PQC); Online - full text ed.: (from EBSCO Publishing, Gale Group, IngentaConnect, ScienceDirect, Swets Information Services).
Indexed: ASCA, ASFA, ApMecR, BrCerAb, C&ISA, CerAb, CivEngAb, CorrAb, CurCont, E&CAJ, EEA, EMA, EPB, ESPM, Englnd, FLUIDEX, GEOBASE, GeotechAb, H&SSA, IAA, ICEA, ISR, Inspec, M&TEA, MBF, METADEX, RefZh, SCI, SWRA, SolStAb, WAA.
—BLDSC (8322.225000), AskIEEE, CISTI, Ei, IDS, IE, Infotrieve, ingenta, Linda Hall. **CCC.**
Published by: Pergamon (Subsidiary of: Elsevier Science & Technology), The Boulevard, Langford Ln, East Park, Kidlington, Oxford OX5 1GB, United Kingdom. TEL 44-1865-843000, FAX 44-1865-843010, http://www.elsevier.com/locate/soildyn. Ed. M Erdik. Circ: 500.
Subscr. to: Elsevier BV, PO Box 211, Amsterdam 1000 AE, Netherlands. TEL 31-20-485-3757, FAX 31-20-485-3432, nlinfo-f@elsevier.nl, http://www.elsevier.nl.

➤ **SOLAR-GEOPHYSICAL DATA. PART 1 - PROMPT REPORTS.** see *ASTRONOMY*

➤ **SOLAR-GEOPHYSICAL DATA: PART 2 - COMPREHENSIVE REPORTS.** see *ASTRONOMY*

551 USA ISSN 1046-1914
SOLAR INDICES BULLETIN. Text in English. m. USD 17 (effective 1998). **Document type:** *Bulletin, Government.*
Description: Contains monthly compilations of sunspot numbers and solar radio flux from radio observatories around the world.
Published by: (National Oceanic and Atmospheric Administration), U.S. National Geophysical Data Center, 325 Broadway, E CG4, Boulder, CO 80303-3328. TEL 303-497-6836, FAX 303-497-6958, info@ngdc.noaa.gov, http://www.ngdc.noaa.gov. Ed. John McKinnon.

551.22 ZAF
SOUTH AFRICA. COUNCIL FOR GEOSCIENCE. SEISMOLOGIC SERIES. Text in Afrikaans, English. 1972. irreg., latest vol.24. price varies. **Document type:** *Bulletin, Government.*
Description: Documents natural and man-induced earthquakes occurring in Southern Africa and provides a forum for publishing research work in this field.
Formerly: South Africa. Geological Survey. Seismologic Series
Published by: Council for Geoscience, Private Bag X112, Pretoria, 0001, South Africa. TEL 27-12-841-1911, FAX 27-12-841-1203, rprice@geoscience.org.za.

SOUTHEASTERN GEOLOGY. see *EARTH SCIENCES—Geology*

551 SWE ISSN 0348-0755
CODEN: RGINE8
STATENS GEOTEKNISKA INSTITUT. RAPPORT/SWEDISH GEOTECHNICAL INSTITUTE. REPORT. Text in English, Swedish; Summaries in English. 1977. irreg. (2-3/yr.), latest vol.64, 2003. price varies. back issues avail. **Document type:** *Monographic series, Government.* **Description:** Presents the research and development work of the Institute.
Formed by the merger of (1946-1972): Statens Geotekniska Institut. Meddelanden; (1960-1977): Statens Geotekniska Institut. Saertryck och Preliminaera Rapporter (0562-0953); (1950-1975): Statens Geotekniska Institut. Proceedings (0081-5705)
Indexed: DokStr, GeotechAb.
—CISTI, Linda Hall.
Published by: Statens Geotekniska Institut/Swedish Geotechnical Institute, Olaus Magnus Vaeg 35, Linkoeping, 58193, Sweden. TEL 46-13-201800, sgi@swedgeo.se, http://www.swedgeotek.se, http://www.swedgeo.se. Ed. Bengt Rydell. Circ: 1,000.

332.6 THA
STOCK MARKET IN THAILAND. Text in English. 1983. a. THB 70; USD 8 in Asia; USD 9.50 elsewhere. **Document type:** *Trade.*
Published by: Stock Exchange of Thailand, 62 Rachadapisek Rd, Klongtoey, Bangkok, 10110, Thailand. TEL 662-229-2000, FAX 662-654-5649, webmaster@setinter1.set.or.th, http://www.set.or.th.

551.22 JPN ISSN 0563-7902
STRONG-MOTION EARTHQUAKE RECORDS IN JAPAN/KYOSHIN KIROKU. Text in English. 1960. s-a. per issue exchange basis. stat. **Document type:** *Government.*
Indexed: EEA.
Published by: Science and Technology Agency, National Research Institute for Earth Science and Disaster Prevention/Kagaku Gijutsucho Bosai Kagaku Gijutsu Kenkyujo, 3-1 Tenno-Dai, Tsukuba-shi, Ibaraki-ken 305-0006, Japan. TEL 0298-51-1611, FAX 0298-51-1622, TELEX 3652595 NIED J. Ed. Makoto Miyamoto.

551.4 POL ISSN 0081-6434
QE260 CODEN: SGCAAE
STUDIA GEOMORPHOLOGICA CARPATHO-BALCANICA. Text in English. 1967. a. price varies. **Document type:** *Academic/Scholarly.*
—BLDSC (8482.700000).
Published by: (Polska Akademia Nauk, Oddzial w Krakowie, Komisja Nauk Geograficznych), Polska Akademia Nauk, Oddzial w Krakowie, ul sw Jana 28, Krakow, 31018, Poland. TEL 48-12-224853, FAX 48-12-222791. Ed. Leszek Starkel.

551 526 CZE ISSN 0039-3169
QC801 CODEN: SGEGA8
➤ **STUDIA GEOPHYSICA ET GEODAETICA**; a journal of geophysics, geodesy, meteorology and climatology. Text and summaries in English, French, German, Russian. 1957. q. EUR 1,113, USD 1,113, GBP 696 combined subscription to institutions print & online eds. (effective 2005). abstr.; charts; illus.; maps. index. reprint service avail. from PSC. **Document type:** *Journal, Academic/Scholarly.* **Description:** Publishes papers on original research into geophysics, geodesy, meteorology and climatology.
Related titles: Online - full text ed.: ISSN 1573-1626 (from EBSCO Publishing, Gale Group, IngentaConnect, Kluwer Online, O C L C Online Computer Library Center, Inc., Ovid Technologies, Inc., Springer LINK, Swets Information Services).
Indexed: ASCA, BibLing, ChemAb, CurCont, FLUIDEX, GEOBASE, IAA, ISR, Inspec, M&GPA, PetrolAb, SCI.
—BLDSC (8482.800000), AskIEEE, CASDDS, CISTI, IDS, IE, Infotrieve, ingenta, Linda Hall. **CCC.**
Published by: Akademie Ved Ceske Republiky, Geofyzikalni Ustav, Bocni II/1401, Prague, 14131, Czech Republic. TEL 420-2-67103383, FAX 420-2-72761549, studia@ig.cas.cz, http://www.ig.cas.cz/studia. Ed. Milan Bursa. Circ: 800.
Subscr. to: Plenum US, 233 Spring St, New York, NY 10013.

551 USA ISSN 0743-0213
STUDIES IN GEOPHYSICS. Text in English. irreg. **Document type:** *Monographic series.*
Indexed: Inspec.
Published by: (National Research Council), National Academy Press, 2101 Constitution Ave, N W, Lockbox 285, Washington, DC 20055. TEL 202-334-3313, 888-624-8373, FAX 202-334-2451, zjones@nas.edu.

551 ROM ISSN 1220-5265
QE500 CODEN: SCGGBP
STUDII SI CERCETARI DE GEOFIZICA. Text in Romanian. 1963. a.
Former titles (until 1990): Studii si Cercetari de Geologie, Geofizica, Geografie. Seria Geofizica (0378-6021); (until 1964): Studii si Cercetari de Geofizica (1220-1626)
Indexed: Inspec.
—AskIEEE, CASDDS, CISTI, Linda Hall.
Published by: (Academia Romana), Editura Academiei Romane/Publishing House of the Romanian Academy, Calea 13 Septembrie 13, Sector 5, Bucharest, 76117, Romania. TEL 40-21-4119008, FAX 40-21-4103983, edacad@ear.ro, http://www.ear.ro. Ed. Liviu Constaninescu. **Dist. by:** Rodipet S.A., Piata Presei Libere 1, sector 1, PO Box 33-57, Bucharest 3, Romania. TEL 40-21-2224126, 40-21-2226407, rodipet@rodipet.ro.

526 FIN ISSN 0085-6932
QB296.F5 CODEN: VFGIAG
SUOMEN GEODEETTISEN LAITOS. JULKAISUJA/FINNISCHES GEODAETISCHES INSTITUT. VEROEFFENTLICHUNGEN/ FINNISH GEODETIC INSTITUTE. PUBLICATIONS. Text and summaries in English, French, German. 1923. irreg. price varies. **Document type:** *Government.*
—BLDSC (7062.600000), Linda Hall.
Published by: Geodeettinen Laitos/Finnish Geodetic Institute, Geodeetinrinne 2, Masala, 02430, Finland. Circ: 300.

551 FIN ISSN 0355-1962
SUOMEN GEODEETTISEN LAITOS. TIEDONANTOJA/FINNISH GEODETIC INSTITUTE. REPORTS. Text in English. 1973. irreg. price varies. **Document type:** *Government.*
—BLDSC (7470.950000), CISTI.
Published by: Geodeettinen Laitos/Finnish Geodetic Institute, Geodeetinrinne 2, Masala, 02430, Finland.

551.2 ISL ISSN 0585-9999
QH166 CODEN: SURPAS
SURTSEY RESEARCH PROGRESS REPORT. Text in English. 1964. irreg.
—CISTI.
Published by: Surtsey Research Society, PO Box 352, Reykjavik, 121, Iceland. TEL 354-562-9822, FAX 354-562-0815. Ed. Steingrimur Hermannsson.

551 NLD ISSN 0169-3298
QE1 CODEN: SUGEEC
➤ **SURVEYS IN GEOPHYSICS**; an international review journal of geophysics and planetary sciences. Text in English. 1973. bi-m. EUR 698, USD 708, GBP 458 combined subscription to institutions print & online eds. (effective 2005). bk.rev. illus. back issues avail.; reprint service avail. from PSC. **Document type:** *Journal, Academic/Scholarly.* **Description:** Publishes articles covering the study of the physical processes of the atmosphere, oceans and interior of the Earth, Moon and other planets of the solar system.
Formerly (until 1986): Geophysical Surveys (0046-5763)
Related titles: Microform ed.: (from PQC); Online - full text ed.: ISSN 1573-0956 (from EBSCO Publishing, Gale Group, IngentaConnect, Kluwer Online, O C L C Online Computer Library Center, Inc., Ovid Technologies, Inc., Springer LINK, Swets Information Services).
Indexed: A&AAb, AESIS, ASCA, ASFA, ApMecR, BibLing, CMCI, CivEngAb, CurCont, ESPM, Englnd, GEOBASE, IAA, ISR, Inspec, M&GPA, OceAb, PetrolAb, PhysBer, PollutAb, RefZh, SCI, SWRA.
—BLDSC (8549.377000), AskIEEE, CISTI, Ei, IDS, IE, Infotrieve, ingenta, Linda Hall. **CCC.**
Published by: (European Geophysical Society USA), Springer-Verlag Dordrecht (Subsidiary of: Springer Science+Business Media), Van Godewijckstraat 30, Dordrecht, 3311 GX, Netherlands. TEL 31-78-6576050, FAX 31-78-6576474, http://springerlink.metapress.com/openurl.asp?genre=journal&issn=0169-3298, http://www.springeronline.com.

551 SWE ISSN 0284-169X
SWEDISH INSTITUTE OF SPACE PHYSICS. ANNUAL REPORT. Text in Swedish. 1985. a. free. **Document type:** *Academic/Scholarly.*
Formerly: Kiruna Geophysical Institute. Annual Report (0283-1686)
Related titles: Online - full text ed.
Published by: Institutet foer Rymdfysik/Swedish Institute of Space Physics, PO Box 812, Kiruna, 98128, Sweden. TEL 46-980-79000, FAX 46-980-79050, rick.mcgregor@irf.se, irf@irf.se, http://www.irf.se/publications. Ed. Rick McGregor. Circ: 1,000.

551 SWE ISSN 0284-1703
SWEDISH INSTITUTE OF SPACE PHYSICS. SCIENTIFIC REPORT. Text in English. 1973. irreg. free. charts. back issues avail. **Document type:** *Academic/Scholarly.*
Description: Features investigations of various phenomena of concern to physicists.
Former titles: Kiruna Geophysical Institute. Scientific Report (0283-1694); Kiruna Geophysical Institute. Report (0347-6405)
Related titles: Online - full text ed.
—BLDSC (4567.808900).
Published by: Institutet foer Rymdfysik/Swedish Institute of Space Physics, PO Box 812, Kiruna, 98128, Sweden. TEL 46-980-79000, FAX 46-980-79050, irf@irf.se, http://www.irf.se/publications.

550 539 SWE ISSN 0284-1738
SWEDISH INSTITUTE OF SPACE PHYSICS. TECHNICAL REPORT. Text and summaries in English, Swedish. 1969. irreg. free. back issues avail. **Document type:** *Academic/Scholarly.*
Former titles (until 1988): Kiruna Geophysical Institute. Technical Report (0349-2672); (until 1980): K G I Teknisk Rapport; (until 1974): Technical Report
Related titles: Online - full text ed.
Published by: Institutet foer Rymdfysik/Swedish Institute of Space Physics, PO Box 812, Kiruna, 98128, Sweden. TEL 46-980-79000, FAX 46-980-79050, irf@irf.se, http://www.irf.se/publications.

TECHNIKA POSZUKIWAN GEOLOGICZNYCH, GEOSYNOPTYKA I GEOTERMIA/EXPLORATION TECHNOLOGY, GEOSYNOPTICS AND GEOTHERMAL ENERGY. see *EARTH SCIENCES—Geology*

551 USA ISSN 0278-7407
QE601 CODEN: TCTNDM
➤ **TECTONICS.** Text in English. 1982. bi-m. USD 360 to institutions (effective 2005 - 2006). charts; illus. Index. back issues avail.; reprints avail. **Document type:** *Journal, Academic/Scholarly.* **Description:** Contains leading papers on the structure and evolution of the lithosphere; analytical, synthetic, and integrative tectonics; and tectonic process.
Related titles: Microfiche ed.: (from AGU, AIP); Microform ed.: (from AGU); Online - full content ed.: USD 360 to institutions; USD 580 combined subscription to institutions print & online eds. (effective 2005); Online - full text ed.: (from EBSCO Publishing).
Indexed: AESIS, ASCA, CurCont, Englnd, GEOBASE, IAA, ISR, Inspec, PetrolAb, RefZh, SCI, SPINweb.
—BLDSC (8763.003500), AskIEEE, CISTI, Ei, IDS, IE, Infotrieve, ingenta, Linda Hall, PADDS. **CCC.**
Published by: American Geophysical Union, 2000 Florida Ave, NW, Washington, DC 20009-1277. TEL 202-462-6900, 800-966-2481, FAX 202-328-0566, institutions@agu.org, service@agu.org, http://www.agu.org/journals/tc/. Ed. Kip V Hodges. **Co-sponsor:** European Geophysical Society.

551.8 NLD ISSN 0040-1951
CODEN: TCTOAM
➤ **TECTONOPHYSICS.** Text in English, French, German. 1964. 68/yr. EUR 4,639 in Europe to institutions; JPY 616,700 in Japan to institutions; USD 5,190 to institutions except Europe and Japan; EUR 451 in Europe to qualified personnel; JPY 59,400 in Japan to qualified personnel; USD 504 to qualified personnel except Europe and Japan (effective 2006). adv. bk.rev. abstr.; charts; illus. back issues avail.; reprints avail. **Document type:** *Journal, Academic/Scholarly.* **Description:** Publishes original research studies and comprehensive reviews in the field of geotectonics and structural geology.

E

Related titles: Microform ed.: (from PQC); Online - full text ed.: (from EBSCO Publishing, Gale Group, IngentaConnect, ScienceDirect, Swets Information Services).
Indexed: AESIS, AJEE, ASCA, ASFA, C&ISA, CIN, CIS, CMCI, ChemAb, ChemTitl, CurCont, E&CAJ, EEA, ESPM, EngInd, GEOBASE, GeosDoc, GeotechAb, IAA, IBR, ISR, Inspec, M&GPA, MinerAb, OceAb, PetrolAb, PhysBer, PollutAb, RefZh, SCI, SPPI, SSCI, SWRA.
—BLDSC (8763.020000), AskIEEE, CASDDS, CISTI, Ei, IDS, IE, Infotrieve, ingenta, Linda Hall, PADDS. **CCC.**
Published by: Elsevier BV (Subsidiary of: Elsevier Science & Technology), Radarweg 29, Amsterdam, 1043 NX, Netherlands. TEL 31-20-4853911, FAX 31-20-4852457, nlinfo-f@elsevier.nl, http://www.elsevier.com/locate/tecto, http://www.elsevier.nl. Eds. H Thybo, J P Burg, K P Furlong, M Sandiford.

---

551   DNK   ISSN 0280-6495
QC880   CODEN: TSAOD8
➤ **TELLUS. SERIES A: DYNAMIC METEOROLOGY AND OCEANOGRAPHY.** Text in English, French, German; Summaries in English. 1949. bi-m., latest vol.54, no.5, 2002. EUR 156 combined subscription in Europe to individuals print & online eds.; USD 175 combined subscription in the Americas to individuals & Carribean, print & online eds.; GBP 104 combined subscription elsewhere to individuals print & online eds.; USD 285 combined subscription in the Americas to institutions & Carribean, print & online eds.; GBP 170 combined subscription elsewhere to institutions print & online eds. (effective 2006). adv. abstr.; charts; illus. stat. index. reprint service avail. from ISI,PSC. **Document type:** *Journal, Academic/Scholarly.*
Supersedes in part: Tellus (0040-2826)
Related titles: Online - full text ed.: ISSN 1600-0870. EUR 149 in Europe to individuals; USD 166 in the Americas to individuals & Caribbean; GBP 99 elsewhere to individuals; USD 271 in the Americas to institutions & Caribbean; GBP 162 elsewhere to institutions (effective 2006) (from Blackwell Synergy, EBSCO Publishing, Gale Group, IngentaConnect, O C L C Online Computer Library Center, Inc., Swets Information Services).
Indexed: APD, ASCA, ASFA, ApMecR, BiolAb, BrCerAb, C&ISA, CerAb, ChemAb, CorrAb, CurCont, E&CAJ, EMA, ESPM, EnvAb, EnvInd, ExcerpMed, FCA, FLUIDEX, GEOBASE, I&DA, IAA, IBR, IBZ, ISR, Inspec, M&GPA, M&TEA, MBF, METADEX, MathR, OceAb, S&F, SCI, SWRA, WAA.
—BLDSC (8789.000100), AskIEEE, CASDDS, CISTI, Ei, IDS, IE, ingenta, Linda Hall. **CCC.**
Published by: (Svenska Geofysiska Foerening SWE), Blackwell Munksgaard (Subsidiary of: Blackwell Publishing Ltd.), Rosenoerns Alle 1, PO Box 227, Copenhagen V, 1502, Denmark. TEL 45-77-333333, FAX 45-77-333377, info@mks.blackwellpublishing.com, http:// www.blackwellpublishing.com/journals/TEA, http://www.munksgaard.dk/chemica/toc.html. Ed. Harald Lejenas. Circ: 1,470.

---

551   DNK   ISSN 0280-6509
QC879.6   CODEN: TSBMD7
➤ **TELLUS. SERIES B: CHEMICAL AND PHYSICAL METEOROLOGY.** Text in English, French, German; Summaries in English. 1949. bi-m., latest vol.54, no.5, 2002. EUR 156 combined subscription in Europe to individuals print & online eds.; USD 175 combined subscription in the Americas to individuals & Caribbean, print & online eds.; GBP 104 combined subscription elsewhere to individuals print & online eds.; USD 285 combined subscription in the Americas to institutions & Caribbean, print & online eds.; GBP 170 combined subscription elsewhere to institutions print & online eds. (effective 2006). adv. abstr.; charts; illus.; stat. index. reprint service avail. from ISI,PSC. **Document type:** *Journal, Academic/Scholarly.*
Supersedes in part: Tellus (0040-2826)
Related titles: Online - full text ed.: ISSN 1600-0889. EUR 149 in Europe to individuals; USD 166 in the Americas to individuals & Caribbean; GBP 99 elsewhere to individuals; USD 271 in the Americas to institutions & Caribbean; GBP 162 elsewhere to institutions (effective 2006) (from Blackwell Synergy, EBSCO Publishing, Gale Group, IngentaConnect, O C L C Online Computer Library Center, Inc., Swets Information Services).
Indexed: APD, ASFA, ApMecR, BIOSIS Prev, BiolAb, CIN, ChemAb, ChemTitl, CurCont, ESPM, EngInd, EnvAb, EnvInd, ExcerpMed, FCA, FLUIDEX, GEOBASE, IAA, IBR, IBZ, INIS AtomInd, ISR, Inspec, M&GPA, OceAb, PollutAb, S&F, SCI, SWRA.
—BLDSC (8789.000150), AskIEEE, CASDDS, CISTI, Ei, IDS, IE, Infotrieve, ingenta, Linda Hall. **CCC.**
Published by: (Swedish Geophysical Society SWE), Blackwell Munksgaard (Subsidiary of: Blackwell Publishing Ltd.), Rosenoerns Alle 1, PO Box 227, Copenhagen V, 1502, Denmark. TEL 45-77-333333, FAX 45-77-333377, info@mks.blackwellpublishing.com, http:// www.blackwellpublishing.com/journals/TEB, http://www.munksgaard.dk/. Ed. H Rodhe. Circ: 1,000.

---

551   JPN   ISSN 0040-8794
QC801   CODEN: TGJOD3
➤ **TOHOKU GEOPHYSICAL JOURNAL;** The science reports of the Tohoku University, fifth series. Text in English. 1949. irreg. (3-4/yr.), latest vol.36, no.3, 2002. free exchange basis. bibl.; charts; illus. index. 50 p./no. 1 cols./p.; back issues avail. **Document type:** *Journal, Academic/Scholarly.*

Formerly: Tohoku University. Science Reports. Series 5: Geophysics
Related titles: Microform ed.: (from PMC).
Indexed: ChemAb, Inspec, M&GPA.
—BLDSC (8859.994400), AskIEEE, CISTI, Linda Hall.
Published by: Tohoku Daigaku, Daigakuin Rigaku-Kenkyuka Chikyu-butsurigaku Senko/Department of Geophysics, Graduate School of Science, Tohoku University, Aoba, Aramaki, Sendai-shi, Miyagi-ken, 980 8578, Japan. FAX 81-22-217-5775. Ed. Hiroshi Fukunishi. Circ: 700.

---

551   JPN   ISSN 0917-6217
TOHOKU NO YUKI TO SEIKATSU/SNOW AND LIFE IN TOHOKU. Text in Japanese. 1986. a. JPY 1,500. **Document type:** *Academic/Scholarly.*
Published by: Nihon Seppyo Gakkai, Tohoku Shibu/Japanese Society of Snow and Ice, Tohoku Branch, c/o University, Civil and Environmental Dept, 4-3-5 Ueda, Morioka-shi, Iwate-ken 020-0066, Japan. Ed. Masami Kitamura.

---

551   CZE
TRAVAUX GEOPHYSIQUES. Text in Czech. a. **Description:** Includes original articles in geophysics, meteorology, climatology and geodesy.
Formerly: Geofysikalni Sbornik
Published by: Akademie Ved Ceske Republiky, Geofyzikalni Ustav, Bocni II/1401, Prague, 14131, Czech Republic. TEL 420-2-67103383, FAX 420-2-72761549, studia@ig.cas.cz, gfu@ig.cas.cz, http://www.ig.cas.cz. Ed. Vladimir Cermak.

U.S. ARMY ENGINEER RESEARCH AND DEVELOPMENT CENTER. TECHNICAL REPORT. see *ENGINEERING—Civil Engineering*

551.22   USA   ISSN 0364-7072
U.S. GEOLOGICAL SURVEY. NATIONAL EARTHQUAKE INFORMATION SERVICE. PRELIMINARY DETERMINATION OF EPICENTERS, MONTHLY LISTING. Key Title: Preliminary Determination of Epicenters, Monthly Listing. Text in English. m. **Document type:** *Government.* **Description:** Compiles earthquakes recorded throughout the world, listing location, depth, and magnitude.
Media: Online - full content. **Related titles:** Microfiche ed.
Published by: U.S. Department of the Interior, Geological Survey, National Earthquake Information Service, Box 25046, MS 967, Denver Federal Center, Denver, CO 80225. TEL 303-273-8500, FAX 303-273-8450, TELEX 510-601-4123 ESL UD, person@neis.cr.usgs, http://www.neic.cr.usgs.gov/neis/ data_services/ftp_files.htm1, http://earthquake.usgs.gov. Ed. Waverly J Person.

---

551   USA   ISSN 0190-860X
U.S. NATIONAL GEOPHYSICAL DATA CENTER. KEY TO GEOPHYSICAL RECORDS DOCUMENTATION. Text in English. 1972. irreg. **Document type:** *Monographic series.*
Published by: U.S. National Geophysical Data Center, 325 Broadway, E CG4, Boulder, CO 80303-3328. TEL 303-497-6826, FAX 303-497-6513, ngdc.info@noaa.gov, http://www.ngdc.noaa.gov.

551.22   USA   ISSN 0091-1429
QE535.2.U6   CODEN: XGEQAP
UNITED STATES EARTHQUAKES. Text in English. 1928. a. price varies. illus. **Document type:** *Government.* **Description:** Lists earthquakes that occurred in the U.S. during the year and describes their effects.
Related titles: Microfilm ed.
Published by: U.S. Department of the Interior, Geological Survey, Open File Services Section, Box 25425, Federal Center, Denver, CO 80225. TEL 303-273-8419. Ed. James W Dewey.

---

551   MEX
UNIVERSIDAD NACIONAL AUTONOMA DE MEXICO. INSTITUTO DE GEOFISICA. BOLETIN SISMOLOGICO. Text in Spanish. 1949. m. USD 30.
Published by: Universidad Nacional Autonoma de Mexico, Instituto de Geofisica, Circuito Exterior, Ciudad Universitaria, Mexico, DF 20, Mexico. Ed. Francisco Graffe.

---

551   MEX   ISSN 0076-7204
UNIVERSIDAD NACIONAL AUTONOMA DE MEXICO. INSTITUTO DE GEOFISICA. MONOGRAFIAS. Text in Spanish. 1959-1963; resumed 1981. irreg.
Published by: Universidad Nacional Autonoma de Mexico, Instituto de Geofisica, Circuito Exterior, Ciudad Universitaria, Mexico, DF 20, Mexico. Ed. Francisco Graffe.

---

551   DEU   ISSN 0343-7493
QC830.F8
UNIVERSITAET MUENCHEN. GEOPHYSIKALISCHES OBSERVATORIUM, FUERSTENFELDBRUCK. VEROEFFENTLICHUNGEN. SERIE A. Text in German. 1959. a. per issue exchange basis. **Document type:** *Academic/Scholarly.*
Indexed: RefZh.
—BLDSC (9185.600000), CISTI.
Published by: Universitaet Muenchen, Geophysikalisches Observatorium, Ludwigshoehe 8, Fuerstenfeldbruck, 82256, Germany.

---

551 551.5   DEU   ISSN 0069-5882
QC801
➤ **UNIVERSITAET ZU KOELN. INSTITUT FUER GEOPHYSIK UND METEOROLOGIE. MITTEILUNGEN.** Text in English, German. 1965. irreg., latest vol.143, 2002. EUR 10 per vol. (effective 2002). **Document type:** *Monographic series, Academic/Scholarly.*
Related titles: CD-ROM ed.: 2002; Online - full text ed.: 2002.
Indexed: GEOBASE, M&GPA.
Published by: Universitaet zu Koeln, Institut fuer Geophysik und Meteorologie, Albertus Magnus Platz, Cologne, 50923, Germany. TEL 49-221-4702552, FAX 49-221-4705198, biblio@geo.uni-koeln.de, http://www.rrz.uni-koeln.de/math-nat-fak/geomet/mitteilungen.html. R&P Martin Paetzold. Circ: 135.

---

551   HUN   ISSN 0237-2738
QC801
UNIVERSITATIS SCIENTIARUM BUDAPESTINENSIS DE ROLANDO EOTVOS NOMINATAE. ANNALES. SECTIO GEOPHYSICA ET METEOROLOGICA. Text in Hungarian. 1985. irreg.
—CISTI, Linda Hall.
Published by: Eotvos Lorand Tudomanyegyetem, Allam- es Jogtudomanyi Kara/Eotvos Lorand University, Egyetem ter 1-3, Budapest, 1364, Hungary. TEL 1-174-930.

UNIVERSITEIT TE GENT. STERRENKUNDIG OBSERVATORIUM. MEDEDELINGEN: METEOROLOGIE EN GEOFYSICA. see *METEOROLOGY*

551.22   USA   ISSN 0041-946X
UNIVERSITY OF CALIFORNIA. SEISMOGRAPHIC STATIONS. BULLETIN. Text in English. 1910. s-a. USD 10. charts. **Document type:** *Bulletin.* **Description:** Lists local, regional and worldwide earthquakes recorded by the seismographic network.
Media: Duplicated (not offset). **Related titles:** Microfiche ed.
Published by: University of California at Berkeley, Seismographic Station, 475 Earth Sciences Bldg, Berkeley, CA 94720. TEL 415-642-3977, FAX 643-5811. Ed. Robert A Uhrhammer. Circ: 450 (controlled).

551.22   USA   ISSN 0092-4288
QE531
UNIVERSITY OF NEVADA. SEISMOLOGICAL LABORATORY. BULLETIN. Key Title: Bulletin of the Seismological Laboratory (Reno). Text in English. 1970. irreg., latest 1987. free. illus. **Document type:** *Catalog.*
Indexed: CurCont.
Published by: University of Nevada, Seismological Laboratory, Makay School of Mines, Reno, NV 89557. TEL 702-784-4975. Ed. Diane Depolo. Circ: 100.

551.22   JPN   ISSN 0040-8972
QE531   CODEN: TDJKAZ
UNIVERSITY OF TOKYO. EARTHQUAKE RESEARCH INSTITUTE. BULLETIN/TOKYO DAIGAKU JISHIN KENKYUJO IHO. Text in Japanese. 1926. q. price varies. **Document type:** *Bulletin.*
Indexed: AJEE, EEA, EngInd, Inspec, JPI, JTA.
—AskIEEE, CISTI, Ei, Linda Hall.
Published by: University of Tokyo, Earthquake Research Institute/Tokyo Daigaku Jishin Kenkyujo, 1-1-1 Yayoi, Bunkyo-ku, Tokyo, 113-0032, Japan. TEL 81-3-5841-5669, FAX 81-3-5800-3859, libro@eri.u-tokyo.ac.jp, http://www.eri.u-tokyo.ac.jp. Ed. T Kato. R&P M Shibao. Circ: 1,150. **Subscr. to:** Maruzen Booknet Service, 2-3-10 Nihonbashi, Chuo-ku, Tokyo 103-0027, Japan. FAX 81-3-3274-2118.

551.22   JPN   ISSN 0915-0862
UNIVERSITY OF TOKYO. EARTHQUAKE RESEARCH INSTITUTE. SPECIAL BULLETIN. Text in English, Japanese. 1943. irreg. price varies. **Document type:** *Bulletin.*
—CISTI, Linda Hall.
Published by: University of Tokyo, Earthquake Research Institute/Tokyo Daigaku Jishin Kenkyujo, 1-1-1 Yayoi, Bunkyo-ku, Tokyo, 113-0032, Japan. TEL 81-3-5841-5669, FAX 81-3-5800-3859, libro@eri.u-tokyo.ac.jp, http://www.eri.u-tokyo.ac.jp. Ed. T Kato. R&P M Shibao. Circ: 1,150. **Subscr. to:** Maruzen Booknet Service, 2-3-10 Nihonbashi, Chuo-ku, Tokyo 103-0027, Japan. FAX 81-3-3274-2118.

---

551   JPN   ISSN 0285-3175
QE1   CODEN: ARITDH
UNIVERSITY OF TSUKUBA. INSTITUTE OF GEOSCIENCE. ANNUAL REPORT. Text in English. 1975. a.
Indexed: M&GPA, RefZh, ZooRec.
—BLDSC (1302.983000), CISTI, IE, ingenta, Linda Hall.
Published by: University of Tsukuba, Institute of Geoscience/Tsukuba Daigaku Chikyu Kagakukei, 1-1 Tenno-Dai 1-chome, Tsukuba-shi, Ibaraki-ken 305-0006, Japan.

VERMONT DIVISION OF GEOLOGY AND MINERAL RESOURCES. ECONOMIC GEOLOGY REPORT. see *EARTH SCIENCES—Geology*

551.2 JPN ISSN 0453-4360
CODEN: KAZAAX
VOLCANOLOGICAL SOCIETY OF JAPAN. BULLETIN/KAZAN. Text in English, Japanese; Summaries in English. 1957. bi-m. JPY 2,500 per issue (effective 2001). 80 p./no.; **Document type:** *Bulletin, Academic/Scholarly.*
Indexed: ChemAb, INIS AtomInd, JPI, MSB.
—CASDDS.
Published by: Volcanological Society of Japan/Nihon Kazan Gakkai, c/o Earthquake Research Institute, University of, 1-1-1 Yayoi, Bunkyo-ku, Tokyo, 113-0032, Japan. TEL 81-3-3813-7421, FAX 81-3-5684-2549, kazan@eri.u-tokyo.ac.jp, http://hakone.eri.u-tokyo.ac.jp/kazan/jishome/VSJ1.html.

551 SVK ISSN 0231-7737
CODEN: RGOOE7
VYSLEDKY GEOMAGNETICKYCH POZOROVANI V GEOMAGNETICKOM OBSERVATORIU V HURBANOVE V ROKU (YEAR)/RESULTS OF GEOMAGNETIC OBSERVATIONS AT THE HURBANOVO GEOMAGNETIC OBSERVATORY IN (YEAR). Text in English, Russian, Slovak. 1953. a. free. back issues avail. **Document type:** *Bulletin.*
Description: Contains tables with results of geomagnetic observations performed on the Geomagnetic Observatory in Hurbanovo.
Indexed: Inspec.
Published by: Slovenska Akademia Vied, Geograficky Ustav/Slovak Academy of Science, Institute of Geography, Dubravska Bratislava, Bratislava, 842 28, Slovakia. TEL 421-7-373768, FAX 421-7-375278, geoflabi@savba.sk. Ed. Magdalena Vaczyova. R&P M Hvozdara. Circ: 300.

VYSOKA SKOLA BANSKA. SBORNIK VEDECKYCH PRACI: RADA HORNICKA-GEOLOGICKA. see *EARTH SCIENCES—Geology*

551 DEU ISSN 0947-7144
ZENTRUM FUER MEERES- UND KLIMAFORSCHUNG. BERICHTE. REIHE C: GEOPHYSIK. Text in German. 1962. irreg. **Document type:** *Monographic series.*
Supersedes in part (in 1992): Universitaet Hamburg. Zentrum fuer Meeres- und Klimaforschung. Berichte (0936-949X); Which was formerly (until 1988): Universitaet Hamburg. Instituts fuer Meereskunde. Mitteilungen (0017-6907)
Indexed: ESPM.
Published by: (Universitaet Hamburg, Institut fuer Geophysik/University of Hamburg, Institute of Geophysics), Universitaet Hamburg, Zentrum fuer Meeres- und Klimaforschung/University of Hamburg, Center for Marine and Climate Research, Bundesstr. 55, Hamburg, 20146, Germany. TEL 49-40-42838-4523, FAX 49-40-42838-5235, http://www.uni-hamburg.de/Wiss/SE/ZMK.

551.22 CHN ISSN 1001-4683
ZHONGGUO DIZHEN/CHINESE SEISMOLOGY. Text in Chinese. q.
Related titles: Online - full text ed.: (from East View Information Services); English ed.
Published by: (Zhongguo Dizhen Bianjibu), Guojia Dizhen-ju/State Seismological Bureau, Editorial Office of Chinese Seismology, 63 Fuxing Lu, Beijing, 100036, China. TEL 811398. Ed. Ding Guoyu.

EARTH SCIENCES—Hydrology

A M S NEWSLETTER (ONLINE EDITION). see *METEOROLOGY*

551.48 AUS ISSN 1037-2512
A S L NEWSLETTER. (Australian Society for Limnology) Text in English. 1984. irreg. **Document type:** *Newsletter, Academic/Scholarly.*
Formerly (until 1987): Limnology Newsletter (1037-2504)
Published by: Australian Society for Limnology, Murray-Darling Freshwater Research Centre, PO Box 921, Albury, NSW 2640, Australia. TEL 61-2-6058-2331, FAX 61-2-6043-1626, Rhonda.Sinclair@csiro.au. Ed. Rhonda Sinclair.

ACTA GEOLOGICA. see *EARTH SCIENCES—Geology*

551.4807 POL ISSN 0208-6158
QH162
ACTA UNIVERSITATIS LODZIENSIS: FOLIA LIMNOLOGICA. Text in Polish; Summaries in Multiple languages. 1955-1974; N.S. 1983. irreg. **Document type:** *Academic/Scholarly.*
Description: Publishes the original works in the field of limnology: taxonomy, morphology, biology, ecology and biogeography of organisms living in inland waters.
Supersedes in part: Uniwersytet Lodzki. Zeszyty Naukowe. Seria 2: Nauki Matematyczno-Przyrodnicze (0076-0366)
Indexed: ZooRec.
—CISTI, KNAW, Linda Hall.
Published by: Wydawnictwo Uniwersytetu Lodzkiego/Lodz University Press, ul Jaracza 34, Lodz, 90262, Poland. TEL 331671. **Dist. by:** Ars Polona, Krakowskie Przedmiescie 7, Warsaw, Poland.

551.48 POL ISSN 0208-5348
QH96.A1 CODEN: AUNLD5
ACTA UNIVERSITATIS NICOLAI COPERNICI. PRACE LIMNOLOGICZNE. Text in Polish. 1965. irreg. price varies. **Document type:** *Academic/Scholarly.*
Indexed: BIOSIS Prev, BiolAb, RefZh, ZooRec.
Published by: Uniwersytet Mikolaja Kopernika/Nicolaus Copernicus University, Wydawnictwo, ul Gagarina 39, Torun, 87100, Poland. TEL 48-56-14295. **Dist. by:** Osrodek Rozpowszechniania Wydawnictw Naukowych PAN, Palac Kultury i Nauki, Warsaw 00901, Poland.

551.48 DEU ISSN 1612-166X
QH98 CODEN: ERLIA6
ADVANCES IN LIMNOLOGY; archiv fur hydrobiologie, special issues. Text in English, German. 1964. irreg., latest vol.58, 2003. EUR 105 per issue domestic (effective 2005). adv. **Document type:** *Monographic series, Academic/Scholarly.*
Formerly: Ergebnisse der Limnologie (0071-1128)
Related titles: ♦ Supplement to: Archiv fuer Hydrobiologie. ISSN 0003-9136.
Indexed: ASFA, B&BAb, BIOSIS Prev, BiolAb, CIN, ChemAb, ChemTitl, ESPM, GEOBASE, RefZh, SFA, WildRev, ZooRec.
—BLDSC (0709.285000), CASDDS, CISTI, IE, Infotrieve, ingenta, Linda Hall. **CCC.**
Published by: (Internationale Vereinigung fuer Theoretische und Angewandte Limnologie), E. Schweizerbart'sche Verlagsbuchhandlung, Johannesstr 3A, Stuttgart, 70176, Germany. TEL 49-711-3514560, FAX 49-711-35145699, mail@schweizerbart.de, http://www.schweizerbart.de/j/advances-in-limnology. Ed. W Lampert.

ADVANCES IN POROUS MEDIA. see *EARTH SCIENCES*

AFRICAN JOURNAL OF AQUATIC SCIENCE; official journal of the Southern African Society of Aquatic Scientists. see *BIOLOGY*

AKITA-KEN KAJU SHIKENJUO KENKYUU HUOKOKU/AKITA FRUIT-TREE EXPERIMENT STATION. BULLETIN. see *AGRICULTURE*

AKITA KENRITSU DAIGAKU TANKI DARGAKUBU KIYO/AKITA PREFECTURAL COLLEGE OF AGRICULTURE. BULLETIN. see *AGRICULTURE*

ALGOLOGICAL STUDIES; Archiv fur Hydrobiologie, Supplementbaende. see *BIOLOGY*

551.48 ESP ISSN 1134-5535
ALQUIBLA. Text in Spanish. 1990. s-a. free (effective 2006). back issues avail. **Document type:** *Bulletin, Academic/Scholarly.*
Related titles: Online - full text ed.
Published by: Asociacion Espanola de Limnologia, Los Angeles, 33, Mislanta, Valencia, 46920, Spain. FAX 34-963-799053, ael@ya.com, ael@miracle.microb.uv.es, http://www.uv.es/ael/alquibla.htm, http://www.aelimno.org/. Ed. Dr. Joan Armengol.

AMERICAN INSTITUTE OF HYDROLOGY. BULLETIN. see *WATER RESOURCES*

AMERICAN METEOROLOGICAL SOCIETY. BULLETIN. see *METEOROLOGY*

AMERICAN RIVERS; bringing rivers to life. see *CONSERVATION*

551.48 FRA ISSN 0003-4088
CODEN: ANLIB3
➤ **ANNALES DE LIMNOLOGIE.** Text in English, French. 1965. 4/yr. EUR 100.61 domestic; EUR 125 foreign (effective 2002). bk.rev. reprint service avail. from ISI. **Document type:** *Academic/Scholarly.* **Description:** Covers continental waters ecology with respect to microorganisms, sea weeds, vertebrate and invertebrate macrophytes, and ecosystems, as well as to the physical and chemical aspects of aquatic environment.
Indexed: ASFA, BIOBASE, BIOSIS Prev, BiolAb, CurCont, ESPM, EntAb, ExcerpMed, ForAb, GEOBASE, HelmAb, I&DA, IABS, MBA, PollutAb, S&F, SFA, SWRA, TDB, WeedAb, WildRev, ZooRec.
—BLDSC (0981.050000), CASDDS, CISTI, IDS, IE, Infotrieve, ingenta, Linda Hall. **CCC.**
Published by: Universite de Toulouse III (Paul Sabatier), 118 Rue de Narbonne, Toulouse III, Toulouse, 31062 Cedex 4, France. limnol@cict.fr, http://www.ups-tlse.fr.

➤ **APPLIED HYDROLOGY MONOGRAPHS.** see *ENGINEERING—Hydraulic Engineering*

551 551.46 ITA ISSN 0394-6568
AQUA; mensile di acqua, natura, vita. Text in Italian. 1986. m. (11/yr.). bk.rev. **Document type:** *Magazine, Consumer.*
Published by: Editrice Portoria Srl, Via Chiossetto, 1, Milan, MI 20122, Italy. TEL 39-2-783541, FAX 39-2-782601. Ed. Luca Oriani.

551.48 ARG ISSN 0327-7755
AQUATEC. Text in Spanish. 1993. irreg. **Document type:** *Monographic series.*
Indexed: ESPM, ZooRec.
Published by: Instituto de Limnologia "Dr. Raul A. Ringuelet", Casilla de Correos 712, La Plata, BA 1900, Argentina. TEL 54-11-4275-8564, FAX 54-11-4275-7799, postmaster@ilpla.edu.ar, http://www.ilpla.edu.ar/.

551.4 CHE ISSN 1015-1621
GB651 CODEN: AQSCEA
➤ **AQUATIC SCIENCES**; research across boundaries. Text in English. 1920. q. EUR 458 combined subscription to institutions print & online eds. (effective 2005). back issues avail. **Document type:** *Journal, Academic/Scholarly.*
Description: Covers the fields of theoretical and applied water research and fisheries sciences.
Former titles (until 1989): Swiss Journal of Hydrology (0036-7842); (until 1948): Zeitschrift fuer Hydrologie, Hydrographie, Hydrobiologie, Fischereiwissenschaft (1011-8497)
Related titles: Online - full text ed.: ISSN 1420-9055. 1997 (from EBSCO Publishing, Springer LINK, Swets Information Services).
Indexed: ASCA, ASFA, AgBio, AgrForAb, AnBrAb, B&BAb, BIOBASE, BIOSIS Prev, BioCN&I, BiolAb, ChemAb, CurCont, ESPM, EnvAb, EnvEAb, ExcerpMed, FLUIDEX, FPA, ForAb, GEOBASE, HelmAb, I&DA, IABS, ISR, IndVet, NutrAb, OceAb, PollutAb, ProtozoAb, RM&VM, RRTA, RefZh, S&F, SCI, SFA, SWRA, VetBull, WAE&RSA, WildRev, ZooRec.
—BLDSC (1582.430000), CASDDS, CISTI, IDS, IE, Infotrieve, ingenta, Linda Hall. **CCC.**
Published by: (Limnological Research Center), Birkhaeuser Verlag AG (Subsidiary of: Springer Science+Business Media), Viaduktstr 42, Postfach 133, Basel, 4051, Switzerland. TEL 41-61-2050707, FAX 41-61-2050799, info@birkhauser.ch, http://link.springer.de/link/service/journals/00027/index.htm, http://www.birkhauser.ch/journals. Ed. Barbara Sulzberger TEL 41-1-823-5459. Circ: 600. **Subscr. in the Americas to:** Springer-Verlag New York, Inc., Journal Fulfillment, PO Box 2485, Secaucus, NJ 07096-2485. TEL 800-777-4643, 201-348-4033, FAX 201-348-4505, journals@birkhauser.com. **Dist. by:** Springer GmbH Auslieferungsgesellschaft.

551.4 DEU
ARBEITSHEFTE WASSER. Text in German. irreg. EUR 18 per issue domestic (effective 2005). **Document type:** *Monographic series, Academic/Scholarly.*
Published by: E. Schweizerbart'sche Verlagsbuchhandlung, Johannesstr 3A, Stuttgart, 70176, Germany. TEL 49-711-3514560, FAX 49-711-35145699, mail@schweizerbart.de, http://www.schweizerbart.de.

ARCHIV FUER HYDROBIOLOGIE; Official journal of the International Association of Theoretical and Applied Limnology. see *BIOLOGY*

ARCHIV FUER HYDROBIOLOGIE. SUPPLEMENT-BAND: LARGE RIVERS. see *BIOLOGY*

ARCHIV FUER HYDROBIOLOGIE. SUPPLEMENT-BAND: UNTERSUCHUNGEN DES ELBE-AESTUARS. see *BIOLOGY*

ARCHIV FUER HYDROBIOLOGIE. SUPPLEMENT VOLUMES, MONOGRAPHIC STUDIES. see *BIOLOGY*

ARCHIVIO DI OCEANOGRAFIA E LIMONOLOGIA. see *EARTH SCIENCES—Oceanography*

551.4 FRA ISSN 1027-4820
ASSOCIATION SCIENTIFIQUE EUROPEENNE POUR L'EAU ET LA SANTE. CAHIERS. Text in French. 1996. a.
Indexed: BrCerAb, C&ISA, CerAb, CorrAb, E&CAJ, EMA, IAA, M&TEA, MBF, METADEX, WAA.
—BLDSC (2947.705000), Linda Hall.
Published by: Association Scientifique Europeenne pour l'Eau et la Sante, 4 ave de l'Observatoire, Paris Cedex, 75270, France. gilles.husson@univ-paris5.fr.

ATMOSPHERE - OCEAN. see *METEOROLOGY*

551.48 AUS ISSN 0156-8426
AUSTRALIAN SOCIETY FOR LIMNOLOGY. SPECIAL PUBLICATION. Text in English. irreg.
Indexed: ZooRec.
Published by: Australian Society for Limnology, Murray-Darling Freshwater Research Centre, PO Box 921, Albury, NSW 2640, Australia. TEL 61-2-6058-2331, FAX 61-2-6043-1626, Rhonda.Sinclair@csiro.au.

551.4 GBR
B H S OCCASIONAL PAPER. Text in English. 1988. irreg., latest vol.10, 1999. price varies. **Document type:** *Monographic series.*
Published by: (British Hydrological Society), C E H Wallingford, Maclean Bldg., Crowmarsh Gifford, Wallingford, Oxon OX10 8BB, United Kingdom. TEL 44-1491-838800, FAX 44-1491-692424, b.h.s@ceh.ac.uk, http://www.salford.ac.uk/civils/bhs. Ed. John Griffin.

BAYERISCHES LANDESAMT FUER WASSERWIRTSCHAFT. INFORMATIONSBERICHTE. see *WATER RESOURCES*

BAYERISCHES LANDESAMTES FUER WASSERWIRTSCHAFT. SCHRIFTENREIHE. see *WATER RESOURCES*

E

551.48 DEU ISSN 0067-8643
QH96.A1 CODEN: BNGWAU
DIE BINNENGEWAESSER; Einzeldarstellungen aus der Limnologie und ihren Grenzgebieten. Text in English, German. 1926. irreg. price varies. **Document type:** *Monographic series, Academic/Scholarly.*
Indexed: BiolAb.
—CISTI.
Published by: E. Schweizerbart'sche Verlagsbuchhandlung, Johannesstr 3A, Stuttgart, 70176, Germany. TEL 49-711-3514560, FAX 49-711-35145699, mail@schweizerbart.de, http://www.schweizerbart.de. Ed. W Lampert.

BIOLOGIYA VNUTRENNIKH VOD. see *WATER RESOURCES*

BIOLOGY OF INLAND WATERS. see *WATER RESOURCES*

551.48 CRI ISSN 0067-9747
BOLETIN HIDROLOGICO. Text in Spanish. 1962. a. charts; illus.; stat. index. **Document type:** *Bulletin, Government.*
Published by: Instituto Costarricense de Electricidad (ICE), Apdo 10032, San Jose, 1000, Costa Rica. TEL 506-2-207531, FAX 506-2-208204. Ed. Sadi Laporte. Circ: (controlled).

551.447 GBR
THE BRITISH CAVER. Text in English. 1936. q. GBP 6 (effective 2000). adv.
Published by: The British Caver, Riverside Mews, Cardigan, SA43 1DH, United Kingdom. anne.oldham@virgin.net. Ed., Pub. Tony Oldham. adv.: B&W page GBP 50. Circ: 3,000.

551.4 CHE ISSN 1421-4946
GB658.8.S9
BULLETIN D'HYDROGEOLOGIE. Text in French, German. 1976. a. CHF 35; EUR 25 in Austria & Germany; EUR 23 in Europe; GBP 16, USD 28 (effective 2006). **Document type:** *Journal, Academic/Scholarly.* **Description:** Studies the hydrogeology of fissured and karstified rocks, the hydrochemistry and isotopes of groundwater, pollution and protection of groundwater, groundwater resources exploration, the modelling of underground flow and mass transport, geophysical methods applied to hydrogeology, regional studies and technical notes.
Formerly (until 1995): Universite de Neuchatel. Centre d'Hydrogeologie. Bulletin (0724-7087)
Published by: (Universite de Neuchatel, Centre d'Hydrogeologie), Verlag Peter Lang AG, Hochfeldstr. 32, Postfach 746, Bern 9, 3000, Switzerland. TEL 41-31-3061717, FAX 41-31-3061727, info@peterlang.com, http://www.peterlang.com. Ed. Francois Vuataz. Circ: 450.

C M O S BULLETIN/BULLETIN S C M O. see *METEOROLOGY*

551.4 AUS
CODEN: DRDOEB
➤ **C S I R O LAND AND WATER. TECHNICAL REPORT.** Text in English. 1980. irreg. free. back issues avail. **Document type:** *Academic/Scholarly.*
Former titles: C S I R O Land and Water. Scientific Report; (until 1997): C S I R O Division of Water Resources. Divisional Report (1033-5579); (until 1988): C S I R O Division of Water Resources Research. Divisional Report (1030-2433); (until 1987): C S I R O Division of Water and Land Resources. Divisional Report (0812-7204); (until 1983): C S I R O Division of Land Use Research. Divisional Report (0726-660X)
Indexed: AESIS, ESPM, MBA, SWRA.
Published by: C S I R O Land and Water, GPO Box 1666, Canberra, ACT 2601, Australia. FAX 61-6-2465800, andrew.bell@cbr.clw.csiro.au. Ed., R&P Andrew Bell. Circ: 300.

551.4 USA
TD224.C3 CODEN: RUCCD8
CALIFORNIA. WATER RESOURCES CENTER. REPORT. Text in English. 1959. a. free. illus. back issues avail. **Document type:** *Government.* **Description:** Provides summaries of water research projects, information transfer activities, conferences, and othe ractivities sponsored by the California water resources academics and other interested groups and agencies.
Formerly (until 1994): California. Water Resources Center. Annual Report (0575-4968)
Indexed: Agr.
—CISTI, Ei.
Published by: University of California at Davis, Center for Water and Wildland Resources, 1 Shields Ave, Davis, CA 95616-8750. TEL 530-752-8050, FAX 530-752-8345, jlwoled@ucdavis.edu, http://www.cwwr.ucdavis.edu. Ed., R&P Jeff Woled. Circ: 480 (controlled).

551.4 333.9 CAN ISSN 0318-5877
GB1230.A4
CANADA. INLAND WATERS DIRECTORATE. HISTORICAL STREAMFLOW SUMMARY, ALBERTA. Text in English. 1970. biennial. **Document type:** *Government.*
—Linda Hall.
Published by: Environment Canada, Inland Waters Directorate, Water Planning and Management Branch, Ottawa, ON K1A 0H3, Canada. TEL 819-953-1518, FAX 819-997-8701.

551.4 333.9 CAN ISSN 0318-5885
CANADA. INLAND WATERS DIRECTORATE. HISTORICAL STREAMFLOW SUMMARY, ATLANTIC PROVINCES. Text in English. 1970. triennial. **Document type:** *Government.*
—Linda Hall.
Published by: Environment Canada, Inland Waters Directorate, Water Planning and Management Branch, Ottawa, ON K1A 0H3, Canada. TEL 819-953-1518, FAX 819-997-8701.

551.4 333.9 CAN ISSN 0318-5893
CANADA. INLAND WATERS DIRECTORATE. HISTORICAL STREAMFLOW SUMMARY, BRITISH COLUMBIA. Text in English. 1970. triennial. **Document type:** *Government.*
—Linda Hall.
Published by: Environment Canada, Inland Waters Directorate, Water Planning and Management Branch, Ottawa, ON K1A 0H3, Canada. TEL 819-953-1518, FAX 819-997-8701.

551.4 333.9 CAN ISSN 0318-5907
CANADA. INLAND WATERS DIRECTORATE. HISTORICAL STREAMFLOW SUMMARY, MANITOBA. Text in English. 1970. triennial. **Document type:** *Government.*
Published by: Environment Canada, Inland Waters Directorate, Water Planning and Management Branch, Ottawa, ON K1A 0H3, Canada. TEL 819-953-1518, FAX 819-997-8701.

551.4 333.9 CAN ISSN 0318-5915
CANADA. INLAND WATERS DIRECTORATE. HISTORICAL STREAMFLOW SUMMARY, ONTARIO. Text in English. 1970. triennial. **Document type:** *Government.*
Incorporates in part: Canada. Division des Releves Hydrologiques. Sommaire Chronologique de l'Ecoulement. Quebec (0706-4527)
—Linda Hall.
Published by: Environment Canada, Inland Waters Directorate, Water Planning and Management Branch, Ottawa, ON K1A 0H3, Canada. TEL 819-953-1518, FAX 819-997-8701.

551.4 333.9 CAN ISSN 0706-3393
CANADA. INLAND WATERS DIRECTORATE. HISTORICAL WATER LEVELS SUMMARY. ATLANTIC PROVINCES. Text in English. 1976. triennial. **Document type:** *Government.*
—Linda Hall.
Published by: Environment Canada, Inland Waters Directorate, Water Planning and Management Branch, Ottawa, ON K1A 0H3, Canada. TEL 819-953-1518, FAX 819-997-8701.

551.4 333.9 CAN ISSN 0706-3474
CANADA. INLAND WATERS DIRECTORATE. HISTORICAL WATER LEVELS SUMMARY. BRITISH COLUMBIA. Text in English. 1976. triennial. **Document type:** *Government.*
—Linda Hall.
Published by: Environment Canada, Inland Waters Directorate, Water Planning and Management Branch, Ottawa, ON K1A 0H3, Canada. TEL 819-953-1518, FAX 819-997-8701.

333.9 551.4 CAN ISSN 0225-0934
CANADA. INLAND WATERS DIRECTORATE. HISTORICAL WATER LEVELS SUMMARY. QUEBEC/SOMMAIRE CHRONOLOGIQUE DES NIVEAUX D'EAU. QUEBEC. Text in English. 1976. triennial. **Document type:** *Government.*
—Linda Hall.
Published by: Environment Canada, Inland Waters Directorate, Water Planning and Management Branch, Ottawa, ON K1A 0H3, Canada. TEL 819-953-1518, FAX 819-997-8701.

333.9 551.4 CAN ISSN 0706-3423
CANADA. INLAND WATERS DIRECTORATE. HISTORICAL WATER LEVELS SUMMARY. SASKATCHEWAN. Text in English. 1976. triennial. **Document type:** *Government.*
—Linda Hall.
Published by: Environment Canada, Inland Waters Directorate, Water Planning and Management Branch, Ottawa, ON K1A 0H3, Canada. TEL 819-953-1518, FAX 819-997-8701.

333.9 551.4 CAN ISSN 0706-3466
CANADA. INLAND WATERS DIRECTORATE. HISTORICAL WATER LEVELS SUMMARY. YUKON AND NORTHWEST TERRITORIES. Text in English. 1976. triennial. **Document type:** *Government.*
—Linda Hall.
Published by: Environment Canada, Inland Waters Directorate, Water Planning and Management Branch, Ottawa, ON K1A 0H3, Canada. TEL 819-953-1518, FAX 819-997-8701.

CANADIAN METEOROLOGICAL AND OCEANOGRAPHIC SOCIETY. ANNUAL CONGRESS PROGRAM AND ABSTRACTS. see *METEOROLOGY*

551.4 FRA ISSN 1624-7396
CENTRE D'ETUDES TECHNIQUES MARITIME ET FLUVIALES. REVUE TECHNIQUE. Key Title: Revue Technique du CETMEF. Text in French. 1966. q.
Former titles (until 2000): Revue Techniques des Phares et Balises (1164-6799); (until 1989): Revue Technique du Service des Phares et Balises (0338-1919)
Indexed: ESPM.
Published by: Centre d'Etudes Techniques Maritimes et Fluviales, 2, boulevard Gambetta, BP 60039, Compiegne, 60321, France. TEL 33-3-44926000, FAX 33-3-44200675, www.cetmef.equipement.gouv.fr.

551.4 363.7394 GBR
CENTRE FOR ECOLOGY AND HYDROLOGY. REPORT. Text in English. irreg.
Formerly (until 2000): Institute of Freshwater Ecology. Report
Published by: Natural Environment Research Council, Centre for Ecology & Hydrology, CEH Windermere, The Ferry House, Far Sawrey, Ambleside, Cumbria LA22 0LP, United Kingdom. TEL 44-15394-42468, FAX 44-15394-46914, ccap@ceh.ac.uk, http://www.ceh.ac.uk.

551.4 USA
CHESAPEAKE RESEARCH CONSORTIUM. PUBLICATIONS. Text in English. 1974. irreg.
Published by: Chesapeake Research Consortium, 645 Contees Wharf Rd, Edgewater, MD 21037. TEL 410-798-1283, FAX 301-261-4500, http://www.chesapeake.org/.

551.4 JPN
CHIKA SUII JIBAN CHINKA KANSOKU KIROKU/ OBSERVATIONS OF UNDERGROUND WATER LEVEL AND SUBSIDENCE OF GROUND IN HOKKAIDO. Text in Japanese. 1976. a. **Document type:** *Academic/Scholarly.* **Description:** Contains observation records of underground water level and subsidences.
Published by: Hokkaidoritsu Chishitsu Kenkyusyo/Geological Survey of Hokkaido, N19 W12, Kita-ku, Sapporo, Hokkaido 060-0819, Japan. TEL 81-11-747-2211, FAX 81-11-737-9071, gsh@gsh.pref.hokkaido.jp, http://www.gsh.pref.hokkaido.jp. Ed., Pub. Toru Wake. R&P Kunihiko Kurosawa.

551.4 333.9 JPN ISSN 0913-4182
GB1001
➤ **CHIKASUI GAKKAISHI/JOURNAL OF GROUNDWATER HYDROLOGY.** Text in English, Japanese. 1959. q. membership. adv. bk.rev. index. 120 p./no.; **Document type:** *Journal, Academic/Scholarly.*
Formerly (until 1986): Nippon Chikasui Gakkai Kaishi/Japanese Association of Groundwater Hydrology. Journal (0029-0602)
Indexed: ExcerpMed, RefZh.
—BLDSC (4996.521050), IE, ingenta. **CCC.**
Published by: Japanese Association of Groundwater Hydrology/Nippon Chikasui Gakkai, 2-15-15, Tsukiji, Chuo-ku, Tokyo, 104-0045, Japan. lep04505@nifty.ne.jp, http://www.groundwater.jp/jagh/journal/index.htm. Ed. Norio Tase. R&P Yasunori Mahara. Adv. contact Yasuo Sakura. Circ: 1,500 (paid).

➤ **CHINESE JOURNAL OF OCEANOLOGY AND LIMNOLOGY/ZHONGGUO HAIYANG YU HUZHAO XUEBAO.** see *EARTH SCIENCES—Oceanography*

551.4 FRA ISSN 1274-6991
CLUB D A L I. BULLETIN. (Dessin Automatique des Lignes Isobathes) Text in French. 1984. a.
Formerly (until 1994): L' Echo de D A L I (0763-0344)
Published by: Association D A L I, 3, place Gabriel, Bordeaux, 33075 Cedex, France. TEL 33-5-56905972, FAX 33-5-56905878, Dali@equipement.gouv.fr, http://www.cetmef.equipement.gouv.fr/projets/simulexploit/dali/bandeau.html.

COASTAL AND ESTUARINE STUDIES. see *EARTH SCIENCES—Oceanography*

COMPENSATION IN GROUND WATER SCIENCE AND ENGINEERING ORGANIZATIONS. see *BUSINESS AND ECONOMICS—Labor And Industrial Relations*

553.79 USA ISSN 0094-9671
GB1001
CONFERENCE ON GROUND WATER. PROCEEDINGS. Key Title: Proceedings - Conference on Ground Water. Text in English. biennial. **Document type:** *Proceedings, Academic/Scholarly.*
Published by: University of California, Riverside, Center for Water Resources, Rubidoux Hall - 094, Riverside, CA 02521-0436. TEL 909-787-4327, FAX 909-787-5295, cwwr@ucdavis.edu, cwr@ucrac1.ucr.edu, cwres@pop.ucr.edu, http://www-cwwr.ucdavis.edu, http://waterresources.ucr.edu. R&P Melanie Carlson. **Co-sponsor:** California Department of Water Resources. State Water Resources Control Board Water Education Foundation.

DEUTSCHES GEWAESSERKUNDLICHES JAHRBUCH. DONAUGEBIET. see *WATER RESOURCES*

DEUTSCHES GEWAESSERKUNDLICHES JAHRBUCH. KUESTENGEBIET DER NORDSEE. see *WATER RESOURCES*

DEUTSCHES GEWAESSERKUNDLICHES JAHRBUCH. RHEINGEBIET TEIL 2: MAIN. see *WATER RESOURCES*

DEVELOPMENTS IN HYDROBIOLOGY. see *BIOLOGY*

DEVELOPMENTS IN WATER SCIENCE. see *WATER RESOURCES*

DIRECTORIO ESPANOL DE ACUICULTURA. see *EARTH SCIENCES—Oceanography*

E

551.48 USA ISSN 0424-1932
QC929.S7
EASTERN SNOW CONFERENCE. ANNUAL MEETING PROCEEDINGS. Text in English. 1966. a. price varies.
—BLDSC (1087.741000), CISTI, Linda Hall.
Published by: Eastern Snow Conference, c/o Mr. Ken Rancourt, Mount Washington Observatory, 2936 White Mountain Highway, P.O. Box 2310, North Conway, NH 03860. k.rancourt@mountwashington.org, http://www.easternsnow.org.

551.4 570 577 POL ISSN 1642-3593
QH541.15.E19 CODEN: EHC YA7
➤ **ECOHYDROLOGY & HYDROBIOLOGY.** Text in English. 2001. q. EUR 60 in Europe to individuals; USD 70 elsewhere to individuals; EUR 100 in Europe to institutions; USD 120 elsewhere to institutions (effective 2005). **Document type:** *Journal, Academic/Scholarly.* **Description:** Publishes original research papers, invited or submitted review papers, short communications in every field of ecohydrology and hydrobiology, especially invited are contributions which provide an integrative (also interdisciplinary) approach to aquatic sciences, explaning ecological and hydrological processes at a river-basin scale, or propose practical applications of this knowledge.
Formed by the merger of (1926-2001): Polskie Archiwum Hydrobiologii (0032-3764); Which was formerly (until 1953): Archiwum Hydrobiologii i Rybactwa (1642-8935); (1954-2001): Acta Hydrobiologica (0065-132X); Which was formerly (until 1959): Polska Akademia Mauk. Zaklad Biologii Stawow. Biuletyn (0866-9678)
Related titles: Online - full content ed.
Indexed: ASFA, ESPM, EntAb, GEOBASE, OceAb, PollutAb, SWRA, WRCInf.
—BLDSC (3648.627500), CISTI, Linda Hall.
Published by: Polska Akademia Nauk, Miedzynarodowe Centrum Ekologii/Polish Academy of Sciences, International Centre of Ecology, ul Tylna 3, Lodz, 90364, Poland. TEL 48-42-6817007, ehjournal@mcepan.lodz.pl. Eds. Dr. David M Harper, Dr. Richard D Robarts, Dr. Maciej Zalewski, Dr. Pawel Bijok. R&P Dr. Pawel Bijok.

551.48 ECU
ECUADOR. INSTITUTO NACIONAL DE METEOROLOGIA E HIDROLOGIA. ANUARIO HIDROLOGICO. Text in Spanish. 1963. a. USD 20.40. index. **Document type:** *Government.*
Supersedes: Ecuador. Servicio Nacional de Meteorologia e Hidrologia. Anuario Hidrologico (0070-8933)
Published by: Instituto Nacional de Meteorologia e Hidrologia, Inaquito 700 y Corea, Quito, Ecuador. TEL 593-2-433934.

551.4 CHE
EIDGENOESSISCHE TECHNISCHE HOCHSCHULE ZUERICH. VERSUCHSANSTALT FUER WASSERBAU, HYDROLOGIE UND GLAZIOLOGIE. JAHRESBERICHT. Text in German. 1970. a. free. illus. **Document type:** *Magazine, Academic/Scholarly.* **Description:** Includes information on hydraulics, water engineering, and glaciology.
Published by: Eidgenoessische Technische Hochschule Zuerich, Versuchsanstalt fuer Wasserbau, Hydrologie und Glaziologie, ETH-Zentrum, Zuerich, 8092, Switzerland. minor@vaw.baug.ethz.ch. Ed. H E Minor.

551.4 627 CHE ISSN 0374-0056
EIDGENOESSISCHE TECHNISCHE HOCHSCHULE ZUERICH. VERSUCHSANSTALT FUER WASSERBAU, HYDROLOGIE UND GLAZIOLOGIE. MITTEILUNGEN. Text in English, German. 1971. a. free. illus. **Document type:** *Magazine, Academic/Scholarly.* **Description:** Includes information on glaciology, water engineering, and hydraulics.
Indexed: FLUIDEX.
—Linda Hall.
Published by: Eidgenoessische Technische Hochschule Zuerich, Versuchsanstalt fuer Wasserbau, Hydrologie und Glaziologie, ETH-Zentrum, Zuerich, 8092, Switzerland. minor@vaw.baug.ethz.ch. Ed. H E Minor.

ENGINEERING SURVEYING SHOWCASE. see *GEOGRAPHY*

363.7 USA ISSN 1067-3997
ENVIRONMENTAL HYDROLOGY REPORT. Text in English. 1990. irreg. USD 90 (effective 2000). bk.rev. **Document type:** *Academic/Scholarly.*
Formerly (until 1993): Environmental Hydrology (1053-8208)
Media: Online - full text.
Published by: International Association for Environmental Hydrology, PO Box 35324, San Antonio, TX 78235-5324. TEL 210-344-5418, FAX 210-344-9941, hydroweb@mail.org, http://www.hydroweb.com. Ed. Roger W Peebles. Circ: 300 (paid).

ESTUARINE AND COASTAL SCIENCES ASSOCIATION. BULLETIN. see *EARTH SCIENCES—Oceanography*

551.4 NLD ISSN 0928-9542
EUROPEAN GEOPHYSICAL SOCIETY SERIES ON HYDROLOGICAL SCIENCES. Text in English. 1992. irreg. price varies. **Document type:** *Monographic series.*
Published by: (European Geophysical Society USA), Elsevier BV (Subsidiary of: Elsevier Science & Technology), Radarweg 29, Amsterdam, 1043 NX, Netherlands. TEL 31-20-4853911, FAX 31-20-4852457, nlinfo-f@elsevier.nl, http://www.elsevier.nl.

368 USA
FLOOD REPORT✶. Text in English. 1983. m. looseleaf. USD 89. back issues avail.
Published by: (Emergency Management Marketing Analysis, Inc.), E M M A, Inc., c/o ELSEY, P O Box 230487, Centrevilley, VA 20120-0487. Circ: 1,000.

551.4 USA
➤ **G E W E X NEWS**; Global Energy and Water Cycle Experiment. Text in English. 1990. q. **Document type:** *Newsletter, Academic/Scholarly.*
Related titles: Online - full text ed.
Published by: International G E W E X Project Office, 1010 Wayne Ave, Ste 450, Silver Spring, MD 20910. TEL 301-565-8345, FAX 301-565-8279, gewex@gewex.org, http://www.gewex.org/gewex_nwsltr.html, http://www.gewex.org/igpo.html. Ed. Paul Twitchell. Circ: 3,000.

➤ **GEO-OEKO.** see *GEOGRAPHY*

➤ **GEOLOGIA APPLICATA E IDROGEOLOGIA.** see *EARTH SCIENCES—Geology*

➤ **GEOLOGISCHES JAHRBUCH. REIHE C: HYDROGEOLOGIE. INGENIEURGEOLOGIE.** see *EARTH SCIENCES—Geology*

➤ **GEOMATICS WORLD**; the geomatics journal for land, engineering and hydrographic survey. see *GEOGRAPHY*

➤ **GESELLSCHAFT DER GEOLOGIE- UND BERGBAUSTUDENTEN. MITTEILUNGEN.** see *EARTH SCIENCES—Geology*

➤ **GIDROBIOLOGICHESKII ZHURNAL/HIDROBIOLOHICHNYI ZHURNAL**; nauchnyi zhurnal. see *BIOLOGY*

➤ **GROTTE D'ITALIA.** see *EARTH SCIENCES—Geology*

551.49 628.11 USA ISSN 0017-467X
GB1001 CODEN: GRWAAP
➤ **GROUND WATER.** Variant title: Journal of Ground Water. Text in English. 1963. bi-m. USD 395 combined subscription in the Americas to institutions; GBP 237 elsewhere to institutions; USD 30 domestic to members; USD 40 in Canada to members; USD 60 elsewhere to members (effective 2006). adv. bk.rev.; software rev. abstr.; bibl.; charts; illus. index. back issues avail.; reprint service avail. from PSC. **Document type:** *Journal, Academic/Scholarly.*
Related titles: Microform ed.: (from PQC); Online - full text ed.: ISSN 1745-6584. USD 375 in the Americas to institutions; GBP 225 elsewhere to institutions (effective 2006) (from bigchalk, Blackwell Synergy, EBSCO Publishing, Florida Center for Library Automation, Gale Group, Northern Light Technology, Inc., O C L C Online Computer Library Center, Inc., ProQuest Information & Learning).
Indexed: AESIS, APD, AS&TI, ASCA, ASFA, Agr, AnalAb, BIOBASE, BibAg, BiolAb, BrCerAb, BrGeoL, C&ISA, CIN, CerAb, ChemAb, ChemTitl, CivEngAb, CorrAb, CurCont, E&CAJ, EIA, EMA, EPB, ESPM, EnerInd, EnerRev, EngInd, EnvAb, EnvEAb, EnvInd, ExcerpMed, FLUIDEX, GEOBASE, GeotechAb, I&DA, IAA, IABS, ICEA, INIS AtomInd, ISMEC, ISR, IndMed, M&TEA, MBF, MEDLINE, METADEX, PetrolAb, PollutAb, Repind, S&F, SCI, SJW, SWRA, SolStAb, WAA, WRCInf, WasteInfo.
—BLDSC (4219.450000), CASDDS, CISTI, Ei, IDS, IE, Infotrieve, ingenta, Linda Hall, PADDS. **CCC.**
Published by: National Ground Water Association, 601 Dempsey Rd, Westerville, OH 43081-8978. TEL 800-551-7379, FAX 614-898-7786, ngwa@ngwa.org, http://www.ngwa.org/publication/gw/gw-menu.html. Ed. Dr. Mary P Anderson. Pub. Thad Plumley. R&P Linett Adell. Adv. contact Cindi Taylor. B&W page USD 1,850; trim 7.5 x 10. Circ: 11,000. **Subscr. to:** Blackwell Publishing, Inc.. http://www.blackwellpublishing.com.

551.49 USA ISSN 1069-3629
GB1001 CODEN: GWMREV
➤ **GROUND WATER MONITORING & REMEDIATION.** Text in English. 1981. q. USD 195 combined subscription in the Americas to institutions print & online eds.; GBP 162 combined subscription elsewhere to institutions print & online eds.; USD 30 domestic to members; USD 40 in Canada to members; USD 60 elsewhere to members (effective 2006). adv. abstr.; charts; illus.; tr.lit. 150 p./no.; back issues avail.; reprint service avail. from PSC. **Document type:** *Journal, Academic/Scholarly.*
Formerly: Ground Water Monitoring Review (0277-1926)
Related titles: Online - full text ed.: ISSN 1745-6592. USD 180 in the Americas to institutions; GBP 155 elsewhere to institutions (effective 2006) (from Blackwell Synergy, EBSCO Publishing, O C L C Online Computer Library Center, Inc.).
Indexed: AEA, AESIS, APIAb, AS&TI, ASCA, ASFA, Agr, AnBrAb, BIOBASE, BibAg, BiolAb, CIN, ChemAb, ChemTitl, CivEngAb, CurCont, EIA, EPB, ESPM, EnerRev, EngInd, EnvAb, EnvEAb, ExcerpMed, FLUIDEX, FPA, ForAb, GEOBASE, HerbAb, HortAb, I&DA, IABS, ICEA, INIS AtomInd, ISR, M&TEA, MBA, NemAb, PN&I, PollutAb, RefZh, Repind, S&F, SCI, SWRA, WAE&RSA, WRCInf, WasteInfo, WeedAb.
—BLDSC (4219.559000), CASDDS, CISTI, Ei, IDS, IE, Infotrieve, ingenta, Linda Hall. **CCC.**
Published by: National Ground Water Association, 601 Dempsey Rd, Westerville, OH 43081-8978. TEL 800-551-7379, FAX 614-898-7786, ngwa@ngwa.org, http://www.ngwa.org/publication/gwmr/gwmr-menu.html. Ed. Paul Johnson. Pub. Thad Plumley. R&P Linett Adell. Adv. contact Vickie Wiles. B&W page USD 1,850; trim 7 x 10. Circ: 11,000. **Subscr. to:** Blackwell Publishing, Inc.. http://www.blackwellpublishing.com.

➤ **HABITAT - CALABRIA.** see *METEOROLOGY*

551.4 JPN ISSN 0914-3009
HAIDOROROJI/HYDROLOGY. Text in English, Japanese; Summaries in English. 1967. 4/yr. JPY 8,000.
—CCC.
Published by: Nihon Suimon Kagakkai/Japanese Association of Hydrological Science, Tsukuba Daigaku Chikyu Kagakukei, 1-1 Tenno-Dai 1-chome, Tsukuba-shi, Ibaraki-ken 305-0006, Japan.

HAIYANG YU HUZHAO/OCEANOLOGIA ET LIMNOLOGIA SINICA. see *EARTH SCIENCES—Oceanography*

551.4 CHN ISSN 1000-1980
TC1 CODEN: HEDXEP
➤ **HEHAI DAXUE XUEBAO/HOHAI UNIVERSITY. JOURNAL.** Text in Chinese; Abstracts in English. 1957. bi-m. USD 80 (effective 2000 - 2001). **Document type:** *Academic/Scholarly.* **Description:** Publishes original papers in the field of development, management and protection of water resources.
Related titles: CD-ROM ed.; Online - full text ed.: (from East View Information Services).
Indexed: ASFA, ESPM, EnvEAb, M&GPA, MathR, MathSciNet, PollutAb, RefZh, WRCInf.
—BLDSC (4758.435000).
Published by: Hehai Daxue, 1 Xikang Rd, Nanjing, Jiangsu 210098, China. TEL 86-25-3713777, FAX 86-25-33150335, kkb@hhu.edu.cn, http://www.hhu.edu.cn/kkb/kkb.htm. Ed., Pub. Guo Zhiping. Circ: 1,200. **Dist. by:** China International Book Trading Corp, 35 Chegongzhuang Xilu, Haidian District, PO Box 399, Beijing 100044, China. TEL 86-10-68412045, FAX 86-10-68412023, cibtc@mail.cibtc.com.cn, http://www.cibtc.com.cn/.

621.4 NLD ISSN 1385-4569
VK588
HYDRO INTERNATIONAL. Text in Dutch. 1997. 8/yr. EUR 48 in Europe to non-members; USD 65 elsewhere to non-members (effective 2001). adv. **Document type:** *Journal, Trade.* **Description:** Reports the latest news and developments in the technology and mangement of hydrography and surveying related industries and markets all over the world.
Indexed: ASFA, ESPM, FLUIDEX, GEOBASE, M&TEA, OceAb, RICS, SWRA.
—BLDSC (4342.750000), IE, ingenta.
Published by: Geomatics Information & Trading Centre BV, PO Box 112, Lemmer, 8530 AC, Netherlands. TEL 31-514-561854, FAX 31-514-563898, mailbox@gitc.nl, http://www.hydro-international.nl, http://www.gitc.nl. Ed. Egon Bakker. Pub., R&P Johan Boesjes. Adv. contact Wilmiene Bakker. Circ: 9,150.

HYDROBIOLOGIA; the international journal on limnology and marine sciences. see *BIOLOGY*

HYDROBIOLOGICAL JOURNAL. see *BIOLOGY*

551.4 DEU ISSN 1431-2174
GB1001
➤ **HYDROGEOLOGY JOURNAL.** Text in English, French. 1992. bi-m. EUR 518 combined subscription to institutions print & online eds. (effective 2005). adv. illus. Index. reprint service avail. from PSC. **Document type:** *Journal, Academic/Scholarly.* **Description:** Covers a wide range of hydrogeological specialities. Provides new information and theoretical papers of merit for practicing hydrogeologists. Official journal of the International Association of Hydrogeologists.
Formerly: Applied Hydrogeology (0941-2816)
Related titles: Online - full text ed.: ISSN 1435-0157 (from EBSCO Publishing, Swets Information Services).
Indexed: ASFA, BrCerAb, C&ISA, CerAb, CivEngAb, CorrAb, CurCont, E&CAJ, EMA, ESPM, EnvEAb, GEOBASE, IAA, ICEA, ISR, M&TEA, MBF, METADEX, PollutAb, SCI, SWRA, SolStAb, WAA.
—CISTI, IDS, IE, Infotrieve. **CCC.**
Published by: (International Association of Hydrogeologists GBR), Springer-Verlag (Subsidiary of: Springer Science+Business Media), Tiergartenstr 17, Heidelberg, 69121, Germany. TEL 49-6221-3450, FAX 49-6221-345229, http://link.springer.de/link/service/journals/10040/index.htm. Adv. contact Stephan Kroeck TEL 49-30-827875739. **Subscr. in N. America to:** Springer-Verlag New York, Inc., Journal Fulfillment, PO Box 2485, Secaucus, NJ 07096-2485. TEL 800-777-4643, 201-348-4033, FAX 201-348-4505, journals@springer-ny.com, http://www.springer-ny.com; **Subscr. to:** Springer GmbH Auslieferungsgesellschaft, Haberstr 7, Heidelberg 69126, Germany. TEL 49-6221-345-0, FAX 49-6221-345-4229, subscriptions@springer.de.

E

551 GBR ISSN 0885-6087
GB651 CODEN: HYPRE3
➤ **HYDROLOGICAL PROCESSES**; an international journal. Text in English. 1987. 20/yr. USD 3,455 to institutions; USD 3,801 combined subscription to institutions print & online eds. (effective 2006). adv. bk.rev. illus.; maps. back issues avail.; reprint service avail. from PSC. **Document type:** *Journal, Academic/Scholarly.* **Description:** Reflects the findings on environmental hydrology, with an emphasis on field processes, their modelling and forecasting.
Related titles: Microform ed.: (from PQC); Online - full content ed.: ISSN 1099-1085. USD 3,455 to institutions (effective 2006); Online - full text ed.: (from EBSCO Publishing, Swets Information Services, Wiley InterScience).
Indexed: AEA, AESIS, ASCA, ASFA, AgrForAb, C&ISA, CPA, CivEngAb, CurCont, DSA, E&CAJ, EPB, ESPM, EngInd, EnvAb, FCA, FLUIDEX, FPA, ForAb, GEOBASE, GeotechAb, HerbAb, HortAb, I&DA, ICEA, ISR, Inspec, M&GPA, M&TEA, MaizeAb, NemAb, PBA, PGegResA, PN&I, PollutAb, ProtozoAb, RA&MP, RDA, RPP, RRTA, RiceAb, S&F, SCI, SJW, SWRA, SolStAb, TriticAb, WAE&RSA, WeedAb.
—BLDSC (4347.625600), AskIEEE, CISTI, Ei, IDS, IE, Infotrieve, ingenta, Linda Hall. **CCC.**
Published by: John Wiley & Sons Ltd. (Subsidiary of: John Wiley & Sons, Inc.), The Atrium, Southern Gate, Chichester, West Sussex PO19 8SQ, United Kingdom. TEL 44-1243-779777, FAX 44-1243-775878, customer@wiley.co.uk, http://www3.interscience.wiley.com/cgi-bin/jhome/4125, http://www.wiley.co.uk. Ed. M G Anderson. adv.: B&W page GBP 650, color page GBP 1,550; trim 200 x 260. Circ: 600. **Subscr. to:** John Wiley & Sons, Inc., 111 River St, Hoboken, NJ 07030-5774. TEL 201-748-6645, 800-225-5945, subinfo@wiley.com.

➤ **HYDROLOGICAL SCIENCE AND TECHNOLOGY.** see *WATER RESOURCES*

551.4 GBR ISSN 0262-6667
GB651 CODEN: HSJODN
➤ **HYDROLOGICAL SCIENCES JOURNAL/JOURNAL DES SCIENCES HYDROLOGIQUES.** Text in English, French. 1956. bi-m. GBP 180 domestic; USD 300 foreign (effective 2004). bk.rev. illus. index. back issues avail.; reprint service avail. from ISI. **Document type:** *Journal, Academic/Scholarly.* **Description:** Provides a forum for original papers and significant developments in hydrology.
Former titles (until 1981): Hydrological Sciences Bulletin (0303-6936); (until 1971): International Association of Scientific Hydrology. Bulletin (0020-6024)
Related titles: Online - full text ed.: (from EBSCO Publishing, Swets Information Services).
Indexed: AEA, APD, ASCA, ASFA, C&ISA, CIN, CRFR, ChemAb, ChemTitl, CivEngAb, CurCont, E&CAJ, ESPM, EngInd, ExcerpMed, FCA, FLUIDEX, ForAb, GEOBASE, GeotechAb, HerbAb, I&DA, IAOP, IBR, IBZ, ICEA, ISMEC, M&GPA, M&TEA, MaizeAb, PollutAb, RDA, RRTA, RefZh, RiceAb, S&F, SWRA, SolStAb, SoyAb, TDB, WAE&RSA, WRCInf.
—BLDSC (4347.628100), CASDDS, CISTI, Ei, IDS, IE, Infotrieve, ingenta, Linda Hall. **CCC.**
Published by: (International Association of Hydrological Sciences/Association Internationale des Sciences Hydrologiques), I A H S Press, Centre for Ecology and Hydrology, Wallingford, Oxon OX10 8BB, United Kingdom. TEL 44-1491-692442, FAX 44-1491-692448, zkundze@man.poznan.pl, frances@iahs.demon.co.uk, http://www.cig.ensmp.fr/~iahs/, http://iahs.info. Ed. Zbigniew Kundzewicz. R&P, Adv. contact Frances Watkins. Circ: 700.

551.48 ISR ISSN 0073-4217
GB1359.P3
HYDROLOGICAL YEARBOOK OF ISRAEL/SHENATON HIDROLOGI LE-YISRAEL. Text in English, Hebrew. 1946. a. USD 50 (effective 2000). **Document type:** *Government.* **Description:** Data on streamflow and springflow in Israel.
Published by: Ministry of Infrastructure, Water Commission, Hydrological Service, P O Box 6381, Jerusalem, 91063, Israel. TEL 972-2-5381101, FAX 972-2-5388704. Ed. Dr. Isabella Shentsis. Circ: 250.

HYDROLOGIE UND WASSERBEWIRTSCHAFTUNG. see *WATER RESOURCES*

551.4 DEU ISSN 1027-5606
GB651
➤ **HYDROLOGY AND EARTH SYSTEM SCIENCES.** Text in English. 1997. q. EUR 500; EUR 85 newsstand/cover (effective 2005). **Document type:** *Journal, Academic/Scholarly.* **Description:** International and interdisciplinary journal for the publication of original research in hydrology.
Related titles: Online - full text ed.: ISSN 1607-7938. free (effective 2005).
Indexed: ASFA, Agr, CurCont, ESPM, EnvEAb, GEOBASE, M&GPA, PollutAb, SWRA, WRCInf.
—BLDSC (4352.070000), IE, ingenta. **CCC.**
Published by: (European Geosciences Union), Copernicus GmbH, Max-Planck Str 13, Katlenburg-Lindau, 37191, Germany. TEL 49-5556-91099, info@copernicus.org, http://www.copernicus.org/EGU/hess/hess.html.

551.4 DEU ISSN 1812-2108
▼ ➤ **HYDROLOGY AND EARTH SYSTEM SCIENCES DISCUSSIONS.** Text in English. 2005. irreg. **Document type:** *Journal, Academic/Scholarly.* **Description:** It encourages and supports fundamental and applied research that seeks to understand the interactions between water, earth, ecosystems and man.
Related titles: Online - full text ed.: ISSN 1812-2116. free (effective 2005).
Published by: (European Geosciences Union), Copernicus GmbH, Max-Planck Str 13, Katlenburg-Lindau, 37191, Germany. TEL 49-5556-91099, info@copernicus.org, http://www.copernicus.org/EGU/hess/hess.html.

➤ **HYDROTITLES**; hydroscience bibliography. see *EARTH SCIENCES—Abstracting, Bibliographies, Statistics*

551.4 CHN
I A H S INFORMATION. Text in Chinese. 1989. s-a. free. adv. **Document type:** *Academic/Scholarly.* **Description:** Aims to be a bridge between IAHS and Chinese hydrologists and to disseminate information on IAHS activities, symposia, and publications. Includes selected papers and meeting reports.
Related titles: ♦ Partial translation of: I A H S Proceedings and Reports. ISSN 0144-7815.
Published by: (International Association of Hydrological Sciences/Association Internationale des Sciences Hydrologiques GBR), Shensheng Dai Ed. & Pub., Yellow River Hydrology Bureau, No. E12 Chengbei Rd, Zhengzhou, Henan 450004, China. TEL 86-371-6305805. Ed., Pub., R&P Dai Shensheng. Circ: 1,400.

551.4 GBR
I A H S NEWSLETTER. Text in English. 1980. 3/yr. **Document type:** *Newsletter, Academic/Scholarly.* **Description:** Includes news from IAHS officers, Scientific Commissions, Committees and Working Groups, and press as well as from governmental and nongovernmental organizations and other water-related associations. Covers meetings and information on fothcoming meetings organized or sponsored by IAHS.
Related titles: Online - full text ed.
Published by: (International Association of Hydrological Sciences FRA), I A H S Press, Centre for Ecology and Hydrology, Wallingford, Oxon OX10 8BB, United Kingdom. TEL 44-1491-692442, FAX 44-1491-692448, http://iahs.info.

551.4 GBR ISSN 0144-7815
GB651 CODEN: IAPUEP
➤ **I A H S PROCEEDINGS AND REPORTS.** Variant title: I A H S Publication. Text in English; Text occasionally in French. 1924. irreg., latest vol.284, 2003. price varies. back issues avail. **Document type:** *Proceedings, Academic/Scholarly.*
Related titles: ♦ Partial Chinese translation(s): I A H S Information.
Indexed: ASFA, BIOSIS Prev, CivEngAb, ESPM, GEOBASE, Inspec, M&GPA, M&TEA, RefZh, SWRA.
—BLDSC (4359.521240), CASDDS, CISTI, IE, Infotrieve, ingenta. **CCC.**
Published by: (International Association of Hydrological Sciences FRA), I A H S Press, Centre for Ecology and Hydrology, Wallingford, Oxon OX10 8BB, United Kingdom. TEL 44-1491-692442, FAX 44-1491-692448, frances@iahs.demon.co.uk, http://iahs.info. R&P, Adv. contact Frances Watkins.

551.4 GBR ISSN 1024-4891
CODEN: ISPUFG
➤ **I A H S SPECIAL PUBLICATIONS.** Text in English. 1989. irreg., latest vol.6, 2002. price varies. back issues avail. **Document type:** *Academic/Scholarly.* **Description:** Aims to provide a forum for short scientific reports which have been prepared by individuals or working groups within the framework of the association, but which do not fit into the Series of Proceedings and Reports.
Indexed: RefZh.
—BLDSC (4359.521250), CASDDS.
Published by: (International Association of Hydrological Sciences FRA), I A H S Press, Centre for Ecology and Hydrology, Wallingford, Oxon OX10 8BB, United Kingdom. TEL 44-1491-692442, FAX 44-1491-692448, frances@iahs.demon.co.uk, http://iahs.info. Eds. H Salz, Zbigniew Kundzewicz.

551.4 333.91 USA ISSN 0741-8507
I G W M C GROUND WATER MODELING NEWSLETTER. Text in English. 1981. a. free. adv. bk.rev.; software rev. back issues avail. **Document type:** *Newsletter.* **Description:** Concerns technical level of interest for engineers and water resources experts in groundwater modeling. Contains announcements of new publications, events and short courses.
Related titles: Online - full text ed.
Published by: International Ground Water Modeling Center, Colorado School of Mines, Institute for Ground Water Research and Education, Golden, CO 80401. TEL 303-273-3103, FAX 303-384-2037, igwmc@mines.edu, http://www.mines.edu/igwmc/. Ed. Ed Eileen Poeter. Pub. A Keith Turner. Adv. contact Eileen Poeter. Circ: 12,000.

551.48 JPN ISSN 0289-9531
IBARAKI UNIVERSITY. ITAKO HYDROBIOLOGICAL STATION. PUBLICATIONS. Text in English. 1984. a.
Published by: (Itako Hydrobiological Station), Ibaraki University, Faculty of Science/Ibaraki Daigaku Rigakubu Fuzoku Itako Rinko Jikkenjo, 1375, Ou, Namekata-gun, Itako-cho, Ibaraki-ken 311-24, Japan.

551.48 IND ISSN 0970-6984
TC503
INDIAN WATER RESOURCES SOCIETY. JOURNAL. Text in English. 1980. q. USD 500 (effective 2000). **Document type:** *Academic/Scholarly.*
Published by: (Indian Water Resources Society), H P C Publishers Distributors Pvt. Ltd., 4805 Bharat Ram Rd, 24 Darya Ganj, New Delhi, 110 002, India. TEL 91-11-3254401, FAX 91-11-619-3511, hpcpd@nda.vsnl.net.in, hpcpd@hpc.cc, http://www.hpc.cc, http://www.bizdelhi.com/publisher/hpc, http://www.indianindustry.com.

INSTITUT FUER WASSERWIRTSCHAFT, HYDROLOGIE UND LANDWIRTSCHAFTLICHEN WASSERBAU. MITTEILUNGEN. see *WATER RESOURCES*

551.4 GBR ISSN 0264-8709
INSTITUTE OF HYDROLOGY. REPORT. Text in English. 1967. irreg. price varies. **Document type:** *Monographic series.*
Indexed: I&DA, S&F.
Published by: C E H Wallingford, Maclean Bldg., Crowmarsh Gifford, Wallingford, Oxon OX10 8BB, United Kingdom. TEL 44-1491-838800, FAX 44-1491-692424, http://www.nwl.ac.uk/ih/www/products/bbooklisting.html, http://www.nwl.ac.uk/ih/www/main.html.

INSTITUTO HIDROGRAFICO. ANAIS. see *WATER RESOURCES*

551.4 627 ROM ISSN 1223-5083
INSTITUTUL POLITEHNIC DIN IASI. BULETINUL. SECTIA 7: HIDROTEHNICA. Text in English, French, German, Italian, Russian, Spanish. 1946. s-a. per issue exchange basis. bk.rev.
Related titles: Series of: Institutul Politehnic din Iasi. Buletinul.
Published by: Institutul Politehnic din Iasi "Gh Asachi", Bd Copou 11, Iasi, 6600, Romania. TEL 40-81-46577, FAX 40-81-47923. Eds. Alfred Braier, Hugo Rosman.

INSTYTUT METEOROLOGII I GOSPODARKI WODNEJ. GAZETA OBSERWATORA/JOURNAL OF I M W M OBSERVER. see *METEOROLOGY*

551.4 POL ISSN 0239-6297
GB651
INSTYTUT METEOROLOGII I GOSPODARKI WODNEJ. MATERIALY BADAWCZE. SERIA: HYDROLOGIA I OCEANOLOGIA/INSTITUTE OF METEOROLOGY AND WATER MANAGEMENT. RESEARCH PAPERS. SERIES: HYDROLOGY AND OCEANOLOGY. Text in Polish; Summaries in English. 1977. irreg. USD 15 (effective 2002). abstr.; charts; illus. **Document type:** *Monographic series.* **Description:** Articles on hydrology, oceanology, methodics, forecastings, measurements, instruments and research works.
Indexed: AgrLib, M&GPA, RefZh.
Published by: Instytut Meteorologii i Gospodarki Wodnej/Institute of Meteorology and Water Management, Ul Podlesna 61, Warsaw, 01673, Poland. TEL 48-22-8341651, FAX 48-22-8345466, bointe@imgw.pl. Pub. Jan Zielinski. R&P Maria Storozynska. Circ: 200.

INTERAFRICAN COMMITTEE FOR HYDRAULIC STUDIES. LIAISON BULLETIN. see *WATER RESOURCES*

INTERNATIONAL AND NATIONAL WATER LAW AND POLICY SERIES. see *LAW—International Law*

551.48 DEU ISSN 0538-4680
QH96.A1 CODEN: IVTMAS
INTERNATIONAL ASSOCIATION OF THEORETICAL AND APPLIED LIMNOLOGY. COMMUNICATIONS/ INTERNATIONALE VEREINIGUNG FUER THEORETISCHE UND ANGEWANDTE LIMNOLOGIE. MITTEILUNGEN. Text in English, German. 1953. irreg., latest vol.25, 1996. EUR 64 per issue domestic; EUR 66.90 per issue foreign (effective 2005). **Document type:** *Monographic series, Academic/Scholarly.*
Indexed: ASFA, BiolAb, ESPM, S&F.
—BLDSC (3352.000000), CASDDS, CISTI, KNAW, Linda Hall. **CCC.**
Published by: (International Association of Theoretical and Applied Limnology), E. Schweizerbart'sche Verlagsbuchhandlung, Johannesstr 3A, Stuttgart, 70176, Germany. TEL 49-711-3514560, FAX 49-711-35145699, mail@schweizerbart.de, http://www.schweizerbart.de/j/mitteilungen-der-ivl. Ed. Robert Wetzel.

E

551.48 DEU ISSN 0368-0770
QH98 CODEN: IVTLAP
INTERNATIONAL ASSOCIATION OF THEORETICAL AND APPLIED LIMNOLOGY. PROCEEDINGS/INTERNATIONALE VEREINIGUNG FUER THEORETISCHE UND ANGEWANDTE LIMNOLOGIE. VERHANDLUNGEN. Text in English, French, German. 1922. irreg., latest vol.28, 2003. EUR 150 per issue domestic; EUR 157.20 per issue foreign (effective 2005). index. **Document type:** *Proceedings, Academic/Scholarly.*
Description: Contains papers and discussions relating to particular fields and subdisciplines of limnology, freshwater science, and aqueous ecology.
Indexed: ASFA, BiolAb, ChemAb, ESPM, ExcerpMed, RefZh, SFA, WildRev, ZooRec.
—BLDSC (6728.000000), CASDDS, CISTI, IE, Infotrieve, ingenta, KNAW, Linda Hall. **CCC.**
Published by: (International Association of Theoretical and Applied Limnology), E. Schweizerbart'sche Verlagsbuchhandlung, Johannesstr 3A, Stuttgart, 70176, Germany. TEL 49-711-3514560, FAX 49-711-35145699, mail@schweizerbart.de, http://www.schweizerbart.de/j/verhandlungen-der-sil. Ed. Robert Wetzel. Circ: 3,000.

551.4 551 NLD ISSN 0936-3912
INTERNATIONAL CONTRIBUTIONS TO HYDROGEOLOGY. Text in English. 1984. irreg. price varies. **Document type:** *Monographic series, Academic/Scholarly.*
—BLDSC (4539.439600), IE.
Published by: (International Union of Geological Sciences NOR, International Association of Hydrogeologists GBR), A A Balkema (Subsidiary of: Taylor & Francis The Netherlands), PO Box 1675, Rotterdam, 3000 BR, Netherlands. TEL 31-10-414-5822, FAX 31-10-413-5947, balkema@balkema.nl, http://www.balkema.nl.

INTERNATIONAL HYDROGRAPHIC CONFERENCE. REPORTS OF PROCEEDINGS. see *EARTH SCIENCES—Oceanography*

551.46 MCO
INTERNATIONAL HYDROGRAPHIC ORGANIZATION. ANNUAL REPORT. Text in English. a.
Related titles: French ed.; Spanish ed.
Published by: International Hydrographic Bureau, 4 quai Antoine 1er, B.P. 445, Monte Carlo, MC 98011 Cedex, Monaco. TEL 377-93108100, info@ihb.mc, http://www.iho.shom.fr.

INTERNATIONAL HYDROGRAPHIC ORGANIZATION. YEARBOOK. see *EARTH SCIENCES—Oceanography*

551.4 USA ISSN 0257-6236
INTERNATIONAL RIVERS AND LAKES. Text in English. irreg. **Document type:** *Newsletter.*
Published by: (Comision Economica para America Latina y el Caribe/Economic Commission for Latin America and the Caribbean CHL), United Nations, Department of Economic and Social Affairs, Secretariat, New York, NY 10017.

551.4 ITA ISSN 1120-3080
ISTITUTO DI IDROBIOLOGIA E ACQUACOLTURA G. BRUNELLI. QUADERNI. Text in Multiple languages. 1980. irreg.
Indexed: ESPM.
Published by: Istituto di Idrobiologia e Acquacoltura G. Brunelli, Casali di Paola, Sabaudia, LT, Italy. TEL 39-0773-596703, FAX 39-06-3217582, isbrunel@tin.it.

JOKULL; journal of the glaciological and geological societies of Iceland. see *EARTH SCIENCES—Geology*

551.48 IND ISSN 0971-670X
JOURNAL OF APPLIED HYDROLOGY. Text in English. 1988. q. USD 100 (effective 2003).
—BLDSC (4942.619000).
Published by: Association of Hydrologists of India, Department of Geophysics, Andhra University, Visakhapatnam, Andhra Pradesh 530 003, India. **Subscr. to:** Scientific Publishers, 5-A New Pali Rd., Near Hotel Taj Hari Mahal, PO Box 91, Jodhpur, Rajasthan 342 003, India. TEL 91-291-2433323, FAX 91-291-2512580, info@scientificpub.com, http://www.scientificpub.com.

JOURNAL OF CONTAMINANT HYDROLOGY. see *ENVIRONMENTAL STUDIES—Pollution*

551.48 363.7 USA ISSN 1058-3912
GB651
JOURNAL OF ENVIRONMENTAL HYDROLOGY. Text in English. irreg. USD 48 to individuals; USD 180 to institutions (effective 2005). **Document type:** *Journal, Academic/Scholarly.*
Media: Online - full text.
Indexed: ASFA, BrCerAb, C&ISA, CerAb, CivEngAb, CorrAb, E&CAJ, EMA, EPB, ESPM, IAA, M&TEA, MBF, METADEX, PollutAb, SWRA, SolStAb, WAA.
Published by: International Association for Environmental Hydrology, PO Box 35324, San Antonio, TX 78235-5324. TEL 210-344-5418, FAX 210-344-9941, hydroweg@mail.org, http://www.hydroweb.com/journal-hydrology.html. Ed. Roger W Peebles.

333.91 USA ISSN 0270-5060
QH541.5.F7 CODEN: JFREDW
➤ **JOURNAL OF FRESHWATER ECOLOGY.** Text in English. 1981. q. USD 87 domestic; USD 97 foreign (effective 2005). 210 p./no. 1 cols./p.; back issues avail. **Document type:** *Journal, Academic/Scholarly.*
Indexed: AEA, ASCA, ASFA, AgBio, AnBrAb, ApEcolAb, B&BAb, BIOBASE, BIOSIS Prev, BioCN&I, BiolAb, CIN, CRFR, ChemAb, ChemTitl, CivEngAb, CurCont, EPB, ESPM, EntAb, EnvAb, EnvInd, FLUIDEX, FPA, ForAb, GEOBASE, GenetAb, HGA, HelmAb, HerbAb, I&DA, IABS, ISR, IndVet, MBA, NutrAb, PollutAb, PoultAb, ProtozoAb, RM&VM, RefZh, RevApplEntom, S&F, SCI, SFA, SWRA, VetBull, WeedAb, WildRev, ZooRec.
—BLDSC (4986.540000), CASDDS, IDS, IE, Infotrieve, ingenta.
Published by: Oikos Publishers, Inc., PO Box 2558, La Crosse, WI 54602-2558. TEL 608-526-9577, FAX 608-526-9477, oikosjourn@aol.com, oikosjour@aol.com, http://www.jfreshwaterecol.com/. Ed. Joseph A Kawatski. Circ: 500 (paid).

➤ **JOURNAL OF HYDROLOGIC ENGINEERING.** see *ENGINEERING—Civil Engineering*

551.4 NLD ISSN 0022-1694
GB651 CODEN: JHYDA7
➤ **JOURNAL OF HYDROLOGY.** Text in English, French, German. 1963. 64/yr. EUR 4,859 in Europe to institutions; JPY 646,200 in Japan to institutions; USD 5,438 elsewhere to institutions (effective 2006). adv. bk.rev. charts; illus. Index. back issues avail.; reprint service avail. from ISI. **Document type:** *Journal, Academic/Scholarly.* **Description:** Presents original studies, research results and reviews on the chemical and physical aspects of surface and groundwater hydrology, hydrometeorology, hydrogeology, parametric and stochastic hydrology, agrohydrology, hydrology of arid zones, and applied hydrology.
Related titles: Microform ed.: (from PQC); Online - full text ed.: (from EBSCO Publishing, Gale Group, IngentaConnect, ScienceDirect, Swets Information Services).
Indexed: AEA, AESIS, APD, ASCA, ASFA, AgBio, Agr, AgrForAb, ApMecR, BIOBASE, BIOSIS Prev, BibAg, BiolAb, BrCerAb, C&ISA, CIN, CIS, CPA, CRFR, CerAb, ChemAb, ChemTitl, CivEngAb, CorrAb, CurCont, E&CAJ, EIA, EMA, ESPM, EnvAb, EnvEAb, EnvInd, ExcerpMed, FCA, FLUIDEX, FPA, ForAb, GEOBASE, GeotechAb, HerbAb, HortAb, I&DA, IAA, IABS, ICEA, ISMEC, ISR, M&GPA, M&TEA, MBF, METADEX, MaizeAb, NemAb, OceAb, OrnHort, PGegResA, PollutAb, RDA, RRTA, RefZh, Repind, RiceAb, S&F, SCI, SFA, SIA, SJW, SPPI, SWRA, SeedAb, SolStAb, TDB, TriticAb, VITIS, WAA, WAE&RSA, WRCInf, WeedAb, WildRev.
—BLDSC (5003.700000), CASDDS, CISTI, Ei, IDS, IE, Infotrieve, ingenta, Linda Hall. **CCC.**
Published by: Elsevier BV (Subsidiary of: Elsevier Science & Technology), Radarweg 29, Amsterdam, 1043 NX, Netherlands. TEL 31-20-4853911, FAX 31-20-4852457, nlinfo-f@elsevier.nl, http://www.elsevier.com/locate/jhydrol, http://www.elsevier.nl. Eds. C Neal, M Sophocleous, R Krzysztofowicz. **Subscr. to:** Elsevier, Subscription Customer Service, 6277 Sea Harbor Dr, Orlando, FL 32887-4800. TEL 407-345-4020, 877-839-7126, FAX 407-363-1354.

551.49 551.5 NZL ISSN 0022-1708
GB651 CODEN: JLHYAD
➤ **JOURNAL OF HYDROLOGY. NEW ZEALAND.** Text in English. 1962. s-a. NZD 55 domestic to individuals; NZD 70 foreign to individuals; NZD 100 domestic to institutions; NZD 100 foreign to institutions; NZD 40 domestic to students; NZD 55 foreign to students (effective 2004). adv. bk.rev. abstr.; charts; illus. cum.index every 5 yrs. back issues avail. **Document type:** *Journal, Academic/Scholarly.* **Description:** Covers all aspects of hydrology including climatology, land use effects and water quality.
Indexed: AEA, ASFA, ApMecR, BIOSIS Prev, BiolAb, ESPM, EngInd, ExcerpMed, FLUIDEX, GEOBASE, I&DA, ICEA, INIS AtomInd, M&GPA, PollutAb, S&F, SWRA, SoftAbEng, WAE&RSA.
—BLDSC (5003.750000), CISTI, IE, ingenta, Linda Hall. **CCC.**
Published by: New Zealand Hydrological Society, PO Box 12300, Wellington, 6038, New Zealand. TEL 64-3-3197211, admin@hydrologynz.org.nz, http://www.hydrologynz.org.nz. Ed. Dr. Richard Hawke. R&P, Adv. contact Mr. Lindsay Rowe TEL 64-3-3197211. Circ: 500 (paid).

551.57 USA ISSN 1525-755X
GB2801
➤ **JOURNAL OF HYDROMETEOROLOGY.** Abstracts and contents page in English. 1999. bi-m. USD 154 to institutions; USD 206 combined subscription to institutions print & online eds. (effective 2005). back issues avail. **Document type:** *Journal, Academic/Scholarly.* **Description:** Publishes research related to the modeling, observing, and forecasting of processes related to water and energy fluxes and storages terms, including interactions with the boundary layer and lower atmosphere, and including processes related to precipitation, radiation, and other meteorological units.
Related titles: Online - full text ed.: ISSN 1525-7541. Online available upon request (from EBSCO Publishing, O C L C Online Computer Library Center, Inc.).
Indexed: ASFA, CurCont, ESPM, FCA, GEOBASE, M&GPA, RefZh, SWRA.
—BLDSC (5003.770000), CISTI, IE, Infotrieve, ingenta, Linda Hall. **CCC.**
Published by: American Meteorological Society, 45 Beacon St, Boston, MA 02108. TEL 617-227-2425, FAX 617-742-8718, amsinfo@ametsoc.org, http://ams.allenpress.com. Eds. Dara Entekhabi, Dennis P Lettenmaier, Efi Fouroula-Georgiou. R&P Melissa Weston TEL 617-227-2426.

551.48 JPN ISSN 0914-8272
GC369
KAIJO HOANCHO. SUIROBU KANSOKU HOKOKU. CHORYU HEN/DATA REPORT OF HYDROGRAPHIC OBSERVATIONS. SERIES OF TIDAL STREAM. Text in English, Japanese. 1987. a. per issue exchange basis. **Document type:** *Government.*
Published by: Kaijo Hoancho, Suirobu/Maritime Safety Agency, Hydrographic Department, 3-1 Tsuki-Ji 5-chome, Chuo-ku, Tokyo, 104-0045, Japan. TEL 81-3-3541-4296, FAX 81-3-3245-2885, consult@cue.jhd.go.jp, http://www.jhd.go.jp/.

551.48 JPN ISSN 0448-3308
KAIJO HOANCHO. SUIROBU KANSOKU HOKOKU. CHOSEKI HEN/DATA REPORT OF HYDROGRAPHIC OBSERVATIONS. SERIES OF TIDE. Text in English. 1965. a. per issue exchange basis. **Document type:** *Government.*
Published by: Kaijo Hoancho, Suirobu/Maritime Safety Agency, Hydrographic Department, 3-1 Tsuki-Ji 5-chome, Chuo-ku, Tokyo, 104-0045, Japan. TEL 81-3-3541-4296, FAX 81-3-3545-2885, consult@cue.jhd.go.jp, http://www.jhd.go.jp/.

551.48 JPN ISSN 0910-9102
QC811
KAIJO HOANCHO. SUIROBU KANSOKU HOKOKU. HACHIJO SUIRO KANSOKUJO CHIJIKI KANSOKU NENPO/DATA REPORT OF HYDROGRAPHIC OBSERVATIONS. HATIZYO HYDROGRAPHIC OBSERVATORY. GEOMAGNETIC OBSERVATIONS. Text in English. 1981. a. per issue exchange basis. **Document type:** *Government.*
Published by: Kaijo Hoancho, Suirobu/Maritime Safety Agency, Hydrographic Department, 3-1 Tsuki-Ji 5-chome, Chuo-ku, Tokyo, 104-0045, Japan. TEL 81-3-3541-4296, FAX 81-3-3545-2885, ico@cue.jhd.go.jp, http://www.jhd.go.jp/. Circ: 280.

551.48 JPN
KAIJO HOANCHO. SUIROBU KANSOKU HOKOKU. HARO HEN/DATA REPORT OF HYDROGRAPHIC OBSERVATIONS. WAVE OBSERVATIONS. Text in English, Japanese. 1987. a. per issue exchange basis. **Document type:** *Government.*
Published by: Kaijo Hoancho, Suirobu/Maritime Safety Agency, Hydrographic Department, 3-1 Tsuki-Ji 5-chome, Chuo-ku, Tokyo, 104-0045, Japan. TEL 81-3-3541-4296, FAX 81-3-3545-2885, consult@cue.jhd.go.jp, http://www.jhd.go.jp/.

551.48 JPN ISSN 0448-3316
KAIJO HOANCHO. SUIROBU KANSOKU HOKOKU. KAIYO HEN/DATA REPORT OF HYDROGRAPHIC OBSERVATIONS. SERIES OF OCEANOGRAPHY. Text in English, Japanese. 1965. a. **Document type:** *Government.*
Published by: Kaijo Hoancho, Suirobu/Maritime Safety Agency, Hydrographic Department, 3-1 Tsuki-Ji 5-chome, Chuo-ku, Tokyo, 104-0045, Japan. TEL 81-3-3541-4296, FAX 81-3-3545-2885, consult@cue.jhd.go.jp, http://www.jhd.go.jp/.

551.48 NGA ISSN 0331-9296
KAINJI LAKE RESEARCH INSTITUTE. ANNUAL REPORT. Text in English. a.
Indexed: ESPM.
Published by: National Institute for Freshwater Fisheries Research, PMB 6006, New Bussa, Nigeria. TEL 234-31-670444.

KARST WATERS INSTITUTE. SPECIAL PUBLICATIONS. see *EARTH SCIENCES—Geology*

KASEN JOHO KENKYUJO HOKOKU/INSTITUTE OF RIVER AND BASIN INTEGRATED COMMUNICATIONS. REPORT. see *WATER RESOURCES*

551.4 JPN ISSN 0912-7402
KOKUSAI KOSHO KANKYO IINKAI. NYUSURETA✶. Text in Japanese. 1986. irreg. **Document type:** *Newsletter.*
Related titles: ♦ English ed.: International Lake Environment Committee Foundation. Newsletter. ISSN 0912-7410.
Published by: Kokusai Kosho Kankyo Iinkai/International Lake Environment Committee Foundation, 1091 Oroshimo-cho, Kusatsu-shi, Shiga-ken 525-0001, Japan. TEL 81-77 568-4567, FAX 81-77-568-4568, info@mail.ilec.or.jp, http://www.ilec.or.jp/.

KYOTO UNIVERSITY. CENTER FOR ECOLOGICAL RESEARCH. COLLECTED PAPERS. see *BIOLOGY*

551.48 JPN ISSN 0289-3363
➤ **LAKE BIWA STUDY MONOGRAPHS/BIWAKO KENKYU MONOGURAFU.** Text in English; Summaries in English, Japanese. 1984. irreg. free. **Document type:** *Monographic series, Academic/Scholarly.*
Published by: Lake Biwa Research Institute/Shigaken Biwako Kenkyujo, 1-10 Uchide-Hama, Otsu-shi, Shiga-ken 520-0806, Japan. TEL 81-775-26-4800, FAX 81-775-26-4803. Ed. Masahisa Nakamura. Circ: 600 (controlled).

E

▼ new title ➤ refereed ✶ unverified ♦ full entry avail.

551.4 LSO
LESOTHO. MINISTRY OF NATURAL RESOURCES. HYDROLOGICAL YEARBOOK. Text in English. 1970. quinquennial. LSL 5 (effective Apr. 1998). back issues avail. **Document type:** *Government.*
Published by: Ministry of Natural Resources, Department of Water Affairs, PO Box MS 772, Maseru, 100, Lesotho. TEL 266-317102, FAX 266-310437, TELEX 4431, wateraff@lesoff.co.za. Circ: 100 (controlled).

LEVEL NEWS. see *WATER RESOURCES*

551.48 ESP ISSN 0213-8409
➤ **LIMNETICA.** Text and summaries in English, Spanish. 1985. q. EUR 45 elsewhere to individual members; EUR 100 elsewhere to institutions (effective 2005). index. back issues avail. **Document type:** *Journal, Academic/Scholarly.* **Description:** Covers research and studies in limnology from the Iberian peninsula.
Related titles: CD-ROM ed.; Online - full text ed.
Indexed: ASFA, ESPM, IECT, RefZh, ZooRec.
—CINDOC.
Published by: (Asociacion Espanola de Limnologia), Universitat de Barcelona, Servei de Publicacions, Gran Via Corts Catalanes 585, Barcelona, 08007, Spain. TEL 34-93-4021100, ael@ya.com, http://www.uv.es/ael/limnetica.htm, http://www.publicacions.ub.es. Ed. Isabel Munoz. Pub. Dr. Joan Armengol. Circ: 600 (paid and controlled).

551.48 DEU ISSN 0075-9511
QH96.A1 CODEN: LMNOA8
LIMNOLOGICA. Text in English. 1962. 4/yr. EUR 105 in Europe to individuals; JPY 13,000 in Japan to individuals; USD 103 to individuals except Europe and Japan; EUR 328 to institutions; EUR 364 in Europe to institutions; JPY 48,400 in Japan to institutions; USD 402 to institutions except Europe and Japan (effective 2006). adv. back issues avail. **Document type:** *Journal, Academic/Scholarly.* **Description:** Publishes original contributions, news, and reviews dealing with any aspect of ecology and hydrobiology of inland waters and adjacent biotops.
Related titles: Online - full text ed.: (from EBSCO Publishing, ScienceDirect).
Indexed: ASFA, BIOSIS Prev, BiolAb, CIN, ChemAb, ChemTitl, CurCont, ESPM, EntAb, ExcerpMed, FLUIDEX, GEOBASE, M&TEA, PollutAb, SFA, SJW, SWRA, WildRev, ZooRec.
—BLDSC (5219.450000), CASDDS, CISTI, IE, Infotrieve, ingenta, Linda Hall. **CCC.**
Published by: (Deutsche Gesellschaft fuer Limnologie), Elsevier GmbH, Urban & Fischer Verlag (Subsidiary of: Elsevier Science & Technology), Loebdergraben 14a, Jena, 07743, Germany. TEL 49-3641-626430, FAX 49-3641-626432, journals@urbanfischer.de, http://www.elsevier.com/locate/limno, http://www.urbanfischer.de. Ed. Rainer Koschel. R&P Martin Huber TEL 49-3641-626430. Adv. contact Sabine Schroeter TEL 49-3641-626445. B&W page EUR 400, color page EUR 1,345; trim 175 x 240. Circ: 300 (paid and controlled).
Non-German speaking countries subscr. to: Nature Publishing Group, Brunel Rd, Houndmills, Basingstoke, Hamps RG21 6XS, United Kingdom. TEL 44-1256-302629, FAX 44-1256-476117

551.48 DEU ISSN 0937-2881
LIMNOLOGIE AKTUELL. Text in Multiple languages. 1990. irreg. EUR 40 per vol. domestic; EUR 44 per vol. foreign (effective 2005). **Document type:** *Monographic series, Academic/Scholarly.*
Indexed: ZooRec.
—CISTI. **CCC.**
Published by: E. Schweizerbart'sche Verlagsbuchhandlung, Johannesstr 3A, Stuttgart, 70176, Germany. TEL 49-711-3514560, FAX 49-711-35145699, mail@schweizerbart.de, http://www.schweizerbart.de/j/limnologie-aktuell.

E

551.48 JPN ISSN 1439-8621
QH96.A1 CODEN: LIMNC8
➤ **LIMNOLOGY.** Text in English. 2000. 3/yr. EUR 188 combined subscription to institutions print & online eds. (effective 2005). back issues avail. **Document type:** *Journal, Academic/Scholarly.* **Description:** Covers physical, chemical, biological, or related research, including environmental issues, on any aspect of theoretical or applied limnology.
Related titles: Online - full text ed.: ISSN 1439-863X (from EBSCO Publishing, Springer LINK, Swets Information Services).
Indexed: ASFA, BIOSIS Prev, BiolAb, CurCont, ESPM, EntAb, EnvEAb, GEOBASE, PollutAb, RefZh, SWRA, ZooRec.
—CISTI, IE, Infotrieve. **CCC.**
Published by: (Nihon Rikusui Gakkai/Japanese Society of Limnology), Springer-Verlag Tokyo (Subsidiary of: Springer Science+Business Media), 3-13 Hongo 3-chome, Bunkyo-ku, Tokyo, 113-0033, Japan. TEL 81-3-38120331, FAX 81-3-38187454, limnology@svt-ebs.co.jp, orders@svt-ebs.co.jp, http://link.springer.de/link/service/journals/10201/index.htm, http://www.springer-tokyo.co.jp/. Ed. Dr. Takahito Yoshioka. Adv. contact Stephan Kroeck TEL 49-30-827875739.
Subscr. in the Americas to: Springer-Verlag New York, Inc., Journal Fulfillment, PO Box 2485, Secaucus, NJ 07096-2485. TEL 800-777-4643, 201-348-4033, FAX 201-348-4505, journals@springer-ny.com, http://www.springer-ny.com; **Subscr. to:** Springer GmbH Auslieferungsgesellschaft, Haberstr 7, Heidelberg 69126, Germany. TEL 49-6221-345-0, FAX 49-6221-345-4229, subscriptions@springer.de.

551.48 551.46 USA ISSN 0024-3590
GC1 CODEN: LIOCAH
➤ **LIMNOLOGY AND OCEANOGRAPHY.** Text in English. 1956. 8/yr. USD 378 to institutions (effective 2005). bk.rev. charts; illus. index. back issues avail.; reprints avail. **Document type:** *Journal, Academic/Scholarly.* **Description:** Covers all areas of aquatic research (except fisheries and pollution) at research level or advanced graduate studies.
Related titles: CD-ROM ed.: USD 560 in North America to libraries; USD 565 elsewhere to libraries (effective 2001); Online - full text ed.: (from EBSCO Publishing, H.W. Wilson, JSTOR (Web-based Journal Archive), O C L C Online Computer Library Center, Inc.).
Indexed: ABIPC, AESIS, APD, ASCA, ASFA, AnBeAb, ApEcolAb, B&AI, BIOBASE, BIOSIS Prev, BiolAb, CIN, CIS, CRFR, Cadscan, ChemAb, ChemTitl, CurCont, EIA, ESPM, EnerInd, EntAb, EnvAb, EnvEAb, EnvInd, ExcerpMed, FLUIDEX, GEOBASE, GSI, I&DA, IABS, INIS AtomInd, ISR, IndVet, LeadAb, M&GPA, MBA, MSB, MSCT, OceAb, PollutAb, ProtozoAb, RM&VM, RefZh, RiceAb, S&F, SCI, SFA, SJW, SPPI, SWRA, WRCInf, WildRev, Zincscan, ZooRec.
—BLDSC (5219.500000), CASDDS, CISTI, IDS, IE, Infotrieve, ingenta, Linda Hall. **CCC.**
Published by: American Society of Limnology and Oceanography, Inc., 1444 Eye St. NW #200, Washington, DC 20005. TEL 202-289-1972, 254-399-9635, 800-929-2756, FAX 202-628-1509, 254-776-3767, business@aslo.org, http://aslo.org/lo/, http://www.aslo.org. Circ: 5,300 (paid).
Subscr. to: c/o Karen Hickey.

551.48 ESP
➤ **LISTA FAUNISTICA Y BIBLIOGRAFICAS.** Text in Spanish. 1984. a. **Document type:** *Academic/Scholarly.*
Formerly: Listas de la Flora y Faunas de las Aguas Continentales de la Peninsula Iberica (1134-5470)
Indexed: ZooRec.
Published by: Asociacion Espanola de Limnologia, Los Angeles, 33, Mislanta, Valencia, 46920, Spain. TEL 34-963-799053, FAX 34-963-935205, ael@miracle.microb.uv.es, http://www.aelimno.org/. Pub. Eugenio Rico.

➤ **LOUISIANA WATER RESOURCES RESEARCH INSTITUTE. ANNUAL REPORT.** see *WATER RESOURCES*

551.48 USA
MAINE GEOLOGICAL SURVEY. U S G S HYDROLOGIC INVESTIGATIONS. Text in English. irreg. **Document type:** *Bulletin, Government.*
Published by: Maine Geological Survey, 22 State House Station, Augusta, ME 04333.

MEMORIE DI SCIENZE GEOLOGICHE. see *EARTH SCIENCES—Geology*

MISSOURI. DIVISION OF GEOLOGICAL SURVEY AND WATER RESOURCES. WATER RESOURCES REPORT. see *WATER RESOURCES*

MONO LAKE NEWSLETTER. see *WATER RESOURCES*

551.4 DNK ISSN 0900-0267
N H P RAPPORT. (Nordisk Hydrologisk Program) Text in Danish, Norwegian, Swedish. 1978. irreg. price varies. illus.
Formerly (until 1981): Nordic I H D Report (0800-7357)
—CISTI.
Published by: Nordisk Hydrologisk Forening/Nordic Association for Hydrology, c/o Danish Water Resources Committee, Geological Survey of Denmark and Greenland (GEuS), Thoravej 8, Copenhagen Nv, 2400, Denmark. TEL 35-38-142000, FAX 35-38-142050, lfj@geus.dk, http://www.vandressource.dk/nhp-dk.htm#reports.

NANCHANG SHUIZHAN XUEBAO/NANCHANG COLLEGE OF WATER CONSERVANCY AND HYDROELECTRIC POWER. see *ENERGY—Hydroelectrical Energy*

NATIONAL DRILLER. see *WATER RESOURCES*

551.4 USA ISSN 0733-4044
GB705.G73
NATIONAL OCEANIC AND ATMOSPHERIC ADMINISTRATION. ENVIRONMENTAL RESEARCH LABORATORIES. GREAT LAKES ENVIRONMENTAL RESEARCH LABORATORY. DATA REPORT. Key Title: N O A A Data Report. E R L-G L E R L. Text in English. 1979. irreg. **Document type:** *Monographic series.*
Indexed: ASFA, ESPM, OceAb.
—CISTI.
Published by: U.S. National Oceanic and Atmospheric Administration, Great Lakes Environmental Research Laboratory, 2205 Commonwealth Blvd, Ann Arbor, MI 48105-2945. TEL 734-741-2235, FAX 734-741-2055, http://www.glerl.noaa.gov. **Orders to:** U.S. Department of Commerce, National Technical Information Service, 5285 Port Royal Rd, Springfield, VA 22161. TEL 800-363-2068, subscriptions@ntis.gov.

551.4 USA ISSN 1060-1929
NATIONAL OCEANIC AND ATMOSPHERIC ADMINISTRATION. ENVIRONMENTAL RESEARCH LABORATORIES. PACIFIC MARINE ENVIRONMENTAL LABORATORY. DATA REPORT. Key Title: N O A A Data Report. E R L-P M E L. Text in English. 1980. irreg. **Document type:** *Monographic series.*
Published by: U.S. National Oceanic and Atmospheric Administration, Pacific Marine Environmental Laboratory, 7600 Sand Point Way NE, Seattle, WA 98115. TEL 206-526-6239, FAX 206-526-6815, http://www.pmel.noaa.gov. **Orders to:** U.S. Department of Commerce, National Technical Information Service, 5285 Port Royal Rd, Springfield, VA 22161. TEL 800-363-2068, subscriptions@ntis.gov.

NATIONAL WATER CONDITIONS. see *WATER RESOURCES*

NEW INTERNATIONAL HYDROGRAPHIC BULLETIN/NOUVEAU BULLETIN HYDROGRAPHIQUE INTERNATIONAL/NUEVO BOLETIN HIDROGRAFICO INTERNACIONAL. see *EARTH SCIENCES—Oceanography*

NEW MEXICO GEOLOGY. see *EARTH SCIENCES—Geology*

NEW WAVES (COLLEGE STATION). see *WATER RESOURCES*

551.48 NZL ISSN 1175-1355
GB651
NEW ZEALAND HYDROLOGICAL SOCIETY. CURRENT. Text in English. 1993. s-a.
Indexed: M&GPA.
—Linda Hall.
Published by: New Zealand Hydrological Society, PO Box 12300, Wellington, 6038, New Zealand. TEL 64-3-3197211, admin@hydrologynz.org.nz, http://www.hydrologynz.org.nz.

NEW ZEALAND JOURNAL OF MARINE AND FRESHWATER RESEARCH. see *EARTH SCIENCES—Oceanography*

NIHON RIKUSUI GAKKAI KOEN YOSHISHU/JAPANESE SOCIETY OF LIMNOLOGY. ABSTRACTS OF MEETING. see *EARTH SCIENCES—Abstracting, Bibliographies, Statistics*

441.48 JPN ISSN 0913-4859
NIHON RIKUSUI GAKKAI KOSHIN'ETSU SHIBUKAI KAIHO/LIMNOLOGICAL SOCIETY OF KOSHIN'ETSU DISTRICT. BULLETIN. Text in Japanese; Summaries in English, Japanese. 1977. a.
Published by: Nihon Rikusui Gakkai, c/o Shiga University, 2-5-1 Hiratsu, Otsu, Shiga-ken 520-0862, Japan. TEL 81-775-37-7735, endoh@sue.shiga-u.ac.jp.

551.48 GBR ISSN 0029-1277
GB651 CODEN: NOHYBB
➤ **NORDIC HYDROLOGY;** an international journal. Text and summaries in English. 1970. 5/yr. GBP 199, USD 325, EUR 286 combined subscription to institutions print & online (effective 2005). bk.rev. bibl.; charts; illus. annual index. back issues avail. **Document type:** *Journal, Academic/Scholarly.* **Description:** Publishes articles within all fields of hydrology in its widest sense, including surface water hydrology, ground water hydrology, hydrometeorology, snow and ice and hydrodynamics. Physics and chemistry of water is also covered.
Related titles: Online - full text ed.: (from EBSCO Publishing, Swets Information Services).
Indexed: AEA, ASCA, ASFA, BIOSIS Prev, BiolAb, BrCerAb, C&ISA, CIN, CIS, CPA, CerAb, ChemAb, ChemTitl, CivEngAb, CorrAb, CurCont, E&CAJ, EIA, EMA, ESPM, EngInd, EnvAb, EnvInd, ExcerpMed, FCA, FLUIDEX, FPA, ForAb, GEOBASE, I&DA, IAA, IBR, ICEA, ISR, M&GPA, M&TEA, MBF, METADEX, OceAb, PollutAb, RRTA, RefZh, S&F, SCI, SWRA, SoftAbEng, SolStAb, TriticAb, WAA, WRCInf.
—BLDSC (6117.920000), CASDDS, CISTI, Ei, IDS, IE, Infotrieve, ingenta, Linda Hall. **CCC.**
Published by: (Nordisk Hydrologisk Forening/Nordic Association for Hydrology DNK), I W A Publishing (Subsidiary of: International Water Association), Alliance House, 12 Caxton St, London, SW1H 0QS, United Kingdom. TEL 44-20-76545500, FAX 44-20-76545555, publications@iwap.co.uk, http://www.iwapublishing.com/template.cfm?name=iwapnordichydrology. Ed. Dan Rosbjerg TEL 45-45-251449. Circ: 325. **subscr. to:** Portland Customer Services, Commerce Way, Colchester CO2 8HP, United Kingdom. TEL 44-1206-796351, FAX 44-1206-799331, sales@portland-services.com, http://www.portland-services.com. **Dist. by:** Portland Press Ltd., Commerce Way, Colchester CO2 8HP, United Kingdom.

551.48 NOR ISSN 0801-955X
NORSK INSTITUTT FOR VANNFORSKNING. AARSBERETNING. Text in Norwegian. 1958. a. free. illus.
Formerly: Norsk Institutt for Vannforskning. Aarbok

Published by: Norsk Institutt for Vannforskning/Norwegian Institute for Water Research, Postboks 173, Kjelsas, Oslo, 0411, Norway. TEL 47-22-18-51-00, FAX 47-22-18-52-00. Ed. Borgny Iversen.

551.48 NOR
NORSK INSTITUTT FOR VANNFORSKNING. REPORTS. Text in Norwegian. irreg. NOK 150. charts; illus.
Published by: Norsk Institutt for Vannforskning/Norwegian Institute for Water Research, Postboks 173, Kjelsas, Oslo, 0411, Norway. TEL 47-22-18-52-00. Ed. Borgny Iversen.

551.48 JPN
OMIA/LAKE BIWA RESEARCH INSTITUTE. NEWS. Text in Japanese. 1982. irreg.
Published by: Shigaken Biwako Kenkyujo/Lake Biwa Research Institute, 1-10 Uchide-Hama, Otsu-shi, Shiga-ken 520-0806, Japan.

551.48 CHE ISSN 0379-1335
QC851 CODEN: WMOHBC
OPERATIONAL HYDROLOGY REPORT. Text in English. 1973. irreg., latest vol.42. price varies. **Document type:** *Monographic series.* **Description:** Technical reports about operational hydrology.
Indexed: I&DA, S&F.
—Linda Hall.
Published by: World Meteorological Organization, 7 bis Avenue de la Paix, Case postale 2300, Geneva 2, 1211, Switzerland. TEL 41-22-7308111, FAX 41-22-7308022, pubsales@gateway.wmo.ch, http://www.wmo.int. **Dist. in U.S. by:** American Meteorological Society, 45 Beacon St, Boston, MA 02108. TEL 617-227-2425.

PROFESSIONAL GEOLOGIST. see *EARTH SCIENCES—Geology*

551.4 ITA ISSN 1121-1059
QUADERNI TECNICI DI ACQUACOLTURA. Text in Multiple languages. 1989. irreg. **Document type:** *Monographic series.*
Indexed: ESPM.
Published by: Ente per le Nuove Tecnologie, l'Energia e l'Ambiente (ENEA), Lungotevere Thaon di Revel 76, Rome, 00196, Italy. TEL 39-06-36272625, FAX 39-06-36272230, http://www.enea.it.

551.49 PRT ISSN 0870-1741
RECURSOS HIDRICOS. Text in Portuguese. 1980. q. EUR 10 (effective 2002).
Indexed: ESPM.
Published by: Associacao Portuguesa dos Recursos Hidricos, a/c LNEC, Av do Brasil, 101, Lisbon, 1700-066, Portugal. TEL 351-21-844 34 28, FAX 351-21-844 30 17, aprh@aprh.pt, http://www.aprh.pt.

REFERATIVNYI ZHURNAL. GIDROGEOLOGIYA, INZHENERNAYA GEOLOGIYA, MERZLOTOVEDENIE. see *EARTH SCIENCES—Abstracting, Bibliographies, Statistics*

REPORTS OF INVESTIGATIONS ABOUT LAKE BIWA. see *PUBLIC HEALTH AND SAFETY*

REVISTA GEOFISICA. see *EARTH SCIENCES—Geophysics*

551.4 628.167 FRA ISSN 0992-7158
CODEN: RSEAEX
➤ **REVUE DES SCIENCES DE L'EAU**; journal of water science. Text in English, French; Summaries in English, French. 1982. q. EUR 112 in the European Union; EUR 132 elsewhere (effective 2003). bk.rev. abstr.; bibl.; illus.; maps. 120 p./no.; back issues avail.; reprints avail. **Document type:** *Academic/Scholarly.* **Description:** Devoted to water sciences.
Formed by the 1988 merger of: Revue Internationale des Sciences de l'Eau (0830-9590); Sciences de l'Eau (0298-6663); Which was formerly (until 1986): Revue Francaise des Sciences de l'Eau (0750-7186)
Indexed: ASFA, BIOSIS Prev, BiolAb, ChemAb, ChemTitl, CivEngAb, EPB, ESPM, EngInd, EnvAb, EnvEAb, FLUIDEX, GEOBASE, IBR, IBZ, M&GPA, OceAb, PollutAb, RefZh, SFA, SWRA, WRCInf, WTA.
—BLDSC (7947.650000), CASDDS, CISTI, Ei, IE, ingenta, Linda Hall. **CCC.**
Published by: Lavoisier, 11 rue Lavoisier, Paris, 75008, France. TEL 33-1-42653995, FAX 33-1-42650246, info@lavoisier.fr, http://www.sciencesdeleau.org, http://www.lavoisier.fr. Ed. M Dorange. R&P Chantal Arpino. Circ: 1,000. **Subscr. to:** Lavoisier - Dept Abonnements, 14 rue de Provigny, Cachan 94236, France. TEL 33-1-47406700, FAX 33-1-47406702, abo@lavoisier.fr.

551.48 JPN ISSN 0021-5104
CODEN: RIZAAU
RIKUSUI GAKU ZASSHI/JAPANESE JOURNAL OF LIMNOLOGY. Text in English, Japanese. 1931. 3/yr. JPY 10,000 for membership to individuals; JPY 20,000 for membership to institution (effective 2004). adv. bk.rev. charts; illus. **Document type:** *Journal, Academic/Scholarly.* **Description:** Cotnains research articles, note, reviews and information on aspect of limnology.
Indexed: ASFA, BIOSIS Prev, BiolAb, CTO, ChemAb, ESPM, EntAb, ExcerpMed, GEOBASE, PollutAb, RefZh, SFA, SWRA, WildRev, ZooRec.
—BLDSC (4656.000000), CASDDS, CISTI, IE, ingenta, KNAW, Linda Hall.
Published by: Nihon Rikusui Gakkai/Japanese Society of Limnology, c/o Business Center for Academic Societies Japan, Honkomagome 5-16-9, Bunkyo-ku, Tokyo, Shiga-ken 113-8622, Japan. TEL 81-3-58145810, FAX 81-3-58145825, endoh@sue.shiga-u.ac.jp, ban@ses.usp.ac.jp, http://wwwsoc.nii.ac.jp/jslim/. Ed. O Mitamura. Adv. contact Seiichi Nohara. Circ: 1,200.

RUSSIAN METEOROLOGY AND HYDROLOGY. see *METEOROLOGY*

S A S A Q S NEWSLETTER. see *WATER RESOURCES*

551.4 SWE ISSN 0283-7722
S M H I HYDROLOGI. Text in English, Swedish. 1974. irreg. **Document type:** *Monographic series.*
Supersedes in part (in 1985): Sveriges Meteorologiska och Hydrologiska Institut. Hydrologiska/Oceanografiska Avdelningen (0282-2601); Formerly (until 1982): HB Rapport
Published by: Sveriges Meteorologiska och Hydrologiska Institut/Swedish Meteorological and Hydrological Institute, Folkborgvaegen 1, Norrkoeping, 60176, Sweden. TEL 46-11-495-80-00, FAX 46-11-495-80-01, smhi@smhi.se, http://www.smhi.se.

551.4 SWE ISSN 0283-1104
S M H I REPORTS. HYDROLOGY. Text in English, Swedish. 1963. irreg.
Supersedes in part (in 1985): S M H I Rapporter. Hydrologi och Oceanografi (0347-7827); Which was formerly (until 1973): Notiser och Preliminary Rapporter. Serie Hydrologi (0586-1659); Incorporates (1979-1985): Institute of Hydrographic Research Goteborg Serie (0349-523X)
Published by: Sveriges Meteorologiska och Hydrologiska Institut/Swedish Meteorological and Hydrological Institute, Folkborgvaegen 1, Norrkoeping, 60176, Sweden. TEL 46-11-495-80-00, FAX 46-11-495-80-01, http://www.smhi.se.

SAVE THE HARBOR - SAVE THE BAY NEWSLETTER. see *ENVIRONMENTAL STUDIES*

551.4 CZE ISSN 0036-5289
GB1001 CODEN: SGVHAS
➤ **SBORNIK GEOLOGICKYCH VED: HYDROGEOLOGIE, INZENYRSKA GEOLOGIE/JOURNAL OF GEOLOGICAL SCIENCES: HYDROGEOLOGY, ENGINEERING GEOLOGY.** Text and summaries in Czech, English, French, German, Russian. 1964. irreg., latest vol.21, 2001. price varies. charts; illus. 120 p./no. 2 cols./p.; back issues avail. **Document type:** *Journal, Academic/Scholarly.* **Description:** Publishes papers on hydrogeology and engineering geology.
Indexed: GEOBASE.
—Linda Hall.
Published by: Ceska Geologicka Sluzba/Czech Geological Survey, Klarov 3, Prague, 11821, Czech Republic. TEL 42-02-57320438, hrkal@natur.cuni.cz, http://www.geology.cz. Ed. Zbynek Hrkal. Circ: 600. **Subscr. to:** Myris Trade, V Stihlach 1311, PO Box 2, Prague 4 14201, Czech Republic. TEL 420-2-34035200, FAX 420-2-34035207.

551.4 CHE
SERIES ON SNOW AND ICE. (Includes: Fluctuations of Glaciers, Glacier Mass Balance Bulletins) Text in English. 1967. irreg., latest 1994. **Document type:** *Monographic series, Academic/Scholarly.* **Description:** Covers topics related to ice and snow. Titles contain data on glaciers, and guides for collecting and assembling data on seasonal snow cover, perennial ice, and snow masses and glaciers.
Published by: (International Association of Hydrological Sciences, International Commission on Snow and Ice GBR), W. Haeberli, Department of Geography, University of Zurich - IRCHEL, Winterthurerstr 190, Zuerich, 8057, Switzerland. TEL 41-1-6355120, FAX 41-1-6356844, haeberli@geo.unizh.ch. **Co-sponsor:** UNESCO.

551.48 JPN ISSN 0914-3068
SHIGA DAIGAKU KYOIKUGAKUBU KOSHO JISSHU SHISETSU RONBUNSHU/SHIGA UNIVERSITY. FACULTY OF EDUCATION. INSTITUTE OF LAKE SCIENCES. ANNUAL REPORT. Text in Japanese; Summaries in English, Japanese. 1961. a. **Document type:** *Academic/Scholarly.*
Published by: (Kosho Jisshu Shisetsu), Shiga Daigaku, Kyoikugakubu/Shiga University, Faculty of Education, 5-1 Hiratsu 2-chome, Otsu-shi, Shiga-ken 520-0862, Japan. FAX 81-77-537-7840. Ed. Michiko Tachibana.

551.48 JPN ISSN 0289-7636
SHIGA KENRITSU BIWAKO BUNKAKAN KENKYU KIYO/BIWAKO BUNKAKAN. ANNUAL REPORT. Text in Japanese. 1983. a.
Published by: Shiga Kenritsu Biwako Bunkakan, 1-1 Uchide-Hama, Otsu-shi, Shiga-ken 520-0806, Japan.

551.48 JPN ISSN 0288-1330
QH98
SHIGAKEN BIWAKO KENKYUJO SHOHO/LAKE BIWA RESEARCH INSTITUTE. BULLETIN. Text in English. 1982. a. **Document type:** *Bulletin.*
Published by: Shigaken Biwako Kenkyujo/Lake Biwa Research Institute, 1-10 Uchide-Hama, Otsu-shi, Shiga-ken 520-0806, Japan.

551.48 570 JPN ISSN 0916-3255
SHINSHU DAIGAKU RIGAKUBU FUZOKU SUWA RINKO JIKKENJO HOKOKU/SHINSHU UNIVERSITY. SUWA HYDROBIOLOGICAL STATION. REPORT. Text in English, Japanese; Summaries in English. 1976. irreg.
Published by: (Fuzoku Suwa Rinko Jikkenjo), Shinshu Daigaku, Rigakubu/Shinshu University, Faculty of Science, Suwa Hydrobiological Station, 2-4 Kogandori 5-chome, Suwa-shi, Nagano-ken 392-0027, Japan.

627 CHN ISSN 1001-6791
GB651
SHUI KEXUE JINZHAN/ADVANCES IN WATER SCIENCE. Text in Chinese. 1990. q. CNY 6 newsstand/cover (effective 2002). **Document type:** *Academic/Scholarly.*
Related titles: Online - full text ed.: (from East View Information Services).
Indexed: M&TEA.
—BLDSC (0712.140000), IE, ingenta.
Published by: Zhongguo Shuili Shuidian Shubanshe/China WaterPower Press, Xikang Lu 1-Hao, Nanjing, 210024, China. Ed. Guowei Lui. **Dist. by:** China International Book Trading Corp, 35 Chegongzhuang Xilu, Haidian District, PO Box 399, Beijing 100044, China. TEL 86-10-68412045, FAX 86-10-68412023, cibtc@mail.cibtc.com.cn, http://www.cibtc.com.cn.

SHUILI KEJI YU JINGJI/WATER CONSERVANCY SCIENCE AND TECHNOLOGY AND ECONOMY. see *CONSERVATION*

SHUISHENG SHENGWU XUEBAO/ACTA HYDROBIOLOGICA SINICA. see *BIOLOGY*

551.4 CHN ISSN 1000-0852
SHUIWEN/HYDROLOGY. Text in Chinese; Abstracts in English. bi-m. 64 p./no.; **Document type:** *Trade.* **Description:** Covers both theoretical and practical issues related to hydrology and water resources.
Related titles: Online - full text ed.: (from East View Information Services).
—Linda Hall.
Published by: Shuiwen Zazhishe, Baiguang Lu 2 Tiao, Xuanwu-qu, Beijing, 100761, China. **Dist. overseas by:** China International Book Trading Corp, 35 Chegongzhuang Xilu, Haidian District, PO Box 399, Beijing 100044, China.

551.4 CHN ISSN 1000-3665
SHUIWEN DIZHI GONGCHENG DIZHI/HYDROGEOLOGY AND ENGINEERING GEOLOGY. Text in Chinese; Abstracts in English. 1957. bi-m. CNY 16.80 (effective 1994). adv. **Document type:** *Academic/Scholarly.*
Related titles: Online - full text ed.: (from East View Information Services).
Indexed: ASFA, BrCerAb, C&ISA, CerAb, CorrAb, E&CAJ, EEA, EMA, ESPM, IAA, M&TEA, MBF, METADEX, RefZh, SWRA, WAA.
—Linda Hall.
Published by: Dizhi Kuangchan Bu/Ministry of Geology and Mineral Products, 20 Dahui Si, Haidian District, Beijing, 100081, China. TEL 86-10-8950262, FAX 86-10-8350261. Ed. Yu Huanxin. Adv. contact Gao Yansong. page USD 500. **Subscr. to:** 504 Anhuali, Andingmenwai, Beijing, China.

551.4 LKA
SRI LANKA. IRRIGATION DEPARTMENT. HYDROLOGY DIVISION. HYDROLOGICAL ANNUAL. Text in English. a. illus. **Document type:** *Government.*
Published by: Irrigation Department, Hydrology Division, Bauddhaloka Mawatha, Colombo, 7, Sri Lanka.

551.48 USA ISSN 0376-4826
CODEN: SBHYA8
STEIRISCHE BEITRAEGE ZUR HYDROGEOLOGIE. Text in English. a. price varies. reprint service avail. from ISI.
Indexed: IBR.
—CCC.
Published by: Springer-Verlag New York, Inc. (Subsidiary of: Springer Science+Business Media), 233 Spring St, New York, NY 10013. TEL 212-460-1500. Ed. Josef Zoetl.

551.48 FRA ISSN 0081-7449
CODEN: IHSRB9
STUDIES AND REPORTS IN HYDROLOGY SERIES. (Consists of: Discharge of Selected Rivers of Africa, Discharge of Selected Rivers of the World, Limnology and Hydrology of Lake Victoria) Text in English. 1969. irreg., latest vol.56, 1998. price varies.
Related titles: Microform ed.
—BLDSC (8489.370000), CISTI.

E

Published by: UNESCO Publishing, 7 place de Fontenoy, Paris, 75352, France. TEL 33-1-45684300, FAX 33-1-45685741, http://www.unesco.org/publications. **Dist. in U.S. by:** Bernan Associates, Bernan, 4611-F Assembly Dr., Lanham, MD 20706-4391. TEL 800-274-4447, FAX 800-865-3450.

STUDIES IN VERMONT GEOLOGY. see *EARTH SCIENCES—Geology*

551.4 628.1   JPN
SUIMON MIZU SHIGEN GAKKAI NYUSU/JAPAN SOCIETY OF HYDROLOGY AND WATER RESOURCES NEWS. Text in Japanese. 1988. s-a.
Published by: Suimon Mizu Shigen Gakkai, Nihon Gakkai Jimu Senta, 16-9 Honkomagome 5-chome, Bunkyo-ku, Tokyo, 113-0021, Japan.

551.4 628.1   JPN   ISSN 0915-1389
SUIMON MIZU SHIGEN GAKKAISHI/JAPAN SOCIETY OF HYDROLOGY AND WATER RESOURCES. JOURNAL. Text in Japanese; Summaries in English, Japanese. 1988. bi-m. adv. **Document type:** *Academic/Scholarly.*
Related titles: Online - full text ed.: ISSN 1349-2853 (from J-Stage).
Indexed: ASFA, ESPM, M&GPA, SWRA.
—CCC.
Published by: Suimon Mizu Shigen Gakkai, Nihon Gakkai Jimu Senta, 16-9 Honkomagome 5-chome, Bunkyo-ku, Tokyo, 113-0021, Japan. Ed. Masaki Sawomoto. Adv. contact Nobuhiko Takeda.

551.4   JPN   ISSN 0288-5301
SUIROBU GIHO/TECHNICAL BULLETIN ON HYDROGRAPHY. Text in Japanese. 1982. a. **Description:** Contains reports of technical research and developments of JHD.
Published by: Kaijo Hoancho, Suirobu/Maritime Safety Agency, Hydrographic Department, 3-1 Tsuki-Ji 5-chome, Chuo-ku, Tokyo, 104-0045, Japan.

551.48   FRA   ISSN 0082-2310
GB651   CODEN: TPHYAF
TECHNICAL PAPERS IN HYDROLOGY SERIES. Text in French. 1970. irreg., latest 1992-94, 27th. price varies.
Related titles: Microform ed.
—CISTI. **CCC.**
Published by: UNESCO Publishing, 7 place de Fontenoy, Paris, 75352, France. TEL 33-1-45684300, FAX 33-1-45685737, http://www.unesco.org/publications. **Dist. in U.S. by:** Bernan Associates, Bernan, 4611-F Assembly Dr., Lanham, MD 20706-4391. TEL 800-274-4447, FAX 800-865-3450.

551.49   USA
TENNESSEE VALLEY AUTHORITY. REPORT. Variant title: T V A Report. Text in English. irreg.
Published by: Tennessee Valley Authority, 400 W Summit Hill Dr, Knoxville, TN 37902-1499. TEL 865-632-2101, tvainfo@tva.gov, http://www.tva.gov.

U N A M. INSTITUTO DE CIENCIAS DEL MAR Y LIMNOLOGIA. ANALES. see *EARTH SCIENCES—Oceanography*

551.4   USA
U.S. ARMY CORPS OF ENGINEERS. WATERWAYS EXPERIMENT STATION. ENVIRONMENTAL LABORATORY. COMPLETION REPORT. Text in English. irreg.
Published by: U.S. Army Corps of Engineers, Waterways Experiment Station Environmental Laboratory, 3909 Halls Ferry Rd, Vicksburg, MS 39180-6199. http://www.wes.army.mil/el/homepage.html. **Orders to:** U.S. Department of Commerce, National Technical Information Service, 5285 Port Royal Rd, Springfield, VA 22161. TEL 800-363-2068, subscriptions@ntis.gov.

U.S. GEOLOGICAL SURVEY. NATIONAL WATER SUMMARY. see *WATER RESOURCES*

551.4   USA
U.S. GEOLOGICAL SURVEY. WATER-DATA REPORTS. Text in English. irreg.
Published by: U.S. Department of the Interior, Geological Survey, 12201 Sunrise Valley Dr, Reston, VA 20192. TEL 888-275-8747, ask@usgs.gov, http://water.usgs.gov/pubs/wdr/. **Subscr. to:** USGS Information Services, Denver Federal Center, Box 25286, Denver, CO 80225-0046. TEL 303-202-4210, FAX 303-202-4693.

553.7   USA   ISSN 0092-332X
GB701   CODEN: WRIND3
U.S. GEOLOGICAL SURVEY. WATER RESOURCES INVESTIGATIONS. Key Title: Water-Resources Investigations. Text in English. 1978 (no.121). irreg., latest 1983. **Document type:** *Government.*
Related titles: Microfiche ed.: 1978 (no.121).
Indexed: ASFA, ESPM, I&DA, S&F, SFA.
Published by: U.S. Department of the Interior, Geological Survey, 12201 Sunrise Valley Dr, Reston, VA 20192. TEL 888-275-8747, ask@usgs.gov, http://water.usgs.gov/pubs/. **Subscr. to:** USGS Information Services, Denver Federal Center, Box 25286, Denver, CO 80225-0046. FAX 303-202-4693, infoservices@usgs.gov.

333.91   USA   ISSN 0886-9308
TC801   CODEN: XIWSAX
U.S. GEOLOGICAL SURVEY. WATER SUPPLY PAPER. Text in English. 1896. irreg. back issues avail. **Document type:** *Monographic series, Government.*
Former titles (until 1982): Geological Survey. Water Supply Paper (0083-1131); (until 1950): U.S. Geological Survey. Water Supply Paper (0887-7149); (until 1908): U.S. Geological Survey. Water-Supply and Irrigation Papers (0888-4765)
Related titles: Microfiche ed.: 1896 (from BHP, PMC); Microfilm ed.: 1896 (from BHP); ♦ Series: U.S. Geological Survey. National Water Summary. ISSN 0892-3469; ♦ U.S. Geological Surveys. Selected Papers in Hydrolic Sciences. ISSN 0892-3450.
Indexed: AESIS, ASFA, FLUIDEX, GEOBASE, I&DA, S&F. —CASDDS, CISTI.
Published by: U.S. Department of the Interior, Geological Survey, 12201 Sunrise Valley Dr, Reston, VA 20192. TEL 703-648-4000, 888-275-8747, FAX 703-648-4888, ask@usgs.gov, http://water.usgs.gov/pubs/. **Subscr. to:** USGS Information Services, Denver Federal Center, Box 25286, Denver, CO 80225-0046. FAX 303-202-4693, infoservices@usgs.gov.

U.S. GEOLOGICAL SURVEYS. SELECTED PAPERS IN HYDROLIC SCIENCES. see *WATER RESOURCES*

551.46   USA   ISSN 0276-4849
VK589
U.S. HYDROGRAPHIC CONFERENCE. BIENNIAL MEETING. PROCEEDINGS. Text in English. 1984. biennial. price varies. back issues avail. **Document type:** *Proceedings.*
Related titles: ♦ Series of: Hydrographic Society. International Headquarters. Special Publications. ISSN 0309-8303.
Published by: Hydrographic Society of America, PO Box 732, Rockville, MD 20848-0732. TEL 301-460-4768, FAX 301-460-4768.

551.4   DEU
GB731
UNESCO INTERNATIONALES HYDROLOGISCHES PROGRAMM: OPERATIONELLES HYDROLOGISCHES PROGRAMM: JAHRBUCH BUNDESREPUBLIK DEUTSCHLAND/UNESCO. INTERNATIONAL HYDROLOGICAL PROGRAMME: OPERATIONAL HYDROLOGY PROGRAMME: YEARBOOK FEDERAL REPUBLIC OF GERMANY. Text in English, German. 1965; N.S. 1968. a. **Document type:** *Government.* **Description:** Surveys hydrological processes in Germany by means of selected stations.
Former titles: Internationales Hydrologisches Programm: Operationelles Hydrologisches Programm: Jahrbuch Bundesrepublik Deutschland und Berlin (West) (1430-6255); (until 1983): Internationales Hydrologisches Programm: Jahrbuch Bundesrepublik Deutschland und Berlin (West) (0344-5259); Internationale Hydrologische Dekade: Jahrbuch der Bundesrepublik Deutschland (0538-7779)
Published by: Bundesanstalt fuer Gewaesserkunde, Am Mainzer Tor 1, Koblenz, 56068, Germany. TEL 49-261-13060, FAX 49-261-13065302, posteingang@bafg.de, http://www.bafg.de. Circ: 1,000.

UNIVERSIDADE FEDERAL DO RIO GRANDE DO NORTE. CENTRO DE BIOCIENCIAS. DEPARTAMENTO DE OCEANOGRAFIA E LIMNOLOGIA. BOLETIM. see *BIOLOGY*

551.4 627   ROM   ISSN 1224-6042
TC160
UNIVERSITATEA POLITEHNICA DIN TIMISOARA. BULETINUL STIINTIFIC. SERIA HIDROTEHNICA. Text in English, French, German, Romanian. 1992. s-a. USD 20 (effective 2000). bk.rev. **Document type:** *Bulletin.*
—Linda Hall.
Published by: Universitatea Politehnica din Timisoara, Piata Victoriei 2, Timisoara, 1900, Romania. TEL 40-56-200349, FAX 40-56-190321. Ed. Ioan David. Circ: 500.

551.4 526   POL   ISSN 1429-799X
➤ **UNIWERSYTET SLASKI W KATOWICACH. PRACE NAUKOWE. LANDFORM ANALYSIS.** Text in English. 1997. a., latest vol.3, 2002. price varies. **Document type:** *Monographic series, Academic/Scholarly.* **Description:** Covers scientific and practical aspect of geomorphology: stratigraphy, lithology, physical and chemical composition of deposits, cartography, geodesy, remote sensing.
Indexed: RefZh.
Published by: (Uniwersytet Slaski w Katowicach), Wydawnictwo Uniwersytetu Slaskiego w Katowicach, Ul Bankowa 12B, Katowice, 40007, Poland. TEL 48-32-2596915, FAX 48-32-2582735, TELEX 0315584 uskpl, wydawus@us.edu.pl, http://www.us.edu.pl/uniwersytet/jednostki/ogolne/wydawnictwo. Circ: 750. **Dist. by:** CHZ Ars Polona, Biblioteka PAN w Warszawie, PO Box 1001, Warsaw 00950, Poland.

➤ **VERMONT DIVISION OF GEOLOGY AND MINERAL RESOURCES. SPECIAL PUBLICATION.** see *EARTH SCIENCES—Geology*

➤ **VODNI HOSPODARSTVI.** see *ENGINEERING—Hydraulic Engineering*

➤ **VODNYE RESURSY.** see *WATER RESOURCES*

551.4 628   SVK   ISSN 0042-790X
GB772.C95   CODEN: VOCAAZ
➤ **VODOHOSPODARSKY CASOPIS/JOURNAL OF HYDROLOGY AND HYDROMECHANICS.** Text in Czech, English, Slovak; Summaries in Czech, English, Slovak. 1953. q. USD 97 foreign (effective 2005). adv. bk.rev. charts; illus. index, cum.index: 1953-1982. 100 p./no. 1 cols./p.; back issues avail. **Document type:** *Academic/Scholarly.* **Description:** Presents original research results and short communications in the fields of hydrology and hydromechanics, including hydrodynamics of porous media and non-Newtonian fluids.
Related titles: Online - full text ed.
Indexed: ASFA, ApMecR, CIN, ChemAb, ChemTitl, ESPM, FLUIDEX, GeotechAb, ICEA, M&GPA, PollutAb, S&F, WRCInf. —BLDSC (5003.720000), CASDDS, CISTI, Linda Hall.
Published by: Slovenska Akademia Vied, Ustav Hydrologie/Slovak Academy of Sciences, Institute of Hydrology, Racianska 75, PO Box 94, Bratislava, 83811, Slovakia. FAX 42-12-44259404, kozumplikova@uh.savba.sk, myska@ih.cas.cz, http://www.ih.savba.sk/jhh. Eds. Jiri Myska, Viliam Novak. Pubs. Julius Sutor TEL 42-12-44259383, Pavel Vlasak TEL 42-12-49268279. R&P Julius Sutor TEL 42-12-44259383. Circ: 320 (paid and controlled). **Dist. by:** Slovart G.T.G. s.r.o., Krupinska 4, PO Box 152, Bratislava 85299, Slovakia. http://www.slovart-gtg.sk. **Co-sponsor:** Akademie Ved Ceske Republiky, Ustav pro Hydrodynamiku/Academy of Sciences of Czech Republic, Institute of Hydrodynamics.

551.4   NGA   ISSN 0795-6495
WATER RESOUCES. Text in English. 1988. s-a.
Indexed: ESPM.
Published by: Nigerian Association of Hydrogeologists, University of Benin, Benin City, Nigeria.

WATER RESOURCES. see *WATER RESOURCES*

WATER RESOURCES DATA FOR ALASKA. see *WATER RESOURCES*

WATER RESOURCES DATA FOR COLORADO. see *WATER RESOURCES*

WATER RESOURCES DATA FOR GEORGIA. see *WATER RESOURCES*

WATER RESOURCES DATA FOR IDAHO. see *WATER RESOURCES*

WATER RESOURCES DATA FOR ILLINOIS. see *WATER RESOURCES*

WATER RESOURCES DATA FOR INDIANA. see *WATER RESOURCES*

WATER RESOURCES DATA FOR IOWA. see *WATER RESOURCES*

WATER RESOURCES DATA FOR KANSAS. see *WATER RESOURCES*

WATER RESOURCES DATA FOR KENTUCKY. see *WATER RESOURCES*

WATER RESOURCES DATA FOR MARYLAND AND DELAWARE. see *WATER RESOURCES*

WATER RESOURCES DATA FOR MINNESOTA. see *WATER RESOURCES*

WATER RESOURCES DATA FOR MONTANA. see *WATER RESOURCES*

WATER RESOURCES DATA FOR NEBRASKA. see *WATER RESOURCES*

WATER RESOURCES DATA FOR NEW MEXICO. see *WATER RESOURCES*

WATER RESOURCES DATA FOR NORTH CAROLINA. see *WATER RESOURCES*

WATER RESOURCES DATA FOR NORTH DAKOTA. see *WATER RESOURCES*

WATER RESOURCES DATA FOR PENNSYLVANIA. see *WATER RESOURCES*

WATER RESOURCES DATA FOR SOUTH CAROLINA. see *WATER RESOURCES*

WATER RESOURCES DATA FOR SOUTH DAKOTA. see *WATER RESOURCES*

WATER RESOURCES DATA FOR TEXAS. see *WATER RESOURCES*

E

WATER RESOURCES DATA FOR VIRGINIA. see *WATER RESOURCES*

WATER RESOURCES DATA FOR WASHINGTON. see *WATER RESOURCES*

WATER RESOURCES DATA FOR WISCONSIN. see *WATER RESOURCES*

WATER RESOURCES DATA FOR WYOMING. see *WATER RESOURCES*

WATER RESOURCES DATA. MISSOURI. see *WATER RESOURCES*

WATER RESOURCES DATA. PUERTO RICO AND THE U.S. VIRGIN ISLANDS. see *WATER RESOURCES*

WATER RESOURCES RESEARCH. see *WATER RESOURCES*

WATER RESOURCES SUMMARY. see *WATER RESOURCES*

WATER RESOURCES WORLDWIDE. see *WATER RESOURCES—Abstracting, Bibliographies, Statistics*

WATERPOWER. see *ENGINEERING—Civil Engineering*

WEATHER AND FORECASTING. see *METEOROLOGY*

551.4 USA ISSN 0161-0589
QC929.S7 CODEN: PWSCA9
WESTERN SNOW CONFERENCE. PROCEEDINGS. Text in English. 1948. a. USD 30 domestic; USD 37.50 foreign (effective 2005). **Document type:** *Proceedings, Academic/Scholarly.*
Indexed: EngInd.
—BLDSC (1087.919500), CISTI, Linda Hall.
Published by: Western Snow Conference, PO Box 2646, Portland, OR 97208-2646. TEL 503-641-7142, marrone@teleport.com. Ed. Charles Troendle. R&P James Marron TEL 503-414-3047. Circ: 800.

EARTH SCIENCES—Oceanography

551.46 AUS ISSN 1033-6974
A I M S REPORT. Text in English. 1989. irreg. AUD 10 per issue (effective 2000). **Document type:** *Bulletin.*
Indexed: ASFA, ESPM, ZooRec.
Published by: Australian Institute of Marine Science, PMB No 3, Townsville Mail Centre, Townsville, QLD 4810, Australia. TEL 61-7-47534409, w.ellery@aims.gov.au, http://www.aims.gov.au. Ed. S Clarke W Ellery.

A M S NEWSLETTER (ONLINE EDITION). see *METEOROLOGY*

A S F A MARINE BIOTECHNOLOGY ABSTRACTS (ONLINE EDITION). see *BIOLOGY—Abstracting, Bibliographies, Statistics*

551.46 CUB ISSN 1010-450X
ACADEMIA DE CIENCIAS DE CUBA. INSTITUTO DE OCEANOLOGIA. REPORTE DE INVESTIGACION. Text in Spanish; Summaries in English. 1982. irreg. free. illus.
Supersedes (after no.187): Academia de Ciencias de Cuba. Instituto de Oceanologia. Informes Cientificos Tecnicos
Indexed: ASFA.
Published by: Academia de Ciencias de Cuba, Instituto de Oceanologia, Avda. 1ra. no. 18406,, La Playa, Ciudad de La Habana, Cuba. TEL 21-9988, TELEX 511290. Ed. Guillermo Garcia Montero.

551.46 MLT
ACROSS THE OCEANS. Text in English. 1982. irreg. free. **Document type:** *Newsletter.*
Incorporates: I O I News
Published by: International Ocean Institute, PO Box 3, Gzira, GZR 01, Malta. TEL 356-346529, FAX 356-346502, ioihq@ioihq.org.mt, http://www.ioist.org. Ed. Anita Coady.

551.46 HRV ISSN 0001-5113
QH93 CODEN: AADRAY
➤ **ACTA ADRIATICA.** Text in English; Summaries in Croatian. 1932. s-a. per issue exchange basis. 150 p./no. 2 cols./p.; back issues avail. **Document type:** *Journal, Academic/Scholarly.* **Description:** Publishes original scientific papers on the oceanography, mostly of the Adriatic and Mediterranean Seas.
Related titles: Diskette ed.; E-mail ed.; Fax ed.
Indexed: ASFA, BiolAb, ChemAb, ESPM, OceAb, RefZh, SWRA, ZooRec.
—BLDSC (0588.000000), CASDDS, IE, ingenta.
Published by: Institut za Oceanografiju i Ribarstvo/Institute of Oceanography and Fisheries, Setaliste Ivana Mestrovica 63, Split, 21000, Croatia. TEL 385-21-358688, FAX 385-21-358650, office@izor.hr, http://www.izor.hr/acta/eng/index.html. Ed., R&P Mira Zore-Armanda. Pub. Ivona Marasovic. Circ: 400 (paid and controlled). **Co-sponsor:** Ministartsvo Znanosti i Tehnologije.

551.46 ECU
CODEN: AAECFX
ACTA ANTARTICA ECUATORIANA. Text in Spanish. 1993. irreg., latest vol.4, 1998.
Indexed: INIS AtomInd.
Published by: Instituto Oceanografico de la Armada, Via al Puerto Maritimo, Av 25 de Julio, Apdo 5940, Guayaquil, Guayas, Ecuador. TEL 593-4-2481300, FAX 593-4-2485166, inocar@inocar.mil.ec, http://www.inocar.mil.ec/public/antart.php.

551.46 ECU ISSN 1010-4402
GC771
ACTA OCEANOGRAFICA DEL PACIFICO. Text in Spanish; Summaries in English, Spanish. 1980. a. free. **Document type:** *Bulletin.* **Description:** Covers physical, biological, chemical, geological oceanography, and their incidence in living resources, weather and climate.
Indexed: CTO.
Published by: Instituto Oceanografico de la Armada, Via al Puerto Maritimo, Av 25 de Julio, Apdo 5940, Guayaquil, Guayas, Ecuador. TEL 593-4-480033, FAX 593-4-484723, TELEX 3572 ED, inocar@inocar.mil.ec. Ed. Jose Almedo Moran. Circ: 3,000 (controlled).

551.4 TWN ISSN 0379-7481
GC1 CODEN: AOTADS
ACTA OCEANOGRAPHICA TAIWANICA. Text in English; Summaries in Chinese, English. 1971. irreg. USD 30 (effective 2000); free to academic institutions. bk.rev. **Document type:** *Academic/Scholarly.* **Description:** Contains original articles, notes, and letters on oceanographic research.
Indexed: ASFA, BAS, CIN, ChemAb, ChemTitl, ESPM, M&GPA, OceAb, ZooRec.
—BLDSC (0641.620000), CASDDS, IE, ingenta, Linda Hall.
Published by: (Institute of Oceanography), National Taiwan University, College of Science, PO Box 23-13, Taipei, 106, Taiwan. TEL 886-2-3625983, FAX 886-2-3636092, ctliu@ccms.ntu.edu.tw, winyang@ms.cc.ntu.edu.tw. Ed. Wung Yang Shieh. Circ: 800.

551.46 CHN ISSN 0253-505X
GC1 CODEN: AOSIEE
➤ **ACTA OCEANOLOGICA SINICA.** Text in English. 1979. bi-m. USD 420 (effective 2006). **Document type:** *Journal, Academic/Scholarly.* **Description:** Publishes scholarly papers on marine science and technology, including physics, chemistry, biology, hydrology, meteorology, aquaculture, engineering, remote sensing, instrumentation and meters.
Related titles: ♦ Chinese ed.: Haiyang Xuebao. ISSN 0253-4193.
Indexed: ASFA, B&BAb, CTO, ChemAb, CurCont, EPB, ESPM, FLUIDEX, GEOBASE, M&GPA, OceAb, RefZh, SWRA, ZooRec.
—BLDSC (0641.623050), CASDDS, CISTI, IE, ingenta. **CCC.**
Published by: (Chinese Society of Oceanography), Haiyang Chubanshe/Ocean Press, International Department, 8 Dahuisi Rd, Haidian District, Beijing, 100081, China. TEL 86-01-62179976, FAX 86-01-62173569, TELEX 22536 NBO CN, hyxb1@263.net,hyxb2@263.net; hyxb3@263.net; hyxbe@263.net, oceanpress@china.com. Ed. Su Jilan. Circ: 1,500.

➤ **ADVANCED SERIES ON OCEAN ENGINEERING.** see *ENGINEERING*

➤ **ADVANCES IN COASTAL AND OCEAN ENGINEERING.** see *ENGINEERING*

➤ **ADVANCES IN MARINE BIOLOGY.** see *BIOLOGY*

551.46 NLD ISSN 0952-1798
➤ **ADVANCES IN UNDERWATER TECHNOLOGY, OCEAN SCIENCE AND OFFSHORE ENGINEERING.** Text in English. irreg., latest vol.33, 1994. price varies. back issues avail. **Document type:** *Monographic series, Academic/Scholarly.*
Formerly (until 1986): Advances in Underwater Technology and Offshore Engineering
—BLDSC (0711.678200), ingenta.
Published by: (Society for Underwater Technology GBR), Springer-Verlag Dordrecht (Subsidiary of: Springer Science+Business Media), Van Godewijckstraat 30, Dordrecht, 3311 GX, Netherlands. TEL 31-78-6576050, FAX 31-78-6576474, http://www.springeronline.com.

551.46 USA ISSN 1060-202X
CODEN: AWAQE4
➤ **ADVANCES IN WORLD AQUACULTURE.** Text in English. 1990. irreg., latest vol.6, 1997. price varies. **Document type:** *Monographic series, Academic/Scholarly.*
Indexed: ZooRec.
Published by: World Aquaculture Society, 143 J M Parker Coliseum, Louisiana State University, Baton Rouge, LA 70803. TEL 225-388-3137, FAX 225-388-3493.

➤ **AMERICAN METEOROLOGICAL SOCIETY. BULLETIN.** see *METEOROLOGY*

➤ **AMERICAN SHORE AND BEACH PRESERVATION ASSOCIATION. NEWSLETTER.** see *ENVIRONMENTAL STUDIES*

578.77 COL ISSN 0120-8241
ANALES DEL INSTITUTO DE INVESTIGACIONES MARINAS DE PUNTA BETIN. SUPLEMENTO. Text in Spanish. 1967. irreg.
Supersedes in part (in 1977): Mitteilungen aus dem Instituto Colombo-Aleman de Investigaciones Cientificas Punta de Betin (0120-825X)
Related titles: ♦ Supplement to: Boletin de Investigaciones Marinas y Costeras. ISSN 0122-9761.
Published by: Instituto de Investigacions Marinas y Costeras, Cerro de Punta de Bertin, Santa Marta, Magdalena 1016, Colombia. TEL 575-4214774, FAX 575-4215181, boletin@invemar.edu.co.

551.46 IND ISSN 0066-1686
ANDHRA UNIVERSITY MEMOIRS IN OCEANOGRAPHY. Text in English. 1954. irreg. price varies.
Published by: (Andhra University), Andhra University Press and Publications, Waltair, Visakhapatnam, Andhra Pradesh 530 003, India. Ed. E C La Fond.

ANNUAIRE DES MAREES POUR L'AN. TOME 1. PORTS DE FRANCE. see *TRANSPORTATION—Ships And Shipping*

551.46 620 GBR ISSN 0141-1187
TC1501 CODEN: AOCRDS
➤ **APPLIED OCEAN RESEARCH.** Text in English. 1979. 6/yr. EUR 885 in Europe to institutions; JPY 117,500 in Japan to institutions; USD 988 to institutions except Europe and Japan (effective 2006). adv. abstr. back issues avail. **Document type:** *Journal, Academic/Scholarly.* **Description:** Provides current information about various aspects of ocean research and development, especially those related to offshore engineering.
Related titles: Microform ed.: (from PQC); Online - full text ed.: (from EBSCO Publishing, Gale Group, IngentaConnect, ScienceDirect, Swets Information Services).
Indexed: AJEE, ASFA, ApMecR, BMT, CTO, CivEngAb, CurCont, E&PHSE, EEA, EPB, ESPM, EngInd, FLUIDEX, GEOBASE, GP&P, ICEA, Inspec, M&GPA, M&TEA, OceAb, OffTech, PetrolAb, SWRA.
—BLDSC (1576.240000), AskIEEE, CISTI, Ei, IDS, IE, Infotrieve, ingenta, Linda Hall, PADDS. **CCC.**
Published by: Pergamon (Subsidiary of: Elsevier Science & Technology), The Boulevard, Langford Ln, East Park, Kidlington, Oxford OX5 1GB, United Kingdom. TEL 44-1865-843000, FAX 44-1865-843010, http://www.elsevier.com/locate/apor, http://www.elsevier.nl. Eds. J Witz, M. Ohkusu, S K Chakrabarti. **Subscr. to:** Elsevier BV, PO Box 211, Amsterdam 1000 AE, Netherlands. TEL 31-20-485-3757, FAX 31-20-485-3432, nlinfo-f@elsevier.nl.

➤ **AQUA**; mensile di acqua, natura, vita. see *EARTH SCIENCES—Hydrology*

551.46 BEL ISSN 1018-9661
AQUACULTURE EUROPE MAGAZINE. Text in English. 1976. q. EUR 60 to members (effective 2005). adv. bk.rev. back issues avail. **Document type:** *Bulletin.* **Description:** Aims at providing a variety of information in this rapidly growing field. Contains general as well as personal information related to developments in aquaculture.
Formerly (until 1992): European Aquaculture Society Quarterly Newsletter (0773-6940)
Indexed: ASFA, ESPM.
—CINDOC.
Published by: European Aquaculture Society (EAS), Slijkensesteenweg 4, Oostende, 8400, Belgium. TEL 32-59-323859, FAX 32-59-321005, eas@unicall.be, http://www.easonline.org/publications/en/AquacultureEuropeMagazine.asp. Ed. Patrick Lavens. Circ: 1,000.

AQUAPHYTE. see *BIOLOGY—Botany*

AQUATIC CONSERVATION; marine and freshwater ecosystems. see *CONSERVATION*

551.46 660.6 333.91 GBR ISSN 1477-903X
QH541.5.W3
▼ ➤ **AQUATIC RESOURCES, CULTURE AND DEVELOPMENT.** Text in English. 2005. q. USD 265 in the Americas to individuals; GBP 150 elsewhere to individuals; USD 440 in the Americas to institutions; GBP 250 elsewhere to institutions non-member country; USD 290 combined subscription in the Americas to individuals; GBP 165 combined subscription elsewhere to individuals; USD 480 combined subscription in the Americas to institutions print & online; GBP 275 combined subscription elsewhere to institutions non-member country, print & online (effective 2005). **Document type:** *Journal, Academic/Scholarly.* **Description:** Provide a new and interconnected body of knowledge to support the management of aquatic resources for human benefit in the developing and developed worlds.
Related titles: Online - full content ed.: ISSN 1479-0696. 2005. USD 140 in the Americas to individuals; GBP 80 elsewhere to individuals; USD 395 in the Americas to institutions; GBP 225 elsewhere to institutions non-member country (effective 2005); Online - full text ed.: (from Gale Group, IngentaConnect, Ovid Technologies, Inc.).
—BLDSC (1582.425000). **CCC.**

E

▼ new title ➤ refereed ✶ unverified ♦ full entry avail.

Published by: CABI Publishing (Subsidiary of: CAB International), CAB International, Wallingford, Oxfordshire OX10 8DE, United Kingdom. TEL 44-1491-832111, FAX 44-1491-833508, cabi@cabi.org, http://www.cabi-publishing.org/Journals.asp?SubjectArea=&Subject=&PID=26. Ed. J F Muir. Pub. Katy Christomanou TEL 44-1491-829187.

551.46 FRA ISSN 1261-6818
AQUITAINE OCEAN. Text in French. 1966. irreg.
Formerly (until 1994): Institut de Geologie du Bassin d'Aquitaine. Bulletin (0524-0832)
Indexed: ESPM.
Published by: Universite de Bordeaux I, Departement de Geologie et Oceanographie, Ave des Facultes, Talence, 33405, France. TEL 05-56-84-60-00, FAX 05-56-84-08-48, sec.geocean@epoc.u-bordeaux.fr, http://www.epoc.u-bordeaux.fr.

ARCHAEONAUTICA. see *ARCHAEOLOGY*

551.46 551.48 ITA ISSN 0066-667X
CODEN: AOLVAE
ARCHIVIO DI OCEANOGRAFIA E LIMONOLOGIA. Text in Italian; Summaries in English, Italian. 1941. irreg., latest vol.21, no.3, 1989. bk.rev. **Document type:** *Journal, Academic/Scholarly.*
Indexed: BiolAb.
—CASDDS, Linda Hall.
Published by: Istituto di Biologia del Mare, Castello 1364-A, Venice, 30122, Italy. TEL 39-041-2404711, FAX 39-041-5204126, biomar@ibm.ve.cnr.it, http://www.ibm.ve.cnr.it. Ed. S Rabitti. Circ: 500.

551.4 BRA ISSN 0374-5686
QH91.A1 CODEN: AQCMBP
➤ **ARQUIVOS DE CIENCIAS DO MAR.** Text and summaries in English, Portuguese. 1961. a., latest vol.35, 2002. BRL 20 domestic; USD 15 foreign (effective 2003). back issues avail. **Document type:** *Journal, Academic/Scholarly.* **Description:** This serial comprises papers on subjects mainly related to oceanography, fish technology and population dynamics and is intended for the academic and private sectors relating to the fishing sector of Northwest Brazil.
Former titles (until 1968): Arquivos da Estacao de Biologia Marinha da Universidade Federal do Ceara (0100-5987); (until 1965): Arquivos da Estacao Biologia Marinha da Universidade do Ceara (0532-2588)
Related titles: E-mail ed.; Fax ed.
Indexed: ASFA, BiolAb, CTO, ChemAb, RefZh, SFA, ZooRec.
—CISTI, Linda Hall.
Published by: Universidade Federal do Ceara, Laboratorio de Ciencias do Mar, Av da Universidade, 2853, Benfica, Fortaleza, CE 60020-181, Brazil. TEL 55-85-2426422, FAX 55-85-2428355, afontele@ufc.br. Ed. Antonio Adauto Fonteles Filho. R&P Antonio Adauto Fonteles-Filho. Circ: 1,500; 800 (controlled).

➤ **ASIAN MARINE BIOLOGY.** see *BIOLOGY*

551.46 578.77 PRI
ASSOCIATION OF MARINE LABORATORIES OF THE CARIBBEAN. NEWSLETTER. Some issues in English, Spanish. 1986. q. USD 5. adv. bk.rev. index. **Document type:** *Newsletter.*
Published by: Association of Marine Laboratories of the Caribbean, University of Puerto Rico, Dept of Marine Sciences, Mayaguez, 00708, Puerto Rico. FAX 787-834-3031.

578.77 PRI
ASSOCIATION OF MARINE LABORATORIES OF THE CARIBBEAN. PROCEEDINGS. Text in English. 1957. irreg., latest vol.22, 1989. USD 5.
Formerly: Association of Island Marine Laboratories of the Caribbean. Proceedings (0066-9571)
Indexed: ASFA.
Published by: Association of Marine Laboratories of the Caribbean, University of Puerto Rico, Dept of Marine Sciences, Mayaguez, 00708, Puerto Rico. FAX 787-265-2880, TELEX UPR MAY 3452024. Ed. Lucy Bunkley Williams. Circ: 500.

551.46 BRA ISSN 0102-1656
QH117
ATLANTICA. Text in English, Portuguese. 1976. irreg.
Indexed: ESPM, ZooRec.
Published by: Fundacao Universidade Federal do Rio Grande, Departamento de Oceanografia, Rua Eng Alfredo Huch, 475 Centro, Rio Grande, 96201-900, Brazil. TEL 55-53-233-6500, reitoria@furg.br, http://www.furg.br.

ATMOSPHERE - OCEAN. see *METEOROLOGY*

ATMOSPHERIC AND OCEANOGRAPHIC SCIENCES LIBRARY. see *EARTH SCIENCES*

551.46 AUS ISSN 1037-3314
AUSTRALIAN INSTITUTE OF MARINE SCIENCE. ANNUAL REPORT. Text in English. 1972. a. charts; illus. **Document type:** *Corporate.*
Formerly: Australian Institute of Marine Science. Yearly Report (0311-4716)
Indexed: AESIS, ASFA, ESPM.
Published by: Australian Institute of Marine Science, PMB No 3, Townsville Mail Centre, Townsville, QLD 4810, Australia. TEL 61-7-47534409, w.ellery@aims.gov.au, http://www.aims.gov.au. Eds. S Clarke, W Ellery. Circ: 2,000.

551.46 AUS ISSN 1036-1650
AUSTRALIAN INSTITUTE OF MARINE SCIENCE. PROJECTED RESEARCH AND DEVELOPMENT ACTIVITIES. Text in English. 1997. biennial. **Document type:** *Corporate.*
Formerly (until 1991): Australian Institute of Marine Science. Projected Research Activities (0814-1452)
Indexed: AESIS, ESPM.
Published by: Australian Institute of Marine Science, PMB No 3, Townsville Mail Centre, Townsville, QLD 4810, Australia. TEL 61-7-47534409, w.ellery@aims.gov.au, http://www.aims.gov.au. Eds. S Clarke, W Ellery.

551.46 AUS
AUSTRALIAN MARINE SCIENCE BULLETIN. Text in English. 1962. q. membership. adv. bk.rev. **Document type:** *Bulletin.*
Former titles: Australian Marine Sciences Association. Bulletin (0157-6429); (until 1970): Australian Marine Science Newsletter
Indexed: ASFA, CTO, ESPM, SFA.
Published by: Australian Marine Sciences Association Inc., Zoology Department, University Of Melbourne, VIC 3052, Australia. FAX 61-3-9344-7909. Ed. E Johnston. Circ: 1,200.

AUSTRALIAN METEOROLOGICAL AND OCEANOGRAPHIC SOCIETY. BULLETIN. see *METEOROLOGY*

551.46 CAN ISSN 1499-9951
GC59.15 CODEN: SRHAEI
BEDFORD INSTITUTE OF OCEANOGRAPHY. IN REVIEW. Text in English. 1968. a. free. adv. **Document type:** *Government.* **Description:** Describes the federal marine science and fisheries research programs performed by the Institute, the Halifax Fisheries Research Laboratory, and the St. Andrews Biological Station.
Former titles (until 2001): Bedford Institute of Oceanography (1496-6557); (until 1995): Bedford Institute of Oceanography. Science Review (0846-9121); (until 1987): Bedford Institute of Oceanography. Review (0229-8910); (until 1981): Bedford Institute of Oceanography. Biennial Review (0067-480X); (until 1968): Bedford Institute of Oceanography. Annual Report (0575-7797)
Related titles: French ed.
Indexed: ASFA, ESPM.
—CISTI. **CCC.**
Published by: Department of Fisheries and Oceans, Bedford Institute of Oceanography, PO Box 1035, Dartmouth, NS B2Y 4T3, Canada. TEL 902-426-4093, FAX 902-426-2256. Ed. Anna Fiander. Adv. contact Brian Nicolls. Circ: 5,000 (controlled).

551.46 DEU ISSN 0940-8096
BEOBACHTUNGEN AUF DEN DEUTSCHEN MESSSTATIONEN DER NORD- UND OSTSEE. Text in German. 1953. a. **Document type:** *Monographic series, Government.*
Former titles (until 1990): Beobachtungen auf den Deutschen Messstationen der Nord- und Ostsee sowie Monatsmittelwerte von Temperatur und Salzgehalt (0934-6066); (until 1987): Beobachtungen auf den Deutschen Feuerschiffen der Nord- und Ostsee sowie Monatsmittelwerte von Temperatur und Salzgehalt (0343-1754); (until 1958): Beobachtungen auf den Deutschen Feuerschiffen der Nord- und Ostsee (0343-1940)
Published by: Bundesamt fuer Seeschiffahrt und Hydrographie, Bernhard-Nocht-Str 78, Hamburg, 20359, Germany. TEL 49-40-31900, FAX 49-40-31905000, posteingang@bsh.de, http://www.bsh.de.

551.46 910.02 DEU ISSN 1618-3193
BERICHTE ZUR POLAR- UND MEERESFORSCHUNG. Text in English, German. 1982. irreg. **Document type:** *Monographic series, Academic/Scholarly.* **Description:** Covers investigations in polar regions and the seas.
Formerly (until 2000): Berichte zur Polarforschung (0176-5027)
Indexed: ASFA, BIOSIS Prev, BiolAb, ESPM, IBR, IBZ, M&GPA, RefZh.
—CISTI.
Published by: Alfred-Wegener-Institut fuer Polar- und Meeresforschung/Alfred Wegener Institute for Polar and Marine Research, Columbusstr., Bremerhaven, 27568, Germany. TEL 49-471-48310, FAX 49-471-48311149, TELEX 238695 POLAR D, http://www.awi-bremerhaven.de/BIB/BerPolarforsch/. Ed. Franz Riemann. **Dist. by:** Kamloth Fachbuchhandlunga, Ostertorstrasse 25-29, Postfach 104340, Bremen 28203, Germany.

551.46 DEU ISSN 0930-8148
BIOLOGISCHE ANSTALT HELGOLAND. BERICHTE. Text in German. 1986. irreg. free to students and scientists. abstr.; bibl.; charts; illus. **Document type:** *Academic/Scholarly.*
Indexed: ASFA, ApicAb, ESPM.
Published by: Biologische Anstalt Helgoland, Postfach 180, Helgoland, 27483, Germany. TEL 49-4725-819-0, FAX 49-4725-819283. Ed. Dr. W Hickel.

551.46 DEU ISSN 0949-9946
BIOLOGISCHE ANSTALT HELGOLAND. ZWEIJAHRESBERICHT. Text in German. 1965. biennial. **Document type:** *Monographic series, Academic/Scholarly.*
Formerly (until 1993): Biologische Anstalt Helgoland. Jahresbericht (0344-6573)
Indexed: ESPM.
Published by: Biologische Anstalt Helgoland, Postfach 180, Helgoland, 27483, Germany. TEL 49-4725-819-0, FAX 49-4725-819283, http://www.awi-bremerhaven.de/Management/kontakt-helgoland-e.html.

BIOLOGIYA MORYA/MARINE BIOLOGY. see *BIOLOGY*

551.42 JPN
GC1 CODEN: JACCEJ
BLUE EARTH. Text in Japanese. 1989. s-m. (q. until Apr. 2000). per issue exchange basis only. **Document type:** *Bulletin.*
Formerly (until Apr. 2000): J A M S T E C (0915-2636)
Related titles: CD-ROM ed.
Published by: Japan Marine Science and Technology Center, Scientific Information Service/Kaiyo Kagaku Gijutsu Senta, 2-15 Natsushima-cho, Yokosuka-shi, Kanagawa-ken 237-0061, Japan. TEL 81-468-67-5525, FAX 81-468-66-6169, info@jamstec.go.jp, http://www.jamstec.go.jp/. Ed. Toshio Tsuchiya. Circ: 1,300.

578.77 COL ISSN 0122-9761
Q33
BOLETIN DE INVESTIGACIONES MARINAS Y COSTERAS. Text in Spanish. 1967. s-a.
Formerly: Instituto de Investigaciones Marinas Punta de Betin. Anales (0120-3959); Which was Superseded in part (in 1977): Mitteilungen aus dem Instituto Colombo-Aleman de Investigaciones Cientificas Punta de Betin (0120-825X)
Related titles: ♦ Supplement(s): Anales del Instituto de Investigaciones Marinas de Punta Betin. Suplemento. ISSN 0120-8241.
Indexed: BIOSIS Prev, BiolAb, ESPM, ZooRec.
—CINDOC.
Published by: Instituto de Investigacions Marinas y Costeras, Cerro de Punta de Bertin, Santa Marta, Magdalena 1016, Colombia. TEL 575-4214774, FAX 575-4215181, boletin@invemar.edu.co.

578.77 USA ISSN 0007-4977
GC1 CODEN: BMRSAW
➤ **BULLETIN OF MARINE SCIENCE.** Text in English. 1951. bi-m. USD 155 domestic to individuals print & online eds.; USD 180 foreign to individuals print & online eds.; USD 370 domestic to institutions print & online eds.; USD 390 foreign to institutions print & online eds. (effective 2005). bk.rev. back issues avail.; reprints avail. **Document type:** *Journal, Academic/Scholarly.*
Formerly (until 1964): Bulletin of Marine Science of the Gulf and Caribbean (0096-8900)
Related titles: Online - full text ed.: ISSN 1553-6955 (from Gale Group, H.W. Wilson, IngentaConnect, O C L C Online Computer Library Center, Inc.).
Indexed: ASCA, ASFA, AnBeAb, AnBrAb, ApEcolAb, B&AI, BIOBASE, BIOSIS Prev, BiolAb, CPA, CRFR, ChemAb, CurCont, E&PHSE, ESPM, EnvAb, ExcerpMed, ForAb, GEOBASE, GP&P, HelmAb, HerbAb, I&DA, IABS, IBR, ISR, IndVet, M&GPA, NutrAb, OceAb, OffTech, PBA, PGegResA, PetrolAb, PollutAb, ProtozoAb, RRTA, RefZh, RevApplEntom, S&F, SCI, SFA, SPPI, SWRA, VetBull, WAE&RSA, WildRev, ZooRec.
—BLDSC (2866.990000), CASDDS, CISTI, IDS, IE, Infotrieve, ingenta, Linda Hall, PADDS.
Published by: Rosenstiel School of Marine and Atmospheric Science, 4600 Rickenbacker Causeway, Miami, FL 33149-1098. TEL 305-361-4624, FAX 305-361-4600, bms@rsmas.miami.edu, http://www.rsmas.miami.edu/bms, http://www.rsmas.miami.edu/bms/. Ed., R&P Samuel C Snedaker. Circ: 1,000 (paid). **Subscr. to:** PO Box 971, Key Biscayne, FL 33149-0971.

551.46 DEU ISSN 0938-8559
VK597.G4 CODEN: JDHIDE
BUNDESAMT FUER SEESCHIFFAHRT UND HYDROGRAPHIE. JAHRESBERICHT. Text in German. 1947. a. **Document type:** *Yearbook, Trade.*
Formerly (until 1991): Deutsches Hydrographisches Institut. Jahresbericht (0070-4458)
Indexed: ASFA, ESPM.
—CISTI.
Published by: Bundesamt fuer Seeschiffahrt und Hydrographie, Bernhard-Nocht-Str 78, Hamburg, 20359, Germany. TEL 49-40-31900, FAX 49-40-31905000, posteingang@bsh.de, http://www.bsh.de. Circ: 1,700.

551.46 639.3 AUS ISSN 1023-4063
QH95.58
C C A M L R SCIENCE. Text in English. 1994. a.
Related titles: Online - full text ed.
Indexed: CurCont, ESPM, ZooRec.
—BLDSC (3095.843500).
Published by: Commission for the Conservation of Antartic Marine Living Resources, P.O. Box 213, North Hobart, N.T. 7002, Australia.

E

C - C O R E NEWS. (Center for Cold Ocean Resources Engineering) see *ENGINEERING*

551.46 620 USA
THE C E R CULAR; information exchange bulletin. Text in English. 1976. q. free. bibl.; charts; illus. **Document type:** *Bulletin, Government.* **Description:** Presents reports on activities of the laboratory.
Indexed: FLUIDEX.
Published by: U.S. Coastal Engineering Research Center, US Army Engineer Waterways Experiment Station, 3909 Halls Ferry Rd, Bldg 3296, Vicksburg, MS 39180-6199. TEL 601-634-2012, FAX 601-634-2055, CAMFIELD@coafs1.wes.army.mil. Circ: 2,700.

551.46 USA
C G O U TECHNICAL REPORT✶. (Coast Guard Oceanographic Unit) Text in English. 1964. irreg.
Published by: (U.S. Coast Guard, Oceanographic Unit), U.S. Department of Commerce, National Technical Information Service, 5285 Port Royal Rd, Springfield, VA 22161. Circ: 300.

578.77 ITA ISSN 0007-8603
C M A S BULLETIN D'INFORMATION/C M A S NEWSLETTER. (Confederation Mondiale des Activites) Text in French. 1959. 4/yr. bk.rev. illus. **Document type:** *Newsletter.*
Published by: World Underwater Federation, Viale Tiziano, 74, Rome, RM 00196, Italy. Circ: 2,000.

C M F R I BULLETIN. see *FISH AND FISHERIES*

C M F R I SPECIAL PUBLICATION. (Central Marine Fisheries Research Institute) see *FISH AND FISHERIES*

C M O S BULLETIN/BULLETIN S C M O. see *METEOROLOGY*

C M S NEWS. (Center for Maritime Studies) see *ARCHAEOLOGY*

C S I R O DIVISION OF FISHERIES. RESEARCH REPORT. (Commonwealth Scientific and Industrial Research Organisation) see *FISH AND FISHERIES*

551.46 540 IND ISSN 0971-8605
C S M C R I NEWSLETTER. Text in English, Hindi, Gujarati; Summaries in Hindi. 1982. q. free. adv. bk.rev. **Document type:** *Newsletter.* **Description:** Deals with dissemination of R & D activities, such as desalination, biosalinity, membrane science and technology to user groups in India and abroad.
Published by: Central Salt and Marine Chemicals Research Institute, Waghawadi Rd., Bhavnagar, Gujarat 364 002, India. TEL 91-278-562615, FAX 91-278-566970, TELEX 0182-230 ABC SALT IN, general@cscsmcri.ren.nic.in. Ed. Shri K D Padia. Pub. S D Gomkale. Circ: 700.

551.46 ESP ISSN 0213-6708
CODEN: CACME6
CADERNOS DA AREA DE CIENCIAS MARINAS. Text in Spanish. 1984. irreg. price varies. **Document type:** *Monographic series.*
Indexed: IECT, ZooRec.
—CASDDS, CINDOC.
Published by: Seminario de Estudos Galegos, Apdo. 215, Santiago De Compostela, (La Coruna) 15080, Spain.

CALANUS. see *BIOLOGY*

551.46 578.77 USA
CALIFORNIA SEA GRANT COLLEGE PROGRAM. REPORT SERIES. Text in English. irreg.
Published by: California Sea Grant College Program, University of California, 9500 Gilman Dr, La Jolla, CA 92093-0232. TEL 858-534-4446, publications@seamail.ucsd.edu, http://www-csgc.ucsd.edu/PUBLICATIONS/pubs-sgseries.html.

CALYPSO LOG. see *ENVIRONMENTAL STUDIES*

551.46 CAN ISSN 0711-6748
CANADIAN CONTRACTOR REPORT OF HYDROGRAPHY AND OCEAN SCIENCES. Text in English. 1982. irreg.
Indexed: ESPM.
—BLDSC (3019.476000), CISTI.
Published by: (Canada. Department of Fisheries and Oceans, Bedford Institute of Oceanography), Department of Fisheries and Oceans, Communications Directorate, 200 Kent St, 13th Fl, Sta 13228, Ottawa, ON K1A 0E6, Canada. TEL 613-993-0999, FAX 613-990-1866, info@dfo-mpo.gc.ca, http://www.ncr.dfo.ca.

551.46 CAN ISSN 0711-6721
CANADIAN DATA REPORT OF HYDROGRAPHY AND OCEAN SCIENCES. Text in English. 1965. irreg. **Document type:** *Monographic series.*
Formerly (until 1982): Bedford Institute of Oceanography. Data Series (0067-4788)
Indexed: ESPM.
—CISTI.
Published by: (Canada. Department of Fisheries and Oceans, Bedford Institute of Oceanography), Department of Fisheries and Oceans, Communications Directorate, 200 Kent St, 13th Fl, Sta 13228, Ottawa, ON K1A 0E6, Canada. TEL 613-993-0999, FAX 613-990-1866, info@dfo-mpo.gc.ca, http://www.ncr.dfo.ca.

CANADIAN INDUSTRY REPORT OF FISHERIES AND AQUATIC SCIENCES. see *FISH AND FISHERIES*

CANADIAN METEOROLOGICAL AND OCEANOGRAPHIC SOCIETY. ANNUAL CONGRESS PROGRAM AND ABSTRACTS. see *METEOROLOGY*

551.46 CAN ISSN 0711-6764
CODEN: CRHSDV
CANADIAN TECHNICAL REPORT OF HYDROGRAPHY AND OCEAN SCIENCES. Text in English. 1982. irreg.
Indexed: ESPM.
—CISTI.
Published by: (Canada. Department of Fisheries and Oceans, Bedford Institute of Oceanography), Department of Fisheries and Oceans, Communications Directorate, 200 Kent St, 13th Fl, Sta 13228, Ottawa, ON K1A 0E6, Canada. TEL 613-993-0999, FAX 613-990-1866, info@dfo-mpo.gc.ca, http://www.ncr.dfo.ca.

623.894 CAN ISSN 0576-2103
VK785
CANADIAN TIDE AND CURRENT TABLES. ATLANTIC COAST. (Continues publication with the same title issued by the Hydrographic Service) Text in English. a. CND 0.50.
(until 1966): Atlantic Coast Tide and Current Tables (0576-2111); (until 1953): Tide Tables for the Atlantic Coast of Canada (0702-9934); (until 193?): Tide Tables for the Eastern Coasts of Canada
Published by: Department of Fisheries and Oceans, Canadian Hydrographic Service, 615 Booth St, Ottawa, ON K1A 0E6, Canada. TEL 613-995-3065.

551.46 DEU
CATALOGUE OF CRETACEOUS CORALS. Text in English. irreg.
Published by: CPress Verlag, PF 19 2409, Dresden, D-01282, Germany. FAX 49-0-351-3100951, info@cp-v.de. Ed. Hannes Loeser.

551.46 MDG
CENTRE D'INFORMATION ET DE DOCUMENTATION SCIENTIFIQUE ET TECHNIQUE. ARCHIVES DU CENTRE NATIONAL DE RECHERCHES OCEANOGRAPHIQUES. Text in French. a.
Published by: Centre d'Information et de Documentation Scientifique et Technique, BP 6224, Antananarivo, 101, Madagascar. TEL 33288, TELEX 225 39 MRS-MG.

551.46 639 AUS
CENTRE FOR RESEARCH ON INTRODUCED MARINE PESTS. PROJECT AND CONSULTANCY REPORT. Text in English. irreg.
Published by: C S I R O Marine Laboratories, GPO Box 1538, Hobart, TAS 7001, Australia. TEL 61-2-62325259, FAX 61-2-62325103, m.newman@marine.csiro.au, http://www.marine.csiro.au.

551.46 639 AUS ISSN 1324-3543
CENTRE FOR RESEARCH ON INTRODUCED MARINE PESTS. TECHNICAL REPORT. Text in English. 1995. irreg.
Indexed: ZooRec.
Published by: C S I R O Marine Laboratories, GPO Box 1538, Hobart, TAS 7001, Australia. TEL 61-2-62325259, FAX 61-2-62325103, m.newman@marine.csiro.au, http://www.marine.csiro.au.

551.46 MDG ISSN 0252-189X
CENTRE NATIONAL DE RECHERCHES OCEANOGRAPHIQUES. DOCUMENT. Text in French. irreg.
Published by: Centre National de Recherches Oceanographiques, BP 68, Nosy-Be, 207, Madagascar. TEL 261-20-8661373, http://www.refer.mg/madag_ct/rec/cnro/cnro.htm.

551.46 ARG ISSN 0328-0535
CENTRO OCEANOGRAFICO BUENOS AIRES. SERIE CIENCIA Y TECNICA. Text in Spanish. 1993. irreg.
Indexed: ESPM.
Published by: Instituto Tecnologico de Buenos Aires, Centro Oceanografico de Buenos Aires, Av. Eduardo Madero 399, Buenos Aires, C1106AD, Argentina. TEL 54-11-4314-7778.

551.46 USA
CHESAPEAKE BAY PROGRAM. TECHNICAL REPORT SERIES. Text in English. irreg.
Published by: Chesapeake Bay Program, 410 Severn Ave, Suite 109, Annapolis, MD 21403. TEL 800-968-7229, FAX 410-267-5777, http://www.chesapeakebay.net.

CHESAPEAKE RESEARCH CONSORTIUM. PUBLICATIONS. see *EARTH SCIENCES—Hydrology*

CHINA OCEAN ENGINEERING. see *ENGINEERING*

551.46 CHN ISSN 1671-2463
GC1
CHINA OCEAN UNIVERSITY. JOURNAL. Text in English. 1959; N.S. 2002. s-a. USD 100 (effective 2003). 110 p./no.; **Document type:** *Journal, Academic/Scholarly.* **Description:** Features ocean sciences, papers in basic research, applied basic research and high and new technology development.
Formerly (until 2002): Ocean University of Qingdao. Journal
Related titles: ♦ Chinese ed.: Qingdao Haiyang Daxue Xuebao. ISSN 1001-1862.
Indexed: ASFA, ESPM, M&GPA, OceAb, PollutAb, RefZh, SWRA.
—BLDSC (4834.490000), IE, ingenta.
Published by: Qingdao Haiyang Daxue, Xuebao Bianjibu/Ocean University of China, Journal Editorial Office, No 5, Yushan Lu, Qingdao, Shandong, China. TEL 86-532-2032256, xbywb@mail.ouc.edu.cn, http://www.ouqd.edu.cn/xbywb/, http://www.ouc.edu.cn/. Ed. Shengchang Wen. Pub. Wei Yu. R&P Fegnqi Li.

551.46 551.48 CHN ISSN 0254-4059
CODEN: CJOLEO
➤ **CHINESE JOURNAL OF OCEANOLOGY AND LIMNOLOGY/ZHONGGUO HAIYANG YU HUZHAO XUEBAO.** Text in English. 1982. q. USD 132 to individuals; USD 264 to institutions (effective 2005). adv. **Document type:** *Journal, Academic/Scholarly.* **Description:** Covers hydrophysics, hydrochemistry, hydrobiology, geomorphology, apparatus research and manufacture, comprehensive reviews, and academic activities.
Related titles: Online - full content ed.: (from WanFang Data Corp.); Online - full text ed.: (from East View Information Services); ♦ Chinese ed.: Haiyang yu Huzhao. ISSN 0029-814X.
Indexed: ASFA, AnBrAb, B&BAb, BIOSIS Prev, BiolAb, CIN, ChemAb, ChemTitl, ESPM, MBA, OceAb, RefZh, SFA, SWRA, ZooRec.
—BLDSC (3180.450000), CASDDS, CISTI, IE, ingenta, Linda Hall. **CCC.**
Published by: Kexue Chubanshe/Science Press, 16 Donghuang Cheng Genbei Jie, Beijing, 100717, China. TEL 86-10-64000246, FAX 86-10-64030255, http://www.maney.co.uk/search?fwaction=show&fwid=357, http://www.sciencep.com/. Ed. C K Tseng. Circ: 6,000.
Subscr. outside China to: Maney Publishing, China Journal Distribution Services, Hudson Rd, Leeds LS9 7DI, United Kingdom. TEL 44-113-2497481, FAX 44-113-2486983, subscriptions@maney.co.uk. **Dist. by:** China International Book Trading Corp, 35 Chegongzhuang Xilu, Haidian District, PO Box 399, Beijing 100044, China. TEL 86-10-68412045, FAX 86-10-68412023, cibtc@mail.cibtc.com.cn, http://www.cibtc.com.cn.

551.46 JPN
CHOI NENPO/YEARBOOK OF TIDAL RECORDS. Text in Japanese. 1966. a. **Document type:** *Government.*
Published by: Kokudo Chiriin/Geographical Survey Institute, Ministry of Construction, 1 Kita-Sato, Tsukuba-shi, Ibaraki-ken 305-0811, Japan. Circ: 400.

551.46 JPN
CHOSEKI KANSOKU/TIDAL OBSERVATIONS. Text in English, Japanese. 1925. a.
Published by: Kishocho/Japan Meteorological Agency, 3-4 Ote-Machi 1-chome, Chiyoda-ku, Tokyo, 100-0004, Japan.

551.46 JPN ISSN 0910-0458
CHOSEKIHYO 1. NIHON OYOBI FUKIN/TIDE TABLES 1. JAPAN AND ITS VICINITIES. Text in English, Japanese. 1920. s-a. JPY 3,000 per issue. **Document type:** *Government.*
Published by: Kaijo Hoancho, Suirobu/Maritime Safety Agency, Hydrographic Department, 3-1 Tsuki-Ji 5-chome, Chuo-ku, Tokyo, 104-0045, Japan. TEL 81-3-3541-4296, FAX 81-3-3545-2885, consult@cue.jhd.go.jp, http:/www.jhd.go.jp/, http://www.jhd.go.jp/.

551.46 JPN ISSN 0910-0466
CHOSEKIHYO 2. TAIHEIYO OYOBI INDOYO/TIDE TABLES 2. PACIFIC AND INDIAN OCEANS. Text in English, Japanese. 1920. a. JPY 2,900 per issue. **Document type:** *Government.*
Published by: Kaijo Hoancho, Suirobu/Maritime Safety Agency, Hydrographic Department, 3-1 Tsuki-Ji 5-chome, Chuo-ku, Tokyo, 104-0045, Japan. TEL 81-3-3541-4296, FAX 81-3-3245-2885, consult@cue.jhd.go.jp, http://www.jhd.go.jp/.

551.46 CHL ISSN 0716-2006
GC1 CODEN: CTEMED
➤ **CIENCIA Y TECNOLOGIA DEL MAR.** Text in Spanish; Summaries in English. 1975. a. free. back issues avail. **Document type:** *Academic/Scholarly.* **Description:** Presents articles on biological, physical and chemical oceanography, marine geology, fisheries, aquaculture, pollution, coastal zone management.
Indexed: ASFA, ESPM, SFA, WildRev, ZooRec.
Published by: Comite Oceanografico Nacional, Playa Archd., Errauriz, 232, Valparaiso, Chile. TEL 56-32-266521, FAX 56-32-266522-266542, TELEX 23-0362 HIDRO CL, cona@shoa.cl. Circ: 600.

E

551.46 MEX ISSN 0185-3880
GC858 CODEN: CIMAD7
➤ **CIENCIAS MARINAS.** Text in English, Spanish. 1974. q. MXP 580 domestic to individuals; USD 84 in the Americas to individuals; USD 100 elsewhere to individuals; MXP 1,360 domestic to institutions; USD 252 in the Americas to institutions; USD 294 elsewhere to institutions (effective 2005). adv. back issues avail. **Document type:** *Academic/Scholarly.*
Description: Dedicated to the publication of original papers on research in the four main areas of marine science: biology, chemistry geology and physics.
Related titles: Online - full text ed.: (from EBSCO Publishing).
Indexed: ASCA, ASFA, AgBio, AnBrAb, BIOSIS Prev, BiolAb, Biostat, CIN, CRFR, ChemAb, ChemTitl, CurCont, EPB, ESPM, EnvAb, FLUIDEX, GEOBASE, HelmAb, HortAb, ISR, IndVet, MAB, MSCT, NutrAb, RM&VM, S&F, SCI, SFA, SWRA, SoyAb, TDB, VetBull, WAE&RSA, WildRev, ZooRec.
—BLDSC (3198.204100), CASDDS, CISTI, IE, ingenta, Linda Hall.
Published by: Universidad Autonoma de Baja California, Instituto de Investigaciones Oceanologicas, Apdo. Postal 423, Ensenada, Baja California, Mexico. TEL 52-646-1745451, cmarinas@uabc.mx, http://rcmarinas.ens.uabc.mx/, http://iio.ens.uabc.mx/. Ed., Adv. contact Ana Luz Quintanilla-Montoya. R&P Ana Luz Quintanilla Montoya.

351.46 JPN ISSN 1341-0091
CLASS N K MAGAZINE. Text in English. 1973. a., latest 2002, 54th ed. free. **Document type:** *Trade.*
Former titles (until 1994): Overseas (0913-204X); (until 1980): N K Overseas (0913-2422)
Published by: Nippon Kaiji Kyokai, 4-7 Kioi-cho, Chiyoda-ku, Tokyo, 102-8567, Japan. TEL 81-43-2945451, FAX 81-43-2947204, isd@classnk.or.jp, http://www.classnk.or.jp/. Ed., R&P S Ogawa. Circ: 7,000 (controlled).

551.46 USA ISSN 1068-3364
COAST AND SEA; marine and coastal research in Louisiana's universities. Text in English. 1972. 3/yr. free. bk.rev. illus. back issues avail. **Document type:** *Consumer.*
Supersedes (in 1992): Aquanotes (0744-4656)
Indexed: EnvAb, FLUIDEX.
Published by: Louisiana State University, Louisiana Sea Grant College Program, 239 Sea Grant Bldg, Baton Rouge, LA 70803-7507. TEL 225-388-6449, FAX 225-388-6331. Ed. Elizabeth B Coleman. Circ: 2,500.

551.46 551.4 USA ISSN 0733-9569
➤ **COASTAL AND ESTUARINE STUDIES.** Text in English. 1992. irreg., latest vol.58, 2001. price varies. back issues avail. **Document type:** *Monographic series, Academic/Scholarly.*
Description: Fosters the development of coastal and estuarine science on an international multidisciplinary basic and designed to be of interest to persons concerned with coastal and estuarine resource managment of interest to researchers, ocean engineers, environmental consultants and regulatory agencies.
Indexed: BIOSIS Prev, Inspec, ZooRec.
—BLDSC (3292.402100), CISTI, IE, ingenta. **CCC.**
Published by: American Geophysical Union, 2000 Florida Ave, NW, Washington, DC 20009-1277. TEL 202-462-6900, 800-966-2481, FAX 202-328-0566, http://www.agu.org.

➤ **COASTAL ENGINEERING CONFERENCE. PROCEEDINGS OF THE INTERNATIONAL CONFERENCE.** see *ENGINEERING—Civil Engineering*

551.46 620 USA ISSN 0193-5992
COASTAL ENGINEERING RESEARCH CENTER. MISCELLANEOUS REPORT. Key Title: U.S. Army Corps of Engineers. Coastal Engineering Research Center. Miscellaneous Report. Text in English. 1964. irreg. price varies. back issues avail. **Document type:** *Monographic series, Government.*
Formerly (until 1976): U.S. Coastal Engineering Research Center. Miscellaneous Papers (0565-1611)
Indexed: ASFA.
—CISTI.
Published by: U.S. Coastal Engineering Research Center, US Army Engineer Waterways Experiment Station, 3909 Halls Ferry Rd, Bldg 3296, Vicksburg, MS 39180-6199. TEL 601-634-2021, camfield@coafsl.wes.army.mil. **Subscr. to:** National Technical Information Service, Government Research Center, 5285 Port Royal Rd, Springfield, VA 22161. TEL 703-605-6060, 800-363-2068, http://www.ntis.gov.

551.46 USA ISSN 0892-0753
HT392 CODEN: CMANEF
➤ **COASTAL MANAGEMENT**; an international journal of marine environment, resources, law and society. Text in English. 1973. q. USD 609, GBP 396 combined subscription to institutions print & online eds. (effective 2006). adv. bk.rev. abstr.; bibl.; charts; illus.; stat. index, cum.index. reprint service avail. from WSH,PSC. **Document type:** *Journal, Academic/Scholarly.* **Description:** Explores the technical, legal, political, social, and policy issues surrounding the utilization of valuable and unique coastal environments and resources.
Formerly: Coastal Zone Management Journal (0090-8339)
Related titles: Microfiche ed.: (from WSH); Online - full text ed.: ISSN 1521-0421. USD 579, GBP 351 to institutions (effective 2006) (from EBSCO Publishing, Gale Group, IngentaConnect, O C L C Online Computer Library Center, Inc., Swets Information Services).
Indexed: ABRCLP, ASCA, ASFA, AnBrAb, ArtHuCI, BrCerAb, C&ISA, CLI, CTO, CerAb, CivEngAb, CorrAb, CurCont, E&CAJ, EIA, EMA, EPB, ESPM, EnerRev, EngInd, EnvAb, EnvEAb, EnvInd, FLUIDEX, GEOBASE, IAA, ILP, IPARL, ISR, IndVet, M&GPA, M&TEA, MAB, MBF, METADEX, OceAb, PAIS, PetrolAb, PollutAb, RDA, RRTA, S&F, SCI, SFA, SSCI, SUSA, SWRA, SolStAb, WAA, WAE&RSA, WildRev.
—BLDSC (3292.413150), CIS, CISTI, Ei, IDS, IE, Infotrieve, ingenta, Linda Hall, PADDS. **CCC.**
Published by: Taylor & Francis Inc. (Subsidiary of: Taylor & Francis Group), 325 Chestnut St, Ste 800, Philadelphia, PA 19016. TEL 215-625-8900, FAX 215-625-2940, coastjnl@u.washington.edu, info@taylorandfrancis.com, http://www.tandf.co.uk/journals/titles/08920753.asp, http://www.taylorandfrancis.com. Ed. Marc J Hershman. **Subscr. outside N. America to:** Taylor & Francis Ltd, Journals Customer Service, Rankine Rd, Basingstoke, Hants RG24 8PR, United Kingdom. TEL 44-1256-813000, FAX 44-1256-330245, enquiry@tandf.co.uk.

551.46 USA ISSN 0271-5376
➤ **COASTAL RESEARCH.** Text in English. 1962. 3/yr. USD 6; USD 7 foreign (effective 1998). bk.rev. back issues avail. **Document type:** *Newsletter, Academic/Scholarly.*
Description: Covers science, engineering and other matters of coastal interest.
Formerly: Coastal Research Notes (0578-5677)
Indexed: AESIS.
—Linda Hall.
Published by: Florida State University, Geology Department, Tallahassee, FL 32306-3026. TEL 904-644-5860, FAX 904-644-4214. Ed. W F Tanner. R&P W.F. Tanner. Circ: 400.

551.46 NLD ISSN 0928-2734
COASTLINE. Text in English. 1992. q. EUR 20 to individuals; EUR 50 to libraries. adv. **Document type:** *Journal, Academic/Scholarly.* **Description:** Covers coastal conservation and integrated coastal zone management throughout Europe.
—IE, Infotrieve.
Published by: (European Union for Coastal Conservation), E U C C Network Services, PO Box 11232, Leiden, 2301 EE, Netherlands. TEL 31-71-512-2900, FAX 31-71-512-4069, admin@coastalguide.org, http://www.eucc.nl, http://www.coastalguide.org. R&P A Salman. Adv. contact E Malta. Circ: 1,000 (paid).

551.46 USA ISSN 1062-3442
COASTLINES (STONY BROOK). Text in English. 1971. q. free. **Document type:** *Academic/Scholarly.* **Description:** Reports on research, education and outreach efforts concerning marine and Great Lakes resources.
Published by: New York Sea Grant Institute, 121 Discovery Hall, State University of New York at Stony Brook, Stony Brook, NY 11794-5001. TEL 516-632-9124, nyseagrant@ccmail.sunysb.edu, http://flounder.seagrant.sunysb.edu.

551.46 363.7063 639.2 USA ISSN 1068-784X
COASTWATCH. Text in English. 1970. bi-m. USD 15; USD 3.75 newsstand/cover (effective 2001). bk.rev. abstr. 32 p./no.; **Document type:** *Magazine, Consumer.* **Description:** Examines coastal policy issues, marine science topics, and the people and places that make the North Carolina coast unique.
Formerly: University of North Carolina. Sea Grant College Newsletter (0161-8369)
Published by: North Carolina Sea Grant College Program, Box 8605, North Carolina State University, Raleigh, NC 27695-8605. TEL 919-515-2454, FAX 919-515-7095, katie_mosher@ncsu.edu, http://www.ncsu.edu/seagrant. Ed., R&P Katie Mosher. Circ: 4,000.

COLLECTANEA MARITIMA. see *HISTORY—History Of Europe*

551.46 MCO ISSN 1017-4907
CODEN: CABYE3
COLLECTION ABYSSES. Text in French. 1989. irreg. price varies.
Indexed: ASFA, ESPM.
Published by: Musee Oceanographique, Service des Publications, Av. Saint-Martin, Monte Carlo, MC 98000, Monaco. TEL 377-93-15-36-07, FAX 377-93-50-52-97, biblio@oceano.mc, http://www.oceano.mc/fr/.

551.46 597 AUS ISSN 1031-2889
COMMISSION FOR THE CONSERVATION OF ANTARCTIC MARINE LIVING RESOURCES. REPORT OF THE MEETING OF THE SCIENTIFIC COMMITTEE. Text in English. 1982. a.
Related titles: Spanish ed.: Comision para la Conservacion de los Recursos Vivos Marinos Antarticos. Informe de la Reunion del Comite Cientifico. ISSN 1031-8852; Russian ed.: Naucnyj Komitet po Sohraneniu Morskih Zivyh Resursov Antartiki. Otcet Sovesania Naucnogo Komiteta. ISSN 1031-8860; French ed.: Comite Scientifique pour la Conservation de la Faune et la Flore Marines de l'Antarctique. Rapport de la Reunion du Comite Scientifique. ISSN 1031-8844.
Indexed: ESPM.
Published by: Commission for the Conservation of Antarctic Marine Living Resources, PO Box 213, North Hobart, TAS 7002, Australia. TEL 61-3-6231-0168, FAX 61-3-6234-9965, 61-3-6234-9965.

551.46 FRA ISSN 0251-6047
COMMISSION OCEANOGRAPHIQUE INTERGOUVERNEMENTALE. MANUELS ET GUIDES. Text in French. 1974. 3/w.
Published by: UNESCO, Intergovernmental Oceanographic Commission, 1, rue Miollis, Paris, 75015, France. TEL 33-1-4568-3984, FAX 33-1-4568-5812, ioc.secretariat@unesco.org, http://ioc.unesco.org/iocweb/index.php.

551.46 639 AUS ISSN 0725-4598
CODEN: RCMLDR
COMMONWEALTH SCIENTIFIC AND INDUSTRIAL RESEARCH ORGANIZATION. MARINE LABORATORIES. REPORT. Text in English. 1956. irreg. free. **Document type:** *Monographic series.*
Supersedes: Commonwealth Scientific and Industrial Research Organization. Division of Fisheries and Oceanography. Report (0069-7370)
Indexed: ASFA, BiolAb, ESPM, M&GPA, PollutAb, RefZh, ZooRec.
—BLDSC (7410.132000), CASDDS.
Published by: C S I R O Marine Laboratories, GPO Box 1538, Hobart, TAS 7001, Australia. TEL 61-2-62325259, FAX 61-2-62325103, m.newman@marine.csiro.au, http://www.marine.csiro.au. R&P Don Michel TEL 61-2-62325478. Circ: 600.

551.46 GBR ISSN 0278-4343
GC85 CODEN: CSHRDZ
➤ **CONTINENTAL SHELF RESEARCH.** Text in English. 1982. 20/yr. EUR 1,985 in Europe to institutions; JPY 263,700 in Japan to institutions; USD 2,220 to institutions except Europe and Japan; EUR 244 in Europe to qualified personnel; JPY 32,600 in Japan to qualified personnel; USD 274 to qualified personnel except Europe and Japan (effective 2006). abstr. back issues avail. **Document type:** *Academic/Scholarly.*
Description: Presents research results in physical oceanography, chemistry, ecology, sedimentology, and applied aspects of continental shelf research.
Related titles: Microfilm ed.: (from PQC); Online - full text ed.: (from EBSCO Publishing, Gale Group, IngentaConnect, ScienceDirect, Swets Information Services).
Indexed: ASCA, ASFA, BIOBASE, CTO, CurCont, DSA, EPB, ESPM, FLUIDEX, GEOBASE, I&DA, IABS, ISR, IndVet, Inspec, M&GPA, M&TEA, OceAb, PollutAb, RefZh, S&F, SCI, SFA, SWRA, VetBull, WRCInf, ZooRec.
—BLDSC (3425.640000), AskIEEE, CASDDS, CISTI, IDS, IE, Infotrieve, ingenta, Linda Hall. **CCC.**
Published by: Pergamon (Subsidiary of: Elsevier Science & Technology), The Boulevard, Langford Ln, East Park, Kidlington, Oxford OX5 1GB, United Kingdom. TEL 44-1865-843000, FAX 44-1865-843010, csr@ocean.washington.edu, http://www.elsevier.com/locate/csr. Eds. Michael B Collins, Richard W Sternberg. **Subscr. to:** Elsevier BV, PO Box 211, Amsterdam 1000 AE, Netherlands. TEL 31-20-485-3757, FAX 31-20-485-3432, nlinfo-f@elsevier.nl, http://www.elsevier.nl.

551.46 DEU ISSN 0722-4028
QH95.8 CODEN: CORFDL
➤ **CORAL REEFS.** Text in English. 1982. 4/yr. EUR 798 combined subscription to institutions print & online eds. (effective 2005). adv. reprint service avail. from ISI. **Document type:** *Journal, Academic/Scholarly.* **Description:** Covers reef structure and morphology, biogeochemical cycles, behavioral ecology, sedimentology, and evolutionary ecology of the reef biota.
Formerly: International Society for Reef Studies. Journal
Related titles: Microform ed.: (from PQC); Online - full text ed.: ISSN 1432-0975 (from EBSCO Publishing, Springer LINK, Swets Information Services).
Indexed: ASCA, ASFA, BIOBASE, BIOSIS Prev, BiolAb, CTO, CurCont, EPB, ESPM, GEOBASE, IABS, ISR, OceAb, PollutAb, RM&VM, SCI, SFA, SPPI, SWRA, ZooRec.
—BLDSC (3470.325000), CASDDS, CISTI, IDS, IE, Infotrieve, ingenta, Linda Hall. **CCC.**
Published by: (International Society for Reef Studies), Springer-Verlag (Subsidiary of: Springer Science+Business Media), Tiergartenstr 17, Heidelberg, 69121, Germany. TEL 49-6221-3450, FAX 49-6221-345229, http://link.springer.de/link/service/journals/00338/index.htm. Eds. Dr. Peter K Swart, Dr. Richard E Dodge TEL 954-262-4027. Adv. contact Stephan Kroeck TEL 49-30-827875739. **Subscr. in the Americas to:** Springer-Verlag New York, Inc., Journal Fulfillment, PO Box 2485, Secaucus, NJ 07096-2485. TEL 800-777-4643, 201-348-4033, FAX 201-348-4505, journals@springer-ny.com, http://www.springer-ny.com; **Subscr. to:** Springer GmbH Auslieferungsgesellschaft, Haberstr 7, Heidelberg 69126, Germany. TEL 49-6221-345-0, FAX 49-6221-345-4229, subscriptions@springer.de.

551.46 DEU ISSN 0945-7275
QE778
CORAL RESEARCH BULLETIN. Text in English, German. 1994. irreg.
Indexed: ZooRec.

E

Published by: CPress Verlag, PF 19 2409, Dresden, D-01282, Germany. FAX 49-0-351-3100951, info@cp-v.de. Ed. Hannes Loeser.

551.46 ESP ISSN 0213-7208
CUADERNOS MARISQUEROS. PUBLICACION TECNICA. Text in Spanish. 1978. irreg. free.
Indexed: ASFA.
Published by: Centro Experimental de Vilaxoan, Apartado 208, Vilagarcia De Arousa, Pontevedra 36600, Spain.

551.46007 USA ISSN 0889-5546
➤ **CURRENT**; the journal of marine education. Text in English. 1976. q. USD 40 membership; USD 250 membership corporate (effective 2005). adv. bk.rev. bibl.; charts; illus.; stat. back issues avail. **Document type:** *Academic/Scholarly.*
Description: Features in-depth articles about marine, physical, earth, and life sciences and marine education and research.
Indexed: CIJE, GSS&RPL.
Published by: National Marine Educators Association, David Niebuhr, Mote Marine Laboratory, 1600 Ken Thompson Pkwy., Sarasota, FL 34236. http://www.marine-ed.org. Ed., Adv. contact Lisa Tooker TEL 707-944-8430. Circ: 1,500.

623 USA
CURRENTS (COLUMBIA). Text in English. bi-m. back issues avail.
Related titles: Online - full text ed.
Published by: Marine Technology Society, Inc., 5565 Sterrett Pl, Ste 108, Columbia, MD 21044. TEL 410-884-5330, FAX 410-884-9060, mtspubs@erols.com, http://www.case.org/CURRENTS/2003/March/, http://www.mtsociety.org.

551.460711 USA
CURRICULA IN THE ATMOSPHERIC, OCEANIC, HYDROLOGIC AND RELATED SCIENCES. Text in English. 1963. biennial. USD 40. adv. **Document type:** *Monographic series.*
Description: Contains description of the curricula in atmospheric, oceanic and related sciences at the major colleges and universities in the U.S., Canada and Puerto Rico.
Former titles: Curricula in the Atmospheric, Oceanic and Related Sciences; Curricula in the Atmospheric and Oceanographic Sciences
Published by: American Meteorological Society, 45 Beacon St, Boston, MA 02108. FAX 617-742-8718, http://ams.allenpress.com. R&P Melissa Weston TEL 617-227-2426. Adv. contact Mary McMahon. **Co-sponsor:** University Corporation for Atmospheric Research.

D B C P TECHNICAL DOCUMENT SERIES. see *METEOROLOGY*

551.46 CAN ISSN 1202-0974
DALHOUSIE UNIVERSITY. DEPARTMENT OF OCEANOGRAPHY. BIENNIAL REPORT. Text in English. biennial.
Former titles (until 1984): Dalhousie University. Institute of Oceanography. Biennial Report (1202-0966); (until 1980): Dalhousie University. Institute of Oceanography. Annual Report (0418-3029)
Indexed: ESPM.
Published by: Dalhousie University, Department of Oceanography, Halifax, NS B3H 4J1, Canada. TEL 902-494-3557, FAX 902-494-3877, oceanography@dal.ca, http://www.dal.ca/~wwwocean/ocean_974.html, http://www.dal.ca/~wwwocean/index.html.

551.46 GBR ISSN 0967-0637
GC1 CODEN: DRORE7
➤ **DEEP-SEA RESEARCH. PART 1: OCEANOGRAPHIC RESEARCH PAPERS.** Text in English. 1953. 12/yr. EUR 2,304 in Europe to institutions; JPY 305,900 in Japan to institutions; USD 2,578 elsewhere to institutions; EUR 156 in Europe to qualified personnel; JPY 20,800 in Japan to qualified personnel; USD 175 elsewhere to qualified personnel (effective 2006). adv. bk.rev. abstr.; bibl.; charts; illus. index. reprints avail. **Document type:** *Journal, Academic/Scholarly.*
Description: Devoted to the publication of the results of original scientific research, the solution of instrumental problems, and new laboratory methods in the marine sciences.
Supersedes in part (until 1993): Deep-Sea Research. Part A: Oceanographic Research Papers (0198-0149); Which had former titles (until 1979): Deep-Sea Research (New York, 1977) (0146-6291); (until 1977): Deep-Sea Research and Oceanographic Abstracts (0011-7471); (until 1961): Deep-Sea Research (New York, 1953) (0146-6313)
Related titles: Microfilm ed.: (from PQC); Online - full text ed.: (from EBSCO Publishing, Gale Group, IngentaConnect, ScienceDirect, Swets Information Services).
Indexed: ASFA, AnBrAb, BIOBASE, BIOSIS Prev, BiolAb, CIN, CTO, ChemAb, ChemTitl, CurCont, EPB, ESPM, EngInd, ExcerpMed, FLUIDEX, GEOBASE, HelmAb, IABS, ISR, Inspec, M&GPA, MBA, NemAb, OceAb, PetrolAb, ProtozoAb, RefZh, SCI, SFA, SPPI, SWRA, WildRev, ZooRec.
—BLDSC (3540.955500), AskIEEE, CASDDS, CISTI, Ei, IDS, IE, Infotrieve, ingenta, Linda Hall, PADDS. **CCC.**
Published by: Pergamon (Subsidiary of: Elsevier Science & Technology), The Boulevard, Langford Ln, East Park, Kidlington, Oxford OX5 1GB, United Kingdom. TEL 44-1865-843000, FAX 44-1865-843010, http://www.elsevier.com/locate/dsri. Ed. M Bacon. **Subscr. to:** Elsevier BV, PO Box 211, Amsterdam 1000 AE, Netherlands. TEL 31-20-485-3757, FAX 31-20-485-3432, nlinfo-f@elsevier.nl, http://www.elsevier.nl.

551.46 GBR ISSN 0967-0645
GC1 CODEN: DSROEK
➤ **DEEP-SEA RESEARCH. PART 2: TOPICAL STUDIES IN OCEANOGRAPHY.** Text in English. 1993. 26/yr. EUR 3,122 in Europe to institutions; JPY 414,400 in Japan to institutions; USD 3,491 elsewhere to institutions; EUR 168 in Europe to qualified personnel; JPY 22,400 in Japan to qualified personnel; USD 189 elsewhere to qualified personnel (effective 2006). abstr. back issues avail. **Document type:** *Journal, Academic/Scholarly.* **Description:** Provides a forum for collected papers on specific topics reflecting important international and interdisciplinary research projects undertaken.
Supersedes in part (in 1993): Deep-Sea Research. Part A, Oceanographic Research Papers (0198-0149); Which was formerly (until 1978): Deep-Sea Research (New York, 1977) (0146-6291); (until 1976): Deep-Sea Research and Oceanographic Abstracts (0011-7471); (until 1961): Deep-Sea Research (New York, 1953) (0146-6313)
Related titles: Microfilm ed.: (from PQC); Online - full text ed.: (from EBSCO Publishing, Gale Group, IngentaConnect, ScienceDirect, Swets Information Services).
Indexed: ASCA, ASFA, AnBrAb, BIOBASE, CIN, ChemAb, ChemTitl, CurCont, EPB, ESPM, EngInd, GEOBASE, HelmAb, IABS, ISR, Inspec, M&GPA, MBA, NemAb, OceAb, RPP, RefZh, RevApplEntom, S&F, SCI, WeedAb, ZooRec.
—BLDSC (3540.955503), AskIEEE, CASDDS, CISTI, Ei, IDS, IE, Infotrieve, ingenta, Linda Hall, PADDS. **CCC.**
Published by: Pergamon (Subsidiary of: Elsevier Science & Technology), The Boulevard, Langford Ln, East Park, Kidlington, Oxford OX5 1GB, United Kingdom. TEL 44-1865-843000, FAX 44-1865-843010, http://www.elsevier.com/locate/dsr2. Ed. John Milliman. **Subscr. to:** Elsevier BV, PO Box 211, Amsterdam 1000 AE, Netherlands. TEL 31-20-485-3757, FAX 31-20-485-3432, nlinfo-f@elsevier.nl, http://www.elsevier.nl.

➤ **A DELAWARE SEA GRANT TECHNICAL REPORT.** see *CONSERVATION*

➤ **DELFT MARINE TECHNOLOGY SERIES.** see *ENGINEERING—Mechanical Engineering*

551.46 DEU ISSN 0946-2015
VK588
DEUTSCHE HYDROGRAPHISCHE ZEITSCHRIFT. ERGAENZUNGSHEFT/GERMAN JOURNAL OF HYDROGRAPHY. SUPPLEMENT. Text in English, German. irreg., latest vol.5, 1996. **Document type:** *Academic/Scholarly.*
Formed by the merger of (1952-1994): Deutsche Hydrographische Zeitschrift. Ergaenzungsheft. Reihe A (0070-4164); (1956-1994): Deutsche Hydrographische Zeitschrift. Ergaenzungsheft. Reihe B (0070-4172)
Indexed: ASFA, ESPM, RefZh.
—Linda Hall.
Published by: Bundesamt fuer Seeschiffahrt und Hydrographie, Bernhard-Nocht-Str 78, Hamburg, 20359, Germany. TEL 49-40-31900, FAX 49-40-31905000. Eds. G Becker, G Heise.

551.46 578.77 NLD ISSN 0163-6995
CODEN: DMBIDF
➤ **DEVELOPMENTS IN MARINE BIOLOGY.** Text in Dutch. 1979. irreg., latest vol.4, 1995. price varies. **Document type:** *Monographic series, Academic/Scholarly.* **Description:** Reports on news and developments in the field of marine biology.
Indexed: BIOSIS Prev, CIN, ChemAb, ChemTitl.
—CASDDS, CISTI. **CCC.**
Published by: Elsevier BV (Subsidiary of: Elsevier Science & Technology), Radarweg 29, Amsterdam, 1043 NX, Netherlands. TEL 31-20-4853911, FAX 31-20-4852457, nlinfo-f@elsevier.nl, http://www.elsevier.nl.

➤ **DEVELOPMENTS IN MARINE TECHNOLOGY.** see *ENGINEERING—Mechanical Engineering*

551.46 COL ISSN 0120-0542
GC860.C7 CODEN: BCCHDR
DIRECCION GENERAL MARITIMA. CENTRO DE INVESTIGACIONES OCEANOGRAFICAS E HIDROGRAFICAS. BOLETIN CIENTIFICO. Text in Spanish. 1977. 3/w.
Indexed: ESPM.
Published by: Direccion General Maritima, Centro de Investigaciones Oceanograficas e Hidrograficas, Cartagena, 982, Colombia. TEL 95-6694427, FAX 95-6694390.

551.4 ESP
DIRECTORIO ESPANOL DE ACUICULTURA. Text in Spanish. 1995. irreg. EUR 21.64 newsstand/cover (effective 2003). **Document type:** *Directory.* **Description:** Lists research centers, companies, and existing species.
Published by: Centro de Informacion y Documentacion Cientifica/Center for Scientific Information and Documentation, Joaquin Costa 22, Madrid, 28002, Spain. TEL 34-91-5635482, FAX 34-91-5642644, sdi@cindoc.csic.es, http://www.cindoc.csic.es.

590 551.46 NCL ISSN 1297-9635
DOCUMENTS SCIENTIFIQUES ET TECHNIQUES - I R D. Text in French. 1978.
Former titles (until 1999): Documents Scientifiques et Techniques - ORSTOM (1245-222X); (until 1995): Rapports Scientifiques et Techniques Sciences de la Mer. Biologie Marine (1169-162X); (until 1987): Rapports Scientifiques et Techniques - Office de la Recherche Scientifique et Technique Outre-Mer, Centre de Noumea Oceanographie (0750-7070)
Indexed: ESPM.
Published by: Institut de Recherche pour le Developpement, Centre de Noumea, 101 Promenade Roger Laroque - Anse Vata, Noumea, BP A5 - 98848, New Caledonia. TEL 687 26 10 00, FAX 687 26 43 26, http://www.ird.nc.

551.46 CHN ISSN 1001-909X
DONGHAI HAIYANG/DONGHAI MARINE SCIENCE. Text in Chinese. 1983. q. CNY 5 domestic (effective 2000). **Document type:** *Academic/Scholarly.*
Related titles: Online - full content ed.: (from WanFang Data Corp.); Online - full text ed.: (from East View Information Services).
Indexed: ASFA, ESPM.
—BLDSC (3619.226000).
Published by: (Guojia Haiyangju Di-2 Haiyang Yanjiusuo, Zhejiang Sheng Haiyang Xuehui), Haiyang Chubanshe, 1 Fuxingmenwai Dajie, Beijing, 100860, China.

DYNAMICS OF ATMOSPHERES AND OCEANS. see *METEOROLOGY*

551.46 MEX ISSN 0188-4840
QH92.3
E P O M E X SERIE CIENTIFICA. Text in Spanish. 1990. 2/yr. **Document type:** *Journal, Academic/Scholarly.*
Published by: Universidad Autonoma de Campeche, Programa de Ecologia, Pesquerias y Oceanografia del Golfo de Mexico, Ave. Agustin Melgar y Juan de la Barrera, Apartado Postal 520, Campeche, 24030, Mexico. FAX 52-981-65954.

551.46 USA ISSN 1068-2678
EARTH SYSTEM MONITOR. Text in English. 1991. q. free. **Document type:** *Government.* **Description:** Reports on N.O.A.A. environmental data and information management programs and activities, describes new NOAA data and information products and services.
Indexed: ASFA, BiolDig, ESPM, EnvAb, GEOBASE, M&TEA, OceAb, PollutAb, RefZh, SWRA.
—Linda Hall.
Published by: U.S. National Oceanographic Data Center, NOAA NESDIS E/OC, SSMC3, 4th Flr, 1315 East-West Hwy, Silver Spring, MD 20910-3282. TEL 301-713-3277, FAX 301-713-3302, services@nodc.noaa.gov, nodc.services@noaa.gov, http://www.nodc.noaa.gov. Ed. Sheri Phillips.

551.46 SYC
EAST AFRICAN REGIONAL SEAS TECHNICAL REPORT SERIES. Text in English. irreg.
Published by: Regional Seas Program in Eastern Africa, Eastern Africa Regional Coordinating Unit, PO Box 487, Victoria, Mahe, Seychelles. TEL 248-324-525, FAX 248-342-573, uneprcu@seychelles.net.

578.77 COL ISSN 0122-3313
QH121 CODEN: BOECE5
ECOTROPICA. ECOSISTEMAS TROPICALES. Text in Spanish; Summaries in English, Spanish. 1970. s-a. price varies. bibl.; illus. **Document type:** *Bulletin.*
Former titles (until 1995): Boletin Ecotropica (0120-8993); (until 1985): Universidad de Bogota Jorge Tadeo Lozano. Museo del Mar. Boletin (0120-0240)
Media: Cards.
Indexed: ASFA, ApEcolAb, BioCN&I, ESPM, EntAb, FPA, ForAb, HortAb, IndVet, OrnHort, PGegResA, RevApplEntom, S&F, SFA, SeedAb, WeedAb, ZooRec.
—CINDOC, CISTI, Linda Hall.
Published by: Universidad de Bogota Jorge Tadeo Lozano, Museo del Mar, Carrera 4 No. 22-61, Bogota, CUND, Colombia. TEL 57-1-3426581, FAX 57-1-2826197. Ed. Elvira Maria Alvarado Chacon. Circ: 1,200 (controlled).

551.46 GBR
ELSEVIER OCEAN ENGINEERING SERIES. Text in English. irreg. **Document type:** *Monographic series.*
—BLDSC (3732.377000), ingenta.
Published by: Elsevier Ltd., Books Division (Subsidiary of: Elsevier Science & Technology), Kidlington, PO Box 800, Oxford, OX2 1DX, United Kingdom. TEL 44-1865-843891, FAX 44-1865-843920. Eds. M E McCormick, R Bhattacharyya.

E

▼ new title ➤ refereed ✶ unverified ♦ full entry avail.

551.46 NLD ISSN 0422-9894
CODEN: ELOSA9
➤ **ELSEVIER OCEANOGRAPHY SERIES.** Text in English. 1964. irreg., latest vol.70, 2004. price varies. back issues avail. **Document type:** *Monographic series, Academic/Scholarly.* **Description:** Disseminates research in all areas of oceanography.
Supersedes (in 1965): Oceanography Series (0078-3226)
Indexed: ASFA, BIOSIS Prev, BiolAb, ChemAb, ESPM, Inspec, MathR, ZooRec.
—BLDSC (3732.380000), CASDDS, CISTI, IE, ingenta. **CCC.**
Published by: Elsevier BV (Subsidiary of: Elsevier Science & Technology), Radarweg 29, Amsterdam, 1043 NX, Netherlands. TEL 31-20-4853911, FAX 31-20-4852457, nlinfo-f@elsevier.nl, http://www.elsevier.nl. Ed. David Halpern.

551.46 GBR
EMARINE; news, articles, jobs and information for the professional marine community. Text in English. 2002 (Sept.). m. free (effective 2003). **Document type:** *Newsletter, Trade.* **Description:** Published for the benefit of the professional marine community and provides, news articles, worldwide event listings and free sample articles.
Media: E-mail.
Published by: Institute of Marine Engineering, Science and Technology, 80 Coleman St, London, EC2R 5BJ, United Kingdom. TEL 44-20-73822600, FAX 44-20-73822669, info@imarest.org, http://www.imarest.org/emarine/.

551.46 JPN
ENGAN KAIYO KENKYU. Text in Japanese; Summaries in English, Japanese. 1962. s-a. JPY 3,800 (effective 1999). **Document type:** *Bulletin, Academic/Scholarly.* **Description:** Contains articles dealing with the results of fundamental and original research in coastal oceanography including engineering.
Formerly (until Feb. 1995): Engan Kaiyo Kenkyu Noto - Bulletin on Coastal Oceanography (0914-3882)
Published by: Nihon Kaiyo Gakkai, Engan Kaiyo Kenkyu Bukai/Oceanographical Society of Japan, Coastal Oceanography Research Committee, Tokai Daigaku Kaiyogakubu, 20-1 Ori-Do 3-chome, shimizu-shi, Shizuoka-ken 424-0902, Japan. TEL 81-543-34-0411. Ed. Shin-ichi Uye.

551.46 EST ISSN 1406-023X
GC59.68.E75
ESTONIAN MARINE INSTITUTE. REPORT SERIES. Text in English, Estonian. 1995. irreg. **Document type:** *Monographic series, Academic/Scholarly.*
Indexed: ESPM.
Published by: Eesti Mereinstituut, Viljandi mnt. 18B, Tallinn, 11216, Estonia. TEL 372-6281569, FAX 372-6281563.

551.46 551.4 GBR ISSN 1352-4615
ESTUARINE AND COASTAL SCIENCES ASSOCIATION. BULLETIN. Cover title: E C S A Bulletin. Text in English. 1972. 3/yr. bk.rev. **Description:** Provides information on meetings, symposia and workshops, and also news relevant to estuarine and coastal science.
Formerly (until 1989): Estuarine and Brackish-Water Sciences Association. Bulletin (0963-2077)
Published by: Estuarine and Coastal Sciences Association, c/o Trevor Telfer, Institute of Aquaculture, University of Stirling, Stirling, FK9 4LA, United Kingdom. t.c.telfer@stir.ac.uk, http://www.ecsa.ac.uk/. Ed. Jim Wilson.

551.46 GBR ISSN 0272-7714
GC96 CODEN: ECSSD3
➤ **ESTUARINE, COASTAL AND SHELF SCIENCE.** Text in English. 1973. 20/yr. EUR 2,708 in Europe to institutions; JPY 292,700 in Japan to institutions; USD 2,408 elsewhere to institutions (effective 2006). adv. bk.rev. illus. Index. reprints avail. **Document type:** *Journal, Academic/Scholarly.* **Description:** Devoted to the analysis of saline water phenomena ranging from the outer edge of the continental shelf to the upper limits of the tidal zone.
Formerly (until 1982): Estuarine and Coastal Marine Science (0302-3524)
Related titles: Online - full text ed.: ISSN 1096-0015. USD 2,188 (effective 2002) (from EBSCO Publishing, Gale Group, IngentaConnect, O C L C Online Computer Library Center, Inc., ScienceDirect, Swets Information Services).
Indexed: ABIPC, AEA, AESIS, ASCA, ASFA, AgBio, AnBrAb, BIOBASE, BIOSIS Prev, BiolAb, CIN, CPA, CTO, Cadscan, ChemAb, ChemTitl, CivEngAb, CurCont, E&PHSE, EPB, ESPM, EnvAb, EnvEAb, ExcerpMed, FLUIDEX, FPA, ForAb, GEOBASE, GP&P, HerbAb, HortAb, I&DA, IABS, ISR, IndVet, LeadAb, M&GPA, M&TEA, NemAb, NutrAb, OceAb, OffTech, PetrolAb, PollutAb, RRTA, RefZh, S&F, SCI, SFA, SWRA, SeedAb, TDB, WAE&RSA, WRCInf, WeedAb, Zincscan, ZooRec.
—BLDSC (3812.599200), CASDDS, CISTI, IDS, IE, Infotrieve, ingenta, Linda Hall, PADDS. **CCC.**
Published by: Academic Press (Subsidiary of: Elsevier Science & Technology), Harcourt Pl, 32 Jamestown Rd, London, NW1 7BY, United Kingdom. TEL 44-20-7424-4200, FAX 44-20-7483-2293, apsubs@acad.com, http://www.elsevier.com/locate/ecss. Eds. D. S. McLusky, E. Wolanski, S. D. Sulkin. R&P Catherine John. Adv. contact Nik Screen. **Subscr. to:** Harcourt Publishers Ltd., Foots Cray High St, Sidcup, Kent DA14 5HP, United Kingdom. TEL 44-208-3085700, FAX 44-20-83090807.

551.4 CHL ISSN 0071-173X
➤ **ESTUDIOS OCEANOLOGICOS.** Text and summaries in English, Spanish. 1965-1966; resumed 1983. a., latest vol.20, 2001. USD 30; or exchange basis. bk.rev. charts; illus.; stat. **Document type:** *Academic/Scholarly.* **Description:** Provides research in aquatic sciences, with emphasis on the Pacific Ocean.
Related titles: Online - full text ed.: (from EBSCO Publishing).
Indexed: ASFA, ESPM, MBA, SFA, SWRA, ZooRec.
Published by: Universidad de Antofagasta, Facultad de Recursos del Mar, Casilla 170, Antofagasta, Chile. TEL 56-55-637404, FAX 56-55-637804, meoliva@uantof.cl, moliva@uantof.cl. Ed., R&P Marcelo E Oliva. Circ: 600 (controlled).

551.46 USA
EXPERIMENTAL LONG LEAD FORECAST BULLETIN. Text in English. q. free. back issues avail. **Document type:** *Bulletin.*
Media: Online - full text.
Published by: Center for Ocean Land Atmosphere Studies, 4041 Powder Mill Rd., Ste. 302, Calverton, MD 20705-3106. TEL 301-595-7000, FAX 301-595-9793, ellfb@cola.iges.org, ellbf@cola.iges.org, www..igesorg/ellgb, http://grads.iges.org/ellfb. Ed. Ben Kirtman. **Co-sponsor:** Institute for Global Environment and Society.

551.46 USA ISSN 1075-2560
GC58
EXPLORATIONS (LA JOLLA); global discoveries for tomorrow's world. Text in English. 1994. q. free to Scripps alumni and other qualified persons. illus. back issues avail. **Document type:** *Journal, Academic/Scholarly.*
Incorporates (in 1994): Scripps Institution of Oceanography. Annual Report (1046-9443); Which was formerly (until 1984): Scripps Institution of Oceanography (Year) (0194-2816); (until 1978): S I O Scripps Institution of Oceanography (0160-7596); (until 1976): Scripps Institution of Oceanography. Annual Report (0147-6203); (until 1972): S I O: A Report on the Work and Programs of Scripps Institution of Oceanography (0091-1518)
Indexed: ASFA, RefZh, SFA.
—BLDSC (3842.194900), CISTI, KNAW, Linda Hall. **CCC.**
Published by: Scripps Institution of Oceanography, Technical Publications Office, University of California at San Diego, 9500 Gilman Dr, Department 0233B, La Jolla, CA 92093-0233. TEL 619-534-1295, techpubs@sio.uscd.edu. Ed. Nan P Criqui. Circ: 18,000.

FISHES OF THE WESTERN NORTH ATLANTIC. MEMOIRS. see *BIOLOGY*

551.46 USA
FLORIDA SEA GRANT COLLEGE PROGRAM. TECHNICAL PAPER. Text in English. irreg.
Published by: Florida Sea Grant College Program, University of Florida, PO Box 110409, Gainesville, FL 32611-0409. TEL 352-392-2801, skearl@ufl.edu, http://www.flseagrant.org.

551.46 USA ISSN 0888-6857
FLORIDA SEA GRANT COLLEGE. REPORT. Text in English. 1974. irreg. price varies. **Document type:** *Monographic series.*
Formerly (until 1979): Florida Sea Grant Program. Report (0733-3714)
—BLDSC (7473.680000), Linda Hall.
Published by: Florida Sea Grant College Program, University of Florida, PO Box 110409, Gainesville, FL 32611-0409. TEL 352-392-2801, kawagner@mail.ifas.ufl.edu, http://www.flseagrant.org.

551.46 DEU ISSN 1432-797X
FORSCHUNGSZENTRUM TERRAMARE. BERICHTE. Text in German. irreg. price varies.
Published by: Forschungszentrum Terramare, Schleusenstr. 1, Wilhelmshaven, 26382, Germany. TEL 49-4421-944-0, FAX 49-4421-944199, http://www.terramare.de/.

551.46 570 JPN ISSN 0917-8147
➤ **FUKUYAMA DAIGAKU FUZOKU NAIKAI SEIBUTSU SHIGEN KENKYUJO HOKOKU/FUKUYAMA UNIVERSITY. RESEARCH INSTITUTE OF MARINE BIORESOURCES. REPORT.** Text in English, Japanese. 1991. irreg. free. **Document type:** *Academic/Scholarly.*
—CCC.
Published by: Fukuyama Daigaku, Fuzoku Naikai Seibutsu Shigen Kenkyujo, Ohama-cho, Innoshima-shi, Hiroshima-ken 722-2101, Japan. TEL 81-849-36-2111, FAX 81-849-36-2023. Eds. Akinori Amenura, Eiji Okimasu. Circ: 100.

551.46 BRA ISSN 0101-7748
FUNDACAO UNIVERSIDADE DO RIO GRANDE. DEPARTAMENTO DE OCEANOGRAFIA. DOCUMENTOS TECNICOS. Text in Portuguese. 1980. irreg. **Document type:** *Monographic series.*
Indexed: ESPM, ZooRec.
Published by: Fundacao Universidade Federal do Rio Grande, Departamento de Oceanografia, Rua Eng Alfredo Huch, 475 Centro, Rio Grande, 96201-900, Brazil. TEL 55-53-233-6500, reitoria@furg.br, http://www.furg.br.

GAYANA. see *BIOLOGY—Zoology*

551.46 JPN
GEKKAN AKUA RAIFU/AQUAL LIFE. Text in Japanese. 1979. m. JPY 760 per issue.
Published by: Marin Kikaku/Marine Planning Co., Ltd., 2-3 Sarugaku-cho 2-chome, Chiyoda-ku, Tokyo, 101-0064, Japan.

551.46 JPN ISSN 0916-2011
GC1
GEKKAN KAIYO/OCEANOGRAPHY MONTHLY. Text in Japanese. 1969. m. JPY 2,000 per issue.
Published by: Kaiyo Shuppan Co. Ltd., 675-5 Misawa, Hino-shi, Tokyo-to 191-0032, Japan.

GEO-MARINE LETTERS; an international journal of marine geology. see *EARTH SCIENCES—Geology*

551.46 USA
GEORGIA SEA GRANT COLLEGE PROGRAM. MARINE EXTENSION BULLETIN. Text in English. irreg.
Published by: University of Georgia, Georgia Sea Grant, 220 Marine Sciences Bldg, Athens, GA 30602. TEL 706-542-6009, FAX 706-542-3652, http://www.marsci.uga.edu/gaseagrant/sgpubs.html.

GEORGIAN GEOPHYSICAL SOCIETY. JOURNAL. see *EARTH SCIENCES—Geophysics*

551.46 DEU ISSN 1619-0092
GEZEITENKALENDER. Text in German. 1947. a. EUR 2.20 (effective 2005). **Document type:** *Journal, Academic/Scholarly.*
Formerly (until 1995): Hoch- und Niedrigwasserzeiten fuer die Deutsche Bucht und deren Flussgebiete (0172-8253)
Published by: Bundesamt fuer Seeschiffahrt und Hydrographie, Bernhard-Nocht-Str 78, Hamburg, 20359, Germany. TEL 49-40-31900, FAX 49-40-31905000, posteingang@bsh.de, http://www.bsh.de.

551.4 DEU ISSN 0084-9774
VK603
GEZEITENTAFELN. Text in German. 1879. a. EUR 17.50 (effective 2005). **Document type:** *Journal, Academic/Scholarly.*
Published by: Bundesamt fuer Seeschiffahrt und Hydrographie, Bernhard-Nocht-Str 78, Hamburg, 20359, Germany. TEL 49-40-31900, FAX 49-40-31905000, posteingang@bsh.de, http://www.bsh.de/de/Produkte/Buecher/Gezeitentafeln/index.jsp.

GREAT BARRIER REEF MARINE PARK AUTHORITY RESEARCH PUBLICATION SERIES. see *BIOLOGY*

551.46 AUS ISSN 0810-6983
GREAT BARRIER REEF MARINE PARK AUTHORITY. SPECIAL PUBLICATION SERIES. Text in English. 1983. irreg.
Indexed: ESPM.
Published by: Great Barrier Reef Marine Park Authority, 2-68 Flinders St, PO Box 1379, Townsville, QLD 4810, Australia. TEL 61-7-47500700, FAX 61-7-47726093, http://www.gbrmpa.gov.au.

GREAT BARRIER REEF MARINE PARK AUTHORITY TECHNICAL MEMORANDUM. see *BIOLOGY*

551.46 AUS ISSN 0156-5842
GREAT BARRIER REEF MARINE PARK AUTHORITY WORKSHOP SERIES. Text in English. 1978. irreg., latest no.25, 1999. price varies. **Document type:** *Proceedings, Academic/Scholarly.* **Description:** Covers workshops on marine sciences held by the Marine Park Authority.
Related titles: Online - full content ed.
Indexed: ASFA, ESPM, ZooRec.
Published by: Great Barrier Reef Marine Park Authority, 2-68 Flinders St, PO Box 1379, Townsville, QLD 4810, Australia. TEL 61-7-47500700, FAX 61-7-47726093, registry@gbrmpa.gov.au, http://www.gbrmpa.gov.au/corp_site/info_services/publications/workshop_series/index.html. Circ: 250.

GUIDES TO THE IDENTIFICATION OF THE MICROINVERTEBRATES OF THE CONTINENTAL WATERS OF THE WORLD. see *BIOLOGY—Zoology*

551.46 593 USA ISSN 1528-0470
GC1 CODEN: GURRA4
➤ **GULF AND CARIBBEAN RESEARCH.** Text in English. 1961. a., latest vol.15, 2003. USD 10; free to qualified personnel (effective 2005). bk.rev. abstr. back issues avail.; reprint service avail. from PQC. **Document type:** *Journal, Academic/Scholarly.*
Formerly (until 2000): Gulf Research Reports (0072-9027)
Indexed: ASFA, BIOSIS Prev, BiolAb, CurCont, EPB, ESPM, MSCT, OceAb, RefZh, SFA, SWRA, WildRev, ZooRec.
—BLDSC (4230.356500), IE, ingenta, Linda Hall.
Published by: (Gulf Coast Research Laboratory), University of Southern Mississippi, Gulf Coast Research Laboratory, P O Box 7000, Ocean Springs, MS 39566-7000. TEL 228-872-4200, FAX 228-872-4204, dawne.hard@usm.edu, mpeters@seahorse.ims.usm.edu, linda.skupien@usm.edu, http://www.ims.usm.edu/grsrep01.htm. Ed. Dr. Mark S Peterson. Circ: 500.

E

551.46 USA ISSN 1087-688X
GC1 CODEN: NGSCDE
➤ **GULF OF MEXICO SCIENCE.** Text in English. 1969. s-a. USD 4 (effective 2002). bk.rev. abstr.; bibl.; illus.; maps; stat. back issues avail. **Document type:** *Academic/Scholarly.*
Former titles (until 1996): Northeast Gulf Science (0148-9836); (until 1977): Journal of Marine Science (0364-1988)
Indexed: ASFA, BIOSIS Prev, BiolAb, CTO, CurCont, ESPM, GEOBASE, M&GPA, OceAb, PollutAb, RefZh, SFA, WildRev, ZooRec.
—BLDSC (4230.374300), IE, ingenta, Linda Hall.
Published by: Marine Environmental Sciences Consortium of Alabama, Dauphin Island Sea Lab, Box 369 370, Dauphin Island, AL 36528. TEL 251-861-2141, wschroed@jaguar1.usouthal.edu, http://www.disl.org. Ed., R&P William W Schroeder. Circ: 300 (paid); 100 (controlled).

551.46 KOR ISSN 1229-8905
HAEYANG JO'SA YEONBO/ANNUAL REPORT OF OCEANOGRAPHIC OBSERVATIONS. Text in English. 1954. a.
Published by: Gugrib Su-san Jinheung-weon/National Fisheries Research and Development Institute, 408-1 Sirang-ri, Gijang-eup, Gijang-gun, Busan, 619-902, Korea, S. TEL 82-51-720-2114, FAX 82-51-720-2054, http://www.nfrda.re.kr/.

HAFRANNSOKNIR. see *FISH AND FISHERIES*

551.46 CHN ISSN 1002-3682
HAIAN GONGCHENG/COASTAL ENGINEERING. Text in Chinese. 1982. q. CNY 5 newsstand/cover (effective 2004). **Document type:** *Journal, Academic/Scholarly.*
Related titles: Online - full text ed.: (from East View Information Services, WanFang Data Corp.).
—BLDSC (3292.404200).
Published by: Guojia Haiyang-ju, Di 1 Haiyang Yanjiusuo, 6, Xianxialing Lu, Qingdao, 266061, China. hbhh@chinajournal.net.cn, http://hagc.periodicals.net.cn/default.html. **Dist. by:** China International Book Trading Corp, 35 Chegongzhuang Xilu, Haidian District, PO Box 399, Beijing 100044, China. TEL 86-10-68412045, FAX 86-10-68412023, cibtc@mail.cibtc.com.cn, http://www.cibtc.com.cn.

HAIYANG DIZHI YU DISIJI DIZHI/MARINE GEOLOGY & QUATERNARY GEOLOGY. see *EARTH SCIENCES—Geology*

HAIYANG GONGCHENG/OCEAN ENGINEERING. see *ENGINEERING*

HAIYANG HUANJING KEXUE/MARINE ENVIRONMENTAL SCIENCE. see *ENVIRONMENTAL STUDIES*

551.46 CHN ISSN 1003-2029
HAIYANG JISHU/OCEAN TECHNOLOGY. Text in Chinese; Abstracts in English. 1982. q. CNY 12; USD 12 foreign. **Document type:** *Academic/Scholarly.* **Description:** Subject matter includes oceanographic instrumentation; buoy technology; coastal engineering; marine environment monitoring, observation and protection technology; ocean remote sensing; and sea technology news.
Related titles: Online - full text ed.: (from East View Information Services).
Indexed: ASFA, ESPM.
—BLDSC (4238.308200), IE.
Published by: Guojia Haiyang-ju, Haiyang Jishu Yanjiusuo/State Oceanic Administration, Institute of Ocean Technology, 60 Xianyang Rd, Tianjin 300111, China. TEL 86-22-736-7821, TELEX 23174 TJPTB CN, iotsoa@v7610.tisti.ac.cn. Ed. Hui Shaotang. Circ: 1,500.

551.46 CHN ISSN 1000-3096
CODEN: HAKEE9
HAIYANG KEXUE/MARINE SCIENCES. Text in Chinese; Summaries in English. 1977. bi-m. CNY 180 (effective 2004). adv. **Document type:** *Journal, Academic/Scholarly.* **Description:** Covers marine physics, geology, chemistry, biology, engineering, instruments, and environmental protection. Devoted to the construction and modernization of China.
Related titles: Online - full content ed.: (from WanFang Data Corp.); Online - full text ed.: (from East View Information Services).
Indexed: ASFA, ESPM, M&TEA, SFA, WildRev, ZooRec.
—BLDSC (5378.144000), CISTI, IE, ingenta.
Published by: (Zhongguo Kexueyuan, Haiyang Yanjiusuo), Kexue Chubanshe/Science Press, 16 Donghuang Cheng Genbei Jie, Beijing, 100717, China. TEL 86-10-64000246, FAX 86-10-64030255, msj@ms.qdio.ac.cn, http://hykx.periodicals.net.cn/default.html, http://www.sciencep.com/. Ed. Hai-ou Zhou. Circ: 10,000. **Dist. by:** China International Book Trading Corp, 35 Chegongzhuang Xilu, Haidian District, PO Box 399, Beijing 100044, China. TEL 86-10-68412045, FAX 86-10-68412023, cibtc@mail.cibtc.com.cn, http://www.cibtc.com.cn.

551.46 CHN ISSN 0438-380X
QH91.A1 CODEN: HYKHAC
HAIYANG KEXUE JIKAN/STUDIA MARINA SINICA. Text in Chinese. 1962. irreg. **Document type:** *Journal, Academic/Scholarly.*
Indexed: ESPM, ZooRec.
—CISTI, Linda Hall.
Published by: Zhongguo Kexueyuan Haiyang Yanjiusuo, 7, Nanhai Road, Qingdao, Shandong 266071, China. TEL 86-532-2898618, http://www.qdio.ac.cn/.

551.46 CHN ISSN 1671-6647
GC811 CODEN: HUHAEK
HAIYANG KEXUE JINZHAN/ADVANCES IN MARINE SCIENCE. Text in Chinese. 1983. q. CNY 15 newsstand/cover (effective 2004). **Document type:** *Journal, Academic/Scholarly.*
Formerly: Huang Bohai Haiyang/Journal of Oceanography of Huanghai & Bohai Seas (1000-7199)
Related titles: Online - full text ed.: (from East View Information Services, WanFang Data Corp.).
Indexed: ASFA, ESPM, RefZh, ZooRec.
—BLDSC (0709.340500), IE.
Published by: Guojia Haiyang-ju, Di 1 Haiyang Yanjiusuo, 6, Xianxialing Lu, Qingdao, 266061, China. hbhh@chinajournal.net.cn, http://hbhhy.periodicals.net.cn/default.html. **Dist. by:** China International Book Trading Corp, 35 Chegongzhuang Xilu, Haidian District, PO Box 399, Beijing 100044, China. TEL 86-10-68412045, FAX 86-10-68412023, cibtc@mail.cibtc.com.cn, http://www.cibtc.com.cn.

551.46 CHN ISSN 1001-5043
HAIYANG SHIJIE/OCEAN WORLD. Text in Chinese. 1975. m. CNY 3.60 newsstand/cover. adv. **Description:** Publishes articles on all aspects of ocean popular science, such as geography, geology, biology and physics.
Published by: (Zhongguo Haiyang Xuehui/Chinese Society of Oceanography), Haiyang Chubanshe/Ocean Press, International Department, 8 Dahuisi Rd, Haidian District, Beijing, 100081, China. TEL 86-10-62174871, FAX 86-10-62173569. Ed. Chen Zeqing. Adv. contact Guo Wei. B&W page USD 1,000, color page USD 3,500. Circ: 20,000.

551.46 CHN ISSN 1001-6392
HAIYANG TONGBAO/MARINE SCIENCE BULLETIN. Text in Chinese; Summaries in English. 1982. bi-m. USD 180 (effective 2003 - 2004). 96 p./no.; **Document type:** *Bulletin, Academic/Scholarly.* **Description:** Includes basic marine research on hydrology, climatology, biology, chemistry, geology, marine engineering, marine techniques & methods, marine development, marine management and environmental protection, etc.
Related titles: ♦ CD-ROM ed.: Chinese Academic Journals Full-Text Database. Science & Engineering, Series A. ISSN 1007-8010; Online - full text ed.: (from East View Information Services); ♦ English ed.: Marine Science Bulletin. ISSN 1000-9620.
Indexed: ASFA, CivEngAb, ESPM, M&TEA, ZooRec.
—BLDSC (5378.134100), IE, ingenta.
Published by: Guojia Haiyang Xinxi Zhongxin/National Marine Data & Information Service, 93 Liuwei Rd, Hedong District, Tianjin, 300171, China. TEL 86-22-24010823, FAX 86-22-24010825, hytb@mail.nmdis.gov.cn. Ed. Hong Wang.

551.46 CHN ISSN 1001-0157
HAIYANG WENZHAI/OCEANIC ABSTRACTS. Text in Chinese. 1962. bi-m. USD 120 (effective until 2003). 64 p./no.; **Document type:** *Abstract/Index.* **Description:** Contains abstracts dealing with basic marine science, marine surveying & observation, marine hydrology, marine meteorology, marine biology, marine chemistry, marine geology & geomorphology, and marine environmental protection, etc.
Published by: Guojia Haiyang Xinxi Zhongxin/National Marine Data & Information Service, 93 Liuwei Rd, Hedong District, Tianjin, 300171, China. TEL 86-22-24010826, FAX 86-22-24010825, library@mail.nmdis.gov.cn. Ed. Chengde Xu.

551.65 CHN ISSN 1005-1724
HAIYANG XINXI/MARINE INFORMATION. Text in Chinese. 1986. q. USD 60 (effective 2003 - 2004). adv. 32 p./no.; **Document type:** *Journal, Academic/Scholarly.* **Description:** Covers various information, reviews research news, technique and management on oceanography.
Related titles: Online - full text ed.: (from East View Information Services).
Published by: Guojia Haiyang Xinxi Zhongxin/National Marine Data & Information Service, 93 Liuwei Rd, Hedong District, Tianjin, 300171, China. TEL 86-22-24011287, FAX 86-22-24010825, hytb@mail.nmdis.gov.cn. Ed. Shaohua Lin.

551.46 CHN ISSN 0253-4193
GC1 CODEN: HYPADJ
➤ **HAIYANG XUEBAO.** Text in Chinese. bi-m. **Document type:** *Journal, Academic/Scholarly.* **Description:** Publishes scholarly papers on marine science and technology, including physics, chemistry, biology, hydrology, meteorology, aquaculture, engineering, remote sensing, instrumentation and meters.
Related titles: Online - full text ed.: (from East View Information Services); ♦ English ed.: Acta Oceanologica Sinica. ISSN 0253-505X.
Indexed: ASFA, CIN, ChemAb, ChemTitl, M&TEA.
—BLDSC (0641.623000), CASDDS, KNAW, Linda Hall.
Published by: (Chinese Society of Oceanography), Haiyang Chubanshe/Ocean Press, International Department, 8 Dahuisi Rd, Haidian District, Beijing, 100081, China. TEL 86-10-62174871, FAX 86-10-62173569, oceanpress@china.com. Ed. Chao Jiping.

551.46 551.48 CHN ISSN 0029-814X
GC1 CODEN: HYHCAG
➤ **HAIYANG YU HUZHAO/OCEANOLOGIA ET LIMNOLOGIA SINICA.** Text in Chinese; Summaries in English. 1957. bi-m. CNY 132 (effective 2004). adv. **Document type:** *Academic/Scholarly.* **Description:** Covers hydrophysics, hydrochemistry, hydrobiology, geomorphology, equipment and apparatus research and manufacture, comprehensive reviews, and academic activities.
Related titles: Online - full content ed.: (from WanFang Data Corp.); Online - full text ed.: (from East View Information Services); ♦ English ed.: Chinese Journal of Oceanology and Limnology. ISSN 0254-4059.
Indexed: ASFA, AgBio, AnBrAb, BioCN&I, BiolAb, CIN, ChemAb, ChemTitl, ESPM, ForAb, HortAb, I&DA, IndVet, Inspec, M&TEA, NemAb, NutrAb, PBA, PoultAb, ProtozoAb, RDA, RefZh, RevApplEntom, S&F, SFA, VetBull, WAE&RSA, WeedAb, WildRev, ZooRec.
—BLDSC (6234.150000), AskIEEE, CASDDS, CISTI, IE, ingenta, Linda Hall.
Published by: (Zhongguo Haiyang Huzhao Xuehui), Kexue Chubanshe/Science Press, 16 Donghuang Cheng Genbei Jie, Beijing, 100717, China. TEL 86-10-64000246, FAX 86-10-64030255, bsun@ms.qdio.ac.cn, http://hyyhz.periodicals.net.cn/default.html, http://www.sciencep.com/. Circ: 7,000. **Dist. by:** China International Book Trading Corp, 35 Chegongzhuang Xilu, Haidian District, PO Box 399, Beijing 100044, China. TEL 86-10-68412045, FAX 86-10-68412023, cibtc@mail.cibtc.com.cn, http://www.cibtc.com.cn.

551.46 CHN ISSN 1003-0239
HAIYANG YUBAO/MARINE FORECASTS. Text in Chinese. 1985. q. CNY 5 (effective 2000).
Related titles: Online - full content ed.: (from WanFang Data Corp.); Online - full text ed.: (from East View Information Services).
Indexed: ASFA, ESPM.
Published by: Guojia Haiyang Huanjing Yubao Zhongxin, 8 Dahui Si, Beijing, 100081, China. TEL 86-1-8313947, xjwu@nmefc.gov.cn. Ed. Du Bilan.

551.46 JPN
HAKODATE KAIYO KISHODAI. KAIYO SOKUHO/HAKODATE MARINE OBSERVATORY. OCEANOGRAPHIC OBSERVATION REPORT. Text in Japanese. 1963. q.
Published by: Kishocho, Hakodate Kaiyo Kishodai/Japan Meteorological Agency, Hakodate Marine Observatory, 3-4-4 Mihara, Hakodate-shi, Hokkaido 041-0806, Japan.

551.46 KOR ISSN 1226-2978
GC1
➤ **HANGUG HAEYANG HAGHOE JI - BADA/KOREAN SOCIETY OF OCEANOGRAPHY. JOURNAL - SEA.** Key Title: Ba'da. Text and summaries in English, Korean. 1996. q. KRW 20,000; USD 20 foreign. adv. index. back issues avail. **Document type:** *Bulletin, Academic/Scholarly.* **Description:** Publishes articles covering every aspect of oceanography and related subjects, focusing on oceanographic studies in the Korean coastal regions, Yellow Sea, East Sea, Pacific Ocean, and the Antarctic region.
Indexed: ZooRec.
—BLDSC (8213.509000).
Published by: Hangug Haeyang Haghoe, c/o Dept. of Oceanography, Seoul National University, Seoul, 151742, Korea, S. TEL 82-2-871-5032, FAX 82-2-887-0255, kso@bada0.snu.ac.kr, http://bada0.snu.ac.kr/ ksohome.htm. Ed. Chang Bok Lee. Pub. Sung Yoon Hong. Adv. contact S B Kim. Circ: 750 (paid); 100 (controlled).

551.46 KOR ISSN 1225-1283
GC1 CODEN: HHHCAX
➤ **HAN'GUG HAEYANG HAGHOEJI/KOREAN SOCIETY OF OCEANOGRAPHY. JOURNAL.** Text in English, Korean. 1966. q. KRW 30,000 to non-members; USD 50 foreign to non-members; KRW 20,000 to members; USD 15 foreign to members (effective 1999). adv. 25 p./no.; back issues avail. **Document type:** *Academic/Scholarly.* **Description:** Oceanographic studies of the coastal regions around the Korean peninsula, the Yellow Sea, the East Sea, the Pacific, and the Antarctic regions.
Formerly (until vol.28, 1993): Oceanological Society of Korea. Journal (0374-8049)
Indexed: ASFA, ESPM, ZooRec.
—BLDSC (4812.346330), CASDDS, IE, ingenta.
Published by: Hangug Haeyang Haghoe, c/o Dept. of Oceanography, Seoul National University, Seoul, 151742, Korea, S. TEL 82-2-872-5032, FAX 82-2-872-0311, edit@bada.snu.ac.kr, http://www.kso.snu.ac.kr. Ed. Hyun Kim Ki. Pub. Sang Oh Im. Adv. contact S B Kim. page KRW 20,000; trim 21 x 28.5. Circ: 700.

551.46 USA
HARBOR BRANCH NEWS. Text in English. 1986. fortn. back issues avail. **Document type:** *Newsletter.*
Published by: Harbor Branch Oceanographic Institution, Inc., 5600 U S 1 N, Fort Pierce, FL 34946. TEL 561-465-2400, FAX 561-465-2446, TELEX 52-2886. Circ: 700.

HARMFUL ALGAE NEWS. see *BIOLOGY*

E

551.46 JPN
HARO CHOSA HOKOKUSHO/RESEARCH REPORT OF WAVES. Text in Japanese. 1966. biennial.
Published by: Suisancho, Gyokobu/Fisheries Agency, Oceanic Fisheries Department, 2-1 Kasumigaseki 1-chome, Chiyoda-ku, Tokyo, 100-0013, Japan.

551.2 DEU ISSN 1438-387X
QH301 CODEN: HMREFR
➤ **HELGOLAND MARINE RESEARCH.** Text in English, German. 1937. q. EUR 148 combined subscription to institutions print & online eds. (effective 2005). adv. bk.rev. abstr.; bibl.; charts; illus. **Document type:** *Journal, Academic/Scholarly.* **Description:** Publishes original contributions, reviews, and short notes on all aspects of marine biology.
Former titles (until 1999): Helgolaender Meeresuntersuchungen (0174-3597); (until 1980): Helgolaender Wissenschaftliche Meeresuntersuchungen (0017-9957)
Related titles: Online - full text ed.: ISSN 1438-3888 (from EBSCO Publishing, Springer LINK, Swets Information Services).
Indexed: ASCA, ASFA, BIOSIS Prev, BiolAb, CRFR, CTO, ChemAb, CurCont, ESPM, ExcerpMed, GEOBASE, IBR, ISR, MSCT, NemAb, RefZh, SCI, SWRA, ZooRec.
—BLDSC (4284.940000), CASDDS, CISTI, IE, Infotrieve, ingenta, Linda Hall. **CCC.**
Published by: (Biologische Anstalt Helgoland), Springer-Verlag (Subsidiary of: Springer Science+Business Media), Tiergartenstr 17, Heidelberg, 69121, Germany. TEL 49-6221-3450, FAX 49-6221-345229, http://link.springer.de/link/service/journals/10152. Ed. Heinz-Dieter Franke TEL 49-4725-819346. Adv. contact Stephan Kroeck TEL 49-30-827875739. Circ: 750. **Subscr. in the Americas to:** Springer-Verlag New York, Inc., Journal Fulfillment, PO Box 2485, Secaucus, NJ 07096-2485. TEL 800-777-4643, 201-348-4033, FAX 201-348-4505, journals@springer-ny.com, http://www.springer-ny.com; **Subscr. to:** Springer GmbH Auslieferungsgesellschaft, Haberstr 7, Heidelberg 69126, Germany. TEL 49-6221-345-0, FAX 49-6221-345-4229, subscriptions@springer.de.

551.46 HRV ISSN 0439-0938
HIDROGRAFSKI GODISNJAK. Text in Croatian. 1954. a.
Indexed: ESPM.
Published by: Drzavni Hidrografski Institut/State Bureau of Hydrography, Zrinsko - Frankopanska 161, Split, 58000, Croatia. TEL 385-58-44433, FAX 385-58-47045.

551.46 570 JPN ISSN 0285-9416
HIROSAKI DAIGAKU RIGAKUBU FUZOKU FUKAURA RINKAI JISSHUJO HOKOKU/HIROSAKI UNIVERSITY. FUKAURA MARINE BIOLOGICAL LABORATORY. REPORT. Text in English, Japanese; Summaries in English. 1969. biennial.
Indexed: ASFA, ESPM, JPI, ZooRec.
Published by: Hirosaki Daigaku, Rigakubu/Hirosaki University, Faculty of Science, 3 Bunkyo-cho, Hirosaki-shi, Aomori-ken 036-8224, Japan.

551.46 570 JPN ISSN 0289-2197
HIROSHIMA UNIVERSITY. MUKAISHIMA MARINE BIOLOGICAL STATION. CONTRIBUTIONS. Text in English; Summaries in English, Japanese. 1933. a.
Indexed: SFA.
Published by: Hiroshima University, Mukaishima Marine Biological Station/Hiroshima Daigaku Rigakubu Fuzoku Mukaishima Rinkai Jikkenjo, Mitsugi-gun, Mukaishimacho, Hiroshima-ken 722, Japan.

551.46 639.2 JPN ISSN 0439-3511
GC791
HOKKAIDO UNIVERSITY. FACULTY OF FISHERIES. DATA RECORD OF OCEANOGRAPHIC OBSERVATIONS AND EXPLORATORY FISHING/KAIYO CHOSA GYOGYO SHIKEN YOHO. Text in Japanese, Multiple languages. 1957. a. per issue exchange basis.
Indexed: RefZh, SFA, ZooRec.
—CINDOC, Linda Hall.
Published by: Hokkaido University, Graduate School of Fisheries Sciences. Faculty of Fisheries, 3-1-1 Minato-cho, Hakodate, 041-8611, Japan. Circ: 600.

551.46 JPN ISSN 0385-6054
QK564
HOKKAIDO UNIVERSITY. INSTITUTE OF ALGOLOGICAL RESEARCH. SCIENTIFIC PAPERS/HOKKAIDO DAIGAKU RIGAKUBU KAISO KENKYUJO OBUN HOKOKU. Text in English. 1935. irreg. per issue exchange basis. **Document type:** *Academic/Scholarly.*
Indexed: ASFA, BiolAb.
—CISTI.
Published by: Hokkaido University, Faculty of Science - Institute of Algological Research/Hokkaido Daigaku Rigakubu Kaiso Kenkyujo, 1-13 Bokoi-Minami-Machi, Muroran-shi, Hokkaido 051-0003, Japan.

551.46 CAN
HUNTSMAN MARINE SCIENCE CENTRE. ANNUAL REPORT. Text in English. 1970. a. free. bibl.; charts; illus.; stat. back issues avail. **Document type:** *Yearbook, Academic/Scholarly.* **Description:** Publishes news of interest to oceanographers and others interested in the marine life of coastal New Brunswick.
Indexed: ASFA.
Published by: Huntsman Marine Science Centre, 1 Lower Campus Rd, St Andrews, NB E5B 2L7, Canada. TEL 506-529-1200, FAX 506-529-1212. Ed. Mark J Castello.

551.46 USA
HYDROWIRE. Text in English. 1998. d. **Document type:** *Academic/Scholarly.* **Description:** Functions as a communication link for the broad aquatic sciences community.
Media: Online - full text.
Published by: University of South Florida, Ocean Modeling and Prediction Laboratory linae@kelvin.marine.usf.edu, http://www.hydrowire.org/.

551.46 639.2 USA ISSN 0193-9254
I A M S L I C NEWSLETTER. Text in English. q. USD 35 (effective 2000). back issues avail. **Document type:** *Newsletter, Academic/Scholarly.*
Published by: International Association of Aquatic and Marine Science Libraries and Information Centers, c/o Harbor Branch Oceanographic Institute Library, 5600 U S 1 N, Fort Pierce, FL 34946. TEL 772-465-2400, FAX 772-465-2446, iamslic@ucsd.edu, http://siolibrary.ucsd.edu/iamslic/. Eds. Elizabeth Fuseler, Roger Kelly.

551.46 347.75 ITA ISSN 1027-4529
I C C O P S NEWSLETTER. Text in English. 1993. s-a.
Published by: International Centre for Coastal and Ocean Policy Studies, c/o University of Genoa, Department Polis, Stradone di S Agostino, 37, Genoa, 16123, Italy. iccops@polis.unige.it.

551.46072 DNK ISSN 0906-0596
I C E S ANNUAL REPORT. Text in English. 1960. irreg. back issues avail.
Formerly (until 1990): Proces-Verbal de la Reunion - Conseil International pour l'Exploration de la Mer (0538-6861)
Related titles: CD-ROM ed.
Indexed: ESPM.
Published by: International Council for the Exploration of the Sea, H. C. Andersens Boulevard 44-46, Copenhagen K, 1553, Denmark. TEL 45-33-386700, FAX 45-33-934215, info@ices.dk, http://www.ices.dk/products/annualreports.asp.

551.46 639.3 GBR ISSN 1054-3139
GC1 CODEN: ICESEC
➤ **I C E S JOURNAL OF MARINE SCIENCE.** Text and summaries in English, French. 1926. 9/yr. EUR 265 in Europe to individuals; JPY 28,700 in Japan to individuals; USD 250 elsewhere to individuals; EUR 985 in Europe to institutions; JPY 106,300 in Japan to institutions; USD 873 elsewhere to institutions (effective 2006). adv. bk.rev. cum.index: vols.1-25. back issues avail.; reprints avail. **Document type:** *Journal, Academic/Scholarly.* **Description:** Contains original papers within the broad field of marine and fisheries science. References subjects including ecology, population studies, plankton research, and physical and chemical oceanography.
Former titles (until 1991): Conseil International pour l'Exploration de la Mer. Journal (0020-6466); (until 1968): Conseil Permanent International pour l'Exploration de la Mer. Journal (0902-3232)
Related titles: Online - full text ed.: ISSN 1095-9289. USD 884 (effective 2002) (from EBSCO Publishing, Gale Group, IngentaConnect, O C L C Online Computer Library Center, Inc., ScienceDirect, Swets Information Services).
Indexed: AEA, ASCA, ASFA, AgBio, AnBrAb, B&BAb, BIOBASE, BIOSIS Prev, BiolAb, CIS, ChemAb, CivEngAb, CurCont, EPB, ESPM, EnvAb, GEOBASE, HelmAb, HortAb, I&DA, IABS, ISR, IndVet, M&TEA, NutrAb, OceAb, PollutAb, PoultAb, ProtozoAb, RDA, RM&VM, RRTA, RefZh, RevApplEntom, S&F, SCI, SFA, SWRA, VetBull, WAE&RSA, WeedAb, WildRev, ZooRec.
—BLDSC (4361.491000), CISTI, IDS, IE, Infotrieve, ingenta, Linda Hall. **CCC.**
Published by: (International Council for the Exploration of the Sea DNK), Academic Press (Subsidiary of: Elsevier Science & Technology), Harcourt Pl, 32 Jamestown Rd, London, NW1 7BY, United Kingdom. TEL 44-20-7424-4200, FAX 44-20-7483-2293, apsubs@acad.com, http://www.elsevier.com/locate/icesjms. Ed. A. I. L. Payne. Circ: 1,000.

➤ **I C E S MARINE SCIENCE SYMPOSIA.** see *FISH AND FISHERIES*

551.46 DNK ISSN 1684-0011
I C E S NEWSLETTER. (International Council for the Exploration of the Sea) Text in English. 198?. q. back issues avail. **Document type:** *Academic/Scholarly.*
Formerly (until 2001): I C E S Information (1027-9032)
Published by: International Council for the Exploration of the Sea, H. C. Andersens Boulevard 44-46, Copenhagen K, 1553, Denmark. TEL 45-33-386700, FAX 45-33-934215, info@ices.dk, http://www.ices.dk/products/newsletter.asp. Ed. Neil Fletcher.

I E E E JOURNAL OF OCEANIC ENGINEERING. see *ENGINEERING—Electrical Engineering*

551.46 USA ISSN 1522-3167
GC67 CODEN: PSATFF
I E E E SYMPOSIUM ON AUTONOMOUS UNDERWATER VEHICLE TECHNOLOGY. Text in English. 1990. a. USD 144; USD 72 to members (effective 2004). **Document type:** *Proceedings, Trade.*
Related titles: Online - full text ed.: (from I E E E).
Published by: Institute of Electrical and Electronics Engineers, Inc., 3 Park Ave, 17th Fl, New York, NY 10016-5997. TEL 800-678-4333, customer.service@ieee.org, http://www.ieee.org.

551.46 621.3 USA ISSN 1085-7990
I E E E WORKING CONFERENCE ON CURRENT MEASUREMENT TECHNOLOGY. PROCEEDINGS. Text in English. 1978. quinquennial. USD 176; USD 88 to members (effective 2004). **Document type:** *Proceedings, Trade.* **Description:** Focuses on addressing problems associated with measuring currents in the oceans.
Formerly: I E E E Working Conference on Current Measurement. Proceedings
Related titles: Microfiche ed.
—BLDSC (6844.169240).
Published by: Institute of Electrical and Electronics Engineers, Inc., 3 Park Ave, 17th Fl, New York, NY 10016-5997. TEL 212-419-7900, 800-678-4333, FAX 212-752-4929, customer.service@ieee.org, http://www.ieee.org. **Co-sponsor:** Oceanic Engineering Society.

551.46 FRA ISSN 0761-3962
CODEN: ACIFE7
I F R E M E R CENTRE DE BREST. ACTES DE COLLOQUES. Text in French, English, Spanish. 1971. irreg., latest 2003. price varies. back issues avail. **Document type:** *Proceedings, Academic/Scholarly.*
Formerly: Centre National pour l'Exploitation des Oceans. Actes de Colloques (0335-8259)
Indexed: ASFA, BiolAb, ChemAb, ESPM, ZooRec.
—BLDSC (0675.113340), CASDDS, CISTI, IE, ingenta. **CCC.**
Published by: (France. Institut Francais de Recherche pour l'Exploitation de la Mer, France. Centre de Brest), Editions IFREMER, BP 70, Plouzane, 29280, France. TEL 33-2-98224586, FAX 33-2-98224586, editions@ifremer.fr, http://www.ifremer.fr. Ed. Patrick Phliponeau. Adv. contact Nelly Courtay.

551.46 FRA ISSN 1279-8339
I F R E M E R CENTRE DE BREST. BILANS & PROSPECTIVES. (Institut Francais de Recherche pour l'Exploitation de la Mer) Text in French. 1997. irreg., latest 2002. price varies. back issues avail. **Document type:** *Monographic series.*
Indexed: ASFA, ESPM, ZooRec.
Published by: (Institut Francais de Recherche pour l'Exploitation de la Mer (IFREMER), Centre de Brest), Editions IFREMER, BP 70, Plouzane, 29280, France. TEL 33-2-98224586, FAX 33-2-98224586, editions@ifremer.fr, http://www.ifremer.fr. Ed. Patrick Phliponeau. Adv. contact Nelly Courtay.

578.77 FRA ISSN 0020-7918
I M S NEWSLETTER. (International Marine Science) Text in English. 1963. q. (online ed. biennial). free to qualified personnel. **Document type:** *Newsletter.*
Formerly (until 1970): International Marine Science (1013-2813)
Related titles: Online - full text ed.; Arabic ed.; Chinese ed.; Russian ed.; Spanish ed.: Boletin Internacional de Ciencias del Mar. ISSN 0379-5276; French ed.: Bulletin International des Sciences de la Mer. ISSN 0251-4451.
Indexed: RASB, SFA.
—CISTI, Linda Hall.
Published by: (Environment and Development in Coastal Regions and in Small Islands), UNESCO S C - C S I, 1 rue Miollis, Paris, Cedex 15 75732, France. TEL 33-1-45683934, FAX 33-1-45685808, g.archibald@unesco.org, http://www.unesco.org/ioc/IMSNewsletteron-line. Ed. Gail Archibald. Circ: 5,000 (controlled).

ILLINOIS-INDIANA SEA GRANT COLLEGE PROGRAM. REPORT. see *BIOLOGY*

578.77 IND ISSN 0379-5136
GC721 CODEN: IJMNBF
➤ **INDIAN JOURNAL OF MARINE SCIENCES.** Text in English. 1972. q. USD 200 to institutions (effective 2006). illus. **Document type:** *Academic/Scholarly.* **Description:** Devoted to research communication in biological, physical, geological and chemical oceanography.
Indexed: ASCA, ASFA, AbHyg, AgBio, AgrForAb, AnBrAb, BIOSIS Prev, BiolAb, CIN, CPA, CRFR, CTO, ChemAb, ChemTitl, CivEngAb, CurCont, DSA, ESPM, FLUIDEX, ForAb, GEOBASE, HelmAb, HortAb, IndVet, Inspec, M&GPA, NutrAb, PGrRegA, PollutAb, ProtozoAb, RA&MP, RM&VM, RPP, RefZh, S&F, SFA, SWRA, TDB, VetBull, WAE&RSA, WeedAb, ZooRec.
—BLDSC (4416.050000), AskIEEE, CASDDS, CISTI, IDS, IE, Infotrieve, ingenta, Linda Hall.

E

Published by: (India. Council of Scientific and Industrial Research, Publications & Information Directorate), Scientific Publishers, 5-A New Pali Rd., Near Hotel Taj Hari Mahal, PO Box 91, Jodhpur, Rajasthan 342 003, India. TEL 91-291-2433323, FAX 91-291-2512580, info@scientificpub.com, http://www.scientificpub.com/bookdetails.php?booktransid=322&bookid=318. Ed. K Satyanarayana. **Dist. by:** H P C Publishers Distributors Pvt. Ltd. **Co-sponsor:** Indian National Science Academy.

551.46 639.2 GRC ISSN 0255-4720
INSTITOUTON OKEANOGRAFIKON KAI ALIEUTIKON EREUNON. EIDIKE EKDOSE/INSTITUTE OF OCEANOGRAPHIC AND FISHERIES RESEARCH. SPECIAL PUBLICATION. Text in English, Greek. 1979. 3/w.
Indexed: ESPM.
Published by: Institouton Okeanografikon kai Alieutikon Ereunon, National Center for Marine Research, Agios Kosmas, Hellinikon 16604, Athens, Greece. TEL 30-1-9820214, FAX 30-1-9833095.

551.46 NCL
INSTITUT DE RECHERCHE POUR LE DEVELOPPEMENT. CENTRE DE NOUMEA. SCIENCES DE LA MER: OCEANOGRAPHIE PHYSIQUE. CONVENTIONS. Text in French. irreg.
Published by: Institut de Recherche pour le Developpement, Centre de Noumea, 101 Promenade Roger Laroque - Anse Vata, Noumea, BP A5 - 98848, New Caledonia. TEL 687 26 10 00, FAX 687 26 43 26, http://www.ird.nc.

551.46 NCL
INSTITUT DE RECHERCHE POUR LE DEVELOPPEMENT. CENTRE DE NOUMEA. SCIENCES DE LA MER: OCEANOGRAPHIE PHYSIQUE. NOTES TECHNIQUES. Text in French. irreg.
Published by: Institut de Recherche pour le Developpement, Centre de Noumea, 101 Promenade Roger Laroque - Anse Vata, Noumea, BP A5 - 98848, New Caledonia. FAX 687 26 43 26, http://www.ird.nc.

551.46 COG
INSTITUT DE RECHERCHE POUR LE DEVELOPPEMENT. CENTRE DE POINTE-NOIRE. DOCUMENTS SCIENTIFIQUES. Text in French. irreg.
Published by: Institut de Recherche pour le Developpement, Centre de Pointe-Noire, BP 1286, Pointe-Noire, Congo, Republic. TEL 242-94-02-38, FAX 242-94-39-81.

551.46 MCO ISSN 0304-5722
CODEN: BULCAA
INSTITUT OCEANOGRAPHIQUE. BULLETIN. Text in English, French. 1904. irreg., latest vol.76, no.1444, 1999. price varies. illus. back issues avail. **Document type:** *Bulletin.*
Description: Monographic studies on taxonomy of marine animals. Catalogues of the oceanographic museum collection.
Related titles: ♦ Supplement(s): Institut Oceonographique. Bulletin. Numero Special. ISSN 1606-1160.
Indexed: ASFA, B&BAb, BIOSIS Prev, BiolAb, ESPM, IBR, M&GPA, MBA, RefZh, SFA, WildRev, ZooRec.
—BLDSC (2574.000000), CISTI, ingenta, KNAW, Linda Hall.
Published by: Musee Oceanographique, Service des Publications, Av. Saint-Martin, Monte Carlo, MC 98000, Monaco. TEL 377-93-15-36-00, FAX 377-93-50-52-97, mcmobiblio@meditnet.com.

551.46 MCO ISSN 0304-5714
CODEN: MIOGA6
INSTITUT OCEANOGRAPHIQUE. MEMOIRES. Text in English, French. 1970. irreg., latest vol.19, 1999. price varies. illus. back issues avail. **Document type:** *Monographic series.*
Description: Monographic studies on taxonomy of marine animals.
Indexed: ASFA, BiolAb, ESPM, M&GPA, PollutAb, RefZh, SFA, WildRev, ZooRec.
—CINDOC, KNAW.
Published by: Musee Oceanographique, Service des Publications, Av. Saint-Martin, Monte Carlo, MC 98000, Monaco. TEL 377-93-15-36-00, FAX 377-93-50-52-97, mcmobiblio@meditnet.com. Circ: 850.

551.46 MCO ISSN 1606-1160
INSTITUT OCEONOGRAPHIQUE. BULLETIN. NUMERO SPECIAL. Text in English, French. 1962. irreg., latest vol.19, 1999. price varies. **Document type:** *Monographic series, Academic/Scholarly.*
Related titles: ♦ Supplement to: Institut Oceanographique. Bulletin. ISSN 0304-5722.
Indexed: BiolAb, ZooRec.
Published by: (Institut Oceanographique, Fondation Albert - 1er Prince de Monaco FRA), Musee Oceanographique, Service des Publications, Av. Saint-Martin, Monte Carlo, MC 98000, Monaco.

551.4 BGR
GC1 CODEN: OKEADB
INSTITUT PO OKEANOLOGIIA. TRUDOVE/INSTITUTE OF OCEANOLOGY. PROCEEDINGS. Text in Bulgarian. 1975. irreg. BGL 500, USD 6.50 per issue (effective 1999). reprint service avail. from IRC. **Document type:** *Academic/Scholarly.*
Formerly (until 1992): Okeanologiia (0324-0878)
Indexed: BSLBiol, ChemAb, CurCont, RefZh.
—CASDDS, Linda Hall.
Published by: Bulgarska Akademiya na Naukite, Institut po Okeanologiia, PO Box 152, Varna, 9000, Bulgaria. TEL 359-52-774256, 359-52-370484, FAX 359-52-370483, http://www.io-bas.bg/products/publications.htm. Ed. Veliko Dachev. Circ: 300.

551.46 HRV ISSN 0561-6360
CODEN: IORBA4
INSTITUT ZA OCEANOGRAFIJU I RIBARSTVO SPLIT. BILJESKE/INSTITUTE OF OCEANOGRAPHY AND FISHERIES SPLIT. NOTES. Text in English. 1951. irreg. **Document type:** *Monographic series, Academic/Scholarly.*
Indexed: ASFA, ESPM, ZooRec.
—BLDSC (2060.250000).
Published by: Institut za Oceanografiju i Ribarstvo/Institute of Oceanography and Fisheries, Setaliste Ivana Mestrovica 63, Split, 21000, Croatia. TEL 385-21-358688, FAX 385-21-358650, office@izor.hr, http://www.izor.hr.

578.77 ESP ISSN 1136-193X
INSTITUTO CANARIO DE CIENCIAS MARINAS. INFORMES TECNICOS. Text in Spanish. 1996. irreg.
Indexed: ESPM, IECT.
—CINDOC, CISTI.
Published by: Instituto Canario de Ciencias Marinas, Apdo. de Correso, 56, Telde, Canarias 35200, Spain. TEL 34-928-132900, FAX 34-928-132908, http://neptuno.iccm.rcanaria.es/.

551.46 ESP ISSN 1578-410X
INSTITUTO ESPANOL DE OCEANOGRAFiA. TESIS DOCTORALES. Text in Spanish; Abstracts in English. 1994. irreg. price varies. **Document type:** *Monographic series.*
Formerly (until 2000): Instituto Espanol de Oceanografia. Microfichas (1135-8491)
Media: CD-ROM.
Indexed: ASFA, ESPM, GEOBASE, OceAb, SFA.
—Linda Hall.
Published by: Instituto Espanol de Oceanografia, Avda Brasil, 31, Madrid, 28020, Spain. TEL 34-1-5974443, FAX 34-1-5974770. Ed. Concha Mosquera de Arancibia. R&P Juan Jose Garcia Garzon TEL 34-1-3475543. **Dist. by:** Centro de Publicaciones, Ministerio de Agricultura, Pesca y Alimentacion, Paseo Infanta Isabel, 1, Madrid 28014, Spain. TEL 34-1-3475551, FAX 34-1-3475722.

551.46 ESP ISSN 0074-0195
GC1 CODEN: BOEA3
INSTITUTO ESPANOL DE OCEANOGRAFIA. BOLETIN. Text in English, Spanish; Abstracts in Multiple languages. 1948. s-a. price varies. **Document type:** *Bulletin.* **Description:** Dedicated to the marine sciences and oceanography.
Indexed: ASFA, BIOSIS Prev, BiolAb, ESPM, FLUIDEX, GEOBASE, IECT, RefZh, SFA, WildRev, ZooRec.
—BLDSC (2171.000000), CINDOC, IE, ingenta, Linda Hall.
Published by: Instituto Espanol de Oceanografia, Avda Brasil, 31, Madrid, 28020, Spain. TEL 34-1-5974443, FAX 34-1-5974770. Ed. Concha Mosquera de Arancibia. R&P Juan Jose Garcia Garzon TEL 34-1-3475543. **Distr. by:** Centro de Publicaciones, Ministerio de Agricultura, Pesca y Alimentacion, Paseo Infanta Isabel, 1, Madrid 28014, Spain. TEL 34-1-3475551, FAX 34-1-3475722.

551.46 ESP ISSN 0212-1565
CODEN: ITIOE3
INSTITUTO ESPANOL DE OCEANOGRAFIA. INFORMES TECNICOS. Text in English, Spanish; Abstracts in Multiple languages. 1982. irreg. price varies. **Document type:** *Monographic series.*
Indexed: ASFA, ESPM, GEOBASE, IECT.
—CINDOC.
Published by: Instituto Espanol de Oceanografia, Avda Brasil, 31, Madrid, 28020, Spain. TEL 34-1-5974443, FAX 34-1-5974770. Ed. Concha Mosquera de Arancibia. R&P Juan Jose Garcia Garzon TEL 34-1-3475543. **Dist. by:** Centro de Publicaciones, Ministerio de Agricultura, Pesca y Alimentacion, Paseo Infanta Isabel, 1, Madrid 28014, Spain. TEL 34-1-3475551, FAX 34-1-3475722.

551.46 ESP ISSN 0214-7378
CODEN: PEIOE9
INSTITUTO ESPANOL DE OCEANOGRAFIA. PUBLICACIONES ESPECIALES. Text in English, Spanish; Abstracts in Multiple languages. 1988. irreg. price varies. **Document type:** *Monographic series.*
Indexed: ASFA, BIOSIS Prev, ESPM, IABS, IECT, SFA, WildRev, ZooRec.
Published by: Instituto Espanol de Oceanografia, Avda Brasil, 31, Madrid, 28020, Spain. TEL 34-1-5974443, FAX 34-1-5974770. Ed. Concha Mosquera de Arancibia. R&P Juan Jose Garcia Garzon TEL 34-1-3475543. **Dist. by:** Centro de Publicaciones, Ministerio de Agricultura, Pesca y Alimentacion, Paseo Infanta Isabel, 1, Madrid 28014, Spain. TEL 34-1-3475551, FAX 34-1-3475722.

551.46 VEN ISSN 0798-0639
CODEN: BOVOEO
➤ **INSTITUTO OCEANOGRAFICO DE VENEZUELA. BOLETIN.** Key Title: Boletin del Instituto Oceanografico de Venezuela. Text in Spanish, English; Abstracts in English, Spanish. 1961. s-a. VEB 8,500, USD 15 (effective 2003). adv. bk.rev. abstr.; bibl.; charts; illus. 100 p./no.; back issues avail. **Document type:** *Bulletin, Academic/Scholarly.* **Description:** Covers studies on the Caribbean Sea and Atlantic Ocean.
Formerly (until 1983): Universidad de Oriente. Instituto Oceanografico. Boletin (0020-417X)
Indexed: ASFA, BiolAb, ESPM, SFA, SWRA, WRCInf, WildRev, ZooRec.
—CASDDS, CISTI, Linda Hall.
Published by: (Biblioteca), Universidad de Oriente, Instituto Oceanografico de Venezuela, Avenida Universidad, Cerro Colorado, Apartado 80, Cumana, Sucre 6101A, Venezuela. TEL 58-293-302156, FAX 58-293-512276, jeiovudo@sucre.udo.edu.ve, http://www.udo.edu.ve. Ed., R&P Juan Pablo Blanco Rambla TEL 58-293-4302156. Circ: 1,000.

➤ **INSTYTUT METEOROLOGII I GOSPODARKI WODNEJ. GAZETA OBSERWATORA/JOURNAL OF I M W M OBSERVER.** see *METEOROLOGY*

➤ **INSTYTUT METEOROLOGII I GOSPODARKI WODNEJ. MATERIALY BADAWCZE. SERIA: HYDROLOGIA I OCEANOLOGIA/INSTITUTE OF METEOROLOGY AND WATER MANAGEMENT. RESEARCH PAPERS. SERIES: HYDROLOGY AND OCEANOLOGY.** see *EARTH SCIENCES—Hydrology*

551.46 POL
INSTYTUT METEOROLOGII I GOSPODARKI WODNEJ. ODDZIAL MORSKI W GDYNI. MATERIALY. WARUNKI SRODOWISKOWE POLSKIEJ STREFY POLUDNIOWEGO BALTYKU. Text in English, Polish. 1987. a. USD 20. charts; illus. **Description:** Covers physics, chemistry and pollution of sea water in the Polish zone of Southern Baltic Sea.
Published by: Instytut Meteorologii i Gospodarki Wodnej, Oddzial Morski w Gdyni/Institute of Meteorology and Water Management, Maritime Branch in Gdynia, Ul Waszyngtona 42, Gdynia, 81342, Poland. TEL 4858-205221, FAX 4858-201641. Circ: 120.

551.46 POL
INSTYTUT METEOROLOGII I GOSPODARKI WODNEJ. ODDZIAL MORSKI W GDYNI. MATERIALY. ZLODZENIE POLSKIEJ STREFY PRZYBRZEZNEJ. Text in English, Polish. 1987. a. USD 20. illus.; maps. **Description:** Covers ice-conditions in the Polish coastal zone of the Baltic Sea.
Published by: Instytut Meteorologii i Gospodarki Wodnej, Oddzial Morski w Gdyni/Institute of Meteorology and Water Management, Maritime Branch in Gdynia, Ul Waszyngtona 42, Gdynia, 81342, Poland. TEL 4858-20701, FAX 4858-201641. Ed. Alicja Wisniewska Michalska. Circ: 120.

641.392 USA ISSN 1532-7337
SH351.T8
INTER-AMERICAN TROPICAL TUNA COMMISSION. STOCK ASSESSMENT REPORT. Text in English, Spanish. 2001. a. price varies. abstr.; charts; maps; stat. back issues avail. **Document type:** *Bulletin, Academic/Scholarly.*
Indexed: ASFA, ESPM, OceAb, ZooRec.
—Linda Hall.
Published by: Inter-American Tropical Tuna Commission, 8604 La Jolla Shores Dr, La Jolla, CA 92037-1508. TEL 858-546-7100, FAX 858-546-7133, wbaylife@lattc.ucsd.edu, http://www.iattc.org/StockAssessmentReport2000ENG.htm. Ed. William H Bayliff. Circ: 1,200 (controlled).

551.46 USA
INTERCOAST NETWORK; international newsletter of coastal management. Text in English. 3/yr. **Document type:** *Newsletter.*
Related titles: Online - full text ed.
Published by: University of Rhode Island, Coastal Resources Center, Narragansett Bay Campus, Narragansett, RI 02882. TEL 401-874-6870, FAX 401-789-4670, http://www.crc.uri.edu/comm/htmlpubs/ic/. **Co-sponsor:** U.S. Agency for International Development.

551.46 FRA ISSN 1020-4040
INTERGOVERNMENTAL OCEANOGRAPHIC COMMISSION. ANNUAL REPORT. Variant title: I O C Annual Report Series. Text in English. a. **Description:** Provides an overview of the commission's activities for the previous year.
Related titles: Online - full text ed.; French ed.: Commission Oceanographique Intergouvernementale. Rapport Annuel. ISSN 1020-4032.
Published by: (Intergovernmental Oceanographic Commission USA), UNESCO Publishing, 7 place de Fontenoy, Paris, 75352, France. FAX 33-1-45685737, http://ioc.unesco.org/iocweb/default.htm, http://www.unesco.org/publishing, http://www.unesco.org/ioc.

551.46 628.5 FRA ISSN 0251-6020
INTERGOVERNMENTAL OCEANOGRAPHIC COMMISSION. MANUALS AND GUIDES. Text in English. 1974. 3/w. **Document type:** *Monographic series.*

E

Published by: (Intergovernmental Oceanographic Commission USA), UNESCO Publishing, 7 place de Fontenoy, Paris, 75352, France. FAX 33-1-45685737, http://ioc.unesco.org/iocweb/IOCpub/elibmg.htm, http://www.unesco.org/publishing.

551.46 FRA ISSN 0074-1175
INTERGOVERNMENTAL OCEANOGRAPHIC COMMISSION. TECHNICAL SERIES. Text in English. 1965. irreg., latest vol.53, 1998. price varies.
Related titles: French ed.: Commission Oceanographique Intergouvernementale. Serie Technique. ISSN 0251-9607; Russian ed.: Mezpravitel'stvennaja Okeanograficeskaja Komissija. Mehaniceskaja Serija. ISSN 0251-9593; Spanish ed.: Comision Oceanografica Intergubernamental. Coleccion Tecnica. ISSN 0538-3900.
Indexed: ASFA, BiolAb, ESPM.
—BLDSC (8726.150000), CISTI, IE, ingenta, Linda Hall.
Published by: (Environment and Development in Coastal Regions and in Small Islands), UNESCO Publishing, 7 place de Fontenoy, Paris, 75352, France. TEL 33-1-45683982, h.guillemain@unesco.org, http://ioc.unesco.org/iocweb/IOCpub/IOCpub.htm, http://www.unesco.org/ioc. **Dist. in U.S. by:** Bernan Associates, Bernan, 4611-F Assembly Dr., Lanham, MD 20706-4391.

551.46 FRA ISSN 1014-2568
INTERGOVERNMENTAL OCEANOGRAPHIC COMMISSION. TRAINING COURSE REPORTS. Text in English. 1982. irreg.
Published by: (Intergovernmental Oceanographic Commission USA), UNESCO Publishing, 7 place de Fontenoy, Paris, 75352, France. FAX 33-1-45685737, http://ioc.unesco.org/iocweb/IOCpub/elibtc.htm, http://www.unesco.org/publishing.

551.46 FRA ISSN 0251-9569
INTERGOVERNMENTAL OCEANOGRAPHIC COMMISSION. WORKSHOP REPORT. Text in English. 1974. irreg. **Document type:** *Monographic series.* **Description:** Includes recommendations, suggested workplans, and scientific papers presented during the workshops.
Published by: (Intergovernmental Oceanographic Commission USA), UNESCO Publishing, 7 place de Fontenoy, Paris, 75352, France. FAX 33-1-45685737, http://ioc.unesco.org/iocweb/IOCpub/elibwr.htm, http://www.unesco.org/publishing.

551.46 USA ISSN 0254-2005
INTERNATIONAL ASSOCIATION FOR THE PHYSICAL SCIENCES OF THE OCEANS. PROCES VERBAUX. Text in English, French. 1934. quadrennial. free. back issues avail. **Document type:** *Proceedings.*
Formerly: International Association for the Physical Science of Oceanography. Proces-Verbaux
Published by: International Association for the Physical Sciences of the Oceans, c/o Dr Fred E Camfield, Box 820440, Vicksburg, MS 39182-0440. TEL 601-636-1363, FAX 601-629-9640, camfield@vicksburg.com, http://www.olympus.net/IAPSO/. Circ: 1,000.

551.46 USA
INTERNATIONAL ASSOCIATION FOR THE PHYSICAL SCIENCES OF THE OCEANS. PUBLICATIONS SCIENTIFIQUES. Text in English. irreg., latest vol.36, 1996. free. **Document type:** *Academic/Scholarly.*
Published by: International Association for the Physical Sciences of the Oceans, c/o Dr Fred E Camfield, Box 820440, Vicksburg, MS 39182-0440. TEL 601-636-1363, FAX 601-629-9640, camfield@vicksburg.com, http://www.olympus.net/IAPSO/.

INTERNATIONAL ASSOCIATION OF AQUATIC AND MARINE SCIENCE LIBRARIES AND INFORMATION CENTERS CONFERENCE SERIES. see *LIBRARY AND INFORMATION SCIENCES*

INTERNATIONAL ASSOCIATION OF THEORETICAL AND APPLIED LIMNOLOGY. PROCEEDINGS/INTERNATIONALE VEREINIGUNG FUER THEORETISCHE UND ANGEWANDTE LIMNOLOGIE. VERHANDLUNGEN. see *EARTH SCIENCES—Hydrology*

INTERNATIONAL CONFERENCE ON OFFSHORE MECHANICS AND ARCTIC ENGINEERING. PROCEEDINGS. see *ENGINEERING—Mechanical Engineering*

551.48 MCO ISSN 0074-6274
INTERNATIONAL HYDROGRAPHIC CONFERENCE. REPORTS OF PROCEEDINGS. Text in English. 1919. quinquennial. reprint service avail. from PQC,ISI. **Document type:** *Proceedings.*
Related titles: French ed.
Published by: International Hydrographic Bureau, 4 quai Antoine 1er, B.P. 445, Monte Carlo, MC 98011 Cedex, Monaco. TEL 377-93108100, FAX 377-93252003, ihb@unice.fr, info@ihb.mc, http://www.iho.shom.fr.

INTERNATIONAL HYDROGRAPHIC ORGANIZATION. ANNUAL REPORT. see *EARTH SCIENCES—Hydrology*

551.46 MCO
INTERNATIONAL HYDROGRAPHIC ORGANIZATION. YEARBOOK. Text in English, French. 1928. a. reprint service avail. from PQC,ISI. **Document type:** *Catalog.*
Formerly: International Hydrographic Bureau. Yearbook (0074-6282)
Indexed: ASFA, ESPM.
Published by: International Hydrographic Bureau, 4 quai Antoine 1er, B.P. 445, Monte Carlo, MC 98011 Cedex, Monaco. TEL 377-93108100, FAX 377-93252003, ihb@unice.fr, info@ihb.mc, http://www.iho.shom.fr. Circ: 550.

INTERNATIONAL JOURNAL OF OFFSHORE AND POLAR ENGINEERING. see *ENGINEERING—Mechanical Engineering*

551.46 MLT
INTERNATIONAL OCEAN INSTITUTE. OCCASIONAL PAPERS. Short title: I O I Occasional Papers. Text in English. 1973. irreg., latest vol.8, 1981. price varies. **Document type:** *Monographic series, Academic/Scholarly.* **Description:** Research papers and commissioned studies on various aspects of international law of the sea and NIED.
Formerly: University of Malta. International Ocean Institute. Occasional Papers
Indexed: ChemAb.
Published by: International Ocean Institute, PO Box 3, Gzira, GZR 01, Malta. TEL 356-346529, FAX 356-346502, ioihq@ioihq.org.mt, http://www.ioist.org. Circ: 200.

551.46 341 MLT
INTERNATIONAL OCEAN INSTITUTE. PACEM IN MARIBUS. PROCEEDINGS. Text in English. 1971. a. price varies. **Document type:** *Proceedings, Academic/Scholarly.* **Description:** Collected papers and discussion of issues under consideration at PIM. Always related to international law and NIED.
Published by: International Ocean Institute, PO Box 3, Gzira, GZR 01, Malta. TEL 356-346529, FAX 356-346502, ioihq@ioihq.org.mt, http://www.ioist.org. Circ: 200.

551.4 623.82 GBR ISSN 1471-0188
TC1501
INTERNATIONAL OCEAN SYSTEMS. Text in English. 1979. bi-m. GBP 80 domestic; USD 195 in United States; GBP 100 elsewhere (effective 2003). adv. bk.rev. 52 p./no.; back issues avail. **Document type:** *Magazine, Trade.* **Description:** Discusses underwater surveying, instrumentation, and ocean data gathering.
Former titles (until 2000): International Ocean Systems Design (1460-4892); (until 1997): International Underwater Systems Design (0267-1085); (until 1991): Underwater System Design
Indexed: ASFA, BMT, FLUIDEX, GEOBASE, OceAb.
—BLDSC (4544.575000), CISTI, IE, Infotrieve, ingenta, Linda Hall.
Published by: Underwater World Publications Ltd., 55 High St, Teddington, Middx TW11 8HA, United Kingdom. TEL 44-20-89434288, FAX 44-20-89434312, astrid@divermag.co.uk, http://www.intoceansys.co.uk. Ed. Daniel Johnson. Pub., Adv. contact Astrid Powell. R&P Nigel Eaton. B&W page USD 1,960, color page USD 2,765; 210 x 297. Circ: 10,250.

INTERNATIONAL OFFSHORE AND POLAR ENGINEERING CONFERENCE. PROCEEDINGS. see *ENGINEERING—Mechanical Engineering*

INTERNATIONAL SEAWEED SYMPOSIUM. PROCEEDINGS. see *BIOLOGY—Botany*

INTERNATIONAL W O C E NEWSLETTER. (World Ocean Circulation Experiment) see *METEOROLOGY*

551 USA ISSN 1067-8174
CODEN: IMMSEK
IRENE MCCULLOCH FOUNDATION. MONOGRAPH SERIES. Text in English. 1992. irreg., latest vol.4, 1999. **Document type:** *Monographic series, Academic/Scholarly.*
Indexed: ASFA, ZooRec.
Published by: (Irene McCulloch Foundation), Hancock Library of Biology and Oceanography, University of Southern California, University Park, Los Angeles, CA 90089-0372. TEL 213-740-7542, FAX 213-740-5142, http://www.usc.edu/isd/locations/science/hancock/.

551.46 RUS ISSN 0368-007X
ISSLEDOVANIYA FAUNY MOREY/EXPLORATIONS OF THE FAUNA OF THE SEAS. Text in Russian. 1961. irreg. **Document type:** *Monographic series, Academic/Scholarly.*
Indexed: ESPM, ZooRec.
—CISTI.
Published by: Rossiiskaya Akademiya Nauk, Zoologicheskii Institut/Russian Academy of Sciences, Zoological Institute, Universitetskaya nab 1, St Petersburg, 199034, Russian Federation. TEL 7-812-3280011, FAX 7-812-3282941, admin@zin.ru, http://www.zin.ru.

ISTITUTO RICERCHE PESCA MARITTIMA. QUADERNI. see *FISH AND FISHERIES*

551.46 ITA ISSN 0082-6456
➤ **ISTITUTO SPERIMENTALE TALASSOGRAFICO DI TRIESTE. PUBBLICAZIONE.** Text in Italian. 1919. irreg., latest vol.700, 1994. per issue exchange basis. **Document type:** *Academic/Scholarly.* **Description:** Reprints of articles prepared by researchers of the institute and published in the journals of different publishers.
—CISTI.
Published by: Consiglio Nazionale delle Ricerche, Istituto Sperimentale Talassografico di Trieste, Viale Romolo Gessi, 2, Trieste, TS 34123, Italy. TEL 39-40-305312, FAX 39-40-308941.

550 551.42 JPN
GC1
J A M S T E C JOURNAL OF DEEP SEA RESEARCH. Text in Japanese; Summaries in English, Japanese. 1985. s-a. JPY 2,000 (effective 2001). **Document type:** *Academic/Scholarly.*
Former titles: J A M S T E C Journal of Deep Sea Research (I) Biology; J A M S T E C Shinkai Kenkyu (1340-7848); (until 1994): Shinkai Shinpojiumu Hokokusho (0918-3221); (until 1992): Shinkai 2000 Kenkyu Sinpojiumu Hokokusho
Related titles: Online - full text ed.
Indexed: ASFA, ESPM, ZooRec.
—BLDSC (4645.862300).
Published by: Japan Marine Science and Technology Center, Scientific Information Service/Kaiyo Kagaku Gijutsu Senta, 2-15 Natsushima-cho, Yokosuka-shi, Kanagawa-ken 237-0061, Japan. TEL 81-468-67-5525, FAX 81-468-66-6169, info@jamstec.go.jp, http://www.jamstec.go.jp. Ed. Toshio Tsuchiya. Circ: 900.

551.46 JPN
J A M S T E C JOURNAL OF DEEP SEA RESEARCH (II) GEOLOGY, GEOCHEMISTRY, GEOPHYSICS AND DIVE SURVEY. Text in Japanese; Summaries in English, Japanese. s-a. JPY 1,200 (effective 2000). **Document type:** *Academic/Scholarly.*
Related titles: Online - full text ed.
Published by: Japan Marine Science and Technology Center, Scientific Information Service/Kaiyo Kagaku Gijutsu Senta, 2-15 Natsushima-cho, Yokosuka-shi, Kanagawa-ken 237-0061, Japan. TEL 81-468-67-5525, FAX 81-468-66-6169, info@jamstec.go.jp, http://www.jamstec.go.jp. Ed. Toshio Tsuchiya.

J G R: JOURNAL OF GEOPHYSICAL RESEARCH. see *EARTH SCIENCES—Geophysics*

551.46 JPN ISSN 1343-0823
J I M S T E F NEWS★. (Japan International Marine Science and Technology Federation) Text in English, Japanese. 1982. q.
Former titles (until 1997): Science and Technology (0914-6105); (until 1987): E C O R. Engineering Committee on Oceanic Resources (0289-7229)
Published by: Kokusai Kaiyo Kagaku Gijutsu Kyokai/Japan International Marine Science and Technology Federation, 1-1-17 Akasaka, Minato-ku, Tokyo, 107-0052, Japan. LEM06031@nifty.ne.jp, http://homepage3.nifty.com/JIMSTEF/.

551.46 JPN
J O D C CATALOGUE. (Japan Oceanographic Data Center) Text in Japanese. 1981. irreg. **Document type:** *Catalog.*
Published by: Maritime Safety Agency Hydrographic Department, Japan Oceanographic Data Center/Kaijo Hoancho Suirobu Nihon Kaiyo Deta Senta, 3-1 Tsuki-Ji 5-chome, Chuo-ku, Tokyo, 104-0045, Japan.

551.46 JPN ISSN 0287-2609
J O D C NEWS. (Japan Oceanographic Data Center) Text in Japanese. 1971. s-a.
Published by: Maritime Safety Agency Hydrographic Department, Japan Oceanographic Data Center/Kaijo Hoancho Suirobu Nihon Kaiyo Deta Senta, 3-1 Tsuki-Ji 5-chome, Chuo-ku, Tokyo, 104-0045, Japan.

J O I D E S JOURNAL. see *PETROLEUM AND GAS*

378 MEX ISSN 0188-4700
QH92.3
JAINA. Text in Spanish. 1990. q. **Document type:** *Journal, Academic/Scholarly.*
Indexed: ESPM.
—Linda Hall.
Published by: Universidad Autonoma de Campeche, Programa de Ecologia, Pesquerias y Oceanografia del Golfo de Mexico, Ave. Agustin Melgar y Juan de la Barrera, Apartado Postal 520, Campeche, 24030, Mexico. FAX 52-981-65954.

JANE'S SEA AND SYSTEMS LIBRARY. see *MILITARY*

627.7005 551.46 GBR ISSN 1464-0805
JANE'S UNDERWATER TECHNOLOGY. Text in English. 1998. a. USD 495 per issue in the Americas for 2001-2002 Ed.; GBP 315 per issue elsewhere for 2001-2002 Ed.; USD 525 per issue in the Americas for 2002-2003 Ed.; GBP 335 per issue elsewhere for 2002-2003 Ed. (effective 2002); 2002-2003 Ed. available Feb/Mar 2002. **Document type:** *Yearbook, Trade.* **Description:** Provides a wealth of up-to-date, accurate information on current underwater technologies around the world, including Europe, North America, Japan, Russia and South Korea.

E

Related titles: CD-ROM ed.: USD 1,305 in the Americas; GBP 815 elsewhere (effective 2002); Online - full text ed.: USD 1,435 in the Americas; GBP 895 elsewhere (effective 2002).
Published by: Jane's Information Group, Sentinel House, 163 Brighton Rd, Coulsdon, Surrey CR5 2YH, United Kingdom. TEL 44-20-87003700, FAX 44-20-87631006, http://catalogue.janes.com/underwatertech.shtml, http://www.janes.com. **Dist. in Asia by:** Jane's Information Group Asia, 60 Albert St, #15-01 Albert Complex, Singapore 189969, Singapore. TEL 65-331-6280, FAX 65-336-9921; **Dist. in Australia by:** Jane's Information Group Australia, PO Box 3502, Rozelle, NSW 2039, Australia. TEL 61-2-8587-7900, FAX 61-2-8587-7901, info@janes.thomson.com.au; **Dist. in the Americas by:** 1340 Braddock Pl, Ste 300, Alexandria, VA 22314-1651. TEL 703-683-3700, 800-824-0768, FAX 703-836-0297, 800-836-0297, info@janes.com.

JANE'S UNDERWATER WARFARE SYSTEMS. see *MILITARY*

551.46 KOR ISSN 1225-5734
JEJU DAEHAGGYO. YEON-GU BO-GO/CHEJU NATIONAL UNIVERSITY. MARINE RESEARCH INSTITUTE. BULLETIN. Text in English, Korean. 1976. a. **Document type:** *Monographic series, Academic/Scholarly.*
Indexed: ESPM.
Published by: Cheju Daehaggyo Haeyang Yeon-guso/Cheju National University, Marine Research Institute, 1 Ara 1-dong, Cheju City, Cheju-do 690-756, Korea, S. TEL 82-64-83-9260, FAX 82-64-83-6066, http://www.cheju.ac.kr.

551.46 FRA ISSN 0397-5347
CODEN: JROCDR
JOURNAL DE RECHERCHE OCEANOGRAPHIQUE. Text in French. 197?. q. EUR 45.73 to individuals; EUR 22.87 to students (effective 2002). **Document type:** *Journal, Academic/Scholarly.*
Formerly (until 1976): Union des Oceanographes de France. Bulletin de Liaison (0398-7531)
Indexed: ESPM, ZooRec.
—CISTI.
Published by: Union des Oceanographes de France, 195 rue Saint-Jacques, Paris, 75005, France. TEL 33-1-46331690, secretariat@uof-assoc.org, http://www.uof-assoc.org/Publications/publicationssommaire.htm.

551.4 CIV ISSN 1018-0354
GC1
JOURNAL IVOIRIEN D'OCEANOLOGIE ET DE LIMNOLOGIE. Text in French; Summaries in English. 19??. q. free. illus. **Document type:** *Journal, Academic/Scholarly.*
Former titles (until 1991): Centre de Recherches Oceanographiques d'Abidjan. Documents Scientifiques (1018-0346); (until 1970): Centre de Recherches Oceanographique Abidjan. Document Scientifique Provisoire (0374-7077)
Indexed: ESPM, SFA, SWRA.
Published by: Centre de Recherches Oceanographiques d'Abidjan, 29, rue des Pecheurs, BP V18, Abidjan, Ivory Coast. TEL 225-355014, FAX 225-351155, abe@cro.ird.ci. Ed. Jacques Abe. Circ: 300.

551.46 GBR ISSN 1741-7538
GC190
➤ **JOURNAL OF ATMOSPHERIC AND OCEAN SCIENCE.** Text in English. 1986. q. GBP 615, USD 903 combined subscription to institutions print & online eds. (effective 2006). illus. back issues avail.; reprint service avail. from PSC. **Document type:** *Journal, Academic/Scholarly.*
Former titles: The Global Atmosphere and Ocean System (1023-6732); (until 1995): Atmosphere - Ocean System (1063-7184); (until 1993): Ocean - Air Interactions (0743-0876)
Related titles: CD-ROM ed.: ISSN 1026-7514. 1995; Microfilm ed.; Online - full text ed.: ISSN 1741-7546. GBP 584, USD 858 to institutions (effective 2006) (from EBSCO Publishing, Gale Group, IngentaConnect, O C L C Online Computer Library Center, Inc., Swets Information Services).
Indexed: ASFA, EPB, ESPM, GEOBASE, IAA, M&GPA, OceAb, PollutAb, SWRA.
—BLDSC (4195.350150), CISTI, IE, ingenta. **CCC.**
Published by: Taylor & Francis Ltd (Subsidiary of: Taylor & Francis Group), 4 Park Sq, Milton Park, Abingdon, OX14 4RN, United Kingdom. TEL 44-1235-828600, FAX 44-1235-829000, info@tandf.co.uk, http://www.tandf.co.uk/journals/titles/17417538.asp. Ed. Dr. Neil C Wells. **Subscr. to:** Journals Customer Service, Rankine Rd, Basingstoke, Hants RG24 8PR, United Kingdom. TEL 44-1256-813000, FAX 44-1256-330245.

➤ **JOURNAL OF ATMOSPHERIC AND OCEANIC TECHNOLOGY.** see *METEOROLOGY*

613.7 551.46 USA ISSN 0749-0208
GB450 CODEN: JCRSEK
➤ **JOURNAL OF COASTAL RESEARCH**; an international forum for the littoral sciences. Text in English. 1985. q. USD 85 domestic to members; USD 95 foreign to members; USD 70 domestic to students; USD 80 foreign to students (effective 2005). adv. bk.rev. bibl.; charts; illus.; stat. index. back issues avail.; reprints avail. **Document type:** *Journal, Academic/Scholarly.* **Description:** Dedicated to all aspects of coastal (marine) research. Encourages the dissemination of knowledge and understanding of the coastal zone by promoting cooperation and communication between specialists in various disciplines.
Formerly (until 1984): Litoralia (0742-6054)
Related titles: Online - full text ed.: ISSN 1551-5036 (from BioOne, C S A, EBSCO Publishing, Gale Group, H.W. Wilson, O C L C Online Computer Library Center, Inc.); ♦ Special ed(s).: Journal of Coastal Research. Special Issue.
Indexed: AS&TI, ASCA, ASFA, AgBio, AnBrAb, BIOBASE, BIOSIS Prev, BiolAb, BiolDig, BrCerAb, C&ISA, CPA, CRFR, CerAb, CivEngAb, CorrAb, CurCont, E&CAJ, EMA, EPB, ESPM, EnvEAb, ExcerpMed, FLUIDEX, ForAb, GEOBASE, HerbAb, I&DA, IAA, IABS, ISR, Inspec, M&GPA, M&TEA, MBF, METADEX, MSCT, OceAb, PBA, PGegResA, PollutAb, RA&MP, RRTA, RefZh, S&F, SCI, SPPI, SSCI, SWRA, SeedAb, SolStAb, WAA, WAE&RSA, WeedAb, ZooRec.
—BLDSC (4958.793700), AskIEEE, CISTI, IDS, IE, Infotrieve, ingenta, Linda Hall. **CCC.**
Published by: Coastal Education & Research Foundation, Inc., PO Box 210187, Royal Palm Beach, FL 33421-0187. TEL 561-391-8102, FAX 561-391-9116, cfinkl@gate.net, http://www.cerf-jcr.com. Ed. Charles W Finkl Jr. Adv. contact Karen Hickey. Circ: 1,500. **Subscr. to:** Allen Press Inc., PO Box 1897, Lawrence, KS 66044.

613.7 551.46 USA
JOURNAL OF COASTAL RESEARCH. SPECIAL ISSUE. Text in English. 1986. irreg. price varies.
Related titles: ♦ Special ed. of: Journal of Coastal Research. ISSN 0749-0208.
Published by: Coastal Education & Research Foundation, Inc., PO Box 210187, Royal Palm Beach, FL 33421-0187. cfinkl@gate.net, http://www.cerf-jcr.com. Ed. Charles W Finkl Jr. **Subscr. to:** Allen Press Inc., PO Box 1897, Lawrence, KS 66044. TEL 785-843-1235, FAX 785-843-1274.

551.46 IND ISSN 0970-9967
GC1
➤ **JOURNAL OF MARINE AND ATMOSPHERIC RESEARCH**; a multidisciplinary journal in marine and atmospheric sciences. Text in English. 1963. q. INR 100, USD 30 to individuals; INR 500, USD 200 to institutions (effective 2000). back issues avail. **Document type:** *Academic/Scholarly.*
Former titles (until 1988): University of Cochin. School of Marine Sciences. Bulletin (0970-9886); (until 1986): University of Cochin. Department of Marine Sciences. Bulletin (0970-9878); (until 1973): University of Cochin. Department of Marine Biology and Oceanography. Bulletin (0970-986X); (until 1971): University of Kerala. Central Research Institute. Bulletin, Series C
Indexed: ASFA.
Published by: Cochin University of Science and Technology, School of Marine Sciences, Fine Arts Ave., Cochin, Kerala 682 016, India. Ed. N R Menon. Circ: 200.

➤ **JOURNAL OF MARINE ENVIRONMENTAL ENGINEERING.** see *ENVIRONMENTAL STUDIES*

551.46 USA ISSN 0022-2402
GC1 CODEN: JMMRAO
➤ **JOURNAL OF MARINE RESEARCH.** Text in English. 1937. bi-m. USD 60 to individuals; USD 140 to institutions (effective 2004). abstr.; bibl.; charts; illus. index, cum.index every 5 yrs. back issues avail.; reprints avail. **Document type:** *Journal, Academic/Scholarly.*
Related titles: Microform ed.: (from PMC, PQC); Online - full text ed.: ISSN 1543-9542 (from EBSCO Publishing, Gale Group, IngentaConnect).
Indexed: ASCA, ASFA, ApMecR, B&AI, B&BAb, BiolAb, CIN, CRFR, CTO, ChemAb, ChemTitl, CivEngAb, CurCont, EPB, ESPM, ExcerpMed, FLUIDEX, GEOBASE, GSI, ISR, M&GPA, OceAb, PetrolAb, PollutAb, SCI, SFA, SPPI, SWRA, WildRev, ZooRec.
—BLDSC (5012.000000), CASDDS, CISTI, IDS, IE, Infotrieve, ingenta, Linda Hall.
Published by: Sears Foundation for Marine Research, Kline Geology Laboratory, Yale University, Box 208109, New Haven, CT 06520-8109. TEL 203-432-3154, jmr@yale.edu, http://www.geology.yale.edu/~jmr/. Ed. George Veronis. Circ: 1,000.

551.46 620 JPN ISSN 0948-4280
GC1000 CODEN: JMATF9
➤ **JOURNAL OF MARINE SCIENCE AND TECHNOLOGY.** Text in English. 1996. q. (in 1 vol., 4 nos./vol.). EUR 178 combined subscription to institutions print & online eds. (effective 2005). reprint service avail. from PSC. **Document type:** *Journal, Academic/Scholarly.* **Description:** Discusses current topics in marine science technology, both research and developments.
Related titles: Online - full text ed.: ISSN 1437-8213 (from EBSCO Publishing, Springer LINK, Swets Information Services).
Indexed: ASFA, BMT, CurCont, ESPM, EngInd, M&TEA, OceAb.
—BLDSC (5012.031000), CISTI, IE, Infotrieve, ingenta, Linda Hall. **CCC.**
Published by: (Society of Naval Architects of Japan), Springer-Verlag Tokyo (Subsidiary of: Springer Science+Business Media), 3-13 Hongo 3-chome, Bunkyo-ku, Tokyo, 113-0033, Japan. TEL 81-3-38120331, FAX 81-3-38187454, http://link.springer.de/link/service/journals/00773/index.htm, http://www.springer-tokyo.co.jp/. Ed. Hideaki Miyata. Adv. contact Stephan Kroeck TEL 49-30-827875739. **Subscr. in the Americas to:** Springer-Verlag New York, Inc., Journal Fulfillment, PO Box 2485, Secaucus, NJ 07096-2485. TEL 800-777-4643, 201-348-4033, FAX 201-348-4505, journals@springer-ny.com, http://www.springer-ny.com; **Subscr. to:** Springer GmbH Auslieferungsgesellschaft, Haberstr 7, Heidelberg 69126, Germany. TEL 49-6221-345-0, FAX 49-6221-345-4229, subscriptions@springer.de.

551.46 TWN ISSN 1023-2796
JOURNAL OF MARINE SCIENCE AND TECHNOLOGY. Text in English. 1993. q. **Document type:** *Journal, Academic/Scholarly.*
Related titles: Online - full content ed.
—BLDSC (5012.030500).
Published by: National Taiwan Ocean University, 2, Pei-Ning Rd, Keelung, 20224, Taiwan. TEL 886-2-2462-2192 ext 5116, FAX 886-2-2462-0106, b0037@mail.ntou.edu.tw, po@mail.ntou.edu.tw, http://140.121.155.217/marine/1024.htm, http://www.ntou.ed.tw. Ed. K K Lee, Email: b0092@mail.ntou.edu.tw. Pub. R R Hwang.

551.46 363.7 GBR
▼ **JOURNAL OF MARINE SCIENCE & THE ENVIRONMENT.** Variant title: Proceedings of the Institute of Marine Engineering, Science and Technology. Text in English. 2003 (Dec.). s-a. **Document type:** *Proceedings, Academic/Scholarly.*
Published by: Institute of Marine Engineering, Science and Technology, 80 Coleman St, London, EC2R 5BJ, United Kingdom. TEL 44-20-73822600, FAX 44-20-73822670, info@imarest.org, http://www.imarest.org/proceedings/. Ed. Richard Allen.

551.46 NLD ISSN 0924-7963
GC1 CODEN: JMASE5
➤ **JOURNAL OF MARINE SYSTEMS.** Text in English. 1990. 20/yr. EUR 2,160 in Europe to institutions; JPY 286,800 in Japan to institutions; USD 2,417 elsewhere to institutions (effective 2006). adv. bk.rev. charts; illus. back issues avail.; reprints avail. **Document type:** *Journal, Academic/Scholarly.* **Description:** Aims to provide a medium of exchange for those engaged in marine research where there exists an interplay between geology, chemistry, biology, and physics.
Related titles: Microform ed.: (from PQC); Online - full text ed.: (from EBSCO Publishing, Gale Group, IngentaConnect, ScienceDirect, Swets Information Services).
Indexed: ASCA, ASFA, BIOBASE, CurCont, EPB, ESPM, EngInd, EnvAb, FLUIDEX, GEOBASE, HelmAb, I&DA, IABS, ISR, Inspec, M&GPA, MSCT, OceAb, PollutAb, RefZh, RevApplEntom, S&F, SCI, SFA, SWRA, ZooRec.
—BLDSC (5012.033000), CISTI, Ei, IDS, IE, Infotrieve, ingenta. **CCC.**
Published by: (European Association of Marine Sciences and Techniques), Elsevier BV (Subsidiary of: Elsevier Science & Technology), Radarweg 29, Amsterdam, 1043 NX, Netherlands. TEL 31-20-4853911, FAX 31-20-4852457, J.Marine.Systems@misc.ulg.ac.be, nlinfo-f@elsevier.nl, http://www.elsevier.com/locate/jmarsys, http://www.elsevier.nl. Eds. J L Largier, W Fennel.

551.46 JPN ISSN 0387-5504
VM4
JOURNAL OF NAVAL ARCHITECTURE AND OCEAN ENGINEERING. Text in English. 1968. a. JPY 4,000 per issue (effective 2005). **Document type:** *Journal, Academic/Scholarly.* **Description:** Cover all aspects of naval architecture and ocean engineering, including fluid dynamics, strength of structure, welding materials, and equipment.
Formerly: Journal of the Society of Naval Architects of Japan. Selected Papers
Indexed: EngInd.
—CISTI, Linda Hall. **CCC.**
Published by: Nihon Zosen Gakkai/Society of Naval Architects of Japan, 1Hamamatsucho Yazaki White Bldg., 2-12-9 Shibadaimon, Minato-ku, Tokyo, 105-0012, Japan. TEL 81-3-34382014, FAX 81-3-34382016, info@snaj.or.jp, http://www.snaj.or.jp/.

551.46 NLD ISSN 0916-8370
GC1 CODEN: JOOCE7
➤ **JOURNAL OF OCEANOGRAPHY.** Text in English. 1941. bi-m. EUR 638, USD 648, GBP 425 combined subscription to institutions print & online eds. (effective 2005). adv. bk.rev. abstr.; charts; illus.; maps. index. reprint service avail. from PSC. **Document type:** *Journal, Academic/Scholarly.* **Description:** Publishes original research papers on all aspects of oceanography: physical, chemical, biological, theoretical, applied, fisheries, palaeo-, or geological.
Supersedes in part (in 1992): Oceanographical Society of Japan. Journal (0029-8131)

E

▼ new title ➤ refereed ✶ unverified ♦ full entry avail.

Related titles: Online - full text ed.: ISSN 1573-868X (from EBSCO Publishing, Gale Group, IngentaConnect, Kluwer Online, O C L C Online Computer Library Center, Inc., Springer LINK, Swets Information Services).
Indexed: ASFA, BibLing, BiolAb, CIN, ChemAb, ChemTitl, CurCont, ESPM, FLUIDEX, GEOBASE, INIS AtomInd, M&GPA, OceAb, PollutAb, RefZh, SFA, SWRA, ZooRec.
—BLDSC (5026.151000), CASDDS, CISTI, IE, Infotrieve, ingenta, Linda Hall. **CCC.**
Published by: Springer-Verlag Dordrecht (Subsidiary of: Springer Science+Business Media), Van Godewijckstraat 30, Dordrecht, 3311 GX, Netherlands. TEL 31-78-6576050, FAX 31-78-6576474, http://springerlink.metapress.com/openurl.asp?genre=journal&issn=0916-8370, http://www.springeronline.com. Ed. K Hanawa. Circ: 2,100.

551.46 USA ISSN 0022-3670
GC1 CODEN: JPYOBT
➤ **JOURNAL OF PHYSICAL OCEANOGRAPHY.** Text in English. 1971. m. USD 428 to institutions; USD 503 combined subscription to institutions print & online eds. (effective 2005). adv. abstr.; bibl.; charts; illus.; stat. index. back issues avail.; reprints avail. **Document type:** *Journal, Academic/Scholarly.*
Description: Publishes research related to the physics of the ocean and of the processes operating at its boundaries.
Related titles: Online - full text ed.: ISSN 1520-0485. Online available upon request (from bigchalk, EBSCO Publishing, Northern Light Technology, Inc., O C L C Online Computer Library Center, Inc., ProQuest Information & Learning).
Indexed: ASCA, ASFA, ApMecR, BiolAb, BiolDig, CCMJ, CMCI, ChemAb, CurCont, EPB, ESPM, EngInd, FLUIDEX, GEOBASE, IAA, ISR, Inspec, M&GPA, MathR, MathSciNet, OceAb, PetrolAb, RefZh, SCI, SPPI, SWRA.
—BLDSC (5036.210000), AskIEEE, CISTI, Ei, IDS, IE, Infotrieve, ingenta, Linda Hall. **CCC.**
Published by: American Meteorological Society, 45 Beacon St, Boston, MA 02108. FAX 617-742-8718, amsinfo@ametsoc.org, http://ams.allenpress.com. Ed. Peter Muller. R&P Melissa Weston TEL 617-227-2426. Adv. contact Mary McMahon. Circ: 1,397. **Subscr. to:** Allen Press Inc., PO Box 1897, Lawrence, KS 66044. http://www.allenpress.com.

➤ **JOURNAL OF PLANKTON RESEARCH.** see *BIOLOGY*

578.77 NLD ISSN 1385-1101
GC1 CODEN: JSREFN
➤ **JOURNAL OF SEA RESEARCH.** Text in English. 1961. 8/yr. EUR 547 in Europe to institutions; JPY 72,500 in Japan to institutions; USD 613 elsewhere to institutions; EUR 124 in Europe to qualified personnel; JPY 16,600 in Japan to qualified personnel; USD 139 elsewhere to qualified personnel (effective 2006). back issues avail. **Document type:** *Journal, Academic/Scholarly.* **Description:** Contains papers on marine research with an emphasis on non-applied aspects, as well as contributions to the understanding of the functioning of marine ecosystems, including abiotic aspects.
Formerly (until vol.35, 1996): Netherlands Journal of Sea Research (0077-7579)
Related titles: Online - full text ed.: (from EBSCO Publishing, Gale Group, IngentaConnect, ScienceDirect, Swets Information Services).
Indexed: ASCA, ASFA, BIOBASE, BIOSIS Prev, BiolAb, CIN, CRFR, CTO, ChemAb, ChemTitl, CurCont, EIA, ESPM, EnvAb, EnvInd, ExcerpMed, GEOBASE, IABS, ISR, M&GPA, OceAb, RefZh, SCI, SFA, ZooRec.
—BLDSC (5062.400000), CASDDS, CIS, CISTI, IDS, IE, Infotrieve, ingenta, Linda Hall. **CCC.**
Published by: (Netherlands Institute for Sea Research/ Nederlands Instituut voor Onderzoek der Zee), Elsevier BV (Subsidiary of: Elsevier Science & Technology), Radarweg 29, Amsterdam, 1043 NX, Netherlands. TEL 31-20-4853911, FAX 31-20-4852457, nlinfo-f@elsevier.nl, http://www.elsevier.com/locate/seares, http://www.elsevier.nl. Eds. C. J.M. Philippart, J J Beukema. Circ: 600.

➤ **K W M NEWSLETTER**; the quarterly journal of the kendall whaling museum. see *MUSEUMS AND ART GALLERIES*

551.46 USA
KA PILI KAI. Text in English. 1979. q. free. bk.rev. **Document type:** *Journal, Academic/Scholarly.*
Former titles (until 2004): Makai (0745-2896); University of Hawaii. Sea Grant College Program. Sea Grant Newsletter
Indexed: EnvAb, SFA.
Published by: University of Hawaii, Sea Grant College Program, Communications Office, 2525 Correa Rd., HIG 238, Honolulu, HI 96822. FAX 808-956-3014, uhsgcomm@hawaii.edu, http://www.soest.hawaii.edu/seagrant/communication/kapilikai/kapilikai.html, http://www.soest.hawaii.edu/SEAGRANT/. Circ: 2,000.

551.46 JPN
KAIGAN SHOKO KENCHI SENTA CHOI NENPO/COAST RISE AND FALL SURVEY CENTER. ANNUAL TIDAL OBSERVATIONS. Text in Japanese. 1967. a.
Published by: Kokudo Chiriin/Geographical Survey Institute, Ministry of Construction, 1 Kita-Sato, Tsukuba-shi, Ibaraki-ken 305-0811, Japan.

551.46 JPN ISSN 1346-5066
KAIJOU GIJUTSU ANZEN KENKYUUJO HOUKOKU/NATIONAL MARITIME RESEARCH INSTITUTE. PAPERS. Text in English. 2002. irreg. **Document type:** *Journal, Academic/Scholarly.*
Indexed: RefZh.
—BLDSC (6390.585000), Linda Hall.
Published by: Kaijou Gijutsu Anzen Kenkyuujo/National Maritime Research Institute, 6-38-1, Shinkawa, Mitaka-shi, Tokyo, 181-0004, Japan. TEL 81-422-413005, FAX 81-422-413247, info@nmri.go.jp, http://www.nmri.go.jp/index.html.

KAISHO NENPO/ANNUAL REPORT OF MARITIME METEOROLOGY. see *METEOROLOGY*

551 JPN ISSN 0472-4666
KAISHO TO KISHO/OCEANOGRAPHY AND METEOROLOGY. Text in English, Japanese. 1947. irreg.
Indexed: ASFA.
Published by: Kishocho, Nagasaki Kaiyo Kishodai/Japan Meteorological Agency, Nagasaki Marine Observatory, 11-51 Minami-Yamate-Machi, Nagasaki-shi, Nagasaki-ken 850-0931, Japan.

551.46 JPN ISSN 0915-2997
➤ **KAIYO CHOSA GIJUTSU/JAPAN SOCIETY FOR MARINE SURVEYS AND TECHNOLOGY. JOURNAL.** Text in Japanese; Summaries in English. 1989. s-a. adv. **Document type:** *Academic/Scholarly.* **Description:** R&D on marine surveys and their technical development.
Published by: Kaiyo Chosa Gijutsu Gakkai/Japan Society for Marine Surveys and Technology, Nihon Suiro Kyokai, 3-1 Tsuki-Ji 5-chome, Chuo-ku, Tokyo, 104-0045, Japan. TEL 81-3-3545-6255, FAX 81-3-3545-6255. Ed. Yoshio Iwabuchi. Circ: 800.

551.46 JPN
KAIYO CHOSA YOHO/DATA RECORD OF OCEANOGRAPHIC OBSERVATIONS. Text in English. biennial.
Indexed: RefZh.
Published by: Hokkaidoritsu Chuo Suisan Shikenjo/Hokkaido Central Fisheries Experimental Station, 238 Hamanaka-cho, Yoichi-gun, Yoichi-cho, Hokkaido 046-0021, Japan.

551.46 JPN
KAIYO ENKAKU TANSA. KAIYO RIMOTO SENSHINGU GIJUTSU NO KENKYU. KENKYU SEIKASHU/REPORT OF MARINE REMOTE SENSING TECHNIQUE. Text in Japanese. a.
Published by: (Kenkyu Kaihatsukyoku), Kagaku Gijiutsu-cho/Science and Technology Agency, 2-1 Kasumigaseki 2-chome, Chiyoda-ku, Tokyo, 100-0013, Japan.

551.46 JPN
KAIYO KAGAKU GIJUTSU SENTA NENPO/JAPAN MARINE SCIENCE AND TECHNOLOGY CENTER. ANNUAL REPORT. Text in Japanese. 1972. a. free.
Related titles: CD-ROM ed.
Indexed: ASFA.
Published by: Kaiyo Kagaku Gijutsu Senta/Japan Marine Science and Technology Center, 2-15 Natsushima-cho, Yokosuka-shi, Kanagawa-ken 237-0061, Japan. TEL 81-468-67-5525, FAX 81-468-66-6169, info@jamstec.go.jp, http://www.jamstec.go.jp/. Circ: 900.

551.46 JPN ISSN 0387-382X
GC1 CODEN: KKKHEJ
KAIYO KAGAKU GIJUTSU SENTA SHIKEN KENKYU HOKOKU/JAPAN MARINE SCIENCE AND TECHNOLOGY CENTER. REPORT. Text in English, Japanese. 1977. s-a. JPY 1,200 (effective 2001).
Indexed: ASFA, ESPM, ZooRec.
—BLDSC (7526.754000), CISTI.
Published by: Kaiyo Kagaku Gijutsu Senta/Japan Marine Science and Technology Center, 2-15 Natsushima-cho, Yokosuka-shi, Kanagawa-ken 237-0061, Japan. TEL 81-468-67-5525, FAX 81-468-66-6169, info@jamstec.go.jp, http://www.jamstec.go.jp/. Circ: 700.

551.46 JPN ISSN 0912-4829
KAIYO KAGAKU KENKYU/RESEARCH INSTITUTE OF OCEANOCHEMISTRY. TRANSACTIONS. Text in English, Japanese. 1986. s-a. free. adv. **Document type:** *Bulletin.*
Published by: Kaiyo Kagaku Kenkyujo/Research Institute of Oceanochemistry, Kyoto Daigaku Rigakubu Kakaku, Kita-Shirakawa Oiwakecho, Kyoto-shi, 606, Japan. Ed. Toshitaka Hori. Adv. contact Takashi Kimoto.

551.46 JPN
KAIYO KAIHATSU SUISHIN KEIKAKU/MARINE SCIENCE AND TECHNOLOGY DEVELOPMENT IN JAPAN. Text in Japanese. 1970. a. JPY 4,854 (effective 2000). **Document type:** *Government.*
Published by: (Kaiyo Kagaku Gijutsu Kaihatsu Suishin Renraku Kaigi/Coordinating Committee for the Promotion and Development of Marine Science and Technology), Okurasho Insatsukyoku/Ministry of Finance, Printing Bureau, 2-4 Toranomon 2-chome, Minato-ku, Tokyo, 105-0001, Japan.

551.4 JPN ISSN 0287-2293
KAIYO KANSOKU DETA/DATA OF OCEANIC OBSERVATIONS. Text in Japanese. 1980. a.

Published by: Tokai Daigaku, Kaiyogakubu/Tokai University, Faculty of Marine Science and Technology, 20-1 Ori-Do 3-chome, shimizu-shi, Shizuoka-ken 424-0902, Japan.

551.46 623.82 JPN
KAIYO KOGAKU SHINPOJUMU/OCEAN ENGINEERING SYMPOSIUM. Text in English, Japanese; Summaries in English. 1975. biennial.
Published by: Nihon Zosen Gakkai/Society of Naval Architects of Japan, 1Hamamatsucho Yazaki White Bldg., 2-12-9 Shibadaimon, Minato-ku, Tokyo, 105-0012, Japan.

551.46 JPN ISSN 0910-5425
KAIYO KYOKAIHO/JAPAN OCEAN DEVELOPMENT CONSTRUCTION ASSOCIATION. NEWS. Text in Japanese. 1976. q.
Published by: Nihon Kaiyo Kaihatsu Kensetsu Kyokai/Ocean Development Construction Association, Kensetsu Kaikan, 5-1 Haccho-Bori 2-chome, Chuo-ku, Tokyo, 104-0032, Japan.

KAIYO SEIBUTSU KANKYO KENKYUJO KENKYU HOKOKU/MARINE ECOLOGY RESEARCH INSTITUTE. REPORT. see *BIOLOGY*

551.46 570 JPN
KANAZAWA DAIGAKU RIGAKUBU FUZOKU NOTO RINKAI JIKKENJO KENKYU GAIYO NENJI HOKOKU/KANAZAWA UNIVERSITY. NOTO MARINE LABORATORY. ANNUAL PROGRESS REPORTS. Text in Japanese. 1987. a.
Published by: (Fuzoku Noto Rinkai Jikkenjo), Kanazawa Daigaku, Rigakubu/Kanazawa University, Faculty of Science, Ogi, Suzu-gun, Uchiura-machi, Ishikawa-ken 927-0553, Japan.

551.46 JPN
KENCHO KIROKU/TIDAL RECORD. Text in Japanese. 1930. a.
Published by: Kokudo Chiriin/Geographical Survey Institute, Ministry of Construction, 1 Kita-Sato, Tsukuba-shi, Ibaraki-ken 305-0811, Japan.

551.46 SAU ISSN 1021-1802
KING ABDULAZIZ UNIVERSITY. FACULTY OF MARINE SCIENCE. JOURNAL. Text in English. 1983. irreg. **Document type:** *Journal, Academic/Scholarly.*
Indexed: ESPM.
Published by: King Abdulaziz University, Faculty of Marine Science, P.O. Box 80207, Jedda, 21589, Saudi Arabia. TEL 966-2-6952383, FAX 966-2-6401747, http://www.kaau.edu.sa/Faculties/marine/faculty%20page.htm.

551.46 JPN
KISHOCHO KAIHYO KANSOKU SHIRYO/RESULTS OF SEA ICE OBSERVATIONS. Text in Japanese. 1983. a.
Published by: Kishocho/Japan Meteorological Agency, 3-4 Ote-Machi 1-chome, Chiyoda-ku, Tokyo, 100-0004, Japan.

551 JPN ISSN 0368-5969
CODEN: KKKIAI
➤ **KOBE KAIYO KISHODAI. IHO/KOBE MARINE OBSERVATORY. BULLETIN.** Text in Japanese; Summaries in English. 1925. a. free to qualified personnel. adv. **Document type:** *Bulletin, Academic/Scholarly.*
Indexed: ASFA, ESPM, M&GPA.
—BLDSC (2600.100000).
Published by: Kobe Kaiyo Kishodai/Kobe Marine Observatory (Subsidiary of: Japan Meteorological Agency/Kishocho), 1-4-3 Wakinohama-Kaigandori, Chuo-ku, Kobe, 651-0073 , Japan. Ed. Minoru Satomi. Adv. contact Yoshio Yokota. Circ: 400.

551.46 JPN
KOBE KAIYO KISHODAI. KAIYO SOKUHO/KOBE MARINE OBSERVATORY. OCEANOGRAPHIC PROMPT REPORT. Text in Japanese. 1956. irreg.
Published by: Kobe Kaiyo Kishodai/Kobe Marine Observatory (Subsidiary of: Japan Meteorological Agency/Kishocho), 1-4-3 Wakinohama-Kaigandori, Chuo-ku, Kobe, 651-0073 , Japan.

551.46 JPN
CODEN: RUMUDA
➤ **KOCHI UNIVERSITY. MARINE SCIENCES AND FISHERIES. BULLETIN.** Text in Japanese, English. 1979. a. per issue exchange basis. **Document type:** *Bulletin, Academic/Scholarly.* **Description:** Covers marine biology, fishery and oceanography.
Formerly (until Dec. 1993): Kochi University. USA Marine Biological Institute. Report (0387-9763); Which was formed by the merger of (1954-1977): Usa Marine Biological Station. Reports (0452-2478); (1974-1978): Kochi Daigaku Suisan Jikkenjo Kenkyu Hokoku (0387-9755)
Indexed: ASFA, BIOSIS Prev, BiolAb, ESPM, RefZh, SFA, ZooRec.
—CASDDS, CISTI.
Published by: Kochi University, Usa Marine Biological Institute, Usa-cho, Tosa, Kochi 781-11, Japan. TEL 0888-56-0422, FAX 0888-56-0425, http://www.kochi-u.ac.jp/kaiyo/kankou.html. Ed. Kosuku Yamaoka. Circ: 300.

551.46 JPN ISSN 0916-3522
KOKUNAI KAIYO CHOSA HOKOKU ICHIRAN/NATIONAL OCEANOGRAPHIC PROGRAM OF JAPAN. Text in Japanese. 1972. a. **Document type:** *Government.*
Formerly: Kaiyo Chosa Hokoku Ichiran

E

Published by: (Japan. Nihon Kaiyo Deta Senta), Kaijo Hoancho, Suirobu/Maritime Safety Agency, Hydrographic Department, 3-1 Tsuki-Ji 5-chome, Chuo-ku, Tokyo, 104-0045, Japan. TEL 81-3-3541-4296, FAX 81-3-3545-2885, consult@cue.jhd.go.jp, http://www.jhd.go.jp/.

363.7 DEU ISSN 0452-7739
TC203 CODEN: KUSTAP
DIE KUESTE; Archiv fuer Forschung und Technik an der Nord- und Ostsee. Text in German. 1952. irreg. (1-2/yr.). price varies. illus. **Document type:** *Academic/Scholarly.*
Indexed: ASFA, ESPM, FLUIDEX, GEOBASE, IBR, RefZh.
—CISTI, IE, Infotrieve, Linda Hall.
Published by: (Kuratorium fuer Forschung im Kuesteningenieurwesen), Westholsteinische Verlagsanstalt Boyens und Co., Am Wulf Isebrand Platz, Heide, 25746, Germany. TEL 49-481-6886162, FAX 49-481-6886467. Ed. Harald Goehren.

551.46 JPN ISSN 0913-1302
KUROSHIO/KOCHI UNIVERSITY. INSTITUTE OF THE KUROSHIO SPHERE. REPORT. Text in Japanese. 1986. a.
Published by: (Kuroshioken Kenkyujo), Kochi Daigaku/Kochi University, 5-1 Akebono-cho 2-chome, Kochi-shi, Kochi-ken 780-8520, Japan.

551.46 JPN
KUROSHIO NO KAIHATSU RIYO CHOSA KENKYU SEIKA HOKOKUSHO/KUROSHIO EXPLOITATION RESEARCH AND UTILIZATION REPORT. Text in Japanese; Summaries in English, Japanese. 1978. a. **Document type:** *Government.*
Description: Covers the ecological effect on plankton and fishes, and on subtropical high pressure.
Published by: (Kenkyu Kaihatsukyoku), Kagaku Gijutsucho/Science and Technology Agency, Planning Bureau, 2-1 Kasumigaseki 2-chome, Chiyoda-ku, Tokyo, 100-0013, Japan. TEL 81-3-3580-6561, FAX 81-3-3581-7442. Circ: 200.

551.46 JPN ISSN 0914-7225
KUROSHIO. TOKUBETSUGO/KOCHI UNIVERSITY. INSTITUTE OF THE KUROSHIO SPHERE. REPORT. SPECIAL SERIES. Text in Japanese. 1987. a.
Published by: (Kuroshioken Kenkyujo), Kochi Daigaku/Kochi University, 5-1 Akebono-cho 2-chome, Kochi-shi, Kochi-ken 780-8520, Japan.

551.46 639.3 JPN
KYOTO FURITSU KAIYO SENTA JIGYO GAIYO/KYOTO INSTITUTE OF OCEANIC AND FISHERY SCIENCE. REPORT. Text in Japanese. a.
Published by: Kyoto Furitsu Kaiyo Senta, Odashiyukuno, Miyazu-shi, Kyoto-Fu 626-0052, Japan.

551.46 639.2 JPN ISSN 0289-9515
KYOTO FURITSU KAIYO SENTA KENKYU GYOSEKISHU/ KYOTO INSTITUTE OF OCEANIC AND FISHERY SCIENCE. CONTRIBUTIONS. Text in English, Japanese. 1983. irreg.
Published by: Kyoto Furitsu Kaiyo Senta, Odashiyukuno, Miyazu-shi, Kyoto-Fu 626-0052, Japan.

639.2 JPN ISSN 0386-5290
KYOTO FURITSU KAIYO SENTA KENKYU HOKOKU/KYOTO INSTITUTE OF OCEANIC AND FISHERY SCIENCE. BULLETIN. Text in English, Japanese. 1977. a. **Document type:** *Bulletin.*
Indexed: ASFA, Agrind, ESPM.
Published by: Kyoto Furitsu Kaiyo Senta, Odashiyukuno, Miyazu-shi, Kyoto-Fu 626-0052, Japan.

551.46 639.2 JPN ISSN 0286-617X
KYOTO FURITSU KAIYO SENTA KENKYU RONBUN/KYOTO INSTITUTE OF OCEANIC AND FISHERY SCIENCE. SPECIAL REPORT. Text in English, Japanese. 1982. irreg.
Published by: Kyoto Furitsu Kaiyo Senta, Odashiyukuno, Miyazu-shi, Kyoto-Fu 626-0052, Japan.

LIMNOLOGY AND OCEANOGRAPHY. see *EARTH SCIENCES—Hydrology*

551.46 USA ISSN 1539-607X
LIMNOLOGY AND OCEANOGRAPHY BULLETIN. Text in English. 1990. q. USD 90 (effective 2000). adv. back issues avail. **Document type:** *Newsletter.* **Description:** Informs members of society events and provides a forum to discuss issues.
Formerly (until 2001): A S L O Bulletin (1536-352X)
Related titles: Online - full text ed.: ISSN 1539-6088.
Published by: American Society of Limnology and Oceanography, Inc., 1444 Eye St. NW #200, Washington, DC 20005. TEL 202-289-1972, 800-929-2756, FAX 202-628-1509, bulletin-editor@also.org, business@also.org, http://www.aslo.org. Ed. Gregory A Cutter. Adv. contact Helen Schneider Lemay. Circ: 3,800 (paid). **Subscr. to:** 5400 Bosque Blvd, Ste 680, Waco, TX 76710-4446.

551.46 USA ISSN 1541-5856
GC1
▼ **LIMNOLOGY AND OCEANOGRAPHY: METHODS.** Text in English. 2003. m. USD 378 (effective 2003). **Document type:** *Academic/Scholarly.*
Media: Online - full content.
Published by: American Society of Limnology and Oceanography, Inc., 5400 Bosque Blvd, Ste 680, Waco, TX 76710-4446. TEL 254-399-9635, 800-929-2756, FAX 254-776-3767, business@aslo.org, http://www.aslo.org/lomethods.

LIVING WITH THE SHORE. see *ENVIRONMENTAL STUDIES*

599 USA
LONG ISLAND SOUND STUDY UPDATE. Text in English. 1988. bi-m. membership. adv.
Former titles: Long Island Sound Report; Taffrail
Published by: Long Island Sound Study, 888 Washington Blvd, Stamford, CT 06904. Ed. Mark Tedesco. Circ: 6,200.

551.46 AUS ISSN 1327-0184
LONG-TERM MONITORING OF THE GREAT BARRIER REEF. STANDARD OPERATIONAL PROCEDURE. Text in English. irreg.
Indexed: ESPM, ZooRec.
Published by: Australian Institute of Marine Science, PMB No 3, Townsville Mail Centre, Townsville, QLD 4810, Australia. TEL 61-7-47534444, FAX 61-7-47725852, http://www.aims.gov.au.

LONG-TERM MONITORING OF THE GREAT BARRIER REEF: STATUS REPORT. see *ENVIRONMENTAL STUDIES*

551.46 USA
THE LOOKDOWN. Text in English. 1980. q. membership. back issues avail. **Description:** Presents information to members about museum programs and trips, Virginia's marine environment and museum research, and promotes ecological awareness.
Published by: Virginia Marine Science Museum, 717 General Booth Blvd, Virginia Beach, VA 23451. TEL 804-437-4949, FAX 804-437-4976. Ed. Mary Reid Barrow.

551.46 GRC ISSN 1011-7148
M A P TECHNICAL REPORTS SERIES. Text in English. 1986. irreg. price varies.
—BLDSC (5369.318110), IE, ingenta.
Published by: (World Meteorological Organization CHE, Intergovernmental Oceanographic Commission USA), United Nations Environment Programme, Mediterranean Action Plan, PO Box 18019, Athens, 116 10, Greece. TEL 30-01-7273100, FAX 30-01-72531965, unepmedu@unepmap.org, http://195.97.105.164/sample/Final/MTSFull.htm, http://www.unepmap.org.

M E R. MARINE ENGINEERS REVIEW. see *ENGINEERING*

551.46 IND ISSN 0542-0938
GC1 CODEN: MHSGAJ
MAHASAGAR (GOA). Text in English. 1968. a. USD 40 (effective 2000). adv. bk.rev. bibl.; charts; illus. **Document type:** *Academic/Scholarly.*
Incorporates: International Indian Ocean Expedition
Related titles: Microfilm ed.
Indexed: ASFA, CTO, ChemAb, ZooRec.
—CASDDS, CISTI, Linda Hall. **CCC.**
Published by: National Institute of Oceanography, Dona Paula, Goa, Goa 403 004, India. Circ: 400. **Dist. by:** H P C Publishers Distributors Pvt. Ltd., 4805 Bharat Ram Rd, 24 Darya Ganj, New Delhi 110 002, India. TEL 91-11-325-4401, FAX 91-11-686-3511. **Affiliate:** Council of Scientific and Industrial Research.

551.46 639.2 USA
MAINE SEA GRANT. TECHNICAL REPORT. Text in English. irreg.
Published by: Maine Sea Grant Program, University of Maine, Coburn Hall, Orono, ME 04469-5715. TEL 207-581-1435, FAX 207-581-1426, umseagrant@maine.edu, http://www.seagrant.umaine.edu/Publication/.

551.46 JPN ISSN 0022-7811
MAIZURU KAIYO KISHODAI. KAIYO SOKUHO/MAIZURU MARINE OBSERVATORY. OCEANOGRAPHIC PROMPT REPORTS. Text in Japanese. 1952. irreg. bk.rev. abstr.; charts.
Published by: Kishocho, Maizuru Kaiyo Kishodai/Japan Meteorological Agency, Maizuru Marine Observatory, 901 Shimo-Fukui, Maizuru-shi, Kyoto-Fu 624-0946, Japan.

551.46 ESP ISSN 1131-9240
MAR (MADRID, 1965). Text in Spanish. 1965. m. free. adv.
Formerly (until 1987): Hoja del Mar
—CINDOC.
Published by: Ministerio de Trabajo y Seguridad Social, Instituto Social de la Marina, Genova, 20 - 5a planta, Madrid, 28004, Spain. TEL 34-91-7006658, FAX 34-91-3199134, TELEX 23743. Ed. Vidal Mate Herreros. Circ: 350,000.

551.46 DEU ISSN 1432-928X
MARE; die Zeitschrift der Meere. Text in German. 1997. bi-m. EUR 39; EUR 7.50 newsstand/cover (effective 2003). adv. bk.rev.; film rev.; music rev. 140 p./no.; back issues avail. **Document type:** *Magazine, Consumer.* **Description:** Covers all aspects of life from the unique perspective of the ocean.
Published by: Dreiviertel Verlag GmbH & Co. KG, Am Sandtorkai 1, Hamburg, 20457, Germany. TEL 49-40-369859-0, FAX 49-40-36985990, mare@mare.de, service@mare.de, http://www.mare.de. Ed., Pub. Nikolaus Gelpke. Adv. contact Friederike Tinzmann. B&W page EUR 3,525, color page EUR 4,850; trim 180 x 250. Circ: 36,500 (paid).

551.46 JPN ISSN 1341-6928
MARIN PABIRION/MARINE PAVILION. Text in Japanese. 1971. m. JPY 1,500 per issue (effective 2001). 6 p./no.; back issues avail. **Document type:** *Journal, Academic/Scholarly.*
Description: Covers mainly ecology of local marine animals.
Published by: Kushimoto Kaichu Koen/Kushimoto Marine Park Center, 1157 Arita, Nishimuro-gun, Kushimoto-cho, Wakayama-ken 649-3514, Japan. TEL 81-735-61-4875, FAX 81-735-62-7170, kmpc@gold.acn.ne, http://www.kushimoto.co.jp. Ed. Hiro-omi Uchida. Circ: 100 (paid); 300 (controlled).

551.46 JPN ISSN 0289-6095
MARINE. Text in Japanese. 1969. m. JPY 1,130 per issue.
Published by: Nikkan Kaiji Tsushinsha/Daily the Kaiji, 23-6 Nishi-Shinbashi 3-chome, Minato-ku, Tokyo, 105-0003, Japan.

551.46 AUS ISSN 1323-1650
GC1 CODEN: MFREFX
➤ **MARINE AND FRESHWATER RESEARCH.** Text in English. 1950. 8/yr. AUD 165 combined subscription in Australia & New Zealand to individuals print & online eds.; USD 165 combined subscription elsewhere to individuals print & online eds.; AUD 880 combined subscription in Australia & New Zealand to institutions print & online eds.; USD 795 combined subscription elsewhere to institutions print & online eds. (effective 2004). adv. illus.; charts; maps. Index. back issues avail.; reprints avail. **Document type:** *Journal, Academic/Scholarly.* **Description:** Presents research in physical oceanography, marine chemistry, marine and estuarine biology and limnology.
Formerly (until 1995): Australian Journal of Marine and Freshwater Research (0067-1940)
Related titles: Microform ed.: (from PQC); Online - full text ed.: AUD 135, USD 135 to individuals; AUD 790, USD 715 to institutions (effective 2004) (from EBSCO Publishing, Gale Group, O C L C Online Computer Library Center, Inc., Swets Information Services).
Indexed: AEA, AESIS, ASCA, ASFA, AgBio, AgrForAb, AnBeAb, AnBrAb, ApEcolAb, B&BAb, BIOBASE, BIOSIS Prev, BioCN&I, BiolAb, BrCerAb, C&ISA, CPA, CRFR, CTO, Cadscan, CerAb, ChemAb, ChemTitl, CivEngAb, CorrAb, CurCont, E&CAJ, EMA, EPB, ESPM, EntAb, EnvAb, ExcerpMed, FCA, FLUIDEX, FS&TA, ForAb, GEOBASE, HelmAb, HerbAb, HortAb, I&DA, IAA, IABS, INIS AtomInd, ISR, IndVet, LeadAb, M&GPA, M&TEA, MBF, METADEX, NutrAb, OceAb, PGegResA, PollutAb, RA&MP, RDA, RRTA, RevApplEntom, S&F, SCI, SFA, SIA, SPPI, SWRA, SeedAb, SolStAb, VetBull, WAA, WAE&RSA, WeedAb, WildRev, Zincscan, ZooRec.
—BLDSC (5373.625700), CASDDS, CIS, CISTI, IDS, IE, Infotrieve, ingenta, Linda Hall. **CCC.**
Published by: (C S I R O Australia), C S I R O Publishing, 150 Oxford St, PO Box 1139, Collingwood, VIC 3066, Australia. TEL 61-3-96627618, FAX 61-3-96627611, agrant@publish.csiro.au, publishing@csiro.au, http://www.publish.csiro.au/journals/mfr/. Circ: 700.

➤ **MARINE BIOLOGICAL ASSOCIATION OF INDIA. JOURNAL.** see *BIOLOGY*

▼ ➤ **MARINE BIOLOGY RESEARCH.** see *BIOLOGY*

➤ **MARINE CONSERVATION NEWS;** "for all at last returns to the sea - the beginning and the end." Rachel Carson. see *CONSERVATION*

▼ ➤ **MARINE DRUGS.** see *PHARMACY AND PHARMACOLOGY*

➤ **MARINE ENGINEERING/MARIN ENJINIARINGU.** see *ENGINEERING*

551.46 GBR
MARINE ENVIRONMENTAL MANAGEMENT. Text in English. a. GBP 42. **Document type:** *Bulletin.*
Address: Candle Cottage, Kempley, Glos GL18 2BU, United Kingdom. TEL 44-1531-890415. Ed. Bob Earll.

MARINE ENVIRONMENTAL RESEARCH. see *ENVIRONMENTAL STUDIES—Pollution*

MARINE GEODESY; an international journal of ocean surveys, mapping and sensing. see *GEOGRAPHY*

E

551.46 NLD ISSN 0025-3227
QE39 CODEN: MAGEA6
➤ **MARINE GEOLOGY.** Text in English, French, German. 1964. 44/yr. EUR 3,341 in Europe to institutions; JPY 443,900 in Japan to institutions; USD 3,738 to institutions except Europe and Japan; EUR 199 in Europe to qualified personnel; JPY 26,500 in Japan to qualified personnel; USD 223 to qualified personnel except Europe and Japan (effective 2006). adv. bk.rev. abstr.; bibl.; charts; illus. index per vol. reprints avail. **Document type:** *Journal, Academic/Scholarly.* **Description:** Presents original research and comprehensive reviews in the field of marine geology, geochemistry, and geophysics.
Related titles: Microform ed.: (from PQC); Online - full text ed.: (from EBSCO Publishing, Gale Group, IngentaConnect, ScienceDirect, Swets Information Services).
Indexed: AESIS, ASCA, ASFA, BIOBASE, BrGeoL, CIN, ChemAb, ChemTitl, CurCont, E&PHSE, EEA, ESPM, EngInd, FLUIDEX, GEOBASE, GP&P, IABS, ISR, M&GPA, M&TEA, OceAb, OffTech, PetrolAb, PollutAb, RefZh, SCI, SFA, SPPI.
—BLDSC (5375.400000), CASDDS, CISTI, Ei, IDS, IE, Infotrieve, ingenta, Linda Hall, PADDS. **CCC.**
Published by: Elsevier BV (Subsidiary of: Elsevier Science & Technology), Radarweg 29, Amsterdam, 1043 NX, Netherlands. TEL 31-20-4853911, FAX 31-20-4852457, nlinfo-f@elsevier.nl, http://www.elsevier.com/locate/margeo, http://www.elsevier.nl. Eds. D. J.W. Piper, G de Lange, John T Wells.

551.46 551 NLD ISSN 0025-3235
QE501 CODEN: MGYRA7
➤ **MARINE GEOPHYSICAL RESEARCHES;** an international journal for the study of the earth beneath the sea. Text in Dutch. 1970. q. EUR 548, USD 578, GBP 365 combined subscription to institutions print & online eds. (effective 2005). adv. bk.rev. illus. reprint service avail. from PSC. **Document type:** *Journal, Academic/Scholarly.* **Description:** Emphasizes the description and analysis of structures that can be investigated with geophysical methods, and the study of the physical processes that led to these structures.
Related titles: Microform ed.: (from PQC); Online - full text ed.: ISSN 1573-0581 (from EBSCO Publishing, Gale Group, IngentaConnect, Kluwer Online, O C L C Online Computer Library Center, Inc., Ovid Technologies, Inc., Springer LINK, Swets Information Services).
Indexed: ASCA, ASFA, BibLing, CTO, ChemAb, CurCont, E&PHSE, EngInd, GEOBASE, GP&P, GeophysAb, ISR, Inspec, M&GPA, MSCT, OceAb, OffTech, PetrolAb, PhysBer, RefZh, SCI.
—BLDSC (5375.500000), AskIEEE, CISTI, Ei, IDS, IE, Infotrieve, ingenta, Linda Hall, PADDS. **CCC.**
Published by: Springer-Verlag Dordrecht (Subsidiary of: Springer Science+Business Media), Van Godewijckstraat 30, Dordrecht, 3311 GX, Netherlands. TEL 31-78-6576050, FAX 31-78-6576474, http://springerlink.metapress.com/openurl.asp?genre=journal&issn=0025-3235, http://www.springeronline.com. Eds. Peter Clift, Y John Chen.

551.46 623 USA ISSN 1064-119X
TN264 CODEN: MGGEEI
➤ **MARINE GEORESOURCES AND GEOTECHNOLOGY.** Text in English. 1993. q. GBP 252, USD 417 combined subscription to institutions print & online eds. (effective 2006). adv. bk.rev. abstr.; charts; illus.; stat. index. reprint service avail. from PQC,PSC. **Document type:** *Journal, Academic/Scholarly.* **Description:** Devoted to all scientific and engineering aspects of seafloor sediment and rocks.
Formed by the merger of (1975-1993): Marine Geotechnology (0360-8867); (1977-1993): Marine Mining (0149-0397)
Related titles: Microform ed.: (from PQC); Online - full text ed.: ISSN 1521-0618. GBP 239, USD 396 to institutions (effective 2006) (from EBSCO Publishing, Gale Group, IngentaConnect, O C L C Online Computer Library Center, Inc., Swets Information Services).
Indexed: AESIS, AS&TI, ASCA, ASFA, BIOSIS Prev, BiolAb, BrCerAb, BrGeoL, C&ISA, CerAb, ChemAb, ChemTitl, CivEngAb, CorrAb, CurCont, E&CAJ, E&PHSE, EMA, EPB, ESPM, EngInd, EnvAb, EnvEAb, FLUIDEX, GEOBASE, GP&P, GeotechAb, IAA, IMMAb, ISMEC, ISR, M&TEA, MBF, METADEX, MSB, MSCT, MinerAb, OceAb, OffTech, PetrolAb, PollutAb, SCI, SWRA, SolStAb, WAA.
—BLDSC (5375.520000), CASDDS, CIS, CISTI, Ei, IDS, IE, Infotrieve, ingenta, Linda Hall, PADDS. **CCC.**
Published by: Taylor & Francis Inc. (Subsidiary of: Taylor & Francis Group), 325 Chestnut St, Ste 800, Philadelphia, PA 19016. TEL 215-625-8900, 800-354-1420, FAX 215-625-2940, info@taylorandfrancis.com, http://www.tandf.co.uk/journals/titles/1064119X.asp, http://www.taylorandfrancis.com. Eds. Michael J Cruickshank, Ronald C Chaney. Circ: 260. **Subscr. addr. in Europe:** Taylor & Francis Ltd, Journals Customer Service, Rankine Rd, Basingstoke, Hants RG24 8PR, United Kingdom. TEL 44-1256-813000, FAX 44-1256-330245, enquiry@tandf.co.uk.

➤ **MARINE LAWS;** navigation and safety. see *LAW—Maritime Law*

➤ **MARINE MAMMAL SCIENCE.** see *BIOLOGY—Zoology*

➤ **MARINE OBSERVER;** a quarterly journal of maritime meteorology. see *METEOROLOGY*

343.09 GBR ISSN 0308-597X
GC1000
➤ **MARINE POLICY.** Text in English. 1977. 6/yr. EUR 873 in Europe to institutions; JPY 116,000 in Japan to institutions; USD 977 to institutions except Europe and Japan (effective 2006). adv. bk.rev. abstr.; illus. Index. back issues avail.; reprints avail. **Document type:** *Academic/Scholarly.* **Description:** Offers researchers, analysts and policy makers a combination of legal, political, social and economic analysis. Major articles are written by international lawyers, political scientists, fishery specialists and marine economists.
Related titles: Microform ed.: (from PQC); Online - full text ed.: (from EBSCO Publishing, Gale Group, IngentaConnect, ScienceDirect, Swets Information Services).
Indexed: APEL, ASCA, ASFA, CJA, CTO, CurCont, EIA, ELLIS, EPB, ESPM, EnerInd, EnerRev, EnvAb, ExcerpMed, FLUIDEX, FutSurv, GEOBASE, IBSS, ISR, KES, MAB, OceAb, PAIS, PCI, RASB, RDA, SFA, SPPI, SSCI, WAE&RSA.
—BLDSC (5377.250000), CIS, CISTI, IDS, IE, Infotrieve, ingenta. **CCC.**
Published by: Pergamon (Subsidiary of: Elsevier Science & Technology), The Boulevard, Langford Ln, East Park, Kidlington, Oxford OX5 1GB, United Kingdom. TEL 44-1865-843000, FAX 44-1865-843010, http://www.elsevier.com/locate/marpol. Ed. E D Brown. **Subscr. to:** Elsevier BV, PO Box 211, Amsterdam 1000 AE, Netherlands. TEL 31-20-485-3757, FAX 31-20-485-3432, nlinfo-f@elsevier.nl, http://www.elsevier.nl.

551.4 IDN ISSN 0216-2873
GC1 CODEN: MRINAQ
MARINE RESEARCH IN INDONESIA. Text in English, German. 1956. irreg. USD 10 per issue.
Formerly (until 1976): Penelitian Laut di Indonesia (0079-0435)
Indexed: ASFA, BAS, BIOSIS Prev, BiolAb, ESPM, OceAb, SFA.
Published by: Centre for Oceanological Research and Development, Documentation and Information Division/Pusat Penelitian dan Pengembangan Oseanologi, Ancol Timur, Jalan Pasir Putih 1, PO Box 580, Jakarta, 11001, Indonesia. TEL 683850, TELEX 45879-PDIN-IA. Ed. Kasijan Romimohtarto. Circ: 500.

551.46 USA ISSN 0738-1360
SH328 CODEN: JMREDD
➤ **MARINE RESOURCE ECONOMICS.** Text in English. 1983. q. USD 50 to individuals; USD 150 to institutions; USD 30 to students (effective 2004). adv. bk.rev. abstr. back issues avail. **Document type:** *Journal, Academic/Scholarly.* **Description:** Devoted to publishing creative and scholarly analyses of a range of issues related to natural resource use in the global marine environment.
Indexed: ASFA, AnBrAb, CREJ, EPB, ESPM, EnerRev, IBR, IBSS, IndVet, JEL, MSCT, OceAb, PollutAb, RRTA, SFA, WAE&RSA.
—BLDSC (5378.104300), IE, Infotrieve, ingenta. **CCC.**
Published by: University of Rhode Island, Department of Environmental and Natural Resource Economics, Lippitt Hall, 5 Lippitt Rd., Kingston, RI 02881. TEL 401-874-2471, FAX 401-782-4766, http://www.uri.edu/cels/enre/mre/mre.htm. Eds. Jon G Sutinen, James L Anderson. R&P, Adv. contact Barbara S Gardiner. Circ: 300. **Subscr. to:** Marine Resources Foundation, PO Box 1828, Kingston, RI 02881. TEL 401-874-4583, FAX 401-782-4766, mre1@etal.uri.edu.

551.46 CHN ISSN 1000-9620
MARINE SCIENCE BULLETIN. Text and summaries in English. 1999. s-a. USD 80 (effective 2003 - 2004). 96 p./no.; **Document type:** *Bulletin, Academic/Scholarly.* **Description:** Includes the basic marine research on hydrology, climatology, biology, chemistry and geology, marine engineering, marine technique & method, marine development, marine management and environmental protection, etc.
Related titles: Online - full text ed.: (from East View Information Services); ♦ Chinese ed.: Haiyang Tongbao. ISSN 1001-6392.
Indexed: ZooRec.
—BLDSC (5378.134000), IE, ingenta.
Published by: Guojia Haiyang Xinxi Zhongxin/National Marine Data & Information Service, 93 Liuwei Rd, Hedong District, Tianjin, 300171, China. TEL 86-22-24010823, FAX 86-22-24010825, hytb@mail.nmdis.gov.cn. Ed. Hong Wang.

551.46 GBR ISSN 1478-1328
MARINE SCIENTIST. Text in English. 2002. q. GBP 26, EUR 43 to non-members; GBP 10, EUR 16 to members (effective 2003). bk.rev.; software rev.; Website rev. back issues avail. **Document type:** *Journal, Trade.* **Description:** Contains news, research, analysis, debates and views from the scientific community, reader letters, interviews, job advertisements, and marine science conferences worldwide.
Indexed: ASFA.
—BLDSC (5378.159000).
Published by: Institute of Marine Engineering, Science and Technology, 80 Coleman St, London, EC2R 5BJ, United Kingdom. TEL 44-20-73822600, FAX 44-20-73822669, info@imarest.org, http://www.imarest.org/scientist/. Ed. John Butchers. Adv. contact Ian Glen TEL 44-20-73822649.

338.476 GBR ISSN 1353-6486
MARINE TECHNOLOGY DIRECTIONS. Text in English. irreg.
Supersedes in part (in 1993): Underwater and Marine Technology News (0965-5468); Which was formerly (until 1992): Marine Technology Research News (0951-6778)
Published by: Marine Technology Directorate Ltd., Innovation Center, Exploration Dr., Offshore Technology Park, Bridge on Don, Aberdeen AB23 8GX, United Kingdom. TEL 44-244-827-005, FAX 44-244-827-017, http://itri.loyala.edu/subsea/e_mtd.htm.

623 USA ISSN 0025-3324
GC1 CODEN: MTSJBB
➤ **MARINE TECHNOLOGY SOCIETY JOURNAL;** the international, interdisciplinary society devoted to ocean and marine engineering, science and policy. Text in English. 1966. q. USD 120 domestic; USD 135 foreign (effective 2002). adv. bk.rev. abstr.; bibl.; charts; illus.; stat. Index. back issues avail.; reprints avail. **Document type:** *Journal, Academic/Scholarly.* **Description:** Represents an international interdisciplinary journal about ocean and marine engineering, science, and policy.
Formerly (until 1968): Journal of Ocean Technology (0099-4529); Incorporated: Ocean Soundings (0048-1386)
Related titles: Microfilm ed.; Online - full text ed.: (from H.W. Wilson, Northern Light Technology, Inc., O C L C Online Computer Library Center, Inc., ProQuest Information & Learning).
Indexed: AS&TI, ASCA, ASFA, B&AI, BMT, BiolAb, CISA, CTO, ChemAb, CivEngAb, CurCont, EIA, EPB, ESPM, EngInd, EnvAb, ExcerpMed, FLUIDEX, GEOBASE, GeotechAb, HRIS, ISR, Inspec, M&GPA, M&TEA, METADEX, MSCT, OceAb, PetrolAb, SCI, SFA, SSCI, SWRA, ZooRec.
—BLDSC (5378.700000), CIS, CISTI, Ei, IDS, IE, Infotrieve, ingenta, Linda Hall, PADDS. **CCC.**
Published by: Marine Technology Society, Inc., 5565 Sterrett Pl, Ste 108, Columbia, MD 21044. TEL 410-884-5330, FAX 410-884-9060, mtspubs@erols.com, http://www.mtsociety.org/publications/journal.cfm. Ed. Dan Walker. Pub., R&P, Adv. contact Melissa Corley TEL 410-884-5330. Circ: 3,200.

➤ **MARINER'S MIRROR.** see *HISTORY*

➤ **MARINERS WEATHER LOG;** a climatic review of North Atlantic and North Pacific Ocean and Great Lake areas. see *METEOROLOGY*

➤ **MARITIME I T & ELECTRONICS.** see *EARTH SCIENCES—Computer Applications*

551.46 USA ISSN 0025-3472
GC1 CODEN: MRTMBB
➤ **MARITIMES.** Text in English. 1957. q. free. charts; illus. index. reprints avail. **Document type:** *Academic/Scholarly.* **Description:** Reports the activities of the school and the work of its faculty and staff, including independent studies and cooperative participation in international programs.
Indexed: ASFA, BiolAb, SFA, WildRev, ZooRec.
Published by: University of Rhode Island, Graduate School of Oceanography, URI Bay Campus Box 43, Narragansett, RI 02882-1197. TEL 401-874-6211, FAX 401-874-6486, jack@gsosun1.gso.uri.edu, http://www.gso.uri.edu/maritimes. Ed., R&P Jackleen de La Harpe TEL 401-874-6499. Circ: 4,500.

551.46 GRC ISSN 1108-393X
MEDITERRANEAN MARINE SCIENCE. Text in Multiple languages. 1976. s-a. EUR 20 (effective 2003). **Description:** Publishes articles on all aspects of oceanography, limnology, fisheries, and aquatics.
Formerly (until 1999): Thalassografika (0250-3298)
—BLDSC (5534.738500), CISTI, IE.
Published by: Institouton Okeanografikon kai Alieutikon Ereunon, National Center for Marine Research, Agios Kosmas, Hellinikon 16604, Athens, Greece. TEL 30-210-9821354, FAX 30-210-9811713, publ@ncmr.gr, http://atlantis.ncmr.gr/publ/index2.htm, http://www.hcmr.gr. Ed. Dr. E Papathanassiou.

551.46 DEU ISSN 0433-7670
MEERESKUNDLICHE BEOBACHTUNGEN UND ERGEBNISSE. Text in German. 1953. irreg. **Document type:** *Monographic series, Academic/Scholarly.*
Indexed: ESPM.
Published by: Bundesamt fuer Seeschiffahrt und Hydrographie, Bernhard-Nocht-Str 78, Hamburg, 20359, Germany. TEL 49-40-31900, FAX 49-40-31905000, posteingang@bsh.de, http://www.bsh.de.

551.46 DEU ISSN 0939-396X
MEERESWISSENSCHAFTLICHE BERICHTE. Text in Multiple languages. 1991. irreg. **Document type:** *Monographic series.*
Indexed: ESPM.
Published by: Institut fuer Meereskunde, Duesternbrooker Weg 20, Kiel, 24105, Germany. TEL 49-431-6000, FAX 49-431-6001515, ifm@ifm.uni-kiel.de, http://www.ifm.uni-kiel.de.

MEMOIRS OF THE HOURGLASS CRUISES. see *BIOLOGY*

578.77 ITA ISSN 0390-492X
QH152 CODEN: MBMOA5
MEMORIE DI BIOLOGIA MARINA E DI OCEANOGRAFIA. Text and summaries in English, French, German, Italian. 1930-1940; N.S. 1971. bi-m. adv. bk.rev. back issues avail.

E

Indexed: ASFA, BiolAb, ChemAb, SFA.
—Linda Hall.
Published by: (Stazione di Biologia Marina), Universita degli Studi di Messina, Istituto di Zoologia, Messina, ME, Italy. Ed. Carmelo Cavallaro. Circ: 350.

551.46   FIN   ISSN 1238-5328
MERI - REPORT SERIES OF THE FINNISH INSTITUTE OF MARINE RESEARCH. Text in English, Finnish, Swedish; Summaries in English. 1975. irreg. (2-4/yr.), latest 2001, nos. 43-44. price varies. back issues avail. **Document type:** *Government.*
Formerly (until 1995): Meri (0356-0023)
—Linda Hall.
Published by: Finnish Institute of Marine Research, PL 33, Helsinki, 00931, Finland. TEL 358-9-61-39-41, FAX 358-9-61-39-44-94, info@fimr.fi, http://www.fimr.fi. Ed. Leena Parkkonen TEL 358-9-613-94463. Circ: 400.

551.46   DEU   ISSN 0936-8957
METEOR-BERICHTE. Text in English, German. irreg.
Indexed: ESPM, M&GPA.
Published by: Leitstelle Meteor, Institut fuer Meereskunde, Troplowitzstrasse 7, Hamburg, 22529, Germany. TEL 49-40-428-38-3974, FAX 49-40-428-38-4644, leitstelle@ifm.uni-hamburg.de.

MICHIGAN SEA GRANT COLLEGE PROGRAM. TECHNICAL REPORT. see *BIOLOGY*

MIROVOI OKEAN. INFORMATSIONNO-ANALITICHESKII SBORNIK. see *EARTH SCIENCES—Abstracting, Bibliographies, Statistics*

551.46 639.2   USA
MISSISSIPPI-ALABAMA SEA GRANT CONSORTIUM. REPORT. Text in English. irreg.
Published by: Mississippi-Alabama Sea Grant Consortium, Caylor Bldg, Ste 200, 703 E Beach Dr, PO Box 7000, Ocean Springs, MS 39566-7000. TEL 228-818-8836, FAX 228-818-8841, http://www.masgc.org/.

333.9   USA   ISSN 0095-6783
GC1021.M7
MISSISSIPPI MARINE RESOURCES COUNCIL. ANNUAL REPORT✱. Key Title: Annual Report - Mississippi Marine Resources Council. Text in English. a. free. illus.
Published by: Mississippi Marine Resources Council, Department of Marine Resources, 1141 Bayview Ave 101, Biloxi, MS 39530-1601. TEL 601-864-4602.

551.4 797.2   ITA   ISSN 0026-9573
MONDO SOMMERSO; international ocean magazine. Text in English, Italian. 1959. m. EUR 44 domestic (effective 2004). adv. video rev. maps. 144 p./no.; back issues avail.; reprints avail. **Document type:** *Magazine, Consumer.* **Description:** Spreads scientific and biological news related to seas, lakes, rivers and their inhabitants. Covers diving resorts worldwide and diving techniques. Also includes people, news, tourism, archeology, photography and environment news.
Published by: Gruppo Editoriale Olimpia SpA, Via E Fermi 24, Loc Osmannoro, Sesto Fiorentino, FI 50129, Italy. TEL 39-055-30321, FAX 39-055-3032280, mondo.sommerso@edolimpia.it, http://www.mondosommerso-online.it, http://www.edolimpia.it. Ed. Sabina Cupi. Pub. Renato Cacciapuoti. Adv. contact Daniela Gatti TEL 39-055-30321. color page EUR 3,615; 210 x 275. Circ: 38,000. **Dist. by:** Parrini & C, Piazza Colonna 361, Rome RM 00187, Italy. TEL 39-06-695141.

551.46   FRA   ISSN 0077-104X
                                          CODEN: MNOMAP
MONOGRAPHS ON OCEANOGRAPHIC METHODOLOGY SERIES. (Consists of: Phytoplankton Pigments in Oceanography) Text in French. 1966. irreg., latest vol.10, 1997. **Document type:** *Monographic series.*
Related titles: Microform ed.
Indexed: BiolAb, ZooRec.
—CASDDS, CISTI.
Published by: UNESCO Publishing, 7 place de Fontenoy, Paris, 75352, France. TEL 33-1-45684300, FAX 33-1-45685737, http://www.unesco.org/publications. **Dist. in U.S. by:** Bernan Associates, Bernan, 4611-F Assembly Dr., Lanham, MD 20706-4391. TEL 800-274-4447, FAX 800-865-3450.

551.46   JPN
NAGASAKI KAIYO KISHODAI. KAIYO SOKUHO/NAGASAKI MARINE OBSERVATORY. OCEANOGRAPHIC PROMPT REPORT. Text in Japanese. 1950. irreg.
Published by: Kishocho, Nagasaki Kaiyo Kishodai/Japan Meteorological Agency, Nagasaki Marine Observatory, 11-51 Minami-Yamate-Machi, Nagasaki-shi, Nagasaki-ken 850-0931, Japan.

551.46   JPN
NAGOYA UNIVERSITY. WATER RESEARCH INSTITUTE. PUBLICATION LIST. Text in English, Japanese. 1983. a.
Published by: Nagoya Daigaku, Suiken Kagaku Kenkyujo/Nagoya University, Water Research Institute, Furo-cho, Chikusa-ku, Nagoya-shi, Aichi-ken 464-0814, Japan.

551.46   CHN   ISSN 1000-8624
NANHAI HAIYANG KEXUE JIKAN/NANHAI STUDIA MARINA SINICA. Text in Chinese. 1980. q.
Indexed: ZooRec.
Published by: (Zhongguo Kexueyuan, Nanhai Haiyang Yanjiusuo/Chinese Academy of Sciences, South China Sea Institute of Oceanology), Kexue Chubanshe/Science Press, 16 Donghuang Cheng Genbei Jie, Beijing, 100717, China.

NASE MORE; pomorski znanstveni casopis. see *ENVIRONMENTAL STUDIES*

551.46 639.2   EGY   ISSN 1110-0354
NATIONAL INSTITUTE OF OCEANOGRAPHY AND FISHERIES. BULLETIN. Text in English. 1939. a. **Document type:** *Bulletin, Academic/Scholarly.*
Former titles (until 1988): Institute of Oceanography and Fisheries. Bulletin (0374-6267); (until 1970): Marine Biological Station, al-Ghardaqa, Red Sea. Publications (0370-0534)
Indexed: ZooRec.
Published by: National Institute of Oceanography and Fisheries, 101 Kasr El Aini St, Cairo, Egypt. TEL 20-2-5941342, FAX 20-2-5941341, http://derp.sti.sci.eg/data/0094.htm. Ed. Dr. Ekram Muhammad Amin.

551.46   IND   ISSN 0547-7530
GC1
NATIONAL INSTITUTE OF OCEANOGRAPHY. ANNUAL REPORT. Text in English. a.
Published by: National Institute of Oceanography, Dona Paula, Goa, Goa 403 004, India. FAX 91-832-223340, ocean@darya.nio.org, http://www.nio.org.

551.46   IND
NATIONAL INSTITUTE OF OCEANOGRAPHY. TECHNICAL REPORT. Text in English. irreg.
Published by: National Institute of Oceanography, Dona Paula, Goa, Goa 403 004, India. FAX 91-832-223340, ocean@darya.nio.org, http://www.nio.org.

551.468   JPN
➤ **NATIONAL INSTITUTE OF POLAR RESEARCH. MEMOIRS. SERIES D: OCEANOGRAPHY.** Text and summaries in English. 1964. irreg., latest vol.1, 1964. per issue exchange basis. **Document type:** *Monographic series, Academic/Scholarly.*
Supersedes: Japanese Antarctic Research Expedition, 1956-1962. Scientific Reports. Series D: Oceanography (0075-3386)
Indexed: ASFA.
Published by: National Institute of Polar Research/Kokuritsu Kyokuchi Kenkyujo, Publications, 9-10, Kiga 1-chome, Itabashi-ku, Tokyo, 173, Japan. TEL 81-3-3962-2214, FAX 81-3-3962-2225, publication@nipr.ac.jp. Ed. Okitsugu Watanabe. Circ: 1,000.

551.46   NZL
GC1   CODEN: NZOMAI
➤ **NATIONAL INSTITUTE OF WATER AND ATMOSPHERIC RESEARCH. BIODIVERSITY MEMOIRS.** Short title: N I W A Biodiversity Memoirs. Text in English. 1955. irreg. price varies. index. **Document type:** *Monographic series, Academic/Scholarly.* **Description:** Features taxonomic monographs.
Formerly: New Zealand Oceanographic Institute. Memoir (0083-7903)
Indexed: ASFA, ChemAb, ZooRec.
—CASDDS, CISTI, Linda Hall.
Published by: National Institute of Water and Atmospheric Research Ltd., PO Box 14-901, Kilbirnie, Wellington, New Zealand. TEL 64-4-3860388, FAX 64-4-3862153, d.gordon@niwa.cri.nz, d.gordon@niwa.co.nz, http://www.niwa.cri.nz, http://www.niwa.co.nz. Ed. Dennis P Gordon. R&P Dennis Gordon. Circ: 500 (controlled).

551.46   USA
NATIONAL OCEANIC AND ATMOSPHERIC ADMINISTRATION. SPECIAL REPORT. Text in English. irreg.
Published by: National Oceanic and Atmospheric Administration, Office of Oceanic and Atmospheric Research, Silver Spring Metro Center, Bldg 3, Rm 11627, 1315 East-West Hwy, Silver Spring, MD 20910. TEL 301-713-2458, http://www.oar.noaa.gov. **Orders to:** U.S. Department of Commerce, National Technical Information Service, 5285 Port Royal Rd, Springfield, VA 22161. TEL 800-363-2068, subscriptions@ntis.gov.

NATIONAL UNDERSEA RESEARCH PROGRAM STUDY. see *ENGINEERING*

551.46   JPN
NATSUSHIMA/JAPAN MARINE SCIENCE AND TECHNOLOGY CENTER NEWS. Text in Japanese. 1973. m.
Published by: Kaiyo Kagaku Gijutsu Senta/Japan Marine Science and Technology Center, 2-15 Natsushima-cho, Yokosuka-shi, Kanagawa-ken 237-0061, Japan. TEL 81-468-67-5525, FAX 81-468-66-6169, info@jamstec.go.jp, http://www.jamstec.go.jp/.

551.46   GBR
NATURAL ENVIRONMENT RESEARCH COUNCIL. PROUDMAN OCEANOGRAPHIC LABORATORY. CRUISE REPORT. Text in English. irreg.

Published by: Natural Environment Research Council, Proudman Oceanographic Laboratory, Bidston Observatory, Birkenhead, CH43 7RA, United Kingdom. TEL 44-151-643-8633, FAX 44-151-653-6269, http://www.pol.ac.uk/.

551.46   GBR
NATURAL ENVIRONMENT RESEARCH COUNCIL. PROUDMAN OCEANOGRAPHIC LABORATORY. REPORT. Text in English. 1988. irreg. price varies.
Published by: Natural Environment Research Council, Proudman Oceanographic Laboratory, Bidston Observatory, Birkenhead, CH43 7RA, United Kingdom. TEL 44-151-643-8633, FAX 44-151-653-6269, http://www.pol.ac.uk/home/polrepts.html.

623.82   POL   ISSN 0548-0523
VK4
NAUTOLOGIA. Text in Polish. 1966. q. EUR 25 foreign (effective 2005). reprints avail. **Document type:** *Journal, Academic/Scholarly.* **Description:** Devoted to maritime problems.
Indexed: AgrLib, CTO, RASB.
Published by: Polskie Towarzystwo Nautologiczne/Polish Nautological Society, ul H Sienkiewicza 3, Gdynia, 81374, Poland. TEL 48-58-6204975. Ed. Zbigniew Machalinsk. **Dist. by:** Ars Polona, Krakowskie Przedmiescie 7, Warsaw, Poland. TEL 48-22-9263914, FAX 48-22-9265334, arspolona@arspolona.com.pl, http://www.arspolona.com.pl.

551.46   BRA   ISSN 0102-6224
QH91.A1   CODEN: NERIEE
➤ **NERITICA.** Text in English, Portuguese, Spanish. 1986. a. back issues avail. **Document type:** *Academic/Scholarly.*
Related titles: Fax ed.
Indexed: ASFA, B&BAb, ESPM, OceAb, SWRA, ZooRec.
Published by: Editora da Universidade Federal do Parana, Centro Politecnico, CX Postal 19029, Curitiba, PARANA, Brazil. TEL 55-41-366-2323, FAX 55-41-267-5973. Ed., R&P Paulo Lana TEL 55-41-4551333. Circ: 500.

551.46   NLD   ISSN 0165-9162
GC59.54
NETHERLANDS INSTITUTE FOR SEA RESEARCH. ANNUAL REPORT. Text in English. 1971. a. free. charts; illus.; stat. **Document type:** *Corporate.* **Description:** Outlines the activities, accomplishments, and plans of the Netherlands Institute for Sea Research.
Indexed: ASFA, ESPM, OceAb, RefZh.
—BLDSC (1371.730000), IE, ingenta, KNAW, Linda Hall.
Published by: Netherlands Institute for Sea Research/Nederlands Instituut voor Onderzoek der Zee (Subsidiary of: Nederlandse Organisatie voor Wetenschappelijk Onderzoek/Netherlands Organization for Scientific Research), PO Box 59, Den Burg, Texel 1790 AB, Netherlands. TEL 31-222-369362, FAX 31-222-319674, http://www.nioz.nl.

551.4   MCO
NEW INTERNATIONAL HYDROGRAPHIC BULLETIN/NOUVEAU BULLETIN HYDROGRAPHIQUE INTERNATIONAL/NUEVO BOLETIN HIDROGRAFICO INTERNACIONAL. Text in English, French, Spanish. 2000. 10/yr. bk.rev. bibl.; illus. index. reprint service avail. from PQC,ISI.
Formed by the merger of (1928-2000): International Hydrographic Bulletin (0020-6938); (1923-2000): International Hydrographic Review (0020-6946)
Indexed: ASFA, CTO, ESPM, FLUIDEX, RefZh.
—BLDSC (6084.254250), CISTI, Linda Hall.
Published by: International Hydrographic Bureau, 4 quai Antoine 1er, B.P. 445, Monte Carlo, MC 98011 Cedex, Monaco. TEL 377-93108100, FAX 377-93252003, TELEX 479164MC-INHORG, ihb@unice.fr, info@ihb.mc, http://www.iho.shom.fr. Circ: 600.

NEW YORK SEA GRANT INSTITUTE. REPORT SERIES. see *BIOLOGY*

578.77   NZL   ISSN 0028-8330
QH91.A1   CODEN: NZJMBS
➤ **NEW ZEALAND JOURNAL OF MARINE AND FRESHWATER RESEARCH.** Text in English. 1967. q. NZD 210, USD 140 combined subscription to individuals print & online eds.; NZD 445, USD 320 combined subscription to institutions print & online eds. (effective 2006). adv. abstr.; bibl.; charts; illus. Index. back issues avail. **Document type:** *Journal, Academic/Scholarly.* **Description:** Publishes papers on all fields of fisheries and aquatic science in the Pacific and Antarctic region.
Related titles: Online - full text ed.: NZD 180, USD 120 to individuals; NZD 380, USD 275 to institutions (effective 2006) (from EBSCO Publishing)
Indexed: ASCA, ASFA, AnBeAb, AnBrAb, ApEcolAb, BIOBASE, BIOSIS Prev, BiolAb, CIN, CTO, ChemAb, ChemTitl, CivEngAb, CurCont, DSA, EIA, EPB, ESPM, EngInd, EntAb, EnvAb, EnvEAb, ExcerpMed, FLUIDEX, FS&TA, ForAb, GEOBASE, HerbAb, I&DA, IABS, INIS AtomInd, ISR, IndVet, M&GPA, MBA, OceAb, PollutAb, ProtozoAb, S&F, SCI, SFA, SPPI, SWRA, VetBull, WeedAb, ZooRec.
—BLDSC (6094.550000), CASDDS, CISTI, Ei, IDS, IE, ingenta, Linda Hall. **CCC.**

E

Published by: R S N Z Publishing, PO Box 598, Wellington, New Zealand. TEL 64-4-4727421, FAX 64-4-4731841, sales@rsnz.org, http://www.rsnz.govt.nz/publish/nzjmfr/. Ed. S Stanislawek. Circ: 500. **Subscr. to:** R S N Z Publishing, PO Box 7075, Lawrence, KS 66044-7075. TEL 785-843-1235, FAX 785-843-1274, sir@allenpress.com.

➤ **NEW ZEALAND MARINE SCIENCES SOCIETY REVIEW.** see *BIOLOGY*

➤ **NEWSLETTER GOLD, SILVER AND URANIUM FROM SEAS AND OCEANS PROGRESS UPDATE.** see *ENGINEERING—Chemical Engineering*

551.46 NGA
NIGERIAN INSTITUTE FOR OCEANOGRAPHY AND MARINE RESEARCH. ANNUAL REPORT. Text in English. a.
Published by: Nigerian Institute for Oceanography and Marine Research, 1 Wilmot Point Road Bar Beach, Victoria Island, PMG 12729, Lagos, Nigeria. TEL 234-1-2617530, FAX 234-1-2629517, niomr@linkserve.com.ng, niomr@hyperia.com.

551.46 621.3 JPN ISSN 0369-4550
GC821 CODEN: NKAGBU
NIHON KAISUI GAKKAISHI/SOCIETY OF SEA WATER SCIENCE, JAPAN. BULLETIN. Text in English, Japanese. 1947. bi-m. JPY 6,000 membership (effective 2005). cum.index. back issues avail. **Document type:** *Journal, Academic/Scholarly.*
Indexed: ASFA, ChemAb, ESPM, INIS Atomlnd, JPI, MSB.
—CASDDS, CISTI, Linda Hall. **CCC.**
Published by: Nihon Kaisui Gakkai/Society of Sea Water Science, Japan, 4-13-20, Sakawa, Odawara-shi, Kanagawa 256-0816, Japan. http://www.ic.it-chiba.ac.jp/kaisuigakkai/p3/frame.html. Circ: 1,000.

NIHON KOKAI GAKKAI RONBUNSHU/JAPAN INSTITUTE OF NAVIGATION. JOURNAL. see *TRANSPORTATION—Ships And Shipping*

551.46 JPN ISSN 0287-623X
NIHONKAIIKI KENKYUJO HOKOKU/KANAZAWA UNIVERSITY. JAPAN SEA RESEARCH INSTITUTE. BULLETIN. Text in Japanese. 1969. a. **Document type:** *Academic/Scholarly.*
Indexed: ESPM, ZooRec.
Published by: Kanazawa Daigaku, Chigaku Kyoshitsu/Kanazawa University, Department of Earth Sciences, Faculty of Science, Kakuma-machi, Kanazawa, 920-1192, Japan. http://earth.s.kanazawa-u.ac.jp/homeJPN.html.

551.46 CAN ISSN 1192-7771
GC781
NORTH PACIFIC MARINE SCIENCE ORGANIZATION. ANNUAL REPORT. Text in English. a.
Indexed: ESPM.
Published by: North Pacific Marine Science Organization, PICES Secretariat, c/o Institute of Ocean Sciences, 9860 W Saanich Rd, PO Box 6000, Sidney, BC V8L 4B2, Canada. TEL 250-363-6364, FAX 250-363-6827, http://www.pices.int/index.asp.

551.46 570 ITA ISSN 0369-5271
NOVA THALASSIA. Text in Italian. 1948. irreg.
Indexed: ESPM.
Published by: (Universita degli Studi di Trieste, Facolta di Scienze Matematiche, Fisiche e Naturali, Laboratorio di Biologia Marina/Marine Biology Laboratory), Edizioni Lint Trieste, Viale Ortles 54a, Milan, 20139, Italy. TEL 39-02-5220181, FAX 39-02-52201820, lint@lint.it.

551.46 KEN
O D I N AFRICA ANNUAL REPORT. Text in English. a.
Formerly (until 2001): RECOSCIX-WIO. Annual Report
Published by: Ocean Data and Information Network for Africa, Kenya Marine and Fisheries Research Institute, PO Box 95832, Mombasa, Kenya. TEL 254-11-472527, FAX 254-11-475157, m.odido@unesco.org, http://www.odinafrica.org.

551.46 JPN ISSN 0289-9078
O D P NYUSU RETA/O D P NEWSLETTER. (Ocean Drilling Program) Text in English, Japanese. 1984. irreg. **Document type:** *Newsletter.*
Published by: O D P Kokunai Kenkyu Renrakukai/National Committee for Ocean Drilling Program, Daigaku Kaiyo Kenkyujo, 15-1 Minami-Dai 1-chome, Nakano-ku, Tokyo, 164-0014, Japan.

551.46 NCL
O.R.S.T.O.M. RESUMES DES TRAVAUX. OCEANOGRAPHIE. Text in French; Summaries in English, French. 1969. biennial. avail. on exchange. **Document type:** *Bibliography.*
Formerly: O.R.S.T.O.M. Recueils des Travaux. Oceanographie (0078-2130)
Indexed: ASFA, SFA.
Published by: Office de la Recherche Scientifique et Technique Outre-Mer, Centre O.R.S.T.O.M., PO Box A5, Noumea, New Caledonia. TEL 687-261000, FAX 687-264326, TELEX 3193 NM ORSTOM, http://www.ird.nc, grandper@noumea.ird.nc, grandper@noumea.ird.nc, http://www.ird.nc. Ed. Rene Grandperrin. Circ: 270.

551.46 USA
▼ **OCEAN;** to celebrate and protect. Text in English. 2004. q. USD 15.50; USD 3.95 newsstand/cover (effective 2004). adv. **Document type:** *Magazine, Consumer.* **Description:** Publishes scientific articles, stories, experiences and poems about the ocean.
Published by: d b productions, 23213 Sudie Payne Rd, PO Box 84, Rodanthe, NC 27968. TEL 252-987-2985, FAX 252-987-2985, diane@oceanmag.org, http://www.oceanmag.org. Ed., Pub., R&P, Adv. contact Diane Buccheri.

551.46 GBR ISSN 0964-5691
GC1000 CODEN: OCMAEU
➤ **OCEAN & COASTAL MANAGEMENT.** Text in English. 1973. 12/yr. EUR 1,375 in Europe to institutions; JPY 182,600 in Japan to institutions; USD 1,538 to institutions except Europe and Japan (effective 2006). adv. bk.rev. charts; illus. back issues avail.; reprints avail. **Document type:** *Academic/Scholarly.* **Description:** Covers all aspects of ocean and coastal management at local, regional, national and international levels.
Former titles (until 1992): Ocean and Shoreline Management (0951-8312); (until 1988): Ocean Management (0302-184X)
Related titles: Microform ed.: (from PQC); Online - full text ed.: (from EBSCO Publishing, Gale Group, IngentaConnect, ScienceDirect, Swets Information Services).
Indexed: ASCA, ASFA, BIOBASE, BibInd, BiolAb, CivEngAb, CurCont, EIA, EPB, ESPM, EnerInd, EnerRev, EngInd, EnvAb, EnvEAb, ExcerpMed, FLUIDEX, GEOBASE, IABS, IPSA, KES, M&GPA, M&TEA, MAB, MSCT, OceAb, PAIS, PollutAb, SFA, SSCI, SWRA, WAE&RSA, ZooRec.
—BLDSC (6231.271920), CISTI, Ei, IDS, IE, Infotrieve, ingenta, Linda Hall. **CCC.**
Published by: Pergamon (Subsidiary of: Elsevier Science & Technology), The Boulevard, Langford Ln, East Park, Kidlington, Oxford OX5 1GB, United Kingdom. TEL 44-1865-843000, FAX 44-1865-843010, http://www.elsevier.com/locate/ocecoaman. Eds. B Cicin-Sain, I P Jolliffe, R W Knecht. **Subscr. to:** Elsevier BV, PO Box 211, Amsterdam 1000 AE, Netherlands. TEL 31-20-485-3757, FAX 31-20-485-3432, nlinfo-f@elsevier.nl, http://www.elsevier.nl.

551.46 KOR ISSN 1598-141X
GC59.81.K6
OCEAN AND POLAR RESEARCH. Text in Korean. 2001. q. **Document type:** *Journal, Academic/Scholarly.*
Formed by the merger of (1990-2001): Han'gug Geugji Yeon'gu/Korean Journal of Polar Research (1225-021X); (1985-2001): Haeyang Yeon'gu/Ocean Research (1011-2723); Which was formerly (1979-1984): Haeyang Yeon'guso So'bo/Korea Ocean Research and Development Institute. Bulletin (0254-1777); Hainyan Gaibar Nyenguso Sobo/Korea Ocean Research and Development Institute. Bulletin (0253-6161)
Indexed: ASFA, ESPM, FLUIDEX, GEOBASE, M&GPA, OceAb, ZooRec.
Published by: Korea Ocean Research and Development Institute, P.O. Box 29, Ansan, 425-600, Korea, S. TEL 82-31-400-6000, FAX 82-31-408-5820, http://www.kordi.re.kr/.

551.46 570 USA
OCEAN BIOCOENOSIS SERIES. Text in English. 1992 (no.5). irreg. price varies. **Document type:** *Monographic series.*
Published by: (Mail Stop No. 5), Woods Hole Oceanographic Institution, Mail Stop 5, Woods Hole, MA 02543-1050. TEL 508-289-2865, FAX 508-289-2156, http://www.whoi.edu/. Ed. Susumu Honjo. **Subscr. to:** WHOI Publication Services, PO Box 50145, New Bedford, MA 02745-0005. TEL 800-291-6458.

551.46 GBR ISSN 0959-0161
GC1 CODEN: OCCHEZ
OCEAN CHALLENGE. Text in English. 1990. 3/yr. GBP 80, USD 152 (effective 2000). adv. bk.rev. **Document type:** *Academic/Scholarly.* **Description:** Contains articles of wide interest on marine science, accounts of the meetings of the Challenger Society and other oceanographic organizations, together with notices of new marine science publications.
Supersedes (in 1990): Challenger Society. Newsletter (0306-7335); Which superseded (in 1975): Challenger Society. Proceedings
—BLDSC (6231.272500). **CCC.**
Published by: (Challenger Society for Marine Science), Parjon Information Services, Parjon Information Services, Haywards Heath, W Sussex RH16 2YX, United Kingdom. TEL 44-444-483661, FAX 44-151-6536269, http://www.soc.soton.ac.uk/others/csms/ochal/chall.htm. Ed., R&P, Adv. contact Angela Colling. Pub. Jon Parry. Circ: 600.

551.46 USA ISSN 0090-8320
K15
➤ **OCEAN DEVELOPMENT AND INTERNATIONAL LAW.** Text in English. 1973. q. GBP 354, USD 584 combined subscription to institutions print & online eds. (effective 2006). adv. bk.rev. abstr.; charts; stat. index, cum.index. reprint service avail. from WSH,PSC. **Document type:** *Journal, Academic/Scholarly.* **Description:** Focuses on the international aspects of ocean regulation, affairs, and all forms of ocean utilization.
Formerly (until 1973): Ocean Development and International Law Journal (0883-4873)
Related titles: Microfiche ed.: (from WSH); Microform ed.: (from WSH); Online - full text ed.: ISSN 1521-0642. GBP 336, USD 555 to institutions (effective 2006) (from EBSCO Publishing, Gale Group, IngentaConnect, O C L C Online Computer Library Center, Inc., Swets Information Services).
Indexed: ABS&EES, APEL, ASCA, ASFA, BrCerAb, C&ISA, CJA, CLI, CTA, CerAb, CorrAb, CurCont, E&CAJ, ELJI, EMA, EPB, ESPM, EnvAb, EnvEAb, FLP, GEOBASE, IAA, IBSS, ILP, IPARL, IPSA, IndIslam, JEL, KES, LJI, LRI, LegCont, M&TEA, MAB, MBF, METADEX, OceAb, PAIS, PRA, PSA, RASB, SFA, SPPI, SSCI, SolStAb, WAA, WildRev.
—BLDSC (6231.275000), IDS, IE, Infotrieve, ingenta, Linda Hall. **CCC.**
Published by: Taylor & Francis Inc. (Subsidiary of: Taylor & Francis Group), 325 Chestnut St, Ste 800, Philadelphia, PA 19016. TEL 215-625-8900, 800-354-1420, FAX 215-625-2940, info@taylorandfrancis.com, http://www.tandf.co.uk/journals/titles/00908320.asp, http://www.taylorandfrancis.com. Ed. Ted L McDorman. **Subscr. addr. in Europe:** Taylor & Francis Ltd, Journals Customer Service, Rankine Rd, Basingstoke, Hants RG24 8PR, United Kingdom. TEL 44-1256-813000, FAX 44-1256-330245, enquiry@tandf.co.uk.

551.46 USA ISSN 0884-5883
QE39 CODEN: PODRET
OCEAN DRILLING PROGRAM. PROCEEDINGS. INITIAL REPORTS. Text in English. irreg. (approx. 6/yr.), latest vol.210, 2004, Oct. free (effective 2005). adv. cum.index. back issues avail. **Document type:** *Proceedings.* **Description:** Reports on the results of investigations of the Earth's crust beneath the world's ocean basins, as determined from core samples.
Formerly (until 1987): Scripps Institution of Oceanography. Deep Sea Drilling Project. Initial Reports (0080-8334)
Related titles: CD-ROM ed.: ISSN 1096-2522; Online - full text ed.: ISSN 1096-2158. free (effective 2005).
Indexed: ChemAb, Inspec, PetrolAb, ZooRec.
—AskIEEE, CASDDS, CISTI, Linda Hall.
Published by: Texas A&M University, Ocean Drilling Program, 1000 Discovery Dr, College Station, TX 77845-9547. TEL 979-845-2016, FAX 979-862-3527, TELEX 62760290, distribution@odemailp.tamu.edu, http://www-odp.tamu.edu/publications/pubs.htm, http://www-odp.tamu.edu/pulications/. Ed. Angie Miller. R&P, Adv. contact Kathy Phillips TEL 979-845-1911. Circ: 50 (paid); 1,550 (controlled).

551.46 USA ISSN 0884-5891
QE39 CODEN: POSRE2
➤ **OCEAN DRILLING PROGRAM. SCIENTIFIC RESULTS. PROCEEDINGS. SCIENTIFIC RESULTS.** Text in English. 1988. irreg. (approx. 6/yr.). price varies. cum.index. back issues avail. **Document type:** *Proceedings, Academic/Scholarly.* **Description:** Report on the results of investigations of the Earth's crust beneath the world's ocean basins, as determined from core samples.
Related titles: CD-ROM ed.: ISSN 1096-2514; Online - full text ed.: ISSN 1096-7451. free (effective 2005).
Indexed: AESIS, CIN, ChemAb, ChemTitl, GEOBASE, Inspec, MSB, PetrolAb, ZooRec.
—AskIEEE, CASDDS, CISTI, Linda Hall.
Published by: Texas A&M University, Ocean Drilling Program, 1000 Discovery Dr, College Station, TX 77845-9547. TEL 979-845-2016, FAX 979-862-3527, distribution@odpemail.tamu.edu, jennifer_rumford@odpemail.tamu.edu, http://www-odp.tamu.edu/publications/. Ed. Angie Miller. R&P Kathy Phillips TEL 979-845-1911. Circ: 50 (paid); 1,550 (controlled).

551.48 DEU ISSN 1616-7341
VK588 CODEN: DHYZA7
➤ **OCEAN DYNAMICS/GERMAN JOURNAL OF HYDROGRAPHY;** theoretical, computational oceanography and monitoring. Text in English. 1873. bi-m. EUR 360 combined subscription to institutions print & online eds. (effective 2005). adv. bk.rev. bibl.; charts; illus. index. back issues avail. **Document type:** *Journal, Academic/Scholarly.* **Description:** Devoted to the study of dynamic processes in the oceans with emphasis given to shelf areas.
Formerly (until 2001): Deutsche Hydrographische Zeitschrift (0012-0308); Which superseded in part (in 1948): Annalen der Hydrographie und Maritimen Meteorologie (0174-8114); Which was formerly (until 1874): Hydrographische Mitteilungen (0933-6508)
Related titles: Online - full text ed.: ISSN 1616-7228 (from EBSCO Publishing, ProQuest Information & Learning, Springer LINK, Swets Information Services).
Indexed: ASFA, BibCart, BiolAb, ChemAb, CurCont, ESPM, ExcerpMed, FLUIDEX, IBR, M&GPA, OceAb, RefZh, SWRA.
—BLDSC (6231.278000), CISTI, IE, ingenta, Linda Hall. **CCC.**
Published by: (Bundesamt fuer Seeschiffahrt und Hydrographie), Springer-Verlag (Subsidiary of: Springer Science+Business Media), Tiergartenstr 17, Heidelberg, 69121, Germany. TEL 49-6221-3450, FAX 49-6221-345229, http://link.springer.de/link/service/journals/10236/index.htm. Ed. Joerg-Olaf Wolff TEL 49-441-798-3404. Adv. contact Stephan Kroeck TEL 49-30-827875739. Circ: 450. **Subscr. in the Americas to:** Springer-Verlag New York, Inc., Journal Fulfillment, PO Box 2485, Secaucus, NJ 07096-2485. TEL 800-777-4643, 201-348-4033, FAX 201-348-4505, journals@springer-ny.com, http://www.springer-ny.com; **Subscr. to:** Springer GmbH Auslieferungsgesellschaft, Haberstr 7, Heidelberg 69126, Germany. TEL 49-6221-345-0, FAX 49-6221-345-4229, subscriptions@springer.de.

623 GBR ISSN 0029-8018
TC1501 CODEN: OCENBQ
➤ **OCEAN ENGINEERING.** Text in English. 1968. 18/yr. EUR 2,344 in Europe to institutions; JPY 311,400 in Japan to institutions; USD 2,622 to institutions except Europe and Japan; EUR 252 in Europe to qualified personnel; JPY 33,400 in Japan to qualified personnel; USD 282 to qualified personnel except Europe and Japan (effective 2006). adv. bk.rev. bibl.; charts; illus. Index. reprints avail. **Document type:** *Academic/Scholarly.* **Description:** Covers the design and building of ocean structures; submarine soil mechanics; coastal engineering; ocean energy; underwater instrumentation, marine resources and other related issues.
Related titles: Microfilm ed.: (from PQC); Online - full text ed.: (from EBSCO Publishing, Gale Group, IngentaConnect, ScienceDirect, Swets Information Services).
Indexed: AS&TI, ASFA, ApMecR, BMT, C&ISA, CTO, ChemAb, CivEngAb, CurCont, E&CAJ, EPB, ESPM, EnerRev, EngInd, ExcerpMed, FLUIDEX, GEOBASE, H&SSA, ICEA, ISMEC, ISR, Inspec, M&TEA, OceAb, PetrolAb, S&VD, SCI, SWRA, SolStAb.
—BLDSC (6231.280000), CISTI, Ei, IDS, IE, Infotrieve, ingenta, Linda Hall, PADDS. **CCC.**
Published by: Pergamon (Subsidiary of: Elsevier Science & Technology), The Boulevard, Langford Ln, East Park, Kidlington, Oxford OX5 1GB, United Kingdom. TEL 44-1865-843000, FAX 44-1865-843010, http://www.elsevier.com/locate/oceaneng. Eds. Michael E McCormick, Rameswar Bhattacharyya. Circ: 1,200. **Subscr. to:** Elsevier BV, PO Box 211, Amsterdam 1000 AE, Netherlands. TEL 31-20-485-3757, FAX 31-20-485-3432, nlinfo-f@elsevier.nl, http://www.elsevier.nl.

551.46 USA ISSN 1463-5003
GC201.2
➤ **OCEAN MODELLING.** Text in English. 1999. 20/yr. EUR 501 in Europe to institutions; JPY 66,500 in Japan to institutions; USD 561 to institutions except Europe and Japan (effective 2006). back issues avail. **Document type:** *Academic/Scholarly.* **Description:** Provides rapid communication between those interested in ocean modelling, whether through direct observation or through analytical, numerical or laboratory models.
Related titles: Online - full text ed.: Ocean Modelling (OMOD). ISSN 1463-5011 (from Gale Group, IngentaConnect, ScienceDirect, Swets Information Services).
Indexed: ASFA, CurCont, ESPM, GEOBASE, M&GPA, RefZh.
—BLDSC (6231.315760), CISTI, IE, ingenta, Linda Hall. **CCC.**
Published by: Elsevier Inc. (Subsidiary of: Elsevier Science & Technology), 360 Park Ave. S, New York, NY 10010-1710. TEL 212-633-3730, 888-437-4636, usinfo-f@elsevier.com, http://www.elsevier.com/locate/ocemod. Ed. Peter Killworth.

551.46 USA ISSN 1082-6106
CODEN: WAVEEP
OCEAN NEWS & TECHNOLOGY. Text in English. 1981; N.S. 1995. bi-m. USD 29 domestic; USD 45 in Canada; USD 80 elsewhere; free to qualified personnel (effective 2005). adv. bk.rev. back issues avail. **Document type:** *Magazine, Trade.* **Description:** Focuses on international underwater ocean technology and trends. Covers defense, offshore oil and gas, underwater vehicles, diving, and advanced imaging. Includes calendar of events, shows and conferences as well as information on people in the industry.
Former titles (until Sep. 1995): Underwater News and Technology (1069-6547); (until June 1993): Waves (1055-0348); (until Jan. 1991): Subnotes (0889-7166)
Related titles: Online - full text ed.: (from bigchalk, Northern Light Technology, Inc., ProQuest Information & Learning).
Indexed: ASFA, ESPM, OceAb.
—IE, Infotrieve.
Published by: Technology Systems Corporation, 7897 S W Jack James Dr, Ste A, Ste 130, Stuart, FL 34997. TEL 772-221-7720, FAX 772-221-7715, techsystems@sprintmail.com, http://www.ocean-news.com. Ed. Dan White. Adv. contact Mj McDuffee. B&W page USD 2,300, color page USD 2,800; trim 11 x 8.5. Circ: 21,000 (paid and controlled).

551.46 USA ISSN 1041-8091
GC2
OCEAN PERSPECTIVES JOURNAL. Text in English. 1987. q.?. **Published by:** Ocean Church, 481 8th Ave, Box G21, New York, NY 10001.

OCEAN REALM; international magazine of the sea. see *CONSERVATION*

551.46 DEU ISSN 1812-0784
▼ ➤ **OCEAN SCIENCE.** Text in English. 2005. irreg. **Document type:** *Journal, Academic/Scholarly.* **Description:** Dedicated to the publication and discussion of research articles, short communications and review papers on all aspects of ocean science, experimental, theoretical and laboratory.
Related titles: Online - full text ed.: ISSN 1812-0792. 2005. free (effective 2005).
Published by: Copernicus GmbH, Max-Planck Str 13, Katlenburg-Lindau, 37191, Germany. TEL 49-5556-91099, info@copernicus.org, http://www.copernicus.org.

551.46 DEU ISSN 1812-0806
▼ ➤ **OCEAN SCIENCE DISCUSSIONS.** Text in English. 2004. irreg. **Document type:** *Journal, Academic/Scholarly.* **Description:** Dedicated to the publication and discussion of research articles, short communications and review papers on all aspects of ocean science.
Related titles: Online - full text ed.: ISSN 1812-0822. free (effective 2005).
Published by: Copernicus GmbH, Max-Planck Str 13, Katlenburg-Lindau, 37191, Germany. TEL 49-5556-91099, info@copernicus.org, http://www.copernicus.org/EGU/os/os.html.

551.46 333.91 USA
OCEAN SCIENCE, RESOURCES AND TECHNOLOGY. Text in English. 1980. irreg., latest 1986. reprint service avail. from ISI.
Published by: Academic Press (Subsidiary of: Elsevier Science & Technology), 525 B St, Ste 1900, San Diego, CA 92101-4495. apsubs@acad.com, http://www.academicpress.com. Ed. D S Cronan.

551.46 333.9 USA ISSN 0191-8575
GC1000
➤ **OCEAN YEARBOOK.** Text in English. 1978. irreg., latest vol.16, 2002. price varies. bibl. index. back issues avail.; reprint service avail. from PQC,ISI. **Document type:** *Journal, Academic/Scholarly.* **Description:** Devoted to assessing the resources, ecology, technology, and strategic importance of the world's oceans.
Related titles: Microform ed.: (from PMC, PQC).
Indexed: ASFA, BAS, BIOSIS Prev, BiolAb, ESPM, MAB, OceAb, SFA, WildRev.
—BLDSC (6231.398000), Linda Hall.
Published by: (International Ocean Institute MLT), University of Chicago Press, Journals Division, Journals Division, PO Box 37005, Chicago, IL 60637. TEL 773-702-7600, FAX 773-702-0172, subscriptions@journals.uchicago.edu, mr@press.uchicago.edu, http://www.press.uchicago.edu/.

➤ **OCEANIC ENGINEERING INTERNATIONAL.** see *ENGINEERING—Hydraulic Engineering*

551.46 578.77 MEX ISSN 1560-8433
➤ **OCEANIDES.** Text and summaries in English, Spanish. 1984. s-a. MXP 400 domestic; USD 75 foreign (effective 2003). back issues avail. **Document type:** *Journal, Academic/Scholarly.* **Description:** Presents clinical papers on research in marine science related to physical and chemical oceanography, marine geology, marine biology and ecology and fisheries.
Formerly (until 1996): Investigaciones Marinas CICIMAR (0186-5102)
Related titles: Online - full text ed.
Indexed: ASFA, BIOSIS Prev, BiolAb, ESPM, FLUIDEX, GEOBASE, ZooRec.
Published by: Instituto Politecnico Nacional, Centro Interdisciplinario de Ciencias Marinas, Av. IPN s-n, Col. Playa Palo de Sta. Rita, La Paz, B.C.S. 23000, Mexico. TEL 52-612-1225344, FAX 52-612-1225322, oceanide@ipn.mx, oceanide@ipn.mex, http://www.cicimar.ipn.mx. Ed. Juan F Elorduy Garay. Pub. Juan F Elorduy-Garay. Circ: 500.

551.46 FRA ISSN 0182-0745
GC1 CODEN: OCAND8
OCEANIS; serie de documents oceanographiques. Variant title: Revue des Seminaires de l'Institut Oceanographique. Text in French. 1976. q. (plus 1 special issue). EUR 97 in the European Union; EUR 115 elsewhere (effective 2005). bk.rev. illus. back issues avail. **Document type:** *Journal, Academic/Scholarly.*
Indexed: ASFA, BIOSIS Prev, BiolAb, CIN, CTO, ChemAb, ChemTitl, ESPM, GEOBASE, M&GPA, MSCT, RefZh, SFA, WildRev, ZooRec.
—BLDSC (6231.600000), CASDDS, CISTI, IE, ingenta, Linda Hall. **CCC.**
Published by: Institut Oceanographique, Fondation Albert - 1er Prince de Monaco, 195 rue Saint Jacques, Paris, 75005, France. TEL 33-1-44321070, FAX 33-1-40517316, cdlb@oceano.org, http://www.oceano.org. Ed. Catherine de la Bigne. Circ: 250.

OCEANOGRAPHIC LITERATURE REVIEW. see *EARTH SCIENCES—Abstracting, Bibliographies, Statistics*

551.46 ZAF
OCEANOGRAPHIC RESEARCH INSTITUTE. SPECIAL PUBLICATION. Text in English. irreg., latest vol.7, 2002. price varies. **Document type:** *Monographic series, Academic/Scholarly.* **Description:** Reports on expeditions surveys and workshops or provides bibliographic and technical information.
Indexed: ASFA, SFA, ZooRec.
—BLDSC (8379.645000).
Published by: Oceanographic Research Institute, Marine Parade, PO Box 10712, Durban, KwaZulu-Natal 4056, South Africa. TEL 27-31-3373536, FAX 27-31-3372132, ori@ori.org.za, http://www.ori.org.za. R&P R P Van der Elst. Circ: 350 (controlled).

551.46 JPN ISSN 0369-707X
GC1 CODEN: OCMAAQ
OCEANOGRAPHICAL MAGAZINE/KISHOCHO OBUN KAIYO HOKOKU. Text in English. 1949. a. JPY 1,900.
Indexed: ASFA.
—CASDDS, CISTI, Linda Hall.
Published by: Kishocho/Japan Meteorological Agency, 3-4 Ote-Machi 1-chome, Chiyoda-ku, Tokyo, 100-0004, Japan. Circ: 788.

OCEANOGRAPHICAL SOCIETY OF JAPAN. ABSTRACTS ON THE CONFERENCE/NIHON KAIYO GAKKAI TAIKAI KOEN YOSHISHU. see *EARTH SCIENCES—Abstracting, Bibliographies, Statistics*

551.46 USA ISSN 1042-8275
GC1
➤ **OCEANOGRAPHY**; serving ocean science and its applications. Text in English. 1988. q. free to members (effective 2004). adv. bk.rev. illus. reprints avail. **Document type:** *Journal, Academic/Scholarly.*
Indexed: ASFA, M&GPA, OceAb, ZooRec.
—BLDSC (6233.620000), IE, ingenta.
Published by: Oceanography Society, 1931, Rockville, MD 20849-1931. TEL 804-464-0131, FAX 804-683-5550, anne@ccpo.odu.edu, http://tos.org/. Ed. Larry Atkinson. R&P Annee West Valle. Circ: 2,000 (paid).

578.77 GBR ISSN 0078-3218
GC1 CODEN: OCMBAT
OCEANOGRAPHY AND MARINE BIOLOGY; an annual review. Text in English. 1963. a., latest 2004, Jul. price varies. **Document type:** *Monographic series, Academic/Scholarly.* **Description:** Current volume contains analysis of convective chimneys in the Greenland Sea, spawning aggregations of coral reef fishes, exopolymers in aquatic systems, the marine insect Halobates, and much more.
Indexed: ASCA, ASFA, BiolAb, ChemAb, ISR, M&GPA, OceAb, SCI, SFA, ZooRec.
—BLDSC (6233.996000), CASDDS, CISTI, IE, ingenta, Linda Hall.
Published by: Taylor & Francis Ltd (Subsidiary of: Taylor & Francis Group), 4 Park Sq, Milton Park, Abingdon, OX14 4RN, United Kingdom. TEL 44-1235-828600, FAX 44-1235-829000, http://www.tandf.co.uk/books/. Eds. Margaret Barnes, R N Gibson, R J A Atkinson.

551.46 POL ISSN 0078-3234
GC1 CODEN: OCEGA4
➤ **OCEANOLOGIA.** Text in English. 1971. q. USD 96 foreign (effective 2005). bk.rev. abstr.; bibl.; illus. 130 p./no.; back issues avail.; reprint service avail. from PQC. **Document type:** *Journal, Academic/Scholarly.* **Description:** Presents works concerning maritime biology, physics, chemistry and other problems connected with maritime phenomena.
Related titles: Online - full text ed.: free (effective 2005).
Indexed: ASFA, AgrAg, AgrLib, ApMecR, CTO, CurCont, ESPM, EnvAb, FLUIDEX, GEOBASE, M&GPA, OceAb, PollutAb, RefZh, SWRA, ZooRec.
—Linda Hall.
Published by: Polska Akademia Nauk, Instytut Oceanologii/Polish Academy of Sciences, Institute of Oceanology, ul Powstancow Warszawy 55, Sopot, 81712, Poland. TEL 48-58-5517281, FAX 48-58-5512130, editor@iopan.gda.pl, http://www.iopan.gda.pl/oceanologia/. Ed., R&P Jerzy Dera TEL 48-58-5503232. **Co-sponsor:** Polska Akademia Nauk, Komitet Badan Morza/Polish Academy of Sciences, National Scientific Committee on Oceanic Research.

551.46 FRA ISSN 0399-1784
GC1 CODEN: OCACD9
➤ **OCEANOLOGICA ACTA**; European journal of oceanology - revue europeene de oceanologie. Text in English, French; Abstracts in English, French. 1978. bi-m. EUR 325 domestic; EUR 335 in the European Union; EUR 370 elsewhere (effective 2004). adv. abstr. back issues avail. **Document type:** *Journal, Academic/Scholarly.* **Description:** Presents results of works in all sections of oceanography and from all parts of the oceans and their adjacent estuaries and brackish water systems.
Related titles: Microform ed.; Online - full text ed.: (from EBSCO Publishing, Gale Group, IngentaConnect, ScienceDirect, Swets Information Services).
Indexed: ASCA, ASFA, AnBrAb, BIOBASE, BiolAb, CTO, ChemAb, ChemTitl, CurCont, ESPM, ExcerpMed, GEOBASE, HelmAb, IABS, INIS AtomInd, ISR, IndVet, Inspec, M&GPA, MBA, NutrAb, RefZh, S&F, SCI, SFA, SPPI, SWRA, ZooRec.
—BLDSC (6234.155000), AskIEEE, CASDDS, CISTI, IDS, IE, Infotrieve, ingenta, Linda Hall. **CCC.**
Published by: (Institute Franceis de Recherche pour l'Exploitation de la Mer (IFREMER)), E D P Sciences, 17 Ave du Hoggar, Parc d'Activites de Courtaboeuf, BP 112, Cedex A, Les Ulis, F-91944, France. TEL 33-1-69187575, FAX 33-1-69860678, subscribers@edpsciences.org, http://www.edpsciences.org.

E

▼ *new title* ➤ *refereed* ✶ *unverified* ♦ *full entry avail.*

551.46 POL ISSN 1730-413X
GC1 CODEN: OHSCBU
➤ **OCEANOLOGICAL AND HYDROBIOLOGICAL STUDIES.** Text in English. 1972. q. USD 50. abstr.; bibl.; charts; illus.; maps. 100 p./no. 1 cols./p.; **Document type:** *Journal, Academic/Scholarly.* **Description:** A series of sheets on various problems of the sea, including sea dynamics, sea physics, ecology of all kinds of water.
Former titles (until 2002): Oceanological Studies (1505-232X); (until 1996): Studia i Materialy Oceanologiczne (0208-421X)
Indexed: ASFA, AgrAg, CIN, ChemAb, ChemTitl, ESPM, GEOBASE, IBR, M&GPA, PollutAb, RefZh, ZooRec.
—CASDDS.
Published by: Uniwersytet Gdanski, Instytut Oceanologii/ University of Gdansk, Institute of Ocenography, ul Wladyslawa Andersa 27, Sopot, 81824, Poland. ohs@gnu.univ.gda.pl. Ed. Marcin Plinski. Circ: 320 (paid).

551.46 FRA ISSN 0985-3057
OCEANORAMA. Text in French. 1974. irreg.
Former titles (until 1985): Fondation Oceanographique Ricard. Revue (0243-6663); (until 1978): Fondation Scientifique Ricard. Observatoire de la Mer. Bulletin (0220-7257)
Indexed: ESPM.
Published by: Institut Oceanographique Paul Ricard, BP 308, Marseille, 13309 Cedex 14, France. TEL 33-4-91111061, FAX 33-4-91111557, http://www.institut-paul-ricard.org.

551.46 JPN
OCEANS CHOSA HOKOKU/JAPAN MARINE SCIENCE AND TECHNOLOGY CENTER. RESEARCH REPORT ON OCEANS. Text in Japanese. irreg., latest Occans '96 Chosa Hokokusho.
Published by: Kaiyo Kagaku Gijutsu Senta/Japan Marine Science and Technology Center, 2-15 Natsushima-cho, Yokosuka-shi, Kanagawa-ken 237-0061, Japan. TEL 81-468-67-5525, FAX 81-468-66-6169, info@jamstec.go.jp, http://www.jamstec.go.jp/.

551.46 636.0832 333.72 GBR
OCEANS ILLUSTRATED; giving voice to the silent world. Text in English. 2000. q. GBP 25 in United Kingdom; GBP 35 in Europe; USD 35 in North America; GBP 45 rest of world (effective 2001); Subscription only. bk.rev. illus.; maps; stat. back issues avail. **Document type:** *Magazine, Consumer.* **Description:** A celebration of the sea with photography and writing from the foremost marine photographers and writers in the world.
Published by: Dive International Publishing Ltd., Aaron House, 6 Bardolph Road, Richmond, Surrey TW9 2LH, United Kingdom. TEL 44-20-8332 2709, FAX 44-20-8332-9307, email@dive.uk.com, http://www.oceansillustrated.com. Ed. Douglas Seifert. Pub. Graeme Gourlay. Circ: 5,000 (paid).

551.46 USA ISSN 0029-8182
GC1 CODEN: OCEAAK
➤ **OCEANUS**; reports on research at the Woods Hole Oceanographic Institution. Text in English. 1952. s-a. USD 15 domestic; USD 18 in Canada; USD 25 elsewhere (effective 2000). adv. charts; illus. index, cum.index: vols.1-14. 16 p./no.; back issues avail.; reprint service avail. from PQC. **Document type:** *Magazine, Academic/Scholarly.* **Description:** Covers marine science and policy for the educated lay reader and specialist alike. Each issue provdes several articles on a single theme such as biodiversity, Atlantic Ocean circulation, or research in the Artctic.
Incorporates in 1994: Woods Hole Oceanographic Institution. Reports on Research (1062-2160)
Media: Magnetic Tape. **Related titles:** Microform ed.: (from PQC); Online - full text ed.: free (effective 2005) (from Florida Center for Library Automation, Gale Group, H.W. Wilson, Northern Light Technology, Inc., O C L C Online Computer Library Center, Inc., ProQuest Information & Learning); ♦ Supplement(s): Woods Hole Currents.
Indexed: AS&TI, ASCA, ASFA, Acal, B&AI, BiolAb, BiolDig, CRFR, CTO, ChemAb, CurCont, EPB, ESPM, EnvAb, EnvInd, ExcerpMed, FLUIDEX, FutSurv, GEOBASE, GSI, M&GPA, MASUSE, MSCT, OceAb, PollutAb, RefZh, SCI, SFA, SSCI, WildRev, ZooRec.
—BLDSC (6234.400000), IDS, IE, Infotrieve, ingenta, Linda Hall. **CCC.**
Published by: Woods Hole Oceanographic Institution, Mail Stop 5, Woods Hole, MA 02543-1050. TEL 508-289-3516, FAX 508-289-2182, http://www.whoi.edu, http://www.whoi.edu/oceanus. Ed. Laurence Lippsett. Circ: 6,000. **Subscr. to:** WHOI Publication Services, PO Box 50145, New Bedford, MA 02745-0005. TEL 800-291-6458, FAX 508-992-4556.

551.46 570 JPN
OCHANOMIZU UNIVERSITY. TATEYAMA MARINE LABORATORY. CONTRIBUTIONS. Text in English. 1975. a. **Document type:** *Academic/Scholarly.*
Published by: Ochanomizu University, Tateyama Marine Laboratory/Ochanomizu Joshi Daigaku Rigakubu Tateyama Rinkai Jikkenjo, 11-12 Koya-Tsu, Tateyama-shi, Chiba-ken 294-0301, Japan. TEL 0470-29-0838, FAX 0470-29-2123. Ed. Shin Ichi Nemoto.

551.46 ITA ISSN 0392-6613
GC1 CODEN: OEBAEN
OEBALIA. Text in Italian. 1975. 3/w.
Indexed: BIOSIS Prev, BiolAb, ESPM, ZooRec.
—BLDSC (6235.248140).
Published by: Istituto Sperimentale Talassografico Attilio Cerruti, Via Roma 3, Taranto, 74100, Italy. TEL 39-099-4542111, FAX 39-099-4542215, istta@istta.le.cnr.it, http://www.istta.le.cnr.it.

551.46 ESP ISSN 0210-9352
QH171
OECOLOGIA AQUATICA. Text in Spanish. 1973. irreg. price varies. **Document type:** *Journal, Academic/Scholarly.*
Indexed: ASFA, ESPM, IECT, ZooRec.
—CINDOC.
Published by: (Universitat de Barcelona, Facultat de Biologia), Universitat de Barcelona, Servei de Publicacions, Gran Via Corts Catalanes 585, Barcelona, 08007, Spain. TEL 34-93-4021100, http://www.publicacions.ub.es.

551.46 639.3 IDN ISSN 0125-9830
GC861
OSEANOLOGI DI INDONESIA. Text and summaries in English, Indonesian. 1974. q. IDR 3,200, USD 3. back issues avail.
Indexed: BAS.
Published by: Indonesian Institute of Sciences, Centre for Oceanological Research and Development/Lembaga Ilmu Pengetahuan Indonesia, Pusat Penelitian dan Pengembangan Oseanologi, Jl. Pasir Putih No. 1, Ancol Timur, Box 580 - DAK, Jakarta Utara, Indonesia. Ed. Dr. Subagjo Soemodihardjo. Circ: 450.

551.46 JPN ISSN 0388-5747
OTSUCHI RINKAI KENKYU SENTA HOKOKU/OTSUCHI MARINE RESEARCH CENTER REPORT. Text in English, Japanese; Summaries in Japanese. 1974. a.
Published by: (Otsuchi Rinkai Kenkyu Senta), Tokyo Daigaku, Kaiyo Kenkyujo/University of Tokyo, Ocean Research Institute, 106-1 Akahama 2-chome, Kamihei-gun, Otsuchi-cho, Iwate-ken 028-1102, Japan.

551.46 USA
PACIFIC RIM RESEARCH SERIES✱. Text in English. 1977 (vol.2). irreg. price varies. index. **Document type:** *Monographic series.*
Published by: D.C. Heath & Company, 222 Berkeley St, Boston, MA 02116-3748. TEL 617-862-6650.

PACIFIC SOCIETY. JOURNAL/TAIHEIYO GAKKAI SHI. see *ANTHROPOLOGY*

551.46 PAK ISSN 1019-8415
GC1
PAKISTAN JOURNAL OF MARINE SCIENCES. Text in English. 1992. s-a.
Indexed: ASFA, ESPM, M&GPA, OceAb, ZooRec.
—BLDSC (6341.500000).
Published by: (University of Karachi, Marine Reference and Resource Collection Centre), University of Karachi, University Campus, Karachi, 75270, Pakistan. TEL 92-21-479001, FAX 92-21-473226, http://www.ku.edu.pk.

560 551.783 USA ISSN 0883-8305
QE39.5.P25 CODEN: POCGEP
➤ **PALEOCEANOGRAPHY.** Text in English. 1986. m. USD 310 to institutions (effective 2006). abstr.; illus. Index. back issues avail.; reprints avail. **Document type:** *Journal, Academic/Scholarly.* **Description:** Deals with the history of the ocean system and its plants and animal life. Publishes studies based on marine sedimentary sections from the ocean basin and margins and from those ancient sediments exposed on the continents.
Related titles: Microfiche ed.: USD 345 (effective 2000) (from AGU, AIP); Microform ed.: (from AGU); Online - full content ed.; Online - full text ed.: (from EBSCO Publishing).
Indexed: AESIS, ASCA, ASFA, CurCont, ESPM, EngInd, GEOBASE, ISR, Inspec, M&GPA, OceAb, PetrolAb, SCI, SPINweb, ZooRec.
—BLDSC (6345.295000), AskIEEE, CISTI, Ei, IDS, IE, Infotrieve, ingenta, Linda Hall, PADDS. **CCC.**
Published by: American Geophysical Union, 2000 Florida Ave, NW, Washington, DC 20009-1277. TEL 202-462-6900, 800-966-2481, FAX 202-328-0566, institutions@agu.org, http://www.agu.org/journals/pa/. Eds. Larry Peterson, Lisa Sloan.

551.46 570 DZA ISSN 0031-4137
PELAGOS. Text in French; Summaries in English. 1963. s-a. DZD 60. illus. **Document type:** *Journal, Academic/Scholarly.*
Indexed: BiolAb.
—Linda Hall.
Published by: Institut des Sciences de la Mer et de l'Ameagement du Littoral, Sidi Fredj, B P 54, Algiers, 42321, Algeria. TEL 213-2-377076, FAX 213-2-376806, infos@ismal.net, http://www.ismal.net. **Dist. in U.S. by:** African & Caribbean Imprint Library Services, PO Box 2780, South Portland, ME 04116-2780. TEL 207-767-5333, FAX 207-767-5335, ailscils@msn.com, http://www.africanbooks.com/.

551.46 USA
GC1 CODEN: POHCAY
➤ **PHYSICAL OCEANOGRAPHY (ONLINE EDITION).** Text in English. 1987. bi-m. EUR 695, USD 708 to institutions (effective 2005). back issues avail.; reprint service avail. from PSC. **Document type:** *Journal, Academic/Scholarly.* **Description:** Provides coverage of recent advances in physical oceanography research.
Former titles (until 2003): Physical Oceanography (Print Edition) (0928-5105); (until 1993): Soviet Journal of Physical Oceanography (0920-5047)
Media: Online - full text (from Gale Group, IngentaConnect, O C L C Online Computer Library Center, Inc., Swets Information Services). **Related titles:** Translation of: Morskoi Gidrofizicheskii Zhurnal. ISSN 0233-7584.
Indexed: ASFA, BibLing, ESPM, FLUIDEX, GEOBASE, M&GPA, M&TEA, OceAb, SWRA.
—BLDSC (0416.823000), CISTI, IE, Infotrieve, ingenta. **CCC.**
Published by: Consultants Bureau (Subsidiary of: Springer-Verlag New York, Inc.), 233 Spring St, New York, NY 10013. TEL 212-460-1500, FAX 212-460-1575, service@springer-ny.com, http://springerlink.metapress.com/openurl.asp?genre=journal&issn=0928-5105, http://www.springeronline.com. Ed. Valery N Eremeev.

551.46 CAN ISSN 1195-2512
GC781
PICES PRESS. Text in English. 1993. q.
Indexed: ESPM.
Published by: North Pacific Marine Science Organization, PICES Secretariat, c/o Institute of Ocean Sciences, 9860 W Saanich Rd, PO Box 6000, Sidney, BC V8L 4B2, Canada. TEL 250-363-6364, FAX 250-363-6827, http://www.pices.int/index.asp.

551.46 CAN ISSN 1198-273X
PICES SCIENTIFIC REPORT. Text in English. irreg.
Indexed: ESPM.
Published by: North Pacific Marine Science Organization, PICES Secretariat, c/o Institute of Ocean Sciences, 9860 W Saanich Rd, PO Box 6000, Sidney, BC V8L 4B2, Canada. TEL 250-363-6364, FAX 250-363-6827, http://www.pices.int/index.asp.

551.46 GBR ISSN 1466-0369
PORCUPINE MARINE NATURAL HISTORY SOCIETY. NEWSLETTER. Text in English. 1976. 3/yr. GBP 10 to individuals; GBP 5 to students. **Document type:** *Newsletter.*
Formerly (until 1998): Porcupine Newsletter (0309-3085)
Indexed: ZooRec.
Published by: Porcupine Marine Natural History Society, 163 High Rd W., Felixstowe, Suffolk IP11 9BD, United Kingdom.

551.46 JPN
PRELIMINARY REPORT OF THE HAKUHO MARU CRUISE. Text in English. 1968. a.
Indexed: RefZh, SFA.
Published by: Tokyo Daigaku, Kaiyo Kenkyujo/University of Tokyo, Ocean Research Institute, 15-1 Minami-Dai 1-chome, Nakano-ku, Tokyo, 164-0014, Japan.

551.46 AUS ISSN 1326-4834
PROBE NEWSLETTER. Text in English. m. **Document type:** *Newsletter.*
Published by: Australian Oceanographic Data Center, Maritime Headquarters, Wylde St, Potts Point, NSW, Australia. TEL 61-2-9359-3115, FAX 61-2-9359-3120, aodc@aodc.gov.au, http://www.aodc.gov.au.

551.46 NLD ISSN 1568-2692
PROCEEDINGS IN MARINE SCIENCE. Text in English. 2000. irreg. price varies. **Document type:** *Proceedings, Academic/Scholarly.*
Indexed: ASFA, ESPM.
—BLDSC (6847.263300), CISTI.
Published by: Elsevier BV (Subsidiary of: Elsevier Science & Technology), Radarweg 29, Amsterdam, 1043 NX, Netherlands. TEL 31-20-4853911, FAX 31-20-4852457, nlinfo-f@elsevier.nl, http://www.elsevier.nl.

551.46 GBR ISSN 0079-6611
GC1 CODEN: POCNA8
➤ **PROGRESS IN OCEANOGRAPHY.** Text in English. 1963. 16/yr. EUR 2,369 in Europe to institutions; JPY 314,500 in Japan to institutions; USD 2,650 to institutions except Europe and Japan; EUR 168 in Europe to qualified personnel; JPY 22,600 in Japan to qualified personnel; USD 189 to qualified personnel except Europe and Japan (effective 2006). adv. illus. index. reprints avail. **Document type:** *Academic/Scholarly.* **Description:** Publishes extended reviews of specific topics in oceanography and treatises on oceanographic subjects.
Related titles: Microfilm ed.: (from PQC); Online - full text ed.: (from EBSCO Publishing, Gale Group, IngentaConnect, ScienceDirect, Swets Information Services).
Indexed: ASCA, ASFA, ApMecR, BIOBASE, BiolAb, CTO, ChemAb, CurCont, EPB, ESPM, EnerRev, EngInd, GEOBASE, IABS, ISR, Inspec, M&GPA, M&TEA, OceAb, PollutAb, SCI, SFA, SWRA, ZooRec.
—BLDSC (6871.300000), AskIEEE, CISTI, Ei, IDS, IE, Infotrieve, ingenta, Linda Hall. **CCC.**

E

Published by: Pergamon (Subsidiary of: Elsevier Science & Technology), The Boulevard, Langford Ln, East Park, Kidlington, Oxford OX5 1GB, United Kingdom. TEL 44-1865-843000, FAX 44-1865-843010, http:// www.elsevier.com/locate/pocean. Eds. Charles B. Miller, Detlef R. Quadfasel. **Subscr. to:** Elsevier BV, PO Box 211, Amsterdam 1000 AE, Netherlands. TEL 31-20-485-3757, FAX 31-20-485-3432, nlinfo-f@elsevier.nl, http://www.elsevier.nl.

551.46 341   NLD   ISSN 0924-1922
➤ **PUBLICATIONS ON OCEAN DEVELOPMENT;** a series of studies on the international, legal, institutional and policy aspects of the ocean development. Text in English. 1976. irreg., latest vol.38, 2005. price varies. back issues avail. **Document type:** *Monographic series, Academic/Scholarly.*
Formerly (until 1983): Sijthoff Publications on Ocean Development (0167-5362)
—BLDSC (7132.900000), IE, ingenta.
Published by: Martinus Nijhoff (Subsidiary of: Brill Academic Publishers), Brill Academic Publishers, PO Box 9000, Leiden, 2300 PA, Netherlands. TEL 31-71-5353500, FAX 31-71-5317532, http://www.nijhoff.nl.

551.46   CHN   ISSN 1001-1862
GC1   CODEN: QHDXE9
QINGDAO HAIYANG DAXUE XUEBAO/OCEAN UNIVERSITY OF QINGDAO. JOURNAL. Text in Chinese; Abstracts in English. 1959. bi-m. USD 7 per issue (effective 2004). 164 p./no.; **Document type:** *Journal, Academic/Scholarly.* **Description:** Features ocean sciences, papers in basic research, applied basic research and high- and new- technology developments.
Formerly (until 1988): Shandong Haiyangxue Yuan Xuebao/Shandong College of Oceanology. Journal (0253-3588)
Related titles: Online - full text ed.: (from East View Information Services); ♦ English ed.: China Ocean University. Journal. ISSN 1671-2463.
Indexed: ASFA, CCMJ, ChemAb, ESPM, M&TEA, MathR, MathSciNet, RefZh, ZentMath, ZooRec.
—BLDSC (4834.480000), CASDDS, CISTI, IE, ingenta.
Published by: Qingdao Haiyang Daxue, Xuebao Bianjibu/Ocean University of China, Journal Editorial Office, No 5, Yushan Lu, Qingdao, Shandong, China. TEL 86-532-2032256, xbzrb@mail.ouc.edu.cn, http://www.ouc.edu.cn/xbzrb. Ed. Shengchang Wen. Pub. Wei Yu. R&P Fegnqi Li. **Dist. overseas by:** China International Book Trading Corp, 35 Chegongzhuang Xilu, Haidian District, PO Box 399, Beijing 100044, China. TEL 86-10-68412045, FAX 86-10-68412023, cibtc@mail.cibtc.com.cn, http://www.cibtc.com.cn.

551   JPN   ISSN 0915-9851
GC38
R N O D C ACTIVITY REPORT. Text in Japanese. 1990. a. **Document type:** *Newsletter, Government.* **Description:** Covers JODC activities for data contributors, data users, oceanographic communities and other national oceanographic data centers.
Published by: (Responsible National Oceanographic Data Center), Japan Oceanographic Data Center, Hydrographic Department, Maritime Safety Agency, 5-3-1 Tsuki-Ji, Chuo-ku, Tokyo, 104-0045, Japan. TEL 81-3-3541-4295. Ed. Goro Matsura. Circ: 600.

551.46   JPN   ISSN 0287-5098
R N O D C NEWSLETTER FOR WESTPAC. Text in English. 1982. a. **Document type:** *Newsletter.*
Published by: (Responsible National Oceanographic Data Center, Hydrographic Department), Japan Oceanographic Data Center, Hydrographic Department, Maritime Safety Agency, 5-3-1 Tsuki-Ji, Chuo-ku, Tokyo, 104-0045, Japan. TEL 81-3-3541-4295. Ed. Goro Matsura.

551.46   JPN
R O V CHOSA HOKOKUSHO/TECHNICAL REPORT OF REMOTELY OPERATED VEHICLE. Text in Japanese. irreg.
Published by: Kaiyo Kagaku Gijutsu Senta/Japan Marine Science and Technology Center, 2-15 Natsushima-cho, Yokosuka-shi, Kanagawa-ken 237-0061, Japan. TEL 81-468-66-3811, FAX 81-468-66-6169, info@jamstec.go.jp, http://www.jamstec.go.jp/.

551.46   NCL   ISSN 1244-6432
RAPPORTS SCIENTIFIQUES ET TECHNIQUES. SCIENCES DE LA MER. OCEANOGRAPHIE PHYSIQUE. Text in Multiple languages. 1989. irreg.
Published by: Institut de Recherche pour le Developpement, Centre de Noumea, 101 Promenade Roger Laroque - Anse Vata, Noumea, BP A5 - 98848, New Caledonia. TEL 687 26 10 00, FAX 687 26 43 26, http://www.ird.nc.

551.46   IND
RECENT RESEARCH DEVELOPMENTS IN PHYSICAL OCEANOGRAPHY. Text in English. a.
—BLDSC (7305.087570).
Published by: Transworld Research Network, T C 36-248 (1), Trivandrum, Kerala 695 008, India. http:// www.transworldresearch.com.

551.46   CHN   ISSN 1009-5470
GC880   CODEN: REHAEI
➤ **REDAI HAIYANG XUEBAO/TROPIC OCEANOLOGY.** Text in Chinese; Summaries in English. 1982. q. CNY 48 (effective 2004). adv. **Document type:** *Journal, Academic/Scholarly.* **Description:** Publishes papers and research results on the tropical and sub-tropical zones, mainly in the South China Sea and its adjacent oceans. Covers physical oceanography and meteorology, marine physics, geotectonics, sedimentation, coasts and estuaries, marine biology, chemistry, and pollution.
Formerly: Redai Haiyang (1000-3053)
Related titles: Online - full text ed.: (from East View Information Services, WanFang Data Corp.).
Indexed: ASFA, CIN, ChemAb, ChemTitl, ESPM, RefZh, SFA, ZooRec.
—BLDSC (5071.070000), CASDDS, CISTI.
Published by: (Zhongguo Kexueyuan, Nanhai Haiyang Yanjiusuo/Chinese Academy of Sciences, South China Sea Institute of Oceanology), Kexue Chubanshe/Science Press, 16 Donghuang Cheng Genbei Jie, Beijing, 100717, China. TEL 86-10-64000246, FAX 86-10-64030255, rdhy@scsio.ac.cn, http://rdhy.periodicals.net.cn/default.html, http:// www.sciencep.com/. Circ: 4,000. **Dist. by:** China International Book Trading Corp, 35 Chegongzhuang Xilu, Haidian District, PO Box 399, Beijing 100044, China. TEL 86-10-68412045, FAX 86-10-68412023, cibtc@mail.cibtc.com.cn, http://www.cibtc.com.cn.

➤ **REFERATIVNYI ZHURNAL. OKEANOLOGIYA. GIDROLOGIYA SUSHI. GLYATSIOLOGIYA.** see *EARTH SCIENCES—Abstracting, Bibliographies, Statistics*

551.46   FRA   ISSN 1240-1153
GC1
REPERES OCEAN. Text in French, English. 1992. irreg., latest 2000. price varies. charts; stat. back issues avail. **Document type:** *Academic/Scholarly.*
Formed by the 1992 merger of: Campagnes Oceanographiques Francaises (0761-3989); Which was formerly (1971-1984): France. Centre National pour l'Exploitation des Oceans. Publications. Serie: Resultats des Campagnes a la Mer (0339-2902); And: France. IFREMER. Publications. Serie: Rapports Economiques et Juridiques (0761-3938); Which was formerly (1984-1987): France. Centre National pour l'Exploitation des Oceans. Publications. Serie: Rapports Economiques et Juridiques (0339-2910); And: France. IFREMER. Publications. Serie: Rapports Scientifique et Techniques (0761-3970); Which was formerly (1971-1984): France. Centre National pour l'Exploitation des Oceans. Publications. Serie: Rapports Scientifiques et Techniques (0339-2899)
Indexed: ASFA, BiolAb, ChemAb, ESPM, ZooRec.
—CINDOC, CISTI, Linda Hall. **CCC.**
Published by: (France. Institut Francais de Recherche pour l'Exploitation de la Mer, France. Centre de Brest), Editions IFREMER, BP 70, Plouzane, 29280, France. TEL 33-2-98224586, FAX 33-2-98224586, editions@ifremer.fr, http://www.ifremer.fr. Ed. Patrick Phliponeau. Adv. contact Nelly Courtay.

551.48   JPN
RESULTS OF OCEANOGRAPHICAL OBSERVATIONS. Text in English. 1947. a.
Published by: Kishocho/Japan Meteorological Agency, 3-4 Ote-Machi 1-chome, Chiyoda-ku, Tokyo, 100-0004, Japan.

551.46   BRA   ISSN 1413-7739
QH1   CODEN: BOCNAO
REVISTA BRASILEIRA DE OCEANOGRAFIA. Text in Multiple languages; Summaries in English. 1950. s-a. USD 17; or exchange basis.
Former titles (until 1996): Universidade de Sao Paulo. Instituto Oceanografico. Boletim (0373-5524); (until 1952): Instituto Paulista de Oceanografia. Boletim (0100-4239)
Indexed: ASFA, BIOSIS Prev, BiolAb, ESPM, M&GPA, RefZh, SFA, WRCInf, ZooRec.
—CASDDS, CISTI.
Published by: Universidade de Sao Paulo, Instituto Oceanografico, Praca do Oceanografico, 191 Cidade Universitaria, Sao Paulo, SP 05508-900, Brazil. TEL 55-11-3091-6501, FAX 55-11-3032-3092, io@edu.usp.br, http://www.io.usp.br. Circ: 650.

REVISTA GEOFISICA. see *EARTH SCIENCES—Geophysics*

ROCZNIKI SOCJOLOGII MORSKIEJ. see *SOCIOLOGY*

ROSSIISKAYA AKADEMIYA NAUK. INSTITUT OBSHCHEI FIZIKI. TRUDY. see *PHYSICS*

ROSSIISKAYA AKADEMIYA NAUK. IZVESTIYA. SERIYA FIZIKA ATMOSFERY I OKEANA. see *METEOROLOGY*

551.46   RUS   ISSN 0030-1574
GC1.A47   CODEN: OKNOAR
➤ **ROSSIISKAYA AKADEMIYA NAUK. OKEANOLOGIYA.** Key Title: Okeanologiya. Text in Russian. 1961. bi-m. RUR 1,270 for 6 mos. domestic (effective 2004). bk.rev. index. **Document type:** *Journal, Academic/Scholarly.* **Description:** Publishes original papers on all fields of theoretical and experimental research in physical, chemical, biological, geological, and technical oceanology, and reviews and information about conferences, symposia, cruises, and other events of interest to the oceanographic community.
Formerly: Akademiya Nauk S.S.S.R. Okeanologiya
Related titles: Online - full text ed.; ♦ English Translation: Russian Academy of Sciences. Oceanology. ISSN 0001-4370.
Indexed: ASCA, ASFA, BIOSIS Prev, BiolAb, ChemAb, CurCont, Inspec, M&GPA, M&TEA, RefZh, SCI, ZooRec.
—CASDDS, CISTI, East View, IDS, KNAW, Linda Hall. **CCC.**
Published by: (Rossiiskaya Akademiya Nauk/Russian Academy of Sciences), Izdatel'stvo Nauka, Profsoyuznaya ul 90, Moscow, 117864, Russian Federation. TEL 7-095-3347151, FAX 7-095-4202220, secret@naukaran.ru, http://www.maik.rssi.ru/cgi-bin/list.pl?page=okean, http://www.naukaran.ru.

➤ **ROSTOCKER MEERESBIOLOGISCHE BEITRAEGE.** see *BIOLOGY*

➤ **RUSSIAN ACADEMY OF SCIENCES. IZVESTIYA. ATMOSPHERIC AND OCEANIC PHYSICS.** see *METEOROLOGY*

551.46   RUS   ISSN 0001-4370
GC1   CODEN: ONLGAE
RUSSIAN ACADEMY OF SCIENCES. OCEANOLOGY. Key Title: Oceanology (Washington, 1965). Text in English. 1961. bi-m. USD 1,127 in North America; USD 1,208 elsewhere (effective 2004). index. reprint service avail. from ISI. **Document type:** *Journal, Academic/Scholarly.* **Description:** Publishes original papers on all fields of theoretical and experimental research in physical, chemical, biological, geological, and technical oceanology, and reviews and information about conferences, symposia, cruises, and other events of interest to the oceanographic community.
Formerly: Academy of Sciences of the U S S R. Oceanology; Supersedes: Soviet Oceanography (0584-5556)
Related titles: ♦ Translation of: Rossiiskaya Akademiya Nauk. Okeanologiya. ISSN 0030-1574.
Indexed: ASFA, CurCont, ESPM, GEOBASE, ISR, Inspec, M&GPA, OceAb, SCI.
—BLDSC (0416.645000), AskIEEE, CISTI, IE, Infotrieve, ingenta, Linda Hall. **CCC.**
Published by: (Rossiiskaya Akademiya Nauk/Russian Academy of Sciences), M A I K Nauka - Interperiodica, Profsoyuznaya ul 90, Moscow, 117997, Russian Federation. TEL 7-095-3347420, FAX 7-095-3360666, compmg@maik.ru, http://www.maik.rssi.ru/journals/ocean.htm, http://www.maik.ru. Ed. Mikhail E Vinogradov. **Subscr. to:** Interperiodica, PO Box 1831, Birmingham, AL 35201-1831. TEL 205-995-1567, 800-633-4931, FAX 205-995-1588.

551.46   USA   ISSN 0575-4488
                                     CODEN: SIORA
S I O REFERENCE SERIES. (Scripps Institution of Oceanography) Text in English. irreg. price varies. **Document type:** *Monographic series.*
Related titles: ♦ Series: S I O Reference Series. Bibliography. ISSN 0730-8191.
Indexed: ASFA.
Published by: Scripps Institution of Oceanography, Technical Publications Office, University of California at San Diego, 9500 Gilman Dr, Department 0233B, La Jolla, CA 92093-0233. TEL 619-534-1295.

551.43 011   USA   ISSN 0730-8191
Z6004.P6
S I O REFERENCE SERIES. BIBLIOGRAPHY. (Scripps Institution of Oceanography) Text in English. 1968. irreg. **Document type:** *Bibliography.*
Related titles: ♦ Series of: S I O Reference Series. ISSN 0575-4488.
—Linda Hall.
Published by: Scripps Institution of Oceanography, Technical Publications Office, University of California at San Diego, 9500 Gilman Dr, Department 0233B, La Jolla, CA 92093-0233. TEL 619-534-1295.

551.46   SWE   ISSN 0283-7714
S M H I OCEANOGRAFI. Text in Swedish. 1974. irreg. **Document type:** *Monographic series.*
Supersedes in part (in 1985): Sveriges Meteorologiska och Hydrologiska Institut. Hydrologiska/Oceanografiska Avdelningen (0282-2601); Formerly (until 1982): HB Rapport
Published by: Sveriges Meteorologiska och Hydrologiska Institut/Swedish Meteorological and Hydrological Institute, Folkborgvaegen 1, Norrkoeping, 60176, Sweden. TEL 46-11-495-80-00, FAX 46-11-495-80-01, smhi@smhi.se, http://www.smhi.se.

551.46   SWE   ISSN 0283-1112
S M H I REPORTS. OCEANOGRAPHY. Text in English, Swedish. 1963. irreg.

E

Supersedes in part (in 1985): S M H I Rapporter. Hydrologi och Oceanografi (0347-7827); Which was formerly (until 1973): Notiser och Preliminara Rapporter. Serie Hydrologi (0586-1659); Incorporates (1979-1985): Institute of Hydrographic Research Goteborg Series (0349-523X)
Indexed: ESPM.
Published by: Sveriges Meteorologiska och Hydrologiska Institut/Swedish Meteorological and Hydrological Institute, Folkborgvaegen 1, Norrkoeping, 60176, Sweden. TEL 46-11-495-80-00, FAX 46-11-495-80-01, http://www.smhi.se.

SCIENCE OF TSUNAMI HAZARDS. see *METEOROLOGY*

351.46 639 ESP ISSN 0214-8358
SH285 CODEN: SCIMEM
➤ **SCIENTIA MARINA**; international journal on marine sciences. Text in English, Spanish. 1955. 4/yr. EUR 155 domestic; EUR 190 in Europe; USD 195 elsewhere (effective 2005). adv. bk.rev. bibl.; charts; illus. index. back issues avail. **Document type:** *Journal, Academic/Scholarly.* **Description:** Contains articles of multi-disciplinary nature related to marine biology and ecology, fisheries, physical and chemical oceanography, and marine geology.
Formerly (until 1988): Investigacion Pesquera (0020-9953)
Related titles: Online - full text ed.: 2002. free (effective 2005).
Indexed: ASCA, ASFA, AnBrAb, BIOSIS Prev, BiolAb, ChemAb, ChemTitl, CurCont, ESPM, FS&TA, GEOBASE, HGA, HelmAb, IECT, IndVet, NemAb, NutrAb, OceAb, RefZh, SFA, VetBull, WAE&RSA, WildRev, ZooRec.
—BLDSC (8172.550000), CASDDS, CINDOC, CISTI, IDS, IE, ingenta. **CCC.**
Published by: Consejo Superior de Investigaciones Cientificas, Instituto de Ciencias, Passeig Maritim de la Barceloneta 37-49, Barcelona, 08003, Spain. TEL 34-93-2309500, FAX 34-93-2309555, scimar@icm.csic.es, http://www.icm.csic.es/scimar/sci_index.html. Ed. Pere Abello. Circ: 400.
Co-sponsor: Institut de Ciencies del Mar de Barcelona.

551.46 AUS
SCIENTIFIC DIVING NEWS. Text in English. 1990. irreg.
Related titles: Online - full text ed.
Published by: Australian Scientific Divers Association, Castletown, PO Box 361, Townsville, QLD 4810, Australia. TEL 61-77-724452, FAX 61-77-213538, edrew@ultra.net.au, http://www.ozemail.com.au/~edrew/news.htm. Ed. Ed Drew.

551.46 GBR
QH91.A1
SCOTTISH ASSOCIATION FOR MARINE SCIENCE. REPORT AND ACCOUNTS. Text in English. 1896. a. **Document type:** *Corporate.*
Former titles (until 1998): Dunstaffnage Marine Laboratory and Scottish Association for Marine Science. Centre for Coastal and Marine Sciences. Report and Accounts (1468-1544); (until 1997): Dunstaffnage Marine Laboratory and Scottish Association for Marine Science. Report and Accounts (1468-1536); (until 1995): Dunstaffnage Marine Laboratory. Report (1366-834X); (until 1992): Scottish Marine Biological Association. Annual Report (0375-2062); (until 1914): Marine Biological Association of the West of Scotland. Annual Report
Related titles: Microfiche ed.
Indexed: ASFA, BiolAb.
Published by: Scottish Association for Marine Science, Dunstaffnage Marine Laboratory, PO Box 3, Oban, Argyll PA34 4AD, United Kingdom. TEL 44-1631-559000, FAX 44-1631-559001, mail@dml.ac.uk, http://www.sams.ac.uk/publicat.html. Ed. Robin Harvey. Circ: 1,000.

551.46 USA ISSN 0080-8318
QH95 CODEN: BUUNAK
➤ **SCRIPPS INSTITUTION OF OCEANOGRAPHY. BULLETIN.** Text in English. 1927. irreg., latest vol.29, 1995. price varies. back issues avail. **Document type:** *Monographic series, Academic/Scholarly.* **Description:** Publishes research on deep-sea flora and fauna.
Indexed: ASFA, BiolAb, SFA, ZooRec.
—CISTI, Linda Hall.
Published by: (Scripps Institution of Oceanography), University of California Press, Book Series, 2120 Berkeley Way, Berkeley, CA 94720. TEL 510-642-4247, FAX 510-643-7127, askucp@ucpress.edu, http://www.ucpress.edu/books/BSIO.ser.html, http://www.ucpress.edu/books/series.html. **Orders to:** California - Princeton Fulfillment Services, 1445 Lower Ferry Rd, Ewing, NJ 08618. TEL 800-777-4726, FAX 800-999-1958.

551.46 USA
SCRIPPS INSTITUTION OF OCEANOGRAPHY. CONTRIBUTIONS. NEW SERIES. Text in English. 1930. a. per issue exchange basis only.
Formerly: Scripps Institution of Oceanography. Contributions (0080-8326)
Indexed: SFA.
—CISTI, KNAW, Linda Hall.
Published by: Scripps Institution of Oceanography, Technical Publications Office, University of California at San Diego, 9500 Gilman Dr, Department 0233B, La Jolla, CA 92093-0233. TEL 619-534-1295.

551.46 USA
THE SEA; the global coastal ocean. Text in English. irreg., latest vol.12, 2002. price varies. **Document type:** *Monographic series, Academic/Scholarly.*
Published by: John Wiley & Sons, Inc., 111 River St, Hoboken, NJ 07030-5774. TEL 201-748-6000, 800-825-7550, FAX 201-748-5915, uscs-wis@wiley.com, http://www.wiley.com. Ed. Allan Robinson.

SEA TECHNOLOGY; for design engineering and application of equipment and services for the marine and defense environment. see *ENGINEERING*

SEA TECHNOLOGY BUYERS GUIDE - DIRECTORY. see *ENGINEERING*

SEA WIND. see *ENVIRONMENTAL STUDIES*

551.46 IND ISSN 0971-7560
SEAWEED RESEARCH AND UTILISATION. Text in English. 1979. a.
Indexed: ESPM.
—CISTI.
Published by: Seaweed Research and Utilisation Association, Mandapam Camp, Namakkal, Ramnad District, Tamil Nadu, India.

551.46 USA ISSN 1522-8789
GC178.2 CODEN: SWPSFC
SEAWIFS POSTLAUNCH TECHNICAL REPORT SERIES. (Sea-Viewing Wide Field-of-View Sensor) Text in English. 1992. bi-m.
Formerly (until 1998): SeaWIFS Technical Report Series (1522-094X)
Indexed: GEOBASE.
Published by: N A S A Goddard Space Flight Center, Code 970.2, Greenbelt, MD 20771. TEL 301-386-4553, http://seawifs.gsfc.nasa.gov/SEAWIFS/TECH_REPORTS/, http://seawifs.gsfc.nasa.gov/SEAWIFS.html. Ed. Elaine Firestone. **Subscr. to:** U.S. Department of Commerce, National Technical Information Service, 5285 Port Royal Rd, Springfield, VA 22161. TEL 703-605-6060, FAX 703-605-6880, subscriptions@ntis.gov, http://www.ntis.gov/ordering.htm.

551.46 DEU ISSN 0937-7395
GC214.H4
SEEGANGSMESSUNGEN IN DER DEUTSCHEN BUCHT. Text in German. 1990. a. **Document type:** *Monographic series, Government.*
Published by: Bundesamt fuer Seeschiffahrt und Hydrographie, Bernhard-Nocht-Str 78, Hamburg, 20359, Germany. TEL 49-40-31900, posteingang@bsh.de, http://www.bsh.de.

578.77 DEU ISSN 0080-889X
QE39 CODEN: SEMADJ
➤ **SENCKENBERGIANA MARITIMA.** Text and summaries in German, English. 1969. 2/yr. EUR 56 domestic; EUR 60 foreign (effective 2005). back issues avail.; reprints avail. **Document type:** *Journal, Academic/Scholarly.* **Description:** Contains papers on marine geology, biology, paleontology, and ecology of the marine environment.
Indexed: ASFA, BIOSIS Prev, BiolAb, ESPM, GEOBASE, IBR, IBZ, RefZh, SFA, ZooRec.
—BLDSC (8241.040000), CISTI, IE, ingenta, Linda Hall. **CCC.**
Published by: (Senckenbergische Naturforschende Gesellschaft, Deutsche Forschungsgemeinschaft), E. Schweizerbart'sche Verlagsbuchhandlung, Johannesstr 3A, Stuttgart, 70176, Germany. TEL 49-711-3514560, FAX 49-711-35145699, mail@schweizerbart.de, http://www.schweizerbart.de/j/senckenbergiana-maritima. Ed. G Hertweck. R&P Peter Koenigshof TEL 49-69-97075686. Circ: 650.

551.46 578.77 SEN ISSN 0850-1602
SENEGAL. CENTRE DE RECHERCHE OCEANOGRAPHIQUE. DOCUMENT SCIENTIFIQUE. Text in French. 1966. irreg., latest vol.146, 1997. adv. bibl. back issues avail. **Document type:** *Monographic series, Academic/Scholarly.*
Related titles: Microfiche ed.
Published by: Centre de Recherche Oceanographique de Dakar-Thiaroye, BP 2241, Dakar, Senegal. TEL 221-8340536, FAX 221-8342792, adiallo@crodt.isra.sn. R&P, Adv. contact Anis Diallo.

551.46 ESP ISSN 1130-4766
➤ **SERIES DE QUIMICA OCEANOGRAFIA. SERIE I. MONOGRAFIAS.** Text in Spanish. 1991. irreg. **Document type:** *Monographic series, Academic/Scholarly.*
Indexed: IECT.
—CINDOC.
Published by: Universidad de Cadiz, Escuela Universitaria de Ingenieria Tecnica, CASEM. Dpto. C. Navales, Puerto Real (Cadiz), 11510, Spain. TEL 34-956-016096, FAX 34-956-016104, jose.lopezruiz@uca.es.

551.46 ESP ISSN 1130-4774
➤ **SERIES DE QUIMICA OCEANOGRAFICA. SERIE II. CUADERNOS.** Text in Spanish. 1991. irreg. **Document type:** *Journal, Academic/Scholarly.*
Indexed: IECT.
—CINDOC.
Published by: Universidad de Cadiz, Escuela Universitaria de Ingenieria Tecnica, CASEM. Dpto. C. Navales, Puerto Real (Cadiz), 11510, Spain. TEL 34-956-016096, FAX 34-956-016104, jose.lopezruiz@uca.es.

551.46 570 JPN ISSN 1342-4181
SESSILE ORGANISMS. Text in English, Japanese. 1979. s-a. JPY 5,000 membership (effective 2005). **Document type:** *Journal, Academic/Scholarly.*
Formerly (until 1996): Fuchaku Seibutsu Kenkyu/Marine Fouling (0388-3531)
—BLDSC (8253.097219). **CCC.**
Published by: Nihon Fuchaku Seibutsu Gakkai/Sessile Organisms Society of Japan, Marine Ecology Research Institute, Central Laboratory, 300 Iwawada Onjuku-machi, Isumi-gun, Chiba 299-5105, Japan. TEL 81-470-685111, FAX 81-470-585115, sessileorg@kaiseiken.or.jp, http://wwwsoc.nii.ac.jp/sosj/.

SHIPPING AND MARINE INDUSTRIES JOURNAL; devoted to shipping and shipbuilding industries, fisheries and oceanography. see *TRANSPORTATION—Ships And Shipping*

SHUISHENG SHENGWU XUEBAO/ACTA HYDROBIOLOGICA SINICA. see *BIOLOGY*

551.46 USA ISSN 0196-0768
CODEN: SCSCD7
SMITHSONIAN CONTRIBUTIONS TO THE MARINE SCIENCES. Text in English. 1977. irreg., latest vol.37, 1996. price varies. abstr.; bibl.; charts; illus. back issues avail.; reprint service avail. from PQC. **Document type:** *Monographic series.*
Indexed: ASFA, BIOSIS Prev, BiolAb, OceAb, SFA, ZooRec.
—BLDSC (8311.605000), CISTI, Linda Hall. **CCC.**
Published by: Smithsonian Institution Press, PO Box 37012, Washington, DC 20013-7012. TEL 202-633-3017, schol.press@si.edu, http://www.si.edu/publications/. Circ: 1,400.

SNOWY MOUNTAINS COUNCIL. ANNUAL REPORT. see *ENGINEERING*

SOCIETE DES SCIENCES NATURELLES DE LA CHARENTE-MARITIME. see *BIOLOGY—Ornithology*

SOCIETY FOR MARINE MAMMALOGY NEWSLETTER (ONLINE EDITION). see *BIOLOGY—Zoology*

551.46 GBR ISSN 1352-8289
SOCIETY FOR UNDERWATER TECHNOLOGY. NEWS. Variant title: S U T News. Text in English. q. membership. **Document type:** *Newsletter, Academic/Scholarly.*
Supersedes in part (in 1993): Underwater and Marine Technology News (0965-5468); Which was formerly (until 1992): Marine Technology Research News (0951-6778)
Published by: Society for Underwater Technology, 80 Coleman St, London, EC2R 5BJ, United Kingdom. TEL 44-20-7382-2601, FAX 44-20-7382-2684, daniel@sutpubs.demon.co.uk, http://www.sut.org.uk.

SORA TO UMI/SKY AND MARINE. see *AERONAUTICS AND SPACE FLIGHT*

551.46 639.2 USA
SOUTH CAROLINA. MARINE RESOURCES DIVISION. TECHNICAL REPORT. Text in English. 1970. irreg., latest vol.79, 1992. **Document type:** *Monographic series, Government.*
Indexed: ASFA, SFA, WildRev.
Published by: South Carolina Department of Natural Resources, PO Box 167, Columbia, SC 29202. TEL 803-734-3972, http://www.scwildlife.com. Circ: 100 (controlled).

551.46 GBR
SOUTH WALES PORTS TIDES TABLES. Text in English. a. GBP 2. **Document type:** *Bulletin.*
Published by: Associated British Ports (Cardiff), Pierhead Bldg,, Bute Docks, Cardiff, CF1 5TH, United Kingdom. TEL 44-1222-471311, FAX 44-1222-471100. Circ: 5,000.

551.46 GBR
SOUTHAMPTON OCEANOGRAPHY CENTRE. ANNUAL REPORT. Text in English. 1995. a. GBP 8 (effective 2001). **Document type:** *Corporate.*
Former titles (until 1995): Institute of Oceanographic Sciences. Deacon Laboratory. Annual Report; Institute of Oceanographic Sciences. Annual Report (0309-4472)
Indexed: ASFA, BiolAb.
—BLDSC (8352.219700).
Published by: Southampton Oceanography Centre, University of Southampton Waterfront Campus, European Way, Southampton, S014 3ZH, United Kingdom. TEL 44-2380-596111, FAX 44-2380-596667, nol@soc.soton.ac.uk, http://www.soc.soton.ac.uk. Ed. Pauline Simpson.

551.46 GBR ISSN 1461-7684
SOUTHAMPTON OCEANOGRAPHY CENTRE. CRUISE REPORT. Text in English. 1996. irreg. **Document type:** *Monographic series.*
Formerly: Institute of Oceanographic Sciences. Cruise Report
Indexed: ASFA, GEOBASE.

E

—BLDSC (3489.876230).
Published by: Southampton Oceanography Centre, University of Southhampton Waterfront Campus, European Way, Southampton, S014 3ZH, United Kingdom. TEL 44-2380-596111, FAX 44-2380-596667, nol@soc.soton.ac.uk, http://www.soc.soton.ac.uk.

551.46 GBR ISSN 1461-7668
SOUTHAMPTON OCEANOGRAPHY CENTRE. REPORT. Text in English. 1996. irreg. **Document type:** *Monographic series.*
Indexed: GEOBASE.
Published by: Southampton Oceanography Centre, University of Southhampton Waterfront Campus, European Way, Southampton, S014 3ZH, United Kingdom. FAX 44-2380-596667, http://www.soc.soton.ac.uk.

551.46 GBR
SOUTHAMPTON PORT TIDE TABLES. Text in English. 1927. a. GBP 1.25 (effective 1997). **Document type:** *Bulletin.*
Published by: Association British Ports (Southampton), Ocean Gate, Ocean Way, Southampton, Hants SO14 3QN, United Kingdom. Circ: 6,000.

551.46 ITA ISSN 0390-4415
IL SUBACQUEO. Text in Italian. 1973. m. (11/yr.). EUR 56 domestic; EUR 85 foreign (effective 2005). adv. **Document type:** *Magazine, Consumer.*
Published by: La Cuba Srl, Via Orti della Farnesina 137, Rome, RM 00194, Italy. TEL 39-063-629021, FAX 39-063-6309950, http://www.subacqueo.it/home/images/subacqueo.htm. Ed. Calogero Cascio. Circ: 70,000.

526.3 551.46 USA ISSN 0270-8876
SUPPLEMENTAL TIDAL PREDICTIONS, ANCHORAGE, NIKISHKA, SELDOVIA, AND VALDEZ, ALASKA. Text in English. a.
Published by: U.S. Department of Commerce, National Geodetic Survey, SSMC-3 # 9202, 1315 E W Highway, Silver Spring, MD 20910-3282. TEL 301-713-3242, FAX 301-713-4172, http://www.ngs.noaa.gov/.

551.46 POL ISSN 0860-6692
SZCZECINSKIE ROCZNIKI NAUKOWE, NAUKI MORSKIE. Variant title: Annales Scientiarum Stetinenses, Nauki Morskie. Text in Polish. 1987. irreg.
Published by: Szczecinskie Towarzystwo Naukowe, ul Wojska Polskiego 96, Szczecin, 71481, Poland. wtarc@univ.szczecin.pl.

551.46 CHN ISSN 1000-8160
TAIWAN HAIXIA/JOURNAL OF OCEANOGRAPHY IN TAIWAN STRAIT. Text in Chinese; Abstracts in English. 1982. q. USD 10 per issue. bk.rev. **Document type:** *Academic/Scholarly.* **Description:** Covers researches on oceanography in East China Sea, especially the Taiwan Strait and its adjacent sea area.
Related titles: Online - full text ed.: (from East View Information Services).
Indexed: ASFA, ESPM, ZooRec.
—BLDSC (5026.153000), IE, ingenta.
Published by: Guojia Haiyang-ju, Disan Haiyang Yanjiusuo/State Oceanic Administration, Third Institute of Oceanography, P.O. Box 0570, Xiamen, Fujian 361005, China. TEL 0592-2085880, FAX 0592-2086646. Ed. Zhang Jinbiao. Circ: 1,000 (controlled).

TECNOLOGIE E TRANSPORTI MARE; international magazine of advanced marine technology, transportation and logistics. see *TRANSPORTATION—Ships And Shipping*

TERRA ET AQUA. see *TRANSPORTATION—Ships And Shipping*

551.46 USA ISSN 0069-9640
GC1
➤ **TEXAS A & M UNIVERSITY. COLLEGE OF GEOSCIENCES. CONTRIBUTIONS IN OCEANOGRAPHY.** Text in English. 1950. irreg. per issue exchange basis. abstr. **Document type:** *Academic/Scholarly.* **Description:** A collection of reprints.
Published by: Texas A & M University, Department of Oceanography, College Station, TX 77843-3146. TEL 409-845-7327, FAX 979-845-6331, workingcollection@ariel.met.tamu.edu, http://www-ocean.tamu.edu/.

551.46 USA ISSN 0272-6076
TEXAS A & M UNIVERSITY. DEPARTMENT OF OCEANOGRAPHY. TECHNICAL REPORT. Text in English. 196?. irreg. **Document type:** *Monographic series.*
Published by: Texas A & M University, Department of Oceanography, College Station, TX 77843-3146. TEL 979-845-7211, FAX 979-845-6331, http://www-ocean.tamu.edu

551.46 639.2 USA
TEXAS A & M UNIVERSITY. SEA GRANT COLLEGE PROGRAM. REPORT. Text in English. irreg.
Published by: Texas A & M University, Sea Grant College Program, 2700 Earl Rudder Freeway S, Ste 1800, College Station, TX 77845. FAX 979-862-3786, http://texas-sea-grant.tamu.edu.

THALASSAS; revista de ciencias del mar. see *BIOLOGY*

623.8949 DNK ISSN 0907-743X
VK623
TIDEVANDSTABELLER. DANMARK. Text in Danish, English. 1977. a. DKK 100 (effective 2000). **Document type:** *Government.*
Formerly (until 1984): Tidevandstabeller for Danmark (0106-8334)
Published by: Farvandsvaesenet, Oceanografisk Tjeneste, Overgaden O Vandet 62 B, Copenhagen K, 1023, Denmark. TEL 45-32-68-95-00, FAX 45-32-57-43-41, pbn@fomfrv.dk. Ed., R&P Palle Bo Nielsen.

623.8949 DNK ISSN 0907-7502
VK614.F2
TIDEVANDSTABELLER. FAEROERNE. Text in Danish. 1977. a. DKK 50 (effective 1997). **Document type:** *Government.*
Formerly (until 1984): Tidevandstabeller for Faeroerne (0106-8342)
Published by: Farvandsvaesenet, Oceanografisk Tjeneste, Overgaden O Vandet 62 B, Copenhagen K, 1023, Denmark. TEL 45-32-68-95-00, FAX 45-32-57-43-41, pbn@fomfrv.dk. Ed., R&P Palle Bo Nielsen.

623.8949 DNK ISSN 0907-7510
VK614.G7
TIDEVANDSTABELLER. GROENLAND. Text in Danish, English. 1966. a. DKK 75 (effective 1997). **Document type:** *Government.*
Formerly (until 1984): Tidevandstabeller for Groenland (0107-0398)
Published by: Farvandsvaesenet, Oceanografisk Tjeneste, Overgaden O Vandet 62 B, Copenhagen K, 1023, Denmark. TEL 45-32-68-95-00, FAX 45-32-57-43-41, pbn@fomfrv.dk. Ed., R&P Palle Bo Nielsen.

TIKHOOKEANSKAYA GEOLOGIYA/GEOLOGY OF THE PACIFIC OCEAN. see *EARTH SCIENCES—Geology*

551.46 JPN ISSN 0287-2099
TOKAI DAIGAKU KAIYO KAGAKU HAKUBUTSUKAN NENPO/TOKAI UNIVERSITY. MARINE SCIENCE MUSEUM. ANNUAL REPORT. Text in English, Japanese. 1972. a.
Indexed: SFA.
Published by: Tokai Daigaku, Kaiyo Kagaku Hakubutsukan, 2389 Miho, shimizu-shi, Shizuoka-ken 424-0901, Japan.

551.46 JPN ISSN 0289-680X
GC1
TOKAI DAIGAKU KAIYO KENKYUJO KENKYU HOKOKU/TOKAI UNIVERSITY. INSTITUTE OF OCEANIC RESEARCH AND DEVELOPMENT. BULLETIN. Text in English, Japanese. 1979. a. **Document type:** *Bulletin.*
Indexed: SFA, ZooRec.
Published by: Tokai Daigaku, Kaiyo Kenkyujo, 20-1 Ori-Do 3-chome, shimizu-shi, Shizuoka-ken 424-0902, Japan.

551.46 JPN ISSN 0287-1467
TOKAI DAIGAKU KAIYO KENKYUJO NENPO/TOKAI UNIVERSITY. INSTITUTE OF OCEANIC RESEARCH AND DEVELOPMENT. ANNUAL REPORT. Text in Japanese. 1979. a.
Published by: Tokai Daigaku, Kaiyo Kenkyujo, 20-1 Ori-Do 3-chome, shimizu-shi, Shizuoka-ken 424-0902, Japan.

551.46 JPN ISSN 0389-2050
CODEN: TDKGCU
TOKAI DAIGAKU KAIYOGAKUBU GYOSEKISHU/TOKAI UNIVERSITY. FACULTY OF MARINE SCIENCE AND TECHNOLOGY. COLLECTED REPRINTS. Text in English, Japanese. a. **Document type:** *Academic/Scholarly.*
Indexed: SFA, WildRev.
Published by: Tokai Daigaku, Kaiyogakubu/Tokai University, Faculty of Marine Science and Technology, 20-1 Ori-Do 3-chome, shimizu-shi, Shizuoka-ken 424-0902, Japan.

551.46 JPN ISSN 0375-3271
GC1 CODEN: TDKYBF
TOKAI DAIGAKU KIYO. KAIYOGAKUBU/TOKAI UNIVERSITY. FACULTY OF MARINE SCIENCE AND TECHNOLOGY. JOURNAL. Text in English, Japanese. 1966. s-a. **Document type:** *Academic/Scholarly.*
Indexed: ASFA, Agrind, BIOSIS Prev, BiolAb, ESPM, JPI, SFA, WildRev, ZooRec.
—CASDDS, CISTI.
Published by: Tokai Daigaku, Kaiyogakubu/Tokai University, Faculty of Marine Science and Technology, 20-1 Ori-Do 3-chome, shimizu-shi, Shizuoka-ken 424-0902, Japan.

551.46 570 JPN
TOKYO DAIGAKU RIGAKUBU FUZOKU RINKAI JIKKENJO NENPO/UNIVERSITY OF TOKYO. MISAKI MARINE BIOLOGICAL STATION. ANNUAL REPORT. Text in Japanese. 1951. a. **Document type:** *Bulletin.*
Published by: (Fuzoku Rinkai Jikkenjo), Tokyo Daigaku, Rigakubu, 1024, Koajiro, Misaki-machi, Miura-shi, Kanagawa-ken 238-0225, Japan. jimu@mmbs.s.u-tokyo.ac.jp. Circ: 300.

551.46 JPN ISSN 0916-4820
GC214.T6
TOKYOKO HARO KANSOKU NENPO/ANNUAL REPORT OF OBSERVATION WAVES IN TOKYO BAY. Text in Japanese. a.
Published by: Tokyoto Kowankyoku/Tokyo Metropolitan Government, Bureau of Port and Harbour, 8-1 Nishi-Shinjuku 2-chome, Shinjuku-ku, Tokyo, 160-0023, Japan.

TROPICAL OCEANOGRAPHY. see *BIOLOGY*

551.46 JPN
TSUKUBA DAIGAKU ENGAN KANSOKU HOKOKU/UNIVERSITY OF TSUKUBA. REPORT OF COASTAL OBSERVATION. Text in Japanese. a.
Published by: Tsukuba Daigaku, Shimoda Rinkai Jikken Senta/University of Tsukuba, Shimoda Marine Research Center, 10-1, Shimodashi 5-chome, Tsukuba, Shizuoka-ken 415, Japan.

TSUKUBA INSTITUTE. TECHNICAL REPORT/TSUKUBA KENKYUJO GIHO. see *TRANSPORTATION—Ships And Shipping*

551.46 639.3 TUN
QH90.A1 CODEN: INOBAG
TUNISIA. INSTITUT NATIONAL DES SCIENCES ET TECHNOLOGIES DE LA MER. BULLETIN. Text in French; Summaries in Arabic, English, French. N.S. 1966. a. **Document type:** *Bulletin, Academic/Scholarly.*
Former titles: Tunisia. Institut National Scientifique et Technique d'Oceanographie et de Peche. Bulletin (0579-7926); Tunisia. Station Oceanographique de Salammbo
Published by: Institut National des Sciences et Technologies de la Mer, 28, rue du 2 mars 1934, Salammbo, 2025, Tunisia. TEL 216-1-730-420, FAX 216-1-732-622. R&P Amor Elabed TEL 216-1-730-548. Circ: 1,150 (controlled).

551.46 TUR ISSN 1300-7122
TURKISH JOURNAL OF MARINE SCIENCES. Text in English. irreg.
Indexed: ASFA, ESPM, OceAb.
Published by: Institute of Marine Sciences and Management, Istanbul University, Istanbul, 34470 VEFA, Turkey.

551.46 USA
CODEN: MSGMDN
TWO IF BY SEA. Text in English. 1996. q. **Document type:** *Newsletter.* **Description:** Highlights recent research, advisory activities, relevant news from the Commonwealth, new publications, and art or poetry related to the sea.
Formerly (until 1997): M I T Sea Grant Report (0271-244X)
Indexed: ASFA, EnvAb, SFA.
—CASDDS.
Published by: Massachusetts Institute of Technology, Sea Grant College Program, 292 Main St, Bldg E38-300, Cambridge, MA 02139. TEL 617-253-5944, alcohen@mit.edu, http://web.mit.edu/seagrant/2ifbysea/. Ed. Andrea Cohen. Circ: 2,000.

551.48 MEX ISSN 0185-3287
QH91.A1 CODEN: AICME6
U N A M. INSTITUTO DE CIENCIAS DEL MAR Y LIMNOLOGIA. ANALES. Text in Spanish. 1967. a. MXP 25, USD 3 newsstand/cover (effective 2000). back issues avail.
Supersedes (in 1980): U N A M. Centro de Ciencias del Mar y Limnologia. Anales (0186-3428); Which was formerly (until 1970): U N A M. Instituto de Biologia. Anales. Serie Ciencias del Mar y Limnologia (0368-8305)
Related titles: Online - full text ed.; Supplement(s): U N A M. Instituto de Ciencias del Mar y Limnologia. Publicaciones Especiales. ISSN 0185-3279. 1978.
Indexed: ASFA, ESPM.
—CISTI, Linda Hall.
Published by: Universidad Nacional Autonoma de Mexico, Biblioteca del Instituto de Ciencias del Mar y Limnologia, Unidad de Bibliotecas, Circuito Exterior, Ciudad Universitaria, Mexico, DF, 04510, Mexico. TEL 52-5-6225804, FAX 52-5-6225804. Ed. Agustin A Castanares.

551.46 KEN ISSN 1014-8647
U N E P REGIONAL SEAS REPORTS AND STUDIES. (United Nations Environment Programme) Text in English. 1982. 10/yr. free. **Document type:** *Academic/Scholarly.* **Description:** Contains reports and studies of the Kenyan waters concerning marine and riparian environments, pollution, conservation, and marine mammals.
Related titles: Microfiche ed.: (from CIS).
Indexed: ASFA, IIS, SFA, ZooRec.
Published by: (United Nations Environment Programme) United Nations Environment Programme, Oceans and Coastal Areas (Subsidiary of: United Nations Environment Programme), Programme Activity Centre, P.O. Box 30552, Nairobi, Kenya. Circ: 500.

551.46 620 USA
U.S. COASTAL ENGINEERING RESEARCH CENTER. INSTRUCTION REPORTS. Text in English. irreg. price varies. back issues avail. **Document type:** *Monographic series, Government.*
Published by: U.S. Coastal Engineering Research Center, US Army Engineer Waterways Experiment Station, 3909 Halls Ferry Rd, Bldg 3296, Vicksburg, MS 39180-6199. TEL 601-634-2021, camfield@coafs1.wes.army.mil. **Subscr. to:** National Technical Information Service, Government Research Center, 5285 Port Royal Rd, Springfield, VA 22161. TEL 703-605-6060, 800-363-2068, http://www.ntis.gov.

E

551.46 627 USA
U.S. COASTAL ENGINEERING RESEARCH CENTER. TECHNICAL REPORTS. Text in English. irreg. price varies. back issues avail. **Document type:** *Monographic series, Government.*
Indexed: ASFA.
Published by: U.S. Coastal Engineering Research Center, US Army Engineer Waterways Experiment Station, 3909 Halls Ferry Rd, Bldg 3296, Vicksburg, MS 39180-6199. TEL 601-634-2021, camfield@coafsl.wes.army.mil. **Subscr. to:** National Technical Information Service, Government Research Center, 5285 Port Royal Rd, Springfield, VA 22161. TEL 703-605-6060, 800-363-2068, http://www.ntis.gov.

551.46 USA ISSN 0501-8234
U.S. NATIONAL OCEAN SERVICE. TIDAL CURRENT TABLES. ATLANTIC COAST OF NORTH AMERICA. Text in English. 1923. a.
Formerly (until 1957): Current Tables. Atlantic Coast, North America (0743-7064)
Published by: U.S. National Ocean Service, SSMC4, Room 13632, 1305 EW Hway, Silver Spring, MD 20910. TEL 301-713-3074, FAX 301-713-3066, nos.media@noaa.gov, http://www.oceanservice.noaa.gov/.

551.46 USA
U.S. NATIONAL OCEANIC AND ATMOSPHERIC ADMINISTRATION. ENGINEERING SUPPORT OFFICE. TECHNICAL MEMORANDUM✶. Text in English. 1969. irreg. free.
Former titles: U.S. National Oceanic and Atmospheric Administration. Test and Evaluation Office. Technical Memorandum; U.S. National Oceanographic Instrumentation Center. Technical Memorandum
Indexed: ASFA, ZooRec.
Published by: U.S. National Oceanic and Atmospheric Administration, Engineering Support Office, Washington, DC 20232. TEL 301-655-4000. Circ: 3,000.

551.46 USA
U.S. NATIONAL OCEANIC AND ATMOSPHERIC ADMINISTRATION. TECHNICAL BULLETIN✶. Text in English. 1964. irreg. free.
Former titles: U.S. National Oceanic and Atmospheric Administration. Test and Evaluation Laboratory. Technical Bulletin; U.S. National Oceanographic Instrumentation Center. Technical Bulletin
Published by: U.S. National Oceanic and Atmospheric Administration, Engineering Support Office, Washington, DC 20232. TEL 301-655-4000. Circ: 3,000.

551.46 USA ISSN 0730-3610
U.S. OCEANOGRAPHIC DATA CENTER. ANNUAL REPORT. Text in English. 1980. a.
Published by: U.S. National Oceanographic Data Center, NOAA NESDIS E/OC, SSMC3, 4th Flr, 1315 East-West Hwy, Silver Spring, MD 20910-3282. TEL 301-713-3277, FAX 301-713-3302, nodc.services@noaa.gov, http://www.nodc.noaa.gov/General/NODCPubs/.

551.46 JPN ISSN 0386-4197
UMI NO HAKUBUTSUKAN/TOKAI UNIVERSITY. MARINE SCIENCE MUSEUM. JOURNAL. Text in Japanese. 1971. bi-m. JPY 800. **Document type:** *Academic/Scholarly.*
Published by: Tokai Daigaku, Kaiyo Kagaku Hakubutsukan, 2389 Miho, shimizu-shi, Shizuoka-ken 424-0901, Japan.

551.46 JPN ISSN 0916-8362
UMI NO KENKYU. Variant title: Nihon Kaiyo Gakkai Kikanshi. Text in Japanese. 1942. bi-m. **Document type:** *Journal, Academic/Scholarly.*
Supersedes in part (in 1992): Nihon Kaiyo Gakkaishi (0029-8131)
Indexed: ESPM, INIS AtomInd.
—CISTI. **CCC.**
Published by: Nihon Kaiyo Gakki/Oceanographic Society of Japan, MK Bldg. 202, 1-6-14, Minamidai, Nakano-ku, Tokyo, 164-0014, Japan. FAX 81-3-3378-9419.

UMI NO KISHO/MARINE METEOROLOGY. see *METEOROLOGY*

551.46 JPN ISSN 0385-5597
UMI TO NINGEN/TOBA MARITIME MUSEUM. ANNUAL. Text in Japanese. 1973. a.
Published by: Umi no Hakubutsukan/Toba Maritime Museum, 1731 Okitsu-Uramuracho, Toba-shi, Mie-ken 517-0000, Japan.

UMI TO SORA/SEA AND SKY. see *METEOROLOGY*

551.46 USA ISSN 1061-5776
UNDERCURRENTS. Text in English. 1992. q. USD 10 to non-members; USD 6 to members. **Document type:** *Newsletter.* **Description:** Describes classes, trips and programs available to members of the Foundation as well as news of undersea archaeological expeditions by the Institute for Exploration. Contains articles on marine life and aquatic habitats.
Published by: (Sea Research Foundation), Mystic Aquarium, Attn: Education Dept, 55 Coogan Blvd, Mystic, CT 06355-1997. TEL 860-572-5955, FAX 860-572-5984, wkelly@mysticaquarium.org. Ed., R&P William J Kelly. Circ: 17,300.

591 USA ISSN 0041-6606
QH91.A1 CODEN: UWNAAX
UNDERWATER NATURALIST. Text in English. 1962. irreg. (2-3/yr.). USD 25 to individuals; USD 30 to institutions; USD 45 foreign to institutions (effective 1999). adv. bk.rev. charts; illus. Index. reprint service avail. from PQC. **Document type:** *Newsletter, Academic/Scholarly.*
Related titles: Microform ed.: (from PQC); Online - full text ed.: (from Gale Group).
Indexed: ASFA, BRI, BiolAb, BiolDig, CBRI, EPB, ESPM, SFA, SWRA, WildRev, ZooRec.
—BLDSC (9090.013000), IE, ingenta, Linda Hall.
Published by: American Littoral Society, Sandy Hook, Highlands, NJ 07732. TEL 908-291-0055, http://www.bullit.org/als.htm. Ed. D W Bennett. Circ: 9,000.

551.46 GBR
➤ **UNDERWATER TECHNOLOGY.** Text in English. 1975. q. Please contact publisher for prices.. adv. bk.rev. illus. **Document type:** *Journal, Academic/Scholarly.* **Description:** Keeps readers informed of current technology and developments in underwater technology, ocean science and offshore engineering.
Formerly (until 1984): Society for Underwater Technology. Journal (0141-0814)
Indexed: ASCA, ASFA, BMT, CivEngAb, ESPM, EngInd, FLUIDEX, GEOBASE, IMMAb, Inspec, OceAb.
—BLDSC (9090.017900), CISTI, Ei, IDS, IE, ingenta, Linda Hall. **CCC.**
Published by: Society for Underwater Technology, 80 Coleman St, London, EC2R 5BJ, United Kingdom. FAX 44-20-7382-2684, paula@sutadmin.demon.co.uk, http://www.sut.org.uk. Circ: 2,000.

551.46 GBR ISSN 1367-3548
UNITED KINGDOM. DEPARTMENT OF THE ENVIRONMENT. MARINE RESEARCH PROGRAMME. REPORT. Variant title: D O E Marine Research Programme. Report. Text in English. 1990. irreg. **Document type:** *Government.*
—BLDSC (3614.603100).
Published by: United Kingdom. Department of the Environment, Marine Research Programme, Romney House RmB452, 43 Marsham St, London, SW1P 3PY, United Kingdom. TEL 44-171-276-8634, doe.marine@gtnet.gov.uk.

551.46 USA ISSN 0098-9002
VK947
UNITED STATES COAST PILOT. 7, PACIFIC COAST. CALIFORNIA, OREGON, WASHINGTON, AND HAWAII. Text in English. 1903. a., latest 2005, 37th ed.
Formerly (until 1951): United States Coast Pilot. Pacific Coast. California, Oregon, and Washington (8755-9234)
Published by: (U.S. National Ocean Service), U.S. Government Printing Office, 732 N Capitol St NW, Washington, DC 20401. TEL 202-512-1530, 888-293-6498, FAX 202-512-1262, http://nauticalcharts.noaa.gov/nsd/coastpilot7.htm.

551.46 MEX ISSN 0187-7305
UNIVERSIDAD AUTONOMA DE BAJA CALIFORNIA. INSTITUTO DE INVESTIGACIONES OCEANOLOGICAS. REPORTE MENSUAL. Text in Spanish. 1988. m.
Indexed: ESPM.
Published by: Universidad Autonoma de Baja California, Instituto de Investigaciones Oceanologicas, Apdo. Postal 423, Ensenada, Baja California, Mexico. TEL 52-66-61745451, FAX 52-66-61745303, cmarinas@bahia.ens.uabc.mx.

551.46 MEX ISSN 0187-7046
UNIVERSIDAD AUTONOMA DE BAJA CALIFORNIA. INSTITUTO DE INVESTIGACIONES OCEANOLOGICAS. REPORTE TECNICO. Text in Spanish. 1985. irreg. **Document type:** *Monographic series.*
Published by: Universidad Autonoma de Baja California, Instituto de Investigaciones Oceanologicas, Apdo. Postal 423, Ensenada, Baja California, Mexico. TEL 52-66-61745451, FAX 52-66-61745303, iio@uabc.mx, http://iio.ens.uabc.mx/.

551.46 MEX
UNIVERSIDAD AUTONOMA DE BAJA CALIFORNIA SUR. AREA DE CIENCIAS DEL MAR. SERIE CIENTIFICA. Text in Spanish. 1989. irreg. **Document type:** *Monographic series.*
Published by: Universidad Autonoma de Baja California Sur, Area de Ciencias del Mar, Carretera al Sur, Km. 5.5, Apdo. Postal 19-B, La Paz, Baja California Sur, 23081, Mexico.

551.46 MEX ISSN 0188-9591
UNIVERSIDAD AUTONOMA DE BAJA CALIFORNIA SUR. REVISTA DE INVESTIGACION CIENTIFICA. SERIE CIENCIAS DEL MAR. Text in Spanish. 1988. irreg. **Document type:** *Monographic series.*
Published by: Universidad Autonoma de Baja California Sur, Carretera al Sur Km. 5.5, La Paz, Baja California Sur, 23080, Mexico. TEL 52-1-1280440, FAX 52-1-1280880, http://www.uabcs.mx/.

551.46 CHL ISSN 0716-159X
QH91.A1
UNIVERSIDAD DE VALPARAISO. INSTITUTO DE OCEANOLOGIA. PUBLICACIONES OCASIONALES. Text in Spanish. 1982. irreg. **Document type:** *Monographic series.*
Indexed: ESPM.
Published by: Universidad de Valparaiso, Facultad de Ciencias del Mar, Avenida Borgono, Montemar, Vina del Mar, Chile. TEL 56-32-507820, FAX 56-32-507859, jeanette.santana@uv.cl, http://www.uv.cl.

550 BRA ISSN 0100-5146
UNIVERSIDADE DE SAO PAULO. INSTITUTO OCEANOGRAFICO. PUBLICACAO ESPECIAL. Text in Portuguese. 1972. irreg., latest vol.4, 1977. per issue exchange basis.
Indexed: ASFA, ESPM, SWRA, ZooRec.
—CISTI.
Published by: Universidade de Sao Paulo, Instituto Oceanografico, Praca do Oceanografico, 191 Cidade Universitaria, Sao Paulo, SP 05508-900, Brazil. Circ: 650.

551 BRA ISSN 0100-5197
GC1
UNIVERSIDADE DE SAO PAULO. INSTITUTO OCEANOGRAFICO. RELATORIO DE CRUZEIROS. Text in Multiple languages; Summaries in English. 1976. irreg., latest vol.6, 1985. per issue exchange basis.
Published by: Universidade de Sao Paulo, Instituto Oceanografico, Praca do Oceanografico, 191 Cidade Universitaria, Sao Paulo, SP 05508-900, Brazil. TEL 55-11-3091-6501, FAX 55-11-3032-3092, io@edu.usp.br, http://www.io.usp.br. Ed. W Besuard. Circ: 650.

551 BRA ISSN 1413-7747
UNIVERSIDADE DE SAO PAULO. INSTITUTO OCEANOGRAFICO. RELATORIOS TECNICOS. Text in Multiple languages; Summaries in English. 1974. irreg., latest vol.14, 1985. price varies; exchange basis. **Document type:** *Monographic series, Academic/Scholarly.*
Formerly (until 1995): Universidade de Sao Paulo. Instituto Oceanografico. Relatorio Interno (0100-5243)
Indexed: ASFA, ESPM, OceAb, PollutAb, RefZh, SFA, ZooRec.
—CISTI.
Published by: Universidade de Sao Paulo, Instituto Oceanografico, Praca do Oceanografico, 191 Cidade Universitaria, Sao Paulo, SP 05508-900, Brazil. Circ: 200.

551.46 DEU ISSN 0935-6215
UNIVERSITAET KIEL. INSTITUT FUER MEERESKUNDE. JAHRESBERICHT. Text in German. 1969. a. **Document type:** *Yearbook, Academic/Scholarly.*
Indexed: ESPM.
Published by: Universitaet Kiel, Leibniz Institut fuer Meereswissenschaften, Wischhofstr 1-3, Kiel, 24148, Germany. TEL 49-431-5973902, FAX 49-431-565876, ifm-geomar@ifm-geomar.de.

551.46 DEU
UNIVERSITAET KIEL. LEIBNIZ INSTITUT FUER MEERESWISSENSCHAFTEN. BERICHTE. Text in English, German; Summaries in English. 1973. bi-m. free. bibl.; illus.; maps; stat. **Document type:** *Journal, Academic/Scholarly.* **Description:** Contains reports, dissertations and monographs on all aspects of the marine sciences.
Formerly (until 2004): Universitaet Kiel. Institut fuer Meereskunde. Berichte (0341-8561)
Indexed: ASFA, ESPM, RefZh, ZooRec.
—BLDSC (1920.483000), IE, ingenta, Linda Hall. **CCC.**
Published by: Universitaet Kiel, Leibniz Institut fuer Meereswissenschaften, Wischhofstr 1-3, Kiel, 24148, Germany. TEL 49-431-6000, FAX 49-431-6002805, ifm-geomar@ifm-geomar.de, http://www.ifm-geomar.de. Ed. Gerhard Kortum. Circ: 250 (controlled).

551.46 NOR ISSN 0525-4760
UNIVERSITY OF BERGEN. INSTITUTE OF GEOPHYSICS. DEPARTMENT OF PHYSICAL OCEANOGRAPHY. REPORT. Cover title: Report - University of Bergen. Geophysical Institute. Division A Physical Oceanography. Text in English. 1962. irreg. **Document type:** *Monographic series.*
Indexed: ASFA, ESPM.
—CISTI.
Published by: Universitetet i Bergen, Geofysisk Institutt/University of Bergen, Geophysical Institute, Allegaten 70, Bergen, 5007, Norway. TEL 47-55-582602, FAX 47-55-589883, http://www.gfi.uib.no/middle_and_right_e.html.

551.46 CAN ISSN 0068-1830
UNIVERSITY OF BRITISH COLUMBIA. INSTITUTE OF OCEANOGRAPHY. DATA REPORT. Text in English. 1951. irreg. **Document type:** *Monographic series.*
Indexed: ESPM.
—CISTI.
Published by: University of British Columbia, Institute of Oceanography, c/o Department of Earth and Ocean Sciences, 6339 Stores Rd, Vancouver, BC V6T 1Z4, Canada. TEL 604-822-2449, FAX 604-822-6088, http://www.eos.ubc.ca.

551.46 USA
UNIVERSITY OF CALIFORNIA, SANTA CRUZ. INSTITUTE FOR MARINE SCIENCES. SPECIAL PUBLICATION. Text in English. 1974. irreg., latest vol.9, 1978. price varies.
Former titles: University of California, Santa Cruz. Center for Marine Studies. Special Publication; University of California, Santa Cruz. Coastal Marine Laboratory. Special Publication

Published by: University of California, Santa Cruz, Institute of Marine Sciences, 1156 High St, Santa Cruz, CA 95064. TEL 408-429-2464, FAX 408-429-0146. Circ: 500 (controlled).

551.46   DNK
UNIVERSITY OF COPENHAGEN. DEPARTMENT OF PHYSICAL OCEANOGRAPHY. REPORT. Text in Danish. 1968. irreg. free. illus. **Document type:** *Academic/Scholarly.*
Formerly: University of Copenhagen. Institute of Physical Oceanography. Report
Published by: Koebenhavns Universitet, Department of Physical Oceanography/Copenhagen University, Rockefeller Complex, Juliane Maries Vej 30, Copenhagen O, 2100, Denmark. TEL 45-35-32-06-02, FAX 45-35-36-53-57, nkh@qfy.ku.dk. Circ: 250.

551.46   USA
UNIVERSITY OF HAWAII. SEA GRANT COLLEGE PROGRAM. TECHNICAL REPORT. Text in English. irreg.
Published by: University of Hawaii, Sea Grant College Program, Communications Office, 2525 Correa Rd., HIG 238, Honolulu, HI 96822. TEL 808-956-7410, FAX 808-956-2880, http://www.soest.hawaii.edu/SEAGRANT/.

551.46   USA
UNIVERSITY OF MARYLAND. SEA GRANT PROGRAM. PUBLICATIONS. Text in English. irreg.
Published by: University of Maryland, Sea Grant Program, 4321 Hartwick Rd, Suite 300, College Park, MD 20740. TEL 301-403-4220, FAX 301-403-4255, mdsg@mdsg.umd.edu, http://www.mdsg.umd.edu/store/pubs.html.

551.46   USA
UNIVERSITY OF MARYLAND. SEA GRANT PROGRAM. TECHNICAL REPORT. Text in English. irreg.
Published by: University of Maryland, Sea Grant Program, 4321 Hartwick Rd, Suite 300, College Park, MD 20740. TEL 301-403-4220, FAX 301-403-4255, mdsg@mdsg.umd.edu, http://www.mdsg.umd.edu/store/pubs.html.

UNIVERSITY OF MIAMI. ROSENSTIEL SCHOOL OF MARINE & ATMOSPHERIC SCIENCE. TECHNICAL REPORT. see *METEOROLOGY*

551.46 639.2   USA
UNIVERSITY OF NEW HAMPSHIRE. SEA GRANT COLLEGE PROGRAM. REPORT. Text in English. irreg.
Supersedes in part: Maine-New Hampshire Sea Grant College Program. Report
Published by: University of New Hampshire Sea Grant Program, Kingman Farm, Durham, NH 03824-3512. TEL 603-749-1565, FAX 603-743-3997, http://www.seagrant.unh.edu/pubs.htm, http://www.seagrant.unh.edu/index.html.

551.46   USA   ISSN 0893-0058
UNIVERSITY OF NORTH CAROLINA SEA GRANT COLLEGE PROGRAM. SEA GRANT PUBLICATION. Variant title: U N C Sea Grant Publication. Text in English. 197?. irreg. **Document type:** *Monographic series.*
Published by: North Carolina Sea Grant College Program, North Carolina State University, 1911 Bldg., Rm. 100B, Box 8605, Raleigh, NC 27695-8605. TEL 919-515-2454, FAX 919-515-7095, http://www.ncsu.edu/seagrant/.

551.46   USA
UNIVERSITY OF RHODE ISLAND. SEA GRANT COLLEGE PROGRAM. MARINE MEMORANDUM SERIES. Text in English. irreg.
Published by: University of Rhode Island, Sea Grant College Program, Bay Campus, Narragansett, RI 02882. TEL 401-874-6842, FAX 401-874-6817, allard@gso.uri.edu, http://seagrant.gso.uri.edu.

551.46   USA
UNIVERSITY OF RHODE ISLAND. SEA GRANT COLLEGE PROGRAM. MARINE TECHNICAL REPORT SERIES. Text in English. irreg.
Published by: University of Rhode Island, Sea Grant College Program, Bay Campus, Narragansett, RI 02882. TEL 401-874-6842, FAX 401-874-6817, allard@gso.uri.edu, http://seagrant.gso.uri.edu.

551.46 578.77   SLE
UNIVERSITY OF SIERRA LEONE. FOURAH BAY COLLEGE. INSTITUTE OF MARINE BIOLOGY AND OCEANOGRAPHY. BULLETIN. Text in English. irreg.
Published by: University of Sierra Leone, Fourah Bay College Institute of Marine Biology and Oceanography, Mount Aureol, Freetown, Sierra Leone. TEL 010-232-22-227924, FAX 010-232-22-224260.

551.46   USA
UNIVERSITY OF SOUTH CAROLINA. BELLE W. BARUCH LIBRARY IN MARINE SCIENCE AND COASTAL RESEARCH. COLLECTED PAPERS. Text in English. 1973. irreg. (approx. 2/yr.). USD 49.95. charts; illus. **Document type:** *Academic/Scholarly.*
Published by: (University of South Carolina, Belle W. Baruch Institute for Marine Biology & Coastal Research), University of South Carolina Press, c/o Dianne Smith, Rights & Permissions, Columbia, SC 29208. TEL 803-777-5243.

551.46 578.77   USA
UNIVERSITY OF SOUTHERN CALIFORNIA SEA GRANT PROGRAM. REPORT. Text in English. irreg. price varies.
Published by: University of Southern California, Sea Grant Program, AHF 209, Los Angeles, CA 90089-0373. TEL 213-740-1961, FAX 213-740-5936, http://www.usc.edu/org/seagrant/Publications/publicationpubs.html.

551.46   JPN   ISSN 0564-6898
                                   CODEN: BUORB3
➤ **UNIVERSITY OF TOKYO. OCEAN RESEARCH INSTITUTE. BULLETIN/TOKYO DAIGAKU KAIYO KENKYUJO.** Text in English. 1967. irreg. per issue exchange basis. stat. **Document type:** *Bulletin, Academic/Scholarly.* **Description:** Covers all aspects related to oceanography, such as physical, chemical, geological, biological, and fisheries.
Indexed: ASFA, BiolAb, ESPM, SFA, ZooRec.
—CISTI, Linda Hall.
Published by: University of Tokyo, Ocean Research Institute/Tokyo Daigaku Kaiyo Kenkyujo, 1-15-1 Minami-Dai, Nakano-ku, Tokyo, 164-0014, Japan. TEL 81-3-5351-6476, FAX 81-3-5351-6836, shomu@ori.u-tokyo.ac.jp, http://www.ori.u-tokyo.ac.jp. Ed., R&P Shuhei Nishida TEL 81-3-5351-6476. Circ: 1,000.

551.48   JPN
UNIVERSITY OF TOKYO. OCEAN RESEARCH INSTITUTE. PUBLICATION LIST. Text in English. a.
Published by: Tokyo Daigaku, Kaiyo Kenkyujo/University of Tokyo, Ocean Research Institute, 15-1 Minami-Dai 1-chome, Nakano-ku, Tokyo, 164-0014, Japan.

551.46 570   JPN
UNIVERSITY OF TSUKUBA. SHIMODA MARINE RESEARCH CENTER. CONTRIBUTIONS. Text in English, Japanese. 1954. irreg.
Published by: Tsukuba Daigaku, Shimoda Rinkai Jikken Senta/University of Tsukuba, Shimoda Marine Research Center, 10-1, Shimodashi 5-chome, Tsukuba, Shizuoka-ken 415, Japan.

551.46   USA   ISSN 0191-3336
                                   CODEN: UWSGA8
UNIVERSITY OF WISCONSIN. SEA GRANT COLLEGE PROGRAM. TECHNICAL REPORT. Cover title: Sea Grant College Technical Report. Text in English. 1973. irreg. **Document type:** *Monographic series.*
Published by: University of Wisconsin, Sea Grant Institute, Goodnight Hall, 1975 Willow Dr., Madison, WI 53706-1177. TEL 608-263-3259, FAX 608-262-0591, linda@seagrant.wisc.edu, http://www.seagrant.wisc.edu/.

551.46   DNK   ISSN 1602-9313
▼ **VAND OG DATA;** nyhedsbrev fra GEUS. Key Title: Vand & Data. Text in Danish. 2003. irreg. free. back issues avail. **Document type:** *Journal, Academic/Scholarly.*
Related titles: Online - full text ed.
Published by: Miljoeministeriet, Danmarks og Groenlands Geologiske Undersoegelse (GEUS)/Danish Ministry of the Environment. Geological Survey of Denmark and Greenland, Oester Voldgade 10, Copenhagen K, 1350, Denmark. TEL 45-38-142000, FAX 45-38-142050, geus@geus.dk, http://www.geus.dk/vand-og-data/vd-dk.htm, htpp://www.geus.dk.

VICTORIA. DEPARTMENT OF NATURAL RESOURCES AND ENVIRONMENT. MARINE AND FRESHWATER RESOURCES INSTITUTE. REPORT. see *BIOLOGY*

551.46   USA   ISSN 0882-7427
                                   CODEN: SEVSDG
VIRGINIA INSTITUTE OF MARINE SCIENCE, GLOUCESTER POINT. SPECIAL REPORT IN APPLIED MARINE SCIENCE AND OCEAN ENGINEERING. Text in English. 1955. irreg., latest 1998. price varies. **Document type:** *Monographic series.*
Indexed: ASFA.
Published by: Virginia Institute of Marine Science, PO Box 3146, Gloucester, VA 23062. TEL 804-684-7116, FAX 804-684-7113, http://www.vims.edu. R&P Eugene Burreson TEL 804-684-7000.

VIRGINIA MARINE RESOURCE BULLETIN; a sea grant advisory service. see *FISH AND FISHERIES*

551.46   USA
VIRGINIA SEA GRANT CONSORTIUM. PUBLICATIONS. Text in English. irreg.
Published by: Virginia Sea Grant Consortium, University of Virginia, Madison House, 170 Rugby Rd, Charlottesville, VA 22903. TEL 434-924-5965, FAX 434-982-3694, http://www.virginia.edu/virginia-sea-grant/.

551.46   RUS
VSESOYUZNYI NAUCHNO-ISSLEDOVATEL'SKII INSTITUT MORSKOGO RYBNOGO KHOZYAISTVA I OKEANOGRAFII (V N I R O). TRUDY. Text in Russian. 1976 (vol.117). irreg. price varies.
Indexed: BiolAb, ChemAb, FS&TA, RASB, SFA.

Published by: Vsesoyuznyi Nauchno-Issledovatel'skii Institut Morskogo Rybnogo Khozyaistva i Okeanografii, Ul Verkhnyaya Krasnoselskaya 17, Moscow, 107140, Russian Federation. Ed. K Yablonskaya. Circ: 500.

551.46   FRA   ISSN 1020-4598
W E S T P A C INFORMATION. (Western Pacific) Text in English. irreg. **Document type:** *Newsletter.*
Published by: (I O C Regional Secretariat for the Western Pacific THA), UNESCO, Intergovernmental Oceanographic Commission, 1, rue Miollis, Paris, 75015, France. TEL 33-1-4568-3984, FAX 33-1-4568-5812, ioc.secretariat@unesco.org, http://ioc.unesco.org/iocweb/index.php.

551.46   KEN   ISSN 1024-4158
QC721
W I N D O W. WESTERN INDIAN OCEAN WATERS. Text in English. 1990. irreg.
Indexed: ESPM.
Published by: UNESCO, c/o Mika Odido, Ed, ODINAFRICA Regional Coordinator, PO Box 95832, Mombasa, 80106, Kenya. TEL 254-11-472527, FAX 254-11-475157. Ed. Mika Odido.

551.46   USA
WASHINGTON LETTER OF OCEANOGRAPHY. Text in English. 1973. fortn. USD 56 domestic; USD 60 in Canada; USD 78 elsewhere (effective 2003). bk.rev. bibl. reprint service avail. from PQC. **Document type:** *Newsletter.* **Description:** Contains comprehensive, factual news on plans and programs in both government and industry, particularly marketing information, legislation, contracts, proposals and interpretations of significant news in oceanology.
Published by: Compass Publications, Inc. (Arlington), 1501 Wilson Blv, Ste 1001, Arlington, VA 22209. TEL 703-524-3136, FAX 703-841-0852, oceanbiz@sea-technology.com. Ed. Michele B. Umansky.

WASHINGTON SEA GRANT PROGRAM. REPORT. see *FISH AND FISHERIES*

WATER & ATMOSPHERE. see *METEOROLOGY*

551.46   AUS   ISSN 1323-6229
WESTERN AUSTRALIAN RESEARCH ACTIVITIES. Text in English. 1993. a. **Document type:** *Corporate.*
Published by: Australian Institute of Marine Science, PMB No 3, Townsville Mail Centre, Townsville, QLD 4810, Australia. TEL 61-7-47534409, w.ellery@aims.gov.au, http://www.aims.gov.au. Eds. S Clarke, W Ellery.

WHALING ACCOUNT. see *BIOLOGY—Zoology*

551.46   USA
WOODS HOLE CURRENTS. Text in English. q. USD 25 domestic includes Oceanus; USD 30 in Canada includes Oceanus; USD 40 elsewhere includes Oceanus (effective 2000). **Description:** Offers descriptions of oceanographic expeditions and laboratory accomplishments, profiles WHOI people, discusses marine policy issues, and reports Institution news.
Related titles: ♦ Supplement to: Oceanus. ISSN 0029-8182.
Indexed: RefZh, SFA.
Published by: Woods Hole Oceanographic Institution, Mail Stop 5, Woods Hole, MA 02543-1050. TEL 508-289-3516, FAX 508-289-2182, http://whoi.edu/oceanus. **Subscr. to:** WHOI Publication Services, PO Box 50145, New Bedford, MA 02745-0005. TEL 800-291-6458.

351.46   USA   ISSN 1062-2152
GC1
WOODS HOLE OCEANOGRAPHIC INSTITUTION - ANNUAL REPORT. Text in English. 1932. a. **Document type:** *Corporate.*
Former titles (until 1990): Woods Hole Oceanographic Institution (1053-9352); (until 1989): Woods Hole Oceanographic Institution. Annual Report (0099-3808)
Indexed: ASFA.
Published by: Woods Hole Oceanographic Institution, Mail Stop 5, Woods Hole, MA 02543-1050. TEL 508-289-2719, FAX 508-289-2182, http://www.whoi.edu. Ed. Vicky Cullen.

551.46   USA   ISSN 0730-9694
                                   CODEN: WOTRAC
WOODS HOLE OCEANOGRAPHIC INSTITUTION. TECHNICAL REPORT. Text in English. 1949. irreg. **Document type:** *Monographic series.*
Published by: Woods Hole Oceanographic Institution, Mail Stop 5, Woods Hole, MA 02543-1050. pgs@whoi.edu, http://www.whoi.edu.

551.46   USA   ISSN 1041-5602
SH1   CODEN: WOAQEK
WORLD AQUACULTURE. Text in English. q. USD 65 to non-members; USD 65 to libraries (effective 2004). adv. **Document type:** *Academic/Scholarly.* **Description:** Contains aquaculture science and technology news and information.
Formerly: World Aquaculture Society. Newsletter
Indexed: ASFA, Agr, B&BAb, ESPM, FS&TA, M&TEA, MBA, OceAb, RefZh, SFA, ZooRec.
—BLDSC (9352.912430), CISTI, IE, ingenta.

E

Published by: World Aquaculture Society, 143 J M Parker Coliseum, Louisiana State University, Baton Rouge, LA 70803. TEL 225-388-3137, FAX 225-388-3493, wasmas@aol.com, http://www.was.org. Ed. Robert R Stickney. R&P Juliette Massey. Adv. contact John Cooksey.

551.46 USA ISSN 0893-8849
SH138 CODEN: JWASE7

➤ **WORLD AQUACULTURE SOCIETY. JOURNAL.** Text in English. 1986. q. USD 135 to non-members; USD 135 to libraries (effective 2004). illus. back issues avail.; reprints avail. **Document type:** *Journal, Academic/Scholarly.* **Description:** Covers all aspects of the culture of plants and animals: culture systems, nutrition, water quality, disease, economics and marketing, physiology, reproduction and breeding and genetics.
Former titles: World Mariculture Society. Journal (0735-0147); World Mariculture Society. Proceedings
Indexed: AEA, ASFA, AgBio, Agr, AnBrAb, B&BAb, BIOSIS Prev, BioCN&I, BiolAb, CurCont, DSA, ESPM, ForAb, GEOBASE, HelmAb, HerbAb, HortAb, ISR, IndVet, MBA, MaizeAb, NutrAb, OceAb, OrnHort, PBA, PN&I, PotatoAb, PoultAb, ProtozoAb, RA&MP, RM&VM, RiceAb, S&F, SCI, SFA, SoyAb, TriticAb, VetBull, WAE&RSA, WeedAb, WildRev, ZooRec.
—BLDSC (4917.434000), CASDDS, CISTI, IDS, IE, Infotrieve, ingenta, Linda Hall.
Published by: World Aquaculture Society, 143 J M Parker Coliseum, Louisiana State University, Baton Rouge, LA 70803. TEL 225-388-3137, FAX 225-388-3493, wasmas@aol.com, http://www.was.org. Ed. Craig Tucker.

551.46 USA

WORLD AQUACULTURE SOCIETY. WORKSHOP SERIES. Text in English. 1991. a. price varies. **Document type:** *Proceedings.*
Published by: World Aquaculture Society, 143 J M Parker Coliseum, Louisiana State University, Baton Rouge, LA 70803. TEL 225-388-3137, FAX 225-388-3493. R&P Juliette Massey.

WORLD METEOROLOGICAL ORGANIZATION. COMMISSION FOR HYDROLOGY. ABRIDGED FINAL REPORT OF THE (NO.) SESSION. see *METEOROLOGY*

551.46 CHE ISSN 0084-2001

WORLD METEOROLOGICAL ORGANIZATION. REPORTS ON MARINE SCIENCE AFFAIRS. Text in English. 1970. irreg., latest vol.16, 1991. price varies. **Document type:** *Monographic series.*
Indexed: BiolAb.
Published by: World Meteorological Organization, 7 bis Avenue de la Paix, Case postale 2300, Geneva 2, 1211, Switzerland. TEL 41-22-7308111, FAX 41-22-7308022, pubsales@gateway.wmo.ch, http://www.wmo.int. **Dist. in U.S. by:** American Meteorological Society, 45 Beacon St, Boston, MA 02108. TEL 617-227-2425.

WORLD SURVEY OF CLIMATOLOGY. see *METEOROLOGY*

551.46 DEU ISSN 0947-7136

ZENTRUM FUER MEERES- UND KLIMAFORSCHUNG. BERICHTE. REIHE B: OZEANOGRAPHIE. Text in German. 1962. irreg. **Document type:** *Monographic series.*
Supersedes in part (in 1992): Universitaet Hamburg. Zentrum fuer Meeres- und Klimaforschung. Berichte (0936-949X); Which was formerly (until 1988): Universitaet Hamburg. Instituts fuer Meereskunde. Mitteilungen (0017-6907)
Indexed: ESPM.
Published by: (Universitaet Hamburg, Institut fuer Meereskunde/University of Hamburg, Institute of Oceanography), Universitaet Hamburg, Zentrum fuer Meeres- und Klimaforschung/University of Hamburg, Center for Marine and Climate Research, Bundesstr. 55, Hamburg, 20146, Germany. TEL 49-40-42838-4523, FAX 49-40-42838-5235, http://www.uni-hamburg.de/Wiss/SE/ZMK.

ZENTRUM FUER MEERES- UND KLIMAFORSCHUNG. BERICHTE. REIHE Z: INTERDISZIPLINAERE ZENTRUMSBERICHTE. see *METEOROLOGY*

551.46 CHN

ZHONGGUO HAIYANG BAO/CHINA OCEANOLOGY REVIEW. Text in Chinese. 1989. 2/w. CNY 72 (effective 2004). **Document type:** *Academic/Scholarly.*
Published by: Zhongguo Haiyang Baoshe, Xicheng-qu, 1, Fuxingmenwei Dajie, Beijing, 100860, China. TEL 86-10-68032211 ext 5823, 5827, 5829 or 5831, FAX 86-10-68033233, hyb3@263.net, http://www.coi.gov.cn/oceannews/. **Dist. by:** China International Book Trading Corp, 35 Chegongzhuang Xilu, Haidian District, PO Box 399, Beijing 100044, China. TEL 86-10-68412045, FAX 86-10-68412023, cibtc@mail.cibtc.com.cn, http://www.cibtc.com.cn.

551.46 USA

41 DEGREES N. Text in English. 2000. 3/yr. free Rhode Island residents; USD 5 out of state (effective 2003). **Document type:** *Journal, Academic/Scholarly.*
Related titles: Online - full text ed.
Published by: University of Rhode Island, Sea Grant College Program, Bay Campus, Narragansett, RI 02882. TEL 401-874-6842, FAX 401-874-6817, http://www.uri.edu/41N, http://seagrant.gso.uri.edu. Ed. Malia Schwartz.

EASTERN ORTHODOX

see RELIGIONS AND THEOLOGY—Eastern Orthodox

ECONOMIC SITUATION AND CONDITIONS

see BUSINESS AND ECONOMICS—Economic Situation And Conditions

ECONOMIC SYSTEMS AND THEORIES, ECONOMIC HISTORY

see BUSINESS AND ECONOMICS—Economic Systems And Theories, Economic History

ECONOMICS

see BUSINESS AND ECONOMICS

EDUCATION

see also CHILDREN AND YOUTH—About ; EDUCATION—Adult Education ; EDUCATION—Computer Applications ; EDUCATION—Guides To Schools And Colleges ; EDUCATION—Higher Education ; EDUCATION—International Education Programs ; EDUCATION—School Organization And Administration ; EDUCATION—Special Education And Rehabilitation ; EDUCATION—Teaching Methods And Curriculum

A A T G NEWSLETTER. see *LINGUISTICS*

A A T S E E L NEWSLETTER. see *LINGUISTICS*

370.82 USA ISSN 1522-340X

A A U W IN ACTION. Text in English. 1981. q. USD 20 to non-members. adv. illus. back issues avail. **Document type:** *Newsletter.* **Description:** Spotlights A A U W's impact on local, state and national levels.
Formerly: Leader in Action (8755-2620)
Published by: American Association of University Women, 1111 16th St, NW, Washington, DC 20036. TEL 202-785-7737, FAX 202-872-1425, editor@aauw.org, ads@aauw.org, http://www.aauw.org. Ed., R&P Jodi Lipson. Circ: 110,000.

372.4 CHN ISSN 1006-1622

A B C PINPIN DUDU HUABAO/A B C SPELLING AND READING PICTORIAL. Text in Chinese. m. CNY 210, USD 24. **Document type:** *Academic/Scholarly.* **Description:** Contains fables, tales, poems and songs for primary school students.
Published by: Shanghai Jiaoyu Chubanshe/Shanghai Educational Publishing House, 123 Yongfu Rd, Shanghai, 200031, China. TEL 4377165. Ed. Zhang Wenjie. Circ: 36,000.

370.72 THA

A C E I D NEWS. Text in English. 1974. 3/yr. free or exchange basis. **Document type:** *Newsletter.*
Formerly: A C E I D Newsletter (0251-4818)
Published by: (Asia-Pacific Centre of Educational Innovation for Development), UNESCO, Principal Regional Office for Asia and the Pacific, PO Box 967, Prakanong Post Office, Bangkok, 10110, Thailand. TEL 662-391-0577, FAX 662-391-0866. Ed. Ian Birch. Circ: 1,900.

613.7 AUS ISSN 1321-0394
GV201

➤ **A C H P E R HEALTHY LIFESTYLES JOURNAL.** (Australian Council for Health Physical Education and Recreation) Text in English. 1954. q. AUD 48 domestic; AUD 64 foreign (effective 2005). adv. bk.rev.; film rev. charts; illus.; stat. back issues avail.; reprint service avail. from PQC. **Document type:** *Magazine, Consumer.* **Description:** For specialists in physical education, health, dance, community fitness, and recreation, doctors, physiotherapists, university lecturers, schools and colleges.
Former titles (until 1994): A C H P E R National Journal (0813-2283); (until 1983): A J H P E R. Australian Journal for Health, Physical Education and Recreation (0813-2275); (until 1977): Australian Journal for Health, Physical Education and Recreation (0312-827X); (until 1975): Australian Journal of Physical Education (0312-8261); Which was formerly (until 1960): Physical Education Journal (0004-9492)
Related titles: Microform ed.: (from PQC).
Indexed: AEI, AbHyg, CPE, ERA, ETA, MEA, NutrAb, RHEA, RRTA, SEA, SENA, SOMA, SportS, TEA, WAE&RSA.
—BLDSC (0576.545000), IE, ingenta. **CCC.**
Published by: Australian Council for Health, Physical Education and Recreation Inc., 214 Port Rd, PO Box 304, Hindmarsh, SA 5007, Australia. TEL 61-8-83403388, FAX 61-8-83403399, membership@achper.org.au, http://www.achper.org.au/. Adv. contact Lyndall Bryden. Circ: 3,500.

371 USA ISSN 0194-8849

A E A ADVOCATE. Text in English. 1914. q. adv. bk.rev. bibl.; illus. **Document type:** *Magazine, Trade.* **Description:** Covers current issues in public education affected Arizona schools: trends, practices, professional events and objectives, legislation, and labor.
Former titles (until 1979): Arizona Educator Advocate; Arizona Teacher (0004-1653)
Related titles: Microfilm ed.: (from LIB); Microform ed.: (from PQC).
Published by: Arizona Education Association, 4000 N. Central Ave, Ste 1600, Phoenix, AZ 85012-1907. TEL 602-264-1774, FAX 602-240-6887, daphne.atkeson@arizonaea.org, datkeson@nea.org, http://www.arizonaea.org. Ed. Daphne Atkeson. adv.: B&W page USD 1,565; 8.25 x 10.75. Circ: 32,000 (controlled).

370 AUS

A E U NEWS - VICTORIA. Text in English. 1990. fortn. AUD 40 to non-members (effective 2000). adv. bk.rev. illus. index. back issues avail. **Document type:** *Newspaper.*
Formed by the merger of (1980-1995): Victorian Secondary Teachers' Association. News; (1990-1995): Federated Teacher's Union of Victoria. Federation News (1036-3904); Which was formed by the merger of (1982-1990): Tech Teacher; (1985-1990): V T U Journal; Which was formerly (1917-1984): Teachers' Journal (0040-0483)
Indexed: AEI.
Published by: Australian Education Union, Victorian Branch, 112 Trenerry Cress, Abbotsford, VIC 3067, Australia. TEL 61-3-94172822, FAX 61-3-94176198. adv.: page AUD 2,000; 370 x 257. Circ: 32,000.

370 AUS

A F MAGAZINE. Text in French; Summaries in English. 1976. m. AUD 45 membership individual; AUD 65 membership family; AUD 25 membership student (effective 2000). adv. reprints avail. **Document type:** *Newsletter.*
Former titles: Ce Mois-Ci; Ce Mois-Ci a l'Alliance; (until 1988): Chantecler
Published by: Alliance Francaise de Canberra Inc., PO Box 125, O'connor, ACT 2602, Australia. TEL 61-2-6247-5027, FAX 61-2-6257-6696, af_de_c@robillent.com.au, http://www.robillent.com.au/alliance/. Ed. Marc Faugeras. Circ: 1,000.

372.3 USA ISSN 1557-9743

A I M S MAGAZINE; your k-9 math and science classroom activities resource. (Activities Integrating Mathematics and Science) Text in English. 1986. 10/yr. USD 19.95 domestic (effective 2006). **Document type:** *Magazine.*
Formerly (until 1993): A I M S Newsletter (0895-3155)
Published by: A I M S Education Foundation, 1595 S. Chestnut Ave., Fresno, CA 93702. TEL 888-733-2467, aimsed@aimsedu.org, http://www.aimsedu.org/.

372.3 USA

A I M S NEWS. (Activities Integrating Mathematics & Science) Text in English. 8/yr. free (effective 2006). **Document type:** *Newsletter.*
Media: E-mail.
Published by: A I M S Education Foundation, 1595 S. Chestnut Ave., Fresno, CA 93702. TEL 888-733-2467, aimsed@aimsedu.org, http://www.aimsedu.org/.

370.1 AUS

A L E A TODAY. (Australian Literacy Educators' Association) Text in English. 3/yr. c/w membership. **Document type:** *Newsletter.* **Description:** Contains news from the organisation, articles on critical issues facing teachers, reviews, and publication details.
—BLDSC (0786.824000).
Published by: Australian Literacy Educators' Association, PO Box 3203, Norwood, SA 5067, Australia. TEL 61-8-83322845, FAX 61-8-83330394, alea@netspace.net.au, http://www.alea.edu.au/today/index.htm.

A L N MAGAZINE. (Asynchronous Learning Networks) see *COMPUTERS—Computer Networks*

370 USA

A M C NEWSLETTER. Text in English. 1996. m. bk.rev.; software rev. **Document type:** *Newsletter.* **Description:** Offers parents and teachers a way to keep up with what is new and relevant in the Montessori community.
Media: Online - full text. **Related titles:** E-mail ed.
Published by: American Montessori Consulting, PO Box 5062, Rossmoor, CA 90720. TEL 562-598-2321, amonco@aol.com, amcnews1@aol.com, http://www.amonco.org/newsletter_collection.html.

370 USA ISSN 0882-438X

A M S STUDIES IN EDUCATION. Text in English. 1974. irreg., latest vol.8, 1987. price varies. back issues avail. **Description:** Series of monographs, reference works and bibliographies on various aspects of education.
Published by: A M S Press, Inc., 63 Flushing Ave., # 417, Brooklyn, NY 11205-1005. TEL 212-777-4700, FAX 212-995-5413.

E

610 370 USA ISSN 0746-9217
A M T EVENTS. Text in English. 1940. 4/yr. USD 50 domestic; USD 60 foreign (effective 2005); includes subsc. to Journal of Continuing Education Topics & Issues. adv. bk.rev. back issues avail. **Document type:** *Journal, Trade.* **Description:** Contains technical and industry news for clinical laboratory and allied health professionals.
Supersedes in part (in 1984): American Medical Technologists. Journal (0002-9963); Which was formerly (until 1966): American Medical Technologists. Official Journal (0092-6485); (until 1959): American Medical Technologists. Journal (0360-0645)
Indexed: CINAHL.
—CISTI, GNLM.
Published by: American Medical Technologists, 710 Higgins Rd, Park Ridge, IL 60068-5765. TEL 847-939-3365, 800-275-1268, FAX 847-823-0458, mail@amt1.com, http://www.amt1.com. Ed. Diane Powell TEL 847-823-5169 ext. 215. adv.: B&W page USD 975. Circ: 25,000 (paid).

370 510.7 USA
A M T N Y S NEWS. Text in English. 3/yr. **Document type:** *Newsletter, Academic/Scholarly.*
Published by: Association of Mathematics Teachers of New York State, c/o John Bailey, Data Manager, PO Box 631, Lake Katrine, NY 12449. http://www.amtnys.org/pubs/journal1.html. Ed. Sal Scire.

370 BRA ISSN 0101-5028
A N D E. Text in Portuguese. 1981. 2/yr. USD 30 (effective 1997). bk.rev. index. back issues avail. **Document type:** *Academic/Scholarly.* **Description:** Covers educational politics, adult education, school organization and administration, teaching methods and curriculum, and educational research.
Related titles: Microform ed.
Published by: Associacao Nacional de Educacao, Rua Joao Jacinto, 118, Luz, SP 01104-010, Brazil. TEL 011-864-0111. Ed. Cesar Augusto Minto. Circ: 8,000 (paid).

296.7 USA ISSN 1075-4601
A O J T NEWSLETTER. Text in English. 1965. q. USD 18 to non-members (effective 2003). adv. bk.rev. 12 p./no. 3 cols./p.; back issues avail. **Document type:** *Newsletter, Newspaper-distributed.* **Description:** Contains essays and articles on events in the New York City public school system. The emphasis is on matters that impact Jewish personnel and students in the schools.
Published by: Association of Orthodox Jewish Teachers, 1577 Coney Island Ave, Brooklyn, NY 11230. TEL 718-258-3585, FAX 718-258-3586, aojt@juno.com, http://www.aojtnyc.org. Ed., R&P Max Zakon. Adv. contact Joyce Hochberg. B&W page USD 500. Circ: 9,000.

A P E F NEWSLETTER. (Association Provinciale des Enseignantes et Enseignants des Ecoles Fransaskoises) see *LINGUISTICS*

A R E E. (Annual Review of Environmental Education) see *ENVIRONMENTAL STUDIES*

372 GBR ISSN 1367-5605
A S P E PAPERS: MANAGING PRIMARY EDUCATION SERIES. Text in English. irreg., latest vol.8, 1999. GBP 4.95 (effective 2001). **Document type:** *Monographic series, Academic/Scholarly.*
—BLDSC (1745.804000).
Published by: (Association for the Study of Primary Education), Trentham Books Ltd., Westview House, 734 London Rd, Stoke-on-Trent, Staffs ST4 5NP, United Kingdom. TEL 44-1782-745567, FAX 44-1782-745553, tb@trentham-books.co.uk, http://www.trentham-books.co.uk. Ed. Colin Richards.

A S T C DIMENSIONS. see *SCIENCES: COMPREHENSIVE WORKS*

378.0072 USA ISSN 1093-1295
A S U RESEARCH; magazine of scholarship and creativity. (Arizona State University) Text in English. 1985. s-a. free. 48 p./no.; **Document type:** *Magazine, Consumer.* **Description:** Covers science research, fine arts, scholarship of all kinds.
Related titles: Online - full text ed.
Published by: Arizona State University, A S U Research Publications, PO Box 878206, Tempe, AZ 85387-8206. TEL 480-965-1266, FAX 480-965-9684, cstorad@asu.edu, http://researchmag.asu.edu. Ed., R&P Conrad J Storad. Circ: 40,000.

370.1 USA ISSN 0889-6488
A T E A JOURNAL. Text in English. 1958. 4/yr. USD 50 to individual members; USD 200 to institutional members; USD 300 to corporations (effective 2003). adv. bk.rev.; software rev. illus.; stat.; tr.lit. 3 cols./p.; back issues avail. **Document type:** *Journal, Trade.* **Description:** Professional development articles for persons involved in post secondary technical education.
Formerly (until 1973): Technical Education Newsletter (0040-0939)
Indexed: CIJE, CPE.
Published by: American Technical Education Association, Inc., North Dakota State College of Science, 800 N 6th St, Wahpeton, ND 58075. TEL 701-671-2240, FAX 701-671-2260, betty.krump@ndscs.nodak.edu, http://www.ateaonline.org. Ed. Charles Mann. Pub., R&P, Adv. contact Betty Krump TEL 701-671-2240. Circ: 2,000.

373 GBR
A T L REPORT. Text in English. 1978. 8/yr. GBP 10 domestic; GBP 13 in Europe; GBP 22 elsewhere (effective 2000). adv. charts. **Document type:** *Trade.* **Description:** Provides news and analysis of events in British (excluding Scottish) education.
Incorporates: A M M A Report (0142-3134); Which was formed by the 1988 merger of: A M A (0001-1819); A A M Journal (0143-943X); Which was formerly: Association of Assistant Mistresses. Journal
Indexed: HECAB, RehabLit.
Published by: Association of Teachers and Lecturers, 7 Northumberland St, London, WC2N 5DA, United Kingdom. TEL 44-171-930-6441, FAX 44-171-930-1359. Ed. Richard Margrave. Adv. contact Sarah Rooth. Circ: 161,000 (controlled).

370.1 ESP ISSN 1137-3350
A TU SALUD; revista de educacion para la salud. Variant title: A tu Salud. Revista de Educacion para la Salud. Text in Spanish. 1992. q. back issues avail.
—CINDOC.
Published by: Alezeia Asociacion de Educacion para la Salud, Apartado Correos 393, Segovia, 40080, Spain. http://www.alezeia.org/a3.html. Ed. Mariea Isabel Serrano Gonzales.

370.72 USA
A V K O NEWSLETTER. Text in English. 1974. q. USD 25 to members (effective 2000). bk.rev. back issues avail. **Document type:** *Newsletter.* **Description:** Contains news and information to assist members of the foundation.
Published by: A V K O Educational Research Foundation, Inc., 3084 W Willard Rd, Ste C, Clio, MI 48420-7801. TEL 810-686-9283, FAX 810-686-1101. Ed. R J Rayl.

370.72 340 DEU ISSN 1433-0911
ABHANDLUNGEN ZU BILDUNGSFORSCHUNG UND BILDUNGSRECHT. Text in German. 1998. irreg., latest vol.11, 2002. price varies. **Document type:** *Monographic series, Academic/Scholarly.*
Published by: Duncker und Humblot GmbH, Carl-Heinrich-Becker-Weg 9, Berlin, 12165, Germany. TEL 49-30-7900060, FAX 49-30-79000361, info@duncker-humblot.de, http://www.duncker-humblot.de.

370 DEU ISSN 0936-7233
ABHANDLUNGEN ZUM STUDENTEN- UND HOCHSCHULWESEN. Text in German. irreg., latest vol.9, 2000. **Document type:** *Monographic series, Academic/Scholarly.*
Published by: (Gemeinschaft fuer Deutsche Studentengeschichte), S H Verlag GmbH, Osterather Str 42, Cologne, 50739, Germany. TEL 49-221-9561740, FAX 49-221-9561741, info@sh-verlag.de, http://www.sh-verlag.de.

370.1 DEU ISSN 0065-0366
ABHANDLUNGEN ZUR PHILOSOPHIE, PSYCHOLOGIE UND PAEDAGOGIK. Text in German. 1954. irreg., latest vol.242, 1996. price varies. **Document type:** *Monographic series.*
Published by: Bouvier Verlag Herbert Grundmann, Am Hof 28, Bonn, 53113, Germany. TEL 49-228-7290184, FAX 49-228-630872, verlag@books.de.

372 SWE ISSN 0280-2414
ABRAKADABRA; vuxenlaesning om barnkultur. Text in Swedish. 1981. bi-m. SEK 280 (effective 1990).
Formerly: Vaar Skola Barnkultur
Indexed: ChLitAb.
Published by: Vaar Skola Foerlag AB, c/o Hulen, Djurgardsvagen 27, Saltsjo-boo, 13246, Sweden. TEL 46-8-715-95-98, FAX 46-8-662-18-43. **Subscr. to:** Riddargatan 17, Stockholm 11457, Sweden. TEL 46-8-662-33-51, FAX 46-8-662-31-24.

370 URY ISSN 1688-1362
EL ABROJO. Text in Spanish. irreg. free (effective 2004).
Media: Online - full text.
Published by: El Abrojo Instituto de Educacion Popular, Maldonado 1162, Montevideo, 11100, Uruguay. TEL 598-2-9030144, FAX 598-2-9009123, elabrojo@elabrojo.org.uy, http://www.elabrojo.org.uy/. Pub. Jose Querejeta.

ABSTRACTS OF BULGARIAN SCIENTIFIC LITERATURE. PHILOSOPHY, SOCIOLOGY, SCIENCE OF SCIENCES, PSYCHOLOGY AND PEDAGOGICS. see *EDUCATION—Abstracting, Bibliographies, Statistics*

ABSTRACTS OF EDUCATIONAL STUDIES AND RESEARCH. see *EDUCATION—Abstracting, Bibliographies, Statistics*

370 CHL ISSN 0716-0526
F3099
ACADEMIA★. Text in Spanish. 1981. s-a. CLP 2,000, USD 25. adv.
Published by: Universidad Metropolitana de Ciencias de la Educacion, Ave. Jose Pedro Alessandri, 774, Nunoa, Santiago, Chile. Ed. Tomas P MacHale. Circ: 1,500.

372 DEU
ACADEMIA. Text in German. 1888. bi-m. EUR 12.50 domestic; EUR 14 foreign; EUR 2.05 newsstand/cover (effective 2004). adv. bk.rev. **Document type:** *Journal, Academic/Scholarly.* **Description:** Articles about the Catholic church and religious questions, politics, higher education, contemporary problems and questions in common. News and information about the Cartellverband, its members, member fraternities and circles.
Published by: Cartellverband der Katholischen Deutschen Studentenverbindungen, Linzer Str 82, Bad Honnef, 53604, Germany. TEL 49-2224-960020, FAX 49-2224-9600220, sekretariat@cartellverband.de, http://www.cartellverband.de/academia/. Ed. Johannes Leclerque. R&P Richard Weiskorn. Adv. contact Thomas Thamm. B&W page EUR 1,480, color page EUR 1,945; trim 185 x 255. Circ: 30,980.

370.1 USA ISSN 1533-7812
➤ **ACADEMIC LEADERSHIP (HERNANDO).** Text in English. 2000. q. free (effective 2005). bk.rev.; software rev.; video rev. back issues avail. **Document type:** *Journal, Academic/Scholarly.* **Description:** Aims to provide insight and commentary on the major issues facing those in positions of leadership in the academic world.
Media: Online - full content.
Published by: AcademicLeadership.org, 3594 E. Arbor Lakes Dr., Hernando, FL 34442. TEL 615-898-2841, drleaming@yahoo.com, http://www.academicleadership.org/index.html. Ed., Pub., R&P, Adv. contact Deryl R. Leaming TEL 352-726-5324.

➤ **ACADIENSIS**; journal of the history of the Atlantic region. see *HISTORY—History Of North And South America*

➤ **ACCELERATOR.** see *SCIENCES: COMPREHENSIVE WORKS*

370 ESP ISSN 0214-2546
ACCION EDUCATIVA. Variant title: Boletin Informativo de Accion Educativa. Text in Spanish. 1979. m.
—CINDOC.
Address: Principe, 35, Madrid, 28012, Spain. TEL 34-91-4295029.

370 VEN ISSN 1315-401X
➤ **ACCION PEDAGOGICA.** Text in Spanish. 1989. s-a. **Document type:** *Journal, Academic/Scholarly.* **Description:** Publishes articles on theoretical, methodological and practical aspects of education.
Related titles: Online - full text ed.: 1999. free (effective 2005).
Published by: Universidad de los Andes, Tachira, Apart Postal 273, San Cristobal, 5001-A, Venezuela. FAX 58-276-3562609, accionpe@tach.ula.ve, http://www.saber.ula.ve/accionpe/.

➤ **ACCORDIONISTS AND TEACHERS GUILD, INTERNATIONAL. BULLETIN.** see *MUSIC*

➤ **ACTA COLLOQUII DIDACTICI CLASSICI**; didactica classica gandensia. see *LINGUISTICS*

370 HUN ISSN 0230-6476
➤ **ACTA PAEDAGOGICA DEBRECINA.** Text in Hungarian; Summaries in German, English. 1962. a. bk.rev. bibl.; charts; illus.; maps; stat. 200 p./no.; back issues avail. **Document type:** *Yearbook, Academic/Scholarly.* **Description:** Studies in the history, psychology, and sociology of education.
Supersedes in part (in 1980): Neveles, Muvelodes. Acta Paedagogica Debrecina (0324-6957); Which was formerly (until 1967): Acta Paedagogica Debrecina (0567-7912); Which superseded in part (in 1963): Acta Marxistica et Pedagogica Debrecina
Published by: (Nevelestudomanyi Tanszek/Department of Educational Studies), Kossuth Lajos Tudomanyegyetem, PF 37, Debrecen, 4010, Hungary. TEL 36-52-316666, nevtud@tigris.klte.hu, rector@admin.unideb.hu. Ed., R&P, Adv. contact Tamas Kozma. Circ: 500 (controlled).

➤ **ACTA UNIVERSITATIS LODZIENSIS: FOLIA ARCHAEOLOGICA.** see *ARCHAEOLOGY*

➤ **ACTA UNIVERSITATIS LODZIENSIS: FOLIA BOTANICA.** see *BIOLOGY—Botany*

➤ **ACTA UNIVERSITATIS LODZIENSIS: FOLIA CHIMICA.** see *CHEMISTRY*

➤ **ACTA UNIVERSITATIS LODZIENSIS: FOLIA ETHNOLOGICA.** see *ANTHROPOLOGY*

➤ **ACTA UNIVERSITATIS LODZIENSIS: FOLIA GEOGRAPHICA.** see *GEOGRAPHY*

➤ **ACTA UNIVERSITATIS LODZIENSIS: FOLIA HISTORICA.** see *HISTORY*

E

➤ ACTA UNIVERSITATIS LODZIENSIS: FOLIA IURIDICA. see *LAW*

➤ ACTA UNIVERSITATIS LODZIENSIS: FOLIA LIMNOLOGICA. see *EARTH SCIENCES—Hydrology*

➤ ACTA UNIVERSITATIS LODZIENSIS: FOLIA LINGUISTICA. see *LINGUISTICS*

➤ ACTA UNIVERSITATIS LODZIENSIS: FOLIA LITTERARIA POLONICA. see *LITERATURE*

➤ ACTA UNIVERSITATIS LODZIENSIS: FOLIA MATHEMATICA. see *MATHEMATICS*

➤ ACTA UNIVERSITATIS LODZIENSIS: FOLIA OECONOMICA. see *BUSINESS AND ECONOMICS*

370   POL
L51
ACTA UNIVERSITATIS LODZIENSIS: FOLIA PAEDAGOGICA.
Text in German, Polish; Summaries in English, German. 1955-1974; N.S. 1980; N.S. 1995. irreg. charts. **Document type:** *Academic/Scholarly.* **Description:** Contains articles from the fields of history, theory of social education, didactics, social pedagogics, as well as reports and proceedings of scientific conferences organized by Department of Pedagogics and Psychology in the University of Lodz.
Supersedes in part (in 1995): Acta Universitatis Lodziensis: Folia Paedagogica et Psychologica (0208-6093); Which superseded in part: Uniwersytet Lodzki. Zeszyty Naukowe. Seria 1: Nauki Humanistyczno-Spoleczne (0076-0358)
—KNAW.
Published by: (Uniwersytet Lodzki, Wydzial Pedagogiki i Psychologii), Wydawnictwo Uniwersytetu Lodzkiego/Lodz University Press, ul Jaracza 34, Lodz, 90262, Poland. TEL 331671.

ACTA UNIVERSITATIS LODZIENSIS: FOLIA PHILOSOPHICA. see *PHILOSOPHY*

ACTA UNIVERSITATIS LODZIENSIS: FOLIA PHYSICA. see *PHYSICS*

ACTA UNIVERSITATIS LODZIENSIS: FOLIA SOCIOLOGICA. see *SOCIOLOGY*

ACTA UNIVERSITATIS LODZIENSIS: FOLIA ZOOLOGICA. see *BIOLOGY—Zoology*

370   POL   ISSN 0208-5313
L53
ACTA UNIVERSITATIS NICOLAI COPERNICI. NAUKI HUMANISTYCZNO-SPOLECZNE. PEDAGOGIKA. Text in Polish. 1971. irreg. price varies.
Formerly (until 1973): Uniwersytet Mikolaja Kopernika w Toruniu. Nauki Humanistyczno-Spoleczne. Zeszyty Naukowe. Pedagogika (0208-5372)
Published by: Uniwersytet Mikolaja Kopernika/Nicolaus Copernicus University, Wydawnictwo, ul Gagarina 39, Torun, 87100, Poland. TEL 48-56-14295. **Dist. by:** Osrodek Rozpowszechniania Wydawnictw Naukowych PAN, Palac Kultury i Nauki, Warsaw 00901, Poland.

370   POL   ISSN 0208-5267
LC191
ACTA UNIVERSITATIS NICOLAI COPERNICI. NAUKI HUMANISTYCZNO-SPOLECZNE. SOCJOLOGIA WYCHOWANIA. Text in Polish; Summaries in English. 1976. irreg. price varies. **Document type:** *Academic/Scholarly.*
Former titles (until 1976): Acta Universitatis Nicolai Copernici. Nauki Humanistyczno-Spoleczne. Socjologia (0208-5275); Uniwersytet Mikolaja Kopernika w Torun. Nauki Humanistyczno-Spoleczne. Zeszyty Naukowe. Socjologia (0208-5399)
Indexed: RASB.
Published by: Uniwersytet Mikolaja Kopernika/Nicolaus Copernicus University, Wydawnictwo, ul Gagarina 39, Torun, 87100, Poland. TEL 48-56-24295. **Dist. by:** Osrodek Rozpowszechniania Wydawnictw Naukowych PAN, Palac Kultury i Nauki, Warsaw 00901, Poland.

370   POL   ISSN 0137-1096
LA843
ACTA UNIVERSITATIS WRATISLAVIENSIS. PRACE PEDAGOGICZNE. Text in Polish; Summaries in English, French, Russian. 1973. irreg. price varies. **Document type:** *Academic/Scholarly.*
Indexed: RASB, RRTA, WAE&RSA.
—KNAW.
Published by: (Uniwersytet Wroclawski), Wydawnictwo Uniwersytetu Wroclawskiego Spolka z o.o., Pl Uniwersytecki 9-13, Wroclaw, 50-137, Poland. TEL 48-71-441006, FAX 48-71-402735. Ed. Mieczyslaw J Adamczyk. Circ: 600.

378.711   USA   ISSN 0162-6620
LB1715
ACTION IN TEACHER EDUCATION. Text in English. 1978. q. USD 130 to institutions (effective 2004). adv. bibl.; charts; stat.; illus. Index. reprints avail. **Document type:** *Trade.* **Description:** Focuses on research and practice in teacher education.
Related titles: Microfilm ed.: (from PQC); Online - full text ed.: (from H.W. Wilson, O C L C Online Computer Library Center, Inc.).
Indexed: ABIn, CIJE, CPE, ChPerl, EduInd, MEA, SRRA.
—BLDSC (0675.748000), IE, Infotrieve, ingenta.
Published by: Association of Teacher Educators, 1900 Association Dr, Ste ATE, Reston, VA 20191-1502. TEL 703-620-3110, FAX 703-620-9530, ate1@aol.com, http://www.ou.edu/action, http://www.ate1.org. Eds. John J Chiodo, Priscilla Griffith. R&P, Adv. contact Lynn Montgomery. Circ: 4,000.

370.72   GBR   ISSN 1476-7333
▼ ➤ **ACTION LEARNING**; research and practice. Text in English. 2004. s-a. GBP 112, USD 185 combined subscription to institutions print & online eds. (effective 2006). **Document type:** *Journal, Academic/Scholarly.*
Related titles: Online - full text ed.: ISSN 1476-7341. GBP 185, USD 176 to institutions (effective 2006) (from EBSCO Publishing, Gale Group, IngentaConnect, O C L C Online Computer Library Center, Inc., Swets Information Services).
Published by: Routledge (Subsidiary of: Taylor & Francis Group), 4 Park Sq, Milton Park, Abingdon, Oxon OX14 4RN, United Kingdom. TEL 44-1235-828600, FAX 44-1235-829000, info@routledge.co.uk, http://www.tandf.co.uk/journals/titles/14767333.asp, http://www.routledge.com. Ed. Mike Pedler.
Subscr. to: Taylor & Francis Ltd, Journals Customer Service, Rankine Rd, Basingstoke, Hants RG24 8PR, United Kingdom. TEL 44-1256-813000, FAX 44-1256-330245.

370   BFA
ACTION - REFLEXION - CULTURE. Text in French. 1968. 4/yr. XOF 2,000 domestic; XOF 4,000 in Africa; XOF 6,000 in France; XOF 8,000 in Switzerland; XOF 9,000 in United States (effective 2000); XOF 500 newsstand/cover (effective 2003). bk.rev. bibl. **Document type:** *Government.* **Description:** Discusses topics in education.
Published by: Ministere de l'Enseignement de Base et de l'Alphabetisation, Institut Pedagogique du Burkina, BP 7043, Ouagadougou, 03, Burkina Faso. TEL 226-324710. Ed. Congo Issouf. Circ: 4,300.

370.72   USA   ISSN 0001-7620
ACTIVITY. Text in English. 1960. q. free. back issues avail. **Description:** Covers education at all levels, career planning, and educational measurement research.
Indexed: CurCont.
Published by: A C T, 2201 N. Dodge St., Box 168, Iowa, IA 52243-0168. TEL 319-337-1410, FAX 319-337-1014. Circ: 105,000.

370   NLD   ISSN 0165-0246
ACTU ECO; werkkrant voor het economie-onderwijs. Text in Dutch. 1974. 5/yr. price varies. illus.
Published by: Wolters-Noordhoff Groningen (Subsidiary of: Wolters Kluwer N.V.), Postbus 58, Groningen, 9700 MB, Netherlands. TEL 31-50-5226524, FAX 31-50-5264866.

370   ESP   ISSN 0210-2714
ACTUALIDAD DOCENTE. Text in Spanish. 1978. m. **Document type:** *Academic/Scholarly.*
—CINDOC.
Published by: Confederacion Espanola de Centros de Ensenanza, Marques de Mondejar 29-31 1o. Piso, Madrid, 28028, Spain. TEL 34-91-7252340, FAX 34-91-7268558. Ed. Pilar Martinez.

ACTUAPRESS (ENGLISH-DUTCH EDITION). see *LINGUISTICS*

ACTUAPRESS (ENGLISH-FRENCH EDITION). see *LINGUISTICS*

ADOLESCENCE (SAN DIEGO); an international quarterly devoted to the physiological, psychological, psychiatric, sociological, and educational aspects of the second decade of human life. see *CHILDREN AND YOUTH—About*

370   USA   ISSN 1538-2052
ADOLESCENCE AND EDUCATION. Text in English. 2002. a.
Published by: Information Age Publishing, Inc., 411 W Putnam Ave, Ste 205, PO Box 4967, Greenwich, CT 06831. TEL 203-661-7602, FAX 203-661-7952, http://www.infoagepub.com. Eds. Frank Pajares, Tim Urdan.

370.15   USA
ADVANCES IN COGNITION AND EDUCATIONAL PRACTICE. Text in English. 1992. irreg., latest vol.7, 2002. price varies. back issues avail. **Document type:** *Monographic series, Academic/Scholarly.* **Description:** Dedicated to publishing state-of-the-art developments in the cognitive sciences as they relate to educational practice.
Indexed: e-psyche.
—BLDSC.

Published by: J A I Press Inc. (Subsidiary of: Elsevier Science & Technology), 360 Park Ave S, New York, NY 10010-1710. TEL 212-989-5800, FAX 212-633-3990, usinfo-f@elsevier.com, http://www.elsevier.com/wps/find/bookdescription.cws_home/BS_ACEP/description#description. Ed. Jerry Carlson.

370   USA   ISSN 1052-0554
                              CODEN: TSSSE9
ADVANCES IN CONTEMPORARY EDUCATIONAL THOUGHT SERIES. Text in English. 1988. irreg. **Document type:** *Monographic series.*
—BLDSC (0704.141000), IE.
Published by: Teachers College Press, 1234 Amsterdam Ave, New York, NY 10027. TEL 212-678-3929, FAX 212-678-4149, tcpress@tc.columbia.edu, http://www.teacherscollegepress.com/advances_in_contemporary.html.

372.21   USA   ISSN 0270-4021
HV854
ADVANCES IN EARLY EDUCATION AND DAY CARE; a research annual. Text in English. 1980. a., latest vol.14, 2005. price varies. back issues avail. **Document type:** *Monographic series, Academic/Scholarly.* **Description:** Designed to provide an academic forum for the publication of original research, critical reviews and conceptual analyses of theoretical and substantive issues related to the education, care and development of young children.
Related titles: Online - full text ed.: (from ScienceDirect).
Indexed: PsycholAb, SSA.
—BLDSC (0704.340000). CCC.
Published by: J A I Press Inc. (Subsidiary of: Elsevier Science & Technology), 360 Park Ave S, New York, NY 10010-1710. TEL 212-989-5800, FAX 212-633-3990, usinfo-f@elsevier.com, http://www.elsevier.com/wps/find/bookdescription.cws_home/BS_AEEDC/description#description. Ed. R Reifel.

370   IND   ISSN 0001-8694
ADVANCES IN EDUCATION. Text in English. 1970 (vol.5). q. bk.rev. bibl.
Published by: Maharaja Sayajirao University of Baroda, Centre for Advanced Study in Education, Faculty of Education and Psychology, Baroda, Gujarat 390 002, India. Ed. Dr. A S Patel.

ADVANCES IN PHYSIOLOGY EDUCATION. see *BIOLOGY—Physiology*

372.4   USA   ISSN 0735-0171
LB1049.9
ADVANCES IN READING - LANGUAGE RESEARCH. Text in English. 1982. irreg., latest vol.8, 2000. price varies. back issues avail. **Document type:** *Monographic series, Academic/Scholarly.*
Indexed: PsycholAb.
—BLDSC (0711.315000). CCC.
Published by: J A I Press Inc. (Subsidiary of: Elsevier Science & Technology), 360 Park Ave S, New York, NY 10010-1710. TEL 212-989-5800, FAX 212-633-3990, usinfo-f@elsevier.com, http://www.elsevier.com/wps/find/bookdescription.cws_home/BS_ARLR/description#description. Ed. P B Mosenthal.

371.19   USA   ISSN 1537-3657
ADVANCES IN SERVICE LEARNING. Text in English. 2002. a.
Published by: Information Age Publishing, Inc., 411 W Putnam Ave, Ste 205, PO Box 4967, Greenwich, CT 06831. TEL 203-661-7602, FAX 203-661-7952, http://www.infoagepub.com. Eds. Andrew Furco, Shelley H. Billig.

371.14   USA
THE ADVOCATE (PITTSBURGH). Text in English. q. free to members; USD 5 to non-members (effective 2005). adv. bk.rev. **Document type:** *Newspaper, Trade.*
Formerly (until 1992): Pennsylvania Teacher
Published by: Pennsylvania Federation of Teachers, 10 S 19th St, Pittsburgh, PA 15203-1842. TEL 412-431-5900, FAX 412-431-6882. Ed. John Tarka. Circ: 43,000 (paid).

371.14   USA
ADVOCATE'S VOICE. Text in English. 1979 (vol.9). 9/yr. USD 2. adv.
Formerly: N E A - N M Advocate
Published by: National Education Association of New Mexico, 130 S Capitol, Santa Fe, NM 87504. TEL 505-982-1916. Ed. Steve Lemken. Circ: 8,500.

AFFINITY. see *RELIGIONS AND THEOLOGY—Other Denominations And Sects*

AFRICAN STUDIES ASSOCIATION. OCCASIONAL PAPERS. see *ETHNIC INTERESTS*

AGAZEN; environment and population. see *CONSERVATION*

370   PER
AGENDA EDUCATIVA. Text in Spanish. 1993. irreg.
Published by: Foro Educativo, Ave. Grau, 1123, 3 Lima, Lima, 4, Peru. TEL 51-14-770640. Ed. Hernan Silva Santisteban Larco. Circ: 1,000.

370.9 AUS ISSN 0044-6726
AGORA. Text in English. 1966. q. AUD 80 domestic; USD 50 foreign (effective 1999). adv. bk.rev.; film rev.; software rev.; video rev. illus.
Incorporates (in Feb. 1981): Journal of History for Senior Students
Indexed: AEI, PROMT.
Published by: History Teacher's Association of Victoria, 402 Smith St, Collingwood, VIC 3006, Australia. TEL 61-3-9417-3422, FAX 61-3-9419-4713, htav@netspace.net.au. Ed. Jacqualine Hollingworth. adv.: page AUD 275. Circ: 1,200.

THE AGRICULTURAL EDUCATION MAGAZINE. see *AGRICULTURE*

AGROBOREALIS. see *AGRICULTURE*

370 JPN ISSN 0288-4712
AICHI KYOIKU DAIGAKU TAIIKU KYOSHITSU KENKYU KIYO/AICHI UNIVERSITY OF EDUCATION. BULLETIN OF THE PHYSICAL EDUCATION AND SPORT RESEARCH. Text in English, Japanese; Summaries in English. 1976. a. **Document type:** *Bulletin.*
Indexed: IBSS.
Published by: Aichi Kyoiku Daigaku, Taiiku Kyoshitsu/Aichi University of Education, Department of Physical Education, 1 Hirosawa-Igayacho, Kariya-shi, Aichi-ken 448-0000, Japan. TEL 0566-36-6997, FAX 0566-36-3111. Circ: 300.

371.15 150 JPN
AIIKU TSUSHIN/LETTERS OF HUMAN GROWTH. Text in Japanese. 1975. q. looseleaf. JPY 4,000 (effective 2001). bk.rev. 8 p./no.; **Document type:** *Newsletter, Academic/Scholarly.* **Description:** Contains Dr. Kokubu Yasutaka's editorial on humanistic psychology and Dr. Hori Shinichiro's presentation of his thoughts and practice at Kinokuni Kodomonomura Gakuen (Japanese Summer Hill School), Wakayama-ken, Japan. Also included are member reports of their application of humanistic philosophy in living and working areas.
Indexed: e-psyche.
Published by: Shin Aiiku Shinri Kenkyukai/Japanese Study Group of Humanistic Education, c/o Mr Masahiro Makino, 3-41-39 kugayama, Suginami-ku, Tokyo, 168-0082, Japan. makino@kgc.keio.ac.jp. Ed. Yasutaka Kokubu. R&P Mr. Masahiro Makino.

371.192 SWE ISSN 1401-8594
AKTIVA SKOLFOERAELDRAR. Text in Swedish. 1995. q. SEK 156 (effective 2000). adv. **Document type:** *Magazine, Consumer.* **Description:** Dedicated to providing parents with information about their children's schools.
Published by: Kommunikationsstrategerna AB, Karlaplan 2, Stockholm, 114 60, Sweden. TEL 46-8-665-38-22, FAX 46-8-665-38-08, maud@aktivaskol.se, http://www.aktivaskol.se. Ed. Maud Hoffsten. adv.: color page SEK 25,500; trim 210 x 280. Circ: 31,200.

370 LBY
AL-FATEH UNIVERSITY. FACULTY OF EDUCATION. BULLETIN. Text in English. a. **Document type:** *Bulletin.*
Published by: Al-Fateh University, Faculty of Education, P O Box 13040, Tripoli, Libya. TEL 36010, TELEX 20629.

370 USA ISSN 0002-435X
ALABAMA SCHOOL JOURNAL. Text in English. 1921. bi-m. USD 24 to non-members; free to members (effective 2005). adv. bk.rev. charts; illus.; tr.lit. index. **Document type:** *Journal, Trade.*
Published by: Alabama Education Association, PO Box 4177, Montgomery, AL 36103-4177. TEL 334-834-9790, FAX 334-262-8377, prdept@alaedu.org, http://www.myaea.org/. Ed. Paul R Hubbert. Circ: 47,000.

370.72 CAN ISSN 0002-4805
LB1028 CODEN: AJEDAQ
➤ **ALBERTA JOURNAL OF EDUCATIONAL RESEARCH.** Abbreviated title: A J E R. Text in English. 1955. q. CND 44.94 domestic to individuals; USD 35 foreign to individuals; CND 53.50 domestic to institutions; USD 40 foreign to institutions (effective 2006). bk.rev. bibl.; charts. index. back issues avail. **Document type:** *Journal, Academic/Scholarly.* **Description:** Devoted to the dissemination, criticism, interpretation, and encouragement of all forms of systematic enquiry into education and fields related to or associated with education.
Related titles: Microfiche ed.: (from MML); Microform ed.: (from MML); Online - full text ed.: (from Micromedia ProQuest, ProQuest Information & Learning).
Indexed: ASCA, CEI, CIJE, CPE, CWPI, CurCont, EAA, ERA, ETA, Faml, L&LBA, MEA, PsycInfo, PsycholAb, RASB, RHEA, SEA, SENA, SOMA, SOPODA, SRRA, SSA, SSCI, SWA, TEA, V&AA, e-psyche.
—BLDSC (0786.585000), IDS, IE, Infotrieve, ingenta. **CCC.**
Published by: University of Alberta, Faculty of Education, 845 Education South, Edmonton, AB T6G 2G5, Canada. TEL 780-492-7941, FAX 780-492-0236, ajer@ualberta.ca, http://www.education.ualberta.ca/educ/journals/ajer.html. Ed., R&P Dr. George H Buck. Circ: 400.

370 CAN ISSN 1492-9716
ALBERTA LEARNING. ANNUAL REPORT. Text in English. 2000. a.
Published by: Alberta Learning, 12360 142nd St, Edmonton, AB T5L 4X9, Canada. TEL 780-427-4681, FAX 780-427-6683.

ALEMANNIA STUDENS. see *HISTORY—History Of Europe*

370 GBR ISSN 0953-9700
ALL-IN SUCCESS. Text in English. 1981. 3/yr. GBP 60 (effective 2000). adv. back issues avail. **Document type:** *Magazine, Consumer.* **Description:** Educational information for secondary schools.
Formerly (until 1988): Contributions (0269-3895)
Indexed: BrEdI, CPE.
—BLDSC (0788.873500), IE.
Published by: University of Leicester, Centre for the Study of Comprehensive Schools, The Weens Blgd, Barrack Rd, Northampton, NN2 6AF, United Kingdom. TEL 44-1604-24969, FAX 44-1604-29735, lizacscs@rmplc.co.uk, http://www.rmplc.co.uk/orgs/cscs/. Ed. Paul Bland. Circ: 1,600.

370 USA ISSN 0002-6093
ALLIANCE REVIEW. Text in English. 1947 (vol.12). a. membership. bk.rev. illus. **Document type:** *Bulletin.* **Description:** Highlights the activities and projects of the Alliance Israelite Universelle and its network of schools in Europe, the Middle East and Canada.
Published by: American Friends of the Alliance Israelite Universelle Inc., 15 W. 16th St., # 6, New York, NY 10011-6301. TEL 212-808-5437, FAX 212-983-0094. Ed., R&P Warren Green. Circ: 5,000.

373 RUS
ALMA MATER. Text in Russian. bi-m. USD 115 in United States.
Indexed: RRTA.
Published by: Rossiiskii Universitet Druzhby Narodov, Ul Miklukho Maklaya 6, Moscow, 117198, Russian Federation. TEL 7-095-3357516. Ed. O Dolzhenko. **US dist. addr.:** East View Information Services, 3020 Harbor Ln. N., Minneapolis, MN 55447. TEL 612-550-0961.

370 ESP ISSN 1133-0163
ALMINAR. Text in Spanish. 1984. q.
Indexed: RILM.
—CINDOC.
Published by: Junta de Andalucia, Consejeria de Educacion y Ciencia, Edif. Torretriana, C. Juan Antonio de Vizarron s-n, Isla de Cartuja, Sevilla, 41092, Spain. FAX 34-955-064003, infomacion@cec.junta-andalucia.es, http://www3.cec.junta-andalucia.es/.

370 ISR ISSN 0334-5076
PJ5007
ALON LAMORAH LESIFRUT. Text in Hebrew. 1972. a.
Indexed: IHP.
Published by: Atlas Ltd., 49 Chelnov St., Tel Aviv, Israel.

ALON SHEVUT; bulletin of graduates. see *RELIGIONS AND THEOLOGY—Judaic*

ALPHA; Mathematik als Hobby. see *MATHEMATICS*

370.72 PER
AMAUTA; revista de investigacion educacional. Text in Spanish. 1971. s-a.
Related titles: Online - full text ed.: ISSN 1682-4946. 2001.
Published by: Universidad Nacional de Trujillo, Departamento Academico de Ciencias de la Educacion, Ciudad Universitaria, Apdo Postal 152, Trujillo, Peru. http://www.minedu.gob.pe/gestion_pedagogica/dir_forma_docente/dir.php?obj=presentacion_formacion.htm#amauta. Ed. Yeconias Culquichicon Gomez.

AMERICAN CLASSICAL LEAGUE. NEWSLETTER. see *CLASSICAL STUDIES*

370.72 USA ISSN 1535-0584
LA205
➤ **AMERICAN EDUCATIONAL HISTORY JOURNAL.** Text in English. 1972. a. USD 60 to individuals; USD 80 to institutions; USD 40 to students; USD 25 newsstand/cover (effective 2006). **Document type:** *Journal, Academic/Scholarly.* **Description:** Publishes current research in all aspects of the history of education.
Formerly (until 1999): Midwest History of Education Society. Journal (0092-2986)
Related titles: Online - full text ed.: (from ProQuest Information & Learning).
Indexed: AmH&L, HistAb.
Published by: (Midwest History of Education Society), Information Age Publishing, Inc., 411 W Putnam Ave, Ste 205, PO Box 4967, Greenwich, CT 06831. TEL 203-661-7602, FAX 203-661-7952, order@infoagepub.com, http://www.infoagepub.com. Ed. Joseph Watros. Circ: 100.

370.72 USA ISSN 0163-9676
CODEN: NFBLBF
AMERICAN EDUCATIONAL RESEARCH ASSOCIATION. ANNUAL MEETING PROGRAM. Text in English. 1969. a. USD 15 (effective 2005).
—BLDSC (0719.728340). **CCC.**
Published by: American Educational Research Association, 1230 17th St, N W, Washington, DC 20036-3078. Circ: 3,500.

370.72 USA ISSN 0002-8312
L11
➤ **AMERICAN EDUCATIONAL RESEARCH JOURNAL.** Text in English. 1964. q. USD 48 to individuals; USD 140 to institutions (effective 2005). adv. bk.rev. abstr.; bibl.; illus. index. reprints avail. **Document type:** *Journal, Academic/Scholarly.* **Description:** Reports original research, both empirical and theoretical, and brief synopses of research.
Related titles: Microform ed.: (from PQC); Online - full text ed.: (from bigchalk, H.W. Wilson, JSTOR (Web-based Journal Archive), O C L C Online Computer Library Center, Inc., ProQuest Information & Learning).
Indexed: ABIn, AMHA, ASCA, ArtHuCI, CIJE, CIS, CJA, CPE, CommAb, CurCont, DIP, ECER, ERA, ETA, EduInd, Faml, HEA, IBR, IBZ, Inspec, L&LBA, MEA, MEA&I, PsycInfo, PsycholAb, RASB, RHEA, RILM, SEA, SOMA, SOPODA, SSA, SSCI, SWA, TEA, e-psyche.
—BLDSC (0813.650000), IDS, IE, Infotrieve, ingenta. **CCC.**
Published by: American Educational Research Association, 1230 17th St, N W, Washington, DC 20036-3078. FAX 202-775-1824, http://www.aera.net/pubs/aerj/, http://aera.net. Adv. contact Camille Coy. Circ: 19,800.

371.1 USA ISSN 0148-432X
AMERICAN EDUCATOR. Text in English. 1977. q. USD 8 (effective 2005). adv. bk.rev. illus. reprint service avail. from PQC. **Document type:** *Journal, Trade.*
Indexed: ABS&EES, CIJE, CPE, MLA-IB, MagInd, PMR.
—BLDSC (0813.670000), IE, Infotrieve, ingenta.
Published by: American Federation of Teachers, 555 New Jersey Ave, NW, Washington, DC 20001. TEL 202-879-4400, FAX 202-879-4534, amered@aft.org, online@aft.org, http://www.aft.org/pubs-reports/american_educator/index.htm. Ed. Ruth Wattenberg. Adv. contact Sandy Hendricks. B&W page USD 7,240, color page USD 9,240; trim 8 x 11. Circ: 700,000.

AMERICAN FORENSIC ASSOCIATION NEWSLETTER. see *COMMUNICATIONS*

370.1 USA ISSN 0195-6744
L11
➤ **AMERICAN JOURNAL OF EDUCATION.** Text in English. 1893. q. USD 37 combined subscription to individuals print & online eds.; USD 126 combined subscription to institutions print & online eds.; USD 14 per issue to individuals; USD 40 per issue to institutions (effective 2006). adv. bk.rev. charts; illus.; stat. Index. 144 p./no.; reprint service avail. from PQC,PSC. **Document type:** *Magazine, Academic/Scholarly.* **Description:** Integrates the intellectual, methodological, and substantive diversity of educational scholarship. Encourages dialogue between scholars and practitioners.
Formerly (until vol.88, Nov. 1979): School Review (0036-6773)
Related titles: Microform ed.: (from PMC, PQC); Online - full text ed.: ISSN 1549-6511. USD 113 to institutions (effective 2006) (from bigchalk, EBSCO Publishing, Florida Center for Library Automation, Gale Group, JSTOR (Web-based Journal Archive), O C L C Online Computer Library Center, Inc., ProQuest Information & Learning).
Indexed: ABIn, APC, ASCA, AmH&L, ArtHuCI, BRI, CBRI, CIJE, CPE, ChPerI, CurCont, DIP, EAA, ERA, ETA, EduInd, Faml, HistAb, IBR, IBZ, IMFL, IPARL, L&LBA, MEA, MEA&I, PCI, PhilInd, PsycInfo, PsycholAb, RASB, RHEA, SEA, SENA, SOMA, SOPODA, SRRA, SSA, SSCI, SociolAb, TEA, e-psyche.
—BLDSC (0824.360000), IDS, IE, Infotrieve, ingenta. **CCC.**
Published by: University of Chicago Press, Journals Division, 1111 E. 60th St, Chicago, IL 60637. TEL 773-753-3347, FAX 773-753-0811, subscriptions@press.uchicago.edu, orders@press.uchicago.edu, http://www.journals.uchicago.edu/AJE/home.html. Ed. William Lowe Boyd. Adv. contact Cheryl Jones. page USD 475; trim 6 x 9. Circ: 1,800 (paid).

372.4 USA ISSN 0895-3562
LB2842.4.N4 CODEN: YARFFV
➤ **AMERICAN READING FORUM. YEARBOOK.** Text in English. 1981. a. USD 20 (effective 1999). **Document type:** *Academic/Scholarly.*
Indexed: CIJE, SOPODA.
Published by: American Reading Forum, c/o Woodrow Trathen, Ed, Appalachian State University, College of Education, Boone, NC 28608. telferr@uwwvax.uww.edu, http://coe2.tsuniv.edu/arf. Ed. Woodrow Trathen. Circ: 200.

➤ **AMERICAN STRING TEACHER.** see *MUSIC*

➤ **AMERICAN TEACHER.** see *LABOR UNIONS*

371.8 ITA ISSN 1124-4275
AMICIZIA.STUDENTI ESTERI. Text in Italian. 1964. m. adv. bk.rev. charts; illus. index. **Document type:** *Academic/Scholarly.* **Description:** Includes articles on students studying in Italy, various exchange programs, and new numbers of students in Italy.
Formerly (until 1974): Amicizia (0003-1720)

▼ new title ➤ refereed ✶ unverified ♦ full entry avail.

Published by: Ufficio Centrale Studenti Esteri in Italia, Lungotevere dei Vallati 14, Rome, 00186, Italy. TEL 39-06-68804062, FAX 39-06-68804063, http://www.ongue.unimondo.org/UCSEI.html. Ed. Nuccio Fava. R&P R Musaragno. Adv. contact Remigio Musaragno.

370 FIN ISSN 1457-6996
AMMATTI+. Variant title: Ammatti Plus. Text in Finnish. 2000. q.
Related titles: Online - full text ed.: ISSN 1457-6015; ♦ Supplement to: Opettaja. ISSN 0355-3965.
Published by: Opetusalan Ammattijarjesto ry/Trade Union of Education in Finland, Rautatielaisenkatu 6, PO Box 20, Helsinki, 00521, Finland. TEL 358-20-7489600, FAX 358-9-145821, oaj@oaj.fi, http://www.oaj.fi.

AMOEBA. see *BIOLOGY*

370 DEU ISSN 0003-2190
AMTLICHES SCHULBLATT FUER DEN REGIERUNGSBEZIRK DUESSELDORF. Text in German. 1909. m. adv. **Document type:** *Bulletin, Government.*
Published by: Bezirksregierung Duesseldorf, Cecilienallee 2, Duesseldorf, 40474, Germany. TEL 49-211-4750, FAX 49-211-4752671, poststelle@brd.nrw.de, http://www.brd.nrw.de/BezRegDdorf/hierarchie/index.php.

ANGLISTIK UND ENGLISCHUNTERRICHT. NEUE FOLGE. see *LINGUISTICS*

371 CHN ISSN 1001-5116
ANHUI JIAOYU XUEYUAN XUEBAO (SHEHUI KEXUE BAN)/ANHUI INSTITUTE OF EDUCATION. JOURNAL (PHILOSOPHY AND SOCIAL SCIENCE EDITION). Text in Chinese. 1985. q. CNY 3; USD 3 foreign. adv. **Document type:** *Academic/Scholarly.* **Description:** Covers education and teaching theory for basic, higher, and adult education. Includes language and literature, history, and humanities teaching, and scientific research results.
Related titles: Online - full text ed.: (from East View Information Services).
Published by: Anhui Jiaoyu Xueyuan/Anhui Institute of Education, 327 Jinzhai Lu, Hefei, Anhui 230061, China. TEL 86-551-2827203. Ed. Li Liangyu. Pub., R&P Wang Gaoxin. Adv. contact Liu Zhencui. Circ: 1,200.

370 FRA ISSN 0395-0840
ANIMATION ET EDUCATION. Text in French. 1976. bi-m. adv.
Published by: Office Central de la Cooperation a l'Ecole, 101 bis rue du Ranelagh, Paris, 75016, France. TEL 33-1-44149330. Ed. Yves Potel. Pub. Francois Bourguignon. Adv. contact Nicole Pinbouen.

370.15 POL ISSN 0867-2040
ANNALES UNIVERSITATIS MARIAE CURIE-SKLODOWSKA. SECTIO J. PAEDAGOGIA - PSYCHOLOGIA. Text and summaries in English, Polish. 1988. a. price varies. **Document type:** *Academic/Scholarly.*
Indexed: L&LBA, SOPODA, e-psyche.
Published by: Uniwersytet Marii Curie-Sklodowskiej w Lublinie, Wydawnictwo, pl M Curie Sklodowskiej 5, Lublin, 20031, Poland. TEL 48-81-375304, FAX 48-81-336699. Ed. Stanislaw Popek. Circ: 500.

370.15 USA ISSN 1075-1211
➤ **ANNALS OF BEHAVIORAL SCIENCE AND MEDICAL EDUCATION.** Text in English. 1994. s-a. USD 95 membership; USD 25 to students (effective 2005). bk.rev.; software rev. **Document type:** *Academic/Scholarly.* **Description:** Includes original articles, a curriculum and evaluation section, and behavioral science teaching rounds.
Indexed: e-psyche.
Published by: Association for the Behavioral Sciences and Medical Education, 1460 N Center Rd, Burton, MI 48509. TEL 810-715-4365, FAX 810-715-4371, admin@absame.org, http://www.absame.org. R&P James Campell. Circ: 300.

372 FRA ISSN 0245-2030
ANNUAIRE DES COMMUNAUTES D'ENFANTS. Text in French. 1954. a.
Published by: Association Nationale des Communautes Educatives, 145 bd. de Magenta, Paris, 75010, France. TEL 33-1-44635115, FAX 33-1-42855614.

372 USA ISSN 0272-4456
LB1140.A1
➤ **ANNUAL EDITIONS: EARLY CHILDHOOD EDUCATION.** Text in English. 1977. a., latest 2004, 25rd ed. USD 20.31 per vol. (effective 2004). illus. **Document type:** *Academic/Scholarly.*
Formerly (until 1981): Readings in Early Childhood Education (0272-8001)
Published by: McGraw-Hill - Dushkin (Subsidiary of: McGraw-Hill Higher Education), 2460 Kerper Blvd, Dubuque, IA 52001. TEL 800-243-6532, customer.service@mcgraw-hill.com, http://www.dushkin.com/text-data/catalog/0072861266.mhtml. Eds. Joyce Huth Munro, Karen Menke Paciorek. Pub. Ian Nielsen. R&P Cheryl Greenleaf.

370 USA ISSN 0272-5010
LB41
➤ **ANNUAL EDITIONS: EDUCATION.** Text in English. 1973. a., latest 2003, 31st ed. USD 20.31 per vol. (effective 2004). illus. **Document type:** *Academic/Scholarly.*
Formerly (until 1981): Annual Editions: Readings in Education (0095-5787)
Published by: McGraw-Hill - Dushkin (Subsidiary of: McGraw-Hill Higher Education), 2460 Kerper Blvd, Dubuque, IA 52001. TEL 800-243-6532, customer.service@mcgraw-hill.com, http://www.dushkin.com/text-data/catalog/007286138x.mhtml. Ed. Fred Schultz. Pub. Ian Nielsen. R&P Cheryl Greenleaf.

370.15 USA ISSN 0731-1141
LB1051
➤ **ANNUAL EDITIONS: EDUCATIONAL PSYCHOLOGY.** Text in English. 1981. a., latest 2004, 19th ed. USD 20.31 per vol. (effective 2004). illus. **Document type:** *Academic/Scholarly.*
Indexed: e-psyche.
Published by: McGraw-Hill - Dushkin (Subsidiary of: McGraw-Hill Higher Education), 2460 Kerper Blvd, Dubuque, IA 52001. TEL 800-243-6532, customer.service@mcgraw-hill.com, http://www.dushkin.com/text-data/catalog/007286379x.mhtml. Eds. Fredric Linder, James McMillan, Kathleen M. Cauley. Pub. Ian Nielsen. R&P Cheryl Greenleaf.

370 USA ISSN 0085-4077
LA337
ANNUAL EDUCATIONAL SUMMARY, NEW YORK STATE. Text in English. 1904. a., latest covers 1992-1993. free. charts; stat. back issues avail. **Document type:** *Government.*
Media: Duplicated (not offset). **Related titles:** Microfiche ed.: (from CIS).
Indexed: SRI.
Published by: Education Department, Information, Reporting & Technology Services, Education Bldg Annex, Rm 962, Albany, NY 12234. TEL 518-474-7082, FAX 518-474-4351. Circ: (controlled).

ANNUAL REPORT ON ALLIED DENTAL HEALTH EDUCATION. see *MEDICAL SCIENCES—Dentistry*

370 DEU
ANTENNE AKTUELL. Text in German. 1972. 3/yr. EUR 11 (effective 2005). back issues avail. **Document type:** *Magazine, Consumer.*
Formerly: Antenne
Published by: Gemeinschaften Christlichen Lebens Jugendverbaende, Sterngasse 3, Augsburg, 86150, Germany. TEL 49-821-3199804, FAX 49-821-3199805, mail@j-gcl.org, http://j-gcl.org. Circ: 1,500.

ANTHROPOLOGY & EDUCATION QUARTERLY. see *ANTHROPOLOGY*

370.9495 GRC
ANTITETRADIA TIS EKPAEDEFSIS. Text in Greek, English. irreg. **Description:** Presents articles on education in Hellas.
Media: Online - full text.
Address: Greece. heraclitos@iname.com, http://www.forthnet.gr/antitetradia/.

370 371.3 MEX ISSN 1665-6180
APERTURA. Text in Spanish. 2001. 2/yr. MXP 250 domestic; USD 30 foreign (effective 2004). **Document type:** *Journal, Academic/Scholarly.* **Description:** Distance education in general. Use of new technologies for information and communication. Evaluation of non conventional education programs.
Published by: Universidad de Guadalajara, Coordinacion General del Sistema para la Innovacion del Aprendizaje, Escuela Militar de Aviacion 16, Col Ladron de Guevara, Guadalajara, Jalisco 44270, Mexico. TEL 52-133-36301444, FAX 52-133-36300085, avallin@cencar.udg.mx, htpp://www.innova.udg.mx. Ed. Angelina Vallin Gallegos. Pub. Manuel Moreno Castaneda. R&P Andres Lopez Diaz.

APPLESEEDS. see *CHILDREN AND YOUTH—For*

APPLIED ENVIRONMENTAL EDUCATION AND COMMUNICATION; an international journal. see *ENVIRONMENTAL STUDIES*

370.287 USA ISSN 0895-7347
LB3051
➤ **APPLIED MEASUREMENT IN EDUCATION.** Text in English. 1988. q., latest vol.16. USD 470 in US & Canada to institutions; USD 500 elsewhere to institutions; USD 495 combined subscription in US & Canada to institutions print & online eds.; USD 525 combined subscription elsewhere to institutions print & online eds. (effective 2006). adv. illus. back issues avail.; reprint service avail. from PSC. **Document type:** *Journal, Academic/Scholarly.* **Description:** Provides information to improve measurement practice by enhancing the communication between academicians and educational measurement practitioners. Describes original research studies, innovative strategies and integrative reviews of current approaches.
Related titles: Online - full text ed.: ISSN 1532-4818. USD 445 worldwide to institutions (effective 2006) (from EBSCO Publishing, Gale Group, O C L C Online Computer Library Center, Inc., Swets Information Services).
Indexed: ABIn, ASCA, CIJE, CPE, CurCont, EAA, ERA, ETA, EduInd, MEA, PCI, PsycInfo, PsycholAb, RHEA, SEA, SENA, SOMA, SSCI, SWA, TEA, e-psyche.
—BLDSC (1574.300000), IE, Infotrieve, ingenta. **CCC.**

Published by: (Buros Institute of Mental Measurements), Lawrence Erlbaum Associates, Inc., 10 Industrial Ave, Mahwah, NJ 07430-2262. TEL 201-258-2200, 800-926-6579, FAX 201-236-0072, journals@erlbaum.com, http://www.leaonline.com/loi/ame. Eds. Barbara S Plake, James C Impara. adv.: page USD 450; trim 5 x 8.

370 500 700 TUN
ARAB LEAGUE EDUCATIONAL, SCIENTIFIC, AND CULTURAL ORGANIZATION. INFORMATION NEWSLETTER. Text in Arabic, English. 1972. 3/yr. USD 20. bk.rev. illus. **Document type:** *Newsletter.*
Formerly: A L E S C O Newsletter
Related titles: Microfiche ed.
Published by: Arab League Educational, Scientific, and Cultural Organization, Department of Documentation and Information, B P 1120, Tunis, Tunisia. Ed. Raouf Ali Hafez.

370 POL ISSN 0066-6831
ARCHIWUM Z DZIEJOW OSWIATY. Text in Polish. 1959. irreg., latest vol.11, 1994. price varies. **Document type:** *Academic/Scholarly.*
Published by: Polska Akademia Nauk, Instytut Historii Nauki, Palac Staszica, ul Nowy Swiat 72, pok 9, Warsaw, 00330, Poland. TEL 48-22-8268754, FAX 48-22-8266137. Ed. Kalina Bartnicka. Circ: 1,000. **Dist. by:** Ars Polona, Krakowskie Przedmiescie 7, Warsaw, Poland.

370 ARG ISSN 0066-7021
ARGENTINA. DEPARTAMENTO DE ESTADISTICA EDUCATIVA. BOLETIN INFORMATIVO.✱. Text in Spanish. 1965. a. free. charts; stat. **Document type:** *Government.*
Published by: Ministerio de Educacion, Pizzurno 935, Buenos Aires, 1020, Argentina. TEL 54-11-41291000, info@me.gov.ar, http://www.me.gov.ar/.

ARGENTINA. MINISTERIO DE CULTURA Y EDUCACION. BOLETIN BIBLIOGRAFICO. see *EDUCATION—Abstracting, Bibliographies, Statistics*

ARGENTINA. MINISTERIO DE CULTURA Y EDUCACION. ESTADISTICAS DE LA EDUCACION. see *EDUCATION—Abstracting, Bibliographies, Statistics*

371 FRA ISSN 0995-2187
ARGOS; revue des B C D et C D I. Text in French. 1989. 3/yr. adv. **Document type:** *Academic/Scholarly.* **Description:** Provides themes and practices to be discussed among participants in the school system (from kindergarden to university).
Published by: Centre Regional de Documentation Pedagogique (Creteil), 20 rue D. Casanova, Le Perreux-sur-Marne, 94170, France. TEL 33-1-43247500, FAX 33-1-48726072, sgoffard@ac-idf.jussieu.fr. Ed. Serge Goffard. Pub. Annick Loran Jolly. Adv. contact Jacqueline Legros.

ARGUMENTATION & ADVOCACY; journal of the American Forensic Association. see *LINGUISTICS*

371.82 USA
ARIZONA DEPARTMENT OF EDUCATION. MIGRANT CHILD EDUCATION. STATE PLAN. Text in English. 1967. a. free. illus.; stat. **Document type:** *Government.*
Formerly: Arizona State Plan for the Education of Migratory Children
Published by: Department of Education, Education Bldg, 1535 W Jefferson, Phoenix, AZ 85007. TEL 602-542-5138, FAX 602-542-3013. Ed. Jane Hunt. Circ: 75.

ARIZONA EDUCATION LAWS ANNOTATED. see *LAW*

370 USA ISSN 1555-5895
LB1050
▼ **ARIZONA EDUCATION REVIEW**; language, reading and culture. Abbreviated title: A E R. Text in English. 2003. a. USD 12 per vol. (effective 2005).
Related titles: Online - full text ed.: ISSN 1553-765X.
Published by: University of Arizona, Department of Language, Reading & Culture, P O Box 210069, Tucson, AZ 85721-0069. TEL 520-621-1311, FAX 520-621-1853, aer_lrc@yahoo.com, lrcinfo@email.arizona.edu, http://www.ed.arizona.edu/aer/, http://www.ed.arizona.edu/lrc/index.html.

370 USA ISSN 0161-7753
L11
ARKANSAS EDUCATOR. Text in English. 1923. 8/yr. USD 4 to non-members; free to members (effective 2005). adv. bk.rev. charts; illus. reprint service avail. from PQC. **Document type:** *Newsletter, Trade.*
Formerly (until 1975): Journal of Arkansas Education (0021-9061)
Related titles: Microfilm ed.: (from PQC).
Published by: Arkansas Education Association, 1500 W Fourth St, Little Rock, AR 72201. TEL 501-375-4611, 800-632-0624, FAX 501-375-4620, tomaliguy@earthlink.net, http://www.aeaonline.org. Ed. Tish Talbot. R&P Pat Jones. Circ: 18,672.

ART EDUCATION. see *ART*

ARTLINK; Australian contemporary art quarterly. see *ART*

E

ARTS (NEW BRIGHTON); the arts in religious and theological studies. see *ART*

ARTS AND LEARNING RESEARCH; journal of the Arts and Learning Special Interest Group. see *ART*

370   KOR   ISSN 1598-1037
ASIA PACIFIC EDUCATION REVIEW. Text in English. s-a. (Jul. & Dec.). reprints avail. **Document type:** *Journal, Academic/Scholarly.* **Description:** Covers the research and professional development of Asian-Pacific education and culture.
—BLDSC (1742.260340), IE.
Published by: The Institute of Asia Pacific Education Development, Dept. of Education, Seoul National University, San 56-1, Shinlim-dong, Kwanak-gu, Seoul, 151-742, Korea, S. TEL 82-2-8805883, FAX 82-2-8716883, aped@plaza.snu.ac.kr, http://aped.snu.ac.kr/. Ed. Shinil Kim.

ASIA PACIFIC EXECUTIVE EDUCATION DIRECTORY. see *BUSINESS AND ECONOMICS—Management*

370   GBR   ISSN 0218-8791
LA1239.5
ASIA PACIFIC JOURNAL OF EDUCATION. Text in English. s-a. GBP 204, USD 307, AUD 543 combined subscription to institutions print & online eds. (effective 2006). **Document type:** *Journal, Academic/Scholarly.* **Description:** Focuses is on major shifts in educational policy and governance, curriculum and pedagogy, and in the everyday lives and practices of students and teachers in the Asia-Pacific Rim.
Related titles: Online - full text ed.: ISSN 1742-6855. GBP 194, USD 292, AUD 516 to institutions (effective 2006) (from EBSCO Publishing).
Indexed: CPE, ERA, ETA, MEA, RHEA, SEA, SENA, SOMA, TEA.
Published by: (National Institute of Education, Nanyang Technological University SGP), Routledge (Subsidiary of: Taylor & Francis Group), 4 Park Sq, Milton Park, Abingdon, Oxon OX14 4RN, United Kingdom. TEL 44-1235-828600, FAX 44-1235-829000, info@routledge.co.uk, http://www.tandf.co.uk/journals/titles/02188791.asp, http://www.routledge.com. Eds. Allan Luke, Allan Luke, S Gopinathan, S Gopinathan.

370.15   IND   ISSN 0971-2909
ASIAN JOURNAL OF PSYCHOLOGY AND EDUCATION. Text in English. 1976. 6/yr. USD 39.50. adv. bk.rev. reprint service avail. from ISI.
Indexed: IBR, PsychoLab, e-psyche.
—BLDSC (1742.570000), IE, ingenta.
Published by: Agra Psychological Research Cell, Tiwari Kothi, Belanganj, Agra, Uttar Pradesh 282 004, India. Eds. B V Patel, N S Chauhan.

371.14   PRI
ASOMA. Text in Spanish. 1977 (vol.6). membership. charts; illus.
Formerly: Vocero Informativo
Published by: Asociacion de Maestros de Puerto Rico, Ave Ponce de Leon 452, Hato Rey, 00918, Puerto Rico. TEL 787-767-2020, http://www.amaestros.edu. Ed. Wanda Garcia.

371   GBR   ISSN 0969-594X
LB3050   CODEN: AEPPFJ
➤ **ASSESSMENT IN EDUCATION: PRINCIPLES, POLICY AND PRACTICE.** Text in English. 1994. 3/yr. GBP 364, USD 619 combined subscription to institutions print & online eds. (effective 2006). adv. bibl.; charts; illus.; stat. index. reprint service avail. from PSC. **Document type:** *Journal, Academic/Scholarly.* **Description:** Explores new approaches to the assessment of student achievement from an international perspective.
Related titles: Microfiche ed.; Online - full text ed.: ISSN 1465-329X. GBP 346, USD 588 to institutions (effective 2006) (from EBSCO Publishing, Gale Group, IngentaConnect, O C L C Online Computer Library Center, Inc., ProQuest Information & Learning, Swets Information Services).
Indexed: BrEdI, CPE, ERA, ETA, MEA, PsycInfo, PsycholAb, RHEA, SEA, SENA, SOMA, SOPODA, SWA, TEA, WBA, WMB.
—BLDSC (1746.637550), IE, Infotrieve, ingenta. **CCC.**
Published by: Routledge (Subsidiary of: Taylor & Francis Group), 4 Park Sq, Milton Park, Abingdon, Oxon OX14 4RN, United Kingdom. TEL 44-1235-828600, FAX 44-1235-829000, info@routledge.co.uk, http://www.tandf.co.uk/journals/titles/0969594X.asp, http://www.routledge.com. Ed. Dr. Gordon Stobart. adv.: B&W page GBP 175, color page GBP 800; 130 x 210. **Subscr. in N. America to:** Taylor & Francis Inc., Customer Services Dept, 325 Chestnut St, 8th Fl, Philadelphia, PA 19106. TEL 215-625-8900, 800-354-1420, FAX 215-625-8914, customerservice@taylorandfrancis.com; **Subscr. to:** Taylor & Francis Ltd, Journals Customer Service, Rankine Rd, Basingstoke, Hants RG24 8PR, United Kingdom. TEL 44-1256-813000, FAX 44-1256-330245, enquiry@tandf.co.uk.

370.1   PRT   ISSN 0872-1998
ASSOCIACAO DOS MUNICIPIOS DO DISTRITO DE SETUBAL. REVISTA. Text in Portuguese. 1989. 12/yr. adv. bk.rev.
Published by: Associacao dos Municipios do Distrito de Setubal, Ave. DR MANUEL DE ARRIAGA, 6-2o Esq, Setubal, 2900, Portugal. TEL 351-265-34221, FAX 351-265-37392. Ed. Antonio Matos. Circ: 12,500.

370   NLD   ISSN 0165-0343
ASSOCIATIE MEMORIAAL. Text in Dutch. 1972. 4/yr.
Published by: (Stichting Nederlandse Associate voor Praktijkexamens), Wolters-Noordhoff Groningen (Subsidiary of: Wolters Kluwer N.V.), Postbus 58, Groningen, 9700 MB, Netherlands. TEL 31-50-5226524, FAX 31-50-5264866. Circ: 3,300.

370   CAN   ISSN 0004-5306
ASSOCIATION CANADIENNE D'EDUCATION. BULLETIN. Text in English. 1965. 8/yr. CND 20 domestic; USD 20 foreign. adv. bk.rev. illus. back issues avail. **Document type:** *Newsletter.* **Description:** Covers education policies and initiatives, curriculum changes, developments, new publications, events and conventions.
Related titles: ◆ English ed.: C E A Newsletter. ISSN 1498-4393.
Published by: Canadian Education Association/Association Canadienne d'Education, 252 Bloor St W, Ste 8 200, Toronto, ON M5S 1V5, Canada. TEL 416-924-7721, FAX 416-924-3188, cea-ace@acea.ca, http://www.acea.ca. Ed. Daniel Fitzerald. Pub., R&P Suzanne Tanguay. Circ: 1,100.

370   USA   ISSN 1054-352X
ASSOCIATION CONTACT. Text in English. fortn.
Formerly: Connecticut Education Association. News Bulletin
Published by: Connecticut Education Association, Capitol Place, Ste 500, 21 Oak St, Hartford, CT 06106-8001. TEL 860-525-5641, FAX 203-725-6323. Ed. Cheryl Yost.

371.02   CAN   ISSN 0228-7730
ASSOCIATION DES COLLEGES PRIVES DU QUEBEC ANNUAIRE. Text in English. 1968. a. free. adv.
Formerly: Association des Colleges du Quebec Annuaire
Published by: Association des Colleges Prives du Quebec, 1940 Blvd Henri Bourassa Est, Montreal, PQ H2B 1S2, Canada. TEL 514-381-8891. Circ: 3,000.

370   CAN   ISSN 1197-7523
ASSOCIATION DES ENSEIGNANTES ET DES ENSEIGNANTS FRANCOPHONES DU NOUVEAU-BRUNSWICK. NOUVELLES. Text in French. 1970. m. adv. bk.rev. back issues avail. **Document type:** *Newsletter.* **Description:** Publishes for francophone teachers who work in the public school systems of New Brunswick.
Formerly: Federation des Enseignants du Nouveau-Brunswick. Nouvelles (0229-7558)
Published by: Association des Enseignantes et des Enseignants Francophones du Nouveau-Brunswick, C P 712, Fredericton, NB E3B 5B4, Canada. TEL 506-452-1749, FAX 506-453-9795, duperen@nbnet.nb.ca. Ed., R&P Nicole Dupere. adv.: B&W page USD 450; trim 235 x 177. Circ: 3,500 (controlled).

370   USA   ISSN 1081-647X
ASSOCIATION FOR INTEGRATIVE STUDIES NEWSLETTER. Variant title: A I S Newsletter. Text in English. 1979. q. free to members. adv. bk.rev. **Document type:** *Newsletter, Academic/Scholarly.* **Description:** Provides a forum for the exchange of ideas among scholars and administrators in the arts and sciences on intellectual and organizational issues related to furthering integrative or interdisciplinary studies.
Published by: Association for Integrative Studies, Miami University, Oxford, OH 45056. TEL 513-529-2213, FAX 513-529-5849, newellwh@muohio.edu, http://www.units.muohio.edu/aisorg/pubs/news/news.html. Circ: 550 (paid).

ASSOCIATION FOR LANGUAGE LEARNING. NEWSLETTER. see *LINGUISTICS*

370   FRA   ISSN 0765-9482
ASSOCIATION NATIONALE DES COMMUNAUTES EDUCATIVES. BULLETIN HEBDOMADAIRE D'INFORMATIONS. Text in French. w.
Published by: Association Nationale des Communautes Educatives, 145 bd. de Magenta, Paris, 75010, France. TEL 33-1-44635115, FAX 33-1-42855614. Circ: (controlled).

370   FRA   ISSN 0245-5668
ASSOCIATION NATIONALE DES COMMUNAUTES EDUCATIVES. BULLETIN MENSUEL D'INFORMATIONS. Text in French. m.
Published by: Association Nationale des Communautes Educatives, 145 bd. de Magenta, Paris, 75010, France. TEL 33-1-44635115, FAX 33-1-42855614. Circ: (controlled).

371.1   USA   ISSN 0001-2718
LB2157.A3
ASSOCIATION OF TEACHER EDUCATORS NEWSLETTER. Variant title: A T E Newsletter. Text in English. 1973. bi-m. free to members. adv. **Document type:** *Newsletter.*
Formerly: A S T Newsletter
Published by: Association of Teacher Educators, 1900 Association Dr, Ste ATE, Reston, VA 20191-1502. TEL 703-620-3110, FAX 703-620-9530, ate1@aol.com, http://www.ate1.org. R&P Lynn Montgomery. Circ: 3,500.

370.945   ITA
ASSOCIAZIONE PEDAGOGICA ITALIANA. BOLLETTINO; periodico d'informazione per la cultura pedagogica. Text in Italian. 1972. q. cum.index. **Document type:** *Bulletin, Academic/Scholarly.*

Published by: (Associazione Pedagogica Italiana (As.Pe.I.)), Tecnodid Editrice Srl, Piazza Carlo III, 42, Naples, NA 80137, Italy. TEL 39-081-441922, FAX 39-081-210893, http://www.tecnodid.it. Ed. Vittorio Telmon.

370.72   FRA   ISSN 0297-9373
➤ **ASTER;** recherches en didactique des sciences experimentales. Text in French. 1985. 2/yr. **Document type:** *Journal, Academic/Scholarly.*
Published by: Institut National de Recherche Pedagogique, Place du Pentacle, BP 17, Saint-Fons, 69195 Cedex, France. TEL 33-4-72898300, FAX 33-4-72898329, publica@inrp.fr, http://www.inrp.fr. Ed. Anne Verin. Circ: 1,000.

370   DNK   ISSN 1601-5754
➤ **ASTERISK;** universitetsmagasinet. Text in Danish. 2001. 6/yr. free (effective 2004). **Document type:** *Academic/Scholarly.* **Description:** Research subjects and results from the university.
Related titles: Online - full text ed.
Published by: Danmarks Paedagogiske Universitet/Danish University of Education, Emdrupvej 101, Copenhagen NV, 2400, Denmark. TEL 45-88-889000, FAX 45-88-889001, asterisk@dpu.dk, http://www.dpu.dk/site.asp?p=162. Ed. Lars-Henrik Schmidt. Circ: 14,000.

➤ **ASTRONOMIE UND RAUMFAHRT.** see *ASTRONOMY*

➤ **ATATURK UNIVERSITESI. ILAHIYAT FAKULTESI. DERGISI.** see *RELIGIONS AND THEOLOGY—Islamic*

370   ITA   ISSN 1593-5949
ATENEI. Text in Italian. 2001. bi-m. EUR 46.48 domestic; EUR 61.97 foreign (effective 2003). **Document type:** *Journal, Academic/Scholarly.*
Published by: Casa Editrice Edumond Le Monnier, Via Antonio Meucci 2, Grassina, FI 50015, Italy. TEL 39-055-64910, FAX 39-055-643983, lemonnier@lemonnier.it, http://www.lemonnier.it.

373   GRC
ATHENS COLLEGE BULLETIN. Text in Greek. 1959. 3/yr. free. bk.rev. illus. **Document type:** *Bulletin.*
Published by: Athens College, PO Box 650 05, Psyhico, Athens 154 10, Greece. Ed. Dimitris Karamanos. Circ: 10,000.

370.72   IDN
ATMA JAYA RESEARCH CENTRE. ANNUAL REPORT. Text in English. 1973. a. illus.
Related titles: Microfiche ed.
Published by: Atma Jaya Research Centre/Pusat Penelitian Atma Jaya, Jalan Jenderal Sudirman 51, PO Box 2639, Jakarta, 10001, Indonesia.

370.72   IDN
ATMA JAYA RESEARCH CENTRE. EDUCATION DEVELOPMENT RESEARCH REPORT/PUSAT PENELITIAN ATMA JAYA. STUDI TENTANG PENGEMBANGAN PENDIDIKAN. Text in English. 1980. irreg. **Document type:** *Monographic series.*
Published by: Atma Jaya Research Centre/Pusat Penelitian Atma Jaya, Jalan Jenderal Sudirman 51, PO Box 2639, Jakarta, 10001, Indonesia.

370.9661   MRT
ATTAALIM/REVUE ATTAALIM; majallah tarbawiyyah thiqafiyyah - revue pedagogique et culturelle. Text in Arabic, French. 1976. a., latest vol.25, 1994. **Document type:** *Academic/Scholarly.* **Description:** Publishes original articles on cultural topics and pedagogical matters, with emphasis on conditions in Mauritania.
Published by: Institut Pedagogique National/Al-Mahad al-Tarbawi al-Watani, B.P. 616, BP 616, Nouakchott, Mauritania. TEL 222-51517, FAX 222-53562. Ed. Mohamed El Hafez Ould Tolba.

370   CAN   ISSN 0225-1965
AU FIL DES EVENEMENTS. Text in French. 1965. w. free. adv. bk.rev. **Document type:** *Academic/Scholarly.*
Related titles: Microform ed.
Published by: Universite Laval, Communication Department, Quebec, PQ G1K 7P4, Canada. TEL 418-656-2571, FAX 418-656-2809. Ed. Jean Eudes Landry. Adv. contact Karine Fleurant. B&W page CND 1,200; trim 14.31 x 10.31. Circ: 15,000.

370.1   BGR   ISSN 1311-0845
LA950
AUDITORIUM. Text in Bulgarian. 1997. q. BGL 1 newsstand/cover domestic (effective 2002). **Description:** Supports and promotes university graduates as the natural elite of society; presents associations, clubs and groups working for a democratic and anthropocentric society; discovers aesthetic and scientific phenomena; publishes information on Bulgarian academic life.
Media: Online - full content.
Published by: Pro BA Roumen Spassov ST TEL 359-2-9882557, rou@art.bg, http://auditorium.art.bg. Ed. Roumen Spassov.

E

371 ESP ISSN 0214-3402
LA910
AULA; revista de ensenanza e investigacion educativa. Text in Spanish. 1985. a., latest vol.9, 1997. bk.rev. **Document type:** *Academic/Scholarly.* **Description:** Contains studies on pedagogy, humanities and science.
Related titles: Online - full text ed.: (from Blackwell Synergy).
Indexed: RILM.
—CINDOC.
Published by: Ediciones Universidad de Salamanca, Apartado 325, Salamanca, 37080, Spain. TEL 34-923-294598, FAX 34-923-262579, http://www3.usal.es/~eus/indexsp.htm. Ed. Jose del Canto.

370 ESP ISSN 1137-8778
LA910
AULA DE ENCUENTRO; revista de investigacion y comunicacion de experiencias educativas. Text in Spanish. 1997. s-a.
—CINDOC.
Published by: Escuela Universitaria del Magisterio "Sagrada Familia", Ave. Cristo Rey, 25, Ubeda, Jean, 23400, Spain. TEL 34-953-750240, FAX 34-953-754829. Ed. Antonio Almagro Garcia.

370 ESP ISSN 1130-4979
AULA LIBRE. Text in Spanish. 1975. q.
—CINDOC.
Published by: Movimiento de Renovacion Pedagogica Aula Libre, Apdo. de Correos 88, Fraga (Huesca), Aragon 22520, Spain. http//www.cgt.es/fedens/aulalibre.html.

370 CHL ISSN 0716-9299
AULA XXI. Text in Spanish. irreg.?.
Published by: Universidad Metropolitana de Ciencias de la Educacion, Ave. Jose Pedro Alessandri, 774, Nunoa, Santiago, Chile.

AUSTRALIA. BUREAU OF STATISTICS. SCHOOLS, AUSTRALIA. see *EDUCATION—Abstracting, Bibliographies, Statistics*

370 AUS ISSN 1443-4628
AUSTRALIA.EDU; online magazine. Text in English. irreg. **Description:** Presents articles on education and curriculum matters.
Media: Online - full text.
Published by: Education Channel International, Inc, 15 Albert Ave, Ste 403, Broadbench, QLD 4818, Australia. TEL 63-7-5527-6899, FAX 63-7-5526-2999, http://www.australia.edu/magazine/. Ed. Jacqui Ryall.

AUSTRALIAN & NEW ZEALAND JOURNAL OF LAW & EDUCATION. see *LAW*

370.994 AUS ISSN 0813-3085
AUSTRALIAN COLLEGE OF EDUCATION. NEW SOUTH WALES CHAPTER NEWSLETTER. Text in English. 1966. 3/yr. AUD 16 to non-members (effective 2000). adv. bk.rev. back issues avail. **Document type:** *Newsletter.* **Description:** Features Chapter activities, and broad coverage of educational issues in all sectors of education.
Published by: Australian College of Education, New South Wales Chapter, 54 Hawthorne Ave, Chatswood, NSW 2067, Australia. TEL 61-2-9419-4466, FAX 61-2-9411-5483. Ed. Mrs. Rae Mitchell. R&P, Adv. contact Miss Ruby Riach. Circ: 1,800.

370.994 AUS
AUSTRALIAN COUNCIL FOR EDUCATIONAL RESEARCH. ANNUAL REPORT. Text in English. a. **Document type:** *Corporate.* **Description:** Financial, divisional reports with administrative organization and staff list.
Published by: Australian Council for Educational Research, 347 Camberwell Rd, Private Bag 55, Camberwell, VIC 3124, Australia. TEL 61-3-9835-7447, 800-338-402, FAX 61-3-9835-7499, sales@acer.edu.au, http://www.acer.edu.au. Ed. Julia Robinson.

370.72 AUS
AUSTRALIAN COUNCIL FOR EDUCATIONAL RESEARCH. RESEARCH MONOGRAPH. Text in English. irreg. **Document type:** *Monographic series.* **Description:** Monograph series consisting of individual titles covering the research activities of the Australian Council for Educational Research and some work of non-ACER authors.
Formerly: Australian Council for Educational Research. Research Series
Published by: Australian Council for Educational Research, 347 Camberwell Rd, Private Bag 55, Camberwell, VIC 3124, Australia. TEL 61-3-9835-7447, 800-338-402, FAX 61-3-9835-7499, sales@acer.edu.au, http://www.acer.edu.au. Ed. Graeme Withers. R&P Deirdre Morris.

372.21 AUS
AUSTRALIAN EARLY CHILDHOOD ASSOCIATION. VICTORIAN BRANCH. NEWSLETTER. Text in English. 1960. q. AUD 20 (effective 2003). adv. bk.rev. 8 p./no.; back issues avail. **Document type:** *Newsletter, Academic/Scholarly.* Australian Pre-School Association. Victoria Branch. Newsletter
Indexed: AEI.
Published by: Australian Early Childhood Association, Victorian Branch, 9-11 Steward St, Richmond, VIC 3121, Australia. TEL 61-3-94299252, FAX 61-3-94278474, aecavic@aeca.org.au. Ed. Berenice Nyland. Circ: 360.

370 AUS ISSN 0311-6875
AUSTRALIAN EDUCATION REVIEW. Text in English. 1974. irreg., latest no.47. price varies. adv. stat. **Document type:** *Monographic series, Academic/Scholarly.* **Description:** Devoted to topics on educational interest.
Formerly: Quarterly Review of Australian Education. (0033-5762)
Indexed: AEI.
—BLDSC (1798.720000). **CCC.**
Published by: Australian Council for Educational Research, 347 Camberwell Rd, Private Bag 55, Camberwell, VIC 3124, Australia. TEL 61-3-9835-7447, 800-338-402, FAX 61-3-9835-7499, sales@acer.edu.au, http://www.acer.edu.au/scripts/Product.php3?family_code=AER. Ed. Laurence Splitter. R&P Deirdre Morris. Adv. contact Maria Bonaccurso. Circ: 1,000.

370.72 AUS ISSN 0311-6999
AUSTRALIAN EDUCATIONAL RESEARCHER. Text in English. 1974. 3/yr. AUD 105 to individual members; AUD 75 to institutional members. bk.rev. **Document type:** *Academic/Scholarly.* **Description:** Aims to promote the understanding of educational issues through the publication of original research and scholarly essays.
Formerly: A.A.R.E. Newsletter
Related titles: Online - full text ed.: free (effective 2005) (from IngentaConnect).
Indexed: AEI, AusPAIS, CPE, CurCont, ERA, ETA, MEA, RHEA, SEA, SENA, SOMA, SSCI, TEA.
—BLDSC (1798.740000), IE, ingenta.
Published by: Australian Association for Research in Education, OO Box 71, Coldstream, VIC 3770, Australia. TEL 61-3-59649031, FAX 61-3-59649586, aare@aare.edu.au, http://www.aare.edu.au/aer/aer.htm. Ed. Jane Kenway. R&P Ruth Jeffrey. Circ: 1,200. **Subscr. to:** Mr. P. Jeffrey, University of New England, PO Box 210, Hawthorn, VIC 3122, Australia.

371.1 AUS
AUSTRALIAN EDUCATOR. Text in English. 1982. q. AUD 17.60 domestic (effective 2005). adv. bk.rev. **Document type:** *Magazine, Trade.* **Description:** Educational, industrial and other news, analysis and resource information for teachers.
Formerly: Australian Teacher (0728-8387)
Indexed: AEI, CPE.
Published by: (Australian Education Union), Hardie Grant Magazines, 85 High St, Prahran, VIC 3181, Australia. TEL 61-3-85206444, FAX 61-3-85206422, info@hardiegrant.com.au, http://www.hardiegrant.com.au. Ed. Tracey Evans. Circ: 120,000.

370.994 AUS ISSN 0004-9441
L91
➤ **AUSTRALIAN JOURNAL OF EDUCATION.** Text in English. 1957. 3/yr. AUD 99 domestic to individuals; AUD 138 foreign to individuals; AUD 164 domestic to institutions; AUD 194 foreign to institutions (effective 2005). adv. bk.rev. abstr.; illus. index. reprints avail. **Document type:** *Journal, Academic/Scholarly.* **Description:** Papers on theory and practice of education.
Related titles: Online - full text ed.: (from Florida Center for Library Automation, Gale Group, H.W. Wilson, R M I T Publishing).
Indexed: AEI, AMHA, ASCA, AgeL, AusPAIS, CIJE, CPE, CurCont, DIP, EAA, ERA, ETA, HEA, IBR, IBZ, MEA, MLA-IB, PCI, PsycholAb, RASB, RHEA, SEA, SENA, SOMA, SOPODA, SSA, SSCI, SWA, SociolAb, TEA.
—BLDSC (1807.600000), IDS, IE, Infotrieve, ingenta. **CCC.**
Published by: Australian Council for Educational Research, 347 Camberwell Rd, Private Bag 55, Camberwell, VIC 3124, Australia. TEL 61-3-9835-7447, 800-338-402, FAX 61-3-9835-7499, sales@acer.edu.au, http://www.acer.edu.au/acerpress/journals/aje.html. Ed. Simon Marginson. R&P Deirdre Morris. Adv. contact Stephanie Rankin. Circ: 1,000.

➤ **AUSTRALIAN JOURNAL OF EDUCATION OF THE DEAF.** see *HANDICAPPED—Hearing Impaired*

370.15 AUS ISSN 1446-5442
LB1051
➤ **AUSTRALIAN JOURNAL OF EDUCATIONAL AND DEVELOPMENTAL PSYCHOLOGY.** Text in English. 2001. a. free (effective 2005). back issues avail. **Document type:** *Academic/Scholarly.* **Description:** Publishes research and scholarly reports from the broad areas of educational and developmental psychology.
Media: Online - full text.
Published by: University of Newcastle, Faculty of Education, Callaghan Campus, Callaghan, NSW 2308, Australia. TEL 61-2-4921-5000, ajedp@newcastle.edu.au, http://www.newcastle.edu.au/journal/ajedp/. Ed. Robert Cantwell.

➤ **AUSTRALIAN JOURNAL OF ENVIRONMENTAL EDUCATION.** see *CONSERVATION*

370.1 371.4 158 AUS ISSN 1037-2911
➤ **AUSTRALIAN JOURNAL OF GUIDANCE & COUNSELLING.** Text in English. 1990. s-a. AUD 22 domestic to individuals; AUD 30 foreign to individuals; AUD 27.50 domestic to institutions; AUD 35 foreign to institutions (effective 2003); AUD 34.50 domestic to individuals; AUD 47 foreign to individuals; AUD 63.50 domestic to institutions; AUD 84 foreign to institutions (effective 2004). adv. **Document type:** *Journal, Academic/Scholarly.* **Description:** Presents articles of relevance to all areas of guidance and counselling that address theoretical, practical and training issues that impact upon guidance and counselling professionals today.
Indexed: AEI.
—BLDSC (1808.375000), IE, ingenta.
Published by: (Australian Guidance & Counselling Association Ltd.), Australian Academic Press Pty. Ltd., 32 Jeays St, Bowen Hills, QLD 4006, Australia. TEL 61-7-32571176, FAX 61-7-32525908, info@australianacademicpress.com.au, http://www.australianacademicpress.com.au/Publications/AGCA/AGCA.html. Eds. Dr. Ivan Watson, Dr. Robyn Gillies. Circ: 1,200.

370.8991 305.8 AUS ISSN 1326-0111
LC3501.A3
➤ **THE AUSTRALIAN JOURNAL OF INDIGENOUS EDUCATION.** Text in English. 1974. a. AUD 35 per issue domestic GST included; AUD 40 per issue foreign GST exempt (effective 2004). adv. bk.rev. **Document type:** *Journal, Academic/Scholarly.* **Description:** Publishes articles in the field of Indigenous education. Devoted specifically to issues of practice, pedagogy and policy in Indigenous education in Australia.
Formerly (until 1996): The Aboriginal Child at School (0310-5822)
Related titles: Online - full text ed.: (from R M I T Publishing).
Indexed: AEI, CPE, ERA, MEA, REE&TA, SENA, SOMA.
Published by: Aboriginal and Torres Strait Islander Studies Unit, University Of Queensland, Brisbane, QLD 4072, Australia. TEL 61-7-3365-6699, FAX 61-7-3365-6855, ajie@uq.edu.au, http://www.atsis.uq.edu.au/ajie/. Eds. Elizabeth Mackinlay, Jackie Huggins. Pub., R&P Sean Ulm. Circ: 1,000.

370 796 AUS ISSN 1324-1486
➤ **AUSTRALIAN JOURNAL OF OUTDOOR EDUCATION.** Text in English. 1995. s-a. AUD 45 domestic to individuals; AUD 65 foreign to individuals; AUD 85 to institutions (effective 2003). Index. **Document type:** *Journal, Academic/Scholarly.* **Description:** Covers the scholarly examination of issues in the field of outdoor education, linking theory, research and practice for classroom teachers, academics or practitioners in the field.
—BLDSC (1810.820000).
Published by: Australian Outdoor Education Council, Griffith University, Nathan, QLD 4111, Australia. TEL 603-862-3047, FAX 603-862-0154, james.neill@unh.edu, http://www.wilderdom.com/ajoe/index.htm. Ed. James Neill. Pub. Tonia Gray. Circ: 700 (paid).

➤ **AUSTRALIAN MUSIC CENTRE UPDATE.** see *MUSIC*

370 AUS ISSN 1326-0286
AUSTRALIAN PRIMARY MATHEMATICS CLASSROOM. Text in English. 1996. q. AUD 5.50 newsstand/cover (effective 2002). adv. **Document type:** *Journal, Academic/Scholarly.*
Related titles: Online - full text ed.: (from EBSCO Publishing).
Indexed: CIJE.
—BLDSC (1818.270000).
Published by: Australian Association of Mathematics Teachers Inc., GPO Box 1729, Adelaide, SA 5001, Australia. TEL 61-8-83630288, FAX 61-8-83629288, office@aamt.edu.au. adv.: B&W page AUD 220, color page AUD 275; 210 x 297. Circ: 1,500 (paid).

372 AUS ISSN 1320-6648
➤ **AUSTRALIAN RESEARCH IN EARLY CHILDHOOD EDUCATION.** Text in English. 1994. s-a. AUD 66 (effective 2004). **Document type:** *Journal, Academic/Scholarly.*
Published by: Monash University, Faculty of Education, PO Box 6, Monash University, VIC 3800, Australia. TEL 61-3-99052819, FAX 61-3-99055400, info@education.monash.edu, http://www.education.monash.edu.au. Ed. Marilyn Fleer.

370.994 AUS
AUSTRALIAN TRAINING REVIEW (ONLINE). Text in English. 1991. q. free. **Document type:** *Journal, Trade.* **Description:** Contains articles and information on industry case studies, policy plans, training techniques and materials, and conferences in Australia and overseas.
Formerly: Australian Training Review (Print) (1037-3292)
Media: Online - full content.
Indexed: AEI.
Published by: National Centre for Vocational Education Research Ltd., 252 Kensington Rd, Leabrook, SA 5068, Australia. TEL 61-8-8333-8416, FAX 61-8-8331-9211, orderit@ncver.edu.au, http://www.ncver.edu.au/articles/index.htm. Ed. Carol Cheshire. Circ: 10,000.

AUSTRALIAN YEARBOOK OF MUSIC AND MUSIC EDUCATION. see *MUSIC*

370 BRA ISSN 1414-4077
AVALIACAO. Text in Portuguese. 1996. q.

E

Published by: Universidade Estadual de Campinas, Pro-Reitoria de Graduacao, Cidade Universitaria Zeferino Vaz, Campinas, SP 13083-970, Brazil. TEL 55-19-37884877, FAX 55-19-37884757. Ed. Jose Dias Sobrinho.

200 371.07   BEL   ISSN 0776-2461
AVIMO INFO. Variant title: Audiovisuele Missie en Ontwikkelingswerking Info. Text in Dutch. 1981. q. film rev. back issues avail. **Document type:** Catalog. **Description:** Covers audio-visual materials relating to mission, education and development issues in the Third World, spirituality and world religions.
Published by: Avimo v.z.w., Kardinaal Mercierplein 3, Leuven, 3000, Belgium. TEL 32-16-234293, FAX 32-16-293165, Avimo@kerknet.be, http://www.kerknet.be/avimo. Ed., Pub., R&P, Adv. contact Joanna van Beek. Circ: 5,000.

AWASIS JOURNAL. see NATIVE AMERICAN STUDIES

AWASIS NEWSLETTER. see NATIVE AMERICAN STUDIES

370   NGA   ISSN 0331-426X
AWORERIN. Text in English. 1952. q. **Document type:** Government.
Published by: Ministry of Education, General Publishing Section, Ibadan, Oyo, Nigeria. Circ: 125,000.

649.124   USA   ISSN 1526-9310
AYUDANDO A LOS ESTUDIANTES A APRENDER (ESCUELA INTERMEDIA). Text in Spanish. m. USD 195 (effective 2003).
Related titles: Online - full text ed.: ISSN 1527-1064; ◆ English ed.: Helping Students Learn (Middle School English Edition). ISSN 1526-9272.
Published by: Parent Institute, PO Box 7474, Fairfax, VA 22039-7474. TEL 703-323-9170, 800-756-5525, FAX 703-323-9173, webmaster@parent-institute.com, http://www.parent-institute.com. Ed. Pat Hodgdon. Pub. John H Wherry.

649.124   USA   ISSN 1526-9329
AYUDANDO A LOS ESTUDIANTES A APRENDER (ESCUELA SECUNDARIA). Text in Spanish. m. USD 195 (effective 2003). **Document type:** Journal, Academic/Scholarly.
Related titles: Online - full text ed.: ISSN 1527-1072; ◆ English ed.: Helping Students Learn (High School English Edition). ISSN 1526-9280.
Published by: Parent Institute, PO Box 7474, Fairfax, VA 22039-7474. TEL 703-323-9170, 800-756-5525, FAX 703-323-9173, webmaster@parent-institute.com, http://www.parent-institute.com. Ed. Pat Hodgdon. Pub. John H Wherry.

649.124   USA   ISSN 1526-9302
AYUDANDO A LOS NINOS A APRENDER (ESCUELA PRIMARIA). Text in Spanish. 1999. m. USD 195 (effective 2003). **Document type:** Newsletter, Academic/Scholarly.
Related titles: Online - full text ed.: ISSN 1527-1056; ◆ English ed.: Helping Children Learn (Elementary School Edition). ISSN 1526-9264.
Published by: Parent Institute, PO Box 7474, Fairfax, VA 22039-7474. TEL 703-323-9170, 800-756-5525, FAX 703-323-9173, webmaster@parent-institute.com, http://www.parent-institute.com. Ed. Pat Hodgdon. Pub. John H Wherry.

649.124   USA   ISSN 1526-9299
AYUDANDO A LOS NINOS A APRENDER (PREPARACION PARALA ESCUELA). Text in Spanish. m. USD 195 (effective 2003). **Document type:** Newsletter, Academic/Scholarly.
Related titles: Online - full text ed.: ISSN 1527-1048; ◆ English ed.: Helping Children Learn (School Readiness English Edition). ISSN 1526-9256.
Published by: Parent Institute, PO Box 7474, Fairfax, VA 22039-7474. TEL 703-323-9170, 800-756-5525, FAX 703-323-9173, webmaster@parent-institute.com, http://www.parent-institute.com. Ed. Pat Hodgdon. Pub. John H Wherry.

370   BGR   ISSN 0861-3990
AZBUKI/ALPHABET. Text in Bulgarian. 1991. w. BGL 0.25 newsstand/cover; BGL 13 (effective 2002). **Document type:** Newspaper. **Description:** Covers the activities of the Bulgarian Ministry of Education; publishes decrees, decisions, etc. related to the system of education and science; comments on current debates in the field, educational materials, including ones in arts and culture, and advice regarding labor law for workers in education and science.
Published by: Ministerstvo na Obrazovanieto i Naukata na Republika Bulgaria/Ministry of Education and Sciences of the Republic of Bulgaria, 125 Tzarigradsko Shosse Blvd., Bl. 5, PO Box 336, Sofia, 1113, Bulgaria. TEL 359-2-705298, http://www.minedu.government.bg. Ed. Olga Markova.

370   USA
B C E A REPORTER. Text in English. q. membership. **Document type:** Newsletter.
Published by: Bergen County Education Association, 210 W Englewood Ave, Teaneck, NJ 07666. TEL 201-833-9166. Ed. Barbara R Duhig.

370   DEU   ISSN 0171-8495
B L L V BAYERISCHE SCHULE. Key Title: Bayerische Schule. Text in German. 1947. 11/yr. adv. bk.rev. **Document type:** Magazine, Trade.
Published by: Bayerischer Lehrer und Lehrerinnen Verband, Bavariaring 37, Munich, 80336, Germany. TEL 49-89-7210010, FAX 49-89-7250324, bllvbsred@vbe.de, bllv@bllv.de, http://www.bayerische-schule.de, http://www.bllv.de. Ed. Karl Herrmann. adv.: B&W page EUR 1,425.50, color page EUR 2,734.40. Circ: 49,027 (controlled).

373.52   DEU
B L L V - HANDBUCH FUER LEHRER IN BAYERN. Text in German. 1979. 4 base vols. plus updates 2/yr. EUR 33.23 (effective 2004). adv. **Document type:** Directory, Trade.
Published by: Walhalla Fachverlag, Haus an der Eisernen Bruecke, Regensburg, 93042, Germany. TEL 49-941-56840, FAX 49-941-5684111, walhalla@walhalla.de, http://www.walhalla.de. adv.: B&W page EUR 615. Circ: 3,000 (controlled).

370.97296   BHS
BAHAMAS. MINISTRY OF EDUCATION AND CULTURE. ANNUAL REPORT. Text in English. a. illus.
Published by: Ministry of Education and Culture, PO Box N 7147, Nassau, Bahamas.

BAHRAIN. EDUCATIONAL DOCUMENTATION LIBRARY. ACQUISITIONS LIST. see EDUCATION—Abstracting, Bibliographies, Statistics

BAHRAIN. EDUCATIONAL DOCUMENTATION LIBRARY. BIBLIOGRAPHIC LISTS. see EDUCATION—Abstracting, Bibliographies, Statistics

BAIJIA ZUOWEN ZHIDAO. see LINGUISTICS

BALDWIN'S OHIO SCHOOL LAW JOURNAL. see LAW

371   USA
BALTIMORE CITY PUBLIC SCHOOLS STAFF NEWSLETTER∗. Text in English. 1948. s-m. free. **Document type:** Newsletter.
Formerly: Baltimore City Public Schools Staff Newsletter and Community Newsletter (0005-4488)
Published by: Baltimore City Public Schools, Division of Publications and Public Information, 200 E North Ave, Baltimore, MD 21202. TEL 301-396-8700. Eds. John A Robbins Jr., Sandra P Jubilee. Circ: 16,500.

BANGLADESH EDUCATION IN STATISTICS (YEAR). see EDUCATION—Abstracting, Bibliographies, Statistics

305.23   SWE   ISSN 0005-6006
BARN I HEM, SKOLA, SAMHAELLE. Text in Swedish. 1945. 8/yr.
Related titles: Audio cassette/tape ed.
Published by: Riksfoerbundet Hem o Skola (RHS), Fack 38400, Stockholm, 10064, Sweden. TEL 46-8-84-03-15, FAX 46-8-668-79-57. Ed. Jan Erik Carlstedt. Pub. Lars H Gustavsson. adv.: B&W page SEK 11,850, color page SEK 14,850; trim 265 x 190. Circ: 18,400.

BARN & KULTUR/CHILDREN AND CULTURE; tidskrift foer barn- och skolbibliotek. see LIBRARY AND INFORMATION SCIENCES

BASIC SKILLS. see EDUCATION—Adult Education

371.07   BEL
BASIS; Christene School. Text in Dutch. 1893. s-m. USD 58 (effective 2000). adv. bk.rev. illus. index. 40 p./no.; back issues avail. **Document type:** Newsletter. **Description:** Contains articles of interest for teachers of primary schools, e.g. social, juridical, political matters as well as matters aspiring to the aims of a teacher's union in accordance with the Christian and democratic principles.
Formerly: Christene School
Related titles: Online - full content ed.
Published by: Christelijk Onderwijzersverbond, Koningsstraat 203, Brussels, 1210, Belgium. TEL 32-2-2274111, FAX 32-2-2194761, basiswissel.cov@acv_csc.be, cov@acv-csc.be, http://www.cov.be. Ed., Pub. Romain Maes TEL 32-2-2274135. R&P, Adv. contact Marie Jeanne Bollen. Circ: 40,000.

373   KAZ   ISSN 0207-5474
BASTAUYSH MEKTEP. Text in Kazakh. m. USD 207 in the Americas (effective 2000).
Published by: Ministry of Education, Ul Zhambyla 25, Almaty, 480100, Kazakstan. TEL 3272-616912. Ed. A Abdulina. **Dist. by:** East View Information Services, 3020 Harbor Ln. N., Minneapolis, MN 55447. TEL 763-550-0961, FAX 763-559-2931.

379   DEU   ISSN 0931-4059
LA405
BAYERISCHEN STAATSMINISTERIEN FUER UNTERRICHT UND KULTUS UND WISSENSCHAFT UND KUNST. AMTSBLATT. TEIL 1. Text in German. 1865. irreg. index. **Document type:** Monographic series, Academic/Scholarly.

Former titles (until 1986): Bayerisches Staatsministerium fuer Unterricht und Kultus. Amtsblatt. Teil 1 (0722-5105); Supersedes in part (in 1974): Bayerisches Staatsministerium fuer Unterricht und Kultus. Amtsblatt (0005-7207)
Related titles: Online - full content ed.
Published by: Bayerischen Staatsministerium fuer Unterricht und Kultus, Salvatorstr. 2, Munich, 80333, Germany. TEL 49-89-21860, FAX 49-89-21862800, peter.kosak@stmuk.bayern.de, http://www.stmuk.bayern.de. Circ: 7,600.

407 370   USA
BEACON (STATESBORO). Text in English. 1966. s-a. USD 20 to members. adv. bk.rev. bibl. **Document type:** Academic/Scholarly. **Description:** Presents language study and teaching methods.
Formerly: Foreign Language Beacon (0015-7198)
Published by: Georgia Southern University, Department of Foreign Languages, PO Box 8081, Statesboro, GA 30460. TEL 912-681-5278, FAX 912-681-062, hkurz@gsvms2.cc.gasou.edu. Ed., R&P Judy Schomber. Adv. contact Horst Kurz. page USD 125. Circ: 1,100 (controlled).
Co-sponsor: Foreign Language Association of Georgia.

BEAMER; Kulturzeitschrift junger Menschen. see CHILDREN AND YOUTH—For

370.72 379   GBR   ISSN 0261-0078
BEDFORD WAY PAPERS. Text in English. 1980. a. price varies. **Document type:** Monographic series, Academic/Scholarly. **Description:** Focuses on topics in education policy and research.
—BLDSC (1872.813000).
Published by: University of London, Institute of Education, 20 Bedford Way, London, WC1H OAL, United Kingdom. TEL 44-20-76126000, FAX 44-20-76126126, info@ioe.ac.uk, http://www.ioe.ac.uk.

370   CHN   ISSN 1000-7997
BEIJING JIAOYU/BEIJING EDUCATION. Text in Chinese. m. CNY 18.
Related titles: Online - full text ed.: (from East View Information Services)
Published by: (Beijing Jiaoyu-ju/Beijing Education Bureau), Beijing Jiaoyu Zazhishe/Beijing Education Magazine Office, 201 Qianmen Dajie, Beijing, 100050, China. TEL 3015815. Ed. Niu Chensheng. adv.: B&W page CNY 1,000, color page CNY 1,200.

BEIJING TIYU DAXUE XUEBAO/BEIJING UNIVERSITY OF PHYSICAL EDUCATION. JOURNAL. see PHYSICAL FITNESS AND HYGIENE

BEITRAEGE ZUR HISTORISCHEN BILDUNGSFORSCHUNG. see HISTORY—History Of Europe

BELGIUM. MINISTERE DE L'EDUCATION, DE LA RECHERCHE ET DE LA FORMATION. ANNUAIRE STATISTIQUE. see EDUCATION—Abstracting, Bibliographies, Statistics

370.2109493   BEL
BELGIUM. MINISTERE DE L'EDUCATION, DE LA RECHERCHE ET DE LA FORMATION. TABLEAU DE BORD DE L'ENSEIGNEMENT. Text in French. N.S. 1994. a. charts; stat. **Document type:** Government. **Description:** Publishes statistical information on education for the French-speaking community in Belgium.
Former titles: Belgium. Ministere de l'Education Nationale. Rapport Annuel; Belgium. Ministere de l'Education Nationale et de la Culture Francaise. Rapport Annuel (0067-5598)
Published by: Ministere de l'Education, de la Recherche et de la Formation, Service des Statistiques, Bd Pacheco 19, Bte 0, Brussels, 1010, Belgium. TEL 32-2-210-5546, FAX 32-2-210-5538.

370   BEL
BELGIUM. MINISTERE DE L'EDUCATION NATIONALE. REVUE. Text in French. 10/yr.
Former titles: Belgium. Ministere de l'Education Nationale et de la Culture Francaise. Revue; Belgium. Ministere de l'Education Nationale et de la Culture Francaise. Bulletin d'Information (0026-5284)
Published by: Ministere de l'Education Nationale, Administrative de l'Etat, Bd Pacheco, Brussels, 1010, Belgium. **Subscr. to:** Rue Royale 123, Brussels 1000, Belgium.

370   AUT   ISSN 0005-9471
BERUF UND GESINNUNG. Text in German. 1946. m. (except July & Aug). membership. adv. bk.rev. illus. index.
Published by: Lehrerbund der O V P Steiermark, Keplerstrasse 92, Graz, St 8020, Austria. Ed. Hermann Thueringer. Circ: 4,000.

373.246   DEU   ISSN 0005-9536
BERUFSBILDUNG; Zeitschrift fuer Praxis und Theorie in Betrieb und Schule. Text in German. 1946. bi-m. EUR 64.80; EUR 11 newsstand/cover (effective 2004). adv. bk.rev. abstr.; bibl.; charts; illus.; stat. **Document type:** Journal, Academic/Scholarly.
Indexed: DIP, IBR, IBZ, ILD, RASB.
—IE, Infotrieve.

E

Published by: Kallmeyersche Verlagsbuchhandlung GmbH, Im Brande 19, Seelze, 30926, Germany. TEL 49-511-40004175, FAX 49-511-40004176, leserservice@kallmeyer.de, http://www.kallmeyer.de. Eds. Ernst Uhe, Joerg Peter Pahl. Adv. contact Bernd Schrader. B&W page EUR 915, color page EUR 1,370. Circ: 3,000 (paid).

370.15 DEU ISSN 1436-7769
BEWEGUNG UND KOMMUNIKATION. Text in German. 1999. irreg., latest vol.2, 2000. EUR 12.70 per vol. (effective 2003). **Document type:** *Monographic series, Academic/Scholarly.*
Published by: Waxmann Verlag GmbH, Steinfurter Str 555, Muenster, 48159, Germany. TEL 49-251-26504-0, FAX 49-251-2650426, info@waxmann.com, http://www.waxmann.com. Ed. Guenther Rebel.

BIBLIOGRAPHIC GUIDE TO EDUCATION. see *EDUCATION—Abstracting, Bibliographies, Statistics*

371.1 ESP
BIBLIOTECA BASICA DEL PROFESORADO. Text in Spanish. a.
Related titles: ♦ Supplement to: Cuadernos de Pedagogia. ISSN 0210-0630.
Published by: Praxis, Principe de Asturias, 61 7a Planta, Barcelona, Cataluna 08012, Spain. TEL 34-93-3444700, FAX 34-93-3444701, educacion@praxis.es, http://www.praxis.es/.

BIBLIOTECA DE EDUCACAO. see *LIBRARY AND INFORMATION SCIENCES*

BIBLIOTHEQUE DE TRAVAIL. see *CHILDREN AND YOUTH—For*

373 027.626 FRA ISSN 0005-3414
BIBLIOTHEQUE DE TRAVAIL 2EME DEGRE. Short title: B T 2. Text in French. 1968. 10/yr.
Published by: Publications de l'Ecole Moderne Francaise, Mouans-Sartoux, Cedex 06376, France. TEL 33-4-92921757, FAX 33-4-92921804. Ed. Jean Pierre Jaubert.

372 027.625 FRA ISSN 0005-3120
BIBLIOTHEQUE DE TRAVAIL JUNIOR. Short title: B T J. Text in French. 1965. 10/yr.
Published by: Publications de l'Ecole Moderne Francaise, Mouans-Sartoux, Cedex 06376, France. TEL 33-4-92921757, FAX 33-4-92921804. Ed. Patrick Bensa.

370 CHN ISSN 1003-7667
BIJIAO JIAOYU. Text in Chinese. bi-m. CNY 11 (effective 1999). **Document type:** *Academic/Scholarly.*
Formerly: Waiguo Jiaoyu Dongtai
Related titles: Online - full text ed.: (from East View Information Services).
Published by: Beijing Shifan Daxue/Beijing Normal University, Xinjiekouwai Beitaipingzhuang, Beijing, 100875, China. TEL 2011144. Ed. Gu Mingyuan.

BILD I SKOLAN. see *ART*

BILDUNG IM ZAHLENSPIEGEL. see *EDUCATION—Abstracting, Bibliographies, Statistics*

370 DEU ISSN 0006-2456
➤ **BILDUNG UND ERZIEHUNG.** Text in German. 1948. q. EUR 59.90; EUR 39.90 to students; EUR 16.50 newsstand/cover (effective 2004). adv. bk.rev. **Document type:** *Journal, Academic/Scholarly.*
Indexed: DIP, IBR, IBZ, RASB, RILM.
—IE, Infotrieve. **CCC.**
Published by: Boehlau Verlag GmbH & Cie, Ursulaplatz 1, Cologne, 50668, Germany. TEL 49-221-913900, FAX 49-221-9139011, vertrieb@boehlau.de, http://www.boehlau.de. Adv. contact Julia Beenken. B&W page EUR 720. Circ: 1,000.

379.43 DEU ISSN 0172-0171
L31
BILDUNG UND WISSENSCHAFT. Abbreviated title: B & W. Text in German. 1965. q. free. bk.rev. index. reprint service avail. from PQC. **Document type:** *Journal, Academic/Scholarly.* **Description:** Publishes articles on German educational developments and policies of the German government. Focuses on higher education, grade schools, and vocational education.
Formerly: Education in Germany
Related titles: Arabic ed.: ISSN 0177-4212; French ed.: ISSN 0178-2991; Russian ed.; Spanish ed.: ISSN 0178-3009.
Indexed: CIJE, CPE, DIP, IBR, IBZ.
Published by: Inter Nationes e.V., Kennedyallee 91-103, Bonn, 53175, Germany. TEL 49-228-880-0, FAX 49-228-880457, bw@inter-nationes.de, http://www.inter-nationes.de. Ed. Ivan Tapia. Circ: 3,000.

370 DEU ISSN 0944-937X
BILDUNG UND WISSENSCHAFT (LUDWIGSBURG); Zeitschrift fuer Gewerkschaft Erziehung und Wissenschaft. Short title: B & W. Text in German. m. EUR 44; EUR 4 newsstand/cover (effective 2004). adv. 48 p./no.; back issues avail. **Document type:** *Journal, Academic/Scholarly.*
Formerly: Lehrerzeitung Baden-Wuerttemberg (0170-4605)
Published by: (G E W Baden-Wuerttemberg), Sueddeutscher Paedagogischer Verlag GmbH, Silcherstr 7a, Stuttgart, 70176, Germany. TEL 49-711-26345690, FAX 49-711-263456990, info@spv-lb.de, http://www.spv-lb.de. Adv. contact Juergen Kienzler. page EUR 1,700; trim 185 x 257. Circ: 38,295 (paid and controlled).

370.1175 USA ISSN 1523-5882
LC3701 CODEN: BREJED
➤ **BILINGUAL RESEARCH JOURNAL.** Text in English. 1975. q. USD 40 (effective 2005). adv. bk.rev. illus. reprints avail. **Document type:** *Journal, Academic/Scholarly.*
Former titles (until 1992): N A B E Journal (0885-5072); (until 1979): N A B E (0888-1685)
Related titles: Online - full content ed.: ISSN 1523-5890. free (effective 2005); Online - full text ed.: (from O C L C Online Computer Library Center, Inc.).
Indexed: ABIn, CIJE, ChPerI, EduInd, LT&LA, MLA-IB, SOPODA.
—BLDSC (2059.880000), IE, ingenta. **CCC.**
Published by: National Association for Bilingual Education, 1030 15th St N W, Ste 470, Washington, DC 20005. TEL 202-898-1829, FAX 202-789-2866, nabe@nabe.org, http://brj.asu.edu, http://www.nabe.org. Ed. Josue Gonzales. R&P, Adv. contact Nancy Zelasko.

372.651 800 USA ISSN 0094-5366
P115
➤ **BILINGUAL REVIEW/REVISTA BILINGUE.** Text in English. 1974. 3/yr. USD 25 (effective 2005). adv. bk.rev. illus. reprint service avail. from PQC. **Document type:** *Journal, Academic/Scholarly.* **Description:** Devoted to the linguistics and literature of bilingualism and bilingual education, primarily Spanish-English, in the United States.
Related titles: Microform ed.: (from PQC); Online - full text ed.: (from EBSCO Publishing, Gale Group).
Indexed: ABIn, AmHI, ArtHuCI, CIJE, ChPerI, CurCont, EduInd, HAPI, IAPV, IBR, L&LBA, LIFT, MEA&I, MLA, MLA-IB, PCI, RILM, SOPODA.
—BLDSC (2059.900000).
Published by: Bilingual Review Press, Hispanic Research Center, Arizona State University, Box 872702, Tempe, AZ 85287-2702. TEL 480-965-3867, FAX 480-965-8309, brp@asu.edu, http://www.asu.edu/brp. Ed., Pub. Gary D Keller. R&P Barbara Firoozye. Adv. contact Karen Vanhooft. Circ: 1,500.

570.7 CZE ISSN 1210-3349
BIOLOGIE, CHEMIE, ZEMEPIS. Text in Czech, Slovak. 1949. 5/yr. CZK 60, USD 22.90. **Document type:** *Academic/Scholarly.*
Formerly (until 1991): Prirodni Vedy ve Skole (0231-5130)
Indexed: ApicAb.
Published by: (Czechoslovakia. Ministerstvo Skolstvi, Mladezy a Telovychovy Ceske Republiky), Statni Pedagogicke Nakladatelstvi, Ostrovni 30, Prague, 11301, Czech Republic. TEL 42-2-203850, FAX 42-2-293883. Ed. Hana Fricova. Circ: 6,500.

BIOLOGY EDUCATION. see *BIOLOGY*

BIOLOGY TEACHING/SHENGWUXUE JIAOXUE. see *BIOLOGY*

BIOTECHNOLOGY EDUCATION. see *BIOLOGY—Biotechnology*

370 ISR ISSN 0523-1469
BISDEH HEMED. Text in Hebrew. 1957. m. USD 25. bk.rev. **Document type:** *Bulletin.* **Description:** Covers educational and instructional issues.
Indexed: IHP.
Published by: Organizations of Religious Teachers in Israel, 8 Ben Saruk, Tel Aviv, 62969, Israel. TEL 972-3-5442151, FAX 972-3-5468942, http://daat.ac.il. Ed. Y Eisenberg. **Subscr. in U.S. to:** Associated Talmud Toras, 2828 W Pratt Blvd, Chicago, IL 60645.

370 DEU
BISMARCKSCHULE. Text in German. 1932. a. bk.rev. **Document type:** *Magazine, Consumer.* **Description:** News concerning school and education, forum for young writers.
Address: Bismarckstr 2, Elmshorn, 25335, Germany. TEL 49-4121-2310. Adv. contact Torben Schneider. Circ: 1,450.

BLACK EMPLOYMENT AND EDUCATION. see *BUSINESS AND ECONOMICS—Labor And Industrial Relations*

370.82 AUS
BLACK WOMEN'S ACTION IN EDUCATION NEWSLETTER*. Text in English. q. AUD 20. **Document type:** *Newsletter.* **Description:** Publishes articles for persons interested in Australian indigenous people's issues, particularly pursuit of education opportunities.
Published by: Black Women's Action in Education Foundation, PO Box 1784, Strawberry Hills, NSW 2012, Australia. TEL 61-2-9699-1201, FAX 61-2-9699-1201, bwaef@telstra.easymail.com.au, http://home.vicnet.net.au/~bwaef/. Ed. R Sykes. Circ: 500.

370 DEU ISSN 0723-6182
BLICKPUNKT SCHULE. Text in German. 1949. 5/yr. free to members (effective 2005). adv. bk.rev. bibl.; illus.; stat.; tr.lit. back issues avail. **Document type:** *Journal, Academic/Scholarly.*
Formerly (until 1980): H P H V Mitteilungsblatt (0343-5296)
Indexed: DIP, IBR, IBZ.
Published by: Hessischer Philologenverband, Schlichterstr 18, Wiesbaden, 65185, Germany. TEL 49-611-307445, FAX 49-611-376905, brief@hphv.de, http://www.hphv.de/bps/bps.html. Ed. Werner Meyer. adv.: B&W page EUR 540, color page EUR 870; trim 187 x 260. Circ: 6,000 (controlled).

362.709489 DNK ISSN 0006-5633
BOERN & UNGE. Text in Danish. 1970. 51/yr. DKK 990 (effective 2003). adv. bk.rev. illus. back issues avail. **Document type:** *Academic/Scholarly.*
Incorporates (1962-1991): Vi Klubfolk (0900-033X); Formed by the merger of (1965-1970): Boernehaven; (1966-1970): Fritidspaedagogen
Related titles: Online - full text ed.
Published by: (Boerne- og Ungdomspaedagogernes Landsforbund), Fagbladet Boern og Unge, Blegdamsvej 124, 4, Copenhagen Oe, 2100, Denmark. TEL 45-35-465400, FAX 45-35-465099, http://www.boernogunge.dk. Eds. Lone Riis Karkov, Tom Nissen. adv.: B&W page DKK 16,960; trim 320 x 220. Circ: 69,200 (controlled).

372.210948 DNK ISSN 0908-1682
BOERNS HVERDAG; tidsskrift for foraeldre, paedagoger og bestyrelsesmedlemmer. Text in Danish. 1971. 10/yr. DKK 134.20. adv. illus.
Former titles (until 1992): D L O - Bladet (0904-5104); (until 1989): Daginstitutionen (0107-6345); (until 1981): Vore Daginstitutioner (0107-6353)
Published by: Daginstitutionernes Lands-Organisation, Blaagaardsgade 17, Copenhagen N, 2200, Denmark.

370.113 URY
BOLETIM TECNICO INTERAMERICANO DE FORMACION PROFESIONAL. Text in Spanish. 1969. 4/yr. USD 50. cum.index.
Formerly (until 1994): Centro Interamericano de Investigacion y Documentacion sobre Formacion Profesional. Boletin (0577-2907); Supersedes: C I N T E R F O R Noticias
Published by: Centro Interamericano de Investigacion y Documentacion Sobre Formacion Profesional, Av. Uruguay, 1238, Casilla de Correos 1761, Montevideo, 11106, Uruguay. FAX 921305, dirmvd@cinterfor.org.uy.

370 BRA
BOLETIM U E R J. Text in Portuguese. 1966. 3/yr. free. bk.rev. bibl.; charts; stat.
Formerly: U E G Boletim (0041-5057)
Media: Cards.
Published by: Universidade do Estado do Rio de Janeiro, R. Sao Francisco Xavier, 524 sala T-01, Maracana, Rio de Janeiro CEP 20550, Brazil. Circ: 2,000 (controlled).

370 PER ISSN 1682-4849
BOLETIN UMC. (Boletin Unidad de Medicion de la Calidad Educativa) Text in Spanish. 1999. irreg.
Formerly (until 2001): Boletin Crecer (1682-4830)
Media: Online - full text.
Published by: Ministerio de Educacion, Unidad de Medicion de la Calidad Educativa, Van de Velde, 160, San Borja, Lima, Peru. http://www.minedu.gob.pe/. Ed. Nancy Torrejon.

370 MNG
BOLOVSROL/EDUCATION. Text in Mongol. 10/yr.
Published by: Ministry of Education, Ulan Bator, Mongolia.

BORE DA. see *CHILDREN AND YOUTH—For*

BRAZIL. SERVICO DE ESTATISTICA DA EDUCACAO E CULTURA. SINOPSE ESTATISTICA DA EDUCACAO PRE-ESCOLAR. see *EDUCATION—Abstracting, Bibliographies, Statistics*

BRAZIL. SERVICO DE ESTATISTICA DA EDUCACAO. SINOPSE ESTATISTICA DO ENSINO REGULAR DE 1O GRAU. see *EDUCATION—Abstracting, Bibliographies, Statistics*

373.246 BRA ISSN 0102-549X
HF1135.B7
BRAZIL. SERVICO NACIONAL DE APRENDIZAGEM COMERCIAL. BOLETIM TECNICO. Text in Portuguese. 1974. 3/yr. free. adv. bk.rev. back issues avail. **Document type:** *Bulletin.* **Description:** Presents previously unpublished papers on education, labor and vocational training.
Published by: Servico Nacional de Aprendizagem Comercial, Rua Dona Mariana, 48 Andar 7, Botafogo, Rio De Janeiro, RJ 22280-020, Brazil. TEL 55-21-5375898, FAX 55-21-2860645, TELEX 021-31129, cedoc@marlin.com.br, http://www.senac.br. Ed. Ana Lucia Bosisio. Pub. Arthur Bosisio Junior. Adv. contact Sidney Dasilva Cunha. Circ: 3,000 (controlled).

371.42 GBR
BREAKOUT SERIES. Text in English. 1986. irreg. Teacher's Notes), 3 base vols. plus irreg. updates. GBP 6.99 per vol.. **Description:** Emphasizes student involvement in the process of discovery in three areas: self-awareness, opportunity awareness, and social awareness.

E

Published by: (Careers Research and Advisory Centre), Lifetime Careers Wiltshire, 7 Ascot Ct, White Horse Business Park, Trowbridge, Wilts BA14 OXA, United Kingdom. TEL 44-1225-216000. Dist. by: Biblios Publishers' Distribution Services Ltd., Star Rd, Partridge Green, W Sussex RH13 8LD, United Kingdom. TEL 44-1403-710851, FAX 44-1403-711143.

▼ **BREATHE**; continuing medical education for respiratory professionals. see *MEDICAL SCIENCES—Respiratory Diseases*

BRIGHAM YOUNG UNIVERSITY EDUCATION AND LAW JOURNAL. see *LAW*

371 USA
BRIGHT IDEAS. Text in English. s-a. free. **Description:** Informs elementary and secondary school teachers in north-central New Jersey about GPU Energy's school programs, contests, tours, and teacher workshops.
Published by: G P U Energy, Consumer Relations, 300 Madison Ave, Morristown, NJ 07962. TEL 201-455-8783.

BRITISH EDUCATION INDEX. see *EDUCATION—Abstracting, Bibliographies, Statistics*

370.72 GBR ISSN 0141-1926
LB1028 CODEN: BERJEL
➤ **BRITISH EDUCATIONAL RESEARCH JOURNAL.** Text in English. 1975. bi-m. GBP 772, USD 1,602 combined subscription to institutions print & online eds. (effective 2006). adv. bk.rev. illus.; stat. index. back issues avail.; reprint service avail. from PSC. **Document type:** *Journal, Academic/Scholarly.*
Formerly (until vol.4, 1978): Research Intelligence (0307-9023)
Related titles: Microfiche ed.; Online - full text ed.: ISSN 1469-3518. GBP 733, USD 1,522 to institutions (effective 2006) (from EBSCO Publishing, Gale Group, IngentaConnect, Northern Light Technology, Inc., O C L C Online Computer Library Center, Inc., ProQuest Information & Learning, Swets Information Services).
Indexed: BrEdI, CIJE, CPE, ChLitAb, CurCont, DIP, EAA, ERA, ETA, HECAB, IBR, IBSS, IBZ, L&LBA, LT&LA, MEA, PCI, PsycInfo, PsycholAb, RHEA, SEA, SENA, SFSA, SOMA, SOPODA, SSA, SSCI, SWA, SociolAb, TEA, V&AA, WBA, WMB.
—BLDSC (2299.250000), IE, Infotrieve, ingenta. **CCC.**
Published by: (British Educational Research Association), Routledge (Subsidiary of: Taylor & Francis Group), 4 Park Sq, Milton Park, Abingdon, Oxon OX14 4RN, United Kingdom. http://www.tandf.co.uk/journals/titles/01411926.asp. Ed. Pat Sikes. **Subscr. in N. America to:** Taylor & Francis Inc., Customer Services Dept, 325 Chestnut St, 8th Fl, Philadelphia, PA 19106. TEL 215-625-8900, 800-354-1420, FAX 215-625-8914, customerservice@taylorandfrancis.com; **Subscr. to:** Taylor & Francis Ltd, Journals Customer Service, Rankine Rd, Basingstoke, Hants RG24 8PR, United Kingdom. TEL 44-1256-813000, FAX 44-1256-330245, enquiry@tandf.co.uk.

➤ **BRITISH JOURNAL OF EDUCATIONAL PSYCHOLOGY.** see *PSYCHOLOGY*

370.941 GBR ISSN 0007-1005
L16
➤ **BRITISH JOURNAL OF EDUCATIONAL STUDIES.** Text in English. 1952. q. GBP 60, EUR 90 combined subscription in Europe to individuals print & online eds.; USD 133 combined subscription in the Americas to individuals & Caribbean, print & online eds.; GBP 79 combined subscription elsewhere to individuals print & online eds.; GBP 257 combined subscription in Europe to institutions print & online eds.; USD 529 combined subscription in the Americas to institutions & Caribbean, print & online eds.; GBP 315 combined subscription elsewhere to institutions print & online eds. (effective 2006). adv. bk.rev. illus. index. reprint service avail. from PSC. **Document type:** *Journal, Academic/Scholarly.*
Related titles: Microform ed.: (from PQC); Online - full text ed.: ISSN 1467-8527. GBP 244 in Europe to institutions; USD 502 in the Americas to institutions & Caribbean; GBP 299 elsewhere to institutions (effective 2006) (from Blackwell Synergy, EBSCO Publishing, Gale Group, IngentaConnect, JSTOR (Web-based Journal Archive), O C L C Online Computer Library Center, Inc., Swets Information Services).
Indexed: ABIn, ASCA, AmH&L, ArtHuCI, BAS, BrEdI, CPE, CurCont, DIP, EAA, ERA, ETA, EduInd, FamI, HECAB, HistAb, IBR, IBSS, IBZ, L&LBA, MEA, PCI, RASB, RHEA, SEA, SENA, SOMA, SOPODA, SRRA, SSA, SSCI, SociolAb, TEA, WBA, WMB.
—BLDSC (2307.720000), IDS, IE, Infotrieve, ingenta. **CCC.**
Published by: (Society for Educational Studies), Blackwell Publishing Ltd., 9600 Garsington Rd, Oxford, OX4 2ZG, United Kingdom. TEL 44-1865-776868, FAX 44-1865-714591, customerservices@oxon.blackwellpublishing.com, http://www.blackwellpublishing.com/journals/BJES. Ed. Paul Croll TEL 44-118-9318875. Circ: 1,300.

➤ **BRITISH JOURNAL OF ENGINEERING EDUCATION.** see *ENGINEERING*

370.1 658.3 GBR ISSN 1479-2613
THE BRITISH JOURNAL OF OCCUPATIONAL TRAINING. Text in English. 2000. s-a. GBP 40 (effective 2003).
Formerly (until 2002): Institute of Training & Occupational Learning. Journal (1469-977X)
—BLDSC (2312.405000), IE.
Published by: Institute of Training & Occupational Learning, Hazel grove, PO Box 69, Stockport, Cheshire SK7 4FR, United Kingdom. TEL 44-161-4834577, FAX 44-161-4840576, enquiries@itol.co.uk, http://www.traininginstitute.co.uk.

BRITISH JOURNAL OF RELIGIOUS EDUCATION. see *RELIGIONS AND THEOLOGY*

306.43 GBR ISSN 0142-5692
LC191.8.G7
➤ **BRITISH JOURNAL OF SOCIOLOGY OF EDUCATION.** Text in English. 1980. 5/yr. GBP 731, USD 1,408 combined subscription to institutions print & online eds. (effective 2006). adv. bk.rev. illus. index. back issues avail.; reprint service avail. from PSC. **Document type:** *Journal, Academic/Scholarly.*
Related titles: Microfiche ed.; Online - full text ed.: ISSN 1465-3346. GBP 731, USD 1,338 to institutions (effective 2006) (from EBSCO Publishing, Gale Group, IngentaConnect, JSTOR (Web-based Journal Archive), Northern Light Technology, Inc., O C L C Online Computer Library Center, Inc., ProQuest Information & Learning, Swets Information Services).
Indexed: ASCA, ASSIA, ArtHuCI, BrEdI, CIJE, CPE, ChLitAb, CurCont, DIP, EAA, ERA, ETA, FamI, HECAB, IBR, IBSS, IBZ, MEA, PSA, PsycInfo, PsycholAb, REE&TA, RHEA, RILM, SEA, SENA, SOMA, SOPODA, SRRA, SSA, SSCI, SWA, SociolAb, TEA, WBA, WMB.
—BLDSC (2324.803000), IDS, IE, Infotrieve, ingenta. **CCC.**
Published by: Routledge (Subsidiary of: Taylor & Francis Group), 4 Park Sq, Milton Park, Abingdon, Oxon OX14 4RN, United Kingdom. TEL 44-1235-828600, FAX 44-1235-829000, info@routledge.co.uk, http://www.tandf.co.uk/journals/titles/01425692.asp, http://www.routledge.com. Ed. Len Barton.

370.941 GBR ISSN 0141-5972
L915
BRITISH QUALIFICATIONS. Text in English. 1969. a. GBP 48 hardcover ed.; GBP 32.50 paperback ed.. adv. **Document type:** *Directory, Academic/Scholarly.* **Description:** Comprehensive listing of all academic, educational, technical and professional qualifications available in Britain today.
—BLDSC (2340.380000).
Published by: Kogan Page Ltd., 120 Pentonville Rd, London, N1 9JN, United Kingdom. FAX 44-20-7837-6348. R&P Caroline Gomm. Adv. contact Linda Batham.

370.15 ESP ISSN 1578-701X
LA BRUJULA DE PAPEL; revista de iniciacion a la investigacion psicoeducativa. Text in Spanish. 2000. a. **Document type:** *Journal, Academic/Scholarly.*
Published by: (Universidad de Cordoba, Facultad de Ciencias de la Educacion), Universidad de Cordoba, Servicio de Publicaciones, Ave. Menendez Pidal, s-n, Cordoba, 14071, Spain. TEL 34-957-218125, FAX 34-957-218196, publicaciones@uco.es, http://www.uco.es/. Ed. Luz Gonzalez Ballesteros.

BUILDER (SCOTTDALE). see *RELIGIONS AND THEOLOGY*

649.124 USA ISSN 1531-4901
BUILDING READERS (ELEMENTARY SCHOOL EDITION). Text in English. 2000. m. (Sep.-May). USD 195 to schools; USD 305 to school districts with up to 2,500 students; USD 470 to school districts with up to 25,000 students; USD 635 to school districts with over 25,000 students (effective 2003). **Description:** Provides parents with helpful ideas, tips and guidance, including recommended books for family reading, reading quizzes, games, fun activities, reading tips that work from parents and kids, and other related subjects.
Related titles: Online - full text ed.: ISSN 1533-3302; ISSN 1533-3329; Spanish ed.: Desarrollando La Lectura (Escuela Primaria). ISSN 1531-4928.
Published by: Parent Institute, PO Box 7474, Fairfax, VA 22039-7474. TEL 703-323-9170, 800-756-5525, FAX 703-323-9173, http://www.parent-institute.com/products/newsletters/br(es).htm. Ed. Betsie Millar. Pub. John H Wherry.

649.124 USA ISSN 1531-4898
BUILDING READERS (READING READINESS EDITION). Text in English. 2000. m. (Sep.-May). USD 195 to schools; USD 305 to school districts with up to 2,500 students; USD 470 to school districts with up to 25,000 students; USD 635 to school districts with over 25,000 students (effective 2003). **Document type:** *Newsletter, Academic/Scholarly.* **Description:** Shows parents exactly what to do to help their kids learn to read, and to read more proficiently, providing the guidance, the steps to take, specific direction and concrete recommendations.
Related titles: Online - full content ed.: ISSN 1533-3299; ♦ Spanish ed.: Desarrollando la Lectura (Preparacidon Para la Lectura). ISSN 1531-491X.
Published by: Parent Institute, PO Box 7474, Fairfax, VA 22039-7474. TEL 703-323-9170, 800-756-5525, FAX 703-323-9173, http://www.parent-institute.com/products/newsletters/br(rr).htm. Ed. Betsie Millar. Pub. John H Wherry.

370 AUS
THE BULLETIN OF GOOD PRACTICE IN POPULAR EDUCATION. Text in English. 1993. irreg., latest vol.6. AUD 16.50 per vol. to individuals; AUD 22 per vol. to institutions (effective 2004). back issues avail.
Formerly: National Bulletin of Good Practice in Adult and Community Education (1325-233X)
Related titles: Online - full text ed.: (from EBSCO Publishing).
Published by: University of Technology, Sidney, Faculty of Education, Centre for Popular Education, PO Box 123, Broadway, NSW 2007, Australia. http://www.cpe.uts.edu.au.

370 CYP ISSN 0007-5019
BULLETIN OF PAEDAGOGICAL RESEARCH✶ /DELTION PAEDAGOGIKON EREVNON. Text in Greek; Summaries in English. 1960. s-a. USD 2.50. bk.rev. bibl.; stat.
Published by: Omilos Pedagogikon Erevnon Kyprou/Cyprus Educational Research Association, 18 Makarios Ave, Flat 8, 2nd Fl, Nicosia, Cyprus. Ed. A D Christodoulides. Circ: 800.

BUNDESZENTRALE FUER POLITISCHE BILDUNG. SCHRIFTENREIHE. see *POLITICAL SCIENCE*

370 USA ISSN 1042-5217
BUSINESS & MANAGEMENT EDUCATION FUNDING ALERT. Text in English. 1989. m. USD 495 (effective 2003). **Document type:** *Journal, Academic/Scholarly.* **Description:** Identifies, collects and disseminates information on funding opportunities for business school research, education and training.
Related titles: E-mail ed.; Online - full content ed.
Published by: The Association to Advance Collegiate Schools of Business, 600 Emerson Rd., Ste. 300, St. Louis, MO 63141-6762. TEL 314-872-8481, FAX 314-872-8495, http://www.aacsb.edu/publications/FundingAlert/index.asp.

BUTSURI KYOIKU/PHYSICS EDUCATION SOCIETY OF JAPAN. JOURNAL. see *PHYSICS*

371.02 USA ISSN 0271-1451
C A P E OUTLOOK✶. Text in English. m. USD 10. back issues avail. **Document type:** *Newsletter.*
Published by: (Council for American Private Education), Serif Press, 4091 Fifth Rd N, Arlington, VA 22203-2102. TEL 202-737-4650, FAX 202-783-1931. Ed. David Early. Circ: 3,400. **Subscr. to:** 1726 M St, N W, Ste 1102, Washington, DC 20036-4502.

370 CAN ISSN 1183-1995
C. A. P. JOURNAL. (Canadian Association of Principals Journal) Text in English. 1991. a.
Indexed: CEI.
Published by: Canadian Association of Principals, 300 Earl Grey Dr Ste 220, Kanata, ON K2T 1C1, Canada. TEL 613-259-5005, FAX 613-259-5685, cap@bellnet.ca, http://www.cdnprincipals.org/.

371 658 USA
C A S B O JOURNAL OF SCHOOL BUSINESS MANAGEMENT. Text in English. 1969. bi-m. adv. **Document type:** *Journal, Academic/Scholarly.*
Published by: (California Association of School Business Officials), Naylor Publications, Inc., 9851 Horn Rd., Ste. 240, Sacramento, CA 95827-1949. TEL 800-873-4800, http://www.casbo.org/Journal.htm, http://www.naylor.com. Pub. Gail Kelly. adv.: B&W page USD 1,489; trim 8.375 x 10.875. Circ: 47,000.

370 USA
C B E REPORT. Text in English. 1976. m. USD 30. bk.rev. index. back issues avail. **Description:** Keeps community-based educators informed about literacy, community-organizing, economic development issues, federal policies, funding opportunities, fellowships, awards, program ideas, resource materials, workshops and conferences.
Published by: Association for Community Based Education, 70587, Washington, DC 20024-0587. TEL 202-462-6333. Ed. V Fay Mays. Circ: 200.

370 USA ISSN 0007-8050
CODEN: CAOCAW
C E A ADVISOR. Text in English. 1958. 8/yr. free to members. adv. bk.rev. 16 p./no. 5 cols./p.; **Document type:** *Newsletter, Trade.* **Description:** Written for kindergarten through 12th grade public school teachers in Connecticut.
Published by: Connecticut Education Association, Capitol Place, Ste 500, 21 Oak St, Hartford, CT 06106-8001. TEL 860-525-5641, 800-842-4316, FAX 860-725-6323, mikel@cea.org, http://www.cea.org. Ed. Michael G Lydick. adv.: B&W page USD 2,000; trim 11.375 x 14.5. Circ: 36,000 (free).

370.971 CAN ISSN 0068-8657
C E A HANDBOOK/KI-ES-KI. Text in English, French. 1949. a. CND 40 (effective 1998). **Document type:** *Directory.* **Description:** Names, titles and addresses of the Canadian Ministries of Education, school boards, teacher training institutions, community colleges and universities, educational organizations and associations, federal departments involved in education and education publications.
Formerly: Directory of Administrative Officials in Public Education - Canada

E

Published by: Canadian Education Association/Association Canadienne d'Education, 252 Bloor St W, Ste 8 200, Toronto, ON M5S 1V5, Canada. TEL 416-924-7721, FAX 416-924-3188, cea-ace@acea.ca, http://www.acea.ca. R&P Suzanne Tanguay. Circ: 3,000.

C E A I NEWSLETTER. see *RELIGIONS AND THEOLOGY*

370 CAN ISSN 1498-4393
C E A NEWSLETTER. Text in English. 1947. 8/yr. CND 20 domestic; USD 20 in United States; CND 29 elsewhere. bk.rev. illus.; stat. reprints avail. **Document type:** *Newsletter, Trade.* **Description:** Covers events, people and policies in Canadian elementary and secondary education.
Former titles (until 2000): Canadian Education Association. Newsletter (0008-3445); (until 1972): C E A Newsletter (0382-6910); (until 1968): Canadian Education Association. Information Service. News Letter (0382-6902)
Related titles: Microfiche ed.: (from MML); Microfilm ed.: (from MML); Microform ed.: (from MML); ♦ English ed.: Association Canadienne d'Education. Bulletin. ISSN 0004-5306.
Indexed: CEI.
Published by: Canadian Education Association/Association Canadienne d'Education, 252 Bloor St W, Ste 8 200, Toronto, ON M5S 1V5, Canada. TEL 416-924-7721, FAX 416-924-3188, cea-ace@acea.ca, http://www.acea.ca. Ed. Suzanne Tanguay. Circ: 6,000.

370 USA ISSN 0882-5017
C E A VOICE. Text in English. 1970 (vol.51). q. membership. bk.rev. illus.
Formerly (until 1985): C E A Spotlight (0007-8107)
Published by: Columbus Education Association, 929 E Broad St, Columbus, OH 43205. TEL 614-253-4731, FAX 614-253-0465. Ed. Bob Buelow. Circ: 10,000.

371.07 USA ISSN 1098-5204
C E CONNECTION COMMUNIQUE. Text in English. 1996. m. free (effective 2004). adv. bk.rev. **Document type:** *Trade.* **Description:** Includes market news, ideas, and practical help.
Media: E-mail.
Published by: (Creative Christian Ministries), C C M Publishing, PO Box 12624, Roanoke, VA 24027. TEL 540-342-7511, FAX 540-342-7929, ccmbbr@juno.com, http://www.EquippingForMinistry.org. Ed., R&P Betty Robertson. Circ: 3,000.

370.72 BRA ISSN 0101-3262
LA555
C E D E S CADERNOS. Text in Portuguese; Abstracts in English. 1980. irreg. BRL 30 to individuals; BRL 40 to institutions. back issues avail. **Document type:** *Academic/Scholarly.* **Description:** Directed to professionals and researchers from the education field, aiming at approaching significant and current issues in that field.
Related titles: Online - full text ed.: free (effective 2005) (from SciELO).
Indexed: SociolAb.
Published by: Centro de Estudos de Educacao e Sociedade, C Universitaria, Caixa Postal 6022, Campinas, SP 13084-971, Brazil. TEL 55-19-289-1598, http://www.cedes.unicomp.br. Ed. Ernesta Zamboni.

C E E PRESIDENTS REPORT. see *RELIGIONS AND THEOLOGY—Protestant*

370 BRA ISSN 1533-6476
C E P A O S REVIEW; interdisciplinary journal on human development, culture and education. Text in Portuguese, English. 2000. s-a. bk.rev. back issues avail. **Description:** Publishes original works that explore interdisciplinary issues on human development, culture and education.
Related titles: Online - full text ed.
Published by: Centro de Estudos e Pesquisas Armando de Oliveira Souza, Caixa Postal 12833, Sao Paulo, 04009-970, Brazil. TEL 55-11-50837182, 55-11-50837182, cepaos@yahoo.com, http://www.cepaosreview.cjb.net/. Ed. Marcelo Lima.

370 CUB
C I C. BOLETIN INFORMATIVO. Text in Spanish. s-m.
Published by: Ministerio de Comunicaciones, Centro de Informacion de Comunicaciones, Obispo no. 527, Apdo. 605, Havana, Cuba.

370 IND ISSN 0007-8425
C I E NEWSLETTER∗. Text in English. 1967 (no.48). irreg. (3-4/yr.). bk.rev. **Document type:** *Newsletter, Academic/Scholarly.*
Published by: Central Institute of Education, Patel Marg, University Campus, New Delhi, 110 016, India. Ed. Dr. R S Vashishj.

370.113 URY ISSN 0577-2931
C I N T E R F O R ESTUDIOS Y MONOGRAFIAS. Text in Spanish. 1967. irreg. price varies.
Indexed: CIRFAb.
Published by: Centro Interamericano de Investigacion y Documentacion Sobre Formacion Profesional, Av. Uruguay, 1238, Casilla de Correos 1761, Montevideo, 11106, Uruguay. FAX 921305, dirmvd@cinterfor.org.uy.

C I R C M E LECTURE SERIES. see *MUSIC*

C I S POLICY MONOGRAPHS. see *POLITICAL SCIENCE*

C M E A MAGAZINE. see *MUSIC*

370.91734 COD
C R I D E CAHIERS. Text in French. 1974. 5/yr. USD 4.
Published by: Universite de Kisangani, Centre de Recherches Interdisciplinaires pour le Developpement de l'Education (CRIDE), BP 1386, Kisangani, Congo, Dem. Republic. Ed. Mbaya Mudimba. Circ: 150.

370 GBR
C S C S JOURNAL. Text in English. 3/yr. GBP 10 per issue (effective 2002). back issues avail. **Document type:** *Journal, Academic/Scholarly.*
Formerly: All in Success
—BLDSC (3490.177920), ingenta.
Published by: University of Leicester, Centre for Supporting Comprehensive Schooling, Moulton College, Moulton, Northhampton, NN3 7RR, United Kingdom. TEL 44-1604-492337, FAX 44-1604-492524, cscs@rmplc.co.uk, http://www.cscs.org.uk/page2.html. Ed. Paul Bland.

C S L A JOURNAL. see *LIBRARY AND INFORMATION SCIENCES*

370 USA
C S S P NEWS. Text in English. 1986. q. bk.rev. back issues avail. **Document type:** *Newsletter.* **Description:** A forum for exchange of ideas on science policy, education, ethics, and scientific research.
Related titles: Online - full text ed.
Published by: Council of Scientific Society Presidents, 1155 16th St, N W, Washington, DC 20036. TEL 202-872-4452, FAX 202-872-4079, cssp@acs.org, http://www.science-presidents.org. Ed. Martin Apple. Circ: 1,500 (controlled).

▼ **C S T A VOICE.** (Computer Science Teachers Association) see *COMPUTERS*

370.72 BRA ISSN 0100-1574
LC4095.B7
➤ **CADERNOS DE PESQUISA;** revista de estudos e pesquisas em educacao. Text in Portuguese; Summaries in English, Portuguese. 1971. 3/yr. BRL 47 domestic; USD 27 foreign (effective 2000 - 2001). adv. bk.rev. bibl.; charts. 240 p./no.; **Document type:** *Academic/Scholarly.* **Description:** Aims to disseminate scientific studies and discussions about educational questions and gender and race issues; focusing mainly on the relationship between Brazilian social problems and perspectives, the state's role and the action of social forces in the development of public policies and educational evaluation.
Related titles: Online - full text ed.: free (effective 2005).
Indexed: BBO, IBR.
Published by: (Fundacao Carlos Chagas, Departamento de Pesquisas Educacionais), Editora Autores Associados, R. Antonio Augusto de Almeida 678, Campinas SP, CEP 13084-070, Brazil. editores@autoresassociados.com.br, http://www.autoresassociados.com.br. Ed. Elba Siqueira de Sa Barreto. Adv. contact Flavio Baldy dos Reis. Circ: 1,500 (paid and controlled).

➤ **CADERNOS DE POS-GRADUACAO EM EDUCACAO, ARTE E HISTORIA DA CULTURA.** see *HUMANITIES: COMPREHENSIVE WORKS*

370 BRA
CADERNOS PEDAGOGICOS. Text in Portuguese. 3/yr. BRL 100. illus.
Published by: Centro Educacional, Av Ernani do Amaral Peixoto, 836, Centro, Niteroi, RJ 24020-077, Brazil. Ed. Roberto Ballalai.

370 FRA ISSN 0293-1729
LES CAHIERS DE L'EDUCATION NATIONALE. Text in French. 1982. m.
Published by: (Centre National de Documentation Pedagogique), Berger-Levrault Editions, 17 Rue Remy Dumoncel, Paris, 75014, France. TEL 33-1-40644232, FAX 33-1-40644230, blc@berger-levrault.fr, http://www.berger-levrault.fr.

370 FRA ISSN 0339-8080
LES CAHIERS DE L'IFOREP. (Cahiers de l'Institut de Formation, de Recherche et de Promotion) Text in English. 1975. irreg.
Published by: Institut de Formation, de Recherche et de Promotion, 8, rue de Rosny, Bp 149, Montreuil, 93104, France. TEL 44-1-48-186915, FAX 44-1-48-186944.

370 FRA ISSN 0008-042X
➤ **CAHIERS PEDAGOGIQUES.** Text in French. 1946. 10/yr. EUR 56 domestic; EUR 72 in Europe; EUR 88 elsewhere (effective 2003). adv. bk.rev. **Document type:** *Academic/Scholarly.* **Description:** Offers suggestions, theories and studies on new teaching approaches at primary and secondary school levels.
Indexed: AmH&L, DIP, HistAb, IBR, IBZ, RASB.
—IE, Infotrieve.
Published by: Cercle de Recherche et d'Action Pedagogiques (CRAP), 10 rue Chevreul, Paris, 75011, France. TEL 33-1-43482230, FAX 33-1-43485321, cahier.peda@wanadoo.fr, http://www.cahiers-pedagogiques.com. Ed. J M Zakhartchouk. R&P Noelle Villatte. Adv. contact Catherine Tilly. Circ: 10,000.

371 USA ISSN 1081-8936
LB2831
CALIFORNIA SCHOOLS. Text in English. 1944. q. USD 20 domestic; USD 40 foreign (effective 2005). adv. charts; illus.; maps; stat.; tr.lit. cum.index. back issues avail. **Document type:** *Magazine, Trade.* **Description:** Explores issues vital to state education, providing issue analysis and advise to education leaders.
Former titles (until 1994): California School Boards Journal (0895-6073); (until 1988): California School Boards (0008-1507)
Indexed: CIJE.
Published by: California School Boards Association, 3100 Beacon Blvd, Box 1660, West Sacramento, CA 95691. TEL 916-371-4691, 800-266-3382, FAX 916-372-3369, mfasulo@csba.org, cwarfe@csba.org, http://www.csba.org/csmag/default.cfm. Ed. Doug Herndon. Pub. Mina G Fasulo. adv.: B&W page USD 1,256, color page USD 1,856; trim 9 x 11. Circ: 9,000 (paid).

371.1009794 USA ISSN 0410-3556
CALIFORNIA TEACHER. Text in English. 1948. 5/yr., latest vol.55. USD 15 to non-members; free to members (effective 2005). adv. bk.rev. charts; illus.; stat.; tr.lit. 12 p./no.; back issues avail.
Published by: California Federation of Teachers, One Kaiser Plaza, Ste 1440, Oakland, CA 94612. TEL 510-832-8812, FAX 510-832-5044, janehun@igc.org. Circ: 70,000 (controlled).

371.071 378 PHL ISSN 0008-252X
CAMPUS LEADER. Text in English, Tagalog, Spanish. 1927. m. USD 1. adv. bk.rev.; play rev. charts; illus.
Published by: University of Manila, 546 Dr. M.V. de los Santos St, Sampaloc, Manila, D-403, Philippines. Ed. Honorato A Victoria. Circ: 8,000 (controlled).

CANADA. DEPARTMENT OF FISHERIES AND OCEANS. GENERAL EDUCATION SERIES. see *FISH AND FISHERIES*

CANADA. STATISTICS CANADA. EDUCATION IN CANADA/CANADA. STATISTIQUE CANADA. L'EDUCATION AU CANADA. see *EDUCATION—Abstracting, Bibliographies, Statistics*

370 CAN ISSN 1195-2261
CANADA. STATISTICS CANADA. EDUCATION QUARTERLY REVIEW/CANADA. STATISTIQUE CANADA. REVUE TRIMESTRIELLE DE L'EDUCATION. Text in English, French. 1993. q. CND 68. **Document type:** *Government.*
Related titles: Microform ed.: (from MML); Online - full text ed.: (from EBSCO Publishing, Micromedia ProQuest).
Indexed: CEI.
Published by: Statistics Canada, Operations and Integration Division, Circulation Management, Jean Talon Bldg, 2 C12, Tunney's Pasture, Ottawa, ON K1A 0T6, Canada. TEL 613-951-7277, 800-267-6677, FAX 613-951-1584, http://www.statcan.ca. Circ: 800 (paid).

370 CAN ISSN 1701-8587
CANADIAN ART TEACHER. Text in English. 1970. s-a. CND 65 (effective 2000). bk.rev. **Document type:** *Academic/Scholarly.*
Formerly (until 2000): Canadian Society for Education Through Art. Journal (1196-4081); (until 1988): C S E A Journal (1196-4073); (until 1986): Canadian Society for Education through Art. Annual Journal (0068-9645)
Indexed: CEI.
—BLDSC (3017.255000).
Published by: Canadian Society for Education Through Art, Faculty of Education, Queen's University, A321 Duncan McArthur Hall, Kingston, ON K7L 3N6, Canada. TEL 613-533-6000 ext 78401, FAX 613-5333-2331, csea@educ.queensu.ca, http://www.csea-scea.ca. Ed. Roger Clark. Circ: 400.

372.21 CAN ISSN 0833-7519
➤ **CANADIAN CHILDREN.** Text in English. 1975. s-a. CND 40 to individual members; CND 85 to institutional members (effective 2005). adv. bk.rev. **Document type:** *Journal, Academic/Scholarly.* **Description:** Targets decision-makers in the field of early childhood education, primary education and child development.
Formerly (until 198?): Canadian Association for Young Children. Journal (0384-1413)
Indexed: CEI.
—CCC.
Published by: Canadian Association for Young Children, c/o Angie Bothe, #302-1775 West 11th Ave, Vancouver, BC V6J 2C1, Canada. editor@cayc.ca, http://www.cayc.ca/Journal.html. Ed. Mabel Higgins. Circ: 700.

370 CAN
AS4.U825
CANADIAN COMMISSION FOR UNESCO. SECRETARY GENERAL'S LETTER/COMMISSION CANADIENNE POUR L'UNESCO. LETTRE DU SECRETAIRE GENERAL. Text and summaries in English, French. 1965. 4/yr. free. bibl.; illus.
Formerly: Canadian Commission for UNESCO. Bulletin (0008-4557)
Published by: Canadian Commission for UNESCO/Commission Canadienne pour l'UNESCO, 350 Albert St, 7th Fl, PO Box 1047, Ottawa, ON K1P 5V8, Canada. TEL 613-566-4414, FAX 613-566-4405. Circ: 5,200.

CANADIAN JOURNAL OF BEHAVIOURAL SCIENCE/REVUE CANADIENNE DES SCIENCES DU COMPORTEMENT. see *PSYCHOLOGY*

CANADIAN JOURNAL OF COUNSELLING/REVUE CANADIENNE DE COUNSELING. see *PSYCHOLOGY*

970.1 CAN ISSN 0710-1481
CODEN: CJNEFX
➤ **CANADIAN JOURNAL OF NATIVE EDUCATION.** Text in English. 1973. q. CND 26.75 domestic to individuals; USD 24 foreign to individuals (effective 2004). adv. bk.rev. bibl.; illus. index. back issues avail.; reprints avail. **Document type:** *Academic/Scholarly.*
Formerly: Indian-Ed (0318-8647)
Related titles: Microfiche ed.: (from MML); Microform ed.: (from MML); Online - full text ed.: (from Micromedia ProQuest, Northern Light Technology, Inc., O C L C Online Computer Library Center, Inc., ProQuest Information & Learning).
Indexed: CEI, CIJE, CPE, ERA, ETA, L&LBA, MEA, RHEA, SEA, SENA, SOMA, SOPODA, SRRA, SSA, TEA.
—BLDSC (3033.200000), IE, ingenta. **CCC.**
Published by: University of Alberta, Educational Policy Studies, 7 104 Education Centre North, Edmonton, AB T6G 2G5, Canada. TEL 403-465-3480, FAX 403-492-2024, kproehl@ualberta.ca, naomi@phys.ualberta.ca, http://www.lights.com/sifc/cjne.htm. R&P, Adv. contact Naomi Stinson. Circ: 700 (paid).

370.15 CAN ISSN 0829-5735
CANADIAN JOURNAL OF SCHOOL PSYCHOLOGY. Text in English. 1985. 2/yr. CND 42 to individuals; CND 80 to institutions (effective 2005). adv. bk.rev. back issues avail. **Document type:** *Journal, Academic/Scholarly.* **Description:** For psychologists, counsellors, teachers and administrators involved in any type of work in schools or other educational institutions.
Related titles: Microfiche ed.: (from MML); Microform ed.: (from MML); Online - full text ed.: (from Micromedia ProQuest).
Indexed: CEI, PsycInfo, PsycholAb, e-psyche.
—BLDSC (3035.518000), IE, ingenta. **CCC.**
Published by: Canadian Association of School Psychologists, c/o Joseph Snyder PhD, McGill University, Faculty of Education, 3700 McTavish St, Montreal, PQ H3A 1Y2, Canada. jsnyder@vax2.concordia.ca, http://www.cpa.ca/CASP/CJSP.htm. R&P, Adv. contact Joseph Snyder. Circ: 500.

CANADIAN MODERN LANGUAGE REVIEW/REVUE CANADIENNE DES LANGUES VIVANTES. see *LINGUISTICS*

CANADIAN MUSIC EDUCATOR. see *MUSIC*

CANADIAN REVIEW OF ART EDUCATION. RESEARCH AND ISSUES/REVUE CANADIENNE D'EDUCATION ARTISTIQUE RECHERCHE ET QUESTIONS D'ACTUALITE ARTISTIQUE. see *ART*

707 CAN
CANADIAN SOCIETY FOR EDUCATION THROUGH ART. VIEWPOINTS. Text in English. 1955. 3/yr. CND 65 (effective 2000). bk.rev. **Document type:** *Newsletter.*
Formerly: Canadian Society for Education Through Art. Newsletter (1200-2151)
Related titles: Microform ed.: (from PQC).
Indexed: WMB.
Published by: Canadian Society for Education Through Art, Faculty of Education, Queen's University, A321 Duncan McArthur Hall, Kingston, ON K7L 3N6, Canada. TEL 613-533-6000 ext 78401, FAX 613-5333-2331, csea@julian.uwo.ca, csea@educ.queensu.ca, http://www.csea-scea.ca. Ed. Roger Clark. Circ: 400.

370.113 CAN ISSN 0045-5520
CANADIAN VOCATIONAL JOURNAL. Text in English. 1965. q. CND 50 domestic; CND 60 in United States; CND 70 elsewhere (effective 2002). adv. bk.rev. index. **Document type:** *Trade.*
Related titles: Microfiche ed.: (from MML); Microfilm ed.: (from MML); Microform ed.: (from MML).
Indexed: CBCARef, CBPI, CEI, CIJE, CPE, ERA, RASB, RHEA, TEA.
—BLDSC (3046.120000), IE, ingenta.
Published by: Canadian Vocational Association, P O Box 3435, Stn D, Ottawa, ON K1P 6L4, Canada. TEL 613-838-6012, FAX 613-838-6012, cva_acfp@magi.com, http://www.cva.ca. Ed. Bob Louks. Circ: 1,000.

370.113 USA ISSN 1554-754X
➤ **CAREER AND TECHNICAL EDUCATION RESEARCH.** Abbreviated title: C T E R. Text in English. 1976. 3/yr. USD 57 domestic; USD 67 foreign (effective 2004). adv. bk.rev. bibl.; charts. back issues avail. **Document type:** *Journal, Academic/Scholarly.* **Description:** Publishes articles dealing with research and research-related topics in vocational education.
Formerly (until 2005): Journal of Vocational Education Research (0739-3369)
Related titles: Online - full text ed.: ISSN 1554-7558 (from H.W. Wilson, O C L C Online Computer Library Center, Inc.).
Indexed: ABIn, CIJE, CPE, EduInd, HEA, TEA.
—BLDSC (5072.512000), IE, Infotrieve, ingenta. **CCC.**
Published by: Association for Career and Technical Education Research, c/o Dr. Morgan Lewis, The Ohio State University, 1900 Kenny Rd, Columbus, OH 43210-1016. TEL 614-292-8796, FAX 614-688-3258, lewis1@osu.edu, rojewski@uga.cc.uga.edu, http://scholar.lib.vt.edu/ejournals/JVER/, http://www.cete.org/. Ed. Joe Kotrlik. adv.: page USD 250. Circ: 600 (paid).

➤ **CAREER WORLD.** see *OCCUPATIONS AND CAREERS*

➤ **CARMELUS;** commentarii ab Instituto Carmelitano editi. see *RELIGIONS AND THEOLOGY—Roman Catholic*

371 USA ISSN 0271-3624
CARNEGIE FOUNDATION FOR THE ADVANCEMENT OF TEACHING. ANNUAL REPORT. Text in English. 1906. a. free. **Document type:** *Corporate.* **Description:** Features a message from the President of the foundation, and financial information about the foundation.
Formerly (until 1933): Carnegie Foundation for the Advancement of Teaching. Annual Report of the President and Treasurer (1045-0467)
Related titles: Microfiche ed.: 1906 (from BHP).
Published by: Carnegie Foundation for the Advancement of Teaching, 51 Vista Ln, Stanford, CA 94305. TEL 650-566-5100, FAX 650-326-0278, publications@carnegiefoundation.org, http://www.carnegiefoundation.org/annualreport/index.htm. Circ: 1,700.

370 ESP ISSN 1133-0848
LA CARPETA. Text in Spanish. 1988. q.
Formerly (until 1990): Centros de Profesores La Rioja (1133-0856)
Published by: Centro de Profesores y de Recursos de Logrono, Ave. de la Paz, 9, Logrono, 26203, Spain. TEL 34-941-254103, FAX 34-941-251954, cpr.logrono@larioja.org, http://www.educarioja.com/cpr.logrono.

370 USA
CASE STUDIES IN EDUCATION AND CULTURE. Text in English. irreg. price varies.
Published by: Holt, Rinehart and Winston, Inc., c/o Harcourt Brace Jovanovich, 6277 Sea Harbor Dr, Orlando, FL 32887. TEL 407-345-2500.

370.113 URY ISSN 0069-1046
CATALOGO DE PUBLICACIONES LATINOAMERICANAS SOBRE FORMACION PROFESIONAL. Text in Spanish. 1964. a. price varies.
Indexed: CIRFAb.
Published by: Centro Interamericano de Investigacion y Documentacion Sobre Formacion Profesional, Av. Uruguay, 1238, Casilla de Correos 1761, Montevideo, 11106, Uruguay. FAX 921305, dirmvd@cinterfor.org.uy.

THE CATECHIST'S CONNECTION (ONLINE EDITION). see *RELIGIONS AND THEOLOGY—Roman Catholic*

282 371.07 GBR
CATHOLIC EDUCATION. Text in English. 1960. biennial. GBP 10. **Document type:** *Directory.*
Published by: Catholic Education Service for England and Wales, 39 Eccleston Sq, London, W13 0RA, United Kingdom. FAX 44-171-233-9802. Ed. M.M. Smart. R&P M M Smart. Circ: 1,000.

371.07 USA ISSN 1097-9638
LC461
➤ **CATHOLIC EDUCATION;** a journal of inquiry and practice. Text in English. 1997. q. USD 39.95 domestic to individuals; USD 50 foreign to individuals; USD 80 domestic to institutions; USD 92 foreign to institutions (effective 2005). **Document type:** *Journal, Academic/Scholarly.*
Indexed: CPL.
Published by: University of Notre Dame, 538 Grace Hall, Notre Dame, IN 46556.

371.0712 AUS ISSN 1324-5333
CATHOLIC EDUCATION CIRCULAR. Text in English. 1978. 8/yr. AUD 1 (effective 2003). index. **Document type:** *Academic/Scholarly.*
Published by: Catholic Education Office of W.A., 50 Ruislip St, Leederville, W.A. 6007, Australia. TEL 61-8-92129212, FAX 61-8-93813201, ceowa@ceo.wa.edu.au. Ed. Alec O'Connelle. R&P Irene Jipp TEL 61-8-92129210. Circ: 1,650.

CATHOLIC SPIRIT (AUSTIN). see *RELIGIONS AND THEOLOGY—Roman Catholic*

371.0712 GBR
CATHOLIC TEACHERS GAZETTE. Text in English. 1997. w. (during school year). GBP 4 per issue to individuals; free to Catholic schools in England and Wales. **Document type:** *Directory, Trade.* **Description:** Lists vacancies for teachers, administrators, and support personnel at Catholic schools throughout England and Wales.
Published by: Cartref Communications, 57 Lake Rd W, Cardiff, S Glam, Wales CF2 5PH, United Kingdom. http://www.cartrefc.demon.co.uk/othrpgs/about.htm, ctg@cartrefc.demon.co.uk, http://www.cartrefc.demon.co.uk.

370.972921 CYM ISSN 0303-8777
CAYMAN ISLANDS. EDUCATION DEPARTMENT. REPORT OF THE CHIEF EDUCATION OFFICER. Text in English. a. illus.
Published by: Education Department, Grand Cayman, Cayman Isl.

373 USA
CELO EDUCATION NOTES. Text in English. 1962. a. looseleaf. free. 8 p./no.; back issues avail. **Document type:** *Newsletter, Academic/Scholarly.* **Description:** Provides information on alternative education to alumni, parents and persons interested in that field.
Published by: Arthur Morgan School, 1901 Hannah Branch Rd, Burnsville, NC 28714. TEL 828-675-4262, FAX 828-676-0003, ams@yancey.main.nc.us, http://www.arthurmorganschool.org. Eds. Julie Kessler, Sarah Hennessey. Pub. Frederick Martin. Circ: 2,500.

CENTER FOR PEACE AND CONFLICT STUDIES - DETROIT COUNCIL FOR WORLD AFFAIRS. NEWSLETTER. see *POLITICAL SCIENCE—International Relations*

370 CAN ISSN 0710-5568
CENTRALE DE L'ENSEIGNEMENT DU QUEBEC. NOUVELLES. Key Title: Nouvelles - C E Q. Text in French. 1970. 5/yr. free. adv. bk.rev. back issues avail. **Document type:** *Academic/Scholarly.*
Former titles: Mouvements (0823-5651); Magazine C E Q (0710-300X); Ligne Directe (0315-4998); Enseignement (0046-211X)
Indexed: PdeR.
Published by: Centrale de l'Enseignement du Quebec, 9405 Sherbrooke St E, Montreal, PQ H1L 6P3, Canada. TEL 514-356-8888, FAX 514-356-9999. Ed. Luc Allaire. R&P, Adv. contact Jacques Fleurent. Circ: 100,000.

370.1 CAN ISSN 1491-2252
CENTRE DE RECHERCHE ET D'INTERVENTION SUR LA REUSSITE SCOLAIRE. ETUDES ET RECHERCHES. Text in French. 1994. irreg., latest vol.5, 2000.
Published by: Universite Laval, Centre de Recherche et d'Intervention sur la Reussite Scolaire, TSE-746, Sainte-Foy, PQ G1S 1R4, Canada. TEL 418-656-3856, FAX 418-656-7770, crires@fse.ulaval.ca, http://www.ulaval.ca/crires/html/etuetrech.html.

CENTRE FOR INDEPENDENT STUDIES. OCCASIONAL PAPERS. see *BUSINESS AND ECONOMICS—Economic Systems And Theories, Economic History*

371.3 FRA ISSN 0395-6601
AP20
CENTRE NATIONAL DE DOCUMENTATION PEDAGOGIQUE. TEXTES ET DOCUMENTS POUR LA CLASSE. Text in French. 1956. 20/yr. adv. bk.rev. charts; illus. **Description:** Committed to offering its readers well-rounded cultural knowledge. Intended primarily for students.
Formerly: France. Institut National de Recherche et de Documentation Pedagogiques. Textes et Documents pour la Classe (0040-4799)
Published by: Centre National de Documentation Pedagogique, 29 rue de l'Ulm, Paris, Cedex 5 75230, France. TEL 33-1-46349000, FAX 33-1-46345544. Ed. Evelyne Lattanzio. Circ: 40,000. **Subscr. to:** CNDP - Abonnement, B.P. 750, Sainte Genevieve Cedex 60732, France. FAX 33-3-44033013.

370.944862 FRA ISSN 0069-2069
CENTRE REGIONAL DE DOCUMENTATION PEDAGOGIQUE DE TOULOUSE. ANNALES; dossier d'information et de perfectionnement (Francais-Mathematiques). Text in French. 1970. irreg. price varies. **Document type:** *Bulletin, Academic/Scholarly.*
Related titles: Supplement(s): Bulletin Regional d'Informations Universitaires.
Published by: Centre Regional de Documentation Pedagogique de Toulouse, 3 rue Roquelaine, Toulouse, 31000, France.

370 ESP ISSN 0212-3975
CENTRO DE ESTUDIOS DEL MAESTRAZGO. BOLETIN DE DIVULGACION CULTURAL. Text in Spanish. 1983. 3/yr. back issues avail.
Related titles: Online - full text ed.
Indexed: RILM.
—CINDOC.
Published by: Centro de Estudios del Maestrazgo, C. Santa Candida, 11, Benicarlo, 12580, Spain. TEL 34-964-461400, cemaestrat@teletine.es, http://www.cemaestrat.org/.

E

370.113 URY
CENTRO INTERAMERICANO DE INVESTIGACION Y DOCUMENTACION SOBRE FORMACION PROFESIONAL. OFICINA TECNICA. PAPELES. Text in Spanish. 1996. irreg. price varies.
Published by: Centro Interamericano de Investigacion y Documentacion Sobre Formacion Profesional, Av. Uruguay, 1238, Casilla de Correos 1761, Montevideo, 11106, Uruguay. FAX 921305, dirmvd@cinterfor.org.uy.

370.1 CZE ISSN 1213-6018
CESKA SKOLA. Text in Czech. 1999. d. adv. **Document type:** *Trade.*
Media: Online - full content.
Published by: Computer Press a.s., Pod Vinici 23, Prague 4, 143 11, Czech Republic. TEL 420-2-225273930, FAX 420-2-225273934, zdenek.ogrodnik@cpress.cz, webmaster@cpress.cz, http://www.ceskaskola.cz, http://www.cpress.cz. Ed. Vit Sebor.

370 CZE ISSN 0009-0786
CESKY JAZYK A LITERATURA; casopis pro metodiku. Text in Czech; Contents page in German. 1950. 5/yr. CZK 57.50. bk.rev. **Document type:** *Academic/Scholarly.*
Indexed: BibLing, LingAb, RASB.
Published by: (Czechoslovakia. Ministerstvo Skolstvi, Mladezy a Telovychovy Ceske Republiky), Statni Pedagogicke Nakladatelstvi, Ostrovni 30, Prague, 11301, Czech Republic. TEL 2-203787, FAX 2-293883. Ed. Marie Cechova. **Subscr. to:** Pelit, Opatoricka 22, Prague 1, Czech Republic.

370 AUS ISSN 1441-9319
➤ **CHANGE. TRANSFORMATIONS IN EDUCATION.** Text in English. 1942. s-a. AUD 40 to individuals; AUD 50 domestic to institutions; AUD 65 foreign to institutions (effective 2000). adv. bk.rev. **Document type:** *Academic/Scholarly.*
Description: Covers theory, policy and practice of education.
Formerly (until 1997): Forum of Education (0015-8542)
Indexed: AEI, AusPAIS, RHEA, SOPODA.
—BLDSC (3129.647450).
Published by: University of Sydney, Faculty of Education, Sydney, NSW 2066, Australia. TEL 61-2-93516311, FAX 61-2-93516249, change@edfac.usyd.edu.au. Ed. Judyth Sachs. R&P Stephen Crump. Adv. contact Janet Egan. Circ: 400.

372.4 GBR ISSN 1358-684X
PR31 CODEN: CENGF4
CHANGING ENGLISH; studies in culture and education. Text in English. 1994. 3/yr. GBP 277, USD 458 combined subscription to institutions print & online eds. (effective 2006). reprint service avail. from PSC. **Document type:** *Journal, Academic/Scholarly.*
Related titles: Online - full text ed.: ISSN 1469-3585. GBP 263, USD 435 to institutions (effective 2006) (from EBSCO Publishing, Gale Group, IngentaConnect, O C L C Online Computer Library Center, Inc., Swets Information Services).
Indexed: BrEdI, CPE, ERA, ETA, L&LBA, MEA, MLA-IB, RHEA, SEA, SENA, SOMA, SOPODA, TEA.
—BLDSC (3129.664100), IE, Infotrieve, ingenta. **CCC.**
Published by: Routledge (Subsidiary of: Taylor & Francis Group), 4 Park Sq, Milton Park, Abingdon, Oxon OX14 4RN, United Kingdom. TEL 44-1235-828600, FAX 44-1235-829000, info@routledge.co.uk, http://www.tandf.co.uk/journals/titles/1358684X.asp, http://www.routledge.com. Ed. Jane Miller. **Subscr. in N America to:** Taylor & Francis Inc., Customer Services Dept, 325 Chestnut St, 8th Fl, Philadelphia, PA 19106. TEL 215-625-8900, 800-354-1420, FAX 215-625-8914, customerservice@taylorandfrancis.com; **Subscr. outside N america to:** Taylor & Francis Ltd, Journals Customer Service, Rankine Rd, Basingstoke, Hants RG24 8PR, United Kingdom. TEL 44-1256-813000, FAX 44-1256-330245, enquiry@tandf.co.uk.

CHAPEAU. see *LINGUISTICS*

370 RUS ISSN 1026-1303
➤ **CHASTNAYA SHKOLA.** Text in Russian. 1992. s-m. RUR 144,000, USD 62 (effective 1998). adv. bibl.; illus.; stat.; tr.lit. back issues avail. **Document type:** *Academic/Scholarly.*
Related titles: Diskette ed.
Published by: Izdatel'stvo Chastnaya Shkola, Marshala Katykova ul 15, korp 1, Moscow, 123181, Russian Federation. TEL 7-095-4995295, FAX 7-095-4995295. Ed. Vladimir Zhukov. **US dist. addr.:** East View Information Services, 3020 Harbor Ln. N., Minneapolis, MN 55447. TEL 612-550-0961.

➤ **CHEF EDUCATOR TODAY.** see *FOOD AND FOOD INDUSTRIES*

370 RUS
CHELOVEK I KAR'ERA. Text in Russian. 1993. 24/yr. USD 145 in the Americas (effective 2000).
Indexed: RASB.
Published by: Izdatel'skii Dom Chelovek i Kar'era, Ul. Seleznevskaya, 24, str.3, Moscow, 103473, Russian Federation. TEL 7-095-9784346, FAX 7-095-9784633. Ed. M V Zherebkin. **Dist. by:** East View Information Services, 3020 Harbor Ln. N., Minneapolis, MN 55447. TEL 763-550-0961, FAX 763-559-2931.

370 792.8 GBR
CHELSEA SCHOOL RESEARCH CENTRE EDITION. Text in English. irreg.
—BLDSC (3133.455385).
Published by: Meyer & Meyer Sport (UK) Ltd., 11B the Boundary, Wheatley Rd, Garsington, Oxford OX44 9EJ, United Kingdom. TEL 44-1865-361122, FAX 44-1865-361133.

THE CHEMICAL EDUCATOR. see *CHEMISTRY*

CHEMICAL EDUCATOR ANNUAL. see *CHEMISTRY*

CHEMISTRY EDUCATION. see *CHEMISTRY*

370.1 DEU ISSN 1617-2507
CHEMNITZER BEITRAEGE ZUR SOZIALPAEDAGOGIK. Text in German. 2001. irreg. price varies. **Document type:** *Monographic series, Academic/Scholarly.*
Published by: Verlag Dr. Kovac, Arnoldstr 49, Hamburg, 22763, Germany. TEL 49-40-3988800, FAX 49-40-39888055, info@verlagdrkovac.de, http://www.verlagdrkovac.de/7-13.htm.

CHICAGO UNION TEACHER. see *LABOR UNIONS*

CHILD CARE IN PRACTICE. see *CHILDREN AND YOUTH—About*

372 GBR ISSN 0009-3947
CHILD EDUCATION. Text in English. 1924. m. GBP 37.50 domestic; GBP 49.95 foreign (effective 2004). adv. bk.rev. illus. index. reprints avail. **Document type:** *Magazine, Trade.*
Description: The magazine for teachers of children 3 to 8.
Related titles: Microform ed.: (from PQC).
Indexed: ABIn, CPE, ChLitAb, EduInd, RASB.
—IE, Infotrieve. **CCC.**
Published by: Scholastic Ltd., Villiers House, Clarendon Ave, Leamington Spa, Warks CV32 5PR, United Kingdom. TEL 44-1926-887799, FAX 44-1926-817727, magazines@scholastic.co.uk, enquiries@scholastic.co.uk, http://www.scholastic.co.uk/magazines/childed.htm. Circ: 59,926. **Subscr. to:** Westfield Rd, Southam, Leamington Spa CV33 0JH, United Kingdom. TEL 44-1926-813910.

CHILD LIFE; the children's own magazine. see *CHILDREN AND YOUTH—For*

155.4 USA ISSN 0009-4005
LB1101 CODEN: CSJOD2
➤ **CHILD STUDY JOURNAL.** Text in English. 1970. q. USD 25 domestic to individuals; USD 47 domestic to institutions; USD 52 foreign to institutions (effective 2002). bk.rev. illus. index. back issues avail.; reprint service avail. from PQC. **Document type:** *Journal, Academic/Scholarly.* **Description:** Serves as a venue to discuss theory and research on child and adolescent development.
Formerly: Child Study Center Bulletin
Related titles: Microfilm ed.: (from PQC); Online - full text ed.: (from EBSCO Publishing, Florida Center for Library Automation, Gale Group, H.W. Wilson, O C L C Online Computer Library Center, Inc.).
Indexed: ABIn, AgeL, CDA, CIJE, CPE, CurCont, DIP, ECER, ERA, ETA, EduInd, FamI, IBR, IBZ, IMFL, L&LBA, MEA, PsySCDP, PsycInfo, PsycholAb, RHEA, RefZh, SEA, SENA, SOMA, SOPODA, SSA, SSCI, TEA, e-psyche.
—BLDSC (3172.949000), IE, Infotrieve, ingenta.
Published by: State University of New York, Buffalo State College, Department of Educational Foundations, Bacon Hall 306, 1300 Elmwood Ave, Buffalo, NY 14222-1095. TEL 716-878-5302, FAX 716-878-5833. Ed. Donald E Carter. R&P Glenda Leyonmark. Circ: 500.

372 USA ISSN 1091-7578
LC4091
CHILDREN AND FAMILIES. Text in English. 1989. q. free to members. adv. **Document type:** *Trade.* **Description:** Features legislative information, research, teaching tips and other information of interest to Head Start directors, staff, parents, volunteers and anyone else in the child development and social services fields.
Formerly: N H S A Journal (1056-7313)
Indexed: CIJE.
Published by: National Head Start Association, 1651 Prince St, Alexandria, VA 22314. TEL 703-739-0875, FAX 703-739-0878, http://www.nhsa.org. Ed., R&P Julie Konieczny. Adv. contact Townsend Group. Circ: 15,000 (controlled).

CHILDREN & SCHOOLS; a journal of social work practice. see *SOCIAL SERVICES AND WELFARE*

CHILDREN'S HOUSE - CHILDREN'S WORLD; a magazine for parents, teachers and professionals about today's children. see *CHILDREN AND YOUTH—About*

CHILDREN'S LITERATURE IN EDUCATION; an international quarterly. see *CHILDREN AND YOUTH—About*

373 300 323.6 GBR ISSN 1357-4019
LB1585
➤ **CHILDREN'S SOCIAL & ECONOMICS EDUCATION**; an international journal. Text in English. 1996. 3/yr. GBP 90, USD 145 to institutions (effective 2001). adv. bk.rev. back issues avail. **Document type:** *Journal, Academic/Scholarly.*
Description: Publishes papers covering formal and informal education and learning up to the age of 14, with a particular emphasis on the teaching and learning of social, economic and political aspects of the curriculum.
Indexed: BrEdI, CPE, ERA, ETA, MEA, PSA, RHEA, SEA, SENA, SOMA, SWA, TEA.
Published by: International Association for Children's Social and Economics Education, 22 Willows Dr, Meir Heath, Stokes-on-Trent, Staffs ST3 7LZ, United Kingdom. iacsee@aol.com, http://www.iacsee.org. Ed. Alistair Ross. Pub. John Price.

370.1 300 CHN
CHINESE ACADEMIC JOURNALS FULL-TEXT DATABASE. EDUCATION & SOCIAL SCIENCES. Text in Chinese, English. m. USD 4,510 (effective 2003). **Document type:** *Academic/Scholarly.* **Description:** Includes 501,483 articles from over 892 academic journals, covering education, society, psychology, nation, religion, population, talent, books information.
Media: CD-ROM (from Tsinghua Tongfang Optical Disc Co., Ltd.).
Related titles: ♦ Online - full content ed.: C N K I Web; Online - full text ed.: (from East View Information Services); ♦ Print ed.: Anhui Shida Xuebao. ISSN 1001-2443.
Published by: Tsinghua Tongfang Optical Disc Co., Ltd., Room 1300, Huaye Building, Tsing Hua University, PO BOX 84-48, Beijing, 100084, China. TEL 86-1-62791819, FAX 86-1-62791944, Beijing@cnki.net, http://www.cnki.net.
Co-sponsor: Tsinghua University.

370.951 USA ISSN 1061-1932
LA1130
➤ **CHINESE EDUCATION AND SOCIETY**; a journal of translations. Text in English. 1968. bi-m. USD 149 domestic to individuals; USD 221 foreign to individuals; USD 1,180 domestic to institutions; USD 1,300 foreign to institutions (effective 2006). adv. illus. index. back issues avail.; reprint service avail. from PSC. **Document type:** *Journal, Academic/Scholarly.* **Description:** Presents unabridged translations of articles on Chinese education and society from Chinese journals, newspapers, and anthologies.
Formerly (until Jan. 1993): Chinese Education (0009-4560)
Related titles: Microform ed.: (from PQC); Online - full text ed.: 2004 (Apr.) (from EBSCO Publishing, H.W. Wilson, O C L C Online Computer Library Center, Inc., Swets Information Services).
Indexed: ABIn, ASCA, AgeL, BAS, CIJE, CPE, CurCont, DIP, EAA, ERA, ETA, EduInd, IBR, IBZ, MEA, PCI, RASB, REE&TA, SEA, SSCI, WBA, WMB.
—BLDSC (3180.278050), IDS, IE, ingenta. **CCC.**
Published by: M.E. Sharpe, Inc., 80 Business Park Dr, Armonk, NY 10504. TEL 914-273-1800, 800-541-6563, FAX 914-273-2106, custserv@mesharpe.com, http://www.mesharpe.com/mall/results1.asp. Ed. Stanley Rosen. Adv. contact Barbara Ladd TEL 914-273-1800 ext 121. page USD 300.

➤ **CHINESE LANGUAGE TEACHERS ASSOCIATION. JOURNAL.** see *LINGUISTICS*

➤ **CHINESE LANGUAGE TEACHERS ASSOCIATION. MONOGRAPH SERIES.** see *LINGUISTICS*

➤ **CHINESE LANGUAGE TEACHERS ASSOCIATION. NEWSLETTER.** see *LINGUISTICS*

370 BGR ISSN 0324-0746
CHITALISHTE. Text in Bulgarian. 1870. bi-m. USD 44 foreign (effective 2002). adv. illus. **Document type:** *Journal.*
Description: Covers information about the cultural clubs in Bulgaria and abroad.
Indexed: RASB.
Published by: Komitet za Izkustvo i Kultura, Foreign Trade Co "Hemus", 1-B Raiko Daskalov pl, Sofia, 1000, Bulgaria. TEL 359-2-871686, FAX 359-2-9803319. Ed. Slavcho Vasev.

CHOUETTE. see *LINGUISTICS*

370.15 POL ISSN 0137-706X
➤ **CHOWANNA.** Text in Polish; Summaries in English. 1929; N.S. 1993. s-a. EUR 18 foreign (effective 2005). **Document type:** *Journal, Academic/Scholarly.* **Description:** Covers theoretical and applied aspects of pedagogy and psychology.
Indexed: e-psyche.
Published by: (Kuratorium Oswiaty i Wychowania w Katowicach), Wydawnictwa Szkolne i Pedagogiczne, Biuro Regionu Slaskiego, Ul kard Stefana Wyszynskiego 9, Katowice, 40132, Poland. wsip@wsip.com.pl, http://www.edukacja.torun.pl/baza/chowanna.html, http://www.wsip.com.pl. Ed. Zofia Ratajczak. R&P Barbara Woznica. Circ: 275. **Dist. by:** Ars Polona, Krakowskie Przedmiescie 7, Warsaw, Poland. TEL 48-22-9263914, FAX 48-22-9265334, arspolona@arspolona.com.pl, http://www.arspolona.com.pl.

E

370 GBR ISSN 1350-6781
➤ **CHREODS.** Text in English. 1986. irreg. (approx. 2/yr.). GBP 6 for 2 issues. **Document type:** *Academic/Scholarly.*
Description: Covers education and practitioner development.
Related titles: Online - full text ed.
Address: c/o Manchester Metropolitan University, School of Education, 799 Wilmslow Rd, Didsbury, Manchester M20 2RR, United Kingdom. A.M.Brown@mmu.ac.uk, D.Wilson@mmu.ac.uk, http://s13a.math.aca.mmu.ac.uk/Chreods/Chreods_intro.html. Eds. Dennis Atkinson, Tony Brown. Circ: 150.

371.07 USA
CHRISTIAN CLASSROOM. Text in English. 1997. q. USD 19.95 (effective 2000 - 2001). adv. software rev. **Document type:** *Magazine, Trade.* **Description:** Brings information on issues and concerns facing the teacher in a Christian classroom.
Published by: Great River Publishing, Inc., 2191 Windy Oaks Dr., Germantown, TN 38139-5207. TEL 901-624-5911, 800-567-6912, FAX 901-624-5910, tcc@grtriver.com, http://www.grtriver.com/tcc/. Ed., R&P Sherry Campbell. adv.: B&W page USD 3,520, color page USD 4,495; trim 10.88 x 8.13.

CHRISTIAN EDUCATION COUNSELOR. see *RELIGIONS AND THEOLOGY*

371.07 230.071 371.67 USA
▼ **CHRISTIAN SCHOOL PRODUCTS.** Text in English. 2005. m. free to qualified personnel (effective 2005). adv. **Document type:** *Magazine, Trade.*
Published by: Valor Media Concepts, Inc., PO Box 36577, Birmingham, AL 35236. TEL 205-620-2888, 888-548-2567, FAX 205-620-4040, info@cspmag.com, http://www.cspmag.com/. Pub. Loren Stiffler TEL 205-620-2888 ext 225. adv.: color page USD 2,950; trim 8 x 10.5.

371.07 AUS ISSN 1443-735X
CHRISTIAN TEACHERS JOURNAL. Text in English. 1984. q. AUD 20 domestic; AUD 28 foreign (effective 2005). adv. bk.rev. 32 p./no.; back issues avail. **Description:** Addresses issues relevant to Christian teachers. Recent editions have focussed on professional development, youth culture, discipline, post modernism, sexuality and environmental education.
Former titles: Partners in Education (0818-6197); (until 1985): Curriculum News (0818-6227)
Published by: Christian Parent Controlled Schools Ltd., PO Box 7000, Blacktown, NSW 2148, Australia. TEL 61-2-06713311, FAX 61-2-96715968, smitchell@cpcs.edu.au, http://www.cpcs.edu.au. Ed., R&P Suzanne Mitchell. Adv. contact Mrs. Sally Winsor. Circ: 2,500.

CHRISTOPHORUS. see *RELIGIONS AND THEOLOGY—Roman Catholic*

370.1 HKG ISSN 1025-1944
LA1134.H6
CHUDENG JIAOYU XUEBAO/JOURNAL OF BASIC EDUCATION. Text in English. 1990. s-a. HKD 100 to individuals; HKD 150 to institutions (effective 2005).
Document type: *Journal, Academic/Scholarly.* **Description:** Aims at the study, promotion, and improvement of basic education in Hong Kong. It seeks contribution in terms of theoretical writing, explorations of educations issues, as well as exchanges in practical experiences in the field of basic education. In addition feature reporting of educational activities and book or article reviews are also welcome.
Indexed: EAA.
—BLDSC (4951.118500).
Published by: Hong Kong Institute of Educational Research (Subsidiary of: Chinese University of Hong Kong), The Chinese University of Hong Kong, Ho Tim Building, Room 204, Shatin, New Territories, Hong Kong. TEL 852-2609-6754, FAX 852-2603-6850, hkier@cuhk.edu.hk, http://www.fed.cuhk.edu.hk/ceric/pej/intro.htm, http://www.fed.cuhk.edu.hk/~hkier/. Ed. Chi-kin John Lee.

371.07 268 USA ISSN 0164-5625
CHURCH EDUCATOR. Text in English. 1976. m. USD 28 domestic; USD 30 in Canada (effective 2001). **Document type:** *Trade.*
Published by: Educational Ministries (Subsidiary of: American Baptist Churches in the U S A), 165 Plaza Dr, Prescott, AZ 86303. TEL 520-771-8601, FAX 520-771-8621, info@educationalministries.com, edmin2@aol.com. Ed. Linda Davidson. Circ: 4,500.

370 CHN
CHUZHONGSHENG SHUXUE XUEXI (CHU YI BAN). Text in Chinese. 1984. m. CNY 2 newsstand/cover (effective 2005).
Document type: *Journal, Academic/Scholarly.*
Supersedes in part: Chuzhongsheng Shuxue Xuexi (1006-7752)
Published by: Jiangsu Jiaoyu Chubanshe/Jiangsu Education Publishing House, 47, Nunan Lu, 1011-shi, Nanjing, Jiangsu 210009, China. TEL 86-25-3279331, FAX 86-25-6630399, maths.m@edu_publisher.com, http://czssxxx-cy.periodicals.net.cn/default.html.

370 CHN
CHUZHONGSHENG SHUXUE XUEXI (CHUSAN BAN). Text in Chinese. 1984. m. CNY 3 newsstand/cover (effective 2005).
Document type: *Journal, Academic/Scholarly.*
Supersedes in part: Chuzhongsheng Shuxue Xuexi (1006-7752)
Published by: Jiangsu Jiaoyu Chubanshe/Jiangsu Education Publishing House, 47, Nunan Lu, 1011-shi, Nanjing, Jiangsu 210009, China. TEL 86-25-3279331, FAX 86-25-6630399, maths-study@263.net, http://czssxxx-cs.periodicals.net.cn/default.html.

370 CUB
CIENCIAS PEDAGOGICAS. Text in Spanish. 1980. s-a. USD 12. bk.rev. bibl.; charts; illus.
Related titles: Online - full text ed.: ISSN 1605-5888. 1999.
Published by: (Cuba. Ministerio de Educacion, Cuba. Instituto Central de Ciencias Pedagogicas), Ediciones Cubanas, Obispo No. 527, Apdo. 605, Havana, Cuba. Circ: 3,000.

371 SWE ISSN 1652-1595
CIRKELN. Text in Swedish. 1980. 6/yr.
Formerly (until 2003): Studie-Cirkeln (0282-6135); Which incorporated (1980-1986): Spaar (0349-9413)
Published by: Studiefraemjandet/Study Promotion Association, PO Box 49013, Stockholm, 10028, Sweden. TEL 46-8-54570700, FAX 46-8-54570739, sfr@sfr.se, http://www.sfr.se. Ed. Hetty Rooth. Pub. Annaa Mattsson. Circ: 20,000.

CITIZENSHIP EDUCATOR. see *LAW*

CIVIL ENGINEERING EDUCATION. see *ENGINEERING—Civil Engineering*

370 CZE ISSN 1210-0811
CIZI JAZYKY; casopis pro teorii a praxi vyucovani cizim jazykum. Text in Czech, Slovak; Contents page in English, French, German, Russian. 1957. 10/yr. CZK 30, USD 15. bk.rev. abstr.; charts; illus. index.
Formerly: Cizi Jazyky ve Skole (0009-8205)
Indexed: BEL&L, BibLing, LT&LA, MLA, MLA-IB, RASB.
Published by: Nakladatelstvi KVARTA, Legerova 25, Prague 2, 120 00, Czech Republic. Ed. Radana Skacelove. **Subscr. to:** PNS, Ustredni Expedice a Dovoz Tisku Praha, Administrace Vyvozu Tisku, Kovpakova 26, Zavod 1, Prague 6 160 00, Czech Republic.

CLASSICAL OUTLOOK. see *CLASSICAL STUDIES*

370 FRA ISSN 1243-4450
CLE...S A VENIR; l'innovation on sait faire. Text in French. 1992. 3/yr.
Published by: Centre National de Documentation Pedagogique, 29 rue de l'Ulm, Paris, Cedex 5 75230, France. TEL 33-1-46349000, FAX 33-1-46345544. **Co-sponsor:** Centre Regional de Documentation Pedagogique (Nancy).

CLEARING; environmental education resources for teachers. see *ENVIRONMENTAL STUDIES*

370 362.7 AUS ISSN 1321-8697
CLEARING HOUSE. Text in English. 1991. q. AUD 31.50 domestic; AUD 42 foreign. **Document type:** *Newsletter.*
Published by: Free Kindergarten Association of Victoria Inc., 1st Flr., 9-11 Stewart St, Richmond, VIC 3121, Australia. TEL 61-3-94284471, FAX 61-3-94299252. Ed. Dr. Rosemary Milne. Circ: 450.

373 USA ISSN 0009-8655
L11 CODEN: TOKIDC
➤ **THE CLEARING HOUSE**; a journal of educational strategies, issues, and ideas. Text in English. 1925. bi-m. USD 49 domestic to individuals; USD 65 foreign to individuals; USD 105 domestic to institutions; USD 121 foreign to institutions; USD 17.50 per issue (effective academic year 2005 - 2006). adv. charts; illus. Index. back issues avail.; reprint service avail. from PSC. **Document type:** *Journal, Academic/Scholarly.* **Description:** It offers a variety of articles for teachers and administrators ofmiddle schools and junior and senior high schools.
Related titles: CD-ROM ed.: (from ProQuest Information & Learning); Microform ed.; Online - full text ed.: (from EBSCO Publishing, Florida Center for Library Automation, Gale Group, H.W. Wilson, Northern Light Technology, Inc., O C L C Online Computer Library Center, Inc., ProQuest Information & Learning, SoftLine Information).
Indexed: ABIn, ASIP, Acal, BusEdI, CERDIC, CIJE, CPE, EAA, ENW, EduInd, LRI, MagInd, SENA, V&AA.
—BLDSC (3278.530000), IE, Infotrieve, ingenta. **CCC.**
Published by: (Helen Dwight Reid Educational Foundation), Heldref Publications, 1319 18th St, NW, Washington, DC 20036-1802. TEL 202-296-6267, 800-365-9753, FAX 202-293-6130, tch@heldref.org, subscribe@heldref.org, http://www.heldref.org/tch.php. Adv. contact Chante Douglas. page USD 525; trim 7 x 10. Circ: 1,112 (paid).

➤ **CLUB CONNECTION.** see *RELIGIONS AND THEOLOGY—Other Denominations And Sects*

371.192 USA
CO-OPERATIVELY SPEAKING. Text in English. 1970. 3/yr., latest vol.31. USD 25 in U S & Canada; USD 35 elsewhere (effective 2001). adv. bk.rev. illus. index. 4 p./no.; back issues avail.
Document type: *Newsletter.*
Formerly (until 1984): Parent Cooperative Preschools International Journal (0048-2978)
Indexed: AgeL.
Published by: Parent Cooperative Preschools International, 1401 New York Ave, N W, Ste 1100, Washington, DC 20005-2102. TEL 800-636-6222, pcpi@ncba.org. Ed., Adv. contact Kathy Ems. Circ: 2,300.

COGNITION AND LANGUAGE; a series in psycholinguistics. see *LINGUISTICS*

370 ESP
COLECCION HISTORIA DE LA EDUCACION EN ZAMORA. Text in Spanish. 1980. a.
Published by: Instituto de Estudios Zamoranos "Florian de Ocampo", Plaza de Viariato, s-n, Zamora, 49071, Spain. TEL 34-980-530486, FAX 34-980-514329, iez@helcom.es, http://www.helcom.es/iez/. Ed. Carmen Seisdedos Sanchez.

370 BRA ISSN 0080-3103
COLEGIO MILITAR DO RIO DE JANEIRO. REVISTA DIDACTICA. Text in Portuguese. 1902. a. free.
Published by: Colegio Militar do Rio de Janeiro, Rua Sao Francisco Xavier 267, Maracana, RJ 20550-010, Brazil. TEL 55-21-2949652, FAX 39-21-2646096. Circ: 1,000.

370.15 FRA ISSN 0246-4950
COLLECTION ORIENTATIONS* . Text in French. irreg. price varies.
Indexed: e-psyche.
Published by: Editions Scientifiques et Psychologiques, c/o Office de Justification de la Diffusion Controle (O J D), 40 Bd. Malesherbes, Paris, 75008, France. TEL 46-45-38-12, FAX 40-95-73-32. Ed. G Pihouee.

370 FRA
COLLECTION SCIENCES DE L'EDUCATION* . Text in French. irreg. price varies.
Published by: Editions Scientifiques et Psychologiques, c/o Office de Justification de la Diffusion Controle (O J D), 40 Bd. Malesherbes, Paris, 75008, France.

370 FRA
COLLECTIONS EDUCATION - PEDAGOGIE* . Text in French. irreg. price varies.
Published by: Editions Scientifiques et Psychologiques, c/o Office de Justification de la Diffusion Controle (O J D), 40 Bd. Malesherbes, Paris, 75008, France. TEL 46-45-38-12, FAX 40-95-73-32. Ed. J L Bernaud.

COLLEGE AND CAREER PROGRAMS FOR DEAF STUDENTS. see *HANDICAPPED—Hearing Impaired*

COLLEGE CATALOG COLLECTION ON MICROFICHE. see *EDUCATION—Abstracting, Bibliographies, Statistics*

370 GBR
COLLEGE OF TEACHERS. NEWSLETTER. Text in English. q. free to members; GBP 12 domestic to non-members; GBP 16 in Europe to non-members; GBP 20 elsewhere to non-members (effective 2004). **Document type:** *Newsletter, Academic/Scholarly.* **Description:** Covers the College events, news, courses, meetings, research projects.
Published by: College of Teachers, University of London, Institute of Education, 57 Gordon Sq, London, WC1H 0NU, United Kingdom. enquiries@cot.ac.uk, http://www.collegeofteachers.ac.uk/newsletter.htm.

370 USA ISSN 0279-3326
COLORADO EDUCATION ASSOCIATION. JOURNAL. Text in English. 1885. bi-m. free domestic to members; USD 12 domestic to non-members (effective 2005). adv. **Document type:** *Journal, Trade.*
Published by: Colorado Education Association, 1500 Grant St., Denver, CO 80203-1800. TEL 303-837-1500, FAX 303-837-9006, http://www.coloradoea.org. Ed., Pub. Jeanne L Beyer. adv.: B&W page USD 1,300. Circ: 30,000 (controlled).

COLORADO MUSIC EDUCATOR. see *MUSIC*

370 GBR ISSN 0010-1842
COLSTONIAN. Text in English. 1894. a. adv. illus. **Document type:** *Consumer.* **Description:** Records activities of the school year, together with literary and artistic contributions by pupils.
Published by: Colston's Collegiate School, Stapleton Rd, Bristol, BS5 0RB, United Kingdom. TEL 44-1272-655207. Ed. M E Davies. Adv. contact M.E. Davies. Circ: 500.

371 CAN ISSN 0703-4628
COMMUNICATE. Text in English. 1976. 8/yr. CND 10. adv. bk.rev.
Formerly: Northwest Territories Association Newsletter
Published by: Northwest Territories Teachers Association, P O Box 761, Iqaluit, NT X0A 0H0, Canada. TEL 403-873-8501, FAX 403-873-2236. Ed. John Maurice. Circ: 900.

E

371.897 USA ISSN 1536-9129
PN4788
COMMUNICATION, JOURNALISM EDUCATION TODAY. Short title: C: J E T. Text in English. 1967. q. USD 45 to institutions; USD 30 to libraries; USD 35 to students. adv. bk.rev. bibl.; charts; illus.; stat. index. reprints avail. **Document type:** *Trade.* **Description:** Journal for scholastic journalism educators and anyone interested in scholastic journalism.
Former titles (until 1997): C: JET (0198-6554); (until 1977): Communication: Journalism Education Today (0010-3535)
Indexed: CIJE.
—CCC.
Published by: Journalism Education Association, Inc., Kedzie Hall 103, Kansas State University, Manhattan, KS 66506. TEL 785-532-5532, FAX 785-532-5563, jea@spub.ksu.edu, http://www.jea.org. Ed. Bradley Wilson. Circ: 1,900.

370.1 USA ISSN 0363-7751
PN4077
➤ **COMMUNICATION MONOGRAPHS.** Text in English. 1934. q. GBP 133, USD 214 combined subscription to institutions print & online eds. (effective 2006). bibl.; illus. index, cum.index: vols.1-36 (1934-1969). reprint service avail. from PQC,PSC. **Document type:** *Monographic series, Academic/Scholarly.*
Formerly (until vol.42): Speech Monographs (0038-7169)
Related titles: Microform ed.: (from PQC); Online - full text ed.: ISSN 1479-5787. GBP 126, USD 203 to institutions (effective 2006) (from EBSCO Publishing, Gale Group, IngentaConnect, Northern Light Technology, Inc., O C L C Online Computer Library Center, Inc., Swets Information Services).
Indexed: ABIn, ASCA, AcaI, AmH&L, ArtHuCI, BAS, BiolAb, CIJE, CommAb, CurCont, ECER, EduInd, FamI, HistAb, IJCS, L&LBA, LT&LA, MEA&I, MLA, MLA-IB, PsycInfo, PsycholAb, SFSA, SOPODA, SPAA, SSA, SSCI, SociolAb, V&AA, e-psyche.
—BLDSC (3361.150000), IDS, IE, Infotrieve, ingenta. **CCC.**
Published by: (National Communication Association), Routledge (Subsidiary of: Taylor & Francis Ltd), 270 Madison Ave, New York, NY 10016. TEL 212-216-7800, FAX 212-564-1563, info@routledge-ny.com, http://www.tandf.co.uk/journals/titles/03637751.asp, http://www.routledge-ny.com. Circ: 3,400.

370 GBR ISSN 1740-4622
COMMUNICATIONS TEACHER. Text in English. q. GBP 19, USD 32 to institutions (effective 2006). **Document type:** *Journal, Academic/Scholarly.* **Description:** Dedicated to the identification, assessment and promotion of quality teaching practices in the K-12, community college, and university communication classrooms.
Media: Online - full content. **Related titles:** Online - full text ed.: (from Gale Group, IngentaConnect, O C L C Online Computer Library Center, Inc., Swets Information Services); Cumulative ed(s).: ISSN 1740-4630. GBP 20, USD 34 combined subscription to institutions print & online eds. (effective 2006).
—IE.
Published by: (National Communication Association USA), Routledge (Subsidiary of: Taylor & Francis Group), 4 Park Sq, Milton Park, Abingdon, Oxon OX14 4RN, United Kingdom. TEL 44-1235-828600, FAX 44-1235-829000, journals@routledge.com, http://www.tandf.co.uk/journals/titles/17404622.asp, http://www.routledge.com. Ed. Kent Menzel.

370 USA ISSN 0045-7736
LB2820
➤ **COMMUNITY EDUCATION JOURNAL.** Text in English. 1971-1975; resumed 19??. q. USD 25 (effective 2004). adv. bk.rev. index. **Document type:** *Journal, Academic/Scholarly.* **Description:** Provides a forum for the exchange of ideas and practices in community education, including reports of successful programs and research projects of interest to community educators.
Related titles: Microform ed.: (from PQC).
Indexed: AgeL, CIJE, EAA, MEA.
—BLDSC (3363.624150), IE, ingenta.
Published by: National Community Education Association, 3929 Old Lee Hwy, Ste 91 A, Fairfax, VA 22030-2401. TEL 703-359-8973, FAX 703-359-0972, ncea@ncea.com, http://www.ncea.com. Ed., R&P Ursula Ellis. Circ: 3,300.

371 USA ISSN 0744-4575
COMMUNITY EDUCATION TODAY. Text in English. 1966. m. (9/yr.). USD 25 (effective 2005). adv. bk.rev. back issues avail. **Document type:** *Newsletter, Consumer.* **Description:** Includes news about association events, legislative updates, practical information, and ideas for practitioners.
Published by: National Community Education Association, 3929 Old Lee Hwy, Ste 91 A, Fairfax, VA 22030-2401. TEL 703-359-8973, FAX 703-359-0972, ncea@ncea.com, http://www.ncea.com. Ed. Valerie Romney. Adv. contact Ursula Ellis. page USD 250; trim 15 x 11. Circ: 3,000.

371 USA
COMMUNITY UPDATE. Text in English. m. free (effective 2005). charts; illus. back issues avail. **Document type:** *Newsletter, Government.* **Description:** Reports on various issues in public education, with emphasis on U.S. Department of Education and other Federal initiatives. Informs educators of government books, Web sites, and other resources available.
Related titles: Online - full text ed.
Published by: U.S. Department of Education, 400 Maryland Ave, S W, Washington, DC 20202. FAX 202-205-0676, OIIA_Community_Update@ed.gov, http://bcol01.ed.gov/CFAPPS/OIIA/communityupdate/page1.cfm, http://www.ed.gov. Circ: 200,000.

370.9 GBR ISSN 0305-0068
L16
➤ **COMPARATIVE EDUCATION**; an international journal of comparative studies. Text in English. 1965. q. GBP 680, USD 1,314 combined subscription to institutions print & online eds. (effective 2006). adv. bk.rev. illus. index. back issues avail.; reprint service avail. from PSC. **Document type:** *Journal, Academic/Scholarly.*
Related titles: Microfiche ed.; Online - full text ed.: ISSN 1360-0486. GBP 646, USD 1,248 to institutions (effective 2006) (from EBSCO Publishing, Gale Group, IngentaConnect, JSTOR (Web-based Journal Archive), Northern Light Technology, Inc., O C L C Online Computer Library Center, Inc., ProQuest Information & Learning, Swets Information Services).
Indexed: ABIn, ASCA, BAS, BrEdI, CIJE, CPE, CurCont, DIP, EAA, ERA, ETA, EduInd, GEOBASE, HECAB, IBR, IBSS, IBZ, L&LBA, MEA, MEA&I, PCI, RASB, RDA, REE&TA, RHEA, RRTA, SEA, SENA, SOMA, SOPODA, SPPI, SSA, SSCI, SWA, SociolAb, TEA, WAE&RSA, WBA, WMB.
—BLDSC (3363.760000), IDS, IE, Infotrieve, ingenta. **CCC.**
Published by: Routledge (Subsidiary of: Taylor & Francis Group), 4 Park Sq, Milton Park, Abingdon, Oxon OX14 4RN, United Kingdom. TEL 44-1235-828600, FAX 44-1235-829000, info@routledge.co.uk, http://www.tandf.co.uk/journals/titles/03050068.asp, http://www.routledge.com. Ed. Michael Crossley. Circ: 1,200. **Subscr. in N. America to:** Taylor & Francis Inc., Customer Services Dept, 325 Chestnut St, 8th Fl, Philadelphia, PA 19106. TEL 215-625-8900, 800-354-1420, FAX 215-625-8914, customerservice@taylorandfrancis.com; **Subscr. to:** Taylor & Francis Ltd, Journals Customer Service, Rankine Rd, Basingstoke, Hants RG24 8PR, United Kingdom. TEL 44-1256-813000, FAX 44-1256-330245.

370.9 USA ISSN 0010-4086
L11
➤ **COMPARATIVE EDUCATION REVIEW.** Text in English. 1957. q. USD 60 combined subscription to individuals print & online eds.; USD 209 combined subscription to institutions print & online eds. (effective 2006); USD 18 per issue to individuals; USD 55 per issue to institutions (effective 2005). adv. bk.rev. bibl.; charts; illus. Index. 144 p./no.; reprint service avail. from PQC,ISI,PSC. **Document type:** *Journal, Academic/Scholarly.* **Description:** Publishes interdisciplinary research on educational policies and problems throughout the world, covering practical, theoretical, and methodological issues.
Related titles: Microform ed.: (from PQC); Online - full text ed.: ISSN 1545-701X (from bigchalk, EBSCO Publishing, Florida Center for Library Automation, Gale Group, JSTOR (Web-based Journal Archive), ProQuest Information & Learning).
Indexed: ABIn, ABS&EES, ASCA, BAS, CIJE, CPE, ChPerI, CurCont, DIP, EAA, ERA, ETA, EduInd, FamI, HECAB, IBR, IBZ, L&LBA, MEA, MEA&I, PAIS, PCI, RASB, RDA, REE&TA, RHEA, RRTA, SEA, SENA, SOMA, SOPODA, SSA, SSCI, SociolAb, TEA, WAE&RSA.
—BLDSC (3363.780000), IDS, IE, Infotrieve, ingenta, Linda Hall. **CCC.**
Published by: (Comparative and International Education Society), University of Chicago Press, Journals Division, Journals Division, PO Box 37005, Chicago, IL 60637. TEL 773-753-3347, FAX 773-753-0811, subscriptions@press.uchicago.edu, http://www.journals.uchicago.edu/CER/home.html. Eds. David Post, Mark Ginsburg. Adv. contact Cheryl Jones. page USD 430; trim 6.75 x 10. Circ: 2,200 (paid).

370.9 ESP ISSN 0588-9049
COMPARATIVE EDUCATION SOCIETY IN EUROPE. PROCEEDINGS OF THE GENERAL MEETING. Text in English, French. 1963. biennial. **Document type:** *Proceedings.*
Published by: Comparative Education Society in Europe (CESE), c/o Dr. Miguel Pereira, Secy., Universidad de Granada, Facultad de Filosofia y Letras, Campus Univ. "La Cartuja, Granada, 18071, Spain. FAX 34-58-236761, mpereyra@platon.ugr.es.

370.9 GBR ISSN 0305-7925
➤ **COMPARE**; a journal of comparative education. Text in English. 1971. q. GBP 731, USD 1,516 combined subscription to institutions print & online eds. (effective 2006). adv. bk.rev. illus. index. back issues avail.; reprint service avail. from PSC. **Document type:** *Journal, Academic/Scholarly.* **Description:** Publishes such research as it relates to educational development and change in different parts of the world.
Related titles: Microfiche ed.; Online - full text ed.: ISSN 1469-3623. GBP 694, USD 1,440 to institutions (effective 2006) (from EBSCO Publishing, Gale Group, IngentaConnect, Northern Light Technology, Inc., O C L C Online Computer Library Center, Inc., ProQuest Information & Learning, Swets Information Services).
Indexed: BAS, BrEdI, CIJE, CPE, CurCont, DIP, EAA, ERA, ETA, HECAB, IBR, IBZ, L&LBA, MEA, PCI, PSA, REE&TA, RHEA, SEA, SENA, SOMA, SOPODA, SSCI, SWA, SociolAb, TEA.
—BLDSC (3363.890000), IE, Infotrieve, ingenta. **CCC.**
Published by: (British and International Comparative Education Society), Routledge (Subsidiary of: Taylor & Francis Group), 4 Park Sq, Milton Park, Abingdon, Oxon OX14 4RN, United Kingdom. compare@man.ac.uk, info@routledge.co.uk, http://www.tandf.co.uk/journals/titles/03057925.asp, http://www.routledge.com. Eds. Anna Robinson-Pant, Karen Evans. **Subscr. in N. America to:** Taylor & Francis Inc., Customer Services Dept, 325 Chestnut St, 8th Fl, Philadelphia, PA 19106. TEL 215-625-8900, 800-354-1420, FAX 215-625-8914, customerservice@taylorandfrancis.com; **Subscr. to:** Taylor & Francis Ltd, Journals Customer Service, Rankine Rd, Basingstoke, Hants RG24 8PR, United Kingdom. TEL 44-1256-813000, FAX 44-1256-330245.

370 USA ISSN 1522-7502
COMPOSITION FORUM; a journal of pedagogical theory in rhetoric and composition. Text in English. 1998. s-a. USD 25 domestic to individuals; USD 35 domestic to institutions; USD 50 foreign (effective 2005). **Document type:** *Journal, Academic/Scholarly.*
Published by: Association of Teachers of Advanced Composition, c/o Lynn Worsham, English Department, University of South Florida, Tampa, FL 33620. http://www2.hawaii.edu/~weisser/cf/index.html, http://www.cas.usf.edu/JAC/index.html. Ed. Joe Hardin.

370 FRA ISSN 1564-1546
COMPTE A REBOURS/COUNTDOWN. Text in French. q. free.
Related titles: Online - full text ed.
Published by: UNESCO Publishing, 7 place de Fontenoy, Paris, 75352, France. http://www.unesco.org/education/educnews/ouvcr.htm.

378 CRI ISSN 0379-3974
COMUNICACION. Text in Spanish. 1978. q. back issues avail. **Description:** Includes articles on education, social sciences and other topics.
Published by: Instituto Tecnologico de Costa Rica, Apdo 159, Cartago, 7050, Costa Rica. FAX 506-551-5348, 506-551-5348, http://www.itcr.ac.cr/. Ed. Esteban Leiva.

370 BRA ISSN 0104-8481
COMUNICACOES. Text in Portuguese. 1994. s-a.
Indexed: PSA, SociolAb.
Published by: (Universidade Metodista de Piracicaba, Faculdade de Ciencias Humanas), Universidade Metodista de Piracicaba, Rodovia do Acucar, Km. 156, Piracicaba, SP 13400911, Brazil. revcomunicacoes@unimep.br, editora@unimep.br, http://www.unimep.br/fch/revcomunica/.

370 ESP ISSN 1134-3478
LB1043.2.S7
COMUNICAR; revista cientifica iberoamericana de comunicacion y educacion. Text in Spanish. 1993. s-a.
Formerly (until 1994): Comunica (1133-3219)
Related titles: Online - full text ed.
—CINDOC.
Published by: Grupo Comunicar, Colectivo Andaluz de Educacion en Medios de Comunicacion, Apdo. de Correos 527, Huelva, 21080, Spain. TEL 34-959-248330, comunica@teletine.es, http://www2.uhu.es/comunicar/colecciones_textos/edicion-electronica-01.htm, http://www.grupo-comunicar.com/.

370 ESP ISSN 0212-2650
COMUNIDAD EDUCATIVA. Text in Spanish. 1970. m.
—CINDOC.
Published by: Instituto Calasanz de Ciencias de la Educacion, C. Eraso, 3, Madrid, 28028, Spain. TEL 34-91-7257200, FAX 34-91-3611052, info@ciberaula.net, http://www.icceciberaula.net/.

370 ESP
CON CIENCIA-SOCIAL. Text in Spanish. 1997. q.
Formerly: Anuario de Didactica de la Geografia, la Historia y otras Ciencias Sociales
—CINDOC.
Published by: Diada Editora, Urbanizacion los Pinos, Biq 4-4o D, Montequinto-Sevilla, 41089, Spain. http://www.diadaeditora.com. Ed. Paloma Espejo Roig.

371.8 GBR ISSN 1359-1983
CONCEPT; the journal of contemporary community education practice theory. Text in English. 3/yr. GBP 20 domestic to individuals; GBP 25 foreign to individuals; GBP 25 domestic to institutions; GBP 32 foreign to institutions; GBP 12 to students & unwaged (effective 2003). **Document type:** *Journal.* **Description:** Contains articles on a wide range of interest to those involved in educational activities in communities; and promotes debate on issues of current interest and represents a range of perspectives from a wide variety of settings.
Indexed: BrEdI.
Published by: The National Institute of Adult Continuing Education (NAICE), Renaissance House, 20 Princess Rd. W, Leicester, Leics LE1 6TP, United Kingdom. TEL 44-116-2044200, 44-116-2044201, FAX 44-116-2854514, enquiries@niace.org.uk, http://www.niace.org.uk/Publications/Periodicals/Concept/Default.htm. Ed. Mae Shaw.

THE CONDITION OF EDUCATION; a statistical report on the condition of American education. see *EDUCATION—Abstracting, Bibliographies, Statistics*

E

371 AUS ISSN 0158-4995
CONNECT; supporting student participation. Text in English. 1979. bi-m. AUD 20 domestic to individuals; AUD 30 domestic to institutions; AUD 30 foreign to individuals; AUD 40 foreign to institutions (effective 2001). bk.rev. charts; illus. back issues avail. **Document type:** *Newsletter, Academic/Scholarly.*
Description: Contains information on documentation, sharing and support of school-based programs promoting the active participation of students in decision-making (both in curriculum and governance) through reflective case studies, reviews and development of resources etc.
—Infotrieve.
Address: 12 Brooke St, Northcote, VIC 3070, Australia. TEL 61-3-94899052, FAX 61-3-83449632, r.holdsworth@edfac.unimelb.edu.au, http://yarn.edfac.unimelb.edu.au/yrcn/home_pages/connect.html. Ed., Pub., R&P Roger Holdsworth. Circ: 500 (paid); 200 (controlled).

CONNECTICUT EDUCATION ASSOCIATION. LEGISLATIVE BULLETIN. see *LAW*

CONNECTICUT ENGLISH JOURNAL. see *LINGUISTICS*

371.192 USA
LC1046.C8
CONNECTICUT. STATE COUNCIL ON VOCATIONAL-TECHNICAL EDUCATION. VOCATIONAL EDUCATION EVALUATION REPORT✶ . Text in English. 1969. a. USD 10.
Description: Includes an evaluation of the vocational - technical education program delivery systems assisted under the Carl D. Perkins Vocational Education Act (PL 98-524), and the Job Training Partnership Act (PL 97-300) in terms of their adequacy and effectiveness in achieving their respective purposes.
Formerly: Connecticut. Advisory Council on Vocational and Career Education. Vocational Education Evaluation Report (0363-650X)
Related titles: Microfiche ed.: 1969.
Published by: Advisory Council on Vocational-Technical Education, 59 Dyer Ave., No.R, Colinsville, CT 06022-1215. TEL 203-232-1961. Ed. Richard G Rausch. Circ: 1,000.

371 USA
CONNECTION (DETROIT). Text in English. 1980. m.
Formerly: Call to Action; Which superseded: Detroit Public Schools Reporter; Detroit Schools (0011-9679)
Published by: Board of Education, 5057 Woodward, Detroit, MI 48202. TEL 313-494-1399. Ed. Arthur Carter. Circ: 22,000 (controlled).

372 AUS ISSN 1440-2076
CONNECTIONS NEWSLETTER. Text in English. 1992. q. abstr. back issues avail. **Document type:** *Newsletter.* **Description:** Outlines the latest in information services and information technology relevant to schools and school libraries.
Related titles: Online - full text ed.
Published by: Curriculum Corporation, Casselden Place, Level 5, 2 Lonsdale St, Melbourne, VIC 3000, Australia. TEL 61-3-9207-9600, FAX 61-3-9639-1616, scisinfo@curriculum.edu.au, http://www.curriculum.edu.au/scis/connect/connect.htm. Ed. Keith Gove.

371.192 USA
CONTACT (COLUMBIA). Text in English. 1921. m. (Sep.-May). USD 5. adv. bk.rev. **Document type:** *Bulletin.*
Formerly: Missouri Parent-Teacher
Published by: Missouri Congress of Parents and Teachers Associations, Tina Zubeck, President, 2100 I-70 Drive Southwest, Columbia, MO 65203. mo_pres@pta.org. Ed. Coni Hadden. Circ: 3,000.

CONTACT (SCORESBY). see *RELIGIONS AND THEOLOGY—Roman Catholic*

371.207 MLI
CONTACT: BULLETIN PEDAGOGIQUE✶ . Text in French. 1973. q. MLF 700. charts; illus.; stat. **Description:** Covers information regarding educational programs.
Published by: Ministere de l'Enseignement Superieur Secondaire et de la Recherche Scientifique, Institut Pedagogique National, BP 1583, Bamako, Mali. Ed. S Tounkara.

370 GBR ISSN 0951-2330
➤ **CONTEMPORARY ANALYSES IN EDUCATION**✶ . Text in English. 1979. 3/yr. GBP 21, USD 52. adv. bk.rev. back issues avail. **Document type:** *Academic/Scholarly.*
Formerly (until 1984): Educational Analysis (0260-0994)
Indexed: ETA, REE&TA, SWA.
—CCC.
Published by: RoutledgeFalmer Press (Subsidiary of: Taylor & Francis Group), 11 New Fetter Ln, London, EC4P 4EE, United Kingdom. TEL 44-20-7583-9855, FAX 44-20-7842-2298, info@tandf.co.uk, http://www.routledgefalmer.com. Eds. C Richards, P Taylor. Circ: 750.

370 USA ISSN 1088-498X
PN4177
➤ **CONTEMPORARY ARGUMENTATION AND DEBATE.** Text in English. a. free to members (effective 2004). **Description:** Publishes material related to the theory and practice of academic debate, public argumentation and debate, diversity issues, and other areas of interest to the academic debate community.
Related titles: Online - full text ed.: (from EBSCO Publishing).
Published by: Cross Examination Debate Association, Dr. Jeffrey Jarman, CEDA Executive Secretary, Elliott School of Communication, Wichita State University, 1845 Fairmount, Wichita, KS 67260-0031. http://cedadebate.org.

370.15 USA ISSN 0361-476X
LB1051 CODEN: CEPOCZ
➤ **CONTEMPORARY EDUCATIONAL PSYCHOLOGY.** Text in English. 1976. 4/yr. EUR 316 in Europe to individuals; JPY 33,100 in Japan to individuals; USD 263 to individuals except Europe and Japan; EUR 698 in Europe to institutions; JPY 72,900 in Japan to institutions; USD 582 to institutions except Europe and Japan; EUR 142 in Europe to students; JPY 14,800 in Japan to students; USD 124 to students except Europe and Japan (effective 2006). illus. index. back issues avail. **Document type:** *Academic/Scholarly.* **Description:** Demonstrates the application of psychological methods and research to problems in education. Covers the process of education through the life span, and presents a clear relationship of topic to data and theory.
Related titles: Online - full text ed.: ISSN 1090-2384. USD 587 (effective 2002) (from EBSCO Publishing, Gale Group, IngentaConnect, O C L C Online Computer Library Center, Inc., ScienceDirect, Swets Information Services).
Indexed: ABIn, ASCA, ArtHuCI, CDA, CIJE, CPE, ChPerI, CurCont, ERA, ETA, EduInd, FamI, IBR, MEA, MEDLINE, PsycInfo, PsycholAb, RHEA, SENA, SOMA, SSCI, TEA, e-psyche.
—BLDSC (3425.181000), IDS, IE, Infotrieve, ingenta. **CCC.**
Published by: Academic Press (Subsidiary of: Elsevier Science & Technology), 525 B St, Ste 1900, San Diego, CA 92101-4495. TEL 619-231-6616, 800-894-3434, apsubs@acad.com, http://www.elsevier.com/locate/cedpsych, http://www.academicpress.com. Ed. P. A. Alexander.

070.5 USA
▼ **CONTENT PROVIDER MEDIA NEWSLETTER.** Text in English. 2003. a. USD 7 per issue (effective 2003). **Document type:** *Newsletter, Consumer.*
Published by: Alfreda Doyal, PO Box 416, Denver, CO 80201. TEL 303-575-5676, FAX 970-292-2136, mail@contentprovidermedia.com, http://www.contentprovidermedia.com. Ed. A Doyle. R&P A. Doyle.

CONTENTS PAGES IN EDUCATION. see *EDUCATION—Abstracting, Bibliographies, Statistics*

370 ARG ISSN 1515-7458
CONTEXTO EDUCATIVO; revista digital de educacion y nuevas technologias. Text in Spanish. 1998. m. back issues avail.
Media: Online - full text.
Published by: Nal Educativa, S.A., Uruguay 112, 6o., Buenos Aires, 1016, Argentina. TEL 54-114-5810121, editor@contexto-educativo.com.ar, http://contexto-educativo.com.ar/.

370.1 370.72 ESP ISSN 1575-023X
CONTEXTOS EDUCATIVOS; revista de educacion. Text in Spanish. 1998. a., latest vol.4, 2001. EUR 15.02 domestic; EUR 18.03 foreign (effective 2004). **Description:** Presents information on education in all its dimensions and perspectives. Includes investigations and related experiences at all levels and areas of learning.
Related titles: Online - full text ed.: ISSN 1695-5714.
Published by: Universidad de la Rioja, Servicio de Publicaciones, C/ Piscinas s/n, Logrono, La Rioja 26004, Spain. TEL 34-941-299187, FAX 34-941-299193, publicaciones@adm.unirioja.es, http://publicaciones.unirioja.es/revistas/contextos.html, http://www.publicaciones.unirioja.es.

371 NLD ISSN 1384-1181
➤ **CONTEXTS OF LEARNING**; classrooms, schools and society. Text in English. 1996. irreg., latest vol.12, 2003. price varies. **Document type:** *Monographic series, Academic/Scholarly.*
Description: Examines issues in teaching and learning from various perspectives.
Published by: Taylor & Francis The Netherlands (Subsidiary of: Taylor & Francis Group), Schipolweg 107 C, PO Box 447, Leiden, 2316 XC, Netherlands. TEL 31-715-243080, FAX 31-715-234571, pub@swets.nl, http://www.tandf.co.uk/swets.asp.

370 USA ISSN 0196-707X
CONTRIBUTIONS TO THE STUDY OF EDUCATION. Text in English. 1981. irreg., latest vol.82, 2002. price varies. **Document type:** *Monographic series, Academic/Scholarly.*
—BLDSC (3461.454000), IE, ingenta.
Published by: Greenwood Publishing Group Inc. (Subsidiary of: Harcourt International), 88 Post Rd W, PO Box 5007, Westport, CT 06881. TEL 203-226-3571, FAX 203-226-1502, webmaster@greenwood.com, http://www.greenwood.com.

370.9 USA ISSN 0010-843X
COOPERATIVE EDUCATION ASSOCIATION NEWSLETTER. Text in English. 1969. 4/yr. USD 25 (effective 1998). **Document type:** *Newsletter.*
Published by: Cooperative Education and Internship Association, Inc., 4190 Highland Dr., Ste. 211, Salt Lake Cty, UT 84124-2675. TEL 410-290-3666, FAX 410-290-7084. Ed. Dawn E Pettit. Circ: 3,000.

370 ITA ISSN 0010-8502
COOPERAZIONE EDUCATIVA. Text in Italian. 1952. q.
Indexed: RASB.
Published by: La Nuova Italia Editrice S.p.A, Via Ernesto Codignola 1, Florence, 50018, Italy. nib.reviews@lanuovaitalia.it, http://www.lanuovaitalia.it. Ed. Giorgio Testa.

370 ZMB
COPPERBELT EDUCATION. Text in English. irreg. (1-2/yr.). illus.
Address: PO Box 1552, Ndola, Zambia.

COUNCIL FOR RESEARCH IN MUSIC EDUCATION. BULLETIN. see *MUSIC*

COUNCIL OF ONTARIO UNIVERSITIES. APPLICATION STATISTICS. see *EDUCATION—Abstracting, Bibliographies, Statistics*

305 USA ISSN 1056-0335
COUNCILOR. Text in English. 19??. a. **Document type:** *Journal, Academic/Scholarly.*
Indexed: CIJE.
Published by: Illinois Council for the Social Studies, c/o Dr. Frederick D Drake, Department of History, Illinois State University, Normal, IL 61790-4420. TEL 309-438-7212, http://coe.ilstu.edu/icss/.

371.4 150.4 USA ISSN 0193-7375
BF637.C6
COUNSELING AND HUMAN DEVELOPMENT. Text in English. 1968. 9/yr. USD 36 to individuals; USD 48 to institutions (effective 2005). bk.rev. index. 16 p./no.; back issues avail.; reprint service avail. from PQC. **Document type:** *Journal, Academic/Scholarly.*
Formerly (until Sep. 1977): Focus on Guidance (0015-5136)
Related titles: Microform ed.: (from PQC); Online - full text ed.: (from bigchalk, Florida Center for Library Automation, Gale Group, O C L C Online Computer Library Center, Inc., ProQuest Information & Learning).
Published by: Love Publishing Co., PO Box 22353, Denver, CO 80222. TEL 303-221-7333, FAX 303-221-7444, http://www.lovepublishing.com. Ed. S F Love. Circ: 1,500.

371.4 USA ISSN 0011-0035
LB1731.75 CODEN: CESUDZ
➤ **COUNSELOR EDUCATION AND SUPERVISION.** Text in English. 1961. q. USD 50 domestic to individuals; USD 75 domestic to institutions; USD 13 per issue; free to members (effective 2005). adv. bk.rev. illus.; abstr.; bibl. index. 80 p./no.; back issues avail.; reprint service avail. from PQC,PSC. **Document type:** *Journal, Academic/Scholarly.* **Description:** Covers theory, practice and research on counselor education and supervision.
Related titles: Microform ed.: (from PQC); Online - full text ed.: ISSN 1556-6978 (from EBSCO Publishing, Florida Center for Library Automation, Gale Group, H.W. Wilson, O C L C Online Computer Library Center, Inc., ProQuest Information & Learning).
Indexed: ABIn, AD&D, AgeL, CIJE, CPE, CurCont, ERA, ETA, EduInd, FamI, MEA, PsycInfo, PsycholAb, RHEA, SEA, SENA, SOMA, SSCI, SWA, TEA, e-psyche.
—BLDSC (3481.350000), IE, Infotrieve, ingenta. **CCC.**
Published by: (Association for Counselor Education and Supervision), American Counseling Association, 5999 Stevenson Ave, Alexandria, VA 22304-3300. TEL 800-347-6647, FAX 800-473-2329, http://www.counseling.org. Ed. William Kline. R&P Cynthia Peay TEL 703-823-9800 ext 249. Adv. contact Kathy Maguire TEL 703-823-9800 ext 207. Circ: 3,500.

371.4 USA ISSN 0271-5368
L901
➤ **COUNSELOR PREPARATION (YEARS)**; programs, faculty, trends. Text in English. 1971. triennial, latest 2003. USD 90.95 per vol. (effective 2005). adv. stat. back issues avail. **Document type:** *Directory, Academic/Scholarly.* **Description:** Lists all counselor-education programs in the United States. Program areas include: counseling psychology, counseling, pastoral counseling, marriage and family therapy, and counselor education.
Formerly: Counselor Education Directory: Personnel and Programs (0190-2199)
—Infotrieve.
Published by: (National Board for Certified Counselors, Inc.), Routledge (Subsidiary of: Taylor & Francis Ltd), 270 Madison Ave, New York, NY 10016. TEL 212-216-7800, FAX 212-564-1563, info@routledge-ny.com, http://www.routledge-ny.com/books.cfm?isbn=0415935539&CFID=68417&CFTOUEN=1515576. Eds. Donna Henderson, Thomas W Clawson, Wendi Schweiger. Circ: 800 (paid).

E

370.72 USA ISSN 1058-1634
COUNTERPOINTS (NEW YORK); studies in the postmodern theory of education. Text in English. 1993. irreg., latest vol.283, 2005. price varies. back issues avail. **Document type:** *Monographic series, Academic/Scholarly.* **Description:** Focuses on issues and concepts in the postmodern theory of education.
Published by: Peter Lang Publishing, Inc., 275 Seventh Ave, 28th Fl, New York, NY 10001. TEL 212-647-7700, 212-647-7706, 800-770-5264, FAX 212-647-7707, customerservice@plang.com, http://www.peterlang.com. Eds. Joe L Kincheloe, Shirley Steinberg. Pub. Christopher Myers. R&P Stephanie Archer. Adv. contact Patricia Mulrane.

COUP DE FOUDRE. see *LINGUISTICS*

COVERING THE EDUCATION BEAT; a current guide for editors & writers. see *JOURNALISM*

370.154 USA ISSN 1053-170X
CODEN: CTTEEU
CREATIVE TRAINING TECHNIQUES; a newsletter of tips, tactics and how-tos for delivering effective training. Text in English. 1988. m. USD 99 domestic; USD 109 in Canada; USD 119 elsewhere (effective 2005). **Document type:** *Newsletter, Trade.* **Description:** Provides tips, tactics and techniques that enliven training and improve end results.
Related titles: Online - full text ed.
—CASDDS, IE. **CCC.**
Published by: V N U Business Publications (Subsidiary of: V N U Business Media), 50 S Ninth St, Minneapolis, MN 55402. TEL 612-333-0471, 800-328-4329, FAX 612-333-6526, bmcomm@vnuinc.com, http://www.vnubusinessmedia.com/. **Subscr. to:** 2980 Commers Dr, Ste 400, Egan, MN 55121. TEL 800-707-7792, FAX 651-686-4883.

370.15 USA ISSN 0093-5263
CREATIVITY IN ACTION. Text in English. 1972. bi-m. USD 50 domestic; USD 55 in Canada & Mexico; USD 60 elsewhere (effective 2000). bk.rev. illus. back issues avail. **Document type:** *Newsletter.* **Description:** Helps readers learn more about and practice more of many important ideas and techniques that enhance creative thinking and action.
Related titles: Online - full text ed.
Indexed: e-psyche.
Published by: Creative Education Foundation, Inc., 289 Bay Rd., Hadley, MA 01035-9780. TEL 716-675-3181, FAX 716-675-3209, cefhq@cef-cpsi.org, http://www.cef-cpsi.org. R&P Grace Guzzutta. Circ: 500.

370 USA ISSN 0011-1171
CRESCENDO (INTERLOCHEN). Text in English. 1964. 2/yr. free. illus. **Document type:** *Newspaper.* **Description:** Guide to art camp and academy programs, news, photos, student and staff profiles, and alumni news.
Published by: Interlochen Center for the Arts, PO Box 199, Interlochen, MI 49643. TEL 231-276-7200, FAX 231-276-6321, http://www.interlochen.org. Ed. Paul Heaton. R&P Bill Morgan TEL 231-276-7601. Circ: 70,000 (controlled).

370 AUS ISSN 1033-808X
LC189.8
CRITICAL PEDAGOGY NETWORKER. Text in English. 1988. q. AUD 20. **Document type:** *Academic/Scholarly.* **Description:** Aims to reintroduce into the schooling debate, issues that highlight the inherently political, historical and theoretical nature of what transpires in schools.
Indexed: AEI.
—CCC.
Published by: Flinders University of South Australia, School of Education, PO Box 2100, Adelaide, SA 5001, Australia. TEL 61-8-82012277, John.Smyth@flinders.edu.au, http://wwwed.stort.flinders.edu.au/edweb/FIST/fist.html. Ed., R&P John Smyth. Circ: 500.

370.1 USA ISSN 1064-8615
CRITICAL STUDIES IN EDUCATION AND CULTURE. Text in English. 1983. irreg. price varies. bibl.; charts; illus. back issues avail. **Document type:** *Magazine, Academic/Scholarly.* **Description:** Examines the interactions between pedagogy and education.
Published by: Bergin & Garvey (Subsidiary of: Greenwood Publishing Group Inc.), 88 Post Rd W, Box 5007, Westport, CT 06881-5007. TEL 203-226-3571, FAX 203-222-1502, http://www.greenwood.com.

370 CHL ISSN 0716-0496
CUADERNOS DE EDUCACION. Text in Spanish. 1973. m. CLP 250, USD 17.50. adv. bk.rev. bibl.; charts; illus. index. **Document type:** *Academic/Scholarly.*
Indexed: IBR.
Published by: Centro de Investigacion y Desarrollo para la Accion Educativa, Casilla 13608, Santiago, 1, Chile. TEL 6987153, cide@reuna.cl. Ed. Francisco Alvarez Martin. Circ: 1,000.

370 ESP ISSN 1131-8074
CUADERNOS DE GRADO MEDIO. Text in Spanish. 1981. a.
Formerly (until 1986): Grado Medio (1131-8082)
—CINDOC.
Published by: Institucion Cultural El Brocense, Complejo Cultural San Francisco, Ronda de San Francisco, s-n, Caceres, Extremadura 10005, Spain. http://www.brocense.com/.

370 ESP ISSN 0210-0630
CUADERNOS DE PEDAGOGIA; revista mensual de educacion. Text in Spanish. 1975. m. (11/yr.). EUR 75 print & online eds. (effective 2002). bibl.; illus.; stat.
Related titles: ♦ CD-ROM ed.: Cuadernos de Pedagogia (CD-ROM Edition). ISSN 1137-4241; Online - full text ed.; ♦ Supplement(s): Biblioteca Basica del Profesorado.
Indexed: PCI, RILM.
—CINDOC, IE, Infotrieve. **CCC.**
Published by: Praxis, Principe de Asturias, 61 7a Planta, Barcelona, Cataluna 08012, Spain. TEL 34-93-3444700, FAX 34-93-3444701, educacion@praxis.es, http://www.praxis.es/. Circ: 20,000.

370 ESP ISSN 1137-4241
CUADERNOS DE PEDAGOGIA (CD-ROM EDITION). Text in Spanish. 1995. biennial.
Media: CD-ROM. **Related titles:** Online - full text ed.; ♦ Print ed.: Cuadernos de Pedagogia. ISSN 0210-0630.
Published by: Praxis, Principe de Asturias, 61 7a Planta, Barcelona, Cataluna 08012, Spain. TEL 34-93-3444700, FAX 34-93-3444701, educacion@praxis.es, http://www.praxis.es/.

370 ESP ISSN 1135-6405
LB1139.L3
➤ **CULTURA Y EDUCACION**; revista de teoria, investigacion y practica. Text in Spanish. 1989. q. EUR 80 per issue to individuals; EUR 325 per issue to institutions (effective 2004). adv. **Document type:** *Journal, Academic/Scholarly.* **Description:** Covers topics on all language and representational systems and their educational treatment.
Formerly (until 1996): Comunicacion, Lenguaje y Educacion (0214-7033)
Related titles: Online - full text ed.: ISSN 1578-4118. 2001 (from EBSCO Publishing, Gale Group, IngentaConnect, Swets Information Services).
Indexed: RILM, e-psyche.
—CINDOC, IE, Infotrieve. **CCC.**
Published by: Fundacion Infancia y Aprendizaje, Naranjo de Bulnes 69, Ciudalcampo, San Sebastian de los Reyes, Madrid, 28707, Spain. cultured@usal.es, fundacion@fia.es, http://www.fia.es/. Ed. Amelia Alvarez. Circ: 2,000.

➤ **CULTURAL CRITIQUE (NEW YORK).** see *SOCIAL SCIENCES: COMPREHENSIVE WORKS*

➤ **CURRENT**; the journal of marine education. see *EARTH SCIENCES—Oceanography*

370 USA ISSN 0011-3131
AP2
➤ **CURRENT (WASHINGTON, 1960).** Text in English. 1960. m. (except Mar.-Apr., Jul.-Aug. combined). USD 45 domestic to individuals; USD 63 foreign to individuals; USD 102 domestic to institutions; USD 120 foreign to institutions; USD 10.20 per issue (effective academic year 2005 - 2006). adv. abstr.; bibl.; charts; illus. index. back issues avail.; reprint service avail. from PSC. **Document type:** *Journal, Academic/Scholarly.* **Description:** This journal presents significant ideas on a wide range of topics, including education, ploitics, and other social issues.
Related titles: CD-ROM ed.: (from ProQuest Information & Learning); Microform ed.; Online - full text ed.: (from O C L C Online Computer Library Center, Inc.).
Indexed: ABS&EES, AmH&L, ArtHuCI, CPE, CurCont, DIP, GSS&RPL, HRA, IBR, IBZ, LRI, MEA&I, MagInd, RGAb, RGPR, SENA, SSCI.
—IDS, Infotrieve.
Published by: (Helen Dwight Reid Educational Foundation), Heldref Publications, 1319 18th St, NW, Washington, DC 20036-1802. TEL 202-296-6267, 800-365-9753, FAX 202-293-6130, cur@heldref.org, subscribe@heldref.org, http://www.heldref.org/current.php. Adv. contact Chante Douglas. page USD 515; trim 7 x 10. Circ: 1,041 (paid).

➤ **CURRENT (WASHINGTON, 1980)**; The Public Telecommunications Newspaper. see *COMMUNICATIONS—Television And Cable*

➤ **CURRENT EVENTS.** see *CHILDREN AND YOUTH—For*

➤ **CURRENT INDEX TO JOURNALS IN EDUCATION.** see *EDUCATION—Abstracting, Bibliographies, Statistics*

➤ **CURRENT INDEX TO JOURNALS IN EDUCATION SEMIANNUAL CUMULATION.** see *EDUCATION—Abstracting, Bibliographies, Statistics*

370.9 USA ISSN 1523-1615
CURRENT ISSUES IN COMPARATIVE EDUCATION (CISE). Text in English. 1998. s-a. free (effective 2005). back issues avail. **Document type:** *Journal, Academic/Scholarly.* **Description:** Publishes single-topic issues on comparative education.
Media: Online - full text.
Published by: Columbia University, Teachers College, 525 W 120th St, New York, NY 10027. TEL 212-678-3774, FAX 212-678-3790, http://www.tc.columbia.edu/cice/index.htm.

370 USA ISSN 1099-839X
L11
➤ **CURRENT ISSUES IN EDUCATION.** Abbreviated title: C I E. Text in English. 1998. irreg. free (effective 2005). **Document type:** *Journal, Academic/Scholarly.* **Description:** Publishes articles that contribute to influencing and expanding the body of knowledge in education, as well as articles that enhance dialogue among graduate students, researchers, educators in the classroom, and policy makers.
Media: Online - full text.
Indexed: EduInd.
Published by: Arizona State University, College of Education, PO Box 870211, Tempe, AZ 85287-0211. cie@cie.ed.asu.edu, http://cie.ed.asu.edu/. Ed. Leslie Poynor.

373 USA ISSN 1059-7107
LB1623.5
➤ **CURRENT ISSUES IN MIDDLE LEVEL EDUCATION.** Text in English. 1992. 2/yr. USD 15 to individuals; USD 30 to institutions. bk.rev. **Document type:** *Academic/Scholarly.* **Description:** Focuses on discussion of issues in middle level education, philosophy, curriculum and instruction, and research.
Published by: State University of West Georgia, College of Education, 1600 Maple St, Carrollton, GA 30118. TEL 770-836-6560, FAX 770-836-4643, jmyers@westga.edu. Ed., R&P John W Myers. Circ: 300.

370 USA
CURRENT POPULATION REPORTS: POPULATION CHARACTERISTICS. EDUCATIONAL ATTAINMENT IN THE UNITED STATES. Text in English. a. **Document type:** *Government.*
Related titles: Online - full content ed.
Published by: U.S. Bureau of the Census (Subsidiary of: U.S. Department of Commerce), Customer Services, Washington, DC 20233. TEL 310-457-4100, http://www.census.gov.

CURRENT SCIENCE. see *CHILDREN AND YOUTH—For*

373 AUS
CURRICULUM COUNCIL - SYLLABUS MANUAL YEAR 11 AND YEAR 12 SUBJECTS; subject accreditation and review - assessment, grading and moderation. Text in English. 1991. a. AUD 80 (effective 1999). **Document type:** *Government.* **Description:** Provides support documentation for developing a school assessment policy, including topics such as assessment and grading requirements, and principles of assessment which support inclusivity and the assessment of out-of-school learning.
Former titles: Curriculum Council - Syllabus Manual Year 11 and Year 12 Accredited Subjects (1440-1452); (until 1997): Secondary Education Authority - Year 11 and Year 12 Accredited Courses (1323-2541)
Published by: Curriculum Council, 27 Walters Dr, Osborne Park, W.A. 6017, Australia. TEL 61-8-927-36300, FAX 61-8-9273-6371, info@curriculum.wa.edu.au, http://www.curriculum.wa.edu.au. Ed. Graeme Quelch. R&P Danny McEvoy TEL 6189-273-6337.

CYPRUS. DEPARTMENT OF STATISTICS AND RESEARCH. EDUCATION STATISTICS. see *EDUCATION—Abstracting, Bibliographies, Statistics*

370 CYP ISSN 0045-9429
DS54.A2
CYPRUS TO-DAY. Text in English. 1963. q. free. adv. bk.rev. illus. **Document type:** *Government.*
Indexed: RASB.
—BLDSC (3506.735000).
Published by: Press and Information Office, Editorial Office, Nicosia, Cyprus. TEL 357-2-446981, FAX 357-2-453730. Ed. Stelios Hadjistylis TEL 357-2-801104. Circ: 15,000.

D G U NACHRICHTEN. see *ENVIRONMENTAL STUDIES*

DAN CHUA MAGAZINE. see *RELIGIONS AND THEOLOGY*

DANCE TEACHER; the magazine for dance professionals. see *DANCE*

370 DNK ISSN 0904-2393
DANSK PAEDAGOGISK TIDSSKRIFT/DANISH JOURNAL OF EDUCATION. Text in Danish. 1879. 4/yr. DKK 350 to individual members; DKK 400 (effective 2005). adv. bk.rev. illus. index. back issues avail. **Document type:** *Journal, Academic/Scholarly.*
Former titles (until 1986): D P T (0904-2385); (until 1973): Dansk Paedagogisk Tidsskrift (0011-6408); Formed by the merger of (1879-1953): Vor Ungdom (0902-3178); (1940-1953): Paedagogisk-Psykologisk Tidsskrift (0909-6701)
Indexed: RASB.
Published by: (Paedagogisk Forum), Christian Ejlers Forlag, Soelvgade 38, Copenhagen K, 1307, Denmark. TEL 45-33-122114, FAX 45-33-122884, redaktion@dpt.dk, http://www.dpt.dk, http://www.ejlers.dk. Eds. Trine Oeland, Tomas Ellegaard. Adv. contact Axel Neubert. B&W page DKK 3,400. Circ: 2,000.

E

DANYAG; journal of studies in the humanities, education and the sciences, basic and applied. see *HUMANITIES: COMPREHENSIVE WORKS*

370.0210946 ESP ISSN 0070-2897
DATOS Y CIFRAS DE LA ENSENANZA EN ESPANA. Text in Spanish. 1978. a. free.
Published by: Ministerio de Educacion, Cultura y Deporte, Centro de Publicaciones, c/o Ciudad Universitaria, S/N, Madrid, 28040, Spain. FAX 34-91-4539884.

370 USA ISSN 1540-4595
HF1101
▼ ➤ **DECISION SCIENCES JOURNAL OF INNOVATIVE EDUCATION.** Text in English. 2003 (Spr.). s-a. USD 255 combined subscription in the Americas to institutions print & online; GBP 191 combined subscription elsewhere to institutions print & online (effective 2004); included with subscr. to Decision Sciences. back issues avail. **Document type:** *Journal, Academic/Scholarly.* **Description:** Publishes significant research relevant to teaching and learning issues in the decision sciences.
Related titles: Online - full text ed.: ISSN 1540-4609. 2003. USD 242 in the Americas to institutions; GBP 181 elsewhere to institutions (effective 2004) (from Blackwell Synergy, EBSCO Publishing, IngentaConnect, O C L C Online Computer Library Center, Inc., Swets Information Services).
—BLDSC (3537.150500), IE. **CCC.**
Published by: (Decision Sciences Institute), Blackwell Publishing, Inc. (Subsidiary of: Blackwell Publishing Ltd.), Commerce Place, 350 Main St, Malden, MA 02148. TEL 781-388-8206, FAX 781-388-8232, subscrip@blackwellpub.com, http://www.blackwellpublishing.com/journal.asp?ref=1540-4595&site=1. Ed. Barbara B Flynn.

370.2509751 USA ISSN 0091-6188
LB2803.D3
DELAWARE. DEPARTMENT OF PUBLIC INSTRUCTION. EDUCATIONAL PERSONNEL DIRECTORY. Text in English. 1921. a. USD 7.50. **Document type:** *Directory, Government.*
Published by: (Delaware. Division of Planning, Research & Evaluation), Department of Public Instruction, Townsend Bldg, Dover, DE 19903. Ed. Wilmer E Wise. Circ: 3,500.

DELAWARE SCHOOL LAWS. see *LAW*

370.72 NZL ISSN 0110-4748
➤ **DELTA RESEARCH MONOGRAPH.** Text in English. 1967. s-a. NZD 25. bk.rev. back issues avail. **Document type:** *Academic/Scholarly.*
Formerly (until 1977): Delta (Palmerston North) (0419-9855)
Indexed: CPE, ERA, MEA, SEA.
—BLDSC (3548.290000). **CCC.**
Published by: Massey University, College of Education, Private bag 11-222, Palmerston North, New Zealand. TEL 64-6-3509261, FAX 64-6-35505635. Ed., R&P John A Codd. Circ: 500.

370 DNK ISSN 0905-7501
DENMARK. STATENS PAEDAGOGISKE FORSOEGSCENTER. PROJEKTBESKRIVELSER. Text in Danish. 1979. a. free. illus. back issues avail. **Document type:** *Academic/Scholarly.*
Formerly (until 1988): Denmark. Statens Paedagogiske Forsoegscenter. Arbejdsbeskrivelse (0107-4652)
Published by: Statens Paedagogiske Forsoegscenter, Skolen paa Forsoegscentret, Islevgaard Alle 5, Roedovre, 2610, Denmark. TEL 45-44-570630, FAX 45-44-570666, spf@school.dk, http://www.inet-spf.dk.

373 DNK ISSN 1600-0366
DENMARK. UNDERVISNINGSMINISTERIET. UDDANNELSESSTYRELSEN. BERETNING OM GYMNASIET OG H F. Text in Danish. 1990. a. back issues avail. **Document type:** *Monographic series, Government.*
Formerly (until 1999): Denmark. Undervisningsministeriet. Gymnasieafdelingen. Beretning (0906-9240)
Related titles: Online - full text ed.: ISSN 1600-0374; ♦ Series of: Denmark Undervisningsministeriet. Uddannelsesstyrelsen. Temahaefteserie. ISSN 1399-2279.
Published by: Undervisningsministeriet, Uddannelsesstyrelsen, Frederiksholms Kanal 21, Copenhagen K, 1220, Denmark. TEL 45-33-925300, FAX 45-33-925608, http://www.uvm.dk.

370 DNK ISSN 1399-2260
DENMARK. UNDERVISNINGSMINISTERIET. UDDANNELSESSTYRELSEN. HAANDBOGSSERIE. Text in Danish. 1995. irreg. price varies. back issues avail. **Document type:** *Monographic series, Government.*
Former titles (until 1999): Denmark. Undervisningsministeriet. Uddannelsesstyrelsen. Haandbogshaefte (1399-0780); (until 1998): Denmark. Undervisningsministeriet. Erhvervsskoleafdelingen. Haandbogshaefte (1395-7600)
Related titles: Online - full text ed.: ISSN 1399-7394; ♦ Series: Proever, Evaluering, Undervisning. ISSN 1603-6735.
Published by: Undervisningsministeriet, Uddannelsesstyrelsen, Frederiksholms Kanal 21, Copenhagen K, 1220, Denmark. TEL 45-33-925300, FAX 45-33-925608, http://www.uvm.dk.

370 DNK ISSN 1399-2279
DENMARK UNDERVISNINGSMINISTERIET. UDDANNELSESSTYRELSEN. TEMAHAEFTESERIE. Text in Danish. 1999. irreg. back issues avail. **Document type:** *Monographic series, Government.*
Related titles: Online - full text ed.: ISSN 1399-7386; ♦ Series: Denmark. Undervisningsministeriet. Uddannelsesstyrelsen. Beretning om Gymnasiet og H F. ISSN 1600-0366.
Published by: Undervisningsministeriet, Uddannelsesstyrelsen, Frederiksholms Kanal 21, Copenhagen K, 1220, Denmark. TEL 45-33-925300, FAX 45-33-925608, http://www.uvm.dk.

649.124 USA ISSN 1531-491X
DESARROLLANDO LA LECTURA (PREPARACIDON PARA LA LECTURA). Text in Spanish. m. (Sep.-May). USD 195 (effective 2003). **Document type:** *Newsletter, Academic/Scholarly.*
Related titles: Online - full text ed.: ISSN 1533-3310; ♦ English ed.: Building Readers (Reading Readiness Edition). ISSN 1531-4898.
Published by: Parent Institute, PO Box 7474, Fairfax, VA 22039-7474. TEL 703-323-9170, 800-756-5525, FAX 703-323-9173, webmaster@parent-institute.com, http://www.parent-institute.com. Ed. Betsie Millar. Pub. John H Wherry.

DESKBOOK ENCYCLOPEDIA OF AMERICAN SCHOOL LAW. see *LAW*

371 USA ISSN 0011-9695
DETROIT TEACHER. Text in English. 1975 (vol.37). s-m. USD 4 to non-members. adv. bk.rev. charts; illus. **Document type:** *Newspaper.*
Published by: Detroit Federation of Teachers, A F L - C I O, Local 231, 2875 W. Grand Blvd., Detroit, MI 48202-2623. TEL 313-875-3500, FAX 313-875-3512. Ed., R&P Susan Watson. Circ: 16,500.

370 DEU ISSN 0012-0731
DIE DEUTSCHE SCHULE; Zeitschrift fuer Erziehungswissenschaft, Bildungspolitik und paedagogische Praxis. Text in German. 1908. q. EUR 53; EUR 43 to students; EUR 16.50 newsstand/cover (effective 2005). adv. bk.rev. index. 128 p./no.; reprints avail. **Document type:** *Magazine, Trade.*
Indexed: DIP, IBR, IBZ, RASB.
—IE, Infotrieve. **CCC.**
Published by: (Gewerkschaft Erziehung und Wissenschaft), Juventa Verlag GmbH, Ehretstr 3, Weinheim, 69469, Germany. TEL 49-6201-90200, FAX 49-6201-902013, juventa@juventa.de, http://www.juventa.de. Adv. contact Annette Hopp. page EUR 250; trim 113 x 193. Circ: 1,000 (paid and controlled).

370 DEU ISSN 0012-1460
PT61
DEUTSCHUNTERRICHT. Text in German. 1948. 6/yr. EUR 39; EUR 9.50 newsstand/cover (effective 2005). adv. bk.rev. abstr. index. **Document type:** *Journal, Academic/Scholarly.*
Indexed: BibLing, DIP, IBR, IBZ.
—IE, Infotrieve.
Published by: Westermann Schulbuchverlag GmbH, Georg-Westermann-Allee 66, Braunschweig, 38104, Germany. TEL 49-531-7080, FAX 49-531-708209, schulservice@westermann.de, http://www.deutschunterricht-westermann.de, http://www.westermann.de. Ed. Burkhard Wetekam. Adv. contact Petra Klein. B&W page EUR 500, color page EUR 800. Circ: 1,900 (paid and controlled).
Subscr. to: CVK Cornelsen Verlagskontor, Postfach 100271, Bielefeld 33502, Germany. TEL 49-521-9719-0.

DER DEUTSCHUNTERRICHT (SEELZE); Beitraege zu seiner Praxis und wissenschaftlichen Grundlegung. see *LINGUISTICS*

DEUTSCHUNTERRICHT IM SUEDLICHEN AFRIKA. see *LINGUISTICS*

DEVELOPMENT EDUCATION. see *ENVIRONMENTAL STUDIES*

370.1 GBR ISSN 1354-0742
THE DEVELOPMENT EDUCATION JOURNAL. Text in English. 1990. 3/yr. GBP 25 in United Kingdom to individuals; GBP 30 elsewhere to individuals; GBP 30 in United Kingdom to institutions; GBP 35 elsewhere to institutions (effective 2002); Subscr. includes free online access.. back issues avail. **Document type:** *Journal, Academic/Scholarly.* **Description:** Forum for debate on development education with reports on current practice, theory and research in Britain and overseas.
Indexed: BrEdI, CPE, ETA, MEA, RHEA, SEA, SENA, SOMA, TEA.
—BLDSC (3579.027200), IE, ingenta.
Published by: (Development Education Association), Trentham Books Ltd., Westview House, 734 London Rd, Stoke-on-Trent, Staffs ST4 5NP, United Kingdom. TEL 44-1782-745567, FAX 44-1782-745553, tb@trentham-books.co.uk, http://www.trentham-books.co.uk. Ed. Christine Parsons.

370.95491 PAK ISSN 0080-1321
DEVELOPMENT OF EDUCATION IN PAKISTAN. Variant title: Report on the Progress of Education in Pakistan. Text in English. 1965. a.
Published by: Ministry of Education, Documentation Section, Curriculum Wing, Sector H-9, P.O. Shaigan, Industrial Area, Islamabad, Pakistan.

DEVELOPMENTS IN SCHOOL LAW. see *LAW*

370.1 DEU ISSN 1615-7516
DIALOG (ESSEN). Text in German. 1999. 3/yr. adv. **Document type:** *Magazine, Trade.*
Published by: (Gewerkschaft Erziehung und Wissenschaft), Stamm Verlag GmbH, Goldammerweg 16, Essen, 45134, Germany. TEL 49-201-843000, FAX 49-201-472590, info@stamm.de, http://www.stamm.de. adv.: B&W page EUR 828, color page EUR 1,116. Circ: 23,000 (controlled).

370 LTU ISSN 1392-1916
DIALOGAS. Text in Lithuanian. 1953. w. LTL 84, USD 21; USD 70 foreign. adv. **Document type:** *Newspaper.*
Former titles (until 1992): Tevynes Sviesa; (until 1989): Tarybinis Mokytojas
Published by: (Lithuania. Lithuanian Ministry of Education and Science), Polilogas, Antakalnio 31, Vilnius, 2000, Lithuania. TEL 370-2-341571, FAX 370-2-748943, dialogas@dialvno.soros.lt, root@dlg1.vno.osf.lt. Ed. Elena Tervidyte. Pub., R&P, Adv. contact Nijole Buciniene. Circ: 6,000.

370 NLD ISSN 1386-7245
DIDAKTIEF EN SCHOOL; opinieblad voor de onderwijspraktijk. Text in Dutch. 1997. 10/yr. (9/yr.). EUR 40 domestic; EUR 60 foreign; EUR 32.50 to students (effective 2002). adv. illus. **Document type:** *Journal, Trade.* **Description:** Covers developments concerning education for persons connected with elementary and higher education.
Formed by the merger of (1973-1997): School (0377-5054); (1981-1997): Didaktief (0169-4820); Which was formerly (1971-1981): O-Vier (0166-8978)
—IE, KNAW.
Published by: Uitgeverij School, Postbus 41, Meppel, 7940 AA, Netherlands. TEL 31-522-855333, FAX 31-522-855300, uitg@gmgroep.nl. Ed. C Schoor. Circ: 10,000.

370.1 DEU ISSN 1616-5586
DIDAKTIK IN FORSCHUNG UND PRAXIS. Text in German. 2000. irreg., latest vol.22, 2005. price varies. **Document type:** *Monographic series, Academic/Scholarly.*
Published by: Verlag Dr. Kovac, Arnoldstr 49, Hamburg, 22763, Germany. TEL 49-40-3988800, FAX 49-40-39888055, info@verlagdrkovac.de, http://www.verlagdrkovac.de/7-11.htm.

DIDASKALIA; recherches sur la communication et l'apprentissage des sciences et des techniques. see *SCIENCES: COMPREHENSIVE WORKS*

DIMENSIO. see *MATHEMATICS*

DIRASAT. EDUCATIONAL SCIENCES. see *EDUCATION—Abstracting, Bibliographies, Statistics*

370 FJI ISSN 1011-5846
➤ **DIRECTIONS**; journal of educational studies. Text in English. 1979. 2/yr. FJD 10 domestic; FJD 20 foreign (effective 2001). bk.rev. 100 p./no.; back issues avail. **Document type:** *Journal, Academic/Scholarly.* **Description:** Essays, research findings, and critical comments on education and education-related matters.
Indexed: CPE, ERA, ETA, MEA, SEA, TEA.
Published by: University of South Pacific, Institute of Education, Suva, Fiji. TEL 679-313900, FAX 679-302409, TELEX 2276 USPFJ, benson_c@usp.ac.fj. Ed. Cliff Benson. Circ: 500.

➤ **DIRECTORY OF DAY SCHOOLS IN THE UNITED STATES AND CANADA.** see *RELIGIONS AND THEOLOGY—Judaic*

370.113 SEN
DIRECTORY OF DEVELOPMENT AND TRAINING INSTITUTES IN AFRICA. Text in English, French. 1983. a. USD 35 (effective 2000). **Document type:** *Directory, Academic/Scholarly.*
Published by: Council for the Development of Social Science Research in Africa, BP 3304, Dakar, Senegal. TEL 221-825-9822, FAX 221-824-1289, TELEX 3339 CODES SG24, codesria@sonatel.senet.net, http://www.sas.upenn.edu/African_Studies/codesria/codes_Menu.html. Circ: 1,000.

DIRECTORY OF INTERNATIONAL MUSIC EDUCATION DISSERTATIONS IN PROGRESS. see *MUSIC*

DIRECTORY OF MUSIC FACULTIES IN COLLEGES & UNIVERSITIES U S AND CANADA. see *MUSIC*

372.025 USA ISSN 1041-6331
L901
DIRECTORY OF PUBLIC ELEMENTARY AND SECONDARY EDUCATION AGENCIES. Text in English. irreg., latest 1989-1990. price varies. **Document type:** *Directory, Government.*
Former titles: Education Directory. Local Education Agencies (0273-4346); Education Directory. Public Schools Systems (0083-2677)

E

Published by: U.S. Department of Education, National Center for Education Statistics, 1990 K St N W, Washington, DC 20006. TEL 202-219-1828, http://nces.ed.gov. **Dist. by:** U.S. Government Printing Office, Superintendent of Documents, PO Box 371954, Pittsburgh, PA 15250-7954. TEL 202-512-1800, FAX 202-512-2250, orders@gpo.gov, http://www.access.gpo.gov. **Dist. by:** Box 1398, Jessup, MD 20794-1398. TEL 877-433-7827, FAX 301-470-1244.

370.82 USA
DIRECTORY OF WOMEN IN SCIENCE AND ENGINEERING PH.D. CANDIDATES AND RECIPIENTS AND POSTDOCTORAL APPOINTEES. Text in English. 1994. a. USD 25 (effective 2000). **Document type:** *Directory.*
Published by: Committee on Institutional Cooperation, 1819 S. Neil St., Ste. D, Champaign, IL 61820-7271. TEL 217-333-8475, FAX 217-244-7127, cic@uiuc.edu, http://www.cic.uiuc.edu.

378.3 CHL
DIRIGIBLE. Text in Spanish. w.
Related titles: Online - full text ed.
Published by: Consorcio Periodistico de Chile S.A., Vicuna Mackenna 1870, Santiago, Chile. TEL 56-2-550-7000, FAX 56-2-550-7999, dirigible@copesa.cl, http://www.copesa.cl.

372 ITA ISSN 0012-3382
DIRITTI DELLA SCUOLA; mensile per la scuola primaria. Text in Italian. 1899. 10/yr. EUR 26 (effective 2005). adv. bk.rev. bibl.; charts; illus. index. **Document type:** *Magazine, Consumer.*
Published by: De Agostini Editore, Via G da Verrazzano 15, Novara, 28100, Italy. TEL 39-0321-4241, FAX 39-0321-424305, info@deagostini.it, http://www.idirittidellascuola.it/, http://www.deagostini.it.

DISCOURSE; learning and teaching in philosophical and religious studies. see *RELIGIONS AND THEOLOGY*

371.2 USA
DISPATCH (DES MOINES). Text in English. 1930. 11/yr. free to qualified personnel. **Document type:** *Newsletter.* **Description:** Focuses on educational administration.
Former titles: D P I Dispatch; Educational Bulletin (0013-1679)
Published by: Department of Education, Office of the Director, Grimes State Office Bldg, Des Moines, IA 50319-0146. TEL 515-682-1151. Ed. Klark Jessen. Circ: 2,600.

371.35 CHN ISSN 1672-0008
➤ **DISTANCE EDUCATION JOURNAL.** Text in Chinese; Section in Chinese, English. 1983. bi-m. CNY 36 domestic; USD 40 foreign; CNY 6 newsstand/cover (effective 2002). maps. cum.index: 2000-. back issues avail. **Document type:** *Journal, Academic/Scholarly.* **Description:** Covers the development of the modern distance education market and introduces new knowledge and technology. Subjects include: Concept, overseas practice, technology, media, service, software, and hardware. Targeted audiences are: higher education organizations, middle schools, open universities, adult education organizations, education technology institutions, education management institutions, education researches, companies of distance education, institutions of education by the Internet, and other organizations and individuals who are interested in distance education.
Formerly (until 2002): Dianda Jiaoxue (1671-7392)
Related titles: Online - full text ed.: (from East View Information Services).
Address: Jiaogong Road, no.42, Hangzhou City, Zhejiang Province 310012, China. TEL 86-571-88822392, FAX 86-571-88842657, shener@zjtvu.edu.cn, zz@zjtvu.edu.cn. Circ: 4,000 (paid). **Dist. by:** China International Book Trading Corp, 35 Chegongzhuang Xilu, Haidian District, PO Box 399, Beijing 100044, China. TEL 86-10-68412045, FAX 86-10-68412023, cibtc@mail.cibtc.com.cn, http://www.cibtc.com.cn.

370 FRA ISSN 0298-2196
DITS ET VECUS POPULAIRES. Text in French. 1983. 6/yr.
Published by: Ecole Moderne Francaise - Pedagogie Freinet, B.P. 109, Cannes - La Bocca, Cedex 06322, France.

DJIBOUTI. MINISTERE DE L'EDUCATION NATIONALE. ANNUAIRE STATISTIQUE. see *EDUCATION—Abstracting, Bibliographies, Statistics*

379.82 ESP ISSN 1578-3154
DJOVENES DEL SIGLO XXI. Text in Spanish. 1998. q.
Formerly (until 2001): Dejovenes (1139-1162)
Published by: Comunidad de Madrid, Servicio de Publicaciones, Gran Via, 3, Madrid, 28013, Spain. TEL 34-91-7200952, FAX 34-91-7200831, http://www3.madrid.org/edupubli/.

373.246 DNK ISSN 1603-4945
▼ **DLT & LVA.** (Dansk Teknisk Laererforbund. Laerersammenslutningen ved Arbejdsmarkedsuddannelserne) Text in Danish. 2003. 6/yr. adv. bk.rev. index. **Document type:** *Magazine, Trade.*
Formed by the merger of (1980-2003): LvA - Bladet (0906-382X); (1977-2003): D T L - Nyt (0105-9157); Which superseded in part (1975-2002): Teknisk Skole (0107-2846); Which was formed by the merger of (1908-1975): Cirklen (0906-320X); (1893-1975): Teknisk Skoletidende (0040-2338)
Published by: (Laerersammenslutningen ved Arbejdsmarkedsuddannelserne), Dansk Teknisk Laererforbund, Rosenvaengets Hovedvej 14, Copenhagen Oe, 2100, Denmark. TEL 45-35-427888, FAX 45-35-422822, dtl@dtl.dk, http://www.dtl.dk. Circ: 3,200.

371.1 ITA ISSN 0391-6324
DOCETE. Text in Italian. 1946. m. adv. bk.rev. index. **Description:** Covers educational issues, aimed especially at headmasters and teachers of free Italian schools.
Published by: Federazione Istituti di Attivita Educative, Via Della Pigna, 13-A, Rome, RM 00186, Italy. TEL 39-6-6791341, FAX 39-6-6791097. Ed. Giuseppe Lupo. Adv. contact Laura Belisari. Circ: 4,000.

370 BRA
DOCUMENTA. Text in Portuguese; Summaries in English, French, Spanish. 1962. m. BRL 8,800, USD 219.
Published by: (Conselho Federal de Educacao), Fundacao Mariana Rezende Costa, Av Dom Jose Gaspar, 500, C Eucaristico, Belo Horizonte, MG 30535-610, Brazil.

DOCUMENTATION PAR L'IMAGE; revue d'historie, geographie and sciences. see *SCIENCES: COMPREHENSIVE WORKS*

372 ITA
DOCUMENTI DELLA SCUOLA. Text in Italian. m.
Address: Viale Isonzo, 60, Milan, MI 20135, Italy. TEL 02-5454313. Ed. Giovanni Girgenti.

DOMINICA. MINISTRY OF FINANCE. CENTRAL STATISTICAL OFFICE. ANNUAL EDUCATION STATISTICS. see *EDUCATION—Abstracting, Bibliographies, Statistics*

371 UKR ISSN 0321-1401
LB1140
DOSHKIL'NE VIKHOVANNYA; naukhovo-metodychnyi zhurnal. Text in Ukrainian. 1931. m. UAK 40.32 domestic; UAK 3.36, USD 1 newsstand/cover (effective 2001). illus. Index. back issues avail.; reprints avail. **Document type:** *Magazine, Trade.*
—CCC.
Published by: Redaktsiya Doshkil'ne Vikhovannya, Yuriya Kotsubinskogo, 7, Kiev, 04053, Ukraine. TEL 380-60-2169114, 380-60-2161119, dv@fm.com.ua. Ed., Pub., R&P Nina O Andrusich.

372.21 RUS
DOSHKOL'NOE VOSPITANIE I OBUCHENIE. Text in Russian. s-a. USD 45 foreign (effective 2000). bk.rev. illus.; bibl.
Published by: Izdatel'stvo Shkola Press, Rustaveli ul 10-3, Moscow, 127254, Russian Federation. TEL 7-095-2198380, FAX 7-095-2195289. Ed. L V Kuznetsova. Circ: 80,000 (paid). **US dist. addr.:** East View Information Services, 3020 Harbor Ln. N., Minneapolis, MN 55447. TEL 612-550-0961.

370 FRA ISSN 1296-2104
LES DOSSIERS DES SCIENCES DE L'EDUCATION. Text in French. 1998. s-a.
Published by: Presses Universitaires du Mirail, Universite de Toulouse II (Le Mirail), 5, Allee Antonio Machado, Toulouse, 31058, France.

370 USA ISSN 1098-6448
DRAGON LODE. Text in English. 1980. s-a. USD 20 (effective 2004). back issues avail. **Document type:** *Magazine, Academic/Scholarly.*
—CCC.
Published by: International Reading Association, Children's Literature and Reading Special Interest Group, c/o Abadiano/Kurkjian, Central Connecticut State University, Dept. of Reading & Language Arts, 1615 Stanley St, New Britain, CT 06050. http://www.csulb.edu/org/childrens-lit/proj/dragon/dl-intro.html. Ed. Helen R Abadiano.

DROPOUT. see *CHILDREN AND YOUTH—For*

370.1 USA ISSN 1530-8774
➤ **DUKE GIFTED LETTER.** Text in English. q. USD 24 (effective 2006). back issues avail. **Document type:** *Newsletter, Academic/Scholarly.* **Description:** It is a joint project between Duke University Press and the Duke Talent Identification Program (TIP). TIP identifies gifted students, offers educational opportunities, and serves as a resource for these bright children, enabling them to participate in precollege high-level educational programs geared to the intellectually gifted child. The Duke Gifted Letter is aimed at the parents of gifted students.
Related titles: Online - full text ed.
Published by: Duke University Press, 905 W Main St, Ste 18 B, Durham, NC 27701. TEL 919-687-3600, FAX 919-688-4574, subscriptions@dukeupress.edu, http://dukeupress.edu/journals/j_titles.php3?user_id=, http://www.dukeupress.edu. Ed. Kristen R Stephens. Circ: 5,200.

370 DEU ISSN 0070-7767
DURCH STIPENDIEN STUDIEREN. Text in German. 1964. a. adv.
Published by: Verein Freunde und Foerderer der Deutschen Studentenschaft e.V., Untere Hausbreite 11, Munich, 80939, Germany. Ed. Gundolf Seidenspinner.

372 DEU
DURCHBRUCH; Zeitung der kreisschueler innenvertretung des Main - Taunus - Kreises. Text in German. 1986. q. adv. bk.rev.
Published by: Kreisschueler Innenvertretung des Main - Taunus - Kreises, Gartenstr 28, Hofheim Am Taunus, 65719, Germany. TEL 06192-24322. Ed. Stefan Diefenbach.

371 UKR
DZHMIL'; dityam: zhivopis, muzika i literatura. Text in Ukrainian, English; Summaries in Ukrainian. 1997. q. UAK 14.92 domestic; USD 55 foreign; UAK 3.73, UAK 1 newsstand/cover (effective 2001). illus. Index. back issues avail.; reprints avail. **Document type:** *Magazine, Consumer.*
Published by: Redaktsiya Doshkil'ne Vikhovannya, Yuriya Kotsubinskogo, 7, Kiev, 04053, Ukraine. TEL 380-60-2169114, 380-60-2161119, dv@fm.com.ua. Ed., Pub., R&P Nina O Andrusich.

370 POL ISSN 1644-292X
DZIENNIK URZEDOWY MINISTRA EDUKACJI NARODOWEJ I SPORTU. Text in Polish. 1988. irreg. EUR 22 foreign (effective 2005). **Document type:** *Government.*
Former titles (until 2001): Dziennik Urzedowy Ministra Edukacji Narodowej (1644-2911); (until 2000): Poland. Ministerstwo Edukacji Narodowej. Dziennik Urzedowy (0860-701X); Which was formed by the merger of (1972-1988): Poland. Ministerstwo Oswiaty i Wychowania. Dziennik Urzedowy (0209-2433); Which was formerly: Poland. Ministerstwo Oswiaty i Szkolnictwa Wyzszego. B, Dzial Oswiaty. Dziennik Urzedowy (0554-4629); (unti 1967): Poland. Ministerstwo Oswiaty. Dziennik Urzedowy (0477-1664); (1944-1945): Poland. Resort Oswiaty. Dziennik Urzedowy (0867-1001); and of (1972-1988): Poland. Ministerstwo Nauki, Szkolnictwa Wyzszego i Techniki. Dziennik Urzedowy (0137-5385); Which was formerly: Poland. Ministerstwo Oswiaty i Szkolnictwa Wyzszego. Dzial Szkolnictwa Wyzszego. Dziennik Urzedowy (0554-4610); (until 1967): Poland. Ministerstwo Szkolnictwa Wyzszego. Dziennik Urzedowy (0551-2689); (1954-1960): Dziennik Urzedowy Ministerstwa Szkolnictwa Wyzszego i Centralnej Komisji Kwalifikacyjnej dla Pracownikow Nauki (0867-0706)
Published by: (Poland. Ministerstwo Edukacji Narodowej), Wydawnictwa Szkolne i Pedagogiczne, Pl Dabrowskiego 8, Warsaw, 00950, Poland. TEL 48-22-8279280, wsip@wsip.com.pl, http://www.wsip.com.pl. **Dist. by:** Ars Polona, Krakowskie Przedmiescie 7, Warsaw, Poland. TEL 48-22-9263914, FAX 48-22-9265334, arspolona@arspolona.com.pl, http://www.arspolona.com.pl.

370 USA
E D INFO. (Education Department) Text in English. irreg. (2-3/wk.). free. back issues avail. **Document type:** *Newsletter, Government.* **Description:** Discusses issues in education of professional and national interest.
Media: E-mail. **Related titles:** Fax ed.
Published by: U.S. Department of Education, Office of Intergovernmental and Intraagency Affairs, Federal Office Bldg 6, Rm 5E217, 400 Maryland Ave, S W, Washington, DC 20202. TEL 877-433-7827, peter.kickbush@ed.gov, http://www.ed.gov/news/newsletters/edinfo/index.html. Eds. Kirk Winters, Peter Kickbush.

370 USA
E D INITIATIVES. (Education Department) Text in English. 1995. bi-w. free. back issues avail. **Document type:** *Newsletter, Trade.* **Description:** Discusses a wide variety of issues and topics pertinent in teaching and learning.
Media: Online - full text.
Published by: U.S. Department of Education, Office of the Undersecretary, Federal Office Bldg 6, Rm 7W114, 400 Maryland Ave, S W, Washington, DC 20202. TEL 202-401-3132, FAX 202-401-3036, kirk_winters@ed.gov, http://www.ed.gov/pubs/EDInitiatives. Ed. Kirk Winters.

E D U NEWS. see *ENGINEERING*

E E F - N E T. (Education and Ecumenical Formation) see *RELIGIONS AND THEOLOGY*

370.72 GBR ISSN 1358-5851
E E R A BULLETIN. Text in English. 1995. 3/yr. membership. **Document type:** *Bulletin, Academic/Scholarly.* **Description:** Informs scholars and practitioners of national associations of educational research, specialized European educational research associations, institutes for research in education of news and events of interest.
Published by: European Educational Research Association, c/o Professional Development Unit, Faculty of Education, University of Strathclyde, 76 Southbrae Dr, Glasgow, Scotland G13 1PP, United Kingdom. TEL 44-141-950-3772, FAX 44-141-950-3210, eera@strath.ac.uk, http://www.eera.ac.uk/membership.html.

370 344.07 FRA ISSN 1564-1562
L10
E F A - 2000; the global newsletter for the Education for All movement. (Education for All) Text in English. 1993. q. **Document type:** *Newsletter.*

E

Related titles: Online - full text ed.: ISSN 1564-1554; Arabic ed.: At- Tarbiyat Li-l-Gami 2000. ISSN 1564-2666; Chinese ed.: ISSN 1564-264X; French ed.: ISSN 1026-0323; Spanish ed.: ISSN 1564-2658.
Published by: UNESCO, International Consultative Forum on Education for All, 7 Place de Fontenoy, Paris, 75352, France. TEL 33-1-45682364, FAX 33-1-45685629, a.muller@unesco.org, http://www.education.unesco.org/efa. Ed. Anne Muller.

370   BEL   ISSN 1027-2194
E I MONTHLY MONITOR. Text in English. m. membership only. Document type: Bulletin.
Related titles: Online - full text ed.; French ed.; Spanish ed.
Published by: Education International, 5 bd du Roi Albert II, 8e etage, Brussels, 1210, Belgium. TEL 32-2-2240611, FAX 32-2-2240606, educint@ei-ie.org, http://www.ei-ie.org. R&P Patrice Vezina.

370.1   USA
THE E-JOURNAL OF STUDENT RESEARCH. Text in English. 1992. q.
Media: Online - full text.
Published by: National Student Research Center, 2024 Livingston St, Mandeville, LA 70448. nsrcmms@communique.net, http://youth.net/nsrc/nsrc-info.html, http://www.youth.net/nsrc/.

370   USA   ISSN 1545-9055
LB1051
▼ ➤ E-JOURNAL OF TEACHING AND LEARNING IN DIVERSE SETTINGS. Text in English. 2003 (Dec). s-a. free (effective 2004). Document type: Journal, Academic/Scholarly.
Media: Online - full content.
Published by: Southern University at Baton Rouge, College of Education, PO Box 11241, Baton Rouge, LA 70813-1241. TEL 225-771-3950, FAX 225-771-5652, http://www.subr.edu/coeducation/ejournal. Ed. Jimmy D. Lindsey.

344.07   USA
E L A NOTES. Text in English. 1954. 4/yr., latest vol.36, 2001. looseleaf. USD 125; USD 135 in Canada; USD 145 elsewhere (effective 2001); includes School Law Reporter. adv. bk.rev. Document type: Newsletter.
Formerly: N O L P E Notes (0047-8997).
Published by: Education Law Association, 300 College Park, Dayton, OH 45469-0528. TEL 937-229-3589, FAX 937-229-3845, ela@udayton.edu, http://www.educationlaw.org. R&P Mandy Bingaman TEL 937-229-3589. Circ: 1,800.

E-NEWS (NEWTON). see HOUSING AND URBAN PLANNING

370   USA
E Q DISPATCH. Text in English. bi-m. Document type: Newsletter, Academic/Scholarly. Description: Covers EQUIP Reports, News, Events, and other EQUIP products.
Media: E-mail.
Published by: Educational Quality Improvement Program, c/o Jane Benbow, Project Director, American Institutes for Research, 1000 Thomas Jefferson St. NW, Washington, DC 20007. http://www.equip123.net/webarticles/anmviewer.asp?a=328&z=7.

370   USA
▼ E Q REVIEW. Text in English. 2003 (Dec.). q. back issues avail. Document type: Newsletter, Academic/Scholarly. Description: Communicates issues fundamental to improving educational quality and to communicate the successes, challenges, & lessons learned by USAID Missions.
Related titles: Online - full content ed.
Published by: Educational Quality Improvement Program, c/o Jane Benbow, Project Director, American Institutes for Research, 1000 Thomas Jefferson St. NW, Washington, DC 20007. http://www.equip123.net/webarticles/anmviewer.asp?a=322&z=7.

E R I C. (Education Resource Information Center) see EDUCATION—Abstracting, Bibliographies, Statistics

371.8   USA   ISSN 0889-8022
E R I C - C U E TRENDS AND ISSUES. Text in English. 1985. irreg., latest no.20, 199?. price varies. bibl. stat. back issues avail. Document type: Monographic series, Academic/Scholarly. Description: Explores timely social and educational developments which are changing the nature of schooling for urban and minority students.
Media: Online - full text. Related titles: Microfiche ed.
Published by: Educational Resource Information Center, Clearinghouse on Urban Education, Box 40, Teachers College, Columbia University, New York, NY 10027. TEL 212-678-3433, eric-cue@columbia.edu, http://eric-web.tc.columbia.edu. Ed. Wendy Schwartz. Co-sponsor: Institute for Urban and Minority Education.

E R I C - C U E URBAN DIVERSITY SERIES. see EDUCATION—Abstracting, Bibliographies, Statistics

372   USA   ISSN 1093-0426
E R I C / E E C E NEWSLETTER (ONLINE EDITION). Text in English. 1993. s-a. 6 p./no.; Document type: Newsletter. Description: Provides information on ERIC and ERIC/EECE as well as articles on topics related to early childhood education.
Media: Online - full text. Related titles: ♦ Print ed.: E R I C / E E C E Newsletter (Print Edition). ISSN 1093-5746.
Published by: E C A P Collaborative (Subsidiary of: University of Illinois at Urbana-Champaign, Children's Research Center), 51 Gerty Dr, Champaign, IL 61820-7469. TEL 217-333-1386, 877-275-3227, FAX 217-333-3767, ecap@uiuc.edu, http://ecap.crc.uiuc.edu/. Ed. Laurel Preece.

370   USA   ISSN 1093-5746
E R I C / E E C E NEWSLETTER (PRINT EDITION). Text in English. 1989. s-a. free. back issues avail. Document type: Newsletter, Academic/Scholarly. Description: Contains articles on topics of interest to early childhood, elementary school, and middle-level educators. Provides updates on Clearinghouse activities, including publications and websites.
Formerly: E R I C - E E C E Bulletin (0883-4148)
Related titles: ♦ Online - full text ed.: E R I C / E E C E Newsletter (Online Edition). ISSN 1093-0426.
Published by: E C A P Collaborative (Subsidiary of: University of Illinois at Urbana-Champaign, Children's Research Center), 51 Gerty Dr, Champaign, IL 61820-7469. TEL 217-333-1386, 877-275-3227, FAX 217-333-3767, ecap@uiuc.edu, http://ecap.crc.uiuc.edu/. Ed. Laurel Preece. Circ: 2,000.

E R I C IDENTIFIER AUTHORITY LIST. see EDUCATION—Abstracting, Bibliographies, Statistics

370.72   USA   ISSN 0740-7874
LB2805
E R S SPECTRUM; the journal of school research and information. Text in English. 1983. q. USD 65 (effective 2003). index. Document type: Journal, Academic/Scholarly.
Indexed: CIJE.
—Infotrieve.
Published by: Educational Research Service, 2000 Clarendon Blvd, Arlington, VA 22201-2908. TEL 703-243-2100, 800-791-9308, FAX 703-243-1985, 800-791-9309, ers@ers.org, http://www.ers.org. R&P Deborah Perkins Gough. Circ: 2,700 (paid).

370.72   USA
E T S RESEARCH REPORTER. Text in English. 3/yr. free. Document type: Newsletter. Description: Keeps E.T.S. staff and colleagues up-to-date on E.T.S. research projects and activities.
Published by: Educational Testing Service, Rosedale Rd, Princeton, NJ 08541-0001. TEL 609-921-9000. Dist. by: Office of Research Administration, E T S, 19 D, Rosedale Rd, Princeton, NJ 08541.

370   USA
E T S TODAY. Text in English. a.?. free.
Published by: Educational Testing Service, Rosedale Rd, Princeton, NJ 08541-0001. TEL 609-921-9000. Institutional subscr. to: Warner Books Inc, Special Sales, Time & Life Bldg, 1271 Ave of the Americas, New York, NY 10020. TEL 212-522-7381; Subscr. to: Little Brown, 200 West St, Waltham, MA 02254. TEL 800-759-0190.

E U D I S E D - EUROPEAN EDUCATIONAL RESEARCH YEARBOOK; project reports - people - contacts. (European Documentation and Information System for Education) see EDUCATION—Abstracting, Bibliographies, Statistics

370.1   USA
E Z - E C NEWSLETTER. Text in English. 1998. q. membership. Document type: Newsletter.
Published by: (Empowerment Zone - Enterprise Community), U.S. Department of Education, Mary E Switzer Bldg, Rm 3030, 330 C St, S W, Washington, DC 20202. TEL 202-401-6224, http://www.ed.gov.

EARLY CHILDHOOD CONNECTIONS. see CHILDREN AND YOUTH—About

372.21   NLD   ISSN 1082-3301
LB1139.25   CODEN: ECEJFA
➤ EARLY CHILDHOOD EDUCATION JOURNAL. Text in English. 1973. 6/yr. EUR 565, USD 578, GBP 368 combined subscription to institutions print & online eds. (effective 2005). adv. bk.rev. illus. back issues avail.; reprint service avail. from PQC,ISI,PSC. Document type: Journal, Academic/Scholarly. Description: Provides a practical and lively forum for early childhood teachers, program administrators, day care workers, and other professionals concerned with the education of young children.
Formerly (until 1995): Day Care and Early Education (0092-4199)
Related titles: Microform ed.: (from PQC); Online - full text ed.: ISSN 1573-1707 (from EBSCO Publishing, Gale Group, IngentaConnect, Kluwer Online, O C L C Online Computer Library Center, Inc., Ovid Technologies, Inc., Springer LINK, Swets Information Services).
Indexed: ABIn, BRI, BehAb, BibLing, CBRI, CIJE, CPE, EAA, ECER, ERA, ETA, EduInd, ExcerpMed, FamI, L&LBA, MEA, MRD, PsycInfo, PsycholAb, RHEA, RefZh, SEA, SENA, SOMA, SOPODA, SWR&A, TEA.

—BLDSC (3642.957300), IE, Infotrieve, ingenta. CCC.
Published by: (Early Childhood Education Journal USA), Springer-Verlag Dordrecht (Subsidiary of: Springer Science+Business Media), Van Godewijckstraat 30, Dordrecht, 3311 GX, Netherlands. TEL 31-78-6576050, FAX 31-78-6576474, mjalongo@iup.edu, http://springerlink.metapress.com/openurl.asp?genre=journal&issn=1082-3301, http://www.springeronline.com. Ed. Mary Renck Jalongo. Circ: 10,000 (paid).

155.4   USA   ISSN 1524-5039
LB1139.2
➤ EARLY CHILDHOOD RESEARCH & PRACTICE; an internet journal on the development, care, and education of young children. Text in English. 1999. s-a. free (effective 2005). Document type: Journal, Academic/Scholarly. Description: Features articles related to the development and care of children from birth to approximately age 8.
Media: Online - full text.
Published by: E C A P Collaborative (Subsidiary of: University of Illinois at Urbana-Champaign, Children's Research Center), 51 Gerty Dr, Champaign, IL 61820-7469. TEL 217-333-1386, 877-275-3227, FAX 217-333-3767, ecap@uiuc.edu, http://ecrp.uiuc.edu/, http://ecap.crc.uiuc.edu/. Ed. Lilian Katz.

372   GBR   ISSN 0885-2006
➤ EARLY CHILDHOOD RESEARCH QUARTERLY. Text in English. 1986. 4/yr. EUR 124 in Europe to individuals; JPY 16,400 in Japan to individuals; USD 138 elsewhere to individuals; EUR 312 in Europe to institutions; JPY 41,400 in Japan to institutions; USD 349 elsewhere to institutions (effective 2006). adv. bk.rev. illus. index. reprints avail. Document type: Academic/Scholarly. Description: Provides information for scholars, researchers, practitioners, parents, and others interested in scholarly treatment of issues and concerns.
Related titles: Online - full text ed.: (from EBSCO Publishing, Gale Group, IngentaConnect, ScienceDirect, Swets Information Services).
Indexed: ABIn, ASCA, CIJE, CPE, CurCont, ERA, EduInd, FamI, MEA, PsycInfo, PsycholAb, SEA, SENA, SSCI, TEA, e-psyche.
—BLDSC (3642.960300), IE, Infotrieve, ingenta. CCC.
Published by: Pergamon (Subsidiary of: Elsevier Science & Technology), The Boulevard, Langford Ln, East Park, Kidlington, Oxford OX5 1GB, United Kingdom. TEL 44-1865-843000, FAX 44-1865-843010, http://www.elsevier.com/locate/ecresq. Ed. K. E. Diamond. Circ: 1,700. Subscr. to: Elsevier BV, PO Box 211, Amsterdam 1000 AE, Netherlands. nlinfo-f@elsevier.nl, http://www.elsevier.nl.

➤ EARLY CHILDHOOD UPDATE. see PSYCHOLOGY

370.15   USA   ISSN 1040-9289
LB1101   CODEN: EEDEF4
EARLY EDUCATION AND DEVELOPMENT. Text in English. 1989. q. USD 270 in US & Canada to institutions; USD 300 elsewhere to institutions; USD 285 combined subscription in US & Canada to institutions print & online eds.; USD 315 combined subscription elsewhere to institutions print & online eds. (effective 2006). adv. bk.rev. Document type: Journal, Academic/Scholarly. Description: Presents empirical research in early childhood education and child development, with emphasis on practical implications for practitioners.
Related titles: Online - full text ed.: ISSN 1556-6935. USD 260 worldwide to institutions (effective 2006).
Indexed: ABIn, CDA, CIJE, EduInd, L&LBA, PsycInfo, PsycholAb, SOPODA, e-psyche.
—BLDSC (3642.964800), IE, Infotrieve, ingenta. CCC.
Published by: Lawrence Erlbaum Associates, Inc., 10 Industrial Ave, Mahwah, NJ 07430-2262. TEL 201-258-2200, 800-926-6579, FAX 201-236-0072, eed@widerange.com, journals@erlbaum.com, http://www.erlbaum.com, http://www.leaonline.com. Ed. Richard Abidin. Circ: 350.

372.357   USA   ISSN 1060-5053
EARTHWORK. Text in English. 1991. 11/yr. (11/yr.). USD 31.95 domestic; USD 37.95 foreign; USD 3.95 newsstand/cover (effective 2001). adv. Document type: Bulletin, Consumer. Description: Provides environmental and natural resource management job listings and career information.
Published by: Student Conservation Association, PO Box 550, Charlestown, NH 03603. TEL 603-543-1700, FAX 603-543-1828, earthwork@sca.inc.org, http://www.sca-mc.org/. Ed., R&P Lisa K Younger. Pub. Scott Izzo. Adv. contact Sherry L Aldrich. B&W page USD 683, color page USD 1,050; trim 10.75 x 8.25. Circ: 2,500 (paid).

370   USA   ISSN 0899-0247
LA620
EAST-WEST EDUCATION. Text in English. 1977-1989; resumed 1992. s-a. USD 22 to individuals; USD 28 foreign to individuals; USD 42 to institutions; USD 48 foreign to institutions. adv. bk.rev. bibl. back issues avail. Document type: Academic/Scholarly.
Formerly (until 1986): Slavic and European Education Review (0149-9858)
Indexed: ABS&EES, AmH&L, BAS, CPE, HistAb, PCI.

E

Published by: Office of East-West Education, Dept of History, Andrews University, Berrien Springs, MI 49104. TEL 269471-3291, FAX 269-428-4775, jjmarko@andrews.edu. Ed. Carol Gayle. Adv. contact John J Merkovic. Circ: 400.
Co-sponsor: Arbeitsstelle fuer Vergleichende Bildungsforschung, Ruhr-Universitaet, Bochum, GW.

ECHO. see *HOME ECONOMICS*

373 DEU
ECKENBRUELLER; Schuelerzeitung am Gymnasium Balingen. Text in German. 1983. 3/yr. USD 1.20. back issues avail. **Document type:** *Newsletter, Consumer.*
Published by: Gymnasium Balingen, Gymnasiumstr 31, Balingen, 72336, Germany. TEL 49-7433-90000, info@gymnasium-balingen.de, http://www.balingen.de/gymbl/. Circ: 500.

370 ITA ISSN 0012-9496
ECO DELLA SCUOLA NUOVA. Text in Italian. 1945. m. adv. bk.rev. bibl.; tr.lit.
Published by: Federazione Nazionale Insegnanti, Via Cavour 238, Rome, 00184, Italy. TEL 39-06-4828218, http://www.fnism.it. Circ: 3,000.

372.1 BEL ISSN 1377-8595
L'ECOLE DES ANNEES 2000. Text in French. 1986. 6/yr. (Sep.-June). adv. illus. **Description:** Publishes articles on topics and projects of interest to early childhood educators and elementary school teachers.
Former titles (until 1999): L' Ecole 2000 (0774-8132); (until 1986): L' Ecole Belge 2000 (0774-1308); Which was formed by the merger of (1956-1986): L' Ecole Belge (0771-6648); (1962-1986): L' Ecole Maternelle Belge (0771-6672)
Published by: Editions Labor, Quai du Commerce 29, Brussels, 1000, Belgium. TEL 32-2-250-0670, FAX 32-2-217-7197, labor@labor.be, http://www.labor.be/cgi-bin/WebObjects/labor.woa. Ed. Marie-Paule Eskenazi.

370 FRA ISSN 0759-2914
ECOLE ET LA NATION-ACTUALITES. Text in French. 1975. q. adv. **Document type:** *Academic/Scholarly.*
Published by: Parti Communiste Francais, Comite National, 2 place du Colonel Fabien, Paris, Cedex 19 75167, France. TEL 33-1-40401213, FAX 33-1-40401356. Ed. Jean Paul Legrand. Adv. contact Nicole Borvo.

370 LUX ISSN 1022-8896
ECOLE ET VIE; bulletin syndical, pedagogique, culturel. Text in French, German. 1945. 8/yr. adv. bk.rev.
Former titles: Syndicat National des Enseignants. Ecole et Vie; Association des Instituteurs Reunis du Grand-Duche de Luxembourg. Bulletin d'Information (1022-8888); Horizons Nouveaux (1022-8705)
Published by: Syndicat National des Enseignants, 5 rue des Ardennes, Luxembourg, 1133, Luxembourg. Ed. Roby Schmitz. Circ: 2,500.

370 FRA ISSN 1763-5551
▼ **L'ECOLE GLOBALE.** Variant title: L' Ecole Globale la Revue. La Revue de l'Ecole Globale. Text in French. 2003. s-a. **Document type:** *Journal, Academic/Scholarly.*
Published by: L' Harmattan, 5 rue de l'Ecole Polytechnique, Paris, 75005, France. TEL 33-1-43257651, FAX 33-1-43258203, http://www.editions-harmattan.fr.

330 370 USA
ECON ED AND THE FED. Text in English. q. **Document type:** *Newsletter.* **Description:** Provides resources and information for teachers.
Related titles: Online - full content ed.
Published by: Federal Reserve Bank of San Francisco, PO Box 7702, San Francisco, CA 94120. TEL 415-974-2000, FAX 415-974-3341, http://www.sf.frb.org/publications/education/newsletter, http://www.frbsf.org.

ECON-EXCHANGE. see *BUSINESS AND ECONOMICS*

ECUADOR. INSTITUTO NACIONAL DE ESTADISTICA Y CENSOS. ENCUESTA ANUAL DE RECURSOS Y ACTIVIDADES DE SALUD. see *EDUCATION—Abstracting, Bibliographies, Statistics*

ED. LINES; official publication of the Australian education union Tasmanian branch. see *LABOR UNIONS*

370 USA
ED.NET BRIEFS. Text in English. 1995. w. free. **Description:** Contains summaries of the week's education news stories gathered from a variety of sources. Includes full source citation.
Media: Online - full text.
Published by: Simpson Communications info@edbriefs.com, http://www.edbriefs.com. Ed. Steven W Simpson.

373 USA ISSN 0740-0357
EDCAL. Variant title: Education California. Text in English. w. free to members (effective 2004). **Document type:** *Newspaper.*
Published by: Association of California School Administrators, 1517 L St, Sacramento, CA 95814. TEL 916-444-3216, 800-890-0325, FAX 916-444-3739, http://www.acsa.org. Ed. London Roberts.

370 GBR ISSN 0013-0893
EDINBURGH ACADEMY CHRONICLE. Text in English. 1893. a. (plus s-a. bulletins). adv. illus. index. **Document type:** *Newspaper.* **Description:** Contains school news and reviews of events.
Published by: Edinburgh Academy, 42 Henderson Row, Edinburgh, EH3 5BL, United Kingdom. TEL 44-131-5564603, FAX 44-131-6244994, http://www.edinburghacademy.org.uk/. Ed. A M Jarman. R&P, Adv. contact A.M. Jarman TEL 44-131-556-4603. Circ: 1,500.

EDITOR. see *PSYCHOLOGY*

370 USA
EDPRESS NEWS. Text in English. 1939. m. membership. illus.; stat.; tr.lit. **Document type:** *Newsletter.* **Description:** Covers news about EdPress and its members, educational issues, print communication and technology, and professional development.
Formerly: EdPress Newsletter (0013-1024)
Published by: EdPress - the Association of Educational Publishers, Rowan University, 201 Mullica Hill Rd, Glassboro, NJ 08028-1701. TEL 856-256-4610, FAX 856-256-4926, edpress@aol.com, http://www.edpress.org. Ed. Charlene Gaynor. R&P Jeri Hendrie. Circ: 900.

371 ZAF
EDU-NEWS/EDU-NUUS; a monthly newspaper for the educators of S.A. - 'n maandelikse koerant vir die onderwys van S.A. Text in Afrikaans, English. 1994. m. adv. illus. **Document type:** *Newspaper.*
Address: PO Box 2874, Alberton, 1450, South Africa.

370 PRT ISSN 0871-6412
EDUCACAO. Text in Portuguese. 1990. 2/yr.
Published by: Porto Editora, Ld, Rua Restauracao, 365, Porto, 4099-023, Portugal. TEL 351-22-6088300, FAX 351-22-6088301, http://www.portoeditora.pt/. Circ: 15,000.

EDUCACAO; indicadores sociais. see *EDUCATION—Abstracting, Bibliographies, Statistics*

370.1 100 BRA ISSN 0102-6801
EDUCACAO E FILOSOFIA. Text in Portuguese. 1986. s-a. BRL 15 (effective 2004). **Document type:** *Journal, Academic/Scholarly.*
Indexed: PhilInd.
Published by: Universidade Federal de Uberlandia, Av Engenheiro Diniz 1178, Uberlandia, MG 38400-902, Brazil. http://www.ufu.br.

370 BRA ISSN 1517-9702
LB2213.S26
➤ **EDUCACAO E PESQUISA.** Text in Portuguese; Summaries in English. 1975. s-a. BRL 10 to individuals; BRL 12 to institutions (effective 1999). bk.rev. back issues avail. **Document type:** *Academic/Scholarly.* **Description:** Covers psychology, methodology, philosophy, history, and administration of education, and comparative education.
Formerly (until 1999): Universidade de Sao Paulo. Faculdade de Educacao. Revista (0102-2555)
Related titles: Online - full text ed.: free (effective 2005) (from SciELO).
Indexed: ERA, ETA, MEA, PSA, RHEA, SEA, SENA, SOMA, SSA, SociolAb, TEA.
Published by: Universidade de Sao Paulo, Faculdade de Educacao, Av. da Universidade, 308, Sao Paulo, SP 05508-900, Brazil. TEL 55-11-8183525, FAX 55-11-8183148, revedu@edu.usp.br, http://www.scielo.br/. Ed. Afranio Mendes Catani. Circ: 1,500.

370.72 BRA ISSN 0100-3143
LA559.R56
EDUCACAO E REALIDADE. Text in Portuguese. 1976. s-a. BRL 10 (effective 2000); or exchange basis. bk.rev. illus. **Document type:** *Academic/Scholarly.* **Description:** Covers research, studies and debates on various topics from a critical perspective.
Published by: Universidade Federal do Rio Grande do Sul, Faculdade de Educacao, Predio 12201 9o andar Sala 901, Av Paulo Gama, S/N, Farroupilha, Porto Alegre, RGS 90040-060, Brazil. TEL 55-51-3163268, FAX 55-51-3163985, educreal@edu.ufrgs.br, http://www.ufrgs.br/faced/revista. Ed. Rosa Maria Bueno Fischer. Circ: 1,500.

370.72 BRA ISSN 0101-7330
LC189.8
➤ **EDUCACAO E SOCIEDADE/EDUCATION AND SOCIETY**; revista quadrimestral de ciencia da educacao. Text in Portuguese; Abstracts in English. 1983. 4/yr. USD 53 (effective 2002). adv. bk.rev.; film rev. 20 p./no.; back issues avail. **Document type:** *Magazine, Academic/Scholarly.* **Description:** Designed to be an incentive to academic research and an instrument of broad debate on education.
Incorporates (1980-1981): Journal Educacao (0101-2339)
Related titles: Online - full text ed.: free (effective 2005) (from SciELO).
Indexed: CPE, ERA, ETA, IBR, MEA, RHEA, SEA, SENA, SOMA, SociolAb, TEA.
Published by: Centro de Estudos de Educacao e Sociedade, C Universitaria, Caixa Postal 6022, Campinas, SP 13084-971, Brazil. TEL 55-19-2391598, FAX 55-19-2891598, revista@cedes.unicomp.br, revista@cedes.unicamp.br, http://www.cedes.unicomp.br. Ed. Ivany Rodriguez Pino. Adv. contact Elias Paulino. Circ: 400 (paid); 600 (controlled).

370 PRT ISSN 0872-7643
EDUCACAO, SOCIEDADE & CULTURAS. Text in Portuguese. 1994. irreg. price varies. back issues avail. **Document type:** *Journal, Academic/Scholarly.*
Published by: Edicoes Afrontamento, Lda., Rua de Costa Cabral, 859, Porto, 4200-225, Portugal. TEL 351-22-5074220, FAX 351-22-5074229, editorial@edicoesafrontamento.pt, http://www.edicoesafrontamento.pt/. Ed. Jose Alberto Correia.

370 ESP ISSN 0212-3169
EDUCACIO I CULTURA. Text in Multiple languages. 1968. a.
Supersedes in part (in 1981): Mayurqa (0301-8296)
—CINDOC.
Published by: Universitat de les Illes Balears, Servei de Publicacions i Intercanvi Cientific, Carr. de Valdemosa, Km. 7.5, Palma de Mallorca, 07071, Spain. TEL 34-971-173000, FAX 34-971-173190, informacio@uib.es, http://www.uib.es/ca/servgenerals/.

370 PRI ISSN 0013-1067
EDUCACION. Text occasionally in English. 1960. 3/yr. free. bk.rev. bibl.; illus. **Document type:** *Academic/Scholarly.* **Description:** Contains articles on education and other related fields. Focuses on research articles and educational innovations and projects.
Published by: Department of Education, PO Box 190759, Hato Rey, 00919, Puerto Rico. TEL 787-754-8610, FAX 787-753-7926. Ed. Jose Galarza Rodriguez. Circ: 40,000.

370 MEX ISSN 0185-0547
EDUCACION. Text in Spanish. 1957. 4/yr. bibl.; charts.
Published by: Consejo Nacional Tecnico de la Educacion, Calle Luis Gonzalez Obregon No. 21, Mexico City, DF 06020, Mexico. Circ: 5,000.

370.9291 CUB ISSN 0138-8029
LA485
➤ **EDUCACION (HAVANA)**; una revista cubana que hace esencia de pensamiento. Text in Spanish. 1971. 3/yr. CUP 18 domestic (effective 2003). adv. bk.rev. bibl.; charts; illus. index. 64 p./no.; back issues avail. **Document type:** *Magazine, Academic/Scholarly.* **Description:** Contains articles on education science: teaching and learning experiences, research issues, acknowledgement of outstanding Cuban educators and their writings.
Published by: Editorial Pueblo y Educacion, Av 3ra A No 4601, entre 46 y 60, La Playa, Ciudad de La Habana 11300, Cuba. TEL 537-2021490, 537-2095401, FAX 537-2040844, revistaeduc@epe.edu.cu. Ed. Maria Eugenia de la Vega. Pub., R&P Catalina Lajud. Adv. contact Mario Naito Lopez. B&W page USD 200; trim 2.3 x 1.75. Circ: 2,200.

370 PER ISSN 1019-9403
➤ **EDUCACION (LIMA, 1992).** Text in Spanish. 1992. s-a. USD 30 (effective 2003). bk.rev. **Document type:** *Academic/Scholarly.*
Published by: Pontificia Universidad Catolica del Peru, Fondo Editorial, Plaza Francia 1164, Cercado de Lima, Lima, 1, Peru. feditor@pucp.edu.pe, http://www.pucp.edu.pe. Ed. Irma Encinas Ramirez.

370 MEX ISSN 1405-2075
LA420
EDUCACION 2001. Text in Spanish. 1995. m. back issues avail. **Document type:** *Academic/Scholarly.*
Related titles: Online - full text ed.
Indexed: PAIS.
Published by: Instituto Mexicano de Investigaciones Educativas, CUAUTLA 10, Col Condesa, Mexico City, DF 06140, Mexico. TEL 52-5-2865171, FAX 52-5-2860851, edu2001@serpiente.dgsca.unam.mx, http://www.unam.mx/2001/. Ed. Gilberto Guevara Niebla.

378 ESP ISSN 1137-7623
EDUCACION CANARIA. Text in Spanish. 1990. irreg.
—CINDOC.
Published by: Gobierno de Canarias. Consejeria de Educacion, Cultura y Deportes, Residencia Anagua, Ave. de Anaga, Santa Cruz de Tenerife, Canarias 38001, Spain. infoedu@gobiernodecanarias.org, http://www.educa.rcanaria.es/.

370 ARG
EDUCACION CUYO. Text in Spanish. s-a.
Published by: Universidad Nacional de Cuyo, Departamento de Ciencias de la Educacion y Formacion, Centro Universitario, Mendoza, 5500, Argentina.

370 COL ISSN 0120-8446
EDUCACION HOY. Text in Spanish. 1945. q. COP 65 domestic; USD 50 in the Americas; USD 70 in Europe (effective 2005).
Former titles (until 1990): Educacion Hoy. Perspectivas Latinoamericanas; (until 1971): Revista Interamericana de Educacion Catolica; (until 1945): Revista Pedagogica
Indexed: HAPI.

E

—IE, Infotrieve.
Published by: Confederacion Interamericana de Educacion Catolica, Calle 78, No.12-16, Oficina 101, Bogota, Santa Fe, Colombia. TEL 57-1-2553676, FAX 57-1-2550513, ciec@cable.net.co, http://www.ciec.to/revista. Ed. Luis Ernesto Solano.

EDUCACION MEDICA; aprender y ensenar en las profesiones sanitarias. see *MEDICAL SCIENCES*

370.91734 URY
EDUCACION PARA EL DESARROLLO. Text in Spanish. ceased 1978; resumed 19??. q. free. illus.
Published by: Confederacion Latinoamericana de Asociaciones Cristianas de Jovenes/Latin American Confederation of YMCAs, Colonia, 1884 Piso 1, Montevideo, 11205, Uruguay. Ed. Edgardo G Crovetto.

370 ESP ISSN 1135-8629
EDUCACION SOCIAL; revista de intervencion socioeducativa. Text in Spanish. 1995. q.
—CINDOC.
Published by: Fondation Pere Tarres, C. Enteca, 157, Barcelona, 08029, Spain. TEL 34-934-101602, FAX 34-934-394515, if@peretarres.org, http://www.peretarres.org/.

370 ESP ISSN 1139-613X
LA910
EDUCACION XXI. Text in Spanish. 1998. a.
—CINDOC.
Published by: Universidad Nacional de Educacion a Distancia, Bravo Murillo No. 38, Madrid, Spain. TEL 34-91-3986000, FAX 34-91-3986600, infouned@adm.uned.es, http://www.uned.es/.

370.115 VEN ISSN 1315-1762
➤ **EDUCACION Y CIENCIAS HUMANAS.** Text in Spanish. 1993. s-a. VEB 2,800, USD 40 to individuals; USD 45 to institutions (effective 2000). bk.rev. bibl. **Document type:** *Monographic series, Academic/Scholarly.* **Description:** Provides reviews and interpretations on education and social science issues.
Published by: Universidad Simon Rodriguez, Decanato de Postgrado, Calle 5 entre 7ma y 8va Transversal, Edif. El Caney, La Urbina, Caracas, DF 1073, Venezuela. TEL 58-2-2676786, FAX 58-2-2674033, ggarci@telcel.net.ve, postusr@conicit.ve, Mbriceno@UNESR.edu.ve. Ed., R&P Magally Briceno. Adv. contact Nora Sanchez. Circ: 500 (paid); 500 (controlled).

370.711 ESP ISSN 0013-1113
EDUCADORES. Text in Spanish. 1958. q. USD 75 (effective 2002). adv. bk.rev. bibl. index, cum.index. **Document type:** *Academic/Scholarly.* **Description:** Contains articles and studies in all areas of education. Covers teacher training, curriculum and methods, foundations of education, moral and religious education, and social education.
Indexed: AmH&L, HistAb.
—CINDOC.
Published by: Federacion Espanola de Religiosos de Ensenanza, Hacienda de Pavones 5, 1o, Madrid, 28030, Spain. TEL 34-91-3288000, FAX 34-91-3288001. Ed. Millan Arroyo. Adv. contact Rafael Ortiz. Circ: 1,750.

371.1 IND
EDUCADORES DEL MUNDO✶ . Text in Spanish. 1978. q. USD 5; to individuals and teachers; $10 to institutions. adv. bk.rev.
Related titles: ♦ English ed.: Teachers of the World. ISSN 0863-0070; French ed.: Revue Internationale des Enseignants. 1951; German ed.: Lehrer der Welt. 1951.
Published by: World Federation of Teachers' Unions (FISE), PPH Bldg, 5-E Rahi Jhansi Rd, New Delhi, 110055, India. TEL 4800591. Ed. Gabriele Vavra. Circ: 19,000.

370 ESP ISSN 0211-819X
EDUCAR. Text in Spanish. 1981. s-a. abstr. back issues avail. **Document type:** *Journal, Academic/Scholarly.*
Formerly (until 1982): Universitat Autonoma de Barcelona. Seccio de Ciencies de l'Educacio. Anuari (0211-6413)
—CINDOC.
Published by: Universitat Autonoma de Barcelona, Servei de Publicacions, Edifici A, Bellaterra, Cardanyola del Valles, 08193, Spain. TEL 34-93-5811022, FAX 34-93-5813239, sp@uab.es, http://dewey.uab.es/paplicada/Publiscions.htm, http://www.uab.es/publicacions/.

370 MEX ISSN 1405-4787
EDUCAR. Text in Spanish. 1996. q. USD 15; USD 2.50 newsstand/cover (effective 2005). back issues avail. **Document type:** *Journal, Government.*
Related titles: Online - full text ed.
Published by: (Direccion de Ediciones y Publicaciones), Gobierno del Estado de Jalisco, Secretaria de Educacion, Ave Prolongacion alcalde, 1351, Edificio B Piso 8, Guadalajara, Jalisco 44280, Mexico. TEL 52-33-38192701, FAX 52-33-38192702, revistaeducar@yahoo.com.mx, jsaras@jalisco.gob.mx, http://educacion.jalisco.gob.mx/index.html. Ed. Baudelio Lara. Circ: 3,000.

370 COL ISSN 0120-162X
EDUCAR✶ . Text in Spanish. 1977. m. illus.
Published by: Ministerio de Educacion Nacional, Division de Documentacion e Informacion Educativa, Avda Eldorado, Of. 501, Bogota, CUND, Colombia.

370 BRA ISSN 0104-4060
L45
EDUCAR EM REVISTA. Text in Portuguese. 1981. s-a. **Description:** Publishes original articles and unpublished research reports in the area of education, including reviews of important books, special documents and translations.
Formerly (until 1993): Educar (0101-4358)
Indexed: MLA-IB.
Published by: (Universidade Federal do Parana, Setor de Educacao), Editora da Universidade Federal do Parana, Centro Politecnico, CX Postal 19029, Curitiba, PARANA, Brazil. TEL 55-41-3613380, FAX 55-41-2675973, educar@ufpr.br, editora@cce.ufpr.br, http://www.educaremrevista.ufpr.br/. Ed. Dr. Marcus Bencostta.

370 FRA ISSN 0154-2524
L'EDUCATEUR. SUPPLEMENT PERIODIQUE DE TRAVAIL ET DE RECHERCHES. Text in French. 1974.
Formerly (until 1975): B.T.R. Bibliotheque de Travail et de Recherches (0154-2516)
Related titles: ♦ Supplement to: Le Nouvel Educateur. ISSN 0991-9708.
Published by: Ecole Moderne Francaise - Pedagogie Freinet, B.P. 109, Cannes - La Bocca, Cedex 06322, France.

370 IND ISSN 0013-1180
EDUCATION. Text and summaries in English, Hindi. 1921. m. INR 40. adv. bk.rev. bibl. cum.index 1948-1978. **Document type:** *Academic/Scholarly.*
Related titles: Online - full text ed.: (from Northern Light Technology, Inc.).
Published by: S. Kumar and Associates, Mass Communications Division, 32 Sarojini Debi Ln., Maqboolganj, Lucknow, Uttar Pradesh 226 078, India. TEL 91-52-224-1010. Ed. Parimal Mandke. Circ: 2,000 (controlled).

370 IRL ISSN 0790-6161
EDUCATION. Text in English. 1980. q. EUR 50 (effective 2002). adv. **Document type:** *Magazine, Academic/Scholarly.* **Description:** Contains information on current events and news involving Second and Third level education in Ireland and the U.K.
Formerly (until 1985): Education Yearbook (0790-6153)
Published by: Keelaun Ltd., 9 Maypark, Malahide Rd., Dublin, 5, Ireland. TEL 353-1-8329249, FAX 353-1-8329246, education@clubi.ie, http://www.educationmagazine.ie/keelaun/keelaun.htm. adv.: B&W page EUR 1,600, color page EUR 2,000; trim 210 x 297.

370 USA ISSN 0013-1172
L11 CODEN: EDUCD6
EDUCATION. Text in English. 1880. q. USD 34 to individuals; USD 40 to institutions (effective 2005). adv. bk.rev. index. 210 p./no. 2 cols./p.; back issues avail.; reprint service avail. from PQC. **Document type:** *Magazine, Trade.* **Description:** Contains articles on curriculum, instructional procedures, practices, trends, philosophy, and literature of education.
Related titles: Microform ed.: (from PMC, PQC); Online - full text ed.: (from EBSCO Publishing, Florida Center for Library Automation, Gale Group, H.W. Wilson, Northern Light Technology, Inc., O C L C Online Computer Library Center, Inc., ProQuest Information & Learning).
Indexed: ABIn, AcaI, CIJE, CPE, ChLitAb, EAA, EduInd, HECAB, L&LBA, PsycholAb, SOPODA, SSA, SociolAb.
—BLDSC (3661.162000), IDS, IE, Infotrieve, ingenta. **CCC.**
Published by: Dr. George E. Uhlig, PO Box 8826, Spring Hill Sta, Mobile, AL 36689. Ed. Phil Feldman. Circ: 3,500 (paid).

370 AUS ISSN 0013-1156
EDUCATION (SYDNEY). Text in English. 1919. fortn. (during school term). AUD 52 (effective 2000). adv. bk.rev. index. **Document type:** *Newspaper.*
Incorporates: Teacher Feedback (0311-2772)
Indexed: AEI, BrEdI.
Published by: New South Wales Teachers Federation, 23-33 Mary St, Surry Hills, NSW 2010, Australia. TEL 61-2-92172100, FAX 61-2-92172470, TELEX 71402 TEFED. Ed., R&P Dennis Long. Adv. contact Carol Leeming. B&W page AUD 2,650. Circ: 65,000.

370.94585 MLT ISSN 1027-7773
EDUCATION 2000. Text in English. 1982. 2/yr. USD 6 (effective 1999). **Document type:** *Trade.* **Description:** Publishes practical articles about education generally, looking at issues affecting teachers in Malta and elsewhere in the World.
Formerly: Education (1022-551X)
Indexed: CPE.
Published by: University of Malta, Faculty of Education, Msida, MSD 06, Malta. TEL 356-32902931, FAX 356-317938, TELEX 407 HIEDUC, cmif2@educ.um.edu.mt, http://www.ilands.com/education2000. Ed. C L Mifsud. Circ: 7,000.

372 GBR ISSN 0300-4279
➤ **EDUCATION 3-13**; the professional journal for primary education. Text in English. 1973. 3/yr. GBP 35 domestic to individuals; EUR 67.50 in Europe to individuals; GBP 45 elsewhere to individuals; GBP 55 domestic to institutions; EUR 97.50 in Europe to institutions; GBP 65 elsewhere to institutions; GBP 144 combined subscription print & online eds. (effective 2005). adv. bk.rev. charts; illus. index. back issues avail.; reprint service avail. from PQC. **Document type:** *Journal, Academic/Scholarly.* **Description:** Focuses on a stimulating ways of teaching rather than relying on a series of tips.
Related titles: Microfiche ed.: (from PQC); Microfilm ed.; Online - full content ed.: ISSN 1475-7575; Online - full text ed.: (from EBSCO Publishing).
Indexed: BrEdI, CIJE, CPE, ChLitAb, EAA, ERA, ETA, MEA, RHEA, SEA, SENA, SOMA, TEA.
—BLDSC (3661.356000), IE, Infotrieve, ingenta. **CCC.**
Published by: (Primary Schools Research and Development Group), Trentham Books Ltd., Westview House, 734 London Rd, Stoke-on-Trent, Staffs ST4 5NP, United Kingdom. TEL 44-1782-745567, FAX 44-1782-745553, tb@trentham-books.co.uk, http://www.trentham-books.co.uk/pages/educ313.htm. Eds. Mark Brundrett, Rosie Turner-Bisset. adv.: page GBP 280; 176 x 280. Circ: 3,000.

➤ **EDUCATION ABSTRACTS (CD-ROM).** see *EDUCATION—Abstracting, Bibliographies, Statistics*

371.4 CAN
EDUCATION ADVISORY. Text in English. 1975. irreg. (approx. 2/yr.). CND 3. bk.rev.
Address: 2267 Kings Ave, West Vancouver, BC V7V 2C1, Canada. Ed. Tunya Audain. Circ: 3,000.

370 GBR ISSN 0265-1602
EDUCATION AND HEALTH; a quarterly journal. Text in English. 1983. q. GBP 20 to individuals (effective 2005). adv. bk.rev. charts. **Document type:** *Journal, Academic/Scholarly.* **Description:** For teachers and health-care professionals.
Related titles: E-mail ed.
Indexed: BrEdI, BrNI, CINAHL, CPE.
—BLDSC (3661.187000). **CCC.**
Published by: Schools Health Education Unit, Renslade House, Bonhay Rd, Exeter, Devon EX4 3AY, United Kingdom. TEL 44-1392-667272, FAX 44-1392-667269, sheu@sheu.org.uk, http://www.sheu.org.uk/pubs/eh.htm. Ed., R&P David McGeorge. Adv. contact Michelle Dickinson. Circ: 5,250 (controlled).

EDUCATION & LAW JOURNAL. see *LAW*

370 150 IND ISSN 0046-1385
EDUCATION AND PSYCHOLOGY REVIEW. Text in English. 1961. q. INR 10, USD 3. bk.rev. stat.
Indexed: BAS, CPE, PsycholAb, e-psyche.
Published by: Maharaja Sayajirao University of Baroda, Faculty of Education and Psychology, Baroda, Gujarat 390 002, India. Ed. D M Desal. Circ: 400.

370.115 GBR ISSN 1464-2689
EDUCATION AND SOCIAL JUSTICE. Text in English. 1998. 3/yr. GBP 30 in United Kingdom to individuals; GBP 40 elsewhere to individuals; GBP 40 in United Kingdom to institutions; GBP 50 elsewhere to institutions (effective 2002); Subscr. includes free online access.. back issues avail. **Document type:** *Journal, Academic/Scholarly.*
Indexed: CPE, ERA.
—BLDSC (3661.195000), IE, ingenta.
Published by: Trentham Books Ltd., Westview House, 734 London Rd, Stoke-on-Trent, Staffs ST4 5NP, United Kingdom. TEL 44-1782-745567, FAX 44-1782-745553, tb@trentham-books.co.uk, http://www.trentham-books.co.uk. Eds. Ken Jones, Martin Allen.

E

370 USA ISSN 0894-0940
EDUCATION AND SOCIETY. Text in English. 1988. q.
Published by: Anti-Defamation League of B'nai B'rith, 823 United Nations Plaza, New York, NY 10017. TEL 212-885-7950, 800-343-5540, FAX 212-867-0779.

370.115 AUS ISSN 0726-2655
LC189.8
➤ **EDUCATION AND SOCIETY.** Text in English. 1983. s-a. AUD 396 domestic to institutions; AUD 360 in New Zealand to institutions; GBP 178 in Europe to institutions; USD 276 elsewhere to institutions (effective 2005). adv. Index. back issues avail.; reprints avail. **Document type:** *Journal, Academic/Scholarly.* **Description:** Examines the relationship between schooling and society, and its impact on culture, ideology and power. Explores social, cultural and economic factors affecting schooling and society.
Indexed: AEI, CPE, ERA, ETA, L&LBA, MEA, RHEA, SEA, SENA, SOMA, SOPODA, SSA, SWA, SociolAb, TEA.
—BLDSC (3661.196500), IE, Infotrieve, ingenta.
Published by: James Nicholas Publishers, Pty. Ltd., PO Box 244, Albert Park, VIC 3206, Australia. TEL 61-3-96905955, FAX 61-3-96992040, custservice@jamesnicholaspublishers.com.au, http://www.jamesnicholaspublishers.com.au/esjrnl.htm. Ed. Dr. Joseph Zajda. Pub. Rea Zajda. R&P Mary Berchmans. Adv. contact Irene Schevchenko.

370.9 NLD ISSN 0926-6070
EDUCATION AND SOCIETY IN THE MIDDLE AGES AND RENAISSANCE. Text in Dutch. 1992. irreg., latest vol.16, 2002. price varies. back issues avail. **Document type:** *Monographic series, Academic/Scholarly.*
Published by: Brill Academic Publishers, PO Box 9000, Leiden, 2300 PA, Netherlands. TEL 31-71-53-53-500, FAX 31-71-53-17-532, cs@brill.nl, http://www.brill.nl. R&P Elizabeth Venekamp. **Subscr. in N. America to:** PO Box 605, Herndon, VA 20172. TEL 703-661-1585, 800-337-9255, FAX 703-661-1501, cs@brillusa.com. **Distr. outside N. America by:** c/o Turpin Distribution, Stratton Business Park, Pegasus Drive, Biggleswade, Bedfordshire SG 18 8TQ, United Kingdom. TEL 44-1767-604-954, FAX 44-1767-601-640, brill@turpin-distribution.com.

EDUCATION AND THE LAW. see *LAW*

370 GBR ISSN 1358-4812
EDUCATION & TRAINING PARLIAMENTARY MONITOR. Text in English. 1994. m. GBP 175 (effective 2005). **Document type:** *Newsletter, Academic/Scholarly.* **Description:** Details the activities and publications of higher education and employment training policy, legislation and regulation, in the UK and the European Union.
Related titles: Online - full content ed.
Published by: Cadmus Newsletters Ltd., 4 Churchill Mews, Dennett Rd, Croydon, CR0 3JH, United Kingdom. TEL 44-20-86656700, FAX 44-20-86656561, cadmus@cadmus.co.uk, http://www.cadmus.co.uk/education_info.asp. Ed. Val Webster.

370.210941 GBR
EDUCATION AND TRAINING STATISTICS FOR THE UNITED KINGDOM. Text in English. 1967. a. price varies. **Document type:** *Government.*
Formerly: Education Statistics for the United Kingdom (0963-3324)
Published by: Stationery Office, 51 Nine Elms Ln, London, SW8 5DA, United Kingdom. TEL 44-20-7873-0011, FAX 44-20-7873-8247, book.orders@theso.co.uk, http://www.national-publishing.co.uk.

372 USA ISSN 0748-8491
LA217 CODEN: ETRCE2
➤ **EDUCATION AND TREATMENT OF CHILDREN.** Abbreviated title: ETC. Text in English. 1978. q., latest vol.25, 2002. USD 45 domestic to individuals; USD 60 foreign to individuals; USD 85 domestic to institutions; USD 100 foreign to institutions (effective 2004). bk.rev. charts; illus.; stat. index. 100 p./no.; back issues avail. **Document type:** *Journal, Academic/Scholarly.*
Formerly: School Applications of Learning Theory
Related titles: Microform ed.: (from PQC); Online - full text ed.: (from EBSCO Publishing, Florida Center for Library Automation, Gale Group, H.W. Wilson, O C L C Online Computer Library Center, Inc., ProQuest Information & Learning).
Indexed: ABIn, CDA, CIJE, ECER, EduInd, FamI, L&LBA, PsySCBA&T, PsycInfo, PsycholAb, RILM, SOPODA, SSA, e-psyche.
—BLDSC (3661.203500), IE, ingenta.
Published by: Family Services of Western Pennsylvania, 310 Central City Plaza, New Kensington, PA 15068-6441. TEL 724-335-9883, FAX 724-335-2730, bdfabry@aol.com, http://www.educationandtreatmentofchildren.net/edit/sub.html, http://www.fswp.org/etc/. Ed. Dan Hursh. R&P Bernard D Fabry. Circ: 600 (paid). **Co-sponsors:** California University of Pennsylvania; West Virginia University.

307.1416 USA ISSN 0013-1245
LC5101
➤ **EDUCATION AND URBAN SOCIETY**; an independent quarterly journal of social research. Text in English. 1968. q. USD 533, GBP 344 to institutions; USD 555, GBP 359 combined subscription to institutions print & online eds. (effective 2006). adv. bk.rev. illus. index. back issues avail.; reprint service avail. from PQC. **Document type:** *Journal, Academic/Scholarly.* **Description:** Contains theme-organized articles prepared by guest editors on education as a social institution within urban contexts.
Related titles: Microfilm ed.: (from PQC); Online - full text ed.: ISSN 1552-3535. USD 528, GBP 341 to institutions (effective 2006) (from C S A, EBSCO Publishing, Gale Group, O C L C Online Computer Library Center, Inc., Sage Publications, Inc., Swets Information Services).
Indexed: ABCPolSci, ABIn, AMHA, ASCA, ASSIA, AmH&L, CIJE, CJA, CPE, ChPerl, CurCont, DIP, EAA, ERA, ETA, EduInd, FamI, HRA, HistAb, IBR, IBSS, IBZ, IMFL, L&LBA, MEA, MEA&I, PAIS, RHEA, SEA, SENA, SFSA, SOMA, SOPODA, SPAA, SRRA, SSA, SSCI, SSI, SUSA, SWA, SWR&A, SociolAb, TEA, UAA.
—BLDSC (3661.204000), IDS, IE, Infotrieve, ingenta. **CCC.**
Published by: Corwin Press, Inc. (Subsidiary of: Sage Publications, Inc.), 2455 Teller Rd, Thousand Oaks, CA 91320-2218. TEL 805-499-9734, FAX 805-499-0871, 800-4-1-SCHOOL (800-417-2466), info@sagepub.com, http://www.sagepub.com/journal.aspx?pid=37. adv.: B&W page USD 350. Circ: 600 (paid). **Subscr. in Asia & India to:** Sage Publications India Pvt. Ltd., M-32 Market, Greater Kailash-I, PO Box 4215, New Delhi 110 048, India. TEL 91-11-645-3915, FAX 91-11-647-2426, journalsubs@indiasage.com; **Subscr. in UK to:** Sage Publications Ltd., 1 Oliver's Yard, 55 City Rd, London EC1 1SP, United Kingdom. TEL 44-20-73740645, FAX 44-20-73748741, subscription@sagepub.co.uk.

370 ZAF ISSN 1682-3206
LA1535
EDUCATION AS CHANGE. Text in English. 1980. q. ZAR 190 to institutions; USD 72 foreign (effective 2000). **Document type:** *Academic/Scholarly.* **Description:** Recognizes the role of education as the conscience of society and its role in transforming society.
Related titles: Online - full text ed.
Published by: South African Bureau for Scientific Publications, PO Box 11663, Pretoria, Hatfield 0028, South Africa. TEL 27-12-322-6404, FAX 27-12-320-7803, bspman@icon.co.za, http://www.journals.co.za/ej/ejour_edchange.html, http://www.safest.org.za/bsp. Ed. E Henning. Circ: 450.

370.994 AUS ISSN 1031-444X
EDUCATION AUSTRALIA. Text in English. 1988. q. bk.rev. back issues avail. **Document type:** *Trade.* **Description:** Freatures opinions, essays and reviews on educational issues.
Related titles: Online - full text ed.: ISSN 1441-5801. 1997.
Indexed: AEI, CPE.
Published by: Centre for Workplace Communication and Culture, PO Box K481, Haymarket, NSW 2000, Australia. TEL 61-2-2981-6575, FAX 61-2-9281-6587, editor@edoz.com.au, http://ww.edoz.com.au/index.html, http://www.edoz.com.au/index.html. Ed. Lorrain Murphy.

370.25 GBR ISSN 0070-9131
L915
EDUCATION AUTHORITIES' DIRECTORY AND ANNUAL. Text in English. 1902. a. GBP 58; GBP 68 hardcover. adv. **Document type:** *Directory.* **Description:** Lists the names, addresses and telephone numbers of more than 13,500 local education authorities, secondary and independent schools, colleges and other educational institutions in the United Kingdom.
Related titles: Microform ed.; Online - full text ed.
—BLDSC (3661.210000).
Published by: School Government Publishing Co. Ltd., Darby House, Bletchingley Rd, Merstham, Redhill, Surrey RH1 3DN, United Kingdom. TEL 44-1737-642223, FAX 44-1737-644283. Ed. Marjorie McCormack. Circ: 8,000.

370 GBR ISSN 0960-9644
EDUCATION BULLETIN. Text in English. 1988. fortn. GBP 95 domestic; GBP 110 foreign (effective 2002). **Document type:** *Abstract/Index.* **Description:** Covers the education and training.
Published by: London Research Centre, Research Library, 81 Black Prince Rd, London, SE1 7SZ, United Kingdom. TEL 020-7983-4672, FAX 020-7983-4674, sue.williams@london.gov.uk. Ed. Jan Fitches. Adv. contact Sue Williams.

370 CAN ISSN 0013-1253
L11
EDUCATION CANADA. Text mainly in English; Text occasionally in French. 1961. q. CND 33 domestic; CND 53 in United States; CND 73 elsewhere (effective 2004). bk.rev. illus. Index. reprint service avail. from PQC. **Document type:** *Journal, Trade.* **Description:** Covers current issues and trends in elementary and secondary education in Canada.
Formerly (until 1969): Canadian Education and Research Digest (0315-1514); Which was formed by the merger of (1945-1961): Canadian Education (0382-8581); (1959-1961): Canadian Research Digest (0576-6028)
Related titles: Microfiche ed.: (from MML); Microform ed.: (from MML, PQC); Online - full text ed.: (from H.W. Wilson, Micromedia ProQuest, O C L C Online Computer Library Center, Inc., ProQuest Information & Learning).
Indexed: ABIn, CBCARef, CBPI, CEI, CIJE, CPE, CPerl, CWPI, CurCont, EAA, ERA, EduInd, MEA, SENA, SOMA, SRRA.
—BLDSC (3661.220000), IE, Infotrieve, ingenta. **CCC.**
Published by: Canadian Education Association/Association Canadienne d'Education, 252 Bloor St W, Ste 8 200, Toronto, ON M5S 1V5, Canada. TEL 416-591-6300, FAX 416-591-5345, cea-ace@acea.ca, http://www.acea.ca. Ed. Suzanne Tanguay. Circ: 4,400.

370 362.4 USA ISSN 0013-1261
EDUCATION DAILY; the American educator's independent, daily news service. Text in English. 1968. d. (Mon.-Fri.). looseleaf. USD 1,200 (effective 2006). q. index. reprint service avail. from PQC. **Document type:** *Newsletter, Trade.* **Description:** Covers current reports on national, state and local events pertinent to top-level education officials everywhere. Includes news from the Education Department, Congress, the White House and the courts. Reports on the latest education research, education of handicapped children, and higher education.
Incorporates: Higher Education Daily (0194-2239)
Related titles: Microform ed.: (from PQC); Online - full text ed.: (from bigchalk, EBSCO Publishing, Florida Center for Library Automation, Gale Group, ProQuest Information & Learning).
—**CCC.**
Published by: L R P Publications, 747 Dresher Rd, PO Box 980, Horsham, PA 19044. TEL 215-784-0860, FAX 215-784-9639, educationdaily@lrp.com, custserve@lrp.com, http://www.educationdaily.net/ED/splash.jsp, http://www.lrp.com.

370 USA ISSN 0424-5407
EDUCATION DEVELOPMENT CENTER. ANNUAL REPORT. Text in English. 1967. a. free. illus. **Document type:** *Corporate.*
Published by: Education Development Center, Publications Office, 55 Chapel St, Newton, MA 02160. TEL 617-969-7100, FAX 617-969-5979. Ed. Dan Tobin. R&P Ellen Lubell. Circ: 2,500.

370 USA ISSN 0013-127X
THE EDUCATION DIGEST; essential readings condensed for quick review. Text in English. 1934. m. (9/yr., Sep.-May), latest vol.68. USD 48 domestic; USD 58 foreign (effective 2005). adv. bk.rev.; software rev.; Website rev.; video rev. illus.; stat.; abstr. index. 80 p./no. 2 cols./p.; back issues avail.; reprint service avail. from PQC. **Document type:** *Magazine, Academic/Scholarly.* **Description:** Condenses outstanding articles on education and includes features on new resources, news from Washington, education briefs, and web resources.
Related titles: CD-ROM ed.: (from ProQuest Information & Learning); Microform ed.: (from PQC); Online - full text ed.: (from bigchalk, EBSCO Publishing, H.W. Wilson, Northern Light Technology, Inc., O C L C Online Computer Library Center, Inc., ProQuest Information & Learning).
Indexed: ABIn, AMHA, ARG, Acal, DIP, ECER, EduInd, HlthInd, IBR, IBZ, JHMA, LRI, MagInd, PCI, PMR, RGAb, RGPR, RGYP, RILM, TOM.
—BLDSC (3661.240000), IE, Infotrieve, ingenta.
Published by: Prakken Publications, Inc., 832 Phoenix Dr, Ann Arbor, MI 48108-2221. kschroeder@eddigest.com, http://www.eddigest.com. Ed., R&P Kenneth Schroeder TEL 734-975-2800 ext. 207. Pub. George F Kennedy. Adv. contact Alice B. Augustus. B&W page USD 775, color page USD 1,369; 4 x 6.75. Circ: 9,500 (paid and free).

372.9498 ROM ISSN 1453-2530
LA970
➤ **EDUCATION EN ROUMANIE/EDUCATION IN ROMANIA.** Text in English, French. 1978. a., latest vol.13, 2000. ROL 40,000 domestic; USD 50 foreign (effective 2002). bk.rev. abstr.; bibl. index. 250 p./no.; back issues avail. **Document type:** *Journal, Academic/Scholarly.* **Description:** Covers secondary and higher education in Rumania.
Formerly: Enseignement et la Pedagogie en Roumanie (0256-5129)
Published by: Biblioteca Pedagogica Nationala/National Library of Education, Str. Zalomit 12, Sector 1, Bucharest, 70714, Romania. TEL 40-01-3110323, FAX 40-01-3110323, bpn@fx.ro. Ed. Cristina Vintila. Circ: 150.

372 FRA ISSN 0013-1288
EDUCATION ENFANTINE; revue des ecoles maternelles, classes enfantines, cours preparatoires. Text in French. 1904. 10/yr. illus.
—**CCC.**
Published by: Editions Nathan, Departement des Revues, 9 rue Mechain, Paris, Cedex 14 75676, France. TEL 33-1-45875000, FAX 33-1-45875791, TELEX 204 525. Ed. Anick Lestage. Circ: 100,000.

370.9414471 CAN ISSN 1192-3318
EDUCATION ET FORMATION AU QUEBEC. Text in English. biennial. CND 44.95 (effective 2001). **Document type:** *Directory.* **Description:** Contains listings of post high school establishments, scholarly commissions, textbook editors, and professional associations in Quebec.
Published by: Quebec dans le Monde, C P 8503, Sainte Foy, PQ G1V 4N5, Canada. TEL 418-659-5540, FAX 418-659-4143.

370 FRA ISSN 0294-0868
LA690
EDUCATION ET FORMATIONS. Text in French. 1967. q.
Formerly (until 1982): Ministere de l'Education Nationale. Etudes et Documents (0247-5049)
—BLDSC (3661.263000), IE, ingenta.
Published by: Ministere de l'Education Nationale, de l'Enseignement Superieur et de la Recherche, 110 rue de Grenelle, Paris, 75357, France.

EDUCATION ET FRANCOPHONIE; revue d'education des communautes francophones canadiennes. see *LINGUISTICS*

306.43 BEL ISSN 1373-847X
➤ **EDUCATION ET SOCIETES**; revue internationale de sociologie de l'education. Text in French; Summaries in French, Dutch, English, Spanish, Russian. 1998. s-a. EUR 60 (effective 2005). bk.rev. abstr. 128 p./no.; back issues avail. **Document type:** *Monographic series, Academic/Scholarly.* **Description:** Reviews topics and research into the sociology of education. Includes reflections by teachers.
Indexed: DIP, IBR, IBZ, SSA, SociolAb.
Published by: (I.N.R.P. - Group d'Etudes Sociologiques), De Boeck Universite, Fond Jean-Paques 4, Louvain-la-Neuve, 1348, Belgium. TEL 32-10-482511, FAX 32-10-482519, info@universite.deboeck.com, http://universite.deboeck.com/livre/?GCOI=28011100609670&fa=sommaire. Ed. Frederic Jongen.

E

373 CAN ISSN 0840-9269
EDUCATION FORUM; the magazine for secondary school professionals. Text in English. 1922. 4/yr. (during school year). CND 20; CND 24 foreign (effective 1999). adv. bk.rev. illus. reprints avail.
Former titles: Forum (Toronto) (0319-2121); (until 1984): O S S T F Forum; (until 1975): O S S T F Bulletin (0029-7275)
Related titles: Microfiche ed.: (from MML); Online - full text ed.: (from Micromedia ProQuest).
Indexed: CBPI, CEI, CPerl.
Published by: Ontario Secondary School Teachers' Federation, 60 Mobile Dr, Toronto, ON M4A 2P3, Canada. TEL 416-751-8300, FAX 416-751-3394, walkern@osstf.co.ca. Ed., R&P Pierre Cote. Adv. contact Renate Brandon. Circ: 46,000 (controlled).

EDUCATION FULL TEXT. see *EDUCATION—Abstracting, Bibliographies, Statistics*

EDUCATION GUIDELINES. see *EDUCATION—Abstracting, Bibliographies, Statistics*

370 KEN ISSN 0046-1423
EDUCATION IN EASTERN AFRICA∗. Text in English. 1970. s-a. KES 28, USD 8. adv. bk.rev. stat.
Indexed: CPE.
Published by: (Regional Council for Education), Kenya Literature Bureau, PO Box 30022, Nairobi, Kenya. Ed. John C B Bigala. Circ: 2,000.

370 USA ISSN 1049-7250
EDUCATION IN FOCUS. Text in English. 1990. s-a. USD 18 for 3 yrs. in North America; USD 28 for 3 yrs. elsewhere (effective 2001). adv. bk.rev. 6 p./no.; back issues avail. **Document type:** *Newsletter, Trade.* **Description:** Focuses on education: its failures and, its successes.
Published by: Books for All Times, Inc (Subsidiary of: F & W Publications, Inc.), PO Box 2, Alexandria, VA 22313. TEL 703-548-0457, staff@bfat.com, http://www.bfat.com. Ed. Joe David. Circ: 1,000.

370.954 IND
EDUCATION IN INDIA. Text in English. 1950. irreg. (in 2 vols.). price varies.
Published by: Ministry of Education and Social Welfare, Department of Education, Shastri Bhavan, New Delhi, 110 001, India. **Subscr. to:** Controller of Publications, Civil Lines, New Delhi 110 006, India.

370.952 JPN ISSN 0070-9220
L611
EDUCATION IN JAPAN; a graphic presentation. Text in English. 1954. irreg., latest vol.8, 1971. JPY 1,400.
Indexed: BAS.
Published by: Ministry of Education, 3-2-2 Kasumigaseki, Chiyoda-ku, Tokyo, 100-0013, Japan. **Subscr. to:** Government Publications Service Center, 2-1 Kasumigaseki 1-chome, Chiyoda-ku, Tokyo 100-0013, Japan. TEL 81-3-3504-3889, 81-3-3504-3885, FAX 81-3-3504-3889.

370.9519 KOR ISSN 0531-6634
EDUCATION IN KOREA∗. Text in English. 1978. biennial. free. bk.rev. charts; stat. **Description:** Features major highlights of educational system to develop a general understanding of the Republic of Korea.
Published by: Ministry of Education, National Institute of Educational Research and Training, 77, Sejong-ro, Chongro-ku, Chongno-gu, Seoul, 110-760, Korea, S. nitea@nitea.or.kr, http://www.nitea.or.kr, http://www.moe.go.kr/. Ed. Pyong Ho Park. Circ: 3,500.

370 370.917 AUS ISSN 1036-0026
LC5148.A8
➤ **EDUCATION IN RURAL AUSTRALIA.** Text in English. 1991. s-a. AUD 50 (effective 2001). adv. bk.rev. back issues avail. **Document type:** *Academic/Scholarly.* **Description:** Examines all aspects of educational provision to rural areas.
Indexed: AEI, CIJE.
—BLDSC (3661.333600).
Published by: Society for the Provision of Education in Rural Australia, PO Box 379, Darling Heights, QLD 4350, Australia. TEL 61-2-6933-2441, FAX 61-2-6933-2888, cboylan@csu.edu.au. Ed., Pub., R&P Colin Boylan. adv.: B&W page AUD 250; trim 18 x 10. **Co-sponsor:** Charles Sturt University, School of Education.

370.947 GBR ISSN 1351-0371
LA832
➤ **EDUCATION IN RUSSIA, THE INDEPENDENT STATES AND EASTERN EUROPE.** Text in English. 1982. s-a. GBP 10 domestic to individuals; GBP 14 foreign to individuals; GBP 12 domestic to institutions; GBP 22 foreign to institutions. bk.rev. bibl. back issues avail. **Document type:** *Academic/Scholarly.* **Description:** Covers all matters relating to education in the former Soviet Union, Tsarist Russia, the C.I.S. and Eastern Europe.
Formerly (until 1995): Soviet Education Study Bulletin (0264-4967)
Indexed: BrEdI, CPE, ERA.
Published by: Study Group on Education in Russia the Independent States and Eastern Europe, c/o Department of Languages and International Studies, University Of Central Lancashire, Preston, Lancs PR1 2HE, United Kingdom. TEL 44-1772-893124, http://www.kingston.ac.uk/~hs_s113/sgerisee/index.htm. Ed. James Muckle. **Co-sponsor:** University of London, School of Slavonic and East European Studies.

507 GBR ISSN 0013-1377
➤ **EDUCATION IN SCIENCE.** Text in English. 1962. 5/yr. free to members; GBP 42 domestic to libraries; GBP 49.50 in Europe to libraries; GBP 59.50 elsewhere to libraries (effective 2005). adv. reprint service avail. from PQC. **Document type:** *Journal, Academic/Scholarly.* **Description:** Intended to provide a means of communication between all sections of the membership - member to member - as well as being an important vehicle for keeping members informed about what ASE is doing on their behalf.
Related titles: Microform ed.: (from PQC).
Indexed: BrEdI, CADCAM, CIJE, CPE, ERA, ETA, EngInd, EnvAb, HECAB, MEA, RHEA, SEA, SENA, SOMA, TEA.
—BLDSC (3661.334000), Ei, IE, Infotrieve, ingenta. **CCC.**
Published by: Association for Science Education, College Ln, Hatfield, Herts AL10 9AA, United Kingdom. TEL 44-1707-283000, FAX 44-1707-266532, http://www.ase.org.uk/htm/journals/eis/index.php. Ed. Carol Abbott. R&P Jane Hanrott. Adv. contact Tracy Hague. B&W page GBP 440. Circ: 24,000.

370.9411 GBR ISSN 0424-5512
➤ **EDUCATION IN THE NORTH**; the journal of Scottish education. Text in English. 1965-1988; resumed 1993 (New Series). a., latest no.9. GBP 5 per issue (effective 2001). adv. bk.rev. abstr. 2 cols./p.; back issues avail. **Document type:** *Journal, Academic/Scholarly.* **Description:** Covers all aspects of education in Scotland.
Indexed: BrEdI, HECAB.
—BLDSC (3661.306000), IE, ingenta.
Published by: Northern College of Education, Hilton Pl, Aberdeen, AB24 4FA, United Kingdom. d.w.hay@norcol.ac.uk, http://www.norcol.ac.uk. Eds. D W Hay TEL 44-1224-283703, S W Cunningham. adv.: page GBP 130; 210 x 297. Circ: 1,000.

370.94229 GBR ISSN 0261-8966
EDUCATION IN THE ROYAL COUNTY OF BERKSHIRE. Text in English. 1981. irreg. illus.
Published by: (Berkshire Education Department), Coles & Sons, 223 Southampton St, Reading, Berks RG1 2RB, United Kingdom.

EDUCATION INDEX. see *EDUCATION—Abstracting, Bibliographies, Statistics*

371 BEL ISSN 1027-2143
➤ **EDUCATION INTERNATIONAL QUARTERLY MAGAZINE.** Text in English. 1959; N.S. 1993. q. illus. **Document type:** *Academic/Scholarly.*
Formerly: Echo (0012-9143)
Related titles: French ed.: Internationale de l'Education. ISSN 1027-216X; Spanish ed.: Internacional de la Educacion. ISSN 1027-2151.
Published by: Education International, 5 bd du Roi Albert II, 8e etage, Brussels, 1210, Belgium. TEL 32-2-2240611, FAX 32-2-2240606, educint@ei-ie.org. Ed., R&P Dominique Marlet. Circ: 12,000.

➤ **EDUCATION LAW.** see *LAW*

370.1 340 GBR
EDUCATION LAW MONITOR. Text in English. m. GBP 186; GBP 210, USD 420 foreign (effective 2000). adv. **Document type:** *Newsletter.* **Description:** Provides a succinct update on all the major legal issues and a summary of the latest legislation and how it affects professionals within education, whether working in LEAs, universities, schools, or colleges and local government.
Published by: Monitor Press Ltd. (Subsidiary of: T & F Informa plc), Suffolk House, Church Field Rd, Sudbury, Suffolk CO10 2YA, United Kingdom. TEL 44-1787-378607, FAX 44-1787-881147, http://www.monitorpress.co.uk. Adv. contact Caroline Gasking.

EDUCATION LAW REPORTER FOR ELEMENTARY & SECONDARY STUDIES. see *LAW*

EDUCATION LAW REPORTER, POST-SECONDARY STUDIES. see *LAW*

EDUCATION LAW REPORTS. see *LAW*

370 USA ISSN 1532-0723
LB1025.3
➤ **EDUCATION LEADERSHIP REVIEW.** Text in English. 2000. 3/yr. USD 20 (effective 2005). **Document type:** *Journal, Academic/Scholarly.*
—CCC.
Published by: Sam Houston State University, National Council of Professors of Educational Administration, PO Box 2119, Huntsville, TX 77341-2119. TEL 936-294-4981, FAX 936-294-3886, creitheo@shsu.edu, http://www.ncpea.net/ELR.html.

➤ **EDUCATION LIBRARIES.** see *LIBRARY AND INFORMATION SCIENCES*

➤ **EDUCATION LIBRARIES JOURNAL.** see *LIBRARY AND INFORMATION SCIENCES*

➤ **EDUCATION PAR LE JEU ET L'ENVIRONNEMENT.** see *ENVIRONMENTAL STUDIES*

370 GBR ISSN 1366-302X
EDUCATION PARLIAMENTARY MONITOR. Text in English. 1996. w. (Mon.). **Description:** Gives brief details of all educational activity in all five parliamentary institutions in the UK in the previous week and the week ahead.
Related titles: CD-ROM ed.; Online - full content ed.; Online - full text ed.: (from EBSCO Publishing).
Published by: The Education Publishing Co. Ltd., Devonia House, 4 Union Terrace, Crediton, Devon EX17 3DY, United Kingdom. TEL 44-1363-774455, FAX 44-1363-776592, info@educationpublishing.com, http://www.educationpublishing.com.

379 USA ISSN 1068-2341
LC71
➤ **EDUCATION POLICY ANALYSIS ARCHIVES.** Text in English. 1993. irreg. free. back issues avail. **Document type:** *Journal, Academic/Scholarly.* **Description:** Contains analysis of education policy at all levels and in all nations.
Related titles: Online - full content ed.: free (effective 2005).
Indexed: CIJE, EduInd, HEA.
Published by: Arizona State University, College of Education, Education Policy Studies Laboratory, PO Box 872411, Tempe, AZ 85287-2411. TEL 480-965-1886, FAX 480-965-0303, glass@asu.edu, http://epaa.asu.edu. Eds. Gene V Glass, Sherman Dorn.

370 USA ISSN 1540-5125
EDUCATION POLICY IN PRACTICE; critical cultural studies. Text in English. 2002. irreg.
Published by: Praeger Publishers (Subsidiary of: Greenwood Publishing Group Inc.), 88 Post Rd W, Box 5007, Westport, CT 06881-5007. TEL 203-226-3571, FAX 203-222-1502, info@greenwood.com, http://www.greenwood.com.

EDUCATION, PUBLIC LAW AND THE INDIVIDUAL. see *LAW*

EDUCATION REPORTER. see *JOURNALISM*

371.04 USA
THE EDUCATION REVOLUTION. Text in English. 1989. q. USD 15 domestic; USD 20 foreign; USD 4.95 newsstand/cover (effective 2002). bk.rev. back issues avail. **Document type:** *Magazine, Consumer.* **Description:** Provides networking information for alternative educators, including homeschoolers.
Formerly: Aero-gramme (1067-9219)
Published by: Aero, 417 Roslyn Rd, Roslyn, NY 11577. TEL 516-621-2195, FAX 516-625-3257, jerryaero@aol.com, http://www.edrev.org. Ed., Pub. Jerry Mintz. Circ: 5,000. **Dist. by:** Tower Magazine, 2550 Del Monte St, West Sacramento, CA 95691.

370.91734 FRA ISSN 0395-7691
EDUCATION RURALE. Text in French. 1946. 5/yr. adv. bk.rev.
Published by: Association Nationale des Maitres Agricoles, Lycee Horticole, BP 329, Lomme, Cedex 59463, France. TEL 33-3-20170390, FAX 33-3-20092799. Ed. Michel Enchery. Circ: 1,500.

370 USA
EDUCATION SAN DIEGO COUNTY. Text in English. 1943. 4/yr. free to qualified personnel.
Formerly: Education Newsletter (0013-144X)
Published by: Department of Education, Superintendent of Schools, 6401 Linda Vista Rd, San Diego, CA 92111. TEL 619-292-3500. Ed. Doug Langdon. Circ: 13,000 (controlled).

370 RWA
EDUCATION, SCIENCE ET CULTURE/UBUREZI, UBUHANGA N'UMUCO. Text in French. 1978. q. USD 3. adv.
Former titles (until 1982): Education et Culture - Uburezi n'Uburere; Vie Familiale; Vie Feminine et Enseignement Familial
Published by: Ministere de l'Enseignement Superieur et de la Recherche Scientifique, BP 624, Kigali, Rwanda. FAX 250-82162.

370 150 GEO ISSN 1512-1801
EDUCATION SCIENCES AND PSYCHOLOGY. Text in Russian, Georgian, English. 2002. irreg. free (effective 2005). **Document type:** *Journal, Academic/Scholarly.* **Description:** The journal publishes articles containing new scientific results in the field of theoretical and applied problems regarding education, pedagogical psychology and the psychology of information.
Media: Online - full text.

E

Published by: Georgian Internet Academy, 272a, 4th Fl, Block 2, Iv Javakhishvili State University, 3 Chavchavadze Ave, Tbilisi, 01280, Georgia. TEL 995-32-290812, http://gesj.internet-academy.org.ge/en/title_en.php?b_sec=&section_l=edu.

EDUCATION STATISTICS, NEW YORK STATE; prepared especially for members of the Legislature. see *EDUCATION—Abstracting, Bibliographies, Statistics*

370.1 GBR
➤ **EDUCATION THROUGH PARTNERSHIP**; excellence through collaboration. Text in English. 1996. s-a. GBP 21 per academic year in United Kingdom; GBP 22 per academic year overseas (effective 2001). **Document type:** *Journal, Academic/Scholarly.*
Formerly (until 2000): Journal of Education Through Partnership (1364-4203)
Indexed: BrEdI.
—BLDSC (3661.311800), IE, ingenta.
Published by: Anglia Polytechnic University, Bishop Hall Lane, Chelmsford, Essex CM1 1SQ, United Kingdom. TEL 44-1245-493131, FAX 44-1245-490835, http://www.anglia.ac.uk/etp/. Eds. Graham Badley, Rebecca Bunting, Dr. Vernon Trafford.

371 AUS
EDUCATION TIMES. Text in English. 1993. fortn. (during school term). AUD 70 (effective 1999). adv. bk.rev. 24 p./no. 5 cols./p.; **Document type:** *Newspaper, Government.*
Former titles: Victorian School News (1323-5915); (until 1995): Victorian School Education News (1039-4990); Which was formed by the merger of (1991-1993): E Q News (1037-4310); (1991-1993): Schools Bulletin (1036-160X); Which incorporated (1990-1991): Victoria Education Gazette and Teachers' Aid (0013-1342); (1991-1993): Education Quarterly (1036-5427); Which was formerly (until 1991): Education Victoria (0817-0975); (1972-1986): Polycom (0311-1962)
Indexed: AEI.
Published by: Department of Education, GPO Box 4367, Melbourne, VIC 3001, Australia. TEL 61-3-6372868, FAX 61-3-6372626, http://www.sofweb.vic.edu.au/news/vsn. Ed. David Ahern. Adv. contact Heather Parry. page AUD 2,220. Circ: 65,000.

370 GBR ISSN 0013-1547
➤ **EDUCATION TODAY (LONDON).** Text in English. 1950. 4/yr. GBP 120 domestic to non-members; GBP 130 in Europe to non-members; GBP 135 elsewhere to non-members (effective 2004). adv. bk.rev. back issues avail.; reprint service avail. from PQC. **Document type:** *Journal, Academic/Scholarly.*
Description: Features articles on relevant teaching and education issues and research.
Related titles: Microfiche ed.; Microfilm ed.
Indexed: CPE, RI-1, RI-2, SWA.
—BLDSC (3661.346000), IE, ingenta. **CCC.**
Published by: College of Teachers, University of London, Institute of Education, 57 Gordon Sq, London, WC1H 0NU, United Kingdom. enquiries@cot.ac.uk, http://www.collegeofteachers.ac.uk/educationtoday.htm. Circ: 3,900.

370 GBR ISSN 0969-0069
EDUCATION U S A. Text in English. 1991. a. GBP 30 per issue (effective 2003). adv. **Document type:** *Journal, Trade.*
Description: Provides information to promote English language learning in the US language schools. Includes information and advice to students considering English language courses in the USA including information on courses, visa requirements, accommodation and other valuable information.
Published by: Nexus Media Ltd. (Subsidiary of: Highbury House Communications PLC), Nexus House, Azalea Dr, Swanley, Kent BR8 8HU, United Kingdom. TEL 44-1322-660070, FAX 44-1322-616311, info@nexusmedia.com, http://www.hhc.co.uk/educationusa. adv.: B&W page GBP 2,480, color page GBP 3,775; trim 214 x 279. Circ: 27,000.

370 USA ISSN 1091-2622
L11
EDUCATION UPDATE (ALEXANDRIA). Text in English. 1980. 8/yr. USD 36; free to members (effective 2005). charts; illus. **Document type:** *Newsletter, Trade.* **Description:** Reports on ASCD projects and conferences, and discusses important contemporary trends and issues influencing education.
Incorporates (1981-2005): Curriculum Update (0734-0044); Formerly: A S C D Update (0733-3293)
Related titles: Online - full text ed.; ♦ Supplement(s): Curriculum Update. ISSN 0734-0044.
—**CCC.**
Published by: Association for Supervision and Curriculum Development, 1703 N Beauregard St, Alexandria, VA 22311. TEL 703-578-9600, FAX 703-575-5400, update@ascd.org, http://www.ascd.org/cms/index.cfm?TheViewID=368. Ed. Scott Willis. Circ: 190,000.

370 USA
EDUCATION UPDATE (NEW YORK); education news for a better world tomorrow. Text in English. 1999 (vol.4, no.12). m. USD 30. **Document type:** *Newspaper.*
Published by: Education Update, Inc., 276 Fifth Ave, Ste 1005, New York, NY 10001. TEL 212-481-5519, FAX 212-481-3919, ednews@aol.com, http://www.educationupdate.com. Ed., Pub. Pola Rosen. **Subscr. to:** PO Box 20005, New York, NY 10001.

370 USA ISSN 0277-4232
EDUCATION WEEK; American education's newspaper of record. Text in English. 1981. 44/yr. USD 79.94 domestic to individuals; USD 135.94 in Canada to individuals; USD 208.94 elsewhere to individuals (effective 2005). adv. bk.rev. illus. index. reprints avail. **Document type:** *Newspaper, Trade.*
Description: Weekly review of state and federal K-12 education policy news.
Related titles: Microfilm ed.; Online - full text ed.: Education Week on the Web (from bigchalk, EBSCO Publishing, Factiva, O C L C Online Computer Library Center, Inc., ProQuest Information & Learning).
Indexed: ABIn, EduInd, SRI.
—**CCC.**
Published by: Editorial Projects in Education Inc., 6935 Arlington Rd, Ste 100, Bethesda, MD 20814-5233. TEL 301-280-3100, 800-346-1834, FAX 301-280-3200, ewletter@epe.org, http://www.edweek.org/ew/. Ed., Pub. Ms. Virginia B Edwards. R&P Kay Dorko. Adv. contact Cheryl Staab. Circ: 54,000. **Subscr. to:** Kable Fulfillment Services, Trade Fulfillment Services, Kable Sq, Mount Morris, IL 61054-1473. TEL 740-382-3322, 800-728-2790, FAX 740-389-6720, edwk@kable.com, http://www.kable.com/.

370 GBR ISSN 0143-5469
EDUCATION YEAR BOOK. Text in English. 1939. a. GBP 89 (effective 1999). adv. **Document type:** *Directory.*
Formerly: Education Committees Year Book (0070-9158)
Published by: Pearson Education, 128 Long Acre, London, WC2E 9AN, United Kingdom. TEL 44-20-7447-2000, FAX 44-20-7240-5771. Ed. Claire Rees. Adv. contact Alan Burfoot. B&W page GBP 455; trim 135 x 203.

EDUCATIONAL ABSTRACTS FOR TANZANIA. see *EDUCATION—Abstracting, Bibliographies, Statistics*

370.15 SWE ISSN 0070-9263
LB1051 CODEN: EPINDT
EDUCATIONAL AND PSYCHOLOGICAL INTERACTIONS. Text in English. 1964. irreg. back issues avail. **Document type:** *Journal, Academic/Scholarly.*
Indexed: CDA, CPE, ETA, MEA, PsycholAb, SENA, e-psyche.
—BLDSC (3661.365000), IE, ingenta.
Published by: Malmoe University, Department of Education, Fack 23501, Malmo, 20045, Sweden. FAX 46-40-325-210.

EDUCATIONAL AND PSYCHOLOGICAL MEASUREMENT; devoted to the development and application of measures of individual differences. see *PSYCHOLOGY*

370.72 USA ISSN 1062-7197
LB3051
EDUCATIONAL ASSESSMENT. Text in English. 1993. q., latest vol.9. USD 300 in US & Canada to institutions; USD 330 elsewhere to institutions; USD 315 combined subscription in US & Canada to institutions print & online eds.; USD 345 combined subscription elsewhere to institutions print & online eds. (effective 2006). adv. reprint service avail. from PSC. **Document type:** *Journal, Academic/Scholarly.* **Description:** Publishes original research and scholarship on the assessment of individuals, groups and programs in educational settings. Covers a broad range of issues related to theory, empirical research, and practice in the appraisal of educational achievements by students and teachers, young children and adults, and novices and experts.
Related titles: Online - full text ed.: ISSN 1532-6977. USD 285 worldwide to institutions (effective 2006) (from EBSCO Publishing, Gale Group, O C L C Online Computer Library Center, Inc., Swets Information Services).
Indexed: ABIn, CIJE, CPE, ERA, ETA, EduInd, MEA, PsycInfo, PsycholAb, RHEA, SEA, SENA, SOMA, TEA, e-psyche.
—BLDSC (3661.366800), IE, Infotrieve, ingenta.
Published by: Lawrence Erlbaum Associates, Inc., 10 Industrial Ave, Mahwah, NJ 07430-2262. TEL 201-258-2200, 800-926-6579, FAX 201-236-0072, journals@erlbaum.com, http://www.leaonline.com/loi/ea, http://www.erlbaum.com. Ed. Joan Herman. adv.: page USD 325; trim 5 x 8.

370 USA ISSN 0146-9282
LC1047.822.K2
➤ **EDUCATIONAL CONSIDERATIONS.** Text in English. 1973. 2/yr. USD 13 (effective 2001). bk.rev. charts; illus.; stat. back issues avail. **Document type:** *Journal, Academic/Scholarly.*
Related titles: Online - full content ed.
Indexed: AgeL, EAA.
—BLDSC (3661.382500), IE, ingenta.
Published by: Kansas State University, College of Education, Bluemont Hall 369, Manhattan, KS 66506. TEL 913-532-5543, FAX 913-532-7304, finance@ksu.edu, http://www2.educ.ksu.edu/projects/edconsiderations/. Ed., R&P David C Thompson. Circ: 1,200 (paid).

370 GBR
EDUCATIONAL COURSES IN GREAT BRITAIN AND AMERICA✶. Text in English. 1980. bi-m.
Published by: Dominion Press Ltd., Dominion House, Signal House, Lyon Rd, Harrow, Mddx HA1 2QE, United Kingdom.

370 CAN ISSN 0046-1482
EDUCATIONAL DIGEST. Text in English. 1969. q. CND 65, USD 65 (effective 1999). adv. bk.rev.; film rev. tr.lit. reprint service avail. from PQC. **Document type:** *Trade.*
Incorporates (in 1973): Canadian University & College (0008-526X); Which was formerly (1966-1969): Canadian University (0315-1565); (1932-1972): School Progress (0036-6757); Which incorporated (19??-1971): Educational Media (0013-1814); Which was formerly (until 1969): Canadian Audio-Visual Review
Related titles: Microform ed.: (from PQC); Online - full text ed.: (from Micromedia ProQuest, Northern Light Technology, Inc., ProQuest Information & Learning).
Indexed: BRI, CBRI, CEI, CPE, RILM.
—IE, Infotrieve.
Published by: Zanny Publications Ltd., 11966 Woodbine Ave, Gormley, ON L0H 1G0, Canada. TEL 905-887-5048, FAX 905-887-0764. Ed. Amy Margaret. Pub., R&P, Adv. contact Janet Gardiner. B&W page CND 3,270, color page CND 4,395; trim 10.75 x 8.25. Circ: 18,506.

371.6 USA ISSN 1059-7417
EDUCATIONAL FACILITY PLANNER. Text in English. 1969. q. USD 40 to non-members (effective 2000). adv. bk.rev. illus. reprint service avail. from PQC.
Formerly (until 1989): C E F P Journal (0007-8220)
Media: Duplicated (not offset). **Related titles:** Microform ed.: 1969 (from PQC).
Indexed: CIJE, EAA.
—BLDSC (3661.407500), IE, ingenta.
Published by: Council of Educational Facility Planners, 9180 E Desert Cove Dr, Ste 104, Scottsdale, AZ 85260-6231. TEL 480-391-0840, FAX 480-391-0940, contact@cefpi.org, http://www.cefpi.org/. Circ: (controlled).

370 USA ISSN 0013-175X
L11
➤ **EDUCATIONAL HORIZONS.** Text in English. 1921. q. USD 18 domestic; USD 25 foreign (effective 2004). adv. bk.rev.; software rev. illus. index. reprint service avail. from PQC. **Document type:** *Journal, Academic/Scholarly.*
Related titles: Microform ed.: (from PQC); Online - full text ed.: (from H.W. Wilson, O C L C Online Computer Library Center, Inc.).
Indexed: ABIn, CIJE, CPE, CurCont, ECER, ERA, ETA, EduInd, MEA, MEA&I, PCI, RHEA, SEA, SENA, SOMA, SOPODA, TEA.
—BLDSC (3661.417000), IE, ingenta.
Published by: Pi Lambda Theta, Inc., 4101 E Third St, Box 6626, Bloomington, IN 47407-6626. TEL 812-339-3411, FAX 812-339-3462, root@pilambda.org, http://www.pilambda.org/. Ed. Juli Knutson. R&P Rob Ehrgott. Circ: 13,000.

➤ **EDUCATIONAL INDEX OF ARABIC PERIODICALS.** see *EDUCATION—Abstracting, Bibliographies, Statistics*

➤ **EDUCATIONAL INDEX OF FOREIGN PERIODICALS.** see *EDUCATION—Abstracting, Bibliographies, Statistics*

370 IND ISSN 0013-1768
EDUCATIONAL INDIA. Text in English. 1965 (vol.32). m. INR 5.50. adv. bk.rev. illus. index.
Indexed: BAS.
Address: Vidya Bhavan, Jagannath Puram, Masulipatnam, Andhra Pradesh, India. Ed. M Venkatarangaiya.

EDUCATIONAL INDICATIVE ABSTRACTS. see *EDUCATION—Abstracting, Bibliographies, Statistics*

EDUCATIONAL INFORMATION ABSTRACTS. see *EDUCATION—Abstracting, Bibliographies, Statistics*

370.9 CHE ISSN 0259-3904
LB1027.3
EDUCATIONAL INNOVATION AND INFORMATION. Text in English. 1975. q. free. bibl. reprint service avail. from PQC. **Document type:** *Newsletter.* **Description:** Provides information about developments in education worldwide.
Incorporates: Innovation (0251-6128); I B E D O C Information Newsletter (0251-5792); Communication Newsletter
Related titles: Microfilm ed.: (from PQC); Online - full text ed.; Spanish ed.: Informacion y Innovacion Educacionales. ISSN 1014-3548; French ed.: Information et Innovation en Education. ISSN 1014-353X.
Indexed: PROMT.
—BLDSC (3661.421000).
Published by: UNESCO, International Bureau of Education, Case Postale 199, Geneva 20, 1211, Switzerland. TEL 41-22-9177837, FAX 41-22-9177801, http://www.ibe.unesco.org. Ed. Jacques Hallak. R&P John Fox. Circ: 5,000.

370.72 CAN
➤ **EDUCATIONAL INSIGHTS**; electronic journal of graduate student research. Text in English. 1992. irreg. bk.rev. **Document type:** *Journal, Academic/Scholarly.* **Description:** Provides graduate students a forum for publishing their research in education.
Media: Online - full content.

E

Published by: (Centre for the Study of Curriculum and Instruction), University of British Columbia, Faculty of Education, 2329 West Mall, Vancouver, BC V6T 1Z4, Canada. TEL 604-822-6502, FAX 604-822-8234, jhu@interchange.ubc.ca, http://www.csci.educ.ubc.ca/publication/insights/. Ed., Adv. contact Jim Hu.

370 ZAF
EDUCATIONAL JOURNAL. Text in English. 8/yr. ZAR 2. adv.
Indexed: EAA.
Published by: Teachers' League of South Africa, Upper Bloem St, Cape Town, 8001, South Africa. Ed. H N Kies.

EDUCATIONAL LAW JOURNAL. see *LAW*

EDUCATIONAL LEGISLATION INDEX. see *LAW—Abstracting, Bibliographies, Statistics*

▼ **EDUCATIONAL LINGUISTICS.** see *LINGUISTICS*

371.26 USA ISSN 0731-1745
LB3051
➤ **EDUCATIONAL MEASUREMENT: ISSUES AND PRACTICE.** Text in English. 1982. q. USD 25 to individuals; USD 30 to institutions (effective 2004). bk.rev. illus. reprint service avail. from PQC,PSC. **Document type:** *Journal, Academic/Scholarly.*
Supersedes: National Council on Measurement in Education. Measurement News (0025-6315); Formerly: N C M E Newsletter
Related titles: Online - full text ed.: ISSN 1745-3992 (from Blackwell Synergy, EBSCO Publishing, O C L C Online Computer Library Center, Inc., ProQuest Information & Learning, Swets Information Services).
Indexed: ABIn, CIJE, CPE, EduInd, PsycInfo, PsycholAb, e-psyche.
—BLDSC (3661.446000), IE, Infotrieve, ingenta. **CCC.**
Published by: (National Council on Measurement in Education), Blackwell Publishing, Inc. (Subsidiary of: Blackwell Publishing Ltd.), Commerce Place, 350 Main St, Malden, MA 02148. TEL 781-388-8206, FAX 781-388-8232, subscrip@blackwellpub.com, http://www.ncme.org/pubs/emip.ace, http://www.blackwellpublishing.com. Ed. Jeffrey Smith. Pub. Thomas Campbell. R&P Meredith Scott. Circ: 2,600.

370 IND
EDUCATIONAL MISCELLANY. Text in English. s-a.
Published by: Directorate of Higher Education, Publications Unit, Old Flowers Corner Bldg., Melarmath, Agartala, Tripura 799 001, India.

370.1 USA ISSN 1539-5367
EDUCATIONAL PATHWAYS. Text in English. 2002. m. USD 119 to individuals; USD 238 to institutions (effective 2005). **Document type:** *Journal, Trade.* **Description:** Covers distance learning and teaching in higher education.
Related titles: Online - full content ed.; Online - full text ed.: (from EBSCO Publishing).
Published by: Lorenzo Associates, Inc., 6011 Railroad St., PO Box 74, Clarence Center, NY 14032. TEL 716-741-2271, FAX 716-741-2272, info@edpath.com, http://www.edpath.com/. Ed., Pub. George Lorenzo.

371.7 USA ISSN 0013-1849
LB2278.H3
EDUCATIONAL PERSPECTIVES. Text in English. 1962. s-a. USD 10; USD 5 per issue (effective 2005). bk.rev. illus. back issues avail.; reprint service avail. from PQC. **Document type:** *Journal, Academic/Scholarly.*
Related titles: Microform ed.: (from PQC).
Indexed: CIJE, CPE, ERA, ETA, MEA, RHEA, SEA, SENA, SOMA, SPPI, TEA.
Published by: University of Hawaii at Manoa, College of Education, 1776 University Ave, Honolulu, HI 96822. TEL 808-956-4242, FAX 808-956-9100, hunter@hawaii.edu, http://www.hawaii.edu/edper. Ed., R&P Hunter McEwan. Circ: 1,000.

370.1 GBR ISSN 0013-1857
LB1025.2
➤ **EDUCATIONAL PHILOSOPHY AND THEORY.** Text in English. 1969. bi-m. EUR 95 combined subscription in Europe to individuals print & online eds.; USD 106 combined subscription in the Americas to individuals & Caribbean (print & online eds.); AUD 95 combined subscription in Australia & New Zealand to individuals print & online eds.; GBP 63 combined subscription elsewhere to individuals print & online eds.; USD 511 combined subscription in the Americas to institutions & Caribbean (print & online eds.); AUD 441 combined subscription in Australia & New Zealand to institutions print & online eds.; GBP 304 combined subscription elsewhere to institutions print & online eds. (effective 2006). bk.rev. back issues avail.; reprint service avail. from PQC,PSC. **Document type:** *Journal, Academic/Scholarly.* **Description:** Publishes articles concerned with all aspects of educational philosophy.
Related titles: Microfiche ed.: (from PQC); Online - full text ed.: ISSN 1469-5812. USD 486 in the Americas to institutions & Caribbean; AUD 419 in Australia & New Zealand to institutions; GBP 289 elsewhere to institutions (effective 2006) (from Blackwell Synergy, EBSCO Publishing, Gale Group, IngentaConnect, O C L C Online Computer Library Center, Inc., R M I T Publishing, Swets Information Services).
Indexed: AEI, AusPAIS, CPE, EAA, ERA, ETA, HECAB, L&LBA, MEA, PCI, PhilInd, RHEA, SEA, SENA, SOMA, TEA.
—BLDSC (3661.480000), IE, Infotrieve, ingenta. **CCC.**
Published by: (Philosophy of Education Society of Australasia), Blackwell Publishing Ltd., 9600 Garsington Rd, Oxford, OX4 2ZG, United Kingdom. TEL 44-1865-776868, FAX 44-1865-714591, customerservices@oxon.blackwellpublishing.com, http://www.blackwellpublishing.com/journals/EPAT. Circ: 700.

371.207 USA ISSN 0315-9388
CODEN: SUOPAD
➤ **EDUCATIONAL PLANNING.** Text in English. 1972-1975; resumed 1985. q. USD 35 membership (effective 2005). adv. bk.rev. **Document type:** *Journal, Academic/Scholarly.*
Formerly: Education Tomorrow
—BLDSC (3661.482000), IE. **CCC.**
Published by: International Society for Educational Planning, c/o Dr. Walter S. Polka, Superintendent, Lewiston-Porter Central School, 4061 Creek Rd, Youngstown, NY 14174. http://web.ics.purdue.edu/~bmcinern/. Ed. P. Rudy Mattai. Circ: 700.

➤ **EDUCATIONAL PSYCHOLOGIST.** see *PSYCHOLOGY*

370.15 GBR ISSN 0144-3410
LB1051 CODEN: EDPSFV
➤ **EDUCATIONAL PSYCHOLOGY;** an international journal of experimental educational psychology. Text in English. 1981. bi-m. GBP 930, USD 1,781 combined subscription to institutions print & online eds. (effective 2006). adv. bk.rev. stat. index. reprint service avail. from PSC. **Document type:** *Journal, Academic/Scholarly.* **Description:** Provides an international forum for the discussion and rapid dissemination of research findings in psychology relevant to education. Aims to be a primary source for articles dealing with the psychological aspects of education ranging from pre-school to tertiary provision and the education of children with special needs.
Related titles: Microfiche ed.; Online - full text ed.: ISSN 1469-5820. GBP 884, USD 1,692 to institutions (effective 2006) (from EBSCO Publishing, Gale Group, IngentaConnect, Northern Light Technology, Inc., O C L C Online Computer Library Center, Inc., ProQuest Information & Learning, Swets Information Services).
Indexed: BAS, BrEdI, CDA, CIJE, CPE, ChLitAb, DIP, ERA, ETA, FamI, IBR, IBZ, L&LBA, MEA, PsycInfo, PsycholAb, RHEA, RILM, SEA, SENA, SOMA, SOPODA, SWA, TEA.
—BLDSC (3661.535000), IE, Infotrieve, ingenta. **CCC.**
Published by: Routledge (Subsidiary of: Taylor & Francis Group), 4 Park Sq, Milton Park, Abingdon, Oxon OX14 4RN, United Kingdom. TEL 44-1235-828600, FAX 44-1235-829000, info@routledge.co.uk, http://www.tandf.co.uk/journals/titles/01443410.asp, http://www.routledge.com. Eds. Kevin Wheldall, Dr. Richard Riding. Circ: 1,000. **Subscr. in N. America to:** Taylor & Francis Inc., Customer Services Dept, 325 Chestnut St, 8th Fl, Philadelphia, PA 19106. TEL 215-625-8900, 800-354-1420, FAX 215-625-8914, customerservice@taylorandfrancis.com; **Subscr. to:** Taylor & Francis Ltd, Journals Customer Service, Rankine Rd, Basingstoke, Hants RG24 8PR, United Kingdom. TEL 44-1256-813000, FAX 44-1256-330245.

370.15 USA
EDUCATIONAL PSYCHOLOGY. Text in English. irreg., latest 2003. price varies. **Document type:** *Monographic series, Academic/Scholarly.*
Indexed: e-psyche.
Published by: Lawrence Erlbaum Associates, Inc., 10 Industrial Ave, Mahwah, NJ 07430-2262. TEL 201-258-2200, 800-926-6579, FAX 201-236-0072, journals@erlbaum.com, http://www.erlbaum.com.

370.15 GBR ISSN 0266-7363
➤ **EDUCATIONAL PSYCHOLOGY IN PRACTICE.** Text in English. q. GBP 200, USD 330 combined subscription to institutions print & online eds. (effective 2006). adv. bk.rev. bibl.; illus. index. back issues avail.; reprint service avail. from PQC,PSC. **Document type:** *Journal, Academic/Scholarly.* **Description:** Features new ideas and the latest developments, plus informational articles about the practical aspects of educational psychology.
Formerly: A E P Journal (0309-3573)
Related titles: Microfilm ed.; Online - full text ed.: ISSN 1469-5839. GBP 190, USD 314 to institutions (effective 2006) (from EBSCO Publishing, Gale Group, IngentaConnect, O C L C Online Computer Library Center, Inc., Swets Information Services).
Indexed: BrEdI, CPE, EAA, ERA, ETA, MEA, PsycInfo, PsycholAb, RHEA, SEA, SENA, SOMA, SWA, TEA, V&AA, e-psyche.
—BLDSC (3661.540000), IE, Infotrieve, ingenta. **CCC.**
Published by: (Association of Educational Psychologists), Routledge (Subsidiary of: Taylor & Francis Group), 4 Park Sq, Milton Park, Abingdon, Oxon OX14 4RN, United Kingdom. TEL 44-1235-828600, FAX 44-1235-829000, info@routledge.co.uk, http://www.tandf.co.uk/journals/titles/02667363.asp, http://www.routledge.com. Ed. Jeremy Monsen. Circ: 2,800. **Subscr. to:** Taylor & Francis Ltd, Journals Customer Service, Rankine Rd, Basingstoke, Hants RG24 8PR, United Kingdom. TEL 44-1256-813000, FAX 44-1256-330245.

370.15 USA ISSN 1040-726X
LB1051 CODEN: EPSREO
➤ **EDUCATIONAL PSYCHOLOGY REVIEW.** Text in English. 1989. q. EUR 558, USD 578, GBP 328 combined subscription to institutions print & online eds. (effective 2005). adv. illus. back issues avail.; reprint service avail. from PSC. **Document type:** *Journal, Academic/Scholarly.* **Description:** Publishes review articles in general education psychology: learning, cognition, measurement, school-related counseling, and development.
Related titles: Microfilm ed.: (from PQC); Online - full text ed.: ISSN 1573-336X (from EBSCO Publishing, Gale Group, IngentaConnect, Kluwer Online, O C L C Online Computer Library Center, Inc., Springer LINK, Swets Information Services).
Indexed: ABIn, ASCA, BibLing, CJA, CPE, CurCont, ERA, ETA, EduInd, FamI, L&LBA, MEA, PsycInfo, PsycholAb, RHEA, RefZh, SEA, SENA, SOMA, SOPODA, SSCI, SWA, TEA, e-psyche.
—BLDSC (3661.545000), IDS, IE, Infotrieve, ingenta. **CCC.**
Published by: Plenum US (Subsidiary of: Springer Science+Business Media), 233 Spring St, New York, NY 10013. TEL 212-460-1500, FAX 212-460-1575, service@springer-ny.com, http://springerlink.metapress.com/openurl.asp?genre=journal&issn=1040-726X, http://www.springeronline.com. Ed. Kenneth A Kierwa.

➤ **EDUCATIONAL RANKINGS ANNUAL.** see *EDUCATION—Abstracting, Bibliographies, Statistics*

370.72 GBR ISSN 0013-1881
CODEN: EDURAE
➤ **EDUCATIONAL RESEARCH.** Text in English. 1958. 3/yr. GBP 197, USD 324 combined subscription to institutions print & online eds. (effective 2006). adv. bk.rev. illus. Index. back issues avail.; reprint service avail. from PSC. **Document type:** *Journal, Academic/Scholarly.* **Description:** Presents research findings in all levels of education from policy-making to classroom teaching.
Related titles: Microfiche ed.: (from SWZ); Online - full text ed.: ISSN 1469-5847. GBP 187, USD 308 to institutions (effective 2006) (from EBSCO Publishing, Gale Group, IngentaConnect, O C L C Online Computer Library Center, Inc., Swets Information Services).
Indexed: ABIn, AMHA, ASCA, ArtHuCI, BrEdI, CDA, CIJE, CJA, CMCI, CPE, ChLitAb, CurCont, DIP, EAA, ERA, ETA, EduInd, FamI, HECAB, IBR, IBSS, IBZ, LT&LA, MEA, MEA&I, PCI, PsycInfo, PsycholAb, REE&TA, RHEA, SEA, SENA, SOMA, SRRA, SSCI, SWA, TEA, e-psyche.
—BLDSC (3661.840000), IDS, IE, Infotrieve, ingenta. **CCC.**
Published by: (National Foundation for Educational Research), Routledge (Subsidiary of: Taylor & Francis Group), 4 Park Square, Milton Park, Abingdon, Oxon OX14 4RN, United Kingdom. TEL 44-1235-828600, FAX 44-1235-829000, info@routledge.co.uk, http://www.tandf.co.uk/journals/routledge/00131881.asp, http://www.routledge.co.uk. Ed. Dr. Seamus Hegarty. R&P Sally Sweet. adv.: page GBP 200; trim 213 x 122. Circ: 2,500.

370.72 NLD ISSN 1380-3611
L21 CODEN: EREVFF
➤ **EDUCATIONAL RESEARCH AND EVALUATION;** an international journal on theory and practice. Text and summaries in English. 1995. 6/yr. GBP 313, USD 534 combined subscription to institutions print & online eds. (effective 2006). adv. bk.rev. index. back issues avail.; reprint service avail. from PSC. **Document type:** *Journal, Academic/Scholarly.* **Description:** Publishes research from all nations relating to the practice of education. Communicates findings from many perspectives, national contexts and methodologies.
Related titles: Microfilm ed.: (from SWZ); Online - full text ed.: ISSN 1744-4187. GBP 297, USD 507 to institutions (effective 2006) (from EBSCO Publishing, Gale Group, IngentaConnect, O C L C Online Computer Library Center, Inc., Swets Information Services).
Indexed: BrEdI, CIJE, CPE, ERA, ETA, MEA, PsycInfo, PsycholAb, RHEA, SEA, SENA, SOMA, TEA.
—BLDSC (3661.844500), IE, Infotrieve, ingenta. **CCC.**
Published by: (European Educational Research Association GBR), Taylor & Francis The Netherlands (Subsidiary of: Taylor & Francis Group), Schipolweg 107 C, PO Box 447, Leiden, 2316 XC, Netherlands. pub@swets.nl, http://www.tandf.co.uk/journals/titles/13803611.asp, http://www.tandf.co.uk/swets.asp. Ed. Bert P M Creemers. adv.: page EUR 225; trim 160 x 240. Circ: 500 (paid).

370.72 NLD ISSN 1570-2081
EDUCATIONAL RESEARCH FOR POLICY AND PRACTICE. Text in English. 2002. 3/yr. EUR 161, USD 161, GBP 106 combined subscription to institutions print & online eds. (effective 2005). adv. reprint service avail. from PSC.

E

▼ *new title* ➤ *refereed* ✶ *unverified* ♦ *full entry avail.*

Related titles: Online - full text ed.: ISSN 1573-1723. USD 45 to individuals (effective 2003); USD 161 to institutions (effective 2005) (from EBSCO Publishing, Gale Group, IngentaConnect, Kluwer Online, O C L C Online Computer Library Center, Inc., Springer LINK, Swets Information Services).
Indexed: BibLing.
—BLDSC (3661.953150), IE, ingenta. **CCC.**
Published by: Springer-Verlag Dordrecht (Subsidiary of: Springer Science+Business Media), Van Godewijckstraat 30, Dordrecht, 3311 GX, Netherlands. TEL 31-78-6576050, FAX 31-78-6576474, http://springerlink.metapress.com/openurl.asp?genre=journal&issn=1570-2081, http://www.springeronline.com. Ed. Colin N Power.

370.72 GBR
EDUCATIONAL RESEARCH MONOGRAPH SERIES. Text in English. 1994. irreg., latest vol.7. adv. **Document type:** *Monographic series.*
Published by: (Research Support Unit), University of Exeter, School of Education, School Of Education, Heavitree Rd, Exeter, EX1 2LU, United Kingdom. TEL 01392-264781. Ed. Hilary Radnor. Adv. contact J Barrett.

370.72 GBR
EDUCATIONAL RESEARCH NETWORK JOURNAL. Text in English. 1987. a. GBP 6 (effective 1999). adv. **Document type:** *Academic/Scholarly.*
Former titles (until 1992): Educational Research Network of Northern Ireland. Journal (0957-8064); (until 1988): Educational Research Network of Northern Ireland. Bulletin (0959-2563)
—BLDSC (3661.947000).
Published by: Educational Research Network of Northern Ireland, University of Ulster at Jordantown, Shore Rd, Newtownabbey, Antrim, United Kingdom. TEL 44-232-365131, B.Hutchinson@ulst.ac.uk. Ed. Dr. Peter Whitehouse. Circ: 80.

370.72 USA ISSN 0196-5042
L11
➤ **EDUCATIONAL RESEARCH QUARTERLY.** Text in English. 1950. q. USD 76.50 to individuals; USD 120 to institutions; USD 140 foreign to institutions (effective Jun. 1999). adv. bk.rev. bibl.; charts. index. reprint service avail. from PQC. **Document type:** *Academic/Scholarly.*
Formerly (until 1976): California Journal of Educational Research (0008-1213)
Related titles: Microfilm ed.: (from PQC); Online - full text ed.: (from EBSCO Publishing, Northern Light Technology, Inc., ProQuest Information & Learning).
Indexed: ABIn, CIJE, CPE, ChPerl, CurCont, ERA, ETA, EduInd, FamI, MEA&I, PsycholAb, RHEA, SEA, SENA, SOMA, SOPODA, SSA, SSCI, TEA.
—BLDSC (3661.953200), IE, Infotrieve, ingenta.
Address: 113 Greenbriar Dr, West Monroe, LA 71291. TEL 318-274-2355, hashway@alphagram.edu. Ed. Robert M Hashway. Circ: 1,500.

370 USA ISSN 1747-938X
▼ **EDUCATIONAL RESEARCH REVIEW.** Text in English. forthcoming 2006. s-a. **Document type:** *Journal, Academic/Scholarly.* **Description:** Aimed at researchers and various agencies interested to review studies in education and instruction at any level. The journal will accept meta-analytic reviews, narrative reviews and best-evidence syntheses.
Published by: Academic Press (Subsidiary of: Elsevier Science & Technology), 525 B St, Ste 1900, San Diego, CA 92101-4495. TEL 619-231-6616, FAX 619-699-6422, http://www.elsevier.com/wps/find/journaldescription.cws_home/706817/description#description, http://www.academicpress.com. Ed. F Dochy.

E

370 USA ISSN 0013-189X
L11
➤ **EDUCATIONAL RESEARCHER.** Text in English. 1972. 9/yr. USD 48 to individuals; USD 150 to institutions (effective 2005). adv. bk.rev. illus. Index. reprint service avail. from PQC. **Document type:** *Journal, Academic/Scholarly.* **Description:** Contains news and features of general significance in educational research.
Media: Duplicated (not offset). **Related titles:** Microform ed.: (from PQC); Online - full content ed.: E R Online; Online - full text ed.: (from H.W. Wilson, JSTOR (Web-based Journal Archive), O C L C Online Computer Library Center, Inc., ProQuest Information & Learning).
Indexed: ABIn, AMHA, CIJE, CPE, DIP, EAA, ECER, ERA, ETA, EduInd, HEA, IBR, IBZ, MEA, MEA&I, RHEA, SEA, TEA.
—BLDSC (3661.955000), IE, Infotrieve, ingenta. **CCC.**
Published by: American Educational Research Association, 1230 17th St, N W, Washington, DC 20036-3078. TEL 202-223-9485, FAX 202-775-1824, http://aera.net. Eds. Michele L Foster, Stafford Hood. Adv. contact Barbara Leitham. Circ: 22,500 (controlled).

370 GBR ISSN 0013-1911
➤ **EDUCATIONAL REVIEW.** Text in English. 1948. q. GBP 736, USD 1,627 combined subscription to institutions print & online eds. (effective 2006). adv. bk.rev. bibl. index. back issues avail.; reprint service avail. from PSC. **Document type:** *Journal, Academic/Scholarly.* **Description:** Publishes articles and report research across a range of education fields including curriculum, inclusive and special education, educational psychology, policy, management and international and comparative education.
Related titles: Microfiche ed.: (from SWZ); Online - full text ed.: ISSN 1465-3397. GBP 699, USD 1,546 to institutions (effective 2006) (from EBSCO Publishing, Gale Group, IngentaConnect, Northern Light Technology, Inc., O C L C Online Computer Library Center, Inc., ProQuest Information & Learning, Swets Information Services).
Indexed: ABIn, ArtHuCI, BrEdI, CIJE, CPE, ChLitAb, CurCont, DIP, EAA, ERA, ETA, EduInd, FamI, IBR, IBSS, IBZ, L&LBA, LT&LA, MEA, PCI, PRA, PsycInfo, PsycholAb, RHEA, SEA, SENA, SOMA, SOPODA, SSA, SSCI, SWA, TEA, V&AA, WBA, WMB.
—BLDSC (3661.960000), IDS, IE, Infotrieve, ingenta. **CCC.**
Published by: (University of Birmingham, School of Education), Routledge (Subsidiary of: Taylor & Francis Group), 4 Park Sq, Milton Park, Abingdon, Oxon OX14 4RN, United Kingdom. TEL 44-1235-828600, FAX 44-1235-829000, info@routledge.co.uk, http://www.tandf.co.uk/journals/titles/00131911.asp, http://www.routledge.com. Ed. Deirdre M Martin. adv.: B&W page GBP 350, color page GBP 1,200; trim 130 x 210. Circ: 800 (paid and controlled). **Subscr. in N America to:** Taylor & Francis Inc., Customer Services Dept, 325 Chestnut St, 8th Fl, Philadelphia, PA 19106. TEL 215-625-8900, 800-354-1420, FAX 215-625-8914, customerservice@taylorandfrancis.com; **Subscr. to:** Taylor & Francis Ltd, Journals Customer Service, Rankine Rd, Basingstoke, Hants RG24 8PR, United Kingdom. TEL 44-1256-813000, FAX 44-1256-330245.

370 USA ISSN 1542-5703
▼ **EDUCATIONAL SALES AND MARKETING INSIDER.** Text in English. 2003 (Feb.). m. USD 395 (effective 2003).
Related titles: E-mail ed.: ISSN 1542-5711.
Published by: Quality Education Data, Inc., 1625 Broadway Ste. 250, Denver, CO 80202. TEL 800-525-5811, FAX 303-860-0238, info@qeddata.com, http://www.qeddata.com.

EDUCATIONAL SELECTIVE ABSTRACTS. see *EDUCATION—Abstracting, Bibliographies, Statistics*

370 USA ISSN 0013-1946
L11
➤ **EDUCATIONAL STUDIES**; a journal of the American Educational Studies Associations. Text in English. 1970. bi-m. (in 2 vols.). USD 335 in US & Canada to institutions; USD 380 elsewhere to institutions; USD 350 combined subscription in US & Canada to institutions print & online eds.; USD 395 combined subscription elsewhere to institutions print & online eds. (effective 2006). adv. bk.rev. illus. index. back issues avail.; reprint service avail. from PSC. **Document type:** *Journal, Academic/Scholarly.* **Description:** Covers academic articles providing members of the American Educational Studies Association and other foundations of education scholars another vehicle for the dissemination of their research. Includes poetry, essay reviews and submisions dealing with the Social Foundations Classroom.
Related titles: Microfilm ed.: (from PQC); Online - full text ed.: ISSN 1532-6993. USD 315 worldwide to institutions (effective 2005) (from EBSCO Publishing, Gale Group, H.W. Wilson, O C L C Online Computer Library Center, Inc., Swets Information Services).
Indexed: ABIn, ABS&EES, ArtHuCI, BRD, BRI, CBRI, CIJE, CPE, ChLitAb, CurCont, ETA, EduInd, PhilInd, PsycInfo, PsycholAb, RHEA, SSCI.
—BLDSC (3662.512000), IE, Infotrieve. **CCC.**
Published by: (American Educational Studies Association), Lawrence Erlbaum Associates, Inc., 10 Industrial Ave, Mahwah, NJ 07430-2262. TEL 201-258-2200, 800-926-6579, FAX 201-236-0072, journals@erlbaum.com, http://www.leaonline.com/loi/es. Ed. Rebecca Martusewicz. adv.: page USD 350; trim 5 x 8. Circ: 1,300.

370 GBR ISSN 0305-5698
L16
➤ **EDUCATIONAL STUDIES.** Text in English. 1975. q. GBP 645, USD 1,313 combined subscription to institutions print & online eds. (effective 2006). adv. bk.rev. abstr. index. back issues avail.; reprint service avail. from PSC. **Document type:** *Journal, Academic/Scholarly.* **Description:** Aims to provide a forum for original investigations and theoretical studies in education.
Related titles: Microfiche ed.; Online - full text ed.: ISSN 1465-3400. GBP 613, USD 1,247 to institutions (effective 2006) (from EBSCO Publishing, Gale Group, IngentaConnect, O C L C Online Computer Library Center, Inc., ProQuest Information & Learning, Swets Information Services).
Indexed: ABIn, BRI, BrEdI, CIJE, CPE, CurCont, DIP, EAA, ERA, ETA, EduInd, FamI, HECAB, IBR, IBSS, IBZ, L&LBA, LT&LA, MEA, MEA&I, PCI, PSA, PsycInfo, PsycholAb, RHEA, RILM, SEA, SENA, SOMA, SOPODA, SSA, SSCI, SWA, SociolAb, TEA.
—BLDSC (3662.513000), IDS, IE, Infotrieve, ingenta. **CCC.**
Published by: Routledge (Subsidiary of: Taylor & Francis Group), 4 Park Sq, Milton Park, Abingdon, Oxon OX14 4RN, United Kingdom. TEL 44-1235-828600, FAX 44-1235-829000, info@routledge.co.uk, http://www.tandf.co.uk/journals/titles/03055698.asp, http://www.routledge.com. Ed. Derek Cherrington. **Subscr. to:** Taylor & Francis Ltd, Journals Customer Service, Rankine Rd, Basingstoke, Hants RG24 8PR, United Kingdom. TEL 44-1256-813000, FAX 44-1256-330245.

370 FRA ISSN 0070-9344
EDUCATIONAL STUDIES AND DOCUMENTS SERIES. Text in French. 1953. irreg., latest vol.68, 1998. price varies.
Related titles: Microfiche ed.: (from CIS); French ed.: Etudes et Documents d'Education. ISSN 0501-3550.
Indexed: IIS, RRTA, WAE&RSA.
Published by: UNESCO Publishing, 7 place de Fontenoy, Paris, 75352, France. TEL 33-1-45684300, FAX 33-1-45685737, http://www.unesco.org/publications. **Dist. in U.S. by:** Bernan Associates, Bernan, 4611-F Assembly Dr., Lanham, MD 20706-4391. TEL 800-274-4447, FAX 800-865-3450.

EDUCATIONAL STUDIES IN MATHEMATICS; an international journal. see *MATHEMATICS*

370 GBR ISSN 1463-9394
EDUCATIONAL TECHNOLOGY RESEARCH PAPERS SERIES. Text in English. 1998. irreg. **Document type:** *Monographic series, Academic/Scholarly.*
—BLDSC (3662.531600).
Published by: University of Birmingham, Education and Technology Research Group, c/o Professor Mike Sharples, Kodak/Royal Academy of Engineering, School of Electronic & Electrical Engineering, Edgbaston, Birmingham B15 2TT, United Kingdom. TEL 44-121-414-3966, FAX 44-121-414-4291, m.sharples@bham.ac.uk, http://www.eee.bham.ac.uk/et_gr/publications/pub.htm. Ed. Theodoros N Arvanitis.

370 GBR ISSN 1463-9416
EDUCATIONAL TECHNOLOGY TECHNICAL REPORT SERIES. Text in English. 1998. irreg. **Document type:** *Monographic series, Academic/Scholarly.*
Related titles: Online - full text ed.: ISSN 1463-9424.
—BLDSC (3662.533200).
Published by: University of Birmingham, Education and Technology Research Group, c/o Professor Mike Sharples, Kodak/Royal Academy of Engineering, School of Electronic & Electrical Engineering, Edgbaston, Birmingham B15 2TT, United Kingdom. TEL 44-121-414-3966, FAX 44-121-414-4291, m.sharples@bham.ac.uk, http://www.eee.bham.ac.uk/et_gr/publications/pub.htm. Ed. Theodoros N Arvanitis.

EDUCATIONAL THEATRE NEWS. see *THEATER*

370 USA ISSN 0013-2004
L11
➤ **EDUCATIONAL THEORY**; a medium of expression. Text in English. 1951. q. USD 53 combined subscription in the Americas to individuals & Caribbean (print & online eds.); EUR 66 combined subscription in Europe to individuals print & online eds.; GBP 44 combined subscription elsewhere to individuals print & online eds.; USD 119 combined subscription in the Americas to institutions & Caribbean (print & online eds.); GBP 102 combined subscription elsewhere to institutions print & online eds. (effective 2006). adv. bk.rev. illus. index. 1 cols./p.; reprint service avail. from PQC. **Document type:** *Journal, Academic/Scholarly.* **Description:** Publishes work in the philosophy of education, along with related research in other areas.
Related titles: Microform ed.: (from PQC); Online - full text ed.: ISSN 1741-5446. USD 113 in the Americas to institutions & Caribbean; GBP 97 elsewhere to institutions (effective 2006) (from Blackwell Synergy, EBSCO Publishing, Gale Group, IngentaConnect, O C L C Online Computer Library Center, Inc., ProQuest Information & Learning, Swets Information Services).
Indexed: ABIn, BRI, CBRI, CIJE, CPE, CurCont, DIP, ERA, ETA, EduInd, IBR, IBZ, IPB, MEA, PhilInd, RHEA, SEA, SENA, SOPODA, SSA, SSCI, SWA.
—BLDSC (3662.550000), IE, Infotrieve, ingenta. **CCC.**
Published by: Blackwell Publishing, Inc. (Subsidiary of: Blackwell Publishing Ltd.), Commerce Place, 350 Main St, Malden, MA 02148. TEL 781-388-8206, FAX 781-388-8232, edtheory@uiuc.edu, subscrip@blackwellpub.com, http://www.blackwellpublishing.com/journals/EDTH. adv.: page USD 100. Circ: 2,200 (paid).

370.72 IND
EDUCATIONAL TRENDS✶. Text in English. 1972 (vol.6). s-a. INR 10, USD 2. bk.rev. bibl.; charts.
Published by: (Alumni Association), National Council of Educational Research and Training, Regional College of Education, Sri Aurobindo Marg, New Delhi, India. Ed. G N Bhardwaj. Circ: 1,000.

371.1 IND
EDUCATOR. Text in Panjabi. 1960. d. adv. 8 cols./p., **Document type:** *Newspaper.*

Address: 104 DSIDC Complex, Okhla Industrial Area, Phase1, New Delhi, 110 020, India. TEL 6817927, FAX 6810297. Ed. Mastan Singh. Pub. Pritam Singh. Adv. contact Amar Pal Singh. Circ: 31,492.

371.1 ITA ISSN 0391-6375
EDUCATORE. Text in Italian. 1953. fortn. adv.
Formerly (until 1976): Educatore Italiano
Published by: R C S Libri (Subsidiary of: R C S Mediagroup), Via Mecenate, 91, Milan, MI 20138, Italy. TEL 39-02-5095-2248, FAX 39-02-5095-2975, http://rcslibri.corriere.it/libri/index.htm. Ed. Sergio Neri. Circ: 50,000.

371.1 USA ISSN 0013-2047
EDUCATORS' ADVOCATE. Text in English. 1884. bi-m. USD 5 to non-members (effective 2005). adv. **Document type:** *Newsletter, Trade.*
Related titles: Online - full text ed.
Published by: S D E A - N E A, 411 E Capital Ave, Pierre, SD 57501. TEL 605-224-9263, FAX 605-224-5810, scottallen@sdea.org, bstevens@nea.org, http://www.sdea.org. Ed. Jerry Wilson. Circ: 8,400 (controlled).

EDUCATORS GUIDE TO FREE INTERNET RESOURCES (ELEMENTARY-MIDDLE SCHOOL EDITION). see *COMPUTERS—Internet*

EDUCATORS GUIDE TO FREE INTERNET RESOURCES (SECONDARY EDITION). see *COMPUTERS—Internet*

371.192 USA ISSN 1527-4306
EDUCATOR'S NOTEBOOK ON FAMILY INVOLVEMENT. Text in English. 1990. 10/yr. (m. Sep.-June), latest vol.3. USD 98 (effective 2003). bk.rev. 6 p./no. 3 cols./p.; back issues avail. **Document type:** *Newsletter.* **Description:** Practical ideas for schools to promote parent involvement in the education of their children.
Formerly (until 1999): What's Working in Parent Involvement (1053-2609)
Related titles: Online - full text ed.: ISSN 1527-1080; Supplement(s): Ideas Staff Can Use.
Published by: Parent Institute, PO Box 7474, Fairfax, VA 22039-7474. TEL 703-323-9170, 800-756-5525, FAX 703-323-9173, http://www.parent-institute.com. Ed. Betsie Millar. Pub. John H Wherry.

370 VEN ISSN 1316-4910
➤ **EDUCERE**; la revista venezolana de educacion. Text in Spanish. 1997. q. free (effective 2005). **Document type:** *Journal, Academic/Scholarly.*
Media: Online - full text.
Published by: Universidad de los Andes, Merida, Av 3, Independencia, Merida, 5101, Venezuela. TEL 58-275-401111, FAX 58-275-527704, info@saber.ula.ve, http://www.saber.ula.ve/educere/revista/, http://www.ula.ve.

370 POL ISSN 0239-6858
EDUKACJA. Text in Polish. 1975. q. USD 40. **Document type:** *Academic/Scholarly.* **Description:** Covers education issues. For scientists, teachers and students of pedagogy.
Formerly (until 1983): Badania Oswiatowe (0137-1258)
Published by: Instytut Badan Edukacyjnych, ul Gorczewska 8, Warsaw, 01-180, Poland. TEL 48-22-6321868. Ed. Miroslaw Szymanski. **Dist. by:** Ars Polona, Krakowskie Przedmiescie 7, Warsaw, Poland. **Co-sponsor:** Ministerstwo Edukacji Narodowej.

EDUKACJA OGOLNOTECHNICZNA. see *TECHNOLOGY: COMPREHENSIVE WORKS*

EDUKACJA PRAWNICZA. see *LAW*

370 USA
EDUPAGE. Text in English. 1993. 3/w. free (effective 2005). back issues avail. **Document type:** *Bulletin, Trade.* **Description:** Contains summaries of information technology news.
Media: E-mail. **Related titles:** Chinese ed.; Estonian ed.; German ed.; Greek ed.; Hebrew ed.; Italian ed.; Hungarian ed.; Korean ed.; Lithuanian ed.; Portuguese ed.; Romanian ed.; Slovak ed.; Spanish ed.
Published by: Educause, 4772 Walnut St, Ste 206, Boulder, CO 80301-2536. TEL 303-449-4430, FAX 303-440-0461, info@educause.com, http://www.educause.edu/pub/edupage/edupage.html. Ed., R&P Greg Dobbin TEL 303-939-0327.

370 FRA ISSN 1634-359X
EDUQUER. Text in French. 2002. q. **Document type:** *Journal, Academic/Scholarly.*
Published by: L' Harmattan, 5 rue de l'Ecole Polytechnique, Paris, 75005, France. TEL 33-1-43257651, FAX 33-1-43258203, http://www.editions-harmattan.fr.

370 BEL ISSN 1371-1261
➤ **EDUQUER & FORMER**; theories et pratiques. Text in English. 1934; N.S. 1995. q. bk.rev. bibl.; charts. reprint service avail. from PQC,ISI. **Document type:** *Academic/Scholarly.*
Formed by the 1995 merger of: Formations et Technologies (0777-8465); Recherche en Education (0777-0820); Which was formerly (until 1990): Revue Belge de Psychologie et de Pedagogie (0035-0826); (until 1950): Revue des Sciences Pedagogiques (0771-6249)
Indexed: PsycholAb.
Published by: Institut Superieur de Pedagogie de la Region de Bruxelles - Capitale, Bd de Waterloo 100-103, Brussels, 1000, Belgium. TEL 32-2-5428351, FAX 32-2-5428390. Ed. Rene Cousin. **Co-sponsor:** Commission Communitaire Francaise.

370.115 USA ISSN 1552-9029
EDUTOPIA; the new world of learning. Text in English. 1994. bi-m. free to qualified personnel; USD 29.99 domestic; USD 40 in Canada; USD 59 elsewhere (effective 2005). **Document type:** *Magazine, Trade.* **Description:** Covers the latest tools, techniques, and technologies used by educators and students. In September 2004 Edutopia changed its format from the semiannual newsletter to the bimonthly magazine.
Related titles: Online - full text ed.
Published by: George Lucas Educational Foundation, PO Box 3494, San Rafael, CA 94912. TEL 415-507-0399, FAX 415-507-0499, edutopia@glef.org, http://www.edutopia.org/magazine/index.php, http://glef.org/. Ed. James Daly.

370 TUR
EGITIM BULTENI/EDUCATION BULLETIN. Text in Turkish. 1972. m. **Document type:** *Bulletin.*
Indexed: CPE.
Published by: Ministry of National Education & Culture, Lefkosa - Nicosia, Mersin 10, Turkey. TEL 520-83136, FAX 520-82334. Circ: 3,000.

370 DEU
EIBE. Text in German. 1973. q. EUR 2 newsstand/cover (effective 2005). bk.rev. **Document type:** *Bulletin, Trade.* **Description:** Contains information on pedagogical matters.
Formerly: Rund um die Eibe
Published by: Rudolf-Steiner-Schulverein Ottersberg e.V., Amtshof 5, Ottersberg, 28870, Germany. TEL 49-4205-31680, FAX 49-4205-8510. Ed. Bert Blumenthal. Adv. contact Peter Stuehl. Circ: 1,300 (controlled).

372.86 DEU
EINHARD INTERN; Schulzeitschrift des staedtischen Einhard-Gymnasiums Aachen. Text in German. 1978. s-a. adv. bk.rev. back issues avail. **Document type:** *Academic/Scholarly.*
Published by: Staedtisches Einhard-Gymnasium, Robert-Schuman-Str 4, Aachen, 52066, Germany. TEL 49-241-67017. Ed. Juergen Lauer. Circ: 1,000.

EKONOMIKA. VOPROSY SHKOL'NOGO EKONOMICHESKOGO OBRAZOVANIYA. see *BUSINESS AND ECONOMICS*

EL-HI TEXTBOOKS AND SERIALS IN PRINT; including related teaching materials K-12. see *EDUCATION—Abstracting, Bibliographies, Statistics*

370 USA ISSN 1556-5378
LB1028.3
➤ **ELECTRONIC JOURNAL FOR THE INTEGRATION OF TECHNOLOGY IN EDUCATION.** Text in English. 2001. s-a. **Document type:** *Journal, Academic/Scholarly.*
Media: Online - full content.
Published by: Idaho State University, College of Education, Box 8059, Pocatello, ID 83209. http://ejite.isu.edu/.

370.72 USA
➤ **ELECTRONIC JOURNAL OF LITERACY THROUGH SCIENCE.** Text in English. 2002. m. free (effective 2005). **Document type:** *Journal, Academic/Scholarly.* **Description:** Devoted to addressing science education by focusing on issues related to literacy through science for a diverse community.
Media: Online - full content.
Published by: San Jose State University, College of Education, One Washington Sq, San Jose, CA 95192. http://sweeneyhall.sjsu.edu/ejlts/. Ed. Dr. Sharon Parsons.

372.35 USA ISSN 1087-3430
Q181.A1
➤ **ELECTRONIC JOURNAL OF SCIENCE EDUCATION.** Text in English. 1996. q. **Document type:** *Journal, Academic/Scholarly.* **Description:** Offers the science education community, a publication devoted to the earth-friendly, timely sharing of ideas,, information, methods, and research relating to the teaching of science.
Media: Online - full text (from H.W. Wilson, O C L C Online Computer Library Center, Inc.).
Indexed: ABIn, CIJE, CPE, ERA, EduInd.
Published by: University of Nevada at Reno, Department of Curriculum Instruction, College of Education, Mail Stop 282, Reno, NV 89557. TEL 702-784-4961, FAX 702-327-5220, majordomo@unr.edu, jcannon@equinox.unr.edu, http://unr.edu/homepage/jcannon/ejse/ejse.html. Ed., Pub., R&P John R Cannon.

372 155.4 USA ISSN 0013-5984
L11 CODEN: ELSJA2
➤ **THE ELEMENTARY SCHOOL JOURNAL.** Abbreviated title: E S J. Text in English. 1900. 5/yr., latest vol.99, 1998, Sep. USD 43 combined subscription to individuals print & online eds.; USD 158 combined subscription to institutions print & online eds.; USD 14 per issue to individuals; USD 40 per issue to institutions (effective 2006). adv. bk.rev. abstr.; illus. Index. 116 p./no.; back issues avail.; reprint service avail. from PQC,ISI,PSC. **Document type:** *Journal, Academic/Scholarly.* **Description:** Covers student and teacher behavior and interactions in elementary school settings, discusses curricula.
Former titles (until 1914): Elementary School Teacher (1545-5858); (until 1902): Elementary School Teacher and Course of Study (1545-5904); (until 1901): Course of Study (1545-5890)
Related titles: Microform ed.: (from PMC, PQC); Online - full text ed.: ISSN 1554-8279. USD 142 (effective 2005) (from EBSCO Publishing, Gale Group, JSTOR (Web-based Journal Archive), ProQuest Information & Learning).
Indexed: ABIn, ASCA, Acal, CIJE, CPE, ChPerI, CurCont, DSHAb, EAA, ECER, ERA, ETA, EduInd, FamI, L&LBA, MEA, PCI, PsycInfo, PsycholAb, RHEA, SEA, SENA, SOMA, SOPODA, SRRA, SSCI, TEA, e-psyche.
—BLDSC (3727.200000), IDS, IE, Infotrieve, ingenta. **CCC.**
Published by: University of Chicago Press, Journals Division, 1111 E. 60th St, Chicago, IL 60637. subscriptions@press.uchicago.edu, http://www.journals.uchicago.edu/ESJ/home.html. Ed. Thomas L Good. Adv. contact Cheryl Jones. B&W page USD 475; trim 6.75 x 10. Circ: 2,200 (paid). **Subscr. to:** Journals Division, PO Box 37005, Chicago, IL 60637. TEL 773-753-3347, 877-705-1878, FAX 773-753-0811, 877-705-1879.

➤ **ELEMENTARY SCHOOL LIBRARY COLLECTION.** see *LIBRARY AND INFORMATION SCIENCES*

➤ **ELEMENTARY SCIENCE THIS MONTH.** see *CHILDREN AND YOUTH—For*

371.8 SWE ISSN 0283-3395
ELEVFORUM. Text in Swedish. 1982. q.
Formerly (until 1984): Nya Elevforum (0281-1510); Which was formed by the merger of (1957-1981): S E C O Aktuellt (0347-996X); (1972-1981): Elevforum (0345-2557)
Published by: Elevorganisationen i Sverige, Malmgaardsvaegen 63, Stockholm, 11638, Sweden. TEL 46-8-644-45-00, FAX 46-8-644-45-02, info@elevorg.se. Ed. Niklas Johansson.

016.02 016.37 CAN
ELIBRARY CANADA. Text in English. 1981. d. CND 2,000 to libraries (effective 2005). **Document type:** *Bibliography.* **Description:** Contains K-12 periodical and multimedia resources for students.
Media: Online - full text.
Published by: Micromedia ProQuest (Subsidiary of: ProQuest Information & Learning), 20 Victoria St, Toronto, ON M5C 2N8, Canada. TEL 416-362-5211, 800-387-2689, FAX 416-362-6161, info@micromedia.ca, http://www.micromedia.ca/Products_Services/eLibrary/eLibrary.htm.

ELTERN. see *CHILDREN AND YOUTH—About*

ELTERN FOR FAMILY. see *CHILDREN AND YOUTH—About*

370 DEU ISSN 0934-8662
ELTERNFORUM; Zeitschrift fuer Eltern und alle, die an Erziehung und Schule interressiert sind. Text in German. 1967. q. EUR 12.80; EUR 3.60 newsstand/cover (effective 2003). adv. bk.rev. index. back issues avail. **Document type:** *Journal, Academic/Scholarly.*
Published by: Katholische Elternschaft Deutschlands e.V., Am Hofgarten 12, Bonn, 53112, Germany. TEL 49-228-650052, FAX 49-228-696217, info@ked-bonn.de, http://www.ked-bonn.de. Ed. Walter Eykmann. R&P, Adv. contact Sigrid Kessens. Circ: 3,000.

370.981 BRA ISSN 0104-1037
LA555
➤ **EM ABERTO.** Text in Portuguese. 1981-1996; resumed 2000. irreg. looseleaf. free (effective 2003). adv. bk.rev. bibl. cum.index: 1981-1987. back issues avail. **Document type:** *Monographic series, Academic/Scholarly.* **Description:** Looks at relevant and current issues related to Brazilian education.
Related titles: Online - full text ed.
Published by: Instituto Nacional de Estudos e Pesquisas Educacionais, Centro de Informacoes e Biblioteca em Educacao (C I B E C)/Center of Information and Library in Education, Esplanada dos Ministerios, Bloco L, Terreo, Brasilia, DF, Brazil. TEL 55-61-4108438, FAX 55-61-2235137, cibec@inep.gov.br, http://www.inep.gov.br/pesquisas/publicacoes, http://www.inep.gov.br/cibec. Ed. Antonio Danilo Morais Barbosa. Circ: 5,000.

370 USA ISSN 1074-5254
EMPHASIS. Text in English. 9/yr. free to members (effective 2004). adv. bk.rev. **Document type:** *Newsletter, Trade.* **Description:** Informs members of education news and association news.
Former titles (until 1991): S C E A Emphasis (0273-7906); South Carolina Education News Emphasis (0038-3066)
Indexed: CINAHL.

E

Published by: South Carolina Education Association, 421 Zimalcrest Dr, Columbia, SC 29210. TEL 803-772-6553, FAX 803-772-0922, http://www.thescea.org/. Ed. Sandor I Ketzis. Circ: 20,000.

370 ITA ISSN 1590-492X
ENCYCLOPAIDEIA. Text in Italian. 1997. s-a.
Published by: Casa Editrice C L U E B, Via Marsala 31, Bologna, BO 40126, Italy. TEL 39-051-220736, FAX 39-051-237758, clueb@clueb.com, http://www.clueb.com.

ENGLISCH; Zeitschrift fuer Englischlehrerinnen und Englischlehrer. see *LINGUISTICS*

ENGLISH ACADEMY REVIEW. see *LITERATURE*

ENGLISH LANGUAGE COURSE VISITORS TO THE U K. see *LINGUISTICS*

ENGLISH LANGUAGE TEACHER EDUCATION AND DEVELOPMENT. see *EDUCATION—Teaching Methods And Curriculum*

ENGLISH PAGES. see *LINGUISTICS*

ENGLISH TEACHING AND RESEARCH FOR ELEMENTARY AND SECONDARY SCHOOLS/ZHONGXIAOXUE YINGYU JIAOXUE YU YANJIU. see *LINGUISTICS*

370 NZL ISSN 1175-8708
➤ **ENGLISH TEACHING: PRACTICE AND CRITIQUE.** Text in English. 2002. irreg. free (effective 2005). **Document type:** *Journal, Academic/Scholarly.* **Description:** It seeks to promote theorizing about English/literacy that is grounded in a range of contexts: classrooms, schools and wider educational constituencies.
Media: Online - full text.
Published by: University of Waikato, School of Education, Private Bag 3105, Hamilton, New Zealand. TEL 64-07-838-4288, FAX 64-07-838-4898, teach@waikato.ac.nz, http://education.waikato.ac.nz/journal/english_journal/index.php. Ed. Terry Locke.

370 CAN ISSN 0046-2101
ENSEIGNANTS; mensuel national d'information pedagogique. Text in English. 1970. m. CND 18. adv. bk.rev.
Related titles: Microfilm ed.: (from BNQ).
Published by: Journal "Les Enseignants" Limitee, 767 Demers, Saint-jean, PQ J3B 4W1, Canada. TEL 514-348-8718. Ed. Fernand Houde. Circ: 4,500.

370 FRA ISSN 0223-5986
ENSEIGNEMENT PUBLIC. Text in French. 1945. m. adv.
Published by: Federation de l'Education Nationale, 48 rue la Bruyere, Paris, Cedex 9 75440, France. TEL 33-4-0167800, FAX 33-4-0167879, TELEX FENTELX 648 356 F. Ed. Yannick Simbron. Circ: 418,100.

370 ESP ISSN 0212-5374
L41
ENSENANZA; anuario interuniversitario de didactica. Text in Spanish. 1983. a., latest vol.16, 8. **Document type:** *Academic/Scholarly.*
Published by: Ediciones Universidad de Salamanca, Apartado 325, Salamanca, 37080, Spain. TEL 34-923-294598, FAX 34-923-262579, http://www3.usal.es/~eus/indexsp.htm. Eds. Antonio Medina Rivilla, Jose Luis Rodriguez Dieguez.

370 ESP ISSN 0212-4521
ENSENANZA DE LAS CIENCIAS. Text in Spanish, English. 1983. 3/yr. EUR 31 domestic to individuals; EUR 55 foreign to individuals; EUR 47 domestic to institutions; EUR 74 foreign to institutions (effective 2002). back issues avail. **Document type:** *Journal, Academic/Scholarly.*
Related titles: Online - full text ed.: EUR 26 (effective 2002) (from EBSCO Publishing).
Indexed: PsycInfo, PsycholAb.
—CINDOC, IE, Infotrieve.
Published by: (Universitat Autonoma de Barcelona, Institut de Ciencies de l'Educacio), Universitat Autonoma de Barcelona, Servei de Publicacions, Edifici A, Bellaterra, Cardanyola del Valles, 08193, Spain. TEL 34-93-5811022, FAX 34-93-5813239, sp@uab.es, http://www.uab.es/publicacions/. Eds. Berta Gutierrez Reno, Neus San Marti.

370 ESP ISSN 1137-7275
ENTRE LINEAS (MADRID); apuntes para la educacion popular. Text in Spanish. 1987. a.
—CINDOC.
Published by: Federacion Espanola de Universidades Populares, C. Los Madrazo 3, 1, Madrid, 28014, Spain. TEL 34-91-5219108, FAX 34-91-5231087, feup@mimosa.pntic.mec.es.

ENVIRONMENTAL COMMUNICATOR. see *ENVIRONMENTAL STUDIES*

ENVIRONMENTAL EDUCATION. see *ENVIRONMENTAL STUDIES*

ENVIRONMENTAL EDUCATION RESEARCH. see *ENVIRONMENTAL STUDIES*

ENVIRONMENTAL STUDIES RESEARCH FUNDS REPORT. see *ENVIRONMENTAL STUDIES*

371.822 USA
EQUITY; for the education of women & girls. Text in English. 1996. 3/yr. USD 21 domestic to individuals; USD 31 foreign to individuals; USD 35 domestic to institutions; USD 45 foreign to institutions. bk.rev. **Document type:** *Newsletter, Academic/Scholarly.* **Description:** Features discussion of research and major ideas in gender equity today.
Published by: Marymount Institute for the Education of Women and Girls, Marymount College Tarrytown, 100 Marymount Ave, Tarrytown, NY 10591. TEL 914-332-4917, FAX 914-631-8586, webmastr@mmc.marymt.edu, http://www.marymt.edu/womens_college/women_institute.html. Ed. Robin Dellabough. Pub. Ellen Silber.

370.193 USA ISSN 1066-5684
LB3062 CODEN: EEEDE5
EQUITY & EXCELLENCE IN EDUCATION. Text in English. 1963. q. GBP 88, USD 144 combined subscription to institutions print & online eds. (effective 2006). adv. bk.rev. reprint service avail. from PSC. **Document type:** *Journal, Academic/Scholarly.* **Description:** Deals with issues confronting American educators now and in the future. Reports on the practical efforts being made to educate all members of our diverse society equitably.
Former titles: Equity and Excellence (0894-0681); Integrateducation (0020-4862)
Related titles: Online - full text ed.: ISSN 1547-3457. GBP 84, USD 137 to institutions (effective 2006) (from EBSCO Publishing, Gale Group, IngentaConnect, Swets Information Services).
Indexed: ABIn, AcaI, CIJE, CPE, ChPerI, CurCont, DIP, EAA, EduInd, FamI, HEA, IBR, IBZ, IIBP, LRI, PAIS, SOPODA, SSA, SWA, V&AA.
—BLDSC (3794.759500), IE, ingenta. **CCC.**
Published by: (Valley Women's Voice, School of Education), Taylor & Francis Inc. (Subsidiary of: Taylor & Francis Group), 325 Chestnut St, Ste 800, Philadelphia, PA 19016. TEL 215-625-8900, 800-354-1420, FAX 215-625-2940, equity@educ.umass.edu, info@taylorandfrancis.com, http://www.eee-journal.com, http://www.taylorandfrancis.com. Ed. Kim Martin. adv.: B&W page USD 225. Circ: 1,500 (paid).

370 DNK ISSN 1604-0570
ERHVERVSSKOLEN.DK. Text in Danish. 1975. q. DKK 187.50 (effective 2004). adv. back issues avail. **Document type:** *Magazine, Trade.* **Description:** Of interest to educators in technical schools.
Former titles (until 2004): Erhvervsskolen (1602-8767); (until 2002): Teknisk skole (0107-2846); Which was formed by the merger of (1908-1975): Cirklen (0906-320X); (1893-1975): Teknisk Skoletidende (0040-2338)
Related titles: Online - full text ed.: ISSN 1399-6525.
Published by: Danmarks Erhvervsskoleforening, Munkehatten 28, Odense SOE, 5220, Denmark. TEL 45-63-151700, FAX 45-63-151777, http://www.erhvervsskolen.dk/magasin/?SID=10&M=10, http://www.de-f.dk. Ed. Lars Mahler. Adv. contact Lone Jensen TEL 45-63-151774. page DKK 6,200; bleed 210 x 290. Circ: 7,500.

ERHVERVSUDDANNELSERNE. see *EDUCATION—Abstracting, Bibliographies, Statistics*

372 CHN ISSN 1002-4042
ERTONG CHUANGZHAO/CHILDREN'S CREATION. Text in Chinese. 1987. m. CNY 0.50 per issue.
Published by: Nanning Shi Jiaoyu Ju/Nanning Municipal Bureau of Education, Minle Lu, Nanning, Guangxi 530012, China. TEL 207323, FAX 0771-205614. Ed. Ma Zuowen. Circ: 250,000.

370 DEU ISSN 0340-6288
ERZIEHEN HEUTE. Text in German. 1974. q. **Document type:** *Journal, Academic/Scholarly.*
Published by: Gemeinschaft Evangelischer Erzieher, Franzstr 9, Duisburg, 47166, Germany. TEL 49-203-547244, erziehen-heute@gee-online.de, gee@cityweb.de, http://www.ekir.de/gee/redaktio.htm. Ed. Horst Herget. Circ: 3,600 (controlled).

370.15 AUT ISSN 1022-2294
ERZIEHUNG HEUTE; Die oesterreichische Zeitschrift fuer Schule, Bildung und Erziehung. Text in German. 1975. 4/yr. EUR 18; EUR 5.50 newsstand/cover (effective 2005). **Document type:** *Journal, Academic/Scholarly.*
Indexed: DIP, IBR, IBZ.
Published by: StudienVerlag, Amraser Str 118, Innsbruck, 6020, Austria. TEL 43-512-395045, FAX 43-512-39504515, order@studienverlag.at, http://www.studienverlag.at.

370 AUT ISSN 0014-0325
ERZIEHUNG UND UNTERRICHT; Oesterreichische paedagogische Zeitschrift. Text in German. 1850. 5/yr. EUR 76 (effective 2003). adv. bk.rev. abstr.; bibl.; charts; illus. Supplement avail. **Document type:** *Magazine, Academic/Scholarly.*
Indexed: DIP, IBR, IBZ.
Published by: Oe B V & H P T Verlagsgesellschaft mbH & Co. KG, Frankgasse 4, Vienna, W 1090, Austria. FAX 43-1-40136185, http://www.oebvhpt.at. Circ: 3,400.

370 DEU ISSN 0342-0671
ERZIEHUNG UND WISSENSCHAFT; allgemeine Deutsche Lehrer-Zeitung. Text in German. 1948. m. adv. bk.rev. illus.; stat. 48 p./no. 3 cols./p.; reprints avail. **Document type:** *Journal, Trade.*
Formerly (until 1971): Allgemeine Deutsche Lehrerzeitung (0002-5836)
Related titles: Online - full text ed.
Indexed: ApicAb, DIP, IBR, IBZ.
Published by: (Gewerkschaft Erziehung und Wissenschaft), Stamm Verlag GmbH, Goldammerweg 16, Essen, 45134, Germany. TEL 49-201-843000, FAX 49-201-472590, info@stamm.de, http://www.gew.de, http://www.stamm.de. Ed. Steffen Welzel. adv.: B&W page EUR 4,992, color page EUR 7,104; trim 202 x 280. Circ: 251,797 (paid and controlled).

371 DEU ISSN 0170-0723
ERZIEHUNG UND WISSENSCHAFT NIEDERSACHSEN. Text in German. m. adv. **Document type:** *Journal, Academic/Scholarly.* **Description:** Deals with issues important to teachers in Niedersachsen.
Published by: (Gewerkschaft Erziehung und Wissenschaft, Landesverband Niedersachsen), Stamm Verlag GmbH, Goldammerweg 16, Essen, 45134, Germany. TEL 49-201-843000, FAX 49-201-472590, info@stamm.de, http://www.stamm.de. Ed. Joachim Tiemer. adv.: B&W page EUR 1,727.80. Circ: 29,674 (paid and controlled).

370.1 DEU ISSN 0945-487X
ERZIEHUNG, UNTERRICHT, BILDUNG. Text in German. 1991. irreg., latest vol.116, 2005. price varies. **Document type:** *Monographic series, Academic/Scholarly.*
Published by: Verlag Dr. Kovac, Arnoldstr 49, Hamburg, 22763, Germany. TEL 49-40-3988800, FAX 49-40-39888055, info@verlagdrkovac.de, http://www.verlagdrkovac.de/7-1.htm.

370 DEU ISSN 0014-0333
ERZIEHUNGSKUNST; Monatsschrift zur Paedagogik R. Steiners. Text in German. 1927. m. adv. bk.rev. illus. index. **Document type:** *Academic/Scholarly.*
Indexed: DIP, IBR, IBZ.
—CCC.
Published by: (Bund der Freien Waldorfschulen e.V.), Verlag Freies Geistesleben GmbH, Landhausstr 82, Stuttgart, 70190, Germany. TEL 49-711-2853200, FAX 49-711-2853210, http://www.geistesleben.com. Eds. Klaus Schickert, Mathias Maurer. R&P Jean Claude Lin. Adv. contact Alexandra Ernst. Circ: 9,000.

370 DEU ISSN 0938-5363
ERZIEHUNGSWISSENSCHAFT. Text in German. 2/yr. EUR 22; EUR 13 newsstand/cover (effective 2004). back issues avail. **Document type:** *Journal, Academic/Scholarly.*
Indexed: IBR, IBSS, IBZ.
Published by: V S - Verlag fuer Sozialwissenschaften (Subsidiary of: Springer Science+Business Media), Abraham-Lincoln-Str 46, Wiesbaden, 65189, Germany. TEL 49-2171-49070, FAX 49-2171-490711, info@vs-verlag.de, http://www.vs-verlag.de. Circ: 2,200 (paid); 2,200 (controlled).

370.94619 ESP
ESCUELA ASTURIANA; periodico de informacion educativa. Text in Spanish. 1984. m.?. free. 28 p./no. 5 cols./p.; **Document type:** *Newspaper, Academic/Scholarly.* **Description:** Contains education information from Asturias, or under auspices of the ministry.
Published by: Ministerio de Educacion y Ciencia, Direccion Provincial, Plaza Espana, 5 2a planta, Oviedo, Asturias 33007, Spain. TEL 34-85-244704, FAX 34-85-75354. Circ: 10,000.

370 ESP ISSN 0214-1515
ESCUELA UNIVERSITARIA DEL PROFESORADO DE E G B. PUBLICACIONES. Text in Spanish. 1981. s-a. back issues avail.
Related titles: Online - full text ed.
Indexed: RILM.
—CINDOC.
Published by: Universidad de Granada - Melilla, Facultad de Educacion y Humanidades, Carr. Alfonso XIII, s-n, Melilla, 52071, Spain. TEL 34-952-698700, FAX 34-952-972881, aliciabb@goliat.ugr.es, http://www.ugr.es/~faedumel/publica/ppal.htm, http://www.ugr.es/~faedumel/inicio.html.

370 BEL
ESPACE DE LIBERTES. Text in French. 1969. m. EUR 20 domestic; EUR 32 foreign (effective 2005).
Published by: Centre d'Action Laique, Campus de la Plaine ULB, Bd du Triomphe, CP 236, Brussels, 1050, Belgium. TEL 32-2-627-6868, FAX 32-2-627-6861, espace@cal.ulb.ac.be, http://www.ulb.ac.be/cal/magazineedl.html. Ed. Michele Michiels. Pub. Patrice Dartevelle.

370 ITA
ESPERIENZE E PROGETTI. Text in Italian. 1974. q. EUR 15 (effective 2005). **Document type:** *Magazine, Consumer.*
Related titles: Online - full text ed.

E

Published by: Centro Studi Esperienze Scout Baden-Powell, Via Alessandro Bonci 4, Bologna, BO 40137, Italy. TEL 39-051-780291, FAX 39-051-63216752, http://www.baden-powell.it. Ed. Guido Palombi. Circ: 3,000 (paid).

054 FRA ISSN 1168-0733
L'ESPRIT DU TEMPS; revue de culture humaine inspiree de l'enseignement de Rudolf Steiner. Text in French. 1953. q. adv. bk.rev. abstr.; illus. index.
Formerly (until 1992): Triades (0041-252X)
Indexed: RASB.
Published by: Esprit du Temps, 15 rue Albert Joly, B.P. 46, Montesson, 78362 Cedex, France. Circ: 2,000.

ESPRIT LIBRE. see *PSYCHOLOGY*

370 USA ISSN 1527-9359
L11
➤ **ESSAYS IN EDUCATION.** Text in English. 2002 (Spring). q. free (effective 2005). **Document type:** *Academic/Scholarly.* **Description:** Seeks to explore the multitude of issues that impact and influence education.
Media: Online - full content.
Published by: Columbia College, Department in Education, 1301 Columbia College Dr, Columbia, SC 29203. http://www.columbiacollegesc.edu/essays/home.html. Ed. Timothy Lintner.

➤ **ESTADISTICA BASICA DEL SISTEMA EDUCATIVO NACIONAL.** see *EDUCATION—Abstracting, Bibliographies, Statistics*

➤ **ESTADISTICA PANAMENA. SITUACION CULTURAL. SECCION 511. EDUCACION.** see *EDUCATION—Abstracting, Bibliographies, Statistics*

➤ **ESTADISTICA PANAMENA. SITUACION ECONOMICA. SECCION 343. HACIENDA PUBLICA.** see *BUSINESS AND ECONOMICS—Abstracting, Bibliographies, Statistics*

370.2109469 PRT
ESTATISTICAS DA EDUCACAO. CONTINENTE, ACORES E MADEIRA. Text in Portuguese. 1940. a.
Formerly: Portugal. Instituto Nacional de Estatistica. Estatisticas de Educacao (0079-4155)
Published by: Instituto Nacional de Estatistica, Ave. Antonio Jose de Almeida 2, Lisbon, 1000-043, Portugal. TEL 351-21-8426100, FAX 351-21-8426380, ine@ine.pt, http://www.ine.pt/. **Orders to:** Imprensa Nacional, Direccao Comercial, rua D. Francisco Manuel de Melo 5, Lisbon 1100, Portugal.

371.5 ESP ISSN 1132-8479
ESTUDIOS DE PEDAGOGIA Y PSICOLOGIA. Text in Spanish. 1989. a.
Formerly (until 1992): Notas y Estudios de Ciencias de la Educacion, Psicologia y Filosofia (1131-6616)
—CINDOC.
Published by: Universidad Nacional de Educacion a Distancia, Bravo Murillo No. 38, Madrid, Spain. TEL 34-91-3986000, FAX 34-91-3986600, infouned@adm.uned.es, http://www.uned.es/. Ed. Angel Saenz Moreno.

370 ESP ISSN 1578-7001
ESTUDIOS SOBRE EDUCACION. Abbreviated title: E S E. Text in Esperanto. 2001. a. EUR 35 in Europe; USD 50 elsewhere (effective 2004). **Document type:** *Academic/Scholarly.*
Related titles: Online - full text ed.: (from EBSCO Publishing).
Indexed: ERA, ETA, MEA, RHEA, SEA, SENA, SOMA, TEA.
Published by: Universidad de Navarra, Servicio de Publicaciones, Edificio de Bibliotecas, Campus Universitario, Pamplona, Navarra 31080, Spain. TEL 34-948-525600, FAX 34-948-425636, ese@unav.es, http://www.unav.es/educacion/ese/.

371 BRA ISSN 0103-6831
LA555
ESTUDOS EM AVALIACAO EDUCACIONAL. Text in Portuguese. s-a. charts; stat.
Formerly (until 1990): Educacao e Selecao (0101-3823)
Published by: (Nucleo de Testes e Medidas), Fundacao Carlos Chagas, Av Professor Francisco Morato, 1565, Butanta, Sao Paulo, SP 05513-100, Brazil. TEL 011-813-4511, FAX 011-815-1059, fcc@fcc.org.br. Ed. Heraldo Marelim Vianna.

370.1 BRA ISSN 1415-2800
LA555
ESTUDOS LEOPOLDENSES. SERIE EDUCACAO. Text in Portuguese. 1966. s-a. USD 20 or exchange basis. bk.rev. abstr.; bibl.; charts; illus.
supersedes in part (in 1997): Estudos Leopoldenses (0014-1607)
Indexed: DIP, IBZ.
Published by: (Universidade do Vale do Rio dos Sinos), Unisinos, Av Unisinos, 950, Sao Leopoldo, RS 93022-000, Brazil. TEL 55-51-5908239, FAX 55-51-5908238.

370 CAN ISSN 0842-6678
L'ETAT ET LES BESOINS DE L'EDUCATION. RAPPORT ANNUEL. Text in French. 1981. a.
Former titles (until 1987): l' Etat et les Besoins de l'Education. Rapport (0839-2471); (until 1983): Conseil Superieur de l'Education. Rapport (0715-1276); Which was formed by the merger of (1965-1981): Conseil Superieur de l'Education. Rapport des Activites (0709-2776); Which was formerly (until 1976): Conseil Superieur de l'Education. Rapport Annuel (0380-5433); (1976-1981): Etat et les Besoins de l'Education (0709-2806)
Related titles: English ed.: The State and Needs of Education. Annual Report. ISSN 0848-581X. 1965.
Published by: Conseil Superieur de l'Education, 1175, avenue Lavigerie, Bureau 180, Quebec, PQ G1V 5B2, Canada. TEL 418-643-3851, FAX 418-644-2530, panorama@cse.gouv.qc.ca, http://www.cse.gouv.qc.ca.

▼ **ETHICS AND EDUCATION.** see *SOCIOLOGY*

370.14 USA
ETHICS TODAY. Text in English. 1991. m. free. bk.rev. back issues avail. **Document type:** *Newsletter, Consumer.* **Description:** Discusses corporate and governmental ethics policies and programs, as well as values education in schools.
Formerly (until 1996): Ethics Journal (1060-0698)
Media: Online - full content.
Published by: Ethics Resource Center, Inc., 1747 Pennsylvania Ave, N W, Ste 400, Washington, DC 20006-4604. TEL 202-737-2258, FAX 202-737-2227, ethics@ethics.org, http://www.ethics.org. Ed. Lauren Larson. R&P Jerry Brown. Adv. contact Jennie Ziegler. Circ: 17,000.

ETHIK IM UNTERRICHT. see *PHILOSOPHY*

370.963 ETH ISSN 0425-4414
➤ **ETHIOPIAN JOURNAL OF EDUCATION.** Text in English. 1967. 2/yr. USD 16 to individuals; USD 20 to institutions (effective 2003). adv. bk.rev. back issues avail. **Document type:** *Journal, Academic/Scholarly.*
Indexed: PLESA.
Published by: Addis Ababa University, Institute of Educational Research, P.O. Box 1176, Addis Ababa, Ethiopia. TEL 251-01-113235, FAX 251-01-551368, ier.aau@telecom.net.et. Ed., Pub. Amare Asgedom. R&P Kahsay Gebre TEL 251-09-402201. Adv. contact Derebssa Dufera TEL 251-01-560083. Circ: 2,000.

370 301 GBR ISSN 1745-7823
▼ ➤ **ETHNOGRAPHY AND EDUCATION.** Text in English. forthcoming 2006. 3/yr. GBP 132, USD 218 combined subscription to institutions print & online eds. (effective 2006). adv. **Document type:** *Journal, Academic/Scholarly.* **Description:** Publishes articles illuminating educational practices through empirical methodologies, which prioritise the experiences and perspectives of those involved.
Related titles: Online - full content ed.: ISSN 1745-7831. forthcoming 2006. GBP 125, USD 207 to institutions (effective 2006).
Published by: Routledge (Subsidiary of: Taylor & Francis Group), 4 Park Sq, Milton Park, Abingdon, Oxon OX14 4RN, United Kingdom. TEL 44-1235-828600, FAX 44-1235-829000, info@routledge.co.uk, http://www.tandf.co.uk/journals/titles/17457823.asp, http://www.routledge.com. Ed. Dr. Geoff Troman. Adv. contact Linda Hann.

➤ **L'ETUDIANT.** see *COLLEGE AND ALUMNI*

➤ **L'ETUDIANT. GUIDE PRATIQUE.** see *COLLEGE AND ALUMNI*

➤ **L'ETUDIANT PLUS.** see *COLLEGE AND ALUMNI*

370 COL
EUREKA; revista electronica de educacion. Text in Spanish. s-a. **Document type:** *Journal, Academic/Scholarly.* **Description:** Reports on local issues and research in education.
Published by: Universidad del Norte, Division de Humanidades y Ciencias Sociales, Apdo Aereo 1569, Barranquilla, Colombia. liceduca@uninorte.edu.co, http://www.uninorte.edu.co/publicacion/eureka.

372.21 GBR ISSN 1350-293X
➤ **EUROPEAN EARLY CHILDHOOD EDUCATION RESEARCH JOURNAL.** Text in English. 1993. s-a. GBP 35 to individual members; GBP 58 to non-members (effective 2000). adv. bk.rev. index. back issues avail. **Document type:** *Academic/Scholarly.* **Description:** Publishes research and provides a forum for ideas on early childhood education in Europe. Publishes annual conference papers.
Indexed: BrEdI, CIJE, CPE, ERA, ETA, MEA, RHEA, SEA, SENA, SOMA, SWA, TEA.
—BLDSC (3829.692800), IE, ingenta.
Published by: (European Early Childhood Education Research Association), Amber Publishing, University College Worchester, Henwick Grove, Worcester, Worcs WR2 6AJ, United Kingdom. TEL 44-1905-855068, FAX 44-1905-855068, t.bertram@worc.ac.uk, http://www.worc.ac.uk/eecera. Ed. Christine Pascal. R&P A D Bertram. Adv. contact Ann Ball. Circ: 325 (paid).

370.94 USA ISSN 1056-4934
➤ **EUROPEAN EDUCATION**; issues and studies. Text in English. 1969. q. USD 149 domestic to individuals; USD 207 foreign to individuals; USD 850 domestic to institutions; USD 934 foreign to institutions (effective 2006). adv. illus. back issues avail.; reprint service avail. from PSC. **Document type:** *Journal, Academic/Scholarly.* **Description:** Contains articles selected and translated from leading European journals. Includes research reports and documents from research centers and school authorities.
Formerly (until 1991): Western European Education (0043-3675)
Related titles: Online - full text ed.: 2004 (Apr.) (from EBSCO Publishing, H.W. Wilson, O C L C Online Computer Library Center, Inc., Swets Information Services).
Indexed: ABIn, CIJE, CPE, CurCont, DIP, ERA, ETA, EduInd, IBR, IBZ, MEA, MEA&I, PsycholAb, RASB, RHEA, SEA, SENA, SOMA, TEA, WBA, WMB.
—BLDSC (3829.697730), IE, Infotrieve, ingenta. **CCC.**
Published by: M.E. Sharpe, Inc., 80 Business Park Dr, Armonk, NY 10504. TEL 914-273-1800, 800-541-6563, FAX 914-273-2106, custserv@mesharpe.com, http://www.mesharpe.com/mall/results1.asp. Ed. Bernhard Streitwieser. Adv. contact Barbara Ladd TEL 914-273-1800 ext 121. page USD 300; 8 x 5. Circ: 220 (paid).

370.72 GBR ISSN 1474-9041
LB1028
➤ **EUROPEAN EDUCATIONAL RESEARCH JOURNAL.** Text in English. 2002. q. GBP 160 domestic to libraries; USD 246 foreign to libraries (effective 2005). bk.rev. abstr.; illus. **Document type:** *Journal, Academic/Scholarly.*
Media: Online - full text.
Published by: (European Educational Research Association), Symposium Journals (Subsidiary of: wwwords Ltd), PO Box 204, Didcot, Oxford, OX11 9ZQ, United Kingdom. TEL 44-1235-818062, FAX 44-1235-817275, info@symposium-journals.co.uk, subscriptions@symposium-journals.co.uk, http://www.wwwords.co.uk/eerj/, http://www.symposium-journals.co.uk/. Ed. Martin Lawn.

370.72 GBR
➤ **EUROPEAN EDUCATIONAL RESEARCHER.** Text in English. irreg. **Document type:** *Journal, Academic/Scholarly.*
Media: Online - full content.
Published by: European Educational Research Association, c/o Professional Development Unit, Faculty of Education, University of Strathclyde, 76 Southbrae Dr, Glasgow, Scotland G13 1PP, United Kingdom. http://www.eera.ac.uk/publications/eer/.

➤ **EUROPEAN ESSAY.** see *POLITICAL SCIENCE*

370.72 GBR ISSN 0141-8211
L101.A2 CODEN: EJEDE6
➤ **EUROPEAN JOURNAL OF EDUCATION**; research, development and policies. Text in English. 1964. q. EUR 254 combined subscription in Europe to individuals print & online eds.; USD 284 combined subscription in the Americas to individuals & Caribbean (print & online eds.); GBP 169 combined subscription elsewhere to individuals print & online eds.; USD 1,335 combined subscription in the Americas to institutions & Caribbean (print & online eds.); GBP 795 combined subscription elsewhere to institutions print & online eds. (effective 2006). adv. bk.rev. illus. index. back issues avail.; reprint service avail. from PSC. **Document type:** *Journal, Academic/Scholarly.* **Description:** Examines educational policies, trends, reforms programs of European countries in an international perspective. Audience consists of academics, researchers, practitioners and students of education sciences.
Formerly: Paedagogica Europaea (0078-7787)
Related titles: Microfiche ed.; Online - full text ed.: ISSN 1465-3435. USD 1,268 in the Americas to institutions & Caribbean; GBP 755 elsewhere to institutions (effective 2006) (from Blackwell Synergy, EBSCO Publishing, Gale Group, IngentaConnect, O C L C Online Computer Library Center, Inc., Swets Information Services).
Indexed: ABIn, BrEdI, CIJE, CPE, DIP, EAA, ERA, ETA, EduInd, HEA, HECAB, IBR, IBZ, MEA, PCI, RASB, RHEA, SENA, SOMA, SOPODA, SSA, SWA, TEA, WBA, WMB.
—BLDSC (3829.728400), IE, Infotrieve, ingenta. **CCC.**
Published by: (Universitat de Valencia, Department of Applied Economics ESP, European Institute of Education and Social Policy, Paris FRA), Blackwell Publishing Ltd., 9600 Garsington Rd, Oxford, OX4 2ZG, United Kingdom. TEL 44-1865-776868, FAX 44-1865-714591, customerservices@oxon.blackwellpublishing.com, http://www.blackwellpublishing.com/journals/EJED. Eds. Jean Gordon, Jean-Pierre Jallade TEL 33-1-44-05-40-11. R&P Melanie Charge TEL 44-1865-382352.

➤ **EUROPEAN JOURNAL OF ENGINEERING EDUCATION.** see *ENGINEERING*

E

370.15 PRT ISSN 0256-2928
CODEN: EJPDER

➤ **EUROPEAN JOURNAL OF PSYCHOLOGY OF EDUCATION/JOURNAL EUROPEEN DE PSYCHOLOGIE DE L'EDUCATION.** Text in English. 1986. q. EUR 70.64 in Europe to individuals; EUR 107.96 in Europe to institutions; EUR 77.31 elsewhere to individuals; EUR 115.96 elsewhere to institutions (effective 2005). adv. bk.rev. bibl.; charts.
Document type: *Journal, Academic/Scholarly.* **Description:** Publishes empirical research results, theoretical and methodological articles and critical literature reviews with a focus on the psychological perspective in education.
Related titles: Online - full text ed.: (from EBSCO Publishing).
Indexed: ASCA, CDA, CIJE, CPE, CurCont, EAA, ERA, ETA, FamI, L&LBA, MEA, PsycInfo, PsycholAb, RHEA, SEA, SENA, SOMA, SOPODA, SSCI, SWA, TEA, e-psyche.
—BLDSC (3829.738000), IDS, IE, Infotrieve, ingenta. **CCC.**
Published by: (Universite de Provence FRA), Instituto Superior de Psicologia Aplicada, Rua Jardim do Tabaco 34, Lisbon, 1149-041, Portugal. TEL 351-21-881-1700, FAX 351-21-886-0954, info@ispa.pt, http://www.ispa.pt. Ed. Felice Carugati.

371.1 GBR ISSN 0261-9768

➤ **EUROPEAN JOURNAL OF TEACHER EDUCATION.** Text in English. 1978. q. GBP 936, USD 1,547 combined subscription to institutions print & online eds. (effective 2006). bk.rev. illus. index. back issues avail.; reprint service avail. from PSC.
Document type: *Journal, Academic/Scholarly.* **Description:** Provides a forum for the examination of policies, theories and practices related to the education and training of teachers at pre-service and in-service levels in the countries of Europe.
Formerly (until vol.4, 1981): Revue A T E E Journal (0379-606X)
Related titles: Microfiche ed.; Online - full text ed.: ISSN 1469-5928. GBP 889, USD 1,470 to institutions (effective 2006) (from EBSCO Publishing, Gale Group, IngentaConnect, O C L C Online Computer Library Center, Inc., ProQuest Information & Learning, Swets Information Services).
Indexed: BrEdI, CIJE, CPE, CommAb, DIP, EAA, ERA, ETA, IBR, IBZ, MEA, RHEA, SEA, SENA, SOMA, SWA, TEA.
—BLDSC (3829.746000), IE, Infotrieve, ingenta. **CCC.**
Published by: (Association for Teacher Education in Europe), Routledge (Subsidiary of: Taylor & Francis Group), 4 Park Sq, Milton Park, Abingdon, Oxon OX14 4RN, United Kingdom. TEL 44-1235-828600, FAX 44-1235-829000, info@routledge.co.uk, http://www.tandf.co.uk/journals/titles/02619768.asp, http://www.routledge.co.uk. Ed. James McCall. **Subscr. to:** Taylor & Francis Ltd, Journals Customer Service, Rankine Rd, Basingstoke, Hants RG24 8PR, United Kingdom. TEL 44-1256-813000, FAX 44-1256-330245.

370.113 GRC
LC1041

➤ **EUROPEAN JOURNAL VOCATIONAL TRAINING.** Text in English. 1977. 3/yr. EUR 15 (effective 2003). bk.rev. abstr. 100 p./no.; back issues avail. **Document type:** *Journal, Academic/Scholarly.* **Description:** Specialized source of reference for all those involved in vocational training (decision making, program planning, and administration).
Formerly: Vocational Training (0378-5068)
Related titles: French ed.: Revue Europeenne Formation Professionnelle. ISSN 0378-5092. 1977. EUR 15 (effective 2003); German ed.: Europaeische Zeitschrift Berufsbildung. ISSN 0378-5106. 1977. EUR 15 (effective 2003); Spanish ed.: Revista Europea Formacion Profesional. ISSN 0258-7483. 1986. EUR 15 (effective 2003).
Indexed: CIJE, CPE, ERA, IBSS, TEA.
—BLDSC (9250.480000), IE, ingenta (VOCATRA).
Published by: European Centre for the Development of Vocational Training, 123 Europis, Thessaloniki, 55102, Greece. TEL 30-2310-490111, FAX 30-2310-490102, info@cedefop.eu.int, http://www.cedefop.eu.int. Ed., R&P Eric Fries Guggenheim. Circ: 10,000.

370.1 DEU ISSN 0946-6797
EUROPEAN STUDIES IN EDUCATION. Text in German, English, French. 1995. irreg., latest vol.17, 2003. EUR 19.90 per vol. (effective 2003). **Document type:** *Monographic series, Academic/Scholarly.* **Description:** Provides an international forum for the publication of educational research in English, German and French.
Published by: Waxmann Verlag GmbH, Steinfurter Str 555, Muenster, 48159, Germany. TEL 49-251-26504-0, FAX 49-251-2650426, info@waxmann.com, http://www.waxmann.com. Ed. Christoph Wulf.

370 LUX ISSN 1016-5428
EUROPEAN UNIVERSITY INSTITUTE. ACADEMIC YEAR. Text in English. a.
—BLDSC (0570.517100).
Published by: (European University Institute ITA), European Commission, Office for Official Publications of the European Union, 2 Rue Mercier, Luxembourg, L-2985, Luxembourg. TEL 352-29291, info-info-opoce@cec.eu.int, http://europa.eu.int.

370.72 GBR ISSN 0950-0790
L16 CODEN: EREEV
EVALUATION AND RESEARCH IN EDUCATION. Abbreviated title: ERiE. Text in English. 1950. 4/yr. GBP 190, USD 330, EUR 270 to institutions (effective 2005). bk.rev. bibl. index. back issues avail. **Document type:** *Journal, Academic/Scholarly.* **Description:** Makes methods of evaluation and research in education available to teachers, administrators and research workers.
Former titles: Durham and Newcastle Research Review (0141-108X); Durham Research Review (0419-8506)
Related titles: Online - full text ed.: (from EBSCO Publishing, Gale Group, Swets Information Services).
Indexed: BrEdI, BrHumI, CJA, CPE, EAA, ERA, ETA, HECAB, LT&LA, MEA, RHEA, SEA, SENA, SOMA, SOPODA, SSCI, SWA, TEA.
—BLDSC (3830.568000), IE, Infotrieve, ingenta. **CCC.**
Published by: Multilingual Matters Ltd., Frankfurt Lodge, Clevedon Hall, Victoria Rd, Clevedon, North Somerset BS21 7HH, United Kingdom. TEL 44-1275-876519, FAX 44-1275-871673, info@multilingual-matters.com, http://www.multilingual-matters.com/multi/journals/journals_erie.asp?TAG=&CID=, http://www.catchword.co.uk. Ed. Keith Morrison. R&P Marjukka Grover. Adv. contact Kathryn King. Circ: 750. **Subscr. to:** Portland Press Ltd., Commerce Way, Colchester CO2 8HP, United Kingdom. TEL 44-1206-796351, FAX 44-1206-799331, sales@portland-services.com.

371.07 DEU ISSN 0344-1466
EVANGELISCHE FACHHOCHSCHULEN DARMSTADT, FREIBURG, LUDWIGSHAFEN, REUTLINGEN. HOCHSCHULBRIEF. Text in German. 1963. a. **Document type:** *Journal, Academic/Scholarly.* **Description:** Provides information on all educational aspects of the schools.
Formerly (until 1974): Darmstaedter Rundbrief (0344-1474)
Published by: Evangelische Fachhochschulen Darmstadt Freiburg Ludwigshafen Reutlingen, Zweifalltorweg 12, Darmstadt, 64293, Germany. TEL 49-6151-879833, FAX 49-6151-879878, presse@efh-darmstadt.de, http://www.efh-darmstadt.de.

372.21 AUS ISSN 1322-0659
EVERY CHILD. Text in English. 1996. q. AUD 47.20 domestic; AUD 50 foreign (effective 2002). adv. bk.rev.; Website rev. index. back issues avail. **Document type:** *Magazine, Consumer.* **Description:** Provides news and features of interest to everyone working with, and interested in the education, care and development of young children.
Indexed: AEI, CPE.
Published by: Early Childhood Australia Inc., Knox St, PO Box 105, Watson, ACT 2602, Australia. TEL 61-2-6241-6900, FAX 61-2-6241-5547, publishing@aeca.org.au. Ed. Alison Elliott. R&P Penelope Craswell. Adv. contact Amenda Mason.

370.115 USA
EX CHANGE. Text in English. 1995. irreg.
Media: Online - full content.
Published by: University of Illinois at Urbana-Champaign, College of Education, 1310 S Sixth St, Champaign, IL 61820. http://deil.lang.uiuc.edu/exchange.

370 USA
EXCELLENCE IN EDUCATION. Text in English. m. free (effective 2005). **Document type:** *Newsletter.*
Published by: Mississippi Department of Education, PO Box 771, Jackson, MS 39205-0771. TEL 601-359-3519, FAX 601-359-3033, kblanton@mdek12.state.ms.us, http://www.mde.k12.state.ms.us. Ed. Karen Blanton. Circ: 2,000 (free).

EXCEPTIONAL CHILDREN. see *EDUCATION—Special Education And Rehabilitation*

371.1 CAN ISSN 1196-9490
EXEMPLARY PRACTICES. RECIPIENTS. Variant title: Prime Minister's Awards for Teaching Excellence in Science, Technology and Mathematics. Text in English. 1994. a.
Published by: (Industry Canada, Prime Minister's Awards for Teaching Excellence), Industry Canada/Industrie Canada, Distribution Services, Communications & Marketing Branch, Rm 268D, West Tower, C.D. Howe Bldg, 235 Queen St, Ottawa, ON K1A 0H5, Canada. publications@ic.gc.ca, http://pma-ppm.ic.gc.ca/exemp-e.asp, http://www.ic.gc.ca.

370.72 IND
EXPERIMENTS IN EDUCATION. Text in English. 1972. m. INR 25 domestic to individuals; USD 25 foreign to individuals; INR 50 domestic to institutions; USD 35 foreign to institutions (effective 2000). **Document type:** *Academic/Scholarly.*
Published by: S I T U Council of Educational Research, 3, 1st Trust Link St., Mandavalipakkam, Chennai, Tamil Nadu 600 028, India. TEL 91-44-4942881, neelakantan@eth.net. Ed. Dr. D Raja Ganesan. Pub. P C Vaidhyanathan.

370 USA
EXPLORATORIUM MAGAZINE ONLINE. Text in English. 1995. m.
Media: Online - full content.
Published by: The Exploratorium, 3601 Lyon St., San Francisco, CA 94123. http://www.exploratorium.edu/exploring.

371.0209599 PHL ISSN 0115-8090
F A P E REVIEW. Text in English. 1970. s-a. free. bk.rev. illus.
Description: Serves as a forum for the articulation of issues and problems affecting private education in the Philippines.
Indexed: IPP.
Published by: Fund for Assistance to Private Education, M.C.P.O. Box 947, Makati, 1299, Philippines. FAX 818-0013. Ed. Bettina R Olmedo. Circ: 2,000.

F F. (Fremdsprachen Fruehbeginn) see *LINGUISTICS*

F F A ADVISORS MAKING A DIFFERENCE. see *AGRICULTURE*

370 DEU
F H PRESSE. Text in German. 1979. bi-m. free. adv. bk.rev. back issues avail. **Document type:** *Newspaper.*
Published by: Fachhochschule Dortmund, Sonnenstr 96, Dortmund, 44139, Germany. TEL 49-231-9112-0, FAX 49-231-9112313. Ed., Adv. contact Juergen Andrae. Pub. Hans Juergen Kottmann. Circ: 3,000.

F I P L V WORLD NEWS. see *LINGUISTICS*

370.1 301 SWE ISSN 0345-3405
F L S - AKTUELLT. Text in Swedish. 1960. q.
Formerly (until 1963): F L S - Nytt
Published by: Foereningen Laerare i Samhaells- och Socialkunskap, c/o Lena Persson, Lutavaegen 7, Staffanstorp, 24542, Sweden. TEL 46-046-25 63 73. Ed. Lena Persson.

371.822 ZAF ISSN 0014-9489
F W I NEWS. Text in English. 1951. m. membership. adv. bk.rev. illus.
Published by: Federation of Women's Institutions, PO Box 153, Pietermaritzburg, KwaZulu-Natal 3200, South Africa. Ed. M Eldridge. Circ: 8,500.

FACHBUCHVERZEICHNIS GEISTESWISSENSCHAFTEN. see *EDUCATION—Abstracting, Bibliographies, Statistics*

370 DEU
FACHHOCHSCHULE AALEN. INFO. Text in German. 1971. q. free. adv. bk.rev. **Document type:** *Bulletin.*
Formerly: Fachhochschule Aalen. Bulletin
Published by: Fachhochschule Aalen, Beethovenstr 1, Aalen, 73430, Germany. TEL 07361-5760. Ed. Joerg Linser. Circ: 1,400.

FACT BOOK; a statistical handbook. see *EDUCATION—Abstracting, Bibliographies, Statistics*

FACTOR D; kwartaalblad voor het economie-onderwijs en zijn didactiek. see *BUSINESS AND ECONOMICS*

370 GBR
FALMER PRESS. QUALITATIVE STUDIES SERIES*. Variant title: Qualitative Studies Series. Text in English. irreg., latest vol.2. **Document type:** *Monographic series, Academic/Scholarly.*
Published by: RoutledgeFalmer Press (Subsidiary of: Taylor & Francis Group), 11 New Fetter Ln, London, EC4P 4EE, United Kingdom. TEL 44-20-7583-9855, FAX 44-20-7842-2298, info@tandf.co.uk, http://www.routledgefalmer.com. **Subscr. in Europe to:** Taylor & Francis Ltd, Journals Customer Service, Rankine Rd, Basingstoke, Hants RG24 8PR, United Kingdom. TEL 44-1256-813000, FAX 44-1256-330245, enquiry@tandf.co.uk; **Subscr. in US to:** Taylor & Francis Inc., Customer Services Dept, 325 Chestnut St, 8th Fl, Philadelphia, PA 19106. TEL 800-354-1420, FAX 215-625-8914.

FAMILIENMAGAZIN. see *CHILDREN AND YOUTH—About*

370 USA
FAMILIES & SCHOOLS. Text in English. q.
Published by: Academic Development Institute, 121 N Kickapoo St, Lincoln, IL 62656g. TEL 217-732-6462, FAX 217-732-3696, adi@adi.org, http://www.families-schools.org/solidfoundations/newsletter.htm, http://www.adi.org.

370 FRA ISSN 1249-2329
FAMILLE ET EDUCATION; le magazine des parents d'eleves de l'enseignement libre. Text in French. 1947. bi-m. free to members (effective 2005). bk.rev.; film rev. bibl.; illus.; stat.; tr.lit.; tr.mk. **Document type:** *Magazine, Consumer.*
Formerly (until 1993): Nouvelle Famille Educatrice (0029-4748)
Published by: Association des Parents d'Eleves de l'Enseignement Libre (APEL), 277 rue Saint Jacques, Paris, 75005, France. TEL 33-1-53737390, FAX 33-1-53737400, http://www.appel.asso.fr. Ed. Sylvie Bocquet. Circ: 775,000 (paid).

FAMILY/JIATING. see *MATRIMONY*

FAMILY MEDICINE. see *MEDICAL SCIENCES*

E

306.85 USA ISSN 0197-6664
CODEN: FCOOBE

➤ **FAMILY RELATIONS**; interdisciplinary journal of applied family studies. Text in English. 1952. 5/yr. USD 114 combined subscription in the Americas to individuals & Caribbean (print & online eds); EUR 137 combined subscription in Europe to individuals print & online eds; GBP 91 combined subscription elsewhere to individuals print & online eds (effective 2006); USD 551 combined subscription in the Americas to institutions & Caribbean (print & online eds.); GBP 420 combined subscription elsewhere to institutions print & online eds (effective 2005); USD 50 combined subscription in the Americas to students & Caribbean (print & online eds); EUR 72 combined subscription in Europe to students print & online eds; GBP 48 combined subscription elsewhere to students print & online eds (effective 2006). adv. bk.rev. charts; abstr.; illus.; stat. index. back issues avail.; reprint service avail. from PQC,PSC. **Document type:** *Journal, Academic/Scholarly.* **Description:** Covers applied scholarly articles with emphasis on family relationships across the life cycle with implications for intervention, education and public policy.
Former titles (until 1979): Family Coordinator (0014-7214); (until 1967): Family Life Coordinator (0886-0394); (until 1959): The Coordinator (1540-8256)
Related titles: CD-ROM ed.: (from National Information Services Corp. (N I S C)); Microform ed.: (from PQC); Online - full text ed.: ISSN 1741-3729. USD 523 in the Americas to institutions & Caribbean; GBP 399 elsewhere to institutions (effective 2005) (from bigchalk, Blackwell Synergy, EBSCO Publishing, IngentaConnect, JSTOR (Web-based Journal Archive), Northern Light Technology, Inc., O C L C Online Computer Library Center, Inc., ProQuest Information & Learning, Swets Information Services, The Dialog Corporation).
Indexed: AC&P, AMHA, ASCA, ASG, AgeL, Agr, BRI, CBRI, CDA, CERDIC, CIJE, CJA, CLFP, CurCont, Faml, HRA, MEA, MEA&I, MRD, PCI, PsycInfo, PsycholAb, RASB, RHEA, RI-1, RI-2, RefZh, SFSA, SRRA, SSA, SSCI, SSI, SWA, SWR&A, SociolAb, V&AA, e-psyche.
—BLDSC (3865.576100), IDS, IE, Infotrieve, ingenta. **CCC.**
Published by: (National Council on Family Relations), Blackwell Publishing, Inc. (Subsidiary of: Blackwell Publishing Ltd.), Commerce Place, 350 Main St, Malden, MA 02148. TEL 781-388-8206, FAX 781-388-8232, subscrip@blackwellpub.com, http://www.blackwellpublishing.com/journals/FARE. Ed. Joyce A Arditti. Pub. Otis Dean. adv.: B&W page USD 600; trim 11 x 8.5. Circ: 4,200 (paid).

371.0712 CAN ISSN 0700-9070
FEDERATION OF CATHOLIC PARENT-TEACHER ASSOCIATIONS OF ONTARIO. NEWSLETTER. Text in English. 1974. q. CND 15 to members. adv. bk.rev. **Document type:** *Newsletter.*
Published by: Ontario Association of Parents in Catholic Education, 2275 Wellesly Ave, Windsor, ON N8W 2G1, Canada. TEL 519-258-4459, FAX 519-258-5455. Circ: 12,000.

371.1 CAN
FEDERATION QUEBECOISE DES DIRECTEURS ET DIRECTRICES D'ECOLE. REVUE INFORMATION. Text in English. 1963. 5/yr. CND 15. adv. illus. back issues avail.
Formerly: Federation Quebecoise des Directeurs d'Ecole. Revue Information
Published by: Federation Quebecoise des Directeurs et Directrices d'Ecole, 7855 Bd L H Lafontaine, Ste 100, Anjou, PQ H1K 4E4, Canada. TEL 514-353-7511, FAX 514-353-2064. Circ: 5,000.

370 HUN ISSN 0209-9608
LC5256.H9
FELNOTTNEVELES, MUVELODES. ACTA ANDRAGOGIAE ET CULTURAE. Text in Hungarian. irreg., latest vol.12, 1991. bibl. **Document type:** *Academic/Scholarly.*
Supersedes in part (in 1980): Neveles, Muvelodes. Acta Paedagogica Debrecina (0324-6957); Which was formerly (until 1963): Acta Paedagogica Debrecina (0567-7912)
Published by: Kossuth Lajos Tudomanyegyetem, Egyetem ter 1, Debrecen, 4010, Hungary. TEL 0036-52-416666, FAX 0036-52-412336. Ed. Kalman Rubovszky. Circ: 500.

FEUILLETS D'INFORMATIONS PEDAGOGIQUES. see *GEOGRAPHY*

371.8 DEU ISSN 1610-2592
F(H)OCUS. Text in German. 2001. 3/yr. adv. **Document type:** *Magazine, Trade.*
Published by: Fachhochschule Muenster, Huefferstr 27, Muenster, 48149, Germany. TEL 49-251-830, FAX 49-251-8364015, verwaltung@fh-muenster.de, http://www.fh-muenster.de/IUP/publikationen/fhocus/.

371.8 DEU ISSN 1615-3677
F(H)ORUM. Text in German. 2000. 2/yr. adv. **Document type:** *Newspaper, Trade.*
Published by: Fachhochschule Muenster, Huefferstr 27, Muenster, 48149, Germany. TEL 49-251-830, FAX 49-251-8364015, verwaltung@fh-muenster.de, http://www.fh-muenster.de/IUP/publikationen/fhorum/.

370 FJI
FIJI. MINISTRY OF EDUCATION, SCIENCE AND TECHNOLOGY. ANNUAL REPORT. Text in English. 1918. a. FJD 10. **Document type:** *Government.* **Description:** Activities of all functional units of the ministry in the year reported on.
Former titles: Fiji. Ministry of Education. Report; (until 1977): Fiji. Ministry of Education, Youth and Sport. Report (0377-3728)
Published by: Ministry of Education Science and Technology, Suva, Fiji. TEL 679-314477, FAX 679-303511. Circ: 500.

FILM UND FERNSEHEN IN FORSCHUNG UND LEHRE. see *MOTION PICTURES*

370.1 RUS
FILOSOFIYA OBRAZOVANIYA. Text in Russian. 2002. q. RUR 280 for 6 mos. domestic; USD 60 foreign (effective 2005). **Document type:** *Journal, Academic/Scholarly.*
Published by: (Rossiiskaya Akademiya Nauk, Sibirskoe Otdelenie, Institut Filosofii Obrazovaniya), Izdatel'stvo Sibirskogo Otdeleniya Rossiiskoi Akademii Nauk/Publishing House of the Russian Academy of Sciences, Siberian Branch, Morskoi pr 2, a/ya 187, Novosibirsk, 630090, Russian Federation. TEL 7-3832-300570, FAX 7-3832-333755, sprice@ad-sbras.nsc.ru, psb@ad-sbras.nsc.ru, http://www-psb.ad-sbras.nsc.ru/phyledu.htm. Ed. N B Nalivaiko.

370.15 HRV ISSN 0352-6798
B1 CODEN: RFFPEQ
➤ **FILOZOFSKI FAKULTET - ZADAR. RAZDIO FILOZOFIJE, PSIHOLOGIJE, SOCIOLOGIJE I PEDAGOGIJE. RADOVI.** Text in Croatian, English; Summaries in English. 1985. a. USD 20 foreign (effective 2000). index, cum.index no.1-2. back issues avail. **Document type:** *Academic/Scholarly.* **Description:** Interdisciplinary journal covers philosophy, psychology, sociology, and education.
Indexed: L&LBA, LingAb, RASB, SOPODA, SSA, SociolAb, e-psyche.
Published by: Sveuciliste u Splitu, Filozofski Fakultet Zadar, Obala P Kresimira IV 2, Zadar, 23000, Croatia. TEL 385-23-316-311, FAX 385-23-316882, radovi-razdio_fpsp@ffzd.hr. Ed. Erma Ivos Niksic. Circ: 500.
Co-sponsor: Ministarstva Znanosti i Tehnologije Republike Hrvatske.

371.1 CAN ISSN 1480-932X
FINE F A C T A. Text in English. 1964. s-a. included in subscription to: Fine. bk.rev. bibl.; illus. **Document type:** *Journal, Academic/Scholarly.* **Description:** Covers the fields of art, dance, drama and music.
Formerly (until 1998): F A C T A Newsletter (0014-5556)
Related titles: Online - full text ed.: (from Micromedia ProQuest).
Indexed: CEI.
Published by: Alberta Teachers' Association, Fine Arts Council, Barnett House, 11010 142 St, Edmonton, AB T5N 2R1, Canada. http://www.fineartscouncil.ca/index.php?section=finefacta&page=index. Ed. Claire Klug TEL 403-777-7400. Circ: 617.

373.246 USA
FIRST OPPORTUNITY. Text in English. 1985. q. USD 9.60 (effective 2000). adv. **Description:** Provides information for young adults with a desire to pursue a vocational-technical career.
Related titles: Special ed(s).: First Opportunity (Black Students' Edition). ISSN 1050-7175; First Opportunity (Hispanic Students' Edition). ISSN 1050-7167.
Published by: Communications Publishing Group, Inc., 660 Penn Tower, 3100 Broadway St. Ste 660, Kansas City, MO 64111-2413. TEL 913-317-2888, FAX 816-960-1989. Ed. Jeanine Meiers. Pub. Georgia Lee Clarke. adv.: B&W page USD 19,000, color page USD 22,800. Circ: 500,000.

372.218 USA ISSN 0744-7434
FIRST TEACHER; for people who care for young children. Text in English. 1979. 6/yr. USD 34 (effective 2004). adv. bk.rev. back issues avail. **Document type:** *Trade.* **Description:** Includes practical articles, ideas, and recipes for preschool and kindergarten teachers.
Published by: First Teacher, Inc., PO Box 180, Wilmington, NC 28402. TEL 800-677-6644, FAX 910-763-0066. Ed. Lisa L Durkin. Circ: 15,000. **Subscr. to:** PO Box 189, Vandalia, OH 45377-0189.

THE FIRST WORD BULLETIN. see *CONSERVATION*

371.192 DEU
DER FISCH; Mitteilungen fuer Eltern und Freunde. Text in German. 1981. 2/yr. free. adv. illus. **Document type:** *Newsletter.*
Published by: Freies Katholisches Schulwerk Friedrichshafen e.V., Bodensee-Schule St. Martin, Zeisigweg 1, Friedrichshafen, 88045, Germany. TEL 07541-2109193. Circ: 1,500.

373 USA
FLORIDA. DEPARTMENT OF EDUCATION. FLORIDA STATEWIDE ASSESSMENT PROGRAM: STATE, DISTRICT AND REGIONAL REPORT OF STATEWIDE ASSESSMENT RESULTS. Text in English. 1976. s-a. free. stat. **Document type:** *Government.* **Description:** Reports the results of the high school competing test.
Formerly: Florida. Department of Education. Florida Statewide Assessment Program: Capsule Report (0094-1468)
Published by: (Florida. Student Assessment Section), Department of Education, Division of Public Schools, Turlington Building, 325 W Gaines St, Tallahassee, FL 32399. TEL 904-448-8198, FAX 904-487-1889.

371 USA
FLORIDA. DEPARTMENT OF EDUCATION. PROFESSIONAL PRACTICES COUNCIL. REPORT. Text in English. 1969. a. free.
Published by: Department of Education, Professional Practices Council, Turlington Building, 325 W Gaines St, Tallahassee, FL 32304. TEL 904-488-2481. Ed. Hugh Ingram. Circ: 300.

370 USA
➤ **FLORIDA EDUCATIONAL RESEARCH COUNCIL. RESEARCH BULLETIN.** Text in English. 1965. q. USD 15 (effective 2003). abstr.; bibl. **Document type:** *Bulletin, Academic/Scholarly.*
Formerly: Florida Educational Research and Development Council. Research Bulletin (0015-4024)
Related titles: Microfiche ed.
Indexed: CIJE.
—BLDSC (7722.620000), IE, ingenta.
Published by: Florida Educational Research Council, Inc., PO Box 506, Sanibel, FL 33957. TEL 238-472-8211, FAX 238-472-0267, chacouncil@aol.com, http://www.firn.edu/webfiles/others/ferc/default.htm. Ed. Charlie T Council. R&P C.T. Council. Circ: 5,100.

370.72 USA
➤ **FLORIDA JOURNAL OF EDUCATIONAL RESEARCH.** Text in English. 1996. a. **Document type:** *Journal, Academic/Scholarly.*
Media: Online - full content.
Published by: Florida Educational Research Association, University of South Florida, College of Education, 4202 E Fowler Ave, Tampa, FL 33620. http://www.coedu.usf.edu/fjer/default.htm. Ed. Dr. Jeff Kromrey.

➤ **FLORIDA MUSIC DIRECTOR.** see *MUSIC*

371.192 USA ISSN 0733-8007
FLORIDA P T A BULLETIN. Text in English. 1927. 7/yr. USD 7 (effective 2001). adv. bk.rev. **Document type:** *Bulletin.*
Published by: Florida Congress of Parents and Teachers, 1747 Orlando Central Parkway, Orlando, FL 32809. TEL 407-855-7604. Ed., R&P Marlene Carls. Adv. contact Anne Thompson. Circ: 4,000.

371.12 USA ISSN 0071-5999
FLORIDA REQUIREMENTS FOR TEACHER CERTIFICATION. Text in English. 1923. irreg. free.
Published by: Florida Department of Education, Office of the Commissioner, Turlington Building, Ste 1514, 325 West Gaines St, Tallahassee, FL 32399. edcert@fldoe.org. Ed. Ralph D Turlington.

FOCUS. see *MATHEMATICS*

FOCUS ON SURGICAL EDUCATION. see *MEDICAL SCIENCES—Surgery*

370 SWE ISSN 0015-6167
FOENSTRET. Text in Swedish. 1922. 12/yr. SEK 150; SEK 20 newsstand/cover (effective 2001). adv. bk.rev. illus. **Document type:** *Magazine, Consumer.*
Formerly (until 1954): A.B.F.
Related titles: Audio cassette/tape ed.
Indexed: RILM.
Published by: Arbetarnas Bildningsfoerbund - ABF, Fack 522, Stockholm, 10130, Sweden. TEL 46-8-613-50-00, FAX 46-8-24-69-56, fonstret@abf.se, http://turture.abf.se/index.htm, http://www.abf.se. Ed., Pub. Eva Swedenmark. Adv. contact Birgitta Olsson. B&W page SEK 13,500, color page SEK 17,500; trim 190 x 255. Circ: 35,100. **Subscr. to:** Pressdata, Fack 3263, Stockholm 10365, Sweden. TEL 46-8- 799-63-11, FAX 46-8-28-59-74.

372.21 SWE ISSN 0015-5292
FOERSKOLAN. Text in Swedish. 1918. 10/yr. SEK 260 (effective 2003). adv. bk.rev. charts; illus. index. **Document type:** *Magazine, Trade.*
Former titles (until 1969): Barntraedgaarden; (until 1940): Tidskrift - Svenska Froebelfoerbundet
Related titles: Online - full text ed.
Published by: Laerarfoerbundet, Tidningsafdelning, Segelbaatsvaegen 15, Box 12229, Stockholm, 10226, Sweden. TEL 46-8-7376500, FAX 46-8-7376569, forskolan@lararforbundet.se, kansli@lararforbundet.se, http://www.forskolan.net/default.asp, http://www.lararforbundet.se. Ed., Pub. Annica Grimlund. Adv. contact Ann Spaak TEL 46-8-7376509. B&W page SEK 17,200, color page SEK 23,500; trim 185 x 264. Circ: 65,200 (paid).

372.9489 DNK ISSN 0015-5837
FOLKESKOLEN. Text in Danish. 1884. w. adv. bk.rev. index. reprints avail. **Document type:** *Trade.*

E

Formerly (until 1906): Danmarks Laererforenings Medlemsblad (0901-4683)
Related titles: Online - full text ed.
Published by: Danmarks Laererforening, Vandkunsten 12, PO Box 2139, Copenhagen K, 1015, Denmark. TEL 45-33-696300, FAX 45-33-696426, folkeskolen@dlf.org, dlf@dlf.org, http://www.folkeskolen.dk, http://www.dlf.org. Ed. Thorkild Thejsen. Adv. contact Lars Juul Nielsen TEL 45-89-398833. B&W page DKK 17,727, color page DKK 24,292; 183 x 265. Circ: 88,299 (controlled).

FOLKESKOLEN. KATALOG. see *EDUCATION—Abstracting, Bibliographies, Statistics*

373 USA
FOR SENIORS ONLY; a magazine for H.S. seniors. Text in English. 1970. s-a. free to qualified high-school students. adv. bk.rev.; film rev.; rec.rev.; software rev.; video rev. illus. 64 p./no.; **Document type:** *Magazine, Consumer.* **Description:** Provides information directed toward high-school seniors and juniors. Includes special single-sponsor editions for seniors only that are developed and tailored for individual corporations or institutions.
Published by: Campus Communications, Inc., 5820 N. Federal Hwy., Ste. D-2, Boca Raton, FL 33487. TEL 561-995-5353, 561-995-5353, FAX 561-995-5354, 561-995-5354, campusmag@aol.com. Ed. Judi Oliff. Pub. Darryl G. Elberg. R&P, Adv. contact Darryl G Elberg. B&W page USD 11,350; 4.5 x 7.25. Circ: 350,000 (controlled).

FOR THE LEARNING OF MATHEMATICS; an international journal of mathematics education. see *MATHEMATICS*

370 800 DEU ISSN 1437-3157
FOREIGN LANGUAGE TEACHING IN EUROPE. Text in English, German. 1999. irreg., latest vol.8, 2003. price varies. **Document type:** *Monographic series, Academic/Scholarly.*
Indexed: MLA-IB.
Published by: Peter Lang GmbH Europaeischer Verlag der Wissenschaften, Eschborner Landstr 42-50, Frankfurt Am Main, 60489, Germany. TEL 49-69-78070550, FAX 49-69-78070550, zentrale.frankfurt@peterlang.com, http://www.peterlang.de. **Dist. by:** Verlag Peter Lang AG, Moosstr. 1, Postfach 350, Pieterlen 2542, Switzerland. TEL 41-32-3761717, FAX 41-32-3761727.

FORENSIC. see *COMMUNICATIONS*

373 USA ISSN 0196-304X
FORENSIC QUARTERLY. Text in English. 1928. q. USD 6 (effective 2003). back issues avail. **Document type:** *Academic/Scholarly.*
Published by: National Federation of State High School Associations, PO Box 690, Indianapolis, IN 46206-0690. TEL 317-972-6900, FAX 317-822-5700, http://www.nfhs.org. Ed. Richard G Fawcett. R&P Fritz McGinness. **Subscr. to:** 361246, Indianapolis, IN 46236-5324. TEL 800-776-3462.

FOREST OF EDUCATION/KYOIKU-NO-MORI. see *FORESTS AND FORESTRY*

370 ESP
FORJA. Text in Spanish. 1964. q. free.
Published by: Colegio Nacional General Primo de Rivera, Leon, 7, Albacete, 02001, Spain.

370.1 DEU ISSN 1435-9839
FORSCHUNG, STUDIUM UND PRAXIS. Text in German. 2002. irreg., latest vol.8, 2003. EUR 16.90 per issue (effective 2003). **Document type:** *Monographic series, Academic/Scholarly.*
Published by: Waxmann Verlag GmbH, Steinfurter Str 555, Muenster, 48159, Germany. TEL 49-251-26504-0, FAX 49-251-2650426, info@waxmann.com, http://www.waxmann.com.

371.14 DNK ISSN 0902-3518
FORTVIVL-IKKE. Text in Danish. 1980. irreg. (5-6/yr.). membership. illus.
Formerly (until 1980): Fortvivl (0109-1425)
Published by: Invandrerlearerforeningen, c/o Dan Saederup, Danmarksgade 16, Odense C, 5000, Denmark.

370 DEU ISSN 1430-3671
FORUM. Text in German. 1957. bi-m. **Document type:** *Journal, Consumer.*
Former titles (until 1995): Novalis-Forum (1420-3251); (until 1994): Der Elternbrief (0013-645X)
Published by: Trithemius Verlag, Kunigundenstr 4, Munich, 80802, Germany. laurin@bigfoot.de. Ed., Pub. Lorenzo Ravagli. Circ: 3,000.

371.0712 BEL
FORUM; contactblad voor inrichtende machten, pedagogische begeleiders en directies van het Katholieke Onderwijs. Text in Dutch. 1970. m. (except July-August). EUR 22.10; free to qualified personnel (effective 2005). **Document type:** *Academic/Scholarly.* **Description:** Publishes policy positions, information on pedagogical research, congresses and other information relevant to Catholic schools.
Related titles: Online - full content ed.
Published by: Vlaams Secretariaat van het Katholiek Onderwijs, Guimardstraat 1, Brussel, 1040, Belgium. TEL 32-2-507-0619, FAX 32-2-513-3645, forum@vsko.be, info@licafr.be, http://ond.vsko.be/portal/page?_pageid=654,1&_dad=portal&_schema=portal&p_portal_id=1. Ed. Willy Bombeek. Pub. A de Wolf. R&P Andre Peeters.

FORUM NEWSLETTER. see *RELIGIONS AND THEOLOGY—Roman Catholic*

370.711 DEU
FORUM SCHULE; magazin fuer lehrerinnen und lehrer. Text in German. m.
Published by: Landesinstitut fuer Schule, Paradieser Weg 64, Soest, 59494, Germany. TEL 49-0-29216831, redaktion.forumschule@mail.lsw.nrw.de, http://www.forum-schule.de/index.html.

370 JPN
FOUR CORNERS*. Text in Japanese. 1983. 3/yr. bk.rev. back issues avail.
Published by: Doshisha International High School/Doshi-sha Kokusai Koko, Tatara, Tanabe-cho, Tsuzuki-gun, Kyoto-shi, 610-03, Japan. Eds. Hillel Weintraub, Masahiko Amenomiya.

370 DEU
FRAENKISCHE SCHULE. Text in German. 1965. bi-m. adv. bk.rev. illus. back issues avail. **Document type:** *Journal, Academic/Scholarly.*
Published by: B L L V Oberfranken, Eichenwaldstr 22, Pinzberg, 91361, Germany. TEL 49-9191-5754, fs-bllv@onlinehome.de, http://oberfranken.bllv.de. Ed. Gerald Lippert. Circ: 5,000. **Subscr. to:** Postfach 135, Schoenwald 95170, Germany.

371 FRA ISSN 0015-9395
PC2065
LE FRANCAIS DANS LE MONDE. Text in French. 1961. 6/yr. EUR 78 (effective 2005). adv. bk.rev. illus. back issues avail.; reprints avail. **Document type:** *Journal, Trade.* **Description:** Covers culture, language and society of France, and surveys pedagogical developments. For French teachers.
Incorporates (1981-1998): Diagonales (0982-9644); Which was formerly (until 1987): Reponses (0292-9554)
Related titles: Microfilm ed.; ♦ Supplement(s): Le Francais dans le Monde. Recherches et Applications. ISSN 0994-6632.
Indexed: BibInd, CIJE, L&LBA, LT&LA, MLA, MLA-IB, RASB, SOPODA.
—BLDSC (4032.160000), IE, Infotrieve, ingenta. **CCC.**
Published by: C L E International, 27 Rue de la Glaciere, Paris, 75013, France. TEL 33-1-45874326, FAX 33-1-45874410, contact@fdlm.org, cle@vuef.fr, http://www.fdlm.org, http://www.cle-inter.com/. Ed. Francoise Ploquin. Circ: 12,000.

371 FRA ISSN 0994-6632
LE FRANCAIS DANS LE MONDE. RECHERCHES ET APPLICATIONS. Text in French. 1987. s-a.
Related titles: ♦ Supplement to: Le Francais dans le Monde. ISSN 0015-9395.
Published by: Hachette Edicef, 58 rue Jean Bleuzen, Vanves, Cedex 92178, France. TEL 33-1-46621050, FAX 33-1-40951975, Fdmdiag@hachette_livre.fr, http://www.fdm.hachette-livre.fr.

370 ZAF ISSN 0042-9228
FREE STATE EDUCATIONAL NEWS/VRYSTAATSE ONDERWYSNUUS. Text in Afrikaans, English. 1968. s-a. free. charts; illus.; stat. **Document type:** *Government.*
Published by: (Education Department), Ficksburg Press (Pty) Ltd., PO Box 521, Bloemfontein, 9300, South Africa. Circ: 1,000 (controlled).

FREIE UNIVERSITAET BERLIN. OSTEUROPA-INSTITUT. ERZIEHUNGSWISSENSCHAFTLICHE VEROEFFENTLICHUNGEN. see *POLITICAL SCIENCE*

370 AUT
FREIHEITLICHER OBEROESTERREICHISCHER LEHRERVEREIN. ZEITSCHRIFT. Text in German. 1956. q. adv. bk.rev. **Document type:** *Journal, Trade.*
Formerly: Freiheitlicher Oberoesterreichischer Landeslehrer Verein. Zeitschrift (0016-0903)
Published by: Freiheitlicher Oberoesterreichischer Lehrerverein, Bluetenstrasse 21-1, Linz, O 4044, Austria. Circ: 10,000.

370 DNK ISSN 0109-9108
FREINET NYT. Text in Danish. 1980. q. DKK 75 to members. illus. **Document type:** *Academic/Scholarly.*
Published by: Arbejdsgruppen af Freinetpaedagoger, c/o Michael Cain, Vestervangen 13, Esbjerg N, 8715, Denmark. TEL 45-75-13-32-51, FAX 45-75-13-49-94. Circ: 200.

370.1 USA ISSN 1544-0370
▼ **FREIRE ONLINE**; a journal of the Paulo Freire Institute/UCLA. Text mainly in English. 2003 (Jan.). q. free (effective 2003).
Media: Online - full content.
Published by: University of California at Los Angeles, Paulo Freire Institute, UCLA School of Education, 2171 Campus Rd., Los Angeles, CA 90041. TEL 323-547-0797, FAX 323-259-8643, http://www.paulofreireinstitute.org/freireonline/. Ed. Saul Duarte.

FREMDSPRACHENUNTERRICHT. see *LINGUISTICS*

DER FREMDSPRACHLICHE UNTERRICHT. ENGLISCH; Grundlagen Unterrichtsvorschlaege Materialien. see *LINGUISTICS*

372 DNK ISSN 1397-517X
FRIE GRUNDSKOLER. Text in Danish. 1898. 18/yr. adv. **Document type:** *Trade.*
Supersedes (in 1998): Tidens Skoler (0108-6278); Which was formerly (until 1972): Den Danske Realskole (0045-964X)
Related titles: Online - full text ed.
Published by: Frie Grundskolers Laererforening, Ravnsoevej 6, Risskov, 8240, Denmark. TEL 45-87-469110, FAX 45-87-469111, redaktionen@fgl.dk, fgl@fgl.dk, http://www.friegrundskoler.dk, http://www.fgl.dk. Ed. Maria Larsen TEL 45-87-469125. adv.: color page DKK 9,200, B&W page DKK 5,800; 225 x 176.

370 DNK ISSN 0109-8632
DEN FRIE LAERERSKOLE. Text in Danish. 1952. q.
Published by: Den Frie Laererskole, Svendborgvej 15, Vester Skerninge, 5762, Denmark. TEL 45-62-24-10-66, FAX 45-62-24-14-85. Ed. Kent Iversen.

371.1 SWE ISSN 0349-2478
FRITIDSPEDAGOGEN. Text in Swedish. 1972-1975; resumed 1980. 10/yr. SEK 200 (effective 2003). adv. 28 p./no. 4 cols./p.; **Document type:** *Magazine, Trade.*
Related titles: Online - full text ed.
Published by: Laerarfoerbundet, Tidningsafdelning, Segelbaatsvaegen 15, Box 12229, Stockholm, 10226, Sweden. TEL 46-8-7376500, FAX 46-8-7376569, fritidspedagogen@lararforbundet.se, kansli@lararforbundet.se, http://www.lararforbundet.se. Pub. Helena Gaardsaeter. adv.: B&W page SEK 7,600, color page SEK 11,400; trim 182 x 266. Circ: 16,100.

370 ESP ISSN 1575-7072
FUENTES. Text in Spanish. 1999. a., latest 2000. EUR 20 per issue (effective 2005). **Document type:** *Journal, Academic/Scholarly.*
Published by: Universidad de Sevilla, Secretariado de Publicaciones, Porvenir 27, Sevilla, 41013, Spain. TEL 34-95-4487444, FAX 34-95-4487443, secpub10@us.es, http://www.us.es/publius/inicio.html.

371.224 USA
FUNDING YOUR EDUCATION. Abbreviated title: F Y E. Text in English. a. free. **Document type:** *Government.* **Description:** Provides general information about the federal student financial aid programs and how to apply for them.
Related titles: Spanish ed.
Published by: U.S. Department of Education, Federal Student Aid Programs, Federal Student Aid Information Center, PO Box 84, Washington, DC 20044-0084 . http://studentaid.ed.gov/students/publications/FYE/index.html, http://studentaid.ed.gov/PORTALSWebApp/students/english/index.jsp.

G A NEWS. (Geographical Association) see *GEOGRAPHY*

370 DEU ISSN 0938-6173
G D S ARCHIV FUER HOCHSCHUL- UND STUDENTENGESCHICHTE. Variant title: G D S Archiv fuer Hochschul- und Studentengeschichte (GA). Text in German. 1992. irreg., latest vol.6, 2002. price varies. **Document type:** *Monographic series, Academic/Scholarly.*
Indexed: DIP, IBR, IBZ.
Published by: (Gemeinschaft fuer Deutsche Studentengeschichte), S H Verlag GmbH, Osterather Str 42, Cologne, 50739, Germany. TEL 49-221-9561740, FAX 49-221-9561741, info@sh-verlag.de, http://www.sh-verlag.de.

370 DEU ISSN 0938-6688
G D S ARCHIV FUER HOCHSCHUL- UND STUDENTENGESCHICHTE. BEIHEFTE. Text in German. 1990. irreg., latest vol.12, 2001. price varies. **Document type:** *Monographic series, Academic/Scholarly.*
Published by: (Gemeinschaft fuer Deutsche Studentengeschichte), S H Verlag GmbH, Osterather Str 42, Cologne, 50739, Germany. TEL 49-221-9561740, FAX 49-221-9561741, info@sh-verlag.de, http://www.sh-verlag.de.

370 USA
G E A EDUCATOR. Text in English. 1966. bi-m. free to members. **Document type:** *Newsletter.* **Description:** Contains information for teachers regarding education within the district and at the state and national levels.
Former titles: Grossmont Educator (0016-3635); G U H S D T A News
Media: Duplicated (not offset).
Published by: Grossmont Education Association, 9015 Grossmont Blvd, La Mesa, CA 91941-4028. TEL 619-460-3465, FAX 619-460-9325. Ed. Aaron Landau. Circ: 900.

▼ **G E F A M E**; journal of African studies. see *HISTORY—History Of Africa*

E

370 DEU
G E W LEHRERKALENDER NORDRHEIN-WESTFALEN. Text in German. a. **Document type:** *Bulletin.*
Published by: (Gewerkschaft Erziehung und Wissenschaft), Vereinigte Verlagsanstalten GmbH, Hoeherweg 278, Duesseldorf, 40231, Germany. TEL 49-211-7357589, FAX 49-211-7357507, am@vva.de, info@vva.de, http://www.vva.de. Circ: 50,000 (controlled).

707 DNK ISSN 0109-9442
G L B. Text in Danish. q. DKK 100. illus.
Published by: Gymnasiets Laerere i Billedkunst, Soroe, Denmark.

370 384.558 USA
G P N EDUCATIONAL MEDIA CATALOG. (Great Plains National) Text in English. 199?. a. USD 20 (effective 2000 - 2001). **Document type:** *Catalog, Academic/Scholarly.* **Description:** Lists educational media products for elementary, secondary and higher education.
Formed by the 1991 merger of: G N P Educational Video Catalog. College - Adult; Which was formerly: G N P Educational Media. College - Adult; G N P Educational Video Catalog. Elementary - Secondary; Which was formerly: G N P Educational Media. Elementary - Secondary; Both of which superseded in part: Great Plains National Instructional Television Library. Recorded Visual Instruction (0740-2732); Which was formerly (1967-1973): Catalog of Recorded Instruction for Television
Related titles: Online - full content ed.
Published by: Great Plains National Instructional Television Library, PO Box 80669, Lincoln, NE 68501. TEL 800-228-4630, FAX 402-472-4076, gpn@unl.edu, http://www.gpn.unl.edu. Circ: 30,000.

370 MEX ISSN 0016-3848
GACETA POLITECNICA★. Text in Spanish. 1963. s-m. free. bk.rev. charts; illus.
Published by: (Direccion de Relaciones Publicas), Instituto Politecnico Nacional, Division de Comunicacion Social, Unidad Profesional Zacatenco, Col Lindavista, Mexico City, DF 07738, Mexico. Ed. Lourdes Jimenez Vidal.

GAMBIA. CENTRAL STATISTICS DEPARTMENT. EDUCATION STATISTICS. see *EDUCATION—Abstracting, Bibliographies, Statistics*

371.822 TGO
GAME SU. Text in Ewe. 1972. m. **Description:** For the newly literate.
Published by: Ministry of Social and Women's Affairs, 19 ave de la Nouvelle Marche, BP1247, Lome, Togo. TEL 21-28-44. Circ: 6,000.

370 CHN ISSN 1002-5111
GAODENG SHIFAN JIAOYU YANJIU. Text in Chinese. bi-m. CNY 12 (effective 1999). **Document type:** *Academic/Scholarly.*
Related titles: Online - full text ed.: (from East View Information Services).
Published by: Beijing Shifan Daxue/Beijing Normal University, Xinjiekouwai Beitaipingzhuang, Beijing, 100875, China. TEL 20110867. Ed. Gu Mingyuan.

GASTROHEP. see *MEDICAL SCIENCES—Gastroenterology*

370 330 POL ISSN 1508-6593
GAZETA SZKOLNA. Text in Polish. w. PLZ 63.70 (effective 2001). **Document type:** *Newspaper.*
Published by: Grupa Wydawnicza INFOR Sp. z o.o., Ul Okopowa 58/72, Warsaw, 01042, Poland. TEL 48-22-5304208, 48-22-5304450, bok@infor.pl. Ed. Janusz Zatorski. Adv. contact Waldemar Krakowiak.

305.307 GBR ISSN 0954-0253
LC212.8 CODEN: GEEDER
➤ **GENDER AND EDUCATION.** Text in English. 1989. 6/yr. GBP 778, USD 1,451 combined subscription to institutions print & online eds. (effective 2006). adv. bk.rev. illus. reprint service avail. from PSC. **Document type:** *Journal, Academic/Scholarly.* **Description:** Covers all aspects of education in relation to gender.
Related titles: Microfiche ed.; Online - full text ed.: ISSN 1360-0516. GBP 739, USD 1,378 to institutions (effective 2006) (from EBSCO Publishing, Gale Group, IngentaConnect, O C L C Online Computer Library Center, Inc., ProQuest Information & Learning, Swets Information Services).
Indexed: ASSIA, BrEdI, CIJE, CPE, CWI, ChLitAb, CurCont, DIP, EAA, ERA, ETA, FamI, FemPer, IBR, IBSS, IBZ, IndIslam, LT&LA, MEA, PCI, RHEA, SEA, SENA, SOMA, SOPODA, SSA, SSCI, SWA, SociolAb, TEA, V&AA.
—BLDSC (4096.401200), IE, Infotrieve, ingenta. **CCC.**
Published by: Routledge (Subsidiary of: Taylor & Francis Group), 4 Park Sq, Milton Park, Abingdon, Oxon OX14 4RN, United Kingdom. TEL 44-1235-828600, FAX 44-1235-829000, info@routledge.co.uk, http://www.tandf.co.uk/journals/titles/09540253.asp, http://www.routledge.co.uk. Eds. Becky Francis, Christine Skelton. **Subscr. in N. America to:** Taylor & Francis Inc., Customer Services Dept, 325 Chestnut St, 8th Fl, Philadelphia, PA 19106. TEL 215-625-8900, 800-354-1420, FAX 215-625-8914, customerservice@taylorandfrancis.com; **Subscr. to:** Taylor & Francis Ltd, Journals Customer Service, Rankine Rd, Basingstoke, Hants RG24 8PR, United Kingdom. TEL 44-1256-813000, FAX 44-1256-330245.

372.4 IND ISSN 0072-0720
GENERAL EDUCATION READING MATERIAL SERIES★. Text in English, Hindi. 1959. irreg. Price varies.
Published by: Aligarh Muslim University, Aligarh, Uttar Pradesh 202 002, India.

GEOGRAFIJA V SOLI. see *GEOGRAPHY*

GEOGRAFIYA V SHKOLE. see *GEOGRAPHY*

GEOGRAPHY TEACHER. see *GEOGRAPHY*

371.192 USA
GEORGIA CONGRESS OF PARENTS AND TEACHERS. ANNUAL LEADERSHIP TRAINING CONFERENCE. WORKSHOP FOR P T A LEADERS. Text in English. a. USD 3.
Formerly: Georgia Congress of Parents and Teachers. Annual Summer Institute. Handbook for P T A Leaders (0072-1220)
Published by: (Georgia Congress of Parents and Teachers), University of Georgia, Center for Continuing Education, 1197 S Lumpkin St, Athens, GA 30602-3603. TEL 404-542-1725. Circ: 700.

GERMAN LIFE AND LETTERS. see *LITERATURE*

THE GERMAN QUARTERLY. see *LINGUISTICS*

GERMANY. STATISTISCHES BUNDESAMT. FACHSERIE 11: BILDUNG UND KULTUR. see *EDUCATION—Abstracting, Bibliographies, Statistics*

372.89 DEU ISSN 0176-943X
GESCHICHTE BETRIFFT UNS. Text in German. 1983. 6/yr. looseleaf. EUR 48; EUR 12 newsstand/cover (effective 2005). adv. bk.rev. back issues avail. **Document type:** *Journal, Academic/Scholarly.* **Description:** Includes educational planning material for teachers of grades 9-13. Covers topics in the history of politics, sociology, economy or technology and aims to involve students actively in these subjects.
Published by: Bergmoser und Hoeller Verlag GmbH, Karl-Friedrich-Str 76, Aachen, 52072, Germany. TEL 49-241-93888123, FAX 49-241-93888134, kontakt@buhv.de, http://www.buhv.de/index_.php4?page=s_3-1&pid=41&cat=4. Ed. Dieter Tiemann. Circ: 2,600.

370 DEU ISSN 0933-3096
D16.4.G3
GESCHICHTE LERNEN. Text in German. 1978. bi-m. EUR 60.60; EUR 10 newsstand/cover (effective 2005). adv. bk.rev. index. back issues avail. **Document type:** *Journal, Academic/Scholarly.*
Formerly (until 1988): Geschichtsdidaktik (0341-8987); Incorporates (1948-1998): Geschichte, Erziehung, Politik (0863-4378); Which was formerly (until 1990): Geschichtsunterricht und Staatsbuergerkunde (0016-9072); (until 1959): Geschichte in der Schule (0323-7893)
Indexed: AmH&L, DIP, HistAb, IBR, IBZ.
—**CCC.**
Published by: Erhard Friedrich Verlag GmbH, Im Brande 17, Seelze, 30926, Germany. TEL 49-511-400040, FAX 49-511-40004170, info@friedrich-verlag.de, http://www.friedrich-verlag.de. Ed. Michael Sauer. adv.: B&W page EUR 1,200, color page EUR 1,800. Circ: 8,800.

GESCHICHTE, POLITIK UND IHRE DIDAKTIK. see *HISTORY—History Of Europe*

370 DEU ISSN 1619-6910
JA86 CODEN: GEGEF7
➤ **GESELLSCHAFT, WIRTSCHAFT, POLITIK;** Sozialwissenschaften fuer politische Bildung. Text in German. 1951. q. EUR 33 domestic; EUR 36.50 foreign; EUR 26 domestic to students; EUR 29.50 foreign to students; EUR 9 newsstand/cover (effective 2004). adv. bk.rev. charts; illus.; stat. back issues avail. **Document type:** *Journal, Academic/Scholarly.* **Description:** Scientific information for teachers on economical, political and sociological matters.
Formerly (until 2002): Gegenwartskunde (0016-5875)
Indexed: AmH&L, DIP, ELLIS, HistAb, IBR, IBSS, IBZ, IPSA, SSCI.
—BLDSC (4162.640050), IDS, IE, ingenta. **CCC.**
Published by: V S - Verlag fuer Sozialwissenschaften (Subsidiary of: Springer Science+Business Media), Abraham-Lincoln-Str 46, Wiesbaden, 65189, Germany. TEL 49-611-78780, FAX 49-611-7878400, info@vs-verlag.de, http://www.vs-verlag.de. adv.: page EUR 650; 125 x 190. Circ: 2,200 (paid).

➤ **DIE GESTALT;** Vierteljahreszeitschrift fuer bildnerische Erziehung. see *ART*

370 DEU ISSN 0943-5689
GEWERKSCHAFT ERZIEHUNG UND WISSENSCHAFT BADEN-WUERTTEMBERG. JAHRBUCH. Text in German. 1981. a. EUR 19.50 (effective 2003). adv. **Document type:** *Journal, Academic/Scholarly.*
Formerly (until 1991): Jahrbuch fuer Lehrer (0721-5940)
Published by: (G E W Baden-Wuerttemberg), Sueddeutscher Paedagogischer Verlag GmbH, Silcherstr 7a, Stuttgart, 70176, Germany. info@spv-lb.de, http://www.spv-lb.de. Adv. contact Juergen Kienzler. page EUR 920; trim 120 x 170. Circ: 25,000.

373.246 DEU
GEWERKSCHAFTLICHE BILDUNGSPOLITIK; Stellungnahmen - Analysen - Informationen. Text in German. 1973. m. free. bk.rev. stat. **Document type:** *Government.*
Formerly: Berufliche Bildung (0005-948X)
Indexed: IBZ, ILD.
—BLDSC (4165.594700).
Published by: Deutscher Gewerkschaftsbund, Bundesvorstand, Hans-Boeckler-Str 39, Duesseldorf, 40476, Germany. TEL 0211-4301-0, FAX 0211-4301410. Circ: 35,000.

370 GHA
GHANA JOURNAL OF EDUCATION★. Text in English. 1973 (vol.4). q. per no. adv. bk.rev. bibl.; illus.
Formerly: Ghana Teacher's Journal (0016-9595)
Published by: Ministry of Education, Higher Education Division, PO Box M 45, Accra, Ghana.

370.72 GHA ISSN 0855-0875
LC5258.G4
GHANA JOURNAL OF LITERACY AND ADULT EDUCATION. Text and summaries in English. 1992. s-a. GHC 60,000 domestic; USD 50 foreign (effective 2001). **Document type:** *Academic/Scholarly.*
Published by: (University of Ghana, Institution of Adult Education), Ghana Universities Press, PO Box GP 4219, Accra, Ghana. TEL 233-21-500300, ext. 6135, FAX 233-21-501930. Ed. S. K. Badu-Nyarko. Pub. K M Ganu. Circ: 500 (paid).

GHANA. MINISTRY OF EDUCATION. EDUCATIONAL STATISTICS. see *EDUCATION—Abstracting, Bibliographies, Statistics*

GISTER EN VANDAG/YESTERDAY AND TODAY; journal for history teaching - tydskrif vir Geskiedenisonderrig. see *HISTORY*

370.72 NGA ISSN 1596-6224
➤ **GLOBAL JOURNAL OF EDUCATIONAL RESEARCH.** Text in English. 2002. s-a. NGN 750 domestic; USD 25 foreign (effective 2003). bk.rev. back issues avail.; reprints avail. **Document type:** *Journal, Academic/Scholarly.*
Published by: Global Journal of Pure and Applied Sciences, c/o Prof. Barth N. Ekwueme, University of Calabar, Department of Geology, PO Box 3651, Calabar, Nigeria. ekwueme@unical.anpa.net.ng, http://www.inasp.info/ajol/. Eds. J U Emeh, Barth N Ekwueme.

➤ **GLOBAL MEDIA JOURNAL.** see *COMMUNICATIONS—Television And Cable*

370 GBR ISSN 1476-7724
▼ **GLOBALISATION, SOCIETIES AND EDUCATION.** Text in English. 2003. 3/yr. GBP 194, USD 321 combined subscription to institutions print & online eds. (effective 2006). **Document type:** *Journal, Academic/Scholarly.* **Description:** Aims to fill the gap between the study of education and broader social, economic and political forces by analysing the complexities of globalisation.
Related titles: Online - full text ed.: ISSN 1476-7732. GBP 184, USD 305 to institutions (effective 2006) (from EBSCO Publishing, Gale Group, IngentaConnect, O C L C Online Computer Library Center, Inc., Swets Information Services).
Indexed: BrEdI, DIP, IBR, IBZ, PSA, SociolAb.
—BLDSC (4195.477955), IE.
Published by: Routledge (Subsidiary of: Taylor & Francis Group), 4 Park Sq, Milton Park, Abingdon, Oxon OX14 4RN, United Kingdom. TEL 44-1235-828600, FAX 44-1235-829000, info@routledge.co.uk, http://www.tandf.co.uk/journals/titles/14767724.asp, http://www.routledge.co.uk. Eds. Roger Dale, Susan Robertson. **Subscr. to:** Taylor & Francis Ltd, Journals Customer Service, Rankine Rd, Basingstoke, Hants RG24 8PR, United Kingdom. TEL 44-1256-813000, FAX 44-1256-330245.

370.9438 USA ISSN 1042-3745
LC3650.P6
GLOS NAUCZYCIELA; kwartalnik. Text in Polish. 1986. q. USD 20 to individuals; USD 25 to institutions (effective 2005). adv. bk.rev. bibl.; illus. back issues avail. **Document type:** *Journal, Consumer.* **Description:** Covers educational and instructional materials about Poland, its culture, literature, language, customs, geography, Polish and Polish-American history.
Published by: Polish American Congress, Commission of Education/Komisja Oswiatowa Kongresu Polonii Amerykanskiej, 5631 W Waveland Ave, Chicago, IL 60634. TEL 773-545-6522. Ed., R&P, Adv. contact Helena Ziolkowska. B&W page USD 300. Circ: 1,300.

E

370 331.8 POL ISSN 0017-1263
GLOS NAUCZYCIELSKI. Text in Polish. 1917. w. USD 23. adv. illus. index. **Document type:** *Newsletter.*
Indexed: AgrLib.
Published by: (Zwiazek Nauczycielstwa Polskiego/Polish Teachers' Union), Glos Nauczycielski, Ul Spasowskiego 6-8, Warsaw, 00389, Poland. TEL 48-22-263420. Ed. Wojciech Sierakowski. Circ: 59,900. **Dist. by:** Ars Polona, Krakowskie Przedmiescie 7, Warsaw, Poland.

371.4 DNK ISSN 1397-8586
GODT I GANG/GOOD START. Text in Danish. 1987. a. free (effective 2005). **Document type:** *Consumer.*
Formerly (until 1997): Godt Begyndt (0906-7930)
Related titles: Online - full text ed.
Published by: Raadet for Uddannelses- og Erhvervsvejledning (R.U.E.)/Danish National Council for Educational and Vocational Guidance, Vester Voldgade 123, Copenhagen V, 1552, Denmark. TEL 45-33-955300, FAX 45-33-955349, r-u-e@r-u-e.dk, http://www.r-u-e.dk.

370 SWE ISSN 0436-1121
GOETEBORG STUDIES IN EDUCATIONAL SCIENCES. Text in English, Swedish. 1966. irreg., latest vol.191, 2003. price varies; also exchange basis. **Document type:** *Monographic series, Academic/Scholarly.*
Related titles: ♦ Series of: Acta Universitatis Gothoburgensis. ISSN 0346-7740.
Published by: Acta Universitatis Gothoburgensis, Renstroemsgatan 4, P O Box 222, Goeteborg, 40530, Sweden. TEL 46-31-773-17-33, FAX 46-31-163-797. Eds. Ference Marton, Ingemar Emanuelsson, Jan-Eric Gustafsson.

GOODWILL DIMENSIONS. see *OCCUPATIONS AND CAREERS*

GOPHER MUSIC NOTES. see *MUSIC*

371.07 USA ISSN 0746-0880
THE GOSPEL HERALD AND SUNDAY SCHOOL TIMES. Text in English. 1902. q. **Document type:** *Consumer.*
Formerly: Sunday School Times and Gospel Herald
Published by: Union Gospel Press, PO Box 6059, Cleveland, OH 44101. TEL 216-749-2100, FAX 216-459-1337. Ed. Beryl C Bidlen. Circ: 50,000 (controlled).

372.2 USA ISSN 0743-5606
GREAT ACTIVITIES NEWSPAPER; an elementary and middle school physical education publication. Text in English. 1984. bi-m. USD 21 domestic; USD 25.30 in Canada & Mexico; USD 31.50 elsewhere. adv. bk.rev. **Document type:** *Newsletter.* **Description:** For kindergarten through grade eight.
Published by: Great Activities Publishing Co., Inc., PO Box 51158, Durham, NC 27717-1158. TEL 919-493-6977. Ed., Pub., Adv. contact Artie Kamiya. R&P Jacki Epperson. Circ: 5,000.

370 GBR
GREAT BRITAIN. DEPARTMENT FOR EDUCATION AND EMPLOYMENT. CIRCULAR. Text in English. irreg. **Document type:** *Government.*
Formerly (until 1995): Department for Education. Circular
—BLDSC (3214.040000).
Published by: Great Britain Department for Education, Sanctuary Bldgs, Sanctuary Buildings, Great Smith St, London, SW1P 3BT, United Kingdom. TEL 44-171-925-6310, FAX 44-171-925-6985. **Dist. by:** DFEE Publications Centre, PO Box 2193, London E15 2EU, United Kingdom. TEL 44-171-510-0150, FAX 44-171-510-0196.

370 GBR
GREAT BRITAIN. DEPARTMENT FOR EDUCATION AND SKILLS. RESEARCH BRIEF. Text in English. irreg.
—BLDSC (7717.455846).
Published by: Great Britain Department for Education, Sanctuary Bldgs, Sanctuary Buildings, Great Smith St, London, SW1P 3BT, United Kingdom. TEL 44-171-925-6310, FAX 44-171-925-6985.

GREAT BRITAIN. DEPARTMENT FOR EDUCATION. STATISTICS OF EDUCATION. see *EDUCATION—Abstracting, Bibliographies, Statistics*

370.941 GBR
GREAT BRITAIN. DEPARTMENT OF EDUCATION AND SCIENCE. ANNUAL REPORT. Text in English. a. price varies. **Document type:** *Government.*
Formerly: Education and Science (0070-9115)
Published by: H.M.S.O., 51 Nine Elms Ln, London, Surrey SW8 5DA, United Kingdom. TEL 44-20-7873-0011, FAX 44-20-7873-8247. **Co-sponsor:** Department of Education and Science.

370.941 GBR ISSN 0072-7121
GREAT BRITAIN. SCHOOLS COUNCIL PUBLICATIONS. EXAMINATIONS BULLETINS. Text in English. 1963. irreg. price varies. **Document type:** *Bulletin.*
Published by: (Schools Council), Routledge (Subsidiary of: Taylor & Francis Group), 4 Park Square, Milton Park, Abingdon, Oxon OX14 4RN, United Kingdom. TEL 44-20-7583-9855, FAX 44-207-583-0701.

370.941 GBR ISSN 0072-713X
GREAT BRITAIN. SCHOOLS COUNCIL PUBLICATIONS. WORKING PAPERS. Text in English. 1965. irreg. price varies. **Document type:** *Bulletin.*
Published by: (Schools Council), Routledge (Subsidiary of: Taylor & Francis Group), 4 Park Square, Milton Park, Abingdon, Oxon OX14 4RN, United Kingdom. TEL 44-20-7583-9855, FAX 44-207-583-0701.

371.1 USA ISSN 1056-2192
GREENWOOD EDUCATORS' REFERENCE COLLECTION. Text in English. 1992. irreg. price varies. **Document type:** *Monographic series, Academic/Scholarly.*
Published by: Greenwood Publishing Group Inc. (Subsidiary of: Harcourt International), 88 Post Rd W, PO Box 5007, Westport, CT 06881. TEL 203-226-3571, FAX 203-226-1502, webmaster@greenwood.com, http://www.greenwood.com.

370 USA ISSN 0271-9509
GREENWOOD ENCYCLOPEDIA OF AMERICAN INSTITUTIONS. Text in English. 1977. irreg. price varies. **Document type:** *Monographic series, Academic/Scholarly.*
Published by: Greenwood Publishing Group Inc. (Subsidiary of: Harcourt International), 88 Post Rd W, PO Box 5007, Westport, CT 06881. TEL 203-226-3571, FAX 203-226-1502, webmaster@greenwood.com, http://www.greenwood.com.

GRENADA SCHOOL DIRECTORY AND BASIC EDUCATIONAL STATISTICS. see *EDUCATION—Abstracting, Bibliographies, Statistics*

GRIP. see *CHILDREN AND YOUTH—For*

GRIP MAGAZINE (CARLSBAD). see *CHILDREN AND YOUTH—For*

GRLICA/TURTLEDOVE; revija za glasbeno vzgojo. see *MUSIC*

370.15 USA ISSN 1059-6011
HM134 CODEN: GOSTDA
➤ **GROUP & ORGANIZATION MANAGEMENT;** an international journal. Text in English. 1976. bi-m. USD 712, GBP 459 to institutions; USD 741, GBP 479 combined subscription to institutions print & online eds. (effective 2006). adv. bk.rev. illus. index. back issues avail.; reprint service avail. from PQC. **Document type:** *Journal, Academic/Scholarly.* **Description:** Aims to bridge the gap between research and practice for psychologists, group facilitators, educators, and consultants involved in the broad field of human relations training.
Formerly (until Mar. 1992): Group and Organization Studies (0364-1082)
Related titles: Microform ed.: (from PQC); Online - full text ed.: ISSN 1552-3993. USD 704, GBP 455 to institutions (effective 2006) (from C S A, EBSCO Publishing, Florida Center for Library Automation, Gale Group, O C L C Online Computer Library Center, Inc., ProQuest Information & Learning, Sage Publications, Inc., Swets Information Services).
Indexed: ABIn, ASCA, BPIA, BusI, CIJE, CINAHL, CommAb, CurCont, Emerald, ErgAb, HRA, IBSS, IMFL, ManagCont, PersLit, PsySCAP, PsycInfo, PsycholAb, SFSA, SPAA, SSCI, SWA, TEA, V&AA, e-psyche.
—BLDSC (4220.173900), CISTI, IDS, IE, Infotrieve, ingenta. **CCC.**
Published by: (Eastern Academy of Management), Sage Publications, Inc., 2455 Teller Rd, Thousand Oaks, CA 91320. TEL 805-499-0721, FAX 805-499-8096, info@sagepub.com, http://www.sagepub.com/journal.aspx?pid=80. Ed. Alison M Konrad. Pub. Sara Miller McCune. R&P Tanya Udin TEL 805-499-0721 ext 7716. Adv. contact Kirsten Beaulieu TEL 805-499-0721 ext 7160. page USD 350. Circ: 600 (paid). **Subscr. overseas to:** Sage Publications Ltd., 1 Oliver's Yard, 55 City Rd, London EC1 1SP, United Kingdom. TEL 44-20-73740645, FAX 44-20-73748741, subscription@sagepub.co.uk.

371.07 200 USA
GROUP MAGAZINE. Text in English. 1974. bi-m. **Document type:** *Trade.*
Published by: Group Publishing, Inc., 1515 Cascade Ave, Loveland, CO 80538-3274. TEL 970-669-3836, FAX 970-679-4372, info@grouppublishing.com, http://www.grouppublishing.com. Ed. Rick Lawrence. Circ: 55,000.

370.72 FRA ISSN 0245-9442
GROUPE DE RECHERCHE POUR L'EDUCATION ET LA PROSPECTIVE. POUR. Text in French. 1972. q. **Document type:** *Journal, Academic/Scholarly.*
—BLDSC (6571.353000).
Published by: (Groupe de Recherche pour l'Education et la Prospective), L' Harmattan, 5 rue de l'Ecole Polytechnique, Paris, 75005, France. TEL 33-1-43257651, FAX 33-1-43258203, http://www.editions-harmattan.fr. Ed. Maurice Gueneau. Pub. Jean Marie Marx.

370 DEU ISSN 0937-2172
➤ **GRUNDLAGEN DER WEITERBILDUNG.** Text in German. 1990. bi-m. EUR 87; EUR 54.90 to students; EUR 15.50 newsstand/cover (effective 2005). adv. **Document type:** *Journal, Academic/Scholarly.*
Indexed: DIP, IBR, IBZ.
Published by: Hermann Luchterhand Verlag GmbH (Subsidiary of: Wolters Kluwer Deutschland GmbH), Heddesdorfer Str 31, Neuwied, 56564, Germany. TEL 49-2631-8012222, FAX 49-2631-8012223, info@luchterhand.de, http://www.luchterhand.de. Ed. Joerg E. Feuchthofen. Adv. contact Gabriele Pannwitz.

370 DEU ISSN 0945-2079
GRUNDSCHULUNTERRICHT. Text in German. 1954. 14/yr. EUR 59.50; EUR 39 to students; EUR 7.20 newsstand/cover (effective 2003). adv. bk.rev. charts; illus. index. **Document type:** *Journal, Academic/Scholarly.*
Formerly: Unterstufe (0042-0638)
Indexed: DIP, IBR, IBZ.
Published by: Paedagogischer Zeitschriftenverlag GmbH & Co. KG, Axel-Springer-Str. 54b, Berlin, 10117, Germany. TEL 49-30-20183592, FAX 49-30-20183593, info@pzv-berlin.de, http://www.pzv-berlin.de. Ed. Ortrud Mentzel-Gruen. Adv. contact Constanze Richter. B&W page EUR 1,200, color page EUR 1,920. Circ: 8,000 (paid and controlled). **Subscr. to:** CVK Cornelsen Verlagskontor, Postfach 100271, Bielefeld 33502, Germany. TEL 49-521-9719-0.

370 CHN
GUANGDONG JIAOYU/GUANGDONG EDUCATION. Text in Chinese. m.
Published by: Guangdong Sheng Jiaoyu Weiyuanhui/Guangdong Provincial Education Commission, No 14, Guangwei Lu, 7th Fl, Guangzhou, Guangdong 510030, China. TEL 330351. Ed. Liu Dazhong.

370 CHN
GUANGZHOU JIAOYU/GUANGZHOU EDUCATION. Text in Chinese. bi-m.
Published by: Guangzhou Shi Jiaoyu-ju/Guangzhou Municipal Bureau of Education, 83-503 Xihu Lu, Guangzhou, Guangdong 510030, China. TEL 345161. Ed. Shao Haiqiang.

796 CHN ISSN 1007-323X
GUANGZHOU TIYU XUEYUAN XUEBAO/GUANGZHOU PHYSICAL EDUCATION INSTITUTE. JOURNAL. Text in Chinese. 1981. q.
Related titles: Online - full text ed.: (from East View Information Services, WanFang Data Corp.).
—BLDSC (4757.657500).
Published by: Guangzhou Tiyu Xueyuan/Guangzhou Physical Education Institute, 458, Guangzhou Dadao Bei, Guangzhou, 510075, China. http://gztyxyxb.periodicals.net.cn/default.html. **Dist. by:** China International Book Trading Corp, 35 Chegongzhuang Xilu, Haidian District, PO Box 399, Beijing 100044, China. TEL 86-10-68412045, FAX 86-10-68412023, cibtc@mail.cibtc.com.cn, http://www.cibtc.com.cn.

372.21 JPN
GUIDANCE OF INFANTS/YOJI-NO-SHIDO. Text in Japanese. 1955. m. JPY 8,160.
Published by: Gakken Co. Ltd., 40-5 Kami-Ikedai 4-chome, Ota-ku, Tokyo, 145-0064, Japan. Ed. Toshiyuki Fuse.

370 FRA ISSN 1166-7419
LE GUIDE DES METIERS. Text in French. 1986. a.
Related titles: ♦ Supplement to: L' Etudiant. ISSN 0766-6330.
Published by: Editions Generation, 27 rue du Chemin Vert, Paris, Cedex 11 75543, France. TEL 33-1-48074141, FAX 33-1-47007980.

001.3 371.4 GBR
A GUIDE FOR POSTGRADUATE AWARD HOLDERS IN THE ARTS AND HUMANITIES. Text in English. a.
—BLDSC (4229.850400).
Published by: Arts and Humanities Research Board, 10 Carlton House Terrace, London, SW1Y 5AH, United Kingdom. TEL 44-20-79695205, FAX 44-20-79695405, http://www.ahrb.ac.uk.

370.25 USA ISSN 0072-8225
GUIDE TO AMERICAN EDUCATIONAL DIRECTORIES. Text in English. 1972. biennial. USD 75 (effective 2000). adv. **Document type:** *Directory.*
Published by: Todd Publications, 500, Millwood, NY 10546-0500. TEL 914-358-6213, FAX 914-358-1059, toddpub@aol.com, http://www.toddpublications.com. Ed., Pub., R&P, Adv. contact Barry Klein.

371.4 001.3 GBR
GUIDE TO APPLICANTS FOR POSTGRADUATE AWARDS IN ARTS AND HUMANITIES. Text in English. a. **Document type:** *Directory, Academic/Scholarly.*
Formerly: Guide to Postgraduate Studentships in the Humanities
—BLDSC (4225.237150).
Published by: Arts and Humanities Research Board, 10 Carlton House Terrace, London, SW1Y 5AH, United Kingdom. http://www.ahrb.ac.uk.

E

373.243 USA ISSN 0732-3034
U408.3
GUIDE TO THE EVALUATION OF EDUCATIONAL EXPERIENCES IN THE ARMED SERVICES (YEAR). Text in English. 1946. biennial (plus s-a. updates) (in 3 vols.). USD 35 per vol. (effective 1999). **Document type:** *Academic/Scholarly.* **Description:** Standard reference work for recognizing learning acquired in military life. Lists and describes courses offered by the military and makes recommendations for college credit where appropriate.
Published by: (Center for Adult Learning and Educational Credentials), American Council on Education, One Dupont Circle, N W, Ste 250, Washington, DC 20036-1193. TEL 202-939-9470, FAX 202-775-8578. Ed. Eugene Sullivan. Circ: 20,000. **Dist. by:** Oryx Press, 4041 N Central Ave, Phoenix, AZ 85012-3397. TEL 800-279-6799.

371 331.8 MYS ISSN 0127-0176
GURU MALAYSIA✶ . Text in English, Malay. 1964. m. MYR 2.40. adv. bk.rev. illus.; stat.
Formerly: Educator (0013-2012)
Published by: Kesatuan Perkhidmatan Perguruan Kebangsaan/National Union of Teaching Profession, 13-15, Jalan Murai Dua, Kompleks Batu, Off Jalan Ipoh, Kuala Lumpur, 51100 , Malaysia. TEL 60-3-62510621, FAX 60-3-62511060, nutp@tm.net.my, http://www.nutp.org/. Ed. Francis Mathews. Circ: 20,000.

GYMNASIEMUSIK; medlemsorientering. see *MUSIC*

373 DNK ISSN 0017-5927
GYMNASIESKOLEN. Text in Danish. 1916. 22/yr. DKK 500 (effective 2004). adv. bk.rev. index. **Document type:** *Trade.* **Description:** Acts as a trade journal for high school teachers in Denmark.
Related titles: Online - full text ed.
Published by: Gymnasieskolernes Laererforening/Danish National Union of Secondary School Teachers, Vesterbrogade 16, Copenhagen V, 1620, Denmark. TEL 45-33-290900, FAX 45-33-290901, gymnasieskolen@gl.org, gl@gl.org, http://www.gl.org./GL-Sites/WWW/Forside/Om_GL/Gymnasieskolen. Ed. Torben Lynge Hansen. adv.: B&W page DKK 7,730, color page DKK 9,530; trim 249 x 168. Circ: 12,322.

GYMNASIET OG HF. see *EDUCATION—Abstracting, Bibliographies, Statistics*

373 CHE ISSN 0017-5951
GYMNASIUM HELVETICUM; Zeitschrift fuer die schweizerische Mittelschule. Text in French, German. 1947. 6/yr. CHF 100; CHF 108 foreign (effective 1999). bk.rev. charts. index. **Document type:** *Academic/Scholarly.* **Description:** Information and evaluation of secondary education in Switzerland, and comparisons to that in other countries. Includes reports of events, and positions available.
Indexed: DIP, IBR, IBZ.
—CCC.
Published by: (Verein Schweizerischer Gymnasiallehrer), Sauerlaender AG, Laurenzenvorstadt 89, Aarau, 5001, Switzerland. FAX 41-62-8245780. Ed. Verena Mueller. adv.: B&W page CHF 1,025; trim 260 x 177. Circ: 5,100.

373 DEU
DAS GYMNASIUM IN BAYERN. Text in German. m.
Published by: Bayerische Philologenverband, Implerstr 25A, Munich, 81371, Germany. TEL 089-774004-05.

370 DEU ISSN 0945-7372
H D Z INFO. Text in German. 1994. 2/yr. **Document type:** *Academic/Scholarly.*
Published by: (Alice-Salomon-Fachhochschule Berlin, Hochschuldidaktischen Zentrum), Schibri Verlag, Dorfstr 60, Milow, 17337, Germany. TEL 039753-22757, FAX 039753-22757.

370 DEU ISSN 1431-5335
H L Z - ZEITSCHRIFT DER G E W HAMBURG. Text in German. 1922. 10/yr. bk.rev. index. **Document type:** *Journal, Trade.*
Former titles (until 1992): H L Z (1431-5327); (until 1984): Hamburger Lehrerzeitung (0017-6966)
Published by: Gewerkschaft Erziehung und Wissenschaft, Landesverband Hamburg, Rothenbaumchaussee 15, Hamburg, 20148, Germany. TEL 49-40-4146330, FAX 49-40-440877, hlz@gew-hamburg.de, info@gew-hamburg.de, http://gew-hamburg.de/hlz/index.htm. Ed. Joachim Geffers. Circ: 10,000.

371.042 USA
H S A HAPPENINGS. Text in English. 1986. m. USD 25 (effective 1999). adv. bk.rev.; Website rev. 20 p./no. 2 cols./p.; **Document type:** *Newsletter.* **Description:** Provides news and information on homeschooling to the community of King and Pierce counties.
Formerly: Homeschoolers' Voice
Published by: Homeschoolers' Support Association, PO Box 413, Maple Valley, WA 98038. TEL 206-432-9805. Ed., R&P Sherry Wiltsey TEL 253-931-3875. Adv. contact Teresa Sparling. Circ: 400 (paid).

370 ISR ISSN 0334-4568
HA-HINNUKH HA-MESHUTAF. Text in Hebrew. 1958. q. ILS 7.50, USD 4.
Indexed: IHP.
Published by: Ha-Kibbutz ha-Artzi, Department of Education, Rehov Leonardo de Vinci 13, Tel Aviv, 61400, Israel. Ed. Yehiel Kadmi. Circ: 2,000.

370 ISR ISSN 0792-223X
HA-HINNUKH USEVIVO. Text in Hebrew. 1977. a. free. bk.rev. **Document type:** *Newsletter, Government.*
Published by: College of Education, Kibbutz Seminar, 149 Namir Rd., Tel Aviv, Israel. FAX 410269. Ed. Karniel Zvi.

370 ISR
HADRACHA DIGEST. Text in English. 1982. s-a. **Description:** Intended for youth leaders and community workers around the world.
Related titles: French ed.; Spanish ed.
Published by: Pedagogic Center, Department for Jewish Zionist Education, Kiryat Moriah, 3 HaAskan St., Jerusalem, Israel. TEL 972-2-6759059, FAX 972-2-6759133, TELEX SUMINIL 25375, pedagog@jajz-ed.org.il, http://www.jajz-ed.org.il. Ed. Henrique Cymerman. Circ: 1,500.

▼ **HAEFFT TIMER.** see *CHILDREN AND YOUTH—For*

792 370 AUS
HALF MASK. Text in English. irreg. free to members. **Document type:** *Newsletter, Academic/Scholarly.*
Published by: Drama Victoria Inc., Office 6, Artshouse, 117 Sturt St., Southbank, VIC 3001, Australia. TEL 61-3-96866829, FAX 61-3-96866839, dramavic@netspace.net.au, http://www.dramavictoria.vic.edu.au/news/newsletter/index.htm.

370.1 DEU
HAMBURGER SCHRIFTENREIHE ZUR SCHUL- UND UNTERRICHTSGESCHICHTE. Text in German. irreg., latest vol.10, 2003. price varies. **Document type:** *Monographic series, Academic/Scholarly.*
Published by: Verlag Dr. Kovac, Arnoldstr 49, Hamburg, 22763, Germany. TEL 49-40-3988800, FAX 49-40-39888055, info@verlagdrkovac.de, http://www.verlagdrkovac.de/7-7.htm.

370 USA ISSN 1537-3711
THE HANDBOOK OF RESEARCH IN MIDDLE LEVEL EDUCATION. Text in English. 2002. a.
Published by: Information Age Publishing, Inc., 411 W Putnam Ave, Ste 205, PO Box 4967, Greenwich, CT 06831. TEL 203-661-7602, order@infoagepub.com, http://www.infoagepub.com.

373 USA ISSN 0743-0221
QA16 CODEN: HSONDB
HANDS ON! (CAMBRIDGE). Text in English. 1977. 2/yr. USD 20 contribution (effective 2001). **Document type:** *Bulletin.* **Description:** For elementary through college level educators and administrators. Each issue contains feature articles on science, math, and technology in education.
Related titles: Online - full text ed.
Indexed: Inspec.
—AskIEEE.
Published by: T E R C, 2067 Massachusetts Ave, Cambridge, MA 02140. TEL 617-547-0430, FAX 617-349-3535, communications@terc.edu, http://www.terc.edu. Ed. Peggy Kapisovsky. Circ: 25,000.

370.1 EST ISSN 0235-9146
HARIDUS. Text in Estonian. 1940. m. **Document type:** *Magazine, Trade.*
Formerly (until 1989): Noukogude Kool (0134-5656)
Address: Parnu mnt 8, Tallinn, 10148, Estonia. TEL 372-644-0587, FAX 372-644-4617. Ed. Tiia Penjam.

370.72 USA ISSN 8755-3716
HARVARD EDUCATION LETTER. Text in English. 1985. bi-m. looseleaf. USD 38 domestic to individuals; USD 49 domestic to institutions (effective 2005). index. back issues avail. **Document type:** *Newsletter, Consumer.* **Description:** Applies the latest educational research to practical concerns in education today; for parents and educators.
Related titles: Online - full text ed.: (from EBSCO Publishing).
Indexed: ABIn, EduInd.
—CCC.
Published by: Harvard University, Graduate School of Education, Gutman Library, 8 Story St, 1st Fl, Cambridge, MA 02138. TEL 617-495-3432, FAX 617-496-3584, orders@edletter.org, hepg@harvard.edu, http://www.edletter.org, http://gseweb.harvard.edu/~hepg/her.htm/. Ed. Michael Sadowski. Circ: 14,000 (paid and controlled).

370.7 USA ISSN 0017-8055
L11 CODEN: HVERA
➤ **HARVARD EDUCATIONAL REVIEW.** Text in English. 1931. q. USD 59 domestic to individuals; USD 79 in Canada to individuals; USD 99 elsewhere to individuals; USD 139 domestic to institutions; USD 159 in Canada to institutions; USD 179 elsewhere to institutions (effective 2005). adv. bk.rev. bibl.; charts; illus. index. reprints avail. **Document type:** *Journal, Academic/Scholarly.*
Formerly (until 1937): Harvard Teachers Record (0361-8021)
Related titles: Microform ed.: (from PQC); Online - full text ed.: (from EBSCO Publishing, Northern Light Technology, Inc., O C L C Online Computer Library Center, Inc., ProQuest Information & Learning).
Indexed: ABIn, ASCA, AgeL, AmH&L, ArtHuCI, BAS, BRD, BRI, CBRI, CIJE, CPE, CurCont, DIP, EAA, ECER, ERA, ETA, EduInd, HECAB, HistAb, IBR, IBZ, IPARL, IPSA, L&LBA, MEA, MEA&I, PAIS, PCI, PSA, PhilInd, PsycInfo, PsycholAb, RASB, RHEA, RefZh, SEA, SENA, SOMA, SOPODA, SSA, SSCI, SWA, SWR&A, SociolAb, TEA, e-psyche.
—BLDSC (4265.900000), IDS, IE, Infotrieve, ingenta. **CCC.**
Published by: Harvard University, Graduate School of Education, Gutman Library, 8 Story St, 1st Fl, Cambridge, MA 02138. TEL 617-495-3432, FAX 617-496-3584, hepg@harvard.edu, http://gseweb.harvard.edu/~hepg/her.htm/. Circ: 9,750 (paid and free).

370.7 USA ISSN 0046-6905
HARVARD UNIVERSITY. GRADUATE SCHOOL OF EDUCATION. BULLETIN. Text in English. 1956. 2/yr. free. adv. bk.rev. **Document type:** *Journal, Academic/Scholarly.* **Description:** Articles on topical educational issues and news about the Harvard Graduate School of Education and its alumni.
Published by: Harvard University, Graduate School of Education, Appian Way, Cambridge, MA 02138. TEL 617-495-3432, FAX 617-496-3584, hepg@harvard.edu, http://gseweb.harvard.edu/~hepg/her.htm/. Ed. Andrew Hrycyna. Circ: 20,500 (controlled).

370.2509969 USA ISSN 0092-1777
L903.H3
HAWAII. DEPARTMENT OF EDUCATION. EDUCATIONAL DIRECTORY: STATE & DISTRICT OFFICE. Text in English. 1924. a. USD 1.50. illus.
Published by: Department of Education, Office of Business Services, PO Box 2360, Honolulu, HI 96804.

370.72 UAE
HAWLIYAH KULLIYAH AL-TARBIYYAH/EDUCATIONAL JOURNAL. Text in Arabic. 1986. a. per issue exchange basis. **Document type:** *Academic/Scholarly.* **Description:** Publishes research in education and conference reports.
Published by: United Arab Emirates University, College of Education, P.O. Box 15551, Al-ain, Abu-Dhabi, United Arab Emirates. j.education@uaeu.ac.ae, http://www.fedu.uaeu.ac.ae/cej. Ed. Abdelmoneim Ahmed Hassan. Circ: 1,000.

371.1 GBR ISSN 0017-873X
HEAD TEACHERS REVIEW. Text in English. 1910. 3/yr. GBP 6 (effective 1999). adv. bk.rev. **Document type:** *Academic/Scholarly.*
Indexed: BrEdI, CPE, SOMA.
Published by: National Association of Head Teachers, 1 Heath Sq, Boltro Rd, Haywards Heath, W Sussex RH16 1BL, United Kingdom. TEL 44-1444-472472, FAX 44-1444-472473. Ed. David M Hart. R&P Peter Hellyer. Adv. contact Lauren Rogers. Circ: 42,000.

372 USA
HEADBONE EDUCATIONAL GAZETTE. Text in English. 1994. irreg. adv. back issues avail. **Document type:** *Newsletter, Trade.* **Description:** Offers many features of value to educators in the classroom.
Media: Online - full text.
Published by: Headbone Interactive, Inc., 3104 Western Ave, Seattle, WA 98121. TEL 206-378-1259, FAX 206-378-0188, tmc@classroom.com, http://www.headbone.com/. Ed. Elizabeth Ward. Adv. contact Mike Selman. Circ: 150,000.

613.7 370 JPN ISSN 0018-3350
HEALTH AND PHYSICAL EDUCATION/HOKEN TAIIKU KYOSHITSU. Text in Japanese. 1967. q. JPY 300 per issue. adv. bk.rev. charts. **Document type:** *Academic/Scholarly.*
Published by: Taishukan Publishing Co. Ltd., 3-24 Kanda-Nishiki-cho, Chiyoda-ku, Tokyo, 101-8466, Japan. FAX 81-3-3295-4108, physic-edu@taishukan.co.jp, hanbai@fa.mbn.or.jp, http://www.taishukan.co.jp. Eds. Kazuyuki Suzuki, Shoichi Tamaki. Pub. Shigeo Suzuki. Circ: 5,000 (controlled).

371.7 USA ISSN 1540-2479
HEALTH IN ACTION. Text in English. 2002 (Aug./Sept.). q. USD 19.95 to individual members; USD 39.95 to institutions (effective 2004).
Published by: American School Health Association, 7263 State Rte 43, PO Box 708, Kent, OH 44240. TEL 330-678-1601, 800-445-2742, FAX 330-678-4526, asha@ashaweb.org, http://www.ashaweb.org. Ed. Deborah R. Schoeberlein.

370 CHN ISSN 1004-6208
HEBEI JIAOYU/HEBEI EDUCATION. Text in Chinese. 1949. m. CNY 18 (effective 1994). adv. bk.rev.
Related titles: Online - full text ed.: (from East View Information Services).
Published by: Hebei Sheng Jiaoyu Weiyuanhui/Hebei Provincial Education Commission, 4, Shigang Dajie, Shijiazhuang, Hebei 050061, China. TEL 86-311-743498. Ed. Liu Xinzong. Adv. contact Yan Zhanji. Circ: 130,000.

371.2 CHN ISSN 1008-9519
HEBEI VOCATION-TECHNICAL TEACHERS COLLEGE. JOURNAL. Text in Chinese. irreg.

E

Related titles: Online - full text ed.: (from East View Information Services).
Indexed: AgBio, AnBrAb, BioCN&I, CPA, DSA, FCA, FPA, FS&TA, ForAb, HelmAb, HerbAb, HortAb, I&DA, MaizeAb, NutrAb, OrnHort, PBA, PGegResA, PGrRegA, PHN&I, PN&I, PotatoAb, RDA, RM&VM, RRTA, RiceAb, SIA, SoyAb, TDB, WAE&RSA, WeedAb.
—BLDSC (4757.987500).
Published by: Hebei Vocational and Technical Teachers College, Hebei, Qinhuangdao, China.

HEBREW UNION COLLEGE ANNUAL. see *RELIGIONS AND THEOLOGY—Judaic*

HEBREW UNION COLLEGE ANNUAL SUPPLEMENTS. see *RELIGIONS AND THEOLOGY—Judaic*

370 ISR ISSN 0017-9493
HED HACHINUCH. Text in Hebrew. 1926. m. adv. bk.rev. charts; illus.; stat. index.
Indexed: IHP.
Published by: Israel Teachers Union/Histadrut Hamorim, 8 Ben Sarouk St., Tel Aviv, Israel. TEL 03-5432911, FAX 03-5432928. Ed. Dalia Lachman. Circ: 40,000.

372 ISR ISSN 0334-2263
HED HAGAN; bulletin for early childhood. Text in Hebrew. 1935. s-a. ILS 32. bk.rev.
Indexed: IHP.
Published by: Israel Teachers Union/Histadrut Hamorim, 8 Ben Sarouk St., Tel Aviv, Israel. TEL 03-543911, FAX 03-5432928. Ed. Ziva Pedahzur. Circ: 6,300.

370 CHN ISSN 0438-9050
HEILONGJIANG JIAOYU/HEILONGJIANG EDUCATION. Text in Chinese. m.
Published by: Heilongjiang Sheng Jiaoyu Weiyuanhui/ Heilongjiang Education Commission, Fu 4, Xuefu Lu, Harbin, Heilongjiang 150080, China. TEL 53562. Ed. Zhu Mantang.

HEILPAEDAGOGIK. see *MEDICAL SCIENCES*

▼ **HEILPAEDAGOGIK IN FORSCHUNG UND PRAXIS.** see *MEDICAL SCIENCES*

649.124 USA ISSN 1526-9264
HELPING CHILDREN LEARN (ELEMENTARY SCHOOL EDITION); tips families can use to help children to do better in school. Text in English. m. (Sep.-May). USD 195 (effective 2003). **Document type:** *Newsletter, Academic/Scholarly.*
Related titles: Online - full text ed.; ♦ Spanish ed.: Ayudando a los Ninos a Aprender (Escuela Primaria). ISSN 1526-9302.
Published by: Parent Institute, PO Box 7474, Fairfax, VA 22039-7474. TEL 703-323-9170, 800-756-5525, FAX 703-323-9173, http://www.parent-institute.com. Ed. Pat Hodgdon. Pub. John H Wherry.

649.124 USA ISSN 1526-9256
HELPING CHILDREN LEARN (SCHOOL READINESS ENGLISH EDITION); tips families can use to help children do better in school. Text in English. m. (Sep.-May). USD 195 (effective 2003). **Document type:** *Newsletter, Academic/Scholarly.*
Related titles: Online - full text ed.: ISSN 1527-1005; ♦ Spanish ed.: Ayudando a los Ninos a Aprender (Preparacion Parala Escuela). ISSN 1526-9299.
Published by: Parent Institute, PO Box 7474, Fairfax, VA 22039-7474. TEL 703-323-9170, 800-756-5525, FAX 703-323-9173, http://www.parent-institute.com. Ed. Pat Hodgdon. Pub. John H Wherry.

649.124 USA ISSN 1526-9280
HELPING STUDENTS LEARN (HIGH SCHOOL ENGLISH EDITION); tips families can use to help students do better in school. Text in English. 1999. m. (Sep.-May). USD 195 (effective 2003).
Related titles: Online - full text ed.; ♦ Spanish ed.: Ayudando a los Estudiantes a Aprender (Escuela Secundaria). ISSN 1526-9329.
Published by: Parent Institute, PO Box 7474, Fairfax, VA 22039-7474. TEL 703-323-9170, 800-756-5525, FAX 703-323-9173, http://www.parent-institute.com. Ed. Pat Hodgdon. Pub. John H Wherry.

649.124 USA ISSN 1526-9272
HELPING STUDENTS LEARN (MIDDLE SCHOOL ENGLISH EDITION). Text in English. m. (Sep.-May). USD 195 (effective 2003). **Document type:** *Academic/Scholarly.*
Related titles: Online - full text ed.: ISSN 1527-1021; ♦ Spanish ed.: Ayudando a los Estudiantes a Aprender (Escuela Intermedia). ISSN 1526-9310.
Published by: Parent Institute, PO Box 7474, Fairfax, VA 22039-7474. TEL 703-323-9170, 800-756-5525, FAX 703-323-9173, http://www.parent-institute.com. Ed. Pat Hodgdon. Pub. John H Wherry.

370.113 URY
HERRAMIENTAS PARA LA TRANSFORMACION. Text in Spanish. 1996. irreg. price varies.
Published by: Centro Interamericano de Investigacion y Documentacion Sobre Formacion Profesional, Av. Uruguay, 1238, Casilla de Correos 1761, Montevideo, 11106, Uruguay. FAX 921305, dirmvd@cinterfor.org.uy.

373 USA ISSN 0018-1498
L11
➤ **THE HIGH SCHOOL JOURNAL.** Text in English. 1917. bi-m. (Oct.-May). USD 30 to individuals; USD 40 to institutions (effective 2005). bk.rev. illus. index. back issues avail.; reprint service avail. from PSC. **Document type:** *Journal, Academic/Scholarly.* **Description:** Concerned with teaching, learning, and administration in the secondary schools.
Related titles: Microform ed.: (from PQC); Online - full text ed.: ISSN 1534-5157 (from EBSCO Publishing, Florida Center for Library Automation, Gale Group, H.W. Wilson, Northern Light Technology, Inc., O C L C Online Computer Library Center, Inc., Project MUSE, ProQuest Information & Learning, Swets Information Services).
Indexed: ABIn, AMHA, CIJE, CLFP, CPE, CurCont, EAA, ERA, ETA, EduInd, MEA, PCI, PsycInfo, PsycholAb, RASB, RHEA, SEA, SENA, SOMA, SWA, TEA, e-psyche.
—BLDSC (4307.358000), IE, Infotrieve, ingenta. **CCC.**
Published by: (University of North Carolina at Chapel Hill, School of Education), University of North Carolina Press, PO Box 2288, Chapel Hill, NC 27515-2288. TEL 919-962-3017, FAX 919-962-3520, uncpress_journals@unc.edu, http://www.uncpress.unc.edu. Ed. Howard Machtinger. R&P Vicky Wells. Circ: 1,200 (paid and free).

370 GBR ISSN 1475-3669
HIGHER QUALITY. Text in English. 1997. s-a. **Document type:** *Bulletin, Academic/Scholarly.* **Description:** Provides the latest news on the work and reports on key decisions taken by the Board.
Formerly: Quality Assurance Agency for Higher Education. Bulletin
Related titles: Online - full content ed.
—CCC.
Published by: Quality Assurance Agency for Higher Education, Southgate House, Southgate Street, Gloucester, GL1 1UB, United Kingdom. TEL 44-1452-557000, FAX 44-1452-557070, http://www.qaa.ac.uk/public/hq/higherquality.htm, http://www.qaa.ac.uk.

HIROSHIMA JOURNAL OF MATHEMATICS EDUCATION/ SUGAKU KYOIKU GAKUJUTSU ZASSHI. see *MATHEMATICS*

HISPANORAMA. see *LITERATURE*

370.9 FRA ISSN 0221-6280
LA691
HISTOIRE DE L'EDUCATION. Text in French. 1978. 3/yr. **Document type:** *Journal, Academic/Scholarly.*
Indexed: AmH&L, DIP, HistAb, IBR, IBZ, PCI.
—IE, Infotrieve.
Published by: Institut National de Recherche Pedagogique, Place du Pentacle, BP 17, Saint-Fons, 69195 Cedex, France. TEL 33-4-72898300, FAX 33-4-72898329, publica@inrp.fr, http://www.inrp.fr. Ed. Pierre Caspard. Circ: 1,000.

370.9 ESP ISSN 0212-0267
LA911
HISTORIA DE LA EDUCACION. Text in Spanish. 1982. a., latest vol.19, 2000. **Document type:** *Academic/Scholarly.*
—CINDOC.
Published by: Ediciones Universidad de Salamanca, Apartado 325, Salamanca, 37080, Spain. TEL 34-923-294598, FAX 34-923-262579, http://www3.usal.es/~eus/indexsp.htm. Ed. Agustin Escolano Benito.

370.9 CAN ISSN 0843-5057
LA410
➤ **HISTORICAL STUDIES IN EDUCATION/REVUE D'HISTOIRE DE L'EDUCATION.** Text in English, French. 1989. s-a. CND 30 domestic to individuals; USD 35 foreign to individuals; CND 45 domestic to institutions; USD 50 foreign to institutions (effective 2002). adv. bk.rev. bibl. 100 p./no.; back issues avail. **Document type:** *Journal, Academic/Scholarly.*
Indexed: AmH&L, CEI, CPE, HistAb, MEA.
—BLDSC (4317.055000), IE, ingenta.
Published by: Canadian History of Education Association/Association Canadienne d'Histoire de l'Education, University of Western Ontario, Faculty of Education, 1137 Western Rd, London, ON N6G 1G7, Canada. hse-rhe@uwo.ca, http://www.edu.uwo.ca/HSE. Eds. Rebecca Coulter, Stephane Levesque, Wyn Millar TEL 519-661-2111 ext 88624. R&P Wyn Millar TEL 519-661-2111 ext 88624. adv.: B&W page CND 350; trim 7.5 x 4.5.

➤ **HISTORIENS ET GEOGRAPHES.** see *HISTORY*

370.9 GBR ISSN 0046-760X
LA5
➤ **HISTORY OF EDUCATION.** Text in English. 1972. bi-m. GBP 724, USD 1,195 combined subscription to institutions print & online eds. (effective 2006). adv. bk.rev. back issues avail.; reprint service avail. from PSC. **Document type:** *Journal, Academic/Scholarly.* **Description:** Intended for social historians and others interested in the development of education worldwide. Articles range from schooling in Britain and abroad to teaching in schools and universities, to government policy and to philosophy of education.
Incorporates (1978-2003): Journal of Sources of Educational History (0140-671X)
Related titles: Online - full text ed.: ISSN 1464-5130. 199?. GBP 688, USD 1,135 to institutions (effective 2006) (from EBSCO Publishing, Gale Group, IngentaConnect, O C L C Online Computer Library Center, Inc., Swets Information Services).
Indexed: AmH&L, BAS, BrEdI, CIJE, CPE, ChLitAb, DIP, ERA, ETA, HistAb, IBR, IBZ, MEA, RHEA, SEA, SENA, SOMA, SRRA, TEA.
—BLDSC (4318.110000), IE, Infotrieve, ingenta. **CCC.**
Published by: (History of Education Society USA), Routledge (Subsidiary of: Taylor & Francis Group), 4 Park Sq, Milton Park, Abingdon, Oxon OX14 4RN, United Kingdom. TEL 44-1235-828600, FAX 44-1235-829000, info@routledge.co.uk, http://www.tandf.co.uk/journals/titles/0046760X.asp, http://www.routledge.co.uk. Eds. Jane Martin, Joyce Goodman. **Subscr. in N. America to:** Taylor & Francis Inc., Customer Services Dept, 325 Chestnut St, 8th Fl, Philadelphia, PA 19106. TEL 215-625-8900, 800-354-1420, FAX 215-625-8914, customerservice@taylorandfrancis.com; **Subscr. to:** Taylor & Francis Ltd, Journals Customer Service, Rankine Rd, Basingstoke, Hants RG24 8PR, United Kingdom. TEL 44-1256-813000, FAX 44-1256-330245, enquiry@tandf.co.uk.

370 USA ISSN 0018-2680
L11
➤ **HISTORY OF EDUCATION QUARTERLY.** Text in English. 1949. q. USD 40 domestic to individuals; USD 47 foreign to individuals; USD 78 domestic to institutions; USD 84 foreign to institutions; USD 20 domestic to students; USD 27 foreign to students (effective 2004). adv. bk.rev. illus. cum.index: 1961-1990. 150 p./no. 1 cols./p.; back issues avail.; reprint service avail. from PQC. **Document type:** *Academic/Scholarly.*
Formerly (until 1961): History of Education Journal (0162-8607)
Related titles: Microfilm ed.: 1961 (from PQC); Online - full text ed.: (from EBSCO Publishing, JSTOR (Web-based Journal Archive), ProQuest Information & Learning).
Indexed: ABIn, ASCA, AmH&L, ArtHuCI, BAS, BHA, CERDIC, CIJE, CPE, CurCont, DIP, ETA, EduInd, HistAb, IBR, IBZ, MEA&I, PCI, RASB, RHEA, RILM, SSCI.
—BLDSC (4318.125000), IDS, IE, Infotrieve, ingenta.
Published by: (History of Education Society), Slippery Rock University, College of Education, 220 McKay Education Building, Slippery Rock, PA 16057-1326. FAX 724-738-4548, heq@sru.edu, http://academics.sru.edu/ history_of_ed_quarterly/heshome.htm, http://www.sru.edu/. Ed. Richard Altenbaugh TEL 724-738-2862. R&P, Adv. contact Bruce C Nelson TEL 724-738-4556. page USD 200. Circ: 1,800.

370 GBR ISSN 1740-2433
LA630
HISTORY OF EDUCATION RESEARCHER. Text in English. 1968. s-a. GBP 70 membership fully waged; GBP 188 to libraries membership (effective 2003). adv. bibl. **Document type:** *Bulletin.* **Description:** Discusses the history of education.
Formerly (until 2003): History of Education Society Bulletin (0018-2699)
Related titles: Microform ed.: (from PQC).
Indexed: BrEdI, CPE, ChLitAb.
—BLDSC (4318.128000), IE, ingenta.
Published by: History of Education Society, Secretariat, 1 Arun House, River Way, Uckfield, TN22 1SL, United Kingdom. http://www.maney.co.uk/search?fwaction=show&fwid=312. Eds. Kevin Myers, Stephanie Spencer. Circ: 500.

370.9 AUS ISSN 0819-8691
➤ **HISTORY OF EDUCATION REVIEW.** Text in English. 1972. s-a. AUD 70 to non-members (effective 2005); free to members. adv. bk.rev. cum.index: 1972-1988. back issues avail. **Document type:** *Journal, Academic/Scholarly.* **Description:** Publishes research and reviews of the history of education.
Formerly (until 1983): A N Z H E S Journal (0311-3248)
Related titles: Online - full content ed.: AUD 20 (effective 2005) (from R M I T Publishing).
Indexed: AEI, AmH&L, AusPAIS, CPE, ERA, HistAb, PCI, SEA.
—BLDSC (4318.130000), IE, ingenta.
Published by: Australian and New Zealand History of Education Society, c/o Dr Craig Campbell, Faculty of Education & Social Work, University of Sydney, Sydney, NSW 2006, Australia. TEL 61-2-93516361, c.campbell@edfac.usyd.edu.au, http://www.her-anzhes.co.nz/index.html, http://www-faculty.edfac.usyd.edu.au/projects/anzhes/index.html. Eds. Malcolm Vick TEL 61-7-77814229, Tanya Fitzgerald. adv.: page AUD 100. Circ: 400.

➤ **HISTORY OF SCHOOLS AND SCHOOLING.** see *HISTORY*

➤ **HISTORY TEACHER.** see *HISTORY*

E

373 DEU
HOCHSCHULE BREMEN. FACHBEREICH WIRTSCHAFT. VERANSTALTUNGSVERZEICHNIS. Text in German. 1982. 2/yr.
Published by: Hochschule Bremen, Fachbereich Wirtschaft, Werderstr 73, Bremen, 28195, Germany. TEL 0421-5905102. Ed. Leuthold.

HOCHSCHULGESETZE DES BUNDES UND DER LAENDER. see *LAW*

370 JPN ISSN 0386-4499
HOKKAIDO KYOIKU DAIGAKU KIYO. DAI-1-BU, C. KYOIKUGAKU HEN/HOKKAIDO UNIVERSITY OF EDUCATION. JOURNAL. SECTION 1 C. EDUCATION. Text in Japanese. 1982 (vol.32). s-a. per issue exchange basis. **Document type:** *Bulletin.*
Published by: Hokkaido University of Education/Hokkaido Kyoiku Daigaku, Ainosato 5-jo, 3-chome, Kita-ku, Sapporo-shi, Hokkaido 002, Japan.

370 JPN ISSN 0387-074X
HOKURIKU DAIGAKU KIYO/HOKURIKU UNIVERSITY. BULLETIN. Text in Japanese. 1978. irreg., latest 2003. **Document type:** *Journal, Academic/Scholarly.*
Incorporates (in 1993): Hokuriku Daigaku Gaikokugo Gakubu Kiyo/Hokuriku University. Faculty of Foreign Languages. Bulletin (0919-6978)
—BLDSC (2555.302300).
Published by: Hokuriku Daigaku/Hokuriku University, 1-1 Taiyogaoka, Kanazawa, 920-1180, Japan. http://www.hokuriku-u.ac.jp/.

370 USA
HOME EDUCATOR'S FAMILY TIMES. Text in English. 1993. bi-m. USD 12 (effective 2004). **Document type:** *Magazine, Consumer.* **Description:** Covers the research on education and homeschool issues, strategies, tips and how -to and curriculum.
Published by: Home Educator's Family Times, Inc., PO Box 6442, Brunswick, ME 04039. TEL 207-657-2800, famtimes@homeeducator.com, http://www.homeeducator.com/FamilyTimes/index.htm.

371.042 USA ISSN 1054-8033
LC40
➤ **HOME SCHOOL RESEARCHER.** Text in English. 1985. q. USD 25 in North America to individuals; USD 37 elsewhere to individuals; USD 40 in North America to institutions; USD 60 elsewhere to institutions (effective 2003). adv. bk.rev. Index. back issues avail. **Document type:** *Journal, Academic/Scholarly.* **Description:** Covers research topics relating to homeschooling, parent involvement, and family in the US and in other countries.
Published by: National Home Education Research Institute, PO Box 13939, Salem, OR 97309. TEL 503-364-1490, FAX 503-364-2827, mail@nheri.org, http://www.nheri.org. Ed. Brian D Ray.

371.042 344.730791 USA ISSN 1094-9631
KF4222
HOME SCHOOLING LAWS AND RESOURCE GUIDE FOR ALL FIFTY STATES. Variant title: Home Schooling Laws. Text in English. 1986. biennial. USD 24.95 (effective 2001). 330 p./no.; back issues avail.; reprints avail. **Document type:** *Academic/Scholarly.* **Description:** Describes state laws on educating a child at home. Name, address and telephone number for each state contact is listed as well as the application process, curriculum, record-keeping, testing and teacher requirements.
Formerly (until 1996): Home Schooling Laws in All Fifty States (1051-5771)
Published by: Vision Publishing, 940 Monticeto Way, Ramona, CA 92065. TEL 800-984-7466, visioncc@hotmail.com.

372 USA
HOMESCHOOLER'S GUIDE TO FREE VIDEOTAPES. Text in English. 1999. a. (4th Ed.), latest 2002-2003. USD 34.95 per issue (effective 2002). 272 p./no.; **Document type:** *Directory.* **Description:** Lists free videotapes expressly available to homeschoolers.
Published by: Educators Progress Service, Inc., 214 Center St, Randolph, WI 53956. TEL 920-326-3126, FAX 920-326-3127, http://www.freeteachingaids.com/hg_877083452.html. Ed. Kathleen Suttles Nehmer.

370 CAN ISSN 1499-187X
HOMESCHOOLING HORIZONS MAGAZINE. Text in English. 2000. m. (10/yr.). CND 23.95 domestic; USD 23.95 (effective 2004). **Document type:** *Magazine, Consumer.* **Description:** Contains articles, tips, activities and stories on homeschooling.
Related titles: Online - full content ed.
Published by: A H M B Horizons, 42 Prevost RR 7, Vaudreuil-Dorion, PQ J7V 8P5, Canada. TEL 450-424-3222, staff@homeschoolinghorizons.com, http://www.homeschoolinghorizons.com/.

371.042 USA ISSN 1073-2217
HOMESCHOOLING TODAY. Text in English. 1992. bi-m. USD 21.99 domestic; USD 26.99 in Canada; USD 31.99 elsewhere (effective 2004). adv. bk.rev.; software rev.; video rev. back issues avail. **Document type:** *Magazine, Consumer.* **Description:** Provides teaching tools to homeschoolers and parents who wish to supplement their children's education.
Published by: Family Reformation, LLC., PO Box 436, Barker, TX 77413. TEL 281-492-6050, 866-804-4478, publisher@homeschooltoday.com, http://www.homeschooltoday.com. adv.: B&W page USD 1,795, color page USD 2,095; trim 8.375 x 10.875. Circ: 30,000.

HORIZONS; news, reviews, practice and policy in outdoor learning. see *SPORTS AND GAMES—Outdoor Life*

370 PHL ISSN 0018-5019
HORIZONS UNLIMITED. Text in English. 1970 (vol.10). q. PHP 3. bk.rev. charts.
Indexed: IPP.
Published by: Foundation University, Dumaguete City, Negros Oriental 6200, Philippines. TEL 37-44.

370 CHN ISSN 1000-5560
HUADONG SHIFAN DAXUE XUEBAO (JIAOYU BAN)/EAST CHINA NORMAL UNIVERSITY. JOURNAL (EDUCATION EDITION). Text in Chinese. q.
Related titles: Online - full text ed.: (from East View Information Services).
Published by: Huadong Shifan Daxue/East China Normal University, 3663 Zhongshan Beilu, Shanghai, 200062, China. FAX 86-21-2578367, http://www.ecnu.edu.cn.

HUARTE DE SAN JUAN. PSICOLOGIA Y PEDAGOGIA. see *PSYCHOLOGY*

370 CZE ISSN 1210-3683
HUDEBNI VYCHOVA. Text in Czech, Slovak; Summaries in English, French, German, Russian. 1970. q. CZK 60, USD 24.20 (effective 2000). bk.rev. abstr.; illus. index, cum.index.
Supersedes in part (in 1992): Esteticka Vychova (0014-1283)
Published by: Universita Karlova, Pedagogicka Fakulta, M D Rettigove 4, Prague, 11639, Czech Republic. Ed. Frantisek Sedlak. **Subscr. to:** PNS, Ustredni Expedice a Dovoz Tisku Praha, Administrace Vyvozu Tisku, Kovpakova 26, Zavod 1, Prague 6 160 00, Czech Republic.

HUMAN SERVICE EDUCATION. see *SOCIAL SERVICES AND WELFARE*

370 MNG
HUN BOLOH BAGAASAA/GROWING UP. Text in Mongol. bi-m.
Published by: Ministry of Education, Ulan Bator, Mongolia. Ed. N Tsevgee. Circ: 23,400.

370 CHN ISSN 1671-6124
HUNAN SHIFAN DAXUE. JIAOYU KEXUE XUEBAO/JOURNAL OF EDUCATIONAL SCIENCE OF HUNAN NORMAL UNIVERSITY. Text in Chinese. w. CNY 8, USD 3.40 per issue (effective 2003). **Document type:** *Journal, Academic/Scholarly.*
Related titles: Online - full text ed.: (from East View Information Services).
—BLDSC (4973.254000).
Published by: Hunan Shifan Daxue/Hunan Normal University, Yuelushan, Changsha, Hunan 410081, China. TEL 86-731-8872472, xbj@hunnu.edu.cn, xb@hunnu.edu.cn, http://www.hunnu.edu.cn/. **Dist. by:** China International Book Trading Corp, 35 Chegongzhuang Xilu, Haidian District, PO Box 399, Beijing 100044, China. TEL 86-10-68412045, FAX 86-10-68412023, cibtc@mail.cibtc.com.cn, http://www.cibtc.com.cn.

370 USA
I C S S NEWSLETTER. Text in English. q. **Document type:** *Newsletter.*
Published by: Illinois Council for the Social Studies, c/o Dr. Frederick D Drake, Department of History, Illinois State University, Normal, IL 61790-4420. TEL 309-438-7212, http://coe.ilstu.edu/icss/. Ed. Barry Witten.

371.14 USA
I E A - N E A ADVOCATE. Text in English. 1971. m. (8/yr.). USD 10 to non-members (effective 1997). adv. bk.rev. illus. **Document type:** *Trade.*
Formerly: Advocate (Springfield) (0097-6164)
Published by: Illinois Education Association, National Education Association, 100 E Edwards St, Springfield, IL 62704. TEL 217-544-0706, FAX 217-544-6423. Ed. Gordon R Jackson. R&P Gordon Jackson. Adv. contact Denise Ward. Circ: 85,000.

371.14 USA ISSN 1059-7743
I E A REPORTER (YEAR). Text in English. 1972 (vol.27). m. (Sep.-May). USD 10. **Document type:** *Newspaper.*
Former titles: I E A - N E A Reporter; I E A Reporter (0046-8495); Idaho Education News (0019-1183)
Published by: Idaho Education Association, 620 N Sixth St, Box 2638, Boise, ID 83701. TEL 208-344-1341, FAX 208-336-6967, info@idahoea.org, http://www.idahoea.org. Ed. Gayle L Moore. Circ: 8,653.

370 USA
I E E E INTERNATIONAL CONFERENCE ON MULTIMEDIA ENGINEERING AND EDUCATION. PROCEEDINGS. Text in English. a. **Document type:** *Proceedings, Trade.*
Indexed: Englnd.
Published by: Institute of Electrical and Electronics Engineers, Inc., 3 Park Ave, 17th Fl, New York, NY 10016-5997. TEL 212-419-7900, 800-678-4333, FAX 212-752-4929, customer.service@ieee.org, http://www.ieee.org.

370 ETH
I E R FLAMBEAU. (Institute of Educational Research) Text in English. 1990. s-a. USD 16 (effective 2003). adv. **Document type:** *Academic/Scholarly.*
Supersedes: Addis Ababa University. Institute of Educational Research. News Bulletin; Which was formerly: Addis Ababa University. Educational Research Centre. News Bulletin
Published by: Addis Ababa University, Institute of Educational Research, P.O. Box 1176, Addis Ababa, Ethiopia. TEL 251-01-113235, FAX 251-01-551368, ier.aau@telecom.net.et. Ed., Pub. Amare Asgedom. R&P Kahsay Gebre TEL 251-09-402201. Adv. contact Derebssa Dufera TEL 251-01-560083.

370.1 ETH
I E R NEWSLETTER. (Institute of Educational Research) Text in English. 1994. s-a. looseleaf. free. **Document type:** *Newsletter.* **Description:** Covers major activities of IER and the Faculty of Education to inform the academic community, and authorities about research, testing and publications under IER.
Published by: Addis Ababa University, Institute of Educational Research, P.O. Box 1176, Addis Ababa, Ethiopia. TEL 251-01-113235, FAX 251-01-551368, ier.aau@telecom.net.et. Ed. Amare Asgedom. Pub., R&P, Adv. contact Kahsay Gebre TEL 251-09-402201. Circ: 300.

370 BEL ISSN 0018-9715
I F M - S E I BULLETIN. Text in English. 1970. 2/yr. **Document type:** *Bulletin.* **Description:** Aims to encourage and develop international understanding and foster co-operation.
Related titles: Spanish ed.
Indexed: RASB.
Published by: International Falcon Movement - Socialist Educational International, Rue Quinaux 3, Brussels, 1030, Belgium. TEL 32-2-2157927, FAX 32-2-2450083, ifm-sei@infonie.be. Ed. Odetke Lambert.

370 USA ISSN 1087-982X
I F T INSIGHT. (Illinois Federation of Teachers) Text in English. 1995. 3/yr. USD 10 (effective 2005). back issues avail. **Document type:** *Magazine, Trade.* **Description:** Explores issues that impact union members to help them understand their job responsibilities.
Related titles: Online - full text ed.
Published by: Illinois Federation of Teachers, PO Box 390, Westmont, IL 60559. TEL 630-571-0100, 800-942-9242, FAX 630-571-1204, gpurkey@ift-aft.org, info@ift-aft.org, http://www.ift-aft.org/news/insight.htm. Circ: 49,000 (paid); 280 (free).

370 FRA ISSN 1564-2356
I I E P NEWSLETTER. Text in English. 1983. q. free (effective 2004). back issues avail. **Document type:** *Newsletter.*
Related titles: Online - full content ed.: ISSN 1564-2364.
Published by: International Institute for Educational Planning, 7-9 rue Eugene Delacroix, Paris, 75116, France. TEL 33-1-45037700, FAX 33-1-40728366, information@iiep.unesco.org, http://www.unesco.org/iiep/eng/newsletter/news.htm.

370 USA ISSN 0019-0624
I S E A COMMUNIQUE. Text in English. 1962. 8/yr. USD 4 to non-members. adv. illus. back issues avail. **Document type:** *Newspaper.*
Published by: Iowa State Education Association, 777 3d St, Des Moines, IA 50309. TEL 515-471-8000, 800-445-9358, http://www.isea.org. Ed. Lana O Schlapkohl. Circ: 37,000.

370.15 IND
I S P T JOURNAL OF RESEARCH IN EDUCATIONAL & PSYCHOLOGICAL TESTING & MEASUREMENT. Text in English. 1977. s-a. INR 200, USD 250. adv. bk.rev. back issues avail. **Document type:** *Academic/Scholarly.* **Description:** Devoted to the fields of educational, psychological measurement, evaluation, testing and other allied subjects.
Formerly: I S P T Journal of Research in Educational and Psychological Measurement (0251-0146)
Indexed: IPsyAb, e-psyche.
Published by: Institute for Studies in Psychological Testing, 101 Doon, Jakhan, Rajpur Rd., Dehra Dun, Uttar Pradesh 248 001, India. TEL 91-135-684551. Ed. S P Kulshrestha. Circ: 500.

370.82 USA ISSN 1063-8725
I T R O W NEWS. (Institute for Teaching & Research on Women) Text in English. 1992. q. USD 5 (effective 2000). **Document type:** *Newsletter.* **Description:** Contains up-to-date information about women's issues, events, and other relevant topics.

E

▼ new title ➤ refereed ✶ unverified ♦ full entry avail.

Published by: Institute for Teaching & Research on Women, Institute for Teaching & Research on Women, Towson State University, LLT 317, Towson, MD 21252. TEL 401-830-2334, FAX 410-830-3469, vanfoss@midget.towson.edu. Ed. Beth E Vanfossen. Circ: 500.

IAW. see *CHILDREN AND YOUTH—For*

370 USA ISSN 1049-2437
IDAHO. DEPARTMENT OF EDUCATION. NEWS AND REPORTS. Text in English. 1972. 5/yr. free. bk.rev. **Document type:** *Newspaper.*
Published by: Department of Education, Len B Jordan Bldg, Boise, ID 83720. TEL 208-334-3300, FAX 208-334-2228. Ed. Lindy High. Circ: 20,000.

370 USA ISSN 0073-4497
IDAHO EDUCATION ASSOCIATION. PROCEEDINGS. Text in English. a. membership. **Document type:** *Proceedings.*
Published by: Idaho Education Association, 620 N Sixth St, Box 2638, Boise, ID 83701. TEL 208-344-1341, FAX 208-336-6967.

370 ARG ISSN 0327-2788
IDEA. Text in Spanish. 1986. s-a. **Document type:** *Journal, Academic/Scholarly.*
Indexed: L&LBA, PSA, SSA, SociolAb.
Published by: Universidad Nacional de San Luis, Facultad de Ciencias de la Educacion, Ejercito de los Andes 950, San Luis, D5700HHW, Argentina. TEL 54-2652-424027, FAX 54-2652-430224, http://www.unsl.edu.ar.

370 IND ISSN 0019-1353
IDEAL EDUCATION✶. Text in English. 1964. m. INR 10, USD 2. adv. bk.rev. charts; tr.lit.
Published by: V.M. Sinkar, Ed. & Pub., "Prabhat", 47-A Gophale Rd. (North), Dadar, Mumbai, Maharashtra 400 028, India. Circ: 2,000.

IGAKU KYOIKU/MEDICAL EDUCATION. see *MEDICAL SCIENCES*

370 ESP ISSN 1137-4446
LA919.P34
IKASTARIA. Text in Spanish. 1985. irreg. price varies. **Document type:** *Monographic series, Academic/Scholarly.*
Formerly (until 1997): Sociedad de Estudios Vascos. Cuadernos de Seccion. Educacion (0213-3636)
Published by: Eusko Ikaskuntza/Sociedad de Estudios Vascos, Palacio Miramar, Miraconcha 48, Donostia, San Sebastian 20007, Spain. TEL 34-943-310855, FAX 34-943-213956, ei-sev@sc.ehu.es, http://www.eusko-ikaskuntza.org/.

372 TUR
➤ **ILKOEGRETIM ONLINE.** Text in Turkish. irreg. free (effective 2004). **Document type:** *Journal, Academic/Scholarly.*
Media: Online - full content.
Published by: Bilkent University, Bilkent, Ankara, 06800, Turkey. TEL 90-312-2904000, FAX 90-312-2664127, ioo@ibu.edu.tr, bilinfo@bilkent.edu.tr, http://ilkogretim-online.org.tr/, http://bilkent.edu.tr. Ed. Dr. Petek Askar.

370 907 USA
ILLINOIS HISTORY TEACHER. Text in English. 1994. 3/yr. **Description:** Provides a thorough examination of themes in Illinois history and includes essays by experts in the field along with lesson plans and class activities.
Related titles: Online - full content ed.
Published by: Illinois Historic Preservation Agency, 1 Old State Capitol Plaza, Springfield, IL 62701. TEL 217-785-9130, FAX 217-524-6973, keith_sculle@ihpa.state.il.us, info@ihpa.state.il.us, http://www.state.il.us/hpa/illinoishistoryteacher.htm, http://www.illinoishistory.gov/.

E

370 800 USA ISSN 1082-555X
ILLINOIS READING COUNCIL JOURNAL. Text in English. 1973. q. free to members. **Document type:** *Journal, Academic/Scholarly.*
Related titles: Online - full text ed.: (from EBSCO Publishing).
Published by: Illinois Reading Council, 1210 Fort Jesse Rd, Ste B2, Normal, IL 61761. TEL 888-454-1341, FAX 309-454-3512, ircread@dave-world.net, http://www.illinoisreadingcouncil.org/.

370 USA ISSN 0019-2236
L11
ILLINOIS SCHOOLS JOURNAL. Text in English. 1967. 3/yr. free to qualified personnel (effective 2005). bibl.; charts; illus.; stat. index, cum.index. reprint service avail. from PQC.
Supersedes: Chicago Schools Journal
Related titles: Microform ed.: (from PQC).
Indexed: CIJE, CurCont, ECER, SOPODA.
Published by: Chicago State University, 95th St at King Dr, Chicago, IL 60628. TEL 312-995-2000, http://www.illinoisschooljournal.org/. Ed. G Lopardo. Circ: 7,000.

ILLUSTRATOR. see *ART*

371.5 ESP ISSN 0212-4599
IN-FAN-CI-A (CATALAN EDITION). Text in Catalan. 1981. bi-m.
Related titles: Ed.: In-fan-ci-a (Spanish Edition). ISSN 1130-6084. 1990.
Indexed: RILM.
—CINDOC.
Published by: Asociacio de Mestres Rosa Sensat, Corsega, 271, Barcelona, 08008, Spain. FAX 34-93-4153680, pescolar@mrp.pangea.org. Ed. Irene Balaguer.

370.72 ZAF ISSN 1560-2265
INDEPENDENT EDUCATION. Text in English. 1998. q. adv. **Document type:** *Academic/Scholarly.* **Description:** Provides information for staff and parents associated with private education. The official magazine of the Independent Schools' Association of Southern Africa.
Indexed: ISAP.
Published by: (Independent Schools' Association of Southern Africa), Malnor (Pty) Ltd., Private Bag X20, Auckland Park, Johannesburg 2006, South Africa. TEL 27-11-7263081, FAX 27-11-7263017, malnor@iafrica.com. Ed. Mark Henning. Pub. Ken Nortje. adv.: B&W page ZAR 6,160, color page ZAR 7,210; trim 210 x 297.

370 USA ISSN 0145-9635
LC47
INDEPENDENT SCHOOL. Text in English. 1941. 3/yr. USD 25 to members; USD 35 to non-members (effective 2005). adv. bk.rev. index. reprint service avail. from PQC. **Document type:** *Magazine, Trade.*
Formerly (until 1976): Independent School Bulletin (0019-3755)
Related titles: Microfilm ed.: (from PQC); Online - full text ed.: (from EBSCO Publishing, H.W. Wilson, O C L C Online Computer Library Center, Inc.).
Indexed: ABIn, CIJE, EduInd, MRD.
Published by: National Association of Independent Schools, 1620 L St, N W, Washington, DC 20036-5605. TEL 202-973-9700, FAX 202-973-9790, info@nais.org, http://www.nais.org. Ed. Michael Brosnan. Pub. Peter Relic. Adv. contact David O'Leary. Circ: 7,500 (paid).

371.02 GBR
INDEPENDENT SCHOOLS YEARBOOK. Text in English. 1991. a. GBP 26 (effective 1999). adv. index. **Document type:** *Academic/Scholarly.* **Description:** Contains full details of all the schools in the Headmasters' Conference, Girls' Schools Association, the Incorporated Association of Preparatory Schools, Independent Schools Association Incorporated, and the Society of Headmasters and Headmistresses of Independent Schools.
Formed by the merger of (1986-1991): Independent Schools Yearbook. Girls' Schools (0951-5909); Which was formerly (1906-1985): Girls' School Year Book (0072-4564); (1986-1991): Independent Schools Yearbook. Boys' Schools, Co-educational Schools and Preparatory Schools (0951-5917); Which was formerly (1935-1985): Public and Preparatory Schools Yearbook (0079-7537)
—CCC.
Published by: A. & C. Black (Publishers) Ltd., Eaton Socon, Howard Rd, St Neots, Huntingdon, Cambs PE19 3EZ, United Kingdom. TEL 44-1480-212666, FAX 44-1480-405014. Ed. G Harries.

INDIA. MINISTRY OF EDUCATION AND SOCIAL WELFARE. PROVISIONAL STATISTICS OF EDUCATION IN THE STATES. see *EDUCATION—Abstracting, Bibliographies, Statistics*

370 IND
INDIA. MINISTRY OF HUMAN RESOURCE DEVELOPMENT. DEPARTMENT OF EDUCATION. REPORT. Text in English. 1948. a. free. **Document type:** *Government.*
Formerly: India. Ministry of Education and Social Welfare. Department of Education. Report (0073-6201)
Published by: Ministry of Human Resource Development, Department of Education, Shastri Bhavan, New Delhi, 110 001, India. Circ: 3,500. **Subscr. to:** Assistant Educational Adviser (Publications), Ministry of Human Resource Development, Department of Education, Ex. AFO Hutments, Dr. Rajendra Prasad Rd., New Delhi 110 001, India.

370 IND ISSN 0019-4689
INDIAN EDUCATION (KANPUR)✶. Text in English. 1960. m. INR 25, USD 8. adv. bk.rev.
Indexed: CPE.
Published by: All India Federation of Educational Associations, Iha Seshadri Khattry Bhanan, P O Box 52, Kanpur, Uttar Pradesh 208 001, India. Ed. V P Rghavachari. Circ: 2,000.

370 IND ISSN 0019-4700
CODEN: IEREDE
INDIAN EDUCATIONAL REVIEW. Text in English. 1966. q. INR 26, USD 18. bk.rev.
Indexed: BAS, CIS, CPE, EAA, IPsyAb, PsycholAb, REE&TA, RHEA, SEA.
Published by: National Council of Educational Research and Training, Publication Department, Sri Aurbindo Marg, New Delhi, 110 016, India. Ed. R P Singh. Circ: 1,000.

INDIAN JOURNAL OF PSYCHOMETRY AND EDUCATION. see *PSYCHOLOGY*

370.72 622.07 IND ISSN 0304-1158
TN213.D52
INDIAN SCHOOL OF MINES. ANNUAL REPORT. Key Title: Annual Report - Indian School of Mines. Text in English. 1968. a. free. adv. illus. **Document type:** *Corporate.* **Description:** Reports the school's annual education and research activities.
Published by: Indian School of Mines, Dhanbad, Bihar 826 004, India. FAX 0326-203042, TELEX 0629-214.

INDIANA DIRECTORY OF MUSIC TEACHERS. see *MUSIC*

371.82997 USA
INDIANA EDUCATION INSIGHT. Text in English. bi-w. USD 179 (effective 2000). **Document type:** *Newsletter.* **Description:** Source for readers to monitor or participate in education policy development in the state.
Related titles: Fax ed.
Published by: Edward D. Feigenbaum, Ed. & Pub., PO Box 383, Noblesville, IN 46061-0383. TEL 317-817-9997, FAX 317-817-9998, info@ingrouponline.com, http://www.ingrouponline.com.

370.113 USA
INDIANA FEDERAL PLAN FOR VOCATIONAL - TECHNICAL EDUCATION. Text in English. 1970. irreg. illus.
Former titles: Indiana. Indiana Commission on Vocational and Technical Education; Indiana. Council on Vocational Education. Annual Report; Indiana. State Advisory Council for Vocational Technical Education. Annual Report (0091-8970)
Published by: Indiana Commission on Vocational and Technical Education, I G C S E 204, 10 N Senate St, Indianapolis, IN 46204-2277. TEL 317-232-1981. Ed. Pamela B Peterson.

THE INDIANA HISTORIAN. see *HISTORY—History Of North And South America*

INDIANA MEDIA JOURNAL. see *LIBRARY AND INFORMATION SCIENCES*

379 USA ISSN 1520-6920
INDIANA STATE TEACHERS ASSOCIATION ADVOCATE. Abbreviated title: I S T A Advocate. Text in English. 1972. q. free membership (effective 2005). adv. **Document type:** *Magazine, Trade.* **Description:** Provides timely information on state and national education issues.
Former titles (until 1997): I S T A Advocate; (until 1981): Teacher Advocate (0300-6298); Which superseded: Indiana Teacher (0019-6797); I S T A News
Published by: Indiana State Teachers Association, 150 W Market St, Indianapolis, IN 46204. TEL 317-263-3400, 800-382-4037, FAX 317-655-3700, http://www.ista-in.org. Ed. Mark Shoup. Circ: 52,000 (controlled).

▼ **INDIVIDUAL DIFFERENCES RESEARCH.** see *PSYCHOLOGY*

371.195 USA ISSN 0091-8601
INDUSTRIAL EDUCATION✶. Text in English. 1914. m. (Sept.-May). USD 20. adv. bk.rev. bibl.; charts; illus.; tr.lit. index. **Description:** Serving vocational-technical education at high school, junior college, community college, vocational school and college-university level.
Formerly: Industrial Arts and Vocational Education (0019-8005); Incorporates: Occupational Education News
Related titles: Microfilm ed.: 1914 (from PQC); Special ed(s).: Industrial Education. Product Suppliers Directory.
Indexed: ABIn, CIJE, CPE, EduInd, IHTDI, MRD, MagInd, PCI, RASB.
—Linda Hall.
Published by: Cummins Publishing Co., 6557 Forest Park Dr, Troy, MI 48098-1954. Ed. Kelley Callaghan. Circ: 46,500.

370.15 ESP ISSN 0210-3702
LB1051
➤ **INFANCIA Y APRENDIZAJE/JOURNAL FOR THE STUDY OF EDUCATION AND DEVELOPMENT;** journal for the study of education and development. Text in English, Spanish. 1977. q. EUR 85 per issue to individuals; EUR 360 per issue to institutions (effective 2005). adv. **Document type:** *Academic/Scholarly.* **Description:** Concerned with the psychology of development-education processes. Publishes original articles on empirical research and literary reviews and theoretical essays.
Related titles: Online - full text ed.: ISSN 1578-4126. 2001 (from EBSCO Publishing, Gale Group, IngentaConnect, Swets Information Services).
Indexed: CDA, PCI, PsycInfo, PsycholAb, RILM, e-psyche.
—CINDOC, IE, Infotrieve. **CCC.**
Published by: Fundacion Infancia y Aprendizaje, Naranjo de Bulnes 69, Ciudalcampo, San Sebastian de los Reyes, Madrid, 28707, Spain. fundacion@fia.es, http://www.fia.es/. Ed. Emilio Sanchez. Circ: 3,000.

➤ **INFORMATION ALERTS.** see *EDUCATION—Abstracting, Bibliographies, Statistics*

344.07 USA ISSN 0020-0115
INFORMATION LEGISLATIVE SERVICE. Text in English. 1961. w. USD 375 to non-members; USD 150 to members (effective 2001). index. back issues avail. **Document type:** *Newsletter.*

Published by: Pennsylvania School Boards Association, 774 Limekiln Rd, New Cumberland, PA 17070-2398. TEL 717-774-2331, FAX 717-774-0718, http://www.psba.org. Circ: 13,800 (controlled).

370 USA ISSN 1538-6694
INFORMATION PLUS REFERENCE SERIES. EDUCATION; reflecting our society?. Text in English. 1980. biennial, latest 2004. USD 40 per vol. (effective 2005). **Document type:** *Monographic series, Academic/Scholarly.*
Related titles: Online - full content ed.; ♦ Series of: Information Plus Reference Series.
Published by: Gale Group (Subsidiary of: Thomson Corporation), 27500 Drake Rd, Farmington Hills, MI 48331-3535. TEL 248-699-4253, 800-877-4253, FAX 248-699-8035, 800-414-5043, galeord@gale.com, http://www.galegroup.com.

INFORMATION SEARCHER; the newsletter for CD-ROM, online searching and the Internet in schools. see *COMPUTERS—Internet*

370.1 004 AUS ISSN 1037-616X
➤ **INFORMATION TECHNOLOGY, EDUCATION AND SOCIETY.** Text in English. 2000. s-a. AUD 374 domestic to institutions; AUD 340 in New Zealand to institutions; GBP 168 in Europe to institutions; USD 260 elsewhere to institutions (effective 2005). adv. bk.rev. index. **Document type:** *Journal, Academic/Scholarly.* **Description:** Covers major and current issues in information technology and its relation to education and society, by critically examining the nexus between both formal and informal educational processes and outcomes and information technology.
Indexed: CPE, ERA, ETA, MEA, RHEA, SEA, SENA, SOMA, TEA.
—BLDSC (4496.368816), IE, ingenta.
Published by: James Nicholas Publishers, Pty. Ltd., PO Box 244, Albert Park, VIC 3206, Australia. TEL 61-3-96905955, FAX 61-3-96992040, custservice@jamesnicholaspublishers.com.au, http://www.jamesnicholaspublishers.com.au/itesjrnl.htm. Ed. Dr. Joseph Zajda. Pub. Rea Zajda. R&P Mary Berchmans. Adv. contact Irene Schevchenko.

➤ **INFORMATIONEN ZUR DEUTSCHDIDAKTIK**; Zeitschrift fuer den Deutschunterricht in Wissenschaft und Schule. see *LINGUISTICS*

➤ **INFORMATIONEN ZUR POLITISCHEN BILDUNG/ INFORMATION FOR CIVIC EDUCATION.** see *POLITICAL SCIENCE*

➤ **INFORMATIONEN ZUR POLITISCHEN BILDUNG.** see *POLITICAL SCIENCE*

➤ **INFORMATIONEN ZUR POLITISCHEN BILDUNG - AKTUELL.** see *POLITICAL SCIENCE*

371.14 ESP ISSN 1578-0678
INFORMATIVO ENSENANZA ANDALUZA. Cover title: Ensenanza Andaluza. Text in Spanish. 1981. 12/yr. free to qualified personnel. adv. **Document type:** *Trade.*
Published by: Union de Sindicatos de Trabajadores de la Ensenanza de Andalucia, C. Aparejo 2, 1o A-B,, Apdo. de Correos 3127, Malaga, 29010, Spain. TEL 34-52-392412, FAX 34-52-286443, ustea_prensa@teleline.es, ustea_ma@teleline.es, http://www.ustea.org/. Ed. Dalmiro Garcia. Circ: 8,500.

370 ESP ISSN 1130-8656
LB1027
➤ **INNOVACION EDUCATIVA.** Text in Spanish; Summaries in English, Spanish. 1991. a. EUR 9.01 (effective 2003). back issues avail. **Document type:** *Journal, Academic/Scholarly.*
—CINDOC.
Published by: Universidad de Santiago de Compostela, Servicio de Publicacions, Campus Universitario Sur, Santiago de Compostela, 15782, Spain. TEL 34-981-593500, FAX 34-981-593963, spublic@usc.es, http://www.usc.es/spubl/revinnovacion.htm. Circ: 500 (paid).

370 USA ISSN 1552-3233
▼ ➤ **INNOVATE**; journal of online education. Text in English. 2004. bi-m. free (effective 2005). **Document type:** *Journal, Academic/Scholarly.* **Description:** Focuses on the creative use of information technology (IT) to enhance educational processes in academic, commercial, and government settings.
Media: Online - full text.
Published by: Nova Southeastern University, Fischler School of Education, 1750 NE 167 St, North Miami, FL 33162. TEL 800-541-6682, http://innovateonline.info/index.php, http://www.nova.edu.

370 NLD ISSN 1572-1957
▼ **INNOVATION AND CHANGE IN PROFESSIONAL EDUCATION.** Text in English. 2003. a. **Document type:** *Journal, Academic/Scholarly.*
—BLDSC (4515.480280).
Published by: Kluwer Academic Publishers (Subsidiary of: Candover Investments plc), van Godewijckstraat 30, PO Box 17, Dordrecht, 3300 AA, Netherlands. TEL 31-78-639-2392, FAX 31-78-654-2254, http://www.wkap.nl.

372.21 USA ISSN 1542-2216
INNOVATIONS IN EARLY EDUCATION; the international Reggio exchange. Text in English. 1992 (Fall). q. USD 30 domestic; USD 35 foreign; USD 25 domestic to students; USD 30 foreign to students (effective 2002).
Published by: Merrill - Palmer Institute, 71 E. Ferry Ave., Detroit, MI 48202. TEL 313-872-1790, FAX 313-875-0947, mpi@wayne.edu, http://www.mpi.wayne.edu. Ed. Judith Allen Kaminsky.

INSEGNARE RELIGIONE. see *RELIGIONS AND THEOLOGY—Roman Catholic*

373 USA
INSIGHT (HUBBARD). Text in English. 1965. 4/yr. free. bk.rev. charts; illus. **Document type:** *Newsletter.*
Formerly (until 1976): Hubbard School System Office of Curriculum and Instruction. Digest Newsletter (0018-6961)
Published by: Hubbard Exempted Village School District, Office of Superintendent, 150 Hall Ave, Hubbard, OH 44425. TEL 216-534-1921. Ed. Kevin S Turner. Circ: 6,000.

370 CAN ISSN 0073-8123
INSIGHTS. Text in English. 1964. irreg. (2-4/yr.). USD 40 membership individual; USD 50 membership corporate (effective 2005). bk.rev. **Document type:** *Academic/Scholarly.* **Description:** Focuses on themes of cultural and educational interest.
Published by: John Dewey Society, Graduate Student Education, Brock University, St Catharines, ON L2S 3A1, Canada. jon.bradley@mcgill.ca, http://www.johndeweysociety.org/Insights/index.htm. Ed. Jon G Bradley. Circ: 400. **Subscr. to:** Robert C. Morris, Secondary Education, West Georgia College, 1600 Maple St, Carrollton, GA 30118.

370 CAN ISSN 0020-2029
INSITE (SASKATOON). Text in English. 1968. 2/yr. CND 20 (effective 2000). adv. bk.rev.; film rev. illus. **Document type:** *Bulletin.*
Media: Duplicated (not offset).
Indexed: CEI.
Published by: (Saskatchewan Industrial Education Association), Saskatchewan Teachers' Federation, 2317 Arlington Ave., Saskatoon, SK S7J 2H8, Canada. stf@stf.sk.ca. Circ: 500.

370 ESP ISSN 0214-1302
L41
INSTITUCION LIBRE DE ENSENANZA. BOLETIN. Text in Spanish. 1877-1936; resumed 1987. q. EUR 19 domestic; EUR 32 foreign (effective 2004). **Document type:** *Bulletin, Academic/Scholarly.* **Description:** Deals with subjects related to education and its ties with culture and contemporary intellectual history.
Indexed: PCI.
—CINDOC.
Published by: Fundacion Francisco Giner de los Rios, General Martinez Campos 14, Madrid, Spain. TEL 34-91-4460197, FAX 34-91-4468068, bile@fundacionginer.org. Ed. Juan Marichal. **Dist. by:** Asociacion de Revistas Culturales de Espana, Hortaleza, 75, Madrid 28004, Spain. TEL 34-91-3086066, FAX 34-91-3199267, info@arce.es, http://www.arce.es.

370 SWE ISSN 0348-8381
INSTITUTIONEN FOR INTERNATIONELL PEDAGOGIK. PUBLICATIONS/INSTITUTE FOR THE STUDY OF INTERNATIONAL PROBLEMS IN EDUCATION. PUBLICATIONS. Text in Multiple languages. 1973. irreg. **Document type:** *Monographic series.*
—BLDSC (4520.757500).
Published by: Stockholms Universitet, Psykologiska Institutionen, Stockholm, 10691, Sweden. http://www.su.se.

370 BRA ISSN 0020-367X
AS80.I52
INSTITUTO BRASIL - ESTADOS UNIDOS. BOLETIM. Text in English, Portuguese. 1943. q. free. adv. bk.rev.; music rev. bibl.; illus. **Document type:** *Bulletin.* **Description:** Reports on IBEU events, original articles on teaching English as a foreign language and classroom management and methodology, students' pages and lists of library acquisitions.
Published by: Instituto Brasil - Estados Unidos, Av. N.S. de Copacabana, 690 - 11 andar, Rio De Janeiro, RJ 22050-000, Brazil. TEL 55-21-5488332, FAX 55-21-2559355. Ed. Luis Monteiro. Circ: 10,000 (controlled).

370 PER
INSTITUTO CULTURAL PERUANO NORTEAMERICANO. NEWSLETTER. Text in English, Spanish. 1939. m. free. illus. **Document type:** *Newsletter.* **Description:** Calendar of events, plus description of highlights.
Formerly: Instituto Cultural Peruano Norteamericano. Boletin (0020-3718)
Published by: Instituto Cultural Peruano Norteamericano, Jiron Cuzco 446, Avda. Arequipa 4798, Apdo 304, Lima, Peru. TEL 54-14-283530. Ed. Mary de Ortiz de Villate. Circ: 3,000.

370.15 ROM
INSTITUTUL DE SUBINGINERI ORADEA. LUCRARI STIINTIFICE: SERIA PEDAGOGIE, PSIHOLOGIE, METODICA. Text in Romanian; Text occasionally in English, French; Summaries in English, French, German, Romanian. 1967. irreg. **Document type:** *Academic/Scholarly.*
Formerly: Institutul Pedagogic Oradea. Lucrari Stiintifice: Seria Pedagogie, Psihologie, Metodica; Which superseded in part (in 1973): Institutul Pedagogica Oradea. Lucrari Stiintifice: Seria Istorie, Stiinte Sociale, Pedagogie; Which superseded in part (in 1971): Institutul Pedagogica Oradea. Lucrari Stiintifice: Seria A si Seria B; Which was formerly (until 1969): Institutul Pedagogic Oradea. Lucrari Stiintifice
Indexed: e-psyche.
Published by: Institutul de Subingineri Oradea, Calea Armatei Rosii 5, Oradea, 3700, Romania.

372 USA ISSN 1532-0200
LB1537
INSTRUCTOR (NEW YORK, 1999). (Published in 2 editions: Primary, Intermediate) Text in English. 1981-1996; resumed 1999. 8/yr. USD 9.99 domestic; USD 32 foreign; USD 3 newsstand/cover (effective 2005). adv. bk.rev.; film rev.; software rev. illus. index. reprints avail. **Document type:** *Magazine, Trade.* **Description:** Features articles on a variety of topics of interest to elementary school teachers. Includes articles on computer applications for teaching techniques, educational software reviews and children's fiction book reviews.
Formed by the merger of (1996-1999): Instructor: Primary Edition; (1996-1999): Instructor: Intermediate Edition; Both of which superseded in part (1981-1996): Instructor (New York, 1990) (1049-5851); Which was formerly (until 1989): Instructor and Teacher (Cleveland) (1048-583X); (until 1989): Instructor (Cleveland) (0892-9122); (until 1986): Instructor and Teacher (Dansville) (0279-3369); Which was formed by the merger of (1931-1981): Instructor (Dansville) (0020-4285); (1972-1981): Teacher (Stamford) (0148-6578); Which was formerly: Grade Teacher (0017-2782)
Related titles: Microform ed.: (from PQC); Online - full text ed.: In School (from EBSCO Publishing, Gale Group, H.W. Wilson, Northern Light Technology, Inc., O C L C Online Computer Library Center, Inc., ProQuest Information & Learning); ♦ Includes: Electronic Learning.
Indexed: ABIn, AcaI, BRI, BusI, CBRI, CIJE, CPerI, ECER, EduInd, ICM, JHMA, MRD, MagInd, T&II.
Published by: Scholastic Inc., 557 Broadway, New York, NY 10012-0399. TEL 212-343-6100, 800-724-6527, FAX 212-343-6333, instructor@scholastic.com, http://teacher.scholastic.com/products/instructor.htm, http://www.scholastic.com. Ed. Terry Cooper. Pub. Michelle Robinson. Adv. contact Gerry Woodworth. B&W page USD 10,220, color page USD 12,680. Circ: 254,361 (paid). **Subscr. to:** PO Box 420235, Palm Coast, FL 32142-0235.

372 USA
INSTRUCTOR NEW TEACHER. Text in English. 2001. s-a. free (effective 2003 - 2004). adv. **Document type:** *Magazine, Trade.* **Description:** Contains information on everything new teachers need to succeed in the classroom, including effective lesson-planning, how to communicate with parents, advice from veteran educators, new educational software, and timesaving tips and activities.
Published by: Scholastic Inc., 557 Broadway, New York, NY 10012-0399. TEL 212-343-6100, http://teacher.scholastic.com/professional/newteachers/index.htm, http://www.scholastic.com. **Subscr. to:** 2931 E McCarthy St, PO Box 3710, Jefferson City, MO 65102-9957. TEL 800-724-6527, classmags@scholastic.com.

370.15 RUS
INTEGRAL'NOE ISSLEDOVANIE INDIVIDUAL'NOSTI. Text in Russian. 1977. irreg.
Indexed: e-psyche.
Published by: Permskii Gosudarstvennyi Pedagogicheskii Institut, Perm, Russian Federation. TEL 32-85-90. Ed. Bronislaw Aleksandrovich Vyatkin. Circ: 700.

INTEGRATING TECHNOLOGY INTO COMPUTER SCIENCE EDUCATION. PROCEEDINGS. see *COMPUTERS*

INTER-AFRICAN CONFERENCE ON INDUSTRIAL COMMERCIAL AND AGRICULTURAL EDUCATION MEETING. see *AGRICULTURE*

370 USA ISSN 0074-0829
F1405.5 1959
INTER-AMERICAN COUNCIL FOR EDUCATION, SCIENCE, AND CULTURE. FINAL REPORT. Text in English, French, Portuguese, Spanish. a. USD 4.
Related titles: Microfiche ed.: (from CIS).
Indexed: IIS.
Published by: Organization of American States/Organizacion de los Estados Americanos, Department of Publications, 1889 F St, N W, Washington, DC 20006. TEL 703-941-1617. Circ: 2,000.

▼ **INTERACTIONS (LOS ANGELES)**; UCLA journal of education and information studies. see *SOCIAL SCIENCES: COMPREHENSIVE WORKS*

E

370 NLD ISSN 0826-4805
L11 CODEN: INDOE4
➤ **INTERCHANGE**; a quarterly review of education. Text in English. 1970. q. EUR 298, USD 318, GBP 188 combined subscription to institutions print & online eds. (effective 2005). adv. bk.rev. charts. reprint service avail. from PQC,PSC. **Document type:** *Journal, Academic/Scholarly.* **Description:** Specializes in frank argumentative articles on the fundamental purposes of education. Its articles typically challenge conventional assumptions about schools and schooling and do so from perspectives in philosophy of the social sciences.
Formerly (until 1984): Interchange on Education (0822-9856); (until 1983): Interchange on Educational Policy (0822-9848); (until 1979): Interchange (0020-5230)
Related titles: Microform ed.: (from PQC); Online - full text ed.: ISSN 1573-1790 (from EBSCO Publishing, Gale Group, IngentaConnect, Kluwer Online, O C L C Online Computer Library Center, Inc., Springer LINK, Swets Information Services).
Indexed: ABIn, BibLing, CEI, CIJE, CPE, CommAb, CurCont, DIP, EAA, ERA, ETA, EduInd, HRA, IBR, IBSS, IBZ, L&LBA, MEA, PhilInd, PsycholAb, RASB, RHEA, RILM, SEA, SENA, SOMA, SOPODA, SSA, SWA, TEA, V&AA.
—BLDSC (4532.500000), IDS, IE, Infotrieve, ingenta. **CCC.**
Published by: (Ontario Institute for Studies in Education CAN), Springer-Verlag Dordrecht (Subsidiary of: Springer Science+Business Media), Van Godewijckstraat 30, Dordrecht, 3311 GX, Netherlands. TEL 31-78-6576050, FAX 31-78-6576474, http://springerlink.metapress.com/openurl.asp?genre=journal&issn=0826-4805, http://www.springeronline.com. Ed. Ian Winchester. Circ: 1,000.

370 USA ISSN 1541-5015
▼ **THE INTERDISCIPLINARY JOURNAL OF PROBLEM-BASED LEARNING.** Text in English. forthcoming 2006 (Jan.). q.
Media: Online - full content.
Published by: Purdue University Press, Purdue University Libraries, 1531 Stewart Cntr., W. Lafayette, IN 47907. TEL 765-494-0297, 800-933-9637, http://www.lib.purdue.edu/IJ_PBL, http://www.thepress.purdue.edu. Eds. Alexius Smith Macklin, Joseph M. La Lopa.

370 BRA ISSN 1414-3283
RA440.5
INTERFACE; comunicacao, saude e educacao. Text in Multiple languages. 1997. s-a. **Document type:** *Journal, Academic/Scholarly.*
Related titles: Online - full text ed.: free (effective 2005).
Indexed: SSA, SociolAb.
Published by: Universidade Estadual Paulista "Julio de Mesquita Filho" , Fundacao U N I, CP 592, Botucatu, 18 618-000, Brazil. intface@fmb.unesp.br, http://www.interface.org.br/.

370.1175 DEU ISSN 1613-1266
INTERKULTURELL UND GLOBAL; forum fuer interkulturelle Kommunikation, Erziehung und Beratung. Text in German. 1980. q. EUR 53 (effective 2005). adv. bk.rev. bibl. index. **Document type:** *Journal, Academic/Scholarly.* **Description:** For teachers and social workers: focus on bilingual and intercultural education.
Former titles (until 2002): Interkulturell (0935-0993); (until 1988): Auslaenderkinder (0720-2857)
Indexed: L&LBA, SOPODA, SSA, SociolAb.
Published by: Forschungsstelle Migration und Integration, Paedagogische Hochschule, Kunzenweg 21, Freiburg Im Breisgau, 79117, Germany. TEL 49-761-682311, FAX 49-761-682402, gschmitt@rufeuni-freiburg.de. Ed. Guido Schmitt. Circ: 450; 250 (paid).

E

INTERKULTURELLE BILDUNGSFORSCHUNG. see *SOCIOLOGY*

INTERKULTURELLE BILDUNGSGAENGE. see *SOCIOLOGY*

373.246 FRA
INTERNATIONAL ASSOCIATION FOR EDUCATIONAL AND VOCATIONAL INFORMATION. STUDIES AND REPORTS. Text in French. irreg.
Published by: International Association for Educational and Vocational Information, 20 rue de l'Estrapade, Paris, 75005, France.

370 CHE
INTERNATIONAL CONFERENCE ON EDUCATION. FINAL REPORT/CONFERENCE INTERNATIONAL DE L'EDUCATION. RAPPORT FINAL. Text in Arabic, Chinese, Russian, Spanish. irreg. free. **Document type:** *Proceedings.* **Description:** Publishes deliberations, speeches at opening and closing ceremonies, and lists of documents and reports distributed.
Former titles: International Conference on Education. Proceedings (0074-3275); (until no.32, 1970): International Conference on Public Education. Proceedings
Related titles: Microfiche ed.
Published by: UNESCO, International Bureau of Education, Case Postale 199, Geneva 20, 1211, Switzerland. TEL 41-22-9177821, FAX 41-22-9177801. Ed. Jacques Hallak. R&P Victor Adamets.

371.3 FRA ISSN 1020-0908
LC1035
INTERNATIONAL CONSULTATIVE FORUM ON EDUCATION FOR ALL. STATUS AND TRENDS; an annual report on new trends in basic education. Variant title: Education for All. Status and Trends. Text in English. 1993. a.
Related titles: Online - full text ed.; French ed.: Education pour Tous. Situation et Tendances. ISSN 1020-1165; Spanish ed.: Educacion para Todos. Situation et Tendencias. ISSN 1020-6930; Arabic ed.: ISSN 1020-7511.
Indexed: IIS.
Published by: UNESCO, International Consultative Forum on Education for All, 7 Place de Fontenoy, Paris, 75352, France. TEL 33-1-45682364, FAX 33-1-45685629, efa@unesco.org, http://wwweducation.unesco.org/efa, http://www.education.unesco.org.

370 USA
INTERNATIONAL EDUCATION DAILY. Text in English. d. **Document type:** *Magazine.* **Description:** Covers news and information important to educators such as technology and articles from international educators.
Media: Online - full content.
Published by: International Educators' Network Association, c/o Bucknell, 25 Tudor City Place, New York, NY 10017. http://members.iteachnet.org/webzine/index.php. Ed. David M Bucknell.

370.72 AUS ISSN 1443-1475
LC1090
➤ **INTERNATIONAL EDUCATION JOURNAL.** Text in English. 1999. irreg. free (effective 2003). **Document type:** *Journal, Academic/Scholarly.* **Description:** Encompasses research and review articles. Education is interpreted in a wide manner and includes human development, learning, school education, formal and informal education, tertiary and vocational education, industry training and lifelong learning.
Related titles: Online - full content ed.: free (effective 2005).
Published by: Flinders University, Institute of International Education, School of Education, Bedford Park, SA, Australia. http://iej.cjb.net/.

370 USA
INTERNATIONAL EDUCATION WEBZINE. Text in English. 1996. bi-m.
Media: Online - full content.
Published by: International Educators' Network Association, c/o Bucknell, 25 Tudor City Place, New York, NY 10017. http://members.iteachnet.org/webzine/, http://members.iteachnet.org/webzine/index.php.

370 CAN ISSN 1206-9620
LB2799
➤ **INTERNATIONAL ELECTRONIC JOURNAL FOR LEADERSHIP IN LEARNING.** Text in English. 1997. a. (w/frequent updates). free (effective 2005). **Document type:** *Journal, Academic/Scholarly.* **Description:** Promotes the study and discussion of substantive leadership issues that are of current concern in educational communities.
Media: Online - full text.
Indexed: CEI, EduInd.
Published by: University of Calgary Press, University of Calgary, Faculty of Education ETD 722, 2500 University Dr N W, Calgary, AB T2N 1N4, Canada. TEL 403-220-7736, FAX 403-282-0085, IEJLL@ucalgary.ca, whildebr@ucalgary.ca, http://www.ucalgary.ca/~iejll, http://www.uofcpress.com. Eds. Charles F Webber, J. Kent Donlevy.

370.72 USA ISSN 1092-3640
➤ **INTERNATIONAL JOURNAL: CONTINUOUS IMPROVEMENT MONITOR**; the peer-reviewed journal of quality in education. Text in English. 1996. irreg. **Document type:** *Journal, Academic/Scholarly.*
Media: Online - full text.
Published by: University of Texas Pan American, 1201 W University Dr, Edinburg, TX 78539-2999. TEL 956-381-3415, FAX 956-383-3662, http://llanes.panam.edu/journal/cim1.

370.72 GBR ISSN 1360-144X
INTERNATIONAL JOURNAL FOR ACADEMIC DEVELOPMENT. Text in English. 1996. s-a. GBP 200, USD 330 combined subscription to institutions print & online eds. (effective 2006). reprint service avail. from PSC. **Document type:** *Journal, Academic/Scholarly.* **Description:** Reports on advances in theory and practice and includes discussions on the development of models and theories for supporting and leading improvements in teaching and learning, and debates current issues at the forefront of educational change.
Formerly: International Journal of Education Development
Related titles: Online - full text ed.: ISSN 1470-1324. GBP 190, USD 314 to institutions (effective 2006) (from EBSCO Publishing, Gale Group, IngentaConnect, O C L C Online Computer Library Center, Inc., Swets Information Services).
Indexed: BrEdI, CPE, ERA, ETA, MEA, RHEA, SEA, SENA, SOMA, TEA.
—BLDSC (4541.515000), IE, Infotrieve, ingenta. **CCC.**
Published by: Routledge (Subsidiary of: Taylor & Francis Group), 4 Park Sq, Milton Park, Abingdon, Oxon OX14 4RN, United Kingdom. TEL 44-1235-828600, FAX 44-1235-829000, journals@routledge.com, http://www.tandf.co.uk/journals/titles/1360144X.asp, http://www.routledge.co.uk. Eds. Dr. Angela Brew, Lynn McAlpine, Rhona Sharpe. R&P Sally Sweet. **Subscr. to:** Taylor & Francis Ltd, Journals Customer Service, Rankine Rd, Basingstoke, Hants RG24 8PR, United Kingdom. TEL 44-1256-813000, FAX 44-1256-330245, enquiry@tandf.co.uk.

INTERNATIONAL JOURNAL FOR MATHEMATICS TEACHING AND LEARNING. see *MATHEMATICS*

371.4 USA ISSN 0165-0653
BF637.C6 CODEN: IJACER
➤ **INTERNATIONAL JOURNAL FOR THE ADVANCEMENT OF COUNSELLING.** Text in English. 1978. q. EUR 358, USD 378, GBP 225 combined subscription to institutions print & online eds. (effective 2005). adv. bk.rev. back issues avail.; reprint service avail. from PSC. **Document type:** *Journal, Academic/Scholarly.* **Description:** Promotes the exchange of information about counselling activities throughout the world.
Related titles: Microform ed.: (from PQC); Online - full text ed.: ISSN 1573-3246 (from EBSCO Publishing, Gale Group, IngentaConnect, Kluwer Online, O C L C Online Computer Library Center, Inc., Springer LINK, Swets Information Services).
Indexed: ASCA, BAS, BibLing, ChPerI, CurCont, DIP, EAA, ERA, ETA, FamI, HRA, IBR, IBZ, IMFL, MEA, PsycInfo, PsycholAb, RHEA, SEA, SENA, SFSA, SOMA, SSA, SSCI, TEA, V&AA, e-psyche.
—BLDSC (4541.573000), IDS, IE, Infotrieve, ingenta. **CCC.**
Published by: Plenum US (Subsidiary of: Springer Science+Business Media), 233 Spring St, New York, NY 10013. TEL 212-460-1500, FAX 212-460-1575, service@springer-ny.com, http://springerlink.metapress.com/openurl.asp?genre=journal&issn=0165-0653, http://www.springeronline.com. Ed. Gary L Hermansson. **Co-sponsors:** International Association for Educational and Vocational Guidance; International Round Table for the Advancement of Counselling.

➤ **INTERNATIONAL JOURNAL OF ARTIFICIAL INTELLIGENCE IN EDUCATION.** see *COMPUTERS—Artificial Intelligence*

370.1175 GBR ISSN 1367-0050
LC3701
➤ **INTERNATIONAL JOURNAL OF BILINGUAL EDUCATION AND BILINGUALISM.** Text in English. 1998. bi-m. GBP 350, USD 640, EUR 525 to institutions (effective 2005); includes online ed.. **Document type:** *Journal, Academic/Scholarly.* **Description:** Aims to promote and disseminate applied research into bilingual education and bilingualism.
Related titles: Online - full text ed.: (from EBSCO Publishing, Gale Group, Swets Information Services).
Indexed: BrEdI, CIJE, CPE, DIP, ERA, ETA, IBR, IBZ, L&LBA, LT&LA, MEA, MLA-IB, PsycInfo, PsycholAb, RHEA, SEA, SENA, SOMA, TEA, e-psyche.
—BLDSC (4542.129550), IE, Infotrieve, ingenta. **CCC.**
Published by: Multilingual Matters Ltd., Frankfurt Lodge, Clevedon Hall, Victoria Rd, Clevedon, North Somerset BS21 7HH, United Kingdom. TEL 44-1275-876519, FAX 44-1275-871673, info@multilingual-matters.com, http://www.multilingual-matters.com. Ed. Colin Baker. R&P Marjukka Grover. Adv. contact Kathryn King.

➤ **INTERNATIONAL JOURNAL OF CHILDREN'S SPIRITUALITY.** see *PSYCHOLOGY*

370 GBR ISSN 1467-1069
INTERNATIONAL JOURNAL OF CLINICAL LEGAL EDUCATION. Text in English. 2000. s-a. GBP 25, USD 50, CND 70, AUD 70 to individuals; GBP 50, USD 100, CND 140, AUD 140 to institutions (effective 2003). **Document type:** *Journal, Academic/Scholarly.* **Description:** Provides a forum for exchange of ideas between clinical programmes throughout the world as well as a basis for academic development of this field.
Published by: (Northumbria University, School of Law), Northumbria Law Press, Sutherland Building, School of Law, University of Northumbria, Newcastle Upon Tyne, NE1 8ST, United Kingdom. TEL 44-191-2437587, FAX 44-191-2437506, suzanne.thomas@unn.ac.uk, http://nlp.unn.ac.uk/journals.asp?jnlid=1. Ed. Tessa Green.

370 384 USA ISSN 1539-3100
LC5800 CODEN: IJDECC
▼ ➤ **INTERNATIONAL JOURNAL OF DISTANCE EDUCATION TECHNOLOGIES**; the international source for technological advances in distance education. Text in English. 2003. q. USD 90 to individuals; USD 225 to institutions (effective 2005). adv. bk.rev. Index. reprints avail. **Document type:** *Journal, Academic/Scholarly.* **Description:** Provides a primary forum for researchers and practitioners to disseminate practical solutions to the automation of open and distance learning.
Related titles: Online - full text ed.: ISSN 1539-3119 (from O C L C Online Computer Library Center, Inc., ProQuest Information & Learning).
Indexed: ABIn, BrCerAb, C&ISA, CerAb, CompLI, CorrAb, E&CAJ, EMA, IAA, Inspec, M&TEA, MBF, METADEX, SolStAb, WAA.

—BLDSC (4542.186350), IE, Linda Hall.
Published by: (Information Resources Management Association), Idea Group Publishing (Subsidiary of: Idea Group Inc.), 701 E Chocolate Ave, Ste 200, Hershey, PA 17033-1240. TEL 717-533-8845, 866-342-6657, FAX 717-533-7115, cust@idea-group.com, http://www.idea-group.com/journals/details.asp?id=498. Eds. Shi Kuo Chang, Timothy K Shih. R&P Jan Travers. adv.: B&W page USD 350; trim 7 x 10.

370 KOR ISSN 1226-9557
INTERNATIONAL JOURNAL OF EARLY CHILDHOOD EDUCATION. Text in English. 1996. irreg. USD 15 domestic to individuals; USD 20 foreign to individuals; USD 35 domestic to institutions; USD 40 foreign to institutions. **Document type:** *Journal, Academic/Scholarly.*
—BLDSC (4542.192000).
Published by: Korean Society for Early Childhood Education, Department of Early Childhood Education, Chonnam National University, 300 Yongbong-dong, Buk-gu, Gwang-ju, 500-757, Korea, S. TEL 82-62-5300610, FAX 82-62-5300611, ksece@hanmail.net. Ed. Ok Kim Young.

370.72 GBR ISSN 0966-9760
LB1139.2
INTERNATIONAL JOURNAL OF EARLY YEARS EDUCATION. Text in English. 1993. 3/yr. GBP 269, USD 444 combined subscription to institutions print & online eds. (effective 2006). adv. bk.rev. back issues avail.; reprint service avail. from PSC. **Document type:** *Journal, Academic/Scholarly.* **Description:** Provides an international forum for researchers and practitioners to debate the theories, research, policies and practices which sustain effective early years education worldwide.
Related titles: Online - full text ed.: ISSN 1469-8463. GBP 256, USD 422 to institutions (effective 2006) (from EBSCO Publishing, Gale Group, IngentaConnect, O C L C Online Computer Library Center, Inc., Swets Information Services).
Indexed: BrEdI, CIJE, CPE, ERA, ETA, FamI, L&LBA, MEA, PsycInfo, PsycholAb, RHEA, SEA, SENA, SOMA, SOPODA, SWA, TEA.
—BLDSC (4542.193000), IE, Infotrieve, ingenta. **CCC.**
Published by: Routledge (Subsidiary of: Taylor & Francis Group), 4 Park Sq, Milton Park, Abingdon, Oxon OX14 4RN, United Kingdom. TEL 44-1235-828600, FAX 44-1235-829000, info@routledge.co.uk, http://www.tandf.co.uk/journals/titles/09669760.asp, http://www.routledge.co.uk. Ed. Iram Siraj-Blatchford. adv.: page GBP 200; trim 250 x 171. Circ: 1,000. **Subscr. in N. America to:** Taylor & Francis Inc., Customer Services Dept, 325 Chestnut St, 8th Fl, Philadelphia, PA 19106. TEL 215-625-8900, 800-354-1420, FAX 215-625-8914, customerservice@taylorandfrancis.com; **Subscr. to:** Taylor & Francis Ltd, Journals Customer Service, Rankine Rd, Basingstoke, Hants RG24 8PR, United Kingdom. TEL 44-1256-813000, FAX 44-1256-330245.

370 004 BRB ISSN 1814-0556
▼ **INTERNATIONAL JOURNAL OF EDUCATION AND DEVELOPMENT USING INFORMATION AND COMMUNICATION TECHNOLOGY.** Text in English. 2005. irreg. free (effective 2005). **Document type:** *Journal, Academic/Scholarly.* **Description:** It aims to strengthen links between research and practice in Information and Communication Technology in education and development in less developed parts of the world, e.g., developing countries, especially small states, and rural and remote regions of developed countries.
Media: Online - full text.
Published by: University of the West Indies, Distance Education Centre, Cavehill Campus, Bridgetown, Barbados. TEL 246-417-4497, FAX 246-421-6753, http://ijedict.dec.uwi.edu//index.php.

370 700 USA ISSN 1529-8094
N81
➤ **INTERNATIONAL JOURNAL OF EDUCATION AND THE ARTS.** Text in English. free (effective 2005). abstr. **Document type:** *Journal, Academic/Scholarly.*
Media: Online - full text.
Indexed: EduInd.
Published by: Arizona State University, Box 870211, Tempe, AZ 85287-0211. TEL 480-965-1243, FAX 480-965-8484, http://ijea.asu.edu. Eds. Liora Bresler, Tom Barone.

370 700 GBR ISSN 1743-5234
▼ ➤ **INTERNATIONAL JOURNAL OF EDUCATION THROUGH ART.** Text in English. 2005. 3/yr. GBP 140 in the European Union to institutions; GBP 148 elsewhere to institutions (effective 2005). **Document type:** *Journal, Academic/Scholarly.* **Description:** Presents research that questions and evaluates the ways in which art is produced, disseminated and interpreted across a diverse range of educational contexts through debates on: education in art, craft and design; formal and informal education contexts; and pedagogy. Policy and practice, research, comparative education, and transcultural issues are all considered.
Related titles: Online - full text ed.: (from EBSCO Publishing).
—BLDSC (4542.198800).
Published by: Intellect Ltd., PO Box 862, Bristol, BS99 1DE, United Kingdom. TEL 44-117-9589910, FAX 44-117-9589911, journals@intellectbooks.com, info@intellectbooks.com, http://www.intellectbooks.co.uk/journals.php?issn=17435234, http://www.intellectbooks.com. Ed. Dr. Rachel Mason. R&P, Adv. contact Mr. Robin Beecroft.

371.264 GBR ISSN 1744-6511
➤ **INTERNATIONAL JOURNAL OF EDUCATIONAL ADVANCEMENT.** Short title: J E A. Text in English. 2000. q. GBP 140 in Europe; USD 250 in North America; GBP 165 elsewhere (effective 2005). abstr. 96 p./no. 2 cols./p.; back issues avail. **Document type:** *Journal, Academic/Scholarly.* **Description:** Publishes thought-provoking, topical articles from academic researchers and advancement professionals working in schools, colleges, and universities, thus providing a forum for the equally important aspects of alumni relations, fund raising, communications, public relations, and marketing.
Formerly (until 2004): The C A S E International Journal of Educational Advancement (1467-3657)
Related titles: Online - full text ed.: ISSN 1740-214X (from Gale Group, IngentaConnect, O C L C Online Computer Library Center, Inc.).
Published by: Palgrave Macmillan Ltd. (Subsidiary of: Macmillan Publishers Ltd.), Houndmills, Basingstoke, Hants RG21 6XS, United Kingdom. TEL 44-1256-329242, FAX 44-1256-810526, journal-info@palgrave.com, http://www.palgrave-journals.com/. Ed. Vince Maniaci. Circ: 800 (paid).

370.9 GBR ISSN 0738-0593
L16
➤ **INTERNATIONAL JOURNAL OF EDUCATIONAL DEVELOPMENT.** Text in English. 1981. 6/yr. EUR 823 in Europe to institutions; JPY 109,200 in Japan to institutions; USD 921 to institutions except Europe and Japan (effective 2006). adv. bk.rev. index. back issues avail. **Document type:** *Journal, Academic/Scholarly.* **Description:** Reports key developments in national systems of education as they emerge, including new structures of schooling, curriculum innovation and change, new approaches to educational management, and studies of achievement and student participation rates, as well as research and analysis of theoretical, practical and planning issues.
Related titles: Microform ed.: (from PQC); Online - full text ed.: (from EBSCO Publishing, Gale Group, IngentaConnect, ScienceDirect, Swets Information Services).
Indexed: ASCA, ArtHuCI, BAS, BrEdI, CPE, CurCont, ERA, ETA, GEOBASE, MEA, RASB, RDA, REE&TA, RHEA, SEA, SENA, SOMA, SSCI, SWA, TEA, WAE&RSA.
—BLDSC (4542.199500), IDS, IE, Infotrieve, ingenta. **CCC.**
Published by: Pergamon (Subsidiary of: Elsevier Science & Technology), The Boulevard, Langford Ln, East Park, Kidlington, Oxford OX5 1GB, United Kingdom. TEL 44-1865-843000, FAX 44-1865-843010, http://www.elsevier.com/locate/ijedudev. Ed. Keith Watson. **Subscr. to:** Elsevier BV, PO Box 211, Amsterdam 1000 AE, Netherlands. nlinfo-f@elsevier.nl, http://www.elsevier.nl.

370 USA ISSN 1056-7879
L11
➤ **INTERNATIONAL JOURNAL OF EDUCATIONAL REFORM.** Text in English. 1992. q. USD 138 domestic; USD 178 foreign (effective 2004). bk.rev. illus.; tr.lit. back issues avail. **Document type:** *Journal, Academic/Scholarly.* **Description:** Keep up with worldwide developments in education reform with current information and analysis from recognized authorities you can trust. The journal combines the voices of the right and left on the political spectrum, and provides you with a balanced view of both sides of the political and educational mainstream.
Indexed: CIJE, CPE, ERA, ETA, MEA, RHEA, SEA, SENA, SOMA, TEA.
—BLDSC (4542.199780), IE, ingenta. **CCC.**
Published by: Scarecrow Education (Subsidiary of: Scarecrow Press, Inc.), 4501 Forbes Blvd, Ste 200, PO Box 191, Lanham, MD 20706. TEL 301-459-3366, 800-462-6420, FAX 800-338-4550, tmiller@rowman.com, custserv@rowman.com, http://www.scarecroweducation.com/Journals/IJER/Index.shtml. Ed. Dr. Steve Permuth. Pub. Dr. Thomas Koerner. R&P Ms. Kelly Rogers. Circ: 230 (paid).

370.72 GBR ISSN 0883-0355
LB2845 CODEN: EIRSD6
➤ **INTERNATIONAL JOURNAL OF EDUCATIONAL RESEARCH.** Text in English. 1977. 12/yr. EUR 1,081 in Europe to institutions; JPY 143,600 in Japan to institutions; USD 1,209 elsewhere to institutions (effective 2006). back issues avail. **Document type:** *Journal, Academic/Scholarly.* **Description:** Publishes results of importance for educational policy, practice, and reseach.
Former titles (until 1985): Evaluation in Education (0191-765X); (until 1979): Evaluation in Education - International Progress (0145-9228)
Related titles: Microfilm ed.: (from PQC); Online - full text ed.: (from EBSCO Publishing, Gale Group, IngentaConnect, ScienceDirect, Swets Information Services); ♦ Series: Learning and Instruction. ISSN 0959-4752.
Indexed: BrEdI, CIJE, CIS, CPE, ERA, ETA, PsycholAb, RASB, RHEA, TEA.
—BLDSC (4542.199800), IE, Infotrieve, ingenta. **CCC.**
Published by: Pergamon (Subsidiary of: Elsevier Science & Technology), The Boulevard, Langford Ln, East Park, Kidlington, Oxford OX5 1GB, United Kingdom. TEL 44-1865-843000, FAX 44-1865-843010, http://www.elsevier.com/locate/ijedures. Ed. Neil Mercer. **Subscr. to:** Elsevier BV, PO Box 211, Amsterdam 1000 AE, Netherlands. TEL 31-20-485-3757, FAX 31-20-485-3432, nlinfo-f@elsevier.nl, http://www.elsevier.nl.

370.72 IND ISSN 0252-8576
INTERNATIONAL JOURNAL OF EDUCATIONAL SCIENCES. Text in English. 1984. a. INR 200, USD 250. adv. bk.rev. back issues avail. **Document type:** *Academic/Scholarly.* **Description:** Forum for research in the educational sciences.
Published by: Institute for Studies in Psychological Testing, 101 Doon, Jakhan, Rajpur Rd., Dehra Dun, Uttar Pradesh 248 001, India. TEL 91-135-684551. Ed. Sr S P Kulshrestha. Circ: 1,000.

370 AUS
➤ **INTERNATIONAL JOURNAL OF EDUCOLOGY (CD-ROM EDITION).** Text in English. 1987. 2/yr. AUD 40 (effective 2003). bk.rev. index. back issues avail. **Document type:** *Academic/Scholarly.* **Description:** Examines various aspects of the educational process from an educological perspective.
Formerly: International Journal of Educology (Print Edition) (0818-0563)
Media: CD-ROM.
Indexed: AEI.
Published by: Educology Research Associates, 11 Sandringham Close, Terrigal, NSW 2260, Australia. TEL 61-2-43653120, FAX 61-2-43650014, jaemar@bigpond.com. Eds. James E Fisher, James Christensen. R&P James E Christensen. Circ: 1,500 (controlled).

➤ **INTERNATIONAL JOURNAL OF ENGINEERING EDUCATION.** see *ENGINEERING*

▼ ➤ **INTERNATIONAL JOURNAL OF ENTREPRENEURSHIP EDUCATION.** see *BUSINESS AND ECONOMICS*

➤ **INTERNATIONAL JOURNAL OF HEALTH PROMOTION AND EDUCATION.** see *PHYSICAL FITNESS AND HYGIENE*

370.72 GBR ISSN 1360-3116
LC1200
➤ **INTERNATIONAL JOURNAL OF INCLUSIVE EDUCATION.** Text in English. 1997. bi-m. GBP 367, USD 601 combined subscription to institutions print & online eds. (effective 2006). adv. reprint service avail. from PSC. **Document type:** *Journal, Academic/Scholarly.* **Description:** Provides a multidisciplinary forum for reporting and evaluating innovative inclusive educational practices and research across a range of educational settings.
Related titles: Online - full text ed.: ISSN 1464-5173. GBP 349, USD 601 to institutions (effective2006) (from EBSCO Publishing, Gale Group, IngentaConnect, O C L C Online Computer Library Center, Inc., Swets Information Services).
Indexed: CPE, ERA, ETA, MEA, RHEA, SEA, SENA, SOMA, TEA.
—BLDSC (4542.302800), IE, Infotrieve, ingenta. **CCC.**
Published by: Routledge (Subsidiary of: Taylor & Francis Group), 4 Park Sq, Milton Park, Abingdon, Oxon OX14 4RN, United Kingdom. TEL 44-1235-828600, FAX 44-1235-829000, info@routledge.co.uk, http://www.tandf.co.uk/journals/titles/13603116.asp, http://www.routledge.co.uk. Ed. Roger Slee. **Subscr. in N. America to:** Taylor & Francis Inc., Customer Services Dept, 325 Chestnut St, 8th Fl, Philadelphia, PA 19106. TEL 800-354-1420; **Subscr. to:** Taylor & Francis Ltd, Journals Customer Service, Rankine Rd, Basingstoke, Hants RG24 8PR, United Kingdom. TEL 44-1256-813000, FAX 44-1256-330245, enquiry@tandf.co.uk.

370 USA ISSN 1550-1876
▼ **INTERNATIONAL JOURNAL OF INFORMATION AND COMMUNICATION TECHNOLOGY EDUCATION.** Text in English. 2005. q. USD 85 to individuals; USD 195 to institutions (effective 2005). **Document type:** *Journal, Academic/Scholarly.* **Description:** Publishes articles, papers, and manuscripts promoting the advancement of teaching with technology at all levels of education encompassing all domains of learning.
Related titles: Online - full text ed.: ISSN 1550-1337. forthcoming 2005.
Indexed: C&ISA, E&CAJ, IAA.
Published by: (Information Resources Management Association), Idea Group Publishing (Subsidiary of: Idea Group Inc.), 701 E Chocolate Ave, Ste 200, Hershey, PA 17033-1240. TEL 866-342-6657, FAX 717-533-7115, cust@idea-group.com, http://www.idea-group.com/journals/details.asp?id=4287.

▼ **INTERNATIONAL JOURNAL OF INTERACTIVE TECHNOLOGY AND SMART EDUCATION;** promoting innovation and a human touch. see *TECHNOLOGY: COMPREHENSIVE WORKS*

E

370 GBR ISSN 1360-3124
LB2806
➤ **INTERNATIONAL JOURNAL OF LEADERSHIP IN EDUCATION**; theory & practice. Text in English. 1998. q. GBP 243, USD 402 combined subscription to institutions print & online eds. (effective 2006). adv. reprint service avail. from PSC. **Document type:** *Journal, Academic/Scholarly.* **Description:** A progressive alternative in the field of educational leadership, educational administration, instructional supervision, curriculum leadership, teacher education and professional staff development in primary through tertiary levels of schooling.
Related titles: Online - full text ed.: ISSN 1464-5092. GBP 231, USD 382 to institutions (effective 2006) (from EBSCO Publishing, Gale Group, IngentaConnect, O C L C Online Computer Library Center, Inc., Swets Information Services).
Indexed: BrEdI, CIJE, CPE, ERA, ETA, MEA, RHEA, SEA, SENA, SOMA, TEA.
—BLDSC (4542.314500), IE, Infotrieve, ingenta. **CCC.**
Published by: Taylor & Francis Ltd (Subsidiary of: Taylor & Francis Group), 4 Park Sq, Milton Park, Abingdon, OX14 4RN, United Kingdom. TEL 44-1235-828600, FAX 44-1235-829000, ijle@txstate.edu, info@tandf.co.uk, http://www.tandf.co.uk/journals/titles/13603124.asp. Ed. Dr. Duncan Waite. **Subscr. in N. America to:** Taylor & Francis Inc., Customer Services Dept, 325 Chestnut St, 8th Fl, Philadelphia, PA 19106. TEL 215-625-8900, 800-354-1420, FAX 215-625-8914, customerservice@taylorandfrancis.com; **Subscr. to:** Journals Customer Service, Rankine Rd, Basingstoke, Hants RG24 8PR, United Kingdom. TEL 44-1256-813000, FAX 44-1256-330245, enquiry@tandf.co.uk.

370 AUS ISSN 1447-9494
➤ **INTERNATIONAL JOURNAL OF LEARNING.** Text in English. 2002. a., latest vol.10, 2003. AUD 300 (effective 2004). Index. back issues avail. **Document type:** *Journal, Academic/Scholarly.* **Description:** Sets out to foster inquiry, invite dialogue and build a body of knowledge on the nature and future of learning.
Related titles: CD-ROM ed.; Online - full content ed.
Published by: Common Ground, PO Box 463, Altona, VIC 3018, Australia. kathryn@commongroundpublishing.com, http://learningconference.publisher-site.com/, http://commongroundgroup.com/. Eds. Howard Dare, Mary Kalantzis. Pub. Kathryn Otte.

370 GBR ISSN 1471-4426
THE INTERNATIONAL JOURNAL OF MEDIA JUSTICE. Text in English. 2001 (Nov.). 3/yr. GBP 40 in United Kingdom; GBP 50 elsewhere; GBP 75 in United Kingdom; GBP 85 elsewhere (effective 2002); Subscr. includes free online access.. back issues avail. **Document type:** *Journal, Academic/Scholarly.* **Description:** Provides a forum for research and scholarship by focusing on learning and teaching about media at all levels of education.
Published by: Trentham Books Ltd., Westview House, 734 London Rd, Stoke-on-Trent, Staffs ST4 5NP, United Kingdom. TEL 44-1782-745567, FAX 44-1782-745553, tb@trentham-books.co.uk, http://www.trentham-books.co.uk. Ed. Andrew Hart.

INTERNATIONAL JOURNAL OF MUSIC EDUCATION. see *MUSIC*

▼ **INTERNATIONAL JOURNAL OF NURSING EDUCATION SCHOLARSHIP.** see *MEDICAL SCIENCES—Nurses And Nursing*

INTERNATIONAL JOURNAL OF PEACE STUDIES. see *POLITICAL SCIENCE*

370.72 GBR ISSN 0951-8398
LB1028 CODEN: QSEEEY
➤ **INTERNATIONAL JOURNAL OF QUALITATIVE STUDIES IN EDUCATION.** Text in English. 1988. bi-m. GBP 439, USD 724 combined subscription to institutions print & online eds. (effective 2005). adv. reprint service avail. from PSC. **Document type:** *Journal, Academic/Scholarly.* **Description:** Aims to enhance the theory and practice of qualitative research in education by reporting experience of a variety of techniques, including ethnographic observation and interviewing, grounded theory, life history, qualitative evaluation, curriculum criticism and phenomenology.
Related titles: Online - full text ed.: ISSN 1366-5898. GBP 417, USD 688 to institutions (effective 2006) (from EBSCO Publishing, Gale Group, IngentaConnect, O C L C Online Computer Library Center, Inc., Swets Information Services).
Indexed: BrEdI, CPE, DIP, ERA, ETA, IBR, IBZ, MEA, PCI, PsycInfo, PsycholAb, RASB, RHEA, SEA, SENA, SOMA, SSA, SociolAb, TEA.
—BLDSC (4542.509700), IE, Infotrieve, ingenta. **CCC.**
Published by: Routledge (Subsidiary of: Taylor & Francis Group), 4 Park Sq, Milton Park, Abingdon, Oxon OX14 4RN, United Kingdom. TEL 44-1235-828600, FAX 44-1235-829000, info@routledge.co.uk, http://www.tandf.co.uk/journals/titles/09518398.asp, http://www.routledge.co.uk. Eds. Angela Valenzuela, James Scheurich, James Scheurich, M Carolyn Clark. **Subscr. in N. America to:** Taylor & Francis Inc., Customer Services Dept, 325 Chestnut St, 8th Fl, Philadelphia, PA 19106. TEL 215-625-8900, 800-354-1420, FAX 215-625-8914, customerservice@taylorandfrancis.com; **Subscr. to:** Taylor & Francis Ltd, Journals Customer Service, Rankine Rd, Basingstoke, Hants RG24 8PR, United Kingdom. TEL 44-1256-813000, FAX 44-1256-330245, enquiry@tandf.co.uk, info@tandf.co.uk, http://www.tandf.co.uk/journals.

370 GBR ISSN 1743-727X
L16
➤ **INTERNATIONAL JOURNAL OF RESEARCH AND METHOD IN EDUCATION.** Text in English. 1978. s-a. GBP 490, USD 1,145 combined subscription to institutions print & online eds. (effective 2006). bk.rev. illus.; stat. back issues avail.; reprint service avail. from PSC. **Document type:** *Journal, Academic/Scholarly.* **Description:** Publishes empirical studies and scholarly discussions where the focus is on innovative or problematic aspects of teaching, learning, assessment and evaluation as these occur in a wide variety of formal and informal settings.
Formerly (until 2005): Westminster Studies in Education (0140-6728)
Related titles: Microfiche ed.; Online - full text ed.: ISSN 1743-7288. GBP 466, USD 1,088 to institutions (effective 2006) (from EBSCO Publishing, Gale Group, IngentaConnect, O C L C Online Computer Library Center, Inc., ProQuest Information & Learning, Swets Information Services).
Indexed: BrEdI, CIJE, CPE, DIP, ERA, ETA, HECAB, IBR, IBZ, MEA, PSA, PsycholAb, RHEA, SEA, SENA, SOMA, SSA, SWA, SociolAb, TEA.
—BLDSC (9304.770000), IE, Infotrieve, ingenta. **CCC.**
Published by: Routledge (Subsidiary of: Taylor & Francis Group), 4 Park Sq, Milton Park, Abingdon, Oxon OX14 4RN, United Kingdom. TEL 44-1235-828600, FAX 44-1235-829000, info@routledge.co.uk, http://www.tandf.co.uk/journals/titles/1743727x.asp, http://www.routledge.co.uk. Eds. Birgit Pepin, Gary Thomas. **Subscr. to:** Taylor & Francis Ltd, Journals Customer Service, Rankine Rd, Basingstoke, Hants RG24 8PR, United Kingdom. TEL 44-1256-813000, FAX 44-1256-330245.

370.72 GBR ISSN 0950-0693
Q181.A1 CODEN: ISEDEB
➤ **INTERNATIONAL JOURNAL OF SCIENCE EDUCATION.** Text in English; Summaries in French, German. 1979. 15/yr. GBP 1,122, USD 1,849 combined subscription to institutions print & online eds. (effective 2006). adv. bk.rev. bibl.; charts; illus. index. back issues avail.; reprint service avail. from PSC. **Document type:** *Journal, Academic/Scholarly.* **Description:** Aims to bridge the gap between research and practice; provides information, ideas and opinions that serve as media for placing these research findings in the context of the classroom.
Formerly (until 1987): European Journal of Science Education (0140-5284)
Related titles: Microfiche ed.; Online - full text ed.: ISSN 1464-5289. GBP 1,066, USD 1,757 to institutions (effective 2006) (from EBSCO Publishing, Gale Group, IngentaConnect, O C L C Online Computer Library Center, Inc., Swets Information Services).
Indexed: ABIn, ASCA, ArtHuCI, BiolAb, BrEdI, CDA, CIJE, CPE, CurCont, ERA, ETA, EduInd, EngInd, ExcerpMed, IBSS, Inspec, MEA, PCI, RASB, RHEA, SEA, SENA, SOMA, SSCI, SWA, TEA.
—BLDSC (4542.544000), AskIEEE, CISTI, Ei, IDS, IE, Infotrieve, ingenta. **CCC.**
Published by: Routledge (Subsidiary of: Taylor & Francis Group), 4 Park Sq, Milton Park, Abingdon, Oxon OX14 4RN, United Kingdom. TEL 44-1235-828600, FAX 44-1235-829000, info@routledge.co.uk, http://www.tandf.co.uk/journals/titles/09500693.asp, http://www.routledge.co.uk. Ed. John K Gilbert. Circ: 700. **Subscr. in N. America to:** Taylor & Francis Inc., Customer Services Dept, 325 Chestnut St, 8th Fl, Philadelphia, PA 19106. TEL 800-354-1420, FAX 215-625-8914; **Subscr. to:** Taylor & Francis Ltd, Journals Customer Service, Rankine Rd, Basingstoke, Hants RG24 8PR, United Kingdom. TEL 44-1256-813000, FAX 44-1256-330245, enquiry@tandf.co.uk.

➤ **INTERNATIONAL JOURNAL OF SOCIAL EDUCATION.** see *SOCIAL SCIENCES: COMPREHENSIVE WORKS*

➤ **INTERNATIONAL JOURNAL OF TESTING.** see *PSYCHOLOGY*

373.246 AUS ISSN 1448-0220
➤ **INTERNATIONAL JOURNAL OF TRAINING RESEARCH.** Text in English. 1985. s-a. AUD 25 per issue. bk.rev. abstr. **Document type:** *Journal, Academic/Scholarly.* **Description:** Provides articles based on vocational education and training research and development activities in Australia and New Zealand.
Former titles: Australian and New Zealand Journal of Vocational Education Research (1039-4001); (until May 1993): Australian Journal of T A F E Research and Development (0816-2018)
Indexed: AEI, CIJE, CPE, ERA, ETA, MEA, RHEA, TEA.
—BLDSC (4542.695880), IE, ingenta.
Published by: Australian Vocational Education and Training Research Association, PO Box 5009, Nowra DC, NSW 2541, Australia. TEL 61-2-44222207, FAX 61-2-44223878, avetra@welldone.com.au, http://www.avetra.org.au/journals.htm. Circ: 300.

370.113 USA ISSN 1075-2455
LC1041
➤ **INTERNATIONAL JOURNAL OF VOCATIONAL EDUCATION AND TRAINING.** Text in English. 1993. s-a. USD 50 to non-members; USD 60 to institutions; free to members (effective 2004). adv. bk.rev. back issues avail. **Document type:** *Journal, Academic/Scholarly.* **Description:** Provides a forum for the discussion of vocational education and training issues and practices.
Published by: International Vocational Education and Training Association, University of Tennessee, Dept of Human Resource Development, 310 Jesseie Harris Bldg, 1215 W Cumberland Ave, Knoxville, TN 37996-1900. TEL 865-974-8924, FAX 865-974-2048, iveta@visi.com, http://www.iveta.org/journals.htm. Ed. Ernest W Brewer.

370 USA ISSN 1710-2146
LC1200
▼ ➤ **INTERNATIONAL JOURNAL OF WHOLE SCHOOLING.** Text in English. 2004. s-a. free. **Document type:** *Journal, Academic/Scholarly.*
Media: Online - full content.
Published by: Whole Schooling Consortium, c/o 217 Education, Wayne State University, Detroit, MI 48202. Wholeschool@comcast.net, http://www.wholeschooling.net/Journal_of_Whole_Schooling/IJWSIndex.html, http://www.wholeschooling.net/WSC.html. Eds. Billie Jo Clausen, Tim Loreman.

➤ **INTERNATIONAL NEWSLETTER ON CHEMICAL EDUCATION.** see *CHEMISTRY*

370 USA
INTERNATIONAL PERSPECTIVES ON EDUCATION AND SOCIETY. Text in English. irreg., latest vol.5, 2002. price varies. back issues avail. **Document type:** *Monographic series, Academic/Scholarly.*
Related titles: Online - full text ed.
Published by: (International Association for the Evaluation of Educational Achievement. NLD), J A I Press Inc. (Subsidiary of: Elsevier Science & Technology), 360 Park Ave S, New York, NY 10010-1710. TEL 212-989-5800, FAX 212-633-3990, usinfo-f@elsevier.com, http://www.elsevier.com/wps/find/bookseriesdescription.cws_home/BS_IPES/description.

370.72 USA ISSN 0278-2731
Q179.98 CODEN: IRCDES
INTERNATIONAL RESEARCH CENTERS DIRECTORY. Text in English. 1982. biennial, latest 2004. USD 635 (effective 2005). **Description:** Guide to research centers worldwide.
—BLDSC (4545.830800), CASDDS.
Published by: Gale Group (Subsidiary of: Thomson Corporation), 27500 Drake Rd, Farmington Hills, MI 48331-3535. TEL 248-699-8061, 800-877-4253, FAX 248-699-4253, galeord@gale.com, http://www.gale.com. Ed. Anthony L Gerring. **Dist. by:** Current Pacific Ltd., PO Box 36-536, Northcote, Auckland, New Zealand. TEL 64-9-480-1388, FAX 64-9-480-1387, info@cplnz.com, http://www.cplnz.com.

INTERNATIONAL RESEARCH IN GEOGRAPHICAL AND ENVIRONMENTAL EDUCATION. see *GEOGRAPHY*

371 NLD ISSN 0020-8566
L18
➤ **INTERNATIONAL REVIEW OF EDUCATION/ INTERNATIONALE ZEITSCHRIFT FUER ERZIEHUNGSWISSENSCHAFT/REVUE INTERNATIONALE DE L'EDUCATION.** Text and summaries in English, French, German; Abstracts in English, French, German, Spanish, Russian. 1955. bi-m. EUR 318, USD 325, GBP 208 combined subscription to institutions print & online eds. (effective 2005). adv. bk.rev. illus. index. reprint service avail. from PSC. **Document type:** *Journal, Academic/Scholarly.* **Description:** Provides departments and institutes of education, teacher training institutions and professional readers worldwide with scholarly information on major educational innovations, research projects and trends.
Related titles: Microform ed.: (from PQC); Online - full text ed.: ISSN 1573-0638 (from EBSCO Publishing, Gale Group, IngentaConnect, Kluwer Online, O C L C Online Computer Library Center, Inc., Springer LINK, Swets Information Services).
Indexed: ABIn, ASCA, AgeL, BAS, BibLing, BrEdI, CIJE, CPE, ChPerI, CurCont, DIP, ERA, ETA, EduInd, FamI, GEOBASE, HECAB, IBR, IBSS, IBZ, IIS, ILD, IndIslam, L&LBA, LT&LA, MEA, MEA&I, PCI, RASB, RDA, REE&TA, RHEA, RefZh, SEA, SENA, SOMA, SOPODA, SSA, SSCI, SociolAb, TEA, WAE&RSA.
—BLDSC (4547.100000), IDS, IE, Infotrieve, ingenta. **CCC.**
Published by: (UNESCO Institute for Education DEU), Springer-Verlag Dordrecht (Subsidiary of: Springer Science+Business Media), Van Godewijckstraat 30, Dordrecht, 3311 GX, Netherlands. TEL 31-78-6576050, FAX 31-78-6576474, http://springerlink.metapress.com/openurl.asp?genre=journal&issn=0020-8566, http://www.springeronline.com.

E

370 GBR
INTERNATIONAL STUDY GUIDE. Text in English. q. GBP 60 (effective 2003). **Document type:** *Academic/Scholarly.* **Description:** Provides information for students around the world and serves as a platform for schools, colleges and universities to present themselves to international students seeking undergraduate, postgraduate, MBA and other Masters, English language learning and information on boarding schools.
Published by: Nexus Media Ltd. (Subsidiary of: Highbury House Communications PLC), Nexus House, Azalea Dr, Swanley, Kent BR8 8HU, United Kingdom. TEL 44-1322-660070, FAX 44-1322-616311, info@nexusmedia.com, http://www.hhc.co.uk/studyguides. Circ: 30,000.

370 PRT ISSN 1645-2194
INTERVIR; online journal of education, technology and politics. Text in Portuguese. 2001 (Sep.). 3/yr. **Document type:** *Journal, Academic/Scholarly.* **Description:** Provides information on educaton topics and issues for portuguese teachers.
Media: Online - full content. **Related titles:** English ed.
Address: http://www.intervir.org/, http://www.intervir.org/i. Eds. Fernando A. C. Canastra, Maria Manuela F. Goncalves, Nelson A. F. Goncalves.

370.72 ESP ISSN 0213-7771
INVESTIGACION EN LA ESCUELA. Text in Spanish. 1987. 3/yr. **Document type:** *Journal, Academic/Scholarly.*
—CINDOC, IE, Infotrieve.
Published by: Diada Editora, Urbanizacion los Pinos, Biq 4-4o D, Montequinto-Sevilla, 41089, Spain. http://www.diadaeditora.com.

INVESTIGACION Y DESARROLLO. see *SCIENCES: COMPREHENSIVE WORKS*

370 NLD ISSN 0021-0307
INZICHT; Onderwysmagazine. Text in Dutch. 1878. 7/yr. EUR 25 to institutions (effective 2005). adv. bk.rev. illus. 36 p./no. 3 cols./p.; **Document type:** *Magazine.*
Formerly: Volksonderwijs
Published by: Vereniging voor Openbaar Onderwijs, Blekerstraat 20, Postbus 10241, Almere, 1301 AE, Netherlands. TEL 31-36-5331500, FAX 31-36-5340464, voo@voo.nl, http://www.voo.nl/actueel/voo_inzicht.html. Circ: 35,000.

IOWA MEDIA MESSAGE. see *LIBRARY AND INFORMATION SCIENCES*

IOWA MUSIC EDUCATOR. see *MUSIC*

370.9567 IRQ
IRAQ. MINISTRY OF EDUCATION. AL-MU'ALLEM AL-JADID✶. Text in Arabic. 1935. 4/yr. IQD 600 to individuals; IQD 1,000 to students. bk.rev. **Document type:** *Government.*
Published by: Ministry of Education, Adhamiya, P O Box 258, Baghdad, Iraq. Ed. Ahmed Shahhath. Circ: 180,000.

372 USA ISSN 1527-3849
THE IRASCIBLE PROFESSOR. Text in English. 1999. irreg. (approx. 2/week). back issues avail. **Document type:** *Newsletter.* **Description:** Includes articles on K-12 and higher education in the United States.
Media: Online - full content.
Published by: The Irascible Professor, c/o Dr. Mark H. Shapiro, 1624 Evergreen Ave, Fullerton, CA 92835-2004. TEL 714-350-3575, FAX 714-529-0415, http://www.irascibleprofessor.com. Ed., Pub. Dr. Mark H Shapiro.

370 GBR ISSN 0332-3315
LA640
IRISH EDUCATIONAL STUDIES. Text in English. 1981. 3/yr. GBP 143, USD 258 combined subscription to institutions print & online eds. (effective 2006).
Related titles: Online - full text ed.: ISSN 1747-4965. GBP 136, USD 245 to institutions (effective 2006).
Indexed: BrEdI.
—BLDSC (4571.328000), IE.
Published by: (Educational Studies Association of Ireland IRL), Taylor & Francis Ltd (Subsidiary of: Taylor & Francis Group), 4 Park Sq, Milton Park, Abingdon, OX14 4RN, United Kingdom. info@tandf.co.uk, http://www.tandf.co.uk/journals.

370.9417 IRL ISSN 0021-1257
➤ **IRISH JOURNAL OF EDUCATION/IRIS EIREANNACH AN OIDEACHAIS.** Text in English. 1967. a., latest vol.34, 2003. EUR 7 in Europe; USD 10 elsewhere (effective 2005). charts; stat.; illus. cum.index every 2 yrs. reprint service avail. from PQC. **Document type:** *Journal, Academic/Scholarly.*
Related titles: Microform ed.: (from PQC); Online - full text ed.: (from H.W. Wilson).
Indexed: BrEdI, CPE, ERA, ETA, EduInd, L&LBA, MEA, PCI, PsycholAb, RHEA, SEA, SOMA, SOPODA, SSA, SSCI, e-psyche.
—BLDSC (4571.950000).
Published by: St. Patrick's College, Educational Research Centre, Drumcondra, Dublin, 9, Ireland. TEL 353-1-8373789, FAX 353-1-8378997, info@erc.ie, http://www.erc.ie/IJE.htm. Ed., R&P Thomas Kellaghan. Circ: 1,000.

➤ **ISLAMIC EDUCATION.** see *RELIGIONS AND THEOLOGY—Islamic*

➤ **ISRAEL. CENTRAL BUREAU OF STATISTICS. SCHOOLS AND KINDERGARTENS.** see *EDUCATION—Abstracting, Bibliographies, Statistics*

305 300 USA ISSN 1086-2005
ISSUES CURRENT IN THE SOCIAL STUDIES. Text in English. bi-m. **Document type:** *Journal, Academic/Scholarly.*
Published by: Illinois Council for the Social Studies, c/o Dr. Frederick D Drake, Department of History, Illinois State University, Normal, IL 61790-4420. TEL 309-438-7212, http://coe.ilstu.edu/icss/. Ed. Bob Lombard TEL 309-697-1629.

ISSUES IN APPLIED LINGUISTICS. see *LINGUISTICS*

370 USA ISSN 0278-0216
ISSUES IN CHRISTIAN EDUCATION. Text in English. 3/yr.
Published by: Concordia Teachers College, 800 N Columbia, Seward, NE 68434. TEL 402-643-3651.

370.15 USA ISSN 1080-9724
LB1051 CODEN: ISEDFC
➤ **ISSUES IN EDUCATION;** contributions from educational psychology. Text in English. 1995. s-a. USD 80 to individuals; USD 185 to institutions; USD 55 to students; USD 20 per vol. to individuals; USD 40 per vol. to institutions (effective 2003). back issues avail. **Document type:** *Journal, Academic/Scholarly.* **Description:** Contains articles which are broad in scope and of significance to a wide audience of scholars and practitioners interested or professionally involved in education.
Indexed: CPE, L&LBA, SOPODA, e-psyche.
—BLDSC (4584.232200), ingenta. **CCC.**
Published by: Information Age Publishing, Inc., 411 W Putnam Ave, Ste 205, PO Box 4967, Greenwich, CT 06831. TEL 203-661-7602, FAX 203-661-7952, order@infoagepub.com, http://www.infoagepub.com.

370 GBR ISSN 1367-0174
ISSUES IN EDUCATION SERIES. Text in English. irreg., latest vol.5, 1999. **Document type:** *Monographic series, Academic/Scholarly.*
—BLDSC (4584.237000).
Published by: Trentham Books Ltd., Westview House, 734 London Rd, Stoke-on-Trent, Staffs ST4 5NP, United Kingdom. TEL 44-1782-745567, FAX 44-1782-745553, tb@trentham-books.co.uk, http://www.trentham-books.co.uk.

370 AUS ISSN 0313-7155
LA2100
➤ **ISSUES IN EDUCATIONAL RESEARCH.** Text in English. 1995. irreg. AUD 30 to individuals; AUD 50 to institutions; AUD 20 to members (effective 2003). **Document type:** *Journal, Academic/Scholarly.* **Description:** Covers general educational issues in Australia, including topics such as educational programs, homework, research, school systems and finances.
Related titles: Online - full text ed.: free (effective 2005).
Published by: Western Australian Institute for Educational Research Inc., c/o Dr Clare McBeath, Faculty of Education, Curtin University of Technology, GPO Box U1987, Perth, W.A. 6845, Australia. TEL 61-8-9266-2182, FAX 61-8-9266-2547, 61-8-9266-2547, http://education.curtin.edu.au/iier/iier.html. Eds. Clare McBeath TEL 61-8-9266-2182, Tony Fetherston TEL 61-8-9370-6373. **Subscr. to:** Issues in Educational Research, c/o Dr John McCormick, School of Education Studies, University of NSW, Sydney, NSW 2052, Australia. TEL 61-02 9385 4917, FAX 61-2 9385 6153, j.mccormick@unsw.edu.au. **Co-publishers:** New South Wales Institute of Educational Research Inc.; South Australia Institute for Educational Research; Northern Territory Institute for Educational Research.

➤ **ISSUES IN LANGUAGE EDUCATION.** see *LINGUISTICS*

370.72 GBR ISSN 1476-6868
ISSUES IN PRACTICE. Text in English. 2000. irreg., latest 2002, June. price varies. **Document type:** *Monographic series, Academic/Scholarly.* **Description:** Focuses on the practical outcomes and applications of research.
Published by: University of London, Institute of Education, 20 Bedford Way, London, WC1H OAL, United Kingdom. TEL 44-20-76126000, FAX 44-20-76126126, info@ioe.ac.uk, http://www.ioe.ac.uk.

370 USA
▼ ➤ **ISSUES IN THE UNDERGRADUATE MATHEMATICS PREPARATION OF SCHOOL TEACHERS.** Text in English. 2003. irreg., latest vol.4, 2004. free. **Document type:** *Journal, Academic/Scholarly.*
Media: Online - full content.
Address: c/o Gary A. Harris, Department of Mathematics, College of Arts & Sciences, Texas Tech University, Lubbock, TX 79409. gary.harris@ttu.edu, http://www.k-12prep.math.ttu.edu/site.shtml. Ed. Gary Harris.

➤ **ITALICA.** see *LITERATURE*

➤ **ITALY. ISTITUTO NAZIONALE DI STATISTICA. STATISTICHE DELLA SCUOLA MATERNA ED ELEMENTARE.** see *EDUCATION—Abstracting, Bibliographies, Statistics*

➤ **ITALY. ISTITUTO NAZIONALE DI STATISTICA. STATISTICHE DELLA SCUOLA MEDIA INFERIORE.** see *EDUCATION—Abstracting, Bibliographies, Statistics*

➤ **ITALY. ISTITUTO NAZIONALE DI STATISTICA. STATISTICHE DELLE SCUOLE SECONDARIE SUPERIORI.** see *EDUCATION—Abstracting, Bibliographies, Statistics*

370.157 USA ISSN 0098-7549
IT'S HAPPENING. Text in English. 1974. irreg. membership. adv. reprint service avail. from PQC.
Published by: National Association for Creative Children and Adults, 8080 Springvalley Dr, Cincinnati, OH 45236-1395. TEL 513-631-1777. Ed. Ann F Isaacs. Circ: 2,000.

370.1 ESP
IT'S MAGAZINE (STUDENT EDITION). Text in Spanish. bi-m. **Document type:** *Academic/Scholarly.* **Description:** Contains articles and features related to current news, movies, fashion, and music. Also includes games, puzzles, discussions, and self-study exercises.
Related titles: Online - full text ed.
Published by: IT's Magazines, Apartado de Correos 5096, Barcelona, 08080, Spain. FAX 34-93-265-4253, crc@its-online.com, http://www.its-online.com.

370.1 ESP
IT'S MAGAZINE (TEACHER'S EDITION). Text in Spanish. 1990. bi-m. **Document type:** *Academic/Scholarly.* **Description:** Contains teaching notes with step-by-step instructions, key to the teaching materials, and also information on other related materials.
Published by: IT's Magazines, Apartado de Correos 5096, Barcelona, 08080, Spain. FAX 34-93-265-4253, crc@its-online.com, http://www.its-online.com.

IT'S ON-LINE. see *LINGUISTICS*

370 JPN ISSN 0367-7370
AS552.I9 CODEN: IDKKBM
IWATE UNIVERSITY. FACULTY OF EDUCATION. ANNUAL REPORT/IWATE DAIGAKU KYOIKUGAKUBU KENKYU NENPO. Text in Japanese. 1950. a. index. back issues avail.
Indexed: BiolAb, INIS AtomInd, RILM, RefZh.
—BLDSC (1248.553500).
Published by: Iwate University, Faculty of Education/Iwate Daigaku Kyoikubu, 3-18-8 Ueda, Morioka-shi, Iwate-ken 020-0066, Japan. Ed. Y Saito. Circ: 450.

370 FRA ISSN 0246-8298
J D I; revue de ecoles elementaires. (Journal des Instituteurs et des Institutrices) Text in French. 1965 (vol.112). 10/yr. adv. bk.rev. bibl.; illus.
Formerly (until 1980): Journal des Instituteurs et des Institutrices (0021-8073)
—**CCC.**
Published by: Editions Nathan, Departement des Revues, 9 rue Mechain, Paris, Cedex 14 75676, France. TEL 33-1-45875000, FAX 33-1-45875791.

370.72 CAN ISSN 0022-0701
➤ **J E T: JOURNAL OF EDUCATIONAL THOUGHT/REVUE DE LA PENSEE EDUCATIVE.** Text in English; Text occasionally in French. 1967. 3/yr. CND 80 domestic to individuals; USD 80 foreign to individuals; CND 90 domestic to institutions; USD 90 foreign to institutions; CND 30 per issue (effective 2005). adv. bk.rev. bibl.; illus. back issues avail.; reprint service avail. from PQC,PSC. **Document type:** *Academic/Scholarly.* **Description:** Promotes speculative, critical and historical research concerning the theory and practice of education in a variety of areas.
Formerly: Journal of Educational Thought
Related titles: Microfiche ed.: (from MML); Microfilm ed.: (from MML, PQC); Microform ed.: (from MML); Online - full text ed.: (from H.W. Wilson, Micromedia ProQuest, O C L C Online Computer Library Center, Inc., ProQuest Information & Learning).
Indexed: ABIn, CEI, CIJE, CPE, CWPI, EAA, ERA, ETA, EduInd, MEA, MEA&I, PhilInd, RASB, RHEA, SEA, SENA, SOMA, SOPODA, SSA, SSCI, SWA, SociolAb, TEA.
—BLDSC (4973.260000), IE, Infotrieve, ingenta. **CCC.**
Published by: University of Calgary, Faculty of Education, 2500 University Dr NW, Calgary, AB T2N 1N4, Canada. TEL 403-220-7498, 403-220-5629, FAX 403-284-4162, jet@ucalgary.ca, http://www.educ.ucalgary.ca/research/jet, http://external.educ.ucalgary.ca/jet/jetaug.html. Ed. Ian Winchester. R&P Linda Lentz. Circ: 575.

➤ **J U M A.** see *LINGUISTICS*

370 DEU ISSN 0941-1461
LA720
JAHRBUCH FUR PAEDAGOGIK. Text in German. 1992. a. CHF 34; EUR 23 in Austria & Germany; EUR 22 in Europe; GBP 16, USD 26 (effective 2006). **Document type:** *Yearbook, Academic/Scholarly.*
Indexed: DIP, IBR, IBZ.

E

▼ new title ➤ refereed ✶ unverified ♦ full entry avail.

Published by: Peter Lang GmbH Europaeischer Verlag der Wissenschaften, Eschborner Landstr 42-50, Frankfurt Am Main, 60489, Germany. TEL 49-69-7807050, FAX 49-69-78070543, zentrale.frankfurt@peterlang.com, http://www.peterlang.de. R&P Ruediger Brunsch.

JAHRBUCH JUGENDFORSCHUNG. see *CHILDREN AND YOUTH—About*

JAIL OPERATIONS BULLETIN. see *CRIMINOLOGY AND LAW ENFORCEMENT*

370 EGY
JAMI'AT AL-MANUFIYYAH. KULLIYYAT AL-TARBIYYAH. MAJALLAH/MENOUFIA UNIVERSITY. FACULTY OF EDUCATION. JOURNAL. Text in Arabic. 1986. irreg.
Published by: Jami'at al-Manufiyyah, Kulliyyat al-Tarbiyyah/Manoufia University, Faculty of Education, Shebeen El-Kom, Menoufia, Egypt.

370.9 JPN ISSN 0289-405X
JAPAN COMPARATIVE EDUCATION SOCIETY. BULLETIN. Text in Japanese. 1975. a. JPY 3,000, USD 15. adv. bk.rev. back issues avail.
Published by: Japan Comparative Education Society, c/o Fac of Education, Bukkyo University, 96 Murasakino-Kitahananobo-cho, Kita-ku, Kyoto-shi, 603-8301, Japan. Ed. Keijiro Tanaka. Circ: 700.

JAZZYBOOKS - SECONDARY SCHOOLS. see *CHILDREN AND YOUTH—For*

THE JERUSALEM TIMES; biladу. see *POLITICAL SCIENCE—International Relations*

JEWISH EDUCATIONAL STATISTICS. see *EDUCATION—Abstracting, Bibliographies, Statistics*

JEZYKI OBCE W SZKOLE. see *LINGUISTICS*

371 CHN
JIANGXI JIAOYU XUEYUAN XUEBAO/JIANGXI INSTITUTE OF EDUCATION. JOURNAL. Text in Chinese. q. CNY 4.
Description: Presents basic theoretical research in secondary and adult education. Includes teaching materials and methods, education science and management, psychology, school history, philosophy, history, politics, economics, Marxist-Leninist theory, and political education.
Published by: Jiangxi Jiaoyu Xueyuan/Jiangxi Institute of Education, 87 Beijing Donglu, Nanchang, Jiangxi 330029, China.

370 CHN
JIAOYU KEXUE/SCIENCE OF EDUCATION. Text in Chinese. q.
Published by: Liaoning Shifan Daxue/Liaoning Normal University, 850 Huanghe Lu, Dalian, Liaoning 116022, China. TEL 401181. Ed. Zhao Hanzhang.

370.72 CHN
JIAOYU PINGLUN/EDUCATION REVIEW. Text in Chinese. bi-m. CNY 7.20. **Description:** Publishes results of scientific research on education, introduces up-to-date educational information at home and abroad and presents institutional and personal experience.
Indexed: BrEdI.
Published by: Fujian Jiaoyu Kexue Yanjiusuo/Fujian Institute of Education Science, No 104, Wusi Lu, Fuzhou, Fujian 350003, China. TEL 556730. Ed. Lin Tianqing. **Dist. overseas by:** Jiangsu Publications Import & Export Corp., 56 Gao Yun Ling, Nanjing, Jiangsu, China. **Co-sponsor:** Fujian Jiaoyu Xuehui.

370 HKG ISSN 1025-1936
L64
➤ **JIAOYU XUEBAO/EDUCATION JOURNAL.** Text in Chinese, English. 1972. s-a. HKD 115, USD 15 per issue (effective 2001). adv. 170 p./no.; **Document type:** *Journal, Academic/Scholarly.* **Description:** Publishes articles on empirical and theoretical studies, research reports, and commentaries that attempt a systematic analysis of educational processes and systems from different viewpoints and approaches.
Indexed: CIJE, EAA, HongKongiana.
—BLDSC (3661.288300), IE, ingenta.
Published by: (Chinese University of Hong Kong, Hong Kong Institute of Educational Research), Zhongwen Daxue Chubanshe/Chinese University Press, The Chinese University of Hong Kong, Shatin, New Territories, Hong Kong. TEL 852-2609-6508, FAX 852-2603-7355, hkier@cuhk.edu.hk, cup@cuhk.edu.hk, http://www.chineseupress.com/. Ed., R&P Wing-Kwong Tsang. Adv. contact Angelina Wong TEL 852-26096500. page HKD 1,500.

370 CHN ISSN 1002-5731
LA1130
➤ **JIAOYU YANJIU/EDUCATIONAL RESEARCH.** Text in Chinese; Contents page in English. 1979. m. CNY 33.60, USD 21.60. adv. bk.rev. abstr.; bibl.; charts. back issues avail. **Document type:** *Academic/Scholarly.*
Related titles: Online - full text ed.: (from East View Information Services).
Indexed: RASB.

Published by: (Zhongyang Jiaoyu Kexue Yanjiusuo/China National Institute for Educational Research), Jiaoyu Yanjiu Zazhishe, 46 Beisanhuan Zhonglu, Beijing, 100088, China. TEL 86-10-6201-1873, FAX 86-10-6203-3132. Ed. Ruiqing Lian. R&P Yongsong Zhao. Adv. contact Yuming Ni. Circ: 25,000. **Dist. in US by:** China Books & Periodicals Inc, 360 Swift Ave., Ste. 48, S San Fran, CA 94080-6220. TEL 415-282-2994; **Dist. outside China by:** China International Book Trading Corp, 35 Chegongzhuang Xilu, Haidian District, PO Box 399, Beijing 100044, China. TEL 86-10-68412045, FAX 86-10-68412023, cibtc@mail.cibtc.com.cn, http://www.cibtc.com.cn.

370 CHN ISSN 0254-8682
JIAOYU ZHANWANG/EDUCATIONAL PROSPECTS. Text in Chinese. 1984. q.
Published by: Zhongguo Duiwai Fanyi Chuban Gongsi, 4 Taipingqiao Dajie, Beijing, 100810, China. TEL 662134. Ed. Mei Zupei.

371.042 CHN
JIATING JIAOYU DAOBAO. Text in Chinese. w. CNY 36 (effective 2004). 96 p./no.; **Document type:** *Magazine, Consumer.* **Description:** Covers home education theories and methods.
Published by: Zhejiang Ribao Baoye Jituan/Zhejiang Daily Newspaper Group, 178, Tiyuchang Lu, Hangzhou, Zhejiang 310039, China. TEL 86-571-85311124, FAX 86-571-85195207, http://www.zjdaily.com.cn/jtjydb/. **Dist. by:** China International Book Trading Corp, 35 Chegongzhuang Xilu, Haidian District, PO Box 399, Beijing 100044, China. TEL 86-10-68412045, FAX 86-10-68412023, cibtc@mail.cibtc.com.cn, http://www.cibtc.com.cn.

370.19312 CHN ISSN 1009-7481
JIATING JIAOYU DAODU/GUIDE TO FAMILY EDUCATION. Text in Chinese. 1978. m. CNY 54 (effective 2004). **Document type:** *Journal, Academic/Scholarly.*
Formerly: Jiating Jiaoyu (1001-3091)
Published by: Zhongguo Renmin Daxue, Shubao Zilio Zhongxin/Renmin University of China, Information Center for Social Server, Dongcheng-qu, 3, Zhangzizhong Lu, Beijing, 100007, China. TEL 86-10-84043003, FAX 86-10-64015080, http://www.confucius.cn.net/bkdetail.asp?fzt=V2. **Dist. by:** China International Book Trading Corp, 35 Chegongzhuang Xilu, Haidian District, PO Box 399, Beijing 100044, China. TEL 86-10-68412045, FAX 86-10-68412023, cibtc@mail.cibtc.com.cn, http://www.cibtc.com.cn.

370 JPN ISSN 0912-9111
JISSEN KYOIKU/PRACTICAL TECHNOLOGY EDUCATION. Text in Japanese. 1986. 3/yr.
Published by: Jissen Kyoiku Kikaikei Kenkyukai/Society for the Practical Technology Education, Tokyo Shokugyo Kunren Tanki Daigakko, 32-1 Ogawa-Nishi-Machi 2-chome, Kodaira-shi, Tokyo-to 187-0035, Japan.

THE JOB SEARCH HANDBOOK FOR EDUCATORS. see *BUSINESS AND ECONOMICS—Labor And Industrial Relations*

371.383 371.42 USA
JOBS CLEARINGHOUSE ONLINE. Text in English. s-w. free (effective 2003). adv. **Document type:** *Bulletin.* **Description:** Lists jobs and internships available nationwide and abroad in the experiential and outdoor education fields.
Media: Online - full text.
Published by: Association for Experiential Education, 3775 Iris Ave, Ste 4, Boulder, CO 80301-2043. TEL 303-440-8844, FAX 303-440-9581, http://www.aee.org/memberpages/jchview.php.

JOHANN WILHELM KLEIN; literarische Zeitschrift fuer Blinde. see *HANDICAPPED—Visually Impaired*

370 GBR ISSN 1740-2743
LC71
▼ ➤ **JOURNAL FOR CRITICAL EDUCATION POLICY STUDIES.** Text in English. 2003. irreg. free (effective 2005). **Document type:** *Journal, Academic/Scholarly.*
Media: Online - full text.
Published by: Institute for Education Policy Studies, c/o Dave Hill (IEPS), University College Northampton, Boughton Green Rd, Northampton, NN2 7AL, United Kingdom. dave.hill@northampton.ac.uk, http://www.jceps.com, http://www.ieps.org.uk.

371.4 USA ISSN 1080-6385
BF637.C6
➤ **JOURNAL FOR THE PROFESSIONAL COUNSELOR.** Text in English. 198?. s-a. USD 30 (effective 2005). adv. bk.rev. **Document type:** *Journal, Academic/Scholarly.* **Description:** Publishes research articles advancing the study and development of the counseling profession.
Indexed: CIJE.
—CCC.
Published by: New York Counseling Association, PO Box 12636, Albany, NY 12212-2636. TEL 877-692-2462, FAX 518-235-0910, nycaoffice@nycounseling.org, http://www.nycounseling.org. Ed., R&P Eugene Goldin. Adv. contact Joella Rand.

370.113 USA ISSN 0195-7597
➤ **JOURNAL FOR VOCATIONAL SPECIAL NEEDS EDUCATION.** Text in English. 1978. 3/yr. USD 48 domestic to non-members; USD 60 foreign to non-members; USD 16 per issue domestic; USD 20 per issue foreign; free to members (effective 2004). adv. bk.rev. charts; stat.; illus. back issues avail.; reprints avail. **Document type:** *Journal, Academic/Scholarly.*
Related titles: Microform ed.: 1978 (from PQC).
Indexed: CIJE, CPE, ERA, ETA, MEA, SENA, TEA.
—BLDSC (5072.512500), IE, ingenta.
Address: c/o John Gugerty, Ed., Center for Education and Work, Univ of Wisconsin, 1025 W Johnson St, Madison, WI 53706-1796. TEL 608-262-3050, FAX 608-263-2724, JohnC.Hodge@ky.gov, jgugerty@education.wisc.edu, http://www.cew.wisc.edu/jvsne/. Ed. Kelli Crane TEL 301-424-2002 ext 233. Adv. contact John C Hodge TEL 859-234-5286. Circ: 2,000 (paid).

➤ **JOURNAL FUER MATHEMATIK-DIDAKTIK**; Zeitschrift der Gesellschaft fuer Didaktik der Mathematik. see *MATHEMATICS*

370 USA ISSN 1534-6536
THE JOURNAL OF ACCELERATED LEARNING AND TEACHING. Variant title: J A L T. Text in English. 1996. q.
Published by: International Alliance for Learning, PO Box 374, Lawrenceville, GA 30043-7638. TEL 678-518-4034, 800-426-2989, FAX 770-277-3649, http://www.ialearn.org/jalt/. Ed. Lylle Palmer.

JOURNAL OF ADULT THEOLOGICAL EDUCATION. see *RELIGIONS AND THEOLOGY*

JOURNAL OF ADVENTURE EDUCATION AND OUTDOOR LEARNING. see *SPORTS AND GAMES—Outdoor Life*

370 100 USA ISSN 0021-8510
N1 CODEN: JAEDBT
➤ **JOURNAL OF AESTHETIC EDUCATION.** Text in English. 1966. q. USD 40 domestic to individuals; USD 50 foreign to individuals; USD 75 domestic to institutions; USD 85 foreign to institutions (effective 2005). adv. bk.rev. charts; illus. Index. 128 p./no.; back issues avail.; reprint service avail. from PQC. **Document type:** *Journal, Academic/Scholarly.* **Description:** Focuses on how to impart to the young the understanding, skills, and attitudes prerequisite for the aesthetic mode of experience and for knowledgeable cultural participation. For educators, philosophers of art, and educational administrators and policymakers.
Related titles: Microform ed.: (from MIM, PQC); Online - full text ed.: ISSN 1543-7809 (from Northern Light Technology, Inc., O C L C Online Computer Library Center, Inc., Project MUSE, ProQuest Information & Learning, Swets Information Services).
Indexed: ABIn, ABM, ASCA, ArtHuCI, ArtInd, BAS, BEL&L, BHA, BRI, CBRI, CIJE, CPE, CurCont, DIP, ETA, EduInd, FLI, IBR, IBRH, IBZ, MAG, PCI, PhilInd, PsycholAb, RASB, RILM, SSCI.
—BLDSC (4919.984000), IDS, IE, Infotrieve, ingenta. **CCC.**
Published by: University of Illinois Press, 1325 S Oak St, Champaign, IL 61820-6903. TEL 866-244-0626, FAX 217-244-9910, alowry@uiuc.edu, journals@uillinois.edu, http://www.press.uillinois.edu/journals/jae.html. Ed. Pradeep A. Dhillon. R&P Heather Munson TEL 217-244-6488. Adv. contact Clydette Wantland TEL 217-244-6496. B&W page USD 275. Circ: 900 (paid).

630.7 USA ISSN 1042-0541
➤ **JOURNAL OF AGRICULTURAL EDUCATION.** Text in English. 1959. 4/yr. free to members; USD 120 domestic to non-members; USD 150 foreign to non-members (effective 2005). adv. back issues avail. **Document type:** *Journal, Academic/Scholarly.* **Description:** Covers current trends and issues, descriptions and, or analyses of innovations, evaluations, philosophical concerns, and research in agricultural education.
Formerly: American Association of Teacher Educators in Agriculture. Journal (0002-7480)
Indexed: Agr, BibAg, CIJE.
—BLDSC (4920.870000), CISTI, IE, ingenta.
Published by: American Association for Agricultural Education, c/o Blannie E. Bowen, 323 Agricultural Administration Bldg, Pennsylvania State University, University Park, PA 16802. TEL 814-865-1688, http://pubs.aged.tamu.edu/jae/, http://aaaeonline.org/. Ed., R&P Blannie E. Bowen. Adv. contact Wade Miller TEL 515-294-0895. Circ: 500 (paid).

➤ **JOURNAL OF AMERICAN INDIAN EDUCATION.** see *NATIVE AMERICAN STUDIES*

➤ **JOURNAL OF APPLIED DEVELOPMENTAL PSYCHOLOGY.** see *PSYCHOLOGY*

➤ **JOURNAL OF ASYNCHRONOUS LEARNING NETWORKS.** see *COMPUTERS—Computer Networks*

370 LTU ISSN 1648-3898
JOURNAL OF BALTIC SCIENCE EDUCATION. Text in English. 2002. s-a. back issues avail. **Document type:** *Journal, Academic/Scholarly.* **Description:** Emphasizes on theoretical, experimental and methodical studies in the field of science education.
Related titles: Online - full text ed.: (from EBSCO Publishing).
Indexed: BrEdI.
Published by: Scientific Methodical Center "Scientia Educologica", Pagegiu str 43-1, Shiauliai, LT-5410, Lithuania. TEL 370-687-95668, http://vingis.ktu.lt/~jbse/journal.htm. Ed. Vicentas Lamanauskas.

370.153 USA ISSN 1053-0819
LB1060.2 CODEN: JBEDE5
➤ **JOURNAL OF BEHAVIORAL EDUCATION.** Text in English. 1991. q. EUR 347, USD 347, GBP 223 combined subscription to institutions print & online eds. (effective 2005). adv. reprint service avail. from PSC. **Document type:** *Journal, Academic/Scholarly.* **Description:** Serves as a forum for research on the application of behavioral principles and technology to education.
Related titles: Online - full text ed.: ISSN 1573-3513 (from EBSCO Publishing, Gale Group, IngentaConnect, Kluwer Online, O C L C Online Computer Library Center, Inc., Springer LINK, Swets Information Services).
Indexed: ABIn, BibLing, CPE, ERA, ETA, EduInd, FamI, IBSS, MEA, PsySc BA&T, PsycInfo, PsycholAb, RHEA, SEA, SENA, SOMA, TEA, e-psyche.
—BLDSC (4951.260000), IE, Infotrieve, ingenta. **CCC.**
Published by: Plenum US (Subsidiary of: Springer Science+Business Media), 233 Spring St, New York, NY 10013. TEL 212-460-1500, FAX 212-460-1575, service@springer-ny.com, http://springerlink.metapress.com/openurl.asp?genre=journal&issn=1053-0819, http://www.springeronline.com. Eds. Christopher H Skinner, Phillip J Belfiore.

371.07 GBR ISSN 1361-7672
JOURNAL OF BELIEFS AND VALUES. Text in English. 1980. 3/yr. GBP 276, USD 509 combined subscription to institutions print & online eds. (effective 2006). adv. bk.rev. reprint service avail. from PSC. **Document type:** *Journal, Academic/Scholarly.* **Description:** Aimed at teachers of religious education and religious studies in higher and continuing education.
Related titles: Online - full text ed.: ISSN 1469-9362. GBP 262, USD 484 to institutions (effective 2006) (from EBSCO Publishing, Gale Group, IngentaConnect, O C L C Online Computer Library Center, Inc., Swets Information Services).
Indexed: BrEdI, CPE, ERA, ETA, MEA, R&TA, RHEA, SEA, SENA, SOMA, SWA, TEA.
—IE, Infotrieve. **CCC.**
Published by: (University of Wales, Department of Theology & Religious Studies USA), Routledge (Subsidiary of: Taylor & Francis Group), 4 Park Sq, Milton Park, Abingdon, Oxon OX14 4RN, United Kingdom. TEL 44-1235-828600, FAX 44-1235-829000, info@routledge.co.uk, http://www.tandf.co.uk/journals/titles/13617672.asp, http://www.routledge.co.uk. Ed. Dr. William S. Campbell. **Subscr. to:** Taylor & Francis Ltd, Journals Customer Service, Rankine Rd, Basingstoke, Hants RG24 8PR, United Kingdom. TEL 44-1256-813000, FAX 44-1256-330245.

JOURNAL OF BIOLOGICAL EDUCATION. see *BIOLOGY*

370 USA ISSN 1548-3185
THE JOURNAL OF BORDER EDUCATIONAL RESEARCH. Text in English. 2002. a.
Published by: Texas A & M International University, College of Education, 5201 University Blvd., Laredo, TX 78041. http://www.tamiu.edu/coedu/index.htm. Ed. Carolyn McCreight.

JOURNAL OF BROADCASTING AND ELECTRONIC MEDIA. see *COMMUNICATIONS—Television And Cable*

JOURNAL OF CHEMICAL EDUCATION. see *CHEMISTRY*

JOURNAL OF CHEMICAL EDUCATION: SOFTWARE. SERIES C; for Apple Macintosh computers. see *CHEMISTRY—Computer Applications*

JOURNAL OF CHEMICAL EDUCATION: SOFTWARE. SERIES D; for windows. see *CHEMISTRY—Computer Applications*

JOURNAL OF CHEMICAL EDUCATION: SOFTWARE. SPECIAL ISSUE SERIES. see *CHEMISTRY—Computer Applications*

THE JOURNAL OF CHIROPRACTIC EDUCATION. see *MEDICAL SCIENCES—Chiropractic, Homeopathy, Osteopathy*

JOURNAL OF CHRISTIAN EDUCATION. see *RELIGIONS AND THEOLOGY—Protestant*

JOURNAL OF CHRISTIAN EDUCATION. see *RELIGIONS AND THEOLOGY*

371.1 USA ISSN 0749-4025
LB1034
➤ **JOURNAL OF CLASSROOM INTERACTION.** Text in English. 1965. s-a. USD 40 in North America to individuals; USD 43 elsewhere to individuals; USD 45 in North America to institutions; USD 48 elsewhere to institutions; USD 67 combined subscription in North America for print & online; USD 76 combined subscription elsewhere for print & online (effective 2005). bk.rev. abstr.; bibl.; charts; stat.; illus. Index. 40 p./no. 2 cols./p.; Supplement avail.; back issues avail.; reprint service avail. from PQC. **Document type:** *Journal, Academic/Scholarly.* **Description:** Covers the empirical investigations and theoretical papers dealing with observation techniques, research on student and teacher behavior, and other issues relevant to the domain of classroom interaction.
Formerly: Classroom Interaction Newsletter (0009-8485)
Related titles: Microform ed.: (from PQC); Online - full text ed.: 2000 (Spring) (from H.W. Wilson, O C L C Online Computer Library Center, Inc., ProQuest Information & Learning).
Indexed: ABIn, CIJE, CPE, ERA, ETA, EduInd, MEA, PsycInfo, PsycholAb, SEA, e-psyche.
—BLDSC (4958.369700), IE, Infotrieve, ingenta.
Address: c/o Dr H Jerome Freiberg, Ed, College of Education, University of Houston, Farish Hall, Rm 452, Houston, TX 77204-5872. TEL 713-743-5919, FAX 713-743-8664, jci@uh.edu, http://pdts.uh.edu/~freiberg/, http://www.coe.uh.edu/. R&P Dr. H Jerome Freiberg. Circ: 1,000 (paid and controlled).

370 USA ISSN 1522-7529
➤ **JOURNAL OF CLINICAL PROBLEM-BASED LEARNING.** Text in English. q. **Document type:** *Journal, Academic/Scholarly.* **Description:** Devoted to further the development and application of problem-based learning in the health sciences, and publishes original case materials, descriptive reports, scholarly research, editorials, and letters concerning problem-based learning in the health sciences.
Media: Online - full content.
Published by: University of Mississippi, School of Pharmacy, Dept of Clinical Pharmacy Practice, 2500 N State Street, Jackson, MS 39216-4505. http://www.jclinpbl.org/high/index.htm. Ed. David S Ziska.

370 USA ISSN 1549-6953
LB1060
▼ ➤ **JOURNAL OF COGNITIVE AFFECTIVE LEARNING.** Abbreviated title: J C A L. Text in English. 2004 (Fall). q. free (effective 2004). **Document type:** *Journal, Academic/Scholarly.*
Media: Online - full content.
Published by: Emory University, Oxford College, 100 Hamill St, Oxford, GA 30054. TEL 770-784-8888, http://www.jcal.emory.edu, http://www.emory.edu/OXFORD. Ed. Ken Carter.

370.152 GBR ISSN 1360-6352
JOURNAL OF COGNITIVE EDUCATION. Text in English. 1990. 3/yr. GBP 30 domestic to individuals; GBP 32 in Europe to individuals; GBP 34 elsewhere to individuals; GBP 60 domestic to institutions; GBP 64 in Europe to institutions; GBP 68 elsewhere to institutions (effective 2000). **Document type:** *Academic/Scholarly.* **Description:** Disseminates theory, research and methodology, policies, and practices relating to cognitive education, taken in the broadest sense.
Formerly: International Journal of Cognitive Education and Mediated Learning (0957-4964)
Related titles: Online - full text ed.
Indexed: CPE, ECER, PsycInfo, SWR&A, e-psyche.
—**CCC.**
Published by: Questions Publishing Company Ltd., 1st Fl, Leonard House, 321 Bradford St, Digbeth, Birmingham, Warks B1 3ET, United Kingdom. TEL 44-121-6667878, FAX 44-121-6667879, rchima@qiis.co.uk, http://www.education-quest.com, http://www.education-quest.com/. Ed. Adrian Ashman. Circ: 350.

370 418.4 USA ISSN 1539-4220
LB1050.455
➤ **JOURNAL OF CONTENT AREA READING.** Text in English. 2002. a. bibl.; charts; stat. 100 p./no.; back issues avail. **Document type:** *Journal, Academic/Scholarly.*
Published by: International Reading Association, Special Interest Group: Content Area Reading, 1533 Blackhall Ln., SE, Decatur, AL 35601. TEL 256-824-2338, FAX 256-351-9818, http://www.content-reading.org. Ed. Mary W. Spor.

616 370 USA ISSN 1522-8606
JOURNAL OF CONTINUING EDUCATION TOPICS & ISSUES. Text in English. 1940. 3/yr. USD 50 domestic; USD 60 foreign (effective 2004); includes subscr. to AMT Events. **Document type:** *Journal, Academic/Scholarly.*
Supersedes in part (in 1999): A M T Events (0746-9217); Which superseded in part (in 1984): Journal of the American Medical Technologists (0002-9963); Which was formerly (until 1966): Official Journal of the American Medical Technologists (0092-6485); (until 1959): Journal of the American Medical Technologists (0360-0645)
Indexed: CINAHL.
—CISTI.
Published by: American Medical Technologists, 710 Higgins Rd, Park Ridge, IL 60068-5765. TEL 847-939-3365, 800-275-1268, FAX 847-823-0458, mail@amt1.com, http://www.amt1.com. Eds. Diane Powell TEL 847-823-5169 ext. 215, Dr. Gerard P Boe. Circ: 25,000 (paid).

370 USA
LB1029.C6
JOURNAL OF COOPERATIVE EDUCATION AND INTERSHIPS. Text in English. 1964. 3/yr. USD 50 (effective 2005). stat. reprint service avail. from PQC.
Formerly: Journal of Cooperative Education (0022-0132)
Related titles: Microform ed.: (from PQC); Online - full text ed.: (from ProQuest Information & Learning).
Indexed: ABIn, CIJE, CPE, EduInd, PersLit.
—BLDSC (4965.280000), IE, ingenta.
Published by: Cooperative Education and Internship Association, Inc., 16 Santa Ana Place, Walnut Creek, CA 94598. TEL 925-947-5581, FAX 925-906-0922, jleim@aol.com, http://www.ceiainc.org/journal/. Ed. Patricia Rowe. Circ: 3,000 (controlled).

JOURNAL OF CORRECTIONAL EDUCATION. see *CRIMINOLOGY AND LAW ENFORCEMENT*

150 370 USA ISSN 0022-0175
BF408
➤ **THE JOURNAL OF CREATIVE BEHAVIOR.** Text in English. 1967. q. USD 75 to individuals; USD 85 elsewhere to individuals; USD 105 to institutions; USD 120 elsewhere to institutions (effective 2005). adv. bk.rev. bibl.; charts; illus.; stat. index. reprint service avail. from PQC. **Document type:** *Academic/Scholarly.*
Related titles: Microform ed.: (from PQC).
Indexed: ABIn, ABS&EES, AMHA, ASCA, CIJE, CPE, CommAb, CurCont, ECER, ERA, ETA, EduInd, MEA, PersLit, PsycInfo, PsycholAb, RASB, RHEA, RILM, RefZh, SEA, SENA, SOMA, SOPODA, SSCI, SSI, SWR&A, TEA, e-psyche.
—BLDSC (4965.500000), IDS, IE, Infotrieve, ingenta, Linda Hall.
Published by: Creative Education Foundation, Inc., 289 Bay Rd, Hadley, MA 01035. TEL 413-559-6614, FAX 800-447-2774, cefhq@cef-cpsi.org, contact@cef-cpsi.org, http://www.creativeeducationfoundation.org/jcb.shtml, http://www.cef-cpsi.org. Ed. Thomas B Ward. R&P Grace Guzzutta. Circ: 2,000.

➤ **JOURNAL OF CRITICAL PEDAGOGY.** see *SOCIOLOGY*

➤ **JOURNAL OF CULTURAL RESEARCH IN ART EDUCATION.** see *ART*

▼ ➤ **JOURNAL OF CULTURE AND ITS TRANSMISSION IN THE AFRICAN WORLD.** see *ANTHROPOLOGY*

➤ **JOURNAL OF DRUG EDUCATION.** see *DRUG ABUSE AND ALCOHOLISM*

372.21 USA
➤ **JOURNAL OF EARLY CHILDHOOD EDUCATION AND FAMILY REVIEW.** Text in English. 1993. q. (5/yr until Sep. 2003). USD 129 domestic to individuals; USD 149 foreign to individuals; USD 195 domestic to institutions; USD 215 foreign to institutions; USD 370 for 2 yrs. domestic to institutions; USD 390 for 2 yrs. foreign to institutions (effective 2004). 40 p./no. 2 cols./p.; back issues avail. **Document type:** *Journal, Academic/Scholarly.* **Description:** Provides a medium for the discussion of major issues, ideas, scholarship and practice trends in the early childhood education profession. It also debates and analyzes public policy and economic issues impacting children and families. Seeks to help low and moderate income children reach their fullest potential.
Former titles (until May 2004: The Journal of Early Education and Family Review (1084-6603); (until 1993): The Journal of Early Education (1083-8902)
Related titles: Fax ed.
Indexed: FamI.
—BLDSC (4970.700000), IE, ingenta.
Published by: Oxford Publishing Company, 110 Oxford Ln, Ste 200, Charles Town, WV 25414. TEL 304-728-0418, 888-327-5933, FAX 304-728-6610. Ed. Denise Lindjord. Circ: 4,000 (paid).

372.4 649 GBR ISSN 1468-7984
LB1139.5.L35
➤ **JOURNAL OF EARLY CHILDHOOD LITERACY.** Text in English. 2001 (Apr.). 3/yr. GBP 250, USD 437 to institutions; GBP 260, USD 455 combined subscription to institutions print & online eds. (effective 2006). **Document type:** *Journal, Academic/Scholarly.* **Description:** Serves as a research publication forum for studies within the field of early childhood literacy, publishing relevant contributions in English from researchers in all countries and in all disciplines. There is particular interest in papers which provide cross-disciplinary perspectives on early childhood literacy.
Related titles: Online - full text ed.: ISSN 1741-2919. 2001. GBP 247, USD 433 to institutions (effective 2006) (from C S A, EBSCO Publishing, O C L C Online Computer Library Center, Inc., Sage Publications, Inc., Swets Information Services).
Indexed: BrEdI, EAA, ERA, FamI, PsycInfo, PsycholAb, e-psyche.
—BLDSC (4970.701500), IE. **CCC.**

E

Published by: Sage Publications Ltd. (Subsidiary of: Sage Publications, Inc.), 1 Oliver's Yard, 55 City Rd, London, EC1 1SP, United Kingdom. TEL 44-20-73248500, FAX 44-20-73248600, info@sagepub.co.uk, http://www.sagepub.co.uk/journal.aspx?pid=105634. Eds. Ann Browne, Anne Haas Haas Dyson, Nigel Hall. **Subscr. in the Americas to:** Sage Publications, Inc., 2455 Teller Rd, Thousand Oaks, CA 91320. TEL 805-499-0721, FAX 805-499-0871, journals@sagepub.com.

▼ ➤ **JOURNAL OF EARLY CHILDHOOD RESEARCH.** see *MEDICAL SCIENCES—Pediatrics*

➤ **JOURNAL OF EARLY CHILDHOOD TEACHER EDUCATION.** see *EDUCATION—Higher Education*

370 CAN ISSN 0022-0566
JOURNAL OF EDUCATION. Text in English. 1866. irreg. **Document type:** *Academic/Scholarly.*
—CCC.
Published by: Nova Scotia Department of Education, Nova Scotia Provincial Library, 3770 Kempt Rd, Halifax, NS B3K 4X8, Canada. TEL 902-424-2478, FAX 902-424-0633, webstegs@gov.ns.ca, http://www.library.ns.ca.

370 USA ISSN 0022-0574
CODEN: JEBUA
JOURNAL OF EDUCATION. Text in English. 1875. 3/yr. USD 35 domestic to individuals; USD 49 in Canada & Mexico to individuals; USD 52 elsewhere to individuals; USD 38 domestic to institutions; USD 53 in Canada & Mexico to institutions; USD 56 elsewhere to institutions; USD 15 newsstand/cover domestic (effective 2001); USD 19 newsstand/cover in Canada & Mexico; USD 21 newsstand/cover elsewhere. adv. bk.rev. charts; illus. back issues avail.; reprint service avail. from PQC. **Document type:** *Academic/Scholarly.*
Related titles: Microform ed.: (from PQC); (from PQC); Online - full text ed.: (from EBSCO Publishing).
Indexed: ABIn, Acal, BRI, CBRI, CIJE, CPE, CommAb, EAA, ERA, ETA, EduInd, L&LBA, MEA, MEA&I, PAIS, PsycholAb, SEA, SENA, SOPODA, SRRA, SWA.
—BLDSC (4973.100000), IE, Infotrieve, ingenta.
Published by: Boston University, School of Education, 605 Commonwealth Ave, Boston, MA 02215. TEL 617-353-3230, FAX 617-353-3924, bjued@bu.edu, http://www.bu.edu/education/news/jedindex.html. Ed. Joan Dee. R&P Melissa Doyle. Circ: 2,000.

370 150 IND ISSN 0022-0590
L61
➤ **JOURNAL OF EDUCATION AND PSYCHOLOGY.** Text in English. 1943. q. looseleaf. adv. bk.rev. index. back issues avail. **Document type:** *Journal, Academic/Scholarly.*
Indexed: BAS, CurCont, e-psyche.
Published by: Sardar Patel University, Department of Education, Vallabh Vidyanagar, Gujarat 388 120, India. TEL 91-2792-30379. Ed. Pallavi P Patel. Circ: 300 (paid).

➤ **JOURNAL OF EDUCATION AND SOCIAL CHANGE.** see *SOCIOLOGY*

371.195 GBR ISSN 0260-7476
LB1725.G6 CODEN: JETEF3
➤ **JOURNAL OF EDUCATION FOR TEACHING;** international research and pedagogy. Abbreviated title: J E T. Text in English. 1975. q. GBP 615, USD 1,086 combined subscription to institutions print & online eds. (effective 2006). adv. bk.rev. index. back issues avail.; reprint service avail. from PSC. **Document type:** *Journal, Academic/Scholarly.*
Formerly (until 1980): British Journal of Teacher Education (0305-8913)
Related titles: Microfiche ed.; Online - full text ed.: ISSN 1360-0540. GBP 584, USD 1,032 to institutions (effective 2006) (from EBSCO Publishing, Gale Group, IngentaConnect, Northern Light Technology, Inc., O C L C Online Computer Library Center, Inc., ProQuest Information & Learning, Swets Information Services).
Indexed: ABIn, ASCA, BrEdI, CIJE, CPE, CurCont, ERA, ETA, EduInd, HEA, HECAB, L&LBA, LT&LA, MEA, PCI, RHEA, SEA, SENA, SOMA, SOPODA, SSCI, SWA, TEA, WBA, WMB.
—BLDSC (4973.152500), IDS, IE, Infotrieve, ingenta. **CCC.**
Published by: Routledge (Subsidiary of: Taylor & Francis Group), 4 Park Sq, Milton Park, Abingdon, Oxon OX14 4RN, United Kingdom. TEL 44-1235-828600, FAX 44-1235-829000, info@routledge.co.uk, http://www.tandf.co.uk/journals/titles/02607476.asp, http://www.routledge.co.uk. Eds. Edgar Stones, Peter Gilroy. **Subscr. to:** Taylor & Francis Ltd, Journals Customer Service, Rankine Rd, Basingstoke, Hants RG24 8PR, United Kingdom. TEL 44-1256-813000, FAX 44-1256-330245.

370 USA ISSN 1531-4278
QA76.27
➤ **JOURNAL OF EDUCATION RESOURCES IN COMPUTING.** Abbreviated title: J E R I C. Text in English. 6/yr. USD 150 to non-members; USD 39 to members; USD 34 to students (effective 2006). back issues avail. **Document type:** *Journal, Academic/Scholarly.* **Description:** Provides access to high quality, archival resources suitable for use in support for computing education.
Media: Online - full content.
Indexed: CompR.
—CCC.
Published by: Association for Computing Machinery, Inc., 1515 Broadway, 17th Fl, New York, NY 10036-5701. TEL 212-626-0500, 212-626-0520, 800-342-6626, FAX 212-869-0481, sigs@acm.org, usacm@acm.org, http://www.acm.org/pubs/jeric/. Eds. Edward A Fox TEL 540-231-5113, Lillian Cassel TEL 610-519-7341.

➤ **JOURNAL OF EDUCATIONAL AND BEHAVIORAL STATISTICS.** see *EDUCATION—Abstracting, Bibliographies, Statistics*

370.15 USA ISSN 1047-4412
LB2799 CODEN: JEPCFB
➤ **JOURNAL OF EDUCATIONAL AND PSYCHOLOGICAL CONSULTATION.** Text in English. 1990. q. USD 450 in US & Canada to institutions; USD 480 elsewhere to institutions; USD 475 combined subscription in US & Canada to institutions print & online eds.; USD 505 combined subscription elsewhere to institutions print & online eds. (effective 2006). adv. bk.rev. back issues avail.; reprint service avail. from PSC. **Document type:** *Journal, Academic/Scholarly.* **Description:** Serves as a forum for the exchange of ideas, theories, and research among the fields of school psychology, special education, and reading.
Related titles: Online - full text ed.: ISSN 1532-768X. USD 430 worldwide to institutions (effective 2006) (from EBSCO Publishing, Gale Group, O C L C Online Computer Library Center, Inc., Swets Information Services).
Indexed: ASCA, CIJE, CPE, CurCont, ECER, ERA, ETA, Faml, IMFL, L&LBA, MEA, PsycInfo, PsycholAb, RHEA, SEA, SENA, SOMA, SOPODA, SSCI, TEA, e-psyche.
—BLDSC (4973.154050), IE, Infotrieve, ingenta. **CCC.**
Published by: (Association for Educational and Psychological Consultants), Lawrence Erlbaum Associates, Inc., 10 Industrial Ave, Mahwah, NJ 07430-2262. TEL 201-258-2200, 800-926-6579, FAX 201-236-0072, journals@erlbaum.com, http://www.leaonline.com/loi/jepc. Ed. Emilia Lopez. adv.: page USD 400; trim 5 x 8.

370.72 NLD ISSN 1389-2843
LB1027
➤ **JOURNAL OF EDUCATIONAL CHANGE.** Text in English. 2000. q. EUR 307, USD 307, GBP 192 combined subscription to institutions print & online eds. (effective 2005). adv. back issues avail.; reprint service avail. from PSC. **Document type:** *Journal, Academic/Scholarly.* **Description:** Deals with issues like educational innovation, reform and restructuring, school improvement and effectiveness, culture-building, inspection, school-review, and change management.
Related titles: Online - full text ed.: ISSN 1573-1812 (from EBSCO Publishing, Gale Group, IngentaConnect, Kluwer Online, O C L C Online Computer Library Center, Inc., Springer LINK, Swets Information Services).
Indexed: BibLing, BrEdI, CPE, EAA.
—BLDSC (4973.154300), IE, Infotrieve, ingenta. **CCC.**
Published by: Springer-Verlag Dordrecht (Subsidiary of: Springer Science+Business Media), Van Godewijckstraat 30, Dordrecht, 3311 GX, Netherlands. TEL 31-78-6576050, FAX 31-78-6576474, http://springerlink.metapress.com/openurl.asp?genre=journal&issn=1389-2843, http://www.springeronline.com. Ed. Andy Hargreaves.

370 AUS ISSN 1444-5530
JOURNAL OF EDUCATIONAL ENQUIRY. Text in English. 2000. 3/yr. free (effective 2005). **Description:** Dedicated to publishing original contributions on all aspects of education with a particular emphasis on articles that are research based.
Media: Online - full text.
Published by: University of South Australia, Centre for Research in Education, Equity and Work, Holbrooks Rd, Underdale, SA 5032, Australia. TEL 61-8-83026246, FAX 61-8-83026832, http://www.education.unisa.edu.au/JEE/. Ed. Bruce Johnson.

371 USA ISSN 1077-0550
CODEN: VEPEEC
THE JOURNAL OF EDUCATIONAL ISSUES OF LANGUAGE MINORITY STUDENTS. Text in English. 3/yr.
Indexed: CIJE.
Published by: Boise State University, Bilingual Education Teacher Preaparation Program, Boise, ID 83725.

371.26 USA ISSN 0274-838X
LB1131.A1 CODEN: JEDMAA
➤ **JOURNAL OF EDUCATIONAL MEASUREMENT.** Short title: J E M. Text in English. 1964. q. USD 294 combined subscription in the Americas to institutions print & online eds.; GBP 203 elsewhere to institutions print & online eds. (effective 2006). adv. bk.rev. abstr.; illus. cum.index. reprint service avail. from PQC. **Document type:** *Journal, Academic/Scholarly.* **Description:** Publishes original measurement research and reports of applications of measurement in an educational context, and reviews of current standardized educational and psychological tests.
Formerly (until 1978): Journal of Educational Measurement (0022-0655); Supersedes: National Council on Measurement in Education. Yearbook
Related titles: Microform ed.: (from PQC); Online - full text ed.: ISSN 1745-3984. USD 279 in the Americas to institutions; GBP 171 elsewhere to institutions (effective 2006) (from Blackwell Synergy, EBSCO Publishing, IngentaConnect, O C L C Online Computer Library Center, Inc., ProQuest Information & Learning, Swets Information Services).
Indexed: ABIn, ASCA, CIJE, CIS, CPE, ChPerI, CurCont, DIP, EduInd, HEA, IBR, IBZ, PersLit, PsycInfo, PsycholAb, RASB, RHEA, SOPODA, SSCI, e-psyche.
—BLDSC (4973.157000), IDS, IE, Infotrieve, ingenta. **CCC.**
Published by: (National Council on Measurement in Education), Blackwell Publishing, Inc. (Subsidiary of: Blackwell Publishing Ltd.), Commerce Place, 350 Main St, Malden, MA 02148. TEL 781-388-8206, FAX 781-388-8232, subscrip@blackwellpub.com, http://www.blackwellpublishing.com/journal.asp?ref=0022-0655&site=1. Ed. Michael J Kolen. Circ: 3,500.

370.15 USA ISSN 0022-0663
➤ **JOURNAL OF EDUCATIONAL PSYCHOLOGY.** Text in English. 1910. q. USD 139 domestic to individuals; USD 157 foreign to individuals; USD 350 domestic to institutions; USD 385 foreign to institutions; USD 67 domestic to members; USD 80 foreign to members (effective 2005). adv. bibl.; charts; illus. index. reprint service avail. from PQC,PSC. **Document type:** *Journal, Academic/Scholarly.* **Description:** Deals with learning and cognition, psychological development, relationships, and adjustment of the individual, especially as related to the problems of instruction. Articles pertain to all levels of education and to all age groups.
Related titles: Microform ed.: (from PMC, PQC); Online - full text ed.: (from C S A, EBSCO Publishing, O C L C Online Computer Library Center, Inc., Ovid Technologies, Inc., ScienceDirect).
Indexed: ABIn, AMHA, ASCA, Acal, AgeL, ArtHuCI, BDM&CN, BiolAb, CIJE, CIS, CPE, CommAb, CurCont, DIP, EAA, ECER, ERA, ETA, EduInd, Faml, HEA, HECAB, IBR, IBZ, IndMed, L&LBA, LT&LA, MEA, MEA&I, MEDLINE, MLA-IB, PCI, PsySCDP, PsycInfo, PsycholAb, RASB, RHEA, SENA, SFSA, SOMA, SSA, SSCI, SWA, TEA, e-psyche.
—BLDSC (4973.200000), IDS, IE, Infotrieve, ingenta. **CCC.**
Published by: American Psychological Association, 12884 Harbor Dr., Woodbridge, VA 22192-2921. TEL 800-374-2721, journals@apa.org, http://www.apa.org/journals/edu.html. Ed. Karen R Harris. R&P Karen Thomas. Adv. contact Jodi Ashcraft TEL 202-336-5500. Circ: 6,000 (paid).

370 USA ISSN 0022-0671
L11 CODEN: JEDRAP
➤ **THE JOURNAL OF EDUCATIONAL RESEARCH.** Text in English. 1920. bi-m. USD 68 domestic to individuals; USD 84 foreign to individuals; USD 150 domestic to institutions; USD 166 foreign to institutions; USD 25 per issue (effective academic year 2005 - 2006). adv. bibl.; charts; illus. index. back issues avail.; reprint service avail. from PSC. **Document type:** *Journal, Academic/Scholarly.* **Description:** For teachers, counselors, supervisors, administrators, planners and educational researchers.
Related titles: CD-ROM ed.: (from ProQuest Information & Learning); Microform ed.: (from PMC); Online - full text ed.: (from Chadwyck-Healey Inc., EBSCO Publishing, Florida Center for Library Automation, Gale Group, H.W. Wilson, O C L C Online Computer Library Center, Inc., ProQuest Information & Learning).
Indexed: ABIn, ASCA, BAS, CDA, CIJE, CPE, CurCont, DIP, EAA, ECER, ERA, ETA, EduInd, Faml, GSS&RPL, HEA, HECAB, IBR, IBZ, Inspec, L&LBA, MEA, PCI, PsycInfo, PsycholAb, RASB, RHEA, SEA, SENA, SOMA, SOPODA, SRRA, SSCI, SWA, TEA, V&AA, e-psyche.
—BLDSC (4973.250000), AskIEEE, IDS, IE, Infotrieve, ingenta. **CCC.**
Published by: (Helen Dwight Reid Educational Foundation), Heldref Publications, 1319 18th St, NW, Washington, DC 20036-1802. TEL 202-296-6267, 800-365-9753, FAX 202-293-6130, jer@heldref.org, subscribe@heldref.org, http://www.heldref.org/jer.php. Adv. contact Chante Douglas. B&W page USD 355; trim 7 x 10. Circ: 1,877 (paid).

373 IND ISSN 0022-068X
JOURNAL OF EDUCATIONAL RESEARCH AND EXTENSION. Text in English. 1963. q. INR 100 to individuals; INR 200 to institutions (effective 2000). adv. bk.rev. bibl. index. back issues avail. **Document type:** *Academic/Scholarly.* **Description:** Covering primary, secondary and further education, it is for all education professionals.
Indexed: BAS, CPE.
—BLDSC (4973.250000).
Published by: Sri Ramakrishna Mission Vidyalaya College of Education, c/o The Principal, Sri Ramakrishna Vidyalaya P.O., Coimbatore, Tamil Nadu 641 020, India. TEL 91-422-892441, FAX 91-422-895066. Eds. M N G Mani, Swami Bhaktirupananda. Circ: 500.

THE JOURNAL OF ENVIRONMENTAL EDUCATION. see *ENVIRONMENTAL STUDIES*

E

378 USA ISSN 1077-5315

➤ **JOURNAL OF EXTENSION (ONLINE EDITION).** Text in English. 1963. bi-m. free (effective 2005). bk.rev. bibl. index, cum.index. reprint service avail. from PQC. **Document type:** *Journal, Academic/Scholarly.* **Description:** Covers successful educational applications, original and applied research findings, scholarly opinions, educational resources, and challenges on issues of critical importance to adult educators.
Former titles (until 1994): Journal of Extension (Print Edition) (0022-0140); (until 1970): Journal of Cooperative Extension (0449-2382).
Media: Online - full text.
Indexed: Agr, CIJE, CPE, CurCont, F&GI, FamI, RRTA, SWR&A, WAE&RSA.
—CISTI, Linda Hall.
Published by: (National Association of Land-Grant Colleges and State Universities), Extension Journal, Inc., c/o Virginia Tech, Blacksburg, VA 24061-0452. TEL 614-688-4729, joe-ed@joe.org, http://www.joe.org. Ed. Laura Hoelscher. Circ: 12,500. **Co-sponsor:** Extension Committee on Organization.

370.1 USA ISSN 1541-0889
LC192.6

▼ ➤ **JOURNAL OF GAY & LESBIAN ISSUES IN EDUCATION**; an international quarterly devoted to research, theory, and practice. Text in English. 2003. q. USD 250 combined subscription domestic to institutions print & online eds.; USD 337.50 combined subscription in Canada to institutions print & online eds.; USD 362.50 combined subscription elsewhere to institutions print & online eds. (effective academic year 2005 - 2006). adv. reprint service avail. from HAW. **Document type:** *Journal, Academic/Scholarly.* **Description:** Contains current information on what's happening in educational policy, curriculum development, professional practice, and pedagogy involving gay and lesbian studies.
Related titles: Online - full text ed.: ISSN 1541-0870. forthcoming; N.S. (from EBSCO Publishing, O C L C Online Computer Library Center, Inc., Swets Information Services).
Indexed: EAA, FamI, IBR, IBZ, PAIS, RefZh, SWA.
—Haworth, IE. **CCC.**
Published by: Haworth Press, Inc., 10 Alice St, Binghamton, NY 13904-1580. TEL 607-722-5857, 800-429-6784, FAX 607-722-1424, 800-895-0582, getinfo@haworthpress.com, http://www.haworthpress.com/web/JGLED. Ed. James T Sears. R&P Ruth Ann Heath TEL 607-722-5857 ext 316. Adv. contact Rebecca Miller-Baum TEL 607-722-5857 ext 337.

378 USA ISSN 0021-3667
L11

➤ **JOURNAL OF GENERAL EDUCATION.** Abbreviated title: J G E. Text in English. 1946. q. USD 30 to individuals; USD 60 to institutions; USD 84 to institutions print & online eds. (effective 2006). bk.rev. charts. Index. back issues avail.; reprint service avail. from PQC,PSC. **Document type:** *Journal, Academic/Scholarly.* **Description:** Addresses the general education concerns of community colleges, four-year colleges, universities, and state systems.
Related titles: Microform ed.: (from PQC); Online - full text ed.: ISSN 1527-2060. 2000. USD 60 to institutions (effective 2006) (from EBSCO Publishing, O C L C Online Computer Library Center, Inc., Project MUSE, Swets Information Services).
Indexed: ABIn, AES, AMHA, AmH&L, BRI, CBRI, CIJE, CPE, DIP, ECER, EduInd, HEA, HistAb, IBR, IBZ, MLA, MLA-IB, PCI, PhilInd, RI-1, RI-2, SOPODA, SSA.
—IE, Infotrieve. **CCC.**
Published by: Pennsylvania State University Press, 820 N University Dr, USB-1, Ste C, University Park, PA 16802-1003. TEL 814-865-1327, FAX 814-863-1408, JGENED@PSU.edu, info@psupress.org, http://www.psupress.org/journals/jnls_jge.html. Ed. Claire Major. Circ: 1,300 (paid). **Dist. by:** The Johns Hopkins University Press, Journals Publishing Division, PO Box 19966, Baltimore, MD 21211-0966. TEL 410-516-6987, FAX 410-516-6968.

➤ **JOURNAL OF GEOGRAPHY.** see *GEOGRAPHY*

➤ **THE JOURNAL OF HOLOCAUST EDUCATION.** see *HISTORY*

➤ **JOURNAL OF HOSPITALITY, LEISURE, SPORTS & TOURISM EDUCATION.** see *TRAVEL AND TOURISM*

➤ **JOURNAL OF HUMANISTIC COUNSELING, EDUCATION AND DEVELOPMENT.** see *PSYCHOLOGY*

370.954 IND ISSN 0377-0435
LA1150

JOURNAL OF INDIAN EDUCATION. Text in English. 1975. bi-m. INR 16, USD 17.
Supersedes: N I E Journal (0027-6634)
Indexed: CPE, ERA.
—BLDSC (5005.305000), IE, ingenta.
Published by: National Council of Educational Research and Training, Publication Department, Sri Aurbindo Marg, New Delhi, 110 016, India. TEL 662708. Ed. R P Singh. Circ: 1,200. **Dist. by:** International Publications Inc., 303 Park Ave S, New York, NY 10010.

371.195 745.2 604 USA ISSN 0022-1864
LB1736

➤ **JOURNAL OF INDUSTRIAL TEACHER EDUCATION.** Text in English. 1963. 4/yr. USD 55 in North America to libraries; USD 60 elsewhere to libraries (effective 2005). bk.rev. illus.; stat. index. reprint service avail. from PQC. **Document type:** *Journal, Academic/Scholarly.* **Description:** Reports scholarly inquiry and commentary broadly related to industrial and technical teacher education, military training, and industrial training.
Related titles: Microform ed.: (from PQC); Online - full text ed.: free (effective 2005) (from EBSCO Publishing, H.W. Wilson, O C L C Online Computer Library Center, Inc.).
Indexed: ABIn, CIJE, CPE, CurCont, ERA, EduInd, TEA.
—BLDSC (5006.400000), IE, ingenta.
Published by: National Association of Industrial and Technical Teacher Educators, c/o Caren Juneau, JITE, University of Southern Mississippi, Dept of Technology Educa, 118 College Dr # 5036, Hattiesburg, MS 39406-0001. TEL 601-266-5588, FAX 601-266-5957, gerogers@tech.purdue.edu, http://scholar.lib.vt.edu/ejournals/JITE/. Ed. George Rogers. Circ: 1,400.

370.15 USA ISSN 0094-1956
LB1051

➤ **JOURNAL OF INSTRUCTIONAL PSYCHOLOGY.** Text in English. 1974. q. USD 34 domestic to individuals; USD 44 foreign to individuals; USD 40 domestic to institutions; USD 50 foreign to institutions (effective 2005). bk.rev. back issues avail.; reprint service avail. from PQC. **Document type:** *Journal, Academic/Scholarly.*
Related titles: Microform ed.: (from PQC); Online - full text ed.: (from EBSCO Publishing, Florida Center for Library Automation, Gale Group, H.W. Wilson, O C L C Online Computer Library Center, Inc., ProQuest Information & Learning).
Indexed: ABIn, CIJE, CPE, ChPerI, ERA, ETA, EduInd, FamI, HEA, L&LBA, MEA, PsycInfo, PsycholAb, RHEA, RILM, RefZh, SEA, SENA, SOMA, SOPODA, SWA, TEA, e-psyche.
—BLDSC (5007.513000), IE, Infotrieve, ingenta. **CCC.**
Published by: Dr. George E. Uhlig, PO Box 8826, Spring Hill Sta, Mobile, AL 36689. Circ: 400 (paid).

➤ **JOURNAL OF INTERNATIONAL BUSINESS EDUCATION.** see *BUSINESS AND ECONOMICS—International Commerce*

370.15 USA ISSN 1060-6041
LB1025.3

➤ **JOURNAL OF INVITATIONAL THEORY AND PRACTICE.** Text in English. 1992. s-a. USD 35 to non-members; free to members (effective 2004). bk.rev. back issues avail. **Document type:** *Journal, Academic/Scholarly.* **Description:** Invitational theory and practice in schools and other organizations. Theory founded on self-concept and perceptual psychology.
Related titles: Online - full text ed.: (from EBSCO Publishing).
Indexed: CIJE, e-psyche.
—BLDSC (5008.055000), IE, ingenta.
Published by: International Alliance for Invitational Education, c/o Radford University Center for Invitational Education, College of Education and Human Development, Radford University, PO Box 7009, Radford, VA 24142. TEL 336-334-3431, FAX 336-334-3433, http://www.invitationaleducation.net/publications/journal/. Ed., R&P Phil Riner. Circ: 3,000.

296.68 USA ISSN 1524-4113
LC701

JOURNAL OF JEWISH EDUCATION. Text in English. 1929. 3/yr. USD 85 to individuals; USD 139 to institutions (effective 2006). adv. bk.rev. index, cum.index: 5 yrs. and 25 yrs. (vols.1-43). reprint service avail. from PQC. **Document type:** *Journal, Academic/Scholarly.*
Formerly (until 1994): Jewish Education (0021-6429)
Related titles: Microform ed.: (from PQC); Online - full text ed.: ISSN 1554-611X. GBP 81, USD 132 (effective 2006) (from H.W. Wilson, O C L C Online Computer Library Center, Inc.).
Indexed: ABIn, CPE, EduInd, IBZ, IJP, JewAb, MEA&I, PCI, PsycholAb, R&TA.
—Infotrieve. **CCC.**
Published by: (Council for Jewish Education), Taylor & Francis Inc. (Subsidiary of: Taylor & Francis Group), 325 Chestnut St, Ste 800, Philadelphia, PA 19106. TEL 215-625-8900, 800-354-1420, FAX 215-625-2940. Ed. Michael Zeldin. Circ: 1,500.

370 401 USA ISSN 1534-8458
P35

JOURNAL OF LANGUAGE, IDENTITY, AND EDUCATION. Text in English. 2002. q. USD 285 in US & Canada to institutions; USD 315 elsewhere to institutions; USD 300 in US & Canada to institutions print & online eds.; USD 330 elsewhere to institutions print & online eds. (effective 2006). adv. back issues avail. **Document type:** *Journal, Academic/Scholarly.* **Description:** Seeks out cutting edge interdisciplinary research from around the world, reflecting diverse theoretical and methodological frameworks and topical areas.
Related titles: Online - full content ed.: ISSN 1532-7701. 2002 (Mar.). USD 270 worldwide to institutions (effective 2006); Online - full text ed.: (from EBSCO Publishing, Gale Group, O C L C Online Computer Library Center, Inc., Swets Information Services).
Indexed: CommAb, PsycInfo, PsycholAb, SFSA.
—BLDSC (5010.097200), IE. **CCC.**
Published by: Lawrence Erlbaum Associates, Inc., 10 Industrial Ave, Mahwah, NJ 07430-2262. TEL 201-258-2200, 800-926-6579, FAX 201-236-0072, journals@erlbaum.com, http://www.leaonline.com/loi/jlie, http://www.erlbaum.com. Eds. Terrence G Wiley, Thomas Ricento. adv.: page USD 350; trim 5 x 8.

305.86 305.868 370.1 USA ISSN 1534-8431
LC2667

➤ **JOURNAL OF LATINOS AND EDUCATION.** Text in English. 2002 (Mar.). q. USD 260 in US & Canada to institutions; USD 290 elsewhere to institutions; USD 275 combined subscription in US & Canada to institutions print & online eds.; USD 305 combined subscription elsewhere to institutions print & online eds. (effective 2006). adv. back issues avail. **Document type:** *Journal, Academic/Scholarly.* **Description:** Provides a cross, multi and interdisciplinary forum for scholars and writers from diverse disciplines who share a common interest in the analysis, discussion, critique, and dissemination of educational issues that impact Latinos.
Related titles: Online - full text ed.: ISSN 1532-771X. 2002. USD 250 per issue worldwide to institutions (effective 2006) (from EBSCO Publishing, Gale Group, O C L C Online Computer Library Center, Inc., Swets Information Services).
Indexed: HAPI, PsycInfo, PsycholAb.
—BLDSC (5010.111000), IE. **CCC.**
Published by: Lawrence Erlbaum Associates, Inc., 10 Industrial Ave, Mahwah, NJ 07430-2262. TEL 201-258-2200, 800-926-6579, FAX 201-236-0072, journals@erlbaum.com, http://www.leaonline.com/loi/jle. Ed. Enrique Murillo. adv.: page USD 400; trim 5 x 8.

➤ **JOURNAL OF LAW AND EDUCATION.** see *LAW*

➤ **JOURNAL OF LEGAL STUDIES EDUCATION.** see *LAW*

370.72 USA ISSN 1086-296X
LB1050 CODEN: JLREF8

➤ **JOURNAL OF LITERACY RESEARCH.** Text in English. 1969. q. USD 100 in US & Canada to institutions; USD 130 elsewhere to institutions; USD 110 combined subscription in US & Canada to institutions print & online eds.; USD 140 combined subscription elsewhere to institutions print & online eds. (effective 2006). adv. bk.rev. index. reprint service avail. from PQC. **Document type:** *Journal, Academic/Scholarly.*
Formerly (until Mar. 1996): Journal of Reading Behavior (0022-4111)
Related titles: Microform ed.: (from PQC); Online - full text ed.: ISSN 1554-8430. USD 90 worldwide to institutions (effective 2006) (from ProQuest Information & Learning).
Indexed: ABIn, ASCA, ArtHuCI, CIJE, CPE, CommAb, CurCont, EAA, EduInd, FamI, PsycInfo, PsycholAb, SEA, SOPODA, SSCI, TEA, e-psyche.
—BLDSC (5010.512000), IE, Infotrieve, ingenta.
Published by: (National Reading Conference, Inc.), Lawrence Erlbaum Associates, Inc., 10 Industrial Ave, Mahwah, NJ 07430-2262. TEL 201-258-2200, 800-926-6579, FAX 201-236-0072, jlr@tamu-commerce.edu, journals@erlbaum.com, http://www.leaonline.com/loi/jlr, http://www.erlbaum.com. Eds. Elizabeth G Sturtevant, Nancy D Padak, Timothy V Rasinski, Wayne M Linek. Circ: 2,000.

370 MLT ISSN 1726-9725

▼ ➤ **JOURNAL OF MALTESE EDUCATION RESEARCH.** Text in English. 2003. s-a. free (effective 2005). **Document type:** *Journal, Academic/Scholarly.* **Description:** This journal provides established and emerging scholars and practitioners with a space for critical and empirical analysis of issues central to Maltese education policy, curriculum reform and pedagogy.
Media: Online - full text.
Published by: University of Malta, Faculty of Education, Msida, MSD 06, Malta. http://www.educ.um.edu.mt/jmer/.

373.246 USA ISSN 1056-2818
U405

JOURNAL OF MILITARY PREPARATORY SCHOOL EDUCATION. Text in English. 1988. a. cum.index. back issues avail. **Document type:** *Academic/Scholarly.* **Description:** Contains articles related to the professional activities associated with military preparatory school education at the secondary and postsecondary levels.
Published by: U.S.A.F. Academy Preparatory School, U S A F Academy, CO 80840. TEL 719-472-2580, FAX 719-472-3648. Ed. Capt John M Bell. Circ: 300 (paid).

JOURNAL OF MOTOR BEHAVIOR. see *PSYCHOLOGY*

JOURNAL OF MUSEUM EDUCATION. see *MUSEUMS AND ART GALLERIES*

JOURNAL OF MUSIC TEACHER EDUCATION (ONLINE EDITION). see *MUSIC*

E

370 301.451 USA ISSN 0022-2984 CODEN: JNEEAK
➤ **JOURNAL OF NEGRO EDUCATION**; a Howard University quarterly review of issues incident to the education of black people. Text in English. 1932. q. USD 55 domestic to individuals; USD 110 foreign to individuals; USD 95 domestic to institutions; USD 155 foreign to institutions (effective 2005). adv. bk.rev. illus. index, cum.index: 1963-1979; 1980-1989. back issues avail.; reprint service avail. from PQC,PSC. **Document type:** *Journal, Academic/Scholarly.* **Description:** Collects and disseminates information about the education of blacks and other minorities in the US.
Related titles: Microform ed.: (from MIM, PMC, PQC); Online - full text ed.: (from JSTOR (Web-based Journal Archive), Northern Light Technology, Inc., O C L C Online Computer Library Center, Inc., ProQuest Information & Learning).
Indexed: ABIn, ASCA, AgeL, AmH&L, BRI, CBRI, CIJE, CPE, ChPerI, CurCont, EAA, ECER, ERA, EduInd, FamI, HEA, HistAb, IBR, IIBP, IMFL, L&LBA, MEA, MagInd, PAIS, PCI, PhilInd, PsycInfo, PsycholAb, RILM, SEA, SFSA, SOPODA, SRRA, SSA, SSCI, SWR&A, SociolAb, e-psyche.
—BLDSC (5021.395000), IDS, IE, Infotrieve, ingenta.
Published by: (Howard University), Howard University Press, Marketing Department, 2600 Sixth St, N W, Washington, DC 20059. TEL 202-806-8120, FAX 202-806-8434, jne@howard.edu, http://www.journalnegroed.org/mainindex.html. Ed. R C Saravanabhavan. R&P Geraldin Bradner. Adv. contact Kamily Anderson. page USD 450; trim 5.5 x 8.5. Circ: 2,300 (paid).

➤ **JOURNAL OF NUTRITION EDUCATION AND BEHAVIOR.** see *NUTRITION AND DIETETICS*

➤ **JOURNAL OF PARALEGAL EDUCATION AND PRACTICE.** see *LAW*

▼ ➤ **JOURNAL OF PEACE EDUCATION.** see *POLITICAL SCIENCE—International Relations*

371.144 NLD ISSN 0920-525X
LB2838
➤ **JOURNAL OF PERSONNEL EVALUATION IN EDUCATION.** Text in English. 1987. q. EUR 402, USD 402, GBP 252 combined subscription to institutions print & online eds. (effective 2005). adv. bk.rev. illus. Index. back issues avail.; reprint service avail. from PQC,PSC. **Document type:** *Journal, Academic/Scholarly.* **Description:** Publishes research and applied scholarship on current issues in the evaluation of teacher and administrator performance.
Related titles: Microform ed.: (from PQC); Online - full text ed.: ISSN 1573-0425 (from EBSCO Publishing, Gale Group, IngentaConnect, Kluwer Online, O C L C Online Computer Library Center, Inc., ProQuest Information & Learning, Springer LINK, Swets Information Services).
Indexed: ABIn, AgeL, BibLing, CIJE, CPE, EAA, ERA, ETA, HEA, MEA, PsycInfo, PsycholAb, RHEA, SEA, SENA, SOMA, SOPODA, TEA, e-psyche.
—BLDSC (5030.970000), IE, Infotrieve, ingenta. **CCC.**
Published by: Springer-Verlag Dordrecht (Subsidiary of: Springer Science+Business Media), Van Godewijckstraat 30, Dordrecht, 3311 GX, Netherlands. TEL 31-78-6576050, FAX 31-78-6576474, http://springerlink.metapress.com/openurl.asp?genre=journal&issn=0920-525X, http://www.springeronline.com.

▼ ➤ **JOURNAL OF POLITICAL SCIENCE EDUCATION.** see *POLITICAL SCIENCE*

370 AUS ISSN 1443-1483
➤ **JOURNAL OF POSTCOLONIAL EDUCATION.** Text in English. s-a. AUD 374 domestic; AUD 340 in New Zealand; GBP 168 in Europe; USD 260 elsewhere (effective 2005). **Document type:** *Journal, Academic/Scholarly.* **Description:** The term 'postcolonial' refers to the process of domination, originating in Europe's colonizing foundation, but which also extends beyond the period of direct colonization to take on new forms, notably those of neo-colonialism, dependency and the intensification of globalization.
Published by: James Nicholas Publishers, Pty. Ltd., 342 Park St, South Melbourne, VIC 3205, Australia. TEL 61-3-96905955, FAX 61-3-96992040, editor.jpe@jnponline.com, http://www.jamesnicholaspublishers.com.au. Pub. Rea Zajda. R&P Mary Berchmans. Adv. contact Irene Schevchenko.

370 USA
THE JOURNAL OF POSTSECONDARY EDUCATION AND DISABILITY. Text in English. 3/yr. **Document type:** *Journal.*
Indexed: CIJE.
Published by: (Association on Higher Education and Disability), Journal of Postsecondary Education & Disability, University of Connecticut, Dept of Educational Psychology, Ctr on Postsecondary Ed. & Disability, Hall Bldg, 362 Fairfield Rd, Unit 2064, Storrs, CT 06269-2064. http://www.ahead.org/publications/jped.html.

371 GBR ISSN 1355-3097
➤ **JOURNAL OF PRACTICE IN EDUCATION FOR DEVELOPMENT.** Text in English. 1995. 3/yr. GBP 20, USD 35 (effective 1998). **Document type:** *Academic/Scholarly.* **Description:** Practice of education in developing countries, including general papers and papers on successful practice at all levels of education from pre-school to higher education.
Indexed: CPE, ERA, ETA, MEA, RHEA, SEA, SENA, SOMA, TEA.
Published by: (School of Education), University of Manchester, Dept. of English Language and Literature, Manchester, M13 9PL, United Kingdom. TEL 44-161-275-3458, FAX 44-161-275-3932, john.turner@man.ac.uk. R&P John Turner. Circ: 100 (paid); 1,000 (controlled).

370.72 USA ISSN 1088-484X
➤ **JOURNAL OF PRECISION TEACHING AND CELERATION.** Text in English. 1980. biennial. USD 25 domestic; USD 30 foreign (effective 2002). adv. bk.rev. back issues avail. **Document type:** *Academic/Scholarly.* **Description:** Multidisciplinary journal devoted to the science of human behavior which includes direct, continous and standard measurement.
Formerly (until 1995): Journal of Precision Teaching (0271-8200)
Indexed: CIJE.
Published by: Standard Celeration Society, Dept of Edecational and School Psychology and Spec. Education, Pennsylvania State University, 231 CEDAR Bldg, University Park, PA 16802-3109. TEL 814-863-2400, FAX 814-863-1002, cmcdade@jsucc.jsu.edu, RMK11@psu.edu. Ed. Richard Kubina. Circ: 250.

370 USA ISSN 1556-6382
BF637.C6
JOURNAL OF PROFESSIONAL COUNSELING, PRACTICE, THEORY & RESEARCH. Text in English. 1972. s-a. USD 90 membership; USD 45 to students (effective 2005). adv. bk.rev. charts; illus. index. reprint service avail. from PQC. **Document type:** *Journal.*
Former titles (until 2004): T C A Journal (1556-4223); (until 1992): T A C D Journal (1046-171X); (until 1984): Texas Personnel and Guidance Association Journal (0364-3409)
Related titles: Microform ed.: (from PQC); Online - full text ed.: (from EBSCO Publishing).
Indexed: CIJE, HEA, PsycInfo, PsycholAb, e-psyche.
—BLDSC (8612.518000).
Published by: Texas Counseling Association, 1204 San Antonio St., # 201, Austin, TX 78701-1869. TEL 800-580-8144, http://www.txca.org/. Ed. Phyllis Erdman. R&P, Adv. contact Charlotte McKay. Circ: 3,000.

370 CAN ISSN 1201-3307
JOURNAL OF PROFESSIONAL STUDIES. Text in English. 1993. s-a. CND 20 to individuals; CND 25 to institutions (effective 2004). **Document type:** *Journal, Academic/Scholarly.* **Description:** Provides a forum for a research-based exchange of ideas about teacher education and its place in the process of becoming a teacher. Promotes professional development of teachers at all levels by featuring the lived experiences of students, cooperating teachers and faculty involved in teacher education.
Indexed: CEI.
Published by: University of Regina, Faculty of Education, Regina, SK S4S 0A2, Canada. TEL 306-585-5142, FAX 306-585-4880, jps@uregina.ca, http://education.uregina.ca/research/jps. Ed. Louisa Kozey.

370.15 USA ISSN 0734-2829 CODEN: JPSAES
LB1131
➤ **JOURNAL OF PSYCHOEDUCATIONAL ASSESSMENT.** Text in English. 1982. q. (Mar., June, Sep.& Dec.). USD 375, GBP 242 to institutions; USD 390, GBP 252 combined subscription to institutions print & online eds. (effective 2006). adv. bk.rev. bibl.; charts; illus. index. back issues avail. **Document type:** *Journal, Academic/Scholarly.*
Related titles: Online - full text ed.: ISSN 1557-5144. USD 371, GBP 240 to institutions (effective 2006) (from HighWire Press).
Indexed: ASCA, ChPerI, CurCont, FamI, IBR, L&LBA, PsycInfo, PsycholAb, RefZh, SOPODA, SSCI, e-psyche.
—BLDSC (5043.275000), IE, Infotrieve, ingenta. **CCC.**
Published by: Sage Publications, Inc., 2455 Teller Rd, Thousand Oaks, CA 91320. TEL 805-499-0721, FAX 805-499-0871, info@sagepub.com, http://www.sagepub.com/journal.aspx?pid=11615. Circ: 700. **Subscr. to:** Sage Publications Ltd., 1 Oliver's Yard, 55 City Rd, London EC1 1SP, United Kingdom. TEL 44-20-73740645, FAX 44-20-73748741, subscription@sagepub.co.uk.

418.4 USA ISSN 0886-5701
JOURNAL OF READING EDUCATION. Text in English. 198?. 3/yr. **Document type:** *Journal, Academic/Scholarly.* **Description:** Intended as a forum to reflect current theory, research, and practice.
Indexed: CPE, ERA, ETA, MEA, RHEA, SEA, SENA, SOMA, TEA.
—BLDSC (5047.620000), IE, ingenta.
Published by: Organization of Teacher Educators in Reading, c/o Dr. Susan Davis Lenski, Editor, Campus Box 5330, Illinois State University, Normal, IL 61790-5330. sjlensk@ilstu.edu, http://www.ed.uno.edu/Faculty/rspeaker/OTER/Journal.html.

302.224 418.4 GBR ISSN 1743-0534
▼ ➤ **THE JOURNAL OF READING, WRITING AND LITERACY.** Text in English. forthcoming 2006. 3/yr. GBP 55 to individuals; GBP 70 to institutions (effective 2004). **Document type:** *Journal, Academic/Scholarly.* **Description:** Papers are invited on reading, writing and literacy, including creative writing and reader development. Contains articles and news items of interest as well as reviews of newly published texts on reading, writing and literacy.
Published by: Pied Piper Publishing Ltd., 80 Birmingham Rd, Shenstone, Lichfield, Staffs WS14 0JU, United Kingdom. debbie@piedpiperpublishing.com, glen@piedpiperpublishing.com, http://www.piedpiperpublishing.com/journals.htm, http://www.piedpiperpublishing.cam. Eds. Ms. Debbie Mynott, Dr. Glen Mynott.

➤ **JOURNAL OF RELIGIOUS EDUCATION.** see *RELIGIONS AND THEOLOGY—Roman Catholic*

372.072 USA ISSN 0256-8543
LB1028
JOURNAL OF RESEARCH IN CHILDHOOD EDUCATION; an international journal of research on the education of children. Text in English. 1986. q. USD 79 domestic to non-members; USD 95 foreign to non-members; USD 34 domestic to members; USD 50 foreign to members (effective 2005). adv. reprints avail. **Document type:** *Academic/Scholarly.* **Description:** Publishes practical and theoretical research into child development from infancy through early adolescence.
Related titles: Online - full text ed.: (from bigchalk, Florida Center for Library Automation, Gale Group, H.W. Wilson, O C L C Online Computer Library Center, Inc., ProQuest Information & Learning).
Indexed: ABIn, CIJE, CPE, ETA, EduInd, FamI, IMFL, MEA, PsycInfo, PsycholAb, SEA, TEA, e-psyche.
—BLDSC (5052.003500), IE, Infotrieve, ingenta. **CCC.**
Published by: Association for Childhood Education International, 17904 Georgia Ave, Ste 215, Olney, MD 20832-2277. TEL 301-570-2111, 800-423-3563, FAX 301-570-2212, aceihq@aol.com, http://www.acei.org/jrcehp.htm. Ed. Doris Bergen.

372.4 GBR ISSN 0141-0423
LB1050.6
➤ **JOURNAL OF RESEARCH IN READING.** Text and summaries in English, French. 1978. q. EUR 89 combined subscription in Europe to individuals print & online eds.; USD 99 combined subscription in the Americas to individuals & Caribbean (print & online eds.); GBP 59 combined subscription elsewhere to individuals print & online eds.; GBP 319 combined subscription in Europe to institutions print & online eds.; USD 468 combined subscription in the Americas to institutions & Caribbean (print & online eds.); GBP 339 combined subscription elsewhere to institutions print & online eds. (effective 2006). adv. bk.rev. abstr.; bibl.; charts. reprint service avail. from PQC,PSC. **Document type:** *Journal, Academic/Scholarly.*
Related titles: Microform ed.: (from PQC); Online - full text ed.: ISSN 1467-9817. GBP 283 in Europe to institutions; USD 415 in the Americas to institutions & Caribbean; GBP 301 elsewhere to institutions (effective 2005) (from Blackwell Synergy, EBSCO Publishing, Gale Group, IngentaConnect, O C L C Online Computer Library Center, Inc., Swets Information Services).
Indexed: BrEdI, CDA, CIJE, CPE, ChLitAb, CurCont, DIP, EAA, ERA, ETA, HECAB, IBR, IBZ, L&LBA, LT&LA, MEA, PCI, PsycInfo, PsycholAb, RHEA, SEA, SENA, SOMA, SOPODA, SSCI, TEA, e-psyche.
—BLDSC (5052.027000), IE, Infotrieve, ingenta. **CCC.**
Published by: (The United Kingdom Literacy Association), Blackwell Publishing Ltd., 9600 Garsington Rd, Oxford, OX4 2ZG, United Kingdom. TEL 44-1865-776868, FAX 44-1865-714591, customerservices@oxon.blackwellpublishing.com, http://www.blackwellpublishing.com/journals/JRIR. Ed. Dr. Morag Stuart. Circ: 1,250.

370 USA ISSN 1551-0670
▼ ➤ **JOURNAL OF RESEARCH IN RURAL EDUCATION (ONLINE).** Text in English. 2004. 3/yr. free (effective 2005). back issues avail. **Document type:** *Journal, Abstract/Index.*
Media: Online - full content.
Published by: University of Maine, College of Education and Human Development, 5766 Shibles Hall, Orono, ME 04469-5766. TEL 207-581-2485, FAX 207-581-2423, http://www.umaine.edu/jrre/, http://www.edumaine.edu.edhd. Eds. Amy Cates, Theodore Coladarci.

➤ **JOURNAL OF RESEARCH IN SCIENCE TEACHING**; the official journal of the National Association for Resarch in Science Teaching. see *SCIENCES: COMPREHENSIVE WORKS*

➤ **JOURNAL OF RESEARCH METHODOLOGY.** see *SOCIAL SCIENCES: COMPREHENSIVE WORKS*

E

371.07 200 USA ISSN 1065-6219
BV1460
JOURNAL OF RESEARCH ON CHRISTIAN EDUCATION. Text in English. 1992. s-a. USD 65 to individuals; USD 110 to institutions; USD 50 to students; USD 25 per issue to individuals; USD 45 per issue to institutions (effective 2006). adv. **Document type:** *Journal, Academic/Scholarly.*
Description: Provides a scholarly interchange of research findings relative to every level of Christian education.
Related titles: Online - full text ed.: (from EBSCO Publishing, H.W. Wilson, O C L C Online Computer Library Center, Inc., ProQuest Information & Learning).
Indexed: ABIn, CIJE, EduInd, RI-1.
—**CCC.**
Published by: (Andrews University, School of Education), Information Age Publishing, Inc., 411 W Putnam Ave, Ste 205, PO Box 4967, Greenwich, CT 06831. TEL 203-661-7602, FAX 203-661-7952, order@infoagepub.com, http://www.andrews.edu/JRCE, http://www.infoagepub.com. Ed. Lyndon G. Furst. Pub., R&P, Adv. contact George F. Johnson. B&W page USD 100.

JOURNAL OF SCHOOL HEALTH. see *PUBLIC HEALTH AND SAFETY*

370 USA ISSN 1052-6846
LB2805
➤ **JOURNAL OF SCHOOL LEADERSHIP.** Text in English. 1991. bi-m. USD 95 domestic to individuals; USD 155 foreign to individuals; USD 205 domestic to institutions; USD 265 foreign to institutions; USD 33 per issue domestic to individuals; USD 40 per issue foreign to individuals; USD 40 per issue domestic to institutions; USD 48 per issue foreign to institutions (effective 2004). illus.; tr.lit. back issues avail. **Document type:** *Journal, Academic/Scholarly.* **Description:** Explores the meaning of school leaderhip in the 21st Century and examines how diversity and issues of social justice affect schools and their leadership.
Indexed: CIJE, CPE, EAA, ERA, SWA.
—BLDSC (5052.660000), IE, ingenta. **CCC.**
Published by: Scarecrow Education (Subsidiary of: Scarecrow Press, Inc.), 4501 Forbes Blvd, Ste 200, PO Box 191, Lanham, MD 20706. TEL 301-459-3366, 800-462-6420, FAX 800-338-4550, ctursman@scarecroweducation.com, custserv@rowman.com, http://www.scarecroweducation.com/journals/JSL/Index.shtml. Ed. Dr. Ulrich C Reitzug. Pub. Dr. Thomas Koerner. R&P Ms. Kelly Rogers. Circ: 385 (paid).

➤ **JOURNAL OF SCHOOL NURSING.** see *MEDICAL SCIENCES—Nurses And Nursing*

370 USA
LB2847
➤ **JOURNAL OF SCHOOL PUBLIC RELATIONS.** Text in English. 1975. 4/yr. USD 55 domestic to individuals; USD 95 foreign to individuals; USD 68 domestic to institutions; USD 108 foreign to institutions (effective 2004). bk.rev. illus. index. 80 p./no.; back issues avail.; reprint service avail. from PQC. **Document type:** *Journal, Academic/Scholarly.* **Description:** Promotes student achievement through positive school-home-community relationships.
Former titles: School Public Relations Journal; Relations (Camp Hill); Journal of Educational Relations (1084-726X); (until 1995): Journal of Educational Public Relations (0741-3653); (until 1984): Journal of Educational Communication (0745-4058)
Related titles: Microform ed.: (from PQC).
Indexed: CIJE, CPE, EAA, ERA, SOPODA.
—**CCC.**
Published by: Scarecrow Education (Subsidiary of: Scarecrow Press, Inc.), 4501 Forbes Blvd, Ste 200, PO Box 191, Lanham, MD 20706. TEL 301-459-3366, 800-462-6420, FAX 800-338-4550, tmiller@rowman.com, http://www.scarecroweducation.com/journals/JSPR/Index.shtml. Ed. Dr. Theodore J Kowalski. Pub. Dr. Thomas Koerner. R&P Ms. Kelly Rogers. Circ: 400 (paid).

➤ **JOURNAL OF SCHOOL SOCIAL WORK.** see *PSYCHOLOGY*

371.7 USA ISSN 1538-8220
LB3013.3
➤ **JOURNAL OF SCHOOL VIOLENCE.** Text in English. 2002. q. USD 250 combined subscription domestic to institutions print & online eds.; USD 337.50 combined subscription in Canada to institutions print & online eds.; USD 362.50 combined subscription elsewhere to institutions print & online eds. (effective 2006). adv. reprint service avail. from HAW. **Document type:** *Journal, Academic/Scholarly.* **Description:** Contains information on the latest strategies for school violence threat assessment, prevention, and intervention.
Related titles: Online - full text ed.: ISSN 1538-8239. free to institutions (effective 2003); free with print subs. (from EBSCO Publishing, O C L C Online Computer Library Center, Inc., Swets Information Services).
Indexed: CJA, EAA, ERA, ESPM, ETA, FamI, H&SSA, MEA, PAIS, RHEA, RefZh, RiskAb, SEA, SENA, SFSA, SOMA, SSA, SociolAb, TEA, V&AA, e-psyche.
—BLDSC (5052.690000), Haworth, IE.
Published by: (International School Violence Prevention Association), Haworth Press, Inc., 10 Alice St, Binghamton, NY 13904-1580. TEL 607-722-5857, 800-429-6784, FAX 607-722-1424, 800-895-0582, getinfo@haworthpress.com, http://www.haworthpress.com/web/JSV. Ed. Edwin R Gerler. adv.: B&W page USD 315, color page USD 550; trim 4.375 x 7.125. Circ: 73 (paid).

391 500 USA ISSN 1530-7859
LC4031
THE JOURNAL OF SCIENCE EDUCATION FOR PERSONS WITH DISABILITIES. Text in English. 199?. a. free membership (effective 2005). **Document type:** *Journal.*
Indexed: CIJE.
Published by: Science Education for Students with Disabilities, c/o David Bartlett, 225 North Ely Dr, Northville, MI 48167. lkq9999@rit.edu, http://www.sesd.info.

372.35 NLD ISSN 1046-560X
Q181.A1 CODEN: JTEAFL
➤ **JOURNAL OF SCIENCE TEACHER EDUCATION.** Text in English. 1989. q. EUR 263, USD 263, GBP 173 combined subscription to institutions print & online eds. (effective 2005). adv. reprint service avail. from PSC. **Document type:** *Journal, Academic/Scholarly.* **Description:** Serves as a forum for disseminating research and theoretical position statements concerning the preparation and inservice education of science teachers.
Related titles: Online - full text ed.: ISSN 1573-1847 (from EBSCO Publishing, Gale Group, IngentaConnect, Kluwer Online, O C L C Online Computer Library Center, Inc., Springer LINK, Swets Information Services).
Indexed: ABIn, AEI, BibLing, CIJE, EduInd.
—BLDSC (5056.600000), IE, Infotrieve, ingenta. **CCC.**
Published by: (Association for the Education of Teachers in Science (AETS)), Springer-Verlag Dordrecht (Subsidiary of: Springer Science+Business Media), Van Godewijckstraat 30, Dordrecht, 3311 GX, Netherlands. TEL 31-78-6576050, FAX 31-78-6576474, http://springerlink.metapress.com/openurl.asp?genre=journal&issn=1046-560X, http://www.springeronline.com. Ed. Charlene M Czerniak.

365.34 371.7 363.119371 USA ISSN 1550-7890
HV8290
▼ **JOURNAL OF SECURITY EDUCATION**; new directions in education, training, and accreditation. Text in English. 2004 (Fall). q. (vol.1, no.1 Fall 2004; vol.1, no.2 Fall 2005). USD 450 combined subscription domestic to institutions print & online eds.; USD 607.50 combined subscription in Canada to institutions print & online eds.; USD 652.50 combined subscription elsewhere to institutions print & online eds. (effective 2006). reprint service avail. from HAW. **Document type:** *Journal, Academic/Scholarly.* **Description:** Comprehensive, one-stop resource on security education and training programs that will help educators, practitioners, and students meet the increasing need for security in the United States.
Related titles: Online - full content ed.: ISSN 1550-7904; Online - full text ed.: (from EBSCO Publishing, O C L C Online Computer Library Center, Inc., Swets Information Services).
Indexed: BrCerAb, C&ISA, CerAb, CorrAb, E&CAJ, EMA, IAA, Inspec, M&TEA, MBF, METADEX, WAA.
—Haworth, IE.
Published by: Haworth Press, Inc., 10 Alice St, Binghamton, NY 13904-1580. TEL 607-722-5857, 800-429-6784, FAX 607-722-1424, 800-895-0582, getinfo@haworthpress.com, http://www.haworthpress.com/web/JSE. Ed. John I Kostanoski. Pub. William Cohen. R&P Ruth Ann Heath TEL 607-722-5857 ext 316.

JOURNAL OF SOCIAL WORK EDUCATION. see *SOCIAL SERVICES AND WELFARE*

370 THA ISSN 1513-4601
LA1250
JOURNAL OF SOUTHEAST ASIAN EDUCATION. Text in English. 2000. s-a. THB 790, USD 18 (effective 2004). back issues avail. **Document type:** *Journal, Academic/Scholarly.*
Published by: Southeast Asian Ministers of Education Organization, 920 Sukhumvit Rd, Bangkok, 10110, Thailand. TEL 66-2-3910144, FAX 66-2-3812587, secretariat@seameo.org, http://www.seameo.org/journal/. Circ: 1,000 (paid); 200 (controlled). **Dist. by:** Pearson Education Indochina Ltd., 2390 Pattanakarn Road, Suanluang, Bangkok 10250, Thailand. TEL 66-2-722-7301, FAX 66-2-722-7307, cserv@pearson-indochina.com, http://www.pearson-indochina.com/.

JOURNAL OF STRATEGIC MANAGEMENT EDUCATION. see *BUSINESS AND ECONOMICS—Management*

378.3 USA ISSN 0884-9153
L11
JOURNAL OF STUDENT FINANCIAL AID. Text in English. 1971. 3/yr. USD 45; USD 15 per issue (effective 2005).
Indexed: CIJE, HEA.
Published by: National Association of Student Financial Aid Administrators, 1129 20th St NW, Suite 400, Washington, DC 20036-3453. TEL 202-785-0453, FAX 202-785-1487, http://www.nasfaa.org.

370.711 USA ISSN 0022-4871
LB1705 CODEN: JTEDA
➤ **JOURNAL OF TEACHER EDUCATION**; the journal of policy, practice, and research in teacher education. Text in English. 1950. 5/yr. USD 359, GBP 232 to institutions; USD 373, GBP 241 combined subscription to institutions print & online eds. (effective 2006). adv. bk.rev. illus. back issues avail.; reprint service avail. from PQC. **Document type:** *Journal, Academic/Scholarly.* **Description:** Explores social and professional issues affecting teachers at all levels. It covers themes like gender issues in teacher education; teacher education and curriculum standards; teaching ethics and morality in the 21st century; field experiences and teacher education; cognitive science and critical thinking; preparing teachers for urban schools; teachers' beliefs; professional ethics in teacher education; and restructuring teacher education.
Related titles: Microform ed.: (from PQC); Online - full text ed.: ISSN 1552-7816. USD 355, GBP 229 to institutions (effective 2006) (from C S A, EBSCO Publishing, Florida Center for Library Automation, Gale Group, O C L C Online Computer Library Center, Inc., Sage Publications, Inc., Swets Information Services).
Indexed: ABIn, ASCA, AcaI, ArtHuCI, BRI, CBRI, CIJE, CPE, ChPerI, CurCont, DIP, EAA, ECER, ERA, ETA, EduInd, FamI, IBR, IBZ, MEA, PCI, PsycholAb, RASB, RHEA, SEA, SENA, SOMA, SOPODA, SSCI, SWA, TEA.
—BLDSC (5068.285000), IE, Infotrieve, ingenta. **CCC.**
Published by: (American Association of Colleges for Teacher Education), Corwin Press, Inc. (Subsidiary of: Sage Publications, Inc.), 2455 Teller Rd, Thousand Oaks, CA 91320-2218. TEL 805-499-9734, FAX 805-499-0871, 800-4-1-SCHOOL (800-417-2466), info@sagepub.com, http://www.sagepub.com/journal.aspx?pid=211, http://www.corwinpress.com. Eds. Dan Liston, Hilda Borko, Jennifer Whitcomb. Pub. Gracia Alkema. R&P Jackie Paciulan. Adv. contact Kristen Beaulieu. B&W page USD 590, color page USD 1,180; trim 8.5 x 11. Circ: 7,876 (paid). **Subscr. in Europe to:** Sage Publications Ltd., 1 Oliver's Yard, 55 City Rd, London EC1 1SP, United Kingdom. TEL 44-20-73740645, FAX 44-20-73748741, subscription@sagepub.co.uk.

➤ **JOURNAL OF TEACHING IN INTERNATIONAL BUSINESS.** see *BUSINESS AND ECONOMICS—International Commerce*

808.025 USA ISSN 0047-2816
T11 CODEN: JTWCAA
➤ **JOURNAL OF TECHNICAL WRITING AND COMMUNICATION.** Text in English. 1971. q. USD 67 to individuals; USD 274 domestic to institutions; USD 282 foreign to institutions (effective 2005). bk.rev. abstr.; charts; illus. Index. back issues avail.; reprints avail. **Document type:** *Journal, Academic/Scholarly.* **Description:** Contains essays on oral, as well as written communication, for purposes from pure research to needs of business and industry.
Related titles: Online - full text ed.: ISSN 1541-3780 (from EBSCO Publishing).
Indexed: ASCA, ArtHuCI, CIJE, CPE, CommAb, CurCont, ERA, ETA, EngInd, IAA, IBR, IBZ, L&LBA, MEA, PerIslam, RHEA, RefZh, SEA, SENA, SOMA, SOPODA, SSCI, TEA.
—BLDSC (5068.295000), CISTI, Ei, IDS, IE, Infotrieve, ingenta, Linda Hall. **CCC.**
Published by: Baywood Publishing Co., Inc., 26 Austin Ave, PO Box 337, Amityville, NY 11701-0337. TEL 631-691-1270, FAX 631-691-1770, info@baywood.com, http://www.baywood.com/Journals/PreviewJournal.asp?Id=0047-2816. Ed. Charles H Sides. R&P Julie Krempa. Adv. contact Rochelle Grant.

➤ **JOURNAL OF THE ASSEMBLY FOR EXPANDED PERSPECTIVES ON LEARNING.** see *LINGUISTICS*

300 USA
JOURNAL OF THE ILLINOIS COUNCIL FOR THE SOCIAL STUDIES. Text in English. bi-m. **Document type:** *Journal.*
Published by: Illinois Council for the Social Studies, c/o Dr. Frederick D Drake, Department of History, Illinois State University, Normal, IL 61790-4420. TEL 309-438-7212, http://coe.ilstu.edu/icss/. Ed. Bob Lombard TEL 309-697-1629.

370.15 USA ISSN 1050-8406
L11 CODEN: JLSBE3
➤ **JOURNAL OF THE LEARNING SCIENCES**; a journal of ideas and their applications. Text in English. 1991. q. USD 525 in US & Canada to institutions; USD 555 elsewhere to institutions; USD 550 combined subscription in US & Canada to institutions print & online eds.; USD 580 combined subscription elsewhere to institutions print & online eds. (effective 2006). adv. back issues avail.; reprint service avail. from PSC. **Document type:** *Journal, Academic/Scholarly.* **Description:** Provides a multidisciplinary forum for the presentation and discussion of research on teaching and learning.
Related titles: Online - full text ed.: ISSN 1532-7809. USD 495 worldwide to institutions (effective 2006) (from EBSCO Publishing, Gale Group, O C L C Online Computer Library Center, Inc., Swets Information Services).
Indexed: ASCA, CIJE, CPE, CurCont, ERA, ETA, FamI, Inspec, L&LBA, MEA, PsycInfo, PsycholAb, RHEA, SEA, SENA, SOMA, SOPODA, SSCI, SWA, TEA, e-psyche.
—BLDSC (5010.231000), IE, Infotrieve, ingenta. **CCC.**

E

▼ new title ➤ refereed ✶ unverified ♦ full entry avail.

Published by: Lawrence Erlbaum Associates, Inc., 10 Industrial Ave, Mahwah, NJ 07430-2262. TEL 201-258-2200, 800-926-6579, FAX 201-236-0072, journals@erlbaum.com, http://www.leaonline.com/loi/jls. Ed. Janet L Kolodner. adv.: page USD 500; trim 5 x 8.

370 USA ISSN 1541-3446
LC5225.L42
▼ ➤ **JOURNAL OF TRANSFORMATIVE EDUCATION.** Text in English. 2003 (Jan.). q. USD 421, GBP 272 to institutions; USD 438, GBP 283 combined subscription to institutions print & online eds. (effective 2006). adv. **Document type:** *Journal, Academic/Scholarly.*
Related titles: Online - full text ed.: ISSN 1552-7840. USD 417, GBP 269 to institutions (effective 2006) (from C S A, EBSCO Publishing, O C L C Online Computer Library Center, Inc., Sage Publications, Inc., Swets Information Services).
Indexed: CPE, ERA.
—BLDSC (5069.853000), IE. **CCC.**
Published by: Sage Publications, Inc., 2455 Teller Rd, Thousand Oaks, CA 91320. TEL 805-499-0721, 800-818-7243, FAX 805-499-8096, 800-583-2665, info@sagepub.com, http://www.sagepub.com/journal.aspx?pid=9184. Eds. Allyson Washburn, Will McWhinney. Adv. contact Kirsten Beaulieu TEL 805-499-0721 ext 7160. B&W page USD 325, color page USD 1,150. **Subscr. to:** Sage Publications Ltd., 1 Oliver's Yard, 55 City Rd, London EC1 1SP, United Kingdom. TEL 44-20-73740645, FAX 44-20-73748741, subscription@sagepub.co.uk.

370.1 USA ISSN 1546-3206
▼ **JOURNAL OF URBAN EDUCATION;** focus on enrichment. Text in English. 2004 (Fall). s-a. USD 15 (effective 2004). **Document type:** *Academic/Scholarly.*
Published by: Southern University at New Orleans, College of Education, 6400 Press Dr., New Orleans, LA 70126. TEL 504-286-5000, FAX 504-286-5299, http://www.suno.edu/college_edu/college_of_education.htm. Eds. Ashraf Esmail, Rose Duhon-Sells.

371.2 USA ISSN 1541-6224
LB2831.8
▼ ➤ **JOURNAL OF WOMEN IN EDUCATIONAL LEADERSHIP.** Text in English. 2003. q. USD 49 to individuals; USD 89 to institutions; USD 29 to students; USD 25 per issue (effective 2003). **Document type:** *Academic/Scholarly.*
—BLDSC (5072.633550).
Published by: ProActive Publications, 1148 Elizabeth Ave. Ste. 2, Lancaster, PA 17601. TEL 717-290-1660, FAX 717-509-6100, info@proactivepublications.com, http://www.proactivepublications.com. Ed. Marilyn L. Grady.

370.9 DNK
JOURNAL OF WORLD EDUCATION. Text in English. 1970. q. DKK 100. adv. bk.rev. back issues avail.
Published by: Association for World Education, Nordenfjord World University, Thy, Snedsted, 7752, Denmark. Ed. Aage R Nielsen. Circ: 3,000.

JOURNAL OF YOUTH STUDIES. see *CHILDREN AND YOUTH—About*

THE JOURNALS OF LEGAL SCHOLARSHIP. ISSUES IN LEGAL SCHOLARSHIP. see *LAW*

JUCO REVIEW. see *SPORTS AND GAMES*

371.076 DEU ISSN 1616-0037
JUEDISCHE BILDUNGSGESCHICHTE IN DEUTSCHLAND. Text in German. 2001. irreg., latest vol.5, 2002. EUR 34.90 per vol. (effective 2003). **Document type:** *Monographic series, Academic/Scholarly.*
Published by: Waxmann Verlag GmbH, Steinfurter Str 555, Muenster, 48159, Germany. TEL 49-251-26504-0, FAX 49-251-2650426, lohmann@erzwiss.uni-hamburg.de, info@waxmann.com, http://www.erzwiss.uni-hamburg.de/Inst01/Projekt/JF/Schriftenreihe.htm, http://www.waxmann.com. Ed. Ingrid Lohmann.

JUGEND - RELIGION - UNTERRICHT; Beitraege zu einer dialogischen Religionspaedagogik. see *RELIGIONS AND THEOLOGY*

370 DNK ISSN 0107-8887
JULEHILSEN. Text in Danish. 1962. a. illus.
Published by: Elevforeningen for Hoven Ungdomsskole, Tarm, 6880, Denmark.

370 LBR
JULIUS C. STEVENS ANNUAL LECTURES IN EDUCATION★. Text in English. irreg.
Published by: University of Liberia, William V.S. Tubman Teachers College, Monrovia, Liberia.

373 GBR ISSN 0309-3484
JUNIOR EDUCATION. Text in English. 1977. m. GBP 37.50 domestic; GBP 49.95 foreign (effective 2001). adv. bk.rev. illus. **Document type:** *Magazine, Academic/Scholarly.* **Description:** Contains up-to-the-minute ideas and information for teachers of children aged 7-11.
Incorporates (in 1982): Pictorial Education (0048-4121); Supersedes: Teachers World (0049-3139)
Indexed: CPE, ChLitAb, ICM.
—BLDSC (5075.137000), IE, ingenta.
Published by: Scholastic Ltd., Villiers House, Clarendon Ave, Leamington Spa, Warks CV32 5PR, United Kingdom. TEL 44-1926-887799, FAX 44-1926-817727, enquiries@scholastic.co.uk, http://www.scholastic.co.uk. Ed. Terry Saunders. Adv. contact Chris Pratt. Circ: 30,510. **Subscr. to:** Westfield Rd, Southam, Leamington Spa CV33 0JH, United Kingdom. TEL 44-1926-813910.

370 AUS ISSN 0819-6168
JUNIOR TOPICS. Text in English. 1982. 8/yr. AUD 45; AUD 50 foreign (effective 2000). **Document type:** *Trade.*
Published by: Scholastic Pty. Ltd., Railway Crescent, Lisarow, NSW 2250, Australia. TEL 61-2-4328-3555, FAX 61-2-4328-2205, http://www.scholastic.com.au. Ed. Jane Campbell. Adv. contact Ken McLachlan. Circ: 5,000.

372.1 DNK ISSN 1604-8334
JURAINFORMATION. DAGTILBUD FOR BOERN OG UNGE. NYHEDSBREV. Text in Danish. 1993. 10/yr. DKK 480 Print edition; DKK 240 Online edition (effective 2005). **Document type:** *Newsletter, Trade.*
Former titles (until 2004): Dagtilbud til Boern og Unge. Nyhedsbrev (1395-332X); (until 1995): Dagsinstitutionerne. Nyhedsbrev (0908-3049)
Related titles: Online - full text ed.
Published by: Jurainformation, Sommerstedsgade 7, Copenhagen V, 1718, Denmark. TEL 45-70-230102, FAX 45-70-230103, post@jurainformation.dk, http://www.jurainformation.dk. Ed. Erik Voelund Mortensen.

JURISTISCHE SCHULUNG; Zeitschrift fuer Studium und praktische Ausbildung mit JuS-Kartei und JuS-Lernbogen. see *LAW*

370.15 FIN ISSN 0075-4625
CODEN: JYSEAV
JYVASKYLA STUDIES IN EDUCATION, PSYCHOLOGY AND SOCIAL RESEARCH. Text in English, Finnish; Summaries in English. 1962. irreg. price varies. **Document type:** *Monographic series.*
Indexed: CPE, ERA, ETA, MEA, PsycholAb, RASB, RHEA, SEA, SENA, SOMA, TEA, e-psyche.
—BLDSC (5078.500000).
Published by: Jyvaskylan Yliopisto/University of Jyvaskyla, PO Box 35, Jyvaeskylae, 40014, Finland. TEL 941-601-211, FAX 603-371, TELEX 28219JYK SF. Eds. Paula Lyytinen, Paula Maatta. Circ: 450.

370 613.7 USA ISSN 1071-2577
K A H P E R D JOURNAL. Text in English. 1964. 2/yr. USD 5 per issue. adv. bk.rev. bibl. **Document type:** *Academic/Scholarly.*
Formerly: K A H P E R Journal (0022-7269)
Indexed: SportS.
Published by: Kentucky Association for Health, Physical Education, Recreation and Dance, c/o Burch E Oglesby, Western Kentucky University, Bowling Green, KY 42101. TEL 502-742-3347, TELEX 745-6043. Ed. Dr. Randy Deere. Circ: 1,000.

372 IND
K A P T UNION PATHRIKA. Text in Malayalam, English. 1975. m. INR 20. adv. **Document type:** *Bulletin.*
Supersedes: Vijnanevedi
Published by: Kerala Aided Primary Teachers' Union, Carrier Station Rd., Cochin, Kerala 682 016, India. Ed. M Chellappan. R&P V Pazhani. Adv. contact A P Jose. Circ: 3,500.

370 USA ISSN 0164-3959
K E A NEWS. Text in English. 1964. 10/yr. USD 5. illus. **Document type:** *Newsletter, Trade.*
Formerly: Kentucky Education News (0023-0170)
Published by: Kentucky Education Association, 401 Capitol Ave, Frankfort, KY 40601-2836. TEL 800-231-4532, http://www.kea.org/news/index.cfm. Ed. Charles Main. Circ: 36,000.

K E A RESEARCH PUBLICATIONS. see *EDUCATION—Abstracting, Bibliographies, Statistics*

370.1 JPN ISSN 0386-4553
➤ **KAGAKU KYOIKU KENKYU/JOURNAL OF SCIENCE EDUCATION IN JAPAN.** Text in English, Japanese; Summaries in English. 1977. q. JPY 8,000 to members (effective 2003). adv. bk.rev. **Document type:** *Journal, Academic/Scholarly.* **Description:** Covers disciplinary areas of science education including theory, methods and instructions.
—CCC.
Published by: Nihon Kagaku Kyoiku Gakkai/Japan Society for Science Education, 5-22 Shimo-Meguro 6-chome, Meguro-ku, Tokyo, 153-8681, Japan. FAX 81-3-3714-0986, fujitakc@cue.e.chiba-u.ac.jp. Ed. Kanji Akahori. R&P Takeshi Fuita. Adv. contact Masaru Sakayauchi. Circ: 1,200.

➤ **KAGAKU TO KYOIKU/CHEMICAL EDUCATION.** see *CHEMISTRY*

370.1 JPN ISSN 0389-3057
AS552.K24 CODEN: KDKDAM
KAGAWA DAIGAKU KYOIKUGAKUBU KENKYU HOKOKU. DAI-2-BU/KAGAWA UNIVERSITY. FACULTY OF EDUCATION. MEMOIRS. PART 2. Text in English, Japanese; Summaries in English. 1950. s-a.
Indexed: JPI.
—CASDDS.
Published by: Kagawa Daigaku, Kyoikugakubu/Kagawa University, Faculty of Education, 1-1 Saiwai-cho, Takamatsu-shi, Kagawa-ken 760-0016, Japan.

370 JPN
KANAZAWA UNIVERSITY. FACULTY OF EDUCATION. BULLETIN: HUMANITIES, SOCIAL AND EDUCATIONAL SCIENCES/KANAZAWA DAIGAKU KYOIKUGAKUBU KIYO. JINBUN, SHAKAI KYOIKU KAGAKU. Text in Japanese; Summaries in English. irreg.
Published by: Kanazawa Daigaku, Kyoikugakubu/Kanazawa University, Faculty of Education, 1-1 Marunochi, Kanazawa-shi, Ishikawa-ken 920-0937, Japan.

371.07 NLD ISSN 0022-8354
KANDELAAR. Text in Dutch. 1947. m. bk.rev.
Published by: Nederlandse Vereniging van Vrijzinnige Zondagsscholen, c/o M Spyker v.d. Laan, Maskweg 28, Renkum, 6871 KX, Netherlands. Ed. C van Santen-Teeling. Circ: 1,200.

KANSAS BIOLOGY TEACHER. see *BIOLOGY*

370 USA ISSN 0022-8834
KANSAS TEACHER. Text in English. 1914. m. (8/yr.). USD 5 to non-members; USD 3 to members. adv. charts; illus.; stat. index.
Published by: Kansas-National Education Association, 715 W 10th St, Topeka, KS 66612. TEL 913-232-8271. Ed. Anna Mary Lyle. Circ: 26,000.

KAR'ERA. see *OCCUPATIONS AND CAREERS*

KAR'ERA - KAPITAL. see *OCCUPATIONS AND CAREERS*

370.7 IND ISSN 0022-4979
KARNATAK UNIVERSITY. COLLEGE OF EDUCATION. JOURNAL. Text in English, Kannada. 1972 (vol.19). s-a. INR 10. bk.rev. charts.
Published by: Karnatak University, College of Education, Dharwad, Karnataka 580 003, India. Ed. T K Hiregange.

KARUNUNGAN; a journal of philosophy. see *PHILOSOPHY*

370 FIN ISSN 0022-927X
L56
KASVATUS/FINNISH JOURNAL OF EDUCATION; Suomen kasvatustieteellinen aikakauskirja. Text mainly in Finnish; Summaries in English, Finnish. 1970. 5/yr. adv. bk.rev. charts. index. back issues avail. **Document type:** *Academic/Scholarly.* **Description:** Presents articles on educational research projects as well as articles on educational issues in general.
Formed by the merger of (1914-1969): Kasvatus ja Koulu (0783-1552); (1937-1969): Kasvatusopillinen Aikakauskirja (0783-1587); Which was formerly (1926-1936): Suomen kasvatusopillinen Yhdistyksen Aikakauskirja (0783-1579)
Indexed: RASB, RHEA, SOPODA.
Published by: Jyvaskylan Yliopisto, Koulutuksen Tutkimuslaitos/University of Jyvaskyla, Institute for Educational Research, PO Box 35, Jyvaskyla, 40014, Finland. TEL 358-14-2603200, FAX 358-14-2603201, http://www.jyu.fi/ktl/journal.htm.

KATALOG FOR SKOLEBIBLIOTEKER. ELEVERNE. see *EDUCATION—Abstracting, Bibliographies, Statistics*

KATALOG FOR SKOLEBIBLIOTEKER. SKOLEBIBLIOTEKAREN. see *EDUCATION—Abstracting, Bibliographies, Statistics*

KATOLICKI UNIWERSYTET LUBELSKI. ZESZYTY NAUKOWE. see *RELIGIONS AND THEOLOGY—Roman Catholic*

370 KAZ
KAZAKHSTAN ZHOGARY MEKTEBI; vestnik vysshei shkoly kazakhstana. Text in Kazakh, Russian. bi-m. USD 181 in North America (effective 2000).
Published by: Ministry of Education, Ul Zhambyla 25, Almaty, 480100, Kazakstan. TEL 3272-617851. **Dist. by:** East View Information Services, 3020 Harbor Ln. N., Minneapolis, MN 55447. TEL 763-550-0961, FAX 763-559-2931.

371.192 USA
KEEPING CHILDREN AT THE CENTER. Text in English. 1976. m. (except July-Aug.). free to members (effective 2004). bk.rev. index. **Document type:** *Newsletter.* **Description:** Provides information regarding parent-community-business partnerships including education policy issues, legislation, research, funding sources, and innovative programs.
Former titles: Partnership Progressions; Partners in Education (1041-1542); Volunteer in Education; School Volunteer; V A S T; Volunteer Views (0042-868X)

E

Published by: National Association of Partners in Education, Inc., 741, Harvard, MA 01451-0741. napehq@napehq.org, http://www.napehq.org/, http://www.partnersineducation.org. Ed. Pamela A McRae. R&P Cathleen Healy. Circ: 6,000.

370   JPN
KENKYU SHUROKU. Text in Japanese. 2/yr. free or on exchange basis.
Published by: (Section of Research Dissemination), National Institute for Educational Research, 6-5-22 Shino-Meguro, Meguro-ku, Tokyo, 153, Japan. Ed. T Chichibu.

KENTUCKY ENGLISH BULLETIN. see *LINGUISTICS*

KENTUCKY SCHOOL LAWS ANNOTATED. see *LAW*

379.1   USA   ISSN 1526-3584
KENTUCKY TEACHER. Text in English. 1972. 9/yr. free (effective 2005). bk.rev. illus. back issues avail. **Document type:** *Newsletter, Trade.* **Description:** News and features that support high levels of innovation and instruction in public school classrooms.
Former titles (until 1992): EdNews; School News (0036-6692)
Related titles: Online - full text ed.
Published by: Kentucky Department of Education, Office of Communication Services, 500 Mero St, Frankfort, KY 40601. TEL 502-564-4770, FAX 502-564-6470, fsalyers@kde.state.ky.us, http://www.kde.state.ky.us. Ed. Faun S Fishback. Circ: 58,000 (controlled and free).

370.96762   KEN   ISSN 0075-5869
KENYA. MINISTRY OF EDUCATION. ANNUAL REPORT. Text in English. a. **Document type:** *Government.*
Published by: (Slovakia. Ministry of Education), Government Printing and Stationery Department, PO Box 30128, Nairobi, Kenya.

370.96762   KEN
KENYA. MINISTRY OF EDUCATION. NEWSLETTER. Text in English. 1974. bi-m. **Document type:** *Newsletter, Government.*
Formerly: Kenya. Ministry of Education, Science and Technology Newsletter
Published by: Ministry of Education Science and Technology, Public Relations Officer, Commercial House, Moi Ave., PO Box 30040, Nairobi, Kenya.

372   USA
KIDS COURIER. Text in English. m. adv. **Description:** Encourages young students to read and write. Features stories written by and for students in grades 3-7. Also contains puzzles, games, problems and contests.
Related titles: Online - full text ed.
Published by: National Childrens Literacy Project, 24 Union St, Hamburg, NY 14075. Ed. C F Kluckhohn.

372.358   USA   ISSN 1079-3070
KIDTECH NEWS. Text in English. 1993. bi-m. USD 16.95; USD 29.95 foreign (effective 2000). bk.rev. **Document type:** *Newsletter.* **Description:** Addresses the existing partnership linking learning and technology for youngsters from ages 2 - 16, in all educational environments. Focus is technology and tools for education that naturally incorporates migration of content to the Wprld Wide Web.
Related titles: Online - full text ed.: 1994.
Published by: KidTECH-BG Associates, 5500 Friendship Blvd, Ste 1614N, Chevy Chase, MD 20815-3625. TEL 301-657-4497, kidtech@ix.netcom.com, KidTECHBG@yahoo.com, http://www.kidtechnews.net, http://www.kidtech-bg.com. Ed., Pub. Barbara A Gollon.

370   ESP   ISSN 1133-0589
KIKIRIKI. Text in Spanish. 1988. q.
—CINDOC.
Published by: Kikiriki Cooperacion Educativa, Apdo. de Correos 117, Moron de la Frontera, Sevilla, 41530, Spain. TEL 34-95-5854850, http://www.cooperacioneducativa.com/.

KINDER IN TAGESEINRICHTUNGEN. see *CHILDREN AND YOUTH—About*

KINDEROPVANG. see *CHILDREN AND YOUTH—About*

KINDERSPIEL. see *CHILDREN AND YOUTH—About*

372.218   DEU   ISSN 0934-6570
KINDERZEIT. Text in German. 1950. bi-m. EUR 18.40 domestic; EUR 23 foreign (effective 2005). adv. bk.rev.; play rev. index. back issues avail. **Document type:** *Magazine, Consumer.*
Former titles (until 1989): Sozialpaedagogischer Blaetter (0342-815X); Kindergarten; (until 1976): Blaetter des Pestalozzi-Froebel-Verbandes (0342-8141)
Indexed: DIP, IBR, IBZ.
—CCC.
Published by: (Pestalozzi-Froebel-Verband), B und B Verlagsgesellschaft mbH, Grunerstr 31, Duesseldorf, 40239, Germany. TEL 49-211-4229185, FAX 49-211-5192175, info@bb-medien.de, http://www.kinderzeit.com, http://www.bb-medien.de. adv.: B&W page EUR 1,850, color page EUR 3,080. Circ: 3,700.

KING SAUD UNIVERSITY JOURNAL. EDUCATIONAL SCIENCES AND ISLAMIC STUDIES/JAMI'AT AL-MALIK SA'UD. MAJALLAH. AL-'ULUM AL-TARBAWIYYAH WAL-DIRASAT AL-ISLAMIYYAH. see *RELIGIONS AND THEOLOGY—Islamic*

KITA KINDERTAGESEINRICHTUNGEN AKTUELL. AUSGABE BADEN-WUERTTEMBERG. see *CHILDREN AND YOUTH—About*

KITA KINDERTAGESEINRICHTUNGEN AKTUELL. AUSGABE BAYERN. see *CHILDREN AND YOUTH—About*

KITA KINDERTAGESEINRICHTUNGEN AKTUELL. AUSGABE BRANDENBURG, MECKLENBURG-VORPOMMERN, SACHSEN, SACHSEN-ANHALT, THUERINGEN UND BERLIN. see *CHILDREN AND YOUTH—About*

KITA KINDERTAGESEINRICHTUNGEN AKTUELL. AUSGABE HESSEN, RHEINLAND-PFALZ, SAARLAND. see *CHILDREN AND YOUTH—About*

KITA KINDERTAGESEINRICHTUNGEN AKTUELL. AUSGABE NIEDERSACHSEN, SCHLESWIG-HOLSTEIN, HAMBURG, BREMEN. see *CHILDREN AND YOUTH—About*

KITA KINDERTAGESEINRICHTUNGEN AKTUELL. AUSGABE NORDRHEIN-WESTFALEN. see *CHILDREN AND YOUTH—About*

KITA RECHT. see *CHILDREN AND YOUTH—About*

KITA SPEZIAL. see *CHILDREN AND YOUTH—About*

371.92   BEL
KLASSE FOR PARENTS. Text in Dutch. 1996. 9/yr. EUR 6 (effective 2005). adv. **Document type:** *Newsletter, Government.* **Description:** For parents with schoolgoing children up to age 14.
Published by: Vlaamse Ministerie van Onderwijs, H. Consciencegebouw, Koning Albert II-laan 15, Brussel, 1210, Belgium. TEL 32-2-553-9686, FAX 32-2-553-9685, info@klasse.be, http://www.klasse.be. Ed. Leo Bormans. R&P Marc Impens. Adv. contact Diana Decaluwe. Circ: 650,000.

370   DEU
DER KLECKS; Schuelerzeitung des Thomas-Morus-Gymnasiums Daun. Text in German. 1966. 2/yr. **Document type:** *Newspaper, Consumer.*
Published by: Thomas-Morus-Gymnasium Daun, Michael Reineke Str 6, Daun, 54550, Germany. TEL 49-6592-4117, FAX 49-6592-3639, tmg.schule@t-online.de, http://www.tmg-daun.de.

KLEIO; the magazine for history teachers. see *HISTORY*

KNOW YOUR WORLD EXTRA. see *CHILDREN AND YOUTH—For*

370   GBR
KNOWLEDGE, IDENTITY AND SCHOOL LIFE SERIES✳. Text in English. 1992. irreg., latest 1998. price varies. **Document type:** *Monographic series, Academic/Scholarly.* **Description:** Combines an empirical focus on school life with a theoretical interest in the meaning of contemporary social and cultural changes for education. Moves between macro and micro levels, and between empirical and theoretical analyses in order to illuminate identity and knowledge processes in school life.
Published by: RoutledgeFalmer Press (Subsidiary of: Taylor & Francis Group), 11 New Fetter Ln, London, EC4P 4EE, United Kingdom. TEL 44-20-7583-9855, FAX 44-20-7842-2298, info@tandf.co.uk, http://www.routledgefalmer.com. Eds. Ivor Goodson, Philip Wexler. **subsc. in Europe & Asia:** Taylor & Francis Ltd, Taylor & Francis Customer Services, ITPS, Cheriton House, North Way, Andover, Hampshire SP10 5BE, United Kingdom. TEL 44-1264-343071, FAX 44-1264-343005, book.orders@tandf.co.uk; **subsc. in N. America:** Taylor & Francis Inc., 7625 Empire Dr., Florence, KY 41042-2919. cserve@routledge-ny.com.

KNOWLEDGE QUEST. see *LIBRARY AND INFORMATION SCIENCES*

370   AUS   ISSN 1448-2673
HD5715.5.A8
THE KNOWLEDGE TREE; an e - journal of flexible learning in vocational education and training (V E T). Text in English. 2002. irreg. free (effective 2005). **Document type:** *Journal, Academic/Scholarly.*
Media: Online - full text.
Published by: Australian Flexible Learning Framework, Locked Mail Bag 527 GPO, Brisbane, QLD 4001, Australia. TEL 61-07-32475511, FAX 61-07-32370419, enquiries@flexiblelearning.net.au, http://www.flexiblelearning.net.au/knowledgetree/index.html.

370   FRA   ISSN 1764-5476
▼ **KNOWLEDGE, WORK & SOCIETY/SAVOIR, TRAVAIL & SOCIETE.** Text in Multiple languages. 2003. q. **Document type:** *Journal, Academic/Scholarly.*

Published by: L' Harmattan, 5 rue de l'Ecole Polytechnique, Paris, 75005, France. TEL 33-1-43257651, FAX 33-1-43258203, http://www.editions-harmattan.fr.

KOBLENZER GEOGRAPHISCHES KOLLOQUIUM. see *GEOGRAPHY*

370   JPN   ISSN 0389-0449
Q77   CODEN: KDKDDP
KOCHI DAIGAKU KYOIKUGAKUBU KENKYU HOKOKU. DAI-3-BU/KOCHI UNIVERSITY. FACULTY OF EDUCATION. BULLETIN. SERIES 3. Text in Japanese; Summaries in English. 1951. a. **Document type:** *Academic/Scholarly.*
Indexed: JPI, RASB.
—CASDDS.
Published by: (Kyoikugakubu), Kochi Daigaku/Kochi University, 5-1 Akebono-cho 2-chome, Kochi-shi, Kochi-ken 780-8520, Japan. TEL 81-888-44-0111.

KOCHNIANO ANEES/ANEES FOR CHILDREN. see *CHILDREN AND YOUTH—For*

372.948   DNK   ISSN 0023-253X
KOEBENHAVNS KOMMUNESKOLE. Text in Danish. 1908. 40/yr. adv. **Description:** News for Copenhagen's Teachers' Union.
Published by: Koebenhavns Laererforening, Frydendalsvej 24, Frederiksberg C, 1809, Denmark. TEL 45-33-22-33-22, http://www.klf-net.dk/kk/kk%20main.htm. Ed. Peter Garde TEL 45-33-31-41-39. Circ: 4,500.

KOGNITION OG PAEDAGOGIK. see *PSYCHOLOGY*

371.7   DNK   ISSN 1395-6124
KOMMUNALE SUNDHEDSORDNINGER. SKOLESUNDHEDSTJENESTEN. Text in Danish. 1994. a. stat.
Related titles: ◆ Series of: Sundhedsstatistikken (Year). ISSN 0909-4156.
Published by: Sundhedsstyrelsen/Danish Board of Health, Islands Brygge 67, PO Box 1881, Copenhagen S, 2300, Denmark. TEL 45-72-227400, FAX 45-72-227411, sst@sst.dk, http://www.sst.dk.

371.07   DEU
KORRESPONDENZBLATT EVANGELISCHER SCHULEN UND HEIME. Text in German. 1960. bi-m. **Document type:** *Newsletter, Trade.*
Published by: Arbeitsgemeinschaft Evangelischer Schulbuende, Herrenhaeuser Str 12, Hannover, 30419, Germany. TEL 49-511-2796240, FAX 49-511-2796277. Circ: 1,850.

372   FIN   ISSN 0357-2714
KOULULAINEN. Text in Finnish. 1945. 11/yr. EUR 50 (effective 2005). adv. illus. **Document type:** *Magazine, Consumer.* **Description:** For school children aged 7 to 13.
Published by: Yhtyneet Kuvalehdet Oy/United Magazines Ltd., Maistraatinportti 1, Helsinki, 00015, Finland. TEL 358-9-15661, FAX 358-9-145650, http://www.kuvalehdet.fi/. Ed. Sirkku Kuusava. Circ: 39,274.

370   ROM   ISSN 1221-5732
KOZOKTATAS. Text in Hungarian. 1957. m. ROL 6,000 per issue (effective 2000). bk.rev. **Document type:** *Academic/Scholarly.*
Formerly (until 1989): Tanugyi Ujsag
Published by: Cultural Association Transylvania, Piata Presei Libere 1, Bucharest, 71341, Romania. TEL 4-093-412980, 40-1-2244629, euromedia@gmx.net, http://www.euromedia.com.bi. Ed. Gergely Laszlo. Circ: 2,500.
Co-sponsor: Council for National Minorities.

370   DEU
KRANICH. Text in German. 1955. q. back issues avail. **Document type:** *Newsletter.*
Published by: Kranich Gymnasium, An der Windmuehle 23-25, Salzgitter, 38226, Germany. TEL 49-5341-4097-0. Ed. Joerg Hoffmeister. Circ: 800.

370.157   SWE   ISSN 1100-9691
KREATIV PEDAGOGIK; foer ett temaorienterat arbetssaett i foerskolan, grundskolans laagstadium och fritidshem. Text in Swedish. 1989. q. SEK 296 (effective 1996).
Published by: Foerlag Mary Ekdahl AB, A C Lindblads Gata 6, Goeteborg, 41871, Sweden. TEL 46-31-53-61-89, FAX 46-31-53-61-89.

796.07   NOR   ISSN 0333-0141
KROPPSOEVING. Text in Norwegian. 1951. 8/yr. NOK 300 (effective 1998). adv. bk.rev. **Document type:** *Journal, Academic/Scholarly.* **Description:** Devoted to physical education and sports in Norwegian schools.
Published by: Landslaget Fysisk Fostring i Skolen, Mollegaten 10, Toensberg, 3111, Norway. TEL 47-33-31-53-00, FAX 47-33-31-52-66, lff@lff.no. Ed. John Elvestad. Pub. Karl-Johan Lowe. Circ: 2,700 (controlled).

371.07   SWE   ISSN 0347-5409
KRUT; kritisk utbildningstidskrift. Variant title: Kritisk Utbildningstidskrift. Text in Swedish. 1977. q. SEK 240 to individuals; SEK 280 to institutions (effective 2004).

E

Published by: Foereningen Kritisk Utbildningstidskrift, Torpedverkstaden, Skeppsholmen, Stockholm, 11149, Sweden. TEL 46-8-6117010, FAX 46-8-6116260, tidskriften.krut@telia.com, http://www.krut.a.se. Ed. Goeran Folin.

370 POL ISSN 1230-266X
KULTURA I EDUKACJA. Text in Polish. 1992. q. EUR 81 foreign (effective 2005). **Document type:** *Journal, Academic/Scholarly.*
Published by: Wydawnictwo Adam Marszalek, ul Lubicka 44, Torun, 87100, Poland. info@marszalek.com.pl, http://www.marszalek.com.pl. **Dist. by:** Ars Polona, Krakowskie Przedmiescie 7, Warsaw, Poland. TEL 48-22-9263914, FAX 48-22-9265334, arspolona@arspolona.com.pl, http://www.arspolona.com.pl.

KULTURSMOCKEN. see *MUSIC*

KUMAR. see *ART*

370 TUR ISSN 1303-0485
KURAM VE UYGULAMADA EDYTYM BYLYMLERY/ EDUCATIONAL SCIENCES: THEORY & PRACTICE. Text in Turkish. s-a. **Document type:** *Journal.*
Related titles: Online - full text ed.: (from EBSCO Publishing, ProQuest Information & Learning).
Indexed: CPE, ERA, ETA, MEA, PsycInfo, PsycholAb, RHEA, SEA, SENA, SOMA, TEA.
Published by: Educational Consultancy Ltd., Kysykly Mh. Alemdao Cd. Ysn Yol Sk., SBK Yp Merkezi No 5, Kat 1 Uskudar, Istanbul, 81190, Turkey. TEL 90-216-4813023, FAX 90-216-4813136, edam@edam.com.tr, http://www.edam.com.tr/kuyeb.asp, http://www.edam.com.tr/estp.asp. Ed. Muhsin Hesapcyadlu.

370 RUS
KUR'YER OBRAZOVANIYA/COURIER OF EDUCATION. Text in Russian. 1997. w.
Media: Online - full content.
Published by: Redaktsiya Zhurnala Kur'yer Obrazovaniya, B. Vlas'yevskii Per. 11, komn. 111, Moscow, Russian Federation. TEL 7-095-2410500, ext. 130, courier ed@mail.ru, http://www.courier.com.ru. Ed. Mikhail Arapov. **Co-sponsor:** Rossiiskii Gumanitarnyi Nauchnyi Fond.

370 POL ISSN 0023-5938
L51
KWARTALNIK PEDAGOGICZNY. Text in Polish; Summaries in English. 1956. q. EUR 41 foreign (effective 2005). bk.rev. **Document type:** *Journal, Academic/Scholarly.*
Indexed: CPE, RASB.
Published by: (Uniwersytet Warszawski, Wydzial Pedagogiczny), Wydawnictwa Uniwersytetu Warszawskiego, ul Nowy Swiat 4, Warsaw, 00497, Poland. TEL 48-22-5531319, FAX 48-22-5531318, kwartalnik@kp.edu.pl, wuw@uw.edu.pl, http://www.kp.edu.pl. Ed. Andrea Folkierska. Circ: 1,000. **Dist. by:** Ars Polona, Krakowskie Przedmiescie 7, Warsaw, Poland. TEL 48-22-9263914, FAX 48-22-9265334, arspolona@arspolona.com.pl, http://www.arspolona.com.pl.

370 JPN ISSN 0023-5997
KYOIKU HYORON/EDUCATIONAL REVIEW. Text in Japanese. 1951. m. JPY 6,000. adv. bk.rev.; film rev.; play rev. charts; illus.; stat.
Published by: Japan Teachers' Union/Nikkyoso, Nihon Kyoiku-Kaikan, 2-6-2 Hitotsubashi, Kanda, Chiyoda-ku, Tokyo, Japan. Ed. Masato Miyake. Circ: 20,000 (controlled).

E

370 JPN ISSN 0452-3318
L67
KYOIKU KENKYU/EDUCATIONAL STUDIES. Text in English, Japanese. 1958. a. USD 5. back issues avail.
Published by: International Christian University, Institute for Educational Research and Service/Kokusai Kirisutokyo Daigaku, 3-10 Osawa, Mitaka-shi, Tokyo-to 181-0015, Japan. FAX 0422-33-9887. Ed. Terumi Nakano. Circ: 500.

370 JPN ISSN 0387-3145
➤ **KYOIKU SHAKAIGAKU KENKYU/JOURNAL OF EDUCATIONAL SOCIOLOGY.** Text in Japanese; Abstracts in English. 1951. s-a. **Document type:** *Journal.*
Indexed: ERA, ETA, MEA, RHEA, SEA, SENA, SOMA, SSA, SociolAb, TEA.
Published by: Nihon Kyoiku Shakai Gakkai/Japan Society of Educational Sociology, Business Center for Academic Societies Japan, 5-16-9, Honkomagome, Bunkyo-ku, Tokyo, 113-8622, Japan. TEL 81-3-58145810, FAX 81-3-58145825, jses2@wwwsoc.nii.ac.jp, http://wwwsoc.nii.ac.jp/jses2/.

➤ **KYOIKU SHINRIGAKU KENKYU/JAPANESE JOURNAL OF EDUCATIONAL PSYCHOLOGY.** see *PSYCHOLOGY*

370.15 JPN ISSN 0452-9650
KYOIKU SHINRIGAKU NENPO/ANNUAL REPORT OF EDUCATIONAL PSYCHOLOGY IN JAPAN. Text in Japanese. 1961. a. JPY 4,000 (effective 2000). adv. **Document type:** *Academic/Scholarly.*
Indexed: e-psyche.
—BLDSC (1511.030000).
Published by: Nihon Kyoiku Shinri Gakkai/Japanese Association of Educational Psychology, Yamazaki Bldg 602, 2-40-14 Hongo, Bunko-ku, Tokyo, 113-0033, Japan. Ed. Akio Kikuchi. Adv. contact Seijun Takano.

370 JPN ISSN 0387-3161
KYOIKUGAKU KENKYU/JAPANESE JOURNAL OF EDUCATIONAL RESEARCH. Text in Japanese. 1932. q. JPY 10,000 membership (effective 2003). **Document type:** *Journal, Academic/Scholarly.*
—BLDSC (4651.760000). **CCC.**
Published by: Nihon Kyoiku Gakkai/Japan Society for the Study of Education, U.K's Bil. 2-29-3, Hongo, Bunkyo-ku, Tokyo, 113-0033, Japan. TEL 81-3-38182505, FAX 81-3-38166898, jsse@oak.ocn.ne.jp, http://wwwsoc.nii.ac.jp/jsse4/kikansi-j.html, http://wwwsoc.nii.ac.jp/jsse4/index-j.html.

371.1 USA ISSN 0162-3052
L A E NEWS. Text in English. 1977. 4/yr. USD 25 to non-members; free to members (effective 2005). adv. **Document type:** *Magazine, Trade.* **Description:** Publication directed to the education community in Louisiana, seeking to update educators on important happenings within the LAE-NEA, as well as cover education news of a more general nature.
Formerly: Louisiana Teachers' Tabloid
Published by: Louisiana Association of Educators, PO Box 479, Baton Rouge, LA 70821. carol.davis@lae.org, http://www.lae.org. adv.: B&W page USD 800; trim 11 x 15. Circ: 20,000 (paid).

370 GBR
L G I U POLICY BRIEFING. (Local Government Information Unit) Text in English. irreg.
—BLDSC (5186.104100).
Published by: Local Government Information Unit, The Education Network, 22 Upper Woburn Place, London, WC1H 0TB, United Kingdom. TEL 44-20-75542810, FAX 44-20-75542801, info@ten.info, http://www.ten.info/.

L M S - LINGUA. see *LINGUISTICS*

370 USA
L U N O. Text in English. 1985. 9/yr. looseleaf. USD 10. bk.rev. back issues avail.
Published by: Learning Unlimited Network of Oregon, 31960 S E Chin St, Boring, OR 97009. Ed. Gene Lehman. Circ: 250 (paid).

370 400 NLD ISSN 1567-6617
L1 EDUCATIONAL STUDIES IN LANGUAGE AND LITERATURE. Variant title: Educational Studies in Language and Literature. Text in English. 2001. 3/yr. EUR 221, USD 221, GBP 139 combined subscription to institutions print & online eds. (effective 2005). adv. reprint service avail. from PSC. **Document type:** *Journal, Academic/Scholarly.* **Description:** Aims to enhance the learning and teaching of mother tongues and deals with language education situations that often are referred to as mother tongue education, the teaching of the standard language or national language education.
Related titles: Online - full text ed.: ISSN 1573-1731 (from EBSCO Publishing, Gale Group, IngentaConnect, Kluwer Online, O C L C Online Computer Library Center, Inc., Springer LINK, Swets Information Services).
Indexed: BibLing, ERA, ETA, MEA, PsycInfo, PsycholAb, RHEA, SEA, SENA, SOMA, TEA.
—BLDSC (5312.540000), IE, Infotrieve, ingenta. **CCC.**
Published by: Springer-Verlag Dordrecht (Subsidiary of: Springer Science+Business Media), Van Godewijckstraat 30, Dordrecht, 3311 GX, Netherlands. TEL 31-78-6576050, FAX 31-78-6576474, http://springerlink.metapress.com/openurl.asp?genre=journal&issn=1567-6617, http://www.springeronline.com. Eds. Gert Rijlaarsdam, Mary Kooy.

370 USA ISSN 0023-7140
LADUE PUBLIC SCHOOLS BULLETIN. Text in English. 1960. bi-m. free. **Document type:** *Newsletter.*
Published by: Ladue Board of Education, c/o Linda Morice, Ed, School District of the City of Ladue, 9703, Conway, MO 63124. TEL 314-994-7080, FAX 314-994-0441. Eds. Erica Abbett, Linda Morice. Circ: 12,000 (controlled).

372 331 FIN ISSN 0356-7842
LAERAREN/TEACHER. Text in Swedish. 1894. 30/yr. EUR 60 (effective 2004). adv. bk.rev.; film rev. illus. back issues avail. **Document type:** *Trade.*
Formerly (until 1975): Skolnytt (0049-0660)
Related titles: Online - full text ed.
Published by: Finlands Svenska Laerarfoerbund/Trade Union of Teachers in Swedish Finland, Jaernvaegsmannagatan 6, Helsinki, 00520, Finland. TEL 358-20-7489410, FAX 358-9-142748, carl.erik.rusk@fsl.fi, http://www.fsl.fi/index.php?action=tidningen. Ed. Carl Erik Rusk TEL 358-20-7489468. Adv. contact Bo Gerkman. Circ: 5,400 (paid).

370 SWE ISSN 1101-2633
LAERARNAS TIDNING. Variant title: L T. Text in Swedish. 1990. 22/yr. SEK 460 (effective 2003). adv. bk.rev. illus.; stat. index. 5 cols./p.; **Document type:** *Newsletter, Trade.*
Formed by the merger of (1953-1990): Facklaeraren (0014-6463); (1967-1990): Laerartidningen, Svensk Skoltidning (0023-849X); Which was formed by the merger of (1957-1967): Laerartidningen (0455-1613); (1944-1967): Svensk Skoltidning
Related titles: Online - full text ed.
Indexed: RASB.
Published by: Laerarfoerbundet, Tidningsafdelning, Segelbaatsvaegen 15, Box 12229, Stockholm, 10226, Sweden. TEL 46-8-7376500, FAX 46-8-7376569, lararnas.tidning@lararforbundet.se, kansli@lararforbundet.se, http://www.lararnastidning.net/default.asp, http://www.lararforbundet.se. Ed. Sten Svensson. Adv. contact Camilla Lundberg TEL 46-8-7376806. B&W page SEK 40,000, color page SEK 53,000; trim 236 x 320. Circ: 222,800.

370.72 NGA ISSN 0331-9237
LA1631 CODEN: MNCEED
LAGOS EDUCATION REVIEW. Text in English. 1978. biennial. USD 10. adv. bk.rev. **Document type:** *Academic/Scholarly.* **Description:** Presents discussions of topics on all areas of education and reports of research.
Published by: Joja Educational Research and Publishers Limited, 13 B Ikorodu Rd, PMB 21526, Ikeja, Maryland, Lagos, Nigeria. TEL 234-64-933866. Ed. M N Okenimkpe. Circ: 3,000 (controlled). **Subscr. to:** Office of the Dean, Faculty of Education, University of Lagos, Akoka, Yaba, Lagos State, Nigeria.

LAMISHPAHA. see *RELIGIONS AND THEOLOGY—Judaic*

LANCASTER'S EDUCATION EMPLOYMENT LAW NEWS. see *LAW*

LANGUAGE & LITERACY; a Canadian educational e-journal. see *LITERATURE*

LANGUAGE LEARNING; a journal of research in language studies. see *LINGUISTICS*

LANGUAGE LEARNING JOURNAL. see *LINGUISTICS*

LANGUAGE MAGAZINE. see *LINGUISTICS*

LANGUAGE TODAY. see *LINGUISTICS*

370 ZAF ISSN 0023-8422
AP18
LANTERN; cultural journal. Text in Afrikaans, English. 1949. q. ZAR 30 (effective 1994). illus.
Incorporates: Young Academic
Related titles: Online - full text ed.: (from EBSCO Publishing).
Indexed: BEL&L, ISAP.
Published by: Foundation for Education Science and Technology, PO Box 1758, Pretoria, 0001, South Africa. TEL 27-12-322-6404, FAX 27-12-320-7803. Ed. Johan van Rooyen. Circ: 5,000.

371.58 USA
LAST RESORT✶ **.** Text in English. 1973. q. USD 10. bk.rev. **Document type:** *Newsletter.* **Description:** Publishes researches regarding the relationship between physical punishment and behavior problems. Promotes alternative methods of raising and educating children.
Published by: End Violence Against the Next Generation, Inc., 6 Gardenia Ct, Gaithersburg, MD 20879-4640. TEL 510-527-0454, adahm@aol.com. Ed. Adah Maurer. Circ: 1,000.

THE LAW HANDBOOK; your practical guide to the law in Victoria. see *CONSUMER EDUCATION AND PROTECTION*

373 USA ISSN 1531-3174
LB2805
LEADERSHIP (SACRAMENTO). Text in English. 1971. bi-m. free to members (effective 2005). adv. bk.rev. bibl.; charts; illus. index. reprint service avail. from PQC. **Document type:** *Trade.* **Description:** Covers curriculum, technology, staff development, at-risk students, school finance, student assessment, school safety, instructional leadership and school reform.
Former titles (until 2000): Thrust for Educational Leadership (1055-2243); (until 1990): Thrust (Sacramento) (0145-2061); Which superseded: Journal of Secondary Education (0022-4464)
Related titles: Microform ed.: (from PQC); Online - full text ed.: (from EBSCO Publishing, Florida Center for Library Automation, Gale Group, H.W. Wilson, O C L C Online Computer Library Center, Inc., ProQuest Information & Learning).
Indexed: ABIn, CalPI, ChPerI, EduInd, PCI.
—BLDSC (5162.863200), IE, ingenta.
Published by: Association of California School Administrators, 1517 L St, Sacramento, CA 95814. TEL 916-444-3216, 800-890-0325, FAX 916-444-3739, http://www.acsa.org. Ed., R&P Susan Davis. Adv. contact Diana Granger. B&W page USD 1,353, color page USD 2,153; trim 11 x 8.5. Circ: 16,000 (paid).

371.8 USA ISSN 1040-5399
LA229
LEADERSHIP FOR STUDENT ACTIVITIES. Text in English. 1974. m. (Sep.-May). free to members (effective 2005). adv. reprint service avail. from PQC. **Document type:** *Magazine, Trade.* **Description:** Articles of interest to student councils, honor societies and other student activity advisers and participants at the middle and high school level.
Former titles: Leadership (Reston); Student Activities (0746-3545); (until 1983): Student Advocate (0094-0836); Supersedes (1962-1974): Student Life Highlights (0039-2766); Student Life
Related titles: Online - full text ed.: (from bigchalk, O C L C Online Computer Library Center, Inc., ProQuest Information & Learning).
Published by: National Association of Secondary School Principals, 1904 Association Dr, Reston, VA 20191-1537. TEL 703-860-0200, FAX 703-476-5432, leadershipmag@principals.org, http://www.nasc.us/leadershipmag/, http://www.nassp.org. adv.: B&W page USD 4,100, color page USD 5,700. Circ: 40,000 (paid).

LEARN ENGLISH IN BRITAIN WITH A R E L S; your assurance of quality English teaching. see *LINGUISTICS*

370.15 GBR ISSN 1041-6080
LB1051 CODEN: LIDIEI
➤ **LEARNING AND INDIVIDUAL DIFFERENCES.** Text in English. 1989. 4/yr. EUR 119 in Europe to individuals; JPY 15,700 in Japan to individuals; USD 132 to individuals except Europe and Japan; EUR 287 in Europe to institutions; JPY 38,200 in Japan to institutions; USD 322 to institutions except Europe and Japan (effective 2006). back issues avail. **Document type:** *Academic/Scholarly.* **Description:** Devoted to publishing articles that make a substantial contribution to an understanding of individual differences within an educational context.
Related titles: Microform ed.: (from PQC); Online - full text ed.: (from EBSCO Publishing, Gale Group, IngentaConnect, ScienceDirect, Swets Information Services).
Indexed: ABIn, ASCA, AgeL, CDA, CPE, CurCont, EduInd, FamI, L&LBA, PsycInfo, PsycholAb, RefZh, SOPODA, SSCI, e-psyche.
—BLDSC (5179.325880), IDS, IE, Infotrieve, ingenta. **CCC.**
Published by: Pergamon (Subsidiary of: Elsevier Science & Technology), The Boulevard, Langford Ln, East Park, Kidlington, Oxford OX5 1GB, United Kingdom. TEL 44-1865-843000, FAX 44-1865-843010, http://www.elsevier.com/locate/lindif. Ed. J. B. Cooney. **Subscr. to:** Elsevier BV, PO Box 211, Amsterdam 1000 AE, Netherlands. TEL 31-20-485-3757, FAX 31-20-485-3432, nlinfo-f@elsevier.nl, http://www.elsevier.nl.

370.1523 GBR ISSN 0959-4752
LA620 CODEN: LEAIE9
➤ **LEARNING AND INSTRUCTION.** Text in English. 1991. 6/yr. EUR 558 in Europe to institutions; JPY 74,100 in Japan to institutions; USD 624 to institutions except Europe and Japan (effective 2006). index. back issues avail. **Document type:** *Journal, Academic/Scholarly.* **Description:** Presents papers and review articles on the processes of learning, development, instruction, and teaching representing a variety of theoretical perspectives and different methodological approaches.
Related titles: Microfilm ed.: (from PQC); Online - full text ed.: (from EBSCO Publishing, Gale Group, IngentaConnect, ScienceDirect, Swets Information Services); ♦ Series of: International Journal of Educational Research. ISSN 0883-0355; Supplement(s): Research Dialogue in Learning and Instruction. ISSN 1461-8222.
Indexed: BrEdI, CIJE, CPE, CurCont, ERA, ETA, MEA, PCI, PsycInfo, PsycholAb, RHEA, SEA, SENA, SOMA, SSCI, SWA, TEA, e-psyche.
—BLDSC (5179.325890), IDS, IE, Infotrieve, ingenta. **CCC.**
Published by: (European Association for Research on Learning and Instruction), Pergamon (Subsidiary of: Elsevier Science & Technology), The Boulevard, Langford Ln, East Park, Kidlington, Oxford OX5 1GB, United Kingdom. TEL 44-1865-843000, FAX 44-1865-843010, http://www.elsevier.com/locate/learninstruc. Ed. Wolfgang Schnotz. **Subscr. to:** Elsevier BV, PO Box 211, Amsterdam 1000 AE, Netherlands. TEL 31-20-485-3757, FAX 31-20-485-3432, nlinfo-f@elsevier.nl, http://www.elsevier.nl.

150 370 USA ISSN 0023-9690
BF1 CODEN: LNMVAV
➤ **LEARNING AND MOTIVATION.** Text in English. 1970. 4/yr. EUR 387 in Europe to individuals; JPY 40,400 in Japan to individuals; USD 261 elsewhere to individuals; EUR 854 in Europe to institutions; JPY 89,100 in Japan to institutions; USD 575 elsewhere to institutions; EUR 193 in Europe to students; JPY 20,200 in Japan to students; USD 131 elsewhere to students (effective 2006). adv. charts; illus. back issues avail. **Document type:** *Academic/Scholarly.* **Description:** Features original experimental research studies devoted to the analysis of basic phenomena and mechanisms of learning, memory, and motivation.
Related titles: Online - full text ed.: ISSN 1095-9122. USD 650 (effective 2002) (from EBSCO Publishing, Gale Group, IngentaConnect, O C L C Online Computer Library Center, Inc., ScienceDirect, Swets Information Services).
Indexed: AMHA, ASCA, ASFA, AnBeAb, B&BAb, BIOSIS Prev, BiolAb, CPE, ChemoAb, CommAb, CurCont, DIP, IBR, IBZ, L&LBA, MEA&I, MEDLINE, NSCI, PCI, PsySCBA&T, PsycInfo, PsycholAb, RASB, SOPODA, SSCI, SSI, SWA, TEA, e-psyche.
—BLDSC (5179.326000), IDS, IE, Infotrieve. **CCC.**
Published by: Academic Press (Subsidiary of: Elsevier Science & Technology), 525 B St, Ste 1900, San Diego, CA 92101-4495. TEL 619-231-6616, 800-894-3434, FAX 619-699-6422, apsubs@acad.com, http://www.elsevier.com/locate/l&m, http://www.academicpress.com. Ed. W A Roberts.

370 NLD ISSN 1387-1579
L11 CODEN: LEREFF
LEARNING ENVIRONMENTS RESEARCH. Text in Dutch. 1998. 3/yr. EUR 242, USD 242, GBP 160 combined subscription to institutions print & online eds. (effective 2005). adv. reprint service avail. from PSC. **Document type:** *Journal, Academic/Scholarly.* **Description:** Publishes original academic papers dealing with the study of learning environments, including theoretical reflections, reports of quantitative and qualitative research, critical and integrative literature reviews and meta-analyses, discussion of methodological issues, reports of the development and validation of assessment instruments, and reviews of books and evaluation instruments.
Related titles: Online - full text ed.: ISSN 1573-1855 (from EBSCO Publishing, Gale Group, IngentaConnect, Kluwer Online, O C L C Online Computer Library Center, Inc., Springer LINK, Swets Information Services).
Indexed: AEI, BibLing, ERA, ETA, MEA, PsycInfo, PsycholAb, RHEA, RefZh, SEA, SENA, SOMA, TEA.
—BLDSC (5179.326522), IE, Infotrieve, ingenta. **CCC.**
Published by: Springer-Verlag Dordrecht (Subsidiary of: Springer Science+Business Media), Van Godewijckstraat 30, Dordrecht, 3311 GX, Netherlands. TEL 31-78-6576050, FAX 31-78-6576474, http://springerlink.metapress.com/openurl.asp?genre=journal&issn=1387-1579, http://www.springeronline.com. Ed. Barry J Fraser.

372.6 USA ISSN 1083-5415
LEARNING LANGUAGES. Text in English. 1987. 3/yr. USD 30 domestic membership; USD 40 foreign membership (effective 2005). **Document type:** *Journal, Academic/Scholarly.*
Formerly (until 1995): F L E S News (1064-3540)
Indexed: L&LBA.
Published by: National Network for Early Language Learning, B205 Tribble Hall, Wake Forest University, Box 7266, Winston-Salem, NC 27109. nnell@wfu.edu, http://nnell.org/nnelljournal.htm. Ed. Dr. Teresa Kennedy.

LEBANON LIGHT. see *CHILDREN AND YOUTH—For*

LEBENDE SPRACHEN; Zeitschrift fuer fremde Sprachen in Wissenschaft und Praxis. see *LINGUISTICS*

LEBLANC BELL. see *MUSIC*

370 330 USA
LEDGER (BOSTON). Text in English. 3/yr. **Description:** Contains economic education resources for teachers and the general public, a well as articles of economic terms.
Published by: Federal Reserve Bank of Boston, 55882, Boston, MA 02205-5882. http://www.bos.frb.org/genpubs/ledger/ledger.htm. Ed. Bob Jabaily.

372.4 NLD ISSN 0921-2388
➤ **LEESGOED**; wat en hoe kinderen (leren) lezen. Text in Dutch. 1973. 8/yr. EUR 47.64 to individuals; EUR 30.99 to students; EUR 8.40 per issue (effective 2005). adv. bk.rev.; software rev. **Document type:** *Academic/Scholarly.* **Description:** For professionals in the field of reading education in the Netherlands and Flanders.
Incorporates (1995-2001): Boekidee (1381-1665); (1977-2001): De Schoolmediatheek (0165-1099); Formerly (until 1987): En Nu over Jengdliteratuur (0165-2788)
Related titles: CD-ROM ed.
—IE, Infotrieve.
Published by: Biblion Uitgeverij, Postbus 437, Leidschendam, 2260 AK, Netherlands. leesgoed@planet.nl, info@nbdbiblion.nl, http://www.nbdbiblion.nl/. Ed. Herman Verschuren. Pub. Andre Henderickx. Circ: 2,000.

370 DEU ISSN 0341-8294
LEHREN UND LERNEN. Text in German. 1975. m. EUR 39.90; EUR 3.80 newsstand/cover (effective 2003). adv. **Document type:** *Journal, Academic/Scholarly.*
Published by: (Landesinstitut fuer Erziehung und Unterricht Stuttgart), Neckar Verlag GmbH, Postfach 1820, Villingen-Schwenningen, 78008, Germany. TEL 49-7721-89870, FAX 49-7721-898750, service@neckar-verlag.de, http://www.neckar-verlag.de. Adv. contact Peter Walter. page EUR 282. Circ: 2,146 (paid and controlled).

370 DEU
LEHRERINNEN- UND LEHRERKALENDER. Text in German. 1977. a. EUR 9.80 (effective 2005). adv. bk.rev. **Document type:** *Bulletin, Trade.*
Published by: Anabas-Verlag Guenter Kaempf KG, Friesstr 20-24, Frankfurt Am Main, 60388, Germany. TEL 49-69-94219871, FAX 49-69-94219872, http://www.txt.de/anabas/. Ed. Vilma Link Kaempf. Pub., R&P Guenter Kaempf. Adv. contact Vilma Link-Kaempf. Circ: 20,000.

370.1 DEU ISSN 1430-2675
LERNEN FUER EUROPA. Text in German. 1996. irreg., latest vol.8, 2001. EUR 15.30 per vol. (effective 2003). **Document type:** *Monographic series, Academic/Scholarly.*
Published by: Waxmann Verlag GmbH, Steinfurter Str 555, Muenster, 48159, Germany. TEL 49-251-26504-0, FAX 49-251-2650426, info@waxmann.com, http://www.waxmann.com. Ed. Georg Hansen.

370.1 DEU ISSN 1434-3770
LERNEN, ORGANISIERT UND SELBSTGESTEUERT. Text in German. irreg., latest vol.3, 2002. EUR 29.90 per vol. (effective 2003). **Document type:** *Magazine, Academic/Scholarly.* **Description:** Focuses on philosophical, cultural, educational, psychological, sociological, organizational, behavioral, motivational, and emotional aspects of self-directed learning.
Published by: Waxmann Verlag GmbH, Steinfurter Str 555, Muenster, 48159, Germany. TEL 49-251-26504-0, FAX 49-251-2650426, info@waxmann.com, http://www.waxmann.com. Ed. Gerald A. Straka.

LESBIAN & GAY TEACHERS' ASSOCIATION NEWSLETTER. see *HOMOSEXUALITY*

LESLEY UNIVERSITY SERIES IN ART AND EDUCATION. see *ART*

370.96885 LSO
LESOTHO. MINISTRY OF EDUCATION, SPORTS AND CULTURE. ANNUAL REPORT OF THE PERMANENT SECRETARY. Text in English. 1966. a. **Document type:** *Government.*
Formerly: Lesotho. Ministry of Education and Culture. Annual Report of the Permanent Secretary
Published by: Ministry of Education Sports and Culture, PO Box 47, Maseru, Lesotho.

LETTRE D'INFORMATION JURIDIQUE. see *LAW—Judicial Systems*

LEVENDE TALEN MAGAZINE. see *LINGUISTICS*

LEVENDE TALEN TIJDSCHRIFT. see *LINGUISTICS*

370 CHN ISSN 1002-8196
LIAONING JIAOYU/LIAONING EDUCATION. Text in Chinese. 1972. m. CNY 18.
Related titles: Online - full text ed.: (from East View Information Services).
Published by: (Liaoning Sheng Jiaoyu Ting/Liaoning Provincial Bureau of Education), Liaoning Jiaoyu Zazhishe, 29 Ningshan Zhonglu, Huangu-qu, Shenyang, Liaoning 110031, China. TEL 6853324. Ed. Wei Guanghua.

371.04 GBR ISSN 0267-8500
LIB ED; a magazine for the liberation of learning. Text in English. 1967. 3/yr. USD 29 to individuals; USD 46 to institutions. adv. bk.rev. **Document type:** *Academic/Scholarly.* **Description:** News items and feature articles on the practical and philosophic issues associated with freedom in education and learning in schools and colleges through alternatives to authoritarianism and elitism; contains lists of sources and associations.
Formerly: Libertarian Education
Address: Phoenix House, 157 Wells Rd, Bristol, BS4 2BU, United Kingdom. FAX 44-1272-778453, editors@libed.demon.co.uk, http://www.libed.demon.uk. Circ: 1,500.

371.07 002 ROM ISSN 1454-265X
Z665.2.R6
➤ **LIBER**; revista pentru bibliotecile pedagogice si scolare. Text in Romanian. 1990. q. ROL 30,000 per issue domestic; USD 20 per issue foreign (effective 2002). bk.rev. abstr.; illus.; maps; stat. 100 p./no.; back issues avail. **Document type:** *Bulletin, Academic/Scholarly.* **Description:** Provides articles on bibliology, school libraries and pedagogy.
Related titles: E-mail ed.
Published by: Biblioteca Pedagogica Nationala/National Library of Education, Str. Zalomit 12, Sector 1, Bucharest, 70714, Romania. TEL 40-01-3110323, FAX 40-01-3110323, bpn@fx.ro. Ed. George Anca. Circ: 100.

370 ITA
LIBERTA DI EDUCAZIONE; rivista di cultura e politica scolastica. Text in Italian. 1976. m. adv. bk.rev. **Document type:** *Journal, Academic/Scholarly.*
Published by: Centro Servizi Didattici, Via Gian Antonio Boltraffio, 21, Milan, MI 20159, Italy. TEL 39-2-606377, FAX 39-2-6880981, red@enter.it, http://www.diesse.org. Ed. Nicola Itri. Pub. Giuseppe Meroni. Adv. contact Valeria Ambrosino. Circ: 5,500.

370 GBR ISSN 0953-7775
LIBERTARIAN ALLIANCE. EDUCATIONAL NOTES. Text in English. irreg. GBP 15, USD 30 (effective 1998). **Document type:** *Monographic series.*

E

Published by: Libertarian Alliance, 2 Landsdowne Row, Ste 35, London, W1J 6HL, United Kingdom. TEL 44-20-7821-5502, FAX 44-20-7834-2031, liberty@capital.demon.co.uk, nigel@libertarian.co.uk, http://www.digiweb.com/igeldard/la. R&P Chris Tame.

LIBRARY AND INFORMATION SCIENCE EDUCATION STATISTICAL REPORT. see *LIBRARY AND INFORMATION SCIENCES—Abstracting, Bibliographies, Statistics*

613.7 POL ISSN 0867-7697
LIDER. Text in Polish. 1991. m. **Document type:** *Journal, Academic/Scholarly.*
Published by: Szkolny Zwiazek Sportowy, Mazowiecka 7, Warsaw, 00052, Poland. TEL 48-22-8278907, zgszs.warszawa@wp.pl. **Dist. by:** Ars Polona, Krakowskie Przedmiescie 7, Warsaw, Poland. TEL 48-22-9263914, FAX 48-22-9265334, arspolona@arspolona.com.pl, http://www.arspolona.com.pl.

371.042 CAN ISSN 1499-7533
LIFE LEARNING; the international magazine of self-directed learning. Text in English. 2002 (March). bi-m. CND 24 domestic individuals & institutions; USD 24 in United States to individuals; USD 30 in United States to institutions (effective 2003 - 2004). **Document type:** *Magazine.* **Description:** Contains information and inspiration about unschooling, self-directed learning and distance learning opportunities for people of all ages.
Published by: Life Media, 508-264 Queen's Quay W, Toronto, ON M5J 1B5, Canada. TEL 416-260-0303, 800-215-9574, editor@lifelearningmagazine.com, http://www.lifelearningmagazine.com.

370 ARG ISSN 0024-354X
LIMEN✶; revista de orientacion didactica. Text in Spanish. 1963. 4/yr. free. adv. bk.rev. charts; illus.
Published by: Kapeluz Revistas S.A.I.C., Moreno 376, Buenos Aires, 1091, Argentina. Ed. Jorge Kapelusz. Circ: 200,000.

LINGUISTICS AND EDUCATION. see *LINGUISTICS*

371.83 CAN
LINK (BURNABY). Text in English. 1966. bi-w. CND 20. adv. bk.rev.
Published by: British Columbia Institute of Technology, Student Association, 3700 Willingdon Ave, Burnaby, BC V5G 3H2, Canada. TEL 604-434-5734. Ed. Paul Dayson. Circ: 5,000.

L'INTERPRETE. see *LINGUISTICS*

372 GBR ISSN 1741-4350
LB1050
➤ **LITERACY.** Text in English. 1967. 3/yr., latest vol.36, no.3, 2002. EUR 89 combined subscription in Europe to individuals print & online eds.; USD 110 combined subscription in the Americas to individuals & Caribbean, print & online eds.; GBP 59 combined subscription elsewhere to individuals print & online eds.; GBP 153 combined subscription in Europe to institutions print & online eds.; USD 294 combined subscription in the Americas to institutions & Caribbean, print & online eds.; GBP 175 combined subscription elsewhere to institutions print & online eds. (effective 2006). adv. bk.rev. back issues avail.; reprint service avail. from PQC,PSC. **Document type:** *Journal, Academic/Scholarly.*
Formerly (until 2004): Reading (0034-0472)
Related titles: Microform ed.: (from MIM, PQC); Online - full text ed.: ISSN 1467-9345. GBP 145 in Europe to institutions; USD 279 in the Americas to institutions & Caribbean; GBP 166 elsewhere to institutions (effective 2006) (from Blackwell Synergy, EBSCO Publishing, IngentaConnect, O C L C Online Computer Library Center, Inc., Swets Information Services).
Indexed: BrEdI, CIJE, CPE, ChLitAb, ERA, ETA, HECAB, L&LBA, LT&LA, MEA, PsycInfo, PsycholAb, RHEA, RILM, SEA, SENA, SOMA, SOPODA, TEA, e-psyche.
—BLDSC (5276.630002), IE, Infotrieve, ingenta. **CCC.**
Published by: Blackwell Publishing Ltd., 9600 Garsington Rd, Oxford, OX4 2ZG, United Kingdom. TEL 44-1865-776868, FAX 44-1865-714591, customerservices@oxon.blackwellpublishing.com, http://www.blackwellpublishing.com/journals/Literacy. Ed. Teresa M Grainger TEL 44-1227-767700. Circ: 2,200.

302.224 GBR
LITERACY NEWS. Text in English. 1971. q. **Document type:** *Newsletter, Academic/Scholarly.*
Former titles (until 2003): Language and Literacy News (0958-8140); (until 1990): U K R A Newsletter (0951-9505); (until 1986): United Kingdom Reading Association. Newsletter (0307-8191)
—BLDSC (5155.696150).
Published by: The United Kingdom Literacy Association, Upton House, Baldock St, Royston, Herts SG8 5AY, United Kingdom. TEL 44-1763-241188, FAX 44-1763-243785, admin@ukla.org.

370 RUS
LITSEISKOE I GIMNAZICHESKOE OBRAZOVANIE. Text in Russian. 1998. bi-m. USD 99 in North America.
Published by: Moskovskii Kul'turologicheskii Litsei, Ul. Nizhnyaya Pervomaiskaya, 52, Moscow, 105203, Russian Federation. TEL 7-095-4652656. **Dist. by:** East View Information Services, 3020 Harbor Ln. N., Minneapolis, MN 55447. TEL 763-550-0961, FAX 763-559-2931.

THE LIVING LIGHT; an interdisciplinary review of Catholic religious education, catechesis and pastoral ministry. see *RELIGIONS AND THEOLOGY—Roman Catholic*

330 IND ISSN 0024-5917
LOK RAJYA. Text in Marathi. 1945. s-m. INR 10. bk.rev. illus. back issues avail.
Related titles: English ed.
Published by: Directorate of Information and Public Relations, Sachivalaya, Mumbai, Maharashtra 400 032, India. Ed. Shri S K Sagane. Circ: 13,250.

370.1 GBR ISSN 0959-8731
PB1011
LONDON ASSOCIATION FOR CELTIC EDUCATION. DIRECTORY. Text in English. 1989. a. GBP 2 (effective 1999). **Document type:** *Directory.*
Published by: London Association for Celtic Education, Eastgate Bldg, 131 St John's Way, London, N19 3RQ, United Kingdom. Ed. Pauline Preece. Circ: 500.

370.1 GBR ISSN 1474-8460
▼ **LONDON REVIEW OF EDUCATION.** Text in English. 2003. 3/yr. GBP 164, USD 271 combined subscription to institutions print & online eds. (effective 2006). **Document type:** *Journal, Academic/Scholarly.* **Description:** Deals with the promotion and dissemination of informed analysis of major issues in education.
Related titles: Online - full text ed.: ISSN 1474-8479. 2003. GBP 156, USD 257 to institutions (effective 2006) (from EBSCO Publishing, Gale Group, IngentaConnect, O C L C Online Computer Library Center, Inc., Swets Information Services).
Indexed: BrEdI, CPE, DIP, ERA, IBR, IBZ.
—BLDSC (5294.094200), IE.
Published by: (University of London, Institute of Education USA), Routledge (Subsidiary of: Taylor & Francis Group), 4 Park Sq, Milton Park, Abingdon, Oxon OX14 4RN, United Kingdom. TEL 44-1235-828600, FAX 44-1235-829000, info@routledge.co.uk, http://www.tandf.co.uk/journals/titles/14748460.asp, http://www.routledge.co.uk. Eds. Dr. David Halpin, David Halpin. **Subscr. to:** Taylor & Francis Ltd, Journals Customer Service, Rankine Rd, Basingstoke, Hants RG24 8PR, United Kingdom. TEL 44-1256-813000, FAX 44-1256-330245.

300 USA ISSN 1040-2748
H62.A1
LOUISIANA SOCIAL STUDIES JOURNAL. Text in English. 1986. a. **Document type:** *Journal.*
Indexed: CIJE.
Published by: Loiusiana Council for the Social Studies, University of New Orleans, Department of Curriculum and Instruction, New Orleans, LA 70148. http://ss.uno.edu/SS/Less/Journal.

LUMEN VITAE; revue internationale de catechese et de pastorale. see *RELIGIONS AND THEOLOGY—Roman Catholic*

370 CAN
LUMINUS. Text in English. s-a. **Document type:** *Magazine, Consumer.*
Related titles: Online - full content ed.
Published by: Memorial University of Newfoundland Alumni Association, Office of Alumni Affairs and Development, St. John"s, NF A1C 5S7, Canada. TEL 709-737-4354, 877-700-4081, FAX 709-737-2008, munalum@mun.ca, http://www.mun.ca/munalum/magazine.html. Ed. Wade Kearley.

370 SWE
LUND STUDIES IN EDUCATION. Text in English, Swedish. irreg., latest vol.4, 1997. price varies.
Published by: Lunds Universitet, Department of Education/Lund University, Box 199, Lund, 22100, Sweden.

LUTHERAN EDUCATION. see *RELIGIONS AND THEOLOGY—Protestant*

370.1 USA
M E A - M F T TODAY. Text in English. 1924. 5/yr. membership. adv. bk.rev. illus. **Document type:** *Newsletter.*
Former titles: M E A Today; Montana Education (0026-993X)
Related titles: Microfilm ed.: (from PQC).
Published by: Montana Education Association - Montana Federation of Teachers, 1232 E Sixth Ave, Helena, MT 59601. TEL 406-442-4250, 800-398-0826, FAX 406-443-5081, sporte@mea-mft.org, http://www.mea-mft.org/. Ed., R&P Sanna Porte. Circ: 15,000.

370.1 AUS
➤ **M E R G A. ANNUAL CONFERENCE PROCEEDINGS.** Text in English. 1992. a. price varies. **Document type:** *Proceedings, Academic/Scholarly.*
Published by: M E R G A, c/o Helen Chick, MERGA VP Membership, Dept Science and Mathematics Education, University of Melbourne, Melbourne, VIC 3010, Australia. TEL 61-3-83448324, FAX 61-3-83448739, h.chick@unimelb.edu.au, http://www.deakin.edu.au/education/numeracy_and_merino/merga/homepage.html.

370.1 AUS
M E R G A. MEMBERSHIP DIRECTORY. (Mathematics Education Research Group of Australasia) Text in English. biennial. **Document type:** *Directory.* **Description:** Contains contact information as well as a description of members' research interests.
Published by: M E R G A, c/o Helen Chick, MERGA VP Membership, Dept Science and Mathematics Education, University of Melbourne, Melbourne, VIC 3010, Australia. TEL 61-3-83448324, FAX 61-3-83448739, h.chick@unimelb.edu.au, http://www.deakin.edu.au/education/numeracy_and_merino/merga/homepage.html.

370 USA ISSN 0898-2481
CODEN: POPREL
M T A TODAY. Text in English. 1972. m. free domestic to members (effective 2005). adv. **Document type:** *Magazine, Trade.*
Published by: Massachusetts Teachers Association, 20 Ashburton Pl, Boston, MA 02108-2727. TEL 617-742-7950, FAX 617-742-7046, http://www.massteacher.org. Ed. Jim Sacks. Circ: 97,000 (controlled).

370.113 USA ISSN 0464-2082
M V A VIEWPOINTS. Text in English. 1947. 4/yr. USD 2. adv. bk.rev. charts; illus.; stat.; tr.lit.
Published by: Minnesota Vocational Association, 6016 Oakland Ave, Minneapolis, MN 55417. TEL 612-866-6574. Ed. James Lee. Circ: 3,200.

320.071 NLD ISSN 1566-1555
MAATSCHAPPIJ & POLITIEK; vakblad voor maatschappijleer. Text in Dutch. 1983. 8/yr. EUR 36.95; EUR 32.25 to students; EUR 41.50 to institutions; EUR 4.75 per issue (effective 2003). **Document type:** *Journal, Academic/Scholarly.*
Formerly (until 1998): Politieke en Sociale Vorming (0167-9538); Which incorporated (1983-1985): Verenigingsorgaan Politieke en Sociale Vorming (0169-1031)
—IE, Infotrieve.
Published by: Instituut voor Publiek en Politiek, Prinsengracht 911-915, Amsterdam, 1017 KD, Netherlands. TEL 31-20-5217600, FAX 31-20-6383118, http://www.publiek-politiek.nl. Ed. Willem Rasing. R&P Eddy M Habben Jansen.

MABAT SHELANU/OUR REVIEW. see *HANDICAPPED—Hearing Impaired*

MACAO. DIRECCAO DOS SERVICOS DE ESTATISTICA E CENSOS. INQUERITO AO ENSINO/MACAO. CENSUS AND STATISTICS DEPARTMENT. EDUCATION SURVEY. see *EDUCATION—Abstracting, Bibliographies, Statistics*

MACHBERET HAMENAHEL. see *RELIGIONS AND THEOLOGY—Judaic*

371.07 ITA
MAESTRI FRIULANI. Text in Italian. 1967. m. free.
Published by: (Associazione Italiana Maestri Cattolici di Udine), A I M C, Vicolo Sillio, 3, Udine, UD 33100, Italy. TEL 0432-295442. Circ: 2,000.

IL MAESTRO. see *RELIGIONS AND THEOLOGY—Roman Catholic*

370 EGY ISSN 1110-1237
MAGALAT KULIYYAT AL-TARVIYAT GAMI'AT TANTA/TANTA UNIVERSITY. FACULTY OF EDUCATION. JOURNAL. Text in Arabic. 1982. s-a. **Document type:** *Journal, Academic/Scholarly.*
Published by: Tanta University, Faculty of Education, c/o Mahmoud El-Tayeb, Tanta, Egypt. TEL 20-40-3318537, FAX 20-40-3359368, http://derp.sti.sci.eg/data/0041.htm. Ed. Dr. Mahmoud Abdel-Zhaher El-Tayeb.

370 150 EGY ISSN 1110-7626
MAGALLAT KOLLIYAT AL-TARBIYAT. TARBIYA WA'ILM NAFS/FACULTY OF EDUCATION. EDUCATION AND PSYCHOLOGY JOURNAL. Text in Arabic. 198?. irreg. free (effective 2004).
Published by: Ain Shams University, Faculty of Education, Heliopolis, Cairo, Egypt. TEL 20-2-4506842, http://derp.sti.sci.eg/data/0293.htm. Ed. Yusri Afifi Afifi.

E

370.72   UAE   ISSN 1684-9507
LA1437
➤ **MAGALLAT KULLIYYAH AL-TARBIYAH/JOURNAL OF FACULTY OF EDUCATION.** Text in English, Arabic; Summaries in Arabic. 1986. a. AED 30 domestic to individuals; AED 40 to individuals Arab countries; AED 60 elsewhere to individuals; AED 100 domestic to institutions; AED 150 foreign to institutions; AED 30 newsstand/cover (effective 2003). bk.rev. abstr.; bibl.; charts; illus.; stat. cum. index: 1986-1999. back issues avail. **Document type:** *Journal, Academic/Scholarly.* **Description:** Covers education, curriculum, instruction, educational reform, students, teachers, schools and so forth.
Related titles: Online - full text ed.
Published by: United Arab Emirates University, College of Education, P.O. Box 15551, Al-ain, Abu-Dhabi, United Arab Emirates. TEL 971-3-7633963, FAX 971-3-7629988, j.education@uaeu.ac.ae, http://www.fedu.uaeu.ac.ae/cej. Ed. Abdelmoneim Ahmed Hassan.

370   EGY   ISSN 1110-3248
MAGALLAT RABETAT AL-TARBIYYAT AL-HADITHAT/JOURNAL OF MODERN EDUCATIONAL LEAGUE. Text in Arabic. 1993. 3/yr. EGP 10 domestic; USD 20 foreign (effective 2004). **Document type:** *Journal, Academic/Scholarly.*
Published by: Tanta University, Faculty of Education, c/o Mahmoud El-Tayeb, Tanta, Egypt. TEL 20-40-3318537, FAX 20-40-3359368, http://derp.sti.sci.eg/data/0283.htm. Ed. Dr. Mahmoud Abdel-Zhaher El-Tayeb.

370   LUX
THE MAGAZINE. Text in English. 1994. q. **Description:** Reports on European Union policies in the fields of education, training, youth, audiovisual technology, culture, languages, sport, and civil society.
Formerly (until no.20, 2003): Le Magazine (1023-3725)
Related titles: Spanish ed.: El Magazine; Ed.: Das Magazin; Ed.: La Rivista.
—BLDSC (5332.695000).
Published by: (European Commission, Directorate-General for Education and Culture BEL), European Commission, Office for Official Publications of the European Union, 2 Rue Mercier, Luxembourg, L-2985, Luxembourg. eac-info@cec.eu.int, info-info-opoce@cec.eu.int, http://europa.eu.int/comm/dgs/education_culture/mag/index_en.html, http://www.eurunion.org/publicat/index.htm. Eds. Francis Gutmann, Jaime Andreu Romeo.

MAGAZINE OF HISTORY; for teachers of history. see *HISTORY*

MAGISTER; revista de la escuela universitaria de magisterio. see *HUMANITIES: COMPREHENSIVE WORKS*

372   ESP
MAGISTERIO. Text in Spanish. 1866. w. adv. bk.rev. **Document type:** *Newspaper.* **Description:** Presents information about education, especially elementary and secondary levels.
Formerly: Magisterio Espanol (1131-8333)
Published by: Siena S.A., Pantoja, 14, Madrid, 28002, Spain. TEL 34-1-5199640, FAX 34-1-5611200. Ed. Miguel A Souto. Circ: 24,228.

370   HUN   ISSN 0025-0260
L56
➤ **MAGYAR PEDAGOGIA**; Hungarian journal of educational research. Text in Hungarian; Summaries in English. 1892. q. HUF 2,800 domestic; USD 14 foreign (effective 2004). bk.rev. 60 p./no. 1 cols./p.; back issues avail. **Document type:** *Journal, Academic/Scholarly.* **Description:** Publishes empirical, theoretical, methodological, and state of the art studies and papers.
Indexed: CPE, CurCont, ERA, ETA, L&LBA, MEA, RHEA, RILM, SEA, SENA, SOMA, SOPODA, TEA.
Published by: (Magyar Tudomanyos Akademia/Hungarian Academy of Sciences), Szegedi Tudomanyegyetem, Pedagogiai Tanszek/University of Szeged, Department of Education, Petofi sgt 30-34, Szeged, 6722, Hungary. TEL 36-62-544354, FAX 36-62-420034, csapo@edpsy.u-szeged.hu, http://www.arts.u-szeged.hu/mped, http://www.arts.u-szeged.hu/education. Ed. Beno Csapo. R&P Maria B Nemeth TEL 36-62-544354. Circ: 1,000 (paid). **Subscr. in Hungary to:** Magyar Posta Rt., Hirlapuzletagi Igazgatosag, Budapest 1846, Hungary. **Dist. by:** Kultura Kulkereskedemi Rt., Kerek utca 80, Budapest 1035, Hungary.

370   IND
MAHARASHTRA STATE INSTITUTE OF EDUCATION. RESEARCH BULLETIN. Text in English. 1975 (vol.5). q. free. bk.rev. bibl.; charts; illus.
Published by: Maharashtra State Institute of Education, Pune, Maharashtra 411030, India. Ed. M S Sadashiv Peth. Circ: 500.

370   USA   ISSN 0025-0775
MAINE TEACHER. Text in English. 1940. 9/yr. (Sep.-May). USD 6 to non-members. adv. charts; illus.
Published by: Maine Teachers' Association, 35 Community Dr, Augusta, ME 04330. TEL 207-622-5866. Ed. Keith C Harvie. Circ: 21,000.

LA MAISON - DIEU; revue de science liturgique. see *RELIGIONS AND THEOLOGY*

370.72   KWT
➤ **AL-MAJALLAH AT-TARBAWIYAH/EDUCATIONAL JOURNAL.** Text in Arabic, English. 1984. q. KWD 3 domestic to individuals; USD 15 foreign to individuals; KWD 15 domestic to institutions; USD 60 foreign to institutions (effective 2005). bk.rev. **Document type:** *Journal, Academic/Scholarly.* **Description:** Includes local and national research and studies.
Published by: Academic Publication Council, Kuwait University/Majliss an-Nushir al-Elmi, P O Box 13411, Keifan, 71955, Kuwait. TEL 965-4847961, FAX 965-4837794, tej@kuc01.kuniv.edu.kw, http://www.pubcouncil.kuniv.edu.kw/joe/english/default.asp. Ed. Abdullah Al Sheikh.

371.02   UAE
MAJALLAT AL-ANSHITTAH AL-TARBAWIYYAH/EDUCATIONAL ACTIVITIES MAGAZINE. Text in Arabic. 1988. irreg. free. **Description:** Discusses the state of private education in the U.A.E., focusing on present activities of private educational institutions and future projects.
Published by: Ministry of Education, Private Education Administration, PO Box 295, Abu Dhabi, United Arab Emirates. TEL 330216. Circ: 1,000.

372   DEU
MAL UND BASTELSTUNDE; Arbeitsblaetter fuer bildhaftes und konstruktives Gestalten. Text in German. 1978. 3/yr. looseleaf. EUR 13 (effective 2005). illus. cum.index: 1978-1999. back issues avail. **Document type:** *Journal, Academic/Scholarly.*
Published by: A L S Verlag GmbH, Voltastr 3, Dietzenbach, 63128, Germany. TEL 49-6074-82160, FAX 49-6074-27322, info@als-verlag.de, http://www.als-verlag.de. Ed. Ingrid Kreide. R&P Maria Landji.

MALTA. CENTRAL OFFICE OF STATISTICS. EDUCATION STATISTICS. see *EDUCATION—Abstracting, Bibliographies, Statistics*

370   IND
MAMANE. Text in English, Kannada. 1970. m. INR 10, USD 2. adv. bk.rev.
Published by: Mamane International Academy, 265-I-N Block, Rajajinagar, Bangalore, Karnataka 560 010, India. Ed. V K Javali. Circ: 500.

MANAGEMENT KINDEROPVANG. see *CHILDREN AND YOUTH—About*

371   GBR   ISSN 0968-1558
MANAGING SCHOOLS TODAY. Text in English. 1987. 6/yr. GBP 48 domestic to individuals; GBP 60 foreign to individuals; GBP 65 domestic to institutions; GBP 85 foreign to institutions (effective 2003). bk.rev.; film rev. **Document type:** *Academic/Scholarly.* **Description:** Independent magazine dealing with all aspects of a changing educational system in Britain.
Supersedes (in 1991): School Governor (0957-2775)
Related titles: Online - full text ed.: (from Swets Information Services).
Indexed: BrEdI, CPE.
—BLDSC (5359.303000), IE, ingenta.
Published by: Questions Publishing Company Ltd., 1st Fl, Leonard House, 321 Bradford St, Digbeth, Birmingham, Warks B1 3ET, United Kingdom. TEL 44-121-6667878, FAX 44-121-6667879, rchima@qiis.co.uk, http://www.education-quest.com/. Ed. Howard Sharron. Circ: 5,000.

371.1   GBR
MANCHESTER TEACHER✱. Text in English. 1980. bi-m.
Published by: Manchester Teachers' Association, c/o Whalley Range High School, Wilbraham Rd, Manchester, Lancs M16 8GW, United Kingdom. Ed. R Flint. Circ: 3,750.

371.042   CAN
MANITOBA ASSOCIATION FOR SCHOOLING AT HOME NEWSLETTER. Text in English. 1984. bi-m. CND 20. adv. **Document type:** *Newsletter.* **Description:** Provides information on events, resources and legislation on education at home. Includes a contact directory.
Published by: Manitoba Association for Schooling at Home, 98 Baltimore Rd, Winnipeg, MB R3L 1H1, Canada. TEL 204-334-4763. Ed. Keith Michaelson. Circ: 100.

371.1   CAN   ISSN 0025-228X
MANITOBA TEACHER. Text in English. 1919. 9/yr. CND 12. adv.
Related titles: Microfiche ed.: (from MML); Microfilm ed.: (from MML); Microform ed.: (from MML).
Indexed: CEI.
Published by: Manitoba Teachers Society, 191 Harcourt St, Winnipeg, MB R3J 3H2, Canada. TEL 204-888-7961, FAX 204-831-0877. Ed. Judy Edmond. Adv. contact Manav Agarwal. Circ: 17,000.

370   NZL
MAORI EDUCATION TRUST. ANNUAL REPORT. Text in English. 1962. a. NZD 30 (effective 1999).
Formerly: Maori Education Foundation. Annual Report (0076-4280)
Published by: Maori Education Trust, P.O. Box 11255, Wellington, New Zealand. TEL 64-4-499-8041, FAX 64-4-499-8006. **Subscr. to:** GP Legislation Services, P.O. Box 12418, Thorndon, Wellington, New Zealand.

370   DEU   ISSN 0178-1804
MARBURGER GELEHRTEN GESELLSCHAFT. ABHANDLUNGEN. Text in German. 1971. irreg. latest vol.24. **Document type:** *Monographic series.*
Published by: Wilhelm Fink Verlag, Ohmstr 5, Munich, 80802, Germany. TEL 49-89-348017, FAX 49-89-341378, http://www.fink.de. R&P Marlene Braun.

MARYLAND MUSIC EDUCATOR. see *MUSIC*

370.193   USA   ISSN 0025-4339
MARYLAND P T A BULLETIN. Text in English. 1950. m. (9/yr.). bk.rev. illus. **Document type:** *Newsletter.*
Published by: Maryland Congress of Parents and Teachers, 3121 Saint Paul St, Ste 25, Baltimore, MD 21218-3857. TEL 301-685-0865. Ed. Diane Thau. Circ: (controlled).

370   MYS   ISSN 0126-5024
MASALAH PENDIDIKAN; bulletin on current issues in education. Text in English, Malay. 1965. a. MYR 10. **Document type:** *Journal, Academic/Scholarly.*
Published by: (University of Malaya, Faculty of Education), University of Malaya/Perpustakaan Universiti Malaya, Lembah Pantai, Kuala Lumpur, 59100, Malaysia. Ed. Raja Maznah Raja Hussain. Circ: 800.

370   CZE   ISSN 1211-6971
MASARYKOVA UNIVERZITA. FILOZOFICKA FAKULTA. SBORNIK PRACI. U: RADA PEDAGOGICKA. Text in Czech; Summaries in Multiple languages. 1996. a. price varies. bk.rev. **Document type:** *Academic/Scholarly.* **Description:** Covers all aspects of pedagogics.
Supersedes in part (in 1996): Masarykova Univerzita. Filozoficka Fakulta. Sbornik Praci. I: Rada Pedagogicko - Psychologicka; Which was formerly: Univerzita J.E. Purkyne. Filozoficka Fakulta. Sbornik Praci. I: Rada Pedagogicko - Psychologicka (0068-2705)
Indexed: IBR, PsycholAb.
Published by: Masarykova Univerzita, Filozoficka Fakulta, A Novaka 1, Brno, 66088, Czech Republic. TEL 420-5-41121102, FAX 420-5-41121406, exchange@phil.muni.cz. R&P Milos Stedron TEL 420-5-41121337.

MASSACHUSETTS MUSIC NEWS. see *MUSIC*

371.1   USA   ISSN 0889-6259
MASTER TEACHER. Text in English. 1970. w. USD 17.64 (effective 2004). charts. **Document type:** *Academic/Scholarly.* **Description:** In-service program provided to teachers by principals and superintendents.
Published by: Master Teacher, Inc., Leadership Lane, Box 1207, Manhattan, KS 66502-0013. TEL 913-539-0555, FAX 913-539-7739, http://www.masterteacher.com/publication. Ed. Alice King. Circ: 214,000.

510.7   CZE   ISSN 1210-1761
MATEMATIKA, FYZIKA, INFORMATIKA; casopis pro zakladni a stredni skoly. Text in Czech, Slovak; Summaries in English. 1970. 10/yr. CZK 230, USD 7.40 (effective 1999). adv. bk.rev. **Document type:** *Academic/Scholarly.*
Formerly (until 1991): Matematika a Fyzika ve Skole (0323-1690); Formed by the merger of: Fyzika ve Skole (0016-3376); Matematika ve Skole
Published by: (Czech Republic. Jednota Ceskych Matematiku a Fyziku), Prometheus, spol. s r.o., Cestmirova 10, Prague 4, 140 00, Czech Republic. mfi@risc.upol.cz, http://www.upol.cz/exfyz/mfi.htm. Ed., R&P, Adv. contact Oldrich Lepil.

370   DEU   ISSN 0173-3842
MATERIALIEN AUS DER BILDUNGSFORSCHUNG. Text in German, English; Summaries in English. 1972. irreg. latest vol.71, 2001. price varies. **Document type:** *Monographic series, Academic/Scholarly.* **Description:** Monographic series of reports on works-in-progress at the institute.
Published by: Max-Planck-Institut fuer Bildungsforschung, Lentzeallee 94, Berlin, 14195, Germany. TEL 49-30-82406-0.

371.3   DEU   ISSN 0177-4018
MATERIALIEN ZUR BERUFS- UND ARBEITSPAEDAGOGIK. Text in German. 1984. irreg. latest vol.11. price varies. **Document type:** *Monographic series, Academic/Scholarly.*
Published by: Neckar Verlag GmbH, Postfach 1820, Villingen-Schwenningen, 78008, Germany. TEL 49-7721-89870, FAX 49-7721-898750, service@neckar-verlag.de, http://www.neckar-verlag.de.

MATERIALY HOMILETYCZNE. see *RELIGIONS AND THEOLOGY—Roman Catholic*

MATH NOTEBOOK. see *MATHEMATICS*

MATHEMATICAL PIE. see *MATHEMATICS*

MATHEMATICAL THINKING AND LEARNING; an international journal. see *MATHEMATICS*

THE MATHEMATICS EDUCATION. see *MATHEMATICS*

E

▼ *new title*   ➤ *refereed*   ✱ *unverified*   ◆ *full entry avail.*

MATHEMATICS EDUCATION LIBRARY. see *LIBRARY AND INFORMATION SCIENCES*

370 AUS ISSN 1442-3901
QA11.A1
➤ **MATHEMATICS TEACHER EDUCATION AND DEVELOPMENT.** Text in English. 1999. a. free to members. **Document type:** *Journal, Academic/Scholarly.* **Description:** Presents papers on issues related to teaching and learning in pre-service and in-service mathematics teacher education.
Indexed: AEI.
Published by: M E R G A, c/o Helen Chick, MERGA VP Membership, Dept Science and Mathematics Education, University of Melbourne, Melbourne, VIC 3010, Australia. TEL 61-3-83448324, FAX 61-3-83448739, h.chick@unimelb.edu.au, http://www.deakin.edu.au/education/numeracy_and_merino/merga/homepage.html. Eds. Len Sparrow, Merrilyn Goos, Sandra Frid.

➤ **MATHEMATIQUE ET PEDAGOGIE.** see *MATHEMATICS*

▼ ➤ **THE MATRON;** for matrons and their colleagues. see *CHILDREN AND YOUTH—About*

370.96982 MUS
MAURITIUS INSTITUTE OF EDUCATION. ANNUAL REPORT. Text in English. a. free. **Document type:** *Academic/Scholarly.*
Published by: Mauritius Institute of Education, Reduit, Mauritius. TEL 230-454-1031, FAX 230-454-1037, osmie@intnet.mu.

370.96982 MUS
MAURITIUS INSTITUTE OF EDUCATION. JOURNAL. Text in English. 1977. a. free. **Document type:** *Journal, Academic/Scholarly.*
Indexed: PLESA.
Published by: Mauritius Institute of Education, Reduit, Mauritius. TEL 230-454-1031, FAX 230-454-1037, osmie@intnet.mu.

370 USA ISSN 0025-6110
MAXWELL REVIEW. Text in English. 1965. s-a.
Published by: Maxwell Graduate Student Association, 225 Eggers Hall, Maxwell School of Syracuse University, Syracuse, NY 13244-1090. Ed. Ralph S Hambrick Jr.

370 CAN ISSN 0024-9033
➤ **MCGILL JOURNAL OF EDUCATION/REVUE DES SCIENCES DE L'EDUCATION DE MCGILL.** Text in English, French. 1966. 3/yr. CND 37.50 domestic; CND 55 foreign; CND 25 to students (effective 2005). bk.rev. bibl.; charts; illus.; stat. cum.index. **Document type:** *Academic/Scholarly.*
Related titles: Microfiche ed.: (from MML); Microfilm ed.: (from MML, PQC); Microform ed.: (from MML); Online - full text ed.: (from H.W. Wilson, Micromedia ProQuest, O C L C Online Computer Library Center, Inc., ProQuest Information & Learning).
Indexed: ABIn, CEI, CIJE, CPE, ERA, ETA, EduInd, MEA, RHEA, SEA, SENA, SOMA, SRRA, SWA, TEA.
—BLDSC (5413.427500), IE, Infotrieve, ingenta. **CCC.**
Published by: McGill University, Faculty of Education, 3700 McTavish St, Montreal, PQ H3A 1Y2, Canada. TEL 514-398-4246, FAX 514-398-4529, keenana@education.mcgill.ca, http://www.education.mcgill.ca/edmje.htm. Ed. Dr. Ann Beer. R&P Ann Keenan. Circ: 500.

371.4 USA ISSN 0748-1756
LB1027.5
➤ **MEASUREMENT AND EVALUATION IN COUNSELING AND DEVELOPMENT.** Text in English; Abstracts in Spanish. 1968. q. USD 63 to individuals; USD 75 to institutions; USD 16 per issue; free to members (effective 2005). adv. bk.rev. abstr.; charts; stat.; bibl. index. 64 p./no.; back issues avail.; reprint service avail. from PQC,PSC. **Document type:** *Journal, Academic/Scholarly.* **Description:** Focuses on the latest research and applications for counselors, administrators, educators, researchers and students.
Formerly (until 1984): Measurement and Evaluation in Guidance (0025-6307)
Related titles: Microform ed.: (from PQC); Online - full text ed.: (from EBSCO Publishing, Florida Center for Library Automation, Gale Group, H.W. Wilson, O C L C Online Computer Library Center, Inc., ProQuest Information & Learning).
Indexed: ABIn, ASCA, AgeL, CIJE, CurCont, EduInd, FamI, HEA, HRA, IMFL, PsycInfo, PsycholAb, SENA, SSCI, SWR&A, e-psyche.
—BLDSC (5413.560800), IDS, IE, Infotrieve, ingenta. **CCC.**
Published by: (Association for Assessment in Counseling), American Counseling Association, 5999 Stevenson Ave, Alexandria, VA 22304-3300. TEL 800-347-6647, FAX 800-473-2329, http://www.counseling.org. Ed. Patricia B Elmore. R&P Cynthia Peay TEL 703-823-9800 ext 249. Adv. contact Kathy Maguire TEL 703-823-9800 ext 207. Circ: 2,000.

➤ **MEDIA LAW NOTES.** see *JOURNALISM*

371.33 HUN ISSN 1218-4004
MEDIAKOMMUNIKACIO/MEDIA COMMUNICATIONS. Text in Hungarian. 1964. 10/yr. HUF 980. adv. bibl. index.
Former titles (until 1994): A V Kommunikacio (0237-9740); (until 1987): Audio-Vizualis Kozlemenyek - Audio-Visual Review (0231-2379); Supersedes (in 1973): Audio-Vizualis Technikai es Modszertani Kozlemenyek (0004-7600)
Published by: Orszagos Muszaki Informacios Kozpont es Konyvtar/National Technical Information Centre and Library, Muzeum utca 17, PO Box 12, Budapest, 1428, Hungary. TEL 36-1-1382300. Ed. Ivan Arkos. Circ: 3,100. **Subscr. to:** Kultura, PO Box 149, Budapest 1389, Hungary.

371.3 FRA ISSN 0997-3702
MEDIALOG. Text in French. 1969. q. bk.rev. abstr. back issues avail. **Description:** Explores new technologies in the world of education.
Formerly: Media (0025-6889)
Indexed: CurCont.
Published by: Centre National de Documentation Pedagogique, 29 rue de l'Ulm, Paris, Cedex 5 75230, France. TEL 33-1-46349000, FAX 33-1-46345544. Circ: 15,000. **Subscr. to:** CNDP - Abonnement, B.P. 750, Sainte Genevieve Cedex 60732, France. FAX 33-3-44033013.

MEDICAL TEACHER. see *MEDICAL SCIENCES*

MEDIELAERERFORENINGEN FOR GYMNASIET OG H F. MEDDELELSER. see *MOTION PICTURES*

370 DEU ISSN 0931-9808
MEDIENCONCRET; Magazin fuer die paedagogische Praxis. Text in German. 1987. irreg. bk.rev. **Document type:** *Magazine, Academic/Scholarly.*
Formerly (until 1987): Spektrum Film (0176-4594)
Published by: Jugendfilmclub Koeln, Hansaring 82-86, Cologne, 50670, Germany. TEL 49-221-120093, FAX 49-221-132592. Ed. Sabine Sonnenschein. Circ: 2,000.

370.72 MLT ISSN 1024-5375
L56
➤ **MEDITERRANEAN JOURNAL OF EDUCATIONAL STUDIES.** Text in English; Summaries in Arabic, English, French. 1996. 2/yr. USD 42 to individuals; USD 84 to institutions (effective 2001). adv. abstr. back issues avail. **Document type:** *Academic/Scholarly.* **Description:** Reports educational research carried out in Mediterranean countries as well as studies relating to the diaspora of Mediterranean people world-wide.
Indexed: BrEdI, CIJE, CPE, ERA, ETA, L&LBA, MEA, PerIslam, RHEA, SEA, SENA, SOMA, SOPODA, SSA, SociolAb, TEA.
—BLDSC (5534.734500), IE, ingenta.
Published by: University of Malta, Faculty of Education, Msida, MSD 06, Malta. TEL 356-32902936, FAX 356-338126, rsul1@educ.um.edu.mt, http://www.edu.um.edu.mt/mep/mep.htm. Eds. Dr. Peter Mayo, Ronald G. Sultana. R&P Ronald G. Sultana. adv.: page USD 100.

➤ **MEDUCATOR.** see *MEDICAL SCIENCES*

306.43 SWE ISSN 1652-9464
MEDVIND; medborgarskolan - daer intresse blir kunskap. Text in Swedish. 1941. 4/yr. adv. **Document type:** *Magazine, Consumer.*
Former titles (until 2005): Tidsspegel (0346-3222); (until 1957): Studienytt; (until 1949): Gimokamraten; Incorporates (1976-1986): Spraaknytt
Related titles: Online - full text ed.
Published by: Studiefoerbundet Medborgarskolan, Sysslomansgatan 15 A, PO Box 2028, Uppsala, 75002, Sweden. TEL 46-18-569500, FAX 46-18-569501, annika.timmerman@medborgarskolen.se, http://www.medborgarskolan.se. Ed. Annika Timmerman. Adv. contact Lars Olson.

MEDYCYNA DYDAKTYKA WYCHOWANIE. see *MEDICAL SCIENCES*

MEGAMOT; behavioural sciences journal. see *SOCIOLOGY*

MEIYU TIANDI/WORLD OF ENGLISH. see *LINGUISTICS*

370 PER ISSN 1682-4962
MEJORAMIENTO DE LA CALIDAD DE LA EDUCACION. DOCUMENTO DE TRABAJO. Key Title: Documento de Trabajo - MECEP. Text in Spanish. 2001. irreg. back issues avail.
Media: Online - full text.
Published by: Ministerio de Educacion, Mejoramiento de la Calidad de la Educacion, C. Van de Velde, 160, San Borja, Lima, Peru. TEL 51-1-2155808, http://www.minedu.gob.pe/web/mecep/publicaciones.htm.

370 AUS ISSN 0076-6275
L101.A8 CODEN: MSEDFM
➤ **MELBOURNE STUDIES IN EDUCATION.** Text in English. 1957. s-a. AUD 90 to individuals; AUD 100 to institutions; AUD 70 to students (effective 2003). bk.rev. back issues avail. **Document type:** *Journal, Academic/Scholarly.* **Description:** Favors discursive writing related to the historical, cultural, administrative, comparative, political, sociological and philosophical areas of education.
Indexed: AEI, AusPAIS, PCI, SOPODA.
—CCC.
Published by: (University of Melbourne), Monash University, Faculty of Education, PO Box 527, Frankston, VIC 3199, Australia. TEL 61-3-99044291, FAX 61-3-99044027, mse@education.monash.edu.au, info@education.monash.edu, http://www.education.monash.edu.au/projects/mse. Eds. Bob Bessant, Gale Trevor. Pub. Gale Trevor. Circ: 2,000. **Subscr. to:** Arena Printing and Publications Pty. Ltd., 2 Kerr St., Fitzroy, VIC 3065, Australia. TEL 61-3-94160232, FAX 61-3-94160684.

370 CAN
MENTOR. Text in English, French. 1985. irreg. price varies. **Document type:** *Monographic series, Academic/Scholarly.* **Description:** Studies all aspects of education (philosophy, history, psychology).
Formerly: Education
Published by: University of Ottawa Press, 542 King Edward, Ottawa, ON K1N 6N5, Canada. TEL 613-562-5246, FAX 613-562-5247, press@uottawa.ca. Ed. Aline Giroux.

MERRILL - PALMER QUARTERLY; journal of developmental psychology. see *PSYCHOLOGY*

370 GAB
MESSAGE✶ ; bulletin de liaison des enseignants gabonais. Text in French. irreg. XOF 600.
Formerly: Tam-Tam
Published by: Direction de l'Enseignement du Premier Degre, BP 221, Libreville, Gabon.

370 ALB
MESUESI/INSTITUTEUR. Text in Albanian. w. USD 175 in Europe; USD 247 elsewhere.
Published by: Ministria e Arsimit dhe e Kultures/Ministry of Education and Culture, Tirana, Albania. TEL 355-42-27206, TELEX 4203. Ed. Thoma Qendro. **Dist. by:** Agjencia Qendrore e Tregtimit, Te Librit Artistik e Shkencor, Rruga e Kavajes, Nr 42, Tirana, Albania. FAX 355-42-27246.

370 CAN ISSN 0823-3993
MESURE ET EVALUATION EN EDUCATION. Text in French. 1978. q.
Formerly: Mesure en Education (0225-4654)
Published by: Association pour le Developpement de la Mesure et de l'Evaluation en Education (ADMEE), 5, 6e Ave, Aylmer, PQ J9H 5C7, Canada. TEL 819-682-9696, FAX 819-682-2633, http://www.umoncton.ca/raicheg/sitemee, http://www.umoncton.ca/raicheg/sitemee/revue-infolect.htm.

370.1 HRV ISSN 0353-765X
METODICKI OGLEDI. Text in Croatian; Summaries in English. 1990. s-a. **Description:** Aims to foster a dialogue between philosophical and scientific approaches to education.
Indexed: PhilInd.
Published by: Hratsko Filozofsko Drustvo/Croatian Philosophical Society, Djure Salaja 3, Zagreb, 41000, Croatia. Ed. Milan Polic. Circ: 600.

379.15 USA ISSN 0026-153X
METROPOLITAN NASHVILLE BOARD OF EDUCATION. NEWS AND VIEWS; official publication of the public schools of metropolitan Nashville Davidson County. Text in English. 1954. q. free. **Description:** Information on events and activities in the public schools of Nashville including recognition of outstanding individuals, awards and new school construction.
Published by: Metropolitan Nashville Board of Education, 2601 Bransford Ave, Nashville, TN 37204. TEL 615-259-8400. Circ: 7,500 (controlled).

MEXICO. INSTITUTO NACIONAL DE ESTADISTICA, GEOGRAFIA E INFORMATICA. ENCUESTA NACIONAL DE EDUCACION CAPACITACION Y EMPLEO. see *EDUCATION—Abstracting, Bibliographies, Statistics*

370.972 MEX ISSN 0188-0446
MEXICO. SECRETARIA DE EDUCACION PUBLICA. INFORME DE LABORES. Text in Spanish. 1970. a. **Document type:** *Government.* **Description:** Reports activities regarding organization and administration of education in Mexico.
Published by: Secretaria de Educacion Publica, Direccion General de Planeacion, Programacion y Presupuesto, Mexico City, DF, Mexico.

373 USA ISSN 0026-2013
MICHIGAN ASSOCIATION OF SECONDARY SCHOOL PRINCIPALS' BULLETIN. Text in English. 1974 (vol.16). m. (Sep.-May). looseleaf. membership. adv. bk.rev. reprint service avail. from PQC. **Document type:** *Bulletin.*
Formerly: Journal of Secondary Education
Related titles: Microfilm ed.
Published by: Michigan Association of Secondary School Principals, 418 Erickson Hall, Michigan State University, East Lansing, MI 48823. Ed. Jock Bittle. Circ: (controlled).

370 371.9142 USA ISSN 1081-4086
➤ **MICHIGAN ASSOCIATION OF SPEECH COMMUNICATION JOURNAL.** Text in English. 1964. a. USD 6 (effective 1998). back issues avail. **Document type:** *Academic/Scholarly.*
Formerly (until 1984): Michigan Speech Association Journal (0543-9965)

E

Published by: Michigan Association of Speech Communication, Eastern Michigan University, Communication & Theater Arts Dept, Ypsilanti, MI 48197. TEL 517-577-8727. Ed. Kathleen Stacey. Circ: 250.

➤ **MICHIGAN LAW REVIEW.** see *LAW*

➤ **MICHIGAN READING JOURNAL.** see *LINGUISTICS—Abstracting, Bibliographies, Statistics*

370 GUM
➤ **MICRONESIAN EDITOR.** Text in English. 1990. a. bk.rev. back issues avail. **Document type:** *Academic/Scholarly.*
Description: Includes articles and research about education activities in the Eastern Pacific area known as Micronesia.
Related titles: Online - full text ed.
Published by: (University of Guam USA, College of Education USA), University of Guam Press, UOG Sta, Mangilao, 96923, Guam. TEL 671-735-2803, FAX 671-734-7930, millhoff@uog9.uog.edu, http://uog2.uog.edu/coe/educator/, http://uog2.uog.edu/up/micronesica/. Ed. Bridget Dalton.

370.72 GUM ISSN 1061-088X
➤ **MICRONESIAN EDUCATOR;** a journal of research and practice on education in Guam and Micronesia. Text in English. 1990. a. USD 10 (effective 1999). adv. bk.rev.
Document type: *Academic/Scholarly.* **Description:** Serves as a forum to share current research, theoretical perspectives, practical applications, innovative practices and book reviews in education, with particular focus on Guam and Micronesia.
Published by: (University of Guam USA, Department of Education USA), University of Guam Press, UOG Sta, Mangilao, 96923, Guam. TEL 671-735-2171, FAX 671-734-2296, gdmo@uog9.uog.edu. Ed. Bridget Dalton. R&P B. Dalton. Adv. contact B Dalton.

370.72 USA ISSN 1056-3997
LB1028.25.U6
MID-WESTERN EDUCATIONAL RESEARCHER. Text in English. 1991. 3/yr. **Document type:** *Journal, Academic/Scholarly.*
Indexed: CIJE.
—BLDSC (5761.448200), IE, ingenta.
Published by: Mid-Western Educational Research Association, c/o Kim Metcalf, Smith Research Str, Ste 174, 2805 E 10th St, Bloomington, IN 47408. kmetcalf@indiana.edu, http://www.mwera.org. Ed. James Salzman.

370.956 GBR
MIDDLE EAST EDUCATION & TRAINING BUYERS GUIDE. Text in English. 1982. a. USD 60. adv. **Document type:** *Trade.*
Related titles: Arabic ed.
Published by: International Business Publications Ltd., Queensway House, 2 Queensway, Redhill, Surrey RH1 1QS, United Kingdom. Ed. Geoff Napier.

370 EGY
MIGALIT KULIYAT AL-TARBIYAT. GAMI' AT AL-MANSUWRAT/ MANSOURA UNIVERSITY. FACULTY OF EDUCATION. JOURNAL. Text in Arabic. 3/yr. free (effective 2004).
Document type: *Journal, Academic/Scholarly.*
Published by: Mansoura University, Faculty of Education, University Campus, Mansoura, Egypt. TEL 20-50-344852, FAX 20-50-344385, http://derp.sti.sci.eg/data/0040.htm, http://www.mans.edu.eg. Ed. Dr. Talaat Hasan Abdel-Rahim.

MIMESIS (BAURU); revista da area de ciencias humanas. see *SOCIAL SCIENCES: COMPREHENSIVE WORKS*

MINISTRY OF EDUCATION. BASIC STATISTICS OF EDUCATION. see *EDUCATION—Abstracting, Bibliographies, Statistics*

370.1 NZL ISSN 1174-8788
MINISTRY OF EDUCATION. RESEARCH REPORT SERIES. Text in English. 1999. irreg. **Document type:** *Academic/Scholarly.*
—BLDSC (7769.547100).
Published by: Ministry of Education, Research Division, Research Unit, PO Box 1666, Wellington, New Zealand.

370.25 USA
MINNESOTA EDUCATION DIRECTORY*✱*. Text in English. a.
Document type: *Directory.*
Published by: Minnesota Department of Education, State Dept. Of Children Families, 1500 Highway 36 W., St. Paul, MN 55113-4266. TEL 612-296-6104.

370 USA ISSN 1521-9062
THE MINNESOTA EDUCATOR. Text in English. 1971. m. USD 20 (effective 2005). **Document type:** *Newspaper, Academic/Scholarly.* **Description:** Contains articles, opinion and photos covering K-12 and postsecondary education topics.
Formerly titles (until 1998): Minnesota Education Association. Transitions (1096-2239); (until 1997): Minnesota Education Association. Advocate (1053-3362); (until 1990): M E A Advocate (Minnesota Education Association) (0889-2474)
Published by: Education Minnesota, 41 Sherburne Ave, St. Paul, MN 55103-2196. TEL 651-652-9073, FAX 651-227-9541, educator@educationminnesota.org, http://www.educationminnesota.org. Ed. Judy Bergland. Circ: 70,000 (paid).

MINNESOTA GEOLOGICAL SURVEY. EDUCATIONAL SERIES. see *EARTH SCIENCES—Geology*

370.1 CHN ISSN 1001-7178
MINZU JIAOYU YANJIU/ETHNIC EDUCATION STUDIES. Text in Chinese. 1989. q. USD 9.12. **Document type:** *Academic/Scholarly.* **Description:** Covers the theory, administration, economics and history of ethnic education.
Related titles: Online - full text ed.: (from East View Information Services).
Published by: (Zhongyang Minzu Xueyuan/Central University of National Minorities), Minzu Jiaoyu Yanjiu Bianjibu, Zhongyang Minzu Daxue, 27 Baishiqiao, Beijing, 100081, China. TEL 8420077-2754, FAX 01-8422954. Ed. Geng Jinsheng. Circ: 2,000. **Dist. overseas by:** China International Book Trading Corp, 35 Chegongzhuang Xilu, Haidian District, PO Box 399, Beijing 100044, China.

370 RUS
MIR OBRAZOVANIYA. Text in Russian. m. USD 159 in United States.
Published by: Firma Novaya Shkola, Pr-t Marshala Zhukova 2, etazh 3, ofis 9, Moscow, 123308, Russian Federation. TEL 7-095-1919147, FAX 7-095-9467811. Ed. V S Girshovich. **US dist. addr.:** East View Information Services, 3020 Harbor Ln. N., Minneapolis, MN 55447. TEL 612-550-0961.

MIRA; a monthly journal of Indian culture. see *LITERARY AND POLITICAL REVIEWS*

371.192 USA ISSN 0076-9460
MISSISSIPPI CONGRESS OF PARENTS AND TEACHERS. PROCEEDINGS. Text in English. a. **Document type:** *Proceedings.*
Published by: Mississippi Congress of Parents and Teachers, PO Box 1937, Jackson, MS 39215-1937. TEL 601-352-7383, 800-795-6123. Circ: (controlled).

371.192 USA ISSN 0076-9479
MISSISSIPPI CONGRESS OF PARENTS AND TEACHERS. YEARBOOK. Text in English. a. **Document type:** *Bulletin.*
Published by: Mississippi Congress of Parents and Teachers, PO Box 1937, Jackson, MS 39215-1937. TEL 601-352-7383, 800-795-6123. Circ: (controlled).

370.15 USA ISSN 0164-8683
MISSISSIPPI EDUCATOR. Text in English. 1976. 5/yr. adv. bk.rev.; film rev. illus. **Document type:** *Magazine, Trade.*
Incorporates (vol.67, no.5, 1976): Mississippi Educational Advance (0026-6183); Supersedes: Mississippi Educational Journal (0026-6191)
Published by: Mississippi Association of Educators, 775 N State St, Jackson, MS 39202. TEL 601-354-4463, 800-530-7998, FAX 601-352-7054, bsanders@nea.org, http://www.ms.nea.org. Eds. Beverly Sanders, Thelma Hickman. Circ: 9,000 (paid).

268 370 DEU
MITEINANDER GOTT ENTDECKEN. Text in German. 1971. q. EUR 20.40; EUR 5.10 newsstand/cover (effective 2003). bk.rev. stat. index. **Document type:** *Magazine, Consumer.*
Formerly: Sonntagschulmitarbeiter (0012-2580); Which was formed by the merger of: Dienst am Kinde; Sonntags Schulhelfer
—CCC.
Published by: Oncken Verlag GmbH, Muendener Str 13, Kassel, 34123, Germany. TEL 49-561-520050, FAX 49-561-5200554, zeitschriften@oncken.de, http://www.oncken.de. Ed. Volkmar Hamp. Circ: 5,800.

MIXED MEDIA. see *ART*

613.7 370 CHE ISSN 1422-7851
MOBILE/EDUCATION PHYSIQUE. Text in German. 1998. bi-m. CHF 35 domestic; CHF 40 foreign (effective 2004). adv. bk.rev. charts; illus. index. **Document type:** *Journal, Academic/Scholarly.*
Formed by the merger of (1923-1998): Sporterziehung in der Schule (0251-7213); Which was formerly (until 1978): Koerpererziehung (0023-2696); Which was formed by the merger of (1920-1923): Pro Corpore (1422-0792); (1890-1923): Monatsblaetter fuer die Physische Erziehung der Jugend (1422-0784); Which was formerly (until 1912): Monatsblaetter fuer das Schulturnen (1422-089X); (1944-1998): Magglingen (0254-1246); Which was formerly (until 1983): Jugend und Sport (0254-1254); (until 1967): Starke Jugend, Freies Volk (1423-3363)
Related titles: French ed.: ISSN 1422-7878; Italian ed.: ISSN 1422-7894.
Indexed: DIP, IBR, IBZ, RRTA.
—CCC.
Published by: (Bundesamt fuer Sport Magglingen), Zollikofer AG, Fuerstenlandstr 122, Postfach 2362, St. Gallen, 9001, Switzerland. TEL 41-71-2727370, FAX 41-71-2727586, leserservice@zollikofer.ch, http://www.baspo.ch/d/publikationen/mobile/mobile.htm, http://www.zollikofer.ch. Circ: 7,000.

371.07 USA ISSN 0026-914X
LC461
MOMENTUM (WASHINGTON). Text in English. 1970. 4/yr. USD 20 (effective 2006); USD 5 per issue (effective 2005). bk.rev. bibl.; charts; illus. cum.index. reprint service avail. from PQC.
Document type: *Magazine, Consumer.*
Formerly: Catholic School Bulletin
Related titles: Microfilm ed.: (from PQC); Online - full text ed.: (from H.W. Wilson, O C L C Online Computer Library Center, Inc., ProQuest Information & Learning).
Indexed: ABIn, CIJE, CPL, ChPerl, CurCont, EduInd, PAIS.
—BLDSC (5901.590000), IE, Infotrieve, ingenta.
Published by: National Catholic Educational Association, 1077 30 St, N W, Ste 100, Washington, DC 20007. TEL 202-337-6232, FAX 202-333-6706, nceaadmin@ncea.org, http://www.ncea.org. Ed. Brian E. Gray. Circ: 25,000.

370.944 FRA
LB5
LE MONDE DE L'EDUCATION, DE LA CULTURE ET DE LA FORMATION. Text in French. 1975. m. **Document type:** *Newspaper.* **Description:** Analyses the different methods of teaching and training in France and abroad.
Formerly: Monde de l'Education (0337-9213)
Related titles: Microfilm ed.: (from RPI).
Indexed: CERDIC, DIP, ELLIS, HECAB, RASB.
—BLDSC (5906.915000), IE, ingenta.
Published by: Le Monde S.A., 21 bis, rue Claude Bernard, Paris, 75242 Cedex 5, France. TEL 33-1-42172901, FAX 33-1-42172121. Ed. Jean Michel Djian. Pub. Jean Marie Colombani. Circ: 115,000. **Subscr. to:** Le Monde - Service Abonnements, 24 av. du General Leclerc, Chantilly Cedex 60646, France. TEL 33-1-42173290.

370 ARG ISSN 1515-9671
EL MONITOR DE LA EDUCACION. Text in Spanish. 2000. q. back issues avail.
Related titles: Online - full text ed.
Published by: Ministerio de Educacion, Pizzurno 935, Buenos Aires, 1020, Argentina. TEL 54-11-41291000, elmonitor@me.gov.ar, info@me.gov.ar, http://www.me.gov.ar/.

373 USA ISSN 0190-9185
HQ796
MONITORING THE FUTURE; questionnaire responses from the nation's high school seniors. Text in English. 1975. a. USD 60 (effective 2003). back issues avail. **Document type:** *Journal, Academic/Scholarly.*
Published by: Institute for Social Research, University of Michigan, Box 1248, Ann Arbor, MI 48106. TEL 734-998-9900, FAX 734-998-9889, mtfinfo@isr.umich.edu, isr-info@isr.umich.edu, http://www.monitoringthefuture.org, http://www.isr.umich.edu.

370.1 USA ISSN 0026-9808
MONMOUTH EDUCATOR*✱*; M C E A monitor. Text in English. 1948. 10/yr. membership. illus.
Published by: Monmouth County Education Association, 1049 Broadway, West Long Branch, NJ 07764-1307. TEL 908-542-8254. Circ: 7,500.

371.0109786 USA
MONTANA SCHOOLS. Text in English. 1956. q. free. illus.
Document type: *Government.*
Published by: Office of Public Instruction, PO Box 202501, Helena, MT 59620-2501. TEL 406-444-4397. Ed. Beth Satre. Circ: 12,000.

370 JPN
MONTHLY EDUCATION JOURNAL/GEKKAN KYOIKU JOURNAL. Text in Japanese. 1963. m. JPY 1,800.
Published by: Gakken Co. Ltd., 40-5 Kami-Ikedai 4-chome, Ota-ku, Tokyo, 145-0064, Japan. Ed. Mitsunobu Hayakawa.

371.82997 USA ISSN 0047-8121
MORNING STAR PEOPLE. Text in English. 1965. 4/yr. free.
Document type: *Newsletter.* **Description:** Informative newsletter from the St. Labre Indian School about the activities of its Native American pupils, both attending and alumni.
Published by: St. Labre Indian School, Tongue River Rd, Ashland, MT 59003. Ed. Mary Jo Burkholder.

370 USA ISSN 1547-7061
LB1027
MOSAIC (NEWTON). Text in English. 1999 (Spr.). irreg. free (effective 2003).
Published by: Education Development Center, Publications Office, 55 Chapel St, Newton, MA 02160. TEL 617-969-7100, FAX 617-969-5979, http://main.edc.org/mosaic/index.asp, http://www.edc.org. Ed. Dan Tobin.

370.72 BWA ISSN 1021-559X
LA1600
➤ **MOSENODI.** Text in English. 1993. s-a. BWP 15 to non-members individuals; BWP 25 to non-members institutions (effective 2000). bk.rev. abstr. **Document type:** *Academic/Scholarly.* **Description:** Disseminates findings in educational research.

E

▼ new title ➤ refereed ✱ unverified ♦ full entry avail.

Published by: Botswana Educational Research Association, University of Botswana, UB Box 70205, Gaborone, Botswana. TEL 267-355-2838, FAX 267-355-2838, bera@noka.ub.bw. Ed., R&P R B Prophet TEL 267-355-2163.

370.1 RUS
MOSKOVSKII GOSUDARSTVENNYI UNIVERSITET. VESTNIK. SERIYA 20: PEDAGOGICHESKOE OBRAZOVANIE. Text in Russian. 2002. s-a. USD 85 foreign (effective 2004). **Document type:** *Journal, Academic/Scholarly.*
Published by: (Moskovskii Gosudarstvennyi Universitet im. M.V. Lomonosova, Fakul'tet Pedagogicheskogo Obrazovaniya), Izdatel'stvo Moskovskogo Gosudarstvennogo Universiteta im. M. V. Lomonosova/Publishing House of Moscow State University, B Nikitskaya 5/7, Moscow, 103009, Russian Federation. TEL 7-095-2295091, FAX 7-095-2036671, kd_mgu@rambler.ru, http://www.msu.ru/depts/MSUPubl. **Dist. by:** East View Information Services, 3020 Harbor Ln. N., Minneapolis, MN 55447. TEL 800-477-1005, FAX 800-800-3839, eastview@eastview.com, http://www.eastview.com.

370 USA ISSN 1555-7200
▼ ➤ **MOUNTAINRISE.** Text in English. 2003. s-a. free (effective 2005). **Document type:** *Journal, Academic/Scholarly.* **Description:** Its purpose is to be an international vehicle for the Scholarship of Teaching & Learning.
Media: Online - full content.
Published by: Western Carolina University, Coulter Faculty Center for Excellence in Teaching & Learning, 166 Hunter Bldg, Cullowhee, NC 28723. TEL 828-227-7196, FAX 828-227-7340, jkneller@mail.wcu.edu, http://mountainrise.wcu.edu, http://www.facctr.wcu.edu. Ed. John Habel.

370 UAE
AL-MU'ALLIM. Text in Arabic. 1982. m. **Description:** Covers international and local educational issues, and society activities.
Formerly: Sawt al-Mu'allim
Published by: Sharjah Teachers Society, PO Box 839, Sharjah, United Arab Emirates. TEL 248877. Ed. Salih Al Marzogi. Circ: 3,500.

MULLI KYOYUK/PHYSICS TEACHING. see *PHYSICS*

MULTIMEDIA INFORMATION & TECHNOLOGY. see *LIBRARY AND INFORMATION SCIENCES*

DER MULTIMEDIA REPORTER; aktuelles News-Magazine fuer den Multimedia Fachhandel. see *COMPUTERS—Computer Games*

MUSIC TEACHER. see *MUSIC*

MUSIK IN DER SCHULE; Zeitschrift fuer Theorie und Praxis des Musikunterrichts. see *MUSIC*

372 DEU
MUSISCHES SPIEL; Unterrichtshilfen fuer Bewegungserziehung, Spielgestaltung, Musikalische Frueherziehung, Darstellung und Tanz. Text in German. 1985. 2/yr. looseleaf. EUR 13.50 (effective 2005). cum.index: 1985-1999. back issues avail. **Document type:** *Journal, Academic/Scholarly.*
Formerly: Musische Stunde
Published by: A L S Verlag GmbH, Voltastr 3, Dietzenbach, 63128, Germany. TEL 49-6074-82160, FAX 49-6074-27322, info@als-verlag.de, http://www.als-verlag.de. Ed. Ingrid Kreide. R&P Maria Landji.

MUSLIM EDUCATION QUARTERLY. see *RELIGIONS AND THEOLOGY—Islamic*

MUSLIMISCHE BILDUNGSGAENGE. see *RELIGIONS AND THEOLOGY—Islamic*

370.1175 USA ISSN 0896-8349
N A B E NEWS. Text in English. 6/yr. USD 60 to individual members; USD 125 to institutional members (effective 2005). adv. illus. **Document type:** *Newsletter.*
Related titles: Online - full text ed.
—BLDSC (6001.754500).
Published by: National Association for Bilingual Education, 1030 15th St N W, Ste 470, Washington, DC 20005. TEL 202-898-1829, FAX 202-789-2866, nabe@nabe.org, http://www.nabe.org. Ed. Josue Gonzales. Adv. contact Jeff Spence.

N A E A NEWS. see *ART*

371.26 USA ISSN 0094-0208
N A E P NEWSLETTER. Text in English. 1967. 4/yr. free. charts. **Document type:** *Newsletter.*
Published by: (Educational Testing Service), National Assessment of Educational Progress, CN 6710, Princeton, NJ 08541-6710. Ed. Eleanor Driscoll. Circ: 40,000.

372 USA ISSN 1522-9734
LB775.M8
THE N A M T A JOURNAL; the Montessori teachers' professional journal. (North American Montessori Teacher's Association) Text in English. 1970. 3/yr. USD 48 domestic membership; USD 58 foreign membership (effective 2005). **Document type:** *Journal, Trade.* **Description:** Provides articles on a particular theme, NAMTA news and Classified advertising (jobs, schools for sale, etc).
Indexed: CIJE.
—BLDSC (6015.332488), IE, ingenta.
Published by: North American Montessori Teacher's Association, 13693 Butternut Rd., Burton, OH 44021-9571. TEL 440-834-4011, http://www.montessori-namta.org/NAMTA/NAMServs/journal.html.

370 CAN ISSN 0317-5227
N B T A NEWS. Text in English. 1969. m. CND 18 to non-members. adv. **Document type:** *Newsletter.*
Indexed: CEI.
Published by: New Brunswick Teachers' Association, P O Box 752, Fredericton, NB E3B 5B4, Canada. TEL 506-452-8921, FAX 506-453-9795. Ed., R&P, Adv. contact Jim Dysart. Circ: 8,200 (controlled).

370 USA ISSN 0027-6189
N C A E NEWS BULLETIN. Text in English. 1970. 8/yr. free to members. 16 p./no.; **Document type:** *Magazine, Trade.*
Incorporates: North Carolina Education (0029-2451); Formerly: N C E A News Bulletin
Published by: North Carolina Association of Educators, 700 S Salisbury St, Box 27347, Raleigh, NC 27611. TEL 919-832-3000, 800-662-7924, FAX 919-829-1626, http://www.ncae.org/. Ed., R&P Jacqueline Vaughn TEL 919-832-3000 ext 216. Adv. contact Linda Powell Jones. Circ: 72,000.

371.0712 USA ISSN 1060-8575
N C E A NOTES. Text in English. 1968. 5/yr. membership. **Description:** For members in elementary and secondary schools and superintendents-diocesan administrators.
Published by: National Catholic Educational Association, 1077 30 St, N W, Ste 100, Washington, DC 20007. TEL 202-337-6232, FAX 202-333-6706, nceaadmin@ncea.org, http://www.ncea.org.

370.72 IND ISSN 0302-508X
N C E R T NEWSLETTER; a monthly house journal. Text in English. 1974. m. bk.rev. **Document type:** *Newsletter.*
Published by: National Council of Educational Research and Training, Publication Department, Sri Aurbindo Marg, New Delhi, 110 016, India. TEL 662708. Ed. T S Sarma. Circ: 5,500.

371.02 AUS
N C I S A ANNUAL REVIEW. Text in English. 1982. a. free. **Document type:** *Corporate.* **Description:** Provides assistance, information to strengthen and promote the interests of independent schools.
Formerly (until 1994): N C I S A Annual Report
Published by: National Council of Independent Schools' Associations, PO Box 324, Deakin West, ACT 2600, Australia. TEL 61-2-6282-3488, FAX 61-2-6286-2926. Circ: 3,500.

370.711 USA ISSN 1054-7673
N C R T L SPECIAL REPORT. Text in English. 1988. irreg., latest 1997. price varies. **Document type:** *Monographic series.* **Description:** Research on teacher education, with a focus on teacher learning.
Formerly (until 1991): N C R T E Colloquy (0896-3932)
Published by: National Center for Research on Teacher Learning, Michigan State University, 116 Erickson Hall, E, Lansing, MI 48824-1034. TEL 517-355-9302, FAX 517-432-2795, http://ncrtl.msu.edu. Ed. Robert Floden.

373 USA ISSN 1084-6522
Q183.3.A1
N C S S S M S T JOURNAL. (National Consortium for Specialized Secondary Schools of Mathematics, Science & Technology) Text in English. 1995. s-a. USD 50 domestic; USD 75 foreign (effective 2003). adv. **Document type:** *Journal, Academic/Scholarly.* **Description:** Disseminates information about Consortium schools and provide a forum for the discussion of innovation in secondary mathematics, science and technology education.
Related titles: Online - full content ed.
Indexed: CIJE.
Published by: National Consortium for Specialized Secondary Schools of Mathematics, Science & Technology, 3020 Wards Ferry Rd, Lynchburg, VA 24502. TEL 434-582-1104, FAX 434-239-4140, clindema@cvgs.k12.va.us, http://www.ncssmst.org/publications/journal.html, http://www.ncsssmst.org/. Eds. Art Williams TEL 318-357-3174, Martin Shapiro TEL 813-893-2926. adv.: B&W page USD 350, color page USD 500.

373 USA
N C S S S M S T NEWSLETTER. (National Consortium for Specialized Secondary Schools of Mathematics, Science & Technology) Text in English. q. **Document type:** *Newsletter.*
Published by: National Consortium for Specialized Secondary Schools of Mathematics, Science & Technology, 3020 Wards Ferry Rd, Lynchburg, VA 24502. TEL 434-582-1104, FAX 434-239-4140, http://www.ncsssmst.org/publications/current.html.

370 DEU ISSN 0720-9673
N D S; Die Fachzeitschrift fuer Bildungsprofis. (Neue Deutsche Schule) Text in German. 1949. s-m. adv. bk.rev. back issues avail. **Document type:** *Magazine, Trade.*
Formerly (until 1981): Neue Deutsche Schule (0344-6158)
Indexed: DIP, IBR, IBZ.
Published by: (Gewerkschaft Erziehung und Wissenschaft, Landesverband Nordrhein-Westfalen), Neue Deutsche Schule Verlagsgesellschaft mbH, Nuenningstr 11, Essen, 45141, Germany. TEL 49-201-2940306, FAX 49-201-2940314, info@nds-verlag.de, http://www.nds-verlag.de/zeitschrift/index.html. Circ: 42,500.

370 USA
N E A NEW YORK. Text in English. 1976. 9/yr. USD 10. adv. illus. **Document type:** *Newsletter.*
Formerly: N Y E A Advocate (0161-7982)
Published by: National Education Association of New York, 217 Lark St, Albany, NY 12210. TEL 518-462-6451, FAX 518-462-1731. Ed., R&P Mollie T Marchione. Pub. Gregory S Nash. Adv. contact Lee St John. Circ: 35,000.

370 USA ISSN 0734-7219
N E A TODAY. Text in English. 1982. 9/yr. (Sep.-May). USD 35 domestic to institutions; USD 54 foreign to institutions (effective 2005). adv. charts; illus. back issues avail.; reprint service avail. from PQC. **Document type:** *Newspaper.* **Description:** Features insights on the education challenges facing our nation today.
Supersedes: N E A Reporter (0027-6405); Supersedes in part (1913-1987): Today's Education (Annual Edition) (0737-1888); Which was formerly: Today's Education (General Edition) (0272-3573); Which superseded in part: Today's Education (0040-8484); Which was formerly: N E A Journal
Related titles: Microform ed.: (from PQC); Online - full text ed.: (from EBSCO Publishing, Florida Center for Library Automation, Gale Group, O C L C Online Computer Library Center, Inc., ProQuest Information & Learning); ◆ Special ed(s).: N E A Today: Educational Support Edition.
Indexed: ABIn, ARG, ChPerI, EduInd, LRI, MagInd, PCI, PSI, RASB, RGAb, RGPR, TOM.
—BLDSC (6067.941500), IE, ingenta.
Published by: National Education Association of the United States, 1201 16th St, N W, Washington, DC 20036-3290. TEL 202-833-4000, FAX 202-822-7974, NEAToday@nea.org, http://www.nea.org/neatoday. Ed. Bill Fischer. Pub. Sam Pizzigati. Adv. contact Richard Dotz. Circ: 2,300,000.

370 GBR
N F E R ANNUAL REPORT. Text in English. a. **Document type:** *Corporate.*
Published by: National Foundation for Educational Research, The Mere, Upton Park, Slough, Berks SL1 2DQ, United Kingdom. TEL 44-1753-574123, FAX 44-1753-691632.

370.1 700 USA
N G C S A NARRATIVE REPORT. (National Guild of Community Schools of the Arts) Text in English. a. USD 70 to individual members; USD 200 to institutional members. back issues avail. **Document type:** *Consumer.* **Description:** Offers statistical information on the development of the organization and deals with community, music and art centers.
Published by: National Guild of Community Schools of Art, 520 Eighth Ave, 3rd Fl, Ste 302, New York, NY 10018. TEL 212-268-3337, FAX 212-268-3995, almayadas@worldnet.att.net, info@natguild.org, http://www.nationalguild.org. Ed. Lolita Mayadas. Circ: 500 (paid).

370.72 JPN
N I E R OCCASIONAL PAPER. Text in English. 1981. irreg. (1-3/yr.). free.
Published by: (Section for International Cooperation in Education), National Institute for Educational Research, 6-5-22 Shino-Meguro, Meguro-ku, Tokyo, 153, Japan. TEL 81-3-5721-5074, FAX 81-3-5721-5517. Ed. R Watanabe. Circ: 500.

370 USA ISSN 0027-6758
L11
N J E A REVIEW. Text in English. 1927. 9/yr. (Sep.-May). free to members; USD 250 to non-members (effective 2005). adv. bk.rev. illus. **Document type:** *Magazine, Trade.* **Description:** Discusses all educational topics for active and retired New Jersey public school employees. Reports on union news and political and social issues affecting teachers and public schools. Offers timely teaching and classroom management tips for new and experienced teachers.
Related titles: Microform ed.: (from PQC).
Indexed: CIJE.
Published by: New Jersey Education Association, 180 W State St, Box 1211, Trenton, NJ 08607-1211. TEL 609-599-4561, FAX 609-599-1201, njeareview@njea.org, http://www.njea.org/publications/review.asp. Ed. Lisa Galley. Circ: 188,000 (controlled).

E

370.25 USA ISSN 0275-9357
L913
N R C S A DIRECTORY OF EDUCATIONAL PROGRAMS. Text in English. irreg. (2-3/yr.). USD 10 per issue. bk.rev.
Document type: *Directory.*
Related titles: Diskette ed.
Published by: National Registration Center for Study Abroad, P O Box 1393, Milwaukee, WI 53201. TEL 414-278-0631, FAX 414-271-8884, inquiries@nrcsa.com, http://www.nrcsa.com. Ed. Mary Croy.

373 FRA ISSN 1636-3566
N R P LETTRES LYCEE. (Nouvelle Revue Pedagogique) Text in French. 1975. 9/yr. adv.
Formerly (until 2002): Nouvelle Revue Pedagogique (0398-0367); Which was formed by the 1975 merger of: N R P Edition Scientifique (0398-0383); N R P Edition Litteraire (0398-0375); Which superseded (in 1969): Nouvelle Revue Pedagogique (1247-9691)
Published by: Editions Nathan, Departement des Revues, 9 rue Mechain, Paris, Cedex 14 75676, France. Circ: 76,000.

370 USA
N S C T E MONOGRAPHS. (National Society of College Teachers of Education) Text in English. a. price varies.
Document type: *Newsletter.*
Published by: Society of Professors of Education, c/o Dr Robert Morris, Dept of Ed Ldshp, UWG, 1600 Maple St, Carrollton, GA 30118-5160. TEL 770-836-4426, FAX 770-836-4439. Ed. Robert C Morris.

372.3 USA
N S T A REPORTS. Text in English. 6/yr. free to members. adv. 48 p./no. 4 cols./p.; back issues avail. **Document type:** *Newspaper, Trade.* **Description:** Presents information of interest to K-12 science teachers.
Published by: National Science Teachers Association, 1840 Wilson Blvd, Arlington, VA 22201. TEL 703-243-7100, nstareports@nsta.org, http://www.nsta.org/reports. Ed. Jodi Peterson. Circ: 55,000 (controlled).

N T U BULLETIN. (Newark Teachers Union) see *LABOR UNIONS*

370 ZAF
N U E COMMENT. Text in English. 1998. 4/yr. (during school year). ZAR 23; ZAR 37 foreign. adv. bk.rev. back issues avail. **Document type:** *Newsletter.* **Description:** Includes material aimed at assisting teachers in the classroom with research results on relevant educational topics, coverage of labor issues, and commentary.
Formed by the 1998 merger of: South African Teachers' Association. Education News; Which superseded in part (1890-1992): Education (0013-1202); Association of Professional Teachers. A P T Comment; Which superseded (1904-1995): Transvaal Education News
Published by: National Union of Educators, PO Box 1309, Houghton, Johannesburg 2041, South Africa. nueho@iafrica.com. Ed. Chris Pretorius. Pub. Mike Ryburgh. R&P Miss H Sieborger. Circ: 5,000.

370.7 NZL
N Z C E R RESEARCHED NEWS. Text in English. 1965. s-a. free. bibl.; illus. **Document type:** *Newsletter.* **Description:** Accounts of educational research in progress and completed, staff movements, and general news.
Formerly (until 1995): N Z C E R Newsletter (0111-2821)
Related titles: Microfilm ed.: (from PQC).
Published by: New Zealand Council for Educational Research, PO Box 3237, Wellington, New Zealand. TEL 64-4-3847939, FAX 64-4-3847933, subscriptions@nzcer.org.nz, http://www.nzcer.org.nz. Circ: 5,000.

370 NZL ISSN 0114-8206
LA2120
N Z E I ROUROU. Text in English. 1990. 21/yr. NZD 20. adv. bk.rev. charts; illus.; stat. **Document type:** *Trade.*
Description: Provides industrial news and professional information to NZEI members in the primary education sector.
Formed by the 1990 merger of: National Education (0027-9188); Nat Ed Newsletter (0111-395X)
Indexed: CPE.
—CCC.
Published by: New Zealand Educational Institute, PO Box 466, Wellington 1, New Zealand. TEL 04-384-9689, FAX 04-385-1772. Ed. Cathy Jackson. Adv. contact Alastair Duncan. Circ: 16,000.

370 NZL ISSN 1176-6662
▼ ➤ **N Z JOURNAL OF TEACHERS' WORK.** Text in English. 2004. s-a. free (effective 2005). **Document type:** *Journal, Academic/Scholarly.* **Description:** Contains articles of interest to Early Childhood, Primary, Secondary and Tertiary teachers. It aims to disseminate New Zealand research on and by teachers and also other articles on current issues which may be of interest to teachers.
Media: Online - full text.
Published by: Massey University, College of Education, Private bag 11-222, Palmerston North, New Zealand. TEL 64-6-0800MASSEY, http://www.teacherswork.ac.nz/twjournal.html.

370 BGR
NACHALNO OBRAZOVANIE. Text in Bulgarian. bi-m. USD 36 foreign (effective 2002).
Published by: Ministerstvo na Obrazovanieto i Naukata na Republika Bulgaria/Ministry of Education and Sciences of the Republic of Bulgaria, 125 Tzarigradsko Shosse Blvd., Bl. 5, PO Box 336, Sofia, 1113, Bulgaria. TEL 359-2-705298, http://www.minedu.government.bg. **Dist. by:** Sofia Books, ul Silivria 16, Sofia 1404, Bulgaria. TEL 359-2-9586257, info@sofiabooks-bg.com, http://www.sofiabooks-bg.com.

372 RUS
NADEZHDA. Text in Russian. m. USD 129.95 in United States.
Address: Bersenevskaya nab 6-2, Moscow, 103790, Russian Federation. TEL 7-095-2301861, FAX 7-095-9590321. Ed. G Ya Kuz'micheva. **US dist. addr.:** East View Information Services, 3020 Harbor Ln. N., Minneapolis, MN 55447. TEL 612-550-0961.

370 HRV ISSN 1330-0059
NAPREDAK; journal for pedagogical theory and practice. Text in Croatian; Summaries in English, German. 1859. bi-m. HRK 450 domestic; USD 75 foreign; USD 20 newsstand/cover (effective 2001). bk.rev. abstr.; bibl.; charts; illus.; maps; stat. Index. back issues avail. **Document type:** *Journal.*
Formerly (until 1991): Pedagoski Rad (0031-384X)
Indexed: DIP, IBR, IBZ.
Published by: Hrvatski Pedagosko-Knijevni Zbor/Croatian Educational Literary Union, Trg M Tita 4, Zagreb, Croatia. hpkz@zg.hinet.hr. Ed. Vlatko Previsic. Pub., R&P Hrvoje Vrgoc. Circ: 5,000.

371.0712 NLD ISSN 1569-3015
NARTHEX; tijdschrift voor levensbeschouwing en educatie. Text in Dutch. 1930; N.S. 2001. bi-m. EUR 27 (effective 2005). illus.
Formed by the merger of (1930-1999): Verbum (0166-6002); (1984-2000): Voorwerk (0168-8286)
Indexed: CERDIC.
Published by: (Katholieke Bond van Besturen voor Voortgezet Onderwijs, Unie voor Christelijk Onderwijs), Uitgeverij Damon, Luchthavenweg 6, Budel, 6021 PX, Netherlands. TEL 31-495-499319, FAX 31-495-499889, info@damon.nl, http://www.damon.nl/isbn/15693015.html. Ed. P Boersma. Circ: 1,000.

NASH MALYSH. see *CHILDREN AND YOUTH—About*

370 SCG ISSN 0547-3330
NASTAVA I VASPITANJE. Text in Serbo-Croatian. 1952. 6/yr. bk.rev. bibl. **Document type:** *Journal, Academic/Scholarly.*
Published by: Pedagosko Drustvo Srbije, Terazije 26, Belgrade, 11000. pds_bgd@eunet.yu, http://www.pedagog.org.yu/casopissrp.htm.

372 USA
NATIONAL ASSOCIATION FOR THE EDUCATION OF YOUNG CHILDREN. RESEARCH INTO PRACTICE SERIES. Text in English. irreg., latest vol.5, 1992. price varies. **Document type:** *Monographic series.*
Formerly: National Association for the Education of Young Children. Research Monographs
Published by: National Association for the Education of Young Children, 1509 16th St, N W, Washington, DC 20036-1426. TEL 202-232-8777, FAX 202-328-1846. Ed. Carol Copple. R&P Debra Liebson.

371.04 USA ISSN 0550-7421
L13
NATIONAL ASSOCIATION OF INDEPENDENT SCHOOLS. ANNUAL REPORT. Text in English. 1963. a. stat. reprint service avail. from PQC.
Published by: National Association of Independent Schools, 1620 L St, N W, Washington, DC 20036-5605.

371.4 GBR ISSN 0263-9696
NATIONAL ASSOCIATION OF INSPECTORS AND EDUCATIONAL ADVISORS. JOURNAL. Text in English. 1974. s-a. GBP 3.
Published by: National Association of Inspectors and Educational Advisors, New Inn, Nebo House, Devauden, Chepstow, Gwent NP6 6NW, United Kingdom. Ed. Eric Williams. Circ: 1,600.

371.04 USA
NATIONAL ASSOCIATION OF LABORATORY SCHOOLS. JOURNAL. Text in English. 1976. 2/yr. free to members. bk.rev. back issues avail.; reprints avail. **Document type:** *Journal, Trade.*
Published by: National Association of Laboratory Schools, c/o Patricia Diebold, Miller Research Learning Center, Edinboro University, Edinboro, PA 16444. TEL 814-732-6257, FAX 814-732-2807, http://www.edinboro.edu/cwis/education/nals/journal.htm, http://www.edinboro.edu/cwis/education/nals/nalshome.htm. Eds. Kenneth Miller, Ron Tibbetts, Sharon Carver. R&P, Adv. contact John R Johnson. Circ: 600 (paid).

371.04 USA
NATIONAL COALITION NEWS. Variant title: N C A C S News. Text in English. q. USD 30 domestic to non-members; USD 38 foreign to non-members (effective 2003). illus. **Document type:** *Newsletter.* **Description:** Contains events, happenings, thoughts, and opinions from around the coalition and the world of alternative education. Includes international news.

Published by: National Coalition of Alternative Community Schools, 1289 Jewett, Ann Arbor, MI 48104-6205 . TEL 734-668-9171, 888-771-9171, ncacs1@earthlink.net, http://www.ncacs.org/. R&P Alan Benard.

370 USA
➤ **NATIONAL COLLEGIATE HONORS COUNCIL. JOURNAL.** Text in English. s-a. USD 20 (effective 2005). **Document type:** *Journal, Academic/Scholarly.* **Description:** Contains scholarly articles on honors education, including analyses of trends in teaching methodology, articles on interdisciplinary efforts, discussions of problems common to honors programs, items on the national higher education agenda, and presentations of emergent issues relevant to honors education.
Published by: National Collegiate Honors Council, Iowa State University, 2130 Jischke Honors Bldg., Ames, IA 50011-1150. TEL 515-294-9188, FAX 515-294-9194, nchc@iastate.edu, http://www.nchchonors.org/journal.htm. Eds. Ada Long, D W Mullins Jr.

➤ **NATIONAL DIRECTORY FOR EMPLOYMENT IN EDUCATION.** see *BUSINESS AND ECONOMICS—Labor And Industrial Relations*

➤ **NATIONAL DIRECTORY OF HIGH SCHOOL COACHES.** see *SPORTS AND GAMES*

370 USA ISSN 8755-1829
L13
NATIONAL EDUCATION ASSOCIATION. HANDBOOK. Abbreviated title: N E A Handbook. Text in English. 1945. a. USD 125 per vol. to non-members; USD 5.95 per vol. to members (effective 2004).
Former titles (until 1976): Nationa Education Association. Handbook for Local, State and National Associations; (until 1950): National Education Association. Handbook and Manual for Local, State, and National Associations; (until 1947): National Education Association. Handbook (0147-2240)
Published by: National Education Association, 1201 16th St NW, Washington, DC 20036-3290. TEL 202-833-4000, FAX 202-822-7974, http://www.nea.org.

371.14 USA
NATIONAL EDUCATION ASSOCIATION OF THE UNITED STATES. PROCEEDINGS OF THE REPRESENTATIVE ASSEMBLY. Text in English. 1860. a. USD 15.95 to non-members; USD 5 to members. index. **Document type:** *Proceedings.*
Former titles: National Education Association of the United States. Proceedings of the Annual Meeting (0190-7662); National Education Association of the United States. Addresses and Proceedings (0077-4243)
—BLDSC (6789.180000).
Published by: National Education Association of the United States, 1201 16th St, N W, Washington, DC 20036-3290. TEL 202-822-7207, FAX 202-822-7206. Ed. Carolyn Cruise.
Subscr. to: NEA Professional Library, PMDS, 9050 Junction Dr, Annapolis, MD 20701. TEL 800-229-4200.

371.14 USA ISSN 0886-9979
NATIONAL EDUCATION ASSOCIATION RHODE ISLAND. NEWSLINE. Text in English. m. (8/yr.). membership. adv.
Former titles: National Education Association Rhode Island. Journal; National Education Association. Journal (0080-2751)
Published by: National Education Association Rhode Island, 99 Bald Hill Rd, Cranston, RI 02920-2631. TEL 401-463-9630. Ed. Karen Comiskey Jenkins. Circ: 9,500.

370.95493 LKA ISSN 0085-3747
NATIONAL EDUCATION SOCIETY OF SRI LANKA. JOURNAL. Text in English. a.
Published by: National Education Society of Sri Lanka, The University, Colombo, 3, Sri Lanka. Ed. Chandra Gunawardena.

NATIONAL EDUCATOR. see *GENERAL INTEREST PERIODICALS—United States*

370.72 USA ISSN 0895-3880
➤ **NATIONAL FORUM OF APPLIED EDUCATIONAL RESEARCH JOURNAL.** Short title: National Forum A E R J. Text in English. 1987. 2/yr., latest vol.14, 2001. USD 44 to individuals; USD 88 to institutions (effective 2004). adv. back issues avail. **Document type:** *Journal, Academic/Scholarly.* **Description:** Scholarly articles bridging the gap between educational theoreticians and practitioners in schools.
Related titles: Online - full content ed.: 1997. USD 144 to individuals and libraries (effective 2004).
Indexed: CDA, EAA, V&AA.
—CCC.
Published by: National Forum Journals, PO Box 7400, Lake Charles, LA 70605-7400. TEL 337-477-0008, FAX 337-562-2848, wakritsonis@aol.com, http://www.nationalforum.com/TOCaer10e3.html. Ed., Pub., R&P, Adv. contact Dr. William Kritsonis TEL 337-477-0008.

E

371.1 USA ISSN 1049-2658
LB1715
➤ **NATIONAL FORUM TEACHER EDUCATION JOURNAL.** Short title: N F T E J. Text in English. 1990. s-a. USD 44, USD 88 domestic (effective 2005); USD 144 foreign (effective 2002). adv. **Document type:** *Journal, Academic/Scholarly.* **Description:** Addresses the roles, problems and progress of teacher education.
Related titles: Online - full content ed.
Indexed: EAA.
—IE. **CCC.**
Published by: (California State University, Los Angeles), National Forum Journals, 17603 Bending Post Dr, Houston, TX 77095. TEL 281-550-5700, http://www.nationalforum.com. Ed., Pub., R&P, Adv. contact Dr. William Kritsonis TEL 337-477-0008. page USD 800.

370.72 JPN ISSN 0385-1990
NATIONAL INSTITUTE FOR EDUCATIONAL REREARCH. NEWSLETTER; UNESCO-NIER programme for educational research in Asia. Text in English. 1969. 3/yr. free. back issues avail. **Document type:** *Newsletter.*
Published by: National Institute for Educational Research, 6-5-22 Shino-Meguro, Meguro-ku, Tokyo, 153, Japan. TEL 81-3-5721-5074, FAX 81-3-5721-5517. Ed. R Watanabe. Circ: 1,000.

370.72 JPN ISSN 0085-378X
L67 CODEN: RBNRD9
NATIONAL INSTITUTE FOR EDUCATIONAL RESEARCH. RESEARCH BULLETIN. Text in English. 1959. irreg. free. charts; illus.; stat. **Document type:** *Bulletin.*
Indexed: BAS, CPE, IBSS, PsycholAb, SEA.
Published by: (Section of Research Dissemination), National Institute for Educational Research, 6-5-22 Shino-Meguro, Meguro-ku, Tokyo, 153, Japan. TEL 81-3-5721-5074, FAX 81-3-5721-5517. Circ: (controlled).

370.72 PNG
NATIONAL RESEARCH INSTITUTE. DIVISION OF EDUCATIONAL RESEARCH. OCCASIONAL PAPERS. Text in English. 1977. irreg. price varies. **Document type:** *Monographic series, Academic/Scholarly.*
Published by: (National Research Institute, Division of Educational Research), National Research Institute, PO Box 5854, Boroko, Papua New Guinea. TEL 675-26-0300, FAX 675-26-0213. Ed. Jim Robbins.

370.72 PNG
NATIONAL RESEARCH INSTITUTE. DIVISION OF EDUCATIONAL RESEARCH. RESEARCH PAPERS. Text in English. 1972. irreg. price varies. **Document type:** *Academic/Scholarly.*
Published by: (National Research Institute, Division of Educational Research), National Research Institute, PO Box 5854, Boroko, Papua New Guinea. TEL 675-26-0300, FAX 675-26-0213. Ed. Jim Robbins.

370.72 PNG
NATIONAL RESEARCH INSTITUTE. DIVISION OF EDUCATIONAL RESEARCH. SPECIAL REPORT. Text in English. 1985. irreg. price varies. **Document type:** *Academic/Scholarly.*
Published by: (National Research Institute, Division of Educational Research), National Research Institute, PO Box 5854, Boroko, Papua New Guinea. TEL 675-26-0300, FAX 675-26-0213. Ed. Jim Robbins.

370.72 PNG
NATIONAL RESEARCH INSTITUTE. DIVISION OF EDUCATIONAL RESEARCH. WORKING PAPERS. Text in English. irreg. price varies. **Document type:** *Academic/Scholarly.*
Published by: (National Research Institute, Division of Educational Research), National Research Institute, PO Box 5854, Boroko, Papua New Guinea. TEL 675-26-0300, FAX 675-26-0213. Ed. Jim Robbins.

370.1 USA ISSN 0036-0023
LC5146
NATIONAL RURAL EDUCATION NEWS. Text in English. 1948. q. USD 50; USD 65 foreign (effective 1999 - 2000); includes Rural Educator. adv. bk.rev. **Document type:** *Newsletter, Trade.*
Incorporates (1976-1980): Rural - Regional Education News (0276-072X); Formerly: Rural Education News
Related titles: Online - full text ed.
Indexed: CIJE.
—BLDSC (8052.434400).
Published by: National Rural Education Association, University of Oklahoma, 820 Van Vleet Oval, Rm 227, Norman, OK 73019. bmooneyham@ou.edu, http://www.nrea.net. Ed., Pub., R&P, Adv. contact Joseph T Newlin. Circ: 1,200 (paid).

370 USA ISSN 0077-5762
LB5
NATIONAL SOCIETY FOR THE STUDY OF EDUCATION. YEARBOOK. Text in English. 1902. a. (in 2 parts). USD 136 combined subscription in the Americas to institutions print & online eds.; GBP 84 combined subscription elsewhere to institutions print & online eds. (effective 2006). **Document type:** *Yearbook, Trade.*
Related titles: Online - full text ed.: ISSN 1744-7984. USD 129 in the Americas to institutions; GBP 80 elsewhere to institutions (effective 2006) (from Blackwell Synergy, EBSCO Publishing, O C L C Online Computer Library Center, Inc.).
Indexed: ABIn, EduInd, RI-1, RI-2.
—BLDSC (9394.100000), IE, ingenta. **CCC.**
Published by: (National Society for the Study of Education), Blackwell Publishing, Inc. (Subsidiary of: Blackwell Publishing Ltd.), Commerce Place, 350 Main St, Malden, MA 02148. TEL 781-388-8206, FAX 781-388-8232, http://www.blackwellpublishing.com. Ed., R&P Kenneth J Rehage. Circ: 1,500. **Subscr. to:** Secretary.

371.12 GBR ISSN 0077-5940
NATIONAL UNION OF TEACHERS. ANNUAL REPORT. Text in English. 1871. a. free (effective 2003). **Document type:** *Corporate.*
Formerly (until 1887): National Union of Elementary Teachers. Annual Report
Published by: National Union of Teachers, Hamilton House, Mabledon Pl, London, WC1H 9BD, United Kingdom. TEL 44-20-73804713, FAX 44-20-73878458, j.friedlander@nut.org.uk, http://www.teachers.org.uk.

NATIONAL VOCATIONAL EVALUATION AND WORK ADJUSTMENT JOURNAL. see *OCCUPATIONS AND CAREERS*

NATUR OG SAMFUNN; environmental magazine. see *ENVIRONMENTAL STUDIES*

370 USA
▼ **NAVIGO.** Text in English. 2005. bi-m. USD 40 (effective 2005). **Document type:** *Magazine, Consumer.* **Description:** Focuses on a specific editorial theme with feature articles written from historical, cultural and scientific perspectives. Includes travel features, product reviews, news and events, and personal interviews with individuals and families exemplifying the spirit of experiential learning.
Address: PO Box 310, Charlton, MA 01507. TEL 508-248-1113, http://www.navigo-online.com/home.htm.

372.86 USA
NEBRASKA JOURNAL. Text in English. s-a. USD 10. adv. back issues avail.
Published by: Nebraska Association for Health, Physical Education, Recreation & Dance, Dept of Health, Kinesiology and Leisure Studies, Lambert Gym, Purdue University, West Lafayette, IN 47907-1362. TEL 402-554-2670. Ed. Tom Sharpe. Circ: 350.

NEBRASKA MUSIC EDUCATOR. see *MUSIC*

371.829 USA ISSN 0548-1457
LC2701
➤ **NEGRO EDUCATIONAL REVIEW**; a forum for discussion of Afro-American issues. Text in English. 1950. q. USD 30 (effective 2005). adv. bk.rev. illus. index, cum.index every 25 yrs. reprints avail. **Document type:** *Journal, Academic/Scholarly.*
Related titles: Online - full text ed.: (from EBSCO Publishing, H.W. Wilson, O C L C Online Computer Library Center, Inc., ProQuest Information & Learning).
Indexed: ABIn, CIJE, CPE, ERA, ETA, EduInd, HEA, IIBP, MEA, PCI, RHEA, SEA, SENA, SOMA, TEA.
—BLDSC (6075.160000), IE, ingenta.
Published by: Negro Educational Review, Inc., Florida A & M University, 676 Gamble St, Tallahassee, FL 32307. TEL 850-599-8446, FAX 850-561-2100, ner@famu.edu. Ed. Mac A Stewart. R&P Charles U Smith. Adv. contact Barbara J Dunn. Circ: 1,000.

370.9492 NLD
NETHERLANDS. MINISTERIE VAN ONDERWIJS EN WETENSCHAPPEN. ONDERWIJSVERSLAG. Text in Dutch. 1973. a. price varies. **Document type:** *Government.*
Published by: (Netherlands. Ministerie van Onderwijs en Wetenschappen), Sdu Uitgevers bv, Christoffel Plantijnstraat 2, The Hague, 2515 TZ, Netherlands.

NETHERLANDS. MINISTERIE VAN ONDERWIJS EN WETENSCHAPPEN. PEDAGOGISCHE BIBLIOGRAFIE. see *EDUCATION—Abstracting, Bibliographies, Statistics*

370 GBR
NETWORK (EXHALL). Text in English. 1981. 5/yr. GBP 60 for membership to schools (effective 2003); subscr. incld. in membership. adv. bk.rev. charts; illus. 4 p./no. 3 cols./p.; **Document type:** *Newsletter.* **Description:** Covers national policy changes, reports good practice and stimulates discussion on a wide range of community-related issues.
Former titles: The Magazine For Community News Network; (until 2000): Community Education Network (0262-706X)
Related titles: Online - full text ed.
Published by: (Community Education Development Centre), Community Schools Network, c/o Julian Piper, CSN Manager, CEDC, Unit C1 Grovelands Court, Grovelands Estate, Longford Rd, Exhall, Coventry CV7 9NE, United Kingdom. TEL 44-2476-588440, FAX 44-2476-588441, info@cedc.org.uk, http://www.cedc-csn.org.uk/. Ed., Adv. contact Amanda Kay. Circ: 1,000.

NETWORK (ROCKVILLE). see *ADVERTISING AND PUBLIC RELATIONS*

370 DEU ISSN 1435-2516
NEUE SAECHSISCHE LEHRERZEITUNG. Text in German. 1990. bi-m. EUR 16 (effective 2003). **Document type:** *Newspaper, Academic/Scholarly.*
Published by: (Saechsischer Lehrerverband e.V.), Satztechnik Meissen GmbH, Am Sand 1c, Nieschuetz, 01665, Germany. TEL 49-3525-71860, FAX 49-3525-718612, info@satztechnik-meissen.de, http://www.satztechnik-meissen.de. Circ: 8,150 (paid).

370 DEU ISSN 0028-3355
AP30
NEUE SAMMLUNG; Vierteljahres-Zeitschrift fuer Erziehung und Gesellschaft. Text in German. 1945. q. EUR 74.40; EUR 20.50 newsstand/cover (effective 2005). adv. bk.rev. bibl. index. reprints avail. **Document type:** *Journal, Academic/Scholarly.*
Formerly (until 1961): Die Sammlung (0179-3128)
Indexed: DIP, HistAb, IBR, IBZ, MLA-IB, RASB.
—IE, Infotrieve. **CCC.**
Published by: Erhard Friedrich Verlag GmbH, Im Brande 17, Seelze, 30926, Germany. TEL 49-511-400040, FAX 49-511-40004170, info@friedrich-verlag.de, http://www.friedrich-verlag.de/index.cfm?2E2F490102824800A37A2C2E31B4A91B. Ed. Gerold Becker. adv.: page EUR 350. Circ: 1,200.

NEUSPRACHLICHE MITTEILUNGEN AUS WISSENSCHAFT UND PRAXIS. see *LINGUISTICS*

370 CAN ISSN 0382-2850
NEW BRUNSWICK. DEPARTMENT OF EDUCATION. ANNUAL REPORT. Text in English. 1936. a.
Former titles (until 1974): Province of New Brunswick. Minister of Education. Annual Report (0382-2869); (until 1968): Annual Report of the Department of Education of the Province of New Brunswick (0382-2877)
—CISTI.
Published by: New Brunswick. Department of Education, Place 2000, 250 King St, Fredericton, NB E3B 9M9, Canada. TEL 506-453-3678, FAX 506-453-3325, http://www.gnb.ca/0000/index-e.asp.

370 POL ISSN 1732-6729
▼ **THE NEW EDUCATIONAL REVIEW.** Text in Polish. 2003. s-a. PLZ 20 per issue (effective 2005). **Document type:** *Journal, Academic/Scholarly.*
Published by: (Uniwersytet Slaski w Katowicach), Wydawnictwo Adam Marszalek, ul Lubicka 44, Torun, 87100, Poland. info@marszalek.com.pl, http://www.marszalek.com.pl.

370 USA ISSN 1547-688X
▼ ➤ **THE NEW EDUCATOR.** Text in English. 2005 (Jan.-Mar.). q. USD 128, GBP 78 combined subscription to institutions print & online eds. (effective 2006). **Document type:** *Journal, Academic/Scholarly.* **Description:** Publishes original contributions that focus on the challenges of building and sustaining professional community in the education of new educators. Aims to address the concerns of teacher educators, school administrators, teacher support staff, school counselors, student advisors and all those who educate outside of the classroom.
Related titles: Online - full text ed.: ISSN 1549-9243. GBP 74, USD 122 to institutions (effective 2006) (from EBSCO Publishing).
Published by: Taylor & Francis Inc. (Subsidiary of: Taylor & Francis Group), 325 Chestnut St, Ste 800, Philadelphia, PA 19016. TEL 215-625-8900, 800-354-1420, FAX 215-625-2940, info@taylorandfrancis.com, http://www.tandf.co.uk/journals/titles/1547688x.asp, http://www.taylorandfrancis.com. Ed. Beverly Falk.

372.4 USA ISSN 0028-4882
➤ **NEW ENGLAND READING ASSOCIATION. JOURNAL.** Text in English. 1966. 3/yr. USD 30 domestic; USD 35 in Canada; USD 45 elsewhere (effective 2005). adv. bk.rev. reprint service avail. from PQC. **Document type:** *Academic/Scholarly.*
Related titles: Microform ed.: (from PQC); Online - full text ed.: (from H.W. Wilson, O C L C Online Computer Library Center, Inc., ProQuest Information & Learning).
Indexed: ABIn, EduInd.
Published by: New England Reading Association, c/o Duane Small, Business Mgr, PO Box 997, Portland, ME, ME 04104-0997. info@nereading.org, http://www.nereading.org. Ed. Robert F O'Neill. Circ: 3,000.

370 GBR ISSN 0957-0942
L16
➤ **NEW ERA IN EDUCATION.** Text in English. 1920. 3/yr. GBP 18 domestic to individuals; GBP 21 foreign to individuals; GBP 30 domestic to institutions; GBP 33 foreign to institutions (effective 2004). adv. bk.rev. index. back issues avail.; reprint service avail. from PQC. **Document type:** *Academic/Scholarly.* **Description:** Covers the progress in educational practice and research around the world.
Formerly (until 1988): New Era (0028-5048); Which incorporated: World Studies Bulletin and Ideas
Related titles: Microform ed.: (from PQC).

E

Indexed: BrEdI, CPE, ChLitAb, DIP, ERA, ETA, IBR, IBZ, MEA, RHEA, SEA, SENA, SOMA, TEA.
—BLDSC (6084.112000), IE, ingenta.
Published by: World Education Fellowship, University Of Hertfordshire, Wall Hall, Aldenham, Watford, Herts WD2 8AT, United Kingdom. TEL 44-1707-285677, FAX 44-1707-285616. Ed. Dave Hinton. R&P, Adv. contact George John. B&W page GBP 64. Circ: 2,000. **Subscr. to:** Treasurer, 58 Dickens Rise, Chigwell, Essex IG7 6NY, United Kingdom. TEL 44-181-281-7122.

➤ **NEW HAMPSHIRE EDUCATION LAWS ANNOTATED.** see *LAW*

370 USA ISSN 0889-5678
NEW HORIZONS (MILWAUKEE). Text in English. q. USD 18 for 2 yrs.. **Document type:** *Newsletter.*
Published by: National Registration Center for Study Abroad, P O Box 1393, Milwaukee, WI 53201. TEL 414-278-0631, FAX 414-271-8884, inquiries@nrcsa.com. Ed. Mary Croy.

370 AUS ISSN 0028-5382
➤ **NEW HORIZONS IN EDUCATION.** Text in English. 1937. s-a. AUD 8 per issue domestic; AUD 10.50 per issue foreign (effective 2000). adv. bk.rev. **Document type:** *Academic/Scholarly.* **Description:** Covers policies, practices and paradigms in/of education, especially new initiative in, and new directions for, education. Includes education narratives of teachers, students, parents, and other interested participants; also contains reports of events and activities.
Indexed: AEI, CPE, PCI, RASB.
Published by: World Education Fellowship (Australia), 21 Ridgway Dr, Flagstaff Hill, SA 5159, Australia. TEL 61-8-82703541, FAX 61-8-83370220. Ed. David Massey TEL 61-7-38644744. Circ: 1,000 (paid).

➤ **NEW JERSEY EDUCATION LAW REPORT**; the authority on labor relations in New Jersey schools. see *LAW*

371.192 USA ISSN 0028-5897
NEW JERSEY PARENT TEACHER. Text in English. 1915. 8/yr. (Sep.-Jun.). USD 7. adv. illus.; stat. **Document type:** *Bulletin.* **Description:** Provides news of local and national issues affecting youth and public education, parental involvement in schools and communities, legislation for public education, and news regarding PTA events.
Published by: New Jersey Congress of Parents and Teachers, 900 Berkeley Ave, Trenton, NJ 08618. TEL 609-393-6709, FAX 609-393-8471, nj_office@pta.org. Ed., Adv. contact Pat Frey. R&P Ginny Hintz. Circ: 4,000 (paid).

794.8 USA
NEW LITERACIES AND DIGITAL EPISTEMOLOGIES. Text in English. 2002. irreg., latest 2004. price varies. back issues avail. **Document type:** *Monographic series.*
Published by: Peter Lang Publishing, Inc., 275 Seventh Ave, 28th Fl, New York, NY 10001. TEL 212-647-7700, 800-770-5264, FAX 212-647-7707, customerservice@plang.com, http://www.peterlangusa.com. Eds. Chris Bigum, Colin Lankshear, Michael Peters, Michele Knoebel.

NEW PLAINS REVIEW. see *LITERATURE*

371.1 PAK ISSN 0077-8826
NEW TEACHER. Text in English, Urdu, Pushto. 1952. a. PKR 8.
Published by: University of Peshawar, College of Education, Peshawar, Pakistan.

371.1 USA ISSN 1070-7379
NEW TEACHER ADVOCATE. Text in English. 1993. q. USD 10 domestic to non-members; USD 12 foreign to non-members; USD 8 domestic to members; USD 10 foreign to members (effective 2005). adv. illus. 12 p./no. 2 cols./p.; back issues avail. **Document type:** *Newsletter, Trade.* **Description:** Contains practical tips and reflections focused on the needs of beginning educators.
Published by: Kappa Delta Pi, 3707 Woodview Trace, Indianapolis, IN 46268-1158. TEL 317-871-4900, 800-284-3167, FAX 317-704-2323, pubs@kdp.org, http://www.kdp.org/publications/advocate.php. Ed., Adv. contact Karen Allen. color 1/2 page USD 1,150. Circ: 26,000 (paid and controlled).

NEW YORK AFRICAN STUDIES ASSOCIATION NEWSLETTER. see *HISTORY—History Of Africa*

NEW YORK EDUCATION LAW REPORT. see *LAW*

NEW YORK STATE ASSOCIATION OF SCHOOL NURSES COMMUNICATOR. see *MEDICAL SCIENCES—Nurses And Nursing*

370 510.7 USA
NEW YORK STATE MATHEMATICS TEACHERS' JOURNAL. Text in English. 3/yr. adv.
Indexed: CIJE.
Published by: Association of Mathematics Teachers of New York State, c/o John Bailey, Data Manager, PO Box 631, Lake Katrine, NY 12449. Ed. Edward Wallace. Adv. contact John Balzano.

371.1 USA ISSN 1074-0503
NEW YORK TEACHER (CITY EDITION). Text in English. 1917. bi-w. (Sep.-Jun.). USD 12 (effective 2005). adv. **Document type:** *Newspaper, Trade.* **Description:** Alerts teachers in New York City public schools to national and union issues of interest and concern.
Formerly: New York Teacher. U F T Bulletin (1064-6744)
Published by: New York State United Teachers, 800 Troy-Schenectady Rd., Latham, NY 12210-2455. TEL 518-213-6000, FAX 518-213-6415, nyteach@nysutmail.org, http://www.nysut.org/newyorkteacher/index.html. Ed. Lance Howland. adv.: B&W page USD 5,184. Circ: 500,000 (paid and controlled).

NEW YORK TEACHER (STATE EDITION). see *LABOR UNIONS*

THE NEW YORK TIMES UPFRONT; the news magazine for teens. see *CHILDREN AND YOUTH—For*

370.72 NZL ISSN 1171-3283
LA2100
➤ **NEW ZEALAND ANNUAL REVIEW OF EDUCATION.** Text in English. a. NZD 39.95 domestic; NZD 45 foreign (effective 2003). back issues avail. **Document type:** *Journal, Academic/Scholarly.* **Description:** Includes articles on current issues and developments in education, a diary of educational events, communications on policy initiatives and legislative changes, and a list of publications and conferences.
Indexed: INZP.
Published by: New Zealand Council for Educational Research, PO Box 3237, Wellington, New Zealand. TEL 64-4-3847939, FAX 64-4-3847933, subscriptions@nzcer.org.nz, http://www.nzcer.org.nz.

372.1 NZL ISSN 0114-166X
NEW ZEALAND CHILDCARE ASSOCIATION. REPORT TO ANNUAL CONFERENCE. Text in English, Maori. 1963. a. back issues avail. **Document type:** *Corporate.*
Related titles: Diskette ed.; Record ed.
Published by: New Zealand Childcare Association, P.O. Box 11-863, Wellington, New Zealand. Ed. Rose Cole. Circ: 800 (controlled).

370 NZL
THE NEW ZEALAND EDUCATION GAZETTE. Text in English. 22/yr. NZD 120 domestic; NZD 184 in Australia; NZD 256 in North America and Asia; NZD 288 elsewhere (effective 2001). **Document type:** *Government.* **Description:** Provides information on courses, conferences, awards, employment opportunities, and other education- and teaching-related news.
Indexed: INZP.
Published by: (Slovakia. Ministry of Education KEN), GP Legislation Services, P.O. Box 12418, Thorndon, Wellington, New Zealand. TEL 64-4-496-5655, FAX 64-4-496-5698, http://www.gplegislation.co.nz.

370 NZL ISSN 0028-8276
LA2120 CODEN: NZESDN
➤ **NEW ZEALAND JOURNAL OF EDUCATIONAL STUDIES.** Text in English. 1966. s-a. NZD 48 domestic; NZD 95 foreign (effective 2004). adv. bk.rev. charts; illus.; stat. cum.index. **Document type:** *Journal, Academic/Scholarly.* **Description:** Contains quality essays, research reports, and critical comment in all fields of education.
Related titles: Online - full text ed.
Indexed: ASCA, ArtHuCI, CPE, CurCont, ERA, ETA, INZP, L&LBA, MEA, PsycInfo, PsycholAb, RHEA, SEA, SENA, SOMA, SOPODA, SPPI, SSA, SSCI, SWA, SociolAb, TEA, e-psyche.
—BLDSC (6093.540000), IDS, IE, ingenta. **CCC.**
Published by: New Zealand Council for Educational Research, PO Box 3237, Wellington, New Zealand. TEL 64-4-3847939, FAX 64-4-3847933, subscriptions@nzcer.org.nz, https://www.nzcer.org.nz/default.php?cPath=139_134_182, http://www.nzcer.org.nz.

370.1 310 NZL
NEW ZEALAND. STATISTICS NEW ZEALAND. FIGURES AND FACTS (YEAR). Text in English. irreg., latest 1998. NZD 10 (effective 2000). stat. **Document type:** *Government.* **Description:** Contains a resource book for schools with data grouped around a number of themes that weave into different areas of the curriculum. It is specially packaged for primary, intermediate and secondary schools and where possible, data and facts are selected that are of special relevance to younger people.
Related titles: Online - full content ed.
Published by: Statistics New Zealand/Te Tari Tatau, PO Box 2922, Wellington, New Zealand. TEL 64-4-495-4600, FAX 64-4-473-2626, info@stats.govt.nz, http://www.stats.govt.nz.

371.14 CAN ISSN 1189-9662
NEWFOUNDLAND AND LABRADOR TEACHERS' ASSOCIATION. BULLETIN. Abbreviated title: N L T A Bulletin. Text in English. 1954. 7/yr. (during school yr.). CND 15 (effective 1998). adv. **Document type:** *Newsletter.*
Formerly: Newfoundland Teachers' Association. Bulletin (0380-1047)
Indexed: CEI.
Published by: Newfoundland and Labrador Teachers' Association, 3 Kenmount Rd, St. John's, NF A1B 1W1, Canada. TEL 709-726-3223, FAX 709-726-4302. Ed. Lesley Ann Browne. Adv. contact Michelle Lamarche. page CND 450.

371 USA
NEWSLINER✶. Text in English. q. **Description:** Exchange of information among members.
Published by: National Association of State Education, Department Information Officers, RR1 Box 55B, Bigelow, AR 72016-9705. TEL 501-378-2344. Ed. Mary Laurie.

370 ESP ISSN 1137-6880
NEXO. Text in Spanish. 1985. irreg.
—CINDOC.
Published by: Junta de Andalucia, Consejeria de Educacion y Ciencia, Edif. Torretriana, C. Juan Antonio de Vizarron s-n, Isla de Cartuja, Sevilla, 41092, Spain. FAX 34-955-064003, infomacion@cec.junta-andalucia.es, http://www3.cec.junta-andalucia.es/.

NICHE - BULLETIN VOOR NET ANDER WIJS IN DE BIOLOGIE. see *BIOLOGY*

370.9669 NGA ISSN 0189-2916
LA1630
NIGERIA EDUCATIONAL FORUM. JOURNAL. Text in English. 1974. s-a. NGN 240. adv. bk.rev. Supplement avail. **Document type:** *Academic/Scholarly.* **Description:** Deals with a variety of educational topics on school subjects.
Formerly: Ahmadu Bello University. Institute of Education. Paper (0065-4752)
Indexed: REE&TA.
Published by: Ahmadu Bello University, Institute of Education, Samaru-Zaria, Kaduna, Nigeria. TEL 234-69-51216. Ed. R A Omojuwa. Circ: 500.

370 NGA ISSN 0029-0157
NIGERIAN SCHOOLMASTER. Text in English. 1969. 3/yr. adv. bk.rev.; play rev. illus. **Document type:** *Trade.* **Description:** Contains organization news.
Published by: Nigeria Union of Teachers, PMB 1044, Yaba, Lagos State, Nigeria. Ed. Gabriel O Falade. Circ: 20,000.

NIHON KYOIKUHO GAKKAI NENPO. see *LAW*

NIIGATAKEN SEIBUTSU KYOIKU KENKYUKAISHI/NIIGATA PREFECTURAL BIOLOGICAL SOCIETY FOR EDUCATION. BULLETIN. see *BIOLOGY*

370 331.8 JPN ISSN 0029-0505
NIKKYOSO KYOIKU SHINBUN. Text in Japanese. 1949. w. JPY 1,500. adv. charts; illus.; stat. **Document type:** *Newspaper.*
Published by: Japan Teachers' Union/Nikkyoso, Nihon Kyoiku-Kaikan, 2-6-2 Hitotsubashi, Kanda, Chiyoda-ku, Tokyo, Japan. Circ: 450,000.

370 USA ISSN 1551-2223
NO CHILD LEFT BEHIND COMPLIANCE INSIDER. Text in English. m. USD 267 domestic print or online ed. (effective 2005). **Document type:** *Newsletter, Consumer.*
Related titles: Online - full text ed.: USD 387 (effective 2004).
Published by: Brownstone Publishers, Inc., 149 Fifth Ave, 16th Fl, New York, NY 10010-6801. TEL 212-473-8200, FAX 212-473-8786, http://www.brownstone.com. Ed. Marion Walsh.

371.02 USA ISSN 0077-9253
NONPUBLIC SCHOOL ENROLLMENT AND STAFF, NEW YORK STATE. Text in English. 1966. a. free. charts; stat. back issues avail. **Document type:** *Government.*
Formerly: Survey of Nonpublic Schools in New York State
Published by: Education Department, Information, Reporting & Technology Services, Education Bldg Annex, Rm 962, Albany, NY 12234. TEL 518-474-7082, FAX 518-474-4351. Circ: (controlled).

370 NOR ISSN 0901-8050
L46 CODEN: NOPEFT
NORDISK PEDAGOGIK. Text in Danish, English, Norwegian, Swedish; Summaries in English. 1980. q. NOK 410 to individuals; NOK 660 to institutions; NOK 200 to students; NOK 98 per issue (effective 2004). bk.rev. **Document type:** *Journal, Academic/Scholarly.* **Description:** Publishes scholarly articles, debates and information on issues in education in the Nordic countries.
Formerly (until 1986): Tidskrift foer Nordisk Foerening foer Pedagogisk Forskning (0349-6732)
Indexed: DIP, IBR, IBZ, L&LBA, SOPODA, SSA, SociolAb.
—**CCC.**
Published by: (Nordisk Forening for Pedagogisk Forskning (NFPF)), Universitetsforlaget AS/Scandinavian University Press (Subsidiary of: Aschehoug & Co.), Sehesteds Gate 3, Postboks 508, Oslo, 0105, Norway. TEL 47-24-147500, FAX 47-24-147501, post@universitetsforlaget.no, http://www.universitetsforlaget.no/tidsskrifter/article.jhtml?articleID=330, http://www.universitetesforlaget.no. Ed. Bjoern Hasselgren.

E

370 NOR ISSN 0029-2052
NORSK PEDAGOGISK TIDSSKRIFT/NORWEGIAN JOURNAL OF EDUCATION. Text in Norwegian. 1916. bi-m. NOK 370 to individuals; NOK 650 to institutions; NOK 200 to students; NOK 75 per issue (effective 2004). adv. bk.rev. abstr. index. back issues avail. **Document type:** *Journal, Academic/Scholarly.* **Description:** Deals with theoretical and practical issues in education.
Indexed: IBR, IBZ.
Published by: (Laererforbundet/Teaching Association, Utdanningsforbundet/Union of Education Norway), Universitetsforlaget AS/Scandinavian University Press (Subsidiary of: Aschehoug & Co.), Sehesteds Gate 3, Postboks 508, Oslo, 0105, Norway. TEL 47-24-147500, FAX 47-24-147501, post@universitetsforlaget.no, http://www.universitetsforlaget.no/tidsskrifter/article.jhtml?articleID=338, http://www.universitesforlaget.no. Eds. Finn Daniel Raaen, Tone Solbrekke.

NORTH AMERICAN JOURNAL OF PSYCHOLOGY. see *PSYCHOLOGY*

371 USA
NORTH DAKOTA CENTURY SCHOOL CODE. Text in English. w/ CD ROM), latest 2001, base vol. plus biennial updates. USD 95 (effective 2003). 659 p./no.
Published by: Michie Company (Subsidiary of: LexisNexis North America), 701 E Water St, Charlottesville, VA 22902-5389. TEL 434-972-7600, 800-446-3410, FAX 434-972-7677, http://www.michie.com.

370.1 USA ISSN 0048-0681
NORTH DAKOTA EDUCATION NEWS. Text in English. 1968. 7/yr. free to members. adv. 12 p./no. 4 cols./p.; **Document type:** *Journal, Academic/Scholarly.*
Published by: North Dakota Education Association, 410 E. Thayer, Bismarck, ND 58501-4049. TEL 701-223-0450, 800-369-6332, FAX 701-224-8535, http://www.ndea.org. Ed. Linda L Harsche. Circ: 8,500 (controlled).

370 CAN ISSN 0029-3253
NORTHIAN★. Text in English. 1964. q. CND 6. bk.rev. illus. index.
Related titles: Microfilm ed.: (from MML); Microform ed.: 1964 (from MML, PQC).
Indexed: CEI, CIJE.
Published by: Society for Indian and Northern Education, Univ of Saskatchewan, College of Educ, 28 Campus Dr, Saskatoon, SK S7N 0X1, Canada. TEL 306-343-2100. Circ: 500.

370.1 USA
NORTHWEST ASSOCIATION OF SCHOOLS AND COLLEGES. REPORT. Text in English. 1968. s-a. membership. bibl.; charts; illus.; tr.lit. **Document type:** *Newsletter, Trade.*
Former titles: Northwest Association of Schools and Colleges. Newsletter; Northwest Association of Schools and Colleges. Committee on Research and Service. Newsletter; Northwest Association of Secondary and Higher Schools. Committee on Research and Service. Newsletter. (0029-3326)
Published by: (Northwest Association of Schools and of Colleges and Universities), Commission on Schools, 1910 University Dr, Boise, ID 83725-1060. TEL 208-426-5727, FAX 208-334-3228, sclemens@boisestate.edu, http://www2.boisestate.edu/nasc. Ed. Shelli D. Clemens. Pub., R&P David G Steadman. Circ: (controlled).

370 USA ISSN 1546-5020
L11
NORTHWEST EDUCATION. Text in English. q., latest vol.7, no.3. **Document type:** *Magazine.*
Related titles: Online - full text ed.
Indexed: CIJE.
Published by: Northwest Regional Education Laboratory, 101 S W Main St,, Ste 500, Portland, OR 97204. TEL 503-275-9500, http://www.nwrel.org/nwedu.

371 USA ISSN 1041-6463
NORTHWEST REPORT (PORTLAND). Text in English. bi-m. **Document type:** *Newsletter.*
Related titles: Online - full text ed.
Published by: Northwest Regional Education Laboratory, 101 S W Main St,, Ste 500, Portland, OR 97204. TEL 503-275-9500, http://www.nwrel.org/nwreport. Ed. Denise Jarrett Weeks TEL 503-275-9191.

NORWAY. STATISTISK SENTRALBYRAA. UTDANNINGSSTATISTIKK. GRUNNSKOLAR. see *EDUCATION—Abstracting, Bibliographies, Statistics*

NORWAY. STATISTISK SENTRALBYRAA. VIDEREGAENDE SKOLER. see *EDUCATION—Abstracting, Bibliographies, Statistics*

370 ITA ISSN 0029-3792
NOSTRI RAGAZZI; incontri tra scuola elementare e famiglia. Text in Italian. 1958. 7/yr.
Published by: Associazione Genitori, P.O. Box 217, Bologna, BO 40100, Italy. Circ: 15,000.

378 PHL ISSN 0048-0932
DS651
➤ **NOTRE DAME JOURNAL.** Text in English. 1965. s-a. PHP 250. bk.rev. **Document type:** *Academic/Scholarly.* **Description:** Publishes papers, research reports and thesis abstracts on education.
Indexed: CurCont, IPP.
Published by: Notre Dame University, Cotabato City, Maguindanao 9600, Philippines. TEL 63-64-421-4312, FAX 63-64-421-4312, ndu@phil.gn.apc.org. Ed. Eliseo R Mercado. Circ: 500.

370 FRA ISSN 0991-9708
LE NOUVEL EDUCATEUR. Text in French. 1939. m. **Description:** Discusses the problems facing children in school.
Formerly (until 1988): L' Educateur (0013-113X); Which was formed by the 1970 merger of: L' Educateur. 1er Degre (0151-119X); L' Educateur. 2nd Degre (0151-1181); Which superseded in part (in 1969): L' Educateur (0420-7661)
Related titles: ♦ Supplement(s): L' Educateur. Supplement Periodique de Travail et de Recherches. ISSN 0154-2524.
Indexed: DIP, IBR, IBZ.
—IE, Infotrieve.
Published by: Publications de l'Ecole Moderne Francaise, Mouans-Sartoux, Cedex 06376, France. TEL 33-4-92921757, FAX 33-4-92921804, pemf@wanadoo.fr, http://www.pemf.fr. Ed. Monique Ribis. Pub. Pierre Guerin.

378 BEL ISSN 0378-8172
NOUVELLES UNIVERSITAIRES EUROPEENES/EUROPEAN UNIVERSITY NEWS. Text in Dutch, English, French, German, Italian. 1965. 5/yr. bk.rev. back issues avail. **Document type:** *Newsletter.* **Description:** Carries news for and from universities in Europe, especially on courses and lectures in European studies and research, calendar of forthcoming events and useful addresses.
Related titles: Online - full text ed.
Indexed: CPE, ECI, RASB.
Published by: European Commission, University Information, Rue de la Loi, 200, Brussels, B-1049, Belgium. marie-francoise.nicaise@dg10.cec.be, http://www.epms.nl/www/ecsa/eun.htm. Circ: 8,000. **Subscr. to:** European Commission, Office for Official Publications of the European Union, 2 Rue Mercier, Luxembourg L-2985, Luxembourg. **Dist. in U.S. by:** European Community Information Service, 2100 M St, NW Ste 707, Washington, DC 20037.

372.11 BRA ISSN 0103-0116
LA557
NOVA ESCOLA. Text in Portuguese. 1986. 10/yr. BRL 26 domestic; USD 43 foreign (effective 2005). adv. bk.rev. charts; illus. back issues avail. **Document type:** *Magazine, Trade.* **Description:** Contains articles and features for elementary school teachers.
Related titles: Online - full text ed.
Published by: Editora Abril, S.A., Av. das Nacoes Unidas, 7221, 11 andar Pinheiros, Sao Paulo, SP 05425-902, Brazil. TEL 55-11-50872112, FAX 55-11-50872100, novaescola.abril@atleitor.com.br, http://revistaescola.abril.com.br/, http://www.abril.com.br/. adv.: page BRL 25,982. Circ: 505,283.

370 USA
➤ **NOVATIONS**; explorations in learning and education. Text in English. irreg. bk.rev. **Document type:** *Journal, Academic/Scholarly.*
Media: Online - full content.
Published by: University of Colorado at Denver, Educational Leadership and Innovation doctoral program, School of Education, Campus Box 106, PO Box 173364, Denver, CO 80217-3364. http://novationsjournal.org/content/, http://www.cudenver.edu/Academics/Colleges/School+of+Education/Programs+and+Degrees/Doctorate+Degree/Educational+Leadership+and+Innovation/default.htm. Ed. Ellen Stevens.

370 POL ISSN 0029-537X
NOWA SZKOLA; miesiecznik spoleczno-pedagogiczny. Text in Polish. 1945. 10/yr. USD 42. bk.rev. illus. index. **Description:** Focuses on contemporary problems of instruction and education, presents teachers' experiences, publishes reports on educational research and experiments undertaken at schools, and reports on the life of schools and other educational institutions.
Indexed: AgrLib.
Published by: (Poland. Ministerstwo Edukacji Narodowej), Korporacja Polonia, ul Rozbrat 6/10, Warsaw, 00-450, Poland. TEL 48-22-6224524. Ed. Julian Radziewicz. **Dist. by:** Ars Polona, Krakowskie Przedmiescie 7, Warsaw, Poland.

370 PAN
NUEVA ESCUELA. Text in Spanish. N.S. 1990. q.
Published by: Instituto de Estudios Nacionales, La Colina, Estafeta Universitaria, Universidad de Panama, Panama City, Panama. TEL 69-1412. Ed. Alfredo Figueroa Navarro. Circ: 500.

370 DEU
NUMERUS CLAUSUS - FINESSEN. Text in German. 1973. a. adv.
Former titles: Numerus Clausus - Alternativen; Numerus Clausus - Ersatzstudiengaenge
Published by: Verein Freunde und Foerderer der Deutschen Studentenschaft e.V., Untere Hausbreite 11, Munich, 80939, Germany. Ed. Gundolf Seidenspinner.

373 ITA
NUOVA SECONDARIA. Text in Italian. 1983. m. EUR 60 domestic; EUR 79 in Europe; EUR 102 elsewhere (effective 2005). adv. **Document type:** *Magazine, Trade.*
Published by: Editrice La Scuola SpA, Via Luigi Cadorna 11, Brescia, BS 25124, Italy. TEL 39-030-29931, FAX 39-030-2993299, http://www.lascuola.it. Ed. Evandro Agazzi. Circ: 25,000.

NURSE EDUCATION IN PRACTICE. see *MEDICAL SCIENCES—Nurses And Nursing*

NURSE EDUCATION IN PRACTICE. see *MEDICAL SCIENCES—Nurses And Nursing*

NURSING AND HEALTH SCIENCE EDUCATION. see *MEDICAL SCIENCES—Nurses And Nursing*

371.07 AUS ISSN 1443-7368
NURTURE; journal for home and school. Text in English. 1966. q. AUD 19 domestic; AUD 28 foreign (effective 2005). adv. bk.rev.; film rev. maps. 24 p./no.; back issues avail. **Document type:** *Journal, Academic/Scholarly.* **Description:** Aims to challenge the community in Christian education. Recent editions have featured bullying education, parents, agricultural programs.
Published by: Christian Parent Controlled Schools Ltd., PO Box 7000, Blacktown, NSW 2148, Australia. TEL 61-2-96713311, FAX 61-2-96715968, smitchell@cpcs.edu.au, http://www.cpcs.edu.au. Ed., R&P Suzanne Mitchell. Adv. contact Mrs. Sally Winsor. B&W page AUD 550, color page AUD 750. Circ: 9,800 (paid).

370 DNK
NYHEDER FRA UVM.DK. Text in Danish. 1991. irreg. free (effective 2005).
Formerly (until 2005): Denmark. Undervisningsministeriet. Nyhedsbrev (1398-3598)
Media: Online - full text.
Published by: Undervisningsministeriet/Ministry of Education, Frederiksholms Kanal 21, Copenhagen K, 1220, Denmark. TEL 45-33-925000, FAX 45-33-925567, http://www.uvm.dk/nyheder/seneste.htm?menuid=6410. Ed. Nicolai Kampmann.

O C T M NEWSLETTER. (Ohio Council of Teachers of Mathematics) see *MATHEMATICS*

370.1 USA ISSN 0743-7986
O E A FOCUS★. (Oklahoma Education Association) Text in English. 1919. 10/yr. USD 5 to non-members. adv. bk.rev. illus. index. reprint service avail. from PQC. **Document type:** *Newspaper.*
Formerly (until 1982): Oklahoma Teacher (0030-1884)
Related titles: Microform ed.: 1919 (from PQC).
Published by: Oklahoma Education Association, Public Affairs Center, 323 E Madison, Box 18485, Oklahoma City, OK 73154. TEL 405-528-7785, FAX 405-524-0350. Ed. Marty Bull. Adv. contact Bill Guy. Circ: 49,500.

371.0712 BEL ISSN 0770-1683
LC461
O I E C BULLETIN. Text in English, French, Spanish. 1969; N.S. 1993. q. USD 25 in Europe; USD 35 elsewhere (effective 2001). adv. bk.rev. **Document type:** *Bulletin.* **Description:** Aim is to make widely known the major trends affecting education in schools today and shaping tomorrow's educational policies.
Former titles: Catholic International Education Office. Bulletin Nouvelle Serie; Catholic International Education Office. Bulletin Trimestriel (0084-8638)
Media: Duplicated (not offset). **Related titles:** Spanish ed.: ISSN 1021-0172.
Indexed: HRIR.
Published by: Office International de l'Enseignement Catholique/Catholic International Education Office, 60 Rue des Eburons, Brussels, 1000, Belgium. TEL 32-2-2307252, FAX 32-2-2309745, oiec@pophost.eunet.be. Ed., R&P Fr. Andres Delgado Hernandez. Pub. Marguerite Lagoueyte. Adv. contact Rodrigo dos Santos Alves Garcia. Circ: 1,000.

371.4 CAN ISSN 1193-9524
O S C A REPORTS. Text in English. 1976. 3/yr. membership. adv. bk.rev. illus. **Document type:** *Newsletter.*
Former titles (until 1990): O S C A R. Ontario School Counsellors' Association Reports (0843-154X); (until 1980): O S C A Reports (0383-9931); (until 1976): Ontario School Counsellors' Association. Newsletter (0317-3992)
Published by: (Ontario School Counsellors' Association), Naylor Communications Ltd., 920 Yonge St, Ste 600, Toronto, ON M4W 3C7, Canada. TEL 416-449-9321, maurthom@enoreo.on.ca, http://ouacinfo.ouac.on.ca/osca/osca.htm. Ed. Kira Vermond. R&P Maureen Thompson. Adv. contact Rob Reid. Circ: 1,200.

370 USA ISSN 0095-6694
L13
O S S C BULLETIN✶. Text in English. 1957. q. USD 75; USD 100 foreign (effective 1999). adv. charts; illus. back issues avail. **Document type:** *Bulletin, Academic/Scholarly.*
Description: Each issue reports on a single, important educational topic or issue.
Formerly: Oregon School Study Council. Bulletin
Related titles: Online - full text ed.
Indexed: CIJE.
Published by: University of Oregon College of Education, Oregon School Study Council, 1215 University of Oregon, Eugene, OR 97403-1215. TEL 541-346-1397, FAX 541-346-5818, bobbiesmith@oregon.uoregon.edu, http://interact.uoregon.edu/ossc/index.html. Pub., Adv. contact Bobbie Smith. Circ: 300 (paid).

370 BGR ISSN 0861-976X
OBRAZOVANIE I KVALIFIKATSIA. Text in Bulgarian. 1993. bi-m. USD 30 foreign (effective 2002). **Description:** Covers problems of the educational system and professional work of the teachers in Bulgaria.
Published by: Universitetsko Izdatelstvo Sv. Kliment Okhridski/Publishing House of the Sofia University St. Kliment Ohridski, Akad G Bonchev 6, Sofia, 1113, Bulgaria. TEL 359-2-9792914. **Dist. by:** Sofia Books, ul Silivria 16, Sofia 1404, Bulgaria. TEL 359-2-9586257, info@sofiabooks-bg.com, http://www.sofiabooks-bg.com.

OBRAZOVANIE V REPUBLIKA BULGARIA/EDUCATION IN THE REPUBLIC OF BULGARIA. see *STATISTICS*

370 RUS
OBSHCHESTVOZNANIE V SHKOLE. Text in Russian. bi-m. USD 54 foreign (effective 2000).
Published by: Izdatel'stvo Shkola Press, Rustaveli ul 10-3, Moscow, 127254, Russian Federation. TEL 7-095-2198380, FAX 7-095-2195289. Ed. A Yu Lazebnikova. **US dist. addr.:** East View Information Services, 3020 Harbor Ln. N., Minneapolis, MN 55447. TEL 612-550-0961.

370 CZE ISSN 0231-7060
OGNIWO. Text in Polish. 1945. 10/yr. CZK 10.
Formerly (until vol.22, 1966): Praca Szkolna (0032-6194)
Published by: Uniwersytet Ostrawski, Dvorakova 76, Ostrava, 701 00, Czech Republic. Ed. Henryka Zabinska. Circ: 2,700. **Subscr. to:** PNS, Ustredni Expedice a Dovoz Tisku Praha, Administrace Vyvozu Tisku, Kovpakova 26, Zavod 1, Prague 6 160 00, Czech Republic.

372.1 TUR
OGRETMEN. Text in Turkish. 1972. 3/yr. **Document type:** *Newspaper.* **Description:** Examines events, problems and developments in the field of teaching in Northern Cyprus at the secondary school level.
Published by: Kibris Turk Orta Egitim Ogretmenler Sendikasi/Cyprus Turkish Secondary School Teachers Union, Abdullah Parla Sokagi, Lefkosa Kibris, Mersin 10, Turkey. TEL 90-392-2287971, FAX 90-392-2288648. Circ: 1,500.

371.192 USA ISSN 0199-0918
OHIO P T A NEWS. Text in English. 1923. 8/yr. USD 10 (effective 2002). adv. charts; illus. **Document type:** *Newsletter.*
Formerly (until vol.57, May 1979): Ohio Parent Teacher (0030-1019)
Published by: Ohio Congress of Parents & Teachers, Inc., 40 Northwoods Blvd, Columbus, OH 43235. TEL 614-781-6344, FAX 614-781-6349, oh_office@pta.org, http://www.ohiopta.org. Ed. Barbara Sprague. Adv. contact Susan Owen. Circ: 2,500.

370.1 USA ISSN 0030-1086
OHIO SCHOOLS. Text in English. 1923. 9/yr. USD 18 to institutions (colleges, universities, public libraries) (effective 2005). bibl.; illus. reprint service avail. from PQC. **Document type:** *Journal, Academic/Scholarly.*
Related titles: Microform ed.: (from PQC).
Published by: Ohio Education Association, PO Box 2550, Columbus, OH 43215. TEL 614-228-4526, FAX 614-228-8771, communic@ohea.org, http://www.ohea.org. Ed., R&P Julie Newhall. Adv. contact Crystal Phillips. Circ: 131,000 (paid and controlled).

OIKOGENEIA KAI SKOLEIO/FAMILY AND SCHOOL; dimenaio pedagogiko periodiko. see *CHILDREN AND YOUTH—About*

371.192 USA
OKLAHOMA P T A TODAY. (Parent Teacher Association) Text in English. 1923. q. **Document type:** *Newsletter.*
Formerly: Oklahoma Parent - Teacher (0030-1817)
Published by: Oklahoma Congress of Parents and Teachers, 1601 S W 89th St, Ste B 200, Oklahoma City, OK 73159-6357. Circ: 1,500.

370 NLD
HET ONDERWIJSBLAD. Text in Dutch. 1850. bi-w. adv. bk.rev. **Document type:** *Trade.*
Formerly: Schoolblad (0036-6889)
Published by: Algemene Onderwijsbond, PO Box 2875, Utrecht, 3500 GW, Netherlands. TEL 31-30-2989898, FAX 31-30-2989877, aob@fnv.nl. Circ: 75,000.

ONE EARTH (HONG KONG). see *ENVIRONMENTAL STUDIES*

370.2509713 CAN ISSN 0316-8549
ONTARIO DIRECTORY OF EDUCATION. Text in English. a. CND 10 per issue.
Published by: Ministry of Education, 880 Bay St, 5th Fl, Toronto, ON M7A 1N8, Canada. TEL 416-326-5300.

370 AUS
OPEN BOOK. Text in English. 1972. irreg. AUD 5.
Indexed: CCR.
Address: 21 Smith St, Thornbury, VIC 3071, Australia.

370 FIN ISSN 0355-3965
OPETTAJA/TEACHER. Text in Finnish. 1973. w. adv. bk.rev. **Document type:** *Newsletter, Trade.*
Formed by the merger of (1906-1973): Opettajain Lehti (0783-3849); (1951-1973): Oppikoululehti (0048-2005)
Related titles: Online - full text ed.: ISSN 1458-4395; ♦ Supplement(s): Ammatti+. ISSN 1457-6996.
Published by: Opetusalan Ammattijarjesto ry/Trade Union of Education in Finland, Rautatielaisenkatu 6, PO Box 20, Helsinki, 00521, Finland. TEL 358-20-7489600, FAX 358-9-145821, opettaja@oaj.fi, oaj@oaj.fi, http://www.oaj.fi. Ed. Hannu Laaksola TEL 358-20-7489720. Adv. contact Jyrki Ehnqvist. Circ: 84,304.

371.192 USA ISSN 1066-2855
OPTIONS IN LEARNING; public, home, private. Text in English. 1990. irreg. USD 50 domestic (effective 2005). bk.rev. back issues avail. **Document type:** *Newsletter.* **Description:** Offers parents information about educational options (public, private, and homeschooling), resources, and encouragement.
Published by: Alliance for Parental Involvement in Education, Inc., 1444 Eye St NW Ste 800, Washington, DC 20005. TEL 202-835-3600, allpie@taconic.net, http://www.aspira.org, http://www.croton.com/allpie. Eds. Katharine Houk, Seth Rockmuller. R&P Seth Rockmuller. Circ: 2,000 (paid).

371.0712 ITA ISSN 1121-1563
L'ORA DI RELIGIONE. Text in Italian. 9/yr. EUR 31.50 in Europe; EUR 37.18 in Africa; EUR 42.35 in Australasia; EUR 32.02 Mediterranean basin; EUR 38.22 The Americas & Asia (effective 2002). **Description:** For use in teaching religion in elementary schools.
Published by: Editrice ELLEDICI, Corso Francia 214, Leumann, TO 10096, Italy. TEL 39-11-9552164, FAX 39-11-9574048, mail@elledici.org, http://www.elledici.org.

370 CAN ISSN 0030-4433
ORBIT; commentary on the world of education. Text in English. 1970. q. CND 33 domestic; USD 33 foreign (effective 2005). reprint service avail. from PQC. **Description:** Discusses major issues in Ontario education from assessment and school councils to technology.
Related titles: Microform ed.: (from PQC); Online - full text ed.: (from Micromedia ProQuest).
Indexed: CEI, CIJE, CPE, RDA.
—Infotrieve. **CCC.**
Published by: University of Toronto, Ontario Institute for Studies in Education, 252 Bloor St W, Toronto, ON M5S 1V6, Canada. TEL 416-693-0253, Heather.Berkeley@oise.utoronto.ca/orbit, http://www.oise.utoronto.ca/orbit/. Ed. Heather Berkeley. Circ: 7,000 (paid). **Subscr. to:** CNS Circulation, P O Box 10, Stn F, Toronto, ON M4Y 2L4, Canada. TEL 416-447-8186, 416-693-7818.

370 ITA ISSN 0030-5391
L36
➤ **ORIENTAMENTI PEDAGOGICI**; rivista internazionale di scienze dell'educazione. Text in Italian; Summaries in Multiple languages. 1954. bi-m. EUR 41.31 domestic; EUR 67.13 foreign; EUR 10.32 per issue domestic; EUR 11.87 per issue foreign (effective 2002). bk.rev. bibl. back issues avail. **Document type:** *Academic/Scholarly.* **Description:** Presents an international review of the science of education with an audience represented by educators, undergraduates, psychological and teaching centers.
Indexed: CERDIC, DIP, IBR, IBZ, MLA-IB.
Published by: (Universita Pontificia Salesiana VAT), Societa Editrice Internazionale, Corso R. Margherita 176, Turin, TO 10152, Italy. TEL 39-011-52271, FAX 39-011-5211320, editoriale@seieditrice.com. Ed. Sergio Giordani. Circ: 3,000.

371.4 ITA
ORIENTAMENTO SCOLASTICO PROFESSIONALE. Text in Italian. 1976 (vol.16). q. abstr.; bibl.; charts. **Document type:** *Academic/Scholarly.*
Indexed: ILD.
Published by: Associazione Italiana di Orientamento Scolastico e Professionale, Via Leopoldo Serra, 5, Rome, RM 00153, Italy. TEL 39-6-5885634. Ed. Guido Giugni.

370.7 RUS
ORIENTIR. ZHURNAL PO PROBLEMAM VOINSKOGO VOSPITANIYA. Text in Russian. m. USD 129.95 in United States.
Related titles: Microfiche ed.: (from EVP).
Published by: Ministerstvo Oborony Rossiiskoi Federatsii/Ministry of Defence of Russian Federation, Khoroshevskoe shosse 38, Moscow, 123826, Russian Federation. FAX 7-095-9414066, http://www.mil.ru. Ed. N N Efimov. **US dist. addr.:** East View Information Services, 3020 Harbor Ln. N., Minneapolis, MN 55447. TEL 800-477-1005, FAX 800-800-3839, eastview@eastview.com, http://www.eastview.com.

370 SVN ISSN 0030-6681
OTROK IN DRUZINA; revija za druzinsko in druzbeno vzgojo. Text in Slovenian. 1952. m. SIT 20.
Published by: Zveza Prijateljev Mladine Slovenije, Miklosiceva 16-II, Ljubljana, 61000, Slovenia. Ed. Biserka Marolt Meden. Circ: 18,000. **Co-sponsor:** Zveza Pedagoskih Drustev Slovenije.

OUR CHILDREN. see *CHILDREN AND YOUTH—About*

370 CAN ISSN 0384-6636
OUR SCHOOLS. Text in English. 1972. 5/yr. free. illus. **Document type:** *Newspaper.*
Formerly: Focus on Winnipeg Schools (0384-6628)
Published by: Winnipeg School Division No. 1, 1577 Wall T E, Winnipeg, MB R3E 2S5, Canada. TEL 204-775-0231. Ed., R&P Linda Wilson. Circ: 24,500.

370.971 CAN ISSN 0840-7339
LA410
OUR SCHOOLS, OUR SELVES; a magazine for Canadian education activists. Text in English. 1988. bi-m. CND 40.66 domestic to individuals; CND 50 foreign to individuals; CND 53.50 domestic to institutions; CND 60 foreign to institutions; CND 7.98 newsstand/cover (effective 2000). adv. **Document type:** *Academic/Scholarly.*
Related titles: Microfiche ed.: (from MML); Microform ed.: (from MML); Online - full text ed.: (from Micromedia ProQuest).
Indexed: AltPI, CEI.
Published by: Our Schools, Our Selves Education Foundation, 107 Earl Grey Rd, Toronto, ON M4J 3L6, Canada. TEL 416-463-6978, 800-565-1975. Ed., R&P Satu Repo. Adv. contact George Martell. **Subscr. to:** 5502 Atlantic St, Halifax, NS B3H 9Z9, Canada.

THE OUTDOOR SOURCE BOOK (YEAR). see *SPORTS AND GAMES—Outdoor Life*

370.951 KOR
OUTLINE OF EDUCATION IN KOREA✶. Text in English. biennial. illus. **Description:** Pictorial that covers education in Korea.
Published by: Ministry of Education, National Institute of Educational Research and Training, 77, Sejong-ro, Chongro-ku, Chongno-gu, Seoul, 110-760, Korea, S. http://www.moe.go.kr/. Ed. Pyong Ho Park.

OXFORD. see *LITERARY AND POLITICAL REVIEWS*

370 GBR ISSN 0305-4985
L16
➤ **OXFORD REVIEW OF EDUCATION.** Text in English. 1975. 5/yr. GBP 434, USD 745 combined subscription to institutions print & online eds. (effective 2006). adv. index. back issues avail.; reprint service avail. from PSC. **Document type:** *Journal, Academic/Scholarly.* **Description:** Promotes the elaboration and evaluation of a body of speculative and empirical theory, the development of which might improve educational practice.
Related titles: Microfiche ed.; Online - full text ed.: ISSN 1465-3915. GBP 412, USD 708 to institutions (effective 2006) (from bigchalk, EBSCO Publishing, Gale Group, IngentaConnect, JSTOR (Web-based Journal Archive), Northern Light Technology, Inc., O C L C Online Computer Library Center, Inc., ProQuest Information & Learning, Swets Information Services).
Indexed: ABIn, ASCA, BrEdI, CIJE, CPE, ChLitAb, ChPerI, CurCont, ERA, ETA, EduInd, FamI, HECAB, IBSS, L&LBA, MEA, PCI, RHEA, SEA, SENA, SOMA, SOPODA, SSA, SSCI, SWA, SociolAb, TEA, WBA, WMB.
—BLDSC (6321.017000), IDS, IE, Infotrieve, ingenta. **CCC.**
Published by: Routledge (Subsidiary of: Taylor & Francis Group), 4 Park Sq, Milton Park, Abingdon, Oxon OX14 4RN, United Kingdom. TEL 44-1235-828600, FAX 44-1235-829000, info@routledge.co.uk, http://www.tandf.co.uk/journals/titles/03054985.asp, http://www.routledge.co.uk. Ed. Geoffrey Walford. **Subscr. to:** Taylor & Francis Ltd, Journals Customer Service, Rankine Rd, Basingstoke, Hants RG24 8PR, United Kingdom. TEL 44-1256-813000, FAX 44-1256-330245.

370.9 GBR ISSN 0961-2149
CODEN: OSCEE2
➤ **OXFORD STUDIES IN COMPARATIVE EDUCATION.** Text in English. 1991. s-a. GBP 42 domestic to individuals; USD 70 foreign to individuals; GBP 98 domestic to libraries; USD 170 foreign to libraries (effective 2005). illus. **Document type:** *Monographic series, Academic/Scholarly.* **Description:** Devotes each volume to a specific topic.
Indexed: BrEdI, CPE, DIP, EAA, ERA, ETA, IBR, IBZ, MEA, RHEA, SEA, SENA, SOMA, SOPODA, SSA, SociolAb, TEA.
—BLDSC (6321.021900), IE, ingenta. **CCC.**

E

Published by: Symposium Books (Subsidiary of: wwwords Ltd), Didcot, PO Box 204, Oxford, OX11 9ZQ, United Kingdom. TEL 44-1235-818062, FAX 44-1235-817275, orders@symposium-books.co.uk, http://www.triangle.co.uk/osc, http://www.symposium-books.co.uk/. Ed. Dr. David Phillips.

➤ **P C TEACH IT**; integrating technology into the classroom. see *COMPUTERS*

372.2   USA
P E A ALERT. Text in English. 1970. 4/yr. free. bk.rev. bibl. **Document type:** *Newsletter.* **Description:** Devoted to issues affecting the education of children in the New York City public school system, grades pre-K through 12. Presents summaries and extracts of the organization's research, analysis, coalition-building, model programs, legal action and extensive information program.
Former titles: Public Education Alert; (until 1986): P E A Reports; Public Education Association Newsletter
Published by: Public Education Association, 39 W 32nd St, New York, NY 10001-3803. TEL 212-868-1640, FAX 212-268-7344. Ed. Jessica Wolff. Circ: 5,000 (controlled).

371   CAN   ISSN 0383-199X
P E I T F NEWSLETTER. Text in English. 1948. q. free. back issues avail. **Document type:** *Newsletter.* **Description:** Describes and comments on activities of the federation and education in the province and nationally.
Published by: Prince Edward Island Teachers Federation, P O Box 6000, Charlottetown, PE C1A 8B4, Canada. TEL 902-569-4157, FAX 902-569-3682, peitf@pei.sympatico.ca. Ed. Robert MacRae. Circ: 2,400 (controlled).

371   USA   ISSN 0161-956X
L11   CODEN: PJEDFQ
➤ **P J E, PEABODY JOURNAL OF EDUCATION.** Variant title: Peabody Journal of Education. Text in English. 1923. q. USD 355 domestic to institutions; USD 385 foreign to institutions; USD 375 combined subscription domestic to institutions print & online eds.; USD 405 combined subscription foreign to institutions print & online eds. (effective 2006). adv. illus.; abstr. back issues avail.; reprint service avail. from PQC,PSC. **Document type:** *Journal, Academic/Scholarly.* **Description:** Publishes symposia in the broad area of education and human development. It contains the work of social scientists, humanists, practitioners, and policy makers.
Formerly (until 1970?): Peabody Journal of Education (0031-3432)
Related titles: Microform ed.: 1923 (from PQC); Online - full text ed.: ISSN 1532-7930. USD 340 worldwide to institutions (effective 2006) (from EBSCO Publishing, Gale Group, H.W. Wilson, O C L C Online Computer Library Center, Inc., Swets Information Services).
Indexed: ABIn, AgeL, BAS, CIJE, CPE, CurCont, ECER, ERA, ETA, EduInd, FamI, L&LBA, PCI, PhilInd, RHEA, SOMA, SOPODA, SSA, SSCI, SociolAb, e-psyche.
—BLDSC (6413.750000), IE, Infotrieve, ingenta. **CCC.**
Published by: (Vanderbilt University, George Peabody College for Teachers), Lawrence Erlbaum Associates, Inc., 10 Industrial Ave, Mahwah, NJ 07430-2262. TEL 201-258-2200, 800-926-6579, FAX 201-236-0072, journals@erlbaum.com, http://www.leaonline.com/loi/pje. Eds. Camilla Benbow, James W Guthrie. adv.: page USD 500; trim 5 x 8. Circ: 2,000 (paid).

➤ **P M E A NEWS**; the official journal of the Pennsylvania Music Educators Association. see *MUSIC*

371   SWE
P M KOMPETENS - LEDARSKAP - UTVECKLING. Text in Swedish. 1996. 5/yr.
Published by: Kompetens Media Foerlag AB, World Trade Center B5, Stockholm, 11156, Sweden. TEL 46-8-20-21-10, FAX 46-8-20-78-10. Ed., Pub. Anders Akerman. adv.: B&W page SEK 15,000, color page SEK 20,000; trim 260 x 175. Circ: 17,400.

370 305.86   CHL
P R E A L INFORMA. (Programa de Promocion de la Reforma Educativa en America Latina y el Caribe) Text in Spanish. 1998. 3/yr.
Related titles: Online - full text ed.
Published by: Programa de Promocion de la Reforma Educativa en America Latina y el Caribe, Santa Magdalena 75, piso 10, oficina 1002, Providencia, Chile. http://www.preal.cl/infor-spi.php.

P T A COMMUNICATOR. see *CHILDREN AND YOUTH—About*

371.192   USA
P T A PERSPECTIVES. (Parent-Teacher Association) Text in English. 1970. 9/yr. USD 6. adv. **Document type:** *Newsletter.*
Formerly (until 1995): Sound-Off; Which superseded: Utah P T A Bulletin (0042-1472)
Published by: Utah Congress of Parents & Teachers, 1037 E South Temple, Salt Lake City, UT 84102. TEL 801-359-3875. Ed. Camille Elkins. Adv. contact Kim Best. Circ: 3,200.

649   USA   ISSN 1523-2417
LOS PADRES AUN HACEN LA DIFERENCIA! (ESCUELA SECUNDARIA). Text in Spanish. m. USD 97 (effective 2003).

Related titles: Online - full content ed.: ISSN 1523-133X; ◆ Translation of: Parents Still Make the Difference! (High School Edition). ISSN 1523-2395.
Published by: Parent Institute, PO Box 7474, Fairfax, VA 22039-7474. TEL 703-323-9170, 800-756-5525, FAX 703-323-9173, webmaster@parent-institute.com, http://www.parent-institute.com. Ed. Pat Hodgdon. Pub. John H Wherry.

649.124   USA   ISSN 1523-2379
LOS PADRES HACEN LA DIFERENCIA! (ELEMENTARY EDITION). Text in Spanish. m. USD 97 (effective 2003).
Related titles: Online - full text ed.: ISSN 1523-1313; ◆ English ed.: Parents Make the Difference!. ISSN 1046-0446.
Published by: Parent Institute, PO Box 7474, Fairfax, VA 22039-7474. TEL 703-323-9170, 800-756-5525, FAX 703-323-9173, webmaster@parent-institute.com, http://www.parent-institute.com. Ed. Pat Hodgdon. Pub. John H Wherry.

371.192   ESP   ISSN 0210-4679
➤ **PADRES Y MAESTROS**; revista de orientacion educativa. Text in Spanish. 1965. 8/yr. USD 100 (effective 1999). bk.rev.; play rev.; software rev.; Website rev. illus.; maps; tr.lit. index. **Document type:** *Magazine, Academic/Scholarly.*
—CINDOC.
Published by: Instituto Padres y Maestros, Fonseca-Ipyma, Fonseca 8, La Coruna, 15004, Spain. TEL 34-981216096, FAX 34-981216861, pym@jesgalicia.org. Ed. Maria Vigites. Adv. contact Dolores Vazquez. Circ: 2,500 (paid).

370.9   GBR   ISSN 0030-9230
L10
➤ **PAEDAGOGICA HISTORICA**; international journal of the history of education. Text in English, French, German. 1961. bi-m. GBP 238, USD 386 combined subscription to institutions print & online eds. (effective 2006). bk.rev. reprint service avail. from PSC. **Document type:** *Journal, Academic/Scholarly.* **Description:** Publishes international methodological articles on intellectual history and social, cultural, economic and political aspects of the history of education, conference reports, announcements, review articles and an overview of contents of national journals in the history of education.
Related titles: Microform ed.; Online - full text ed.: ISSN 1477-674X. GBP 226, USD 367 to institutions (effective 2006) (from EBSCO Publishing, IngentaConnect, O C L C Online Computer Library Center, Inc., Swets Information Services).
Indexed: AmH&L, BAS, BibInd, BrEdI, CIJE, CPE, DIP, ERA, ETA, HistAb, IBR, IBZ, MEA, PCI, RASB, RHEA, SEA, SENA, SOMA, TEA.
—IE, Infotrieve, KNAW.
Published by: Routledge (Subsidiary of: Taylor & Francis Group), 4 Park Sq, Milton Park, Abingdon, Oxon OX14 4RN, United Kingdom. TEL 44-1235-828600, FAX 44-1235-829000, info@routledge.co.uk, http://www.tandf.co.uk/journals/titles/00309230.asp, http://www.routledge.co.uk. Eds. Frank Simon, Mark Depaepe. Circ: 700. **Subscr. to:** Taylor & Francis Ltd, Journals Customer Service, Rankine Rd, Basingstoke, Hants RG24 8PR, United Kingdom. TEL 44-1256-813000, FAX 44-1256-330245.

370   DEU   ISSN 0933-422X
➤ **PAEDAGOGIK.** Text in German. 1988. m. EUR 59; EUR 6 newsstand/cover (effective 2003). adv. bk.rev. index. reprints avail. **Document type:** *Journal, Academic/Scholarly.*
Formerly: Paedagogik Heute - Paedagogische Beitraege; Which was formed by the merger of (1949-1988): Westermanns Paedagogische Beitraege (0043-3446); (1968-1988): Paedagogik Heute (0179-9401); Which was formerly (until 1986): Be - Betrifft Erziehung (0340-2177); (until 1974): Betrifft - Erziehung (0045-1789)
Indexed: DIP, IBR, IBZ, L&LBA, RASB, SOPODA.
—IE, Infotrieve. **CCC.**
Published by: Julius Beltz GmbH & Co. KG, Werderstr 10, Weinheim, 69469, Germany. TEL 49-6201-60070, FAX 49-6201-6007382, info@beltz.de, http://www.beltz-paedagogik.de, http://www.beltz.de. Ed. Johannes Bastian. R&P Katrin Wolter. Adv. contact Brigitte Bell. B&W page EUR 1,430. Circ: 15,000.

370   DEU   ISSN 0943-5484
DER PAEDAGOGISCHE BLICK. Text in German. 1978. q. EUR 33.20 domestic; EUR 39.50 foreign (effective 2003). adv. **Document type:** *Journal, Academic/Scholarly.*
Formerly (until 1993): B A G Mitteilungen (0178-0514)
Indexed: DIP, IBR, IBZ.
Published by: (Bundesverband der Diplom-Paedagoginnen und Diplom-Paedagogen e.V.), Juventa Verlag GmbH, Ehretstr 3, Weinheim, 69469, Germany. TEL 49-6201-90200, FAX 49-6201-902013, juventa@juventa.de, http://www.juventa.de. Adv. contact Karola Weiss. page EUR 250; trim 113 x 193. Circ: 800.

370.15   DEU   ISSN 1430-2977
PAEDAGOGISCHE PSYCHOLOGIE UND ENTWICKLUNGSPSYCHOLOGIE. Text in German. 1996. irreg., latest vol.34, 2002. EUR 25.50 per vol. (effective 2003). **Document type:** *Monographic series, Academic/Scholarly.*

Published by: Waxmann Verlag GmbH, Steinfurter Str 555, Muenster, 48159, Germany. TEL 49-251-26504-0, FAX 49-251-2650426, info@waxmann.com, http://www.waxmann.com. Ed. Detlef H. Rost.

370   DEU   ISSN 0030-9273
PAEDAGOGISCHE RUNDSCHAU. Text in German. 1946. bi-m. CHF 102; EUR 70 in Austria & Germany; EUR 66 in Europe; GBP 46, USD 79; CHF 72 to students; EUR 49 to students in Austria & Germany; EUR 46 in Europe to students; GBP 32, USD 55 to students (effective 2006). bk.rev. abstr.; illus. index. **Document type:** *Journal, Academic/Scholarly.*
Indexed: DIP, IBR, IBSS, IBZ, RASB, SSCI.
—IE, Infotrieve. **CCC.**
Published by: Peter Lang GmbH Europaeischer Verlag der Wissenschaften, Eschborner Landstr 42-50, Frankfurt Am Main, 60489, Germany. TEL 49-69-7807050, FAX 49-69-78070550, zentrale.frankfurt@peterlang.com, http://www.peterlang.de. Eds. Dr. Birgit Ofenbach, Rudolf Lassahn. R&P Ruediger Brunsch. Adv. contact Melanie Marburger TEL 49-69-78070521. Circ: 950. **Dist. by:** Verlag Peter Lang AG, Hochfeldstr. 32, Postfach 746, Bern 9 3000, Switzerland. FAX 41-32-3761727, customerservice@peterlang.com.

370   NLD   ISSN 0165-0645
L21
PAEDAGOGISCHE STUDIEN; tijdschrift voor onderwijskunde en opvoedkunde. Text in Dutch. 1920. 6/yr. to individuals; institutions fl.265; students fl.99.50 (effective 1998). abstr. **Document type:** *Academic/Scholarly.*
Incorporates (1975-2000): Tijdschrift voor Onderwijsresearch (0166-591X)
Indexed: PsycInfo, PsycholAb, e-psyche.
—BLDSC (6417.427000), IE, Infotrieve, ingenta, KNAW.
Published by: Wolters-Noordhoff Groningen (Subsidiary of: Wolters Kluwer N.V.), Postbus 58, Groningen, 9700 MB, Netherlands. TEL 31-50-5226524, FAX 31-50-5264866. Ed. Dr. J Lowyck. Circ: 2,700.

370   AUT   ISSN 0030-9281
PAEDAGOGISCHES INSTITUT DER STADT WIEN. MITTEILUNGEN. Text in German. 1962. 10/yr. **Document type:** *Journal, Academic/Scholarly.*
Published by: Paedagogisches Institut der Stadt Wien, Burggasse 14-16, Vienna, W 1070, Austria. TEL 43-1-5236222, FAX 43-1-5236222, piwien@m56ssr.wien.at, http://www.pi-wien.at. Ed. Johanna Juna. Circ: 1,500.

370   CYP
PAEDIKI CHARA/CHILDREN'S JOY. Text in Greek. m. **Description:** Developed for Greek-Cypriot children.
Published by: Pan-Cyprian Greek Teachers Union, 18 Archbishop Makarios III Ave, Nicosia, Cyprus. TEL 02-442683. Ed. Costas Protopapas. Circ: 15,000.

370.1   USA   ISSN 0190-1176
B1
PAIDEIA (BUFFALO). Text in English. 1972. a. USD 10. adv. bk.rev. **Document type:** *Academic/Scholarly.*
Indexed: MLA, MLA-IB.
Published by: State University of New York at Buffalo, Department of Foundational Studies, 1300 Elmwood Ave, Buffalo, NY 14222. TEL 716-878-4303, FAX 716-675-2315. Ed., R&P Albert Grande. Circ: 1,000.

PAKISTAN. CENTRAL BUREAU OF EDUCATION. EDUCATIONAL STATISTICS BULLETIN SERIES. see *EDUCATION—Abstracting, Bibliographies, Statistics*

370.95491   PAK   ISSN 0078-8287
PAKISTAN. MINISTRY OF EDUCATION. YEARBOOK. Text in English. a.
Formerly: Pakistan. Central Bureau of Education. Yearbook (0078-7922)
Published by: Ministry of Education, Documentation Section, Curriculum Wing, Sector H-9, P.O. Shaigan, Industrial Area, Islamabad, Pakistan.

371   UKR   ISSN 1680-449X
PALITRA PEDAGOGA. Text in Ukrainian; Text occasionally in English. q. UAK 14.92 domestic; USD 55 foreign; UAK 3.92, USD 1 newsstand/cover (effective 2001). Index. back issues avail.; reprints avail.
Published by: Redaktsiya Doshkil'ne Vikhovannya, Yuriya Kotsubinskogo, 7, Kiev, 04053, Ukraine. TEL 380-60-2169114, 380-60-2161119, dv@fm.com.ua. Ed., Pub. R&P Nina O Andrusich.

370.1523   USA   ISSN 1092-5619
➤ **PALO ALTO REVIEW**; journal of ideas. Text in English. 1992. s-a. USD 10; USD 5 newsstand/cover (effective 1999). bk.rev.; film rev.; software rev.; tel.rev.; video rev. illus. back issues avail. **Document type:** *Academic/Scholarly.* **Description:** Contains articles, poems, and stories about people, places, and events dealing with living and learning.
Indexed: e-psyche.
Published by: Palo Alto College, 1400 W Villaret Blvd, San Antonio, TX 78224-2499. TEL 210-921-5017, FAX 210-921-5008. Eds. Bob Richmond, Ellen Shull. Circ: 600.

E

370 ESP ISSN 1130-846X
PANEL (BURGOS). Text in Spanish. 1986. s-a.
—CINDOC.
Published by: Universidad de Valladolid, Escuela Universitaria de Formacion del Profesorado de E.G.B. de Burgos, Carr. de Valladolid, s-n, Burgos, Castilla y Leon 09001, Spain.

370 ISR
PANIM LEKHAN ULEKHAN. Text in Hebrew. 1988. bi-m. ILS 25.
Published by: Institute for Education in Democracy, Levinsky College, Tel Aviv, Israel. FAX 972-3-6993546. Ed. Shlomo Tzidkiyahu. Circ: 2,000.

370 CHE ISSN 1011-5218
PANORAMA. Text and summaries in French, German. 1987. bi-m. CHF 72 domestic; CHF 87 foreign; CHF 18 newsstand/cover (effective 2001). adv. bk.rev.; film rev. bibl.; charts; illus.; stat. index. **Document type:** *Magazine, Academic/Scholarly.*
Incorporates (1915-1996): Berufsberatung und Berufsbildung (0005-9501)
Indexed: RASB.
Published by: Schweizerischer Verband fuer Berufsberatung/ Association Suisse pour l'Orientation Scolaire et Professionnelle, Zuerichstr 98, Duebendorf, 8600, Switzerland. TEL 41-1-2661111, FAX 41-1-2661100, ewettstein@panorama.ch, http://www.panorama.ch. Ed. Emil Wettstein. adv.: B&W page CHF 1,800; trim 280 x 200. Circ: 4,000.

370 PNG ISSN 0048-2919
PAPUA AND NEW GUINEA EDUCATION GAZETTE. Text in English. 1967. m. (exc. Jan.& Dec.). free. bk.rev.
Indexed: AEI.
Published by: Department of Education, P.S.A. Haus, Private Mail Bag, Boroko, Papua New Guinea. Ed. J Oberlenter. Circ: 8,000.

370 PNG ISSN 0031-1472
LA2270.P3
PAPUA NEW GUINEA JOURNAL OF EDUCATION. Text in English. 1961. s-a. PGK 10 domestic; USD 40 foreign. adv. bk.rev. bibl.; charts; illus.; stat. **Document type:** *Academic/Scholarly.*
Indexed: CPE, ERA, MEA, REE&TA.
Published by: National Research Institute, PO Box 5854, Boroko, Papua New Guinea. TEL 675-3260300, FAX 675-3260213. Ed. Richard Guy. Circ: 400. **Subscr. to:** Education Research Officer, Policy, Research & Evaluation, NDOW, PSA HAUS, Private Mail Bag, Boroko, NCD, Papua New Guinea.

PARENT & CHILD; the learning link between home & school. see *CHILDREN AND YOUTH—About*

371.192 AUS ISSN 0726-7126
PARENT AND CITIZEN. Text in English. 1939. q. AUD 10 (effective 2000). adv. bk.rev. **Document type:** *Newsletter.* **Description:** Aimed at informing parents on school and educational matters.
Indexed: AEI.
Published by: Federation of Parents & Citizens Associations of New South Wales, 210 Crown St, East Sydney, PO Box 789, Dalinghurst, 2000, Australia. TEL 61-2-93602481, FAX 61-2-93616835, pandc@australis.net.au, mail@pandc.org.au. Ed. Vicki Scott. Adv. contact Fay Stern. Circ: 1,300.

371.03 USA
PARENT COOPERATIVE PRESCHOOLS INTERNATIONAL. DIRECTORY. Text in English. 1969. a. membership. adv. bk.rev. **Document type:** *Directory.* **Description:** Listing of cooperative preschool programs and cooperative preschool councils in the US and Canada.
Published by: Parent Cooperative Preschools International, 1401 New York Ave, N W, Ste 1100, Washington, DC 20005-2102. TEL 800-636-6222. Circ: 6,500.

649.124 371.192 USA ISSN 1046-0446
PARENTS MAKE THE DIFFERENCE!; practical ideas for parents to help their children. Text in English. 1989. m. (Sep.-May). looseleaf. USD 97 (effective 2003). back issues avail. **Document type:** *Newsletter.* **Description:** Contains practical ideas for parents of children in grades K through 6 to help their children do better in school.
Related titles: Online - full text ed.: Parents Make the Difference! (Elementary Edition). ISSN 1523-1275; ♦ Spanish ed.: Los Padres Hacen la Diferencia! (Elementary Edition). ISSN 1523-2379.
Published by: Parent Institute, PO Box 7474, Fairfax, VA 22039-7474. TEL 703-323-9170, 800-756-5525, FAX 703-323-9173, http://www.parent-institute.com. Ed. Pat Hodgdon. Pub. John H Wherry.

PARENTS MAKE THE DIFFERENCE! (SCHOOL READINESS EDITION); practical ideas for parents to help their children. see *CHILDREN AND YOUTH—About*

371.192 USA ISSN 1523-2395
PARENTS STILL MAKE THE DIFFERENCE! (HIGH SCHOOL EDITION); practical ideas for parents to help their children. Text in English. 1997. m. (Sep.-May). looseleaf. USD 97 (effective 2003). bk.rev. 4 p./no.; back issues avail. **Document type:** *Newsletter.* **Description:** Presents ideas for parents of children in grades 10 through 12, to help their children do better in school.
Related titles: Online - full text ed.: ISSN 1523-1291; ♦ Spanish Translation: Los Padres aun Hacen la Diferencia! (Escuela Secundaria). ISSN 1523-2417.
Published by: Parent Institute, PO Box 7474, Fairfax, VA 22039-7474. TEL 703-323-9170, 800-756-5525, FAX 703-323-9173, http://www.parent-institute.com/nl/login.htm. Ed. Pat Hodgdon.

PARENTS STILL MAKE THE DIFFERENCE! (MIDDLE SCHOOL EDITION); practical ideas for parents to help their children. see *CHILDREN AND YOUTH—About*

371.0712 USA ISSN 1060-8567
PARISH COORDINATORS - DIRECTORS OF RELIGIOUS EDUCATION. Text in English. 1979. q. membership.
Formerly: Parish Coordinator of Religious Education
Published by: (National Forum of Religious Educators), National Catholic Educational Association, 1077 30 St, N W, Ste 100, Washington, DC 20007. TEL 202-337-6232, FAX 202-333-6706, nceaadmin@ncea.org, http://www.ncea.org.

371.07 GBR ISSN 0264-3944
➤ **PASTORAL CARE IN EDUCATION**; the journal for pastoral care and personal and social education. Text in English. 1983. q. GBP 87, EUR 131 combined subscription in Europe to individuals print & online eds.; USD 163 combined subscription in the Americas to individuals & Caribbean, print & online eds.; GBP 97 combined subscription elsewhere to individuals print & online eds.; GBP 210 combined subscription in Europe to institutions print & online eds.; USD 405 combined subscription in the Americas to institutions & Caribbean, print & online eds.; GBP 241 combined subscription elsewhere to institutions print & online eds. (effective 2006). reprint service avail. from PSC. **Document type:** *Academic/Scholarly.*
Related titles: Microform ed.: (from PQC); Online - full text ed.: ISSN 1468-0122. GBP 200 in Europe to institutions; USD 385 in the Americas to institutions & Caribbean; GBP 229 elsewhere to institutions (effective 2006) (from Blackwell Synergy, EBSCO Publishing, Gale Group, IngentaConnect, O C L C Online Computer Library Center, Inc., Swets Information Services).
Indexed: BrEdI, CPE, ERA, ETA, HECAB, MEA, RHEA, SEA, SENA, SOMA, TEA.
—BLDSC (6409.230000), IE, Infotrieve, ingenta. **CCC.**
Published by: Blackwell Publishing Ltd., 9600 Garsington Rd, Oxford, OX4 2ZG, United Kingdom. TEL 44-1865-776868, FAX 44-1865-714591, customerservices@oxon.blackwellpublishing.com, http://www.blackwellpublishing.com/journals/PAST. Ed. Colleen McLaughlin TEL 44-1223-369631. Circ: 4,500.

➤ **PATHWAYS**; the Ontario journal of outdoor education. see *CONSERVATION*

➤ **PECHES ET OCEANS. SERIE DE L'EDUCATION GENERALE.** see *FISH AND FISHERIES*

370 ITA ISSN 0031-3777
PEDAGOGIA E VITA. Text in Italian. 1933. bi-m. EUR 56 domestic; EUR 86.50 foreign (effective 2005). adv. bk.rev. bibl. index. **Document type:** *Journal, Academic/Scholarly.*
Indexed: CERDIC.
Published by: Editrice La Scuola SpA, Via Luigi Cadorna 11, Brescia, BS 25124, Italy. TEL 39-030-29931, FAX 39-030-2993299, http://www.lascuola.it. Ed. Luigi Morgano.

370 ESP ISSN 1139-1723
PEDAGOGIA SOCIAL. Text in Spanish. 1986. s-a.
Formerly (until 1991): Revista de Pedagogia Social (0213-7682)
—CINDOC.
Published by: Universidad de Murcia, Servicio de Publicaciones, Edificio Saavedra Fajardo, C/ Actor Isidoro Maiquez 9, Murcia, 30007, Spain. TEL 34-968-363013, FAX 34-968-363414, servpubl@um.es, http://www.um.es/spumweb.

370 CUB ISSN 1609-4808
PEDAGOGIA UNIVERSITARIA. Text in Spanish. 1996. 3/yr.
Media: Online - full text.
Published by: Ministerio de Educacion Superior, Direccion de Formacion de Profesionales, Ave. 23 Esq. F, Vedado, Havana, Cuba.

370.72 RUS ISSN 1728-8894
▼ **PEDAGOGICHESKIE NAUKI.** Text in Russian. 2003. bi-m. **Document type:** *Journal, Academic/Scholarly.* **Description:** Publishes scientific research articles written by students and applicants for graduate degrees in Education.
Published by: Izdatel'stvo Kompaniya Sputnik+, Ryazanskii pr-kt, dom 8a, Moscow, 109428, Russian Federation. TEL 7-095-7304774, sputnikplus2000@mail.ru, http://www.sputnikplus.ru.

370 RUS
PEDAGOGICHESKII KALEIDOSKOP. Text in Russian. w. USD 199.95 in United States.
Published by: Chastnaya Obrazovatel'naya Firma Novaya Shkola, 3-ya Grazhdanskaya ul 1, Moscow, 107258, Russian Federation. TEL 7-095-1621884, FAX 7-095-1628139. Ed. V S Girshovich. **US dist. addr.:** East View Information Services, 3020 Harbor Ln. N., Minneapolis, MN 55447. TEL 612-550-0961.

370 RUS
PEDAGOGICHESKII VESTNIK. Text in Russian. 26/yr. USD 217.95 in United States.
Indexed: RASB.
Address: Profsoyuznaya ul 62, Moscow, 117390, Russian Federation. TEL 7-095-1993280, FAX 7-095-2881923. Ed. L I Ruvinskii. **US dist. addr.:** East View Information Services, 3020 Harbor Ln. N., Minneapolis, MN 55447. TEL 612-550-0961.

370 NLD ISSN 1567-7109
PEDAGOGIEK. Text in Dutch. 2000. q. EUR 41.90 domestic to individuals; EUR 53.90 foreign to individuals; EUR 60.90 domestic to institutions; EUR 70.75 foreign to institutions; EUR 33 to students; EUR 14.75 newsstand/cover (effective 2005). adv. bk.rev. **Document type:** *Academic/Scholarly.*
Formed by the merger of (1984-1999): Nederlands Tijdschrift voor Opvoeding, Vorming, en Onderwijs (0169-1872); (1981-1999): Comenius (0167-9163)
Indexed: CPE, ERA, ETA, MEA, RHEA, SEA, SENA, SOMA, TEA.
—IE, KNAW.
Published by: Koninklijke Van Gorcum BV/Royal Van Gorcum BV, PO Box 43, Assen, 9400 AA, Netherlands. TEL 31-592-379555, FAX 31-592-372064, info@vangorcum.nl, http://www.vangorcum.nl. Ed. Daniel Lechner. Adv. contact Bel Jorine de Bruin. B&W page EUR 400; 140 x 215. Circ: 1,300.

370 SCG ISSN 0031-3807
L51
PEDAGOGIJA; casopis Saveza pedagoskih drustava. Text in Serbo-Croatian. 1963. q. **Document type:** *Journal, Academic/Scholarly.*
Published by: Savez Pedagoskih Drustava Srbije, Institut za Pedagoska Istrazivanja, Dobrinjska 11/III, PF 546, Belgrade, 11000.

370 CZE ISSN 0031-3815
L51
PEDAGOGIKA/PEDAGOGY; casopis pro pedagogicke vedy. Text in Czech, Slovak; Summaries in English, German, Russian. 1951. bi-m. bk.rev. abstr.; bibl.; charts; illus.; stat. index. **Description:** Contains original articles from all spheres of pedagogical sciences; general pedagogical theory, theory of education, educational psychology, history of education, etc.
Indexed: CPE, ETA, PsycholAb, RASB.
Published by: Universita Karlova, Pedagogicka Fakulta, M D Rettigove 4, Prague, 11639, Czech Republic. Ed. Jarmila Skalkova. **Dist. in Western countries by:** Kubon & Sagner Buchexport - Import GmbH, Postfach 24, Munich 34 8000, Germany.

370 RUS ISSN 0869-561X
L51
➤ **PEDAGOGIKA.** Text in Russian; Contents page in English. 1937. 8/yr. RUR 240; USD 88 foreign (effective 1999). bk.rev. bibl.; illus. index. reprints avail. **Document type:** *Academic/Scholarly.*
Formerly: Sovetskaya Pedagogika (0038-5093)
Indexed: PsycholAb, RASB, RefZh.
Published by: Rossiiskaya Akademiya Pedagogicheskikh Nauk, Nauchno-Issledovatel'skii Institut Pedagogicheskoi Metodologii Standartov, Pogodinskaya ul 8, Moscow, 119905, Russian Federation. TEL 7-095-2485198, FAX 7-095-2485149. Ed. Vladimir Borissenkov. Circ: 75,000. **Dist. by:** M K - Periodica, ul Gilyarovskogo 39, Moscow 129110, Russian Federation. TEL 7-095-2845008, FAX 7-095-2813798, info@periodicals.ru, http://www.mkniga.ru; **Dist. in U.S. by:** Victor Kamkin Inc., 220 Girard St, Ste 1, Gaithersburg, MD 20877. http://www.kamkin.com.

➤ **PEDAGOGIKA DETSTVA.** see *CHILDREN AND YOUTH—About*

370.15 BEL ISSN 0169-2127
PEDAGOGISCH TIJDSCHRIFT. Text in French. 1967. 4/yr. bk.rev. index. **Document type:** *Trade.*
Formerly: Pedagogisch Tijdschrift - Forum voor Opvoedkunde (0166-5855); Which was formed by the merger of: Pedagogisch Forum (0031-3823); Tijdschrift voor Opvoedkunde (0040-7577)
—IE, Infotrieve, KNAW.
Published by: Institute of Psychology, Tiensestraat 102, Leuven, 3000, Belgium. TEL 32-16-326102, FAX 32-16-326000, paulsmeyers@ped.kuleuven.ac.be. Ed. Paul Smeyers. Circ: 400.

370 SWE ISSN 1401-6788
➤ **PEDAGOGISK FORSKNING I SVERIGE.** Text in Multiple languages. 1996. q. SEK 500 to individuals; SEK 600 to institutions; SEK 250 to students; SEK 125 per issue (effective 2004). **Document type:** *Journal, Academic/Scholarly.*

E

Published by: Goeteborgs Universitet, Institutionen foer Pedagogik och Didaktik/University of Goeteborg. Department of Education and Educational Research, PO Box 300, Goeteborg, 40530, Sweden. TEL 46-31-7731000, FAX 46-31-7732100, pedagogisk.forsknin@ped.gu.se, http://www.ped.gu.se. Eds. Jan-Erik Johansson TEL 46-31-7732456, Bioern Hasselgren.

370.72 SWE ISSN 1401-3320
PEDAGOGISKA MAGASINET. Text in Swedish. 1996. q. SEK 210 (effective 2003). adv. **Document type:** *Magazine, Trade.* **Description:** Forum for pedagogic research and debate.
Related titles: Online - full text ed.
Published by: Laerarfoerbundet, Tidningsafdelning, Segelbaatsvaegen 15, Box 12229, Stockholm, 10226, Sweden. TEL 46-8-7376500, FAX 46-8-7376569, pedagogiska.magasinet@lararforbundet.se, kansli@lararforbundet.se, http://www.pedagogiskamagasinet.net/default.asp, http://www.lararforbundet.se. Ed., Pub. Lena Fejan Ljunghill. Adv. contact Annelie Bjoernsdotter Lundqvist. B&W page SEK 20,600, color page SEK 27,500; trim 171 x 228. Circ: 225,900.

370 SWE ISSN 0281-6776
PEDAGOGISKA RAPPORTER/EDUCATIONAL REPORTS. Text in English, Swedish. 1969; N.S. 1984. irreg. free. **Document type:** *Academic/Scholarly.*
Formerly: Pedagogiska Rapporter Umeaa (0348-9388)
Published by: Umeaa Universitet, Pedagogiska Institutionen, Umeaa, 90187, Sweden. FAX 46-90166203, TELEX 54005. Ed. Jarl Backman. Circ: 200.

371.14 HUN ISSN 0133-2260
PEDAGOGUSOK LAPJA. Text in Hungarian. 1945. fortn. USD 21.
Former titles (until 1957): Nevelok Lapja (0324-2846); (until 1950): Ertesito (0324-2943)
Published by: Hungarian Union of Teachers, Gorkij Fasor 10, Budapest, 1068, Hungary. Circ: 20,000.

PEER HEALTH NEWS. see *CHILDREN AND YOUTH—About*

372.6 CAN ISSN 0031-4315
PENMEN'S NEWS LETTER. Text in English. 1950. 6/yr. USD 15. bk.rev.
Published by: (International Association of Master Penmen and Teachers of Handwriting), Eileen Richardson, Ed. & Pub., 34 Broadway Ave, Ottawa, ON K1S 2V6, Canada. TEL 613-232-3014. Circ: 300 (controlled).

371.01 USA ISSN 0079-0508
PENNSYLVANIA SCHOOL STUDY COUNCIL. REPORTS. Text in English. 1947. irreg. (20-25/yr.). price varies. bk.rev. **Document type:** *Academic/Scholarly.*
Published by: Pennsylvania School Study Council, 212 Rackley Bldg, Pennsylvania State University, University Park, PA 16802. TEL 814-865-0321. Ed. Seldon V Whitaker Jr. Circ: 250.

370 GBR ISSN 1358-6297
HF5549
PEOPLE MANAGEMENT; magazine for professionals in personnel training and development. Text in English. 1995. 25/yr. GBP 90 domestic; USD 230 in United States; GBP 150 in Europe (effective 2004). adv. bk.rev. illus. reprints avail. **Document type:** *Trade.* **Description:** Committed to providing personnel and development professionals with the information, advice, stimulation and support they need in order to contribute effectively to their organizations.
Formed by the merger of (1982-1995): Training and Development (0264-1739); (1969-1992): Personnel Management (0031-5761); (1985-1995): Transition (0267-8950); Which was formerly: B A C I E Journal (0005-2612)
Related titles: Online - full text ed.: P M Online (from EBSCO Publishing, Florida Center for Library Automation, Gale Group, H.W. Wilson, Northern Light Technology, Inc., O C L C Online Computer Library Center, Inc., ProQuest Information & Learning).
Indexed: ABIn, BPI, BldManAb, BrHumI, CPE, CPM, ERA, ETA, Emerald, H&TI, Inspec, M&MA, RASB, RHEA, SWA, TEA, TMA, WBA, WMB.
—BLDSC (6422.876650), AskIEEE, IE, Infotrieve, ingenta. **CCC.**
Published by: (Institute of Personnel and Development), Permanent Press, 1 Benjamin St, London, EC1M 5EA, United Kingdom. editorial@peoplemanagement.co.uk, http://www.peoplemanagement.co.uk/. Ed. Steven Brabb. Adv. contact Ben Flory TEL 44-20-78808546.

370 FRA
PERISCOPE. Text in French. 1983. 5/yr.
Published by: Publications de l'Ecole Moderne Francaise, Mouans-Sartoux, Cedex 06376, France. TEL 33-4-92921757, FAX 33-4-92921804.

370 BRA ISSN 0102-5473
PERSPECTIVA. Text in Portuguese. 1983. s-a. BRL 35 for 2 yrs.; BRL 10 newsstand/cover (effective 2004).
Indexed: MLA-IB.
Published by: Universidade Federal de Santa Catarina, Centro de Ciencias da Educacao, Campus Universitario Trindade, Florianopolis, SC 88010-970, Brazil. TEL 55-48-3319336, FAX 55-48-3319752, http://www.ced.ufsc.br/nucleos/nup/perspectiva.html, http://www.ced.ufsc.br/nova/homepage.php.

370 ESP ISSN 0210-2331
PERSPECTIVA ESCOLAR. Text in Catalan. 1974. m. adv. bk.rev. bibl.; illus. cum.index: 1974-1985, 1986-1995.
Indexed: RILM.
—CINDOC.
Published by: Asociacio de Mestres Rosa Sensat, Ave de Drassanes, 3, Barcelona, 08001, Spain. TEL 34-93-4817373, FAX 34-93-4817550, pescolar@mrp.pangea.org, rsensat@pangea.org, http://www.pangea.org/rsensat. Circ: 4,000.

PERSPECTIVE ON PHYSICIAN ASSISTANT EDUCATION. see *MEDICAL SCIENCES*

370.9 FRA ISSN 0304-3045
PERSPECTIVES; revue trimestrielle de l'education comparee. Text in French. 1971. q. price varies. bk.rev. bibl.; charts.
Formerly: Perspectives de l'Education (1010-6952)
Related titles: ♦ English ed.: Prospects. ISSN 0033-1538; Chinese ed.; Russian ed.; Spanish ed.: Perspectivas. ISSN 0304-3053. 1971; Arabic ed.: Mustaqbaliyyat. ISSN 0254-119X. 1971.
Indexed: IBR.
—BLDSC (6927.810000), IE.
Published by: (International Bureau of Education), UNESCO Publishing, 7 place de Fontenoy, Paris, 75352, France. TEL 33-1-45684300, FAX 33-1-45685737, http://www.unesco.org/publications. Circ: 2,125. **Dist. in U.S. by:** Bernan Associates, Bernan, 4611-F Assembly Dr., Lanham, MD 20706-4391. TEL 800-274-4447, FAX 800-865-3450.

370 FRA ISSN 1148-4519
L26
PERSPECTIVES DOCUMENTAIRES EN EDUCATION. Text in French. 1983. 3/yr. **Document type:** *Journal, Academic/Scholarly.*
Former titles (until 1990): Perspectives Documentaires en Sciences de l'Education (0760-7962); (until 1983): Informations Bibliographiques en Sciences de l'Education (0760-7970)
—IE, Infotrieve.
Published by: Institut National de Recherche Pedagogique, Place du Pentacle, BP 17, Saint-Fons, 69195 Cedex, France. TEL 33-4-72898300, FAX 33-4-72898329, publica@inrp.fr, http://www.inrp.fr. Ed. Christiane Eteve. Circ: 1,000.

370 ZAF ISSN 0258-2236
L81
➤ **PERSPECTIVES IN EDUCATION/PERSPEKTIEWE IN OPVOEDKUNDE.** Text mainly in English. 1978. q. ZAR 220 domestic to individuals; ZAR 275 domestic to institutions; EUR 85 foreign (effective 2005). bk.rev. back issues avail. **Document type:** *Journal, Academic/Scholarly.* **Description:** Discusses issues and research in education.
Incorporates (1967-2000): Tydskrif vir Opvoeding en Opleiding; Which was formerly (until June 1997): Pedagogiekjoernaal - Journal of Pedagogics (0256-520X); (until 1980): Suid-Afrikaanse Tydskrif vir die Pedagogiek (0039-4815)
Indexed: CPE, CurCont, ERA, ETA, IBSS, ISAP, MEA, PsycholAb, RHEA, SEA, SENA, SOMA, SSCI, TEA.
—BLDSC (6428.142305).
Published by: University of Pretoria, Faculty of Education/Universiteit van Pretoria, Pretoria, 0001, South Africa. TEL 27-12-4204732, FAX 27-12-4203003, perspect@postino.up.ac.za, http://www.education.up.ac.za/perspectives. Ed. J G Maree. Circ: 550 (paid and controlled).

370.15 IND ISSN 0971-1562
PERSPECTIVES IN PSYCHOLOGICAL RESEARCHES. Text in English, Hindi. 1978. s-a. free. adv. bk.rev. stat. **Document type:** *Academic/Scholarly.*
Indexed: IPsyAb, e-psyche.
—BLDSC (6428.161200).
Address: 53 Dalsingar, Azamgarh, 276 001, India. TEL 91-546-222006. Ed. Dr. Ramji Srivastava. Circ: 1,000.

370.9 RUS
PERSPEKTIVNYE MATERIALY. Text in Russian. bi-m. USD 225 in United States.
Indexed: METADEX, RefZh.
—BLDSC (0129.404500).
Published by: Interkontakt Nauka, Leninskii pr-t 49, Moscow, 117911, Russian Federation. TEL 7-095-1359408, FAX 7-095-1354540. Ed. N P Lyakishev. **US dist. addr.:** East View Information Services, 3020 Harbor Ln. N., Minneapolis, MN 55447. TEL 612-550-0961.

370.9 RUS
PERSPEKTIVY (MOSCOW); mysliteli obrazovaniya. Text in Russian. q. USD 85 in United States. bibl.
Related titles: Arabic ed.; English ed.; French ed.; Spanish ed.
Published by: YUNESKO, Zubovskii bulv 17, Moscow, 119847, Russian Federation. TEL 7-095-2471794. Ed. E Ol'shevskaya. **US dist. addr.:** East View Information Services, 3020 Harbor Ln. N., Minneapolis, MN 55447. TEL 612-550-0961.

370.985 PER
PERU. MINISTERIO DE EDUCACION PUBLICA. OFICINA SECTORIAL DE PLANIFICACION. PLAN BIENAL. Text in Spanish. irreg. illus.
Published by: Ministerio de Educacion Publica, Oficina Sectorial de Planificacion, Lima, Peru.

370 USA ISSN 8756-6494
L11
PHI DELTA KAPPA FASTBACKS. Text in English. 1972. 12/yr. USD 4 per issue (effective 2003). bibl. back issues avail. **Document type:** *Monographic series, Academic/Scholarly.*
Related titles: Online - full text ed.: (from H.W. Wilson, O C L C Online Computer Library Center, Inc., ProQuest Information & Learning).
Indexed: ABIn, CIJE, DIP, EduInd, IBR, IBZ.
—**CCC.**
Published by: (Phi Delta Kappa Educational Foundation), Phi Delta Kappa International, 408 N Union St, Bloomington, IN 47402-0789. TEL 812-339-1156, FAX 812-339-0018, kappan@kiva.net, http://www.pdkintl.org. Ed. Donovan Walling. R&P Terri Hampton TEL 812-339-1156.

371 USA ISSN 0031-7217
LJ121
PHI DELTA KAPPAN. Variant title: The Kappan. Text in English. 1915. m. (Sep.-June), latest vol.84, 2002. USD 58 domestic to individuals; USD 70.50 foreign to individuals; USD 65 domestic to institutions; USD 77.50 foreign to institutions; USD 5.50 newsstand/cover (effective 2005). adv. stat.; illus. index. 80 p./no. 3 cols./p.; reprint service avail. from PQC. **Document type:** *Journal, Academic/Scholarly.* **Description:** Addresses all issues in education, many of them controversial, such as inclusion, class size, and high-stakes testing.
Formerly: Phi Delta Kappan Magazine (1045-1749)
Related titles: Microfiche ed.: (from CIS); Microfilm ed.: (from PQC); Online - full text ed.: (from bigchalk, EBSCO Publishing, Florida Center for Library Automation, Gale Group, H.W. Wilson, Northern Light Technology, Inc., O C L C Online Computer Library Center, Inc., ProQuest Information & Learning).
Indexed: ABIn, ABS&EES, ASCA, Acal, ArtHuCI, BRD, BRI, CBRI, CIJE, CPE, ChPerI, CurCont, EAA, ECER, ERA, EduInd, FamI, FutSurv, IBR, IBZ, IPARL, LRI, MEA, MagInd, PMR, PSI, RASB, RGAb, RGPR, RHEA, SEA, SOMA, SPAA, SRI, SSCI, TOM.
—BLDSC (6449.400000), IDS, IE, Infotrieve, ingenta.
Published by: Phi Delta Kappa International, 408 N Union St, Bloomington, IN 47402-0789. TEL 812-339-1156, FAX 812-339-0018, information@pdkintl.org, kappan@kiva.net, http://www.pdkintl.org/kappan/kappan.htm. Adv. contact Carol Bucheri. Circ: 95,000 (paid).

370 PHL ISSN 0031-7527
PHILIPPINE EDUCATIONAL FORUM. Text in English. s-a. PHP 26, USD 4.50.
Indexed: IPP.
Published by: Philippine Women's University, Taft Ave, Manila, 2801, Philippines. Ed. Ester Vallado Daroy. Circ: 1,000.

370.1 USA ISSN 0160-7561
L107
➤ **PHILOSOPHICAL STUDIES IN EDUCATION.** Text in English. 1968. a. reprint service avail. from PQC. **Document type:** *Proceedings, Academic/Scholarly.* **Description:** Contains essays and articles considering important topics relating to school and schooling from a philosophical perspective.
Formerly (until 1976): Ohio Valley Philosophy of Education Society. Proceedings of the Annual Meetings (0078-4044)
Related titles: Microfiche ed.
Indexed: DIP, IBR, IBZ, PhilInd.
Published by: Ohio Valley Philosophy of Education Society, c/o Jaylynne Hutchinson, Mng Editor, McCracken Hall, Ohio University, Athens, OH 45701. TEL 740-593-9827, http://www.ovpes.org/journal.htm. Eds. Deron Boyles, Jaylynne Hutchinson. R&P Jaylynne Hutchinson. Circ: 120 (paid).

370.1 NLD ISSN 0923-9065
➤ **PHILOSOPHY AND EDUCATION.** Text in English. 1988. irreg., latest vol.14, 2005. price varies. back issues avail. **Document type:** *Monographic series, Academic/Scholarly.* **Description:** Identifies the philosophical dimensions of problems in education, coupled with a philosophical approach to them.
—BLDSC (6464.540000).
Published by: Springer-Verlag Dordrecht (Subsidiary of: Springer Science+Business Media), Van Godewijckstraat 30, Dordrecht, 3311 GX, Netherlands. TEL 31-78-6576050, FAX 31-78-6576474, http://www.springeronline.com. Eds. Kenneth R Howe, Robert E Floden.

976.07 ISR ISSN 0333-5259
➤ **PHYSICAL EDUCATION AND SPORT.** Text in Hebrew. 1944. bi-m. USD 45 (effective 1999). adv. bk.rev. **Document type:** *Academic/Scholarly.* **Description:** Information, research and applied material for Israeli physical education instructors and coaches.
Indexed: IHP.
Published by: Wingate Institute, Wingate Post, 42902, Israel. TEL 972-9-8639480, FAX 972-9-8639482. Ed. Tilman Elinor. Adv. contact Maital Cohen. Circ: 3,500.

E

371   USA
PINE TORCH. Text in English. 1992 (vol.52, no.4). q. **Document type:** *Newsletter.* **Description:** News and activities of the school, its staff and alumni.
Published by: Piney Woods Country Life School, PO Box, Piney Woods, MS 39148. Ed. Bevelyn D Young.

370   ESP   ISSN 1133-052X
PISSARRA. Text in Spanish, Catalan. 1977. bi-m. —CINDOC.
Published by: Sindicat de Treballadors de L'Ensenyanca de les Illes, Vinsanya, Palma de Mallorca, Isla Baleares 07005, Spain.

370.72   COD   ISSN 1022-8632
PISTES ET RECHERCHES. Text in French. 1986. 2/yr.
Indexed: PLESA.
Published by: Institut Superieur Pedagogique, BP 258, Kikwit, Congo, Dem. Republic.

PLAY GUITAR; the ultimate practical course on CD. see *MUSIC*

370   NLD   ISSN 1389-2371
PLEIN PRIMAIR. Text in Dutch. 1999. m. EUR 40.45 domestic to individuals; EUR 44.10 in Belgium to individuals; EUR 59.55 foreign to individuals; EUR 33.65 to students (effective 2005). adv.
Incorporates (1885-1999): Vacature (0042-2053)
Published by: Ten Brink Meppel B.V., Postbus 41, Meppel, 7940 AA, Netherlands. TEL 31-522-855333, FAX 31-522-855300, pleinp@euronet.nl, http://www.pleinprimair.nl/. adv.: B&W page EUR 797; trim 190 x 270. Circ: 7,000.

379   ITA
POLITICA DELLA SCUOLA. Text in Italian. 1972. s-a.
Published by: Associazione Nazionale per Il Progresso della Scuola Italiana, Piazza SS, Apostoli N. 80, Rome, RM, Italy.

370   POL   ISSN 0137-9585
POLSKA AKADEMIA NAUK. KOMITET NAUK PEDAGOGICZNYCH. ROCZNIK PEDAGOGICZNY. Text in Polish. 1971. a., latest 2002. price varies. **Document type:** *Academic/Scholarly.* **Description:** Presents pedagogical dissertations.
Indexed: RASB.
Published by: Polska Akademia Nauk, Komitet Nauk Pedagogicznych, ul Mokotowska 16/20, Warsaw, 01561, Poland. TEL 48-22-6283461. Ed. Maria Dudzik.

370   POL   ISSN 0079-340X
POLSKA AKADEMIA NAUK. ODDZIAL W KRAKOWIE. KOMISJA NAUK PEDAGOGICZNYCH. PRACE. Text in Polish; Summaries in English, Russian. 1958. irreg., latest vol.21, 2000. price varies. **Document type:** *Monographic series, Academic/Scholarly.*
Published by: (Polska Akademia Nauk, Oddzial w Krakowie, Komisja Nauk Pedagogicznych), Polska Akademia Nauk, Oddzial w Krakowie, ul sw Jana 28, Krakow, 31018, Poland. TEL 48-12-4224853, FAX 48-12-4222791.

370.72   POL   ISSN 0079-3418
L53
POLSKA AKADEMIA NAUK. ODDZIAL W KRAKOWIE. KOMISJA NAUK PEDAGOGICZNYCH. ROCZNIK. Text in Polish; Summaries in English, French, German, Russian. 1961. a. price varies. **Document type:** *Yearbook, Academic/Scholarly.* **Description:** Presents original works in all areas of basic educational research, particularly on topics spanning history, theory, methodology and application.
Indexed: RASB.
Published by: (Polska Akademia Nauk, Oddzial w Krakowie, Komisja Nauk Pedagogicznych), Polska Akademia Nauk, Oddzial w Krakowie, ul sw Jana 28, Krakow, 31018, Poland. TEL 48-12-4224853, FAX 48-12-4222791.

371.07   BRA   ISSN 0101-465X
PONTIFICIA UNIVERSIDADE CATOLICA DO RIO GRANDE DO SUL. EDUCACAO. Text in Portuguese. 1978. 2/yr. BRL 10, USD 9. bk.rev. charts.
Published by: (Pontificia Universidade Catolica do Rio Grande do Sul), Editora da P U C R S, c/o Antoninho M. Naime, Partenon, Caixa Postal 12001, Porto Alegre, RGS 90651-970, Brazil. Circ: 1,000.

POPULATION EDUCATION ACCESSIONS LIST. see *EDUCATION—Abstracting, Bibliographies, Statistics*

370   SWE   ISSN 1652-5221
▼ **PORTFOLIONYTT;** om pedagogisk dokumentation i foerskola och skola. Text in Swedish. 2004. q. SEK 295; SEK 90 per issue (effective 2004). adv. **Document type:** *Magazine.*
Published by: Borda Foerlag och Texttjaenst, Strandgatan 2, Linkoeping, 58226, Sweden. TEL 46-13-129230, FAX 46-13-129213, portfolionytt@borda.se, info@borda.se, http://www.portfolionytt.se/, http://www.borda.se. Ed. Bo Forkman. adv.: page SEK 7,500.

370.157   USA   ISSN 1040-0494
POSITIVE INK. Text in English. 1985. m. USD 25 domestic to individuals; USD 30 foreign (effective 2000). adv. bk.rev.
Document type: *Newsletter.* **Description:** Contains motivational articles and ideas for educators, classroom strategies, staff development ideas and more.
Formerly (until 1988): P O P S Ink (0887-5839)
Published by: Power of Positive Students International Foundation, 4325 Dick Pond Rd, Myrtle Beach, SC 29575. TEL 803-650-7677, 800-521-2741, FAX 803-650-7681, http://www.pops.com. Ed., R&P, Adv. contact Michael A Mitchell. Circ: 10,000 (paid).

370   FRA
POURQUOI, COMMENT; pedagogie Freinet. Text in French. 1982. 5/yr.
Published by: Ecole Moderne Francaise - Pedagogie Freinet, B.P. 109, Cannes - La Bocca, Cedex 06322, France.

370   USA   ISSN 1531-7714
➤ **PRACTICAL ASSESSMENT, RESEARCH & EVALUATION.** Text in English. 1999. irreg. free (effective 2005). **Document type:** *Academic/Scholarly.* **Description:** Publishes scholarly syntheses of research and ideas about issues and practices in education.
Media: Online - full content.
Indexed: e-psyche.
Published by: University of Maryland, Department of Measurement, Statistics, and Evaluation, 1230 Benjamin Building, College Park, MD 20742-1115. TEL 301-405-3624, FAX 301-314-9245, http://pareonline.net/, http://www.education.umd.edu/EDMS/. Eds. Lawrence M Rudner, William D Schafer.

372.210941   GBR   ISSN 1366-610X
PRACTICAL PRE-SCHOOL. Text in English. 1997. m. GBP 39.50 (effective 2001). **Description:** Contains news and latest reports; practical activities covering all six areas of learning within the foundation stage of education.
—CCC.
Published by: Step Forward Publishing Ltd, Coach House, Cross Rd, Milverton, Learnington Spa, CV32 5PB, United Kingdom. TEL 44-1926-420046, FAX 44-1926-420042, enquiries@practicalpreschool.com, http://www.practicalpreschool.com/. Pub. Gil Wilton. Adv. contact Belinda Harvey TEL 44-1235-772007. Circ: 7,000.

370   ESP   ISSN 1139-2533
PRAXIS (ALCALA DE HENARES). Text in Spanish. 1998. q. —CINDOC.
Published by: Universidad de Alcala de Henares, Instituto de Ciencias de la Educacion, C.ibreros, 13, Alcala de Henares, Madrid 28801, Spain. TEL 34-91-8854372, FAX 34-91-8854378, http://www.uah.es/. Ed. Isabel Brincones Calvo.

370.15   DEU   ISSN 0934-5256
PRAXIS SPIEL UND GRUPPE. Text in German. q. EUR 25.20; EUR 23 to students (effective 2003). adv. back issues avail.
Document type: *Magazine, Academic/Scholarly.*
Formerly (until 1988): Schwalbacher Blaetter
Indexed: e-psyche.
Published by: Matthias Gruenewald Verlag GmbH, Max-Hufschmidt-Str 4A, Mainz, 55130, Germany. TEL 49-6131-9286-0, FAX 49-6131-928626, mail@gruenewaldverlag.de, http://www.engagementbuch.de. Ed. Hiltraud Laubach. Adv. contact Nina Baab TEL 49-6131-928620. B&W page EUR 550; trim 135 x 200. Circ: 900.

370   DEU
PRAXIS VERKEHRSERZIEHUNG. (In two editions for different scholastic levels) Text in German. 1965. 6/yr. adv. bk.rev.
Formerly (until 1990): Lehrer-Briefe zur Verkehrserziehung (0075-8612)
Published by: Rot-Gelb-Gruen Lehrmittel GmbH, Theodor-Heuss-Str 3, Braunschweig, 38122, Germany. FAX 0531-80907-21. Circ: 10,000.

372.21   SVK   ISSN 0032-7220
PREDSKOLSKA VYCHOVA; casopis pre rodicov, jasle a materskych skol. Text in Czech, Slovak. 1946. 5/yr. SKK 135; USD 14 foreign (effective 2000). adv. bk.rev. charts; illus.
Indexed: RASB.
Address: Rovniankova 11, Bratislava, 82102, Slovakia. TEL 421-7-823430, FAX 421-7-5229277. Ed., Pub., Adv. contact Katarina Domastova. Page SKK 5,000. Circ: 30,000.

370   BGR   ISSN 0204-7004
PREDUCHILISHTNO VUZPITANIE. Text in Bulgarian. 10/yr. USD 44 foreign (effective 2002). **Document type:** *Journal, Academic/Scholarly.* **Description:** Covers theory and practice of pre-school education in Bulgaria.
Published by: Ministerstvo na Obrazovanieto i Naukata na Republika Bulgaria/Ministry of Education and Sciences of the Republic of Bulgaria, 125 Tzarigradsko Shosse Blvd., Bl. 5, PO Box 336, Sofia, 1113, Bulgaria. TEL 359-2-705298, http://www.minedu.government.bg. **Dist. by:** Sofia Books, ul Silivria 16, Sofia 1404, Bulgaria. TEL 359-2-9586257, info@sofiabooks-bg.com, http://www.sofiabooks-bg.com.

PREHLED PEDAGOGICKE LITERATURY. RADA A. see *EDUCATION—Abstracting, Bibliographies, Statistics*

PREHLED PEDAGOGICKE LITERATURY. RADA B. see *EDUCATION—Abstracting, Bibliographies, Statistics*

PRESENCE DE L'ENSEIGNEMENT AGRICOLE PRIVE. see *AGRICULTURE*

372.21   ITA
PRIMA I BAMBINI. Text in Italian. 1975. bi-m. free to members.
Document type: *Magazine, Consumer.*
Published by: Federazione Italiana Scuole Materne, Via della Pigna 13 A, Rome, 00186, Italy. TEL 39-06-69870511, FAX 39-06-69925248, http://www.fism.net. Ed. Nico de Vincentiis. Circ: 19,500.

372.11   AUS
THE PRIMARY AND MIDDLE YEARS EDUCATOR. Text in English. 1995. 3/yr. AUD 68 domestic; AUD 72 elsewhere; AUD 57 to students (effective 2003). back issues avail.
Document type: *Journal, Academic/Scholarly.* **Description:** Practical journal for teachers providing up-to-date information which crosses the primary-secondary divide in all key learning areas.
Formerly (until 2003): The Primary Educator (1324-4825); Which incorporated (in 1997): Primary Updates (1328-3634)
Related titles: Online - full text ed.: (from EBSCO Publishing).
Indexed: AEI, WBA, WMB.
Published by: Australian Curriculum Studies Association Inc., PO Box 331, Deakin West, ACT 2600, Australia. TEL 61-2-62605660, FAX 61-2-62605665, acsa@acsa.edu.au, http://www.acsa.edu.au. Circ: 1,000.

PRIMARY ENGLISH; die Fachzeitschrift fuer Englisch in der Grundschule. see *LINGUISTICS*

372.35   GBR   ISSN 0269-2465
➤ **PRIMARY SCIENCE REVIEW.** Text in English. 1986. q. GBP 53 domestic to libraries; GBP 60.50 in Europe to libraries; GBP 70.50 elsewhere to libraries (effective 2005). adv. bk.rev. 32 p./no.; back issues avail. **Document type:** *Journal, Academic/Scholarly.* **Description:** Contains reference material and practical ideas for science primary teachers.
Indexed: BrEdI, CIJE, CPE.
—BLDSC (6612.912900), IE, ingenta. **CCC.**
Published by: Association for Science Education, College Ln, Hatfield, Herts AL10 9AA, United Kingdom. TEL 44-1707-283000, FAX 44-1707-266532, info@ase.org.uk, http://www.ase.org.uk/htm/journals/psr/index.php. Ed. W Harlen. R&P Jane Hanrott. Adv. contact Tracy Hague. B&W page GBP 340, color page GBP 505. Circ: 7,000.

370   ESP   ISSN 1136-7733
PRIMERAS NOTICIAS COMUNICACION Y PEDAGOGIA. Text in Spanish. 1978. 8/yr. EUR 42 (effective 2005). adv. bk.rev. **Document type:** *Academic/Scholarly.*
Formerly (until 1991): Primeras Noticias. Periodico de Comunicaciones (1136-7725); Which superseded in part (in 1988): Primeras Noticias (1136-7709)
—CINDOC.
Published by: Centro de Comunicacion y Pedagogia, C Arago, 466, Entresuelo, Barcelona, 08013, Spain. TEL 34-93-2075052, FAX 34-93-2076133, info@comunicacionypedagogia.com, http://www.comunicacionypedagogia.com/. Ed. Raul Mercadal. Pub. Jose Domingo Aliaga Serrano. Adv. contact Angeles Lopez.

370   CAN   ISSN 1208-0888
PRINCE EDWARD ISLAND. DEPARTMENT OF EDUCATION. ANNUAL REPORT. Text in English. 1994. a.
Former titles (until 1993): Prince Edward Island. Department of Education and Human Resources. Annual Report (1190-8610); (until 1992): Province of Prince Edward Island. Department of Education. Annual Report (0382-2753); (until 1931): Province of Prince Edward Island. Chief of Superintendent of Education. Annual Report (0382-2761)
Published by: Prince Edward Island, Department of Education, Box 2000, Charlottetown, PE C1A 7N6, Canada. TEL 902-368-5556, FAX 902-368-6144.

370 659.2   USA
PRINCIPAL COMMUNICATOR. Text in English. 1941. 10/yr. USD 90 domestic; USD 100 in Canada; USD 105 elsewhere (effective 2005). **Document type:** *Newsletter, Trade.*
Former titles: It Starts on the Frontline; It Starts in the Classroom (0021-2717)
Published by: National School Public Relations Association, 15948 Derwood Rd, Rockville, MD 20855-2123. TEL 301-519-0496, FAX 301-519-0494, nspra@nspra.org, http://www.nspra.org/cgi-bin/catalog.exe?ft=e&ef=viewdetail.htm&iid=48. Eds. Andy Grunig, Rich Bagin. Circ: 2,400 (paid).

E

▼ *new title*   ➤ *refereed*   ✳ *unverified*   ◆ *full entry avail.*

373.1 USA ISSN 1538-9251
LA201
PRINCIPAL LEADERSHIP (HIGH SCHOOL EDITION). (Middle School edition avail.) Text in English. 2000. m. (Sep.-May). USD 148 to individuals; USD 180 to libraries (effective 2005); subscr. package also includes: NASSP Newsleader, NASSP Bulletin, NASSP Legal Memorandum, Principal Leadership (Middle School Editions) and Connections. adv. **Document type:** *Trade.* **Description:** Focuses on school leaders' real needs, offering them practical strategies for improving their schools in a constantly evolving educational environment.
Formed by the merger of (1993-2000): The High School Magazine (1070-9533); (1981-2000): Schools in the Middle (0276-4482)
Related titles: Online - full text ed.: (from H.W. Wilson, O C L C Online Computer Library Center, Inc., ProQuest Information & Learning).
Indexed: ABIn, BRI, CBRI, CPE, EduInd.
—BLDSC (6612.969150), IE. **CCC.**
Published by: National Association of Secondary School Principals, 1904 Association Dr, Reston, VA 20191-1537. TEL 703-860-0200, 866-647-7253, FAX 703-476-5432, http://www.nassp.org, http://nasccms.principals.org. Ed. Patricia George. adv.: B&W page USD 4,100, color page USD 5,700; trim 8.375 x 10.875.

373.1 USA ISSN 1529-8957
LB2831.9
PRINCIPAL LEADERSHIP (MIDDLE SCHOOL EDITION). (High School Edition avail.) Text in English. 2000. m. (Sep. - May). USD 148 to individuals; USD 180 to libraries (effective 2005); subscr. package also includes: NASSP Newsleader, NASSP Bulletin, NASSP Legal Memorandum, Principal Leadership (High School Edition) and Connections. **Description:** Focuses on school leaders' real needs, offering them practical strategies for improving their schools in a constantly evolving educational environment.
Related titles: Online - full text ed.: (from H.W. Wilson, O C L C Online Computer Library Center, Inc., ProQuest Information & Learning).
Indexed: ABIn, EduInd.
—**CCC.**
Published by: National Association of Secondary School Principals, 1904 Association Dr, Reston, VA 20191-1537. TEL 703-860-0200, 866-647-7253, FAX 703-476-5432, http://www.nassp.org, http://nasccms.principals.org.

373.1 AUS
PRINCIPALS' PERSPECTIVES. Text in English. 1976. a. AUD 3. **Document type:** *Academic/Scholarly.* **Description:** Publishes articles of interest to secondary principals.
Formerly: W.A.S.P.A. Journal
Published by: Western Australian Secondary Principals Association, Australind Senior High School, Break O'Day Dr., Australind, W.A. 6230, Australia. TEL 61-97-971800, FAX 61-97-971811, tomt@bunbury.iap.net.au. Ed. Tom Tuffin. adv.: page AUD 250. Circ: 300 (controlled).

371.12 CAN ISSN 1188-8644
PRISM. Text in English. 1980 (vol.69). a. CND 5 (effective 1998). adv. bk.rev. charts; illus. **Document type:** *Academic/Scholarly.*
Former titles (until 1992): Professional Development Journal (0834-0633); (until 1984): N T A Journal (0027-7037)
Indexed: CEI, CPerI, M&MA.
Published by: Newfoundland and Labrador Teachers' Association, 3 Kenmount Rd, St. John's, NF A1B 1W1, Canada. TEL 709-726-3223, FAX 709-726-4302. Ed. Lesley Ann Browne. R&P Lesley-Ann Browne. Adv. contact Michelle Lamarche. Circ: 5,000.

PRISMA (KASSEL). see *SCIENCES: COMPREHENSIVE WORKS*

371.071 NOR ISSN 0032-8847
PRISMET; pedagogisk tidsskrift. Text in Norwegian. 1950. bi-m. adv. bk.rev. index. **Document type:** *Academic/Scholarly.* **Description:** Examines the pedagogy of religion, particularly the place and function of Christian beliefs in the bringing up of children at school and in the home and parish.
Published by: Institutt for Kristen Oppseding, c/o Harald Leenderts, PO Box 2633, St. Hanshaugen, Oslo, 0131, Norway. TEL 47-22-595312.

PRIVATE EDUCATION LAW REPORT. see *LAW*

PRIVATE SCHOOL LAW IN AMERICA. see *LAW*

371.02 CAN ISSN 1188-777X
LE PRIVE. Text in English. 1973-1996 (vol.5, no.4); resumed 1998. 4/yr. free. bk.rev. abstr.; bibl.; charts; stat. index. **Document type:** *Newsletter.* **Description:** Covers private education in elementary and high schools.
Formerly (until 1992): Bivoie (0315-2138)
Published by: Federation des Associations de l'Enseignement Prive, 1940 Est, bd Henri Bourassa, Montreal, PQ H2B 1S2, Canada. TEL 514-381-8891, FAX 514-381-4086, desrosiersr@cadre.qc.ca, http://www.cadre.qc.ca. Ed. Auguste Servant. Circ: 1,000.

370 BRA ISSN 0103-7307
PRO-POSICOES. Text in Portuguese. 1990. 3/yr. **Document type:** *Academic/Scholarly.*
Published by: Universidade Estadual de Campinas, Faculdade de Educacao, Ave Bertrand Russell, 801, Cidade Universitaria "Zeferino Vaz', Sao Paulo, Campinas 13083-865, Brazil. TEL 55-19-3289-1463, FAX 55-19-3788-5566, http://www.unicamp.br/.

370 150 301 ROM ISSN 1220-8825
➤ **PROBLEME DE PEDAGOGIE CONTEMPORANA.** Text in Romanian; Contents page in English. 1970. a., latest vol.14, 2000. ROL 40,000 domestic; USD 30 foreign (effective 2002). bk.rev. index. back issues avail. **Document type:** *Journal, Academic/Scholarly.* **Description:** Provides reviews of articles or books tackling problems of secondary education in the world.
Supersedes: Buletin de Informare Pedagogica (0007-3792)
Published by: Biblioteca Pedagogica Nationala/National Library of Education, Str. Zalomit 12, Sector 1, Bucharest, 70714, Romania. TEL 40-01-3110323, FAX 40-01-3110323, bpn@fx.ro. Ed. Cristina Vintila. Circ: 5,000.

370 ITA ISSN 0032-9347
PROBLEMI DELLA PEDAGOGIA. Text in Italian. 1955. bi-m. adv. bk.rev.; film rev. charts; illus.; stat. cum.index 1955-1965.
Indexed: RASB.
Published by: Marzorati Editore, Via Pordoi, 8, Settimo Milanese, MI 20019, Italy. TEL 02-33501314, FAX 02-33500046. Ed. Ignazio Volpicelli. Circ: 2,500.

373.222 POL ISSN 0552-2188
PROBLEMY OPIEKUNCZO-WYCHOWAWCZE. Text in Polish. 1961. m. USD 35. **Description:** For teachers in boarding schools, foster parents and inter-school educational centres.
Indexed: RASB.
Published by: Instytut Rozwoju Sluzb Spolecznych, ul Marszalkowska 34/50, Warsaw, 00-554, Poland. TEL 48-22-6294018. Ed. Jadwiga Rzczkowska. **Dist. by:** Ars Polona, Krakowskie Przedmiescie 7, Warsaw, Poland. **Co-sponsor:** Ministerstwo Edukacji Narodowej.

370 POL ISSN 1428-5991
➤ **PROBLEMY OSWIATY I WYCHOWANIA.** Text in Polish. 1976. m. PLZ 36. Website rev. bibl.; illus. 16 p./no. 2 cols./p.; **Document type:** *Journal, Academic/Scholarly.*
Related titles: Online - full text ed.
Published by: Orsodek Ksztalcenia Ustawicznego Nauczycieli, Ul Chrobrego 15, Leszno, 64100, Poland. TEL 48-65-5299062, FAX 48-65-5293109, swodniku@ids.pl, http://www.swodniku.leszno.ids.pl. Eds. Krystyna Chorostecka, Krzysztof Nowaczyk.

370 AUS ISSN 1447-3607
PROFESSIONAL EDUCATOR. Text in English. 2002. q. AUD 143 (effective 2003). 28 p./no.; **Document type:** *Magazine, Academic/Scholarly.* **Description:** Covers the education profession with data-driven and evidence-based approaches to learning and teaching.
Published by: Australian College of Educators, PO Box 323, Deakin West, ACT 2600, Australia. TEL 61-2-62811677, FAX 61-2-62851262, ace@austcolled.com.au, http://www.austcolled.com.au. Ed. Steve Holden.

370.72 USA ISSN 0196-786X
➤ **THE PROFESSIONAL EDUCATOR.** Text in English. 1978. s-a. USD 20; USD 10 per issue (effective 2005). bk.rev. charts; illus.; stat. **Document type:** *Academic/Scholarly.* **Description:** Publishes research and discussions related to developments, issues and trends in teacher education, on the professional development of teachers, and on teacher-researcher and school-university collaboration.
Related titles: Online - full text ed.: (from EBSCO Publishing).
Published by: Auburn University, College of Education, 3084 Haley Ctr, Auburn, AL 36849-5218. TEL 334-844-4446, FAX 334-844-5785, professionaleducator@auburn.edu, http://education.auburn.edu/resourcesservices/trumanpierceinstitute/theprofessionaleducator. Ed. Miles L DeMott. Circ: 200 (paid). **Co-sponsor:** Auburn University, Truman Pierce Institute.

370 GBR ISSN 1476-6833
PROFESSIONAL LECTURES. Text in English. irreg., latest 2003, Spring. GBP 5 per issue (effective 2003). **Document type:** *Academic/Scholarly.* **Description:** Features inaugural lectures from the Institute's newly appointed professors.
Published by: University of London, Institute of Education, 20 Bedford Way, London, WC1H OAL, United Kingdom. TEL 44-20-76126000, FAX 44-20-76126126, info@ioe.ac.uk, http://www.ioe.ac.uk.

371.4 USA ISSN 1096-2409
LB1027.5
➤ **PROFESSIONAL SCHOOL COUNSELING.** Text in English. 1997. 5/yr. USD 90 to non-members; free to members (effective 2005). adv. bk.rev. illus. Index. reprint service avail. from PQC. **Document type:** *Academic/Scholarly.* **Description:** Keeps the reader up-to-date with ideas and techniques on how to deal with current issues in elementary, middle, and secondary school counseling.
Formed by the merger of (1965-1997): Elementary School Guidance and Counseling (0013-5976); (1954-1997): School Counselor (0036-6536); Which superseded (1953-1954): Elementary Counselor (0013-5941)
Related titles: Microform ed.: 1997 (from PQC); Online - full text ed.: (from EBSCO Publishing, Florida Center for Library Automation, Gale Group, H.W. Wilson, Northern Light Technology, Inc., O C L C Online Computer Library Center, Inc., ProQuest Information & Learning).
Indexed: ABIn, AgeL, CIJE, CPE, ChPerI, ERA, ETA, EduInd, FamI, MEA, PsycInfo, PsycholAb, RHEA, SEA, SENA, SFSA, SOMA, SWR&A, TEA, e-psyche.
—BLDSC (6864.220100), IE, ingenta. **CCC.**
Published by: American School Counselor Association, 1101 King St., Ste. 625, Alexandria, VA 22314-2957. TEL 800-306-4722, http://www.schoolcounselor.org/content.asp?contentid=235, http://www.schoolcounselor.org/index.cfm. Eds. Kathleen M Rakestraw TEL 703-864-8734, Pamelia Brott TEL 703-538-8347. **Subscr. to:** PO Box 18136, Merrifield, VA 22118-0136.

372.21 649 GBR ISSN 1468-6759
PROFESSIONALISM IN PRACTICE: THE P A T JOURNAL. Text in English. 2000. q. GBP 9.20; GBP 2 per issue (effective 2004). adv. bk.rev. **Document type:** *Journal, Trade.* **Description:** News, views, matters of interest to teachers, lecturers, nursery nurses and nannies.
Formed by the merger of (1996-2000): Professional Lecturer (1363-3600); (1971-2000): Professional Teacher (0269-0411); (1996-2000): Professional Nursery Nurse (1364-5641); Which was formerly (1995-1996): Nursery Nurse (1360-8053)
Related titles: Online - full content ed.
Published by: Professional Association of Teachers, 2 St James' Court, Friar Gate, Derby, DE1 1BT, United Kingdom. editor@pat.org.uk, pressoffice@pat.org.uk, http://www.pat.org.uk. Ed., Adv. contact Richard Fraser. Circ: 34,000 (controlled).

370.1 CAN
PROFESSIONALLY SPEAKING. Text in English. 1997. q. CND 10 domestic; CND 20 foreign (effective 2000). bk.rev.; software rev.; Website rev. **Document type:** *Magazine.*
Published by: Ontario College of Teachers, 121 Bloor St East, 6th Fl, Toronto, ON M4W 3M5, Canada. TEL 416-961-8800 ext 228, ps@oct.on.ca, ps@oct.ca, http://www.oct.on.ca. Circ: 200 (paid); 170,000 (controlled).

PROFESSIYA. see *OCCUPATIONS AND CAREERS*

371.1 PRT ISSN 0870-841X
PROFESSOR. Text in Portuguese. 1971. 12/yr.
Address: Rua de S. Bernardo 14, Lisbon, 1200, Portugal. TEL 1-670193, FAX 1-668793, TELEX 65791.

378 DEU ISSN 0945-7666
PROFIL. Text in German. 1947. 10/yr. EUR 9.50 newsstand/cover (effective 2003). adv. bk.rev. index. **Document type:** *Journal, Academic/Scholarly.*
Formerly: Hoehere Schule (0018-3083)
Indexed: DIP, IBR, IBZ.
Published by: (Deutscher Philologenverband e.V.), Vereinigte Verlagsanstalten GmbH, Hoeherweg 278, Duesseldorf, 40231, Germany. TEL 49-211-73570, FAX 49-211-7357123, info@vva.de, http://www.vva.de. adv.: B&W page EUR 2,350, color page EUR 3,910.

370.72 IND
PROGRAM EVALUATION KIT. Text in English. (in 9 vols.). USD 200 for complete set (effective 2004). **Description:** A practical step-by-step guide to planning and conducting a program evaluation. Its nine volumes and 1368 pages contain every technique necessary to evaluate any program. It includes tips, exercise, data collection forms, flow charts, graphs, measurement instruments, plus many other illustrative items.
Published by: Sage Publications India Pvt. Ltd. (Subsidiary of: Sage Publications, Inc.), M-32 Market, Greater Kailash-I, PO Box 4215, New Delhi, 110 048, India. TEL 91-11-6444958, FAX 91-11-6472426, sageind@nda.vsnl.net.in, editors@indiasage.com, http://www.indiasage.com/. Ed. Joan L Herman.

370 305.86 CHL
PROGRAMA DE PROMOCION DE LA REFORMA EDUCATIVA EN AMERICA LATINA Y EL CARIBE. DOCUMENTOS DE TRABAJO. Text in Spanish. 1996. irreg.
Related titles: Online - full text ed.
Published by: Programa de Promocion de la Reforma Educativa en America Latina y el Caribe, Santa Magdalena 75, piso 10, oficina 1002, Providencia, Chile. http://www.preal.cl/public-dt01.php.

370 305.86 CHL
PROGRAMA DE PROMOCION DE LA REFORMA EDUCATIVA EN AMERICA LATINA Y EL CARIBE. RESUMENES EJECUTIVOS. Text in Spanish. 1999. irreg.
Related titles: Online - full text ed.
Published by: Programa de Promocion de la Reforma Educativa en America Latina y el Caribe, Santa Magdalena 75, piso 10, oficina 1002, Providencia, Chile. http://www.preal.cl/infor-re.php.

370 305.86 CHL
PROGRAMA DE PROMOCION DE LA REFORMA EDUCATIVA EN AMERICA LATINA Y EL CARIBE. SERIE MEJORES PRACTICAS. Text in Spanish. 1999. 3/yr.
Related titles: Online - full text ed.

E

Published by: Programa de Promocion de la Reforma Educativa en America Latina y el Caribe, Santa Magdalena 75, piso 10, oficina 1002, Providencia, Chile. http://www.preal.cl/informsmp.php.

370 320 CHL
PROGRAMA DE PROMOCION DE LA REFORMA EDUCATIVA EN AMERICA LATINA Y EL CARIBE. SERIE POLITICAS. Text in Spanish. 1998. irreg.
Related titles: Online - full text ed.
Published by: Programa de Promocion de la Reforma Educativa en America Latina y el Caribe, Santa Magdalena 75, piso 10, oficina 1002, Providencia, Chile. http://www.preal.cl/inforsp.php.

PROGRESS OF EDUCATION IN SAUDI ARABIA; a statistical review. see *EDUCATION—Abstracting, Bibliographies, Statistics*

370.1 USA ISSN 0033-0825
PROGRESSIVE TEACHER. Text in English. 1894. q. USD 6.95. adv. bk.rev.; film rev.; rec.rev. illus. index. **Document type:** *Academic/Scholarly.*
Indexed: CurCont.
Published by: Progressive Publishing Co., 2678 Henry St, Augusta, GA 30904. Ed. M S Adcock. Circ: 10,450.

PROJECTIONS OF EDUCATION STATISTICS. see *EDUCATION—Abstracting, Bibliographies, Statistics*

370.9 FRA ISSN 0033-1538
L11
PROSPECTS; quarterly review of comparative education. Text in English. 1969. q. EUR 100, USD 100, GBP 66 combined subscription to institutions print & online eds. (effective 2005). bk.rev. bibl.; illus. reprint service avail. from PSC. **Document type:** *Journal, Academic/Scholarly.*
Formerly: Prospects in Education (1014-4560)
Related titles: Online - full text ed.: ISSN 1573-9090 (from EBSCO Publishing, Gale Group, IngentaConnect, Kluwer Online, O C L C Online Computer Library Center, Inc., Springer LINK, Swets Information Services); ♦ French ed.: Perspectives. ISSN 0304-3045; Chinese ed.; Arabic ed.: Mustaqbaliyyat. ISSN 0254-119X. 1971; Spanish ed.: Perspectivas. ISSN 0304-3053. 1971; Russian ed.; ♦ Persian, Modern Translation: Nama-Ye Tarbiyat.
Indexed: ABIn, BibLing, BrEdI, CIJE, CPE, DIP, ETA, EduInd, HECAB, IBR, IBZ, PCI, RASB, REE&TA, SSCI.
—BLDSC (6927.810000), IE, Infotrieve, ingenta. **CCC.**
Published by: (International Bureau of Education), UNESCO Publishing, 7 place de Fontenoy, Paris, 75352, France. TEL 33-1-45684300, FAX 33-1-45685741, http://www.unesco.org/publications. Circ: 2,125. **Dist. in U.S. by:** Bernan Associates, Bernan, 4611-F Assembly Dr., Lanham, MD 20706-4391. TEL 800-274-4447, FAX 800-865-3450.

370 ITA ISSN 1125-3975
PROSPETTIVA E P. (Educazione Permanente) Text in Italian. 1978. q. EUR 42 domestic; EUR 52 foreign (effective 2005). **Document type:** *Journal, Academic/Scholarly.*
Indexed: DIP, IBR, IBZ.
Published by: Bulzoni Editore, Via dei Liburni 14, Rome, 00185, Italy. TEL 39-06-4455207, FAX 39-06-4450355, bulzoni@bulzoni.it, http://www.bulzoni.it. Ed. Sira Macchietti.

370 SCG ISSN 0033-1651
PROSVETNI PREGLED; list prosvetnih, naucnih i kulturnih radnika SR Srbije. Text in Serbo-Croatian. 1944. w. YUN 140.
Published by: Privredni Pregled, Marsala Birjuzova 3-5, Belgrade, 11000. Ed. Rade Vukovic.

370 MKD ISSN 0033-1635
PROSVETNI RABOTNIK. Text in Macedonian. 1953. fortn.
Address: Rabotnicki Dom II-VIII, Soba 185, Skopje, 91000, Macedonia. Ed. Miso Kitanoski.

370 BIH ISSN 0033-1678
PROSVJETNI LIST. Text in Serbo-Croatian. 1952. fortn. BAD 80, USD 6.25.
Published by: Sindikat Radnika Drustvenih Djelatnosti SR Bosne i Hercegovine, Dure Dakovica 4, Sarajevo, Bosnia Herzegovina. Ed. Nikola Nikic.

370 SCG ISSN 0033-1686
PROSVJETNI RAD; list prosvjetnih radnika. Text in Serbo-Croatian. 195?. bi-w.
Published by: Institut za Medije Crne Gore/Montenegro Media Institute, Balsica 4, Podgorica, 81000. http://www.mminstitute.org. Ed. Miroje Vukovic.

370.15 ITA ISSN 0392-680X
PSICOLOGIA E SCUOLA; giornale italiano di psicologia dell'educazione e pedagogia sperimentale. Text in Italian. 1980. bi-m. EUR 25 domestic; EUR 32.50 foreign (effective 2005). charts; illus.; stat. back issues avail. **Document type:** *Magazine, Trade.* **Description:** Covers a variety of topics in educational psychology: research and theory in the field, implications of psychology for education, teacher training, and practical tools for teachers.
Indexed: DIP, e-psyche.
Published by: Giunti Gruppo Editoriale SpA, Via Bolognese 165, Florence, 50139, Italy. TEL 39-055-5062376, FAX 39-055-5062397, informazioni@giunti.it, http://www.giunti.it. Ed. Massimo Casini.

PSICOLOGIA EDUCATIVA; revista de los psicologos de la educacion. see *PSYCHOLOGY*

370.15 ARG ISSN 1515-1182
PSICOLOGIA Y PSICOPEDAGOGIA. Text in Spanish. 2000. q. back issues avail.
Media: Online - full text.
Published by: Universidad del Salvador, Facultad de Psicologia y Psicopedagogia, Marcelo T. de Alvear 1314, 1er. Piso, Buenos Aires, 1058, Argentina. uds-psic@salvador.edu.ar, http://www.salvador.edu.ar/ual-9-pub.htm. Ed. Bernardo Beget.

PSYCHOLOGIA A PATOPSYCHOLOGIA DIETATA. see *PSYCHOLOGY*

370.15 FRA ISSN 1148-9502
PSYCHOLOGIE & EDUCATION. Text in French. 1962. q. bk.rev. back issues avail. **Document type:** *Academic/Scholarly.*
Former titles (until 1990): Psychologie Scolaire (0291-8382); (until 1969): Association Francaise des Psychologues Scolaires. Bulletin (0999-2243)
Indexed: e-psyche.
Published by: Association Francaise des Psychologues Scolaires, c/o Alain Brabant, 3 rue des 4 Assiettes, Smarves, 86240, France. TEL 33-5-49559927, FAX 33-5-49559927, afps@infonie.fr, http://webhome.infonie.fr/afps/. Ed. Michel Monville. R&P Alma Braban. Circ: 2,000.

370.15 155.4 DEU ISSN 0342-183X
LB1051 CODEN: PEUNDV
➤ **PSYCHOLOGIE IN ERZIEHUNG UND UNTERRICHT**; Organ der Deutschen Gesellschaft fuer Psychologie. Text in German. 1954. q. EUR 73; EUR 58.40 to students; EUR 19.90 newsstand/cover (effective 2005). adv. bk.rev. reprint service avail. from PQC,ISI. **Document type:** *Journal, Academic/Scholarly.*
Formerly (until 1972): Schule und Psychologie (0582-1428)
Indexed: ASCA, CPE, CurCont, DIP, ERA, ETA, GJP, IBR, IBZ, MEA, PsycInfo, PsycholAb, RASB, RHEA, RILM, SEA, SENA, SOMA, SSCI, SWA, TEA, e-psyche.
—BLDSC (6946.532000), IDS, IE, ingenta. **CCC.**
Published by: Ernst Reinhardt Verlag, Kemnatenstr 46, Munich, 80639, Germany. TEL 49-89-1780160, FAX 49-89-17801630, webmaster@reinhardt-verlag.de, http://www.reinhardt-verlag.de/deutsch/zeitschriften/fi_komplett.htm. adv.: page EUR 550. Circ: 900.

➤ **PSYCHOLOGY & EDUCATION**; an interdisciplinary journal. see *PSYCHOLOGY*

➤ **PSYCHOLOGY IN THE SCHOOLS.** see *PSYCHOLOGY*

370.15 GBR ISSN 1463-9807
➤ **THE PSYCHOLOGY OF EDUCATION REVIEW.** Text in English. 1979. s-a. GBP 8 to non-members (effective 2003). bk.rev. reprint service avail. from ISI. **Document type:** *Journal, Academic/Scholarly.* **Description:** Publishes material in educational psychology likely to be of general interest to members. Includes the "open dialogue" section in which there is a simultaneous exchange of views on an issue of substantial interest. This consists of an initial paper, peer review, and an author's reply.
Formerly (until 1998): British Psychological Society. Education Section. Review (0262-4087)
Indexed: BrEdI, CPE, SOMA, e-psyche.
—BLDSC (6946.535584), IE, ingenta.
Published by: The British Psychological Society, St Andrews House, 48 Princess Rd E, Leicester, LE1 7DR, United Kingdom. TEL 44-116-2549568, FAX 44-116-2470787, mail@bps.org.uk, http://www.bps.org.uk. Ed. Sue Palmer. R&P Geoff Ellis TEL 44-116-2529523. Adv. contact Z Terry TEL 44-116-252-9562. Circ: 850.

➤ **PSYCHOLOGY TEACHING REVIEW.** see *PSYCHOLOGY*

➤ **PSYKOLOGISK PAEDAGOGISK RAADGIVNING/JOURNAL OF SCHOOL PSYCHOLOGY**; tidsskrift for paedagogisk psykologi og raadgivning. see *PSYCHOLOGY*

370 CAN ISSN 1180-1751
PUBLIC AND INDEPENDENT SCHOOLS BOOK. Text in English. a.
Former titles (until 1989): Public Schools in British Columbia (0712-0176); (until 1979): List of Schools in British Columbia with Names and Addresses of Secretary-Treasures and Principals or Head Teachers (0704-5891)
Published by: British Columbia, Ministry of Education, Stn Prou Gout, Box 9041, Victoria, BC V8W 9E1, Canada. TEL 604-387-1715, FAX 604-387-0087, http://www.gov.bc.ca/.

379.2 USA
PUBLIC POLICY FORUM; researching community issues. Text in English. 1913. irreg. (8-18/yr.). USD 50. charts; stat. **Description:** Covers the five-county Milwaukee area.
Formerly: C G R B Bulletin (Citizen's Governmental Research Bureau)
Address: 633 W Wisconsin Ave, Milwaukee, WI 53203-1918. TEL 414-276-8240, FAX 414-276-9962, http://www.publicpolicyforum.org. Ed. Jean B Tyler. Circ: 1,500.

371.01 USA ISSN 0077-9229
PUBLIC SCHOOL PROFESSIONAL PERSONNEL REPORT, NEW YORK STATE. Text in English. 1967. a. free. charts; illus. back issues avail. **Document type:** *Government.*
Formerly: New York (State) Education Department. Public School Professional Personnel Report (0077-9245)
Published by: Education Department, Information, Reporting & Technology Services, Education Bldg Annex, Rm 962, Albany, NY 12234. TEL 518-474-7082, FAX 518-474-4351. Circ: (controlled).

370 CAN ISSN 0709-6607
PUBLIC SCHOOL PROGRAMS (YEAR)/PROGRAMMES DES ECOLES PUBLIQUES. Text in English. 1954. a.
Formerly (until 1977): Program of Studies in the Schools of Nova Scotia (0709-6593)
Published by: Nova Scotia Department of Education, 2021 Brunswick St, Halifax, NS B3J 2S9, Canada. TEL 902-424-5168, FAX 902-424-0511, http://www.ednet.ns.ca.

370 ESP ISSN 1132-7707
PUERTANUEVA. Text in Spanish. 1986. q.
Related titles: ♦ Supplement(s): Puertanueva. Anexo. ISSN 1132-7715.
—CINDOC.
Published by: Junta de Andalucia, Consejeria de Educacion y Ciencia, Edif. Torretriana, C. Juan Antonio de Vizarron s-n, Isla de Cartuja, Sevilla, 41092, Spain. FAX 34-955-064003, infomacion@cec.junta-andalucia.es, http://www3.cec.junta-andalucia.es/.

370 ESP ISSN 1132-7715
PUERTANUEVA. ANEXO. Text in Spanish. 1987. a.
Related titles: ♦ Supplement to: Puertanueva. ISSN 1132-7707.
Published by: Junta de Andalucia, Consejeria de Educacion y Ciencia, Edif. Torretriana, C. Juan Antonio de Vizarron s-n, Isla de Cartuja, Sevilla, 41092, Spain. FAX 34-955-064003, infomacion@cec.junta-andalucia.es, http://www3.cec.junta-andalucia.es/.

370.72 URY ISSN 0797-4248
PUNTO 21. Text in Spanish. 1974. q. charts.
Indexed: RASB.
Published by: Centro de Investigacion y Experimentacion Pedagogica, Jaime Cibils, 2810, Montevideo, 11616, Uruguay. **Subscr. to:** Libreria Adolfo Linardi, Juan Carlos Gomez, 1435, Montevideo 11004, Uruguay.

370 USA ISSN 0734-3612
PURPLE AND GOLD. Text in English. 1884. q. membership. **Document type:** *Journal, Academic/Scholarly.* **Description:** Educational journal of the Chi Psi Educational Trust.
Published by: Chi Psi Educational Trust, 147 Maple Row Blvd., Ste. 200, Hendersonvlle, TN 37075-3830. Ed. William J Green. Circ: 17,000; 17,000 (controlled).

370 GBR
Q U A S E TECHNICAL REPORT. (Quantitative Analysis for Self-Evaluation) Text in English. irreg. **Document type:** *Monographic series, Academic/Scholarly.*
Formerly (until 1996): Q U A S E Technical Report of Analysis
Published by: National Foundation for Educational Research, The Mere, Upton Park, Slough, Berks SL1 2DQ, United Kingdom. TEL 44-1753-574123, FAX 44-1753-691632. Ed. Ian Schagen.

370.15 ITA
QUALE SCUOLA?; periodico di educazione per una scuola diversa. Text in Italian. 1982. q. **Description:** Covers primary and elementary education and the psychological development of children.
Indexed: e-psyche.
Address: Traversa T. de Amicis 41 2-A, Naples, NA 80145, Italy. TEL 39-81-5466406. Ed. Salvatore Alosco.

370 ITA
QUALEDUCAZIONE; rivista internazionale di pedagogia. Text in Italian. q. EUR 25.82 (effective 2004). **Document type:** *Journal, Academic/Scholarly.*
Published by: Editrice Pellegrini, Via de Rada 67c, Cosenza, CS 87100, Italy. TEL 39-0984-795065, FAX 39-0984-792672, http://www.pellegrinieditore.it.

370 GBR
QUALITY ASSURANCE AGENCY FOR HIGHER EDUCATION. ANNUAL REPORT. Text in English. 1997. a. **Document type:** *Academic/Scholarly.* **Description:** Provides an overview of the activity of the Agency in the previous year, including financial summary, details of Board and Committee membership and a listing of quality audits and outcomes undertaken during the year.
Related titles: Online - full content ed.
Published by: Quality Assurance Agency for Higher Education, Southgate House, Southgate Street, Gloucester, GL1 1UB, United Kingdom. TEL 44-1452-557000, FAX 44-1452-557070, http://www.qaa.ac.uk/aboutqaa/annualreports.htm, http://www.gaa.ac.uk.

E

▼ new title ➤ refereed ✶ unverified ♦ full entry avail.

371.144 GBR ISSN 0968-4883
LB2806.22
QUALITY ASSURANCE IN EDUCATION. Text in English. 1993. q. EUR 5,153.66 in Europe; USD 5,529 in North America; AUD 6,889 in Australasia; GBP 3,609.41 in UK & elsewhere (effective 2006). reprint service avail. from PSC. **Document type:** *Journal, Academic/Scholarly.* **Description:** Tackles the problems which must be overcome if students are to receive the high standards of education they need to meet the demands of the international employment market.
Incorporates (1995-1996): Innovation and Learning in Education (1356-3297)
Related titles: CD-ROM ed.; Online - full text ed.: (from EBSCO Publishing, Emerald Group Publishing Limited, Gale Group, IngentaConnect, O C L C Online Computer Library Center, Inc., ProQuest Information & Learning, Swets Information Services).
Indexed: BrEdI, CPE, EAA, ERA, ETA, EmerIntel, Emerald, MEA, RHEA, SEA, SENA, SOMA, TEA.
—BLDSC (7168.139354), IE, Infotrieve, ingenta. **CCC.**
Published by: Emerald Group Publishing Limited, 60-62 Toller Ln, Bradford, W Yorks BD8 9BY, United Kingdom. TEL 44-1274-777700, FAX 44-1274-785200, infomation@emeraldinsight.com, http://www.emeraldinsight.com/qae.htm. Ed. John Dalrymple. **Subscr. addr. in N America:** Emerald Group Publishing Ltd., 44 Brattle St, 4th Fl, Cambridge, MA 02138. TEL 617-497-2175, 888-622-0075, FAX 617-354-6875.

370 CHN
QUANGUO ZHONGXUE YOUXIU ZUOWEN XUAN (CHUZONG BAN)/SELECTED EXCELLENT COMPOSITIONS FROM NATIONWIDE MIDDLE SCHOOLS (JUNIOR HIGH SCHOOL EDITION). Text in Chinese. 1984. m. CNY 2 newsstand/cover (effective 2005). **Document type:** *Magazine, Academic/Scholarly.*
Supersedes in part (in 2001): Quanguo Zhongxue Youxiu Zuowen Xuan (1004-0293)
Published by: Jiangsu Jiaoyu Chubanshe/Jiangsu Education Publishing House, 47, Nunan Lu, 1011-shi, Nanjing, Jiangsu 210009, China. TEL 86-25-3311794, zwx@edu-publisher.com, http://qgzxyxzwx-c.periodicals.net.cn/default.html.

420.07 USA ISSN 0033-5630
PN4071
➤ **QUARTERLY JOURNAL OF SPEECH.** Text in English. 1915. q. GBP 133, USD 214 combined subscription to institutions print & online eds. (effective 2006). adv. bk.rev. illus. index, cum.index: vols.1-55 (1915-1969). reprint service avail. from PQC,PSC. **Document type:** *Journal, Academic/Scholarly.* **Description:** Presents research that is original, significant, and designed to further understanding of the processes of human communication, particularly in its rhetorical and cultural dimensions.
Former titles (until 1927): Quarterly Journal of Speech Education; (until 1917): Quarterly Journal of Public Speaking
Related titles: Microform ed.: (from PMC, PQC); Online - full text ed.: ISSN 1479-5779. GBP 126, USD 203 to institutions (effective 2006) (from EBSCO Publishing, IngentaConnect, Northern Light Technology, Inc., O C L C Online Computer Library Center, Inc., Swets Information Services).
Indexed: ABS&EES, AES, ASCA, AcaI, AmH&L, AmHI, ArtHuCI, BEL&L, BRI, CBRI, CIJE, CPE, CommAb, CurCont, DIP, ECER, FamI, HRA, HistAb, HumInd, IBR, IBZ, IJCS, L&LBA, LT&LA, MLA, MLA-IB, PCI, PRA, PSA, PhilInd, PsycInfo, PsycholAb, RASB, RI-1, RI-2, RILM, SOPODA, SPAA, SSA, SSCI, SUSA, SociolAb, V&AA, e-psyche.
—BLDSC (7195.930000), IDS, IE, Infotrieve, ingenta. **CCC.**
Published by: (National Communication Association), Routledge (Subsidiary of: Taylor & Francis Ltd), 325 Chestnut St., Suite 800, Philadelphia, PA 19106. TEL 215-625-8900, 800-354-1420, FAX 215-625-8914, journals@routledge.com, http://www.tandf.co.uk/journals/titles/00335630.asp, http://www.routledge.com. Ed. David Henry. Adv. contact Jennifer Peltak. Circ: 5,400. **Subscr. to:** Taylor & Francis Inc., Customer Services Dept, 325 Chestnut St, 8th Fl, Philadelphia, PA 19106. TEL 215-625-8900, FAX 215-625-8914.

371.042 CAN ISSN 0033-5967
QUEBEC HOME & SCHOOL NEWS. Text in English. 1948. 4/yr. CND 15 membership (effective 2003). bk.rev. **Document type:** *Newspaper, Academic/Scholarly.* **Description:** Communication and information medium for parents and others interested in education in Quebec and in Canada.
Published by: Quebec Federation of Home and School Associations, 3285 Cavendish Blvd, Ste 560, Montreal, PQ H4B 2L9, Canada. TEL 514-481-5619, FAX 514-481-5610, info@qfhsa.org, http://www.qfhsa.org/news.html. Ed. Helene Koeppe. Adv. contact Donna Sauriol. Circ: 5,600 (paid); 2,000 (controlled).

371.042 CAN
QUEBEC HOMESCHOOLING ADVISORY NEWSLETTER/ CONSEIL POUR L'EDUCATION A DOMICILE AU QUEBEC. Text in English, French. 1983. 4/yr. looseleaf. CND 15. adv. back issues avail. **Document type:** *Newsletter.* **Description:** Provides legal and pedagogical advice, as well as local contacts regarding home schooling in Quebec.
Published by: Quebec Homeschooling Advisory, 1002 Rosemarie, Box 1278, Val David, PQ J0T 2N0, Canada. TEL 819-322-6495. Ed. Elizabeth Edwards. Circ: 80.

370.72 AUS
QUEENSLAND. DEPARTMENT OF EDUCATION. RESEARCH AND EVALUATION UNIT. EDUCATIONAL RESEARCH REPORT. Text in English. 1975. irreg.
Former titles (until May 1987): Queensland. Department of Education. Research Services. Research Series (0816-3782); (Until 1983): Queensland. Department of Education. Research Branch. Research Series
Published by: Department of Education, Research and Evaluation Unit, 50 Albert St., PO Box 33, Brisbane, QLD 4002, Australia. TEL 07-237-0970, FAX 07-237-0203.

370.72 AUS ISSN 1329-0703
➤ **QUEENSLAND JOURNAL OF EDUCATIONAL RESEARCH.** Abbreviated title: Q J E R. Text in English. 1973. s-a. (3/yr. until 1997). AUD 50 (effective 2002). adv. 120 p./no.; back issues avail. **Document type:** *Journal, Academic/Scholarly.* **Description:** Publishes feature articles and papers on topics in educational research and evaluation.
Former titles (until 1996): Queensland Researcher (0818-545X); (until 1985): Q I E R Journal (0311-2349)
Indexed: AEI, CIJE.
Published by: Queensland Institute of Educational Research, School of Education, University of Queensland, Brisbane, QLD 4072, Australia. TEL 61-7-3365-6506, FAX 61-7-3365-7199, c.sim@mailbox.gu.edu.au@mailbox.uq.edu.au. Ed., R&P Graham Maxwell. Circ: 200.

371.1 AUS ISSN 0033-6238
QUEENSLAND TEACHERS' JOURNAL. Text in English. 1895. 8/yr. AUD 22 (effective 1997). adv. bk.rev. index. **Document type:** *Newspaper, Trade.* **Description:** For teachers in Queensland's State Education system. Covers industrial and professional issues in Queensland education.
Indexed: AEI.
Published by: Queensland Teachers' Union, PO Box 1750, Milton, QLD 4064, Australia. TEL 61-7-33690088, FAX 61-7-33690022, jul@qtu.asn.au, http://www.qtu.asn.au. Ed. John Battams. R&P Brett Young. Adv. contact Margaret Hinchliffe. Circ: 35,000 (controlled).

370 ITA ISSN 0033-6262
QUERCE; informativo semestrale. Text in Italian. 1945. s-a. free. adv. bk.rev. **Document type:** *Academic/Scholarly.* **Description:** For students, alumni and their families. Provides news regarding the school and alumni.
Published by: Collegio alla Querce, Via Della Piazzola, 44, Florence, FI 50133, Italy. TEL 39-55-573621, FAX 39-55-579655. Ed. Giovanni Scalese. Circ: 2,000 (controlled).

370 CAN ISSN 0380-240X
➤ **QUERY**; young Saskatchewan writers. Text in English. 1970. 3/yr. CND 20 (effective 2000). bk.rev. **Document type:** *Academic/Scholarly.*
Indexed: CEI, CPerI.
Published by: (Saskatchewan Reading Council), Saskatchewan Teachers' Federation, 2317 Arlington Ave., Saskatoon, SK S7J 2H8, Canada. stf@stf.sk.ca. Ed. Adele Owatz. Circ: 1,000.

➤ **QUILL & SCROLL.** see *JOURNALISM*

370 ESP ISSN 1130-5371
QURRICULUM; revista de teoria, investigacion y practica educativa. Text in Spanish. 1990. s-a. EUR 14 (effective 2005).
—CINDOC.
Published by: Universidad de la Laguna, Secretariado de Publicaciones, Campus Central, La Laguna-Tenerife, Canary Islands 38071, Spain. TEL 34-922-319198, FAX 34-922-258127, svpubli@ull.es, http://www.ull.es/. Ed. Ma. de los Angeles Padilla Baucells.

370.1175 USA ISSN 1091-6822
R E A D PERSPECTIVES. Text in English. 1993. a. free membership (effective 2005). reprint service avail. from PSC. **Document type:** *Journal, Academic/Scholarly.* **Description:** Reviews current research on the education of immigrant, migrant and refugee children in US public schools, and reports on effective English language programs.
Indexed: CIJE, SOPODA.
—**CCC.**
Published by: Institute for Research in English Acquisition and Development, 14 Pigeon Hill Dr, Suite 500, Sterling, VA 20165. TEL 703-421-5443, FAX 703-421-6401, http://www.ceousa.org/READ/readper.html.

370 MYS ISSN 0377-3450
Q183.4.A7
R E C S A M ANNUAL REPORT. (Regional Centre for Education in Science and Mathematics) Text in English. 1972. a. free. illus.
Published by: Southeast Asian Ministers of Education Organisation, Regional Centre for Education in Science and Mathematics, Glugor, Penang 11700, Malaysia. TEL 604-6583266, FAX 604-6572541. Circ: 150.

370 ESP ISSN 1579-1513
R E E C. REVISTA ELECTRONICA DE ENSENANZA DE LAS CIENCIAS. Text in Multiple languages. 2002. 3/yr. free (effective 2005). **Document type:** *Journal, Academic/Scholarly.* **Description:** Devoted to innovation and research on science teaching and learning in the various educational levels (kindergarden, primary and secondary school and university).
Media: Online - full text.
Published by: Universidade de Vigo, Servicio de Publicacions, Rua Oporto 1, Vigo, 36201, Spain. TEL 34-986-812000, informacion@uvigo.es, http://www.uvigo.es.

R E L C JOURNAL; a journal of language teaching and research in Southeast Asia. (Regional English Language Centre) see *LINGUISTICS*

370.72 ESP ISSN 1134-4032
LB1028
➤ **R E L I E V E: REVISTA ELECTRONICA DE INVESTIGACION Y EVALUACION EDUCATIVA/ ELECTRONIC JOURNAL OF EDUCATIONAL RESEARCH, ASSESSMENT AND EVALUATION.** Variant title: Revista Electronica de Investigacion y Evaluacion Educativa. Text in Spanish, English. 1994. s-a. free (effective 2005). **Document type:** *Academic/Scholarly.* **Description:** Contains articles about educational research, assessment and evaluation topics.
Media: Online - full content.
Published by: Asociacion Interuniversitaria de Investigacion Pedagogica, Ave. Blasco Ibanez No. 30, Valencia, 46010, Spain. relieve@uv.es, francisco.aliaga@uv.es, http://www.uv.es/RELIEVE/, http://wwwuca.es/RELIEVE/. Ed. Francisco M Aliaga.

371.0712 GBR ISSN 0266-7738
R E TODAY. (Religious Education) Text in English. 1983. 3/yr. GBP 25 (effective 2003). adv. bk.rev.; Website rev.; software rev. illus. 48 p./no. 5 cols./p.; **Document type:** *Magazine, Academic/Scholarly.* **Description:** Offers practical help to classroom teachers with a religious curriculum. Includes features on current topics in religion and stories from a wide variety of traditions along with approaches, teaching points, and sample questions that can be used to promote discussion.
Indexed: ChLitAb.
Published by: R E Today Services (Subsidiary of: Christian Education), 1020 Bristol Rd, Selly Oak, Birmingham, B29 6LB, United Kingdom. TEL 44-121-4724242, FAX 44-121-4727575, retoday@retoday.org.uk, http://www.retoday.org.uk/retodaymag.htm. Ed. Rev. Colin Johnson. R&P Elizabeth Bruce-Whitehorn. Adv. contact Lian Purcell. Circ: 5,600 (paid).

370 ESP
R E U. (Revista de Ensenanza Universitaria) Text in Spanish. 1991. irreg. price varies. **Document type:** *Academic/Scholarly.*
Formerly (until 1991): Revista de Ensenanza Universitaria (1131-5245)
—CINDOC.
Published by: Universidad de Sevilla, Secretariado de Publicaciones, Porvenir 27, Sevilla, 41013, Spain. TEL 34-95-4487444, FAX 34-95-4487443, secpub10@us.es, http://www.us.es/publius/inicio.html.

R E: VIEW; rehabilitation and education for blindness and visual impairment. (Rehabilitation and Education) see *HANDICAPPED—Visually Impaired*

370.72 ESP ISSN 0212-4068
R I E. (Revista Investigacion Educativa) Key Title: RIE. Revista Investigacion Educativa. Text in Spanish. 1983. s-a. **Document type:** *Journal, Academic/Scholarly.*
—CINDOC, IE, Infotrieve.
Published by: (Universitat de Barcelona, Facultat de Pedagogia), Universitat de Barcelona, Servei de Publicacions, Gran Via Corts Catalanes 585, Barcelona, 08007, Spain. TEL 34-93-4021100, http://www.publicacions.ub.es.

R I F NEWSLETTER. see *LITERATURE*

370.72 USA
R M L E ONLINE: RESEARCH IN MIDDLE LEVEL EDUCATION. Text in English. irreg. (1-3/yr.). free. **Document type:** *Newsletter, Academic/Scholarly.* **Description:** Publishes research syntheses, integrative reviews, interpretations of research literature, case studies, action-research, and data-based qualitative and quantitative studies.
Media: Online - full content.
Published by: National Middle School Association, 4151 Executive Pkwy, Ste 300, Westerville, OH 43081-3871. TEL 614-895-4730, 800-528-6672, FAX 614-895-4750, info@nmsa.org, http://www.nmsa.org/research/rmle/rmle.html.

371.4 DNK ISSN 0109-0984
R.U.E.-REVUE; nyt fra Raadet for Uddannelses- og Erhvervsvejledning. Text in Danish. 1983. q. free. illus. **Document type:** *Academic/Scholarly.*

E

Published by: Raadet for Uddannelses- og Erhvervsvejledning (R.U.E.)/Danish National Council for Educational and Vocational Guidance, Vester Voldgade 123, Copenhagen V, 1552, Denmark. TEL 45-39-95-53-00, FAX 45-39-95-53-49, r-u-e@r-u-e.dk, http://www.r-u-e.dk. Ed. Taus Randsholt. Circ: 11,000.

370 DNK ISSN 1395-7929
R.U.E. SKRIFTSERIE. Text in Danish. 1995. irreg. price varies. **Document type:** *Monographic series.*
Published by: Raadet for Uddannelses- og Erhvervsvejledning (R.U.E.)/Danish National Council for Educational and Vocational Guidance, Vester Voldgade 123, Copenhagen V, 1552, Denmark. TEL 45-39-95-53-00, FAX 45-39-95-53-49, r-u-e@r-u-e.dk.

R W I : MATERIALIEN. see *SOCIAL SCIENCES: COMPREHENSIVE WORKS*

305.8 GBR ISSN 1361-3324
LC3701
RACE, ETHNICITY AND EDUCATION. Text in English. 1998. q. GBP 371, USD 607 combined subscription to institutions print & online eds. (effective 2006). reprint service avail. from PSC. **Document type:** *Journal, Academic/Scholarly.* **Description:** Explores the dynamics of race and ethnicity in education theory, policy and practice. Welcomes work which focuses on the interconnections between race and ethnicity and multiple forms of oppression.
Related titles: Online - full text ed.: ISSN 1470-109X. GBP 352, USD 577 to institutions (effective 2006) (from EBSCO Publishing, Gale Group, IngentaConnect, O C L C Online Computer Library Center, Inc., Swets Information Services).
Indexed: BrEdI, CPE, ERA, ETA, GEOBASE, IBSS, L&LBA, MEA, RHEA, SEA, SENA, SOMA, SSA, SWA, SociolAb, TEA.
—BLDSC (7225.899000), IE, Infotrieve, ingenta. **CCC.**
Published by: Routledge (Subsidiary of: Taylor & Francis Group), 4 Park Sq, Milton Park, Abingdon, Oxon OX14 4RN, United Kingdom. TEL 44-1235-828600, FAX 44-1235-829000, info@routledge.co.uk, http://www.tandf.co.uk/journals/titles/13613324.asp, http://www.routledge.co.uk. Ed. David Gilborn. **Subscr. to:** Taylor & Francis Ltd, Journals Customer Service, Rankine Rd, Basingstoke, Hants RG24 8PR, United Kingdom. TEL 44-1256-813000, FAX 44-1256-330245.

371.8 USA ISSN 0085-4093
RACIAL - ETHNIC DISTRIBUTION OF PUBLIC SCHOOL STUDENTS AND STAFF, NEW YORK STATE. Text in English. 1968. irreg., latest 1993-1994. free. charts; stat. back issues avail. **Document type:** *Government.*
Published by: Education Department, Information, Reporting & Technology Services, Education Bldg Annex, Rm 962, Albany, NY 12234. TEL 518-474-7082, FAX 518-474-4351. Circ: (controlled).

370.1 BEL ISSN 1375-4459
RAISONS EDUCATIVES; pari des sciences de l'education. Text in French. 2/yr. **Document type:** *Academic/Scholarly.*
Published by: (Universite de Geneve/University of Geneva CHE), De Boeck Universite, Fond Jean-Paques 4, Louvain-la-Neuve, 1348, Belgium. TEL 32-10-482511, FAX 32-10-482519, info@universite.deboeck.com, http://universite.deboeck.com. Ed. Jean-Michel Baudouin. **Subscr. to:** Acces S.P.R.L., Fond Jean-Paques 4, Louvain-la-Neuve 1348, Belgium. TEL 32-10-482500, FAX 32-10-482519.

373 IND ISSN 0033-9083
RAJASTHAN BOARD JOURNAL OF EDUCATION. Text in English, Hindi. 1964. q. INR 25; INR 15 to libraries. adv. bk.rev. stat. index. **Description:** Provides teachers and educational administrators with the latest developments in the field of secondary education.
Published by: Board of Secondary Education, Ajmer, Rajasthan, India. TEL 20346. Ed. Panna Lal Verma. Circ: 20,000.

373 ITA ISSN 1125-9612
RASSEGNA DELL'ISTRUZIONE; bimestrale d'informazione e di politica scolastica. Text in Italian. 1946. bi-m. EUR 29 domestic (effective 2003). adv. bk.rev.
Former titles (until 1982): Rassegna dell'Istruzione Secondaria (0033-9466); (until 1966): Rassegna dell'Istruzione Media (1125-9604)
Published by: Casa Editrice Edumond Le Monnier, Via Antonio Meucci 2, Grassina, FI 50015, Italy. TEL 39-055-64910, FAX 39-055-643983, lemonnier@lemonnier.it, http://www.lemonnier.it. Circ: 5,000.

370 ITA ISSN 0033-9571
RASSEGNA DI PEDAGOGIA/PAEDAGOGISCHE UMSCHAU. Text in French, German, Italian; Summaries in English, French, German, Italian. 1941. q. EUR 140 domestic to individuals; EUR 240 foreign to individuals; EUR 195 domestic to institutions; EUR 340 foreign to institutions (effective 2004). bk.rev. bibl. index. **Description:** Includes research on theory and practice in the field of pedagogy.
Related titles: Online - full text ed.
Published by: (Universita degli Studi di Trieste, Istituto di Pedagogia), Istituti Editoriali e Poligrafici Internazionali (Subsidiary of: Libra Web), Via Giosue' Carducci, 60, Ghezzano - La Fontina, PI 56010, Italy. TEL 39-050-878066, FAX 39-050-878732, iepi@iepi.it, http://www.iepi.it. Circ: 1,200.

371.07 USA
REACH (NEW HAVEN)✶. Text in English. 1970. q. membership. **Document type:** *Newsletter.*
Published by: (Religious Education Association), Scholars Press, PO Box 15299, Atlanta, GA 30333-0399. TEL 404-727-2320, 888-747-2354, FAX 404-727-2348, scholars@emory.edu. Ed. Ron Cram. Circ: 1,000 (controlled).

READING AND WRITING; an interdisciplinary journal. see *LINGUISTICS*

372.4 USA ISSN 1096-1232
LB1049.9
➤ **READING ONLINE.** Text in English. 1997. m. free (effective 2005). bk.rev.; software rev.; Website rev. **Document type:** *Journal, Academic/Scholarly.* **Description:** Communicates critical issues in early reading research and instruction, developments in literacy, technology relevant to reading instruction, research results and reviews of professional materials, both print and nonprint. Scholars and educators are welcome and encouraged to participate and contribute to the journal.
Media: Online - full text.
—**CCC.**
Published by: International Reading Association, Inc., 800 Barksdale Rd, Newark, DE 19714-8139. TEL 302-731-1600, 800-336-7323, FAX 302-368-2449, journals@reading.org, http://www.readingonline.org, http://www.reading.org.

370.15 USA ISSN 0270-2711
BF456.R2 CODEN: RRPSDW
➤ **READING PSYCHOLOGY**; an international quarterly. Text in English. 1979. 5/yr. GBP 262, USD 433 combined subscription to institutions print & online eds. (effective 2006). adv. bk.rev. bibl.; charts; stat. index. back issues avail.; reprint service avail. from PQC,PSC. **Document type:** *Journal, Academic/Scholarly.* **Description:** Publishes original manuscripts in the field of literacy, reading, and related psychology disciplines.
Related titles: Online - full text ed.: ISSN 1521-0685. GBP 249, USD 411 to institutions (effective 2006) (from EBSCO Publishing, Gale Group, IngentaConnect, O C L C Online Computer Library Center, Inc., Swets Information Services).
Indexed: AgeL, CDA, CIJE, CPE, EAA, ERA, ETA, FamI, L&LBA, MEA, MLA, MLA-IB, PsycInfo, PsycholAb, RHEA, SEA, SENA, SOMA, SOPODA, SWA, TEA, e-psyche.
—BLDSC (7301.260000), IE, Infotrieve, ingenta. **CCC.**
Published by: (University of North Texas, College of Education, Pupil Appraisal Center), Routledge (Subsidiary of: Taylor & Francis Ltd), 325 Chestnut St., Suite 800, Philadelphia, PA 19106. TEL 215-625-8900, 800-354-1420, FAX 215-625-8914, journals@routledge.com, http://www.tandf.co.uk/journals/titles/02702711.asp, http://www.routledge.com. Ed. William H Rupley. Circ: 275. **Subscr. addr. in Europe:** Taylor & Francis Ltd, Journals Customer Service, Rankine Rd, Basingstoke, Hants RG24 8PR, United Kingdom. TEL 44-1256-813000, FAX 44-1256-330245, enquiry@tandf.co.uk.

372.4 USA ISSN 0034-0553
LB1050 CODEN: RRQUA6
➤ **READING RESEARCH QUARTERLY.** Text in English; Summaries in French, German, Japanese, Spanish. 1965. q. USD 61 to individuals; USD 122 to institutions (effective 2005). adv. bk.rev. abstr.; charts; illus.; stat. Index. back issues avail.; reprint service avail. from PQC. **Document type:** *Magazine, Academic/Scholarly.* **Description:** Contains articles on current research in reading theory and practice, conduced with a variety of methodologies.
Related titles: Microform ed.: (from PQC); Online - full text ed.: (from EBSCO Publishing, Florida Center for Library Automation, Gale Group, H.W. Wilson, JSTOR (Web-based Journal Archive), Northern Light Technology, Inc.).
Indexed: ABIn, ASCA, AgeL, ArtHuCI, CDA, CIJE, CPE, ChLitAb, CommAb, CurCont, EAA, ECER, ERA, ETA, EduInd, FamI, HECAB, L&LBA, LT&LA, MEA, MEA&I, MLA-IB, PCI, PsycInfo, PsycholAb, RHEA, SEA, SENA, SFSA, SOMA, SOPODA, SSCI, TEA, e-psyche.
—BLDSC (7301.310000), IDS, IE, Infotrieve, ingenta. **CCC.**
Published by: International Reading Association, Inc., 800 Barksdale Rd, Newark, DE 19714-8139. TEL 302-731-1600, FAX 302-368-2449, journals@reading.org, http://www.reading.org/publications/journals/RRQ/. Eds. David Reinking, Donna E. Alvermann. R&P Janet Parrack. Circ: 13,000 (paid).

372.4 USA ISSN 0034-0561
LB1573 CODEN: REDTAH
➤ **THE READING TEACHER**; a journal of the International Reading Association. Text in English. 1948. 8/yr. (Sep.-May; except Dec.-Jan. combined). USD 61 to individuals print & online eds.; USD 122 to institutions (effective 2005). adv. bk.rev. charts; illus. index. reprint service avail. from PQC. **Document type:** *Journal, Academic/Scholarly.* **Description:** Discusses important issues and research on the teaching of reading and other language arts (whether whole language or phonics), primarily at the pre- and primary-school levels.
Related titles: Microform ed.: (from PQC); Online - full text ed.: (from EBSCO Publishing, Florida Center for Library Automation, Gale Group, H.W. Wilson, Northern Light Technology, Inc., O C L C Online Computer Library Center, Inc., ProQuest Information & Learning).
Indexed: ABIn, ASCA, AcaI, AgeL, ArtHuCI, BRI, CBRI, CIJE, CPE, ChLitAb, ChPerI, CurCont, ECER, ETA, EduInd, FamI, JHMA, L&LBA, MEA, MEA&I, MLA-IB, MRD, PsycholAb, RHEA, RILM, SEA, SENA, SOMA, SOPODA, SSCI, TEA.
—BLDSC (7301.400000), IDS, IE, Infotrieve, ingenta. **CCC.**
Published by: International Reading Association, Inc., 800 Barksdale Rd, Newark, DE 19714-8139. TEL 800-336-7323, journals@reading.org, http://www.reading.org. Eds. D Ray Reutzel, Judith Mitchell. R&P Janet Parrack. Adv. contact Linda Hunter. Circ: 55,000 (paid).

372.4 USA
READING TODAY; your source for news about the reading profession. Text in English. 1983. bi-m. USD 18 in developing nations; USD 36 elsewhere (effective 2005). adv. bk.rev. illus. back issues avail.; reprint service avail. from PQC. **Document type:** *Newspaper, Trade.* **Description:** News and features about the reading profession and information for educators and parents about association activities, publications and meetings.
Formerly: Reading (0737-4208); Which was formed by the merger of (1977-1983): Reading Today (0149-1490); (1972-1983): Reading Today International (0149-1482)
Related titles: Online - full text ed.: (from EBSCO Publishing, Gale Group, Northern Light Technology, Inc., O C L C Online Computer Library Center, Inc., ProQuest Information & Learning).
Indexed: BRI, ChLitAb, JHMA, L&LBA, SOPODA.
—BLDSC (7301.445000), IE. **CCC.**
Published by: International Reading Association, Inc., 800 Barksdale Rd, Newark, DE 19714-8139. jmicklos@reading.org, journals@reading.org, http://www.reading.org/publications/rty/. Ed. John Micklos. Pub. Joan Irwin. Adv. contact Linda Hunter. Circ: 80,000 (paid).

371.82 USA ISSN 0270-1448
LC4091
➤ **READINGS ON EQUAL EDUCATION.** Text in English. 1970. a. USD 79.50 (effective 2005). bk.rev. charts. index. 350 p./no.; back issues avail. **Document type:** *Academic/Scholarly.* **Description:** Contains articles on education policy toward minorities in the United States.
Formerly: Educating the Disadvantaged (0531-8327)
Published by: A M S Press, Inc., 63 Flushing Ave., # 417, Brooklyn, NY 11205-1005. TEL 212-777-4700, FAX 212-995-5413, amserve@earthlink.net. Eds. Charles Teddlie, Elizabeth A Kemper.

370 GBR ISSN 1476-2374
RECENT ADVANCES IN CONDUCTIVE EDUCATION. Text in English. 2001 (Dec.). s-a. GBP 12 in Europe; GBP 16 elsewhere (effective 2005). **Document type:** *Journal, Academic/Scholarly.* **Description:** Concentrates on developments in the actual practice of conductive education.
—BLDSC (7303.814150).
Published by: Foundation for Conductive Education, Cannon Hill House, Russell Rd, Moseley, Birmingham, B13 8RD, United Kingdom. TEL 44-121-4491569, FAX 44-121-4491611, foundation@conductive-education.org.uk, http://www.conductive-education.org.uk/.

RECHT DER JUGEND UND DES BILDUNGSWESENS; Zeitschrift fuer Schule, Berufsbildung und Jugenderziehung. see *CHILDREN AND YOUTH—About*

371.01 SDN
REGIONAL EDUCATIONAL BUILDING INSTITUTE FOR AFRICA. LETTER✶ **/INSTITUT REGIONAL POUR LES CONSTRUCTIONS SCOLAIRES EN AFRIQUE. LETTRE.** Text in English. q. illus.
Published by: Regional Educational Building Institute of Africa, Section de Documentation, P O Box 1720, Khartoum, Sudan.

REGISTER OF MUSICIANS IN EDUCATION. see *MUSIC*

REGISTER OF PROFESSIONAL PRIVATE MUSIC TEACHERS. see *MUSIC*

371.07 FRA ISSN 0222-4259
RELIGIEUSES EN MISSION EDUCATIVE. Text in French. 1968. 4/yr. adv.
Formerly (until 1978): Religieuses Enseignantes (0222-4267)
Address: 10 bis rue Jean Bart, Paris, 75006, France. Ed. S Denizet.

371.07 USA ISSN 1550-7394
LC405
➤ **RELIGION & EDUCATION.** Text in English. 1974. 2/yr. USD 25 (effective 2005). adv. bk.rev. back issues avail. **Document type:** *Journal, Academic/Scholarly.* **Description:** Aims to provide readers with an overview of issues and curriculum related to the academic study of religion.
Former titles (until 1995): Religion & Public Education (1056-7224); (until 1984): National Council on Religion and Public Education. Bulletin (1550-7386)
Indexed: CIJE, FamI, RI-1, RI-2, RILM.
Address: University of Northern Iowa, 508 Schindler Education Center, Cedar Falls, IA 50614-0604. TEL 319-273-2605, FAX 319-273-5175, jrae@uni.edu, http://www.uni.edu/jrae. Ed. Michael D Waggoner.

E

371.07   DEU   ISSN 0722-9151
RELIGION HEUTE. Text in German. 1982. q. EUR 53.20; EUR 10 newsstand/cover (effective 2005). adv. bk.rev. **Document type:** *Journal, Academic/Scholarly.*
Formed by the merger of (1970-1982): Informationen zum Religions-Unterricht (0342-5398); (1970-1982): Z R - Zeitschrift fuer Religionspaedagogik (0344-1962); Which was formerly (until 1977): Zeitschrift fuer Religions-Paedagogik (0344-1954)
Indexed: DIP, IBR, IBZ.
Published by: Erhard Friedrich Verlag GmbH, Im Brande 17, Seelze, 30926, Germany. TEL 49-511-400040, FAX 49-511-40004170, info@friedrich-verlag.de, http://www.friedrich-verlag.de/index.cfm?65E3A9AA576349209BA60EB3EAEC7314. adv.: color page EUR 1,200, B&W page EUR 800. Circ: 4,000 (paid and controlled).

371.07   USA
RELIGION IN AMERICA (PRINCETON). Text in English. 1967. biennial. USD 40. back issues avail.
Published by: Princeton Religion Research Center, 502 Carnegie Ctr., Ste. 300, Princeton, NJ 08540-6289, TEL 609-921-8112, FAX 609-924-0228, marie-swirsky@gallup.com, http://www.prrc.com.

371.07   SWE   ISSN 0347-2159
RELIGION & LIVSFRAAGOR (ROL). Key Title: R o L. Religion och Livsfraagor. Text in Swedish. 1967. 4/yr. SEK 200 (effective 2003). adv. **Document type:** *Bulletin.* **Description:** Presents a guide to schools and colleges from a religious perspective.
Former titles (until 1977): F L R - Aktuellt (0345-3391); (until 1970): Meddelande fraan Foereningen Laerare i Religionskunskap (0282-3950)
Published by: Foereningen Laerare i Religionskunskap (FLR), Djupadavaegen 18, Esloev, 24136, Sweden. TEL 46-4-13555544, rune.larsson@teol.lu.se, http://www.gamdat.se/flr/flr4.htm. Ed. Gunnar Iselau. Circ: 825.

RELIGIONE E SCUOLA; rivista dell'insegnante di religione. see *RELIGIONS AND THEOLOGY—Roman Catholic*

RELIGIONSPAEDAGOGIK IN EINER MULTIKULTURELLEN GESELLSCHAFT. see *RELIGIONS AND THEOLOGY*

RELIGIONSPAEDAGOGISCHE BEITRAEGE. see *RELIGIONS AND THEOLOGY—Roman Catholic*

RELIGIONSUNTERRICHT AN HOEHEREN SCHULEN. see *RELIGIONS AND THEOLOGY—Roman Catholic*

370.951   CHN   ISSN 0448-9365
LA1130
RENMIN JIAOYU/PEOPLE'S EDUCATION. Text in Chinese. 1950. m. CNY 4.20 newsstand/cover (effective 1999). adv. back issues avail. **Description:** Covers all aspects of education in China.
Related titles: Diskette ed.; Online - full text ed.: (from East View Information Services).
Published by: (Guojia Jiaoyu Weiyuanhui/State Education Commission), China Education Press Agency, No10 Wenhuiyuan North Rd, Haidian District, China. TEL 86-010-62236797, FAX 86-010-62242984, pej@263.net. Pub. Fu Guoliang. Adv. contact Xu Mei. B&W page CNY 10,000, color page CNY 30,000; trim 260 x 185. Circ: 210,000 (paid).

370 360   USA
REPORTS MAGAZINE. Text in English. irreg., latest vol.32, 1997. USD 7.50 to individuals; USD 10 to institutions (effective 2001). back issues avail. **Document type:** *Academic/Scholarly.* **Description:** Promotes self-sufficiency among community organizations throughout the world.
Published by: World Education, Inc., 44 Farnsworth St, Boston, MA 02210. wei@worlded.org. R&P Peta Gordon.

REPUBLICKI ZAVOD ZA UNAPREDJIVANJE VASPITANJA I OBRAZOVANJA. BIBLIOGRAFIJA; lista bibliografskih podataka novonabavljenih knjiga i clanaka iz domace i inostrane pedagoske literature. see *EDUCATION—Abstracting, Bibliographies, Statistics*

371   USA   ISSN 1046-3364
➤ RESEARCH AND TEACHING IN DEVELOPMENTAL EDUCATION. Short title: R T D E. Text in English. 1984. s-a. (in 1 vol., 2 nos./vol.). USD 35 membership (effective 2005). adv. bk.rev.; software rev.; Website rev. 100 p./no.; back issues avail. **Document type:** *Journal, Academic/Scholarly.* **Description:** Interdisciplinary journal which focuses on theoretically based articles on pedagogy, evaluation, program design and delivery in the areas of mathematics, writing and reading, developmental education.
Related titles: Online - full text ed.: (from ProQuest Information & Learning).
Indexed: CIJE, CPE, ERA, ETA, MLA-IB, SENA, TEA.
—BLDSC (7716.075000), IE, ingenta.
Published by: New York College Learning Skills Association, Finger Lakes Community College, 4355 Lake Shore Dr, Canandaigua, NY 14424. TEL 585-394-3500, FAX 585-394-5005, http://www.rit.edu/~jwsldc/NYCLSA/publications/rtde/issue_contents.shtml. Ed., R&P, Adv. contact Patricia A Malinowski. Circ: 800.

➤ RESEARCH IN DANCE EDUCATION. see *DANCE*

➤ RESEARCH IN DRAMA EDUCATION. see *THEATER*

370   GBR
RESEARCH IN EDUCATION (EDINBURGH). Text in English. 1968. s-a. back issues avail. **Document type:** *Journal, Academic/Scholarly.* **Description:** Contains short feature articles, listings of new research projects and publications, and news from across Scotland.
Former titles: S C R E Newsletter (0951-1369); (until 1983): Research in Education (0486-493X)
Related titles: Online - full content ed.
Published by: Scottish Council for Research in Education, 15 St John St, Edinburgh, EH8 8JR, United Kingdom. TEL 44-131-5572944, FAX 44-131-5569454, scre@scre.ac.uk, http://www.scre.ac.uk/Newsletters.html. Ed. Jon Lewin.

370.72   GBR   ISSN 0034-5237
LB1028.A1
RESEARCH IN EDUCATION (MANCHESTER). Text in English. 1969. s-a. GBP 21, EUR 36, USD 40 to individuals; GBP 90, EUR 148, USD 168 to institutions includes Online access (effective 2005). adv. back issues avail.; reprints avail. **Document type:** *Journal, Academic/Scholarly.* **Description:** Sociology and psychology of education, with emphasis on current practical issues in teaching.
Related titles: Online - full text ed.: (from EBSCO Publishing, Northern Light Technology, Inc., ProQuest Information & Learning, Swets Information Services).
Indexed: ABIn, BrEdI, CPE, ChLitAb, CurCont, EI, ERA, ETA, EduInd, HECAB, IBSS, L&LBA, LT&LA, MEA, PCI, PsycholAb, RHEA, SEA, SENA, SOMA, SOPODA, SSA, SSCI, SWA, SociolAb, TEA.
—BLDSC (7738.930000), IE, ingenta. **CCC.**
Published by: Manchester University Press, Oxford Rd, Manchester, Lancs M13 9NR, United Kingdom. TEL 44-161-2752310, FAX 44-161-2743346, mup@man.ac.uk, http://www.manchesteruniversitypress.co.uk/information_areas/journals/res_in_ed/Res_in_Ed.htm. Eds. David Hustler, Hilary Constable. Pub. David Rodgers. Circ: 700.

370.1   AUS
RESEARCH IN MATHEMATICS EDUCATION IN AUSTRALASIA. Text in English. quadrennial. AUD 40 to non-members & institutions; AUD 25 to members (effective 2003). **Document type:** *Academic/Scholarly.*
Published by: M E R G A, c/o Helen Chick, MERGA VP Membership, Dept Science and Mathematics Education, University of Melbourne, Melbourne, VIC 3010, Australia. TEL 61-3-83448324, FAX 61-3-83448739, h.chick@unimelb.edu.au, http://www.deakin.edu.au/education/numeracy_and_merino/merga/homepage.html.

370.72   GBR   ISSN 0263-5143
➤ RESEARCH IN SCIENCE & TECHNOLOGICAL EDUCATION. Text in English. 1983. s-a. GBP 481, USD 941 combined subscription to institutions print & online eds. (effective 2006). adv. illus.; stat. index. back issues avail.; reprint service avail. from PSC. **Document type:** *Journal, Academic/Scholarly.* **Description:** Publishes original research from throughout the world dealing with science education and/or technological education.
Related titles: Microfiche ed.; Online - full text ed.: ISSN 1470-1138. GBP 457, USD 894 to institutions (effective 2006) (from EBSCO Publishing, Gale Group, IngentaConnect, Northern Light Technology, Inc., O C L C Online Computer Library Center, Inc., ProQuest Information & Learning, Swets Information Services).
Indexed: BrEdI, CIJE, CPE, ERA, ETA, EngInd, MEA, PsycInfo, PsycholAb, RASB, RHEA, SEA, SENA, SOMA, SWA, TEA, WBA, WMB, e-psyche.
—BLDSC (7769.692500), CISTI, IE, Infotrieve, ingenta. **CCC.**
Published by: Routledge (Subsidiary of: Taylor & Francis Group), 4 Park Sq, Milton Park, Abingdon, Oxon OX14 4RN, United Kingdom. TEL 44-1235-828600, FAX 44-1235-829000, info@routledge.co.uk, http://www.tandf.co.uk/journals/titles/02635143.asp, http://www.routledge.co.uk. Ed. Chris Botton.
Subscr. to: Taylor & Francis Ltd, Journals Customer Service, Rankine Rd, Basingstoke, Hants RG24 8PR, United Kingdom. TEL 44-1256-813000, FAX 44-1256-330245.

370.72 500   NLD   ISSN 0157-244X
➤ RESEARCH IN SCIENCE EDUCATION. Text in English. 1971. q. EUR 184, USD 184, GBP 115 combined subscription to institutions print & online eds. (effective 2005). adv. reprint service avail. from PSC. **Document type:** *Journal, Academic/Scholarly.* **Description:** Publishes internationally refereed and edited versions of research papers from Australasian and international researches.
Related titles: Online - full text ed.: ISSN 1573-1898 (from EBSCO Publishing, Gale Group, IngentaConnect, O C L C Online Computer Library Center, Inc., Springer LINK, Swets Information Services).
Indexed: AEI, BibLing, CIJE, CPE, CurCont, ERA, SSCI.
—BLDSC (7769.693000), IE, Infotrieve, ingenta. **CCC.**

Published by: (Australasian Science Education Research Association AUS), Springer-Verlag Dordrecht (Subsidiary of: Springer Science+Business Media), Van Godewijckstraat 30, Dordrecht, 3311 GX, Netherlands. TEL 31-78-6576050, FAX 31-78-6576474, http://springerlink.metapress.com/openurl.asp?genre=journal&issn=0157-244x, http://www.springeronline.com. Ed. Campbell McRobbie. Circ: 300 (paid).

306.43   USA   ISSN 1479-3539
LC189.8
RESEARCH IN SOCIOLOGY OF EDUCATION. Text in English. 1979. a., latest vol.14, 2003. price varies. back issues avail. **Document type:** *Monographic series, Academic/Scholarly.* **Description:** Offers original empirical papers, critical reviews, and commentaries, advancing our knowledge on pivotal topics related to schools, learning, and families.
Formerly (until vol.13, 2002): Research in Sociology of Education and Socialization (0197-5080)
Related titles: Online - full text ed.: (from ScienceDirect).
Indexed: SOPODA, SSA.
—BLDSC (7770.710000). **CCC.**
Published by: J A I Press Inc. (Subsidiary of: Elsevier Science & Technology), 360 Park Ave S, New York, NY 10010-1710. TEL 212-989-5800, FAX 212-633-3990, usinfo-f@elsevier.com, http://www.elsevier.com/wps/find/bookdescription.cws_home/BS_RSES/description#description. Eds. B Fuller, E Hannum.

370.72   USA   ISSN 1085-5300
LB1028
➤ RESEARCH IN THE SCHOOLS. Text in English. 1994. s-a. USD 25 domestic to individuals; USD 50 foreign to individuals; USD 30 domestic to institutions; USD 55 foreign to institutions (effective 2005). **Document type:** *Journal, Academic/Scholarly.* **Description:** Covers varies issues on education.
Indexed: CIJE, PsycInfo, PsycholAb.
—BLDSC (7769.691650).
Published by: Mid-South Educational Research Association, c/o Larry Daniel, College of Education and Human Services, University of North Florida, 4567 St. Johns Bluff Road, South, Jacksonville, FL 32224-2676. TEL 904-620-2520, http://www.msstate.edu/org/msera/rits.htm. Ed. Larry Daniel.

370   CAN   ISSN 1203-3308
RESEARCH MATTERS. Text in English. 1996. 3/yr. **Document type:** *Corporate.*
Related titles: Online - full content ed.
Published by: Memorial University of Newfoundland, Division of University Relations for the Office of the Vice-President, Ground Fl, Spencer Hall, St. John's, NF A1B 3X5, Canada. http://www.mun.ca/research/rmatters/menu.html. Ed. Deborah Inkpen.

370   USA   ISSN 1531-2828
LB1065
RESEARCH ON SOCIOCULTURAL INFLUENCES ON MOTIVATION AND LEARNING. Text in English. 2001. a. USD 73.25 per vol. hard cover; USD 34.95 per vol. paperback (effective 2004).
Published by: Information Age Publishing, Inc., 411 W Putnam Ave, Ste 205, PO Box 4967, Greenwich, CT 06831. TEL 203-661-7602, FAX 203-661-7952, order@infoagepub.com, http://www.infoagepub.com/products/product1/McInerneycombo.pdf. Eds. Dennis M McInerney, Shawn Van Etten.

370.72   GBR   ISSN 0267-1522
RESEARCH PAPERS IN EDUCATION. Text in English. 1986. q. GBP 438, USD 724 combined subscription to institutions print & online eds. (effective 2006). adv. bk.rev. illus.; stat. index, cum.index. reprint service avail. from PSC. **Document type:** *Journal, Academic/Scholarly.* **Description:** Provides authoritative research reports on educational policy and practice.
Related titles: Microfiche ed.; Online - full text ed.: ISSN 1470-1146. GBP 416, USD 688 to institutions (effective 2006) (from EBSCO Publishing, Gale Group, IngentaConnect, O C L C Online Computer Library Center, Inc., Swets Information Services).
Indexed: BrEdI, CIJE, CPE, ERA, ETA, IBSS, MEA, RHEA, SEA, SENA, SOMA, SWA, TEA.
—BLDSC (7755.034960), IE, Infotrieve, ingenta. **CCC.**
Published by: (National Foundation for Educational Research), Routledge (Subsidiary of: Taylor & Francis Group), 4 Park Sq, Milton Park, Abingdon, Oxon OX14 4RN, United Kingdom. TEL 44-1235-828600, FAX 44-1235-829000, info@routledge.co.uk, http://www.tandf.co.uk/journals/titles/02671522.asp, http://www.routledge.co.uk. Eds. Peter Preece, Ted Wragg. R&P Sally Sweet. adv.: page GBP 150; trim 200 x 126. **Subscr. to:** Taylor & Francis Ltd, Journals Customer Service, Rankine Rd, Basingstoke, Hants RG24 8PR, United Kingdom. TEL 44-1256-813000, FAX 44-1256-330245, enquiry@tandf.co.uk.

RESONANCE - JOURNAL OF SCIENCE EDUCATION. see *SCIENCES: COMPREHENSIVE WORKS*

615 649   AUS   ISSN 1031-3796
RESOURCE. Text in English. 1988. q. AUD 21 domestic; AUD 36.75 foreign. **Document type:** *Newsletter.*

E

Published by: F K A Multicultural Resource Centre, Level 1, 9-11 Stewart St, Richmond, VIC 3121, Australia. TEL 61-3-94284471, FAX 61-3-94299252.

370 USA ISSN 0147-7501
RESOURCES FOR CHANGE. Text in English. 1976. a.
Published by: (Fund for the Improvement of Postsecondary Education), U.S. Government Printing Office, 732 N Capitol St NW, Washington, DC 20401. TEL 888-293-6498, FAX 202-512-1262, gpoaccess@gpo.gov, http://www.gpo.gov.

RESOURCES IN EDUCATION. see *EDUCATION—Abstracting, Bibliographies, Statistics*

RESOURCES IN EDUCATION ANNUAL CUMULATION. see *EDUCATION—Abstracting, Bibliographies, Statistics*

RESUMENES ANALITICOS EN EDUCACION. see *EDUCATION—Abstracting, Bibliographies, Statistics*

RETHINKING CHILDHOOD. see *CHILDREN AND YOUTH—About*

371.0091732 USA ISSN 0895-6855
LA390
RETHINKING SCHOOLS; an urban educational journal. Text in English. 1987. 4/yr. (during school yr.). USD 15 domestic; USD 20 in Canada; USD 25 elsewhere (effective 2004). adv. bk.rev. back issues avail. **Document type:** *Newspaper, Trade.* **Description:** Independent, nonprofit, educational journal published by classroom teachers and educators. Grassroots advocate for educational reform in theory and practice.
Indexed: AltPI, SRRA.
—CCC.
Published by: Rethinking Schools Limited, 1001 E Keefe Ave, Milwaukee, WI 53212. TEL 414-694-9646, FAX 414-964-7220, rsbusiness@aol.com, http://www.rethinkingschools.org. Ed. Catherine Capellaro. R&P Stacie Williams. Adv. contact Michael Trokan TEL 414-964-9646. Circ: 8,000 (paid); 34,000 (controlled).

REVIEW OF ALLIED HEALTH EDUCATION. see *MEDICAL SCIENCES*

370.954 IND
REVIEW OF EDUCATION IN INDIA. Text in English. 1950. a.
Published by: Ministry of Education and Social Welfare, Department of Education, Shastri Bhavan, New Delhi, 110 001, India. **Subscr. to:** Assistant Educational Adviser (Publications), Ministry of Human Resource Development, Department of Education, Ex. AFO Hutments, Dr. Rajendra Prasad Rd., New Delhi 110 001, India.

THE REVIEW OF EDUCATION - PEDAGOGY - CULTURAL STUDIES. see *EDUCATION—Abstracting, Bibliographies, Statistics*

370.72 USA ISSN 0034-6543
L11 CODEN: REDRAB
➤ **REVIEW OF EDUCATIONAL RESEARCH.** Text in English. 1931. q. USD 48 to individuals; USD 140 to institutions (effective 2005). adv. bibl.; illus. index. reprint service avail. from PQC. **Document type:** *Journal, Academic/Scholarly.* **Description:** Contains integrative reviews and interpretations of the research literature on substantive and methodological issues.
Related titles: Microform ed.: (from PMC, PQC); Online - full text ed.: (from H.W. Wilson, JSTOR (Web-based Journal Archive), Northern Light Technology, Inc., O C L C Online Computer Library Center, Inc., ProQuest Information & Learning).
Indexed: ABIn, AMHA, ASCA, CDA, CIJE, CIS, CPE, ChPerl, CommAb, CurCont, DIP, EAA, ECER, ERA, ETA, EduInd, FamI, HEA, HECAB, IBR, IBZ, L&LBA, LT&LA, MEA, MEA&I, PCI, PsycInfo, PsycholAb, RASB, RHEA, SEA, SENA, SOMA, SOPODA, SSA, SSCI, SociolAb, TEA, e-psyche.
—BLDSC (7790.300000), IDS, IE, Infotrieve, ingenta. **CCC.**
Published by: American Educational Research Association, 1230 17th St, N W, Washington, DC 20036-3078. TEL 202-223-9485, FAX 202-775-1824, margaret.lecompte@colorado.edu, http://aera.net/pubs/rer/. Ed. Margaret LeCompte TEL 303-492-7951. Circ: 18,400.

370.72 USA ISSN 0091-732X
LB1028
➤ **REVIEW OF RESEARCH IN EDUCATION.** Text in English. 1973. a. USD 48 to individuals non-members; USD 67 to institutions non-members; USD 20 to members (effective 2005). adv. index. reprints avail. **Document type:** *Academic/Scholarly.* **Description:** Surveys research, development, and theory in education through critical, synthesizing essays.
Related titles: Online - full text ed.: (from JSTOR (Web-based Journal Archive)).
Indexed: ASCA, SSCI.
—BLDSC (7794.530000), IDS, IE, Infotrieve, ingenta. **CCC.**
Published by: American Educational Research Association, 1230 17th St, N W, Washington, DC 20036-3078. TEL 202-223-9485, FAX 202-775-1824, http://www.aera.net/pubs/rre/, http://aera.net. Ed. Bill Ayers TEL 517-355-3486. Circ: 8,000.

370 SCG ISSN 0351-0697
REVIJA OBRAZOVANJA. Text in Serbo-Croatian; Summaries in English, French, Russian. 1957-1971; resumed 19??. 6/yr. YUN 10,000, USD 50. bk.rev. abstr.; bibl.; charts. index.
Formerly (until 1977): Revija Skolstva i Prosvetna Dokumentacija (0034-6896)
Published by: Republicki Zavod za Unapredjivanje Vaspitanja i Obrazovanja, Draze Pavlovica 15, Belgrade, 11124. TEL 765-366. Ed. Cedo Nedeljkovic. Circ: 1,000.

370.15 ARG
REVISTA ARGENTINA DE PSICOPEDAGOGIA. Text in Portuguese, Spanish; Abstracts in English. 1981. q. USD 30 (effective 2000). adv. bk.rev. abstr.; bibl. **Document type:** *Academic/Scholarly.*
Supersedes (1975-1981): Revista de Psicopedagogia
Published by: Fundacion Suzuki, Charlone, 1689, San Miguel, Buenos Aires 1663, Argentina. TEL 54-11-664-0771, FAX 54-11-667-1476. Ed. Elizabeth J Calvo de Suzuki. Circ: 500.

370 BRA ISSN 0034-7183
L45
➤ **REVISTA BRASILEIRA DE ESTUDOS PEDAGOGICOS.** Short title: R B E P. Text in Portuguese; Summaries in English, French, Portuguese, Spanish. 1944-1980; resumed 1983. 3/yr. free. bk.rev. abstr.; bibl.; stat. cum.index: 1944-1984. **Document type:** *Academic/Scholarly.* **Description:** Covers research, study and debates of various topics in education.
Related titles: Online - full text ed.
Indexed: HAPI, L&LBA, SSA.
Published by: Instituto Nacional de Estudos e Pesquisas Educacionais, Centro de Informacoes e Biblioteca em Educacao (C I B E C)/Center of Information and Library in Education, MEC-Esplanada dos Ministerios, Bloco L, Anexos I e II, 4 Andar, sala 416, CEP 70047-900, Brasilia, DF, Brazil. TEL 55-61-4108562, FAX 55-61-2235137, cibec@inep.gov.br, http://www.inep.gov.br/cibec. Ed. Jair Santana Moraes. Circ: 2,500.

370.72 ESP ISSN 0210-9581
REVISTA DE CIENCIAS DE LA EDUCACION. Text in Spanish. 1888. q. EUR 33.08 domestic; EUR 65.25 foreign (effective 2002).
Formerly (until 1970): Revista Calasancia (0484-6583)
Related titles: Online - full text ed.
—CINDOC.
Published by: Instituto Calasanz de Ciencias de la Educacion, C. Eraso, 3, Madrid, 28028, Spain. TEL 34-91-7257200, FAX 34-91-3611052, info@ciberaula.net, http://www.icceciberaula.net/. Ed. Pedro Manuel Alonso Maranon.

371.0712 BRA ISSN 0104-0537
LC505.B7
REVISTA DE EDUCACAO A E C. Text in Portuguese. 1945. q. USD 8. bk.rev.
Formerly (until 1971): Associacao de Educacao Catolica do Brasil. Boletim
Published by: Associacao de Educacao Catolica do Brasil, SBN Quadra 1, Bloco H, loja 40, Brasilia, DF 70040, Brazil. TEL 061-223-2947. Ed. Jose Paulo II. Circ: 6,000.

370 CRI ISSN 0379-7082
L45 CODEN: ERURFF
REVISTA DE EDUCACION. Text in Spanish. 1977. s-a. CRC 1,000 domestic; USD 30 foreign (effective 2000). adv. **Document type:** *Academic/Scholarly.*
Related titles: Online - full text ed.: (from Gale Group).
Indexed: DIP, HAPI, IBR, IBZ, SOPODA, SociolAb.
Published by: Editorial de la Universidad de Costa Rica, Apdo. 75-2060, Ciudad Universitaria Rodrigo Facio Brenes, San Pedro de Montes de Oca, San Jose, 2050, Costa Rica. TEL 506-207-4000, FAX 506-207-5535, cmmoreno@cariari.ucr.ac.cr, http://www.ucr.ac.cr/. Ed. Marta Rojas. R&P Mario Murillo TEL 506-2075003. Adv. contact Cristina Moreno Murillo.

370 ESP ISSN 0034-8082
REVISTA DE EDUCACION (MADRID). Text in Spanish. 1967 (vol.66). 3/yr. EUR 27.86 domestic; EUR 36.87 foreign (effective 2002). bk.rev. abstr.
—CINDOC, IE, Infotrieve.
Published by: (Spain. Secretaria General Tecnica), Ministerio de Educacion, Cultura y Deporte, Centro de Publicaciones, c/o Ciudad Universitaria, S/N, Madrid, 28040, Spain. FAX 34-91-4539884.

370 ARG ISSN 0325-2736
L45
REVISTA DE EDUCACION Y CULTURA✶. Text in Spanish. 1858; N.S. 1956. q. free to schools, institutions & libraries. bk.rev. illus. index. **Document type:** *Government.*
Supersedes (in 197?): Revista de Educacion (0034-8074)
Published by: Ministerio de Educacion, Pizzurno 935, Buenos Aires, 1020, Argentina. TEL 54-11-41291000, info@me.gov.ar, http://www.me.gov.ar/.

370 VEN ISSN 0798-9792
REVISTA DE PEDAGOGIA. Text in Spanish. 1976. irreg.
Related titles: Online - full text ed.: free (effective 2005).
Published by: Universidad Central de Venezuela, Facultad de Humanidades y Educacion, Edificio Trasbordo, Planta Baja, Calle Minerva, Urb los Chaguaramos, Caracas, 1051, Venezuela.

370 ROM ISSN 0034-8678
L56
REVISTA DE PEDAGOGIE. Text in Romanian; Summaries in English, French, Russian. 1952. m. adv. bk.rev. abstr.; charts; illus.; stat. index.
Related titles: Supplement(s): Technologii Educationale Moderne. ISSN 1221-1680. 1992; Invatamintul Primar. ISSN 1220-6431. 1991.
Indexed: CDA, PsycholAb, RASB.
Published by: Institutul de Stiinte ale Educatiei/Institute of Educational Sciences, 37 Stirbei-Voda Str, Bucharest, 70732, Romania. Ed. Anton Vasilescu. Circ: 33,000. **Subscr. to:** ILEXIM, Str. 13 Decembrie 3, PO Box 136-137, Bucharest 70116, Romania.

370.15 ESP ISSN 1136-1034
REVISTA DE PSICODIDACTICA. Text in Spanish. 1996. s-a. back issues avail.
Related titles: Online - full text ed.
—CINDOC.
Published by: Universidad del Pais Vasco, Escuela Universitaria de Magisterio, C. Juan Ibanez de Sto. Domingo, 1, Victoria - Gasteiz, 01006, Spain. TEL 34-945-183281, FAX 34-945-142798, http://www.vc.ehu.es/deppe/revista.html. Ed. Alfredo Goni Grandmontagne.

370 CHL ISSN 0259-5400
LB1028.3
REVISTA DE TECNOLOGIA EDUCATIVA. Text in Spanish. 1978. q. free. back issues avail. **Document type:** *Academic/Scholarly.*
Published by: (Organization of American States NLD), Ministerio de Educacion, Centro de Perfeccionamiento Experimentacion e Investigaciones Pedagogica, Camino Nido de Aguilas s/n, Apartado 16162, Santiago de Chile, Santiago, Chile. pmet@cpeip.mic.cl. Ed. Maria Eugenia Nordenflycht. Circ: 2,000.

REVISTA DE TEORIA Y DIDACTICA DE LAS CIENCIAS SOCIALES. see *SOCIAL SCIENCES: COMPREHENSIVE WORKS*

370 COL ISSN 0121-7593
➤ **REVISTA EDUCACION Y PEDAGOGIA.** Text in Spanish; Summaries in English, French, Spanish. 1989. 3/yr. COP 90,000 domestic (effective 2003). bk.rev. abstr.; charts. back issues avail. **Document type:** *Academic/Scholarly.* **Description:** Presents research or theoretical reflection on pedagogy, didactics, teaching, and the history of education.
Published by: Universidad de Antioquia, Calle 67, 53-108, Apartado Aereo 1226, Medellin, Colombia. TEL 57-4-2630011, FAX 57-4-2638282, reveyp@ayura.udea.edu.co, comunicaciones@udea.edu.co, http://www.udea.edu.co. Ed. Jesus Alberto Echaverry Sanchez. Circ: 850 (paid); 150 (controlled).

370 150 ESP ISSN 1696-2095
LB1051
▼ ➤ **REVISTA ELECTRONICA DE INVESTIGACION EDUCATIVA Y PSICOPEDAGOGICA/ELECTRONIC JOURNAL OF RESEARCH IN EDUCATIONAL PSYCHOLOGY.** Text in Spanish, English. 2003. s-a. free (effective 2005). **Document type:** *Journal, Academic/Scholarly.*
Media: Online - full text.
Published by: Universidad de Almeria, Servicio de Publicaciones, Carretera Sacramento sn, La Canada de San Urbano, Almeria, Spain. TEL 34-950-015182, http://www.investigacion-psicopedagogica.org/revista, http://www.ual.es.

370 ESP ISSN 1137-8654
REVISTA ESPANOLA DE EDUCACION COMPARADA. Text in Spanish. 1995. a. EUR 12.02 (effective 2002).
—CINDOC.
Published by: Universidad Nacional de Educacion a Distancia, Bravo Murillo No. 38, Madrid, Spain. TEL 34-91-3986000, FAX 34-91-3986600, infouned@adm.uned.es, http://www.uned.es/.

370.15 ESP ISSN 1139-7853
REVISTA ESPANOLA DE ORIENTACION Y PSICOPEDAGOGIA. Text in Spanish. 1990. s-a. **Document type:** *Journal, Academic/Scholarly.*
Former titles (until 1998): Revista de Orientacion y Psicopedagogia (1136-4270); (until 1996): Revista de Orientacion Educativa y Vocacional (1130-2666)
Related titles: Online - full text ed.
—CINDOC.
Published by: Universidad Nacional de Educacion a Distancia, Bravo Murillo No. 38, Madrid, Spain. TEL 34-91-3986000, FAX 34-91-3986600, http://www.uned.es/aeop/revsta.html. Ed. Carlos Velasco Murviedo.

370 ESP ISSN 0034-9461
L41
REVISTA ESPANOLA DE PEDAGOGIA. Text in Spanish. 1943. q. adv. bk.rev. bibl.; charts; illus. cum.index. **Description:** Contains articles on all aspects of teaching.

E

Indexed: AmH&L, CPE, DIP, ERA, ETA, HistAb, IBR, IBZ, MEA, PCI, RHEA, RILM, SEA, SENA, SOMA, TEA.
—CINDOC, IE, Infotrieve. **CCC.**
Published by: Consejo Superior de Investigaciones Cientificas, Vitruvio, 8, Madrid, 28006, Spain. TEL 34-91-5932817, publ@csic.es, http://www.csic.es/publica. Ed. Jose A Ibanez Martin. Circ: 1,000.

370.15 ESP ISSN 1138-1663
REVISTA GALEGO-PORTUGUESA DE PSICOLOXIA E EDUCACION/GALICIAN-PORTUGUESE JOURNAL FOR THE STUDY OF PSYCHOLOGY AND EDUCATION. Text in Gallegan, Portuguese. 1997. a. EUR 18.03 (effective 2003). **Document type:** *Journal, Academic/Scholarly.*
—CINDOC.
Published by: (Universidade da Coruna, Departamento de Socioloxia e Ciencia Politica), Universidade da Coruna, Servicio de Publicacions, Campus de Elvina, Coruna, 15071, Spain. TEL 34-981-167000, FAX 34-981-167041, publica@six.udc.es, http://www.six.udc.es.

370 ESP ISSN 1022-6508
LA540
REVISTA IBEROAMERICANA DE EDUCACION/REVISTA IBERO - AMERICANA DE EDUCACAO. Text in Spanish, Portuguese. 1993. 3/yr. USD 30. **Description:** Contains research studies on educational subjects.
—CINDOC.
Published by: Organizacion de Estados IberoAmericanos para la Educacion la Ciencia y la Cultura, Bravo Murillo 38, Madrid, 28015, Spain. TEL 34-91-5944382, FAX 34-91-5943286, oeimad@oei.es, http://www.oei.es. Circ: 3,000.

370.72 MEX ISSN 1405-9525
REVISTA INTERNACIONAL DE ESTUDIOS EN EDUCACION. Text in Spanish. 2001. s-a. USD 35 (effective 2003).
Published by: Universidad de Montemorelos, Apdo. Postal 16, Montemorelos, Nuevo Leon, 67530, Mexico. TEL 52-826-2630900, FAX 52-826-2636185, http://www.um.edu.mx/revistaedu/. Ed. Victor Andres Korniejczuk.

370 MEX ISSN 0185-1284
L43
REVISTA LATINOAMERICANA DE ESTUDIOS EDUCATIVOS. Text in Spanish; Summaries in English, Spanish. 1971. q. MXP 150; USD 75 in Latin America; USD 85 elsewhere. adv. bk.rev. abstr.; charts; stat. index, cum.index. back issues avail.
Formerly (until 1979): Centro de Estudios Educativos. Revista (0045-6128)
Indexed: CurCont, HAPI, IBR, ILD, RHEA, SSCI.
—IE.
Published by: Centro de Estudios Educativos, A.C., Av. Revolucion 1291, Deleg. Alvaro Obregon, Mexico City, DF 01040, Mexico. TEL 525-5935977, FAX 525-6643039. Ed. Salvador Martinez Licon. Circ: 1,500.

370 ARG
REVISTA LATINOAMERICANA DE INNOVACIONES EDUCATIVAS. Text in Spanish. irreg. back issues avail.
Published by: Ministerio de Educacion, Pizzurno 935, Buenos Aires, 1020, Argentina. TEL 54-11-41291000, info@me.gov.ar, http://www.me.gov.ar/.

370 MEX ISSN 1405-6666
LA420
➤ **REVISTA MEXICANA DE INVESTIGACION EDUCATIVA/MEXICAN JOURNAL OF EDUCATIONAL RESEARCH.** Text in Spanish; Abstracts in English. 1996. 3/yr. USD 45 in Latin America to individuals; USD 65 elsewhere to individuals; USD 90 in Latin America to institutions; USD 130 elsewhere to institutions (effective 2003).
Related titles: Online - full content ed.: free (effective 2005); Online - full text ed.: (from EBSCO Publishing).
Indexed: HAPI.
Published by: Consejo Mexicano de Investigacion Educativa, A.C., San Lorenzo de Almagro #116, Col. Arboledas del Sur, Deleg., Tlalpan, 14376 D.F., Mexico. comie@servidor.unam.mx, http://www.comie.org.mx.

370 ARG ISSN 0328-6002
REVISTA NORDESTE. SERIE: DOCENCIA. Text in Spanish. 1960. s-a. **Document type:** *Journal, Academic/Scholarly.*
Supersedes in part (in 1995): Nordeste (0029-1242)
Published by: Universidad Nacional del Nordeste, Facultad de Humanidades, 25 de Mayo 868, Corrientes, 3400, Argentina. TEL 54-3783-425060, FAX 54-3783-425064, http://www.unne.edu.ar/.

370 ALB ISSN 0304-3509
REVISTA PEDAGOGJIKE. Text in Albanian. q. USD 19. bk.rev. bibl.
Indexed: RASB.
Published by: Institutit te Studimeve Pedagogjike/Pedagogical Research Institute, Rr Naim Frasheri 37, Tirana, Albania. TEL 355-42-23860, FAX 355-42-23860. Circ: 4,850.

370 CUB
REVISTA REFERATIVA DE EDUCACION. Text in Spanish. 1974-1975; resumed 1980. 3/yr. free. bk.rev. bibl.
Published by: Ministerio de Educacion, Direccion de Divulgacion y Publicaciones, Obispo 160, Havana, Cuba. Circ: 2,000.

370 CUB
REVISTA VARONA. Text in Spanish. s-a. USD 9 in the Americas; USD 11 in Europe; USD 12 elsewhere.
Published by: (Cuba. Ministerio de Educacion), Ediciones Cubanas, Obispo No. 527, Apdo. 605, Havana, Cuba.

REVISTA VIRTUAL MATEMATICA, EDUCACION E INTERNET. see *MATHEMATICS*

370 COD
REVUE AFRICAINE DES SCIENCES DE L'EDUCATION/ AFRICAN REVIEW OF EDUCATIONAL SCIENCES. Text and summaries in English, French. 1976. s-a. XAF 80, USD 35.
Published by: African Bureau of Educational Sciences, BP 14, Ksangani, Congo, Dem. Republic. Ed. A S Mungala. Circ: 150.

370 DZA ISSN 1111-0015
Q91.A47
REVUE DE L'INFORMATION SCIENTIFIQUE ET TECHNIQUE. Text in French. 1991. s-a. DZD 150 (effective 2004).
Related titles: Online - full text ed.: (from International Network for the Availability of Scientific Publications, African Journals Online).
Published by: Centre de Recherche sur l'Information Scientitique et Technique, 03 Rue des Freres Aissiou, Ben Aknoun, Algeria. TEL 213-21910209, rist@mail.cerist.dz, http://www.inasp.info/ajol/journals/rist/index.html, http://rist.cerist.dz/revue.asp. Ed. Dahmane Madjid.

378 DZA
REVUE DE L'ENSEIGNEMENT SUPERIEUR ET DE LA RECHERCHE SCIENTIFIQUE. Text in French. 1956. q. illus. index.
Formerly: Revue de l'Enseignement Superieur (0035-1407)
Address: 11 Chemin Mokhtar Doudou, Ben-aknoun, Algiers, Algeria. TEL 78-87-18. Circ: 8,000.

370.15 CAN ISSN 1706-4503
REVUE DE PSYCHOEDUCATION. Text in French; Summaries in English, French. 1964. s-a. CND 20 domestic to individuals; CND 35 domestic to institutions; CND 25 foreign to individuals; CND 45 foreign to institutions (effective 2004). bk.rev. bibl. **Document type:** *Journal, Academic/Scholarly.*
Former titles (until 2001): Revue Canadienne de Psycho-Education (0080-2492); (until 1969): Revue Canadienne d'Education Specialisee (0700-4613)
Indexed: PdeR, PsycInfo, PsycholAb, e-psyche.
—BLDSC (7944.562000), IE.
Published by: Universite de Montreal, Ecole de Psycho-Education, Succ Centre Ville, CP 6128, Montreal, PQ H3C 3J7, Canada. rpo@attcanada.ca, http://www.fas.umontreal.ca/psyced/RPO/, http://www.psyced.umontreal.ca. Ed. Serge Larivee. Circ: 600.

372 BEL ISSN 0035-1997
REVUE DES ECOLES. Text in French. 1880. bi-m. adv. bk.rev.; film rev.; play rev.; rec.rev. bibl.; charts. index.
Formerly (until 1966): Bulletin des Ecoles Primaires (0773-5898)
Published by: Imprimerie Artistic, Av de Maire 179, Tournai, 7500, Belgium. Ed. A Gille. Circ: 2,200.

370.193 FRA
LA REVUE DES PARENTS. Text in French. 1952. bi-m. EUR 12.96 to non-members (effective 2005). bk.rev. **Document type:** *Magazine, Consumer.* **Description:** Covers children's issues in education, health, sports, and many other areas.
Former titles (until 1988): Pour l'Enfant vers l'Homme (0223-0232); (until 1975): P E V H (0395-9090)
Published by: Federation des Conseils de Parents d'Eleves, 108 av. Ledru Rollin, Paris, Cedex 11 75544, France. TEL 33-1-43571616, FAX 33-1-43574078, fcpe@fcpe.asso.fr, http://www.fcpe.asso.fr. Ed. Francois Albertini. Circ: 300,000.

370.72 CAN ISSN 0318-479X
REVUE DES SCIENCES DE L'EDUCATION. Text in English. 1975. 3/yr.
Indexed: CEI.
Published by: Association Canadienne-Francaise pour l'Avancement des Sciences, 425 rue de la Gauchetiere E, Montreal, PQ H2L 2M7, Canada. TEL 514-849-0045, FAX 514-849-5558.

370 FRA ISSN 0556-7807
L26
REVUE FRANCAISE DE PEDAGOGIE. Text in French; Summaries in English. 1967. q. adv. bk.rev. abstr.; bibl. index. back issues avail. **Document type:** *Journal, Academic/Scholarly.*
Indexed: CPE, ERA, ETA, MEA, RASB, RHEA, SEA, SENA, SOMA, TEA.
—BLDSC (7904.215000), IE, Infotrieve.
Published by: Institut National de Recherche Pedagogique, Place du Pentacle, BP 17, Saint-Fons, 69195 Cedex, France. TEL 33-4-72898300, FAX 33-4-72898329, publica@inrp.fr, http://www.inrp.fr. Ed. Andre Robert. R&P Philippe Meirieu. Circ: 2,500.

370 FRA ISSN 1254-4590
REVUE INTERNATIONALE D'EDUCATION SEVRES. Text in French. 1994. q.
Published by: Centre International d'Etudes Pedagogiques, 1 Ave Leon Journault, Sevres, 92310, France. TEL 33-1-45076000, FAX 33-1-45076001.

371.1 HTI
REVUE L'EDUCATEUR. Text in French. m.
Address: Grand Rue, B.P. 164, Port-au-Prince, Haiti. TEL 1-2-2297, TELEX 0533. Circ: 8,000.

370.15 COD
REVUE ZAIROISE DE PSYCHOLOGIE ET DE PEDAGOGIE. Text in French; Abstracts occasionally in English. 1972. 2/yr. USD 8 per issue.
Indexed: e-psyche.
Published by: Universite de Kisangani, Faculte de Psychologie et des Sciences de l'Education, BP 1386, Kisangani, Congo, Dem. Republic. Ed. Bamwisho Mihia.

RHODE ISLAND EDUCATION LAWS AND RULES. see *LAW*

370 ITA ISSN 0035-5046
RICERCHE DIDATTICHE. Text in Italian. 1951. m. **Description:** Explores diverse didatic tactics and arguments regarding the discipline of studying.
Indexed: IBR, IBZ.
—IE.
Published by: Movimento Circoli della Didattica, Via Crescenzio, 25, Rome, RM 00193, Italy. Ed. Carlo Santonocito.

370 PER
RIDECAB; boletin informativo. Text in Spanish. 1980. s-a.
Published by: Instituto Nacional de Investigacion y Desarrollo de la Educacion, Centro Nacional de Documentacion e Informacion Educacional, Van De Velde, 160, San Borja, Lima, 100, Peru.

THE RIGHT OF AESTHETIC REALISM TO BE KNOWN; a periodical of hope and information. see *HUMANITIES: COMPREHENSIVE WORKS*

370.1 USA
RITENOUR NEWS. Text in English. 1971. q. free. **Document type:** *Newspaper.* **Description:** Information, feature articles and sports schedules concerning the Ritenour School District.
Former titles (until 1979): Ritenour School District News (0035-5631); Ritenour School Bulletin
Published by: Ritenour School District, 2420 Woodson Rd., Overland, MO 63114. TEL 314-429-3500, FAX 314-426-7144. Ed. Cindy L Gibson. Circ: 25,000.

371.2 ITA ISSN 0394-8447
RIVISTA DELL'ISTRUZIONE; sistema formativo e produttivita scolastica. Text in Italian. 1985. bi-m. EUR 39 to individuals; EUR 100 to institutions (effective 2005). **Document type:** *Magazine, Trade.* **Description:** Provides the teacher and school administrator with information about all issues of education including: standardized examinations, educational reform legislation, and teaching methods.
Published by: Maggioli Editore, Via del Carpino 8/10, Santarcangelo di Romagna, RN 47822, Italy. TEL 39-0541-628111, FAX 39-0541-622020, editore@maggioli.it, http://www.maggioli.it.

RIVISTA DI CULTURA CLASSICA E MEDIOEVALE. see *CLASSICAL STUDIES*

ROCCA. see *RELIGIONS AND THEOLOGY—Roman Catholic*

370 SVK ISSN 0231-6463
RODINA A SKOLA; casopis pro rodinu a skolu. Text in Slovak. 1953. 10/yr.
Indexed: RASB.
Published by: (Slovakia. Ministry of Education KEN), Parents, Sutazna 18, Bratislava, 82108, Slovakia. TEL 697-64. Ed. Viera Chrostekova. Circ: 37,000. **Subscr. to:** Slovart G.T.G. s.r.o., Krupinska 4, PO Box 152, Bratislava 85299, Slovakia. TEL 421-2-63839472, FAX 421-2-63839485, http://www.slovart-gtg.sk.

370 028.5 DEU ISSN 0940-1997
ROLF KAUKAS BUSSI BAER; fuer Ihr Kind: lesen - malen - lachen - basteln - lernen. Text in German. 1967. m. EUR 27.60; EUR 2.30 newsstand/cover (effective 2005). adv. bk.rev. **Document type:** *Magazine, Consumer.* **Description:** Contains stories, puzzles and other games to entertain and educate young children.
Formerly: Bussi Baer (0007-7208)
Published by: Pabel-Moewig Verlag KG (Subsidiary of: Heinrich Bauer Verlag), Karlsruherstr 31, Rastatt, 76437, Germany. TEL 49-7222-130, FAX 49-7222-13218, bussi.baer@vpm.de, empfang@vpm.de, http://bussibaer.de, http://www.vpm-online.de. Ed. Ulrike Edelmann. Adv. contact Rainer Gross. page EUR 6,187. Circ: 150,723 (paid).

ROLLSTUHLSPORT. see *SPORTS AND GAMES*

306.432 MEX
ROMPAN FILAS; familia, escuela y sociedad. Text in Spanish. bi-m. MXP 132 (effective 1999). back issues avail.
Related titles: Online - full text ed.: ISSN 1605-4091. 1996.

Published by: Investigaciones y Servicios Educativos S.C., ADOLFO PRIETO 1147-A, Col Del Valle, Delegacion Benito Juarez, Mexico City, DF 03100, Mexico. TEL 52-5-5597035, FAX 52-5-5758433, http://www.unam.mx/rompan/. Ed. Jorge Sanchez Azcona.

371.03   USA
ROUGH ROCK NEWS. Text in English. 1966. bi-m. (during school year). USD 6. adv. bk.rev.; play rev. illus. **Document type:** Newspaper.
Published by: Rough Rock Community School, RRDS Box 217, Chinle, AZ 86503. TEL 520-728-3243, FAX 520-728-3215. Ed. Ray Ann Terry. Circ: 400.

370.9438   POL   ISSN 0080-4754
ROZPRAWY Z DZIEJOW OSWIATY. Text in Polish. 1958. a., latest vol.38, 1998. price varies. bk.rev. **Document type:** Academic/Scholarly. **Description:** Papers on the history and problems of education in Poland and abroad.
Indexed: IBR, RASB.
Published by: (Zaklad Dziejow Oswiaty), Polska Akademia Nauk, Instytut Historii Nauki, Palac Staszica, ul Nowy Swiat 72, pok 9, Warsaw, 00330, Poland. TEL 48-22-8268754, FAX 48-22-8266137, ihn@ihnpan.waw.pl. Ed. Jozef Miaso. Circ: 600. Dist. by: Ars Polona, Krakowskie Przedmiescie 7, Warsaw, Poland.

370.91734   USA   ISSN 0273-446X
LB1567
RURAL EDUCATOR; journal for rural and small schools. Text in English. 1980. 3/yr. USD 50 domestic to libraries; USD 100 foreign to libraries (effective 2005); includes National Rural Education News. adv. bk.rev. illus. back issues avail.; reprint service avail. from PQC. **Document type:** Journal, Trade.
Related titles: Microfiche ed.; Online - full text ed.: (from ProQuest Information & Learning).
Indexed: ABIn, CIJE, CPE, EduInd, MEA.
—BLDSC (8052.434500), IE, ingenta.
Published by: National Rural Education Association, University of Oklahoma, 820 Van Vleet Oval, Rm 227, Norman, OK 73019. bmooneyham@ou.edu, http://www.nrea.net/Rural%20Educator.htm. Ed. Dr. Patti Chance. Circ: 1,200 (paid).

370.91734   USA   ISSN 1537-4696
RURAL POLICY MATTERS. Text in English. m. **Document type:** Newsletter.
Related titles: Online - full text ed.
Published by: Rural School and Community Trust, 1530 Wilson Blvd., Ste. 240, Arlington, VA 22209-2466. TEL 202-955-7177, FAX 202-955-7179, info@ruraledu.org, http://www.ruraledu.org/. Ed. Alison Yaunches.

370.91734   USA   ISSN 1532-642X
RURAL ROOTS. Text in English. 2000. bi-m. back issues avail. **Document type:** Newsletter. **Description:** Emphasizes on practice or rural education rooted in school and community projects.
Related titles: Online - full text ed.
Published by: Rural School and Community Trust, 1530 Wilson Blvd., Ste. 240, Arlington, VA 22209-2466. TEL 202-955-7177, FAX 202-955-7179, info@ruraledu.org, http://www.ruraledu.org/. Ed. Alison Yaunches.

RUSISTIKA. see LINGUISTICS

370.1   USA   ISSN 1060-9393
L11
➤ RUSSIAN EDUCATION AND SOCIETY; a journal of translations. Text in English. 1958. m. USD 175 domestic to individuals; USD 216 foreign to individuals; USD 1,245 domestic to institutions; USD 1,380 foreign to institutions (effective 2006). adv. illus. index. back issues avail.; reprint service avail. from PSC. **Document type:** Journal, Academic/Scholarly. **Description:** Presents world readers with post-Soviet writing on pedagogical theory and practice, education policy, youth and the family. The articles are gleaned from a wide variety of monographs and journals.
Formerly (until 1992): Soviet Education (0038-5360)
Related titles: Online - full text ed.: 2004 (Feb.) (from EBSCO Publishing, H.W. Wilson, O C L C Online Computer Library Center, Inc., Swets Information Services).
Indexed: ABIn, ASCA, ArtHuCI, CIJE, CJA, CPE, CurCont, EAA, ETA, EduInd, FamI, MEA, PAIS, RHEA, RILM, SEA, SENA, SOMA, SSCI, TEA.
—BLDSC (8052.698000), IDS, IE, Infotrieve, ingenta. **CCC.**
Published by: M.E. Sharpe, Inc., 80 Business Park Dr, Armonk, NY 10504. TEL 914-273-1800, 800-541-6563, FAX 914-273-2106, custserv@mesharpe.com, http://www.mesharpe.com/mall/results1.asp. Ed. Anthony Jones. Adv. contact Barbara Ladd TEL 914-273-1800 ext 121. page USD 300; 8 x 5.

---

371   USA
RUTGERS INVITATIONAL SYMPOSIA ON EDUCATION. Abbreviated title: R I S E. Text and summaries in English. 1987. a. **Document type:** Proceedings, Academic/Scholarly. **Description:** Publishes papers presented at the annual Rutgers Invitational Symposia on Education on a variety of topics in education, each year following a particular theme.

Published by: Rutgers University, Graduate School of Education, 10 Seminary Pl, New Brunswick, NJ 08901-1183. TEL 732-932-7496, FAX 732-932-8206, lwilkin@rci.rutgers.edu, http://www.gse.rutgers.edu/announce/rise.htm. Ed. Louise C Wilkinson.

RWANDA. MINISTERE DE L'ENSEIGNEMENT PRIMAIRE ET SECONDAIRE. DIRECTION DE LA PLANIFICATION. BULLETIN DES STATISTIQUES DE L'ENSEIGNEMENT. see EDUCATION—Abstracting, Bibliographies, Statistics

---

370.72   LKA   ISSN 1391-1880
S A A R C JOURNAL OF EDUCATIONAL RESEARCH. Text in English. 1995. a. LKR 75; USD 10 foreign. **Document type:** Academic/Scholarly.
Published by: National Institute of Education, Department of Educational Research, Maharagama, Sri Lanka. TEL 94-1-851301-5, FAX 94-1-851300. Ed. Upali Gunasekera.

THE S A L T PROGRAMME FOR 8 TO 10. (Sharing and Learning Together) see RELIGIONS AND THEOLOGY

S A S C A NEWSLETTER. see COLLEGE AND ALUMNI

S C R C SPIRIT. see RELIGIONS AND THEOLOGY—Roman Catholic

S C W E A NEWSLETTER. see OCCUPATIONS AND CAREERS

---

371   THA   ISSN 1513-1165
S E A M E O HORIZON; the official voice of Southeast Asia's Ministers of Education. Text in English. 1998. q. free. bk.rev. back issues avail. **Document type:** Newsletter. **Description:** Provides information on the policies, partnerships, programs, research, and activities of the Ministry of Education in Southeast Asia.
Related titles: Online - full text ed.
Published by: Southeast Asian Ministers of Education Organization, 920 Sukhumvit Rd, Bangkok, 10110, Thailand. TEL 66-2-3910144, FAX 66-2-3812587, secretariat@seameo.org, http://www.seameo.org. Ed. Wilfredo Pascual. Circ: 500 (controlled).

S E E JOURNAL. see ENVIRONMENTAL STUDIES

---

391   USA
S E S D NEWSLETTER. Text in English. 3/yr. **Document type:** Newsletter.
Published by: Science Education for Students with Disabilities, c/o Susan K Blizard, 3200 E Cheyenne Ave, S2B, N Las Vegas, NV 89030. TEL 209-278-0239. Ed. Susan K Blizard TEL 702-651-4135.

370.72   SWZ
S I E R BULLETIN. Text in English. 1979 (no.2). a. USD 10. **Document type:** Bulletin.
Indexed: IBSS, PLESA.
Published by: University of Swaziland, Swaziland Institute for Educational Research, Private Bag, Kwaluseni, Swaziland. TEL 268-85108, FAX 268-85276, TELEX 2087 WD. Ed. B Putsoa.

---

788   USA
S I G SYNERGY. (Special Interest Group) Text in English. w. **Document type:** Newspaper.
Published by: A P I C S Communications, 5301 Shawnee Rd, Alexandria, VA 22312-2317. TEL 703-354-8851, 800-444-2742, FAX 703-354-8106.

S I L - A A I B OCCASIONAL PAPERS. see LINGUISTICS

---

371   USA   ISSN 0882-1100
S P E MONOGRAPH SERIES. Text in English. irreg. **Document type:** Monographic series.
Formerly: National Society of College Teachers of Education. Monographs
Indexed: EngInd.
—Ei.
Published by: Society of Professors of Education, c/o Dr Robert Morris, Dept of Ed Ldshp, UWG, 1600 Maple St, Carrollton, GA 30118-5160. TEL 770-836-4426, FAX 770-836-4646. Ed. Robert C Morris.

371.14   USA   ISSN 1068-1752
LB1025.3
➤ S R A T E JOURNAL. Text in English. 1991. a. USD 20. bk.rev. **Document type:** Academic/Scholarly.
Indexed: CPE.
Published by: Southeastern Regional Association of Teacher Educators, c/o W S Hopkins, Department of Curriculum & Instruction, College of Education, University of South Alabama, Mobile, AL 36688-0002. TEL 205-380-2895. R&P W S Hopkins TEL 334-380-2894. Circ: 300.

➤ S R C D NEWSLETTER. see CHILDREN AND YOUTH—About

306.43   ISR
SADA-A-TARBIYA; educational and social problems in Israel. Text in Arabic. m.

Published by: Israel Teachers Union/Histadrut Hamorim, 8 Ben Sarouk St., Tel Aviv, Israel. TEL 03-543911, FAX 03-5432928.

371.7   USA   ISSN 1524-878X
SAFE SCHOOLS, SAFE STUDENTS. Text in English. 1999. m.
Published by: School to Work Publications, Inc., 303 E. Gurley St., Ste. 506, Prescott, AZ 86301. TEL 520-443-9941, FAX 520-443-9942, safety@stwnews.org. Ed. Mary Beaumont.

---

370   GBR   ISSN 0955-3517
➤ ST. CATHERINE'S CONFERENCE REPORT. Text in English. 1987. irreg., latest vol.70, 1999. GBP 2, USD 5 (effective 2000). **Document type:** Proceedings, Academic/Scholarly.
—BLDSC (8070.152450).
Published by: King George VI and Queen Elizabeth Foundation of St. Catharine's, Cumberland Lodge, The Great Park, Windsor, Berks SL4 2HP, United Kingdom. TEL 44-1784-432316, FAX 44-1784-438507. geoffreywilliams@cumberlandlodge.ac.uk, http://www.cumberlandlodge.ac.uk. Ed. Geoffrey Williams. Circ: 500.

➤ SAITAMA SEIBUTSU/SAITAMA BIOLOGICAL SOCIETY OF HIGH SCHOOL TEACHERS. see BIOLOGY

➤ SANTUARIO DE APARECIDA. see RELIGIONS AND THEOLOGY

---

370   ESP   ISSN 1138-5863
➤ SARMIENTO; anuario galego de historia da educacion. Text in Multiple languages. 1997. a. EUR 12.02 (effective 2003). **Document type:** Academic/Scholarly.
Published by: (Universidade da Coruna, Servicio de Publicacions, Universidade de Vigo, Servicio de Publicacions, Universidad de Santiago de Compostela, Servicio de Publicacions, Campus Universitario Sur, Santiago de Compostela, 15782, Spain. TEL 34-981-593500, FAX 34-981-593963, spublic@usc.es, http://www.usc.es/spubl/revsarmiento.htm. Circ: 500 (paid).

---

370   CAN   ISSN 0036-4886
SASKATCHEWAN BULLETIN. Text in English. 1933. fortn. CND 7. adv. bk.rev.; film rev. illus.; stat. **Document type:** Bulletin.
Related titles: Microfilm ed.: (from CML, MML); Microform ed.: (from MML).
Indexed: CEI.
Published by: Saskatchewan Teachers' Federation, 2317 Arlington Ave., Saskatoon, SK S7J 2H8, Canada. stf@stf.sk.ca, http://www.stf.sk.ca. Ed. Frank Garritty. Circ: 22,300 (controlled).

371.4   CAN   ISSN 0048-9190
SASKATCHEWAN GUIDANCE AND COUNSELLING ASSOCIATION. GUIDELINES. Text in English. 1964. s-a. CND 50 to individuals; CND 30 to libraries (effective 2000). adv. bk.rev. **Document type:** Newsletter.
Indexed: CEI.
Published by: (Saskatchewan Guidance and Counselling Association), Saskatchewan Teachers' Federation, 2317 Arlington Ave., Saskatoon, SK S7J 2H8, Canada. stf@stf.sk.ca. Circ: 250.

371.4   CAN   ISSN 0833-2916
SASKATCHEWAN GUIDANCE AND COUNSELLING ASSOCIATION. NEWSLETTER. Text in English. s-a. CND 50 to individuals; CND 30 to libraries (effective 2000). **Document type:** Newsletter.
Published by: (Saskatchewan Guidance and Counselling Association), Saskatchewan Teachers' Federation, 2317 Arlington Ave., Saskatoon, SK S7J 2H8, Canada. stf@stf.sk.ca.

SAUDI ARABIA. MINISTRY OF EDUCATION. ANNUAL STATISTICAL REPORT. see EDUCATION—Abstracting, Bibliographies, Statistics

---

370.9538   SAU   ISSN 1319-0067
SAUDI ARABIA. MINISTRY OF EDUCATION. EDUCATIONAL DOCUMENTATION/SAUDI ARABIA. WIZARAT AL-MA'ARIF. AL-TAWTHIQ AL-TARBAWI. Text in Arabic, English. 1968. s-a. **Document type:** Government.
Published by: Ministry of Education, P O Box 2871, Riyadh, Saudi Arabia. TEL 401-2900, FAX 402-1154.

SAUDI ARABIA. MINISTRY OF EDUCATION. EDUCATIONAL STATISTICS. see EDUCATION—Abstracting, Bibliographies, Statistics

---

SAUDI ARABIA. WIZARAT AL-MA'ARIF. AL-ISTIKHLASAT AL-TARBAWIYYAH/SAUDI ARABIA. MINISTRY OF EDUCATION. EDUCATIONAL ABSTRACTS. see EDUCATION—Abstracting, Bibliographies, Statistics

---

370   FRA   ISSN 0769-6094
SAVOIRS ET FORMATION. Text in French. irreg.
Published by: Federation des Associations Departementales pour l'Enseignement et la Formation des Travailleurs Immigres et de leurs Familles, 16 rue de Valmy, Montreuil, 93100, France. TEL 33-1-42870220. Ed. Camel Jendoubi. Pub. Jean Bellanger.

E

▼ new title   ➤ refereed   ✳ unverified   ◆ full entry avail.

370 GBR ISSN 0031-3831
CODEN: SJERAS
➤ **SCANDINAVIAN JOURNAL OF EDUCATIONAL RESEARCH.** Text in English. 1957. 5/yr. GBP 450, USD 744 combined subscription to institutions print & online eds. (effective 2006). adv. bk.rev. bibl.; charts. index. reprint service avail. from PSC. **Document type:** *Journal, Academic/Scholarly.* **Description:** Focuses on central ideas and themes in educational thinking and research.
Formerly: Pedagogisk Forskning
Related titles: Microform ed.: (from PQC); Online - full text ed.: ISSN 1470-1170. GBP 428, USD 707 to institutions (effective 2006) (from EBSCO Publishing, Gale Group, IngentaConnect, Northern Light Technology, Inc., O C L C Online Computer Library Center, Inc., ProQuest Information & Learning, Swets Information Services).
Indexed: BrEdI, CDA, CIJE, CPE, DIP, EAA, ERA, ETA, IBR, IBZ, L&LBA, MEA, PsycInfo, PsycholAb, RASB, RHEA, SEA, SENA, SOMA, SOPODA, SSA, SWA, SociolAb, TEA, V&AA, e-psyche.
—BLDSC (8087.506000), IE, Infotrieve, ingenta. **CCC.**
Published by: Routledge (Subsidiary of: Taylor & Francis Group), 4 Park Sq, Milton Park, Abingdon, Oxon OX14 4RN, United Kingdom. TEL 44-1235-828600, FAX 44-1235-829000, journals@routledge.com, http://www.tandf.co.uk/journals/titles/00313831.asp, http://www.routledge.co.uk. Ed. Asmund L Stromnes. **Subscr. to:** Taylor & Francis Ltd, Journals Customer Service, Rankine Rd, Basingstoke, Hants RG24 8PR, United Kingdom. TEL 44-1256-813000, FAX 44-1256-330245.

370 DEU
SCHECKHEFT STUDIUM. Text in German. 1980. a. adv. bk.rev. **Document type:** *Academic/Scholarly.*
Published by: Verein Freunde und Foerderer der Deutschen Studentenschaft e.V., Untere Hausbreite 11, Munich, 80939, Germany. Ed. Gundolf Seidenspinner. Circ: 100.

028.1 ITA ISSN 0036-5955
SCHEDARIO; periodico di letteratura giovanile. Text in Italian. 1970 (vol.17). q. adv. bk.rev. bibl.; illus.
Related titles: Microfiche ed.
Published by: Biblioteca di Documentazione Pedagogica, Sezione di Letteratura Giovanile, Via M. Buonarroti 10, Florence, FI 50122, Italy. Ed. Antonio Augenti. Circ: 8,000. **Co-sponsor:** Ministero Pubblica Istruzione.

370 DEU ISSN 0945-2923
SCHLESWIG-HOLSTEIN. MINISTERIN FUER WISSENSCHAFT, FORSCHUNG UND KULTUR. NACHRICHTENBLATT; als besondere Ausgabe des Amtsblatts fuer Schleswig-Holstein. Text in German. 1949. m. bk.rev. index. back issues avail.; reprints avail. **Document type:** *Government.* **Description:** Government publication listing laws and regulations of schools, higher education, and trade schools concerning exams and organization. Includes positions available.
Former titles: Schleswig-Holstein. Ministerin fuer Bildung, Wissenschaft, Kultur und Sport. Nachrichtenblatt (0943-8343); (until 1992): Schleswig-Holstein. Ministerin fuer Bildung, Wissenschaft, Jugend und Kultur. Nachrichtenblatt (0937-0005); (until 1989): Schleswig-Holstein. Kulturminister. Nachrichtenblatt (0023-7868); (until 1960): Schleswig-Holsteinische Schulwesen. Nachrichtenblatt
Published by: Ministerin fuer Wissenschaft Forschung und Kultur, Duesternbrooker Weg 64, Kiel, 24105, Germany. TEL 49-431-9885807, FAX 49-431-9885815, pressestelle@kumi.landsh.de. Circ: 2,900. **Subscr. to:** Schmidt und Klaunig, Ringstr 19, Kiel 24114, Germany.

370 DEU
SCHO WIDA. Text in German. 1979. irreg. bk.rev.; film rev.; play rev. illus. back issues avail.
Address: Chiemgau Gymnasium, Brunnwiese 1, Traunstein, 83278, Germany. Circ: 650.

370 USA ISSN 1540-9392
LC196
SCHOLAR-PRACTITIONER QUARTERLY. Text in English. 2002 (Fall). q. USD 75 to individuals; USD 175 to institutions (effective 2005).
Indexed: CPE, ERA.
Published by: Caddo Gap Press, 3145 Geary Blvd,, PMB 275, San Francisco, CA 94118. TEL 415-666-3012, FAX 415-666-3552, info@caddogap.com, http://www.caddogap.com. Ed. Patrick M. Jenlink. Pub. Alan H Jones.

370 USA
SCHOLASTIC MATH TEACHER'S EDITION. Text in English. 12/yr. teacher's edition incl. with 10 or more student editions. **Document type:** *Magazine, Trade.*
Published by: Scholastic Inc., 557 Broadway, Rm. 367, New York, NY 10012-3949. TEL 212-343-6100, http://www.scholastic.com. Ed. Jack Silbert.

SCHOLASTIC NEWS. GRADE 5 / 6 EDITION. see *CHILDREN AND YOUTH—For*

SCHOLE; a journal of leisure studies and recreation education. see *LEISURE AND RECREATION*

370.1 USA ISSN 0036-6447
CODEN: CSPAEP
SCHOOL AND COMMUNITY. Text in English. 1915. q. USD 15 domestic; USD 20 foreign (effective 2005). adv. bk.rev. illus. index. reprint service avail. from PQC. **Document type:** *Magazine, Trade.* **Description:** Touches upon school projects, activities, association activities affecting the Missouri school systems and teachers; educational news.
Related titles: Microform ed.: (from PQC).
Published by: Missouri State Teachers Association, 407 S Sixth St, Columbia, MO 65201. TEL 573-442-3127, 800-392-0532, FAX 573-443-5079, msta_mail@msta.org, http://www.msta.org. Ed., R&P Letha Albright. Adv. contact Jennifer Bacon. Circ: 44,000 (paid).

SCHOOL BAND AND ORCHESTRA. see *MUSIC*

370 USA ISSN 1059-308X
LC215
SCHOOL COMMUNITY JOURNAL. Text in English. 1991. s-a. USD 22 to individuals; USD 52 to institutions; USD 12 newsstand/cover (effective 2005). **Description:** Includes research and field reports related to the school as a community of teachers, students, parents, and staff.
Indexed: CIJE, PsycInfo, PsycholAb.
—BLDSC (8092.702700), IE, ingenta.
Published by: Academic Development Institute, 121 N Kickapoo St, Lincoln, IL 62656g. TEL 217-732-6462, FAX 217-732-3696, adi@adi.org, http://www.adi.org/publications.html. Ed. Lori Thomas.

370.72 NLD ISSN 0924-3453
CODEN: SEFIE9
➤ **SCHOOL EFFECTIVENESS AND SCHOOL IMPROVEMENT;** an international journal of research, policy and practice. Text in English. 1990. q. GBP 276, USD 470 combined subscription to institutions print & online eds. (effective 2006). adv. back issues avail.; reprint service avail. from PSC. **Document type:** *Journal, Academic/Scholarly.* **Description:** Explores all facts of school effectiveness and school improvement.
Related titles: Online - full text ed.: ISSN 1744-5124. GBP 262, USD 447 to institutions (effective 2006) (from EBSCO Publishing, Gale Group, IngentaConnect, O C L C Online Computer Library Center, Inc., Swets Information Services).
Indexed: ASCA, BrEdI, CIJE, CJA, CPE, CurCont, DIP, EAA, ERA, ETA, FamI, IBR, IBZ, MEA, PsycInfo, PsycholAb, RHEA, SEA, SENA, SOMA, SSCI, TEA.
—BLDSC (8092.734000), IDS, IE, Infotrieve, ingenta, KNAW. **CCC.**
Published by: (International Congress for School Effectiveness and Improvement), Taylor & Francis The Netherlands (Subsidiary of: Taylor & Francis Group), Schipolweg 107 C, PO Box 447, Leiden, 2316 XC, Netherlands. TEL 31-715-243080, FAX 31-715-234571, pub@swets.nl, infoho@swets.nl, http://www.tandf.co.uk/journals/titles/09243453.asp, http://www.tandf.co.uk/swets.asp. Eds. Bert P M Creemers, David Reynolds. R&P J van der Valk. Adv. contact Miranda Mauritz. page EUR 225; trim 160 x 240.

➤ **SCHOOL LAW REPORTER.** see *LAW*

370 UGA
SCHOOL LEAVER. Text in English. 1973. 3/yr. UGX 100, USD 45. adv. bk.rev. illus.
Published by: Uganda School Leavers Association, PO Box 5145, Kampala, Uganda. Ed. John Ken Lukyamuzi. Circ: 8,500.

SCHOOL LIBRARIAN. see *LIBRARY AND INFORMATION SCIENCES*

SCHOOL LIBRARY JOURNAL; the magazine of children, young adults & school librarians. see *LIBRARY AND INFORMATION SCIENCES*

SCHOOL LIBRARY MEDIA RESEARCH. see *LIBRARY AND INFORMATION SCIENCES*

SCHOOL PHOTOGRAPHER. see *PHOTOGRAPHY*

SCHOOL PSYCHOLOGIST. see *PSYCHOLOGY*

SCHOOL PSYCHOLOGY QUARTERLY. see *PSYCHOLOGY*

370 USA ISSN 1066-341X
SCHOOL SCENE. Text in English. 1968. q. USD 10. adv. bk.rev. **Document type:** *Newsletter.* **Description:** Provides networking news and opportunities for members.
Published by: Technology Student Association, 1914 Association Dr, Reston, VA 22091. TEL 703-860-9000, FAX 703-620-4483. Ed. Jane Wright. Circ: 60,000.

SCHOOL SCIENCE; quarterly journal for secondary schools. see *SCIENCES: COMPREHENSIVE WORKS*

371.67 USA ISSN 1070-3586
SCHOOL TRANSPORTATION NEWS. Text in English. 1991. m. USD 29.95; free to qualified personnel (effective 2005). adv. bk.rev. **Document type:** *Magazine, Trade.* **Description:** Focuses on news developments in school transportation at all academic levels.
Related titles: Online - full content ed.
Published by: School Transportation News Media Co., 700 Torrance Blvd, Ste C, PO Box 789, Redondo Beach, CA 90277. TEL 310-792-2226, FAX 310-792-2231, ryan@stnonline.com, bpaul@stnonline.com, http://www.stnonline.com. Ed., Pub., R&P Bill Paul. Adv. contact Anthony Corpin. Circ: 22,000 (paid and free).

371.0712 NLD ISSN 0924-8129
SCHOOLBESTUUR. Text in Dutch. 10/yr. adv. bk.rev. **Document type:** *Trade.*
Incorporates (1981-1989): School en Besturen (0167-7772); Supersedes: Schoolbestuur (0036-6870)
—KNAW.
Published by: Vereniging van Besturenorganisaties van Katholieke Onderwijsinstellingen (VBKO), Postbus 82158, The Hague, 2508 ED, Netherlands. TEL 31-70-3568600, FAX 31-70-3616052. Ed. J M M van de Ven. Circ: 7,250.

370 NLD ISSN 1386-3266
SCHOOLJOURNAAL. Text in Dutch. 1997. w. adv. illus.
Formed by the 1997 merger of: Katholieke Schoolblad (0165-7674); Which incorporated (in 1986): Bernardus (0005-9390); Which was formerly (until 1968): Nijverheidsschool (0920-0258); P C O - Magazine (0165-7933); Which incorporated (1982-1986): Protestants Christelijke Onderwijsvakorganisatie. Special (0920-7252); (1937-1986): Magazine Voortgezet Onderwijs (0920-5276); Which was formerly (until 1979): Magazine Beroepsonderwijs (0165-7682); (until 1976): Ons Beroepsonderwijs (0920-5519)
—KNAW.
Published by: Onderwijsbonden C N V, Boerhaavelaan 5, Zoetermeer, 2713 HA, Netherlands. TEL 31-79-3202020, FAX 31-79-3202195, redactie@ocnv.nl, http://www.ocnv.nl. Ed. Cees V Overbeek. R&P Laurens Reitsma.

SCHOOLS AND THE COURTS; briefs of selected court cases involving secondary and elementary schools. see *LAW*

SCHOOLS OF PRAYER. see *RELIGIONS AND THEOLOGY—Roman Catholic*

370.15 DEU ISSN 1610-0743
SCHRIFTEN ZUR PAEDAGOGISCHEN PSYCHOLOGIE. Text in German. 2002. irreg., latest vol.17, 2005. price varies. **Document type:** *Monographic series, Academic/Scholarly.*
Published by: Verlag Dr. Kovac, Arnoldstr 49, Hamburg, 22763, Germany. TEL 49-40-3988800, FAX 49-40-39888055, info@verlagdrkovac.de, http://www.verlagdrkovac.de/7-10.htm.

370.72 DEU ISSN 1619-3814
SCHRIFTEN ZUR REFORMPAEDAGOGIK. Text in German. 2002. irreg., latest vol.2, 2004. price varies. **Document type:** *Monographic series, Academic/Scholarly.*
Published by: Verlag Dr. Kovac, Arnoldstr 49, Hamburg, 22763, Germany. TEL 49-40-3988800, FAX 49-40-39888055, info@verlagdrkovac.de, http://www.verlagdrkovac.de.

SCHUELERINNEN, SCHUELER UND STUDIERENDE - ELEVES, ETUDIANTES ET ETUDIANTS. see *EDUCATION—Abstracting, Bibliographies, Statistics*

371 DEU ISSN 0722-7094
SCHULE IM BLICKPUNKT. Text in German. 1967. 8/yr. EUR 10.65; EUR 1.95 newsstand/cover (effective 2003). **Document type:** *Journal, Academic/Scholarly.*
Published by: Neckar Verlag GmbH, Postfach 1820, Villingen-Schwenningen, 78008, Germany. TEL 49-7721-89870, FAX 49-7721-898750, service@neckar-verlag.de, http://www.neckar-verlag.de.

SCHULE IN EVANGELISCHER TRAEGERSCHAFT. see *RELIGIONS AND THEOLOGY—Protestant*

371.33 DEU ISSN 0036-7125
SCHULFERNSEHEN (MUNICH)✶. Text in German. 1964. m. play rev. charts; illus.
Media: Cards.
Published by: (Bayerischer Rundfunk), T R - Verlagsunion, Postfach 260202, Munich, 80059, Germany. Ed. Rosemarie V Hornstein. Circ: 8,000.

370.15 AUT
SCHULHEFT. Text in German. 1976. 4/yr. EUR 23.50; EUR 9 newsstand/cover (effective 2005). **Document type:** *Journal, Academic/Scholarly.*
Published by: StudienVerlag, Amraser Str 118, Innsbruck, 6020, Austria. TEL 43-512-395045, FAX 43-512-39504515, order@studienverlag.at, http://www.studienverlag.at/titel.php3?TITNR=1065.

371.109433 DEU ISSN 0586-965X
SCHULREPORT; Tatsachen und Meinungen zur Bildungspolitik in Bayern. Text in German. 1970. 4/yr. **Document type:** *Government.* **Description:** For educators and teachers in Bavaria.
Indexed: DIP, IBZ.
Published by: Bayerisches Staatsministerium fuer Unterricht und Kultus, Salvatorstr 2, Munich, 80333, Germany. TEL 49-89-2186-1511, FAX 49-89-2186-1803, TELEX 898300-0, http://www.stmukwk.bayern.de. Ed. Hartmut Pramstaller. Circ: 90,000.

372.4 DEU
DER SCHWAMM. Text in German. 1955. irreg. (3-4/yr.). free. back issues avail. **Document type:** *Newsletter, Consumer.*
Published by: Gottlieb-Daimler-Gymnasium, Kattowitzer Str 8, Stuttgart, 70374, Germany. TEL 49-711-9528300, FAX 49-711-952830123, sekretariat@gdg-stuttgart.de, http://www.gdg-stuttgart.de. Ed. Franziska Kellner. R&P Jochen Schorn. Adv. contact Lars Oberg. Circ: 350.

370 CHE ISSN 1422-0660
SCHWEIZER LEHRERINNEN- UND LEHRERZEITUNG. Text in German. 1855. m. CHF 85; CHF 120 foreign (effective 1999). bk.rev. bibl.; illus. index. back issues avail. **Document type:** *Trade.*
Former titles (until 1992): Schweizerische Lehrerzeitung (0036-7656); (until 1862): Padagogische Monatsschrift fuer die Schweiz (1422-0687)
Related titles: ♦ Supplement(s): Zeichnen und Gestalt.
Published by: Dachverband Schweizer Lehrerinnen und Lehrer, Postfach 189, Zuerich, 8057, Switzerland. TEL 41-1-3155454, FAX 41-1-3118315, lch@lch.ch, http://www.lch.ch. Ed. Daniel Mover. adv.: B&W page CHF 2,313. Circ: 15,000 (controlled).

371.071 CHE ISSN 0036-7443
SCHWEIZER SCHULE. Text in German. 1914. s-m. CHF 68. adv. bk.rev.; rec.rev. bibl.; charts; illus. index.
Published by: Brunner Druck AG, Arsenalstr 24, Kriens, 6010, Switzerland. Circ: 4,500.

370 CHE ISSN 1424-3946
L56
SCHWEIZERISCHE ZEITSCHRIFT FUER BILDUNGSWISSENSCHAFTEN/REVUE SUISK DES SCIENCES DE L'EDUCATION/RIVISTA SVIZZERA DI SCIENZE DELL'EDUCAZIONE. Text in French, German, Italian. 1979. 3/yr. CHF 53 (effective 2004). **Document type:** *Journal, Academic/Scholarly.*
Formerly (until 2000): Bildungsforschung und Bildungspraxis (0252-9955)
Related titles: Online - full text ed.
Indexed: DIP, IBR, IBZ.
—BLDSC (8121.870000), IE, ingenta.
Published by: Academic Press Fribourg, Perolles 42, Fribourg, 1705, Switzerland. TEL 41-26-4264311, FAX 41-26-4264300, info@paulusedition.ch, http://www.paulusedition.ch/academic_press/. Ed. Franz Baeriswyl.

SCIENCE & EDUCATION; contributions from history, philosophy & sociology of science and mathematics. see *SCIENCES: COMPREHENSIVE WORKS*

SCIENCE & TECHNOLOGY EDUCATION LIBRARY. see *LIBRARY AND INFORMATION SCIENCES*

SCIENCE EDUCATION NEWS. see *SCIENCES: COMPREHENSIVE WORKS*

371.04 BEL ISSN 0582-2351
L10 CODEN: SPEXDN
➤ **SCIENTIA PAEDAGOGICA EXPERIMENTALIS**; international journal. Short title: S P E. Text in English, French. 1964. s-a. EUR 38 (effective 2003). adv. bk.rev. abstr. back issues avail. **Document type:** *Journal, Academic/Scholarly.*
Indexed: BrEdI, CurCont, ERA, ETA, IBR, L&LBA, MEA, PhilInd, PsycholAb, RHEA, RILM, SEA, SENA, SOMA, SOPODA, SSCI, SWA, TEA.
—BLDSC (8172.800000), IE, Infotrieve, ingenta, KNAW.
Published by: (Universiteit Gent, Dept. Pedagogiek), Communication and Cognition, Blandijnberg 2, Ghent, 9000, Belgium. TEL 32-9-2643952, FAX 32-9-2644197, Marc.Spoelders@rug.ac.be. Ed. M Spoelders. R&P M. Spoelders TEL 32-9-2646381. Circ: 600.

372.4 USA ISSN 1088-8438
LB1050 CODEN: SSTRFZ
SCIENTIFIC STUDIES OF READING. Text in English. 1997. q. USD 400 in US & Canada to institutions; USD 430 elsewhere to institutions; USD 420 combined subscription in US & Canada to institutions print & online eds.; USD 450 combined subscription elsewhere to institutions print & online eds. (effective 2006). adv. back issues avail.; reprint service avail. from PSC. **Document type:** *Journal, Academic/Scholarly.* **Description:** Publishes original empirical investigations dealing with all aspects of reading and its related areas.
Related titles: Online - full text ed.: ISSN 1532-799X. USD 380 worldwide to institutions (effective 2006) (from EBSCO Publishing, Gale Group, O C L C Online Computer Library Center, Inc., Swets Information Services).
Indexed: CurCont, L&LBA, PsycInfo, PsycholAb, SOPODA, SSCI, e-psyche.
—BLDSC (8204.152000), IE, Infotrieve, ingenta. **CCC.**
Published by: (Society for the Scientific Study of Reading), Lawrence Erlbaum Associates, Inc., 10 Industrial Ave, Mahwah, NJ 07430-2262. TEL 201-258-2200, 800-926-6579, FAX 201-236-0072, journals@erlbaum.com, http://www.leaonline.com/loi/ssr. Ed. Frank Manis. adv.: page USD 300; trim 5 x 8.

SCOTTISH EDUCATION DEPARTMENT. STATISTICAL BULLETIN. see *EDUCATION—Abstracting, Bibliographies, Statistics*

370.9411 GBR ISSN 0036-9179
SCOTTISH EDUCATIONAL JOURNAL. Abbreviated title: S E J. Text in English. 1876. 6/yr. GBP 15 in Europe; GBP 18 elsewhere (effective 2001); Free to EIS members. adv. bk.rev. back issues avail. **Document type:** *Magazine.* **Description:** Features the latest EIS (Educational Institute of Scotland) developments and also covers wider areas of educational interest and trade union interest.
Indexed: RASB.
Published by: Educational Institute of Scotland, 46 Moray Pl, Edinburgh, Midlothian EH3 6BH, United Kingdom. TEL 44-131-225-6244, FAX 44-131-220-3151, Kblackwell@eis.org.uk, http://www.eis.org.uk. Ed. Simon G Macaulay. adv.: color page GBP 1,660; trim 216 x 303. Circ: 60,000.

370 ITA ISSN 1590-3206
SCUOLA DELL'INFANZIA. Text in Italian. 2000. m. (11/yr.). EUR 36 domestic; EUR 54 foreign (effective 2005). **Document type:** *Magazine, Trade.*
Published by: Giunti Gruppo Editoriale SpA, Via Bolognese 165, Florence, 50139, Italy. TEL 39-055-5062376, FAX 39-055-5062397, informazioni@giunti.it, http://www.giunti.it.

371.07 ITA
SCUOLA DOMENICALE. Text in Italian. 1879. q. bk.rev.
Published by: (Federazione dell Chiese Evangeliche in Italia), Servizio Istruzione ed Educazione, Via Porro Lambertenghi 28, Milano, 20159, Italy. TEL 39-02-69000883, FAX 39-02-6682645, sie.fcei@iol.it.

370 ITA ISSN 0036-9853
L36
SCUOLA E CITTA; rivista de problemi educativi e di politica scolastica. Text in Italian. 1950. m. bibl.; illus. index.
Indexed: RASB.
—BLDSC (8213.330000), IE, Infotrieve.
Published by: La Nuova Italia Editrice S.p.A, Via Ernesto Codignola 1, Florence, 50018, Italy. TEL 39-55-75901, FAX 39-55-757318, nib.reviews@lanuovaitalia.it, http://www.lanuovaitalia.it. Circ: 4,500.

372 ITA ISSN 0036-9861
SCUOLA E DIDATTICA. Text in Italian. 1955. fortn. EUR 61 domestic; EUR 97 in Europe; EUR 141 elsewhere (effective 2005). adv. illus. index. **Document type:** *Magazine, Trade.*
Indexed: RASB.
—IE, Infotrieve.
Published by: Editrice La Scuola SpA, Via Luigi Cadorna 11, Brescia, BS 25124, Italy. TEL 39-030-29931, FAX 39-030-2993299, http://www.lascuola.it. Ed. Giuseppe Vico. Circ: 40,000.

371.071 ITA ISSN 0036-987X
LA SCUOLA E L'UOMO. Text in Italian. 1944. m. EUR 27 (effective 2004). adv. bk.rev. 32 p./no.; back issues avail. **Document type:** *Magazine, Academic/Scholarly.* **Description:** Covers education in a global sense as welll as in the context of religious and social education. Also addresses teacher and headmaster training.
Published by: Unione Cattolica Italiana Insegnanti Medi, Via Crescenzio, 25, Rome, RM 00193, Italy. FAX 39-06-68802701, uci.im@flashnet.it, http://www.uciim.it. Adv. contact Luciano Corradini. Circ: 22,000.

370 ITA ISSN 1123-8100
SCUOLA INSIEME. Text in Italian. 1994. 5/yr. EUR 10 (effective 2005). **Document type:** *Magazine, Trade.*
Published by: Casa Editrice La Tecnica della Scuola, Via Tripolitania 12, Catania, CT 95127, Italy. TEL 39-095-448780, FAX 39-095-503256, info@tecnicadellascuola.it, http://www.tecnicadellascuola.it. Ed. Gabriella Girgenti.

372 ITA ISSN 0036-9888
SCUOLA ITALIANA MODERNA. Text in Italian. 1893. fortn. EUR 53 domestic; EUR 89 in Europe; EUR 133 elsewhere (effective 2005). adv. charts; illus. index. **Document type:** *Magazine, Trade.*
Related titles: Supplement(s): Direzione Scuola. ISSN 0392-2812. 1981.
Indexed: RASB.
Published by: Editrice La Scuola SpA, Via Luigi Cadorna 11, Brescia, BS 25124, Italy. TEL 39-030-29931, FAX 39-030-2993299, http://www.lascuola.it. Ed. Giorgio Chiosso. Circ: 80,000.

372.218 ITA
SCUOLA MATERNA. Text in Italian. 1913. fortn. EUR 51 domestic; EUR 86 in Europe; EUR 127 elsewhere (effective 2005). adv. bk.rev. **Document type:** *Magazine, Trade.*
Published by: Editrice La Scuola SpA, Via Luigi Cadorna 11, Brescia, BS 25124, Italy. TEL 39-030-29931, FAX 39-030-2993299, http://www.lascuola.it. Ed. Giovanni Cattanei. Circ: 40,000.

370.1 CHE
➤ **SCUOLA TICINESE.** Text in Italian. 1972. bi-m. CHF 20 domestic; CHF 25 foreign (effective 2001). adv. 24 p./no. 3 cols./p.; back issues avail. **Document type:** *Magazine, Academic/Scholarly.* **Description:** Contains articles and information concerning schools and education.
Related titles: Online - full text ed.
Published by: Divisione Scuola, Viale Portone 12, Bellinzona, 6501, Switzerland. TEL 41-91-8143455, FAX 41-91-8144492, diego.erba@ti.ch, http://www.ti.ch/dic/ds. Ed. Diego Erba. adv.: B&W page CHF 900. Circ: 8,000 (paid).

370 ITA ISSN 0036-9926
SCUOLA VIVA; mensile per educatori. Text in Italian. 1964. q. free. adv. bk.rev.; play rev. bibl.; illus. **Document type:** *Academic/Scholarly.*
Published by: Societa Editrice Internazionale, Corso R. Margherita 176, Turin, TO 10152, Italy. TEL 39-011-52271, FAX 39-011-5211320. Ed. Sergio Giordani. Circ: 2,000.

SECOND PENNY. see *WOMEN'S INTERESTS*

373 USA ISSN 0160-6778
LB1607.52.M5
SECONDARY EDUCATION TODAY. Text in English. 1958. q. USD 40. adv. bk.rev. reprint service avail. from PQC. **Document type:** *Academic/Scholarly.*
Formerly (until 1972): Michigan Journal of Secondary Education (0026-2226)
Related titles: Microform ed.: (from PQC).
Indexed: HistAb.
Published by: Michigan Association of Secondary School Principals, 418 Erickson Hall, Michigan State University, East Lansing, MI 48823. Ed. Dr. Philip Cusick. Circ: 2,460.

370.1 297 AUS ISSN 1329-6701
SECONDARY SCHOOLS NETWORK, CATHOLIC CURRICULUM COORDINATORS. NEWSLETTER. Text in English. q. looseleaf. adv. **Document type:** *Newsletter.* **Description:** Provides information about teaching, learning, and assessment.
Formerly (until 199?): Curriculum Co-ordinators' Network, Catholic Secondary Schools. Newsletter (1039-2025)
Published by: Catholic Education Office, Victoria, James Wood House, PO Box 3, East Melbourne, VIC 3002, Australia. TEL 61-3-9267-0228, FAX 61-3-9415-9325, director@ceo.melb.catholic.edu.au.

SEGUE. see *MUSIC*

SEIBUTSU KENKYU/JAPAN ASSOCIATION OF BIOLOGY EDUCATION. RESEARCH REPORT. see *BIOLOGY*

SEIBUTSU KYOIKU/JAPANESE JOURNAL OF BIOLOGICAL EDUCATION. see *BIOLOGY*

370.954 IND
SELECTIONS FROM EDUCATIONAL RECORDS OF THE GOVERNMENT OF INDIA. Text in English. 1976. irreg. bibl.
Published by: Jawaharlal Nehru University, Zakir Husain Centre for Educational Studies, New Delhi, 110 067, India. Ed. Joseph Bara. Circ: 100.

370 PRT ISSN 0037-203X
SEMPRE PRONTO; mensario escotista. Text in Portuguese. 1945. m. adv.
Published by: Associacao dos Escoteiros de Portugal, Travessa das Galeotas, 1, Lisbon, 1300-264, Portugal. TEL 351-21-3639339, FAX 351-21-3623722, international@aep.pt, http://escoteiros.net/site/. Ed. Joaquim Xavier Lopes. Circ: 2,000.

371.042 RUS ISSN 0131-7377
L51
SEM'YA I SHKOLA. Text in Russian. 1871. m. USD 163 foreign (effective 2005). adv. index. **Document type:** *Magazine, Consumer.*
Related titles: Microfiche ed.: (from IDC).
Indexed: CDSP.
—East View.
Published by: Redaktsiya Zhurnala Sem'ya i Shkola, ul Pavla Korchagina 7, Moscow, 129278, Russian Federation. TEL 7-095-2838009, FAX 7-095-2838614. Ed. Petr Gelazoniya. adv.: color page RUR 20,000. Circ: 6,000. **Dist. by:** East View Information Services, 3020 Harbor Ln. N., Minneapolis, MN 55447. TEL 763-550-0961, FAX 763-559-2931, eastview@eastview.com, http://www.eastview.com.

SEQUENCES; la revue de cinema. see *MOTION PICTURES*

370 DEU ISSN 0138-2497
SERBSKA SULA. Text in German. 10/yr. EUR 1.50 per issue (effective 2003). **Document type:** *Journal, Academic/Scholarly.*

E

Published by: Domowina Verlag GmbH, Tuchmacherstr 27, Bautzen, 02625, Germany. TEL 49-3591-5770, FAX 49-3591-577207, domowinaverlag@t-online.de, http://www.domowinaverlag.de.

370 URY ISSN 0797-650X
LA544.S68
SERIE: EDUCACION Y MERCOSUR. Text in Spanish. 1992. a. **Document type:** *Government.*
Published by: Ministerio de Educacion y Cultura, Direccion de Educacion, Reconquista, 535 Piso 6, Montevideo, 11007, Uruguay. TEL 95-38-57, FAX 96-26-32. Ed. Carlos Romero.

370 USA
SERIE MONOGRAFIAS Y ESTUDIOS DE LA EDUCACION. (Published by host country) Text in Spanish. 1974. irreg. back issues avail. **Document type:** *Monographic series, Academic/Scholarly.*
Published by: Organization of American States/Organizacion de los Estados Americanos, 1889 F St N W, 2nd Fl, Washington, DC 20006-4499. TEL 703-789-3319. Circ: 2,000.

▼ **SERIES ON MATHEMATICS EDUCATION.** see *MATHEMATICS*

370.15 USA ISSN 1556-9128
THE SERIES ON SOCIAL EMOTIONAL LEARNING. Text and summaries in English. irreg. price varies. illus. **Document type:** *Monographic series, Academic/Scholarly.* **Description:** Examines the psychological aspects of issues in teaching and learning.
Published by: Teachers College Press, Teachers College, Columbia University, 525 W 120th St, Box 303, New York, NY 10027-6694. http://tc-press.tc.columbia.edu. **Dist. by:** Eurospan University Press Group, Order Dept, 3 Henrietta St, London WC2E 8LU, United Kingdom. TEL 44-20-7240-0856, FAX 44-20-7379-0609, http://www.eurospan.co.uk; Pademelon Press, Pty Ltd, 7-10 Anella Ave, PO Box 229, Castle Hill, NSW 2154, Australia. TEL 61-2-9634-2558, FAX 61-2-9680-4634; Transdex International, Pte Ltd, Block 1, Farrer Rd 307-05, Singapore 268817, Singapore. TEL 65-468-6242, FAX 65-462-5457.

370.72 NZL ISSN 0110-6376
➤ **SET (WELLINGTON);** research information for teachers. Text in English. 1974. 3/yr. looseleaf. NZD 56 to individuals; NZD 80 to institutions; NZD 56 to students (effective 2003). bibl. **Document type:** *Journal, Academic/Scholarly.*
Related titles: Microfilm ed.: (from PQC).
—CCC.
Published by: New Zealand Council for Educational Research, PO Box 3237, Wellington, New Zealand. TEL 64-4-3847939, FAX 64-4-3847933, subscriptions@nzcer.org.nz, http://www.nzcer.org.nz/publications/journals/index.htm. R&P Bev Webber TEL 64-4-8021445. Circ: 1,000.

➤ **SEVIVOT/ENVIRONMENTS;** semi-annual on questions in environmental education. see *ENVIRONMENTAL STUDIES*

613.9071 GBR ISSN 1468-1811
➤ **SEX EDUCATION;** sexuality, society and learning. Text in English. 2001. q. GBP 194, USD 317 combined subscription to institutions print & online eds. (effective 2006). reprint service avail. from PSC. **Document type:** *Journal, Academic/Scholarly.* **Description:** Covers the research into sex education in educational institutions, families, media influence, peer influence and other areas.
Related titles: Online - full text ed.: ISSN 1472-0825. 2001. GBP 184, USD 301 to institutions (effective 2006) (from EBSCO Publishing, Gale Group, IngentaConnect, O C L C Online Computer Library Center, Inc., Swets Information Services).
Indexed: BrEdI, CPE, ERA, ETA, FamI, MEA, PsycInfo, PsycholAb, RHEA, SEA, SENA, SOMA, SSA, SociolAb, TEA.
—BLDSC (8254.456100), Infotrieve. **CCC.**
Published by: Routledge (Subsidiary of: Taylor & Francis Group), 4 Park Sq, Milton Park, Abingdon, Oxon OX14 4RN, United Kingdom. TEL 44-1235-828600, FAX 44-1235-829000, journals@routledge.com, http://www.tandf.co.uk/journals/titles/14681811.asp, http://www.routledge.co.uk. Ed. Michael Reiss. **Subscr. in N America to:** Taylor & Francis Inc., Customer Services Dept, 325 Chestnut St, 8th Fl, Philadelphia, PA 19106. TEL 215-625-8900, 800-354-1420, FAX 215-625-8914, customerservice@taylorandfrancis.com; **Subscr. to:** Taylor & Francis Ltd, Journals Customer Service, Rankine Rd, Basingstoke, Hants RG24 8PR, United Kingdom. TEL 44-1256-813000, FAX 44-1256-330245.

370 CHN
SHANGHAI JIAOYU (XIAOXUE BAN)/SHANGHAI EDUCATION (ELEMENTARY SCHOOL EDITION). Text in Chinese. m.
Published by: Shanghai Shi Jiaoyu-ju/Shanghai Municipal Bureau of Education, 500 Shaanxi Beilu, Shanghai, 200041, China. TEL 2534408. Ed. Song Xuhui.

370 CHN
SHANGHAI JIAOYU (ZHONGXUE BAN)/SHANGHAI EDUCATION (MIDDLE SCHOOL EDITION). Text in Chinese. m.
Published by: Shanghai Shi Jiaoyu-ju/Shanghai Municipal Bureau of Education, 500 Shaanxi Beilu, Shanghai, 200041, China. TEL 2534408. Ed. Shen Mianrong.

370.72 CHN ISSN 1007-2020
➤ **SHANGHAI JIAOYU KEYAN/SHANGHAI EDUCATION RESEARCH.** Text in Chinese. 1982. m. CNY 9 per issue (effective 2004). adv. bk.rev. 64 p./no.; **Document type:** *Magazine, Academic/Scholarly.* **Description:** Contains research information, methods, and research papers on education.
Published by: Shanghai Shi Putong Jiaoyu Kexue Yanjiusuo/Shanghai Institute of General Educational Research, 21 Chaling Beilu, Shanghai, 20032, China. TEL 86-21-64167677, 86-21-64438001, FAX 86-21-64032692, Shanghai-edu@vip.163.com, http://www.pjky.com. Adv. contact Zhang Zhaofeng. Circ: 8,000.

370 CHN ISSN 1000-5498
SHANGHAI TIYU XUEYUAN XUEBAO/SHANGHAI PHYSICAL EDUCATION INSTITUTE. JOURNAL. Text in English. 1981. q. **Document type:** *Journal, Academic/Scholarly.*
Related titles: Online - full text ed.: (from East View Information Services).
Indexed: PEI, RefZh.
—BLDSC (4874.795000), IE, ingenta.
Published by: Shanghai Tiyu Xueyuan/Shanghai Institute of Physical Education, 650 Qingyuan Huanlu, Shanghai, 200433, China.

SHANGHAI ZHONGXUE SHUXUE/SHANGHAI SECONDARY SCHOOL MATHEMATICS. see *MATHEMATICS*

370 CHN ISSN 1004-6739
SHANXI JIAOYU/SHANXI EDUCATION. Text in Chinese. m. CNY 3 newsstand/cover.
Related titles: Online - full text ed.: (from East View Information Services).
Published by: Shanxi Jiaoyu Baokan She, 17 Jiefang Lu, Dongtou Daoxiang, Taiyuan, Shanxi 030009, China. TEL 86-351-3082165. Circ: 1,200,000.

370 CHN
SHANXI JIAOYU BAO/SHANXI EDUCATION NEWSPAPER. Text in Chinese. w. CNY 0.60 newsstand/cover. **Document type:** *Newspaper.*
Published by: Shanxi Jiaoyu Baokan She, 17 Jiefang Lu, Dongtou Daoxiang, Taiyuan, Shanxi 030009, China. TEL 0351-3047730.

370.72 CHN ISSN 1000-260X
AS452.S5327
SHENZHEN DAXUE XUEBAO (RENWEN SHEKE BAN)/SHENZHEN UNIVERSITY. JOURNAL (HUMANITIES, SOCIAL SCIENCES EDITION). Text in Chinese; Summaries in English. 1984. 4/yr. CNY 12. **Document type:** *Academic/Scholarly.* **Description:** Contains academic papers. Aims to reflect research results in education and to promote academic exchange.
Related titles: Online - full text ed.: (from East View Information Services).
Published by: Journal of Shenzhen University, Shenzhen University, Shenzhen, Guangdong 518060, China. TEL 6660277, gongqh@szu.edu.cn. Ed. Zhang Bigong.

371.33 JPN ISSN 0037-3664
SHICHOKAKU KYOIKU/AUDIO-VISUAL EDUCATION. Text in Japanese. 1947. m. JPY 9,440 (effective 1999). adv. bk.rev.; play rev. abstr.; bibl.; pat.; stat.; tr.lit. index, cum.index. **Document type:** *Trade.* **Description:** Features study and teaching manuals and materials on audio-visual education.
Published by: Japan Audio-Visual Education Association/Nihon Shichokaku Kyoiku Kyokai, 1-17-1 Toranomon, Minato-ku, Tokyo, 105-0001, Japan. FAX 81-3-3597-0564. Ed. M Okabe. Circ: 5,000 (controlled).

370 JPN ISSN 1342-9280
SHIGA DAIGAKU KYOIKU GAKUBU KIYO. KYOIKU KAGAKU/SHIGA UNIVERSITY. FACULTY OF EDUCATION. MEMOIRS. PEDAGOGIC SCIENCE. Text in Japanese. 1978. irreg. **Document type:** *Journal, Academic/Scholarly.*
Supersedes in part (in 1995): Shiga Daigaku Kyoiku Gakubu Kiyo. Jinbun Kagaku, Shakai Kagaku, Kyoiku Kagaku/Shiga University. Faculty of Education. Memoirs. Humanities, Social Science and Pedagogic Science (0583-0044); Which was formed by the merger of (1952-1978): Shiga Daigaku Kyoiku Gakubu Kiyo. Kyoiku Kagaku/Shiga University. Faculty of Education. Memoirs. Educational Science (0385-7840); (1952-1978): Shiga Daigaku Kyoiku Gakubu Kiyo. Jinbun Kagaku, Shakai Kagaku/Shiga University. Faculty of Education. Memoirs. Cultural Science and Social Science (0385-7859); Both of which superseded in part (in 1975): Shiga Daigaku Kyoiku Gakubu Kiyo. Jinbun Kagaku. Shakai Kagaku, Kyoiku Kagaku/Shiga University. Faculty of Education. Memoirs. Cultural Science, Social Science and Educational Science (1342-9175); Which was formerly (until 1966): Shiga Daigaku Gakugei Gakubu Kenkyu Ronshu (0488-6275)
Published by: Shiga Daigaku, Kyoikugakubu/Shiga University, Faculty of Education, 5-1 Hiratsu 2-chome, Otsu-shi, Shiga-ken 520-0862, Japan. FAX 81-77-537-7840.

370 CHN
SHIJIE YANJIU DONGTAI. Text in Chinese. m. CNY 14.40. bk.rev.
Address: Wangfujing Dajie, 1 Dongchang Hutong, Beijing, 100006, China. **Dist. outside China by:** China International Book Trading Corp, 35 Chegongzhuang Xilu, Haidian District, PO Box 399, Beijing 100044, China. TEL 86-10-68412045, FAX 86-10-68412023, cibtc@mail.cibtc.com.cn, http://www.cibtc.com.cn/.

370 JPN ISSN 0286-732X
L67
SHIZUOKA DAIGAKU KYOIKUGAKUBU KENKYU HOKOKU. KYOKA KYOIKUGAKU HEN/SHIZUOKA UNIVERSITY. FACULTY OF EDUCATION. BULLETIN. EDUCATIONAL RESEARCH SERIES. Text in English, Japanese. a. **Document type:** *Monographic series.*
Supersedes in part (in 1964): Shizuoka Daigaku Kyoiku Gakubu Kenkyu Hokoku (0488-6852)
Published by: Shizuoka Daigaku, Kyoikugakubu, 836 Oya, shizuoka-shi, 422-8017, Japan. TEL 81-54-238-4572, FAX 81-54-238-5422.

370 RUS ISSN 0037-4024
SHKOLA I PROIZVODSTVO. Text in Russian. 1957. bi-m. USD 49 foreign (effective 2000). adv. bk.rev. illus.
—East View.
Published by: Izdatel'stvo Shkola Press, Rustaveli ul 10-3, Moscow, 127254, Russian Federation. TEL 7-095-2198380, FAX 7-095-2195289. Ed. Yu Ye Rives Korobkov. Pub., R&P Irina Kozlova TEL 7-095-2195287. Adv. contact Vladimir Kolyshev.

370 610 RUS
SHKOLA ZDOROV'YA. Text in Russian. q. USD 85 in United States.
Indexed: RefZh.
Published by: Izdatel'stvo Dyagnostika Adaptatsiya Razvitie, Ul Arkhitektora Vlasova 19, Moscow, 117335, Russian Federation. TEL 7-095-1283987, FAX 7-095-1284865. Ed. V N Kasatkin. **US dist. addr.:** East View Information Services, 3020 Harbor Ln. N., Minneapolis, MN 55447. TEL 612-550-0961.

370 330 RUS
SHKOL'NYI EKONOMICHESKII ZHURNAL. Text in Russian. 8/yr. USD 105 in United States.
Published by: Mezhdunarodnaya Pedagogicheskaya Akademiya, Mezhdunarodnyi Fond Ekonomicheskikh i Sotsyal'nykh Reform, Kotel'nicheskaya nab 17, ofis 411, Moscow, 109240, Russian Federation. TEL 7-095-9159677. **US dist. addr.:** East View Information Services, 3020 Harbor Ln. N., Minneapolis, MN 55447. TEL 612-550-0961.

370 CHN
SICHUAN JIAOYU/SICHUAN EDUCATION. Text in Chinese. m.
Published by: Sichuan Sheng Jiaoyu Weiyuanhui/Sichuan Commission of Education, 44 Xuedao Jie, Chengdu, Sichuan 610016, China. TEL 28782. Ed. Li Ruolin.

370 SLE ISSN 0022-0582
SIERRA LEONE JOURNAL OF EDUCATION. Text in English. 1966. s-a. USD 0.42 per issue. adv. bk.rev. bibl.; charts. **Document type:** *Consumer.*
Indexed: CIJE, ECER, PsycholAb.
Published by: Ministry of Education, c/o Publications Branch, New England, Freetown, Sierra Leone.

370.9664 SLE
SIERRA LEONE. MINISTRY OF EDUCATION. MONTHLY NEWSLETTER. Text in English. 1966. m. **Document type:** *Newsletter, Government.*
Published by: Ministry of Education, c/o Publications Branch, New England, Freetown, Sierra Leone. Circ: 250.

370.9664 SLE ISSN 0080-9551
SIERRA LEONE. MINISTRY OF EDUCATION. REPORT. Text in English. 1961. a. **Document type:** *Government.*
Published by: Ministry of Education, c/o Publications Branch, New England, Freetown, Sierra Leone. Circ: 1,200.

370 IND ISSN 0037-5160
SIKSHA - O - SAHITYA; teachers' journal. Text in Bengali, English. 1921. m. INR 48 (effective 2003). adv. bk.rev. abstr.; charts; stat. index. **Document type:** *Bulletin, Academic/Scholarly.* **Description:** Constitutes a journal for teachers and education.
Published by: All Bengal Teachers' Association, Satyapriya Bhavan, P-14, Ganesh Chandra Ave, Kolkata, West Bengal 700 013, India. TEL 91-33-22368158, FAX 91-33-22369932. Ed. Prasanta Dhar. Circ: 12,500.

372.21 CUB
SIMIENTES; circulos infantiles. Text in Spanish. 1962. 3/yr. USD 16 in South America; USD 18 in North America; USD 20 elsewhere. bk.rev. bibl.; charts; illus.
Published by: (Cuba. Ministerio de Educacion, Cuba. Direccion de Divulgacion y Publicaciones), Ediciones Cubanas, Obispo No. 527, Apdo. 605, Havana, Cuba. Circ: 8,000.

E

370.95957 SGP ISSN 0129-4776
LA1239.5
SINGAPORE JOURNAL OF EDUCATION. Text in English. 1978. s-a. SGD 15, USD 22. adv. bk.rev. illus. **Document type:** *Academic/Scholarly.* **Description:** Contains articles, research papers, and reviews on educational developments and pedagogy.
Indexed: CPE, ERA, ETA, MEA, SEA, SOMA, TEA.
Published by: (National Institute of Education, Nanyang Technological University), Longman Singapore Publishers (Pte) Ltd., 25 First Lok Yang Rd, Singapore, 629734, Singapore. Ed. Ngiau Maru Gi. Circ: 1,500.

SISTEMA DE INDICADORES SOCIO-ECONOMICOS Y EDUCATIVOS DE LA O E I. see *EDUCATION—Abstracting, Bibliographies, Statistics*

370.115 CHN ISSN 1001-2753
SIXIANG ZHENGZHI JIAOYU/IDEOLOGICAL AND POLITICAL EDUCATION. Text in Chinese. 1978. m. CNY 84 (effective 2004). 112 p./no.; **Document type:** *Journal, Academic/Scholarly.* **Description:** Covers ideological education.
Indexed: RASB.
Published by: Zhongguo Renmin Daxue, Shubao Zilio Zhongxin/Renmin University of China, Information Center for Social Server, Dongcheng-qu, 3, Zhangzizhong Lu, Beijing, 100007, China. TEL 86-10-64039458, FAX 86-10-64015080, kyes@163.net, http://www.confucius.cn.net/bkdetail.asp?fzt=G2. **Dist. in US by:** China Publications Service, PO Box 49614, Chicago, IL 60649. TEL 312-288-3291, FAX 312-288-8570**; Dist. by:** China International Book Trading Corp, 35 Chegongzhuang Xilu, Haidian District, PO Box 399, Beijing 100044, China. TEL 86-10-68412045, FAX 86-10-68412023, cibtc@mail.cibtc.com.cn, http://www.cibtc.com.cn.

370 CHN ISSN 1002-588X
SIXIANG ZHENGZHIKE JIAOXUE. Text in Chinese. m. CNY 18 (effective 1999). **Document type:** *Academic/Scholarly.*
Related titles: Online - full text ed.: (from East View Information Services).
Published by: Beijing Shifan Daxue/Beijing Normal University, Xinjiekouwai Beitaipingzhuang, Beijing, 100875, China. TEL 2012288. Ed. He Yunqing.

370 DNK ISSN 1602-8155
SKOLEN I NORDEN (ONLINE). Text in Multiple languages. 2001. s-a. **Document type:** *Academic/Scholarly.*
Formed by the merger of (1978-2001): Skolan i Norden (Print Edition) (0109-8985); Which was formerly (until 1984): Information om Skolan i Norden (0106-2107); (1977-2001): Pohjoismaiden Kouluoloista (Finnish Edition) (0109-8993); Which was formerly (until 1984): Tietoja Pohjoismaiden Koulusta (0106-2433)
Media: Online - full content.
Published by: Nordisk Ministerraad/Nordic Council of Ministers, Store Strandstraede 18, Copenhagen K, 1255, Denmark. TEL 45-33-960200, FAX 45-33-960202, http://www.skolen.odin.dk, http://www.norden.dk. Ed. Ingrid Yrvin.

SKOLHISTORISKT ARKIV; uppsatser och urkunder. see *HISTORY—History Of Europe*

370 SWE ISSN 0037-6515
SKOLLEDAREN. Text in Swedish. 1930. 10/yr. SEK 300 (effective 2001). adv. bk.rev. **Document type:** *Magazine, Trade.*
Formerly (until 1966): Svensk Skolledartidning
Published by: Skolledarna/Swedish Association of Schoolprincipals and Directors of Education, Box 3266, Stockholm, 10365, Sweden. TEL 46-8-567-06-200, FAX 46-8-567-06-299, info@skolledarna.se, http://www.skolledarna.se/skolledaren. Ed., Pub. Kerstin Loeoev. Adv. contact Lena Elison. B&W page SEK 11,000, color page SEK 19,900; trim 189 x 260. Circ: 7,200.

370 HRV ISSN 0037-6531
SKOLSKE NOVINE. Text in Croatian. 1950. w. **Document type:** *Magazine, Academic/Scholarly.* **Description:** Contains educational news from Croatia and abroad, as well as other cultural information.
Related titles: Microfiche ed.
Address: A Hebranga 40, PO Box 785, Zagreb, 10000, Croatia. TEL 385-1-4855720, FAX 385-1-4855712. Ed. Ivan Zigic. Circ: 15,000.

371 SWE ISSN 0037-6566
SKOLVAERLDEN. Variant title: Skol Vaerlden. Text in Swedish. 1901. 22/yr. SEK 600; SEK 30 newsstand/cover (effective 2001). adv. bk.rev. charts; illus. **Document type:** *Magazine, Trade.*
Formerly (until 1963): Tidningen foer Sveriges Laeroverk
Published by: Laerarnas Riksfoerbund, Box 3529, Stockholm, 10369, Sweden. TEL 46-8-613-27-00, FAX 46-8-411-01-75, redaktionen@lr.se, lr@lr.se, http://www.lr.se. Ed., Pub. Kerstin Weyler. Adv. contact IngMarie Ahlstrand. B&W page SEK 25,950, color page SEK 36,500; trim 230 x 324. Circ: 76,000 (controlled).

370 300 ESP ISSN 1578-486X
SKRIBUAK; working paper. Text in Spanish. 2001. irreg. EUR 7.50 per issue (effective 2003). 70 p./no.; **Document type:** *Monographic series, Academic/Scholarly.*
Published by: (Universidad del Pais Vasco, Departamento de Sociologia), Universidad del Pais Vasco, Servicio Editorial, Apartado 1397, Bilbao, 48080, Spain. TEL 34-94-6015126, FAX 34-94-4801314, luxedito@lg.ehu.es, http://www.ehu.es/servicios/se_az/pags/p43.htm. Ed. Mr. Andres Davila. R&P, Adv. contact Mr. Juan J Rodriguez.

SLEUTELGAT. see *LINGUISTICS*

370.115 TWN
SOCIAL EDUCATION YEARLY✶ . Text in Chinese. a. abstr.; charts; stat. index, cum.index.
Media: Duplicated (not offset).
Published by: Social Education Society of China, Ministry of Education, Social Education Dept., Chungshan S. Rd., Taipei, Taiwan. Ed. Shing Chou Wang.

370.15 NLD ISSN 1381-2890
LC189.8 CODEN: SPEDFX
➤ **SOCIAL PSYCHOLOGY OF EDUCATION**; an international journal. Text in English. 1996. q. EUR 288, USD 288, GBP 180 combined subscription to institutions print & online eds. (effective 2005). adv. reprint service avail. from PSC. **Document type:** *Journal, Academic/Scholarly.* **Description:** Fills the gap between the disciplines of psychology and sociology, covering a wide variety of content concerns, theoretical interests and research methods.
Related titles: Online - full text ed.: ISSN 1573-1928 (from EBSCO Publishing, Gale Group, IngentaConnect, Kluwer Online, O C L C Online Computer Library Center, Inc., Springer LINK, Swets Information Services).
Indexed: AEI, BibLing, CPE, ERA, PsycInfo, PsycholAb, SSA, SociolAb, e-psyche.
—BLDSC (8318.146100), IE, Infotrieve, ingenta. **CCC.**
Published by: Springer-Verlag Dordrecht (Subsidiary of: Springer Science+Business Media), Van Godewijckstraat 30, Dordrecht, 3311 GX, Netherlands. TEL 31-78-6576050, FAX 31-78-6576474, http://springerlink.metapress.com/openurl.asp?genre=journal&issn=1381-2890, http://www.springeronline.com. Ed. Lawrence J Saha.

➤ **SOCIALNA PEDAGOGIKA.** see *SOCIOLOGY*

➤ **SOCIALPAEDAGOGEN.** see *SOCIAL SERVICES AND WELFARE*

➤ **SOCIETY FOR RESEARCH IN CHILD DEVELOPMENT. MONOGRAPHS.** see *PSYCHOLOGY*

370.1 USA
SOCIETY OF PROFESSORS OF EDUCATION. NEWSLETTER. Text in English. irreg. membership. **Document type:** *Newsletter.*
Former titles: Society of Professors of Education. Quarterly Review (0028-0194); National Society of College Teachers of Education Newsletter
Published by: Society of Professors of Education, c/o Dr Robert Morris, Dept of Ed Ldshp, UWG, 1600 Maple St, Carrollton, GA 30118-5160. TEL 770-836-4426, FAX 770-836-4646. Ed., R&P Robert C Morris. Circ: 150.

371.1 USA ISSN 0882-7141
SOCIETY OF PROFESSORS OF EDUCATION. OCCASIONAL PAPERS. Text in English. 1974. irreg. price varies. **Document type:** *Monographic series.*
Formerly: National Society of College Teachers of Education. Occasional Papers
Published by: Society of Professors of Education, c/o Dr Robert Morris, Dept of Ed Ldshp, UWG, 1600 Maple St, Carrollton, GA 30118-5160. TEL 770-836-4426, FAX 770-836-4646. R&P Robert C Morris. Circ: (controlled).

370.15 USA ISSN 0038-0407
L11 CODEN: SCYEB7
➤ **SOCIOLOGY OF EDUCATION**; a journal of research in socialization and social structure. Text in English. 1927. q. USD 75 in US & Canada to individuals; USD 95 foreign to individuals; USD 155 in US & Canada to institutions; USD 175 foreign to institutions; USD 30 in US & Canada to members; USD 50 foreign to members (effective 2005). adv. charts; illus. Index. back issues avail.; reprint service avail. from PQC. **Document type:** *Journal, Academic/Scholarly.* **Description:** Publishes papers on educational processes and human development. The research may focus on the individual, institutions, or structural arrangements among institutions which have a bearing on education and human development.
Formerly (until 1963): Journal of Educational Sociology (0885-3525)
Related titles: Microform ed.: (from PMC, PQC); Online - full text ed.: (from EBSCO Publishing, Gale Group, IngentaConnect, JSTOR (Web-based Journal Archive), O C L C Online Computer Library Center, Inc., ProQuest Information & Learning).
Indexed: ABIn, AMHA, ASCA, ASSIA, AgeL, AmH&L, CIJE, CPE, CurCont, DIP, EAA, ERA, ETA, EduInd, FamI, HEA, HECAB, HistAb, IBR, IBZ, MEA, MEA&I, PAIS, PCI, PRA, PsycInfo, PsycholAb, RASB, RHEA, SEA, SENA, SOMA, SOPODA, SRRA, SSA, SSCI, SSI, SWA, SociolAb, TEA, e-psyche.
—BLDSC (8319.678000), IDS, IE, Infotrieve, ingenta.
Published by: American Sociological Association, 1307 New York Ave, N W, Ste 700, Washington, DC 20005-4701. TEL 202-383-9005, FAX 202-638-0882, socofed@jhu.edu, publications@asanet.org, http://ceres.ingentaselect.com/vl=1844302/cl=41/nw=1/rpsv/cw/asoca/00380407/contp1.htm, http://www.asanet.org. Ed. Karl L Alexander. Adv. contact Redante Asuncion Reed. B&W page USD 300; 5.312 x 7.5. Circ: 3,000.

370 PRI ISSN 0034-933X
EL SOL. Text in Spanish. 4/yr. adv. bk.rev. charts; illus.
Published by: Asociacion de Maestros de Puerto Rico, Ave Ponce de Leon 452, Hato Rey, 00918, Puerto Rico. TEL 787-767-2020, http://www.amaestros.edu. Ed. Evelyn Cruz de Soto. Circ: 35,000.

SOLIDARITY NEWSLETTER. see *LABOR UNIONS*

SOLOMON GOLDMAN LECTURES. see *RELIGIONS AND THEOLOGY—Judaic*

370.949 SVN ISSN 1318-6728
LB5
➤ **SOLSKA KRONIKA/SCHOOL CHRONICLE**; zbornik za zgodovino solstva in vzgoje. Text in Slovenian; Summaries in English, German. 1964. a. SIT 3,000; SIT 1,500 per issue (effective 2005). bk.rev. bibl.; illus. back issues avail. **Document type:** *Journal, Academic/Scholarly.* **Description:** Disseminates articles, discussions, viewpoints, and reviews on all aspects on the history of schools and education.
Supersedes in part (in 1992): Zbornik za Povijest Skolstva i Prosvjete (0352-7972); Which was formerly (until 1984): Zbornik za Historiju Skolstva i Prosvjete (0514-6151)
Related titles: E-mail ed.; Fax ed.; Online - full text ed.
Indexed: AmH&L, HistAb, IBZ.
Published by: Slovenski Solski Muzej, Plecnikov trg 1, Ljubljana, 1000, Slovenia. solski.muzej@guest.arnes.si, http://www.ssolski-muzej.si. Ed. Stane Okolis. Pub. Branko Sustar. Circ: 800 (controlled).

370 SVN
SOLSKI RAZGLEDI. Text in Slovenian. 1950. 20/yr. SIT 2,700 (effective 2000). adv. bk.rev. **Document type:** *Newspaper.*
Formerly (until 1992): Prosvetni Delavec (0033-1643)
Published by: Prosvetni Delavec d.d., Poljanski nasip 28, Ljubljana, 1000, Slovenia. TEL 386-61-315585. Ed., Adv. contact Lucka Lesnik. Circ: 7,000.

371.912 DEU
➤ **SONDERPAEDAGOGISCHE FOERDERUNG.** Text in German. 1956. bi-m. EUR 39; EUR 25.50 to students; EUR 12 newsstand/cover (effective 2003). adv. bk.rev. abstr.; charts; illus. index. reprints avail. **Document type:** *Journal, Academic/Scholarly.*
Former titles (until 2003): Die Neue Sonderschule; Sonderschule (0323-4592)
Indexed: IBR, IBZ.
Published by: Julius Beltz GmbH & Co. KG, Werderstr 10, Weinheim, 69469, Germany. TEL 49-6201-60070, FAX 49-6201-6007393, info@beltz.de, http://www.beltz.de. Ed. Gabriele Pannwitz. R&P Heiko Ernst. adv.: page EUR 730. Circ: 9,500.

370 USA
➤ **THE SOURCE (LOS ANGELES)**; a journal of education. Text in English. 1999. irreg. free (effective 2004). **Document type:** *Academic/Scholarly.* **Description:** Aims at disseminating the most current research and fresh ideas in all areas of education.
Media: Online - full text.
Published by: University of Southern California, Rossier School of Education, White Phillips Hall, 1100C, Los Angeles, CA 90089-0031. source@usc.edu, http://www.usc.edu/dept/education/TheSource/.

370 300 FRA ISSN 1683-2310
SOURCE O C D E. ENSEIGNEMENT ET COMPETENCES. (Organisation de Cooperation et Developpement Economiques) Text in French. irreg. EUR 590, USD 678, GBP 389, JPY 79,700 (effective 2005).
Related titles: Online - full content ed.: ISSN 1684-2960. EUR 410, USD 471, GBP 272, JPY 55,400 (effective 2005); Online - full text ed.: (from EBSCO Publishing, Gale Group, IngentaConnect, Swets Information Services); ♦ English ed.: Source O E C D. Education & Skills. ISSN 1608-0165.
Published by: Organization for Economic Cooperation and Development, 2 Rue Andre Pascal, Paris, 75775 Cedex 16, France. TEL 33-1-45248200, FAX 33-1-45248500, http://www.oecd.org. **Dist. by:** Extenza - Turpin, Pegasus Dr, Stratton Business Park, Biggleswade, Beds SG18 8TQ, United Kingdom. TEL 44-1462-687552, FAX 44-1462-480947, subscriptions@extenza-turpin.com; O E C D Turpin North America, PO Box 194, Downingtown, PA 19335-0194. TEL 610-524-5361, 800-456-6323, FAX 610-524-5417, journalscustomer@turpinna.com.

370 300 FRA ISSN 1608-0165
SOURCE O C D E. EDUCATION & SKILLS. Text in English. irreg. EUR 590, USD 678, GBP 389, JPY 79,700 (effective 2005). **Document type:** *Government.*

E

▼ *new title* ➤ *refereed* ✶ *unverified* ♦ *full entry avail.*

Related titles: Online - full content ed.: ISSN 1681-5327. EUR 410, USD 471, GBP 272, JPY 55,400 (effective 2005); Online - full text ed.: 2000 (from EBSCO Publishing, Gale Group, IngentaConnect, Swets Information Services); ♦ French ed.: Source O C D E. Enseignement et Competences. ISSN 1683-2310.
Published by: Organization for Economic Cooperation and Development, 2 Rue Andre Pascal, Paris, 75775 Cedex 16, France. TEL 33-1-45248200, FAX 33-1-45248500, http://www.oecd.org. **Dist. by:** Extenza - Turpin, Pegasus Dr, Stratton Business Park, Biggleswade, Beds SG18 8TQ, United Kingdom. TEL 44-1462-687552, FAX 44-1462-480947, subscriptions@extenza-turpin.com; O E C D Turpin North America, PO Box 194, Downingtown, PA 19335-0194. TEL 610-524-5361, 800-456-6323, FAX 610-524-5417, journalscustomer@turpinna.com.

370.968 ZAF ISSN 0256-0100 CODEN: SAJEDM
SOUTH AFRICAN JOURNAL OF EDUCATION/SUID-AFRIKAANSE TYDSKRIF VIR OPVOEDKUNDE. Text and summaries in Afrikaans, English. 1981-1993 (vol.13, no.4); resumed. q. ZAR 175 to individuals; ZAR 290 to institutions (effective 2003). bk.rev. back issues avail. **Document type:** *Academic/Scholarly.*
Related titles: Online - full text ed.: (from International Network for the Availability of Scientific Publications, African Journals Online).
Indexed: CPE, DIP, ERA, ETA, IBSS, ISAP, MEA, SEA, SENA, TEA.
—BLDSC (8338.865000), IE, ingenta.
Published by: (South African Association for the Advancement of Education), Foundation for Education Science and Technology, PO Box 1758, Pretoria, 0001, South Africa. TEL 27-12-322-6422, http://www.inasp.info/ajol/journals/saje/about.html. Ed. C H Swanepoel. Circ: 500.

SOUTH AFRICAN MUSIC TEACHER/SUID-AFRIKAANSE MUSIEKONDERWYSER. see *MUSIC*

370.954 PHL ISSN 0038-3600
AS539.5
SOUTHEAST ASIA JOURNAL. Text in English. s-a. PHP 30, USD 5. adv. bibl.
Indexed: BAS, IPP, MLA-IB, RASB.
Published by: Central Philippine University, PO Box 231, Iloilo City, Iloilo Province 5000, Philippines. Ed. Elma S Herradura.

SOUTHERN AFRICAN JOURNAL OF MATHEMATICS AND SCIENCE EDUCATION. see *MATHEMATICS*

SOUTHERN BAPTIST EDUCATOR. see *RELIGIONS AND THEOLOGY—Protestant*

370 AUT ISSN 0038-6146
SOZIALISTISCHE ERZIEHUNG; Zeitschrift fuer Erziehung, Bildung, Kultur. Text in German. 1921. 4/yr. adv. bk.rev. abstr.; bibl.; charts; stat. index, cum.index. **Document type:** *Journal, Academic/Scholarly.*
Published by: Kinderfreunde Oesterreich, Rauhensteingasse 5-5, Vienna, W 1010, Austria. TEL 43-1-5121298, FAX 43-1-512129862, kind-und-co@kinderfreunde.at, http://www.kinderfreunde.at. Ed. Ute Pichler. Circ: 6,000.

370 DEU ISSN 0932-3244
HM5 CODEN: SINFEY
SOZIALWISSENSCHAFTLICHE INFORMATIONEN. Text in German. 1972. q. EUR 40; EUR 12.50 newsstand/cover (effective 2005). adv. **Document type:** *Journal, Academic/Scholarly.*
Formerly (until 1986): Sozialwissenschaftliche Informationen fuer Unterricht und Studium (0340-2304)
Indexed: AmH&L, DIP, HistAb, IBR, IBZ.
Published by: (Arbeitskreis Sozialwissenschaftliche Informationen), Erhard Friedrich Verlag GmbH, Im Brande 17, Seelze, 30926, Germany. TEL 49-511-400040, FAX 49-511-40004170, info@friedrich-verlag.de, http://www.friedrich-verlag.de/index.cfm?692FD9AEC9D940248B56DB0897BB4474. adv.: color page EUR 350, B&W page EUR 230. Circ: 3,000.

370.946 ESP
SPAIN. MINISTERIO DE EDUCACION Y CULTURA. BOLETIN. Text in Spanish. m. **Document type:** *Bulletin, Government.*
Formed by the 1997 merger of: Spain. Ministerio de Educacion y Ciencia. Boletin Oficial: Actos Administrativos; Spain. Ministerio de Educacion y Ciencia. Boletin Oficial: Coleccion Legislativa
Published by: Ministerio de Educacion, Cultura y Deporte, Centro de Publicaciones, c/o Ciudad Universitaria, S/N, Madrid, 28040, Spain. TEL 34-91-453-9800.

370 ESP
SPAIN. MINISTERIO DE EDUCACION Y CULTURA. GUIA. Text in Spanish. m. **Document type:** *Bulletin, Government.*
Formerly: Spain. Ministerio de Educacion y Ciencia. Guia
Published by: Ministerio de Educacion, Cultura y Deporte, Centro de Publicaciones, c/o Ciudad Universitaria, S/N, Madrid, 28040, Spain. FAX 34-91-4539884.

SPEAK OUT!. see *THEATER*

371.85 USA
PN4009
SPEAKER AND GAVEL (ONLINE EDITION). Text in English. 1964. q. USD 5 (effective 2005). reprint service avail. from PQC.
Formerly: Speaker and Gavel (Print Edition) (0584-8164)
Media: Online - full content. **Related titles:** Microform ed.: 1964 (from PQC).
Published by: Delta Sigma Rho-Tau Kappa Alpha - National Honorary Forensic Society, c/o James Weaver, Pres, 230 Armstrong Hall, Minnesota State University, Mankato, MN 56001. TEL 507-389-6160, daniel.cronn-mills@mnsu.edu. Ed. Daniel Cronn-Mills. Circ: 1,200.

371 ZAF
SPECIFILE SCHOOLS COMMUNICATOR. Variant title: Schools Communicator. Text in English. 1993. 3/yr. adv. illus. **Document type:** *Trade.*
Published by: Communications Group, PO Box 7870, Johannesburg, 2000, South Africa.

370 USA
SPECTRA (ANNANDALE). Text in English. 1964. m. USD 45 domestic; USD 50 foreign (effective 2000). **Document type:** *Newsletter.*
Published by: National Communication Association, 1765 N St, N W, Washington, DC 20036. smorreale@natcom.org, http://www.natcom.org. Circ: 6,000.

370 AUS ISSN 1037-2040
SPECTRUM (HOBART). Text in English. 1967. bi-m. free to qualified personnel. bk.rev. index. **Document type:** *Newspaper, Government.* **Description:** Covers departmental issues in education and state library service.
Former titles (until May 1991): Tasmania. Department of Education and the Arts. Gazette (1035-5014); Tasmanian Education Gazette (0039-9760)
Related titles: Online - full text ed.
Published by: Department of Education, 116 Bathurst St, Hobart, TAS 7000, Australia. TEL 61-3-6233-7721, FAX 61-3-6233-7300, http://www.tased.edu.au. Ed., R&P Zoe Furman. Circ: 3,300 (controlled).

SPEECH AND DRAMA. see *THEATER*

373 RUS ISSN 0869-5210
LC1047.R9 CODEN: SSOBET
SPETSIALIST. Text in Russian. 1954. m. USD 72 (effective 1999). adv. bk.rev. index. **Document type:** *Academic/Scholarly.*
Formerly (until 1991): Srednee Spetsial'noe Obrazovanie (0131-9590)
—East View.
Address: A-ya 35, Moscow, 129090, Russian Federation. TEL 7-095-2815404. Ed., Adv. contact Eugene N Kolosov. Circ: 6,000.

372 DEU ISSN 0344-8754
SPIELEN UND LERNEN. Text in German. 1968. m. EUR 3.75 newsstand/cover (effective 2002). adv. **Document type:** *Magazine, Consumer.*
Published by: Velber im OZ Verlag GmbH, Guenterstalstr. 57, Freiburg, 79102, Germany. TEL 49-761-705780, FAX 49-761-7057839, butsch@oz-bpv.de, http://www.oz-verlag.com. Adv. contact Bernd Sandvoss. B&W page EUR 4,140, color page EUR 7,670. Circ: 125,139 (paid).

370.72 FRA ISSN 0994-3722
➤ **SPIRALE;** revue de recherches en education. Text in French. 1988. 2/yr. bk.rev. back issues avail. **Document type:** *Monographic series, Academic/Scholarly.* **Description:** Contains articles on education research. For researchers and educators.
Indexed: CBCARef.
Published by: Universite de Lille III (Charles de Gaulle), Sciences de l'Education, B.P. 149, Villeneuve d'Ascq, Cedex 59653, France. TEL 33-3-20416491, FAX 33-3-20416203, brassart@univ-lille3.fr. Ed. Dominique Guy Brassart. Circ: 450.

➤ **SPORT, EDUCATION AND SOCIETY.** see *SPORTS AND GAMES*

➤ **SPORT SUPPLEMENT.** see *SPORTS AND GAMES*

➤ **SPORTS BIOMECHANICS.** see *SPORTS AND GAMES*

➤ **SPORTS TEACHER.** see *SPORTS AND GAMES*

➤ **SPOT.** see *PHOTOGRAPHY*

370 BHS
SPOTLIGHT. Text in English. 1976. irreg. USD 1 per issue.
Published by: Ministry of Education and Culture, PO Box N 7147, Nassau, Bahamas.

SPRAKPEDAGOGIK. see *LINGUISTICS*

370 AUS ISSN 1448-6156
▼ ➤ **SPREADSHEETS IN EDUCATION.** Text in English. 2003. a. free (effective 2005). **Document type:** *Journal, Academic/Scholarly.* **Description:** Studies of the role that spreadsheets can play in education.
Media: Online - full text.
Published by: Bond University, Faculty of Information Technology, c/o Dr Steve Sugden, EIC - eJSiE, Gold Coast, QLD 4229, Australia. TEL 61-7-55953325, FAX 61-7-55953320, http://www.sie.bond.edu.au. Ed. Steve Sugden.

370 NLD
SPRINGER INTERNATIONAL HANDBOOKS OF EDUCATION SERIES. Text in English. 1996. irreg., latest vol.13, 2005. price varies. **Document type:** *Monographic series.*
Formerly: Kluwer International Handbooks of Education Series
Published by: Springer-Verlag Dordrecht (Subsidiary of: Springer Science+Business Media), Van Godewijckstraat 30, Dordrecht, 3311 GX, Netherlands. TEL 31-78-6576050, FAX 31-78-6576474, http://www.springeronline.com.

SRBIJA I CRNA GORA ZAVOD ZA STATISTIKU. OSNOVNA I SREDNJE. see *EDUCATION—Abstracting, Bibliographies, Statistics*

370.72 LKA ISSN 1391-1589
SRI LANKAN JOURNAL OF EDUCATIONAL RESEARCH. Text in English. 1990. a. LKR 75; USD 10 foreign. **Document type:** *Academic/Scholarly.*
Published by: National Institute of Education, Department of Educational Research, Maharagama, Sri Lanka. TEL 94-1-851301-5, FAX 94-1-851300. Ed. Upali Gunasekara.

370 IND ISSN 0970-7425
SRIARVIMDA AMTARASTRIYA SIKSHA KEMDRA PATRIKA/SRI AUROBINDO INTERNATIONAL CENTRE OF EDUCATION BULLETIN. Text in Hindi, English, French. 1949. q. INR 80 domestic; USD 12 foreign; INR 20 newsstand/cover (effective 2003). adv. bk.rev. illus. back issues avail. **Document type:** *Magazine, Academic/Scholarly.*
Related titles: ♦ English ed.: Sri Aurobindo International Centre of Education. Bulletin. ISSN 0970-7417.
Published by: Sri Aurobindo Ashram Trust, c/o Manoj Das Gupta, Pondicherry, Tamil Nadu 605 002, India. TEL 91-413-2334980, FAX 91-413-2223328, sabda@sriaurobindoashram.org, http://sabda.sriaurobindoashram.org. Ed., Pub., R&P Manoj Das Gupta.

370.1 IND ISSN 0971-9008
STAFF AND EDUCATIONAL DEVELOPMENT INTERNATIONAL. Text in English. 1997. 3/yr. **Description:** Provides a forum for debate, disscussion and exchange of idea practices, and research on staff and educational development.
Indexed: ERA, ETA, MEA, RHEA, SEA, SENA, SOMA, TEA.
—BLDSC (8426.304000).
Published by: Network for Staff and Educational Development (NetSED), Indira Gandhi National Open University, Maidan Garhi, Delhi, 110 068, India. FAX 91-11-685-7062, stride@del2.vsnl.net.in. Ed. Santosh Panda.

371.8 910.91 GBR ISSN 0953-9115
STAFFROOM GUIDE TO SCHOOL JOURNEYS. Text in English. 1987. a. GBP 25. adv. **Document type:** *Directory.* **Description:** Helps school teachers plan educational trips.
Published by: E M A P Automotive, Wentworth House, Wentworth St, Peterborough, Cambs PE1 1DS, United Kingdom. TEL 44-1733-467048, FAX 44-1733-467002. Ed., Pub. Mark Barton. Adv. contact Marc Bates. B&W page GBP 1,995, color page GBP 2,350; trim 210 x 297. Circ: 5,000 (controlled).

370.9544 IND
STATE INSTITUTE OF EDUCATION, RAJASTHAN. ANNUAL REPORT. Text in English. a.
Published by: State Institute of Education, Udaipur, Rajasthan, India.

372.6 USA ISSN 1077-3584
THE STATE OF READING. Text in English. 1994. s-a. **Document type:** *Journal.* **Description:** Provides a forum for the exchange of information and opinion on current theory, research, and classroom applications in literacy education.
Published by: Texas State Reading Association, 2700 Pecan St W, No 424, Pflugerville, TX 78660. TEL 512-371-3826, 800-326-5274, FAX 512-371-0232, http://www.tsra.us/publications.html.

STATISTICS OF EDUCATION AND TRAINING IN WALES: SCHOOLS. see *EDUCATION—Abstracting, Bibliographies, Statistics*

370.21096773 SOM
STATISTICS OF EDUCATION IN SOMALIA✶. Text in English. irreg. illus.; stat.
Published by: Ministry of Education, Department of Planning, SB 2503, Mogadishu, Somalia.

STATISTICS OF EDUCATION. TEACHERS. ENGLAND AND WALES. see *EDUCATION—Abstracting, Bibliographies, Statistics*

STATISTICS ON SOCIAL WORK EDUCATION IN THE UNITED STATES. see *SOCIAL SERVICES AND WELFARE—Abstracting, Bibliographies, Statistics*

STATISTIK AUSTRIA. KRIPPEN, KINDERGAERTEN UND HORTE (KINDERTAGESHEIME). see *EDUCATION—Abstracting, Bibliographies, Statistics*

305.4 CAN ISSN 1183-0735
STATUS OF WOMEN AND EMPLOYMENT EQUITY IN ONTARIO SCHOOL BOARDS. Text in English. 1986. a.
Formerly (until 1988): Status of Women and Affirmative Action - Employment Equity in Ontario School Boards (0843-4077)
Published by: Ontario. Ministry of Training Colleges and Universities, Mowat Block, 900 Bay St, Toronto, ON M7A 1L2, Canada. TEL 416-325-2929, FAX 416-325-6348, info@edu.gov.cn.ca, http://www.edu.gov.on.ca/eng/welcome.html.

370.1 310 NZL
STATZING. Text in English. stat. **Document type:** *Newsletter, Government.* **Description:** Provides ideas for primary and secondary school teachers on how to access and use Statistics New Zealand data in the class room.
Media: Online - full content. **Related titles:** E-mail ed.
Published by: Statistics New Zealand/Te Tari Tatau, PO Box 2922, Wellington, New Zealand. info@stats.govt.nz, http://www.stats.govt.nz.

370 GBR ISSN 1361-7400
STEINER EDUCATION. Text in English. 1930. s-a. GBP 5.60; USD 11.10 in United States; CND 14.25 in Canada (effective 2000). adv. bk.rev. illus. **Document type:** *Academic/Scholarly.*
Formerly (until 1995): Child and Man (0009-3890)
Indexed: BrEdI, CPE.
Published by: Steiner Waldorf Schools Fellowship, Kidbrooke Park, Forest Row, Sussex, RH18 5JB, United Kingdom. TEL 44-1342-822758, FAX 44-1342-826004. Ed. Dr. Brien Masters. Adv. contact Peter Ramm TEL 44-1342-824564. Circ: 3,000.

STEPPING UP. see *RELIGIONS AND THEOLOGY—Protestant*

370 SWE ISSN 1403-4972
➤ **STOCKHOLM STUDIES OF CURRICULUM STUDIES.** Text in Multiple languages. 1998. irreg. **Document type:** *Monographic series, Academic/Scholarly.*
Published by: H L S Foerlag/Stockholm Institute of Education Press, PO Box 34103, Stockholm, 10026, Sweden. TEL 46-8-7375662, FAX 46-8-6561153, hls-forlag@lhs.se, http://www.lhs.se/forl/. Ed. Staffan Selander.

371.192 GBR
STOP PRESS. Text in English. m. GBP 25 non-photocopiable ed.; GBP 150 photocopiable ed. (effective 2001). **Description:** Summarizes the main education stories published in the national press of the previous month.
Published by: Advisory Centre for Education (A C E) Ltd., 1c Aberdeen Studios, 22 Highbury Grove, London, N5 2DQ, United Kingdom. TEL 44-20-73548318, FAX 44-20-73549069, enquiries@ace.dialnet.com, http://www.ace-ed.org.uk.

THE STORY (DELAWARE). see *RELIGIONS AND THEOLOGY—Protestant*

STORY FRIENDS. see *RELIGIONS AND THEOLOGY*

STORY TIME STORIES THAT RHYME NEWSLETTER. see *CHILDREN AND YOUTH—For*

▼ **STRATEGIC ORGANIZATION.** see *BUSINESS AND ECONOMICS—Management*

371.224 USA
THE STUDENT AID AUDIO GUIDE. Text in English. a. free. **Document type:** *Government.* **Description:** Contains audio files covering various federal student loan questions and answers.
Media: Online - full content.
Published by: U.S. Department of Education, Federal Student Aid Programs, Federal Student Aid Information Center, PO Box 84, Washington, DC 20044-0084 . http://studentaid.ed.gov/students/publications/student_audio_guide/index.html, http://studentaid.ed.gov/PORTALSWebApp/students/english/index.jsp.

▼ **STUDENT GROUP TOUR MAGAZINE.** see *TRAVEL AND TOURISM*

371.224 USA
THE STUDENT GUIDE. Text in English. a. free. **Document type:** *Government.* **Description:** Informs on how to apply for student financial aid.
Related titles: Online - full content ed.; Spanish ed.
Published by: U.S. Department of Education, Federal Student Aid Programs, Federal Student Aid Information Center, PO Box 84, Washington, DC 20044-0084 . http://studentaid.ed.gov/students/publications/student_guide/index.html, http://studentaid.ed.gov/PORTALSWebApp/students/english/index.jsp.

371.42 GBR
STUDENT HELPBOOKS SERIES. Text in English. irreg. price varies. **Description:** Advises students on career options and study skills.
Published by: (Careers Research and Advisory Council), Lifetime Careers Wiltshire, 7 Ascot Ct, White Horse Business Park, Trowbridge, Wilts BA14 OXA, United Kingdom. TEL 44-1225-216000. **Dist. by:** Biblios Publishers' Distribution Services Ltd., Star Rd, Partridge Green, W Sussex RH13 8LD, United Kingdom. TEL 44-1403-710851, FAX 44-1403-711143.

371.8 ZAF ISSN 1022-7938
STUDENT LIFE. Text in English. 1994. bi-m. ZAR 33. adv. illus.
Related titles: Online - full text ed.: (from LexisNexis).
Published by: Studentwise Marketing and Publishing, PO Box 23525, Claremont, Cape Town 7735, South Africa.

371.8 GBR ISSN 1471-6291
THE STUDENT MAGAZINE; international magazine for students of all ages. Text in English. 2000. s-a. GBP 20 in Europe; USD 60 in United States; GBP 25 elsewhere (effective 2002).
Published by: Fern Publications, Casa Alba, 24 Frosty Hollow, E Hunsbury, Northants NN4 0SY, United Kingdom. Ed., Pub. Jacqueline Gonzalez-Marina. Circ: 1,000 (paid).

371.9947 IRL ISSN 1393-9947
STUDENT XPRESS. Text in English. 1999. m. adv. **Document type:** *Newspaper, Consumer.*
Address: PO Box 7433, Dublin, 16, Ireland. editor@studentxpress.ie, http://www.studentxpress.ie. adv.: B&W page EUR 1,790, color page EUR 2,476; 260 x 345. Circ: 50,000 (controlled).

370 DEU ISSN 0931-0444
STUDENTEN KURIER. Text in German. 1981. q. bk.rev. back issues avail. **Document type:** *Journal, Academic/Scholarly.*
Published by: Gemeinschaft fuer Deutsche Studentengeschichte, Oberstr 45, Essen, 45134, Germany. TEL 49-201-843469, FAX 49-201-843499, gds@gmx.de, http://www.gds-web.dem. Ed. Detlef Frische. Circ: 2,000 (paid).

STUDENTIDROTT. see *SPORTS AND GAMES*

371.8 SWE
STUDENTLIV. Text in Swedish. 5/yr. adv. **Document type:** *Magazine, Consumer.*
Published by: Tjaenstemaennens Centralorganisation, Stockholm, 11494, Sweden. TEL 46-8-782-93-12, FAX 46-8-662-36-79, studentliv@tco.se, http://www.tco.se/studentliv. Ed., Pub. Alexander Armiento. adv.: B&W page SEK 41,800, color page SEK 46,400; trim 210 x 290. Circ: 188,900 (controlled).

373 JOR
STUDENT'S MESSAGE✶ /RISALAT AL-TALIB. Text in Arabic. 1963. m.
Address: P O Box 2087, Amman, Jordan. Ed. Abdullah Abu Mughly.

STUDENTS WORLD. see *COLLEGE AND ALUMNI*

370.15 ITA ISSN 0393-6163
STUDI DI PSICOLOGIA DELL'EDUCAZIONE. Text in Italian. 1982. 3/yr. EUR 28.50 domestic; EUR 51.07 foreign (effective 2005). bibl.; charts; illus.; stat. **Document type:** *Journal, Academic/Scholarly.*
Indexed: DIP, IBR, IBZ, PsycholAb, e-psyche.
Published by: (Pontificia Universita della Santa Croce), Armando Editore Srl, Viale Trastevere 236, Rome, 00153, Italy. TEL 39-06-5894525, FAX 39-06-5818564, info@armandoeditore.com, http://www.armando.it. Ed. Roberto Truzoli.

370 ITA ISSN 0392-2146
STUDI SULL'EDUCAZIONE. Text in Italian. 1981. irreg., latest vol.46, 1999. price varies. adv. **Document type:** *Monographic series.*
Published by: Liguori Editore srl, Via Posillipo 394, Naples, 80123, Italy. TEL 39-81-7206111, FAX 39-81-7206244, http://www.liguori.it. Eds. Paolo Orefice, Raffaele Laporta. Pub. Guido Liguori. Adv. contact Maria Liguori.

370.1 BEL
STUDIA PAEDAGOGICA. Text in English. 1973. irreg., latest vol.30, 2001. price varies. back issues avail. **Document type:** *Monographic series, Academic/Scholarly.* **Description:** Examines topics of pedagogical inquiry.
—BLDSC (8483.097700).
Published by: Leuven University Press, Blijde Inkomststraat 5, Leuven, 3000, Belgium. TEL 32-16-325345, FAX 32-16-325352, university.press@upers.kuleuven.ac.be, http://www.kuleuven.ac.be/upers.

370 POL ISSN 0081-6795
STUDIA PEDAGOGICZNE. Text in Polish. 1954. irreg. price varies. **Document type:** *Monographic series, Academic/Scholarly.*
Published by: Polska Akademia Nauk, Komitet Nauk Pedagogicznych, ul Mokotowska 16/20, Warsaw, 01561, Poland. TEL 48-22-6283461. Ed. Tadeusz Lewowicki.

370.15 SWE ISSN 0346-5926
STUDIA PSYCHOLOGICA ET PAEDAGOGICA; series altera. Text in English, Swedish; Summaries in English. 1947. irreg. price varies. back issues avail. **Document type:** *Journal, Academic/Scholarly.*
Indexed: e-psyche.
Published by: Malmoe University, Department of Education, Fack 23501, Malmo, 20045, Sweden. FAX 46-40-325-210.
Co-sponsor: Malmoe Institute of Education.

370.15 ROM ISSN 1221-8111
BF30
STUDIA UNIVERSITATIS "BABES-BOLYAI". PSYCHOLOGIA - PAEDAGOGIA. Text in English, Romanian; Summaries in English, French, German. 1990. s-a. per issue exchange basis. **Document type:** *Academic/Scholarly.*
Indexed: IBSS, RASB, e-psyche.
Published by: Universitatea "Babes-Bolyai", Biblioteca Centrala Universitara/Babes-Bolyai University, Central University Library in Cluj-Napoca, Mihail Kogalniceanu 1B, Cluj-Napoca, 3400, Romania. TEL 40-64-194315, FAX 40-64-191906, puc@hera.ubbcluj.ro, staff@staff.ubbcluj.ro. Ed. A Marga.

370 DEU ISSN 0076-5627
STUDIEN UND BERICHTE. Text mainly in German; Summaries in English. 1965. irreg., latest vol.68, 2000. price varies. **Document type:** *Monographic series, Academic/Scholarly.*
Published by: Max-Planck-Institut fuer Bildungsforschung, Lentzeallee 94, Berlin, 14195, Germany. TEL 49-30-82406-0.

370.1 DEU ISSN 1435-6538
STUDIEN ZUR SCHULPAEDAGOGIK. Text in German. 1994. irreg., latest vol.46, 2005. price varies. **Document type:** *Monographic series, Academic/Scholarly.*
Published by: Verlag Dr. Kovac, Arnoldstr 49, Hamburg, 22763, Germany. TEL 49-40-3988800, FAX 49-40-39888055, info@verlagdrkovac.de, http://www.verlagdrkovac.de/7-3.htm.

370 DEU
DER STUDIENBEGINN. Text in German. 1968. a. adv.
Published by: Verein Freunde und Foerderer der Deutschen Studentenschaft e.V., Untere Hausbreite 11, Munich, 80939, Germany. Ed. Gundolf Seidenspinner.

370 SWE ISSN 0348-212X
STUDIER I IDE- OCH LAERDOMSHISTORIA. Text in Multiple languages. 1978. irreg., latest vol.3, 1988. price varies. **Document type:** *Monographic series, Academic/Scholarly.*
Related titles: ♦ Series of: Acta Universitatis Upsaliensis. ISSN 0346-5462.
Published by: (Uppsala Universitet), Uppsala Universitet, Acta Universitatis Upsaliensis/University Publications from Uppsala, PO Box 256, Uppsala, 75105, Sweden. TEL 46-18-4713922, http://www.ub.uu.se/upu/auu. Ed. Bengt Landgren. **Dist. by:** Almqvist & Wiksell International, PO Box 614, Soedertaelje 15127, Sweden. TEL 46-8-5509497, FAX 46-8-55016710.

370.9 FRA ISSN 0251-5865
STUDIES AND SURVEYS IN COMPARATIVE EDUCATION. Text in French. a. **Document type:** *Academic/Scholarly.*
Related titles: ♦ Series of: I B E Studies Series.
Published by: (International Bureau of Education), UNESCO Publishing, 7 place de Fontenoy, Paris, 75352, France. TEL 33-1-45684300, FAX 33-1-45685737, http://www.unesco.org/publications. **Dist. in US by:** Bernan Associates, Bernan, 4611-F Assembly Dr., Lanham, MD 20706-4391. TEL 800-274-4447, FAX 800-865-3450.

STUDIES IN ART EDUCATION; a journal of issues and research in art education. see *ART*

370.9 USA
STUDIES IN COMPARATIVE EDUCATION. Text in English. 1978. irreg. price varies. **Document type:** *Monographic series.*
Published by: Praeger Publishers (Subsidiary of: Greenwood Publishing Group Inc.), 88 Post Rd W, Box 5007, Westport, CT 06881-5007. TEL 203-226-3571, FAX 203-222-1502.

STUDIES IN COMPOSITION AND RHETORIC. see *LITERATURE*

371.334 IND ISSN 0254-0185
STUDIES IN EDUCATION AND TEACHING TECHNIQUES. Text in English. 1979. irreg. price varies. **Document type:** *Monographic series, Academic/Scholarly.* **Description:** Studies of education and information about educational software innovations.
Published by: Bahri Publications, 1749A/5, Gobindpuri Extension, Kalkaji, P O Box 4453, New Delhi, 110 019, India. TEL 91-11-644-5710, FAX 91-11-6448606, bahrius@ndf.vsnl.net.in, bahrius@del6.vsnl.net.in. Ed. Ujjal Singh Bahri.

370 SWE ISSN 1652-2729
L46
STUDIES IN EDUCATIONAL POLICY AND EDUCATIONAL PHILOSOPHY DISCOURSE. Text in Danish, English, Norwegian, Swedish. 2002. s-a. (1-3/yr.). free. **Document type:** *Journal, Academic/Scholarly.*
Media: Online - full content.

E

Published by: Studies in Educational Policy and Educational Philosophy, Pedagogiska institutionen, Uppsala universitet, Box 2109, Uppsala, 750 02, Sweden. marie.ols@ilu.uu.se, ulf_p.lundgren@ped.uu.se, http://www.upi.artisan.se/Pages/cgi-bin/PUB_Latest_Version.exe?allFrameset=1&pageId=3, http://130.238.25.247/ILU_portal/externt/forskning/STEP/Index_Eng.htm. Ed. Ulf P Lundgren.

370.15   SWE   ISSN 1400-478X
STUDIES IN EDUCATIONAL SCIENCES. Text in Multiple languages. 1977. irreg. price varies. back issues avail. **Document type:** Monographic series, Academic/Scholarly.
Formerly (until 1992): Studies in Education and Psychology (0348-291X)
Indexed: e-psyche.
Published by: (Laerarhoegskolan i Stockholm, Institutionen foer Individ, Omvaerld och Laerande/Stockholm Institute of Education), H L S Foerlag/Stockholm Institute of Education Press, PO Box 34103, Stockholm, 10026, Sweden. TEL 46-8-7375662, FAX 46-8-6561153, hls-forlag@lhs.se, http://www.lhs.se/forl/.

STUDIES IN JEWISH EDUCATION. see RELIGIONS AND THEOLOGY—Judaic

370   AUS   ISSN 1832-2050
▼ ➤ **STUDIES IN LEARNING, EVALUATION, INNOVATION AND DEVELOPMENT.** Text in English. 2004. irreg. free (effective 2005). **Document type:** Journal, Academic/Scholarly. **Description:** It supports emerging scholars and the development of evidence-based practice and publishes research and scholarship about teaching and learning in formal, semi-formal and informal educational settings and sites.
Media: Online - full text.
Published by: Central Queensland University, Division of Teaching and Learning Services, Learning, Evaluation, Innovation and Development Centre, Rockhampton, QLD 4702, Australia. TEL 61-7-49306417, FAX 61-7-49309792, http://www.sleid.cqu.edu.au/index.php.

➤ **STUDIES IN MATHEMATICS EDUCATION SERIES.** see MATHEMATICS

370.1   NLD   ISSN 0039-3746
L11   CODEN: SPYEAT
➤ **STUDIES IN PHILOSOPHY AND EDUCATION;** an international quarterly. Text in English. 1960. bi-m. EUR 438, USD 448, GBP 278 combined subscription to institutions print & online eds. (effective 2005). adv. bk.rev. back issues avail.; reprint service avail. from PSC. **Document type:** Journal, Academic/Scholarly. **Description:** Focuses on philosophical, normative and conceptual problems and issues in educational research, policy and practice.
Related titles: Microform ed.: (from PQC); Online - full text ed.: ISSN 1573-191X (from EBSCO Publishing, Gale Group, IngentaConnect, Kluwer Online, O C L C Online Computer Library Center, Inc., Springer LINK, Swets Information Services).
Indexed: AEI, BibLing, BrEdI, CPE, DIP, ERA, ETA, HEA, IBR, IBSS, IBZ, IPB, MEA, PCI, PhilInd, RHEA, SEA, SENA, SOMA, SOPODA, SSA, SociolAb, TEA.
—BLDSC (8491.220000), IE, Infotrieve, ingenta. **CCC.**
Published by: Springer-Verlag Dordrecht (Subsidiary of: Springer Science+Business Media), Van Godewijckstraat 30, Dordrecht, 3311 GX, Netherlands. TEL 31-78-6576050, FAX 31-78-6576474, http://springerlink.metapress.com/openurl.asp?genre=journal&issn=0039-3746, http://www.springeronline.com. Ed. Gert Biesta.

370   GBR   ISSN 1742-5964
▼ ➤ **STUDYING TEACHER EDUCATION;** a journal of self-study of teacher education practices. Text in English. 2005 (May). s-a. GBP 106, USD 160 combined subscription to institutions print & online eds. (effective 2006). **Document type:** Journal, Academic/Scholarly. **Description:** Publishes research in the study of teaching and teacher education practices, with a goal of encouragement and wide dissemination. The journal is a forum for educators to make contributions to self-study research design and practice, the knowledge base of teaching and teaching about teaching, enhanced understandings of learning to teach, the nature of teacher education, and the professional development of teachers and teacher educators.
Related titles: Online - full text ed.: ISSN 1742-5972. GBP 101, USD 152 to institutions (effective 2006) (from EBSCO Publishing).
Published by: Routledge (Subsidiary of: Taylor & Francis Group), 4 Park Sq, Milton Park, Abingdon, Oxon OX14 4RN, United Kingdom. TEL 44-1235-828600, FAX 44-1235-829000, info@routledge.co.uk, http://www.tandf.co.uk/journals/titles/17425964.asp, http://www.routledge.co.uk. Eds. John Loughran, Tom Russell. **Subscr. to:** Taylor & Francis Ltd, Journals Customer Service, Rankine Rd, Basingstoke, Hants RG24 8PR, United Kingdom. TEL 44-1256-813000, FAX 44-1256-330245.

370   CHN   ISSN 1009-7597
SUIZHI JIAOYU (XIAOXUE BAN)/QUALITY EDUCATION (PRIMARY SCHOOL EDITION). Text in Chinese. m. CNY 42 (effective 2004). **Document type:** Journal, Academic/Scholarly.

Related titles: Alternate Frequency ed(s).: a. USD 26.60 (effective 2002).
Published by: Zhongguo Renmin Daxue, Shubao Zilio Zhongxin/Renmin University of China, Information Center for Social Server, Dongcheng-qu, 3, Zhangzizhong Lu, Beijing, 100007, China. TEL 86-10-64039458, FAX 86-10-64015080, kyes@163.net, http://www.confucius.cn.net/bkdetail.asp?fzt=V7. **Dist. in the US by:** China Publications Service, PO Box 49614, Chicago, IL 60649. TEL 312-288-3291, FAX 312-288-8570; **Dist. outside of China by:** China International Book Trading Corp, 35 Chegongzhuang Xilu, Haidian District, PO Box 399, Beijing 100044, China. TEL 86-10-68412045, FAX 86-10-68412023, cibtc@mail.cibtc.com.cn, http://www.cibtc.com.cn/.

370   CHN
SUIZHI JIAOYU (ZHONGXUE BAN)/QUALITY EDUCATION (MIDDLE SCHOOL EDITION). Text in Chinese. m. CNY 42 (effective 2004). **Document type:** Journal, Academic/Scholarly.
Related titles: Alternate Frequency ed(s).: a. USD 26.60 (effective 2001).
Published by: Zhongguo Renmin Daxue, Shubao Zilio Zhongxin/Renmin University of China, Information Center for Social Server, Dongcheng-qu, 3, Zhangzizhong Lu, Beijing, 100007, China. TEL 86-10-64039458, FAX 86-10-64015080, kyes@163.net, http://www.confucius.cn.net/bkdetail.asp?fzt=V4. **Dist. in the US by:** China Publications Service, PO Box 49614, Chicago, IL 60649. TEL 312-288-3291, FAX 312-288-8570; **Dist. outside of China by:** China International Book Trading Corp, 35 Chegongzhuang Xilu, Haidian District, PO Box 399, Beijing 100044, China. TEL 86-10-68412045, FAX 86-10-68412023, cibtc@mail.cibtc.com.cn, http://www.cibtc.com.cn.

THE SUMMIT. see RELIGIONS AND THEOLOGY—Roman Catholic

371.1   USA   ISSN 0094-2308
LB2833.3.D4
SUPPLY AND DEMAND: EDUCATIONAL PERSONNEL IN DELAWARE. Variant title: Educational Personnel in Delaware. Text in English. a. illus.
Formerly: Delaware. Department of Public Instruction. Teacher Supply and Demand
Published by: (Delaware. Division of Planning, Research & Evaluation), Department of Public Instruction, Townsend Bldg, Dover, DE 19903. TEL 302-736-4583.

371   USA
SUPPORT AND ASSISTANCE UPDATE; a newsletter offering support and assistance to educators implementing Project Construct. Text in English. 1995. s-a. bk.rev. bibl.; illus. **Document type:** Newsletter, Academic/Scholarly. **Description:** Each issue focuses on a central theme or issue in education. Offers elementary and secondary educators practical tips and alerts them to forthcoming conferences.
Published by: University of Missouri - Columbia, Project Construct National Center, 27 S Tenth St, Ste 202, Columbia, MO 65211-8010. TEL 800-335-PCNC, FAX 573-884-5580, http://www.projectconstruct.org. Ed. Bill Sutherland.
Co-sponsor: Missouri Department of Elementary and Secondary Education.

370   ESP   ISSN 0210-1955
SURGAM∗. Text in Spanish. 6/yr.
—CINDOC.
Address: Carretera Betera s-n, Valencia, 46110, Spain. Ed. Tomas Roca.

THE SURVEY KIT. see MEDICAL SCIENCES

370.72   IND
SURVIVAL SKILLS FOR SCHOLARS. Text in English. **Description:** For anyone contemplating a career in teacher education in special education. It informs decisions about their personal and professional future.
—BLDSC (8553.061000).
Published by: Sage Publications India Pvt. Ltd. (Subsidiary of: Sage Publications, Inc.), M-32 Market, Greater Kailash-I, PO Box 4215, New Delhi, 110 048, India. TEL 91-11-6444958, FAX 91-11-6472426, sageind@nda.vsnl.net.in, editors@indiasage.com, http://www.indiasage.com/.

370.15   HRV   ISSN 0353-4448
SVEUCILISTE U ZAGREBU. FILOZOFSKI FAKULTET. INSTITUT ZA PEDAGOGIJSKA ISTRAZIVANJA. ZBORNIK RADOVA∗. Text in Croatian; Summaries in English, Russian. 1981. a. USD 5.
Formerly: Odgoj i Samoupravljanje (0351-4889)
Indexed: RILM, RefZh, e-psyche.
Published by: Sveuciliste u Zagrebu, Filozofski Fakultet, Institut za Pedagogijska Istrazivanja, Savska 77, Zagreb, 10000, Croatia. Circ: 1,000.

SWAZILAND. CENTRAL STATISTICAL OFFICE. EDUCATION STATISTICS. see EDUCATION—Abstracting, Bibliographies, Statistics

SWEDEN. STATISTISKA CENTRALBYRAAN. STATISTISKA MEDDELANDEN. SERIE U, UTBILDNING OCH FORSKNING. see EDUCATION—Abstracting, Bibliographies, Statistics

370.2109485   SWE   ISSN 0348-6397
LA902
SWEDEN. STATISTISKA CENTRALBYRAAN. UTBILDNINGSSTATISTISK AARSBOK/SWEDISH EDUCATIONAL STATISTICS YEARBOOK. Text in Swedish. a. price varies.
Published by: Statistiska Centralbyraan/Statistics Sweden, Publishing Unit, Orebro, 70189, Sweden.

SYSTEMS ENGINEERING OF EDUCATION SERIES. see ENGINEERING

371.0712   POL   ISSN 1234-9356
SZKOLY POBOZNE; mlodziezowy kwartalnik katolicki. Short title: S P. Text in Polish. 1988. q. bk.rev. **Document type:** Bulletin. **Description:** Promotes Christian values for high school and college students.
Published by: Kuria Prowincjalna Zakonu Pijarow, Ul Pijarska 2, Krakow, 31015, Poland. schp@kr.onet.pl. Ed. Fr Jozef Tarnawski. Circ: 2,500. **Subscr. to:** Redakcja eSPe, ul Meissnera 20, Krakow 31457, Poland. TEL 48-12-112851, FAX 48-12-112851.

370.1   USA   ISSN 0039-8306
T E A NEWSLETTER; a professional journal for a united education profession. Text in English. 1957. m. USD 10. **Document type:** Newsletter.
Published by: Tucson Education Association, 4625 E Second St, Tucson, AZ 85711. TEL 520-795-8870. Circ: 3,800.

370   USA
T.I.C. NEWSLETTER. Text in English. 1969. m. USD 20. charts. **Document type:** Newsletter.
Formerly: T.D.O.C. Newsletter
Published by: Teacher Information Center, 61 Surrey Ln, Sudbury, MA 01776. TEL 617-443-0424. Eds. Deanna Solo, Len Solo.

370   NLD   ISSN 0927-8982
T I N F O N; tijdschrift voor informatica-onderwijs. Text in Dutch. 1992. q. EUR 35 to individuals; EUR 55 to institutions (effective 2003).
—Infotrieve.
Published by: D I N F O R, Redactiesecretariaat, Postbus 207, Doetinchem, 7000 AE, Netherlands. TEL 31-314-382259, 31-26-3251395, info@tinfon.nl, dinfor@planet.nl, http://www.tinfon.nl.

T L E. (Theorie Litterature Enseignement) see LITERATURE

T O M. (Text on Microfilm) see EDUCATION—Abstracting, Bibliographies, Statistics

T R A C E NEWS. see RELIGIONS AND THEOLOGY

371.1   USA   ISSN 0279-022X
T S T A ADVOCATE. Text in English. 1981. q. membership. illus. **Document type:** Magazine, Trade.
Formerly: Advocate
Published by: Texas State Teachers Association, 316 W 12th St, Austin, TX 78701. TEL 512-476-5355, FAX 512-469-0766, debbiem@tsta.org, http://www.tsta.org. Ed. Deborah Mohondro. Circ: 80,000 (controlled and free).

370   ESP   ISSN 0214-7742
TABANQUE. Text in Spanish. 1985. a. **Document type:** Academic/Scholarly.
—CINDOC.
Published by: (Escuela Universitaria del Profesorado de E.G.B. de Palencia), Universidad de Valladolid, Secretariado de Publicaciones, Juan Mambrilla, 14, Valladolid, 47003, Spain. TEL 34-83-294499, FAX 34-83-290300.

306.73   USA   ISSN 1080-5400
LB45
➤ **TABOO;** the journal of culture and education. Text in English. 1995. s-a. USD 40 to individuals (effective 2005); USD 60 to institutions (effective 2002). adv. 96 p./no. 1 cols./p.; back issues avail. **Document type:** Journal, Academic/Scholarly. **Description:** Academic forum for the study of teaching and pedagogy that focuses on the relationship between education and its sociocultural context.
Indexed: CPE, DIP, IBR, IBZ, MLA-IB.
—BLDSC (8597.743000).
Published by: Caddo Gap Press, 3145 Geary Blvd,, PMB 275, San Francisco, CA 94118. TEL 415-666-3012, FAX 415-666-3552, info@caddogap.com, http://www.caddogap.com. Ed. Shirley Steinberg. Pub., R&P Alan H Jones. adv.: page USD 200; trim 4.5 x 7. Circ: 200 (paid).

370   TWN
T'AI-WAN CHIAO YU/TAIWAN EDUCATION REVIEW. Text in Chinese. 1952. m. TWD 500 (effective 1992).
Published by: Taiwan Provincial Education Association/Taiwan Sheng Chiao Yu Hui, 2F, No 51, Tsingtao E. Rd, Taipei, Taiwan. TEL 02-3519671, FAX 02-3519242. Ed. Kao Wen Yi.

E

370 USA ISSN 1091-8817
LA217.2 .T34
TAKING SIDES: CLASHING VIEWS ON CONTROVERSIAL EDUCATIONAL ISSUES. Text in English. irreg., latest 2002, 12th ed. USD 22.50 per vol. (effective 2004). illus. **Document type:** *Academic/Scholarly.*
Published by: McGraw-Hill - Dushkin (Subsidiary of: McGraw-Hill Higher Education), 2460 Kerper Blvd, Dubuque, IA 52001. TEL 800-243-6532, customer.service@mcgraw-hill.com, http://www.dushkin.com/text-data/catalog/0072822821.mhtml. Ed. James William Noll. Pub. David Dean. R&P Cheryl Greenleaf.

TALKABOUT. see *LINGUISTICS*

370 HUN ISSN 0082-1632
TANULMANYOK A NEVELESTUDOMANY KOREBOL. Text in Hungarian; Summaries in English, Russian. 1958. irreg. price varies.
Published by: (Magyar Tudomanyos Akademia/Hungarian Academy of Sciences), Osiris Kiado, Veres Palne u 4-6, Budapest, 1053, Hungary. konyveshaz@osiriskiado.hu, http://www.osiriskiado.hu.

370 TZA ISSN 0039-9477
TANZANIA EDUCATION JOURNAL. Text in English; Text occasionally in Swahili. 1964. 3/yr. TZS 9. adv. bk.rev. illus.; mkt. **Document type:** *Government.*
Indexed: CPE.
Published by: Ministry of National Education, Institute of Education, PO Box 9121, Dar Es Salaam, Tanzania. Ed. A Rugumyemheto. Circ: 8,000.

370 ESP ISSN 1132-6239
LA910
TARBIYA. Text in Spanish. 1980. s-a.
Formerly (until 1991): Instituto de Ciencias de la Educacion. Boletin (1131-6365)
—CINDOC.
Published by: Universidad Autonoma de Madrid, Instituto Universitario de Ciencias de la Educacion, Carr. Colmenar Viejo, Km. 15, Cantoblanco, Madrid, 28049, Spain. TEL 34-91-3974973, FAX 34-91-3975020, http://www.uam.es/.

370 UAE
AT-TARBIYYAH/EDUCATION. Text in Arabic. 1979. m.
Description: Covers education issues and developments in the U.A.E. and the Arab world.
Published by: Wizarat al-Tarbiyyah wal-Ta'lim, Idarat al-Ilaqat al-Aama/Ministry of Education, Public Relations Department, PO Box 295, Abu Dhabi, United Arab Emirates. TEL 321950. Ed. Da'in Jum'ah Ahmad al-Qubaisi. Circ: 2,000.

370 QAT
➤ **AT-TARBIYYAH/EDUCATION.** Text in Arabic, English. 1972. q. free. bk.rev. **Document type:** *Academic/Scholarly.*
Description: Presents educational innovations, strategies, policies, exchange of ideas and experience with the aim of disseminating the findings of the Qatari experiment in the field of education.
Related titles: Microfilm ed.
Published by: Qatar National Commission for Education Culture and Science, P O Box 9865, Doha, Qatar. TEL 974-861412, FAX 974-880911, TELEX 4672 NATCOM DH. Ed. Abdul Aziz F Al Ansari. Circ: 2,500.

370 PER ISSN 0252-8819
F3401
TAREA; revista de educacion y cultura. Text in Spanish. 1980. 3/yr. PEN 20 domestic; USD 25 in Latin America; USD 30 elsewhere (effective 2003). bk.rev. bibl. back issues avail. **Document type:** *Academic/Scholarly.*
Former titles: Chaski; Tarea
Related titles: Supplement(s): Alerta Tarea. 1991. free.
Indexed: IBR.
Published by: Tarea, Asociacion de Publicaciones Educativas, Parque Osores, antes Parque Borgono161, Lima, 100, Peru. TEL 51-14-4240997, FAX 51-14-3327404, postmaster@tarea.org.pe, http://www.tarea.org.pe. Ed. Manuel Iguiniz Echevarria.

371.7 340 DEU ISSN 1430-225X
TASCHENLEXIKON SCHUL- UND HOCHSCHULRECHTLICHER ENTSCHEIDUNGEN. Text in German. 1996. irreg. price varies. **Document type:** *Monographic series, Trade.*
Published by: Erich Schmidt Verlag GmbH & Co. (Berlin), Genthiner Str 30G, Berlin, 10785, Germany. TEL 49-30-250085-0, FAX 49-30-25008511, esv@esvmedien.de, http://www.erich-schmidt-verlag.de.

TAUSCH; textanalyse in universitaet und schule. see *LITERATURE*

370 ESP ISSN 0214-137X
TAVIRA; ciencias de la educacion. Text in Spanish. 1984. a. back issues avail.
Indexed: RILM.
—CINDOC.
Published by: Universidad de Cadiz, Servicio de Publicaciones, Rectorado Ancha 16, Cadiz, 11001, Spain. TEL 34-956-0150000, http://www.uca.es/.

371.1 AUS ISSN 1328-2484
TAX GUIDE (GLEN WAVERLEY)✶. Text in English. 1978. a. AUD 5.
Former titles (until 1995): Teachers' Tax Guide (0728-554X); (until 1980): Taxation Advice for Teachers (0813-0671)
Published by: Victorian Affiliated Teachers' Federation, 11 Glenwood Ave, PO Box 200, Glen Waverley, VIC 3150, Australia. TEL 61-3-8200766, FAX 61-3-8200766. Ed. Alan W Kidd. Circ: 2,000.

372.1 NZL
TE TARI PUNA ORA O AOTEAROA. ITIREAREA/NEW ZEALAND CHILDCARE ASSOCIATION. NEWSLETTER. Text in English, Maori. 1990. bi-m. NZD 60. back issues avail. **Document type:** *Newsletter.*
Related titles: Diskette ed.
Published by: New Zealand Childcare Association, P.O. Box 11-863, Wellington, New Zealand. Ed. Rose Cole. Circ: 800.

370.1 USA ISSN 0039-8292
TEACH. Text in English. 1969. m. (except Jul.). membership. back issues avail.; reprint service avail. from PQC. **Document type:** *Newspaper, Trade.*
Related titles: Microform ed.: (from PQC).
Indexed: CIJE.
Published by: Tennessee Education Association, 801 Second Ave N, Nashville, TN 37201-1099. TEL 615-242-8392, FAX 615-259-4581, bguy@tea.nea.org, http://www.teateachers.org. Ed. Bill Guy. Circ: 43,000.

370 MLT ISSN 1028-5717
➤ **THE TEACHER.** Text in English, Maltese. 1920. q. free. adv. bk.rev. bibl.; illus.; tr.lit. back issues avail. **Document type:** *Newsletter, Academic/Scholarly.* **Description:** Contains editorial and trade union matters and is distributed to teachers, school libraries and overseas teachers' organizations.
Related titles: Fax ed.
Published by: Malta Union of Teachers, Teachers' Institute, 213 Republic St., Valletta, Malta. TEL 356-222663, FAX 356-244074, mut1@maltanet.net. Ed. John D Jones. R&P Victor Fenech. Adv. contact Irene Fenech. Circ: 5,000.

371.1 CAN ISSN 0841-9574
TEACHER (VANCOUVER). Text in English. 1960. m. CND 25 domestic; CND 30 foreign (effective 2005). **Document type:** *Magazine, Trade.*
Former titles (until 1988): B C T F Newsletter (0709-9800); (until 1979): British Columbia Teachers' Federation. Newsletter (0005-2965)
Related titles: Online - full text ed.
Indexed: CEI.
—CCC.
Published by: British Columbia Teachers' Federation, 100-550 W 6th Ave, Vancouver, BC V5Z 4P2, Canada. TEL 604-871-2283, 800-663-9163, newsmag@bctf.ca, http://www.bctf.ca/newsmag. Ed. Peter Owens. Circ: 41,000.

TEACHER AND LIBRARIAN. see *LIBRARY AND INFORMATION SCIENCES*

371.12 USA ISSN 1063-7508
TEACHER CERTIFICATION REQUIREMENTS IN ALL FIFTY STATES. Text in English. 1990. a.
Published by: Teacher Certification Publications, 7756, Sebring, FL 33872-0113.

370.711 IND ISSN 0379-3400
TEACHER EDUCATION. Text in English. 1960. q. INR 40 to non-members; INR 24 to members. adv. bk.rev. bibl.
Description: Deals with problems of teacher education, education and education research.
Published by: Indian Association of Teacher Educators, 8B Bundh Rd., Allenganj, Allahabad, Uttar Pradesh, India. Ed. D D Tewari. Circ: 1,000.

371.1 USA
TEACHER EDUCATION REPORTS. Text in English. 1979. 24/yr. USD 297 (effective 2005). **Document type:** *Newsletter.*
Description: Provides information on teaching and teacher education at the federal, state and local levels.
Published by: Feistritzer Publications, 4401 A Connecticut Ave, N W, Ste 212, Washington, DC 20088. TEL 202-362-3444, FAX 202-362-3493, dchester@ncei.com. Pub. Emily Feistritzer.

021.24 USA ISSN 1481-1782
Z675.S3
➤ **TEACHER LIBRARIAN JOURNAL;** the journal for school library professionals. Text in English. 1973. 5/yr. USD 54 (effective 2005). adv. bk.rev.; software rev.; video rev.; Website rev. bibl.; illus. 72 p./no. 3 cols./p.; back issues avail.; reprint service avail. from PQC. **Document type:** *Journal, Academic/Scholarly.* **Description:** Provides challenging articles addressing the practical concerns of the teacher-librarian, and the answers, tips and information needed to stay up-to-date in the profession.
Formerly (until 1998): Emergency Librarian (0315-8888)
Related titles: Microfiche ed.: (from MML, PQC); Microform ed.: (from MML); Online - full text ed.: (from bigchalk, EBSCO Publishing, Florida Center for Library Automation, Gale Group, H.W. Wilson, Micromedia ProQuest, O C L C Online Computer Library Center, Inc., ProQuest Information & Learning).
Indexed: ABIn, BRI, CBCARef, CBPI, CBRI, CEI, CIJE, CPE, CPerI, ChLitAb, ChPerI, EduInd, ICM, InfoSAb, LISA, LibLit, NPI, RGYP, WBA, WMB.
—BLDSC (8613.487000), IE, ingenta. **CCC.**
Published by: Ken Haycock & Associates, Inc., 15200 NBN Way, Blue Ridge Summit, PA 17214. TEL 717-794-3800, FAX 717-794-3833, admin@teacherlibrarian.com, http://www.teacherlibrarian.com. Ed. David Loertscher. Pub. Ken Haycock. R&P Kim Tabor. adv.: B&W page USD 1,100, color page USD 1,725. Circ: 10,000 (paid). **Subscr. to:** Department 343, Box 34069, Seattle, WA 98124-1069. subs@teacherlibrarian.com.

371.109759 USA
TEACHER SUPPLY AND DEMAND IN FLORIDA. Text in English. a.
Formerly: Areas of Critical Teacher Needs in Florida
Published by: Florida Department of Education, Office of the Commissioner, Turlington Building, Ste 1514, 325 West Gaines St, Tallahassee, FL 32399. http://www.fldoe.org.

370.1 USA ISSN 0161-4681
L11
➤ **TEACHERS COLLEGE RECORD;** a professional journal of ideas, research and informed opinion. Text in English. 1900. m. USD 89 combined subscription in the Americas to individuals & Carribean, print & online eds.; EUR 137 combined subscription in Europe to individuals print & online eds.; GBP 91 combined subscription elsewhere to individuals print & online eds.; USD 621 combined subscription in the Americas to institutions & Carribean, print & online eds.; GBP 472 combined subscription elsewhere to institutions print & online eds.; USD 63 combined subscription in the Americas to students & Carribean, print & online eds.; EUR 93 combined subscription in Europe to students print & online eds.; GBP 62 combined subscription elsewhere to students print & online eds. (effective 2006). adv. bk.rev.; film rev. bibl.; charts; illus. index. reprint service avail. from PQC. **Document type:** *Journal, Academic/Scholarly.*
Former titles (until 1970): The Record, Teachers College, Columbia University (0161-6161); (until 1967): Teachers College Record (0040-0475)
Related titles: Microform ed.: (from MIM, PQC); Online - full text ed.: ISSN 1467-9620. USD 590 in the Americas to institutions & Caribbean; GBP 449 elsewhere to institutions (effective 2006) (from Blackwell Synergy, EBSCO Publishing, Gale Group, H.W. Wilson, IngentaConnect, O C L C Online Computer Library Center, Inc., Swets Information Services).
Indexed: ABIn, ASCA, AmH&L, ArtHuCI, BRD, BRI, CBRI, CIJE, CPE, CurCont, DIP, EAA, ECER, ERA, ETA, EduInd, FamI, FutSurv, HEA, HistAb, IBR, IBZ, MEA, MLA-IB, PhilInd, PsycInfo, PsycholAb, RHEA, SEA, SENA, SOMA, SOPODA, SRRA, SSA, SSCI, SWA, SociolAb, TEA, V&AA, e-psyche.
—BLDSC (8613.710000), IDS, IE, Infotrieve, ingenta. **CCC.**
Published by: (Columbia University, Teachers College), Blackwell Publishing, Inc. (Subsidiary of: Blackwell Publishing Ltd.), Commerce Place, 350 Main St, Malden, MA 02148. TEL 781-388-8206, FAX 781-388-8232, subscrip@blackwellpub.com, http://www.blackwellpublishing.com/journals/TCR. Eds. Amy Stuart Wells, Clifford Hill, Lyn Corno. Circ: 2,500.

370 NGA ISSN 0331-1376
TEACHERS' FORUM✶. Text in English. 1955. bi-m. charts. **Document type:** *Government.*
Formerly: Teachers' Monthly
Published by: Ministry of Education, General Publishing Section, Ibadan, Oyo, Nigeria.

TEACHER'S INTERACTION; a magazine for Sunday school teachers. see *RELIGIONS AND THEOLOGY—Protestant*

371.1 NGA
TEACHERS JOURNAL. Text in English. bi-m. **Document type:** *Trade.*
Address: PO Box 139, Lagos, Nigeria.

TEACHERS OF HISTORY IN THE UNIVERSITIES OF THE UNITED KINGDOM. see *HISTORY*

371.1 IND ISSN 0863-0070
TEACHERS OF THE WORLD✶; international pedagogical and trade union review. Text in English. 1951. q. USD 5 to individuals; USD 10 to institutions. adv. bk.rev. charts; illus.
Description: Worldwide educational issues and problems discussed from FISE's point of view. Covers all levels of education.
Related titles: ♦ Spanish ed.: Educadores del Mundo; French ed.: Revue Internationale des Enseignants. 1951; German ed.: Lehrer der Welt. 1951.
Indexed: MEA&I.
Published by: World Federation of Teachers' Unions (FISE), PPH Bldg, 5-E Rahi Jhansi Rd, New Delhi, 110055, India. Circ: 19,000.

TEACHERS OF VISION. see *RELIGIONS AND THEOLOGY*

E

371.1 USA
TEACHERS TRAVEL GAZETTE. Text in English. q.
Published by: Teachers Travel, PO Box 5513, Santa Monica, CA 90405.

370 BGD ISSN 0040-0521
TEACHER'S WORLD; quarterly journal of education and research. Text in Bengali. 1961. q. USD 1.50. bk.rev. bibl. index.
Published by: (Institute of Education and Research), University of Dhaka, Ramna, Dhaka, 1000, Bangladesh. Ed. Noorul Huq. Circ: 1,000.

▼ **THE TEACHING ARTIST JOURNAL.** see *ART*

TEACHING CITIZENSHIP. see *POLITICAL SCIENCE*

371 GBR ISSN 1047-6210
➤ **TEACHING EDUCATION.** Text in English. 1987. q. GBP 211, USD 348, AUD 517 combined subscription to institutions print & online eds. (effective 2006). adv. bk.rev. illus. Index. back issues avail.; reprint service avail. from PSC. **Document type:** *Journal, Academic/Scholarly.* **Description:** Focuses on the challenges and possibilities of rapid social and cultural change for teacher education.
Related titles: Online - full text ed.: ISSN 1470-1286. GBP 200, USD 331, AUD 491 to institutions (effective 2006) (from EBSCO Publishing, Gale Group, H.W. Wilson, IngentaConnect, O C L C Online Computer Library Center, Inc., Swets Information Services).
Indexed: ABIn, CIJE, CPE, ERA, ETA, EduInd, MEA, RHEA, SEA, SENA, SOMA, TEA.
—BLDSC (8614.095000), IE, Infotrieve, ingenta. **CCC.**
Published by: (University of Queensland, Graduate School of Education AUS), Routledge (Subsidiary of: Taylor & Francis Group), 4 Park Sq, Milton Park, Abingdon, Oxon OX14 4RN, United Kingdom. TEL 44-1235-828600, FAX 44-1235-829000, journals@routledge.com, http://www.tandf.co.uk/journals/titles/10476210.asp, http://www.routledge.co.uk. Eds. Allan Luke, Diane Mayer. Circ: 1,200 (controlled). **Subscr. add. in Europe:** Taylor & Francis Ltd, Journals Customer Service, Rankine Rd, Basingstoke, Hants RG24 8PR, United Kingdom. TEL 44-1256-813000, FAX 44-1256-330245.

370.15 USA
▼ **TEACHING EDUCATIONAL PSYCHOLOGY.** Text in English. 2003. q. USD 80 to individuals; USD 185 to institutions; USD 55 to students (effective 2003). **Document type:** *Journal, Academic/Scholarly.*
Published by: Information Age Publishing, Inc., 411 W Putnam Ave, Ste 205, PO Box 4967, Greenwich, CT 06831. TEL 203-661-7602, FAX 203-661-7952, order@infoagepub.com, http://www.infoagepub.com.

TEACHING ELEMENTARY PHYSICAL EDUCATION. see *SPORTS AND GAMES*

371 USA ISSN 0898-6533
TEACHING FOR LEARNING. Text in English. 1985. s-a. USD 15 for 4 issues. **Document type:** *Newsletter.*
Published by: Anderson-Shea, Inc., PO Box 4780, Jackson, WY 83001. TEL 307-734-8207, FAX 307-734-8269, 72460.2362@compuserve.com, http://members.aol.com/casinc/tfl.html. Ed. Charlene Anderson Shea.

370.1 USA
TEACHING FOR SOCIAL JUSTICE SERIES. Text in English. irreg. price varies. back issues avail. **Document type:** *Monographic series, Trade.* **Description:** Examines issues in the teaching for social justice movement and how they can be applied in school management, curriculum development, and classroom teaching.
Published by: Teachers College Press, Teachers College, Columbia University, 525 W 120th St, Box 303, New York, NY 10027-6694. http://www.teacherscollegepress.com. Pub. Carole Saltz. R&P Amy Detjen. **Dist. by:** Eurospan University Press Group, Order Dept, 3 Henrietta St, London WC2E 8LU, United Kingdom. TEL 44-20-7240-0856, FAX 44-20-7379-0609, http://www.eurospan.co.uk; Pademelon Press, Pty Ltd, 7-10 Anella Ave, PO Box 229, Castle Hill, NSW 2154, Australia. TEL 61-2-9634-2558, FAX 61-2-9680-4634; Transdex International, Pte Ltd, Block 1, Farrer Rd 307-05, Singapore 268817, Singapore. TEL 65-468-6242, FAX 65-462-5457.

TEACHING GEOGRAPHY. see *GEOGRAPHY*

371.33 USA
TEACHING LANGUAGES, LITERATURES, AND CULTURES. Text in English. 1998. irreg. price varies. back issues avail. **Document type:** *Monographic series, Academic/Scholarly.* **Description:** Discusses theoretical and applied research on the teaching of world languages at all levels.
Indexed: MLA-IB.
Published by: (Modern Language Association of America), Modern Language Association, Book Publications Program, 26 Broadway, 3rd Fl, New York, NY 10004-1789. TEL 646 576-5000. Ed. Martha Noel Evans.

TEACHING MATHEMATICS. see *MATHEMATICS*

370 AUS ISSN 1449-6313
▼ **TEACHING SCIENCE.** Text in English. 2004. q. **Document type:** *Journal, Academic/Scholarly.*
Formed by the merger of (1985-2004): Investigating the Australian Primary and Junior Science Journal (1442-5556); (1955-2004): Australian Science Teachers Journal (0045-0855)
Related titles: Online - full text ed.: (from EBSCO Publishing, ProQuest Information & Learning).
Published by: Australian Science Teachers Association, Mungga-iri House, Unit 7, 18 Napier Close, Deakin, ACT 2600 , Australia. http://www.asta.edu.au/.

TEACHING SCIENCE. see *SCIENCES: COMPREHENSIVE WORKS*

TEACHING STATISTICS; an international journal for teachers of pupils aged up to 19. see *EDUCATION—Abstracting, Bibliographies, Statistics*

TEACHING TEXTS IN LAW AND POLITICS. see *LAW*

TEACHING THEATRE. see *THEATER*

371.1 GBR ISSN 0968-3062
TEACHING TODAY. Text in English. 1921. 3/yr. GBP 2 to non-members. adv. bk.rev. **Document type:** *Trade.*
Former titles: N A S U W T Career Teacher Journal; Schoolmaster and Career Teacher
Indexed: CPE.
Published by: N A S U W T, 5 King St, London, WC2E 8HN, United Kingdom. TEL 44-171-379-9499, FAX 44-171-497-8262. Ed. Graham Terrell. Adv. contact Liane Carter. Circ: 180,000.

371.07 200 USA
TEAM N Y I MAGAZINE; resourcing Nazarene youth workers. Text in English. 1997. q. **Document type:** *Trade.*
Published by: Nazarene Publishing House, 6401 The Paseo, Kansas City, MO 64131. FAX 816-333-4315, TeamNYI@nazarene.org, http://www.nazarene.org/nyi. Ed. Jeff Edmondson. Circ: 10,000.

TECHNICAL EDUCATION & TRAINING ABSTRACTS. see *EDUCATION—Abstracting, Bibliographies, Statistics*

370.113 USA ISSN 1527-1803
LC1041
TECHNIQUES. Text in English. 1926. 8/yr. USD 48 domestic to non-members; USD 81 foreign to non-members (effective 2005). adv. index. back issues avail.; reprints avail. **Document type:** *Magazine, Trade.* **Description:** Focuses on trends and professional issues affecting career and technical education, business and industry, school counselors and administrators.
Former titles (until 1996): American Vocational Association.Techniques (1091-0131); (until 1996): Vocational Education Journal (0884-8009); (until 1985): VocEd (0164-9175); (until 1978): American Vocational Journal (0003-1496)
Related titles: CD-ROM ed.: (from ProQuest Information & Learning); Microform ed.: (from PQC); Online - full text ed.: (from EBSCO Publishing, Florida Center for Library Automation, Gale Group, H.W. Wilson, O C L C Online Computer Library Center, Inc., ProQuest Information & Learning).
Indexed: ABIn, AcaI, BRI, BusEdI, CIJE, ChPerI, EduInd, MRD, PEI.
—BLDSC (8743.070000), IE, Infotrieve, ingenta, Linda Hall. **CCC.**
Published by: Association for Career and Technical Education, 1410 King St, Alexandria, VA 22314. TEL 800-826-9972, FAX 703-683-7424, cweiss@acteonline.org, http://www.acteonline.org/members/techniques/index.cfm. Ed. Susan Reese. Adv. contact Rich Vizard. Circ: 32,000 (paid).

373 USA
TECHNOLOGY EDUCATION. Text in English. a. adv. **Description:** Covers a wide range of topics for vocational school educators (grades 9-12).
Published by: Studentaware Communications, 305 SW 140th Ter, Newberry, FL 32669. TEL 352-332-9600.

372.3 GBR ISSN 0952-889X
TECHNOLOGY IN EDUCATION; devoted to the teaching of science and design technology including art & design, business studies, craft design technology, home economics, and information technology. Text in English. 1985. 7/yr. GBP 20. tr.lit. back issues avail. **Document type:** *Journal, Academic/Scholarly.* **Description:** Presents a forum for teachers involved with sciences and technology.
Published by: B & S Publications, 3 Crescent Terr, Cheltenham, Glos GL50 3PE, United Kingdom. TEL 44-1242-510760, FAX 44-1242-22626, Bernardhubbard@msn.com. Ed. Bernard Hubbard. adv.: B&W page GBP 760, color page GBP 995; trim 210 x 297. Circ: 8,000 (controlled).

TEKSTIILIOPETTAJA/TEXTILLAREN. see *TEXTILE INDUSTRIES AND FABRICS*

370 COL
TEMAS DE EDUCACION. Text in Spanish. q. COP 45,000 domestic; USD 30 foreign (effective 2003). **Document type:** *Monographic series.* **Description:** Presents pedagogic proposals and research works from faculty members.
Published by: Universidad Externado de Colombia, Departamento de Publicaciones, Calle 12, No 0-38 Este, Apartado Aereo 034141, Santafe de Bogota, Colombia. publicaciones@uexternado.edu.co, http://www.uexternado.edu.co.

TEMPO. see *MUSIC*

370 ITA ISSN 0392-2804
TEMPO SERENO. Text in Italian. 1962. bi-m. adv. **Document type:** *Magazine, Trade.*
Published by: Editrice La Scuola SpA, Via Luigi Cadorna 11, Brescia, BS 25124, Italy. TEL 39-030-29931, FAX 39-030-2993299, http;//www.lascuola.it. Ed. Luigi Morgano.

370 ESP ISSN 0214-7351
TEMPS D'EDUCACIO. Text in Catalan. 1989. s-a. **Document type:** *Journal, Academic/Scholarly.*
Indexed: SSA, SociolAb.
—CINDOC.
Published by: (Universitat de Barcelona, Facultat de Pedagogia), Universitat de Barcelona, Servei de Publicacions, Gran Via Corts Catalanes 585, Barcelona, 08007, Spain. TEL 34-93-4021100, sipu-sec@org.ub.es, http://www.publicacions.ub.es. Ed. Gloria Bordons.

371.192 USA
TENNESSEE PARENT - TEACHER BULLETIN. Text in English. 1924. 10/yr. (Aug.-May). USD 4. film rev. **Document type:** *Bulletin.*
Supersedes (in 197?): Tennessee Parent - Teacher (0049-3392)
Media: Duplicated (not offset).
Published by: Tennessee Congress of Parents and Teachers, 1905 Acklen Ave, Nashville, TN 37212. TEL 615-383-9740. Ed. Pat Gammon. Circ: 1,400 (controlled).

373.246 USA ISSN 0093-9889
LC1046.T4
TENNESSEE. STATE BOARD FOR VOCATIONAL EDUCATION. INFORMATION SERIES. Key Title: Information Series - Tennessee State Board of Vocational Education. Text in English. irreg.
Published by: State Board for Vocational Education, Nashville, TN 37219. TEL 615-741-3446.

370.1 USA ISSN 0040-3407
TENNESSEE TEACHER. Text in English. 1934. m. (Aug.-Apr.). USD 5. adv. bk.rev. illus. reprint service avail. from PQC.
Related titles: Microform ed.: (from PQC).
Published by: Tennessee Education Association, 801 Second Ave N, Nashville, TN 37201-1099. TEL 615-242-8392. Ed. Dawn Charles. Circ: 42,000.

TENRAG; student journal for secondary school students. see *MATHEMATICS*

370.1 ESP ISSN 1130-3743
LB14.7
TEORIA DE LA EDUCACION. Text in Spanish; Abstracts in English. 1986. a., latest vol.11, 1999. **Document type:** *Academic/Scholarly.*
—CINDOC.
Published by: Ediciones Universidad de Salamanca, Apartado 325, Salamanca, 37080, Spain. TEL 34-923-294598, FAX 34-923-262579, http://www3.usal.es/~eus/indexsp.htm. Ed. Joaquin Garcia Carrasco.

TEXAS SCHOOL LAW BULLETIN. see *LAW*

373 USA ISSN 0040-4705
TEXAS STUDY OF SECONDARY EDUCATION RESEARCH BULLETIN. Text in English. 1948. s-a. USD 15. adv. charts; illus.; stat. **Document type:** *Trade.*
Formerly: Texas Journal of Secondary Education
Published by: Texas Association of Secondary School Principals, 1833 South 1 H 35, Austin, TX 78741. TEL 512-442-2100, FAX 512-443-3343. Ed. Julian Shaddix. Circ: 4,000.

TEXTILARBEIT UND UNTERRICHT. see *CLOTHING TRADE—Fashions*

370 CHE ISSN 1422-1187
TEXTILARBEIT UND WERKEN. Text in German. 1918. 10/yr. adv. bk.rev. illus. **Document type:** *Trade.*
Formerly (until 1993): Schweizerische Arbeitslehrerinnen Zeitung (0036-7214)
Indexed: DIP, IBR, IBZ.
Published by: (Verein Lehrer und Lehrerinnen Schweiz fuer Textilarbeit und Werken), Kretz AG, Postfach, Feldmeilen, 8706, Switzerland. TEL 41-1-9237656, FAX 41-1-9237657, kretz_ag@bluewin.ch. Circ: 5,700.

THEATRE JOURNAL (BALTIMORE). see *THEATER*

THEMA IM UNTERRICHT. see *POLITICAL SCIENCE*

E

370.1 ESP ISSN 0212-8365
THEMATA. Text in Spanish. 1984. s-a., latest vol.26, 2001. EUR 15 per issue (effective 2005). **Document type:** *Journal, Academic/Scholarly.*
Indexed: IPB, PhilInd.
—CINDOC.
Published by: Universidad de Sevilla, Secretariado de Publicaciones, Porvenir 27, Sevilla, 41013, Spain. TEL 34-95-4487444, FAX 34-95-4487443, secpub10@us.es, http://www.us.es/publius/inicio.html.

THEMENBLAETTER IM UNTERRICHT. see *POLITICAL SCIENCE*

THEOLOGICAL EDUCATION. see *RELIGIONS AND THEOLOGY*

370 GBR ISSN 1477-8785
LB2326.3
➤ **THEORY AND RESEARCH IN EDUCATION.** Text in English. 1990. 3/yr. GBP 215, USD 375 to institutions; GBP 223, USD 391 combined subscription to institutions print & online eds. (effective 2006). bk.rev. **Document type:** *Journal, Academic/Scholarly.* **Description:** Provides a focus for educationalists who are hungry for a truly multi-disciplinary approach to education theory. The aim of the journal is to situate the issue of education in the context of contemporary theoretical debates by questioning its usual boundaries and discuss general conceptions that corresponds to current social changes and the development of educational theory.
Formerly (until 2002): The School Field (0353-6807)
Related titles: CD-ROM ed.: ISSN 1580-2213; Online - full content ed.: (from C S A, EBSCO Publishing); Online - full text ed.: ISSN 1580-2205. GBP 212, USD 371 to institutions (effective 2006) (from O C L C Online Computer Library Center, Inc., Sage Publications, Inc., Swets Information Services).
Indexed: AEI, BrEdI, CIJE, CPE, DIP, EAA, ERA, IBR, IBSS, IBZ, L&LBA, MEA, PSA, PhilInd, RHEA, SEA, SociolAb.
—BLDSC (8814.628900), IE, ingenta. **CCC.**
Published by: (Slovene Society of Researchers in the School Field SVN), Sage Publications Ltd. (Subsidiary of: Sage Publications, Inc.), 1 Oliver's Yard, 55 City Rd, London, EC1 1SP, United Kingdom. TEL 44-20-73248500, FAX 44-20-73248600, info@sagepub.co.uk, http://www.sagepub.co.uk/journal.aspx?pid=105794. Ed. Mitja Sardoc. **Subscr. in the Americas to:** Sage Publications, Inc., 2455 Teller Rd, Thousand Oaks, CA 91320. TEL 805-499-0721, FAX 805-499-0871, journals@sagepub.com.

370 USA ISSN 0040-5841
LB1028 CODEN: THPRAC
➤ **THEORY INTO PRACTICE.** Text in English. 1962. q., latest vol.43, 2004. USD 120 in US & Canada to institutions; USD 150 elsewhere to institutions; USD 125 combined subscription in US & Canada to institutions print & online eds.; USD 155 combined subscription elsewhere to institutions print & online eds. (effective 2006). adv. illus. index. 80 p./no. 2 cols./p.; back issues avail.; reprints avail. **Document type:** *Journal, Academic/Scholarly.* **Description:** Contains thematic issues relating to education.
Supersedes: Educational Research Bulletin (1555-4023)
Related titles: CD-ROM ed.: Theory Into Practice - Digital. ISSN 1527-2532; Microform ed.: (from PQC); Online - full text ed.: ISSN 1543-0421. USD 115 worldwide to institutions (effective 2006) (from bigchalk, EBSCO Publishing, Florida Center for Library Automation, Gale Group, H.W. Wilson, Northern Light Technology, Inc., O C L C Online Computer Library Center, Inc., Project MUSE, ProQuest Information & Learning, Swets Information Services).
Indexed: ABIn, AMHA, ASCA, CIJE, CJA, CPE, CurCont, EAA, ERA, EduInd, FamI, MEA, PsycholAb, RASB, SEA, SFSA, SOMA, SOPODA, SSCI.
—BLDSC (8814.632000), IDS, IE, Infotrieve, ingenta. **CCC.**
Published by: (Ohio State University, College of Education), Lawrence Erlbaum Associates, Inc., 10 Industrial Ave, Mahwah, NJ 07430-2262. TEL 201-258-2200, 800-926-6579, FAX 201-236-0072, journals@erlbaum.com, http://www.leaonline.com/loi/tip. Ed. Anita Woolfolk Hoy. adv.: page USD 550; trim 7 x 10. Circ: 1,500.

370.3 USA ISSN 1051-2993
Z695.1.E3
THESAURUS OF E R I C DESCRIPTORS. (Educational Resources Information Center) Text in English. 1967. irreg., latest vol.13, 1995. USD 69.50 domestic; USD 83.40 foreign. index. **Document type:** *Abstract/Index.* **Description:** Lists the vocabulary of descriptors and terms used by the ERIC system in indexing and abstracting education literature. Has an extensive introduction describing the ERIC system providing keys for using the thesaurus.
Related titles: CD-ROM ed.: (from National Information Services Corp. (N I S C)); Online - full text ed.: (from National Information Services Corp. (N I S C)).
Published by: Oryx Press (Subsidiary of: Greenwood Publishing Group Inc.), 1434 E. San Miguel Ave., Phoenix, AZ 85014-2422. TEL 602-265-2651, 800-279-6799, FAX 602-265-6250, info@oryxpress.com, http://www.oryxpress.com. Ed. Anne Thompson. Pub. Phyllis Steckler. R&P Lori Cavanaugh TEL 602-265-2651 ext 662. Circ: 6,000.

370 USA
➤ **THINKING CLASSROOM**; a journal of reading, writing and critical reflection. Text in English. q. USD 12.50 in developing nations (effective 2003). **Document type:** *Journal, Academic/Scholarly.* **Description:** Publishes manuscripts of interest to those seeking to promote active inquiry, student-centered learning, problem solving, critical thinking, cooperative learning and alternative assessment.
Related titles: Russian Translation: Peremena.
Published by: International Reading Association, Inc., 800 Barksdale Rd, Newark, DE 19714-8139. TEL 302-731-1600, FAX 302-368-2449, journals@reading.org, http://www.rwct.org/journal, http://www.reading.org. Eds. Inna Valkova, Daiva Penkauskiene. Circ: 2,000 (paid).

370 GBR ISSN 1871-1871
THINKING SKILLS AND CREATIVITY. Text in English. a. EUR 30 in Europe to individuals; JPY 3,500 in Japan to individuals; USD 30 elsewhere to individuals; EUR 160 in Europe to institutions; JPY 18,900 in Japan to institutions; USD 159 elsewhere to institutions (effective 2006). **Document type:** *Journal, Academic/Scholarly.* **Description:** Provides a peer-reviewed forum for communication and debate for the community of researchers interested in teaching for thinking and creativity. Papers may represent a variety of theoretical perspectives and methodological approaches and may relate to any age level in a diversity of settings: formal and informal, education and work-based.
Published by: Pergamon (Subsidiary of: Elsevier Science & Technology), The Boulevard, Langford Ln, East Park, Kidlington, Oxford OX5 1GB, United Kingdom. TEL 44-1865-843000, FAX 44-1865-843010, http://www.elsevier.com/wps/find/journaldescription.cws_home/706922/description#description, http://www.elsevier.nl. Ed. R Wegerif.

370.72 USA ISSN 0196-9641
LA267
➤ **THRESHOLDS IN EDUCATION.** Text in English. 1975. q. USD 25 domestic; USD 29 foreign; USD 10 per issue (effective 2004). adv. bk.rev. index. back issues avail. **Document type:** *Journal, Academic/Scholarly.* **Description:** Informs educators about future trends and contemporary issues related to research and practice in education.
Formerly: Thresholds in Secondary Education (0361-106X)
Indexed: CIJE.
—BLDSC (8820.342300), IE, ingenta.
Published by: Thresholds in Education Foundation, Northeast Illinois University, 225 Graham Hall, Dekalb, IL 60115. TEL 815-753-9359, FAX 815-753-8750, thresh@niu.edu, http://www.cedu.niu.edu/epf/foundations/thresholds/jrnl.htm. Ed. Wilma F Miranda. Adv. contact Betty Lahti. page USD 200; 7.25 x 9. Circ: 500. **Subscr. and Adv. to:** Department of Leadership, Educational Psychology and Foundations, Northern Illinois University, DeKalb, IL 60115.

➤ **TIJDSCHRIFT VOOR ONDERWIJSRECHT EN ONDERWIJSBELEID.** see *LAW*

370 302.23 NOR ISSN 1502-2471
➤ **TILT**; mediepedagogisk tidsskrift. Text in Norwegian. 1986. q. NOK 250 to individuals; NOK 300 to institutions (effective 2003).
Former titles (until 2002): Media i Skole og Samfunn (1502-3710); (until 1999): Media i Skolen (0802-1252); (until 1988): LMU-kontakten (0801-4760)
Related titles: Online - full text ed.
Published by: Landslaget for Medieundervisning, Filips gate 4, Oslo, 0655, Norway. TEL 47-22-474664, FAX 47-22-474694, http://www.lmu.no. Ed. Trygve Panhoff.

371.8 640.73 GBR ISSN 0957-8110
TIME OUT STUDENT GUIDE. Text in English. 1977. a. free to students; GBP 2 newsstand/cover (effective 2001). adv. 132 p./no.; **Document type:** *Magazine, Consumer.* **Description:** Student survival guide full of advice and information for first-time students in London.
Published by: Time Out Group Ltd., Universal House, 251 Tottenham Court Rd, London, WIT 7AB, United Kingdom. FAX 44-20-7813-6001, net@timeout.co.uk, http://www.timeout.com. Ed. Sharon Loughel. Pub. Tony Elliott. R&P Mike Hardwick. Adv. contact Mark Phillipps. B&W page GBP 2,890, color page GBP 3,510; 210 x 273. Circ: 120,000 (controlled).

370 GBR ISSN 0040-7887
L16
TIMES EDUCATIONAL SUPPLEMENT. Text in English. 1910. w. GBP 56; GBP 1.20 newsstand/cover (effective 2004). adv. bk.rev. illus. Index. reprints avail. **Document type:** *Journal, Academic/Scholarly.* **Description:** Provides news and opinions on issues at all levels of education from nursery schools to universities.
Related titles: CD-ROM ed.: (from Chadwyck-Healey Inc.); Microfilm ed.: (from RPI); Online - full text ed.; Regional ed(s).: Times Educational Supplement Scotland. ISSN 0143-8492. 1965.
Indexed: ABIn, AcaI, BNI, BRI, BrEdI, CBRI, ChLitAb, EduInd, HECAB, LT&LA, RASB, RHEA, RILM, SRRA, WBA, WMB.
—BLDSC (8853.500000). **CCC.**
Published by: T S L Education Ltd., Admiral House, 66-68 E Smithfield, London, E1 1BX, United Kingdom. TEL 44-20-7782-3000, FAX 44-20-7782-3300, sales@tes.co.uk, http://www.tes.co.uk, http://www.tsleducation.co.uk. Ed. Patricia Rowan. Adv. contact John Ladbrook. Circ: 135,000.

370.15 AUT
➤ **TIROLER SCHULE.** Text in German. 1890. q. EUR 14.50 (effective 2005). bk.rev.; tel.rev.; video rev. bibl.; illus.; abstr. back issues avail. **Document type:** *Newsletter, Academic/Scholarly.*
Indexed: e-psyche.
Published by: Katholischer Tiroler Lehrerverein, Riedgasse 9, Innsbruck, T 6020, Austria. TEL 43-512-2230521, FAX 43-512-2230528, tirolerschule@ktlv.at, ktlv@dioezese-innsbruck.at, http://www.ktlv.at/tiroler_schule/portal_ts.html. Ed. Franz Steinbacher. Circ: 3,500 (paid and controlled).

➤ **TIYU XUEKAN/JOURNAL OF PHYSICAL EDUCATION.** see *PHYSICAL FITNESS AND HYGIENE*

371.0712 USA ISSN 0040-8441
LC461
TODAY'S CATHOLIC TEACHER. Text in English. 1967. bi-m. USD 14.95 domestic; USD 19.95 foreign (effective 2005). adv. bk.rev.; film rev. charts; illus.; stat. reprints avail. **Document type:** *Magazine, Trade.* **Description:** Articles, columns, and announcements on Catholic education for teachers and administrators.
Related titles: Online - full text ed.: (from Northern Light Technology, Inc., ProQuest Information & Learning).
Indexed: BiolDig, CERDIC, CPL.
Published by: Peter Li Education Group, 2621 Dryden Rd, Ste 300, Dayton, OH 45439-1661. TEL 937-293-1415, 800-523-4625, FAX 937-293-1310, tcteditor@peterli.com, service@peterli.com, http://www.peterli.com. Ed., R&P Mary Noschang. Pub., Adv. contact Bret Thomas. Circ: 50,000 (paid).

TODAY'S CHRISTIAN TEEN; college prep guide. see *RELIGIONS AND THEOLOGY*

370.1 USA ISSN 1525-3589
TODAY'S O E A. Text in English. 1926. 6/yr. (Oct.-June). USD 10 (effective 2005). charts; illus. **Document type:** *Magazine, Trade.*
Formerly (until 1998): Oregon Education (0030-4689)
Published by: Oregon Education Association, 6900 S W Atlanta St, Portland, OR 97223. TEL 503-684-3300, FAX 503-684-8063, janineleggett@oregoned.org, http://www.oregoned.org/. Ed. Amber Cole-Hall. Circ: 39,445 (paid and controlled).

TODAY'S SCHOOL PSYCHOLOGIST. see *PSYCHOLOGY*

TODAY'S SCIENCE ON FILE. see *SCIENCES: COMPREHENSIVE WORKS*

371.07 NLD ISSN 1568-8763
TOER; impulsen voor inspirerend kerk-zijn. Text in Dutch. 1959. 6/yr. EUR 24; EUR 5.50 newsstand/cover (effective 2005). adv. **Document type:** *Bulletin.* **Description:** For church members and group leaders. Discusses educational issues.
Formerly (until 2001): Toerusting (0166-3461)
Published by: (Landelijk Dienstencentrum van de Samen Op Weg-Kerken), Boekencentrum Uitgevers, Goudstraat 50, Postbus 29, Zoetermeer, 2700 AA, Netherlands. TEL 31-79-3615481, FAX 31-79-3615489, j.van.dijk@pkn.nl, info@boekencentrum.nl, http://www.boekencentrum.nl.

370 JPN ISSN 1346-910X
LC3987.J3
TOKUSHU KYOUIKU KENKYUU SHISETSU KENKYUU HOUKOKU/RESEARCH INSTITUTE FOR THE EDUCATION OF EXCEPTIONAL CHILDREN. RESEARCH REPORT. Abbreviated title: R I E E C Research Report. Text in Japanese. 2002. a. **Document type:** *Academic/Scholarly.*
Formed by the merger of (1994-2000): Tokushu Kyoiku Kenkyu Shisetsu Kenkyu Nempo/RIEEC Annual Report (1341-0563); (1997-2001): Tokushu Kyoiku Kenkyu Shisetsu Kenkyusei Kenkyu Hokoku (1342-7504)
—BLDSC (7970.541000).
Published by: Toukyou Gakugei Daigaku, Tokushu Kyoiku Kenkyu Shisetsu Hokoku/Tokyo Gakugei University, Research Institute for the Education of Exceptional Children, 4-1-1 Nukuikitamachi, Koganei, Tokyo, 184-8501, Japan. TEL 81-423-297671, FAX 81-423-297672, http://www.u-gakugei.ac.jp/~rieechom/index-j.html.

372 USA
TOO COOL FOR GROWNUPS; bringing the power of the Internet into the classroom. Abbreviated title: T C F G. Text in English. 1996. bi-w. USD 29 to individuals; USD 99 to institutions. **Description:** Designed to help upper elementary and middle school teachers and students integrate the Web into their curriculum.
Related titles: Online - full text ed.
Published by: T C F G Publishing, Inc., PO Box 17116, Chapel Hill, NC 27516. TEL 919-969-7130, FAX 919-969-4116, publisher@tcfg.com, http://www.tcfg.com/. Ed. Alec M Bodzin.

E

370.72 GBR ISSN 0953-895X
TOPIC (SLOUGH); practical applications of research in education. Text in English. 1989. s-a. looseleaf. GBP 29.50 (effective 2001). **Document type:** *Academic/Scholarly.* **Description:** Highlights the practical implications of research findings for teachers.
Published by: National Foundation for Educational Research, The Mere, Upton Park, Slough, Berks SL1 2DQ, United Kingdom. TEL 44-1753-574123, FAX 44-1753-691632. Ed., R&P David Upton. Circ: 1,000.

TORAH EDUCATION. see *RELIGIONS AND THEOLOGY—Judaic*

370 JPN ISSN 1345-3327
TOTTORI UNIVERSITY. FACULTY OF EDUCATION AND REGIONAL SCIENCES. EDUCATIONAL SCIENCE AND THE HUMANITIES/TOTORRI DAIGAKU KYOIKU CHIIKI KAGAKUBU KIYO. KYOIKU JIMBUN KAGAKU. Text in Japanese, English. 1999. a.
Published by: Tottori Daigaku, Kyoiku Chiiki Kagakubu/Tottori University, Faculty of Education and Regional Sciences, 4-101 Minami-Koyama-cho, Tottori-shi, 680-8551, Japan. TEL 81-857-31-5498, FAX 81-857-31-5076, http://www.fed.tottori-u.ac.jp.

TOURISM EDUCATION DIRECTORY. see *TRAVEL AND TOURISM*

370.1 JPN ISSN 1344-6401
TOYAMA DAIGAKU KYOUIKUGAKUBU KENKYUROSHU/ TOYAMA UNIVERSITY. FACULTY OF EDUCATION. BULLETIN. Text in English, Japanese; Summaries in English. 1952. a. **Document type:** *Academic/Scholarly.*
Formed by the 1999 merger of part of: Toyama Daigaku Kyoikugakubu Kiyo, A. Bunkakei - Toyama University. Faculty of Education. Memoirs, A. Literature (0285-9602); part of: Toyama Daigaku Kyoikugakubu Kiyo, B. Rikakei - Toyama University. Faculty of Education. Memoirs, B. Natural Science (0285-9610); Which both superseded (in 1978): Toyama Daigaku Kyoiku Gakubu Kiyo (0495-9841)
Indexed: ZooRec.
Published by: Toyama Daigaku, Kyoikugakubu/Toyama University, Faculty of Education, 3190 Gofuku, Toyama-shi, 930-0887, Japan. TEL 81-764-41-1271, FAX 81-764-32-4212. Ed. Masato Yamashita.

370.1 JPN ISSN 1344-641X
CODEN: TDKKFB
TOYAMA DAIGAKU KYOUIKUGAKUBU KIYO/TOYAMA UNIVERSITY. FACULTY OF EDUCATION. MEMOIRS. Text in English, Japanese; Summaries in English. 1952. a. **Document type:** *Academic/Scholarly.*
Formed by the 1999 merger of part of: Toyama Daigaku Kyoikugakubu Kiyo, A. Bunkakei - Toyama University. Faculty of Education. Memoirs, A. Literature (0285-9602); part of: Toyama Daigaku Kyoikugakubu Kiyo, B. Rikakei - Toyama University. Faculty of Education. Memoirs, B. Natural Science (0285-9610); Which both superseded (in 1978): Toyama Daigaku Kyoiku Gakubu Kiyo (0495-9841)
Indexed: ZooRec.
—BLDSC (5593.330000).
Published by: Toyama Daigaku, Kyoikugakubu/Toyama University, Faculty of Education, 3190 Gofuku, Toyama-shi, 930-0887, Japan. TEL 81-764-41-1271, FAX 81-764-32-4212. Ed. Masato Yamashita.

TOYAMAKEN KOTO GAKKO KYOIKU KENKYUKAI SEIBUTSU BUNKAIHO/TOYAMA BIOLOGICAL EDUCATION SOCIETY. REPORT. see *BIOLOGY*

370 ESP ISSN 1131-9615
TRABAJADORES DE LA ENSENANZA. Key Title: T.E. Trabajadores de la Ensenanza. Text in Spanish. 1979. m.
—CINDOC.
Published by: Federacion de Ensenanza de Comisiones Obreras, Plaza Cristino Martos, 4, Madrid, 28015, Spain. Ed. Fernando Lezcano Lopez.

370.25 ZAF
TRAINING & DEVELOPMENT ORGANISATIONS DIRECTORY. Abbreviated title: T D O D. Text in English. 1994. a. ZAR 91.20. **Document type:** *Directory.*
Published by: Human Sciences Research Council, Programme for Development Research, Private Bag X41, Pretoria, 0001, South Africa. TEL 27-12-302-2999, FAX 27-12-302-2445, yzettet@beauty.hsrc.ac.za.

370.29 GBR
TRAINING AND ENTERPRISE DIRECTORY. Text in English. 1985. a. GBP 27.50. adv. **Document type:** *Directory.*
Former titles: Training Directory (0958-9856); (until 1989): Trainer's Yearbook; Directory of Trainer Support Services
Published by: (Confederation of British Industry), Kogan Page Ltd., 120 Pentonville Rd, London, N1 9JN, United Kingdom. FAX 44-20-7837-6348. R&P Caroline Gromm. Adv. contact Linda Batham. **Co-sponsor:** T E C National Council.

370 ZAF
TRANSITION. Text in English. 1994. irreg. **Document type:** *Government.*
Published by: Education and Culture Service, Private Bag X54330, Durban, KwaZulu-Natal 4000, South Africa.

TREELINES. see *FORESTS AND FORESTRY*

TRENDS (NEW YORK). see *RELIGIONS AND THEOLOGY—Judaic*

370 SVN ISSN 0041-2724
TRIBUNA; studentski list. Text in Slovenian. 1952-1992; resumed 19??. s-m. SIT 350.
Address: Kersnikova 4, Ljubljana, 61000, Slovenia. TEL 386-61-319496, FAX 386-61-319448. Circ: 5,000.

370 ROM
TRIBUNA INVATAMANTULUI. Text in Romanian. 1970. w. USD 102 in Europe; USD 150 elsewhere.
Formerly (until 1989): Tribuna Scolii
Published by: (Rumania. Ministerul di Educatie si Stiinti), Megapress, Piata Presei Libere 1, Bucharest, 71341, Romania. TEL 40-12225115, FAX 40-12243733. Ed. Tirea Doina. Circ: 67,000. **Co-sponsor:** Trade Union of Workers in Education, Science and Cultural Institutions.

THE TRUSTED PROFESSIONAL. see *BUSINESS AND ECONOMICS—Accounting*

373.246 USA ISSN 0271-9746
LB2328
TRUSTEE QUARTERLY. Text in English. 1977. q. USD 30. adv. back issues avail. **Description:** Articles of interest to governing board members of two-year postsecondary institutions.
Related titles: Microfiche ed.
Indexed: HEA.
Published by: Association of Community College Trustees, 1740 N St, N W, Washington, DC 20036. TEL 202-775-4667. Ed. Sally Hutchins. Circ: 7,000 (controlled).

TURKEY. DEVLET ISTATISTIK ENSTITUSU. KAMU KURUMU VE KURULUSLARI HIZMET ONCESI VE HIZMET ICI EGITIM ISTATISTIKLERI/TURKEY. STATE INSTITUTE OF STATISTICS. STATISTICS ON TRAINING IN STATE INSTITUTIONS. see *EDUCATION—Abstracting, Bibliographies, Statistics*

TURKEY. DEVLET ISTATISTIK ENSTITUSU. MILLI EGITIM ISTATISTIKLERI OGRETIM YILI BASI. see *EDUCATION—Abstracting, Bibliographies, Statistics*

TURKEY. DEVLET ISTATISTIK ENSTITUSU. MILLI EGITIM ISTATISTIKLERI ORGUN EGITIM/TURKEY. STATE INSTITUTE OF STATISTICS. NATIONAL EDUCATIONAL STATISTICS FORMAL EDUCATION. see *EDUCATION—Abstracting, Bibliographies, Statistics*

TUTTITALIA. see *LINGUISTICS*

370 ITA ISSN 0391-7967
TUTTOSCUOLA. Text in Italian. 1975. bi-w. EUR 48 to individuals (effective 2005). adv. bk.rev. **Document type:** *Magazine, Consumer.*
Indexed: IBR, IBZ.
Published by: Editoriale Tuttoscuola Srl, Via della Scrofa 39, Rome, 00186, Italy. TEL 39-06-68307851, FAX 39-06-68802728, tuttoscuola@tuttoscuola.com, http://www.tuttoscuola.com. Ed. Giovanni Vinciguerra. Circ: 150,000.

370 POL ISSN 1231-675X
TY I SZKOLA; gazeta rodzinna. Text in Polish. 1994. m. PLZ 14. adv. bk.rev.; film rev.; play rev.; music rev. back issues avail. **Document type:** *Newspaper.* **Description:** Covers regional educational issues.
Published by: Atest - Studio Sp. z o.o., Ul Narutowicza 128, Lodz, 90145, Poland. TEL 48-42-783925, FAX 48-42-406032. Adv. contact Tomasz Radzynkiewicz. page PLZ 250; 290 x 210. Circ: (controlled). **Subscr. to:** ul. Wspolzawodnicza 2, Lodz, Poland.

TYDSKRIF VIR TAALONDERRIG/JOURNAL OF LANGUAGE TEACHING. see *LINGUISTICS*

U C DAVIS JOURNAL OF JUVENILE LAW & POLICY. (University of California) see *CHILDREN AND YOUTH—About*

370.1 USA ISSN 0042-1413
U E A ACTION. Text in English. 1969. q. free to members. adv. bk.rev. charts; illus. index. **Document type:** *Magazine, Trade.* **Description:** Covers national, state and local association activities, and the professional aspects of teaching people in the profession, legislative action involving schools.
Formerly: Utah Educational Review
Related titles: Online - full text ed.
Published by: Utah Education Association, 875 E. 5180 South St., Murray, UT 84107. TEL 800-594-8996, mark.mickelsen@utea.org, mmickelsen@nea.org, http://www.utea.org. Ed. Mark D Mickelsen. Circ: 19,500 (paid).

378 PHL ISSN 0118-3931
➤ **U E TODAY.** Text in English, Tagalog; Summaries in English. 1992. m. free. bk.rev. charts; illus.; bibl. 50 p./no.; back issues avail. **Document type:** *Journal, Academic/Scholarly.* **Description:** Contains feature articles, opinion columns, and reference material that concern the UE community. Subject areas include the academe and the arts, as well as any timely topic as the need arises.
Formerly (until 1996): U E Journal
Related titles: Online - full text ed.
Published by: University of the East, 2219 C.M. Recto Ave, Manila, 1008, Philippines. TEL 63-2-735-5471, FAX 63-2-735-6972, postmaster@ue.edu.ph, webmaster@ue.edu.ph, http://ue.edu.ph/ue/news.htm. Ed. Lourdes C Sanchez. Pub. P O Domingo. Circ: 2,000.

370.72 DEU
U I E ANNUAL REPORT. (UNESCO Institute for Education) Text in English. a. **Document type:** *Academic/Scholarly.*
Related titles: Online - full text ed.
Published by: UNESCO Institute for Education, Feldbrunnenstr 58, Hamburg, 20148, Germany. http://www.unesco.org/education/uie/news/annual.shtml.

370.91734 DEU
U I E STUDIES IN EDUCATION. Text in English, French. 1993. irreg., latest vol.3, 1994. back issues avail. **Document type:** *Monographic series, Academic/Scholarly.* **Description:** Covers international efforts to bring education throughout less-developed areas.
Published by: UNESCO Institute for Education, Feldbrunnenstr 58, Hamburg, 20148, Germany. TEL 49-40-448-0410, FAX 49-40-410-7723, uie@unesco.org.

370 DEU
U I E STUDIES SERIES. Text in French. irreg. price varies.
Related titles: ♦ Series: Alpha (Year): Current Research in Literacy. ISSN 1184-6836.
Published by: UNESCO Institute for Education, Feldbrunnenstr 58, Hamburg, 20148, Germany. TEL 49-40-448-0410, FAX 49-40-410-7723, http://www.education.unesco.org/uie. **Dist. in the U.S. by:** Bernan Associates, Bernan, 4611-F Assembly Dr., Lanham, MD 20706-4391. TEL 800-274-4447, FAX 800-865-3450.

370 USA ISSN 0161-7389
U S A TODAY (VALLEY STREAM). Text in English. 1915. m. USD 29 domestic; USD 35 in Canada; USD 9.50 newsstand/cover (effective 2005). adv. bk.rev. bibl.; illus. index. reprint service avail. from PQC. **Document type:** *Magazine, Consumer.* **Description:** Newsmagazine covering a broad range of subjects.
Former titles (until 1978): Intellect (0149-0095); (until 1972): School and Society (0036-6455); Which incorporated: Educational Review (0190-4191)
Related titles: Microform ed.: (from PMC, PQC); Online - full text ed.: (from EBSCO Publishing, Florida Center for Library Automation, Gale Group, H.W. Wilson, O C L C Online Computer Library Center, Inc., ProQuest Information & Learning, The Dialog Corporation).
Indexed: ABS&EES, Acal, BRI, BiolDig, CBRI, CIJE, CurCont, EAA, FLI, HEA, HlthInd, IPARL, LRI, MASUSE, MagInd, NewsAb, PCI, PMR, PhilInd, RASB, RGAb, RGPR, SSCI, TOM, WSA.
—BLDSC (9124.840000), IE, ingenta. **CCC.**
Published by: (Society for the Advancement of Education), S A E Inc., 500 Bi County Blvd., Ste. 203, Farmingdale, NY 11735-3931. Eds. Robert Rothenberg, Wayne Barrett. Pub. Robert Rothenberg. R&P Frances Eng. Adv. contact Steve Donenfeld. B&W page USD 6,100, color page USD 8,125; trim 10.88 x 8.38. Circ: 257,000.

U.S. DEPARTMENT OF EDUCATION. NATIONAL CENTER FOR EDUCATION STATISTICS. DIGEST OF EDUCATION STATISTICS. see *EDUCATION—Abstracting, Bibliographies, Statistics*

370 USA
U.S. DEPARTMENT OF EDUCATION. NATIONAL CENTER FOR EDUCATION STATISTICS. EARLY ESTIMATES OF PUBLIC ELEMENTARY AND SECONDARY EDUCATION STATISTICS. Text in English. irreg. **Document type:** *Government.*
Related titles: Online - full content ed.
Published by: U.S. Department of Education, National Center for Education Statistics, 1990 K St N W, Washington, DC 20006. http://nces.ed.gov/.

U.S. DEPARTMENT OF EDUCATION. NATIONAL CENTER FOR EDUCATION STATISTICS. PUBLIC ELEMENTARY AND SECONDARY STATE AGGREGATE DATA, BY STATE. see *EDUCATION—Abstracting, Bibliographies, Statistics*

371 USA ISSN 1557-4814
U T D EDGE. Text in English. 1947. m. USD 5 to non-members. adv. bk.rev. charts; illus.; stat. **Document type:** *Newsletter.*
Former titles: U T D Action (1546-6310); (until 2003): U T D Today (1082-8680); Dade County Teacher (0011-524X)
Published by: United Teachers of Dade, 2200 Biscayne Blvd., Miami, FL 33137-5016. TEL 305-854-0220. Ed. Annette Katz. Pub. Pat Tornillo. Circ: 20,000.

E

370 RUS
UCHITEL'SKAYA GAZETA. Text in Russian. 1924. w. USD 145 (effective 2000). **Document type:** *Newspaper, Consumer.*
Related titles: Microfilm ed.: (from EVP, PQC).
Address: Vetoshnyi per 13-15, Moscow, 103012, Russian Federation. TEL 7-095-9288253, ug@ug.ru, http://www.ug.ru. Ed. P Polozhevetz. Pub., R&P Slava Nekrasov. Adv. contact Marina Zeva. **US dist. addr.:** East View Information Services, 3020 Harbor Ln. N., Minneapolis, MN 55447. TEL 612-550-0961.

370 SVK ISSN 0139-5769
UCITEL'SKE NOVINY. Text in Slovak. 1951. w. USD 34 (effective 2000).
Published by: (Slovakia. Ministerstvo Skolstva Slovenskej Republiky), Redakcia Ucitel'ske Noviny, Sasinkova 5, Bratislava, 81560, Slovakia. Ed. Herlinda Novakova. Circ: 30,000.

370 DNK ISSN 0503-0102
L46
➤ **UDDANNELSE**; undervisningsministeriets tidsskrift. Text in Danish. 1968. 10/yr. DKK 725; DKK 85 per issue (effective 2005). **Document type:** *Magazine, Government.*
Related titles: Online - full text ed.: ISSN 1601-7730.
Indexed: RILM.
Published by: Undervisningsministeriet/Ministry of Education, Frederiksholms Kanal 21, Copenhagen K, 1220, Denmark. TEL 45-33-925000, FAX 45-33-925567, http://udd.uvm.dk/?menuid=4515. Ed. Benedicte Kieler TEL 45-33-925306.

370.9489 DNK ISSN 0900-226X
L46
UDDANNELSESHISTORIE (YEAR). Text in Danish. 1967. a. DKK 200; DKK 250 per issue (effective 2003). bk.rev. back issues avail. **Document type:** *Yearbook, Academic/Scholarly.*
Description: Features articles and reviews on Danish educational history.
Formerly (until 1984): Dansk Skolehistorie. Aarbog (0107-1661)
Indexed: RILM.
Published by: (Selskabet for Dansk Skolehistorie), Syddansk Universitetsforlag/University Press of Southern Denmark, Campusvej 55, Odense M, 5230, Denmark. TEL 45-66-157999, FAX 45-66-158126, press@forlag.sdu.dk, http://www.universitypress.dk. Ed. Vagn Skovgaard-Petersen. Circ: 1,000.

370 UGA ISSN 0049-5026
UGANDA SCHOOLS NEWSLETTER. Text in English. 1972 (vol.4). m. free. illus.
Published by: Ministry of Information Broadcasting and Tourism, PO Box 7142, Kampala, Uganda. Circ: 10,000.

ULTIBASE JOURNAL. see *BUSINESS AND ECONOMICS*

UMWELT - BILDUNG - FORSCHUNG. see *ENVIRONMENTAL STUDIES*

UMWELTSTUNDE; Lehrblaetter fuer die Umwelterziehung im Unterricht. see *ENVIRONMENTAL STUDIES*

372.21 GBR ISSN 0969-9481
UNDER FIVE CONTACT. Text in English. 1969. m. (except Aug. & Jan.). GBP 25. adv. bk.rev. index, cum.index. back issues avail. **Document type:** *Bulletin, Academic/Scholarly.*
Description: Covers pre-school education in community groups - quality provisions, training and support for parents.
Formerly: Contact (0308-0633)
Indexed: CERDIC.
Published by: Pre-School Learning Alliance, 69 King's Cross Rd, London, WC1X 9LL, United Kingdom. TEL 44-171-833-0991, FAX 44-171-837-4942. Ed., R&P Ann Henderson. Adv. contact Madison Bell. Circ: 23,000.

UNDERSTANDING CHILDREN'S SOCIAL CARE. see *CHILDREN AND YOUTH—About*

UNDERSTANDING JAPAN. see *GENERAL INTEREST PERIODICALS—Japan*

UNDERSTANDING STATISTICS; statistical issues in psychology, education, and the social sciences. see *STATISTICS*

370 KEN
UNDUGU BULLETIN. Text in Dutch, English, French, German. 1979. q. free. **Document type:** *Bulletin.* **Description:** Covers the progress of the Undugu Society.
Published by: Undugu Society of Kenya, PO Box 40417, Nairobi, Kenya. FAX 254-2-505888. Ed. Herbert Kassamani. Circ: 740.

060 370 PHL ISSN 0041-5294
UNESCO PHILIPPINES✶. Text in English. 1962-1967; resumed 1984. biennial. free. illus. cum.index 1962-1964. **Description:** Features significant programs, projects and activities undertaken by UNESCO, especially the UNESCO National Commission of the Philippines.
Indexed: IPP.
Published by: UNESCO National Commission of the Philippines, No. 2330 Old A D B Bldg, Roxas Blvd, Pasay City, Philippines. TEL 832-03-09, TELEX 40257 UNESCO PM. Ed. Apolinario Y Tating. Circ: 3,000.

UNGDOMS- OG VOKSENUNDERVISNING. see *EDUCATION—Abstracting, Bibliographies, Statistics*

370 DNK ISSN 1602-0324
UNGDOMSFORSKNING. Text in Danish. 2002. q. DKK 150 to individuals; DKK 200 to institutions; DKK 50 per issue (effective 2005). back issues avail. **Document type:** *Monographic series, Academic/Scholarly.*
Related titles: Online - full text ed.: Ungdomsforskning. ISSN 1602-060X. 2000.
Published by: Danmarks Paedagogiske Universitet, Learning Lab Denmark. Center for Ungdomsforskning (CEFU)/Danish University of Education, Emdrupvej 101, Copenhagen NV, 2400, Denmark. TEL 45-39-559933, FAX 45-39-669228, ungdomsforskning@lld.dk, cefu@lld.dk, http://www.cefu.dk/nyhedsbrev/. Ed. Niels-Henrik M Hansen.

370 DNK ISSN 0904-5341
UNGDOMSUDDANNELSER. Text in Danish. 1984. a. DKK 275 (effective 1998). illus. **Document type:** *Academic/Scholarly.*
Formerly (until 1988): Ungdomsuddannelser - Efter 9. og 10. Klasse (0900-1395)
Published by: Ole Camaae Ed. & Pub., Lerbjergstien 18, Birkeroed, 3460, Denmark. TEL 45-48-17-62-82, FAX 45-48-17-78-80.

372 DNK ISSN 0106-5386
➤ **UNGE PAEDAGOGER.** Text in Danish. 1939. 8/yr. (8/yr.). DKK 180 to individuals; DKK 255 to institutions; DKK 140 to students; DKK 30 per issue (effective 2004). adv. bk.rev. index, cum.index. **Document type:** *Academic/Scholarly.*
Description: Concerned with everything related to the Danish state school system of elementary education.
Indexed: RASB.
Published by: Foreningen Unge Paedagoger, Edvard Griegsgade 2, Copenhagen Oe, 2100, Denmark. TEL 45-39-291548, FAX 45-39-291579, http://www.u-p.dk/tidsskrifter.php?s=3&dd=1, http://www.u-p@u-p.dk. Circ: 2,500.

370 AUT
UNI-PRESS. Text in German. 1977. 6/yr. free. adv. bk.rev. illus.; tr.lit.
Supersedes: De Facto (0014-6536)
Published by: Oesterreichische Hochschuelerschaft an der Universitaet Salzburg, Residenzplatz 1, Salzburg, Sa 5020, Austria. Ed. Viktor Mayer Schoenberger. Circ: 4,500.

370 ZAF ISSN 0259-5591
DIE UNIE. Text in Afrikaans. 1905. bi-m. ZAR 30 (effective 1999). adv. bk.rev.
Indexed: ISAP.
Published by: Suid-Afrikaanse Onderwysersunie/South African Teachers Union, PO Box 196, Cape Town, 8000, South Africa. TEL 27-21-461-6340, FAX 27-21-461-9238, saou@new.co.za. Ed. A P J Botha. Adv. contact M Burger. Circ: 7,055 (controlled).

370 USA
UNION CONNECTION. Text in English. 1923. q. USD 10 to non-members; free to members (effective 2005). adv. bk.rev.; film rev. charts; illus.; tr.lit. index. reprint service avail. from PQC. **Document type:** *Magazine, Trade.*
Former titles (until 1993): Forum (Tallahassee) (1063-8393); (until 1987): F E A - United's Forum Magazine (1071-619X); (until 1984): Forum (1071-6181); (until 1984): F E A - U's Forum (0744-6063); (until 1982): F E A United's Forum (0279-862X); (until 1980): Forum (0274-8738); (until 1980): United Teacher; Florida Education (0015-4016)
Related titles: Microform ed.: (from PQC).
Published by: Florida Education Association, 213 S Adams St, Tallahassee, FL 32399-1701. TEL 850-224-1161, FAX 850-681-2905, http://www.feaweb.org. Ed. Mark Pudlow. Circ: 120,000 (controlled).

371.14 USA
UNION LEADER (TALLAHASSEE). Text in English. q. back issues avail. **Document type:** *Newsletter.* **Description:** Covers education issues and union trends in the K-12 area of education.
Former titles: Focus (Tallahassee); Solidarity's Focus
Published by: Florida Education Association, 213 S Adams St, Tallahassee, FL 32399-1701. TEL 904-224-1161, FAX 904-681-2905. Eds. Elisia Norton, Kendra Brown. Circ: 1,500.

370 USA ISSN 1092-8022
UNION NEWS. Text in English. 1995. 6/yr. USD 10 (effective 2005). adv. back issues avail. **Document type:** *Newsletter, Trade.*
Related titles: Online - full text ed.
Published by: Illinois Federation of Teachers, PO Box 390, Westmont, IL 60559. TEL 630-571-0100, 800-942-9242, FAX 630-571-1204, gpurkey@ift-aft.org, http://www.ift-aft.org. Circ: 49,280 (paid and controlled).

UNITAS; a quarterly review for the arts and sciences. see *ART*

370 GBR
UNITED KINGDOM. DEPARTMENT FOR EDUCATION AND SKILLS. RESEARCH REPORT. Text in English. irreg., latest RR 334. GBP 4.95 per paper copy (effective 2002); Free on the internet. **Document type:** *Monographic series.*
Related titles: Online - full text ed.
—BLDSC (7761.341100).
Published by: Great Britain Department for Education, Sanctuary Bldgs, Sanctuary Buildings, Great Smith St, London, SW1P 3BT, United Kingdom. TEL 44-171-925-6310, FAX 44-171-925-6985.

371.192 USA
UNITED PARENTS ASSOCIATION OF NEW YORK CITY. NEWSLETTER✶. Text in English. 1975 (vol.6). m. (during school year). USD 15.
Published by: United Parents Associations of New York City, 391 E 149th St, Ste 205, Bronx, NY 10455. TEL 212-619-0095.

370.954 IND
UNITED SCHOOLS ORGANISATION OF INDIA. ANNUAL REPORT. Text in English. 1969 (19th ed.). a. adv. illus. **Document type:** *Corporate.*
Published by: United Schools Organisation of India, U S O House, USO Rd. 6 Special Institutional Area, New Delhi, 110 067, India. TEL 91-11-656-1103, FAX 91-11-685-6283. R&P Jiya Lal Jain. Adv. contact Ram Nath Tandon.

370 ESP ISSN 0214-0489
UNIVERSIDAD DE GRANADA. REVISTA DE EDUCACION. Text in Spanish. 1987. a. price varies. **Document type:** *Monographic series, Academic/Scholarly.*
Indexed: RILM.
—CINDOC.
Published by: Editorial Universidad de Granada, Antiguo Colegio Maximo, Campus de Cartuja, Granada, 18071, Spain. TEL 34-958-246220, FAX 34-958-243931, comunicacion@editorialugr.com, http://www.editorialugr.com. Ed. Esteban de Mannuel Torres.

378 MEX ISSN 0185-1330
UNIVERSIDAD DE MEXICO. Text in Spanish. 1945. m. MXP 150, USD 90 (effective 2000). back issues avail. **Description:** Covers literature, science and Mexican culture.
Related titles: Online - full text ed.: ISSN 1605-4067. 1996.
Indexed: HAPI, IBR, MLA-IB.
—BLDSC (7835.350000).
Published by: Universidad Nacional Autonoma de Mexico, Coordinacion de Humanidades, c/o Departamento de Publicidad y Relaciones Publicas, Mexico, INSURGENTES SUR 3744, Centro Tlalpan, Mexico City, DF 14000, Mexico. TEL 52-5-6663496, FAX 52-5-6663749, univmex@escaner.dgsca.unam.mx, http://www.unam.mx/. Ed. Alberto Dallal Castillo.

370 ESP ISSN 0212-8322
UNIVERSIDAD DE MURCIA. ANALES DE PEDAGOGIA. Text in Spanish, English. 1955. a., latest vol.17, 1999. back issues avail. **Document type:** *Academic/Scholarly.*
Supersedes in part (in 1983): Universidad de Murcia. Anales. Filosofia y Letras (0463-9863)
—CINDOC, KNAW.
Published by: Universidad de Murcia, Servicio de Publicaciones, Edificio Saavedra Fajardo, C/ Actor Isidoro Maiquez 9, Murcia, 30007, Spain. TEL 34-968-363887, FAX 34-968-363414, servpubl@um.es, http://www.um.es/spumweb. Ed. Fernando Vicente Jara. Circ: 256.

370.946 ESP
UNIVERSIDAD DE NAVARRA. FACULTAD DE CIENCIAS DE LA EDUCACION. COLECCION. Text in Spanish. 1969. irreg., latest vol.31, 1989. price varies.
Formerly: Universidad de Navarra. Instituto de Ciencias de la Educacion. Coleccion I C E (0078-8686)
Published by: (Universidad de Navarra), Ediciones Universidad de Navarra S.A., Pza. Los Sauces, 1-2, Baranain, (Navarra) 31010, Spain. TEL 34-948-256850.

370 ESP
UNIVERSIDAD DE SEVILLA. SERIE: CIENCIAS DE LA EDUCACION. Text in Spanish. irreg., latest vol.16, 2001. price varies. **Document type:** *Monographic series, Academic/Scholarly.*
Published by: (Universidad de Sevilla, Instituto de Ciencias de la Educacion), Universidad de Sevilla, Secretariado de Publicaciones, Porvenir 27, Sevilla, 41013, Spain. TEL 34-95-4487444, FAX 34-95-4487443, secpub10@us.es, http://www.us.es/publius/inicio.html.

370 ITA ISSN 0082-6480
UNIVERSITA DEGLI STUDI DI TRIESTE. ISTITUTO DI PEDAGOGIA. QUADERNI. Text in Italian. 1966. irreg. price varies.
Published by: (Universita degli Studi di Trieste, Universita degli Studi di Trieste, Istituto di Pedagogia), Casa Editrice Edumond Le Monnier, Via Antonio Meucci 2, Grassina, FI 50015, Italy. TEL 39-055-64910, FAX 39-055-643983, lemonnier@lemonnier.it, http://www.lemonnier.it.

UNIVERSITAET MOZARTEUM SALZBURG. JAHRESBERICHT. see *ART*

378 DOM ISSN 0041-9044
UNIVERSITARIO✶. Text in Spanish. 1970. s-m. charts; illus.
Published by: Universidad Autonoma de Santo Domingo, Escuela de Ciencias de la Informacion Publica, Santo Domingo, Dominican Republic. Ed. Dr. Gonzalez Tirado.

E

▼ new title ➤ refereed ✶ unverified ◆ full entry avail.

370 NOR ISSN 0800-6113
UNIVERSITET I OSLO. PEDAGOGISK FORSKNINGSINSTITUTT. RAPPORT. Text in Norwegian. 1977. irreg. price varies. **Document type:** *Academic/Scholarly.*
Published by: Universitetet i Oslo, Pedagogisk Forskningsinstitutt, Postboks 1092, Blindern, Oslo, 0317, Norway. TEL 47-22-85-70-75, FAX 47-22-85-42-50. Circ: 175.

370 331.8 SWE ISSN 0282-4973
UNIVERSITETSLAERAREN. Text in Swedish. 1950. 20/yr. SEK 250 (effective 2001). adv. bk.rev. **Document type:** *Magazine, Trade.*
Formed by the 1985 merger of: S U H A F - Tidningen (0036-2018); U L F
Published by: Sveriges Universitetslaerarfoerbund (SULF), Box 1227, Stockholm, 11182, Sweden. TEL 46-8-698-36-10, FAX 46-8-21-61-82, universitetslararen@sulf.se, http://www.sulf.se. Ed., Pub. Lars-Goeran Heldt. Adv. contact Lena Loewenmark-Andre TEL 46-8-698-36-22. B&W page SEK 13,500, color page SEK 19,500; trim 185 x 260. Circ: 17,300 (paid and controlled).

370 MYS
UNIVERSITI KEBANGSAAN MALAYSIA. LAPURAN TAHUNAN - ANNUAL REPORT. Text mainly in Malay. 1971. a. free. stat.
Published by: Penerbit Universiti Kebangsaan Malaysia, Ukm Bangi, Selangor 43600, Malaysia. TEL 8250001.

UNIVERSITIES ACACDEMIC PENSION PLAN (YEAR) ANNUAL REPORT. see *BUSINESS AND ECONOMICS—Labor And Industrial Relations*

UNIVERSITY OF ALASKA SEA GRANT COLLEGE PROGRAM. EDUCATION PUBLICATION. see *SCIENCES: COMPREHENSIVE WORKS*

370.72 IND ISSN 0084-621X
UNIVERSITY OF ALLAHABAD. EDUCATION DEPARTMENT. RESEARCHES AND STUDIES. Text in English, Hindi. 1950. a., latest vol.45. per issue exchange basis. bk.rev. stat. **Document type:** *Journal, Internal.*
Published by: University of Allahabad, Education Department, Allahabad, Uttar Pradesh 211 002, India. Ed. K S Misra. Circ: (controlled).

370.72 GHA ISSN 0855-0883
LG497.C34
UNIVERSITY OF CAPE COAST. INSTITUTE OF EDUCATION. JOURNAL. Text and summaries in English. s-a. GHC 40,000 domestic; USD 50 foreign (effective 2001). **Document type:** *Academic/Scholarly.*
Indexed: RASB.
Published by: (University of Cape Coast, Institution of Education), Ghana Universities Press, PO Box GP 4219, Accra, Ghana. TEL 233-21-500300, ext. 6135, FAX 233-21-501930. Ed. A E Sosu. Pub. K M Ganu. Circ: 500 (paid).

UNIVERSITY OF DAYTON. SCHOOL OF EDUCATION. WORKSHOP PROCEEDINGS. see *RELIGIONS AND THEOLOGY—Roman Catholic*

370.72 PHL ISSN 0070-8259
UNIVERSITY OF EASTERN PHILIPPINES. RESEARCH CENTER. REPORT. Text in English. 1965. irreg. USD 2 (effective 2000).
Media: Duplicated (not offset).
Published by: University of Eastern Philippines, Research Center, University Town, Northern Samar, 6400, Philippines. Ed. Julita R Calonge. Circ: 3,000.

370 USA ISSN 0733-0375
UNIVERSITY OF HEALING. SYLLABUS. Text in English. a. **Document type:** *Academic/Scholarly.*
Published by: God Unlimited - University of Healing, 1101 Far Valley Rd, Campo, CA 91906. TEL 619-478-5111, FAX 619-478-5013, unihealing@goduni.org, http://www.university-of-healing.edu.

370 FIN ISSN 0359-5749
UNIVERSITY OF HELSINKI. DEPARTMENT OF EDUCATION. RESEARCH BULLETIN. Text in English, French, German. 1957. a. price varies.
Formerly (until 1982): University of Helsinki. Institute of Education. Research Bulletin (0073-179X)
Related titles: Microfiche ed.
Indexed: CIJE, PsycholAb.
Published by: University of Helsinki, Department of Education, University of Helsinki, PL 39, Helsinki, 00014, Finland. TEL 358-0-1911, FAX 358-0-1918073. Circ: 325.

370.966925 NGA ISSN 0331-0817
LB2133.I22
UNIVERSITY OF IBADAN. INSTITUTE OF EDUCATION. ANNUAL REPORT. Text in English. a. **Document type:** *Corporate.*
Published by: University of Ibadan, Institute of Education, Ibadan, Oyo, Nigeria. TEL 234-22-62550-1495. Ed. J D Obemeata.

370 NGA ISSN 0073-4314
UNIVERSITY OF IBADAN. INSTITUTE OF EDUCATION. OCCASIONAL PUBLICATIONS. Text in English. irreg. price varies. **Document type:** *Monographic series.*
Published by: University of Ibadan, Institute of Education, Ibadan, Oyo, Nigeria. TEL 234-22-62550-1495. Ed. J D Obemeata.

370.72 379 GBR ISSN 1476-6841
UNIVERSITY OF LONDON. INSTITUTE OF EDUCATION. VIEWPOINT. Text in English. 1995. irreg., latest 2001, Dec. GBP 3 per issue (effective 2003). **Document type:** *Monographic series, Academic/Scholarly.* **Description:** Presents topical issues in education policy and research accessibly summarized by the Institute's experts.
Published by: University of London, Institute of Education, 20 Bedford Way, London, WC1H OAL, United Kingdom. TEL 44-20-76126000, FAX 44-20-76126126, info@ioe.ac.uk, http://www.ioe.ac.uk.

370.72 GBR
UNIVERSITY OF SUSSEX. INSTITUTE OF EDUCATION. RESEARCH REPORT SERIES. Text in English. irreg., latest vol.8, 1998. GBP 3.95. **Document type:** *Monographic series.* —BLDSC (7769.087870).
Published by: University of Sussex, Institute of Education, Education Development Bldg, University Of Sussex, Falmer, Brighton, E Sussex BN1 9RG, United Kingdom.

378 CAN ISSN 0042-031X
UNIVERSITY OF WATERLOO. GAZETTE. Text in English. 1970 (vol.10). w. CND 30; free on campus. adv. bk.rev. illus. **Document type:** *Newspaper.*
Published by: University of Waterloo, Internal Communications Department, 200 University Ave, W, Waterloo, ON N2L 3G1, Canada. TEL 519-885-1211, FAX 519-746-9875, credmond@watservl.uwaterloo.ca, http://www.adm.uwaterloo.ca/infoipa/gazette.html. Ed. Chris Redmond. Circ: 7,000 (controlled).

370 SVK ISSN 0083-4165
UNIVERZITA KOMENSKEHO. FILOZOFICKA FAKULTA. ZBORNIK: PAEDAGOGICA. Text in Slovak; Summaries in English, German; Some issues in English. 1968. irreg. free domestic (effective 2005). **Document type:** *Academic/Scholarly.*
Indexed: RASB.
Published by: Univerzita Komenskeho, Filozoficka Fakulta, Ustredna Kniznica, Gondova 2, Bratislava, 81801, Slovakia. Ed. Stefan Svec. Circ: 700.

370.15 POL ISSN 0083-4254
UNIWERSYTET IM. ADAMA MICKIEWICZA. PSYCHOLOGIA-PEDAGOGIKA. Text in Polish. 1961. irreg., latest vol.110, 1996. price varies. bk.rev. **Document type:** *Monographic series, Academic/Scholarly.* **Description:** Contains current research results of one author in the field of psychology, including monographs and Ph.D. works.
Formerly: Uniwersytet im. Adama Mickiewicza w Poznaniu. Wydzial Historyczny. Prace. Seria Psychologia-Pedagogika (0860-1380)
Indexed: PsycholAb, e-psyche.
Published by: Wydawnictwo Naukowe Uniwersytetu im. Adama Mickiewicza/Adam Mickiewicz University Press, Nowowiejskiego 55, Poznan, 61-734, Poland. TEL 48-61-527380, FAX 48-61-527701. Pub. Maria Jankowska. R&P Malgorzata Bis.

370 POL ISSN 0239-5436
UNIWERSYTET JAGIELLONSKI. ZESZYTY NAUKOWE. PRACE PEDAGOGICZNE/UNIVERSITAS IAGELLONICA ACTA SCIENTIARUM LITTERARUMQUE. SCHEDAE PAEDAGOGICAE. Text in Polish. 1957. irreg., latest 2001. price varies. illus. **Document type:** *Monographic series, Academic/Scholarly.*
Supersedes in part (in 1984): Uniwersytet Jagiellonski. Zeszyty Naukowe. Prace Psychologiczno-Pedagogiczne (0083-4408)
Indexed: RASB.
Published by: (Uniwersytet Jagiellonski, Instytut Pedagogiki), Wydawnictwo Uniwersytetu Jagiellonskiego/Jagiellonian University Press, ul Grodzka 26, Krakow, 31044, Poland. TEL 48-12-4312364, FAX 48-12-4301995, wydaw@if.uj.edu.pl, http://www.wuj.pl. **Dist. by:** Ars Polona, Krakowskie Przedmiescie 7, Warsaw, Poland. TEL 48-22-9263914, FAX 48-22-9265334, arspolona@arspolona.com.pl, http://www.arspolona.com.pl.

370 DEU
DER UNTERMIETER. Text in German. 1966. irreg. adv.
Published by: Verein Freunde und Foerderer der Deutschen Studentenschaft e.V., Untere Hausbreite 11, Munich, 80939, Germany. Ed. Peter Gantzer.

370 DEU ISSN 0340-4099
L31
UNTERRICHTSWISSENSCHAFT. Text in German. 1973. q. EUR 63.20 domestic; EUR 69.50 foreign (effective 2003). adv. bk.rev. index. 96 p./no.; reprints avail. **Document type:** *Journal, Academic/Scholarly.*
Indexed: DIP, IBR, IBZ.
—BLDSC (9121.325000), IE, Infotrieve, ingenta. **CCC.**
Published by: Juventa Verlag GmbH, Ehretstr 3, Weinheim, 69469, Germany. TEL 49-6201-90200, FAX 49-6201-902013, juventa@juventa.de, http://www.juventa.de. Ed. Guenter Doerr. Adv. contact Karola Weiss. page EUR 250; trim 113 x 193. Circ: 700 (paid and controlled).

371.822 DEU ISSN 0939-5474
UNTERSCHIEDE. Text in German. 1991. q. adv.
Published by: (Neue Bildungswege fuer Frauen e.V.), Kleine Verlag GmbH, Postfach 101668, Bielefeld, 33516, Germany. TEL 0521-15811. Circ: 3,000.

UPDATE: APPLICATIONS OF RESEARCH IN MUSIC EDUCATION (ONLINE EDITION). see *MUSIC*

372 ISL ISSN 1022-5110
UPPELDI; timarit um boern og fleira folk. Text in Icelandic. 1988. q. ISK 1,980.
Published by: Foreldrasamtoeking i Reykjavik, Bolholti 4, Reykjavik, 105, Iceland. TEL 354-568-0709.

370.72 ISL ISSN 1022-4629
➤ **UPPELDI OG MENNTUN**; timarit kennarahaskola Islands. Text in Icelandic. 1992. a. ISK 2,000, USD 30 (effective 2001). abstr.; illus. 170 p./no.; back issues avail. **Document type:** *Academic/Scholarly.* **Description:** Publishes original research in the field of education, and short articles of a personal or practical nature of interest to the Icelandic teaching profession.
Published by: Rannsoknarstofnun Kennarahaskola Islands, Stakkahlid, Reykjavik, 105, Iceland. TEL 354-563-3827, 354-563-3805, FAX 354-563-3833, khirann@khi.is, http://www.khi.is. Ed. Amalie Bjoernsdottir.

370 SWE ISSN 0348-3649
UPPSALA REPORTS ON EDUCATION. Text in English. 1978. irreg. price varies. back issues avail. **Document type:** *Monographic series, Academic/Scholarly.*
Related titles: ♦ Supplement to: Uppsala Studies in Education. ISSN 0347-1314.
Published by: Uppsala Universitet, Pedagogiske Institutionen/University of Uppsala. Department of Education, PO Box 2109, Uppsala, 75002, Sweden. TEL 46-18-4711652, FAX 46-18-4711651, pedagogen@ped.uu.se, http://www.ped.uu.se.

370 SWE ISSN 0347-1314
UPPSALA STUDIES IN EDUCATION. Text in English, Swedish; Summaries in English. 1976. irreg., latest vol.99, 2002. price varies. index. back issues avail. **Document type:** *Monographic series, Academic/Scholarly.*
Supersedes: Studia Scientiae Paedagogicae Upsaliensia (0081-6892)
Related titles: ♦ Series of: Acta Universitatis Upsaliensis. ISSN 0346-5462; ♦ Supplement(s): Uppsala Reports on Education. ISSN 0348-3649.
Indexed: PsycholAb.
Published by: (Uppsala Universitet, Pedagogiska Institutionen), Uppsala Universitet, Acta Universitatis Upsaliensis/University Publications from Uppsala, PO Box 256, Uppsala, 75105, Sweden. TEL 46-18-4713922, http://www.ub.uu.se/upu/auu. Ed. Bengt Landgren. Circ: 750. **Dist. by:** Almqvist & Wiksell International.

370 BGR
UPRAVLENIE I ORGANIZATSIA NA NAUKATA I VISSHETO OBRAZOVANIE. Text in Bulgarian. bi-m. USD 36 foreign (effective 2002). **Document type:** *Bulletin.* **Description:** Covers organization and administration of college and university education.
Published by: Ministerstvo na Obrazovanieto i Naukata na Republika Bulgaria/Ministry of Education and Sciences of the Republic of Bulgaria, 125 Tzarigradsko Shosse Blvd., Bl. 5, PO Box 336, Sofia, 1113, Bulgaria. TEL 359-2-705298, http://www.minedu.government.bg. **Dist. by:** Sofia Books, ul Silivria 16, Sofia 1404, Bulgaria. TEL 359-2-9586257, info@sofiabooks-bg.com, http://www.sofiabooks-bg.com.

370 BGR
UPRAVLENIE NA SREDNOTO OBRAZOVANIE. Text in Bulgarian. m. USD 48 foreign (effective 2002). **Document type:** *Bulletin.*
Published by: Ministerstvo na Obrazovanieto i Naukata na Republika Bulgaria/Ministry of Education and Sciences of the Republic of Bulgaria, 125 Tzarigradsko Shosse Blvd., Bl. 5, PO Box 336, Sofia, 1113, Bulgaria. TEL 359-2-705298, http://www.minedu.government.bg. **Dist. by:** Sofia Books, ul Silivria 16, Sofia 1404, Bulgaria. TEL 359-2-9586257, info@sofiabooks-bg.com, http://www.sofiabooks-bg.com.

UPRAVLENIE SHKOLOI. see *OCCUPATIONS AND CAREERS*

371.0091732 USA ISSN 0042-0859
LC5101
➤ **URBAN EDUCATION.** Text in English. 1966. bi-m. USD 650, GBP 420 to institutions; USD 677, GBP 437 combined subscription to institutions print & online eds. (effective 2006). adv. bk.rev. charts; stat.; illus. index. back issues avail.; reprints avail. **Document type:** *Journal, Academic/Scholarly.* **Description:** Presents urban educators and administrators a well-balanced view of current debates, controversies, and solutions, facing schools in urban environments.

E

Related titles: Microfilm ed.: (from PQC); Online - full text ed.: ISSN 1552-8340. USD 644, GBP 415 to institutions (effective 2006) (from C S A, EBSCO Publishing, O C L C Online Computer Library Center, Inc., Sage Publications, Inc., Swets Information Services).
Indexed: ABIn, AMHA, ASCA, BRI, BiolAb, CIJE, CJA, CPE, ChPerl, CurCont, DIP, EAA, ERA, ETA, EduInd, FamI, HRA, IBR, IBZ, MEA, PsycInfo, PsycholAb, RHEA, SEA, SENA, SFSA, SOMA, SOPODA, SPAA, SRRA, SSA, SSCI, SUSA, SWA, SWR&A, SociolAb, TEA, UAA, V&AA.
—BLDSC (9123.370000), IDS, IE, Infotrieve, ingenta. CCC.
Published by: Corwin Press, Inc. (Subsidiary of: Sage Publications, Inc.), 2455 Teller Rd, Thousand Oaks, CA 91320-2218. TEL 805-499-9734, FAX 805-499-0871, 800-4-1-SCHOOL (800-417-2466), info@sagepub.com, http://www.sagepub.com/journal.aspx?pid=213. Ed. Kofi Lomotey. adv.: B&W page USD 350. Circ: 750 (paid). Subscr. to: Sage Publications Ltd., 1 Oliver's Yard, 55 City Rd, London EC1 1SP, United Kingdom. TEL 44-20-73740645, FAX 44-20-73748741, subscription@sagepub.co.uk.

370　　　　　　URY　　　　　　ISSN 0797-6275
LA600
URUGUAY. DIRECCION DE EDUCACION. REVISTA. Text in Spanish. 1992. s-a. Document type: Government.
Published by: Ministerio de Educacion y Cultura, Direccion de Educacion, Reconquista, 535 Piso 6, Montevideo, 11007, Uruguay.

370.9895　　　　URY　　　　　ISSN 0797-6461
URUGUAY. DIRECCION DE EDUCACION. SERIE LOS DEPARTAMENTOS. Key Title: Serie los Departamentos. Text in Spanish. 1992. m.
Published by: Ministerio de Educacion y Cultura, Direccion de Educacion, Reconquista, 535 Piso 6, Montevideo, 11007, Uruguay. Ed. Carlos Romero.

370　　　　　　NOR　　　　　　ISSN 1502-9778
LA890
UTDANNING. Text in Norwegian. 2002. 26/yr. NOK 500 (effective 2003). adv. bk.rev. index. reprints avail. Document type: Journal, Trade.
Incorporates (1991-2002): Norsk Foerskolelaererblad (1501-4312); Formed by the merger of (1993-2002): Skolefokus (0804-3698); Which was formed by the merger of (1947-1993): Yrke (0049-8475); (1946-1993): Mercator (0800-8957); Which was formerly (until 1973): Tidsskrift for Handelsutdannelse (0801-7727); (until 1953): Mercator (1502-6264); (1892-1993): Skoleforum (0332-7167); Which was formerly (until 1976): Den Hogre Skolen (0018-3075); (until 1899): Filologernes og Realisternes Landsforening. Meddelelser fra Bestyrelsen (1500-0206); (1934-2002): Norsk Skoleblad (0029-2117); Which incorporated (1892-1934): Norsk Skoletidende (0802-6017); (1897-1934): Skolebladet (0802-6025); (1952-1959): Skole og Samfunn (0489-0744)
Related titles: Online - full text ed.
Indexed: RASB.
—CCC.
Published by: Utdanningsforbundet/Union of Education Norway, Hausman Gate 15, PO Box 9191, Groenland, Oslo, 0134, Norway. TEL 47-24-142000, FAX 47-24-142100, redaksjonen@utdanning.ws, post@utdanningsforbundet.no, http://www.utdanning.ws, http://www.utdanningsforbundet.no. Ed. Knut Hovland TEL 47-24-142208. Adv. contact Nina Mietle TEL 47-24-142087. B&W page NOK 20,700, color page NOK 35,000; 197 x 265. Circ: 126,753 (controlled).

370.1　　　　　USA　　　　　　ISSN 0042-1790
V E A NEWS. Text in English. 1966 (vol.8). m. (Sep.-May). membership. illus. Document type: Newspaper.
Published by: Virginia Education Association, 116 S Third St, Richmond, VA 23219. TEL 804-648-5801, FAX 804-775-8379. Ed. Rosmarie Studer. Circ: 50,000.

370　　　　　　GBR
V E T N E T - E C E R. PROCEEDINGS. (Vocational Education and Training NETwork - European Conference of Education Research) Text in English. irreg. back issues avail. Document type: Proceedings.
Published by: (Vocational Education and Training NETwork), European Educational Research Association, Room W307, Faculty of Education, University of Strathclyde, 76 Southbrae Dr, Glasgow, G13 1PP, United Kingdom. eera@strath.ac.uk, http://www.b.shuttle.de/wifo/abstract/lecer00p.htm, http://www.eera.ac.uk/. Eds. David Raffe, Sabine Manning.

V H W MITTEILUNGEN. see SCIENCES: COMPREHENSIVE WORKS

V R IN THE SCHOOLS. (Virtual Reality) see COMPUTERS—Computer Simulation

370　　　　　　FRA　　　　　　ISSN 0396-8669
V S T. (Vie Sociale et Traitements) Text in French. 1973. q. Document type: Journal, Academic/Scholarly.
Published by: Editions Eres, 11 rue des Alouettes, Ramonville Saint-Agne, 31520, France. TEL 33-5-61751576, FAX 33-5-61735289, eres@edition-eres.com, http://www.cemea.asso.fr/vst, http://www.edition-eres.com. Ed. Serge Vallon.

VAEGLEDAREN I UTBILDNING OCH ARBETSLIV. see OCCUPATIONS AND CAREERS

370　　　　　　ESP　　　　　　ISSN 1136-0313
VELA MAJOR. Text in Catalan. 1994. 3/yr.
—CINDOC.
Published by: Editorial Barcanova, Plaza Lesseps, 33 Entre Sol 1a., Barcelona, 08023, Spain. TEL 34-93-2172054, FAX 34-93-2373469, barcanova@barcanova.es, http://www.barcanova.es/.

370　　　　　　ESP　　　　　　ISSN 1133-7974
VELA MAYOR. Text in Spanish. 1993. q.
—CINDOC.
Published by: Anaya Educacion, E. Juan Ignacio Luca de Tena, 15, Madrid, 28027, Spain. TEL 34-91-3938800, FAX 34-91-7426631. Ed. Arsenio Lopez.

370.210987　　　　VEN
VENEZUELA. DEPARTAMENTO DE INVESTIGACIONES EDUCACIONALES. SECCION DE ESTADISTICA. ESTADISTICAS EDUCACIONALES* . Text in Spanish. 1971. a. illus.; stat.
Published by: (Venezuela. Departamento de Investigaciones Educacionales), Ministerio de Educacion, c/o Ministerio de Relaciones Exteriores, Direccion de Relaciones Culturales, Caracas, Venezuela.

372　　　　　　CAN　　　　　　ISSN 0315-2235
VENTURE FORTH. Text in English. 1969. 3/yr. CND 35 (effective 2000). bk.rev. back issues avail. Document type: Bulletin.
Formerly: It's Our Bag
Indexed: CEI.
Published by: (Early Childhood Education Council), Saskatchewan Teachers' Federation, 2317 Arlington Ave., Saskatoon, SK S7J 2H8, Canada. stf@stf.sk.ca. Circ: 1,063.

VERMONT EDUCATION LAWBOOK. see LAW

370.1　　　　　USA
VERMONT - N E A TODAY. Text in English. 1933. m. (Aug.-Jun.). USD 6. Document type: Newspaper.
Former titles: V E A Today; Vermont Blackboard (0042-4137)
Published by: Vermont National Education Association, 10 Wheelock St, Montpelier, VT 05602-3737. http://www.vtnea.org/today.htm. Ed., Pub., R&P, Adv. contact Huse Li. Circ: 9,200.

370　　　　　　NLD　　　　　　ISSN 0922-0194
L21
VERNIEUWING. Text in Dutch. 1987. 9/yr. EUR 33 to individuals; EUR 44 to institutions (effective 2003). adv. bk.rev. charts; illus. Document type: Magazine, Academic/Scholarly.
Formed by the merger of (1949-1987): Onderwijs en Opvoeding (0030-2481); Vernieuwing van Opvoeding, Onderwijs en Maatschappij (0168-986X); Former titles (until 1984): Over Vernieuwing van Opvoeding, Onderwijs en Maatschappij (0165-0599); Which was formed by the 1981 merger of: Over Onderwijs (0166-6509); Vernieuwing van Opvoeding, Onderwijs en Maatschappij (0166-7459); Formerly (1938-1973): Vernieuwing van Opvoeding en Onderwijs (0042-4196)
—IE, Infotrieve, KNAW.
Published by: Koninklijke Van Gorcum BV/Royal Van Gorcum BV, PO Box 43, Assen, 9400 AA, Netherlands. TEL 31-592-379555, FAX 31-592-372064, info@vangorcum.nl, http://www.vangorcum.nl. Circ: 1,800.

370　　　　　　FRA　　　　　　ISSN 0151-1904
VERS L'EDUCATION NOUVELLE. Text in French. 1946. bi-m. (5/yr.).
Indexed: RASB.
Published by: Centre d'Entrainement aux Methodes d'Education Active, c/o Pascale Chesnay, 76 bd. de la Villette, Paris, Cedex 19 75940, France. TEL 33-1-40404341, FAX 33-1-42066650. Ed. Bertrand Chavaroche. Pub. Christian Gautellier.

370　　　　　　ESP　　　　　　ISSN 1130-7471
VETE A SABER!. Text in Spanish. 1986. m. free.
Published by: (Gobierno de Navarra, Departamento de Educacion y Cultura), Instituto Navarro de Deporte y Juventud, Arrieta 25, Pamplona, 31002, Spain. TEL 34-48-427843.

VI FORAELDRE. see CHILDREN AND YOUTH—About

371.192　　　　AUS
VICTORIAN PARENTS COUNCIL NEWSLETTER. Text in English. 1962. q. AUD 22 domestic; AUD 25 foreign (effective 2001). bk.rev. Document type: Newsletter. Description: Informs parents about educational changes, problems and funding.
Published by: Victorian Parents Council Inc., GPO Box 2463 V, Melbourne, VIC 3001, Australia. TEL 61-3-94193693, FAX 61-3-94160707, vicpc@smart.nev.au. Ed., R&P Susan Hughes. Circ: 1,400.

VIDA HISPANICA. see LINGUISTICS

370　　　　　　DEU　　　　　　ISSN 0507-7230
VIERTELJAHRSSCHRIFT FUER WISSENSCHAFTLICHE PAEDAGOGIK. Text in German. 1950. q. EUR 46; EUR 12.80 newsstand/cover (effective 2005). Document type: Journal, Academic/Scholarly.
Indexed: DIP, IBR, IBZ.
Published by: (Goerres-Gesellschaft), Verlag und Druckkontor Kamp GmbH, Kurfuerstenstr 4A, Bochum, 44791, Germany. TEL 49-234-516170, FAX 49-234-5161718, mail@kamp-verlag.de, http://www.kamp-verlag.de.

370.2509755　　　USA　　　　　ISSN 0083-6354
L903.V8
VIRGINIA EDUCATIONAL DIRECTORY. Text in English. a. USD 10. Document type: Directory.
Formerly: Virginia's Public Education Directory
Media: Diskette.
Published by: Department of Education, PO Box 2120, Richmond, VA 23216-2120. TEL 804-225-2400, pwhicks@pen.1212.va.us, http://www.pen.k12.va.us/VDOE/dbpubs/doedir/, http://www.pen.1212.va.us.

VIRGINIA ENGLISH BULLETIN. see LINGUISTICS

370.1　　　　　USA　　　　　　ISSN 0270-837X
　　　　　　　　　　　　　　　　　　　　　　CODEN: KLCBDZ
VIRGINIA JOURNAL OF EDUCATION. Text in English. 1907. m. (Oct.-June). membership. adv. bk.rev. charts; illus.; stat.; tr.lit. 28 p./no.; back issues avail. Document type: Journal, Academic/Scholarly.
Former titles (until 1980): Journal of Virginia Education (0198-3504); (until 1979): Virginia Journal of Education (0042-6563)
Indexed: PCI.
Published by: Virginia Education Association, 116 S Third St, Richmond, VA 23219. TEL 804-648-5801, FAX 804-775-8379, http://www.veaweteach.org/articles_vje.asp. Ed. Tom Allen. Adv. contact Yolanda Morris. page USD 630. Circ: 50,000.

371.192　　　　USA　　　　　　ISSN 0042-6709
VIRGINIA P T A BULLETIN. (Parents and Teachers Association) Text in English. 1973 (vol.56). 8/yr. USD 8. Document type: Newsletter. Description: Serves as the main communication link among national, state, and local levels of the P.T.A. in Virginia.
Published by: Virginia Congress of Parents and Teachers, PO Box 15659, Richmond, VA 23227. TEL 804-264-1234. Ed. Mary S Cottrell. Circ: 6,500.

VIRGINIA SCHOOL LAWS. see LAW

VISIBLE LANGUAGE; the triannual concerned with all that is involved in our being literate. see LINGUISTICS

370　　　　　　USA
VISIONS (TALLAHASSEE); the journal of applied research for the Florida Association of Community Colleges. Text in English. a. back issues avail. Document type: Journal, Academic/Scholarly.
Indexed: CIJE.
Published by: Florida Association of Community Colleges, 113 E. College Ave., Tallahassee, FL 32301-7703. TEL 850-222-3222. Ed. James Wattenberger.

370　　　　　　ITA　　　　　　ISSN 0042-7241
VITA DELL'INFANZIA. Text in Italian. 1952. m. EUR 30 domestic; EUR 45 foreign (effective 2005). bk.rev. bibl.; illus. index, cum.index. Document type: Magazine, Consumer.
Indexed: DIP, e-psyche.
Published by: Opera Nazionale Montessori, Via di San Gallicano 7, Rome, RM 00153, Italy. TEL 39-06-5883320, FAX 39-06-5885434, info@montessori.it, http://www.montessori.it. Ed. Elena Dompe. Circ: 8,000.

370　　　　　　ITA　　　　　　ISSN 0042-7349
LA VITA SCOLASTICA; rassegna quindicinale della istruzione primaria. Text in Italian. 1947. 19/yr. EUR 49 domestic; EUR 87 foreign (effective 2005). adv. bk.rev. bibl.; charts; illus. Document type: Magazine, Trade.
Published by: Giunti Gruppo Editoriale SpA, Via Bolognese 165, Florence, 50139, Italy. TEL 39-055-5062376, FAX 39-055-5062397, informazioni@giunti.it, http://www.giunti.it. Ed. Mario Renzo. Circ: 100,000.

VITAE SCHOLASTICAE; the journal of educational biography. see BIOGRAPHY

370.1　　　　　USA　　　　　　ISSN 0883-573X
VOICE (EAST LANSING). Variant title: M E A Voice. Text in English. 1923. m. free to members (effective 2005). adv. illus. index. Document type: Newspaper, Trade.
Former titles: Teacher's Voice (0026-2129); Michigan Education Journal
Published by: Michigan Education Association, 1216 Kendale Rd, PO Box 2573, E Lansing, MI 48826-2573. TEL 517-332-6551, 517-332-6551, FAX 517-337-5414, drk@mea.org, http://www.mea.org. Adv. contact Gertie Buren. Circ: 160,000 (paid and free).

E

370.193 USA ISSN 1096-1909
A VOICE FOR CHILDREN. Text in English. 1920. m. (Sep.-May).
looseleaf. USD 10. bk.rev. reprints avail. Document type:
Bulletin, Consumer.
Formerly (until 1997): Iowa P T A Bulletin (0021-0617)
Published by: Iowa Congress of Parents and Teachers, 8345
University Blvd, Ste F-1, Des Moines, IA 50325. TEL
515-225-4197, 800-475-4782, ia_office@pta.org,
http://www.iowapta.org. Ed. Cheryl Knapp. Circ: 350.

370 USA ISSN 0896-6605
VOICE FOR EDUCATION. Text in English. 1969. 9/yr.
(Sep.-June). USD 8. charts; illus.; stat.; tr.lit. Document type:
Newsletter.
Formerly: Voice of P S E A (0507-2298)
Published by: Pennsylvania State Education Association, 400 N
Third St, Box 1724, Harrisburg, PA 17105. TEL 717-255-7000,
FAX 717-255-7124. Ed. William H Johnson Jr. Circ: 125,000.

VOICE OF WASHINGTON MUSIC EDUCATORS. see MUSIC

370 USA
VOICES IN EDUCATION∗. Text in English. bi-m.
Published by: Pen & Ink, Inc., 36 Ridge Rd, Andover, CT
06232-1231. TEL 203-635-0522. Ed. John Vecchitto.

370.193 FRA ISSN 0049-6693
VOIX DES PARENTS. Text in French. 1932. 5/yr. EUR 12 to
members; EUR 16 to non-members (effective 2005). bk.rev.;
film rev. bibl.; illus. Document type: Magazine, Consumer.
Indexed: e-psyche.
Published by: Federation des Parents d'Eleves de
l'Enseignement Publique, 91 bd. Berthier, Paris, 75017,
France. TEL 33-1-44151813, FAX 33-1-47663302,
peep@peep.asso.fr, http://www.peep.asso.fr. Ed. Carole
Reminny. Circ: 100,000.

370 RUS
VUZOVSKIE VESTI. Text in Russian. 1994. m. USD 125 in United
States (effective 2000).
Indexed: RASB.
Published by: Moskovskii Gosudarstvennyi Universitet Pechati, Ul
Sadovaya Spasskaya 6, Moscow, 103045, Russian
Federation. TEL 7-095-2073865. Ed. A B Sholokhov. Dist. by:
East View Information Services, 3020 Harbor Ln. N.,
Minneapolis, MN 55447. TEL 763-550-0961, FAX
763-559-2931.

370.15 SVK ISSN 0139-6919
VYCHOVAVATEL. Text in Slovak. 1955. 10/yr.
Indexed: RASB, e-psyche.
Published by: (Slovakia. Ministry of Education of the Slovak
Socialist Republic), Vydavatel'stvo Edocatio, Sasinkova 5,
Bratislava, 81560, Slovakia. TEL 21-42-49. Ed. Jan Farkas.
Circ: 12,500. Subscr. to: Slovart G.T.G. s.r.o., Krupinska 4,
PO Box 152, Bratislava 85299, Slovakia. TEL
421-2-63839472, FAX 421-2-63839485, http://www.slovart-
gtg.sk.

370 CZE ISSN 1210-3691
VYTVARNA VYCHOVA; casopis pro vytvarnou a obecne
estetickouvychovu skoli a mimosklni. Text in Czech, Slovak;
Summaries in English, French, German. 1970. q.
Supersedes in part (in 1992): Esteticka Vychova (0014-1283)
Indexed: BHA.
Published by: Universita Karlova, Pedagogicka Fakulta, M D
Rettigove 4, Prague, 11639, Czech Republic.

370 USA ISSN 8750-8133
W & J MAGAZINE. Text in English. 1972. q. back issues avail.
Formerly: W and J News
Published by: Washington & Jefferson College, 60 S Lincoln St,
Washington, PA 15301. TEL 412-223-6074. Ed. Edward A
Marotta. Circ: 14,500.

370 USA
W E A NEWS. Text in English. 1935. 5/yr. USD 10 to
non-members (effective 2004). adv. illus. 16 p./no. 3 cols./p.;
Document type: Newspaper. Description: Carries articles by
teachers and educators dealing with teaching developments
and news of state, national and international interest.
Formerly: Wyoming Education News (0043-9681)
Published by: Wyoming Education Association, 115 E 22nd St
Ste.1, Cheyenne, WY 82001. TEL 307-634-7991,
800-442-2395, FAX 307-778-8161, http://www.wyoea.org. Ed.
Ron Sniffin. Adv. contact Cheryl Clark. Circ: 7,700 (paid).

370 CHN
WAIGUO JIAOYU YANJIU/STUDIES IN FOREIGN EDUCATION.
Text in Chinese. bi-m. 56 p./no.; Document type:
Academic/Scholarly. Description: Covers foreign elementary,
high school education, adult and special education.
Published by: (Dongbei Shifan Daxue/Northeast Normal
University, Bijiao Jiaoyu Yanjiusuo), Waiguo Jiaoyu Yanjiu
Bianjibu, Changchun, Jilin 130024, China. TEL 685085. Ed.
Liang Zhongyi. Dist. overseas by: China International Book
Trading Corp, 35 Chegongzhuang Xilu, Haidian District, PO
Box 399, Beijing 100044, China.

370 CHN
WAIGUO JIAOYU ZILIAO/FOREIGN EDUCATION MATERIAL.
Text in Chinese. bi-m.

Published by: (Jiaoyu Kexue Xueyuan), Huadong Shifan
Daxue/East China Normal University, 3663 Zhongshan Beilu,
Shanghai, 200062, China. TEL 86-21-2549677,
http://www.ecnu.edu.cn.

WALL STREET JOURNAL (CLASSROOM EDITION). see
BUSINESS AND ECONOMICS

370.1 GBR ISSN 1362-6558
WARWICK PAPERS ON EDUCATION POLICY. Text in English.
1992. irreg., latest vol.9, 2000. GBP 5.95 (effective 2001).
Document type: Monographic series, Academic/Scholarly.
Published by: Trentham Books Ltd., Westview House, 734
London Rd, Stoke-on-Trent, Staffs ST4 5NP, United Kingdom.
TEL 44-1782-745567, FAX 44-1782-745553,
tb@trentham-books.co.uk, http://www.trentham-books.co.uk.

WASHINGTON COUNSELETTER. see OCCUPATIONS AND
CAREERS

370.2509753 USA
WASHINGTON EDUCATION DIRECTORY. Text in English. 1973.
a. USD 15 per vol. payment with order, plus sales tax; USD
16 per vol. billed order, plus sales tax, no invoiced orders
outside WA state (effective 2000 - 2001). Document type:
Directory. Description: Includes all public school districts
(K-12), state-approved private schools (1-12), public and
private universities and colleges, community colleges,
education agencies and associations.
Published by: (Washington (State). Superintendent of Public
Instruction), Barbara Krohn and Associates, 1904 Third Ave.,
Ste 835, Seattle, WA 98101-1162. TEL 206-622-3538. Ed.,
Pub. Barbara Krohn. Circ: 15,000.

370.116 USA ISSN 1522-6786
WASHINGTON SEMESTERS AND INTERNSHIPS; promoting
civic and cultural education in the nation's capital. Text in
English. 1999. a. USD 5 (effective 2003). adv. bk.rev. bibl.;
illus.; tr.lit. back issues avail. Document type: Newsletter,
Academic/Scholarly. Description: Clearinghouse for scholars
and teachers interested in civic and cultural education in
Washington. Provides professional common meeting ground
for the needs of political scientists and others interested in
using the resources of the nation's capital.
Published by: Washington Semesters and Internships
Association, One University Place, 148 Bronson Hall,
Louisiana State University in Shreveport, Shreveport, LA
71115-2301. TEL 318-797-5349, FAX 318-795-4203,
wpederso@pilot.lsu.edu. Ed., R&P, Adv. contact William D
Pederson. B&W page USD 25. Circ: 300 (paid).

370.07 AUS ISSN 1329-881X
LB1028
➤ THE WEAVER; a forum for new ideas in educational research.
Text in English. 1997. s-a. back issues avail. Document type:
Academic/Scholarly. Description: Publishes conventional
articles on research, as well as more experimental pieces and
those on work in process.
Media: Online - full text.
Indexed: AEI.
Published by: La Trobe University, Graduate School of
Education, Kingsbury Dr, Bundoora, VIC 3086, Australia.
gradassoc@latrobe.edu.au, http://www.latrobe.edu.au/www/
graded/weaverindex.html. Ed. Julianne Lynch.

➤ WELSH EDUCATION STATISTICS BULLETINS. see
EDUCATION—Abstracting, Bibliographies, Statistics

370 GBR ISSN 0957-297X
➤ WELSH JOURNAL OF EDUCATION. Text in English, Welsh.
1989. s-a. GBP 20 to individuals; GBP 30 to institutions
(effective 2004). adv. bk.rev. back issues avail. Document
type: Academic/Scholarly.
Related titles: Online - full text ed.: (from Gale Group,
IngentaConnect).
Indexed: BrEdI, CPE, ERA, ETA, MEA, RHEA, SEA, SENA,
SOMA, SWA, TEA.
—BLDSC (9294.652000), IE, ingenta. CCC.
Published by: (University of Wales, Faculty of Education),
University of Wales Press, 10 Columbus Walk, Brigantine Pl,
Cardiff, CF10 4UP, United Kingdom. TEL 44-29-2049-6899,
FAX 44-29-2049-6108, journals@press.wales.ac.uk,
http://www.uwp.co.uk. Eds. John Fitz, Sian Rhiannon Williams.
Circ: 350.

370 NLD ISSN 0165-4772
➤ DE WERELD VAN HET JONGE KIND. Text in Dutch. 1955.
10/yr. EUR 43; EUR 30 to students (effective 2005). adv.
bk.rev. abstr.; bibl. index. reprints avail. Document type:
Journal, Academic/Scholarly.
Formerly (until 1974): Kleuterwereld (0023-2106)
—KNAW.
Published by: Uitgeverij Bekadidact, PO Box 122, Baarn, 3740
AC, Netherlands. TEL 31-35-5482421, FAX 31-35-5421672,
http://www.bekadidact.nl. Pub. J Carla Snip. Circ: 10,000.

370 NGA ISSN 0043-2997
L81
WEST AFRICAN JOURNAL OF EDUCATION. Text in English.
1957. 3/yr. USD 35. adv. bk.rev. illus. Document type:
Academic/Scholarly.
Indexed: ASD.

Published by: University of Ibadan, Institute of Education, Ibadan,
Oyo, Nigeria. TEL 62550-1495. Ed. J D Obemeata. Circ:
2,550.

371.26 NGA ISSN 0331-0515
➤ WEST AFRICAN JOURNAL OF EDUCATIONAL AND
VOCATIONAL MEASUREMENT. Text in English. 1973. s-a.
NGN 5. adv. Document type: Academic/Scholarly.
Indexed: PsycholAb.
Published by: West African Examinations Council, Test
Development and Research Division, PMB 1076, Yaba, Lagos
State, Nigeria. TEL 234-1-861711. Ed. A A Awomolo. Circ:
250.

370.15 IND
WEST BENGAL. BUREAU OF EDUCATIONAL AND
PSYCHOLOGICAL RESEARCH. Text in English. 1971. s-a.
free.
Indexed: e-psyche.
Published by: Bureau of Educational and Psychological
Research, 25-3 Ballygunge Circular Rd., Kolkata, Maharashtra
700 019, India. Ed. Maya Mukherjee.

371.822 USA
WEST SIDE STORY. Text in English. 1968. m. USD 10. adv.
bk.rev.; film rev.; play rev. charts; illus. Description: Serves to
supplement the educational environment of West High School
by providing news and information to the school and all its
components.
Related titles: Microfilm ed.
Published by: Iowa City Community Schools, West High School,
2901 Melrose Ave, Iowa City, IA 52246. TEL 319-339-6817.
Circ: 2,000.

370.2509754 USA ISSN 0085-8099
WEST VIRGINIA EDUCATION DIRECTORY. Text in English.
1934. a. free. charts. Document type: Directory, Government.
Description: Lists schools and personnel in West Virginia by
district and county.
Published by: Department of Education, Capitol Complex, Bldg B
204, Charleston, WV 25305. TEL 304-348-3667. Ed. Kim
Nuzum. Circ: 5,000.

370 USA ISSN 0274-8606
L11
WEST VIRGINIA SCHOOL JOURNAL. Abbreviated title: W V
School Journal. Text in English. 1881. q. USD 10 to
non-members (effective 2005). adv. bk.rev. charts; illus.
Document type: Journal, Academic/Scholarly.
Former titles: W V E A School Journal (0094-176X); West
Virginia School Journal (0043-3322)
Related titles: Microform ed.: (from PQC).
Published by: West Virginia Education Association, 1558 Quarrier
St, Charleston, WV 25311. TEL 304-346-5315, 800-642-8261,
FAX 304-346-4325, mail@wvea.org, http://www.wvea.org. Ed.,
Pub. Kym Randolph. Circ: 17,000 (controlled).

371.1 AUS ISSN 0310-5369
WESTERN TEACHER. Text in English. 1971. every 4 wks.
(except Jan.). AUD 15. adv. bk.rev. abstr.; bibl.; charts; illus.;
stat. Document type: Newspaper.
Formerly: W.A. Teachers' Journal (0042-949X)
Published by: State School Teachers Union of W.A. (Inc.),
150-152 Adelaide Terrace, Perth, Australia. TEL 09-325-5311,
FAX 09-221-2394. Ed. Jerry Maher. Adv. contact Terry Healy.
Circ: 12,000.

371.07 USA ISSN 1049-9792
THE WESTMINSTER TANNER-MCMURRIN LECTURES ON THE
HISTORY AND PHILOSOPHY OF RELIGION AT
WESTMINSTER COLLEGE. Text in English. 1989. irreg.
Published by: Westminster College, 1840 South 1300 E, Salt
Lake City, UT 84105. TEL 801-484-7651.

WEST'S EDUCATION LAW DIGEST. see LAW

WEST'S EDUCATION LAW REPORTER. see LAW

WHAT'S NEW (PHILADELPHIA). see HOME ECONOMICS

▼ WHO'S WHO (YEAR). see MUSIC

373.025 USA
WHO'S WHO AMONG AMERICAN HIGH SCHOOL STUDENTS.
Text in English. 1967. a. (in 18 vols.). USD 44.95. illus.; stat.
Document type: Directory.
Published by: Educational Communications, Inc. (Lake Forest),
1701 Directors Blvd., Ste. 920, Austin, TX 78744-1098. TEL
847-295-6650. Ed. Paul C Krouse.

370.25 011 USA
WHO'S WHO AMONG AMERICA'S TEACHERS. Text in English.
1990. biennial (in 2 vols.). USD 79.95. Document type:
Directory.
Published by: Educational Communications, Inc. (Lake Forest),
1701 Directors Blvd., Ste. 920, Austin, TX 78744-1098. TEL
847-295-6650. Pub. Paul C Krouse.

WHO'S WHO IN AMERICAN EDUCATION. see BIOGRAPHY

E

370.72 GBR ISSN 1476-6876
THE WIDER BENEFITS OF LEARNING. Text in English. 2001. irreg., latest 2002, Summer. GBP 9.95 per issue (effective 2003). **Document type:** *Monographic series, Academic/Scholarly.* **Description:** Promotes discussion on key topics in the currently under-researched area of the non-economic benefits that learning brings to the individual learner and to society as a whole.
Published by: University of London, Institute of Education, 20 Bedford Way, London, WC1H OAL, United Kingdom. TEL 44-20-76126000, FAX 44-20-76126126, info@ioe.ac.uk, http://www.ioe.ac.uk.

WIRKENDES WORT; deutsche Sprache und Literatur in Forschung und Lehre. see *LINGUISTICS*

WIRTSCHAFT UND ERZIEHUNG. see *BUSINESS AND ECONOMICS—Economic Systems And Theories, Economic History*

WIRTSCHAFT UND UNTERRICHT; Informationen fuer Paedagogen in Schule und Betrieb. see *BUSINESS AND ECONOMICS*

WIRTSCHAFTSPAEDAGOGISCHE STUDIEN ZUR INDIVIDUELLEN UND KOLLEKTIVEN ENTWICKLUNG. see *BUSINESS AND ECONOMICS*

370 DEU ISSN 0340-3084
DAS WIRTSCHAFTSSTUDIUM - W I S U; Zeitschrift fuer Studium und Examen. Text in German. 1972. m. EUR 86; EUR 66.20 to students; EUR 8 newsstand/cover (effective 2003). adv. bk.rev. reprints avail. **Document type:** *Magazine, Academic/Scholarly.*
Published by: Lange Verlag GmbH, Poststr 12, Duesseldorf, 40213, Germany. TEL 49-211-864190, FAX 49-211-320000, info@wisu.de, webmaster@langeverlag.de, http://www.wisu.de, http://www.langeverlag.de. Ed. Dieter Geller. Pub. Rainer Lange. adv.: B&W page EUR 3,380, color page EUR 5,340. Circ: 10,000.

WISCONSIN ACADEMY REVIEW. see *LITERARY AND POLITICAL REVIEWS*

371.192 USA
WISCONSIN PARENT TEACHER ASSOCIATION. Text in English. 1938. 9/yr. (Sep.-May). USD 8 (effective 1998). illus. **Document type:** *Newsletter.*
Formerly: Wisconsin Parent Teacher Bulletin (0043-6577)
Published by: Wisconsin Congress of Parents and Teachers Inc., 4797 Hayes Rd, Ste 2, Madison, WI 53704-3256. TEL 608-244-1455. Ed. C J Wunsch. Circ: 3,000.

370.15 DEU ISSN 1613-3544
▼ **WISSEN UND LERNEN IN ORGANISATIONEN.** Text in German. 2004. irreg., latest vol.2, 2004. price varies. **Document type:** *Monographic series, Academic/Scholarly.*
Published by: Verlag Dr. Kovac, Arnoldstr 49, Hamburg, 22763, Germany. TEL 49-40-3988800, FAX 49-40-39888055, info@verlagdrkovac.de, http://www.verlagdrkovac.de/7-21.htm.

WISSENSCHAFTSMANAGEMENT; Zeitschrift fuer Innovation. see *SCIENCES: COMPREHENSIVE WORKS*

370.82 USA ISSN 1552-8650
WOMEN AND MATHEMATICS EDUCATION NEWSLETTER. Text in English. 1979. 3/yr. USD 15. bk.rev. back issues avail. **Document type:** *Newsletter.*
Published by: Mount Holyoke College, Women & Mathematics Education - Summer Math, 302 Shattuck Hall, South Hadley, MA 01075. TEL 413-538-2608. Ed. Eric Kasnowski. R&P Charlene Morrow TEL 413-538-2069. Circ: 400.

306.85 362.8 USA ISSN 1040-0958
WORK AND FAMILY LIFE. Text in English. m.
Related titles: Online - full text ed.: (from ProQuest Information & Learning).
Published by: Bank Street College, 610 W 112th St, New York, NY 10025. TEL 212-875-4400, collegepubs@bankstreet.edu, http://www.bankstreet.edu.

370.72 BEL
WORLD ASSOCIATION FOR EDUCATIONAL RESEARCH. CONGRESS REPORTS. Text in English. 1953. quadrennial (11th 1993, Jerusalem). **Document type:** *Proceedings.* **Description:** Papers and discussions on Congress presented and discussed when Congress meets.
Formerly: International Association for the Advancement of Educational Research. Congress Reports (0074-154X)
Published by: World Association for Educational Research, Henri Dunantlaan 1, Ghent, 9000, Belgium. Ed. M L van Herreweghe.

370.9 GBR
WORLD COUNCIL OF COMPARATIVE EDUCATION SOCIETIES. NEWSLETTER/CONSEIL MONDIAL DES SOCIETES D'EDUCATION COMPAREE. BULLETIN D'INFORMATION. Text in English, French. 1972. q. free. bk.rev.
Published by: World Council of Comparative Education Societies, c/o Raymond Ryba, University of Manchester, Department of Education, Manchester, Lancs M13 9PL, United Kingdom. FAX 061-275-3519. Ed. Douglas Ray. Circ: 3,000.

370.9 FRA ISSN 1020-0479
WORLD EDUCATION REPORT. Text in English. 1991. biennial. EUR 22.87 newsstand/cover (effective 2003). **Description:** Aims to present a broad but concise analysis of major trends and policy issues in education in the world today.
Related titles: Arabic ed.; Chinese ed.; Russian ed.; French ed.: Rapport Mondial sur l'Education. ISSN 1020-0460; Portuguese ed.: Informe Mundial sobre l'Educacao. ISSN 1014-9864; Spanish ed.: Informe Mundial sobre la Educacion. ISSN 1020-0452.
Published by: UNESCO Publishing, 7 place de Fontenoy, Paris, 75352, France. TEL 33-1-45684300, FAX 33-1-45685737, http://www.unesco.org/publications. **Dist. by:** Bernan Associates, Bernan, 4611-F Assembly Dr., Lanham, MD 20706-4391. TEL 800-274-4447, FAX 800-865-3450.

WORLD ENGLISHES; journal of English as an international and intranational language. see *LINGUISTICS*

370 331.88 FRA ISSN 0020-8884
WORLD FEDERATION OF TEACHERS' UNIONS. INFORMATION LETTER*. Text in French. 1969. irreg. free. bk.rev.
Published by: World Federation of Teachers' Unions (F I S E), 263 rue de Paris, Montreuil, Cedex 93160, France. Circ: 1,500.

370 ETH
WORLD OF EDUCATION*. Text in Amharic, English. q.
Published by: Ministry of Education, PO Box 30747, Addis Ababa, Ethiopia.

370.1 AUS ISSN 1441-340X
➤ **WORLD STUDIES IN EDUCATION.** Text in English. 2000. s-a. AUD 374 domestic to institutions; AUD 340 in New Zealand to institutions; GBP 168 in Europe to institutions; USD 260 elsewhere to institutions (effective 2005). adv. bk.rev. index. **Document type:** *Academic/Scholarly.* **Description:** Provides a worldwide forum for international education research and global studies. Focuses on major issues affecting educational policy, curriculum reforms in education, society, and culture in the global economy.
Indexed: ABIn, CPE, ERA, ETA, EduInd, MEA, RHEA, SEA, SENA, SOMA, SociolAb, TEA.
—BLDSC (9360.041980), IE.
Published by: James Nicholas Publishers, Pty. Ltd., 342 Park St, South Melbourne, VIC 3205, Australia. TEL 61-3-96905955, FAX 61-3-96992040, custservice@jamesnicholaspublishers.com.au, http://www.jamesnicholaspublishers.com.au. Ed. Dr. Joseph Zajda. Pub. Rea Zajda. R&P Mary Berchmans. **Subscr. to:** PO Box 244, Albert Park, VIC 3206, Australia.

370 AUS ISSN 1446-2257
➤ **WORLD TRANSACTIONS ON ENGINEERING AND TECHNOLOGY EDUCATION.** Text in English. 2002. s-a. USD 150 to individuals; USD 300 to institutions (effective 2005). **Document type:** *Academic/Scholarly.* **Description:** Publishes high quality international, fully refereed papers on engineering and technology education and covers a wide and diverse range of issues including case studies, regional and country issues, pedagogical issues, etc, thereby facilitating the transfer of information, expertise and research and development on engineering education and thus realizing the UICEE's mission.
—BLDSC (9360.154050), IE.
Published by: UNESCO International Centre for Engineering Education, Monash University, Engineering Bldg. 70, Wellinghon Rd, Clayton, VIC 3800, Australia. TEL 61-3-9905-4977, FAX 61-3-9905-1547, http://www.eng.monash.edu.au/uicee/worldtransactions/WTETE1.html, http://www.eng.monash.edu.au/uicee/index.html.

370.5 GBR ISSN 0084-2508
L101.G8
WORLD YEARBOOK OF EDUCATION. Text in English. 1932. a. adv. **Document type:** *Yearbook, Abstract/Index.* **Description:** Collects articles by international authorities to report on a variety of themes.
Formerly (until 1965): Year Book of Education (0950-1223)
Indexed: BAS, HECAB.
—BLDSC (9360.450000). **CCC.**
Published by: Kogan Page Ltd., 120 Pentonville Rd, London, N1 9JN, United Kingdom. FAX 44-20-7837-6348. Eds. Crispin Jones, David Coulby. R&P Caroline Gomm. Adv. contact Linda Batham.

372.62 USA ISSN 0889-6143
CODEN: WCEJE3
➤ **THE WRITING CENTER JOURNAL.** Text in English. 1979. 2/yr. USD 15.75 domestic; USD 21 foreign (effective 2005). adv. bk.rev. **Document type:** *Journal, Academic/Scholarly.* **Description:** Publishes articles, reviews and announcements to writing center personnel, particularly manuscripts that explore issues or theories related to writing center dynamics or administration.
Indexed: CIJE, MLA-IB.
—BLDSC (9364.757400), IE, ingenta.
Published by: National Writing Centers Association, c/o Neal Lerner, Massachusetts Institute of Technology, Writing/Humanistic Studies, Rm 14E-303, 77 Massachusetts Ave, Cambridge, MA 02139. nlerner@mit.edu, http://www.writing.ku.edu/wcj. Eds. Beth Boquet, Neal Lerner. Circ: 800.

370 USA
➤ **THE WRITING INSTRUCTOR (ONLINE EDITION).** Text in English. 2001. irreg. **Document type:** *Journal, Academic/Scholarly.*
Media: Online - full text (from H.W. Wilson, O C L C Online Computer Library Center, Inc., ProQuest Information & Learning). **Related titles:** Microform ed.: (from PQC).
Published by: The Writing Instructor, c/o Dawn Formo, ed., Literature & Writing Studies Program, California State University, San Marcos, CA 92096-0001. TEL 760-750-4199, http://www.writinginstructor.com/. Eds., Pubs. David Blakesley, Dawn Formo.

➤ **WRITING MATTERS**; the journal and newsletter of the society for italic handwriting. see *ART*

796 CHN ISSN 1000-520X
WUHAN TIYUAN XUEBAO/WUHAN INSTITUTE OF PHYSICAL EDUCATION. JOURNAL. Text in Chinese. 1959. bi-m. USD 25.20; USD 4.20 newsstand/cover (effective 2004).
Related titles: Online - full text ed.: (from East View Information Services).
Indexed: PEI, RefZh.
—BLDSC (4917.469050).
Published by: Wuhan Tiyu Xueyuan/Wuhan Institute of Physical Education, Hongshan-qu, 461, Luoyu, Wuhan, 430079, China. WTXB@chinajournal.net.cn, http://whtyxyxb.periodicals.net.cn/default.html. **Dist. by:** China International Book Trading Corp, 35 Chegongzhuang Xilu, Haidian District, PO Box 399, Beijing 100044, China. TEL 86-10-68412045, FAX 86-10-68412023, cibtc@mail.cibtc.com.cn, http://www.cibtc.com.cn.

WYCHOWANIE MUZYCZNE W SZKOLE. see *MUSIC*

WYCHOWANIE TECHNICZNE W SZKOLE. see *ENGINEERING*

370 POL ISSN 0137-8082
WYCHOWANIE W PRZEDSZKOLU. Text in Polish. 1948. 10/yr. PLZ 75; PLZ 7.50 per issue (effective 2003). **Document type:** *Journal, Academic/Scholarly.* **Description:** Publishes articles on psychology, pedagogy, the history of education, the theory and practice of nursery education, and educational policy in the field, with discussions of experiences in nursery schools, and problems encountered in the dialogue between parents and schools.
Published by: (Poland. Ministerstwo Edukacji Narodowej), Wydawnictwa Szkolne i Pedagogiczne, Pl Dabrowskiego 8, Warsaw, 00950, Poland. TEL 48-22-8279280, wsip@wsip.com.pl, http://www.wsip.com.pl. Ed. Hanna Ratynska. R&P Teresa Dziurzynska. **Dist.by:** Ars Polona, Krakowskie Przedmiescie 7, Warsaw, Poland. TEL 48-22-9263914, FAX 48-22-9265334, arspolona@arspolona.com.pl, http://www.arspolona.com.pl; **Dist. by:** RUCH S.A., ul Jana Kazimierza 31/33, Warsaw 00958, Poland. TEL 48-22-5328731.

370 POL ISSN 0239-6769
WYZSZA SZKOLA PEDAGOGICZNA IM. KOMISJI EDUKACJI NARODOWEJ W KRAKOWIE. PROBLEMY STUDIOW NAUCZYCIELSKICH. Text in Polish. 1964. irreg., latest vol.4, 1990. price varies.
Published by: (Wyzsza Szkola Pedagogiczna im. Komisji Edukacji Narodowej w Krakowie), Wydawnictwo Naukowe W S P, Ul Karmelicka 41, Krakow, 31128, Poland. TEL 33-78-20.
Co-sponsor: Ministerstwo Edukacji Narodowej.

370 POL ISSN 0239-2356
WYZSZA SZKOLA PEDAGOGICZNA IM. KOMISJI EDUKACJI NARODOWEJ W KRAKOWIE. ROCZNIK NAUKOWO-DYDAKTYCZNY. PRACE PEDAGOGICZNE. Text in Polish. 1972. irreg., latest vol.12, 1991. price varies.
Published by: (Wyzsza Szkola Pedagogiczna im. Komisji Edukacji Narodowej w Krakowie), Wydawnictwo Naukowe W S P, Ul Karmelicka 41, Krakow, 31128, Poland. TEL 33-78-20.
Co-sponsor: Ministerstwo Edukacji Narodowej.

370 POL ISSN 0860-1046
WYZSZA SZKOLA PEDAGOGICZNA IM. KOMISJI EDUKACJI NARODOWEJ W KRAKOWIE. ROCZNIK NAUKOWO-DYDAKTYCZNY. PRACE Z HISTORII OSWIATY I WYCHOWANIA. Text in Polish. 1984. irreg., latest vol.2, 1989. price varies.
Published by: (Wyzsza Szkola Pedagogiczna im. Komisji Edukacji Narodowej w Krakowie), Wydawnictwo Naukowe W S P, Ul Karmelicka 41, Krakow, 31128, Poland. FAX 33-78-20.
Co-sponsor: Ministerstwo Edukacji Narodowej.

370 CHN
XIANDAI YUER BAO. Text in Chinese. 1993. w. CNY 49.92 (effective 2004). **Document type:** *Consumer.*
Related titles: Online - full content ed.

E

Published by: Guangzhou Ribao Baoye Jituan/Guangzhou Daily Newspaper Group, 10, Renmin Zhonglu Tongle Lu, Guangzhou, 510121, China. TEL 86-20-81883088. **Dist. by:** China International Book Trading Corp, 35 Chegongzhuang Xilu, Haidian District, PO Box 399, Beijing 100044, China. TEL 86-10-68412045, FAX 86-10-68412023, cibtc@mail.cibtc.com.cn, http://www.cibtc.com.cn.

372 CHN
XIAOXUESHENG XUEXI ZHIDAO/STUDY GUIDE FOR ELEMENTARY STUDENTS. Text in Chinese. m.
Published by: Liaoning Shaonian Ertong Chubanshe, 2, Nanjing Jie 6 Duan 1 Li, Shenyang, Liaoning 110001, China. TEL 365076. Ed. Zhang Fenghe.

370.1 CHN ISSN 1006-5288
XIEZI/HOW TO WRITE CHINESE CHARACTERS. Text in Chinese. 1988. bi-m. CNY 22.80 (effective 2004). **Document type:** *Academic/Scholarly.*
Published by: Shanghai Xinwen Chuban Fazhan Gongsi, Donghu Road, 26 Alley, no.22, Shanghai, 200031, China. TEL 86-21-54038106, cnsbtb@online.sh.cn. **Dist. by:** China International Book Trading Corp, 35 Chegongzhuang Xilu, Haidian District, PO Box 399, Beijing 100044, China. TEL 86-10-68412045, FAX 86-10-68412023, cibtc@mail.cibtc.com.cn, http://www.cibtc.com.cn.

370 CHN ISSN 1002-5308
XUEKE JIAOYU. Text in Chinese. q. CNY 18 (effective 1999). **Document type:** *Academic/Scholarly.*
Related titles: Online - full text ed.: (from East View Information Services).
Published by: Beijing Shifan Daxue/Beijing Normal University, Xinjiekouwai Beitaipingzhuang, Beijing, 100875, China. TEL 2012288. Ed. Yan Jinduo.

370 CHN ISSN 0439-7843
XUEQIAN JIAOYU/PRESCHOOL EDUCATION. Text in Chinese. 1980. m. CNY 0.95 per issue. **Document type:** *Academic/Scholarly.*
Formerly (until 1984): Youjiao Tongxun
Published by: (Beijing Jiaoyu-ju/Beijing Education Bureau), Beijing Jiaoyu Zazhishe/Beijing Education Magazine Office, 201 Qianmen Dajie, Beijing, 100050, China. TEL 3015815. Ed. Niu Chensheng. Pub. Chen Yankang. adv.: B&W page CNY 1,600, color page CNY 2,100.

370 ESP ISSN 1575-0345
XXI; revista de educacion. Text in Spanish. 1999. a. back issues avail.
Related titles: Online - full text ed.
—CINDOC.
Published by: Universidad de Huelva, Servicio de Publicaciones, Campus el Carmen, Ave. de las Fuerzas Armadas, s-n, Huelva, Andalucia 21071, Spain. TEL 34-95-9018000, publica@uhu.es, http://www.uhu.es/publicaciones/index.html. Ed. Emilia Moreno Sanchez.

370 JPN ISSN 0513-4668
YAMAGATA DAIGAKU KIYO (KYOIKU KAGAKU)/YAMAGATA UNIVERSITY. BULLETIN (EDUCATIONAL SCIENCE). Text in Japanese. 1952. a. **Document type:** *Bulletin, Academic/Scholarly.*
Published by: Yamagata Daigaku/Yamagata University, Publicatin Committee, Library, Division of Information Processing & Management, 1-4-12, Kojirakawa, Yamagata, Yamagata 990-9585, Japan. TEL 81-23-6285054, FAX 81-23-6285059, http://www.lib.yamagata-u.ac.jp/kiyou/kiyou.html.

YEARBOOK OF EDUCATIONAL LAW. see *LAW*

370 ETH ISSN 0044-0310
YEMEMHIRAN DIMTS. Text in Amharic. 1962. 2/yr. ETB 2 per issue. adv. bk.rev.
Published by: Ethiopian Teacher's Association, PO Box 1639, Addis Ababa, Ethiopia. Ed. Bisrat Dilnessahu. Circ: 30,000.

370 ERI ISSN 0044-0329
YEMEMHIRAN MELKT∗/TEACHERS' MESSAGE. Text in Amharic. irreg. ETB 1 per issue.
Related titles: English ed.
Published by: Teachers Association of Ethiopia, Eritrea Branch, PO Box 954, Asmara, Eritrea.

YISHI JINXIU ZAZHI/JOURNAL OF POSTGRADUATES OF MEDICINE. see *MEDICAL SCIENCES*

370.1 JPN ISSN 1344-4611
L67
YOKOHAMA KOKURITSU DAIGAKU KYOIKU NINGEN KAGAKUBU KIYO. I, KYOIKU KAGAKU/YOKOHAMA NATIONAL UNIVERSITY. FACULTY OF EDUCATION AND HUMAN SCIENCES. JOURNAL (EDUCATIONAL SCIENCES). Text in Japanese. 1998. a. **Document type:** *Academic/Scholarly.*
Published by: Yokohama National University, Faculty of Education and Human Sciences, 79-2 Tokiwadai, Hodogaya-ku, Yokohama, 240-8501, Japan. http://www.ed.ynu.ac.jp/index.html.

370 JPN ISSN 0513-5656
YOKOHAMA NATIONAL UNIVERSITY. EDUCATIONAL SCIENCES/YOKOHAMA KOKURITSU DAIGAKU KYOIKU KIYO. Text in English, Japanese. 1962. a. per issue exchange basis. cum.index nos. 11-15, 1971-1975. **Document type:** *Academic/Scholarly.*
Published by: Yokohama Kokuritsu Daigaku, Kyoikugakubu/ Yokohama National University, Faculty of Education, 156 Tokiwa-Dai, Hodogaya-ku, Yokohama-shi, Kanagawa-ken 240-0067, Japan.

372.21 CHN ISSN 1009-749X
LB1140.A1
YOU'ER JIAOYU DAODU/GUIDE TO PRESCHOOL EDUCATION. Text in Chinese. 1978. m. CNY 54 (effective 2004). 64 p./no.; **Document type:** *Journal, Academic/Scholarly.*
Formerly: You'er Jiaoyu (1001-327X)
Published by: Zhongguo Renmin Daxue, Shubao Zilio Zhongxin/Renmin University of China, Information Center for Social Server, Dongcheng-qu, 3, Zhangzizhong Lu, Beijing, 100007, China. TEL 86-10-64039458, FAX 86-10-64015080, kyes@163.net, http://www.confucius.cn.net/bkdetail.asp?fzt= G51. **Dist. in US by:** China Publications Service, PO Box 49614, Chicago, IL 60649. TEL 312-288-3291, FAX 312-288-8570; **Dist. by:** China International Book Trading Corp, 35 Chegongzhuang Xilu, Haidian District, PO Box 399, Beijing 100044, China. TEL 86-10-68412045, FAX 86-10-68412023, cibtc@mail.cibtc.com.cn, http://www.cibtc.com.cn.

268.68 USA ISSN 0044-1007
YOUR CHILD. Text in English. 1967. 3/yr. USD 7.50 (effective 2000). bk.rev. **Document type:** *Newsletter.* **Description:** Focuses on issues, problems, and goals involved in raising and educating a young Jewish child in the Conservative tradition.
Published by: United Synagogue of Conservative Judaism, 155 Fifth Ave, New York, NY 10010. TEL 212-533-7800, FAX 212-353-9439, 71263.266@compuserve.com, http://www.uscj.org. Ed. R&P Kay E Pomerantz. Circ: 3,000.

371.07 200 USA
YOUTH AND CHRISTIAN EDUCATION LEADERSHIP. Text in English. 1976. q. USD 8 (effective 2001). bk.rev. 24 p./no.; **Document type:** *Trade.*
Formerly (until 2000): Christian Education Leadership
Published by: Pathway Press, PO Box 2250, Cleveland, TN 37320-2250. TEL 423-478-7597, FAX 423-478-7616, Wanda_Griffith@pathwaypress.org, http:// www.pathwaypress.org. Eds. Tony Lane, Wanda Griffith. R&P Wanda Griffith. Circ: 10,000.

370.96894 ZMB ISSN 0255-0695
ZAMBIA EDUCATIONAL REVIEW∗. Text in English. 1979. s-a. USD 13. adv. bk.rev. abstr. **Document type:** *Academic/Scholarly.*
Indexed: CPE.
Published by: (Zambia. University of Zambia, Department of Education), Unza Press (Subsidiary of: University of Zambia), PO Box 32379, Lusaka, Zambia. TEL 260-1-293029, FAX 260-1-293580. Circ: 400.

370.96894 ZMB ISSN 0084-487X
ZAMBIA. MINISTRY OF EDUCATION. ANNUAL REPORT. Text in English. 1964. a. **Document type:** *Government.*
Published by: Ministry of Education, PO Box 50093, Lusaka, Zambia. **Dist. by:** Government Printer.

370.96894 ZMB ISSN 0556-9001
ZAMBIA. TEACHING SERVICE COMMISSION. ANNUAL REPORT. Text in English. 1963. a. ZMK 150. **Document type:** *Government.* **Description:** Contains information on functions of the commission, appointments, promotions, results of examinations, and other events.
Published by: (Zambia. Teaching Service Commission), Government Printing Department, PO Box 60136, Lusaka, Zambia.

ZEITSCHRIFT FUER BERUFLICHE UMWELTBILDUNG. see *ENVIRONMENTAL STUDIES*

370.1 DEU ISSN 0949-1147
Q181.A1
➤ **ZEITSCHRIFT FUER DIDAKTIK DER NATURWISSENSCHAFTEN.** Text in German; Summaries in English, German. irreg. bk.rev. charts; illus. back issues avail. **Document type:** *Academic/Scholarly.* **Description:** Covers research in science education.
Media: Online - full text.
Indexed: DIP, IBR, IBZ.
Published by: Schmidt and Klaunig, Postfach 3925, Kiel, 24038, Germany. TEL 49-431-62095, FAX 49-431-62097. Ed. Peter Nentwig. Circ: 500.

➤ **ZEITSCHRIFT FUER ENTWICKLUNGSPSYCHOLOGIE UND PAEDAGOGISCHE PSYCHOLOGIE.** see *PSYCHOLOGY*

370 DEU ISSN 1434-663X
L31
➤ **ZEITSCHRIFT FUER ERZIEHUNGSWISSENSCHAFT.** Text in German. 1998. q. EUR 58 domestic to individuals; EUR 61.50 foreign to individuals; EUR 68 domestic to institutions; EUR 71.50 foreign to institutions; EUR 19 newsstand/cover (effective 2004). adv. **Document type:** *Journal, Academic/Scholarly.*
Indexed: DIP, IBR, IBZ.
Published by: V S - Verlag fuer Sozialwissenschaften (Subsidiary of: Springer Science+Business Media), Abraham-Lincoln-Str 46, Wiesbaden, 65189, Germany. TEL 49-611-78780, FAX 49-611-7878400, info@vs-verlag.de, http://www.vs-verlag.de. adv.: page EUR 600; 140 x 200.

370 DEU
ZEITSCHRIFT FUER INTERNATIONALE BILDUNGSFORSCHUNG UND ENTWICKLUNGSPAEDAGOGIK. Text in German. 1978. q. adv. bk.rev. illus. back issues avail. **Document type:** *Academic/Scholarly.*
Former titles: Z E P - Zeitschrift fuer Entwicklungspaedagogik (0175-0488); (until 1983): Zeitschrift fuer Entwicklungspaedagogik (0172-2433)
Indexed: DIP, IBR, IBZ.
Published by: (Gesellschaft zur Foerderung Entwicklungsbezogener Bildung), I K O - Verlag fuer Interkulturelle Kommunikation, Postfach 900421, Frankfurt Am Main, 60044, Germany. TEL 49-69-784808, FAX 49-69-7896575, ikoverlag@t-online.de, http://www.iko-verlag.de. Ed. R&P Walter Suelberg. Adv. contact Barbara Ophoven.

370 DEU ISSN 0044-3247
L31
➤ **ZEITSCHRIFT FUER PAEDAGOGIK.** Text in German. 1949. bi-m. EUR 72; EUR 18 newsstand/cover (effective 2003). adv. bk.rev. index. reprints avail. **Document type:** *Journal, Academic/Scholarly.* **Description:** Provides comprehensive coverage of education and schools.
Related titles: ♦ Supplement(s): Zeitschrift fuer Paedagogik. Beiheft. ISSN 0514-2717.
Indexed: ASCA, ArtHuCI, CIJE, CPE, CurCont, DIP, EAA, ERA, ETA, IBR, IBZ, L&LBA, MEA, RASB, RHEA, RILM, SEA, SENA, SOMA, SOPODA, SSA, SSCI, SWA, SociolAb, TEA. —BLDSC (9475.800000), IDS, IE, Infotrieve, ingenta. **CCC.**
Published by: Julius Beltz GmbH & Co. KG, Werderstr 10, Weinheim, 69469, Germany. TEL 49-6201-60070, FAX 49-6201-6007393, info@beltz.de, http://www.beltz.de. Ed. Dietrich Benner. R&P Micheline Mangold. Adv. contact Brigitte Bell. B&W page EUR 760. Circ: 3,000 (paid and controlled).

268 DEU
ZEITSCHRIFT FUER PAEDAGOGIK UND THEOLOGIE; der Evangelische Erzieher. Text in German. 1945. 4/yr. adv. bk.rev. abstr. index. **Document type:** *Academic/Scholarly.*
Formerly (until 1998): Evangelische Erzieher (0014-3413)
Indexed: DIP, IBR, IBZ, NTA, RILM. —CCC.
Published by: Verlag Moritz Diesterweg GmbH, Hedderichstr 108-110, Frankfurt Am Main, 60596, Germany. TEL 49-69-42081-0, FAX 49-69-1301-100, TELEX 413234-MDD. Circ: 3,500.

ZEITSCHRIFT FUER VERKEHRSERZIEHUNG. see *TRANSPORTATION—Roads And Traffic*

ZEITUNGS - DOKUMENTATION BILDUNGSWESEN. see *EDUCATION—Abstracting, Bibliographies, Statistics*

ZHENGZHI JIAOYU/POLITICAL EDUCATION. see *POLITICAL SCIENCE*

370 CHN
ZHONGGUO CHAOXIANZU JIAOYU/KOREAN CHINESE EDUCATION. Text in Korean. m.
Published by: Yanbian Jiaoyu Weiyuanhui, Yanji, Jilin 133000, China. TEL 512771.

370 CHN
ZHONGGUO JIAOYU BAO/CHINESE EDUCATION DAILY. Text in Chinese. d. CNY 105.84. **Document type:** *Newspaper, Academic/Scholarly.*
Address: Jia-2 Xi Huangchenggen Beijie, Xicheng, Beijing, 100034, China. TEL 86-10-6020836. Ed. Yu Jiaqing. Pub. Li Zhaohan. **Dist. overseas by:** China International Book Trading Corp, 35 Chegongzhuang Xilu, Haidian District, PO Box 399, Beijing 100044, China.

370 CHN
ZHONGGUO JIAOYU NIANJIAN/CHINA EDUCATION YEARBOOK. Text in Chinese. a. CNY 35. **Description:** Summarizes educational policies, activities, and situations nationwide.
Published by: Ministry of Education of China, 55 Sha Tan Hou Street, Beijing, 100009, China.

370 CHN ISSN 1002-4808
ZHONGGUO JIAOYU XUEKAN/CHINA EDUCATION ASSOCIATION. JOURNAL. Text in Chinese. bi-m. CNY 10.
Related titles: Online - full text ed.: (from East View Information Services).

Published by: Zhongguo Jiaoyu Xuehui, 35 Damucang Hutong, Xidan, Beijing, 100816, China. TEL 6097082. Ed. Zhang Jian.

370   CHN   ISSN 1002-5952
ZHONGGUO MINZU JIAOYU/NATIONALITIES EDUCATION OF CHINA. Text in Chinese. bi-m. USD 18.
Formerly (until 1991): Minzu Jiaoyu
Related titles: Online - full text ed.: (from East View Information Services).
Published by: Zhongguo Minzu Jiaoyu Chubanshe/China Nationalities Education Press, Xinan Minzu Xueyuan, Chengdu, Sichuan 610041, China. TEL 028-583730, FAX 028-589294. Ed. Chen Hongtao. **Co-sponsor:** State Education Commission, Department of Education for Minorities.

370   CHN   ISSN 1009-458X
ZHONGGUO YUANCHENG JIAOYU/DISTANCE EDUCATION IN CHINA. Text in Chinese. 1986. s-m. **Document type:** Journal, Academic/Scholarly.
Formerly (until 1998): Zhongguo Dian-da Jiaoyu (1001-9901)
Related titles: Online - full text ed.: (from East View Information Services).
—BLDSC (9512.831570).
Address: Haidian-qu, 45, Xisihuan Zhonglu, Beijing, 100039, China. TEL 86-10-68182512, FAX 86-10-68182520, zzs@crtvu.edu.cn, http://www.chinadisedu.com/.

370   CHN
ZHONGHUA HUOYE WENXUAN (CHENGREN BAN)/CHINESE LOOSE-LEAF SELECTIONS (ADULT EDITION). Text in Chinese. 1998. s-m. looseleaf. CNY 24 (effective 2004). **Document type:** Journal, Academic/Scholarly.
Related titles: ♦ Series: Zhonghua Huoye Wenxuan (Chuzhong Ban). ISSN 1009-7260; ♦ Zhonghua Huoye Wenxuan (Gaozhong Ban). ISSN 1009-7279; ♦ Zhonghua Huoye Wenxuan (Xiaoxue Ban). ISSN 1009-7252.
Published by: Zhonghua Shuju, Fengtai-qu, 38, Taipingqiao Xili, Beijing, 100073, China. TEL 86-10-63431741, 86-10-63431747, huoye870@sohu.com, http:// www.zhbc.com.cn/huoye/huoyechengren.php. **Dist. by:** China International Book Trading Corp, 35 Chegongzhuang Xilu, Haidian District, PO Box 399, Beijing 100044, China. TEL 86-10-68412045, FAX 86-10-68412023, cibtc@mail.cibtc.com.cn, http://www.cibtc.com.cn.

370   CHN   ISSN 1009-7260
ZHONGHUA HUOYE WENXUAN (CHUZHONG BAN)/CHINESE LOOSE-LEAF SELECTIONS (JUNIOR MIDDLE SCHOOL EDITION). Text in Chinese. 1998. s-m. looseleaf. CNY 38.40 (effective 2004). **Document type:** Journal, Academic/Scholarly.
Related titles: ♦ Series: Zhonghua Huoye Wenxuan (Gaozhong Ban). ISSN 1009-7279; ♦ Zhonghua Huoye Wenxuan (Xiaoxue Ban). ISSN 1009-7252; ♦ Zhonghua Huoye Wenxuan (Chengren Ban).
Published by: Zhonghua Shuju, Fengtai-qu, 38, Taipingqiao Xili, Beijing, 100073, China. TEL 86-10-63431741, 86-10-63431747, huoye870@sohu.com, http:// www.zhbc.com.cn/huoye/huoyechuzhong.php. **Dist. by:** China International Book Trading Corp, 35 Chegongzhuang Xilu, Haidian District, PO Box 399, Beijing 100044, China. TEL 86-10-68412045, FAX 86-10-68412023, cibtc@mail.cibtc.com.cn, http://www.cibtc.com.cn.

370   CHN   ISSN 1009-7279
ZHONGHUA HUOYE WENXUAN (GAOZHONG BAN)/CHINESE LOOSE-LEAF SELECTIONS (SENIOR MIDDLE SCHOOL EDITION). Text in Chinese. 24/yr. looseleaf. CNY 38.40 (effective 2004). **Document type:** Journal, Academic/Scholarly.
Related titles: ♦ Series: Zhonghua Huoye Wenxuan (Chuzhong Ban). ISSN 1009-7260; ♦ Zhonghua Huoye Wenxuan (Xiaoxue Ban). ISSN 1009-7252; ♦ Zhonghua Huoye Wenxuan (Chengren Ban).
Published by: Zhonghua Shuju, Fengtai-qu, 38, Taipingqiao Xili, Beijing, 100073, China. TEL 86-10-63431741, 86-10-63431747, huoye870@sohu.com, http:// www.zhbc.com.cn/huoye/huoyegaozhong.php. **Dist. by:** China International Book Trading Corp, 35 Chegongzhuang Xilu, Haidian District, PO Box 399, Beijing 100044, China. TEL 86-10-68412045, FAX 86-10-68412023, cibtc@mail.cibtc.com.cn, http://www.cibtc.com.cn.

370   CHN   ISSN 1009-7252
ZHONGHUA HUOYE WENXUAN (XIAOXUE BAN)/CHINESE LOOSE-LEAF SELECTIONS (PRIMARY SCHOOL EDITION). Text in Chinese. s-m. looseleaf. CNY 38.40 (effective 2004). **Document type:** Journal, Academic/Scholarly.
Related titles: ♦ Series: Zhonghua Huoye Wenxuan (Chuzhong Ban). ISSN 1009-7260; ♦ Zhonghua Huoye Wenxuan (Gaozhong Ban). ISSN 1009-7279; ♦ Zhonghua Huoye Wenxuan (Chengren Ban).
Contact Dist.: China International Book Trading Corp/Zhongguo Guoji Tushu Maoyi Zonggongsi, 35 Chegongzhuang Xilu, Haidian District, PO Box 399, Beijing 100044, China. TEL 86-10-68412045, FAX 86-10-68412023, cibtc@mail.cibtc.com.cn, http://www.zhbc.com.cn/huoye/ huoyexiaoxue.php, http://www.cibtc.com.cn.

ZHONGWEN ZIXIU/CHINESE SELF-STUDY. see LINGUISTICS

ZHONGWEN ZIXUE ZHIDAO/GUIDE TO TEACHING YOURSELF CHINESE. see LINGUISTICS

370   CHN   ISSN 1001-2982
LB1607.53.C6
ZHONGXIAOXUE JIAOYU/MIDDLE AND PRIMARY SCHOOL EDUCATION. Text in Chinese. 1978. m. USD 84 (effective 2004). 96 p./no.; **Document type:** Journal, Academic/Scholarly.
Published by: Zhongguo Renmin Daxue, Shubao Zilio Zhongxin/Renmin University of China, Information Center for Social Server, Dongcheng-qu, 3, Zhangzizhong Lu, Beijing, 100007, China. TEL 86-10-64039458, FAX 86-10-64015080, kyes@163.net, http://www.confucius.cn.net/bkdetail.asp?fzt= G3. **Dist. in US by:** China Publications Service, PO Box 49614, Chicago, IL 60649. TEL 312-288-3291, FAX 312-288-8570.

371   CHN   ISSN 1009-7686
ZHONGXIAOXUE XUEYUAN GUANLI/PRIMARY AND SECONDARY SCHOOL MANAGEMENT. Text in Chinese. bi-m. USD 14.40 (effective 2001). 72 p./no.; **Document type:** Journal, Academic/Scholarly. **Description:** Covers the management of elementary and secondary schools.
Formerly: Zhongxiaoxue Guanli
Published by: Zhongguo Renmin Daxue, Shubao Zilio Zhongxin/Renmin University of China, Information Center for Social Server, Dongcheng-qu, 3, Zhangzizhong Lu, Beijing, 100007, China. TEL 86-10-64039458, FAX 86-10-64015080, kyes@163.net, http://www.confucius.cn.net/bkdetail.asp?fzt= G30. **Dist. in US by:** China Publications Service, PO Box 49614, Chicago, IL 60649. TEL 312-288-3291, FAX 312-288-8570.

ZHONGXIAOXUE YINYUE JIAOYU/MUSIC EDUCATION FOR ELEMENTARY AND HIGH SCHOOLS. see MUSIC

373.01   CHN   ISSN 0412-3921
ZHONGXUE JIAOYU/SECONDARY SCHOOL EDUCATION. Text in Chinese. 1979. m. CNY 14.40 (effective 1993). bk.rev. **Document type:** Academic/Scholarly. **Description:** Covers the theories and practices of secondary school education, including education psychology, and school administration.
Published by: Shanghai Jiaoyu Xueyuan/Shanghai Institute of Education, 1045 Huaihai Zhonglu, Shanghai, 200031, China. TEL 4314823. Ed. Zhang Jiaxiang. Circ: 50,000.

373   CHN   ISSN 1006-0545
ZHONGXUE KEJI/MIDDLE SCHOOL SCIENCE & TECHNOLOGY. Text in Chinese. m. USD 36.80. adv. **Document type:** Academic/Scholarly.
Published by: Shanghai Keji Jiaoyu Chubanshe/Shanghai Science and Technology Education Publishing House, 393 Guanshengyuan Lu, Shanghai, 200233, China. TEL 86-21-4367970, FAX 86-21-4702835. Ed. Hong Ruhui. Adv. contact Wang Yang. **Dist. in US by:** China Books & Periodicals Inc, 360 Swift Ave., Ste. 48, S San Fran, CA 94080-6220. TEL 415-282-2994.

370 910.02 900   CHN   ISSN 1009-2978
ZHONGXUE LISHI, DILI JIAOXUE/TEACHING OF HISTORY AND GEOGRAPHY IN MIDDLE SCHOOL. Text in Chinese. 1997. bi-m. CNY 57.60 (effective 2004). **Document type:** Journal, Academic/Scholarly.
Formerly (until 1999): Zhongxue Lishi Dili Jiaoxue (1007-8355); Which was formed by the merger of (1980-1997): Zhongxue Lishi Jiaoxue (1001-2818); (1980-1997): Zhongxue Dili Jiaoxue (1001-3008)
Related titles: Alternate Frequency ed(s).: a. USD 34.20 newsstand/cover (effective 2002).
Published by: Zhongguo Renmin Daxue, Shubao Zilio Zhongxin/Renmin University of China, Information Center for Social Server, Dongcheng-qu, 3, Zhangzizhong Lu, Beijing, 100007, China. TEL 86-10-64039458, FAX 86-10-64015080, kyes@163.net, http://www.confucius.cn.net/bkdetail.asp?fzt= G32. **Dist. by:** China Publications Service, PO Box 49614, Chicago, IL 60649. TEL 312-288-3291, FAX 312-288-8570; China International Book Trading Corp, 35 Chegongzhuang Xilu, Haidian District, PO Box 399, Beijing 100044, China. TEL 86-10-68412045, FAX 86-10-68412023, cibtc@mail.cibtc.com.cn, http://www.cibtc.com.cn/.

370   CHN   ISSN 1009-296X
ZHONGXUE ZHENGZHI JI QITA GEKE JIAOXUE/TEACHING AND LEARNING OF POLITICS AND OTHER SUBJECTS IN MIDDLE SCHOOL. Text in Chinese. 1998. bi-m. CNY 57.60 (effective 2004). **Document type:** Journal, Academic/Scholarly.
Related titles: Alternate Frequency ed(s).: a. USD 34.20 newsstand/cover (effective 2001).
Published by: Zhongguo Renmin Daxue, Shubao Zilio Zhongxin/Renmin University of China, Information Center for Social Server, Dongcheng-qu, 3, Zhangzizhong Lu, Beijing, 100007, China. TEL 86-10-64039458, FAX 86-10-64015080, kyes@163.net, http://www.confucius.cn.net/bkdetail.asp?fzt= G382. **Dist. by:** China Publications Service, PO Box 49614, Chicago, IL 60649. TEL 312-288-3291, FAX 312-288-8570; China International Book Trading Corp, 35 Chegongzhuang Xilu, Haidian District, PO Box 399, Beijing 100044, China. TEL 86-10-68412045, FAX 86-10-68412023, cibtc@mail.cibtc.com.cn, http://www.cibtc.com.cn/.

373   CHN   ISSN 1003-0204
ZHONGXUESHENG/MIDDLE SCHOOL STUDENT. Text in Chinese. m. USD 21.20.
Published by: Zhongguo Shaonian Ertong Chubanshe, 21 Dongsi 12 Tiao, Beijing, 100708, China. TEL 86-10-6403-2266. Ed. Liu Xiliang. **Dist. in US by:** China Books & Periodicals Inc, 360 Swift Ave., Ste. 48, S San Fran, CA 94080-6220. TEL 415-282-2994.

370   CHN
ZHONGXUESHENG KEXUE JIAOYU/MIDDLE SCHOOL STUDENT SCIENCE EDUCATION. Text in Chinese. m.
Published by: Beijing Keji Ribao/Beijing Science and Technology Daily, A-5, Beiwa Lu, Beijing, 100036, China. TEL 8417774. Ed. Wei Yi.

ZHONGYI JIAOYU/EDUCATION OF TRADITIONAL CHINESE MEDICINE. see ALTERNATIVE MEDICINE

370.720967   ZWE   ISSN 1013-3445
LB1028.25.Z55   CODEN: ZJERE7
➤ **ZIMBABWE JOURNAL OF EDUCATIONAL RESEARCH.** Abbreviated title: Z J E R. Text in English. 1989. q. ZWD 195 domestic to individuals; USD 95 foreign to individuals; ZWD 330 domestic to institutions; USD 135 foreign to institutions (effective 2003). bk.rev. abstr. cum.index 1989-1998. back issues avail. **Document type:** Journal, Academic/Scholarly. **Description:** Publishes scholarly articles reporting on research findings and policy issues relating to education in sub-Saharan Africa, as well as news reports of research initiatives in progress, relevant literature, and organizations of interest.
Related titles: Online - full text ed.: (from International Network for the Availability of Scientific Publications, African Journals Online).
Indexed: ASD, CPE, ERA, L&LBA, MEA, PLESA, SEA, SENA, SOMA, SOPODA, SSA, TEA.
—BLDSC (9513.250300), IE, ingenta.
Published by: University of Zimbabwe, Faculty of Education, Human Resources Research Centre, PO Box MP 167, Mount Pleasant, Harare, Zimbabwe. TEL 263-4-303271, FAX 263-4-302182, nherera@hrrc.uz.zw, http://www.inasp.info/ajol/ journals/zjer/about.html. Ed., R&P Chipo M Nherera.

371   USA   ISSN 1529-5982
ZIP LINES; the voice for adventure education. Text in English. 199?. 3/yr. USD 20 (effective 2005).
Indexed: CIJE.
Published by: Project Adventure, Inc, 701 Cabot St, Beverly, MA 01915. TEL 978-524-4500, FAX 978-524-4501, pub@pa.org.

370   COL   ISSN 1657-2416
ZONA PROXIMA. Text in Spanish. 2001. s-a. COP 12,000 (effective 2002).
Related titles: Online - full text ed.: (from Gale Group).
Published by: Universidad del Norte, Ediciones Uninorte, Km 5 Via a Puerto Colombia, Barranquilla, Colombia. TEL 57-5-3509218, FAX 57-5-3509489, ediciones@uninorte.edu.co, http://www.uninorte.edu.co. Circ: 500.

370   DEU
ZULASSUNGSARBEIT. Text in German. 1972. irreg. adv.
Published by: Verein Freunde und Foerderer der Deutschen Studentenschaft e.V., Untere Hausbreite 11, Munich, 80939, Germany. Ed. Gundolf Seidenspinner.

373   CHN   ISSN 1001-571X
ZUOWEN CHENGGONG ZHI LU/WAYS TO A SUCCESSFUL COMPOSITION. Text in Chinese. 1987. m. CNY 2.30 newsstand/cover; USD 2.30 newsstand/cover foreign. adv. bk.rev. **Document type:** Academic/Scholarly. **Description:** Guides high school students to successful composition.
Published by: (Daqing Jiaoyu Xueyuan/Daqing Institute of Education), Zuowen Chenggong zhi Lu Chubanshe, 4-34 Donggeng Xincun, Daqing, Heilongjiang 163311, China. TEL 86-459-4666092. Ed., R&P Yuhai Wang. Adv. contact Xinyun Wang. Circ: 500,000.

370   DEU
ZUSAMMENSTELLUNG STUDIENEINFUEHRENDER SCHRIFTEN. Text in German. 1974. irreg. adv. bk.rev.
Published by: Verein Freunde und Foerderer der Deutschen Studentenschaft e.V., Untere Hausbreite 11, Munich, 80939, Germany.

372   POL   ISSN 0137-7310
ZYCIE SZKOLY. Text in Polish. 1946. 10/yr. PLZ 75; PLZ 7.50 per issue (effective 2003). bibl.; illus. 64 p./no.; **Description:** Covers issues in elementary education, for teachers, theoreticians of elementary pedagogy and students in pedagogical schools.
Published by: (Poland. Ministerstwo Edukacji Narodowej), Wydawnictwa Szkolne i Pedagogiczne, Pl Dabrowskiego 8, Warsaw, 00950, Poland. TEL 48-22-8279280, wsip@wsip.com.pl, http://www.wsip.com.pl. Ed. Ryszard Wieckowski. Adv. contact Elzbieta Stoj. **Dist. by:** Ars Polona, Krakowskie Przedmiescie 7, Warsaw, Poland. TEL 48-22-9263914, FAX 48-22-9265334, arspolona@arspolona.com.pl, http://www.arspolona.com.pl; **Dist. by:** RUCH S.A., ul Jana Kazimierza 31/33, Warsaw 00958, Poland. TEL 48-22-5328731.

E

370 DEU
ZZAP; Schuelerzeitung Schillerschule. Text in English, German. 1956. 4/yr. free. adv. bk.rev. abstr.; bibl.; charts; illus.; stat.
Supersedes (in 1987): Glocke (0017-1247)
Address: c/o Joerg Thiel, Albert-Schweitzer-Hof 21, Hannover, 30559, Germany. TEL 0511-526462. Circ: 600.

370 NLD ISSN 1385-3538
0 - 25. Text in Dutch. 1996. 10/yr. EUR 46.75 to individuals; EUR 64.50 to institutions; EUR 36.75 to students (effective 2005). adv. bk.rev. abstr.; charts; illus. index. **Document type:** *Academic/Scholarly.*
Formed by the 1996 merger of: Jeugd en Samenleving (0047-1976); Which was formed by the 1971 merger of: Blauwdruk (0520-268X); Fase (0014-861X); And: Tijdschrift voor Jeugdverlening en Jeugdwerk (0924-3496); Which was formerly (until 1989): Tijdschrift voor Jeugdhulpverlening (0924-3488); (until 1986): Tijdschrift voor Jeugdhulpverlening Sjow (0168-8146); Sjow (0165-2974); Which was formed by the 1973 merger of: Koepel; Mozaiek
Indexed: AC&P, CERDIC.
—Infotrieve, KNAW.
Published by: (Stichting Jeugd en Samenleving), Koninklijke Van Gorcum BV/Royal Van Gorcum BV, PO Box 43, Assen, 9400 AA, Netherlands. TEL 31-592-379555, FAX 31-592-372064, redactie.025@nizw.nl, info@vangorcum.nl, http://www.tijdschrift025.nl/, http://www.vangorcum.nl. Ed. Donald Suidman. Adv. contact Bel Jorine de Bruin. Circ: 3,500.

371.07 SWE ISSN 1652-3350
24 TRETTON; pedagogik i svenska kyrkan. Text in Swedish. 1943. 6/yr. SEK 250 (effective 2003). adv. **Document type:** *Newspaper.*
Former titles (until 2003): Barn och Familj (0348-0348); (until vol.4, 1977): Textutkast foer Kyrkans Soendagsskolor (0346-3109)
Related titles: Online - full text ed.
Published by: Svenska Kyrkans Press AB, Goetgatan 22A, PO Box 15412, Stockholm, 10465, Sweden. TEL 46-8-4622800, FAX 46-8-6445604, 24tretton@svenskakyrkan.se, http://www.svenskakyrkan.se/24tretton. Ed. Urban Engvall.

370 FRA ISSN 1637-6900
128. LETTRES. Cover title: Collection 128. Lettres. Variant title: Cent-Vingt-Huit. Lettres. Text in French. 1992. irreg. **Document type:** *Monographic series.*
Related titles: ♦ Series of: Collection 128. ISSN 1160-2422.
Indexed: MLA-IB.
Published by: Editions Nathan, 9 rue Mechain, Paris, 75014, France. TEL 33-1-45875000, FAX 33-1-45875757, http://www.nathan.fr.

EDUCATION—Abstracting, Bibliographies, Statistics

016.378 GBR
A C U BULLETIN. Text in English. 1971. 4/yr. free to members (effective 2003). adv. bk.rev. bibl. 32 p./no. 3 cols./p.; **Document type:** *Bulletin, Academic/Scholarly.* **Description:** Pan Commonwealth digest of higher education news, issues and resources.
Formerly (until 1998): A C U Bulletin of Current Documentation (0044-9563)
Indexed: HECAB, RASB.
Published by: Association of Commonwealth Universities, John Foster House, 36 Gordon Square, London, WC1H 0, United Kingdom. TEL 44-20-73806700, FAX 44-20-73872655, s.cripps@acu.ac.uk, info@acu.ac.uk, http://www.acu.ac.uk/bulletin/. Ed., R&P Sarah Cripps. Adv. contact Reeta Gupta. color page EUR 1,620, B&W 1/2 page EUR 1,130; 267 x 185. Circ: 8,000.

016.37 BGR
ABSTRACTS OF BULGARIAN SCIENTIFIC LITERATURE. PHILOSOPHY, SOCIOLOGY, SCIENCE OF SCIENCES, PSYCHOLOGY AND PEDAGOGICS. Text in English. 1958. q. BGL 3.44, USD 8. abstr. author index. reprint service avail. from IRC.
Formerly: Abstracts of Bulgarian Scientific Literature. Philosophy, Psychology and Pedagogics (0001-3528)
Related titles: Russian ed.
Published by: (Bulgarska Akademiya na Naukite/Bulgarian Academy of Sciences), Universitetsko Izdatelstvo Sv. Kliment Okhridski/Publishing House of the Sofia University St. Kliment Ohridski, Akad G Bonchev 6, Sofia, 1113, Bulgaria. Circ: 390. **Dist. by:** Hemus, 6 Rouski Blvd., Sofia 1000, Bulgaria.

016.37072 NGA
ABSTRACTS OF EDUCATIONAL STUDIES AND RESEARCH✶. Text in English. 1971. w. NGN 1.50, USD 2.25. abstr.; stat. back issues avail.
Published by: (Department of Education), Obafemi Awolowo University, Ile Ife, Osun State, Nigeria. Ed. Adeniji Adaralegbe.

370.21 USA
AMERICAN STATISTICAL ASSOCIATION. SECTION ON STATISTICAL EDUCATION. NEWSLETTER. Text in English. 1995. s-a. membership. back issues avail. **Document type:** *Newsletter.*
Related titles: Online - full text ed.
Published by: (Section on Statistical Education), American Statistical Association, 1429 Duke St, Alexandria, VA 22314-3415. tlking@acad.nwmissouri.edu, http://renoir.vill.edu/cgi-bin/short/StatEd.cgi. Ed. Terry King.

016.37 ARG
ARGENTINA. MINISTERIO DE CULTURA Y EDUCACION. BOLETIN BIBLIOGRAFICO. Text in Spanish. 1976 (no.5). q. free. bibl.
Published by: (Argentina. Ministerio de Cultura y Educacion), Centro de Documentacion e Informacion Educativa, Paraguay, 1657-Piso 1, Capital Federal, 1062, Argentina.

370.21 ARG
ARGENTINA. MINISTERIO DE CULTURA Y EDUCACION. ESTADISTICAS DE LA EDUCACION✶. Text in Spanish. 1974. a. illus.; stat. **Document type:** *Government.*
Formerly: Estadistica Educativa
Published by: (Argentina. Departamento de Estadistica Educativa), Ministerio de Educacion, Pizzurno 935, Buenos Aires, 1020, Argentina. TEL 54-11-41291000, info@me.gov.ar, http://www.me.gov.ar/.

016.378 GHA
ASSOCIATION OF AFRICAN UNIVERSITIES. BIBLIOGRAPHY ON HIGHER EDUCATION IN AFRICA. Text in English. irreg. USD 25 per vol.. **Document type:** *Bibliography.* **Description:** Carries information on lists of publications on higher education in Africa.
Formerly: Association of African Universities. New Acquisitions List
Published by: Association of African Universities, PO Box 5744, Accra - North, Ghana. info@aau.org. Ed. Yawo Assigbley.

016.371335 USA
AUDIOCASSETTE & C D FINDER. Text in English. 1986. irreg., latest vol.3, 1993. USD 125 (effective 2001). abstr. back issues avail. **Description:** Subject guide of 29,000 titles of literary materials on audiocassette.
Former titles (until 1992): Audiocassette Finder; (until 1986): N I C E M Index to Educational Audio Tapes
Related titles: Online - full text ed.
Published by: (National Information Center for Educational Media), Plexus Publishing, Inc., 143 Old Marlton Pike, Medford, NJ 08055. TEL 609-654-6500, FAX 609-654-4309, info@plexuspublishing.com, http://www.plexuspublishing.com. R&P Pat Palatucci.

370.021 AUS
AUSTRALIA. BUREAU OF STATISTICS. A.B.S. CLASSIFICATION OF QUALIFICATIONS. Text in English. 1993. irreg., latest 1993. AUD 30.60 (effective 2002). **Document type:** *Government.* **Description:** Classifies post-school educational qualifications, by level of attainment and field study.
Related titles: Diskette ed.
Published by: Australian Bureau of Statistics, PO Box 10, Belconnen, ACT 2616, Australia. TEL 61-2-6252-5249, FAX 61-2-6252-6778, http://www.abs.gov.au.

370.021 AUS
AUSTRALIA. BUREAU OF STATISTICS. A.B.S CLASSIFICATION OF QUALIFICATIONS: MANUAL CODING SYSTEM. Text in English. 1993. irreg. AUD 30.60 (effective 2002). **Document type:** *Government.* **Description:** Classifies post-school qualifications by level of attainment and field of study.
Related titles: Diskette ed.
Published by: Australian Bureau of Statistics, PO Box 10, Belconnen, ACT 2616, Australia. TEL 61-2-6252-5249, FAX 61-2-6252-6778, http://www.abs.gov.au.

371.3021 AUS
AUSTRALIA. BUREAU OF STATISTICS. A DIRECTORY OF EDUCATION AND TRAINING STATISTICS. Text in English. 1993. irreg., latest 1997. AUD 10 (effective 2003). **Document type:** *Government.*
Related titles: Online - full text ed.
Published by: Australian Bureau of Statistics, PO Box 10, Belconnen, ACT 2616, Australia. TEL 61-2-6252-5249, FAX 61-2-6252-6778, http://www.abs.gov.au.

371.3021 AUS
AUSTRALIA. BUREAU OF STATISTICS. ASPECTS OF LITERACY: ASSESSED SKILL LEVELS, AUSTRALIA. Text in English. 1996. irreg., latest 1996. AUD 30 (effective 2001). **Document type:** *Government.*
Published by: Australian Bureau of Statistics, PO Box 10, Belconnen, ACT 2616, Australia. TEL 61-2-6252-5249, FAX 61-2-6252-6778, http://www.abs.gov.au.

371.3021 AUS
AUSTRALIA. BUREAU OF STATISTICS. ASPECTS OF LITERACY: PROFILES AND PERCEPTIONS, AUSTRALIA. Text in English. 1996. irreg., latest 1996. AUD 20 (effective 2001). **Document type:** *Government.*
Published by: Australian Bureau of Statistics, PO Box 10, Belconnen, ACT 2616, Australia. TEL 61-2-6252-5249, FAX 61-2-6252-6778, http://www.abs.gov.au.

371.3021 AUS
AUSTRALIA. BUREAU OF STATISTICS. AUSTRALIAN STANDARD CLASSIFICATION OF EDUCATION. Text in English. 2001. irreg. AUD 59 (effective 2003). **Document type:** *Government.*
Published by: Australian Bureau of Statistics, PO Box 10, Belconnen, ACT 2616, Australia. TEL 61-2-6252-5249, FAX 61-2-6252-6778, http://www.abs.gov.au.

371.3021 AUS ISSN 1446-3121
AUSTRALIA. BUREAU OF STATISTICS. EDUCATION AND TRAINING INDICATORS, AUSTRALIA. Text in English. 2002. biennial. AUD 36 (effective 2003). **Document type:** *Government.*
Published by: Australian Bureau of Statistics, PO Box 10, Belconnen, ACT 2616, Australia. http://www.abs.gov.au.

370.021 AUS
AUSTRALIA. BUREAU OF STATISTICS. INFORMATION PAPER: A.B.S. CLASSIFICATION OF QUALIFICATIONS. Text in English. 1992. irreg., latest 1992. free. **Document type:** *Government.* **Description:** Provides an overview of the A.B.S.C.Q.
Published by: Australian Bureau of Statistics, PO Box 10, Belconnen, ACT 2616, Australia. TEL 61-2-6252-5249, FAX 61-2-6252-6778, http://www.abs.gov.au.

371.3021 AUS
AUSTRALIA. BUREAU OF STATISTICS. INFORMATION PAPER: AUSTRALIAN STANDARD CLASSIFICATION OF EDUCATION. Text in English. 2000. irreg. AUD 10 (effective 2003). **Document type:** *Government.*
Published by: Australian Bureau of Statistics, PO Box 10, Belconnen, ACT 2616, Australia. TEL 61-2-6252-5249, FAX 61-2-6252-6778, http://www.abs.gov.au.

371.3021 AUS
AUSTRALIA. BUREAU OF STATISTICS. INFORMATION PAPER: EDUCATION AND TRAINING EXPERIENCE, AUSTRALIA, (YEAR) - CONFIDENTIALISED UNIT RECORD FILE. Text in English. 1989. irreg., latest 1997. AUD 10 (effective 2002). **Document type:** *Government.*
Former titles: Australia. Bureau of Statistics. Information Paper: Training and Education Experience, Australia, (Year) - Sample File on Magnetic Tape; (until 1989): Australia. Bureau of Statistics. Information Paper: How Workers Get Their Training, Australia, (Year) - Sample File on Magnetic Tape
Media: Magnetic Tape.
Published by: Australian Bureau of Statistics, PO Box 10, Belconnen, ACT 2616, Australia. TEL 61-2-6252-5249, FAX 61-2-6252-6778, http://www.abs.gov.au.

378.97021 AUS ISSN 0729-171X
AUSTRALIA. BUREAU OF STATISTICS. RESEARCH AND EXPERIMENTAL DEVELOPMENT, HIGHER EDUCATION ORGANISATIONS, AUSTRALIA. Text in English. 1978. a. AUD 19.50 (effective 2003). **Document type:** *Government.* **Description:** Covers expenditure and human resources devoted to research and experimental development carried out by higher education organizations in Australia.
Published by: Australian Bureau of Statistics, PO Box 10, Belconnen, ACT 2616, Australia. TEL 61-2-6252-5249, FAX 61-2-6252-6778, http://www.abs.gov.au.

371.0021 AUS ISSN 1035-3461
AUSTRALIA. BUREAU OF STATISTICS. SCHOOLS, AUSTRALIA. Text in English. 1984. a., latest 1999. AUD 22 (effective 2003). **Document type:** *Government.* **Description:** Covers statistics on schools, students, teaching and non-teaching staff involved in the provision or administration of primary and secondary education, in government and non-government schools.
Formerly: National Schools Statistics Collection (0819-5323); Formed by the merger of: National Schools Collection: Government Schools & Non-Government Schools
Published by: Australian Bureau of Statistics, PO Box 10, Belconnen, ACT 2616, Australia. TEL 61-2-6252-5249, FAX 61-2-6252-6778, http://www.abs.gov.au. Circ: 399.

016.37 AUS
Z5813
AUSTRALIAN EDUCATION INDEX (ONLINE EDITION). Text in English. m. **Document type:** *Database, Abstract/Index.*
Media: Online - full text. **Related titles:** CD-ROM ed.: (from The Dialog Corporation).
Published by: Australian Council for Educational Research, 347 Camberwell Rd, Private Bag 55, Camberwell, VIC 3124, Australia. TEL 61-3-92775555, FAX 61-3-92775500, sales@acer.edu.au, http://www.informit.com.au/show.asp?id=AEIPT, http://www.acer.edu.au.

016.37 BHR
BAHRAIN. EDUCATIONAL DOCUMENTATION LIBRARY. ACQUISITIONS LIST. Text in English. m.
Published by: Ministry of Education, Educational Documentation Library, PO Box 43, Manama, Bahrain. TEL 25840.

016.37 BHR
BAHRAIN. EDUCATIONAL DOCUMENTATION LIBRARY. BIBLIOGRAPHIC LISTS. Text in English. a.
Published by: Ministry of Education, Educational Documentation Library, PO Box 43, Manama, Bahrain. TEL 25840.

E

378.2021 THA ISSN 0067-3498
BANGKOK, THAILAND. COLLEGE OF EDUCATION. THESIS ABSTRACT SERIES✶. Text in English. 1967. a. USD 1.
Related titles: Thai ed.: 1967.
Published by: Suan Sunautha Teacher College, Samsen, Bangkok 4, Thailand.

370.21 BGD
BANGLADESH EDUCATION IN STATISTICS (YEAR). Text in English. a. BDT 100, USD 15. **Document type:** *Government.*
Published by: (Bangladesh. Bureau of Statistics), Ministry of Planning, Statistics Division, Secretariat, Dhaka, 2, Bangladesh.

370.21 BEL
BELGIUM. MINISTERE DE L'EDUCATION, DE LA RECHERCHE ET DE LA FORMATION. ANNUAIRE STATISTIQUE. Text in French. 1957. a. **Document type:** *Government.* **Description:** Publishes statistics on education in French-speaking parts of Belgium.
Former titles (until 1988): Belgium. Ministere de l'Education Nationale. Etudes et Documents (0773-5820); (until 1973): Belgium. Ministere de l'Education Nationale et de la Culture Francaise. Annuaire Statistique de l'Enseignement; (until 1968): Belgium. Institut National de Statistique. Annuaire Statistique de l'Enseignement (0067-5423)
Published by: Ministere de l'Education, de la Recherche et de la Formation, Service des Statistiques, Bd Pacheco 19, Bte 0, Brussels, 1010, Belgium. TEL 32-2-210-5546, FAX 32-2-210-5538.

016.37191 FIN ISSN 0357-2498
BIBLIOGRAFIA ERITYSIRYHMIEN LIIKUNNAN TUTKIMUKSESTA/BIBLIOGRAPHY ON RESEARCH IN PHYSICAL EDUCATION AND SPORT FOR THE HANDICAPPED. Text in English, Finnish. 1975. irreg. bibl.
Published by: Liikunnan ja Kansanterveyden Edistaemisaeaetion Tutkmuslaitos/Research Institute of Physical Culture and Health, Uimahalli, Yliopistonkatu, Jyvaeskylae, 40100, Finland. Circ: 500.

016.37 USA ISSN 0147-6505
Z5813
BIBLIOGRAPHIC GUIDE TO EDUCATION. Text in English. 1975. a. USD 470 (effective 2005). bibl. **Document type:** *Bibliography.* **Description:** Covers all aspects of education. Lists materials recorded on the OCLC tapes of Columbia University Teachers College during the past year, including additional entries from New York Public Library.
Published by: G.K. Hall & Co. (Subsidiary of: Gale Group), 12 Lunar Dr, Woodbridge, CT 06525. TEL 203-397-2600, 800-444-0799, FAX 203-397-8296, remmel.nunn@gale.com, http://www.galegroup.com/gkhall. **Subscr. to:** Simon & Schuster, PO Box 7500, Riverside, NJ 08075-8075. TEL 800-223-2336.

016.37 USA ISSN 0742-6917
BIBLIOGRAPHIES AND INDEXES IN EDUCATION. Text in English. 1984. irreg. price varies. **Document type:** *Bibliography.*
Published by: Greenwood Publishing Group Inc. (Subsidiary of: Harcourt International), 88 Post Rd W, PO Box 5007, Westport, CT 06881. TEL 203-226-3571, FAX 203-226-1502, bookinfo@greenwood.com, http://www.greenwood.com.

016.378 AUS ISSN 0811-0174
Z5815.A8
BIBLIOGRAPHY OF EDUCATION THESES IN AUSTRALIA. Text in English. 1982. a., latest vol.21, 2000. price varies. bibl. back issues avail. **Document type:** *Bibliography.*
Related titles: CD-ROM ed.; Online - full text ed.
—CCC.
Published by: Australian Council for Educational Research, 347 Camberwell Rd, Private Bag 55, Camberwell, VIC 3124, Australia. TEL 61-3-9835-7447, FAX 61-3-9835-7499, forster@acer.edu.au, sales@acer.edu.au, http://www.acer.edu.au. Ed. Margaret Forster. R&P Deirdre Morris. Circ: 350.

370.21 DEU ISSN 0938-1104
LA722
BILDUNG IM ZAHLENSPIEGEL. Text in German. 1974. a. stat. **Document type:** *Government.*
Indexed: RASB.
Published by: Statistisches Bundesamt, Gustav-Stresemann-Ring 11, Wiesbaden, 65180, Germany. TEL 49-611-75-1, FAX 49-611-724000, http://www.statistik-bund.de.

016.37 USA ISSN 1044-7962
BIO-BIBLIOGRAPHIES IN EDUCATION. Text in English. 1989. irreg. price varies. **Document type:** *Monographic series, Bibliography.*
Published by: Greenwood Publishing Group Inc. (Subsidiary of: Harcourt International), 88 Post Rd W, PO Box 5007, Westport, CT 06881. TEL 203-226-3571, FAX 203-226-1502, bookinfo@greenwood.com, http://www.greenwood.com.

BOLETIM ESTATISTICO. RELATORIO DE ACTIVIDADES. see *EDUCATION—Higher Education*

370.21 BWA
BOTSWANA. CENTRAL STATISTICS OFFICE. EDUCATION STATISTICS. Text and summaries in English. a. charts. back issues avail. **Document type:** *Government.* **Description:** Provides statistics on the number of schools, classrooms, teachers, and pupils thoughout Botswana.
Related titles: E-mail ed.; Fax ed.
Published by: Central Statistics Office, c/o Government Statistician, Private Bag 0024, Gaborone, Botswana. TEL 267-31-352200, FAX 267-31-352201, csobots@gov.bw. Ed. G M Charumbira. **Subscr. to:** Government Printer, Private Bag 0081, Gaborone, Botswana.

370.21 BRA
BRAZIL. SERVICO DE ESTATISTICA DA EDUCACAO E CULTURA. SINOPSE ESTATISTICA DA EDUCACAO PRE-ESCOLAR. Text in Portuguese. 1984. irreg.
Supersedes (1968-1973): Brazil. Servico de Estatistica da Educacao e Cultura. Sinopse Estatistica do Ensino Primario.
Published by: Ministerio da Educacao e Cultura, Servico de Estatistica da Educacao e Cultura, Esplanada dos Ministerios, Bloco L - Anexo II - Terreo, Brasilia, DF 70047, Brazil.

378.0021 BRA
BRAZIL. SERVICO DE ESTATISTICA DA EDUCACAO E CULTURA. SINOPSE ESTATISTICA DO ENSINO SUPERIOR. Text in Portuguese. 1954. irreg.
Published by: Ministerio da Educacao e Cultura, Servico de Estatistica da Educacao e Cultura, Esplanada dos Ministerios, Bloco L - Anexo II - Terreo, Brasilia, DF 70047, Brazil.

370.21 BRA
BRAZIL. SERVICO DE ESTATISTICA DA EDUCACAO. SINOPSE ESTATISTICA DO ENSINO REGULAR DE 1O GRAU. Text in Portuguese. irreg. charts; stat.
Published by: (Brazil. Servico de Estadistica da Educacao), Ministerio da Educacao e Cultura, Servico de Estatistica da Educacao e Cultura, Esplanada dos Ministerios, Bloco L - Anexo II - Terreo, Brasilia, DF 70047, Brazil.

016.37 GBR ISSN 0007-0637
Z5813
BRITISH EDUCATION INDEX. Text in English. 1961. a. (plus q. updates). GBP 298 domestic; GBP 322 foreign (effective 2005). illus. reprints avail. **Document type:** *Abstract/Index.* **Description:** Provides a subject and author index to articles of permanent educational interest in a wide range of British and some European periodicals.
Related titles: CD-ROM ed.: (from The Dialog Corporation); Online - full text ed.
Indexed: RASB.
—BLDSC (2299.200000).
Address: Brotherton Library, University of Leeds, Leeds, W Yorks LS2 9JT, United Kingdom. TEL 44-113-3435525, FAX 44-113-3435524, bei@leeds.ac.uk, http://www.leeds.ac.uk/bei/bei.htm. Ed. Philip W Sheffield. Circ: 500.

016.3719 GBR
BRITISH INSTITUTE OF LEARNING DISABILITIES. CURRENT AWARENESS SERVICE. Abbreviated title: C A S. Text in English. 1979. m. GBP 39 domestic to individuals; EUR 70, GBP 44 in Europe to individuals; USD 77, GBP 49 elsewhere to individuals; GBP 57 domestic to institutions; EUR 104, GBP 65 in Europe to institutions; USD 110, GBP 70 elsewhere to institutions (effective 2003). adv. back issues avail. **Document type:** *Bibliography.* **Description:** Bibliography of current books, articles, educational events, and audiovisual materials covering all aspects of learning disabilities.
Formerly: British Institute of Mental Handicap. Current Awareness Service (0143-0289)
Published by: B I L D, Campion House, Green St, Kidderminster, Worcs DY10 1JL, United Kingdom. TEL 44-1562-723010, FAX 44-1562-723029, enquiries@bild.org.uk, http://www.bild.org.uk. Ed. Linda Averill. Circ: 1,000.

370.21 CAN ISSN 0706-3679
CANADA. STATISTICS CANADA. EDUCATION IN CANADA/CANADA. STATISTIQUE CANADA. L'EDUCATION AU CANADA. Text in English, French. 1973. a. CND 52 domestic; USD 52 foreign (effective 1999). **Document type:** *Government.* **Description:** Summarizes information on institutions, enrollment, graduates, teachers and finance for all levels of education and provides an analysis of the data.
Related titles: Microform ed.: (from MML); Online - full text ed.: (from EBSCO Publishing).
Published by: Statistics Canada, Operations and Integration Division, Circulation Management, Jean Talon Bldg, 2 C12, Tunney's Pasture, Ottawa, ON K1A 0T6, Canada. TEL 613-951-7277, 800-267-6677, FAX 613-951-1584, http://statcan.ca:80/cgi-bin/downpub/downpub.cgi. Circ: 800 (paid).

CANADA. STATISTICS CANADA. MINORITY AND SECOND LANGUAGE EDUCATION, ELEMENTARY AND SECONDARY LEVELS/CANADA. STATISTIQUE CANADA. LANGUE DE LA MINORITE ET LANGUE SECONDE DANS L'ENSEIGNEMENT, NIVEAUX ELEMENTAIRE ET SECONDAIRE. see *LINGUISTICS—Abstracting, Bibliographies, Statistics*

016.37 CAN ISSN 1481-7586
CANADIAN BUSINESS AND CURRENT AFFAIRS EDUCATION. Key Title: C B C A Fulltext Education. Abbreviated title: C B C A. Text in English, French. 1996. m. CND 2,100 to libraries (effective 2005). illus. back issues avail.; reprints avail. **Document type:** *Abstract/Index.* **Description:** Covers journal articles from Canadian education journals including daily news sources. Includes federal and provincial government research reports, monographs from educational research communities, provincial curriculum guides, and graduate dissertations in education.
Formerly (until 1998): Canadian Education Index (CD-ROM Edition) (1206-1832)
Media: Online - full content.
Published by: (Canadian Education Association/Association Canadienne d'Education), Micromedia ProQuest (Subsidiary of: ProQuest Information & Learning), 20 Victoria St, Toronto, ON M5C 2N8, Canada. TEL 416-362-5211, 800-387-2689, FAX 416-362-6161, http://www.micromedia.ca/products_services/cbcaedu.htm. Ed. Mr. Tom McGreevy.

CANADIAN MEDICAL EDUCATION STATISTICS. see *MEDICAL SCIENCES—Abstracting, Bibliographies, Statistics*

016.6137 GBR
CENTRE FOR SPORTS SCIENCE AND HISTORY. SERIAL HOLDINGS. Text in English, Multiple languages. 1974. a. free. **Document type:** *Catalog, Abstract/Index.* **Description:** Lists national and international periodicals, abstracts, and indexing journals on sports, physical education, and recreation held in the library of the Centre.
Former titles (until 1993): Sports Documentation Centre. Serial Holdings; Sports Documentation Centre. List of Periodical and Abstracting and Indexing Journal Holdings
Published by: Centre for Sports Science and History, Main Library, University of Birmingham, Edgbaston, Birmingham B15 2TT, United Kingdom. TEL 44-121-414-5843, FAX 44-121-471-4691. Circ: 333.

016.3713 URY
CENTRO INTERAMERICANO DE INVESTIGACION Y DOCUMENTACION SOBRE FORMACION PROFESIONAL. SERIE BIBLIOGRAFICA. Text in Spanish. 1968. irreg. price varies. bk.rev. abstr.; bibl.
Published by: Centro Interamericano de Investigacion y Documentacion Sobre Formacion Profesional, Av. Uruguay, 1238, Casilla de Correos 1761, Montevideo, 11106, Uruguay. FAX 921305, dirmvd@cinterfor.org.uy.

371.206021 GBR ISSN 0309-5614
LA630
CHARTERED INSTITUTE OF PUBLIC FINANCE AND ACCOUNTANCY. EDUCATION STATISTICS. ACTUALS. Text in English. 1948. a. GBP 80. stat. back issues avail.
—CCC.
Published by: (Statistical Information Service), Chartered Institute of Public Finance and Accountancy, 3 Robert St, London, WC2N 6RL, United Kingdom. TEL 44-20-7543-5800, FAX 44-20-7543-5700, http://www.cipfa.org.uk.

371.206021 GBR ISSN 0307-0514
LA630
CHARTERED INSTITUTE OF PUBLIC FINANCE AND ACCOUNTANCY. EDUCATION STATISTICS. ESTIMATES. Text in English. 1974. a. GBP 80. back issues avail.
—CCC.
Published by: (Statistical Information Service), Chartered Institute of Public Finance and Accountancy, 3 Robert St, London, WC2N 6RL, United Kingdom. TEL 44-20-7543-5800, FAX 44-20-7543-5700, http://www.cipfa.org.uk.

016.378 IRN ISSN 1022-7814
CHIKIDAH-I PAYAN'NAMAHHA-YI IRAN/IRANIAN DISSERTATION ABSTRACTS. Text in Persian, Modern. 1973. q. USD 70 (effective 2003). 420 p./no.; back issues avail. **Document type:** *Abstract/Index.* **Description:** Six subjects are covered: Literature & humanities, basic sciences, medicine, engineering, agriculture, and arts.
Published by: Iranian Information & Documentation Center (IRANDOC), 1188 Enqelab Ave., P O Box 13185-1371, Tehran, Iran. TEL 98-21-6494955, FAX 98-21-6462254, journal@irandoc.ac.ir, http://www.irandoc.ac.ir. Ed. Hussein Gharibi.

COLLECTIVE BARGAINING IN HIGHER EDUCATION AND THE PROFESSIONS. ANNUAL BIBLIOGRAPHY. see *LABOR UNIONS—Abstracting, Bibliographies, Statistics*

016.37 USA
COLLEGE CATALOG COLLECTION ON MICROFICHE. Text in English. 1973. s-a. price varies. abstr.; charts; illus.; stat. back issues avail. **Document type:** *Catalog.*
Media: Microfiche.
Published by: Career Guidance Foundation, 8090 Engineer Rd, San Diego, CA 92111. TEL 619-560-8051, FAX 619-278-8960. Circ: 100,000.

E

▼ new title ➤ refereed ✶ unverified ♦ full entry avail.

370.21 USA ISSN 0098-4752
L112
THE CONDITION OF EDUCATION; a statistical report on the condition of American education. Text in English. 1975. a. stat. 442 p./no.; **Document type:** *Government.* **Description:** Monitors and discloses the status of recent progress in American education on the basis of 60 separate indicators.
Related titles: Online - full text ed.
Indexed: AmStI.
Published by: U.S. Department of Education, National Center for Education Statistics, 1990 K St N W, Washington, DC 20006. TEL 202-219-1828, http://nces.ed.gov, http://www.nces.ed.gov. **Subscr. to:** U.S. Government Printing Office, Superintendent of Documents, PO Box 371954, Pittsburgh, PA 15250-7954. TEL 202-512-1800, FAX 202-512-2250, orders@gpo.gov, http://www.access.gpo.gov.

016.37 GBR ISSN 0265-9220
Z5813
CONTENTS PAGES IN EDUCATION. Text in English. 1986. m. GBP 1,113, USD 1,881 combined subscription to institutions print & online eds. (effective 2006). index. back issues avail.; reprint service avail. from PSC. **Document type:** *Journal, Abstract/Index.* **Description:** A computer-based, international current awareness service that shows the contents pages of over 700 of the world's education journals.
Related titles: Microfiche ed.; Online - full text ed.: (from ProQuest Information & Learning).
Indexed: RASB.
—IE, Infotrieve. **CCC.**
Published by: Routledge (Subsidiary of: Taylor & Francis Group), 4 Park Sq, Milton Park, Abingdon, Oxon OX14 4RN, United Kingdom. TEL 44-1235-828600, FAX 44-1235-829000, info@routledge.co.uk, http://www.tandf.co.uk/journals/titles/02659220.asp, http://www.routledge.co.uk. Ed. Angie Davis. **Subscr. to:** Taylor & Francis Ltd.

370.21 CAN ISSN 0382-912X
LA418.O6
COUNCIL OF ONTARIO UNIVERSITIES. APPLICATION STATISTICS. Text in English. 1973. a. reprints avail.
Related titles: Microform ed.: (from MML).
Published by: Council of Ontario Universities, 180 Dundas St W, Ste 1100, Toronto, ON M5G 1Z8, Canada. TEL 416-979-2165, FAX 416-979-8635, acadieux@coupo.cou.on.ca, http://www.cou.on.ca.

016.37 USA ISSN 0011-3565
Z5813 CODEN: CIJEA
CURRENT INDEX TO JOURNALS IN EDUCATION. Text in English. 1969. m. (plus s-a. cumulation). illus. s-a. index. reprints avail. **Document type:** *Journal, Abstract/Index.* **Description:** Annotated index to education literature, including elementary, secondary and higher education, as well as administrative issues and concerns.
Related titles: Microfiche ed.; Online - full text ed.: (from Questel Orbit Inc.); ♦ Cumulative ed(s).: Current Index to Journals in Education Semiannual Cumulation. ISSN 1082-6343.
Indexed: RASB.
—BLDSC (3498.180000).
Published by: Educational Resources Information Center, c/o Computer Sciences Corporation, 4483-A Forbes Blvd, Lanham, MD 20706. http://www.eric.ed.gov/.

016.37 USA ISSN 1082-6343
Z5813
CURRENT INDEX TO JOURNALS IN EDUCATION SEMIANNUAL CUMULATION. Text in English. s-a. USD 245 in North America; USD 280 elsewhere (effective 2001). **Document type:** *Abstract/Index.*
Related titles: ♦ Cumulative ed. of: Current Index to Journals in Education. ISSN 0011-3565.
Published by: Oryx Press (Subsidiary of: Greenwood Publishing Group Inc.), 1434 E. San Miguel Ave., Phoenix, AZ 85014-2422. TEL 602-265-2651, 800-279-6799, FAX 602-265-6250, info@oryxpress.com, http://www.oryxpress.com.

370.72021 CYP
LA1480
CYPRUS. DEPARTMENT OF STATISTICS AND RESEARCH. EDUCATION STATISTICS. Text in English, Greek. 1964. a. CYP 6 (effective 1999). **Document type:** *Government.* **Description:** Presents statistical data on education at all levels.
Formerly: Statistics of Education in Cyprus (0253-8733)
Published by: Ministry of Finance, Department of Statistics and Research, 13 Andreas Araouzos St, Nicosia, 1444, Cyprus. TEL 357-2-309318, FAX 357-2-374830, cydsr@cytanet.com.cy, http://www.pio.gov.cy/dsr.

016.3782 USA
DELTA PI EPSILON. INDEX TO DOCTORAL DISSERTATIONS IN BUSINESS EDUCATION. Text in English. 1975. every 5 yrs. price varies. Supplement avail. **Document type:** *Abstract/Index.*
Published by: Delta Pi Epsilon Graduate Business Education Society, National Office, P O Box 4340, Little Rock, AR 72214. TEL 501-562-1233, FAX 501-562-1293.

370.9489 DNK ISSN 0108-5492
DENMARK. DANMARKS STATISTIK. UDDANNELSE OG KULTUR. Text in Danish. 1983. **Document type:** *Government.*
Supersedes in part (1976-1983): Statistiske Efterretninger A (0105-306X); (1976-1983): Statistiske Efterretninger B (0105-3078); Which both superseded in part (1909-1976): Statistiske Efterretninger (0039-0674)
Related titles: ♦ Series of: Denmark. Danmarks Statistik. Statistiske Efterretninger. Indhold. ISSN 1396-8173.
Published by: Danmarks Statistik, Sejroegade 11, Copenhagen Oe, 2100, Denmark. TEL 45-39-173917, FAX 45-39-173939.

314.021 DNK ISSN 1602-0308
DENMARK. UNDERVISNINGSMINISTERIET. FACTS AND FIGURES; education indicators in Denmark. Text in English. 2000. a., latest 2004. stat. back issues avail. **Document type:** *Government.*
Media: Online - full content. **Related titles:** ♦ Danish ed.: Denmark. Undervisningsministeriet. Tal der Taler. ISSN 1601-4561.
Published by: Undervisningsministeriet/Ministry of Education, Frederiksholms Kanal 21, Copenhagen K, 1220, Denmark. TEL 45-33-925000, FAX 45-33-925567, http://uvm.dk.

370.21 DNK ISSN 1601-4561
DENMARK. UNDERVISNINGSMINISTERIET. TAL DER TALER; uddannelsesnoegletal. Text in Danish. 2000. a., latest 2004. price varies. back issues avail. **Document type:** *Government.*
Related titles: Online - full text ed.: ISSN 1601-5746; ♦ English ed.: Denmark. Undervisningsministeriet. Facts and Figures. ISSN 1602-0308.
Published by: Undervisningsministeriet/Ministry of Education, Frederiksholms Kanal 21, Copenhagen K, 1220, Denmark. TEL 45-33-925000, FAX 45-33-925567, http://pub.uvm.dk/2004/taldertaler/kolofon.html.

016.378 DEU ISSN 0939-0588
Z5055.G29
DEUTSCHE NATIONALBIBLIOGRAPHIE. REIHE H, HOCHSCHULSCHRIFTEN. Text in German. 1972. m. price varies. bibl. index. **Document type:** *Bibliography.*
Incorporates: Deutsche Nationalbibliographie. Reihe C: Dissertationen und Habilitationsschriften (0012-0545); Formerly: Deutsche Bibliographie. Hochschulschriften-Verzeichnis (0301-4665)
Indexed: RASB.
—BLDSC (3573.164000).
Published by: (Deutsche Bibliothek), M V B - Marketing- und Verlagsservice des Buchhandels GmbH, Postfach 100442, Frankfurt Am Main, 60004, Germany. TEL 49-69-1306-243, FAX 49-69-1306255, info@mvb-online.de, http://www.buchhaendler-vereinigung.de.

016.37 JOR ISSN 1026-3713
LA1470 CODEN: DUJOES
➤ **DIRASAT. EDUCATIONAL SCIENCES.** Text in Arabic, English. 1974. s-a. JOD 9 domestic to individuals; JOD 11 domestic to institutions; USD 30 foreign (effective 2005). index, cum.index. **Document type:** *Journal, Academic/Scholarly.* **Description:** Presents research papers and articles in the educational, psychological, and physical sciences.
Supersedes in part (in 1996): Dirasat. Series A: Humanities (0255-8033)
Indexed: HistAb, IBSS, PsycInfo, PsycholAb, e-psyche.
—CASDDS, CISTI.
Published by: University of Jordan, Deanship of Academic Research, Dean of Academic Research, Amman, 11942, Jordan. TEL 962-6-5355000 ext 3200, FAX 962-6-5355599, dirasata@ju.edu.jo, http://dar.ju.edu.jo. Ed. Nabil Shawagfeh. Circ: 1,000 (controlled).

016.378 IRN ISSN 1026-7212
➤ **DISSERTATION ABSTRACTS OF IRANIAN GRADUATES ABROAD/CHIKIDAH-'I PAYAN'NAMAH'HA-YI FARIGH-AL TAHSILAN-I IRANI KHARIJ AZ KISHVAR.** Text and summaries in English. 1995. q. USD 115 (effective 2003). 250 p./no. 2 cols./p.; back issues avail. **Document type:** *Abstract/Index.* **Description:** Contains abstracts of dissertations for the Masters and Doctor of Philosophy degrees of Iranian graduates abroad since 1934.
Related titles: CD-ROM ed.; Diskette ed.; Online - full text ed.
Published by: Iranian Information & Documentation Center (IRANDOC), 1188 Enqelab Ave., P O Box 13185-1371, Tehran, Iran. TEL 98-21-6494955, FAX 98-21-6462254, journal@irandoc.ac.ir, http://www.irandoc.ac.ir. Ed. Hussein Gharibi. Circ: 400.

378.0021 USA ISSN 0077-9210
DISTRIBUTION OF HIGH SCHOOL GRADUATES AND COLLEGE GOING RATE, NEW YORK STATE. Text in English. 1967. a. free. **Document type:** *Government.*
Published by: Education Department, Information, Reporting & Technology Services, Education Bldg Annex, Rm 962, Albany, NY 12234. TEL 518-474-7082, FAX 518-474-4351. Circ: (controlled).

370.21 DJI ISSN 1018-2241
DJIBOUTI. MINISTERE DE L'EDUCATION NATIONALE. ANNUAIRE STATISTIQUE. Text in French. a.
Published by: Ministere de l'Education Nationale, Direction Generale de l'Education Nationale, BP 2102, Djibouti, Djibouti. TEL 35-08-50.

370.21 DMA
DOMINICA. MINISTRY OF FINANCE. CENTRAL STATISTICAL OFFICE. ANNUAL EDUCATION STATISTICS. Text in English. a. USD 13.50. **Document type:** *Government.*
Published by: Ministry of Finance, Central Statistical Office, Kennedy Ave., Roseau, Dominica. Ed. Michael Murphy.

016.37 USA
LB1028
E R I C. (Education Resource Information Center) Variant title: ERIC on CD-ROM. Text in English. base vol. plus q. updates. USD 125 includes online. **Document type:** *Database, Abstract/Index.* **Description:** Provides complete cumulative information from the ERIC database on education, including Resources in Education and Current Index to Journals in Education, the ERIC Digests and the Thesaurus of ERIC Descriptors, and much more.
Media: Online - full text.
—CINDOC.
Published by: E R I C Project, c/o Computer Sciences Corporation, 4483-A Forbes Blvd, Lanham, MD 20706. TEL 800-538-3742, http://www.eric.ed.gov/.

016.37 USA ISSN 0889-8030
E R I C - C U E URBAN DIVERSITY SERIES. Text in English. 1972. irreg., latest vol.110, 1997. price varies. bibl.; stat. back issues avail. **Document type:** *Monographic series.* **Description:** Contains monographs, literature and research reviews, and annotated bibliographies concerning educational socioeconomic and social-psychological issues involved in the development of diverse urban populations.
Related titles: Microfiche ed.
Indexed: CIJE.
Published by: Educational Resource Information Center, Clearinghouse on Urban Education, Box 40, Teachers College, Columbia University, New York, NY 10027. TEL 212-678-3433, eric-cue@columbia.edu, http://eric-web.tc.columbia.edu. Ed., R&P Wendy Schwartz. Circ: 1,000.

016.37 USA ISSN 0737-1578
E R I C CLEARINGHOUSE PUBLICATIONS. Text in English. 1980. a. free (effective 2005).
Published by: (Educational Resources Information Center), U.S. Department of Education, Institute of Education Sciences, 400 Maryland Ave SW, Washington, DC 20202. TEL 800-872-5327, FAX 202-401-0689, customerservice@inet.ed.gov, http://www.ed.gov.

016.37 USA ISSN 1062-0508
Z695.1.E3
E R I C IDENTIFIER AUTHORITY LIST. Text in English. 1987. irreg., latest 1995. USD 59.50 domestic; USD 71.40 foreign (effective 2002). **Document type:** *Abstract/Index.* **Description:** Lists over 45,000 retrieval identifiers for the ERIC database.
Published by: (Educational Resources Information Center), Oryx Press (Subsidiary of: Greenwood Publishing Group Inc.), 1434 E. San Miguel Ave., Phoenix, AZ 85014-2422. TEL 602-265-2651, 800-279-6799, FAX 602-265-6250, info@oryxpress.com, http://www.oryxpress.com. Ed. Anne Thompson. Pub. Phyllis Steckler. R&P Lori Cavanaugh TEL 602-265-2651 ext 662.

016.37 DEU
E U D I S E D - EUROPEAN EDUCATIONAL RESEARCH YEARBOOK; project reports - people - contacts. (European Documentation and Information System for Education) Text in English, French, German. 1976. a. back issues avail. **Document type:** *Monographic series, Academic/Scholarly.* **Description:** Provides latest information on educational research projects.
Formerly (until 1994): E U D I S E D - R & D Bulletin (0378-7192)
Related titles: Microfiche ed.; Online - full text ed.
—**CCC.**
Published by: (Council of Europe/Conseil de l'Europe FRA), K.G. Saur Verlag GmbH (Subsidiary of: Gale Group), Ortlerstr 8, Munchen, 81373, Germany. TEL 49-89-76902-0, FAX 49-89-76902150, customerservice_saur@csi.com, http://www.saur.de. Ed. Wilson Barret. Circ: 500.

370.21 ECU
ECUADOR. INSTITUTO NACIONAL DE ESTADISTICA Y CENSOS. ENCUESTA ANUAL DE RECURSOS Y ACTIVIDADES DE SALUD. Text in Spanish. 1967. a. USD 20 (effective 2001).
Related titles: Diskette ed.; E-mail ed.
Published by: Instituto Nacional de Estadistica y Censos, Juan Larrea N15-36 y Jose Riofrio, Quito, Ecuador. TEL 593-2-529858, FAX 593-2-509836, inec1@ecnet.ec, http://www.inec.gov.ec.

370.21 BRA ISSN 0103-5770
LC70.B6
EDUCACAO; indicadores sociais. Text in Portuguese. 1981. a. BRL 6.90. **Document type:** *Government.* **Description:** Provides information on the education of Brazil's population.

E

Published by: (Centro de Documentacao e Disseminacao de Informacoes), Fundacao Instituto Brasileiro de Geografia e Estatistica, Rua General Canabarro 666, Bloco B, Maracana, Rio de Janeiro, RJ 20271201, Brazil. TEL 55-11-2645424, FAX 55-11-2841109, http://www.ibge.gov.br.

016.37 USA ISSN 1092-1435
Z5813
EDUCATION ABSTRACTS (CD-ROM). Text in English. 1995. m. price varies. **Document type:** *Abstract/Index.* **Description:** Contains abstracts of articles relating to education.
Formerly (until 1997): Wilson Education Abstracts (1084-0214)
Media: CD-ROM. **Related titles:** Online - full text ed.: 1995. USD 3,085 in US & Canada (effective 2006).
Published by: H.W. Wilson Co., 950 University Ave, Bronx, NY 10452-4224. TEL 718-588-8400, 800-367-6770, FAX 718-590-1617, 800-590-1617, custserv@hwwilson.com, http://www.hwwilson.com/Databases/educat.htm.

016.370 USA ISSN 1538-9693
LC5805
EDUCATION AND DISTANCE LEARNING RESOURCES; an internet miniguide. Text in English. 2002. a. USD 95 newsstand/cover (effective 2002).
Published by: InternetMiniGuides.com, P.O. Box 220, Marco Island, FL 34146. TEL 941-434-5113, zillman@internetminiguides.com, http://www.internetminiguides.com. Pub. Marcus P. Zillma.

370 ZAF
EDUCATION AND MANPOWER DEVELOPMENT. Text in English. 1981. a., latest vol.19. ZAR 18 (effective 2003). 24 p./no.; back issues avail.; reprints avail. **Document type:** *Monographic series, Academic/Scholarly.* **Description:** Gives a quantitative overview of the state of education in South Africa. Offers administrators and planners projected numbers of future learners.
Published by: Free State University, Research Institute for Education Planning, UFS, PO Box 339, Bloemfontein, 9300, South Africa. TEL 27-51-401-2856, 27-51-401-9111, FAX 27-51-447-4939, strausjp.hum@mail.uovs.ac.za, http://www.uovs.ac.za/edu/niob/default.htm. Eds. H J van der Linde, J P Strauss, S J Plekker.

016.37 USA
EDUCATION FULL TEXT. Text in English. 1996. 4/w. USD 3,795 in US & Canada (effective 2006). **Document type:** *Abstract/Index.* **Description:** Education -Abstracting, Bibliographies, Statistics; Abstracting And Indexing Services.
Formerly: Education Abstracts - Full Text
Media: Online - full text (from The Dialog Corporation). **Related titles:** ♦ Print ed.: Education Index. ISSN 0013-1385.
Published by: H.W. Wilson Co., 950 University Ave, Bronx, NY 10452-4224. TEL 718-588-8400, 800-367-6770, FAX 718-590-1617, 800-590-1617, custserv@hwwilson.com, http://www.hwwilson.com/databases/educat.htm.

016.37 AUS ISSN 0729-8528
EDUCATION GUIDELINES. Text in English. 1979. 3/yr. (plus a. cumulation). AUD 35.70 (effective 2000). **Document type:** *Abstract/Index.* **Description:** Subject index to Australian education journals and journals of teaching associations.
Published by: Bibliographic Services, PO Box 614, Castlemaine, VIC 3450, Australia. Ed. Keith S Darling. Circ: 500.

016.378 KEN
EDUCATION IN KENYA; index of articles on education. Text in English. 1977. a. USD 70. **Document type:** *Abstract/Index.* **Description:** Indexes various subjects and indicates public response to contemporary issues in education.
Published by: Kenyatta University Library, PO Box 43844, Nairobi, Kenya. Ed. E W Kaberia. Circ: 200.

016.37 USA ISSN 0013-1385
Z5813
EDUCATION INDEX. Text in English. 1929. 10/yr. USD 540 in US & Canada (effective 2006). **Document type:** *Abstract/Index.* **Description:** Author-subject index to educational publications in the English language.
Related titles: CD-ROM ed.: ISSN 1076-707X (from H.W. Wilson, SilverPlatter Information, Inc.); ♦ Online - full text ed.: Education Full Text; USD 2,010 in US & Canada (effective 2006).
—BLDSC (3661.284000).
Published by: H.W. Wilson Co., 950 University Ave, Bronx, NY 10452-4224. TEL 718-588-8400, 800-367-6770, FAX 718-590-1617, 800-590-1617, custserv@hwwilson.com, http://www.hwwilson.com/Databases/educat.htm. Ed. Barbara Berry.

016.37 USA ISSN 1045-0734
EDUCATION LITERATURE REVIEW. Text in English. 1989. m. USD 135 to individuals; USD 179 to libraries. index. **Document type:** *Abstract/Index.* **Description:** Summarizes important articles on all aspects of K-12 education, covering topics in the areas of administration, good teaching practice, curriculum development, and special education.
Related titles: Audio cassette/tape ed.; Online - full content ed.
Published by: Management Development Associates, Inc., PO Box 9328, Drawer G, Winter Haven, FL 33883-9328. TEL 239-293-4882, FAX 239-299-6737, http://www.edlitrev.com. Ed. Tom D Freijo.

370.016 GBR
EDUCATION RESEARCH ABSTRACTS. Variant title: Education Research Abstracts Online. Text in English. base vol. plus m. updates. GBP 3,216, USD 5,307 to institutions (effective 2006). **Document type:** *Database, Abstract/Index.* **Description:** Comprehensive database comprising specially selected abstracts which cover the current international research in education.
Media: Online - full text.
Published by: Routledge (Subsidiary of: Taylor & Francis Group), 4 Park Sq, Milton Park, Abingdon, Oxon OX14 4RN, United Kingdom. TEL 44-1235-828600, FAX 44-1235-829000, info@routledge.co.uk, http://www.tandf.co.uk/era/default.asp, http://www.tandf.co.uk/journals.

370.21 USA
EDUCATION STATISTICS, NEW YORK STATE; prepared especially for members of the Legislature. Text in English. 1968. a. free. charts; stat. back issues avail. **Document type:** *Government.*
Published by: Education Department, Information, Reporting & Technology Services, Education Bldg Annex, Rm 962, Albany, NY 12234. TEL 518-474-7082, FAX 518-474-4351. Circ: (controlled).

370.21 USA ISSN 1524-394X
EDUCATION STATISTICS OF THE UNITED STATES. Text in English. 1999. a.
Published by: Bernan Press, 4611-F Assembly Dr, Lanham, MD 20706-4391. TEL 301-459-2255, FAX 301-459-0056, bpress@bernan.com, http://www.bernan.com.

370.21 USA ISSN 1521-3374
LA201
EDUCATION STATISTICS QUARTERLY. Text in English. 1999. q. free; free. abstr.; bibl.; charts. back issues avail. **Document type:** *Journal, Trade.* **Description:** Offers reliable statistical data and analyses on all aspects of education in the US, along with a comprehensive, in-depth overview of NCES activities.
Related titles: Online - full text ed.: free (effective 2005).
Published by: U.S. Department of Education, National Center for Education Statistics, 1990 K St N W, Washington, DC 20006. TEL 202-219-1828, http://nces.ed.gov, http://nces.ed.gov. **Subscr. to:** U.S. Government Printing Office, Superintendent of Documents, PO Box 371954, Pittsburgh, PA 15250-7954. TEL 202-512-1800, FAX 202-512-2250, orders@gpo.gov, http://www.access.gpo.gov.

016.37 TZA ISSN 0856-0005
EDUCATIONAL ABSTRACTS FOR TANZANIA. Text in English. 1983. s-a. USD 28. **Document type:** *Abstract/Index.*
Published by: Library Services Board, National Documentation Centre, P O Box 9283, Dar es Salaam, Tanzania. TEL 255-51-150048-9. Ed. D A Sekimang'a. Circ: 200.

016.3712 USA ISSN 0013-1601
LB2805
EDUCATIONAL ADMINISTRATION ABSTRACTS. Text in English. 1966. q. USD 772, GBP 498 to institutions (effective 2006). adv. index. back issues avail.; reprint service avail. from PQC,ISI. **Document type:** *Journal, Abstract/Index.* **Description:** Provides abstracts from more than 100 professional journals, books, and other sources relating to education and educational administration.
Formerly: Educational Abstracts
Related titles: Microform ed.: (from PQC); Online - full text ed.: ISSN 1552-3527 (from O C L C Online Computer Library Center, Inc.).
—IE. **CCC.**
Published by: Corwin Press, Inc. (Subsidiary of: Sage Publications, Inc.), 2455 Teller Rd, Thousand Oaks, CA 91320-2218. TEL 805-499-9734, FAX 805-499-0871, 800-4-1-SCHOOL (800-417-2466), info@sagepub.com, http://www.sagepub.com/journal.aspx?pid=35. adv.: B&W page USD 350. Circ: 300 (paid and free). **Subscr. outside the Americas to:** Sage Publications Ltd., 1 Oliver's Yard, 55 City Rd, London EC1 1SP, United Kingdom. TEL 44-20-73740645, FAX 44-20-73748741, subscription@sagepub.co.uk.

016.37 BHR
EDUCATIONAL INDEX OF ARABIC PERIODICALS. Text in English. m.
Published by: Ministry of Education, Educational Documentation Library, PO Box 43, Manama, Bahrain. TEL 25840.

016.37 BHR
EDUCATIONAL INDEX OF FOREIGN PERIODICALS. Text in English. m.
Published by: Ministry of Education, Educational Documentation Library, PO Box 43, Manama, Bahrain. TEL 25840.

016.37 BHR
EDUCATIONAL INDICATIVE ABSTRACTS. Text in English. 3/yr.
Published by: Ministry of Education, Educational Documentation Library, PO Box 43, Manama, Bahrain. TEL 25840, TELEX 9094.

016.37 BHR
EDUCATIONAL INFORMATION ABSTRACTS. Text in English. 3/yr.
Published by: Ministry of Education, Educational Documentation Library, PO Box 43, Manama, Bahrain. TEL 25840.

EDUCATIONAL LEGISLATION INDEX. see *LAW—Abstracting, Bibliographies, Statistics*

016.3712 GBR ISSN 1467-582X
EDUCATIONAL MANAGEMENT ABSTRACTS. Text in English. 1982. a. GBP 604, USD 1,025 combined subscription to institutions print & online eds. (effective 2006). cum.index. back issues avail.; reprint service avail. from PSC. **Document type:** *Abstract/Index.*
Formerly (2000, until vol.18): School Organisation and Management Abstracts (0261-2755)
Related titles: Microfiche ed.; Online - full text ed.: ISSN 1467-5838. GBP 574, USD 974 to institutions (effective 2006) (from ProQuest Information & Learning).
—**CCC.**
Published by: Routledge (Subsidiary of: Taylor & Francis Group), 2 Park Sq, Milton Park, Abingdon, Oxon OX14 4RN, United Kingdom. TEL 44-20-70176000, FAX 44-20-70176699, info@routledge.co.uk, http://www.tandf.co.uk/journals/carfax/1467582x.html, http://www.routledge.co.uk. Ed. Daniel Muijs. **Subscr. to:** Taylor & Francis Ltd, Journals Customer Service, Rankine Rd, Basingstoke, Hants RG24 8PR, United Kingdom. TEL 44-1256-813000, FAX 44-1256-330245.

370.21 USA ISSN 1053-1378
LB2331.63
EDUCATIONAL RANKINGS ANNUAL. Text in English. a., latest 2005. USD 295 (effective 2004).
Published by: Gale Group (Subsidiary of: Thomson Corporation), 27500 Drake Rd, Farmington Hills, MI 48331-3535. TEL 248-699-8061, 800-877-4253, FAX 248-699-4253, galeord@gale.com, http://www.gale.com. Ed. Lynn C Hattendorf.

016.37 GBR ISSN 1467-5900
EDUCATIONAL RESEARCH ABSTRACTS ONLINE. Text in English. m. GBP 2,733, USD 4,509 to institutions (effective 2005). **Document type:** *Abstract/Index.*
Media: Online - full text.
Published by: Taylor & Francis Ltd (Subsidiary of: Taylor & Francis Group), 4 Park Sq, Milton Park, Abingdon, OX14 4RN, United Kingdom. TEL 44-1235-828600, FAX 44-1235-829000, info@tandf.co.uk, http://www.tandf.co.uk/era/default.asp, http://www.tandf.co.uk/journals.

016.37 BHR
EDUCATIONAL SELECTIVE ABSTRACTS. Text in English. bi-m.
Published by: Ministry of Education, Educational Documentation Library, PO Box 43, Manama, Bahrain. TEL 25840.

016.374 GBR ISSN 0266-3368
EDUCATIONAL TECHNOLOGY ABSTRACTS. Text in English. 1985. a. GBP 801, USD 1,319 combined subscription to institutions print & online eds. (effective 2006). adv. bk.rev. index. back issues avail.; reprint service avail. from PSC. **Document type:** *Abstract/Index.* **Description:** Designed to assist teachers, lecturers, educational technologists and instructional designers to identify important recently published material in the field of the technology of education and training.
Related titles: Microfiche ed.; Online - full text ed.: ISSN 1467-5846. GBP 761, USD 1,253 to institutions (effective 2006) (from ProQuest Information & Learning).
—BLDSC (3662.530500). **CCC.**
Published by: Routledge (Subsidiary of: Taylor & Francis Group), 4 Park Sq, Milton Park, Abingdon, Oxon OX14 4RN, United Kingdom. TEL 44-1235-828600, FAX 44-1235-829000, info@routledge.co.uk, http://www.tandf.co.uk/journals/titles/02663368.asp. Ed. Dr. Vivien M Johnsten. **Subscr. to:** Taylor & Francis Ltd, Journals Customer Service, Rankine Rd, Basingstoke, Hants RG24 8PR, United Kingdom. TEL 44-1256-813000, FAX 44-1256-330245.

016.373 USA ISSN 0000-0825
Z5813
EL-HI TEXTBOOKS AND SERIALS IN PRINT; including related teaching materials K-12. Text in English. 1956. a. USD 265 (effective 2004). **Document type:** *Directory, Bibliography.* **Description:** Provides complete bibliographic and ordering information for elementary, junior and senior high school textbooks, text series, periodicals, references, tests, teaching aids, and pedagogical and professional books and serials, arranged by subject and indexed by author, title and series, with a key to book publishers' and distributors' addresses.
Former titles (until 1969): Textbooks in Print (0888-2029); (until 1984): El-Hi Textbooks in Print (0070-9565)
Published by: R.R. Bowker LLC (Subsidiary of: Cambridge Information Group), 630 Central Ave., New Providence, NJ 07974. TEL 908-286-1090, 800-526-9537, FAX 908-219-0098, info@bowker.com, http://www.bowker.com. **Subscr. to:** Order Dept., PO Box 32, New Providence, NJ 07974-9903. TEL 800-521-8110.

016.37 DNK ISSN 0901-9316
ERHVERVSUDDANNELSERNE. Spine title: Erhvervsuddannelserne. Katalog. Text in Danish. 1979. a. DKK 24.30.

E

Formerly (until 1986): Undervisningsmidler for Erhvervsuddannelserne (0106-5963); Formerly: Danske Skole- og Laereboeger
Related titles: Online - full content ed.
Published by: Fonden Undervisnings Information, Siljangade 6, Copenhagen S, 2300, Denmark. http://www.fui.dk/servlet/fui.

370.21 MEX
ESTADISTICA BASICA DEL SISTEMA EDUCATIVO NACIONAL. Text in Spanish. 1970. irreg. **Description:** National statistics on education in Mexico from kindergarten to college.
Published by: Secretaria de Educacion Publica, Direccion General de Planeacion, Programacion y Presupuesto, Mexico City, DF, Mexico.

370.21 PAN ISSN 0378-4967
LA465
ESTADISTICA PANAMENA. SITUACION CULTURAL. SECCION 511. EDUCACION. Text in Spanish. 1957. a. PAB 1.50 domestic (effective 2000). **Document type:** *Bulletin, Government.* **Description:** Includes data on educational establishments, teachers, and enrollment levels.
Published by: Direccion de Estadistica y Censo, Contraloria General, Apdo. 5213, Panama City, 5, Panama. FAX 507-210-4801. Circ: 850.

371.384021 CHL ISSN 0716-0615
ESTADISTICAS DE EDUCACION EXTRAESCOLAR. Text in Spanish. 1976. a. CLP 1,650; USD 10.10 in United States; USD 13.40 elsewhere.
Published by: Instituto Nacional de Estadisticas, Casilla 498, Correo 3, Ave. Bulnes, 418, Santiago, Chile. TEL 56-2-6991441, FAX 56-2-6712169.

ESTETICHESKOE VOSPITANIE; referativno-bibliograficheskaya informatsiya. see *PHILOSOPHY—Abstracting, Bibliographies, Statistics*

016.3719 USA
Z5814.C52
EXCEPTIONAL CHILD EDUCATION RESOURCES (ONLINE EDITION). Text in English. 1968. m. USD 400 (effective 2005). adv. illus. reprints avail. **Document type:** *Abstract/Index.* **Description:** Computerized database containing more than 85,000 abstracts in the field of special education. Every citation gives author, title, source, publication date, availability date, subject terms, and a descriptive summary of the document or journal article.
Former titles (until 2004): Exceptional Child Education Resources (Print Edition) (0160-4309); (until May 1977): Exceptional Child Education Abstracts (0014-4010)
Related titles: CD-ROM ed.: (from SilverPlatter Information, Inc.).
Published by: Council for Exceptional Children, 1110 N. Glebe Rd., Ste. 300, Arlington, VA 22201-4795. TEL 703-264-9481, FAX 703-264-1637, http://www.cec.sped.org/ecer/. Ed. Bernadette Knoblauch. R&P Melinda MacDonald. Adv. contact Victor Erickson.

016.37 DEU
FACHBUCHVERZEICHNIS GEISTESWISSENSCHAFTEN. Text in German. a. **Document type:** *Bibliography.* **Description:** Bibliography of available books for students.
Formerly: Buecher fuer das Studium Geisteswissenschaften
Published by: Rossipaul Kommunikation GmbH, Menzinger Str 37, Munich, 80638, Germany. TEL 49-89-179106-0, FAX 49-89-17910622. Ed. Angela Sendlinger. Circ: 25,000.

370.21 USA
FACT BOOK; a statistical handbook. Text in English. 1967. a. free (effective 2005). charts. **Document type:** *Government, Abstract/Index.* **Description:** Provides statistical information about Maryland's 24 school systems, including enrollment, staff, state aid, per pupil cost, and average teacher salary.
Former titles: Facts about Maryland Public Education (0092-461X); Facts about Maryland Schools
Indexed: SRI.
Published by: Maryland State Department of Education, 200 W Baltimore St, Baltimore, MD 21201. TEL 410-767-0100, FAX 301-333-2017, http://www.marylandpublicschools.org/msde. Ed. Kathie Hiatt. Circ: 8,500.

016.37133 USA
FILMSTRIP AND SLIDE SET FINDER. Text in English. 1976 (vol.6). irreg., latest 1990. USD 225 (effective 1998).
Formerly: N I C E M Index to 35mm Educational Filmstrips
Related titles: CD-ROM ed.; Online - full text ed.
Published by: (National Information Center for Educational Media), Plexus Publishing, Inc., 143 Old Marlton Pike, Medford, NJ 08055. TEL 609-654-6500, FAX 609-654-4309.

370.21 FIN ISSN 1459-8221
FINLAND. TILASTOKESKUS. HENKILOSTOKOULUTUS. Text in Finnish. 1989. irreg. **Document type:** *Government.*
Formerly (until 2003): Finland. Tilastokeskus. Henkilostokoulutus (Print edition) (0785-8493)
Media: Online - full content. **Related titles:** ♦ Series of: Finland. Tilastokeskus. Koulutus. ISSN 1236-4746.
Published by: Tilastokeskus/Statistics Finland, Tyopajakatu 13, Statistics Finland, Helsinki, 00022, Finland. TEL 358-9-17341, FAX 358-9-17342750, http://www.stat.fi/tk/he/henkkoul.html.

370.21 FIN ISSN 0785-0638
FINLAND. TILASTOKESKUS. KORKEAKOULUIHIN HAKENEET JA HYVAKSYTYT. Text in Finnish. 1968. a., latest 2004. EUR 14 (effective 2005). **Document type:** *Government.*
Supersedes in part (in 1988): Finland. Tilastokeskus. KO, Koulutus ja Tutkimus (0355-2268)
Related titles: ♦ Series of: Finland. Tilastokeskus. Koulutus. ISSN 1236-4746.
Published by: Tilastokeskus/Statistics Finland, Tyopajakatu 13, Statistics Finland, Helsinki, 00022, Finland. TEL 358-9-17341, FAX 358-9-17342750, http://www.stat.fi/.

370.21 FIN ISSN 1457-5183
FINLAND. TILASTOKESKUS. KOULUTUKSEN JARJESTAJAT JA OPPILAITOKSET. Text in Finnish, Swedish. 1988. a., latest 2004. EUR 56 (effective 2005). **Document type:** *Government.*
Former titles (until 2000): Finland. Tilastokeskus. Oppilaitosluokitus ja Luettelo. Liitetaulukot (1236-6307); (until 1993): Finland. Tilastokeskus. Oppilatokset (0785-0697); (until 1988): Finland. Tilastokeskus. KO, Koulutus ja Tutkimus (0355-2268)
Related titles: ♦ Series of: Finland. Tilastokeskus. Koulutus. ISSN 1236-4746.
Published by: Tilastokeskus/Statistics Finland, Tyopajakatu 13, Statistics Finland, Helsinki, 00022, Finland. TEL 358-9-17341, FAX 358-9-17342750, http://www.stat.fi/.

370.21 FIN ISSN 1236-4746
LB1028.27.F5
FINLAND. TILASTOKESKUS. KOULUTUS/FINLAND. STATISTICS FINLAND. EDUCATION AND RESEARCH. Text in English, Finnish, Swedish. 1968. biennial. EUR 60 (effective 2005). **Document type:** *Government.*
Supersedes in part (in 1993): Finland. Tilastokeskus. Koulutus ja Tutkimus (0784-8242); Which was formerly (until 1988): Finland. Tilastokeskus. K O Koulutus ja Tutkimus (0355-2268)
Related titles: ♦ Series: Finland. Tilastokeskus. Henkilostokoulutus. ISSN 1459-8221; ♦ Finland. Tilastokeskus. Oppilaitostilastot. ISSN 1455-4402; ♦ Finland. Tilastokeskus. Koulutuksen Jarjestajat ja Oppilaitokset. ISSN 1457-5183; ♦ Finland. Tilastokeskus. Korkeakouluihin Hakeneet ja Hyvaksytyt. ISSN 0785-0638; ♦ Finland. Tilastokeskus. Vaeston Koulutusrakenne Kunnittain. ISSN 0785-0743.
Published by: Tilastokeskus/Statistics Finland, Tyopajakatu 13, Statistics Finland, Helsinki, 00022, Finland. TEL 358-9-17341, FAX 358-9-17342750, http://www.stat.fi/.

370.21 FIN ISSN 1455-4402
FINLAND. TILASTOKESKUS. OPPILAITOSTILASTOT. Text in Finnish. 1997. a., latest 2004. EUR 60 (effective 2005). **Document type:** *Government.*
Formed by the merger of (1992-1997): Finland. Tilastokeskus. Ammatillisten Oppilaitosten Opiskelijat (1235-6220); (1993-1997): Finland. Tilastokeskus. Ammatilliset Oppilaitokset (1237-0258); (1994-1997): Finland. Tilastokeskus. Koulutuksen Kysynka (1237-8097); (1995-1997): Finland. Tilastokeskus. Yleissivistavat Oppilaitokset (1238-3317); (1991-1997): Finland. Tilastokeskus. Korkeakoulut (1237-0177); Which was formerly (until 1994): Finland Tilastokeskus. Koulutus (0788-8066)
Related titles: ♦ Series of: Finland. Tilastokeskus. Koulutus. ISSN 1236-4746.
Published by: Tilastokeskus/Statistics Finland, Tyopajakatu 13, Statistics Finland, Helsinki, 00022, Finland. TEL 358-9-17341, FAX 358-9-17342750.

370.21 FIN ISSN 1239-467X
FINLAND. TILASTOKESKUS. SIJOITTUMISCD. Text in Finnish. biennial. stat. **Document type:** *Government.*
Media: CD-ROM.
Published by: Tilastokeskus/Statistics Finland, Tyopajakatu 13, Statistics Finland, Helsinki, 00022, Finland. TEL 358-9-17341.

370.21 FIN ISSN 0785-0743
FINLAND. TILASTOKESKUS. VAESTON KOULUTUSRAKENNE KUNNITTAIN. Text in English, Finnish, Swedish. 1968. a. EUR 20.18 (effective 2001). **Document type:** *Government.*
Supersedes in part (in 1988): Finland. Tilastokeskus. Tilastotiedotus - Tilastokeskus. KO, Koulutus ja (0355-2268)
Related titles: ♦ Series of: Finland. Tilastokeskus. Koulutus. ISSN 1236-4746.
Published by: Tilastokeskus/Statistics Finland, Tyopajakatu 13, Statistics Finland, Helsinki, 00022, Finland. TEL 358-9-17341, FAX 358-9-17342750, http://www.stat.fi/.

016.37 DNK ISSN 0909-6477
FOLKESKOLEN. KATALOG. Text in Danish. 1979. a.
Former titles (until 1994): Folkeskolen. Oversigtkatalog (0901-9332); (until 1986): Undervisningsmidler for Folkeskolen. Katalog (0106-5823)
Related titles: Online - full content ed.
Published by: Fonden Undervisnings Information, Siljangade 6, Copenhagen S, 2300, Denmark. TEL 45-32-96-10-66, FAX 45-32-96-12-10, http://www.fui.dk/servlet/fui.

370.21 352.74021 FRA
FRANCE. MINISTERE DE L'EDUCATION NATIONALE, DE L'ENSEIGNEMENT SUPERIEUR ET DE LA RECHERCHE. DIRECTION DE L'EVALUATION ET DE LA PROSPECTIVE. NOTE D'INFORMATION. Text in French. 1998. m. EUR 45 domestic; EUR 48 foreign (effective 2004).
Formerly: France. Ministere de l'Education Nationale, de la Recherche et de la Technologie. Direction de la Programmation et du Developpement. Note d'Information (1286-9392)
Published by: France. Ministere de l'Education Nationale, de l'Enseignement Superieur et de la Recherche, Direction de l'Evaluation et de la Prospective, 58, boulevard du Lycee, Vanves, 92170, France. TEL 33-1-55557204, FAX 33-1-55557229, http://www.education.gouv.fr/stateval/ni/ni.htm.

016.37 DNK ISSN 0901-4578
FREMMEDSPROG. Text in Danish. 1985. a.
Related titles: Online - full content ed.
Published by: Fonden Undervisnings Information, Siljangade 6, Copenhagen S, 2300, Denmark. TEL 45-32-96-10-66, FAX 45-32-96-12-10, http://www.fui.dk/servlet/fui.

378.0021 GBR ISSN 0968-5596
LA668
FURTHER AND HIGHER EDUCATION AND TRAINING STATISTICS FOR WALES. Text in English. 1987. a. GBP 7. stat. **Document type:** *Government.* **Description:** Statistics on student numbers in further and higher education, student-staff ratios, teacher training, adult education and expenditure in further education sectors.
Formerly (until 1993): Statistics of Education in Wales: Higher and Further Education (0951-1245); Which supersedes in part (in 1987): Statistics of Education in Wales (0262-8317)
—BLDSC (4059.505800). **CCC.**
Published by: Welsh Funding Councils, c/o Mrs. Frances Good, Linden Court, The Orchards, Ty Glas Ave, Llanishen, Cardiff, S Glam CF4 5DZ, United Kingdom. TEL 44-1222-761861. Circ: 600.

371.021 GMB
GAMBIA. CENTRAL STATISTICS DEPARTMENT. EDUCATION STATISTICS. Text in English. a. GMD 10. stat.
Former titles: Gambia. Education Department. Education Statistics; Gambia. Education Department. Annual Report and Statistics
Published by: Central Statistics Department, Wellington St., Banjul, Gambia.

370.21 DEU ISSN 0072-1778
GERMANY. STATISTISCHES BUNDESAMT. FACHSERIE 11: BILDUNG UND KULTUR. (Consists of several subseries) Text in German. 1960. irreg. Price varies. **Document type:** *Government.*
Published by: Statistisches Bundesamt, Gustav-Stresemann-Ring 11, Wiesbaden, 65180, Germany. TEL 49-611-75-1, FAX 49-611-724000, http://www.statistik-bund.de.

370.21 GHA
GHANA. MINISTRY OF EDUCATION. EDUCATIONAL STATISTICS. Text in English. a. GHC 2. charts. **Document type:** *Government.*
Published by: Ministry of Education, Higher Education Division, PO Box M 45, Accra, Ghana.

016.37 GBR
GLOBAL ACCUMULATIVE BIBLIOGRAPHY OF ACTION LEARNING. Abbreviated title: G A B A L. Text in English. irreg. bk.rev. **Document type:** *Bibliography.* **Description:** Includes papers that present ideas and practice for all action learners worldwide.
Media: Online - full text.
Published by: Internet Free-Press Ltd., 60-62 Toller Ln, Bradford, BD8 9DA, United Kingdom. esandelands@mcb.co.uk, http://www.free-press.com/journals/gabal. Ed. Eric Sandelands.

370.21 GBR
GREAT BRITAIN. DEPARTMENT FOR EDUCATION AND SKILLS. FIRST RELEASE. Text in English. irreg. stat.
Former titles: Department for Education and Employment. First Release; Department for Education and Employment. Statistical First Release
—BLDSC (3934.466273).
Published by: Great Britain Department for Education, Sanctuary Bldgs, Sanctuary Buildings, Great Smith St, London, SW1P 3BT, United Kingdom. TEL 44-171-925-6310, FAX 44-171-925-6985, http://www.dfes.gov.uk/statistics/DB/SFR/index.html.

370.21 GBR ISSN 0072-5900
GREAT BRITAIN. DEPARTMENT FOR EDUCATION. STATISTICS OF EDUCATION. Text in English. 1961. a. (in 6 vols.). GBP 12.95; price varies. **Document type:** *Government.*
Related titles: Microfiche ed.: (from PQC); ♦ Series: Great Britain. Department for Education. Statistics of Education. Further and Higher Education. Student - Staff Ratios and Unit Costs. ISSN 0955-9574.
—**CCC.**

E

Published by: Department for Education, Government Statistical Service, Mowden Hall, Staindrop Rd, Darlington, Durham DL3 9BG, United Kingdom. TEL 0325-392683, FAX 0325-392695. **Subscr. also to:** H.M.S.O., PO Box 276, London SW8 5DT, United Kingdom. TEL 44-20-7873-9090, FAX 44-2078-730011.

378.0021　　　　　**GBR**　　　　　ISSN 0955-9574
GREAT BRITAIN. DEPARTMENT FOR EDUCATION. STATISTICS OF EDUCATION. FURTHER AND HIGHER EDUCATION. STUDENT - STAFF RATIOS AND UNIT COSTS. Text in English. a. GBP 12. **Document type:** *Government.*
Former titles (until 1988): Great Britain. Department for Education. Further and Higher Education. Student - Staff Ratios (0268-8875); (until 1985): Great Britain. Department for Education. Report on the Monitoring of Student Staff Ratios Series.
Related titles: ◆ Series of: Great Britain. Department for Education. Statistics of Education. ISSN 0072-5900.
Published by: Department for Education, Government Statistical Service, Mowden Hall, Staindrop Rd, Darlington, Durham DL3 9BG, United Kingdom. TEL 44-1325-392683, FAX 44-1325-392695. **Subscr. also to:** H.M.S.O., Publications Centre, PO Box 276, London SW8 5DT, United Kingdom. TEL 44-20-7873-9090, FAX 44-207-873-0011.

GREENLAND. GROENLANDS STATISTIK. UDDANNELSE. see *STATISTICS*

371.0021　　　　　**GRD**
GRENADA SCHOOL DIRECTORY AND BASIC EDUCATIONAL STATISTICS. Text in English. a. **Document type:** *Directory, Government.*
Published by: Ministry of Education, Statistical Unit, Young St., St. George's, Grenada.

016.37　　　　　**DNK**　　　　　ISSN 0901-9308
GYMNASIET OG HF. Text in Danish. 1973. a.
Formerly (until 1986): Undervisningsmidler for Gymnasiet og HF (0106-5955); Which supersedes in part (in 1978): Danske Skole- og Laereboeger (0107-6426)
Related titles: Online - full content ed.
Published by: Fonden Undervisnings Information, Siljangade 6, Copenhagen S, 2300, Denmark. TEL 45-32-96-10-66, FAX 45-32-96-12-10, http://www.fui.dk/servlet/fui.

016.378　　　　　**USA**　　　　　ISSN 0748-4364
Z5814.P8
HIGHER EDUCATION ABSTRACTS; abstracts of periodical literature, monographs and conference papers on college students, faculty and administration. Text in English. 1965. q. USD 160 per vol. to individuals; USD 395 per vol. to institutions (effective 2005). adv. bk.rev. abstr.; illus. index. back issues avail.; reprints avail. **Document type:** *Abstract/Index.* **Description:** Synopsis of current research and theory on students, faculty and administrators in higher education institutions, examining teaching, research, planning, and management, as well as the institutional environment, orientation, the role of state and federal governments, and demographic trends.
Formerly (until 1984): College Student Personnel Abstracts (0010-1168)
Related titles: Microform ed.: (from PQC).
Published by: Claremont Graduate University, 145 Dartmouth Place, Claremont, CA 91711. TEL 909-607-3905, FAX 909-621-8390, Judy.Ritchie@cgu.edu, http://www.HigherEducationAbstracts.org. Ed. Bonny M McLaughlin TEL 909-607-3904. Circ: 1,200.

370.21　　　　　**IND**　　　　　ISSN 0579-6105
LA1150
INDIA. MINISTRY OF EDUCATION AND SOCIAL WELFARE. PROVISIONAL STATISTICS OF EDUCATION IN THE STATES. Text in English. 1954. a. free.
Published by: Ministry of Education and Social Welfare, Department of Education, Shastri Bhavan, New Delhi, 110 001, India. Circ: (controlled).

016.370　　　　　**IND**　　　　　ISSN 0019-4697
INDIAN EDUCATION ABSTRACTS. Text in English. 1955. q. INR 15.60, USD 5.62. abstr.; bibl. index. **Document type:** *Abstract/Index.*
Published by: Ministry of Education and Social Welfare, Department of Education, Shastri Bhavan, New Delhi, 110 001, India. Circ: (controlled).

016.374　　　　　**MEX**
INDICE DE ARTICULOS SOBRE EDUCACION Y ADIESTRAMIENTO. Text in Spanish. 1972. q. MXP 80, USD 5. cum.index: 1972-1977.
Related titles: Microfilm ed.
Published by: Servicio Nacional de Adiestramiento Rapido de la Mano de Obra en la Industria, Centro de Informacion Tecnica y Documentacion, Calzada Atzcapotzalco-la Villa 209, Apdo. 16-099, Mexico City, DF, Mexico. Ed. Gilberto Diaz Santana. Circ 2,500.

016.37　　　　　**USA**
INFORMATION ALERTS. Text in English. 1988. irreg., latest vol.75, 1997. **Document type:** *Bibliography.* **Description:** Contains short annotated bibliographies of 10-15 documents and journal articles newly added to the ERIC database on a selected topic.
Published by: Educational Resource Information Center, Clearinghouse on Urban Education, Box 40, Teachers College, Columbia University, New York, NY 10027. TEL 212-678-3433, 800-601-4868, FAX 212-678-4012, eric-due@columbia.edu, http://eric-web.tc.columbia.edu. Ed. Wendy Schwartz. R&P Eva Medina.

016.37　　　　　**ESP**　　　　　ISSN 0211-8335
Z5813
INTERNATIONAL BULLETIN OF BIBLIOGRAPHY ON EDUCATION/BOLETIM INTERNACIONAL DE BIBLIOGRAFIA SOBRE EDUCACAO/BOLETIN INTERNACIONAL DE BIBLIOGRAFIA SOBRE EDUCACION/BULLETIN INTERNATIONAL DE BIBLIOGRAPHIE SUR L'EDUCATION/INTERNATIONALE BIBLIOGRAPHIE ZU DEN ERZIEHUNGSWISSENSCHAFTEN/SERVIZIO INTERNAZIONALE DI BIBLIOGRAFIA SULL'EDUCAZIONE. Text in English, French, German, Italian, Portuguese, Spanish. 1981. q. EUR 224 in Europe; EUR 324 elsewhere (effective 2003). bk.rev. bibl. 300 p./no.; back issues avail. **Document type:** *Bibliography.*
—CINDOC.
Published by: B I B E Project, Apartado 52, San Lorenzo Del Escorial, Madrid 28200, Spain. bbcjcf@hotmail.com. Ed. Miguel Fernandez.

378.0021　　　　　**ISR**　　　　　ISSN 0334-049X
HA1931
ISRAEL. CENTRAL BUREAU OF STATISTICS. INPUTS IN RESEARCH AND DEVELOPMENT IN UNIVERSITIES. Text in English, Hebrew. 1970. irreg., latest 1990-1991. ILS 11. charts; stat. **Document type:** *Government.*
Related titles: Diskette ed.
Published by: Central Bureau of Statistics, PO Box 13015, Jerusalem, 91130, Israel. TEL 972-2-6553364, FAX 972-2-6521340. **Co-sponsor:** National Council for Research and Development.

372.218021　　　　　**ISR**　　　　　ISSN 0075-1065
ISRAEL. CENTRAL BUREAU OF STATISTICS. SCHOOLS AND KINDERGARTENS. Text in English, Hebrew. 1954. irreg., latest 1982. USD 5.50. **Document type:** *Government.*
Published by: Central Bureau of Statistics, PO Box 13015, Jerusalem, 91130, Israel. TEL 972-2-6553364, FAX 972-2-6521340.

372.021　　　　　**ITA**
ITALY. ISTITUTO NAZIONALE DI STATISTICA. STATISTICHE DELLA SCUOLA MATERNA ED ELEMENTARE. Text in Italian. 1992. a. **Document type:** *Government.*
Published by: Istituto Nazionale di Statistica, Via Cesare Balbo 16, Rome, 00184, Italy. FAX 39-06-46735198.

372.021　　　　　**ITA**
ITALY. ISTITUTO NAZIONALE DI STATISTICA. STATISTICHE DELLA SCUOLA MEDIA INFERIORE. Text in Italian. 1992. a.
Published by: Istituto Nazionale di Statistica, Via Cesare Balbo 16, Rome, 00184, Italy. FAX 39-06-46735198.

373.021　　　　　**ITA**
ITALY. ISTITUTO NAZIONALE DI STATISTICA. STATISTICHE DELLE SCUOLE SECONDARIE SUPERIORI. Text in Italian. 1992. a.
Published by: Istituto Nazionale di Statistica, Via Cesare Balbo 16, Rome, 00184, Italy. FAX 39-06-46735198.

371.0025　　　　　**QAT**
JAMI'AT QATAR. AL-TAQRIR AL-IHSA'I AL-SANAWI LIL-AAM AL-JAMI'I/UNIVERSITY OF QATAR. ANNUAL STATISTICAL REPORT FOR THE SCHOOL YEAR. Text in Arabic. a.
Published by: (Qatar. Statistical Section), University of Qatar, Cultural Affairs Administration, P O Box 2173, Doha, Qatar. TEL 83-2222, TELEX 4630.

371.829021 296　　　　　**ISR**
JEWISH EDUCATIONAL STATISTICS. Text in English. irreg., latest vol.5.
Published by: Magnes Press (Subsidiary of: Hebrew University of Jerusalem), Hebrew University, Jerusalem, PO Box 39099, Jerusalem, 91390, Israel. TEL 972-2-5660341, FAX 972-2-5883688.

016.37　　　　　**CHN**
JIAOYUXUE WENZHAI KA/PEDAGOGICS ABSTRACTS ON CARDS. Text in Chinese. q. CNY 20 (effective 2004). abstr. 80 p./no.; **Document type:** *Abstract/Index.*
Media: Cards.

Published by: Zhongguo Renmin Daxue, Shubao Zilio Zhongxin/Renmin University of China, Information Center for Social Server, Dongcheng-qu, 3, Zhangzizhong Lu, Beijing, 100007, China. TEL 86-10-64039458, FAX 86-10-64015080, http://www.confucius.cn.net/bkdetail.asp?fzt=WG1. **Dist. in the US by:** China Publications Service, PO Box 49614, Chicago, IL 60649. TEL 312-288-3291, FAX 312-288-8570; **Dist. outside of China by:** China International Book Trading Corp, 35 Chegongzhuang Xilu, Haidian District, PO Box 399, Beijing 100044, China. TEL 86-10-68412045, FAX 86-10-68412023, cibtc@mail.cibtc.com.cn, http://www.cibtc.com.cn/.

370.21　　　　　**USA**　　　　　ISSN 1076-9986
LB2846
➤ **JOURNAL OF EDUCATIONAL AND BEHAVIORAL STATISTICS.** Abbreviated title: J E B S. Text in English. 1976. q. USD 60 to individuals; USD 75 to institutions (effective 2005). adv. bk.rev. illus. Index. reprint service avail. from PQC. **Document type:** *Academic/Scholarly.* **Description:** Demonstrates how educational statistics can contribute to sound, creative educational decision making and practice.
Formerly (until vol.19, no.3, 1994): Journal of Educational Statistics (0362-9791)
Related titles: Microform ed.: (from PQC); Online - full text ed.: (from H.W. Wilson, JSTOR (Web-based Journal Archive), O C L C Online Computer Library Center, Inc., ProQuest Information & Learning).
Indexed: ABIn, ASCA, Biostat, CIJE, CIS, CPE, CurCont, EduInd, JCQM, ORMS, PsyScAP, PsycInfo, PsycholAb, QC&AS, RASB, RHEA, SSCI, ST&MA, e-psyche.
—BLDSC (4973.154040), IDS, IE, Infotrieve, ingenta. **CCC.**
Published by: American Educational Research Association, 1230 17th St, N W, Washington, DC 20036-3078. TEL 202-223-9485, FAX 202-775-1824, http://www.aera.net/pubs/jebs/, http://aera.net. Ed. Howard Wainer. Adv. contact Camille Coy. Circ: 3,700. **Co-sponsor:** American Statistical Association.

016.37　　　　　**USA**
K E A RESEARCH PUBLICATIONS. Text in English. 1964. s-a. price varies. abstr.; charts; stat. Supplement avail. **Document type:** *Academic/Scholarly.*
Formerly: K E A Publications (0022-7307)
Published by: Kentucky Education Association, 401 Capitol Ave, Frankfort, KY 40601-2836. TEL 800-755-2889, FAX 502-227-8062. Ed. Gretchen Lampe. Circ: 2,500.

016.37　　　　　**DNK**　　　　　ISSN 0904-1893
KATALOG FOR SKOLEBIBLIOTEKER. ELEVERNE. Variant title: Elevernes katalog for skolebiblioteker. Text in Danish. 1986. a. DKK 585 (effective 2004). Supplement avail. **Document type:** *Consumer.*
Formerly (until 1988): Katalog for Skolebiblioteker (0901-666X); Which superseded in part (1975-1985): Katalog for Boerne- og Skolebiblioteker (0106-9829)
Related titles: CD-ROM ed.; Online - full text ed.
Published by: Dansk BiblioteksCenter AS, Tempovej 7-11, Ballerup, 2750, Denmark. TEL 45-44-867777, FAX 45-44-867892, dbc@dbc.dk, http://www.dbc.dk.

016.37　　　　　**DNK**　　　　　ISSN 0904-1907
KATALOG FOR SKOLEBIBLIOTEKER. SKOLEBIBLIOTEKAREN. Text in Danish. 1975. a.
Formerly (1986-1987): Katalog for Skolebiblioteker. (Skolebibliotekarens Katalog) (0901-6678); Which supersedes in part (1975-1985): Katalog for Skolebiblioteker (0106-7583)
Related titles: CD-ROM ed.; Online - full text ed.
Published by: Dansk BiblioteksCenter AS, Tempovej 7-11, Ballerup, 2750, Denmark. TEL 45-44-867777, FAX 45-44-867892, dbc@dbc.dk, http://www.dbc.dk.

378.0021　　　　　**USA**
KENTUCKY COLLEGE AND UNIVERSITY ORIGIN OF ENROLLMENTS. Text in English. 1968. a. free. stat. **Description:** Lists and tables of enrollments of state-supported and independent senior, junior, and community colleges in the state, by the Kentucky county, state, and foreign country of origin of the students and number of first-time freshmen.
Former titles: Kentucky. Council on Higher Education. Origin of Kentucky College and University Enrollments; Kentucky. Council on Public Higher Education. Origin of Enrollments, Accredited Colleges and Universities (0098-9770)
Published by: Kentucky Higher Education Association, P O Box 798, Frankfort, KY 40602-0798. TEL 502-564-3553, FAX 502-564-2063. Ed. Sue D McDade. Circ: 500.

LANGUAGE TEACHING; the international abstracting journal for language teachers and applied linguistics . see *LINGUISTICS—Abstracting, Bibliographies, Statistics*

LIBRARY AND INFORMATION SCIENCE EDUCATION STATISTICAL REPORT. see *LIBRARY AND INFORMATION SCIENCES—Abstracting, Bibliographies, Statistics*

016.37　　　　　**DEU**
LITERATURINFORMATIONEN AUS DER BILDUNGSFORSCHUNG. Text in German. 1968. m. **Document type:** *Abstract/Index.*
Formerly: Literatur aus der Bildungsforschung (0174-0601)
Media: Online - full text.

E

▼ *new title*　　➤ *refereed*　　✱ *unverified*　　◆ *full entry avail.*

Published by: Max-Planck-Institut fuer Bildungsforschung, Lentzeallee 94, Berlin, 14195, Germany. TEL 49-30-82406-0, http://www.mpib-berlin.mpg.de/dok/einfo.htm.

370.21 MAC ISSN 0870-5658
MACAO. DIRECCAO DOS SERVICOS DE ESTATISTICA E CENSOS. INQUERITO AO ENSINO/MACAO. CENSUS AND STATISTICS DEPARTMENT. EDUCATION SURVEY. Text in Chinese, Portuguese. 1984. a. free. **Document type:** *Government.* **Description:** Presents statistics on all levels of education in Macau, including data for public and private schools.
Published by: Direccao dos Servicos de Estatistica e Censos, Rua Inacio Baptista, No. 4-6, P.O. Box 3022, Macau. TEL 853-3995311, FAX 853-307825, info@dsec.gov.mo, http://www.dsec.gov.mo/.

370.21 MLT ISSN 0076-3489
MALTA. CENTRAL OFFICE OF STATISTICS. EDUCATION STATISTICS. Text in English. 1953. a., latest 1997, for years 1995-1996. MTL 4.50. **Document type:** *Government.*
Published by: Central Office of Statistics, Auberge d'Italie, Merchants' St., Valletta, Malta. FAX 356-248483, cos@magent.mt. **Subscr. to:** Publications Bookshop, Castille Place, Valletta, Malta.

016.378 USA ISSN 0898-9095
Z5055.U49
MASTERS ABSTRACTS INTERNATIONAL; catalog of selected masters theses. Text in English. 1962. bi-m. USD 320. index. **Document type:** *Abstract/Index.*
Formerly: Masters Abstracts (0025-5106)
Related titles: CD-ROM ed.: (from ProQuest Information & Learning); Magnetic Tape ed.; Online - full text ed.
Indexed: BiolAb, E&PHSE, GP&P, OffTech, PEI, PetrolAb, SFA, WildRev.
—Linda Hall, PADDS.
Published by: ProQuest Information & Learning, 300 N Zeeb Rd., PO Box 1346, Ann Arbor, MI 48106-1346. TEL 313-761-4700, 800-521-0600, FAX 800-864-0019.

016.378242 USA ISSN 1072-5903
Z5055.U5
MASTER'S THESES DIRECTORIES✶. Text in English. 1952. a. USD 87.95.
Formed by the 1992 merger of (1991-1992): Master's Theses Directories. Education (1072-5911); Which was formerly: Master's Theses in Education (0076-5112); (1991-1992): Master's Theses Directories. The Arts and Social Sciences (1066-9795); Which was formerly: Master's Theses in the Arts and Social Sciences (0160-8797); (1991-1992): Master's Theses Directories. The Natural and Technical Sciences (1069-8973); Which was formerly: Master's Theses in the Natural and Technical Sciences (1053-2110)
Address: P O Box 38, Moorhead, IA 51558-0038. TEL 515-228-5996. Eds. Marvin Silvey, Merrill Silvey.

016.378 USA ISSN 0736-7910
MASTERS THESES IN THE PURE AND APPLIED SCIENCES ACCEPTED BY COLLEGES AND UNIVERSITIES OF THE UNITED STATES AND CANADA. Cover title: Master Theses in the Pure and Applied Sciences. Text in English. 1959. a. price varies.
Formerly (until 1974): Masters Theses in the Pure and Applied Sciences Accepted by Colleges and Universities of the United States (0542-9897)
Published by: (Center for Information and Numerical Data Analysis and Synthesis), Springer-Verlag New York, Inc. (Subsidiary of: Springer Science+Business Media), 233 Spring St, New York, NY 10013. TEL 212-460-1500, FAX 212-460-1575, service@springer-ny.com, http://www.springer-ny.com.

370.21 MUS
MAURITIUS. CENTRAL STATISTICAL OFFICE. DIGEST OF EDUCATIONAL STATISTICS. Text in English. 1984. a., latest 2000. MUR 100 per issue (effective 2001). charts. **Document type:** *Government.* **Description:** Reviews statistical economic data pertaining to all aspects of education in Mauritius.
Published by: Mauritius. Central Statistical Office, L.I.C. Centre, President John Kennedy St, Port Louis, Mauritius. TEL 230-212-2316, FAX 230-212-4150, cso@intnet.mu, http://statsmauritius.gov.mu. **Subscr. to:** Mauritius. Government Printing Office, Ramtoolah Bldg, Sir S Ramgoolam St, Port Louis, Mauritius. TEL 230-234-5294, 230-242-0234, FAX 230-234-5322.

016.374 MEX
MEXICO. CENTRO DE INFORMACION TECNICA Y DOCUMENTACION. INDICE DE REVISTAS. SECCION DE EDUCACION Y COMUNICACION. Text in Spanish. 1973. w. MXP 327, USD 17.
Published by: Servicio Nacional de Adiestramiento Rapido de la Mano de Obra en la Industria, Centro de Informacion Tecnica y Documentacion, Calzada Atzcapotzalco-la Villa 209, Apdo. 16-099, Mexico City, DF, Mexico. Ed. Gilberto Diaz Santana. Circ: 164.

370.21 MEX
MEXICO. INSTITUTO NACIONAL DE ESTADISTICA, GEOGRAFIA E INFORMATICA. ENCUESTA NACIONAL DE EDUCACION CAPACITACION Y EMPLEO. Text in Spanish. irreg.
Published by: Instituto Nacional de Estadistica, Geografia e Informatica, Secretaria de Programacion y Presupuesto, Av. Heroe de Nacozari 2301 Sur, Puerta 11, Acceso, Fracc. Jardines del Parque, Aguascalientes, 20270, Mexico. Circ: 2,050.

370.21 KOR ISSN 1011-8314
MINISTRY OF EDUCATION. BASIC STATISTICS OF EDUCATION✶. Text in Korean. a. charts; stat.
Published by: Ministry of Education, Korean Educational Development Institute, 77, Sejong-ro, Chongro-ku, Seoul, 110-760, Korea, S. http://www.moe.go.kr/.

016.370117 GBR ISSN 0260-9770
LC1099
MULTICULTURAL EDUCATION ABSTRACTS. Text in English. 1982. m. GBP 575, USD 1,011 combined subscription to institutions print & online eds. (effective 2006). adv. bk.rev. cum.index. back issues avail.; reprint service avail. from PSC. **Document type:** *Abstract/Index.* **Description:** Awareness service which draws on a wide range of international sources in order to serve the information needs of those throughout the world, concerned with multicultural education.
Related titles: Microfiche ed.; Online - full text ed.: ISSN 1467-5854. GBP 546, USD 960 to institutions (effective 2006) (from Northern Light Technology, Inc., ProQuest Information & Learning).
—Infotrieve. **CCC.**
Published by: Routledge (Subsidiary of: Taylor & Francis Group), 4 Park Sq, Milton Park, Abingdon, Oxon OX14 4RN, United Kingdom. TEL 44-1235-828600, FAX 44-1235-829000, info@routledge.co.uk, http://www.tandf.co.uk/journals/titles/02609770.asp, http://www.routledge.co.uk. Ed. Derek Cherrington. **Subscr. to:** Taylor & Francis Ltd, Journals Customer Service, Rankine Rd, Basingstoke, Hants RG24 8PR, United Kingdom. TEL 44-1256-813000, FAX 44-1256-330245.

016.37133 USA ISSN 1044-3967
LB1043.Z9
N I C E M INDEX TO A V PRODUCERS AND DISTRIBUTORS. Text in English. 1971. biennial. USD 89. **Description:** Provides the name, address, phone number and type of media produced or distributed of companies and institutions involved in nonprint media.
Published by: (National Information Center for Educational Media), Plexus Publishing, Inc., 143 Old Marlton Pike, Medford, NJ 08055. TEL 609-654-4888, FAX 609-654-4309, custserv@infotoday.com, info@plexuspublishing.com, http://www.infotoday.com, http://www.plexuspublishing.com.

NATIONAL PROFILE OF COMMUNITY COLLEGES: TRENDS & STATISTICS. see *EDUCATION—Guides To Schools And Colleges*

370.21 NLD
NETHERLANDS. CENTRAAL BUREAU VOOR DE STATISTIEK. JAARBOEK ONDERWIJS: FEITEN EN CIJFERS BIJEENGEBRACHT DOOR HET C B S. Text in Dutch. 1980. a. EUR 23.14 (effective 2000). charts. **Document type:** *Government.* **Description:** Reviews the educational situation in the Netherlands, presenting data in tables.
Published by: Centraal Bureau voor de Statistiek, Prinses Beatrixlaan 428, PO Box 4000, Voorburg, 2270 JM, Netherlands. TEL 31-70-3373800, FAX 31-70-3877429, infoservice@cbs.nl, http://www.cbs.nl. **Dist. by:** Samsom Uitgeverij B.V., Postbus 4, Alphen aan den Rijn 2400 MA, Netherlands.

370.021 NLD
NETHERLANDS. CENTRAAL BUREAU VOOR DE STATISTIEK. STANDAARD ONDERWIJS INDELING EDITIE (YEAR). Text in Dutch. a. EUR 22.69 per vol. (effective 2000). charts. **Document type:** *Government.* **Description:** Provides a classification system whereby training for educational levels and education sectors is defined.
Media: CD-ROM.
Published by: Centraal Bureau voor de Statistiek, Prinses Beatrixlaan 428, PO Box 4000, Voorburg, 2270 JM, Netherlands. TEL 31-70-3373800, FAX 31-70-3877429, infoservice@cbs.nl, http://www.cbs.nl.

016.37 NLD ISSN 0028-2987
NETHERLANDS. MINISTERIE VAN ONDERWIJS EN WETENSCHAPPEN. PEDAGOGISCHE BIBLIOGRAFIE. Text in Dutch. 1960. m. bk.rev. bibl. **Document type:** *Bibliography.*
Published by: (Netherlands. Ministerie van Ondewijs en Wetenschappen), Sdu Uitgevers bv, Christoffel Plantijnstraat 2, The Hague, 2515 TZ, Netherlands. Circ: 1,200.

016.37 FRA
Z6483.U5
NEW UNESCO DOCUMENTS AND PUBLICATIONS. Text in English, French, Spanish; Summaries in English. 1973. 4/yr. (plus a. cumulation). free.
Formerly: UNESCO List of Documents and Publications (Print Edition) (0377-631X)
Media: Online - full text. **Related titles:** CD-ROM ed.; Microfiche ed.
Indexed: RASB.
Published by: UNESCO Library, 7 place de Fontenoy, Paris, 75352, France. TEL 33-1-45680356, FAX 33-1-45685617, http://www.unesco.org/publications.

378.669021 NGA ISSN 1117-0603
NIGERIA. NATIONAL UNIVERSITIES COMMISSION. STATISTICAL DIGEST. Short title: N U C Statistical Digest. Text in English. a. free. stat. **Document type:** *Government.* **Description:** Catalogues several tables of useful statistical data on student enrollment and graduation, as well as on faculty and staff.
Published by: National Universities Commission, Information and Public Relations Unit, Aja Nwachukwu House, Plot 430 Aguiyi-Ironsi St.Maitama District Garki G.P.O., Federal, PMB 237, Abuja, Capital Territory, Nigeria. TEL 234-9-523-3176, FAX 234-9-523-3520. Ed. Goddy Nnadi. Circ: 3,000.

379.021 USA
NORTH DAKOTA. DEPARTMENT OF PUBLIC INSTRUCTION. BIENNIAL REPORT OF THE SUPERINTENDENT OF PUBLIC INSTRUCTION. Text in English. 1888. biennial. **Document type:** *Government.*
Published by: Department of Public Instruction, 600 E. Boulevard Ave., Dept. 201, Bismarck, ND 58505-0440. TEL 701-328-2260, FAX 701-328-2461, http://www.dpi.state.nd.us/dpi/index.htm. Ed. Joe Linnertz. Circ: 5,000.

372.021 NOR ISSN 0332-804X
HA1501
NORWAY. STATISTISK SENTRALBYRAA. UTDANNINGSSTATISTIKK. GRUNNSKOLAR. Text in Norwegian. 1972. a. NOK 85 (effective 1998). **Document type:** *Government.*
Indexed: RASB.
Published by: Statistisk Sentralbyraa/Statistics Norway, Kongensgate 6, Postboks 8131, Dep, Oslo, 0033, Norway. TEL 47-22-86-45-00, FAX 47-22-86-49-73.

378.481021 NOR ISSN 0300-5631
HA1501
NORWAY. STATISTISK SENTRALBYRAA. UTDANNINGSSTATISTIKK. UNIVERSITETER OG HOEGSKOLER. Text in Norwegian. 1969. a. NOK 80 (effective 1997). **Document type:** *Government.*
Published by: Statistisk Sentralbyraa/Statistics Norway, Kongensgate 6, Postboks 8131, Dep, Oslo, 0033, Norway. TEL 47-22-86-45-00, FAX 47-22-86-49-73.

373.021 NOR ISSN 0332-8031
HA1501
NORWAY. STATISTISK SENTRALBYRAA. VIDEREGAENDE SKOLER. Text in Norwegian. 1974. a. NOK 70 (effective 1997). **Document type:** *Government.*
Published by: Statistisk Sentralbyraa/Statistics Norway, Kongensgate 6, Postboks 8131, Dep, Oslo, 0033, Norway. TEL 47-22-86-45-00, FAX 47-22-86-49-73.

016.370116 USA ISSN 0029-3962
LA132.A1
NOTES AND ABSTRACTS IN AMERICAN AND INTERNATIONAL EDUCATION. Text in English. 1963. 2/yr., latest vol.92, 2001. USD 20 domestic to individuals; USD 30 foreign to individuals; USD 25 domestic to institutions; USD 35 foreign to institutions (effective 2001). bk.rev. abstr.; bibl. back issues avail. **Document type:** *Journal, Academic/Scholarly.* **Description:** Features news, essays, dissertation abstracts, and other materials relevant to the social foundation of education and international education.
Indexed: RASB.
Published by: (University of Michigan, Law School, Associates in the Social Foundations of Education), Caddo Gap Press, 3145 Geary Blvd,, PMB 275, San Francisco, CA 94118. TEL 415-922-1911, FAX 415-440-4870, caddogap@aol.com. Ed., Pub., R&P Alan H Jones. Circ: 100 (paid).

378.0021 AUT ISSN 0067-2343
OESTERREICHISCHE HOCHSCHULSTATISTIK. Text in German. 1953. a. EUR 36 (effective 2005). **Document type:** *Government.* **Description:** Data on students at universities and at arts colleges.
Related titles: ♦ Series of: Beitraege zur Oesterreichischen Statistik. ISSN 0067-2319.
Published by: Statistik Austria, Guglgasse 13, Vienna, W 1110, Austria. TEL 43-1-711280, FAX 43-1-711287728, info@statistik.gv.at, http://www.statistik.at.

378.771021 USA ISSN 0094-6109
L188
OHIO HIGHER EDUCATION. BASIC DATA SERIES. Text in English. 1970. biennial. free. illus. **Document type:** *Government.*
Indexed: CIJE.
Published by: Board of Regents, 30 E Broad St, 36th Fl, Columbus, OH 43266-0417. TEL 614-466-6000, FAX 614-466-5866, drings@regents.state.oh.us. Ed. Diane Rings. Circ: 500.

E

370.21 PAK ISSN 0078-7914
L578.5
PAKISTAN. CENTRAL BUREAU OF EDUCATION. EDUCATIONAL STATISTICS BULLETIN SERIES. Text in English. 1966. irreg. **Document type:** *Bulletin.*
Published by: Central Bureau of Education, Sector H-9, Cultural Area, Islamabad, Pakistan.

016.6137 USA ISSN 0191-9202
GV341
PHYSICAL EDUCATION INDEX. Text in English. 1978. q. USD 310 combined subscription includes a. cumulative index for print & online eds. (effective 2006). index. back issues avail.; reprints avail. **Document type:** *Abstract/Index.* **Description:** Subject index to health, physical education, recreation, dance, sports, and sports medicine literature in over 180 journals.
Related titles: CD-ROM ed.: USD 645 (effective 2000).
Published by: C S A Journal Division (Subsidiary of: Cambridge Information Group), 7200 Wisconsin Ave, Ste 715, Bethesda, MD 20814. TEL 301-961-6798, 800-843-7751, FAX 301-961-6799, journals@csa.com, http://www.csa.com/factsheets/pei-set-c.php. Ed. Deborah B Whitman.

016.37 THA ISSN 1014-6083
POPULATION EDUCATION ACCESSIONS LIST. Text in English. 1987. 3/yr. **Description:** Output from UNESCO computerized bibliographic data base.
Published by: (Regional Clearing House on Population Education and Communication), UNESCO, Principal Regional Office for Asia and the Pacific, PO Box 967, Prakanong Post Office, Bangkok, 10110, Thailand. TEL 662-391-0577, FAX 662-391-0866, rechpec@unesco-proap.org.

016.37 CZE ISSN 1211-8079
PREHLED PEDAGOGICKE LITERATURY. RADA A. Text in Czech. 1949. bi-m. CZK 570, USD 39. bk.rev. bibl. **Document type:** *Bibliography.* **Description:** Provides annotated bibliography of articles from Czech periodicals and books in the field of education that are available in the Czech Republic.
Supersedes in part (in 1994): Prehled Pedagogicke Literatury (0139-9489); Former titles: Novinky Literatury: Prehled Pedagogicke Literatury (0032-7344); Czechoslovakia. Statni Knihovna. Novinky Literatury: Spolecenske Vedy.
Indexed: RASB.
Published by: Ustav pro Informace ve Vzdelavani, Statni Pedagogicka Knihovna Komenskeho, Mikulandska 5, Prague 1, Czech Republic. TEL 420-2-294062, FAX 420-2-294062, http://www.uiv.cz. Eds. Alice Koskova, Marcela Petrovicova. Circ: 350. **Subscr. to:** Senovazne nam 26, Prague 111 21, Czech Republic.

016.37 CZE ISSN 1211-8087
PREHLED PEDAGOGICKE LITERATURY. RADA B. Text in Czech, Slovak. 1949. bi-m. CZK 894, USD 57. bk.rev. bibl. **Document type:** *Bibliography.* **Description:** Provides annotated bibliography of articles from foreign periodicals and books in the field of education that are available in the Czech Republic and in Slovak Republic.
Supersedes in part (in 1994): Prehled Pedagogicke Literatury (0139-9489); Which was formerly: Novinky Literatury: Prehled Pedagogicke Literatury (0032-7344); Czechoslovakia. Statni Knihovna. Novinky Literature: Spolecenske Vedy
Indexed: RASB.
Published by: Ustav pro Informace ve Vzdelavani, Statni Pedagogicka Knihovna Komenskeho, Mikulandska 5, Prague 1, Czech Republic. TEL 420-2-294062, FAX 420-2-294062, vavrova@uiv.cz, http://www.uiv.cz. Eds. Alice Koskova, Marcela Petrovicova. Circ: 350.

370.9538021 SAU
PROGRESS OF EDUCATION IN SAUDI ARABIA; a statistical review. Text in English. irreg. **Document type:** *Government.*
Published by: Ministry of Education, P O Box 2871, Riyadh, Saudi Arabia. TEL 401-2900, FAX 402-1154.

370.21 USA
PROJECTIONS OF EDUCATION STATISTICS. Text in English. 1964. a. charts; stat. **Document type:** *Government.*
Published by: U.S. Department of Education, National Center for Education Statistics, 1990 K St N W, Washington, DC 20006. TEL 202-219-1828, 202-219-1828. Ed. Debra E Gerald. **Dist. by:** U.S. Government Printing Office, Superintendent of Documents, PO Box 371954, Pittsburgh, PA 15250-7954. TEL 202-512-1800, FAX 202-512-2250, orders@gpo.gov, http://www.access.gpo.gov. **Dist. by:** Box 1398, Jessup, MD 20794-1398. TEL 877-433-7827, FAX 301-470-1244.

371.20021 USA
RANKINGS & ESTIMATES: RANKINGS OF THE STATES AND ESTIMATES OF SCHOOL STATISTICS. Text in English. 1959. a. **Description:** Analyzes data from state departments of education and help clarify trends.
Formed by the merger of: Estimates of School Statistics (0077-4278); Rankings of the States (0077-4332)
Published by: (National Education Association of the United States, Research Division), National Education Association of the United States, 1201 16th St, N W, Washington, DC 20036-3290. TEL 202-833-4000, FAX 202-822-7974, http://www.nea.org/edstats/.

016.37 SCG ISSN 0351-6660
REPUBLICKI ZAVOD ZA UNAPREDJIVANJE VASPITANJA I OBRAZOVANJA. BIBLIOGRAFIJA; lista bibliografskih podataka novonabavljenih knjiga i clanaka iz domace i inostrane pedagoske literature. Text in Serbo-Croatian. 1972. m. YUN 80.
Formerly: Institut za Istrazivanje i Razvoj Obrazovanja. Bibliografija
Published by: Republicki Zavod za Unapredjivanje Vaspitanja i Obrazovanja, Draze Pavlovica 15, Belgrade, 11124. Ed. Marija Sladojevic.

378.0021 CAN
RESEARCH AND STUDIES. Text in English. 1970. biennial (in 4 vols.). free. **Description:** Lists all publications, research projects, grants and research funding awards, and patents of University faculty members, with activities of the organized research units, and comparative statistics for the faculties and departments.
Published by: (Office of Research Administration), Carleton University, Faculty of Graduate Studies and Research, Dunton Tower, Rm 1501, Ottawa, ON K1S 5B6, Canada. TEL 613-788-2516, FAX 613-788-2521. Ed. Anne Burgess.

016.37812 GBR ISSN 0080-1674
RESEARCH IN THE HISTORY OF EDUCATION: A LIST OF THESES FOR HIGHER DEGREES IN THE UNIVERSITIES OF ENGLAND AND WALES. Text in English. 1969. a. GBP 2.40. **Description:** Lists completed research in the history of education accepted by British and Irish universities.
Published by: History of Education Society, Evington, 4 Marydene Dr, Leicester, LE5 6HD, United Kingdom. Ed. V F Gilbert. Circ: 250.

016.378 GBR ISSN 0034-5326
LB2331
RESEARCH INTO HIGHER EDUCATION ABSTRACTS. Text in English. 1966. 3/yr. GBP 557, USD 1,020 combined subscription to institutions print & online eds. (effective 2006). adv. bk.rev. cum.index. back issues avail.; reprint service avail. from PSC. **Document type:** *Abstract/Index.* **Description:** Provides a regular survey of international periodicals relevant to the theory and practice of higher education and also offers a selective coverage of books and monographs. More than 600 abstracts are produced each year.
Related titles: CD-ROM ed.: ISSN 1743-1166. 2004; Microfiche ed.; Online - full text ed.: ISSN 1467-5862. GBP 529, USD 969 to institutions (effective 2006) (from Northern Light Technology, Inc., ProQuest Information & Learning).
—BLDSC (7741.250000). **CCC.**
Published by: (Society for Research into Higher Education), Routledge (Subsidiary of: Taylor & Francis Group), 4 Park Sq, Milton Park, Abingdon, Oxon OX14 4RN, United Kingdom. TEL 44-1235-828600, FAX 44-1235-829000, info@routledge.co.uk, http://www.tandf.co.uk/journals/titles/00345326.asp, http://www.routledge.co.uk. Ed. Ian McNay. **Subscr. to:** Taylor & Francis Ltd, Journals Customer Service, Rankine Rd, Basingstoke, Hants RG24 8PR, United Kingdom. TEL 44-1256-813000, FAX 44-1256-330245.

016.37 USA ISSN 0098-0897
CODEN: JEBOD9
RESOURCES IN EDUCATION. Short title: R I E. Text in English. 1966. m. USD 78 domestic; USD 97.50 foreign (effective 2005). bibl.; illus. s-a.index (until 1994). back issues avail.; reprints avail. **Document type:** *Abstract/Index.* **Description:** Provides up-to-date information about educational resources. Designed to keep teachers, administrators, research specialists, and others in the educational community, as well as the public, informed about educational research and resources.
Formerly (until 1975): Research in Education (0034-5229)
Related titles: CD-ROM ed.: (from National Information Services Corp. (N I S C), SilverPlatter Information, Inc., The Dialog Corporation); Microform ed.: (from PQC); Online - full text ed.: (from National Information Services Corp. (N I S C), The Dialog Corporation); ♦ Cumulative ed(s).: Resources in Education Annual Cumulation. ISSN 0197-9973.
Indexed: ETA, MEA&I, MEDOC, RASB, REE&TA, WAE&RSA.
—BLDSC (7777.608100), CINDOC, Infotrieve.
Published by: (U.S. Department of Education, Office of Educational Research and Improvement), E R I C Processing and Reference Facility, 4483-A Forbes Blvd, Lanham, MD 20706-4354. TEL 301-552-4200, FAX 301-552-4700, ericfac@inet.ed.gov, http://www.ericfacility.org. Ed. Kerri Nine. Circ: 4,000. **Subscr. to:** U.S. Government Printing Office, Superintendent of Documents, PO Box 371954, Pittsburgh, PA 15250-7954. TEL 202-512-1800, FAX 202-512-2250, orders@gpo.gov, http://www.access.gpo.gov.

016.37 USA ISSN 0197-9973
L11
RESOURCES IN EDUCATION ANNUAL CUMULATION. Text in English. 1979. a. USD 415 in North America; USD 470 elsewhere (effective 2001). index. back issues avail. **Document type:** *Journal, Abstract/Index.* **Description:** Index to annotated abstracts of current educational research literature, including technical reports, speeches, books, and unpublished manuscripts.
Related titles: CD-ROM ed.: (from National Information Services Corp. (N I S C)); Online - full text ed.: (from National Information Services Corp. (N I S C)); ♦ Cumulative ed. of: Resources in Education. ISSN 0098-0897.
Published by: (Education Resources Information Center), Oryx Press (Subsidiary of: Greenwood Publishing Group Inc.), 1434 E. San Miguel Ave., Phoenix, AZ 85014-2422. TEL 602-265-2651, 800-279-6799, FAX 602-265-6250, info@oryxpress.com, http://www.oryxpress.com. Ed. Anne Thompson. Pub. Phyllis Steckler. R&P Lori Cavanaugh TEL 602-265-2651 ext 662. Circ: 1,000.

016.37 CHL ISSN 0716-0151
LA540
RESUMENES ANALITICOS EN EDUCACION. Text in Spanish. 1972. 2/yr. USD 60. abstr.; bibl. index. **Document type:** *Academic/Scholarly.*
Indexed: PAIS.
Published by: Centro de Investigacion y Desarrollo para la Accion Educativa, Casilla 13608, Santiago, 1, Chile. TEL 6987153, cide@reuna.cl. Ed. Gonzalo Gutierrez. Circ: 1,500.

016.37 USA ISSN 1071-4413
L11 CODEN: RECSED
➤ **THE REVIEW OF EDUCATION - PEDAGOGY - CULTURAL STUDIES.** Text in English. 1975. q. GBP 252, USD 320 combined subscription to institutions print & online eds. (effective 2006). adv. bk.rev. index. reprint service avail. from PQC,PSC. **Document type:** *Journal, Academic/Scholarly.* **Description:** Publishes critical and integrative essays on recent titles.
Formerly (until vol.16): Review of Education (0098-5597)
Related titles: Microform ed.: (from PQC); Online - full text ed.: ISSN 1556-3022. GBP 239, USD 304 to institutions (effective 2006) (from EBSCO Publishing, Gale Group, IngentaConnect, O C L C Online Computer Library Center, Inc., Swets Information Services).
Indexed: ABIn, ArtHuCI, BRI, CPE, ERA, EduInd, MEA, MLA, RASB, SWA.
—BLDSC (7790.277500), IE, Infotrieve, ingenta. **CCC.**
Published by: Taylor & Francis Inc. (Subsidiary of: Taylor & Francis Group), 325 Chestnut St, Ste 800, Philadelphia, PA 19016. TEL 215-625-8900, 800-354-1420, FAX 215-625-8914, info@taylorandfrancis.com, http://www.tandf.co.uk/journals/titles/10714413.asp, http://www.taylorandfrancis.com. Eds. Henry A Giroux, Patrick Shannon, Susan Searls Giroux.

372.021 RWA ISSN 1019-4940
RWANDA. MINISTERE DE L'ENSEIGNEMENT PRIMAIRE ET SECONDAIRE. DIRECTION DE LA PLANIFICATION. BULLETIN DES STATISTIQUES DE L'ENSEIGNEMENT. Text in French. 1966. a. RWF 10, USD 32. **Document type:** *Government.*
Formerly: Rwanda. Ministere de l'Education Nationale. Direction de la Planification, Statistique et Information. Statistique de l'Enseignement
Published by: Ministere de l'Enseignement Primaire et Secondaire, Direction de la Planification, BP 622, Kigali, Rwanda. Circ: 150.

370.9538021 SAU
SAUDI ARABIA. MINISTRY OF EDUCATION. ANNUAL STATISTICAL REPORT. Text in Arabic. a. **Document type:** *Government.*
Published by: Ministry of Education, P O Box 2871, Riyadh, Saudi Arabia. TEL 401-2900, FAX 402-1154.

370.21 SAU
SAUDI ARABIA. MINISTRY OF EDUCATION. EDUCATIONAL STATISTICS. Text in Arabic, English. irreg. illus. **Document type:** *Government.*
Published by: (Saudi Arabia. Statistics, Research and Education Documents Unit, Statistics Section), Ministry of Education, P O Box 2871, Riyadh, Saudi Arabia. TEL 401-2900, FAX 402-1154.

016.37 SAU ISSN 1319-0768
SAUDI ARABIA. WIZARAT AL-MA'ARIF. AL-ISTIKHLASAT AL-TARBAWIYYAH/SAUDI ARABIA. MINISTRY OF EDUCATION. EDUCATIONAL ABSTRACTS. Key Title: Al-isthlasat al-tarbiwiat. Text in Arabic. 1978. s-a. **Document type:** *Government.*
Published by: Ministry of Education, P O Box 2871, Riyadh, Saudi Arabia. TEL 401-2900, FAX 402-1154.

370.21 USA
SCHOOL FACTS. Text in English. USD 25 newsstand/cover. **Description:** Contains data, by school district, relating to enrollment, tax rates, staffing ratios, scores on state tests, teacher salaries, expenditures and revenues.
Published by: Wisconsin Taxpayers Alliance, 401 North Lawn Ave., Madison, WI 53704-5033. TEL 608-255-4581, wtataxes@itis.com. Ed. Craig Svoboda.

370.21 CHE
SCHUELERINNEN, SCHUELER UND STUDIERENDE - ELEVES, ETUDIANTES ET ETUDIANTS. Text in French, German. 1976. a. CHF 12 (effective 2001). **Document type:** *Government.*
Formerly: Switzerland. Bundesamt fuer Statistik. Schuelerstatistik - Statistique des Eleves

E

Published by: Bundesamt fuer Statistik, Espace de l'Europe 10, Neuchatel, 2010, Switzerland. TEL 41-32-7136011, FAX 41-32-7136012, information@bfs.admin.ch, http://www.admin.ch/bfs.

370.21 GBR ISSN 0143-599X
SCOTTISH EDUCATION DEPARTMENT. STATISTICAL BULLETIN. Text in English. 1977. m. **Document type:** *Government.*
Published by: Scottish Education Department, New St Andrew's House, Rm 5-52, Edinburgh, Midlothian EH1 3TG, United Kingdom. TEL 031-244-4991.

016.375 USA
SECONDARY TEACHERS GUIDE TO FREE CURRICULUM MATERIALS. Text in English. 1934. a. (111th Ed.), latest 2002-2003. USD 47.95 per issue (effective 2002). 379 p./no.; **Document type:** *Directory, Academic/Scholarly.* **Description:** Lists free pamphlets, pictures and chart materials for high school and college levels.
Formerly: Educators Index of Free Materials
Published by: Educators Progress Service, Inc., 214 Center St, Randolph, WI 53956. TEL 920-326-3126, FAX 920-326-3127, http://www.freeteachingaids.com/pm_877083355.html. Ed. Kathleen Suttles Nehmer.

016.378 MEX
SINOPSIS. Text in Spanish. a. MXP 25, USD 10 per issue (effective 2000). **Description:** Compiles and summarizes postgraduate dissertations presented at the University.
Published by: Universidad Nacional Autonoma de Mexico, Coordinacion General de Estudios de Posgrado, Departamento de Publicaciones, Edificio Unidad de Posgrado, P.B., Circuito Interior, Ciudad Universitaria, Mexico City, DF 04510, Mexico. TEL 52-5-6220807, FAX 52-5-6220814, gordon@servidor.unam.mx. Ed. Irma Osnaya Cornejo.

370.21 ESP ISSN 1010-2965
SISTEMA DE INDICADORES SOCIO-ECONOMICOS Y EDUCATIVOS DE LA O E I. Text in Spanish. 1980. a. USD 500. **Document type:** *Directory.*
Formerly: Educacion en Iberoamerica: Sistema de Indicadores Socio-Economicos y Educativos
Related titles: Diskette ed.
Published by: Organizacion de Estados IberoAmericanos para la Educacion la Ciencia y la Cultura, Bravo Murillo 38, Madrid, 28015, Spain. TEL 34-91-5944382, FAX 34-91-5943286, oeimad@oei.es, http://www.oei.es. Circ: 1,000.

016.30642 GBR ISSN 0038-0415
➤ **SOCIOLOGY OF EDUCATION ABSTRACTS.** Text in English. 1965. m. GBP 813, USD 1,339 combined subscription to institutions print & online eds. (effective 2006). cum.index. back issues avail.; reprint service avail. from PSC. **Document type:** *Abstract/Index.* **Description:** Draws on a wide range of international sources as a means of serving the information needs of those concerned with the sociological study of education.
Related titles: Microfiche ed.; Online - full text ed.: ISSN 1467-5870. GBP 772, USD 1,272 to institutions (effective 2006) (from ProQuest Information & Learning).
—CCC.
Published by: Routledge (Subsidiary of: Taylor & Francis Group), 4 Park Sq, Milton Park, Abingdon, Oxon OX14 4RN, United Kingdom. TEL 44-1235-828600, FAX 44-1235-829000, info@routledge.co.uk, http://www.tandf.co.uk/journals/titles/00380415.asp, http://www.routledge.co.uk. Ed. Dr. Chris Shilling. **Subscr. to:** Taylor & Francis Ltd, Journals Customer Service, Rankine Rd, Basingstoke, Hants RG24 8PR, United Kingdom. TEL 44-1256-813000, FAX 44-1256-330245.

370 FRA ISSN 1812-7010
SOURCE O E C D. EDUCATION STATISTICS/SOURCE O C D E STATISTIQUES DE L'EDUCATION. Text in English. 2000. irreg. EUR 135, USD 155, GBP 88, JPY 18,200 (effective 2005). stat. **Description:** Provides comparative education statistics and indicators from OECD and non-OECD countries.
Formerly: Source O E C D. Education at a Glance. O E C D Database (1608-1250)
Media: Online - full content. **Related titles:** Online - full text ed.: (from Gale Group, IngentaConnect).
Published by: Organization for Economic Cooperation and Development, 2 Rue Andre Pascal, Paris, 75775 Cedex 16, France. TEL 33-1-45248200, FAX 33-1-45248500, http://www.oecd.org.

378.106021 ZAF
SOUTH AFRICA. STATISTICS SOUTH AFRICA. STATISTICAL RELEASE. FINANCIAL STATISTICS OF UNIVERSITIES AND TECHNIKONS. Text in English. a., latest 1996. **Document type:** *Government.*
Formerly (until Aug. 1998): South Africa. Central Statistical Service. Statistical Release. Financial Statistics of Universities and Technikons
Published by: Statistics South Africa/Statistieke Suid-Afrika, Private Bag X44, Pretoria, 0001, South Africa. TEL 27-12-310-8911, FAX 27-12-310-8500, info@statssa.pwv.gov.za, http://www.statssa.gov.za.

016.3713 MYS ISSN 0126-7590
SOUTHEAST ASIAN MINISTERS OF EDUCATION ORGANISATION. REGIONAL CENTRE FOR EDUCATION IN SCIENCE AND MATHEMATICS. LIBRARY ACCESSION LIST. Text in English. s-a. free. reprints avail.
Indexed: RILM.
Published by: Southeast Asian Ministers of Education Organisation, Regional Centre for Education in Science and Mathematics, Glugor, Penang 11700, Malaysia. TEL 604-6583266, FAX 604-6572541. Circ: 100.

016.3719 GBR ISSN 0954-0822
➤ **SPECIAL EDUCATIONAL NEEDS ABSTRACTS.** Text in English. 1989. m. GBP 621, USD 1,025 combined subscription to institutions print & online eds. (effective 2006). adv. bk.rev. reprint service avail. from PSC. **Document type:** *Abstract/Index.* **Description:** Draws on a wide range of international sources to identify materials which are of interest to those concerned with special needs education.
Related titles: Microfiche ed.; Online - full text ed.: ISSN 1467-5889. GBP 590, USD 974 to institutions (effective 2006) (from Northern Light Technology, Inc., ProQuest Information & Learning).
—IE, Infotrieve. **CCC.**
Published by: Routledge (Subsidiary of: Taylor & Francis Group), 4 Park Sq, Milton Park, Abingdon, Oxon OX14 4RN, United Kingdom. TEL 44-1235-828600, FAX 44-1235-829000, info@routledge.co.uk, http://www.tandf.co.uk/journals/titles/09540822.asp, http://www.routledge.co.uk. Ed. Derek Cherrington. **Subscr. to:** Taylor & Francis Ltd, Journals Customer Service, Rankine Rd, Basingstoke, Hants RG24 8PR, United Kingdom. TEL 44-1256-813000, FAX 44-1256-330245.

016.6137 GBR ISSN 0142-1794
SPORTS DOCUMENTATION MONTHLY BULLETIN. Text in English, Multiple languages; Summaries in English. 1971. m. GBP 58 in United Kingdom to individuals; GBP 79 in United Kingdom to institutions; GBP 79 elsewhere (effective 2002). index, cum.index. back issues avail. **Document type:** *Bulletin, Abstract/Index.* **Description:** Lists recent periodical articles and conference papers on the scientific and medical aspects of sport, physical education, and recreation, with indexes of authors and subject matter.
Formerly (until 1974): Sports Information Monthly Bulletin
Indexed: ErgAb.
—BLDSC (8419.834000).
Published by: Centre for Sports Science and History, Main Library, University of Birmingham, Edgbaston, Birmingham B15 2TT, United Kingdom. TEL 44-121-414-5843, FAX 44-121-471-4691, CENSSAH@bham.ac.uk. Circ: 330.

370.21 SCG
SRBIJA I CRNA GORA ZAVOD ZA STATISTIKU. OSNOVNA I SREDNJE. Text in Serbo-Croatian. irreg. **Document type:** *Government.*
Formerly: Yugoslavia. Savezni Zavod za Statistiku. Osnovna i Srednje
Related titles: ♦ Series of: Srbija i Crna Gora. Zavod za Statistiku. Statisticki Bilten.
Published by: Srbija i Crna Gora Zavod za Statistiku/Serbia and Montenegro Statistical Office, Kneza Milosa 20, Postanski Fah 203, Belgrade, 11000. http://www.szs.sv.gov.yu. Circ: 1,000.

370.21 GBR ISSN 0968-5588
LA660
STATISTICS OF EDUCATION AND TRAINING IN WALES: SCHOOLS. Text in English. 1975. a. GBP 10 (effective 2000). stat. **Document type:** *Government.* **Description:** Statistics on education provision for under 5's, primary and secondary education, the teaching of Welsh, special education, school meals, and expenditure on the school education service.
Formerly: Statistics of Education in Wales: Schools (0951-1237); Which supersedes in part (in 1987): Statistics of Education in Wales (0262-8317)
—BLDSC (8453.529080). **CCC.**
Published by: (Great Britain. Publication Unit), National Assembly of Wales, Statistical Directorate, Cathays Park, Cardiff, CF10 3NQ, United Kingdom. TEL 44-2920-825054, FAX 44-2920-825350, stats.pubs@wales.gsi.gov.uk. Circ: 625.

370.21 GBR
STATISTICS OF EDUCATION. TEACHERS. ENGLAND AND WALES. Text in English. a. **Document type:** *Government.*
Former titles: Statistics of Education. Teachers in Service. England and Wales (0266-674X); Statistics of Teachers in Service in England and Wales
—BLDSC (8453.534200).
Published by: Great Britain Department for Education, Sanctuary Bldgs, Sanctuary Buildings, Great Smith St, London, SW1P 3BT, United Kingdom. TEL 44-171-925-6310, FAX 44-171-925-6985.

STATISTICS ON SOCIAL WORK EDUCATION IN THE UNITED STATES. see *SOCIAL SERVICES AND WELFARE—Abstracting, Bibliographies, Statistics*

372.021 AUT
STATISTIK AUSTRIA. KRIPPEN, KINDERGAERTEN UND HORTE (KINDERTAGESHEIME). Text in German. a. EUR 20. **Document type:** *Government.* **Description:** Compiles data on all aspects of the development of kindergarten.
Former titles: Austria. Statistisches Zentralamt. Krippen, Kindergaerten und Horte (Kindertagesheime); Austria. Statistisches Zentralamt. Die Kindergaerten (Kindertagesheime) (0259-7969)
Related titles: ♦ Series of: Beitraege zur Oesterreichischen Statistik. ISSN 0067-2319.
Published by: Statistik Austria, Guglgasse 13, Vienna, W 1110, Austria. TEL 43-1-711280, FAX 43-1-711287728, info@statistik.gv.at, http://www.statistik.at.

378.5693021 CYP
SURVEY ON GRADUATING STUDENTS ABROAD. Text in English. irreg. CYP 3 per issue (effective 1999). **Document type:** *Government.* **Description:** Estimates the number of graduates who remain abroad and examines the employment situation of those returning to Cyprus one year after their graduation.
Published by: Ministry of Finance, Department of Statistics and Research, 13 Andreas Araouzos St, Nicosia, 1444, Cyprus. TEL 357-2-309318, FAX 357-2-374830, cydsr@cytanet.com.cy, http://www.pio.gov.cy/dsr.

370.21 SWZ
SWAZILAND. CENTRAL STATISTICAL OFFICE. EDUCATION STATISTICS. Text in English. 1968. a. free. **Document type:** *Government.*
Published by: Central Statistical Office, PO Box 456, Mbabane, Swaziland. TEL 268-43765. Circ: 700.

370.21 SWE ISSN 0282-3470
SWEDEN. STATISTISKA CENTRALBYRAAN. STATISTISKA MEDDELANDEN. SERIE U, UTBILDNING OCH FORSKNING. Text in Swedish; Summaries in English. N.S. 1963. irreg. SEK 910.
Supersedes in part (in 1985): Sweden. Statistiska Centralbyraan. Statistiska Meddelanden. Serie U, Utbildning, Forskning och Kultur
Published by: Statistiska Centralbyraan/Statistics Sweden, Publishing Unit, Orebro, 70189, Sweden. Circ: 2,000.

016.37 USA
T O M. (Text on Microfilm) Text in English. m. price varies. **Document type:** *Abstract/Index.* **Description:** Index and full-text retrieval system for the approximately 154 periodicals most often subscribed to by high schools. Contains 6 years of data.
Media: Microfilm. **Related titles:** CD-ROM ed.
Published by: Gale Group (Subsidiary of: Thomson Corporation), 27500 Drake Rd, Farmington Hills, MI 48331-3535. TEL 248-699-4253, 800-347-4253, FAX 248-699-8035, gale.galeord@thomson.com, http://www.galegroup.com.

TAL OM FORSKNING. see *STATISTICS*

TEACHERS' CHOICES. see *CHILDREN AND YOUTH—Abstracting, Bibliographies, Statistics*

372.021 GBR ISSN 0141-982X
➤ **TEACHING STATISTICS**; an international journal for teachers of pupils aged up to 19. Text in English. 1979. 3/yr. GBP 26, EUR 39 combined subscription in Europe to individuals print & online eds.; USD 47 combined subscription in the Americas to individuals & Caribbean, print & online eds..; GBP 28 combined subscription elsewhere to individuals print & online eds.; GBP 43 combined subscription in Europe to institutions print & online eds.; USD 81 combined subscription in the Americas to institutions & Caribbean, print & online eds.; GBP 48 combined subscription elsewhere to institutions print & online eds.; EUR 24 combined subscription in Europe to students print & online eds.; USD 27 combined subscription in the Americas to students & Caribbean, print & online eds.; GBP 16 combined subscription elsewhere to students print & online eds. (effective 2006). adv. bk.rev. illus. Index. back issues avail.; reprints avail. **Document type:** *Journal, Academic/Scholarly.* **Description:** Seeks to inform, enlighten, stimulate, correct, entertain and encourage. Aimed at teachers and students aged 9-19 who uses statistics in their work. The emphasis is on teaching the subject and addressing problems which arise in the classroom. It seeks to support not only specialist statistics teachers but also those in other disciplines, such as economics, biology and geography, who make widespread use of statistics in their teaching.
Related titles: Online - full text ed.: ISSN 1467-9639. GBP 41 in Europe to institutions; USD 77 in the Americas to institutions & Caribbean; GBP 46 elsewhere to institutions (effective 2006) (from Blackwell Synergy, EBSCO Publishing, Gale Group, IngentaConnect, O C L C Online Computer Library Center, Inc., Swets Information Services).
Indexed: BrEdI, CIJE, CIS, CPE, ORMS, QC&AS, TEA, ZentMath.
—BLDSC (8614.343000), IE, Infotrieve, ingenta. **CCC.**
Published by: (The/Royal Statistical Society), Blackwell Publishing Ltd., 9600 Garsington Rd, Oxford, OX4 2ZG, United Kingdom. TEL 44-1865-776868, FAX 44-1865-714591, customerservices@oxon.blackwellpublishing.com, http://www.blackwellpublishing.com/journals/TEST. Ed. G W Goodall. Circ: 1,050 (paid).

E

016.37 GBR ISSN 0966-162X
T61
TECHNICAL EDUCATION & TRAINING ABSTRACTS. Text in English. 1961. m. GBP 679, USD 1,184 combined subscription to institutions print & online eds. (effective 2006). cum.index. back issues avail.; reprint service avail. from PSC. **Document type:** *Abstract/Index.* **Description:** Designed to serve the information needs of those teaching mathematics, science and design and technology at primary, secondary and higher education levels.
Formerly (until 1993): Technical Education Abstracts (0040-0920)
Related titles: Microfiche ed.; Online - full text ed.: ISSN 1467-5897. GBP 645, USD 1,125 to institutions (effective 2006) (from Northern Light Technology, Inc., ProQuest Information & Learning).
—CCC.
Published by: Routledge (Subsidiary of: Taylor & Francis Group), 4 Park Sq, Milton Park, Abingdon, Oxon OX14 4RN, United Kingdom. TEL 44-1235-828600, FAX 44-1235-829000, info@routledge.co.uk, http://www.tandf.co.uk/journals/titles/0966162X.asp, http://www.routledge.co.uk. Ed. Stuart Trickey. **Subscr. to:** Taylor & Francis Ltd, Journals Customer Service, Rankine Rd, Basingstoke, Hants RG24 8PR, United Kingdom. TEL 44-1256-813000, FAX 44-1256-330245.

016.378 ISR ISSN 0792-7355
T1
TECHNION - ISRAEL INSTITUTE OF TECHNOLOGY. ABSTRACTS OF RESEARCH THESES. Text in English. 1983. a. USD 30 (effective 1998). **Document type:** *Abstract/Index.*
Published by: Technion - Israel Institute of Technology, Graduate School, Technion City, Haifa, 32000, Israel. FAX 972-4-8221600, http://www.technion.ac.il. Circ: 500.

378.764021 USA
TEXAS HIGHER EDUCATION COORDINATING BOARD. STATUS REPORT ON HIGHER EDUCATION AND STATISTICAL REPORT. Text in English. 1965. biennial. free. **Document type:** *Government.*
Former titles: Texas Higher Education Coordinating Board. C B Annual Report and Statistical Supplement; Texas College and University System. Coordinating Board. C B Annual Report and Statistical Supplement; Texas. Coordinating Board. Texas College and University System. C B Annual Report (0082-2981)
Indexed: SRI.
Published by: Texas Higher Education Coordinating Board, PO Box 12788, Capitol Sta, Austin, TX 78711. TEL 512-483-6111, FAX 512-483-6127, restersa@thecb.state.tx.us. Ed. Teri E Flack. Circ: 1,000 (controlled).

310 THA
THAILAND. NATIONAL STATISTICAL OFFICE. REPORT OF THE EDUCATION STATISTICS: ACADEMIC YEAR (YEAR). Text in English, Thai. 1964. a. **Document type:** *Government.* **Description:** Contains statistics on number of schools, classrooms, students and teachers by general education, vocational education, teacher training, and other education types.
Published by: (Thailand. Statistical Data Bank and Information Dissemination Division), National Statistical Office, Larn Luang Rd, Bangkok, 10100, Thailand. TEL 66-2-282-1535, FAX 66-2-281-3814, binfodsm@nso.go.th, http://www.nso.go.th/. Circ: 550.

378.0021 CAN ISSN 0847-5482
TRENDS. Text in English. 1983. a. CND 80 (effective 2004).
Formerly (until 1990): Compendium of University Statistics (0826-2292)
Published by: Association of Universities and Colleges of Canada/Association des Universites et Colleges du Canada, 350 Albert St, Ste 600, Ottawa, ON K1R 1B1, Canada. TEL 613-563-1236, 613-563-3961, FAX 613-563-9745, publications@aucc.ca, http://www.aucc.ca/publications/auccpubs/research/trends/trends_e.html.

378.101 USA ISSN 1520-7161
LB2342
TUITION FACT BOOK. Text in English. 1989. irreg., latest 1998. USD 60 to institutions commercial; USD 40 to institutions academic (effective 2001). bibl.; charts. **Document type:** *Academic/Scholarly.* **Description:** Presents a comprehensive collection of statistics on all facets of college and university tuition, together with key observations.
Published by: Research Associates of Washington, 1200 N Nash St, Apt 1112, Arlington, VA 22209-3612. TEL 703-243-3399, FAX 703-524-6889, http://www.rschassoc.com. Ed., Pub. Kent Halstead.

370.21 TUR ISSN 1300-1043
TURKEY. DEVLET ISTATISTIK ENSTITUSU. KAMU KURUMU VE KURULUSLARI HIZMET ONCESI VE HIZMET ICI EGITIM ISTATISTIKLERI/TURKEY. STATE INSTITUTE OF STATISTICS. STATISTICS ON TRAINING IN STATE INSTITUTIONS. Text in English, Turkish. 1987. a. USD 40 (effective 1998). **Document type:** *Government.*
Published by: Devlet Istatistik Enstitusu/State Institute of Statistics, Necatibey Caddesi 114, Ankara, 06100, Turkey. TEL 90-312-4176440, FAX 90-312-4253387, yayin@die.gov.tr, http://www.die.gov.tr. Circ: 5,000.

370.21 TUR
TURKEY. DEVLET ISTATISTIK ENSTITUSU. MILLI EGITIM ISTATISTIKLERI OGRETIM YILI BASI. Text in Turkish. 1933. a., latest 1986. free or on exchange basis. **Document type:** *Government.*
Published by: Devlet Istatistik Enstitusu/State Institute of Statistics, Necatibey Caddesi 114, Ankara, 06100, Turkey. TEL 90-4-4176440, FAX 90-4-4253387.

370.21 TUR ISSN 1300-0993
HA1911.A3
TURKEY. DEVLET ISTATISTIK ENSTITUSU. MILLI EGITIM ISTATISTIKLERI ORGUN EGITIM/TURKEY. STATE INSTITUTE OF STATISTICS. NATIONAL EDUCATIONAL STATISTICS FORMAL EDUCATION. Text in English, Turkish. 1988. a. USD 75 (effective 1998). **Document type:** *Government.* **Description:** Contains statistical information on state and private education from kindergarten through high school, including vocational and technical high schools.
Related titles: Diskette ed.
Published by: Devlet Istatistik Enstitusu/State Institute of Statistics, Necatibey Caddesi 114, Ankara, 06100, Turkey. TEL 90-312-4185027, FAX 90-312-4170432, yayin@die.gov.tr, http://www.die.gov.tr. Circ: 520.

374.0021 TUR ISSN 1300-1027
TURKEY. DEVLET ISTATISTIK ENSTITUSU. MILLI EGITIM ISTATISTIKLERI YAYGIN EGITIM/TURKEY. STATE INSTITUTE OF STATISTICS. NATIONAL EDUCATION STATISTICS ADULT EDUCATION. Key Title: Milli Egitim Istatistikleri Yaygin Egitim. Text in English, Turkish. 1978. a. USD 50 (effective 1998). **Document type:** *Government.* **Description:** Provides statistical information on private teaching centers, private courses, apprenticeship training programs, Koran courses, illiteracy campaign activities and practical trade schools for girls.
Published by: Devlet Istatistik Enstitusu/State Institute of Statistics, Necatibey Caddesi 114, Ankara, 06100, Turkey. TEL 90-312-4185027, FAX 90-312-4170432, yayin@die.gov.tr, http://www.die.gov.tr. Circ: 925.

378.0021 USA
U.S. DEPARTMENT OF EDUCATION. NATIONAL CENTER FOR EDUCATION STATISTICS. COMPLETIONS IN INSTITUTIONS OF HIGHER EDUCATION. Text in English. 1948. irreg., latest 1987. **Document type:** *Government.*
Formerly: U.S. Department of Education. National Center for Education Statistics. Earned Degrees Conferred (0565-744X)
Published by: U.S. Department of Education, National Center for Education Statistics, 1990 K St N W, Washington, DC 20006. TEL 202-219-1828, http://nces.ed.gov. **Subscr. to:** U.S. Government Printing Office, Superintendent of Documents, PO Box 371954, Pittsburgh, PA 15250-7954. TEL 202-512-1800, FAX 202-512-2250, orders@gpo.gov, http://www.access.gpo.gov.

370.21 USA ISSN 0502-4102
L11
U.S. DEPARTMENT OF EDUCATION. NATIONAL CENTER FOR EDUCATION STATISTICS. DIGEST OF EDUCATION STATISTICS. Short title: Digest of Education Statistics. Text in English. 1962. a., latest vol.38, 2002. free (effective 2003). **Document type:** *Government.* **Description:** Provides statistics on American education from kindergarten through graduate school. Includes statistics on Federal programs for education, library resources and technology, education characteristics of the labor force, and international comparisons.
Formerly: U.S. National Center for Education Statistics. Digest of Educational Statistics (0083-2634)
—CASDDS.
Published by: U.S. Department of Education, National Center for Education Statistics, 1990 K St N W, Washington, DC 20006. TEL 800-424-1616, http://nces.ed.gov/pubs2003/digest02/. **Dist. by:** Office of Education Research and Improvement, U.S. Department of Education, 555 New Jersey Ave, N W, Washington, DC 20208-5500.

370.21 USA
U.S. DEPARTMENT OF EDUCATION. NATIONAL CENTER FOR EDUCATION STATISTICS. DROPOUT RATES IN THE UNITED STATES. Text in English. a., latest 2001. **Document type:** *Government.* **Description:** Presents estimates of high school dropout and completion rates, and includes time series data on high school dropout and completion rates.
Related titles: Online - full content ed.
Published by: U.S. Department of Education, National Center for Education Statistics, 1990 K St N W, Washington, DC 20006. chris.chapman@ed.go, http://nces.ed.gov/. **Dist. by:** Ed Pubs, PO Box 1398, Jessup, MD 20794-1398. TEL 877-433-7827, FAX 301-470-1244, edpubs@inet.ed.gov, http://www.edpubs.org/.

370.21 USA
U.S. DEPARTMENT OF EDUCATION. NATIONAL CENTER FOR EDUCATION STATISTICS. PUBLIC ELEMENTARY AND SECONDARY STATE AGGREGATE DATA, BY STATE. Text in English. 1954. a. **Document type:** *Government.*
Supersedes: U.S. National Center for Education Statistics. Revenues and Expenditures for Public Elementary and Secondary Education (0149-2497); U.S. National Center for Education Statistics. Expenditures and Revenues for Public Elementary and Secondary Education (0090-7618); Incorporates: U.S. National Center for Education Statistics. Statistics of Public Elementary and Secondary School Systems; Which was formerly: U.S. National Center for Education Statistics. Statistics of Public Elementary and Secondary Day Schools
Published by: U.S. Department of Education, National Center for Education Statistics, 1990 K St N W, Washington, DC 20006. TEL 202-219-1828, http://nces.ed.gov. **Subscr. to:** U.S. Government Printing Office, Superintendent of Documents, PO Box 371954, Pittsburgh, PA 15250-7954. TEL 202-512-1800, FAX 202-512-2250, orders@gpo.gov, http://www.access.gpo.gov. **Dist. by:** Box 1398, Jessup, MD 20794-1398. TEL 877-433-7827, FAX 301-470-1244.

378.0021 USA
U.S. DEPARTMENT OF EDUCATION. NATIONAL CENTER FOR EDUCATION STATISTICS. STATE HIGHER EDUCATION PROFILES. Text in English. irreg., latest 1987. price varies. **Document type:** *Government.*
Formerly: U.S. National Center for Education Statistics. Financial Statistics of Institutions of Higher Education (0095-6716)
Published by: U.S. Department of Education, National Center for Education Statistics, 1990 K St N W, Washington, DC 20006. TEL 202-219-1828, http://nces.ed.gov. **Subscr. to:** U.S. Government Printing Office, Superintendent of Documents, PO Box 371954, Pittsburgh, PA 15250-7954. TEL 202-512-1800, FAX 202-512-2250, orders@gpo.gov, http://www.access.gpo.gov. **Dist. by:** Box 1398, Jessup, MD 20794-1398. TEL 877-433-7827, FAX 301-470-1244.

378.0021 500 USA ISSN 0094-7881
Q183.3.A1
U.S. NATIONAL SCIENCE FOUNDATION. SELECTED DATA ON STUDENTS AND POSTDOCTORALS IN SCIENCE & ENGINEERING; detailed statistical tables. Key Title: Graduate Science Education Student Support and Postdoctorals. Text in English. a. **Document type:** *Government.*
Formerly: U.S. National Science Foundation. Graduate Science Education Student Support and Postdoctorals
Related titles: ♦ Series of: U.S. National Science Foundation. Surveys of Science Resources Series. ISSN 0083-2405.
—Linda Hall.
Published by: (Division of Science Resources Studies), U.S. National Science Foundation, 4201 Wilson Blvd, Ste 245, Arlington, VA 22230. TEL 703-306-1780, FAX 703-306-0510, pubs@nsf.gov, srsweb@nsf.gov, http://www.nsf.gov/sbe/srs/stats.htm. Ed. Joan Burrelli.

370.21 DNK
LC53.E85
UNDERVISNINGSMINISTERIET. INSTITUTIONSSTYRELSEN. DE FRIE GRUNDSKOLER I TAL. Text in Danish. 1989-1990; resumed 1992. a. DKK 200; DKK 250 foreign (effective 1998). adv. back issues avail. **Document type:** *Government.*
Formerly (until 1999): De Private Skoler i de Enkelte Kommuner (0905-1449); Which superseded in part (in 1993): Folkeskolen i de Enkelte Kommuner (0106-2530)
Related titles: Diskette ed.; Online - full text ed.
Published by: Undervisningsministeriet, Institutionsstyrelsen, Frederiksholm Kanal 21, Copemhagen K, 1220, Denmark. TEL 45-33-925000, FAX 45-33-925567, uvm@uvm.dk, http://www.uvm.dk. Circ: 1,000.

314.021 DNK ISSN 1395-380X
UNDERVISNINGSMINISTERIET. INSTITUTIONSSTYRELSEN. FOLKESKOLEN I TAL. PLANLAEGNINGSTAL. Text in Danish. 1979. a. **Document type:** *Government.*
Formerly (until 1995): Undervisningsministeriet. Folkeskoleafdelingen. Folkeskolen i de Enkelte Kommuner (0106-2530)
Related titles: Online - full text ed.
Published by: Undervisningsministeriet, Institutionsstyrelsen, Frederiksholm Kanal 21, Copemhagen K, 1220, Denmark. TEL 45-33-925000, FAX 45-33-925567, uvm@uvm.dk, http://www.uvm.dk.

016.37 DNK ISSN 0901-9294
UNGDOMS- OG VOKSENUNDERVISNING. Text in Danish. 1979. a.
Former titles (until 1986): Undervisningsmidler for Ungdoms- og Voksenundervisning (0106-5971); Supersedes in part: Danske Skole- og Laereboeger
Related titles: Online - full content ed.
Published by: Fonden Undervisnings Information, Siljangade 6, Copenhagen S, 2300, Denmark. TEL 45-32-96-10-66, FAX 45-32-96-12-10, http://www.fui.dk/servlet/fui.

378.8134021 BRA
UNIVERSIDADE FEDERAL DE PERNAMBUCO. ANUARIO ESTATISTICO. Text in Portuguese. 1972. a. free. stat. Supplement avail. **Document type:** *Academic/Scholarly.*
Published by: Universidade Federal de Pernambuco, Divisao de Suporte a Decisao, Cidade Universitaria, Av. Prof. Morais Rego, Recife, PERNAMBUCO, Brazil. TEL 55-81-2718126, FAX 55-81-2718128.

E

016.378 USA ISSN 0070-3044
Z5055.U5
UNIVERSITY OF DAYTON. SCHOOL OF EDUCATION. ABSTRACTS OF RESEARCH PROJECTS. Text in English. 1968. irreg., latest vol.8, 1989. free. index. **Document type:** *Abstract/Index.* **Description:** Projects completed by candidates for the M.S.
Published by: University of Dayton, School of Education, 300 College Park, Dayton, OH 45469. TEL 513-229-3146. Ed. L Gordon Fuchs.

016.378 BIH
UNIVERZITET U SARAJEVU. DOKTORSKE DISERTACIJE. REZIMEI. Text in Serbo-Croatian. 1969. a. illus. **Description:** Summary of doctoral dissertations on education.
Published by: Univerzitet u Sarajevu, Obala Vojevode Stepe 7-III, Sarajevo, 71000, Bosnia Herzegovina. TEL 213-296.

371.221 USA
URBAN SCHOOL SUPERINTENDENTS: CHARACTERISTICS, TENURE, AND SALARY. SECOND BIENNIAL SURVEY. Text in English. 1998. biennial. charts. **Description:** Surveys large urban districts to compile data on the salaries, tenure, and demographic profiles of their superintendents.
Related titles: Online - full content ed.
Published by: Council of the Great City Schools, 1301 Pennsylvania Ave, NW, Ste 702, Washington, DC 20004. TEL 202-393-2427, FAX 202-393-2400, http://www.cgcs.org/reports/home/superintendents.htm.

370.21 GBR ISSN 0951-3191
WELSH EDUCATION STATISTICS BULLETINS. Text in English. 1986. irreg. **Document type:** *Government.*
Published by: (Great Britain. Publication Unit), National Assembly of Wales, Statistical Directorate, Cathays Park, Cardiff, CF10 3NQ, United Kingdom. TEL 44-2920-825054, FAX 44-2920-825350, stats.pubs@wales.gsi.gov.uk.

016.37 DEU ISSN 0177-9419
ZEITUNGS - DOKUMENTATION BILDUNGSWESEN. Text in German. 1978. fortn. EUR 68 (effective 2002). index. back issues avail. **Document type:** *Abstract/Index.* **Description:** Contains systematically arranged index of current magazine and newspaper articles on education, including research, politics, schools, teachers, and vocational education.
Indexed: RASB.
Published by: (Deutsches Institut fuer Internationale Paedagogische Forschung), V W B - Verlag fuer Wissenschaft und Bildung, Zossener Str 55, Berlin, 10961, Germany. TEL 49-30-2510415, FAX 49-30-2511136, 100615.1565@compuserve.com, http://www.vwb-verlag.com. Circ: 200. **Co-sponsor:** Zentralstelle fuer Paedagogische Information und Dokumentation.

370.21 ZWE
ZIMBABWE. CENTRAL STATISTICAL OFFICE. EDUCATION REPORT. Text in English. a. ZWD 176.90 in Africa; ZWD 240.20 in Europe; ZWD 285.30 elsewhere (effective 2000). **Document type:** *Government.*
Published by: Central Statistical Office, Causeway, PO Box 8063, Harare, Zimbabwe. TEL 263-4-706681, FAX 263-4-728529.

EDUCATION—Adult Education

374 USA ISSN 1524-7244
A A C E BONUS BRIEFS; connecting careers, education, and work. Text in English. 1991. q. USD 15 to members (effective 2003). back issues avail.; reprints avail. **Document type:** *Consumer.*
Published by: American Association for Career Education, 2900 Amby Pl, Hermosa Beach, CA 90254-2216. TEL 310-376-7378, FAX 310-376-2926. R&P Pat Nellor Wickwire. Circ: 500 (controlled).

374 USA ISSN 1074-9551
A A C E CAREERS UPDATE; connecting careers, education and work. Text in English. 1982. q. USD 15 to non-members (effective 2004). adv. bk.rev. back issues avail.; reprints avail. **Document type:** *Newsletter.* **Description:** Covers education, work, and careers today.
Published by: American Association for Career Education, 2900 Amby Pl, Hermosa Beach, CA 90254-2216. TEL 310-376-7378, FAX 310-376-2926. Ed. Pat Wickwire. R&P, Adv. contact Pat Nellor Wickwire. page USD 150; trim 8.5 x 11. Circ: 500.

374 USA ISSN 1549-0181
A A C E DISTINGUISHED MEMBER SERIES ON CAREER EDUCATION; connecting careers, education, and work. Text in English. 1992. a. USD 15 to members (effective 2003). back issues avail.; reprints avail. **Document type:** *Academic/Scholarly.*
Published by: American Association for Career Education, 2900 Amby Pl, Hermosa Beach, CA 90254-2216. TEL 310-376-7378, FAX 310-376-2926. Ed. Pat Wickwire. R&P, Adv. contact Pat Nellor Wickwire. Circ: 500 (controlled).

374.96 KEN ISSN 0256-5048
A A E A NEWSLETTER. Text in English. 1978. s-a. free. back issues avail. **Document type:** *Newsletter.*
Indexed: RASB.
Published by: African Adult Education Association, PO Box 50768, Nairobi, Kenya. Ed. Paul Wangoola. Circ: 1,200.

374.4 USA
A C S D E RESEARCH MONOGRAPH SERIES. Text in English. 1990. irreg., latest vol.16, 1998. price varies. **Document type:** *Monographic series.* **Description:** Publishes technical or specialized articles, symposium papers and studies on a variety of topics relating to distance education, including computer applications, studies of international interest, and research issues.
—BLDSC (0578.895300).
Published by: (American Center for the Study of Distance Education), Pennsylvania State University, College of Education, 110 Rackley Blvd, University Park, PA 16802-3202. TEL 814-863-3764, FAX 814-865-5878, http://www.ed.psu.edu/acsde/. Ed. Michael G Moore TEL 814-863-3501. R&P Suzanne Bienert.

374.013 DEU ISSN 0937-8375
A K S B - INFORM. Text in German. 1974. bi-m. bk.rev. **Document type:** *Newsletter.*
Published by: Arbeitsgemeinschaft Katholisch-Sozialer Bildungswerke, Heilsbachstr 6, Bonn, 53123, Germany. TEL 49-228-645058, FAX 49-228-6420910, info@aksb.de. Ed. Lukas Rolli. Pub. Johannes Tessmer.

374 IRL
A O N T A S NEWSHEET. Text in English. 5/yr. membership. **Document type:** *Newsletter.*
Published by: A O N T A S National Association of Adult Education, 83-87 Main St., 2nd Flr., Ranelagh, Ireland. TEL 353-1-4754121, FAX 353-1-4780084. Ed. Margaret Purcell.

374 AUS
A R I S MONTHLY MEMO. Text in English. m. free with subscription to ARIS Resources Bulletin. **Document type:** *Newsletter, Academic/Scholarly.* **Description:** Provides a source of information about a range of professional development opportunities for teachers, coordinators and tutors - workshops, conferences, courses and other activities.
Published by: Adult Education Resource and Information Service (Subsidiary of: Language Australia), GPO Box 372F, Melbourne, VIC 3001, Australia. TEL 61-3-9926-4779, FAX 61-3-9926-4780, robynh@la.ames.vic.edu.au, http://sunsite.anu.edu.au/language-australia/aris. **Co-sponsors:** Language Australia; Adult, Community & Further Education Board.

374 AUS ISSN 1035-6932
A R I S RESOURCES BULLETIN. Text in English. 1990. q. AUD 30 domestic; AUD 40 foreign (effective 2001). **Description:** Provides information for adult education teachers, especially those teaching literacy and numeracy. Includes reviews and abstracts of new publications and a list of recently published journal readings.
Indexed: AEI, L&LBA.
Published by: Adult Education Resource and Information Service (Subsidiary of: Language Australia), GPO Box 372F, Melbourne, VIC 3001, Australia. TEL 61-3-9926-4779, FAX 61-3-9926-4780, robynh@la.ames.vic.edu.au, http://sunsite.anu.edu.au/language-australia/aris. Ed. Robyn Hodge. Circ: 1,500.

A R T I NEWS LETTER. see *AGRICULTURE*

ACCESS (GLENSIDE); information and education for the mining and petroleum industry. see *MINES AND MINING INDUSTRY*

374.4 FRA ISSN 0397-331X
ACTUALITE DE LA FORMATION PERMANENTE. Text in French. 1972. 6/yr. bk.rev. bibl.
Indexed: RASB.
Published by: Centre I N F F O, Tour Europe, Paris La Defense, Cedex 92049, France. TEL 33-1-41252222, FAX 33-1-47737420, TELEX 615 383, cinffo1@easynet.fr. Ed. Ambroise Monod. Pub. Patrick Kessel. Circ: 4,400.

ADIESTRAMIENTO. see *LABOR UNIONS*

374.012 USA ISSN 1052-231X
LC5201
➤ **ADULT BASIC EDUCATION**; an interdisciplinary journal for adult literacy educational planning. Text in English. 1977. 3/yr. USD 30 in US & Canada; USD 40 elsewhere (effective 2003). adv. bk.rev. abstr.; bibl.; stat.; illus. index. back issues avail.; reprints avail. **Document type:** *Journal, Academic/Scholarly.*
Formerly (until vol.14, no.3, 1990): Adult Literacy and Basic Education (0147-8354)
Related titles: Microfilm ed.: (from PQC); Online - full text ed.: (from EBSCO Publishing, Northern Light Technology, Inc., ProQuest Information & Learning).
Indexed: ABIn, AgeL, BRI, CIJE, EduInd.
—BLDSC (0696.637000), IE, Infotrieve, ingenta.
Published by: Commission on Adult Basic Education, 1320 Jamesville Ave, Syracuse, NY 13210. TEL 315-426-0645, FAX 315-422-6369, http://www.coabe.org/. Ed., Adv. contact Ken Melichar TEL 706-778-3000 ext. 1264. R&P Larry Ady. Circ: 1,500 (paid).

374 AUS
ADULT, COMMUNITY AND FURTHER EDUCATION BOARD. ANNUAL REPORTS. Text in English. 1998 (Dec 22nd). a. **Document type:** *Government.*
Related titles: Online - full content ed.
Published by: Adult, Community & Further Education Board (Subsidiary of: Adult, Community & Further Education Division), PO Box 266 D, Melbourne, VIC 3001, Australia. TEL 61-3-9637-2675, FAX 61-3-9637-2490, valerie.hazel@dse.vic.gov.au, http://www.acfe.vic.gov.au.

374.7 DEU ISSN 0342-7633
LC2607
ADULT EDUCATION AND DEVELOPMENT. Text in English. 1973. s-a. **Document type:** *Journal, Academic/Scholarly.*
Related titles: Spanish ed.: Educacion de Adultos y Desarrollo. ISSN 0935-8153. 1978; French ed.: Education des Adultes et Developpement. ISSN 0935-8161. 1978.
Indexed: CPE, DIP, ERA, ETA, IBR, IBZ, MEA, RDA, RHEA, RRTA, SEA, SENA, SOMA, SWA, TDB, TEA, WAE&RSA.
—BLDSC (0696.657500), IE, ingenta. **CCC.**
Published by: Institut fuer Internationale Zusammenarbeit des Deutschen Volkshochschul-Verbandes, Obere Wilhelmstr 32, Bonn, 53225, Germany. TEL 49-228-975690, FAX 49-228-9756955, iiz-dvv@iiz-dvv.de, http://www.iiz-dvv.de/deutsch/default.htm. Ed. Heribert Hinzen. Circ: 21,000 (controlled).

374 IRL
ADULT EDUCATION COLLEGE: AN GRIANAN PROGRAMME. Text in English. 1954. a. adv. **Document type:** *Newsletter.* **Description:** Outlines weekly courses for the year taught by the Irish Countrywomen's Association.
Formerly: Irish Countrywomen's Association: An Grianan Programme
Published by: Irish Countrywomen's Association, An Grianan, Termonfechin, Co. Louth, Ireland. TEL 353-41-9822119, FAX 353-41-9822690, admin@an-grianan.ie. Ed. Ann Flanagan. Circ: 5,000.

374.4 GBR
ADULT EDUCATION PROGRAMME. Text in English. 1965. a. free. adv. **Document type:** *Bulletin.* **Description:** For people interested in vocational and nonvocational adult education courses.
Published by: (Marketing - News Group Office), Bradford and Ilkley Community College, Great Horton Rd, Bradford, W Yorks BD7 1AY, United Kingdom. TEL 44-1274-753089, FAX 44-1274-753173, rons@bilk.ac.uk. Ed. Ron T Sweeney. Adv. contact Lynn Tomlinson. B&W page GBP 750. Circ: 50,000.

374 USA ISSN 0741-7136
LC5201
➤ **ADULT EDUCATION QUARTERLY**; a journal of research and theory. Text in English. 1950. q. USD 74, GBP 45 to individuals; USD 237, GBP 153 to institutions; USD 246, GBP 159 combined subscription to institutions print & online eds. (effective 2006). adv. bk.rev. illus. index. reprints avail. **Document type:** *Journal, Academic/Scholarly.* **Description:** Committed to the dissemination of research and theory in adult and continuing education. Articles report research, build theory, interpret and review literature, and ctritique work previously published in the journal.
Formerly (until 1983): Adult Education (0001-8481); Which was formed by the 1950 merger of: Adult Education Journal (0888-5060); Adult Education Bulletin (0733-0766); Which was superseded in part (in 1941): Journal of Adult Education (0888-5044)
Related titles: Microform ed.: (from PQC); Online - full text ed.: ISSN 1552-3047. USD 234, GBP 151 to institutions (effective 2006) (from C S A, EBSCO Publishing, Gale Group, H.W. Wilson, O C L C Online Computer Library Center, Inc., Sage Publications, Inc., Swets Information Services).
Indexed: ABIn, ASCA, AgeL, BRI, BrEdI, CBRI, CIJE, CPE, CurCont, EAA, ERA, ETA, EduInd, HECAB, MEA, MEA&I, MEDLINE, PCI, PsycInfo, PsycholAb, RASB, REE&TA, RHEA, RI-1, RI-2, SEA, SENA, SOMA, SSCI, SWA, TEA, e-psyche.
—BLDSC (0696.667000), IDS, IE, Infotrieve, ingenta. **CCC.**
Published by: (American Association for Adult and Continuing Education), Sage Publications, Inc., 2455 Teller Rd, Thousand Oaks, CA 91320. TEL 805-499-0721, 800-818-7243, FAX 805-499-0871, 800-583-2665, info@sagepub.com, http://www.sagepub.com/journal.aspx?pid=22. Eds. Bradley C Courtenay, Robert J Hill. Adv. contact Kirsten Beaulieu TEL 805-499-0721 ext 7160. B&W page USD 350. Circ: 5,000. **Subscr. to:** Sage Publications Ltd., 1 Oliver's Yard, 55 City Rd, London EC1 1SP, United Kingdom. TEL 44-20-73740645, FAX 44-20-73748741, subscription@sagepub.co.uk.

374 IRL ISSN 0790-8040
THE ADULT LEARNER. Text in English. 1985. a. **Document type:** *Newsletter, Academic/Scholarly.*
Related titles: Online - full text ed.
Published by: A O N T A S National Association of Adult Education, 83-87 Main St., 2nd Flr., Ranelagh, Ireland. TEL 353-1-4068220, FAX 353-1-4068227, mmcmullen@aontas.com, mail@aontas.com, http://www.aontas.com/. **Co-sponsor:** Adult Education Organiser's Association.

E

374 USA ISSN 1045-1595
LC5251
ADULT LEARNING. Text in English. q. USD 29 domestic; USD 34 in Canada; USD 39 elsewhere (effective 2004). adv. reprint service avail. from PQC. **Document type:** *Magazine, Trade.* **Description:** Practical applications of research, innovative instructional strategies.
Former titles (until 1989): Lifelong Learning (0740-0578); (until 1983): Lifelong Learning: The Adult Years (0148-2165); (until 1977): Adult Leadership (0001-8554); (until 1952): A A C E Dateline; Techniques for Teachers of Adults (0040-1358)
Related titles: Microform ed.: (from PQC); Online - full text ed.: (from EBSCO Publishing, Florida Center for Library Automation, Gale Group, H.W. Wilson, Northern Light Technology, Inc., O C L C Online Computer Library Center, Inc., ProQuest Information & Learning).
Indexed: ABIn, ASG, AcaI, AgeL, BRI, BrEdI, CBRI, CIJE, CPE, EduInd, LT&LA, MEDLINE, PCI, T&DA.
—BLDSC (0696.680100), IE, Infotrieve, ingenta.
Published by: American Association for Adult and Continuing Education, 4380 Forbes Blvd, Lanham, MD 20706. TEL 301-918-1913, FAX 301-918-1846, aaace10@aol.com, http://www.aaace.org. Ed. Stacy Hudson. Circ: 4,000 (controlled).

374.8 USA
ADULT LEARNING AND LITERACY - A L L POINTS BULLETIN. Text in English. 199?. bi-m. free. back issues avail. **Document type:** *Newsletter, Government.* **Description:** Publishes articles on adult basic education and literacy, English as a second language for immigrants, and other literacy-related issues, such as workplace literacy.
Published by: U.S. Department of Education, Office of Vocational and Adult Education, 4090 MES, 600 Independence Ave, S W, Washington, DC 20202. TEL 202-205-5451, 800-872-5327, FAX 202-205-8748, http://www.ed.gov/offices/OVAE.

374.8 GBR ISSN 1472-5061
LC5201
ADULT LEARNING YEARBOOK (YEAR). Text in English. 1961. a., latest 2001-2002. GBP 21.95 per issue (effective 2005). bk.rev. bibl. index. 378 p./no.; reprints avail. **Document type:** *Directory, Academic/Scholarly.* **Description:** Directory of organizations in the UK and guide to sources of information.
Former titles (until 2000): Adult Continuing Education Year Book; (until 1988): Yearbook of Adult Continuing Education (0265-1726); (until 1983): Yearbook of Adult Education (0084-3601)
Related titles: Microfiche ed.
—**CCC.**
Published by: The National Institute of Adult Continuing Education (NAICE), Renaissance House, 20 Princess Rd. W, Leicester, Leics LE1 6TP, United Kingdom. TEL 44-116-2044200, 44-116-2044201, FAX 44-116-2854514, enquiries@niace.org.uk, http://www.niace.org.uk/Publications/Periodicals/Yearbook.htm. R&P Virman Man. Circ: 2,000.

374.0124 AUS ISSN 0157-4833
ADULT LITERACY CONTACTS VICTORIA. Text in English. 1983. a. AUD 10 (effective 1999). **Document type:** *Directory.* **Description:** Lists names, addresses and descriptions of Victorian adult literacy programs.
Published by: Victorian Adult Literacy and Basic Education Council (VALBEC), Ross House, 247 Flinders Ln, Melbourne, VIC 3000, Australia. TEL 61-3-96506906, FAX 61-3-96541321, valbec@vicnet.net.au. Ed., Pub., R&P Robert Keith. Circ: 1,000.

374.1822 GBR ISSN 0955-2308
LC5201
ADULTS LEARNING. Text in English. 1989. 10/yr. GBP 34 domestic to individuals; GBP 45 elsewhere to individuals; GBP 56 domestic to institutions; GBP 70 elsewhere to institutions (effective 2003). adv. bk.rev.; Website rev. illus. index. back issues avail.; reprints avail. **Document type:** *Academic/Scholarly.* **Description:** For everyone involved in the education and training of adults, and contains essays, news and special features.
Related titles: Online - full text ed.: (from EBSCO Publishing).
Indexed: BrEdI, CIJE, CPE, ERA, ETA, MEA, RHEA, SEA, SENA, SOMA, TEA.
—BLDSC (0696.684887), IE, Infotrieve, ingenta.
Published by: The National Institute of Adult Continuing Education (NAICE), Renaissance House, 20 Princess Rd. W, Leicester, Leics LE1 6TP, United Kingdom. TEL 44-116-2044200, 44-116-2044201, FAX 44-116-2854514, enquiries@niace.org.uk, http://www.niace.org.uk/Publications/Periodicals/AdultsLearning/Default.htm. Ed., Adv. contact Stephenie Hughes TEL 44-116-2044211. Circ: 3,000.

374 USA
ADVENTURES IN ASSESSMENT. Text in English. a. back issues avail. **Document type:** *Journal, Academic/Scholarly.* **Description:** Examines approaches to literacy education for adults.
Related titles: Online - full content ed.
Published by: (System for Adult Basic Education Support), Massachusetts Department of Education, 350 Main St, Malden, MA 02148-5023. http://www.sabes.org.

374 FIN ISSN 0358-6197
➤ **AIKUISKASVATUS/ADULT EDUCATION.** Text in Finnish; Summaries in English, Finnish. 1981. q. EUR 25, USD 30 (effective 2003). adv. bk.rev. 80 p./no.; back issues avail. **Document type:** *Journal, Academic/Scholarly.* **Description:** Publishes specific themes, mostly scientific, in adult education.
Indexed: AgeL.
Published by: Kansanvalistusseura (KVS Foundation)/The Finnish Adult Education Research Society, Dobelninkatu 2 E 28, Helsinki, 00260, Finland. TEL 358-9-54918855, FAX 358-9-54918811, anneli.kajanto@kvs.fi, info@kvs.fi, http://www.kansanvalistusseura.fi, http://www.kvs.fi. Eds. Anneli Kajanto TEL 358-9-54918833, Anja Heikkinen. R&P, Adv. contact Anneli Kajanto TEL 358-9-54918833. B&W page USD 500. Circ: 2,200.

374.9798 USA
ALASKA ADULT EDUCATION. Text in English. a. **Document type:** *Government.*
Published by: Department of Education, 801 W 10th St, Ste 200, Juneau, AK 99801-1894.

374.013 HKG
THE ALTERNATIVE ROUTE. Text in Chinese. 1986. bi-m. free. **Document type:** *Newsletter.* **Description:** Follows activities and developments of the council and is targeted to readers in government, employment, educational and social services circles.
Formerly (until 1998): Vocational Training News
Published by: Vocational Training Council, Information and Public Relations Section, Vocational Training Council Tower, 27 Wood Rd., 14th Fl., Wanchai, Hong Kong. TEL 852-2836-1046, FAX 852-2591-4809. Circ: 7,000.

AMERICAN COUNCIL ON EDUCATION. CENTER FOR ADULT LEARNING UPDATE. see *MILITARY*

374.4 USA ISSN 0892-3647
LC5805 CODEN: AJDECQ
➤ **AMERICAN JOURNAL OF DISTANCE EDUCATION.** Text in English. 1983. q., latest vol.17. USD 185 in US & Canada to institutions; USD 215 elsewhere to institutions; USD 195 combined subscription in US & Canada to institutions print & online eds. (effective 2006); USD 225 combined subscription elsewhere to institutions print & online eds. (effective 2005). bk.rev. back issues avail.; reprint service avail. from PSC. **Document type:** *Journal, Academic/Scholarly.* **Description:** Serves as a forum for discussion about research in and the practice of distance education in the Americas, examining program ideas, developments in methods and systems for the delivery of education at a distance, management and administration, evaluation and assessment through a variety of technical media..
Formerly (until 1987): Media and Adult Learning (0886-5086)
Related titles: Online - full content ed.: ISSN 1538-9286. USD 175 worldwide to institutions (effective 2006); Online - full text ed.: (from EBSCO Publishing, Gale Group, O C L C Online Computer Library Center, Inc., Swets Information Services).
Indexed: ABIn, CIJE, CPE, ERA, ETA, EduInd, HEA, Inspec, SENA, T&DA, TEA.
—BLDSC (0824.305000), IE, Infotrieve, ingenta. **CCC.**
Published by: (Pennsylvania State University, College of Education), Lawrence Erlbaum Associates, Inc., 10 Industrial Ave, Mahwah, NJ 07430-2262. TEL 201-258-2200, 800-926-6579, FAX 201-236-0072, journals@erlbaum.com, http://www.leaonline.com/loi/ajde. Ed. Michael G Moore TEL 814-863-3501.

374 SCG ISSN 0354-5415
➤ **ANDRAGOSKE STUDIJE**; casopis za proucavanje obrazovanja i ucenja odraslih. Text in Serbo-Croatian, English. 1994. s-a. YUN 175 domestic; USD 20 foreign (effective 2003). adv. bk.rev. abstr. 98 p./no.; back issues avail. **Document type:** *Journal, Academic/Scholarly.*
Published by: Filozofski Fakultet, Institut za Pedagogiju i Andragogiju, Cika Ljubina 18-20, Belgrade, 11000. andragogisimus@yahoo.com, kovesni@eunet.yu. Ed. Dusan Savicevic. Adv. contact Miomir Despotovic TEL 38-11-3206159. Circ: 250.

374 USA ISSN 1527-3970
LC5225.R4
ANNUAL REVIEW OF ADULT LEARNING AND LITERACY. Text in English. a. back issues avail. **Document type:** *Academic/Scholarly.*
Published by: (National Center for the Study of Adult Learning and Literacy), Jossey-Bass Inc., Publishers (Subsidiary of: John Wiley & Sons, Inc.), 989 Market St, San Francisco, CA 94103-1741. TEL 415-433-1740, 800-956-7739, FAX 415-433-0499, http://www.gse.harvard.edu/%7Encsall/ann_rev/index.html, http://www.josseybass.com.

APPROVED PROVIDERS OF CONTINUING PHARMACEUTICAL EDUCATION. see *PHARMACY AND PHARMACOLOGY*

374.84895 DNK ISSN 1395-2471
ASKOV HOEJSKOLE. AARSSKRIFT. Text in Danish. 1904. a. DKK 50. illus.
Formerly (until 1994): Askov Laerlinge (0106-7478)
Published by: Askov Hoejskoles Elevforening, Maltvej 1, Vejen, 6600, Denmark.

ASSOCIATION EDUCATOR. see *BUSINESS AND ECONOMICS—Management*

374 CAN ISSN 0703-5357
ATLANTIC CO-OPERATOR; promoting community ownership. Text in English. 1933. 9/yr. CND 10; CND 20 foreign. adv. bk.rev. back issues avail. **Document type:** *Consumer.*
Formerly: Maritime Co-Operator (0025-3405)
—CISTI.
Address: 123 Halifax Street, Moncton, NB E1C 8N5, Canada. TEL 506-858-6614, FAX 506-858-6615, coop@nbnet.nb.ca, atlcoop@atcom.com. Ed. Ron Levesque. Pub. Euclide Chiasson. Circ: 40,000 (paid and controlled).

374 DEU ISSN 0004-8100
DER AUSBILDER. Text in German. 1952. m. adv. bk.rev. charts. index. **Document type:** *Journal, Trade.*
Indexed: DIP, IBR, IBZ.
—IE, Infotrieve. **CCC.**
Published by: Franz Steiner Verlag Stuttgart GmbH, Birkenwaldstr 44, Stuttgart, 70191, Germany. TEL 49-711-25820, FAX 49-711-2582290, service@steiner-verlag.de, http://www.steiner-verlag.de/Ausbilder/. Ed. Rainer M. Kieslinger. adv.: B&W page EUR 600; trim 148 x 210. Circ: 4,700.

AUSTRALIAN BUSINESS EDUCATION DIRECTORY. see *BUSINESS AND ECONOMICS*

374.994 AUS ISSN 1443-1394
LC5201 CODEN: AJAEED
➤ **AUSTRALIAN JOURNAL OF ADULT LEARNING.** Text in English. 1961. s-a. AUD 70 (effective 2004). adv. bk.rev. index every 3 yrs. 130 p./no.; back issues avail. **Document type:** *Journal, Academic/Scholarly.* **Description:** Provides information concerned with the theory, research and practice of adult and community education, and to promote critical thinking and research in this field.
Former titles (until 2000): Australian Journal of Adult & Community Education (1035-0462); (until 1990): Australian Journal of Adult Education (0004-9387)
Related titles: Microfilm ed.: (from PQC).
Indexed: AEI, AusPAIS, CIJE, CPE, EAA, ERA, ETA, HEA, L&LBA, MEA, PCI, RHEA, SEA, SENA, SOMA, SOPODA, SWA, TEA.
—BLDSC (1801.730000), IE, ingenta.
Published by: Adult Learning Australia, PO Box 260, Canberra City, ACT 2601, Australia. TEL 61-2-62749500, FAX 61-2-62749513, info@ala.asn.au, http://www.ala.asn.au/pubs/AJAL/ajal.htm. Ed., R&P Roger Harris TEL 61-2-8302-6246. Adv. contact Cath Styles. Circ: 900 (paid); 200 (controlled).

374.0124 AUS ISSN 1320-2251
AUSTRALIAN LANGUAGE MATTERS. Text in English. 1993. q. AUD 33 domestic; AUD 55 foreign (effective 2001). adv. bk.rev. back issues avail. **Document type:** *Journal, Academic/Scholarly.* **Description:** Covers English language and literacy education, research and policy development for individuals, organizations, interest groups and research centers involved in LOTE.
Indexed: AEI, L&LBA, SOPODA.
Published by: Language Australia, GPO Box 372 F, Melbourne, VIC 3001, Australia. TEL 61-3-9926-4779, FAX 61-3-9926-4780, languageaustralia@languageaustralia.com.au, davet@la.ames.vic.edu.au, http://sunsite.anu.edu.au/language-australia. Ed. Dave Tout. Circ: 2,200 (paid).

AVIATION EDUCATION NEWS. see *TRANSPORTATION—Air Transport*

374 SWE ISSN 1403-3194
➤ **BALTIC SEA DIALOGUE**; newsletter for adult learning in the Baltic Sea area. Text in English. 1994. s-a. free (effective 2004). **Document type:** *Newsletter.*
Formerly (until 1998): Baltic Dialogue (1401-615X)
Related titles: Online - full text ed.
Published by: Nordens Folkliga Akademi/Nordic Folk Academy, PO Box 12024, Goeteborg, 40242, Sweden. TEL 46-31-695600, FAX 46-31-690950, norden@nfa.se, http://www.nfa.se/index.asp?lid=1&p=7&msid=7&pub_id=27. Ed. Antra Carlsen. Circ: 2,000 (free).

374.95492 BGD ISSN 0070-8135
BANGLADESH. EDUCATION DIRECTORATE. REPORT ON PILOT PROJECT ON ADULT EDUCATION. Text in English. 1964. a. BDT 2 per issue.
Supersedes: East Pakistan. Education Directorate. Adult Education Branch. Report on Pilot Project on Adult Education
Related titles: Bengali ed.: Barshika Bibarani Bayaska Siksha Parikshya Prakalpa Bangladesh.
Published by: Education Directorate, Adult Education Branch, B E E R I, Dhanmond, Dhaka, 5, Bangladesh. Circ: 500.

BANGLADESH JOURNAL OF EXTENSION EDUCATION. see *AGRICULTURE*

BANKING & FINANCIAL TRAINING. see *BUSINESS AND ECONOMICS—Banking And Finance*

E

BAPTIST ADULTS. see *RELIGIONS AND THEOLOGY—Protestant*

374 GBR ISSN 1357-7352
BASIC SKILLS. Text in English. 1978. q. **Description:** Provides information to anyone teaching basic skills to young people and adults in England and Wales, or anyone involved in education and training.
Former titles (until 1994): Adult Literacy and Basic Skills Unit. Newsletter (0260-5104); (until 1980): Adult Literacy Unit. Newsletter (0142-047X)
Indexed: CIJE.
—BLDSC (1864.165000).
Published by: Basic Skills Agency, Flat 1, Commonwealth House, 1-19 New Oxford St, London, WC1A 1NU, United Kingdom. TEL 44-171-405-4017, FAX 44-171-404-5038. Ed. Kate Cowlard.

374 DEU ISSN 0934-3814
BAUSTEINE GRUNDSCHULE. Text in German. 1988. bi-m. looseleaf. EUR 54; EUR 12 newsstand/cover (effective 2005). back issues avail. **Document type:** *Journal, Academic/Scholarly.*
Published by: Bergmoser und Hoeller Verlag GmbH, Karl-Friedrich-Str 76, Aachen, 52072, Germany. TEL 49-241-93888123, FAX 49-241-93888134, kontakt@buhv.de, http://www.buhv.de. Circ: 5,000.

374 CHN ISSN 1002-414X
BEIJING CHENGREN JIAOYU/BEIJING ADULT EDUCATION. Text in Chinese. m. CNY 12.
Related titles: Online - full text ed.: (from East View Information Services).
Published by: Beijing Chengren Jiaoyu Zazhishe, Beijing, 100088, China. TEL 2012890. Ed. Ma Guifeng.

374 DEU ISSN 0005-951X
DIE BERUFSBILDENDE SCHULE. Text in German. 1949. m. EUR 42.57; EUR 3.53 newsstand/cover. adv. bk.rev. bibl.; illus.; stat. index. **Document type:** *Journal, Academic/Scholarly.*
Indexed: DIP, IBR, IBZ, ILD, RASB.
—IE, Infotrieve. **CCC.**
Published by: (Bundesverband der Lehrer an Beruflichen Schulen), Heckner Druck- und Verlagsgesellschaft mbH & Co. KG, Postfach 1559, Wolfenbuettel, 38285, Germany. TEL 49-5331-800840, FAX 49-5331-800820. Eds. P Grothe, R Bader. adv.: B&W page EUR 1,069, color page EUR 2,143; trim 187 x 257. Circ: 19,373 (paid and controlled).

BETRIEBLICHE AUSBILDUNGSPRAXIS; Merkblaetter fuer Ausbilder in der Eisen- und Metallindustrie. see *METALLURGY*

374 DEU ISSN 1617-3287
BOCHUM STUDIES IN INTERNATIONAL ADULT EDUCATION. Abbreviated title: B S I A E. Text in English. 2000. irreg., latest vol.4, 2002. EUR 20.90 per vol.. **Document type:** *Monographic series, Academic/Scholarly.*
Published by: Lit Verlag, Grevener Str. 179, Muenster, 48159, Germany. TEL 49-251-235091, FAX 49-251-231972, lit@lit-verlag.de, http://www.lit-verlag.de/reihe/bostin. Ed. Agnieszka Bron.

BUSINESS EXECUTIVE. see *BUSINESS AND ECONOMICS—Management*

374.4 CAN
C A U C E BULLETIN. Text in English. 1969. q. CND 80 to members. back issues avail. **Document type:** *Bulletin.* **Description:** Reports current developments and noteworthy programs; includes list of regional, national and international conferences.
Published by: (Canadian Association for University Continuing Education), Elizabeth Clarke & Associates, 329 March Rd, Ste 232, P O Box 11, Kanata, ON K2K 2E1, Canada. TEL 613-599-7060, FAX 613-599-7027. Ed., R&P Regina Aulinskas. Circ: 475.

C C E T S W ANNUAL REVIEW. see *SOCIAL SERVICES AND WELFARE*

C C E T S W NEWS. see *SOCIAL SERVICES AND WELFARE*

374.94 GBR
C E D E P EUROPEAN CENTRE FOR CONTINUING EDUCATION ADDRESS BOOK. Text in English. 1982. a. GBP 95 to non-members. **Document type:** *Directory.* **Description:** Lists all alumni from CEDEP according to member company and geographical location.
Related titles: Diskette ed.
Published by: A P Information Services, Marlborough House, 298 Regents Park Rd, London, N3 2UU, United Kingdom. TEL 44-20-83499988, FAX 44-20-83499797, info@apinfo.co.uk, http://www.ap-info.co.uk. Ed. Alan Philipp. Circ: 5,000.

374.0124 IND
C I L ADULT LITERACY SERIES. Text in Assamese, English. 1976. irreg., latest 1983. bibl.
Published by: Ministry of Human Resource Development, Central Institute of Indian Languages, Manasagangotri, Mysore, Karnataka 570 006, India.

374.0124 IND
C I L BORDER AND TRIBAL LANGUAGES. ADULT LITERACY SERIES. Text in English. 1978. irreg., latest 1981. price varies.
Published by: Ministry of Human Resource Development, Central Institute of Indian Languages, Manasagangotri, Mysore, Karnataka 570 006, India.

C M E; South Africa's continuing medical education journal. (Continuing Medical Education) see *MEDICAL SCIENCES*

374.971 CAN ISSN 0835-4944
LC5254
➤ **CANADIAN JOURNAL FOR THE STUDY OF ADULT EDUCATION/REVUE CANADIENNE POUR L'ETUDE DE L'EDUCATION DES ADULTES.** Text in English. 1987. s-a. CND 30 in Canada to individuals; USD 30 in United States to individuals; USD 40 in United States to institutions. bk.rev. **Document type:** *Academic/Scholarly.* **Description:** Committed to the dissemination of knowledge derived from disciplined inquiry in the field of adult and continuing education.
Related titles: Microfiche ed.: (from MML); Microform ed.: (from MML); Online - full text ed.: (from Micromedia ProQuest).
Indexed: CEI, CPE, ERA, ETA, MEA, RHEA, SEA, SENA, SOMA, SWA, TEA.
—BLDSC (3035.780000), IE.
Published by: Canadian Association for the Study of Adult Education/Association Canadienne pour l'Etude de l'Education des Adultes, St Francis Xavier University, Dept of Adult Education, Xavier Hall, P O Box 5000, Antigonish, NS B2G 2W5, Canada. aquigley@stfx.ca. Ed., R&P Allan Quigley. Circ: 500.

➤ **CANADIAN JOURNAL OF CONTINUING MEDICAL EDUCATION.** see *MEDICAL SCIENCES*

374.8 AUS ISSN 0310-1649
CANBERRA PAPERS IN CONTINUING EDUCATION. Text in English. 1972; N.S. 1981. irreg., latest vol.5, 1985. price varies.
Published by: Australian National University, Centre for Continuing Education, c/o The Director, Canberra, ACT 0200, Australia. TEL 61-2-6249-2892, FAX 61-2-6249-2892.

CARAVAN; a resource for those engaged in animating adult faith formation. see *RELIGIONS AND THEOLOGY—Roman Catholic*

374.8 USA ISSN 0736-1920
HF5381.A1
CAREER PLANNING AND ADULT DEVELOPMENT JOURNAL. Text in English. 1983. q. USD 59 domestic membership includes Career Planning and Adult Development Network; USD 74 foreign membership includes Career Planning and Adult Development Network (effective 2004). adv. bk.rev.; film rev. illus. back issues avail.; reprints avail. **Document type:** *Journal, Trade.* **Description:** Contains articles on group and individual career counseling techniques, assessment, and job search skills for career counselors.
Indexed: CIJE, T&DA.
—BLDSC (3051.762000), IE, ingenta. **CCC.**
Published by: Career Planning and Adult Development Network, 4965 Sierra Rd, San Jose, CA 95132. TEL 408-441-9100, FAX 408-441-9101, info@careertrainer.com, http://www.careernetwork.org/. Ed. Steven E Beasley. Pub., R&P Richard L. Knowdell. Circ: 1,000.

374.8 USA ISSN 0898-1353
CAREER PLANNING AND ADULT DEVELOPMENT NETWORK NEWSLETTER; a newsletter for career counselors, educators, and human resource specialists. Text in English. 1979. bi-m. USD 227 (effective 2005). bk.rev.; film rev. back issues avail. **Document type:** *Newsletter.* **Description:** Listing of workshops, conferences, films, books and counseling techniques for career counselors.
Formerly: Career Planning and Adult Development Newsletter (0898-1345)
Indexed: CIJE.
Published by: Career Planning and Adult Development Network, 4965 Sierra Rd, San Jose, CA 95132. TEL 408-441-9100, FAX 408-441-9101, info@careertrainor.com, http://www.careernetwork.org/career_newsletter.html. Ed. Richard L. Knowdell. Circ: 600 (paid); 400 (free).

374 USA
CATALOGUE OF CONFERENCES, SEMINARS, WORKSHOP. Text in English. 1958. 3/yr. USD 5. bk.rev.
Former titles: Trends (Rye); Laymen's Movement Review (0023-9518)
Published by: Wainwright House, Inc., Wainwright House, 260 Stuyvesant Ave, Rye, NY 10580. TEL 914-967-6080, FAX 914-967-6114. Ed. Stacy C Orphanos. Circ: 35,000.

374 USA
LC215
➤ **THE CATALYST (PORTLAND).** Text in English. 1971. 3/yr. USD 50 (effective 2001). bk.rev. back issues avail. **Document type:** *Journal, Academic/Scholarly.*
Formerly (until vol.25, no.1, 1995): Community Services Catalyst (0739-9227)
Related titles: Online - full text ed.
Indexed: CIJE.
Published by: National Council for Continuing Education and Training, Palomar College, 1140 W Mission Rd, San Marcos, CA 92069. TEL 760-753-8375, FAX 760-942-7296, nccet@home.com, nccet@earthlink.net, http://www.nccet.org. Ed., R&P William J Flynn. Pub. Carol Brown. Circ: 1,200 (controlled).

374.8 USA ISSN 0736-3044
CENTER FOR SELF-SUFFICIENCY UPDATE. Text in English. 1984. a. looseleaf. USD 3 (effective 2000). 4 p./no.; back issues avail. **Document type:** *Newsletter.*
Published by: Center for Self-Sufficiency, Publishing Division, c/o Prosperity & Profits Unlimited Distribution Services, Box 416, Denver, CO 80201-0416. mail@besomebodybeyourself.com, www.centerforselfsufficiency.com. Ed. A Doyle. R&P A. Doyle. Circ: 2,000.

CENTRAL COUNCIL FOR EDUCATION AND TRAINING IN SOCIAL WORK. REPORT OF COUNCIL MEETING. see *SOCIAL SERVICES AND WELFARE*

374 FRA ISSN 1166-0600
CENTRE I N F F O. FICHES PRATIQUES. Key Title: Fiches Pratiques de la Formation Continue. Mise a Jour. Text in French. m.
Published by: Centre I N F F O, Tour Europe, Paris La Defense, Cedex 92049, France. TEL 33-1-41252222, FAX 33-1-47737420, cinffo1@easynet.fr.

CENTRE I N F F O. GUIDES TECHNIQUES. see *BUSINESS AND ECONOMICS—Personnel Management*

CHANGNYON UL WIHAN SONGGYONG YONGU. see *RELIGIONS AND THEOLOGY—Protestant*

CHANNEL (MADISON). see *LIBRARY AND INFORMATION SCIENCES*

CHECKMATE INCORPORATING DUNGEONMASTER. see *HOMOSEXUALITY*

CHENG NIAN QING NIAN YAN JING KE CHENG. see *RELIGIONS AND THEOLOGY—Protestant*

374.4 CHN ISSN 1009-7503
CHENGREN JIAOYU XUEKAN/ADULT EDUCATION. Text in Chinese. 1978. m. CNY 69 (effective 2004). 64 p./no.; **Document type:** *Journal, Academic/Scholarly.* **Description:** Covers adult education, occupational training, special education and correspondence education.
Former titles: Chengren Jiaoyu yu Qita Leixing Jiaoyu (1005-4170); (until 1994): Zhigong Jiaoyu yu Qita Leixing Jiaoyu (1001-3288)
Published by: Zhongguo Renmin Daxue, Shubao Zilio Zhongxin/Renmin University of China, Information Center for Social Server, Dongcheng-qu, 3, Zhangzizhong Lu, Beijing, 100007, China. TEL 86-10-64039458, FAX 86-10-64015080, kyes@163.net, http://www.confucius.cn.net/bkdetail.asp?fzt=G5. **Dist. in US by:** China Publications Service, PO Box 49614, Chicago, IL 60649. FAX 312-288-8570, 312-288-8570.

374 UKR
COLLEGIUM. Text in Ukrainian. s-a. USD 80 in United States.
Indexed: RASB.
Published by: Akademiya Evrobiznesa, A-ya 36, Kiev, 254119, Ukraine. **US dist. addr.:** East View Information Services, 3020 Harbor Ln. N., Minneapolis, MN 55447. TEL 612-550-0961.

374 DEU
COMMUNITY EDUCATION INTERNATIONAL. Text in English. 1984. s-a. adv. bk.rev. back issues avail. **Document type:** *Journal.*
Published by: International Community Education Association, c/o Prof. Dr. Juergen Zimmer, Pres. & Pub., International Academy, International Center of ICEA, Koenigin-Luise-Strasse 24-26, Berlin, 14195, Germany. icexicea@zedat.fu-berlin.de, http://www.community-education.de/. adv.: page GBP 300. Circ: 1,000.

COMMUTER PERSPECTIVES. see *EDUCATION—Higher Education*

374.8 USA ISSN 0361-6908
LC5252.C2
CONTINUATION EDUCATION. Text in English. 1975. 3/yr. USD 5 to individuals; USD 10 to institutions. charts; stat.
Formerly: Alternatives (0273-0839)
Published by: California Continuation Education Association, 6501 Balboa Blvd, Van Nuys, CA 91406. Ed. A C Laudon. Circ: 600.

374.8 USA ISSN 0736-1696
CONTINUING EDUCATION ALTERNATIVES UPDATE. Text in English. 1983. biennial. USD 19.95 (effective 2001). adv. bibl. 20 p./no.; back issues avail. **Document type:** *Directory.*
Related titles: Microfiche ed.
—**CCC.**

E

Published by: Prosperity and Profits Unlimited, PO Box 416, Denver, CO 80201-0416. TEL 303-575-5676, FAX 970-292-2136, mail@coursemith.com. Ed., R&P A Doyle TEL 303-575-5676. Circ: 1,000.

CONTINUING MEDICAL EDUCATION DIRECTORY. see *MEDICAL SCIENCES*

374 NLD ISSN 0166-7831
CONTOUR. Text in Dutch. 1922. 8/yr. bk.rev. illus. **Document type:** *Newsletter.*
Formerly: Federatie Contact (0014-9284)
Indexed: AgrForAb, CERDIC, ForAb, I&DA, RevApplEntom, S&F, WeedAb.
Published by: Y W C A of the Netherlands, FC Dondersstraat 23, Utrecht, 3572 JB, Netherlands. TEL 31-30-2715525, FAX 31-30-2722836, ywcanl@worldaccess.nl. Circ: 1,600.

374 CAN ISSN 0010-8146
LC5201 CODEN: COVEE5
➤ **CONVERGENCE**; international journal of adult education. Text and summaries in English, French, Spanish. 1968. q. USD 60, CND 90; USD 40, CND 60 to students (effective 2002). bk.rev. abstr. 92 p./no.; back issues avail. **Document type:** *Journal, Academic/Scholarly.* **Description:** Provides a forum for international exchange on developments in adult education.
Related titles: Microfiche ed.: (from MML); Microfilm ed.: (from MML); Microform ed.: (from MML, PQC); Online - full text ed.: (from EBSCO Publishing, H.W. Wilson, Micromedia ProQuest, O C L C Online Computer Library Center, Inc., ProQuest Information & Learning).
Indexed: ABIn, CEI, CIJE, CPE, CPerI, DSA, ERA, ETA, EduInd, MEA, MEA&I, RDA, REE&TA, RHEA, RRTA, SEA, SENA, SOMA, SOPODA, SSA, TDB, TEA, WAE&RSA.
—BLDSC (3463.550000), IE, Infotrieve, ingenta. **CCC.**
Published by: International Council for Adult Education/Conseil International d'Education des Adultes, 720 Bathurst St, Ste 500, Toronto, ON M5S 2R4, Canada. TEL 416-588-1211, FAX 416-588-5725, icae@icae.ca, http://www.web.net/icae. Ed. Stephan Dobson. Circ: 1,000.

374 USA
CONVERSATIONS. Text in English. 1982. 3/yr. looseleaf. USD 30 to individuals; USD 100 to institutions (effective 2000). back issues avail. **Document type:** *Newsletter.* **Description:** Covers non-formal, non-competitive education and emphasizes individual and community development; inspired by folk-schools of Scandinavia and liberatory education of Latin America.
Former titles: F E A A Newsletter (1067-4233); Folk School Association of America Newsletter
Published by: Folk Education Association of America, 73 Willow St., Florence, MA 01062-2639. TEL 413-585-8755, cspicer@k12Sphast.umass.edu, http://www.peopleseducation.org. Ed., R&P Chris Spicer TEL 413-585-8755. Circ: 350.

CORPORATE TRAINING & DEVELOPMENT ADVISOR; news & analysis for professionals in the corporate training industry. see *PUBLISHING AND BOOK TRADE*

374.8 USA
COURSE TRENDS. Text in English. m. USD 95. back issues avail. **Document type:** *Newsletter.* **Description:** Newsletter of information and trends in continuing education courses, programs, workshops, and seminars in all fields throughout the United States.
Incorporates: Marketing Classes for Adults; Formerly: Course Trends in Adult Learning
Published by: Learning Resources Network, PO Box 9, River Falls, WI 54022-0009. TEL 913-539-5376. Ed. Julie Coates. Circ: 2,000.

374 USA ISSN 1022-1646
CRITICAL PERSPECTIVES. Text in English. 1993. s-a.
Related titles: Online - full text ed.
Published by: Three Continents Press, Box 38009, Colorado Springs, CO 80937-8009.

CUADERNOS C I P C A (SERIE POPULAR). see *AGRICULTURE—Agricultural Economics*

374.8 USA ISSN 0097-952X
BR115.C8
CULTURAL INFORMATION SERVICE; the magazine for lifelong learners. Text in English. 1972. 10/yr. USD 37; USD 49 foreign. bk.rev. index. **Description:** Discusses education and media.
Published by: C I S-tems, Inc., PO Box 786, New York, NY 10159. TEL 212-691-5240. Ed. Frederic A Brussat.

374.013 GBR
DATA NEWS. Text in English. q. **Document type:** *Bulletin, Trade.*
Supersedes (in 1998): Monitor (London); Which was formerly: N V Q Monitor
Indexed: M&MA.
Published by: Qualifications and Curriculum Authority, 29 Bolton St, London, W1Y 7PD, United Kingdom. TEL 44-171-509-5555, info@qca.org.uk, http://www.open.gov.uk/qca/.

430.715 DEU ISSN 0341-3675
DEUTSCH LERNEN; Zeitschrift fuer den Sprachunterricht mit auslaendischen Arbeitnehmern. Text in German. 1976. q. adv. bk.rev. back issues avail.; reprint service avail. from PQC. **Document type:** *Academic/Scholarly.*
Indexed: IBR, L&LBA, LT&LA, SOPODA.
—IE.
Published by: (Sprachverband Deutsch fuer Auslaendische Arbeitnehmer e.V.), Schneider Verlag Hohengehren GmbH, Wilhelmstr 13, Baltmannsweiler, 73666, Germany. FAX 49-7153-48761, schneider-verlag-hohengehren@t-online.de.

374 ESP ISSN 1134-7880
DIALOGOS (EL MANSOU, BARCELONA); educacion y formacion de personas adultas. Text in Spanish. 1994. 3/yr.
—CINDOC.
Published by: Dialogos, C. Amadeo Vives, 7, El Masnou, Barcelona, 08320, Spain. TEL 34-93-5404326, FAX 34-93-540-0504, http://www.dialogosred.org/. Ed. Angel Marzo.

DIASTEMA; rivista di cultura e informazione musicale. see *MUSIC*

THE DISSEMINATOR. see *LIBRARY AND INFORMATION SCIENCES*

374.4 GBR ISSN 0158-7919
LC5800
➤ **DISTANCE EDUCATION**; an international journal. Text in English. 1980. 3/yr. GBP 191, USD 309, AUD 309 combined subscription to institutions print & online eds. (effective 2006). adv. bk.rev. cum.index. back issues avail.; reprint service avail. from PSC. **Document type:** *Journal, Academic/Scholarly.* **Description:** Publishes papers on the philosophy, history, politics, theory, practice and administration of distance education, open learning, and flexible delivery systems.
Related titles: Online - full text ed.: ISSN 1475-0198. 2002. GBP 191, USD 294, AUD 294 to institutions (effective 2006) (from EBSCO Publishing, Gale Group, IngentaConnect, O C L C Online Computer Library Center, Inc., ProQuest Information & Learning, R M I T Publishing, Swets Information Services).
Indexed: ABIn, AEI, CIJE, CPE, ERA, ETA, EduInd, HEA, MEA, RHEA, SEA, SENA, SOMA, TEA.
—BLDSC (3602.520000), IE, Infotrieve, ingenta. **CCC.**
Published by: (Open and Distance Learning Association of Australia AUS), Routledge (Subsidiary of: Taylor & Francis Group), 4 Park Sq, Milton Park, Abingdon, Oxon OX14 4RN, United Kingdom. TEL 44-1235-828600, FAX 44-1235-829000, distance-education@unimelb.edu.au, info@routledge.co.uk, http://www.tandf.co.uk/journals/titles/01587919.asp, http://www.routledge.com. Eds. Som Naidu, Som Naidu. Circ: 1,000. **Subscr. in N. America to:** Taylor & Francis Inc., Customer Services Dept, 325 Chestnut St, 8th Fl, Philadelphia, PA 19106. TEL 215-625-8900, 800-354-1420, FAX 215-625-8914, customerservice@taylorandfrancis.com; **Subscr. to:** Taylor & Francis Ltd, Journals Customer Service, Rankine Rd, Basingstoke, Hants RG24 8PR, United Kingdom. TEL 44-1256-813000, FAX 44-1256-330245.

374 ESP ISSN 1133-1151
A DISTANCIA. Text in Spanish. 1983. s-a. **Document type:** *Academic/Scholarly.*
Formerly (until 1983): U N E D (1135-1721)
Related titles: ◆ Supplement(s): Cuadernos de Cultura. ISSN 1135-1608.
—CINDOC.
Published by: Universidad Nacional de Educacion a Distancia, Bravo Murillo No. 38, Madrid, Spain. TEL 91-3986000, FAX 91-3986600, infouned@adm.uned.es, http://www.uned.es/.

DOSSIER KENNIS EN MEDIA. see *EDUCATION—Teaching Methods And Curriculum*

DRIVING INSTRUCTOR. see *TRANSPORTATION—Automobiles*

DRIVING INSTRUCTOR'S MANUAL. see *TRANSPORTATION—Automobiles*

374.094183 IRL ISSN 0791-7392
DUBLIN'S EVENING CLASSES. Text in English. 1991. a. **Document type:** *Directory, Academic/Scholarly.*
Published by: Oisin Publications, 4 Iona Dr., Dublin, 9, Ireland. TEL 353-1-8305236, FAX 353-1-8307860, oisinpr@iol.ie.

374 DEU ISSN 0341-7905
E B - ERWACHSENENBILDUNG. Text in German. q. EUR 25 (effective 2005). adv. **Document type:** *Journal, Academic/Scholarly.*
Formerly (until 1971): Erwachsenenbildung (0423-3530)
Indexed: DIP, IBR, IBZ.
—CCC.
Published by: Katholische Bundesarbeitsgemeinschaft fuer Erwachsenenbildung, Joachimstr 1, Bonn, 53113, Germany. TEL 49-228-902470, FAX 49-228-9024729, kbe@kbe-bonn.de, http://shop.wbv.de/promoframes/promoframe_EB110202102921.html, http://www.kath.de/kbe/. adv.: B&W page EUR 690, color page EUR 1,207.50. Circ: 2,000 (paid and controlled).

374 371.42 GBR ISSN 0040-0912
T61 CODEN: EDTRDC
➤ **EDUCATION + TRAINING.** Text in English. 1959. 9/yr. EUR 9,112.16 in Europe; USD 7,769 in North America; AUD 11,169 in Australasia; GBP 6,143.29 in UK & elsewhere (effective 2006). bk.rev. illus. index. reprint service avail. from PSC. **Document type:** *Journal, Academic/Scholarly.* **Description:** Research and case study papers relating to vocational education and training worldwide.
Formerly: Technical Education
Related titles: Online - full text ed.: (from EBSCO Publishing, Emerald Group Publishing Limited, Gale Group, IngentaConnect, O C L C Online Computer Library Center, Inc., ProQuest Information & Learning, Swets Information Services).
Indexed: ABIn, ADPA, BrEdI, CIJE, CPE, EAA, ERA, ETA, EmerIntel, Emerald, HECAB, HRA, Inspec, M&MA, MEA, PsycInfo, PsycholAb, RHEA, SEA, SENA, SOMA, SWA, T&DA, TEA.
—BLDSC (3661.198000), IE, Infotrieve, ingenta. **CCC.**
Published by: Emerald Group Publishing Limited, 60-62 Toller Ln, Bradford, W Yorks BD8 9BY, United Kingdom. TEL 44-1274-777700, FAX 44-1274-785200, infomation@emeraldinsight.com, http://www.emeraldinsight.com/et.htm. Ed. Dr. Richard Holden. Pub. Miss Rachel Murawa. R&P Mr. John Eggleton.

374.8 361 FRA ISSN 0339-7513
EDUCATION PERMANENTE. Text in French. 1969. 4/yr. adv. bk.rev. Supplement avail.
Indexed: CPE, ERA, ETA, ILD, MEA, RHEA, SEA, SENA, SOMA, TEA.
—BLDSC (3661.312000), IE, Infotrieve.
Address: 16 rue Berthollet, Arcueil, Cedex 94113, France. TEL 33-1-40499470, FAX 33-1-40499469. Ed. Guy Jobert. Circ: 3,500. **Subscr. to:** 10 bis rue du Fief, Cely En Biere 77930, France.

374.22 USA ISSN 1093-7188
EDUCATION SPECIAL INTEREST SECTION QUARTERLY. Text in English. 1991. q. USD 20 (effective 1999). **Document type:** *Newsletter.*
Formerly (until 1997): Education Special Interest Section Newsletter (1059-0595)
Related titles: ◆ Series: Administration & Management Special Interest Section Quarterly. ISSN 1093-720X; ◆ Developmental Disabilities Special Interest Section Quarterly. ISSN 1093-7196; ◆ Gerontology Special Interest Section Quarterly. ISSN 1093-717X; ◆ Mental Health Special Interest Section Quarterly. ISSN 1093-7226; ◆ Sensory Integration Special Interest Section Quarterly. ISSN 1093-7250; ◆ Work Programs Special Interest Section Quarterly. ISSN 1093-7145; ◆ Physical Disabilities Special Interest Section Quarterly. ISSN 1093-7234; ◆ Technology Special Interest Section Quarterly. ISSN 1093-7137.
Indexed: CINAHL.
Published by: American Occupational Therapy Association, Inc., 4720 Montgomery Ln, Bethesda, MD 20814-3425. TEL 301-652-2682, FAX 301-652-7711.

EDUCATIONAL GERONTOLOGY; an international journal. see *GERONTOLOGY AND GERIATRICS*

EDUCATIONAL OPPORTUNITIES OF GREATER BOSTON. see *EDUCATION—Guides To Schools And Colleges*

EDUCATIONAL TECHNOLOGY ABSTRACTS. see *EDUCATION—Abstracting, Bibliographies, Statistics*

374 POL ISSN 1507-6563
EDUKACJA USTAWICZNA DOROSLYCH. Text in Polish. 1993. q.
Formerly (until 1999): Edukacja Doroslych (1230-9206)
Published by: (Towarzystwo Uniwersytetu Robotniczego, Towarzystwo Wiedzy Powszechnej, Stowarzyszenie Oswiatowcow Polskich, Instytut Technologii Eksploatacji, Osrodek Ksztalcenia i Doskonalenia Kadr), Instytut Technologii Eksploatacji, ul Pulaskiego 6/10, Radom, 26600, Poland. TEL 48-22-3644241, FAX 48-22-3644765, instytut@itee.radom.pl, http://www.itee.radom.pl. Ed. Henryk Bednarczyk TEL 48-22-3644778.

374.016 USA ISSN 1543-4710
ELDERHOSTEL. Variant title: Elderhostel Catalog. Text in English. 1978. 8/yr. free in US & Canada; USD 45 foreign (effective 2005). **Document type:** *Catalog, Consumer.* **Description:** Contains information on domestic and overseas educational programs for adults age 55 and older.
Formerly (until 2003): Elderhostel: U.S. and Canada Catalog (1530-1184)
Published by: Elderhostel, Inc., 11 Avenue de Lafayette, Boston, MA 02111-1746. TEL 978-323-4141, 877-426-8056, FAX 617-426-0701, registration@elderhostel.org, http://www.elderhostel.org. Circ: 900,000.

374 JPN
ENERGETIC LIFE/KASSEI. Text in Japanese. 1977. m. JPY 7,680.
Published by: Gakken Co. Ltd., 40-5 Kami-Ikedai 4-chome, Ota-ku, Tokyo, 145-0064, Japan. Ed. Hiroyoshi Tayama.

▼ *new title* ➤ *refereed* ✶ *unverified* ◆ *full entry avail.*

374 JPN
ENLIGHTENMENT/KEIHATSU. Text in Japanese. 1974. m. JPY 5,980.
Published by: Gakken Co. Ltd., 40-5 Kami-Ikedai 4-chome, Ota-ku, Tokyo, 145-0064, Japan. Ed. Ken'ichi Yamana.

374.4 USA
EXCLAIMER. Text in English. 1973. bi-m. free. **Document type:** *Academic/Scholarly.* **Description:** Contains articles, news and information on the contributions of University Outreach and Extension and continuing professional education throughout Missouri.
Published by: University Outreach & Extension, 817 Clark Hall, Columbia, MO 65211. TEL 573-882-0604, FAX 573-882-2595, http://riker.ps.missouri.edu/deptpubs/extensionlincoln/extensionlincoln.html. Ed. Eileen Bennett. R&P Ileen Bennett. Circ: 10,000 (controlled).

EXPLORE THE BIBLE: ADULT LEARNER GUIDE LARGE PRINT. see *RELIGIONS AND THEOLOGY—Protestant*

374.0124 USA
EXPLORING ADULT LITERACY. Text in English. 1996. m. **Description:** Addresses the needs of adult literacy practitioners in adult basic education, family and workplace literacy.
Media: Online - full text.
Published by: Virginia Commonwealth University, School of Education, Box 842020, Richmond, VA 23284-2020. http://www.vcu.edu/eduweb/CRA/eal.html. Ed. N Boraks.

374 SWE ISSN 1404-7314
➤ **F O V U DIALOG.** (Folkeoplysnings- og Voksenundervisningsarbejde) Text in Danish, Norwegian, Swedish. 1991. 3/yr. free (effective 2004). **Document type:** *Academic/Scholarly.*
Former titles (until 1996): Dialog i Nordisk Folkbildning och Vuxenundervisning (1400-6758); (until 1995): F O V U Dialog (1991) (1102-7797)
Related titles: Finnish ed.
Published by: Nordens Folkliga Akademi/Nordic Folk Academy, PO Box 12024, Goeteborg, 40242, Sweden. TEL 46-31-695600, FAX 46-31-690950, norden@nfa.se, http://www.nfa.se/index.asp?lid=1&p=7&pub=6. Ed. Lis Hellstroem Sveningson. Circ: 4,000. **Co-sponsor:** Nordisk Ministerraad, Styringsgruppen for Nordisk Folkeoplysnings- og Voksenundervisningsarbejde (FOVU)/Nordic Council of Ministers. Committee on General and Adult Education.

➤ **FAMILY BIBLE SERIES: ADULTS.** see *RELIGIONS AND THEOLOGY—Protestant*

➤ **FAMILY BIBLE SERIES: LARGE PRINT.** see *RELIGIONS AND THEOLOGY—Protestant*

374 USA
FIELD NOTES (BOSTON). Text in English. q. **Description:** Covers a variety of topics devoted to adult education, including new educational resources and practices in the field.
Published by: (System for Adult Basic Education Support), Massachusetts Department of Education, 350 Main St, Malden, MA 02148-5023.

FISHERIES EDUCATION AND TRAINING. see *FISH AND FISHERIES*

374.8 USA
FIVE MINUTES WITH A C H E. Text in English. 1977. 10/yr. USD 25 (effective 2001). bk.rev. **Document type:** *Newsletter.*
Former titles: Association for Continuing Higher Education. Newsletter; Association of University Evening Colleges. Newsletter (0004-5845)
Media: Duplicated (not offset).
Published by: Association for Continuing Higher Education, Inc., Community College of Rhode Island, 400 East Ave, Warwick, RI 02886-1807. TEL 843-574-6658, FAX 843-574-6470. Ed. Wayne Whelan. R&P Irene Barrineau. Circ: 1,600.

374.0025 GBR ISSN 0956-3709
FLOODLIGHT; the official guide to part-time day and evening classes in Greater London. Text in English. 1936. a. GBP 3.50 (effective 1999). adv. **Document type:** *Directory.* **Description:** Lists more than 45,000 classes plus enrollment and fee information, for London's 100 universities, colleges and adult educational centers.
Published by: Floodlight Publishing, 242 Vauxhall Bridge Rd, London, SW1V 1AU, United Kingdom. TEL 44-171-222-7799. Ed. Philippa Miller. Circ: 150,000.

FOCUS ON BASICS; innovative teaching practices for adults. see *LINGUISTICS*

374.8489 DNK ISSN 0107-4504
FOLKEHOEJSKOLER✶. Text in Danish. 1971. a. free.
Published by: Kulturministeriet, Folkeoplysningsafdelingen, Nybrogade 2, Copenhagen K, 1203, Denmark. TEL 45-33-92-33-70.

374.9485 SWE ISSN 0348-4769
FOLKHOEGSKOLAN. Text in Swedish. 1920. 8/yr. SEK 250 (effective 2004). adv. bk.rev. **Description:** Covers different issues in adult education, focusing on activities in the Swedish higher education system.
Formerly (until Jan. 1979): Tidskrift foer Svenska Folkhoegskolan (0040-6899)
Published by: Svenska Folkhoegskolans Laerarfoerbund, c/o Staffan Myrbaeck, Lagmannsgatan 33A, Umeaa, 90355, Sweden. http://www.sfhl.se. Ed. Staffan Myrbaeck. Adv. contact Elisabeth Tingdal. page SEK 2,500. Circ: 3,100.

FORSCHUNGSDOKUMENTATION ZUR ARBEITSMARKT- UND BERUFSFORSCHUNG. see *BUSINESS AND ECONOMICS—Labor And Industrial Relations*

374 DEU ISSN 0176-3687
DAS FORUM (MUNICH, 1961). Text in German. 1961. s-a. adv. bk.rev. illus. index. back issues avail. **Document type:** *Journal, Academic/Scholarly.*
Published by: Bayerischer Volkshochschulverband, Faeustlestr 5a, Munich, 80339, Germany. TEL 49-89-510800, FAX 49-89-5023812, bvv@vhs-bayern.de, http://www.vhs-bayern.de. Ed. Josef Roehrer. Adv. contact Gisela Haberer. Circ: 3,000.

374 371.3 POL ISSN 0867-0323
LA840
➤ **FORUM OSWIATOWE.** Text in Polish. 1988. s-a. EUR 15 foreign (effective 2005). bibl.; charts; illus. back issues avail. **Document type:** *Journal, Academic/Scholarly.*
Published by: (Uniwersytet Warminsko-Mazurski), Wydawnictwo U W M, ul J Heweliusza 14, Olsztyn, 10724, Poland. TEL 48-89-5233661, FAX 48-89-5233438, wydawca@uwm.edu.pl, http://www.uwm.edu.pl/wydawnictwo. Ed. Zbigniew Kwiencinski. Pub. Zofia Gawinek. Circ: 300 (paid and controlled). **Dist. by:** Ars Polona, Krakowskie Przedmiescie 7, Warsaw, Poland. TEL 48-22-9263914, FAX 48-22-9265334, arspolona@arspolona.com.pl, http://www.arspolona.com.pl.

374 CHN
FUJIAN ZIXUE KAOSHI/FUJIAN EXAMINATION GUIDE TO THE SELF-TAUGHT. Text in Chinese. bi-m. CNY 6. **Description:** Adult education journal focusing on remedial learning and passing exams.
Published by: Zixue Kaoshi Zhidao Weiyuanhui, Fujian, No24, Xihukou Houcao, Fuzhou, Fujian 350001, China. TEL 557205. **Dist. overseas by:** Jiangsu Publications Import & Export Corp., 56 Gao Yun Ling, Nanjing, Jiangsu, China.

FUJIN NO TOMO/WOMEN'S FRIEND. see *HOME ECONOMICS*

374.8025 GBR ISSN 0967-0165
FULL-TIME FLOODLIGHT; Greater London's guide to full-time courses. Text in English. 1992. a. GBP 5.95. **Document type:** *Directory.* **Description:** Includes 93 public-sector colleges and universities, with over 8,000 courses, leading to A-Levels, BTEC awards, first degrees, GCSEs, and postgraduate degrees.
Published by: Floodlight Publishing, 242 Vauxhall Bridge Rd, London, SW1V 1AU, United Kingdom. TEL 44-171-222-7799. Ed. Philippa Miller. Circ: 10,000.

374.8 USA ISSN 0896-0518
G E D ITEMS. (General Educational Development) Text in English. 1983. 5/yr. free. adv. back issues avail. **Document type:** *Newsletter.* **Description:** For GED examiners, teachers, administrators, program staff; state departments of education and directors; adult educators. Includes teaching tips, program news, research articles.
Published by: (G E D Testing Service), American Council on Education, One Dupont Circle, N W, Ste 250, Washington, DC 20036-1193. TEL 202-939-9490, FAX 202-775-8578, http://www.acenet.edu. Adv. contact Lisa Richards Hone TEL 202-939-9493. Circ: 24,000.

374.016 USA ISSN 1055-3371
HF5549.5.T7
GLOBAL CONNECTOR✶; the complete resource directory for international training. Text in English. 1992. a. USD 245. **Document type:** *Directory.*
Published by: PASport Publications International, PO Box 2706, Sausalito, CA 94965. TEL 415-331-2606, FAX 415-331-3903. Ed. Ellen Mischka.

374 AUS ISSN 0818-8483
CODEN: GGAZEJ
GRIFFITH GAZETTE. Text in English. 1986. m. **Description:** Provides information on research and issues at the university, as well as student and graduate successes.
Indexed: INIS AtomInd.
Published by: Griffith University, External Relations, Kessels Rd, Nathan, QLD 4111, Australia. http://www.gu.edu.au/er/news/gazette.html. Ed. Jenny Waller.

GRIMME. see *COMMUNICATIONS—Television And Cable*

GRIMME INFOSERVICE. see *COMMUNICATIONS—Television And Cable*

374.007 ESP ISSN 0213-0610
AS302.L328
GUINIGUADA. Text in Spanish. 1984. a. USD 15 to individuals; USD 20 to institutions. adv. **Description:** Devoted to educational and pedagogical research.
Indexed: MLA-IB.
—CINDOC.
Published by: (Escuela del Profesorado de E.G.B. (Las Palmas and Tenerife)), Universidad de la Laguna, Secretariado de Publicaciones, Campus Central, La Laguna-Tenerife, Canary Islands 38071, Spain. FAX 34-922-258127.

374 DEU ISSN 0932-8297
H V V RUNDSCHREIBEN. Text in German. 1980. s-m. **Description:** Contains various reports and articles on adult education.
Published by: Hessischer Volkshochschulverband, Winterbachstr 38, Frankfurt Am Main, 60320, Germany. info@hvv.de. Circ: 265.

HEALTH EDUCATION & BEHAVIOR. see *PUBLIC HEALTH AND SAFETY*

374 JPN
HEALTH LIFE. Text in Japanese. 1981. m. JPY 5,400.
Formerly: Gold Life
Published by: Gakken Co. Ltd., 40-5 Kami-Ikedai 4-chome, Ota-ku, Tokyo, 145-0064, Japan. Ed. Kenji Watanabe.

374 ISR
HED HA-ULPAN. Text in Hebrew. 1974. 3/yr.
Published by: (Israel. Division of Adult Education), Ministry of Education, 34 Shivtei Israel St., P O Box 292, Jerusalem, 91911, Israel. Ed. Ido Bassok.

374 DEU ISSN 0018-103X
HESSISCHE BLAETTER FUER VOLKSBILDUNG✶. Text in German. 1951. q. adv. bk.rev. charts; stat. index. **Document type:** *Bulletin, Academic/Scholarly.*
Indexed: DIP, IBR, IBZ, MLA-IB, RASB.
—CCC.
Published by: Hessischer Volkshochschulverband, Winterbachstr 38, Frankfurt Am Main, 60320, Germany. TEL 49-69-5600080, FAX 49-69-56000810, info@hvv.de, http://vhs-hessen.server.de. adv.: page EUR 200. Circ: 2,500.

374.8489 DNK ISSN 0018-3334
HOEJSKOLEBLADET. Text in Danish. 1876. 20/yr. DKK 500 (effective 2005). adv. bk.rev. **Document type:** *Magazine, Consumer.* **Description:** Discusses politics, literature, the arts, education and the church.
Published by: Folkehoejskolernes Forening i Danmark, Hoejskolernes Hus, Nytorv 7, Copenhagen K, 1450, Denmark. TEL 45-33-364040, FAX 45-33-139870, redaktionen@hojskolebladet.dk, kontor@ffd.dk, http://www.ffd.dk/da/main/main.php?menu=158, http://www.ffd.dk/da/main/main.php?menu=100. Eds. Niels Elberling, Anders Wedel Berthelsen TEL 45-66-156210. Adv. contact Bjoern Clausen TEL 45-74-489211. page DKK 5,900. Circ: 2,000.

374.8489 DNK ISSN 1399-2805
HOEJSKOLERNES FAELLESKATALOG. Text in Multiple languages. 1950. a. free (effective 2006). illus. 128 p./no.; **Document type:** *Catalog, Consumer.*
Former titles (until 1999): Danmarks Folkehoejskoler (0108-3082); (until 1975): Danmarks Hoejskoler
Published by: Folkehoejskolernes Forening i Danmark, Hoejskolernes Hus, Nytorv 7, Copenhagen K, 1450, Denmark. TEL 45-33-364040, FAX 45-33-139870, kontor@ffd.dk, http://www.folkehojskoler.dk, http://www.ffd.dk/da/main/main.php?menu=100. Circ: 220.

374 JPN ISSN 0912-1420
HOKEN KANRI SENTA DAYORI. Text in Japanese. 1975. 3/yr. **Document type:** *Bulletin.* **Description:** Contains news of the center.
Published by: Nara Joshi Daigaku, Hoken Kanri Senta/Nara Women's University, Health Administration Center, Kita-Uoyahigashi-Machi, Nara-shi, 630-8285, Japan. Ed. Kimihiro Yamamoto. Circ: 3,000.

374 CAN ISSN 1029-709X
I C A E BULLETIN. Text in English. 1981. q. looseleaf. **Document type:** *Newsletter.* **Description:** Provides forum and information exchange for international adult education movement.
Formerly (until 1998): I C A E News (0834-9789)
Related titles: Spanish ed.: El Boletin del I C A E. ISSN 1029-7111.
Published by: International Council for Adult Education/Conseil International d'Education des Adultes, 720 Bathurst St, Ste 500, Toronto, ON M5S 2R4, Canada. TEL 416-588-1211, FAX 416-588-5725, icae@web.net, http://www.web.net/icae. Circ: 2,000.

E

374 USA ISSN 1058-6962
PS536.2
➤ **I L R JOURNAL.** (Institute for Learning in Retirement) Text in English. 1991. a. USD 10 (effective 2003). 82 p./no.; **Document type:** *Magazine, Academic/Scholarly.* **Description:** Provides original stories, essays, memoirs, poetry and art by older learners.
Published by: Northwestern University, Institute for Learning in Retirement, Walter Annenberg Hall, 2120 Campus Dr, Ste 162, Evanston, IL 60208-2650. TEL 847-491-7724, FAX 847-491-3660, http://www.scs.northwestern.edu/nuilr. Pub., R&P Barbara Reinish. Circ: 900.

374.4 USA
I T C NEWS. Text in English. 1986. m. members. adv. charts; illus.; pat.; stat.; tr.lit. back issues avail. **Document type:** *Newsletter.* **Description:** Covers news and articles related to distance education. It keeps members informed about legislative activities, professional development opportunities and what other distance educators are doing in the field.
Published by: Instructional Telecommunications Council, One Dupont Circle, N W, Ste 410, Washington, DC 20036. TEL 202-293-3110, FAX 202-833-2467. Ed., Adv. contact Christine Dalziel. Circ: 2,000.

374.9796 USA
IDAHO. STATE DIVISION OF VOCATIONAL EDUCATION. ANNUAL PERFORMANCE REPORT. Text in English. 1963. a. **Document type:** *Government.*
Formerly: Idaho. State Board for Vocational Education. Annual Descriptive Report of Program Activities for Vocational Education (0091-5882)
Published by: State Division of Vocational Education, 650 W State St, Boise, ID 83720. TEL 208-334-3216, http://www.sde.state.id.us/ute/index. Ed. Chris Latter. Circ: 40.

IMPROVING SOCIAL WORK EDUCATION AND TRAINING SERIES. see *SOCIAL SERVICES AND WELFARE*

INDEPENDENT STUDY CATALOG. see *EDUCATION—Guides To Schools And Colleges*

374.954 IND ISSN 0019-5006
LC5201
➤ **INDIAN JOURNAL OF ADULT EDUCATION.** Text in English. 1939. q. INR 100, USD 30. adv. bk.rev. abstr.; bibl.; illus. index. reprint service avail. from PQC. **Document type:** *Academic/Scholarly.*
Related titles: Microform ed.: (from PQC).
Indexed: BAS, CIJE, CPE, ILD, MEA, RASB, REE&TA, RRTA, SENA, SWA, WAE&RSA.
—BLDSC (4409.800000), IE, ingenta.
Published by: (Indian Adult Education Association), J.L. Sachdeva Pub., 17-B Indraprastha Marg, New Delhi, 110 002, India. TEL 91-11-3319282, FAX 91-11-3355306. Ed. B S Garg. Adv. contact J L Sachdeva. Circ: 2,000.

374.8 IND ISSN 0537-1996
S544.5.I5
INDIAN JOURNAL OF EXTENSION EDUCATION. Text in English. 1965. s-a. INR 70, USD 30.
Indexed: CPE.
Published by: (Division of Agricultural Extension), Indian Society of Extension Education, Indian Agricultural Research Institute, New Delhi, 110 012, India. Ed. Y P Singh.

INDICE DE ARTICULOS SOBRE EDUCACION Y ADIESTRAMIENTO. see *EDUCATION—Abstracting, Bibliographies, Statistics*

374 GBR
INDUSTRIAL SOCIETY. COURSES & SERVICES (YEAR). Text in English. a. adv. **Document type:** *Directory.*
Formerly (until 1994): Industrial Society. Course Directory (Year)
Published by: Industrial Society, Robert Hyde House, 48 Bryanston Sq, London, W1HY 7LN, United Kingdom. TEL 44-171-839-4300, FAX 44-171-839-3898. Ed., Adv. contact Clive Wood.

374.013 USA ISSN 8755-9269
INFO-LINE. Text in English. 1984. m. USD 129 domestic to non-members; USD 169 foreign to non-members; USD 89 domestic to members; USD 129 foreign to members (effective 2005). bibl.; charts; illus.; tr.lit. back issues avail. **Document type:** *Trade.*
Indexed: T&DA.
—Infotrieve.
Published by: American Society for Training & Development, 1640 King St, Box 1443, Alexandria, VA 22313. TEL 703-683-8100, FAX 703-683-9591, http://www.astd.org/astd/publications/infoline/infoline_home. Ed. Tora Estep.

INFORMATION TECHNOLOGY NEWSLETTER; international newsletter of information technology and libraries. see *COMPUTERS—Information Science And Information Theory*

374 CHE
INFOS. Text in German. 11/yr. **Document type:** *Trade.*
Indexed: AEA, BioCN&I, FS&TA, ForAb, HortAb, PHN&I, WeedAb.
Published by: Kretz AG, Postfach, Feldmeilen, 8706, Switzerland. TEL 41-1-9237656, FAX 41-1-9237657, kretz_ag@bluewin.ch. Circ: 4,200 (controlled).

374.0124 GBR ISSN 0968-1876
INKLING; magazine of the Oxfordshire adult literacy and basic education scheme. Text in English. 1978. irreg. (3-4/yr.). free.
Published by: Oxfordshire County Education Department, Community Education, Macclesfield House, Oxford, United Kingdom.

374.4 CRI ISSN 1022-9825
INNOVACIONES EDUCATIVAS. Text in Spanish. 1993. s-a. USD 3. adv. **Document type:** *Academic/Scholarly.*
Published by: (Escuela de Ciencias de la Educacion), Universidad Estatal a Distancia, Apdo. 474, San Pedro de Montes de Oca, San Jose, 2050, Costa Rica. Ed. Jose Joaquin Villegas. Adv. contact Cristina Pereira.

INSTITUTE OF FINANCE MANAGEMENT. PROSPECTUS. see *BUSINESS AND ECONOMICS—Banking And Finance*

374 USA ISSN 1551-7756
▼ **INSTRUCTIONAL LEADERSHIP ABSTRACTS (ONLINE).** Text in English. 2003. 8/yr. USD 15 to non-members; free to members (effective 2004).
Formerly (until Sep.2004): Instructional Leadership Abstracts (Print) (1542-9717)
Media: Online - full content.
Published by: National Council of Instructional Administrators, Texas Tech University, P O Box 41071, Lubbock, TX 79409-1071. TEL 806-742-1997, 800-782-9698, FAX 806-742-2385, ncia.educ@ttu.edu, http://www.nciaonline.org/resources.html. Ed. Brent D Cejda.

INTAND NEWSLETTER; the newsletter of the international network for transactional analysis, neuro-linguistic programming. see *PSYCHOLOGY*

374 371.2 GBR ISSN 0969-613X
INTERCHANGE (EDINBURGH). Text in English. 1991. irreg. (8-10/yr.). free (effective 2003). back issues avail. **Document type:** *Bulletin, Government.* **Description:** Provides information and explanation about educational practice and clarifies and challenges ideas and assumptions.
Related titles: Online - full text ed.
—BLDSC (4532.729000). **CCC.**
Published by: (Scotland. Educational Research Unit), Scottish Office, Education and Industry Department, Scottish Office, 1-B Victoria Quay, Edinburgh, EH6 6QQ, United Kingdom. TEL 44-131-244-0167, FAX 44-131-244-5581, dissemination@hmis.scotoff.gov.uk, dissemination@scotland.gov.uk, http://www.scotland.gov.uk/publications/search.aspx?key=interchange. Ed. Jane Ogden Smith. Circ: 4,500 (controlled).

374.8 NLD
➤ **INTERNATIONAL JOURNAL FOR EDUCATIONAL AND VOCATIONAL GUIDANCE.** Text in English, French, German. 1959. 3/yr. EUR 230, USD 230, GBP 151 combined subscription to institutions print & online eds. (effective 2005). adv. bk.rev. bibl.; charts; illus. reprint service avail. from PSC. **Document type:** *Journal, Academic/Scholarly.* **Description:** Publishes articles in relation to work and leisure, career development, career counselling and guidance and career education, preferably with international content or topics.
Former titles (until 2000): Educational and Vocational Guidance - Bulletin A I O S P, I A E V G, I V S B B (1023-8921); Bulletin A I O S P-I A E V G-I V S B B (0251-2513); A I O S P Bulletin (0044-9504)
Related titles: Online - full text ed.: (from EBSCO Publishing, Gale Group, IngentaConnect, Kluwer Online, O C L C Online Computer Library Center, Inc., Springer LINK, Swets Information Services).
Indexed: BibLing, CPE, PsycInfo, PsycholAb.
—BLDSC (4542.199200), IE, Infotrieve, ingenta. **CCC.**
Published by: (Association Internationale d'Orientation Scolaire et Professionnelle/International Association for Educational and Vocational Guidance - Internationale Vereinigung fuer Schul- und Berufsberatung BEL), Springer-Verlag Dordrecht (Subsidiary of: Springer Science+Business Media), Van Godewijckstraat 30, Dordrecht, 3311 GX, Netherlands. TEL 31-78-6576050, FAX 31-78-6576474, http://springerlink.metapress.com/openurl.asp?genre=journal&issn=0251-2513, http://www.springeronline.com. Eds. Elvira Repetto, Raoul Van Esbroeck. Circ: 1,500. **Co-sponsors:** International Association for Educational and Vocational Guidance; Internationale Vereinigung fur Schul- und Berufsferatung.

374 GBR ISSN 1478-9736
▼ **THE INTERNATIONAL JOURNAL OF ACADEMY OF EXECUTIVES AND ADMINISTRATORS.** Text in English. 2003. s-a. GBP 7 per issue (effective 2003). adv. **Document type:** *Journal.*
Published by: The Academy of Executives and Administrators (Subsidiary of: The Academy of Multi-Skills), Academy House, Warwick Corner, 42 Warwick Rd, Kenilworth, Warks CV8 1HE, United Kingdom. TEL 44-1926-855498, FAX 44-1926-513100. Adv. contact Prof. H J Manners. B&W page GBP 400.

INTERNATIONAL JOURNAL OF CONTINUING ENGINEERING EDUCATION AND LIFE-LONG LEARNING. see *ENGINEERING*

▼ **INTERNATIONAL JOURNAL OF INFORMATION AND OPERATIONS MANAGEMENT EDUCATION.** see *BUSINESS AND ECONOMICS—Management*

374.8 GBR ISSN 0260-1370
LC5201
➤ **INTERNATIONAL JOURNAL OF LIFELONG EDUCATION.** Text in English. 1982. bi-m. GBP 493, USD 813 combined subscription to institutions print & online eds. (effective 2006). adv. abstr. index. reprint service avail. from PSC. **Document type:** *Journal, Academic/Scholarly.* **Description:** Provides an international forum for the debate of the principles and practice of lifelong, continuing, recurrent, adult and initial education.
Related titles: Online - full text ed.: ISSN 1464-519X. GBP 468, USD 772 to institutions (effective 2006) (from EBSCO Publishing, Gale Group, IngentaConnect, O C L C Online Computer Library Center, Inc., Swets Information Services).
Indexed: ABIn, BrEdI, CIJE, CPE, ERA, ETA, EduInd, HECAB, L&LBA, MEA, PCI, REE&TA, RHEA, SEA, SENA, SOMA, SWA, TEA.
—BLDSC (4542.321300), IE, Infotrieve, ingenta. **CCC.**
Published by: Routledge (Subsidiary of: Taylor & Francis Group), 4 Park Sq, Milton Park, Abingdon, Oxon OX14 4RN, United Kingdom. TEL 44-1235-828600, FAX 44-1235-829000, info@routledge.co.uk, http://www.tandf.co.uk/journals/titles/02601370.asp, http://www.routledge.co.uk. Eds. John Holford, Peter Jarvis, Stella Parker. **Subscr. in N. America to:** Taylor & Francis Inc., Customer Services Dept, 325 Chestnut St, 8th Fl, Philadelphia, PA 19106. TEL 215-625-8900, 800-354-1420, FAX 215-625-8914, customerservice@taylorandfrancis.com; **Subscr. to:** Taylor & Francis Ltd, Journals Customer Service, Rankine Rd, Basingstoke, Hants RG24 8PR, United Kingdom. TEL 44-1256-813000, FAX 44-1256-330245, enquiry@tandf.co.uk.

▼ ➤ **INTERNATIONAL JOURNAL OF MOBILE LEARNING AND ORGANISATION.** see *BUSINESS AND ECONOMICS—Management*

374.4 CAN ISSN 1492-3831
LC5800
➤ **INTERNATIONAL REVIEW OF RESEARCH IN OPEN AND DISTANCE LEARNING.** Text in English. 2000. q. free (effective 2005). back issues avail. **Document type:** *Journal, Academic/Scholarly.* **Description:** Aims to contribute and disseminate to practitioners and scholars worldwide scholarly and open source knowledge in each of the following areas: theory, research, and best practice in open and distance learning.
Media: Online - full text.
—**CCC.**
Published by: Athabasca University, 1 University Dr, Athabasca, AB T9S 3A3, Canada. TEL 780-675-6111, 800-788-9041, FAX 780-675-6437, irrodl@athabascau.ca, http://www.irrodl.org/, http://www.athabascau.ca. Ed. Terry Anderson. R&P, Adv. contact Paula Smith.

374 DEU ISSN 0074-9818
➤ **INTERNATIONALES JAHRBUCH DER ERWACHSENENBILDUNG/INTERNATIONAL YEARBOOK OF ADULT EDUCATION.** Text in German. 1969. a. EUR 39.90 (effective 2004). adv. **Document type:** *Yearbook, Academic/Scholarly.*
Indexed: DIP, IBR, IBZ.
Published by: Boehlau Verlag GmbH & Cie, Ursulaplatz 1, Cologne, 50668, Germany. TEL 49-221-913900, FAX 49-221-9139011, vertrieb@boehlau.de, http://www.boehlau.de. Ed. Joachim Knoll. Adv. contact Julia Beenken.

374.013 CHN
JIAOYU YU ZHIYE/EDUCATION AND OCCUPATION. Text in Chinese. m.
Published by: Zhonghua Zhiye Jiaoyu She, 4 Taipingqiao Dajie, Xicheng-qu, Beijing, 100810, China. TEL 6011155.

374.94 GBR
JOLLI; journal of lifelong learning initiatives. Text in English. 1997. bi-m. GBP 75 domestic; GBP 85 foreign (effective 2000). **Document type:** *Academic/Scholarly.* **Description:** Guide to international thinking, innovation and current practice in lifelong learning.
Published by: Planning Exchange, Tontine House, 8 Gordon St, Glasgow, G1 3PL, United Kingdom. TEL 44-141-248-8541, FAX 44-141-248-8277, publications@planex.co.uk, info@planex.co.uk, http://www.planex.co.uk. Ed. Connie Young.

374 GBR
LC5256.G7
JOURNAL OF ACCESS, POLICY & PRACTICE. Text in English. 1998. s-a. looseleaf. GBP 40 (effective 2003). bk.rev. charts. **Document type:** *Journal, Academic/Scholarly.* **Description:** Offers a forum for informed discussion and debate in the rapidly developing areas of credit, credit frameworks and credit accumulation and transfer systems.
Formerly (until 2003): Journal of Access & Credit Studies (1462-0367)

E

Related titles: E-mail ed.
Indexed: BrEdI, ERA, ETA, MEA, RHEA, SEA, SENA, SOMA, TEA.
—BLDSC (4918.859470), IE, ingenta.
Published by: The National Institute of Adult Continuing Education (NAICE), Renaissance House, 20 Princess Rd. W, Leicester, Leics LE1 6TP, United Kingdom. TEL 44-116-2044200, 44-116-2044201, FAX 44-116-2854514, enquiries@niace.org.uk, http://www.niace.org.uk/Publications/Periodicals/JACS.htm. Ed. Jonathan Brown. R&P Virman Man. Adv. contact Jackie Lawless. **Co-sponsor:** National Open College Network.

374.8 GBR ISSN 1477-9714
JOURNAL OF ADULT & CONTINUING EDUCATION. Text in English. 1951. s-a. GBP 30 domestic to individuals; GBP 40 foreign to individuals; GBP 80 domestic to institutions; GBP 95 foreign to institutions (effective 2003). **Document type:** *Journal, Academic/Scholarly.* **Description:** Includes reports on current research and articles concerned with community based adult and continuing education policies and practice in Scotland and the rest of the world and is aimed at those concerned with community based adult and continuing education and lifelong learning.
Former titles (until 2001): Scottish Journal of Adult & Continuing Education (1361-7788); (until 1994): Scottish Journal of Education (0305-795X); (until 1973): Scottish Adult Education (0950-1762)
Related titles: Online - full text ed.: (from EBSCO Publishing, Gale Group, IngentaConnect).
Indexed: BrEdI, CPE, ERA, ETA, MEA, RHEA, SEA, SENA, SOMA, TEA.
—BLDSC (4918.943580), IE, ingenta.
Published by: The National Institute of Adult Continuing Education (NAICE), Renaissance House, 20 Princess Rd. W, Leicester, Leics LE1 6TP, United Kingdom. TEL 44-116-2044200, 44-116-2044201, FAX 44-116-2854514, enquiries@niace.org.uk, http://www.niace.org.uk/Publications/Periodicals/JACE/Default.htm. Ed. Mike Osborne.

374 TZA ISSN 0856-1109
JOURNAL OF ADULT EDUCATION. Text in English. 1977. a. USD 15. adv. bk.rev. **Document type:** *Academic/Scholarly.* **Description:** Contains articles with one main theme, especially in the field of adult education.
Formerly (until 1977): Fikara
Indexed: CIJE.
Published by: Institute of Adult Education, PO Box 20679, Dar Es Salaam, Tanzania. Ed. Lawrence Kagaruki. Circ: 1,500.

374.007 USA ISSN 0090-4244
LC5201
➤ **JOURNAL OF ADULT EDUCATION.** Text in English. 1972. s-a. USD 20 to members. bk.rev. bibl. **Document type:** *Academic/Scholarly.* **Description:** Provides a regional forum for discussion of current issues and research in adult education, its evolution and future.
Indexed: CIJE.
—BLDSC (4918.944500), IE, ingenta.
Published by: Mountain Plains Adult Education Association, Utah State University, 265 West 1100 South, Brigham City, UT 84302. http://www.mpaea.org/journal.htm. Eds. Dr. Andrew G Shinkle, Dr. Pamela A Dupin-Bryant. Circ: 700.

➤ **JOURNAL OF CAREER AND TECHNICAL EDUCATION.** see *EDUCATION—Higher Education*

➤ **JOURNAL OF CONTINUING EDUCATION IN THE HEALTH PROFESSIONS.** see *MEDICAL SCIENCES*

374.8 USA ISSN 0737-7363
➤ **JOURNAL OF CONTINUING HIGHER EDUCATION.** Text in English. 1952. 3/yr. USD 40 domestic to non-members; USD 50 foreign to non-members. bk.rev. **Document type:** *Academic/Scholarly.* **Description:** Serves as a forum for the reporting and exchange of information based on research, observations, and experiences relevant to continuing higher education.
Formerly: Association for Continuing Higher Education. Newsletter
Indexed: CIJE.
—BLDSC (4965.247940), IE, Infotrieve, ingenta.
Published by: Association for Continuing Higher Education, Inc., Community College of Rhode Island, 400 East Ave, Warwick, RI 02886-1807. TEL 401-825-1000. Circ: 2,800 (paid).

374.4 CAN ISSN 0830-0445
➤ **JOURNAL OF DISTANCE EDUCATION.** Text in English, French. 1986. s-a. (May & Nov.). CND 40 to non-members; CND 60 membership individuals; CND 220 membership institutions; CND 30 membership students (effective 2005). adv. bk.rev. back issues avail. **Document type:** *Journal, Academic/Scholarly.* **Description:** Aims to promote and encourage scholarly work of empirical and theoretical nature relating to distance education in Canada and throughout the world.
Related titles: Microfiche ed.: (from MML); Microform ed.: 1986 (from MML); Online - full text ed.: free (effective 2005) (from Micromedia ProQuest, ProQuest Information & Learning).
Indexed: ABIn, CEI, CIJE, CPE, ERA, ETA, EduInd, HEA, MEA, RHEA, SEA, SENA, SOMA, SWA, TEA.
—BLDSC (4969.840000), IE, Infotrieve, ingenta. **CCC.**
Published by: Canadian Association for Distance Education, 205-1 Stewart St, Ottawa, ON K1N 6H7, Canada. TEL 613-241-0018, FAX 613-241-0019, http://www.cade-aced.ca/en_pub.php. Ed., R&P, Adv. contact Joan Collinge. Circ: 800 (paid).

▼ ➤ **JOURNAL OF LIBRARY & INFORMATION SERVICES IN DISTANCE LEARNING.** see *LIBRARY AND INFORMATION SCIENCES*

➤ **JOURNAL OF STAFF DEVELOPMENT.** see *BUSINESS AND ECONOMICS—Personnel Management*

374.013 GBR ISSN 1363-6820
CODEN: VAEDES
➤ **JOURNAL OF VOCATIONAL EDUCATION AND TRAINING.** Text in English. 1949. q. GBP 316 combined subscription domestic to institutions print & online eds.; USD 491 combined subscription foreign to institutions print & online eds. (effective 2006). bk.rev. abstr.; illus. back issues avail.; reprint service avail. from PSC. **Document type:** *Journal, Academic/Scholarly.* **Description:** Publishes articles on the development of practice and theory in work-related education.
Formerly (until 1996): Vocational Aspect of Education (0305-7879)
Related titles: Online - full text ed.: ISSN 1747-5090. GBP 300, USD 466 to institutions (effective 2006) (from EBSCO Publishing, Swets Information Services).
Indexed: ASSIA, BrEdI, CIJE, CPE, DIP, EAA, ERA, ETA, HECAB, HRA, IBR, IBZ, ILD, MEA, RASB, REE&TA, RHEA, SEA, SENA, SOMA, SOPODA, SWA, TEA.
—BLDSC (5072.511500), IE, Infotrieve, ingenta. **CCC.**
Published by: Routledge (Subsidiary of: Taylor & Francis Group), 4 Park Sq, Milton Park, Abingdon, Oxon OX14 4RN, United Kingdom. TEL 44-1235-828600, FAX 44-1235-829000, journals@routledge.com, http://www.tandf.co.uk/journals/titles/13636820.asp, http://www.routledge.co.uk. Ed. Dr. Jocelyn Robson.

374 DNK ISSN 0905-5487
L V U FAGBLADET. Text in Danish. 1954. 17/yr. DKK 600 membership (effective 2004). adv. bk.rev. **Document type:** *Trade.*
Former titles (until 1990): A og U Fagbladet (0108-2752); (until 1982): Aften- og Ungdomsskolen (0902-4255)
Published by: Landsforbundet af Voksen- og Ungdomsundervisere/National Federation of Teachers in Adult and Youth ducation, Hauser Plads 20,5, Copenhagen K, 1127, Denmark. TEL 45-33-114466, FAX 45-33-140655, lvu@lvu.dk, http://www.lvu.dk/sw879.asp. adv.: B&W page DKK 7,000, color page DKK 11,500; 250 x 175. Circ: 7,494.

LABOUR EDUCATION. see *BUSINESS AND ECONOMICS—Labor And Industrial Relations*

374.8025 DNK ISSN 1397-1824
LAERERHEFTE TIL VI UNDERSOEGER OG MIN VEJ. Text in Danish. 1996. a. free. **Document type:** *Government.*
Related titles: ◆ Supplement(s): Vi Undersoeger. ISSN 1397-1832; ◆ Min Vej. ISSN 1396-9684.
Published by: Raadet for Uddannelses- og Erhvervsvejledning (R.U.E.)/Danish National Council for Educational and Vocational Guidance, Vester Voldgade 123, Copenhagen V, 1552, Denmark. TEL 45-39-95-53-00, FAX 45-39-95-53-49, r-u-e@r-u-e.dk, http://www.r-u-e.dk. Circ: 11,500.

374 NOR
LAERING & KOMPETANSE. Text in Norwegian. 1952. q. bk.rev.
Former titles (until 2004): Curriculum Vitae (1500-760X); (until 1998): Studienytt (0800-7624); (until 1955): Tidsskrift
Published by: (Voksenopplaeringsforbundet/Norwegian Association for Adult Education (NAAE)), Linc Media AS, Toerkoppveien 10, Dilling, 1570, Norway. TEL 47-69-122600, FAX 47-69-122601. Ed. Tor Erik Skaar.

374 CHN
LAONIAN JIAOYU/EDUCATION FOR THE ELDERLY. Text in Chinese. bi-m.
Published by: Shandong Laonian Daxue/Shandong University of the Elderly, No 3 Qianfoshan Xilu, Jinan, Shandong, 250014, China. TEL 614704. Ed. Yuan Shishuo.

374.0124 USA ISSN 1092-8367
LAUBACH LITSCAPE. Text in English. 1971. q. free. bk.rev. bibl.; illus. 12 p./no.; **Document type:** *Newspaper.* **Description:** Includes support and information on tutoring, resource information, trainer and workshop information, new reader personal stories and involvement, program management issues, recruitment and retention of students and volunteers.
Former titles (until 1997): Literacy Advance (0047-4142); Laubach Literacy News
Published by: (Laubach Literacy International), Richard T LaPointe, 1320 Jamesville Ave, Box 131, Syracuse, NY 13210. info@laubach.org, http://www.laubach.org. Ed. Linda Church. Circ: 35,000.

374 AUS ISSN 1329-1440
LEARNING COMMUNITIES; international journal of adult and vocational learning. Text in English. 2000. s-a. **Description:** Publishes occasional editions of original research relating to the learning of groups, communities and organisations with a focus on rural and regional areas.
Media: Online - full text.
Published by: Centre for Research and Learning in Regional Australia, Locked Bag 1-313, Launceston, TAS 7250, Australia. TEL 61-3-63243142, http://www.crlra.utas.edu.au/Pages/Journal/display.html. Ed. Ian Falk.

374 GBR
THE LECTURER. Text in English. 1991. bi-m. GBP 8. adv. bk.rev. back issues avail. **Document type:** *Bulletin.*
Indexed: SRRA.
—BLDSC (5180.870000).
Published by: N A T F H E - The University and College Lecturers' Union, 27 Britannia St, London, WC1X 9JP, United Kingdom. TEL 44-207-837-3636, FAX 44-207-837-4403, http://natfhe.org.uk. Eds. Brenda Kirsch, Midge Purcell. Circ: 70,000 (controlled).

374.013 DNK ISSN 0109-9299
LEDER. KURSUSKATALOG. Text in Danish. a. DKK 32.
Published by: Koebenhavns Universitet, Noerregade 10, Copenhagen, 1017, Denmark. TEL 45-35322626, FAX 45-35322628, http://www.ku.dk.

374 GBR ISSN 0965-0342
LEEDS STUDIES IN CONTINUING EDUCATION. Text in English. 1981. irreg. **Document type:** *Monographic series, Academic/Scholarly.*
Formerly (until 1991): Leeds Studies in Adult and Continuing Education (0261-1406)
—BLDSC (5181.304500).
Published by: (Study of Continuing Education Unit), University of Leeds, School of Education, Parkinson Court, Leeds, W Yorks LS2 9JT, United Kingdom.

THE LIBERATOR (CARTERSVILLE). see *POLITICAL SCIENCE*

LIFE AND WORK PATHWAYS: BIBLE STUDIES FOR ADULTS 70 & UP. see *RELIGIONS AND THEOLOGY—Protestant*

LIFE AND WORK VENTURES: BIBLE STUDIES FOR ADULTS 55-69. see *RELIGIONS AND THEOLOGY—Protestant*

374 DEU
LIFELONG EDUCATION BIBLIOGRAPHY. Text in German. 1980. irreg. back issues avail.; reprints avail. **Document type:** *Monographic series, Bibliography.* **Description:** Provides a bibliography on lifelong education.
Formerly: Lifelong Education Network
Published by: UNESCO Institute for Education, Feldbrunnenstr 58, Hamburg, 20148, Germany. TEL 49-40-448-0410, FAX 49-40-410-7723, uie@unesco.org, http://www.unesco.org/publications. Eds. Ursula Giere, Yasushi Maehira. **Dist. in U.S. by:** Bernan Associates, Bernan, 4611-F Assembly Dr., Lanham, MD 20706-4391. TEL 800-274-4888, FAX 800-865-3450.

374.94 FIN ISSN 1239-6826
➤ **LIFELONG LEARNING IN EUROPE.** Cover title: LLinE. Text in English; Summaries in French, German, Russian. 1996. q. EUR 45, USD 55 to individuals; EUR 70, USD 85 to institutions (effective 2005). adv. bk.rev. 64 p./no.; back issues avail. **Document type:** *Journal, Academic/Scholarly.* **Description:** Publishes articles and interviews on adult learning in various contexts.
Indexed: CPE.
—BLDSC (5208.966222), IE, ingenta.
Published by: Kansanvalistusseura (KVS Foundation)/The Finnish Adult Education Research Society, Dobelninkatu 2 E 28, Helsinki, 00260, Finland. TEL 358-9-54918855, FAX 358-9-54918811, eeva.siirala@kvs.fi, info@kvs.fi, http://www.kvs.fi. Ed. Kauko Hamalainen. Adv. contact Eeva Siirala. Circ: 1,200.

374.4 USA ISSN 1553-1619
LC5201
LIFELONG LEARNING TRENDS; a profile of continuing higher education. Text in English. 1990. biennial. USD 25.
Published by: University Continuing Education Association, 1 Dupont Circle, N W, Ste 615, Washington, DC 20036. TEL 202-659-3130.

374.0124 USA ISSN 1067-0114
LITERACY ADVOCATE. Text in English. 1990. 3/yr. free to qualified personnel. **Document type:** *Newspaper, Academic/Scholarly.*
Published by: ProLiteracy Worldwide, Corporate Communications, 1320 Jamesville Ave, Syracuse, NY 13210. TEL 315-422-9121, FAX 315-422-6369, tcarman@proliteracy.org, http://www.proliteracy.org. Ed. Bethel Kogut. Circ: 16,000 (controlled).

302.224 AUS ISSN 1441-0559
LITERACY & NUMERACY STUDIES; an international journal in the education and training of adults. Text in English. 1990. s-a. USD 33 domestic to individuals; USD 38.50 foreign to individuals; USD 77 domestic to institutions; USD 82.50 foreign to institutions (effective 2002). back issues avail. **Document type:** *Journal.*
Formerly (until 1997): Open Letter (1035-4727)
Indexed: AusPAIS, CIJE, CPE.
—BLDSC (5276.630200).

E

Published by: University of Technology, Sydney, Centre for Language and Literacy, PO Box 123, Broadway, NSW 2007, Australia. TEL 61-2-95143853, FAX 61-2-95143939, cll.education@uts.edu.au, http://www.education.uts.edu.au/centres/cll/lnshome.htm.

374.0124 AUS ISSN 0158-3026
➤ **LITERACY LINK.** Text in English. 1980. q. AUD 44 to individuals; AUD 66 to institutions (effective 2001). bk.rev. back issues avail. **Document type:** *Newsletter, Academic/Scholarly.* **Description:** Brings together a wide range of viewpoints related to adult literacy issues.
Indexed: AEI.
Published by: Australian Council For Adult Literacy, GPO Box 2283, Canberra, ACT 2601, Australia. TEL 61-3-9326-8988, FAX 61-3-9326-8670, http://www.acal.edu.au/. Ed. Jim Thompson. Circ: 400.

374 JPN
LIVE. Text in Japanese. 1971. m. JPY 5,980.
Published by: Gakken Co. Ltd., 40-5 Kami-Ikedai 4-chome, Ota-ku, Tokyo, 145-0064, Japan. Ed. Ken'ichi Yamana.

374 USA
M P A E A NEWSLETTER✶. Text in English. 1975 (no.2). q. USD 20. bk.rev. **Document type:** *Newsletter.*
Published by: Mountain Plains Adult Education Association, Newsletter, c/o Bill Shupe, Box 80 Pinecrest, Clancy, MT 59634. TEL 406-933-8327. Circ: 550.

THE MALVERN EXAMINER; a newsletter for CPCU and IIA students. see *INSURANCE*

THE MANAGEMENT SPECIALIST; the international aid to management specialists and education in Management. see *BUSINESS AND ECONOMICS—Management*

MANAGERSEMINARE; das Weiterbildungsmagazin. see *BUSINESS AND ECONOMICS—Management*

▼ **MEDICAL MASTERCLASS.** see *MEDICAL SCIENCES*

MEXICO. CENTRO DE INFORMACION TECNICA Y DOCUMENTACION. INDICE DE REVISTAS. SECCION DE EDUCACION Y COMUNICACION. see *EDUCATION—Abstracting, Bibliographies, Statistics*

374.9774 USA ISSN 0094-1506
LC1046.M5
MICHIGAN STATE PLAN FOR VOCATIONAL EDUCATION✶. Text in English. 1917. a. free. illus. **Document type:** *Government.*
Published by: Department of Education, Division of Vocational Education, PO Box 30008, Lansing, MI 48909-7508. TEL 517-373-3373, FAX 517-373-8776. Circ: 1,700.

374.8025 DNK ISSN 1396-9684
MIN VEJ. Text in Danish. 1996. a. free. **Document type:** *Academic/Scholarly.*
Formed by the merger of (1984-1995): P Vej (0900-5005); (1990-1995): Gymnasiale Uddannelser (0906-0073); (1991-1995): Erhvervsuddannelser Efter 9 og 10 Klasse (0906-7892); Which was formerly (until 1991) : Erhvervsuddannelser (0906-0065); (until 1990): Om Laerlinge- og E F G - Uddanelserne (0109-9914); (1979-1984): Om E F G - Uddannelserne (0901-5353)
Related titles: ♦ Supplement to: Laererhefte til Vi Undersoeger og Min Vej. ISSN 1397-1824.
Published by: Raadet for Uddannelses- og Erhvervsvejledning (R.U.E.)/Danish National Council for Educational and Vocational Guidance, Vester Voldgade 123, Copenhagen V, 1552, Denmark. TEL 45-39-95-53-00, FAX 45-39-95-53-49, r-u-e@r-u-e.dk, http://www.r-u-e.dk. Ed. Bonnie Hegner. Circ: 85,000.

331.2592 PHL
MINDANAO JOURNAL OF INDUSTRIAL EDUCATION✶. Text in English. 1981. s-a. PHP 60, USD 20. bk.rev. back issues avail.
Published by: (Mindanao State University), School of Industrial Education (Subsidiary of: Mindanao State University), P O Box 5594, Iligan City, 9200, Philippines. Ed. Fedeseria C Camarao. Circ: 500.

374 USA
MYRIN INSTITUTE FOR ADULT EDUCATION PROCEEDINGS. Text in English. 1954. irreg., latest vol.38. USD 2 per issue (effective 2001). bk.rev. bibl. **Document type:** *Proceedings.*
Published by: Myrin Institute, Inc., 187 Main St, Great Barrington, MA 01230-1602. Circ: 2,000.

N A I E C NEWSLETTER. see *BUSINESS AND ECONOMICS—Management*

374 AUT ISSN 0027-7363
NACH DER ARBEIT. Text in German. 1947. 10/yr. bk.rev. **Document type:** *Journal, Consumer.*
Published by: Volkshochschule Linz, Coulinstr 18, Linz, O 4020, Austria. TEL 43-732-604545, FAX 43-732-654625, vhs-bib@mag.linz.at, http://www.linz.at/vhs/. Ed. Erich Leichtenmueller. Circ: 1,300.

NARA JOSHI DAIGAKU HOKEN KANRI SENTA NENPO/NARA WOMEN'S UNIVERSITY. HEALTH ADMINISTRATION CENTER. ARCHIVES OF HEALTH CARE. see *PUBLIC HEALTH AND SAFETY*

374.013 GBR ISSN 0954-3732
NATIONAL ASSOCIATION OF CAREER & GUIDANCE TEACHERS. JOURNAL. Text in English. 1979. 5/yr. GBP 15. adv. bk.rev. back issues avail.
Formerly: Careers and Guidance Teacher
Indexed: CPE.
Published by: National Association of Careers & Guidance Teachers, Stonesfield House, Overthorpe, Banbury, Oxon OX17 2AF, United Kingdom. Ed. G Robb. Circ: 1,000.

NATIONAL DIRECTORY OF ART INTERNSHIPS. see *ART*

NETWORK NEWS (SHERMAN). see *POLITICAL SCIENCE—Civil Rights*

374.8 USA ISSN 1052-2891
LC5251
NEW DIRECTIONS FOR ADULT AND CONTINUING EDUCATION. Text in English. 1979. q. USD 180 domestic; USD 220 in Canada & Mexico; USD 254 elsewhere; USD 198 combined subscription domestic print & online eds.; USD 238 combined subscription in Canada & Mexico print & online eds.; USD 272 combined subscription elsewhere print & online eds. (effective 2006). bibl. Index. back issues avail.; reprint service avail. from PQC. **Document type:** *Journal, Academic/Scholarly.* **Description:** Combines research findings on adult students and programs with the practical experience of continuing education directors and staff.
Formerly: New Directions for Continuing Education (0195-2242)
Related titles: Microform ed.: (from PQC); Online - full text ed.: ISSN 1536-0717. USD 180 (effective 2006) (from EBSCO Publishing, H.W. Wilson, O C L C Online Computer Library Center, Inc., Swets Information Services, Wiley InterScience).
Indexed: ABIn, CIJE, CPE, ChPerl, ERA, ETA, EduInd, HEA, MEA, RHEA, SEA, SENA, SOMA, TEA.
—BLDSC (6083.312500), IE, Infotrieve, ingenta. **CCC.**
Published by: Jossey-Bass Inc., Publishers (Subsidiary of: John Wiley & Sons, Inc.), 989 Market St, San Francisco, CA 94103-1741. TEL 415-433-1740, 888-378-2537, FAX 800-605-2665, 415-433-0499, jbsubs@jbp.com, http://www3.interscience.wiley.com/cgi-bin/jhome/86011352, http://www.josseybass.com. Ed. Susan Imel. Pub. Sue Lewis. R&P Lorri Wimer TEL 415-433-1740. Circ: 775 (paid).

374 USA ISSN 1062-3183
➤ **NEW HORIZONS IN ADULT EDUCATION.** Text in English. 1987. irreg. (2-3/yr.). free (effective 2005). bk.rev. **Document type:** *Journal, Academic/Scholarly.* **Description:** Provides faculty, graduate students, researchers, and practitioners with a means for publishing their current thinking and research within adult education and related fields.
Media: Online - full text.
Published by: Nova Southeastern University, Department of Higher Education Leadership, 1750 N E 167th St, North Miami Beach, FL 33162-3017. horizons@nova.edu, http://www.nova.edu/~aed/newhorizons.html. Ed. Nancy Gadbow.

➤ **NEWFOUNDLAND AND LABRADOR WOMEN'S INSTITUTES. NEWSLETTER.** see *WOMEN'S INTERESTS*

374.22 USA ISSN 0884-3910
NEWS FOR YOU. Text in English. 1959. w. USD 29.95 48 weeks (effective 2003). charts; illus.; stat.; tr.lit. **Document type:** *Newspaper, Consumer.* **Description:** News and information for adults and older youth at reading levels 4-6, including supplementary worksheet.
Formed by the 1985 merger of: News for You (Edition A) (0162-8518); News for You (Edition B) (0162-850X)
Related titles: Online - full text ed.
Indexed: JHMA, MASUSE.
Published by: Richard T LaPointe, 1320 Jamesville Ave, Box 131, Syracuse, NY 13210. TEL 315-422-9121, 800-448-8878, FAX 315-422-5561, nrp@laubach.org, http://www.news-for-you.com/index_h.html. Ed. Heidi Stevens. Circ: 80,000 (paid).

374.8 USA ISSN 0886-0165
NON-CREDIT LEARNING NEWS; the newsletter for directors of non-credit programs. Text in English. 1986. 10/yr. USD 84 (effective 2000). adv. bk.rev. tr.lit. back issues avail. **Document type:** *Newsletter.* **Description:** Information and announcements on continuing education courses, programs, workshops, and seminars in all fields.
Published by: Learning for All Seasons, Inc., PO Box 579X, Lexington, MA 02420. TEL 781-861-0379, FAX 781-860-0237. Ed., Pub. Susan B Capon. Circ: 1,300.

374.013 DEU
NORDBAYERN. LANDESARBEITSAMT. BUNDESANSTALT FUER ARBEIT. BERATUNGS- UND VERMITTLUNGSDIENSTE. INFORMATIONEN. Text in German. 1950. w. bk.rev. **Document type:** *Government.* **Description:** Information for vocational and occupational guidance services of the Bundesanstalt.
Published by: Landesarbeitsamt Nordbayern, Bundesanstalt fuer Arbeit, Regensburgerstr 104, Nuernberg, 90328, Germany. FAX 0911-1792417. Circ: 18,000.

NORTHERN DEVELOPMENT CURRICULUM PROJECT. see *SOCIAL SERVICES AND WELFARE*

374.4 AUS ISSN 1038-8958
OCCASIONAL PAPERS IN OPEN AND DISTANCE LEARNING. Text in English. 1990. irreg. back issues avail. **Document type:** *Abstract/Index.* **Description:** Designed to disseminate ideas which will enhance learning and teaching within the university.
Formerly (until 1993): Occasional Papers in Distance Education (1034-7186)
Related titles: Online - full text ed.
Indexed: AEI.
Published by: Charles Sturt University, Open Learning Institute, 624 Olive St, Albury, NSW 2640, Australia. TEL 61-2-6338-4678, FAX 61-2-6331-8780, http://www.csu.edu.au/division/oli/pubs. Ed. Peter Donnan.

374.4 GBR
OPEN PRAXIS. Text in English. 1983. 2/yr. USD 75 membership (effective 2000). bk.rev. **Document type:** *Bulletin.*
Formerly: International Council for Distance Education. Bulletin (0264-0201)
Indexed: CPE.
—BLDSC (6265.972000), IE, ingenta. **CCC.**
Published by: International Council for Distance Education, c/o Dr. David Sewart Ed, Director Student Academic Services, The Open University, Walton Hall, Milton Keynes, Bucks MK7 6AA, United Kingdom. TEL 44-1908-274066, FAX 44-1908-655143, j.b.meadows@open.ac.uk. R&P David Sewart. Circ: 1,100 (paid).

398.0715 USA
OPTION. (Membership includes Conversations) Text in English. 1977. 2/yr. USD 15 to non-members & students; USD 30 to members; USD 100 to institutions (effective 2000). bk.rev. back issues avail. **Document type:** *Academic/Scholarly.* **Description:** Contains articles on current practice and history of folk and popular education and culture, nationally and internationally.
Published by: Folk Education Association of America, 73 Willow St., Florence, MA 01062-2639. Ed. Mary Cattani. R&P Chris Spicer TEL 413-585-8755. Circ: 350.

374.8 USA ISSN 1554-5903
LC5201
P A A C E JOURNAL OF LIFELONG LEARNING. Text in English. 1995 (vol.4). a. USD 7; USD 7 foreign (effective 1999). bk.rev. back issues avail. **Document type:** *Academic/Scholarly.*
—BLDSC (6327.825000).
Published by: Pennsylvania Association for Adult Continuing Education, c/o Indiana University of Pennsylvania, 206 Stouffer Hall, Indiana, PA 15705-1087. TEL 724-357-2470, FAX 724-357-7821, gjdean@grove.iup.edu, trferro@grove.iup.edu. Circ: 1,400. **Dist. by:** Mary Kay Peterson, 121 Leary Road, Honey Brook, PA 19344. TEL 610-857-9157.

374.01 DEU
P H - F R. Text in German. 1976. s-a. adv. illus. **Document type:** *Academic/Scholarly.*
Published by: Paedagogische Hochschule Freiburg, Kunzenweg 21, Freiburg Im Breisgau, 79117, Germany. TEL 49-761-682-380, FAX 49-761-682-402. Ed. Reinhold Voss. Circ: 1,000.

374 DEU ISSN 0723-7197
PAEDAGOGISCHE ARBEITSSTELLE FUER ERWACHSENENBILDUNG. SCHRIFTEN. Text in German. 1972. irreg., latest vol.21. price varies. **Document type:** *Monographic series, Academic/Scholarly.*
Published by: (Paedagogische Arbeitsstelle fuer Erwachsenenbildung in Baden-Wuerttemberg), Neckar Verlag GmbH, Postfach 1820, Villingen-Schwenningen, 78008, Germany. TEL 49-7721-89870, FAX 49-7721-898750, service@neckar-verlag.de, http://www.neckar-verlag.de.

374 POL ISSN 0137-3943
PAIDEIA; international pedagogical review. Text in English, French, German. 1972. a. price varies. **Document type:** *Academic/Scholarly.* **Description:** Papers on adult education, secondary and academic schools in Europe, U.S.A. and in Third World countries.
Published by: Polska Akademia Nauk, Komitet Nauk Pedagogicznych, ul Mokotowska 16/20, Warsaw, 01561, Poland. TEL 48-22-6283461.

PEDAGOGIA PARA EL ADIESTRAMIENTO. see *BUSINESS AND ECONOMICS—Labor And Industrial Relations*

374 331 POL ISSN 0239-7757
PEDAGOGIKA PRACY. Text in Polish. 1975. s-a. EUR 19 foreign (effective 2005). **Document type:** *Journal, Academic/Scholarly.*
Published by: Instytut Technologii Eksploatacji, ul Pulaskiego 6/10, Radom, 26600, Poland. TEL 48-22-3644241, FAX 48-22-3644765, instytut@itee.radom.pl, http://www.itee.radom.pl/czasopisma/p_p/pp_info.htm. Ed. Stanislaw Kaczor. **Dist. by:** Ars Polona, Krakowskie Przedmiescie 7, Warsaw, Poland. TEL 48-22-9263914, FAX 48-22-9265334, arspolona@arspolona.com.pl, http://www.arspolona.com.pl.

E

▼ *new title* ➤ *refereed* ✶ *unverified* ♦ *full entry avail.*

374 USA
PERSPECTIVE (WHEATON). Variant title: Pioneer Clubs Perspective. Text in English. 1967. 3/yr. USD 6. back issues avail. **Description:** Provides resources for club leaders to develop leadership and relationship skills.
Published by: Pioneer Clubs, PO Box 788, Wheaton, IL 60189-0788. TEL 630-293-1600, FAX 630-293-3053. Ed. Rebecca Powell Parat. Circ: 25,000.

374.007 IND
PRASAR; journal devoted to theory, research and field practices in adult continuing education. Text in English, Hindi. 1973. q. INR 18, USD 10. adv. bk.rev. bibl.; charts; stat.
Published by: University of Rajasthan, Department of Adult & Continuing Education, Gandhi Nagar, Jaipur, 302004, India. Ed. C K Dandiya. Circ: 250.

374 DEU
PRAXIS DER VERKUENDIGUNG. Text in German. q. **Document type:** *Bulletin.*
Published by: J.G. Oncken Nachf. GmbH, Postfach 200152, Kassel, 34080, Germany. TEL 49-561-52005-0, FAX 49-561-5200550. Ed. Rev. Hinrich Schmidt. Circ: 3,200.

PRESERVATION EDUCATION DIRECTORY. see *LIBRARY AND INFORMATION SCIENCES*

374.013 NLD ISSN 1387-6112
PROFIEL; van beroepsonderwijs, educatie en scholing. Text in Dutch. 1992. 10/yr. EUR 62 to individuals; EUR 88 to institutions (effective 2005). adv. software rev. bibl.; illus. back issues avail. **Document type:** *Journal, Academic/Scholarly.* **Description:** For professionals and others who are interested in the field of vocational and adult education, employment programs, and other matters in the field of school and work.
Formerly (until 1997): Profiel van Beroepsonderwijs en Volwasseneneducatie (0927-4898); Which was formed by the merger of (1976-1992): Volwassenen Educatie (0167-0026); (1971-1992): Werking (0924-4115); Which was formerly (until 1990): Interaktie (0165-4470)
—IE, Infotrieve.
Published by: Profiel Producties, Postbus 15150, Utrecht, 3501 BD, Netherlands. TEL 31-30-2735121, FAX 31-30-2734116, http://www.profielvakblad.nl, http://www.profielproducties.nl. Ed. Lex Sanou. Adv. contact Luigi Mascini. page EUR 975; trim 210 x 297.

PROFILE (WHEATON). see *RELIGIONS AND THEOLOGY*

374.0124 USA
PROLITERACY WORLDWIDE. ANNUAL REPORT. Text in English. 1957. a. free to qualified personnel. **Document type:** *Yearbook, Corporate.* **Description:** Documents the organization's annual report and financial statement.
Formerly (until 2002): Laubach Literacy International. Annual Report (1066-7377)
Published by: ProLiteracy Worldwide, Corporate Communications, 1320 Jamesville Ave, Syracuse, NY 13210. TEL 315-422-9121, FAX 315-422-6369, tcarman@proliteracy.org, http://www.proliteracy.org. Ed. Bethel Kogut.

PROSPECT; an Australian journal of TESOL. see *LINGUISTICS*

QUADERNI DI TECNOSTRUTTURA; tecnostruttura delle regioni per il Fondo Sociale Europeo. see *BUSINESS AND ECONOMICS—Labor And Industrial Relations*

374 AUS ISSN 1448-4390
QUEST (CANBERRA CITY). Text in English. 1961. q. AUD 64 (effective 2004). adv. 32 p./no.; back issues avail. **Document type:** *Newsletter, Academic/Scholarly.*
Former titles (until 2003): Adult Learning Australia (1327-8347); (until 1996): A A A C E News (1320-2162); (until 1993): Adult Education News (0727-4386); (until 1981): Australian Association of Adult Education. Newsletter (0727-4378); (until 1975): A A A E Newsletter (0810-2309)
Indexed: AEI.
Published by: Adult Learning Australia, PO Box 260, Canberra City, ACT 2601, Australia. TEL 61-2-62749500, FAX 61-2-62749513, info@ala.asn.au, http://www.ala.asn.au/pubs/ALAn/newsletter.htm. Eds. Cath Styles, Tony Brown. Pub., Adv. contact Cath Styles. Circ: 900 (paid); 200 (controlled).

374.4 ESP ISSN 1131-8783
R E D. (Revista de Educacion a Distancia) Key Title: RED. Revista de Educacion a Distancia. Text in Spanish. 1991. 3/yr.
—CINDOC.
Published by: C I D E A D, C. Argumosa, 43, Madrid, 28012, Spain. TEL 34-91-5271430, FAX 34-91-4299771.

R U S A UPDATE. (Reference & User Services Association) see *LIBRARY AND INFORMATION SCIENCES*

374 ESP ISSN 0213-4969
RADIO Y EDUCACION DE ADULTOS. Text in Spanish. 1986. 3/yr. EUR 12.02 domestic; USD 21 foreign (effective 2004).
—CINDOC.
Published by: Radio y Educacion de Adultos. Radio ECCA, Apdo. de Correso 994, Las Palmas de Gran Canaria, 35080, Spain. TEL 34-928-257400, FAX 34-928-207395, info@radioecca.org, http://www.radioecca.org/publicaciones/boletin.htm.

374.4 DEU ISSN 0938-0345
RATGEBER FUER FERNUNTERRICHT; mit amtlichen Verzeichnis aller zugelassenen Fernlehrgaenge. Text in German. 1980. s-a. **Document type:** *Directory.*
Published by: Staatliche Zentralstelle fuer Fernunterricht, Peter-Welter-Platz 2, Cologne, 50676, Germany. TEL 49-221-921207-0, FAX 49-221-921207-20, m.vennemann@zfu.de, http://www.zfu.de. Ed. Michael Vennemann. Circ: 20,000.

374.0124 USA ISSN 1066-2839
LB1049.9
➤ **THE READING PROFESSOR.** Text in English. 1980. s-a. USD 22 (effective 2003). adv. bk.rev. back issues avail. **Document type:** *Journal, Academic/Scholarly.* **Description:** Publishes articles dealing with topics, issues and events of interest to professors of literacy.
Published by: International Reading Association, Special Interest Group: Professors of Reading Teacher Educators, c/o Dr Lawrence M Kenney, Ed, College of Education, Winther Hall 2040, University of Wisconsin, 800 W Main St, Whitewater, WI 53190. TEL 262-472-4677, FAX 262-472-5716, kenneyl@mail.uww.edu. Pub., R&P Lawrence M Kenney. Adv. contact Terrence V. Stange. Circ: 350.

051 374 USA ISSN 1091-7268
HQ1063.2.U6
READY OR NOT; retirement guide. Text in English. 1993. a. USD 10.95 (effective 2000). bk.rev.
Published by: Manpower Education Institute, 715 Ladd Rd, Bronx, NY 10471-1203. TEL 718-548-4200, FAX 718-548-4202, meiready@aol.com, http://www.manpower-education.org.

374 GBR ISSN 1351-086X
REPORTBACK. Text in English. 1969. s-a. GBP 3.50 (effective 2000). adv. bk.rev. **Document type:** *Magazine.* **Description:** Focuses on issues which are of interest to all involved in adult education.
Formerly (until 1991): W E A News
Published by: Workers' Educational Association, 17 Victoria Park Sq, London, E2 9PB, United Kingdom. TEL 44-208-983-1515, FAX 44-208-983-4840, info@wea.org.uk, http://www.wea.org.uk. Ed. Mel Doyle. Adv. contact Halina Hassett. Circ: 12,000 (controlled).

371.35 ESP ISSN 1138-2783
LC5808.L29
REVISTA IBEROAMERICANA DE EDUCACION A DISTANCIA. Text in Spanish. 1988. s-a. back issues avail.
Formerly (until 1998): Revista Iberoamericana de Educacion Superior a Distancia (0214-3992)
—CINDOC.
Published by: Universidad Nacional de Educacion a Distancia, Instituto Universitario de Educacion a Distancia, C. Bravo Murillo, 38, 2a. Planta, Madrid, 28015, Spain. TEL 34-91-3987576, FAX 34-91-3988086, ried@cu.uned.es, relint@adm.uned.es, http://www.iued.uned.es/iued/Ried.htm. Ed. Lorenzo Garcia Aretio.

374.98 MEX ISSN 1016-8087
REVISTA INTERAMERICANA DE EDUCACION DE ADULTOS. Text in Spanish, Portuguese. 1978. q. USD 5 per issue (effective 2001). back issues avail. **Document type:** *Academic/Scholarly.*
Published by: Centro de Cooperacion Regional para la Educacion de Adultos en America Latina y el Caribe - CREFAL, Ave. Lazaro Cardenas s/n Col.Revolucion, Patzcuaro, Mich. 61609, Mexico. TEL 52-434-21898, FAX 52-434-20092, http://www.crefal.edu.mx. Ed. Jesus Liceaga Angeles. Circ: 1,500.

374.8 388.614 NLD ISSN 0166-6894
RIJ - INSTRUCTIE; onafhankelijk vakblad voor de auto- en motorrijopleiding in Nederland en Vlaanderen. Text in Dutch. 1966. m. (11/yr.). EUR 49; EUR 5.50 newsstand/cover (effective 2005). adv. bk.rev. illus. **Document type:** *Newsletter.* **Description:** Provides professional advice for automobile and motorcycle driving instructors in the Netherlands and the Flemish-speaking northern Belgian province of Flanders.
Published by: Sdu Uitgevers bv, Postbus 20025, The Hague, 2500 EA, Netherlands. TEL 31-70-3789911, FAX 31-70-3854321, sdu@sdu.nl, l, http://www.sdu.nl/. Ed. K Wijdooge. Pub. K Frijters. adv.: color page EUR 1,260, B&W page EUR 760; 210 x 297. Circ: 3,425. **Subscr. to:** Postbus 20014, The Hague 2500 EA, Netherlands. TEL 31-70-3789880, FAX 31-70-3789783.

374 FRA ISSN 1763-4229
▼ **SAVOIRS.** Text in French. 2003. q. EUR 37 (effective 2004). **Document type:** *Journal, Academic/Scholarly.*
Published by: L' Harmattan, 5 rue de l'Ecole Polytechnique, Paris, 75005, France. TEL 33-1-43257651, FAX 33-1-43258203, http://www.editions-harmattan.fr.

374 USA ISSN 0740-2791
SEMINARS, WORKSHOPS & CLASSES. Text in English. 1985. a. USD 21.95 domestic; USD 26.95 in Canada; USD 32.95 elsewhere (effective 2005). back issues avail. **Document type:** *Newsletter.* **Description:** Provides information on educational opportunities, adult education, lifelong learning.
Related titles: Microfiche ed.
Published by: Training Manuals, Etc., P O Box 416, Denver, CO 80201-0416. TEL 303-575-5676, FAX 303-575-1187, mail@coursesmith.com, http://www.contentprovidermedia.com, http://www.coursesmith.com. Ed. A Doyle. R&P A. Doyle. Circ: 1,500 (paid and controlled).

SEX, ETC.; a national newsletter by teens for teens. see *MEN'S INTERESTS*

SEXUAL INTELLIGENCE. see *MEN'S INTERESTS*

374.016 ISR ISSN 0792-8262
T174.3
SHALOM; magazine for alumni of Mashav training courses. Text in Arabic, English, French, Russian, Spanish. 1962. 3/yr. free. adv. illus. **Document type:** *Newsletter, Government.* **Description:** Aimed at the alumni of the Center for International Cooperation.
Related titles: Online - full text ed.
Published by: Society for Transfer of Technology, P O Box 13006, Jerusalem, 91130, Israel. TEL 972-2-6524383, FAX 972-2-6512636, http://www.israel-mfa.gov.il. Ed. Joan Hooper. Circ: 60,000.

374 CHN ISSN 0488-5406
SHANGHAI JIAOYU (CHENGREN JIAOYU BAN)/SHANGHAI EDUCATION (ADULT EDUCATION EDITION). Text in Chinese. m.
Published by: Shanghai Shi Jiaoyu-ju/Shanghai Municipal Bureau of Education, 500 Shaanxi Beilu, Shanghai, 200041, China. TEL 2530739. Ed. Liu Yuanzhang.

374 CHN ISSN 1004-6747
SHANXI CHENGREN JIAOYU/SHANXI ADULT EDUCATION. Text in Chinese. m. CNY 5 newsstand/cover. 48 p./no.;
Related titles: Online - full text ed.: (from East View Information Services).
Published by: Shanxi Jiaoyu Baokan She, 17 Jiefang Lu, Dongtou Daoxiang, Taiyuan, Shanxi 030009, China. TEL 0351-3084241.

SOUTH AFRICAN JOURNAL OF AGRICULTURAL EXTENSION/SUID-AFRIKAANSE TIJDSKRIF VIR LANDBOUVOORLIGTING. see *AGRICULTURE*

SOUTH AFRICAN SOCIETY FOR AGRICULTURAL EXTENSION. CONFERENCE PROCEEDINGS/SUID-AFRIKAANSE VERENIGING VIR LANDBOUVOORLIGTING. KONFERENSIEHANDELINGE. see *AGRICULTURE*

SPEAK UP; the newsmagazine for your English. see *LINGUISTICS*

374.013 DNK ISSN 0107-4733
SPECIALARBEJDERKURSER. Text in Danish. 1973. a. free. illus. **Document type:** *Catalog, Government.*
Formerly: Specialarbejderkurser paa Specialarbejderskolerne
Published by: Arbejdsmarkedsstyrelsen, Blegdamsvej 56, PO Box 2722, Copenhagen Oe, 2100, Denmark. TEL 45-35-28-81-00, FAX 45-35-36-24-11, ams@ams.dk, http://www.ams.dk.

374.95493 LKA
SRI LANKA FOUNDATION INSTITUTE. NEWS. Text in English, Singhalese, Tamil. irreg. LKR 3.
Indexed: SLSI.
Published by: Sri Lanka Foundation Institute, 100 Independence Square, Colombo, 8, Sri Lanka.

374 DEU ISSN 0342-9571
STAATLICHE ZENTRALSTELLE FUER FERNUNTERRICHT. AMTLICHES MITTEILUNGSBLATT. Text in German. 1973. s-a. adv. bk.rev. **Document type:** *Bulletin.*
Published by: Staatliche Zentralstelle fuer Fernunterricht, Peter-Welter-Platz 2, Cologne, 50676, Germany. TEL 49-221-921207-0, FAX 49-221-921207-20, m.vennemann@zfu.de, http://www.zfu.de. Ed. Michael Vennemann.

STANDARD LESSON COMMENTARY KING JAMES VERSION; international Sunday school lessons. see *RELIGIONS AND THEOLOGY*

374 AUT ISSN 0039-1042
DB681
STEIRISCHE BERICHTE. Text in German. 1956. bi-m. EUR 15; EUR 5 newsstand/cover (effective 2005). adv. bk.rev. bibl.; illus. **Document type:** *Magazine, Consumer.*
Formerly: Steirische Berichte zur Volksbildung und Kulturarbeit

E

Published by: Steirisches Volksbildungswerk, Herdergasse 3, Graz, St 8010, Austria. TEL 43-316-321020, FAX 43-316-3210204, redaktion@steirische-berichte.at, office@volksbildungswerk-stmk.at, http://www.steirische-berichte.at, http://www.volksbildungswerk-stmk.at. Ed. Max Mayr. Circ: 6,500 (paid and controlled).

374 ITA ISSN 0039-2057
STRADE APERTE. Text in Italian. 1959. m. membership. adv. bk.rev.; film rev. charts; illus.; stat. index.
Published by: Movimento Adulti Scouts Cattolici Italiani, Via Gualtiero Castellini, 24, Rome, RM 00197, Italy. FAX 06-877647. Circ: 7,000.

374 371.2 BGR ISSN 1310-0270
➤ **STRATEGII NA OBRAZOVATELNATA I NAUCHNATA POLITIKA/STRATEGIES FOR POLICY IN SCIENCE AND EDUCATION.** Text in Bulgarian; Summaries in English. 1993. q. USD 50 foreign (effective 2002). abstr.; charts; bibl.; stat. index. back issues avail. **Document type:** *Journal, Academic/Scholarly.*
Published by: Natsionalen Institut po Obrazovaniye, Tsarigradsko Shosse 125, bl 5, Sofia, 1113, Bulgaria. TEL 359-2-717224, FAX 359-2-702062, director@nie.bg, strategies_nio@yahoo.com, http://www.nie.bg. Ed. Stoyanka Daskalova. Adv. contact Tinka Ivanova-Kotseva TEL 359-2-727596. Circ: 350 (paid and controlled).

331.2592 DEU ISSN 1610-6962
STUDIEN ZUR BERUFSPAEDAGOGIK. Text in German. 2002. irreg., latest vol.15, 2005. price varies. **Document type:** *Monographic series, Academic/Scholarly.*
Published by: Verlag Dr. Kovac, Arnoldstr 49, Hamburg, 22763, Germany. TEL 49-40-3988800, FAX 49-40-39888055, info@verlagdrkovac.de, http://www.verlagdrkovac.de/7-17.htm.

374 DEU ISSN 1435-652X
STUDIEN ZUR ERWACHSENENBILDUNG. Text in German. 1997. irreg., latest vol.22, 2005. price varies. **Document type:** *Monographic series, Academic/Scholarly.*
Published by: Verlag Dr. Kovac, Arnoldstr 49, Hamburg, 22763, Germany. TEL 49-40-3988800, FAX 49-40-39888055, info@verlagdrkovac.de, http://www.verlagdrkovac.de/7-2.htm.

374 TZA ISSN 0856-0560
STUDIES IN ADULT EDUCATION. Text in English. 1971. q. USD 12 per issue. **Document type:** *Academic/Scholarly.* **Description:** Deals with specific issues on adult education.
Indexed: CIJE, ILD, RASB, RHEA.
Published by: Institute of Adult Education, PO Box 20679, Dar Es Salaam, Tanzania. Ed. W I Mjema. Circ: 500.

374.8 GBR ISSN 0158-037X
LC5201
➤ **STUDIES IN CONTINUING EDUCATION.** Text in English. 3/yr. GBP 232, USD 383, AUD 291 combined subscription to institutions print & online eds. (effective 2006). bk.rev. reprint service avail. from PSC. **Document type:** *Journal, Academic/Scholarly.* **Description:** Concerned with all aspects of continuing, professional and lifelong learning.
Related titles: Online - full text ed.: ISSN 1470-126X. GBP 220, USD 364, AUD 273 to institutions (effective 2006) (from EBSCO Publishing, Gale Group, IngentaConnect, O C L C Online Computer Library Center, Inc., Swets Information Services).
Indexed: AEI, CIJE, CPE, ERA, ETA, HEA, MEA, RHEA, SEA, SENA, SOMA, SWA, TEA.
—BLDSC (8490.307280), IE, Infotrieve, ingenta. **CCC.**
Published by: Routledge (Subsidiary of: Taylor & Francis Group), 4 Park Sq, Milton Park, Abingdon, Oxon OX14 4RN, United Kingdom. TEL 44-1235-828600, FAX 44-1235-829000, info@routledge.co.uk, http://www.tandf.co.uk/journals/titles/0158037X.asp, http://www.routledge.co.uk. Eds. Clive Chappell, David Boud, Nicky Solomon. **Subscr. to:** Taylor & Francis Ltd, Journals Customer Service, Rankine Rd, Basingstoke, Hants RG24 8PR, United Kingdom. TEL 44-1256-813000, FAX 44-1256-330245.

374 GBR ISSN 0266-0830
CODEN: SEDAE9
➤ **STUDIES IN THE EDUCATION OF ADULTS.** Text in English. 1969. s-a. GBP 30 domestic to individuals; GBP 40 to individuals Europe, N America, Australasia & Japan; USD 20 elsewhere to individuals; GBP 80 domestic to institutions; GBP 95 to institutions Europe, N America, Australasia & Japan; GBP 30 elsewhere to institutions (effective 2004). adv. bk.rev. bibl.; illus.; abstr. index. back issues avail.; reprints avail. **Document type:** *Journal, Academic/Scholarly.* **Description:** Contains essays and reserach studies in adult continuing education.
Formerly: Studies in Adult Education (0039-3525)
Related titles: Online - full text ed.: (from EBSCO Publishing, Gale Group, H.W. Wilson, IngentaConnect, O C L C Online Computer Library Center, Inc.).
Indexed: ABIn, BrEdI, CIJE, CPE, DIP, ERA, ETA, EduInd, HECAB, IBR, IBZ, L&LBA, MEA, PCI, REE&TA, RHEA, SEA, SENA, SOMA, SOPODA, SRRA, TEA.
—BLDSC (8490.466300), IE, Infotrieve, ingenta. **CCC.**

Published by: The National Institute of Adult Continuing Education (NAICE), Renaissance House, 20 Princess Rd. W, Leicester, Leics LE1 6TP, United Kingdom. TEL 44-116-2044200, 44-116-2044201, FAX 44-116-2854514, enquiries@niace.org.uk, http://www.niace.org.uk/Publications/Periodicals/Studies.htm. Ed. Miriam Zukas. Circ: 750.

374 DEU ISSN 1430-2683
STUDIUM IM ALTER; Forschungen und Dokumentationen. Text in German. 1996. irreg., latest vol.7, 2002. EUR 25.50 per vol. (effective 2003). **Document type:** *Monographic series, Academic/Scholarly.* **Description:** Studies all aspects of adult education and the learning and cognitive abilities of people as they age.
Published by: Waxmann Verlag GmbH, Steinfurter Str 555, Muenster, 48159, Germany. TEL 49-251-26504-0, FAX 49-251-2650426, info@waxmann.com, http://www.waxmann.com. Ed. Gerhard Breloer.

374.8 USA
SUCCEED MAGAZINE; the magazine for continuing education. Text in English. 1994. q. USD 15; USD 5.99 newsstand/cover; CND 7.99 newsstand/cover in Canada (effective 1999). adv. bk.rev.; software rev. charts; illus.; maps; stat. back issues avail. **Document type:** *Magazine, Consumer.* **Description:** For those interested in continuing education, whether it be for changing careers or enhancing their current careers.
Published by: Ramholtz Publishing, Inc., 2071 Clove Rd, Staten Island, NY 10304. TEL 718-273-5700, FAX 718-273-2539, editorial@collegebound.net. Ed. Gina LaGuardia. Pub. Luciano Rammairone. Adv. contact Gina Biancardi. page USD 4,900; trim 8.13 x 10.38. Circ: 155,000. **Dist. by:** Wagner Publishing Services, 1271 Ave of the Americas, New York, NY 10020. TEL 212-522-8900, FAX 212-522-7162.

374.942 GBR ISSN 1352-870X
SUMMERTIME FLOODLIGHT; London's official guide to summer courses. Text in English. 1994. a. GBP 3.75 (effective 1999). adv. back issues avail. **Document type:** *Directory.* **Description:** Guide to day, evening and weekend classes, summer schools and study holidays run between April and August.
Related titles: Online - full text ed.
Published by: Floodlight Publishing, 242 Vauxhall Bridge Rd, London, SW1V 1AU, United Kingdom. TEL 44-171-222-7799, editorial@floodlight.co.uk, http://www.floodlight.co.uk. Ed., Pub. Philippa Miller. R&P Peter Marsden. Circ: 25,000 (paid).

374.4 USA
THE SURVEY OF DISTANCE LEARNING PROGRAMS IN HIGHER EDUCATION. Text in English. irreg. USD 795 domestic; EUR 851 foreign (effective 2003). **Description:** Covers the practices and technologies used in distance learning programs, which provide administrators with useful benchmarking data for making decisions on the financing, scope, and development of distance learning efforts.
Related titles: Online - full text ed.: USD 795 domestic; EUR 851 foreign (effective 2003).
Published by: Primary Research Group, 850 Seventh Avenue, Suite 1200, New York, NY 10019. TEL 212-245-2327, FAX 212-245-1430, primarydat@mindspring.com, http://www.primaryresearch.com. **Dist. by:** Research and Markets Ltd., Guinness Centre, Taylors Lane, Dublin 8, Ireland. TEL 353-1-4957318, FAX 353-86-8797580, orders@researchandmarkets.com, http://www.researchandmarkets.com.

374.948 FIN ISSN 0356-1755
LA1010
SVENSKBYGDEN. Text in Finnish, Swedish. 1922. q. EUR 8 membership (effective 2004).
Published by: Svenska Folkskolans Vaenner, Annegatan 12, Helsinki, 00120, Finland. TEL 358-9-6844570, FAX 358-9-68445715, sfv@sfv.fi, http://www.sfv.fi/.

374.8 USA
SYRACUSE UNIVERSITY PUBLICATIONS IN CONTINUING EDUCATION. LANDMARK AND NEW HORIZONS SERIES✶. Text in English. 1971. irreg.
Published by: Syracuse University, Publications in Continuing Education, 356 Huntington Hall, 150 Marshall St, Syracuse, NY 13244. TEL 315-443-3421.

374.8 USA
SYRACUSE UNIVERSITY PUBLICATIONS IN CONTINUING EDUCATION. NOTES AND ESSAYS. Text in English. 1972 (no.72). irreg. price varies. bibl.; illus.
Published by: Syracuse University, Publications in Continuing Education, 356 Huntington Hall, 150 Marshall St, Syracuse, NY 13244. TEL 315-443-3421.

374.8 USA ISSN 0082-1179
SYRACUSE UNIVERSITY PUBLICATIONS IN CONTINUING EDUCATION. OCCASIONAL PAPERS✶. Text in English. irreg., latest vol.46, 1976.
Published by: Syracuse University, Publications in Continuing Education, 356 Huntington Hall, 150 Marshall St, Syracuse, NY 13244. TEL 315-443-3421.

331.2592 AUS ISSN 1033-8012
T A F E LINK. (Technical and Further Education) Key Title: TAFELINK. Text in English. 1980. m. free. adv. back issues avail. **Document type:** *Newsletter.* **Description:** Designed to keep industry up-to-date with the latest TAFE Plus services and training capabilities.
Former titles (until 1989): T A F E Newsletter (0810-8757); (until 1983): T A F E New South Wales (0156-6083)
Published by: T A F E Plus, Business Development Unit,, Level 15, 1 Oxford St, Darlinghurst, NSW 2010, Australia. TEL 61-2-92445255, FAX 61-2-92445266. Eds. Amanda Sheard, Karin O'Gready. Circ: 13,000.

374.013 DEU
DIE TECHNIKSTUNDE; paedagogische Arbeitsblaetter fuer zeitgemaessen Technikunterricht. Text in German. 1969. 2/yr. EUR 13 (effective 2005). cum.index: 1992-1999. back issues avail. **Document type:** *Journal, Academic/Scholarly.*
Formerly (until 1992): Werkstunde
Published by: A L S Verlag GmbH, Voltastr 3, Dietzenbach, 63128, Germany. TEL 49-6074-82160, FAX 49-6074-27322, info@als-verlag.de, http://www.als-verlag.de. Ed. Ingrid Kreide. R&P Maria Landji.

374 HRV ISSN 1019-7591
CODEN: THMEEU
THELEME; casopis za istrazivanje edukacije i kulture. Text in Croatian; Summaries in English. 1955. q. USD 36. adv. **Document type:** *Academic/Scholarly.*
Former titles (until no.12, 1990): Andragogija (0029-764X); (until 1969): Obrazovanje Odraslih (1330-271X); (until 1959): Narodno Sveuciliste (1330-2701)
Indexed: RASB, SOPODA.
Published by: Andragoski Centar, Vojnoviceva 42-II, Zagreb, 41001, Croatia. TEL 041-412-523. Ed. Vjerocka Ban. Circ: 1,000.

374 GBR
TIME TO LEARN. Text in English. 1949. s-a. GBP 6.45 (effective 2003). adv. reprints avail. **Document type:** *Directory, Academic/Scholarly.* **Description:** Gives details on subjects, venues and costs.
Former titles: Residential Short Courses; Calendar of Residential Short Courses
Published by: City & Guilds, 1 Giltspur St, London, EC1A 9DD, United Kingdom. TEL 44-20-72942800, FAX 44-20-72942400, timetolearn@city-and-guilds.co.uk, enquiry@city-and-guilds.co.uk, http://www.timetolearn.org.uk/, http://www.city-and-guilds.co.uk/. Circ: 9,000.

374 NLD ISSN 0165-9839
TOORTS. Text in Dutch. 1925. 5/yr. EUR 35 to non-members (effective 2005). adv. bk.rev.; film rev. illus. index. **Document type:** *Bulletin, Academic/Scholarly.*
Incorporates: Stuwing (0039-4211)
Published by: Centraal Bestuur NIVON, Hilversumstraat 332, Amsterdam, 1024 MB, Netherlands. TEL 31-20-4350700, FAX 31-20-6376533, toorts@nivon.nl, info@nivon.nl, http://www.pz.nl/nivon/nieuws/toorts/htm. Circ: 21,000.

374 USA
TRAINING TRENDS. Text in English. 1985. q. looseleaf. bk.rev. charts; illus.; stat. back issues avail.
Indexed: BrEdI.
Published by: T P C Training Systems (Subsidiary of: Telemedia Inc.), 750 Lake Crook Rd, Buffalo, IL 60089-5080. TEL 708-537-6610. Ed. Patricia Horn. Circ: 25,000.

TURKEY. DEVLET ISTATISTIK ENSTITUSU. MILLI EGITIM ISTATISTIKLERI YAYGIN EGITIM/TURKEY. STATE INSTITUTE OF STATISTICS. NATIONAL EDUCATION STATISTICS ADULT EDUCATION. see *EDUCATION—Abstracting, Bibliographies, Statistics*

374.8025 USA
UNIVERSITY CONTINUING EDUCATION ASSOCIATION. DIRECTORY. Text in English. 1974. a. USD 54.50 to non-members; USD 20.50 to members. **Document type:** *Directory.*
Former titles (until 1996): National University Continuing Education Association. Directory; National University Continuing Education Association. Handbook and Directory; National University Extension Association. Handbook and Directory (0097-0255)
Published by: University Continuing Education Association, 1 Dupont Circle, N W, Ste 615, Washington, DC 20036. TEL 202-659-3130.

374.8 GBR
UNIVERSITY OF LEEDS. UNIVERSITIES ASSOCIATION FOR CONTINUING EDUCATION. CONFERENCE PROCEEDINGS. Text in English. irreg. **Document type:** *Proceedings.*
Published by: University of Leeds, Universities Association for Continuing Education, Leeds, W Yorks LS2 9JT, United Kingdom. TEL 44-113-233-3184, FAX 44-113-233-3246, j.brownridge@leeds.ac.uk. Ed. Miriam Zukas.

E

▼ new title ➤ refereed ✶ unverified ♦ full entry avail.

374.8 GBR ISSN 0306-1108
➤ **UNIVERSITY OF SUSSEX. CENTRE FOR CONTINUING EDUCATION. OCCASIONAL PAPER.** Text in English. 1975. irreg., latest vol.33, 1995. price varies. **Document type:** *Monographic series, Academic/Scholarly.* **Description:** Contains aspects of local history and social studies; designed to aid tutors and adult students, and often being the result of research done by adult classes.
Published by: University of Sussex, Centre for Continuing Education, University Of Sussex, Falmer, Brighton, Sussex BN1 9RG, United Kingdom. TEL 44-1273-678025, FAX 44-1273-678848. Ed., R&P Fred Gray. Circ: 1,000.

374.96894 ZMB
UNIVERSITY OF ZAMBIA. CENTRE FOR CONTINUING EDUCATION. REPORT OF THE ANNUAL RESIDENT TUTORS' CONFERENCE. Text in English. 1975. a., latest vol.8, 1976. free.
Formerly: University of Zambia. Centre for Continuing Education. Report of the Annual Staff Conference
Published by: University of Zambia, Centre for Continuing Education, PO Box 516, Lusaka, Zambia. Circ: 1,000.

374.8025 DNK ISSN 1397-1832
VI UNDERSOEGER. Text in Danish. 1996. a. free. **Document type:** *Academic/Scholarly.*
Related titles: ◆ Supplement to: Laererhefte til Vi Undersoeger og Min Vej. ISSN 1397-1824.
Published by: Raadet for Uddannelses- og Erhvervsvejledning (R.U.E.)/Danish National Council for Educational and Vocational Guidance, Vester Voldgade 123, Copenhagen V, 1552, Denmark. TEL 45-39-95-53-00, FAX 45-39-95-53-49, r-u-e@r-u-e.dk, http://www.r-u-e.dk. Ed. Jette Stedemann. Circ: 65,000.

374.013 AUS ISSN 1327-4716
VICTORIAN COURSES DIRECTORY 1: HIGHER EDUCATION AND VOCATIONAL EDUCATION AND TRAINING (VET) COURSES. Text in English. 1983. a. AUD 65. **Document type:** *Directory, Government.* **Description:** Designed to assist school students and adults to explore course and career options.
Former titles: J A C Directory 1 Victoria: T A F E and University Courses (1322-686X); (until 1994): J A C Courses Directory Victoria (1323-8043); (until 1991): J A C Courses Directory (1031-7805); (until 1989): Victorian T A F E Courses Directory (0812-5961); (until 1986): T A F E in Victoria (0812-2741)
Published by: Department of Education, Level 1, Central Wing, 2 Treasury Place, East Melbourne, VIC 3002, Australia. TEL 61-3-96372011, FAX 61-3-96372770. Ed. M MacNally. Adv. contact R Johnson. Circ: 7,000.

331.2592 AUS ISSN 1327-4724
VICTORIAN COURSES DIRECTORY 2: SHORT COURSES FOR JOB SKILLS. Text in English. 1992. s-a. AUD 30. **Document type:** *Directory, Government.* **Description:** Provides information regarding short courses for the further development of job skills.
Former titles: J A C Directory 2 Victoria: Short Courses for Job Skills (1322-6878); J A C Skills Development Courses Directory, Victoria (1039-7272); (until 1993): J A C Training Short Courses Directory, Victoria (1038-6122)
Published by: Department of Education, Level 1, Central Wing, 2 Treasury Place, East Melbourne, VIC 3002, Australia. TEL 61-3-96372011, FAX 61-3-96372770. Ed. M MacNally. Adv. contact R Johnson. Circ: 1,000.

374.4 USA ISSN 1099-4262
THE VIRTUAL UNIVERSITY GAZETTE. Short title: V U G. Text in English. 1998. m. free. **Document type:** *Newsletter.* **Description:** Covers new distance learning academic programs, industry-university collaborations, jobs and career opportunities, tips and techniques for administering online learning initiatives and emerging trend and issues related to online learning in colleges at the adult and continuing education levels.
Media: Online - full text.
Published by: Geteducated.com, 4 Carmichael St, #2160, Essex Junction, VT 05452. gazette@geteducated.com, http://geteducated.com. Ed., Pub., R&P Vicky Phillips. Circ: 25,000.

374.013 HKG
VOCATIONAL TRAINING COUNCIL. ANNUAL REPORT. Text in Chinese. a. **Document type:** *Corporate.*
Published by: Vocational Training Council, Information and Public Relations Section, Vocational Training Council Tower, 27 Wood Rd., 14th Fl., Wanchai, Hong Kong. TEL 852-2836-1046, FAX 852-2591-4809.

374 DNK ISSN 0107-8135
VOKSENUDDANNELSE; tidsskrift for amtskommunale enkeltfagkurser. Text in Danish. 1980. 6/yr. DKK 80. adv. bk.rev. illus.
Published by: Benne Vagn Jensen Ed. & Pub., Gyldenrisvej 12, Svebolle, 4470, Denmark. Circ: 2,000.

374 DEU
VOLKSHOCHSCHULE FLENSBURG. ARBEITSPLAN. Text in German. 1949. s-a.
Published by: Volkshochschule Flensburg, Suederhofenden 40-42, Flensburg, 24937, Germany. TEL 0461-852023, FAX 0461-852971.

VOX LATINA. see *LITERATURE*

374.013 USA
W V A VIEWS & VISIONS. Text in English. 1970 (vol.6). 5/yr. membership. adv. bk.rev. illus. **Document type:** *Newsletter.*
Former titles: W V A Lifeline; W A V A E News (0042-9503)
Published by: Wisconsin Vocational Association, 518 Potomac Ln, Madison, WI 53719. TEL 608-833-5858, FAX 608-833-3011. Ed. Bette Lou Esser. Circ: 2,500.

WAKE FOREST UNIVERSITY SCHOOL OF LAW. CONTINUING LEGAL EDUCATION. ANNUAL REVIEW, NORTH CAROLINA. see *LAW*

374.971 CAN ISSN 0822-7225
THE WESTCOAST READER. Text in English. 1981. irreg. **Document type:** *Newspaper.* **Description:** Designed for beginning adult readers in British Columbia. Covers ESL, literacy, special education, high school learning assistance, and upper elementary.
Formerly (until 1982): Westcoaster (0826-0257)
Published by: (British Columbia Association of Teachers of English as an Additional Language), Capilano Press Society, 2055 Purcell Way, North Vancouver, BC V7J 3H5, Canada. TEL 604-984-1712, FAX 604-990-7837, wcreader@capcollege.bc.ca, tcr@capcollege.bc.ca, http://www.capcollege.bc.ca/about/publications/westcoast-reader/index.htm.

374 AUT ISSN 0026-6906
WIENER URANIA. MITTEILUNGEN. Text in German. 1910. q. EUR 7 membership (effective 2005). adv. bk.rev. **Document type:** *Newsletter, Consumer.*
Published by: Wiener Urania, Volksbildungshaus, Uraniastr 1, Vienna, W 1010, Austria. TEL 43-1-71261910, FAX 43-1-712619153, kursanmeldung@urania-wien.at. Ed. Wilhelm Petrasch. Circ: 8,000.

374 DEU ISSN 0942-4946
WIRTSCHAFT UND WEITERBILDUNG. Text in German. 1988. bi-m. EUR 79 domestic; EUR 89 foreign; EUR 7.90 newsstand/cover (effective 2004). adv. bk.rev. **Document type:** *Magazine, Trade.* **Description:** Information on vocational training in management and sales.
Formerly (until 1992): Weiterbildung (0935-3097) —IE, Infotrieve.
Published by: Max Schimmel Verlag GmbH & Co. KG (Subsidiary of: Rudolf Haufe Verlag GmbH & Co. KG), Im Kreuz 9, Wuerzburg, 97076, Germany. TEL 49-931-2791420, FAX 49-931-2791444, info@schimmelverlag.de, http://www.wirtschaftundweiterbildung.de, http://www.schimmelverlag.de. Ed. Sabine Sunter. Pub. Helmut Juenger. Adv. contact Petra Hahn. B&W page EUR 3,480, color page EUR 4,380. Circ: 19,458 (paid and controlled).

374.22 USA ISSN 0361-2848
L216
WISCONSIN LIBRARY SERVICE RECORD. Text in English. 1973. a. free. reprint service avail. from PQC. **Document type:** *Government.*
Related titles: Microfiche ed.: (from CIS).
Indexed: SRI.
Published by: Department of Public Instruction, Division for Library and Technology Community Learning, 125 S Webster St, 5th Fl, P O Box 7841, Madison, WI 53707. TEL 608-266-3939, FAX 608-267-1052.

WORKERS EDUCATION JOURNAL. see *BUSINESS AND ECONOMICS—Labor And Industrial Relations*

WORLD DIRECTORY OF HUMAN RIGHTS RESEARCH AND TRAINING INSTITUTIONS. see *POLITICAL SCIENCE—Civil Rights*

WORLD EDUCATION REPORTS; a journal of program developments in the field of Third World and US nonformal education for community development. see *SOCIOLOGY*

374.0124 CAN ISSN 0820-6686
WORLDLIT. Text in English. 1967. s-a. CND 35. bk.rev. illus. **Document type:** *Newsletter.*
Former titles (until 1982): World Literacy of Canada. Newsletter (0700-5350); World Literacy of Canada, News and Views (0705-8829)
Published by: World Literacy of Canada, 59 Front St E, Toronto, ON M5E 1B3, Canada. TEL 416-863-6262, FAX 416-601-6984. Ed. Mamta Mishra. Circ: 3,000.

374.0025 USA ISSN 0084-2486
L900
WORLDWIDE REGISTER OF ADULT EDUCATION; directory of home study schools. Text in English. 1960. irreg., latest 1973, with 1980 supplement. USD 8.95. **Document type:** *Directory.* **Description:** Lists hundreds of correspondence schools, including those accredited by the National Home Study Council, as well as many other vocational and university extension programs.
Published by: Aurea Publications, 207 Allen Ave, Allenhurst, NJ 07711. TEL 908-531-4535. Ed. Alex Sandri White.

370.113 SWE ISSN 1402-8557
YRKESLAERAREN - RET-INFO. Text in Swedish. 1996. 6/yr. SEK 180 (effective 2003). adv. 32 p./no. 3 cols./p.; **Document type:** *Journal, Trade.*
Formed by the merger of (1985-1995): Yrkeslaeraren (0284-0332); (1979-1995): RET-Info (0283-5568)
Related titles: Online - full text ed.
Indexed: RefZh.
Published by: Laerarfoerbundet, Tidningsafdelning, Segelbaatsvaegen 15, Box 12229, Stockholm, 10226, Sweden. TEL 46-8-7376500, FAX 46-8-7376569, kansli@lararforbundet.se, http://www.yrkeslararen.net/default.asp, http://www.lararforbundet.se. Ed. Bjoern Andersson. Adv. contact Annelie Bjoernsdotter Lundqvist. B&W page SEK 6,150, color page SEK 9,250; trim 182 x 266. Circ: 6,400.

374 CHN
ZI XUE/SELF-TEACHING. Text in Chinese. m. USD 35.
Contact Dist.: China Books & Periodicals Inc TEL 415-282-2994. **Dist. by:** China International Book Trading Corp, 35 Chegongzhuang Xilu, Haidian District, PO Box 399, Beijing 100044, China.

ZIELSPRACHE ENGLISCH; Zeitschrift fuer den Englischunterricht in der Erwachsenbildung. see *LINGUISTICS*

374.8 CHE
ZUERIWOCHE. Text in German. w. **Document type:** *Newsletter.*
Published by: Kretz AG, Postfach, Feldmeilen, 8706, Switzerland. TEL 41-1-9237656, FAX 41-1-9237657, kretz_ag@bluewin.ch. Circ: 288,965 (controlled).

374 DEU
ZWEIWOCHEN DIENST; Bildung - Wissenschaft - Kulturpolitik. Text in German. 1985. fortn. bibl.; stat. back issues avail. **Document type:** *Newsletter.*
Published by: Zweiwochendienst Verlag GmbH, Pressehaus I Rm. 234, Heussallee 2-10, Bonn, 53113, Germany. TEL 0228-217375, FAX 0228-215226. Ed. Karin Dupp. Circ: 1,500.

EDUCATION—Computer Applications

see also COMPUTERS—Computer Assisted Instruction

370.285 USA ISSN 1551-3696
LB1028.3 CODEN: ETREF9
➤ **A A C E JOURNAL.** (Association for the Advancement of Computing in Education) Text in English. 1994. q. free domestic. adv. **Document type:** *Journal, Academic/Scholarly.* **Description:** Publishes articles on the issues and applications of educational technology to enhance learning and teaching in all disciplines and levels.
Former titles (until 2004): Educational Technology Review (Online); (until 2001): Educational Technology Review (1081-8677); (until 1993): Ed - Tech Review (1065-6901)
Media: Online - full content.
Indexed: CIJE, CPE, ERA, ETA, Inspec, MicrocompInd. —BLDSC (3662.531700), AskIEEE, IE. **CCC.**
Published by: Association for the Advancement of Computing in Education, PO Box 3728, Norfolk, VA 23514. TEL 757-623-7588, FAX 703-997-8760, info@aace.org, http://www.aace.org/pubs/aacej/. Ed. Gary H Marks. R&P Sarah D Williams. Adv. contact Ingrid Hoffman. B&W page USD 950; trim 11 x 8.5. Circ: 7,500.

➤ **A L T - J.** (Association for Learning Technology Journal) see *EDUCATION—Higher Education*

370.285 USA ISSN 1094-2602
LB1028.43
➤ **ANNUAL EDITIONS: COMPUTERS IN EDUCATION.** Text in English. 1985. a., latest 2003, 11th ed. USD 20.31 per vol. (effective 2004). illus. **Document type:** *Academic/Scholarly.* **Description:** Features articles on computer applications in education, including computer literacy, software, hardware, programming languages and their effectiveness. Contains discussions on the logistics and administrative problems surrounding the introduction of computers into a school system.
Published by: McGraw-Hill - Dushkin (Subsidiary of: McGraw-Hill Higher Education), 2460 Kerper Blvd, Dubuque, IA 52001. TEL 800-243-6532, customer.service@mcgraw-hill.com, http://www.dushkin.com/text-data/catalog/0072847158.mhtml. Ed. John Hirschbuhl. Pub. Ian Nielsen. R&P Cheryl Greenleaf. Circ: 10,000.

370.285 USA
APPLE EDUCATION NEWS; an information service for educators and trainers. Text in English. q. free. bk.rev. **Description:** For educators and trainers using Apple computers. Features articles on projects and innovative applications created by schools using Apple computers.
Published by: Apple Computer, Inc., 1 Infinite Loop, Cupertino, CA 95014. TEL 408-974-2552. Circ: 100,000.

E

370.285 AUS ISSN 0816-9020
➤ **AUSTRALIAN EDUCATIONAL COMPUTING.** Text in English. 1986. irreg. back issues avail. **Document type:** *Journal, Academic/Scholarly.*
Related titles: Online - full text ed.: ISSN 1443-833X. free (effective 2005).
Indexed: AEI.
Published by: Australian Council for Computers in Education, PO Box 1255, Belonnen, ACT 2616, Australia. TEL 61-8-9370-6331, FAX 61-8-9407-8413, http://lamp.infosys.deakin.edu.au/journals/. Ed. Jeremy Pagram.

➤ **BIBLIOGRAPHIE INFORMATIK, DIDAKTIK UND ELEMENTARE COMPUTERANWENDUNGEN FUER SCHULE, HOCHSCHULE UND WEITERBILDUNG.** see *COMPUTERS—Information Science And Information Theory*

➤ **BIG 6 NEWSLETTER**; teaching technology and information skills. see *EDUCATION—Teaching Methods And Curriculum*

➤ **C A L I C O JOURNAL.** see *COMPUTERS—Computer Assisted Instruction*

➤ **C I T INFOBITS.** see *EDUCATION—Higher Education*

370.285 371.335 USA ISSN 1090-8595
C S S JOURNAL✶. (Computers in the Social Studies) Text in English. 1992. bi-m. USD 10 to individuals; USD 20 to institutions. bk.rev.; software rev. back issues avail. **Document type:** *Journal, Trade.* **Description:** Informs social studies teachers of ways in which they can use personal computers and related technology as a tool for their instruction and students' learning.
Former titles (until 1996): C S S Journal (Paper) (1080-1723); (until 199?): Computers in the Social Studies: A Journal for Teachers (1067-0971)
Media: Online - full content.
Address: 1415 S. Frisco Ave., Tulsa, OK 74119-3425. journalcss@aol.com, http://cssjournal.com.

CAMPUS TECHNOLOGY; new directions in educational technology. see *EDUCATION—Higher Education*

CATALYST (MENLO PARK). see *EDUCATION—Special Education And Rehabilitation*

CLOSING THE GAP. see *EDUCATION—Special Education And Rehabilitation*

372.35 IRL ISSN 1393-7545
COMPUSCHOOL. Text in English. 1998. q. adv. **Document type:** *Magazine.* **Description:** Covers all aspects of technology in education.
Published by: Impact Press, 47 Harrington St., Dublin, 8, Ireland. TEL 353-1-4760031, FAX 353-1-4760033, sales@impact-press.ie. adv.: B&W page EUR 2,000, color page EUR 3,000; 256 x 328. Circ: 14,000 (controlled).

COMPUTER ASSISTED LANGUAGE LEARNING; an international journal. see *COMPUTERS—Computer Assisted Instruction*

370.285 GBR ISSN 0010-4590
QA76.27 CODEN: CPECBK
➤ **COMPUTER EDUCATION**; a journal for teachers (especially classes of 11-18 age range) interested in computers & computing. Text in English. 1969. 3/yr. GBP 14; GBP 24 overseas (effective 1999). adv. bk.rev. index every 2 yrs. **Document type:** *Academic/Scholarly.*
Indexed: CPE, CompC, CurCont, ERA, ETA, HECAB, Inspec, MEA, RHEA, SEA, SENA, SOMA, TEA.
—BLDSC (3393.920000), AskIEEE, IE, Infotrieve, ingenta.
Published by: Staffordshire University, School of Computing, Trent Bldg, College Rd, Stoke on Trent, Staffordshire ST4 2DE, United Kingdom. TEL 44-1782-294000, http://www.staffs.ac.uk. Ed. I Selwood. Adv. contact I. Selwood. Circ: 1,200.

370.285 USA
COMPUTER LEARNING. Text in English. a. (Oct.). free. **Document type:** *Newsletter.* **Description:** Focuses people's attention on the importance of technology in children's learning. Includes tips for parents and teachers.
Published by: Computer Learning Foundation, 4700 Northgate Blvd., Ste. 135, Sacramento, CA 95834-1148. TEL 408-720-8898, FAX 408-720-8777, clf@computerlearning.org, http://www.computerlearning.org.

004.071 GBR ISSN 0899-3408
CODEN: CSEDFE
➤ **COMPUTER SCIENCE EDUCATION.** Text in Dutch. 1988. 4/yr. GBP 246, USD 420 combined subscription to institutions print & online eds. (effective 2006). adv. index. reprint service avail. from PSC. **Document type:** *Journal, Academic/Scholarly.* **Description:** Covers computer science education at college and university levels.
Related titles: Online - full text ed.: GBP 234, USD 399 to institutions (effective 2006) (from EBSCO Publishing, Gale Group, IngentaConnect, O C L C Online Computer Library Center, Inc., Swets Information Services).
Indexed: ABIn, CPE, CompLI, ERA, ETA, EduInd, Inspec, MEA, RHEA, SEA, SENA, SOMA, TEA.
—BLDSC (3394.270170), AskIEEE, IE, Infotrieve. **CCC.**
Published by: Routledge (Subsidiary of: Taylor & Francis Group), 4 Park Sq, Milton Park, Abingdon, Oxon OX14 4RN, United Kingdom. TEL 44-1235-828600, FAX 44-1235-829000, info@routledge.co.uk, http://www.tandf.co.uk/journals/titles/08993408.asp, http://www.routledge.com. Eds. Renee McCauley, Sally Fincher. adv.: page EUR 175; trim 160 x 240. Circ: 300.

370.285 USA ISSN 1573-4552
▼ **COMPUTER-SUPPORTED COLLABORATIVE LEARNING.** Text in English. 2003. irreg., latest vol.5, 2005. price varies. **Document type:** *Monographic series, Academic/Scholarly.* **Description:** Aims to cover all aspects of collaborative learning, from situations ranging from two individuals performing a task together, during a short period of time, to groups of 200 students following the same course and interacting via electronic mail.
—BLDSC (3394.284000).
Published by: Springer-Verlag New York, Inc. (Subsidiary of: Springer Science+Business Media), 233 Spring St, New York, NY 10013. TEL 212-460-1500, FAX 212-473-6272, journals@springer-ny.com, http://www.springer-ny.com. Ed. Pierre Dillenbourg.

370.285 DEU ISSN 0941-519X
COMPUTER UND UNTERRICHT. Text in German. 1991. q. EUR 53; EUR 9.50 newsstand/cover (effective 2004). adv. **Document type:** *Journal, Academic/Scholarly.*
Published by: Erhard Friedrich Verlag GmbH, Im Brande 17, Seelze, 30926, Germany. TEL 49-511-40004-0, FAX 49-511-40004119, info@friedrich-verlag.de, http://www.friedrich-verlag.de. adv.: B&W page EUR 1,156, color page EUR 1,733.

COMPUTERS & EDUCATION. see *EDUCATION—Higher Education*

370.285 USA ISSN 1069-3769
QA75.5 CODEN: CEJOE7
➤ **COMPUTERS IN EDUCATION JOURNAL.** Text in English. 1965. q. USD 45 domestic; USD 65 foreign (effective 2004). adv. bk.rev. illus. back issues avail. **Document type:** *Journal, Academic/Scholarly.* **Description:** Covers transactions, scholarly research papers, applications notes, and teaching methods.
Formerly (until 1991): CoED Journal (0736-8607); Formed by the merger of: A S E E Computers in Education Division. Newsletter; A S E E Computers in Education Division. Application Notes (0736-895X); A S E E Computers in Education Division. CoED Transactions (0271-5902); Which was formerly: Analog-Hybrid Computer Educational Society. A C E S Transactions (0276-8542)
Media: Duplicated (not offset).
Indexed: AIA, CADCAM, CPE, CompC, EngInd, Inspec.
—BLDSC (3394.913500), CISTI, Ei, IE, ingenta, Linda Hall.
Published by: American Society for Engineering Education, Computers in Education Division, PO Box 68, Port Royal Sq, Port Royal, VA 22535. TEL 804-742-5611, FAX 804-742-5030. Ed., R&P W W Everett Jr. Pub. Leanne E Traver. Circ: 1,250 (paid).

370.285 NZL ISSN 0114-4081
➤ **COMPUTERS IN NEW ZEALAND SCHOOLS.** Text in English. 1989. 3/yr. NZD 35; NZD 11.95 newsstand/cover (effective 2001). adv. bk.rev.; software rev. illus.; tr.lit. 56 p./no.; back issues avail. **Document type:** *Academic/Scholarly.* **Description:** Publishes articles on all aspects of computers in education, with emphasis on practical applications.
Indexed: INZP.
Published by: (University of Otago Press, Education Department), University of Otago, Hocken Library, PO Box 56, Dunedin, New Zealand. TEL 64-3-479-8807, FAX 64-3-479-8385, university.press@stonebow.otago.ac.nz. Ed. Kwok Wing Lai. R&P Wendy Harrex. Adv. contact Philippa Jamieson TEL 61-3-479-9094. B&W page NZD 225; trim 275 x 210. Circ: 800 (paid).

370.285 USA ISSN 0738-0569
LB1028.43
➤ **COMPUTERS IN THE SCHOOLS**; the interdisciplinary journal of practice, theory, and applied research. Text in English. 1984. q. USD 500 combined subscription domestic to institutions print & online eds.; USD 675 combined subscription in Canada to institutions print & online eds.; USD 725 combined subscription elsewhere to institutions print & online eds. (effective 2006). adv. bk.rev. bibl.; charts; illus. 120 p./no.; back issues avail.; reprint service avail. from HAW. **Document type:** *Journal, Academic/Scholarly.* **Description:** Features articles that combine theory and practical applications of small computers in schools.
Related titles: Microfiche ed.: (from PQC); Microform ed.; Online - full text ed.: ISSN 1528-7033 (from EBSCO Publishing, O C L C Online Computer Library Center, Inc., Swets Information Services).
Indexed: ABIn, BrCerAb, C&ISA, CIJE, CPE, CerAb, CompC, CompLI, CompR, CorrAb, DIP, E&CAJ, EAA, ECER, EMA, ERA, ETA, EduInd, FamI, IAA, IBR, IBZ, InfoSAb, Inspec, L&LBA, LAMP, M&TEA, MBF, MEA, METADEX, MicrocompInd, RHEA, RefZh, SEA, SENA, SOMA, SOPODA, SRRA, SWR&A, TEA, WAA.
—BLDSC (3394.937500), AskIEEE, Haworth, IE, Infotrieve, ingenta, Linda Hall. **CCC.**
Published by: Haworth Press, Inc., 10 Alice St, Binghamton, NY 13904-1580. TEL 607-722-5857, 800-429-6784, FAX 607-722-1424, 800-895-0582, getinfo@haworthpress.com, http://www.haworthpress.com/web/CITS. Ed. D Lamont Johnson. Pub. William Cohen. R&P Ruth Ann Heath TEL 607-722-5857 ext 316. adv.: B&W page USD 315, color page USD 550; trim 4.375 x 7.125. Circ: 445 (paid).

➤ **CONTEMPORARY ISSUES IN TECHNOLOGY & TEACHER EDUCATION.** see *EDUCATION—Teaching Methods And Curriculum*

370.285 USA
CONVERGE ONLINE. Text in English. 1998. m. free (effective 2005). software rev. illus. **Document type:** *Trade.* **Description:** Explores the role of technology in all areas and at all grade levels of children's education.
Media: Online - full content.
Published by: (Center for Digital Education), e.Republic, Inc., 100 Blue Ravine Rd, Folsom, CA 95630-4703. TEL 916-932-1300, FAX 916-932-1470, getinfo@govtech.net, http://www.centerdigitaled.com/converge/, http://www.govtech.net/. Ed. Wayne Hanson. Circ: 50,000 (controlled).

370.285 371.3 USA ISSN 1091-2703
LB2806.15
CURRICULUM - TECHNOLOGY QUARTERLY. Text in English. 1991. q. USD 39 to members; USD 46 to non-members (effective 2003); USD 10 per issue (effective 2005). bk.rev.; software rev. charts; illus.; tr.lit. back issues avail. **Document type:** *Newsletter, Trade.* **Description:** Explores strategies for using technology for enhancing classroom instruction. Includes pull-out section on curriculum context areas. For K-12 teachers and curriculum developers.
Related titles: Online - full text ed.
—**CCC.**
Published by: (Education & Technology Resource Center), Association for Supervision and Curriculum Development, 1703 N Beauregard St, Alexandria, VA 22311. TEL 703-578-9600, 800-933-2723, FAX 703-575-5400, update@ascd.org, http://www.ascd.org/cms/index.cfm?TheViewID=370. Ed. Larry Mann. R&P Christine Richards TEL 800-933-2723 ext 5749. Circ: 15,000 (paid).

370.285 DNK ISSN 0108-3708
DATALOGI O. Text in Danish. 1973. irreg. free. illus. **Document type:** *Academic/Scholarly.*
Published by: Koebenhavns Universitet, Datalogisk Institut, Universitetsparken 1, Copenhagen Oe, 2100, Denmark. TEL 45-35-32-14-00, FAX 45-35-32-14-01.

370.285 GBR ISSN 1472-4499
LB1028.5 CODEN: EDCODK
E C & T. Variant title: Educational Computing & Technology. Text in English. 1980. m. GBP 6.50, USD 30. back issues avail.
Former titles (until 1999): Educational Computing and Technology (0964-167X); (until 1990): Educational Computing (0143-6058)
Indexed: CPE, CompC, CompD, HECAB, Inspec, RHEA, SOMA.
—BLDSC (3647.241000), IE, ingenta. **CCC.**
Published by: Hobsons PLC, Bateman St, Cambridge, Cambs CB2 1LZ, United Kingdom. TEL 01223-354551, http://www.hobsons.com. Circ: 15,000.

370.285 DEU ISSN 1860-7470
▼ ➤ **E-LEARNING AND EDUCATION.** Text in English. 2005. irreg. free (effective 2005). **Document type:** *Journal, Academic/Scholarly.* **Description:** Offers a platform for new scientific research results from the widespread area of all e-learning aspects.
Media: Online - full content.
Published by: Di P P - N R W, Postfach 270451, Cologne, 50510, Germany. TEL 49-221-40075124, FAX 49-221-40075190, eleed@campussource.de, dipp@hbz-nrw.de, http://eleed.campussource.de, http://www.dipp.nrw.de.

370.25 USA
▼ **ED TECH MAGAZINE.** Text in English. 2003. w. **Document type:** *Magazine, Trade.*
Published by: C D W Government, Inc, 230 N Milwaukee Ave, Vernon Hills, IL 60061. FAX 847-419-6200, 800-808-4239, http://www.cdwg.com/edtech. Ed. Lee Copeland.

370.285 USA ISSN 1061-5008
LB1028.43
EDUCATION TECHNOLOGY NEWS; insiders guide to multimedia in the K-12 classroom. Text in English. 1984. bi-w. looseleaf. USD 217 in US & Mexico; USD 221 elsewhere; USD 247 combined subscription print & email eds. (effective 2005). bk.rev.; software rev. illus. **Document type:** *Newsletter.* **Description:** For teachers and other persons interested in the educational uses of computers in the classroom. Includes feature articles on applications, educational software, and pertinent programs.

E

Formerly (until 1991): Education Computer News (0742-0250); Incorporates (in 2002): Higher Education Technology News (1524-8097)
Related titles: E-mail ed.: ISSN 1545-4886. USD 167 (effective 2005); Online - full text ed.: (from Factiva, Gale Group, Northern Light Technology, Inc.).
—CCC.
Published by: Business Publishers, Inc., 8737 Colesville Rd., Flr. 10, Silver Spring, MD 20910-3976. TEL 800-274-6737, bpinews@bpinews.com, custserv@bpinews.com, http://www.bpinews.com. Ed. Rasheeda Childress. Pub. L A Eiserer.

370.285 USA
EDUCATIONAL SOFTWARE REVIEW. Text in English. 1991. m. USD 33.75. illus.
Published by: Growth Systems, Inc., 855 Normandy Rd, Encinitas, CA 92024. Ed. Stewart Walton.

370.285 371.33 NZL ISSN 1436-4522
LB1028.3 CODEN: ETSDB7
➤ **EDUCATIONAL TECHNOLOGY & SOCIETY.** Text in English. 1998 (Oct.). q. free (effective 2005). adv. bk.rev. back issues avail. **Document type:** *Journal, Academic/Scholarly.* **Description:** Explores issues affecting educators and developers of educational systems, including artificial intelligence researchers.
Media: Online - full text (from H.W. Wilson). **Related titles:** Print ed.: ISSN 1176-3647. NZD 89 to individuals; NZD 107 to institutions (effective 2005).
Indexed: CurCont, EAA, Inspec, SSCI.
—CCC.
Published by: International Forum of Educational Technology & Society, Information Systems Department, Massey University, Private Bag 11-222, Palmerston North, New Zealand. TEL 64-6-350-5799 ext 2090, FAX 64-6-350-5725, kinshuk@ieee.org, http://ifets.ieee.org/periodical. Eds. Ashok Patel, Demetrios G. Sampson, Reinhard Oppermann.

➤ **EDUCAUSE.** see *EDUCATION—Higher Education*

378.00285 USA
EDUCAUSE LEADERSHIP STRATEGIES SERIES. Text in English. 1999. irreg. price varies. **Document type:** *Monographic series, Academic/Scholarly.* **Description:** Explores the challenges and changes advanced technology can bring into a higher-education setting.
Published by: (Educause), Jossey-Bass Inc., Publishers (Subsidiary of: John Wiley & Sons, Inc.), 989 Market St, San Francisco, CA 94103-1741. TEL 415-433-1767, FAX 415-433-0499, info@educause.edu, http://www.educause.edu/pub/pubs.html, http://www.josseybass.com.

378.00285 USA ISSN 1525-2299
EDUCAUSE MONOGRAPH SERIES. Text in English. 1999. irreg. price varies. back issues avail. **Document type:** *Monographic series, Academic/Scholarly.* **Description:** Discusses issues regarding using technology in higher education teaching and learning.
Published by: Educause, 4772 Walnut St, Ste 206, Boulder, CO 80301-2536. TEL 303-449-4430, FAX 303-440-0461, info@educause.edu, http://www.educause.edu/pub/pubs.html. R&P Nancy Hayes TEL 303-939-0321.

378.00285 USA
EDUCAUSE PROFESSIONAL PAPER SERIES. Text in English. 1988. irreg., latest vol.18, 1998. back issues avail. **Document type:** *Monographic series, Academic/Scholarly.* **Description:** Examines the introduction, use, and management of information resources and technologies in teaching, learning, scholarship, research, and institutional management in the context of higher education.
Formerly (until 1999): C A U S E Professional Paper Series
Related titles: Online - full content ed.: free.
Published by: Educause, 4772 Walnut St, Ste 206, Boulder, CO 80301-2536. TEL 303-449-4430, FAX 303-440-0461, info@educause.edu, info@educause.com, http://www.educause.edu/pub/profess.html. Pub., R&P Nancy Hayes TEL 303-939-0321. Circ: 4,200 (paid).

EDUCAUSE QUARTERLY. see *EDUCATION—Higher Education*

EDUCAUSE REVIEW. see *EDUCATION—Higher Education*

370.285 USA
THE EDUHOUND WEEKLY. Text in English. w. **Document type:** *Newsletter.* **Description:** Covers tips on using the Internet in education and special topics with activities and links.
Media: Online - full text.
Published by: 101 Communications, Llc., 9121 Oakdale Ave, Ste 101, Chatsworth, CA 91311. TEL 818-734-1520, FAX 818-734-1522, info@101com.com, http://www.101com.com.

370.285 USA ISSN 1077-9949
ELECTRONIC EDUCATION REPORT; business intelligence on opportunities in the educational software industry. Text in English. 1994. bi-m. USD 625 (effective 2006). 8 p./no.; **Document type:** *Newsletter, Trade.* **Description:** Covers educational software, multimedia CD-ROM, integrated learning systems, videodiscs, distance learning, online services for classrooms, videocassettes, and developments on the Information Superhighway.
Related titles: Online - full text ed.: USD 599 (effective 2005) (from EBSCO Publishing, Factiva, Florida Center for Library Automation, Gale Group).
Indexed: MicrocompInd.
—CCC.
Published by: SIMBA Information (Subsidiary of: R.R. Bowker LLC), 60 Long Ridge Rd., Ste 300, Stamford, CT 06902. TEL 203-325-8193, 800-307-2529, FAX 203-325-8915, info@simbanet.com, http://www.simbanet.com/publications/news_eer.htm.

▼ **ELECTRONIC JOURNAL OF E-LEARNING.** see *EDUCATION—Teaching Methods And Curriculum*

ELECTRONIC LEARNING. see *COMPUTERS—Computer Assisted Instruction*

ELECTRONIC MEDIA FOR THE SCHOOL MARKET (YEAR): REVIEW, TRENDS & FORECAST. see *EDUCATION—Teaching Methods And Curriculum*

370.285 GBR ISSN 0957-2953
ELECTRONICS EDUCATION. Text in English. 1982. 3/yr. USD 20 in the Americas to non-members; GBP 12 elsewhere to non-members; USD 7 per issue in the Americas to non-members; GBP 4 per issue elsewhere to non-members (effective 2003). adv. bk.rev. back issues avail. **Document type:** *Journal, Academic/Scholarly.* **Description:** Geared toward teachers of electronics and computing in schools.
Formerly (until 1990): Electronic Systems News (0265-0096)
Indexed: C&ISA, E&CAJ, Inspec, SolStAb.
—AskIEEE, IE. **CCC.**
Published by: Institution of Electrical Engineers, Michael Faraday House, Six Hills Way, Stevenage, Herts SG1 2AY, United Kingdom. TEL 44-1438-313311, FAX 44-1438-313465, inspec@iee.org, http://www.iee.org/Publish/Journals/MagsNews/Mags/ELED/index.cfm. Ed. A Kuras. R&P Michael McCabe TEL 732-321-5575. Circ: 12,000. **Subscr. to:** INSPEC, I E E, Publication Sales Dept., PO Box 96, Stevenage, Herts SG1 2SD, United Kingdom. TEL 44-1438-313311, FAX 44-1438-742840; **US subscr. addr.:** INSPEC/I E E, 379 Thornall St., Edison, NJ 08837. TEL 732-321-5575, FAX 732-321-5702.

370.285 USA
EXTENDED STUDIES E-ZINE. Text in English. irreg. **Document type:** *Newsletter.* **Description:** Dedicated to extension programs and distance learning education.
Media: Online - full text.
Published by: California State University - San Marcos TEL 760-750-4020, 800-500-9377, jubran@mailhost1.csusm.edu, http://ww2.csusm.edu, http://ww2.csusm.edu/es/ezine. Ed. Janet Jubran.

FLEXIBLE ONLINE LEARNING. see *COMPUTERS—Internet*

378 IND
HANDBOOK OF DISTANCE EDUCATION (YEAR). Text in English. 1927. irreg., latest 1998. USD 20 (effective 2003). **Document type:** *Newsletter.* **Description:** Contains information about distance education.
Published by: Association of Indian Universities, A.I.U. House, 16 Kotla Marg, New Delhi, 110 002, India. TEL 91-11-323-0059, FAX 91-11-323-6105, aiu@del12.vsnl.net.in, http://www.aiuweb.org.

370.285 USA ISSN 1047-5230
HELLER REPORT ON EDUCATION TECHNOLOGY AND TELECOMMUNICATIONS MARKETS. Text in English. 1989. m. USD 395 domestic; USD 435 foreign (effective 2001). adv. back issues avail. **Document type:** *Newsletter.*
Related titles: Online - full text ed.: (from Florida Center for Library Automation, Gale Group).
Indexed: CompD.
—CCC.
Published by: Nelson B. Heller & Associates, 1625 Broadway., Ste. 250, Denver, CO 80202-4765. TEL 847-441-2920, FAX 847-926-0202, anne@HellerReports.com, http://www.HellerReports.com. Ed., Pub., R&P Nelson B Heller TEL 847-674-6282. Adv. contact Robert James. Circ: 1,000.

370.285 USA
I A A V C COMMUNICATOR. Text in English. 1959. 6/yr. USD 60. adv. bk.rev. illus. **Document type:** *Trade.* **Description:** Provides data to producers of corporate, industrial, educational and promotional programs in any individual medium. Focuses on the association's CINDY and VCDY competitions and on their winners.
Former titles: A V C Visions; A V C Communicator; Communicator (South Pasadena); I F P A Communicator (0099-1090); I F P A Newsletter
Published by: International Association of Audio Visual Communicators, 57 W Palo Verde Ave, PO Box 250, Ocotillo, CA 92259-0250. TEL 760-358-7000, sheemonw@cindys.com, http://www.cindys.com, http://www.iaavc.org. Ed., R&P Betty I Lougaris. Pub., Adv. contact Phillip N Shuey. Circ: 65,000.

371.35 IND ISSN 0971-2690
INDIAN JOURNAL OF OPEN LEARNING. Text in English. 1992. s-a. INR 100 domestic to individuals; USD 20 in developing nations to individuals; USD 30 rest of world to individuals; INR 300 domestic to institutions; USD 40 in developing nations to institutions; USD 60 rest of world to institutions (effective 2000). **Description:** Disseminates information about theory, practice and research in the field of open and distance education, including correspondence and multimedia education.
Indexed: CPE, ERA, ETA, MEA, RHEA, SEA, SENA, SOMA, TEA.
—BLDSC (4417.560000), IE, ingenta.
Published by: Indira Gandhi National Open University, Maidan Gharhi, New Delhi, 110 068, India. http://www.ignou.org. Ed. Santosh Panda.

370.285 USA ISSN 1522-8185
LB1028.5 CODEN: ITCAFY
➤ **INFORMATION TECHNOLOGY IN CHILDHOOD EDUCATION ANNUAL.** Text in English. 1989. a. USD 55 domestic to individual members; USD 70 foreign to individual members; USD 95 domestic to institutions; USD 110 foreign to institutions; USD 40 domestic to students; USD 55 foreign to students (effective 2005). adv. abstr. back issues avail. **Document type:** *Academic/Scholarly.* **Description:** Serves as a forum and information source to report the research and applications on using computer technology in the education of children.
Formerly: Journal of Computing in Childhood Education (1043-1055)
Related titles: Microfiche ed.; Online - full text ed.: (from Florida Center for Library Automation, Gale Group, H.W. Wilson, O C L C Online Computer Library Center, Inc.).
Indexed: ABIn, CIJE, CPE, CompD, CompR, ERA, ETA, EduInd, InfoSAb, Inspec, MEA, MicrocompInd, PsycInfo, PsycholAb, RHEA, SEA, SENA, SOMA, SWA, TEA, e-psyche.
—BLDSC (4496.368767), AskIEEE, IE, ingenta. **CCC.**
Published by: Association for the Advancement of Computing in Education, PO Box 3728, Norfolk, VA 23514. TEL 757-623-7588, FAX 703-997-8760, info@aace.org, http://www.aace.org. Ed. Daniel Shade. R&P Sarah D Williams. Adv. contact Garrett Paulin.

370.285 GBR ISSN 1360-1954
INTERACTIVE. Text in English. 5/yr. GBP 25 domestic to individuals; GBP 33 foreign to individuals; GBP 40 domestic to institutions; GBP 60 foreign to institutions (effective 2003). **Document type:** *Academic/Scholarly.* **Description:** Designed to help all primary and secondary teachers get the most from information technology in the classroom.
Related titles: Online - full text ed.: (from Swets Information Services).
—IE.
Published by: Questions Publishing Company Ltd., 1st Fl, Leonard House, 321 Bradford St, Digbeth, Birmingham, Warks B1 3ET, United Kingdom. TEL 44-121-6667878, FAX 44-121-6667879, rchima@qiis.co.uk, http://www.education-quest.com/.

370.285 371.335 NLD ISSN 1049-4820
LB1028.3 CODEN: ILENFR
➤ **INTERACTIVE LEARNING ENVIRONMENTS.** Text in English. 1990. 3/yr. GBP 201, USD 344 combined subscription to institutions print & online eds. (effective 2006). adv. reprint service avail. from PSC. **Document type:** *Journal, Academic/Scholarly.* **Description:** Examines technologies such as the Internet and multimedia in education and training. Covers individual learning, group activity, social and organizational issues, and courseware production.
Formerly (until 1990): Artificial Intelligence and Education
Related titles: Online - full text ed.: ISSN 1744-5191. GBP 191, USD 327 to institutions (effective 2006) (from EBSCO Publishing, Gale Group, IngentaConnect, O C L C Online Computer Library Center, Inc., Swets Information Services).
Indexed: BrEdI, CIJE, CPE, CompLI, CurCont, ERA, ETA, EnvAb, Inspec, MEA, RHEA, SEA, SENA, SOMA, SSCI, TEA.
—BLDSC (4531.872180), IE, Infotrieve, ingenta. **CCC.**
Published by: Taylor & Francis The Netherlands (Subsidiary of: Taylor & Francis Group), Schipolweg 107 C, PO Box 447, Leiden, 2316 XC, Netherlands. TEL 31-715-243080, FAX 31-715-234571, pub@swets.nl, infoho@swets.nl, http://www.tandf.co.uk/journals/titles/10494820.asp, http://www.tandf.co.uk/swets.asp. Eds. Masoud Yazdani, Roy Rada. Adv. contact Miranda Mauritz. page EUR 225; trim 160 x 240. Circ: 300.

371.33 AUS ISSN 1327-7308
LB1028.3
➤ **INTERNATIONAL JOURNAL OF EDUCATIONAL TECHNOLOGY.** Text in English. 1999. s-a. free (effective 2005). **Document type:** *Journal, Academic/Scholarly.* **Description:** Covers articles about computer-based educational technologies.
Media: Online - full text.
Indexed: AEI.
Published by: University of Western Australia, Department of Education, 35 Stirling Highway, Nedlands, W.A. 6907, Australia. http://www.outreach.uiuc.edu/ijet/. Ed. Roger G. Hacker.

➤ **INTERNET TEACHER.** see *COMPUTERS—Internet*

E

370.285 CHN
JISUANJI JIAO YU XUE✶ /COMPUTER TEACHING AND LEARNING. Text in Chinese. 1985. bi-m. CNY 5.28. adv. bk.rev. **Document type:** *Academic/Scholarly.*
Published by: Shanghai Shifan Daxue/Shanghai Teachers University, 10 Guilin Lu, Shanghai, 200234, China. TEL 2531905. Ed. Sun Yuanqing. Circ: 50,000. **Co-sponsor:** Shanghai Jiaoyuju - Shanghai Municipal Bureau of Education.

JOURNAL OF COMPUTER ASSISTED LEARNING. see *COMPUTERS—Computer Assisted Instruction*

JOURNAL OF COMPUTERS IN MATHEMATICS AND SCIENCE TEACHING. see *MATHEMATICS—Computer Applications*

378.00285 USA ISSN 1042-1726
LB2395.7 CODEN: JHIEE2
➤ **JOURNAL OF COMPUTING IN HIGHER EDUCATION.** Text in English. 1989. s-a. USD 40 domestic to individuals; USD 45 in Canada to individuals; USD 65 elsewhere to individuals; USD 80 domestic to institutions; USD 85 in Canada to institutions; USD 95 elsewhere to institutions (effective 2005). adv. bk.rev.; software rev. charts; illus.; abstr. cum.index. 121 p./no.; back issues avail. **Document type:** *Journal, Academic/Scholarly.* **Description:** Publishes scholarly essays, case studies, reviews, reports, and research articles that contribute to the understanding of the issues, problems and research associated with instructional technologies. Covers all aspects of academic computing.
Indexed: CIJE, CompAb, Inspec.
—BLDSC (4963.950000), AskIEEE, IE, ingenta. **CCC.**
Published by: Norris Publishers, PO Box 2593, Amherst, MA 01004-2593. TEL 413-549-5150, FAX 413-253-9525, cmacknight@oit.umass.edu, http://www.jchesite.org. R&P, Adv. contact Carol B MacKnight TEL 419-549-7288. B&W page USD 250; trim 6 x 9. Circ: 400 (controlled).

370.285 USA ISSN 0735-6331
CODEN: JERSEY
➤ **JOURNAL OF EDUCATIONAL COMPUTING RESEARCH.** Text in English. 1984. 8/yr. (in 2 vols.). USD 145 to individuals; USD 400 domestic to institutions; USD 415 foreign to institutions (effective 2005). adv. bk.rev. abstr.; charts; illus. Index. back issues avail.; reprints avail. **Document type:** *Journal, Academic/Scholarly.* **Description:** Includes original research papers, critical analyses, reports on research in progress, design and development studies, article reviews, grant award listings, and readers' opinions.
Related titles: Online - full text ed.: ISSN 1541-4140 (from EBSCO Publishing).
Indexed: ABIn, ASCA, ArtHuCI, CIJE, CPE, CompAb, CompLI, CurCont, DIP, EAA, ERA, ETA, EduInd, IBR, IBZ, Inspec, L&LBA, MEA, PsycInfo, PsycholAb, RASB, RHEA, SEA, SENA, SOMA, SOPODA, SSCI, SWA, TEA, e-psyche.
—BLDSC (4973.154700), AskIEEE, Ei, IDS, IE, Infotrieve, ingenta. **CCC.**
Published by: Baywood Publishing Co., Inc., 26 Austin Ave, PO Box 337, Amityville, NY 11701-0337. TEL 631-691-1270, FAX 631-691-1770, info@baywood.com, http://www.baywood.com/Journals/PreviewJournal.asp?Id=0735-6331. Ed. Robert H Seidman. R&P Julie Krempa. Adv. contact Rochelle Grant.

➤ **JOURNAL OF EDUCATIONAL MULTIMEDIA AND HYPERMEDIA.** see *COMPUTERS—Computer Assisted Instruction*

370.285 USA ISSN 0047-2395
LB1028.3 CODEN: JETSB7
➤ **JOURNAL OF EDUCATIONAL TECHNOLOGY SYSTEMS.** Text in English. 1972. q. USD 274 domestic to institutions; USD 282 foreign to institutions; USD 60 foreign to members (effective 2005). adv. abstr.; charts; illus.; stat. Index. back issues avail.; reprints avail. **Document type:** *Journal, Academic/Scholarly.* **Description:** Deals with the nature of technological devices (i.e., hardware) useful for teaching and learning; focuses on the techniques and approaches (i.e., software) for using technology in all types of educational systems.
Formerly: Journal of Educational Instrumentation
Related titles: Online - full text ed.: ISSN 1541-3810 (from EBSCO Publishing).
Indexed: ABIn, AHCI, BrCerAb, C&ISA, CIJE, CPE, CerAb, CompLI, CorrAb, DIP, E&CAJ, EAA, EMA, ERA, ESPM, ETA, EduInd, EngInd, IAA, IBR, IBZ, InfoSAb, Inspec, L&LBA, M&TEA, MBF, MEA, METADEX, MicrocompInd, RHEA, RefZh, RiskAb, SEA, SENA, SOMA, SOPODA, SolStAb, TEA, WAA, e-psyche.
—BLDSC (4973.259000), AskIEEE, IE, ingenta, Linda Hall. **CCC.**
Published by: (Society for Applied Learning Technology), Baywood Publishing Co., Inc., 26 Austin Ave, PO Box 337, Amityville, NY 11701-0337. TEL 631-691-1270, FAX 631-691-1770, info@baywood.com, http://www.baywood.com/Journals/PreviewJournals.asp?Id=0047-2395. Ed. David C Miller. Adv. contact Rochelle Grant.

370.285 USA ISSN 1055-3096
QA76.27
➤ **JOURNAL OF INFORMATION SYSTEMS EDUCATION.** Text in English. 1988. q. USD 55 domestic to individuals; USD 75 foreign to individuals; USD 110 domestic to institutions; USD 130 foreign to institutions (effective 2005). **Document type:** *Journal, Academic/Scholarly.* **Description:** Contains original articles on current topics of special interest to information systems educators and trainers.
Formerly (until 1991): C I S Educator Forum (1055-310X)
Related titles: Online - full text ed.: (from EBSCO Publishing, H.W. Wilson, O C L C Online Computer Library Center, Inc., ProQuest Information & Learning).
Indexed: ABIn, EduInd.
—BLDSC (5006.777500), IE, ingenta. **CCC.**
Address: c/o Albert L. Harris, Ed., Department of ITOM, Appalachian State University, Boone, NC 28608. TEL 828-262-6180, FAX 828-262-6190, jise@appstate.edu, http://www.jise.appstate.edu/. Ed., Pub., R&P Dr. Albert L Harris.

➤ **JOURNAL OF INTERACTIVE INSTRUCTION DEVELOPMENT.** see *COMPUTERS—Computer Assisted Instruction*

370.285 USA ISSN 1093-023X
LB1028.43 CODEN: JILRFU
➤ **JOURNAL OF INTERACTIVE LEARNING RESEARCH.** Text in English. 1997. q. USD 55 domestic to individual members; USD 70 foreign to individual members; USD 140 domestic to institutions; USD 155 foreign to institutions; USD 40 domestic to students; USD 55 foreign to students (effective 2005). adv. **Document type:** *Academic/Scholarly.* **Description:** Includes articles related to the underlying theory, design, implementation, effectiveness, and impact of interactive learning environments in education and training.
Related titles: Microfiche ed.; Online - full text ed.: (from Gale Group, ProQuest Information & Learning).
Indexed: CIJE, CPE, CompD, CompLI, EAA, ERA, ETA, InfoSAb, Inspec, LISA, MEA, MicrocompInd, PsycInfo, PsycholAb, RHEA, SEA, SENA, SOMA, TEA, e-psyche.
—BLDSC (5007.539550), IE, Infotrieve, ingenta. **CCC.**
Published by: Association for the Advancement of Computing in Education, PO Box 3728, Norfolk, VA 23514. TEL 757-623-7588, FAX 703-997-8760, info@aace.org, http://www.aace.org/pubs/jilr/default.htm. Ed. Tom Reeves. R&P Sarah D Williams. Adv. contact Ingrid Hoffman.

370.285 GBR ISSN 1365-893X
LB1028.55
➤ **JOURNAL OF INTERACTIVE MEDIA IN EDUCATION.** Abbreviated title: J I M E. Text in English. 1996. irreg. free (effective 2005). bk.rev. illus. reprints avail. **Document type:** *Journal, Academic/Scholarly.* **Description:** Aims to foster a multidisciplinary and intellectually rigorous debate on the theoretical and practical aspects of interactive media in education.
Media: Online - full content.
Indexed: PsycInfo.
Published by: Open University, Knowledge Media Institute, Milton Keynes, MK7 6AA, United Kingdom. jime@open.ac.uk, http://www-jime.open.ac.uk. Eds. Simon Buckingham Shum, Tamara Sumner.

370.285 USA
➤ **JOURNAL OF ONLINE LEARNING.** Abbreviated title: J.O.L. Text in English. q. USD 29 domestic to non-members; USD 39 foreign to non-members; USD 20 domestic to members; USD 30 foreign to members; USD 12 domestic to students; USD 22 foreign to students. adv. **Document type:** *Academic/Scholarly.* **Description:** Covers communications, projects, research, publications, international connections and training.
Formerly: Telecommunications in Education News
Media: Online - full content.
Indexed: Inspec.
—BLDSC (5026.315400).
Published by: (S I G Tel), International Society for Technology in Education, 1710 Rhode Island Ave NW, Ste 900, Washington, DC 20036. FAX 541-346-5890, iste@iste.org. Ed. Terresa Gibrey. R&P Jennifer Roland TEL 541-346-2422. Adv. contact J D Fite.

370.285 USA ISSN 1539-1523
LB1715 CODEN: JRCEE8
➤ **JOURNAL OF RESEARCH ON TECHNOLOGY IN EDUCATION.** Text in English. 1967. q. USD 78 domestic to non-members (effective 2001). adv. bk.rev. charts; stat.; abstr. index. back issues avail.; reprint service avail. from PQC. **Document type:** *Academic/Scholarly.* **Description:** Provides a forum for researchers at schools and colleges of education confronting issues of providing computer and technology education for preservice and in-service teachers.
Former titles: Journal of Research on Computing in Education (0888-6504); (until 1986): A E D S Journal (0001-1037)
Related titles: Microform ed.: (from PQC); Online - full text ed.: (from bigchalk, EBSCO Publishing, Florida Center for Library Automation, Gale Group, H.W. Wilson, Northern Light Technology, Inc., O C L C Online Computer Library Center, Inc., ProQuest Information & Learning).
Indexed: ABIn, CIJE, CPE, CompLI, CompR, EAA, ETA, EduInd, Inspec, MEA, MicrocompInd, RHEA, SEA, SENA, SOMA, TEA.
—BLDSC (5052.0358), AskIEEE, IE, ingenta. **CCC.**
Published by: (Special Interest Group for Teacher Educators (SIGTE)), International Society for Technology in Education, 1710 Rhode Island Ave NW, Ste 900, Washington, DC 20036. FAX 541-346-5890, iste@iste.org, http://www.iste.org/jrte/index.html. Eds. Dr. David Ayersman, Dr. Lynne Schrum, Dr. W Michael Reed. R&P Jennifer Roland TEL 541-346-2422. Adv. contact J D Fite. Circ: 2,500.

➤ **JOURNAL OF SPECIAL EDUCATION TECHNOLOGY.** see *EDUCATION—Special Education And Rehabilitation*

370.285 USA ISSN 1059-7069
LB1028.3 CODEN: JTEDFU
➤ **JOURNAL OF TECHNOLOGY AND TEACHER EDUCATION.** Variant title: J T A T E. Text in English. 1993. q. USD 55 domestic to individual members; USD 70 foreign to individual members; USD 140 domestic to institutions; USD 155 foreign to institutions; USD 40 domestic to students; USD 55 foreign to students (effective 2005). adv. back issues avail. **Document type:** *Journal, Academic/Scholarly.* **Description:** Serves as an international forum to report research and applications of technology in teacher education: preservice, in-service, and graduate teacher education.
Related titles: Microfiche ed.; Online - full text ed.: (from Florida Center for Library Automation, Gale Group, H.W. Wilson, O C L C Online Computer Library Center, Inc., ProQuest Information & Learning).
Indexed: ABIn, CIJE, CPE, CompD, CompLI, CompR, EAA, ERA, ETA, EduInd, Inspec, MEA, MicrocompInd, RHEA, SEA, SENA, SOMA, TEA.
—BLDSC (5068.530000), IE, Infotrieve, ingenta. **CCC.**
Published by: Association for the Advancement of Computing in Education, PO Box 3728, Norfolk, VA 23514. TEL 757-623-7588, FAX 703-997-8760, info@aace.org, http://www.aace.org/pubs/jtate/default.htm. Eds. Dee Anna Willis, Jerry Willis. R&P Sarah D Williams. Adv. contact Ingrid Hoffman. **Co-sponsor:** Society for Information Technology and Teacher Education.

371.334 USA ISSN 1082-5754
LB1028.5
➤ **LEARNING AND LEADING WITH TECHNOLOGY.** Text in English. 1979. 8/yr. subscr. incld. with membership. adv. bk.rev. charts; illus. Index. back issues avail.; reprints avail. **Document type:** *Journal, Academic/Scholarly.* **Description:** Provides feature articles and columns in language arts, Logo, science, mathematics, telecommunications, equity and international connections for the K-12 technology-using educator.
Formerly (until 1995): Computing Teacher (0278-9175)
Related titles: Microform ed.: (from PQC); Online - full text ed.: (from Florida Center for Library Automation, Gale Group, H.W. Wilson, O C L C Online Computer Library Center, Inc.).
Indexed: ABIn, CIJE, CPE, CompC, CompD, CybAb, ETA, EduInd, InfoSAb, Inspec, MicrocompInd, PCR2, RASB, TEA.
—BLDSC (5179.325893), IE, Infotrieve, ingenta. **CCC.**
Published by: International Society for Technology in Education, 480 Charnelton St, Eugene, OR 97401-2626. TEL 541-302-3777, 800-336-5191, FAX 541-302-3778, iste@iste.org, http://www.iste.org/LL/31/3/index.cfm. Ed. Kate Conley. Circ: 12,000.

370.285 371.33 NZL ISSN 1438-0625
LEARNING TECHNOLOGY. Text in English. q. adv. back issues avail. **Document type:** *Journal, Academic/Scholarly.* **Description:** Aims to report the activities of the Learning Technology Task Force including various announcements, work in progress, projects, participation opportunities, additions and modifications to the website, and so on.
Media: Online - full text.
Published by: I E E E Computer Society, Learning Technology Task Force, c/o Dr. Kinshuk, Ed., Information Systems Dept. Private Bag 11-222, Massey University, Palmerston North, New Zealand. TEL 64-6-350-5799, FAX 64-6-350-5725, kinshuk@massey.ac.nz, http://lttf.ieee.org/learn_tech.

370.285 DEU ISSN 0720-8642
LOG IN; Informatik und Computer in der Schule. Text in German. 1981. 5/yr. EUR 54 domestic; EUR 60 foreign; EUR 14 newsstand/cover (effective 2005). **Document type:** *Journal, Academic/Scholarly.* **Description:** Devoted to the use of computers and information technology in education. Features practice and methods, application, readers' letters, and a calendar of events.
Indexed: RASB.
—**CCC.**
Published by: Log In Verlag GmbH, Friedrichshaller Str 41, Berlin, 14195, Germany. TEL 49-30-8232339, FAX 49-30-8621645, redaktion@log-in-verlag.de, verlagsmail@log-in-verlag.de, http://www.log-in-verlag.de/wwwredlogin/index.html. Ed. Ingo Ruediger Peters.

370.285 USA ISSN 1097-9778
MERIDIAN (RALEIGH); a middle school computer technologies journal. Text in English. 1998. s-a. free (effective 2005). **Document type:** *Academic/Scholarly.* **Description:** Electronic journal dedicated to the research and practice of computer technology in the middle school.
Media: Online - full text.
Published by: North Carolina State University, Raleigh, NC 27695. beckey@ahlgreen.com, http://www.ncsu.edu/meridian.

E

▼ new title ➤ refereed ✶ unverified ♦ full entry avail.

371.3078 USA ISSN 1546-4636
LB1028.3 CODEN: MSUCCS
MULTIMEDIA & INTERNET@SCHOOLS; the media and technology specialist's guide to electronic tools and resources for K-12. Text in English. 1994. 6/yr. USD 39.95 domestic; USD 54 in Canada & Mexico; USD 63 elsewhere; USD 7.95 newsstand/cover domestic; USD 8.95 newsstand/cover in Canada (effective 2005). adv. bk.rev. illus. **Document type:** *Journal, Trade.* **Description:** Reviews new titles, evaluates hardware and software, offers technical advice and troubleshooting tips, profiles high-tech installations.
Formerly (until 2003): MultiMedia Schools (1075-0479)
Related titles: Online - full text ed.: 1994 (from bigchalk, EBSCO Publishing, Florida Center for Library Automation, Gale Group, H.W. Wilson, Northern Light Technology, Inc., O C L C Online Computer Library Center, Inc., ProQuest Information & Learning).
Indexed: ABIn, CIJE, CPerl, EduInd, InfoSAb, Inspec, MicrocompInd, SoftBase.
—BLDSC (5983.146900), IE, ingenta. **CCC.**
Published by: Information Today, Inc., 143 Old Marlton Pike, Medford, NJ 08055-8750. TEL 609-654-6266, FAX 609-654-4309, custserv@infotoday.com, http://www.infotoday.com/MMSchools/. Ed. David Hoffman. Pub. Thomas H Hogan.

371 USA ISSN 1546-2625
ONLINE CL@SSROOM. Text in English. 2001. m. USD 167 domestic; USD 171 in Canada; USD 177 elsewhere (effective 2005). **Document type:** *Newsletter, Academic/Scholarly.* **Description:** Povides practical advice and examples of proven, research-based pedagogical techniques to help instructors and course developers create and teach outstanding online courses. Includes expert advice on course design, learner-centered pedagogy, synchronous and asynchronous interaction, online learning communities, appropriate use of technology, course management, and assessment.
Related titles: Online - full content ed.: USD 167 (effective 2005); Online - full text ed.: (from EBSCO Publishing, H.W. Wilson).
Indexed: EduInd.
Published by: Magna Publications, Inc., 2718 Dryden Dr, Madison, WI 53704. TEL 608-246-3590, FAX 608-246-3597, custserv@magnapubs.com, http://www.magnapubs.com/pub/magnapubs_oc.

371.334 URY
ONLINE COURSES NEWSLETTER. Text in Spanish. 1998. m. free. back issues avail. **Document type:** *Newsletter.* **Description:** Informs about the existing online courses available on the Internet.
Media: Online - full text.
Published by: Eduardo Peirano, Ed. & Pub., Uruguay. emapey@adinet.com.uy, http://www.paisvirtual.com/educacion/comercial/edu26/online.html, http://members.tripod.com/~enviroline/online.html. Circ: 600.

▼ **ONLINE DEGREES MAGAZINE.** see *EDUCATION—Higher Education*

▼ **PITCH JOURNAL.** see *EDUCATION—Teaching Methods And Curriculum*

PROGRESSIO; newsletter for teaching development - nuusbrief vir onderrigontwikkeling. see *EDUCATION—Teaching Methods And Curriculum*

374.00285 USA ISSN 0895-6537
R I T INDUSTRY EDUCATION PROGRAMS UPDATE. (Rochester Institute of Technology) Variant title: R I T Update. Text in English. a. free. **Document type:** *Catalog.*
Published by: Rochester Institute of Technology, Industry Education Programs, 67 Lomb Memorial Dr, Rochester, NY 14623-5603. TEL 585-475-7429, 800-724-2536, FAX 585-475-5055, krptpd@rit.edu, http://www.seminars.cias.rit.edu.

370.285 CAN ISSN 1497-5572
RESCOL. Text in French. 1995. 3/yr. **Document type:** *Magazine, Government.*
Former titles (until 2000): Rescol Hors Ligne (1206-0054); (until 1996): Rescol (Ottawa, 1995) (1203-4150)
Related titles: Online - full content ed.: ISSN 1206-1603; Online - full text ed.: (from Micromedia ProQuest); ♦ English ed.: SchoolNet Magazine. ISSN 1494-7331.
Indexed: CEI.
Published by: Industry Canada/Industrie Canada, Distribution Services, Communications & Marketing Branch, Rm 268D, West Tower, C.D. Howe Bldg, 235 Queen St, Ottawa, ON K1A 0H5, Canada. TEL 613-947-7466, FAX 613-954-6436, publications@ic.gc.ca, http://www.ic.gc.ca.

370.285 PER ISSN 0034-866X
REVISTA DE TECNOLOGIA EDUCATIVA. Text in English, German, Spanish. 1967. s-a. per issue exchange basis. bk.rev. charts; illus.
Formerly (until vol.9, 1976): Revista de Pedagogia Cibernetica e Instruccion Programada
Published by: (Seccion de Tecnologia Educacional), Universidad Nacional de Trujillo, Apdo Postal 315, Trujillo, Peru. Ed. Atilio Leon Rubio. Circ: 600.

370.285 CAN ISSN 0831-7925
S A C E BULLETIN. Text in English. 2/yr. CND 20; CND 30 out of province (effective 2000). adv. **Document type:** *Bulletin.*
Published by: (Saskatchewan Association for Computers in Education), Saskatchewan Teachers' Federation, 2317 Arlington Ave., Saskatoon, SK S7J 2H8, Canada. stf@stf.sk.ca.

370.285 USA ISSN 1096-3936
QA76.27 CODEN: SIGSD3
S I G C S E BULLETIN INROADS. (Special Interest Group on Computer Science Education) Text in English. 1969. q. USD 30 (effective 2004). **Document type:** *Bulletin, Academic/Scholarly.*
Formerly (until 1997): S I G C S E Bulletin (0097-8418)
Related titles: Online - full text ed.: (from EBSCO Publishing).
Indexed: B&BAb, CompR, EngInd, ErgAb, Inspec.
—BLDSC (8275.265000), AskIEEE, CISTI, Ei, IE, Infotrieve, ingenta.
Published by: Association for Computing Machinery, Inc., 1515 Broadway, 17th Fl, New York, NY 10036-5701. TEL 212-626-0500, 212-626-0520, 800-342-6626, FAX 212-869-0481, inroads@hofstra.edu, sigs@acm.org, usacm@acm.org, http://www.acm.org/sigcse/. Ed. John Impagliazzo.

370.285 USA
S I G T C CONNECTIONS; the journal for technology coordinators. Text in English. q. USD 29 domestic to non-members; USD 39 foreign to non-members; USD 20 domestic to members; USD 30 foreign to members. adv. **Document type:** *Academic/Scholarly.* **Description:** Provides a forum to identify problems and solutions and to share information on issues facing technology coordinators today.
Related titles: Online - full text ed.: 2000.
Published by: (Special Interest Group for Technology Coordinators), International Society for Technology in Education, 1710 Rhode Island Ave NW, Ste 900, Washington, DC 20036. FAX 541-346-5890, iste@iste.org. Ed. Gordon Dahlby. R&P Jennifer Roland TEL 541-346-2422. Adv. contact J D Fite.

616.07 AUS
SCHOOL P C AUSTRALIA. Text in English. 1998. m. AUD 29. adv. bk.rev.; software rev. 52 p./no. 3 cols./p.; back issues avail. **Document type:** *Newspaper.* **Description:** Publishes articles on curriculum and methods for computer education.
Related titles: Online - full text ed.
Published by: A C P Computer Publications, 54-58 Park St., Level 6, Sydney, NSW 1028, Australia. TEL 61-393470300, FAX 61-393475001, schoolpc@acp.com.au, http://www.schoolpc.acp.com.au. Ed. Helen Dancer. Pub. John Alexander. R&P Heather Milley TEL 612-92889162. adv.: B&W page AUD 2,135, color page AUD 2,850; trim 210 x 275.

370.285 CAN ISSN 1494-7331
SCHOOLNET MAGAZINE. Text in English. 1995. 3/yr. **Document type:** *Magazine, Academic/Scholarly.*
Former titles (until 2000): SchoolNet Off-line (1206-0062); (until 1996): SchoolNet (1203-4142)
Related titles: Online - full content ed.: ISSN 1206-159X. 1999; Online - full text ed.: (from Micromedia ProQuest); ♦ French ed.: Rescol. ISSN 1497-5572.
Indexed: CEI.
Published by: Industry Canada/Industrie Canada, Distribution Services, Communications & Marketing Branch, Rm 268D, West Tower, C.D. Howe Bldg, 235 Queen St, Ottawa, ON K1A 0H5, Canada. TEL 613-947-7466, FAX 613-954-6436, publications@ic.gc.ca, http://www.ic.gc.ca.

370.285 USA ISSN 0894-4393
H61.3 CODEN: CSOSE6
➤ **SOCIAL SCIENCE COMPUTER REVIEW.** Text in English. 1983. q. USD 492, GBP 318 to institutions; USD 512, GBP 331 combined subscription to institutions print & online eds. (effective 2006). adv. bk.rev. abstr.; illus. Index. back issues avail.; reprints avail. **Document type:** *Journal, Academic/Scholarly.* **Description:** Disseminates research and teaching applications of microcomputers for social scientists. Features include pertinent software reviews, new product announcements and tutorials for beginners.
Former titles (until 1987): Social Science Microcomputer Review (0885-0011); (until 1985): Social Science Micro Review (8755-3031); Incorporates: Computers and the Social Sciences (0748-9269)
Related titles: Microfilm ed.; Online - full text ed.: ISSN 1552-8286. USD 487, GBP 314 to institutions (effective 2006) (from bigchalk, EBSCO Publishing, O C L C Online Computer Library Center, Inc., Sage Publications, Inc., Swets Information Services).
Indexed: ASCA, ASSIA, AmH&L, ArtHuCI, BRI, BrCerAb, C&ISA, CBRI, CMCI, CPE, CerAb, ChPerI, CompLI, CompR, CorrAb, CurCont, DIP, E&CAJ, EMA, ERA, ETA, FamI, IAA, IBR, IBZ, InfoSAb, Inspec, LISA, M&TEA, MBF, MEA, METADEX, MicrocompInd, PSA, PsycInfo, PsycholAb, RHEA, SEA, SENA, SOMA, SOPODA, SSA, SSCI, SWR&A, SociolAb, SoftBase, SolStAb, TEA, WAA, e-psyche.
—BLDSC (8318.159500), AskIEEE, IDS, IE, Infotrieve, ingenta, KNAW, Linda Hall. **CCC.**
Published by: (North Carolina State University, Social Science Research and Instructional Computing Lab), Sage Publications, Inc., 2455 Teller Rd, Thousand Oaks, CA 91320. TEL 805-499-0721, 800-818-7243, FAX 805-499-0871, 805-499-8096, 800-583-2665, info@sagepub.com, http://www.sagepub.com/journal.aspx?pid=198. Ed. G David Garson. Pub. Sara Miller McCune. R&P Tanya Udin TEL 805-499-0721 ext 7716. Adv. contact Kirsten Beaulieu TEL 805-499-0721 ext 7160. page USD 350. Circ: 500 (paid). **Subscr. to:** Sage Publications Ltd., 1 Oliver's Yard, 55 City Rd, London EC1 1SP, United Kingdom. TEL 44-20-73740645, FAX 44-20-73748741, subscription@sagepub.co.uk.

370.285 USA
SOCIETY FOR APPLIED LEARNING TECHNOLOGY. NEWSLETTER. Text in English. 1972. q. **Document type:** *Newsletter.* **Description:** Primarily for professionals in instructional technology. Includes organizational news, conference information and publications.
Published by: Society for Applied Learning Technology, 50 Culpeper St, Warrenton, VA 20186. TEL 540-347-0055, info@salt.org, http://www.salt.org. Ed. Raymond G Fox. Circ: 27,000.

370.285 CHE
SPEEDUP. Text in Italian. 1987. 2/yr. **Document type:** *Academic/Scholarly.*
Indexed: Inspec.
Published by: Centro Svizzero di Calcolo Scientifico, Galleria 2, via Cantonale, Manno, 6928, Switzerland. speedup@cscs.ch, decker@mit-solutions.com. Ed. Alfred Scheidegger.

370.285 USA
LB1028.7
T E S S. (The Educational Software Selector) Text in English. 1984. a. USD 82.50 for base vol (1996); USD 32.50 for update. index. back issues avail. **Document type:** *Directory, Trade.* **Description:** Contains descriptions of software for all grade levels, preschool through postgraduate.
Former titles: Latest and Best of T E S S; Educational Software Selector (8755-5107)
Media: CD-ROM.
Published by: Educational Products Information Exchange Institute, 103 3 W Montauk Hwy, 3, Hampton, NY 11946-4006. TEL 516-728-9100, FAX 516-728-9228.

370.285 USA
T H E FOCUS. (Technological Horizons in Education) Text in English. bi-w. **Document type:** *Newsletter.* **Description:** Examines a specific area of educational technology through articles written by technology experts.
Media: Online - full text.
Published by: 101 Communications, Llc., 9121 Oakdale Ave, Ste 101, Chatsworth, CA 91311. TEL 818-734-1520, FAX 818-734-1522, info@101com.com, http://www.101com.com.

370.285 USA ISSN 0192-592X
LB1028.3 CODEN: THEJD4
T H E JOURNAL. (Technological Horizons in Education) Text in English. 1973. m. free domestic to qualified personnel (effective 2005). adv. bk.rev. charts; illus.; stat. back issues avail.; reprints avail. **Document type:** *Magazine, Trade.* **Description:** Contains material of interest to educators of all levels; focuses on a specific topic for each issue, as well as technological innovations as they apply to education.
Related titles: Microform ed.: (from PQC); Online - full text ed.: (from EBSCO Publishing, Florida Center for Library Automation, Gale Group, H.W. Wilson, O C L C Online Computer Library Center, Inc., ProQuest Information & Learning).
Indexed: ABIn, CIJE, CPE, CompC, CompD, EAA, ERA, ETA, EduInd, Inspec, LRI, MicrocompInd, SoftBase, TEA.
—**CCC.**
Published by: 101 Communications, Llc., 9121 Oakdale Ave, Ste 101, Chatsworth, CA 91311. TEL 818-734-1520, FAX 818-734-1522, editorial@thejournal.com, info@101com.com, http://www.thejournal.com, http://www.101com.com. adv.: color page USD 12,305, B&W page USD 10,605. Circ: 170,000 (controlled). **Co-sponsor:** Information Access Co.

370.285 USA
T H E'S NEWSLETTER. (Technological Horizons in Education) Text in English. w. **Document type:** *Newsletter.* **Description:** Comprised of recent announcements that affect the education community.
Media: Online - full text.
Published by: 101 Communications, Llc., 9121 Oakdale Ave, Ste 101, Chatsworth, CA 91311. TEL 818-734-1520, FAX 818-734-1522, info@101com.com, http://www.101com.com.

370.285 USA ISSN 1053-6728
LB1028.43
TECHNOLOGY AND LEARNING; the leading magazine of electronic education. Text in English. 1980. m. (10/yr.). USD 29.95 domestic; USD 39.95 in Canada & Mexico; USD 69.95 elsewhere; free to qualified personnel (effective 2005). adv. bk.rev. charts; illus. back issues avail.; reprints avail. **Document type:** *Magazine, Trade.* **Description:** Features, reviews, news, and announcements of educational activities and opportunities in programming, software development, and hardware configurations.

E

Former titles (until 1990): Classroom Computer Learning (0746-4223); (until 1983): Classroom Computer News (0731-9398)
Related titles: Online - full text ed.: (from EBSCO Publishing, Florida Center for Library Automation, Gale Group, H.W. Wilson, LexisNexis, O C L C Online Computer Library Center, Inc., ProQuest Information & Learning, The Dialog Corporation).
Indexed: ABIn, CIJE, CPE, CPerI, CompC, CompD, ERA, ETA, EduInd, ICM, InfoSAb, Inspec, MRD, MagInd, Microcompind, PCR2, PSI, RILM.
—BLDSC (8758.633500), IE, Infotrieve, ingenta. **CCC.**
Published by: C M P Media LLC (Subsidiary of: United News & Media), 600 Harrison St, 6th Fl., San Francisco, CA 94107. TEL 415-947-6746, FAX 415-947-6041, techlearning_editors@cmp.com, http://www.techlearning.com/. Ed. Susan McLester. Pub. Jo-Ann McDevitt. Circ: 83,000 (controlled).

370.285 USA
TECHNOLOGY AND TEACHER EDUCATION ANNUAL (YEAR). Text in English. irreg. **Document type:** *Proceedings.* **Description:** Publishes papers presented at AACE conferences.
—BLDSC (8758.665500), ingenta.
Published by: Association for the Advancement of Computing in Education, PO Box 3728, Norfolk, VA 23514. TEL 757-623-7588, FAX 804-978-7449, info@aace.org, http://www.aace.org.

370.285 USA ISSN 1547-7878
TECHNOLOGY LEADERSHIP NEWS (ONLINE); insights and outlooks for the K-12 educators. Text in English. 1986. 9/yr. free to members (effective 2003). bk.rev. **Document type:** *Newsletter.* **Description:** Covers new applications of computer and other technologies, and their impact on education at primary and secondary school levels. Considers policy, curriculum development, school environment, administrative concerns, and more, as they relate to technology in schools.
Former titles (until 2003): Technology Leadership News (Print) (1098-657X); (until Nov.1997): Insider's Letter
Media: Online - full content.
Published by: (Institute for the Transfer of Technology to Education.), National School Boards Association, 1680 Duke St, Alexandria, VA 22314-3493. TEL 703-838-6722, FAX 703-683-7590, info@nsba.org, http://www.nsba.org/itte, http://www.nsba.org/site/index.asp. Ed. Kathleen Vail. Circ: 5,000.

370.285 USA
LB1028.3
TECHNOS QUARTERLY; journal of the Agency for Instructional Technology. Text in English. 1992. q. free (effective 2003). 36 p./no.; back issues avail. **Document type:** *Journal, Academic/Scholarly.* **Description:** Provides a forum for discussing ideas that concern the use of technology in education, with a focus on reform.
Formerly (Until 2002): Technos (1060-5649)
Related titles: Online - full text ed.: (from Gale Group).
Indexed: CIJE.
—BLDSC (8761.075000), IE, ingenta. **CCC.**
Published by: Agency for Instructional Technology, PO Box A, Bloomington, IN 47402-0120. TEL 812-339-2203, FAX 812-333-4218, info@technos.net, ait@ait.net, http://www.technos.net, http://www.ait.net. Ed. Carole Novak. Pub. Michael F Sullivan. R&P Amy Bond TEL 812-339-2203 ext. 220. Circ: 4,000.

370.285 USA ISSN 8756-3894
LB1043 CODEN: TETREF
➤ **TECHTRENDS**; for leaders in education and training. Text in English. 1956. bi-m. USD 55 domestic; USD 75 foreign (effective 2005). adv. bk.rev. charts; illus. index. back issues avail.; reprint service avail. from PQC. **Document type:** *Magazine, Trade.* **Description:** Features authoritative, practical articles about technology and its integration into the learning environment.
Former titles (until 1985): Instructional Innovator (0196-6979); Audiovisual Instruction with Instructional Resources (0191-3417); Audiovisual Instruction (0004-7635)
Related titles: Online - full text ed.: (from bigchalk, EBSCO Publishing, H.W. Wilson, O C L C Online Computer Library Center, Inc., ProQuest Information & Learning).
Indexed: ABIn, CIJE, CPE, CurCont, ERA, ETA, EduInd, InfoSAb, Inspec, LHTB, MEA, MRD, Microcompind, RASB, RHEA, SEA, SENA, SOMA, TEA, e-psyche.
—BLDSC (8614.727000), AskIEEE, IE, Infotrieve, ingenta, Linda Hall.
Published by: Association for Educational Communications and Technology, 1800 N Stonelake Dr, Ste 2, Bloomington, IN 47404. TEL 812-335-7675, FAX 812-335-7678, aect@aect.org, http://www.aect-members.org/journals/TechTrends.php, http://www.aect.org/. Ed. Elizabeth Boling. Circ: 6,400 (paid and free).

370.285 USA
U C C C TECHNICAL UPDATE. (University of Cincinnati Computing Center) Text in English. 1973. q. free. bk.rev. stat. index.
Published by: University of Cincinnati Computing Center, Instruction and Research Information Technology, B 3 Beecher Hall, ML 88, Cincinnati, OH 45221-0088. TEL 513-556-9022. Ed. Mary J Clark. Circ: 3,250.

371.3 SCG ISSN 0352-2253
UCITELJ✶ /TEACHER. Text in Serbian. 1983. q. YUN 250, USD 15 to individuals; YUN 500, USD 30 to institutions. adv. bk.rev.
Published by: Savez Ucitelja Srbije/Association of Teachers in Serbia, Mose Pijade 6-III, Postanski Fah 628, Belgrade, 11000. TEL 011 683-675. Circ: 4,000.

370.285 410.285 NLD ISSN 0924-1868
QA76.9.H85 CODEN: UMUIEQ
➤ **USER MODELING AND USER-ADAPTED INTERACTION**; an international journal. Text in English. 1991. 5/yr. EUR 548, USD 558, GBP 348 combined subscription to institutions print & online eds. (effective 2005). adv. back issues avail.; reprint service avail. from PSC. **Document type:** *Journal, Academic/Scholarly.* **Description:** Provides interdisciplinary forum for research results in user modelling and user-adapted interaction, including intelligent information retrieval, recognition, conceptual models, response tailoring, and explanation strategies.
Related titles: Microform ed.: (from PQC); Online - full text ed.: ISSN 1573-1391 (from EBSCO Publishing, Gale Group, IngentaConnect, Kluwer Online, O C L C Online Computer Library Center, Inc., ProQuest Information & Learning, Springer LINK, Swets Information Services).
Indexed: ABIn, ASCA, BibLing, CMCI, CompAb, CompLI, CurCont, EngInd, ErgAb, Inspec, PsycInfo, PsycholAb, RefZh, ZentMath, e-psyche.
—BLDSC (9133.045900), AskIEEE, CISTI, Ei, IDS, IE, Infotrieve, ingenta. **CCC.**
Published by: Springer-Verlag Dordrecht (Subsidiary of: Springer Science+Business Media), Van Godewijckstraat 30, Dordrecht, 3311 GX, Netherlands. TEL 31-78-6576050, FAX 31-78-6576474, http://springerlink.metapress.com/openurl.asp?genre=journal&issn=0924-1868, http://www.springeronline.com. Ed. Alfred Kobsa.

378 USA
WASHINGTON UPDATE. Text in English. 1995. m. free (effective 2005). back issues avail. **Document type:** *Newsletter, Trade.* **Description:** Covers legislative, executive branch, and other policy events affecting technology in higher education relevant to Educause's member organizations.
Media: Online - full content. **Related titles:** E-mail ed.
Published by: Educause, 4772 Walnut St, Ste 206, Boulder, CO 80301-2536. TEL 303-449-4430, FAX 303-440-0461, info@educause.edu, http://www.educause.edu/pub/wu. Ed. Garret Sem TEL 202-331-5365.

20.B-INTE. (20 Boletin de Introduccion a las Nuevas Tecnologias en la Educacion) see *EDUCATION—Teaching Methods And Curriculum*

EDUCATION—Guides To Schools And Colleges

371.0025 GBR ISSN 1363-1993
A A B'S GUIDE TO PRIVATE ENGLISH LANGUAGE SCHOOLS IN THE U.K. FOR OVERSEAS STUDENTS. Text in English. 1985. a., latest vol.25, 2001. GBP 29.95 per issue. **Document type:** *Directory, Consumer.*
Related titles: CD-ROM ed.
Published by: Magna Graecia's Publishers (U.K.), AAB The BBHS, PO Box 342, Oxford, OX2 7YF, United Kingdom. editorial@magnagraeciaspublishers.co.uk, http://www.magnagraeciaspublishers.co.uk. Ed. Luigi Gigliotti. Circ: 2,500.

378.071025 USA
A A C S NEWSLETTER✶. Text in English. 1985. m. back issues avail. **Document type:** *Newsletter.*
Published by: American Association of Christian Schools, c/o Waller, 440 First St N W, Ste 310, Washington, DC 20001-2028. Ed. Carl Herbster. Circ: 1,500.

373.025 USA ISSN 0270-1715
L901
ACCREDITED INSTITUTIONS OF POSTSECONDARY EDUCATION. Text in English. 1964. a., latest 2002-2003. USD 80, GBP 52 per issue (effective 2003). **Document type:** *Directory.*
Former titles: Accredited Institutions of Postsecondary Education and Programs (0361-9362); Accredited Institutions of Post Secondary Education; Accredited Institutions of Higher Education (0065-0862)
Published by: Oryx Press (Subsidiary of: Greenwood Publishing Group Inc.), 1434 E. San Miguel Ave., Phoenix, AZ 85014-2422. TEL 602-265-2651, 800-279-6799, FAX 602-265-6250, info@oryxpress.com, http://www.oryxpress.com. Eds. Louanne W Rozek, Anne Thompson. Pub. Phyllis Steckler. R&P Lori Cavanaugh TEL 602-265-2651 ext 662. Circ: 8,000.

AMERICAN ARTIST DIRECTORY OF ART SCHOOLS & WORKSHOPS. see *ART*

378.071025 USA
AMERICAN ASSOCIATION OF CHRISTIAN SCHOOLS. DIRECTORY✶. Text in English. 1972. a. USD 25. **Document type:** *Directory.* **Description:** Listing of all AACS member schools.
Published by: American Association of Christian Schools, c/o Waller, 440 First St N W, Ste 310, Washington, DC 20001-2028. Ed. Carl Herbster. Circ: 1,500.

AMERICAN CHEMICAL SOCIETY. DIRECTORY OF GRADUATE RESEARCH. see *CHEMISTRY*

610.711 USA ISSN 1079-0519
R840
AMERICAN MEDICAL ASSOCIATION. GRADUATE MEDICAL EDUCATION DIRECTORY (YEARS). Variant title: Graduate Medical Education Directory (Years). Text in English. 1914. a., latest 2003-2004. USD 55 per vol. to members; USD 75 per vol. to non-members (effective 2003). reprint service avail. from PQC. **Document type:** *Directory, Trade.*
Former titles (until 1993): American Medical Association. Directory of Graduate Medical Education Programs Accredited by the Accreditation Council for Graduate Medical Education (0892-0109); American Medical Association. Directory of Residency Training Accredited by the Accreditation Council for Graduate Medical Education (0164-1670); American Medical Association. Directory of Residency Training Programs (0097-899X); American Medical Association. Directory of Accredited Residencies; American Medical Association. Directory of Approved Residencies; (until 1975): American Medical Association. Directory of Approved Internships and Residencies (0419-2141)
Related titles: CD-ROM ed.
—BLDSC (4206.836800), GNLM. **CCC.**
Published by: American Medical Association, 515 N State St, Chicago, IL 60610-0946. TEL 800-262-8335, FAX 212-746-8892, 312-464-4184, 800-262-3221, amaa@ama-assn.org, http://www.ama-assn.org/ama/pub/category/9808.html#1.

371.0025 USA ISSN 0517-564X
T73
AMERICAN TRADE SCHOOLS DIRECTORY. Text in English. 1953. base vol. plus updates 10/yr. looseleaf. USD 129.95 base vol(s). (effective 2005). adv. **Document type:** *Directory, Trade.* **Description:** Directory of trade, technical and vocational schools arranged by state.
Published by: Croner Publications, Inc., 10951 Sorrento Valley Rd, Ste 1D, San Diego, CA 92121-1613. TEL 800-441-4033, FAX 800-809-0334, paul@croner.com, http://www.croner.com. Ed. Carol Sixt.

378.73025 USA ISSN 0066-0922
LA226
AMERICAN UNIVERSITIES AND COLLEGES. Text in German. 1928. quadrennial, latest vol.16, 2001. price varies. **Document type:** *Directory, Academic/Scholarly.*
—CISTI. **CCC.**
Published by: (American Council on Education), Greenwood Publishing Group Inc. (Subsidiary of: Harcourt International), 88 Post Rd W, PO Box 5007, Westport, CT 06881. TEL 203-226-3571, 800-225-5800, FAX 603-431-2214, webmaster@greenwood.com, http://www.greenwood.com.

378.73 USA ISSN 1042-8267
LB2331.63
AMERICA'S BEST COLLEGES. Text in English. a.
Formerly (until 1988): America's Best Colleges and Professional Schools (1042-8259)
—**CCC.**
Published by: U S News & World Report Inc., 1050 Thomas Jefferson St, NW, Washington, DC 20007. TEL 202-955-2000, FAX 202-955-2685, letters@usnews.com, http://www.usnews.com.

378.0028 AUS ISSN 1441-0567
N333.A8
ART & DESIGN EDUCATION RESOURCE GUIDE. Text in English. a. AUD 9.90, USD 8 domestic; USD 15 foreign (effective 2003). **Document type:** *Yearbook, Academic/Scholarly.*
Published by: D G International Pty. Ltd., 6 School Rd, Ferny Creek, VIC 3786, Australia. TEL 61-3-97551149, email@designgraphics.com.au, http://www.designgraphics.com.au. Pub. Colin Wood. Adv. contact Colleen Bate.

510.71025 USA ISSN 1040-7650
QA13
ASSISTANTSHIPS AND GRADUATE FELLOWSHIPS IN THE MATHEMATICAL SCIENCES. Text in English. a., latest 2003, Nov. USD 23 (effective 2004). adv. **Description:** Provides information from a broad range of academic institutions for students seeking support for graduate study in the mathematical sciences, and for mathematical sciences departments and faculty.
Published by: American Mathematical Society, 201 Charles St, Providence, RI 02904-2294. TEL 401-455-4000, 800-321-4267, FAX 401-331-3842, ams@ams.org, http://www.ams.org. Adv. contact Anne Newcomb.

E

▼ new title ➤ refereed ✶ unverified ♦ full entry avail.

371.07025 USA
ASSOCIATION OF THEOLOGICAL SCHOOLS IN THE UNITED STATES AND CANADA. MEMBERSHIP LIST. Text in English. 1918. a. USD 14.85 per issue. **Document type:** *Directory.*
Former titles: Association of Theological Schools in the United States and Canada. Directory; American Association of Theological Schools in the United States and Canada. Directory (0065-7379)
Published by: Association of Theological Schools In The United States & Canada, The, 10 Summit Park Dr., Pittsburgh, PA 15275-1103. TEL 412-788-6505. Ed. Nancy Merrill.

BARRON'S GUIDE TO GRADUATE BUSINESS SCHOOLS. see *BUSINESS AND ECONOMICS*

340 USA ISSN 1062-2489
KF266
BARRON'S GUIDE TO LAW SCHOOLS. Text in English. 1967. biennial.
Published by: Barron's Educational Series, Inc., 250 Wireless Blvd., Hauppage, NY 11788. TEL 516-434-3311, 516-921-8750, info@barronseduc.com, http://www.barronseduc.com.

378.0025 USA ISSN 1065-5026
L901
BARRON'S PROFILES OF AMERICAN COLLEGES. Text in English. 1964. biennial. USD 26.95 per issue (effective 2003). **Document type:** *Directory, Consumer.*
Formed by the 1991 merger of: Barron's Profiles of American Colleges. Vol. 1: Descriptions of the Colleges; Barron's Profiles of American Colleges. Vol. 2: Index of College Major Areas of Study; Which were formerly (until 1982): Barron's Profiles of American Colleges (0533-1072)
Related titles: CD-ROM ed.
Published by: Barron's Educational Series, Inc., 250 Wireless Blvd, Hauppauge, NY 11788. TEL 516-434-3311, info@barronseduc.com, http://www.barronseduc.com/0764174363.html.

378.0025 USA
HD5724
BIG BOOK OF MINORITY OPPORTUNITIES. Text in English. 1974. irreg., latest vol.7, 1997. USD 19 per vol. (effective 2003). bibl. **Document type:** *Directory.* **Description:** Lists 2900 educational programs for minorities in specific fields, 580 programs of support for students in any field, and 800 programs for specific minority groups.
Formerly (until 1995): Directory of Special Programs for Minority Group Members: Career Information Services, Employment Skills, Banks, Financial Aid Sources (0093-9501)
Published by: Garrett Park Press, PO Box 190F, Garrett Park, MD 20896. TEL 301-946-2553. Ed. Willis L Johnson.

378.1025 GBR ISSN 1366-8242
BIG OFFICIAL U C A S GUIDE TO UNIVERSITY & COLLEGE ENTRANCE. (Universities and Colleges Admissions Service) Text in English. 1996. a.
—BLDSC (2057.270850).
Published by: U C A S, Rosehill, New Barn Lane, Cheltenham, Gloucestershire GL52 3LZ, United Kingdom. TEL 44-1242-222444, enq@ucas.ac.uk, http://www.ucas.ac.uk.

378.025 DNK ISSN 0908-6293
BILLEDPAEDAGDGISK TIDSSKRIFT. Text in Danish. 1938. q. DKK 300 (effective 2003). adv. **Document type:** *Magazine, Academic/Scholarly.* **Description:** Offers a guide to art schools and colleges, art teaching methods, curriculum and related topics.
Former titles (until 1993): Formning (0109-8616); (until 1962): Tegning
Published by: Danmarks Billedkunstlaerere/Association of Art Teachers in Denmark, Plantanvej 8, Slagelse, 4200, Denmark. teddyandersen@mail.tele.dk, http://www.danmarksbilledkunstlaerere.dk. R&P Finn Tonnesen TEL 4-86-283709. adv.: B&W page USD 300, color page USD 600. Circ: 3,200.

378.0025 GBR ISSN 0951-872X
BOARDING SCHOOLS & COLLEGES. Text in English. 1987. a. GBP 14.95 per issue (effective 2003). adv. charts; illus. back issues avail. **Document type:** *Directory, Academic/Scholarly.* **Description:** Provides a unique ABC's of independent and maintained boarding schools in the UK and Europe.
Published by: John Catt Educational Ltd., Great Glemham, Saxmundham, Suffolk IP17 2DH, United Kingdom. TEL 44-1728-663666, FAX 44-1728-663415, enquiries@johncatt.co.uk, http://www.schoolsearch.co.uk. Ed. Derek Bingham. Adv. contact Sharon Bleese. Circ: 2,000.

BRICKER'S INTERNATIONAL DIRECTORY. see *BUSINESS AND ECONOMICS—Management*

371.0025 GBR
BRITAIN'S INDEPENDENT SCHOOLS; the definitive and essential guide for parents. Text in English. a. GBP 9.95. **Document type:** *Directory.*
Published by: Peerage Publications, Strand-on-the-Green, Peerage Publications, PO Box 5135, London, W4 3WN, United Kingdom. TEL 44-181-7470385, FAX 44-181-9945435, peerage@aol.com. Ed. Sara Marden King. adv.: B&W page GBP 375, color page GBP 475; trim 210 x 297.

THE C R A C STUDENTS' GUIDE TO GRADUATE STUDIES IN THE U K. see *EDUCATION—Higher Education*

371.0025 USA ISSN 0098-5147
L903.C2
CALIFORNIA PRIVATE SCHOOL DIRECTORY. Text in English. 1969. a. USD 17.50 per issue. index. **Document type:** *Directory.* **Description:** Lists private elementary schools and high schools registered with the state superintendent of public instruction. The schools are listed alphabetically within each county. Information provided with each entry includes enrollment, whether affiliated with a religious organization, whether restricted to boys or girls, whether boarding facilities are offered, and whether any special education programs are offered.
Formerly: Directory of Private Elementary Schools and High Schools in California
Published by: Department of Education, Publications Division, C D E Press, 560 J St Ste 355, P O Box 271, Sacramento, CA 95812-0271. TEL 916-445-1260, FAX 916-323-0823. Eds. Bob Klingensmith, Curt Robinson. R&P Cary Gillgrass. Circ: 4,000.

371.0025 USA ISSN 0068-5771
L903.C2
CALIFORNIA PUBLIC SCHOOL DIRECTORY. Text in English. 1928. a., latest 2003. USD 19.50 per vol. (effective 2003). index. **Document type:** *Directory.* **Description:** Lists each public school, school district and county office of education. Other educational organizations, commissions and projects are also listed.
Formerly (until 1970): Directory of Administrative and Supervisory Personnel of California Public Schools
Published by: Department of Education, Publications Division, C D E Press, 560 J St Ste 355, P O Box 271, Sacramento, CA 95812-0271. TEL 916-445-1260, FAX 916-323-0823, http://www.cde.ca.gov/schooldir/. Eds. Bob Klingensmith, Curt Robinson. R&P Cary Gillgrass. Circ: 15,000.

CAMPUS - FREE COLLEGE DEGREES. see *EDUCATION—Higher Education*

CAREERS & COLLEGES. see *OCCUPATIONS AND CAREERS*

378.0025 USA ISSN 1075-3443
L901
CASS & BIRNBAUM'S GUIDE TO AMERICAN COLLEGES; for students, parents and counselors. Text in English. biennial. USD 19.95. **Description:** Takes a consumer view of how to choose a college.
Formerly: Comparative Guide to American Colleges (0893-1216)
Published by: HarperCollins Publishers, Inc., 10 E 53rd St, New York, NY 10022. TEL 800-242-7737.

378.0025 USA ISSN 1084-2128
HD3630.U7
CERTIFICATION AND ACCREDITATION PROGRAMS DIRECTORY. Text in English. 1996. biennial.
Published by: Gale Research Co. (Subsidiary of: Gale Group), 220 Book Tower, Detroit, MI 48226. TEL 248-699-4253, FAX 248-699-8035, http://www.gale.com.

371.0025 USA
CHICAGO SCHOOLS AND CAREERS. Text in English. m. free.
Published by: K B Communications, 2240 W 23rd Pl, Chicago, IL 60608-3904. TEL 630-271-1133, FAX 630-271-1144. Ed. Joe Brar.

378.0025 USA ISSN 0191-3670
L901
CHRONICLE FOUR-YEAR COLLEGE DATABOOK. Text in English. 1979. a. USD 24.99 per vol. 2003-04 ed. (effective 2003); 2004-05 ed. avail. Fall 2004. **Document type:** *Abstract/Index.*
Formerly: Guide to Four-Year College Databook (0361-8927); Supersedes in part: Chronicle College Charts (0163-9242)
Related titles: CD-ROM ed.
Published by: Chronicle Guidance Publications, Inc., PO Box 1190, Moravia, NY 13118. TEL 315-497-0330, 800-622-7284, FAX 315-497-3359, customerservice@chronicleguidance.com, http://www.chronicleguidance.com. Ed. Stephen Thompson. Circ: 6,800.

378.0025 USA ISSN 0191-3662
L901
CHRONICLE TWO-YEAR COLLEGE DATABOOK. Text in English. 1979. a., latest 2003-2004. USD 24.97 per vol. 2003-2004 ed. (effective 2003). **Document type:** *Abstract/Index.*
Former titles (until 1978): Chronicle Guide to Two-Year College Majors and Careers; Guide to Two-Year College Majors and Careers (0362-420X); Supersedes in part: Chronicle College Charts (0163-9242)
Related titles: CD-ROM ed.
Published by: Chronicle Guidance Publications, Inc., PO Box 1190, Moravia, NY 13118. TEL 315-497-0330, 800-622-7284, FAX 315-497-3359, customerservice@chronicleguidance.com, http://www.chronicleguidance.com. Circ: 6,800.

373.025 USA ISSN 0276-0371
L901
CHRONICLE VOCATIONAL SCHOOL MANUAL. Text in English. 1979. a. USD 24.96 per issue (effective 2003). charts.
Formerly: Chronicle Annual Vocational School Manual (0163-4100)
Related titles: CD-ROM ed.
Published by: Chronicle Guidance Publications, Inc., PO Box 1190, Moravia, NY 13118. TEL 315-497-0330, 800-622-7284, FAX 315-497-3359, customerservice@chronicleguidance.com, http://www.chronicleguidance.com. Ed. Stephen Thompson. Circ: 6,200.

378.0025 USA ISSN 1529-367X
LB2351.2
COLLEGE ADMISSIONS INDEX OF MAJORS & SPORTS. Text in English. 1987. a. USD 33 per issue. **Document type:** *Abstract/Index.*
Published by: Riverside Publishing, 425 Spring Lake Dr, Itasca, IL 60143-2076. TEL 630-467-7000, 800-323-9540, FAX 630-467-7192, http://www.riversidepublishing.com. Ed. Mary MacDonald-Murray. Pub., R&P Allan Corderman. Circ: 2,000.

378.1025 USA ISSN 1082-7048
L901
THE COLLEGE BLUE BOOK: DEGREES OFFERED BY COLLEGES AND SUBJECTS. Text in English. 1923. a., latest vol.31, 2003. USD 325 per vol. (effective 2004).
Supesedes in part (in 1972): College Blue Book (0069-5572)
Related titles: CD-ROM ed.: USD 400; Supplement(s): Scholarships, Fellowships, Grants and Loans. ISSN 0198-8409. 1975.
Published by: Gale Group (Subsidiary of: Thomson Corporation), 27500 Drake Rd, Farmington Hills, MI 48331-3535. TEL 248-699-4253, FAX 248-699-8035, gale.galeord@thomson.com, http://www.galegroup.com.

378.1025 USA ISSN 1082-7064
L901
THE COLLEGE BLUE BOOK: NARRATIVE DESCRIPTIONS. Text in English. 1972. a., latest 2004, 32nd edition. USD 350 (effective 2004); for six-volume set.
Formerly (until 1977): The College Blue Book: U S Colleges Narrative Descriptions; Which supersedes in part (in 1972): College Blue Book (0069-5572)
Published by: Gale Group (Subsidiary of: Thomson Corporation), 27500 Drake Rd, Farmington Hills, MI 48331-3535. TEL 248-699-4253, FAX 248-699-8035, gale.galeord@thomson.com, http://www.galegroup.com.

378.1025 USA ISSN 1082-7056
L901
THE COLLEGE BLUE BOOK: TABULAR DATA. Text in English. 1972. a. USD 350 per vol. (effective 2004); for six-volume set.
Formerly (until 1977): The College Blue Book: U S Colleges Tabular Data; Which superseded in part (in 1972): College Blue Book (0069-5572)
Published by: Gale Group (Subsidiary of: Thomson Corporation), 27500 Drake Rd, Farmington Hills, MI 48331-3535. TEL 248-699-4253, FAX 248-699-8035, gale.galeord@thomson.com, http://www.galegroup.com.

378.025 378 USA
COLLEGE BOUND MAGAZINE. Text in English. 1987. 6/yr. (NY/NJ/CT, other states 3/yr.). USD 15 (effective 2001). adv. music rev.; software rev. **Document type:** *Magazine, Consumer.* **Description:** Provides high school juniors and seniors with an inside view of college life. College students from around the country serve as correspondents, providing high school students with personal accounts on all aspects of college life.
Published by: Ramholtz Publishing, Inc., 2071 Clove Rd, Staten Island, NY 10304. TEL 718-273-5700, FAX 718-273-2539, editorial@collegebound.net, http://www.collegeboundmag.com/. Ed. Gina LaGuardia. Pub. Luciano Rammairone. Adv. contact Gina Biancardi.

378.0025 USA ISSN 1073-1075
COLLEGE COST AND FINANCIAL AID HANDBOOK. Text in English. 1975. a. reprints avail. **Description:** For high school students, parents, and counselors. Provides current facts on costs plus financial aid and scholarship availability at 3,200 two- and four-year institutions.
Former titles (until 1993): College Cost Book (Year) (0270-8493); (until 1980): Student Expenses at Postsecondary Institutions (0361-0039)
Published by: College Board, 45 Columbus Ave, New York, NY 10023. TEL 212-713-8000, FAX 212-713-8143.

378.0025 USA ISSN 0069-5688
L901
COLLEGE FACTS CHART. Text in English. 1956. a. USD 7 (effective 2001). **Document type:** *Newsletter.*
Published by: National Beta Club, 151 W Lee St, Spartanburg, SC 29306-3012. TEL 864-583-4553. Ed. Shala Hainer. Circ: 15,000.

378.0025 USA ISSN 1525-4313
COLLEGE SPOTLIGHT. Variant title: Off to College. Text in English. 1996. bi-m. USD 30. bk.rev. **Document type:** *Newsletter.* **Description:** Provides information to help counselors, admission officers, financial aid advisers and others concerned with college planning and admissions. Describes colleges programs and lists financial aid programs in each issue.
Formerly (until 1999): Ferguson's Off to College (1089-9839)

E

Published by: Garrett Park Press, PO Box 190F, Garrett Park, MD 20896. TEL 301-945-2553, FAX 301-949-3955. Ed. Robert Calvert Jr.

378.0025   USA   ISSN 0747-8836
L901
COLLEGE TRANSFER GUIDE. (In 4 regional editions) Text in English. 1976. a. free to students (effective 2003). adv. **Document type:** *Directory.*
Published by: School Guide Publications, 210 North Ave, New Rochelle, NY 10801. TEL 914-632-7771, 800-433-7771, FAX 914-632-3412. Eds. Jeanne Marie Healy, Mari Castrovilla. Pub. Myles Ridder. Adv. contact Tom White. B&W page USD 2,260; 10.75 x 8.25. Circ: 60,000.

371.0025   FRA   ISSN 0291-8242
COMMUNAUTES EDUCATIVES. Text in French. 1972. q. adv.
Published by: Association Nationale des Communautes Educatives, 145 bd. de Magenta, Paris, 75010, France. TEL 33-1-44635115, FAX 33-1-42855614.

COMMUNICATIONS INSTITUTE COMMUNICATIONS LIBRARY (YEAR); worldwide courses in communications. see *COMMUNICATIONS*

378.0025   USA
COMMUNIQUEST INTERACTIVE; a guide to academic programs in the United States and Canada. Text in English.
Media: Online - full text.
Published by: Association for Communication Administration, 5105 F Backlick Rd, Annandale, VA 22003. TEL 703-750-0533, FAX 703-914-9471, http://www.aca.iupui.edu/cq-i/aca-info.html.

378.0025   USA   ISSN 1089-4373
COMMUNITY COLLEGE TIMES. Text in English. 1989. bi-w. (Tue.). USD 53 domestic; USD 62 foreign (effective 2005). adv. **Document type:** *Newspaper.* **Description:** Covers the happenings and people at community, technical, and junior colleges.
Formerly: Community, Technical, and Junior College Times
Published by: American Association of Community Colleges, One Dupont Circle, N W, Ste 410, Washington, DC 20036-1176. TEL 202-728-0200, FAX 202-223-9390, mcoran@aacc.nche.edu, https://bookstore.aacc.nche.edu/times.asp, http://www.aacc.nche.edu/. adv. B&W page USD 1,581, color page USD 2,781, page USD 62. Circ: 6,000 (paid).

CRACKING THE L S A T. see *EDUCATION—Higher Education*

DANCE MAGAZINE COLLEGE GUIDE; a directory to dance in North American colleges and universities. see *DANCE*

371.0025   DNK   ISSN 0909-7872
HF5382.5.D4
DANSK UDDANNELSES & ERHVERVS LEKSIKON/DANISH EDUCATIONAL AND VOCATIONAL ENCYCLOPAEDIA. Variant title: DUEL. Text in Danish. 1994. a. (in 2 vols.). **Document type:** *Directory.* **Description:** Offers information and guidance on all education, training and occupations in Denmark. The information covers jobs, educational and training requirements, prospective finances during and after studies, employment prospects and work environment.
Related titles: CD-ROM ed.; Diskette ed.
Published by: Raadet for Uddannelses- og Erhvervsvejledning (R.U.E.)/Danish National Council for Educational and Vocational Guidance, Vester Voldgade 123, Copenhagen V, 1552, Denmark. TEL 45-39-95-53-00, FAX 45-39-95-53-49, r-u-e@r-u-e.dk, http://www.r-u-e.dk. Eds. Dorte Hansen, Michael Blegvae. Circ: 8,100.

378.0025   GBR   ISSN 0309-0485
DEGREE COURSE GUIDES (YEAR). (Consists of 35 subject guides) Text in English. 1975. biennial (in 2 vols., each offered in alternating yrs.). GBP 5.50 per issue (effective 2002). charts. **Document type:** *Directory.* **Description:** Guides students to first-degree programs and offers detailed comparative course information for each of 35 fields.
—BLDSC (3546.292600).
Published by: (Careers Research and Advisory Centre), Hobsons PLC, Challenger House, 42 Adler St, London, E1 1EE, United Kingdom. TEL 44-1223-460366, FAX 44-1223-301506. **Dist. by:** Biblios Publishers' Distribution Services Ltd., Star Rd, Partridge Green, W Sussex RH13 8LD, United Kingdom. TEL 44-1403-710851, FAX 44-1403-711143.

371.0025   DEU   ISSN 0070-4385
L929
DEUTSCHER HOCHSCHULFUEHRER. Text in German. 1929. irreg., latest vol.57, 2004. price varies. adv. **Document type:** *Monographic series,* Trade.
Published by: Dr. Josef Raabe Verlags GmbH, Rotebuehlstr 77, Stuttgart, 70178, Germany. TEL 49-711-629000, FAX 49-711-6290010, info@raabe.de, http://www.raabe.de. Circ: 3,000.

DIGEST OF LAW SCHOOL TRANSFER POLICIES. see *LAW*

378.861   COL   ISSN 0120-5056
LB2341.8.C7
DIRECTORIO DE LA EDUCACION SUPERIOR EN COLOMBIA. Text in Spanish. 1977. a. COP 500, USD 10.
Related titles: Microfiche ed.
Published by: Instituto Colombiano para el Fomento de la Educacion Superior, Calle 17, 3-40, Bogota, D E, Colombia. TEL 57-1-2819311, FAX 57-1-2868045. Circ: 5,000.

371.0025   USA
DIRECTORY OF ACCREDITED INSTITUTIONS. Text in English. 1953. a. free. **Document type:** *Directory.* **Description:** Lists accredited distance education institutions.
Formerly: Directory of Accredited Private Home Study Schools (0070-5055)
Published by: Distance Education & Training Council, 1601 18th St, N W, Washington, DC 20009. TEL 202-234-5100. Ed. Sally R Welch. Circ: 40,000.

378.71025   CAN   ISSN 0706-2338
THE DIRECTORY OF CANADIAN UNIVERSITIES (YEAR)/REPERTOIRE DES UNIVERSITES CANADIENNES (YEAR). Text in English, French. 1956. a. CND 45 domestic; CND 49 in United States; CND 59 elsewhere (effective 2000). **Document type:** *Directory.*
Former titles: Directory of Canadian Universities and Colleges; Universities and Colleges of Canada (0083-3932)
—CISTI.
Published by: Association of Universities and Colleges of Canada/Association des Universites et Colleges du Canada, 350 Albert St, Ste 600, Ottawa, ON K1R 1B1, Canada. TEL 613-563-1236, FAX 613-563-9745, sales@aucc.ca, http://www.aucc.ca. Ed. Dick Seldenthuis. Circ: 3,000.

371.9025   USA   ISSN 1085-9411
LC4812.6
DIRECTORY OF COLLEGE FACILITIES AND SERVICES FOR PEOPLE WITH DISABILITIES. Text in English. 1983. irreg. (4th ed. 1996). USD 125 domestic; USD 150 foreign. **Document type:** *Directory.* **Description:** Provides information on programs and services available for the disabled in approximately 3600 postsecondary institutions within the U.S., Canada and outlying areas.
Formerly (until 1991): Directory of College Facilities and Services for the Disabled
Published by: Oryx Press (Subsidiary of: Greenwood Publishing Group Inc.), 1434 E. San Miguel Ave., Phoenix, AZ 85014-2422. TEL 602-265-2651, 800-279-6799, FAX 602-265-6250, info@oryxpress.com, http://www.oryxpress.com. Ed. Anne Thompson. Pub. Phyllis Steckler. R&P Lori Cavanaugh TEL 602-265-2651 ext 662.

361.3071   USA   ISSN 1049-5657
HV11
DIRECTORY OF COLLEGES AND UNIVERSITIES WITH ACCREDITED SOCIAL WORK DEGREE PROGRAMS. Text in English. a. USD 10 (effective 2001). **Document type:** *Directory, Academic/Scholarly.*
Former titles: Colleges and Universities with Accredited Social Work Degree Programs; Colleges and Universities with Accredited Undergraduate Social Work Programs
—BLDSC (3593.295900).
Published by: Council on Social Work Education, 1725 Duke St, 500, Alexandria, VA 22314-3457. TEL 703-683-8080, FAX 703-683-8099, permissions@cswe.org, http://www.cswe.org. R&P Michael J. Monti.

378.025   IND
DIRECTORY OF DISTANCE EDUCATION INSTITUTIONS PART II (PAKISTAN & SRI LANKA). Text in English. 1927. irreg. USD 65 (effective 2003). **Document type:** *Directory.*
Published by: Association of Indian Universities, A.I.U. House, 16 Kotla Marg, New Delhi, 110 002, India. TEL 91-11-323-0059, FAX 91-11-323-6105, aiu@del12.vsnl.net, http://www.aiuweb.org.

DIRECTORY OF EDUCATIONAL PROGRAMS IN GERONTOLOGY AND GERIATRICS. see *GERONTOLOGY AND GERIATRICS*

DIRECTORY OF GEOSCIENCE DEPARTMENTS. see *EARTH SCIENCES*

DIRECTORY OF GRADUATE LAW PROGRAMS IN THE UNITED STATES. see *LAW*

DIRECTORY OF HIGHER EDUCATION COURSES. see *EDUCATION—Higher Education*

DIRECTORY OF HIGHER EDUCATION NURSING COURSES. see *MEDICAL SCIENCES—Nurses And Nursing*

378.0025   USA   ISSN 1077-8500
DIRECTORY OF HISTORY DEPARTMENTS AND ORGANIZATIONS (YEAR); colleges, universities, and research institutions in the United States and Canada. Text in English. 1975. a. USD 80 to non-members; USD 58 to members (effective 2003). stat. index. back issues avail. **Document type:** *Directory.* **Description:** Lists programs, faculty, and staff of more than 800 departments and research institutions, including e-mail and Web addresses.

Incorporates (1976-1994): Doctoral Dissertations in History (0145-9929); **Formerly:** Guide to Departments of History (Year)
Published by: American Historical Association, 400 A St, S E, Washington, DC 20003-3889. TEL 202-544-2422, FAX 202-544-8307, aha@theaha.org, http://www.theaha.org. Ed. Liz Townsend. Circ: 2,500.

DIRECTORY OF OSTEOPATHIC POSTDOCTORAL EDUCATION. see *MEDICAL SCIENCES—Chiropractic, Homeopathy, Osteopathy*

DIRECTORY OF POLITICAL SCIENCE FACULTY (YEAR). see *POLITICAL SCIENCE*

373.025   USA   ISSN 0898-2317
L901
DIRECTORY OF POSTSECONDARY INSTITUTIONS. Text in English. 1967. biennial. price varies. **Document type:** *Directory, Government.*
Former titles (until 1986): Education Directory - Colleges and Universities (0730-7896); (until 1976): Education Directory. Higher Education (0083-2669); (until 1970): Education Directory (0733-5520)
Published by: U.S. Department of Education, National Center for Education Statistics, 1990 K St N W, Washington, DC 20006. TEL 202-219-1828, http://nces.ed.gov. **Dist. by:** U.S. Government Printing Office, Superintendent of Documents, PO Box 371954, Pittsburgh, PA 15250-7954. TEL 202-512-1800, FAX 202-512-2250, orders@gpo.gov, http://www.access.gpo.gov. **Dist. by:** Box 1398, Jessup, MD 20794-1398. TEL 877-433-7827, FAX 301-470-1244.

371.0025   USA
DIRECTORY OF PUBLIC SCHOOLS IN THE U S. Text in English. a. USD 70 to non-members. **Document type:** *Directory.*
Published by: American Association for Employment in Education, 3040 Riverside Dr., Ste. 125, Columbus, OH 43221-2575. TEL 847-864-1999, FAX 847-864-8303, aaee@nwu.edu, http://www.aaee.org. Circ: 1,000.

373.025   USA   ISSN 0898-2686
T73
DIRECTORY OF PUBLIC VOCATIONAL TECHNICAL SCHOOLS, COLLEGES AND INSTITUTES. Variant title: Directory of Public Vocational Technical Schools. Text in English. 1982. biennial. USD 65. **Document type:** *Directory.*
Published by: Media Marketing Group, Media, IL 60115. TEL 815-895-6842. Ed., R&P Marcia Gabriel. **Co-publisher:** Minnesota Scholarly Press.

373.025   GBR
T61
DIRECTORY OF VOCATIONAL AND FURTHER EDUCATION. Text in English. 1956. a. GBP 79 (effective 1999). adv. index. **Document type:** *Directory.*
Former titles: Directory of Technical and Further Education (0309-5290); Yearbook of Technical and Further Education; Yearbook of Technical Education and Training for Industry (0084-4020)
—BLDSC.
Published by: Pearson Education, 128 Long Acre, London, WC2E 9AN, United Kingdom. TEL 44-20-7447-2000, FAX 44-20-7240-5771. Adv. contact Alan Burfoot. B&W page GBP 455; trim 128 x 203.

378.025 305.4   IND
DIRECTORY OF WOMEN'S STUDIES IN INDIA (YEAR). Text in English. 1927. irreg., latest 1991. USD 33 (effective 1999). **Document type:** *Directory.*
Published by: Association of Indian Universities, A.I.U. House, 16 Kotla Marg, New Delhi, 110 002, India. TEL 91-11-323-0059, FAX 91-11-323-6105, aiu@del12.vsnl.net, http://www.aiuweb.org.

378.025   USA
DISTANCE DEGREES. Text in English. a. USD 24.90 per vol.; USD 3 updates lifetime subscr. **Document type:** *Directory.* **Description:** Lists more than 900 degree programs available online from accredited colleges and universities.
Published by: Accredited College Degrees by Correspondence, PO Box 209, Oakland, CA 97462. TEL 541-459-9384, FAX 541-459-9535, http://www.collegeathome.com.

378.0025   GBR
E C I S HIGHER EDUCATION DIRECTORY. Text in English. a. GBP 40 per issue (effective 2003). **Document type:** *Directory, Academic/Scholarly.* **Description:** Offers detailed descriptions of more than 350 universities & colleges in Europe and North America, together with a listing of some 400 major fields of study showing which institution offers which.
Published by: (European Council of International Schools), John Catt Educational Ltd., Great Glemham, Saxmundham, Suffolk IP17 2DH, United Kingdom. TEL 44-1728-663666, FAX 44-1728-663415, office@johncatt.co.uk, http://www.schoolsearch.co.uk. Ed. Derek Bingham. Adv. contact Sharon Bleese.

E S R C STUDENTSHIP HANDBOOK; postgraduate studentships in the social sciences. see *SOCIAL SCIENCES: COMPREHENSIVE WORKS*

E

▼ *new title*   ➤ *refereed*   ✳ *unverified*   ◆ *full entry avail.*

371.0025 GBR
EDUCATION & TRAINING NEWS. Text in English. 1988. q. adv. back issues avail. **Document type:** *Newspaper.*
Formerly (until 1993): What Next; Incorporates (1985-199?): News for Industry, Commerce and Education
Published by: (Marketing - News Group Office), Bradford and Ilkley Community College, Great Horton Rd, Bradford, W Yorks BD7 1AY, United Kingdom. TEL 44-1274-753089, FAX 44-1274-753173, rons@bilk.ac.uk. Ed. Ron T Sweeney. Adv. contact Lynn Tomlinson. B&W page GBP 1,560. Circ: 10,350.

374.8025 USA
LC5053.C3
EDUCATIONAL OPPORTUNITIES OF GREATER BOSTON. Text in English. 1923. a. adv. **Document type:** *Directory, Trade.* **Description:** Offers a guide to schools and colleges.
Media: Online - full content. **Related titles:** E-mail ed.; Fax ed.
Published by: Education Resources Institute, Attn: Educational Opportunities, 330 Stuart St, Ste 500, Boston, MA 02116. TEL 617-426-0681, FAX 617-426-7114, online@edinfo.org, http://www.edinfo.org. Ed. Cindy Barthelmess. Pub., R&P Ann Coles. Circ: 3,500.

378.41025 GBR
EXPERIENCE ERASMUS; the U K guide to Socrates-Erasmus programmes (Year). Text in English. a. GBP 13.95 per issue (effective 2003). **Document type:** *Directory.* **Description:** Essential guide for any student who wants to build a European experience into their UK degree course.
Former titles: Socrates - Erasmus - the U K Guide; Erasmus - the U K Guide
Indexed: BHA.
Published by: (Independent Schools Careers Organisation), I S C O Publications, 12a Princess Way, Camberley, Surrey GU15 3SP, United Kingdom. TEL 44-1276-21188, FAX 44-1276-691833, info@isco.org.uk, http://www.isco.org.uk/.

371.0025
FLORIDA EDUCATION DIRECTORY. Text in English. a.
Published by: Florida Department of Education, Office of the Commissioner, Turlington Building, Ste 1514, 325 West Gaines St, Tallahassee, FL 32399. commissioner@fldoe.org.

FLORIDA. STATE BOARD OF INDEPENDENT COLLEGES AND UNIVERSITIES. REPORT. see *EDUCATION—Higher Education*

378.0025 USA ISSN 1544-2330
L901
FOUR-YEAR COLLEGES. Variant title: Peterson's Four-Year Colleges. Text in English. 1970. a. USD 29.95 (effective 2005). **Description:** Includes detailed profiles submitted by more than 2,000 accredited institutions in the United States and Canada that grant baccalaureate degrees provide guidance on selecting the right school, getting in, and financial aid.
Former titles (until 2002): Peterson's Four-Year Colleges; (until 1999): Peterson's Guide to Four-Year Colleges (Year) (0894-9336); (until 1989): Guide to Four-Year Colleges (0737-3163); Which superseded in part (in 1970): Peterson's Annual Guide to Undergraduate Study (0147-8451); Annual Guide to Undergraduate Study (0091-0465)
Related titles: Online - full text ed.: (from CompuServe Inc.).
Published by: Thomson Peterson's (Subsidiary of: Thomson Corporation), Princeton Pike Corporate Center, 2000 Lenox Dr, 3rd Fl, Lawrenceville, NJ 08648. TEL 609-896-1800, FAX 609-896-4531, custsvc@petersons.com, http://www.petersons.com.

378.0025 DEU
G H K PUBLIK. (Gesamt Hochschule Kassel) Text in German. 1978. m. back issues avail. **Document type:** *Newspaper.*
Published by: Universitaet Gesamthochschule Kassel, Moenchebergstr 19, Kassel, 34109, Germany. TEL 49-561-8042216, FAX 49-561-8047216, presse@hrz.uni-kassel.de, http://www.uni-kassel.de/presse/publik/welcome.html, http://www.uni-kassel.de/presse/prisma. Ed. Jens Broemer. Circ: 5,800.

371.071025 USA ISSN 0147-8044
LC501
GANLEY'S CATHOLIC SCHOOLS IN AMERICA. Text in English. 1972. a., latest vol.29. USD 48.50 (effective 2001). **Document type:** *Directory.* **Description:** Lists every diocesan and archdiocesan school office along with names of administrative personnel.
Former titles: Ganley's Catholic Schools in America - Elementary, Secondary; Catholic Schools in the United States (0091-9527)
Related titles: CD-ROM ed.: USD 350 (effective 2001); Online - full content ed.
Published by: (National Catholic Educational Association), Fisher Publishing Company, PO Box 1339, Silverthorne, CO 80498-1339. TEL 800-759-7615, FAX 970-468-8786, publisher@ganleyscatholicschools.com. Ed. Millard T Fisher. Circ: 3,000 (paid).

373.025 USA
GEORGIA'S POSTSECONDARY SCHOOLS. Text in English. 1966. a. free. adv. illus. **Document type:** *Government.* **Description:** Outlines programs of study at Georgia postsecondary schools. Includes information on location, enrollment, admissions, and financial aid.
Former titles: Georgia Postsecondary School Directory: A Guide to Colleges, Vocational-Technical Schools and Special Purpose Institutions; Directory: A Guide to Colleges, Vocational-Technical Schools and Special Purpose Institutions; Directory: A Guide to Colleges, Vocational-Technical and Diploma Schools of Nursing; Directory of Educational Opportunities in Georgia (0419-2559)
Published by: Georgia Student Finance Commission, 2082 E Exchange Pl, Ste 200, Tucker, GA 30084. TEL 707-414-3000, FAX 707-414-3133, http://www.gsfc.org. Ed., R&P Lee Sanford TEL 770-414-3098. Circ: 130,000.

GLOBAL DIRECTORY OF SCHOOLS OF LAW OUTSIDE OF THE UNITED STATES OF AMERICA. see *LAW*

378 USA ISSN 1528-591X
GRADUATE PROGRAMS IN ARTS AND ARCHITECTURE. Text in English. 1999. a. USD 19.95 (effective 2004). **Description:** Provides a comparison of programs in fine and performing arts, architecture, photography, and others.
Supersedes in part: Peterson's U-Wire Graduate Studies in Arts, Humanities & Archaeology (1522-6018)
Published by: Thomson Peterson's (Subsidiary of: Thomson Corporation), Princeton Pike Corporate Center, 2000 Lenox Dr, 3rd Fl, Lawrenceville, NJ 08648. TEL 609-896-1800, FAX 609-896-4531, custsvc@petersons.com, http://www.petersons.com.

378 USA ISSN 1528-5960
Q183.3.A1
GRADUATE PROGRAMS IN PHYSICAL SCIENCES. Variant title: Peterson's Graduate Programs in Physical Sciences. Text in English. 1999. a. USD 19.95 (effective 2004).
Supersedes in part: Peterson's U-Wire Graduate Studies in Physical Sciences, Mathematics & Environmental Sciences (1522-6050)
Published by: Thomson Peterson's (Subsidiary of: Thomson Corporation), Princeton Pike Corporate Center, 2000 Lenox Dr, 3rd Fl, Lawrenceville, NJ 08648. TEL 609-896-1800, FAX 609-896-4531, custsvc@petersons.com, http://www.petersons.com.

378 USA ISSN 1528-5987
L901
GRADUATE PROGRAMS IN SOCIAL SCIENCES. Text in English. 1999. a. USD 19.95 (effective 2004).
Supersedes in part: Peterson's U-Wire Graduate Studies in Social Sciences & Social Work (1522-6069)
Published by: Thomson Peterson's (Subsidiary of: Thomson Corporation), Princeton Pike Corporate Center, 2000 Lenox Dr, 3rd Fl, Lawrenceville, NJ 08648. TEL 609-896-1800, FAX 609-896-4531, custsvc@petersons.com, http://www.petersons.com.

378.0025 USA
GRADUATE SCHOOL GUIDE. (Published in 9 regional editions) Text in English. 1970. a. free to qualified persons (effective 2003). adv. stat. **Document type:** *Directory.*
Published by: School Guide Publications, 210 North Ave, New Rochelle, NY 10801. TEL 914-632-7771, 800-433-7771, FAX 914-632-3412. Eds. Jeanne Marie Healy, Mari Castrovilla. Pub. Myles Ridder. Adv. contact Tom White. B&W page USD 2,260; 10.75 x 8.25. Circ: 150,000.

GRADUATE STUDY IN PSYCHOLOGY. see *PSYCHOLOGY*

371.0712 ESP ISSN 0211-4410
GUIA DE CENTROS EDUCATIVOS CATOLICOS. Text in Spanish. 1970. triennial. adv. stat. **Document type:** *Directory.* **Description:** Provides information on all Catholic centers of education at all levels, from preschool to university.
Formerly (until 1979): Guia de Centros Docentes de la Iglesia
Published by: (Servicio Estadistico), Federacion Espanola de Religiosos de Ensenanza, Hacienda de Pavones 5, 1o, Madrid, 28030, Spain. TEL 34-91-3288000, FAX 34-91-3288001. Circ: 1,000.

378.7284025 SLV
GUIA UNIVERSITARIA SALVADORENA. Text in Spanish. a. **Document type:** *Directory.*
Published by: Instituto Salvadoreno de Estudios Politicos, 1a Calle Poniente No. 3549, Col. Escalon,, Apdo. Postal 2687, San Salvador, El Salvador. Circ: 500.

GUIDA RAGIONATA ALLE SCUOLE D'INGLESE IN ITALIA. see *LINGUISTICS*

378.1025 CAN ISSN 0820-2788
GUIDE PRATIQUE DES ETUDES UNIVERSITAIRES AU QUEBEC. Text in French. 1986. a. **Document type:** *Directory, Consumer.*
Formerly (until 1987): Guide Pratique des Etudes Universitaires (0820-277X)
Published by: Service Regional d'Admission du Montreal Metropolitain, CP 11028, Centre Ville, Montreal, PQ, Canada. TEL 514-271-2454, http://www.sram.qc.ca.

378.0025 AUS ISSN 1037-6666
GUIDE TO CAMPUS RECRUITING. Text in English. 1981. a. AUD 15. adv. **Document type:** *Newsletter.*
Formerly: Employers Guide to Recruiting in Australian Universities and Colleges of Advanced Education
Published by: Graduate Careers Council of Australia Ltd., PO Box 28, Parkville, VIC 3052, Australia. TEL 61-3-93444666, FAX 61-3-93477298. Ed. Jacqueline Vidot. Circ: 2,500.

GUIDE TO COLLEGE PROGRAMS IN HOSPITALITY & TOURISM; a directory of CHRIE member colleges and universities. see *TRAVEL AND TOURISM*

THE GUIDE TO COOKING SCHOOLS. see *NUTRITION AND DIETETICS*

378.025 USA ISSN 1546-590X
LC5805
THE GUIDE TO DISTANCE LEARNING PROGRAMS. Text in English. a. USD 26.95. **Document type:** *Directory.* **Description:** Provides information for potential students and university personnel on current electronic distance learning programs in higher education. Includes practical advice, interviews and details on associate, baccalaureate, master's, and doctoral programs, as well as undergraduate and graduate certificate programs.
Published by: (University Continuing Education Association), Thomson Peterson's (Subsidiary of: Thomson Corporation), Princeton Pike Corporate Center, 2000 Lenox Dr, 3rd Fl, Lawrenceville, NJ 08648. TEL 609-243-9111, 800-338-3282, FAX 609-243-9150, http://www.petersons.com.

GUIDE TO DOCTORAL PROGRAMS IN BUSINESS AND MANAGEMENT. see *BUSINESS AND ECONOMICS*

GUIDE TO GRADUATE STUDY IN BOTANY FOR THE UNITED STATES AND CANADA. see *BIOLOGY—Botany*

340.0711 NLD ISSN 1374-478X
GUIDE TO LEGAL STUDIES IN EUROPE (YEAR). Text in Dutch. 1993. a., latest 2001. USD 43.50 per vol. (effective 2004). **Document type:** *Directory, Academic/Scholarly.* **Description:** Offers a guide to more than 240 law schools in 32 European nations, with information on the city, country, and legal system of the locale for each school, along with the addresses of the faculty, student associations, courses offered, and admissions requirements.
Published by: (European Law Students' Association BEL), Kluwer Law International (Subsidiary of: Aspen Publishers, Inc.), Laan van Meerdervoort 70, PO Box 85889, The Hague, 2508 CN, Netherlands. TEL 31-70-3081500, FAX 31-70-3081515, sales@kluwerlaw.com, http://www.kluwerlaw.com.

GUIDE TO PROGRAMS IN GEOGRAPHY IN NORTH AMERICA - A A G HANDBOOK AND DIRECTORY OF GEOGRAPHERS. see *GEOGRAPHY*

371.0025 USA ISSN 0072-8705
GV193
GUIDE TO SUMMER CAMPS AND SUMMER SCHOOLS; an objective, comprehensive reference source. Text in English. 1924. biennial, latest 29th edition. USD 27 per issue paper ed.; USD 45 per issue cloth ed. (effective 2004 - 2005). adv. illus.; stat.; mkt. index. 560 p./no.; **Document type:** *Directory, Consumer.* **Description:** Covers 1300 recreational and educational summer opportunities, including specialized programs for those with special needs or learning disabilities.
Formerly (until 1936): Summert Camps
Published by: Porter Sargent Publishers, Inc., 11 Beacon St, Ste 1400, Boston, MA 02108. TEL 617-523-1670, 800-342-7470, FAX 617-523-1021, info@portersargent.com, http://www.summerprograms.us/, http://www.portersargent.com. Ed. Daniel P. McKeever. Pub., Adv. contact John Yonce. page USD 540; 3.625 x 6. Circ: 4,000.

GUIDE TO SUMMER SCHOOLS (YEAR). see *MUSIC*

378.025 BEL ISSN 1561-1965
GUIDE TO UNIVERSITIES & COLLEGES IN CANADA. Text in English. 1999. a.
Published by: Education International, 5 bd du Roi Albert II, 8e etage, Brussels, 1210, Belgium. TEL 32-2-224-0611, FAX 32-2-224-0606, educint@ei-ie.org, http://www.ei-ie.org.

378.0025 GBR
HALIFAX / EQUITABLE STUDENT BOOK (YEAR). Text in English. 1979. a. GBP 14.99 (effective 2001). **Document type:** *Directory, Consumer.* **Description:** One-stop guide for all applicants to university and college in the UK.
Former titles (until 2001): The NatWest Student Book (Year); (until 1994): Student Book (Year) (0143-0068)
—BLDSC (8479.730000).
Published by: Trotman & Co. Ltd., 2 The Green, Richmond, Surrey TW9 1PL, United Kingdom. TEL 44-20-8486 1150, FAX 44-20-8486 1161, mail@trotman.co.uk, http://www.trotmanpublishing.co.uk. Eds. Jenny Lees Spalding, Klaus Boehm. R&P Amanda Williams. Adv. contact Alistair Rogers. **Dist. by:** Plymbridge Distributors Ltd, Plymbridge House, Estover Rd, Plymouth, Devon PL6 7PY, United Kingdom. TEL 44-1752-202300, FAX 44-1752-202330, enquiries@plymbridge.com.

E

371.0025 USA ISSN 0072-9884
L901
HANDBOOK OF PRIVATE SCHOOLS; an annual descriptive survey of independent education. Text in English. 1914. a., latest 2005, 86th edition. USD 99 per issue (effective 2005). adv. illus.; stat.; charts; maps. index. 1408 p./no.; **Document type:** *Directory, Consumer.* **Description:** Contains current facts on more than 1600 elementary and secondary boarding and day schools throughout the nation.
Former titles (until 1977): Private Schools; (until 1926): American Private Schools; (until 1915): The Best Private Schools
Published by: Porter Sargent Publishers, Inc., 11 Beacon St, Ste 1400, Boston, MA 02108. TEL 617-523-1670, 800-342-7470, FAX 617-523-1021, info@portersargent.com, http://www.privateschools.us, http://www.portersargent.com. Ed. Daniel P. McKeever. Pubs. Jane Culver Sargent, John Yonce. Adv. contact John Yonce. page USD 540; 3.75 x 6. Circ: 3,500 (paid).

HEALTH PROFESSIONS CAREER AND EDUCATION DIRECTORY. see *MEDICAL SCIENCES*

378.0025 USA ISSN 0160-4961
RA440.7.U6
HEALTH SERVICES ADMINISTRATION EDUCATION✶. Text in English. 1979. biennial. USD 35. **Document type:** *Directory.* **Description:** Contains higher education and continuing education health administration program information, featuring admission requirement, application, curriculum, cost, and student aid information.
Published by: Association of University Programs in Health Administration, 2000 14th St North, Ste 780, Arlington, VA 22201. TEL 202-822-8550, FAX 202-822-8555, ahacala@aupha.org, aupha@aupha.org aupha@aupha.org aupha@aupha.org, http://www.aupha.org. Ed. Cindy Liedpke.

371.07025 USA ISSN 1090-4859
BM60
HILLEL GUIDE TO JEWISH LIFE ON CAMPUS (YEAR). Text in English. 1981. biennial. USD 18. adv. index. **Document type:** *Directory.* **Description:** Description of Jewish life on approximately 500 college campuses designed to assist students in choosing colleges.
Published by: (Princeton Review), Princeton Review Publishing, L.L.C., 2315 Broadway, New York, NY 10024. Ed. Ruth Fredman Cernea. Circ: 10,000.

371.0025 GBR
I S I S MAGAZINE. Text in English. 1972. s-a. GBP 4 domestic; GBP 7.50 foreign. adv. bk.rev. back issues avail. **Document type:** *Newsletter.* **Description:** Targeted to parents and staff of British independent schools: senior and junior, day and boarding, girls', boys' and coeducational. News and features about independent education.
Former titles: I S I S News; (until 1986): I S I S Newsletter
Published by: Independent Schools Information Service, 56 Buckingham Gate, London, SW1E 6AG, United Kingdom. TEL 44-171-630-8793, national@isis.org.uk, info@iscis.uk.net. Ed. R C Davison. Circ: 25,000.

371.02025 USA
I S S DIRECTORY OF INTERNATIONAL SCHOOLS. Text in English. 1981. a. USD 45.95 per issue (effective 2003). **Document type:** *Directory.* **Description:** Comprehensive guide to American and International schools around the globe with over 500 listings that include the address, phone, fax, e-mail, and chief school officer for each school.
Formerly: I S S Directory of Overseas Schools (0732-7862)
Published by: International Schools Services, Inc., PO Box 5910, Princeton, NJ 08543. TEL 609-452-0990, FAX 609-452-2690, directory@iss.edu, http://www.iss.edu. Ed., R&P, Adv. contact Judy Seltz. Circ: 4,000.

371.0025 USA
IDAHO EDUCATIONAL DIRECTORY. Text in English. 1919. a. USD 6.50. **Document type:** *Directory.*
Published by: Department of Education, Division of Finance and Special Services, PO Box 83720, Boise, ID 83720-0027. TEL 208-332-6841, FAX 209-334-3484. Circ: 5,000.

378.0025 GBR
INDEPENDENT COLLEGES - DIRECTORY OF COURSES. Text in English. irreg. GBP 6.50 (effective 2000). **Document type:** *Directory.* **Description:** Contains details of more than 400 colleges.
Formerly: Directory of Independent Further Education
Indexed: EEA.
Published by: (Independent Schools Careers Organisation), I S C O Publications, 12a Princess Way, Camberley, Surrey GU15 3SP, United Kingdom. TEL 44-1276-21188, FAX 44-1276-691833, info@isco.org.uk, http://www.isco.org.uk/. Ed. Philip Gray TEL 44-1276-21188.

373.25 370.025 USA ISSN 0073-5779
INDEPENDENT SCHOOLS ASSOCIATION OF THE SOUTHWEST. MEMBERSHIP LIST. Text in English. 1966. a. free. **Document type:** *Directory.* **Description:** Lists schools accredited by the Association.
Published by: Independent Schools Association of the Southwest, PO Box 52297, Tulsa, OK 74152-0297. TEL 918-749-5927, FAX 918-749-5937. Ed. Richard W Ekdahl. Circ: 700.

378.0025 USA ISSN 0733-6020
LC5951
INDEPENDENT STUDY CATALOG. Text in English. 1964. biennial. USD 21.95. **Document type:** *Directory.* **Description:** Covers over 13,000 high school, undergraduate, graduate and non-credit correspondence courses offered by over 140 accredited schools and institutions.
Former titles (until 1977): Guide to Independent Study Through Correspondence Instruction (0149-1083); Guide to Correspondence Studies in Colleges and Universities (0072-8322)
—CCC.
Published by: (University Continuing Education Association), Thomson Peterson's (Subsidiary of: Thomson Corporation), Princeton Pike Corporate Center, 2000 Lenox Dr, 3rd Fl, Lawrenceville, NJ 08648. TEL 609-243-9111, FAX 609-243-9150, http://www.petersons.com. Ed. Barbara Lawrence.

371.025 DEU
DAS INGENIEURSTUDIUM. Text in German. 1979. triennial. **Document type:** *Directory.*
Published by: Staufenbiel Institut fuer Studien- und Berufsplanung GmbH, Konrad-Adenauer-Ufer 33, Cologne, 50668, Germany. TEL 49-221-9126630, FAX 49-221-9126639, info@staufenbiel.de, http://www.staufenbiel.de. Ed. Joerg Staufenbiel. Circ: 7,500.

INSIDER'S GUIDE TO GRADUATE PROGRAMS IN CLINICAL AND COUNSELING PSYCHOLOGY (YEARS). see *PSYCHOLOGY*

371.0025 FRA ISSN 0242-2999
INTER - C D I; revue des centres de documentation et d'information de l'enseignement secondaire. Text in French. 1972. bi-m. EUR 58 domestic; EUR 69.50 in Europe; EUR 88 elsewhere (effective 2003). bk.rev. 84 p./no.; back issues avail. **Document type:** *Magazine, Trade.*
Formerly (until 1974): Inter S D I (1154-7758)
Related titles: Online - full text ed.
Published by: Centre d'Etude de la Documentation et de l'Information Scolaires (C E D I S), 16 rue des Belles-Croix, Etampes, 91150, France. TEL 33-1-64943951, FAX 33-1-64944935, cedis@fr.inter.net, http://www.cedis.org. Eds. Chantal Nicolas, Jose Frances. Pub. Jose Frances. R&P Chantal Nicolas. Adv. contact Valerie Devay.

INTERNATIONAL DIRECTORY OF MODEL - TALENT AGENCIES AND SCHOOLS (YEAR). see *CLOTHING TRADE—Fashions*

378.025 BEL ISSN 1561-7564
THE INTERNATIONAL GUIDE TO UNIVERSITIES & 4-YEAR COLLEGES IN THE U S A. Text in English. 1998. irreg., latest 1999.
Published by: Education International, 5 bd du Roi Albert II, 8e etage, Brussels, 1210, Belgium. TEL 32-2-224-0611, FAX 32-2-224-0606, educint@ei-ie.org, http://www.ei-ie.org.

378.0025 GBR
INTERNATIONAL SCHOOLS DIRECTORY (YEAR). Text in English. a. GBP 35, USD 57 per issue to non-members (effective 2003). **Document type:** *Directory.* **Description:** Lists and describes more than 500 ECIS member schools and another 397 international are listed in brief.
Published by: (European Council of International Schools), John Catt Educational Ltd., Great Glemham, Saxmundham, Suffolk IP17 2DH, United Kingdom. TEL 44-1728-663666, FAX 44-1728-663415, office@johncatt.co.uk, enquiries@johncatt.co.uk, http://www.schoolsearch.co.uk. Ed. Derek Bingham. Adv. contact Sharon Bleese.

371.025 GBR ISSN 1470-4862
INTERNATIONAL SCHOOLS, THE DATABASE. Text in English. 2000 (Apr.). a., latest 2001. GBP 14 (effective 2001). adv. charts; illus.; maps. **Document type:** *Directory, Consumer.* **Description:** Contains details of 1,800 schools worldwide that cater for international students.
Related titles: CD-ROM ed.: ISSN 1470-4897; Online - full content ed.
Published by: International Schools Ltd., Tilshead House, Tilshead, Salisbury, Wilts SP3 4RX, United Kingdom. TEL 44-1980-620575, FAX 44-1980-621090, book@internationalschools.net, http://www.internationalschools.net, http://www.earl.org.uk/isbi/international/. Ed. Mr. Bob Findlay. Pub. Mr. Richard Essberger. Adv. contact Mr. Tony Evans TEL 44-1494-512919.

371.025 371.9 GBR ISSN 1472-0744
ISBI.COM. (Independent Schools of the British Isles) Text in English. 1996. s-a. GBP 18 worldwide (effective 2001). **Document type:** *Directory, Academic/Scholarly.* **Description:** Directory of all the independent and fee-paying schools and residential special needs schools in the British Isles, special language schools, summer schools and educational suppliers, organizations and consultants.
Former titles (until 2000): I S B I, the Education Database (1463-3574); (until 1998): I S B I, the Database (1366-4654)
Media: CD-ROM.
Published by: (Independent Schools of the British Isles), Which School Ltd., Tilshead House, High St, Tilshead, Salisbury, Wilts SP3 4RX, United Kingdom. TEL 44-1980-620575, FAX 44-1980-621090, cdrom@isbi.com, http://www.isbi.com. Ed. Richard Essberger. Adv. contact Mrs. Pamela Wickham TEL 44-1926-641231.

370.1 371.025 USA ISSN 1558-2159
▼ ➤ **JOURNAL OF SCHOOL CHOICE**; charters, vouchers, home schooling, and alternative education. Text in English. forthcoming 2006 (Spring). q. USD 400 combined subscription domestic to institutions print & online eds.; USD 540 combined subscription in Canada to institutions print & online eds.; USD 580 combined subscription elsewhere to institutions print & online eds. (effective 2006). **Document type:** *Journal, Academic/Scholarly.* **Description:** Offers informed and unbiased perspectives on the effectiveness of school choice on student achievement, parental satisfaction, and the teaching profession as a whole.
Related titles: Online - full content ed.: ISSN 1558-2167. forthcoming 2006.
Published by: Haworth Press, Inc., 10 Alice St, Binghamton, NY 13904-1580. TEL 607-722-5857, 800-429-6784, FAX 607-722-1424, 800-895-0582, getinfo@haworthpress.com, http://www.haworthpress.com/web/JSC. Ed. Steve A Rollins. Pub. William Cohen. R&P Ruth Ann Heath TEL 607-722-5857 ext 316.

➤ **JOURNALISM AND MASS COMMUNICATION DIRECTORY.** see *JOURNALISM*

➤ **JOURNALIST'S ROAD TO SUCCESS.** see *JOURNALISM*

378.072025 DEU
KATHOLISCHE UNIVERSITAET EICHSTAETT. VORLESUNGSVERZEICHNIS. Text in German. 1960. s-a. EUR 4 newsstand/cover (effective 2002). adv. bibl.; stat. **Document type:** *Directory, Academic/Scholarly.*
Published by: Katholische Universitaet Eichstaett, Ostenstr 26, Eichstaett, 85072, Germany. TEL 08421-20246. adv.: B&W page EUR 205, color page EUR 565. Circ: 5,400.

371.0025 USA ISSN 0091-0775
L152
KENTUCKY SCHOOL DIRECTORY. Text in English. 1975. a. USD 25 per issue includes CD-ROM (effective 2003). stat. **Document type:** *Directory, Trade.* **Description:** Lists all public and private schools within the state of Kentucky, broken out by school district. Includes the principal name, address, phone number and various statistical data for each school.
Media: Duplicated (not offset).
Published by: Department of Education, Office of Communication Services, Capital Plaza Tower, 500 Mero St, 19th Fl, Frankfort, KY 40601. TEL 502-564-3421, wnewton@kde.state.ky.us. Ed. Windy Newton. Circ: 6,000.

378.0025 USA
KEY - A GUIDE TO COLLEGE AND CAREERS. (In 3 editions: High School Junior, High School Senior, Junior-Community College Transfer) Text in English. biennial. free to qualified personnel. adv. **Description:** Focuses on educational options, campus life, financial aid sources and military and career opportunities.
Published by: Target Marketing, Inc., 1 Liberty Bell Circle, Ste 200, Liberty, MO 64068. TEL 816-781-7557, FAX 816-792-3892. Ed., Pub. Lyle Kraft. Circ: 1,400,000 (controlled).

LAERERHEFTE TIL VI UNDERSOEGER OG MIN VEJ. see *EDUCATION—Adult Education*

LAW SCHOOL SUMMER SCHOOL PROGRAMS AT HOME AND ABROAD. see *LAW*

378.0025 USA ISSN 0076-132X
LA226
LOVEJOY'S COLLEGE GUIDE. Text in English. 1940. s-a. **Document type:** *Directory, Consumer.*
Published by: Macmillan General Reference, 300 Park Ave., S, New York, NY 10010-5313. TEL 212-654-8500. Ed. Barbarasue Lovejoy Straughn.

378.0025 USA ISSN 0024-7022
LOVEJOY'S GUIDANCE DIGEST. Text in English. 1946. 10/yr. USD 60. adv. index. **Document type:** *Newsletter.*
Published by: Lovejoy's College Guide Inc., PO Box 485, Dover, DE 19903-0485. TEL 302-698-0597, FAX 302-698-0597. Ed. Charles T Straughn II. Pub. Barbara Lovejoy Straughn. R&P B L Straughn. Circ: 5,000 (paid).

371.0025 USA
L903.W27
M D R'S SCHOOL DIRECTORIES. Text in English. 1976. a. (in 51 vols.). USD 1,214 National Set (includes 50 states and the District of Columbia); USD 3,761 combined subscription National Set (includes 50 states and the District of Columbia); print & CD-ROM (effective 2003).
Former titles (until 1995): C I C's State School Directory (Regional Ed.) (0162-9646); (until 1979): School Universe Data Book. Library Edition (0146-4329)

E

▼ *new title* ➤ *refereed* ✶ *unverified* ♦ *full entry avail.*

Related titles: CD-ROM ed.: USD 3,210 National set (effective 2003); Regional ed(s).: M D R's School Directory. Alaska. ISSN 1077-7407. 1992. USD 44 print; USD 131 CD-ROM; USD 149 combined subscription print & CD-ROM (effective 2003); M D R's School Directory. Alabama. ISSN 1077-7393. 1992. USD 59 print; USD 171 CD-ROM; USD 196 combined subscription print & CD-ROM (effective 2003); M D R's School Directory. Arizona. ISSN 1077-7415. 1992. USD 44 print; USD 131 CD-ROM; USD 149 combined subscription print & CD-ROM (effective 2003); M D R's School Directory. Arkansas. ISSN 1077-7423. 1992. USD 59 print; USD 171 CD-ROM; USD 196 combined subscription print & CD-ROM (effective 2003); M D R's School Directory. California. ISSN 1077-7431. 1992. USD 86 print; USD 243 CD-ROM; USD 279 combined subscription print & CD-ROM (effective 2003); M D R's School Directory. Colorado. ISSN 1077-744X. 1992. USD 59 print; USD 171 CD-ROM; USD 196 combined subscription print & CD-ROM (effective 2003); M D R's School Directory. Connecticut. ISSN 1077-7458. 1979. USD 59 print; USD 171 CD-ROM; USD 196 combined subscription print & CD-ROM (effective 2003); M D R's School Directory. District of Columbia. ISSN 1077-7474. 1992. USD 44 print; USD 131 CD-ROM; USD 149 combined subscription print & CD-ROM (effective 2003); M D R's School Directory. Delaware. ISSN 1077-7466. 1992. USD 44 print; USD 131 CD-ROM; USD 149 combined subscription print & CD-ROM (effective 2003); M D R's School Directory. Florida. ISSN 1077-7482. 1992. USD 71 print; USD 207 CD-ROM; USD 237 combined subscription print & CD-ROM (effective 2003); M D R's School Directory. Georgia. ISSN 1077-7490. 1992. USD 59 print; USD 171 CD-ROM; USD 196 combined subscription print & CD-ROM (effective 2003); M D R's School Directory. Hawaii. ISSN 1077-7504. 1992. USD 44 print; USD 131 CD-ROM; USD 149 combined subscription print & CD-ROM (effective 2003); M D R's School Directory. Idaho. ISSN 1077-7512. 199?. USD 44 print; USD 131 CD-ROM; USD 149 combined subscription print & CD-ROM (effective 2003); M D R's School Directory. Illinois. USD 86 print; USD 243 CD-ROM; USD 279 combined subscription print & CD-ROM (effective 2003); M D R's School Directory. Indiana. ISSN 1077-7539. 1992. USD 59 print; USD 171 CD-ROM; USD 196 combined subscription print & CD-ROM (effective 2003); M D R's School Directory. Iowa. ISSN 1077-7547. 1992. USD 59 print; USD 171 CD-ROM; USD 196 combined subscription print & CD-ROM (effective 2003); M D R's School Directory. Kansas. ISSN 1077-7555. 1992. USD 59 print; USD 171 CD-ROM; USD 196 combined subscription print & CD-ROM (effective 2003); M D R's School Directory. Kentucky. ISSN 1077-7563. 199?. USD 59 print; USD 171 CD-ROM; USD 196 combined subscription print & CD-ROM (effective 2003); M D R's School Directory. Louisiana. ISSN 1077-7571. 1992. USD 59 print; USD 171 CD-ROM; USD 196 combined subscription print & CD-ROM (effective 2003); M D R's School Directory. Maine. ISSN 1077-758X. 19??. USD 44 print; USD 131 CD-ROM; USD 149 combined subscription print & CD-ROM (effective 2003); M D R's School Directory. Maryland. ISSN 1077-7598. 1992. USD 59 print; USD 171 CD-ROM; USD 196 combined subscription print & CD-ROM (effective 2003); M D R's School Directory. Massachusetts. ISSN 1077-7601. 19??. USD 71 print; USD 207 CD-ROM; USD 237 combined subscription print & CD-ROM (effective 2003); M D R's School Directory. Michigan. ISSN 1077-761X. 1992. USD 71 print; USD 207 CD-ROM; USD 237 combined subscription print & CD-ROM (effective 2003); M D R's School Directory. Minnesota. ISSN 1077-7628. 1992. USD 71 print; USD 207 CD-ROM; USD 237 combined subscription print & CD-ROM (effective 2003); M D R's School Directory. Mississippi. ISSN 1077-7636. 1992. USD 59 print; USD 171 CD-ROM; USD 196 combined subscription print & CD-ROM (effective 2003); M D R's School Directory. Missouri. ISSN 1077-7644. 1992. USD 59 print; USD 171 CD-ROM; USD 19 combined subscription print & CD-ROM (effective 2003); M D R's School Directory. Montana. ISSN 1077-7652. 1992. USD 44 print; USD 131 CD-ROM; USD 149 combined subscription print & CD-ROM (effective 2003); M D R's School Directory. Nebraska. ISSN 1077-7660. 1992. USD 59 print; USD 171 CD-ROM; USD 196 combined subscription print & CD-ROM (effective 2003); M D R's School Directory. Nevada. ISSN 1077-7679. 1992. USD 44 print; USD 131 CD-ROM; USD 149 combined subscription print & CD-ROM (effective 2003); M D R's School Directory. New Hampshire. ISSN 1077-7687. 19??. USD 44 print; USD 131 CD-ROM; USD 149 combined subscription print & CD-ROM (effective 2003); M D R's School Directory. New Jersey. ISSN 1077-7695. 1992. USD 71 print; USD 207 CD-ROM; USD 237 combined subscription print & CD-ROM (effective 2003); M D R's School Directory. New Mexico. ISSN 1077-7709. 1992. USD 44 print; USD 131 CD-ROM; USD 149 combined subscription print & CD-ROM (effective 2003); M D R's School Directory. New York. ISSN 1077-7717. 1992. USD 86 print; USD 243 CD-ROM; USD 279 combined subscription print & CD-ROM (effective 2003); M D R's School Directory. North Carolina. ISSN 1077-7725. 1992. USD 59 print; USD 171 CD-ROM; USD 196 combined subscription print & CD-ROM (effective 2003); M D R's School Directory. North Dakota. ISSN 1077-7733. 1992. USD 44 print; USD 131 CD-ROM; USD 149 combined subscription print & CD-ROM (effective 2003); M D R's School Directory. Ohio. ISSN 1077-7741. 1992. USD 74 print; USD 207 CD-ROM; USD 237 combined subscription print & CD-ROM (effective 2003); M D R's School Directory. Oklahoma. ISSN 1077-775X. 1992. USD 59 print; USD 171 CD-ROM; USD 196 combined subscription print & CD-ROM (effective 2003); M D R's School Directory. Oregon. ISSN 1077-7768. 19??. USD 59 print; USD 171 CD-ROM; USD 196 combined subscription print & CD-ROM (effective 2003); M D R's School Directory. Pennsylvania. ISSN 1077-7776. 19??. USD 71 print; USD 207 CD-ROM; USD 237 combined subscription print & CD-ROM (effective 2003); M D R's School Directory. Rhode Island. ISSN 1077-7784. 19??. USD 44 print; USD 131 CD-ROM; USD 149 combined subscription print & CD-ROM (effective 2003); M D R's School Directory. South Carolina. ISSN 1077-7792. 1992. USD 59 print; USD 171 CD-ROM; USD 196 combined subscription print & CD-ROM (effective 2003); M D R's School Directory. South Dakota. ISSN 1077-7806. 1992. USD 44 print; USD 131 CD-ROM; USD 149 combined subscription print & CD-ROM (effective 2003); M D R's School Directory. Tennessee. ISSN 1077-7814. 1992. USD 59 print; USD 171 CD-ROM; USD 196 combined subscription print & CD-ROM (effective 2003); M D R's School Directory. Texas. ISSN 1077-7822. 19??. USD 86 print; USD 243 CD-ROM; USD 279 combined subscription print & CD-ROM (effective 2003); M D R's School Directory. Utah. ISSN 1077-7830. 1992. USD 44 print; USD 131 CD-ROM; USD 149 combined subscription print & CD-ROM (effective 2003); M D R's School Directory. Vermont. ISSN 1077-7849. 19??. USD 44 print; USD 131 CD-ROM; USD 149 combined subscription print & CD-ROM (effective 2003); M D R's School Directory. Virginia. ISSN 1077-7857. 19??. USD 59 print; USD 171 CD-ROM; USD 196 combined subscription print & CD-ROM (effective 2003); M D R's School Directory. Washington. ISSN 1077-7865. 1992. USD 59 print; USD 171 CD-ROM; USD 196 combined subscription print & CD-ROM (effective 2003); M D R's School Directory. West Virginia. ISSN 1077-7873. 1992. USD 44 print; USD 131 CD-ROM; USD 149 combined subscription print & CD-ROM (effective 2003); M D R's School Directory. Wisconsin. ISSN 1077-7881. 197?. USD 59 print; USD 171 CD-ROM; USD 196 combined subscription print & CD-ROM (effective 2003); M D R's School Directory. Wyoming. ISSN 1077-789X. 1992. USD 44 print; USD 131 CD-ROM; USD 149 combined subscription print & CD-ROM (effective 2003).

Published by: Market Data Retrieval, Inc., PO Box 907, Shelton, CT 06484-0947. TEL 203-926-4800, FAX 203-929-5253, morinfo@dnb.com, http://www.schooldata.com.

MACLEAN'S GUIDE TO CANADIAN UNIVERSITIES & COLLEGES. see *EDUCATION—Higher Education*

378.0025 USA
MAJOR DECISIONS; a guide to college majors. Text in English. 1990. biennial. USD 22.
Published by: Riverside Publishing, 425 Spring Lake Dr, Itasca, IL 60143-2076. TEL 630-467-7000, 800-323-9540, FAX 630-467-7192, http://www.riversidepublishing.com. Eds. Joseph Despres, Richard Blumenthal. Pub., R&P Allan Corderman. Circ: 2,000.

796.025 USA
MARKETING RECREATION CLASSES. Text in English. 1987. m. USD 95. **Description:** Newsletter and articles on art, music, personal skills, health, business, and other nonacademic-oriented courses, seminars, workshops, and programs throughout the United States.
Published by: Learning Resources Network, PO Box 9, River Falls, WI 54022-0009. TEL 913-539-5376.

373.025 USA ISSN 0363-7433
LB2351
MICHIGAN POSTSECONDARY ADMISSIONS & FINANCIAL ASSISTANCE HANDBOOK. Text in English. a. illus.
Former titles (until 1976): Michigan College Admissions and Financial Assistance Handbook (0887-0462); (until 1974): Michigan. Department of Education. College Admissions and Financial Assistance Handbook (0094-3754)
Published by: Department of Education, PO Box 30008, Lansing, MI 48909. TEL 517-373-0457.

MIN VEJ. see *EDUCATION—Adult Education*

371.0025 USA ISSN 0092-7899
L903.M6
MISSISSIPPI EDUCATIONAL DIRECTORY. Text in English. 1977. a. USD 8. **Document type:** *Directory.*
Formerly: Educational Directory of Mississippi Schools (0363-874X)
Published by: Department of Education, c/o Management Information System, Box 771, Jackson, MS 39205. TEL 601-359-3487, FAX 601-359-2027. Ed. Jayne Lloyd. Circ: 1,600.

371.0025 USA ISSN 1062-0869
L901
NATIONAL DIRECTORY OF ALTERNATIVE SCHOOLS. Text in English. biennial. USD 16. adv. bibl. **Document type:** *Directory.* **Description:** Contains a list of alternative schools and colleges in the United States and foreign countries, with descriptions of programs and resources.
Published by: National Coalition of Alternative Community Schools, 1289 Jewett, Ann Arbor, MI 48104-6205 . TEL 734-668-9171, 888-771-9171, ncacs1@earthlink.net, http://www.ncacs.org/. Ed., R&P, Adv. contact Alan Benard.

340 USA
NATIONAL DIRECTORY OF LAW SCHOOLS. Text in English. a. USD 60 to non-members (effective 2001). **Document type:** *Directory.* **Description:** Interprets student resumes, grading systems, standards for honors recognition, and lists law school placement office contacts.
Former titles: Employers Guide to Law Schools; Employers Guide to A B A Approved N A L P Member Law Schools (0275-2832)
Related titles: Online - full text ed.
Published by: National Association for Law Placement, 1666 Connecticut Ave, N W, Ste 325, Washington, DC 20009-1039. TEL 202-667-1666, FAX 202-265-6735, info@nalp.org, http://www.nalp.org.

378.0025 USA
NATIONAL PROFILE OF COMMUNITY COLLEGES: TRENDS & STATISTICS. Text in English. 1950. a. USD 45 to non-members; USD 35 to members. adv. charts; stat. **Document type:** *Directory, Consumer.* **Description:** Aims to be a tool for speech-writing, creating public information-media relations, materials, and supporting basic research. Includes national and statewide analysis of data. Information is presented in both tabular and graphic forms.
Former titles: A A C C Statistical Yearbook (Year); A A C J C Statistical Yearbook; Community, Technica, and Junior Colleges Directory: A Statistical Analysis; Community, Technical, and Junior College Directory; Community and Junior College Directory; Junior College Directory (0075-4552)
Indexed: CIJE, SRI.
Published by: American Association of Community Colleges, One Dupont Circle, N W, Ste 410, Washington, DC 20036-1176. TEL 800-250-6557, FAX 301-604-0158. Ed. Kent Phillippe. Pub. David Pierce. R&P Barbara Daniels. Adv. contact Norma Kent. **Subscr. to:** Community College Press, PO Box 311, Annapolis, MD 20701. TEL 301-490-8116.

371.0025 AUS
NATIONAL REGISTER OF INDEPENDENT SCHOOLS OF AUSTRALIA. Text in English. 1978. a. AUD 65. **Document type:** *Directory.*
Published by: Educare, P.O. Box 266, Burwood, VIC 3125, Australia. TEL 03-98889722. Ed. Paul Fenton. Circ: 3,000.

THE NEXT STEP MAGAZINE; college - careers - life. see *OCCUPATIONS AND CAREERS*

NO LIMITS; life after high school in Wisconsin. see *CHILDREN AND YOUTH—About*

371.0025 GBR
NORVICENSIAN. Text in English. 1873. a. adv. **Document type:** *Corporate.*
Published by: Norwich School, Norwich School, 71a The Close, Norwich, NR1 4DD, United Kingdom. Ed. P J Carpmael. Adv. contact T Hilton. Circ: 2,200.

NURSING PROGRAMS. see *MEDICAL SCIENCES—Nurses And Nursing*

378.0025 USA ISSN 0731-8650
OCCUPATIONAL PROGRAMS IN CALIFORNIA PUBLIC COMMUNITY COLLEGES. Text in English. 1980. biennial. USD 28. adv. index. **Document type:** *Directory.* **Description:** Reference lists for vocational counselors, administrators, libraries, students, and career centers, providing general information, charts of program locations, and information about all California community colleges.
Published by: Leo A. Meyer Associates, Inc., 2381 Sleepy Hollow Ave., Hayward, CA 94545-3429. TEL 510-785-1091, FAX 510-785-1099, lama@best.com, http://www.lamabooks.com. Ed. Carol Markos. Adv. contact Deborah Schultz. Circ: 2,000.

OFFICIAL GUIDE TO DENTAL SCHOOLS. see *MEDICAL SCIENCES—Dentistry*

OPPORTUNITIES FOR MINORITY STUDENTS IN THE U.S. DENTAL SCHOOLS. see *EDUCATION—Higher Education*

371.0025 USA ISSN 0078-5679
OREGON SCHOOL DIRECTORY. Text in English. 1972. a. USD 10. **Document type:** *Directory.*
Formerly (until 1973): Oregon School-Community College Directory
Related titles: Microfiche ed.
Published by: Department of Education, 255 Capitol St, N E, Salem, OR 97310. TEL 503-378-3310, FAX 503-373-7968, barbara.slimak@state.or.us. Ed. Sharon Lesh. Circ: 10,000.

OVERBACHER BRUECKE. see *CHILDREN AND YOUTH—For*

PARALEGAL SCHOOL DIRECTORY. see *LAW*

378.0025 USA
PAREGIAN DIRECTORY OF COLLEGES. Text in English. bi-w. USD 2 newsstand/cover (effective 2005). **Document type:** *Directory.*
Published by: Moushegh George Paregian, 8 Timber Ln, Paoli, PA 19301-1721. TEL 610-407-9086, FAX 610-407-4078, mgparegian@prodigy.net.

371.0025 USA
PAREGIAN DIRECTORY OF INDEPENDENT - PRIVATE SCHOOLS. Text in English. bi-w. USD 2 newsstand/cover (effective 2005). **Document type:** *Directory.*
Published by: Moushegh George Paregian, 8 Timber Ln, Paoli, PA 19301-1721. TEL 610-407-9086, FAX 610-407-4078, mgparegian@prodigy.net.

371.0025 USA ISSN 0079-0230
L901
PATTERSON'S AMERICAN EDUCATION. Text in English. 1904. a. USD 87 to individuals. index. **Document type:** *Directory, Academic/Scholarly.* **Description:** Directory to more than 11,000 public school districts; 34,000 public, private and Catholic high, junior high and middle schools; 300 parochial superintendents; and 400 State Department of Education personnel.
Published by: Educational Directories Inc., PO Box 199, Mount Prospect, IL 60056-0199. TEL 847-459-0605, FAX 847-459-0608. Ed. Wayne Moody.

371.0025 USA ISSN 1044-1417
L901
PATTERSON'S ELEMENTARY EDUCATION. Text in English. 1989. a. USD 87 to individuals. **Document type:** *Directory, Academic/Scholarly.* **Description:** Directory to more than 13,000 public school districts and 71,000 public, private and Catholic elementary and middle schools.
Published by: Educational Directories Inc., PO Box 199, Mount Prospect, IL 60056-0199. TEL 847-459-0605, FAX 847-459-0608. Ed. Wayne Moody.

371.0025 USA ISSN 0553-4054
L901
PATTERSON'S SCHOOLS CLASSIFIED. Text in English. 1951. a. USD 15. **Document type:** *Directory, Academic/Scholarly.* **Description:** Directory to more than 7,000 accredited postsecondary schools. Schools are commingled under 50 academic disciplines but retain their school type identification.
Media: Duplicated (not offset).
Published by: Educational Directories Inc., PO Box 199, Mount Prospect, IL 60056-0199. TEL 847-459-0605, FAX 847-459-0608. Ed. Wayne Moody.

378.0025 DEU
PERSONAL- UND VORLESUNGSVERZEICHNIS DER UNIVERSITAET WUERZBURG. Text in German. s-a. back issues avail. **Document type:** *Journal, Academic/Scholarly.*
Published by: Julius Maximilian Universitaet Wuerzburg, Sanderring 2, Wuerzburg, 97070, Germany. TEL 49-931-312750, FAX 49-931-312610, presse@zv.uni-wuerzburg.de, http://www.uni-wuerzburg.de. Circ: 9,800.

378.0025 USA ISSN 1089-831X
LB2337.2
PETERSON'S COLLEGE MONEY HANDBOOK (YEAR). Text in English. 1983. a. USD 26.95. **Description:** Details costs and financial aid information at more than 1,600 accredited four-year colleges in the United States.
Former titles (until 1997): Peterson's Paying Less for College (Year) (1070-616X); (until 1994): Paying Less for College (Year) (1062-3205); College Money Handbook (0894-9395)
Published by: Thomson Peterson's (Subsidiary of: Thomson Corporation), Princeton Pike Corporate Center, 2000 Lenox Dr, 3rd Fl, Lawrenceville, NJ 08648. TEL 609-243-9111, FAX 609-243-9150, http://www.petersons.com. Ed. Barbara Lawrence.

378.0025 USA ISSN 0887-0152
LB2351.2
PETERSON'S COMPETITIVE COLLEGES (YEAR). Text in English. 1981. a. USD 16.95. **Description:** Provides objective criteria to compare more than 375 colleges and universities in the United States that admit the nation's highest achieving students.
Published by: Thomson Peterson's (Subsidiary of: Thomson Corporation), Princeton Pike Corporate Center, 2000 Lenox Dr, 3rd Fl, Lawrenceville, NJ 08648. TEL 609-243-9111, FAX 609-243-9150, http://www.petersons.com. Ed. Barbara Lawrence.

378.0025 USA ISSN 1521-2874
L901
PETERSON'S DIRECTORY OF COLLEGE & UNIVERSITY ADMINISTRATORS (YEAR). Text in English. 1988. a. USD 49.95 (effective 2001). **Document type:** *Directory.* **Description:** Identifies contact names, titles, addresses, e-mail, and phone and fax numbers of 91,000 key adminstrative officials at some 3,700 US degree-granting undergraduate and graduate institutions.
Former titles (until 1999): Peterson's Register of Higher Education (Year) (1046-2406); (until 1990): Peterson's Higher Education Directory (Year) (0896-2944)
Published by: Thomson Peterson's (Subsidiary of: Thomson Corporation), Princeton Pike Corporate Center, 2000 Lenox Dr, 3rd Fl, Lawrenceville, NJ 08648. TEL 609-243-9111, FAX 609-243-9150, http://www.petersons.com. Ed. Barbara Lawrence.

378.0025 USA ISSN 1520-4359
L901
PETERSON'S GRADUATE AND PROFESSIONAL PROGRAMS: AN OVERVIEW (YEAR) (BOOK 1). Text in English. 1966. a., latest vol.38, 2004. USD 49.95 per issue (effective 2004). 1344 p./no.; **Document type:** *Directory.* **Description:** Provides a look at the array of graduate and professional programs in more than 1,600 accredited colleges and institutions offering postbaccalaureate programs in the United States and Canada.
Former titles (until 1996): Peterson's Guide to Graduate and Professional Programs: An Overview (Year) (Book 1) (0894-9344); (until 1989): Peterson's Annual Guides to Graduate Study. Book 1. Graduate and Professional Programs (0887-8366); (until 1982): Peterson's Annual Guides to Graduate Study. Book 1. Accredited Institutions Offering Graduate Work (0887-8358); (until 1980): Peterson's Annual Guides to Graduate Study. Book 1: Graduate Institutions of the U.S. and Canada (0887-834X)
Related titles: CD-ROM ed.: (from SilverPlatter Information, Inc.); Online - full text ed.
Published by: Thomson Peterson's (Subsidiary of: Thomson Corporation), Princeton Pike Corporate Center, 2000 Lenox Dr, 3rd Fl, Lawrenceville, NJ 08648. TEL 609-243-9111, FAX 609-243-9150, http://www.petersons.com. Ed. Barbara Lawrence.

378.0025 USA ISSN 1088-9442
L901
PETERSON'S GRADUATE AND PROFESSIONAL PROGRAMS: BUSINESS, EDUCATION, HEALTH, INFORMATION STUDIES, LAW, AND SOCIAL WORK (YEAR) (BOOK 6). Text in English. 1966. a., latest vol.38, 2004. USD 49.95 per issue (effective 2004). 2336 p./no.; **Document type:** *Directory.* **Description:** Covers postbaccalaureate programs in the professional areas of business, education, allied health, information studies, law, and social work in the United States and Canada.
Formerly: Peterson's Guide to Graduate Programs in Business, Education, Health, and Law (Year) (Book 6) (0897-6023)
Related titles: CD-ROM ed.: (from SilverPlatter Information, Inc.); Online - full text ed.
Published by: Thomson Peterson's (Subsidiary of: Thomson Corporation), Princeton Pike Corporate Center, 2000 Lenox Dr, 3rd Fl, Lawrenceville, NJ 08648. TEL 609-243-9111, FAX 609-243-9150, http://www.petersons.com. Ed. Barbara Lawrence.

PETERSON'S GRADUATE AND PROFESSIONAL PROGRAMS: ENGINEERING AND APPLIED SCIENCES (YEAR) (BOOK 5). see *ENGINEERING*

570.71025 USA ISSN 1088-9434
L901
PETERSON'S GRADUATE AND PROFESSIONAL PROGRAMS: THE BIOLOGICAL SCIENCES (YEAR) (BOOK 3). Text in English. 1966. a. USD 44.95. **Document type:** *Directory.* **Description:** Covers nearly 4,000 programs in such areas as oncology, conservation, biology, pharmacology, and zoology in the United States and Canada.
Former titles: Peterson's Guide to Graduate Programs in the Biological and Agricultural Sciences (Year) (Book 3) (0894-9360); (until 1989): Peterson's Annual Guides - Graduate Study. Book 3. Graduate Programs in the Biological, Agricultural, and Health Sciences (0887-8412); (until 1984): Peterson's Annual Guides to Graduate Study. Book 3. Biological, Agricultural, and Health Sciences. (0278-5358); (1976-1977): Peterson's Annual Guides to Graduate Study. Book 3: Biological and Health Sciences (0887-8404)
Related titles: CD-ROM ed.: (from SilverPlatter Information, Inc.); Online - full text ed.
Published by: Thomson Peterson's (Subsidiary of: Thomson Corporation), Princeton Pike Corporate Center, 2000 Lenox Dr, 3rd Fl, Lawrenceville, NJ 08648. TEL 609-243-9111, FAX 609-243-9150, http://www.petersons.com. Ed. Barbara Lawrence.

PETERSON'S GRADUATE AND PROFESSIONAL PROGRAMS: THE HUMANITIES, ARTS, AND SOCIAL SCIENCES (YEAR) (BOOK 2). see *HUMANITIES: COMPREHENSIVE WORKS*

PETERSON'S GRADUATE AND PROFESSIONAL PROGRAMS: THE PHYSICAL SCIENCES, MATHEMATICS, AGRICULTURAL SCIENCES, THE ENVIRONMENT & NATURAL RESOURCES. see *SCIENCES: COMPREHENSIVE WORKS*

378.74025 USA ISSN 0742-4973
L903.N38
PETERSON'S GUIDE TO COLLEGES IN NEW ENGLAND (YEAR). Text in English. 1984. a. USD 16.95. **Description:** Covers all accredited four-year and private two-year colleges in New England.
Published by: Thomson Peterson's (Subsidiary of: Thomson Corporation), Princeton Pike Corporate Center, 2000 Lenox Dr, 3rd Fl, Lawrenceville, NJ 08648. TEL 609-243-9111, FAX 609-243-9150, http://www.petersons.com. Ed. Barbara Lawrence.

378.747025 USA ISSN 0742-4965
L903.N7
PETERSON'S GUIDE TO COLLEGES IN NEW YORK (YEAR). Text in English. 1984. a. USD 16.95. **Description:** Covers all accredited four-year and private two-year colleges in New York State.
Published by: Thomson Peterson's (Subsidiary of: Thomson Corporation), Princeton Pike Corporate Center, 2000 Lenox Dr, 3rd Fl, Lawrenceville, NJ 08648. TEL 609-243-9111, FAX 609-243-9150, http://www.petersons.com. Ed. Barbara Lawrence.

378.74025 USA ISSN 0742-4957
L903.M54
PETERSON'S GUIDE TO COLLEGES IN THE MIDDLE ATLANTIC STATES (YEAR). Text in English. 1984. a. USD 16.95. **Description:** Covers all accredited four-year and private two-year colleges in the Middle Atlantic states.
Published by: Thomson Peterson's (Subsidiary of: Thomson Corporation), Princeton Pike Corporate Center, 2000 Lenox Dr, 3rd Fl, Lawrenceville, NJ 08648. TEL 609-243-9111, FAX 609-243-9150, http://www.petersons.com. Ed. Barbara Lawrence.

378.77025 USA ISSN 0742-4949
L903.M57
PETERSON'S GUIDE TO COLLEGES IN THE MIDWEST (YEAR). Text in English. 1984. a. USD 16.95. **Description:** Covers all accredited four-year and private two-year colleges in the Midwest.
Published by: Thomson Peterson's (Subsidiary of: Thomson Corporation), Princeton Pike Corporate Center, 2000 Lenox Dr, 3rd Fl, Lawrenceville, NJ 08648. TEL 609-243-9111, FAX 609-243-9150, http://www.petersons.com. Ed. Barbara Lawrence.

378.75025 USA ISSN 1069-0085
L903.S84
PETERSON'S GUIDE TO COLLEGES IN THE SOUTH (YEAR). Text in English. 1985. a. USD 16.95. **Description:** Covers all accredited four-year and private two-year colleges in the southern U.S.
Formerly (until 1993): Peterson's Guide to Colleges in the Southeast (Year) (0882-309X)
Published by: Thomson Peterson's (Subsidiary of: Thomson Corporation), Princeton Pike Corporate Center, 2000 Lenox Dr, 3rd Fl, Lawrenceville, NJ 08648. TEL 609-243-9111, FAX 609-243-9150, http://www.petersons.com. Ed. Barbara Lawrence.

378.78025 USA ISSN 0888-8159
L903.W39
PETERSON'S GUIDE TO COLLEGES IN THE WEST (YEAR). Text in English. 1986. a. USD 16.95. **Description:** Covers all accredited four-year and private two-year colleges in the western United States.
Published by: Thomson Peterson's (Subsidiary of: Thomson Corporation), Princeton Pike Corporate Center, 2000 Lenox Dr, 3rd Fl, Lawrenceville, NJ 08648. TEL 609-243-9111, FAX 609-243-9150, http://www.petersons.com. Ed. Barbara Lawrence.

378.0025 USA ISSN 1080-2533
PETERSON'S GUIDE TO M B A PROGRAMS. Text in English. 1995. a.
Published by: Thomson Peterson's (Subsidiary of: Thomson Corporation), Princeton Pike Corporate Center, 2000 Lenox Dr, 3rd Fl, Lawrenceville, NJ 08648. TEL 609-243-9111, FAX 609-243-9150, http://www.petersons.com.

373.025 USA
L900
PETERSON'S PRIVATE SECONDARY SCHOOLS (YEAR). Text in English. 1980. a. USD 29.95. **Description:** Guide to 1,400 schools worldwide: military, religious, day, boarding, special needs, and traditional.
Former titles (until 1997): Peterson's Guide to Private Secondary Schools (1066-5366); (until 1993): Peterson's Guide to Independent Secondary Schools (Year) (0894-9409); (until 1988): Guide to Independent Secondary Schools (0894-9069); (until 1984): Peterson's Annual Guide to Independent Secondary Schools (0196-7495)
—CCC.
Published by: Thomson Peterson's (Subsidiary of: Thomson Corporation), Princeton Pike Corporate Center, 2000 Lenox Dr, 3rd Fl, Lawrenceville, NJ 08648. TEL 609-243-9111, FAX 609-243-9150, http://www.petersons.com. Ed. Barbara Lawrence.

378.0025 USA ISSN 1069-1383
PETERSON'S SPORTS SCHOLARSHIPS AND COLLEGE ATHLETIC PROGRAMS. Text in English. 1994. biennial. price varies. **Document type:** *Directory, Consumer.*
Published by: Thomson Peterson's (Subsidiary of: Thomson Corporation), Princeton Pike Corporate Center, 2000 Lenox Dr, 3rd Fl, Lawrenceville, NJ 08648. TEL 609-243-9111, FAX 609-243-9150, http://www.petersons.com.

378.0025 610 USA ISSN 1089-3342
PETERSON'S U.S. & CANADIAN MEDICAL SCHOOLS. Text in English. 1997. a.

E

▼ new title ➤ refereed ✶ unverified ♦ full entry avail.

Published by: Thomson Peterson's (Subsidiary of: Thomson Corporation), Princeton Pike Corporate Center, 2000 Lenox Dr, 3rd Fl, Lawrenceville, NJ 08648. TEL 609-243-9111, FAX 609-243-9150, http://www.petersons.com.

PHARMACY SCHOOL ADMISSION REQUIREMENTS. see *PHARMACY AND PHARMACOLOGY*

POLITIK UND UNTERRICHT; Zeitschrift fuer die Praxis der politischen Bildung. see *POLITICAL SCIENCE*

POSTGRAD SERIES - THE DIRECTORY. see *EDUCATION—Higher Education*

371.0025 GBR ISSN 0950-4508
PRIMARY EDUCATION DIRECTORY. Text in English. 1986. a. GBP 36. **Document type:** *Directory.* **Description:** Lists 26,000 state and independent schools in the UK.
Related titles: Online - full text ed.
Published by: School Government Publishing Co. Ltd., Darby House, Bletchingley Rd, Merstham, Redhill, Surrey RH1 3DN, United Kingdom. TEL 44-1737-642223, FAX 44-1737-644283. adv.: page GBP 100; trim 106 x 178. Circ: 1,600.

378.0025 GBR ISSN 0951-6883
PRISM. Text in English. 1986. every 4 wks. free. adv. **Document type:** *Newsletter.*
Published by: University of Strathclyde, External Affairs and Development Office, McCance Bldg, 16 Richmond St, Glasgow, G1 1XQ, United Kingdom. TEL 44-141-552-4400, FAX 44-141-552-0775, http://www.strath.ac.uk/campus/prism/prism.html. Circ: 4,800.

371.0025 USA ISSN 0079-5399
L901
PRIVATE INDEPENDENT SCHOOLS (YEAR); the Bunting and Lyon blue book. Text in English. 1943. a. USD 105 (effective 2001). **Document type:** *Directory.* **Description:** Provides a comprehensive guide to more than 1,200 elementary and secondary private schools and summer programs in the United States, Canada, and elsewhere.
Published by: Bunting and Lyon, Inc, 238 N Main St, Wallingford, CT 06492. TEL 203-269-3333, FAX 203-269-5697, bandlblubk@aol.com, http://www.buntingandlyon.com. Pub. Peter G Bunting.

378.0025 USA ISSN 0097-5206
L901
RANDAX EDUCATION GUIDE; to colleges seeking students. Text in English. 1971. a. USD 21.95. adv. bk.rev. **Document type:** *Directory.*
Published by: Education Guide, Inc., PO Box 421, Randolph, MA 02368. TEL 617-376-0066, FAX 617-376-0067. Ed. Stephen E Marshall. Circ: 20,000.

378.0025 USA
RECREATIONAL SPORTS DIRECTORY. Text in English. 1975. a. price varies. **Document type:** *Directory.* **Description:** Lists recreational sports programs in colleges and universities in the U.S., Canada, and within U.S. military installations.
Published by: National Intramural - Recreational Sports Association Foundation, 4185 S W Research Way, Corvallis, OR 97333-1067. TEL 541-766-8211, FAX 541-766-8284, nirsa@nirsa.org, http://nirsa.org. Ed. Natalie Kovac. Circ: 2,000.

371.0025 USA
SCHOOL GUIDE. (Regional editions avail.: New England; Connecticut; New York Metro; Long Island; Upper New York State; New Jersey; Philadelphia & Eastern PA; Pittsburgh & Western PA; Ohio-Michigan-Indiana; Delaware-Maryland-Virginia; Florida; Chicago-Milwaukee Areas; Minneapolis-St. Paul Area; St. Louis Area Areas) Text in English. 1935. a. USD 10; free to high school counselors (effective 2005). adv. stat. **Document type:** *Directory.*
Published by: School Guide Publications, 210 North Ave, New Rochelle, NY 10801. TEL 914-632-7771, 800-433-7771, FAX 914-632-3412, info@schoolguides.com, http://www.schoolguides.com/. Ed. Amy Enright. Pub. Myles Ridder. Adv. contact Tom White. Circ: 375,000.

371.025 USA ISSN 1042-3044
SCHOOLHOUSE MAGAZINE; regional guide to Minnesota schools. Text in English. 1984. a. USD 7.95 newsstand/cover (effective 2003). adv. **Document type:** *Magazine, Consumer.* **Description:** Provides descriptions and detailed information on all public school districts and private schools.
Address: 15500 Wayzata Blvd., Ste. 902, Wayzata, MN 55391-1415. TEL 800-224-3642, teresa@schoolhousemagazine.com, http://www.schoolhousemagazine.com. Ed., Pub., R&P, Adv. contact Ms. Teresa Woodward.

SCHOOLS IN THE UNITED STATES AND CANADA OFFERING GRADUATE EDUCATION IN PHARMACOLOGY. see *PHARMACY AND PHARMACOLOGY*

SCHWENDEMAN'S DIRECTORY OF COLLEGE GEOGRAPHY OF THE UNITED STATES. see *GEOGRAPHY*

371.02571 CAN ISSN 1487-119X
SCOTT'S DIRECTORY OF CANADIAN SCHOOLS. Text in English. 1984. a. (in Apr.). CND 199 per issue (effective 2004). **Document type:** *Directory, Trade.* **Description:** Lists contacts, titles, addresses, phone and fax numbers, email addresses, and all the statistics on over 16,000 schools in Canada.
Former titles (until 1999): Southam's Directory of Canadian Schools (1207-4098); (until 1996): Directory of Canadian Schools (0832-1442)
Related titles: CD-ROM ed.: Scott's Directory of Canadian Schools Select. CND 199 per issue (effective 2004).
Published by: Business Information Group, 12 Concorde Pl, Ste 800, Toronto, ON M3C 4J2, Canada. TEL 416-442-5600, 800-668-2374, FAX 416-442-2191, http://www.businessinformationgroup.ca.

SEI MARIANNA IKA DAIGAKU KIYO/ST. MARIANNA UNIVERSITY SCHOOL OF MEDICINE. BULLETIN. see *MEDICAL SCIENCES*

378.0025 ESP
SERIE GUIAS DE LOS ESTUDIOS UNIVERSITARIOS. Text in Spanish. 1977. irreg., latest vol.13, 1984.
Published by: (Universidad de Sevilla, Instituto de Ciencias de la Educacion, Universidad de Navarra), Ediciones Universidad de Navarra S.A., Pza. Los Sauces, 1-2, Baranain, (Navarra) 31010, Spain. TEL 34-948-256850.

SEX EDUCATION MATTERS. see *CHILDREN AND YOUTH—For*

371.0025 GBR
STAFFROOM JOURNAL✶. Text in English. 1980. 2/school-academic yr. free. adv. bk.rev. back issues avail.
Published by: E M A P Automotive, Wentworth House, Wentworth St, Peterborough, Cambs PE1 1DS, United Kingdom. Ed. Lynn Dorward. Circ: 32,000.

STATE-APPROVED SCHOOLS OF NURSING - L.P.N. - L.V.N. see *MEDICAL SCIENCES—Nurses And Nursing*

STATE-APPROVED SCHOOLS OF NURSING - R.N. see *MEDICAL SCIENCES—Nurses And Nursing*

371.025 DEU ISSN 1434-727X
STUDIENANGEBOTE DEUTSCHER HOCHSCHULEN. Text in German. 2/yr. **Document type:** *Directory, Academic/Scholarly.* **Description:** Documents all degree courses offered by state-maintained and state-recognised higher education institutions in Germany.
Published by: Verlag K.H. Bock, Reichenbergerstr 11 e, Bad Honnef, 53604, Germany. TEL 49-2224-5443, FAX 49-2224-78310, verlag@bock-net.de, http://www.bock-net.de. Pub. Karl Heinrich Bock. R&P Bernhard Wambach.

371.025 DEU
STUDIEREN FUER EUROPA. Text in German. 1984. biennial. **Document type:** *Directory.*
Formerly (until 1997): Europaeische Studiengaenge und MBA Programme in Europe
Published by: Staufenbiel Institut fuer Studien- und Berufsplanung GmbH, Konrad-Adenauer-Ufer 33, Cologne, 50668, Germany. TEL 49-221-9126630, FAX 49-221-9126639, info@staufenbiel.de, http://www.staufenbiel.de. Ed. Joerg Staufenbiel. Circ: 5,000.

THE STUDY U K HANDBOOK. see *EDUCATION—Higher Education*

373.025 USA ISSN 1045-6171
T73.1
TECHNICAL, TRADE & BUSINESS SCHOOL DATA HANDBOOK. Text in English. 1984. biennial (in 4 vols.). USD 150.
Published by: Riverside Publishing, 425 Spring Lake Dr, Itasca, IL 60143-2076. TEL 630-467-7000, 800-323-9540, FAX 630-467-7192, 630-467-7192, http://www.riversidepublishing.com. Ed. Cory Decker. Pub., R&P Allan Corderman. Circ: 4,500.

371.0025 USA ISSN 0363-4566
L903.T4
TEXAS SCHOOL DIRECTORY. Text in English. 1915. a. USD 35 to individuals; USD 20 to non-profit organizations. **Document type:** *Directory, Government.*
Former titles: Public School Directory of the State of Texas; Texas Public School Directory
Related titles: CD-ROM ed.: 2001. USD 7 (effective 2001).
Published by: (Resource Center Library), Texas Education Agency, 1701 N Congress Ave, Austin, TX 78701-1494. TEL 512-463-9734, cbaylor@tea.state.tx.us, http://www.tea.state.tx.us. Circ: 15,000.

378.0025 GBR
U C A S ANNUAL REPORT. Text in English. a. **Document type:** *Corporate.*
Formerly: Universities Central Council on Admissions. Report
Published by: Universities and Colleges Admissions Service, Rosehill, New Barn Ln, Cheltenham, Glos GL52 3LZ, United Kingdom. TEL 44-1242-227788, http://www.ucas.com.

371.025 USA
U.S. NEWS & WORLD REPORT BEST GRADUATE SCHOOLS (YEAR). Text in English. a. USD 7.95 newsstand/cover (effective 2002).
Published by: U.S. News & World Report, Inc., 1050 Thomas Jefferson St., N W, Washington, DC 20007. TEL 202-955-2000, 800-436-6520, FAX 202-955-2049, usnews@palmcoasted.com, http://www.usnews.com. Ed. Mortimer B Zuckerman.

371.025 SVK
UCITELSKE NOVINY. Text in Slovak. 1950. 43/yr. SKK 225, USD 6.20; SKK 9 newsstand/cover (effective 1999). adv. back issues avail. **Description:** Includes articles and criticism, as well as teachers' responses.
Indexed: RASB.
Published by: (Slovenske Pedagogicke Naklad./Ministry of Education of Slovakia), Media Trade s.r.o., Sasinkova 5, Bratislava, 81560, Slovakia. TEL 42-17-55561685, FAX 42-17-55571894. Adv. contact Ludmila Farkasova. B&W page SKK 28,000. **Subscr. to:** Zahradnicka 151, Bratislava 82005, Slovakia.

378.45025 ITA ISSN 0392-8411
L935
UNIVERSITA DEGLI STUDI IN ITALIA. ANNUARIO. Text in Italian. 1981. biennial. EUR 77.47 (effective 2004). adv. **Document type:** *Directory.* **Description:** Provides information on Italian universities, including faculties, curricula, and degrees offered.
Related titles: Diskette ed.
Published by: (Istituto Nazionale dell'Informazione), Editoriale Italiana, Via Vigliena 10, Rome, 00192, Italy. TEL 39-06-3230177, FAX 39-06-3211359, info@editoriale.it, http://www.editoriale.it. Ed. Giordano Treveri Gennari. Circ: 50,000.

378.0025 AUT
DIE UNIVERSITAET. Text in English, German. bi-m. bk.rev. **Document type:** *Newsletter, Consumer.*
Related titles: Online - full text ed.
Published by: Universitaet Wien, Aussensinstitut, Dr Karl-Lueger-Ring 1, Vienna, W 1010, Austria. TEL 43-1-427718131, FAX 43-1-42779181, zeitung.ausseninstitut@univie.ac.at, http://www.univie.ac.at/dieuniversitaet/, http://www.univie.ac.at/dieuniversitaet/. Ed. Bernd Matouschek. Circ: 8,000 (controlled).

378 IND ISSN 0377-6336
UNIVERSITIES HANDBOOK (YEAR). Text in English. 1927. irreg., latest vol.27, 1997. USD 300 (effective 2003). **Document type:** *Newsletter.* **Description:** Contains information on 229 university-level institutions, including 39 'deemed universities' in India.
Published by: Association of Indian Universities, A.I.U. House, 16 Kotla Marg, New Delhi, 110 002, India. TEL 91-11-323-0059, FAX 91-11-323-6105, aiu@del2.vsnl.net.in, http://www.aiuweb.org. Circ: 1,600.

UNIVERSITY CONTINUING EDUCATION ASSOCIATION. DIRECTORY. see *EDUCATION—Adult Education*

378.0025 GBR
UNIVERSITY OF LIVERPOOL POST GRADUATE PROSPECTUS. Text in English. 1985. a. free. **Document type:** *Bulletin.* **Description:** Information on postgraduate degree courses, entry requirements, application procedures and general information.
Formerly (until 1989): Postgraduate Study at the University of Liverpool (0268-0645)
Published by: University of Liverpool, Committee Secretariat, Liverpool, University Of Liverpool, Liverpool, L69 3BX, United Kingdom. TEL 44-151-794-5926, FAX 44-151-794-2060, uksro@liverpool.ac.uk, http://www.liv.ac.uk/uksro/uksro.html. Ed. G Kelly. Circ: 30,000.

378.429025 GBR
➤ **UNIVERSITY OF WALES, ABERYSTWYTH. UNDERGRADUATE PROSPECTUS.** Text in English. 1872. a. free. **Document type:** *Bulletin, Academic/Scholarly.*
Former titles: University of Wales, Aberystwyth. Prospectus (0309-8192); (until 1977): University College of Wales, Aberystwyth. General Prospectus (0309-1244)
—BLDSC (9087.599000).
Published by: University of Wales, Admissions and Recruitment Office, Old College, King St, Aberystwyth, Ceredigion SY23 2AX, United Kingdom. TEL 44-1970-622021, FAX 44-1970-627410, hwd@aber.ac.uk, http://www.aber.ac.uk. Ed. R Davies.

371.0025 USA
UTAH PUBLIC SCHOOL DIRECTORY. Text in English. a. USD 10. **Document type:** *Directory, Government.*
Published by: Utah State Office of Education, PO Box 144200, Salt Lake City, UT 84114-4200. TEL 801-538-7782, FAX 801-538-7768. Circ: 2,000.

371.0025 DNK ISSN 0909-3044
LC1047.D4
VEJLEDNING OG VEJLEDERE, ADRESSER. Text in Danish. 1973. a. **Document type:** *Academic/Scholarly.*

E

Former titles (until 1993): Uddannelse og Erhverv. Adresser (0906-0480); Supersedes in part (in 1985): Uddannelse og Erhverv (0900-3479)
Published by: Raadet for Uddannelses- og Erhvervsvejledning (R.U.E.)/Danish National Council for Educational and Vocational Guidance, Vester Voldgade 123, Copenhagen V, 1552, Denmark. TEL 45-39-95-53-00, FAX 45-39-95-53-49, r-u-e@r-u-e.dk, http://www.r-u-e.dk. Ed. Leif Hammelev. Circ: 11,000.

378.0025 DEU
VERANSTALTUNGSKALENDER. Text in German. 1972. 7/yr. free. **Document type:** *Catalog.*
Published by: Ludwig Maximilians Universitaet Muenchen, Geschwister-Scholl-Platz 1, Munich, 80539, Germany. TEL 49-89-21803423, FAX 49-89-338297, http://www.uni-muenchen.de. Eds. Dietmar Schmidt, Doris Bayer. Circ: 3,400.

VI UNDERSOEGER. see *EDUCATION—Adult Education*

VISUAL AND PERFORMING ARTS. see *ART*

WHERE SHALL I GO TO STUDY ADVERTISING & PUBLIC RELATIONS?. see *ADVERTISING AND PUBLIC RELATIONS*

378.0025 USA
WHERE THE COLLEGES RANK✶. Text in English. irreg., latest 1973. USD 2.
Published by: College-Rater, Inc., 2121 South 12th St, Allentown, PA 18103.

378.0025 GBR
WHICH DEGREE. ENGINEERING, TECHNOLOGY, GEOGRAPHY. Text in English. 196?. a. GBP 20.95 per issue (effective 2002). **Document type:** *Directory.* **Description:** Guides students and career counselors to degree programs in engineering and geography with concise course descriptions.
Formerly: Which Degree. Engineering, Technology, Environment
Published by: (Careers Research and Advisory Centre), Hobsons PLC, Challenger House, 42 Adler St, London, E1 1EE, United Kingdom. TEL 44-1223-460366, FAX 44-1223-301506. **Dist. by:** Biblios Publishers' Distribution Services Ltd., Star Rd, Partridge Green, W Sussex RH13 8LD, United Kingdom. TEL 44-1403-710851, FAX 44-1403-711143.

378.0025 GBR
WHICH DEGREE. SCIENCES, MEDICINE, MATHEMATICS. Text in English. 196?. a. GBP 20.95 per issue (effective 2002). **Document type:** *Directory.* **Description:** Guides students and career counselors to degree programs in the natural sciences, along with medicine and mathematics, with concise course descriptions.
Published by: (Careers Research and Advisory Centre), Hobsons PLC, Challenger House, 42 Adler St, London, E1 1EE, United Kingdom. TEL 44-1223-460366, FAX 44-1223-301506. **Dist. by:** Biblios Publishers' Distribution Services Ltd., Star Rd, Partridge Green, W Sussex RH13 8LD, United Kingdom. TEL 44-1403-710851, FAX 44-1403-711143.

378.0025 GBR
WHICH DEGREE. SOCIAL SCIENCES, BUSINESS, EDUCATION. Text in English. 196?. a. GBP 20.95 per issue (effective 2002). **Document type:** *Directory.* **Description:** Guides students and career counselors to degree programs in business, education, and the social sciences, with concise course descriptions.
Published by: (Careers Research and Advisory Centre), Hobsons PLC, Challenger House, 42 Adler St, London, E1 1EE, United Kingdom. TEL 44-1223-460366, FAX 44-1223-301506. **Dist. by:** Biblios Publishers' Distribution Services Ltd., Star Rd, Partridge Green, W Sussex RH13 8LD, United Kingdom. TEL 44-1403-710851, FAX 44-1403-711143.

371.0025 GBR ISSN 0952-083X
L915
WHICH SCHOOL?. Text in English. 1924. a. GBP 22.95 per issue (effective 2003). adv. **Document type:** *Directory, Academic/Scholarly.* **Description:** Lists over 2000 British independent schools in Britain for children and is fully comprehensive.
Former titles (until 1986): Schools (0080-6897); (until 1982): Directory of Catholic Schools and Colleges (0070-5233)
—BLDSC (9310.897000), IE, ingenta.
Published by: John Catt Educational Ltd., Great Glemham, Saxmundham, Suffolk IP17 2DH, United Kingdom. TEL 44-1728-663666, FAX 44-1728-663415, enquiries@johncatt.co.uk, http://www.schoolsearch.co.uk. Ed. Derek Bingham. Adv. contact Sharon Bleese. Circ: 2,500.

371.9025 GBR ISSN 0965-1004
WHICH SCHOOL? FOR SPECIAL NEEDS. Text in English. 1992. a. GBP 19.95 per issue (effective 2003). **Document type:** *Directory, Academic/Scholarly.* **Description:** Lists independent and maintained schools in Britain for pupils with learning, educational and behavioral difficulties, physical or mental handicaps, or dyslexia.
Published by: John Catt Educational Ltd., Great Glemham, Saxmundham, Suffolk IP17 2DH, United Kingdom. TEL 44-1728-663666, FAX 44-1728-663415, enquiries@johncatt.co.uk, http://www.schoolsearch.co.uk. Ed. Derek Bingham. Adv. contact Sharon Bleese. Circ: 2,000.

378.0025 GBR
WHICH SCHOOL? FOR THE SIXTH FORM. Text in English. 1994. a. GBP 12.95 per issue (effective 2003). **Document type:** *Directory, Academic/Scholarly.* **Description:** Lists independent schools and colleges offering A-level courses, as well as schools and colleges offering the International Baccalaureate diploma.
Formerly: Which School? For A Levels (1354-5302)
Published by: John Catt Educational Ltd., Great Glemham, Saxmundham, Suffolk IP17 2DH, United Kingdom. TEL 44-1728-663666, FAX 44-1728-663415, enquiries@johncatt.co.uk, http://www.schoolsearch.co.uk. Ed. Derek Bingham. Adv. contact Sharon Bleese. Circ: 2,000.

WHICH UNIVERSITY - ON CD-ROM. see *EDUCATION—Higher Education*

371.025 DEU
WIRTSCHAFT STUDIEREN. Text in German. 1977. biennial. EUR 15 per issue (effective 2002). adv. **Document type:** *Directory, Trade.*
Formerly (until 1998): Wirtschaftswissenschaftlichen Fakultaeten
Published by: Staufenbiel Institut fuer Studien- und Berufsplanung GmbH, Konrad-Adenauer-Ufer 33, Cologne, 50668, Germany. TEL 49-221-9126630, FAX 49-221-9126639, info@staufenbiel.de, http://www.staufenbiel.de. Ed. Joerg Staufenbiel. adv.: B&W page EUR 1,750, color page EUR 2,680. Circ: 10,000.

WORLD DIRECTORY OF MEDICAL SCHOOLS. see *MEDICAL SCIENCES*

370.025 378.0025 GBR ISSN 0084-1889
L900
WORLD LIST OF UNIVERSITIES, OTHER INSTITUTIONS OF HIGHER EDUCATION AND UNIVERSITY ORGANISATIONS/LISTE MONDIALE DES UNIVERSITES. Variant title: World List of Universities. Text in English. 1952. triennial. GBP 85 (effective 1998). index. **Document type:** *Directory.* **Description:** Contains information on more than 11,000 universities, university organizations, and other centers of higher learning in 171 countries.
Published by: (International Association of Universities), Macmillan Reference Ltd., 25 Eccleston Pl, London, W13 0RA, United Kingdom. TEL 44-171-881-8000, FAX 44-171-881-8001. Ed. Julian Ashby.

378.0025 GBR ISSN 0084-2117
AS2 CODEN: WOLED4
WORLD OF LEARNING (YEAR). Text in English. 1947. a., latest 2002. **Document type:** *Directory.* **Description:** Guide and directory of over 30,000 academic institutions including universities and colleges, learned societies, research institutes, libraries, and museums throughout the world.
Related titles: Online - full text ed.: GBP 365 (effective 2005).
Indexed: RASB.
—BLDSC (9356.400000), CASDDS, KNAW. **CCC.**
Published by: Europa Publications Limited (Subsidiary of: Taylor & Francis Group), 11 New Fetter Ln, London, EC4P 4EE, United Kingdom. TEL 44-20-7822-4300, FAX 44-20-7842-2249, sales.europa@tandf.co.uk, http://www.worldoflearning.com/, http://www.europapublications.com. Ed. Michael Salzman. **Dist. by:** Taylor & Francis Inc., 7625 Empire Dr., Florence, KY 41042-2919. cserve@routledge-ny.com.

371.0025 GBR
A YEAR OFF - A YEAR ON. Text in English. 1983. irreg. GBP 7.99. **Document type:** *Directory.*
Published by: Lifetime Careers Wiltshire, 7 Ascot Ct, White Horse Business Park, Trowbridge, Wilts BA14 OXA, United Kingdom. TEL 44-1223-354551, FAX 44-1223-321454. **Dist. by:** Biblios Publishers' Distribution Services Ltd., Star Rd, Partridge Green, W Sussex RH13 8LD, United Kingdom. TEL 44-1403-710851, FAX 44-1403-711143.

378.0025 FIN ISSN 0355-1784
LB2353.26.F5
YLIOPPILASAINEITA. Text in Finnish. 1948. a. price varies. **Document type:** *Yearbook.*
Formerly (until 1968): Valioaineita (0504-9776)
Published by: Suomalaisen Kirjallisuuden Seura/Finnish Literature Society, Hallituskatu 1, PO Box 259, Helsinki, 00171, Finland. TEL 358-9-131231, FAX 358-9-13123220, sks-fl@finlit.fi, http://www/finlit.fi. Circ: 15,000.

378.0025 USA ISSN 1541-5066
L901
2 YEAR COLLEGES. Text in English. 1960. a. USD 21.95. **Description:** Profiles of more than 1,500 accredited institutions in the United States offering associate degree programs, arranged alphabetically by state.
Former titles (until 2002): Peterson's 2 Year Colleges; (until 1999): Peterson's Guide to Two-Year Colleges (Year) (0894-9328); (until 1989): Peterson's Annual Guides/Undergraduate Study: Guide to Two-Year Colleges (0737-3171); Which supersedes in part (in 1970): Peterson's Annual Guide to Undergraduate Study (0147-8451)
Related titles: Online - full text ed.: (from CompuServe Inc.).
Published by: Thomson Peterson's (Subsidiary of: Thomson Corporation), Princeton Pike Corporate Center, 2000 Lenox Dr, 3rd Fl, Lawrenceville, NJ 08648. TEL 609-243-9111, FAX 609-243-9150, http://www.petersons.com. Ed. Barbara Lawrence.

EDUCATION—Higher Education

see also COLLEGE AND ALUMNI

378.111 USA ISSN 1040-8924
A A C R A O DATA DISPENSER. Text in English. 1981. 10/yr. USD 30 domestic to non-members; USD 40 foreign to non-members (effective 2001). adv. bk.rev. back issues avail. **Document type:** *Newsletter.* **Description:** For professional higher education administrators, covering Association news, issues in higher education, and international education.
Related titles: Diskette ed.
Published by: American Association of Collegiate Registrars and Admissions Officers, One Dupont Circle, N W, Ste 520, Washington, DC 20036-1135. TEL 202-293-9161, FAX 202-872-8857, pubs@aacrao.org, http://www.aacrao.com. Ed. Saira Burki. Pub. Casandra Tate. R&P Barmak Nassirian. Adv. contact Sairi Burki. Circ: 9,200.

378.1 USA ISSN 0360-697X
HF1101
A A C S B NEWSLINE. (Association to Advance Collegiate Schools of Business) Text in English. 1971. q. USD 15 domestic; USD 20 foreign (effective 2001). adv. **Document type:** *Newsletter.* **Description:** Reports on activities of the association, as well as trends and issues in management education.
Incorporates (in Apr. 1977): International Dimension
Indexed: SRI.
Published by: The Association to Advance Collegiate Schools of Business, 600 Emerson Rd., Ste. 300, St. Louis, MO 63141-6762. TEL 314-872-8481, FAX 314-872-8495, http://www.aacsb.edu. Ed., R&P Howard Hoskins TEL 314-872-8507. Adv. contact Rosemarie Kroscher. Circ: 8,000.

A A E E CONNECTIONS. see *BUSINESS AND ECONOMICS—Labor And Industrial Relations*

A A T T BULLETIN. see *LINGUISTICS*

378.101 GHA ISSN 0855-0174
LA1503
A A U NEWSLETTER. Text in English. 3/yr. free. **Document type:** *Newsletter, Academic/Scholarly.* **Description:** Carries information on the activities of AAU member universities and the AAU secretariat and lists vacancy announcements, as well as applications for employment in African universities and new publications.
Formerly: Association of African Universities. Information Bulletin
Published by: Association of African Universities, PO Box 5744, Accra - North, Ghana. info@aau.org. Ed. Yawo Assigbley.

378.19822 USA ISSN 1044-5706
LC1756.A2
A A U W OUTLOOK. Text in English. 1962. q. USD 15 to non-members (effective 2005). adv. bk.rev. illus. reprint service avail. from PQC. **Document type:** *Magazine, Trade.*
Former titles (until 1988): Graduate Woman (0161-5661); (until 1978): A A U W Journal (0001-0278)
Related titles: Microfilm ed.: (from PQC).
Indexed: AgeL, CIJE, PAIS, PMR.
Published by: American Association of University Women, 1111 16th St, NW, Washington, DC 20036. TEL 202-785-7728, FAX 202-872-1425, editor@aauw.org, ads@aauw.org, http://www.aauw.org/outlook/index.cfm. Ed. Jodi Lipson. Circ: 150,000 (paid and free).

378.19822 USA
A A W C J C NEWSLETTER. Text in English. q.
Indexed: HEA.
Published by: American Association of Women in Community and Junior Colleges, c/o Barb Cannell North Campus, Milwaukee Area Technical College, 5555 W, Highland, WI 53092. TEL 414-242-6500.

378.07 USA
BV4019
A B H E NEWSLETTER. Text in English. 1957. 5/yr. USD 10 newsstand/cover domestic to members; USD 15 newsstand/cover domestic to non-members; USD 20 newsstand/cover foreign (effective 2000 - 2001). 8 p./no.; **Document type:** *Newsletter, Consumer.*
Former titles (until 2004): A A B C Newsletter; (until 196?): American Association of Bible Colleges. Newsletter (0094-260X)
Published by: The Association for Biblical Higher Education, 5575 S Semoran Blvd, Ste 26, Orlando, FL 32822-1781. TEL 407-207-0808, FAX 407-207-0840, info@abhe.org, http://www.abhe.org. Eds. Larry J. McKinney, Randall E Bell. Circ: 1,200.

E

378.007 AUS
A C E R NEWSLETTER. Text in English. 1969. 3/yr. free. back issues avail. **Document type:** *Newsletter.* **Description:** Includes articles on ACER's research and features on new publications.
Published by: Australian Council for Educational Research, 347 Camberwell Rd, Private Bag 55, Camberwell, VIC 3124, Australia. TEL 61-3-9835-7447, 800-338-402, FAX 61-3-9835-7499, sales@acer.edu.au, http://www.acer.edu.au. Ed. Julia Robinson. R&P Deirdre Morris. Circ: 22,000.

A C H A ACTION. see *PHYSICAL FITNESS AND HYGIENE*

364.0711 USA
A C J S PROGRAM BOOK. Text in English. a. **Description:** Complete program and abstracts of annual meeting.
Published by: Academy of Criminal Justice Sciences, 7339 Hanover Pkwy., Ste. A, Greenbelt, MD 20770-3640. info@acjs.org, http://www.acjs.org. Circ: 2,000 (controlled).

378 USA
A C T ANNUAL REPORT. Text in English. 1959. a. free.
Formerly (until 1990): American College Testing Program. Annual Report (0517-0680)
Published by: A C T, 2201 N Dodge St, Box 168, Iowa City, IA 52243-0168. TEL 319-337-1028.

378 USA ISSN 0569-3993
CODEN: ACRRCI
A C T RESEARCH REPORT. Text in English. 1965. irreg. free.
Formerly: A C T Research Service Report (0065-7840)
Related titles: Microfiche ed.
Indexed: CIJE, HEA, PsycholAb.
—BLDSC (0578.955000).
Published by: A C T, 2201 N Dodge St, Box 168, Iowa City, IA 52243-0168. TEL 319-337-1077. Circ: 3,354.

A C U BULLETIN. see *EDUCATION—Abstracting, Bibliographies, Statistics*

378.111 USA ISSN 1097-8658
LB2342.75
A C U T A JOURNAL OF TELECOMMUNICATIONS IN HIGHER EDUCATION. Text in English. 1997. q. USD 80 to non-members; USD 60 to members (effective 2004). adv. **Document type:** *Academic/Scholarly.* **Description:** Focuses on telecommunications issues of significance to administrators, managers, and technical staff in higher education environments.
Published by: Association of College and University Telecommunications Administrators, 152 W Zandale Dr, Ste 200, Lexington, KY 40503-2486. TEL 606-278-3338, FAX 606-278-3268, pscott@acuta.org, http://www.acuta.org. Ed. Pat Scott. Pub. Jeri A Semer. Adv. contact Kevin Adkins.

378.155 420.07 USA ISSN 0001-0898
PE68.U5
A D E BULLETIN. Text in English. 1964. 3/yr. USD 27 to individuals; USD 30 to institutions (effective 2005). adv. bk.rev. charts; stat. reprint service avail. from PQC. **Document type:** *Academic/Scholarly.* **Description:** Presents articles and surveys dealing with professional, pedagogical, curricular, and departmental issues.
Related titles: Microform ed.: (from MIM, PQC).
Indexed: BibInd, CIJE, MLA-IB.
—BLDSC (0680.250000), IE, ingenta.
Published by: Association of Departments of English (Subsidiary of: Modern Language Association), 26 Broadway, 3rd fl, New York, NY 10004-1789. TEL 646-576-5137, FAX 646-458-0030, ade@mla.org, http://www.ade.org/bulletin/index.htm, http://www.ade.org/index.htm. Ed. David Laurence. Pub. Phyllis Franklin. R&P Marcia Reid. Adv. contact James Papp. Circ: 2,500. **Affiliate:** Modern Language Association of America.

E

378.155 407.11 USA ISSN 0148-7639
➤ **A D F L BULLETIN.** Text in English. 1969. 3/yr. USD 27 to individuals; USD 30 to libraries (effective 2005). adv. bk.rev. bibl.; tr.lit. reprint service avail. from PQC. **Document type:** *Academic/Scholarly.*
Formerly: Association of Departments of Foreign Languages. Bulletin (0148-8066)
Related titles: Microfiche ed.; Microfilm ed.: (from PQC).
Indexed: CIJE, L&LBA, MLA, MLA-IB, PSI, RASB.
—BLDSC (0680.470000), IE, ingenta.
Published by: Association of Departments of Foreign Languages (Subsidiary of: Modern Language Association), 26 Broadway, 3rd fl, New York, NY 10004-1789. TEL 646-576-5134, FAX 646-458-0030, adfl@mla.org, http://www.adfl.org/bulletin/bulletin_home.htm. Ed. Elizabeth Welles. Pub. Phyllis Franklin. R&P Marcia Reid. Adv. contact David Goldberg. Circ: 1,870. **Affiliate:** Modern Language Association.

➤ **A E J M C NEWS.** see *JOURNALISM*

➤ **A G H E EXCHANGE.** see *GERONTOLOGY AND GERIATRICS*

➤ **A I C P ROSTER.** see *HOUSING AND URBAN PLANNING*

378 USA ISSN 8756-6168
THE A I R PROFESSIONAL FILE. Text in English. 1978. q. free membership (effective 2005).
Published by: Association for Institutional Research, 222 Stone Bldg, Florida State University, Tallahassee, FL 32306-4462. TEL 850-644-4470, FAX 850-644-8824, air@mailer.fsu.edua, http://airweb.org/page.asp?page=57. Ed. Gerald W McLaughlin.

378.0085 GBR ISSN 0968-7769
LB1028.5
➤ **A L T - J.** (Association for Learning Technology Journal) Text in English. 1993. 3/yr. GBP 166, USD 248 combined subscription to institutions print & online eds. (effective 2006). 80 p./no. 1 cols./p.; **Document type:** *Journal, Academic/Scholarly.* **Description:** Devoted to research and good practice in the use of learning technologies in higher education.
Related titles: Online - full text ed.: ISSN 1741-1629. GBP 158, USD 236 to institutions (effective 2006) (from EBSCO Publishing, Gale Group, IngentaConnect, O C L C Online Computer Library Center, Inc., Swets Information Services).
Indexed: BrEdI, CPE, ERA, ETA, MEA, RHEA, SEA, SENA, SOMA, TEA.
—BLDSC (0802.404050), IE, ingenta. **CCC.**
Published by: (Association for Learning Technology), Routledge (Subsidiary of: Taylor & Francis Group), 4 Park Sq, Milton Park, Abingdon, Oxon OX14 4RN, United Kingdom. TEL 44-1235-828600, FAX 44-1235-829000, journals@routledge.com, http://www.tandf.co.uk/journals/titles/09687769.asp, http://www.routledge.com. Eds. Grainne Conole, Dr. Jane K Seale, Dr. Martin Oliver. Circ: 925 (paid).
Subscr. to: Taylor & Francis Ltd, Journals Customer Service, Rankine Rd, Basingstoke, Hants RG24 8PR, United Kingdom. TEL 44-1256-813000, FAX 44-1256-330245.

➤ **A M A T Y C REVIEW.** see *MATHEMATICS*

➤ **A N U REPORTER ONLINE.** see *COLLEGE AND ALUMNI*

378 USA
LB3223.3
A P P A: THE ASSOCIATION OF HIGHER EDUCATION FACILITIES OFFICERS. PROCEEDINGS OF THE ANNUAL MEETING. Text in English. 1929. a. price varies. adv. charts; illus. **Document type:** *Proceedings.*
Formerly (until 1992): Association of Physical Plant Administrators of Universities and Colleges. Proceedings of the Annual Meeting (0738-3835)
Published by: A P P A: The Association of Higher Education Facilities Officers, 1643 Prince St, Alexandria, VA 22314-2818. TEL 703-684-1446, FAX 703-549-2772. Ed. Medea Ranck. R&P Steve Glazner. Adv. contact Cotrenia Aytch. **Subscr. to:** PO Box 1201, Alexander, VA 22313-1201.

378 USA ISSN 1081-3985
A R A NEWSLETTER. Text in English. 1986. 2/yr. (Spring & Fall). USD 70 to members (effective 2000). adv. back issues avail. **Document type:** *Newsletter.* **Description:** For persons interested in Romanian art, literature, science and Romanian affairs.
Related titles: Online - full text ed.
Published by: (American Romanian Academy of Arts and Sciences), A R A Publications (Tempe), c/o Aleksandra Gruzinska, Ed, Foreign Languages Department, Arizona State University, P O Box 870202, Tempe, AZ 85287-0202. TEL 480-965-6281, FAX 480-965-0135, gruzinska@asu.edu, http://www.public.asu.edu/~gzl747. Ed., R&P Aleksandra Gruzinska TEL 408-965-3873. Circ: 250. **Subscr. to:** Mr. Miron Bonca, Treasurer, 3153 Country Club Dr, Costa Mesa, CA 92626.

A R I E L. (A Review of International English Literature) see *LITERATURE*

378.59 THA ISSN 0066-9695
A S A I H L SEMINAR REPORTS. Text in Thai. 1963. irreg. USD 6. **Document type:** *Academic/Scholarly.*
Published by: Association of Southeast Asian Institutions of Higher Learning, Ratasastra Bldg, Chulalongkorn University, Henri Dunant Rd, Bangkok, 10330, Thailand. TEL 66-2-251-6966, FAX 66-2-253-7909. Circ: 1,000.

A S E E PRISM. see *ENGINEERING*

378 USA ISSN 1551-6970
➤ **A S H E HIGHER EDUCATION REPORT SERIES.** Variant title: A S H E - E R I C Higher Education Reports. Text in English. 1971. bi-m. USD 185 domestic to institutions; USD 245 in Canada & Mexico to institutions; USD 296 elsewhere to institutions; USD 204 combined subscription domestic to institutions print & online eds.; USD 264 combined subscription in Canada & Mexico to institutions print & online eds.; USD 315 combined subscription elsewhere to institutions print & online eds. (effective 2006). index. back issues avail.; reprints avail. **Document type:** *Journal, Academic/Scholarly.* **Description:** Definitive analysis of tough higher education problems, based on thorough investigation of research, literature and institutional experiences.
Former titles (until 2004): A S H E - E R I C Higher Education Report Series (0884-0040); A S H E - E R I C Higher Education Research Report Series; A S H E - E R I C Higher Education Research Reports (0737-1292); (until 1982): A A H E - E R I C Higher Education Research Report Series (0737-1764); E R I C - A A H E Research Reports
Related titles: Microfiche ed.; Online - full content ed.: ISSN 1554-6306. USD 185 to institutions (effective 2006); Online - full text ed.: (from EBSCO Publishing, H.W. Wilson, O C L C Online Computer Library Center, Inc., Swets Information Services, Wiley InterScience).
Indexed: ABIn, DIP, EduInd, HEA, IBR, IBZ, SRI.
—BLDSC (1742.047900), IE, Infotrieve, ingenta. **CCC.**
Published by: (Association for the Study of Higher Education), Jossey-Bass Inc., Publishers (Subsidiary of: John Wiley & Sons, Inc.), 989 Market St, San Francisco, CA 94103-1741. TEL 415-433-1740, 888-378-2537, FAX 800-605-2665, 415-433-0499, jbsubs@jbp.com, http://www.josseybass.com/WileyCDA/WileyTitle/productCd-AEHE.html. Ed. Adriana J Kezar. Pub. Sue Lewis. Circ: 750 (paid).

378 USA
A S H E NEWSLETTER. Text in English. q. membership only. **Document type:** *Academic/Scholarly.*
Formerly: A S H E Notes
Published by: Association for the Study of Higher Education, c/o Center for International Higher Education, 207 Champion Hall, Boston College, Chestnut Hill, MA 02167. TEL 617-552-4236.

378.6216 EGY
A U C TODAY. Text in English. 1979. 3/yr. free. **Description:** Provides news of the University for alumni, friends and former faculty and staff.
Former titles: American University in Cairo. News; American University in Cairo. President's Review
Published by: American University in Cairo, 113 Sharia Kasr el Aini, Cairo, Egypt. TEL 20-2-354-2966, FAX 20-2-355-3565, auctoday@aucegypt.edu, http://aucpress.com.

A U P H A EXCHANGE. see *HEALTH FACILITIES AND ADMINISTRATION*

378.101 GBR ISSN 1468-5663
A U T LOOK. Text in English. 1962. 5/yr. free to members (effective 2005). adv. 32 p./no. 2 cols./p.; back issues avail. **Document type:** *Magazine, Academic/Scholarly.* **Description:** Covers issues relevant to university academic membership, especially professional and policy matters.
Formerly (until 1999): A U T Bulletin (0001-2823)
Indexed: SRRA.
Published by: Association of University Teachers, Egmonk House, 25-31 Tavistock Pl, London, WCIH 9UT, United Kingdom. TEL 44-20-76709700, FAX 44-20-76709799, publications@aut.org.uk, hq@aut.org.uk, http://www.aut.org.uk. Ed., R&P Zoe Stagg TEL 44-20-76709706. Adv. contact Lynne Jones TEL 44-151-3349802. Circ: 52,000 (controlled).

A W P JOB LIST. see *OCCUPATIONS AND CAREERS*

378 USA
A W U PIPELINE. Text in English. 1994. q. free. **Description:** Reports AWU corporate and program activities.
Published by: Associated Western Universities, Inc., 535 E. 4500 S., Ste. D120, Salt Lake Cty, UT 84107-2988. TEL 801-273-8948, FAX 801-277-5632, becky@awu.org. Ed. Becky McKean. Circ: 1,500.

378 USA ISSN 1086-4822
LA226
ABOUT CAMPUS; enriching the student learning experience. Text in English. 1996. bi-m. USD 145 domestic to institutions; USD 205 in Canada & Mexico to institutions; USD 256 elsewhere to institutions; USD 160 combined subscription domestic to institutions print & online eds.; USD 220 combined subscription in Canada & Mexico to institutions print & online eds.; USD 271 combined subscription elsewhere to institutions print & online eds. (effective 2006). bk.rev. Index. 32 p./no.; back issues avail.; reprints avail. **Document type:** *Journal, Academic/Scholarly.* **Description:** Offers thoughtful and challenging analysis, suggestions, resources, and debate on wide-ranging topics affecting student life and learning on campus.
Related titles: Online - full text ed.: ISSN 1536-0687. USD 145 to institutions (effective 2006) (from EBSCO Publishing, O C L C Online Computer Library Center, Inc., Swets Information Services, Wiley InterScience).
Indexed: CIJE, CPE, HEA.
—IE. **CCC.**
Published by: (American College Personnel Association), Jossey-Bass Inc., Publishers (Subsidiary of: John Wiley & Sons, Inc.), 989 Market St, San Francisco, CA 94103-1741. TEL 415-433-1740, FAX 415-433-0499, 415-433-0499, jbsubs@jbp.com, http://www.josseybass.com/cda/product/0,,ABC,00.html. Circ: 8,000 (paid).

378 USA ISSN 0190-2946
➤ **ACADEME.** Text in English. 1915. bi-m. USD 68 domestic; USD 72 foreign (effective 2005). adv. bk.rev. illus. index. back issues avail.; reprints avail. **Document type:** *Journal, Academic/Scholarly.* **Description:** Offers features on current topics and reports on developments in higher education, and reports on the business of the AAUP.

Incorporates (1967-1978): Academe (0001-3749); Former titles (until 1978): A A U P Bulletin (0001-026X); (until 1955): American Association of University Professors. Bulletin (0883-1610)
Related titles: Microform ed.: (from PMC, PQC); Online - full text ed.: (from EBSCO Publishing, Northern Light Technology, Inc., O C L C Online Computer Library Center, Inc., ProQuest Information & Learning).
Indexed: ABIn, ASCA, AbAn, AgeL, AmH&L, CIJE, CPE, CurCont, EAA, ERA, ETA, EduInd, HEA, HistAb, IPARL, MEA, MLA-IB, PAIS, RASB, RHEA, RI-1, RI-2, SEA, SENA, SOMA, SRI, SSCI, TEA.
—BLDSC (0570.467000), IDS, IE, Infotrieve, ingenta.
Published by: American Association of University Professors, 1012 14th St, N W, Ste 500, Washington, DC 20005-3465. TEL 202-737-5900, FAX 202-737-5526, aaup@aaup.org, http://www.aaup.org/academe.htm. R&P Wendi A Maloney TEL 202-737-5900 ext 3014. Adv. contact Tim McCormack. B&W page USD 1,865, color page USD 2,865. Circ: 45,000 (paid). **Dist. by:** Ingram Periodicals, PO Box 7000, La Vergne, TN 37086-7000. TEL 800-627-6247.

378.107 USA
ACADEME THIS WEEK. Text in English. 1994. w.
Media: Online - full content.
Published by: Chronicle of Higher Education, Inc., 1255 23rd St, NW, Ste 700, Washington, DC 20037. http://thisweek.chronicle.com.

378.12 USA ISSN 8750-7730
ACADEMIC LEADER; the newsletter for academic deans and department chairs. Text in English. 1985. m. USD 198 domestic; USD 202 in Canada; USD 208 elsewhere (effective 2005). adv. bk.rev. back issues avail. **Document type:** *Newsletter, Academic/Scholarly.*
Related titles: Online - full content ed.: USD 198 (effective 2005); Online - full text ed.: (from EBSCO Publishing, H.W. Wilson, O C L C Online Computer Library Center, Inc.).
Indexed: ABIn, EduInd.
—CCC.
Published by: Magna Publications, Inc., 2718 Dryden Dr, Madison, WI 53704. TEL 608-246-3590, FAX 608-246-3597, editor@magnapubs.com, http://www.magnapubs.com/pub/magnapubs_al. Ed. Rob Kelly. Pub. David Burns. Circ: 2,000 (paid).

378 USA ISSN 1086-1149
LB2341
ACADEMIC LEADERSHIP (MESA); journal for community and technical college leaders. Text in English. 1993. 3/yr. USD 60 domestic; USD 75 foreign (effective 2002). **Document type:** *Journal, Academic/Scholarly.* **Description:** Dedicated to disseminating research based and practical information to assist community and technical college leaders achieve academic excellence.
Published by: The Chair Academy, 145 N. Centennial Way, Mesa, AZ 85201. TEL 480-461-6270, FAX 480-461-6275, chair.academy@mcmail.maricopa.edu, http://www.mc.maricopa.edu/chair/journal/index.html. Ed. Jennifer Ramirez.

ACADEMIC MEDICINE. see *MEDICAL SCIENCES*

ACADEMIC PHYSICIAN AND SCIENTIST. see *MEDICAL SCIENCES*

ACADEMIC PSYCHIATRY. see *MEDICAL SCIENCES—Psychiatry And Neurology*

378.34 USA ISSN 0895-4852
AS30 CODEN: ACQUEO
➤ **ACADEMIC QUESTIONS.** Text in English. 1988. q. USD 70 to individuals print or online (effective 2004); USD 220 to institutions print or online; USD 77 combined subscription to individuals print & online; USD 242 combined subscription to institutions print & online (effective 2003). adv. bk.rev. reprint service avail. from PSC. **Document type:** *Journal, Academic/Scholarly.* **Description:** Explores interdisciplinary issues related to politics, ideology, and scholarship in higher education.
Related titles: Microform ed.: (from PQC); Online - full text ed.: A Q Online (from EBSCO Publishing, Florida Center for Library Automation, Gale Group, O C L C Online Computer Library Center, Inc., Swets Information Services).
Indexed: DIP, HEA, IBR, IBZ, PhilInd, SOPODA, SSA.
—CCC.
Published by: (National Association of Scholars), Transaction Publishers, 390 Campus Dr, Somerset, NJ 07830. TEL 888-999-6778, FAX 732-748-9801, trans@transactionpub.com, http://www.transactionpub.com. Ed. Bradford P Wilson. Pub. Mary Curtis. R&P Marlena Davidian TEL 732-445-2280 ext 100. Adv. contact Alicja Garbie. page USD 700; 5.25 x 8. Circ: 6,500.

➤ **ACADEMIC YEAR ABROAD.** see *EDUCATION—International Education Programs*

378 FIN ISSN 1455-1608
ACATIIMI. Text in Finnish. 1987. 10/yr. adv. back issues avail. **Document type:** *Magazine, Trade.*
Formerly (until 1997): Tieteentekijae (0784-6800)
Related titles: Online - full text ed.
Published by: Professoriliitto/Finnish Union of University Professors, Rautateilaeisenkatu 6, Helsinki, 00520, Finland. TEL 358-9-4250700, FAX 358-9-42507030, professoriliitto@professorilitto, http://www.acatiimi.fi/, http://www.professoriliitto.fi. Ed. Ann-Marie Rosloef. adv.: B&W page EUR 750, color page EUR 1,110; 174 x 250.

378 ITA ISSN 0393-859X
ACCADEMIA NAZIONALE DI SAN LUCA. ANNUARIO. Text in Italian. biennial.
Published by: Accademia Nazionale di San Luca, Piazza Dell' Accademia Di San Luca, 77, Rome, RM 00187, Italy. FAX 06-6790324.

ACCOUNTING AND FINANCE. see *BUSINESS AND ECONOMICS—Accounting*

ACCOUNTING EDUCATION. see *BUSINESS AND ECONOMICS—Accounting*

378.16 USA
ACCREDITATION FACT SHEET. Text in English. 1980. irreg. USD 6 per issue. **Description:** Information concerning accreditation criteria for private, nontraditional schools and colleges with history and general facts about accreditation.
Published by: National Association of Private Non-Traditional Schools and Colleges, 182 Thompson Rd, Grand Junction, CO 81503. TEL 303-243-5441. Ed. H Earl Heusser.

378.03 IRL
ACCREDITATION OF UNIVERSITIES AND DISTANT LEARNING UNIVERSITIES. Text in English. 1996. a. looseleaf. USD 450. **Document type:** *Newsletter, Academic/Scholarly.* **Description:** Provides guidelines for accrediting worldwide universities and Distance Learning Universities (DLUs).
Published by: Royal University, Ltd., 6 Lower Hatch St., Dublin, 2, Ireland. FAX 353-1-6686632. Ed. C V Ramasastry.

378 POL ISSN 0866-9279
ACTA UNIVERSITATIS WRATISLAVIENSIS. STUDIA I MATERIALY Z DZIEJOW UNIWERSYTETU WROCLAWSKIEGO. Text in Polish. 1989. irreg. price varies. **Document type:** *Academic/Scholarly.*
Indexed: RASB.
Published by: (Uniwersytet Wroclawski), Wydawnictwo Uniwersytetu Wroclawskiego Spolka z o.o., Pl Uniwersytecki 9-13, Wroclaw, 50-137, Poland. TEL 48-71-441006, FAX 48-71-402735. Eds. Teresa Kulak, Wojciech Wrzesinki.

378 USA ISSN 0001-7442
ACTION LINE (ANNAPOLIS). Variant title: M S T A Action Line. Text in English. 1968. 8/yr. free to members. adv. charts; illus. **Document type:** *Magazine, Trade.*
Published by: Maryland State Teachers Association, 140 Main St, Annapolis, MD 21401-2020. TEL 410-263-6600, FAX 410-263-3605, http://www.mstanea.org., http://www.msta.nea.org. Ed. Casey Newton. Circ: 51,000.

378 FRA ISSN 0065-177X
ACTION UNIVERSITAIRE. Text in French. 1970; N.S... m. bk.rev. **Description:** Forum for students, teachers and personnel at the University.
Published by: Union Nationale Inter-Universitaire, 8 rue de Musset, Paris, 75016, France. TEL 45-25-34-65. Ed. Frederic Deloffre. Circ: 45,000.

378.00285 GBR ISSN 1469-7874
LB2300
➤ **ACTIVE LEARNING IN HIGHER EDUCATION**; the journal of the Institute for Learning and Teaching. Text in English. 2000. 3/yr. GBP 46, USD 84 to individuals; GBP 269, USD 471 to institutions; GBP 280, USD 490 combined subscription to institutions print & online eds. (effective 2006). **Document type:** *Journal, Academic/Scholarly.* **Description:** Focuses on all aspects of developments, innovations and good practice in higher education teaching and learning worldwide, including the use of information and communication technologies.
Related titles: Online - full text ed.: ISSN 1741-2625. GBP 266, USD 466 to institutions (effective 2006) (from C S A, EBSCO Publishing, O C L C Online Computer Library Center, Inc., Sage Publications, Inc., Swets Information Services).
Indexed: ABIn, BrEdI, CPE, EAA, ERA, ETA, EduInd, MEA, MLA-IB, PsycInfo, PsycholAb, RHEA, SEA, SENA, SOMA, TEA.
—BLDSC (0676.031450), IE. **CCC.**
Published by: (Institute for Learning and Teaching), Sage Publications Ltd. (Subsidiary of: Sage Publications, Inc.), 1 Oliver's Yard, 55 City Rd, London, EC1 1SP, United Kingdom. TEL 44-20-73248500, FAX 44-20-73248600, info@sagepub.co.uk, http://www.sagepub.co.uk/journal.aspx?pid=105463. Ed. Lynne P Baldwin. **Subscr. in the Americas to:** Sage Publications, Inc., 2455 Teller Rd, Thousand Oaks, CA 91320. TEL 805-499-0721, FAX 805-499-0871, journals@sagepub.com.

➤ **THE ACUTA JOURNAL OF TELECOMMUNICATIONS IN HIGHER EDUCATION.** see *COMMUNICATIONS—Telephone And Telegraph*

378.12 USA ISSN 1078-5264
LB2843.P3
THE ADJUNCT ADVOCATE. Text in English. 1992. bi-m. USD 35 to individuals; USD 100 to institutions (effective 2004). adv. bk.rev. **Document type:** *Journal, Trade.* **Description:** For college educators, part-time faculty, and administrators focusing on issues of interest to and about adjunct or part-time college faculty.
Related titles: Online - full text ed.
Published by: Adjunct Advocate, Inc., PO Box 130117, Ann Arbor, MI 48113-0117. TEL 734-930-6854, FAX 734-665-9001. Ed. P.D. Lesko. Adv. contact P D Lesko. B&W page USD 2,660, color page USD 4,660; trim 11 x 8.5. Circ: 91,000.

ADMINISTRATIVE COMPENSATION SURVEY. see *BUSINESS AND ECONOMICS—Labor And Industrial Relations*

ADVANCES IN ACCOUNTING EDUCATION; teaching and curriculum innovations. see *BUSINESS AND ECONOMICS—Accounting*

ADVANCES IN HEALTH SCIENCES EDUCATION. see *MEDICAL SCIENCES*

AFFILIATES IN TRAINING. see *MEDICAL SCIENCES—Cardiovascular Diseases*

378.744 USA
AFRICAN-AMERICAN GRADUATES OF KENTUCKY DIRECTORY. Text in English. 1970. a. free. **Document type:** *Directory, Government.*
Formerly (until 1993): Black Graduates of Kentucky Directory
Published by: Kentucky Commission on Human Rights, 332 W Broadway, 7th Fl, Louisville, KY 40202. TEL 502-595-4024, FAX 502-595-4801. Ed. Eric W George. Circ: 3,000.

378.17 VEN ISSN 1315-3013
➤ **AGENDA ACADEMICA.** Text in Spanish. 1994. s-a. VEB 10,000 (effective 2005). adv. bk.rev. **Document type:** *Journal, Academic/Scholarly.* **Description:** Promotes intellectual work on academic topics done at the university, research on the modernization of universities, teaching innovations, and the improvement of quality in higher education.
Related titles: Online - full text ed.
Published by: (Sistema de Actualizacion Docente del Profesorado), Universidad Central de Venezuela, Vicerrectorado Academico, Ave. Neveri, Centro Los Chaguaramos, Piso 10, Apartado Postal 47149, Caracas, DF 1041-A, Venezuela. TEL 58-2-6629383, FAX 58-2-6627455, academia@rect.ucv.ve, sadpro@reacciun.ve, http://www.sadpro.ucv.ve/agenda. Ed. Eleazar Navaez. Pub., R&P Gladys Villaroel.

378 IND ISSN 0044-6734
AGRA UNIVERSITY. BULLETIN✶. Text in English, Hindi. 1970. q. bk.rev. bibl.; charts; stat. **Document type:** *Bulletin.*
Published by: Agra University, Agra, Uttar Pradesh 282 004, India. Ed. Rajeshwar Prasad.

330.0711 POL ISSN 1640-0550
AKADEMIA EKONOMICZNA, KRAKOW. BIBLIOTEKA GLOWNA. BIULETYN INFORMACYJNY (ONLINE EDITION). Text in English, Polish. 1993. irreg., latest vol.25, 2004. free. **Document type:** *Bulletin, Internal.*
Formerly (until 1997): Akademia Ekonomiczna, Krakow. Biblioteka Glowna. Biuletyn Informacyjny (Print Edition) (1640-0542)
Media: Online - full content.
Published by: Akademia Ekonomiczna w Krakowie, Biblioteka Glowna/Main Library of the Cracow University of Economics, ul Rakowicka 27, Krakow, 31510, Poland. TEL 48-12-2935009, FAX 48-12-2935010, agogut@bibl.ae.krakow.pl, http://kangur.ae.krakow.pl/Biblioteka/Biuletyn/. Circ: 250.

378.1 DEU ISSN 0178-2479
AKADEMISCHE REDEN UND KOLLOQUIEN. Text in German. 1985. irreg., latest vol.21, 2003. price varies. **Document type:** *Monographic series, Academic/Scholarly.*
Published by: Universitaetsbibliothek Erlangen-Nuernberg, Universitaetsstr. 4, Erlangen, 91054, Germany. TEL 49-9131-8522160, FAX 49-9131-8529309, direktion@bib.uni-erlangen.de, http://www.ub.uni-erlangen.de.

378 SWE ISSN 0283-0345
AKADEMIX; nyhetsbrev fraan SACO studentraad. Text in Swedish. 1985. 8/yr.
Published by: S A C O - Sveriges Akademikers Centralorganisation, Fack 2206, Stockholm, 10315, Sweden.

378.761 USA
ALABAMA. COMMISSION ON HIGHER EDUCATION. ANNUAL REPORT✶. Text in English. 1973. a. free. illus. reprints avail. **Document type:** *Government.* **Description:** Highlights activities of the Higher Education Commission on academic and financial aid issues.
Formerly (until 1978): Alabama. Commission on Higher Education. Biennial Report to the Governor and the Legislature (0095-1285)
Published by: Commission on Higher Education, PO Box 302000, Montgomery, AL 36103. TEL 205-269-2700, FAX 205-240-3349. Ed. Henry J Hector.

E

▼ *new title* ➤ *refereed* ✶ *unverified* ♦ *full entry avail.*

378 PER ISSN 1021-9633
AS88.L77
ALMA MATER. Text in Spanish. a.
Related titles: Online - full text ed.: ISSN 1609-9036.
Published by: Universidad Nacional Mayor de San Marcos, Direccion de Biblioteca y Publicaciones, Rep. de Chile 295, Of. 508, Lima, Peru. http://www.unmsm.edu.pe/.

378.05 POL ISSN 1427-1176
LF4203
ALMA MATER; kwartalnik Uniwersytetu Jagiellonskiego. Text in Polish. 1996. q. 70 p./no.;
Related titles: Online - full content ed.: ISSN 1689-0426.
Published by: Wydawnictwo Uniwersytetu Jagiellonskiego/ Jagiellonian University Press, ul Grodzka 26, Krakow, 31044, Poland. TEL 48-12-4312364, FAX 48-12-4301995, alma@jubileum.uj.edu.pl, wydaw@if.uj.edu.pl, http://www3.uj.edu.pl/alma/alma/index.html, http://www.wuj.pl. Ed. Adam Michajlow.

ALPHA COMMUNICATIONS MONTHLY. see *COMMUNICATIONS*

378.17 USA
ALVERNO MAGAZINE. Text in English. 1983. 2/yr. free. **Document type:** *Academic/Scholarly.* **Description:** Explores issues of teaching and learning in higher education.
Published by: Alverno College, 3401 S 39th St, Box 343922, Milwaukee, WI 53234-3922. TEL 414-382-6166, FAX 414-382-6167. R&P Kathleen A Mulvey. Circ: 17,000.

378.12 USA ISSN 0731-602X
AMERICAN ASSOCIATION OF COLLEGES FOR TEACHER EDUCATION. BRIEFS. Text in English. 1980. 17/yr. USD 30 domestic; USD 40 foreign; USD 15 to students (effective 2005). adv. illus. back issues avail. **Document type:** *Newsletter, Trade.* **Description:** Association and member news for deans and professors of education.
Supersedes: American Association of Colleges for Teacher Education. Legislative Briefs; American Association of Colleges for Teacher Education. Bulletin (0002-7413)
Published by: American Association of Colleges for Teacher Education, 1307 New York Ave, NW. Ste 300, Washington, DC 20005-4701. TEL 202-293-2450, FAX 202-457-8095, emf@aacte.nche.edu, http://www.aacte.org. Ed. Kristin McCabe. R&P Deborah Hinrichs. Adv. contact Danielle Underferth. B&W page USD 320. Circ: 6,400 (paid).

378.12 USA ISSN 0516-9313
LB1715
AMERICAN ASSOCIATION OF COLLEGES FOR TEACHER EDUCATION. DIRECTORY. Text in English. a. USD 50. **Document type:** *Directory.* **Description:** Documents members, committee and board of directors member's list.
Published by: American Association of Colleges for Teacher Education, 1307 New York Ave, NW. Ste 300, Washington, DC 20005-4701. TEL 202-293-2450, FAX 202-457-8095, nnc@aacte.nche.edu, http://www.aacte.org. R&P Deborah Hinrichs.

AMERICAN ASSOCIATION OF ENGINEERING SOCIETIES. ENGINEERING WORKFORCE COMMISSION. SALARIES OF ENGINEERS IN EDUCATION (YEAR). see *ENGINEERING*

THE AMERICAN BIOLOGY TEACHER. see *BIOLOGY*

378.145 USA ISSN 1079-7599
AMERICAN COMMUNITY COLLEGES. Text in English. 1984. irreg. (10th ed.). USD 149.95 per issue (effective 2004). 920 p./no.;
Formerly (until 1984): American Community, Technical, and Junior Colleges (0749-2650)
Published by: (American Council on Education), Oryx Press (Subsidiary of: Greenwood Publishing Group Inc.), 4041 N Central Ave, Phoenix, AZ 85012-3397. TEL 602-265-2651, FAX 602-265-6250, info@oryxpress.com, http://www.oryxpress.com. Ed. Robert H Atwell.

378.12 USA ISSN 0065-809X
Z5055.U49
AMERICAN DOCTORAL DISSERTATIONS. Text in English. 1934. a. **Document type:** *Academic/Scholarly.* **Description:** Lists dissertations accepted by U.S. and Canadian universities.
Former titles (until 1963): Index to American Doctoral Dissertations (1046-9230); (until 1955): Doctoral Dissertations Accepted by American Universities (1046-9222)
Related titles: CD-ROM ed.: (from ProQuest Information & Learning); Microfiche ed.; Online - full text ed.: (from Data-Star).
—BLDSC (0812.770000), Linda Hall.
Published by: (Association of Research Libraries), ProQuest Information & Learning, 300 N Zeeb Rd., PO Box 1346, Ann Arbor, MI 48106-1346. TEL 313-761-4700, 800-521-0600, FAX 800-864-0019.

378 USA ISSN 0278-6990
LA227.3
THE AMERICAN FRESHMAN: NATIONAL NORMS (YEAR). Text in English. 1966. a., latest 2004. USD 25 per issue (effective 2005).
Formerly (until 1971): National Norms for Entering College Freshmen
Published by: University of California at Los Angeles, Higher Education Research Institute, 3005 Moore Hl, Los Angeles, CA 90095-1521. TEL 310-825-1925, FAX 310-206-2228, heri@ucla.edu, http://www.gseis.ucla.edu/heri/american_freshman.html, http://www.gseis.ucla.edu/heri/heri.

AMERICAN JOURNAL OF PHARMACEUTICAL EDUCATION. see *PHARMACY AND PHARMACOLOGY*

AMERICAN MEDICAL ASSOCIATION. GRADUATE MEDICAL EDUCATION DIRECTORY (YEARS). see *EDUCATION—Guides To Schools And Colleges*

AMERICAN SCHOOL & UNIVERSITY; shaping facilities & business decisions. see *EDUCATION—School Organization And Administration*

AMERICAN UNIVERSITIES AND COLLEGES. see *EDUCATION—Guides To Schools And Colleges*

378.5695 JOR
ANBA AL-JAMI'AH/JORDAN UNIVERSITY NEWS. Text in Arabic. 1971. m. free. **Document type:** *Newsletter.*
Published by: Jordan University, Department of Cultural and Public Relations, P O Box 1682, Amman, 11943, Jordan. TEL 962-6-843555, FAX 962-6-840150, TELEX 21629 UNVJ JO, http://www.ju.edu.jo/publications/aljami.htm. Ed. Mohammad Khair Mamser. Circ: 3,000.

378 USA ISSN 0882-7133
ANNUAL DEGARMO LECTURES. Text in English. 1975. a. price varies. **Document type:** *Monographic series.*
Formerly: DeGarmo Lectures
Published by: Society of Professors of Education, c/o Dr Robert Morris, Dept of Ed Ldshp, UWG, 1600 Maple St, Carrollton, GA 30118-5160. TEL 770-836-4426, FAX 770-736-4646. R&P Robert C Morris.

378.33 USA ISSN 0066-4049
AS911.A2
ANNUAL REGISTER OF GRANT SUPPORT; a directory of funding resources. Text in English. 1967. a., latest vol.38, 2005. USD 249 (effective 2006). index. 1500 p./no.; **Document type:** *Directory, Trade.* **Description:** Offers a guide to more than 3,500 programs offering billions of dollars in grant support. Shows how to unlock the funding potential of these sources. Organized by 11 major subject areas with 61 specific areas.
Formerly: Grant Data Quarterly (0436-3159)
—CCC.
Published by: Information Today, Inc., 143 Old Marlton Pike, Medford, NJ 08055-8750. TEL 609-654-6266, FAX 609-654-4309, custserv@infotoday.com, http://www.infotoday.com.

378.1982 USA ISSN 1061-2947
LC3727
ANNUAL STATUS REPORT ON MINORITIES IN HIGHER EDUCATION. Text in English. a. USD 26.95 to members; USD 29.95 to non-members (effective 2005).
Published by: (Office of Minorities in Higher Education), American Council on Education, Office of Research, One Dupont Circle, Washington, DC 20036. TEL 202-939-9380, FAX 202-833-4760.

378 ITA ISSN 0393-6368
L935
ANNUARIO D E A DELLE UNIVERSITA E ISTITUTI DI STUDIO E RICERCA IN ITALIA/D E A DIRECTORY OF UNIVERSITIES, SCIENTIFIC AND CULTURAL INSTITUTIONS IN ITALY. Text in Italian. 1983. a. USD 135. adv. bk.rev. **Document type:** *Directory.*
Related titles: CD-ROM ed.: Annuario D E A delle Universita e Istituti di Studio e Ricerca in Italia (version D). ISSN 1591-4054. 1997. USD 135 (effective 2001); Annuario D E A delle Universita e Istituti di Studio e Ricerca in Italia (version M). ISSN 1593-2362.
Published by: D E A Editrice, Via Lima, 28, Rome, RM 00198, Italy. TEL 39-06-8551441, FAX 39-06-8543228, deanet@deanet.it, http://www.deanet.it. R&P Anna Ligi TEL 39-06-8419801. Adv. contact Gabriella Gerboni TEL 39-06-8417564. Circ: 2,000.

ANSAETZE; E S G - Nachrichten. see *RELIGIONS AND THEOLOGY*

378.2 USA
ANTIOCH NEW ENGLAND NOTES. Text in English. 1973. 2/yr. bk.rev. back issues avail. **Document type:** *Newsletter, Academic/Scholarly.* **Description:** Alumini newsletter for practice-oriented master's and doctoral programs for adult learners.
Published by: Antioch New England Graduate School, Department of Environmental Studies, 40 Avon St, Keene, NH 03431-3516. TEL 603-357-3122, FAX 603-357-0718, ebelleisle@antiochne.edu. Ed. Elizabeth Belle Isle. Circ: 7,500 (controlled).

378.007 807 USA ISSN 1059-1133
APPROACHES TO TEACHING WORLD LITERATURE. Text in English. 1986. irreg. price varies. back issues avail. **Document type:** *Monographic series, Academic/Scholarly.* **Description:** Compiles within each volume various points of view on teaching a literary subject, either a work or a writer, to undergraduate students.
Indexed: MLA-IB.
—BLDSC (1580.560000), IE, ingenta.
Published by: (Modern Language Association of America), Modern Language Association, Book Publications Program, 26 Broadway, 3rd Fl, New York, NY 10004-1789. TEL 646 576-5000, FAX 646 458-0030, evans@mla.org, http://www.mla.org/store/CID39. Ed. Martha Noel Evans.

APPROVED COURSES FOR ACCOUNTANCY EDUCATION. see *BUSINESS AND ECONOMICS—Accounting*

378 JPN ISSN 0493-4342
AS552.T685
AREA AND CULTURE STUDIES. Text in Japanese. 1951. a. per issue exchange basis. **Document type:** *Monographic series.* **Description:** Faculty member's monographs on various cultures in the world, especially on languages and literatures.
Formerly: Tokyo University of Foreign Studies. Summary (0082-4844)
Indexed: MLA-IB, RASB.
Published by: Tokyo University of Foreign Studies/Tokyo Gaikogugo Daigaku, 4-51-21 Nishigahara, Kita-ku, Tokyo, 114-0024, Japan. Circ: 1,000.

ART, DESIGN & COMMUNICATION IN HIGHER EDUCATION. see *ART*

ARTS AND HUMANITIES IN HIGHER EDUCATION; an international journal of theory, research and practice. see *HUMANITIES: COMPREHENSIVE WORKS*

378 JPN
ASAHIKAWA NATIONAL COLLEGE OF TECHNOLOGY. JOURNAL. Text in Japanese. 1964. a. **Document type:** *Journal, Academic/Scholarly.*
Formerly: Asahikawa Kogyo Koto Senmon Gakko kenkyu Hobun/Asahikawa Technical College. Journal (0389-9306)
Indexed: MathR, MathSciNet.
—BLDSC (4701.290000).
Published by: Asahikawa National College of Technology, Syunkoudai 2-2-1-6, Asahikawa, Hokkaido 071-8142 , Japan. TEL 81-166-558000, FAX 81-166-558082, http://www.asahikawa-nct.ac.jp/.

378.016 USA ISSN 1077-114X
ASIA - PACIFIC EXCHANGE JOURNAL. Variant title: A P Ex - J. Text in English. 1994. s-a. **Description:** For college faculty, staff, and administrators who are developing or promoting international, multicultural education programs, courses, or activities.
Related titles: Online - full text ed.: A P E X - J.
Published by: University of Hawaii, Kapiolani Community College jamess@hawaii.edu, listserv@uhccvm.uhcc.hawaii.edu, http://leahi.kcc.hawaii.edu/pub/apexj/.

378 GBR ISSN 0260-2938
CODEN: AEHEED
➤ **ASSESSMENT & EVALUATION IN HIGHER EDUCATION;** an international journal. Text in English. 1976. bi-m. GBP 990, USD 1,716 combined subscription to institutions print & online eds. (effective 2006). adv. bk.rev. reprint service avail. from PQC,PSC. **Document type:** *Journal, Academic/Scholarly.* **Description:** All aspects of assessment and evaluation relevant to the generalist in higher education.
Formerly: Assessment in Higher Education (0307-1367)
Related titles: Microfiche ed.; Online - full text ed.: ISSN 1469-297X. GBP 941, USD 1,630 to institutions (effective 2006) (from EBSCO Publishing, Gale Group, IngentaConnect, Northern Light Technology, Inc., O C L C Online Computer Library Center, Inc., ProQuest Information & Learning, Swets Information Services).
Indexed: BrEdI, CIJE, CPE, EAA, ERA, ETA, HEA, HECAB, MEA, PsycInfo, PsycholAb, RASB, RHEA, SEA, SENA, SOMA, SOPODA, TEA, WBA, WMB.
—BLDSC (1746.637000), IE, Infotrieve, ingenta. **CCC.**
Published by: (University of Bath, School of Education), Routledge (Subsidiary of: Taylor & Francis Group), 4 Park Sq, Milton Park, Abingdon, Oxon OX14 4RN, United Kingdom. TEL 44-1235-828600, FAX 44-1235-829000, info@routledge.co.uk, http://www.tandf.co.uk/journals/titles/02602938.asp, http://www.routledge.com. Ed. William Scott. Circ: 200. **Subscr. in N. America to:** Taylor & Francis Inc., Customer Services Dept, 325 Chestnut St, 8th Fl, Philadelphia, PA 19106. TEL 215-625-8900, 800-354-1420, FAX 215-625-8914, customerservice@taylorandfrancis.com; **Subscr. to:** Taylor & Francis Ltd, Journals Customer Service, Rankine Rd, Basingstoke, Hants RG24 8PR, United Kingdom. TEL 44-1256-813000, FAX 44-1256-330245, enquiry@tandf.co.uk.

E

378.007 USA ISSN 1041-6099
LB2822.75
ASSESSMENT UPDATE; progress, trends, and practices in higher education. Text in English. 1989. bi-m. USD 140 domestic to institutions; USD 200 in Canada & Mexico to institutions; USD 251 elsewhere to institutions; USD 154 combined subscription domestic to institutions print & online eds.; USD 214 combined subscription in Canada & Mexico to institutions print & online eds.; USD 265 combined subscription elsewhere to institutions print & online eds. (effective 2006). bk.rev. Index. 16 p./no.; back issues avail. **Document type:** *Newsletter, Academic/Scholarly.* **Description:** Offers academic leaders up-to-date information and practical advice on conducting assessments in a range of areas, including student learning and outcomes, faculty instruction, academic programs and curricula, student services, and overall institutional functioning.
Related titles: Microform ed.: (from PQC); Online - full text ed.: ISSN 1536-0725. USD 140 to institutions (effective 2006) (from EBSCO Publishing, O C L C Online Computer Library Center, Inc., Swets Information Services, Wiley InterScience).
Indexed: HEA.
—IE. **CCC.**
Published by: Jossey-Bass Inc., Publishers (Subsidiary of: John Wiley & Sons, Inc.), 989 Market St, San Francisco, CA 94103-1741. TEL 415-433-1740, FAX 415-433-0499, jbsubs@jbp.com, http://www.josseybass.com/cda/product/0,,AU,00.html. Ed. Trudy W Banta. Pub. Sue Lewis. R&P Lorri Wimer TEL 415-433-1740. Circ: 1,100 (paid).

ASSOCIACAO DOS ANTIGOS ALUNOS DO COLEGIO MILITAR. REVISTA. see *MILITARY*

378 USA ISSN 0066-8729
ASSOCIATED COLLEGES OF ILLINOIS. REPORT. Text in English. a. charts; illus.; stat.
Published by: Associated Colleges of Illinois, 20 N. Wacker Dr., Ste. 1456, Chicago, IL 60606-2902. TEL 312-263-2391, FAX 312-263-3424.

378 USA
ASSOCIATED WESTERN UNIVERSITIES. PROGRAM GUIDE. Text in English. biennial. **Document type:** *Corporate.*
Former titles: Associated Western Universities. Program Report; Associated Western Universities. Biennial Report; Associated Western Universities. Annual Report (0066-877X)
Published by: Associated Western Universities, Inc., 535 E. 4500 S., Ste. D120, Salt Lake Cty, UT 84107-2988. FAX 801-277-5632. Ed. Thomas G Squires.

378.158 USA
ASSOCIATION FOR CONTINUING HIGHER EDUCATION. PROCEEDINGS. Text in English. 1939. a. USD 17 in North America; USD 20 elsewhere (effective 2001). **Document type:** *Proceedings.*
Formerly: Association of University Evening Colleges. Proceedings (0066-9741)
—BLDSC (6841.324000).
Published by: Association for Continuing Higher Education, Inc., Community College of Rhode Island, 400 East Ave, Warwick, RI 02886-1807. TEL 843-574-6658, FAX 803-574-6470. R&P Irene Barrineau. Circ: 1,500.

378 USA
ASSOCIATION FOR EDUCATORS AND COUNSELORS IN GOVERNMENT. NEWSLETTER✶. Text in English. 1978. q. USD 20; USD 25 foreign. adv. bk.rev. charts; stat. **Document type:** *Newsletter.* **Description:** Focuses on professional counseling issues for those employed in government and the military; provides professional development and networking information for members and others.
Formerly (until 1994): Military Educators and Counselors Association Newsletter
Published by: Association for Counselors and Educators in Government (ACEG), 5999 Stevenson A, Alexandria, VA 22394. Ed. Mary F Koss. Circ: 900.

378.07 USA
ASSOCIATION FOR PROFESSIONAL EDUCATION FOR MINISTRY. REPORT OF THE BIENNIAL MEETING. Text in English. 1950. biennial. USD 10.
Published by: Association for Professional Education for Ministry, c/o Oliver Williams, Pres, University of Notre Dame, Notre Dame, IN 46556. TEL 219-239-5000. Ed. Gaylord Noyce. Circ: 400. **Subscr. to:** Joseph Kelly, Treas, St Bernard s Seminary, 2260 Lake Ave, Rochester, NY 14612.

378.079 USA
ASSOCIATION OF ADVANCED RABBINICAL AND TALMUDIC SCHOOLS. ACCREDITATION COMMISSION. HANDBOOK. Text in English. a. **Description:** Accreditation standards.
Published by: Association of Advanced Rabbinical and Talmudic Schools, 175 Fifth Ave, New York, NY 10010. TEL 212-477-0950, FAX 212-533-5335.

378.6 GHA
ASSOCIATION OF AFRICAN UNIVERSITIES. ANNUAL REPORT. Text in English. a. free. **Document type:** *Corporate.* **Description:** Publishes information about the implementation of AAU's projects and programs during the year.
Published by: Association of African Universities, PO Box 5744, Accra - North, Ghana. info@aau.org. Ed. Yawo Assigbley.

ASSOCIATION OF AFRICAN UNIVERSITIES. BIBLIOGRAPHY ON HIGHER EDUCATION IN AFRICA. see *EDUCATION—Abstracting, Bibliographies, Statistics*

378.6 GHA
ASSOCIATION OF AFRICAN UNIVERSITIES. C O R E V I P PROCEEDINGS. (Conference of Rectors, Vice-Chancellors and Presidents) Text in English. biennial. free. **Document type:** *Proceedings, Academic/Scholarly.* **Description:** Contains information about the proceedings of the Conference of Rectors, Vice-Chancellors and Presidents of African universities, which is held every two years for African leaders and partners in higher education to reflect on the performance of universities in Africa and to consider appropriate measures for their revitalization.
Published by: Association of African Universities, PO Box 5744, Accra - North, Ghana. info@aau.org. Ed. Yawo Assigbley.

378.6 GHA
ASSOCIATION OF AFRICAN UNIVERSITIES. GUIDE TO HIGHER EDUCATION IN AFRICA. Text in English. biennial. USD 57 per vol. (effective 2000). **Document type:** *Directory.* **Description:** Contains general information about African universities, including principal officers, academic staff, faculties and institutes, degrees, certificates and diplomas awarded, duration of studies, and admission requirements.
Supersedes: A A U Handbook
Published by: (International Association of Universities FRA), Association of African Universities, PO Box 5744, Accra - North, Ghana. info@aau.org. Eds. Claudine Langlois, Yawo Assigbley.

378.6 GHA
ASSOCIATION OF AFRICAN UNIVERSITIES. REPORT OF THE GENERAL CONFERENCE. Text in English. 1967. quadrennial. free. **Document type:** *Proceedings, Academic/Scholarly.* **Description:** Carries information on the proceedings of the AAU General Conference, which brings together member universities, regional organizations, donors, and international organizations to discuss problems facing higher education in Africa and how to solve these problems.
Published by: Association of African Universities, PO Box 5744, Accra - North, Ghana. Ed. Yawo Assigbley.

ASSOCIATION OF AMERICAN LAW SCHOOLS. NEWSLETTER. see *LAW*

ASSOCIATION OF AMERICAN MEDICAL COLLEGES. PROCEEDINGS OF THE ANNUAL CONFERENCE. RESEARCH IN MEDICAL EDUCATION. see *MEDICAL SCIENCES*

378.07 GBR ISSN 0952-6889
ASSOCIATION OF CHRISTIANS IN HIGHER EDUCATION. FORUM. Text in English. a. GBP 14 (effective 2001). bk.rev. back issues avail. **Document type:** *Journal, Academic/Scholarly.*
Formerly (until 1987): University Staffs' Christian Fellowship Broadsheet (0268-2826)
Published by: (Association of Christians in Higher Education), Universities and Colleges Christian Fellowship, 38 De Montfort St, Leicster, LE1 7GP, United Kingdom. TEL 44-116-255-1700, FAX 44-116-255-5672, ache@uccf.org.uk. Ed. Gwynne Davies. R&P Patricia Deacon.

378.101 USA ISSN 0004-5659
L13.A6994
ASSOCIATION OF COLLEGE UNIONS - INTERNATIONAL. BULLETIN. Text in English. 1933. bi-m. USD 50 domestic to libraries; USD 65 foreign to libraries; USD 10 newsstand/cover; free to members (effective 2005). adv. bk.rev. charts; illus. **Document type:** *Trade.* **Description:** Publishes articles for college union and student activities personnel dealing with program, operations, and student development.
Related titles: Microfiche ed.
Indexed: HEA.
Published by: Association of College Unions - International, 120 W Seventh St, Ste 200, Bloomington, IN 47404. TEL 812-855-8550, FAX 812-855-0162, acui@indiana.edu, http://acuiweb.org. Ed., R&P Chad R Sievers TEL 812-855-8480. Pub. Marshar Herman Betzen. Adv. contact Gerry Van Treeck. Circ: 4,500.

378 USA
ASSOCIATION OF COLLEGE UNIONS - INTERNATIONAL. DIRECTORY & CATALOG. Text in English. a. USD 100 to non-members (effective 1999). adv. **Document type:** *Directory, Trade.* **Description:** Lists the names, addresses, and telephone numbers of all individual, institutional, honarary, subscriber, and affiliate members, along with ACUI officers. Describes publications, videotapes, and microfiche available for sale.
Media: Online - full content.
Published by: Association of College Unions - International, 120 W Seventh St, Ste 200, Bloomington, IN 47404. TEL 812-855-8550, FAX 812-855-0162, acui@indiana.edu, i, http://acuiweb.org. Pub. Marsha Herman Betzen. R&P Ann H Vest. Adv. contact Robb McPhail.

378 USA ISSN 0004-5667
ASSOCIATION OF COLLEGE UNIONS - INTERNATIONAL. UNION WIRE. Text in English. 1968. bi-m. membership. bk.rev. **Document type:** *Newsletter.* **Description:** Lists building projects, conferences and new members.
Published by: Association of College Unions - International, 120 W Seventh St, Ste 200, Bloomington, IN 47404. TEL 812-855-8550, FAX 812-855-0162, acui@indiana.edu, http://unionwire.acuiweb.org, http://acuiweb.org. Ed. Chad R Sievers TEL 812-855-8480. Pub. Marsha Herman Betzen. Circ: 1,800.

378 GBR ISSN 0307-2274
LA637
ASSOCIATION OF COMMONWEALTH UNIVERSITIES. ANNUAL REPORT OF THE COUNCIL TOGETHER WITH THE ACCOUNTS OF THE ASSOCIATION. Text in English. 1964. a. free (effective 2003). 52 p./no.; **Document type:** *Corporate.* **Description:** Reviews association activities over the previous year.
Formerly: Association of Commonwealth Universities. Report of the Council Together with the Accounts of the Association (0571-6241)
Published by: Association of Commonwealth Universities, John Foster House, 36 Gordon Square, London, WC1H 0, United Kingdom. TEL 44-20-73806700, FAX 44-20-73872655, info@acu.ac.uk, http://www.acu.ac.uk. Ed. Sarah Cripps.

378.12 GBR
ASSOCIATION OF COMMONWEALTH UNIVERSITIES. WHO'S WHO (YEAR). Variant title: Who's Who (Year). Text in English. 1988. every 30 mos. GBP 25 per issue (effective 2003). **Document type:** *Directory.* **Description:** Contains detailed bibliographical notes on over 450 executive heads of institutions which are members of the Association of Commonwealth Universities.
Former titles (until 2001): (Year) Who's Who of Executive Heads: Vice-Chancellors, Presidents, Principals, Rectors (1463-4198); (until 1998): Who's Who of Vice-Chancellors, Presidents and Rectors of Commonwealth Universities (1362-4628)
Published by: Association of Commonwealth Universities, John Foster House, 36 Gordon Square, London, WC1H 0, United Kingdom. TEL 44-20-73806700, FAX 44-20-73872655, s.kirkland@acu.ac.uk, info@acu.ac.uk, http://www.acu.ac.uk/publications. Ed., R&P, Adv. contact Sue Kirkland TEL 44-20-73806700.

378.072 USA ISSN 1053-8941
LC493
ASSOCIATION OF JESUIT COLLEGES AND UNIVERSITIES AND JESUIT SECONDARY EDUCATION ASSOCIATION DIRECTORY. Text in English. 1970. a. USD 10. **Document type:** *Directory.*
Published by: Association of Jesuit Colleges and Universities, 1 Dupont Cir, N W, Ste 405, Washington, DC 20036-1110. TEL 202-862-9893. Ed. George Chen. Circ: 2,500.

378 GBR ISSN 0964-4229
ASSOCIATION OF OPEN UNIVERSITY GRADUATES. JOURNAL. Text in English. 1991. a.
—BLDSC (4705.030000).
Published by: Association of Open University Graduates, RAF Hut, Walton Hall, Milton Keynes, MK7 6AA, United Kingdom. TEL 44-1908-653316, http://www.ougrads.org.uk, FAX 44-1908-638130, aoug@open.ac.uk.

378.54 THA ISSN 0066-9687
L961.A2
ASSOCIATION OF SOUTHEAST ASIAN INSTITUTIONS OF HIGHER LEARNING. HANDBOOK: SOUTHEAST ASIAN INSTITUTIONS OF HIGHER LEARNING. Text in English. 1966. triennial. USD 55. **Document type:** *Directory.* **Description:** Covers member institutions in Brunei, Hong Kong, Indonesia, Malaysia, Philippines, Singapore, Thailand, Vietnam and associate members in Australia, Japan, Canada, New Zealand, Sweden and the United States. Includes name, address, phone, chief officers, faculties and deans, libraries, courses, fees, publications, and more.
Published by: Association of Southeast Asian Institutions of Higher Learning, Ratasastra Bldg, Chulalongkorn University, Henri Dunant Rd, Bangkok, 10330, Thailand. TEL 66-2-251-6966, FAX 66-2-253-7909. Ed. Ninnat Olanvoravuth. Circ: 1,500.

378.59 THA ISSN 0572-4325
ASSOCIATION OF SOUTHEAST ASIAN INSTITUTIONS OF HIGHER LEARNING. NEWSLETTER. Text in Thai. 1969. s-a. USD 5. **Document type:** *Newsletter.*
Published by: Association of Southeast Asian Institutions of Higher Learning, Ratasastra Bldg, Chulalongkorn University, Henri Dunant Rd, Bangkok, 10330, Thailand. TEL 66-2-251-6966, FAX 66-2-253-7909. Circ: 1,500.

ASSOCIATION OF TEACHERS OF JAPANESE. NEWSLETTER. see *LINGUISTICS*

378 USA ISSN 0066-975X
ASSOCIATION OF UNIVERSITY SUMMER SESSIONS. SUMMARY OF REPORTS. Text in English. 1919. a. membership only.
Formerly: Association of Summer Session Deans and Directors. Summary of Reports

E

▼ *new title* ➤ *refereed* ✶ *unverified* ♦ *full entry avail.*

Published by: Association of University Summer Sessions, Office of Summer Sessions and Special Programs, Indiana University, Bloomington, IN 47405. TEL 812-855-5048, FAX 812-855-3815. Ed. Leslie J Coyne. Circ: 50.

378 IDN ISSN 0126-1584
ATMA JAYA RESEARCH CENTRE. NEWSLETTER. Text in English. 1975. bi-m. illus. **Document type:** *Newsletter.*
Published by: Atma Jaya Research Centre/Pusat Penelitian Atma Jaya, Jalan Jenderal Sudirman 51, PO Box 2639, Jakarta, 10001, Indonesia.

340 378 AUS ISSN 1327-0583
KVC46
THE AUSTRALASIAN LEGAL EDUCATION YEARBOOK. Text in English. a. AUD 50 domestic; AUD 54.50 in Asia & the Pacific; AUD 56.50 elsewhere (effective 2000). stat. **Document type:** *Directory.* **Description:** Provides statistical and other information on legal education and professional training in Australia, New Zealand, and Papua New Guinea.
Published by: Centre for Legal Education, c/o Faculty of Law, University of Newcastle, Callaghan, NSW 2308, Australia. TEL 61-2-4921-6778, FAX 61-2-4921-6931, cle@mail.newcastle.edu.au, http://www.law.newcastle.edu.au/cle/. **Dist. in N. America by:** Wm. W. Gaunt & Sons Inc., Gaunt Bldg, 3011 Gulf Dr, Holmes Beach, FL 34217-2199. TEL 941-778-5211, 941-778-5252.

378 AUS ISSN 1323-2770
THE AUSTRALASIAN PROFESSIONAL LEGAL EDUCATION DIRECTORY. Text in English. a. **Document type:** *Directory.* **Description:** Lists the addresses and telephone and fax numbers, of practical training courses and continuing legal education providers in Australia, New Zealand and Papua New Guinea.
Published by: Centre for Legal Education, c/o Faculty of Law, University of Newcastle, Callaghan, NSW 2308, Australia. TEL 61-2-4921-5419, FAX 61-2-4921-6931, cle@mail.newcastle.edu.au, http://www.law.newcastle.edu.au/cle/. **Dist. in N. America by:** Wm. W. Gaunt & Sons Inc., Gaunt Bldg, 3011 Gulf Dr, Holmes Beach, FL 34217-2199. TEL 941-778-5211.

AUSTRALIA. BUREAU OF STATISTICS. EDUCATION AND WORK, AUSTRALIA. see *OCCUPATIONS AND CAREERS—Abstracting, Bibliographies, Statistics*

AUSTRALIA. BUREAU OF STATISTICS. RESEARCH AND EXPERIMENTAL DEVELOPMENT, HIGHER EDUCATION ORGANISATIONS, AUSTRALIA. see *EDUCATION—Abstracting, Bibliographies, Statistics*

378.9425 AUS ISSN 1038-6432
L981
AUSTRALIAN DIRECTORY OF ACADEMICS; who's who in Australian universities. Text in English. 1991. a. AUD 169.95. back issues avail. **Document type:** *Directory.* **Description:** Lists information on 15000 Australian academics including fax, telephone, e-mail numbers and teaching, research and consulting interests.
Related titles: Diskette ed.; Online - full text ed.
Published by: Universal Consultancy Services, PO Box 683, Kenmore, QLD 4069, Australia. TEL 61-7-32028404, FAX 61-7-32028393. Eds. Glyn Edwards, Terese Sullivan. Circ: 1,500.

378.94025 AUS ISSN 1038-6440
L981
AUSTRALIAN DIRECTORY OF FACULTIES. Text in English. 1992. a. AUD 127.95. back issues avail. **Document type:** *Directory.* **Description:** Provides alphabetical listing of Australian academic staff. Contains 35000 names indexed by subject specialties.
Related titles: Diskette ed.; Online - full text ed.
Published by: Universal Consultancy Services, PO Box 683, Kenmore, QLD 4069, Australia. TEL 61-7-32028404, FAX 61-7-32028393. Eds. Glyn Edwards, Terese Sullivan. Circ: 1,000.

AUSTRALIAN FILM, TELEVISION AND RADIO SCHOOL ANNUAL REPORT. see *COMMUNICATIONS—Radio*

AUSTRALIAN FILM, TELEVISION AND RADIO SCHOOL HANDBOOK. see *COMMUNICATIONS—Radio*

378.12 AUS ISSN 0313-5373
LB1727.A7
➤ **AUSTRALIAN JOURNAL OF TEACHER EDUCATION.** Text in English. 1975. 2/yr. AUD 20 domestic to individuals; AUD 25 foreign to individuals; AUD 30 domestic to institutions; AUD 35 foreign to institutions. adv. bk.rev. **Document type:** *Academic/Scholarly.* **Description:** Aims to enhance the quality of teacher education in Australia through the publication of research reports, learned points of view and commentaries.
Indexed: AEI, CPE, ERA, IBR, SEA, TEA.
—BLDSC (1812.900000).
Published by: (Edith Cowan University, School of Education), Social Science Press, PO Box 624, Katoomba, NSW 2780, Australia. TEL 61-2-47822909, socsci@ozemail.com.au, http://www.cowan.edu.au/ecuwis/docs/ajte/ajte.html. Ed., Pub., R&P David Barlow. Circ: 100.

378.94 AUS ISSN 0818-8068
➤ **AUSTRALIAN UNIVERSITIES' REVIEW.** Text in English. 1957. 2/yr. AUD 50 domestic; AUD 60 foreign (effective 2000). adv. bk.rev. bibl.; charts; illus.; stat. index. **Document type:** *Academic/Scholarly.* **Description:** Deals with current educational debates in Australia.
Formerly (until 1986): Vestes (0042-4560)
Related titles: Online - full text ed.
Indexed: AEI, AusPAIS, CIJE, CPE, HEA, RHEA, TEA.
—BLDSC (1823.700000), IE, ingenta.
Published by: National Tertiary Education Union, PO Box 1323, South Melbourne, VIC 3205, Australia. TEL 61-3-92541880, FAX 61-3-9254-1915, sroberts@nteu.org.au, http://www.nteu.org.au/services/publics/aur/aur.html. Ed. Simon Marginson. Circ: 25,000.

378.436 AUT
AUSTRIA. BUNDESMINISTERIUM FUER WISSENSCHAFT UND VERKEHR. HOCHSCHULBERICHT. Text in German. triennial. free. stat. **Document type:** *Government.* **Description:** Report by the Austrian minister for science and transportation on higher education.
Former titles: Austria. Bundesministerium fuer Wissenschaft, Verkehr und Kunst. Hochschulbericht; Austria. Bundesministerium fuer Wissenschaft, Forschung und Kunst. Hochschulbericht; Austria. Bundesministerium fuer Wissenschaft und Forschung. Hochschulbericht
Published by: Bundesministerium fuer Wissenschaft und Verkehr, Bankgasse 1, Vienna, W 1014, Austria. TEL 43-1-53120-0, FAX 43-1-531205860, service@bmwf.gv.at. R&P Wolfgang Fingernagel.

378.436 AUT
AUSTRIA. BUNDESMINISTERIUM FUER WISSENSCHAFT UND VERKEHR. UNIVERSITAETEN - HOCHSCHULEN, STUDIUM UND BERUF. Text in German. 1976. a. free. **Document type:** *Government.*
Formerly: Austria. Bundesministerium fuer Wissenschaft, Verkehr und Kunst. Universitaeten - Hochschulen, Studium und Beruf
Indexed: RASB.
Published by: Bundesministerium fuer Wissenschaft und Verkehr, Bankgasse 1, Vienna, W 1014, Austria. TEL 43-1-53120-0, FAX 43-1-531205860, christine.kampl@bmwf.gv.at, http://www.bmwf.gv.at. Ed. Eva Knollmayer. R&P Wolfgang Fingernagel.

378 DEU ISSN 0937-6569
AUSZEIT; Informationen, Berichte und Dokumentation zum Auslaenderstudium. Text in German. 1964. q. USD 10. bk.rev. back issues avail. **Document type:** *Academic/Scholarly.*
Published by: World University Service, German Committee, Goebenstr 35, Wiesbaden, 65195, Germany. TEL 49-611-446648, FAX 49-611-446489, wusgermany@aol.com. Ed. Kambiz Ghawami.

AVIATION MEDICAL EDUCATION SERIES. see *AERONAUTICS AND SPACE FLIGHT*

B C I T UPDATE. (British Columbia Institute of Technology) see *TECHNOLOGY: COMPREHENSIVE WORKS*

B D I C JOURNAL. (Bund Deutscher Ingenieur Corporationen) see *CLUBS*

378 POL ISSN 1509-9849
B.E.S.T. (Biuletyn Efektywnie Studiujacych Talentow) Text in Polish. 1996. q. 24 p./no.; **Document type:** *Bulletin, Academic/Scholarly.*
Related titles: Online - full content ed.: ISSN 1689-0574. 1999; Supplement(s): B.E.S.T. Plus. ISSN 1509-9857. 1999.
Published by: Akademia Ekonomiczna im. Oskara Langego we Wroclawiu, ul Komandorska 118-120, Wroclaw, 53345, Poland. TEL 48-71-3680100, FAX 48-71-3672778, redakcja@credit.ae.wroc.pl, www@ae.wroc.pl, http://best.ae.wroc.pl, http://www.ae.wroc.pl. Ed. Wioletta Woznica. Circ: 3,000.

378 AUS
B - H E R T NEWSLETTER. (Business Higher Education Round Table Newsletter) Text in English. 1998. q. AUD 7.70 per issue (effective 2003).
Media: Online - full text.
Published by: Business Higher Education Round Table, 24 Brunswik St 1st Fl, Fitzroy, VIC 3065, Australia. TEL 61-3-9419-8068, FAX 61-3-9419-8276, http://www.bhert.com/publications_News.htm.

B M C MEDICAL EDUCATION. (BioMed Central) see *MEDICAL SCIENCES*

BANGKOK, THAILAND. COLLEGE OF EDUCATION. THESIS ABSTRACT SERIES. see *EDUCATION—Abstracting, Bibliographies, Statistics*

378 DEU ISSN 0171-645X
LB2300
BEITRAEGE ZUR HOCHSCHULFORSCHUNG. Text in German; Abstracts in English. 1974. q. free. reprints avail. **Document type:** *Newsletter, Academic/Scholarly.*
Formerly (until 1978): Ad Acta (0342-8338)
Indexed: ERA, RHEA.
—BLDSC (1884.238000).
Published by: Bayerisches Staatsinstitut fuer Hochschulforschung und Hochschulplanung, Prinzregentenstr 24, Munich, 80538, Germany. TEL 49-89-21234405, FAX 49-89-21234450, sekretariat@ihf.bayern.de, http://www.ihf.bayern.de.

BIBLIOGRAPHY OF EDUCATION THESES IN AUSTRALIA. see *EDUCATION—Abstracting, Bibliographies, Statistics*

378.016 USA ISSN 1537-338X
BIZED. Text in English. 2001. bi-m. USD 72 domestic; USD 82 in Canada; USD 92 elsewhere (effective 2005). adv. **Document type:** *Magazine, Trade.* **Description:** Covers trends, practices, ideas, issues, and hard facts related to management education.
Related titles: Online - full text ed.: (from EBSCO Publishing, H.W. Wilson, O C L C Online Computer Library Center, Inc.).
Indexed: EduInd.
Published by: The Association to Advance Collegiate Schools of Business, 777 South Harbour Island Blvd, Ste 750, Tampa, FL 33602. TEL 813-769-6500, FAX 813-769-6559, bized@aacsb.edu, http://www.aacsb.edu/publications/bized/default.asp. Eds. Sharon Shinn, Tricia Bisoux. Adv. contact William Cotner. B&W page USD 4,690, color page USD 6,090; trim 8.375 x 10.875. Circ: 15,000 (paid and controlled).

378.021 BRA
BOLETIM ESTATISTICO. RELATORIO DE ACTIVIDADES. Text in Portuguese. 1992. a. **Document type:** *Corporate.*
Published by: Pontificia Universidade Catolica de Minas Gerais, Av Dom Jose Gaspar, 500, C Eucaristico, Belo Horizonte, MG 30535-610, Brazil. TEL 55-31-33194271, FAX 55-31-33194129, proex@pucminas.br, http://www.pucminas.br.

378 IRL
(YEAR) BOOK OF MODULES. Text in English. a. **Document type:** *Monographic series, Academic/Scholarly.*
—BLDSC (2248.129250).
Published by: University College Cork, College Rd, Cork, Ireland. TEL 353-21-490-3000, downtown@sec.ucc.ie, http://www.ucc.ie.

BRAZIL. SERVICO DE ESTATISTICA DA EDUCACAO E CULTURA. SINOPSE ESTATISTICA DO ENSINO SUPERIOR. see *EDUCATION—Abstracting, Bibliographies, Statistics*

378 GBR
BRITISH COUNCIL ANNUAL REPORT AND ACCOUNTS (YEAR). Text in English. 1940. a. free to qualified personnel. back issues avail. **Description:** Reports on work of British Council worldwide.
—BLDSC (1121.200000).
Published by: British Council, 10 Spring Gardens, London, SW1A 2BN, United Kingdom. TEL 44-20-7930-8466, FAX 44-20-7493-5035, publications.information@britishcouncil.org, http://www.britcoun.org. Ed. Paul Howson. Circ: 20,000 (controlled).

378 ARG ISSN 0328-0918
LA BRUJULA (COMODORO RIVADAVIA). Text in Spanish. 1994. a.
Published by: Universidad Nacional de la Patagonia San Juan Bosco, Direccion de Orientacion Educativa, Ciudad Universitaria Km 4, Comodoro Rivadavia, Chubut 9005, Argentina. TEL 54-297-4557169, FAX 54-297-4550934, webmaster@unp.edu.ar, http://www.unp.edu.ar. Ed. Lidia Silvestrini.

378 GBR ISSN 1368-2164
BRUNEL UNIVERSITY. VICE-CHANCELLOR'S REPORT TO COURT (YEAR). Text in English. 1967. a. free. **Document type:** *Corporate.* **Description:** Covers events, aims and activities of the year.
Former titles (until 1992): Brunel University. Vice-Chancellor's Annual Report (0953-4903); (until 1991): Brunel University. Annual Report (0306-9990)
—BLDSC (9232.257000).
Published by: Brunel University, Brunel University, Kingston Ln, Uxbridge, Mddx UB8 3PH, United Kingdom. TEL 44-1895-274000, FAX 44-1895-232806, http://www.brunel.ac.uk. Ed. M Judge. Circ: 1,000.

BULLETIN OF DENTAL EDUCATION. see *MEDICAL SCIENCES—Dentistry*

378.51249 TWN
BULLETIN OF EDUCATIONAL RESEARCH. Text in Chinese, English. 1959. s-a. USD 9. bk.rev. **Document type:** *Academic/Scholarly.*
Former titles (until 1997): Bulletin of Education Research; National Taiwan Normal University. Graduate Institute of Education. Bulletin
Published by: (Department of Education), National Taiwan Normal University/Tai-wan Shih Fan Ta Hsueh, 162 Ho-Ping E. Rd, Sec 1, Taipei, 10610, Taiwan. TEL 886-2-2322-5146, FAX 886-2-2393-9468. Ed. Hsiu-Chuan Lee TEL 886-2-23636143 ext 242. Circ: 1,500.

BUSINESS EDUCATION FORUM. see *BUSINESS AND ECONOMICS*

E

378 USA ISSN 0147-877X
LB2341
BUSINESS OFFICER. Text in English. 1967. m. USD 94.95 membership (effective 2005). adv. bk.rev. **Document type:** *Magazine, Trade.* **Description:** News magazine of the association.
Former titles: College and University Business Officer (0010-0919); College and University Business (0010-0900)
Media: Duplicated (not offset).
Indexed: CIJE.
—BLDSC (2934.475550), IE, Infotrieve, ingenta.
Published by: National Association of College and University Business Officers, 2501 M St, NW, Ste 400, Washington, DC 20037. TEL 202-861-2500, FAX 202-861-2583, dklinger@nacubo.nche.edu, http://www.nacubo.org/business_officer. Ed., R&P Donna J Klinger. Adv. contact David Rupp. Circ: 20,000 (controlled).

650.07 IRL ISSN 0790-5742
BUSINESS STUDIES. Variant title: Business Studies for Leaving Certificate Students. Text in English. 1983. 7/yr. adv. **Document type:** *Academic/Scholarly.*
Published by: C.J. Fallon Educational Publishers, Lucan Rd., Palmerstown, PO Box 1054, Dublin, 20, Ireland. TEL 353-1-6166490, FAX 353-1-6166499. Adv. contact Gertie Fagan. B&W page EUR 950, color page EUR 1,020. Circ: 14,000 (controlled).

378.17334 USA
C A L I C O. MONOGRAPH SERIES. Text in English. 1986. irreg. price varies. adv. charts. back issues avail. **Document type:** *Monographic series.* **Description:** Brochure on journals, monographs, software, programs, and symposia offered by the consortium.
Published by: Computer Assisted Language Instruction Consortium, Southwest Texas State University, 116 Centennial Hall, San Marcos, TX 78666. TEL 512-245-1417, FAX 512-245-8298, execdir@calico.org, info@calico.org, http://www.calico.org. Ed. Robert Fischer.

378.101 CAN ISSN 0834-9614
C A U T BULLETIN/A C P P U BULLETIN. Text in English, French. 1953. 10/yr. CND 37.45 domestic; CND 45 in United States; CND 55 elsewhere (effective 2005). adv. bk.rev. **Document type:** *Bulletin.* **Description:** Promotes the interests of teachers, professional librarians and researchers in Canadian universities and colleges; advances the standards of the higher education profession and seeks to improve the quality of higher education in Canada.
Former titles (until 1974): Canadian Association of University Teachers. Bulletin (0834-9606); (until 1974): C A U T Bulletin (0007-7887)
Related titles: Microfilm ed.: (from MML); Microform ed.: (from MML); Online - full text ed.: (from Micromedia ProQuest).
Indexed: CBPI, CEI.
Published by: Canadian Association of University Teachers, 2675 Queensview Dr, Ottawa, ON K2B 8K2, Canada. TEL 613-820-2270, FAX 613-820-2417, duhaime@caut.ca, http://www.caut.ca. R&P Liza R Duhaime. Adv. contact Johanne Smith. Circ: 31,000 (controlled).

378.05 USA ISSN 0146-5813
LB2341.6.T4
C B REPORT; quarterly notes from the Coordinating Board. Text in English. 1966. q. free. charts; stat. back issues avail. **Document type:** *Newsletter, Government.* **Description:** Covers the actions of the board and other issues in higher education.
Published by: Higher Education Coordinating Board, PO Box 12788, Capitol Sta, Austin, TX 78711. TEL 512-483-6111, FAX 512-483-6127, http://www.thecb.state.tx.us. Ed. Teri E Flack. Circ: 1,000 (controlled).

378.12 USA
C C A ADVOCATE; the official newspaper of the Community College Association. (Community College Association) Text in English. 1966. 5/yr. membership. bk.rev. back issues avail. **Document type:** *Newspaper, Trade.* **Description:** News articles on legislative and policy issues that affect the Community College Association chapters of the California Teachers Association.
Formerly (until 1979): California Professor (0008-1418)
Related titles: Online - full content ed.
Published by: Community College Association, P.O. Box 41927, Sacramento, CA 95841-0927. TEL 916-726-4207, FAX 916-726-4238, rockycca@aol.com, http://www.ccafca.org. Circ: 8,000. **Affiliate:** California Teachers Association.

378 USA
C C A S NEWSLETTER. Text in English. 1965. bi-m. membership. **Document type:** *Newsletter.*
Published by: Council of Colleges of Arts & Sciences, Arizona State University, College of Liberal Arts and Sciences, Box 873901, Tempe, AZ 85287-3901. TEL 480-727-6064, FAX 480-727-6078, ccas@asu.edu. Ed. Richard J Hopkins. R&P Ernie Peck. Circ: 1,800 (controlled).

378.1982 USA
C C D M MINORITY STUDENT RECRUITMENT GUIDE. Text in English. 1973. biennial. USD 150. **Document type:** *Directory.*
Former titles: Handbook for Recruiting Minority College Students; Handbook for Recruiting at Minority Colleges (0163-2795); (until 1979): Handbook for Recruiting at the Historically Black Colleges (0146-5104)
Published by: Council on Career Development for Minorities, Inc., 1341 W Mockingbird Ln, Ste 412E, Dallas, TX 75247. TEL 214-631-3677, FAX 214-905-2046. Ed. Verna Green Bennett. Circ: 2,500.

378 USA
C C U M C ANNUAL REPORT. Text in English. 1993. a. membership. back issues avail.
Related titles: Online - full content ed.
Published by: Consortium of College and University Media Centers, Iowa State University, Instructional Technology Center, 1200 Communications Bldg, Ames, IA 50011-3243. TEL 515-294-1811, FAX 515-294-8089, ccumc@ccumc.org, http://www.indiana.edu/~ccumc/.

378 USA
C C U M C CONFERENCE PROCEEDINGS. Text in English. a. membership.
Published by: Consortium of College and University Media Centers, Iowa State University, Instructional Technology Center, 1200 Communications Bldg, Ames, IA 50011-3243. TEL 515-294-1811, FAX 515-294-8089, ccumc@ccumc.org, churt@library.unt.edu, http://www.indiana.edu/~ccumc/. Ed. Cecilia Hurt.

371.3 USA
C C U M C LEADER. Variant title: The Leader. Text in English. 1972. q. membership. bk.rev.; film rev.; software rev.; video rev. 20 p./no.; **Document type:** *Newsletter.* **Description:** Reports news, information and events of the consortium and to facilitate networking among the membership.
Formerly: C U F C Leader
Published by: Consortium of College and University Media Centers, Iowa State University, Instructional Technology Center, 1200 Communications Bldg, Ames, IA 50011-3243. TEL 515-294-1811, FAX 515-294-8089, ccumc@ccumc.org, http://www.indiana.edu/~ccumc/. Ed. John P Kerstetter. R&P Donald Rieck TEL 515-294-1811. Circ: 600.

C E A CRITIC. see *LITERATURE*

810 USA ISSN 1547-3821
PE11
C E A FORUM (ONLINE EDITION). (College English Association) Text in English. 2000. 2/yr. bk.rev. bibl.; illus. back issues avail.
Media: Online - full content. **Related titles:** Microform ed.: (from PQC).
Published by: College English Association, c/o Joan Frederick, Dept of English, James Madison University, Harrisonburg, VA 22807. TEL 540-568-3753, FAX 540-568-2983, frederjx@jmu.edu. Ed., R&P Bege K Bowers.

378 USA ISSN 1521-9275
C I T INFOBITS. Text in English. 1993. m. free. bk.rev. back issues avail. **Document type:** *Newsletter.* **Description:** Reports on noteworthy articles published in the information and instructional technology trade literature.
Formerly: I A T Infobits
Media: Online - full text.
Published by: University of North Carolina at Chapel Hill, Center for Instructional Technology, Campus Box 3420, Chapel Hill, NC 27514. TEL 919-962-6042, FAX 919-962-5334, cit@unc.edu, carolyn_kotlas@unc.edu, http://www.unc.edu/cit/infobits/, http://www.unc.edu/cit/infobits/infobits.html. Ed., R&P Carolyn Kotlas TEL 919-962-9287. Circ: 5,355.

C M E - CONTINUING MEDICAL EDUCATION. see *MEDICAL SCIENCES*

C O T H REPORT. see *MEDICAL SCIENCES*

378.41 GBR
THE C R A C STUDENTS' GUIDE TO GRADUATE STUDIES IN THE U K. Abbreviated title: S E G R A S. Text in English. 1982. a. GBP 19.99 (effective 1999). **Document type:** *Directory.* **Description:** Provides insight into all postgraduate opportunities.
Published by: (Careers Research and Advisory Centre), Hobsons PLC, Bateman St, Cambridge, Cambs CB2 1LZ, United Kingdom. TEL 44-1223-460366, FAX 44-1223-301506. **Dist. by:** Biblios Publishers' Distribution Services Ltd., Star Rd, Partridge Green, W Sussex RH13 8LD, United Kingdom. TEL 44-1403-710851, FAX 44-1403-711143.

378.17 USA
C R L A NEWSLETTER. Text in English. 1977. 3/yr. USD 40. bk.rev. **Document type:** *Newsletter.* **Description:** Addresses learning needs in colleges and universities: reading, learning assistance, developmental education and tutorial assistance.
Former titles: W C R L A Newsletter; W C R A Newsletter
Published by: College Reading and Learning Association, 382, El Dorado, KS 67042-0382. http://www.crla.net/. Ed. Thomas L Pasternack. Circ: 900.

378 CAN ISSN 0836-7973
C S S H E PROFESSIONAL FILE. (Canadian Society for the Study of Higher Education) Text in English. 1986. irreg., latest vol.24, 2003. CND 95 academic membership; CND 50 student membership (effective 2005).
Media: Online - full text (from Micromedia ProQuest).
Indexed: CEI.
—CCC.
Published by: Canadian Society for the Study of Higher Education, PO Box 34091, RPO Fort Richmond, Winnipeg, MB R3T 5T5, Canada. TEL 204-474-6211, FAX 204-474-7607, csshe@cc.umanitoba.ca, http://umanitoba.ca/outreach/csshe.

378.1 USA ISSN 1046-9508
LB2335.5.A1
C U P A JOURNAL. Text in English. 1949. 2/yr. USD 75 to non-members; USD 40 to members; USD 20 newsstand/cover (effective 2000). adv. bk.rev. bibl.; charts; stat. index, cum.index: vol.1-15 (1949-1964). back issues avail.; reprint service avail. from PQC. **Document type:** *Academic/Scholarly.* **Description:** Focuses on human resource themes such as benefits, EEO, early retirement, administrative contracts, employee recruitment, and sexual harassment.
Formerly (until 1986): College and University Personnel Association. Journal (0010-0935)
Related titles: Microform ed.: (from PQC); Online - full text ed.
Indexed: ABIn, CIJE, CPE, CurCont, EAA, EduInd, HEA, SSCI.
—BLDSC (3493.245000), IE.
Published by: College and University Personnel Association, 1233 20th St, N W, Ste 301, Washington, DC 20036. TEL 202-429-0311, FAX 202-429-0149, http://www.cupa.org. Ed. Melissa Edeburn. R&P Audrey Rothstein. Circ: 1,200.

378 FRA ISSN 0248-9430
CAHIERS DE L'APLIUT. (Cahiers de l'Association des Professeurs de Languages des Instituts Universitaires de Technologie) Text in French. 1980. q. **Document type:** *Academic/Scholarly.*
Indexed: L&LBA.
—BLDSC (2948.622820), IE.
Published by: A P L I U T, 1, ave Leon Journault, Sevres, 92310, France. TEL 33-1-45076000, FAX 33-1-45076001, contact@ciep.fr, http://www.ciep.fr/.

378.12 USA ISSN 1091-6148
CALIFORNIA EDUCATOR. Text in English. 1962. 9/yr. USD 10 to non-members; free to members (effective 2005). adv. **Document type:** *Magazine, Trade.* **Description:** Publishes news, announcements, and articles on legislative, policy, and educational issues that affect the association.
Supersedes: C T A Action (0896-7326); Which was formerly (until 1987): Action (0742-2121); C T A - N E A Action (0164-9760); C T A Action (0007-9200)
Published by: California Teachers Association, 1705 Murchison Dr, Burlingame, CA 94010-4583. TEL 650-697-1400, editor@cta.org, http://www.cta.org. Ed., R&P Trudy Willis. Adv. contact Caroline Johnson. B&W page USD 4,089. Circ: 300,000 (controlled).

378 USA ISSN 1099-5811
AS30
➤ **CALIFORNIA STATE UNIVERSITY, STANISLAUS JOURNAL OF RESEARCH.** Variant title: Journal of Research. Text in English. 1996. a. free. **Document type:** *Academic/Scholarly.* **Description:** Covers scholarly and research articles.
Related titles: Online - full text ed.
Indexed: CIS.
Published by: California State University, Stanislaus, 801 W Monte Vista Ave, Turlock, CA 95382-0299. TEL 209-667-3082, http://www.csustan.edu/graduate_studies. Ed. Diana Mayer Demetrulias.

378 GBR ISSN 0305-764X
LB1725.G4 CODEN: CJEDEI
➤ **CAMBRIDGE JOURNAL OF EDUCATION.** Text in English. 1971. q. GBP 429, USD 781 combined subscription to institutions print & online eds. (effective 2006). adv. bk.rev. bibl. reprint service avail. from PSC. **Document type:** *Journal, Academic/Scholarly.*
Related titles: Microfiche ed.; Online - full text ed.: ISSN 1469-3577. GBP 408, USD 742 to institutions (effective 2006) (from EBSCO Publishing, Gale Group, IngentaConnect, Northern Light Technology, Inc., O C L C Online Computer Library Center, Inc., ProQuest Information & Learning, Swets Information Services).
Indexed: BrEdI, CPE, ChLitAb, EAA, ERA, ETA, HECAB, MEA, MLA-IB, PCI, PsycInfo, PsycholAb, RHEA, RI-1, RI-2, SEA, SENA, SOMA, SOPODA, SSA, SWA, SociolAb, TEA, V&AA, WBA, WMB, e-psyche.
—BLDSC (3015.957000), CINDOC, IE, Infotrieve, ingenta. **CCC.**
Published by: (Cambridge Institute of Education), Routledge (Subsidiary of: Taylor & Francis Group), 4 Park Sq, Milton Park, Abingdon, Oxon OX14 4RN, United Kingdom. TEL 44-1235-828600, FAX 44-1235-829000, info@routledge.co.uk, http://www.tandf.co.uk/journals/titles/0305764X.asp, http://www.routledge.com. Ed. Paula Peachey. **Subscr. outside N. America to:** Taylor & Francis Inc., Customer

E

Services Dept, 325 Chestnut St, 8th Fl, Philadelphia, PA 19106. TEL 215-625-8900, 800-354-1420, FAX 215-625-8914, customerservice@taylorandfrancis.com; **Subscr. to:** Taylor & Francis Ltd, Journals Customer Service, Rankine Rd, Basingstoke, Hants RG24 8PR, United Kingdom. TEL 44-1256-813000, FAX 44-1256-330245, enquiry@tandf.co.uk.

378 GBR
CAMBRIDGE UNIVERSITY REPORTER. Text in English. 1870. irreg. price varies.
Indexed: RASB.
Published by: Cambridge University Press, The Edinburgh Bldg, Shaftesbury Rd, Cambridge, CB2 2RU, United Kingdom. TEL 44-1223-312393, FAX 44-1223-315052, information@cambridge.org, http://www.cup.cam.ac.uk/. R&P Linda Nicol TEL 44-1223-325757.

378 USA ISSN 0746-2328
PN2016.N32
CAMPUS ACTIVITIES PROGRAMMING. Text in English. 1968. 8/yr. USD 40 (effective 2005). adv. bk.rev. illus. reprint service avail. from PQC. **Document type:** *Trade.*
Former titles: Student Activities Programming (0098-1664); N E C Newsletter (0093-3643)
Related titles: Microform ed.: (from PQC).
Indexed: CIJE, HEA.
Published by: National Association for Campus Activities, 13 Harbison Way, Columbia, SC 29212-3401. TEL 803-732-6222, FAX 803-749-1047, http://www.naca.org/NACA. Ed. Glenn Farr. Adv. contact Jeff Nemens. B&W page USD 1,095. Circ: 6,500 (controlled).

378.19 USA ISSN 1054-3821
HV8291.U6
CAMPUS CRIME. Text in English. 1991. m. looseleaf. USD 217 in US & Mexico; USD 21 elsewhere; USD 247 combined subscription print & email eds. (effective 2005). tr.lit. back issues avail.; reprints avail. **Document type:** *Newsletter.* **Description:** Offers advice for university security officers and university officials on reducing incidents of crime on campus. Tracks federal crime reporting legislation.
Related titles: CD-ROM ed.; E-mail ed.: ISSN 1545-4738. USD 187 (effective 2005); Online - full text ed.: (from Gale Group).
—**CCC.**
Published by: Business Publishers, Inc., 8737 Colesville Rd., Flr. 10, Silver Spring, MD 20910-3976. TEL 800-274-6737, bpinews@bpinews.com, http://www.bpinews.com. Ed. Rasheeda Childress. Pub. L A Eiserer.

378 PER ISSN 1682-3001
CAMPUS DE SAN MARCOS. Text in Spanish. 1990. m.
Formerly (until 2001): Actualidad Sanmarquina (1609-9028)
Media: Online - full text.
Published by: Universidad Nacional Mayor de San Marcos, Oficina General de Relaciones Publicas, Ave. German Amezaga, s-n, Lima, Peru. TEL 51-1-6197000, rrpp@unmsm.edu.pe, http://www.unmsm.edu.pe/rrpp/index_2.html.

378.154 SWE ISSN 1401-5382
CAMPUS EKONOMI. Text in Swedish. 1986. q. SEK 125 (effective 2005). adv. bk.rev.; music rev.; play rev.; software rev. charts; illus.; stat. back issues avail. **Document type:** *Magazine, Consumer.*
Formerly (until 1996): Fri Ekonomi (0284-0928)
Related titles: Online - full text ed.
Published by: Universum International AB, Karlavaegen 108, PO Box 7053, Stockholm, 10386, Sweden. TEL 46-8-56293000, FAX 46-8-56293050, campus@universum.se, info@campus.se, http://www.campusnet.com. Ed. Sofia Eriksson. Adv. contact Martin Stromquist. B&W page SEK 36,600, color page SEK 36,600; trim 215 x 280. Circ: 20,000.

▼ **CAMPUS FACILITY MAINTENANCE**; promoting a healthy and productive learning environment. see *BUSINESS AND ECONOMICS—Management*

378.0028 USA ISSN 1043-2086
LC6251
CAMPUS - FREE COLLEGE DEGREES. Text in English. 1986. biennial. USD 31.95, USD 38.95, USD 50.95 (effective 2000 - 2001). adv. **Document type:** *Directory, Consumer.* **Description:** Describes accredited distance college degree programs for adults.
Published by: Thorson Guides, L.L.C., PO Box 470886, Tulsa, OK 74147-0886. TEL 918-294-1297, 800-741-7771, FAX 918-294-1297, thorson@tulsa.com, http://www.college-distancedegree.com. Ed., Pub., R&P, Adv. contact Marcie Thorson. Circ: 5,000 (paid).

378 GBR
CAMPUS REPORT. Text in English. 1982. 3/yr. free. back issues avail. **Document type:** *Newsletter.*
Published by: University of Salford, Campus Office, Maxwell Bldg, Salford, Lancs M5 4WT, United Kingdom. TEL 44-161-743-1727, FAX 44-161-745-5109. Ed. Anna Thornton. Circ: 6,000.

378 USA ISSN 0890-4618
LC72.2
CAMPUS REPORT. Text in English. 1985. m. USD 30. adv. bk.rev. back issues avail.; reprints avail. **Document type:** *Newspaper.* **Description:** Investigates and exposes abuses of First Amendment freedoms on college campuses, including cases of political classroom indoctrination, discrimination, and political correctness.
Formerly (until 1986): Accuracy in Academia
Related titles: Online - full text ed.
Published by: Accuracy in Academia, Inc., 4455 Connecticut Ave, N W, Ste 330, Washington, DC 20008. TEL 202-364-4401, 800-787-0429, FAX 202-364-4098, cr@take.aim.org, http://take.aim.org/. Ed. Reed J Irvine. R&P, Adv. contact Brandan Slattery. Circ: 176,500.

378 AUS
CAMPUS REVIEW. Text in English. 1991. w. AUD 210 domestic; AUD 341 foreign (effective 2004). adv. **Document type:** *Newspaper, Trade.* **Description:** Reports on issues related to higher education and vocational education and training in Australasia.
Formerly (until 1993): Campus: Higher Education News (1037-034X)
Related titles: Online - full content ed.
Address: PO Box 6097, North Sydney, NSW 2060, Australia. TEL 61-2-99368666, FAX 61-2-99540565, http://www.camrev.com.au. Ed. Julie Hare. Adv. contact Emma Knox. Circ: 93,000.

CAMPUS SECURITY REPORT. see *CRIMINOLOGY AND LAW ENFORCEMENT—Security*

378.00285 USA ISSN 1553-7544
LB1028.43
CAMPUS TECHNOLOGY; new directions in educational technology. Text in English. 1988. q. USD 24 in Canada & Mexico; USD 75 elsewhere; free (effective 2004). adv. bk.rev. illus. back issues avail.; reprints avail. **Document type:** *Magazine, Trade.* **Description:** Covers how technology can improve teaching and learning at the post secondary level. Features technology overviews, case studies, interviews, product information, news, and resources for instructors and software developers.
Formerly (until 2004): Syllabus (Sunnyvale) (1065-2051); Which incorporated (1991-199?): Higher Education Product Companion (1065-2086); (1992-1993): Computer Science Syllabus (1065-2078)
Related titles: Diskette ed.; Online - full text ed.
—BLDSC (3016.406102), IE.
Published by: Syllabus Press (Subsidiary of: 101 Communications, Llc.), 9121 Oakdale Ave., Ste. 101, Chatsworth, CA 91311-6526. TEL 800-773-0670, mgrush@syllabus.com, http://www.campus-technology.com, http://www.syllabus.com. Ed., R&P Mary Grush. Pub. Mark Sande. Adv. contact Lee Conrad. B&W page USD 3,000, color page USD 3,900; trim 8.588 x 10.88. Circ: 55,000.

378.154 SWE ISSN 1401-5196
CAMPUS TEKNIK. Text in Swedish. 1988. q. SEK 125 (effective 2005). adv. music rev.; play rev.; software rev. illus.; stat. back issues avail. **Document type:** *Magazine, Consumer.* **Description:** Presents information on education, careers, and lifestyles, aiming at an audience of university students.
Related titles: Online - full text ed.
Published by: Universum International AB, Karlavaegen 108, PO Box 7053, Stockholm, 10386, Sweden. TEL 46-8-56293000, FAX 46-8-56293050, campustek@universum.se, info@campus.se, http://www.campusnet.com. Ed. Sofia Eriksson. Adv. contact Martin Stromquist. B&W page SEK 39,200, color page SEK 39,200; trim 215 x 280. Circ: 28,000.

378 GBR
CAMPUS U K. (United Kingdom) Text in English. 3/yr. 95 p./no.; **Document type:** *Magazine.*
Published by: (British Council), Hobsons PLC, Challenger House, 42 Adler St, London, E1 1EE, United Kingdom. TEL 44-20-79585000, FAX 44-20-79584972.

CAMPUS WATCH. see *POLITICAL SCIENCE—Civil Rights*

378.3 CAN ISSN 1190-8459
CANADA SCHOLARS IN TECHNOLOGY. TERMS AND CONDITIONS FOR CANADA SCHOLARS. Text in Multiple languages. 199?. a.
Published by: Industry Canada/Industrie Canada, Distribution Services, Communications & Marketing Branch, Rm 268D, West Tower, C.D. Howe Bldg, 235 Queen St, Ottawa, ON K1A 0H5, Canada. TEL 613-947-7466, FAX 613-954-6436, publications@ic.gc.ca, http://www.ic.gc.ca.

378 CAN ISSN 0228-8397
CANADIAN ASSOCIATION OF AFRICAN STUDIES. NEWSLETTER/ASSOCIATION CANADIENNE DES ETUDES AFRICAINES. BULLETIN. Text in English, French. 1975. 3/yr. CND 70 to members. bibl. **Document type:** *Newsletter.* **Description:** Covers African studies at universities.
Indexed: AICP, IBSS.
Published by: Canadian Association of African Studies, c/o Concordia University, 1455 de Maisonneuve O., Montreal, PQ H3G 1M8, Canada. TEL 416-978-7067. Circ: 1,000.

378.71 CAN ISSN 0316-1218
➤ **CANADIAN JOURNAL OF HIGHER EDUCATION/REVUE CANADIENNE D'ENSEIGNEMENT SUPERIEUR.** Text in English, French. 1971. 3/yr. CND 85 foreign to institutions (effective 2005). adv. bk.rev. abstr.; bibl. reprint service avail. from PQC. **Document type:** *Journal, Academic/Scholarly.* **Description:** Presents original research in the field of higher education in Canada and abroad.
Formerly (until 1974): S T O A (0315-6680)
Related titles: Online - full text ed.: (from EBSCO Publishing, Gale Group, H.W. Wilson, IngentaConnect, Micromedia ProQuest, O C L C Online Computer Library Center, Inc.).
Indexed: ABIn, CBPI, CEI, CIJE, CPE, EAA, ERA, ETA, EduInd, HEA, MEA, RHEA, SEA, SENA, SOMA, SRRA, SWA, TEA.
—BLDSC (3031.620000), IE, Infotrieve, ingenta. **CCC.**
Published by: Canadian Society for the Study of Higher Education, PO Box 34091, RPO Fort Richmond, Winnipeg, MB R3T 5T5, Canada. TEL 204-474-6211, FAX 204-474-7607, kaarcher@ucalgary.ca, csshe@cc.umanitoba.ca, http://umanitoba.ca/outreach/csshe/Pub/pub.html. Ed. Keith Archer. Circ: 750.

378 USA
CANADIAN STUDIES UPDATE (ONLINE EDITION). Text in English. 1982. irreg. (2-3/yr.). free to members. **Document type:** *Newsletter.* **Description:** Contains news of interest to the Canadian studies community.
Formerly (until 2004): Canadian Studies Update (Print Edition) (0734-4546)
Media: Online - full content.
Indexed: CEI.
—BLDSC (3044.897500).
Published by: Association for Canadian Studies in the United States, 1424 16th St NW, Ste 502, Washington, DC 20036-2238. info@acsus.org, http://acsus.org/display.cfm?id=276&Sub=296, http://www.acsus.org. Ed., R&P David N Biette. Circ: 1,000.

378 CAN
CAPILANO COLLEGE. ANNUAL REVIEW. Text in English. a.
Related titles: Online - full text ed.
Published by: Capilano Press Society, 2055 Purcell Way, North Vancouver, BC V7J 3H5, Canada. TEL 604-984-1712, FAX 604-990-7837, tcr@capcollege.bc.ca, http://www.capcollege.bc.ca/about/publications/annual-report/index.xhtml.

378.1982 GBR ISSN 1359-2432
CAREERS FOR ETHNIC MINORITY GRADUATES. Variant title: Casebook for Ethnic Minority Graduates. Text in English. a. GBP 9.99 per issue (effective 2002). **Description:** Recent graduates belonging to ethnic minority groups discuss their careers.
Formerly: Racial Equality Casebook
Published by: (Careers Research and Advisory Centre), Hobsons PLC, Challenger House, 42 Adler St, London, E1 1EE, United Kingdom. TEL 44-1223-460366, FAX 44-1223-301506. **Dist. by:** Biblios Publishers' Distribution Services Ltd., Star Rd, Partridge Green, W Sussex RH13 8LD, United Kingdom. TEL 44-1403-710851, FAX 44-1403-7111143.

CAREERS FOR WOMEN GRADUATES. see *OCCUPATIONS AND CAREERS*

CAREERSCOPE. see *OCCUPATIONS AND CAREERS*

378 CAN ISSN 0226-5389
CARLETON UNIVERSITY MAGAZINE. Text in English. 3/yr.
Related titles: Online - full content ed.
Published by: Carleton University, Development and Alumni Services, 1125 Colonel By Dr, Robertson Hall, Rm 510, Ottawa, ON K1S 5B6, Canada. TEL 613-520-3636, FAX 613-520-3587, devalum@carleton.ca, nancylewis@carleton.ca, http://magazine.carleton.ca/, http://www.carleton.ca/alumni. Ed., Adv. contact Nancy Lewis.

378 USA ISSN 1081-7727
BX6201
CARSON - NEWMAN STUDIES. Text in English. 1965. a. free. **Document type:** *Academic/Scholarly.*
Formerly: Carson - Newman College, Jefferson City, Tennessee. Faculty Studies (0069-0783)
Published by: Carson - Newman College, Jefferson City, TN 37760. TEL 423-471-3275, FAX 423-471-3502, olive@cncacc.cn.edu, http://www.cn.edu. Ed., R&P Don H Olive. Circ: 600 (controlled).

378.155 500 001.3 BRA ISSN 1516-7577
CATALOGO DE TESES E DISSERTACOES. Text in Portuguese. 1991. a.
Published by: Universidade Estadual de Maringa, Av. Colombo, 5.790, Maringa, Parana 87020-900, Brazil. TEL 55-44-2614253, FAX 55-44-2222754, http://www.uem.br. Pub. Gilberto Cesar Pavanelli.

378.81 BRA
CATALOGO GERAL DE INSTITUICOES DE ENSINO SUPERIOR. Text in Portuguese. 1973. irreg., latest 1993. charts; stat. **Document type:** *Catalog, Government.* **Description:** Lists all Brazilian higher education institutions, their departments and courses, and statistical information.

E

Formerly: Atividades das Instituicoes Federais de Ensino Superior
Published by: Ministerio da Educacao e do Desporto, Secretaria de Educacao Superior, Esplanada dos Ministerios, Bloco L, 3o andar, Brasilia, DF 70047903, Brazil. TEL 61-223-7965, FAX 61-224-8920, TELEX 61-1860 MBRL-BR.

378.6724 COG
CENTRE D'ENSEIGNEMENT SUPERIEUR DE BRAZZAVILLE. ANNALES. Text in French. 1965. a.
Published by: Centre d'Enseignement Superieur de Brazzaville, BP 69, Brazzaville, Congo, Republic.

378.1 GBR ISSN 1363-9536
CENTRE FOR EQUALITY RESEARCH IN BUSINESS. RESEARCH PAPER. Text in English. 1997. irreg. **Document type:** *Academic/Scholarly.* **Description:** Focuses on the investigation and analysis of issues of equality and diversity in work, organizations and management.
—BLDSC (3106.498800).
Published by: University of North London, Centre for Equality Research in Business, Stapleton House, University Of North London, 277-281 Holloway Rd, London, N7 8HN, United Kingdom. TEL 44-171-753-7063, f.colgan@unl.ac.uk, http://www.unl.ac.uk/cerb/.

378 340 AUS
CENTRE FOR LEGAL EDUCATION. NEWSLETTER. Text in English. 3/yr. free. back issues avail. **Document type:** *Newsletter.* **Description:** Reports on the Centre's work and activities; comments on developments in legal training and education in Australia and worldwide.
Related titles: Online - full text ed.
Published by: Centre for Legal Education, c/o Faculty of Law, University of Newcastle, Callaghan, NSW 2308, Australia. TEL 61-2-4921-6778, 61-2-4921-5419, FAX 61-2-4921-6931, cle@mail.newcastle.edu.au, http://www.law.newcastle.edu.au/cle/.

378 USA ISSN 0009-1383
LB2300
➤ **CHANGE**; the magazine of higher learning. Text in English. 1969. bi-m. USD 58 domestic to individuals; USD 74 foreign to individuals; USD 136 domestic to institutions; USD 152 foreign to institutions; USD 22.67 per issue (effective academic year 2005 - 2006). adv. bk.rev. illus.; charts; stat. index. 50 p./no. 3 cols./p.; back issues avail.; reprint service avail. from PSC. **Document type:** *Journal, Academic/Scholarly.* **Description:** Deals with contemporary issues in higher learning, the award-winning Change spotlights trends, provides new insights, and analyzes the implications of educational programs.
Formerly (until 1970): Change in Higher Education (0363-6291)
Related titles: CD-ROM ed.: (from ProQuest Information & Learning); Microform ed.; Online - full text ed.: (from EBSCO Publishing, Florida Center for Library Automation, Gale Group, H.W. Wilson, Northern Light Technology, Inc., O C L C Online Computer Library Center, Inc., ProQuest Information & Learning, SoftLine Information).
Indexed: ABIn, AcaI, AgeL, AmH&L, BRI, CBRI, CIJE, CPE, DIP, EAA, ERA, EduInd, GSS&RPL, HEA, HistAb, IBR, IBZ, MEA&I, MEDLINE, MagInd, RGAb, RGPR, RHEA, RehabLit, SOMA, SOPODA, e-psyche.
—BLDSC (3129.644000), IDS, IE, Infotrieve, ingenta. **CCC.**
Published by: (American Association of Higher Education), Heldref Publications, 1319 18th St, NW, Washington, DC 20036-1802. TEL 202-296-6267, 800-365-9753, FAX 202-293-6130, ch@heldref.org, subscribe@heldref.org, http://www.heldref.org/change.php. Adv. contact Chante Douglas. Circ: 12,868 (paid). **Co-sponsor:** Helen Dwight Reid Educational Foundation.

➤ **CHEMICAL ENGINEERING EDUCATION.** see *ENGINEERING—Chemical Engineering*

➤ **CHEMICAL ENGINEERING FACULTY DIRECTORY.** see *ENGINEERING—Chemical Engineering*

➤ **CHEMICAL RESEARCH IN CHINESE UNIVERSITIES.** see *CHEMISTRY*

378 USA
CHICAGO CHRONICLE. Text in English. 1981. 20/yr. USD 20 (effective 1999). **Document type:** *Newspaper.*
Published by: University of Chicago, Chicago Chronicle, 5801 S Ellis Ave, Rm 200, Chicago, IL 60637. FAX 773-702-8324, chronicle@uchicago.edu, http://www.news.uchicago.edu/chronicle/. Ed. Laurie Davis. Circ: 12,300.

CHIEF EXECUTIVE COMPENSATION AND BENEFITS SURVEY. see *BUSINESS AND ECONOMICS—Labor And Industrial Relations*

CHIKIDAH-I PAYAN'NAMAHHA-YI IRAN/IRANIAN DISSERTATION ABSTRACTS. see *EDUCATION—Abstracting, Bibliographies, Statistics*

378 USA
THE CHIMES (COLUMBUS). Text in English. w. USD 15. **Document type:** *Newspaper.*
Published by: Capital University, 2199 E Main St, Columbus, OH 43209. TEL 614-236-6716, FAX 614-236-6490. R&P Kelly Messinger TEL 614-236-6423. Circ: 2,300.

378.2 GBR
CHOOSING YOUR DEGREE COURSE & UNIVERSITY. Text in English. 1993. a. GBP 16.99 (effective 2001). **Document type:** *Directory, Consumer.* **Description:** Advice on choosing a UK degree course and university or college.
Formerly: How to Choose Your Degree Course
Published by: Trotman & Co. Ltd., 2 The Green, Richmond, Surrey TW9 1PL, United Kingdom. TEL 44-20-8486 1150, FAX 44-20-8486 1161, mail@trotman.co.uk, http://www.trotmanpublishing.co.uk. Ed. Brian Heap. R&P Amanda Williams. Adv. contact Alistair Rogers. **Dist. by:** Plymbridge Distributors Ltd, Plymbridge House, Estover Rd, Plymouth, Devon PL6 7PY, United Kingdom. TEL 44-1752-202300, FAX 44-1752-202330, enquiries@plymbridge.com.

378.07 GBR
CHRIST'S COLLEGE MAGAZINE. Text in English. 1886. a. free to members. bk.rev.
Published by: Christ's College, Cambridge University, Printing Services University Press, Christs College, Cambridge, CB2 3BU, United Kingdom. FAX 44-1223-334962, aht21@cam.ac.uk, http://www.christs.cam.ac.uk/alumni. Ed. R N Barlow Poole. Circ: 6,500.

378.34 USA ISSN 1063-7915
LB2337.4
CHRONICLE FINANCIAL AID GUIDE. Text in English. 1961. a. USD 24.98 (effective 2000). **Description:** Lists scholarship titles.
Former titles: Chronicle Student Aid Annual (0190-339X); Student Aid Annual (0585-4555); Student Aid Manual (0145-8043)
Related titles: CD-ROM ed.
Published by: Chronicle Guidance Publications, Inc., PO Box 1190, Moravia, NY 13118. TEL 315-497-0330, 800-622-7284, FAX 315-497-3359, customerservice@chronicleguidance.com, http://www.chronicleguidance.com. Circ: 6,300.

378 USA ISSN 0009-5982
LB2300
THE CHRONICLE OF HIGHER EDUCATION. Text in English. 1966. w. (49/yr.). USD 82.50 domestic; USD 135 in Canada; USD 275 elsewhere (effective 2005); includes Almanac of Higher Education. adv. bk.rev. charts; illus.; stat. Index. back issues avail.; reprint service avail. from PQC. **Document type:** *Newspaper, Trade.* **Description:** Provides news reports and editorials on all facets of higher education in the United States, Canada, and abroad, with reference lists of relevant research, books, seminars, workshops, fellowships, and grants; for senior administrative, business, and academic officers.
Related titles: Microfiche ed.: (from CIS); Microfilm ed.: (from PQC); Online - full text ed.: USD 82.50 (effective 2002) (from EBSCO Publishing, LexisNexis, Northern Light Technology, Inc., O C L C Online Computer Library Center, Inc., ProQuest Information & Learning); Supplement(s): Events in Academe; The Chronicle of Higher Education Almanac. ISSN 1043-7967. 1988.
Indexed: A&ATA, ABIn, ABS&EES, AcaI, Agr, BRI, CBRI, CIJE, CWI, ChLitAb, EduInd, EngInd, InfoSAb, LRI, MagInd, NTA, PRA, PSI, RASB, RHEA, RI-1, RI-2, RILM, SRI, SRRA.
—BLDSC (3186.250000), Linda Hall.
Published by: Chronicle of Higher Education, Inc., 1255 23rd St, NW, Ste 700, Washington, DC 20037. TEL 202-466-1080, FAX 202-452-1033, editor@chronicle.com, http://chronicle.com. Ed. Philip Semas. Pub. Robinette Ross. adv.: B&W page USD 8,935, color page USD 12,575; trim 13.5 x 21.25. Circ: 92,000 (paid).

▼ **CO - ED MAGAZINE.** see *MEN'S INTERESTS*

370.711 371.33 USA
COE-MMUNETY. Text in English. s-m. free. **Document type:** *Newsletter.* **Description:** Informs the faculty, staff, students, and alumni of the ASU College of Education of news and developments.
Media: Online - full text.
Published by: Arizona State University, College of Education, PO Box 870211, Tempe, AZ 85287-0211. TEL 602-965-2114, FAX 602-965-9144, hhp@asu.edu. Ed. Heidi Hagen Pearson.

378 ESP
COLECCION ABIERTA. Text in Spanish. 1993. irreg., latest vol.56, 2001. price varies. **Document type:** *Monographic series, Academic/Scholarly.*
Published by: Universidad de Sevilla, Secretariado de Publicaciones, Porvenir 27, Sevilla, 41013, Spain. TEL 34-95-4487444, FAX 34-95-4487443, secpub10@us.es, http://www.us.es/publius/inicio.html.

378 ESP
COLECCION NUEVA AMERICA. Text in Spanish. 1996. irreg., latest 1998. price varies. **Document type:** *Monographic series, Academic/Scholarly.*
Published by: Universidad de Sevilla, Secretariado de Publicaciones, Porvenir 27, Sevilla, 41013, Spain. TEL 34-95-4487444, FAX 34-95-4487443, secpub10@us.es, http://www.us.es/publius/inicio.html.

COLLECTION 128. see *LINGUISTICS*

378 401 FRA ISSN 0764-9169
COLLECTION AMPHI 7. Text in French. 1983. irreg. price varies. **Document type:** *Monographic series.*
Indexed: MLA-IB.
Published by: Presses Universitaires du Mirail, Universite de Toulouse II (Le Mirail), 5, Allee Antonio Machado, Toulouse, 31058, France. TEL 33-05-61503810, FAX 33-05-61503800, pum@univ-tlse2.fr, http://www.univ-tlse2.fr. Ed. d'Odette Gorsse.

378.111 378 USA ISSN 0192-1371
KF4225.A59
COLLEGE ADMINISTRATOR AND THE COURTS; briefs of selected court cases affecting the administration of institutions of higher education. Text in English. 1977. q. USD 63.50 (effective 2003). index. **Document type:** *Newsletter.* **Description:** Presents research briefs on court cases that affect the administrative staff and activities of institutions of higher education.
Published by: College Administration Publications, Inc., 830 Fairview Rd, Ste D, Asheville, NC 28803-1081. TEL 828-277-8777, FAX 828-277-8735, info@collegepubs.com, http://www.collegepubs.com/descrip/3.shtml. Ed. Joseph C Beckham. Circ: 1,200.

378 USA ISSN 0010-0889
LB2300
COLLEGE AND UNIVERSITY. Text in English. 1925. q. USD 50 to non-members; USD 60 foreign to non-members (effective 2001). adv. bk.rev. charts; illus. index. back issues avail.; reprints avail. **Document type:** *Academic/Scholarly.* **Description:** Addresses issues relevant to the association's purposes; looks at emerging issues in higher education; and reports new techniques and technology used by members in handling their responsibilities.
Related titles: Microform ed.: (from PQC); Online - full text ed.: (from ProQuest Information & Learning).
Indexed: ABIn, ASCA, AgeL, BRI, CBRI, CIJE, CPE, CurCont, EAA, EduInd, HEA, SSCI.
—BLDSC (3311.017000), IE, Infotrieve, ingenta.
Published by: American Association of Collegiate Registrars and Admissions Officers, One Dupont Circle, N W, Ste 520, Washington, DC 20036-1135. TEL 202-293-9161, FAX 202-872-8857, pubs@aacrao.org, http://www.aacrao.com. Eds. Roman S Gawkoski, Saira Burki. R&P Saira Burki. Adv. contact Sairi Burki. Circ: 9,500.

378.161 USA ISSN 0147-5894
LB2351
COLLEGE AND UNIVERSITY ADMISSIONS AND ENROLLMENT, NEW YORK STATE. Text in English. 1948. a. free. charts; stat. back issues avail.
Formerly: College and University Enrollment in New York State (0077-9180)
Published by: Education Department, Post-Secondary Policy Analysis, Cultural Education Bldg, Rm 5B44, Albany, NY 12230. TEL 518-474-3874. Circ: (controlled).

378.2 USA ISSN 0077-9172
COLLEGE AND UNIVERSITY DEGREES CONFERRED, NEW YORK STATE. Text in English. 1950. a. free. charts; stat. back issues avail.
Published by: Education Department, Post-Secondary Policy Analysis, Cultural Education Bldg, Rm 5B44, Albany, NY 12230. TEL 518-474-3874. Circ: (controlled).

378.12 USA ISSN 0093-3414
LB2331.7
COLLEGE AND UNIVERSITY EMPLOYEES, NEW YORK STATE. Text in English. 1960. a. charts; stat. back issues avail.
Formerly: New York (State). Education Department. Employees in Colleges and Universities
Published by: Education Department, Office of Post-Secondary Policy Analysis, c/o James J Brady, Chief, Bureau of Post Secondary Statistical Service, Rm 5B44 CEC, Albany, NY 12230. TEL 518-474-3874. Circ: (controlled).

378 600 USA ISSN 1075-8496
LB3044.72 CODEN: CUMRC5
➤ **COLLEGE & UNIVERSITY MEDIA REVIEW**; a look at practices, trends & research. Text in English. 1994. s-a. USD 75 to libraries & non-members (effective 2005). bk.rev.; software rev. **Document type:** *Journal, Academic/Scholarly.* **Description:** Includes articles that focus on media and technology, related research, instructional development, management and supervision, as related to the operation of instructional support service units in higher education.
Related titles: Online - full text ed.: (from H.W. Wilson, O C L C Online Computer Library Center, Inc.).
Indexed: ABIn, EduInd, HEA, Inspec, LISA.
Published by: Consortium of College and University Media Centers, Iowa State University, Instructional Technology Center, 1200 Communications Bldg, Ames, IA 50011-3243. TEL 515-294-1811, FAX 515-294-8089, ccumc@ccumc.org, teach@indiana.edu, http://www.ccumc.org/pubs/c&umr.html, http://www.indiana.edu/~ccumc/. Ed., R&P Jeff Clark.

E

▼ new title ➤ refereed ✶ unverified ♦ full entry avail.

378 USA
COLLEGE BEAT. Text in English. w. **Description:** Features articles and columns for college students all over the country.
Media: Online - full text.
Address: jens@internal.collegebeat.com, http://www.collegebeat.com/home.asp. Ed. Jen Snyder.

378 USA
COLLEGE BOARD NEWS. Text in English. 1972. 4/yr. free to qualified personnel. film rev. charts; illus.; stat.; tr.lit. reprint service avail. from PQC. **Document type:** *Newspaper.*
Published by: College Board, 45 Columbus Ave, New York, NY 10023. TEL 212-713-8000. Ed. Nancy Viggiano. Circ: 107,000.

378.16 USA ISSN 0010-0951
LB2353
COLLEGE BOARD REVIEW. Text in English. 1947. q. USD 25. illus. cum.index every 2 yrs. reprint service avail. from PQC. **Document type:** *Corporate.* **Description:** Focuses on high school counseling, college admissions, financial aid, recruitment and testing.
Related titles: Microform ed.: (from PQC).
Indexed: ABIn, CIJE, CPE, ChPerI, EduInd, HEA.
—BLDSC (3311.025000), IE, ingenta.
Published by: College Board, 45 Columbus Ave, New York, NY 10023. TEL 212-713-8000, http://www.collegeboard.com/. Ed. Paul Barry. Circ: 15,500. **Subscr. to:** College Board Review, PO Box 080419, Great Kills Sta, Staten Island, NY 10308-0005.

378.161 USA ISSN 1068-7912
COLLEGE BOUND. Text in English. 1986. m. USD 59 domestic; USD 69 foreign (effective 2005). bk.rev. tr.lit. back issues avail.; reprints avail. **Document type:** *Newsletter, Consumer.* **Description:** Covers college admissions, financial aid, issues and trends.
Related titles: Online - full text ed.: USD 100 (effective 2004).
Published by: College Bound Publications, Inc., PO Box 6526, Evanston, IL 60204. TEL 773-262-5810, FAX 773-262-5806, http://www.collegeboundnews.com. Ed., Pub. R Craig Sautter. Circ: 2,500 (paid and controlled).

COLLEGE BOUND MAGAZINE. see *EDUCATION—Guides To Schools And Colleges*

378.145 USA ISSN 0740-395X
COLLEGE BY MAIL NEWSLETTER - ETC. NEWSLETTER. Text in English. 1991. a. USD 16.95 (effective 2005). **Document type:** *Newsletter.* **Description:** Publishes lists of colleges, schools and what they offer.
Formerly: College By Mail
Published by: Prosperity & Profits Unlimited, PO Box 416, Denver, CO 80201-0416. TEL 303-575-5676, FAX 303-575-1187. Ed. A. Doyle. Circ: 10,000 (controlled and free).

378.052 CAN ISSN 1203-4789
COLLEGE CANADA. Text in English, French. 1969. q. **Document type:** *Newsletter.* **Description:** Addresses issues of interest to all five of the association's constituent groups: CEOs, faculty, administration, staff and students. Features columns that highlight literacy and human resources development.
Former titles: A C C C Community (0839-0088); (until 1987): College Canada (0045-7361)
Published by: Association of Canadian Community Colleges, 1223 Michael St N, Ste 200, Ottawa, ON K1J 7T2, Canada. TEL 613-746-6626, FAX 613-746-6721, lchevrier@accc.ca, http://www.accc.ca. Circ: 11,000.

E

378 USA ISSN 0733-1355
COLLEGE CATALOG COLLECTION. Text in English. 1973. 3/yr. USD 798.
Media: Microfiche. **Related titles:** CD-ROM ed.
Published by: Career Guidance Foundation, 8090 Engineer Rd, San Diego, CA 92111. TEL 800-854-2670, FAX 619-278-8960. Ed. Ralph Anders.

378 USA ISSN 0588-2699
COLLEGE CHEMISTRY FACULTIES. Text in English. 1965. irreg.
—**CCC.**
Published by: American Chemical Society, 1155 16th St, N W, Washington, DC 20036. TEL 202-872-4614, 800-227-5558, FAX 202-776-8264, http://www.acs.org.

COLLEGE COMPOSITION AND COMMUNICATION. see *EDUCATION—Teaching Methods And Curriculum*

378 FRA ISSN 0069-5580
COLLEGE DE FRANCE. ANNUAIRE; resume des cours et travaux. Variant title: Resume des Cours et Travaux des Professeurs du College de France. Text in French. 1901. a. EUR 25 (effective 2003). **Document type:** *Academic/Scholarly.*
Indexed: BAS, BHA.
Published by: College de France, 11 Place Marcelin Berthelot, Paris, 75231 Cedex 05, France. TEL 33-1-44271101, FAX 33-1-44271109, contact@college-de-france.fr, http://www.college-de-france.fr. Ed. Florence Terrasse-Riou. R&P Florence Terrasse Riou. Circ: 700. **Subscr. to:** C I D, 131 bd. Saint-Michel, Paris 75005, France.

COLLEGE ENGLISH. see *EDUCATION—Teaching Methods And Curriculum*

COLLEGE FACTS CHART. see *EDUCATION—Guides To Schools And Colleges*

378 USA ISSN 1045-3938
COLLEGE HILL. Text in English. 198?. q. **Document type:** *Magazine, Academic/Scholarly.*
Related titles: Online - full text ed.
Published by: Rogers State College, 1701 W. Will Rogers Blvd., Claremore, OK 74017. http://www.rsu.edu/.

COLLEGE INFORMATION BOOKLET. see *MEDICAL SCIENCES—Chiropractic, Homeopathy, Osteopathy*

378.12 CAN
COLLEGE INSTITUTE EDUCATORS' ASSOCIATION. PROFILE. Text in English. 1989. s-a. back issues avail. **Document type:** *Newsletter.* **Description:** Offers analysis and information on policy, labor relations and professional issues affecting community college and institute educators and the higher education system in general.
Published by: College Institute Educators' Association, 301 555 W Eighth Ave, Vancouver, BC V5Z 1C6, Canada. TEL 604-873-8988, FAX 604-873-8865. Ed. Roseanne Moran. Circ: 7,500.

COLLEGE LITERATURE. see *LITERATURE*

COLLEGE MEDIA REVIEW. see *JOURNALISM*

COLLEGE MUSIC SOCIETY. NEWSLETTER. see *MUSIC*

COLLEGE NEWS. see *COMPUTERS—Internet*

378 USA ISSN 1543-7094
▼ **COLLEGE PARENT MAGAZINE.** Text in English. 2003 (Sep.). 10/yr. free (effective 2004). adv. **Document type:** *Magazine, Consumer.* **Description:** Provides expert advice on helping students select, and be selected by, the best colleges and universities at affordable prices.
Published by: College Parent, Inc., 241 North Avenue West, Westfield, NJ 07091. TEL 973-762-5800, info@collegeparenting.com, http://www.collegeparenting.com. adv.: color page USD 3,850.

378 USA ISSN 1523-0910
COLLEGE PLANNING AND MANAGEMENT. Text in English. m. free to qualified personnel (effective 2004). **Document type:** *Magazine, Consumer.* **Description:** Addresses all concerns of higher education administrators, including increased security and safety needs, technology capability, and recreational facilities.
Related titles: Online - full text ed.: (from Gale Group).
Indexed: CIJE.
—**CCC.**
Published by: Peter Li Education Group, 2621 Dryden Rd, Ste 300, Dayton, OH 45439-1661. TEL 937-293-1415, 800-523-4625, FAX 937-293-1310, cpm@peterli.com, http://www.peterli.com. Ed. Deborah P Moore TEL 602-867-2085.

378 USA ISSN 0010-1125
COLLEGE PRESS SERVICE. Text in English. 1962. s-w. price varies. bk.rev. index every 3 years. reprint service avail. from PQC. **Description:** Covers national student, faculty, and higher education news.
Formerly: Collegiate Press Service
Media: Duplicated (not offset). **Related titles:** Microform ed.: (from PQC); Online - full text ed.
Published by: Tribune Media Services, 435 N Michigan Ave, Ste 1417, Chicago, IL 60611-4008. Ed. Carol Monaghan. Circ: 610.

378.3 USA ISSN 1050-7159
COLLEGE PREVIEW. Text in English. 1985. q. USD 9.60. adv. **Description:** Focuses on continuing education, financial aid sources and survival skills for Black and Hispanic high school students who are college bound.
Published by: Communications Publishing Group, Inc., 660 Penn Tower, 3100 Broadway St. Ste 660, Kansas City, MO 64111-2413. TEL 913-317-2888, FAX 816-960-1989. Ed. Jeanine Meiers. Pub. Georgia Lee Clarke. adv.: B&W page USD 22,600, color page USD 25,200. Circ: 600,000.

378 CAN
➤ **THE COLLEGE QUARTERLY (ONLINE EDITION).** Abbreviated title: C Q. Text in English. 1993. q. free (effective 2005). **Document type:** *Journal, Academic/Scholarly.* **Description:** Professional development of college educators.
Formerly (until 1997): The College Quarterly (Print Edition) (1195-4353)
Media: Online - full content.
Indexed: CEI, HEA.
Published by: Seneca College of Applied Arts and Technology, 1750 Finch Ave E, Toronto, ON, Canada. TEL 416-491-5050, FAX 416-491-7745, cq@globalserve.net, http://www.senecac.on.ca/quarterly/index.html. Ed. Katharine Janzen.

378 GBR ISSN 1367-5664
➤ **COLLEGE RESEARCH.** Text in English. 1997. 3/yr. GBP 40 (effective 2001). bk.rev. 60 p./no.; **Document type:** *Journal, Academic/Scholarly.* **Description:** Contains research papers, reports, summaries of work in progress and commentary on topical research issues affecting post-16 education and training.
Indexed: BrEdI, CPE, ERA, ETA, MEA, RHEA, SEA, SENA, SOMA, SWA, TEA.
Published by: Learning and Skills Development Agency, Citadel Pl, Tinworth St, London, SE11 5EF, United Kingdom. TEL 44-20-7840-5400, FAX 44-20-7840-5401, enquiries@LSagency.org.uk, http://www.LSagency.org.uk. Ed. Andrew Morris. R&P Ann Marie Warrender. Circ: 2,500 (paid).

378.111 USA ISSN 1540-8434
LB2342.92
COLLEGE SERVICES. Text in English. 1978. bi-m. USD 100 (effective 2002). adv. bk.rev. **Document type:** *Trade.*
Formerly (until 2001): College Services Administration (0738-7903)
Published by: National Association of College Auxiliary Services, PO Box 5546, Charlottesville, VA 22905-5546. TEL 434-245-8425, http://www.nacas.org, FAX 434-245-8453. Ed., R&P, Adv. contact David Rood. Circ: 2,500.

COLLEGE STORE EXECUTIVE. see *BUSINESS AND ECONOMICS—Marketing And Purchasing*

378 USA ISSN 0145-1472
KF4243.A59
➤ **COLLEGE STUDENT AND THE COURTS**; briefs of selected court cases involving student-institutional relationships in higher education. Text in English. 1973. q. looseleaf. USD 63.50 (effective 2003). index. back issues avail. **Document type:** *Newsletter, Academic/Scholarly.* **Description:** Presents research briefs on court cases that affect the relationship between students and institutions in higher education.
Published by: College Administration Publications, Inc., PO Box 830 Fairview Rd, Ste D, Asheville, NC 28803-1081. TEL 828-277-8777, FAX 828-277-8735, info@collegepubs.com, http://www.collegepubs.com/descrip/1.shtml. Eds. Donald D Gehring, Timothy D Letzring. Circ: 2,200.

378.3 USA ISSN 0146-3934
LA229 CODEN: CSJLAO
➤ **COLLEGE STUDENT JOURNAL**; a journal pertaining to college students. Text in English. 1963. q. USD 27 domestic to individuals; USD 37 foreign to individuals; USD 33 domestic to institutions; USD 43 foreign to institutions (effective 2004). adv. bk.rev. index. **Document type:** *Journal, Academic/Scholarly.*
Formerly: College Student Survey (0010-1184)
Related titles: Microform ed.: (from PQC); Online - full text ed.: (from bigchalk, EBSCO Publishing, Florida Center for Library Automation, Gale Group, H.W. Wilson, O C L C Online Computer Library Center, Inc., ProQuest Information & Learning).
Indexed: ABIn, CIJE, CPE, ChPerI, ERA, ETA, EduInd, HEA, L&LBA, MEA, MLA-IB, PsycInfo, PsycholAb, RHEA, SEA, SENA, SOMA, SOPODA, SSA, SWA, TEA, e-psyche.
—BLDSC (3311.290000), IE, Infotrieve, ingenta. **CCC.**
Published by: Dr. George E. Uhlig, 1362 Santa Cruz Ct, Chula Vista, CA 91910-7114. FAX 334-639-7360, guhlig007@yahoo.com. Circ: 700.

370.711 USA ISSN 8756-7555
L11 CODEN: ICUNA5
➤ **COLLEGE TEACHING.** Text in English. 1953. q. USD 52 domestic to individuals; USD 66 foreign to individuals; USD 113 domestic to institutions; USD 127 foreign to institutions; USD 28.25 per issue (effective academic year 2005 - 2006). adv. bk.rev. illus. index, cum.index: vols.1-10. back issues avail.; reprint service avail. from PSC. **Document type:** *Journal, Academic/Scholarly.* **Description:** Highlights education and training of teachers.
Formerly (until 1985): Improving College and University Teaching (0019-3089)
Related titles: CD-ROM ed.: (from ProQuest Information & Learning); Microform ed.; Online - full text ed.: (from bigchalk, EBSCO Publishing, Florida Center for Library Automation, Gale Group, H.W. Wilson, Northern Light Technology, Inc., O C L C Online Computer Library Center, Inc., ProQuest Information & Learning).
Indexed: ABIn, CIJE, CPE, DIP, EAA, ERA, ETA, EduInd, HEA, IBR, IBZ, MEA, RHEA, SEA, SENA, SOMA, TEA.
—BLDSC (3311.313000), IE, Infotrieve, ingenta. **CCC.**
Published by: (Helen Dwight Reid Educational Foundation), Heldref Publications, 1319 18th St, NW, Washington, DC 20036-1802. TEL 202-296-6267, 800-365-9753, FAX 202-293-6130, ct@heldref.org, subscribe@heldref.org, http://www.heldref.org/ct.php. Adv. contact Chante Douglas. B&W page USD 330; trim 7 x 10. Circ: 1,302 (paid).

➤ **COLLEGE - UNIVERSITY FOODSERVICE WHO'S WHO.** see *FOOD AND FOOD INDUSTRIES*

378.007 USA ISSN 0588-4934
AS36 CODEN: CCSTBG
COLORADO COLLEGE STUDIES. Text in English. 1958. irreg.
Indexed: AmH&L, HistAb.

Published by: Colorado College, 14 E Cache La Poudre St, Colorado Springs, CO 80903-3294. TEL 719-389-6000, FAX 719-389-6256, communications@coloradocollege.edu, http://www.coloradocollege.edu.

378   PER
COMENTARIOS REALES. Text in Spanish. **Document type:** *Academic/Scholarly.* **Description:** Publishes articles, essays and studies on teaching, history, literature, linguistics, geography and other areas of science and research.
Published by: Universidad Inca Garcilaso de la Vega, Escuela de Profesionalizacion Docente, Ave. Arequipa, 3610, San Isidro, Lima 27, Peru. TEL 711421. Ed. Gustavo Armijos.

378.33   LUX   ISSN 1023-3040
COMMISSION OF THE EUROPEAN COMMUNITIES. ERASMUS AND LINGUA ACTION II. DIRECTORY/ERASMUS AND LINGUA ACTION II. REPERTOIRE. Variant title: Erasmus and Lingua Action II. Directory. Text in Multiple languages. 1988. a. USD 55.
—BLDSC (3794.910100).
Published by: European Commission, Office for Official Publications of the European Union, 2 Rue Mercier, Luxembourg, L-2985, Luxembourg. FAX 352-2929-1, opoce-info-info@cec.eu.int, http://publications.eu.int.

378   USA   ISSN 0069-6854
LB2301.C56
COMMITTEE ON INSTITUTIONAL COOPERATION. ANNUAL REPORT. Text in English. 1970. a. free.
Published by: Committee on Institutional Cooperation, 1819 S. Neil St., Ste. D, Champaign, IL 61820-7271. TEL 217-333-8475, FAX 217-244-7127, cic@uiuc.edu, http://www.cic.uiuc.edu. Ed. Russell W Snyder. Circ: (controlled).

378   GBR   ISSN 0069-7745
LB2310
COMMONWEALTH UNIVERSITIES YEARBOOK. Text in English. 1914. a. GBP 200, USD 250 per issue (effective 2003 - 2004). adv. **Document type:** *Directory.* **Description:** Includes extensive profiles of individual institutions covering academic structure and facilities, course information and admissions proceedure, departmental research strengths, listings of senior academic and administrative staff and, in addition, national guides to first and higher degree programmes.
Related titles: Online - full content ed.
Indexed: RASB.
—BLDSC (3341.110000).
Published by: Association of Commonwealth Universities, John Foster House, 36 Gordon Square, London, WC1H 0, United Kingdom. TEL 44-20-73806700, FAX 44-20-73872655, s.kirkland@acu.ac.uk, info@acu.ac.uk, http://www.acu.ac.uk/publications. Ed. Paul Turner. R&P, Adv. contact Sue Kirkland TEL 44-20-73806700. **Dist. in U.S. by:** Grove's Dictionaries Inc., 354 Park Ave S, 10th Fl, New York, NY 10010-1707.

378.052   USA
COMMUNITY COLLEGE COUNCIL PERSPECTIVE. Text in English. bi-m. adv. charts; illus.; stat. back issues avail. **Description:** For all community college faculty and staff who are represented by the California Federation of Teachers. Covers statewide issues including CC legislation, finances, reform, conferences and trends.
Published by: California Federation of Teachers, Community College Council, 1200 W Magnolia Blvd, Burbank, CA 91506. TEL 818-843-8226. Ed. Gail E Myers. Circ: 2,400.

378 371.2   USA   ISSN 1541-0935
LB2328.15.U62
➤ **THE COMMUNITY COLLEGE ENTERPRISE**; a journal of research and practice. Text in English. 1995. 2/yr., latest vol.8. USD 35 to individuals; USD 75 to institutions (effective 2003 - 2004). bk.rev. 120 p./no. 2 cols./p.; back issues avail. **Document type:** *Journal, Academic/Scholarly.* **Description:** Provides sound educational practices based upon scholarship and research for and by the community college practitioners.
Formerly (until May 2002): Michigan Community College Journal (1081-9428)
Related titles: Online - full text ed.: (from ProQuest Information & Learning).
Indexed: CIJE.
Published by: Schoolcraft College, 18600 Haggerty Rd, Livonia, MI 48152. TEL 734-462-4400, FAX 734-462-4679, gwilson@schoolcraft.edu, gwilson@schoolcraft.cc.mi.us, http://www.schoolcraft.edu/cce. Ed. Dr. Louis A Reibling. R&Ps Mr. Gordon L Wilson TEL 734-462-4400 ext 5283, Ms. Ione Skaggs. Circ: 200.

378.052   USA   ISSN 1052-7095
LB2361.5
COMMUNITY COLLEGE EXEMPLARY INSTRUCTIONAL PROGRAMS. Text in English. 1989. a.
Published by: Massachusetts Bay Community College Press, 50 Oakland St, Wellesley, MA 02181.

378.052   USA   ISSN 1067-1803
LB2300
COMMUNITY COLLEGE JOURNAL. Text in English. 1930. bi-m. USD 28 domestic (effective 2005). adv. bk.rev. bibl.; illus. index. reprint service avail. from PQC. **Document type:** *Journal, Academic/Scholarly.* **Description:** Covers the latest trends, innovations, and research affecting two-year colleges. Features exemplary programs, practices, and policies.
Former titles (until 1991): Community, Technical, and Junior College Journal (0884-7169); Community and Junior College Journal (0190-3160); Junior College Journal (0022-653X)
Related titles: Microform ed.: (from PQC); Online - full text ed.: (from ProQuest Information & Learning)
Indexed: ABIn, AgeL, CIJE, CPE, EAA, EduInd, HEA, MEDLINE. —BLDSC (3363.606100), IE, Infotrieve, ingenta.
Published by: American Association of Community Colleges, One Dupont Circle, N W, Ste 410, Washington, DC 20036-1176. TEL 202-728-0200, FAX 202-223-9390, cgamble@aacc.nche.edu, http://www.aacc.nche.edu/. Ed. Cheryl Gamble. adv.: B&W page USD 1,987, color page USD 3,102. Circ: 11,000 (paid).

378.052   USA   ISSN 1066-8926
LB2328   CODEN: CCJPEU
➤ **COMMUNITY COLLEGE JOURNAL OF RESEARCH AND PRACTICE.** Text in English. 1976. 10/yr. GBP 368, USD 607 combined subscription to institutions print & online eds. (effective 2006). adv. bk.rev. abstr.; bibl.; charts; illus. Index. back issues avail.; reprint service avail. from PQC,PSC. **Document type:** *Journal, Academic/Scholarly.* **Description:** Devoted to all aspects, domestic and international, research and practical, of two-year college education.
Former titles (until 1993): Community Junior College Research Quarterly of Research and Practice (0277-6774); (until vol.6, 1981): Community Junior College Research Quarterly (0361-6975)
Related titles: Microform ed.: (from PQC); Online - full text ed.: ISSN 1521-0413. GBP 350, USD 577 to institutions (effective 2006) (from EBSCO Publishing, Gale Group, IngentaConnect, O C L C Online Computer Library Center, Inc., Swets Information Services).
Indexed: ABIn, CIJE, CPE, ChPerl, CurCont, EAA, ERA, ETA, EduInd, HEA, MEA, RHEA, SEA, SENA, SOMA, SWA, TEA, V&AA.
—BLDSC (3363.606200), IE, Infotrieve, ingenta. **CCC.**
Published by: (University of North Texas, Department of Higher Education), Routledge (Subsidiary of: Taylor & Francis Ltd), 325 Chestnut St., Suite 800, Philadelphia, PA 19106. TEL 215-625-8900, 800-354-1420, FAX 215-625-8914, journals@routledge.com, http://www.tandf.co.uk/journals/titles/10668926.asp, http://www.routledge.com. Ed. D Barry Lumsden. Circ: 500. **Subscr. outside N. America to:** Taylor & Francis Ltd, Journals Customer Service, Rankine Rd, Basingstoke, Hants RG24 8PR, United Kingdom. TEL 44-1256-813000, FAX 44-1256-330245, enquiry@tandf.co.uk.

378.052   USA   ISSN 0091-5521
LB2328
➤ **COMMUNITY COLLEGE REVIEW.** Text in English. 1973. q. USD 90 domestic; USD 92 in Canada; USD 94 elsewhere (effective 2005). bk.rev. bibl.; charts; illus. reprints avail. **Document type:** *Academic/Scholarly.* **Description:** Publishes scholarly articles, case studies, models, research, analyses, and literature reviews on the contemporary problems and issues that affect professionals at this educational level.
Related titles: Microfilm ed.: (from PQC); Online - full text ed.: (from bigchalk, EBSCO Publishing, Florida Center for Library Automation, Gale Group, H.W. Wilson, O C L C Online Computer Library Center, Inc., ProQuest Information & Learning).
Indexed: ABIn, CIJE, CPE, EAA, ERA, ETA, EduInd, HEA, MEA, MLA-IB, RHEA, SEA, SENA, SOMA, TEA.
—BLDSC (3363.607000), IE, ingenta.
Published by: North Carolina State University, Department of Adult and Community College Education, PO Box 7801, Raleigh, NC 27695-7801. TEL 919-513-3706, FAX 919-515-6305, http://ced.ncsu.edu/acce. R&P Barbara Scott. Circ: 1,325 (paid).

378.052   USA   ISSN 1041-5726
COMMUNITY COLLEGE WEEK; the independent voice serving community, technical and junior colleges. Text in English. 1988. bi-w. USD 40 domestic; USD 50 in Canada; USD 60 elsewhere (effective 2004). adv. illus.; charts; stat. 5 cols./p.; back issues avail.; reprints avail. **Document type:** *Newspaper, Academic/Scholarly.* **Description:** Provides current information on state and national news affecting community, technical and junior colleges.
Related titles: Online - full text ed.: (from EBSCO Publishing, Florida Center for Library Automation, Gale Group).
Published by: Cox, Matthews & Associates, Inc., 10520 Warwick Ave, Ste B 8, Fairfax, VA 22030. TEL 703-385-2981, FAX 703-385-1839, ccweek@cmabiccw.com, http://www.ccweek.com, http://www.ccw.com. Ed. Scott Cech. Pub. Frank Matthews. R&P Ralph Newell TEL 703-385-2981. Adv. contact Pam Barrett. Circ: 60,000.

378 374   USA
COMMUTER PERSPECTIVES. Text in English. 1973. q. USD 35 (effective 2000). bk.rev. bibl. 8 p./no.; back issues avail. **Document type:** *Consumer.* **Description:** Provides information, issues and services for commuter students at both 2-year and 4-year institutions of higher education.

Published by: National Clearinghouse for Commuter Programs, University of Maryland, 1195 Stamp Student Union, College Park, MD 20742-4621. TEL 301-314-5274, FAX 301-314-9874, nccp@accmail.umd.edu, http://www.umd.edu/nccp. Ed., R&P Richard A Stevens Jr. Circ: 300.

COMPASS POINTS. see *RELIGIONS AND THEOLOGY—Protestant*

378.0025   GBR
COMPENDIUM OF HIGHER EDUCATION. Text in English. irreg., latest 1999. GBP 24.99, USD 64.95 base vol(s). (effective 2003). 400 p./no.: **Document type:** *Directory.* **Description:** A unique guide to the qualifications needed to get onto a higher education course and all undergraduate degrees in the UK.
Formerly: Compendium of Advanced Courses in Colleges of Further and Higher Education
—BLDSC (3363.967970).
Published by: (L A S E R Advisory Council), Butterworth - Heinemann (Subsidiary of: Elsevier Ltd., Books Division), Linacre House, Jordan Hill, Oxford, OX2 8DP, United Kingdom. TEL 44-1865-310366, 44-1865-888180, FAX 44-1865-310898, 44-1865-314091.

COMPUTER SCIENCE & ELECTRICAL ENGINEERING PROGRAMS. see *COMPUTERS*

378.00285   GBR   ISSN 0360-1315
LB2846   CODEN: COMEDR
➤ **COMPUTERS & EDUCATION.** Text in English. 1977. 8/yr. EUR 1,390 in Europe to institutions; JPY 184,400 in Japan to institutions; USD 1,556 to institutions except Europe and Japan; EUR 171 in Europe to qualified personnel; JPY 22,600 in Japan to qualified personnel; USD 190 to qualified personnel except Europe and Japan (effective 2006). adv. bk.rev. charts; illus. index. back issues avail. **Document type:** *Academic/Scholarly.* **Description:** For users of analog, digital and hybrid computers in all aspects of higher education. Presents technical research papers covering a broad range of subjects.
Related titles: Microfilm ed.: (from PQC); Online - full text ed.: (from EBSCO Publishing, Gale Group, IngentaConnect, ScienceDirect, Swets Information Services).
Indexed: ABIn, AHCI, ASCA, BrCerAb, BrEdI, C&ISA, CADCAM, CIJE, CMCI, CPE, CerAb, CompC, CompLI, CompR, CorrAb, CurCont, CybAb, E&CAJ, EMA, ERA, ETA, EduInd, EngInd, ErgAb, HEA, HECAB, IAA, Inspec, LAMP, M&TEA, MBF, MEA, METADEX, MicrocompInd, PCI, RHEA, RefZh, SEA, SENA, SOMA, SSCI, SWA, SolStAb, TEA, WAA.
—BLDSC (3394.677000), AskIEEE, CISTI, Ei, IDS, IE, Infotrieve, ingenta, Linda Hall. **CCC.**
Published by: Pergamon (Subsidiary of: Elsevier Science & Technology), The Boulevard, Langford Ln, East Park, Kidlington, Oxford OX5 1GB, United Kingdom. TEL 44-1865-843000, FAX 44-1865-843010, http://www.elsevier.com/locate/compedu. Eds. J. M. Underwood, R. S. Heller. Circ: 1,100. **Subscr. to:** Elsevier BV, PO Box 211, Amsterdam 1000 AE, Netherlands. TEL 31-20-485-3757, FAX 31-20-485-3432, nlinfo-f@elsevier.nl, http://www.elsevier.nl.

➤ **COMPUTERS IN HIGHER EDUCATION ECONOMICS REVIEW.** see *COMPUTERS—Computer Assisted Instruction*

378.12   IND
CONFERENCE OF VICE-CHANCELLORS. PROCEEDINGS. Text in English. 1961. irreg.
Published by: University Grants Commission, Publication Officer, 35 Ferozeshah Rd., New Delhi, 110 001, India. TEL 386 365. Ed. V Appa Rao. Circ: 6,000.

378.12   IND
CONFERENCE OF VICE-CHANCELLORS. REPORT. Text in English. irreg.?.
Published by: University Grants Commission, Publication Officer, 35 Ferozeshah Rd., New Delhi, 110 001, India.

378   CHE
CONFERENCE UNIVERSITAIRE SUISSE. INFO - C U S/SCHWEIZERISCHE HOCHSCHULKONFERENZ. S H K - INFO. Text in French. 1994. irreg. (5-6/yr.). free. **Document type:** *Bulletin.*
Published by: Conference Universitaire Suisse/Schweizerische Hochschulkonferenz, Sennweg 2, Bern, 3012, Switzerland. TEL 41-31-3066060, FAX 41-31-3021792, shk@shk.ch.

378   CHE
CONFERENCE UNIVERSITAIRE SUISSE. RAPPORT ANNUEL. Text in French. 1969. a. free. **Document type:** *Corporate.*
Related titles: German ed.: Schweizerische Hochschulkonferenz. Jahresbericht.
Published by: Conference Universitaire Suisse/Schweizerische Hochschulkonferenz, Sennweg 2, Bern, 3012, Switzerland. TEL 41-31-3066060, FAX 41-31-3021792, shk@shk.ch. Circ: 350.

378   USA
CONFLICT MANAGEMENT IN HIGHER EDUCATION REPORT. Text in English. 2000. bi-m. free (effective 2000). abstr. back issues avail.
Media: Online - full text.

E

Published by: Wayne State University, College of Urban, Labor and Metro Affairs, 3248 Faculty Admin Bldg, 656 W Kirby, Detroit, MI 48202. TEL 313-993-7482, FAX 313-577-8800, http://www.culma.wayne.edu/CMHER/Newsletter.html. Ed. Bill Warters.

378 MEX ISSN 1560-7348
CONFLUENCIA. Text in Spanish. 1997. m. back issues avail.
Media: Online - full text. **Related titles:** Print ed.: ISSN 1405-2342.
Published by: Asociacion Nacional de Universidades e Institutos de Ensenanza Superior, Tenayuca No. 200, Col. Santa Cruz Atoyac, Mexico, DF, 03310, Mexico. TEL 52-5-4204900, FAX 52-5-6044263, editor@anuies.mx, http://www.anuies.mx/.

378 USA ISSN 0895-6405
LC67.65.N49
CONNECTION (BOSTON); New England's journal of higher education and economic development. Text in English. 1986. q. subscr. avail. with a donation. adv. illus. **Document type:** *Magazine.* **Description:** Covers issues related to higher education and its impact on economic development, particularly the New England area.
Formerly (until 1986): Higher Education in New England (0440-7881)
Related titles: Online - full text ed.: (from EBSCO Publishing, ProQuest Information & Learning).
Indexed: CIJE, IBR, IBZ, PAIS.
Published by: New England Board of Higher Education, 45 Temple Pl, Boston, MA 02111. TEL 617-357-9620, FAX 617-338-1577, connection@nebhe.org, friends@nebhe.org, http://www.nebhe.org/connection.html. Ed. John O Harney. Adv. contact Christine Quinlan.

378.0712 USA
CONNECTIONS (WASHINGTON D.C.). Text in English. 1976. m. (except Jul. and Aug.). USD 25 (effective 2002). back issues avail. **Document type:** *Newsletter.* **Description:** Discusses higher education issues, as well as relevant points of interest concerning the 28 Jesuit institutions in the United States.
Formerly (until 2000): A J C U Higher Education Report (1053-8933)
Published by: Association of Jesuit Colleges and Universities, 1 Dupont Cir, N W, Ste 405, Washington, DC 20036-1110. TEL 202-862-9893, FAX 202-862-8523, blkrobe@aol.com, http://www.ajcunet.edu. Ed. George Chen. Circ: 900.

378.2 VEN
CONSEJO NACIONAL DE INVESTIGACIONES CIENTIFICAS Y TECNOLOGICAS. DEPARTAMENTO DE EDUCACION. DIRECTORIO NACIONAL DE CURSOS DE POSTGRADO. Text in Spanish. irreg.
Published by: Consejo Nacional de Investigaciones Cientificas y Tecnologicas, Departamento de Educacion, Los Ruices, Apdo 70617, Caracas, DF 1071, Venezuela. TEL 2390433, FAX 2398677, TELEX 25205 CONICIT.

378 CRI ISSN 0589-4301
CONSEJO SUPERIOR UNIVERSITARIO CENTROAMERICANO. ACTAS DE LA REUNION ORDINARIA. Text in Spanish. irreg.
Published by: Consejo Superior Universitario Centroamericano, Apdo. Postal 37, Ciudad Univ. R. Facio, San Jose, Costa Rica.

378 ITA
CONSORZIO UNIVERSITARIO. PUBBLICAZIONI. SEZIONE MISCELLANEA. Text in Italian. 1975. irreg. per issue exchange basis. **Document type:** *Monographic series.*
Published by: Consorzio Universitario del Friuli, Via F Mantica, 5, Udine, UD 33100, Italy. TEL 39-432-21924, FAX 39-432-504696.

378 CAN
CONTACT (OTTAWA). Text in English. q. **Description:** Includes general information for and about the university.
Published by: Saint Paul University, Alumni and Development Office, 223 Main, Ottawa, ON K1S 1C4, Canada. TEL 613-236-1393, FAX 613-782-3030, dclapin@ustpaul.uottawa.ca. Ed. Daniel G Caplin.

378 GBR
CONTACT EUROPE. Text in English. 1992. q. **Document type:** *Newsletter.* **Description:** Reports on higher educational programs being funded by the E.U.
Published by: Consortium for Advanced Continuing Education, Enterprise House, Manchester Science Park, Lloyd St N, Manchester, Lancs M2 5ND, United Kingdom. TEL 44-161-226-6586, FAX 44-161-226-4766.

378 USA ISSN 0893-0384
LC6201
CONTINUING HIGHER EDUCATION REVIEW. Variant title: C H E R. Text in English. 1956. a. USD 27; USD 35 foreign (effective 2004). adv. bk.rev. index. **Document type:** *Academic/Scholarly.*
Former titles (until 1986): Continuum (Washington) (0162-4024); (until 1976): N U E A Spectator (0027-7096)
Indexed: CIJE, CPE, ERA, ETA, HEA, SEA, TEA.
—BLDSC (3425.688210), IE, ingenta.
Published by: (University Continuing Education Association), Harvard University, Division of Continuing Education, 51 Brattle Street, Cambridge, MA 02138-3722. TEL 617-495-2478, FAX 617-495-2680, http://www.dce.harvard.edu. Eds. Wayne Ishikawa, Michael Shinagel. Circ: 2,000.

378 ITA ISSN 1722-9480
CONTRIBUTI ALLA STORIA DELL'UNIVERSITA DI PADOVA. Text in Italian. 1964. irreg., latest vol.11, 1979. price varies. **Document type:** *Monographic series, Academic/Scholarly.*
Published by: (Universita degli Studi di Padova), Editrice Antenore, Via Valadier 52, Rome, 00193, Italy. TEL 39-06-32600370, FAX 39-06-3223132, antenore@editriceantenore.it, http://www.editriceantenore.it.

378.0082 USA ISSN 1065-4941
CORNERSTONE (ANN ARBOR). Text in English. 1965. irreg. (1-2/yr.). free. **Document type:** *Newsletter.* **Description:** Studies the role of women in society, with emphasis on education and careers.
Formerly: University of Michigan. Center for Continuing Education of Women Newsletter
Published by: University of Michigan, Center for the Education of Women, 330 E Liberty St, Ann Arbor, MI 48104-2289. TEL 313-998-7080, FAX 313-998-6203, cew.staff@umich.edu. Circ: 13,000.

378.106 CAN ISSN 1486-0929
COUNCIL OF ONTARIO UNIVERSITIES. RESOURCE DOCUMENT. Text in English. 1985. a.
Formerly (until 1997): Financial Position of Ontario Universities (0845-373X)
Published by: Council of Ontario Universities, 180 Dundas St W, Ste 1100, Toronto, ON M5G 1Z8, Canada. TEL 416-979-2165, FAX 416-979-8635, acadieux@coupo.cou.on.ca, http://www.cou.on.ca.

378.154 USA ISSN 1072-5830
➤ **COUNCIL ON UNDERGRADUATE RESEARCH QUARTERLY.** Text in English. 1979. q. USD 40 to individuals; USD 85 to libraries (effective 2005). adv. **Document type:** *Newsletter, Academic/Scholarly.* **Description:** Presents articles by and for faculty members primarily at undergraduate institutions, mainly in the sciences and mathematics. Also presents news items regarding undergraduate faculty and research opportunities, conferences, and sources of funds for research.
Formerly: Council on Undergraduate Research Newsletter (0890-8273)
Published by: Council on Undergraduate Research, 734 15th St NW Ste 550, Washington, DC 20005. TEL 202-783-4810, FAX 202-783-4811, cur@cur.org, http://www.cur.org. Ed. Anant Godbole. R&P Elaine Hoagland. Adv. contact JoAnne Reiche. Circ: 3,400.

378 USA
COUNTERPOINT MAGAZINE. Text in English. 8/yr. USD 20 (effective 2001). adv. bk.rev. back issues avail. **Description:** Explores topics that range from book reviews and university campus life.
Related titles: Online - full text ed.
Address: MIT Room W20-443, 77 Massachusetts Ave, Cambridge, MA 02139. http://counterpoint.mit.edu/. Ed. Kevin Beach. Adv. contact Sarah Ligon. Circ: 7,000.

COURS SPECIALISES. see *MATHEMATICS*

378 CAN ISSN 1709-8076
COURSE GUIDE. Text in English. 1998. a. **Document type:** *Academic/Scholarly.*
Former titles (until 2002): Course Calendar (1709-8068); (until 2000): Bow Valley College. Calendar (1709-805X); (until 1999): Bow Valley College. Career Catalogue (1709-8041)
Published by: Bow Valley College, Student Services, Registrar(UNKNOWN CHARACTER)s Office, 2nd Fl, 332, 6 Avenue SE, Calgary, AB T2G 4S6, Canada. TEL 403-410-1400, 866-428-2669, FAX 403-297-4081, info@bowvalleycollege.ca, http://www.bowvalleycollege.ca/.

378 USA
➤ **COYOTE;** an interdisciplinary undergraduate journal. Text in English. 1998. a. free. **Document type:** *Academic/Scholarly.* **Description:** Publishes academic works of undergraduates in a variety of disciplines.
Media: Online - full text.
Published by: University of South Dakota, 414 E Clark St, Vermillion, SD 57069-2390. TEL 605-677-5434, mrogge@usd.edu, http://www.usd.edu/~ejournal, http://www.usd.edu/ejournal. Ed. Michelle Rogge Gannon.

378.161 USA ISSN 1062-5550
CRACKING THE G M A T. (Cracking the Graduate Management Admission Test) Text in English. 1989. irreg.
Formerly: Cracking the System. The G M A T (1057-8862)
Published by: Villard Books, 299 Park Ave, New York, NY 10171.

378.161 USA ISSN 1062-5534
CRACKING THE G R E. Text in English. 1988. a.
Formerly: Cracking the System. The G R E (1049-622X)
Published by: Villard Books, 299 Park Ave, New York, NY 10171.

CRACKING THE G R E PSYCHOLOGY TEST. see *PSYCHOLOGY*

378.161 373.025 340 USA ISSN 1062-5542
CRACKING THE L S A T. Text in English. 1989. a.
Formerly (until 1993): Cracking the System. The L S A T (1049-6246)
Published by: Villard Books, 299 Park Ave, New York, NY 10171.

CRANFIELD SCHOOL OF MANAGEMENT ADDRESS BOOK. see *COLLEGE AND ALUMNI*

378.3 USA
CREDIT REPORT; linking higher education with business, industry, and government. Text in English. 1990. s-a. free. **Document type:** *Newsletter.* **Description:** Provides information on ACE-College Credit Recommendation Service (CREDIT) which recommends college credit for workplace education and training.
Formerly (until 1997): P O N S I Report (1089-4675)
Published by: (Center for Adult Learning and Educational Credentials), American Council on Education, One Dupont Circle, N W, Ste 250, Washington, DC 20036-1193. TEL 202-939-9731, FAX 202-775-8578, stephen_sattler@ace.nche.edu, http://www.acenet.edu. R&P Stephen Sattler. Circ: 5,000 (controlled).

378 AUS
CRITERIA-BASED ASSESSMENT: THE QUEENSLAND EXPERIENCE. Text in English. 1985. irreg.
Published by: Queensland Board of Senior Secondary School Studies, P.O. Box 307, Spring Hill, QLD 4101, Australia. TEL 61-7-3864-0299, FAX 61-7-3221-2553, office@qbssss.edu.au.

CRITICAL ISSUES IN FACILITIES MANAGEMENT. see *EDUCATION—School Organization And Administration*

378.07 USA ISSN 0011-1953
BR1
➤ **CROSS CURRENTS (NEW YORK).** Text in English. 1950. q. USD 30 domestic to individuals; USD 35 foreign to individuals; USD 50 domestic to libraries; USD 55 foreign to libraries; USD 20 domestic to students; USD 25 foreign to students; USD 10 newsstand/cover (effective 2005). adv. bk.rev. illus. Index. back issues avail.; reprints avail. **Document type:** *Magazine, Academic/Scholarly.* **Description:** An interfaith journal of opinion, representing thought and writing being done within various world religions; Christianity, Judaism, Islam, Buddhims, etc. whithin educational environment.
Former titles (until 1990): Religion and Intellectual Life (0741-0549); (until 1983): N I C M Journal for Jews and Christians in Higher Education (0362-0794)
Related titles: CD-ROM ed.; Magnetic Tape ed.; Microform ed.; Online - full text ed.: (from bigchalk, EBSCO Publishing, Florida Center for Library Automation, Gale Group, H.W. Wilson, O C L C Online Computer Library Center, Inc., Ovid Technologies, Inc., ProQuest Information & Learning).
Indexed: ABM, ABS&EES, AmHI, BAS, BHA, CPL, HumInd, JewAb, MLA-IB, NTA, OTA, PCI, PerIslam, R&TA, RI-1, RI-2.
—BLDSC (3488.850000), IE, Infotrieve, ingenta.
Published by: Association for Religion and Intellectual Life, 475 Riverside Dr, Ste 1945, New York, NY 10115. TEL 212-870-2544, cph@crosscurrents.org, http://www.crosscurrents.org, http://www.aril.org. Ed., R&P Kenneth Arnold. Pub. Charles Henderson. Circ: 5,000.

➤ **CROSSCURRENTS SERIES.** see *LITERATURE*

371.0712 USA
➤ **CURRENT ISSUES IN CATHOLIC HIGHER EDUCATION.** Text in English. 1975. s-a. price varies. reprint service avail. from PQC. **Document type:** *Journal, Academic/Scholarly.*
Supersedes (1975-1980): National Catholic Educational Association. Occasional Papers
Related titles: Microform ed.
Indexed: CIJE.
Published by: Association of Catholic Colleges and Universities, One Dupont Circle, Ste 650, Washington, DC 20036. TEL 202-457-0650, FAX 202-728-0977. Ed., R&P Michael James. Circ: 2,000 (paid and controlled).

378.16 USA ISSN 0748-478X
LB2300
CURRENTS (WASHINGTON). Text in English. 1975. m. (except Aug. and Dec.). USD 115 to non-members (effective 2005). adv. bk.rev. abstr.; illus. index. **Document type:** *Magazine, Trade.* **Description:** Articles on fundraising, alumni administration, institutional relations, management, periodicals, student recruitment, government relations and general interest.
Formerly (until 1983): C A S E Currents (0360-862X)
Related titles: Microform ed.: 1975 (from PQC).
Indexed: CIJE, ChPerI, HEA, PSI.
—BLDSC (3505.040000), IE, ingenta. **CCC.**
Published by: Council for Advancement and Support of Education, 1307 New York Ave, N W, Ste 1000, Washington, DC 20005. TEL 202-328-2273, FAX 202-387-4973, http://www.case.org/Currents. Ed. Deborah Bongiorno. Adv. contact Judy Palmer. Circ: 14,500.

CURRICULA IN THE ATMOSPHERIC, OCEANIC, HYDROLOGIC AND RELATED SCIENCES. see *EARTH SCIENCES—Oceanography*

378 BRA ISSN 1645-1384
➤ **CURRICULO SEM FRONTEIRAS.** Text in Portuguese. 2001. s-a. **Document type:** *Journal, Academic/Scholarly.*
Media: Online - full content.
Address: http://www.curriculosemfronteiras.org/. Pubs. Alvaro Moreira Hypolito, Joao M Paraskeva, Luis Armando Gandin.

378.199 HKG ISSN 1024-0276
➤ **CURRICULUM FORUM/KECHENG LUNTAN.** Text in Chinese, English. 1991. s-a. HKD 240, USD 30. bk.rev. **Document type:** *Academic/Scholarly.* **Description:** Focuses on research, development and innovation in all curriculum areas in the primary, secondary and tertiary levels of education.
Indexed: HongKongiana.
Published by: University of Hong Kong, Department of Curriculum Studies, Pokfulam Rd, Hong Kong, Hong Kong. TEL 852-2859-2517, FAX 852-2858-5649. Ed. Francis Lopez Real.

378 AUS ISSN 0159-7868
LB1570
CURRICULUM PERSPECTIVES (JOURNAL EDITION). Text in English. 1980. s-a. AUD 110 domestic to individuals; AUD 150 domestic to institutions; AUD 130 foreign (effective 2005); subscr. incl. journal & newsletter. **Document type:** *Journal, Academic/Scholarly.*
Indexed: CPE, ERA.
—BLDSC (3505.280200), IE, ingenta. **CCC.**
Published by: Australian Curriculum Studies Association Inc., PO Box 331, Deakin West, ACT 2600, Australia. TEL 61-2-62605660, FAX 61-2-62605665, acsa@acsa.edu.au, http://www.acsa.edu.au.

378 MEX ISSN 1605-4911
CYBER PERIODICO 2000. Text in Spanish. 1998. m. back issues avail. **Document type:** *Newspaper, Academic/Scholarly.*
Media: Online - full text.
Published by: Universidad Regiomontana, Padre Mier Pte. 471, Monterrey, Nuevo Leon, Mexico. TEL 52-8343-1290, FAX 52-8343-3172, cyberperiodico2000@yahoo.com, http://www.geocities.com/cyberperiodico2000/, http://www.ur.mx/.

378.3 IRL
D I T INDEPENDENT. Text in English. m. adv. **Document type:** *Journal, Academic/Scholarly.*
Published by: Dublin Institute of Technology, Fitzwilliam House, 30 Upper Pembroke St., Dublin, 2, Ireland. TEL 353-1-4023352. adv.: B&W page EUR 572, color page EUR 762; 260 x 365. Circ: 23,000 (controlled).

378 DEU ISSN 1437-4234
LA720
D U Z; das unabhaengige Hochschulmagazin. (Deutsche Universitaets Zeitung) Text in German. 1945. s-m. EUR 91.52; EUR 50.11 to students; EUR 5 newsstand/cover (effective 2003). adv. bk.rev. bibl.; charts. index. **Document type:** *Magazine, Consumer.*
Former titles (until 1997): D U Z - Deutsche Universitats-Zeitung, das Hochschulmagazin (0936-4501); (until 1988): D U Z - Universitaets Zeitung (0176-7224); (until 1984): D U Z - Deutsche Universitaets Zeitung (0724-147X); (until 1981): D U Z - H D - Deutsche Universitaets-Zeitung Vereinigt mit Hochschul-Dienst (0343-5563); (until 1972): Deutsche Universitaets-Zeitung Vereinigt mit Hochschul-Dienst (0170-0464)
Indexed: AmH&L, CEABA, CRCL, DIP, HistAb, IBR, IBZ, RASB.
—BLDSC (3633.123500), GNLM, Infotrieve.
Published by: Dr. Josef Raabe Verlags GmbH, Rotebuehlstr 77, Stuttgart, 70178, Germany. TEL 49-711-629000, FAX 49-711-6290099, d.schepens@raabe.de, info@raabe.de, http://www.raabe.de/bn_duz.html. adv.: B&W page EUR 2,400, color page EUR 3,400. Circ: 4,500 (paid and controlled).

378 780 USA
DA-CAPO. Text in English. a. **Document type:** *Newsletter.*
Related titles: Online - full text ed.
Published by: University of South Carolina, School of Music, 813 Assembly St, Columbia, SC 29208. TEL 803-777-4280, FAX 803-777-6508, ugmusic@mozart.sc.edu, http://www.music.sc.edu.

378 USA ISSN 1080-6814
THE DAILY BAROMETER. Text in English. 1896. d. (Mon.-Fri.). USD 66; free (effective 2005). adv. back issues avail. **Document type:** *Newspaper.*
Related titles: Online - full text ed.: (from LexisNexis).
Published by: Oregon State University, Student Media Committee, 118 Memorial Union East, Corvallis, OR 93731-1617. TEL 541-737-3374, FAX 541-737-4999, editor@dailybarometer.com, baro.editor@studentmedia.orst.edu, http://www.dailybarometer.com, http://barometer.orst.edu. Ed. Scott Johnson. adv.: col. inch USD 10. Circ: 10,000 morning (controlled and free). Wire service: AP.

DAKOTA SCIENTIST. see *SCIENCES: COMPREHENSIVE WORKS*

378 USA ISSN 0274-9262
THE DAKOTA STUDENT. Text in English. 1923. w. back issues avail. **Document type:** *Newspaper.*
Related titles: Online - full text ed.: (from LexisNexis).
Published by: University of North Dakota, PO Box 7209, Grand Forks, ND 58202. TEL 701-777-3322, FAX 701-777-2373, ndq@sage.nodak.edu, http://www.und.nodak.edu/org/ndq/.

DANMARKS JOURNALISTHOEJSKOLE. BERETNING. see *JOURNALISM*

378.773 USA ISSN 0098-5279
LA267.5
DATA BOOK ON ILLINOIS HIGHER EDUCATION✶ . Text in English. a., latest 2000. **Document type:** *Directory.*
Indexed: SRI.
Published by: Board of Higher Education, 431 E Adams St Fl 2nd, Springfield, IL 62701-1418. TEL 217-782-2551, http://www.ibhe.state.il.us. R&P Donald Sevener TEL 217-557-7334.

378 CHN ISSN 1002-2678
DAXUESHENG/UNIVERSITY STUDENT. Text in Chinese. 1988. m. USD 36.80.
Published by: Beijing Chubanshe/Beijing Publishing House, 6 Beisanhuan Zhonglu, Beijing, 100011, China. TEL 2016699. Ed. Lin Haoji. **Dist. in US by:** China Books & Periodicals Inc, 360 Swift Ave., Ste. 48, S San Fran, CA 94080-6220. TEL 415-282-2994.

DEBTS AND CAREER PLANS OF OSTEOPATHIC MEDICAL STUDENTS. see *MEDICAL SCIENCES—Chiropractic, Homeopathy, Osteopathy*

DEGREE COURSE GUIDES (YEAR). see *EDUCATION—Guides To Schools And Colleges*

378.2 GBR
DEGREE COURSE OFFERS. Text in English. 1971. a., latest vol.32, 2001. GBP 21.99 (effective 2001). adv. **Document type:** *Directory, Consumer.* **Description:** A guide to entry to UK universities and colleges.
Former titles: Complete Degree Course Offers (0953-122X); (until 1985): Degree Course Offers (0306-5812)
—BLDSC (3364.330000).
Published by: Trotman & Co. Ltd., 2 The Green, Richmond, Surrey TW9 1PL, United Kingdom. TEL 44-20-8486 1150, FAX 44-20-8486 1161, mail@trotman.co.uk, http://www.trotmanpublishing.co.uk. Ed. Brian Heap. R&P Amanda Williams. Adv. contact Alistair Rogers. Circ: 20,000. **Dist. by:** Plymbridge Distributors Ltd, Plymbridge House, Estover Rd, Plymouth, Devon PL6 7PY, United Kingdom. TEL 44-1752-202300, FAX 44-1752-202330, enquiries@plymbridge.com.

378 NLD ISSN 0165-6384
DEKANOLOOG. Text in Dutch. 1965. 10/yr. EUR 80 to non-members (effective 2005). adv. bk.rev.; tel.rev. charts; illus.; stat.; tr.lit. back issues avail. **Document type:** *Journal, Academic/Scholarly.* **Description:** Designed to support career counsellors in schools by informing them and keeping them up-to-date.
—IE, Infotrieve, KNAW.
Published by: N V S-N V L, Mauritsstraat 100, Utrecht, 3583 HW, Netherlands. TEL 31-30-2543929, FAX 31-30-2545274, dekanoloog@nvs-nvl.nl, hinemoa@xs4all.nl, bureau@nvs-nvl.nl, http://www.nvs.nl/index.cgi?F=dekanoloog. Ed. Willem Gebuis. Adv. contact Hielke Van der Werf.

378 USA ISSN 0011-8044
LJ145.D5 CODEN: DKGBF7
➤ **DELTA KAPPA GAMMA BULLETIN.** Text in English. 1934. q. USD 5 (effective 2000). bk.rev. abstr.; charts; illus. index. reprint service avail. from PQC. **Document type:** *Bulletin, Academic/Scholarly.* **Description:** Promotes professional and personal growth of members through publication of their writing.
Related titles: Microform ed.: (from PQC); Online - full text ed.: (from EBSCO Publishing, H.W. Wilson, O C L C Online Computer Library Center, Inc.).
Indexed: ABIn, EduInd, L&LBA, PCI, SOPODA.
—BLDSC (3548.293000), IE, ingenta.
Published by: Delta Kappa Gamma Society International, PO Box 1589, Austin, TX 78767-1589. TEL 512-478-5748, 888-762-4685, FAX 512-478-3961, soceditr@deltakappagamma.org. Ed. Jane L Posten. R&P Genelle Schlickeisen TEL 888-762-4685 ext 408. Circ: 150,000.

➤ **DELTA PI EPSILON. (YEAR) RESEARCH CONFERENCE PROCEEDINGS.** see *BUSINESS AND ECONOMICS*

➤ **DELTA PI EPSILON. INDEX TO DOCTORAL DISSERTATIONS IN BUSINESS EDUCATION.** see *EDUCATION—Abstracting, Bibliographies, Statistics*

378 USA ISSN 0011-8052
HF1101
➤ **DELTA PI EPSILON JOURNAL.** Text in English. 1957. q. USD 65 membership (effective 2005). bibl.; charts. reprint service avail. from PQC. **Document type:** *Academic/Scholarly.* **Description:** Contains abstracts of recently completed research studies and projects.
Related titles: Microfilm ed.: (from PQC); Online - full text ed.: (from EBSCO Publishing, H.W. Wilson, O C L C Online Computer Library Center, Inc.).
Indexed: ABIn, BusEdI, CIJE, EduInd.
—BLDSC (3548.295000), IE, ingenta.
Published by: Delta Pi Epsilon Graduate Business Education Society, National Office, P O Box 4340, Little Rock, AR 72214. TEL 501-562-1233, FAX 501-562-1293. Ed. Nancy Groneman. Circ: 5,000.

➤ **DELTA PI EPSILON. SERVICE BULLETINS.** see *BUSINESS AND ECONOMICS*

378.3409489 DNK ISSN 0903-062X
DENMARK. STATENS UDDANNELSESSTOETTE. HAANDBOG. Text in Danish. 1980. a. DKK 40 (effective 1998). **Document type:** *Government.*
Formerly (until 1987): Denmark. Statens Uddannelsesstoette. Regelsamling for Stoetteaaret (0107-5152)
Published by: Styrelsen for Statens Uddannelsesstoette/Danish Students Grants and Loans Agency, Danasvej 30, Copenhagen V, 1780, Denmark. TEL 45-33-268600, FAX 45-33-268611, su@su.dk, http://www.su.dk. Ed. Jens Christian Klaksvig. Circ: 8,500. **Subscr. to:** Statens Informationstjeneste. TEL 45-33-37-92-00.

THE DEPARTMENT CHAIR; a resource for academic administrators. see *EDUCATION—School Organization And Administration*

378.12 MEX ISSN 1405-2040
DESDE EL SUR; humanismo y ciencia. Text in Spanish. 1994. q. MXP 80 (effective 2000). **Description:** Aims to disseminate teaching methods and experiences at college level.
Published by: Universidad Nacional Autonoma de Mexico, Colegio de Ciencias y Humanidades Plantel Sur, Cataratas y Llanura s-n Edificio B P.B., Col del Pedregal de San Angel, Mexico City, DF 04500, Mexico. TEL 52-5-5683933, FAX 52-5-5681155. Ed. Rodolfo Moreno Gonzalez.

DEUTSCHE NATIONALBIBLIOGRAPHIE. REIHE H, HOCHSCHULSCHRIFTEN. see *EDUCATION—Abstracting, Bibliographies, Statistics*

DEVELOPING INDICATORS FOR ACADEMIC LIBRARY PERFORMANCE; ratios from the A R L statistics. see *LIBRARY AND INFORMATION SCIENCES*

378.07 USA ISSN 0012-2289
DIALOGUE ON CAMPUS; linking the religious and the higher education systems. Text in English. 1950. 4/yr. looseleaf. USD 5. adv. bk.rev. bibl. back issues avail.
Indexed: CIJE, HEA.
Published by: Association for the Coordination of University Religious Affairs, Executive Committee, c/o Robert L Johnson, Cornell United Religious Work, Anabel Taylor Hall, Ithaca, NY 14882. TEL 607-255-6004, FAX 607-255-9412. Circ: 300.

378.12 MEX ISSN 0185-3872
LB1719.M6
DIDAC. Text in Spanish. 1982. s-a. USD 25 (effective 2002). bk.rev. bibl.; illus. 56 p./no.; **Document type:** *Journal, Academic/Scholarly.* **Description:** Tool for higher education teachers to use in their classrooms.
Published by: (Centro de Procesos Docentes), Universidad Iberoamericana, Prol Paseo de la Reforma 880, Col Lomas de Santa Fe, Mexico City, DF 01210, Mexico. TEL 52-5-2674000, FAX 52-5-2674331, minerva.hernandez@uia.mx. Ed. Yolanda Argudin Vazquez. Circ: 1,500.

DIDAKTIEF EN SCHOOL; opinieblad voor de onderwijspraktijk. see *EDUCATION*

DIRECTORIO DE LA EDUCACION SUPERIOR EN COLOMBIA. see *EDUCATION—Guides To Schools And Colleges*

THE DIRECTORY OF CANADIAN UNIVERSITIES (YEAR)/REPERTOIRE DES UNIVERSITES CANADIENNES (YEAR). see *EDUCATION—Guides To Schools And Colleges*

DIRECTORY OF ENGINEERING AND ENGINEERING TECHNOLOGY UNDERGRADUATE PROGRAMS. see *ENGINEERING*

DIRECTORY OF ENGINEERING GRADUATE STUDIES AND RESEARCH. see *ENGINEERING*

DIRECTORY OF FACULTY CONTRACTS AND BARGAINING AGENTS IN INSTITUTIONS OF HIGHER EDUCATION. see *LABOR UNIONS*

378.34 IND ISSN 0084-9936
DIRECTORY OF FULBRIGHT ALUMNI. Text in English. 1969. triennial. free. cum.index 1950-1970.
Published by: United States Educational Foundation in India, Fulbright House, 12 Hailey Rd., New Delhi, 110 001, India. Ed. P D Sayal. Circ: (controlled).

E

378.3 AUS
DIRECTORY OF FUNDING SOURCES. Text in English. a. AUD 40 to non-members; AUD 35 to members. back issues avail. **Document type:** *Directory.* **Description:** Lists funding agencies throughout Australia.
Formerly (until 1989): Directory of Funding Sources for Nursing Projects, Grants and Scholarships (1030-3618)
Media: Diskette.
Published by: Royal College of Nursing Australia, 1 Napier Close, Deakin, ACT 2600, Australia. TEL 61-2-6282-5633, FAX 61-2-6282-3565. Adv. contact Joanne Ramadge.

378.0025 GBR
DIRECTORY OF FURTHER EDUCATION. Abbreviated title: D O F E. Text in English. 1962. a. GBP 76.50 (effective 2002). **Document type:** *Directory.* **Description:** Examines vocational courses in colleges of higher education in the UK, including this year's NVQs, GNVQs, and general SVQs.
Published by: (Careers Research and Advisory Centre), Hobsons PLC, Challenger House, 42 Adler St, London, E1 1EE, United Kingdom. TEL 44-1223-460366, FAX 44-1223-301506. **Dist. by:** Biblios Publishers' Distribution Services Ltd., Star Rd, Partridge Green, W Sussex RH13 8LD, United Kingdom. TEL 44-1403-710851, FAX 44-1403-711143.

378.33 USA ISSN 0887-0551
AZ188.U5
DIRECTORY OF GRANTS IN THE HUMANITIES. Text in English. 1986. a. USD 84.50 domestic; USD 101.40 foreign. **Document type:** *Directory.* **Description:** Lists nearly 4,000 grants and funding programs in the humanities, with sponsoring organizations, application procedures, addresses, and restrictions.
Related titles: Online - full text ed.: (from The Dialog Corporation).
Published by: Oryx Press (Subsidiary of: Greenwood Publishing Group Inc.), 1434 E. San Miguel Ave., Phoenix, AZ 85014-2422. TEL 602-265-2651, 800-279-6799, FAX 602-265-6250, info@oryxpress.com, http://www.oryxpress.com. Eds. Millie Hannum, Anne Thompson. Pub. Phyllis Steckler. R&P Lori Cavanaugh TEL 602-265-2651 ext 662.

378.0025 AUS ISSN 0158-9032
DIRECTORY OF HIGHER EDUCATION COURSES*. Text in English. 1983. a. AUD 34.50. adv. **Document type:** *Directory.* **Description:** Lists all undergraduate and postgraduate degrees by subject. Contains advice on admission to university studies.
Related titles: Diskette ed.: 1983. AUD 29.95.
Published by: New Hobsons Press Pty. Ltd., 2 Elizabeth Pl., Level 4, North Sydney, NSW, NSW 2060, Australia. TEL 02-310-2257, FAX 02-310-2243. Ed. Melody Lord. Adv. contact Colin Ritchie. page AUD 1,350. Circ: 8,500.

378.761 USA
DIRECTORY OF HIGHER EDUCATION IN ALABAMA*. Text in English. 1972. a. illus. reprints avail. **Document type:** *Directory, Government.* **Description:** Overview of public and private colleges and universities in Alabama.
Former titles: Fact Book. Higher Education in Alabama; Fact Book. Alabama Institutions of Higher Education, Universities and Colleges (0095-0637)
Published by: Commission on Higher Education, PO Box 302000, Montgomery, AL 36103. TEL 205-269-2700, FAX 205-240-3349.

378.4025 GBR
DIRECTORY OF HIGHER EDUCATION INSTITUTIONS IN THE EUROPEAN COMMUNITY. Text in English. a. GBP 25. adv. **Document type:** *Directory.*
Published by: Kogan Page Ltd., 120 Pentonville Rd, London, N1 9JN, United Kingdom. FAX 44-20-7837-6348. R&P Caroline Gomm. Adv. contact Linda Batham.

DIRECTORY OF HIGHER EDUCATION NURSING COURSES. see *MEDICAL SCIENCES—Nurses And Nursing*

378.07 USA
DIRECTORY OF MINISTRIES IN HIGHER EDUCATION. Text in English. 1975. a. USD 6 (effective 2000). **Document type:** *Directory.* **Description:** Lists more than 1,700 ministries, campus ministers, and college chaplains by state and college, including denominational affiliation.
Published by: Higher Education Ministries Arena, 7407 Steele Creek Rd, Charlotte, NC 28217. TEL 704-588-2182, FAX 704-588-3652. Ed. Linda Freeman. Circ: 2,000.

378.2 USA
(YEAR) DIRECTORY OF MINORITY DOCTORAL RECIPIENTS AND CANDIDATES IN NEW YORK STATE. Text in English. a.
Published by: State University of New York at Albany, State Education Department - Bureau of Doctoral Program Review, State University Plaza, Albany, NY 12246.

378.1982 USA
DIRECTORY OF MINORITY PH.D. AND M.F.A. CANDIDATES AND RECIPIENTS. Text in English. 1985. a. USD 25 (effective 2000). **Document type:** *Directory.*
Published by: Committee on Institutional Cooperation, 1819 S. Neil St., Ste. D, Champaign, IL 61820-7271. TEL 217-333-8475, FAX 217-244-7127, cic@uiuc.edu, http://www.cic.uiuc.edu.

571.9 USA ISSN 0070-6086
RB123
DIRECTORY OF PATHOLOGY TRAINING PROGRAMS (YEAR). Text in English. 1968. a. USD 25 (effective 2000). **Document type:** *Directory.* **Description:** Describes residency programs and postgraduate subspecialty fellowships in anatomic and clinical pathology in the US and Canada, and post-sophomore fellowships.
—GNLM.
Published by: Intersociety Committee on Pathology Information, 9650 Rockville Pike, Bethesda, MD 20814. TEL 301-571-1880, FAX 301-571-1879, icpi@pathol.faseb.org, http://www.pathologytraining.org. Ed. Eileen Lavine. R&P Frances Pitlick. Circ: 2,500.

378.94 AUS ISSN 1035-5405
DIRECTORY OF POSTGRADUATE STUDY. Text in English. 1990. a. AUD 25; AUD 50 foreign. **Document type:** *Directory.* **Description:** Guide to postgraduate courses in Australia and awards for postgraduate study and research in Australia and overseas.
Published by: Graduate Careers Council of Australia Ltd., PO Box 28, Parkville, VIC 3052, Australia. TEL 61-3-93449333, FAX 61-3-93477298, l.gladman@gcca.unimelb.edu.au, http://www.gradlink.edu.au. Ed. Phillip Coyte. R&P Lyn Gladman.

378.33025 USA ISSN 0146-7336
LB2338
DIRECTORY OF RESEARCH GRANTS. Text in English. 1975. a. USD 135 domestic; USD 162 foreign (effective 2000). **Document type:** *Directory.* **Description:** Lists more than 6,000 grant programs alphabetically by grant title, providing program descriptions, requirements, restrictions, funding amounts, application deadlines, programs, and addresses.
Related titles: CD-ROM ed.: (from The Dialog Corporation); Online - full text ed.: (from The Dialog Corporation).
—BLDSC (3595.057000).
Published by: Oryx Press (Subsidiary of: Greenwood Publishing Group Inc.), 1434 E. San Miguel Ave., Phoenix, AZ 85014-2422. TEL 602-265-2651, 800-279-6799, FAX 602-265-6250, info@oryxpress.com, http://www.oryxpress.com. Eds. Millie Hannum, Anne Thompson. Pub. Phyllis Steckler. R&P Lori Cavanaugh TEL 602-265-2651 ext 662.

DIRECTORY OF STAFF BARGAINING AGENTS IN INSTITUTIONS OF HIGHER EDUCATION. see *BUSINESS AND ECONOMICS—Labor And Industrial Relations*

DIRECTORY OF UNIVERSITY LIBRARIES IN EUROPE. see *LIBRARY AND INFORMATION SCIENCES*

DIRECTORY OF VISITING FULBRIGHT SCHOLARS AND OCCASIONAL LECTURERS. see *EDUCATION—International Education Programs*

DISABILITY COMPLIANCE FOR HIGHER EDUCATION. see *POLITICAL SCIENCE—Civil Rights*

378.198287 GBR
DISABLED GRADUATES CASEBOOK. Text in English. 1994. a. GBP 9.99 per issue (effective 2002). **Document type:** *Directory.* **Description:** Recent graduates discuss their careers.
Formerly: Careers for Disabled Graduates
Related titles: Series of: Equal Opportunities Casebook Series.
Published by: (Careers Research and Advisory Centre), Hobsons PLC, Challenger House, 42 Adler St, London, E1 1EE, United Kingdom. TEL 44-1223-354551, FAX 44-1223-323154. **Dist. by:** Biblios Publishers' Distribution Services Ltd., Star Rd, Partridge Green, W Sussex RH13 8LD, United Kingdom. TEL 44-1403-710851, FAX 44-1403-711143.

378.03 USA ISSN 1094-320X
LC5808.U6
DISTANCE EDUCATION REPORT. Text in English. 1997. s-m. USD 399 domestic; USD 403 in Canada; USD 409 elsewhere (effective 2005). bk.rev. index. back issues avail. **Document type:** *Newsletter.* **Description:** Provides distance educators and administrators with the timely information needed to design, implement and manage distance education programs or courses. Emphasizes practical applications and discusses the latest developments in new technology.
Related titles: Online - full content ed.: USD 399 (effective 2005); Online - full text ed.: (from EBSCO Publishing, H.W. Wilson, O C L C Online Computer Library Center, Inc.).
Indexed: ABIn, EduInd.
—BLDSC (3602.521000). **CCC.**
Published by: Magna Publications, Inc., 2718 Dryden Dr, Madison, WI 53704. TEL 608-246-3590, 800-433-0499, FAX 608-246-3597, editor@magnapubs.com, http://www.magnapubs.com/pub/magnapubs_der. Ed. Farhad Saba. Pub. William H Haight. Circ: 2,000.

DISTRIBUTION OF HIGH SCHOOL GRADUATES AND COLLEGE GOING RATE, NEW YORK STATE. see *EDUCATION—Abstracting, Bibliographies, Statistics*

378.1982 USA ISSN 1557-5411
LC2781
DIVERSE ISSUES IN HIGHER EDUCATION. Text in English. 1984. bi-w. USD 20 domestic; USD 40 in Canada; USD 50 elsewhere (effective 2006). adv. bibl.; charts; stat.; illus. Index. 3 cols./p.; back issues avail.; reprints avail. **Document type:** *Magazine, Academic/Scholarly.* **Description:** Presents news, information, statistics and opinion regarding minorities in higher education.
Formerly (until Aug. 2005): Black Issues in Higher Education (0742-0277)
Related titles: Online - full text ed.: (from bigchalk, Chadwyck-Healey Inc., EBSCO Publishing, Factiva, Florida Center for Library Automation, Gale Group, H.W. Wilson, Northern Light Technology, Inc., O C L C Online Computer Library Center, Inc., ProQuest Information & Learning, SoftLine Information).
Indexed: ABIn, CIJE, ChPerI, DYW, ENW, EduInd, HEA, IIBP, SRRA.
Published by: Cox, Matthews & Associates, Inc., 10520 Warwick Ave, Ste B 8, Fairfax, VA 22030. TEL 703-385-2981, FAX 703-385-1839, 800-783-3199, http://www.diverseeducation.com/. Ed. Hilary Hurd. Pub. Frank Matthews. R&P Ralph Newell TEL 703-385-2981. Adv. contact Pam Barrett. Circ: 200,000.

378.45 ITA ISSN 0391-5018
AS218
DOC ITALIA. Text in Italian. 1972. biennial. EUR 105 (effective 2004). illus. **Document type:** *Directory.* **Description:** Information on cultural and scientific centers in Italy.
Formerly (until 1977): Doc - Documentazione
Related titles: Diskette ed.
Published by: (Istituto Nazionale Informazione), Editoriale Italiana, Via Vigliena 10, Rome, 00192, Italy. TEL 39-06-3230177, FAX 39-06-3211359, info@editoriale.it, http://www.editoriale.it. Circ: 5,000.

378 ESP ISSN 1133-9926
DOCENCIA E INVESTIGACION. Text in Spanish. 1975. a.
Former titles (until 1993): Escuela Universitaria de E.G.B. de Toledo (1133-374X); (until 1992): Escuela Universitaria. Revista (1134-4008); (until 1987): Acibar (1133-3731)
Related titles: Online - full content ed.
Indexed: RILM.
—CINDOC.
Published by: Universidad de Castilla - La Mancha, Escuela Universitaria de Profesorado de E.G.B. de Toledo, Ave. Barber, s-n, Toledo, Castilla-La Mancha 45004, Spain. TEL 34-925-220691, http://www.uclm.es/. Ed. Humildad Munoz Resino.

378 MEX ISSN 0185-3597
DOCENCIA POSTSECUNDARIA. Text in Spanish; Abstracts in English, Spanish. 1973. 3/yr. MXP 110 to individuals; MXP 130 to institutions. adv. illus. **Document type:** *Academic/Scholarly.* **Description:** Provides an international perspective on innovation in contemporary universities, problems and possible solutions.
Indexed: HAPI.
Published by: (Universidad Autonoma de Guadalajara), Ediciones Educativas, Av. Patria No. 1201, Lomas del Valle, Box 1-440, Guadalajara, Jal. 44100, Mexico. TEL 52-36-415051, FAX 52-36-410818, TELEX 682785 UAG PME. Ed. Ricardo Beltran Rojas. Circ: 1,000.

DOKUMENTE ZUM HOCHSCHULSPORT. see *SPORTS AND GAMES*

E C I S HIGHER EDUCATION DIRECTORY. see *EDUCATION—Guides To Schools And Colleges*

378 MEX ISSN 0186-176X
E N P GACETA. (Escuela Nacional Preparatoria) Variant title: Organo Informativo de la Escuela Nacional Preparatoria. Text in Spanish. 1974. m. free. back issues avail.
Related titles: Online - full text ed.
Published by: (Direccion General), Universidad Nacional Autonoma de Mexico, Escuela Nacional Preparatoria, ADOLFO PRIETO 722, Col Del Valle, Mexico City, DF 03100, Mexico. TEL 52-5-6876828, http://dgenp.unam.mx/gaceta.html.

E P R. (Emory Political Review) see *POLITICAL SCIENCE*

378.052 USA
E R I C CLEARINGHOUSE FOR COMMUNITY COLLEGES DIGEST. (Educational Resources Information Center) Text in English. 11/yr. free. **Document type:** *Bulletin, Trade.* **Description:** Provides an overview of topics of current interest in community college education.
Formerly: E R I C Clearinghouse for Junior College Digest
Published by: E R I C Clearinghouse for Community Colleges, 3051 Moore Hall, University of California, Los Angeles, 405 Hilgard Ave, Los Angeles, CA 90024. TEL 800-832-8256, FAX 310-206-8095, http://www.gseis.ucla.edu/eric/pubs.html, http://www.gseis.ucla.edu/ERIC/pubs.htm.

E

378.052 USA
E R I C INFORMATION BULLETIN; clearinghouse for community colleges. Text in English. 1966. q. free. **Document type:** *Bulletin, Trade.* **Description:** Includes abstracts of ERIC documents, data on clearinghouse personnel and activities and list of products currently available.
Former titles: E R I C Clearinghouse for Junior College; E R I C Two-Year College Information Bulletin
Published by: E R I C Clearinghouse for Community Colleges, 3051 Moore Hall, University of California, Los Angeles, 405 Hilgard Ave, Los Angeles, CA 90024. TEL 800-832-8256, FAX 310-206-8095, http://www.gseis.ucla.edu/eric/pubs.html, http://www.gseis.ucla.edu/ERIC/pubs.htm. Circ: 8,359.

378 USA ISSN 1545-5742
E-SOURCE. Text in English. 1987. 6/yr. USD 40 (effective 2003). bk.rev.; Website rev. bibl.; charts; stat. 12 p./no.; back issues avail. **Document type:** *Newsletter, Trade.* **Description:** Reports items of interest to faculty and administrators in higher education involved with first-year students.
Former titles (until 2003): F Y E (1539-9583); (until 2000): The First - Year Experience Newsletter; (until 1998): The Freshman Year Experience Newsletter (1053-2048)
Media: E-mail.
Published by: University of South Carolina, National Resource Center for the First-Year Experience and Students in Transition, 1629 Pendleton St, Columbia, SC 29208. TEL 803-777-6029, FAX 803-777-4699, fye@gwm.sc.edu, http://www.sc.edu/fye. Ed., R&P Tracy Skipper TEL 803-777-6226. Circ: 925.

378.00287 USA ISSN 0046-1547
LB1131
E T S DEVELOPMENTS. Text in English. 1951. q. free. illus.; stat. **Document type:** *Newsletter.* **Description:** Reports news of ETS measurement, research, and related activities of general interest.
Published by: Educational Testing Service, Rosedale Rd, Princeton, NJ 08541-0001. TEL 609-921-9000. Ed. Wendy Miller Nardi. Circ: 85,000. **Dist. by:** Corporate Publications, ETS, 16 D, Princeton, NJ 08541-0001.

378 USA
THE EASTERN PROGRESS. Text in English. 1922. w. USD 38 (effective 1992). adv. **Document type:** *Newspaper.*
Related titles: Microfilm ed.: (from PQC).
Published by: Eastern Kentucky University, Department of Mass Communications, 117 Donovan Annex, Richmond, KY 40475-3113. TEL 606-622-1881, FAX 606-622-2354, progress@acs.eku.edu. Eds. Brian Simms, Jamie Neal. R&P Elizabeth Fraas. Adv. contact Sonja Knight. Circ: 10,000.

378 POL ISSN 1640-842X
ECHO PERYFERII; magazyn studencki wyzszej szkoly handlowej. Text in Polish. 1995. bi-m. 24 p./no.; **Document type:** *Magazine.*
Published by: Wyzsza Szkola Handlowa w Kielcach, ul Peryferyjna 15, Kielce, 25562, Poland. TEL 48-41-3626027, echo@wsh-kielce.edu.pl, http://echo.wsh-kielce.edu.pl. Ed. M Bugajniak. Circ: 1,200.

378 FRA ISSN 0982-5339
ECOLE DU GRAND PARIS. Text in French. 1922. m. (during academic year). adv.
Published by: Syndicat National des Instituteurs et Professeurs du College, 69 rue du Faubourg Saint- Martin, Paris, 75010, France.

378 ZAF ISSN 0070-8976
EDGAR BROOKES ACADEMIC AND HUMAN FREEDOM LECTURE. Text in English. 1965. a.
Published by: University of KwaZulu-Natal, Students Representative Council, PO Box 375, Pietermaritzburg, KwaZulu-Natal, South Africa. Circ: 1,000.

378.1 IRL
EDIT. Text in English. a. adv. **Document type:** *Magazine, Academic/Scholarly.*
Published by: Dublin Institute of Technology, Fitzwilliam House, 30 Upper Pembroke St., Dublin, 2, Ireland. TEL 353-1-4023352, FAX 353-1-4023449. adv.: B&W page EUR 1,905, color page EUR 2,540; bleed 218 x 305. Circ: 23,000 (controlled).

378 CUB ISSN 0256-5110
EDUCACION SUPERIOR CONTEMPORANEA. Text in Spanish. 1975. q. USD 28.
Published by: (Cuba. Ministerio de Educacion Superior), Ediciones Cubanas, Obispo No. 527, Apdo. 605, Havana, Cuba.

378 VEN ISSN 0798-1228
LA543
EDUCACION SUPERIOR Y SOCIEDAD. Text in Spanish; Text occasionally in English, French. 1979. 2/yr. VEB 3,000 domestic; USD 35 foreign. back issues avail.
Former titles (until 1990): Educacion Superior (0251-4664); Higher Education Bulletin
—IE.
Published by: UNESCO (Venezuela), Centro Regional para Educacion Superior en America Latina y el Caribe, Apartado Postal 68394, Caracas, DF 1062-A, Venezuela. FAX 58-2-2612129, TELEX 24642 UNELC VC, a.vila@unesco.org. Circ: 1,500.

378.68 ZAF ISSN 0256-8829
L81
➤ **EDUCARE.** Text in Afrikaans, English. 1972. s-a. ZAR 30, USD 10 (effective 2001). adv. bk.rev. back issues avail. **Document type:** *Journal, Academic/Scholarly.* **Description:** Publishes research reports on theoretical and practical educational issues with special reference to South African educational problems.
Related titles: Online - full text ed.
Indexed: ISAP.
Published by: (University of South Africa), Unisa Press, Periodicals, PO Box 392, Pretoria, 0003, South Africa. TEL 27-12-429-3081, FAX 27-12-429-3221, unisa-press@unisa.ac.za, ttp://www.journals.co.za/ej/ejour_educare.html, http://www.unisa.ac.za/press. Ed. W F Sohnge. Circ: 16,000.

378 GBR ISSN 1477-5557
➤ **EDUCATE (LONDON)**; the London journal of doctoral research in education. Text in English. 2002. s-a. GBP 12; GBP 6 per issue (effective 2004). **Document type:** *Journal, Academic/Scholarly.*
—BLDSC (3661.155800).
Published by: The Doctoral School at the Institute of Eduction (Subsidiary of: University of London), c/o Prof. Ingrid Lunt, 20 Bedford Way, London, WC1H OAL, United Kingdom. i.lunt@ioe.ac.uk.

378 GBR ISSN 1746-1979
▼ **EDUCATION, CITIZENSHIP AND SOCIAL JUSTICE.** Text in English. forthcoming 2006. 3/yr. GBP 234, USD 409 to institutions; GBP 243, USD 426 combined subscription to institutions print & online eds. (effective 2006). **Document type:** *Journal, Academic/Scholarly.* **Description:** Provides a forum for international and multi-disciplinary dialogue for academic educators and educational policy-makers concerned with the meanings and form of citizenship and social justice as realized throughout time spent in educational institutions.
Related titles: Online - full text ed.: ISSN 1746-1987. forthcoming. GBP 231, USD 404 to institutions (effective 2006).
Published by: Sage Publications Ltd. (Subsidiary of: Sage Publications, Inc.), 1 Oliver's Yard, 55 City Rd, London, EC1 1SP, United Kingdom. TEL 44-20-73248500, FAX 44-20-73248600, info@sagepub.co.uk, http://www.sagepub.co.uk/journal.aspx?pid=106981. Eds. Alan Dyson, Peter Clough, Tony Gallagher. **Subscr. to:** Sage Publications, Inc., 2455 Teller Rd, Thousand Oaks, CA 91320. TEL 805-499-0721, FAX 805-499-0871, journals@sagepub.com.

EDUCATION FOR PRIMARY CARE. see *MEDICAL SCIENCES*

375 305.8 USA
EDUCATION HIGHWAY. Text in English. q. adv. **Description:** Focuses on historically black colleges, targeting alumni, educators, and professionals.
Published by: Diversity Publishing Co, 96 Linwood Plaza, PO Box 325, Fort Lee, NJ 07024. TEL 201-862-0206, FAX 201-862-0212, http://www.eduhwy.com.

EDUCATION IN KENYA; index of articles on education. see *EDUCATION—Abstracting, Bibliographies, Statistics*

378.11 GBR ISSN 1352-9722
EDUCATION MARKETING; the marketing magazine for universities and colleges. Text in English. 1993. 3/yr. GBP 20. adv. bk.rev. bibl.; tr.lit. back issues avail. **Document type:** *Trade.* **Description:** Contains a range of case studies in the areas of course marketing, market research, public relations, advertising, alumni relations and fundraising.
Formed by the 1993 merger of: Development in Education (0966-4025); Promoting Education
Indexed: BrEdI.
—BLDSC (3661.297900).
Published by: Heist, The Coach House, 184 Otley Rd, Leeds, LS16 5LW, United Kingdom. TEL 44-113-226-5858, FAX 44-113-226-7878, zwhitby@heist.co.uk, publications@heist.co.uk. Ed. Zoe Whitby. Adv. contact Caron Thomas. B&W page GBP 850, color page GBP 1,100; trim 190 x 262. Circ: 2,000.

378.599 PHL ISSN 0115-1894
EDUCATION QUARTERLY. Text in English. 1953. q. PHP 36, USD 15. bk.rev. abstr.; bibl.
Indexed: IPP.
Published by: University of the Philippines, College of Education, Diliman, Quezon City Mm, 1128, Philippines. Ed. Celeste O Botor. Circ: (controlled).

378 AUS ISSN 0311-2543
LB2300
➤ **EDUCATION RESEARCH AND PERSPECTIVES.** Text in English. 1950. s-a. AUD 30 (effective 2000). bk.rev. **Document type:** *Journal, Academic/Scholarly.* **Description:** Presents articles on all aspects of education research and perspectives.
Formerly: Australian Journal of Higher Education
Related titles: Online - full text ed.
Indexed: AEI, AusPAIS, CPE, ERA, ETA, MEA, RASB, RHEA, SEA, TEA.
—BLDSC (3661.331000), IE, ingenta.
Published by: University of Western Australia, Department of Education, 35 Stirling Highway, Nedlands, W.A. 6907, Australia. TEL 61-8-9380-2385, FAX 61-8-9380-1052, TELEX AA 92992, cwhitehead@ecel.uwa.edu.au, http://www.gse.ecel.uwa.edu.au/gse. Ed., R&P Clive Whitehead. Circ: 300 (paid). **Dist. in US by:** International Scholarly Book Services, PO Box 555, Forest Grove, OR 97116.

378 GBR ISSN 1462-7272
L16
EDUCATION REVIEW. Text in English. 1987. 2/yr. GBP 16 domestic to individuals; GBP 20 in Europe to individuals; USD 35 in United States to individuals; AUD 55 in Australia to individuals; GBP 24 elsewhere to individuals; GBP 55 domestic to institutions; GBP 60 in Europe to institutions; USD 95 in United States to institutions; AUD 149 in Australia to institutions; GBP 65 elsewhere to institutions (effective 2003). adv. bk.rev. **Document type:** *Academic/Scholarly.* **Description:** Addresses subjects such as equal opportunities, special needs, standards, curriculum, management, training, and professional development.
Formerly (until 1997): N U T Education Review (0951-7855); Formed by the merger of (1975-1987): Primary Education Review (0141-6022); (1970-1987): Secondary Education Journal (0143-1749); Which was formerly: Secondary Education (0018-1595); Higher Education Journal
Related titles: Online - full text ed.: (from EBSCO Publishing).
Indexed: BrEdI, CPE, ERA, ETA, MEA, RASB, RHEA, SEA, SENA, SOMA, SWA, TEA.
—BLDSC (3661.333250), IE, ingenta.
Published by: (National Union of Teachers), The Education Publishing Co. Ltd., Devonia House, 4 Union Terrace, Crediton, Devon EX17 3DY, United Kingdom. TEL 44-1363-774455, FAX 44-1363-776592, info@educationpublishing.com, http://www.educationpublishing.com. Ed. Janet Theakston. Circ: 4,000. **Subscr. addr. in Australia:** The Education Publishing Co. of Australia, PO Box 390, Sandy Bay, TAS 7006, Australia. TEL 61-3-62248240, FAX 61-3-62248239, epca@educationpublishing.com.

378 GBR ISSN 1469-3267
➤ **EDUCATIONAL DEVELOPMENTS.** Text in English. 2000. q. GBP 20 domestic to non-members; GBP 23 in Europe to non-members; GBP 25 elsewhere to non-members (effective 2003). adv. bk.rev.; software rev.; Website rev. 28 p./no. 2 cols./p.; back issues avail. **Document type:** *Magazine, Academic/Scholarly.*
Formed by the merger of (1993-2000): S E D A Newsletter (1468-0955); (1991-2000): New Academic Magazine (0964-6353)
Indexed: BrEdI.
—BLDSC (3661.389000), IE, ingenta. **CCC.**
Published by: Staff and Educational Development Association, Selly Wick House, 59/61 Selly Wick Rd, Selly Park, Birmingham B29 7JE, United Kingdom. TEL 44-121-4156801, FAX 44-121-4156802, office@seda.ac.uk, http://www.seda.ac.uk/educational_developments.htm, http://www.seda..ac.uk. R&P, Adv. contact Jill Brookes.

378 USA ISSN 0013-1725
➤ **THE EDUCATIONAL FORUM.** Text in English. 1936. q. USD 20 domestic to non-members; USD 24 foreign to non-members; USD 12 domestic to members; USD 16 foreign to members (effective 2005). adv. bk.rev. bibl.; illus. index. 96 p./no. 2 cols./p.; reprint service avail. from PQC. **Document type:** *Academic/Scholarly.* **Description:** Features scholarly analyses and critical essays on contemporary problems and possibilities in education.
Related titles: Microform ed.: (from MIM, PQC); Online - full text ed.: (from H.W. Wilson, O C L C Online Computer Library Center, Inc., ProQuest Information & Learning).
Indexed: ABIn, BRI, BusEdI, CBRI, CIJE, CPE, EAA, EduInd, MEA, PCI, PhilInd.
—BLDSC (3661.414000), IE, Infotrieve, ingenta.
Published by: Kappa Delta Pi, 3707 Woodview Trace, Indianapolis, IN 46268-1158. TEL 317-871-4900, 800-284-3167, FAX 317-704-2323, pubs@kdp.org, http://www.kdp.org/publications/educational.php. Circ: 7,000.

378.111 USA
➤ **EDUCATIONAL LEADERSHIP AND ADMINISTRATION.** Text in English. a., latest vol.14, 2002. USD 20 to individuals; USD 30 to institutions (effective 2002). adv. back issues avail. **Document type:** *Journal, Academic/Scholarly.* **Description:** Contains articles on the preparation of educational administrators.
Formerly (until 1997): Journal of C A P E A (1064-4474)
Indexed: CIJE, CPE, ERA, IBR, IBZ.

E

▼ new title ➤ refereed ✶ unverified ♦ full entry avail.

Published by: (California Association of Professors of Educational Administration), Caddo Gap Press, 3145 Geary Blvd., PMB 275, San Francisco, CA 94118. TEL 415-922-1911, FAX 415-440-4870, caddogap@aol.com. Ed. Penny Bryan. R&P Alan H Jones. adv.: page USD 200; 4.5 x 7. Circ: 250.

378.16 USA ISSN 1070-4418
LB3051
EDUCATIONAL TESTING SERVICE ANNUAL REPORT. Key Title: Annual Report - Educational Testing Service. Text in English. 1949. a. free. illus. **Description:** An annual review of ETS research, programs, services and finances.
Former titles (until 1981): E T S Annual Report (0732-0507); (until 1977): Educational Testing Service Annual Report (0091-8989); (until 1956): Annual Report to the Board of Trustees - Educational Testing Service (0361-6533)
Published by: Educational Testing Service, Rosedale Rd, Princeton, NJ 08541-0001. TEL 609-921-9000. Ed. Albert Benderson. Circ: 65,000. **Institutions subscr. to:** Warner Books Inc, Special Sales, Time & Life Bldg, 1271 Ave of the Americas, New York, NY 10020. TEL 212-522-7381; **Subscr. to:** Little Brown, 200 West St, Waltham, MA 02254. TEL 800-759-0190.

378.00285 USA
CODEN: EDUPEC
EDUCAUSE★. Text in English. 1992. w. membership. adv. **Document type:** *Bulletin.* **Description:** Aims to enable the transformational changes occuring in higher education through the introduction, use, access to, and management of information resources and technologies in teaching, learning, scholarship, research, and institutional management.
Formerly (until 1998): Educom Update (1069-8183)
Media: Online - full text.
Published by: Educom, 1150 18th St NW #1010, Washington, DC 20036-3824. TEL 202-872-4200, 800-254-4770, FAX 512-335-3083, info@educause.edu, http://www.educause.edu. Ed., R&P, Adv. contact John Gehl.

EDUCAUSE LEADERSHIP STRATEGIES SERIES. see *EDUCATION—Computer Applications*

EDUCAUSE MONOGRAPH SERIES. see *EDUCATION—Computer Applications*

EDUCAUSE PROFESSIONAL PAPER SERIES. see *EDUCATION—Computer Applications*

378.00285 USA ISSN 1528-5324
LB2395.7 CODEN: EQDUAT
➤ **EDUCAUSE QUARTERLY.** Abbreviated title: EQ. Text in English. 1978. q. USD 24 domestic to members; USD 40 foreign to members; USD 52 domestic to non-members; USD 72 foreign to non-members; USD 24 domestic to libraries; USD 40 foreign to libraries (effective 2005). bk.rev. bibl. index. back issues avail. **Document type:** *Journal, Academic/Scholarly.* **Description:** For managers and users of information resources in higher education. Each issue features an article on the management and use of information resources at a EDCAUSE member college or univerisity. Other articles cover practical applications and problem solving, management and organizational issues, and general issues related to the use and evaluation of information resources in higher education.
Formerly (until 1999): Cause - Effect Magazine (0164-534X)
Related titles: Microfilm ed.: (from PQC); Online - full text ed.: free (effective 2005) (from EBSCO Publishing).
Indexed: CIJE, CompLI, HEA, Inspec.
—BLDSC (3662.815000), IE, ingenta.
Published by: Educause, 4772 Walnut St, Ste 206, Boulder, CO 80301-2536. TEL 303-449-4430, FAX 303-440-0461, info@educause.edu, info@educause.com, http://www.educause.edu/apps/eq/index.asp?bhcp=1. Ed., R&P Nancy Hayes TEL 303-939-0321. Circ: 7,300.

378.00285 USA ISSN 1527-6619
LB2300 CODEN: EDREFX
➤ **EDUCAUSE REVIEW.** Text in English. 1966. bi-m. USD 24 in US & Canada; USD 48 elsewhere (effective 2005). adv. bk.rev. charts; illus.; stat. index. back issues avail.; reprints avail. **Document type:** *Journal, Academic/Scholarly.* **Description:** Covers current issues and applications in the planning, management, and use of information technology in higher education.
Former titles (until 1999): Educom Review (1045-9146); (until 1989): Educom Bulletin (1045-9154); (until 1984): Educom (0424-6268)
Related titles: Microfiche ed.; Microfilm ed.; Online - full text ed.: free (effective 2005) (from EBSCO Publishing).
Indexed: ABIn, CIJE, CompLI, CurCont, EduInd, HEA, Inspec, SOPODA.
—BLDSC (3662.821000), AskIEEE, CASDDS, IE, ingenta, KNAW.
Published by: Educause, 4772 Walnut St, Ste 206, Boulder, CO 80301-2536. TEL 303-449-4430, FAX 303-440-0461, info@educause.com, http://www.educause.edu/pub/er/. Ed. Teddy Diggs. Adv. contact Geri Farman. Circ: 20,000.

378 ARG
EDUCYT. Text in Spanish. 1997. w. back issues avail. **Document type:** *Academic/Scholarly.*
Media: Online - full text. **Related titles:** E-mail ed.
Published by: Universidad de Buenos Aires, Facultad de Ciencias Exactas y Naturales, Cuidad Universitaria, Nunez - Pabellon 2, Buenos Aires, 1428, Argentina. TEL 54-11-4573300, info@fcen.uba.ar, http://www.fcen.uba.ar/prensa/educol.htm, http://fcen.uba.ar/. Ed. Carlos Borches.

EDUEXEC. see *EDUCATION—School Organization And Administration*

378 ARG ISSN 1514-6006
➤ **ENFOQUES (LIBERTADOR SAN MARTIN).** Text in Spanish, English, French. 1976. a. ARS 18 in South America; ARS 30 elsewhere (effective 2005). back issues avail. **Document type:** *Journal, Academic/Scholarly.*
Related titles: Online - full text ed.: free (effective 2006).
Indexed: PhilInd.
Published by: Universidad Adventista del Plata, 25 de Mayo 99, Libertador San Martin, Entre Rios 3103, Argentina. TEL 54-343-4910010, FAX 54-343-4910300, uap@uapar.ed.ar, http://redalyc.uaemex.mx/redalyc/src/inicio/HomRevRed.jsp?iCveEntRev=259, http://www.uapar.edu.ar. Ed. Fernando Aranda Fraga.

➤ **ENGINEERING EDUCATION AND RESEARCH.** see *ENGINEERING*

378.6668 CIV
ENSEIGNEMENT SUPERIEUR EN COTE-D'IVOIRE. Text in French. 1980. a. XOF 60. adv.
Published by: Universite Nationale de Cote d'Ivoire, 08 BP 859, Abidjan, Ivory Coast.

378 SWE ISSN 1100-181X
ENTUSIASMEN. Text in Swedish. 1979. bi-m.
Published by: Laerarhoegskolan i Malmoe, Laerarhoegskolans Studentkaar, Fack 23501, Malmoe, S-200 45, Sweden.

378 IND
ENVIRONMENTAL CHALLENGES AND THE UNIVERSITIES (YEAR). Text in English. 1927. irreg., latest 1994. USD 40 (effective 2003). **Document type:** *Newsletter.*
Published by: Association of Indian Universities, A.I.U. House, 16 Kotla Marg, New Delhi, 110 002, India. TEL 91-11-323-0059, FAX 91-11-323-6105, aiu@del12.vsnl.net.in, http://www.aiuweb.org.

378 IND
EQUIVALENCE OF FOREIGN DEGREES (YEAR). Text in English. 1987. irreg., latest 1995. USD 44 (effective 1999). **Document type:** *Newsletter.*
Published by: Association of Indian Universities, A.I.U. House, 16 Kotla Marg, New Delhi, 110 002, India. TEL 91-11-323-0059, FAX 91-11-323-6105, aiu@del12.vsnl.net.in, http://www.aiuweb.org.

ERNEST BLOCH LECTURES. see *MUSIC*

378 CHL ISSN 0716-050X
LB5
ESTUDIOS PEDAGOGICOS. Text in Spanish; Summaries in English, Spanish. 1976. a. CLP 2,000 domestic; USD 8 foreign (effective 2004). abstr.; bibl.; charts; stat.
Related titles: Online - full text ed.: ISSN 0718-0705. free (effective 2005) (from Gale Group).
Indexed: DIP, IBR, IBZ.
Published by: Universidad Austral de Chile, Facultad de Filosofia y Humanidades, Casilla 142, Valdivia, Chile. eped@uach.cl, http://www.scielo.cl/scielo.php?script=sci_serial&pid=0718-0705&nrm=iso&lng=en. Ed. Raul Salas. Circ: 500.

378 BRA ISSN 0425-4082
AS80.A1
ESTUDOS UNIVERSITARIOS. Text in Portuguese; Summaries in French, English. 1962. q. USD 12.
Indexed: IBR, MLA-IB.
Published by: Universidade Federal de Pernambuco, Departamento de Extensao Cultural, Recife, PERNAMBUCO, Brazil.

378.4 DEU
EUROMECUM; European higher education and research institutions. Text in German. 1991. 3 base vols. plus updates 6/yr. price varies. **Document type:** *Directory, Trade.*
Published by: Dr. Josef Raabe Verlags GmbH, Rotebuehlstr 77, Stuttgart, 70178, Germany. TEL 49-711-629000, FAX 49-711-6290010, info@raabe.de, http://www.raabe.de.

EUROPEAN EXECUTIVE EDUCATION DIRECTORY. see *BUSINESS AND ECONOMICS—Management*

THE EUROPEAN JOURNAL OF LEGAL EDUCATION. see *LAW*

650.07 IRL
EXAM & CAREER GUIDE. Text in English. 7/yr. adv. **Document type:** *Magazine, Academic/Scholarly.*
Published by: C.J. Fallon Educational Publishers, Lucan Rd., Palmerstown, PO Box 1054, Dublin, 20, Ireland. TEL 353-1-6166490, FAX 353-1-6166499. Adv. contact Gertie Fagan. B&W page EUR 950, color page EUR 1,020; 178 x 267. Circ: 13,000 (controlled).

378 IND
EXCELLENCE ACHIEVING SOCIAL RELEVANCE IN HIGHER EDUCATION (YEAR). Text in English. 1927. irreg., latest 1993. USD 40 (effective 1999). **Document type:** *Newsletter.*
Published by: Association of Indian Universities, A.I.U. House, 16 Kotla Marg, New Delhi, 110 002, India. TEL 91-11-323-0059, FAX 91-11-323-6105, aiu@del12.vsnl.net.in, http://www.aiuweb.org.

378 USA ISSN 1549-5361
LH1.E234
▼ **EXEMPLAR.** Text in English. 2003 (Fall). 3/yr. **Document type:** *Magazine.*
Published by: Eastern Michigan University, Office of Advancement Communications, 1349 S Huron St Ste 2, Ypsilanti, MI 48197-2214. TEL 734-487-0250, FAX 734-487-7009, exemplar@emich.edu, http://www.emich.edu/exemplar. Ed. Kevin Merrill.

378 AUS
EXIT LINES. Text in English. s-a.
Published by: Queensland Board of Senior Secondary School Studies, P.O. Box 307, Spring Hill, QLD 4101, Australia. TEL 61-7-3864-0299, FAX 61-7-3221-2553, office@qbssss.edu.au.

378.37 USA
EXPERIENCE (COLUMBIA). Text in English. 1990. q. USD 22; USD 30 in Canada & Mexico; USD 36 elsewhere.
Formerly (until 1997): Co-op - Experience - Co-op Magazine
Published by: Cooperative Education and Internship Association, Inc., 4190 Highland Dr., Ste. 211, Salt Lake Cty, UT 84124-2675. TEL 410-290-3666, FAX 410-290-7084.

EXPERIENCE ERASMUS; the U K guide to Socrates-Erasmus programmes (Year). see *EDUCATION—Guides To Schools And Colleges*

EXPOSURE (OXFORD). see *PHOTOGRAPHY*

378 MEX ISSN 1605-4229
EXPRESION. Text in Spanish. 1996. w. back issues avail.
Media: Online - full text. **Related titles:** Print ed.
Published by: Universidad Regiomontana, Padre Mier Pte. 471, Monterrey, Nuevo Leon, Mexico. TEL 52-8343-1290, FAX 52-8343-3172, http://www.ur.mx/expresion/. Ed. Guadalupe Monterde.

378.05 USA ISSN 1535-3273
F A C C C T S. Text in English. 1959. q. membership. adv. bk.rev. Index. **Document type:** *Academic/Scholarly.* **Description:** Features faculty-written essays and articles analyzing community college issues.
Former titles (until Sep. 1994): Faculty Association of California Community Colleges Bulletin (0046-3159); California Junior College Faculty Association C J C F A Bulletin
Related titles: Microfiche ed.; Online - full text ed.
Indexed: CIJE, CalPI.
Published by: Faculty Association of California Community Colleges, 1823, 11th St, Sacramento, CA 95814-6514. TEL 916-447-8555, FAX 916-447-0726, faccc@aol.com, http://www.faccc.org. Ed., R&P Katherine Martinez TEL 916-447-8555. Pub. Jonathan Lightman. Circ: 9,000.

F A T E IN REVIEW. see *ART*

378.3 GBR
F E F C CORPORATE PLAN. Text in English. triennial. free. **Document type:** *Corporate.*
Media: Online - full content.
Published by: Further Education Funding Council, Cheylesmore House, Quinton Rd, Coventry, Warks CV1 2WT, United Kingdom. http://194.66.249.219/documents/othercouncilpublications/index.html, http://www.fefc.ac.uk.

378 GBR ISSN 0260-5058
F E R N JOURNAL. Text in English. 1980. s-a. membership.
Published by: Further Education Research Network, c/o D. G. Rogers, Centre for Postgraduate Studies, Leicester Polytechnic, Scraptoft Campus, Leicester, LE7 9SU, United Kingdom.

378 DEU
FACHHOCHSCHULE COBURG. STUDIENFUEHRER. Text in German. a. EUR 2 newsstand/cover (effective 2002). adv. **Document type:** *Journal, Academic/Scholarly.*
Published by: Fachhochschule Coburg, Friedrich-Streib-Str. 2, Coburg, 96450, Germany. TEL 49-9561-3170, FAX 49-9561-317273, poststelle@fh-coburg.de, http://web.fh-coburg.de. adv.: page EUR 360. Circ: 4,000 (controlled).

378 DEU ISSN 0936-7098
FACHHOCHSCHULE MUENCHEN. STUDIENFUEHRER. Variant title: Studienfuehrer. Text in German. 197?. a. EUR 4.60 newsstand/cover (effective 2002). adv. **Document type:** *Journal, Academic/Scholarly.*
Published by: Verlag Kastner & Zeeb, Schlosshof 2-6, Wolnzach, 85283 , Germany. TEL 49-8442-92530, FAX 49-8442-2289, verlag@kastner.de, http://www.kastner.de. adv.: page EUR 590. Circ: 4,500 (controlled).

378 DEU
FACHHOCHSCHULE WIESBADEN. PUBLIKATIONSREIHE. Text in German. 1987. irreg., latest vol.41. price varies. **Document type:** *Monographic series, Academic/Scholarly.*
Published by: Fachhochschule Wiesbaden, Kurt-Schumacher-Ring 18, Wiesbaden, 65197, Germany. TEL 49-611-949501, FAX 49-611-444696, info@fh-wiesbaden.de, http://fh-web1.informatik.fh-wiesbaden.de.

378.73 USA
FACT BOOK ON HIGHER EDUCATION. Text in English. 1958. irreg., latest 1997. USD 49.95; USD 59.95 foreign (effective 1998). stat. cum.index. **Document type:** *Academic/Scholarly.*
Former titles (until 1982): Fact Book for Academic Administrators (0198-8425); (until 1980): Fact Book for Academic Administration; (until 1977): Fact Book on Higher Education (0363-6720); F B; A Fact Book on Higher Education (0014-6501)
Published by: Oryx Press (Subsidiary of: Greenwood Publishing Group Inc.), 1434 E. San Miguel Ave., Phoenix, AZ 85014-2422. TEL 602-265-2651, 800-279-6799, FAX 602-265-6250, info@oryxpress.com, http://www.oryxpress.com. Ed. Anne Thompson. Pub. Phyllis Steckler. R&P Lori Cavanaugh TEL 602-265-2651 ext 662.

378 USA ISSN 1063-9942
THE FAMUAN. Text in English. w.
Related titles: Online - full content ed.
Published by: Florida Agricultural and Mechanical University, 400 Lee Hall, Tallahassee, FL 32307-3100. TEL 850-599-3225, FAX 850-561-2152, http://www.thefamuan.com/, http://www.famu.edu/famu.asp.

FEDERAL GRANTS & CONTRACTS WEEKLY; funding opportunities in research, training and services. see *LAW*

378.34 USA ISSN 1080-1685
Z668
FINANCIAL ASSISTANCE FOR LIBRARY AND INFORMATION STUDIES. Text in English. 1970. a. USD 4 (effective 2003). **Document type:** *Directory.* **Description:** Lists scholarships and assistantships available from library schools, state associations and agencies, national associations and other sources.
Formerly (until 1994): Financial Assistance for Library Education (0569-6275)
Published by: (American Library Association, Office for Human Resource Development and Recruitment), American Library Association, 50 E Huron St, Chicago, IL 60611-2795. TEL 800-545-2433, FAX 312-944-8741, http://www.ala.org. Circ: 3,000. **Subscr. to:** PO Box 932501, Atlanta, GA 31193-2501. TEL 866-746-7252, FAX 770-442-9742, ala-orders@pbd.com.

378.106 CAN ISSN 0823-5872
LB2342.2.C3
FINANCIAL REPORT OF ONTARIO UNIVERSITIES. Text in English. a. CND 38.
Published by: Council of Ontario Universities, 180 Dundas St W, Ste 1100, Toronto, ON M5G 1Z8, Canada. TEL 416-979-2165, FAX 416-979-8635, acadieux@coupo.cou.on.ca, http://www.cou.on.ca.

378.759025 USA ISSN 0093-1071
LA258.5
FLORIDA. STATE BOARD OF INDEPENDENT COLLEGES AND UNIVERSITIES. REPORT. Key Title: Report of the State Board of Independent Colleges and Universities (Tallahassee). Text in English. 1972. a. free.
Published by: Florida State Board of Independent Colleges and Universities, c/o C Wayne Freeburg, Exec Dir and Ed, 201 Collins Bldg, Tallahassee, FL 32399. TEL 904-488-8695. Circ: 100.

378.56946 ISR
FOCUS. Text in English. 1983. 3/yr. free (effective 2005). **Document type:** *Newspaper.* **Description:** News and features about the University of Haifa.
Former titles: Inside; Carmel: News from Haifa University
Published by: University of Haifa, Department of External Relations and Resource Development, Mt. Carmel, Haifa, 31905, Israel. TEL 972-4-8240093, FAX 972-4-8342104, mzieashr@research.haifa.ac.il, http://www.haifa.ac.il/~focus/focus.html. Ed. A M Goldstein. Circ: 7,000.

378.0076 USA ISSN 0276-0592
LA201
FOCUS (PRINCETON). Text in English. 1976. s-a. free. illus.; stat. **Document type:** *Newsletter.*
Published by: Educational Testing Service, Rosedale Rd, Princeton, NJ 08541-0001. TEL 609-921-9000. Ed. Carol Carlson. Circ: 50,000. **Institutional subscr. to:** Warner Books Inc, Special Sales, Time & Life Bldg, 1271 Ave of the Americas, New York, NY 10020. TEL 212-522-7381; **Subscr. to:** Little Brown, 200 West St, Waltham, MA 02254. TEL 800-759-0190.

FOCUS (WASHINGTON, D.C. 1976). see *COLLEGE AND ALUMNI*

610.711 AUS ISSN 1442-1100
➤ **FOCUS ON HEALTH PROFESSIONAL EDUCATION.** Text in English. 1999. s-a. **Document type:** *Journal, Academic/Scholarly.* **Description:** Covers all aspects of health professional education, including undergraduate, postgraduate, and continuing professional education.
—BLDSC (3964.215688), IE.
Published by: ANZAME, c/o Michele Groves, University of Queensland, School of Medicine, Herston Rd, Herston, QLD 4006, Australia. http://www.anzame.unsw.edu.au/journal.htm. Ed. Ken Jones.

344.0711 USA
FOCUS ON LAW STUDIES; teaching about law in the liberal arts. Text in English. 1985. s-a. free. bk.rev. **Document type:** *Academic/Scholarly.* **Description:** Offers a forum for ideas, resources, analysis, and opinion on teaching about law in liberal arts programs.
Published by: American Bar Association for Public Education, Commission on College and University Legal Studies, 541 N Fairbanks Ct, Chicago, IL 60611-3314. TEL 312-988-5736, FAX 312-988-5494. Ed., Pub., R&P John Paul Ryan. Circ: 5,000.

378.052 USA
FOR GRADUATES ONLY. Text in English. 1979. a. free to qualified personnel. 64 p./no. 2 cols./p.; **Document type:** *Academic/Scholarly.* **Description:** Provides guidance and planning advice to seniors of two-year community and junior colleges.
Published by: Campus Communications, Inc., 5820 N. Federal Hwy., Ste. D-2, Boca Raton, FL 33487. TEL 561-995-5353. Ed. Judi Oliff. Pub., R&P, Adv. contact Darryl G Elberg. Circ: 100,000 (controlled).

378 CAN ISSN 1495-8546
FOR THE RECORD. Text in English. 1998. irreg. **Document type:** *Newsletter.*
Published by: Council of Ontario Universities, Public Affairs Division, 180 Dundas St W, Suite 1100, Toronto, ON M5G 1Z8, Canada. TEL 416-979-2165, FAX 416-979-8635, http://www.cou.on.ca/publications/record.htm.

378 DEU ISSN 0945-5604
LA727.5
FORSCHUNG UND LEHRE; Alles was die Wissenschaft bewegt. Text in German. 1950. m. EUR 76.50 (effective 2005). adv. bk.rev. back issues avail. **Document type:** *Journal, Academic/Scholarly.* **Description:** Presents informative articles on all issues affecting the scientific and academic communities.
Formerly (until 1994): Deutscher Hochschulverband. Mitteilungen (0437-6315)
Indexed: DIP, IBR, IBZ.
Published by: Deutscher Hochschulverband, Rheinallee 18, Bonn, 53173, Germany. TEL 49-228-364002, FAX 49-228-353403, redaktion@forschung-und-lehre.de, dhv@hochschulverband.de, http://www.forschung-und-lehre.de, http://www.hochschulverband.de. Ed. Felix Grigat. Adv. contacts Angelika Miebach, Vera Mueller. B&W page EUR 2,496, color page EUR 3,546; trim 180 x 250. Circ: 23,138 (paid and controlled).

FORSCHUNGEN UND MATERIALIEN ZUR UNIVERSITAETSGESCHICHTE. see *HISTORY—History Of Europe*

378 AUT ISSN 0429-1573
FORSCHUNGEN ZUR INNSBRUCKER UNIVERSITAETSGESCHICHTE✶. Text in German. 1962. irreg., latest vol.10, 1971. price varies.
Related titles: Series of: Universitaet Innsbruck. Veroeffentlichungen.
Published by: (Universitaet Innsbruck), Oesterreichische Kommissionsbuchhandlung, Glasmalereistr 6, Innsbruck, T 6020, Austria. Ed. Franz Huter.

378 DNK ISSN 1399-9648
FORSKERFORUM. Text in Danish. 1985. 10/yr. adv. bk.rev. illus. back issues avail. **Document type:** *Magazine.*
Former titles (until 1998): Universitetslaereren (0902-2619); (until 1987): Magistrenes Universitetslaererforeningen. Beskrivelse (0900-081X)
Related titles: Online - full text ed.
Published by: Dansk Magisterforening, Nimbusparken, Peter Bangs Vej 32, Frederiksberg, 2000, Denmark. TEL 45-38-156633, FAX 45-38-156632, joe@magister.dk, dm@magister.dk, http://www.forskeren.dk, http://www.magister.dk. Ed. Leif Soendergaard. Circ: 8,000.

378.007 DNK ISSN 1601-4480
FORSKNINGSSTYRELSEN. AARSBERETNING. Text in Danish. 1994. a. back issues avail. **Document type:** *Yearbook.*
Former titles (until 2001): Forskningsstyrelsen. Aarsberetning fra Forskningsforum og de seks Statslige Forskningsraad (1600-4213); (until 1999): Forskningsraadene. Aarsberetning (0909-5918)
Published by: Forskningsstyrelsen/Danish Research Agency, Artillerivej 88, Copenhagen S, 2300, Denmark. TEL 45-35-446200, FAX 45-35-446201, forsk@forsk.dk, http://www.forsk.dk.

FORUM (WASHINGTON, 1970). see *COLLEGE AND ALUMNI*

378 SWE ISSN 0348-1522
FORUM FOER DEBATT OCH INFORMATION. Text in Swedish. 1974. 8/yr.
Published by: Laerarhoegskolan i Malmoe, PO Box 23501, Malmoe, S-200 45, Sweden.

378 ROM ISSN 0015-8453
FORUM - REVISTA INVATAMINTULUI SUPERIOR. Text in Romanian; Summaries in English, French, Romanian. 1959. m. ROL 4,000, USD 2 per issue (effective 1999). adv. bk.rev. charts; illus.; stat. index. **Document type:** *Academic/Scholarly.*
Formerly: Revista Invatamintului Superior
Indexed: RASB.
Published by: Redactia Publicatiilor Pentru Strainatate "Romania"/Foreign Languages Press Group "Romania", Uniunea Scriitorilorf, Piata Presei Libere 1, PO Box 33-28, Bucharest, 71341, Romania. TEL 40-1-2719401, FAX 40-1-2243608. Ed. Corneliu Rades. Pub., R&P, Adv. contact Nicolae Sarambei TEL 40-1-2242719. Circ: 4,850.

FOUR-YEAR COLLEGES. see *EDUCATION—Guides To Schools And Colleges*

378.34 USA
FREE ONLINE SCHOLARSHIP NEWSLETTER. Text in English. 2001. w. adv. back issues avail. **Document type:** *Newsletter.* **Description:** Discusses the migration of print scholarship to the Internet.
Media: Online - full text. **Related titles:** E-mail ed.
Published by: Topica, Inc, 650 Folsom St, Ste 300, San Francisco, CA 94107. http://www.earlham.edu/~peters/fos/index.htm. Ed. Peter Suber.

378.34 USA
FULBRIGHT ASSOCIATION NEWSLETTER. Text in English. 1978. irreg. membership. adv. back issues avail. **Document type:** *Newsletter.*
Formerly: Fulbrighters' Newsletter
Published by: Fulbright Association, 666 11th St NW, Ste. 525, Washington, DC 20001-4537. TEL 202-331-1590, FAX 202-331-1979, fulbright@fulbright.org, http://www.fulbright.org. Ed. Jane L Anderson. Circ: 10,000.

FURTHER AND HIGHER EDUCATION AND TRAINING STATISTICS FOR WALES. see *EDUCATION—Abstracting, Bibliographies, Statistics*

378.3 GBR
FURTHER EDUCATION FUNDING COUNCIL. ANNUAL REPORT. Text in English. a. free. back issues avail. **Document type:** *Corporate.*
Media: Online - full content.
—BLDSC (1271.152000).
Published by: Further Education Funding Council, Cheylesmore House, Quinton Rd, Coventry, Warks CV1 2WT, United Kingdom. http://194.66.249.219/documents/othercouncilpublications/index.html, http://www.fefc.ac.uk.

378.3 GBR
FURTHER EDUCATION FUNDING COUNCIL. CIRCULAR. Text in English. irreg. free. back issues avail. **Document type:** *Bulletin.*
—BLDSC (3227.600000).
Published by: Further Education Funding Council, Cheylesmore House, Quinton Rd, Coventry, Warks CV1 2WT, United Kingdom. http://www.fefc.ac.uk.

E

378.3 GBR
FURTHER EDUCATION FUNDING COUNCIL. COLLEGE INSPECTION REPORTS. (Reports are issued for individual colleges.) Text in English. 1993. quadrennial. back issues avail. **Description:** Reports on each college of further education, following a four-year cycle, rating the institution in a variety of categories.
Media: Online - full content.
Published by: Further Education Funding Council, Cheylesmore House, Quinton Rd, Coventry, Warks CV1 2WT, United Kingdom. http://www.fefc.cov.net/documents/inspectionreports, http://www.fefc.ac.uk.

378.3 GBR
FURTHER EDUCATION FUNDING COUNCIL. EVALUATION OF THE WORK OF THE INSPECTORATE (YEAR). Text in English. 1994. a. free. back issues avail.
Media: Online - full content.
Published by: Further Education Funding Council, Cheylesmore House, Quinton Rd, Coventry, Warks CV1 2WT, United Kingdom. http://194.66.249.219/documents/inspectoratepublications/index.html, http://www.fefc.ac.uk.

378.3 GBR
FURTHER EDUCATION FUNDING COUNCIL. FUNDING ALLOCATIONS (YEAR). Text in English. a. free.
Media: Online - full content.
Published by: Further Education Funding Council, Cheylesmore House, Quinton Rd, Coventry, Warks CV1 2WT, United Kingdom. http://194.66.249.219/documents/othercouncilpublications/index.html, http://www.fefc.ac.uk.

378.3 GBR
FURTHER EDUCATION FUNDING COUNCIL. QUALITY AND STANDARDS IN FURTHER EDUCATION IN ENGLAND (YEAR). a. free. back issues avail. **Description:** Reviews the quality and standards in colleges in England.
Published by: Further Education Funding Council, Cheylesmore House, Quinton Rd, Coventry, Warks CV1 2WT, United Kingdom. http://194.66.249.219/documents/insepectoratepublications, http://www.fefc.ac.uk.

378.3 GBR
FURTHER EDUCATION FUNDING COUNCIL. REINSPECTION OF CURRICULUM AREAS (YEAR). Text in English. 1994. a. free. back issues avail.
Media: Online - full content.
Published by: Further Education Funding Council, Cheylesmore House, Quinton Rd, Coventry, Warks CV1 2WT, United Kingdom. http://194.66.249.219/documents/inspectoratepublications/index.html, http://www.fefc.ac.uk.

378.3 GBR
FURTHER EDUCATION FUNDING COUNCIL. REPORT OF THE OMBUDSMAN (YEAR). Text in English. a. free. **Document type:** *Corporate.*
Media: Online - full content.
Published by: Further Education Funding Council, Cheylesmore House, Quinton Rd, Coventry, Warks CV1 2WT, United Kingdom. http://194.249.219/documents/othercouncilpublications/index.html, http://www.fefc.ac.uk.

378.3 GBR
FURTHER EDUCATION FUNDING COUNCIL. RESIDENTIAL BURSARIES (YEAR); funds for residential bursaries and the terms and conditions that apply for the teaching year. Text in English. a. free.
Media: Online - full content.
Published by: Further Education Funding Council, Cheylesmore House, Quinton Rd, Coventry, Warks CV1 2WT, United Kingdom. http://194.66.249.219/documents/othercouncilpublications/index.html, http://www.fefc.ac.uk.

378 AUS ISSN 1325-0574
G C C A NEWSLETTER. Text in English. 1969. s-a. bk.rev.
Published by: Graduate Careers Council of Australia Ltd., PO Box 28, Parkville, VIC 3052, Australia. TEL 61-3-93449333, FAX 61-3-93477298, l.gladman@gcca.unimelb.edu.au, http://www.gradlink.edu.au. Ed. Jacqueline Vidot. R&P Lyn Gladman. Circ: 3,000.

378 USA
G R E EXAM. (Graduate Record Exam) Text in English. 1998. a. USD 22 (effective 2005).
Formerly (until 2001): G R E (1090-9117)
Published by: Simon & Schuster, 1230 Ave of the Americas, New York, NY 10020. TEL 212-698-7000, FAX 212-698-7099, http://www.simonsays.com. **Subscr. to:** PO Box 7500, Riverside, NJ 08075-8075. TEL 800-223-2336, 800-223-2348.

378 URY ISSN 0797-3918
GACETA UNIVERSITARIA. Text in Spanish. 1957. q.
Formerly (until 1969): Gaceta de la Universidad (0016-3759)
Published by: Universidad de la Republica, Av. Dieciocho De Julio, 1968 Piso 2, Montevideo, 11211, Uruguay. TEL 598-2-484901, FAX 598-2-480303, TELEX 26692 UDELAY UY.

378 CHN ISSN 1001-2834
GAODENG JIAOYU/HIGHER EDUCATION. Text in Chinese. 1978. m. CNY 132 (effective 2004). 128 p./no.; **Document type:** *Journal, Academic/Scholarly.*
Published by: Zhongguo Renmin Daxue, Shubao Zilio Zhongxin/Renmin University of China, Information Center for Social Server, Dongcheng-qu, 3, Zhangzizhong Lu, Beijing, 100007, China. TEL 86-10-84043003, FAX 86-10-64015080, kyes@163.net, http://www.confucius.cn.net/bkdetail.asp?fzt=G4. **Dist. in US by:** China Publications Service, PO Box 49614, Chicago, IL 60649. TEL 312-288-3291, FAX 312-288-8570; **Dist. by:** China International Book Trading Corp, 35 Chegongzhuang Xilu, Haidian District, PO Box 399, Beijing 100044, China. TEL 86-10-68412045, FAX 86-10-68412023, cibtc@mail.cibtc.com.cn, http://www.cibtc.com.cn.

GAODENG XUEXIAO HUAXUE XUEBAO/CHEMICAL JOURNAL OF CHINESE UNIVERSITIES. see *CHEMISTRY*

378 CHN ISSN 1002-4409
GAOXIAO LILUN ZHANXIAN/THEORETICAL FRONT OF HIGHER EDUCATION INSTITUTES. Text in Chinese. 1987. m. **Document type:** *Journal, Academic/Scholarly.*
Related titles: Online - full text ed.: (from East View Information Services).
Published by: Zhonghua Renmin Gongheguo Jiaoyubu, 163, Haidian Lu, 7F, Beikeyanlou, Beijing, 100080, China. TEL 86-10-62514709, GXLL@chinajournal.net.cn, http://gxll.chinajournal.net.cn/. **Dist. by:** China International Book Trading Corp, 35 Chegongzhuang Xilu, Haidian District, PO Box 399, Beijing 100044, China. TEL 86-10-68412045, FAX 86-10-68412023, cibtc@mail.cibtc.com.cn, http://www.cibtc.com.cn.

378.12 GBR
GENERAL EDUCATOR. Text in English. 1988. bi-m. GBP 20 (effective 1997). adv. bk.rev. back issues avail. **Document type:** *Newsletter, Trade.*
Indexed: CPE, ERA, TEA.
Published by: (General Education Section), National Association of Teachers in Further and Higher Education in England and Wales, 27 Britannia St, London, WC1X 9JP, United Kingdom. TEL 44-171-837-3636. Adv. contact Colin Waugh. page GBP 100; trim 165 x 255. Circ: 220 (paid).

378 DEU ISSN 0016-8157
AS181
GEORGIA AUGUSTA. Text in German. 1964. s-a. price varies. bk.rev. charts; illus. **Document type:** *Journal, Academic/Scholarly.*
Indexed: BHA, RILM.
—CCC.
Published by: (Universitaet Goettingen), Vandenhoeck und Ruprecht, Robert-Bosch-Breite 6, Goettingen, 37079, Germany. TEL 49-551-508440, FAX 49-551-5084422.

378.4355 DEU
GERHARD-MERCATOR-UNIVERSITAET DUISBURG. DUISBURGER UNIVERSITAETS-REPORT. Text in German. 1982. q. back issues avail. **Document type:** *Journal, Academic/Scholarly.* **Description:** Covers all general issues, news and information of the University of Duisburg.
Former titles: Gerhard-Mercator-Universitaet Gesamthochschule Duisburg. Duisburger Universitaets-Report; Universitaet-Gesamthochschule Duisburg. Universitaets-Report (0722-8481)
Published by: Gerhard-Mercator-Universitaet Duisburg, Lotharstr 65, Duisburg, 47048, Germany. TEL 49-203-379-0, FAX 49-203-3793333, pressestelle@uni-duisburg.de, http://www.uni-duisburg.de. Ed. Beate H Kostka. Adv. contact Josi Kemmann. Circ: 6,000.

610.076 378.1662 USA
GET INTO MEDICAL SCHOOL; a strategic approach. Text in English. 1997. a.
Former titles (until 2003): Medical School Admissions Adviser (1097-5411); (until 1999): Getting into Medical School (1090-9184); (until 1998): Road to Medical School (1083-9879)
Published by: Simon & Schuster, 1230 Ave of the Americas, New York, NY 10020. TEL 212-698-7000, FAX 212-698-7099.

GETTING INTO DENTAL SCHOOL; A S D A's guide for dental students. see *MEDICAL SCIENCES—Dentistry*

GETTING THROUGH DENTAL SCHOOL; A S D A's guide for dental students. see *MEDICAL SCIENCES—Dentistry*

GIJUTSU KYOIKU KENKYU RONBUNSHI/JOURNAL OF TECHNOLOGY AND EDUCATION. see *ENGINEERING—Electrical Engineering*

GILBERT LAW SUMMARIES. MULTISTATE BAR EXAMINATION. see *LAW*

378 GBR
GLASGOW UNIVERSITY STUDENTS' HANDBOOK. Text in English. 1972. a. GBP 1. adv. **Document type:** *Bulletin.*
Formerly: Students Representative Council. Handbook
Published by: Students Representative Council, John McIntyre Bldg, The University, Glasgow, Lanarkshire G12 8QQ, United Kingdom. TEL 041-339-8541, FAX 041-337-3557. Circ: 8,000 (controlled).

378 DEU ISSN 0085-1108
GOETTINGER UNIVERSITAETSREDEN. Text in German. 1941. irreg., latest vol.94, 1999. price varies. **Document type:** *Monographic series, Academic/Scholarly.*
Published by: Vandenhoeck und Ruprecht, Robert-Bosch-Breite 6, Goettingen, 37079, Germany. TEL 49-551-508440, FAX 49-551-5084422, info@v-r.de, http://www.vandenhoeck-ruprecht.de.

378.016 USA ISSN 1049-717X
LB2331.63
GOURMAN REPORT. RATING OF GRADUATE AND PROFESSIONAL PROGRAMS IN AMERICAN AND INTERNATIONAL UNIVERSITIES. Text in English. 1967. biennial. USD 21.95.
Published by: National Education Standards, One Wilshire Bldg, Ste 2900, 624 S Grand Ave, Los Angeles, CA 90017. TEL 213-426-6569, 323-665-6990. Ed., R&P Jack Gourman.

378.016 USA ISSN 1049-7188
LB2331.63
GOURMAN REPORT. RATING OF UNDERGRADUATE PROGRAMS IN AMERICAN AND INTERNATIONAL UNIVERSITIES. Text in English. 1967. biennial. USD 19.95.
Published by: National Education Standards, One Wilshire Bldg, Ste 2900, 624 S Grand Ave, Los Angeles, CA 90017. TEL 213-426-6569, 323-665-6990. Ed., R&P Jack Gourman.

378.4 GBR ISSN 0963-1542
GRADUATE CAREERS SERVICES DIRECTORY. Text in English. a. GBP 15 (effective 1999). adv. **Document type:** *Directory.* **Description:** Lists all U.K. higher education career services personnel.
—CCC.
Published by: C S U Ltd. (Subsidiary of: Higher Education Careers Services Unit), Prospects House, Booth St, E., Manchester, Lancs M13 9EP, United Kingdom. TEL 44-161-277-5200, FAX 44-161-277-5210, http://www.prospects.csu.ac.uk. Adv. contact Susan Rains.

GRADUATE PROGRAMS: PHYSICS, ASTRONOMY, AND RELATED FIELDS (YEAR). see *PHYSICS*

370.91732 USA ISSN 0888-1014
GRADUATE RESEARCH IN URBAN EDUCATION AND RELATED DISCIPLINES. Text in English. 1965. s-a. USD 5. charts; stat. **Document type:** *Academic/Scholarly.*
Formerly (until 1979): Graduate Research in Education and Related Disciplines (0017-2839)
Indexed: PsycholAb.
Published by: City College of New York, School of Education, N A C 6 207, 138th St & Convent Ave, New York, NY 10031. TEL 212-650-5354. Circ: 325.

GRADUATE SCHOOL GUIDE. see *EDUCATION—Guides To Schools And Colleges*

THE GRADUATE SCHOOL JOURNAL. see *ENVIRONMENTAL STUDIES*

378 PHL ISSN 0117-9802
➤ **GRADUATE SCHOOL RESEARCH JOURNAL: UNIVERSITY OF THE EAST.** Text in English. a., latest vol.6, no.1, 2000. 100 p./no.; **Document type:** *Journal, Academic/Scholarly.* **Description:** Contains articles, essays, and research reports by members of faculty and other contributions, including summaries of Master thesis/doctoral dissertations, a list of completed Master theses and doctoral dissertations.
Published by: University of the East, Graduate School, 2219 C.M. Recto Ave, Manila, 1008, Philippines. TEL 63-2-735-5471, FAX 63-2-735-6972, gs@ue.edu.ph, http://ue.edu.ph/. Eds. Cerazen Esclabanan, Lourdes G Tayae.

378.19822 AUS ISSN 1324-2113
➤ **GRADUATE WOMEN✱.** Text in English. 1960. s-a. membership. **Document type:** *Bulletin, Academic/Scholarly.*
Formerly: Australian Federation of University Women. Newsletter (0812-4345)
Published by: Australian Federation of University Women, Inc., PO Box 520, Canberra City, ACT 2601, Australia. afuw@mulga.adelaide.edu.au, afuwact@afuw.org.au, http://www.afuw.org.au/welcome.htm. Ed. Daphne Elliot. Circ: 1,500.

378.33 USA ISSN 0740-5383
GRANT ADVISOR. Text in English. 1983. m. USD 225 to individuals; USD 445 to institutions (effective 2004). adv. **Document type:** *Newsletter.* **Description:** Comprehensive newsletter on federal, foundation, and other philanthropic grant sources available for college and university faculty and their institutions.
Related titles: Diskette ed.; Online - full text ed.: USD 398 (effective 2000).
Address: 248 Marilyn Circle, Cary, NC 27513. TEL 919-461-1649, FAX 815-361-2971, info@grantadvisor.com, http://www.grantadvisor.com. Ed., Pub., Adv. contact Christopher L Watkins.

379.11 361.73 USA ISSN 1553-2453
▼ **GRANT AND SPONSORSHIP TRENDS.** Text in English. 2005. q. USD 89 to non-profit organizations & academic institutions; USD 79 to corporations (effective 2005). **Description:** Provides current information on the rapidly changing landscape of grant and sponsorship fundraising. Prospect researchers, grant writers, fundraising directors, and sponsorship coordinators in all segments of the non-profit world now have this valuable new tool to help focus their development efforts.
Media: Online - full text.
Published by: Regulus Communications, Inc., 3015 Woodsdale Blvd, Lincoln, NE 68502-5053. TEL 402-730-4926, FAX 402-421-9682, research@regulus.com, http://www.regulus.com/.

378.33 361.73 USA ISSN 1542-4472
GRANTS AND FUNDING FOR HIGHER EDUCATION. Text in English. 2001. m. USD 187 (effective 2005). **Document type:** *Directory, Academic/Scholarly.*
Related titles: Online - full text ed.: ISSN 1542-4642.
Published by: Quinlan Publishing Group, Marine Industrial Park, 23 Drydock Ave, 6th Fl, Boston, MA 02210-2387. TEL 617-542-0048, 800-229-2084, FAX 617-345-9646, info@quinlan.com, http://www.quinlan.com/b_hefn.html. Pub. E Michael Quinlan.

E

371.22   USA   ISSN 1045-2761
LB2337.2
GRANTS FOR HIGHER EDUCATION. Text in English. 1982. m. USD 187 per issue (effective 2005). **Document type:** *Newsletter, Trade.* **Description:** Provides a convenient and affordable way to make sure you are among the fire to know about the grants you need to fund your key program.
Related titles: ◆ Series of: Grant Guides.
Published by: Quinlan Publishing Group, Marine Industrial Park, 23 Drydock Ave, 6th Fl, Boston, MA 02210-2387. TEL 617-542-0048, 800-229-2084, FAX 617-345-9646, info@quinlan.com, http://www.quinlan.com. Ed. Annie Archaumbalt. Pub. Dennis Hofmaier.

378.33   USA   ISSN 0072-5471
LB2338
THE GRANTS REGISTER (YEAR). Text in English. 1968. a. (August, 2004), latest 2005, 23rd ed. USD 210 (effective 2005). back issues avail. **Document type:** *Academic/Scholarly.* **Description:** Complete guide to postgraduate and professional funding worldwide.
—BLDSC (4211.120000), CISTI.
Published by: Palgrave Macmillan, 175 Fifth Ave, New York, NY 10010. TEL 212-982-3900, 800-221-7945, 888-330-8477, FAX 212-982-5562. Ed. Ruth Austin.

379.3   USA
GRAPEVINE (NORMAL); state appropriations for higher education; state tax legislation; legislation affecting education beyond the high school. Text in English. 1958. m. looseleaf. free. charts; stat. back issues avail. **Document type:** *Academic/Scholarly.*
Media: Online - full text.
Address: c/o Dr Edward R Hines, Ed & Pub, Educational Admin & Foundations Dept, Illinois State Univ, Campus Box 5900, Normal, IL 61761. TEL 309-438-5405, FAX 309-438-8683, erhines@RS6000.cmp.ilstu.edu, http://coe.ilstu.edu/grapevine/. Circ: 1,000 (paid).

378.33   GBR
GREAT BRITAIN. DEPARTMENT FOR EDUCATION. POSTGRADUATE AWARDS. Text in English. a. stat.
Formerly (until 1992): Great Britain. Department for Education. Guides to Grants - Postgraduate Awards
Published by: Department for Education, Government Statistical Service, Mowden Hall, Staindrop Rd, Darlington, Durham DL3 9BG, United Kingdom. TEL 0325-392683, FAX 0325-392695. **Subscr. to:** H.M.S.O., PO Box 276, London SW8 5DT, United Kingdom. TEL 44-20-7873-9090, FAX 44-2078-730011.

GREAT BRITAIN. DEPARTMENT FOR EDUCATION. STATISTICS OF EDUCATION. FURTHER AND HIGHER EDUCATION. STUDENT - STAFF RATIOS AND UNIT COSTS. see *EDUCATION—Abstracting, Bibliographies, Statistics*

378.1   USA   ISSN 1545-4665
THE GREENTREE GAZETTE; the business magazine for higher education. Text in English. 1994. bi-m. adv.
Published by: Greentree Gazette, 4346, West Palm Bch, FL 33402-4346. http://www.greentreegazette.com. Ed. Richard Hoffmann. Pub. Jeff Wendt.

378.81   BRA   ISSN 0104-480X
GUIA DO ESTUDANTE; cursos & profissoes. Text in Portuguese. 1986. a. price varies. illus. **Document type:** *Magazine, Consumer.* **Description:** Describes all technical and university level professions available in Brazil, as well as all universities and colleges within the country. Includes information on facilities and quality of education with a systematic evaluation of undergraduate courses in the country.
Related titles: Online - full text ed.
Published by: Editora Abril, S.A., Av. das Nacoes Unidas, 7221, 11 andar Pinheiros, Sao Paulo, SP 05425-902, Brazil. TEL 55-11-50872112, FAX 55-11-50872100, guiadoestudante.abril@atleitor.com.br, http://guiadoestudante.abril.com.br/, http://www.abril.com.br/. Ed. Lucila Camargo. Circ: 40,000.

GUIA UNIVERSITARIA SALVADORENA. see *EDUCATION— Guides To Schools And Colleges*

378   FRA   ISSN 0997-1025
LE GUIDE DES ETUDES SUPERIEURES. Text in French. 1986. a.
Related titles: ◆ Supplement to: L' Etudiant. ISSN 0766-6330.
Published by: Editions Generation, 27 rue du Chemin Vert, Paris, Cedex 11 75543, France. TEL 33-1-48074141, FAX 33-1-47007980.

GUIDE TO DEPARTMENTS OF SOCIOLOGY, ANTHROPOLOGY AND ARCHAEOLOGY IN UNIVERSITIES AND MUSEUMS IN CANADA/ANNUAIRE DES DEPARTEMENTS DE SOCIOLOGIE, D'ANTHROPOLOGIE ET D'ARCHEOLOGIE DES UNIVERSITES ET DES MUSEES DU CANADA. see *SOCIOLOGY*

THE GUIDE TO DISTANCE LEARNING PROGRAMS. see *EDUCATION—Guides To Schools And Colleges*

GUIDE TO GRADUATE DEPARTMENTS OF SOCIOLOGY. see *SOCIOLOGY*

GUIDE TO POSTGRADUATE DEGREES, DIPLOMAS AND COURSES IN MEDICINE. see *MEDICAL SCIENCES*

378.3   AUS
GUIDE TO SUCCESSFUL GRANT APPLICATIONS. Text in English. a. AUD 12 to non-members; AUD 10 to members. **Document type:** *Trade.* **Description:** Provides practical advice on how to develop high-quality grant applications.
Published by: Royal College of Nursing Australia, 1 Napier Close, Deakin, ACT 2600, Australia. TEL 61-2-6282-5633, FAX 61-2-6282-3565. Ed. Helen Hamilton. R&P Lisa Howdin. Adv. contact Joanne Ramadge.

GUIDE TO USING THE INTERNET AND THE WORLD WIDE WEB. see *COMPUTERS—Internet*

378   AUS
GUIDELINES FOR THE PREPARATION AND PRESENTATION OF MUSIC SUBMISSIONS FOR CERTIFICATION. Text in English. 1994. a.
Published by: Queensland Board of Senior Secondary School Studies, P.O. Box 307, Spring Hill, QLD 4101, Australia. TEL 61-7-3864-0299, FAX 61-7-3221-2553, office@qbssss.edu.au.

378   AUS
GUIDELINES FOR THE PREPARATION OF SUBMISSIONS - ART. Text in English. 1996. a.
Published by: Queensland Board of Senior Secondary School Studies, P.O. Box 307, Spring Hill, QLD 4101, Australia. TEL 61-7-3864-0299, FAX 61-7-3221-2553, office@qbssss.edu.au.

378   JPN   ISSN 0533-6627
GUNMA UNIVERSITY, FACULTY OF EDUCATION. ANNUAL REPORT: ART, TECHNOLOGY, HEALTH & PHYSICAL EDUCATION, AND SCIENCE OF HUMAN LIVING SERIES. Text in Japanese; Summaries in English. 1966. a. per issue exchange basis.
Indexed: BiolAb, RILM, RefZh.
Published by: Gunma University, Faculty of Education/Gunma Daigaku Kyoikugakubu, Library, 4-2 Aramaki-Machi, Maebashi-shi, Gunma-ken 371-0044, Japan.

378   NLD   ISSN 0167-0468
H B O JOURNAAL. (Hoger Beroepsonderwijs) Text in Dutch. 1978. 9/yr. EUR 49.90; EUR 7 newsstand/cover (effective 2005). adv. **Document type:** *Academic/Scholarly.*
—IE, Infotrieve.
Published by: Koninklijke Van Gorcum BV/Royal Van Gorcum BV, PO Box 43, Assen, 9400 AA, Netherlands. TEL 31-592-379555, FAX 31-592-372064, info@vangorcum.nl, http://www.vangorcum.nl. Circ: 3,100.

378.17   BWA   ISSN 1024-8110
THE H E D U BULLETIN. (Higher Education Development Unit) Text in English. 1989. s-a. free. bk.rev. **Document type:** *Academic/Scholarly.* **Description:** Disseminates findings in higher-education teaching.
Published by: University of Botswana, Higher Education Development Unit, Private Bag 0022, Gaborone, Botswana. TEL 267-351151, FAX 267-356591, TELEX 2429 BD. Circ: 800 (controlled).

378 620   GBR
H E I NEWS. (Higher Education International) Text in English. 1989. s-a. **Document type:** *Newsletter.*
Related titles: Online - full text ed.
Published by: Royal Academy of Engineering, 29 Great Peter St, Westminster, London, SW1P 3LW, United Kingdom. TEL 44-20-7222-2688, FAX 44-20-7233-0054, http://www.raeng.org.uk. Ed. Ian Bowbrick.

378   AUS   ISSN 1323-4021
H E R D S A GOLD GUIDE SERIES. Text in English. 1995. irreg., latest vol.5. AUD 15 to non-members; AUD 10 to members. **Document type:** *Academic/Scholarly.* **Description:** Practical guides for tertiary educators.
Published by: Higher Education Research and Development Society of Australasia, PO Box 516, Jamison, ACT 2614, Australia. TEL 61-262534242, FAX 61-262534246, herdsa.office@effect.net.au. Ed. Susan Hayes.

378.9   AUS   ISSN 0813-524X
H E R D S A GREEN GUIDE SERIES. Text in English. 1984. irreg., latest vol.21, 1997. AUD 15 (effective 2000). back issues avail. **Document type:** *Academic/Scholarly.* **Description:** Brief, practical guides for tertiary educators.
Indexed: TEA.
—BLDSC (4298.81505).
Published by: Higher Education Research and Development Society of Australasia, PO Box 516, Jamison, ACT 2614, Australia. TEL 61-262534242, FAX 61-262534246, herdsa.office@effect.net.au. Ed. Susan Beatty.

378   AUS   ISSN 0157-1826
H E R D S A NEWS. Text in English. 1978. 3/yr. membership. bk.rev. back issues avail. **Document type:** *Newsletter.* **Description:** Informal and practical articles on teaching and learning in higher education.

Indexed: AEI, CPE, HEA.
—BLDSC (4298.815100).
Published by: Higher Education Research and Development Society of Australasia, PO Box 516, Jamison, ACT 2614, Australia. TEL 61-262534242, FAX 61-262534246. Ed. Susan Hayes. Circ: 1,000.

378   GBR
H E S D A. BRIEFING PAPERS. Text in English. irreg., latest vol.47, 1997. GBP 10. **Document type:** *Monographic series, Academic/Scholarly.*
Former titles: Universities' and Colleges' Staff Development Agency Briefing Papers; U S D U Briefing Paper
—BLDSC (4300.650000).
Published by: Higher Education Staff Development Agency, Ingram House, 65 Wilkinson St, University of Sheffield, Sheffield, S Yorks S10 2GJ, United Kingdom. TEL 44-114-222-1335, FAX 44-114-222-1333, ucosda@sheffield.ac.uk, http://www.hesda.org.uk.

HANDBOOK OF COMPUTER EDUCATION (YEAR). see *COMPUTERS*

HANDBOOK OF DISTANCE EDUCATION (YEAR). see *EDUCATION—Computer Applications*

HANDBOOK OF ENGINEERING EDUCATION YEAR). see *ENGINEERING*

378   IND
HANDBOOK OF LIBRARY AND INFORMATION SCIENCE (YEAR). Text in English. 1927. irreg., latest 1997. USD 12 (effective 2003). **Document type:** *Trade.* **Description:** Contains information on library and information science.
Published by: Association of Indian Universities, A.I.U. House, 16 Kotla Marg, New Delhi, 110 002, India. TEL 91-11-323-0059, FAX 91-11-323-6105, aiu@del12.vsnl.net.in, http://www.aiuweb.org.

378   IND
HANDBOOK OF MANAGEMENT EDUCATION (YEAR). Text in English. 1927. irreg., latest 1998. USD 25 (effective 2003). **Document type:** *Newsletter.* **Description:** Contains information in management education.
Published by: Association of Indian Universities, A.I.U. House, 16 Kotla Marg, New Delhi, 110 002, India. TEL 91-11-323-0059, FAX 91-11-323-6105, TELEX 311-66180 AIU IN, aiu@del12.vsnl.net.in, http://www.aiuweb.org.

HANDBOOK OF MEDICAL EDUCATION (YEAR). see *MEDICAL SCIENCES*

378   AUS
HANDBOOK OF PROCEDURES FOR SMALL AND INTERMEDIATE SUBJECT-GROUPS IN SENIOR SCHOOLS. Text in English. 1998. a.
Published by: Queensland Board of Senior Secondary School Studies, P.O. Box 307, Spring Hill, QLD 4101, Australia. TEL 61-7-3864-0299, FAX 61-7-3221-2553, office@qbssss.edu.au.

378   AUS
HANDBOOK OF PROCEDURES FOR THE COMPILATION OF EQUIVALENT OVERALL POSITIONS AND FIELD POSITIONS FOR VISA STUDENTS. Text in English. irreg. AUD 6.
Published by: Queensland Board of Senior Secondary School Studies, P.O. Box 307, Spring Hill, QLD 4101, Australia. TEL 61-7-3864-0299, FAX 61-7-3221-2553, office@qbssss.edu.au.

378   DEU   ISSN 0933-4831
HANDBUCH DER UNIVERSITAETEN UND FACHHOCHSCHULEN BUNDESREPUBLIK DEUTSCHLAND, OESTERREICH, SCHWEIZ. Text in German. 1967. irreg., latest vol.10, 2001. adv. back issues avail. **Document type:** *Directory, Trade.*
Formerly (until 1985): Deutsches Universitaets-Handbuch (0070-4512)
—CISTI. CCC.
Published by: K.G. Saur Verlag GmbH (Subsidiary of: Gale Group), Ortlerstr 8, Munchen, 81373, Germany. TEL 49-89-76902-0, FAX 49-89-76902150, customerservice_saur@csi.com, http://www.saur.de.

HARVARD BUSINESS SCHOOL ALUMNI BULLETIN. see *BUSINESS AND ECONOMICS*

HARVARD BUSINESS SCHOOL CLUB OF LONDON ADDRESS BOOK. see *COLLEGE AND ALUMNI*

HEALTH EDUCATOR. see *PUBLIC HEALTH AND SAFETY*

HEALTH PROFESSIONS REPORT; the independent bi-weekly newsletter on the education & training of medical, nursing and health professionals. see *MEDICAL SCIENCES*

HEBREW UNION COLLEGE - JEWISH INSTITUTE OF RELIGION. CHRONICLE. see *RELIGIONS AND THEOLOGY—Judaic*

E

▼ *new title*   ➤ *refereed*   ✳ *unverified*   ◆ *full entry avail.*

378 FIN
HELSINGIN KAUPPAKORKEAKOULU. JULKAISUSARJA A. VAEITOESKIRJOJA. Text in English, Finnish. irreg.
Published by: Helsinki School of Economics, Runeberginkatu 22-24, Helsinki, 00100, Finland.

378 GHA
HI-ED NEWS; national higher education news. Text in English. bi-m. free. **Document type:** *Bulletin, Government.*
Former titles: H E News; Ghana. National Council for Higher Education. Annual Report
Published by: Ministry of Education, Higher Education Division, PO Box M 45, Accra, Ghana. Ed. Irene Duncan.

378 GBR
THE HIGH FLYERS CASEBOOK. Variant title: Springboard High Flyers. Text in English. a. GBP 9.99 per issue (effective 2002).
Description: Contains case studies of school dropouts who have gone into higher education or work. Gives students insight into where their chosen courses can lead at 18 and beyond.
Formerly: Hobsons Sixth Form Casebook
Published by: (Careers Research and Advisory Centre), Hobsons PLC, Challenger House, 42 Adler St, London, E1 1EE, United Kingdom. TEL 44-1223-460366, FAX 44-1223-301506. **Dist. by:** Biblios Publishers' Distribution Services Ltd., Star Rd, Partridge Green, W Sussex RH13 8LD, United Kingdom. TEL 44-1403-710851, FAX 44-1403-711143.

378 USA ISSN 1523-9551
HIGHER ED; questions about the purpose(s) of colleges and universities. Text in English. 1999. irreg., latest 2004. price varies. **Document type:** *Monographic series, Academic/Scholarly.*
Published by: Peter Lang Publishing, Inc., 275 Seventh Ave, 28th Fl, New York, NY 10001. TEL 212-647-7700, 800-770-5264, FAX 212-647-7707, customerservice@plang.com, http://www.peterlangusa.com. Eds. Joe L Kincheloe, Josef Progler, Norm Denzin, Shirley Steinberg.

378 USA ISSN 0882-4126
LB2300
➤ **HIGHER EDUCATION**; handbook of theory & research. Text in English. 1985. a., latest vol.20, 2005. price varies. bibl.; charts; illus. 500 p./no.; back issues avail. **Document type:** *Yearbook, Academic/Scholarly.* **Description:** Analytical reviews of history, trends and current literature on all aspects of higher education.
Related titles: Online - full text ed.
Indexed: ArtHuCI, CIJE.
—BLDSC (4307.369880), IE, ingenta. **CCC.**
Published by: (Association for Institutional Research - Association for the Study of Higher Education), Springer-Verlag New York, Inc. (Subsidiary of: Springer Science+Business Media), 233 Spring St, New York, NY 10013. TEL 212-460-1500, FAX 212-460-1575, service@springer-ny.com, http://www.springer-ny.com. Ed. John C Smart. Circ: 700 (paid).

378.107 NLD ISSN 0018-1560
LB2300
➤ **HIGHER EDUCATION**; the international journal of higher education and educational planning. Text and summaries in English. 1971. 8/yr. EUR 778, USD 788, GBP 488 combined subscription to institutions print & online eds. (effective 2005). adv. bk.rev. stat.; illus. index, cum.index every 5 yrs. reprint service avail. from PSC. **Document type:** *Journal, Academic/Scholarly.* **Description:** Serves as a forum for exchange of research results, experience and insights on education in universities, polytechnics, technical colleges, research institutes and specialist institutions throughout the world.
Related titles: Microform ed.: (from PQC); Online - full text ed.: ISSN 1573-174X (from EBSCO Publishing, Gale Group, IngentaConnect, Kluwer Online, O C L C Online Computer Library Center, Inc., Springer LINK, Swets Information Services).
Indexed: ABIn, BibLing, BrEdI, CIJE, CPE, CurCont, DIP, EAA, ERA, ETA, EduInd, FamI, HEA, HECAB, IBR, IBSS, IBZ, IPSA, Inspec, LT&LA, MEA, MEA&I, RASB, RHEA, SEA, SENA, SOMA, SOPODA, SSA, SSCI, SWA, TEA, WAE&RSA.
—BLDSC (4307.369900), IDS, IE, Infotrieve, ingenta. **CCC.**
Published by: Springer-Verlag Dordrecht (Subsidiary of: Springer Science+Business Media), Van Godewijckstraat 30, Dordrecht, 3311 GX, Netherlands. TEL 31-78-6576050, FAX 31-78-6576474, http://springerlink.metapress.com/openurl.asp?genre=journal&issn=0018-1560, http://www.springeronline.com. Ed. Grant Harman.

➤ **HIGHER EDUCATION ABSTRACTS**; abstracts of periodical literature, monographs and conference papers on college students, faculty and administration. see *EDUCATION—Abstracting, Bibliographies, Statistics*

378 USA ISSN 0018-1579
HIGHER EDUCATION AND NATIONAL AFFAIRS. Text in English. 1952. s-m. USD 60 (effective 1998). adv. reprint service avail. from PQC. **Document type:** *Newsletter.*
Related titles: Microform ed.: (from PQC).
Indexed: HEA.
Published by: American Council on Education, Office of Research, One Dupont Circle, Washington, DC 20036. TEL 202-939-9365, FAX 202-833-4760. Ed. Janetta Hammock. Adv. contact Lisa Richards Hone TEL 202-939-9493. Circ: 25,000.

378 USA ISSN 0736-0797
HIGHER EDUCATION DIRECTORY (YEAR). Text in English. 1983. a., latest 2004. USD 72 per vol. (effective 2004).
Published by: Higher Education Publications, Inc., 6400 Arlington Blvd, Ste 648, Falls Church, VA 22042. TEL 703-532-2300, 888-349-7715, FAX 703-532-2305, hed@hepinc.com, info@hepinc.com, http://www.hepinc.com.

378 AUT
▼ **HIGHER EDUCATION IN AUSTRIA.** Text in English. 2003. a. free (effective 2003). adv. **Document type:** *Academic/Scholarly.* **Description:** Overview about the Austrian higher education system.
Published by: Oesterreichischer Austauschdienst/Austrian Exchange Service, Alserstrasse 4-1-3-8, Vienna, W 1090, Austria. TEL 43-1-427728101, FAX 43-1-42779281, elisabeth.bessert@oead.ac.at, info@oead.ac.at, http://www.oead.ac.at. Eds. Mrs. Elisabeth I Bessert, Mr. Felix Wilcek. Adv. contact Mrs. Eva Muellner TEL 43-1-427728180.

378.4 GBR ISSN 0379-7724
LA628
HIGHER EDUCATION IN EUROPE. Text in English. 1975. q. GBP 296, USD 490 combined subscription to institutions print & online eds. (effective 2006). adv. bk.rev. back issues avail.; reprint service avail. from PSC. **Document type:** *Journal, Academic/Scholarly.* **Description:** Deals with major problems and trends in contemporary higher education.
Related titles: Online - full text ed.: ISSN 1469-8358. GBP 281, USD 466 to institutions (effective 2006) (from EBSCO Publishing, Gale Group, IngentaConnect, O C L C Online Computer Library Center, Inc., Swets Information Services); French ed.; Russian ed.
Indexed: CIJE, CPE, DIP, ERA, ETA, HEA, IBR, IBZ, MEA, RASB, RHEA, SEA, SENA, SOMA, SWA, TEA.
—IE, Infotrieve. **CCC.**
Published by: (UNESCO ROM, Centre Europeen pour l'Enseignement Superieur (CEPES)), Routledge (Subsidiary of: Taylor & Francis Group), 4 Park Sq, Milton Park, Abingdon, Oxon OX14 4RN, United Kingdom. TEL 44-1235-828600, FAX 44-1235-829000, info@routledge.co.uk, http://www.tandf.co.uk/journals/titles/03797724.asp, http://www.routledge.co.uk. Ed. Daniel Lincoln. Circ: 1,500. **Subscr. in N. America to:** Taylor & Francis Inc., Customer Services Dept, 325 Chestnut St, 8th Fl, Philadelphia, PA 19106. TEL 215-625-8900, 800-354-1420, FAX 215-625-8914, customerservice@taylorandfrancis.com; **Subscr. to:** Taylor & Francis Ltd, Journals Customer Service, Rankine Rd, Basingstoke, Hants RG24 8PR, United Kingdom. TEL 44-1256-813000, FAX 44-1256-330245.

378 IND
HIGHER EDUCATION IN INDIA - IN SEARCH OF QUALITY (YEAR). Text in English. 1927. irreg., latest 1995. USD 60 (effective 1999). **Document type:** *Newsletter.*
Published by: Association of Indian Universities, A.I.U. House, 16 Kotla Marg, New Delhi, 110 002, India. TEL 91-11-323-0059, FAX 91-11-323-6105, aiu@del12.vsnl.net.in, http://www.aiuweb.org.

378 IND
HIGHER EDUCATION IN INDIA: RETROSPECT AND PROSPECT (YEAR). Text in English. 1927. irreg. USD 55 (effective 2003). **Document type:** *Newsletter.*
Published by: Association of Indian Universities, A.I.U. House, 16 Kotla Marg, New Delhi, 110 002, India. TEL 91-11-323-0059, FAX 91-11-323-6105, aiu@del12.vsnl.net.in, http://www.aiuweb.org.

378 USA ISSN 1556-5424
LA227.3
▼ **HIGHER EDUCATION IN REVIEW.** Text in English. 2004. a.
Related titles: Online - full text ed.: ISSN 1556-5750.
Published by: Higher Education Student Association, Penn State University, 400 Rackley Bldg, University Park, PA 16802-3202. TEL 814-865-6346, FAX 814-865-3638, HigherEducationInReview@psu.edu, hesa@psu.edu, http://www.clubs.psu.edu/up/hesa/HER/, http://www.clubs.psu.edu/up/hesa/index.html.

378.106 FRA ISSN 1682-3451
LB2341 CODEN: CRCOCR
HIGHER EDUCATION MANAGEMENT AND POLICY. Text in English. 1977. 3/yr. EUR 104, USD 119, GBP 70, JPY 14,000 (effective 2005). bk.rev. back issues avail. **Description:** Covers management in higher education institutions in different countries.
Former titles (until 2001): Higher Education Management (1013-851X); (until 1988): International Journal of Institutional Management in Higher Education (0253-0058)
Related titles: Online - full content ed.: ISSN 1609-6924. USD 68 (effective 2004); Online - full text ed.: (from EBSCO Publishing, Gale Group, IngentaConnect, O C L C Online Computer Library Center, Inc., Swets Information Services); ♦ French ed.: Politiques et Gestion de l'Enseignement Superieur. ISSN 1682-346X.
Indexed: CIJE, CPE, ERA, ETA, HEA, MEA, PAIS, RHEA, SEA, SENA, SOMA, TEA.
—BLDSC (4307.382600), IE, ingenta. **CCC.**
Published by: Organization for Economic Cooperation and Development, 2 Rue Andre Pascal, Paris, 75775 Cedex 16, France. TEL 33-1-45248200, FAX 33-1-45248500, http://www.oecd.org. Circ: 470. **Dist. by:** Extenza - Turpin, Pegasus Dr, Stratton Business Park, Biggleswade, Beds SG18 8TQ, United Kingdom. TEL 44-1462-687552, FAX 44-1462-480947, subscriptions@extenza-turpin.com; O E C D Turpin North America, PO Box 194, Downingtown, PA 19335-0194. TEL 610-524-5361, FAX 610-524-5417.

378.19822 USA
HIGHER EDUCATION OPPORTUNITIES FOR MINORITIES AND WOMEN: ANNOTATED SELECTIONS. Text in English. a. free.
Published by: U.S. Department of Education, 400 Maryland Ave, S W, Washington, DC 20202.

378.1012 GBR ISSN 0952-8733
➤ **HIGHER EDUCATION POLICY.** Text in English. 1952. q. USD 88 combined subscription in United States to individuals; GBP 54 combined subscription elsewhere to individuals; USD 396 combined subscription in United States to institutions; GBP 240 combined subscription elsewhere to institutions (effective 2005); Combined subscr. includes print & online eds.. illus. index. back issues avail. **Document type:** *Journal, Academic/Scholarly.* **Description:** Focuses on policy issues and the role of higher education in society today; also carries reports on relevant research being carried out in various parts of the world.
Formerly (until 1988): International Association of Universities. Bulletin (0020-6032)
Related titles: Microfiche ed.; Online - full text ed.: ISSN 1740-3863. GBP 198 in Europe; USD 306 elsewhere (effective 2004) (from EBSCO Publishing, Gale Group, IngentaConnect, O C L C Online Computer Library Center, Inc., ProQuest Information & Learning, ScienceDirect, Swets Information Services).
Indexed: BrEdI, CIJE, CPE, ERA, ETA, HEA, IBR, IBSS, IBZ, MEA, RASB, RHEA, SEA, SENA, SOMA, SociolAb, TEA.
—BLDSC (4307.385900), IE, Infotrieve, ingenta. **CCC.**
Published by: (International Association of Universities), Palgrave Macmillan Ltd. (Subsidiary of: Macmillan Publishers Ltd.), Houndmills, Basingstoke, Hants RG21 6XS, United Kingdom. TEL 44-1256-329242, FAX 44-1256-810526, journal-info@palgrave.com, http://www.palgrave-journals.com/hep/index.html. Ed. Guy Neave. Pub. David Bull TEL 44-1256-329242. Adv. contact Robert Sloan TEL 44-20-88827199.

378 GBR ISSN 0951-5224
LA630
➤ **HIGHER EDUCATION QUARTERLY.** Text in English. 1946. q. GBP 56, EUR 84 combined subscription in Europe to individuals print & online eds.; USD 120 combined subscription in the Americas to individuals & Caribbean (print & online eds.); GBP 71 combined subscription elsewhere to individuals print & online eds.; EUR 230 combined subscription in Europe to institutions print & online eds.; USD 468 combined subscription in the Americas to institutions & Caribbean (print & online eds.); GBP 278 combined subscription elsewhere to institutions print & online eds. (effective 2006). adv. bk.rev. bibl. index. reprint service avail. from PQC,PSC. **Document type:** *Journal, Academic/Scholarly.* **Description:** Publishes articles concerned with policy, strategic management and ideas in higher education.
Former titles (until 1986): Universities Quarterly (0263-9769); (until 1982): New Universities Quarterly (0307-8612); (until 1975): Universities Quarterly (0041-9230)
Related titles: Microform ed.: (from PQC); Online - full text ed.: ISSN 1468-2273. GBP 219 in Europe to institutions; USD 445 in the Americas to institutions & Caribbean; GBP 264 elsewhere to institutions (effective 2006) (from Blackwell Synergy, EBSCO Publishing, Gale Group, IngentaConnect, O C L C Online Computer Library Center, Inc., Swets Information Services).
Indexed: ABIn, AgeL, BrEdI, CIJE, CPE, CurCont, ERA, ETA, EduInd, HECAB, IPSA, MEA, MEA&I, PAIS, PCI, PSA, RASB, RHEA, SEA, SENA, SOMA, SOPODA, SSA, SSCI, SociolAb, TEA.
—BLDSC (4307.387000), IE, Infotrieve, ingenta. **CCC.**
Published by: (Society for Research into Higher Education), Blackwell Publishing Ltd., 9600 Garsington Rd, Oxford, OX4 2ZG, United Kingdom. TEL 44-1865-776868, FAX 44-1865-714591, customerservices@oxon.blackwellpublishing.com, http://www.blackwellpublishing.com/journals/HEQU. Ed. Heather Eggins. Circ: 1,000.

378.101 USA ISSN 1086-7260
HIGHER EDUCATION REPORT CARD (YEAR). Text in English. 1995. irreg., latest no.2, 1998. USD 60 to institutions commercial (effective 2001); USD 40 to institutions academic (effective 2000). bibl.; charts; stat. **Document type:** *Academic/Scholarly.* **Description:** Presents 55 measures to compare state public higher education systems. Includes environment, context, performance measures, and operation actions. Charts national trends.

E

Published by: Research Associates of Washington, 1200 N Nash St, Apt 1112, Arlington, VA 22209-3612. TEL 703-243-3399, FAX 703-524-6889, http://www.rschassoc.com. Ed. Kent Halstead.

378.007 GBR ISSN 0729-4360

➤ **HIGHER EDUCATION RESEARCH AND DEVELOPMENT.** Text in English. 1982. q. GBP 331, USD 548, AUD 482 combined subscription to institutions print & online eds. (effective 2006). adv. bk.rev. back issues avail.; reprint service avail. from PSC. **Document type:** *Journal, Academic/Scholarly.* **Description:** Aims to further debate and provide opportunities for more immediate and wider comment.
Related titles: Online - full text ed.: ISSN 1469-8366. GBP 314, USD 521, AUD 458 to institutions (effective 2006) (from EBSCO Publishing, Gale Group, IngentaConnect, O C L C Online Computer Library Center, Inc., Swets Information Services).
Indexed: AEI, CIJE, CPE, ERA, ETA, HEA, MEA, RHEA, SEA, SENA, SOMA, TEA.
—BLDSC (4307.389000), IE, Infotrieve, ingenta. **CCC.**
Published by: (Higher Education Research & Development Society of Australasia AUS), Routledge (Subsidiary of: Taylor & Francis Group), 4 Park Sq, Milton Park, Abingdon, Oxon OX14 4RN, United Kingdom. TEL 44-1235-828600, FAX 44-1235-829000, info@routledge.co.uk, http://www.tandf.co.uk/journals/titles/07294360.asp, http://www.routledge.co.uk. Eds. Linda Hort, Margot Pearson. Circ: 1,000. **Subscr. in N. America to:** Taylor & Francis Inc., Customer Services Dept, 325 Chestnut St, 8th Fl, Philadelphia, PA 19106. TEL 215-625-8900, 800-354-1420, FAX 215-625-8914, customerservice@taylorandfrancis.com; **Subscr. to:** Taylor & Francis Ltd, Journals Customer Service, Rankine Rd, Basingstoke, Hants RG24 8PR, United Kingdom. TEL 44-1256-813000, FAX 44-1256-330245.

378 GBR ISSN 0018-1609
LB2300

➤ **HIGHER EDUCATION REVIEW.** Text in English. 1968. 3/yr. GBP 54, USD 105 (effective 2005). bk.rev. bibl.; charts; illus.; abstr. cum.index every 3 yrs. back issues avail.; reprint service avail. from PQC. **Document type:** *Academic/Scholarly.*
Related titles: Microform ed.: (from PQC).
Indexed: BrEdI, CIJE, CPE, DIP, ERA, ETA, HEA, HECAB, IBR, IBZ, MEA, PCI, RHEA, SEA, SENA, SOMA, SRRA, SSCI, SWA, TEA.
—BLDSC (4307.390000), IE, ingenta.
Published by: Tyrrell Burgess Associates Ltd., 34 Sandilands, Croydon, CR0 5DB, United Kingdom. TEL 44-208-656-1770. Ed. John Pratt. R&P Tyrrell Burgess. Circ: 1,000.

378 CAN ISSN 1496-9424

HIGHER LEARNING MAGAZINE; technology serving education. Text in English. 2001. bi-m. tr.lit. **Document type:** *Magazine, Academic/Scholarly.*
Media: Online - full content.
Published by: Teach Magazine, 258 Wallace Ave, Ste 206, Toronto, ON M6P 3M9, Canada. TEL 416-537-2103, FAX 416-537-3491, teachmag@istar.ca, http://www.teachmag.com. Ed., Pub. Will Liberman.

378.1982 USA ISSN 1054-2337
LC2670.6

➤ **HISPANIC OUTLOOK IN HIGHER EDUCATION.** Variant title: Hispanic Outlook. Text in English. 1990. 25/yr. USD 29.95 (effective 2005); USD 3.75 per issue (effective 2003). adv. bk.rev.; video rev. illus. index. back issues avail.; reprints avail. **Document type:** *Magazine, Academic/Scholarly.* **Description:** Covers Hispanics in higher education, student issues as well as faculty and administration.
Related titles: Online - full text ed.: (from Northern Light Technology, Inc., ProQuest Information & Learning, SoftLine Information).
Indexed: ChPerI, DYW, ENW.
Published by: Hispanic Outlook in Higher Education Publishing Company, Inc., 210 Rt 4 E, Ste 310, Paramus, NJ 07652. TEL 201-587-8800, FAX 201-587-9105, outlook@aol.com, http://www.hispanicoutlook.com. Ed. Adalyn Hixson. Pub. Jose Lopez-Isa. R&P Sue Lopez-Isa. Adv. contact Angel Rodriguez. page USD 395. Circ: 28,000. **Subscr. to:** PO Box 68, Paramus, NJ 07652.

378.009 USA ISSN 0737-2698
LB2300

➤ **HISTORY OF HIGHER EDUCATION ANNUAL.** Text in English. 1981. a. price varies. bk.rev. **Document type:** *Journal, Academic/Scholarly.* **Description:** Articles on the history of higher education in America and overseas.
Related titles: Microform ed.
Indexed: AmH&L, HistAb.
Published by: Pennsylvania State University, Higher Education Program, 403 S Allen St, Ste 115, University Park, PA 16801-5202. TEL 814-863-2690, FAX 814-865-0543, rlg9@psu.edu. Ed., R&P Roger Geiger. Circ: 350.

378.42659 GBR ISSN 0960-2887

HISTORY OF THE UNIVERSITY OF CAMBRIDGE TEXTS AND STUDIES. Text in English. 1990. irreg.
Indexed: RASB.
—BLDSC (4318.612700).

Published by: Boydell Press (Subsidiary of: Boydell & Brewer Ltd.), PO Box 9, Woodbridge, Suffolk IP12 3DF, United Kingdom.

378.009 GBR ISSN 0144-5138
LA173

HISTORY OF UNIVERSITIES. Text in English, French, German, Italian, Spanish. 1981. a., latest 2002. price varies. adv. bk.rev. index. **Document type:** *Academic/Scholarly.*
Indexed: AmH&L, HistAb, IBZ, PCI, RASB, RI-1, RI-2.
—BLDSC (4318.612000), IE, ingenta.
Published by: Oxford University Press, Great Clarendon St, Oxford, OX2 6DP, United Kingdom. TEL 44-1865-556767, FAX 44-1865-556646, enquiry@oup.co.uk, http://www.oup-usa.org/catalogs/general/series/, http://www.oup.co.uk/. Ed. Mordechai Feingold. **Orders in N. America to:** Oxford University Press, 2001 Evans Rd, Cary, NC 27513.

HOBSONS ENGINEERING CASEBOOK. see *ENGINEERING*

HOBSONS FINANCE CASEBOOK. see *BUSINESS AND ECONOMICS—Banking And Finance*

HOBSONS I T CASEBOOK. (Information Technology) see *BUSINESS AND ECONOMICS—Production Of Goods And Services*

HOBSONS LAW CASEBOOK. see *LAW*

HOBSONS MANAGEMENT CASEBOOK. see *BUSINESS AND ECONOMICS—Management*

HOBSONS MARKETING, RETAILING AND SALES CASEBOOK. see *BUSINESS AND ECONOMICS—Marketing And Purchasing*

HOBSONS SCIENCE CASEBOOK. see *SCIENCES: COMPREHENSIVE WORKS*

378 DEU

HOCHSCHULE FUER TECHNIK UND WIRTSCHAFT DES SAARLANDES. STUDIENFUEHRER UND VORLESUNGSVERZEICHNIS. Text in German. a. adv. **Document type:** *Journal, Academic/Scholarly.*
Published by: Hochschule fuer Technik und Wirtschaft des Saarlandes, Goebenstr. 40, Saarbruecken, 66117, Germany. TEL 49-681-58679, pressestelle@htw-saarland.de, http://www.htw-saarland.de. adv.: page EUR 535. Circ: 4,500 (controlled).

HOCHSCHULFUEHRER. see *ENGINEERING*

378 DEU

HOCHSCHULFUEHRER DER FACHHOCHSCHULE WIESBADEN. Text in German. a. EUR 4.50 newsstand/cover (effective 2003). adv. **Document type:** *Journal, Academic/Scholarly.*
Published by: Fachhochschule Wiesbaden, Kurt-Schumacher-Ring 18, Wiesbaden, 65197, Germany. TEL 49-611-949501, FAX 49-611-444696, info@fh-wiesbaden.de, http://fh-web1.informatik.fh-wiesbaden.de. adv.: B&W page EUR 660, color page EUR 1,200. Circ: 1,850 (controlled).

378.7283 HND

HONDURAS. UNIVERSIDAD NACIONAL AUTONOMA. REVISTA DE LA UNIVERSIDAD; publicacion cientifico y cultural. Text in Spanish. 1909. irreg., latest vol.26, 1990. USD 6. bk.rev. reprints avail.
Published by: (Universidad Nacional Autonoma), Editorial Universitaria U N A H, Ciudad Universitaria, Tegucigalpa DC, Honduras. TEL 504-32-4772, FAX 504-31-0675. Circ: 1,000.

378 CAN ISSN 0381-3789
L906.O6

HORIZONS (TORONTO). Text in English. 1966. a.
Incorporates (1974-1983): Registered Private Vocational Schools (0822-0956); Which was formerly (until 1982): Directory of Registered Private Vocational Schools (0318-8221); (1986-19??): Colleges of Applied Arts and Technology. Programs (0383-4743)
Published by: Ontario. Ministry of Training Colleges and Universities, Mowat Block, 900 Bay St, Toronto, ON M7A 1L2, Canada. TEL 416-325-2929, FAX 416-325-6348, info@edu.gov.cn.ca, http://www.edu.gov.on.ca/eng/welcome.html.

HOSPITAL PHYSICIAN; medical practice for staff & resident. see *MEDICAL SCIENCES*

378 USA

HOUGHTON MILIEU. Text in English. 5/yr. free. back issues avail. **Description:** Publishes education and faith-related issues in features, campus news, sport news, notes.
Published by: Houghton College, PO Box 128, Houghton, NY 14744-0128. TEL 716-567-9200, FAX 716-567-9522, milieu@houghton.edu. Ed. Dean Liddick. Circ: 17,500.

378.161 GBR

HOW TO COMPLETE YOUR U C A S FORM (YEAR) ENTRY. Text in English. 1990. a. GBP 9.99 (effective 2001). adv. **Document type:** *Consumer.* **Description:** Advice on applying to UK university.
Formerly: How to Complete Your U C A S Application Form
Related titles: Diskette ed.: GBP 19.99.
Published by: Trotman & Co. Ltd., 2 The Green, Richmond, Surrey TW9 1PL, United Kingdom. TEL 44-20-8486 1150, FAX 44-20-8486 1161, mail@trotman.co.uk, http://www.trotmanpublishing.co.uk. Ed. Tony Higgins. R&P Amanda Williams. Adv. contact Alistair Rogers. Circ: 15,000. **Dist. by:** Plymbridge Distributors Ltd, Plymbridge House, Estover Rd, Plymouth, Devon PL6 7PY, United Kingdom. TEL 44-1752-202300, FAX 44-1752-202330, enquiries@plymbridge.com.

378 USA
LC2851.H83

HOWARD UNIVERSITY MAGAZINE. Text in English. 1973. q. adv. bk.rev. charts; illus. **Document type:** *Magazine, Academic/Scholarly.*
Formerly: New Directions (0047-9616)
Indexed: AIPP, RehabLit.
Published by: Howard University, Department of Publications, Arrupe House, 1400 Shepherd St, NE, Washington, DC 20017. TEL 202-806-0970, FAX 202-806-4577, http://138.238.41.254/communications/HMagazine.htm. Ed. Victor R Lambert. Adv. contact Horace G Dawson Jr. Circ: 10,000 (controlled).

HUMANITIES IN THE SOUTH. see *HUMANITIES: COMPREHENSIVE WORKS*

378 CHN ISSN 1001-6074
CODEN: HJUUEY

➤ **HUNAN JIAOYU XUEYUAN XUEBAO/HUNAN EDUCATIONAL INSTITUTE. JOURNAL.** (Issues 1, 3, 4 and 6 cover social sciences; issues 2 and 5 cover natural sciences) Text in Chinese; Summaries in English. 1983. bi-m. CNY 12; USD 30 foreign. adv. bk.rev. **Document type:** *Academic/Scholarly.*
Indexed: CCMJ, CIN, ChemAb, ChemTitl.
—BLDSC (4759.165000), CASDDS.
Published by: Hunan Jiaoyu Xueyuan, Xuebao Bianjibu, Zuojialong, Changsha, Hunan 410012, China. TEL 86-731-8825923. Ed. Suqin Wang. R&P Wenhua Hai. Adv. contact Ailiang Long. Circ: 1,500. **Dist. overseas by:** International Publishing Trading Corporation of China, PO Box 782, Beijing 100011, China.

378.016 CHE

I B O PUBLICATIONS CATALOGUE. Text in English, French, Spanish. 1996. a. free. **Document type:** *Catalog, Trade.*
Related titles: Online - full text ed.
Published by: International Baccalaureate Organisation/ Organisation du Baccalaureat International, Route des Morillons 15, Le Grand-Saconnex, 1218, Switzerland. TEL 41-22-7917740, FAX 41-22-7910277, ibhg@ibo.org, ibhq@ibo.org, http://www.ibo.org. R&P Pat Adams.

378 CHE ISSN 1560-5795

I B WORLD; the magazine of the international baccalaureate organisation. (International Baccalaureate) Text in English, French, Spanish. 1992. q. CHF 25, GBP 12, USD 16 (effective 2005). **Document type:** *Magazine, Academic/Scholarly.* **Description:** Covers the activities of the International Baccalaureate Organisation, its schools, students and graduates worldwide.
Published by: (International Baccalaureate Organisation/ Organisation du Baccalaureat International), Zidao Communication sarl, Route de Morges 36, St-Prex, 1162, Switzerland. ibhg@ibo.org, http://www.ibo.org. Ed. Ellen Wallace. R&P Pat Adams.

378.07 USA ISSN 1051-2772

I C S A NEWSLETTER. Text in English. 1983. a. USD 10 (effective 2003). adv. 12 p./no. 2 cols./p.; back issues avail. **Document type:** *Newsletter, Academic/Scholarly.* **Description:** Covers Association, conferences, research and publishing news.
Related titles: CD-ROM ed.
Published by: (International Christian Studies Association), Institute for Interdisciplinary Research, 1065 Pine Bluff Dr, Pasadena, CA 91107-1751. TEL 626-351-0419, http://www.jis3.org. Ed., Pub. Oskar Gruenwald. Circ: 1,250.

I E E E POTENTIALS; the magazine for engineering students. see *ENGINEERING—Electrical Engineering*

378 SWE ISSN 1400-1683

I Q VAGVISAREN/I Q STUDENT. Text in Swedish. 1991. 8/yr. adv. **Document type:** *Magazine, Consumer.*
Formerly (until 1994): Vagvisaren (1102-7770)
Published by: Mediafabriken Conny & Teddy Hallin AB, Box 3101, Stockholm, 10362, Sweden. TEL 46-8-587-07-500, FAX 46-8-587-07-501, webmaster@iqstudent.se, http://www.iqstudent.se. Ed. Catharina Arvidsson. Pub. Conny Hallin. Adv. contact Teddy Hallin. color page SEK 42,500; trim 245 x 342.

E

378.3 CAN
IBIDEM: GLENDON COLLEGE STUDENT HANDBOOK. Text in English. a. adv. **Document type:** *Bulletin.*
Published by: Glendon College, Student Union, 2275 Bayview Ave, Toronto, ON M4N 3M6, Canada. TEL 416-487-6720. Circ: 1,000.

378 AUS
IDEOLOGIES, PRINCIPLES AND PHILOSOPHIES UNDERPINNING MODERATION IN AUSTRALIA. Text in English. 1991. a.
Published by: Queensland Board of Senior Secondary School Studies, P.O. Box 307, Spring Hill, QLD 4101, Australia. TEL 61-7-3864-0299, FAX 61-7-3221-2553, office@qbssss.edu.au.

378 305.4 JPN ISSN 0289-3762
IIYAMA RONSO/IIYAMA MEMOIRS. Text in Japanese. 1984. a. **Document type:** *Academic/Scholarly.*
—BLDSC (4363.881140).
Published by: Tokyo Kogei Daigaku, Joshi Tanki Daigakubu/Tokyo Institute of Polytechnics, Women's Junior College, 2184 Iiyama, Atsugi, Kanagawa, 243-0213, Japan. TEL 81-46-2411731, FAX 81-46-2416677, http://www.wjc.t-kougei.ac.jp/.

378.773 USA ISSN 0094-8322
L903.I3
ILLINOIS. BOARD OF HIGHER EDUCATION. DIRECTORY OF HIGHER EDUCATION✱. Key Title: Directory of Higher Education. Text in English. a., latest 2001. **Document type:** *Directory.*
Published by: Board of Higher Education, 431 E Adams St Fl 2nd, Springfield, IL 62701-1418. TEL 217-782-2551, http://www.ibhe.state.il.us. R&P Donald Sevener TEL 217-557-7334.

378.052 USA
ILLINOIS. COMMUNITY COLLEGE BOARD. BIENNIAL REPORT. Text in English. 1967. biennial. free. stat.
Former titles: Illinois. Community College Board. Annual Report; Illinois. Community College Board. Biennial Report; Which supersedes: Illinois. Junior College Board. Annual Report (0092-7783)
Published by: Community College Board, 401 E Capitol Ave, Springfield, IL 62701-1711. TEL 217-785-0123, FAX 217-524-4981, smorse@icob.state.il.us, http://www.icob.state.il.us, http://www.icob@state.il.us. Ed. Steve Morse.

378.052 USA
ILLINOIS. COMMUNITY COLLEGE BOARD. DATA AND CHARACTERISTICS. Text in English. 1981. a. **Description:** Contains data and characteristics of the Illinois public community college system and is designed to serve as a basic reference.
Published by: Community College Board, 401 E Capitol Ave, Springfield, IL 62701-1711. TEL 217-850-0123, FAX 217-524-4981, sparke@iccb.state.il.us, http://www.iccb.state.il.us.

378 USA
IN FOCUS (WASHINGTON, 1996). Text in English. 10/yr. USD 45; USD 60 foreign. **Document type:** *Directory.*
Former titles (until 1996): N U C E A News; National University Extension Association. N U E A Newsletter
Published by: University Continuing Education Association, 1 Dupont Circle, N W, Ste 615, Washington, DC 20036. TEL 202-659-3130. adv.: B&W page USD 300.

IN THE CLUTCH. see *SPORTS AND GAMES*

378 USA
INDEPENDENT (WASHINGTON, 1956). Text in English. 1956. 5/yr. looseleaf. membership only. bk.rev. **Document type:** *Newsletter.*
Formerly: C A S C Newsletter (Council for the Advancement of Small Colleges)
Published by: Council of Independent Colleges, One Dupont Cir, Ste 320, Washington, DC 20036. TEL 202-466-7230, http://www.cic.edu. Ed. Stephen G Pelletier. Circ: 7,000 (controlled).

INDEPENDENT COLLEGES - DIRECTORY OF COURSES. see *EDUCATION—Guides To Schools And Colleges*

379.324 AUS ISSN 0310-7175
INDEPENDENT EDUCATION. Text in English. 1971. 3/yr. AUD 38.50 (effective 2001). bk.rev. 44 p./no.; back issues avail. **Document type:** *Academic/Scholarly.* **Description:** Covers specific issues of current interest and debate on education within state and federal education spheres in the non-government and independent education sector.
Related titles: Online - full content ed.
Indexed: AEI.
Published by: N S W - A C TIndependent Education Union, GPO Box 116, Sydney, NSW 2001, Australia. TEL 61-2-92022600, FAX 61-2-92618850, ieu@nswactieu.labor.net.au, http://www.nswactieu.labor.net.au. Ed. Richard F Shearman. R&P, Adv. contact Tina Delandre. Circ: 45,000. **Co-sponsors:** Victorian Independent Education Union; Queensland Independent Education Union.

371.04 USA ISSN 1066-5633
INDEPENDENT SCHOLAR; a newsletter for independent scholars and their organizations. Text in English. 1987. q. USD 17 domestic; USD 20 in Canada; USD 25 elsewhere (effective 2000). adv. bk.rev.; Website rev. back issues avail. **Document type:** *Newsletter, Academic/Scholarly.* **Description:** Seeks to facilitate the work and enhance the standing of independent scholars.
Published by: National Coalition of Independent Scholars, c/o Patricia A Farrant, Ed, 1050 Woodlawn, Iowa City, IA 52245-4446. TEL 319-337-2928, ncis@mindspring.com, http://www.ncis.org/. Ed., R&P Patricia A Farrant. Circ: 500.

INDEPENDENT STUDY CATALOG. see *EDUCATION—Guides To Schools And Colleges*

378.1 USA ISSN 1065-2787
INDEX OF MAJORS AND GRADUATE DEGREES. Text in English. 1980. a.
Formerly (until 1992): Index of Majors (0192-3242)
—CISTI.
Published by: College Entrance Examination Board, 45 Columbus Ave, New York, NY 10023-6992. TEL 212-713-8000, http://www.collegeboard.org/.

378.107 IND
INDIAN EDUCATION (AGRA); planning and development. Text in English. 1977. q. bk.rev.
Published by: Agra University, Agra, Uttar Pradesh 282 004, India. Ed. S B B B Singh.

INDONESIAN STUDIES NEWSLETTER. see *ASIAN STUDIES*

INDUSTRIAL TEACHER EDUCATION DIRECTORY. see *TECHNOLOGY: COMPREHENSIVE WORKS*

378.37 GBR ISSN 0950-4222
LC1085
➤ **INDUSTRY AND HIGHER EDUCATION.** Text in English. 1987. bi-m. USD 462 combined subscription in United States to institutions print & online eds.; EUR 467 combined subscription to institutions in the Eurozone; print & online eds.; GBP 306 combined subscription elsewhere to institutions print & online eds. (effective 2005). adv. abstr. index. back issues avail. **Document type:** *Journal, Academic/Scholarly.* **Description:** Explores all aspects of the collaboration between business and higher education.
Related titles: Microform ed.: (from PQC); Online - full text ed.: 2000 (from EBSCO Publishing, Gale Group, IngentaConnect, Swets Information Services).
Indexed: BrEdI, CIJE, CPE, ERA, ETA, IBSS, MEA, RASB, RHEA, SEA, SENA, SOMA, TEA.
—BLDSC (4476.285000), IE, Infotrieve, ingenta. **CCC.**
Published by: I P Publishing Ltd., Coleridge House, 4-5 Coleridge Gardens, London, NW6 3HQ, United Kingdom. TEL 44-20-7372-2600, FAX 44-20-7372-2253, JEdmondIP@aol.com, http://www.ippublishing.com/general_industry.htm. Ed. J Edmondson. **Subscr. to:** Extenza - Turpin, Pegasus Dr, Stratton Business Park, Biggleswade, Beds SG18 8TQ, United Kingdom. subscriptions@turpinltd.com.

378.777 USA
INFORMATION DIGEST OF POST-SECONDARY EDUCATION IN IOWA. Text in English. 1967. a. USD 10 (effective 1998). stat. **Document type:** *Directory, Government.*
Former titles (until 1992): Iowa. College Student Aid Commission. Annual Data Digest Report; (until 1991): Iowa. College Student Aid Commission. Annual Report; (until 1986): Iowa. College Aid Commission. Annual Report; (until 1986): Iowa. College Aid Commission. Biennium Report; (until 1978): Iowa. Higher Education Facilities Commission. Biennium Report; Iowa. State of Iowa Scholarships, Tuition Grants. Biennium Report (0091-3588)
Indexed: SRI.
Published by: College Student Aid Commission, 200 10th St, 4th Fl, Des Moines, IA 50309. TEL 515-281-3501. Ed., R&P Keith Greiner. Circ: 1,000.

378 AUT
INFORMATION FUER AUSLAENDISCHE STUDIENBEWERBER AN OESTERREICHISCHEN UNIVERSITAETEN/ INFORMATION FOR INTERNATIONAL STUDENTS INTERESTED IN STUDYING AT AUSTRIAN UNIVERSITIES OR UNIVERSITIES OF THE ARTS. Text in English, German. 1961. irreg. **Document type:** *Academic/Scholarly.*
Former titles: Information fuer Auslaendische Studienwerber an Oesterreichischen Universitaeten und Kunsthochschulen; Information fuer Auslaendische Studienbewerber an Oesterreichischen Hochschulen (0020-0077)
Published by: Oesterreichischer Austauschdienst/Austrian Exchange Service, Alserstrasse 4-1-3-8, Vienna, W 1090, Austria. TEL 43-1-4277-28180, FAX 43-1-4277-28195, info@oead.ac.at, http://www.oead.ac.at. Circ: 12,500.

378 DEU ISSN 0724-9616
INFORMATIONEN DEUTSCH ALS FREMDSPRACHE. Text in German. 1973. 6/yr. EUR 50 domestic; EUR 56 foreign (effective 2003). **Document type:** *Journal, Academic/Scholarly.*
Indexed: BibLing, DIP, IBR, IBZ.
Published by: Iudicium Verlag, Hans-Graessel-Weg 13, Munich, 81375, Germany. TEL 49-89-718747, FAX 49-89-7142039, info@iudicium.de, http://www.iudicium.de. R&P Elisabeth Schaidhammer.

378 DEU
INFORMATIONEN FUER REGENSBURGER STUDENTINNEN UND STUDENTEN. Text in German. 1969. a. back issues avail. **Document type:** *Directory, Consumer.*
Published by: Studentenwerk Niederbayern-Oberpfalz, Albertus-Magnus-Str 4, Regensburg, 93053, Germany. TEL 49-941-9432201, FAX 49-941-9431937, stwno@studentenwerk.uni-regensburg.de, http://www.studentenwerk.uni-regensburg.de.

378 AUT
INFORMATIONEN ZUR AKADEMISCHEN MOBILITAET. Short title: I A M. Text in German. irreg. **Document type:** *Academic/Scholarly.*
Published by: Oesterreichischer Austauschdienst/Austrian Exchange Service, Alserstrasse 4-1-3-8, Vienna, W 1090, Austria. TEL 43-1-4277-28180, FAX 43-1-4277-28195, info@oead.ac.at, http://www.oead.ac.at. Ed. Mr. Felix Wilcek. **Co-sponsor:** Bundesministerium fuer Wissenschaft und Verkehr.

378 CAN
INFORMER; a newsletter for Capilano College employees. Text in English. 10/yr. back issues avail. **Document type:** *Newsletter.*
Related titles: Online - full content ed.
Published by: (Capilano College, Community Relations Department), Capilano Press Society, 2055 Purcell Way, North Vancouver, BC V7J 3H5, Canada. TEL 604-984-1712, FAX 604-990-7837, tcr@capcollege.bc.ca, http://www.capcollege.bc.ca/about/publications/informer/index.html.

378.155 USA ISSN 0363-2601
L901
INNOVATIVE GRADUATE PROGRAMS DIRECTORY. Text in English. 1975. irreg., latest vol.6, 1992. USD 25. **Document type:** *Directory.*
Published by: Empire State College, Educational Materials Distribution Center, Saratoga Springs, NY 12866. TEL 518-587-2100, FAX 518-583-0801. Circ: 1,000.

378 NLD ISSN 0742-5627
LA227.3 CODEN: IHEDDZ
➤ **INNOVATIVE HIGHER EDUCATION.** Text in English. 1976. 5/yr. EUR 628, USD 668, GBP 395 combined subscription to institutions print & online eds. (effective 2005). adv. bibl.; illus. Index. back issues avail.; reprint service avail. from PQC,ISI,PSC. **Document type:** *Journal, Academic/Scholarly.* **Description:** Presents professional and scholarly information and encourages creative practices relevant to the higher education field.
Formerly (until 1983): Alternative Higher Education (0361-6851)
Related titles: Microform ed.: (from PQC); Online - full text ed.: ISSN 1573-1758 (from EBSCO Publishing, Gale Group, IngentaConnect, Kluwer Online, O C L C Online Computer Library Center, Inc., Springer LINK, Swets Information Services).
Indexed: ABIn, BibLing, CIJE, CPE, DIP, ERA, ETA, EduInd, HEA, HECAB, HRA, IBR, IBZ, MEA, PsycholAb, RASB, RHEA, SEA, SENA, SOMA, SOPODA, SWA, TEA.
—BLDSC (4515.487800), IE, Infotrieve, ingenta. **CCC.**
Published by: Springer-Verlag Dordrecht (Subsidiary of: Springer Science+Business Media), Van Godewijckstraat 30, Dordrecht, 3311 GX, Netherlands. TEL 31-78-6576050, FAX 31-78-6576474, http://springerlink.metapress.com/openurl.asp?genre=journal&issn=0742-5627, http://www.springeronline.com. Ed. Libby V Morris.

378 AUT
INNSBRUCKER UNIVERSITAETSREDEN✱. Text in German. 1969. irreg., latest vol.8, 1974. price varies.
Related titles: Series of: Universitaet Innsbruck. Veroeffentlichungen.
Published by: (Universitaet Innsbruck), Oesterreichische Kommissionsbuchhandlung, Glasmalereistr 6, Innsbruck, T 6020, Austria. TEL 43-512-587039, FAX 43-512-5870394, oekobuch@aon.at, http://www.oekobuch.com.

378.145 CAN ISSN 0714-7198
INQUIRY. Text in English. 1977. s-a. free to alumni (effective 2005).
Formerly (until 1981): Inquiry on Business (0707-221X)
—Infotrieve. **CCC.**
Published by: Queen's University, School of Business, 99 University Ave, Kingston, ON K7L 3N6, Canada. TEL 613-533-2330. Ed. Shelley Pleiter.

378.05 USA ISSN 0745-9432
INSIDE U V A. Text in English. 1979. w. (Weekly during the academic year, biweekly during the summer and holiday breaks). free On Grounds; USD 10 (effective 2004).
Published by: University of Virginia, Office of University Relations, P O Box 400229, Charlottesville, VA 22904. TEL 434-924-1400, FAX 434-924-0938, http://www.virginia.edu/insideuva, http://www.virginia.edu/universityrelations.

378 AUS ISSN 0313-3249
INSTEAD✱. Text in English. 1970. irreg. free. back issues avail.

Published by: Western Australian Institute of Educational Administration, 151 Royal St, Perth, W.A. 6000, Australia. Ed. C W Rielly. Circ: 500.

378 FRA ISSN 0751-1418
INSTITUT D'ALLEMAND D'ASNIERES. PUBLICATIONS. Variant title: P I A. Text in French. 1977. irreg., latest vol.32, 2002. price varies. **Document type:** *Monographic series.*
Published by: Institut d'Allemand d'Asnieres, 94 ave des Gresillons, Asnieres, 92600, France. TEL 33-1-46134860, FAX 33-1-46134866, michele.leprettre@univ-paris3.fr, http://www.univ-paris3.fr/recherche/publications/PIA/INDEX.HTM.

378 AUT ISSN 0020-2320
➤ **INSTITUT FUER WISSENSCHAFT UND KUNST. MITTEILUNGEN.** Text in German. 1946. q. EUR 22 domestic; EUR 30 foreign (effective 2002). adv. bk.rev. back issues avail. **Document type:** *Proceedings, Academic/Scholarly.*
Published by: Institut fuer Wissenschaft und Kunst, Berggasse 17, Vienna, W 1090, Austria. TEL 43-1-3174342, FAX 43-1-3174342, iwk.institut@utanet.at, http://homehobel.phl.umivie.ac.at/iwk. Ed., R&P Helga Kaschl. Circ: 1,500 (controlled).

378.03 GBR ISSN 0965-5298
INSTITUTE FOR COMPUTER BASED LEARNING. REPORTS. Text in English. 1992. irreg. **Document type:** *Monographic series.*
—BLDSC (4360.295160).
Published by: Heriot-Watt University, Institute for Computer Based Learning, Edinburgh, EH14 4AS, United Kingdom. TEL http://www.icbl.hw.ac.uk.

378 DOM
INSTITUTO TECNOLOGICO DE SANTO DOMINGO. BOLETIN. Text in Spanish. 1976. 3/yr. DOP 12, USD 12 (effective 1999).
Published by: Instituto Tecnologico de Santo Domingo, Apdo Postal 342-9, Santo Domingo, Dominican Republic. Ed. Antonio Fernandez. Circ: 4,000.

378 BRA ISSN 0101-7136
INTER-ACAO; revista da faculdade de educacao da UFA. Text in Portuguese. 1975. 2/yr. USD 23; or exchange basis. bk.rev. charts.
Published by: Universidade Federal de Goias, Faculdade de Educacao, Praca Universitaria-C.P. 131, Setor Universitario, Goiania, GOIAS 74000, Brazil. Ed. Terezinha Mendonca. Circ: 1,000.

378 USA ISSN 1081-0625
Q4 CODEN: IJEPFJ
➤ **INTERJOURNAL.** Text in English. 1997. irreg. free (effective 2005); free. illus. reprints avail. **Document type:** *Academic/Scholarly.* **Description:** Disseminates research results of quantitative research in the behavior of complex systems. Publishes original research articles, news items, letters, brief reviews, and review articles that might be of interest to the entire scientific community.
Media: Online - full text.
Published by: New England Complex Systems Institute, 24 Mount Auburn St, Cambridge, MA 02138. nesci@necsi.org, http://www.interjournal.org. Ed. Y Bar Yam.

378 USA
INTERNATIONAL ASSOCIATION OF INDEPENDENT SCHOLARS. NEWS & NOTES. Text in English. q. USD 30. **Document type:** *Newsletter.*
Published by: International Association of Independent Scholars, PO Box 1453, Reseda, CA 91337.

378.34 GBR
LB2337.6.G7
INTERNATIONAL AWARDS - SCHOLARSHIPS, FELLOWSHIPS, RESEARCH GRANTS. Text in English. 2001. irreg., latest 2001. GBP 40, USD 70 per issue (effective 2003). adv. 400 p./no. 2 cols./p.; **Document type:** *Directory.* **Description:** Describes 950 international awards open to students or researchers wishing to study abroad in a country other than their own at undergraduate, graduate and postdoctoral levels.
Formed by the merger of (1973-1997): Awards for First Degree Study at Commonwealth Universities (0967-9863); Which was formerly (until 1989): Financial Aid for First Degree Study at Commonwealth Universities (0260-0749); (1972-1997): Awards for Postgraduate Study at Commonwealth Universities (0960-7986); Which was formerly (until 1988): Scholarships Guide for Commonwealth Postgraduate Students (0306-1736); (1971-1997): Awards for University Teachers and Research Workers (0964-2706); Which was formerly (until 1991): Awards for Commonwealth University Academic Staff (0144-4611); (until 1980): Awards for Commonwealth University Staff (0305-8697)
Published by: Association of Commonwealth Universities, John Foster House, 36 Gordon Square, London, WC1H 0, United Kingdom. TEL 44-20-73806700, FAX 44-20-73872655, s.kirkland@acu.ac.uk, info@acu.ac.uk, http://www.acu.ac.uk/publications. Ed., R&P, Adv. contact Sue Kirkland TEL 44-20-73806700.

378.1542 CHE
INTERNATIONAL BACCALAUREATE ORGANISATION. ANNUAL REPORT. Text in English. 1968. a. CHF 11, USD 8. **Document type:** *Corporate.*
Former titles: International Baccalaureate Organisation. Annual Bulletin; International Baccalaureate Office. Annual Bulletin (0074-1973); (until 1972): International Baccalaureate Office. Semi-Annual Bulletin
Published by: International Baccalaureate Organisation/ Organisation du Baccalaureat International, Route des Morillons 15, Le Grand-Saconnex, 1218, Switzerland. TEL 41-22-7917740, FAX 41-22-7910277, ibhq@ibo.org, ibhq@ibo.org, http://www.ibo.org. R&P Pat Adams. Circ: 5,000 (controlled). **U.S. subscr. to:** International Baccalaureate North America, 200 Madison Ave, New York, NY 10016.

378.0712 FRA ISSN 0579-3866
INTERNATIONAL FEDERATION OF CATHOLIC UNIVERSITIES. GENERAL ASSEMBLY. REPORT. Text in French. 1963. every 3 yrs. USD 10 (effective 1999). **Document type:** *Proceedings.* **Description:** Discusses issues relevant to Catholic higher education.
Published by: International Federation of Catholic Universities (IFCU)/Federation Internationale des Universites Catholiques, 21 rue d'Assas, Paris, Cedex 6 75270, France. TEL 33-1-44395226, FAX 33-1-44395228, sgfive@club-internet.fr, http://fiuc.org/. Circ: 500.

378 GBR ISSN 0074-6215
L900
INTERNATIONAL HANDBOOK OF UNIVERSITIES AND OTHER INSTITUTIONS OF HIGHER EDUCATION. Variant title: International Handbook of Universities. Text in English. 1959. irreg., latest 16th Ed. GBP 179 for 16th Ed.. index. **Document type:** *Directory, Academic/Scholarly.* **Description:** Covers more than 5,700 institutions in 171 countries. Presents information on the latest developments in higher education worldwide.
—CISTI, Linda Hall.
Published by: (International Association of Universities), Palgrave Macmillan Ltd. (Subsidiary of: Macmillan Publishers Ltd.), Houndmills, Basingstoke, Hants RG21 6XS, United Kingdom. TEL 44-1256-329242, FAX 44-1256-810526, bookenquiries@palgrave.com, http://www.palgrave.com/catalogue/catalogue.asp?Title_Id=0333945131.

THE INTERNATIONAL JOURNAL OF ACCOUNTING. see *BUSINESS AND ECONOMICS—Accounting*

▼ **INTERNATIONAL JOURNAL OF PHARMACY EDUCATION.** see *PHARMACY AND PHARMACOLOGY*

378.101 GBR ISSN 1467-6370
LB2324
➤ **INTERNATIONAL JOURNAL OF SUSTAINABILITY IN HIGHER EDUCATION.** Text in English. 2000. 4/yr. EUR 1,021.16 in Europe; USD 1,149 in North America; AUD 1,639 in Australasia; GBP 716.66 in UK & elsewhere (effective 2006). reprint service avail. from PSC. **Document type:** *Journal, Academic/Scholarly.* **Description:** Reports on initiatives aimed at environmental improvements in universities, and the increased competitiveness of self-regulatory mechanisms such as environmental auditing and maintaining EMS. Disseminates case studies, projects and programs while still considering the market opportunities available.
Related titles: Online - full text ed.: (from EBSCO Publishing, Emerald Group Publishing Limited, Gale Group, IngentaConnect, O C L C Online Computer Library Center, Inc., ProQuest Information & Learning, Swets Information Services).
Indexed: ESPM, PEI, PollutAb, e-psyche.
—BLDSC (4542.685400), IE, Infotrieve, ingenta. **CCC.**
Published by: Emerald Group Publishing Limited, 60-62 Toller Ln, Bradford, W Yorks BD8 9BY, United Kingdom. TEL 44-1274-777700, FAX 44-1274-785200, infomation@emeraldinsight.com, http://konstanza.emeraldinsight.com/vl=607802/cl=42/nw=1/rpsv/ijshe.htm, http://www.emeraldinsight.com/. Ed. Walter Leal Filho TEL 49-40-766180-56.

➤ **INTERNATIONAL REVIEW OF ECONOMICS EDUCATION.** see *BUSINESS AND ECONOMICS*

➤ **INTERNATIONAL REVIEW OF HISTORY EDUCATION.** see *HISTORY*

378 IND
INTERNATIONAL STUDENTS IN INDIAN UNIVERSITIES (YEAR). Text in English. 1927. irreg., latest 1997. USD 25 (effective 1999). **Document type:** *Newsletter.*
Published by: Association of Indian Universities, A.I.U. House, 16 Kotla Marg, New Delhi, 110 002, India. TEL 91-11-323-0059, FAX 91-11-323-6105, aiu@del12.vsnl.net.in, http://www.aiuweb.org.

378.016 NLD
INTERNATIONAL STUDY PROGRAMS AT THE UNIVERSITEIT VAN AMSTERDAM; come in searching of the reasons. Text in English. 1995. a. free. **Description:** Includes information on certificate programs, masters programs, Ph.D. programs, and postgraduate courses.
Formerly: International Education Programs at the Universiteit van Amsterdam
Published by: Universiteit van Amsterdam, Bureau Campagne en Studievoorlierting, PO Box 19268, Amsterdam, 1000 GG, Netherlands. TEL 31-20-5256062, FAX 31-20-5252771, isp@bdu.uva.nl. Ed. Maria Hagen.

378.016 USA
INTERNATIONAL UNIVERSITY FOUNDATION DIRECTORY. Text in English. 1973. a. looseleaf. USD 600 (effective 2001). **Document type:** *Directory.* **Description:** Information on people active in higher education internationally.
Published by: (International University Foundation), T I U Press, 1301 S Noland Rd, Independence, MO 64055. TEL 816-461-3633. Ed. John Wayne Johnston. Circ: 1,000.

378.016 USA
INTERNATIONAL UNIVERSITY FOUNDATION REPORT. Text in English. 1973. q. looseleaf. USD 400 (effective 2000). **Document type:** *Newsletter.* **Description:** Covers major events in the Foundation's program of facilitating international higher education.
Published by: (International University Foundation), T I U Press, 1301 S Noland Rd, Independence, MO 64055. TEL 816-461-3633. Ed. John Wayne Johnston. Circ: 1,000.

378 USA
INTERNATIONAL UNIVERSITY NEWSLETTER. Text in English. 1973. q. looseleaf. USD 600 (effective 2001). index, cum.index. **Document type:** *Newsletter.*
Published by: T I U Press, 1301 S Noland Rd, Independence, MO 64055. TEL 816-461-3633. Ed. John Wayne Johnston. Circ: 415.

INTERNATIONALE HOCHSCHULSCHRIFTEN/INTERNATIONAL UNIVERSITY STUDIES. see *SOCIAL SCIENCES: COMPREHENSIVE WORKS*

THE INTERNET AND HIGHER EDUCATION. see *COMPUTERS—Internet*

378.12 IRL ISSN 1393-4813
INTOUCH. Text in English. 1868. m. adv. bk.rev. **Document type:** *Magazine, Academic/Scholarly.*
Formed by the merger of (1979-1997): Tuarascail (0790-9136); (1993-1997): Education Today (0791-9336); Which was formerly (until 1993): Muinteoir (0790-9047); (until 1986): Muinteoir Naisiunta (0027-3058); (until 1956): Irish School Monthly (0790-911X); (until 1954): Irish School Weekly (0790-9101); (until 1904): Irish Teachers' Journal (0790-9098)
Published by: Irish National Teacher's Organisation, 35 Parnell Sq., Dublin, 1, Ireland. TEL 353-1-8047700, FAX 353-1-8722462, editor@into.ie, info@into.ie, http://www.into.ie/html/publications/intouch/current.htm. Ed. Sinead Shannon. Adv. contact Cecilia Power. color page EUR 1,900; 182 x 263. Circ: 25,000.

378 EGY
ISHRAQAH. Text in Arabic. 1989. s-a.
Published by: Ministry of Higher Education, General Administration for Cultural Research, Sharia al-Falaki, Cairo, Egypt.

ISRAEL. CENTRAL BUREAU OF STATISTICS. INPUTS IN RESEARCH AND DEVELOPMENT IN UNIVERSITIES. see *EDUCATION—Abstracting, Bibliographies, Statistics*

378 USA ISSN 1081-4760
BD255
➤ **ISSUES IN INTEGRATIVE STUDIES**; an interdisciplinary journal. Text in English. 1982. a. USD 40 to individual members; USD 100 to institutional members; USD 15 to students (effective 2004). adv. bk.rev. **Document type:** *Journal, Academic/Scholarly.* **Description:** Provides articles on interdisciplinary theory and method, integrative research, empirical evaluations of interdisciplinary curricular models and programs, cross-campus surveys on the status of interdisciplinary programs, and pedagogical approaches.
Related titles: Microform ed.; Online - full content ed.
Indexed: HEA.
Published by: Association for Integrative Studies, Miami University, Oxford, OH 45056. TEL 513-529-2213, FAX 513-529-5849, aisorg@muohio.edu, http://www.units.muohio.edu/aisorg/pubs/issues/issues.html. Eds. Dr. Francine Navakas, Dr. Joan Fiscella. Circ: 550 (paid).

➤ **ISSUES IN WRITING**; education, government, arts and humanities, business and industry, science and technology. see *JOURNALISM*

➤ **IWATE UNIVERSITY. FACULTY OF EDUCATION. ANNUAL REPORT/IWATE DAIGAKU KYOIKUGAKUBU KENKYU NENPO.** see *EDUCATION*

378 ISR ISSN 0334-2565
IYYUNIM B'-HINNUKH. Added title page title: Studies in Education. Text in Hebrew; Summaries in English. 1973. s-a. bk.rev. **Document type:** *Academic/Scholarly.*
Indexed: IHP.
Published by: Haifa University, School of Education, Mount Carmel, Haifa, 31999, Israel. Ed. Moshe Zeidner. Circ: 1,000.

E

378 DEU ISSN 0075-2177
LF2901
JAHRBUCH DER ALBERTUS UNIVERSITAET ZU KOENIGSBERG - PR. Text in German. 1951. irreg., latest vol.29, 1995. price varies. reprints avail. **Document type:** *Monographic series, Academic/Scholarly.*
Indexed: MLA-IB.
—BLDSC (4617.300000).
Published by: (Goettinger Arbeitskreis e.V.), Duncker und Humblot GmbH, Carl-Heinrich-Becker-Weg 9, Berlin, 12165, Germany. TEL 49-30-7900060, FAX 49-30-79000631, duh-werbung@duncker-humblot.de, http://www.duncker-humblot.de.

JAPANESE LANGUAGE AND LITERATURE. see *LINGUISTICS*

378 CHN
JIANGSU DAXUE XUEBAO (GAO-JIAO BAN)/JIANGSU UNIVERSITY. JOURNAL (HIGHER EDUCATION STUDY EDITION). Text in Chinese. 1979. q.
Formerly: Zhenjiang Shi-Zhuan Xuebao (Shehui Kexueban) (1004-003X)
Related titles: Online - full text ed.: (from East View Information Services).
Published by: Jiangsu Daxue/Jiangsu University, Editorial Department of Journal of Jiangsu University, 301 Xuefu Road, Zhenjiang, Jiangsu 212013, China. TEL 86-511-8791434, http://www1.ujs.edu.cn/xuebao/index4.php, http://www.ujs.edu.cn/.

378.106 CHN ISSN 1003-8418
JIANGSU GAOJIAO/JIANGSU HIGHER EDUCATION. Text in Chinese. 1985. bi-m. CNY 9 (effective 2003). adv. bk.rev. **Document type:** *Academic/Scholarly.* **Description:** Covers higher education management, research and theory.
Related titles: CD-ROM ed.; Online - full text ed.: (from East View Information Services).
Published by: Jiangsu Sheng Gaodeng Jiaoyu Xuehui/Jiangsu Provincial Department of Education, 15 Beijing West Rd, Nanjing, Jiangsu 210024, China. TEL 86-25-3239209, FAX 86-25-3239107, jsgjz@ec.js.edu.cn, http://www.jsgj.chinajournal.net.cn. Ed. Ge Suowang. Adv. contact Gu Guanhua. Circ: 6,000 (controlled). **Co-sponsor:** Jiangsu Sheng Jiaowei.

378.17 CHN ISSN 1001-5469
JIAOCAI TONGXUN/BULLETIN OF TEACHING MATERIAL. Text in Chinese. bi-m.
Published by: Gaodeng Jiaoyu Chubanshe, 55 Shatan Houjie, Beijing, 100009, China. TEL 4016633. Ed. Jiang Liyin.

378.1 CHN ISSN 1008-3855
➤ **JIAOYU FAZHAN YANJIU/EXPLORING EDUCATION DEVELOPMENT.** Text and summaries in Chinese. 1980. m. CNY 60 (effective 2000); USD 60 foreign; CNY 5 newsstand/cover. stat. back issues avail. **Document type:** *Academic/Scholarly.* **Description:** Covers school education and talents cultivation into the macroeconomics, scientific and social development circumstances, by combining higher-education research with studies in basic education, vocational education and adult education, by delving deeply into the education development and reform from education thinking, policy, system, finance and statutes.
Formerly (until 1998): Shanghai Gaojiao Yanjiu - Shanghai Higher Education Research (1000-4394)
Related titles: Fax ed.; Online - full text ed.: (from East View Information Services).
Published by: Shanghai Jiaoyu Kexue Yanjiuyuan/Shanghai Academy of Educational Sciences, 21 Chaling Rd, Shanghai, 200032, China. TEL 86-21-6403-4824, FAX 86-21-6403-2607. Ed., Pub. Hu Ruiwen. R&P Qingzhang Xiao. Circ: 8,000 (paid). **Co-sponsor:** Shanghai Gaodeng Jiaoyu Xuehui - Shanghai Higher Education Association.

➤ **JOBS IN HIGHER EDUCATION.** see *BUSINESS AND ECONOMICS—Labor And Industrial Relations*

378 DEU ISSN 0302-5926
JOHANN WOLFGANG GOETHE UNIVERSITAET. STUDIENFUEHRER. Text in German. 1973. a. adv. **Document type:** *Academic/Scholarly.*
Published by: Johann Wolfgang Goethe Universitaet, Senckenberganlage 31, Frankfurt Am Main, 60054, Germany. TEL 49-69-79822683, FAX 49-69-79823610. Ed., Adv. contact Maria Marchel. Circ: 3,000.

378 USA ISSN 0190-227X
JOHN SIMON GUGGENHEIM MEMORIAL FOUNDATION. REPORTS OF THE PRESIDENT AND THE TREASURER. Text in English. 1962. a.
Published by: John Simon Guggenheim Memorial Foundation, 900 Park Ave, New York, NY 10016. TEL 212-687-4470, FAX 212-697-3248, fellowships@gf.org.

378.121 170 NLD ISSN 1570-1727
▼ ➤ **JOURNAL OF ACADEMIC ETHICS.** Text in English. 2003. q. EUR 237, USD 237, GBP 149 combined subscription to institutions print & online eds. (effective 2005). adv. reprint service avail. from PSC. **Document type:** *Journal, Academic/Scholarly.* **Description:** Devoted to the examination of ethical issues related to all aspects of post-secondary education, primarily within a university context.
Related titles: Online - full content ed.: ISSN 1572-8544; Online - full text ed.: (from EBSCO Publishing, Gale Group, IngentaConnect, Kluwer Online, O C L C Online Computer Library Center, Inc., Springer LINK, Swets Information Services).
Indexed: BibLing.
—BLDSC (4918.857000), IE. **CCC.**
Published by: Springer-Verlag Dordrecht (Subsidiary of: Springer Science+Business Media), Van Godewijckstraat 30, Dordrecht, 3311 GX, Netherlands. TEL 31-78-6576050, FAX 31-78-6576474, http://springerlink.metapress.com/openurl.asp?genre=journal&issn=1570-1727, http://www.springeronline.com. Ed. Deborah C Poff.

➤ **JOURNAL OF ACCOUNTING EDUCATION.** see *BUSINESS AND ECONOMICS—Accounting*

➤ **JOURNAL OF AGRICULTURAL EDUCATION AND EXTENSION;** international journal on changes in agricultural knowledge and action systems. see *AGRICULTURE*

378.052 USA ISSN 1068-610X
LB2326.3
➤ **JOURNAL OF APPLIED RESEARCH IN THE COMMUNITY COLLEGE.** Text in English. 1993. s-a. USD 35 domestic; USD 50 foreign (effective 2005). **Document type:** *Journal, Academic/Scholarly.* **Description:** Contains articles for and by institutional researchers and planners in the community college.
Indexed: CIJE, HEA.
—CCC.
Published by: (National Community College Council for Research and Planning), New Forums Press, Inc., 1018 S Lewis St, Stillwater, OK 74074. TEL 800-606-3766, FAX 405-377-2237, kinnickm@pdx.edu, info@newforums.com, http://www.nmsu.edu/~NCRP/jarcc.htm, http://www.newforums.com. Ed. Dr. Mary K Kinnick. Pub. Dr. Douglas O Dollar. R&P Dr. Donna Massey.

378.1982 USA ISSN 1077-3711
LC2781
JOURNAL OF BLACKS IN HIGHER EDUCATION. Text in English. 1993. q. USD 36 (effective 2005). adv. bk.rev. illus. 160 p./no. 2 cols./p.; back issues avail. **Document type:** *Journal, Academic/Scholarly.* **Description:** Dedicated to the conscientious investigation of the status and prospects for African Americans in higher education.
Related titles: CD-ROM ed.; Online - full text ed.: (from JSTOR (Web-based Journal Archive), Northern Light Technology, Inc., ProQuest Information & Learning).
Indexed: ASCA, ArtHuCI, CIJE, CurCont, ENW, HEA, IIBP, PAIS, SRRA, SSCI.
—BLDSC (4954.208000), IDS.
Published by: The CH II Foundation, Inc., 200 W 57th St, 15th Fl, New York, NY 10019. TEL 212-399-1084, FAX 212-245-1973, info@jbhe.com, http://www.jbhe.com. Ed. Theodore Cross. Adv. contact Elaine Kursch. B&W page USD 1,275, color page USD 2,370. Circ: 2,500 (paid); 300 (free).

378 374.8 USA ISSN 1531-4952
LC1037.5
➤ **JOURNAL OF CAREER AND TECHNICAL EDUCATION.** Text in English. 1984. s-a. adv. bibl.; charts; illus.; stat. back issues avail. **Document type:** *Journal, Academic/Scholarly.*
Formerly (until 2000): Journal of Vocational and Technical Education (0888-8639)
Related titles: E-mail ed.; Online - full text ed.: ISSN 1533-1830.
Indexed: CIJE.
—BLDSC (4954.873750).
Published by: Omicron Tau Theta, Graduate and Nontraditional Programs, Delta State University, Box 3295, Cleveland, OH 38733. TEL 601-846-4181, FAX 601-846-4215, mjlush@dsu.deltast.edu, http://scholar.lib.vt.edu/ejournals/JCTE/, http://www.ott.vt.edu/pubs.htm. Ed. Myra Womble. Pub., R&P, Adv. contact Mary Jean Lush.

➤ **JOURNAL OF CHEMICAL EDUCATION.** see *CHEMISTRY*

378.161 USA ISSN 0734-6670
LB2351.2
JOURNAL OF COLLEGE ADMISSION. Text in English. 1968. q. USD 65 domestic to non-members; USD 75 foreign to non-members (effective 2005). **Document type:** *Journal, Trade.* **Description:** Aimed at school counselors, admission personnel and others concerned about the transition process.
Formerly (until 1982): National A C A C Journal (0027-8599)
Related titles: Online - full text ed.: (from EBSCO Publishing, H.W. Wilson, O C L C Online Computer Library Center, Inc., ProQuest Information & Learning).
Indexed: ABIn, CIJE, EduInd, HEA.
—BLDSC (4958.799600), IE, ingenta.
Published by: National Association for College Admission Counseling, 1631 Prince St, Alexandria, VA 22314-2818. TEL 703-836-2222, FAX 703-836-8015, http://www.nacac.com/pubs_counselors.html#journal. Ed., R&P Elaina Loveland. Circ: 7,500.

378.3 USA ISSN 0161-827X
LB3226
➤ **JOURNAL OF COLLEGE AND UNIVERSITY STUDENT HOUSING;** A C U H O journal. Text in English. 1971. s-a. USD 30 to non-members; USD 34 foreign to non-members; USD 20 to members; USD 24 foreign to members. adv. bk.rev. reprint service avail. from PQC. **Document type:** *Academic/Scholarly.* **Description:** Contains current research, literature reviews and other scholarly materials related to college and university housing.
Related titles: Microform ed.: (from PQC); Online - full text ed.: (from EBSCO Publishing).
Indexed: CIJE, CPE, HEA.
Published by: Association of College and University Housing Officers' International, 941 Chatham Lane, Ste 318, Columbus, OH 43221-2416. TEL 614-292-0099, FAX 614-292-3205, osuacuho@postobx.acs.ohio-state.edu, http://www.acuho.ohio-state.edu. Ed. Dade Tampke. R&P Mary Ellerbrock. Adv. contact Darcy Lehner. Circ: 3,000 (controlled).

371.4 USA ISSN 1099-0399
LB2343
➤ **JOURNAL OF COLLEGE COUNSELING.** Text in English. 1999. s-a. USD 42 to individuals; USD 50 to institutions; USD 21 per issue; free to members (effective 2005). adv. bk.rev. abstr.; charts; stat. index. 96 p./no.; back issues avail.; reprint service avail. from PSC. **Document type:** *Journal, Academic/Scholarly.* **Description:** Publishes articles that inform the practice of counselors working in higher education settings.
Related titles: Microfilm ed.: (from PQC); Online - full text ed.: (from EBSCO Publishing, Gale Group, H.W. Wilson, O C L C Online Computer Library Center, Inc., ProQuest Information & Learning).
Indexed: ABIn, CIJE, EduInd, PsycInfo, PsycholAb.
—BLDSC (4958.799900), IE. **CCC.**
Published by: American Counseling Association, 5999 Stevenson Ave, Alexandria, VA 22304-3300. TEL 800-347-6647, FAX 800-473-2329, http://www.counseling.org. Ed. Laura Hensley Choate. R&P Cynthia Peay TEL 703-823-9800 ext 249. Adv. contact Kathy Maguire TEL 703-823-9800 ext 207. Circ: 2,500 (paid).

378.17 USA
LB2365.R4
➤ **THE JOURNAL OF COLLEGE LITERACY AND LEARNING.** Text in English. 1983. a. adv. bk.rev. **Document type:** *Academic/Scholarly.* **Description:** Publishes materials related to the teaching of reading and study skills at the college and postsecondary levels. Provides a forum for the exchange of information regarding research, theory, and practice.
Supersedes (in 1998): Forum for Reading (0738-9523)
Indexed: CIJE, PsycholAb.
—CCC.
Published by: (International Reading Association, Inc.), University of Pittsburgh, School of Education, 5T01 Forbes Quadrangle, Pittsburgh, PA 15260. TEL 412-648-1782, biggs@pitt.edu. Ed. Shirley A Biggs. Circ: 650 (controlled).

378 USA ISSN 1079-0195
➤ **JOURNAL OF COLLEGE READING AND LEARNING.** Text in English. 1983. s-a. USD 30 to individuals; USD 50 to institutions (effective 2004). adv. back issues avail. **Document type:** *Journal, Academic/Scholarly.* **Description:** Acts as a forum for current theory, research, practice and policy related to post-secondary reading improvement and learning assistance.
Related titles: Online - full text ed.: (from Gale Group, H.W. Wilson, O C L C Online Computer Library Center, Inc.).
Indexed: ABIn, CEI, EduInd, SOPODA.
—CCC.
Published by: College Reading and Learning Association, 382, El Dorado, KS 67042-0382. http://www.crla.net/journal.htm. Ed., Adv. contact Cynthia Peterson. B&W page USD 200; trim 9 x 6. Circ: 1,300.

➤ **JOURNAL OF COLLEGE SCIENCE TEACHING.** see *SCIENCES: COMPREHENSIVE WORKS*

378.17 371.4 371.8 USA ISSN 0897-5264
LB2343
➤ **JOURNAL OF COLLEGE STUDENT DEVELOPMENT.** Text in English. 1959. bi-m. USD 62 to individuals; USD 125 to institutions; USD 175 combined subscription to institutions print & online eds.; USD 12 per issue to individuals; USD 24 per issue to institutions (effective 2006). adv. bk.rev. abstr.; illus. index. 120 p./no.; reprint service avail. from PQC. **Document type:** *Journal, Academic/Scholarly.* **Description:** In-depth coverage of topics such as student psychosocial and cognitive development, needs of special student populations and career planning.
Formerly (until 1987): Journal of College Student Personnel (0021-9789)
Related titles: Microform ed.: (from PQC); Online - full text ed.: ISSN 1543-3382. USD 125 to institutions (effective 2006) (from bigchalk, O C L C Online Computer Library Center, Inc., Project MUSE, ProQuest Information & Learning, Swets Information Services).
Indexed: ABIn, ASCA, AgeL, CIJE, CPE, ChPerI, CurCont, EAA, ERA, EduInd, FamI, HEA, MEA, PSI, PsycInfo, PsycholAb, SENA, SSCI, SWR&A, TEA, e-psyche.
—BLDSC (4958.816000), IE, Infotrieve, ingenta.

E

Published by: (American College Personnel Association), The Johns Hopkins University Press, Journals Publishing Division, 2715 N Charles St, Baltimore, MD 21218-4363. TEL 410-516-6984, 410-516-6987, 800-548-1784, FAX 410-516-6968, info@acpa.nche.edu, http://www.press.jhu.edu/journals/journal_of_college_student_development/index.html. Ed. Florence Hamrick. Adv. contact Monica Queen TEL 410-516-6984. page USD 375; 5.5 x 8. Circ: 695 (paid).

➤ **JOURNAL OF COLLEGE STUDENT PSYCHOTHERAPY.** see *PSYCHOLOGY*

378.3 USA ISSN 1521-0251
LC148.15
➤ **JOURNAL OF COLLEGE STUDENT RETENTION: RESEARCH, THEORY & PRACTICE.** Text in English. 1999. q. USD 62 to individuals; USD 191 domestic to institutions; USD 199 foreign to institutions (effective 2005). adv. bk.rev. back issues avail.; reprints avail. **Document type:** *Journal, Academic/Scholarly.* **Description:** Provides the educational community, federal and state government officials, and the public with the latest findings regarding the retention of students in higher education.
Related titles: Online - full text ed.: ISSN 1541-4167 (from EBSCO Publishing, ProQuest Information & Learning).
Indexed: ABIn, DIP, ESPM, EduInd, IBR, IBZ, RiskAb.
—BLDSC (4958.840000). **CCC.**
Published by: Baywood Publishing Co., Inc., 26 Austin Ave, PO Box 337, Amityville, NY 11701-0337. TEL 631-691-1270, FAX 631-691-1770, info@baywood.com, http://www.baywood.com/Journals/PreviewJournal.asp?Id=1521-0251. Ed. Dr. Alan Seidman. R&P Julie Krempa. Adv. contact Rochelle Grant.

378 USA ISSN 1544-0389
LB2331
▼ ➤ **JOURNAL OF COLLEGE TEACHING AND LEARNING.** Text in English. 2004 (Jan). m. USD 100 to individuals; USD 495 to institutions (effective 2004). **Document type:** *Journal, Academic/Scholarly.*
Published by: Western Academic Press, PO Box 620760, Littleton, CO 80162. TEL 303-904-4750, FAX 303-978-0413, http://www.wapress.com/JCTLMain.htm.

➤ **JOURNAL OF COMPUTER INFORMATION SYSTEMS.** see *COMPUTERS—Computer Systems*

➤ **JOURNAL OF COMPUTER SCIENCE EDUCATION.** see *COMPUTERS*

➤ **JOURNAL OF COMPUTING IN HIGHER EDUCATION.** see *EDUCATION—Computer Applications*

➤ **JOURNAL OF COMPUTING IN TEACHER EDUCATION.** see *COMPUTERS*

378 004 USA
➤ **JOURNAL OF COMPUTING SCIENCES IN COLLEGES.** Text in English. 5/yr. **Document type:** *Journal, Academic/Scholarly.*
—BLDSC (4963.965000).
Published by: Consortium for Computing Sciences in Colleges, c/o Cathy Bareiss, C.S. Dept, Olivet Nazarene University, One University Ave, Bourbonnais, IL 60914. TEL 815-939-5366, FAX 815-939-5081, cbareiss@olivet.edu, http://www.ccsc.org/publications/pubsJournal.htm, http://www.ccsc.org/index.htm. Ed. John G Meinke.

617.6071 USA ISSN 0022-0337
RK71
➤ **JOURNAL OF DENTAL EDUCATION.** Text in English. 1936. m. USD 125 domestic; USD 150 in Canada; USD 175 elsewhere (effective 2005). adv. bk.rev.; software rev. charts; illus.; stat.; abstr. index. back issues avail.; reprints avail. **Document type:** *Journal, Academic/Scholarly.* **Description:** Contains articles on dental educational research, teaching methods and materials, curriculum, and administration of educational programs.
Related titles: Microform ed.; Online - full text ed.: (from EBSCO Publishing).
Indexed: AgeL, BiolAb, CIJE, CPE, CTD, DentAb, DentInd, ERA, HEA, IndMed, MEDLINE, RHEA, SWA, TEA.
—BLDSC (4968.450000), CISTI, GNLM, IE, Infotrieve, ingenta, KNAW.
Published by: American Dental Education Association, 1625 Massachusetts Ave, N W, Washington, DC 20036-2212. TEL 202-667-9433, FAX 202-667-0642, webmail@adea.org, http://www.jdentaled.org, http://www.adea.org. Ed. Dr. Olav Alvares. R&P Sue Sandmeyer. Circ: 4,143 (paid and controlled).

378.107 USA ISSN 0894-3907
➤ **JOURNAL OF DEVELOPMENTAL EDUCATION.** Text in English. 1978. 3/yr. USD 32 to individuals; USD 37 to institutions (effective 2005). illus. Index. reprint service avail. from PQC. **Document type:** *Academic/Scholarly.* **Description:** Forum for educators concerned with practice, theory, research and news of postsecondary basic skills.
Formerly (until 1984): Journal of Developmental and Remedial Education (0738-9701)
Related titles: CD-ROM ed.; Microfilm ed.; Online - full text ed.: (from bigchalk, EBSCO Publishing, H.W. Wilson, Northern Light Technology, Inc., O C L C Online Computer Library Center, Inc., ProQuest Information & Learning).
Indexed: ABIn, CIJE, CPE, ERA, ETA, EduInd, HEA, MEA, MLA-IB, RHEA, SEA, SENA, SOMA, TEA.
—BLDSC (4969.290500), IE, Infotrieve, ingenta.
Published by: Appalachian State University, National Center for Developmental Education, Reich College of Education, Boone, NC 28608. TEL 828-262-2876, FAX 828-262-2128, http://www.ncde.appstate.edu/journal.htm, http://www.ncde.appstate.edu/index.htm. Ed. Milton G Spann. R&P, Adv. contact Barbara Calderwood TEL 828-262-6101. Circ: 5,000.

372.11 370.3781 GBR ISSN 1090-1027
➤ **JOURNAL OF EARLY CHILDHOOD TEACHER EDUCATION.** Text in English. 1980. 4/yr. GBP 237, USD 393 combined subscription to institutions print & online eds. (effective 2006). bk.rev. back issues avail.; reprints avail. **Document type:** *Journal, Academic/Scholarly.* **Description:** Considers issues and ideas about research and practice in early childhood teacher education.
Related titles: Online - full text ed.: ISSN 1745-5642. GBP 225, USD 373 to institutions (effective 2006) (from EBSCO Publishing, Gale Group, IngentaConnect).
Indexed: CIJE.
—BLDSC (4970.702000), IE, ingenta. **CCC.**
Published by: Routledge (Subsidiary of: Taylor & Francis Group), 4 Park Sq, Milton Park, Abingdon, Oxon OX14 4RN, United Kingdom. TEL 44-1235-828600, FAX 44-1235-829000, info@routledge.co.uk, http://www.tandf.co.uk/journals/titles/10901027.asp, http://www.routledge.co.uk. Ed. Dr. Leslie R Williams.

➤ **JOURNAL OF EDUCATION FOR BUSINESS.** see *BUSINESS AND ECONOMICS*

370.72 MYS ISSN 0126-6020
LA1235
JOURNAL OF EDUCATIONAL RESEARCH/JURNAL PENDIDIKAN. Text in English, Malay. 1970. a. USD 15. **Document type:** *Academic/Scholarly.* **Description:** Contains research, reports, commentaries and articles in the field of teaching and learning: primary, secondary and higher education.
Published by: Penerbit Universiti Kebangsaan Malaysia, Ukm Bangi, Selangor 43600, Malaysia. TEL 8250001, TELEX UNIKEB-MA-31496.

JOURNAL OF ENTREPRENEURSHIP EDUCATION. see *BUSINESS AND ECONOMICS—Management*

378 USA
JOURNAL OF EXCELLENCE IN HIGHER EDUCATION✶. Text in English. 1995. 2/yr.
Related titles: Online - full text ed.: 1995.
Published by: University of Phoenix, Southern California Campus, 10540 Talbert Ave, Ste 100E, Fountain Valley, CA 92708-6027. Ed. Carol J Amato.

378 USA
➤ **THE JOURNAL OF FACULTY DEVELOPMENT.** Text in English. 1983. q. USD 52 domestic; USD 67 foreign (effective 2005). bk.rev. tr.lit. back issues avail. **Document type:** *Journal, Academic/Scholarly.* **Description:** Addresses both the practical and theoretical aspects of the planning, design, implementation and evaluation of practices and programs leading to effective and efficient institutions and individuals.
Formerly (until 2002): Journal of Staff, Program & Organization Development (0736-7627)
Indexed: CIJE, HEA.
—BLDSC (4983.624500), IE, Infotrieve, ingenta. **CCC.**
Published by: New Forums Press, Inc., 1018 S Lewis St, Stillwater, OK 74074. TEL 800-606-3766, FAX 405-377-2237, info@newforums.com, http://www.newforums.com. Ed. Edward Neal. Pub. Dr. Douglas O Dollar.

378.3 USA ISSN 0093-3961
HG174
➤ **JOURNAL OF FINANCIAL EDUCATION.** Text in English. 1972. q. USD 80 to institutions (effective 2004). adv. back issues avail. **Document type:** *Academic/Scholarly.*
Formerly: Financial Education (0190-7654)
Address: c/o Jean L Heck, Ed, Dept of Finance, Villanova University, Villanova, PA 19085. TEL 610-519-4325, http://www.fea.villanova.edu. Circ: 800.

378 GBR ISSN 0309-877X
L16
➤ **JOURNAL OF FURTHER AND HIGHER EDUCATION.** Text in English. 1943. q. GBP 274, USD 456 combined subscription to institutions print & online eds. (effective 2006). adv. bk.rev. bibl.; charts; illus.; stat. index, cum.index. reprint service avail. from PQC,PSC. **Document type:** *Journal, Academic/Scholarly.* **Description:** Publishes articles representing the whole filed of post-16 education and training. Topic areas include management and administration, teacher education and training, curriculum, staff and institutional development, and teaching and learning strategies and processes.
Incorporates: Education for Teaching (0013-1326)
Related titles: Microform ed.: (from PQC); Online - full text ed.: ISSN 1469-9486. GBP 260, USD 433 to institutions (effective 2006) (from EBSCO Publishing, Gale Group, IngentaConnect, O C L C Online Computer Library Center, Inc., Swets Information Services).
Indexed: BrEdI, CPE, ERA, ETA, HECAB, MEA, RASB, RHEA, SEA, SENA, SOMA, SWA, TEA.
—BLDSC (4986.850000), IE, Infotrieve, ingenta. **CCC.**
Published by: (N A T F H E - The University and College Lecturers' Union), Routledge (Subsidiary of: Taylor & Francis Group), 4 Park Sq, Milton Park, Abingdon, Oxon OX14 4RN, United Kingdom. TEL 44-1235-828600, FAX 44-1235-829000, info@routledge.co.uk, http://www.tandf.co.uk/journals/titles/0309877X.asp, http://www.routledge.co.uk. Ed. Jennifer E Rowley. **Subscr. to:** Taylor & Francis Ltd, Journals Customer Service, Rankine Rd, Basingstoke, Hants RG24 8PR, United Kingdom. TEL 44-1256-813000, FAX 44-1256-330245.

➤ **JOURNAL OF GEOGRAPHY IN HIGHER EDUCATION.** see *GEOGRAPHY*

378 USA ISSN 1068-6096
LB2335.4
➤ **THE JOURNAL OF GRADUATE TEACHING ASSISTANT DEVELOPMENT.** Text in English. 1993. 3/yr. USD 20 domestic; USD 35 foreign (effective 2005). tr.lit. back issues avail. **Document type:** *Journal, Academic/Scholarly.* **Description:** Guide to the study of improved training, employment and administration of graduate teaching assistant development programs.
Indexed: HEA.
—**CCC.**
Published by: New Forums Press, Inc., 1018 S Lewis St, Stillwater, OK 74074. TEL 800-606-3766, FAX 405-377-2237, kglewis@mail.utexas.edu, info@newforums.com, http://www.cstudies.ubc.ca/facdev/services/papers/001.html, http://www.newforums.com. Ed. Ka Ron Lewis. Pub. Dr. Douglas O Dollar.

➤ **JOURNAL OF HEALTH ADMINISTRATION EDUCATION.** see *HEALTH FACILITIES AND ADMINISTRATION*

378 IND ISSN 0252-0397
JOURNAL OF HIGHER EDUCATION. Text in English. 4/yr. INR 75, USD 15 (effective 1999). bk.rev. bibl. **Document type:** *Academic/Scholarly.*
Related titles: Online - full text ed.: (from Northern Light Technology, Inc.).
Indexed: ArtHuCI, CIJE, CPE, HECAB, PAA&I, RHEA, SSCI, SWR&A.
Published by: University Grants Commission, Publication Officer, 35 Ferozeshah Rd., New Delhi, 110 001, India.

378 USA ISSN 0022-1546
L11 CODEN: JHIEAW
➤ **JOURNAL OF HIGHER EDUCATION.** Text in English. 1930. bi-m. USD 50 domestic to individuals; USD 73.50 in Canada to individuals; USD 70 elsewhere to individuals; USD 110 domestic to institutions & libraries; USD 137.70 in Canada to institutions & libraries; USD 130 elsewhere to institutions & libraries; USD 32 domestic to students; USD 54.24 in Canada to students; USD 52 elsewhere to students; USD 18 per issue domestic; USD 22 per issue in Canada; USD 21.34 per issue elsewhere (effective 2005). adv. bk.rev. illus. index. back issues avail.; reprint service avail. from PQC,ISI. **Document type:** *Journal, Academic/Scholarly.* **Description:** Investigates issues of higher education teaching, administration, evaluation, and management.
Related titles: CD-ROM ed.: USD 74 (effective 1999) (from ProQuest Information & Learning); Microform ed.: (from PMC, PQC); Online - full text ed.: ISSN 1538-4640. USD 110 domestic to institutions; USD 117.70 in Canada to institutions; USD 110 elsewhere to institutions (effective 2005) (from EBSCO Publishing, Florida Center for Library Automation, Gale Group, H.W. Wilson, JSTOR (Web-based Journal Archive), Northern Light Technology, Inc., O C L C Online Computer Library Center, Inc., Project MUSE, ProQuest Information & Learning, Swets Information Services).
Indexed: ABIn, Acal, AgeL, AmH&L, BRI, CBRI, CIJE, CPE, ChPerI, ChemAb, CurCont, EAA, ERA, ETA, EduInd, HEA, HistAb, MEA, MEA&I, MLA-IB, PCI, PhilInd, PsycholAb, RASB, RHEA, RI-1, RI-2, SEA, SENA, SOMA, SOPODA, SSA, SSCI, SWA, SWR&A, TEA.
—BLDSC (4998.600000), IDS, IE, Infotrieve, ingenta. **CCC.**
Published by: Ohio State University Press, 180 Pressey Hall, 1070 Carmack Rd, Columbus, OH 43210-1002. TEL 614-292-1407, 614-292-6930, FAX 614-292-2065, ohiostatepress@osu.edu, http://www.ohiostatepress.org. Ed. Leonard L Baird. Circ: 4,200 (paid).

378 USA ISSN 1534-6102
LB2331.44
JOURNAL OF HIGHER EDUCATION OUTREACH AND ENGAGEMENT. Text in English. 1996. s-a.
Formerly (until 2000): Journal of Public Service & Outreach (1086-2447)
Indexed: CIJE.
Published by: University of Georgia, Institute of Higher Education, Meigs Hall, Athens, GA 30602-6772. TEL 706-583-0048, FAX 706-583-0281, http://www.uga.edu/jheoe/about.htm. Ed. Melvin Hill Jr.

E

378.1012 GBR ISSN 1360-080X
LB2341 CODEN: JHEMF7
➤ **JOURNAL OF HIGHER EDUCATION POLICY AND MANAGEMENT.** Text in English. 1979. 3/yr. GBP 282, USD 465, AUD 406 combined subscription to institutions print & online eds. (effective 2006). reprint service avail. from PSC. **Document type:** *Journal, Academic/Scholarly.* **Description:** Covers professional experience and ideas in post-secondary education. It supports higher education managers by disseminating ideas, analyses and reports of professional experience relevant to colleagues internationally.
Former titles (until vol.18, 1996): Journal of Tertiary Education Administration (1036-9708); (until 1990): Journal of Tertiary Educational Administration (0157-6038); Supersedes (1976-1978): Australian Institute of Tertiary Educational Administrators Newsletter (0156-5753)
Related titles: Online - full text ed.: ISSN 1469-9508. GBP 268, USD 442, AUD 386 to institutions (effective 2006) (from EBSCO Publishing, Gale Group, IngentaConnect, O C L C Online Computer Library Center, Inc., ProQuest Information & Learning, Swets Information Services).
Indexed: AEI, AusPAIS, CIJE, CPE, ERA, ETA, HEA, JEL, MEA, RHEA, SEA, SENA, SOMA, SOPODA, SSA, TEA.
—BLDSC (4998.660000), IE, Infotrieve, ingenta. **CCC.**
Published by: Routledge (Subsidiary of: Taylor & Francis Group), 4 Park Sq, Milton Park, Abingdon, Oxon OX14 4RN, United Kingdom. TEL 44-1235-828600, FAX 44-1235-829000, info@routledge.co.uk, http://www.tandf.co.uk/journals/titles/1360080X.asp, http://www.routledge.co.uk. Eds. Angel J Calderon, Ian R Dobson. **Subscr. to:** Taylor & Francis Ltd, Journals Customer Service, Rankine Rd, Basingstoke, Hants RG24 8PR, United Kingdom. TEL 44-1256-813000, FAX 44-1256-330245.

305.86 USA ISSN 1538-1927
LC2670.6
➤ **JOURNAL OF HISPANIC HIGHER EDUCATION.** Text in English. 2002. q. USD 322, GBP 208 to institutions; USD 335, GBP 217 combined subscription to institutions print & online eds. (effective 2006). adv. **Document type:** *Journal, Academic/Scholarly.* **Description:** Devoted to the advancement of knowledge and understanding of issues at Hispanic-serving higher education institutions worldwide.
Related titles: Online - full text ed.: ISSN 1552-5716. USD 319, GBP 206 to institutions (effective 2006) (from C S A, EBSCO Publishing, O C L C Online Computer Library Center, Inc., Sage Publications, Inc., Swets Information Services).
Indexed: CPE, EAA, ERA, ETA, HAPI, MEA, PsycInfo, PsycholAb, RHEA, SEA, SENA, SOMA, SociolAb, TEA, e-psyche.
—IE. **CCC.**
Published by: Sage Publications, Inc., 2455 Teller Rd, Thousand Oaks, CA 91320. TEL 805-499-0721, 800-818-7243, FAX 805-499-8096, 800-583-2665, info@sagepub.com, http://www.sagepub.com/journal.aspx?pid=289. Eds. Esther Elena Lopez-Mulnix, Michael William Mulnix. Adv. contact Kirsten Beaulieu TEL 805-499-0721 ext 7160. page USD 350. Circ: 200 (paid). **Subscr. to:** Sage Publications Ltd., 1 Oliver's Yard, 55 City Rd, London EC1 1SP, United Kingdom. TEL 44-20-73740645, FAX 44-20-73748741, subscription@sagepub.co.uk.

378 AUS ISSN 1443-2110
➤ **JOURNAL OF INSTITUTIONAL RESEARCH.** Text in English. 1991. s-a. **Document type:** *Journal, Academic/Scholarly.*
Formerly (until 1999): Journal of Institutional Research in Australia (1322-4298)
—BLDSC (5007.506700), IE, ingenta.
Published by: Monash University, Public Affairs Office, Bldg. 3.1, Wellington Road, Clayton, VIC 3168, Australia. Eds. Angel J Calderon, Ian R Dobson.

➤ **JOURNAL OF INTERDISCIPLINARY STUDIES (POMONA);** a journal of research and innovative activities. see *ENGINEERING*

➤ **JOURNAL OF LEGAL EDUCATION.** see *LAW*

378.00688 USA ISSN 0884-1241
LB2342.82 CODEN: JMHEEW
➤ **JOURNAL OF MARKETING FOR HIGHER EDUCATION.** Abbreviated title: J M H E. Text in English. 1988. s-a. USD 400 combined subscription domestic to institutions print & online eds.; USD 540 combined subscription in Canada to institutions print & online eds.; USD 580 combined subscription elsewhere to institutions print & online eds. (effective 2006). adv. bk.rev. 120 p./no. 1 cols./p.; back issues avail.; reprint service avail. from HAW. **Document type:** *Journal, Academic/Scholarly.* **Description:** Provide guidance for marketing, admissions, public relations, development and planning professionals who have the responsibility for enrollments and image enhancements at institutions of higher education.
Related titles: Microfiche ed.: (from PQC); Microform ed.; Online - full text ed.: ISSN 1540-7144. free to institutions (effective 2003); free with print subs. (from EBSCO Publishing, O C L C Online Computer Library Center, Inc., Swets Information Services).
Indexed: CIJE, CPE, DIP, EAA, ERA, ETA, HEA, IBR, IBZ, MEA, RHEA, SEA, SENA, SOMA, SWA, TEA.
—BLDSC (5012.118000), Haworth, IE, ingenta. **CCC.**
Published by: Best Business Books (Subsidiary of: Haworth Press, Inc.), 10 Alice St, Binghamton, NY 13904. TEL 607-722-5857, 800-429-6784, FAX 607-771-0012, 800-896-0582, getinfo@haworthpress.com, http://www.haworthpress.com/web/JMHE. Eds. Raghu Tadapalli, Thomas J Hayes. Pub. William Cohen. R&P Ruth Ann Heath TEL 607-722-5857 ext 316. Adv. contact Rebecca Miller-Baum TEL 607-722-5857 ext 337. B&W page USD 315, color page USD 550; trim 4.375 x 7.125. Circ: 2,180 (paid).

➤ **JOURNAL OF MATHEMATICS TEACHER EDUCATION.** see *MATHEMATICS*

➤ **JOURNAL OF MEDICAL LICENSURE AND DISCIPLINE.** see *MEDICAL SCIENCES*

➤ **JOURNAL OF NURSING EDUCATION.** see *MEDICAL SCIENCES—Nurses And Nursing*

➤ **JOURNAL OF NURSING SCHOLARSHIP.** see *MEDICAL SCIENCES—Nurses And Nursing*

➤ **JOURNAL OF SCHOOL IMPROVEMENT.** see *EDUCATION—School Organization And Administration*

➤ **JOURNAL OF STATISTICS EDUCATION.** see *STATISTICS*

➤ **THE JOURNAL OF STUDENT CENTERED LEARNING.** see *EDUCATION—Teaching Methods And Curriculum*

378 USA ISSN 1542-3077
LB2343.32
➤ **JOURNAL OF THE FIRST - YEAR EXPERIENCE AND STUDENTS IN TRANSITION.** Text in English. 1989. s-a. USD 40 (effective 2005). bk.rev. bibl.; charts; stat. 100 p./no.; back issues avail. **Document type:** *Journal, Academic/Scholarly.* **Description:** Presents the most current articles and statistical research about the student transition at US and Canadian colleges and universities.
Former titles: Journal of the First - Year Experience; Journal of the Freshman Year Experience (1053-203X)
Indexed: CIJE, CIS, HEA.
—BLDSC (4984.279600), IE.
Published by: University of South Carolina, National Resource Center for the First-Year Experience and Students in Transition, 1629 Pendleton St, Columbia, SC 29208. TEL 803-777-6029, FAX 803-777-4699, fye@gwm.sc.edu, http://www.sc.edu/fye. Ed. Joshua Gold. R&P Tracy Skipper TEL 803-777-6226. Circ: 765.

378 USA ISSN 1527-9316
JOURNAL OF THE SCHOLARSHIP OF TEACHING AND LEARNING. Abbreviated title: Jo So T L. Text in English. 2000. q. free (effective 2005). back issues avail. **Document type:** *Journal, Academic/Scholarly.* **Description:** Includes articles on teaching and learning processes at colleges and universities.
Media: Online - full text.
Published by: Indiana University at South Bend, 1700 Mishiwaka Ave, South Bend, IN 46634. TEL 574-237-4872, http://titans.iusb.edu/josotl/, http://www.iusb.edu/.

378 AUS ISSN 1449-9789
▼ ➤ **JOURNAL OF UNIVERSITY OF TEACHING & LEARNING PRACTICE.** Abbreviated title: J U T L P(Journal of University of Teaching & Learning Practice). Text in English. 2004 (Aug.). s-a. free (effective 2005). back issues avail. **Document type:** *Journal, Academic/Scholarly.* **Description:** Aims to provide a forum for educational practitioners in a wide range of disciplines to communicate their teaching and learning outcomes in a scholarly way. Its purpose is to bridge the gap between journals covering purely academic research and more pragmatic articles and opinions published elsewhere.
Media: Online - full content.
Published by: University of Wollongong, Northfields Ave, Wollongong, NSW 2522, Australia. TEL 61-4221-5659, hbrooks@uow.edu.au, http://jutlp.uow.edu.au. Pub. Mrs. Helen Brooks. R&Ps Geraldine Lefoe, Helen Mandl.

➤ **JOURNAL OF VETERINARY MEDICAL EDUCATION.** see *VETERINARY SCIENCE*

378.125 USA ISSN 1052-4800
LB2331
➤ **JOURNAL ON EXCELLENCE IN COLLEGE TEACHING.** Text in English. 1990. 3/yr. USD 49 domestic; USD 55 foreign (effective 2005). back issues avail. **Document type:** *Journal, Academic/Scholarly.* **Description:** Forum for faculty to share proven, innovating teaching in colleges and universities.
Related titles: Online - full text ed.: USD 250 to institutions under 2,500 students; USD 500 to institutions 2,500-14,999 students; USD 750 to institutions over 15,000 students (effective 2000) (from EBSCO Publishing).
Indexed: CIJE, HEA, MLA-IB.
Published by: Miami University, O A S T, Oxford, OH 45056. TEL 513-529-6648, ject@compuserve.com, http://ject.lib.muohio.edu. Ed. Milton D Cox. Circ: 1,000.

➤ **JOURNALISM AND MASS COMMUNICATION EDUCATOR.** see *JOURNALISM*

378 USA ISSN 1050-723X
JOURNEY (KANSAS CITY). Text in English. 1985-1996; resumed 1998. s-a. USD 3 per issue. adv. **Description:** For Asian-American high school and college students with a desire to pursue a higher education.
Published by: Communications Publishing Group, Inc., 660 Penn Tower, 3100 Broadway St. Ste 660, Kansas City, MO 64111-2413. TEL 816-960-1988, FAX 816-960-1989. Circ: 200,000.

378 USA
JUNGLE LAW MAGAZINE. Text in English. 7/yr. USD 24.97 (effective 2003). adv. **Document type:** *Magazine, Consumer.* **Description:** Covers all aspects of law students' and lawyers' personal and professional lives, from how to ace the bar exam to strategies for job success. Also contains features on lifestyle, trends in fashion, travel, dining, and more.
Related titles: Online - full content ed.
Published by: Jungle Media Group, 632 Broadway, 7th Fl, New York, NY 10012. TEL 212-352-0840, FAX 212-352-9282, smcduffy@junglemediagroup.com, http://www.junglelawonlibe.com, http://www.junglemediagroup.com/. adv.: B&W page USD 21,575, color page USD 26,000; trim 8 x 10.875.

JUNGLE MAGAZINE. see *BUSINESS AND ECONOMICS*

JURISTE. see *LAW*

344.0711 CAN
JUSTICE INSTITUTE OF BRITISH COLUMBIA. ANNUAL REPORT. Text in English. 1979. a. back issues avail. **Document type:** *Corporate.*
Published by: Justice Institute of British Columbia, 715 McBride Blvd, New Westminster, BC V3L 5T4, Canada. Ed. Larry Goble.

JUSTUF; das grosse Magazin fuer junge Juristen. see *LAW*

378.05 UKR ISSN 0453-8048
PG2003 CODEN: VKSGA3
KAHRKIVS'KYI NATSIONAL'NYI UNIVERSYTET. VISNYK. Text in Ukrainian. 1964. s-m.
Indexed: RefZh.
—BLDSC (0040.294000), CISTI, Linda Hall.
Published by: Kharkivs'kyi Natsional'nyi Universytet, Maidan Svobody 4, Kharkiv, 61077, Ukraine. TEL 380-572-436196, FAX 380-572-437044, postmaster@univer.kharkov.ua, http://www-ukr.univer.kharkov.ua.

378 USA
KAPPA GAMMA PI NEWS. Text in English. 1930. 5/yr. membership. back issues avail. **Document type:** *Newsletter, Consumer.*
Published by: Kappa Gamma Pi, 10215 Chardon Rd, Chardon, OH 44024-9700. TEL 440-286-3764, FAX 440-286-4379, kgpnews@aol.com, http://www.kappagammapi.org. Ed., R&P Pamela W Waitinas. Circ: 7,000.

378 USA
THE KAPPA PROFILE. Text in English. 1949. s-a. membership. **Document type:** *Newsletter.*
Former titles: Kappa Kappa Iota Newsletter; Kappa Kappa Iota Bulletin
Published by: National Kappa Kappa Iota, 1875 E 15, Tulsa, OK 74104-4610. TEL 918-744-0389. Ed. Connie Krute. Circ: 9,600.

KATHOLISCHE UNIVERSITAET EICHSTAETT. VORLESUNGSVERZEICHNIS. see *EDUCATION—Guides To Schools And Colleges*

378 JPN ISSN 0910-1381
KEIO UNIVERSITY BULLETIN. Text in English. 1969. biennial.
Published by: Keio Gijuku Daigaku/Keio University, 2-15-45 Mita, Tokyo, Minato-ku 108-8345, Japan. TEL 81-3-3453-4511, www@info.keio.ac.jp, http://www.keio.ac.jp.

378.2 USA
KENTUCKY COLLEGE AND UNIVERSITY DEGREES AND OTHER FORMAL AWARDS (YEAR). Text in English. a. **Description:** Contains data for degrees conferred by Kentucky's state-supported and independent colleges and universities, business colleges, and theological seminaries.
Published by: Kentucky Higher Education Association, P O Box 798, Frankfort, KY 40602-0798. TEL 502-564-3553.

378.3 USA
KENTUCKY COLLEGE AND UNIVERSITY ENROLLMENTS (YEAR). Text in English. a.
Published by: Kentucky Higher Education Association, P O Box 798, Frankfort, KY 40602-0798. TEL 502-564-3553.

KENTUCKY COLLEGE AND UNIVERSITY ORIGIN OF ENROLLMENTS. see *EDUCATION—Abstracting, Bibliographies, Statistics*

KENTUCKY JOURNAL OF EXCELLENCE IN COLLEGE TEACHING AND LEARNING. see *EDUCATION—Teaching Methods And Curriculum*

E

378.007   KEN
KENYATTA UNIVERSITY COLLEGE. DIRECTORY OF RESEARCH. Text in English. 1975. base vol. plus a. updates. free. Supplement avail. **Document type:** *Directory.* **Description:** Annual catalogue of research at Kenyatta University College.
Published by: Kenyatta University Library, PO Box 43844, Nairobi, Kenya. Ed. J M Ng'Ang'A. Circ: 200.

378.1543   USA
KEY COMMUNITY COLLEGE TRANSFER. Text in English. a. adv. **Description:** Helps junior college students make the transition to a four-year university and other schools, as well as information on financial aid and job opportunities.
Published by: Target Marketing, Inc., 1 Liberty Bell Circle, Ste 200, Liberty, MO 64068. TEL 816-781-7557, 800-279-9988, FAX 816-792-3892. Ed. Eddie Cook. Pub. Lyle Kraft.

378   GBR   ISSN 1363-206X
KEY NOTE MARKET REPORT: FURTHER AND HIGHER EDUCATION. Variant title: Further and Higher Education. Text in English. 1996. irreg., latest 2000, July. GBP 340 per issue (effective 2002). **Document type:** *Trade.* **Description:** Provides and overview of a specific UK market segment and includes executive summary, market definition, market size, industry background, competitor analysis, current issues, forecasts, company profiles, and more.
Published by: Key Note Ltd., Field House, 72 Oldfield Rd, Hampton, Mddx TW12 2HQ, United Kingdom. TEL 44-20-8481-8750, FAX 44-20-8783-0049, info@keynote.co.uk, http://www.keynote.co.uk. Ed. Emma Clarke.

KEYING IN. see *BUSINESS AND ECONOMICS*

378   JPN   ISSN 0389-1658
KOBE JOGAKUIN DAIGAKU RONSHU/KOBE COLLEGE STUDIES. Text in Japanese. 1953. 3/yr. **Document type:** *Journal, Academic/Scholarly.*
Indexed: MLA-IB.
—BLDSC (5100.577060).
Published by: Kobe Jogakuin Daigaku, Kenkyujo/Kobe College, Research Institute, 4-1, Okadayama, Nishinomiya City, 662-8505, Japan. TEL 86-798-518544, FAX 86-798-518527.

378.104   AUT
KOOPERATIONEN: HIGHER EDUCATION, SCIENCE & RESEARCH. Text in German. irreg. **Document type:** *Academic/Scholarly.*
Published by: Oesterreichischer Austauschdienst/Austrian Exchange Service, Alserstrasse 4-1-3-8, Vienna, W 1090, Austria. TEL 43-1-4277-28180, FAX 43-1-4277-28195, info@oead.ac.at, http://www.oead.ac.at. Circ: 10,000.
Co-sponsor: Bundesministerium fuer Wissenschaft und Verkehr.

L O E X QUARTERLY. (Library Orientation Exchange) see *LIBRARY AND INFORMATION SCIENCES*

378   GBR
L R D G OCCASIONAL PUBLICATION. Text in English. irreg., latest vol.4, 1993. **Document type:** *Monographic series.*
Published by: (Learning Resources Development Group), Underhill Press, 8 Herriot Way, Thirsk, N Yorks YO7 1FL, United Kingdom. TEL 44-1845-526749, FAX 44-1845-524347, peter.pack@lrdg.octacon.co.uk. Ed. David Scott. R&P Peter Pack.

L S A T. (Law School Admissions Test) see *LAW*

LAW SCHOOL RECORD. see *LAW*

LAWASIA DIRECTORY OF LAW COURSES IN THE ASIA AND WEST PACIFIC REGIONS. see *LAW*

▼ **LEARNING AND TEACHING IN THE SOCIAL SCIENCES.** see *SOCIAL SCIENCES: COMPREHENSIVE WORKS*

378   GBR   ISSN 0268-2125
LEARNING RESOURCES JOURNAL. Abbreviated title: L R J. Text in English. 1979. 3/yr. GBP 48 domestic; GBP 54 overseas (effective 1999); includes Learning Resources News (ISSN 0955-0631). **Document type:** *Academic/Scholarly.*
Formerly (until 1985): L R D G Bulletin (0143-3555)
Indexed: BrEdI, CPE, ETA, LISA, TEA.
—BLDSC (5179.329190), IE.
Published by: (Learning Resources Development Group), Underhill Press, 8 Herriot Way, Thirsk, N Yorks YO7 1FL, United Kingdom. TEL 44-1845-526749, FAX 44-1845-524347, peter.pack@lrdg.octacon.co.uk. Ed. David Scott. R&P Peter Pack. Circ: 300.

378   GBR   ISSN 0955-0631
LEARNING RESOURCES NEWS. Text in English. 1985. 3/yr. GBP 48 domestic; GBP 54 foreign (effective 1999); includes Learning Resources Journal. **Document type:** *Academic/Scholarly.*
Formerly (until 1987): L R D G Newsletter
Published by: (Learning Resources Development Group), Underhill Press, 8 Herriot Way, Thirsk, N Yorks YO7 1FL, United Kingdom. TEL 44-1845-526749, FAX 44-1845-524347, peter.pack@lrdg.octacon.co.uk. Ed. David Scott. Circ: 340.

378 340   AUS   ISSN 1320-0313
LEGAL EDUCATION IN ASIA. Text in English. irreg. (approx. 2/yr). free. **Document type:** *Newsletter.* **Description:** Reports on developments in legal education throughout Asia. Describes the activities of the Law Asia Legal Education Standing Committee.
Related titles: Online - full text ed.
Published by: Centre for Legal Education, c/o Faculty of Law, University of Newcastle, Callaghan, NSW 2308, Australia. TEL 61-2-4921-5419, FAX 61-2-4921-6931, cle@mail.newcastle.edu.au, http://www.lawfoundation.net.au.

LEGAL EDUCATION REVIEW. see *LAW*

378   BRA   ISSN 0101-9635
AS80.S65
LEOPOLDIANUM; revista de estudos e comunicacoes. Text in Portuguese. 1974. 3/yr. USD 2. adv. bk.rev. illus. index. **Document type:** *Academic/Scholarly.*
Indexed: ZooRec.
Published by: (Sociedade Visconde de Sao Leopoldo), Editora Universitaria Leopoldianum, Rua Ceara, 70, J Menino, Santos, SP 11065-430, Brazil. TEL 4373435. Circ: 1,000.

LEX COLLEGII. see *LAW*

378   IND
LIASON CELLS FOR UNIVERSITY - INDUSTRY INTERACTION (YEAR). Text in English. 1927. irreg., latest 1995. USD 20 (effective 1999). **Document type:** *Newsletter.*
Published by: Association of Indian Universities, A.I.U. House, 16 Kotla Marg, New Delhi, 110 002, India. TEL 91-11-323-0059, FAX 91-11-323-6105, aiu@del12.vsnl.net.in, http://www.aiuweb.org.

378   USA   ISSN 0024-1822
L13   CODEN: ARMCAH
LIBERAL EDUCATION. Text in English. 1915. q. USD 50 to non-members; USD 36 to members; USD 14 per issue to non-members; USD 10 per issue to members (effective 2005). bk.rev. illus. Index. back issues avail.; reprints avail. **Document type:** *Trade.* **Description:** Contains insightful essays on the best reports on thinking about innovative developments, liberal learning and academic planning.
Incorporates: Forum for Liberal Education (0734-9793); Former titles (until 1958): Association of American Colleges. Bulletin (0730-899X); (until 1939): Bulletin of the Association of American Colleges (0895-8637)
Related titles: Microform ed.: (from PQC); Online - full text ed.: (from bigchalk, EBSCO Publishing, Florida Center for Library Automation, Gale Group, Northern Light Technology, Inc., ProQuest Information & Learning).
Indexed: ABIn, AgeL, AmH&L, CIJE, CPE, CurCont, EduInd, HEA, HECAB, HistAb, MLA-IB, PSI, RHEA, SEA, SSCI.
—BLDSC (5186.600000), IE, ingenta.
Published by: Association of American Colleges and Universities, 1818 R St, N W, Washington, DC 20009. TEL 202-387-3760, 800-297-3775, FAX 202-265-9532, http://www.aacu.org/liberaleducation/index.cfm. Ed., R&P Bridget Puzon. Circ: 5,000.

378   MEX
LIBERTAS; el periodico universitario de Mexico. Text in Spanish. m. adv. **Document type:** *Newspaper, Academic/Scholarly.*
Related titles: Online - full text ed.: ISSN 1563-7484. 1998.
Published by: Comercial Libertas, SA de CV, Ave de las Vegas No 107, Col de Tarango, Mexico, DF 01610, Mexico. TEL 52-5-602-4238, FAX 52-5-643-0636, libertas@spin.com.mx, http://pp.terra.com.mx/~libertas/periodico/general/. Ed. Ernesto Olmedo-Castelan. Circ: 20,000.

378.076   USA   ISSN 1076-5891
LIFE AND WORK DIRECTIONS: BIBLE STUDIES FOR EARLY ADULTHOOD (18-24). Text in English. q. USD 8.28. **Description:** Contains topical Bible studies for adults ages 18-24.
Formerly: Life and Work Directions: Bible Studies for Adults 18-24; Which supersedes in part (in 1995): Young Adult Bible Study (0162-4814)
Published by: LifeWay Christian Resources, 1 Lifeway Plaza, Nashville, TN 37234. TEL 615-251-2000, 800-458-2772, FAX 615-251-5933, customerservice@lifeway.com, http://www.lifeway.com.

378.076   USA   ISSN 1076-593X
LIFE AND WORK DIRECTIONS: TEACHER EDITION. Text in English. q. USD 16.88. **Description:** Provides guidelines for Sunday school teachers of students 18-24.
Published by: LifeWay Christian Resources, 1 Lifeway Plaza, Nashville, TN 37234. TEL 615-251-2000, 800-458-2772, FAX 615-251-5933, customerservice@lifeway.com, http://www.lifeway.com.

378   DEU
LIFT UNI-TIP. Text in German. 1991. 2/yr. adv. **Document type:** *Magazine, Consumer.*
Published by: P V - Projekt Verlag, Falbenhennenstr 17, Stuttgart, 70180, Germany. TEL 49-711-60171717, FAX 49-711-60171729. adv.: B&W page EUR 1,530, color page EUR 2,430. Circ: 27,340 (controlled).

378   USA   ISSN 0720-8812
LINZER UNIVERSITAETSSCHRIFTEN. Text in English. 1969. irreg. price varies. reprint service avail. from ISI. **Document type:** *Monographic series.*
Formerly: Linzer Hochschulschriften (0075-9724)
Published by: Springer-Verlag New York, Inc. (Subsidiary of: Springer Science+Business Media), 233 Spring St, New York, NY 10013. TEL 212-460-1500, FAX 212-473-6272.

378   DNK   ISSN 1398-6244
LOENMAGASIN. Text in Danish. 198?. a. **Description:** Salary information.
Formerly (until 1998): Loen (1397-8535)
Related titles: ◆ Issued with: Magisterbladet. ISSN 0903-7349.
Published by: Dansk Magisterforening, Nimbusparken, Peter Bangs Vej 32, Frederiksberg, 2000, Denmark. TEL 45-38-156600, FAX 45-38-156666, dm@magister.dk, http://www.magister.dk.

378.0025   GBR
LONDON AND SOUTH EAST REGION ADVISORY COUNCIL FOR EDUCATION AND TRAINING. INDEX OF COURSES. Text in English. 1965. a. GBP 20 (effective 2000). **Document type:** *Directory.*
Former titles: London and South Eastern Regional Advisory Council for Further Education. Index of Courses; London and Home Counties Regional Advisory Council for Technological Education. Index of Courses
Published by: (L A S E R Advisory Council), Butterworth - Heinemann (Subsidiary of: Elsevier Ltd., Books Division), Linacre House, Jordan Hill, Oxford, OX2 8DP, United Kingdom. TEL 44-1865-310366, 44-1865-888180, FAX 44-1865-310898, 44-1865-314091. Circ: 1,000.

LOVEJOY'S COLLEGE GUIDE. see *EDUCATION—Guides To Schools And Colleges*

LOVEJOY'S GUIDANCE DIGEST. see *EDUCATION—Guides To Schools And Colleges*

378.4   DEU   ISSN 0720-7662
LUDOVICO MAXIMILIANEA FORSCHUNGEN. Text in German. 1971. irreg., latest vol.20, 2003. price varies. **Document type:** *Monographic series, Academic/Scholarly.*
Published by: Duncker und Humblot GmbH, Carl-Heinrich-Becker-Weg 9, Berlin, 12165, Germany. TEL 49-30-7900060, FAX 49-30-79000631, info@duncker-humblot.de, http://www.duncker-humblot.de.

378.4   DEU   ISSN 0720-7670
LUDOVICO MAXIMILIANEA QUELLEN. Text in German. 1973. irreg., latest vol.3, 2003. price varies. **Document type:** *Monographic series, Academic/Scholarly.*
Published by: Duncker und Humblot GmbH, Carl-Heinrich-Becker-Weg 9, Berlin, 12165, Germany. TEL 49-30-7900060, FAX 49-30-79000631, info@duncker-humblot.de, http://www.duncker-humblot.de.

378.65   DZA
L'UNIVERSITE∗; revue bimestrielle de l'enseignement superieur et de la recherche scientifique. Text in French. bi-m.
Published by: Universite d'Alger, 2 rue Didouche-Mourad, Algiers, Algeria.

378.155   DEU
DAS M B A STUDIUM. (Masters in Business Administration) Text in German. 1981. a. EUR 18 (effective 2003). adv. **Document type:** *Directory, Academic/Scholarly.*
Formerly (until 1996): M B A Studium und Business Schools in den U S A
Published by: Staufenbiel Institut fuer Studien- und Berufsplanung GmbH, Konrad-Adenauer-Ufer 33, Cologne, 50668, Germany. TEL 49-221-9126630, FAX 49-221-9126639, info@staufenbiel, http://www.staufenbiel.de. Ed. Joerg Staufenbiel. adv.: B&W page EUR 1,625, color page EUR 2,285. Circ: 6,000.

610.076 378.1662   USA   ISSN 1090-901X
R838.5
M C A T COMPREHENSIVE REVIEW. (Medical College Admissions Test) Text in English. 1995. a. USD 65 per issue (effective 2005).
Formerly (until 1998): Kaplan M C A T All-in-One Test Prep Plus Medical School Admissions (1084-9106)
Published by: Simon & Schuster, 1230 Ave of the Americas, New York, NY 10020. TEL 212-698-7000, FAX 212-698-7099, http://www.simonsays.com.

378.072   PER
M I E C SERVICO DE DOCUMENTACION. Text in Spanish. 12/yr. USD 18; includes subscr. to: SPES and America Latina Boletin. bk.rev. bibl.; illus.
Published by: Movimiento Internacional de Estudiantes Catolicos, Centro de Documentacion, Apdo. 3564, Lima, 100, Peru.

378.33   USA   ISSN 1057-2899
M L A DIRECTORY OF SCHOLARLY PRESSES IN LANGUAGE AND LITERATURE. (Modern Language Association of America) Text in English. 1991. irreg.
Published by: Modern Language Association of America, 26 Broadway, 3rd Fl, New York, NY 10004-1789. TEL 646-576-5000, FAX 646-458-0030, http://www.mla.org.

E

▼ *new title*   ➤ *refereed*   ∗ *unverified*   ◆ *full entry avail.*

378.33 USA ISSN 0160-5720
M L A NEWSLETTER (NEW YORK). Text in English. 1969. q. USD 8 domestic; USD 14 foreign (effective 2005). adv. reprint service avail. from PQC. **Document type:** *Newsletter, Trade.* **Description:** Information about the activities of the Modern Language Association, deadlines for fellowships and grants, and news of the language and literature profession.
Published by: Modern Language Association of America, 26 Broadway, 3rd Fl, New York, NY 10004-1789. TEL 646-576-5000, FAX 646-458-0030, newsletter@mla.org, http://www.mla.org. Ed. Rosemary G Feal. Circ: 30,000 (paid and controlled).

378.161 373.025 CAN ISSN 1498-9921
MACLEAN'S GUIDE TO CANADIAN UNIVERSITIES & COLLEGES. Text in English. 2001. a. **Document type:** *Directory, Trade.*
Formed by the merger of (1999-2001): Maclean's Guide to Canadian Colleges (1481-6768); (1996-2001): Maclean's Guide to Canadian Universities (1206-3924); Which was formerly (until 1997): Maclean's Guide to Universities (1203-6668)
Published by: Rogers Media Publishing Ltd, One Mount Pleasant Rd, 11th Fl, Toronto, ON M4Y 2Y5, Canada. TEL 416-764-2000, FAX 416-764-3941, http://www.rogers.com.

378.106 AUS ISSN 0815-578X
MACQUARIE UNIVERSITY ANNUAL REPORT. Text in English. 1964. a., latest 2002. free. **Document type:** *Yearbook, Corporate.* **Description:** Provides information on the activities of the university for the preceding year.
Formerly (until 1975): Macquarie University Council. Report for the Period (Years) (0156-8477)
Related titles: Online - full content ed.
Published by: Macquarie University, Balaclava Rd., North Ryde, NSW 2109, Australia. TEL 61-2-98507377, FAX 61-2-98507391, http://www.mq.edu.au.

MACQUARIE UNIVERSITY CALENDAR OF GOVERNANCE, LEGISLATION & RULES. see *MEETINGS AND CONGRESSES*

378 AUS ISSN 1446-4705
MACQUARIE UNIVERSITY HANDBOOK OF POSTGRADUATE STUDIES. Text in English. 1967. a. AUD 11 domestic; AUD 25 foreign; AUD 8 newsstand/cover domestic (effective 2003). **Document type:** *Academic/Scholarly.*
Supersedes in part (in 2001): Macquarie University Calendar (0810-5049)
Related titles: Online - full text ed.
Published by: Macquarie University, Balaclava Rd., North Ryde, NSW 2109, Australia. TEL 61-2-98507377, FAX 61-2-98507391, http://www.mq.edu.au.

378 AUS ISSN 1446-4713
MACQUARIE UNIVERSITY HANDBOOK OF UNDERGRADUATE STUDIES. Text in English. 1967. a. AUD 13 domestic; AUD 30 foreign; AUD 10 newsstand/cover domestic (effective 2003). **Document type:** *Consumer.*
Supersedes in part (in 2001): Macquarie University Calendar (0810-5049)
Related titles: Online - full text ed.
Published by: Macquarie University, Balaclava Rd., North Ryde, NSW 2109, Australia. TEL 61-2-98507377, FAX 61-2-98507391, http://www.mq.edu.au.

378 AUS
MACQUARIE UNIVERSITY NEWS. Text in English. 10/yr. Free. bk.rev. back issues avail. **Document type:** *Magazine, Academic/Scholarly.*
Related titles: Online - full content ed.
Published by: Macquarie University, Balaclava Rd., North Ryde, NSW 2109, Australia. TEL 61-2-98507377, FAX 61-2-98507391, http://www.pr.mq.edu.au/macnews/, http://www.mq.edu.au. Ed. Kathy Vozella TEL 61-2-985074565.

378.007 AUS ISSN 0159-2165
MACQUARIE UNIVERSITY RESEARCH REPORT. Text in English. 1978. a. free. **Document type:** *Academic/Scholarly.* **Description:** Provides information on the research activites of the university for the preceding year.
Indexed: AESIS.
Published by: Macquarie University, Balaclava Rd., North Ryde, NSW 2109, Australia. TEL 61-2-98507377, FAX 61-2-98507391, http://www.mq.edu.au.

378 EGY ISSN 1110-2411
MAGALLAT KULLIYYAT AL-TARBIYYT BI-BANHA/FACULTY OF EDUCATION JOURNAL. Text in Arabic. 1990. 3/yr. EGP 5 newsstand/cover (effective 2004). **Document type:** *Journal, Academic/Scholarly.*
Published by: Zagazig University, Faculty of Education, Banha Branch, Banha, Egypt. TEL 20-13-227523, FAX 20-13-222777, http://derp.sti.sci.eg/data/0283.htm. Ed. Dr. Hasan El-Beblawi.

370.7 DNK ISSN 0903-7349
MAGISTERBLADET. Text in Danish. 1964. s-m. free membership. adv. back issues avail. **Document type:** *Trade.*
Incorporates (198?-2001): Seminariebladet (1396-8408); Former titles (until 1988): Magisterbladet D M (0108-9609); (until 1977): D M Magisterbladet (0108-9617); Which incorporates (1914-1975): Dansk Seminarieblad (0011-6467); Incorporates (1981-1993): S L F Information (0108-3856); Which was formerly (1978-1979): B F L Information (0904-0218)
Related titles: Online - full text ed.; ◆ Includes: Loenmagasin. ISSN 1398-6244.
Published by: Dansk Magisterforening, Nimbusparken, Peter Bangs Vej 32, Frederiksberg, 2000, Denmark. TEL 45-38-156600, FAX 45-38-156666, magisterbladet@magister.dk, dm@magister.dk, http://www.magister.dk/sw1074.asp. Ed. Mogens Tanggaard. adv.: page DKK 17,500; 176 x 263. Circ: 23,073.

378 IDN ISSN 0216-0161
➤ **MAJALAH U S U/MAJALAH UNIVERSITAS SUMATERA UTARA.** Text in Indonesian. 1975. m. USD 3 (effective 2001). bk.rev. abstr.; charts; stat. 97 p./no.; back issues avail. **Document type:** *Bulletin, Academic/Scholarly.*
Published by: University of North Sumatra, Jl. Dr. Mansur, Kampus USU, Medan, 20155, Indonesia. TEL 62-61-524033, FAX 62-61-520822, http://www.usu.ac.id. Ed. Bachtiar Hasan Mirazu.

378 UGA
MAKERERE UNIVERSITY. FACULTY OF EDUCATION. HANDBOOK. Added title page title: Teacher Education in Uganda. Text in English. a. illus.
Published by: Makerere University, Faculty of Education, PO Box 7062, Kampala, Uganda.

MANCHESTER TRAINING HANDBOOKS. see *PUBLIC ADMINISTRATION*

378 CAN ISSN 0318-8612
MARITIME PROVINCES HIHGER EDUCATION COMMISSION. ANNUAL REPORT. Text in English. 1975. a.
Published by: Canada. Maritime Provinces Higher Education Commission, 82 Westmorland St Ste 401, Fredericton, NB E3B 5H1, Canada. TEL 506-453-2844, FAX 506-453-2106, info@mphec.ca, http://www.mphec.ca/.

658.8 USA ISSN 1052-8008
HF5415.1
MARKETING EDUCATION REVIEW. Text in English. 1992-199?; resumed 1995. 3/yr. USD 32 domestic to individuals; USD 42 foreign to individuals; USD 72 domestic to institutions; USD 82 foreign to institutions (effective 2005). back issues avail. **Document type:** *Journal, Academic/Scholarly.* **Description:** Provides a communications network for marketing educators.
Related titles: Microform ed.: (from PQC); Online - full text ed.: (from EBSCO Publishing).
—BLDSC (5381.641970), IE, ingenta. **CCC.**
Published by: C T C Press, PO Box 200159, Columbia, SC 29229-0159. TEL 803-754-3112, 800-382-8856, FAX 803-754-3013, bruce@sba.pdxedu, cbarnett@ctcpress.com, http://www.ctcpress.com. Ed. Dr. Bruce Stern.

378.107 USA ISSN 0896-7156
MARKETING HIGHER EDUCATION NEWSLETTER. Text in English. 1987. m. USD 395 (effective 2005). bk.rev. back issues avail. **Document type:** *Newsletter, Trade.*
Media: Online - full text.
Published by: Topor & Associates, 282 Nevada St, Redwood City, CA 94062-2136. TEL 650-364-9551, FAX 650-364-6173, topor@marketinged.com, http://www.marketinged.com. Ed., Pub. Robert Topor.

378 USA
MARQUETTE MAGAZINE. Text in English. 1981. q. illus. **Description:** News of Marquette University.
Former titles: Marquette Today; Marquette University Magazine (0025-4002)
Published by: Marquette University, 1212 Building, Rm 315, Box 1881, Milwaukee, WI 53201-1881. TEL 414-288-7448, FAX 414-288-6519. Ed. Margaret E McCormick. Circ: 96,000.

MASTER'S THESES DIRECTORIES. see *EDUCATION—Abstracting, Bibliographies, Statistics*

MATHEMATICS AND COMPUTER EDUCATION. see *MATHEMATICS*

MED IN GERMANY. see *MEDICAL SCIENCES*

MEDICAL EDUCATION. see *MEDICAL SCIENCES*

MEDICAL EDUCATION. SUPPLEMENT. see *MEDICAL SCIENCES*

MEDICAL SCHOOL ADMISSION REQUIREMENTS, UNITED STATES AND CANADA. see *MEDICAL SCIENCES*

MEDICINE NORTHWEST. see *MEDICAL SCIENCES*

378 USA ISSN 0047-6692
MEMO TO THE PRESIDENT✶. Text in English. 1960. w. USD 65 to non-members. bk.rev. **Document type:** *Newsletter.*
Media: Duplicated (not offset).
Published by: American Association of State Colleges and Universities, 1307 New York Ave, N W, 500, Washington, DC 20005-4701. TEL 202-293-7070, FAX 202-296-5819. Ed. Gay Clyburn. R&P Trudy G James. Circ: (controlled).

378 371.102 USA ISSN 1530-8219
THE MENTOR (FAYETTEVILLE); journal of mentoring and field experience. Text in English. 2001 (Dec.). a. USD 15 per issue domestic to individuals; USD 25 per issue foreign to individuals; USD 30 per issue domestic to institutions; USD 40 per issue foreign to institutions; USD 12 per issue domestic to students; USD 22 per issue foreign to students (effective 2002). **Document type:** *Journal, Academic/Scholarly.*
Published by: Fayetteville State University, Department of Psychology, 1200 Murchison Rd, Fayetteville, NC 28301. TEL 910-672-1576, FAX 910-672-1043. Ed. Chris A. Ike.

MER UTDANNING? YRKESORIENTERING. see *OCCUPATIONS AND CAREERS*

378.12 JOR ISSN 0040-0505
L71
➤ **MESSAGE OF THE TEACHER/RISALAT AL-MU'ALLIM.** Text in Arabic. 1956. q. JOD 8 domestic to individuals; JOD 10 foreign to individuals; JOD 10 domestic to institutions; JOD 15 foreign to institutions (effective 1999). bk.rev. cum. index: vols. 1956-1990. back issues avail. **Document type:** *Academic/Scholarly.*
Published by: Ministry of Education, Educational Publications Division, P O Box 1646, Amman, Jordan. TEL 962-5607181, FAX 962-5666019, TELEX 21396, moe@amra.nic.gov.jo. Ed. Salwa Madadha. Circ: 60,000 (paid).

378 USA ISSN 1047-8485
LB2328.4 CODEN: METUEF
METROPOLITAN UNIVERSITIES; an international forum. Text in English. 1990. q. USD 38 domestic to individuals; USD 64 foreign to individuals; USD 78 domestic to institutions; USD 104 foreign to institutions (effective 2004). adv. bk.rev. back issues avail. **Document type:** *Journal, Academic/Scholarly.* **Description:** Provides a forum on issues in higher education, focusing on those relating to metropolitan regions.
Related titles: Microform ed.: (from PQC); Online - full text ed.: (from ProQuest Information & Learning).
Indexed: CIJE, CPE, ERA, ETA, HEA, MEA, RHEA, SEA, SENA, SOMA, SOPODA, TEA.
Published by: (Coalition of Urban and Metropolitan Universities), Indiana University, Purdue University Indianapolis, University College, Office of Development and Operations, 815 W Michigan St, UC 3169, Indianapolis, IN 46202-5164. TEL 317-274-5036, muj@iupui.edu, http://muj.uc.iupui.edu/, http://uc.iupui.edu/. Pub. Harriett L Bennett. Circ: 610 (paid).

378 USA ISSN 0047-7052
MICHIGAN ACADEMY OF SCIENCE, ARTS, AND LETTERS. ACADEMY LETTER. Text in English. 1969. 3/yr. included with membership or with subscr. to Michigan Academician. bk.rev. charts; stat. **Document type:** *Newsletter, Academic/Scholarly.* **Description:** Provides sample abstract and abstract instructions, information on the executive committee and a listing of the sections and current section chairs involved.
Media: Duplicated (not offset). **Related titles:** Online - full text ed.
Published by: Michigan Academy of Science, Arts and Letters, 614 W. Superior St., Alma, MI 48801-1504. http://www.umich.edu/~michacad/newsletter.html. Ed. Kathleen F Duke. Circ: 1,000.

378.052 USA ISSN 1076-0180
LC220.5
➤ **MICHIGAN JOURNAL OF COMMUNITY SERVICE LEARNING.** Text in English. 1994. a. USD 20 per academic year to individuals; USD 26 per academic year to institutions (effective 2004 - 2005). **Document type:** *Journal, Academic/Scholarly.* **Description:** Aims to provide a forum for educators to dicuss issues pertinent to academic service-learning, and a place to publish scholarly articles on service-learning.
Indexed: CIJE.
—BLDSC (5755.280200), IE.
Published by: (University of Michigan, Law School, Center for Learning through Community Service), O C S L Press, 1024 Hill St, Ann Arbor, MI 48109-3310. TEL 313-763-3548, FAX 313-647-7464, jphoward@umich.edu, http://www.umich.edu/~mjcsl/. Ed. Jeffrey Howard.

378.155 USA
MIDWESTERN ASSOCIATION OF GRADUATE SCHOOLS. PROCEEDINGS OF THE ANNUAL MEETING. Text in English. 1949. a. USD 20.
Supersedes: Midwest Conference on Graduate Study and Research. Proceedings
Published by: Midwestern Association of Graduate Schools, Kansas State University, Graduate School, Fairchild 102, Manhattan, KS 66506. TEL 913-532-6191. Ed. R F Kruh. Circ: 200.

MINERVA; a review of science, learning and policy. see *SCIENCES: COMPREHENSIVE WORKS*

MINORITY STUDENT OPPORTUNITIES IN UNITED STATES MEDICAL SCHOOLS. see *MEDICAL SCIENCES*

378 AUS
THE MODERATION HANDBOOK. Text in English. 1999. a.
Published by: Queensland Board of Senior Secondary School Studies, P.O. Box 307, Spring Hill, QLD 4101, Australia. TEL 61-7-3864-0299, FAX 61-7-3221-2553, office@qbssss.edu.au.

378 AUS
MODERATION OF ACHIEVEMENTS IN SCHOOL-BASED ASSESSMENT. Text in English. 1998. irreg.
Published by: Queensland Board of Senior Secondary School Studies, P.O. Box 307, Spring Hill, QLD 4101, Australia. TEL 61-7-3864-0299, FAX 61-7-3221-2553, office@qbssss.edu.au.

378.33 USA
MODERN LANGUAGE ASSOCIATION OF AMERICA. PROCEEDINGS. Text in English. 1887. a. **Document type:** *Proceedings.*
Formerly (until 1887): Modern Language Association of America. Transaction and Proceedings (1539-3682); Which was formed by the 1885 merger of: Modern Language Association of America. Transactions (1539-3674); Modern Language Association of America. Proceedings (1539-3666)
Related titles: Online - full text ed.: (from JSTOR (Web-based Journal Archive)).
Published by: Modern Language Association of America, 26 Broadway, 3rd Fl, New York, NY 10004-1789. TEL 212-614-6321, FAX 212-358-9140, http://www.mla.org.

378 USA
THE MONDAY REVIEW. Short title: T M R. Text in English. 1998. w. free. bk.rev. **Description:** Features news of intellectual affairs, produced for an international university educated audience.
Media: E-mail.
Published by: Monday Review specpres@earthlink.net. Ed. Joan Hartman.

378.44 FRA ISSN 0247-6355
MUTU. Text in French. s-a.
Formerly: Recherches Universitaires
Published by: Mutuelle Nationale des Etudiants de France, 16 av. Raspail, Gentilly, 94250, France. Eds. Jean Michel Grosz, Jean Pierre Alaux.

N A B T E REVIEW. see *BUSINESS AND ECONOMICS*

378 USA ISSN 1046-2929
N A C A C BULLETIN. Text in English. 1963. 10/yr. USD 50 domestic to non-members; USD 60 foreign to non-members; free to members (effective 2005). **Document type:** *Bulletin, Academic/Scholarly.* **Description:** Keeps school and college admission counselors in touch with education issues, people and actions that shape the admission process and profession. Includes interviews, special features and resources.
Formerly (until 1981): N A C ACtion News (0749-7717)
Indexed: ASFA.
Published by: National Association for College Admission Counseling, 1631 Prince St, Alexandria, VA 22314-2818. TEL 703-836-2222, FAX 703-836-8015, bulletin@nacac.com, http://www.nacac.com/news.html. Circ: 7,500.

378 USA ISSN 0271-9517
LB2343
➤ **N A C A D A JOURNAL.** Text in English. 1981. s-a. free membership (effective 2005). reprint service avail. from PQC. **Document type:** *Journal, Academic/Scholarly.* **Description:** Enriches the knowledge, skills and professional development of people concerned with academic advising in higher education.
Related titles: Microform ed.: (from PQC).
Indexed: CIJE, CPE, ETA, HEA, MEA, TEA.
—BLDSC (6001.781500), IE, ingenta.
Published by: National Academic Advising Association, Kansas State University, 2323 Anderson Ave, Ste 225, Manhattan, KS 66502-2912. TEL 785-532-5717, FAX 785-532-7732, Journals@ksu.edu, nacada@ksu.edu, http://www.nacada.ksu.edu/Journal/Journal_home.htm. Eds. Gary M Padak, Terry L Kuhn.

➤ **N A C E JOURNAL**; the international magazine of placement and recruitment. see *BUSINESS AND ECONOMICS—Labor And Industrial Relations*

➤ **N A C T A JOURNAL.** see *AGRICULTURE*

378 USA ISSN 0161-7990
N A E B BULLETIN; the newsletter serving higher education's purchasing professionals. Text in English. 1940. 10/yr. USD 40 to non-members; USD 20 to members (effective 2001). bk.rev. abstr.; tr.lit. **Document type:** *Newsletter.*
Formerly: Buying for Higher Education
Published by: National Association of Educational Buyers, Inc., 5523 Research Park Dr., Catonsville, MD 21228-4680. TEL 516-273-2600, FAX 516-952-3660. Ed., Pub. Joan S Fox. R&P Lorinda Pranzo TEL 516-273-2600 ext.305. Circ: (controlled).

N A S A UNIVERSITY PROGRAMS REPORT. see *AERONAUTICS AND SPACE FLIGHT*

378.3 USA ISSN 0882-4630
N A S F A A NEWSLETTER. Text in English. 1972. fortn. looseleaf. membership only. adv. index. back issues avail. **Document type:** *Newsletter.* **Description:** Covers legislation, regulation and news to promote the effective administration of student financial aid.
Related titles: Online - full text ed.
Published by: National Association of Student Financial Aid Administrators, 1129 20th St NW, Suite 400, Washington, DC 20036-3453. TEL 202-785-0453, FAX 202-785-1487, sheppardj@smtp.nasfaa.org, http://www.nasfaa.org. Ed. Jeffrey Sheppard. Circ: 5,000.

N A S P A FORUM. see *BUSINESS AND ECONOMICS—Personnel Management*

378.111 USA
N A S P A JOURNAL (ONLINE EDITION). Text in English. 1996. q. USD 35 (effective 2005).
Media: Online - full text (from EBSCO Publishing, H.W. Wilson, O C L C Online Computer Library Center, Inc., ProQuest Information & Learning).
Published by: National Association of Student Personnel Administrators, 1875 Connecticut Ave, N W, Ste 418, Washington, DC 20009-5728. TEL 202-265-7500, FAX 202-797-1157, office@naspa.org, http://www.naspa.org.

378.1543 USA
N A S U L G C NEWSLINE✶. Text in English. 1947. 10/yr. free. **Document type:** *Newsletter.*
Supersedes: National Association of State Universities and Land Grant Colleges. Circular Letter
Published by: National Association of State Universities and Land-Grant Colleges, 1307 New York Ave, NW, Ste. 400, Washington, DC 20005-4704. TEL 202-478-6040. Ed. Roz Hiebert. Circ: 7,100.

378.73 USA ISSN 0743-670X
LA227.3
N E A ALMANAC OF HIGHER EDUCATION. Text in English. 1984. a. USD 35 to libraries (effective 1999). adv. stat. **Description:** Surveys the status of US higher education, with special attention to the Association's role in higher education.
Related titles: Microform ed.
Published by: National Education Association of the United States, 1201 16th St, N W, Washington, DC 20036-3290. TEL 202-822-7207, FAX 202-822-7206. Ed. Con Lehane. R&P Sam Pizzigati. Adv. contact Sherida McGhee. Circ: 85,000.

378.73 USA
N E A HIGHER EDUCATION ADVOCATE. Text in English. 1983. 8/yr. USD 35 (effective 1999). **Document type:** *Newsletter.*
Published by: National Education Association of the United States, 1201 16th St, N W, Washington, DC 20036-3290. TEL 202-822-7207, FAX 202-822-7206. Circ: 90,000.

378.19 GBR
N S E. (National Student Extra) Text in English. 1989. 6/yr. GBP 30. adv. film rev. **Document type:** *Consumer.* **Description:** Informative guide to student life in higher education.
Former titles: N S M; National Student
Published by: N U S Services Ltd., Bleaklow House, Howard Town Mills, Mill St, Glossop, Derbys SK13 8HT, United Kingdom. TEL 01457-890900, FAX 01457-890909. Ed. Sarah Clare Davy. Adv. contact Vicki Steward. Circ: 100,000.

378 AUS ISSN 1321-8476
N T E U ADVOCATE. Variant title: Advocate (South Melbourne). Text in English. 1975. bi-m. AUD 50 in Australia & New Zealand (effective 1999); AUD 60 elsewhere. back issues avail. **Document type:** *Newsletter.* **Description:** Union newsletter for academics in higher education institutions.
Formerly: F A U S A Newsletter (0313-430X)
Indexed: AEI.
—IE, Infotrieve.
Published by: National Tertiary Education Union, PO Box 1323, South Melbourne, VIC 3205, Australia. TEL 61-3-9254-1910, FAX 61-3-9254-1915. Ed. Simon Roberts. Circ: 25,000.

378 AUS
➤ **N T E U EXPRESS.** (National Tertiary Education Union) Text in English. m. **Document type:** *Academic/Scholarly.*
Media: Online - full content.
Published by: National Tertiary Education Union, PO Box 1323, South Melbourne, VIC 3205, Australia. http://www.nteu.org.au/.

378 AUS ISSN 1322-2945
N T E U FRONTLINE. Variant title: Frontline. Text in English. 1995. 2/yr. AUD 20 in Australia & New Zealand and Papua New Guinea; AUD 30 elsewhere.
Indexed: AEI.
Published by: National Tertiary Education Union, PO Box 1323, South Melbourne, VIC 3205, Australia. TEL 61-3-9254-1910, FAX 61-3-92541910.

378.669 NGA
N U C PROJECT NEWS. Text in English. 1994. free. **Document type:** *Newsletter, Government.* **Description:** Highlights the activities of the N.U.C. World Bank Project Implementation Unit. Reports on eligibility criteria, financial allocations to Nigerian universities, procurement of facilities and equipment, and staff development.
Formerly (until 1995): World Bank Project News (1117-5524)
Published by: (Nigeria. World Bank Implementation Unit), National Universities Commission, Aja Nwachukwu House, Plot 430 Aguiyi-Ironsi St., Maitama District, Garki G.P.O., Federal Capitol Territory, PMB 237, Abuja, Nigeria. TEL 234-9-5233176, FAX 234-9-5233520, TELEX UNICOMM LAGOS NG. Ed. Goddy Nnadi. Circ: 20,000.

378.052 CAN ISSN 1194-5958
THE NATIONAL ADVOCATE. Text in English, French. 1991. bi-m. **Document type:** *Newsletter.*
Formerly: A C C C National
Published by: Association of Canadian Community Colleges, 1223 Michael St N, Ste 200, Ottawa, ON K1J 7T2, Canada. TEL 613-746-2222, FAX 613-746-6721, lchevrier@accc.ca, http://www.accc.ca.

378.161 USA
LB2343
NATIONAL ASSOCIATION FOR COLLEGE ADMISSION COUNSELING. MEMBERSHIP DIRECTORY. Text in English. a. USD 50 to non-members; USD 10 to members. adv. **Document type:** *Directory.* **Description:** Lists NACAC members, official policy statements, state and regional leaders and annual conferences.
Formerly: National Association of College Admissions Counselors. Membership Directory (0090-3965)
Published by: National Association for College Admission Counseling, 1631 Prince St, Alexandria, VA 22314-2818. TEL 703-836-2222, FAX 703-836-8015, http://www.nacac.com. Ed., R&P Dee Dee Faulkner TEL 703-826-2222 ext 137. Adv. contact Amy Vogt. Circ: 13,000.

NATIONAL ASSOCIATION OF COLLEGES AND EMPLOYERS. SALARY SURVEY; a study of beginning salary offers. see *BUSINESS AND ECONOMICS—Labor And Industrial Relations*

378.1543 USA ISSN 0077-3433
NATIONAL ASSOCIATION OF STATE UNIVERSITIES AND LAND-GRANT COLLEGES. PROCEEDINGS✶. Text in English. 1887. a. free. **Document type:** *Proceedings.*
—BLDSC (6841.539550).
Published by: National Association of State Universities and Land-Grant Colleges, 1307 New York Ave, NW, Ste. 400, Washington, DC 20005-4704. TEL 202-478-6040. Circ: 1,000.

NATIONAL ASSOCIATION OF STUDENT AFFAIRS PROFESSIONALS JOURNAL. see *EDUCATION—School Organization And Administration*

378 USA ISSN 0742-3667
LB2334
NATIONAL CENTER FOR THE STUDY OF COLLECTIVE BARGAINING IN HIGHER EDUCATION AND THE PROFESSIONS. ANNUAL CONFERENCE PROCEEDINGS. Text in English. 1973. a. USD 45; USD 45 foreign (effective 1999). bibl. reprints avail. **Document type:** *Proceedings.*
Formerly: National Center for the Study of Collective Bargaining in Higher Education and the Professions. Annual Conference Proceedings (0095-9294)
Indexed: CIJE.
Published by: National Center for the Study of Collective Bargaining in Higher Education and the Professions, Bernard M Baruch College, City University of New York, 17 Lexington Ave, Box F 1228, New York, NY 10010. TEL 212-802-6751, FAX 212-802-5903. Ed. Ceasar Naples. R&P Beth Johnson. Circ: 310 (paid); 5 (controlled).

331.88 USA ISSN 0737-9285
LB2335.885.U6
NATIONAL CENTER FOR THE STUDY OF COLLECTIVE BARGAINING IN HIGHER EDUCATION AND THE PROFESSIONS. NEWSLETTER. Text in English. 1973. q. USD 35; USD 35 foreign (effective 1999). bibl. reprints avail. **Document type:** *Newsletter.*
Formerly: National Center for the Study of Collective Bargaining in Higher Education. Newsletter (0738-2103)
Indexed: CIJE, HEA.
Published by: National Center for the Study of Collective Bargaining in Higher Education and the Professions, Bernard M Baruch College, City University of New York, 17 Lexington Ave, Box F 1228, New York, NY 10010. TEL 212-802-6751, FAX 212-802-5903. Ed. Beth Johnson. Circ: 165 (paid); 5 (controlled).

378.12 USA ISSN 0191-8133
L901
NATIONAL DEAN'S LIST. Text in English. 1978. a. (in 2 vols.). USD 49.50.
Published by: Educational Communications, Inc. (Lake Forest), 1701 Directors Blvd., Ste. 920, Austin, TX 78744-1098. TEL 847-295-6650.

NATIONAL FACULTY SALARY SURVEY BY DISCIPLINE AND RANK IN PRIVATE COLLEGES AND UNIVERSITIES. see *BUSINESS AND ECONOMICS—Labor And Industrial Relations*

E

378.111 USA ISSN 0888-8132
➤ **NATIONAL FORUM OF EDUCATION ADMINISTRATION AND SUPERVISION JOURNAL.** Short title: N F E A S Journal. Text in English. 1983. 3/yr. USD 44 domestic to individuals; USD 88 domestic to institutions (effective 2005); USD 144 foreign to institutions (effective 2002). adv. bk.rev. back issues avail. **Document type:** *Journal, Academic/Scholarly.*
Formerly: National Forum of Educational Administration and Supervision (0882-9047)
Related titles: Online - full text ed.
Indexed: EAA.
—CCC.
Published by: (California State University, Los Angeles), National Forum Journals, 17603 Bending Post Dr, Houston, TX 77095. TEL 281-550-5700, http://www.nationalforum.com. Ed., Pub., R&P, Adv. contact Dr. William Kritsonis TEL 337-477-0008. page USD 800. Circ: 10,000.

➤ **NATIONAL LAWYERS GUILD DISORIENTATION HANDBOOK**; law for the people. see *LAW*

➤ **NATIONAL ON-CAMPUS REPORT.** see *COLLEGE AND ALUMNI*

➤ **NATIONAL PROFILE OF COMMUNITY COLLEGES: TRENDS & STATISTICS.** see *EDUCATION—Guides To Schools And Colleges*

378.17 USA ISSN 1057-2880
LB1026
NATIONAL TEACHING & LEARNING FORUM. Text in English. 1991. bi-m. USD 49 domestic; USD 55 in Canada; USD 68 elsewhere (effective 2005). **Document type:** *Newsletter, Academic/Scholarly.* **Description:** Provides a forum for dialogue regarding the challenge of teaching and learning in the college classroom.
Indexed: HEA, MLA-IB.
Published by: Oryx Press (Subsidiary of: Greenwood Publishing Group Inc.), 1434 E. San Miguel Ave., Phoenix, AZ 85014-2422. TEL 602-265-2651, 800-279-6799, FAX 602-265-6250, info@oryxpress.com, http://www.ntlf.com. Eds. James Rhem, Anne Thompson. Pub. Phyllis Steckler. R&P Lori Cavanaugh TEL 602-265-2651 ext 662.

378 BLR
NATSIYANAL'NAYA AKADEMIYA NAVUK BELARUSI. NAVINY. Text in Russian, Belorussian. w. USD 159 in North America (effective 2000). **Document type:** *Newspaper.*
Published by: (Natsiyanal'naya Akademiya Navuk Belarusi/National Academy of Sciences of Belarus), Vydavetstvo Belaruskaya Navuka/Publishing House Belaruskaya Navuka, 18 Academician V F Kuprevich St, Minsk, 220141, Belarus. TEL 375-17-2632327, FAX 375-17-2637618, belnauka@infonet.by. **Dist. by:** East View Information Services, 3020 Harbor Ln. N., Minneapolis, MN 55447. TEL 763-550-0961, FAX 763-559-2931.

NATURAL SCIENCES AND ENGINEERING RESEARCH COUNCIL OF CANADA. ANNUAL REPORT. see *SCIENCES: COMPREHENSIVE WORKS*

378.33 500 CAN
NATURAL SCIENCES AND ENGINEERING RESEARCH COUNCIL OF CANADA. LIST OF SCHOLARSHIPS AND GRANTS IN AID OF RESEARCH/CONSEIL DE RECHERCHES EN SCIENCES NATURELLES ET EN GENIE DU CANADA. LISTE DES BOURSES ET SUBVENTIONS DE RECHERCHE. Text and summaries in English, French. 1978. a. free. adv. stat. **Document type:** *Government.*
Former titles: National Research Council of Canada. Annual Report on Scholarships and Grants in Aid of Research (0316-4047); National Research Council of Canada. Annual Report on Support of University Research
Media: Online - full text.
Indexed: BMT, PetrolAb.
—CISTI.
Published by: Natural Sciences & Engineering Research Council of Canada, 350 Albert St, Ottawa, ON K1A 1H5, Canada. TEL 613-995-5992, FAX 613-943-0742, http://www.nserc.ca. Ed. Joyce French. R&P Victor Wallwark. Adv. contact Monique Martin. Circ: 2,200.

378 ISR
NEGBA. Text in Hebrew. 1985. q. free. bk.rev. **Document type:** *Newsletter.*
Published by: Ben Gurion University of the Negev, Department of Public Relations, P O Box 653, Beersheba, 84120, Israel. FAX 972-7-6472937. Ed. Chaya Galai. Circ: 5,000.

378.052 USA ISSN 0194-3081
LB2328
➤ **NEW DIRECTIONS FOR COMMUNITY COLLEGES.** Text in English. 1973. q. USD 180 domestic; USD 220 in Canada & Mexico; USD 254 elsewhere; USD 198 combined subscription domestic print & online eds.; USD 238 combined subscription in Canada & Mexico print & online eds.; USD 272 combined subscription elsewhere print & online eds. (effective 2006). Index. back issues avail.; reprint service avail. from PQC. **Document type:** *Journal, Academic/Scholarly.* **Description:** Provides expert assistance in helping community colleges meet the challenges of their distinctive and expanding educational mission.
Related titles: Microfiche ed.: (from PQC); Online - full text ed.: ISSN 1536-0733. USD 180 (effective 2006) (from EBSCO Publishing, H.W. Wilson, O C L C Online Computer Library Center, Inc., Swets Information Services, Wiley InterScience).
Indexed: ABIn, CIJE, CPE, CurCont, ETA, EduInd, HEA, MLA-IB, SSCI.
—BLDSC (6083.340000), IE, ingenta. **CCC.**
Published by: (E R I C Clearinghouse for Community Colleges), Jossey-Bass Inc., Publishers (Subsidiary of: John Wiley & Sons, Inc.), 989 Market St, San Francisco, CA 94103-1741. TEL 415-433-1740, 888-378-2537, FAX 800-605-2665, 415-433-0499, jbsubs@jbp.com, http://www.josseybass.com/WileyCDA/WileyTitle/productCd-CC.html. Ed. Arthur M Cohen. Pub. Sue Lewis. Circ: 875 (paid).

378 USA ISSN 0271-0560
LB2331.72
NEW DIRECTIONS FOR HIGHER EDUCATION. Text in English. 1973. q. USD 180 domestic; USD 220 in Canada & Mexico; USD 254 elsewhere; USD 198 combined subscription domestic print & online eds.; USD 238 combined subscription in Canada & Mexico print & online eds.; USD 272 combined subscription elsewhere print & online eds. (effective 2006). Index. back issues avail.; reprint service avail. from PQC,PSC. **Document type:** *Journal, Academic/Scholarly.* **Description:** Provides current information and authoritative advice about major issues and administrative problems confronting every institution of higher education.
Related titles: Microform ed.: (from PQC); Online - full text ed.: ISSN 1536-0741. USD 180 (effective 2006) (from EBSCO Publishing, O C L C Online Computer Library Center, Inc., Swets Information Services, Wiley InterScience).
Indexed: ABIn, CIJE, CPE, CurCont, ETA, EduInd, HEA, MLA-IB, PsycholAb, RHEA, SSCI, SWA.
—BLDSC (6083.370000), IE, Infotrieve, ingenta. **CCC.**
Published by: Jossey-Bass Inc., Publishers (Subsidiary of: John Wiley & Sons, Inc.), 989 Market St, San Francisco, CA 94103-1741. TEL 415-433-1740, 888-378-2537, FAX 800-605-2665, 415-433-0499, jbsubs@jbp.com, http://www.josseybass.com/WileyCDA/WileyTitle/productCd-HE.html. Ed. Martin Kramer. Pub. Sue Lewis. Circ: 1,000 (paid).

378 USA ISSN 0271-0579
LA227.3
NEW DIRECTIONS FOR INSTITUTIONAL RESEARCH. Text in English. 1974. q. USD 170 domestic; USD 210 in Canada & Mexico; USD 244 elsewhere; USD 187 combined subscription domestic print & online eds.; USD 227 combined subscription in Canada & Mexico print & online eds.; USD 261 combined subscription elsewhere print & online eds. (effective 2006). stat. Index. back issues avail.; reprint service avail. from PQC,PSC. **Document type:** *Journal, Academic/Scholarly.* **Description:** Provides planners and administrators in all types of academic institutions with guidelines in such areas as resource coordination, information analysis, program evaluation, and institutional management.
Related titles: Microfiche ed.: (from PQC); Online - full text ed.: ISSN 1536-075X. USD 170 (effective 2006) (from EBSCO Publishing, O C L C Online Computer Library Center, Inc., Swets Information Services, Wiley InterScience).
Indexed: ABIn, CIJE, CPE, CurCont, ERA, ETA, EduInd, HEA, MEA, RHEA, SEA, SENA, SOMA, TEA.
—BLDSC (6083.390000), IE, Infotrieve, ingenta. **CCC.**
Published by: (Association for Institutional Research), Jossey-Bass Inc., Publishers (Subsidiary of: John Wiley & Sons, Inc.), 989 Market St, San Francisco, CA 94103-1741. TEL 415-433-1740, 888-378-2537, FAX 800-605-2665, 415-433-0499, jbsubs@jbp.com, http://www.josseybass.com/WileyCDA/WileyTitle/productCd-IR.html. Ed. J Fredericks Volkwein. Pub. Sue Lewis. R&P Lorri Wimer TEL 415-433-1740. Circ: 875.

378.3 USA ISSN 0164-7970
LB1027.5
NEW DIRECTIONS FOR STUDENT SERVICES. Text in English. 1978. q. USD 180 domestic; USD 220 in Canada & Mexico; USD 254 elsewhere; USD 198 combined subscription domestic print & online eds.; USD 238 combined subscription in Canada & Mexico print & online eds.; USD 272 combined subscription elsewhere print & online eds. (effective 2006). Index. back issues avail.; reprint service avail. from PQC. **Document type:** *Journal, Academic/Scholarly.* **Description:** Offers guidelines and programs for aiding students in their total development: emotional, social, and physical, as well as intellectual.
Related titles: Microfiche ed.: (from PQC); Online - full text ed.: ISSN 1536-0695. USD 180 (effective 2006) (from EBSCO Publishing, H.W. Wilson, O C L C Online Computer Library Center, Inc., Swets Information Services, Wiley InterScience).
Indexed: ABIn, CIJE, CPE, ERA, ETA, EduInd, HEA, MEA, PsycholAb, RHEA, SEA, SENA, SOMA, TEA.
—BLDSC (6083.466000), IE, ingenta. **CCC.**
Published by: Jossey-Bass Inc., Publishers (Subsidiary of: John Wiley & Sons, Inc.), 989 Market St, San Francisco, CA 94103-1741. TEL 415-433-1740, 888-378-2537, FAX 800-605-2665, 415-433-0499, jbsubs@jbp.com, http://www.josseybass.com/WileyCDA/WileyTitle/productCd-SS.html. Eds. Elizabeth J Whitt, John H Schuh. Pub. Sue Lewis. Circ: 775.

378.17 USA ISSN 0271-0633
LB1025.2
NEW DIRECTIONS FOR TEACHING AND LEARNING. Text in English. 1980. q. USD 180 domestic; USD 220 in Canada & Mexico; USD 254 elsewhere; USD 198 combined subscription domestic print & online eds.; USD 238 combined subscription in Canada & Mexico print & online eds.; USD 272 combined subscription elsewhere print & online eds. (effective 2006). Index. back issues avail.; reprint service avail. from PQC. **Document type:** *Journal, Academic/Scholarly.* **Description:** Presents ideas and techniques for improving college teaching based on both the practical expertise of seasoned instructors and on the latest research findings of educational and psychological researchers.
Related titles: Microfiche ed.: (from PQC); Online - full text ed.: ISSN 1536-0768. USD 180 (effective 2006) (from EBSCO Publishing, O C L C Online Computer Library Center, Inc., Swets Information Services, Wiley InterScience).
Indexed: ABIn, CIJE, CPE, ChPerI, ERA, ETA, EduInd, HEA, MEA, PsycholAb, RHEA, SEA, SENA, SOMA, SWA, TEA.
—BLDSC (6083.469500), IE, Infotrieve, ingenta. **CCC.**
Published by: Jossey-Bass Inc., Publishers (Subsidiary of: John Wiley & Sons, Inc.), 989 Market St, San Francisco, CA 94103-1741. TEL 415-433-1740, 888-378-2537, FAX 800-605-2665, 415-433-0499, jbsubs@jbp.com, http://www.josseybass.com/WileyCDA/WileyTitle/productCd-TL.html. Ed. Marilla D Svinicki. Pub. Sue Lewis. Circ: 900.

378.161 USA
NEW ENGLAND BOARD OF HIGHER EDUCATION. NEW ENGLAND REGIONAL STUDENT PROGRAM: ENROLLMENT REPORT. Text in English. 1968. a. to qualified personnel free (effective 2001). charts. 88 p./no.; **Document type:** *Catalog, Academic/Scholarly.* **Description:** Report of enrollment in college programs available at reduced tuition for out-of-state students under the Regional Student Program.
Formerly: New England Board of Higher Education. New England Regioanl Student Services: Enrollment Report
Published by: (New England Regional Student Services), New England Board of Higher Education, 45 Temple Pl, Boston, MA 02111. TEL 617-357-9620, FAX 617-338-1577, rsp@nebhe.org, http://www.nebhe.org.

378.74 USA
NEW ENGLAND BOARD OF HIGHER EDUCATION. NEW ENGLAND REGIONAL STUDENT PROGRAM: UNDERGRADUATE AND GRADUATE CATALOG. Text in English. 1957. a. free (effective 2001). **Document type:** *Catalog, Academic/Scholarly.* **Description:** Listing of undergraduate and graduate public college degree programs available to out-of-state New England students for reduced tuition.
Formed by the merger of: New England Board of Higher Education. New England Regional Student Program: Undergraduate Level; New England Board of Higher Education. New England Regional Student Program: Graduate Level
Related titles: E-mail ed.; Online - full text ed.
Published by: New England Board of Higher Education, 45 Temple Pl, Boston, MA 02111. TEL 617-357-9620, FAX 617-338-1577, friends@nebhe.org, nebhe@nebhe.org, http://www.nebhe.org. Circ: 15,000.

378 IND ISSN 0047-9705
LA1153
NEW FRONTIERS IN EDUCATION. Text in English. 1971. q. USD 25. adv. bk.rev. bibl.; tr.lit. reprint service avail. from PQC.
Related titles: Microform ed.: 1971 (from PQC).
Indexed: BAS, CIJE, CPE, ERA, MEA.
Published by: All India Association for Christian Higher Education, Ecumenical House, 39 Institutional Area, D-Block, Janakpuri, New Delhi, 110 058, India. TEL 91-11-5506190, FAX 91-11-5555033, aiache@nda.vsnl.net.in, http://www.aiache.org/. Ed. Mani Jacob. Circ: 1,000.

NEW HAMPSHIRE BUSINESS EDUCATION ASSOCIATION. NEWSLETTER. see *BUSINESS AND ECONOMICS*

378.07 USA ISSN 0028-5374
NEW HORIZONS (NEW YORK). Text in English. 1934. 3/yr. free. bk.rev. illus. **Document type:** *Newsletter.*
Published by: United Board for Christian Higher Education in Asia, 475 Riverside Dr, New York, NY 10115. TEL 212-870-2610, FAX 212-870-2322, staff@ubchea.com. Ed. Ronald G Taylor. Pub. David W Vikner. R&P Ronald Taylor. Circ: 15,000.

THE NEW LEARNING MEDICINE. see *MEDICAL SCIENCES*

378 AUS
NEW SCHOOL FORM, FORMS AND BENCHES; the move to benchmarks and outcomes. Text in English. 1999. irreg.
Published by: Queensland Board of Senior Secondary School Studies, P.O. Box 307, Spring Hill, QLD 4101, Australia. TEL 61-7-3864-0299, FAX 61-7-3221-2553, office@qbsss.edu.au.

378 USA
NEW YORK STATE. EDUCATION DEPARTMENT. COLLEGE AND UNIVERSITY ENROLLMENT. Text in English. 1960. a. stat.; charts. back issues avail.

E

Published by: Education Department, Office of Post-Secondary Policy Analysis, c/o James J Brady, Chief, Bureau of Post Secondary Statistical Service, Rm 5B44 CEC, Albany, NY 12230. TEL 518-474-3874. Circ: 500.

378.106 USA
NEW YORK STATE. EDUCATION DEPARTMENT. COLLEGE AND UNIVERSITY REVENUES AND EXPENDITURES. Text in English. 1960. a. charts; stat.
Published by: Education Department, Office of Post-Secondary Policy Analysis, c/o James J Brady, Chief, Bureau of Post Secondary Statistical Service, Rm 5B44 CEC, Albany, NY 12230. TEL 518-474-3874. Circ: 500.

378.669 NGA ISSN 1117-062X
LA1630
NIGERIA. NATIONAL UNIVERSITIES COMMISSION. ANNUAL REPORT. Short title: N U C Annual Report. Text in English. 1963. a. (in 2 vols.). free. **Document type:** *Government.*
Description: Covers the year-end progress of the N.U.C., including decisions, policies, program reviews, and general activities.
Published by: National Universities Commission, Information and Public Relations Unit, Aja Nwachukwu House, Plot 430 Aguiyi-Ironsi St.Maitama District Garki G.P.O., Federal, PMB 237, Abuja, Capital Territory, Nigeria. TEL 234-9-523-3176, FAX 234-9-523-3520. Ed. Goddy Nnadi. Circ: 3,000.

378.669 NGA ISSN 1117-0611
LA1633
NIGERIA. NATIONAL UNIVERSITIES COMMISSION. CONVOCATION SPEECHES OF NIGERIAN UNIVERSITIES. Text in English. 1988. a. free. **Document type:** *Trade.*
Description: Features speeches and addresses delivered during convocation ceremonies at Nigerian universities.
Published by: National Universities Commission, Information and Public Relations Unit, Aja Nwachukwu House, Plot 430 Aguiyi-Ironsi St.Maitama District Garki G.P.O., Federal, PMB 237, Abuja, Capital Territory, Nigeria. TEL 234-9-523-3176, FAX 234-9-523-3520. Ed. Goddy Nnadi. Circ: 1,000.

378.669 NGA ISSN 1117-0638
LB2337.N6
NIGERIA. NATIONAL UNIVERSITIES COMMISSION. RESEARCH BULLETIN. Text in English. 1989. a. free. **Document type:** *Bulletin, Government.* **Description:** Provides a down-to-earth analysis of research grant allocations from the N.U.C. to Nigerian universities and how they are being used.
Formerly (until 1993): Nigeria. National Universities Commission. Research Directory
Published by: National Universities Commission, Information and Public Relations Unit, Aja Nwachukwu House, Plot 430 Aguiyi-Ironsi St.Maitama District Garki G.P.O., Federal, PMB 237, Abuja, Capital Territory, Nigeria. TEL 234-9-523-3176, FAX 234-9-523-3520. Ed. Goddy Nnadi. Circ: 3,000.

NIGERIA. NATIONAL UNIVERSITIES COMMISSION. STATISTICAL DIGEST. see *EDUCATION—Abstracting, Bibliographies, Statistics*

378.669 NGA ISSN 0795-9931
LA1633
NIGERIA. NATIONAL UNIVERSITIES COMMISSION. UNIVERSITY SYSTEM NEWS. Short title: N U C University System News. Text in English. 1977. q. free. **Document type:** *Newsletter, Government.* **Description:** Covers important news about the Nigerian university system, particularly in the areas of research and development, academic programs, accreditation, and awards.
Formerly: Nigeria. National Universities Commission. Bulletin
Published by: National Universities Commission, Information and Public Relations Unit, Aja Nwachukwu House, Plot 430 Aguiyi-Ironsi St.Maitama District Garki G.P.O., Federal, PMB 237, Abuja, Capital Territory, Nigeria. TEL 234-9-523-3176, FAX 234-9-523-3520, TELEX UNICOMM LAGOS. Ed. Goddy Nnadi. Circ: 20,000.

378.756 USA
NORTH CAROLINA STATE UNIVERSITY. CHANCELLOR'S REPORT. Text in English. 1958. biennial. free. **Document type:** *Corporate.*
Formerly: North Carolina State University. Chancellor's Annual Report; Incorporates (1958-1984): North Carolina State University. Development Board. Report; Which was formerly: North Carolina State University. Development Council. Report (0078-1428); North Carolina University. State College of Agriculture and Engineering, Raleigh. Development Council. Report
Published by: North Carolina State University, Office of Public Affairs, Campus Box 7508, Raleigh, NC 27695-7508. TEL 919-515-9616, FAX 919-515-7946, http://www.ncsu.edu. Ed., R&P Alethea Wieland. Circ: 6,000.

NORWAY. DIREKTORATET FOR ARBEIDSTILSYNET. FORSKRIFTER/REGULATIONS. see *OCCUPATIONAL HEALTH AND SAFETY*

NORWAY. STATISTISK SENTRALBYRAA. UTDANNINGSSTATISTIKK. UNIVERSITETER OG HOEGSKOLER. see *EDUCATION—Abstracting, Bibliographies, Statistics*

378.12 CAN
O T F - F E O INTERACTION (ONLINE). Text in English. 1965. 4/yr. membership. adv. bk.rev. **Document type:** *Newsletter.*
Former titles: O T F - F E O Interaction (Print) (0316-3903); O T F Interaction; Interaction; (until 1974): O T F Reporter (0029-7313)
Media: Online - full text.
Published by: Ontario Teachers' Federation, 1300 Young St, Ste 200, Toronto, ON M4T 1X3, Canada. TEL 416-966-3424, http://www.otffeo.on.ca. Ed., R&P Kathleen Devlin. Circ: 126,000.

378 USA
OAK RIDGE ASSOCIATED UNIVERSITIES. ANNUAL REPORT. Text in English. 1947. a. free. reprint service avail. from NTI.
Formerly: Oak Ridge Institute for Nuclear Studies. Report (0078-2904)
Related titles: Microform ed.: (from NTI).
Published by: Oak Ridge Associated Universities, Inc., Office of Information Services, Box 117, Oak Ridge, TN 37831-0117. TEL 615-576-3146. Ed. Karen Moles. Circ: 2,500.

OCCUPATIONAL PROGRAMS IN CALIFORNIA PUBLIC COMMUNITY COLLEGES. see *EDUCATION—Guides To Schools And Colleges*

378.769 USA ISSN 1076-9447
ODYSSEY (LEXINGTON). Text in English. 1982. s-a. free. illus.; stat. **Document type:** *Academic/Scholarly.*
Supersedes (in 1982): University of Kentucky Research Foundation. Annual Report (0566-8719)
—CISTI.
Published by: University of Kentucky, Communications and Advancement Office, 109 Kinkead Hall, Lexington, KY 40506-0057. TEL 606-257-8297, FAX 606-257-8298, deweis@pop.uky.edu, http://www.rgs.uky.edu/cal/odyssey.html. Ed. Jeff Worley. R&P Lisa Lizer. Circ: 33,000.

OESTERREICHISCHE HOCHSCHULSTATISTIK. see *EDUCATION—Abstracting, Bibliographies, Statistics*

378.07 AUT ISSN 0029-9200
DIE OESTERREICHISCHE HOEHERE SCHULE. Text in German. 1948. 4/yr. adv. bk.rev. index. **Document type:** *Journal, Trade.*
Published by: Vereinigung Christlicher Lehrerinnen und Lehrer an Hoeheren und Mittleren Schulen Oesterreichs, Harmoniegasse 8/19, Vienna, W 1090, Austria. w.r.jahn@aon.at, http://www.vcl-oe.at. Circ: 5,800.

OESTERREICHISCHER KRANKENPFLEGEVERBAND. FORTBILDUNGSPROGRAMM. see *MEDICAL SCIENCES—Nurses And Nursing*

378 378.0076 USA
OFFICIAL GUIDE FOR G M A T REVIEW. (Graduate Management Admission Test) Text in English. 1972. biennial. USD 11.95. back issues avail.
Former titles: Official Guide to G M A T; Guide to Graduate Management Education
Published by: (Graduate Management Admission Council), Educational Testing Service, Rosedale Rd, Princeton, NJ 08541-0001. TEL 609-951-1236. **Institutional subscr. to:** Warner Books Inc, Special Sales, Time & Life Bldg, 1271 Ave of the Americas, New York, NY 10020. TEL 212-522-7381; **Subscr. to:** Little Brown, 200 West St, Waltham, MA 02254. TEL 800-759-0190.

OFFICIAL GUIDE TO A B A-APPROVED LAW SCHOOLS. (American Bar Association) see *LAW*

378.96 GHA ISSN 0855-0913
THE OGUAA EDUCATOR; a journal for the promotion of educational thinking in Africa. Text in English. 1975. irreg. USD 20. bk.rev. **Document type:** *Magazine.*
Formerly: University of Cape Coast. Faculty of Education. Bulletin
Published by: University of Cape Coast, University Post Office, Cape Coast, Ghana. TEL 233-42-32378, FAX 233-42-32485, ucclib@ucc.gn.apc.org. Circ: 500.

OHIO HIGHER EDUCATION. BASIC DATA SERIES. see *EDUCATION—Abstracting, Bibliographies, Statistics*

378 USA
OLD GOLD AND BLACK. Text in English. 1916. w. USD 50. adv. bk.rev.; film rev.; play rev. charts; illus. back issues avail. **Document type:** *Newspaper.*
Published by: Wake Forest University, PO Box 7569, Reynolds Sta, Winston Salem, NC 27109. TEL 910-758-5280, FAX 910-758-4561, letters@tsongas.ogb.wfu.edu, http://www.ogb.wfu.edu/. Ed., R&P Danielle Deaver TEL 336-758-4922. Adv. contact Brad Gilmore. Circ: 5,600.

378 GBR ISSN 0964-4237
OMEGA (MILTON KEYNES). Text in English. 1989. q. free to members (effective 2003).
Published by: Association of Open University Graduates, RAF Hut, Walton Hall, Milton Keynes, MK7 6AA, United Kingdom. TEL 44-1908-653316, http://www.ougrads.org.uk, FAX 44-1908-638130, aoug@open.ac.uk.

378.972 MEX ISSN 0186-4742
OMNIA. Text in Spanish. 1985. q. MXP 100, USD 85 (effective 2000). **Description:** For graduate students at the University.
Published by: Universidad Nacional Autonoma de Mexico, Coordinacion General de Estudios de Posgrado, Departamento de Publicaciones, Edificio Unidad de Posgrado, P.B., Circuito Interior, Ciudad Universitaria, Mexico City, DF 04510, Mexico. TEL 52-5-6220807, FAX 52-5-6220814. Ed. Irma Osnaya Cornejo.

378.19822 USA ISSN 0734-0141
CODEN: VITEFR
ON CAMPUS WITH WOMEN. Text in English. 1971. q. free (effective 2005). bk.rev. illus. back issues avail.; reprint service avail. from PQC. **Document type:** *Newsletter, Academic/Scholarly.* **Description:** Explores the ways women are changing all sectors of higher education; highlights both research and practice.
Related titles: Microform ed.: (from PQC); Online - full text ed.: (from Northern Light Technology, Inc., ProQuest Information & Learning).
Indexed: CIJE, HEA, WSA.
Published by: Association of American Colleges and Universities, 1818 R St, N W, Washington, DC 20009. TEL 202-387-3760, FAX 202-265-9532, info@aacu.nw.dc.us, http://www.aacu.org/ocww/, http://209.29.150.40/index.cfm. Ed. Amy Addams. Circ: 4,000.

378 GBR ISSN 1074-8121
ON THE HORIZON; the strategic planning resource for education professionals. Text in English. 1992. q. EUR 401.29 in Europe; USD 379 in North America; AUD 709 in Australasia; GBP 281.66 in UK & elsewhere (effective 2006). bk.rev. back issues avail.; reprint service avail. from PSC. **Document type:** *Journal, Academic/Scholarly.* **Description:** Provides analysis and comment on the future of post-secondary education.
Related titles: Online - full text ed.: 1998 (from EBSCO Publishing, Emerald Group Publishing Limited, Gale Group, IngentaConnect, O C L C Online Computer Library Center, Inc.).
Indexed: HEA.
—BLDSC (6256.705500), IE, Infotrieve, ingenta. **CCC.**
Published by: (University of North Carolina, Chapel Hill USA), Emerald Group Publishing Limited, 60-62 Toller Ln, Bradford, W Yorks BD8 9BY, United Kingdom. TEL 44-1274-777700, FAX 44-1274-785200, help@emeraldinsight.com, infomation@emeraldinsight.com, http://www.emeraldinsight.com/oth.htm. Ed. Dr. Tom P Abeles. **Subscr. in N America:** Emerald Group Publishing Ltd., 44 Brattle St, 4th Fl, Cambridge, MA 02138. TEL 617-497-2175, 888-622-0075, FAX 617-354-6875.

378.00285 USA
▼ **ONLINE DEGREES MAGAZINE.** Text in English. 2005. s-a. **Document type:** *Magazine, Consumer.* **Description:** Combines expert advice and success stories to inform and inspire readers about cyber learning.
Published by: ClassesUSA, 920 Broadway, 10th Fl, New York, NY 10010. editorial@classesusa.com, info@classesusa.com, http://www.writenews.com/2005/040105_online_degrees.htm, http://www.classesusa.com.

378.713 CAN ISSN 0711-6896
LB2335.C3
ONTARIO UNIVERSITIES BENEFITS SURVEY. Text in English. biennial (in 2 vols.). CND 5.10.
Published by: Council of Ontario Universities, 180 Dundas St W, Ste 1100, Toronto, ON M5G 1Z8, Canada. TEL 416-979-2165, FAX 416-979-8635, acadieux@coupo.cou.on.ca, http://www.cou.on.ca.

378.106 GBR ISSN 0268-0513
LC5808.G7
➤ **OPEN LEARNING.** Text in English. 1974. 3/yr. GBP 160, USD 268 combined subscription to institutions print & online eds. (effective 2006). bk.rev. illus. reprint service avail. from PQC,PSC. **Document type:** *Journal, Academic/Scholarly.* **Description:** Publishes theoretical and practice-based articles reflecting developments in distance, flexible, and open education and training,.
Supersedes (in 1986): Teaching at a Distance (0307-241X)
Related titles: Microform ed.: (from PQC); Online - full text ed.: ISSN 1469-9958. GBP 152, USD 255 to institutions (effective 2006) (from EBSCO Publishing, Gale Group, IngentaConnect, O C L C Online Computer Library Center, Inc., Swets Information Services).
Indexed: BrEdI, CIJE, CPE, ERA, ETA, HEA, HECAB, MEA, RHEA, SEA, SENA, SOMA, TEA.
—BLDSC (6265.960600), IE, Infotrieve, ingenta. **CCC.**
Published by: (Open University), Routledge (Subsidiary of: Taylor & Francis Group), 4 Park Sq, Milton Park, Abingdon, Oxon OX14 4RN, United Kingdom. TEL 44-1235-828600, FAX 44-1235-829000, info@routledge.co.uk, http://www.tandf.co.uk/journals/titles/02680513.asp, http://www.routledge.co.uk. Ed. Anne Gaskell. **Subscr. to:** Taylor & Francis Ltd, Journals Customer Service, Rankine Rd, Basingstoke, Hants RG24 8PR, United Kingdom. TEL 44-1256-813000, FAX 44-1256-330245.

E

617.6071 USA
OPPORTUNITIES FOR MINORITY STUDENTS IN THE U.S. DENTAL SCHOOLS. Text in English. 1995. biennial, latest 4th edition. USD 10 (effective 2003). charts; stat. **Document type:** *Consumer.* **Description:** Provides information on programs available to minority students at U.S. dental schools, admission requirements, admission and graduation statistics.
Published by: American Dental Education Association, 1625 Massachusetts Ave, N W, Washington, DC 20036-2212. TEL 202-667-9433, FAX 202-667-0642, http://www.adea.org. Ed., R&P Sue Sandmeyer. Circ: 3,000.

378.1543 GBR
OPPORTUNITIES IN THE GAP YEAR. Text in English. 1969. a. GBP 6.95 (effective 2003). **Document type:** *Directory.* **Description:** Provides advice for students between high school and college.
Former titles: Jobs in the Gap Year; Temporary Occupations and Employment (0264-7761)
Published by: (Independent Schools Careers Organisation), I S C O Publications, 12a Princess Way, Camberley, Surrey GU15 3SP, United Kingdom. TEL 44-1276-21188, FAX 44-1276-691833, info@isco.org.uk, http://www.isco.org.uk/. Circ: 4,000.

378 CHE
OPTIONS; magazine d'information sur les formations et les metiers. Text in French. 1970. 5/yr. CHF 30. bk.rev. illus. **Document type:** *Academic/Scholarly.*
Formerly (until 1992): Etudes et Carrieres
Indexed: ILD.
Published by: Office d'Orientation et de Formation Professionelle, Service d'Information, Case Postale 457, Geneva 4, 1211, Switzerland. TEL 41-22-7050253, FAX 41-22-7050562. Ed. Yvonne Marie Ruedin. Circ: 28,000.

378 USA ISSN 8755-9366
CODEN: RPMMAG
THE ORACLE. Text in English. s-w.
Published by: Oral Roberts University, Student Publications Department, 7777 S. Lewis Ave, LRC Rm 230, Tulsa, OK 74171. TEL 918-495-6346, FAX 918-495-6345, oracle@oru.edu, http://www.oru.edu/oracle. Ed. Beth Pitts.

ORATORY SCHOOL MAGAZINE. see *LITERATURE*

378 AUT
OST-DOKUMENTATION: BILDUNGS-, WISSENSCHAFTS- UND KULTURPOLITIK IN MITTEL- UND OSTEUROPA. Text in German. 1987. q. abstr. index. **Document type:** *Bulletin, Trade.*
Former titles: Ost-Dokumentation Bildungs- und Wissenschaftspolitik; (until 1991): Ost-Dokumentation Bildungswesen
Published by: Oesterreichisches Ost- und Suedosteuropa Institut, Josefsplatz 6, Vienna, W 1010, Austria. TEL 43-1-5121895, FAX 43-1-512189553, josef.vogl@osi.ac.at, http://www.osi.ac.at. Ed. Peter Bachmaier. Circ: 100.

P R I M U S. (Problems, Resources, and Issues in Mathematics Undergraduate Studies) see *MATHEMATICS*

378 USA
P S C CLARION. (Professional Staff Congress) Text in English. 1972. 9/yr. membership. adv. bk.rev. charts; illus. **Document type:** *Newspaper.*
Former titles: Legislative Conference Reporter (0024-0478); U F C T Action
Published by: Professional Staff Congress, City University of New York, 25 W 43 St, New York, NY 10036. TEL 212-354-1252, FAX 212-302-7815, http://www.psc-cuny.org. Ed., R&P Carol Sims. Circ: 15,000.

378 IND
PANJAB UNIVERSITY NEWS. Text in English. 1958. q. INR 15. adv. charts; illus.
Published by: Panjab University, Publication Bureau, Arts Block No. 3, Panjab University Campus, Chandigarh, Haryana 160 014, India. Ed. R K Malhotra. Circ: 500.

378 MEX ISSN 0186-2766
F1246.3
PANORAMA (LA PAZ). Text in Spanish. 1977. bi-m. back issues avail.
Related titles: Supplement(s): Panorama. Suplemento. ISSN 0186-2774. 1977.
Published by: Universidad Autonoma de Baja California Sur, Carretera al Sur Km. 5.5, La Paz, Baja California Sur, 23080, Mexico. TEL 52-1-1280440, FAX 52-1-1280880, http://www.uabcs.mx/.

378 USA ISSN 1541-1389
LB2335.7
PEER REVIEW; emerging trends and key debates in undergraduate education. Text in English. 1998. q. USD 8 per issue to members; USD 10 per issue to non-members (effective 2005). **Document type:** *Journal, Academic/Scholarly.*
Formerly (until 2001): A A C & U Peer Review (1525-9463)
Related titles: Online - full text ed.: (from bigchalk, EBSCO Publishing, Gale Group, O C L C Online Computer Library Center, Inc., ProQuest Information & Learning).
Indexed: MLA-IB.
Published by: Association of American Colleges and Universities, 1818 R St, N W, Washington, DC 20009. TEL 202-387-3760, 800-297-3775, FAX 202-265-9532, info@aacu.nw.dc.us, http://209.29.150.40/index.cfm. Eds. Bridget Puzon, David Tritelli. R&P Bridget Puzon.

378.72 MEX ISSN 0185-2698
PERFILES EDUCATIVOS. Text in Spanish. 1978; N.S. 1983. q. MXP 60, USD 50 (effective 2000). bk.rev. **Document type:** *Academic/Scholarly.*
Published by: Universidad Nacional Autonoma de Mexico, Centro de Investigaciones y Servicios Educativos, Circuito Exterior, Ciudad Universitaria, Mexico, DF 04510, Mexico. TEL 52-5-622-8702, FAX 52-5-550-1801, sanchez@pompeya.cise-sua.unam.mx. Ed. Jose Manuel Alvarez Manila. Circ: 2,000.

378.12 DEU ISSN 0945-2761
PERSONAL- UND VORLESUNGSVERZEICHNIS. Text in German. 1972. s-a. adv. **Document type:** *Bulletin, Academic/Scholarly.*
Published by: Bergische Universitaet - Gesamthochschule Wuppertal, Gausstr 20, Wuppertal, 42097, Germany. TEL 49-202-4392212, FAX 49-202-4393712, stephan@uni-wuppertal.de, http://www.uni-wuppertal.de. Ed. Rainer Stephan. Adv. contact Volker Reischert TEL 49-211-683313. Circ: 8,000.

378.111 USA ISSN 0888-9732
KF4225.A15
PERSPECTIVE (MADISON); the campus legal monthly. Text in English. 1986. m. USD 249 domestic; USD 253 in Canada; USD 259 elsewhere (effective 2005). adv. back issues avail. **Document type:** *Newsletter.* **Description:** Focuses on legal issues for college and university administrators.
Related titles: Online - full text ed.: USD 249 (effective 2005) (from EBSCO Publishing, H.W. Wilson, O C L C Online Computer Library Center, Inc.).
Indexed: ABIn, EduInd.
—**CCC.**
Published by: Magna Publications, Inc., 2718 Dryden Dr, Madison, WI 53704. TEL 608-246-3590, 800-433-0499, FAX 608-246-3597, editor@magnapubs.com, http://www.magnapubs.com/pub/magnapubs_persy. Ed. Dennis Black. Circ: 1,300.

378.1012 GBR ISSN 1360-3108
LB2341
PERSPECTIVES (LONDON, 1997); policy and practice in higher education. Text in English. 1997. q. GBP 86, USD 143 combined subscription to institutions print & online eds. (effective 2006). adv. reprint service avail. from PSC. **Document type:** *Journal, Academic/Scholarly.* **Description:** Aims to disseminate ideas which enhance the practical aspects of higher education management and administration.
Related titles: Online - full text ed.: ISSN 1460-7018. GBP 82, USD 136 to institutions (effective 2006) (from EBSCO Publishing, Gale Group, IngentaConnect, O C L C Online Computer Library Center, Inc., Swets Information Services).
Indexed: BrEdI, CPE, ERA, ETA, FamI, MEA, RHEA, SEA, SENA, SOMA, TEA.
—BLDSC (6428.136030), IE, Infotrieve, ingenta. **CCC.**
Published by: (Association of University Administrators), Routledge (Subsidiary of: Taylor & Francis Group), 4 Park Sq, Milton Park, Abingdon, Oxon OX14 4RN, United Kingdom. TEL 44-1235-828600, FAX 44-1235-829000, info@routledge.co.uk, http://www.tandf.co.uk/journals/titles/13603108.asp, http://www.routledge.co.uk. Ed. Dr. Giles H Brown. **Subscr. to:** Taylor & Francis Ltd, Journals Customer Service, Rankine Rd, Basingstoke, Hants RG24 8PR, United Kingdom. TEL 44-1256-813000, FAX 44-1256-330245.

378.007 USA ISSN 1542-1422
➤ **PERSPECTIVES IN LEARNING.** Text in English. 2000. a. **Document type:** *Academic/Scholarly.*
Published by: Columbus State University, College of Education, Jordan Hall 131, 4225 University Ave., Columbus, GA 31907. TEL 706-568-2212, http://coe.colstate.edu. Eds. Lisa Shaw, Nancy Tarsi, Virginia Causey.

378.101 USA ISSN 1080-2541
LB2341.93.U6
PETERSON'S CONTRACT SERVICES FOR HIGHER EDUCATION. Text in English. 1995. a. **Document type:** *Directory, Trade.* **Description:** Lists more than 100 areas - from bookstore management to food service - and 2,000 vendors that currently provide these services to colleges and universities in the U.S.
Published by: Thomson Peterson's (Subsidiary of: Thomson Corporation), Princeton Pike Corporate Center, 2000 Lenox Dr, 3rd Fl, Lawrenceville, NJ 08648. TEL 609-243-9111, 800-338-3282, FAX 609-243-9150, http://www.petersons.com. Ed. Barbara Lawrence.

378.33 USA ISSN 1089-1013
LB2337.2
PETERSON'S GRANTS FOR GRADUATE & POSTDOCTORAL STUDY (YEAR). Text in English. 1986. triennial. USD 89.95. **Document type:** *Directory.* **Description:** Lists over 1,400 grant and fellowship programs for graduate and postdoctoral students from associations and other sponsors allowing study at the institution of the students' choice.
Formed by the merger of: Peterson's Grants for Post-doctoral Study; Peterson's Grants for Graduate Study (Year) (1058-6377); Former titles: Peterson's Grants for Graduate Students (Year) (1040-1091); Grants for Graduate Students (Year) (0889-1613)
Published by: Thomson Peterson's (Subsidiary of: Thomson Corporation), Princeton Pike Corporate Center, 2000 Lenox Dr, 3rd Fl, Lawrenceville, NJ 08648. TEL 609-243-9111, FAX 609-243-9150, http://www.petersons.com. Ed. Barbara Lawrence.

PETERSON'S GUIDE TO M B A PROGRAMS. see *EDUCATION—Guides To Schools And Colleges*

378.016 USA ISSN 1069-6504
LB2376
PETERSON'S STUDY ABROAD. Text in English. 1993. a. USD 26.95. **Document type:** *Directory.* **Description:** Provides details on over 1,300 credit programs offered by 350 accredited U.S. and foreign colleges and universities during the regular academic year. Organized geographically by country and city.
Published by: Thomson Peterson's (Subsidiary of: Thomson Corporation), Princeton Pike Corporate Center, 2000 Lenox Dr, 3rd Fl, Lawrenceville, NJ 08648. TEL 609-243-9111, FAX 609-243-9150, http://www.petersons.com. Ed. Barbara Lawrence.

PETERSON'S TOP COLLEGES FOR SCIENCE. see *SCIENCES: COMPREHENSIVE WORKS*

PHARMACY STUDENT. see *PHARMACY AND PHARMACOLOGY*

378.599 PHL
PHILIPPINE NORMAL COLLEGE RESEARCH SERIES. Text in English. 1976. irreg., latest vol.3, 1977. price varies. charts.
Published by: Philippine Normal College, Taft Ave, Manila, 2801, Philippines. Circ: 500.

378.161 GBR
PHOENIX (MANCHESTER). Text in English. 1977. q. GBP 30 (effective 1999). **Description:** Analyzes trends, issues, and events within graduate recruitment and higher-education careers advisory work in the U.K.
Published by: (Association of Graduate Careers Advisory Services), C S U Ltd. (Subsidiary of: Higher Education Careers Services Unit), Prospects House, Booth St, E., Manchester, Lancs M13 9EP, United Kingdom. TEL 44-161-277-5200, FAX 44-161-277-5210, http://www.prospects.csu.ac.uk. adv.: color page GBP 700. Circ: 1,200 (controlled).

378 USA
PITT MAGAZINE. Text in English. 1986. 4/yr. free to qualified personnel; USD 25 (effective 2003). adv. bk.rev. abstr.; charts; illus. back issues avail. **Document type:** *Academic/Scholarly.* **Description:** Covers the University, its alumni, and all subjects encompassed in the educational enterprise.
Indexed: EnvAb.
Published by: University of Pittsburgh, Department of University Relations, 400 Craig Hall, Pittsburgh, PA 15260. TEL 412-624-4147, FAX 412-624-1021, pittmag@pitt.edu, http://www.univ-relations.pitt.edu/pittmag/. Ed., R&P Sally Ann Flecker. Adv. contact Bill Young. Circ: 125,000 (controlled).

378.107 USA ISSN 0736-0983
LA227.3
➤ **PLANNING FOR HIGHER EDUCATION.** Text in English. 1970. q. USD 95 domestic; USD 118 in Canada & Mexico; USD 129 elsewhere (effective 2004). adv. bk.rev. illus. index. back issues avail.; reprint service avail. from PQC. **Document type:** *Journal, Academic/Scholarly.* **Description:** Provides information and ideas for the purpose of advancing state-of-the-art planning.
Supersedes: S C U P News and Journal (0037-9719); Society for College and University Planning Quarterly
Related titles: Microform ed.: 1970 (from PQC); Online - full text ed.: 1970 (from H.W. Wilson, O C L C Online Computer Library Center, Inc.).
Indexed: ABIn, CIJE, CPE, EAA, EduInd, HEA, MEA.
—BLDSC (6509.070000), IE, Infotrieve, ingenta.
Published by: Society for College and University Planning, 311 Maynard St, Ann Arbor, MI 48104-2211. TEL 734-998-7832, FAX 734-998-6532, scup@scup.org, http://www.scup.org/. Ed. Rod Rose. R&P Sharon Morioka. Adv. contact Betty Cobb. Circ: 4,700.

378 IND
POLICIES OF HIGHER EDUCATION (YEAR). Text in English. 1927. irreg., latest 1995. USD 25 (effective 1999). **Document type:** *Newsletter.*
Published by: Association of Indian Universities, A.I.U. House, 16 Kotla Marg, New Delhi, 110 002, India. TEL 91-11-323-0059, FAX 91-11-323-6105, aiu@del12.vsnl.net.in, http://www.aiuweb.org.

POLICJA. see *CRIMINOLOGY AND LAW ENFORCEMENT*

E

378 USA ISSN 0897-1595
POLICY DOCUMENTS AND REPORTS. Text in English. 1968. irreg. USD 26 per issue (effective 2005).
Published by: American Association of University Professors, 1012 14th St, N W, Ste 500, Washington, DC 20005-3465. TEL 202-737-5900, FAX 202-737-5526, aaup@aaup.org, http://www.aaup.org.

378.12 USA
POLICY PERSPECTIVES (WASHINGTON, D.C.); examining public policy issues in teacher education. Text in English. bi-m. USD 99.95 to non-members; USD 85 to members (effective 2005). **Document type:** *Journal, Academic/Scholarly.* **Description:** Focuses on education policy at the state and national levels, with an analysis of legislative activity, detailed examinations of specific issues, and analyses of current topics of critical importance to teacher educators.
Published by: American Association of Colleges for Teacher Education, 1307 New York Ave, NW. Ste 300, Washington, DC 20005-4701. TEL 202-293-2450, FAX 202-457-8095, emf@aacte.nche.edu, http://www.edpolicy.org/perspectives, http://www.aacte.org.

378.12 USA ISSN 1048-194X
LC89
POLICY PERSPECTIVES (WEST CHESTER). Text in English. 198?. q. **Document type:** *Journal, Academic/Scholarly.* **Description:** Provides a forum for discussions of critical issues in higher education derived in part from formal research and analysis and in part from human experience as tested and refined through the workings of national roundtables.
—CCC.
Published by: The Learning Alliance for Higher Education, 1398 Wilmington Pike, West Chester, PA 19382. TEL 610-399-6601, FAX 815-550-8892, zemsky@thelearningalliance.info, http://thelearningalliance.info/mailman/listinfo/polper_thelearningalliance.info, http://www.thelearningalliance.info.

378.106 FRA ISSN 1682-346X
POLITIQUES ET GESTION DE L'ENSEIGNEMENT SUPERIEUR. Text in French. 3/yr. EUR 104, USD 119, GBP 70, JPY 14,000 (effective 2005). **Description:** Covers management in higher education institutions in different countries.
Former titles (until 2001): Gestion de l'Enseignement Superieur (1013-8501); (until 1988): Revue Internationale de Gestion des Etablissements d'Enseignement Superieur (1011-8179)
Related titles: Online - full content ed.: ISSN 1684-3592. EUR 72, USD 82, GBP 48, JPY 9,700 (effective 2005); Online - full text ed.: (from EBSCO Publishing, Gale Group, IngentaConnect, Swets Information Services); ♦ English ed.: Higher Education Management and Policy. ISSN 1682-3451.
Published by: Organization for Economic Cooperation and Development, 2 Rue Andre Pascal, Paris, 75775 Cedex 16, France. TEL 33-1-45248200, FAX 33-1-45248500, http://www.oecd.org. **Dist. by:** Extenza - Turpin, Pegasus Dr, Stratton Business Park, Biggleswade, Beds SG18 8TQ, United Kingdom. TEL 44-1462-687552, FAX 44-1462-480947, subscriptions@extenza-turpin.com; O E C D Turpin North America, PO Box 194, Downingtown, PA 19335-0194. TEL 610-524-5361, 800-456-6323, FAX 610-524-5417, journalscustomer@turpinna.com.

378 AUS ISSN 1444-383X
LB1028.25.A8
POST-SCRIPT. Text in English. 2000. s-a. back issues avail.
Media: Online - full text.
Published by: University of Melbourne, Faculty of Education, Alice hoy Bldg Monash Rd, Gate 4, Melbourne, VIC 3010, Australia. TEL 61-3-8344-8285, FAX 61-3-8344-8529, enquiries@edfac.unimelb.edu.au, http://www.edfac.unimelb.edu.au/insight/pscript.shtml.

POSTEPY NAUK MEDYCZNYCH. see *MEDICAL SCIENCES*

378.41025 GBR ISSN 1366-8323
POSTGRAD SERIES - THE DIRECTORY. Key Title: Directory of Graduate Studies. Text in English. 1972. a. GBP 109.99 per issue (effective 2002). **Document type:** *Directory.* **Description:** Covers all postgraduate study opportunities in the UK.
Formerly (until 1996): Graduate Studies (0309-0949)
Related titles: CD-ROM ed.
Published by: (Careers Research and Advisory Centre), Hobsons PLC, Challenger House, 42 Adler St, London, E1 1EE, United Kingdom. TEL 44-1223-460366, FAX 44-1223-301506. **Dist. by:** Biblios Publishers' Distribution Services Ltd., Star Rd, Partridge Green, W Sussex RH13 8LD, United Kingdom. TEL 44-1403-710851, FAX 44-1403-711143.

378 USA ISSN 1068-9818
POSTSECONDARY EDUCATION OPPORTUNITY. Text in English. 1992. m. USD 160; USD 80 to students (effective 2004). **Document type:** *Journal, Academic/Scholarly.*
Address: PO Box 415, Oskaloosa, IA 52577-0415. TEL 641-673-3401, FAX 641-673-3411, tom@postsecondary.org, http://www.postsecondary.org.

378.0799 ZAF ISSN 0079-4341
CODEN: WBPNBQ
POTCHEFSTROOM UNIVERSITY FOR CHRISTIAN HIGHER EDUCATION. WETENSKAPLIKE BYDRAES. REEKS B: NATUURWETENSKAPPE. SERIES. Text in English. irreg. free.
Indexed: BiolAb.
Published by: Potchefstroom University for Christian Higher Education/Potchefstroomse Universiteit vir Christelike Hoer Onderwys, Pvt Bag X6001, Potchefstroom, 2520, South Africa.

378.07 ZAF
POTCHEFSTROOM UNIVERSITY FOR CHRISTIAN HIGHER EDUCATION. WETENSKAPLIKE BYDRAES. REEKS H: INOUGURELE REDES. Text in Afrikaans; Text occasionally in English. irreg. free.
Published by: Potchefstroom University for Christian Higher Education/Potchefstroomse Universiteit vir Christelike Hoer Onderwys, Pvt Bag X6001, Potchefstroom, 2520, South Africa.

378 IND ISSN 0554-9884
PRAJNA. Text in English. 1974 (no.6). q. bk.rev.
Published by: Banaras Hindu University, Varanasi, Uttar Pradesh, India. Ed. R M Pandey. Circ: 10,000.

378 FRA ISSN 0292-2215
PRATIQUES DE FORMATION-ANALYSES. Text in French. 1981. s-a. **Description:** Provides a forum for the examination of theories of practice for socio-cultural promotion and further adult education.
Published by: (Universite Paris VIII, Service de la Formation Permanente), Presses Universitaires de Vincennes, L'Universite Paris 8, 2, rue de la Liberte, Saint-Denis, 93526 Cedex 02, France. revuepfa@univ-paris8.fr, http://www.puv-univ-paris8.org. Ed. Jacques Ardoino.

378 HND
PRESENCIA UNIVERSITARIA. Text in Spanish. 1964. m. free. illus.
Indexed: RASB.
Published by: (Universidad Nacional Autonoma de Honduras), Editorial Universitaria U N A H, Ciudad Universitaria, Tegucigalpa DC, Honduras. TEL 504-32-4772, FAX 504-31-0675. Circ: 1,000.

378 ITA ISSN 0478-1376
PRESENZA. Text in Italian. 1969. q.
Published by: Universita Cattolica del Sacro Cuore, Largo Gemelli 1, Milan, MI 20123, Italy. TEL 39-02-72341, http://www.unicatt.it/. Ed. Franco Monaco. Circ: 79,000.

378 USA ISSN 1099-3681
LB2341 CODEN: EDREAS
THE PRESIDENCY; the magazine for higher education leaders. Text in English. 1920. 3/yr. USD 40 to non-members; USD 36 to members (effective 2005). adv. bk.rev. charts; illus. index. reprint service avail. from PQC.
Formerly (until 1998): Educational Record (0013-1873)
Related titles: Microform ed.: (from PMC, PQC); Online - full text ed.: (from EBSCO Publishing, O C L C Online Computer Library Center, Inc., ProQuest Information & Learning).
Indexed: ABIn, AgeL, CIJE, CPE, ChPerI, CurCont, EAA, EduInd, HEA, IBZ, MEA&I, PAIS, PCI, PhilInd, PsycholAb, RHEA, SOPODA, SPAA, SSCI.
—BLDSC (6609.794000), IE, Infotrieve, ingenta.
Published by: American Council on Education, Office of Research, One Dupont Circle, Washington, DC 20036. TEL 202-939-9380, FAX 202-833-4760, http://www.acenet.edu/bookstore/pubInfo.cfm?pubID=51. Ed. Wendy Bresler. R&P Lisa Richards Hone TEL 202-939-9493. Circ: 12,000.

378.05 POL
PRESSJE; teki klubu Jagiellonskiego. Text in Polish. 2002. q. 216 p./no.; **Document type:** *Journal, Academic/Scholarly.*
Published by: Jagiellonskie Towarzystwo Kulturalno-Oswiatowe, ul Sw Tomasza 17, Krakow, 31018, Poland. pressje@kj.org.pl, http://www.kj.org.pl. Ed. Arkady Rzegocki. Circ: 1,000.

378 GBR
PRIOR PARK MAGAZINE✶. Text in English. a. adv.
Published by: Prior Park College, Prior Park College, Ralph Allen Dr, Bath, BA2 5AH, United Kingdom. Ed. Angela Webster. Adv. contact B Bane. Circ: 500.

378 ESP ISSN 1130-765X
PROFESIONES Y EMPRESAS; revista de educacion tecnologica y profesional. Text in Spanish. 1974. bi-m. adv. bk.rev. illus.; pat.
—CINDOC.
Published by: Editepsa, Gran Via, 38-9o, Madrid, 28013, Spain. TEL 5223844. Ed. Maria Cruz Mendiola. Circ: 7,000.

378 ITA ISSN 0392-2790
PROFESSIONALITA. Text in Italian. 1980. bi-m. EUR 47 domestic; EUR 58 in Europe; EUR 72 elsewhere (effective 2005). adv. **Document type:** *Magazine, Trade.*
Published by: Editrice La Scuola SpA, Via Luigi Cadorna 11, Brescia, BS 25124, Italy. TEL 39-030-29931, FAX 39-030-2993299, http;//www.lascuola.it. Ed. Luigi Morgano. Circ: 3,000.

378.007 610 USA ISSN 1052-7060
PROFESSIONS EDUCATION RESEARCHER QUARTERLY. Text in English. 1973. q. **Document type:** *Newsletter.*
Former titles (until 1990): Professions Education Researcher Notes (0743-4359); (until 1981): P E R. Professions Education Researcher (0196-0466); (until 1979): H P E E R. Health Professions Educators Exchange of Research (0147-8214)
—CCC.
Published by: American Educational Research Association, Division I: Education in the Professions, 1230 17th St, NW, Washington, DC 20036. TEL 202-223-9485, FAX 202-775-1824, http://www.aera.net/divisions/i/home/DivI.html. Ed. Dr. Ruth Streveler.

PROGRESSIO; newsletter for teaching development - nuusbrief vir onderrigontwikkeling. see *EDUCATION—Teaching Methods And Curriculum*

378 GBR
PROSPECTS POSTGRAD. Text in English. 1987. q. GBP 7.50 to students. adv. **Description:** Discusses options for further study and research for college and university graduates.
Formerly: Postgraduate Bulletin
Published by: C S U Ltd. (Subsidiary of: Higher Education Careers Services Unit), Prospects House, Booth St, E., Manchester, Lancs M13 9EP, United Kingdom. TEL 44-161-277-5200, FAX 44-161-277-5210. adv.: B&W page GBP 1,250. Circ: 50,000.

378.0025 GBR
PROSPECTS POSTGRADUATE DIRECTORY. Text in English. 1973. a. (3 vols./yr.). GBP 30 per vol. (effective 1999). **Document type:** *Directory.*
Formerly (until 1997): Higher Education in the U K - Postgraduate Study; (Until 1995): British Universities' Guide to Graduate Study (0957-9435); Postgraduate Courses in United Kingdom Universities (0263-6182); (until 1982): Schedule of Postgraduate Courses in United Kingdom Universities (0306-1728)
Published by: (C V C P), C S U Ltd. (Subsidiary of: Higher Education Careers Services Unit), Prospects House, Booth St, E., Manchester, Lancs M13 9EP, United Kingdom. TEL 44-161-277-5200, FAX 44-161-277-5210. Ed. Chris Phillips. Pub. Sean Fielding. **Co-sponsor:** United Kingdom Committee of Vice-Chancellors and Principals.

378 MEX ISSN 1606-7908
PROYECCIONES. Text in Spanish. 1999. q. back issues avail. **Document type:** *Academic/Scholarly.*
Media: Online - full content.
Published by: Instituto Tecnologico y de Estudios Superiores de Monterrey, Divisiones de Administracion y Ciencias Sociales, Calz. Lago de Guadalupe Km. 3.5, Atizapan de Zaragoza, Edo. de Mexico, 52926, Mexico. TEL 52-5-8645613, FAX 52-5-8645555, revdacs@campus.cem.itesm.mx, http://www.cem.itesm.mx/dacs/publicaciones/proy/. Ed. Sergio Ortiz Valdez.

PRZEGLAD POLICYJNY. see *CRIMINOLOGY AND LAW ENFORCEMENT*

378.1 USA ISSN 1066-0070
Z479
PUBLISHING FOR THE COLLEGE MARKET: REVIEW, TRENDS & FORECAST. Text in English. 1992. biennial. USD 1,995 (effective 2000). **Document type:** *Trade.* **Description:** Reviews print and electronic markets for college and university publishing. Covers demographics, enrollment, and distribution trends affecting this market.
Published by: SIMBA Information (Subsidiary of: R.R. Bowker LLC), 60 Long Ridge Rd., Ste 300, Stamford, CT 06902. TEL 203-325-8193, 800-307-2529, 888-269-5372, FAX 203-325-8915, info@simbanet.com, http://www.simbanet.com.

378 ITA ISSN 0078-7760
LF3573
QUADERNI PER LA STORIA DELL'UNIVERSITA DI PADOVA. Text in Italian. 1968. a. EUR 32 domestic; EUR 42 foreign (effective 2003). **Document type:** *Academic/Scholarly.*
Indexed: AmH&L, HistAb, IBR.
Published by: (Universita degli Studi di Padova), Editrice Antenore, Via Valadier 52, Rome, 00193, Italy. TEL 39-06-32600370, FAX 39-06-3223132, antenore@editriceantenore.it, http://www.editriceantenore.it.

378 GBR ISSN 1353-8322
LB2331.62 CODEN: QHEDFN
➤ **QUALITY IN HIGHER EDUCATION.** Text in English. 1995. 3/yr. GBP 280, USD 462 combined subscription to institutions print & online eds. (effective 2006). reprint service avail. from PSC. **Document type:** *Journal, Academic/Scholarly.* **Description:** Details theory, practice, and policies relating to the control, management, and quality improvement of higher education.
Related titles: Online - full text ed.: ISSN 1470-1081. GBP 266, USD 439 to institutions (effective 2006) (from EBSCO Publishing, Gale Group, IngentaConnect, O C L C Online Computer Library Center, Inc., Swets Information Services).
Indexed: BrEdI, CIJE, CPE, EAA, ERA, ETA, HEA, MEA, RHEA, SEA, SENA, SOMA, SOPODA, SSA, SociolAb, TEA.
—BLDSC (7168.152280), IE, Infotrieve, ingenta. **CCC.**

E

Published by: Routledge (Subsidiary of: Taylor & Francis Group), 4 Park Sq, Milton Park, Abingdon, Oxon OX14 4RN, United Kingdom. TEL 44-1235-828600, FAX 44-1235-829000, info@routledge.co.uk, http://www.tandf.co.uk/journals/titles/13538322.asp, http://www.routledge.co.uk. Ed. Lee Harvey. **Subscr. to:** Taylor & Francis Ltd, Journals Customer Service, Rankine Rd, Basingstoke, Hants RG24 8PR, United Kingdom. TEL 44-1256-813000, FAX 44-1256-330245.

378 GBR
QUEEN MARY COLLEGE STUDENTS UNION HANDBOOK. Text in English. 1958. a. free. adv. **Document type:** *Academic/Scholarly.*
Published by: University of London, Queen Mary College Students Union, 432 Bancroft Rd, London, E1 4DH, United Kingdom. Circ: 6,000.

378 AUS
QUEENSLAND BOARD OF SENIOR SECONDARY SCHOOL STUDIES: OVERVIEW OF THE PRINCIPAL RESPONSIBILITIES. Text in English. a. **Document type:** *Bulletin.*
Published by: Queensland Board of Senior Secondary School Studies, P.O. Box 307, Spring Hill, QLD 4101, Australia. TEL 61-7-3864-0299, FAX 61-7-3221-2553, office@qbssss.edu.au.

378 AUS ISSN 1329-234X
QUEENSLAND BOARD OF SENIOR SECONDARY SCHOOL STUDIES. PUBLICATIONS LIST. Text in English. s-a. **Document type:** *Government.*
Published by: Queensland Board of Senior Secondary School Studies, P.O. Box 307, Spring Hill, QLD 4101, Australia. TEL 61-7-3864-0299, FAX 61-7-3221-2553, office@qbssss.edu.au. Circ: 500.

378 AUS
QUEENSLAND BOARD OF SENIOR SECONDARY SCHOOL STUDIES: SOME FREQUENTLY ASKED QUESTIONS. Text in English. a. **Document type:** *Bulletin.*
Published by: Queensland Board of Senior Secondary School Studies, P.O. Box 307, Spring Hill, QLD 4101, Australia. TEL 61-7-3864-0299, FAX 61-7-3221-2553, office@qbssss.edu.au.

378 AUS
QUEENSLAND BOARD OF SENIOR SECONDARY SCHOOL STUDIES: SPECIAL CONSIDERATION EXEMPTION AND SPECIAL ARRANGEMENTS IN SENIOR SECONDARY SCHOOL-BASED ASSESSMENT. Text in English. a. **Document type:** *Bulletin.*
Published by: Queensland Board of Senior Secondary School Studies, P.O. Box 307, Spring Hill, QLD 4101, Australia. TEL 61-7-3864-0299, FAX 61-7-3221-2553, office@qbssss.edu.au.

378 AUT
QUELLEN UND DOKUMENTE ZUR GESCHICHTE DER BERUFSBILDUNG IN DEUTSCHLAND. Text in German. irreg., latest vol.8, 2003. price varies. **Document type:** *Monographic series, Academic/Scholarly.*
Published by: Boehlau Verlag GmbH & Co.KG., Sachsenplatz 4-6, Vienna, W 1201, Austria. TEL 43-1-33024270, FAX 43-1-3302432, boehlau@boehlau.at, http://www.boehlau.at.

378.1 USA ISSN 1065-206X
LB2341
QUERY (SUNNYVALE)✶. Text in English. 1991. 10/yr. USD 99. adv. bk.rev. back issues avail. **Document type:** *Newsletter.* **Description:** Covers the integration of computer technology in the administrative area of higher education. Features news, resources, and advice about how campuses can improve the computer environment.
Related titles: Diskette ed.: 1991; Online - full text ed.: 1991.
Published by: Syllabus Press (Subsidiary of: 101 Communications, Llc.), 9121 Oakdale Ave., Ste. 101, Chatsworth, CA 91311-6526. TEL 408-261-7200, 800-773-0670, FAX 408-261-7280, info@syllabus.com, http://www.syllabus.com. Ed., Pub. John P Noon. R&P Mary Grush. Adv. contact David Kastriner. B&W page USD 3,000, color page USD 3,900; trim 10.88 x 8.5.

QUEST; an interdisciplinary journal for Asian Christian scholars. see *RELIGIONS AND THEOLOGY*

378 FRA ISSN 0395-6725
QUINZAINE UNIVERSITAIRE. Text in French. 1905. s-m. adv. bk.rev. abstr. **Document type:** *Bulletin, Academic/Scholarly.*
Published by: Syndicat National des Lycees et Colleges, 4 rue de Trevise, Paris, 75009, France. TEL 33-1-45230514, FAX 33-1-42462660. Ed., R&P Francois Xavier Chardon. Adv. contact Annette Taffin. Circ: 20,000.

378 ZAF ISSN 0033-6785
R A U - RAPPORT. Text in Afrikaans. 1968. 2/yr. free. illus. **Document type:** *Consumer.*
Published by: Rand Afrikaans University, PO Box 524, Auckland Park, Johannesburg 2006, South Africa. FAX 27-11-4892632. Circ: 5,000.

R C N INSTITUTE. REPORT. see *MEDICAL SCIENCES—Nurses And Nursing*

378.6 ZAF
RANDSE AFRIKAANSE UNIVERSITEIT. JAARBOEK. Text in English. 1968. a. free.
Media: Duplicated (not offset).
Published by: Rand Afrikaans University, PO Box 524, Auckland Park, Johannesburg 2006, South Africa. FAX 27-11-4892790. Circ: (controlled).

378.6 ZAF
RANDSE AFRIKAANSE UNIVERSITEIT. OP EN OM DIE KAMPUS✶. Text in English. 1968. a. free. adv.
Media: Duplicated (not offset).
Published by: Rand Afrikaans University, PO Box 524, Auckland Park, Johannesburg 2006, South Africa. Circ: (controlled).

RAPID READERS SERIES. see *BUSINESS AND ECONOMICS*

378.007 FRA ISSN 0988-1824
RECHERCHE ET FORMATION. Text in French. 3/yr. **Document type:** *Journal, Academic/Scholarly.*
Published by: Institut National de Recherche Pedagogique, Place du Pentacle, BP 17, Saint-Fons, 69195 Cedex, France. TEL 33-4-72898300, FAX 33-4-72898329, publica@inrp.fr, http://www.inrp.fr. Ed. Catherine Tauveron. Circ: 800.

378 USA ISSN 0893-889X
AS30
RECORDER (SEARCY). Text in English. 1958. a. free. **Document type:** *Proceedings, Academic/Scholarly.*
Published by: Alpha Chi National Honor Society, Harding University, 900 E. Center, PO Box 12249, Searcy, AR 72149-0001. TEL 501-279-4443, 800-477-4225, FAX 501-279-4589, alphachi@harding.edu, http://www.harding.edu/alphachi/recorder.htm. Ed. Dennis M Organ. Circ: 7,500 (controlled).

378.16 USA ISSN 0891-012X
RECRUITMENT AND RETENTION IN HIGHER EDUCATION. Text in English. 1987. m. USD 237 domestic; USD 241 in Canada; USD 247 elsewhere (effective 2005). index. back issues avail. **Document type:** *Newsletter, Trade.* **Description:** Focuses on student enrollment in colleges and universities.
Incorporates (in 1999): Re-Quest
Related titles: Online - full content ed.: USD 237 (effective 2005); Online - full text ed.: (from EBSCO Publishing, H.W. Wilson, O C L C Online Computer Library Center, Inc.).
Indexed: ABIn, EduInd.
—CCC.
Published by: Magna Publications, Inc., 2718 Dryden Dr, Madison, WI 53704. TEL 608-246-3590, FAX 608-246-3597, editor@magnapubs.com, http://www.magnapubs.com/pub/magnapubs_rr. Ed. Terese Kattner. Pub. David Burns. Circ: 2,000.

378.1982 USA ISSN 0274-8657
LA RED - THE NET; the Hispanic journal of education commentary and reviews. Text in English. 1983. q. USD 60 (effective 2005). adv. bk.rev. **Document type:** *Journal, Academic/Scholarly.* **Description:** Focuses on issues, problems and discussion of current themes in education of Hispanics, with emphasis on higher education. Includes commentaries and reviews of current fiction and nonfiction humanities and social science U.S. Latino titles.
Indexed: ChPerl.
Published by: Floricanto Press, 650 Castro St, Ste 120-331, Mountain View, CA 94041. TEL 415-552-1879, FAX 702-995-1410, info@floricantopress.com, http://floricantopress.com/la.htm. Ed. Roberto Cabello Argandona. Pub. Roberto Cabell Argandona. R&P, Adv. contact Bob Hoffman.

378 MEX ISSN 0188-168X
REENCUENTRO; analisis de problemas universitarios. Variant title: Serie Cuadernos de Reencuentro. Text in Spanish. 1989. s-a. back issues avail.
Related titles: Online - full text ed.
Published by: (Programa de Superacion Academica), Universidad Autonoma Metropolitana - Xochimilco, CALZ DEL HUESO 1100, Col Villa Quietud, Mexico City, DF 04960, Mexico. TEL 52-5-724-5015, FAX 52-5-6716702, 1fbj2235@cueyatl.uam.mx, http://cueyatl.uam.mx/cuaree/index.html.

378 AUS
REPORT OF THE (YEAR) RANDOM SAMPLING PROJECT. Text in English. 1996. a.
Published by: Queensland Board of Senior Secondary School Studies, P.O. Box 307, Spring Hill, QLD 4101, Australia. TEL 61-7-3864-0299, FAX 61-7-3221-2553, office@qbssss.edu.au.

378.007 AUS ISSN 0156-8884
➤ **RESEARCH AND DEVELOPMENT IN HIGHER EDUCATION SERIES.** Text in English. 1979. a. price varies. back issues avail. **Document type:** *Proceedings, Academic/Scholarly.* **Description:** Publishes selected papers from the annual conference of HERDSA.
Formerly (until 1975): Higher Education Research and Development Society of Australasia. Proceedings of the Conference (0155-6223)
Related titles: CD-ROM ed.
—BLDSC (7714.740000).
Published by: Higher Education Research and Development Society of Australasia, PO Box 516, Jamison, ACT 2614, Australia. TEL 61-262534242, FAX 61-262534246. Circ: 400.

➤ **RESEARCH AND STUDIES.** see *EDUCATION—Abstracting, Bibliographies, Statistics*

378 USA
RESEARCH IN DEVELOPMENTAL EDUCATION. Text in English. 1983. 4/yr. USD 12 (effective 2003). reprint service avail. from PQC. **Document type:** *Newsletter, Academic/Scholarly.* **Description:** Summaries and reports of research that influence the field of developmental education.
Former titles: Review of Research in Developmental Education; Research in Developmental Education
Published by: Appalachian State University, National Center for Developmental Education, Reich College of Education, Boone, NC 28608. TEL 828-262-2876, FAX 828-262-2128. Ed. Dr. Patrick Saxon. R&P Barbara Calderwood TEL 828-262-6101.

378.007 NLD ISSN 0361-0365
LB2331.63 CODEN: RHEDAT
➤ **RESEARCH IN HIGHER EDUCATION.** Text in English. 1973. 8/yr. EUR 768, USD 785, GBP 495 combined subscription to institutions print & online eds. (effective 2005). adv. bibl.; charts; illus.; stat. index. reprint service avail. from PQC,PSC. **Document type:** *Journal, Academic/Scholarly.* **Description:** Features original theoretical and in-depth empirical research about the functioning of post-secondary educational institutions.
Related titles: Microform ed.: (from PQC); Online - full text ed.: ISSN 1573-188X. USD 785 (effective 2005) (from EBSCO Publishing, Gale Group, IngentaConnect, Kluwer Online, O C L C Online Computer Library Center, Inc., Springer LINK, Swets Information Services).
Indexed: ABIn, ASCA, AgeL, BibLing, CIJE, CIS, CPE, ChPerl, CurCont, DIP, EAA, ERA, ETA, EduInd, HEA, IBR, IBZ, MEA, PsycholAb, RHEA, SEA, SENA, SOMA, SOPODA, SSCI, SWA, TEA.
—BLDSC (7741.245000), IDS, IE, Infotrieve, ingenta. **CCC.**
Published by: Springer-Verlag Dordrecht (Subsidiary of: Springer Science+Business Media), Van Godewijckstraat 30, Dordrecht, 3311 GX, Netherlands. TEL 31-78-6576050, FAX 31-78-6576474, http://springerlink.metapress.com/openurl.asp?genre=journal&issn=0361-0365, http://www.springeronline.com. Ed. John C Smart. **Co-sponsor:** Association for Institutional Research.

378 GBR ISSN 1359-6748
LC1039
➤ **RESEARCH IN POST-COMPULSORY EDUCATION.** Text in English. 1996. 3/yr. GBP 256, USD 407 combined subscription to institutions print & online eds. (effective 2006). bk.rev. abstr. back issues avail.; reprint service avail. from PSC. **Document type:** *Journal, Academic/Scholarly.* **Description:** Covers all aspects of the organization and structure of post-compulsory education, policy initiatives, funding, assessment and evaluation, and quality management.
Related titles: Online - full text ed.: ISSN 1747-5112. GBP 243, USD 387 to institutions (effective 2006) (from EBSCO Publishing, Swets Information Services).
Indexed: BrEdI, CPE, DIP, EAA, ERA, ETA, IBR, IBZ, MEA, RHEA, SEA, SENA, SOMA, SociolAb, TEA.
—BLDSC (7755.077650), IE, ingenta.
Published by: Routledge (Subsidiary of: Taylor & Francis Group), 4 Park Sq, Milton Park, Abingdon, Oxon OX14 4RN, United Kingdom. TEL 44-1235-828600, FAX 44-1235-829000, info@routledge.co.uk, http://www.tandf.co.uk/journals/titles/13596748.asp, http://www.routledge.co.uk. Ed. Geoffrey Elliott.

➤ **RESEARCH IN THE HISTORY OF EDUCATION: A LIST OF THESES FOR HIGHER DEGREES IN THE UNIVERSITIES OF ENGLAND AND WALES.** see *EDUCATION—Abstracting, Bibliographies, Statistics*

➤ **RESEARCH INTO HIGHER EDUCATION ABSTRACTS.** see *EDUCATION—Abstracting, Bibliographies, Statistics*

378.07 USA
RESEARCH - PENN STATE. Text in English. 1980. 3/yr. free. bk.rev. **Document type:** *Magazine, Academic/Scholarly.*
Indexed: IFP.
Published by: Pennsylvania State University, Vice President for Research, 320 Kern Bldg, University Park, PA 16802. TEL 814-865-3477, FAX 814-863-5368, editor@research.psu.edu, dap1@psu.edu, http://www.rps.psu.edu/. Ed. David Pacchioli. Circ: 25,000 (controlled).

378 GBR
REVIEW. Text in English. 1948. s-a. adv. **Document type:** *Academic/Scholarly.*
Formerly (until 1997): University of Leeds Review (0041-9737)
Indexed: MLA, MLA-IB.
—BLDSC (9111.810000), ingenta.
Published by: University of Leeds, E C Stoner Bldg, Rm 12.68, Leeds, W Yorks LS2 9JT, United Kingdom. TEL 44-113-233-6109, FAX 44-113-233-4029, review@leeds.ac.uk, http://www.leeds.ac.uk/. Ed., R&P Jayne Glennon. Adv. contact Mike King.

THE REVIEW (NORFOLK); the quarterly magazine of Eastern Virginia Medical School. see *MEDICAL SCIENCES*

E

378 USA ISSN 0162-5748
LA226
➤ **THE REVIEW OF HIGHER EDUCATION.** Text in English. 1977. q. USD 60 to individuals; USD 145 to institutions; USD 203 combined subscription to institutions print & online eds.; USD 18 per issue to individuals; USD 42 per issue to institutions (effective 2006). adv. bk.rev. bibl.; charts; illus. 104 p./no.; back issues avail.; reprint service avail. from PQC,PSC. **Document type:** *Journal, Academic/Scholarly.* **Description:** Articles, essays, and reviews discuss issues affecting higher education. Official journal of ASHE.
Formerly (until 1978): Higher Education Review (0148-9585)
Related titles: Microform ed.: (from PQC); Online - full text ed.: ISSN 1090-7009. USD 145 to institutions (effective 2006) (from Chadwyck-Healey Inc., EBSCO Publishing, O C L C Online Computer Library Center, Inc., Project MUSE, ProQuest Information & Learning, Swets Information Services).
Indexed: ASCA, CIJE, CPE, CurCont, DIP, EAA, ERA, ETA, FamI, HEA, IBR, IBZ, MEA, PsycInfo, PsycholAb, RASB, RHEA, SEA, SENA, SOMA, SSCI, SWA, TEA.
—BLDSC (7790.769200), IDS, IE, Infotrieve, ingenta. **CCC.**
Published by: (Association for the Study of Higher Education), The Johns Hopkins University Press, Journals Publishing Division, 2715 N Charles St, Baltimore, MD 21218-4363. TEL 410-516-6984, 410-516-6987, 800-548-1784, FAX 410-516-6968, jlorder@jhupress.jhu.edu, http://www.press.jhu.edu/journals/review_of_higher_education/index.html, http://muse.jhu.edu. Ed. Amaury Nora. Adv. contact Monica Queen TEL 410-516-6984. page USD 270; trim 4.75 x 7.5. Circ: 2,184 (paid). **Subscr. to:** PO Box 19966, Baltimore, MD 21211. jlorder@jhunix.hcf.jhu.edu.

378.12 ESP ISSN 1130-2496
LA910
REVISTA COMPLUTENSE DE EDUCACION. Text in Spanish. 1990. s-a. EUR 33 in the European Union; EUR 40 elsewhere (effective 2004). back issues avail. **Document type:** *Academic/Scholarly.* **Description:** Publishes original articles on education and serves as a communication channel for teachers and students at the university.
—CINDOC.
Published by: (Universidad Complutense de Madrid, Facultad de Educacion), Universidad Complutense de Madrid, Servicio de Publicaciones, C Isaac Peral s/n, Ciudad Universitaria, Madrid, 28040, Spain. TEL 34-91-3946934, FAX 34-91-3946978, felixdid@edu.ucm.es, servicio@publicaciones.ucm.es, http://www.ucm.es/publicaciones. Ed. Julio Ruiz Berrio.

REVISTA CUBANA DE EDUCACION MEDICA SUPERIOR. see *MEDICAL SCIENCES*

378.7291 CUB ISSN 0257-4314
LA488
REVISTA CUBANA DE EDUCACION SUPERIOR. Text in Spanish. 1981. q. USD 14 in North America; USD 16 in Europe; USD 17 elsewhere. abstr.; illus.; stat.
Related titles: Online - full text ed.: (from EBSCO Publishing).
Indexed: RASB.
Published by: (Universidad de Camaguey, Carretera de Circunvalacion), Ediciones Cubanas, Obispo No. 527, Apdo. 605, Havana, Cuba. Circ: 5,000.

378 MEX ISSN 0185-2760
REVISTA DE LA EDUCACION SUPERIOR. Text in Spanish. 1972. q. MXP 300 domestic; USD 70 foreign (effective 2002). bk.rev. back issues avail.
Related titles: Online - full text ed.
Published by: Asociacion Nacional de Universidades e Institutos de Ensenanza Superior, Tenayuca No. 200, Col. Santa Cruz Atoyac, Mexico, DF, 03310, Mexico. TEL 52-5-4204900, FAX 52-5-6044263, editor@anuies.mx, http://www.anuies.mx/. Ed. Alfonso Rangel Guerra. Circ: 5,000.

378 MEX ISSN 1607-4041
L45
➤ **REVISTA ELECTRONICA DE INVESTIGACION EDUCATIVA/ELECTRONIC JOURNAL OF EDUCATIONAL RESEARCH.** Text in English, Spanish. 1999. s-a. free (effective 2005). back issues avail. **Document type:** *Journal, Academic/Scholarly.* **Description:** Publishes articles about educational practice, from different disciplines and from diverse theoretical and methodological perspectives.
Media: Online - full text.
Published by: Universidad Autonoma de Baja California, Instituto de Investigacion y Desarrollo Educativo, Km. 103 Carr. Tijuana - Ensenada, Ensenada, Baja California, Mexico. TEL 52-646-1744905, FAX 52-646-1745600, redie@uabc.mx, http://redie.ens.uabc.mx/.

378 ESP ISSN 0213-8646
LB1725.S7
➤ **REVISTA INTERUNIVERSITARIA DE FORMACION DEL PROFESORADO/INTER-UNIVERSITY JOURNAL OF TEACHER EDUCATION.** Text in Spanish. 1922. q. EUR 66.75 domestic; EUR 90 foreign (effective 2002). bk.rev. back issues avail. **Document type:** *Journal, Academic/Scholarly.*
Former titles (until 1987): Revista de Escuelas Normales (0213-8638); (until 1923): Boletin de Escuelas Normales (1575-9741)
Related titles: Online - full text ed.: Revista Electronica Universitaria de Formacion del Profesorado. ISSN 1575-0965. 1998.
Indexed: RILM.
—CINDOC.
Published by: Asociacion Universitaria de Formacion del Profesorado, Corona de Aragon 22, Zaragoza, 50009, Spain. emipal@posta.unizar.es, http://www.aufop.org.

378 CHL
REVISTA PERSPECTIVA EDUCACIONAL. Text in Spanish. 1980. s-a. USD 90 per issue (effective 2001). **Document type:** *Academic/Scholarly.*
Published by: (Universidad Catolica de Valparaiso, Instituto de Educacion), Ediciones Universitarias de Valparaiso, Casilla 1415, Valparaiso, Chile. TEL 56-32-273086, FAX 56-32-273429, euvsa@ucv.cl, http://www.ucv.cl/web/euv. Ed. Alvaro F Valenzuela. Circ: 250.

378 CHL ISSN 0250-3670
REVISTA UNIVERSITARIA. Text in Spanish. 1915. 4/yr. CLP 9,500, USD 35 to individuals; CLP 7,500, USD 28 to students. adv. bk.rev. illus. **Document type:** *Academic/Scholarly.* **Description:** Scholarly articles on literature, technology, sciences, art and history.
Indexed: ABM, AmH&L, BiolAb, HistAb, IBR.
Published by: Pontificia Universidad Catolica de Chile, Alameda 340, Santiago de Chile, Chile. TEL 56-2-6862415, FAX 56-2-2223116, soporte@puc.cl, http://www.puc.cl. Ed., R&P Cecilia Garcia Huidobro. Circ: 4,000.

378.007 ITA ISSN 0393-3849
AS221
RIVISTA DI SCIENZE DELL'EDUCAZIONE. Text in Italian; Summaries in English, French, Italian, Polish, Spanish. 1963. 3/yr. EUR 30 in Europe; EUR 35 elsewhere (effective 2003). bk.rev. bibl. index. 200 p./no.; back issues avail. **Document type:** *Magazine, Academic/Scholarly.* **Description:** Presents studies and research in the science of education with specific focus on female educational problems during the childhood and adolescent years.
Formerly (until 1972): Rivista di Pedagogia e Scienze Religiose (0393-5655)
Indexed: DIP, IBR, IBZ.
Published by: Pontificia Facolta di Scienze dell'Educazione "Auxilium", Via Cremolino 141, Rome, 00166, Italy. TEL 39-6-6157201, FAX 39-6-61564640, auxilium@pcn.net, http://www.auxilium.urbe.it, http://auxilium.urbe.it. Ed., R&P Enrica Rosanna. Circ: 1,100.

378 AUS
ROAD TO CERTIFICATION. Text in English. a.
Published by: Queensland Board of Senior Secondary School Studies, P.O. Box 307, Spring Hill, QLD 4101, Australia. TEL 61-7-3864-0299, FAX 61-7-3221-2553, office@qbssss.edu.au.

378 JPN ISSN 0287-6000
RYUKOKU DAIGAKU RONSHU/RYUKOKU UNIVERSITY. JOURNAL. Text in Japanese. 1899. s-a. **Document type:** *Journal, Academic/Scholarly.*
Former titles (until 1944): Ryukoku Gakuho (0287-5993); (until 1932): Ryukoku DaigakuRronso (0287-5985); (until 1922): Bukkyo Daigaku Ronso (0287-5977); (until 1921): Rokujo Gakuho (0287-5969)
Indexed: RILM.
Published by: Ryukoku Gakkai/Ryukoku University, 67 Tsukamoto-cho,Fukakusa Fushimi-ku, Kyoto, 612-8577, Japan. http://www.ryukoku.ac.jp/.

378.107 USA
S C U P E-MAIL NEWS. Text in English. 2001. bi-m. back issues avail. **Document type:** *Newsletter.* **Description:** Provides timely and frequent exchange of information for those interested in planning for higher education.
Media: Online - full text. **Related titles:** E-mail ed.
Published by: Society for College and University Planning, 311 Maynard St, Ann Arbor, MI 48104-2211. TEL 734-998-7832, FAX 734-998-6532, scup@scup.org, http://www.scup.org/. Ed. Terry Calhoun.

378.1012 ITA ISSN 0391-8599
S I P E. (Service International de Presse Etudiante) Text in Italian. 1969. m. looseleaf. free. adv. bk.rev. index. back issues avail. **Document type:** *Bulletin, Trade.* **Description:** Deals with the development of cooperation policies in higher education in Italy and other countries. Gives information on the activities of the institute.
Published by: Istituto per la Cooperazione Universitaria/Institute for University Cooperation, Viale Gioacchino Rossini, 26, Rome, RM 00198, Italy. TEL 39-06-85300722, FAX 39-06-8554646. Ed. Pier Giovanni Palla. Circ: 2,200.

378 ITA ISSN 0391-8572
S I P E-FAMIGLIA. (Service International de Presse Etudiante) Text in Italian. 1977. bi-m.
Published by: (Istituto per la Cooperazione Universitaria/Institute for University Cooperation), Casa Editrice Fratelli Palombi, Via dei Gracchi 181-185, Rome, 00192, Italy.

378 FRA
S N E S U P BULLETIN. Text in French. 1947. bi-w. adv. bk.rev.
Published by: Syndicat National de l'Enseignement Superieur, 78 rue du Faubourg Saint Denis, Paris, 75010, France. Ed. Roger Bourderon. Circ: (controlled).

378 USA
LA230.5.S6
S R E B FACT BOOK ON HIGHER EDUCATION. Text in English. 1956. biennial. USD 25 per issue. **Document type:** *Corporate.*
Formerly (until 1986): Fact Book on Higher Education in the South (0191-1643)
Indexed: SRI.
Published by: Southern Regional Education Board, 592 Tenth St, N W, Atlanta, GA 30318-5790. TEL 404-875-9211. Ed., R&P Amy Schneider. Circ: 6,000.

378.007 GBR
S R H E NEWS. Text in English. 1970. 3/yr. free to members (effective 2006). **Document type:** *Newsletter.* **Description:** Contains SRHE news, details of upcoming events and reports on recent activities.
Formerly: S R H E Bulletin (0266-6081)
Related titles: Online - full text ed.
Published by: Society for Research into Higher Education, 76 Portland Pl, London, W1B 1NT, United Kingdom. TEL 44-20-76372766, FAX 44-20-76372781, srheoffice@srhe.ac.uk, http://www.srhe.ac.uk/. Circ: 1,500.

378 EGY ISSN 0036-2654
SAHIFAT AL-TARBIYA✶. Text in Arabic; Summaries in English. 1948. q. bk.rev.
Published by: Association of the Graduates of the Institutes and Faculties of Education, 13 Tahrir Sq., Cairo, Egypt. Ed. Aziz Mohammed Habib. Circ: 3,000.

378 USA
SAINT JOHN'S. Text in English. 1961. q. free to alumni. bk.rev. **Document type:** *Newsletter.* **Description:** Covers college activities and developments of interest to alumni.
Published by: St. John's University, Dir. of Public Affairs, PO Box 2000, Collegeville, MN 56321. bduffy@csbsju.edu, http://www.csbsju.edu/sot. Ed. Gil Hoyes. Circ: 22,000.

378 USA
ST. JOHN'S REPORTER. Text in English. 1974. q. free. bk.rev. illus.
Published by: St. John's College, Office of Public Relations, PO Box 2800, Annapolis, MD 21404. TEL 410-626-2539, FAX 410-295-6937. Ed. Elizabeth Skewes. R&P Barbara Goyette. Circ: 20,000.

378 USA ISSN 0277-4720
AP2
➤ **ST. JOHN'S REVIEW.** Text in English. 1969. s-a. USD 10 (effective 2005). bk.rev. charts; illus. **Document type:** *Journal, Academic/Scholarly.*
Formerly (until Aug. 1980): College (0010-0862)
Related titles: Microform ed.: (from PQC).
Published by: St. John's College, Box 2800, Annapolis, MD 21404. TEL 410-263-2371, FAX 410-263-4828, review@sjca.edu, http://www.stjohnscollege.edu/asp/main.aspx?page=2530&parent=2401, http://www.sjca.edu/. Ed., Pub. Pamela Kraus. R&P P Kraus TEL 410-626-2521. Circ: 9,000.

378 USA ISSN 0745-3582
ST. LAWRENCE. Text in English. 1943. 3/yr. bk.rev. **Document type:** *Academic/Scholarly.* **Description:** Covers topics in education.
Published by: St. Lawrence University, 109 Vilas Hall, Canton, NY 13617. TEL 315-229-5560, FAX 315-229-7422, nburdick@stlaw.edu, nburdick@stlawu.edu. Ed. Neal Burdick. Pub. Lisa Cania. Circ: 27,000 (controlled).

378 PHL ISSN 0048-8992
SAINT LOUIS CHRONICLE. Text in English. 1969. bi-m. free. bk.rev. charts; illus. **Description:** News, opinion and feature articles gathered from the elementary, high school, college and teaching hospital departments of Saint Louis University.
Published by: Saint Louis University, PO Box 71, Baguio City, Benguet 2600, Philippines. TEL 63-74-442-3043, FAX 63-74-442-2842. Ed. Editha Somera Salazar. Circ: 6,000.

SALARY SURVEY (YEARS) (ST. LOUIS). see *BUSINESS AND ECONOMICS—Labor And Industrial Relations*

378 RUS
SAMARSKII UNIVERSITET. Text in Russian. 1978. 10/yr. free (effective 2004). **Document type:** *Newspaper.*
Related titles: Online - full text ed.
Published by: (Samarskii Gosudarstvennyi Universitet), Izdatel'stvo Samarskii Universitet/Publishing House of Samara State University, ul Akademika Pavlova 1, k 209, Samara, 443011, Russian Federation. http://www.ssu.samara.ru/~press. Ed. Nina M Okorkova. Circ: 4,000.

378 DEU ISSN 0344-0591
SAMMLUNG GROOS; Beitraege zur Hoergeschaedigten-Paedagogik. Text in German. 1977. irreg. price varies. adv. back issues avail. **Document type:** *Monographic series, Academic/Scholarly.*

E

Published by: Median-Verlag von Killisch-Horn GmbH, Hauptstr 64, Heidelberg, 69117, Germany. TEL 49-6221-90509-0, FAX 49-6221-9050920, median-verlag@t-online.de, http://www.median-verlag.de. Adv. contact Karin Ball. Circ: 500.

378.04 USA ISSN 1058-7608
SANTA FE INSTITUTE. BULLETIN. Text in English. s-a. **Document type:** *Bulletin, Academic/Scholarly.*
Related titles: Online - full content ed.
—BLDSC (2702.393000).
Published by: Santa Fe Institute, 1399 Hyde Park Road, Santa Fe, NM 87501. TEL 505-984-8800, FAX 505-982-0565, editor@alife.santafe.edu, http://www.santafe.edu/sfi/publications/Bulletins/.

378.34 USA ISSN 1058-5699
LB2338
SCHOLARSHIPS, FELLOWSHIPS AND LOANS. Text in English. a., latest 2004. USD 230 (effective 2004). **Description:** Lists over 2500 financial opportunities for U.S and Canadian students and researchers.
Published by: Gale Group (Subsidiary of: Thomson Corporation), 27500 Drake Rd, Farmington Hills, MI 48331-3535. TEL 248-699-8061, 800-877-4253, FAX 248-699-4253, galeord@gale.com, http://www.gale.com. Ed. Valerie Webster.

378 IND
SCHOLARSHIPS FOR STUDY ABROAD AND AT HOME (YEAR). Text in English. 1927. irreg., latest 1997. USD 12 (effective 2003). **Document type:** *Newsletter.*
Published by: Association of Indian Universities, A.I.U. House, 16 Kotla Marg, New Delhi, 110 002, India. TEL 91-11-323-0059, FAX 91-11-323-6105, aiu@del12.vsnl.net.in, http://www.aiuweb.org.

378.34 USA ISSN 1089-9898
LB2337.4
SCHOLARSHIPS, GRANTS, & PRIZES. Text in English. 1996. a. USD 24.95. **Document type:** *Directory.* **Description:** Profiles of undergraduate scholarships from over 2,000 private aid sources.
Related titles: CD-ROM ed.
Published by: Thomson Peterson's (Subsidiary of: Thomson Corporation), Princeton Pike Corporate Center, 2000 Lenox Dr, 3rd Fl, Lawrenceville, NJ 08648. TEL 609-243-9111, FAX 609-243-9150, http://www.petersons.com. Ed. Barbara Lawrence.

SCHOOL BUSINESS MAGAZINE. see *EDUCATION—School Organization And Administration*

SCHOOL LAW BULLETIN (CHAPEL HILL). see *LAW*

378 GBR
SCHOOL LEAVER*. Text in English. 1968. 8/yr. free. bibl.; illus.
Formerly: Which Course?
Published by: Dominion Press Ltd., Dominion House, Signal House, Lyon Rd, Harrow, Mddx HA1 2QE, United Kingdom.

378 USA ISSN 0898-0748
SCIENCE AND ENGINEERING DOCTORATES. Text in English. 1981. a.
—Linda Hall.
Published by: National Science Foundation, 1800 G St N W, Washington, DC 20550. TEL 202-634-4622.

371.1 IRL
SCIENCE PLUS. Text in English. 7/w. adv. **Document type:** *Magazine, Academic/Scholarly.*
Published by: C.J. Fallon Educational Publishers, Lucan Rd., Palmerstown, PO Box 1054, Dublin, 20, Ireland. TEL 353-1-6166490, FAX 353-1-6166499. adv.: B&W page EUR 950, color page EUR 1,020. Circ: 8,000 (controlled).

378 USA ISSN 0275-8075
SCIENCE, TECHNOLOGY AND SOCIETY; curriculum newsletter. Text in English. 1977. q. USD 8 (effective 2001). bk.rev. bibl. cum.index: 1977-1994. back issues avail. **Document type:** *Newsletter, Academic/Scholarly.* **Description:** Presents curriculum ideas, book reviews, and discussions of topics relating to the relationships between science, technology and society.
Published by: Lehigh University, S T S Program, 327 Maginnes Hall, 9 W Packer Ave, Bethlehem, PA 18015-3082. TEL 610-758-3350, FAX 610-758-6554, shc0@lehigh.edu. Ed. Stephen H Cutliffe. Circ: 400 (paid). **Subscr. to:** Office of the Bursar, Lehigh University, 27 Memorial Dr W, Bethlehem, PA 18015.

378 IND
SELECTIONS FROM UNIVERSITY NEWS. Text in English. 1927. a. price varies. **Document type:** *Monographic series, Academic/Scholarly.*
Published by: Association of Indian Universities, A.I.U. House, 16 Kotla Marg, New Delhi, 110 002, India. TEL 91-11-323-0059, FAX 91-11-323-6105, aiu@del12.vsnl.net.in, http://www.aiuweb.org.

378 IRN
SHAHID CHAMRAN UNIVERSITY EDUCATIONAL JOURNAL. Text in English, Persian, Modern. 1972. s-a. IRR 100.
Formerly (until 1983): Jundi Shapur University Educational Journal
Published by: Shahid Chamran University, Faculty of Education, Ahwaz, Iran. Ed. K C Chehrezad. Circ: 2,000.

378 CHN ISSN 1008-2662
SHANGQIU SHIFAN XUEYUAN XUEBAO/SHANGQIU TEACHERS COLLEGE. Text in Chinese; Contents page in English. 1985. bi-m. **Document type:** *Academic/Scholarly.*
Related titles: Online - full text ed.: (from East View Information Services).
—BLDSC (4874.822500), IE, ingenta.
Published by: Shangqiu Shifan Xueyuan/Shangqiu Teachers College, 298 Wenhua Zhong Lu, Shangqiu, Henan-sheng 476000, China. TEL 86-370-2593016. Ed. Jianli Gao. **Dist. by:** China International Book Trading Corp, 35 Chegongzhuang Xilu, Haidian District, PO Box 399, Beijing 100044, China. TEL 86-10-68412045, FAX 86-10-68412023, cibtc@mail.cibtc.com.cn, http://www.cibtc.com.cn.

SHEFFIELD HALLAM UNIVERSITY. ENGINEERING EDUCATION RESEARCH GROUP. PROCEEDINGS. see *ENGINEERING*

378.42821 GBR
SHEFFIELD UNIVERSITY ANNUAL REPORT. Text in English. 1906. a. free.
Published by: Sheffield University Biomedical Information Service (SUBIS), The University, Sheffield, S Yorks S10 2TN, United Kingdom. Circ: 10,000.

378.42821 GBR ISSN 0307-6202
SHEFFIELD UNIVERSITY CALENDAR. Text in English. 1905. a. GBP 8.
—BLDSC (3002.000000).
Published by: Sheffield University Biomedical Information Service (SUBIS), The University, Sheffield, S Yorks S10 2TN, United Kingdom. Circ: 1,100.

378 GBR
SHEFFIELD UNIVERSITY POSTGRADUATE PROSPECTUS. Text in English. a. free.
Published by: Sheffield University Biomedical Information Service (SUBIS), The University, Sheffield, S Yorks S10 2TN, United Kingdom. Circ: 40,000.

378.154 GBR
SHEFFIELD UNIVERSITY UNDERGRADUATE PROSPECTUS. Text in English. a. free.
Formerly: Sheffield University General Prospectus
Published by: Sheffield University Biomedical Information Service (SUBIS), The University, Sheffield, S Yorks S10 2TN, United Kingdom. Circ: 85,000.

378 USA ISSN 0892-6603
THE SHORTHORN. Text in English. 1919. 4/w. (Tue.-Fri.; s-w.: Tue. & Thu. summer). USD 40. adv. bk.rev. back issues avail. **Document type:** *Newspaper.*
Related titles: Online - full text ed.: (from LexisNexis).
Published by: University of Texas at Arlington, Student Publications, c/o Dorothy Estes, S W University Center, 301 W Second St, Box 19308, Arlington, TX 76019-0038. TEL 817-272-3188, FAX 817-272-5009, http://www.theshorthorn.com. Circ: 15,000.

SI DE KA MAGAZINE. see *LAW*

378 ARG ISSN 0326-3932
AS78.A1
SIGNOS UNIVERSITARIOS. Text in Spanish. 1979. s-a. ARS 25 domestic; USD 40 foreign (effective 2000). adv. bk.rev. bibl.; illus. **Document type:** *Monographic series.* **Description:** Each issue is devoted to a scientific discipline taught at the university. Includes research papers and reviews.
Indexed: SociolAb.
Published by: Universidad del Salvador, Vicerrectorado de Investigacion y Desarrollo, Pena Rodriguez, 770 Piso 2, Buenos Aires, 1020, Argentina. TEL 54-114-8131381, FAX 54-114-8130631, tallered-usal@salvador.edu.ar, http://www.salvador.edu.ar/sv14.htm. Ed. Haydee I Nieto. Adv. contact Fernando Lucero Schmidt.

SINOPSIS. see *EDUCATION—Abstracting, Bibliographies, Statistics*

378 ITA
SISTEMA UNIVERSITA. Text in Italian. 1996. m. free. adv. Website rev. abstr.; stat. 16 p./no.; **Document type:** *Newsletter, Consumer.*
Related titles: E-mail ed.; Online - full text ed.
Published by: Universita degli Studi di Milano, Ufficio Stampa E Publicazioni, Via Festa Del Perdono, 7, Milan, MI 20122, Italy. TEL 39-02-58352249, FAX 39-02-58352627. Circ: 10,000.

378 GBR
THE SIXTHFORMER'S GUIDE TO VISITING UNIVERSITIES AND COLLEGES (YEAR). Text in English. a. GBP 6.95 per issue (effective 2003). **Document type:** *Directory.* **Description:** Provides a guide to visiting universities and colleges in the U.K.; lists all open days, together with contact names and addresses.
Published by: (Independent Schools Careers Organisation), I S C O Publications, 12a Princess Way, Camberley, Surrey GU15 3SP, United Kingdom. TEL 44-1276-21188, FAX 44-1276-691833, info@isco.org.uk, http://www.isco.org.uk/. Ed., R&P Philip Gray TEL 44-1276-21188.

378 SWE ISSN 0502-7454
LF4583 CODEN: AUCHE7
SKRIFTER ROERANDE UPPSALA UNIVERSITET. C, ORGANISATION OCH HISTORIA. Text in Swedish. 1961. irreg., latest vol.72, 2002. price varies. **Document type:** *Monographic series, Academic/Scholarly.*
Related titles: ◆ Series of: Acta Universitatis Upsaliensis. ISSN 0346-5462.
Indexed: MathR.
—BLDSC (0586.530000).
Published by: (Uppsala Universitet), Uppsala Universitet, Acta Universitatis Upsaliensis/University Publications from Uppsala, PO Box 256, Uppsala, 75105, Sweden. TEL 46-18-4713922, http://www.ub.uu.se/upu/auu. Ed. Bengt Landgren. **Dist. by:** Almqvist & Wiksell International.

378 USA ISSN 1047-6229
SMALL COLLEGE CREATIVITY. Text in English. 3/yr. USD 20; USD 30 foreign. **Description:** Publishes articles or short pieces on innovative ideas, projects, curricula or approaches that have been successful at institutions of ten thousand or fewer students.
Published by: Human Technology Interface, Ink Press, 163 Wood Wedge Way, Sanford, NC 27330. TEL 919-499-9216. Ed. Lynn Veach Sadler.

378 AUS
SMITH'S. Text in English. 1960. fortn. AUD 40.
Formerly: Smith's Weekly
Published by: University of New England, Armidale, NSW 2351, Australia. TEL 61-67-732819, FAX 61-67-733482, bdrew@metz.une.edu.au.

SOCIAL WORK EDUCATION REPORTER. see *SOCIAL SERVICES AND WELFARE*

SOCIAL WORK PERSPECTIVES. see *SOCIAL SERVICES AND WELFARE*

378 USA
SOCIETY FOR VALUES IN HIGHER EDUCATION. MONOGRAPH SERIES. Text in English. 1964. irreg. price varies. bk.rev. abstr.; bibl. back issues avail. **Document type:** *Academic/Scholarly.*
Published by: Society for Values in Higher Education, 216 Aconda Ct, University of Tennessee, Knoxville, TN 37996. TEL 503-721-6520, FAX 503-721-6523, svhe@unidial.com. Circ: 1,400 (paid).

378 USA
SOCIETY FOR VALUES IN HIGHER EDUCATION. NEWSLETTER. Key Title: S V H E. Newsletter. Text in English. q. USD 20. **Document type:** *Newsletter.* **Description:** Presents cutting-edge news on topics of collaborative research and alerts readers to conferences in the U.S. and U.K.
Published by: Society for Values in Higher Education, 216 Aconda Ct, University of Tennessee, Knoxville, TN 37996. TEL 503-721-6520, FAX 503-721-6523, svhe@unidial.com, http://www-adm.pdx.edu/user/svhe. R&P Sherry Stock. Circ: 2,000 (paid).

378 ZAF ISSN 1011-3487
➤ **SOUTH AFRICAN JOURNAL OF HIGHER EDUCATION.** Text in English. 1987. s-a. ZAR 150 domestic; USD 100 foreign (effective 2003). adv. bk.rev. index. back issues avail. **Document type:** *Academic/Scholarly.* **Description:** Includes articles of interest to researchers and practitioners in higher education and provides a focal point for the publication of educational research from around the world.
Related titles: Online - full text ed.: (from International Network for the Availability of Scientific Publications, African Journals Online).
Indexed: CIJE, CPE, ERA, ETA, ISAP, MEA, RHEA, SEA, SENA, SOMA, SWA, TEA.
Published by: (South African Association for Research and Development in Higher Education), Unisa Press, Periodicals, PO Box 392, Pretoria, 0003, South Africa. TEL 27-12-429-3081, FAX 27-12-429-3221, unisa-press@unisa.ac.za, higgsp@alpha.unisa.ac.za, http://www.inasp.info/ajl/journals/sajhe/about.html, http://www.unisa.ac.za/press, http://www.saarjhe.ac.za. Ed., R&P, Adv. contact Philip Higgs. B&W page ZAR 1,500. Circ: 1,500.

➤ **SOUTH DAKOTA LAW REVIEW.** see *LAW*

E

378 USA ISSN 0038-3813
CODEN: CSEDFE
SOUTHERN ASSOCIATION OF COLLEGES AND SCHOOLS. PROCEEDINGS. Text in English. 1945. bi-m. (except Dec. & Jan.). USD 10 to non-members. bk.rev. **Document type:** *Newsletter.*
Published by: Southern Association of Colleges and Schools, 1866 Southern Ln, Decatur, GA 30033-4097. TEL 404-679-4500, FAX 404-679-4556, tgreer@sacscoc.org, http://www.sacs.org. Ed., R&P Teresa R Greer. Circ: 18,600.

SPRINGER SERIES ON MEDICAL EDUCATION. see *MEDICAL SCIENCES*

SPRINGER SERIES ON THE TEACHING OF NURSING. see *MEDICAL SCIENCES—Nurses And Nursing*

378 DEU
STADTMAGAZIN HOCHSCHUL-SPECIAL. Text in German. 2/yr. adv. **Document type:** *Magazine, Consumer.*
Published by: M G Medien GmbH, Egerstr. 2-4, Moenchengladbach, 41236, Germany. TEL 49-2166-924092, FAX 49-2166-20327, mgmedien@aol.com, http://www.stadtmagazin.de/hochsch.htm. adv.: B&W page EUR 700, color page EUR 1,300; trim 225 x 300. Circ: 10,000 (controlled).

378 DEU
STADTREVUE HOCHSCHULMAGAZIN. Text in German. 1980. 2/yr. adv. **Document type:** *Magazine, Consumer.*
Published by: StadtRevue Verlag GmbH, Maastrichter Str. 49, Cologne, 50672, Germany. TEL 49-221-951541-0, FAX 49-221-95154111, geschaeftsfuehrung@stadtrevue.de. adv.: B&W page EUR 1,150, color page EUR 2,250. Circ: 36,800 (paid and controlled).

378 IND
STAFF DEVELOPMENT IN INDIAN UNIVERSITIES (YEAR). Text in English. 1927. irreg., latest 1996. USD 30 (effective 1999). **Document type:** *Newsletter.*
Published by: Association of Indian Universities, A.I.U. House, 16 Kotla Marg, New Delhi, 110 002, India. TEL 91-11-323-0059, FAX 91-11-323-6105, aiu@del12.vsnl.net.in, http://www.aiuweb.org.

378 DEU
DER STELLENREPORT - AUSBILDUNGSPLAETZE FUER SCHULABGAENGER. Text in German. 2/yr. free to students. adv. **Document type:** *Magazine, Consumer.*
Published by: Der Stellenreport Verlagsgesellschaft mbH, Echterweg 8, Tegernsee, 83684, Germany. TEL 49-8022-26061, FAX 49-8022-26064, info@stellenreport.de, http://www.stellenreport.de. adv.: B&W page EUR 1,800, color page EUR 3,120; trim 149 x 215. Circ: 15,000 (controlled).

378 DEU
DER STELLENREPORT - FUER HOCHSCHULABSOLVENTEN. Text in German. 2/yr. adv. **Document type:** *Magazine, Consumer.*
Published by: Der Stellenreport Verlagsgesellschaft mbH, Echterweg 8, Tegernsee, 83684, Germany. TEL 49-8022-26061, FAX 49-8022-26064, info@stellenreport.de, http://www.stellenreport.de. adv.: B&W page EUR 2,100, color page EUR 3,420; trim 131 x 185. Circ: 35,000 (controlled).

STERN SPEZIAL CAMPUS UND KARRIERE. see *OCCUPATIONS AND CAREERS*

378 USA
STREET SCENES. Text in English. 1964. q. free. **Document type:** *Newsletter.*
Former titles (until 1989): Bank Street News - Reviews - Reporting; Report from Bank Street; Bank Street Reporting (0045-1509)
Published by: Bank Street College, 610 W 112th St, New York, NY 10025. TEL 212-875-4400, collegepubs@bankstreet.edu, http://www.bankstreet.edu. Circ: 10,000.

378 ZAF ISSN 0258-9044
STUDENT; monthly newspaper-maandelikse studentekoerant. Text in Afrikaans, English. 1970. m. looseleaf. free. adv. bk.rev.; film rev.; play rev. charts; illus.; stat. **Document type:** *Newspaper, Academic/Scholarly.*
Formerly: Trompie (0041-316X)
Published by: Technikon Pretoria, Student Representative Council, Private Bag X680, Pretoria, South Africa. Circ: 1,700.

378.3 USA ISSN 0194-2212
STUDENT AID NEWS; the independent biweekly news service on student financial assistance programs. Text in English. 1974. bi-w. looseleaf. USD 383 (effective 2005). **Document type:** *Newsletter.* **Description:** Covers federal student aid programs and the student aid community. Provides news on federal policies affecting financial aid to post-secondary students, including Pell Grants, Stafford Student Loans and Perkins Loans, College Work-Study, Supplemental Education Opportunity Grants and State Student Incentive Grants.
Related titles: Online - full text ed.: (from bigchalk, Gale Group, ProQuest Information & Learning).
—CCC.

Published by: Aspen Publishers, Inc. (Subsidiary of: Wolters Kluwer N.V.), 111 Eighth Ave., 7th Fl, New York, NY 10011. TEL 212-771-0600, 212-597-0020, FAX 212-771-0885, customer.service@aspenpubl.com, http://www.aspenpublishers.com. Pubs. Jane Coyle Garwood, Marjorie Weiner. Dist. by: Customer Care, 7201 McKinney Circle, Frederick, MD 21704. TEL 800-234-1660, FAX 800-901-9075.

378.3 USA ISSN 1060-2275
LB2338
STUDENT AID NEWSLETTER: FELLOWSHIPS, GRANTS, LOANS, AWARDS AND SCHOLARSHIPS* . Text in English. 1955. q. looseleaf. USD 52.95 in North America; USD 59 elsewhere (effective 1999). bk.rev. bibl. index. back issues avail. **Document type:** *Newsletter.* **Description:** Acts as guidance for counselors, financial aid directors, students and parents. Lists financialaid sources.
Former titles (until 1990): Scholarships, Fellowships and Loan News Service and Counselors Information Services; Scholarships, Fellowships, Loans News Service (0036-6366)
Published by: Scovill, Paterson Inc., PO Box 1725, Jacksonville, OR 97530-1725. TEL 212-673-6090, FAX 212-673-6603. Ed. Archer Irby.

378.3 USA
STUDENT GUIDE - FINANCIAL AID (YEAR). Text in English. a. free. **Document type:** *Government.* **Description:** Offers college and university students in the US comprehensive information on student financial aid from the U.S. Department of Education, covering the major programs, such as Pell Grants, Stafford Loans, and Plus Loans.
Related titles: Online - full text ed.
Published by: U.S. Department of Education, Office of Federal Student Aid, PO Box 84, Washington, DC 20044-0084. TEL 800-433-3213, http://www.ed.gov/prog_info/SFA/StudentGuide.

378.3 GBR
STUDENT PAGES IRELAND. Text in English. a. adv. **Document type:** *Directory, Academic/Scholarly.*
Published by: Hobsons PLC, Challenger House, 42 Adler St, London, E1 1EE, United Kingdom. TEL 44-20-79585000, FAX 44-20-79585001, http://www.hobsons.com. adv.: B&W page EUR 1,841, color page EUR 3,492.

378 AUS
STUDENT PARTICIPATION AND STUDENT OUTCOMES IN THE SOCIAL SCIENCES. Text in English. 1998. irreg.
Published by: Queensland Board of Senior Secondary School Studies, P.O. Box 307, Spring Hill, QLD 4101, Australia. TEL 61-7-3864-0299, FAX 61-7-3221-2553, office@qbssss.edu.au.

378.4891 DNK ISSN 0108-1020
STUDENTERHAANDBOGEN. Text in Danish. 1893. a. DKK 150. adv. illus. **Document type:** *Academic/Scholarly.*
Former titles (until 1973): Studenterhaandbog for Koebenhavns Universitet (0903-3653); (until 1968): Haandbog for Studenter (0903-3661)
Published by: Koebenhavns Universitet, Forenede Studenterraad, Krystalgade 16, Copenhagen K, 1172, Denmark. TEL 45-35-32-38-38, FAX 45-35-32-38-48. Ed. Lars Chr Arnt Joenbech.

331.548 DEU ISSN 0302-6299
STUDIEN- UND BERUFSWAHL. Text in German. 1973. a. EUR 6.50 newsstand/cover (effective 2002). adv. **Document type:** *Magazine, Academic/Scholarly.*
Formed by the merger of (1970-1973): Das Studium an Fachhochschulen (0081-8895); (19??-1973): Hochschulstudium (0171-6247)
Related titles: CD-ROM ed.: ISSN 1436-9516. 1998; Online - full text ed.: ISSN 1436-1752. 1998.
Published by: Bildung und Wissen Verlag und Software GmbH, Postfach 820150, Nuernberg, 90252, Germany. TEL 49-911-9676-0, FAX 49-911-6880301, serviceteam@bwverlag.de, http://www.studienwahl.de, http://www.bwverlag.de. Adv. contact Beate Kindt TEL 49-7131-8885123. page EUR 8,950; trim 99 x 168. Circ: 720,000 (paid and controlled).

STUDIENANGEBOTE DEUTSCHER HOCHSCHULEN. see *EDUCATION—Guides To Schools And Colleges*

STUDIENFUEHRER MATHEMATIK. see *MATHEMATICS*

378.155 DEU
STUDIEREN NACH DEM STUDIUM. Text in German. 1989. triennial. **Document type:** *Directory.*
Published by: Staufenbiel Institut fuer Studien- und Berufsplanung GmbH, Konrad-Adenauer-Ufer 33, Cologne, 50668, Germany. TEL 49-221-9126630, FAX 49-221-9126639, info@staufenbiel.de, http://www.staufenbiel.de. Ed. Joerg Staufenbiel. Circ: 6,000.

STUDIES IN CONTINUING EDUCATION. see *EDUCATION—Adult Education*

STUDIES IN EDUCATION AND SPIRITUALITY. see *RELIGIONS AND THEOLOGY*

378 USA ISSN 1531-8087
STUDIES IN HIGHER EDUCATION. Text in English. 2001. irreg.
Published by: Greenwood Publishing Group Inc. (Subsidiary of: Harcourt International), 88 Post Rd W, PO Box 5007, Westport, CT 06881. TEL 203-226-3571, http://www.greenwood.com.

378 GBR ISSN 0307-5079
LB2300
➤ **STUDIES IN HIGHER EDUCATION.** Text in English. 1976. bi-m. GBP 868, USD 1,953 combined subscription to institutions print & online eds. (effective 2006). adv. bk.rev. illus.; stat. index. back issues avail.; reprint service avail. from PSC. **Document type:** *Journal, Academic/Scholarly.*
Related titles: Microfiche ed.; Online - full text ed.: ISSN 1470-174X, GBP 825, USD 1,855 to institutions (effective 2006) (from EBSCO Publishing, Gale Group, IngentaConnect, Northern Light Technology, Inc., O C L C Online Computer Library Center, Inc., ProQuest Information & Learning, Swets Information Services).
Indexed: ASCA, ArtHuCI, BrEdI, CIJE, CPE, CurCont, DIP, EAA, ERA, ETA, HEA, HECAB, IBR, IBSS, IBZ, MEA, PCI, PsycholAb, RASB, RHEA, SEA, SENA, SOMA, SSCI, SWA, TEA, WBA, WMB.
—BLDSC (8490.633000), IDS, IE, Infotrieve, ingenta. **CCC.**
Published by: (Society for Research into Higher Education), Routledge (Subsidiary of: Taylor & Francis Group), 4 Park Sq, Milton Park, Abingdon, Oxon OX14 4RN, United Kingdom. TEL 44-1235-828600, FAX 44-1235-829000, info@routledge.co.uk, http://www.tandf.co.uk/journals/titles/03075079.asp, http://www.routledge.co.uk. Ed. Malcolm Tight.
Subscr. to: Taylor & Francis Ltd, Journals Customer Service, Rankine Rd, Basingstoke, Hants RG24 8PR, United Kingdom. TEL 44-1256-813000, FAX 44-1256-330245.

➤ **STUDY ABROAD/ESTUDIOS EN EL EXTRANJERO/ETUDES A L'ETRANGER**; scholarships and higher education courses worldwide. see *EDUCATION—International Education Programs*

378.154 AUS ISSN 0727-8225
STUDY AT MACQUARIE. Text in English. 1979. a. free. **Document type:** *Consumer.* **Description:** Provides a summary of undergraduate information for intending students, for the following academic year.
Related titles: Online - full content ed.
Published by: Macquarie University, Balaclava Rd., North Ryde, NSW 2109, Australia. TEL 61-2-98507377, FAX 61-2-98507391, http://www.mq.edu.au.

378.104 AUT
STUDY IN AUSTRIA. Text in English. 1997. irreg. **Document type:** *Academic/Scholarly.*
Published by: Oesterreichischer Austauschdienst/Austrian Exchange Service, Alserstrasse 4-1-3-8, Vienna, W 1090, Austria. TEL 43-1-4277-28180, FAX 43-1-4277-28195, info@oead.ac.at, http://www.oead.ac.at. Circ: 10,000 (controlled).

378.41025 GBR
THE STUDY U K HANDBOOK. Variant title: Studying and Living in the UK. Text in English. 1988. a. GBP 5.99 per issue (effective 2002). **Document type:** *Directory.* **Description:** Helps overseas students choose the right first-degree course at a UK higer-education institution.
Formerly: Which Degree in Britain (Year) (0955-8977)
Published by: (Careers Research and Advisory Centre), Hobsons PLC, Challenger House, 42 Adler St, London, E1 1EE, United Kingdom. TEL 44-1223-4600366, FAX 44-1223-301506. **Dist. by:** Biblios Publishers' Distribution Services Ltd., Star Rd, Partridge Green, W Sussex RH13 8LD, United Kingdom. TEL 44-1403-710971, FAX 44-1403-711143.

378 AUS
STUDYING ASSESSMENT PRACTICES: A RESOURCE FOR TEACHERS IN SCHOOLS. Text in English. 1995. irreg.
Published by: Queensland Board of Senior Secondary School Studies, P.O. Box 307, Spring Hill, QLD 4101, Australia. TEL 61-7-3864-0299, FAX 61-7-3221-2553, office@qbssss.edu.au.

SUM NEWS; the newsletter of the Massachusetts Society of CPAs. see *BUSINESS AND ECONOMICS—Accounting*

378 USA ISSN 1091-8515
LC5715+
➤ **SUMMER ACADEME**; a journal of higher education. Text in English. 1997. a. USD 20 to individuals; USD 30 to institutions (effective 2002). adv. 96 p./no. 1 cols./p.; back issues avail. **Document type:** *Journal, Academic/Scholarly.* **Description:** Includes case studies, research, and administrative and pedagogical issues relating to summer sessions.
Published by: Caddo Gap Press, 3145 Geary Blvd., PMB 275, San Francisco, CA 94118. TEL 415-922-1911, FAX 415-440-4870, caddogap@aol.com. Ed. David Schejbal. Pub., R&P, Adv. contact Alan H Jones. page USD 200; 4.5 x 7. Circ: 800 (paid).

617 AUS
SURGICAL NEWS (ONLINE). Text in English. 1980. 3/yr. bk.rev. charts; illus. back issues avail. **Document type:** *Bulletin.* **Description:** Publishes financial and related issues concerning the Royal College.

E

Formerly (until 2000): R A C S Bulletin (Print Edition) (0728-1048)
Media: Online - full content.
Published by: Royal Australasian College of Surgeons, Spring St, Melbourne, VIC 3000, Australia. TEL 61-3-9249-1200, FAX 61-3-9249-1219, surgical.news@surgeons.org, http://www.medeserv.com.au/racs/open/surgical_news/surg_news.cfm, http://www.surgeons.org/. Ed. Fiona Gillies. Circ: 6,300.

378 AUS
SURVEY OF ASSESSMENT MANAGEMENT PRACTICES IN SENIOR SECONDARY SCHOOLS. Text in English. 1992. irreg.
Published by: Queensland Board of Senior Secondary School Studies, P.O. Box 307, Spring Hill, QLD 4101, Australia. TEL 61-7-3864-0299, FAX 61-7-3221-2553, office@qbsss.edu.au.

THE SURVEY OF COLLEGE MARKETING PROGRAMS. see *BUSINESS AND ECONOMICS—Marketing And Purchasing*

SURVEY ON GRADUATING STUDENTS ABROAD. see *EDUCATION—Abstracting, Bibliographies, Statistics*

378.1012 USA ISSN 1042-0169
KF4225.A15
SYNTHESIS (ASHEVILLE); law and policy in higher education. Text in English. 1988. q. USD 69.50 (effective 2003).
Description: Provides an analysis and commentary on law and policy issues of concern to higher education administrators and faculty.
Published by: College Administration Publications, Inc., 830 Fairview Rd, Ste D, Asheville, NC 28803-1081. TEL 828-277-8777, FAX 828-277-8735, info@collegepubs.com, http://www.collegepubs.com/descrip/14.shtml. Ed. Gary Pavela. Circ: 750.

T H & M A. (Tijdschrift voor Hoger Onderwijs en Management) see *EDUCATION—School Organization And Administration*

378 USA
T M I FOCUS. Text in English. 1983. q. USD 65 membership. bk.rev. **Document type:** *Newsletter.* **Description:** Covers the activities, new programs and products of the institute.
Formerly: T M I Bulletin
Published by: The Monroe Institute, Rte 1, Box 175, Faber, VA 22938. TEL 804-361-1252, FAX 804-361-1237. Ed., R&P Shirley N Bliley. Circ: 2,200.

378 620 DEU
T U CONTACT. (Technischer Universitaet) Text in German. 1997. 2/yr. **Document type:** *Academic/Scholarly.*
Published by: (Technische Universitaet Clausthal), Satztechnik Meissen GmbH, Am Sand 1c, Nieschuetz, 01665, Germany. TEL 49-3525-71860, FAX 49-3525-718612, info@satztechnik-meissen.de, http://www.satztechnik-meissen.de. Circ: 7,200 (paid).

378 USA
TALBOT'S STUDENT PLANNING BOOK. Text in English. 1971. a. price varies. adv. **Document type:** *Consumer.* **Description:** Contains articles on questions students should ask about college and career planning.
Published by: Dexter Publishing Co., Inc., 1 Hollis St, Ste 110, Wellesley, MA 02181. TEL 781-237-0920, FAX 781-235-6654. Ed. Marie Devins. Circ: 400,000.

378 PHL
TARLAC COLLEGE OF TECHNOLOGY. ANNUAL REPORT OF THE PRESIDENT. Text in English. 1966. a. back issues avail.
Published by: Tarlac College of Technology, Tarlac, Philippines. Ed. Lita Nicdao. Circ: 105.

378 USA ISSN 0890-3107
THE TARTAN. Text in English. 1906. w. (throughout academic year). USD 60 (effective 1999). adv. charts; illus. back issues avail. **Document type:** *Newspaper.*
Published by: Carnegie Mellon University, PO Box 17, Pittsburgh, PA 15213. TEL 412-268-2111, FAX 412-268-1596, tartan@andrew.cmu.edu, http://tartan.web.cmu.edu. Ed. Kevin Babbitt. R&P Kevin Babbit. Adv. contact Dinesh Parvani. Circ: 7,000.

378 USA ISSN 1073-4376
➤ **TAYLOR**; a magazine for Taylor University alumni and friends. Text in English. 1907. q. bk.rev. **Document type:** *Academic/Scholarly.* **Description:** Information and continuing education for alumni, friends, parents, faculty and staff of the university.
Formerly: Taylor University Magazine
Published by: Taylor University, 500 W Reade Ave, Upland, IN 46989. TEL 765-998-2751, FAX 765-998-4910, editor@tayloru.edu, http://www.tayloru.edu. Ed. Randy Dillinger. Circ: 23,500 (controlled).

378.12 USA ISSN 0887-8730
➤ **THE TEACHER EDUCATOR.** Text in English. 1965. q. USD 25 domestic to individuals; USD 35 domestic to institutions; USD 40 foreign to institutions (effective 2005). charts; illus. cum.index: 1967-70, 1970-75. 90 p./no.; back issues avail.; reprint service avail. from PQC. **Document type:** *Journal, Academic/Scholarly.* **Description:** Discusses pre- and in-service education of teachers and related matters concerning programs, quantitative and qualitative research, descriptions of policies and practices as it applies to teacher education and allied disciplines.
Formerly: Supervisors Quarterly (0039-5897)
Related titles: Microform ed.: (from PQC); Online - full text ed.: (from H.W. Wilson, O C L C Online Computer Library Center, Inc., ProQuest Information & Learning).
Indexed: ABIn, CIJE, EduInd.
—BLDSC (8613.480000), IE, ingenta.
Published by: Ball State University, Teachers College, TC 1008, Muncie, IN 47306. TEL 765-285-5453, FAX 765-285-5455, lsiler@bsu.edu, http://www.bsu.edu/tte/. Eds. Jerrell Cassidy, Laurie Mullen. R&P Lynn Siler. Circ: 1,000.

➤ **TEACHING AND LEARNING IN MEDICINE**; an international journal. see *MEDICAL SCIENCES*

▼ ➤ **TEACHING AND LEARNING IN NURSING.** see *MEDICAL SCIENCES—Nurses And Nursing*

➤ **TEACHING ENGLISH IN THE TWO-YEAR COLLEGE.** see *LINGUISTICS*

378.12 GBR ISSN 1356-2517
LB2331 CODEN: THEDFM
➤ **TEACHING IN HIGHER EDUCATION.** Text in English. 1996. q. GBP 402, USD 665 combined subscription to institutions print & online eds. (effective 2006). reprint service avail. from PSC. **Document type:** *Journal, Academic/Scholarly.* **Description:** Addresses the roles of teaching, learning and the curriculum in higher education in order to explore and clarify the intellectual challenges which they present.
Related titles: Online - full text ed.: ISSN 1470-1294. GBP 382, USD 632 to institutions (effective 2006) (from EBSCO Publishing, Gale Group, IngentaConnect, Northern Light Technology, Inc., O C L C Online Computer Library Center, Inc., ProQuest Information & Learning, Swets Information Services).
Indexed: BrEdI, CIJE, CPE, CurCont, ERA, ETA, HEA, L&LBA, MEA, PhilInd, PsycInfo, PsycholAb, RHEA, SEA, SENA, SOMA, SOPODA, SSCI, SWA, TEA.
—BLDSC (8614.188000), IE, Infotrieve, ingenta. **CCC.**
Published by: Routledge (Subsidiary of: Taylor & Francis Group), 4 Park Sq, Milton Park, Abingdon, Oxon OX14 4RN, United Kingdom. TEL 44-1235-828600, FAX 44-1235-829000, journals@routledge.com, http://www.tandf.co.uk/journals/titles/13562517.asp, http://www.routledge.co.uk. Ed. Sue Clegg. **Subscr. to:** Taylor & Francis Ltd, Journals Customer Service, Rankine Rd, Basingstoke, Hants RG24 8PR, United Kingdom. TEL 44-1256-813000, FAX 44-1256-330245.

378.12 USA ISSN 0892-2209
LB1025.3
THE TEACHING PROFESSOR. Text in English. 1987. 10/yr. USD 79 domestic; USD 83 in Canada; USD 89 elsewhere (effective 2005). 3 p./no. 8 cols./p.; back issues avail.; reprints avail. **Document type:** *Newsletter.* **Description:** Offers concise information to help faculty members teach more effectively. Topics include giving lectures, testing, planning courses, student passivity and working with teaching assistants.
Related titles: Online - full content ed.: USD 79 (effective 2005); Online - full text ed.: (from EBSCO Publishing, H.W. Wilson).
Indexed: EduInd.
—**CCC.**
Published by: Magna Publications, Inc., 2718 Dryden Dr, Madison, WI 53704. TEL 608-246-3590, FAX 608-246-3597, editor@magnapubs.com, http://www.magnapubs.com/pub/magnapubs_tp. Ed. Maryellen Weimer. Pub. Deborah Harville. Circ: 18,000.

TEACHING PUBLIC ADMINISTRATION. see *PUBLIC ADMINISTRATION*

TEACHING THEOLOGY AND RELIGION. see *RELIGIONS AND THEOLOGY*

378 GBR
TEARS; higher education. Text in English. 1950. irreg.
Published by: University of Exeter, Teaching Service Centre, Streatham Court, Rennes Dr, Exeter, Devon EX4 4PU, United Kingdom.

378 ZAF
TECHNIKON FORUM. Text in Afrikaans, English. 1977. biennial. looseleaf. free. illus. **Document type:** *Academic/Scholarly.*
Formerly: Kamera; Incorporates: Media News
Published by: Technikon Pretoria, Private Bag X680, Pretoria, South Africa. Ed. Willa De Ruyter.

TECHNION - ISRAEL INSTITUTE OF TECHNOLOGY. ABSTRACTS OF RESEARCH THESES. see *EDUCATION—Abstracting, Bibliographies, Statistics*

378 DEU
TECHNISCHE UNIVERSITAET BRAUNSCHWEIG. FORSCHUNGSBERICHT. Text in German. irreg., latest 1995. **Document type:** *Monographic series.*
Formerly: Technische Universitaet Braunschweig. Berichtsband. Forschung
Published by: Technische Universitaet Braunschweig, Presse- und Oeffentlichkeitsarbeit, Pockelsstr 14, Braunschweig, 38106, Germany.

026.378 DEU
TECHNISCHE UNIVERSITAET BRAUNSCHWEIG. UNIVERSITAETSBIBLIOTHEK. VEROEFFENTLICHUNGEN. Text in German. 1988. irreg. free. **Document type:** *Academic/Scholarly.*
Published by: (Universitaetsbibliothek), Technische Universitaet Braunschweig, Presse- und Oeffentlichkeitsarbeit, Pockelsstr 14, Braunschweig, 38106, Germany. TEL 49-531-3915011, FAX 49-531-3915836. Ed. Dietmar Brandes.

TECHNISCHE UNIVERSITAET MUENCHEN. JAHRBUCH. see *TECHNOLOGY: COMPREHENSIVE WORKS*

378.768 USA
TENNESSEE. HIGHER EDUCATION COMMISSION. BIENNIAL REPORT. Text in English. 1970. biennial. free. charts; stat. **Document type:** *Government.* **Description:** Reviews the events and progress of the Tennessee public higher education system and gives statistical information regarding such matters as state appropriations, student population profiles, tuition and other fees, and degrees awarded.
Published by: Higher Education Commission, Pkwy Towers, Ste 1900, 404 James Robertson Pkwy, Nashville, TN 37243-0830. TEL 615-741-7572. Ed. Cathy L Cole. Circ: 1,000.

378.111 NLD ISSN 1358-3883
TERTIARY EDUCATION AND MANAGEMENT. Text in English. 1995. q. EUR 241, USD 241, GBP 151 combined subscription to institutions print & online eds. (effective 2005). adv. back issues avail.; reprint service avail. from PSC. **Document type:** *Academic/Scholarly.* **Description:** Intended for professionals in the area of higher education management.
Related titles: Online - full text ed.: ISSN 1573-1936 (from EBSCO Publishing, Gale Group, IngentaConnect, Kluwer Online, O C L C Online Computer Library Center, Inc., ProQuest Information & Learning, Springer LINK, Swets Information Services).
Indexed: ABIn, BibLing, BrEdI, CPE, RHEA.
—BLDSC (8796.150700), IE, Infotrieve, ingenta. **CCC.**
Published by: (E A I R), Springer-Verlag Dordrecht (Subsidiary of: Springer Science+Business Media), Van Godewijckstraat 30, Dordrecht, 3311 GX, Netherlands. TEL 31-78-6576050, FAX 31-78-6576474, http://springerlink.metapress.com/openurl.asp?genre=journal&issn=1358-3883, http://www.springeronline.com. Ed. Bjorn Stensaker.

378 AUS
THE TERTIARY EDUCATION REPORT. Text in English. fortn. **Document type:** *Academic/Scholarly.*
Media: E-mail.
Published by: National Tertiary Education Union, PO Box 1323, South Melbourne, VIC 3205, Australia. http://www.nteu.org.au/.

378 USA ISSN 1531-7722
TEXAS EDUCATION REVIEW. Text in English. 2000. q.
Published by: Texas Review Society, Inc., 2620 B S Shepherd, PMB 154, Houston, TX 77098. TEL 713-523-9100, FAX 713-523-8004, TXEducationRvw@aol.com, http://www.texaseducationreview.homestead.com. Ed., Pub. Brent Tantillo.

378.764 USA
TEXAS HIGHER EDUCATION COORDINATING BOARD. C B POLICY PAPER. Text in English. 1968. irreg., latest vol.9, 1970. free to qualified personnel. **Document type:** *Government.*
Formerly: Texas College and University System. Coordinating Board. C B Policy Paper (0082-299X)
Published by: Texas Higher Education Coordinating Board, PO Box 12788, Capitol Sta, Austin, TX 78711. TEL 512-483-6111, FAX 512-483-6127, restersa@thecb.state.tx.us. Ed. Teri E Flack. Circ: (controlled).

378.764 USA
TEXAS HIGHER EDUCATION COORDINATING BOARD. C B STUDY PAPER. Text in English. 1968. irreg., latest vol.30, 1983. free to qualified personnel. **Document type:** *Government.*
Formerly: Texas Coordinating Board. Texas College and University System. C B Study Paper (0082-3007)
Published by: Texas Higher Education Coordinating Board, PO Box 12788, Capitol Sta, Austin, TX 78711. TEL 512-483-6111, FAX 512-483-6127, restersa@thecb.state.tx.us. Ed. Teri E Flack. Circ: (controlled).

TEXAS HIGHER EDUCATION COORDINATING BOARD. STATUS REPORT ON HIGHER EDUCATION AND STATISTICAL REPORT. see *EDUCATION—Abstracting, Bibliographies, Statistics*

E

378.2 NGA ISSN 0082-4100
Z965
THESES AND DISSERTATIONS ACCEPTED FOR HIGHER DEGREES IN NIGERIAN UNIVERSITIES. Text in English. 1969. a. index. **Document type:** *Academic/Scholarly.*
Published by: National Library of Nigeria, 4 Wesley St, PMB 12626, Lagos, Nigeria. TEL 234-1-634704.

378 USA ISSN 0748-8475
CODEN: TMRIEY
THOUGHT & ACTION. Text in English. 1984. irreg. USD 35 to libraries. **Document type:** *Journal, Academic/Scholarly.* **Description:** Information and articles on issues of interest to the nation's higher education faculty.
Supersedes: Today's Education: Higher Education Edition
Related titles: Online - full content ed.
Indexed: CIJE, HEA, SRRA.
Published by: National Education Association of the United States, 1201 16th St, N W, Washington, DC 20036-3290. TEL 202-833-4000, FAX 202-822-7974, http://www2.nea.org/he/tanda.html, http://www.nea.org. Ed. Con Lehane. Pub. Sam Pizzigati. Circ: 80,000.

378 SWE ISSN 1400-190X
TIDSKRIFTEN FOLKUNIVERSITETET; ideer och debatt om bildning och kultur. Text in Swedish. 1978. q. SEK 40 (effective 1996).
Former titles (until 1989): Folkuniversitetet (0284-7574); (until 1987): F U - Bladet (0349-3903)
Published by: Folkuniversitetet, Folkuniversitetets Kansli, Fack 26152, Stockholm, 10041, Sweden. TEL 46-8-679-29-50, FAX 46-8-678-15-44.

TIEMPO Y ESPACIO. see *HISTORY—History Of North And South America*

378 NLD ISSN 0168-1095
➤ **TIJDSCHRIFT VOOR HOGER ONDERWIJS.** Text in Dutch. 1982. q. EUR 55 domestic; USD 55 foreign (effective 2002). adv. bk.rev. index. 64 p./no.; back issues avail. **Document type:** *Academic/Scholarly.* **Description:** Publishes studies of higher education and higher education policy.
—IE, Infotrieve.
Published by: Uitgeverij Lemma BV, Postbus 3320, Utrecht, 3502 GH, Netherlands. TEL 31-30-2545652, FAX 31-30-2512496, infodesk@lemma.nl, http://www.lemma.nl. Ed. Henri Christiaans. Pub. Ruud Veen. adv.: B&W page EUR 250. Circ: 500 (paid).

378 GBR ISSN 0049-3929
TIMES HIGHER EDUCATION SUPPLEMENT. Cover title: The Higher. Text in English. 1971. w. free to members (effective 2004). adv. bk.rev. illus. index. reprints avail. **Document type:** *Newspaper, Academic/Scholarly.* **Description:** Contains news, features and commentaries about universities and colleges in Britain and abroad.
Related titles: CD-ROM ed.: (from Chadwyck-Healey Inc.); Microfilm ed.: (from RPI); Online - full text ed.: (from EBSCO Publishing).
Indexed: ABIn, BNI, BRI, BrCerAb, BrEdI, BrHumI, EduInd, HECAB, IndBusRep, LT&LA, MLA-IB, PhilInd, RHEA, WBA, WMB.
—BLDSC (8853.700000). **CCC.**
Published by: T S L Education Ltd., Admiral House, 66-68 E Smithfield, London, E1 1BX, United Kingdom. TEL 44-20-7782-3000, FAX 44-20-7782-3300, editor@thes.co.uk, http://www.thesis.co.uk, http://www.tsleducation.co.uk. Ed. John O'Leary. Adv. contact John Ladbrook. Circ: 25,000.

378 USA ISSN 1065-237X
TO IMPROVE THE ACADEMY. Text in English. 1982. a. USD 15 to members; USD 18 to non-members (effective 2005). **Document type:** *Magazine, Trade.*
Published by: Professional and Organizational Development Network in Higher Education, Box 271370, Ft Collins, CO 80527-1370. TEL 970-377-9269, FAX 970-377-9282, podnetwork@podweb.org, http://www.podweb.org/.

TOPICS IN AUSTRALIAN TEACHER LIBRARIANSHIP. see *LIBRARY AND INFORMATION SCIENCES*

378.016 NLD ISSN 0929-4848
TRANSFER; vakblad over internationalisering in het hoger onderwijs. Text in Dutch. 1971; N.S. 1993. 9/yr. EUR 60 domestic; EUR 65 in Belgium; EUR 65 in Netherlands Antilles; EUR 78 elsewhere (effective 2003). adv. bk.rev. **Document type:** *Academic/Scholarly.* **Description:** Focuses on international cooperation in education and its research.
Formed by the 1993 merger of: Visum (0925-8272); Which was formerly (until 1990): Visum Nieuws (0920-5136); Overzicht (0920-5292); Which was formerly (until 1984): Overzicht Internationale Universitaire Samenwerking (0165-148X)
—IE, Infotrieve.
Published by: (Netherland Universities Foundation for International Cooperation), Reed Business Information bv (Subsidiary of: Reed Business), Van Bylandthuis, Benoordenhoutseweg 46, Den Haag, 2596 BC, Netherlands. TEL 31-70-441-5166, FAX 31-70-441-5916, http://www.reedbusiness.nl. Eds. Dr. A van Vliet, Dr. F Koning. Circ: 2,800.

378 MEX ISSN 1605-4245
TRANSFERENCIA. Text in Spanish. 1988. q. back issues avail. **Document type:** *Academic/Scholarly.*
Related titles: Online - full text ed.: ISSN 1605-4237. 1996.
Published by: Instituto Tecnologico y de Estudios Superiores de Monterrey, Sucursal de Correos "J", Ave. Eugenio Garza Sada No. 2501, Monterrey, Nuevo Leon, 64849, Mexico. TEL 52-81-83582000, http://www.mty.itesm.mx/die/ddre/trasnferencia.

378.1982 970.1 USA ISSN 1052-5505
E97.55
TRIBAL COLLEGE; journal of American Indian higher education. Text in English. 1989. q. USD 24 domestic to individuals; USD 34 domestic to institutions (effective 2005). adv. bk.rev. illus. Index. reprints avail.
Related titles: Online - full text ed.: (from EBSCO Publishing, SoftLine Information).
Indexed: ABIn, CIJE, DYW, ENW, EduInd, HEA.
Published by: American Indian Higher Education Consortium, PO Box 720, Mancos, CO 81328. TEL 970-533-9170, info@tribalcollegejournal.org, 970-533-9145, http://www.tribalcollegejournal.org/. Ed. Marjane Ambler. Adv. contact Rachael Marchbanks.

378.07 PHL ISSN 0304-1972
TRINITY COLLEGE JOURNAL. Text in English, Tagalog, Spanish. 1974. a. PHP 30, USD 8. bk.rev. abstr.; illus.; stat. back issues avail. **Document type:** *Academic/Scholarly.*
Indexed: IPP.
Published by: Trinity College of Quezon City, E. Rodriguez Sr. Blvd, Quezon City, Philippines. TEL 724-46-58. Ed. Erlinda G Rosales. Circ: 300.

371.07 284.1 USA ISSN 0270-2533
TRINITY SEMINARY REVIEW. Text in English. 1979. s-a. free (effective 2005).
Related titles: Online - full content ed.; Online - full text ed.: (from EBSCO Publishing).
Indexed: NTA, RI-1, RILM.
Published by: Trinity Lutheran Seminary, Office of Communications, 2199 E Main St, Columbus, OH 43209. TEL 614-235-4136, FAX 614-238-0263, advancement@trinity.capital.edu, http://www.trinitylutheranseminary.edu/Publications/. Ed. Tim Huffman.

378.101 USA ISSN 1068-1027
LB2341
TRUSTEESHIP. Text in English. 1993. bi-m. USD 65 to members; USD 75 to institutions (effective 2005). back issues avail.; reprint service avail. from PQC. **Document type:** *Trade.* **Description:** Reports trends, issues, and practices in higher education to help board members and chief executives better understand their distinctive and complementary roles and to strengthen board performance.
Formed by the merger of (1958-1993): A G B Reports (0044-961X); (1982-1993): A G B Notes (0738-3460); Which was formerly (1970-1982): A G B News Notes (0199-7939)
Related titles: Microform ed.
Indexed: CIJE, HEA.
—BLDSC (9066.587000), IE, ingenta.
Published by: Association of Governing Boards of Universities and Colleges, One Dupont Circle, Ste 400, Washington, DC 20036. TEL 202-296-8400, FAX 202-223-7053, http://www.agb.org. Ed. Daniel J Levin. Circ: 32,000 (paid).

TUITION FACT BOOK. see *EDUCATION—Abstracting, Bibliographies, Statistics*

378 ZAF ISSN 1022-1786
DIE TUKKIE. Text in Afrikaans, English. 1970. s-a. adv. illus. 40 p./no.; back issues avail. **Document type:** *Magazine, Academic/Scholarly.*
Former titles (until 1993): Tukkie - Werf (0256-6052); (until 1974): Eie Werf (0256-5978)
Published by: University of Pretoria, Marketing and Communication/Universiteit van Pretoria, Pretoria, 0002, South Africa. TEL 27-12-4203047, 27-12-4204111, FAX 27-12-3625088, djacobs@postino.up.ac.za, http://www.up.ac.za. Ed., R&P D C Jacobs. Adv. contact Pieter Bressler. Circ: 45,000.

378.12 ZAF ISSN 1021-9617
TUTOR; bulletin for academic staff. Text in English. 1993. s-a. **Document type:** *Bulletin.*
Published by: Technikon Northern Transvaal, Directorate: Teaching Development, Private Bag X7, Pretoria North, 0116, South Africa. TEL 27-1214-2005, FAX 27-1214-2009.

378 USA
U C DAVIS MAGAZINE. (University of California) Text in English. 1983. q. **Document type:** *Newspaper.* **Description:** Covers news and publishes feature stories about U.C.-Davis research, faculty, teaching programs, and alumni.
Formerly: Spectator (Davis)
Published by: Univ. of California at Davis, One Shields Ave, Davis, CA 95616. TEL 916-752-9839. Ed. Maril Revette Stratton. Circ: 115,000. **Subscr. to:** Cal Aggie Alumni Association, Guilbert House, University of California at Davis, Davis, CA 95616.

378 PHL
U E NEWS. Text in English. 1996. m. free. 4 p./no.; back issues avail. **Document type:** *Newsletter, Internal.* **Description:** Features news items involving faculty members, employees, officials, students and alumni of the university, to disseminate such information to UE's two campuses.
Formerly (until Jun. 2000): U E Newsletter (Manila) (0118-3923)
Related titles: Online - full text ed.
Published by: University of the East, 2219 C.M. Recto Ave, Manila, 1008, Philippines. TEL 63-2-735-5471, FAX 63-2-735-6972, postmaster@ue.edu.ph, http://ue.edu.ph/ue/news.htm. Ed. Lourdes C Sanchez. Pub. P O Domingo. Circ: 5,000.

378 GBR
U K HIGHER EDUCATION RESEARCH YEARBOOK (YEAR). Text in English. a. (in 2 vols.). GBP 195 per issue higher education customers; GBP 245 per issue others (effective 2005). **Document type:** *Yearbook, Academic/Scholarly.* **Description:** Analyses university and college research performance across the UK.
—BLDSC (9082.656900).
Published by: Evidence Ltd., 103 Claredon Rd, Leeds, W Yorks LS2 9DF, United Kingdom. TEL 44-113-3845680, FAX 44-113-3845874, enquiries@evidence.co.uk, http://www.evidence.co.uk.

378.1542 USA ISSN 1084-3043
U - MAGAZINE. (University) Key Title: U., the National College Magazine. Text in English. 1988. m. USD 18 (effective 2000). adv. bk.rev. back issues avail. **Document type:** *Consumer.* **Description:** Focuses on the diverse interests, activities, attitudes and concerns of students attending four-year colleges and universities.
Formerly (until 1992): U: The National College Newspaper
Related titles: Online - full text ed.: free (effective 2005).
Published by: U. Inc., 12707 High Bluff Dr, Ste. 2000, San Diego, CA 92130. TEL 858-847-3350, FAX 858-847-3340, editor@colleges.com, editor@umagazine.com, http://www.colleges.com/Umagazine. Ed., Pub. John Carrieri. Circ: 1,500,000 (controlled).

378 MEX ISSN 0186-2863
U N A M GACETA. (Universidad Nacional Autonoma de Mexico) Text in Spanish. 1966. bi-w. free. back issues avail. **Document type:** *Bulletin.* **Description:** Includes university activities, events and comments.
Related titles: Online - full text ed.: ISSN 1605-4040. 1996; Supplement(s): U N A M Gaceta. Agenda. ISSN 0188-5138. 1989.
Published by: (Unidad de Sistemas y Consulta), Universidad Nacional Autonoma de Mexico, Direccion General de Informacion, Unidad de Sistemas y Consulta, Circuito Interior, Ciudad Universitaria, Mexico, D.F., 04510, Mexico. TEL 525-6220581, FAX 525-6162834, dginfo@condor.unam.mx, http://www.unam.mx/gaceta/.

378.972 MEX ISSN 0188-6630
LH3.U568
U N A M HOY. (Universidad Nacional Autonoma de Mexico) Text in Spanish. 1991. bi-m. MXP 50 (effective 2000). **Description:** Presents all the academic activities, notes and interviews within the university.
Related titles: Online - full text ed.: ISSN 1605-4059.
Published by: Universidad Nacional Autonoma de Mexico, Direccion General de Informacion, Direccion Tecnica, Edificio de Relaciones Laborales,1er. Piso,, Junto a la Torre II de Humanidades, Ciudad Universitaria, Mexico City, DF 04510, Mexico. TEL 52-5-6230406, FAX 52-5-6162834, dginfo@condor.dgsca.unam.mx, http://www.unamhoy.unam.mx.Ed. Virginia Careaga Covarrubias.

378 AUS ISSN 0156-1006
U N E CONVOCATION BULLETIN & ALUMNI NEWS. Text in English. 1957. a. to graduates only. bk.rev. **Document type:** *Bulletin.*
Former titles: U N E Bulletin; University of New England. Bulletin (0084-6740)
Published by: University of New England, Armidale, NSW 2351, Australia. TEL 61-67-7332819, FAX 61-67-733482, bdrew@metz.une.edu.au. Circ: 14,000.

026.378 USA
U.S. DEPARTMENT OF EDUCATION. NATIONAL CENTER FOR EDUCATION STATISTICS. ACADEMIC LIBRARIES. Text in English. irreg., latest 1988. **Document type:** *Directory, Trade.*
Formerly: U.S. Department of Education. National Center for Education Statistics. Library Statistics of Colleges and Universities
Published by: U.S. Department of Education, National Center for Education Statistics, 1990 K St N W, Washington, DC 20006. TEL 202-219-1828, http://nces.ed.gov/. **Subscr. to:** U.S. Government Printing Office, Superintendent of Documents, PO Box 371954, Pittsburgh, PA 15250-7954. TEL 202-512-1800, FAX 202-512-2250, gpoaccess@gpo.gov, http://www.access.gpo.gov. **Dist. by:** Box 1398, Jessup, MD 20794-1398. TEL 877-433-7827, FAX 301-470-1244.

U.S. DEPARTMENT OF EDUCATION. NATIONAL CENTER FOR EDUCATION STATISTICS. COMPLETIONS IN INSTITUTIONS OF HIGHER EDUCATION. see *EDUCATION—Abstracting, Bibliographies, Statistics*

E

378.16 USA ISSN 0362-5036
LA227.3
U.S. DEPARTMENT OF EDUCATION. NATIONAL CENTER FOR EDUCATION STATISTICS. FALL ENROLLMENT IN HIGHER EDUCATION. Text in English. 1947. a. price varies.
Document type: *Government.*
Formerly: Opening Fall Enrollment in Higher Education (0083-2758)
Published by: U.S. Department of Education, National Center for Education Statistics, 1990 K St N W, Washington, DC 20006. TEL 202-219-1828, http://nces.ed.gov. **Subscr. to:** U.S. Government Printing Office, Superintendent of Documents, PO Box 371954, Pittsburgh, PA 15250-7954. TEL 202-512-1800, FAX 202-512-2250, orders@gpo.gov, http://www.access.gpo.gov. **Dist. by:** Box 1398, Jessup, MD 20794-1398. TEL 877-433-7827, FAX 301-470-1244.

U.S. DEPARTMENT OF EDUCATION. NATIONAL CENTER FOR EDUCATION STATISTICS. STATE HIGHER EDUCATION PROFILES. see *EDUCATION—Abstracting, Bibliographies, Statistics*

378.155 332.3 USA
U.S. DEPARTMENT OF EDUCATION. NATIONAL CENTER FOR EDUCATION STATISTICS. STUDENT FINANCING OF GRADUATE AND FIRST-PROFESSIONAL EDUCATION. Text in English. irreg., latest 2002. stat. **Document type:** *Government.* **Description:** Describes how students in selected graduate and first-professional programs pay for their education and compares the use of assistantships across programs and fields of study.
Media: Online - full content. **Related titles:** Print ed.
Published by: U.S. Department of Education, National Center for Education Statistics, 1990 K St N W, Washington, DC 20006. TEL 202-502-7300, Aurora.D'Amico@ed.gov, http://nces.ed.gov/.

378.33 USA
U.S. NATIONAL ENDOWMENT FOR THE ARTS. GRANTS TO ORGANIZATIONS. Text in English. 1997. a. **Document type:** *Government.* **Description:** Covers the new general guideline for grants to be given in four categories: Heritage & Preservation, Creation & Presentation, Education & Access, and Planning & Stabilization. Since guidelines are no longer divided according to disciplines (visual arts, dance, music, theater etc.), this publication covers eligibility and application information for all organizations involved in these areas.
Published by: U.S. National Endowment for the Arts, Public Information Office, 1100 Pennsylvania Ave, N W, Washington, DC 20506. TEL 202-682-5400, http://www.arts.endow.gov, http://www.nea.gov.

U.S. NATIONAL SCIENCE FOUNDATION. SELECTED DATA ON STUDENTS AND POSTDOCTORALS IN SCIENCE & ENGINEERING; detailed statistical tables. see *EDUCATION—Abstracting, Bibliographies, Statistics*

378.489 DNK ISSN 0907-9386
UDDANNELSES- OG ERHVERVSVALGET; orientering for gymnasiet og HF. Text in Danish. 1966. a. **Document type:** *Academic/Scholarly.*
Formerly (until 1992): Studie- og Erhvervsvalget (0108-6944)
Published by: Raadet for Uddannelses- og Erhvervsvejledning (R.U.E.)/Danish National Council for Educational and Vocational Guidance, Vester Voldgade 123, Copenhagen V, 1552, Denmark. TEL 45-39-95-53-00, FAX 45-33-95-53-49, r-u-e@r-u-e.dk, http://www.r-u-e.dk. Ed. Jakob Lange. Circ: 156,000. **Dist. by:** Danske Boghandleres Kommissionsanstalt.

378 GBR
THE ULTIMATE GUIDE. Text in English, Welsh. 1972. a. free. adv. **Document type:** *Consumer.*
Formerly (until 1993): Union Handbook
Published by: University Union Cardiff, c/o Angela Williams, Park Pl, Cardiff, S Glam CF1 3QN, United Kingdom. TEL 44-222-781455, FAX 44-222-781435. Ed., R&P Drew Benvie. Adv. contact Yvonne Thomas. Circ: 5,000.

378 DEU
UNI MAGAZIN PERSPEKTIVEN FUER BERUF UND ARBEITSMARKT. Text in German. 1977. 7/yr. back issues avail. **Document type:** *Magazine, Trade.*
Formerly (until 1991): Uni Berufswahl-Magazin
Published by: (Germany, Federal Republic. Bundeanstalt fuer Arbeit), Transmedia Projekt und Verlags GmbH, Ludolf-Krehl-Str 13-17, Mannheim, 68167, Germany. TEL 49-621-37070, FAX 49-621-3707111, http://www.unimagazin.de, http://www.transmedia-mannheim.de. Ed. Manfred Hammes. Circ: 160,000. **Subscr. to:** DSB Zeitschriften - Abonnements - Verwaltungsgesellschaft mbH, Postfach 1163, Neckarsulm 74148, Germany.

378 DEU
UNI SIEGEN AKTUELL. Text in German. 1973. q. adv. bk.rev. back issues avail. **Document type:** *Newsletter.*
Formerly (until 1996): Siegener Hochschul Zeitung
Published by: Universitaet - Gesamthochschule Siegen, Herrengarten 3, Siegen, 57068, Germany. TEL 49-271-7404864, FAX 49-271-7404911, georgi@vrz.uni-siegen.de, http://uni-siegen.de. Ed. Ullrich Georgi. Circ: 5,000.

378.17 AUS
LA2100
UNICORN ONLINE REFEREED ARTICLES. (Issues numbering changed to ORA01 after title change.) Text in English. 1975; N.S. 2002. irreg. (3/yr. until 2002), latest ORA32. AUD 27.50 per issue (effective 2005). adv. bk.rev. back issues avail. **Document type:** *Academic/Scholarly.* **Description:** Provides information on new ideas and significant developments in education; informs members of the activities of the college.
Formerly (until vol.28, no.3, 2002): Unicorn (0311-4775)
Related titles: Online - full text ed.: free to members (from R M I T Publishing).
Indexed: AEI, AusPAIS, BAS, CIJE, CPE, ERA, ETA, MEA, SEA, SENA, SOMA, SWA, TEA.
—BLDSC (9090.551500), IE, ingenta.
Published by: Australian College of Educators, PO Box 323, Deakin West, ACT 2600, Australia. TEL 61-2-62811677, FAX 61-2-62851262, bpope@austcolled.com.au, http://www.austcolled.com.au/pubs.php?id=98. Circ: 6,500.

378 AUS
UNIKEN. Text in English. 1975. bi-w. free. 12 p./no. 4 cols./p.; **Description:** Material involves research, teaching and administrative news from the staff and students of UNSW's various campuses. Contains hard news, features, sports and letters.
Published by: University of New South Wales, Sydney, NSW 2052, Australia. TEL 61-2-93852866, FAX 61-2-93851650, b.goldie@unsw.edu.au. Ed. Benard Goldie. Pub. Bernard Goldie. Circ: 12,000 (controlled).

378 USA
UNION COLLEGE. Text in English. 1973 (vol.64). 6/yr. free. bk.rev.
Published by: Union College (Schenectady), Lamont House, Schenectady, NY 12308. TEL 518-370-6131. Ed. Peter E Blankman. Circ: 22,000.

378 MEX ISSN 0185-2779
UNION DE UNIVERSIDADES DE AMERICA LATINA. GACETA. Short title: Gaceta U D U A L. Text in Spanish. q. USD 12 (effective 1999). adv. **Description:** Covers general university events.
Published by: Union de Universidades de America Latina, A.P. 70-232 Cd., Universitaria Delg., Coyoacan, Mexico City, DF 04510, Mexico. TEL 52-5-622-00-97, FAX 52-5-616-23-83, vazquezm@servidor.unam.mx, villegas@servidor.unam.mx. Ed. Maria Vazquez Valdez. Adv. contact Juan Jose Sanchez Sosa.

UNION WIRE. see *LABOR UNIONS*

053.1 DEU
UNISPIEGEL (HAMBURG). Text in German. 1998. 6/yr. free to students. adv. **Document type:** *Magazine, Consumer.* **Description:** Contains articles on higher education and other items of interest to university students.
Published by: Spiegel-Verlag Rudolf Augstein GmbH und Co. KG, Brandstwiete 19, Hamburg, 20457, Germany. TEL 49-40-3007-0, FAX 49-30-30072247, uly_foerster@spiegel.de, http://www.spiegel.de/unispiegel/. adv.: B&W page EUR 8,500, color page EUR 10,500; trim 190 x 260. Circ: 211,061 (controlled).

378.16 DEU ISSN 0171-4880
UNISPIEGEL (HEIDELBERG). Text in German. 1969. 6/yr. free. adv. bk.rev. **Document type:** *Newsletter, Academic/Scholarly.* **Description:** Higher education politics, college news, and general interest articles for students.
Formerly: Unispiegel Aktuell
Published by: Rektor der Universitaet Heidelberg, Postfach 105760, Heidelberg, 69047, Germany. TEL 49-6221-542310, FAX 49-6221-542317, presse@urz.uni-heidelberg.de, http://www.uni-heidelberg.de. Ed. Michael Schwarz. Adv. contact Edeltraud Conen. B&W page EUR 1,800. Circ: 25,000.

378.42871 GBR
UNIVERSAL POST✶. Text in English. 1992. fortn. bk.rev.; film rev.; play rev. illus. back issues avail. **Document type:** *Newspaper.* **Description:** Aimed at the students and staff of the University of Sunderland.
Published by: Charlton Allison Publishing, Universal Post, 2 Ashwood Terr, Sunderland, Tyne and Wear SR2 7NB, United Kingdom. Ed. Colin Thorne. Adv. contact Maggie Edge. page GBP 375. Circ: 5,000 (controlled).

378 ESP ISSN 0213-1595
DP302.C217
UNIVERSIDA DE CADIZ. ANALES. Text in Spanish. 1984. s-a. back issues avail.
Published by: Universidad de Cadiz, Servicio de Publicaciones, Rectorado Ancha 16, Cadiz, 11001, Spain. TEL 34-956-0150000, http://minerva.uca.es/publicaciones/seccion.asp?secc=R-AU, http://www.uca.es/.

378 NIC
UNIVERSIDAD. Text in Spanish. a.?.
Published by: Universidad Nacional Autonoma de Nicaragua, Recinto Universitario Ruben Dario, PABELLON, 7, Managua, Nicaragua. TEL 74852. Ed. Lizandro Chavez Alfaro.

378 BOL
UNIVERSIDAD BOLIVIANA JUAN MISAEL SARACHO. INFORME DE LABORES. Text in Spanish. irreg. charts; illus.; stat.
Published by: Universidad Boliviana Juan Misael Saracho, Av. Las Americas, Casilla 51, Tarija, Bolivia.

378.4682 ESP ISSN 0210-5454
AP60
UNIVERSIDAD DE GRANADA. BOLETIN. Text in Spanish. 1929; N.S. 1970. s-a.
Related titles: ♦ Supplement(s): Cuadernos Geograficos. ISSN 0210-5462.
Indexed: BiolAb, HistAb, PCI.
Published by: Universidad de Granada, Servicio de Publicaciones, Antiguo Colegio Maximo, Campus de Cartuja, Granada, 18071, Spain.

378.7291 CUB
UNIVERSIDAD DE LA HABANA. DIRECCION DE EXTENSION UNIVERSITARIA. REVISTA. Text in Spanish. 1977 (no.204). q. per issue exchange basis.
Indexed: HistAb.
Published by: (Universidad de La Habana, Direccion de Extension Universitaria), Ediciones Cubanas, Obispo No. 527, Apdo. 605, Havana, Cuba. Ed. Luisa Campuzano.

378 ESP
UNIVERSIDAD DE LAS PALMAS DE GRAN CANARIA. BOLETIN OFICIAL. Text in Spanish. 2000. irreg.
Media: Online - full text.
Published by: Universidad de las Palmas de Gran Canaria, Campus Universitario de San Cristobal, Edificio anexo a la "Granja", Avenida Maritima del Sur, Las Palmas, 35016, Spain. TEL 34-928452707, FAX 34-928458950, serpubli@infovia.ulpgc.es, http://www.ulpgc.es/cgi-bin/vicerrectorados/secretariageneral/boulpgc/listadoboletines.pl, http://www.ulpgc.es/index1.html.

378.861 COL ISSN 0120-5692
AS82.M4
UNIVERSIDAD DE MEDELLIN. REVISTA. Text in Spanish. 1957. s-a. COP 5,000; COP 10,000 foreign (effective 1999). illus.
Document type: *Academic/Scholarly.*
Indexed: IBR.
Published by: Universidad de Medellin, Apartado Aereo 1983, Medellin, ANT, Colombia. FAX 53-9-2458216. Ed. Jose Gabriel Baona. Circ: 5,000.

378 ESP
UNIVERSIDAD DE SEVILLA. SERIE: TESTIMONIO UNIVERSITARIO. Text in Spanish. irreg., latest vol.10. price varies. **Document type:** *Monographic series, Academic/Scholarly.*
Published by: Universidad de Sevilla, Secretariado de Publicaciones, Porvenir 27, Sevilla, 41013, Spain. TEL 34-95-4487444, FAX 34-95-4487443, secpub10@us.es, http://www.us.es/publius/inicio.html.

378.46 ESP ISSN 0080-6145
UNIVERSIDAD INTERNACIONAL MENENDEZ PELAYO. PUBLICACIONES. Text in Spanish. 1947. biennial.
Published by: Universidad Internacional Menendez Pelayo, Palacio de la Magdalena, Santander, Spain. Circ: 1,000.

UNIVERSIDAD NACIONAL AUTONOMA DE MEXICO. FACULTAD DE QUIMICA. GACETA. see *CHEMISTRY*

378.4 ESP ISSN 0213-117X
UNIVERSIDAD NACIONAL DE EDUCACION A DISTANCIA. CENTRO ASOCIADO DE BARBASTRO. ANALES. Key Title: Anales - Centro de la Universidad Nacional de Educacion a Distancia. Text in Spanish. 1984. a.
Published by: Universidad Nacional de Educacion a Distancia, Centro Asociado de Barbastro, Argensola, 60, Barbastro, Huesca 22300, Spain. TEL 34-974-311448, http://www.uned.es/.

378 PER
UNIVERSIDAD NACIONAL DEL CENTRO DEL PERU. ANALES CIENTIFICOS. Text in Spanish. 1971. a. price varies. illus.
Published by: Universidad Nacional del Centro del Peru, c/o Departamento de Publicaciones, Calle Real, 160, Huancayo, Peru. Circ: 1,000.

378 ARG
UNIVERSIDAD NACIONAL DEL LITORAL. BOLETIN. Text in Spanish. m.
Published by: Universidad Nacional del Litoral, C.c. 353, Santa Fe, S3000, Argentina. TEL 54-342-457-1110, http://www.unl.edu.ar/. Ed. Pedro Sanchez Izquierdo.

378.85 PER
UNIVERSIDAD PERUANA CAYETANO HEREDIA. BOLETIN. Text in Spanish. 1966.
Published by: (Direccion de Biblioteca Publicaciones y Museos), Universidad Peruana Cayetano Heredia, Calle Honorio Delgado 932, Lima, Peru.

UNIVERSIDAD TECNOLOGICA DEL CHOCO. REVISTA. see *TECHNOLOGY: COMPREHENSIVE WORKS*

E

Link to your serials resources and content with ulrichsweb.com

378 BRA
UNIVERSIDADE FEDERAL DE GOIAS. PUBLICACAO. Text in Portuguese. 1955. irreg., latest vol.74, 1983. adv.
Published by: Universidade Federal de Goias, Faculdade de Educacao, Praca Universitaria-C.P. 131, Setor Universitario, Goiania, GOIAS 74000, Brazil. caia@recitoria.ufg.br, http://www.ufg.br. Circ: 1,000.

UNIVERSIDADE FEDERAL DE PERNAMBUCO. ANUARIO ESTATISTICO. see *EDUCATION—Abstracting, Bibliographies, Statistics*

378.81 BRA
UNIVERSIDADE FEDERAL DO PARA. RELATORIO ANUAL. Text in Portuguese. a.
Published by: Universidade Federal do Para, Av Governador Jose Malcher, 1192, Nazare, Belem, Parana 66055260, Brazil.

378.8 MEX ISSN 0041-8935
UNIVERSIDADES. Text in Spanish. 1950. s-a. USD 18 to non-members (effective 1999). adv. bk.rev. bibl.; charts; illus.; stat. index. **Document type:** *Academic/Scholarly.*
Description: Covers dynamics, situations and perspectives in the area of higher education.
Indexed: IBR.
Published by: Union de Universidades de America Latina, A.P. 70-232 Cd., Universitaria Delg., Coyoacan, Mexico City, DF 04510, Mexico. TEL 52-5-622-00-97, FAX 52-5-616-23-83, vazquezm@servidor.unam.mx. Ed. Maria Vazquez Valdez. Adv. contact Juan Jose Sanchez Sosa. Circ: 2,500.

378 ITA
UNIVERSITA DEGLI STUDI DI MILANO. ANNUARIO. Text in Italian. 1924. a. free. **Document type:** *Directory, Academic/Scholarly.*
Indexed: NumL.
Published by: Universita degli Studi di Milano, Ufficio Stampa E Publicazioni, Via Festa Del Perdono, 7, Milan, MI 20122, Italy. TEL 39-02-58352249, FAX 39-02-58352627. Circ: 1,000.

378 DEU ISSN 0942-6884
UNIVERSITAET GOETTINGEN. JAHRESFORSCHUNGSBERICHT. Text in German. 1966. biennial. adv. stat. **Document type:** *Academic/Scholarly.*
Formerly: Universitaet Goettingen. Jahresbericht (0436-1202)
Published by: Universitaet Goettingen, Wilhelmsplatz 1, Goettingen, 37073, Germany. TEL 49-551-394341, FAX 49-551-394251, http://www.uni-goettingen.de.

378.106 DEU
UNIVERSITAET HOHENHEIM. AMTLICHE MITTEILUNGEN. Text in German. 1971. irreg. (10-20/yr.). looseleaf. **Document type:** *Bulletin, Corporate.* **Description:** Internal administration rules for the university.
Published by: Universitaet Hohenheim, Presse und Oeffentlichkeitsarbeit, Schloss, Mittelbau, Stuttgart, 70599, Germany. TEL 49-711-459-2001, FAX 49-711-4593289, presse@uni-hohenheim.de, http://www.uni-hohenheim.de. Circ: 500.

378 DEU
UNIVERSITAET MANNHEIM. STUDIUM GENERALE. Variant title: Studium Generale. Text in German. 2/yr. adv. **Document type:** *Directory, Academic/Scholarly.*
Published by: (Universitaet Mannheim), Grunert Medien & Kommunikation GmbH, Am Paradeplatz 5-6, Mannheim, 68161, Germany. TEL 49-621-400404-0, FAX 49-621-40040488, info@grunert-medien.de, http://www.grunert-medien.de. adv.: B&W page EUR 840, color page EUR 1,120. Circ: 10,500 (controlled).

378 DEU ISSN 0942-2234
LF2525
UNIVERSITAET ZU KOELN. FORSCHUNGSBERICHT. Text in German. 1966. biennial. price varies. adv. **Document type:** *Journal, Academic/Scholarly.*
Formerly (until 1990): Universitaet zu Koeln. Jahrbuch (0069-5890)
—GNLM.
Published by: Universitaet zu Koeln, Pressestelle, Albertus-Magnus-Platz, Cologne, 50923, Germany. TEL 49-221-4702202, FAX 49-221-4705190. Circ: 8,000.

378 DEU ISSN 0179-7514
UNIVERSITAETSFUEHRER. Text in German. 1972. a. **Document type:** *Directory, Consumer.*
Formerly (until 1985): Hochschulfuehrer Universitaet Hohenheim (0179-1923)
Published by: Universitaet Hohenheim, Presse und Oeffentlichkeitsarbeit, Schloss, Mittelbau, Stuttgart, 70599, Germany. TEL 49-711-4592003, FAX 49-711-4593289, presse@uni-hohenheim.de, http://www.uni-hohenheim.de. Ed. Klaus Grabowski. Circ: 3,700. **Subscr. to:** Buchhandlung Wittwer, Fruwirthstr 24, Stuttgart 70599, Germany.

UNIVERSITARIO EJECUTIVO. see *BUSINESS AND ECONOMICS—Management*

378.72 MEX ISSN 0185-4143
AP63
LOS UNIVERSITARIOS. Text in Spanish. m. free. **Description:** Designed for students, teachers and administrative workers at the university.
Published by: Universidad Nacional Autonoma de Mexico, Coordinacion de Difusion Cultural, c/o Secretaria de Comunicacion, Edificio D, 4o. Piso, Zona Cultural, Ciudad Universitaria, Mexico City, DF 04510, Mexico. TEL 52-5-6226240, FAX 52-5-6226243, cazes@servidor.unam.mx. Ed. Gonzalo Celorio.

378 USA ISSN 0146-9061
UNIVERSITAS. Text in English. 1970. m. USD 25 membership; USD 10 to libraries. adv. bk.rev. back issues avail.
Indexed: ABS&EES, RHEA.
Published by: (University Professors for Academic Order (UPAO)), COMCOA, Inc., PO Box Q, Corvallis, OR 97339. Ed. Donald Senese. Circ: 550.

378 GHA ISSN 0049-5530
AS631.A1 CODEN: ECTHEA
UNIVERSITAS; an inter-faculty journal. Text in English. 1971. a. USD 20. adv. bk.rev. bibl.; charts. **Document type:** *Academic/Scholarly.*
Indexed: ASD, AmH&L, CCA, HistAb, IBSS, RASB.
Published by: University of Ghana, Department of English, Legon, Ghana. TEL 233-21-775381. Ed. Elom Dovlo. Circ: 1,000.

378 VEN ISSN 1315-4192
➤ **UNIVERSITAS 2000.** Text in Spanish. 1979. 4/yr., latest vol.24, 2000. VEB 20,000 domestic to individuals; USD 90 foreign to individuals; VEB 22,000 domestic to institutions; USD 750 foreign to institutions (effective 2002). adv. **Document type:** *Academic/Scholarly.* **Description:** Contains critical reviews of research literature and reports of empirical, theoretical and practical studies in Education, Science and Technology.
Related titles: Online - full content ed.
Published by: Fondo Editorial para el Desarrollo de la Educacion Superior/Fund for the Development of Higher Education, Apdo 62532, Caracas, DF 1060-A, Venezuela. TEL 58-212-5554221, FAX 58-212-5526387, universitas2000@iesa.edu.ve, http://www.universitas2000.usb.ve. Ed. Luis Manuel Penalver.
Co-sponsor: Latin American University Group for the Reform and Improvement of Education.

378.71 CAN ISSN 1193-2791
UNIVERSITE. Text in English. 1979. 6/yr. looseleaf. free. adv. bk.rev. back issues avail. **Document type:** *Newspaper.*
Former titles (until 1991): F Q P P U Nouvelles Universitaires; F A P U Q Nouvelles Universitaires (0709-8006); F A P U Q Information (0709-8014)
Published by: Federation Quebecoise des Professeures et Professeurs d'Universite, 4446 bd St Laurent, Bur 405, Montreal, PQ H2W 1Z5, Canada. TEL 514-843-5953, FAX 514-843-6928. Circ: 8,000.

378.73 CIV ISSN 1010-3961
UNIVERSITE D'ABIDJAN. ANNALES. HORS SERIE. Variant title: Universite d'Abidjan. Annales. Volume Hors Serie. Text in French. 1972. irreg. **Document type:** *Journal, Academic/Scholarly.*
Published by: Universite Nationale de Cote d'Ivoire, Institut d'Histoire d'Art et d'Archeologie Africains, 08 BP 865, Abidjan 22, Ivory Coast.

UNIVERSITE DE GENEVE. DEPARTEMENT D'HISTOIRE ECONOMIQUE. BULLETIN. see *BUSINESS AND ECONOMICS—Economic Systems And Theories, Economic History*

378 COG
AS659.C64
UNIVERSITE MARIEN NGOUABI. ANNALES. Text in French; Summaries in English. -1977; resumed 1989. a. XAF 2,000; XAF 4,000 foreign. bk.rev. bibl.; illus. **Description:** Covers the academic publications of the University.
Supersedes: Universite de Brazzaville. Annales (0302-4814)
Indexed: BiolAb, MLA, MLA-IB.
Published by: Universite Marien Ngouabi, BP 69, Brazzaville, Congo, Republic. Ed. Emmanuel B Dongala. Circ: 1,000.

378 FRA ISSN 0751-5839
UNIVERSITE SYNDICALISTE. Text in French. 1928. w. adv. **Document type:** *Bulletin.* **Description:** News about the education system (secondary schools only). Reforms, debates, union views, ideas on current issues, interviews of writers, sociologists, scientists, etc..
Published by: Syndicat National des Enseignements de Second Degre, c/o C.A.G., 36 rue La Bruyere, Paris, 75009, France. TEL 33-01-42809104, FAX 33-01-42809311, http://www.snes.edu. Ed. Gerard Antheaume. Adv. contact Catherine Pinchaux. Circ: 112,225.

378 NLD
UNIVERSITEIT UTRECHT. UNIVERSITEIT MEDIA BULLETIN. Text in Dutch. 1988. s-m. looseleaf. free. illus. **Document type:** *Bulletin.* **Description:** Provides information on new projects and activities at the university.
Published by: Uniiversiteit Utrecht, Postbus 80125, Utrecht, 3584 CL, Netherlands. TEL 31-30-2539111, FAX 31-30-2533388, http://www.uu.nl. Circ: 900 (controlled).

378 CAN ISSN 0226-7454
UNIVERSITES. Text in English. 1980. q. CND 30. **Document type:** *Bulletin.*
Supersedes: A U P E L F Bulletin de Nouvelles Breves (0007-4373); Etudes Francaises dans le Monde (0316-2672); Nouvelles Universitaires Africaines
Related titles: Online - full text ed.
—IE.
Published by: Agence Francophone pour l'Enseignement Superieur et de la Recherche, succ Cote des Neiges, PMB 400, Montreal, PQ H3C 2S7, Canada. TEL 514-343-6630, FAX 514-343-2107, universi@refer.qc.ca, http://www.aupelf-uref.org/UNIVERSITES. Ed. Jean Claude Castelain. Pub. Michel Guillou. R&P Jean-Claude Castelain. Circ: 12,000.

378 RUS
UNIVERSITET ROSSIISKOI AKADEMII OBRAZOVANIYA. VESTNIK. Text in Russian. irreg.
Indexed: RASB.
Published by: Vestnik Universiteta Rossiiskoi Akademii Obrazovaniya, B Polyanka 58, Moscow, 113184, Russian Federation. **US dist. addr.:** East View Information Services, 3020 Harbor Ln. N., Minneapolis, MN 55447. TEL 612-550-0961.

378 DNK ISSN 0106-7141
UNIVERSITETSAVISEN. Text in Danish. 1973. fortn. illus.
Supersedes: Koebenhavns Universitet. Meddelelser (0525-6836)
Indexed: RASB.
Published by: Koebenhavns Universitet, Noerregade 10, Copenhagen, 1017, Denmark. TEL 45-35322626, FAX 45-35322628, http://www.ku.dk. Ed. Gitte Meyer. Circ: 37,000.

379.324 GBR
UNIVERSITIES' AND COLLEGES' STAFF DEVELOPMENT AGENCY GREEN PAPERS. Variant title: U Co S D A Green Papers. Text in English. 1993. irreg., latest vol.14, 1996. GBP 12.50. **Document type:** *Monographic series, Academic/Scholarly.* **Description:** Stimulates and provokes discussion about strategic issues and policy-making in higher education institutions and other organizations and agencies involved in higher education.
Published by: Higher Education Staff Development Agency, Ingram House, 65 Wilkinson St, University of Sheffield, Sheffield, S Yorks S10 2GJ, United Kingdom. TEL 44-114-222-1335, FAX 44-114-222-1333, ucosda@sheffield.ac.uk.

378.12 GBR
UNIVERSITIES' AND COLLEGES' STAFF DEVELOPMENT AGENCY HANDBOOKS. Variant title: U Co S D A Handbooks. Text in English. 1988. irreg., latest vol.30, 1997. GBP 12.50. **Document type:** *Monographic series, Academic/Scholarly.*
Published by: Higher Education Staff Development Agency, Ingram House, 65 Wilkinson St, University of Sheffield, Sheffield, S Yorks S10 2GJ, United Kingdom. TEL 44-114-222-1335, FAX 44-114-222-1333, ucosda@sheffield.ac.uk.

378.12 GBR
UNIVERSITIES' AND COLLEGES' STAFF DEVELOPMENT AGENCY OCCASIONAL LONGER BRIEFING PAPERS. Variant title: U Co S D A Occasional Longer Briefing Papers. Text in English. 1994. irreg., latest vol.6, 1997. GBP 2. **Document type:** *Monographic series, Academic/Scholarly.*
Published by: Higher Education Staff Development Agency, Ingram House, 65 Wilkinson St, University of Sheffield, Sheffield, S Yorks S10 2GJ, United Kingdom. TEL 44-114-222-1335, FAX 44-114-222-1333, ucosda@sheffield.ac.uk.

379.324 GBR
UNIVERSITIES' AND COLLEGES' STAFF DEVELOPMENT AGENCY RESOURCE PACKS AND DISKS. Variant title: U Co S D A Resource Packs and Disks. Text in English. 1989. irreg., latest vol.20, 1997. GBP 60 to non-members; GBP 30 to members. **Document type:** *Monographic series, Academic/Scholarly.*
Published by: Higher Education Staff Development Agency, Ingram House, 65 Wilkinson St, University of Sheffield, Sheffield, S Yorks S10 2GJ, United Kingdom. TEL 44-114-222-1335, FAX 44-114-222-1333, ucosda@sheffield.ac.uk.

UNIVERSITIES HANDBOOK (YEAR). see *EDUCATION—Guides To Schools And Colleges*

UNIVERSITIES SAFETY ASSOCIATION. DIGEST. see *PUBLIC HEALTH AND SAFETY*

378.0025 CAN ISSN 0847-3536
UNIVERSITIES TELEPHONE DIRECTORY (YEAR)/BOTTIN DES UNIVERSITES (YEAR). Text in English, French. a. CND 45 domestic; CND 49 in Canada; CND 59 elsewhere (effective 2000). **Document type:** *Directory.*
Formerly: Academic and Administrative Officers at Canadian Universities (Year) (0711-7051)

E

▼ new title ➤ refereed ✶ unverified ♦ full entry avail.

—CISTI.
Published by: Association of Universities and Colleges of Canada/Association des Universites et Colleges du Canada, 350 Albert St, Ste 600, Ottawa, ON K1R 1B1, Canada. TEL 613-563-1236, FAX 613-563-9745, sales@aucc.ca, http://www.aucc.ca. Circ: 2,000.

378.71 CAN ISSN 0041-9257
LA418.O8
UNIVERSITY AFFAIRS/AFFAIRES UNIVERSITAIRES. Text in English, French. 1959. 10/yr. CND 39 domestic; CND 55 in United States; CND 75 foreign; CND 3.75 newsstand/cover (effective 2000). adv. bk.rev. bibl. **Description:** Carries news about universities across Canada as well as advertisements of career opportunities inside and outside the universities.
Related titles: Microfilm ed.: (from MML); Microform ed.: (from MML).
Indexed: CBCARef, CBPI, CEI, CPE, RHEA.
—CCC.
Published by: Association of Universities and Colleges of Canada/Association des Universites et Colleges du Canada, 350 Albert St, Ste 600, Ottawa, ON K1R 1B1, Canada. TEL 613-563-1236, FAX 613-563-9745, ua@aucc.ca, http://www.aucc.ca. Ed. Christine Tausig Ford. Adv. contact Mary Lu May. Circ: 25,000.

378.161 GBR
LB2351
UNIVERSITY AND COLLEGE ENTRANCE: THE OFFICIAL GUIDE (YEAR). Text in English. 1963. a., latest 9th Ed., 2002. GBP 22.95 (effective 2002). adv. **Document type:** *Directory, Academic/Scholarly.*
Supersedes: University Entrance: The Official Guide (0956-781X); Formerly (until 1987): Compendium of University Entrance Requirements for First Degree Courses in the United Kingdom (0571-625X)
—BLDSC (9103.781000).
Published by: Universities and Colleges Admissions Service, Rosehill, New Barn Ln, Cheltenham, Glos GL52 3LZ, United Kingdom. TEL 44-1242-227788, http://www.ucas.com, http://www.swotbooks.com/ucasbooks/. Ed., R&P Tony Higgins. Circ: 30,000. **Dist. addr.:** U C A S Distribution, PO Box 130, Cheltenham, Glous GL52 3ZF, United Kingdom. TEL 44-1242-544610, FAX 44-1242-544960, distribution@ucas.ac.uk.

UNIVERSITY BOOKMAN; a quarterly review. see *PUBLISHING AND BOOK TRADE*

378.42393 GBR
UNIVERSITY BRISTOL CALENDAR. Text in English. 1910. a. GBP 15. **Document type:** *Directory.*
Published by: University of Bristol, Senate House, Tyndall Ave, Bristol, Avon BS8 1TH, United Kingdom. TEL 44-117-928-9000, FAX 44-117-925-1424, jennifer.clapham@bristol.ac.uk. Ed. Jennifer Clapham. Circ: 400.

378.106 USA ISSN 1097-6671
LB2341.93.U6
UNIVERSITY BUSINESS; solutions for today's higher education. Cover title: U. Text in English. 1998-2001; resumed 2002. 10/yr. USD 72 domestic; USD 144 foreign (effective 2005). adv. bk.rev. charts; stat. back issues avail. **Document type:** *Magazine, Trade.* **Description:** Features strategies for managing the financial, facility-related, technological, and academic aspects of higher education. For senior administrators of colleges and universities including presidents, chancellors, provosts, chief financial officers, and information officers.
Incorporates (2000-2002): Matrix Magazine (1531-0884)
Related titles: Online - full text ed.: (from EBSCO Publishing, Gale Group).
Published by: Educational Media, Inc. (Subsidiary of: Hanson Publishing Group, Inc.), 488 Main Ave, Norwalk, CT 06851 . general@universitybusiness.com, camagazine@aol.com, http://www.universitybusiness.com/, http:// www.districtadministration.com. adv.: B&W page USD 5,620, color page USD 7,230; trim 7.875 x 10.5. Circ: 34,345 (controlled).

378.106 USA
UNIVERSITY BUSINESS DAILY; daily reports from the education revolution. Text in English. d. **Description:** Covers new stories, reports and press releases from the field of higher education.
Media: E-mail.
Published by: Educational Media, Inc. (Subsidiary of: Hanson Publishing Group, Inc.), 488 Main Ave, Norwalk, CT 06851 . camagazine@aol.com, http://www.districtadministration.com.

UNIVERSITY CHEMISTRY EDUCATION. see *CHEMISTRY*

378 IRL ISSN 0332-0863
UNIVERSITY COLLEGE CORK CALENDAR. Text in English. 1909. a.
—BLDSC (2988.600000).
Published by: University College Cork, Academic Secretariat, Office of the Registrar & VP for Academic Affairs, Cork, Ireland. TEL 353-21-4902257, FAX 353-21-4273072, registrar@ucc.ie, http://www.ucc.ie/academic/calendar/ index.html, http://www.ucc.ie/admin/registrar/. Circ: 2,500.

378 IND ISSN 0566-2257
L61
UNIVERSITY NEWS; a weekly chronicle of higher education & research. Text in English. w. (Mon.). USD 140 (effective 2003). adv. **Document type:** *Newsletter.* **Description:** Covers higher education, campus happenings, job opportunities, and award of fellowships and scholarships.
Indexed: PAA&I.
Published by: Association of Indian Universities, A.I.U. House, 16 Kotla Marg, New Delhi, 110 002, India. TEL 91-11-323-0059, FAX 91-11-323-6105, TELEX 31-66180 AIU IN, aiu@del2.vsnl.net.in, http://www.aiuweb.org. Ed. Sutinder Singh. Adv. contact B S Dahiya Aso. page USD 315; 230 x 165.

378 GBR
UNIVERSITY OF BRADFORD. ANNUAL REPORT. Text in English. 1983. a. free. stat. back issues avail. **Document type:** *Corporate.*
Former titles: University of Bradford. Vice-Chancellor's Annual Report (0957-5677); (until 1985): University of Bradford. Vice-Chancellor's Report (0305-8654)
—BLDSC (1479.768500).
Published by: University of Bradford, Public Relations Office, Richmond Rd, Bradford, W Yorks BD7 1DP, United Kingdom. TEL 44-1274-233088, FAX 44-1274-235460, TELEX 51309-UNIBFD-G, public-relations@bradford.ac.uk, http://www.brad.ac.uk/index.html. Ed. Alison Darnbrough. Circ: 16,000.

UNIVERSITY OF CAPE TOWN. COMMITTEE FOR UNDERGRADUATE EDUCATION IN SCIENCE. COLLOQUIUM SERIES. see *SCIENCES: COMPREHENSIVE WORKS*

378.687355 ZAF
➤ **UNIVERSITY OF CAPE TOWN. RESEARCH REPORT.** Text in English. 1976. a. free. back issues avail. **Document type:** *Academic/Scholarly.* **Description:** Reports on research at the University of Cape Town.
Media: Online - full text. **Related titles:** CD-ROM ed.
Published by: University of Cape Town, Department of Research Development, Private Bag, Rondebosch, 7701, South Africa. TEL 27-21-6502434, FAX 27-21-6505768, reamhw@bremner.uct.ac.za, http://www.uct.ac.za/depts/drd/ resrep.html. Ed. Margaret H Ward. Circ: 750 (controlled).

378.77311 USA ISSN 0362-4706
UNIVERSITY OF CHICAGO RECORD. Text in English. 1967. irreg. (3-4/yr.). free. charts. **Document type:** *Academic/Scholarly.*
Indexed: RI-1, RI-2.
Published by: University of Chicago, 5710 S Woodlawn Ave, Chicago, IL 60637. TEL 773-702-8352, FAX 773-702-8174, ellen-mcgrew@uchicago.edu. Ed., R&P Ellen McGrew TEL 773-702-8363. Circ: 21,000.

UNIVERSITY OF DAYTON. SCHOOL OF EDUCATION. ABSTRACTS OF RESEARCH PROJECTS. see *EDUCATION—Abstracting, Bibliographies, Statistics*

378.4127 GBR
UNIVERSITY OF DUNDEE STUDENTS ASSOCIATION HANDBOOK. Text in English. 1968. a. free to new students. adv. **Document type:** *Bulletin.*
Published by: University of Dundee, Students Association, Airlie Pl, Dundee, Angus DD1 4HP, United Kingdom. http://www.dusa.dundee.ac.uk. Circ: 4,000.

378 GBR ISSN 0267-6311
UNIVERSITY OF GLASGOW. NEWSLETTER. Text in English. 1977. m. back issues avail. **Document type:** *Newsletter.* **Description:** Contains news about the University of Glasgow and its students, faculty, and alumni.
Related titles: Online - full content ed.
Published by: University of Glasgow, Publicity Services, No.2 The Square, Glasgow, Lanarkshire, United Kingdom. newsletter@gla.ac.uk, http://www.gla.ac.uk/publications/ newsletter/index.html. Ed. Annie Vaz.

378.669 NGA ISSN 0331-0809
UNIVERSITY OF IBADAN. STUDENT AFFAIRS OFFICE. STUDENT HANDBOOK OF INFORMATION ON UNIVERSITY POLICIES AND PRACTICES. Text in English. irreg. illus.
Published by: University of Ibadan, Student Affairs Office, Ibadan, Oyo, Nigeria.

378.549 IND
UNIVERSITY OF KASHMIR. ANNUAL REPORT. Text in English. a.
Published by: University of Kashmir, Hazratbal, Srinagar, Jammu & Kashmir 190 006, India.

378 657.6 GBR
UNIVERSITY OF LEICESTER. QUALITY AUDIT REPORT. Text in English. irreg.
—BLDSC (9111.815100).
Published by: (University of Leicester), Quality Assurance Agency for Higher Education, Southgate House, Southgate Street, Gloucester, GL1 1UB, United Kingdom. TEL 44-1452-557000, FAX 44-1452-557070, http://www.gaa.ac.uk.

378.42753 GBR ISSN 0305-9227
UNIVERSITY OF LIVERPOOL CALENDAR. Text in English. 1881. a. GBP 18 (effective 2000). **Document type:** *Bulletin.* **Description:** Yearbook of the University of Liverpool; includes statutes, ordinances, committee memberships and staff lists.
Related titles: Microfiche ed.
Published by: University of Liverpool, Committee Secretariat, Liverpool, University Of Liverpool, Liverpool, L69 3BX, United Kingdom. TEL 44-151-794-2023, FAX 44-151-708-6502, sheila.jones@liverpool.ac.uk. Ed. S A Jones. Circ: 825.

UNIVERSITY OF LIVERPOOL POST GRADUATE PROSPECTUS. see *EDUCATION—Guides To Schools And Colleges*

378.161 GBR ISSN 0268-2362
UNIVERSITY OF LIVERPOOL PROSPECTUS. Text in English. 1984. a. free. **Document type:** *Academic/Scholarly.* **Description:** Information on first degree courses, entry requirements, application procedures and general information.
Published by: University of Liverpool, Committee Secretariat, Liverpool, University Of Liverpool, Liverpool, L69 3BX, United Kingdom. TEL 44-151-794-5926, FAX 44-151-794-2060, uksro@liverpool.ac.uk, http://www.liv.ac.uk/uksro/uksro.htm. Ed. G Kelly. Circ: 95,000.

378.3 IND ISSN 0076-2210
UNIVERSITY OF MADRAS. ENDOWMENT LECTURES✶. Text in English. a.
Published by: University of Madras, c/o Director, Publications Division, Chennai, Tamil Nadu 600 005, India. TEL 91-44-568778, FAX 91-44-566693.

378 MLT
UNIVERSITY OF MALTA. ANNUAL REPORT. Text in English. a. **Document type:** *Corporate.*
Published by: University of Malta, Msida, Malta. TEL 356-333903, FAX 356-336450, comms@um.edu.mt, http://www.um.edu.mt/pub/annualreport.html. Ed. Lawrence Ellul. Circ: 1,500.

378.6982 MUS
UNIVERSITY OF MAURITIUS. ANNUAL REPORT. Text in English. 1968. a. stat. back issues avail.
Published by: University of Mauritius, Reduit, Mauritius. Circ: 450.

378 USA ISSN 0041-9842
➤ **UNIVERSITY OF MICHIGAN. DIVISION OF RESEARCH DEVELOPMENT AND ADMINISTRATION. RESEARCH NEWS.** Text in English. 1949. q. USD 6 in Canada & Mexico; USD 15 elsewhere. charts; illus.; stat. back issues avail.; reprint service avail. from PQC. **Document type:** *Academic/Scholarly.* **Description:** Describes research from all areas and disciplines, using nonspecialist language.
Related titles: Microform ed.: (from PQC).
Indexed: BiolAb, IFP, MMI.
—Linda Hall.
Published by: University of Michigan, Division of Research Development and Administration, 3003 S State St, Ann Arbor, MI 48109-1274. TEL 313-763-5587, FAX 313-763-4053, TELEX 43208155. Ed. Suzanne Tainter. Circ: 14,000.

378.74 AUS ISSN 0375-4588
UNIVERSITY OF NEW ENGLAND. ANNUAL REPORT. Text in English. 1968. a. stat. back issues avail. **Document type:** *Corporate.*
Indexed: BiolAb.
Published by: University of New England, Armidale, NSW 2351, Australia. TEL 61-67-732819, FAX 61-67-733482, bdrew@metz.une.edu.au. Circ: 250.

378.12 AUS
UNIVERSITY OF NEW ENGLAND. GUIDE TO EXPERTISE. Text in English. 1979. a. free. **Description:** Provides a list of academic staff and their specialisations.
Former titles: University of New England. Specialists List; University of New England. Public Affairs Specialists List; University of New England. Information Office Specialists List (0158-0604)
Published by: University of New England, Armidale, NSW 2351, Australia. TEL 61-67-732819, FAX 61-67-733482, bdrew@metz.une.edu.au.

378.74 AUS ISSN 1443-3435
UNIVERSITY OF NEW ENGLAND. TEACHING & LEARNING CENTRE. UPDATES. Text in English. 1956. s-a. free. illus. 24 p./no.; **Document type:** *Newsletter.*
Former titles (until 2000): U N E News (1321-3350); (until 1994): Armidale News (1036-594X); (until 1991): Network (Armidale) (1036-5931); (until 1990): External Studies Gazette (0014-5459)
Related titles: Online - full content ed.
Published by: University of New England, Teaching & Learning Centre, Armidale, NSW 2351, Australia. TEL 61-2-6773-2681, FAX 61-2-6773-3269, pmathew@metz.une.edu.au, http://www.une.edu.au/tlc/. Ed., R&P Peter Mathew. Circ: 13,000 (controlled).

E

378   USA
UNIVERSITY OF NEW MEXICO. OFFICE OF RESEARCH SERVICES. RESEARCH NOTES. Text in English. 1971. s-m. **Document type:** *Newsletter.*
Formerly: University of New Mexico. Office of Research Administration. Research Notes
Published by: University of New Mexico, Office of Research Services, 102 Scholes Hall, Albuquerque, NM 87131. TEL 505-277-2256, http://www.unmedu/~ors/rn_main.html. Ed. Denise A Wallen. Circ: 1,500.

378.994   AUS   ISSN 0157-1621
UNIVERSITY OF NEW SOUTH WALES. RESEARCH AND PUBLICATIONS REPORT. Text in English. a.
Formerly: University of New South Wales. Research and Publications (0548-6831)
Published by: University of New South Wales, Sydney, NSW 2052, Australia. TEL 61-2-385-2840, FAX 61-2-662-2163.

378.669   NGA   ISSN 0331-1686
UNIVERSITY OF NIGERIA. ANNUAL REPORT. Text in English. 1958. a. illus.; stat. **Document type:** *Bulletin, Corporate.*
Published by: University of Nigeria, Office of the Registrar, Nsukka, Enugu State, Nigeria. TEL 234-42-771911, FAX 234-42-770644, TELEX 51496 ULIONS NG.

UNIVERSITY OF QUEENSLAND. DOCTOR OF PHILOSOPHY HANDBOOK. see *PHILOSOPHY*

378   AUS
UNIVERSITY OF QUEENSLAND. YEARBOOK. Text in English. 1967. a. AUD 49.95 (effective 2003). stat. index. 300 p./no.; **Document type:** *Directory, Academic/Scholarly.* **Description:** Lists legislation, statutes, senate and other major committees, financial award and prize rules, awards, senior staff,principal dates, benefactions received and a list of centres and units.
Former titles: University of Queensland. Calendar Series. Vol.1: Yearbook (1324-8944); (until 1996): University of Queensland. Calendar (0157-2849)
Published by: University of Queensland, Academic Information and Handbooks Office, Brisbane, QLD 4072, Australia. TEL 61-7-33651111, FAX 61-7-33651199, ewright@admin.uq.edu.au, http://www.uq.edu.au. Circ: 700. **Subscr. to:** University Bookshop, PO Box 6086, St Lucia, QLD 4067, Australia. TEL 61-7-3365-2168, FAX 61-7-3365-1977, geninfo@bookshop.uq.edu.au, http://www.bookshop.uq.edu.au.

378   AUS
UNIVERSITY OF SOUTHERN QUEENSLAND. HANDBOOK. Text in English. a.
Related titles: Online - full text ed.
Published by: University of Southern Queensland, Toowoomba, QLD 4350, Australia. http://www.usq.edu.au/handbook/. Ed. Julie Hillocks.

378   GBR
UNIVERSITY OF STRATHCLYDE. UNIVERSITY REVIEW. Text in English. 1982. a. free. back issues avail. **Document type:** *Corporate.*
Formerly: University of Strathclyde. Annual Report (0305-5574)
Indexed: BiolAb.
Published by: University of Strathclyde, External Affairs and Development Office, McCance Bldg, 16 Richmond St, Glasgow, G1 1XQ, United Kingdom. TEL 44-141-552-4400, FAX 44-141-552-0775, TELEX 77472-UNSLIB-G. Circ: 25,000.

UNIVERSITY OF TECHNOLOGY, SYDNEY. ANNUAL REPORT. see *TECHNOLOGY: COMPREHENSIVE WORKS*

UNIVERSITY OF TECHNOLOGY, SYDNEY. FACULTY OF BUSINESS HANDBOOK. see *BUSINESS AND ECONOMICS*

UNIVERSITY OF TECHNOLOGY, SYDNEY. FACULTY OF DESIGN ARCHITECTURE AND BUILDING HANDBOOK. see *ARCHITECTURE*

378.94   AUS   ISSN 1036-0662
UNIVERSITY OF TECHNOLOGY, SYDNEY. FACULTY OF EDUCATION HANDBOOK. Text in English. 1990. a. AUD 14 domestic; AUD 19 foreign (effective 2000). **Document type:** *Catalog, Academic/Scholarly.* **Description:** Contains detailed information about the faculty, staff, courses and subject synopses.
Published by: University of Technology, Sydney, City Campus, PO Box 123, Broadway, NSW 2007, Australia. TEL 61-2-9514-2000, FAX 61-2-9514-1551, publications@uts.edu.au, http://www.uts.edu.au/div/ publications. Circ: 3,000.

UNIVERSITY OF TECHNOLOGY, SYDNEY. FACULTY OF ENGINEERING HANDBOOK. see *ENGINEERING*

UNIVERSITY OF TECHNOLOGY, SYDNEY. FACULTY OF HUMANITIES AND SOCIAL SCIENCES HANDBOOK. see *SOCIAL SCIENCES: COMPREHENSIVE WORKS*

UNIVERSITY OF TECHNOLOGY, SYDNEY. FACULTY OF MATHEMATICAL & COMPUTING SCIENCES HANDBOOK. see *MATHEMATICS*

UNIVERSITY OF TECHNOLOGY, SYDNEY. FACULTY OF NURSING, MIDWIFERY AND HEALTH HANDBOOK. see *MEDICAL SCIENCES—Nurses And Nursing*

UNIVERSITY OF TECHNOLOGY, SYDNEY. FACULTY OF SCIENCE HANDBOOK. see *SCIENCES: COMPREHENSIVE WORKS*

378   PHL
UNIVERSITY OF THE EAST RESERACH BULLETIN. Text in English. 1995. a. **Document type:** *Bulletin, Academic/Scholarly.* **Description:** Publishes completed and ongoing college, faculty and student research from Manila and Caloocan campuses.
Published by: University of the East, Office of Reserach Coordination, 2219 C.M. Recto Ave, Manila, 1008, Philippines. TEL 63-2-735-5471, FAX 63-2-735-6972, postmater@ue.edu.ph, http://ue.edu.ph/. Ed. Lourdes C Sanchez.

378.599   PHL
UNIVERSITY OF THE PHILIPPINES GAZETTE. Text in English. 1970. q.
Published by: University of the Philippines, Diliman, Quezon City, 1128, Philippines. TEL 63-2-9205301, http://www.upd.edu.ph. Ed. Leonardo de Castro. Circ: 1,000.

378.729   JAM   ISSN 0799-0006
UNIVERSITY OF THE WEST INDIES. VICE-CHANCELLOR'S REPORT. Text in English. 1962. a. (in 1 vol.). free. stat.
Description: Reports on activities and major developments in the University for the report year and projected activities for the ensuing year.
Published by: University of the West Indies, Office of University Registrar, Mona Campus, Kingston, 7, Jamaica. TEL 876-977-2407, FAX 876-977-1422, TELEX 2123 JAMAICA, http://www.uwimona.edu.jm. Circ: 750.

UNIVERSITY OF WALES, ABERYSTWYTH. UNDERGRADUATE PROSPECTUS. see *EDUCATION—Guides To Schools And Colleges*

378   GBR
UNIVERSITY OF WARWICK NEWSLETTER. Text in English. 1977. m. back issues avail. **Document type:** *Newsletter.*
Published by: University of Warwick Business Information Service, University of Warwick Library, Coventry, W Mids CV4 7AL, United Kingdom. TEL 44-1203-522876, FAX 44-1203-524752, j.m.evans@warwick.ac.uk, http://www.warwick.ac.uk/. Ed. Sarah Hordern.

UNIVERSITY OF ZAMBIA. SCHOOL OF HUMANITIES AND SOCIAL SCIENCES. ANNUAL REPORT. see *SOCIAL SCIENCES: COMPREHENSIVE WORKS*

UNIVERSITY URBAN PROGRAMS. see *SOCIOLOGY*

378   BIH   ISSN 0042-0425
UNIVERZITET DANAS. Text in Serbo-Croatian. 1966 (vol.7). m. BAD 60, USD 6.
Published by: Zajednica Jugoslovenskih Univerziteta, Obaca 7, Sarajevo, Bosnia Herzegovina. Ed. Franko Kozul.

UNIVERZITET U SARAJEVU. DOKTORSKE DISERTACIJE. REZIMEI. see *EDUCATION—Abstracting, Bibliographies, Statistics*

378.016   CAN   ISSN 1183-725X
UNIWORLD/UNIMONDE. Text in English, French. 2/yr. CND 39 domestic; CND 55 in United States; CND 75 elsewhere (effective 2000). **Document type:** *Bulletin.* **Description:** Describes Canadian university activities in international development.
Published by: Association of Universities and Colleges of Canada/Association des Universites et Colleges du Canada, 350 Albert St, Ste 600, Ottawa, ON K1R 1B1, Canada. TEL 613-563-1236, FAX 613-563-9745, ua@aucc.ca, http://www.aucc.ca.

378.0025   AUS   ISSN 1320-0283
V T A C GUIDE TO UNIVERSITY AND T A F E COURSES. Text in English. 1987. a. AUD 5.50 newsstand/cover (effective 2000). adv. **Document type:** *Directory.* **Description:** Details of entrance requirements and course summaries for Victorian Universities and TAFE colleges.
Former titles (until 1994): V T A C Guide to Tertiary Courses (1038-7226); (until 1992): V T A C Guide to Courses in Colleges and Universities (0818-6073)
Related titles: Braille ed.; Online - full text ed.
Published by: Victorian Tertiary Admissions Centre, 40 Park St, South Melbourne, VIC 3205, Australia. TEL 1-300-364133, FAX 61-3-96961310, enquiry@vtac.edu.au, http://www.vtac.edu.au. Ed. Dominil Muller. R&P, Adv. contact Dominil Miller TEL 61-3-99543250. page AUD 5,000. Circ: 100,000.

V U - OWNERS. see *COMPUTERS—Internet*

THE VANGUARD (MOBILE). see *COLLEGE AND ALUMNI*

378.12   NLD   ISSN 0925-9384
➤ **VELON;** tijdschrift voor lerarenopleiders. Text in Dutch. 1979. 4/yr. EUR 35 membership (effective 2005). adv. bk.rev. **Document type:** *Academic/Scholarly.* **Description:** Covers topics relating to teacher training, education and continuing education.
Former titles (until 1991): Idee (0925-188X); (until 1989): I D (Informatie- en Documentatievoorziening) (0920-4326) —IE, Infotrieve, KNAW.
Published by: Vereniging voor Lerarenopleiders in Nederland, Zeebruggestraat 9, Eindhoven, 5628 NH, Netherlands. TEL 31-40-2926821, velon@wxs.nl, http://www.velon.nl/ velontijdschrift.htm. Adv. contact Mathilde Van Vliet. Circ: 820 (paid).

378   MEX
VERITAS. Text in Spanish. 1997. a. back issues avail. **Document type:** *Yearbook.*
Media: Online - full text.
Published by: Universidad Regiomontana, Padre Mier Pte. 471, Monterrey, Nuevo Leon, Mexico. TEL 52-8343-1290, FAX 52-8343-3172, http://www.ur.mx/UR/veritas/.

VERMONT ACADEMY OF ARTS AND SCIENCES. STUDENT SYMPOSIUM AND ANNUAL CONFERENCE. OCCASIONAL PAPERS. see *ART*

VESTNIK VYSSHEI SHKOLY. see *BUSINESS AND ECONOMICS*

378.972   MEX
VIDA EN ZARAGOZA. Text in Spanish. q. MXP 80; MXP 20 newsstand/cover (effective 2000). **Description:** Covers activities at the university campus. Features interviews and reportages about services and cultural issues.
Published by: Universidad Nacional Autonoma de Mexico, Facultad de Estudios Superiores Zaragoza, Secretaria Particular, Mexico, Ave. GUELATAO 66, Col Ejercito de Oriente, Mexico City, DF 09230, Mexico. TEL 52-5-6230540, FAX 52-5-7441217, macias@pumaz.zaragoza.unam.mx, http://www.zaragoza.unam.mx/. Ed. Benny Weiss Steider.

378   IDN
VIDYA KARYA. Text in Indonesian. bi-m.
Published by: Lambung Mangkurat University, Fakultas Keguruan, Jl. Veteran No. 268, Banjarmasin, Indonesia.

378.0713   USA
VIEWS ON EDUCATION - NEWS OF EPISCOPAL COLLEGES. Variant title: Views & News. Text in English. 1986. s-a. free. back issues avail. **Document type:** *Newsletter.*
Formerly (until 1983): News of the Episcopal Colleges
Published by: Colleges and Universities of the Anglican Communion, c/o the Assn of Epispocal Colleges, 815 Second Ave, Ste 315, New York, NY 10017-4594. TEL 212-716-6148, FAX 212-986-5039, hclark@cuac.org. Ed., R&P Hal Clark. Circ: 10,000.

378.776   USA   ISSN 0095-5744
LD4827.S62
VIKING. Text in English. 1904. a. USD 10. adv. illus.
Indexed: AIAP.
Published by: St. Olaf College, 1520 St. Olaf Ave, Northfield, MN 55057. Ed. Sara Peterson. Circ: 2,500.

378   USA   ISSN 0731-9649
VIRGINIA TECH RESEARCH. Text in English. 1981. a. free (effective 2000). **Description:** Features articles about specific research projects conducted at the university.
Indexed: BiolAb, CurCont, NutrAb, PBA.
Published by: Virginia Polytechnic Institute and State University, Research and Graduate Studies, 102 Sandy Hall, Blacksburg, VA 24061-0325. TEL 540-231-5646, FAX 540-231-3714, strulove@vt.edu, http://www.rgs.vt.edu/resmag. Ed., R&P Susan Trulove. Circ: 12,000.

VISIONS (KANSAS CITY). see *ETHNIC INTERESTS*

378   USA
VOICE (ALBANY). Text in English. 1973. m. (9/yr.). membership. bk.rev.
Published by: United University Professions, 15143, Albany, NY 12212-5143. TEL 518-458-7935, FAX 518-459-3242. Ed. Peggy L S Barmore. Circ: 20,000 (controlled).

378   RUS
VORONEZHSKII GOSUDARSTVENNYI UNIVERSITET. VESTI. PROBLEMY VYSSHEGO OBRAZOVANIYA. Text in Russian. 2000. irreg.
Related titles: Online - full text ed.
Published by: Voronezhskii Gosudarstvennyi Universitet, Universitetskaya pl 1, Voronezh, 394693, Russian Federation. TEL 7-0732-789657, FAX 7-0732-554308, office@main.vsu.ru, http://www.vsu.ru/dept/science/public/vest_vsu/proedu.html. Ed. S. A. Sklyadnev.

378   RUS
VYSSHAYA I SREDNIAYA PROFESSIONAL'NAYA SHKOLA V ROSSII I ZA RUBEZHOM. Text in Russian. bi-m.
Indexed: RASB.

E

Address: Podsosenskii per 20, Moscow, 103062, Russian Federation. **US dist. addr.:** East View Information Services, 3020 Harbor Ln. N., Minneapolis, MN 55447. TEL 612-550-0961.

378 RUS ISSN 0869-3617
LA839
VYSSHEYE OBRAZOVANIE V ROSSII. Text in Russian. q.
Indexed: RASB, RefZh.
—East View.
Published by: Moskovskaya Gosudarstvennaya Akademiya Pechati, Sadovaya-Spasskaya 6, Moscow, 103045, Russian Federation. TEL 7-095-2089304, FAX 7-095-2073865. Ed. B G Yakovlev. **US dist. addr.:** East View Information Services, 3020 Harbor Ln. N., Minneapolis, MN 55447. TEL 612-550-0961.

306.4 650 AUS
➤ **WACANA.** Text mainly in English; Text occasionally in Indonesian. 1995. irreg., latest vol.5. free. back issues avail. **Document type:** *Proceedings, Academic/Scholarly.* **Description:** Named after the Indonesian linguistic term for discourse, this journal compiles and presents papers presented at conferences and new research on the teaching and study of Indonesian language.
Media: Online - full text.
Published by: Australian Society of Indonesian Language Educators (ASILE), Arts Faculty, University of the Sunshine Coast, Maroochydore, QLD 4558, Australia. TEL 61-7-5430-1254, FAX 61-5430-2448, http://intranet.usc.edu.au/wacana/wacana.html. Ed. Phillip Mahnken.

➤ **WASHINGTON UPDATE.** see *EDUCATION—Computer Applications*

378 DEU
WEGWEISER - STUDIEREN IN FREISING. Text in German. a. adv. **Document type:** *Bulletin, Consumer.*
Published by: Studentenwerk Muenchen, Leopoldstr. 15, Munich, 80802, Germany. TEL 49-89-38196-0, FAX 49-89-38196133, stuwerk@studentenwerk.mhn.de, http://www.studentenwerk.mhn.de. adv.: B&W page EUR 225, color page EUR 505; trim 94 x 130. Circ: 3,000 (controlled).

378 DEU
WEGWEISER - STUDIEREN IN MUENCHEN. Text in German. a. adv. **Document type:** *Bulletin, Consumer.*
Published by: Studentenwerk Muenchen, Leopoldstr. 15, Munich, 80802, Germany. TEL 49-89-38196-0, FAX 49-89-38196133, stuwerk@studentenwerk.mhn.de, http://www.studentenwerk.mhn.de. adv.: B&W page EUR 895, color page EUR 1,520; trim 94 x 130. Circ: 35,000 (controlled).

378 DEU
WEGWEISER - STUDIEREN IN ROSENHEIM. Text in German. a. adv. **Document type:** *Bulletin, Consumer.*
Published by: Studentenwerk Muenchen, Leopoldstr. 15, Munich, 80802, Germany. TEL 49-89-38196-0, FAX 49-89-38196133, stuwerk@studentenwerk.mhn.de, http://www.studentenwerk.mhn.de. adv.: B&W page EUR 200, color page EUR 350; trim 94 x 130. Circ: 1,200 (controlled).

378.07176 USA
WESLEYAN UNIVERSITY ALUMNI MAGAZINE. Text in English. 1916. q. free. bk.rev. back issues avail. **Document type:** *Consumer.* **Description:** Informs alumni of university and alumni developments.
Formerly: Wesleyan University Alumnus
Published by: Wesleyan University, Office of Public Information and Publications, Wesleyan Station, Middletown, CT 06459. TEL 860-685-3699, FAX 860-685-3601, wholder@wesleyan.edu. R&P William Holder. Circ: 30,000.

378.155 USA ISSN 0511-6848
LB2371
WESTERN ASSOCIATION OF GRADUATE SCHOOLS. PROCEEDINGS OF THE ANNUAL MEETING. Text in English. 1977 (19th). a. membership. **Document type:** *Proceedings.*
Published by: Western Association of Graduate Schools, University of Wyoming, The Graduate School, Laramie, WY 82071-3108. TEL 307-766-2287, FAX 307-766-4042. Ed. Thomas G Dunn. Circ: 500 (controlled).

378 AUS
WESTERN AUSTRALIAN DEPARTMENT OF TRAINING. COMMUNITY RELATIONS SECTION. HANDBOOK. Variant title: T A F E Handbook. Text in English. 1948. a. AUD 5.
Former titles: Western Australia. Office of Technical and Further Education. Handbook; Western Australia. Technical Education Division. Handbook
Published by: Western Australian Department of Training, Community Relations Section, 2nd Level., 151 Royal St, East Perth, W.A. 6004, Australia. TEL 61-9-2356022, FAX 61-9-2356014. Circ: 40,000.

378 CAN ISSN 0843-9699
➤ **THE WESTERN JOURNAL OF GRADUATE RESEARCH.** Text in English. 1989. a. **Document type:** *Journal, Academic/Scholarly.*
Published by: (University of Western Ontario, Faculty of Graduate Studies, University of Western Ontario, Society of Graduate Students), University of Western Ontario, 1151 Richmond St., Suite 2, London, ON N6A 5B8, Canada. TEL 519-661-2111, http://www.uwo.ca/sogs/academic/wjgr.htm.

378.1 CAN ISSN 0317-333X
WESTERN SPECTRUM. Text in English. 1974. a. CND 17.95 (effective 2004).
Published by: University of Toronto, Guidance Centre, 5201 Dufferin St, Toronto, ON M3H 5T8, Canada. TEL 416-667-7791, 800-565-9523, FAX 416-667-7832, 800-221-9985, utpbooks@utpress.utoronto.ca, http://www.utpress.utoronto.ca/GCentre/07784spec.html.

WHICH DEGREE. ARTS, HUMANITIES, LANGUAGES. see *HUMANITIES: COMPREHENSIVE WORKS*

WHICH DEGREE. ENGINEERING, TECHNOLOGY, GEOGRAPHY. see *EDUCATION—Guides To Schools And Colleges*

WHICH DEGREE. SCIENCES, MEDICINE, MATHEMATICS. see *EDUCATION—Guides To Schools And Colleges*

WHICH DEGREE. SOCIAL SCIENCES, BUSINESS, EDUCATION. see *EDUCATION—Guides To Schools And Colleges*

WHICH M B A?; a critical guide to the world's best programmes. (Master's in Business Administration) see *BUSINESS AND ECONOMICS—Management*

WHICH SCHOOL? FOR THE SIXTH FORM. see *EDUCATION—Guides To Schools And Colleges*

378.41025 GBR
WHICH UNIVERSITY - ON CD-ROM. Text in English. a. GBP 58 (effective 1999). **Document type:** *Directory.* **Description:** Contains detailed information on UK colleges and universities running first-degree programs.
Former titles: Which Degree. Which University - on CD-ROM; (until 1996): Which Degree. Which University: Universities - Colleges
Media: CD-ROM.
Published by: (Careers Research and Advisory Centre), Hobsons PLC, Bateman St, Cambridge, Cambs CB2 1LZ, United Kingdom. TEL 44-1223-460366, FAX 44-1223-301506.

378.161 USA ISSN 1077-0739
WHO GOT IN?; national survey of college admissions trends. Text in English. 1987. a. USD 14.95 domestic; USD 16.95 foreign (effective 2001). **Document type:** *Directory.* **Description:** Provides current information on more than 120 colleges, including class size, tuition, available scholarships, and financial aid tips.
Formerly: College Bound Admissions Survey
Published by: College Bound Publications, Inc., PO Box 6526, Evanston, IL 60204. TEL 773-262-5810, FAX 773-262-5806. Pub. R. Craig Sautter.

378.1543092 USA ISSN 0511-8891
WHO'S WHO AMONG STUDENTS IN AMERICAN JUNIOR COLLEGES. Text in English. 1966. a. USD 49.95. **Document type:** *Directory.*
Published by: Randall Publishing Company, 3200 Rice Mine Rd, Tuscaloosa, AL 35406. TEL 800-633-5953, FAX 205-391-2081, http://www.randallpub.com.

378.0092 USA
WHO'S WHO AMONG STUDENTS IN AMERICAN UNIVERSITIES AND COLLEGES. Text in English. a., latest vol.62, 1996. USD 49.95. **Document type:** *Directory.*
Published by: Randall Publishing Company, 3200 Rice Mine Rd, Tuscaloosa, AL 35406. TEL 800-633-5953, FAX 205-391-2081, http://www.randallpub.com.

378 GTM ISSN 0257-6449
WINAK. Text in Spanish. 1985. q.
Indexed: IBR, IBZ.
Published by: Universidad Mariano Galvez de Guatemala, 3a Ave 9-00 Zona 2, Interior Finca El Zapote, Guamala City, 01002, Guatemala. TEL 502-288-7592, FAX 502-288-9880, information@umg.edu.gt, http://www.umg.edu.gt/.

WISDOM. see *ETHNIC INTERESTS*

378 DEU
WISSENSCHAFTSPOLITIK UND WISSENSCHAFTSRECHT. Text in German. 2001. irreg., latest vol.6, 2004. price varies. **Document type:** *Monographic series, Academic/Scholarly.*
Published by: Deutscher Hochschulverband, Rheinallee 18, Bonn, 53173, Germany. TEL 49-228-9026666, FAX 49-228-9026680, dhv@hochschulverband.de, http://www.hochschulverband.de.

378 DEU
WO GEHT'S LANG?; Tips und Infos fuer Studenten. Text in German. 1976. a. free. **Document type:** *Bulletin.*
Former titles: Information Nicht nur fuer Studienanfaenger; (until 1982): Informationen fuer Studienanfaenger
Published by: Technische Universitaet Berlin, Universitaetsbibliothek, Str des 17. Juni 135, Berlin, 10623, Germany. TEL 49-30-31423980, FAX 49-30-31423909. Circ: 15,000.

378.19822 USA ISSN 1060-8303
LC1751
WOMEN IN HIGHER EDUCATION. Text in English. 1992. m. USD 73 domestic; USD 83 in Canada; USD 93 elsewhere (effective 2004). adv. bk.rev. 44 p./no.; back issues avail. **Document type:** *Newsletter, Consumer.* **Description:** Contains information to enlighten, encourage, empower, and enrich women on campus in the U.S. and Canada, administrators as well as faculty and students.
Related titles: Online - full text ed.: (from Gale Group, O C L C Online Computer Library Center, Inc.).
Indexed: CWI, FemPer.
Published by: Wenniger Company, 5376 Farmco Dr., Madison, WI 53704-7656. TEL 608-251-3232, FAX 608-284-0601, women@wihe.com, http://www.wihe.com. Ed., Pub., R&P Mary Dee Wenniger TEL 608-251-3232. Adv. contact Helen Conroy TEL 608-251-3232. Circ: 2,500 (paid).

378.33 USA ISSN 0084-1145
WOODROW WILSON NATIONAL FELLOWSHIP FOUNDATION. ANNUAL REPORT. Text in English. 1958. a. free. **Document type:** *Corporate.*
Published by: Woodrow Wilson National Fellowship Foundation, Office of the President, CN5281, Princeton, NJ 08543-5281. TEL 609-452-7007, FAX 609-452-0066, http://www.woodrow.org.

378.33 USA ISSN 0084-1137
WOODROW WILSON NATIONAL FELLOWSHIP FOUNDATION. NEWSLETTER. Text in English. 1963. irreg. (approx. 2/yr.). free. **Document type:** *Newsletter.*
Published by: Woodrow Wilson National Fellowship Foundation, Office of the President, CN5281, Princeton, NJ 08543-5281. TEL 609-452-7007, FAX 609-452-0066, http://www.woodrow.org.

▼ **WORK BASED LEARNING IN PRIMARY CARE.** see *MEDICAL SCIENCES*

370.7 FRA
WORLD DIRECTORY OF TEACHER-TRAINING INSTITUTIONS. Text in English, French, Spanish. irreg., latest 1993. EUR 18.29 newsstand/cover (effective 2003).
Published by: (International Council for Education for Teaching), UNESCO Publishing, 7 place de Fontenoy, Paris, 75352, France. TEL 33-1-45684300, FAX 33-1-45685737, http://www.unesco.org/publications. **Dist. in the US by:** Bernan Associates, Bernan, 4611-F Assembly Dr., Lanham, MD 20706-4391. TEL 800-274-4447, FAX 800-865-3450.

378 FRA
WORLD GUIDE TO HIGHER EDUCATION. Text in French. irreg., latest 1996. EUR 33.54 newsstand/cover (effective 2003).
Published by: UNESCO Publishing, 7 place de Fontenoy, Paris, 75352, France. TEL 33-1-45684300, FAX 33-1-45685737, http://www.unesco.org/publications. **Dist. in the U.S. by:** Bernan Associates, Bernan, 4611-F Assembly Dr., Lanham, MD 20706-4391. TEL 800-274-4447, FAX 800-865-3450.

WORLD MEDICAL JOURNAL. see *MEDICAL SCIENCES*

378.11 USA ISSN 0196-4682
PE1404
WRITING PROGRAM ADMINISTRATION. Short title: W P A. Text in English. 1977. s-a. USD 30 to individuals; USD 50 to institutions (effective 2004). adv. bk.rev. **Description:** Deals with administration of college and university writing programs: theory, research, and professional practices.
Indexed: BibInd, CIJE, MLA-IB.
—BLDSC (9364.539000), IE, ingenta.
Published by: Council of Writing Program Administrators, c/o Jennie Dautermann, Dept. of English, Miami University, Oxford, OH 45046. TEL 513-529-1393, ddhesse@ilstu.edu, dauterjp@muohio.edu, http://www.wpacouncil.org/. Ed., R&P, Adv. contact Douglas Hesse. Circ: 725.

378 CHN ISSN 1671-8267
XI'AN JIATONG UNIVERSITY. ACADEMIC JOURNAL. Text in Chinese. a.
Indexed: C&ISA, E&CAJ, ExcerpMed, IAA, RefZh.
—BLDSC (0570.512550), IE, ingenta.
Published by: Xi'an Jiatong University, 26 Xianning Rd, Xi'an, 710049, China. http://www.xjtu.edu.cn.

XIEZUO/WRITING. see *LITERATURE*

E

378 CHN ISSN 1001-960X
LB2391.C43
XUEWEI YU YANJIUSHENG JIAOYU/ACADEMIC DEGREES AND GRADUATE EDUCATION. Text in Chinese. 1984. bi-m. USD 20.40; USD 1.70 newsstand/cover (effective 2002).
Description: Publishes articles reflecting views concerning graduate education and system of academic degrees in China by summarizing relevant theoretical and practical issues, summing up experiences both at home and abroad, so as to materialize in China a system of academic degrees and graduate education with its own distinguishing features.
Related titles: Online - full text ed.: (from East View Information Services).
Published by: Guowuyuan, Xuewei Weiyuanhui/State Council, Academic Degree Committee, 7 Baishiqiao Lu, Beijing, 100081, China. Ed. Yue Wang. Circ: 18,500 (paid). **Dist. outside China by:** China International Book Trading Corp, 35 Chegongzhuang Xilu, Haidian District, PO Box 399, Beijing 100044, China. TEL 86-10-68412045, FAX 86-10-68412023, cibtc@mail.cibtc.com.cn, http://www.cibtc.com.cn/.

378 USA ISSN 0084-344X
YALE SCENE. Text in English. 1967. irreg. price varies.
Published by: Yale University Press, PO Box 209040, New Haven, CT 06520. TEL 203-432-0940, FAX 616-592-2618, chla@mlc.lib.mi.us, ysm@yale.edu, http://www.yale.edu, http://www.yalepress.yale.edu.

378 USA
YALE UNIVERSITY. BULLETIN. Text in English. 16/yr. **Document type:** *Catalog.*
Published by: Yale University, PO Box 208227, New Haven, CT 06520-8227. Ed. Judith Calvert.

378 CHN ISSN 1007-7162
YANGZHOU DAXUE XUEBAO (GAO JIAO YANJIU BAN)/YANGZHOU UNIVERSITY. JOURNAL (HIGHER EDUCATION STUDY EDITION). Text in Chinese. 1997. q.
Related titles: Online - full text ed.: (from East View Information Services).
Indexed: RefZh.
—BLDSC (4757.655700).
Published by: Yangzhou Daxue/Yangzhou University, 88, Daxue Nanlu, Yangzhou, 225009, China. TEL 86-514-7971606, FAX 86-514-7349817.

378.161 DEU
Z V S - INFO. Text in German. 1973. s-a. free. **Document type:** *Bulletin, Trade.* **Description:** Guide for application to German universities.
Published by: Zentralstelle fuer die Vergabe von Studienplaetzen, Sonnenstr 171, Dortmund, 44137, Germany. TEL 49-231-10810, FAX 49-231-1081227, poststelle@zvs.nrw.de, http://www.zvs.de. Adv. contact Irmgard Goetze TEL 49-251-690574. Circ: 300,000 (paid).

ZAGAZIG UNIVERSITY. FACULTY OF SCIENCE. BULLETIN. see *SCIENCES: COMPREHENSIVE WORKS*

378.6894 ZMB
ZAMBIA EDUCATIONAL JOURNAL✶. Text in English. 1971. a. bk.rev. charts; illus. **Document type:** *Academic/Scholarly.*
Formerly: Educational Front
Published by: (Zambia. University of Zambia, Zambia. School of Education, Zambia. Department of Education), Unza Press (Subsidiary of: University of Zambia), PO Box 32379, Lusaka, Zambia. TEL 260-1-293029, FAX 260-1-293580.

378.51 CHN ISSN 1002-4417
LA1133
ZHONGGUO GAODENG JIAOYU/HIGHER EDUCATION IN CHINA. Text in Chinese. 1965-1966; resumed 1982. m. CNY 42, USD 21.60 (effective 1999). adv. bk.rev. **Description:** Covers China's policy, development and administration of higher education.
Formerly: Higher Educational Front
Related titles: Online - full text ed.: (from East View Information Services).
Published by: (State Educational Commission), Zhongguo Jiaoyu Zazhishe, 10 Wenhuiyuan Beilu, Haidian, Beijing, 100088, China. TEL 86-10-6224-3806, FAX 86-10-6224-3806, chisaditor@chisa.edu.cn. Ed. Zhang Dimei. Circ: 24,000. **Dist. in US by:** China Books & Periodicals Inc, 360 Swift Ave., Ste. 48, S San Fran, CA 94080-6220. info@chinabooks.com, http://www.chinabooks.com/.

EDUCATION—International Education Programs

370.116 USA
A F S - U S A BRIDGES✶; a monthly newsletter for AFS volunteers. Text in English. 1988. m. free to qualified personnel. **Document type:** *Newsletter.* **Description:** Focuses on volunteer training, recruitment, and recognition; offers ideas for expanding AFS' student hosting and sending programs.
Formerly: A F S - U S A Directions (1063-0910)
Published by: A F S Intercultural Programs - U S A, 71 W 23nd St 17 Fl, New York, NY 10010-4102. TEL 212-949-4242, FAX 212-949-9379. Ed. Nancy Stuve. Pub. Jennifer Froistad. Circ: 10,000.

370.116 USA ISSN 1063-0902
A F S WORLD✶. Text in English. 1991. 3/yr. USD 25 membership. charts; illus.; maps. index. back issues avail.
Description: Offers a specific "AFS angle" on international and intercultural subjects, with the intent to educate towards a "global understanding," with an ultimate goal of global - cultural friendship.
Formerly (until 1990): Connections
Published by: A F S Intercultural Programs - U S A, 71 W 23nd St 17 Fl, New York, NY 10010-4102. TEL 212-949-4242, FAX 212-949-9379, TELEX AFSI UI 66379 UW (WUI). Ed. Nancy Struve. Pub. Jennifer Froistad. Circ: 32,000.

378.016 USA ISSN 1047-2576
LB2376
ACADEMIC YEAR ABROAD. Text in English. 1964. a. USD 42.95. index. reprints avail. **Document type:** *Directory.*
Description: Describes more than 2,200 semester and academic-year programs offered by U.S. and foreign universities and private organizations.
Supersedes: Learning Traveler. U S College-Sponsored Programs Abroad: Academic Year; Former titles: U S College-Sponsored Programs Abroad. Academic Year (0082-8602); United States Academic Programs Abroad
Published by: Institute of International Education, PO Box 371, Annapolis, MD 20701-0371. TEL 301-617-7804, FAX 301-953-2838, http://www.iie.org/. Ed. Sara Steen.

370.116 USA ISSN 0895-1101
ADVISING QUARTERLY; for professionals in international education. Text in English. 1987. q. USD 40 domestic; USD 50 foreign (effective 2005). adv. bk.rev.; video rev.; software rev.; Website rev. 32 p./no. 2 cols./p.; back issues avail.
Document type: *Newsletter.* **Description:** Contains articles, academic news, and research questions of interest to educational advisers and guidance counselors both in the U.S. and abroad.
Formerly (until 1987): Amideast Counseling Quarterly
Published by: America-Mideast Educational & Training Services, 1730 M St, N W, Ste 1100, Washington, DC 20036. TEL 202-776-9619, FAX 202-776-7019, TELEX 440160, aq@amideast.org, http://www.advisingquarterly.org, http://www.amideast.org/aq.html. Ed. Juleann Fallgatter. R&P, Adv. contact Lia Hutton TEL 202-776-9619. Circ: 1,100.

370.116 USA
ADVISORY LIST OF INTERNATIONAL EDUCATIONAL TRAVEL AND EXCHANGE PROGRAMS✶. Text in English. 1985. a. USD 8.50. adv. bibl.; charts; stat. **Document type:** *Directory.*
Description: Describes international educational exchange organizations that conduct programs for high-school-age students that have been found to be in compliance with the Council's nine standard areas.
Published by: Council on Standards for International Educational Travel, 212 S Henry St, Alexandria, VA 22314-3522. TEL 703-771-2040, FAX 703-771-2046. Ed. Anne Shattuck.

370.116 DEU
AFRIKANISCH-ASIATISCHE STUDENTENFOERDERUNG. JAHRBUCH. Text in German. a. **Document type:** *Bulletin, Academic/Scholarly.*
Published by: (Afrikanisch-Asiatische Studentenfoerderung e.V.), I K O - Verlag fuer Interkulturelle Kommunikation, Postfach 900421, Frankfurt Am Main, 60444, Germany. TEL 49-69-784808, FAX 49-69-7896575, ikoverlag@t-online.de, http://www.iko-verlag.de.

440.370 GBR ISSN 1356-1332
ALLONS-Y. Text in French. 1966. 6/yr. (during school year, Sep.-May). USD 7.95 Includes workbook (effective 2003 - 2004). illus. **Description:** French-language magazine for beginners.
Former titles (until 1994): Allons! (0957-6215); (until 1990): Boum (0032-0471)
—CCC.
Published by: Mary Glasgow Magazines (Subsidiary of: Scholastic Publications Ltd.), Commonwealth House, 1-19 New Oxford St, London, WC1A 1NU, United Kingdom. TEL 44-20-74219050, FAX 44-20-74219051, http://www.link2english.com. **Subscr. to:** Scholastic Inc., 2931 E McCarthy St, PO Box 3710, Jefferson City, MO 65102-9957. TEL 800-724-6527, classmags@scholastic.com; Westfield Rd, Southam, Leamington Spa, Warks CV33 03H, United Kingdom. orders@maryglasgowmags.co.uk.

ALTERNATIVE TRAVEL DIRECTORY; the complete guide to traveling, studying & living overseas. see *TRAVEL AND TOURISM*

370.116 USA
AMERICAN O R T ANNUAL REPORT. (Organization for Rehabilitation through Training) Text in English. 1952. a. free. stat. index. back issues avail. **Document type:** *Newsletter, Corporate.* **Description:** Reports on the international ORT network of schools and training centers which provide vocational and technical training for 250,000 students in 60 countries throughout the world.
Formerly: American O R T Federation. Yearbook (1062-4392)
Published by: American O R T, 817 Broadway, New York, NY 10003. TEL 212-353-5800, FAX 212-353-5888. Ed., R&P Robert L Kern TEL 212-353-5828. Circ: 22,000.

370.116 USA
AMERICANS FOR THE UNIVERSALITY OF UNESCO NEWSLETTER. Text in English. 1985. q. USD 25 (effective 2001). bk.rev. Supplement avail.; back issues avail.
Document type: *Newsletter.* **Description:** Contains news and commentary on UNESCO, including multilateral cooperation in education, science, culture, and communication, as well as the U.S. role in these matters.
Published by: Americans for the Universality of UNESCO, PO Box 18418, Asheville, NC 28814. TEL 704-253-5383, FAX 704-252-9728. Ed. John E Fobes. Circ: 3,000.

370.117 USA ISSN 1092-924X
LC1099.3
ANNUAL EDITIONS: MULTICULTURAL EDUCATION. Text in English. 1993. a., latest 2003, 11th ed. USD 20.31 per vol. (effective 2003). illus. **Document type:** *Academic/Scholarly.*
Description: Anthology of recent articles.
Published by: McGraw-Hill - Dushkin (Subsidiary of: McGraw-Hill Higher Education), 2460 Kerper Blvd, Dubuque, IA 52001. TEL 800-243-6532, customer.service@mcgraw-hill.com, http://www.dushkin.com/text-data/catalog/0072874376.mhtml. Ed. Fred Schultz.

370.116 AUS ISSN 0819-3053
L981
AUSTRALIAN STUDY OPPORTUNITIES✶. Text mainly in English; Section in Chinese, French, Indonesian, Japanese, Korean, Thai. 1985. a. AUD 19.95. adv. **Document type:** *Directory.* **Description:** Lists accredited courses for international students studying in Australia, including secondary school, TAFE and university courses. Also contains articles on the further education system, admission and visa requirements.
Published by: (International Development Program), New Hobsons Press Pty. Ltd., 2 Elizabeth Pl., Level 4, North Sydney, NSW, NSW 2060, Australia. TEL 61-9-2310-2257, FAX 61-9-2310-2243. Ed. Catherine Etteridge. Adv. contact Colin Ritchie. Circ: 25,000.

371.223 ESP
BANCO DE DATOS DE BECAS Y CURSOS. Text in Spanish. 1980. a. USD 500. **Document type:** *Directory.* **Description:** Contains information on postgraduate courses at higher education institutions in Iberoamerica. Includes financial aid information.
Formerly: Becas y Cursos de Educacion
Related titles: Diskette ed.
Published by: Organizacion de Estados IberoAmericanos para la Educacion la Ciencia y la Cultura, Bravo Murillo 38, Madrid, 28015, Spain. TEL 34-91-5944382, FAX 34-91-5943286, oeimad@oei.es, http://www.oei.es. Circ: 1,000.

370.116 DEU ISSN 0940-3132
BEGEGNUNG (BONN); Deutsche Schulen im Ausland. Text in German. 1977. s-a. **Document type:** *Magazine, Trade.*
Description: Contains information for teachers of the German language sent abroad by the government.
Published by: Bundesverwaltungsamt, Zentralstelle fuer das Auslandsschulwesen, Barbarastr 1, Cologne, 50735, Germany. TEL 49-1888-3581448, FAX 49-1888-358711448, dieter.uesseler@bva.bund.de, http://www.dasan.de/index.php?cat_rec_form=article.php&cat_rec_id=117. Circ: 12,000 (controlled).

370.116 GBR
BRITISH CHEVENING SCHOLARSHIPS PROGRAMME. ANNUAL REPORT. Text in English. 1999. a. free (effective 2001). **Document type:** *Yearbook.* **Description:** Covers the program's efforts to provide scholarships to international students to study in the United Kingdom.
Related titles: Online - full content ed.
Published by: British Council, British Council Publications, Bridgewater House, 58 Whitworth St, Manchester, M1 6BB, United Kingdom. TEL 44-161-9577184, FAX 44-161-9577168, publications.information@britishcouncil.org, http://www.britishcouncil.org/chevening/reports.htm, http://www.britishcouncil.org/publications.

370.116 CAN ISSN 0315-1409
➤ **CANADIAN AND INTERNATIONAL EDUCATION/EDUCATION CANADIENNE ET INTERNATIONALE.** Text and summaries in English, French. 1972. s-a. CND 25 to individuals; CND 30 to institutions; CND 10 to students (effective 2003). bk.rev. bibl. 120 p./no.; **Document type:** *Journal, Academic/Scholarly.*
Description: Provides a forum for articles dealing with education from a comparative and international perspective.
Related titles: Microfiche ed.: (from MML); Microfilm ed.: (from MML); Microform ed.: (from MML, PQC).
Indexed: BAS, CEI, CPE, EAA, ERA, MEA, MEA&I, SEA, SENA, SOMA, SRRA, SWA, TEA.
—BLDSC (3017.140000), IE, Infotrieve, ingenta.
Published by: Comparative and International Education Society of Canada, c/o Faculty of Education, Queens University, Kingston, ON K7L 3N6, Canada. TEL 613-533-6000, FAX 613-533-6584. Ed. Eva Krugly-Smolska. Circ: 400.

370.116 CAN ISSN 1191-9124
CANADIAN BUREAU FOR INTERNATIONAL EDUCATION. ANNUAL REPORT. Text in English. 1971. a. **Document type:** *Corporate.*

E

Related titles: French ed.: Bureau Canadien de l'Education Internationale. ISSN 0708-8728.
Published by: Canadian Bureau for International Education, 220 Laurier Ave W Ste 1100, Ottawa, ON K1P 5Z9, Canada. TEL 613-237-4820, FAX 613-237-1073, http://www.cbie.ca. Ed. Mary Kane.

370.116 CAN ISSN 1484-8678
CANADIAN INTERNATIONALIST. Text in English. 1990. q. CND 40, USD 30 domestic; CND 55 foreign (effective 1999). bk.rev.
Formerly (until 1998): Synthesis (1180-4734)
Related titles: French ed.: Internationaliste Canadien. ISSN 1481-2703.
Indexed: CMCI, CurCont.
Published by: Canadian Bureau for International Education, 220 Laurier Ave W Ste 1100, Ottawa, ON K1P 5Z9, Canada. TEL 613-237-4820, FAX 613-237-1073, http://www.cbie.ca/cdnint.html. Ed. Mary Kane. Circ: 1,400.

370.116 GBR ISSN 1362-6647
CENTRAL BUREAU NEWS. Text in English. 1995. 3/yr. free (effective 2001). **Document type:** *Magazine.* **Description:** Covers programs, activities and good practices about the field of international education.
Related titles: Online - full content ed.
Published by: British Council, Central Bureau, 10 Spring Gardens, London, SW1A 2BN, United Kingdom. TEL 44-20-7389-4880, FAX 44-20-7389-4426, cbresources@britishcouncil.org, publications.information@britishcouncil.org, http://www.britishcouncil.org/cbiet/resource/cbecbn.htm, http://www.britishcouncil.org/publications.

370.116 GBR
CHEVENING CONTACTS; the British Chevening Scholarships newsletter. Text in English. 1995. s-a. **Document type:** *Newsletter.* **Description:** Covers activities of interest to former and current Chevening scholars.
Related titles: Online - full content ed.
Published by: British Council, British Council Publications, Bridgewater House, 58 Whitworth St, Manchester, M1 6BB, United Kingdom. TEL 44-161-9577184, FAX 44-161-9577168, contacts.newsletter@britishcouncil.org, publications.information@britishcouncil.org, http://www.britishcouncil.org/chevening/newsletter.htm, http://www.britishcouncil.org/publications.

370.116 GBR
CONNECT YOUTH INTERNATIONAL. ANNUAL REPORT. Text in English. 2000. a. free (effective 2001). **Document type:** *Yearbook.* **Description:** Covers CYI's activities in promoting exchanges of young people between the United Kingdom and other countries.
Published by: Connect Youth International (Subsidiary of: British Council), 10 Spring Gardens, London, SW1A 2BN, United Kingdom. TEL 44-20-73894030, FAX 44-20-73894033, connectyouth.enquiries@britishcouncil.org, http://www.connectyouthinternational.com/.

370.116 GBR
CONNECT YOUTH INTERNATIONAL. NEWS. Text in English. 1980. 4/yr. free. 8 p./no.; **Document type:** *Newsletter.* **Description:** Touches on exchange programs, grants and seminars.
Former titles: Connect Youth News; (until 2000): Youth Exchange News (0144-7327)
Published by: Connect Youth International (Subsidiary of: British Council), 10 Spring Gardens, London, SW1A 2BN, United Kingdom. TEL 44-20-73894030, FAX 44-20-73894033, connectyouth.enquiries@britishcouncil.org, http://www.connectyouthinternational.com.

E

370.116 PAK ISSN 0070-606X
DIRECTORY OF PAKISTANI SCHOLARS ABROAD. Text in English. 1965. a.
Published by: Ministry of Education, Documentation Section, Curriculum Wing, Sector H-9, P.O. Shaigan, Industrial Area, Islamabad, Pakistan.

378.016 USA
DIRECTORY OF VISITING FULBRIGHT SCHOLARS AND OCCASIONAL LECTURERS. Text in English. a. free. **Document type:** *Directory.*
Former titles (until 1984): Directory of Visiting Fulbright Scholars and Occasional Lecturer Program (0742-079X); Directory of Visiting Fulbright Scholars in the United States (0098-1508); Directory of Visiting Lecturers and Research Scholars in the United States Under the Mutual Educational Exchange Program (the Fulbright-Hays Act); Directory of Visiting Scholars in the United States Awarded Grants Under the Mutual Educational and Cultural Exchange Act (the Fulbright-Hays Act) (0070-6582)
Published by: Council for International Exchange of Scholars, 3007 Tilden St, N W, Ste 5M, Washington, DC 20008-3009. TEL 202-686-8664.

370.117 GBR ISSN 1350-1372
➤ **DONAIRE.** Text and summaries in Spanish, English, Catalan, Gallegan. 1993. s-a. bk.rev. bibl.; illus. back issues avail. **Document type:** *Magazine, Academic/Scholarly.* **Description:** Offers persons teaching Spanish in the United Kingdom articles on Spanish culture, religion, art, and history, with which to enhance the content of their instruction.
Related titles: Online - full text ed.
Published by: Spanish Embassy, London. Education and Science Office/Embajada de Espana, Londres. Consejeria de Educacion en el Reino Unido e Irlanda, 20 Peel St, London, W8 7PD, United Kingdom. TEL 44-20-7727-2462, 44-20-7243-8535, asesores.uk@correo.mec.es, http://www.sqci.mec.es/uk.

370.116 NLD ISSN 1389-0808
E A I E FORUM. Text in English. 1990. 3/yr. membership. adv. bk.rev. **Document type:** *Newsletter.* **Description:** Contains news from membership, news from the secretariat, features, announcements, and calendar of events.
Formerly (until 1999): E A I E Newsletter (0927-572X)
Published by: European Association for International Education, PO Box 11189, Amsterdam, 1001 GD, Netherlands. TEL 31-20-5254999, FAX 31-20-5254998, eaie@eaie.nl, http://www.eaie.org. Ed. Michael Cooper. Pub. Alex Olde Kalter. R&P Belinda Stratton. Adv. contact Janny van Wijk. B&W page EUR 455; 180 x 255. Circ: 2,000.

E C I S HIGHER EDUCATION DIRECTORY. see *EDUCATION—Guides To Schools And Colleges*

370.196 BEL
E F I L LATEST EDITION. Text in Multiple languages. m. bk.rev. **Document type:** *Newsletter.* **Description:** News of EFIL activities and EU matters concerning youth and education and a monthly focus on themes of interest to EFIL partners.
Former titles: E F I L Newsletter; (until 1978): A F S Europa; A F S International Scholarships. European Coordination Letter
Published by: European Federation for Intercultural Learning, Rue des Colonies, Brussels, 1000, Belgium. TEL 32-2-5145250, FAX 32-2-5142929, info@efil.be, http://www.afs.org/efil. Ed. Nele Hiers. Circ: 350.

401 370.116 GBR ISSN 1466-7436
EDUCATION TRAVEL MAGAZINE. Text in English. 1998. q. GBP 20 to individuals; GBP 30 to institutions (effective 2002). adv. back issues avail. **Document type:** *Magazine, Trade.* **Description:** Reports on educational programs of interest to recruiters of international students.
Related titles: Online - full content ed.
Published by: Hothouse Media Ltd, 11-15 Emerald St, London, WC1N 3QL, United Kingdom. TEL 44-20-74404020, FAX 44-20-74404033, http://www.hothousemedia.com/etm/index.htm. adv.: B&W page GBP 1,200, color page GBP 1,350.

370.117 USA ISSN 1549-1056
LC1099
EDUCATORS GUIDE TO FREE MULTICULTURAL MATERIALS. Text in English. 1998. a., latest 5th Edition, 2002-2003. USD 34.95 per issue (effective 2002). 203 p./no.; **Description:** Lists free video tapes, films, web sites, and print materials for multicultural education.
Published by: Educators Progress Service, Inc., 214 Center St, Randolph, WI 53956. TEL 920-326-3126, FAX 920-326-3127, http://www.freeteachingaids.com/mmr_877083444.html. Ed. Kathleen Suttles Nehmer.

ELDERHOSTEL. see *EDUCATION—Adult Education*

370.117 375.006 USA
➤ **ELECTRONIC JOURNAL OF MULTICULTURAL EDUCATION.** Text in English. 1999. s-a. free (effective 2005). bk.rev. back issues avail. **Document type:** *Journal, Academic/Scholarly.* **Description:** Publishes scholarly papers, practitioner essays, instructional ideas, and reviews of multimedia resources pertaining to multicultural education, diversity, cultural pluralism, anthropology and education, global education and related subjects.
Media: Online - full content.
Published by: Eastern University, Education Department, 1300 Eagle Rd, St Davids, PA 19087-3696. emmme@eastern.edu, http://www.eastern.edu/publications/emme/. Ed. Heewon Chang.

370.116 GBR
EMBAJADA DE ESPANA. LONDRES. CONSEJERIA DE EDUCACION Y CIENCIA. BOLETIN. Variant title: Boletin del Espanol. Text in Spanish, English. 1998. q. free. back issues avail. **Document type:** *Bulletin.* **Description:** Reports on topics, themes, and issues of teachers of Spanish in the UK, highlighting both Spanish language and Spanish culture.
Media: Online - full content.
Published by: Spanish Embassy, London. Education and Science Office/Embajada de Espana, Londres. Consejeria de Educacion en el Reino Unido e Irlanda, 20 Peel St, London, W8 7PD, United Kingdom. TEL 44-20-7727-2462, 44-20-7243-8535, asesores.uk@correo.mec.es, http://www.sqci.mec.es/uk.

ESPERANTIC STUDIES. see *LINGUISTICS*

FINANCIAL AID FOR RESEARCH AND CREATIVE ACTIVITIES ABROAD. see *EDUCATION—School Organization And Administration*

FRONTLINE. see *BUSINESS AND ECONOMICS—International Development And Assistance*

371.223 USA
FULBRIGHT SCHOLAR PROGRAM: GRANTS FOR FACULTY AND PROFESSIONALS. Text in English. a. free.
Former titles: Fulbright Scholar Program - Faculty Grants, Research and Lecturing Awards; Fulbright Scholar Program - Research Awards and Lectureships; Fulbright Awards Abroad
Published by: Council for International Exchange of Scholars, 3007 Tilden St, N W, Ste 5M, Washington, DC 20008-3009. TEL 202-686-7877, cies1@ciesnet.cies.org, http://www.cied.org. Circ: 52,000.

370.116 DEU ISSN 0940-3116
G A P P MAGAZIN. (German - American Partnership Program) Text in English, German. 1988. s-a. **Document type:** *Government.* **Description:** Contains information on the German-American Partnership Program involving pupils and teachers.
Published by: (Paedagogischer Austauschdienst), Varus Verlag, Konrad-Zuse-Platz 1-3, Bonn, 53227, Germany. TEL 49-228-94466-0, FAX 49-228-9446666, varus.mail@t-online.de, info@varus.com, http://www.varus.com. Circ: 4,000 (controlled).

GLOBAL CONNECTOR; the complete resource directory for international training. see *EDUCATION—Adult Education*

370.116 USA
▼ ➤ **GLOBAL EDUCATION JOURNAL.** Text in English. 2004 (Mar.). q. USD 185 to individuals (effective 2005 & 2006). **Document type:** *Journal, Academic/Scholarly.* **Description:** Covers global education and all allied fields of scholarship.
Published by: Franklin Publishing Company, 2723 Steamboat Circle, Arlington, TX 76006. TEL 817-548-1124, FAX 817-299-0930, luotto@comcast.net, http://www.franklinpublishing.net/pages/580555/index.htm. Ed. Mrs. Maxime E Knight. Pub. Dr. Ludwig Otto.

370.116 USA
GLOBAL LINKS. Text in English. 1986. q. USD 25 membership; USD 15 to students. adv. bk.rev. **Document type:** *Newspaper.* **Description:** Provides network updates, grassroots development news, resource and calendar listings and more.
Published by: Just Act, 333 Valencia St, Ste 330, San Francisco, CA 94103. TEL 415-431-4204, FAX 415-431-5953, http://www.justact.com. Ed. Mark Rand. R&P Stefano Dezerega. Circ: 600.

370.1163 CHN ISSN 1001-0114
GUOJI RENCAI JIAOLIU/INTERNATIONAL TALENT MAGAZINE. Text in Chinese. m. CNY 96; USD 72 foreign. adv.
Related titles: Online - full text ed.: (from East View Information Services).
Published by: Zhongguo Guoji Rencai Jiaoliu Xinxi Yanjiu Zhongxin, 3 Baishiqiao Ave, Beijing, 100873, China. TEL 86-10-6842-5584, FAX 86-10-6841-6998, intertal@chinaonline.com.cn.net, http://www.china-access.com/sbft/talent.com. Ed. Bi Lianggan. Adv. contact Wang Yang. color page USD 3,000. Circ: 30,000.

370.116 FRA
I B E STUDIES SERIES. Text in French. irreg. price varies. **Document type:** *Academic/Scholarly.*
Related titles: ♦ Series: Studies and Surveys in Comparative Education. ISSN 0251-5865.
Published by: (International Bureau of Education), UNESCO Publishing, 7 place de Fontenoy, Paris, 75352, France. TEL 33-1-45684300, FAX 33-1-45685737, http://www.unesco.org/publications. **Dist. in the US by:** Bernan Associates, Bernan, 4611-F Assembly Dr., Lanham, MD 20706-4391. TEL 800-274-4447, FAX 800-865-3450.

I B O PUBLICATIONS CATALOGUE. see *EDUCATION—Higher Education*

370.116 USA
IIENETWORKER MAGAZINE. Text in English. 2001 (Fall). s-a. USD 14 domestic; USD 20 in Canada & Mexico; USD 28 elsewhere (effective 2004). adv. **Document type:** *Magazine.* **Description:** Publishes pieces on all aspects of international education in the United States and around the world and features new research, as well as resources and articles that deal with everyday practice.
Published by: Institute of International Education, 809 United Nations Plaza, 7th Fl, New York, NY 10017-3580. TEL 212-984-5453, http://www.iienetwork.org/?p=41601, http://www.iie.org/.

370.116 USA
I I E S EXCHANGE. Text in English. 1988 (vol.10). 3/yr. free. adv. bk.rev. **Document type:** *Newsletter.* **Description:** Provides information for IES alumni and friends about the ongoing development of IES programs, updates from IES centers worldwide and reference information.
Former titles: I E S Exchange; News from I E S - I A S; News from I E S

Published by: Institute for the International Education of Students, 33 N LaSalle, 15th Fl, Chicago, IL 60602-4196. TEL 800-995-2300, FAX 312-944-1448, info@iesabroad.org, http://www.iesabroad.org/menus/alumni.html. Ed. Maureen Meyer. Adv. contact Louisa Wales TEL 312-944-1750. Circ: 4,000.

370.116 USA ISSN 0160-0079
INSTITUTE OF INTERNATIONAL EDUCATION. ANNUAL REPORT. Text in English. 1920. a.
Former titles (until 1949): Institute of International Education. Annual Report of the President (0160-0060); (until 1948): Institute of International Education. Annual Report of the Director (0160-0052)
Published by: Institute of International Education, 809 United Nations Plaza, 7th Fl, New York, NY 10017-3580. TEL 212-883-8200, FAX 212-984-5452, http://www.iie.org/Content/NavigationMenu/About_IIE/Annual_Report/Annual_Report.htm.

370.116 620.1 USA ISSN 0195-0193
INTERACTIONS (NORTHBROOK). Text in English. 1975. m. USD 16.80 (effective 1999). adv. bk.rev. charts; illus.; stat. 12 p./no. 3 cols./p.; back issues avail. **Document type:** *Newsletter, Trade.* **Description:** Provides the value of projects and - or services.
Published by: Save International, 60 Revere Dr, Ste 500, Northbrook, IL 60062. TEL 847-480-1730, FAX 847-9282, value@value-eng.com, http://www.value-eng.com. Ed. Kirsten Lambert. R&P, Adv. contact Melanie Epel. Circ: 1,200 (controlled).

370.116 USA ISSN 0047-0457
INTERCHANGE (PORTLAND). Text in English. 1964. 3/yr. USD 40 to members (effective 2001). adv. bk.rev. illus. reprints avail. **Document type:** *Academic/Scholarly.*
Indexed: CLFP.
Published by: Oregon Educational Media Association, PO Box 277, Terrebone, OR 97760. TEL 541-923-0675, FAX 541-923-0675, sporter@oregontrail.net, http://www.teleport.com/~oema. Ed. Zita Podamy. R&P Sharon Porter TEL 541-963-6267. Adv. contact Miriam Mann. Circ: 700 (controlled).

370.116 IRL ISSN 0538-4427
INTERNATIONAL ASSOCIATION FOR THE EXCHANGE OF STUDENTS FOR TECHNICAL EXPERIENCE. ANNUAL REPORT. Short title: I A E S T E Annual Report. Text in French. 1948. a. free. **Document type:** *Corporate.*
Published by: International Association for the Exchange of Students for Technical Experience, P O Box 6104, Co Dublin, Swords, Ireland. jimeidgsiaeste@eircom.net, http://www.iaeste.org. Ed. James E Reid. Circ: 8,000.

370.116 USA ISSN 0160-5429
LC1090
➤ **INTERNATIONAL EDUCATION.** Text in English. 1971. s-a. USD 16 domestic; USD 22 foreign (effective 2000). bk.rev. **Document type:** *Journal, Academic/Scholarly.* **Description:** Contains articles related to educational programs in various countries, including the U.S.
Related titles: Online - full text ed.: (from H.W. Wilson, O C L C Online Computer Library Center, Inc., ProQuest Information & Learning).
Indexed: ABIn, BAS, CPE, DIP, ERA, EduInd, IBR, IBZ, MEA, Perlslam, REE&TA, SENA.
—BLDSC (4539.835000), IE, ingenta.
Published by: University of Tennessee at Knoxville, College of Education, 344 Claxton Complex, Knoxville, TN 37996-3400. TEL 865-974-5252, FAX 865-974-8718, scarey@utk.edu. Eds. Karl Jost, Tricia McClam. R&P Sue Carey. Circ: 350.

370.116 AUS ISSN 1327-9548
➤ **INTERNATIONAL EDUCATION - EJ.** Text in English. 1996. q. back issues avail. **Document type:** *Journal, Academic/Scholarly.* **Description:** Provides an online focus for those involved in research related to international education, the provision of international education programs, information technology in international education, projects related to education and training which have an international dimension and socio-cultural economic policy, policy issues related to international education.
Media: Online - full text.
Indexed: AEI.
Published by: University of Canberra, Faculty of Education, Centre for Research in International Education, PO Box 1, Belconnen, ACT 2616, Australia. TEL 61-6-201-2490, FAX 61-6-201-5065, http://www.canberra.edu.au/uc/educ/crie/ieej_home.html. Ed. Sakari Mattila.

378.016 USA ISSN 1556-1682
▼ **INTERNATIONAL EDUCATION REPORT.** Text in English. 2004 (Sept.). m. USD 349 domestic; USD 353 in Canada; USD 359 elsewhere (effective 2005). **Document type:** *Newsletter.* **Description:** Helps to deal with today's special challenges, manage successful programs and advance the internationalization of higher education.
Related titles: Online - full content ed.: USD 349 (effective 2005).
Published by: Magna Publications, Inc., 2718 Dryden Dr, Madison, WI 53704. TEL 608-246-3590, 800-433-0499, FAX 608-246-3597, editor@magnapubs.com, http://www.magnapubs.com/pub/magnapubs_ier.

370.116 USA ISSN 1059-4221
LC1090
INTERNATIONAL EDUCATOR (WASHINGTON). Text in English. 1991. q. USD 35 to non-members; USD 48 in Canada & Mexico to non-members; USD 63 elsewhere to non-members (effective 2005). **Document type:** *Journal, Academic/Scholarly.* **Description:** Covers professional, political, administrative and social issues pertaining to international educational exchange.
Related titles: Online - full text ed.: (from ProQuest Information & Learning).
Indexed: ABIn, CPE, ERA, EduInd, HEA.
Published by: National Association for Foreign Student Affairs (N A F S A), Association of International Educators, 1307 New York Ave, NW, 8th Fl, Washington, DC 20005-4701. TEL 202-737-3699, 800-836-4994, FAX 202-737-3657, publications@nafsa.org, http://www.nafsa.org/content/ProfessionalandEducationalResources/Publications/IE/IeHome.htm. Ed. Steven B Kennedy. R&P Cary Haney.

370.116 USA ISSN 1044-3509
L10
INTERNATIONAL EDUCATOR (WEST BRIDGEWATER). Text in English. 1986. q. USD 43 combined subscription in US & Canada print & online eds.; USD 53 combined subscription elsewhere print & online eds. (effective 2004). adv. bk.rev. back issues avail. **Document type:** *Newspaper, Academic/Scholarly.* **Description:** Features available teaching and administrative positions in overseas schools. Includes news and developments about global education issues.
Related titles: Online - full content ed.: T I E Online. USD 33 (effective 2004); Supplement(s): Jobs Only.
Published by: International Educator's Institute, PO Box 513, Cummaquid, MA 02637. TEL 508-362-1414, FAX 508-362-1411, tie@tieonline.com, http://www.tieonline.com/. Ed. Sherry Calef. Adv. contact Nikki Gundry. B&W page USD 2,448, color page USD 2,915; 10 x 12. Circ: 15,000.

370.116 GBR ISSN 1366-8048
THE INTERNATIONAL FOUNDATION DIRECTORY (YEAR). Text in English. 1974. a., latest 2001, 10th Edition. GBP 180, USD 280 (effective 2001). bibl. **Document type:** *Directory.* **Description:** Lists and describes more than 1,500 new and established foundations and their executives in 100 nations, including those of the former Soviet Union.
Published by: Europa Publications Limited (Subsidiary of: Taylor & Francis Group), 11 New Fetter Ln, London, EC4P 4EE, United Kingdom. TEL 44-20-7822-4300, FAX 44-20-7842-2249, sales.europa@tandf.co.uk, http://www.europapublications.co.uk, http://www.europapublications.com. Ed. Cathy Hartley. **Subsc. addr. in N. America:** Taylor & Francis Inc., Customer Services Dept, 325 Chestnut St, 8th Fl, Philadelphia, PA 19106. TEL 215-625-8900, 800-354-1420, FAX 215-625-8914; **Subscr. to:** Taylor & Francis Ltd, Journals Customer Service, Rankine Rd, Basingstoke, Hants RG24 8PR, United Kingdom. TEL 44-1256-813000, FAX 44-1256-330245.

370.116 GBR
INTERNATIONAL GUIDE TO QUALIFICATIONS IN EDUCATION. Text in English. irreg., latest vol.4, 1995. GBP 100. **Document type:** *Academic/Scholarly.*
Published by: (British Council, National Academic Recognition Information Centre), Mansell Publishing Ltd., Wellington House, 125 Strand, London, WC2R 0BB, United Kingdom. TEL 44-171-4205555, FAX 44-171-2407261, cassellacad@msn.com, http://www.cassell.co.uk. R&P Gaelle Beauclair TEL 44-171-4205534. **Dist. in US by:** Cassell and Continuum, Books International, 22883 Quicksilver Dr, Dulles, VA 20166.

INTERNATIONAL JOURNAL OF CURRICULUM AND INSTRUCTION. see *EDUCATION—Teaching Methods And Curriculum*

370.116 GBR ISSN 1461-3956
LC1090
THE INTERNATIONAL SCHOOL MAGAZINE. Short title: I S. Text in English. 1998. 3/yr. GBP 15 to non-members (effective 2003); USD 25 to non-members (effective 2002). illus. **Document type:** *Magazine, Trade.* **Description:** Provides teachers and administrators with information on what is happening within ECIS, as well as international education worldwide.
Indexed: BrEdI, CPE.
Published by: (European Council of International Schools), John Catt Educational Ltd., Great Glemham, Saxmundham, Suffolk IP17 2DH, United Kingdom. TEL 44-1728-663666, FAX 44-1728-663415, ChristineEvans@johncatt.co.uk, enquiries@johncatt.co.uk, http://www.schoolsearch.co.uk/magismagdefault.asp. Ed. Caroline Ellwood. Adv. contact Sharon Bleese.

INTERNATIONAL SCHOOLS DIRECTORY (YEAR). see *EDUCATION—Guides To Schools And Colleges*

370.116 GBR ISSN 0264-7281
➤ **INTERNATIONAL SCHOOLS JOURNAL.** Text in English. 1981. s-a. GBP 45, USD 73 to individual members (effective Jul. 2001). adv. bk.rev. bibl.; charts. index every 5 yrs. back issues avail. **Document type:** *Academic/Scholarly.* **Description:** For educators in international schools worldwide. Covers management and administration; bilingualism; multicultural education; international curriculum; and third culture students.
Indexed: BrEdI, CIJE, CPE, ERA.
—BLDSC (4548.840000), IE, ingenta.
Published by: European Council of International Schools, 21 Lavant St, Petersfield, Hamps GU32 3EL, United Kingdom. TEL 44-1730-268244, FAX 44-1730-267914, ecis@ecis.org. Ed. Charles Gellar. R&P Edna Murphy. adv.: page GBP 150. Circ: 2,000.

370.116 USA ISSN 1531-2763
H62.A1
THE INTERNATIONAL SOCIAL STUDIES FORUM. Text in English. 2000. q. USD 65 domestic to individuals; USD 105 foreign to individuals; USD 150 domestic to institutions; USD 190 foreign to institutions; USD 45 domestic to students; USD 85 foreign to students; USD 105 domestic to individuals for print & online eds.; USD 250 domestic to institutions for print & online eds.; USD 65 domestic to students for print & online eds. (effective 2002).
Formerly (until 2002): International Journal of Educational Policy Research & Practice (1528-3534)
Related titles: Online - full text ed.: (from EBSCO Publishing).
Indexed: CPE, ERA.
—BLDSC (4542.199750), IE, ingenta. **CCC.**
Published by: Information Age Publishing, Inc., 411 W Putnam Ave, Ste 205, PO Box 4967, Greenwich, CT 06831. TEL 203-661-7602, FAX 203-661-7952, order@infoagepub.com, http://www.infoagepub.com. Eds. Jeff Passe, Richard A. Diem.

370.116 GBR ISSN 1324-1702
INTERNATIONAL STUDIES IN EDUCATIONAL ADMINISTRATION; journal of the Commonwealth Council for Educational Administration and Management. Text in English. 1972. s-a. GBP 80 in United Kingdom to institutions; GBP 95 to institutions in the Commonwealth; GBP 159 in United States to institutions; GBP 99 elsewhere to institutions (effective 2000); includes 2 issues of Managing Education Matters: newsletter of the CCEAM. adv. bk.rev. back issues avail.
Formerly: Studies in Educational Administration
Related titles: Online - full text ed.: (from EBSCO Publishing); ♦ Includes: Managing Education Matters. ISSN 1463-7081.
Indexed: BrEdI, CIJE, CPE, ERA, ETA, MEA, RHEA, SEA, SENA, SOMA, TEA.
Published by: (Commonwealth Council for Educational Administration & Management), The Education Publishing Co. Ltd., Devonia House, 4 Union Terrace, Crediton, Devon EX17 3DY, United Kingdom. Circ: 6,500.

INTERNATIONAL STUDY PROGRAMS AT THE UNIVERSITEIT VAN AMSTERDAM; come in searching of the reasons. see *EDUCATION—Higher Education*

INTERNATIONAL UNIVERSITY FOUNDATION DIRECTORY. see *EDUCATION—Higher Education*

INTERNATIONAL UNIVERSITY FOUNDATION REPORT. see *EDUCATION—Higher Education*

370.116 USA
INTERNATIONAL VOLUNTEER. Text in English. 1982. a. free (effective 2005). **Document type:** *Newsletter.* **Description:** Summarizes the international workcamp program and contains information about membership.
Formerly: International Workcamper (1066-3541)
Published by: V F P International Workcamps, 1043 Tiffany Rd, Belmont, VT 05730. TEL 802-259-2759, FAX 802-259-2922, vfp@vjp.org, http://www.vfp.org. Ed. Peter Coldwell.

370.116 USA ISSN 0896-565X
INTERNATIONAL WORKCAMP DIRECTORY. Text in English. 1983 (Apr.). a. USD 20 per issue (effective 2005). back issues avail. **Document type:** *Directory.* **Description:** Includes listings of 2,800 International Voluntary Service programs in 90 countries.
Related titles: Online - full content ed.
Published by: V F P International Workcamps, 1043 Tiffany Rd, Belmont, VT 05730. TEL 802-259-2759, FAX 802-259-2922, vfp@vfp.org, http://www.vfp.org. Ed., Pub., R&P, Adv. contact Peter Coldwell. Circ: 5,000.

370.116 USA
ISSUES IN GLOBAL EDUCATION; the information on global, international and foreign language education. Text in English. 1979. bi-m. USD 30 domestic; USD 36 in Canada; USD 48 elsewhere. adv. bk.rev. bibl. back issues avail. **Document type:** *Newsletter, Academic/Scholarly.* **Description:** Serves as an open forum for ideas and inquiries on global education; includes articles, resource reviews, job opportunities, program announcements, teaching aids and a calendar of events for all global educators.
Formerly: Access (New York, 1979)

E

Published by: American Forum for Global Education, 120 Wall St, Ste 2600, New York, NY 10005-4001. TEL 212-624-1300, FAX 212-624-1412. Ed. Cassandra Faulkner. R&P, Adv. contact Donald L Miller. Circ: 2,000.

JOURNAL OF AMERICAN - EAST ASIAN RELATIONS. see *SOCIAL SCIENCES: COMPREHENSIVE WORKS*

370.116 USA ISSN 1554-2262
LC98
➤ **JOURNAL OF EDUCATION FOR INTERNATIONAL DEVELOPMENT.** Text in English. irreg. free (effective 2005). **Document type:** *Journal, Academic/Scholarly.* **Description:** Dedicated to the improvement of education policies and practices promoting lifelong learning for the sustainable economic growth and poverty reduction of developing countries worldwide.
Media: Online - full content.
Published by: Educational Quality Improvement Program, c/o Jane Benbow, Project Director, American Institutes for Research, 1000 Thomas Jefferson St. NW, Washington, DC 20007. JEID@air.org, http://www.equip123.net/JEID/default.htm. Ed. Kimberly J Bolyard.

370.116 USA ISSN 0273-3382
LB2375
JOURNAL OF INTERNATIONAL STUDENT PERSONNEL✶. Text in English. 1980. 4/yr. USD 25. adv. bk.rev. charts.
Published by: Association for International and Cultural Education, c/o Samuel B Olorounto, Ed, Box 1127, Dublin, VA 24084. Ed. Samuel B Olorounto. Circ: 3,000.

370.117 GBR ISSN 0143-4632
P115
➤ **JOURNAL OF MULTILINGUAL & MULTICULTURAL DEVELOPMENT.** Text in English. 1980. bi-m. GBP 265, USD 495, EUR 399 combined subscription to institutions print & online; GBP 55, USD 99, EUR 80 combined subscription to individuals print & online (effective 2005). adv. bk.rev. illus. index. back issues avail.; reprints avail. **Document type:** *Journal, Academic/Scholarly.* **Description:** Publishes research studies about multiculturalism and multilingualism in education, psychology, sociology, second-language learning, and bilingualism.
Related titles: Online - full text ed.: (from EBSCO Publishing, Gale Group, Swets Information Services).
Indexed: BibLing, BrEdI, CIJE, CPE, ChPerI, DIP, ERA, ETA, IBR, IBSS, IBZ, L&LBA, LT&LA, LingAb, MEA, MLA, MLA-IB, PCI, PerIslam, RHEA, RILM, SEA, SENA, SOMA, SOPODA, SSA, SSCI, SWA, SociolAb, TEA.
—BLDSC (5021.060000), IE, Infotrieve, ingenta. **CCC.**
Published by: Multilingual Matters Ltd., Frankfurt Lodge, Clevedon Hall, Victoria Rd, Clevedon, North Somerset BS21 7HH, United Kingdom. TEL 44-1275-876519, FAX 44-1275-871673, info@multilingual-matters.com, http://www.multilingual-matters.com/multi/journals/journals_jmmd.asp, http://www.catchword.co.uk. Ed. John Edwards. R&P Marjukka Grover. Adv. contact Kathryn King. Circ: 800. **Dist. by & subscr. to:** Portland Press Ltd., Commerce Way, Colchester CO2 8HP, United Kingdom. TEL 44-1206-796351, FAX 44-1206-799331, sales@portland-services.com, http://www.portland-services.com.

370 GBR ISSN 1475-2409
LC1090
➤ **JOURNAL OF RESEARCH IN INTERNATIONAL EDUCATION.** Text in English; Abstracts in English, French, Spanish. 2002. 3/yr. GBP 230, USD 402 to institutions; GBP 239, USD 419 combined subscription to institutions print & online eds. (effective 2006). **Document type:** *Journal, Academic/Scholarly.* **Description:** Promotes the relationship between theory and practice, and will be of the highest intellectual and academic quality for those undertaking rigorous and systematic enquiry.
Related titles: Online - full text ed.: ISSN 1741-2943. GBP 228, USD 398 to institutions (effective 2006) (from C S A, EBSCO Publishing, O C L C Online Computer Library Center, Inc., Sage Publications, Inc., Swets Information Services).
Indexed: BrEdI, CPE, EAA, ERA.
—BLDSC (5052.009200), IE. **CCC.**
Published by: Sage Publications Ltd. (Subsidiary of: Sage Publications, Inc.), 1 Oliver's Yard, 55 City Rd, London, EC1 1SP, United Kingdom. TEL 44-20-73248500, FAX 44-20-73248600, info@sagepub.co.uk, http://www.sagepub.co.uk/journal.aspx?pid=105681. Ed. Jeff Thompson. **Subscr. in the Americas to:** Sage Publications, Inc., 2455 Teller Rd, Thousand Oaks, CA 91320. TEL 805-499-0721, FAX 805-499-0871, journals@sagepub.com.

370.116 USA ISSN 1028-3153
LC1090
JOURNAL OF STUDIES IN INTERNATIONAL EDUCATION. Text in English. 1997. q. USD 449, GBP 290 to institutions; USD 467, GBP 302 combined subscription to institutions print & online eds. (effective 2006). **Document type:** *Journal, Academic/Scholarly.* **Description:** Aims to encourage serious research dealing with international education and academic mobility, to stimulate interest in such work (both in the international education community and in academic circles in general), and to develop and promote ways to disseminate this work.
Related titles: Online - full text ed.: ISSN 1552-7808. USD 444, GBP 287 to institutions (effective 2006) (from C S A, EBSCO Publishing, O C L C Online Computer Library Center, Inc., Sage Publications, Inc., Swets Information Services).
Indexed: CIJE, CPE, EAA, ERA, ETA, IBSS, MEA, PAIS, RHEA, SEA, SENA, SOMA, SWA, TEA.
—BLDSC (5066.897300), IE, ingenta. **CCC.**
Published by: Sage Publications, Inc., 2455 Teller Rd, Thousand Oaks, CA 91320. TEL 805-499-0721, 800-818-7243, FAX 805-499-0871, 800-583-2665, info@sagepub.com, http://www.sagepub.com/journal.aspx?pid=254. Ed. Hans de Wit. **Subscr. outside the US to:** Sage Publications Ltd., 1 Oliver's Yard, 55 City Rd, London EC1 1SP, United Kingdom. TEL 44-20-73740645, FAX 44-20-73748741, subscription@sagepub.co.uk.

370.116 DEU ISSN 1615-0228
➤ **JUGENDNACHRICHTEN**; Zeitschrift des Bayerischen Jugendrings. Text in German. 1946. 10/yr. bk.rev.; film rev.; play rev.; software rev.; Website rev. charts; stat. 28 p./no.; **Document type:** *Journal, Academic/Scholarly.* **Description:** Contains information on programs and situations involving youths in relation to educational opportunities, social life and work, political affairs, and cultural matters.
Published by: Bayerischer Jugendring/Bavarian Youth Council, Herzog-Heinrich-Str 7, Munich, 80336, Germany. TEL 49-89-514580, FAX 49-89-5145888, juna@bjr.de, info@bjr.de, http://www.bjr.de/jugendnachrichten. Ed., R&P, Adv. contact Marko Junghaenel TEL 49-89-5145820. Circ: 3,500.

370.117 BEL
KEY TO EUROPE. Text in English, French. 1994. a. adv. **Document type:** *Magazine, Consumer.* **Description:** Provides a forum in which people from different nations can express their viewpoints on social, political and cultural themes.
Formerly: One Europe Magazine (1023-6953)
Published by: Association des Etats Generaux des Etudiants d'Europe, Rue Nestor de Tiere 15, Schaarbeek, 1040, Belgium. TEL 32-2-2452300, FAX 32-2-2456260, headoffice@aegee.org, http://www.aegee.org.

370.117 DEU ISSN 1432-8194
KULTURKONTAKTE. Text in German. 1994. irreg., latest vol.3, 1997. EUR 15.30 per vol. (effective 2003). **Document type:** *Magazine, Academic/Scholarly.*
Published by: Waxmann Verlag GmbH, Steinfurter Str 555, Muenster, 48159, Germany. TEL 49-251-26504-0, FAX 49-251-2650426, info@waxmann.com, http://www.waxmann.com.

LANGUAGE TRAVEL MAGAZINE. see *LINGUISTICS*

370.117 DEU ISSN 0938-1309
MIGRANTENKINDER IN DEN SCHULEN EUROPAS; Versuche und Erfahrungen. Text in German. 1990. irreg., latest vol.10, 1995. EUR 15.30 per vol. (effective 2003). **Document type:** *Monographic series, Academic/Scholarly.* **Description:** Presents papers on multicultural education and the integration of foreign students.
Published by: Waxmann Verlag GmbH, Steinfurter Str 555, Muenster, 48159, Germany. TEL 49-251-26504-0, FAX 49-251-2650426, info@waxmann.com, http://www.waxmann.com. Eds. Hans Reich, Ingrid Gogolin.

MODERN ENGLISH TEACHER; a magazine of practical suggestions for improving the teaching of English as a foreign language. see *EDUCATION—Teaching Methods And Curriculum*

370.116 GBR ISSN 1478-2685
MONOGRAPHS IN INTERNATIONAL EDUCATION. Text in English. 1999. s-a. GBP 80 domestic to libraries; USD 120 foreign to libraries (effective 2005). **Document type:** *Monographic series, Academic/Scholarly.*
Published by: Symposium Books (Subsidiary of: wwwords Ltd), Didcot, PO Box 204, Oxford, OX11 9ZQ, United Kingdom. TEL 44-1235-818062, FAX 44-1235-817275, orders@symposium-books.co.uk, http://www.symposium-books.co.uk/. Ed. Dr. Colin Brock.

370.117 DEU ISSN 1430-8770
MUENCHENER BEITRAEGE ZUR INTERKULTURELLEN KOMMUNIKATION. Text in German. 1996. irreg., latest vol.14, 2003. EUR 19.90 per vol. (effective 2003). **Document type:** *Monographic series, Academic/Scholarly.*
Published by: Waxmann Verlag GmbH, Steinfurter Str 555, Muenster, 48159, Germany. TEL 49-251-26504-0, FAX 49-251-2650426, info@waxmann.com, http://www.waxmann.com.

MULTICULTURAL EDUCATION ABSTRACTS. see *EDUCATION—Abstracting, Bibliographies, Statistics*

370.117 375.006 USA
MULTICULTURAL EDUCATION SERIES. Text in English. irreg. price varies. back issues avail. **Document type:** *Monographic series, Trade.* **Description:** Examines and discusses important issues in teaching students from a wide variety of cultural backgrounds, including the teaching for social justice.
Published by: Teachers College Press, Teachers College, Columbia University, 525 W 120th St, Box 303, New York, NY 10027-6694. http://www.teacherscollegepress.com. Pub. Carole Saltz. R&P Amy Detjen. **Dist. by:** Eurospan University Press Group, Order Dept, 3 Henrietta St, London WC2E 8LU, United Kingdom. TEL 44-20-7240-0856, FAX 44-20-7379-0609, http://www.eurospan.co.uk; Pademelon Press, Pty Ltd, 7-10 Anella Ave, PO Box 229, Castle Hill, NSW 2154, Australia. TEL 61-2-9634-2558, FAX 61-2-9680-4634; Transdex International, Pte Ltd, Block 1, Farrer Rd 307-05, Singapore 268817, Singapore. TEL 65-468-6242, FAX 65-462-5457.

MULTICULTURAL PERSPECTIVES. see *EDUCATION—Teaching Methods And Curriculum*

370.117 USA ISSN 1058-9236
Z711.8 CODEN: MUREF2
MULTICULTURAL REVIEW; dedicated to a better understanding of ethnic, racial and religious diversity. Text in English. 1992. q. USD 29.95 to individuals; USD 65 domestic to institutions; USD 85 foreign to institutions (effective 2005). adv. bk.rev. illus. Index. reprints avail. **Document type:** *Magazine, Academic/Scholarly.* **Description:** Reviews multicultural books and educational curriculum materials. Includes feature articles on related subjects.
Incorporates (1986-1992): Journal of Multicultural Librarianship (0950-1649)
Indexed: ABIn, ABS&EES, BRD, BRI, CBRI, CIJE, ChLitAb, ChPerI, DIP, EduInd, IBR, IBZ, IndIslam, MRD, PAIS, SOPODA.
—BLDSC (5983.084420), IE, Infotrieve, ingenta.
Published by: Goldman Group, 14497 N Dale Mabry Hwy, Ste 205-N, Tampa, FL 33618. TEL 813-264-2772, 800-600-4364, FAX 813-264-2343, editor@mcreview.com, http://www.mcreview.com, http://www.ggpubs.com. Ed. Lynn Miller-Lachmann. Pub. Todd Goldman. adv.: B&W page USD 750, color page USD 1,500; trim 8.25 x 10.88. Circ: 5,000 (paid).

370.116 USA
LA203
N A F S A DIRECTORY OF INSTITUTIONS AND INDIVIDUALS IN INTERNATIONAL EDUCATIONAL EXCHANGE (ONLINE EDITION). Text in English. 1948. biennial. free to members. adv. index. **Document type:** *Directory.*
Former titles: N A F S A Directory of Institutions and Individuals in International Educational Exchange (Print Edition) (0736-4660); (until 1983): National Association for Foreign Student Affairs N A F S A Directory (0077-3190)
Media: Online - full text.
Published by: National Association for Foreign Student Affairs (N A F S A), Association of International Educators, 1307 New York Ave, NW, 8th Fl, Washington, DC 20005-4701. TEL 202-737-3699, 800-836-4994, FAX 202-737-3657, publications@nafsa.org, http://www.nafsa.org. Ed. Steven B Kennedy. Adv. contact Cary Haney. Circ: 10,000.

370.116 USA
N C I V NETWORK NEWS. Text in English. 1956. m. USD 50. bk.rev. **Document type:** *Newsletter.*
Former titles: N C I V Newsletter; (until 1979): C O S E R V Newsletter (National Council for Community Services to International Visitors) (0547-5619)
Published by: National Council for International Visitors, 1420 K St, N W, Ste 800, Washington, DC 20005-2401. TEL 202-842-1414, FAX 202-289-4625. Ed. Dominic O'Brien.

370.116 PHL ISSN 0115-852X
N F E - W I D EXCHANGE - ASIA. NEWSLETTER. Text and summaries in English. 1981. 3/yr. back issues avail. **Document type:** *Newsletter.*
Published by: University of the Philippines at Los Banos, College of Agriculture, College, Laguna, 4031, Philippines. Ed. Lina L Ilag. Circ: 800.

370.116 USA ISSN 0278-3789
L914.5
N R C S A PROGRAM DIRECTORY. EUROPE. Text in English. 1983. q. **Document type:** *Directory.*
Published by: National Registration Center for Study Abroad, P O Box 1393, Milwaukee, WI 53201. TEL 414-278-0631, FAX 414-271-8884, inquiries@nrcsa.com. Ed. Mary Croy.

370.116025 USA
NEW SCHOOLS EXCHANGE. DIRECTORY AND RESOURCE GUIDE. Text in English. 1969. a. USD 5. adv. bk.rev.; film rev. bibl. cum.index. back issues avail.
Published by: New Schools Exchange, Pettigrew, AR 72752. Ed. Grace Dailey Harwood. Circ: 3,000.

370.116 USA ISSN 1043-3724
NEWSLINKS. Text in English. q. USD 35 in US & Canada; USD 45 elsewhere (effective 2003). illus. **Document type:** *Newspaper.*
Published by: International Schools Services, Inc., PO Box 5910, Princeton, NJ 08543. TEL 609-452-0990, FAX 609-452-2690, http://www.iss.edu. Ed. Judy Seltz.

E

371.223 NOR ISSN 0803-8201
NORGE-AMERIKA FORENINGEN. YEARBOOK. Text in Multiple languages. 1945. a. adv. bk.rev. illus. **Document type:** *Corporate.* **Description:** Dedicated to providing scholarship and fellowship opportunities to Americans and Norwegians each year.
Incorporates: Norge-Amerikaforeningen. Annual Report
Published by: Norge-Amerika Foreningen/Norway-America Association, Raadhusgaten 23 B, Oslo, 0158, Norway. TEL 47-23-357160, FAX 47-23-357175, namerika@online.no, http://www.noram.no. Circ: 2,000.

NOTES AND ABSTRACTS IN AMERICAN AND INTERNATIONAL EDUCATION. see *EDUCATION—Abstracting, Bibliographies, Statistics*

370.1163 USA ISSN 1077-0313
O-HAYO SENSEI; the newsletter of English teaching jobs in Japan. Text in English. 1994. bi-w. USD 12 (effective 2005). bk.rev. **Document type:** *Newsletter.* **Description:** Reports English teaching positions at universities and public and private schools across Japan. Articles related to ESL and TESL teaching and living in Japan. Includes school addresses and contact person.
Media: Online - full content. **Related titles:** Online - full text ed.
Address: 1032 Irving St, Ste 508, San Francisco, CA 94122. TEL 415-731-1113, FAX 415-731-1113, editor@ohayosensei.com, http://www.ohayosensei.com. Ed., Pub. Lynn Cullivan. Circ: 6,000.

370.116 RUS
OBUCHENIYE ZA RUBEZHOM/STUDY AND TRAINING ABROAD. Text in Russian. 1998. m.
Related titles: Online - full content ed.
Published by: Mnemo, a/ya 29, Moscow, 121170, Russian Federation. TEL 7-095-2385205, http://www.mnemo.ru/study, http://www.mnemo.ru/about.htm.

370.116 AUT
OESTERREICHISCHER AUSTAUSCHDIENST. RECHENSCHAFTSBERICHT. Text in German. 1961. a. illus.; stat. **Document type:** *Journal, Academic/Scholarly.*
Formerly: Oesterreichischer Auslandsstudentendienst. Rechenschaftsbericht
Published by: Oesterreichischer Austauschdienst/Austrian Exchange Service, Alserstrasse 4-1-3-8, Vienna, W 1090, Austria. TEL 43-1-427728101, FAX 43-1-42779281, info@oead.ac.at, http://www.oead.ac.at. Circ: 350.

370.116 USA ISSN 0078-5172
LB2376
OPEN DOORS; report on international exchange. Text in English. 1955. a. USD 39.95. reprints avail. **Document type:** *Directory.* **Description:** Reports on the IIE's annual census of international students with data on national origin, sources of financial support, fields of study, enrollments and rates of growth at virtually all accredited US colleges and universities.
Indexed: SRI.
—BLDSC (6265.953500).
Published by: Institute of International Education, PO Box 371, Annapolis, MD 20701-0371. TEL 301-617-7804, FAX 301-953-2838, http://www.iie.org/.

370.116 USA
OPEN EXCHANGE. Text in English. 1974. 6/yr. USD 12. adv. bk.rev. illus.
Formerly: Open Education Exchange
Published by: Community Resource Institute, PO Box 7880, Berkeley, CA 94707. TEL 510-526-7190, FAX 510-540-1057. Ed., R&P Bart Brodsky. Pub., Adv. contact Janet Geis. Circ: 102,000.

370.116 USA
OVER THE RAINBOW. Text in English. 1982. s-a. membership. adv. bk.rev. back issues avail. **Document type:** *Newsletter.* **Description:** Provides information on the latest opportunities concerning travel and international exchange programs, and provides information on scholarships,and new publications. Provides details on MIUSA's community service programs and international exchanges.
Related titles: Audio cassette/tape ed.
Published by: Mobility International U S A, PO Box 10767, Eugene, OR 97440-2767. TEL 541-343-1284, FAX 541-343-6812, info@miusa.org, http://www.miusa.org. Ed. Susan Sygall. Adv. contact Pamela Houston TEL 541-343-1284. Circ: 300.

OVERSEAS TRAVEL PLANNER. see *TRAVEL AND TOURISM*

370.116 USA ISSN 1549-0645
LC189.8
▼ **PARALLAX**; a journal of international perspectives. Text in English. 2003 (Fall). a. free (effective 2004). **Document type:** *Journal, Academic/Scholarly.*
Published by: Suffolk University, Center for International Education, 8 Ashburton Pl, Boston, MA 02108. TEL 617-573-8000, http://www.suffolk.edu/international/index.html. Ed. David L Robbins.

379.116 USA ISSN 0031-501X
PEOPLE (KANSAS CITY). Text in English. 1962. a. membership. illus.
Formerly: People-to-People Newsletter
Published by: People To People International, 501 E Armour Blvd, Kansas City, MO 64109-2200. TEL 816-531-4701, FAX 816-561-7502, ptpi@ptpi.org, http://www.ptpi.org. Ed. Laura Sapp. Circ: 24,000.

371.223 USA
PERSPECTIVE (NEW YORK). Text in English. 1970. q. USD 12. adv. bk.rev. **Document type:** *Newsletter, Academic/Scholarly.* **Description:** Provides information on conferences, grants, media, employment, news from universities, and workshops.
Published by: Association of Teachers of Latin American Studies, PO Box 620754, Flushing, NY 11362-0754. TEL 718-428-1237. Ed. Rosa Salinas. R&P D J Mugan. Circ: 1,000.

370.116 USA ISSN 1089-246X
LC6681
PETERSON'S LEARNING ADVENTURES AROUND THE WORLD. Text in English. 1997. a. USD 24.95. **Document type:** *Directory.* **Description:** Contains information on over 1,300 learning opportunities worldwide from cultural tours to gourmet cooking-wine programs to archeological digs.
Published by: Thomson Peterson's (Subsidiary of: Thomson Corporation), Princeton Pike Corporate Center, 2000 Lenox Dr, 3rd Fl, Lawrenceville, NJ 08648. TEL 609-243-9111, FAX 609-243-9150, http://www.petersons.com. Ed. Barbara Lawrence.

PETERSON'S STUDY ABROAD. see *EDUCATION—Higher Education*

370.116 GBR
PORTICO. Text and summaries in Spanish. 1992. 3/yr. illus. back issues avail. **Document type:** *Magazine, Academic/Scholarly.* **Description:** Summarizes articles from the popular press on Spanish and Latin American culture for teachers of Spanish in the UK. Includes instructional activities to teach Spanish in a real-world multicultural context.
Published by: Spanish Embassy, London. Education and Science Office/Embajada de Espana, Londres. Consejeria de Educacion en el Reino Unido e Irlanda, 20 Peel St, London, W8 7PD, United Kingdom. TEL 44-20-7727-2462, 44-20-7243-8535, asesores.uk@correo.mec.es, http://www.sqci.mec.es/uk.

PROLITERACY WORLDWIDE. ANNUAL REPORT. see *EDUCATION—Adult Education*

370.117 GBR ISSN 1478-8551
LC1099.5.G7
RACE EQUALITY TEACHING. Text in English. 1982. 3/yr. GBP 24 in United Kingdom to individuals; GBP 35 elsewhere to individuals; GBP 32 in United Kingdom to institutions; GBP 42 elsewhere to institutions (effective 2003); Subscr. includes online access.. adv. bk.rev. index. back issues avail. **Document type:** *Journal, Academic/Scholarly.* **Description:** Serves all teachers preparing students for life in a multi-ethnic society.
Formerly (until 2002): M C T - Multicultural Teaching (0263-0869)
Related titles: Microform ed.; Online - full text ed.: (from EBSCO Publishing).
Indexed: BrEdI, CPE, ChLitAb, ERA, ETA, LT&LA, MEA, RHEA, SEA, SENA, SOMA, SRRA, TEA.
—BLDSC (7225.898700), IE. **CCC.**
Published by: Trentham Books Ltd., Westview House, 734 London Rd, Stoke-on-Trent, Staffs ST4 5NP, United Kingdom. TEL 44-1782-745567, FAX 44-1782-745553, tb@trentham-books.co.uk, http://www.trentham-books.co.uk/pages/jret.htm. Eds. Gillian Klein, Ros Garside. Adv. contact Barbara Wiggins. Circ: 2,100.

370.116 USA ISSN 0899-2002
L900
SCHOOLS ABROAD OF INTEREST TO AMERICANS; a survey of international primary and preparatory education. Text in English. 1959. triennial, latest 2003-2004, 10th ed. USD 45 per issue (effective 2005). adv. illus.; stat. index. 544 p./no.; **Document type:** *Directory, Consumer.* **Description:** Describes 800 elementary and secondary schools in 130 foreign countries that accept English-speaking students.
Published by: Porter Sargent Publishers, Inc., 11 Beacon St, Ste 1400, Boston, MA 02108. TEL 617-523-1670, 800-342-7470, FAX 617-523-1021, info@portersargent.com, http://www.schoolsabroad.us, http://www.portersargent.com. Ed. Daniel P. McKeever. Pub., Adv. contact John Yonce. page USD 540; 3.125 x 6. Circ: 2,000.

370.116 NLD
SINT MARTEN POST. Text in Dutch. 1977. m. adv. bk.rev. illus. **Document type:** *Newsletter, Academic/Scholarly.* **Description:** Deals with participation of youth in developing projects and international education.
Published by: Stichting Jongeren Tref- en Werkcentrum, Postbus 501, Arnhem, 6800 AM, Netherlands. TEL 31-26-445-4649, iju@dds.nl, http://www.antenna.nl/iju. Ed., Pub., Adv. contact Kees Kentin. Circ: 500.

370.116 IND ISSN 0970-7417
SRI AUROBINDO INTERNATIONAL CENTRE OF EDUCATION. BULLETIN/BULLETIN DU CENTRE INTERNATIONAL D'EDUCATION SRI AUROBINDO. Text in English, French. 1949. q. INR 70 domestic (effective 2003); USD 10 foreign (effective 2002); INR 80 domestic English-French-Hindi ed.; USD 12 foreign English-French-Hindi ed.; INR 20 newsstand/cover English-French-Hindi ed. (effective 2003). adv. bk.rev. illus. back issues avail. **Document type:** *Bulletin, Academic/Scholarly.*
Related titles: ♦ Hindi ed.: Sriarvimda Amtarastriya Siksha Kemdra Patrika. ISSN 0970-7425.
Indexed: RASB.
Published by: (Sri Aurobindo International Center of Education), Sri Aurobindo Ashram Trust, c/o Manoj Das Gupta, Pondicherry, Tamil Nadu 605 002, India. TEL 91-413-2334980, FAX 91-413-2223328, sabda@sriaurobindoashram.org, http://sabda.sriaurobindoashram.org. Ed., Pub., R&P Manoj Das Gupta. Circ: 800.

370.117 DEU ISSN 0948-3357
➤ **STAUFFENBURG DISCUSSION**; Studien zur inter-und multikultur. Text in German. 1995. irreg., latest vol.19, 2002. price varies. adv. **Document type:** *Monographic series, Academic/Scholarly.*
Published by: Stauffenburg Verlag, Postfach 2525, Tuebingen, 72015, Germany. TEL 49-7071-97300, FAX 49-7071-973030, info@stauffenburg.de, http://www.stauffenburg.de/groups/sdiscuss.htm. R&P Brigitte Narr. Adv. contact Birgit Cocoucelli.

370.116 DEU
STERN SPEZIAL OSKAR'S. Text in English, German. 2/yr. **Document type:** *Magazine, Consumer.* **Description:** Contains articles and features on educational and cultural issues for German and American foreign exchange students.
Published by: Gruner und Jahr AG & Co., Am Baumwall 11, Hamburg, 20459, Germany. TEL 49-40-3703-0, FAX 49-40-37036000, ksc@guj.de, http://www.guj.de.

370.116 USA
STUDENT TRAVELS. Text in English. 1992. s-a. free. adv. **Description:** Covers student travel abroad for work and study.
Published by: Council on International Educational Exchange, c/o Campus Agency, LLC, 132 E 28th St, 400, New York, NY 10016. TEL 212-252-8426, FAX 212-252-8427. Ed. Michael Fuller. Adv. contact Stephanie Orange. Circ: 450,000.

378.116 FRA ISSN 0081-895X
LB2338
STUDY ABROAD/ESTUDIOS EN EL EXTRANJERO/ETUDES A L'ETRANGER; scholarships and higher education courses worldwide. Text in English, French, Spanish. 1949. biennial. EUR 18.29 newsstand/cover (effective 2003).
Related titles: CD-ROM ed.: FRF 180.
Indexed: RASB.
—CISTI.
Published by: UNESCO Publishing, 7 place de Fontenoy, Paris, 75352, France. TEL 33-1-45684300, FAX 33-1-45685737, http://www.unesco.org/publications. **Dist. in U.S. by:** Bernan Associates, Bernan, 4611-F Assembly Dr., Lanham, MD 20706-4391. TEL 800-274-4447, FAX 800-865-3450. **Co-publisher:** International Bureau of Education.

378.016 IND
STUDY & TRAVEL INDIA; the resource magazine for international students. Text in English. 2001. q. INR 100, USD 10 (effective 2001). adv. bk.rev.; video rev. back issues avail. **Document type:** *Magazine, Consumer.* **Description:** Deals with education and travel opportunities in India.
Published by: Jaffe Publishing Management Service, Kunnuparambil Bldgs., Kurichy, Kottayam, Kerala 686 549, India. TEL 91-481-434141, FAX 91-481-430470. Ed. Kunnuparambil P Punnoose. Pub. Mrs. Niggy S. Kuriakose. Adv. contact Shaji Jacob. B&W page USD 200; 24 x 18. Circ: 5,000.

370.116 GBR
STUDYING AND LIVING IN THE UNITED KINGDOM. Text in English. 1949. a. GBP 5.99 (effective 2001). 128 p./no.; **Description:** Guide for foreign students studying in the UK.
Former titles: Studying and Living in Britain; How to Live in Britain
Published by: British Council, 10 Spring Gardens, London, SW1A 2BN, United Kingdom. TEL 44-20-7930-8466, FAX 44-20-7493-5035, publications.information@britishcouncil.org, http://www.britishcouncil.org/publications. **Dist. by:** Plymbridge Distributors Ltd, Plymbridge House, Estover Rd, Plymouth, Devon PL6 7PY, United Kingdom. TEL 44-1752-202300, FAX 44-1752-202330, enquiries@plymbridge.com, http://www.plymbridge.com.

378.016 IND
STUDYING & WORKING ABROAD. Text in English. 1999. q. INR 100, USD 10 (effective 2001). adv. back issues avail. **Description:** Deals with education and career opportunities worldwide.
Published by: Jaffe Publishing Management Service, Kunnuparambil Bldgs., Kurichy, Kottayam, Kerala 686 549, India. TEL 91-481-434141, FAX 91-481-430470. Ed. Jaffe K. Punnoose. Pub. Kunnuparambil P Punnoose. adv.: B&W page USD 200; 24 x 18. Circ: 5,300.

E

▼ new title ➤ refereed ✶ unverified ♦ full entry avail.

370.116 401   GBR
STUDYZONE MAGAZINE; education and language learning overseas. Text in English. a. **Document type:** *Magazine, Consumer.* **Description:** Reports on educational programs for international students.
Published by: Hothouse Media Ltd, 11-15 Emerald St, London, WC1N 3QL, United Kingdom. TEL 44-20-74404020, FAX 44-20-74404033, http://www.hothousemedia.com/studyzone/index.htm.

370.116   USA
T A NEWS. (Transitions Abroad) Text in English. 1998. bi-m. **Document type:** *Newsletter.* **Description:** Highlights what's new in international learning opportunities of all kinds.- study abroad programs, internships, volunteer placements, short-term jobs, and all other independent or organized travel-learning opportunities.
Media: Online - full text.
Published by: Transitions Abroad Publishing, PO Box 745, Bennington, VT 05201. TEL 413-256-3414, FAX 413-256-0373, editor@transitionsabroad.com, http://www.transitionsabroad.com. Ed. Nicole Rosenleaf Ritter.

370.116 371.3   AUS   ISSN 1030-8385
➤ **T E S O L IN CONTEXT**; journal of A C T A. (Teachers of English to Speakers of Other Languages) Text in English. 1990. 2/yr. AUD 25 domestic to individuals; AUD 40 foreign to individuals; AUD 50 domestic to institutions; AUD 80 foreign to institutions; AUD 15 newsstand/cover. adv. bk.rev. back issues avail. **Document type:** *Academic/Scholarly.* **Description:** Constitutes a forum of expression of ideas on matters relating to T E S O L. Aims at academics, researchers and school teachers.
Indexed: AEI, L&LBA.
Published by: Australian Council of T E S O L Associations (A C T A), 25 Kimmax St, Sunnybank, QLD 4109, Australia. TEL 61-07-3864 3279, pa.mckay@qut.edu.au, nellis@acue.adelaide.edu.au, http://www.acta.edu.au/. Ed., R&P Kate Cadman TEL 61-08-8303 3957. Pub. Penny McKay. Adv. contact Mark Taylor. B&W page AUD 150; trim 275 x 180. Circ: 2,000. **Subscr. to:** A C U E, University of Adelaide, Adelaide, SA 5069, Australia. TEL 61-08-8303 6035, FAX 61-08-8303 6034.

➤ **TEACHERS' GUIDE TO OVERSEAS TEACHING**; a complete and comprehensive guide of English-language schools and colleges overseas. see *LINGUISTICS*

370.1163   USA   ISSN 0889-8839
TEACHING OPPORTUNITIES OVERSEAS - BULLETIN. Text in English. 1975. m. USD 42. adv. **Document type:** *Newsletter.* **Description:** Provides information on teaching positions at elementary and secondary schools all over the world.
Published by: Overseas Academic Opportunities, PO Box 768, Merrick, NY 11566-0368. Ed., Pub., R&P, Adv. contact Susan Towey. Circ: 2,800 (paid).

370.117   GBR   ISSN 1359-172X
TECLA; texts for learners and teachers of Spanish. Text in Spanish. 1994. w. (during UK academic year). free. illus. index. back issues avail. **Document type:** *Magazine, Trade.* **Description:** Offers teachers and learners of Spanish in the UK and elsewhere culturally relevant authentic texts in Spanish.
Media: Online - full content.
Published by: Spanish Embassy, London. Education and Science Office/Embajada de Espana, Londres. Consejeria de Educacion en el Reino Unido e Irlanda, 20 Peel St, London, W8 7PD, United Kingdom. TEL 44-20-7727-2462, 44-20-7243-8535, asesores.uk@correo.mec.es, http://www.sqci.mec.es/uk.

370.117   DEU   ISSN 0947-9732
LB43
➤ **TERTIUM COMPARATIONIS.** Text in English, German. 1995. 2/yr. EUR 35 in Europe; EUR 39 elsewhere; EUR 20 newsstand/cover (effective 2003). **Document type:** *Journal, Academic/Scholarly.* **Description:** Publishes articles in the fields of comparative education, international education research and intercultural education.
Related titles: Online - full text ed.: ISSN 1434-1697. EUR 16 (effective 2003).
Indexed: DIP, IBR, IBZ.
Published by: Waxmann Verlag GmbH, Steinfurter Str 555, Muenster, 48159, Germany. TEL 49-251-26504-0, FAX 49-251-2650426, tc@waxmann.com, info@waxmann.com, http://www.waxmann.com/zs/tc.html. Ed. Norbert Wenning.

371.3   PER   ISSN 1682-4873
U N E B I BOLETIN. (Unidad de Educacion Bilingue Intercultural Boletin) Key Title: Boletin UNEBI. Text in Spanish. 1998. q.
Media: Online - full text.
Published by: Ministerio de Educacion, Unidad de Educacion Bilingue Intercultural, Van de Velde 160, Lima, 14, Peru. TEL 51-1-4363960, http://www.minedu.gob.pe/gestion_pedagogica/dir_edubilingue/comunica_difus/boletin1.htm. Ed. Juan Carlos Godenzzi Alegre.

370.116   USA
U.S. DEPARTMENT OF EDUCATION. OPPORTUNITIES FOR TEACHERS ABROAD. Text in English. a. price varies. **Document type:** *Directory, Government.*

Formerly: Opportunities Abroad for Teachers (0078-5458)
Published by: U.S. Department of Education, 400 Maryland Ave, S W, Washington, DC 20202. TEL 202-655-4000. **Subscr. to:** U.S. Government Printing Office, Superintendent of Documents. TEL 202-783-3238, FAX 202-512-2233.

370.116   USA
U S FOREIGN STUDENT MAGAZINE. Text in English. 1990. bi-m. USD 3.50. adv. bk.rev. **Description:** Emphasizes the forces that influence the welfare of current and potential incoming foreign students.
Published by: International Family Company, PO Box 1742, Tempe, AZ 85281. TEL 602-966-0304. Circ: 30,000.

370.116   IND   ISSN 0503-4663
UNITED SCHOOLS INTERNATIONAL. DOCUMENTS OF THE BIENNIAL CONFERENCE. Text in English. 1961. biennial. free. adv. **Document type:** *Proceedings.*
Published by: United Schools Organisation of India, U S O House, USO Rd. 6 Special Institutional Area, New Delhi, 110 067, India. TEL 91-11-656-1103, FAX 91-11-685-6283. Ed., Pub., R&P Jiya Lal Jain. Adv. contact Ram Nath Tandon. Circ: 500.

370.116   ITA   ISSN 1121-0370
UNIVERSITA PER STRANIERI. ANNALI. Text in Italian. 1981. s-a. **Document type:** *Academic/Scholarly.*
Indexed: MLA-IB.
Published by: Universita Italiana per Stranieri, Palazzo Gallenga, Piazza Fortebraccio, Perugia, PG 06122, Italy. TEL 075-57461, FAX 075-62014, TELEX 662079 UNSTRA I. Ed. Giorgio Spitella.

370.116   AUS   ISSN 1329-5179
UNIVERSITY OF TECHNOLOGY, SYDNEY. INSTITUTE FOR INTERNATIONAL STUDIES HANDBOOK. Text in English. 1996. a. AUD 14 domestic; AUD 19 foreign (effective 2000). back issues avail. **Document type:** *Catalog, Academic/Scholarly.* **Description:** Presents detailed information about the institute, courses, staff and subject synopses.
Published by: University of Technology, Sydney, City Campus, PO Box 123, Broadway, NSW 2007, Australia. TEL 61-2-9514-2000, FAX 61-2-9514-1551, publications@uts.edu.au, http://www.uts.edu.au/div/publications. Circ: 2,000.

UNIWORLD/UNIMONDE. see *EDUCATION—Higher Education*

370.116   USA
UP WITH PEOPLE REPORTS✷ . Text in English. 1971-1980; resumed 1988. s-a. free. illus. **Document type:** *Newsletter.* **Description:** Contains news of the organization's international student program and other developments.
Formerly (until 1980): Up with People News
Published by: Up with People, Inc., 2380 W Midway Blvd #2, Broomfield, CO 80020-1602. TEL 303-460-7100, FAX 303-438-7300. Ed. Scott Johnson. Circ: 60,000 (controlled).

370.116   USA   ISSN 1046-2104
LB2375
VACATION STUDY ABROAD. Text in English. 1947. a. USD 36.95. **Document type:** *Directory.* **Description:** Provides information on 1600 summer and short-term programs offered by US and foreign higher education institutions and private agencies.
Supersedes: Learning Traveler. Vacation Study Abroad (0271-1702); Formerly: Summer Study Abroad (0081-9379)
Published by: Institute of International Education, PO Box 371, Annapolis, MD 20701-0371. TEL 301-617-7804, FAX 301-953-2838, http://www.iie.org/. Ed. Sara Steen.

370.117   DEU   ISSN 0943-1748
VERGLEICHENDE PAEDAGOGISCHE CHINAFORSCHUNG. Text in German. 1993. irreg., latest vol.4, 1996. EUR 25.50 per vol. (effective 2003). **Document type:** *Monographic series, Academic/Scholarly.* **Description:** Contains discussions on intercultural education and exchanges between China and Germany.
Published by: Waxmann Verlag GmbH, Steinfurter Str 555, Muenster, 48159, Germany. TEL 49-251-26504-0, FAX 49-251-2650426, info@waxmann.com, http://www.waxmann.com. Ed. Kersten Reich.

370.116   USA   ISSN 0271-3195
AS36.W79
WOODROW WILSON INTERNATIONAL CENTER FOR SCHOLARS. ANNUAL REPORT. Key Title: Annual Report - Woodrow Wilson International Center for Scholars. Text in English. 1970. a. free. illus. **Document type:** *Corporate.*
Published by: Woodrow Wilson International Center for Scholars, 1 Woodrow Wilson Plaza, 1300 Pennsylvania Ave, N W, Washington, DC 20004-3027. TEL 202-691-4029. Ed. Steven Lagerfeld. Pub. Kathy Read. R&P James Carman TEL 202-691-4200. Circ: 60,000.

370.116   BHR
WORKSHOP OF PEACE/MUNTADA AS-SALAAM. Text in English. 1980. q. free. adv. illus. **Document type:** *Academic/Scholarly.* **Description:** Dedicated to promoting peace and cooperation. Provides news of international educational issues, cooperative programs and other items of interest.
Published by: United Schools International, Arab Regional Office, PO Box 726, Manama, Bahrain. TEL 973-232576, FAX 973-254805, TELEX 9094 TARBIA BN. Eds. Jiya Lal Jain, Rashid Sulaybikh. adv.: B&W page BHD 160.

370.116   USA
A WORLD AWAITS YOU. Text in English. 1996. a. free (effective 2001). **Description:** Provides resources for including disabled individuals in international exchange programs, including academic, volunteer and community service, research and work abroad programs.
Related titles: Audio cassette/tape ed.; Diskette ed.
Published by: Mobility International U S A, PO Box 10767, Eugene, OR 97440-2767. TEL 541-343-1284, FAX 541-343-6812, clearinghouse@miusa.org, http://www.miusa.org. Ed. Tracy Scharn. Circ: 3,000.

370.116   USA
WORLD LEARNING. ANNUAL REPORT. Text in English. 1960. a. free. **Document type:** *Corporate.*
Former titles: Experiment in International Living. Annual Report; Experiment in International Living. President's Report (0071-3376)
Published by: World Learning, Kipling Rd, Box 676, Brattleboro, VT 05302-0676. TEL 802-257-7751, FAX 802-258-3163. Circ: 8,000.

370.116   USA
▼ **WORLD SCHOLAR.** Text in English. 2005 (Fall). q. free. adv. **Document type:** *Magazine, Consumer.* **Description:** Covers the life issues of foreign students, including insurance, immigration, scholarship, living accommodations, job search, and culture.
Published by: Uni-Recruitment, Inc., 719 Remsen Ave, Ste 2A, Brooklyn, NY 11236. TEL 718-566-2177, FAX 718-566-2178, info@theworldscholar.com, http://www.theworldscholar.com. adv.: B&W page USD 1,575, color page USD 1,990; trim 8.25 x 10.875. Circ: 100,000 (controlled).

370.116   USA
➤ **THE YALE - CHINA REVIEW.** Text in English. 1979. s-a. USD 35. adv. bk.rev. back issues avail. **Document type:** *Academic/Scholarly.* **Description:** Contains articles relating to culture, education, science, and current events in contemporary China, as well as US-China exchange.
Formerly (until 1993): China Update
Indexed: BAS.
Published by: Yale China Association, PO Box 208223, Yale STA, New Haven, CT 06520. TEL 203-432-0880, ycassoc@minerva.cis.yale.edu, http://www.yale.edu/yalechin. Ed., R&P Heather McGray. Adv. contact Judith M Collins. Circ: 3,000.

EDUCATION—School Organization And Administration

371.2   USA   ISSN 0898-252X
THE A A S A PROFESSOR. (American Association of School Administrators) Text in English. 1978. q.
—**CCC.**
Published by: American Association of School Administrators, 801 N Quincy St, Ste 700, Arlington, VA 22208-1730. TEL 703-528-0700, FAX 703-841-1543, http://www.aasa.org. Ed. Frederick Dembowski TEL 561.237.7850.

371.2   GBR   ISSN 0266-6278
A C E BULLETIN. Text in English. 1960. bi-m. GBP 33 domestic; GBP 38 in Europe; GBP 48 elsewhere (effective 2005). adv. bk.rev. abstr. index. back issues avail. **Document type:** *Magazine, Consumer.* **Description:** Contains news, features, and guidelines for school governors and information sheets that reflect the parents' perspective on developments in education, as well as digests of the latest books, pamphlets, journals, and reports on education.
Former titles (until Sep. 1984): Where to Find Out More about Education; Where (0043-4809)
Related titles: Online - full text ed.
Indexed: BrEdI, CPE, ERA, ETA, MEA, RHEA, SEA, SENA, SOMA, SWA, TEA.
—**BLDSC** (0573.781300), IE, ingenta. **CCC.**
Published by: Advisory Centre for Education (A C E) Ltd., 1c Aberdeen Studios, 22 Highbury Grove, London, N5 2DQ, United Kingdom. TEL 44-20-73548318, FAX 44-20-73549069, enquiries@ace.dialnet.com, http://www.ace-ed.org.uk/bulletin.html. Ed. Alison Murdoch. R&P Margaret McGowan. Adv. contact Jill Chandler. B&W page GBP 275, color page GBP 300; trim 190 x 280. Circ: 2,000.

379.94   AUS
A C S S O POLICY DOCUMENT (YEAR). Text in English. a. AUD 10 (effective 2001).
Formerly (until 1994): A C S S O Policy (Year)

E

Published by: Australian Council of State School Organisations, Hughes Primary School, Kent St, Hughes, ACT 2605, Australia. TEL 61-262825150, FAX 61-262851351, acsso@acsso.org.au, http://www.acsso.org.au. Ed., R&P Penny Cook. Circ: 200 (controlled).

371.2 FRA ISSN 0222-674X
A F A E; administration et education. Text in French. 1979. q. adv. bk.rev. **Document type:** *Bulletin, Academic/Scholarly.*
Published by: Association Francaise des Administrateurs de l'Education, 28 rue du General Foy, Paris, 75008, France. TEL 33-1-42931201, FAX 33-1-42941198, AFAE@wanadoo.fr. Ed., Adv. contact Guy Roger Meitinger. Pub. Bernard Toulemonde. R&P Paul Dela Taille. Circ: 1,500.

379.2 USA ISSN 1543-0006
A G E L E NEWS. (Association for Gender Equity Leadership in Education) Text in English. 1984. q. free to members (effective 2003). adv.
Formerly (until 2003): N C S E E News (1537-131X)
Published by: Association for Gender Equity Leadership in Education, 317 S. Division St. PMB 54, Ann Arbor, MI 48104. AGELEbusiness@yahoo.com, http://www.agele.org/newsletter/newsletter.html, http://www.agele.org/index.html. Ed. Pam Miller.

371.6 USA ISSN 0736-7252
A P P A NEWSLETTER. (Association of Physical Plant Administrators) Text in English. 1953. 8/yr. USD 40; includes Facilities Manager. adv. bk.rev. charts; illus. index. **Document type:** *Newsletter.* **Description:** Promotes excellence in the administration, care, operation, planning, and development of higher education facilities.
Media: Online - full text.
Published by: A P P A: The Association of Higher Education Facilities Officers, 1643 Prince St, Alexandria, VA 22314-2818. TEL 703-684-1446, FAX 703-549-2772. Ed. Alycia Eck. Circ: 5,000.

A P P A: THE ASSOCIATION OF HIGHER EDUCATION FACILITIES OFFICERS. PROCEEDINGS OF THE ANNUAL MEETING. see *EDUCATION—Higher Education*

371.2 USA ISSN 1091-014X
LB2804
A S B O ACCENTS. Text in English. 1981. q. free to members. adv. **Document type:** *Newspaper.*
Formerly (until 1980): Newsletter - Association of School Business Officials (0194-5661)
Published by: (Association of School Business Officials), A S B O International, 11401 N Shore Dr, Reston, VA 20190-4200. FAX 703-478-0205, asboreq@asbointl.org, http://www.asbointl.org. Ed. Ceil Goldberg. Pub. Don I Tharpe. R&P Barbara Cook. Adv. contact Tim McCormack. Circ: 6,900.

379.1531 USA ISSN 0001-2408
A S B S D BULLETIN. Text in English. 1946. s-m. USD 25. adv. bk.rev.; film rev. charts; illus.; stat. **Document type:** *Bulletin.*
Published by: Associated School Boards of South Dakota, PO Box 1059, Pierre, SD 57501-1059. TEL 605-773-2500, FAX 605-773-2501, info@asbsd.org, http://www.asbsd.org. Ed. Gene Enck. Circ: 2,800.

371.206 USA
A S S C NEWSLETTER. Text in English. 1976. m. looseleaf. membership. **Document type:** *Newsletter.* **Description:** Research in school finance.
Published by: Arkansas School Study Council, 231 Graduate Education Bldg, University of Arkansas, Box 428, Fayetteville, AR 72701. TEL 501-575-5112. Ed. Martin Schoppmeyer. R&P Sonja Bennett TEL 501-575-4210. Circ: 650.

371.2 NLD ISSN 1384-5608
ACADEMIA. Text in Dutch. 1996. q. **Document type:** *Journal, Trade.*
Formed by the merger of (1992-1996): V S N U Opinie (0928-9100); (1986-1996): U & H (0921-5263); Which was formerly (1954-1986): Universiteit en Hogeschool (0165-5183)
—Infotrieve.
Published by: Vereniging van Samenwerkende Nederlandse Universiteiten, Postbus 19270, Utrecht, 3501 DG, Netherlands. TEL 31-30-2363888, FAX 31-30-2333540, balie@vsnu.nl, http://www.vsnu.nl.

371.2 ESP ISSN 0213-4705
LA910
➤ **ADAXE**; revista de estudos e experiencias educativas. Text in Spanish; Summaries in Gallegan, English. 1984. a. EUR 7.21 (effective 2003). bk.rev. bibl. back issues avail. **Document type:** *Magazine, Academic/Scholarly.*
Indexed: RILM.
—CINDOC.
Published by: Universidad de Santiago de Compostela, Servicio de Publicacions, Campus Universitario Sur, Santiago de Compostela, 15782, Spain. TEL 34-981-593500, FAX 34-981-593963, spublic@usc.es, http://www.usc.es/spubl/revadaxe.htm. Pub. Ramon Sanchez. Circ: 500.

371.2 USA ISSN 1056-1293
ADMINISTRATIVE FOCUS. Text in English. q. **Document type:** *Government.*
Former titles: Superintendent's Newsletter (0149-2322); State Superintendent's Newsletter (0149-2055)
Published by: Oklahoma State Department of Education, 2500 N. Lincoln Blvd., Oklahoma City, OK 73105-4599. TEL 405-521-3301, FAX 405-521-6205, http://www.sde.state.ok.us/home/defaultie.html.

371.201 IDN ISSN 0304-6117
JA26
ADMINISTRATOR. Text in English. 1973. m. IDR 3,500. **Document type:** *Bulletin, Academic/Scholarly.*
Indexed: EI.
Published by: University of Brawijaya, Faculty of Administrative Science/Universitas Brawijaya, Fakultas Ilmu Administrasi, Jalan Mayor Jenderal Haryono 163, Malang, Indonesia. TEL 0341-553737, FAX 341-553737. Circ: 1,000.

371.2 USA
ADMINISTRATOR, RESPONSE TEAM, AND STEERING COMMITTEE MANUAL. Text in English. 1997. biennial. USD 55 (effective 2003). 164 p./no. 2 cols./p.; **Document type:** *Journal, Trade.* **Description:** Facilitates the school's progress through the school improvement planning process.
Published by: (Northwest Association of Schools and of Colleges and Universities), Commission on Schools, 1910 University Dr, Boise, ID 83725-1060. TEL 208-426-5727, FAX 208-334-3228, sclemens@boisestate.edu, http://www2.boisestate.edu/nasc. Ed. Shelli D. Clemens. Pub. David G Steadman.

371.201 USA
ADMINISTRATORS NEWSLETTER. Text in English. 1969. m. USD 29.95. **Document type:** *Newsletter.*
Published by: C M A Microcomputers, 113 Wattenbarger Rd, Sweetwater, TN 37874-6135. TEL 615-337-2525, FAX 615-337-0222, cwmcma@aol.com. Ed. Ray Burr. Circ: 47,123.

371.21 USA ISSN 0884-7398
LB2351:2
ADMISSIONS MARKETING REPORT. Text in English. 1985. m. USD 125 (effective 1997). back issues avail. **Document type:** *Trade.* **Description:** Looks at the admissions marketing programs at colleges and universities across America.
Published by: H M R Publications Group, 3050 Presidential Dr, Ste 111, Atlanta, GA 30340. TEL 770-457-6105. Ed. Bill Gregory. Pub. Jan Michael Lok. Circ: 900.

371.2 USA ISSN 1479-3660
ADVANCES IN EDUCATIONAL ADMINISTRATION. Text in English. 1990. irreg., latest vol.7, 2004. price varies. back issues avail. **Document type:** *Monographic series, Academic/Scholarly.* **Description:** Covers issues in educational administration, leadership, developing topics and ideas.
Related titles: Online - full text ed.: (from ScienceDirect).
Published by: J A I Press Inc. (Subsidiary of: Elsevier Science & Technology), 360 Park Ave S, New York, NY 10010-1710. TEL 800-325-4177, FAX 212-633-3990, usinfo-f@elsevier.com, http://www.elsevier.com/wps/find/bookseriesdescription.cws_home/BS_AEA/description. Ed. R C Hunter.

371.22 USA ISSN 1058-1324
LB2825
AID FOR EDUCATION REPORT. Text in English. 1991. s-m. USD 419 (effective 2005). 18 p./no.; back issues avail. **Document type:** *Newsletter, Trade.* **Description:** Public and private funding opportunities for all levels of education, plus updates on application deadlines, eligibility criteria for upcoming programs, funding levels and budget trends.
—CCC.
Published by: (Community Development Services, Inc.), C D Publications, Inc., 8204 Fenton St, Silver Spring, MD 20910-2889. TEL 301-588-6380, FAX 301-588-6385, afe@cdpublications.com, subscriptions@cdpublications.com, http://www.cdpublications.com. Ed. Mehdi Abdalkhalki. Pub., R&P Mike Gerecht.

371.2 HUN ISSN 0865-9303
AKADEMIAI ERTESITO/HUNGARIAN ACADEMY OF SCIENCES. BULLETIN. Text in Hungarian. 1952. m. USD 72 (effective 2006). 16 p./no.; back issues avail. **Document type:** *Journal, Academic/Scholarly.* **Description:** Contains the legal rules, decisions, and information on applications and grants for the Hungarian Academy of Sciences.
Formerly (until 1990): Akademiai Kozlony (0460-5829)
Related titles: Online - full text ed.: ISSN 1588-2721.
Published by: (Magyar Tudomanyos Akademia/Hungarian Academy of Sciences), Akademiai Kiado Rt. (Subsidiary of: Wolters Kluwer N.V.), Prielle Kornelia U. 19, Budapest, 1117, Hungary. TEL 36-1-4648282, FAX 36-1-4648221, info@akkrt.hu, http://www.akkrt.hu. Ed. Tamas Demcsik.

371.26 DEU ISSN 0720-8618
Z5055.G4
ALBERT-LUDWIGS-UNIVERSITAET FREIBURG. FORSCHUNGSBERICHT. Text in German. 19??. irreg. **Document type:** *Monographic series, Academic/Scholarly.*
Published by: Albert-Ludwigs-Universitaet Freiburg, Fahnenbergplatz, Freiburg, 79085, Germany. TEL 49-761-203-0, FAX 49-761-2034369, info@pr.uni-freiburg.de, http://www.uni-freiburg.de.

371.26 DEU ISSN 0176-909X
LF2601
ALBERT-LUDWIGS-UNIVERSITAET FREIBURG. VORLESUNGSVERZEICHNIS. Text in German. 1972. 2/yr. adv. **Document type:** *Directory, Academic/Scholarly.*
Published by: Albert-Ludwigs-Universitaet Freiburg, Fahnenbergplatz, Freiburg, 79085, Germany. TEL 49-761-203-0, FAX 49-761-2034369, info@pr.uni-freiburg.de, http://www.uni-freiburg.de. adv.: page EUR 472. Circ: 8,000 (controlled).

379.24 DEU ISSN 1184-6836
ALPHA (YEAR): CURRENT RESEARCH IN LITERACY. Text in English. 1990. biennial. price varies. back issues avail. **Document type:** *Monographic series, Academic/Scholarly.* **Description:** Covers efforts to promote literacy worldwide.
Related titles: French ed.: Alpha (Year): Recherches en Alphabetisation. ISSN 0849-2794; ♦ Series of: U I E Studies Series.
Published by: UNESCO Institute for Education, Feldbrunnenstr 58, Hamburg, 20148, Germany. TEL 49-40-448-0410, FAX 49-40-410-7723, uie@unesco.org, http://www.unesco.org/publications. Ed. Christopher McIntosh. **Dist. in the U.S. by:** Bernan Associates, Bernan, 4611-F Assembly Dr., Lanham, MD 20706-4391.

371.12 USA ISSN 1082-1759
LB1771
ALTERNATIVE TEACHER CERTIFICATION. Text in English. 1990. a. USD 110 per vol. (effective 2004).
Published by: National Center for Education Information, 4401 Connecticut Ave Ste 212, Washington, DC 20008. TEL 202-822-8280, 866-778-2784, FAX 202-822-8284, http://www.ncei.com.

371.6 USA
AMERICAN SCHOOL AND HOSPITAL MAINTENANCE. Text in English. 1978. q. adv. **Document type:** *Magazine, Trade.* **Description:** Focuses on the renovation, maintenance, energy, and security of the physical plant and grounds.
Published by: A S & H M, 100-6 Coolidge Hill Rd, Watertown, MA 02472-5031. TEL 617-923-8158, FAX 617-926-7174, http://www.facilitymanagement.com/ashmmag.htm. adv.: B&W page USD 2,750; trim 8.125 x 10.875. Circ: 34,305.

371.2 USA ISSN 0003-0945
AMERICAN SCHOOL & UNIVERSITY; shaping facilities & business decisions. Abbreviated title: A S U. Text in English. 1928. m. USD 50 domestic; USD 75 foreign; free to qualified personnel (effective 2005). adv. bk.rev. bibl.; charts; illus.; mkt.; pat.; tr.mk. index. **Document type:** *Magazine, Trade.* **Description:** For administrators in school districts and colleges concerned with facilities operations and management.
Incorporates (1961-1963): Educational Executives' Overview (0424-575X)
Related titles: Microform ed.: (from PMC, PQC); Online - full text ed.: (from EBSCO Publishing, Florida Center for Library Automation, Gale Group, H.W. Wilson, LexisNexis, Northern Light Technology, Inc., O C L C Online Computer Library Center, Inc., ProQuest Information & Learning).
Indexed: ABIn, AgeL, CIJE, CPE, ConsI, EduInd, LRI, MagInd.
—BLDSC (0856.430000), IE, ingenta. **CCC.**
Published by: Primedia Business Magazines & Media, Inc. (Subsidiary of: Primedia, Inc.), 9800 Metcalf Ave, Overland Park, KS 66212-2216. TEL 913-341-1300, FAX 913-967-7276, asu@primediabusiness.com, inquiries@primediabusiness.com, http://industryclick.com/magazine.asp?magazineid=134&siteid=17, http://www.primediabusiness.com. Ed. Joe Agron. Pub. David George TEL 770-955-2500. adv.: B&W page USD 7,700. Circ: 63,000 (controlled). **Subscr. to:** PO Box 12993, Overland Park, KS 66282-2993. TEL 800-441-0294, FAX 913-967-1331.

379.1531 USA ISSN 0003-0953
AMERICAN SCHOOL BOARD JOURNAL. Text in English. 1891. m. USD 57 (effective 2005). adv. bk.rev. illus. Index. reprint service avail. from PQC. **Document type:** *Magazine, Trade.* **Description:** Offers practical advice on a broad range of topics pertinent to school governance and management, policy making, student achievement, and the art of school leadership.
Related titles: Microform ed.: (from PQC); Online - full text ed.: (from EBSCO Publishing); ♦ Supplement(s): Learning by Design. ISSN 0730-6164.
Indexed: ABIn, CIJE, CPE, EAA, EduInd, PAIS, RILM.
—BLDSC (0856.450000), IE, Infotrieve, ingenta. **CCC.**
Published by: National School Boards Association, 1680 Duke St, Alexandria, VA 22314-3493. TEL 703-838-6722, FAX 703-549-6719, editorial@asbj.com, http://www.asbj.com. Ed. Sally Zakariya. Pub. Marilee C. Rist. Adv. contacts Deborah Cumbo, Leah Burns-Atkins. Circ: 40,000 (paid).

371.2 371.3 USA ISSN 0003-1003
LA222
➤ **AMERICAN SECONDARY EDUCATION.** Text in English. 1970. 3/yr. USD 30 domestic; USD 40 foreign (effective 2005). adv. bk.rev. abstr.; charts; stat. 1 cols./p.; back issues avail.; reprints avail. **Document type:** *Journal, Academic/Scholarly.* **Description:** Covers a broad range of topics that reflect what professional secondary educators and practitioners deal with.

E

Related titles: Microform ed.: (from PQC); Online - full text ed.: (from EBSCO Publishing, H.W. Wilson, O C L C Online Computer Library Center, Inc., ProQuest Information & Learning).
Indexed: ABIn, CIJE, CPE, ERA, ETA, EduInd, MEA, RHEA, SEA, SENA, SOMA, SWA, TEA.
—BLDSC (0857.027000), IE, ingenta. **CCC.**
Address: c/o James A. Rycik, Ed, 401 College Avenue, Ashland University - Weltmer Ctr, Ashland, OH 44805. TEL 419-289-5273, 419-289-5334, FAX 419-289-5097, qvanderz@ashland.edu, http://www.ashland.edu/ase. R&P, Adv. contact Gay Vanderzyden. Circ: 400 (paid).

371.2 USA ISSN 0740-4565
AMERICAN UNIVERSITY STUDIES. SERIES 14. EDUCATION. Text in English. 1984. irreg., latest 2000. price varies. **Document type:** *Monographic series, Academic/Scholarly.* **Description:** Explores theoretical and practical issues in education at all levels.
Indexed: MLA-IB.
—BLDSC (0858.078620).
Published by: Peter Lang Publishing, Inc., 275 Seventh Ave, 28th Fl, New York, NY 10001. TEL 212-647-7700, 212-647-7706, 800-770-5264, FAX 212-647-7707, customerservice@plang.com, http://www.peterlang.com. Ed. David Bergeron. Pub. Christopher Myers. R&P Stephanie Archer. Adv. contact Patricia Mulrane.

379 DEU
AMTLICHES SCHULBLATT FUER DEN REGIERUNGSBEZIRK MUENSTER. Text in German. m. adv. bk.rev. **Document type:** *Journal, Academic/Scholarly.*
Published by: Aschendorffsche Verlagsbuchhandlung, Soester Str 13, Muenster, 48135, Germany. TEL 49-251-690-0, FAX 49-251-690143, buchverlag@aschendorff.de, http://www.aschendorff.de/buch. R&P Dirk F Passmann. Adv. contact Petra Landsknecht. B&W page EUR 346. Circ: 1,600 (controlled).

379 DEU ISSN 1434-5390
AMTSBLATT WISSENSCHAFT, FORSCHUNG UND KUNST. Text in German. 1952. m. **Document type:** *Academic/Scholarly.*
Former titles (until 1996): Amtsblatt Wissenschaft Forschung (0945-1285); (until 1993): Amtsblatt Wissenschaft und Kunst (0721-9229); Which supersedes in part: Kultus und Unterricht (0451-0550)
Published by: Staatsanzeiger fuer Baden-Wuerttemberg GmbH, Breitscheidstr 69, Stuttgart, 70176, Germany. TEL 49-711-6660144, FAX 49-711-6660134, verlag@staatsanzeiger.de.

379.1535 USA ISSN 0077-9342
ANALYSIS OF SCHOOL FINANCES, NEW YORK STATE SCHOOL DISTRICTS. Text in English. 1984. a. USD 2 (effective 2001). **Description:** Provides a perspective to staff in the Division of the Budget, the Legislature and the Education Department concerning school expenditures, state aid and local support.
Published by: Education Department, Fiscal Analysis and Research Unit, University of the State of New York, Education Bldg, Rm 301 EB, 89 Washington Ave, Albany, NY 12234. TEL 518-474-5213. **Co-sponsor:** University of the State of New York.

371.2 DEU
DER ANDREANER; Schuelerzeitung am Gymnasium Andreanum. Text in German, Latin; Summaries in German. 1948. q. adv. bk.rev.; film rev. bibl.; illus.; stat. index. back issues avail. **Document type:** *Newspaper, Consumer.*
Published by: Gymnasium Andreanum, Hagentorwall 17, Hildesheim, 31134, Germany. TEL 49-5121-165910, FAX 49-5121-157124, gymnasium@andreanum.de, http://www.andreanum.de. Circ: 1,500.

379.2 ITA ISSN 1720-4135
ANNALI DELL' ISTRUZIONE. Text in Italian. 1955. bi-m. EUR 21.78 domestic; EUR 31.80 foreign (effective 2003).
Formerly (until 2000): Annali della Pubblica Istruzione (0391-6642)
Indexed: MLA-IB.
Published by: Casa Editrice Edumond Le Monnier, Via Antonio Meucci 2, Grassina, FI 50015, Italy. TEL 39-055-64910, FAX 39-055-643983, lemonnier@lemonnier.it, http://www.annalistruzione.it, http://www.lemonnier.it. Circ: 22,000.

379.2 CRI
APUNTES; boletin de analisis de la administracion educativa y la realidad nacional. Text in Spanish. 1993 (no.2). s-a.?.
Published by: Universidad de Costa Rica, Escuela de Administracion Educativa, San Pedro, San Jose, Costa Rica.

ARBITRATION IN THE SCHOOLS. see *BUSINESS AND ECONOMICS—Labor And Industrial Relations*

379.157 USA ISSN 0095-5310
L120
ARIZONA. DEPARTMENT OF EDUCATION. SUPERINTENDENT OF PUBLIC INSTRUCTION. ANNUAL REPORT. Key Title: Annual Report of the Superintendent of Public Instruction. Text in English. a. USD 1,020 (effective 1994). illus.; stat. **Document type:** *Government.*
Related titles: Microfiche ed.: (from CIS).
Indexed: SRI.
Published by: (Washington (State). Superintendent of Public Instruction), Department of Education, Education Bldg, 1535 W Jefferson, Phoenix, AZ 85007. TEL 602-542-3088, FAX 602-542-3647.

371.2 THA
ASIAN INSTITUTE OF TECHNOLOGY. A I T ANNUAL REPORT. Text in English. 1977. a. free. **Description:** Covers academic affairs, administrative reports, on-going research programs, staff changes, and expansion plans.
Published by: Asian Institute of Technology, Promotional Support Services Unit, PO Box 4, Klong Luang, Pathumthani, 12120, Thailand. TEL 66-2-524-5830, FAX 66-2-524-5883, omis@ait.ac.th, pssu@ait.ac.th, http://www.ait.ac.th, http://www.ait.ac.th/. Ed., R&P Teresita M Padilla TEL 662-524-5880. Circ: 1,500.

379.2 379 USA ISSN 0066-8753
ASSOCIATED PUBLIC SCHOOLS SYSTEMS. YEARBOOK. Text in English. 1951. a. USD 5.
Published by: (Associated Public School Systems), Columbia University, Teachers College, 525 W 120th St, New York, NY 10027. TEL 212-280-1754. Circ: 1,000.

371.8 DEU ISSN 0076-1745
ASTA-PRESS. Text in German. 1971. irreg. adv.
Formerly: M S Z: Muenchener Studentenzeitung
Published by: (Technische Universitaet Muenchen, Studentenvertretung), Asta-Tum, Tsingtauer Str 66A, Munich, 81827, Germany. Ed. Heino Jahn. Circ: 10,000.

371.6 USA ISSN 1554-2033
GV347
ATHLETIC MANAGEMENT. Text in English. 1989. bi-m. USD 24 domestic; CND 30 in Canada; free to qualified personnel (effective 2005). adv. back issues avail. **Document type:** *Magazine, Trade.* **Description:** Aimed at key decision-makers at college and highschool athletic departments. Provides information on how athletic managers can improve their operations, implement new programs and make efficient purchases with respect to equipment, training supplies, facilities and team travel.
Formerly (until 1991): College Athletic Management (1041-5432); Incorporates: Athletic Director (1048-339X)
Indexed: PEI.
Published by: Momentum Media, 2488 N Triphammer Rd, Ithaca, NY 14850-1014. TEL 607-257-6970, FAX 607-257-7328, mg@momentummedia.com, info@momentummedia.com, http://www.athleticsearch.com. Pub., Adv. contact Mark Goldberg TEL 607-257-6970 ext 11. R&P Eleanor Frankel TEL 607-257-6970 ext 18. Circ: 30,552 (controlled).

371.201 AUS
THE AUSTRALIAN EDUCATIONAL LEADER. Text in English. 1972-1978 (no.36); N.S. 1979. q. AUD 60 domestic; AUD 70 foreign (effective 2005). adv. bk.rev. 48 p./no.; back issues avail. **Document type:** *Journal, Trade.* **Description:** Serves as a forum for the exchange of trends and innovation, and allows readers to evaluate developments, share administrative techniques, and otherwise deal with any aspect of the broad spectrum of educational administration at all levels.
Formerly: Practising Administrator (0157-3357)
Indexed: AEI, CPE, ERA, RHEA, SOMA.
—BLDSC (6597.750000), IE, ingenta. **CCC.**
Published by: Australian Council for Educational Administration, PO Box 4268, Winmalee, NSW 2777, Australia. TEL 61-4-7517974, acel@pnc.com.au, http://www.acel.org.au/publications.html. Circ: 5,000.

379.2 AUS ISSN 1038-1562
LB1049.9 CODEN: AJLLEL
➤ **AUSTRALIAN JOURNAL OF LANGUAGE AND LITERACY.** Text in English. 1978. q. AUD 82.50 for membership to individuals; AUD 132 for membership to institutions (effective 2004). adv. bk.rev. tr.lit. cum.index. back issues avail. **Document type:** *Journal, Academic/Scholarly.*
Formerly: Australian Journal of Reading (0156-0301)
Related titles: Online - full text ed.: (from EBSCO Publishing, Florida Center for Library Automation, Gale Group, R M I T Publishing).
Indexed: AEI, CIJE, CPE, ChLitAb, L&LBA, SOPODA.
—BLDSC (1809.130000), IE, ingenta. **CCC.**
Published by: Australian Literacy Educators' Association, PO Box 3203, Norwood, SA 5067, Australia. TEL 61-8-83322845, FAX 61-8-83330394, alea@netspace.net.au, http://www.alea.edu.au/ajll.htm. Ed. Jan Turbill. adv.: B&W page AUD 300; trim 180 x 250. Circ: 3,000.

371.2 DEU ISSN 0944-3207
B L Z. (Berliner Lehrerinnen Zeitung) Text in German. 1931. 10/yr. adv. back issues avail. **Document type:** *Newspaper, Trade.*
Published by: Gewerkschaftliche Wirtschafts Verlags und Veranstaltungs GmbH, Ahornstr 5, Berlin, 10787, Germany. TEL 49-30-21999346, FAX 49-30-21999349, blz@gew-berlin.de, http://www.gew-berlin.de. Ed. Peter Michael Rulff. R&P Klaus Will. Adv. contact Annette Wolff. B&W page EUR 1,239.81. Circ: 23,000 (controlled).

379.44 FRA ISSN 1254-7131
L391
LE B O. BULLETIN OFFICIEL DE L'EDUCATION NATIONALE. Text in French. 1981. w. EUR 77 domestic; EUR 182.50 foreign (effective 2005). **Description:** Publishes current news and decisions affecting the education system.
Formerly (until 1994): France. Ministere de l'Education Nationale. Bulletin Officiel (0291-5871)
Published by: Ministere de l'Education Nationale, de l'Enseignement Superieur et de la Recherche, 110 rue de Grenelle, Paris, 75357, France. TEL 33-1-55551010, http://www.education.gouv.fr/bo/default.htm. Circ: 100,000. **Subscr. to:** CNDP - Abonnement, B.P. 750, Sainte Genevieve Cedex 60732, France. TEL 33-3-44033237, FAX 33-3-44033013.

379.2 USA
BAKER'S HANDBOOK OF OHIO SCHOOL LAW. Text in English. a. USD 59.50 per vol. domestic. **Document type:** *Trade.* **Description:** Acts as a reference for legal matters concerning the management of schools and districts, the role of state and county agencies, school finance, teachers' contracts and other labor issues, the construction and maintenance of school buildings, general liability, and students' issues.
Published by: Anderson Publishing Co (Subsidiary of: LexisNexis North America), 9443 Springboro Pike, Miamisburg, OH 45342-4425. TEL 513-421-4142, 800-582-7295, FAX 513-562-8116, mail@andersonpublishing.com, http://www.andersonpublishing.com. Eds. Kimball H Carey, Robert T Baker.

379.2 USA
BAKER'S OHIO SCHOOL LAW GUIDE. Text in English. a. (plus CD-ROM) (in 3 vols.). USD 189 (effective 2003). **Document type:** *Trade.* **Description:** Offers a comprehensive reference for legal matters concerning the management of schools and districts, the role of state and county agencies, school finance, teachers' contracts and other labor issues, the construction and maintenance of school buildings, general liability, and students' issues. Includes all relevant forms.
Published by: Anderson Publishing Co (Subsidiary of: LexisNexis North America), 9443 Springboro Pike, Miamisburg, OH 45342-4425. TEL 513-421-4142, 800-833-9844, FAX 513-562-8116, mail@andersonpublishing.com, http://www.andersonpublishing.com. Ed. Kimball H Carey.

BANCO DE DATOS DE BECAS Y CURSOS. see *EDUCATION—International Education Programs*

371.2 NLD ISSN 0922-0402
BASISSCHOOLMANAGEMENT. Text in Dutch. 1987. 8/yr. adv. **Document type:** *Trade.*
Incorporates (1987-1998): School Management (0921-4356); (1996-1998): School Management Recent (1384-4253)
—KNAW.
Published by: Samsom H.D. Tjeenk Willink B.V. (Subsidiary of: Wolters Kluwer N.V.), Postbus 316, Alphen aan den Rijn, 2400 AH, Netherlands. TEL 31-1720-66822, FAX 31-1720-66939.

379 DEU ISSN 0931-4075
LA405
➤ **BAYERISCHEN STAATSMINISTERIEN FUER UNTERRICHT UND KULTUS UND WISSENSCHAFT UND KUNST. AMTSBLATT. TEIL 2.** Text in German. 1974. irreg. price varies. **Document type:** *Monographic series, Academic/Scholarly.*
Formerly (until 1986): Bayerisches Staatsministerium fuer Unterricht und Kultus. Amtsblatt. Teil 2 (0722-5113); Supersedes in part (in 1974): Bayerisches Staatsministerium fuer Unterricht und Kultus. Amtsblatt (0005-7207)
Published by: (Bavaria. Bayerischen Staatsministerium fuer Unterricht und Kultus), Oldenbourg Wissenschaftsverlag GmbH, Rosenheimer Str 145, Munich, 81671, Germany. TEL 49-89-45051399, FAX 49-89-45051333, vertrieb-zs@verlag.oldenbourg.de, http://www.oldenbourg.de.

371.2 USA
BECKLEY - CARDY QUARTERLY✶. Text in English. 1988. q. **Document type:** *Catalog.*
Published by: Beckley - Cardy, Inc., 100 Paragon Pkwy, Mansfield, OH 44903-8056. TEL 218-725-2234, FAX 218-725-2414. adv.: page USD 3,745; trim 10.88 x 8.5. Circ: 200,000.

BEDFORD WAY PAPERS. see *EDUCATION*

371.2 DEU ISSN 0938-9288
BEREINIGTE AMTLICHE SAMMLUNG DER SCHULVORSCHRIFTEN. Abbreviated title: B A S S. Text in German. 1984. a. EUR 50.50 (effective 2004). **Document type:** *Journal, Trade.*
Published by: (Ministerium fuer Schule, Jugend und Kinder des Landes Nordrhein-Westfalen), Ritterbach Verlag GmbH, Postfach 1820, Frechen, 50208, Germany. TEL 49-2234-18660, FAX 49-2234-186690, verlag@ritterbach.de, http://www.ritterbach.de.

371.207 ARG ISSN 0067-7922
BIBLIOTECA DEL PLANEAMIENTO EDUCATIVO✶. Text in Spanish. 1961. irreg. **Document type:** *Government.*

E

Published by: (Argentina. Departamento de Documentacion Informacion Educativa), Ministerio de Educacion, Pizzurno 935, Buenos Aires, 1020, Argentina. TEL 54-11-41291000, info@me.gov.ar, http://www.me.gov.ar/.

371.2 DEU ISSN 0341-4922
BILDUNG AKTUELL. Text in German. 1970. 8/yr. adv. **Document type:** *Magazine, Trade.*
Published by: Nordrhein-Westfaelischer Lehrerverband, Graf-Adolf-Str 84, Duesseldorf, 40210, Germany. TEL 49-211-177440, FAX 49-211-161973, info@nrwl.de, http://www.nrwl.de. adv.: B&W page EUR 1,452, color page EUR 2,234. Circ: 19,500 (controlled).

371.2 DEU ISSN 0343-4583
BILDUNG REAL. Text in German. 1957. 8/yr. adv. **Document type:** *Magazine, Trade.*
Formerly (until 1973): Realschulpost (0343-463X)
Published by: Nordrhein-Westfaelischer Lehrerverband, Graf-Adolf-Str 84, Duesseldorf, 40210, Germany. TEL 49-211-177440, FAX 49-211-161973, info@nrwl.de, http://www.nrwl.de. adv.: B&W page EUR 1,452, color page EUR 2,234.

371.2 DEU
BLICKPUNKT BILDUNG; Beitraege zur Schul- und Bildungspolitik. Text in German. 1966. 5/yr. bk.rev. 40 p./no. 2 cols./p.; back issues avail. **Document type:** *Bulletin, Academic/Scholarly.* **Description:** Bulletin for teachers at schools and colleges in the Hamburg area.
Formerly (until 1989): Beitraege zur Schul und Bildungspolitik
Published by: Deutscher Lehrerverband Hamburg, Papenstr 18, Hamburg, 22089, Germany. TEL 49-40-255272, FAX 49-40-2505949, deutscher.lehrerverband@hamburg.de, http://www.dl-hamburg.de. Ed. Helmut P. Hagge. Circ: 4,000.

379.4352 DEU ISSN 0006-9582
BREMER SCHULBLATT. Text in German. 1954. base vol. plus irreg. updates. looseleaf. EUR 66 base vol(s). (effective 2004). abstr. cum.index. **Document type:** *Monographic series, Government.* **Description:** Concerned with education in the cities of Bremen and Bremershaven. Includes decisions, regulations, laws and list of schools.
Related titles: CD-ROM ed.
Published by: (Bremen. Senator fuer Bildung und Wissenschaft), Hermann Luchterhand Verlag GmbH (Subsidiary of: Wolters Kluwer Deutschland GmbH), Heddesdorfer Str 31, Neuwied, 56564, Germany. TEL 49-2631-8012222, FAX 49-2631-8012223, info@luchterhand.de, http://www.luchterhand.de. Circ: 800.

379.711 CAN ISSN 1481-8442
L222.B8
BRITISH COLUMBIA. MINISTRY OF EDUCATION. ANNUAL REPORT. Text in English. 1871. a. free. **Document type:** *Government.* **Description:** Summarizes a wide array of data and survey results, provides descriptions of programs and student activities, describes the effectiveness of the school system.
Supersedes in part (in 1998): British Columbia. Ministry of Education, Skills and Training. Annual Report (1480-2376); Which was formerly (until 1996): British Columbia. Ministry of Education. Annual Report (1198-3175); (until 1993): British Columbia. Ministry of Education and Ministry Responsible for Multiculturalism and Human Rights. Annual Report (1192-9545); (until 1992): British Columbia. Ministry of Education. Annual Report (0711-9410); Which superseded in part (in 1980): British Columbia. Ministry of Education, Science and Technology. Annual Report (0711-9151); Which was formerly (until 1979): Province of British Columbia. Ministry of Education. Annual Report (0709-8383); (until 1977): Province of British Columbia. Department of Education. Annual Report (0709-8375); (until 1945): British Columbia. Department of Education. Public Schools of the Province of British Columbia (0709-8367)
Published by: Ministry of Education, Parliament Bldgs, Victoria, BC V8V 2M4, Canada. TEL 604-356-2500, FAX 604-356-5945. Circ: 6,000 (controlled).

379 USA ISSN 1096-2719
LC89
➤ **BROOKINGS PAPERS ON EDUCATION POLICY (YEAR).** Text in English. 1998. a. USD 30 per issue (effective 2005). bibl. back issues avail. **Document type:** *Academic/Scholarly.* **Description:** Publishes papers on all aspects of public policy on education from leading academic authorities and educators.
Related titles: Online - full text ed.: ISSN 1533-4457. 2000. USD 43.95 (effective 2004) (from EBSCO Publishing, O C L C Online Computer Library Center, Inc., Project MUSE, Swets Information Services).
—BLDSC (2350.075000). **CCC.**
Published by: (Brown Center on Education Policy), Brookings Institution Press, 1775 Massachusetts Ave, NW, Washington, DC 20036-2188. http://www.brook.edu/gs/brown/bpep/index.htm, http://www.brook.edu/press. Ed. Diane Ravitch.
Dist. by: Plymbridge Distributors Ltd, Plymbridge House, Estover Rd, Plymouth, Devon PL6 7PY, United Kingdom. TEL 44-1752-202300, FAX 44-1752-202330, enquiries@plymbridge.com, http://www.plymbridge.com.

379.1531 USA ISSN 1092-1818
C A B E JOURNAL. Text in English. 1979. m. (except Jul.-Aug. combined). USD 60. adv. charts; illus.; stat. back issues avail. **Document type:** *Newspaper.*
Published by: Connecticut Association of Boards of Education, Inc., 81 Wolcott Hill Rd, Wethersfield, CT 06109-1242. TEL 860-571-7446, FAX 860-571-7452, cabeschlbd@aol.com, http://www.cabe.org. Ed. Robert Rader. Adv. contact Bonnie Carney. Circ: 2,500.

371.2 CAN
C A S E A - A C E A S NEWSLETTER. Text in English. 1971. s-a. membership. **Document type:** *Newsletter.*
Published by: (Canadian Association for Studies in Educational Administration), St. Francis Xavier University, PO Box 5000, Antigonish, NS B2G 2W5, Canada. TEL 902-867-2254, FAX 902-867-3887, rmacmillan@stfx.ca, http://juliet.stfx.ca/~rmacmill/. Ed. Robert B Macmillan. Circ: 250 (paid).

371.201 USA
C S A NEWS (BROOKLYN). Text in English. 1966. m. membership. bk.rev. **Document type:** *Newsletter.*
Formerly: C S A Newsletter
—BLDSC (3490.174990).
Published by: Council of Supervisors and Administrators of the City of New York, Local 1, American Federation of School Administrators, AFL CIO, 16 Court St, 4th Fl, Brooklyn, NY 11241. TEL 718-852-3000, FAX 718-403-0278. Ed. Charnia J Adelman. Circ: 12,400 (controlled).

379 USA ISSN 0892-7855
C U P A NEWS; communications update for personnel administrators. Text in English. 1973. 24/yr. USD 80 to non-members; USD 40 to members; USD 55 to institutions (effective 2000). **Document type:** *Newsletter.* **Description:** Keeps members current on the latest legislative, regulatory, and judicial events affecting personnel management.
Indexed: CIJE.
Published by: College and University Personnel Association, 1233 20th St, N W, Ste 301, Washington, DC 20036. TEL 202-429-0311, FAX 202-429-0149, http://www.cupa.org. Ed. Melissa Edeburn. R&P Audrey Rothstein. Circ: 6,400.

371.202 USA ISSN 0008-1515
CALIFORNIA SCHOOL EMPLOYEE. Text in English. 1932. m. (except Aug. & Sept.). USD 2.25 to non-members. adv. bk.rev. illus.; stat. reprint service avail. from PQC.
Related titles: Microform ed.: (from PQC).
Indexed: CalPI.
Published by: California School Employees Association, PO Box 640, San Jose, CA 95106. TEL 408-263-8000, FAX 408-954-0948. Ed. Doug Crooks. Circ: 106,000 (controlled).

379.794 USA ISSN 0094-2057
KFC648.A59
CALIFORNIA SCHOOL LAW DIGEST. Text in English. 1973. m. looseleaf. USD 155 (effective 2006). bk.rev. cum.index. back issues avail. **Document type:** *Newsletter, Academic/Scholarly.* **Description:** Covers news and administrative and court decisions pertaining to the law, the courts and California schools. Emphasizes decisions by the Professional Standards Review Board.
—**CCC.**
Published by: L R P Publications, 747 Dresher Rd, PO Box 980, Horsham, PA 19044. TEL 800-341-7874, FAX 215-784-9639, custserve@lrp.com, http://www.shoplrp.com/product/p-300049.html, http://www.lrp.com. Ed. Jay Kravetz.

CALIFORNIA. TEACHERS' RETIREMENT BOARD. STATE TEACHERS' RETIREMENT SYSTEM; COMPREHENSIVE ANNUAL FINANCIAL REPORT TO THE GOVERNOR AND THE LEGISLATURE. see *BUSINESS AND ECONOMICS—Labor And Industrial Relations*

371.6 USA ISSN 1065-0857
CAMP DIRECTORS PURCHASING GUIDE. Text in English. 1964. a. USD 105 per vol. domestic (effective 2004). adv. bk.rev. 160 p./no. 2 cols./p.; back issues avail. **Document type:** *Directory, Trade.* **Description:** Provides sources of material used in construction and operation of children's summer camps.
Published by: Klevens Publications, Ltd., 411 S Main St, Ste 209, Los Angeles, CA 90013-1321. TEL 213-625-9000, FAX 213-625-5002, mailroom@klevenspub.com, editor@klevenspub.com, http://www.campdirectorsguide.com, http://www.klevenspub.com. Ed. H B Schwartz. Pub. Gilbert George Klevens. Adv. contact Edward Yale Klevens TEL 213-625-9000. Circ: 14,736.

CAMPUS LAW ENFORCEMENT JOURNAL; professional publication for campus law enforcement administrators, campus safety, security adm. see *CRIMINOLOGY AND LAW ENFORCEMENT*

344.07 USA ISSN 1526-9493
CAMPUS SAFETY & STUDENT DEVELOPMENT. Text in English. 1999. bi-m. USD 182.95 domestic; USD 212.95 foreign (effective 2005). **Document type:** *Newsletter.* **Description:** A key resource for professionals in all disciplines working to guide student conduct and to make colleges and universities safer communities.
—**CCC.**
Published by: Civic Research Insitute, 4490 US Route 27, PO Box 585, Kingston, NJ 08528. TEL 609-683-4450, FAX 609-683-7291, order@civicresearchinstitute.com, http://www.civicresearchinstitute.com. Ed. Brett Sokolow.

363.119371 USA ISSN 1551-2800
▼ **CAMPUS SECURITY REPORT (HORSHAM).** Text in English. 2004 (May). m. USD 185 (effective 2006). **Document type:** *Newsletter, Trade.*
Published by: L R P Publications, 747 Dresher Rd, PO Box 980, Horsham, PA 19044. TEL 215-784-0860, 800-341-7874, FAX 215-784-9639, custserve@lrp.com, http://www.shoplrp.com/product/p-31100.html, http://www.lrp.com.

371.2 CAN ISSN 0008-2813
CANADIAN ADMINISTRATOR. Text in English. 1961. m. (Oct.-May). CND 17. bibl. reprint service avail. from PQC. **Document type:** *Abstract/Index.* **Description:** Aims to inform practitioners and scholars about the findings and implications of recent research, to alert them to emerging conditions and trends, and to facilitate the exchange of ideas and perspectives leading to more effective practices in the administration of schools and educational systems.
Related titles: Microform ed.: (from PQC).
Indexed: CEI, CIJE, CPE, EAA, ERA, SEA, SOMA, SRRA, TEA.
Published by: University of Alberta, Department of Educational Policy Studies, 7-104 Education North, Edmonton, AB T6G 2G5, Canada. TEL 780-492-7625, FAX 780-492-2024. Ed., R&P Frank Peters. Circ: 1,200.

379.71 CAN ISSN 0380-2361
LA410
➤ **CANADIAN JOURNAL OF EDUCATION/REVUE CANADIENNE DE L'EDUCATION.** Text in English, French. 1976. q. free to members; CND 100 to non-members; CND 25 per issue (effective 2005). bk.rev. bibl.; illus. Index. reprints avail. **Document type:** *Journal, Academic/Scholarly.* **Description:** Provides a national forum for the discussion of the problems and issues confronting education in Canada.
Related titles: Microfiche ed.: (from MML); Microfilm ed.: 1976 (from MML, PQC); Microform ed.: 1976 (from MML); Online - full text ed.: (from H.W. Wilson, Micromedia ProQuest, O C L C Online Computer Library Center, Inc., ProQuest Information & Learning).
Indexed: ABIn, CBCARef, CBPI, CEI, CIJE, CPE, CPerI, CWPI, DIP, EAA, ERA, ETA, EduInd, IBR, IBZ, L&LBA, MEA, PAIS, PsycInfo, PsycholAb, RASB, RHEA, SEA, SENA, SOMA, SOPODA, SRRA, SSA, SWA, SociolAb, e-psyche.
—BLDSC (3031.250000), IE, ingenta. **CCC.**
Published by: Canadian Society for the Study of Education, 260 Dalhousie, Ste 204, Ottawa, ON K1N 7E4, Canada. TEL 613-241-0018, FAX 613-241-0019, csse@csse.ca, http://www.csse.ca/CJE/home.htm, http://www.scee.ca. Eds. Francois Larose, Samuel Robinson. Circ: 1,460.

371.201 CAN ISSN 1207-7798
➤ **CANADIAN JOURNAL OF EDUCATIONAL ADMINISTRATION AND POLICY.** Text in English. 1995. irreg. free (effective 2005). **Document type:** *Journal, Academic/Scholarly.*
Media: Online - full content.
Indexed: CEI.
Published by: University of Manitoba, Department of Educational Administration, Foundations & Psychology, c/o Kevin L Seigert, Ed, Winnipeg, AB R3T 2N2, Canada. http://www.umanitoba.ca/publications/cjeap/. Ed. Kelvin L Seifert.

371.716 AUS
CANTEEN NEWS. Text in English. 1992. q. AUD 24 domestic; AUD 30 foreign (effective 2000 - 2001). adv. **Description:** Covers studies of different canteen operations and operators; constructive reports on different aspects of canteen organizations; new products and canteen equipment; nutrition in canteens.
Published by: (Federation of Canteens in Schools), Sterling Media, PO Box 6104, North Parramatta, NSW 2150, Australia. TEL 61-2-98901199, FAX 61-2-98907694. Ed. John Allison. Adv. contact Abe Vatner. B&W page AUD 3,795, color page AUD 4,545. Circ: 10,500 (controlled).

379.77311 USA ISSN 1058-6830
LA269.C4
CATALYST (CHICAGO); voices of Chicago school reform. Text in English. 1990. 9/yr. USD 23 to individuals; USD 30 to institutions (effective 2005). adv. illus. index. **Document type:** *Magazine, Consumer.* **Description:** Covers the progress, problems and politics of school reform in Chicago.
Related titles: Online - full text ed.: free (effective 2003) (from SoftLine Information).
Indexed: AltPI.
Published by: Community Renewal Society, 332 S Michigan Ave, Ste 500, Chicago, IL 60604-4301. TEL 312-427-4830, FAX 312-427-6130, editorial@catalyst-chicago.org, http://www.catalyst-chicago.org. Ed., Pub. Linda Lenz. R&P Veronica Audersou. Adv. contact Ericka Moore. Circ: 7,500.

371.3 USA ISSN 0739-2532
CATALYST FOR CHANGE. Text in English. 1971. 3/yr. USD 10. bk.rev. reprint service avail. from PQC. **Document type:** *Academic/Scholarly.*

E

▼ new title ➤ refereed ∗ unverified ◆ full entry avail.

Related titles: Microform ed.: (from PQC); Online - full text ed.: (from H.W. Wilson, O C L C Online Computer Library Center, Inc.).
Indexed: ABIn, CIJE, EAA, EduInd.
—BLDSC (3092.259000), IE, ingenta.
Published by: (National Council of Staff Development), East Texas School Study Council, Texas A & M University Commerce, Commerce, TX 75428. TEL 903-886-5521, FAX 903-886-5507, anita_pankake@tamu-commerce.edu. Ed. Anita Pankake. R&P Stacey Edmonson. Circ: 2,200.

371.201 USA
CHAMPIONS FOR CHILDREN; New Hampshire school administrators newsletter. Text in English. 1955. m. membership. adv. bk.rev. abstr.; charts; illus.; stat. **Document type:** *Newsletter.*
Former titles (until 1993): Granite State School Leader; New Hampshire School Boards Association Newsletter; Granite State School Leader (0027-660X)
Published by: New Hampshire School Administrators Association, Summer Street School, 12 Cross St., Penacock, NH 03303. TEL 603-753-4479, FAX 603-753-4611, m_joyce@cnhec.concord.k12.nh.us, http://www.nhsaa.org/. Ed. Mark V Joyce. Circ: 200.

CHARTERED INSTITUTE OF PUBLIC FINANCE AND ACCOUNTANCY. EDUCATION STATISTICS. ACTUALS. see *EDUCATION—Abstracting, Bibliographies, Statistics*

CHARTERED INSTITUTE OF PUBLIC FINANCE AND ACCOUNTANCY. EDUCATION STATISTICS. ESTIMATES. see *EDUCATION—Abstracting, Bibliographies, Statistics*

371.2 USA ISSN 0164-8527
HV854
CHILD CARE INFORMATION EXCHANGE. Text in English. 1978. bi-m. USD 38 domestic; USD 60 foreign (effective 2001). adv. bk.rev.; Website rev. cum.index: 1978-1998. back issues avail. **Document type:** *Magazine, Consumer.* **Description:** Aims at administrators of early childhood programs.
Indexed: ABIn, CIJE, EduInd, PSI.
—BLDSC (3172.927000), IE, ingenta. **CCC.**
Published by: Exchange Press Inc, PO Box 3249, Redmond, WA 98073-3249. TEL 425-883-9394, FAX 425-867-5217, ccie@ccie.com, http://www.ccie.com/. Ed. Roger Neugebauer. Pub. Bonnie Neugebauer. R&P Beth Dolowy TEL 800-221-2864. Adv. contact Ann Warren. Circ: 26,000.

371.201 USA
CHRISTIAN SCHOOL ADMINISTRATOR. Text in English. 1993. bi-m. USD 15. adv. **Document type:** *Trade.*
Published by: Great River Publishing, Inc., 2191 Windy Oaks Dr., Germantown, TN 38139-5207. TEL 901-624-5911, 800-567-6912, FAX 901-624-5910, csa@grtriver.com, http://www.grtriver.com/csa/. Ed., R&P Sherry Campbell. adv.: B&W page USD 1,640, color page USD 2,490; trim 10.88 x 8.13. Circ: 15,000 (paid and controlled).

371.07 USA ISSN 1523-8202
BV1460
CHRISTIAN SCHOOL EDUCATION; enabling christian educators and schools worldwide. Text in English. 1997. 5/yr. USD 30. bk.rev.; software rev.; video rev. back issues avail. **Document type:** *Academic/Scholarly.* **Description:** Guide magazine for christian school administrators, teachers and school board members.
Published by: Association of Christian Schools International, 731 Chapel Hills Dr, Colorado Springs, CO 80920. TEL 719-528-6906, FAX 719-531-0631, derek-keenan@acsi.org, bonnie-church@acsi.org. Ed. Derek J Keenan. R&P Bonnie Church TEL 719-528-6906 ext 212. Adv. contact David Smitherman TEL 719-528-6906 ext 115. Circ: 11,000. **Subscr. to:** PO Box 35907, Colorado Springs, CO 80935-3509.

379.1535 USA
CITIZEN'S GUIDE TO SCHOOL DISTRICTS* . Text in English. a. USD 25.
Formerly: Citizen's Guide to School District Budgeting
Published by: Washington Research Council, 108 S, Washington St, 406, Seattle, WA 98104-3408. TEL 206-357-6643.

371.6 FRA ISSN 1143-2802
CLASSE. Text in French. 1989. 10/yr.
Address: 12 rue Raymond Poincare, Revigny-sur-Ornain, 55800, France. TEL 33-3-29705633, FAX 33-3-29705744. Ed. Rene Louis Martin. Circ: 25,000.

COLLEGE SERVICES. see *EDUCATION—Higher Education*

COLLEGE - UNIVERSITY FOODSERVICE WHO'S WHO. see *FOOD AND FOOD INDUSTRIES*

COLORADO EDUCATION & LIBRARY DIRECTORY. see *LIBRARY AND INFORMATION SCIENCES*

371.1 USA ISSN 0745-2233
LB2831.92
COMMUNICATOR (ALEXANDRIA, 1981). Text in English. 1977. m. (Sep.-June). free membership (effective 2005). adv. back issues avail. **Document type:** *Newsletter, Trade.* **Description:** For elementary and middle school educators. Covers educational, legislative and other issues.
Formerly (until 1981): N A E S P Communicator (0162-1920)
Related titles: Microfilm ed.
Published by: National Association of Elementary School Principals, 1615 Duke St, Alexandria, VA 22314-3483. TEL 703-684-3345, FAX 703-548-6021, naesp@naesp.org, http://www.naesp.org/comm/commun.htm. Ed. Peter Magnuson. Adv. contact Tim McCormack. Circ: 29,000 (paid and controlled).

THE COMMUNITY COLLEGE ENTERPRISE; a journal of research and practice. see *EDUCATION—Higher Education*

371.2 USA ISSN 1098-8203
LA201
➤ **CONNECTIONS**; journal of principal preparation and development. Text in English. 1998. a. USD 148 to individuals; USD 180 to libraries (effective 2005); subscr. package also includes: NASSP Newsleader, NASSP Bulletin, NASSP Legal Memorandum, Principal Leadership (High School & Middle School Editions). **Document type:** *Journal, Academic/Scholarly.*
Indexed: CIJE.
—CCC.
Published by: National Association of Secondary School Principals, 1904 Association Dr, Reston, VA 20191-1537. TEL 703-860-0200, 866-647-7253, FAX 703-476-5432, connections@principals.org, http://www.nassp.org, http://nasccms.principals.org.

371.2 USA
COUNCIL OF THE GREAT CITY SCHOOLS. ANNUAL REPORT. Text in English. a. free. charts; stat. back issues avail. **Document type:** *Corporate.* **Description:** Details the programs and financial activity of the Council of Great City Schools, which comprises administrators from large US urban school districts.
Related titles: Online - full content ed.
Published by: Council of the Great City Schools, 1301 Pennsylvania Ave, NW, Ste 702, Washington, DC 20004. TEL 202-393-2427, FAX 202-393-2400, http://www.cgcs.org/reports/Annual/index.htm.

371.2 USA
COUNCIL OF THE GREAT CITY SCHOOLS. PRESS RELEASES. Text in English. 1994. irreg. (4-10/yr). back issues avail. **Document type:** *Monographic series.* **Description:** Publicizes and comments on important social and political issues and events facing urban schools and urban educators nationwide.
Media: Online - full content.
Published by: Council of the Great City Schools, 1301 Pennsylvania Ave, NW, Ste 702, Washington, DC 20004. TEL 202-393-2427, FAX 202-393-2400, http://www.cgcs.org/services/media/index.cfm.

371.2 USA ISSN 1041-7877
COUNTY CARE. Text in English. 1975 (vol.11). 7/yr. membership. adv. bk.rev.; film rev.; play rev. bibl.; charts; illus.; stat.; tr.lit. **Document type:** *Newsletter.*
Former titles: Administrative News and Notes; Maine School Administrative District No. 70 News and Notes; Maine School Administrative District No. 29 News and Notes
Media: Duplicated (not offset). **Related titles:** Microfiche ed.
Published by: Consulting Group, Inc., c/o Lloyd R Chase, Ed, Box 323, Houlton, ME 04730-0323. TEL 207-532-4780, FAX 207-532-4780. Circ: 800.

371.2 USA
CRITICAL ISSUES IN EDUCATIONAL LEADERSHIP SERIES. Text in English. irreg. price varies. illus. back issues avail. **Document type:** *Monographic series, Academic/Scholarly.* **Description:** Discusses ways in which school administrators and teachers can create communities of learning.
Published by: Teachers College Press, Teachers College, Columbia University, 525 W 120th St, Box 303, New York, NY 10027-6694. http://www.teacherscollegepress.com. Pub. Carole Saltz. R&P Amy Detjen. **Dist. by:** Eurospan University Press Group, Order Dept, 3 Henrietta St, London WC2E 8LU, United Kingdom. TEL 44-20-7240-0856, FAX 44-20-7379-0609, http://www.eurospan.co.uk; Pademelon Press, Pty Ltd, 7-10 Anella Ave, PO Box 229, Castle Hill, NSW 2154, Australia. TEL 61-2-9634-2558, FAX 61-2-9680-4634; Transdex International, Pte Ltd, Block 1, Farrer Rd 307-05, Singapore 268817, Singapore. TEL 65-468-6242, FAX 65-462-5457.

371.6 USA
CRITICAL ISSUES IN FACILITIES MANAGEMENT. Text in English. irreg., latest vol.8, 1992. USD 30 to non-members; USD 22 to members. **Document type:** *Monographic series, Trade.*
Published by: A P P A: The Association of Higher Education Facilities Officers, 1643 Prince St, Alexandria, VA 22314-2818. TEL 703-684-1446, FAX 703-549-2772. R&P Steve Glazner. **Subscr. to:** PO Box 1201, Alexander, VA 22313-1201.

379 USA
CRITICAL POLICY REFERENCE MANUAL. Text in English. base vol. plus s-a. updates. USD 150 to non-members; USD 75 to members (effective 2000). **Document type:** *Trade.* **Description:** Legal reference information and policy guidelines for effective school district operation.
Published by: New Jersey School Boards Association, 413 W State St, PO Box 909, Trenton, NJ 08605. TEL 609-695-7600, FAX 609-695-0413.

371.2 USA
CRITICAL TRENDS IN URBAN EDUCATION; biennial survey of America's great city schools. Text in English. 1994. biennial. charts; stat. **Description:** Surveys and analyzes trends in urban education, especially regarding the future of urban education, assistance from outside groups, pressing urban school needs, and effective reform strategies and their perceived effectiveness.
Related titles: Online - full content ed.
Published by: Council of the Great City Schools, 1301 Pennsylvania Ave, NW, Ste 702, Washington, DC 20004. TEL 202-393-2427, FAX 202-393-2400, http://www.cgcs.org/reports/home/critical_trends_.htm, http://www.cgcs.org.

CURRICULUM AND TEACHING. see *EDUCATION—Teaching Methods And Curriculum*

371.2 DEU ISSN 1431-2158
D D S. (Die Deutsche Schule) Text in German. 1954. m. **Document type:** *Journal, Academic/Scholarly.*
Formerly (until 1993): Die Demokratische Schule (0011-8311)
Published by: Gewerkschaft Erziehung und Wissenschaft Landesverband Bayern, Schwanthaler Str 64, Munich, 80336, Germany. TEL 49-89-5440810, FAX 49-89-5389487, info@bayern.gew.de, http://www.bayern.gew.de.

371.2 DNK ISSN 1603-1482
▼ **DEN DANSKE SKOLEAARBOG.** Text in Danish. 2003. a. DKK 340 (effective 2004). adv.
Formed by the merger of (1942-2003): Den Danske Skolehaandbog (Year) (0109-3584); (1978-2003): Aarbog for Folkeskolen (0106-0465)
Related titles: CD-ROM ed.: ISSN 1603-4279.
Published by: (Danmarks Laererforening), Kroghs Forlag A-S, Chr Hansensvej 3, Vejle, 7100, Denmark. TEL 45-75-823900, FAX 45-75-823271, kf@kroghsforlag.dk, http://www.kroghsforlag.dk. **Co-publisher:** Kommuneinformation A/S.

379.1531 USA ISSN 0362-8787
LA252
DELAWARE. STATE BOARD OF EDUCATION. REPORT OF EDUCATIONAL STATISTICS. Key Title: Report of Educational Statistics. Text in English. 1921. a.
Related titles: Microfiche ed.: (from CIS).
Indexed: SRI.
Published by: State Board of Education, Townsend Bldg, Box 1402, Dover, DE 19901. TEL 302-736-4629. Circ: 300.

371.22 DNK ISSN 1398-1080
DENMARK. STYRELSEN FOR STATENS UDDANNELSESSTOETTE. HAANDBOG OM SU TIL UNGDOMSUDDANNELSER. Text in Danish. 1998. a.
Media: Online - full content.
Published by: Styrelsen for Statens Uddannelsesstoette/Danish Students Grants and Loans Agency, Danasvej 30, Copenhagen V, 1780, Denmark. TEL 45-33-268600, FAX 45-33-268611, su@su.dk, http://www.su.dk/publikationer/2001/haandbog_uu/index.htm.

378.1542 USA ISSN 1049-3255
➤ **THE DEPARTMENT CHAIR**; a resource for academic administrators. Text in English. 1990. q. USD 99 domestic; USD 109 in Canada; USD 119 elsewhere (effective 2005). adv. bk.rev. 32 p./no. 3 cols./p.; back issues avail. **Document type:** *Newsletter, Trade.* **Description:** Contains original articles, news, and resources for department chairs, division heads, and deans for any discipline at four- or two-year schools.
Indexed: HEA.
Published by: Anker Publishing Company, Inc., 563 main St, Bolton, MA 01740-0249. TEL 978-779-6190, FAX 978-779-6366, info@ankerpub.com, http://www.ankerpub.com. Ed., R&P Carolyn Dumore. Pub. James D Anker. Adv. contact Jennifer Gibson. Circ: 7,500 (paid and controlled).

371.223 USA ISSN 0883-5330
R850.A1
DIRECTORY OF BIOMEDICAL AND HEALTH CARE GRANTS. Text in English. 1985. a. USD 84.50 domestic; USD 101.40 foreign. **Document type:** *Directory.* **Description:** Lists more than 3,000 federal, state and private grants and funding programs in health and related fields, including sponsoring organizations, application procedures, addresses, and restrictions.
Related titles: Online - full text ed.: (from The Dialog Corporation).

E

Published by: Oryx Press (Subsidiary of: Greenwood Publishing Group Inc.), 1434 E. San Miguel Ave., Phoenix, AZ 85014-2422. TEL 602-265-2651, 800-279-6799, FAX 602-265-6250, info@oryxpress.com, http://www.oryxpress.com. Eds. Millie Hannnum, Anne Thompson. Pub. Phyllis Steckler. R&P Lori Cavanaugh TEL 602-265-2651 ext 662.

371.223 USA ISSN 1070-3950
HG177.5.U6
DIRECTORY OF COMPUTER AND HIGH TECHNOLOGY GRANTS. Text in English. 1991. biennial. USD 59.50. **Document type:** *Directory.* **Description:** Contains information for nonprofit organizations seeking funding or donations to purchase or upgrade computers, software and high-tech office equipment.
Published by: Research Grant Guides, PO Box 1214, Loxahatchee, FL 33470. TEL 561-765-6129, FAX 561-795-7794. Ed. Richard M Eckstein.

371.22 USA ISSN 0732-5215
LB2338
DIRECTORY OF FINANCIAL AIDS FOR WOMEN. Text in English. 1978. biennial. USD 45 (effective 2004 - 2005).
Published by: Reference Service Press, 1100 Industrial Rd., Ste 9, San Carlos, CA 94070. TEL 916-939-9620, FAX 916-939-3626, rspinfo@aol.com, http://www.rspfunding.com/products/rspbooks/woman.html. Ed. Gail A Schlachter.

DIRECTORY OF GRANTS FOR ORGANIZATIONS SERVING PEOPLE WITH DISABILITIES; a guide to sources of funding in the United States for programs & services for persons with disabilities. see *EDUCATION—Special Education And Rehabilitation*

379.786 USA
DIRECTORY OF MONTANA SCHOOLS. Text in English. 1980. a. USD 5.95. **Document type:** *Directory, Government.*
Published by: Office of Public Instruction, PO Box 202501, Helena, MT 59620-2501. TEL 406-256-3060. **Orders to:** Printing Center, 117 9th St N, Great Falls, MT 59401-2696. TEL 406-761-1555, FAX 406-771-7777.

371.201025 USA
DIRECTORY OF NONPUBLIC SCHOOLS AND ADMINISTRATORS, NEW YORK STATE. Text in English. a. USD 3. **Document type:** *Directory, Government.*
Published by: Education Department, Information, Reporting & Technology Services, Education Bldg Annex, Rm 962, Albany, NY 12234. TEL 518-474-7082, FAX 518-474-4351. Circ: (controlled).

371.20025 USA ISSN 1044-0453
L901
DIRECTORY OF ORGANIZATIONS IN EDUCATIONAL MANAGEMENT. Text in English. 1968. irreg., latest vol.10, 1998. index. **Document type:** *Directory, Trade.*
Former titles: Directory of Organizations and Researchers in Educational Management (0894-6221); Directory of Organizations and Personnel in Educational Management (0070-6035); Directory of Organizations and Personnel in Educational Administration
Media: Online - full text.
Published by: Clearinghouse on Educational Policy and Management (Subsidiary of: University of Oregon, College of Education), 5207 University of Oregon, Eugene, OR 97403-5207. TEL 541-346-5044, FAX 541-346-2334, directory@eric.uoregon.edu, http://eric.uoregon.edu/directory, http://cepm.uoregon.edu/. Ed. Stuart C Smith. Circ: 1,500.

371.201025 USA
DIRECTORY OF PUBLIC SCHOOLS AND ADMINISTRATORS, NEW YORK STATE. Text in English. 1977. a. USD 4. back issues avail. **Document type:** *Directory, Government.*
Formerly: Directory of New York State Public Schools and Administrators
Published by: Education Department, Information, Reporting & Technology Services, Education Bldg Annex, Rm 962, Albany, NY 12234. TEL 518-474-7965, FAX 518-474-4351.

379.025 USA ISSN 0897-4462
LB2809.A2
DIRECTORY OF STATE EDUCATION AGENCIES. Text in English. a. USD 25 (effective 2001). back issues avail. **Document type:** *Directory.* **Description:** Lists key personnel at the 50 state education departments, the District of Columbia, five US territories, and the Department of Defense education activity. Also provides addresses for U.S. governors, national education associations, and key personnel of the U.S. Department of Education.
Published by: Council of Chief State School Officers, One Massachusetts Ave, N W, Ste 700, Washington, DC 20001. TEL 202-408-5505, FAX 202-408-8072. R&P Billie Rollins. Circ: 3,000.

371.2 RUS
DIREKTOR SHKOLY. Text in Russian. bi-m.
Published by: Izdatel'skaya Firma Sentyabr', A-ya 90, k 50, Moscow, 103050, Russian Federation. TEL 7-095-2687550, FAX 7-095-2857190. Ed. K M Ushakov. **US dist. addr.:** East View Information Services, 3020 Harbor Ln. N., Minneapolis, MN 55447. TEL 612-550-0961.

379 GBR ISSN 0159-6306
L91
➤ **DISCOURSE;** studies in the cultural politics of education. Text in English. 1980. q. GBP 354, USD 583, AUD 530 combined subscription to institutions print & online eds. (effective 2006). adv. bk.rev. illus. back issues avail.; reprint service avail. from PSC. **Document type:** *Journal, Academic/Scholarly.* **Description:** Focuses on cultural, political, economic, philosophical, historical, and policy studies of education.
Related titles: Online - full text ed.: ISSN 1469-3739. GBP 336, USD 554, AUD 504 to institutions (effective 2006) (from EBSCO Publishing, Gale Group, IngentaConnect, O C L C Online Computer Library Center, Inc., Swets Information Services).
Indexed: AEI, CPE, CommAb, ERA, ETA, L&LBA, MEA, MLA-IB, PSA, RHEA, SEA, SENA, SOMA, SOPODA, SSA, SWA, SociolAb, TEA.
—BLDSC (3595.780000), IE, Infotrieve, ingenta. **CCC.**
Published by: (University of Queensland AUS, Department of Education AUS), Routledge (Subsidiary of: Taylor & Francis Group), 4 Park Sq, Milton Park, Abingdon, Oxon OX14 4RN, United Kingdom. TEL 44-1235-828600, FAX 44-1235-829000, info@routledge.co.uk, http://www.tandf.co.uk/journals/titles/01596306.asp, http://www.routledge.com. Eds. Martin Mills, Robert Lingard, Victoria Carrington. Circ: 500. **Subscr. in N. America to:** Taylor & Francis Inc., Customer Services Dept, 325 Chestnut St, 8th Fl, Philadelphia, PA 19106. TEL 215-625-8900, 800-354-1420, FAX 215-625-8914, customerservice@taylorandfrancis.com; **Subscr. to:** Taylor & Francis Ltd, Journals Customer Service, Rankine Rd, Basingstoke, Hants RG24 8PR, United Kingdom. TEL 44-1256-813000, FAX 44-1256-330245.

371.201 CAN ISSN 0831-3318
E A F JOURNAL. Variant title: Journal of Educational Administration and Foundations. Text in English. 1986. 2/yr.
Related titles: Microfiche ed.: (from MML); Microform ed.: 1986 (from MML); Online - full text ed.: (from Micromedia ProQuest).
Indexed: CEI, CIJE, CPE, EAA, ERA, ETA, MEA, RHEA, SEA, SENA, SOMA, TEA.
Published by: University of Manitoba, Department of Educational Administration, Foundations & Psychology, c/o Kevin L Seigert, Ed, Winnipeg, AB R3T 2N2, Canada.

371.201 USA ISSN 1076-1497
LB1028.A1
E R S BULLETIN; a monthly summary of research, data, and information for school administrators and board members. Text in English. 1973. m. price varies. bk.rev. abstr. index. **Document type:** *Bulletin, Trade.*
Published by: Educational Research Service, 2000 Clarendon Blvd, Arlington, VA 22201-2908. TEL 800-791-9308, FAX 800-791-9309. Ed. Deborah Perkins Gough. R&P Deborah Perkins-Gough. Circ: 2,700 (controlled).

379 USA
E T S POLICY INFORMATION REPORT. Text in English. irreg. price varies. **Document type:** *Bulletin.*
Published by: Educational Testing Service, Rosedale Rd, Princeton, NJ 08541-0001. TEL 609-921-9000. **Institutional subscr. to:** Warner Books Inc, Special Sales, Time & Life Bldg, 1271 Ave of the Americas, New York, NY 10020. TEL 212-522-7381; **Subscr. to:** Little Brown, 200 West St, Waltham, MA 02254. TEL 800-759-0190.

379 USA
E T S POLICY NOTES. Text in English. irreg. (2-3/yr.). **Document type:** *Newsletter.* **Description:** Discloses research results relating to education policy.
Published by: Educational Testing Service, Rosedale Rd, Princeton, NJ 08541-0001. TEL 609-921-9000. **Institutional subscr. to:** Warner Books Inc, Special Sales, Time & Life Bldg, 1271 Ave of the Americas, New York, NY 10020. TEL 212-522-7381; **Subscr. to:** Little Brown, 200 West St, Waltham, MA 02254. TEL 800-759-0190.

379 GBR ISSN 0272-7757
LC65
➤ **ECONOMICS OF EDUCATION REVIEW.** Text in English. 1982. 6/yr. EUR 703 in Europe to institutions; JPY 93,300 in Japan to institutions; USD 786 elsewhere to institutions; EUR 188 in Europe to qualified personnel; JPY 24,900 in Japan to qualified personnel; USD 209 elsewhere to qualified personnel (effective 2006). adv. bk.rev. bibl.; illus. index. back issues avail.; reprints avail. **Document type:** *Academic/Scholarly.* **Description:** Publishes theoretical, empirical and policy-oriented research addressing the role of economic analysis in the understanding and solution of educational problems and issues.
Related titles: Microfilm ed.: (from PQC); Online - full text ed.: (from EBSCO Publishing, Gale Group, IngentaConnect, ScienceDirect, Swets Information Services).
Indexed: ASCA, ASG, BAS, CIJE, CPE, CurCont, EAA, ERA, ETA, Faml, GEOBASE, HEA, HRA, JEL, MEA, PCI, RHEA, SEA, SSCI, SWA, TEA.
—BLDSC (3656.990000), IDS, IE, Infotrieve, ingenta. **CCC.**
Published by: Pergamon (Subsidiary of: Elsevier Science & Technology), The Boulevard, Langford Ln, East Park, Kidlington, Oxford OX5 1GB, United Kingdom. TEL 44-1865-843000, FAX 44-1865-843010, http://www.elsevier.com/locate/econedurev. Ed. Dr. Elchanan Cohn. Circ: 525. **Subscr. to:** Elsevier BV, PO Box 211, Amsterdam 1000 AE, Netherlands. TEL 31-20-485-3757, FAX 31-20-485-3432, nlinfo-f@elsevier.nl, http://www.elsevier.nl.

371.2 GBR ISSN 1463-7073
EDUCATION (CREDITON); the professional's voice. Text in English. w. free (effective 2004). **Description:** The main focus is on schools and colleges and the government institutions that work with them bringing news from all parts of the United Kingdom and the world. There are sections on research, conferences, Parliament and reports of the latest documents and opinion columns. Professional development, leadership and management issues will be covered.
Media: Online - full content. **Related titles:** CD-ROM ed.: GBP 240 domestic; USD 350 foreign (effective 2004); Print ed.: GBP 88 domestic; USD 225 foreign (effective 2004).
Published by: The Education Publishing Co. Ltd., Devonia House, 4 Union Terrace, Crediton, Devon EX17 3DY, United Kingdom. TEL 44-1363-774455, FAX 44-1363-776592, info@educationpublishing.com, http://www.educationpublishing.com.

379.794 USA ISSN 1058-4226
EDUCATION BEAT. Text in English. 1990. fortn. USD 145. index. **Document type:** *Newsletter.* **Description:** News of issues in California education from kindergarten through graduate school.
Published by: Political Pulse, 926 J St, Rm 1218, Sacramento, CA 95814. TEL 916-446-3956, FAX 916-498-3195. Ed., R&P Larry Lynch. Circ: 350 (paid).

371.206 GBR ISSN 0964-5292
LC65 CODEN: EDECFU
➤ **EDUCATION ECONOMICS.** Text in English. 1993. q. GBP 685, USD 1,131 combined subscription to institutions print & online eds. (effective 2006). adv. bk.rev. index. back issues avail.; reprint service avail. from PSC. **Document type:** *Journal, Academic/Scholarly.* **Description:** Serves as a forum for debate in all areas of the economics and management of education. Particular emphasis is given to the quantitative aspects of educational management which involve numerate disciplines such as economics and operational research.
Related titles: Microfiche ed.; Online - full text ed.: ISSN 1469-5782. GBP 651, USD 1,074 to institutions (effective 2006) (from EBSCO Publishing, Gale Group, IngentaConnect, Northern Light Technology, Inc., O C L C Online Computer Library Center, Inc., ProQuest Information & Learning, Swets Information Services).
Indexed: BAS, BrEdI, CIJE, CPE, DIP, EAA, ERA, ETA, GEOBASE, HEA, HRA, IBR, IBSS, IBZ, JEL, MEA, RHEA, SEA, SENA, SOMA, SOPODA, SSA, SWA, TEA, WBA, WMB.
—BLDSC (3661.251000), IE, Infotrieve, ingenta. **CCC.**
Published by: Routledge (Subsidiary of: Taylor & Francis Group), 4 Park Square, Milton Park, Abingdon, Oxon OX14 4RN, United Kingdom. TEL 44-1235-828600, FAX 44-1235-829000, info@routledge.co.uk, http://www.tandf.co.uk/journals/titles/09645292.asp, http://www.routledge.com. Ed. Steve Bradley. **Subscr. to:** Taylor & Francis Ltd, Journals Customer Service, Rankine Rd, Basingstoke, Hants RG24 8PR, United Kingdom. TEL 44-1256-813000, FAX 44-1256-330245.

371.2 340 USA ISSN 1556-5734
▼ **EDUCATION EMPLOYMENT LAW BULLETIN.** Text in English. 2005 (May). m. USD 147 (effective 2006). **Document type:** *Newsletter.*
Related titles: Online - full content ed.: ISSN 1556-5726.
Published by: Quinlan Publishing Group, Marine Industrial Park, 23 Drydock Ave, 6th Fl, Boston, MA 02210-2387. TEL 617-542-0048, 800-229-2084, FAX 617-507-1079, info@quinlan.com, http://www.quinlan.com. Ed. Heidi Taylor. Pub. Dennis Hofmaier.

371.2 USA ISSN 1557-3060
▼ **EDUCATION FINANCE AND POLICY.** Text in English. forthcoming 2006 (Jan.). q. USD 112 combined subscription in US & Canada to individuals print & online eds.; USD 132 combined subscription elsewhere to individuals print & online eds.; USD 254 combined subscription in US & Canada to institutions print & online eds.; USD 274 combined subscription elsewhere to institutions print & online eds. (effective 2006). **Document type:** *Journal, Academic/Scholarly.*
Related titles: Online - full text ed.: ISSN 1557-3079. forthcoming 2006 (Jan.). USD 100 to individuals; USD 228 to institutions (effective 2006).
Published by: M I T Press, 55 Hayward St, Cambridge, MA 02142-1493. TEL 617-253-5646, FAX 617-258-6779, journals-info@mit.edu, http://mitpress.mit.edu/efp.

E

▼ *new title* ➤ *refereed* ✶ *unverified* ♦ *full entry avail.*

371.206 USA ISSN 0273-4443
EDUCATION FUNDING NEWS. Text in English. 1971. w. (50/yr.). USD 278. **Document type:** *Newsletter.* **Description:** Details private and federal sources of financial aid and technical assistance for elementary and secondary schools and educational organizations. Provides analyses of pending legislation, funding deadlines, new program regulations, program requirements and major court decisions affecting education.
—CCC.
Published by: Education Funding Research Council (Subsidiary of: Thompson Publishing Group), 1725 K St, N W, Ste 700, Washington, DC 20006. TEL 800-454-2959, FAX 800-999-5661, http://www.thompson.com. Ed. Lisa Hayes. Pub. Daphne Musselwhite. **Subscr. to:** PO Box 22782, Tampa, FL 33622-2782.

371.2 GBR ISSN 1364-4505
EDUCATION JOURNAL. Text in English. 1996. 11/yr. GBP 38 domestic to individuals; USD 79 elsewhere to individuals; AUD 155 in Australia to individuals; GBP 48 domestic to libraries; USD 95 elsewhere to libraries (effective 2004).
Related titles: CD-ROM ed.: GBP 240 domestic; USD 336 elsewhere (effective 2004); Online - full text ed.: GBP 38 domestic to individuals; USD 49 elsewhere to individuals; AUD 99 in Australia to individuals (effective 2004) (from EBSCO Publishing).
Indexed: BrEdI, ERA, ETA, MEA, RHEA, SEA, SENA, SOMA, TEA.
Published by: The Education Publishing Co. Ltd., Devonia House, 4 Union Terrace, Crediton, Devon EX17 3DY, United Kingdom. TEL 44-1363-774455, FAX 44-1363-776592, info@educationpublishing.com, http://www.educationpublishing.com.

379 CAN ISSN 0843-1779
EDUCATION LEADER; news and views on education. Text in English. 1967. s-m. membership Members (effective 2000). adv. bk.rev. index. back issues avail. **Description:** Provides information about broad curriculum and policy issues and developments, and the latest trends in research.
Formerly (until 1987): British Columbia School Trustees Association. Newsletter (0381-5978)
Indexed: CEI.
Published by: British Columbia School Trustees Association, 1580 W Broadway, 4th Fl, Vancouver, BC V6J 5K9, Canada. TEL 604-734-2721, FAX 604-732-4559, bcsta@bcsta.org. Ed. Jennifer Gray Grant. Circ: 7,000.

EDUCATION MARKETING; the marketing magazine for universities and colleges. see *EDUCATION—Higher Education*

379 USA ISSN 1539-9664
➤ **EDUCATION NEXT**; a journal of opinion and research. Text in English. 2001. q. looseleaf. USD 20 domestic; USD 30 in Canada; USD 40 elsewhere; USD 7 newsstand/cover (effective 2005). adv. bk.rev. charts; stat.; illus. back issues avail. **Document type:** *Journal, Academic/Scholarly.* **Description:** Informs the public about current research and developments in education policy and school reform.
Formerly (until Aug. 2001): Education Matters (1532-5148)
Related titles: Online - full text ed.: ISSN 1539-9672. free (effective 2005) (from Florida Center for Library Automation, Gale Group, H.W. Wilson).
Indexed: EduInd.
—BLDSC (3661.305500), ingenta.
Published by: (Thomas B. Fordham Foundation), Hoover Institution, 434 Galvez Mall, Stanford, CA 94305-6010. TEL 650-723-1754, FAX 650-723-1687, Editor_EM@latte.harvard.edu, digest@hoover.stanford.edu, http://www.educationnext.org. Ed. Paul E. Peterson. R&P Carol Peterson. Adv. contact Thomas Polseno TEL 617-495-6954. B&W page USD 750, color page USD 1,000; trim 8.375 x 10.875. Circ: 15,000 (paid and controlled).

371.67 GBR ISSN 1472-0248
EDUCATION RESOURCES & MANAGEMENT. Text in English. 1959. 10/yr. free to qualified personnel. adv. bk.rev. illus. reprint service avail. from PQC. **Document type:** *Journal, Trade.* **Description:** Provides information to secondary and further and higher education establishments in UK.
Formerly (until 1999): Education Equipment (0013-1296)
Related titles: Microform ed.: (from PQC).
Indexed: ERA, ETA.
Published by: Nexus Media Ltd. (Subsidiary of: Highbury House Communications PLC), Nexus House, Azalea Dr, Swanley, Kent BR8 8HU, United Kingdom. TEL 44-1322-660070, FAX 44-1322-616311, info@nexusmedia.com, http://www.hhc.co.uk/erm. Ed. Russell Flanders TEL 44-1322-660070 ext 2445. Adv. contact Mark Tucker TEL 44-1322-660070 ext 2151. Circ: 12,000 (controlled).

371.2 USA ISSN 1521-7434
EDUCATION TECHNOLOGY LITERATURE REVIEW. Text in English. m. USD 99. **Document type:** *Newsletter, Abstract/Index.* **Description:** Summarizes articles on education technology.
Published by: E-School News, 7920 Norfolk Ave, Ste 900, Bethesda, MD 20814. TEL 800-394-0115, FAX 301-913-0119, info@eSchoolNews.com, info@eschoolnews.com, http://www.eschoolnews.com. Pub. Stephen Sanford.

371.2 CAN
EDUCATION TODAY. Text in English. 1969. 3/yr. CND 17.12 domestic; CND 26 foreign; CND 6 newsstand/cover foreign (effective 2000). adv. bk.rev. reprint service avail. from PQC. **Document type:** *Trade.* **Description:** For teachers, principals, school boards, provincial education officials, school trustees and parents who need to know the new developments in education and fresh opinions about what these mean for the school system and the education profession.
Former titles: Ontario Today (0843-5081); Ontario Education (0030-2902)
Related titles: Microform ed.: (from PQC); Online - full text ed.: (from Micromedia ProQuest).
Indexed: CBPI, CEI, CPerI, CurCont, DIP, IBR, IBZ.
Published by: Ontario Public School Board's Association, 439 University Ave, Ste 1850, Toronto, ON M5G 1Y8, Canada. TEL 416-340-2540, FAX 416-340-7571, admin@opsba.org, http://www.opsba.org. Ed., R&P Catherine Watson. Adv. contact Wendy Agostino. Circ: 3,500 (paid); 500 (controlled).

379.1531 USA ISSN 0744-3668
EDUCATION UPDATE (ST. PAUL)✱ . Text in English. 1966. 5/yr. **Document type:** *Newspaper, Government.* **Description:** Communicates policies and programs of Minnesota Department of Education and State Board of Education and information about programs in Minnesota public schools.
Formerly: Minnesota Education Report (0026-5454)
Published by: State Department of Children Families, 1500 Hwy.36, W., St. Paul, MN 55113-4266. TEL 612-297-1928, FAX 612-297-7201. Ed. Bob Anderson. Circ: 64,500.

EDUCATIONAL ADMINISTRATION ABSTRACTS. see *EDUCATION—Abstracting, Bibliographies, Statistics*

371.2 GBR ISSN 0140-0428
EDUCATIONAL ADMINISTRATION AND HISTORY MONOGRAPHS. Text in English. 1973. irreg., latest vol.18, 1990. price varies. **Document type:** *Monographic series.*
—BLDSC (3661.359000).
Published by: University of Leeds, School of Education, Parkinson Court, Leeds, W Yorks LS2 9JT, United Kingdom. TEL 44-113-233-4520. R&P Paul Sharp.

371.2 USA ISSN 0013-161X
LB2805 CODEN: AVSPAC
➤ **EDUCATIONAL ADMINISTRATION QUARTERLY.** Text in English. 1964. 5/yr. USD 543, GBP 350 to institutions; USD 565, GBP 365 combined subscription to institutions print & online eds. (effective 2006). adv. bk.rev. charts; illus. Index. back issues avail.; reprint service avail. from PQC,ISI. **Document type:** *Journal, Academic/Scholarly.* **Description:** Disseminates the latest knowledge about research and practice in educational administration and educational leadership.
Related titles: Microform ed.: (from PQC); Online - full text ed.: ISSN 1552-3519. USD 537, GBP 347 to institutions (effective 2006) (from C S A, EBSCO Publishing, O C L C Online Computer Library Center, Inc., Sage Publications, Inc., Swets Information Services).
Indexed: ABIn, ASCA, CIJE, CPE, ChPerI, CurCont, DIP, EAA, ERA, ETA, EduInd, FamI, IBR, IBZ, MEA, MEA&I, MEDLINE, RHEA, SEA, SENA, SOMA, SPAA, SSCI, SWA, TEA.
—BLDSC (3661.362000), IDS, IE, Infotrieve, ingenta. **CCC.**
Published by: (University Council for Educational Administration), Corwin Press, Inc. (Subsidiary of: Sage Publications, Inc.), 2455 Teller Rd, Thousand Oaks, CA 91320-2218. TEL 805-499-9734, FAX 800-4-1-SCHOOL (800-417-2466), info@sagepub.com, http://www.sagepub.com/journal.aspx?pid=107, http://www.corwinpress.com. Ed. Diana G Pounder. Pub. Sara Miller McCune. R&P Jackie Paciulin. Adv. contact Kristen Beaulieu. B&W page USD 350. Circ: 1,200 (paid). **Subscr. in Asia to:** Sage Publications India Pvt. Ltd., M-32 Market, Greater Kailash-I, PO Box 4215, New Delhi 110 048, India. TEL 91-11-645-3915, FAX 91-11-647-2426, journalsubs@indiasage.com; **Subscr. in Europe to:** Sage Publications Ltd., 1 Oliver's Yard, 55 City Rd, London EC1 1SP, United Kingdom. TEL 44-20-73740645, FAX 44-20-73748741.

➤ **EDUCATIONAL DEALER.** see *BUSINESS AND ECONOMICS—Trade And Industrial Directories*

371.207 USA ISSN 0162-3737
LB1028
➤ **EDUCATIONAL EVALUATION & POLICY ANALYSIS**; a quarterly publication of the American Educational Research Association. Text in English. 1979. q. USD 48 to individuals; USD 140 to institutions (effective 2005). adv. bk.rev. illus. reprint service avail. from PQC. **Document type:** *Academic/Scholarly.* **Description:** Focuses on practical, theoretical, and methodological issues in educational evaluation and educational policy analysis.
Related titles: Microform ed.: (from PQC); Online - full text ed.: (from H.W. Wilson, JSTOR (Web-based Journal Archive), O C L C Online Computer Library Center, Inc., ProQuest Information & Learning).
Indexed: ABIn, ASCA, CIJE, CPE, CurCont, ERA, ETA, EduInd, FamI, MEA, PsycInfo, PsycholAb, SSCI, TEA, e-psyche.
—BLDSC (3661.402000), IDS, IE, Infotrieve, ingenta. **CCC.**
Published by: American Educational Research Association, 1230 17th St, N W, Washington, DC 20036-3078. FAX 202-775-1824, http://aera.net/pubs/eepa/. Ed. Jane Hannaway. Adv. contact Camille Coy. Circ: 6,000.

➤ **EDUCATIONAL MANAGEMENT ABSTRACTS.** see *EDUCATION—Abstracting, Bibliographies, Statistics*

371.2 GBR ISSN 1741-1432
LB2901
➤ **EDUCATIONAL MANAGEMENT, ADMINISTRATION, & LEADERSHIP.** Text in English. 1972. q. GBP 393, USD 688 to institutions; GBP 409, USD 716 combined subscription to institutions print & online eds. (effective 2006). adv. bk.rev. index, cum.index: 1972-1975. reprint service avail. from PQC. **Document type:** *Journal, Academic/Scholarly.* **Description:** Provides a forum for research and analysis on all aspects of management, administration and policy in education.
Former titles (until 2003): Educational Management & Administration (0263-211X); (until 1982): Educational Administration (0305-7496)
Related titles: Microform ed.: (from PQC); Online - full text ed.: ISSN 1741-1440. GBP 389, USD 680 to institutions (effective 2006) (from C S A, EBSCO Publishing, O C L C Online Computer Library Center, Inc., Sage Publications, Inc., Swets Information Services).
Indexed: BrEdI, CIJE, CPE, EAA, ERA, ETA, HECAB, MEA, RHEA, SEA, SENA, SOMA, SWA, TEA, V&AA.
—BLDSC (3661.441950), IE, Infotrieve, ingenta. **CCC.**
Published by: (British Educational Management and Administration Society), Sage Publications Ltd. (Subsidiary of: Sage Publications, Inc.), 1 Oliver's Yard, 55 City Rd, London, EC1 1SP, United Kingdom. TEL 44-20-73248500, FAX 44-20-73248600, info@sagepub.co.uk, http://www.sagepub.co.uk/journal.aspx?pid=105528. Ed. Tony Bush. Adv. contact Jenny Kirby. page GBP 220; trim 200 x 130. Circ: 1,600. **Subscr. in the Americas to:** Sage Publications, Inc., 2455 Teller Rd, Thousand Oaks, CA 91320. TEL 805-499-0721, FAX 805-499-0871, journals@sagepub.com.

379 USA ISSN 0895-9048
LC89
➤ **EDUCATIONAL POLICY**; an interdisciplinary journal of policy and practice. Text in English. 1987. 5/yr. USD 578, GBP 373 to institutions; USD 602, GBP 389 combined subscription to institutions print & online eds. (effective 2006). adv. bk.rev. charts; illus. index. back issues avail. **Document type:** *Journal, Academic/Scholarly.* **Description:** Provides analysis and research on educational policy at the local, national and international level. The focus of the journal encompasses schooling and higher education as well as non-school settings.
Related titles: Microform ed.: (from PQC); Online - full text ed.: ISSN 1552-3896. USD 572, GBP 369 to institutions (effective 2006) (from C S A, EBSCO Publishing, O C L C Online Computer Library Center, Inc., Sage Publications, Inc., Swets Information Services); ♦ Special ed(s).: Politics of Education Association. Yearbook. ISSN 1054-3910.
Indexed: ABIn, ASCA, CIJE, CPE, CurCont, DIP, EAA, ERA, ETA, EduInd, FamI, HEA, IBR, IBZ, L&LBA, MEA, PAIS, PRA, RHEA, SEA, SENA, SOMA, SOPODA, SRRA, SSA, SSCI, SWA, SWR&A, SociolAb, TEA, V&AA.
—BLDSC (3661.483400), IDS, IE, Infotrieve, ingenta. **CCC.**
Published by: Corwin Press, Inc. (Subsidiary of: Sage Publications, Inc.), 2455 Teller Rd, Thousand Oaks, CA 91320-2218. TEL 805-499-9734, FAX 805-499-0871, 800-4-1-SCHOOL (800-417-2466), order@corwin.sagepub.com, info@sagepub.com, http://www.sagepub.com/journal.aspx?pid=186, http://www.corwinpress.com. Ed. Ana M Martinez-Aleman. adv.: B&W page USD 350. **Subscr. in Europe to:** Sage Publications Ltd., 1 Oliver's Yard, 55 City Rd, London EC1 1SP, United Kingdom. TEL 44-20-73740645, FAX 44-20-73748741, subscription@sagepub.co.uk.

379.52 JPN
EDUCATIONAL STANDARDS IN JAPAN. Text in English. 1959. irreg. illus.; stat.
Published by: Ministry of Education, 3-2-2 Kasumigaseki, Chiyoda-ku, Tokyo, 100-0013, Japan.

371.1 USA
EDUCATOR SUPPLY AND DEMAND IN THE UNITED STATES. Text in English. a. USD 15.
Former titles: Teacher Supply and Demand in the United States; Teacher Supply and Demand
Related titles: Microfiche ed.: (from CIS).
Indexed: SRI.
Published by: American Association for Employment in Education, 3040 Riverside Dr., Ste. 125, Columbus, OH 43221-2575. TEL 847-864-1999, FAX 847-864-8303, http://www.ub-careers.buffalo.edu/aaee/, http://www.aaee.org.

378.111 USA
EDUEXEC. Text in English. 1982. m. USD 179 domestic; USD 183 in Canada; USD 189 elsewhere (effective 2005). bk.rev. back issues avail. **Document type:** *Newsletter.* **Description:** Management information for college administrators.
Formerly: Administrator (Madison) (0744-7078)
Related titles: Online - full content ed.: USD 179 (effective 2005); Online - full text ed.: (from EBSCO Publishing, H.W. Wilson, O C L C Online Computer Library Center, Inc.).
Indexed: ABIn, EduInd.

E

—CCC.
Published by: Magna Publications, Inc., 2718 Dryden Dr, Madison, WI 53704. TEL 608-246-3590, FAX 608-246-3597, editor@magnapubs.com, http://www.magnapubs.com/pub/magnapubs_ad. Ed. Chris Hill. Pub. David Burns. Circ: 1,600.

371.2 USA ISSN 0883-1327
EDUTECH REPORT. Text in English. 1985. m. USD 199 domestic; USD 203 in Canada; USD 209 elsewhere (effective 2005). 8 p./no.; back issues avail. **Document type:** *Newsletter, Academic/Scholarly.* **Description:** Covers the issues surrounding information technology in higher education.
Related titles: Online - full content ed.: USD 199 (effective 2005); Online - full text ed.: (from EBSCO Publishing).
Indexed: HEA.
—CCC.
Published by: (Edutech International), Magna Publications, Inc., 2718 Dryden Dr, Madison, WI 53704. TEL 608-246-3590, FAX 608-246-3597, custserv@magnapubs.com, http://www.magnapubs.com/pub/magnapubs_etr/.

371.2 USA ISSN 1554-0464
▼ **EFFECTIVE PRACTICES FOR ACADEMIC LEADERS.** Text in English. forthcoming 2006. m. USD 90 (effective 2005).
Related titles: Online - full text ed.: ISSN 1554-0472. forthcoming 2006.
Published by: Stylus Publishing, 22883 Quicksilver Dr, Herndon, VA 20166-2102. TEL 703-661-1504, FAX 703-661-1547, StylusInfo@StylusPub.com, http://www.styluspub.com.

371.14 USA ISSN 0898-2139
CODEN: FODMD5
EMPLOYERS NEGOTIATING SERVICE✶. Text in English. 1967. s-m. looseleaf. USD 159. bk.rev. index.
Formerly: Educators Negotiating Service (0046-1571)
Published by: E F R Corp., PO Box 15236, Colorado Spring, CO 80935-5236. Ed. Dr. Eric Rhodes. Circ: 1,000.

EMPLOYMENT OPPORTUNITIES (ENGLEWOOD). see *OCCUPATIONS AND CAREERS*

ENGAGEMENT; Zeitschrift fuer Erziehung und Schule. see *EDUCATION—Teaching Methods And Curriculum*

371.2 USA ISSN 1098-0814
LB1044.87
ESCHOOL NEWS. Text in English. 1998. m. USD 30 (effective 2004). adv. software rev. illus. **Document type:** *Journal, Trade.* **Description:** Gives school administrators the information they need to make decisions on integrating technology into their schools and curricula.
Related titles: Online - full text ed.: ISSN 1098-0806.
Indexed: MicrocompInd.
Published by: E-School News, 7920 Norfolk Ave, Ste 900, Bethesda, MD 20814. TEL 800-394-0115, FAX 301-913-0119, info@eSchoolNews.com, info@eschoolnews.com, http://www.eschoolnews.com. Ed., Pub. Gregg W Downey. adv.: B&W page USD 7,000, color page USD 7,310; trim 10.75 x 14.5. Circ: 42,000 (controlled).

371 ESP ISSN 0214-0721
ESCUELA ESPANOLA. Text in Spanish. 1941. w. EUR 54 (effective 2002).
Published by: Praxis, Principe de Asturias, 61 7a Planta, Barcelona, Cataluna 08012, Spain. TEL 34-93-3444700, FAX 34-93-3444701, educacion@praxis.es, http://www.praxis.es/. Circ: 30,000.

371.201 USA ISSN 1092-4841
EXECUTIVE SESSION. Text in English. 1997. m. USD 95 (effective 2001). **Document type:** *Newsletter.*
Related titles: Online - full text ed.
Published by: Nyper Publications, PO Box 662, Latham, NY 12110-0662. TEL 518-786-1654, 518-786-1654, FAX 518-456-8582, nyper@capital.net. Eds. Eric D Randall, Harvey Randall.

371.21 DEU
FACHHOCHSCHULE DARMSTADT. VORLESUNGS- UND PERSONALVERZEICHNIS. Text in German. 2/yr. adv. **Document type:** *Directory, Academic/Scholarly.*
Published by: Fachhochschule Darmstadt, Haardtring 100, Darmstadt, 64295, Germany. TEL 49-6151-1602, FAX 49-6151-1689, webadmin@fh-darmstadt.de, http://www.fh-darmstadt.de. adv.: B&W page EUR 495, color page EUR 1,290. Circ: 4,000 (controlled).

378.196 USA ISSN 0882-7249
FACILITIES MANAGER. Text in English. 1985. q. USD 66 to members; USD 120 to non-members (effective 2005). adv. bk.rev. charts; illus. index. **Document type:** *Trade.* **Description:** Promotes excellence in the administration, care, operation, planning and development of higher education facilities. Covers new products, resource management and data bases.
Indexed: CIJE, Inspec, RefZh.
—Linda Hall.
Published by: A P P A: The Association of Higher Education Facilities Officers, 1446 Duke St, Alexandria, VA 22314-3492. TEL 703-684-1446, FAX 703-549-2772, http://www.appa.org/FacilitiesManager/index.cfm. Ed., R&P Steve Glazner. Adv. contact Cotrenia Aytch. Circ: 5,000.

371.22 USA ISSN 1080-5583
FEDERAL GRANT DEADLINE CALENDAR. A SUPPLEMENT TO THE GUIDE TO FEDERAL FUNDING FOR EDUCATION. Text in English. 1995. s-m.
Related titles: ♦ Supplement to: Guide to Federal Funding for Education. ISSN 0275-8393.
Published by: Education Funding Research Council (Subsidiary of: Thompson Publishing Group), 1725 K St, N W, Ste 700, Washington, DC 20006. TEL 800-454-2959, FAX 800-999-5661, http://www.thompson.com. Ed. Charles Edwards.

371.206 USA
FEDERAL STUDENT AID HANDBOOK. STUDENT ELIGIBILITY. Abbreviated title: F S A Handbook Student Eligibility. Text in English. a.
Formerly (until 2002): Student Financial Aid Handbook. Student Eligibility; Which superseded in part (in 1999): Federal Student Financial Aid Handbook (0730-8922)
Published by: U.S. Department of Education, Office of Federal Student Aid, PO Box 84, Washington, DC 20044-0084. TEL 800-433-7327, fsa.customer.support@ed.gov, http://www.ed.gov/about/offices/list/fsa/index.html.

379.1531 USA ISSN 0015-0037
FERGUSON-FLORISSANT SCHOOLS. Text in English. 1945. q. illus. **Document type:** *Newsletter.*
Published by: Ferguson-Florissant School District, Board of Education, 1005 Waterford Dr, Florissant, MO 63033-3694. FAX 314-831-1525. Ed. Donna Corno. Circ: 32,000.

371.22 305.896 USA ISSN 1099-906X
LB2338
FINANCIAL AID FOR AFRICAN AMERICANS. Text in English. 1999. biennial.
Published by: Reference Service Press, 1100 Industrial Rd., Ste 9, San Carlos, CA 94070. TEL 916-939-9620, FAX 916-939-3626.

371.22 305.895073 USA ISSN 1099-9124
LB2338
FINANCIAL AID FOR ASIAN AMERICANS. Text in English. 1999. biennial. USD 37.50 per vol. (effective 2004). **Document type:** *Directory.*
Supersedes in part (in 1999): Directory of Financial Aids for Minorities (0738-4122)
Published by: Reference Service Press, 1100 Industrial Rd., Ste 9, San Carlos, CA 94070. TEL 916-939-9620, FAX 916-939-3626, rspinfo@aol.com, http://www.rspfunding.com.

371.22 305.897 USA ISSN 1099-9116
LB2338
FINANCIAL AID FOR NATIVE AMERICANS. Text in English. biennial. USD 40 per issue (effective 2004).
Supersedes in part (in 1999): Directory of Financial Aids for Minorities (0738-4122)
Published by: Reference Service Press, 1100 Industrial Rd., Ste 9, San Carlos, CA 94070. TEL 916-939-9620, FAX 916-939-3626, rspinfo@aol.com, http://www.rspfunding.com.

371.22 370.116 USA ISSN 1072-530X
LB2337.2
FINANCIAL AID FOR RESEARCH AND CREATIVE ACTIVITIES ABROAD. Text in English. 1994. biennial. USD 45 per vol. (effective 2004). **Document type:** *Directory, Consumer.*
Published by: Reference Service Press, 1100 Industrial Rd., Ste 9, San Carlos, CA 94070. TEL 916-939-9620, FAX 916-939-3626, rspinfo@aol.com, http://www.rspfunding.com.

371.22 355.3 353.538 USA ISSN 0896-7792
UB403
FINANCIAL AID FOR VETERANS, MILITARY PERSONNEL, AND THEIR DEPENDENTS. Text in English. 1988. biennial. **Document type:** *Directory.*
Published by: Reference Service Press, 1100 Industrial Rd., Ste 9, San Carlos, CA 94070. TEL 916-939-9620, FAX 916-939-3626, rspinfo@aol.com, http://www.rspfunding.com.

379.759 USA ISSN 0898-4387
CODEN: DPTOE9
FLORIDA LEADER; the magazine for Florida students. Text in English. 1983. 3/yr., latest vol.17, no.3. USD 3.50 newsstand/cover. adv. bk.rev. charts; illus. back issues avail. **Document type:** *Consumer.* **Description:** Covers education issues, careers and employment, and college success for Florida students.
Related titles: Online - full text ed.: (from SoftLine Information); Special ed(s).: Florida Leader (College Edition).
Indexed: DYW.
Published by: Oxendine Publishing, Inc., PO Box 14081, Gainesville, FL 32604-2081. TEL 352-373-6907, 888-547-6310, FAX 352-373-8120, info@studentleader.com, http://www.floridaleader.com. Ed., Pub. W.H. Oxendine Jr. Adv. contact W H Oxendine Jr. page USD 3,484; trim 10.88 x 8.38. Circ: 140,000. **Subscr. to:** 412 N W 16th Ave, Gainesville, FL 32607.

THE FOCUS NEWSLETTER. see *EDUCATION—Teaching Methods And Curriculum*

FOCUS ON EDUCATION. see *EDUCATION—Teaching Methods And Curriculum*

371.223 USA ISSN 0071-7274
AS911.F6
FORD FOUNDATION ANNUAL REPORT. Text in English. 1951. a. free. **Document type:** *Corporate.* **Description:** Lists foundation grants and other financial data for the fiscal year. Includes information on grant applications.
Related titles: Microfiche ed.: (from BHP).
Published by: Ford Foundation, Office of Communications, 320 E 43rd St, New York, NY 10017. TEL 212-573-5000, FAX 212-351-3677, office-of-communications@fordfound.org, http://www.fordfound.org. Ed. Thomas Quinn.

371.201 USA
FORTNIGHTER. Variant title: The M A S A Fortnighter. Text in English. 1971. bi-w. looseleaf. USD 40 to members. **Document type:** *Newsletter.* **Description:** Provides legislative updates, news releases, announcements and Association information.
Related titles: Online - full content ed.
Published by: Michigan Association of School Administrators, 1001 Centennial Way, Ste 300, Lansing, MI 48917-9279. TEL 517-327-5910, FAX 517-327-0771, jscofield@gomasa.org, jkeidel@admin.melg.org, http://www.gomasa.org/Newsletter.htm, http://www.melg.org. Ed. Gerard E Keidel. Circ: 1,850.

379 GBR ISSN 0963-8253
L16 CODEN: FPCEEI
FORUM; for promoting 3-19 comprehensive education. Text in English. 1958. 3/yr. GBP 21 domestic to individuals; USD 40 foreign to individuals; GBP 50 domestic to libraries includes online access; USD 78 foreign to libraries includes online access (effective 2003). bk.rev. abstr.; illus. back issues avail. **Document type:** *Journal, Academic/Scholarly.* **Description:** Addresses subjects of immediate concern to teachers and policy-makers.
Formerly (until 1991): Forum for the Discussion of New Trends in Education (0046-4708)
Related titles: Online - full text ed.: (from EBSCO Publishing, Swets Information Services).
Indexed: BrEdI, CIJE, CPE, DIP, ETA, HECAB, IBR, IBZ, L&LBA, MEA, MEA&I, RASB, SEA, TEA.
—BLDSC (4024.095550), IE, ingenta.
Published by: Triangle Journals Ltd., Attn: Roger Osborn-King, Publisher, PO Box 65, Wallingford, Oxon OX10 0YG, United Kingdom. TEL 44-1491-838013, FAX 44-1491-834968, subscriptions@triangle.co.uk, journals@triangle.co.uk, http://www.triangle.co.uk/for. Eds. Annabelle Dixon, Clyde Chitty.

371.2 DNK ISSN 1397-0372
FORUM FOR SKOLELEDELSE; medlemsblad for Danmarks skolelederforening. Text in Danish. 1981. 10/yr. DKK 675; DKK 65 per issue (effective 2004). adv.
Formerly (until 1997): D S - Kontakt (0107-301X)
Published by: Danmarks Skolelederforening/Danish Association of Headmasters, Ved Stranden 16, Copenhagen K, 1061, Denmark. TEL 45-33-142840, FAX 45-33-140329, ds@dsnet.dk. Ed. Marianne Kyed TEL 45-64-761546. Circ: 3,000.

371.223 USA ISSN 1062-4686
FOUNDATION & CORPORATE GRANTS ALERT. Text in English. 1993. m. USD 383 (effective 2002). **Document type:** *Newsletter.* **Description:** Provides guide to private grant opportunities for nonprofit organizations. Tracks developments and trends in funding and provides notification of changes in foundations' funding priorities.
—CCC.
Published by: Aspen Publishers, Inc. (Subsidiary of: Wolters Kluwer N.V.), 5301 Buckeystown Pike, Ste. 400, Frederick, MD 21704-8319. TEL 800-638-8437, customer.service@aspenpubl.com, http://www.aspenpub.com. Ed. Molly Mudd. Pub. Marjorie Weiner. R&P Rossette Graham. **Dist. by:** Distribution Center, 7201 McKinney Circle, Frederick, MD 21701. TEL 301-698-7100, FAX 301-417-7550.

379.1531 DEU
FRANKFURTER LEHRERZEITUNG. Text in German. 1980. bi-m. membership. adv. bk.rev. back issues avail. **Description:** Covers the activities of the teacher's union and the school board in Frankfurt.
Published by: Gewerkschaft Erziehung und Wissenschaft, Bezirksverband Frankfurt, Bleichstr 38A, Frankfurt Am Main, 60313, Germany. TEL 069-291818. Circ: 4,000.

371.2 DNK ISSN 0106-066X
FRISKOLEBLADET. Text in Danish. 1958. irreg. (22-23/yr.). adv. **Document type:** *Academic/Scholarly.*
Formerly (until 1971): Friskolens Tidende (0901-2672)
Published by: Dansk Friskoleforening/Private School Association of Denmark, Prices Havevej 11, Faaborg, 5600, Denmark. TEL 45-75-69-17-02, FAX 45-75-69-17-04. Ed. Lars Skriver. Circ: 5,200.

371.1531 USA
FROM THE BOARD ROOM. Text in English. 1961. 10/yr. USD 25. adv. bk.rev. **Document type:** *Newsletter.*
Former titles: V S B A Newsletter; V S S D A Newsletter (0042-191X)
Media: Duplicated (not offset).

E

▼ new title ➤ refereed ✶ unverified ♦ full entry avail.

Published by: Vermont School Boards Association, 2 Prospect St, Ste 4, Montpelier, VT 05602. TEL 802-223-3580, http://www.vetc.vsc.edu/vsba/index.html. Ed. Edith Miller. Circ: 2,300.

FULBRIGHT SCHOLAR PROGRAM: GRANTS FOR FACULTY AND PROFESSIONALS. see *EDUCATION—International Education Programs*

371.207 FRA ISSN 0071-9862
FUNDAMENTALS OF EDUCATIONAL PLANNING. Text in English. 1966. irreg., latest vol.57, 1998. price varies. **Document type:** *Trade.*
Related titles: French ed.: Principes de la Planification de l'Education. ISSN 0251-4931. 1967; ♦ Series of: I I E P Studies Series.
Indexed: CIJE, RRTA, WAE&RSA.
—BLDSC (4056.094000), IE, ingenta.
Published by: (International Institute for Educational Planning), UNESCO Publishing, 7 place de Fontenoy, Paris, 75352, France. TEL 33-1-45684300, FAX 33-1-45685737, http://www.unesco.org/publications. **Dist. in US by:** Bernan Associates, Bernan, 4611-F Assembly Dr., Lanham, MD 20706-4391.

379.3 USA ISSN 1079-297X
FUNDING PRIVATE SCHOOLS. Text in English. 1994. m. USD 187 (effective 2005). **Document type:** *Newsletter, Trade.*
Related titles: Online - full text ed.: ISSN 1544-5178.
Published by: Quinlan Publishing Group, Marine Industrial Park, 23 Drydock Ave, 6th Fl, Boston, MA 02210-2387. TEL 617-542-0048, 800-229-2084, FAX 617-507-1079, info@quinlan.com, http://www.quinlan.com. Ed. Annie Archaumbalt. Pub. Dennis Hofmaier.

371.2 DEU ISSN 0344-2101
GANZTAGSSCHULE. Text in German. 1961. q. EUR 20 (effective 2005). adv. back issues avail. **Document type:** *Magazine, Trade.*
Formerly (until 1977): Tagesheimschule (0342-7129)
Indexed: DIP, IBR, IBZ.
Published by: Ganztagsschulverband Gemeinnuetzige Gesellschaft Tagesheimschule e.V., Quellhofstr 140, Kassel, 34127, Germany. TEL 49-561-85077, FAX 49-561-85078, gts-informationsstelle@hegelsberg.ksan.de, http://www.ganztagsschulverband.de.

371.2 371.9 371.3 USA
GEORGIA SCHOOL LAW DECISIONS. Text in English. bi-m. looseleaf. USD 298 (effective 2006). **Document type:** *Trade.* **Description:** Reports on administrative law decisions in the field of special education in the state of Georgia. Useful for school districts, law firms and attorneys specializing in this field. Reports on Georgia Board of Education decisions and state and regional hearing officer decisions.
Published by: L R P Publications, 747 Dresher Rd, PO Box 980, Horsham, PA 19044. TEL 215-784-0860, 800-341-7874, FAX 215-784-9639, custserve@lrp.com, http://www.shoplrp.com/product/p-300012.html, http://www.lrp.com.

371.2 DEU
GOETIKUSS. Text in German. 1978. irreg. adv. bk.rev. charts. back issues avail. **Document type:** *Newsletter, Consumer.*
Published by: Goetikuss Goethe-Gymnasium, Seestr 37, Ludwigsburg, 71638, Germany. TEL 49-7141-9102338, FAX 49-7141-9102268, postmaster@goethe.lb.bw.schule.de, http://www.goethe.lb.bw.schule.de/kontakt/kontakt.htm. Circ: 1,000.

379 USA ISSN 1055-825X
GOVERNMENT PROGRAMS✶. Text in English. 1991. q. USD 29.99. adv. Supplement avail. **Document type:** *Consumer.* **Description:** Lists government programs covering education, employment, housing, families, and business.
Announced as: Subsidized Government Programs
Published by: Publishing & Business Consultants, 4427 W Slauson Ave, Los Angeles, CA 90043-2717. TEL 213-732-3477, FAX 213-732-9123. Ed. Andeson Napoleon Atia. Circ: 120,000. **Subscr. to:** PO Box 75392, Los Angeles, CA 90075.

371.22 USA
GRANT GUIDES. Text in English. 1972. a., latest 2003-2004. USD 75 for each of 12 titles included in the series (effective 2004). **Description:** Includes 12 subject-oriented publications. Lists actual foundation grants categorized into 30 key areas of grantmaking.
Formed by the merger of (1972-1991): Comsearch: Broad Topics; (1980-1991): Comsearch: Geographics; (1982-1991): Comsearch: Subjects; Which was formerly: Comsearch Printouts: Subjects; Supersedes in part: Comsearch Printouts; (in 1977): Foundation Grants Index: Subjects on Microfiche (0090-1601); Broad Topics incorporated International Philanthropy
Related titles: Microfiche ed.; ♦ Series: Grants for Higher Education. ISSN 1045-2761; ♦ Grants for Foreign and International Programs. ISSN 1056-649X; ♦ Grants for Women and Girls. ISSN 1064-4377; ♦ Grants for Arts, Culture and the Humanities; ♦ Grants for Children & Youth; ♦ Grants for Elementary & Secondary Education; ♦ Grants for Environmental Protection & Animal Welfare; ♦ Grants for Libraries & Information Services; ♦ Grants for Mental Health, Addictions & Crisis Services; ♦ Grants for Minorities; ♦ Grants for the Physically & Mentally Disabled; ♦ Grants for Religion, Religious Welfare & Religious Education.
Published by: Foundation Center, 79 Fifth Ave, New York, NY 10003. TEL 212-620-4230, 800-424-9836, FAX 212-807-3677, http://www.fdncenter.org.

371.22 USA
GRANTS FOR ARTS, CULTURE AND THE HUMANITIES. Text in English. a., latest 2003-2004. USD 75 per issue (effective 2004). **Description:** Provides indication of foundation giving in the field. Contains descriptions of 22,280 recent grants of $10,000 or more awarded by 920 foundations.
Related titles: ♦ Series of: Grant Guides.
Published by: Foundation Center, 79 Fifth Ave, New York, NY 10003. TEL 212-620-4230, 800-424-9836, FAX 212-807-3677, orders@fdncenter.org, http://www.fdncenter.org.

371.22 649 USA
GRANTS FOR CHILDREN & YOUTH. Text in English. a., latest 2003-2004. USD 75 per issue (effective 2004). **Description:** Provides indication of foundation giving in the field. Presents descriptions of over 28,700 recent grants of $10,000 or more awarded by 913 foundations.
Related titles: ♦ Series of: Grant Guides.
Published by: Foundation Center, 79 Fifth Ave, New York, NY 10003. TEL 212-620-4230, 800-424-9836, FAX 212-807-3677, orders@fdncenter.org, http://www.fdncenter.org.

371.22 USA
GRANTS FOR ELEMENTARY & SECONDARY EDUCATION. Text in English. a., latest 2003-2004. USD 75 per issue (effective 2004). **Description:** Provides indication of foundation giving in the field. Presents descriptions of over 14,800 recent grants of $10,000 or more awarded by 864 foundations.
Related titles: ♦ Series of: Grant Guides.
Published by: Foundation Center, 79 Fifth Ave, New York, NY 10003. TEL 212-620-4230, 800-424-9836, FAX 212-807-3677, orders@fdncenter.org, http://www.fdncenter.org.

371.22 USA
GRANTS FOR ENVIRONMENTAL PROTECTION & ANIMAL WELFARE. Text in English. a., latest 2003-2004. USD 75 per issue (effective 2004).
Related titles: ♦ Series of: Grant Guides.
Published by: Foundation Center, 79 Fifth Ave, New York, NY 10003. TEL 212-620-4230, 800-424-9836, FAX 212-807-3677, orders@fdncenter.org, http://www.fdncenter.org.

371.22 USA ISSN 1056-649X
HC59.8
GRANTS FOR FOREIGN AND INTERNATIONAL PROGRAMS. Text in English. 1991. a., latest 2003-2004. USD 75 per vol. (effective 2004). **Document type:** *Directory.* **Description:** Contains descriptions of over 11,400 recent grants of $10,000 or more awarded by 638 foundations.
Related titles: ♦ Series of: Grant Guides.
Published by: Foundation Center, 79 Fifth Ave, New York, NY 10003. TEL 212-620-4230, 800-424-9836, FAX 212-807-3677, orders@fdncenter.org.

GRANTS FOR HIGHER EDUCATION. see *EDUCATION—Higher Education*

371.223 USA ISSN 1542-4464
GRANTS FOR K-12 HOTLINE. Text in English. 1989. bi-w. USD 187 (effective 2004). back issues avail. **Document type:** *Newsletter, Trade.* **Description:** Provides information on available federal and foundation grants, schools programs and business partnerships throughout the country, of interest to school administrators, grants writers, district officials and superintendents.
Formerly (until 2000): Grants for School Districts Monthly Hotline (1075-8976)
Related titles: Online - full text ed.: ISSN 1542-4529.
—CCC.
Published by: Quinlan Publishing Group, Marine Industrial Park, 23 Drydock Ave, 6th Fl, Boston, MA 02210-2387. TEL 617-542-0048, 800-229-2084, FAX 617-345-9646, info@quinlan.com, http://www.quinlan.com. Ed. Annie Archaumbalt. Pub. Dennis Hofmaier.

371.22 USA
GRANTS FOR LIBRARIES & INFORMATION SERVICES. Text in English. a., latest 2003-2004. USD 75 per issue (effective 2004). **Description:** Provides indication of foundation giving in the field. Presents descriptions of over 3,600 recent grants of $10,000 or more awarded by 633 foundations.
Related titles: ♦ Series of: Grant Guides.
Published by: Foundation Center, 79 Fifth Ave, New York, NY 10003. TEL 212-620-4230, 800-424-9836, FAX 212-807-3677, orders@fdncenter.org, http://www.fdncenter.org.

371.22 USA
GRANTS FOR MENTAL HEALTH, ADDICTIONS & CRISIS SERVICES. Text in English. a., latest 2003-2004. USD 75 per issue (effective 2004). **Description:** Provides indication of foundation giving in the field. Presents descriptions of over 5,500 recent grants of $10,000 or more awarded by 700 foundations.
Related titles: ♦ Series of: Grant Guides.
Published by: Foundation Center, 79 Fifth Ave, New York, NY 10003. TEL 212-620-4230, 800-424-9836, FAX 212-807-3677, orders@fdncenter.org, http://www.fdncenter.org.

371.22 USA
GRANTS FOR MINORITIES. Text in English. a., latest 2003-2004. USD 75 per issue (effective 2004). **Description:** Provides indication of foundation giving in the field. Presents descriptions of over 14,000 recent grants of $10,000 or more awarded by 787 foundations.
Related titles: ♦ Series of: Grant Guides.
Published by: Foundation Center, 79 Fifth Ave, New York, NY 10003. TEL 212-620-4230, 800-424-9836, FAX 212-807-3677, orders@fdncenter.org, http://www.fdncenter.org.

371.22 USA
GRANTS FOR RELIGION, RELIGIOUS WELFARE & RELIGIOUS EDUCATION. Text in English. a., latest 2003-2004. USD 75 per issue (effective 2004). **Description:** Provides indication of foundation giving in the field. Presents descriptions of over 14,000 recent grants of $10,000 or more awarded by 853 foundations.
Related titles: ♦ Series of: Grant Guides.
Published by: Foundation Center, 79 Fifth Ave, New York, NY 10003. TEL 212-620-4230, 800-424-9836, FAX 212-807-3677, orders@fdncenter.org, http://www.fdncenter.org.

371.22 362.4 USA
GRANTS FOR THE PHYSICALLY & MENTALLY DISABLED. Text in English. a., latest 2003-2004. USD 75 per issue (effective 2004). **Description:** Provides indication of foundation giving in the field. Presents descriptions of over 6,600 recent grants of $10,000 or more awarded by 751 foundations.
Related titles: ♦ Series of: Grant Guides.
Published by: Foundation Center, 79 Fifth Ave, New York, NY 10003. TEL 212-620-4230, 800-424-9836, FAX 212-807-3677, orders@fdncenter.org, http://www.fdncenter.org.

371.22 371.822 USA ISSN 1064-4377
AS911.A2
GRANTS FOR WOMEN AND GIRLS. Text in English. 1982. a., latest 2003-2004. USD 75 per vol. (effective 2004). **Document type:** *Directory.* **Description:** Contains descriptions of over 8,600 recent grants of $10,000 or more awarded by 803 foundations.
Related titles: ♦ Series of: Grant Guides.
Published by: Foundation Center, 79 Fifth Ave, New York, NY 10003. TEL 212-620-4230, 800-424-9836, FAX 212-807-3677, http://www.fdncenter.org.

371.6 GBR
GREAT BRITAIN. DEPARTMENT FOR EDUCATION AND EMPLOYMENT. BUILDING BULLETINS. Text in English. 1955; N.S. 1964. irreg. price varies. **Document type:** *Bulletin, Government.*
Formerly: Great Britain. Department of Education and Science. Building Bulletins (0072-5870)
—CCC.
Published by: (Great Britain. Department of Education and Employment), Stationery Office, 51 Nine Elms Ln, London, SW8 5DA, United Kingdom. TEL 44-20-7873-0011, FAX 44-20-7873-8247, book.orders@theso.co.uk, http://www.national-publishing.co.uk.

371.6 GBR ISSN 0260-0471
GREAT BRITAIN. DEPARTMENT OF EDUCATION AND SCIENCE. ARCHITECTS AND BUILDING BRANCH. BROADSHEETS✶. Text in English. 1980. irreg. free.
—CCC.
Published by: (Great Britain. Architects and Building Branch), Department of Education and Science, Sanctuary Bldg, Great Switer St, London, SW1P 3BT, United Kingdom. Ed. J M Brown. Circ: 2,000.

363.119371 GBR ISSN 0262-5229
GREAT BRITAIN. DEPARTMENT OF EDUCATION AND SCIENCE. SAFETY IN EDUCATION✶. Text in English. 1981. irreg. free. bk.rev. bibl.; charts; illus.; stat. back issues avail. **Document type:** *Government.* **Description:** Accounts of local governments' good practice in educational building and management.
—CCC.
Published by: Department of Education and Science, Sanctuary Bldg, Great Switer St, London, SW1P 3BT, United Kingdom. Ed. Bernard McDonnell. Circ: 100,000.

371.6 USA ISSN 0072-8101
GUIDE FOR PLANNING EDUCATIONAL FACILITIES✶. Text in English. 1949. triennial. USD 60. index.
Formerly: Guide for Planning School Plants
Published by: Council of Educational Facility Planners, 9180 E Desert Cove Dr, Ste 104, Scottsdale, AZ 85260-6231. TEL 480-391-0840.

E

371.22 USA ISSN 0275-8393
LB2805
GUIDE TO FEDERAL FUNDING FOR EDUCATION. Text in English. 1975. q. looseleaf. USD 297. **Document type:** *Directory.* **Description:** Details more than 380 federal aid programs available to school districts, colleges and universities, state education departments and non-profit groups. Provides specific information on eligibility requirements, outlook for funding, application deadlines, allowable uses of funds and program contacts (including telephone numbers).
Former titles: Federal Funding Guide for Education; Federal Funding Guide for Elementary and Secondary Education (0095-3342)
Related titles: ♦ Supplement(s): Federal Grant Deadline Calendar. A Supplement to the Guide to Federal Funding for Education. ISSN 1080-5583.
—CCC.
Published by: Education Funding Research Council (Subsidiary of: Thompson Publishing Group), 1725 K St, N W, Ste 700, Washington, DC 20006. TEL 800-424-2959, FAX 800-999-5661, http://www.thompson.com. Eds. Charles Edwards, Lisa Hayes. Pub. Daphne Musselwhite.

GUIDE TO FEDERAL TAX ISSUES FOR COLLEGES AND UNIVERSITIES. see *BUSINESS AND ECONOMICS—Public Finance, Taxation*

GUILDNOTES. see *ART*

371.2 DEU ISSN 0935-0489
H L Z. ZEITSCHRIFT DER G E W HESSEN FUER ERZIEHUNG, BILDUNG, FORSCHUNG. Text in German. 1948. 9/yr. EUR 1.50 newsstand/cover (effective 2005). adv. **Document type:** *Magazine, Trade.*
Former titles (until 1988): Hessische Lehrerzeitung (0722-8201); (until 1982): H L Z (0342-3522); (until 1973): Hessische Lehrerzeitung (0342-4979)
—CCC.
Published by: Gewerkschaft Erziehung und Wissenschaft, Landesverband Hessen, Zimmerweg 12, Frankfurt Am Main, 60325, Germany. TEL 49-69-9712930, FAX 49-69-97129393, info@hessen.gew.de, http://www.gew-hessen.de. Eds. Harald Freiling, Joachim Euler. R&P Harald Freiling. adv.: B&W page EUR 1,280. Circ: 24,460 (paid and controlled).

379.219 USA
HAWAII. DEPARTMENT OF EDUCATION. OFFICE OF BUSINESS SERVICES. PUBLIC AND PRIVATE SCHOOL ENROLLMENT. Text in English. 197?. a.
Formerly: Hawaii. Department of Education. Office of Research and Planning. Information Systems Branch. Public and Private School Enrollment
Published by: Department of Education, Office of Business Services, PO Box 2360, Honolulu, HI 96804. Circ: 650.

371.2012 USA
LA283
HOOSIER PRINCIPAL. Text in English. 1956. s-a. membership. adv. bk.rev. **Document type:** *Trade.* **Description:** Articles on research and curriculum of interest to school building-level administrators.
Formerly: Hoosier Schoolmaster (0018-4810)
Published by: Indiana Association of School Principals, 11025 E. 25th St., Indianapolis, IN 46229-1523. TEL 317-576-5400, FAX 317-576-5408, http://www.iasp.org. Ed. F Edward Wall. Circ: 2,000.

371.22 USA ISSN 1554-4079
LB2338
HOW TO PAY FOR YOUR DEGREE IN BUSINESS & RELATED FIELDS. Text in English. biennial. USD 30 per issue (effective 2005). **Document type:** *Directory, Consumer.*
Published by: Reference Service Press, 1100 Industrial Rd., Ste 9, San Carlos, CA 94070. TEL 916-939-9620, FAX 916-939-3626, rspinfo@aol.com, http://www.rspfunding.com.

379.81 CHN ISSN 1005-6629
HUAXUE JIAOXUE/CHEMISTRY TEACHING. Text in Chinese. 1978. bi-m. CNY 19.20 (effective 1994). adv. **Document type:** *Academic/Scholarly.* **Description:** Covers teaching and learning methods, practices and experiments in education reform.
Related titles: Online - full text ed.: (from East View Information Services).
Published by: (Huaxue Xi), Huadong Shifan Daxue/East China Normal University, 3663 Zhongshan Beilu, Shanghai, 200062, China. TEL 86-21-2577577, FAX 86-21-2576217, http://www.ecnu.edu.cn. Ed. Jin Litong. Circ: 30,000.

371.26 DEU
HUMBOLDT-UNIVERSITAET ZU BERLIN. VORLESUNGSVERZEICHNIS. Text in German. 2/yr. adv. **Document type:** *Directory, Academic/Scholarly.*
Published by: Humboldt-Universitaet zu Berlin, Unter den Linden 6, Berlin, 10099, Germany. TEL 49-30-2093-0, FAX 49-30-20932770, hu-presse@uv.hu-berlin.de, http://www.hu-berlin.de. adv.: page EUR 770. Circ: 14,000 (controlled).

371.207 FRA ISSN 0074-6401
I I E P OCCASIONAL PAPERS. Text in English, French. 1968. irreg., latest vol.79, 1990. price varies.
Indexed: CIJE, RRTA, WAE&RSA.
Published by: International Institute for Educational Planning, 7-9 rue Eugene Delacroix, Paris, 75116, France. TEL 33-1-45037700, FAX 33-1-40728366, TELEX 640032, information@iiep.unesco.org, http://www.unesco.org/iiep/.

371.207 FRA
I I E P RESEARCH REPORTS. Text in English, French. 1975. irreg., latest vol.92, 1991. price varies.
Indexed: CIJE, RRTA, WAE&RSA.
Published by: International Institute for Educational Planning, 7-9 rue Eugene Delacroix, Paris, 75116, France. TEL 33-1-45037700, FAX 33-1-40728366, information@iiep.unesco.org, http://www.unesco.org/iiep/.

371.207 FRA
I I E P SEMINAR PAPERS. Text in English, French. 1975. irreg., latest vol.45, 1986. price varies.
Indexed: CIJE.
Published by: International Institute for Educational Planning, 7-9 rue Eugene Delacroix, Paris, 75116, France. TEL 33-1-45037700, FAX 33-1-40728366, information@iiep.unesco.org, http://www.unesco.org/iiep/.

371.207 FRA
I I E P STUDIES SERIES. Text in French. irreg. price varies. **Document type:** *Academic/Scholarly.*
Related titles: ♦ Series: Fundamentals of Educational Planning. ISSN 0071-9862.
Published by: (International Institute for Educational Planning), UNESCO Publishing, 7 place de Fontenoy, Paris, 75352, France. TEL 33-1-45684300, FAX 33-1-45685737, http://www.unesco.org/publications. **Dist. in the US by:** Bernan Associates, Bernan, 4611-F Assembly Dr., Lanham, MD 20706-4391. TEL 800-274-4447, FAX 800-865-3450.

379.1531 USA ISSN 0019-0586
I S B A JOURNAL. Text in English. 1949. q. USD 30 to non-members (effective 2003). adv. charts; illus.; stat. **Document type:** *Trade.* **Description:** Contains articles of interest to school board members and administrators.
Formerly: H S B Journal
Published by: Indiana School Boards Association, One N Capitol, Ste 1215, Indianapolis, IN 46204. TEL 317-639-0330, FAX 317-639-3591, http://www.isba-ind.org/. Ed., R&P Darci Valentine. Circ: 2,600.

379.796 USA ISSN 0093-7223
E97.65.I2
IDAHO. STATE SUPERINTENDENT OF PUBLIC INSTRUCTION. ANNUAL REPORT. STATE OF IDAHO JOHNSON-O'MALLEY PROGRAM. Key Title: Annual Report: State of Idaho Johnson-O'Malley Program. Cover title: Indian Education Annual Report. Text in English. 1966. irreg. **Document type:** *Government.*
Published by: State Department of Education, Adult Education, 650 W State St, PO Box 83720, Boise, ID 83720-0027. TEL 208-334-3300, FAX 208-334-2228. Circ: 20.

379.24 USA
ILLINOIS LITERACY. Text in English. 1985. q. free. **Document type:** *Newsletter.* **Description:** Discusses literacy campaign activities in Illinois.
Formerly (until Fall 1996): Passing the Word
Published by: Secretary of State, Literacy Office, 431 S Fourth St, Springfield, IL 62701. TEL 217-785-6921, FAX 217-785-6927, jrake@library.sos.state.il.us. Ed., R&P Kristie Metrow TEL 217-785-8232.

379.1531 USA ISSN 0019-221X
ILLINOIS SCHOOL BOARD JOURNAL. Text in English. 1934. bi-m. USD 18 to non-members (effective 2005). adv. bk.rev. charts; illus. index. **Document type:** *Magazine, Trade.* **Description:** Focuses on current issues that affect school board policies and school management.
Published by: Illinois Association of School Boards, 2921 Baker Dr., Springfield, IL 62703-5929. TEL 217-528-9688, FAX 217-528-2831, jbilling@mail.fgi.net, http://www.iasb.com. Eds. Jessica Billings, Linda Dawson. R&P Jessica Billings. Adv. contacts Ruth Ann Ferris, Diane Cape. Circ: 8,100 (paid).

379.1531 USA ISSN 0147-2860
L142
ILLINOIS. STATE BOARD OF EDUCATION. ANNUAL REPORT. Text in English. 1976. a. illus.; stat. **Document type:** *Government.*
Supersedes: Illinois. Department of Public Instruction. Annual State of Education Message (0098-0269)
Published by: State Board of Education, 100 N First St, Springfield, IL 62777. TEL 217-782-4648, http://www.isbe.state.il.us. Circ: 100.

371.2 GBR ISSN 1365-4802
LB2822.84.G7
IMPROVING SCHOOLS. Text in English. 1998. 3/yr. GBP 245, USD 429 to institutions; GBP 255, USD 447 combined subscription to institutions print & online eds. (effective 2006). back issues avail. **Document type:** *Journal, Academic/Scholarly.* **Description:** Publishes research and development articles which show how failing schools can be turned around and good schools can be made even better in a wide range of cultures in Britain and around the world.
Related titles: Online - full text ed.: ISSN 1475-7583. GBP 243, USD 424 to institutions (effective 2006) (from EBSCO Publishing, O C L C Online Computer Library Center, Inc., Sage Publications, Inc., Swets Information Services).
Indexed: BrEdI, CPE, ERA, ETA, MEA, RHEA, SEA, SENA, SOMA, TEA.
—BLDSC (4371.493050), IE, ingenta. **CCC.**
Published by: Sage Publications Ltd. (Subsidiary of: Sage Publications, Inc.), 1 Oliver's Yard, 55 City Rd, London, EC1 1SP, United Kingdom. TEL 44-20-73248500, FAX 44-20-73248600, info@sagepub.co.uk, http://www.sagepub.co.uk/journal.aspx?pid=105834. Eds. Hugh Busher, Terry Wrigley. **Subscr. in the Americas to:** Sage Publications, Inc., 2455 Teller Rd, Thousand Oaks, CA 91320. TEL 805-499-0721, FAX 805-499-0871, journals@sagepub.com.

INDEPENDENT EDUCATION. see *EDUCATION—Higher Education*

371.2012 USA ISSN 1522-9289
INDIANAGRAM. Text in English. 1978 (vol.8). m. membership. bk.rev. **Document type:** *Newsletter.*
Formerly: Indiana Secondary School Administrators. Newsletter
Published by: Indiana Association of School Principals, 11025 E. 25th St., Indianapolis, IN 46229-1523. TEL 317-576-5400, FAX 317-576-5408, http://www.iasp.org/iasp/default.htm. Ed. F Edward Wall. Circ: 2,000.

371.206 USA ISSN 1077-7172
LB2829.2
INFLATION MEASURES FOR SCHOOLS, COLLEGES AND LIBRARIES. Text in English. 1981. a. USD 140 to corporations; USD 120 to institutions academic (effective 2001). adv. **Document type:** *Academic/Scholarly.*
Formerly: Inflation Measures for Schools and Colleges (1057-7394); Formed by the 1991 merger of: Elementary - Secondary School Price Indexes (1057-9915); Higher Education Price Indexes Update (1051-2977); Which was formerly (until 1989): Higher Education Prices and Price Indexes. Supplement (0148-0634)
Related titles: Diskette ed.
Published by: Research Associates of Washington, 1200 N Nash St, Apt 1112, Arlington, VA 22209-3612. TEL 703-243-3399, FAX 703-524-6889, http://www.rschassoc.com. Ed., R&P Kent Halstead. Adv. contact Marjorie Halstead.

379 USA ISSN 1069-0190
INQUIRY & ANALYSIS. Text in English. 1979. 10/yr. USD 120 (effective 2005). back issues avail. **Document type:** *Newsletter.* **Description:** For attorneys representing public schools. Focuses on Supreme Court and national legal issues.
Published by: (National School Boards Association, Council of School Attorneys), National School Boards Association, 1680 Duke St, Alexandria, VA 22314-3493. TEL 703-838-6722, FAX 703-683-7590, https://secure.nsba.org/pubs/item_info.cfm?ID=488, http://www.nsba.org/site/index.asp. Ed. Naomi Gittins. Circ: 3,200.

371.2 USA ISSN 1087-0032
LC49.
INSIDE PRIVATE SCHOOL MANAGEMENT. Text in English. 1996. m. USD 267 (effective 2002). **Document type:** *Newsletter, Trade.* **Description:** Provides solutions to the challenges private school administrators face every day, from finance and board management to technology and planning student achievement.
—CCC.
Published by: Aspen Publishers, Inc. (Subsidiary of: Wolters Kluwer N.V.), 5301 Buckeystown Pike, Ste. 400, Frederick, MD 21704-8319. TEL 800-638-8437, customer.service@aspenpubl.com, http://www.aspenpub.com. Ed. April Moore. **Dist. by:** Distribution Center, 7201 McKinney Circle, Frederick, MD 21701. TEL 301-698-7100, FAX 301-417-7550.

371.2 USA ISSN 1086-2420
INSIDE SCHOOL SAFETY. Text in English. 1996. m. USD 216 (effective 2006). **Document type:** *Newsletter, Trade.* **Description:** Provides news, ideas, tips, and techniques on school safety.
Related titles: Online - full text ed.: (from EBSCO Publishing).
—CCC.
Published by: L R P Publications, 747 Dresher Rd, PO Box 980, Horsham, PA 19044. TEL 215-784-0860, 800-341-7874, FAX 215-784-9639, custserve@lrp.com, http://www.shoplrp.com/product/p-300508.ASP.html, http://www.lrp.com.

E

▼ new title ➤ refereed ✶ unverified ♦ full entry avail.

371.14 USA
INSIDER'S REPORT; a special bulletin for leaders. Text in English. 1983. 3/yr. free. **Document type:** *Newsletter.* **Description:** Discusses the effects of unionism in education, in relation to legislation, litigation and other areas.
Published by: Concerned Educators Against Forced Unionism, 8001 Braddock Rd, Springfield, VA 22160. TEL 703-321-8519, clj@nrtw.org. Ed., R&P Cathy Jones. Circ: 7,500.

379 GBR
INSTITUTE OF EDUCATION. NUFFIELD SERIES. Text in English. irreg. price varies.
Published by: Lifelong Learning Group, Institute of Education, 55 Gordon Square, London, WC1H 0NT, United Kingdom. TEL 44-20-7612-6498, FAX 44-20-7612-6766, k.oliver@ioe.ac.uk, http://k1.ioe.ac.uk.

INTERCHANGE (EDINBURGH). see *EDUCATION—Adult Education*

379.24 DEU
INTERNATIONAL AWARD FOR LITERACY RESEARCH/PREMIO INTERNACIONAL A LA INVESTIGACION EN ALFABETIZACION/PRIX INTERNATIONAL DE RECHERCHE EN ALPHABETISATION. Text in English, French, Spanish. biennial. free. back issues avail. **Document type:** *Academic/Scholarly.* **Description:** Highlights research in the problems and solutions in the campaign for literacy.
Published by: UNESCO Institute for Education, Feldbrunnenstr 58, Hamburg, 20148, Germany. TEL 49-40-448-0410, FAX 49-40-410-7723, uie@unesco.org, http://www.unesco.org/publications.

371.2 GBR ISSN 1358-1511
INTERNATIONAL CENTRE FOR RESEARCH AND ASSESSMENT. RESEARCH MONOGRAPHS. Variant title: I C R A. Research Monographs. Text in English. 1995. irreg.
—BLDSC (4362.068030).
Published by: University of London, Institute of Education, 20 Bedford Way, London, WC1H OAL, United Kingdom. TEL 44-20-76126000, FAX 44-20-76126126, http://www.ioe.ac.uk.

371.2 USA ISSN 1555-5062
▼ **INTERNATIONAL JOURNAL OF EDUCATION POLICY AND LEADERSHIP.** Text in English. forthcoming 2006 (Jan.). m.
Published by: Association for Supervision and Curriculum Development, 1703 N Beauregard St, Alexandria, VA 22311. TEL 703-578-9600, 800-933-2723, FAX 703-575-5400, http://www.ascd.org.

371.22 USA ISSN 0097-871X
GV346
INTERSCHOLASTIC ATHLETIC ADMINISTRATION. Text in English. 1974. q. USD 15 (effective 2005). adv. **Document type:** *Trade.*
Indexed: PEI, SportS.
Published by: National Federation of State High School Associations, PO Box 690, Indianapolis, IN 46206-0690. TEL 317-972-6900, FAX 317-822-5700, http://www.nfhs.org. Ed. Richard G Fawcett. R&P Fritz McGinness. Circ: 6,250.

379.1531 USA ISSN 0021-0668
IOWA SCHOOL BOARD DIALOGUE. Text in English. 1951. bi-m. USD 2 to non-members. adv. illus. **Document type:** *Newsletter.*
Formerly (until 1968): Iowa School Board Bulletin (0444-4736)
Published by: Iowa Association of School Boards, 700 Second Ave, Ste 100, Des Moines, IA 50309-1731. FAX 515-243-4992. Ed. Lisa Bartusek. Circ: 4,700.

E

371.2 ISR
IYYUNIM B'MINHAL HA-HINNUKH. Text in Hebrew. irreg. **Document type:** *Academic/Scholarly.*
Published by: Haifa University, School of Education, Mount Carmel, Haifa, 31999, Israel. FAX 972-4-342101.

JAMI'AT QATAR. AL-TAQRIR AL-IHSA'I AL-SANAWI LIL-AAM AL-JAMI'I/UNIVERSITY OF QATAR. ANNUAL STATISTICAL REPORT FOR THE SCHOOL YEAR. see *EDUCATION—Abstracting, Bibliographies, Statistics*

379.51 CHN ISSN 1001-2869
L64
JIAOYUXUE. Text in Chinese. 1978. m. CNY 150 (effective 2004). 160 p./no.; **Document type:** *Journal, Academic/Scholarly.* **Description:** Covers China's educational guidelines and policies, theories and history.
Published by: Zhongguo Renmin Daxue, Shubao Zilio Zhongxin/Renmin University of China, Information Center for Social Server, Dongcheng-qu, 3, Zhangzizhong Lu, Beijing, 100007, China. TEL 86-10-84043003, FAX 86-10-64015080, kyes@163.net, http://www.confucius.cn.net/bkdetail.asp?fzt=G1. **Dist. in US by:** China Publications Service, PO Box 49614, Chicago, IL 60649. TEL 312-288-3291, FAX 312-288-8570; **Dist. by:** China International Book Trading Corp, 35 Chegongzhuang Xilu, Haidian District, PO Box 399, Beijing 100044, China. TEL 86-10-68412045, FAX 86-10-68412023, cibtc@mail.cibtc.com.cn, http://www.cibtc.com.cn.

371.2 AUT ISSN 1029-2624
JOURNAL FUER SCHULENTWICKLUNG. Text in German. 1997. q. EUR 31 (effective 2005). adv. bk.rev. back issues avail. **Document type:** *Journal, Academic/Scholarly.*
Published by: StudienVerlag, Amraser Str 118, Innsbruck, 6020, Austria. TEL 43-512-395045, FAX 43-512-39504515, order@studienverlag.at, http://www.studienverlag.at. Ed. Bianca Ender. R&P Markus Hatzer.

371.2 GBR ISSN 1740-1348
▼ ➤ **JOURNAL OF ACCESS POLICY & PRACTICE.** Text in English. 2004. s-a. GBP 30 domestic to individuals; GBP 40 to individuals in Europe, N America, Australasia, Japan & Singapore; GBP 20 elsewhere to individuals; GBP 80 domestic to institutions; GBP 95 to institutions in Europe, N America, Australasia, Japan & Singapore; GBP 30 elsewhere to institutions (effective 2004). **Document type:** *Journal, Academic/Scholarly.* **Description:** Shares ideas and practical solutions to create wider and deeper participation in lifelong learning and offers a space for practitioners and academics to critically reflect and debate different perspectives.
Related titles: Online - full text ed.: (from Gale Group, IngentaConnect).
Indexed: ERA.
—BLDSC (4918.859475), IE.
Published by: The National Institute of Adult Continuing Education (NAICE), Renaissance House, 20 Princess Rd. W, Leicester, Leics LE1 6TP, United Kingdom. TEL 44-116-2044200, 44-116-2044201, FAX 44-116-2854514, enquiries@niace.org.uk, http://www.niace.org.uk/Publications/Periodicals/JAPP/Default.htm. Ed. Dr. Mary Stuart.

379.24 USA ISSN 1081-3004
LB1050 CODEN: JADLFI
➤ **JOURNAL OF ADOLESCENT AND ADULT LITERACY.** Text in English. 1957. 8/yr. (Sep.-May; Dec. & Jan. combined). USD 61 to individuals; USD 122 to institutions; USD 12.50 in developing nations (effective 2005). adv. bk.rev. illus. Index. reprint service avail. from PQC. **Document type:** *Journal, Academic/Scholarly.* **Description:** Covers adolescent and adult readers.
Former titles (until 1995): Journal of Reading (0022-4103); (until 1964): Journal of Developmental Reading (0731-3667)
Related titles: Microform ed.: (from PQC); Online - full text ed.: (from bigchalk, EBSCO Publishing, Florida Center for Library Automation, Gale Group, H.W. Wilson, O C L C Online Computer Library Center, Inc., ProQuest Information & Learning).
Indexed: ABIn, ABS&EES, ASCA, Acal, AgeL, ArtHuCI, BEL&L, BRI, BehAb, CBRI, CIJE, CPE, ChLitAb, ChPerI, CurCont, ECER, ERA, ETA, EduInd, FamI, L&LBA, MEA, MLA-IB, MRD, RHEA, RILM, SEA, SENA, SOMA, SOPODA, SSCI, SWA, TEA.
—BLDSC (4918.942400), IDS, IE, Infotrieve, ingenta. **CCC.**
Published by: International Reading Association, Inc., 800 Barksdale Rd, Newark, DE 19714-8139. TEL 302-731-1600, 800-336-7323, FAX 302-368-2449, journals@reading.org, http://www.reading.org/publications/journals/jaal/index.html. Ed. Todd Goodson. R&P Janet Parrack. Adv. contact Linda Hunter. Circ: 15,000 (paid).

371.201 USA ISSN 1555-4589
➤ **JOURNAL OF CASES IN EDUCATIONAL LEADERSHIP.** Text in English. q. USD 295, GBP 191 to institutions (effective 2005). **Document type:** *Journal, Academic/Scholarly.* **Description:** Publishes cases appropriate for use in programs that prepare educational leaders.
Media: Online - full content (from HighWire Press).
Published by: Sage Publications, Inc., 2455 Teller Rd, Thousand Oaks, CA 91320. TEL 805-499-0721, FAX 805-499-0871, info@sagepub.com, http://www.sagepub.com/journal.aspx?pid=11561. Ed. Michael E Dantley.

372.218 USA ISSN 1066-1468
JOURNAL OF CHILD-CARE ADMINISTRATION; A National Publication for Owners and Directors of Early Childhood Centers. (JCCA) Text in English. 1990. 4/yr. USD 48; USD 56 foreign (effective 2002). adv. bk.rev.; video rev. 16 p./no.; back issues avail.; reprints avail. **Document type:** *Magazine, Trade.* **Description:** Offers business and practical guidance to owners and directors of early childhood facilities.
Published by: Christine Kalbaugh, Ed.& Pub., 202 Cirrus Rd, Holbrook, NY 11741-4407. TEL 631-472-8009, FAX 631-472-8009, JCCA@metusa.net, http://www.JCCAjournal.com. Ed., R&P, Adv. contact Christine Kalbaugh. Circ: 1,000.

371.716 USA ISSN 1536-1403
TX945
JOURNAL OF CHILD NUTRITION & MANAGEMENT. Text in English. 1977. s-a. free (effective 2005). bk.rev. index. back issues avail. **Document type:** *Journal, Trade.* **Description:** Covers research concerning school food service and child nutrition.
Formerly (until 1997): School Food Service Research Review (0149-6808)
Media: Online - full content.
Indexed: Agr, H&TI, Hospl.
—BLDSC (4957.630000), CISTI.
Published by: American School Food Service Association, 700 S Washington St, Ste 300, Alexandria, VA 22314-4287. TEL 703-739-3900, FAX 703-739-3915, asfsa@asfsa.org, http://www.schoolnutrition.org/jcnm.asp?id=1086, http://www.asfsa.org. Ed. Jeannie Sneed.

JOURNAL OF COLLEGE ADMISSION. see *EDUCATION—Higher Education*

JOURNAL OF EDUCATION AND WORK. see *EDUCATION—Teaching Methods And Curriculum*

371.206 USA ISSN 0098-9495
LB2825
➤ **JOURNAL OF EDUCATION FINANCE.** Text in English. 1975. q. USD 40 to individuals (effective 2004); USD 48 foreign to individuals; USD 60 to institutions; USD 68 foreign to institutions (effective 2005). adv. bk.rev. reprint service avail. from WSH. **Document type:** *Journal, Academic/Scholarly.* **Description:** Contains original research and analysis on issues such as education reform, judicial intervention in finance, school-social agency linkages, tax limitation measures, and factors influencing teacher salaries.
Related titles: Microfiche ed.: (from WSH); Microfilm ed.: (from PMC, WSH); Microform ed.: (from WSH); Online - full text ed.: (from H.W. Wilson, O C L C Online Computer Library Center, Inc.).
Indexed: ABIn, AgeL, CIJE, CLI, CPE, EAA, EduInd, HEA, ILP, JEL, LRI.
—BLDSC (4973.130000), IE, ingenta. **CCC.**
Published by: University of Illinois Press, 1325 S Oak St, Champaign, IL 61820-6903. TEL 866-244-0626, FAX 217-244-9910, journals@uillinois.edu, http://www.press.uillinois.edu. Ed. Kern Alexander. Circ: 1,200.

379 GBR ISSN 0268-0939
LC73
➤ **JOURNAL OF EDUCATION POLICY.** Text in English. 1985. bi-m. GBP 391, USD 645 combined subscription to institutions print & online eds. (effective 2006). adv. reprint service avail. from PSC. **Document type:** *Journal, Academic/Scholarly.* **Description:** Comments on current, international educational developments in a broad range of areas and provides a forum for wider historical and comparative analysis of policy.
Related titles: Online - full text ed.: ISSN 1464-5106. GBP 371, USD 613 to institutions (effective 2006) (from EBSCO Publishing, Gale Group, IngentaConnect, O C L C Online Computer Library Center, Inc., Swets Information Services).
Indexed: BrEdI, CPE, CurCont, EAA, ERA, ETA, IBSS, MEA, PAIS, PSA, RHEA, SEA, SENA, SOMA, SRRA, SSA, SSCI, SWA, SociolAb, TEA.
—BLDSC (4973.150800), IDS, IE, Infotrieve, ingenta. **CCC.**
Published by: Routledge (Subsidiary of: Taylor & Francis Group), 4 Park Sq, Milton Park, Abingdon, Oxon OX14 4RN, United Kingdom. TEL 44-1235-828600, FAX 44-1235-829000, info@routledge.co.uk, http://www.tandf.co.uk/journals/titles/02680939.asp, http://www.routledge.co.uk. Eds. Ivor Goodson, Stephen J Ball. **Subscr. in N. America to:** Taylor & Francis Inc., Customer Services Dept, 325 Chestnut St, 8th Fl, Philadelphia, PA 19106. TEL 800-354-1420, FAX 215-625-8914.

371.2 GBR ISSN 0957-8234
LB2806
JOURNAL OF EDUCATIONAL ADMINISTRATION. Text in English. 1963. 5/yr. EUR 7,470.04 in Europe; USD 7,689 in North America; AUD 9,049 in Australasia; GBP 5,229.79 in UK & elsewhere (effective 2006). bk.rev. abstr.; bibl.; charts; illus.; stat. index. back issues avail.; reprint service avail. from PQC,PSC. **Document type:** *Journal, Academic/Scholarly.* **Description:** Covers practice and theory of the field, oriented toward principals, inspectors, superintendents, directors, and university teachers and students.
Related titles: CD-ROM ed.; Microform ed.: (from PQC); Online - full text ed.: (from EBSCO Publishing, Emerald Group Publishing Limited, Gale Group, IngentaConnect, O C L C Online Computer Library Center, Inc., ProQuest Information & Learning, Swets Information Services).
Indexed: ABIn, AEI, AusPAIS, CIJE, CPE, CurCont, EAA, ERA, ETA, EmerIntel, Emerald, INZP, MEA, RHEA, SEA, SENA, SOMA, SSCI, TEA.
—BLDSC (4973.153000), IE, Infotrieve, ingenta. **CCC.**
Published by: Emerald Group Publishing Limited, 60-62 Toller Ln, Bradford, W Yorks BD8 9BY, United Kingdom. TEL 44-1274-777700, FAX 44-1274-785200, infomation@emeraldinsight.com, http://www.emeraldinsight.com/jea.htm. Ed. Dr. A Ross Thomas.

371.2 GBR ISSN 0022-0620
L11
JOURNAL OF EDUCATIONAL ADMINISTRATION AND HISTORY. Text in English. 1968. 3/yr. GBP 182, USD 303 combined subscription to institutions print & online eds. (effective 2006). adv. bk.rev. abstr.; charts. reprint service avail. from PQC,PSC. **Document type:** *Journal, Academic/Scholarly.* **Description:** Presents research and literature reviews pertaining to all aspects of the administration and history of education in the nation and abroad.

Related titles: Microform ed.: (from PQC); Online - full text ed.: ISSN 1478-7431. GBP 173, USD 288 to institutions (effective 2006) (from EBSCO Publishing, Gale Group, IngentaConnect, O C L C Online Computer Library Center, Inc., Swets Information Services).
Indexed: AmH&L, BrEdI, CIJE, CPE, ChLitAb, DIP, EAA, ERA, HECAB, HistAb, IBR, IBZ, MEA, PCI, RHEA, SOMA, TEA. —BLDSC (4973.154000), IE, Infotrieve. **CCC.**
Published by: Routledge (Subsidiary of: Taylor & Francis Group), 4 Park Sq, Milton Park, Abingdon, Oxon OX14 4RN, United Kingdom. TEL 44-1235-828600, FAX 44-1235-829000, info@routledge.co.uk, http://www.tandf.co.uk/journals/titles/00220620.asp, http://www.routledge.co.uk. Ed. Roy Lowe. Circ: 300. **Subscr. to:** Taylor & Francis Ltd, Journals Customer Service, Rankine Rd, Basingstoke, Hants RG24 8PR, United Kingdom. TEL 44-1256-813000, FAX 44-1256-330245.

371.207 IND ISSN 0971-3859
LA1150
➤ **JOURNAL OF EDUCATIONAL PLANNING AND ADMINISTRATION.** Text in English. 1977. q., latest vol.15, no.4, 2001, Oct. INR 120, USD 50 to individuals; INR 250, USD 75 to institutions (effective 2001). adv. bk.rev. 125 p./no. 1 cols./p.; back issues avail.; reprints avail. **Document type:** *Journal, Academic/Scholarly.* **Description:** Educational planning, Development, Policy....
Formerly: E P A Bulletin
Indexed: CPE, JEL, PAA&I.
Published by: National Institute of Educational Planning and Administration, 17-B Sri Aurobindo Marg, New Delhi, 110 016, India. TEL 91-11-6861320, FAX 91-11-685-3041, niepa@vsnl.com, http://www.niepaonline.org. Ed. Jandhyala B G Tilak. R&P Jandhyala B.G. Tilak. adv.: page INR 2,000, page USD 100, 1/2 page INR 1,100, 1/2 page USD 55; 17 x 12. Circ: 1,500.

➤ **JOURNAL OF HIGHER EDUCATION POLICY AND MANAGEMENT.** see *EDUCATION—Higher Education*

➤ **JOURNAL OF PUBLIC AFFAIRS EDUCATION.** see *PUBLIC ADMINISTRATION*

371.2 USA ISSN 1058-2622
LB2826.I3
JOURNAL OF SCHOOL BUSINESS MANAGEMENT. Text in English. 1989. q. USD 4.28 per issue to non-members; USD 4 per issue to members. adv. **Document type:** *Academic/Scholarly.*
—BLDSC (5052.648500), IE, ingenta.
Published by: Illinois A S B O, Northern Illinois Univ., Dekalb, IL 60115. TEL 815-753-1276, FAX 815-753-9367, http://www.iasbo.org. Ed. Donald R Johnson. Pub. Ronald E Everett.

371.2 USA ISSN 1530-6631
LB2822.82
➤ **JOURNAL OF SCHOOL IMPROVEMENT.** Text in English. 1926. q. USD 25 (effective 2001). bk.rev. index. **Document type:** *Journal, Academic/Scholarly.*
Former titles: N C A Quarterly (1043-3511); (until 1989): North Central Association Quarterly (0029-2648)
Related titles: Microform ed.: (from PQC).
Indexed: ABIn, CIJE, EduInd.
Published by: North Central Association Commission on Accreditation & School Improvement, Arizona State University, Tempe, AZ 85287-3011. TEL 480-965-8700, tsieditor@ncacasi.org, http://www.ncacasi.org. Ed. Ken Gose. R&P Aida Valenzuela. Circ: 13,000.

▼ ➤ **JOURNAL OF WOMEN IN EDUCATIONAL LEADERSHIP.** see *EDUCATION*

371.2 DEU
JUNGLEHRER. Text in German. 1949. 8/yr. EUR 10 (effective 2003). adv. 24 p./no. 3 cols./p.; **Document type:** *Magazine, Academic/Scholarly.*
Published by: Arbeitsgemeinschaft Bayerischer Junglehrer, Wernher-von-Braun-Str 8, Heidenfeld, 97520, Germany. TEL 49-9723-9370040, FAX 49-9723-9370039, redaktion@junglehrer.de. Ed. Tomi Neikor. Adv. contact Heike Bauer. page EUR 550; trim 188 x 267. Circ: 20,000.

KEJI JINBU YU DUICE/SCIENCE & TECHNOLOGY PROGRESS AND POLICY. see *SCIENCES: COMPREHENSIVE WORKS*

371.2 USA
KEY - HIGH SCHOOL FALL. Text in English. a. **Description:** Helps high school students planning to go to college understand their options and reach their goals.
Published by: Target Marketing, Inc., 1 Liberty Bell Circle, Ste 200, Liberty, MO 64068. TEL 816-781-7557, 800-279-9988, FAX 816-792-3892. Ed. Eddie Cook. Pub. Lyle Kraft.

371.2 USA
KEY - HIGH SCHOOL SPRING. Text in English. a. adv. **Description:** Helps high school juniors planning to go to college with their options and advice on how to achieve their goals.
Published by: Target Marketing, Inc., 1 Liberty Bell Circle, Ste 200, Liberty, MO 64068. TEL 816-781-7557, 800-279-9988, FAX 816-792-3892. Ed. Eddie Cook. Pub. Lyle Kraft.

371.2 GBR ISSN 1356-6172
KEY NOTE MARKET REVIEW: U K EDUCATION INDUSTRY. Variant title: U K Education Industry. Text in English. 1993. irreg., latest vol.2, 1994. GBP 565 per issue (effective 2002). **Document type:** *Trade.*
Related titles: CD-ROM ed.; Online - full text ed.
Published by: Key Note Ltd., Field House, 72 Oldfield Rd, Hampton, Mddx TW12 2HQ, United Kingdom. TEL 44-20-8481-8750, FAX 44-20-8783-0049, info@keynote.co.uk, http://www.keynote.co.uk.

379 BEL ISSN 0777-5954
KLASSE. Text in Dutch. 1989. m. adv. bk.rev. **Document type:** *Government.* **Description:** Covers education issues and government information on education.
Related titles: Online - full content ed.
Indexed: BHA.
Published by: Vlaamse Ministerie van Onderwijs, H. Consciencegebouw, Koning Albert II-laan 15, Brussel, 1210, Belgium. TEL 32-2-5539686, FAX 32-2-5539685, info@klasse.be, http://www.klasse.be. Ed. Leo Bormans. R&P Patrick Debusscher. Adv. contact Diana Decaluwe. Circ: 180,000.

379 DEU ISSN 0933-7776
KULTUS UND UNTERRICHT. AUSGABE A. Text in German. 1952. m. EUR 65.60; EUR 3.75 newsstand/cover (effective 2003). adv. bk.rev. **Document type:** *Journal, Academic/Scholarly.*
Formerly (until 1983): Kultus und Unterricht (0451-0550)
Published by: (Baden-Wuerttemberg. Ministerium fuer Kultus, Jugend und Sport), Neckar Verlag GmbH, Postfach 1820, Villingen-Schwenningen, 78008, Germany. TEL 49-7721-89870, FAX 49-7721-898750, service@neckar-verlag.de, http://www.neckar-verlag.de. Ed. Guenther Hoerz. Adv. contact Peter Walter. page EUR 614. Circ: 7,300.

371.2 DEU ISSN 1432-8267
L A MULTIMEDIA; Magazin fuer Medien und Bildung. (Lehrmittel Aktuell) Text in German. 1969. 4/yr. EUR 34.20; EUR 22.20 to students; EUR 9.50 newsstand/cover (effective 2003). adv. bk.rev. 48 p./no.; back issues avail. **Document type:** *Magazine, Academic/Scholarly.*
Former titles: Lehrmittel Aktuell - Lehrmittel Computer (0931-1998); Lehrmittel Aktuell (0341-8243)
Indexed: RASB, RefZh.
—**CCC.**
Published by: Westermann Schulbuchverlag GmbH, Georg-Westermann-Allee 66, Braunschweig, 38104, Germany. TEL 49-531-7080, FAX 49-531-708209, schulservice@westermann.de, http://www.lamultimedia.de, http://www.westermann.de. Ed. Dr. Ortner. adv.: B&W page EUR 2,600, color page EUR 4,160; trim 187 x 258. Circ: 22,500 (controlled).

LEADER IN THE CHURCH SCHOOL TODAY. see *RELIGIONS AND THEOLOGY—Protestant*

379 USA ISSN 1570-0763
L56
LEADERSHIP AND POLICY IN SCHOOLS. Text in English. q. GBP 197, USD 325 combined subscription to institutions print & online eds. (effective 2006). reprint service avail. from PSC. **Document type:** *Journal, Academic/Scholarly.* **Description:** Feature studies about leadership and policy in primary and secondary education, as well as in tertiary education, where appropriate. Studies that utilize the school-site as their primary unit of analysis are of particular interest. Such studies will include schools from diverse contexts in both the public and private sectors.
Related titles: Online - full text ed.: ISSN 1744-5043. GBP 187, USD 309 to institutions (effective 2006) (from EBSCO Publishing, Gale Group, IngentaConnect, O C L C Online Computer Library Center, Inc., Swets Information Services).
—BLDSC (5162.866070), IE. **CCC.**
Published by: Taylor & Francis Inc. (Subsidiary of: Taylor & Francis Group), 325 Chestnut St, Ste 800, Philadelphia, PA 19016. TEL 215-625-8900, 800-354-1420, FAX 215-625-2940, info@taylorandfrancis.com, http://www.tandf.co.uk/journals/titles/15700763.asp, http://www.taylorandfrancis.com. Eds. David Monk, Kenneth Leithwood, Stephen Jacobson.

371.2 USA ISSN 1546-0169
LB2822.5
▼ **LEADERSHIP COMPASS**; helping principals create and sustain learning communities. Text in English. 2003 (Fall). q. free to members (effective 2005). **Document type:** *Newsletter.*
Published by: National Association of Elementary School Principals, 1615 Duke St, Alexandria, VA 22314-3483. TEL 703-684-3345, FAX 703-548-6021, naesp@naesp.org, http://www.naesp.org. Ed. Rebecca Kesner.

LEARNING BY DESIGN; a school leader's guide to architectural services. see *ARCHITECTURE*

379 USA ISSN 0093-397X
KF4119.A1
LEGAL NOTES FOR EDUCATION✱. Text in English. 1973. m. looseleaf. USD 159 (effective 2003). cum.index. **Document type:** *Newsletter.* **Description:** Reports court decisions and legislation affecting education.
Published by: Oakstone Legal and Business Publishing, PO Box 381205, Birmingham, AL 35238-9950. TEL 800-365-4900, http://www.oakstonelegal.com/. Ed. James A Roth.

371.2 DEU
LEHRER UND SCHULE HEUTE. Text in German. 1950. m. bk.rev. **Document type:** *Newsletter, Trade.* **Description:** Information on education and school related topics and policies.
Published by: Saarlaendischer Lehrerinnen- und Lehrerverband, Lisdorferstr 21b, Saarlouis, 66740, Germany. TEL 49-6831-49440, FAX 49-6831-46601, sllv.ev@t-online.de, http://www.sllv.de. Ed., R&P, Adv. contact Gerhard Berger. Circ: 3,000 (controlled).

371.2 DEU
LERNWELTEN; Projekte-Medien-Schule. Text in German. 1999. q. EUR 29.50; EUR 20 to students; EUR 9.90 newsstand/cover (effective 2003). adv. **Document type:** *Journal, Academic/Scholarly.*
—BLDSC (5183.472000).
Published by: Paedagogischer Zeitschriftenverlag GmbH & Co. KG, Axel-Springer-Str. 54b, Berlin, 10117, Germany. TEL 49-30-20183592, FAX 49-30-20183593, info@pzv-berlin.de, http://www.pzv-berlin.de. Ed. Juergen Walther. Adv. contact Constanze Richter. B&W page EUR 400, color page EUR 640. Circ: 1,000 (paid and controlled). **Subscr. to:** CVK Cornelsen Verlagskontor, Postfach 100271, Bielefeld 33502, Germany.

LOCUS; tidskrift foer barn- och ungdomsvetenskap. see *CHILDREN AND YOUTH—About*

379.1531 USA
LOOK AT US!. Text in English. 1956. q. free. bk.rev. **Document type:** *Newsletter.*
Former titles: V C S Newsletter; Report from Your Vestal Schools; Status of Your Vestal Schools (0039-0755)
Published by: Vestal Board of Education, Vestal Central School District, Vestal, NY 13850. TEL 607-757-2205, FAX 607-757-2227. Ed. Katie Ellis. Circ: 13,500.

379.1531 USA ISSN 1052-2824
M A S B JOURNAL. Text in English. 1949. bi-m. USD 24. adv. bk.rev. illus. reprint service avail. from PQC. **Document type:** *Trade.*
Formerly (until 1986): Michigan School Board Journal (0026-2439)
Indexed: MMI.
Published by: Michigan Association of School Boards, Inc., 1001 Centennial Way, 400, Lansing, MI 48917-9279. TEL 517-371-5700, FAX 517-371-5338. Ed. Gail M Braverman. R&P Gail Braverman. Adv. contact Sherry Nelton. Circ: 9,100.

371.2 USA
M A S C JOURNAL. Text in English. 3/yr. USD 10 to members; USD 25 to non-members (effective 2005). **Document type:** *Magazine, Trade.*
Published by: Massachusetts Association of School Committees, One McKinley Sq., Boston, MA 02109. TEL 617-523-8454, FAX 617-742-4125, masc@masc.org, http://www.masc.org. Ed. Jenifer Handy.

373.1201 USA
MAINE APPRISE. Text in English. 1970 (vol.41). m. (10/yr.). USD 20. adv.
Former titles (until 1992): Maine Principal; Maine Secondary School Principals' Association. Newsletter; Maine Secondary School Principals' Association. Bulletin; State Principals Association. Bulletin (0039-0143)
Media: Duplicated (not offset).
Published by: Maine Secondary School Principals' Association, PO Box 2468, Augusta, ME 04338-2468. FAX 207-622-1513. Ed. Heidi Shott. Circ: 480 (controlled).

371.2 371.9 362.1 USA ISSN 1539-7424
LB3013.3
MAINTAINING SAFE SCHOOLS. Variant title: Practical Strategies for Maintaining Safe Schools. Text in English. m. USD 185 (effective 2006). back issues avail. **Document type:** *Newsletter, Trade.* **Description:** Provides strategies for mediation and crisis management that have worked in schools, security measures being taken by schools to curb violence. Highlights special rules that apply to disciplining students with disabilities.
Formerly: School Violence Alert (1082-4774)
Indexed: e-psyche.
—**CCC.**
Published by: L R P Publications, 747 Dresher Rd, PO Box 980, Horsham, PA 19044. TEL 215-784-0860, 800-341-7874, FAX 215-784-9639, custserve@lrp.com, http://www.shoplrp.com/product/p-300036.html, http://www.lrp.com.

379.2 BEL
MAKS!; klasse for youngsters. Text in Dutch. 1997. 9/yr. EUR 7 (effective 2005). adv. bk.rev. **Document type:** *Newsletter, Government.* **Description:** Covers education issues and government information on education. For ages 14-19.
Formerly: Klasse voor Jongeren (1373-4555)

Published by: Vlaamse Ministerie van Onderwijs, H. Consciencegebouw, Koning Albert II-laan 15, Brussel, 1210, Belgium. TEL 32-2-553-9686, FAX 32-2-553-9685, redactie@maks.be, info@klasse.be, http://new.maks.be, http://www.klasse.be. Ed. Leo Bormans. R&P Leen Mortier. Adv. contact Diana Decaluwe. Circ: 250,000.

371.2 GBR
MANAGEMENT AND LEADERSHIP IN EDUCATION SERIES. Text in English. irreg. GBP 14.95. adv. **Document type:** *Monographic series.*
Published by: Kogan Page Ltd., 120 Pentonville Rd, London, N1 9JN, United Kingdom. FAX 44-20-7837-6348. Ed. Howard Green. R&P Caroline Gromm. Adv. contact Linda Batham.

371.2 GBR ISSN 0892-0206
MANAGEMENT IN EDUCATION. Text in English. 5/yr. GBP 52.25; GBP 58.18 in Europe; GBP 64.12 elsewhere. adv. bk.rev. charts; illus.; stat. back issues avail. **Document type:** *Trade.* **Description:** Provides a forum for the exchange of trends and innovations, where contributors and readers may evaluate development, share management ideas and techniques, and otherwise deal with any aspect of the broad spectrum of education management at all levels.
Related titles: Online - full text ed.: (from EBSCO Publishing).
Indexed: BrEdI, CPE, ERA, ETA, MEA, RHEA, SEA, SENA, SOMA, TEA.
—BLDSC (5359.024200), IE, ingenta. **CCC.**
Published by: (British Educational Management & Administration Society), Pitman Publishing, 128 Long Acre, London, WC2E 9AN, United Kingdom. TEL 44-171-447-2000, FAX 44-171-240-5771. Ed. A Thody. **Subscr. to:** Galleon Ltd., Fulham House, Goldsworth Rd, Woking GU21 1LY, United Kingdom. TEL 44-1483-747008, FAX 44-1483-776573.

371.2 GBR ISSN 1463-7081
MANAGING EDUCATION MATTERS. Abbreviated title: M E M. Text in English. 1971. s-a. free with subscr. to Journal of the CCEAM (ISSN 1324-1702). bk.rev. **Document type:** *Newsletter.*
Former titles: C C E A M Newsletter; (until 1994): C C E A Newsletter (0310-1878)
Related titles: Microfiche ed.; Online - full text ed.: (from EBSCO Publishing); ♦ Issued with: International Studies in Educational Administration. ISSN 1324-1702.
Indexed: CIJE.
Published by: (Commonwealth Council for Educational Administration & Management), The Education Publishing Co. Ltd., Devonia House, 4 Union Terrace, Crediton, Devon EX17 3DY, United Kingdom. Circ: 6,500.

658 658.3 371.2 USA ISSN 1092-2229
MANAGING SCHOOL BUSINESS. Text in English. 1996. s-m. (21/yr.). USD 235 (effective 2006). **Document type:** *Newsletter, Trade.* **Description:** Designed to help school business managers solve the everyday problems they face in managing finance, operations, personnel, and their career. Questions and answers section allows managers to communicate directly with peers.
Related titles: Online - full text ed.: (from LexisNexis).
—**CCC.**
Published by: L R P Publications, 747 Dresher Rd, PO Box 980, Horsham, PA 19044. TEL 800-341-7874, FAX 215-784-9639, custserve@lrp.com, http://www.shoplrp.com/product/p-300052N.html, http://www.lrp.com. Ed. Carol MacDonald.

379.744 USA
MASSACHUSETTS ASSOCIATION OF SCHOOL COMMITTEES. BULLETIN. Text in English. bi-m. USD 10 to members; USD 25 to non-members (effective 2005). adv. back issues avail. **Document type:** *Bulletin, Trade.*
Published by: Massachusetts Association of School Committees, One McKinley Sq., Boston, MA 02109. TEL 617-523-8454, FAX 617-742-4125, masc@masc.org, http://www.masc.org/. Ed., R&P, Adv. contact Jenifer Penfield Handy. Circ: 2,800.

MEGAPHON. see *CHILDREN AND YOUTH—For*

371.21 USA
MEMBERANDA. Text in English. 1983. q. **Description:** Directed to educators of independent school admission; features articles about marketing, demographics, applicant pool and leadership.
Published by: Secondary School Admission Test Board, CN 5339, Princeton, NJ 08543. TEL 609-683-4440. Ed. Regan Kenyon. Circ: 1,000.

371.2 NLD ISSN 0924-8250
MESO MAGAZINE. Text in Dutch. 1980. bi-m.
Formerly (until 1989): Meso (0168-0978)
—Infotrieve.
Published by: Educatieve Partners Nederland, Postbus 666, Houten, 3990 DR, Netherlands. TEL 31-3403-59777, FAX 31-3403-59700, http://www.epn.nl/_theme/EPN/frameset.asp?MID=59&DID=47&.

379.77595 USA
MILWAUKEE PUBLIC SCHOOLS. ANNUAL REPORT. Text in English. a. free. **Document type:** *Government.*
Published by: Milwaukee Public Schools, Department of Communications and Public Affairs, PO Box 2181, Milwaukee, WI 53201-2181. TEL 414-475-8274. Ed. Denise Callaway.

379.44 FRA ISSN 0758-9867
MINISTERE DE L'EDUCATION NATIONALE. RECUEIL DES LOIS ET REGLEMENTS. Text in French. 1963. 10 base vols. plus m. updates.
Published by: (Ministere de l'Education Nationale, de l'Enseignement Superieur et de la Recherche), Centre National de Documentation Pedagogique, 29 rue de l'Ulm, Paris, Cedex 5 75230, France. TEL 33-1-46349000, FAX 33-1-46345544. **Subscr. to:** CNDP - Abonnement, B.P. 750, Sainte Genevieve Cedex 60732, France. FAX 33-3-44033013.

371.2 DEU
MINISTERIUM FUER BILDUNG, FRAUEN UND JUGEND RHEINLAND-PFALZ. AMTSBLATT. Text in German. 1948. s-m. EUR 38.29 (effective 2004). adv. bk.rev. **Document type:** *Newsletter, Government.*
Formerly: Rheinland Pfalz. Kultusministerium. Amtsblatt
Published by: Ministerium fuer Bildung, Frauen und Jugend Rheinland-Pfalz, Wallstr 3, Mainz, 55122, Germany. TEL 49-6131-162854, FAX 49-6131-165499, poststelle@mbfj.rlp.de, http://www.mbfj.rlp.de/amtsblatt_stellen/amtsblatt.html. Ed. Anita Spalteholz. adv.: page EUR 365; trim 170 x 245. Circ: 4,200 (paid and controlled).

371.2 DEU
MINISTERIUM FUER SCHULE, JUGEND UND KINDER DES LANDES NORDRHEIN-WESTFALEN. AMTSBLATT. Text in German. 1948. m. EUR 50.50; EUR 5 newsstand/cover (effective 2004). adv. **Document type:** *Journal, Trade.*
Published by: (Ministerium fuer Schule, Jugend und Kinder des Landes Nordrhein-Westfalen), Ritterbach Verlag GmbH, Postfach 1820, Frechen, 50208, Germany. TEL 49-2234-18660, FAX 49-2234-186690, verlag@ritterbach.de, http://www.ritterbach.de. adv.: B&W page EUR 1,155, color page EUR 1,635. Circ: 11,500 (controlled).

379.1531 USA ISSN 0026-6698
MISSOURI SCHOOL BOARD. Text in English. 1970 (vol.17). m. (except July & Aug.). USD 15. adv. bk.rev.
Published by: Missouri School Boards Association, 2100 Interstate 70 Dr, S W, Columbia, MO 65203. TEL 314-445-9920. Ed. Diana Ranly Juergens. Circ: 3,500.

371.2 USA ISSN 0270-6881
L13
N A E N BULLETIN. Text in English. 1970. m. USD 40.
Formerly: A E N Bulletin (0044-958X)
Published by: National Association of Educational Negotiators, c/o Lyn King, 122 White Pine Dr., Springfield, IL 62707. TEL 217-529-7902, FAX 217-529-7904. Circ: 500.

N A P S A NEWS. see *EDUCATION—Special Education And Rehabilitation*

373.1201 USA ISSN 0192-6365
L13
➤ **N A S S P BULLETIN.** Text in English. 1916. m. (Sep.-May). USD 216 to institutions; USD 225 combined subscription to institutions print & online eds. (effective 2006). adv. bk.rev. bibl.; charts; illus. index. 98 p./no.; back issues avail.; reprint service avail. from PQC. **Document type:** *Journal, Academic/Scholarly.* **Description:** Publishes articles for administrators dealing with all aspects of education.
Formerly: National Association of Secondary School Principals. Bulletin (0027-8653)
Related titles: Microform ed.: (from PQC); Online - full text ed.: USD 214 to institutions (effective 2006) (from H.W. Wilson, O C L C Online Computer Library Center, Inc., ProQuest Information & Learning).
Indexed: ABIn, Acal, BRI, CBRI, CIJE, CJA, CPE, EAA, ECER, EduInd, LRI, MEA, PCI, RILM, SEA, SOMA, SWA, V&AA.
—BLDSC (6015.613000), IE, Infotrieve, ingenta. **CCC.**
Published by: (National Association of Secondary School Principals), Corwin Press, Inc. (Subsidiary of: Sage Publications, Inc.), 2455 Teller Rd, Thousand Oaks, CA 91320-2218. TEL 805-499-9734, FAX 805-499-0871, info@sagepub.com, http://www.sagepub.com/journal.aspx?pid=11636, http://www.corwinpress.com. Ed. Len Foster. adv.: B&W page USD 2,350; trim 6 x 9. Circ: 40,000 (paid).
Co-publisher: National Association of Secondary School Principals.

373.1201 USA
N A S S P LEADERSHIP FOR STUDENT ACTIVITIES. Text in English. 1988. m. USD 85.
Published by: National Association of Secondary School Principals, 1904 Association Dr, Reston, VA 20191-1537. http://www.nassp.org. Ed. Lyn Fiscus.

379 USA ISSN 0192-6152
KF4102
N A S S P LEGAL MEMORANDUM. Key Title: Legal Memorandum. Text in English. 1969. q. USD 148 to individuals; USD 180 to libraries (effective 2005); subscr. package also includes: NASSP Newsleader, NASSP Bulletin, Principal Leadership (High School & Middle School Editions) and Connections. reprint service avail. from PQC. **Document type:** *Newsletter, Trade.* **Description:** Provides in-depth information on prominent topics in education law.
—BLDSC (5181.340000). **CCC.**
Published by: National Association of Secondary School Principals, 1904 Association Dr, Reston, VA 20191-1537. TEL 703-860-0200, 866-647-7253, FAX 703-476-5432, http://www.nassp.org. Ed. James Theisen. Circ: 42,000.

373.1201 USA ISSN 0278-0569
LB2831.92
N A S S P NEWSLEADER. Short title: Newsleader. Text in English. 1971. m. (Sep.-May). USD 148 to individuals; USD 180 to libraries (effective 2005); subscr. package also includes: NASSP Bulletin, Legal Memorandum, Principal Leadership (High School & Middle School Editions) and Connections. adv. bk.rev. illus. Index. reprint service avail. from PQC. **Document type:** *Newspaper, Trade.* **Description:** News of special interest to members of the association.
Formerly: N A S S P Newsletter (0547-034X)
—**CCC.**
Published by: National Association of Secondary School Principals, 1904 Association Dr, Reston, VA 20191-1537. TEL 703-860-0200, 866-647-7253, FAX 703-476-5432, http://www.nassp.org. Ed. James Rourke. Circ: 42,000 (controlled).

379 USA
N E A TODAY: EDUCATIONAL SUPPORT EDITION. Text in English. a.
Formerly: Today's Education - Educational Support Edition (0737-187X)
Related titles: ♦ Special ed. of: N E A Today. ISSN 0734-7219.
Published by: National Education Association of the United States, 1201 16th St, N W, Washington, DC 20036-3290. TEL 202-822-7207, FAX 202-822-7206, NEAToday2@aol.com. Ed. Stephanie Weiss.

373 USA
N F H S NEWS; national voice of high school activities. Text in English. 1983. 9/yr. USD 12 (effective 2005). illus. back issues avail. **Document type:** *Magazine, Trade.*
Formerly: National Federation News
Indexed: SPI, SportS.
Published by: National Federation of State High School Associations, PO Box 690, Indianapolis, IN 46206-0690. TEL 317-972-6900, FAX 317-822-5700, http://www.nfhs.org. Ed. Bruce Howard. R&P Bob Gardner. Circ: 12,000. **Subscr. to:** 361246, Indianapolis, IN 46236-5324. TEL 800-776-3462.

371.2 USA ISSN 0027-674X
N J E A REPORTER. Text in English. m. (Sept-June). **Description:** Focuses on the Association's events and interests. Emphasis is on legislative actions, issues affecting members, member benefits, and NJEA conferences and workshops.
Published by: New Jersey Education Association, 180 W. State St., Trenton, NJ 08608. TEL 609-599-4561, http://www.njea.org.

379.1531 CAN ISSN 1207-5272
N S S B A MATTERS!. Text in English. 1954. m. looseleaf. CND 25 (effective 2000). adv. bk.rev. back issues avail. **Document type:** *Newsletter.* **Description:** Discusses school board member's roles, board governance, curriculum, funding and operations.
Formerly: Nova Scotia School Boards Association Newsletter (0702-9292)
Published by: Nova Scotia School Boards Association, P O Box 605, Sta M, Halifax, NS B3J 2R7, Canada. TEL 902-491-2856, FAX 902-429-7405, sfmacphee@nssba.ednet.ns.ca, http://www.nssba.ednet.ns.ca. Ed. Sharon Findlay-MacPhee. adv.: B&W page CND 500. Circ: 700.

338.0029 USA ISSN 1045-0033
L901
N S S E A MEMBERSHIP DIRECTORY. Variant title: N S S E A Membership Directory & Buyer's Guide. Text in English. 1916. a. membership. **Document type:** *Directory.* **Description:** Lists NSSEA's membership, along with manufacturers, dealers, and representatives in the school market.
Former titles: N S S E A Directory for Members Only (0741-2789); N S S E A Directory of Members, Officers, Committees, Bylaws (0147-2577)
Related titles: Online - full text ed.
Published by: National School Supply & Equipment Association, 8300 Colesville Rd, Ste 250, Silver Spring, MD 20910. TEL 301-485-0240, 800-395-5550, FAX 301-495-3330. Ed. Adrienne Watts. Circ: 3,500 (controlled).

379.1535 POL ISSN 1428-295X
NASZA POLITECHNIKA. Text in Polish. 1997. bi-m. free. adv. bk.rev.; play rev. charts; illus. back issues avail. **Document type:** *Bulletin.* **Description:** Contains information for the academic community.
Related titles: Online - full text ed.
Published by: Politechnika Krakowska/Cracow University of Technology, UL Warszawska 24, Krakow, 31155, Poland. TEL 48-12-6330300, FAX 48-12-6335773, naszapol@usk.pk.edu.pl, http://www.pk.edu.pl. Ed. Ryszard Moszumanski. R&P Elzbieta Barowa. adv.: color page PLZ 5,500.

E

372.1201 USA
NATIONAL ASSOCIATION OF ELEMENTARY SCHOOL PRINCIPALS. PROFESSIONAL RESOURCES CATALOG. Text in English. 1994. biennial. free. **Document type:** *Catalog.* **Description:** Lists publications of interest to elementary and middle school educators on such topics as leadership, parent involvement, and restructuring.
Published by: (Educational Products Division), National Association of Elementary School Principals, 1615 Duke St, Alexandria, VA 22314-3483. TEL 703-684-3345, FAX 703-548-6021.

379.1531 USA
NATIONAL ASSOCIATION OF STATE BOARDS OF EDUCATION. STATE BOARD CONNECTION∗. Text in English. 1982. q. membership. bk.rev. illus.; stat. **Document type:** *Newsletter.*
Supersedes (in 1980): National Association of State Boards of Education. Focus (0015-4962)
Published by: National Association of State Boards of Education, Inc., 277 S Washington St, Ste 100, Alexandria, VA 22314-3646. TEL 703-684-4000, FAX 703-836-2313. Ed. David Kysilko. Circ: 850.

372.1 USA ISSN 1094-6624
CODEN: FAARC8
➤ **NATIONAL ASSOCIATION OF STUDENT AFFAIRS PROFESSIONALS JOURNAL.** Text in English. 1984. a. USD 32 to individual members; USD 250 to institutional members; USD 10 to students (effective 2005). bk.rev. bibl.; charts. **Document type:** *Academic/Scholarly.* **Description:** Provides a forum for sharing innovations in practice. Provides information on research and current issues.
Formerly: National Association of Personnel Workers. Journal
Indexed: HEA.
Published by: National Association of Student Affairs Professionals, Northeastern Illinois University, 5500 N St Louis Ave, P. E. #1124, Chicago, IL 60625-4699. TEL 773-794-2867, FAX 773-794-6515, m-terrell@neiu.edu, http://www.nasap.net/NASAPjournal.html. Ed., Pub., R&P Dr. Melvin C Terrell TEL 773-794-2867.

371.202 USA ISSN 0027-9196
NATIONAL EDUCATIONAL SECRETARY. Text in English. 1934. q. USD 20 to non-members. adv. bk.rev. illus.; stat. reprint service avail. from PQC. **Document type:** *Trade.*
Related titles: Microform ed.: (from PQC).
Published by: National Association of Educational Office Professionals, PO Box 12619, Wichita, KS 67277-2619. FAX 316-942-7100. Ed. Kay Barclay. Circ: 7,000.

371.1 USA ISSN 0077-4472
L901
NATIONAL FACULTY DIRECTORY. Text in English. 1971. a., latest 2004. USD 895 (effective 2004). **Document type:** *Directory, Trade.* **Description:** Cumulation of American faculty members.
Related titles: Supplement(s): Supplement. USD 335 per issue (effective 2003).
—CISTI.
Published by: Gale Group (Subsidiary of: Thomson Corporation), 27500 Drake Rd, Farmington Hills, MI 48331-3535. TEL 248-699-8061, 800-877-4253, FAX 248-699-4253, galeord@gale.com, http://www.gale.com.

371.218 USA ISSN 0275-4142
LB3051
NATIONAL GUIDE TO EDUCATIONAL CREDIT FOR TRAINING PROGRAMS. Text in English. 1976. a., latest 2003-2004. USD 105 (effective 2003). adv. **Description:** Describes more than 2000 educational programs conducted by businesses, labor unions, professional and voluntary associations and government agencies, listing course titles, dates and locations, objectives and methods of instruction.
Formerly: National Guide to Credit Recommendations for Noncollegiate Courses
Related titles: Microfiche ed.
Indexed: CIJE.
Published by: (American Council on Education, Office on Educational Credit), Oryx Press (Subsidiary of: Greenwood Publishing Group Inc.), 1434 E. San Miguel Ave., Phoenix, AZ 85014-2422. TEL 602-265-2651, 800-279-6799, FAX 602-265-6250, info@oryxpress.com, http://www.oryxpress.com. Ed. Anne Thompson. Pub. Phyllis Steckler. R&P Lori Cavanaugh TEL 602-265-2651 ext 662. Circ: 3,000.

371.22 USA ISSN 0548-1384
LB2338
NEED A LIFT?. Text in English. 1951. a. USD 3.95 (effective 2001). adv. 152 p./no.; **Description:** Covers sources of career, scholarship and loan information for not only children of veterans but for all children. Includes information that leads students to sources of scholarships, fellowships, loans and part-time jobs to help finance their education.
Published by: American Legion, Need a Lift, National Emblem Sales, PO Box 1050, Indianapolis, IN 46206. Ed., R&P, Adv. contact Robert K Caudell TEL 317-630-1212. Circ: 100,000.

379.1531 USA ISSN 0039-0070
NEW JERSEY SCHOOL BOARDS ASSOCIATION. SCHOOL BOARD NOTES. Text in English. 1969. w. USD 55 to non-members; USD 27.50 to members (effective 2003). adv. illus.; stat. index. **Document type:** *Newsletter.* **Description:** Provides timely information on state and federal legislation, state board action, recent ethics opinions, local and county school board activities, relevant court decisions, and NJSBA positions, activities and membership services.
Supersedes: School Boards Newsletter (0036-648X)
Published by: New Jersey School Boards Association, 413 W State St, PO Box 909, Trenton, NJ 08605. TEL 609-695-7600, FAX 609-695-0413. Circ: 8,000.

379.1531 USA
NEW JERSEY SCHOOL BOARDS ASSOCIATION. SCHOOL LEADER. Text in English. 1954. bi-m. USD 35 to non-members; USD 17.50 to members (effective 2000). adv. bk.rev. abstr.; charts; illus.; stat. index. **Document type:** *Newsletter, Trade.*
Incorporates: New Jersey School Boards Association. Legislative Bulletin (0024-046X); New Jersey School Boards Association. Legislation News; New Jersey School Boards Association. Negotiations News and School Law Reporter; Which was formerly titled: Negotiations News (0028-2472)
Published by: New Jersey School Boards Association, 413 W State St, PO Box 909, Trenton, NJ 08605. TEL 609-695-7600, FAX 609-695-0413. Ed., R&P Josephine Kane TEL 609-278-5242. Adv. contact Latonya Jackson. Circ: 8,000.

379.1531 USA ISSN 1080-7152
NEW YORK SCHOOL BOARDS. Text in English. 1987. s-m. USD 100. adv. **Document type:** *Newspaper.*
Incorporates: New York State School Boards Association. Employee Relations News; Formerly (until 1995): EducatioNews (0899-7330); Incorporates: New York State School Boards Association. Legislative Bulletin
Published by: New York State School Boards Association, Inc., 119 Washington Ave, Albany, NY 12210. TEL 518-465-3474, 800-342-3360, FAX 518-465-3481, nyssba@nyssba.org. Ed. Nancy Walsh. R&P Janice Romero. Adv. contact Cheryl Brenn. Circ: 11,600.

NEW YORK STATE. EDUCATION DEPARTMENT. COLLEGE AND UNIVERSITY REVENUES AND EXPENDITURES. see *EDUCATION—Higher Education*

371.2012 USA
NEW YORK SUPERVISOR. Text in English. 1945. s-a. USD 1 per issue. adv. bk.rev. illus. **Description:** Of interest to elementary school administrators and principals.
Published by: New York City Elementary School Principals Association, 93-06 63 Drive, Rego Park, NY 11374. TEL 718 459-0844. Ed. Thomas J Hiler. Circ: 2,000.

NEWSMONTH. see *LABOR UNIONS*

NORGE-AMERIKA FORENINGEN. YEARBOOK. see *EDUCATION—International Education Programs*

NORTH DAKOTA. DEPARTMENT OF PUBLIC INSTRUCTION. BIENNIAL REPORT OF THE SUPERINTENDENT OF PUBLIC INSTRUCTION. see *EDUCATION—Abstracting, Bibliographies, Statistics*

NORTHERN IRELAND COUNCIL FOR THE CURRICULUM, EXAMINATIONS AND ASSESSMENT. CORPORATE PLAN. see *EDUCATION—Teaching Methods And Curriculum*

NUTRITION CONNECTION. see *FOOD AND FOOD INDUSTRIES*

379 RUS ISSN 1026-129X
OBRAZOVANIE V DOKUMENTAKH. Text in Russian. 1994. 24/yr. USD 310 in United States. adv. illus.; stat. back issues avail. **Description:** Publishes documents, commentaries, surveys on all aspects of education, including federal policy, legislation and administration.
Related titles: Diskette ed.
Address: Marshala Katykova ul 15, k 1, Moscow, 123181, Russian Federation. TEL 7-095-4995295, FAX 7-095-4995295. Ed. Vladimir Zhukov. **US dist. addr.:** East View Information Services, 3020 Harbor Ln. N., Minneapolis, MN 55447. TEL 612-550-0961.

379.1531 USA ISSN 0893-5289
OHIO SCHOOL BOARDS ASSOCIATION. JOURNAL. Key Title: Journal - Ohio School Boards Association. Text in English. 1956. 10/yr. USD 35. charts; illus.; stat. **Document type:** *Trade.*
Formerly (until 1982): Ohio School Boards Journal (0030-1078)
Media: Duplicated (not offset).
Published by: Ohio School Boards Association, 8050 N High St, Ste 100, Columbus, OH 43235. TEL 614-540-4000, FAX 614-540-4100, http://www.osba-ohio.org. Ed., R&P Scott Ebright. Pub. John Brendt. Adv. contact Phullis Vore. Circ: 6,800.

379.1531 USA ISSN 0030-185X
OKLAHOMA SCHOOL BOARD JOURNAL. Text in English. 1950. m. USD 5. adv. illus.
Published by: Oklahoma State School Boards Association, 2801 N Lincoln Blvd, Oklahoma City, OK 73105. TEL 405-528-3571, FAX 405-528-5695. Ed. Bob Mooneyham. Circ: 4,600 (controlled).

371.2 USA ISSN 1556-3847
LC5805
ONLINE JOURNAL OF DISTANCE LEARNING ADMINISTRATION. Text in English. 1998. irreg. free (effective 2005).
Media: Online - full content.
Published by: State University of West Georgia, 1600 Maple St, Carrollton, GA 30118. http://www.westga.edu/~distance/jmain11.html.

371.02 ESP ISSN 1134-0312
ORGANIZACION Y GESTION EDUCATIVA. Text in Spanish. 1993. bi-m. EUR 36.36 (effective 2002).
—CINDOC.
Published by: Praxis, Principe de Asturias, 61 7a Planta, Barcelona, Cataluna 08012, Spain. TEL 34-93-3444700, FAX 34-93-3444701, educacion@praxis.es, http://www.praxis.es/.

OTWARTA SZKOLA; miesiecznik wielkopolskiej oswiaty. see *EDUCATION—Teaching Methods And Curriculum*

379.1531 USA ISSN 0162-3559
P S B A BULLETIN. Text in English. 1937. bi-m. USD 150 to non-members; USD 60 to members (effective 2005). adv. charts; illus.; stat. **Document type:** *Magazine, Consumer.*
Formerly: Pennsylvania School Boards Association. Bulletin (0031-4668)
Published by: Pennsylvania School Boards Association, 774 Limekiln Rd, New Cumberland, PA 17070-2398. TEL 717-506-2450, FAX 717-506-2475, lynn.mannion@psba.org, http://www.psba.org. Ed. Cindy Cooker. Adv. contact Paula Marinak. color page USD 1,700, B&W page USD 1,100; 7 x 10. Circ: 13,400 (controlled).

371.19 USA ISSN 1548-2936
▼ **P T A FUNDRAISING ESSENTIALS.** (Parent Teacher Association) Text in English. 2004. a.
Published by: National Parent - Teacher Association, 541 N Fairbanks Ct, Ste 1300, Chicago, IL 60611-3396. TEL 312-670-6782, 800-307-4782, FAX 312-670-6783, info@pta.org, http://www.pta.org.

379 USA ISSN 1072-3242
P T A IN PENNSYLVANIA∗. Text in English. 1924. 8/yr. USD 5. **Document type:** *Bulletin.* **Description:** Information on advocacy, public relations, health and safety, AIDS education, secondary education concerns, legislation, and administering a PTA unit.
Former titles: Pennsylvania Parent Teacher Bulletin; P T A in Pennsylvania; Pennsylvania Parent Teacher
Published by: Pennsylvania Congress of Parents and Teachers, 4804 Derby St, Harrisburg, PA 17111-3440. TEL 717-564-8985, FAX 717-564-9046, papta@juno.com. Ed. Jan Moore. R&P Linda Wilczynski. Circ: 1,700.

371.2 649 USA
P T O TODAY. (Parent Teacher Organization) Text in English. 2000. bi-m. USD 20; USD 5 per issue (effective 2005). adv. **Document type:** *Magazine, Consumer.* **Description:** Focuses on providing the expertise parent group leaders need and the programs and services that can help those parent group leaders help their schools.
Published by: P T O Today, Inc., 200 Stonewall Blvd, Ste 6A, Wrentham, MA 02093. TEL 508-384-0394, FAX 508-384-6108, nsousa@PTOtoday.com, http://www.ptotoday.com/. Ed. Craig Bystrinski. Adv. contact John Williams. color page USD 8,360; trim 7.875 x 10.375.

371.2 DEU ISSN 0939-0413
➤ **PAEDAGOGISCHE FUEHRUNG;** Zeitschrift fuer Schulleitung und Schulberatung. Text in German. 1990. 4/yr. EUR 54; EUR 15 newsstand/cover (effective 2005). adv. **Document type:** *Journal, Academic/Scholarly.*
Related titles: ♦ Regional ed(s).: Paedagogische Fuehrung. Ausgabe Bayern. ISSN 0939-1045; ♦ Paedagogische Fuehrung. Ausgabe Rheinland-Pfalz/Saarland. ISSN 0939-1037; ♦ Supplement(s): Die Schulleitung. ISSN 0931-265X.
Indexed: DIP, IBR, IBZ.
Published by: Hermann Luchterhand Verlag GmbH (Subsidiary of: Wolters Kluwer Deutschland GmbH), Heddesdorfer Str 31, Neuwied, 56564, Germany. TEL 49-2631-8012222, FAX 49-2631-8012223, info@luchterhand.de, http://www.luchterhand.de. Ed. Uwe Borchers. Adv. contact Gabriele Pannwitz. B&W page EUR 1,190, color page EUR 2,315. Circ: 7,300 (paid and controlled).

371.2 DEU ISSN 0939-1045
➤ **PAEDAGOGISCHE FUEHRUNG. AUSGABE BAYERN.** Text in German. 1990. 4/yr. EUR 54; EUR 15 newsstand/cover (effective 2005). **Document type:** *Journal, Academic/Scholarly.*
Related titles: ♦ Regional ed(s).: Paedagogische Fuehrung. ISSN 0939-0413; ♦ Paedagogische Fuehrung. Ausgabe Rheinland-Pfalz/Saarland. ISSN 0939-1037; ♦ Supplement(s): Die Schulleitung. ISSN 0931-265X.

E

Published by: Hermann Luchterhand Verlag GmbH (Subsidiary of: Wolters Kluwer Deutschland GmbH), Heddesdorfer Str 31, Neuwied, 56564, Germany. TEL 49-2631-8012222, FAX 49-2631-8012223, info@luchterhand.de, http://www.luchterhand.de.

371.2 DEU ISSN 0939-1053
➤ **PAEDAGOGISCHE FUEHRUNG. AUSGABE BERLIN, BRANDENBURG, MECKLENBURG-VORPOMMERN, SACHSEN, SACHSEN-ANHALT, THUERINGEN.** Variant title: Paedagogische Fuehrung. Ausgabe Neue Laender. Text in German. 1990. 4/yr. EUR 54; EUR 15 newsstand/cover (effective 2005). **Document type:** *Journal, Academic/Scholarly.*
Published by: Hermann Luchterhand Verlag GmbH (Subsidiary of: Wolters Kluwer Deutschland GmbH), Heddesdorfer Str 31, Neuwied, 56564, Germany. TEL 49-2631-8012222, FAX 49-2631-8012223, info@luchterhand.de, http://www.luchterhand.de.

371.2 DEU ISSN 0939-1037
➤ **PAEDAGOGISCHE FUEHRUNG. AUSGABE RHEINLAND-PFALZ/SAARLAND.** Text in German. 1990. 4/yr. EUR 54; EUR 15 newsstand/cover (effective 2005). **Document type:** *Journal, Academic/Scholarly.*
Related titles: ♦ Regional ed(s).: Paedagogische Fuehrung. ISSN 0939-0413; ♦ Paedagogische Fuehrung. Ausgabe Bayern. ISSN 0939-1045.
Published by: Hermann Luchterhand Verlag GmbH (Subsidiary of: Wolters Kluwer Deutschland GmbH), Heddesdorfer Str 31, Neuwied, 56564, Germany. TEL 49-2631-8012222, FAX 49-2631-8012223, info@luchterhand.de, http://www.luchterhand.de.

371.2 DEU ISSN 0944-2901
➤ **PAEDAGOGISCHE FUEHRUNG. HESSEN.** Text in German. 4/yr. EUR 54; EUR 15 newsstand/cover (effective 2005). **Document type:** *Journal, Academic/Scholarly.*
Published by: Hermann Luchterhand Verlag GmbH (Subsidiary of: Wolters Kluwer Deutschland GmbH), Heddesdorfer Str 31, Neuwied, 56564, Germany. TEL 49-2631-8012222, FAX 49-2631-8012223, info@luchterhand.de, http://www.luchterhand.de.

371.2 DEU ISSN 0948-0552
➤ **PAEDAGOGISCHE FUEHRUNG. NORDRHEIN-WESTFALEN.** Text in German. 4/yr. EUR 54; EUR 15 newsstand/cover (effective 2005). **Document type:** *Journal, Academic/Scholarly.*
Published by: Hermann Luchterhand Verlag GmbH (Subsidiary of: Wolters Kluwer Deutschland GmbH), Heddesdorfer Str 31, Neuwied, 56564, Germany. TEL 49-2631-8012222, FAX 49-2631-8012223, info@luchterhand.de, http://www.luchterhand.de.

371.2 USA
➤ **PENNSYLVANIA ADMINISTRATOR.** Text in English. 1998. 2/yr. free to qualified personnel (effective 2003). adv. abstr.; stat.; tr.lit. back issues avail. **Document type:** *Academic/Scholarly.*
Media: Diskette.
Published by: Pennsylvania Association of Elementary and Secondary School Principals, PO Box 39, Summerdale, PA 17093. TEL 717-732-4999, FAX 717-732-4890, houck@paessp.org, http://www.paessp.org. adv.: B&W page USD 600; trim 11 x 8.5. Circ: 4,100.

379.748 USA ISSN 0031-4455
LA355
PENNSYLVANIA EDUCATION. Text in English. 1968. q. looseleaf. free. bk.rev. **Document type:** *Government.* **Description:** Communicates educational information to teachers in Pennsylvania schools, administrators, and the public.
Formerly: Pennsylvania Basic Education
Published by: Department of Education, Bureau of Press and Communications, 333 Market St, Harrisburg, PA 17126-0333. TEL 717-783-9802, FAX 717-783-4517. Ed. Dawn Schaffer. Circ: 190,000.

371.2012 USA
PENNSYLVANIA PRINCIPAL. Text in English. 1995. q. membership. adv. bk.rev. **Document type:** *Newsletter, Academic/Scholarly.* **Description:** Scholarly articles by principals, superintendents and college professors on successful administrative practices.
Formed by the 1995 merger of: Keystone Schoolmaster Newsletter; Pennsylvania Schoolmaster (0190-2385)
Published by: Pennsylvania Association of Secondary School Principals, 122 Valley St, Box 39, Summerdale, PA 17093. TEL 717-732-4999. Ed., R&P, Adv. contact Terri Houck. Circ: 3,200 (controlled).

PERSPECTIVE (NEW YORK). see *EDUCATION—International Education Programs*

379 GBR ISSN 1476-685X
PERSPECTIVES ON EDUCATION POLICY. Text in English. irreg. price varies. **Document type:** *Monographic series, Academic/Scholarly.* **Description:** Presents and reviews research and evidence related to policy developments.
Published by: University of London, Institute of Education, 20 Bedford Way, London, WC1H OAL, United Kingdom. TEL 44-20-76126000, FAX 44-20-76126126, info@ioe.ac.uk, http://www.ioe.ac.uk.

371.2 USA ISSN 0032-0684
LA210
➤ **PLANNING & CHANGING;** an educational leadership and policy journal. Text in English. 1970. s-a. USD 18 domestic; USD 24 foreign (effective 2005). bk.rev. stat. 128 p./no. 1 cols./p.; back issues avail.; reprint service avail. from PQC. **Document type:** *Journal, Academic/Scholarly.* **Description:** This journal attempts to disseminate timely & useful reports of practice and theory, with particular emphasis on change & planning in K - 12 educational settings and higher educational settings.
Related titles: Microform ed.: (from PQC); Online - full text ed.: (from ProQuest Information & Learning).
Indexed: ABIn, CIJE, CPE, EAA, ERA, EduInd, SOMA.
—BLDSC (6508.990000), IE, Infotrieve, ingenta.
Published by: Illinois State University, Department of Educational Administration and Foundations, DeGarmo Hall Rm 331, Campus Box 5900, Normal, IL 61790-5900. TEL 309-438-5422, FAX 309-438-8683, ajredig@ilstu.edu, eafdept@ilstu.edu, http://www.coe.ilstu.edu/eafdept/pandc/pandcmain.htm. Ed. Lucille Eckrich. Circ: 1,000.

379.2 GBR ISSN 1478-2103
▼ ➤ **POLICY FUTURES IN EDUCATION.** Text in English. 2003. q. GBP 160 domestic to libraries; USD 246 foreign to libraries (effective 2005). **Document type:** *Journal, Academic/Scholarly.* **Description:** Promotes debate in education among university academics, practising policy analysts in government and local government, national and international policy advisors, politicians, members of policy think-tanks and world policy agencies such as the World Bank, OECD and the European Union.
Media: Online - full content.
Published by: Symposium Journals (Subsidiary of: wwwords Ltd), PO Box 204, Didcot, Oxford, OX11 9ZQ, United Kingdom. TEL 44-1235-818062, FAX 44-1235-817275, info@symposium-journals.co.uk, subscriptions@symposium-journals.co.uk, http://www.wwwords.co.uk/pfie/, http://www.symposium-journals.co.uk/. Ed. Michael A Peters.

379.1 USA ISSN 1054-3910
POLITICS OF EDUCATION ASSOCIATION. YEARBOOK. Text in English. a.
Related titles: ♦ Special ed. of: Educational Policy. ISSN 0895-9048.
—CCC.
Published by: (Politics of Education Association), Sage Publications, Inc., 2455 Teller Rd, Thousand Oaks, CA 91320. info@sagepub.com, http://www.sagepub.com.

371.2 RUS
PRAKTICHESKII ZHURNAL DLYA UCHITELYA I ADMINISTRATSII SHKOLY/PRACTICAL JOURNAL FOR A TEACHER AND ADMINISTRATION OF THE SCHOOL. Text in Russian. 2002. q. **Document type:** *Journal.*
Published by: Izdatel'stvo Folium, Dmitrovskoe shosse 58, Moscow, 127238, Russian Federation. TEL 7-095-4825544, 7-095-4825590, pj@folium.ru, info@folium.ru, http://www.folium.ru/ru/journals/pract_school.

371.2 GBR ISSN 0967-3865
PRIMARY SCHOOL MANAGER. Text in English. 1994. bi-m. GBP 48; GBP 54 in Europe; GBP 58 elsewhere. adv. bk.rev. **Document type:** *Bulletin.* **Description:** Up-to-date information on the day-to-day running of a primary school.
Published by: Pearson Education, 128 Long Acre, London, WC2E 9AN, United Kingdom. TEL 44-20-7447-2000, FAX 44-20-7240-5771. Ed. Gill Wilton. Adv. contact Alan Burfoot. Circ: 2,000 (controlled).

371.2012 USA ISSN 0271-6062
PRINCIPAL (ALEXANDRIA). Text in English. 1921. 5/yr. USD 8 newsstand/cover to non-members; free to members (effective 2005). bk.rev. illus. index. back issues avail.; reprint service avail. from PQC. **Document type:** *Magazine, Academic/Scholarly.*
Formerly (until Sep. 1980): National Elementary Principal (0027-920X)
Related titles: Microfiche ed.: (from PQC); Microfilm ed.; Online - full text ed.: (from H.W. Wilson, O C L C Online Computer Library Center, Inc.).
Indexed: ABIn, CIJE, CPE, ECER, EduInd, PCI.
—BLDSC (6612.967800), IE, ingenta.
Published by: National Association of Elementary School Principals, 1615 Duke St, Alexandria, VA 22314-3483. TEL 703-684-3345, FAX 703-548-6021, 800-396-2377, lgreene@naesp.org, http://www.naesp.org. Ed. Leon E Greene. Circ: 29,000 (paid and controlled).

PRIVATE SCHOOL DIRECTOR'S LEGAL GUIDE. see *LAW*

372 USA ISSN 1042-0487
PRO PRINCIPAL. Text in English. 1988. m. USD 216 (effective 2002). **Document type:** *Newsletter, Trade.* **Description:** Provides principals network with other principals from across the US and Canada.
Related titles: Online - full text ed.: (from EBSCO Publishing).
—CCC.
Published by: Aspen Publishers, Inc. (Subsidiary of: Wolters Kluwer N.V.), 5301 Buckeystown Pike, Ste. 400, Frederick, MD 21704-8319. TEL 800-638-8437, customer.service@aspenpubl.com, http://www.aspenpub.com. Ed. Darla Struck. **Dist. by:** Distribution Center, 7201 McKinney Circle, Frederick, MD 21701. TEL 301-698-7100, FAX 301-417-7550.

371.26 DNK ISSN 1603-6735
▼ **PROEVER, EVALUERING, UNDERVISNING;** en samlet evaluering af folkeskolernes afsluttede proever. Text in Danish. 2003. a. back issues avail. **Document type:** *Monographic series, Government.* **Description:** Annual testing evaluations.
Formed by the merger of (1996-2003): Proever, Evaluering, Undervisning. Fremmedsprog (1397-2170); (1996-2003): Proever, Evaluering, Undervisning. Matematik, Fysik/Kemi (1397-2189); (1996-2003): Proever, Evaluering, Undervisning. Dansk (1397-2154); (1996-2003): Proever, Evaluering, Undervisning. Praktiske Fag (1397-2162)
Related titles: Online - full text ed.: ISSN 1604-7729; ♦ Series of: Denmark. Undervisningsministeriet. Uddannelsesstyrelsen. Haandbogsserie. ISSN 1399-2260.
Published by: Undervisningsministeriet, Uddannelsesstyrelsen, Frederiksholms Kanal 21, Copenhagen K, 1220, Denmark. TEL 45-33-925300, FAX 45-33-925608, http://www.uvm.dk.

371.2 GBR ISSN 1460-8340
PROFESSIONAL DEVELOPMENT TODAY. Text in English. 1997. 3/yr. GBP 25 domestic; GBP 32 foreign (effective 2003).
Related titles: Online - full text ed.: (from Swets Information Services).
—BLDSC (6857.707000), IE.
Published by: Questions Publishing Company Ltd., 1st Fl, Leonard House, 321 Bradford St, Digbeth, Birmingham, Warks B1 3ET, United Kingdom. TEL 44-121-6667878, FAX 44-121-6667879, rchima@qiis.co.uk, http://www.education-quest.com/.

371.206 USA
PUBLIC EDUCATION FINANCES. Text in English. 1977. a. price varies. back issues avail. **Document type:** *Government.*
Formerly (until 1988): Finances of Public School Systems (0270-8868)
Related titles: Online - full content ed.
Published by: U.S. Bureau of the Census (Subsidiary of: U.S. Department of Commerce), Customer Services, Washington, DC 20233. TEL 310-457-4100, FAX 301-457-4714, http://www.census.gov.

371.21 USA ISSN 0197-2901
L182
PUBLIC SCHOOL ENROLLMENT AND STAFF, NEW YORK STATE. Text in English. 1961. a. free. charts; stat. back issues avail. **Document type:** *Government.*
Formerly: New York (State) Education Department. Survey of Enrollment, Staff and School Housing
Published by: Education Department, Information, Reporting & Technology Services, Education Bldg Annex, Rm 962, Albany, NY 12234. TEL 518-474-7082, FAX 518-474-4351. Circ: (controlled).

379.714 CAN
QUEBEC (PROVINCE). MINISTERE DE L'EDUCATION. DIRECTION GENERALE DU FINANCEMENT ET DES EQUIPEMENTS. REGLES BUDGETAIRES DES COMMISSION SCOLAIRES. Text in English. 1965. a. **Document type:** *Government.*
Former titles: Quebec (Province). Ministere de l'Education. Direction Generale du Financement. Regles Budgetaires des Commission Scolaires; Quebec (Province). Direction Generale des Ressources Materielles et Financieres. Regles Budgetaires des Commission Scolaires et des Commissions Regionales; Quebec (Province). Ministere de l'Education. Regles Budgetaires des Commissions Scolaires et des Commissions Regionales; Quebec (Province). Ministere de l'Education. Direction du Financement. Regles Budgetaires des Commissions Scolaires et des Commissions Regionales.
Published by: Direction Generale du Financement et des Equipements, 1035 rue de la Chevrotiere 14e, Quebec, PQ G1R 5A5, Canada. TEL 418-643-5432, FAX 418-643-9224, jean.bouchard@meq.gouv.qc.ca.

371.2 CAN ISSN 0704-7630
KEQ696.T4
RECUEIL DES SENTENCES DE L'EDUCATION. Text in English. 40/yr. CND 290. cum.index. **Document type:** *Government.*
Published by: Publications du Quebec, P O Box 1005, Quebec, PQ G1K 7B5, Canada. TEL 418-643-5150, FAX 418-643-6177. **Subscr. to:** Christiane Roy, Ministere de l Education, 300 Boul Jean Lesage, Quebec, PQ G1K 8K6, Canada. TEL 418-643-4758.

379.24 USA ISSN 1046-6150
REPORT ON LITERACY PROGRAM; the bi-weekly newsletter on basic skills training and workplace literacy. Text in English. 1989. bi-w. looseleaf. USD 317; USD 367 combined subscription print & email eds. (effective 2005). back issues avail. **Document type:** *Newsletter, Academic/Scholarly.* **Description:** Provides news and information on ways and efforts to improve literacy in the United States, both in the workplace and at home.

E

Related titles: E-mail ed.: ISSN 1545-7842. USD 267 (effective 2005); Online - full text ed.: (from Gale Group).
—CCC.
Published by: Business Publishers, Inc., 8737 Colesville Rd., Flr. 10, Silver Spring, MD 20910-3976. TEL 800-274-6737, bpinews@bpinews.com, custserv@bpinews.com, http://www.bpinews.com. Eds. Marcy Levin-Epstein, C Wright. Pub. L A Eiserer.

REPORT ON PRESCHOOL PROGRAMS; the bi-weekly newsletter on federal programs for early childhood development. see *EDUCATION—Teaching Methods And Curriculum*

098 USA
REPORT TO THE PRINCIPAL. Text in English. 2001. m. USD 102 in US & Canada; USD 109 elsewhere (effective 2001).
Published by: W D & S Publishing, 1200 Tices Lane,, East Brunswick, NJ 08816. TEL 732-545-8600, 800-321-5312, FAX 800-314-4770, http://www.curriculumreview.com.

379.1531 USA ISSN 1041-6757
LB2831
THE REPORTER (LITTLE ROCK). Text in English. 1982. 10/yr. **Document type:** *Newsletter.* **Description:** News and features pertinent to Arkansas School Board members.
Related titles: Online - full content ed.: free (effective 2003).
Published by: Arkansas School Boards Association, 808 Dr M L King Dr, Little Rock, AR 72202-3646. TEL 501-372-1415, FAX 501-375-2454, arsba@arsba.org, dan@arsba.org, http://www.arsba.org/reporters.html. Ed. Dan Farley. Circ: 3,500 (controlled).

371.2 USA ISSN 1047-7071
LB1771
REQUIREMENTS FOR CERTIFICATION OF TEACHERS, COUNSELORS, LIBRARIANS, ADMINISTRATORS FOR ELEMENTARY AND SECONDARY SCHOOLS (YEAR). Text in English. a., latest 2002, 67th ed. USD 43 per vol. (effective 2003). 280 p./no.; **Document type:** *Journal, Trade.*
Formerly (until 1989): Requirements for Certification for Elementary Schools, Secondary Schools, Junior Colleges (1048-9371)
—Infotrieve.
Published by: University of Chicago, 5710 S Woodlawn Ave, Chicago, IL 60637. http://www.press.uchicago.edu/cgi-bin/hfs.cgi/00/15270.ctl. Ed. Elizabeth A Kaye.

371.12 USA ISSN 0080-1429
LB1771
REQUIREMENTS FOR CERTIFICATION OF TEACHERS, COUNSELORS, LIBRARIANS, ADMINISTRATORS FOR ELEMENTARY SCHOOLS, SECONDARY SCHOOLS, JUNIOR COLLEGES. Text in English. 1935. a. price varies. reprint service avail. from PQC,ISI.
Published by: University of Chicago, 5801 S Ellis Ave, Chicago, IL 60637. TEL 773-702-7899, sales@press.uchicago.edu, http://www.press.uchicago.edu. Ed. John Tryneski.

371.2 USA ISSN 1537-3738
RESEARCH AND THEORY IN EDUCATIONAL ADMINISTRATION. Text in English. 2002. a.
Published by: Information Age Publishing, Inc., 411 W Putnam Ave, Ste 205, PO Box 4967, Greenwich, CT 06831. TEL 203-661-7602, FAX 203-661-7952, http://www.infoagepub.com.

371.2012 USA ISSN 8755-2590
RESEARCH ROUNDUP. Text in English. 1984. 3/yr. USD 175 membership; USD 115 to institutions (effective 2000).
Published by: National Association of Elementary School Principals, 1615 Duke St, Alexandria, VA 22314-3483. TEL 703-684-3345, FAX 703-548-6021.

379 USA
RESOLUTIONS, BELIEFS & POLICIES, CONSTITUTION AND BYLAWS. Text in English. 1940. a. free. **Description:** Official policy positions of the association passed annually by the Delegate Assembly.
Published by: National School Boards Association, 1680 Duke St, Alexandria, VA 22314-3493. TEL 703-838-6722, FAX 703-683-6719. Ed. Anne L Bryant. Circ: 2,000.

379 FRA ISSN 1563-4914
REVIEWS OF NATIONAL POLICIES FOR EDUCATION. Text in French. irreg. price varies. **Document type:** *Monographic series.*
Related titles: French ed.: Examens des Politiques Nationales d'Education. ISSN 1563-4922.
Indexed: IIS.
Published by: Organization for Economic Cooperation and Development, 2 Rue Andre Pascal, Paris, 75775 Cedex 16, France. TEL 33-1-45248200, FAX 33-1-45248500, http://www.oecd.org. **Subscr. in N. America to:** O E C D Turpin North America, PO Box 194, Downingtown, PA 19335-0194. TEL 610-524-5361, 800-456-6323, FAX 610-524-5417, bookscustomer@turpinna.com.

379.8151 BRA
REVISTA AMAE EDUCANDO. Text in Portuguese. 1967. 8/yr. BRL 45 (effective 2001). back issues avail. **Description:** Covers all aspects of education in the state of Minas Gerais.
Formerly: Associacao Mineira de Acao Educacional. Revista (0102-0471)
Published by: Fundacao Amae para Educacao e Cultura, Av Bernardo Monteiro, 861, Belo Horizonte, MG 30150-281, Brazil. TEL 351-31-3224-5400, FAX 351-31-3224-5400, fundacaoamae@b.pee.com.br. Circ: 12,000.

REVISTA BRASILEIRA DE SAUDE ESCOLAR/BRAZILIAN JOURNAL OF SCHOOL HEALTH. see *PUBLIC HEALTH AND SAFETY*

371.2 ITA ISSN 1121-0761
RIVISTA DELLA SCUOLA. Text in Italian. 1979. fortn. EUR 38.73 (effective 2001). adv.
Published by: Girgenti Editore s.r.l., Viale Andrea Doria, 10, Casella Postale 10016Casella Postale 10016, Milan, MI 20124, Italy. TEL 39-02-6692195, FAX 39-02-66983333, riscuola@tin.it, info@girgenti.it, http://www.girgenti.it. Ed., R&P, Adv. contact Salvatore Girgenti. B&W page EUR 2,355, color page EUR 3,532.56. Circ: 70,000.

379 LVA ISSN 1407-3617
S. Text in Latvian. 1997. m. **Document type:** *Magazine, Trade.*
Published by: Zurnals Santa, Balasta Dambis 3, PO Box 32, Riga, LV-1081, Latvia. TEL 371-762-8275, FAX 371-746-5450, santa@santa.lv.

371.14 AUS
S A I T JOURNAL. Text in English. 1915; N.S. 1969. every 3 wks. AUD 27. adv. bk.rev. stat. index. **Document type:** *Newspaper.*
Formerly (until Nov., 1990): South Australian Teachers Journal (0038-3015)
Indexed: AEI, CIJE.
Published by: South Australian Institute of Teachers, 163 A Greenhill Rd, Parkside, SA 5063, Australia. TEL 61-8-272-1399, FAX 61-8-373-1254, TELEX 89144. Ed. Andrew Macfarlane. Circ: 16,000.

371.6 CAN ISSN 0834-0455
S I E C C A N NEWSLETTER. Text in English. 1965. irreg. (2-3/yr.). CND 40 in Canada to individuals; USD 50 in United States to individuals; USD 70 elsewhere to individuals; CND 60 in Canada to institutions; USD 70 in United States to institutions; USD 90 elsewhere to institutions; CND 25 in Canada to students; USD 35 in United States to students; USD 55 elsewhere to students (effective 2002); includes subscription for the Canadian Journal of Human Sexuality. adv. bk.rev.; film rev. **Document type:** *Newsletter.* **Description:** Features practical teaching and counselling ideas, articles, media reports and reviews.
Formerly: S I E C C A N Newsletter Toronto (0381-873X)
Indexed: CINAHL.
Published by: Sex Information and Education Council of Canada, 850 Coxwell Ave, Toronto, ON M4C 5R1, Canada. TEL 416-466-5304, FAX 416-778-0785, sieccan@web.net, http://www.sieccan.org. Ed. F Michael Barrett. R&P, Adv. contact Alex McKay. Circ: 1,000.

371.2 USA ISSN 0048-9441
S M S G NEWSLETTER. Text in English. 1970. 8/yr. USD 25. bk.rev. **Document type:** *Newsletter.*
Published by: School Management Study Group, 860 18th Ave, Salt Lake City, UT 84103. TEL 801-532-5340, FAX 801-484-2089. Ed. M Donald Thomas. Circ: 200.

378.33 CAN ISSN 1494-9660
S S H R C GRANT HOLDER'S GUIDE. Variant title: C R S H Guide des Detenteurs du Subventions. Text in English, French. 1994. a.
Published by: Social Sciences and Humanities Research Council of Canada, PO Box 1610, Ottawa, ON K1P 6G4, Canada. TEL 613-992-0691, FAX 613-992-1787, http://www.sshrc.ca/web/using/grant_holder/intro_e.asp.

371.2 USA ISSN 1527-5221
SAFE SCHOOLS TODAY. Text in English. 1998. m. USD 99. **Document type:** *Newsletter.* **Description:** Provides school administrators news and information to help manage safe, secure and healthy schools.
Formerly (until 1999): E-Rate Update (1522-3043)
Published by: E-School News, 7920 Norfolk Ave, Ste 900, Bethesda, MD 20814. TEL 800-394-0115, FAX 301-913-0119, info@eSchoolNews.com, info@eschoolnews.com, http://www.eschoolnews.com.

371.2 RUS ISSN 1681-1941
SANKT-PETERBURGSKII UNIVERSITET. Text in Russian. 1991. m.
Related titles: Online - full content ed.: ISSN 1681-1968.
Published by: Izdatelstvo Sankt-Peterburgskogo Universiteta, Universitetskaya nab 7-9, St Petersburg, 199034, Russian Federation. http://www.spbumag.nw.ru.

371.2 CAN ISSN 0709-8146
THE SASKATCHEWAN EDUCATIONAL ADMINISTRATOR. Text in English. 1967. a. CND 20 (effective 2000). adv. **Document type:** *Bulletin.*
Formerly: Saskatchewan Administrator (0048-914X)
Indexed: CEI.
Published by: (Saskatchewan Council on Educational Administration), Saskatchewan Teachers' Federation, 2317 Arlington Ave., Saskatoon, SK S7J 2H8, Canada. stf@stf.sk.ca.

371.20 CAN ISSN 1205-8343
SASKATCHEWAN SCHOOL BASED ADMINISTRATORS NEWSLETTER. Text in English. 1994. q. CND 35 membership (effective 2000). **Document type:** *Newsletter.*
Published by: (Saskatchewan School Based Administrators), Saskatchewan Teachers' Federation, 2317 Arlington Ave., Saskatoon, SK S7J 2H8, Canada. stf@stf.sk.ca, http://www.stf.sk.ca.

371.223 USA ISSN 1528-9079
LB2337.2
THE SCHOLARSHIP BOOK. Text in English. 1984. a. USD 30 (effective 2005).
Published by: Prentice Hall, One Lake St, Upper Saddle River, NJ 07458. TEL 800-282-0693, FAX 800-835-5327, http://www.prenhall.com.

371.2 USA ISSN 1538-5191
SCHOLASTIC ADMINISTR@TOR. Text in English. 2002. 8/yr. USD 48; USD 6 newsstand/cover; free to qualified personnel (effective 2005). adv. **Document type:** *Magazine, Trade.* **Description:** Provides readers with insight into effective technology and management strategies used by leading school districts today.
Related titles: Online - full text ed.
Published by: Scholastic Inc., 557 Broadway, New York, NY 10012-0399. TEL 212-343-6100, http://www.scholastic.com/administrator/. Ed. Bernadette Grey TEL 212-343-6329. adv.: B&W page USD 10,780, color page USD 14,000; trim 7 x 9.75. Circ: 100,000 (controlled). **Subscr. to:** 2931 E McCarthy St, PO Box 3710, Jefferson City, MO 65102-9957. TEL 800-724-6527, classmags@scholastic.com.

371.201 USA ISSN 0036-6439
LB2805
SCHOOL ADMINISTRATOR; the monthly magazine for school system leaders. Text in English. 1943. m. (11/yr.). USD 10 newsstand/cover to non-members; USD 9 newsstand/cover to members (effective 2005). adv. bk.rev. **Document type:** *Magazine, Trade.*
Incorporates: D C Dateline
Related titles: Online - full text ed.: (from EBSCO Publishing, Gale Group, H.W. Wilson, Northern Light Technology, Inc., O C L C Online Computer Library Center, Inc., ProQuest Information & Learning).
Indexed: ABIn, CIJE, CPE, EduInd, PSI, SOMA.
—BLDSC (8092.570000), IE, ingenta. **CCC.**
Published by: American Association of School Administrators, 801 N Quincy St, Ste 700, Arlington, VA 22208-1730. TEL 703-528-0700, FAX 703-841-1543, magazine@aasa.org, http://www.aasa.org/publications/sa/2004_11/contents.htm. Ed. Jay P Goldman. Adv. contact Bob Solomon TEL 212-683-7905. Circ: (controlled).

371.2 AUS ISSN 0048-9387
SCHOOL BELL✱. Text in English. 1946. 10/yr. adv. bk.rev. back issues avail.
Published by: Victorian Council of School Organisation, c/o Victorian Council for Educational Administration, 1-317 Barkers Rd, Kew, VIC 3101, Australia. Circ: 6,000.

371.1531 USA ISSN 1045-8115
SCHOOL BOARD NEWS; a service for national affiliates. Text in English. 1981. s-m. USD 45. adv. reprint service avail. from PQC. **Document type:** *Newspaper.* **Description:** Provides news from the school board members' perspective on such topics as school policies, legislation, school law, curriculum, and standards.
Related titles: Online - full content ed.
Published by: National School Boards Association, 1680 Duke St, Alexandria, VA 22314-3493. TEL 703-838-6722, FAX 703-683-7590, info@nsba.org, http://www.nsba.org/site/page_sbn.asp?TRACKID=&CID=297&DID=5786, http://www.nsba.org/site/index.asp. Ed. Ellie Ashford. Circ: 21,000.

371.7 USA
SCHOOL BUS BRIEFS. Text in English. q. free.
Formerly: Chrome Yellow
Published by: Department of Public Instruction, Pupil Transportation Service, 125 S Webster St, Box 7841, Madison, WI 53707-7841. Ed. Kathleen J Cole. Circ: (controlled).

371.2 USA ISSN 0036-651X
LB2804
SCHOOL BUSINESS AFFAIRS. Text in English. 1936. m. USD 85 to non-members; free to members (effective 2005). adv. bk.rev. bibl.; charts; illus.; stat. index. reprint service avail. from PQC. **Document type:** *Magazine, Trade.* **Description:** Supplies management information to school administrators in charge of school business operations.
Related titles: Microform ed.: (from PQC).
Indexed: ATI, CIJE, CPE, EAA.
—BLDSC (8092.700000), IE, ingenta.

E

Published by: (Association of School Business Officials), A S B O International, 11401 N Shore Dr, Reston, VA 20190-4200. TEL 703-478-0405, FAX 703-708-7060, asboreq@asbointl.org, http://asbointl.org/Publications/PublicationsOnline/index.asp?bid=79, http://www.asbointl.org. Ed. Ceil Goldberg. Pub. Don I Tharpe. R&P Barbara Cook. Adv. contact Tim McCormack. Circ: 6,500 (paid).

371.2 CAN ISSN 1198-1164
SCHOOL BUSINESS MAGAZINE. Text in English. 1992. bi-m. CND 18; CND 30 in United States. adv. music rev.; software rev.; video rev. tr.lit. back issues avail. **Document type:** *Trade.* **Description:** Covers business, facility management and administrative issues for school and board officials, university and college administrative executives.
Formerly: School Business (1192-4357)
Published by: Momentum Media Management, 4040 Creditview Rd, Unit 11, P O Box 1800, Mississauga, ON L5C 3Y8, Canada. TEL 905-813-7100, FAX 905-813-7117, barwellj@momentummedia.com. Ed. Jay Barwell. Pub., Adv. contact Hugh Parkinson. B&W page CND 1,915, color page CND 2,750; trim 10.88 x 8. Circ: 10,500 (controlled).

371.23 CAN ISSN 0382-7879
SCHOOL CALENDAR/CALENDRIER SCOLAIRE; opening and closing dates, number of working days and prescribed holidays in Canada. Text in English, French. 1969. a. CND 17 (effective 1998). **Document type:** *Monographic series.* **Description:** Official school dates in Canada.
Indexed: CEI.
Published by: Canadian Education Association/Association Canadienne d'Education, 252 Bloor St W, Ste 8 200, Toronto, ON M5S 1V5, Canada. TEL 416-924-7721, FAX 416-924-3188, cea-ace@acea.ca, http://www.acea.ca. Ed. Suzanne Tanguay. Circ: 600.

379 USA ISSN 1526-0178
THE SCHOOL DISCIPLINE ADVISOR. Text in English. m. USD 135 (effective 2006). **Document type:** *Newsletter, Trade.* **Description:** Provides effective, ready-to-use methods that can be adapted in the classroom immediately. It gives latest discipline experiences and practices used by other colleagues. It provides practical tips, how-to-advice, and timely legal updates help to develop alternative discipline strategies that work.
—CCC.
Published by: L R P Publications, 747 Dresher Rd, PO Box 980, Horsham, PA 19044. TEL 215-784-0860, 800-341-7874, FAX 215-784-9639, custserve@lrp.com, http://www.shoplrp.com/product/p-300085.html, http://www.lrp.com.

379 NLD ISSN 0165-2028
SCHOOL EN WET. Text in Dutch. 1956. 10/yr. adv. **Document type:** *Trade.*
Published by: Samsom H.D. Tjeenk Willink B.V. (Subsidiary of: Wolters Kluwer N.V.), Postbus 316, Alphen aan den Rijn, 2400 AH, Netherlands. TEL 31-1720-66822, FAX 31-1720-66639. Circ: 1,800 (paid).

371.2 USA ISSN 1058-6431
SCHOOL EXECUTIVE. Text in English. 1990. 3/yr. USD 35 (effective 2005). **Document type:** *Magazine, Trade.*
Formerly (until 1991): School executive report (1059-7638)
Related titles: Online - full text ed.: (from ProQuest Information & Learning).
Published by: American Society of Educators, 1429 Walnut St, Philadelphia, PA 19102. TEL 215-241-9201, 800-555-5657, FAX 215-587-9706, http://www.schoolexec.com/. Ed. Christine Weiser. Pub. Michele Sokoloff.

371.716 USA ISSN 1075-3885
LB3475.A1 CODEN: SFNUEO
SCHOOL FOODSERVICE AND NUTRITION. Text in English. 1946. 11/yr. USD 75 domestic; USD 125 foreign (effective 2005). adv. bk.rev. tr.lit. index. **Document type:** *Magazine, Trade.* **Description:** Covers legislative and management issues concerning school food service and child nutrition.
Former titles (until Jun. 1994): School Food Service Journal (0160-6271); School Lunch Journal (0036-6641)
Indexed: Agr, H&TI.
—CISTI.
Published by: American School Food Service Association, 700 S Washington St, Ste 300, Alexandria, VA 22314-4287. TEL 703-739-3900, FAX 703-739-3915, asfsa@asfsa.org, http://www.asfsa.org. Ed. Patricia L Fitzgerald. Adv. contact Maria Robertson. Circ: 60,000 (paid).

SCHOOL FOODSERVICE WHO'S WHO. see *FOOD AND FOOD INDUSTRIES*

SCHOOL LAW BRIEFINGS. see *EDUCATION—Special Education And Rehabilitation*

379 USA ISSN 8755-8297
KF4114
SCHOOL LAW BULLETIN (BOSTON). Text in English. 1974. m. looseleaf. USD 147 (effective 2005). Index. reprint service avail. from PQC. **Document type:** *Newsletter, Trade.* **Description:** Summarizes current cases concerning labor relations, tort liability, student searches, student injuries, special education and other issues facing schools and school districts.
Related titles: Microform ed.: (from PQC); Online - full text ed.: ISSN 1544-5011 (from LexisNexis).
Indexed: CLI, LRI.
—CCC.
Published by: Quinlan Publishing Group, Marine Industrial Park, 23 Drydock Ave, 6th Fl, Boston, MA 02210-2387. TEL 617-542-0048, 800-229-2084, FAX 617-345-9646, info@quinlan.com, http://www.quinlan.com. Ed. Heidi Taylor. Pub. Dennis Hofmaier. Circ: 1,000.

379 USA ISSN 0194-2271
KF4102
SCHOOL LAW NEWS; the independent bi-weekly news service on legal developments affecting education. Text in English. 1973. bi-w. USD 383 (effective 2002). s-a. index. **Document type:** *Newsletter.* **Description:** Provides information to school administrators and legal advisors informed of legal decisions, pending court cases and issues that affect schools. Covers the federal judiciary, the US Supreme Court, state courts, and legal developments in federal agencies and Congress.
Incorporates (in Sep. 1987): Equal Opportunity in Higher Education (0194-2344)
Related titles: Online - full text ed.: (from EBSCO Publishing, ProQuest Information & Learning).
—CCC.
Published by: Aspen Publishers, Inc. (Subsidiary of: Wolters Kluwer N.V.), 5301 Buckeystown Pike, Ste. 400, Frederick, MD 21704-8319. customer.service@aspenpubl.com, http://www.aspenpublishers.com. Pubs. Dan Mangan, Marjorie Weiner. R&P Rossette Graham. **Dist. by:** Customer Care, 7201 McKinney Circle, Frederick, MD 21704. TEL 800-234-1660, FAX 800-901-9075.

371.2 GBR ISSN 1363-2434
L16
➤ **SCHOOL LEADERSHIP & MANAGEMENT.** Text in English. 1981. 5/yr. GBP 594, USD 1,084 combined subscription to institutions print & online eds. (effective 2006). adv. bk.rev. index. back issues avail.; reprint service avail. from PSC. **Document type:** *Journal, Academic/Scholarly.* **Description:** Discusses the management and organizational problems faced in primary and secondary schools.
Formerly (until vol.17, 1997): School Organisation (0260-1362)
Related titles: Microfiche ed.; Online - full text ed.: ISSN 1364-2626. GBP 564, USD 1,030 to institutions (effective 2006) (from EBSCO Publishing, Gale Group, IngentaConnect, Northern Light Technology, Inc., O C L C Online Computer Library Center, Inc., ProQuest Information & Learning, Swets Information Services).
Indexed: BrEdI, CIJE, CPE, EAA, ERA, ETA, MEA, PCI, RHEA, SEA, SENA, SOMA, SWA, TEA.
—BLDSC (8092.783000), IE, Infotrieve, ingenta. **CCC.**
Published by: Routledge (Subsidiary of: Taylor & Francis Group), 4 Park Sq, Milton Park, Abingdon, Oxon OX14 4RN, United Kingdom. TEL 44-1235-828600, FAX 44-1235-829000, journals@routledge.com, http://www.tandf.co.uk/journals/titles/13632434.asp, http://www.routledge.co.uk. Ed. Alma Harris. **Subscr. in N America to:** Taylor & Francis Inc., Customer Services Dept, 325 Chestnut St, 8th Fl, Philadelphia, PA 19106. TEL 215-625-8900, 800-354-1420, FAX 215-625-8914, customerservice@taylorandfrancis.com; **Subscr. to:** Taylor & Francis Ltd, Journals Customer Service, Rankine Rd, Basingstoke, Hants RG24 8PR, United Kingdom. TEL 44-1256-813000, FAX 44-1256-330245.

371.2 GBR ISSN 1351-4660
SCHOOL MANAGEMENT HANDBOOK (YEAR). Text in English. a. GBP 16.95. adv. **Document type:** *Directory.*
Published by: Kogan Page Ltd., 120 Pentonville Rd, London, N1 9JN, United Kingdom. FAX 44-20-7837-6348. Ed. Howard Green. R&P Caroline Gromm. Adv. contact Linda Batham.

371.2 USA
SCHOOL MARKETING NEWSLETTER. Text in English. 1981. m. looseleaf. USD 119 (effective 2005). charts; illus.; mkt.; stat.; tr.lit. 12 p./no. 2 cols./p.; back issues avail. **Document type:** *Newsletter, Trade.* **Description:** Covers all aspects of marketing to educators.
Formerly (until Dec. 1987): Direct Response Marketing to Schools Newsletter (0882-701X)
Published by: School Market Research Institute, PO Box 10, Haddam, CT 06438. TEL 860-345-8183, FAX 860-345-3985, info@smriinc.com, http://www.smriinc.com. Ed. Lynn O Stimolo. Pub., R&P Robert Stimolo TEL 860-345-8183. Circ: 500 (paid).

371.207 USA ISSN 1086-4628
SCHOOL PLANNING AND MANAGEMENT. Text in English. 1962. m. USD 23.95 domestic; USD 28.95 foreign (effective 2005). adv. bk.rev.; film rev. charts; illus.; tr.lit. back issues avail.; reprint service avail. from PQC. **Document type:** *Magazine, Trade.* **Description:** Covers construction, facilities, business and technology concerns in K-12 school districts.
Former titles (until 1995): School and College (1045-3970); (until 1986): School and College Product News (0893-4126); School Product News (0036-6749)
Related titles: Microform ed.: (from PQC); Online - full text ed.: (from Florida Center for Library Automation, Gale Group, ProQuest Information & Learning, The Dialog Corporation).
Indexed: BusI, CIJE, T&II.
—BLDSC (8092.923747). **CCC.**
Published by: Peter Li Education Group, 2621 Dryden Rd, Ste 300, Dayton, OH 45439-1661. TEL 937-293-1415, 800-523-4625, FAX 937-293-1310, spmeditor@peterli.com, http://www.webspm.com, http://www.peterli.com. Pub. Deborah P Moore TEL 602-867-2085. Adv. contact Rosemarie Brown. color page USD 8,115, B&W page USD 6,980; 7.875 x 10.875. Circ: 55,000 (controlled).

371.207 USA ISSN 1521-2831
SCHOOL POLICY LEGAL INSIDER. Text in English. 1998. m. USD 255. **Document type:** *Newsletter.* **Description:** Teaches school superintendents, principals and board members nationwide how to formulate and administer policies governing students, staff and outside vendors. Features model policies, notices and dialogues.
Published by: Brownstone Publishers, Inc., 149 Fifth Ave, 16th Fl, New York, NY 10010-6801. TEL 212-473-8200, FAX 212-473-8786. Ed. Marion Walsh. Pub. John M Striker.

371.2 USA ISSN 1522-3035
SCHOOL TECHNOLOGY FUNDING BULLETIN. Text in English. 1998. m. USD 165. **Document type:** *Newsletter, Trade.* **Description:** Informs school administrators on where to obtain grants and funds.
Published by: E-School News, 7920 Norfolk Ave, Ste 900, Bethesda, MD 20814. TEL 800-394-0115, FAX 301-913-0119, info@eschoolnews.com, http://www.eschoolnews.com.

379.1531 CAN ISSN 0036-6854
SCHOOL TRUSTEE. Text in English. 1934. 10/yr. CND 10. adv. bk.rev. abstr.; stat. **Document type:** *Newsletter.*
Indexed: CBPI, CEI, CPerI.
Published by: Saskatchewan School Trustees Association, 400 2222 13th Ave, Regina, SK S4P 3M7, Canada. TEL 306-569-0750, http://www.ssta.sk.ca. Ed. A Stephanson. Circ: 4,000.

371.2 DEU ISSN 0341-8235
SCHUL-MANAGEMENT; die Zeitung fuer Schulleitung und Schulpraxis. Text in German. 1970. bi-m. EUR 37.80; EUR 8.90 newsstand/cover (effective 2003). adv. bk.rev. **Document type:** *Journal, Trade.*
Indexed: DIP, IBR, IBZ.
—IE, Infotrieve. **CCC.**
Published by: Oldenbourg Schulbuchverlag GmbH und Bayerischer Schulbuch Verlag GmbH (Subsidiary of: Oldenbourg Wissenschaftsverlag GmbH), Rosenheimer Str. 145, Munich, 81671, Germany. TEL 49-89-450510, FAX 49-89-45051200, info@oldenbourg-bsv.de, http://www.oldenbourg-bsv.de. adv.: page EUR 665. Circ: 4,000.

371.2 DEU ISSN 1611-9975
▼ **SCHULENTWICKLUNG IN FORSCHUNG UND PRAXIS.** Text in German. 2003. irreg., latest vol.3, 2005. price varies. **Document type:** *Monographic series, Academic/Scholarly.*
Published by: Verlag Dr. Kovac, Arnoldstr 49, Hamburg, 22763, Germany. TEL 49-40-3988800, FAX 49-40-39888055, info@verlagdrkovac.de, http://www.verlagdrkovac.de/7-19.htm.

371.2 DEU ISSN 0931-265X
➤ **DIE SCHULLEITUNG**; ein Lernsystem. Text in German. 1974. 4 base vols. plus irreg. updates. EUR 158 base vol(s). (effective 2004). **Document type:** *Monographic series, Academic/Scholarly.*
Related titles: ♦ Supplement to: Paedagogische Fuehrung. ISSN 0939-0413; ♦ Supplement to: Paedagogische Fuehrung. Ausgabe Bayern. ISSN 0939-1045.
Published by: Hermann Luchterhand Verlag GmbH (Subsidiary of: Wolters Kluwer Deutschland GmbH), Heddesdorfer Str 31, Neuwied, 56564, Germany. TEL 49-2631-8012222, FAX 49-2631-8012223, info@luchterhand.de, http://www.schulleitung.de, http://www.luchterhand.de. Eds. Hans-Joachim Schmidt, Richard Bessoth.

371.2 DEU ISSN 1618-5978
SCHULMANAGEMENT HANDBUCH. Text in German. 1977. q. EUR 50.80; EUR 15.30 newsstand/cover (effective 2004). adv. bk.rev. index. **Document type:** *Journal, Trade.*
Formerly (until 2002): Schulleiter Handbuch (0170-7922)
—CCC.
Published by: Oldenbourg Wissenschaftsverlag GmbH, Rosenheimer Str 145, Munich, 81671, Germany. TEL 49-89-450510, FAX 49-89-45051204, vertrieb-zs@verlag.oldenbourg.de, http://www.oldenbourg.de. Ed. Burkhard Hitz. Circ: 3,500.

SCHULRECHT. see *LAW*

371.2 DEU ISSN 0942-3974
SCHULVERWALTUNG. AUSGABE BADEN-WUERTTEMBERG. Text in German. 1992. 11/yr. EUR 114; EUR 12 newsstand/cover (effective 2005). adv. **Document type:** *Journal, Trade.*
Published by: Carl Link Verlag (Subsidiary of: Wolters Kluwer Deutschland GmbH), Adolf-Kolping-Str 10, Kronach, 96317, Germany. TEL 49-9261-9694000, FAX 49-9261-9694111, info@wolters-kluwer.de, http://www.carllink.de. adv.: B&W page EUR 1,520, color page EUR 2,960. Circ: 2,800 (paid and controlled).

371.2   DEU   ISSN 1433-4674
SCHULVERWALTUNG. AUSGABE BAYERN. Text in German.
1978. 11/yr. EUR 164; EUR 16 newsstand/cover (effective
2005). adv. **Document type:** *Journal, Trade.*
Formerly (until 1990): SchulVerwaltung (0170-091X)
Published by: Carl Link Verlag (Subsidiary of: Wolters Kluwer
Deutschland GmbH), Adolf-Kolping-Str 10, Kronach, 96317,
Germany. TEL 49-9261-9694000, FAX 49-9261-9694111,
info@wolters-kluwer.de, http://www.carllink.de. adv.: B&W page
EUR 1,520, color page EUR 2,960. Circ: 3,020 (paid and
controlled).

371.2   DEU   ISSN 0939-3439
**SCHULVERWALTUNG. AUSGABE BRANDENBURG,
MECKLENBURG-VORPOMMERN, SACHSEN,
SACHSEN-ANHALT, THUERINGEN UND BERLIN.** Text in
German. 1991. 11/yr. EUR 124; EUR 12 newsstand/cover
(effective 2005). adv. **Document type:** *Journal, Trade.*
Published by: Carl Link Verlag (Subsidiary of: Wolters Kluwer
Deutschland GmbH), Adolf-Kolping-Str 10, Kronach, 96317,
Germany. TEL 49-9261-9694000, FAX 49-9261-9694111,
info@wolters-kluwer.de, http://www.carllink.de. adv.: B&W page
EUR 1,520, color page EUR 2,960. Circ: 2,430 (paid and
controlled).

371.2   DEU   ISSN 1618-9159
**SCHULVERWALTUNG. AUSGABE HESSEN,
RHEINLAND-PFALZ, SAARLAND.** Text in German. 2002.
11/yr. EUR 106; EUR 12 newsstand/cover (effective 2005).
adv. **Document type:** *Journal, Trade.*
Formed by the merger of (1997-2002): SchulVerwaltung.
Ausgabe Hessen (1432-9603); (1995-2002): SchulVerwaltung.
Ausgabe Rheinland-Pfalz und Saarland (0949-2550)
Published by: Carl Link Verlag (Subsidiary of: Wolters Kluwer
Deutschland GmbH), Adolf-Kolping-Str 10, Kronach, 96317,
Germany. TEL 49-9261-9694000, FAX 49-9261-9694111,
info@wolters-kluwer.de, http://www.carllink.de. adv.: B&W page
EUR 1,520, color page EUR 2,960. Circ: 2,250 (paid and
controlled).

371.2   DEU   ISSN 1618-9167
**SCHULVERWALTUNG. AUSGABE NIEDERSACHSEN,
SCHLESWIG-HOLSTEIN.** Text in German. 2002. 11/yr. EUR
121; EUR 12 newsstand/cover (effective 2005). adv.
Document type: *Journal, Trade.*
Formed by the merger of (1991-2002): SchulVerwaltung.
Ausgabe Niedersachsen (0940-1369); (1998-2002):
SchulVerwaltung. Ausgabe Schleswig-Holstein, Hamburg,
Bremen (1435-0092)
Published by: Carl Link Verlag (Subsidiary of: Wolters Kluwer
Deutschland GmbH), Adolf-Kolping-Str 10, Kronach, 96317,
Germany. TEL 49-9261-9694000, FAX 49-9261-9694111,
info@wolters-kluwer.de, http://www.carllink.de. adv.: B&W page
EUR 1,520, color page EUR 2,960. Circ: 2,450 (paid and
controlled).

371.2   DEU   ISSN 0937-7239
SCHULVERWALTUNG. AUSGABE NORDRHEIN-WESTFALEN.
Text in German. 1990. 11/yr. EUR 121; EUR 12
newsstand/cover (effective 2005). adv. **Document type:**
Journal, Trade.
Published by: Carl Link Verlag (Subsidiary of: Wolters Kluwer
Deutschland GmbH), Adolf-Kolping-Str 10, Kronach, 96317,
Germany. TEL 49-9261-9694000, FAX 49-9261-9694111,
info@wolters-kluwer.de, http://www.carllink.de. adv.: B&W page
EUR 1,520, color page EUR 2,960. Circ: 3,080 (paid and
controlled).

371.2   DEU   ISSN 1438-1907
SCHULVERWALTUNG SPEZIAL. Text in German. 1999. 4/yr.
EUR 44; EUR 15 newsstand/cover (effective 2005).
Document type: *Journal, Trade.*
Published by: Carl Link Verlag (Subsidiary of: Wolters Kluwer
Deutschland GmbH), Adolf-Kolping-Str 10, Kronach, 96317,
Germany. TEL 49-9261-9694000, FAX 49-9261-9694111,
info@wolters-kluwer.de, http://www.carllink.de.

371.2   DEU   ISSN 0048-9484
SCHULVERWALTUNGSBLATT FUER NIEDERSACHSEN. Text in
German. 1949. m. EUR 33.75; EUR 3.30 newsstand/cover
(effective 2005). adv. bk.rev. **Document type:** *Bulletin, Trade.*
Indexed: DIP, IBR.
Published by: (Niedersachsen. Kultusministerium
Niedersachsen), Verlag Hahnsche Buchhandlung, Leinstr 32,
Hannover, 30159, Germany. TEL 49-511-80718040, FAX
49-511-363698, info@hahnsche-buchhandlung.de. adv.: B&W
page EUR 750, color page EUR 1,125. Circ: 7,130 (paid and
controlled).

379.1531   GBR
SCOTTISH EDUCATION MANUAL. Text in English. 1999. base
vol. plus updates 2/yr. looseleaf. GBP 185 base vol(s).; GBP
135, EUR 203 updates in Europe; GBP 145, USD 263
updates elsewhere (effective 2006). **Document type:** *Trade.*
Related titles: Online - full text ed.: GBP 130 (effective 2005).
Published by: Sweet & Maxwell Ltd., 100 Avenue Road, London,
NW3 3PF, United Kingdom. TEL 44-20-74491111, FAX
44-20-74491144, http://www.sweetandmaxwell.co.uk. **Subscr.
to:** Cheriton House, North Way, Andover, Hants SP10 5BE,
United Kingdom.

SCOTTISH SCHOOLS DRUGS SURVEY. see *DRUG ABUSE
AND ALCOHOLISM*

SECTION 504 COMPLIANCE ADVISOR. see *EDUCATION—
Special Education And Rehabilitation*

379   CHE
SEKTOR ERZIEHUNG. Text in German. 1974. q. CHF 20
(effective 2001). bk.rev.; music rev.; Website rev. back issues
avail. **Document type:** *Newsletter, Trade.* **Description:**
Information about the schools, education, politics and culture
of Basel.
Published by: Gewerkschaft Erziehung Basel, Rebgasse 1,
Postfach, Basel, 4005, Switzerland. TEL 41-61-6921400, FAX
41-61-6839858, ge.basel@freesurf.ch. Ed. Martin Stohler.
Circ: 1,100 (controlled).

371.206   USA   ISSN 0162-9697
LB2825
SELECTED PAPERS IN SCHOOL FINANCE. Text in English.
1974. irreg. **Document type:** *Government.*
Published by: U.S. Department of Education, National Center for
Education Statistics, 1990 K St N W, Washington, DC 20006.
TEL 202-219-1828, http://nces.ed.gov/. Ed. William J Fowler.

379.2   USA
THE SERIES ON SCHOOL REFORM. Text in English. irreg. price
varies. illus. back issues avail. **Document type:** *Monographic
series, Academic/Scholarly.* **Description:** Discusses issues in
school, curriculum, and pedagogic reform.
Published by: Teachers College Press, Teachers College,
Columbia University, 525 W 120th St, Box 303, New York, NY
10027-6694. http://tc-press.columbia.edu. Dist. by: Eurospan
University Press Group, Order Dept, 3 Henrietta St, London
WC2E 8LU, United Kingdom. TEL 44-20-7240-0856, FAX
44-20-7379-0609, http://www.eurospan.co.uk; Pademelon
Press, Pty Ltd, 7-10 Anella Ave, PO Box 229, Castle Hill,
NSW 2154, Australia. TEL 61-2-9634-2558, FAX
61-2-9680-4634; Transdex International, Pte Ltd, Block 1,
Farrer Rd 307-05, Singapore 268817, Singapore. TEL
65-468-6242, FAX 65-462-5457.

371.227   USA
SHARING SPACE. Text in English. 1978. 3/yr. USD 15 (effective
2003). adv. bk.rev. back issues avail. **Document type:**
Newsletter. **Description:** Brings those who seek to develop
an affirming, cooperative classroom atmosphere into a support
network.
Published by: Creative Response to Conflict, Inc., 521 N
Broadway, Box 271, Nyack, NY 10960. TEL 845-353-1796,
FAX 845-358-1924, ccrcnyack@aol.com. Adv. contact Priscilla
Prutzman. Circ: 1,500.

371.207   USA
SIGNAL (OLYMPIA). Text in English. 1948. 12/yr. USD 12. bk.rev.
Document type: *Newsletter.*
Formerly: Washington State School Directors Association
Newsletter (0043-0811)
Indexed: RASB, TelAb.
Published by: Washington State School Directors Association,
221 College St, N E, Olympia, WA 98516. TEL 206-493-9237,
FAX 360-493-9247, http://www.wssda.org. Ed. Susan Lowery.
R&P Linda Lowery. Circ: 3,800.

379.466   ESP
**SITUACION DE LA REFORMA EDUCATIVA EN LA
COMUNIDAD AUTONOMA VASCA.** Text in Spanish. 1994.
a., latest 1994.
Published by: (Basque Region. Hezkuntza, Universitate eta
Ikerketa Saila/Departamento de Educacion, Universidades e
Investigacion), Eusko Jaurlaritzaren Argitalpen-Zerbitzu
Nagusia/Servicio Central de Publicaciones del Gobierno
Vasco, Donostia-San Sebastian, 1, Vitoria-gasteiz, Alava
01010, Spain. TEL 34-945-018561, FAX 34-945-018709,
hac-sabd@ej-gv.es, http://www.ej-gv.net/publicaciones. Circ:
2,000.

371.2   SWE   ISSN 1100-3340
SKOLLEDNINGSNYTT. Text in Swedish. 1989. 8/yr. SEK 190
(effective 2003). adv. 24 p./no. 3 cols./p.; **Document type:**
Magazine, Trade.
Related titles: Online - full text ed.
Published by: Laerarfoerbundet, Tidningsafdelning,
Segelbaatsvaegen 15, Box 12229, Stockholm, 10226,
Sweden. TEL 46-8-7376500, FAX 46-8-7376569,
skolledningsnytt@larerforbundet.se, kansli@lararforbundet.se,
http://www.skolledningsnytt.net/default.asp,
http://www.lararforbundet.se. Ed., Pub. Jonas Almquist. Adv.
contact Annelie Bjoernsdotter Lundqvist. B&W page SEK
9,000, color page SEK 13,500; trim 182 x 266. Circ: 6,900.

379   USA
SOCIAL AND POLICY ISSUES IN EDUCATION. Text in English.
1990. irreg., latest 1996. price varies. **Document type:**
Academic/Scholarly.
Indexed: e-psyche.
Published by: Ablex Publishing Corporation (Subsidiary of:
Greenwood Publishing Group Inc.), 88 Post Rd W, Westport,
CT 06881. TEL 203-226-3571, http://www.ablexbooks.com.

379   USA   ISSN 1530-5473
**SOCIOCULTURAL STUDIES IN EDUCATIONAL POLICY
FORMATION AND APPROPRIATION.** Text in English. 2001.
irreg.
Published by: Ablex Publishing Corporation (Subsidiary of:
Greenwood Publishing Group Inc.), 88 Post Rd W, Westport,
CT 06881. TEL 203-226-3571.

**SOUTH AFRICA. STATISTICS SOUTH AFRICA. STATISTICAL
RELEASE. FINANCIAL STATISTICS OF UNIVERSITIES AND
TECHNIKONS.** see *EDUCATION—Abstracting, Bibliographies,
Statistics*

379.1531   USA   ISSN 0081-3060
**SOUTHERN REGIONAL EDUCATION BOARD. ANNUAL
REPORT.** Text in English. a. USD 5. **Document type:**
Corporate.
Published by: Southern Regional Education Board, 592 Tenth St,
N W, Atlanta, GA 30318-5790. TEL 404-875-9211. Ed., R&P
Amy Schneider. Circ: 4,000.

371.2   GBR   ISSN 1367-6334
SPECIAL EDUCATION HANDBOOK. Text in English. 1983. irreg.
Formerly: A C E Special Education Handbook
—BLDSC (0573.798000).
Published by: Advisory Centre for Education (A C E) Ltd., 1c
Aberdeen Studios, 22 Highbury Grove, London, N5 2DQ,
United Kingdom. TEL 44-20-73548318, FAX 44-20-73549069,
enquiries@ace.dialnet.com, http://www.ace-ed.org.uk.

379.74426   USA   ISSN 0038-8602
SPRINGFIELD PUBLIC SCHOOLS. NEWS AND VIEWS. Text in
English. 1953. q. (during school yr.). free. bk.rev.
Published by: Springfield Public Schools, Board of Education,
940 N Jefferson, Springfield, MO 65802. Ed. Dick
Grosenbaugh. Circ: 50,000 (controlled).

379.1535 371.2   USA   ISSN 1540-8000
LB3060.83
THE STATE EDUCATION STANDARD. Text in English. 2000. q.
USD 35 (effective 2002). **Document type:** *Journal.*
Description: Each issue examines a specific theme at length
through its feature articles and includes departments on the
art of policymaking, innovative state practices, the federal
scene, and summaries of important state education actions
from across the country.
Published by: National Association of State Boards of Education,
Inc., 277 S Washington St, Ste 100, Alexandria, VA
22314-3646. TEL 703-684-4000, FAX 703-836-2313,
http://www.nasbe.org. Ed. David Kysilko. Adv. contact Carolyn
Headen.

371.2   USA   ISSN 0734-5062
LB2832
STATUS OF THE AMERICAN PUBLIC SCHOOL TEACHER. Text
in English. irreg.
Published by: National Education Association, 1201 16th St NW,
Washington, DC 20036-3290. TEL 202-833-4000, FAX
202-822-7974, http://www.nea.org.

**STRATEGII NA OBRAZOVATELNATA I NAUCHNATA
POLITIKA/STRATEGIES FOR POLICY IN SCIENCE AND
EDUCATION.** see *EDUCATION—Adult Education*

379   USA
STUDENT ACCELERATION IN FLORIDA PUBLIC EDUCATION.
Text in English. 1975. a.
Published by: Florida Department of Education, Office of the
Commissioner, Turlington Building, Ste 1514, 325 West
Gaines St, Tallahassee, FL 32399. http://www.fldoe.org.

344.07 371.5   USA   ISSN 1542-4952
STUDENT DISCIPLINE LAW BULLETIN. Text in English. 1999
(Aug.). m. USD 147 (effective 2005). **Document type:**
Newsletter.
Formerly (until 2002): School Violence Prevention Report
Related titles: Online - full text ed.: ISSN 1545-9470.
Published by: Quinlan Publishing Group, Marine Industrial Park,
23 Drydock Ave, 6th Fl, Boston, MA 02210-2387. TEL
617-542-0048, 800-229-2084, FAX 617-507-1079,
info@quinlan.com, http://www.policecenter.com,
http://www.quinlan.com. Ed. Amanda Telford.

379.4   DEU   ISSN 1435-9847
**STUDIEN ZUM BILDUNGSWESEN MITTEL- UND
OSTEUROPAEISCHER STAATEN.** Text in German. 1998.
irreg., latest vol.3, 1999. EUR 19.50 per vol. (effective 2003).
Document type: *Monographic series, Academic/Scholarly.*
Description: Studies various educational issues and policies
in Eastern Europe.
Published by: Waxmann Verlag GmbH, Steinfurter Str 555,
Muenster, 48159, Germany. TEL 49-251-26504-0, FAX
49-251-2650426, info@waxmann.com, http://
www.waxmann.com. Ed. Friedrich Kuebart.

371.2   ISR   ISSN 0334-4770
**STUDIES IN EDUCATIONAL ADMINISTRATION AND
ORGANIZATION.** Text in Hebrew; Summaries in English.
1973. a. USD 7. bk.rev. **Document type:** *Academic/Scholarly.*
Indexed: IHP.

E

Published by: Haifa University, School of Education, Mount Carmel, Haifa, 31999, Israel. FAX 972-4-342101. Ed. Lya Kremer Hayon.

371.2 **ITA** **ISSN 1722-8395**
STUDIUM EDUCATIONIS. Text in Italian. 1996. EUR 60 domestic; EUR 85 foreign (effective 2004). **Description:** Intended to inform students and graduates in education science.
Published by: C E D A M, Via Giuseppe Jappelli 5-6, Padua, PD 35121, Italy. TEL 39-049-8239111, FAX 39-049-8752900, info@cedam.com, http://www.cedam.com. Ed. Diega Orlando Cian. Circ: 4,200.

379 **LAO**
SUKSA MAY. Text in Laotian. m.
Published by: Ministry of Education Sports and Fine Arts, Vientiane, Laos.

372.206 **USA** **ISSN 0094-8268**
L162
SUMMARY OF EXPENDITURE DATA FOR MICHIGAN PUBLIC SCHOOLS. Text in English. a. free. charts; stat.
Published by: Department of Education, PO Box 30009, Lansing, MI 48909. TEL 517-373-0424.

SUNDAY SCHOOL PLANNING & PROMOTION RESOURCE KIT.
see *RELIGIONS AND THEOLOGY—Protestant*

371.2 **FRA**
SYSTEME EDUCATIF FRANCAIS ET SON ADMINISTRATION.
Text in French. q. **Document type:** *Academic/Scholarly.*
Published by: Association Francaise des Administrateurs de l'Education, 28 rue du General Foy, Paris, 75008, France. TEL 33-1-42931201, FAX 33-1-42941198, AFAE@wanadoo.fr. Ed., Adv. contact Guy Roger Meitinger. Pub. Bernard Toulemonde. R&P Paul Dela Taille.

371.2012 **USA** **ISSN 0300-6433**
➤ **T E P S A JOURNAL.** Text in English. 1970. s-a. USD 25. adv. **Document type:** *Academic/Scholarly.* **Description:** Contains current, timely articles by principals and professors on education practices.
Published by: Texas Elementary Principals and Supervisors Association, 501 E Tenth St, Austin, TX 78701-2697. TEL 512-478-5268, 800-252-3621, FAX 512-478-1502. Ed., R&P Dorian Martin. Pub. Sandi Border. Adv. contact Anita Jiles. Circ: 5,500.

378.111 658 **NLD** **ISSN 1380-7110**
T H & M A. (Tijdschrift voor Hoger Onderwijs en Management) Text in Dutch. 1994. 5/yr. EUR 189 domestic; EUR 199 in Belgium; EUR 41 newsstand/cover domestic; EUR 48 newsstand/cover in Belgium (effective 2005). adv. bk.rev. illus. back issues avail. **Document type:** *Academic/Scholarly.* **Description:** Covers issues relating to higher education management and planning.
—IE, Infotrieve.
Published by: Reed Business Information bv (Subsidiary of: Reed Business), Postbus 16500, Den Haag, 2500 BM, Netherlands. TEL 31-70-4415128, FAX 31-70-4415923, info@reedbusiness.nl, http://www.tijdschriftthema.nl/, http://www.reedbusiness.nl. adv.: color page EUR 1,919, B&W page EUR 973; trim 215 x 285. Circ: 1,350.

371.2 **USA**
TABCO BULLETIN. Text in English. m. free (effective 2005). **Document type:** *Newsletter, Trade.*
Formerly: The Advocate
Published by: Teachers Association of Baltimore County, MD., Inc., 305 E Joppa Rd, Towson, MD 21286. TEL 410-828-6403, FAX 410-337-7081. Ed. Angie Leitzer. Circ: 6,000 (controlled).

379.1531 **AUS**
TASMANIAN CERTIFICATE OF EDUCATION MANUAL. Text in English. 1992. a. AUD 15 (effective 2000). **Document type:** *Academic/Scholarly.* **Description:** Provides an overview of the Tasmanian Secondary Assessment Board and its functions, including assessment and moderation.
Published by: Tasmanian Secondary Assessment Board, PO Box 147, Sandy Bay, TAS 7006, Australia. TEL 61-03-62336364, FAX 61-03-62240175, reception@tassab.tased.ed.au, http://www.tassab.tased.edu.au. Circ: 1,000.

371.14 **CAN** **ISSN 0382-408X**
TEACHER (HALIFAX). Text in English, French. 1971. m. CND 22; CND 25 foreign (effective 1998). adv. bk.rev.; software rev.; video rev. charts. **Document type:** *Newsletter.* **Description:** Contains news and articles of interest to members of the union and teachers in general.
Formerly: Nova Scotia Teachers Union Newsletter (0029-5108)
Related titles: Microfiche ed.
Indexed: CBPI, CEI.
Published by: Nova Scotia Teachers Union, 3106 Dutch Village Rd, Halifax, NS B3L 4L7, Canada. TEL 902-477-5621, FAX 902-477-3517, theteacher@nstu.ns.ca, http://www.nstu.ns.ca. Ed. Monica Maloney. R&P Paul McCormick. Adv. contact Sonya Morgan. page CND 131,890; trim 17 x 11. Circ: 13,000.

331.28137 **CAN** **ISSN 0829-917X**
TEACHERS' MONEY MATTERS. Text in English. 1983. 8/yr. CND 20. adv. bk.rev.
Published by: Teachers' Money Matters Ltd., 70 Scriven Rd, Bailieboro, ON K0L 1B0, Canada. TEL 705-939-1203, FAX 705-939-1179. Ed. Michael Pengelley. Adv. contact Paul Cramp. B&W page CND 1,900; trim 10.75 x 8.13. Circ: 1,000 (paid); 33,000 (controlled).

371.26 **DEU** **ISSN 0178-6660**
TECHNISCHE UNIVERSITAET MUENCHEN. VORLESUNGSVERZEICHNIS. Text in German. 1970. 2/yr. adv. **Document type:** *Directory, Academic/Scholarly.*
Published by: Technische Universitaet Muenchen, Arcisstr 21, Munich, 80290, Germany. TEL 49-89-28928601, FAX 49-89-28928622, http://www.tu-muenchen.de. adv.: B&W page EUR 582.87, color page EUR 1,472.52. Circ: 7,500 (controlled).

371.2 **ITA** **ISSN 1123-8097**
LA TECNICA DELLA SCUOLA. Text in Italian. 1949. 15/yr. EUR 29 (effective 2005). adv. bk.rev. charts; illus.; stat. **Document type:** *Magazine, Trade.*
Published by: Casa Editrice La Tecnica della Scuola, Via Tripolitania 12, Catania, CT 95127, Italy. TEL 39-095-448780, FAX 39-095-503256, info@tecnicadellascuola.it, http://www.tecnicadellascuola.it. Ed. Venero Girgenti. Circ: 70,000.

379.768 **USA** **ISSN 0739-0408**
TENNESSEE EDUCATION. Text in English. 1971. s-a. USD 6 domestic; USD 10 foreign. bk.rev. **Document type:** *Academic/Scholarly.* **Description:** Publishes general education articles, some specific to Tennessee schools or systems.
Related titles: Microform ed.: (from PQC).
Indexed: CIJE.
Published by: University of Tennessee at Knoxville, College of Education, 344 Claxton Complex, Knoxville, TN 37996-3400. TEL 865-974-5252, FAX 865-974-8718, scarey@utk.edu. Ed., R&P Sue Carey. Circ: 2,500.

379.1531 **USA** **ISSN 0049-3406**
TENNESSEE SCHOOL BOARDS BULLETIN∗. Variant title: Tennessee School Boards Association Bulletin. Text in English. 1950. 8/yr. USD 10. adv. bk.rev. charts; stat. **Document type:** *Bulletin.*
Published by: Tennessee School Boards Association, 1130 Nelson Merry St, Nashville, TN 37203-2830. TEL 615-741-2824, FAX 615-741-2824. Ed. Beth Garfrerick. Circ: 1,800 (controlled).

379.1531 **USA** **ISSN 0747-6159**
TENNESSEE SCHOOL BOARDS JOURNAL. Text in English. 1983. q. USD 20. back issues avail. **Description:** Informs school board members, school superintendents and other school administrators about education issues.
Published by: Pollock Printing Co., 928 6th Ave, South, Nashville, TN 37203. TEL 615-255-0526. Ed. Holly Hewitt. Circ: 1,700. **Subscr. to:** 500 13th Ave N, Nashville, TN 37203.

379.1531 **USA** **ISSN 0749-9310**
TEXAS LONE STAR. Text in English. 1982. m. USD 30. bk.rev. index. back issues avail. **Document type:** *Journal, Trade.*
Formerly: Texas School Board Journal
Published by: Texas Association of School Boards, 7620 Guadalupe, Austin, TX 78752. lee.williams@tasb.org, http://www.tasb.org. Ed. Roger White. Circ: 13,500.

371.2 **DEU** **ISSN 1436-7696**
THUERINGER SCHULE. Text in German. 1998. q. EUR 16 (effective 2003). adv. **Document type:** *Newspaper, Academic/Scholarly.*
Published by: (Thueringer Lehrerverband e.V.), Satztechnik Meissen GmbH, Am Sand 1c, Nieschuetz, 01665, Germany. TEL 49-3525-71860, FAX 49-3525-718612, info@satztechnik-meissen.de, http://www.satztechnik-meissen.de. adv.: page EUR 782. Circ: 4,500 (paid).

371.2 690.24 **USA**
TIDINGS (SILVER SPRING). Text in English. 1939. bi-m. membership. adv. bk.rev. tr.lit. back issues avail. **Document type:** *Trade.* **Description:** Covers the school maintenance and supply market, listing new products and companies and reporting on industry trends.
Related titles: Online - full text ed.
Published by: National School Supply & Equipment Association, 8300 Colesville Rd, Ste 250, Silver Spring, MD 20910. TEL 800-395-5550, FAX 301-495-3330. Adv. contact Kathy Jentz. Circ: 2,900 (controlled).

371.9 **USA**
TITLE I HANDBOOK: UNDERSTANDING AND IMPLEMENTING THE PROGRAM. Text in English. 1971. q. looseleaf. USD 267. **Document type:** *Trade.* **Description:** Complete reference source on federal government's largest program of financial aid to educationally and economically disadvantaged children. Includes analyses of the laws, amendments and all regulations.
Former titles: Chapter I Handbook: Understanding and Implementing the Program (0737-2094); Chapter I Handbook: Understanding and Implementing the New Regulations (0275-0759); (until 1982): Title I Handbook

—CCC.
Published by: Education Funding Research Council (Subsidiary of: Thompson Publishing Group), 1725 K St, N W, Ste 700, Washington, DC 20006. TEL 800-424-2959, FAX 800-999-5661, http://www.thompson.com. Eds. Charles J Edwards, Lisa Hayes Sierra. Pub. Daphne Musselwhite.

372.22 **USA** **ISSN 1086-2455**
TITLE I MONITOR. Text in English. 1996. m. USD 177. 12 p./no.; **Document type:** *Newsletter.* **Description:** Reports on news and developments in the Title I compensatory education program, the largest program of federal aid for elementary and secondary education.
—CCC.
Published by: Education Funding Research Council (Subsidiary of: Thompson Publishing Group), 1725 K St, N W, Ste 700, Washington, DC 20006. TEL 800-424-2959, FAX 800-999-5661, http://www.thompson.com. Ed. Charles Edwards. Pub. Daphne Musselwhite. R&P Ellen Shindelman.

371.2 **USA**
TODAY'S SCHOOL. Text in English. q. USD 23.95 domestic; USD 28.95 foreign (effective 2003).
Published by: Peter Li Education Group, 2621 Dryden Road, Dayton, OH 45439. TEL 937-293-1415, FAX 937-293-1310, tlumm@peterli.com, http://www.peterli.com. Ed. Tim Lumm.

379 **USA**
TRIANGLE COALITION ELECTRONIC BULLETIN∗. Text in English. 1986. w. USD 100 to non-members. **Document type:** *Bulletin.* **Description:** Covers information about national and affiliate programs in science, mathematics, and technology education reform.
Formerly: Triangle Coalition Network News
Related titles: Online - full text ed.: 1986.
Published by: Triangle Coalition for Science and Technology Education, 1201 New York Ave, N W, Ste 700, Washington, DC 20003-3917. TEL 301-220-3164, FAX 301-474-4381, tricoal@aol.com. Ed., R&P Joanne VanVoorhis. Pub. Walter Purdy. Circ: 3,500.

371.2 **USA** **ISSN 1041-3502**
U C E A MONOGRAPH SERIES. Text in English. 1986. irreg. price varies. back issues avail. **Document type:** *Monographic series, Academic/Scholarly.*
Published by: University Council for Educational Administration, 205 Hill Hall, Columbia, MO 65211-2185. TEL 573-884-8300, FAX 573-884-8302, admnucea@coe.missouri.edu, http://www.ucea.org.

U E NEWS. see *EDUCATION—Higher Education*

379.24 **DEU**
U I E HANDBOOKS. Text in Arabic, English, French, Spanish. 1989. irreg. latest vol.3, 1994. back issues avail. **Document type:** *Monographic series, Academic/Scholarly.* **Description:** Contains practical ideas for undertaking literacy and other local education initiatives.
Published by: UNESCO Institute for Education, Feldbrunnenstr 58, Hamburg, 20148, Germany. TEL 49-40-448-0410, FAX 49-40-410-7723, uie@unesco.org, http://www.unesco.org/publications.

379.24 **DEU** **ISSN 1014-9880**
U I P - BERICHTE/DOSSIERS I U E/U I E REPORTS. (UNESCO Institut fuer Paedagogik) Text in English, French, German. 1990. irreg., latest vol.12, 1993. free. back issues avail. **Document type:** *Monographic series, Academic/Scholarly.* **Description:** Covers the institute's efforts worldwide to promote literacy.
Published by: UNESCO Institute for Education, Feldbrunnenstr 58, Hamburg, 20148, Germany. TEL 49-40-448-0410, FAX 49-40-410-7723, uie@unesco.org, http://www.unesco.org/publications.

379 **USA**
U.S. NATIONAL SCIENCE FOUNDATION. GUIDE TO PROGRAMS. Text in English. a. free. **Document type:** *Government.* **Description:** Provides a compilation of funding opportunities for research and education in science, mathematics, engineering and education. Includes general descriptions of NSF programs and research areas and sources for more information.
Media: Online - full text.
Published by: (Office of Legislative and Public Affairs), U.S. National Science Foundation, 4201 Wilson Blvd, Ste 245, Arlington, VA 22230. TEL 703-306-1070, cbartlet@nsf.gov, pubs@nsf.gov, http://www.nsf.gov/. Ed. Christina Bartlett Whitcomb. Circ: 35,000.

344.07 **USA**
U.S. SUPREME COURT EDUCATION CASES∗. Text in English. 1990. a. USD 84.95. **Document type:** *Trade.* **Description:** Compiles summarized U.S. Supreme Court decisions since 1954 that affect education.
Published by: Oakstone Business and Legal Publishing, 11975 Portland Ave Ste 110, Burnsville, MN 55337-1530. TEL 651-452-8267, FAX 651-452-8694. Ed., R&P Steve McEllistrem. Pub. Joanne E Flore.

371.2 USA
UNIONGRAM. Text in English. 1994. 8/yr. free to members (effective 2005). **Document type:** *Newsletter.*
Published by: AFL-CIO State of Virginia, 3515 W Broad St, Richmond, VA 23230. TEL 804-355-7444, 800-639-8511, FAX 804-353-0442, info@va-aflcio.org, http://www.va-aflcio.org. Ed. Daniel G. LeBlanc. Circ: 112,000 (controlled).

379.5357 UAE
UNITED ARAB EMIRATES. WIZARAT AL-TARBIYYAH WAL-TA'LIM. AL-TAQRIR AL-SANAWI/UNITED ARAB EMIRATES. MINISTRY OF EDUCATION. ANNUAL REPORT. Text in Arabic. 1977. a. stat. **Document type:** *Government.* **Description:** Provides a comprehensive overview of the activities of the departments of the ministry and the educational climate in the U.A.E.
Published by: Wizarat al-Tarbiyyah wal-Ta'lim, Idarat al-I'lam al-Tarbawi/Ministry of Education, Educational Information Department, PO Box 259, Abu Dhabi, United Arab Emirates. TEL 213800. Circ: 1,000 (controlled).

371.26 DEU ISSN 1431-7419
UNIVERSITAET MANNHEIM. VORLESUNGSVERZEICHNIS. Text in German. 1946. 2/yr. EUR 3.10 newsstand/cover (effective 2002). adv. **Document type:** *Directory, Academic/Scholarly.*
Former titles (until 1972): Universitaet und Wirtschaftshochschule Mannheim. Personal- und Vorlesungsverzeichnis (1431-7400); (until 1967): Wirtschaftshochschule Mannheim. Personal- und Vorlesungsverzeichnis (1431-7397)
Published by: (Universitaet Mannheim), Grunert Medien & Kommunikation GmbH, Am Paradeplatz 5-6, Mannheim, 68161, Germany. TEL 49-621-400404-0, FAX 49-621-40040488, info@grunert-medien.de, http://www.uni-mannheim.de/i3v/00022000/00593991.htm, http://www.grunert-medien.de. adv.: B&W page EUR 720, color page EUR 958. Circ: 9,000 (controlled).

371.207 CAN ISSN 1484-2173
UNIVERSITY MANAGER. Text in English. 1992. q. CND 29.95; free to qualified personnel (effective 2005). adv. **Document type:** *Magazine.* **Description:** Covers CAUBO activities and provides articles of a management nature exclusively developed for post-secondary institutions.
Indexed: CEI.
Published by: Canadian Association of University Business Officers, 320-350 Albert St, Ottawa K1R 1B1, ON K1R 1B1, Canada. TEL 613-563-3961, FAX 613-563-7739, jsamson@caubo.ca, http://www.caubo.ca. adv.: B&W page CND 116,950. Circ: 2,500.

UNIVERSITY OF LONDON. INSTITUTE OF EDUCATION. VIEWPOINT. see *EDUCATION*

371.223 USA
UNIVERSITY OF MINNESOTA. CENTER FOR COGNITIVE SCIENCES. REPORT AND FELLOWSHIP OFFERINGS. Text in English. 1965. a. USD 3. **Document type:** *Proceedings.*
Former titles: University of Minnesota. Center for Research in Learning, Perception and Cognition. Report and Fellowship Offerings; University of Minnesota. Center for Research in Human Learning. Report and Fellowship Offerings; University of Minnesota. Center for Research in Human Learning. Report (0076-9282)
Published by: University of Minnesota, Center for Cognitive Sciences, 205 Elliott Hall, Minneapolis, MN 55455. TEL 612-625-9367, crlpc@turtle.psych.umn.edu, http://www.cogsci.psych.umnn.edu/. Circ: 1,000.

379.1531 USA ISSN 1081-8286
LB2806
UPDATING SCHOOL BOARD POLICIES. Text in English. 1970. bi-m. USD 75 (effective 2004). index. back issues avail. **Document type:** *Newsletter.* **Description:** Includes articles, trends, tips and legal analyses on subjects relating to school policies and issues of concern to school boards and superintendents.
Related titles: Supplement(s): Administrative Angle.
Published by: National School Boards Association, 1680 Duke St, Alexandria, VA 22314-3493. TEL 703-838-6722, FAX 703-548-5516, info@nsba.org, http://www.nsba.org/site/index.asp. Ed. Carla Schultz. Circ: 20,000 (paid and controlled).

379.1531 USA
URBAN AFFAIRS (TRENTON). Text in English. q. USD 30 to non-members; USD 15 to members. **Document type:** *Newsletter.*
Published by: New Jersey School Boards Association, 413 W State St, PO Box 909, Trenton, NJ 08605. TEL 609-695-7600, FAX 609-695-0413. R&P Raymond Milan TEL 609-278-5208.

371.2 USA
URBAN EDUCATOR; the nation's voice for urban education. Text in English. m. membership. back issues avail. **Document type:** *Newsletter, Trade.* **Description:** Reports news, issues, and trends of interest to administrators and teachers in large urban districts.
Published by: Council of the Great City Schools, 1301 Pennsylvania Ave, NW, Ste 702, Washington, DC 20004. TEL 202-393-2427, FAX 202-393-2400, http://www.cgcs.org/newslett/educator/about.htm. Ed. Henry Duvall.

379.2 NLD ISSN 0042-0972
LC5101
➤ **THE URBAN REVIEW**; issues and ideas in public education. Text in English. 1966. q. EUR 598, USD 635, GBP 378 combined subscription to institutions print & online eds. (effective 2005). adv. bibl. index. reprint service avail. from PQC,PSC. **Document type:** *Journal, Academic/Scholarly.* **Description:** Intended for urban educators, scholars, administrators and all others concerned with improving public education in urban communities.
Related titles: Microform ed.: (from PQC); Online - full text ed.: ISSN 1573-1960 (from EBSCO Publishing, Gale Group, IngentaConnect, Kluwer Online, O C L C Online Computer Library Center, Inc., Springer LINK, Swets Information Services).
Indexed: ABIn, AMHA, AmH&L, BibLing, CIJE, CPE, ChPerl, EAA, ERA, ETA, EduInd, FamI, MEA, PSA, PsycInfo, PsycholAb, RHEA, RI-1, RI-2, SEA, SENA, SFSA, SOMA, SOPODA, SSA, SUSA, SociolAb, TEA, V&AA, e-psyche. —BLDSC (9123.689700), IE, Infotrieve, ingenta. **CCC.**
Published by: Springer-Verlag Dordrecht (Subsidiary of: Springer Science+Business Media), Van Godewijckstraat 30, Dordrecht, 3311 GX, Netherlands. TEL 31-78-6576050, FAX 31-78-6576474, http://springerlink.metapress.com/openurl.asp?genre=journal&issn=0042-0972, http://www.springeronline.com. Eds. George W Noblit, William T Pink.

➤ **URBAN SCHOOL SUPERINTENDENTS: CHARACTERISTICS, TENURE, AND SALARY. SECOND BIENNIAL SURVEY.** see *EDUCATION—Abstracting, Bibliographies, Statistics*

379.792 USA ISSN 0094-8314
L206
UTAH. STATE OFFICE OF EDUCATION. ANNUAL REPORT OF THE STATE SUPERINTENDENT OF PUBLIC INSTRUCTION. Key Title: Annual Report of the State Superintendent of Public Instruction Utah Public School System. Variant title: Utah Public School System. Text in English. a. illus. **Document type:** *Government.*
Indexed: SRI.
Published by: Utah State Office of Education, PO Box 144200, Salt Lake City, UT 84114-4200. TEL 801-538-7510, FAX 801-538-7768, http://www.usoe.k12.ut.us/.

371.782 USA
VIOLENCE CHRONICLES. Text in English. 1998. m. free (effective 2003). bk.rev. back issues avail. **Document type:** *Newsletter.* **Description:** Aimed at professionals interested in prevention of school violence; includes book reviews, skills, websites, workshops, critical incident debriefing etc.
Media: E-mail.
Published by: Listening Inc., 187, Hobart, IN 46342-0187. TEL 219-938-6962, FAX 219-938-7435, addup@crown.net, http://www.preventviolence.net. Ed. Richard C Bennett. R&P Patricia Work Bennett. Circ: 100,000.

379.1531 USA ISSN 0042-6776
VIRGINIA SCHOOL BOARDS ASSOCIATION NEWSLETTER. Text in English. 1953. 10/yr. membership. bk.rev. illus. **Document type:** *Newsletter.*
Media: Duplicated (not offset).
Published by: Virginia School Boards Association, 2320 Hunters Way, Ste B, Charlottesville, VA 22911-7931. TEL 804-295-8722, FAX 804-295-8785, vsba@comet.net. Ed. Cass Cannon. Circ: 2,300 (controlled).

371.26 371.39 USA
VISION (GREENSBORO). Text in English. 3/school-academic yr. free. bk.rev. charts; illus. back issues avail. **Document type:** *Newsletter, Trade.* **Description:** Discusses ways in which school administrators, along with classroom teachers, in the US Southeast can enhance and maximize teaching and learning efficacy. Reports on professional development programs and workshops. Back issues are available online.
Published by: Serve, PO Box 5367, Greensboro, NC 27435. TEL 336-334-3211, 800-755-3277, FAX 336-334-3268, info@serve.org, http://www.serve.org/publications/vision.htm.

VISUAL LITERACY REVIEW. see *EDUCATION—Teaching Methods And Curriculum*

379.1531 USA ISSN 0744-4583
VOICE OF NORTH CAROLINA SCHOOL BOARDS ASSOCIATION. Text in English. 1953. q. USD 15 domestic; USD 20 foreign (effective 2001). adv. bk.rev. illus. reprints avail. **Document type:** *Trade.* **Description:** Covers schools, school systems, education techniques and various topics related to education and school boards.
Formerly: North Carolina School Boards Association Bulletin (0029-2613)
Published by: North Carolina School Boards Association, 5808 Faringdon Pl, Raleigh, NC 27624-7877. TEL 919-981-2630, FAX 919-981-2637. Ed., R&P, Adv. contact Stacy M Boyette. Circ: 7,500.

W C E R RESEARCH HIGHLIGHTS. see *EDUCATION—Teaching Methods And Curriculum*

WAGES AND BENEFITS. see *BUSINESS AND ECONOMICS—Labor And Industrial Relations*

WHAT WORKS IN TEACHING AND LEARNING. see *EDUCATION—Teaching Methods And Curriculum*

371.2 USA ISSN 1551-2827
▼ **WHAT'S WORKING: DATA-DRIVEN DECISION MAKING IN THE SCHOOLS.** Text in English. 2004 (Mar.). m. USD 235 (effective 2006). **Document type:** *Newsletter, Trade.*
Published by: L R P Publications, 747 Dresher Rd, PO Box 980, Horsham, PA 19044. TEL 215-784-0860, 800-341-7874, FAX 215-784-9639, custserve@lrp.com, http://www.shoplrp.com/product/p-300184.html, http://www.lrp.com.

WIESCI OSWIATOWE; suwalski miesiecznik edukacyjny. see *EDUCATION—Teaching Methods And Curriculum*

379.1531 USA ISSN 0361-2120
LB1044.8
WISCONSIN. EDUCATIONAL COMMUNICATIONS BOARD. BIENNIAL REPORT. Key Title: Biennial Report-Educational Communications Board. Text in English. biennial. free. **Document type:** *Government.* **Description:** Provides a description of agency functions in public broadcasting and a summary of activities over the previous two years.
Published by: Educational Communications Board, 3319 W Beltline Hwy, Madison, WI 53713. FAX 608-264-9622.

379.775 USA
WISCONSIN SCHOOL NEWS. Text in English. 1945. m. USD 30 domestic; USD 50 foreign (effective 2001). adv. bk.rev. mkt.; stat. index. **Document type:** *Journal, Trade.* **Description:** Covers Wisconsin and national educational issues for school boards and educators.
Formerly: Wisconsin School Board News (0043-664X)
Published by: Wisconsin Association of School Boards, 122 W Washington Ave, Madison, WI 53703. TEL 608-257-2622, FAX 608-257-8386, info@wasb.org, http://www.wasb.org/bookstore/schoolnews.html. Ed., R&P, Adv. contact Kathryn Derene. Circ: 5,700 (controlled).

379 USA ISSN 1068-9885
A WORD ON... Text in English. q. free with subscription to Inquiry & Analysis. back issues avail. **Document type:** *Newsletter.* **Description:** Covers both legal and legislative issues affecting education.
Published by: National School Boards Association, 1680 Duke St, Alexandria, VA 22314-3493. TEL 703-838-6722, FAX 703-683-6719. Circ: 3,000.

379.787 USA
WYOMING. DEPARTMENT OF EDUCATION. EDUCATION DIRECTORY. Text in English. a. USD 5 (effective 1999). **Document type:** *Directory, Government.*
Published by: Department of Education, Hathaway Bldg, 2nd Fl, 2300 Capitol Ave, Cheyenne, WY 82002-0050. TEL 307-777-7673.

371.2 USA
YEAR-ROUNDER. Text in English. 1972. q. USD 45 (effective 1999). adv. **Document type:** *Newsletter.* **Description:** Articles and comment regarding the year-round education movement in the U.S. and Canada.
Published by: National Association for Year-Round Education, PO Box 711386, San Diego, CA 92171-1386. TEL 619-276-5296, FAX 619-571-5754, info@nayre.org, http://www.nayre.org. Ed. Charles Ballinger. Circ: 4,000.

379 USA ISSN 0094-0399
KF4102
YOUR SCHOOL AND THE LAW. Text in English. 1972. 22/yr. USD 195 (effective 2006). **Document type:** *Newsletter, Trade.* **Description:** Offers practical information on current judicial decisions affecting schools. Covers student discipline, sexual harassment of employees and students, liability for negligence, legalities surrounding extracurricular and athletic activities, and racial discrimination against employees and students.
Incorporates (in 1990): Athletic Director and Coach; Which was formerly: Coach's Legal Report (8750-9261); Your School District and the Law; School Board Advisor
Related titles: Online - full text ed.: (from LexisNexis). —CCC.
Published by: L R P Publications, 747 Dresher Rd, PO Box 980, Horsham, PA 19044. TEL 215-784-0860, 800-341-7874, FAX 215-784-9639, custserve@lrp.com, http://www.shoplrp.com/product/p-300007.html, http://www.lrp.com. Ed. Jason Wermers.

379.1535 USA ISSN 0044-1112
YOUR SCHOOLS. Text in English. 1957. 10/yr. free to school district residents. adv. **Document type:** *Newspaper.*
Published by: Sweet Home Central School District - Towns of Amherst and Tonawanda, 1901 Sweet Home Rd, Amherst, NY 14228. TEL 716-689-5227, FAX 716-689-5229, http://www.ins1.moran.com/~seethm/. Ed., R&P, Adv. contact Martin P Biniasz. Circ: 16,000.

379 DEU ISSN 0514-2717
ZEITSCHRIFT FUER PAEDAGOGIK. BEIHEFT. Text in German. 1959. a. EUR 29.90 (effective 2004).
Related titles: ♦ Supplement to: Zeitschrift fuer Paedagogik. ISSN 0044-3247.
Indexed: DIP, IBR, IBZ, PCI.

E

—BLDSC (9475.800500), IE.
Published by: Julius Beltz GmbH & Co. KG, Werderstr 10, Weinheim, 69469, Germany. info@beltz.de, http://www.beltz.de.

371.2   CHN   ISSN 1002-2384
                                CODEN: BM4238
ZHONGXIAOXUE GUANLI/ADMINISTRATION OF ELEMENTARY AND SECONDARY SCHOOL. Text in Chinese. 1987. m. CNY 24. adv. **Document type:** *Academic/Scholarly.* **Description:** Covers the latest developments in educational policy, research, and administration of elementary and secondary schools in China.
Related titles: CD-ROM ed.
Published by: Zhongxiaoxue Guanli Zazhishe, A-24 Huangsi Dajie Dewai, Beijing, 100011, China. TEL 2018316. Ed. Tao Xiping. Circ: 65,000 (paid). **Dist. overseas by:** China International Book Trading Corp, 35 Chegongzhuang Xilu, Haidian District, PO Box 399, Beijing 100044, China.

EDUCATION—Special Education And Rehabilitation

see also CRIMINOLOGY AND LAW ENFORCEMENT ; HANDICAPPED ; SOCIAL SERVICES AND WELFARE

371.928   USA
A C R M D ON THE RECORD. (Association for Children with Retarded Mental Development) Text in English. 1960. s-a. free.
Published by: Association for C R M D, Inc., 345 Hudson St, 3rd Fl, New York, NY 10014. TEL 212-627-8318. Ed. Philip Vassallo. Circ: 3,500.

371.9   DEU   ISSN 0934-8417
A F E T - MITGLIEDER - RUNDBRIEF. Text in German. 1948. q. looseleaf. EUR 16.40; EUR 4.60 newsstand/cover (effective 2005). bk.rev. **Document type:** *Newsletter, Consumer.*
Related titles: Diskette ed.
Published by: Arbeitsgemeinschaft fuer Erziehungshilfe (AFET) e.V., Osterstr 27, Hannover, 30159, Germany. TEL 49-511-3539913, FAX 49-511-35399150, info@afet-ev.de, http://www.afet-ev.de. Ed. Cornelie Bauer. Circ: 1,200.

371.9   DEU   ISSN 0344-1695
A F E T NEUE SCHRIFTENREIHE. Text in German. 1947. irreg. price varies. **Document type:** *Monographic series, Academic/Scholarly.*
Formerly (until 1972): Allgemeine Fuersorgeerziehungstag. Neue Schriftenreihe (0516-7213)
Published by: Arbeitsgemeinschaft fuer Erziehungshilfe (AFET) e.V., Osterstr 27, Hannover, 30159, Germany. TEL 49-511-3539913, FAX 49-511-35399150, info@afet-ev.de, http://www.afet-ev.de.

371.9   DEU   ISSN 0932-8874
A F E T WISSENSCHAFTLICHE INFORMATIONSSCHRIFTEN. Text in German. 1973. irreg. price varies. **Document type:** *Monographic series, Academic/Scholarly.*
Published by: Arbeitsgemeinschaft fuer Erziehungshilfe (AFET) e.V., Osterstr 27, Hannover, 30159, Germany. TEL 49-511-3539913, FAX 49-511-35399150, info@afet-ev.de, http://www.afet-ev.de.

371.95   CAN   ISSN 0833-0603
A G A T E. (Alberta Gifted and Talented Education) Text in English. 1987. s-a.
Indexed: CEI.
—BLDSC (0736.010500), IE, ingenta.
Published by: Alberta Teachers' Association, 11010 142 St NW, Edmonton, AB T5N 2R1, Canada. TEL 780-447-9400, FAX 780-455-6481, http://www.teachers.ab.ca.

A H R C CHRONICLE. see *MEDICAL SCIENCES—Psychiatry And Neurology*

371.9   USA
A S C A COUNSELOR∗ . Text in English. 1963. 5/yr. looseleaf. membership. illus. reprint service avail. from PQC.
Formerly: A S C A Newsletter (0001-2416)
Related titles: Microform ed.: 1963 (from PQC).
Published by: American School Counselor Association, 1101 King St., Ste. 625, Alexandria, VA 22314-2957. Ed. Patricia Ferris. Circ: 15,000.

616.21   AUS   ISSN 1441-6727
ACQUIRING KNOWLEDGE IN SPEECH, LANGUAGE AND HEARING. Text in English. 1999 (Feb). N.S. 2000. 3/yr. (Feb., Jun. & Oct.). **Document type:** *Journal, Academic/Scholarly.*
Formerly (until 1997): Australian Communication Quarterly (1036-4994)
—BLDSC (0578.699950).
Published by: The Speech Pathology Association of Australia Ltd., 2nd Fl., 11-19 Bank Pl., Melbourne, VIC 3000, Australia. TEL 61-3-96424899, FAX 61-3-96424922, office@speechpathologyaustralia.org.au, http://www.speechpathologyaustralia.org.au/.

371.9   USA   ISSN 0736-5829
GV445
▶ **ADAPTED PHYSICAL ACTIVITY QUARTERLY.** Short title: A P A Q. Text in English. 1984. q. USD 52 domestic to individuals; USD 62 foreign to individuals; USD 208 domestic to institutions; USD 218 foreign to institutions; USD 73 combined subscription domestic to individuals print & online eds.; USD 83 combined subscription foreign to individuals print & online eds.; USD 291 combined subscription domestic to institutions print & online eds.; USD 301 combined subscription foreign to institutions print & online eds. (effective 2005). adv. bk.rev. abstr.; bibl.; charts; stat.; illus. index. back issues avail.; reprint service avail. from PSC. **Document type:** *Journal, Academic/Scholarly.* **Description:** Communicates scholarly inquiries related to physical activity for at-risk infants, pre-schoolers, and students who receive special educations.
Related titles: Online - full text ed.: ISSN 1543-2777. USD 62 to individuals; USD 250 to institutions (effective 2005) (from EBSCO Publishing).
Indexed: AMED, CINAHL, DIP, ECER, ERA, ExcerpMed, FoSS&M, IBR, IBZ, PEI, PsycInfo, PsycholAb, RILM, RefZh, SENA, SSCI, SportS, e-psyche.
—BLDSC (0678.308000), GNLM, IDS, IE, Infotrieve, ingenta. **CCC.**
Published by: (International Federation for Adapted Physical Activity), International Association for the Philosophy of Sport/Human Kinetics, PO Box 5076, Champaign, IL 61825-5076. TEL 217-351-5078, 800-747-4457, FAX 217-351-2674, orders@hkusa.com, http://www.humankinetics.com. Ed. David L. Porretta. Pub. Rainer Martens. Adv. contact Chad Hoffman. B&W page USD 300. Circ: 977 (paid and free).

▶ **ADULT BIBLE LESSONS FOR THE DEAF.** see *RELIGIONS AND THEOLOGY—Protestant*

371.94   USA   ISSN 0735-004X
RJ506.L4
▶ **ADVANCES IN LEARNING AND BEHAVIORAL DISABILITIES.** Text in English. 1982. a., latest vol.18, 2005. price varies. back issues avail. **Document type:** *Monographic series, Academic/Scholarly.* **Description:** Devoted to new developments in the study of disorders of learning and behavior.
Related titles: Online - full text ed.: (from ScienceDirect).
Indexed: DIP, IBR, IBZ, PsycholAb, SOPODA, e-psyche.
—BLDSC (0709.258000), GNLM, IE, ingenta. **CCC.**
Published by: J A I Press Inc. (Subsidiary of: Elsevier Science & Technology), 360 Park Ave S, New York, NY 10010-1710. TEL 212-989-5800, FAX 212-633-3990, usinfo-f@elsevier.com, http://www.elsevier.com/wps/find/bookdescription.cws_home/BS_ALBD/description#description. Eds. M A Mastropieri, T E Scruggs.

371.9   USA   ISSN 0270-4013
LC3950   CODEN: ASEDEP
ADVANCES IN SPECIAL EDUCATION; a research annual. Text in English. 1980. a., latest vol.16, 2004. price varies. back issues avail. **Document type:** *Monographic series, Academic/Scholarly.*
Related titles: Online - full text ed.: (from ScienceDirect).
Indexed: ABIn, EduInd, PsycholAb.
—BLDSC (0711.530000), IE, ingenta. **CCC.**
Published by: J A I Press Inc. (Subsidiary of: Elsevier Science & Technology), 360 Park Ave S, New York, NY 10010-1710. TEL 212-989-5800, FAX 212-633-3990, usinfo-f@elsevier.com, http://www.elsevier.com/wps/find/bookdescription.cws_home/BS_ASE/description#description. Ed. Anthony F Rotatori.

371.94   USA
ADVOCATE (BETHESDA). Text in English. 1968. bi-m. USD 25 domestic to individual members; USD 40 foreign to individual members; USD 200 to institutions. adv. bk.rev. **Document type:** *Newsletter.* **Description:** Provides the latest news on autism. Features include personal stories. Includes information on medical research and legislative issues.
Formerly (1979): N S A C Newsletter (0047-9101)
Media: Duplicated (not offset).
Indexed: e-psyche.
Published by: Autism Society of America, 7910 Woodmont Ave, Ste 300, Bethesda, MD 20814-3015. TEL 301-657-0881, 800-328-8476, FAX 301-657-0869, http://www.autism-society.org. Circ: 24,000 (paid).

AGING & VISION; a publication for practitioners, researchers and educators. see *HANDICAPPED—Visually Impaired*

371.93   DEU
DIE AKZENTE. Text in German. q. EUR 29; EUR 9.70 newsstand/cover (effective 2003). **Document type:** *Journal, Academic/Scholarly.*
Published by: (Arbeitskreis Ueberaktives Kind e.V.), Paedagogischer Zeitschriftenverlag GmbH & Co. KG, Axel-Springer-Str. 54b, Berlin, 10117, Germany. TEL 49-30-20183592, FAX 49-30-20183593, info@pzv-berlin.de, http://www.pzv-berlin.de.

ALL INDIA INSTITUTE OF SPEECH AND HEARING. JOURNAL. see *HANDICAPPED—Hearing Impaired*

AMERICAN ANNALS OF THE DEAF. see *HANDICAPPED—Hearing Impaired*

AMERICAN ERA. see *HANDICAPPED—Hearing Impaired*

AMERICAN PRINTING HOUSE FOR THE BLIND. DEPARTMENT OF EDUCATIONAL AND TECHNICAL RESEARCH. REPORT OF RESEARCH AND DEVELOPMENT ACTIVITIES. see *HANDICAPPED—Visually Impaired*

AMERICAN SOCIETY FOR ADOLESCENT PSYCHIATRY. NEWSLETTER. see *MEDICAL SCIENCES—Psychiatry And Neurology*

THE ANN CRAFT TRUST BULLETIN. see *SOCIAL SERVICES AND WELFARE*

371.913   USA   ISSN 0736-9387
RJ496.A5   CODEN: ORSBBT
▶ **ANNALS OF DYSLEXIA;** an interdisciplinary journal of specific language disability. Text in English. 1951. a. USD 30 to non-members; USD 24 to members (effective 2004). reprint service avail. from PQC. **Document type:** *Academic/Scholarly.* **Description:** Covers the scientific study of dyslexia, its comorbid conditions; and theory-based practices on remediation, and intervention of dyslexia and related areas of written language disorders including spelling, composing and mathematics.
Formerly (until 1981): Orton Society. Bulletin (0474-7534)
Related titles: Microform ed.: (from PQC); Online - full text ed.: (from bigchalk, EBSCO Publishing, H.W. Wilson, O C L C Online Computer Library Center, Inc., ProQuest Information & Learning).
Indexed: ABIn, ASCA, CDA, CIJE, CurCont, DSHAb, EAA, ECER, EduInd, FamI, L&LBA, PsycInfo, PsycholAb, SOPODA, SSCI, e-psyche.
—BLDSC (1040.357500), IDS, IE, ingenta.
Published by: International Dyslexia Association, Chester Bldg, Suite 382, 8600 LaSalle Rd, Baltimore, MD 21286-2044. TEL 410-296-0232, FAX 410-321-5069, http://www.interdys.org/. Ed. Che Kan Leong. Circ: 10,000.

371.95   USA   ISSN 0198-7518
LC4031
▶ **ANNUAL EDITIONS: EDUCATING EXCEPTIONAL CHILDREN.** Key Title: Educating Exceptional Children. Text in English. 1979. a., latest 2003, 33rd ed. USD 20.31 per vol. (effective 2004). illus. **Document type:** *Academic/Scholarly.*
Published by: McGraw-Hill - Dushkin (Subsidiary of: McGraw-Hill Higher Education), 2460 Kerper Blvd, Dubuque, IA 52001. TEL 800-243-6532, customer.service@mcgraw-hill.com, http://www.dushkin.com/text-data/catalog/0072874481.mhtml. Ed. Dr. Karen L. Freiberg. Pub. Ian Nielsen. R&P Cheryl Greenleaf.

371.9   CAN   ISSN 1189-3958
▶ **APPRENTISSAGE ET SOCIALISATION.** Text in French; Summaries in English. 1965. s-a. CND 20 to individuals; CND 30 to institutions (effective 2000). adv. bk.rev. **Document type:** *Academic/Scholarly.*
Former titles (until 1991): Apprentissage et Socialisation en Piste (0827-1844); (until 1985): Apprentissage et Socialisation (0704-7517); (until 1978): Enfant Exceptionnel (0046-1970)
Indexed: CEI, PdeR, PsycInfo, PsycholAb, e-psyche.
Published by: Universite du Quebec a Hull, C P 1250, succ B, Hull, PQ J8X 3X7, Canada. TEL 819-595-3900, FAX 819-595-4459, therese_deslierres@uqah.uquebec.ca, http://www.uqah.uquebec.ca/apprentisage/index.html. Ed. Therese Des Lierres. Circ: 1,500 (paid).

371.9   USA
ARKANSAS. DIVISION OF REHABILITATION SERVICES. ANNUAL REPORT. Text in English. 1940. a. free. illus.; stat.
Published by: Division of Rehabilitation Services, PO Box 3781, Little Rock, AR 72203. TEL 501-628-8168. Circ: 1,000.

371.95   USA   ISSN 1534-5084
LB3050
▶ **ASSESSMENT FOR EFFECTIVE INTERVENTION.** Text in English. 1976. q. USD 28 domestic; USD 32 foreign (effective 2004). adv. bk.rev. illus. back issues avail.; reprints avail. **Document type:** *Academic/Scholarly.* **Description:** Directed to psychologists, diagnosticians, and special educators who use methods of educational measurement in evaluating exceptional individuals.
Formerly: Diagnostique (0737-2477)
Related titles: Microform ed.: (from PQC).
Indexed: CIJE, CPE, ECER, FamI, PsycInfo, PsycholAb, e-psyche.
—BLDSC (1746.637570), IE, ingenta. **CCC.**
Published by: Council for Educational Diagnostic Services (Subsidiary of: Council for Exceptional Children), 1920 Association Dr., Reston, VA 22091. http://www.unr.edu/educ/ceds/. Ed. Linda K. Elksnin. Circ: 1,800.

E

371.9 USA ISSN 1040-0435
RM698 CODEN: ASTEF2
➤ **ASSISTIVE TECHNOLOGY.** Text in English. 1989. s-a. USD 65 in US & Canada to individuals; USD 80 elsewhere to individuals; USD 75 in US & Canada to institutions; USD 90 elsewhere to institutions (effective 2004). adv. back issues avail. **Document type:** *Journal, Academic/Scholarly.*
Description: Seeks to foster communications among researchers, developers, clinicians, educators, consumers and others working in all aspects of the assistive technology arena.
Indexed: AgeL, CINAHL, CurCont, ExcerpMed, Inspec, MEDLINE, PsycInfo, PsycholAb, SSCI.
—AskIEEE, Ei, GNLM, IDS, Infotrieve.
Published by: R E S N A, 1700 N Moore St, Ste 1540, Arlington, VA 22209-1903. TEL 703-524-6686, journal@resna.org, info@resna.org, http://www.resna.org. Ed. Jeff Jutai. Circ: 1,900. **Subscr. to:** Allen Press Inc., PO Box 1897, Lawrence, KS 66044.

371.9 SWE ISSN 0345-0384
ATT UNDERVISA. Text in Swedish. 1969. 6/yr. SEK 250 (effective 2004). adv.
Published by: Svenska Foerbundet foer Specialpedagogik, c/o Aake Joeneby, Bjoerkdalsvaegen 9, PEREBO, 70230, Sweden. ingabritt.c@telia.com, http://www.awj.se/attundervisa. adv.: B&W page SEK 4,000, color page SEK 6,500; 185 x 260. **Subscr. to:** SFSP-Inform, Spanngatan 5, Linkoeping 587 35, Sweden. TEL 46-13-24-58-15.

371.9142 USA ISSN 0897-9278
AUGMENTATIVE COMMUNICATION NEWS. Text in English. 1988. q. USD 50 in US & Canada to individuals; USD 62 elsewhere to individuals; USD 75 in US & Canada to institutions; USD 88 elsewhere to institutions (effective 2004). **Document type:** *Newsletter, Academic/Scholarly.*
Published by: Augmentative Communication, Inc., One Surf Way, Ste 237, Monterey, CA 93940. TEL 831-649-3050, FAX 831-646-5428, http://www.augcominc.com/acn.html.

371.91 AUS ISSN 1030-0112
AUSTRALASIAN JOURNAL OF SPECIAL EDUCATION. Text in English. 1977. s-a.
Formerly (until 1987): Australian Journal of Special Education (0157-7379)
—BLDSC (1795.170000), IE, ingenta.
Published by: (New Zealand Special Education Association NZL), Australian Association of Special Education Inc., P O Box 226, Bomaderry, NSW 2541, Australia. http://www.aase.edu.au/.

371.91 AUS ISSN 1324-8928
➤ **AUSTRALIAN JOURNAL OF LEARNING DISABILITIES.** Text in English. 1969. q. AUD 73 domestic; AUD 75 to New Zealand & SE Asia; AUD 81 elsewhere (effective 2003). adv. bk.rev.; software rev.; video rev. index. back issues avail.; reprints avail. **Document type:** *Journal, Academic/Scholarly.*
Description: Covers all aspects of special education. Looks at learning disabilities and the intelligent underachiever.
Former titles (until June 1996): Australian Journal of Remedial Education (0311-1954); Remedial Education (0048-7236)
Related titles: E-mail ed.
Indexed: AEI, AusPAIS, CPE, ECER, ERA, ETA, L&LBA, MEA, RHEA, SEA, SENA, SOMA, SOPODA, TEA.
Published by: Learning Difficulties Australia (LDA), 4 Canterbury Rd, Toorak, VIC 3142, Australia. TEL 61-3-98260371, FAX 61-3-98262696, davidson@netspace.org.au, http://www.ldaustralia.org/journal%20past.html. Ed., R&P, Adv. contact Christopher Davidson. page AUD 320. Circ: 1,000.

▼ ➤ **AUTISM SPECTRUM QUARTERLY.** see *MEDICAL SCIENCES—Psychiatry And Neurology*

371.9 DNK ISSN 0109-0135
AVIS 81. Text in Danish. 1982. 11/yr. DKK 242 to members (effective 2002). illus. **Document type:** *Magazine, Trade.*
Published by: Speciallaererforeningen af 1981, Aabenraa 5, 4, Copenhagen K, 1124, Denmark. TEL 45-33-14-50-65, FAX 45-33-91-50-01. Ed. Leif Sort. Circ: 1,800 (paid).

B I L D SEMINAR PAPERS. (British Institute of Learning Disabilities) see *MEDICAL SCIENCES—Psychiatry And Neurology*

BACK TO WORK. see *OCCUPATIONAL HEALTH AND SAFETY*

371.9 DEU ISSN 0170-902X
DAS BAND. Text in German. 1970. bi-m. EUR 15 (effective 2005). adv. bk.rev.; play rev. abstr.; illus.; tr.lit. **Document type:** *Magazine, Consumer.*
Indexed: RefZh.
Published by: Bundesverband fuer Koerper- und Mehrfachbehinderte e.V., Brehmstr 5-7, Duesseldorf, 40239, Germany. TEL 49-211-640040, FAX 49-211-6400420, dasband@bvkm.de, info@bvkm.de, http://www.bvkm.de/0-10/zeitschriften,dasband.html. Ed. Stephanie Wilken Dapper. Circ: 20,000.

616.858842 POL ISSN 1428-7439
BARDZIEJ KOCHANI; magazyn poswiecony problemom osob z zespolem Downa i ich rodzin. Text in Polish. 1997. q. 40 p./no.; **Document type:** *Magazine, Consumer.*
Published by: Stowarzyszenia Rodzin i Opiekunow Osob z Zespolem Downa Bardziej Kochani, Ul Inflancka 8, Warsaw, 00189, Poland. TEL 48-22-6659292, FAX 48-22-6651112, bardziej_kochani@go2.pl. Ed. Ewa Danielewska. Circ: 2,000.

BAUSTEINE KINDERGARTEN. see *EDUCATION—Teaching Methods And Curriculum*

371.94 USA ISSN 0198-7429
➤ **BEHAVIORAL DISORDERS.** Text in English. 1976. q. USD 20 domestic to individuals; USD 50 domestic to institutions; USD 54 foreign (effective 2004). adv. bk.rev. reprint service avail. from PQC. **Document type:** *Academic/Scholarly.* **Description:** Directed to educators, parents, mental health personnel and others concerned with the education and well-being of children and youth with behavioral and emotional disorders.
Related titles: Microform ed.: (from PQC); Online - full text ed.: (from bigchalk, ProQuest Information & Learning).
Indexed: ABIn, ASCA, CIJE, CJA, CurCont, ECER, EduInd, FamI, MEA, PsycInfo, PsycholAb, SENA, SSCI, e-psyche.
—BLDSC (1877.370000), IE, Infotrieve, ingenta.
Published by: (Council for Children with Behavioral Disorders), Council for Exceptional Children, 1110 N. Glebe Rd., Ste. 300, Arlington, VA 22201-4795. TEL 703-264-9481, FAX 703-264-1637, http://www.cec.sped.org/. Eds. Gary Sasso, Jo Hendrickson. R&P Robert Gable. Circ: 9,000.

371.9 DEU ISSN 0171-9718
BEHINDERTENHILFE DURCH ERZIEHUNG, UNTERRICHT UND THERAPIE. Text in German. 1977. irreg., latest vol.18, 1993. price varies. **Document type:** *Monographic series.*
Published by: Ernst Reinhardt Verlag, Kemnatenstr 46, Munich, 80639, Germany. TEL 49-89-1780160, FAX 49-89-17801630. Ed. Otto Speck.

371.9 DEU ISSN 0341-7301
BEHINDERTENPAEDAGOGIK; Vierteljahresschrift fuer Behindertenpaedagogik in Praxis, Forschung und Lehre und Integration Behinderter. Text in German. 1971. q. EUR 35; EUR 28 to students (effective 2003). adv. bk.rev. bibl. index. **Document type:** *Journal, Academic/Scholarly.*
Indexed: DIP, IBR, IBZ, PsycholAb.
Published by: Verlag Jarick Oberbiel GmbH & Co. KG, Postfach 30, Solms-Oberbiel, 35602, Germany. TEL 49-6441-5868, FAX 49-6441-51614, behindertenpaedagogik@jarick-oberbiel.de, info@jarick-oberbiel.de, http://www.jarick-oberbiel.de. Ed. Dr. Peter Roedler. Circ: 2,500.

371.9 DEU ISSN 0723-4511
BEHINDERTENPAEDAGOGIK IN BAYERN. Text in German. 1957. q. adv. bk.rev. back issues avail. **Document type:** *Academic/Scholarly.*
Formerly (until 1981): Sonderschule in Bayern (0723-4503)
Published by: Verband Deutscher Sonderschulen e.V., LV Bayern, Welserstr 11, Nuernberg, 90489, Germany. TEL 49-911-5303861, FAX 49-911-5303861. Circ: 3,000.

371.9 USA
BETHPHAGE MESSENGER. Text in English. 3/yr.
Published by: Bethphage, Lind Center, South 118th St. Suite A, Omaha, NE 681372221. TEL 800-279-1234, 402-896-3884, FAX 402-894-4784, http://www.bethphage.org/organization/newsletter.html. Ed. Carrie L Reed. Circ: 100,000.

371.94 USA ISSN 1074-2956
BEYOND BEHAVIOR. Text in English. 1990. 3/yr. **Document type:** *Journal, Academic/Scholarly.*
Published by: Council for Children with Behavioral Disorders, 1110 N Glebe Rd, Ste 300, Arlington, VA 22201-5704. http://www.ccbd.net/. Ed. Cavin Clark.

BIBLIOGRAFIA ERITYSIRYHMIEN LIIKUNNAN TUTKIMUKSESTA/BIBLIOGRAPHY ON RESEARCH IN PHYSICAL EDUCATION AND SPORT FOR THE HANDICAPPED. see *EDUCATION—Abstracting, Bibliographies, Statistics*

371.93 DEU ISSN 1614-9971
▼ **BILDUNG FUER NACHHALTIGE ENTWICKLUNG.** Text in German. 2005. irreg. price varies. **Document type:** *Monographic series, Academic/Scholarly.*
Published by: Verlag Dr. Kovac, Arnoldstr 49, Hamburg, 22763, Germany. TEL 49-40-3988800, FAX 49-40-39888055, info@verlagdrkovac.de, http://www.verlagdrkovac.de/7-22.htm.

BRITISH ASSOCIATION OF TEACHERS OF THE DEAF. MAGAZINE. see *HANDICAPPED—Hearing Impaired*

BRITISH INSTITUTE OF LEARNING DISABILITIES. CURRENT AWARENESS SERVICE. see *EDUCATION—Abstracting, Bibliographies, Statistics*

371.92 GBR ISSN 0969-7950
RC569.7 CODEN: BJDDE2
➤ **BRITISH JOURNAL OF DEVELOPMENTAL DISABILITIES.** Abbreviated title: B J D D. Text in English. 1952. s-a. GBP 32 in Europe; USD 49 in United States; CND 69 in Canada; AUD 75 in Australia; GBP 36 elsewhere (effective 2002). adv. bk.rev. charts; illus. cum.index every 2 yrs. **Document type:** *Journal, Academic/Scholarly.* **Description:** Provides an international forum for a multidisciplinary approach to the problems posed by mental handicaps and learning disabilities.
Former titles (until 1992): British Journal of Mental Subnormality (0374-633X); Journal of Mental Subnormality (0022-2666)
Indexed: AMHA, ASCA, ASSIA, AgeL, BDM&CN, BiolAb, BrEdI, BrNI, CINAHL, CurCont, ExcerpMed, FamI, L&LBA, MEA&I, PsycInfo, PsycholAb, SENA, SOPODA, SSCI, e-psyche.
—BLDSC (2307.450000), GNLM, IDS, IE, Infotrieve, ingenta, KNAW.
Published by: (British Society for Developmental Disabilities), S E F A (Publications) Ltd., The Globe, 4 Great William St, Stratford-upon-Avon, Warks CV37 6RY, United Kingdom. editor@bjdd.org, http://www.bjdd.org, http://www.sefa.org.uk. Ed. A L Gunzburg. Pub., R&P W H Gunzberg. Adv. contact B Salmons. Circ: 1,500 (paid). **Subscr. to:** British Society for Developmental Disabilities, BJDD Admin., 2 Wellacres Cottages, Draycott, Moreton-in-Marsh B43 6ED, United Kingdom. FAX 44-1386-701142, smc@bjdd.org.

371.9 GBR ISSN 0952-3383
LC3986.G7 CODEN: BJSPEB
BRITISH JOURNAL OF SPECIAL EDUCATION. Text in English. 1974. q. EUR 71 combined subscription in Europe to individuals print & online eds.; USD 79 combined subscription in the Americas to individuals & Caribbean (print & online eds.); GBP 47 combined subscription elsewhere to individuals print & online eds.; GBP 207 combined subscription in Europe to institutions print & online eds.; USD 395 combined subscription in the Americas to institutions & Caribbean (print & online eds.); GBP 235 combined subscription elsewhere to institutions print & online eds. (effective 2006). adv. bk.rev. cum.index: 1974-1983. back issues avail.; reprints avail. **Document type:** *Journal, Academic/Scholarly.*
Formerly (until 1985): Special Education - Forward Trends (0305-7526); Which was formed by the 1974 merger of: Special Education (0038-6707); Forward Trends (0015-8658)
Related titles: Microfiche ed.; Microfilm ed.; Online - full text ed.: ISSN 1467-8578. GBP 196 in Europe to institutions; USD 375 in the Americas to institutions & Caribbean; GBP 223 elsewhere to institutions (effective 2006) (from Blackwell Synergy, EBSCO Publishing, Gale Group, IngentaConnect, O C L C Online Computer Library Center, Inc., Swets Information Services).
Indexed: ASSIA, BrEdI, CDA, CIJE, CPE, ChLitAb, ECER, ERA, ETA, HECAB, L&LBA, LT&LA, MEA, MEDLINE, RASB, RHEA, SEA, SENA, SOMA, SOPODA, TEA, e-psyche.
—BLDSC (2324.850000), GNLM, IE, Infotrieve, ingenta. **CCC.**
Published by: (National Association for Special Educational Needs), Blackwell Publishing Ltd., 9600 Garsington Rd, Oxford, OX4 2ZG, United Kingdom. TEL 44-1865-776868, FAX 44-1865-714591, customerservices@oxon.blackwellpublishing.com, http://www.blackwellpublishing.com/journals/BJSE. Ed. Richard Byers TEL 44-1223369631.

BRITISH JOURNAL OF VISUAL IMPAIRMENT. see *HANDICAPPED—Visually Impaired*

371.91 DEU ISSN 0172-0996
DAS BRUDERHAUS. Text in German. 1949. s-a. free.
Published by: Gustav Werner Stiftung, Ringelbachstr 211, Reutlingen, 72762, Germany. FAX 07121-278300. Ed. I Steudle. Circ: 20,000.

DAS BUERO (MARBURG). see *HANDICAPPED—Visually Impaired*

371.9 DEU
BUNDESARBEITSGEMEINSCHAFT HILFE FUER BEHINDERTE. BERICHTE. JAHRESSPIEGEL. Text in German. a. free. **Document type:** *Academic/Scholarly.*
Formerly: Bundesarbeitsgemeinschaft Hilfe fuer Behinderte. Jahrespiegel
Published by: Bundesarbeitsgemeinschaft Hilfe fuer Behinderte e.V., Kirchfeldstr 149, Duesseldorf, 40215, Germany. Ed. Elfriede Loebel.

C A E D H H JOURNAL/ASSOCIATION CANADIENNE DES ENSEIGNANTS(ES) DES SOURDS(ES) ET DES MALENTENDANTS(ES). REVUE. see *HANDICAPPED—Hearing Impaired*

371.9 USA
C C B D NEWSLETTER. Text in English. 1987. 4/yr. membership only. **Document type:** *Newsletter.* **Description:** Gives information on the council and its activities; includes news, legislation and other developments in the field.
Published by: (Council for Children with Behavioral Disorders), Council for Exceptional Children, 1110 N. Glebe Rd., Ste. 300, Arlington, VA 22201-4795. TEL 703-620-3660, FAX 703-264-9494. Ed. Brenda Scheuermann. R&P Robert Gable. Circ: 8,400.

C D R REPORTS. see *POLITICAL SCIENCE—Civil Rights*

E

C P D NEWS. (Center for Persons with Disabilities) see *HANDICAPPED*

371.9 BRN ISSN 0827-3391
CANADIAN JOURNAL OF SPECIAL EDUCATION. Text in English. 1984. s-a. BND 25. **Document type:** *Academic/Scholarly.*
Related titles: Microfiche ed.: (from MML); Microform ed.: (from MML).
Indexed: CEI, CIJE, ECER.
—CCC.
Published by: Center for Human Development and Research, c/o Dr. Marg Csapo, Special Education Unit, Ministry of Education, Bandar Seri Begawan, Brunei Darussalam. TEL 673-446-553.

THE CAPSTONE (TOWSON); news from the Council, and its accreditation and evaluation systems and ProLerna. see *HANDICAPPED*

371.95 USA ISSN 0885-7288
LC3981
CAREER DEVELOPMENT FOR EXCEPTIONAL INDIVIDUALS. Text in English. 1978. s-a. USD 25 domestic; USD 24 foreign (effective 2004). bk.rev. illus. reprints avail. **Document type:** *Academic/Scholarly.* **Description:** Contains articles on the latest research activities, model programs, and issues in career development and transition planning for exceptional individuals.
Related titles: Microform ed.: (from PQC); Online - full text ed.: ISSN 1557-5047 (from Gale Group, IngentaConnect, ProQuest Information & Learning).
Indexed: CIJE, ECER.
—CCC.
Published by: (Council for Exceptional Children), Pro-Ed Inc., 8700 Shoal Creek Blvd, Austin, TX 78757-6897. TEL 512-451-3246, 800-897-3202, FAX 512-451-8542, 800-397-7633, journals@proedinc.com, http://www.proedinc.com. Eds. Michael Benz, Michael Bullis. Circ: 2,700.

371.90285 USA ISSN 0897-3318
CATALYST (MENLO PARK). Text in English. 1981. q. USD 12 to individuals; USD 18 to institutions. bk.rev. **Document type:** *Newsletter.* **Description:** Directed to educators and administrators interested in microcomputer applications to special education and rehabilitation.
Indexed: CIJE.
Published by: Western Center for Microcomputers in Special Education, Inc., 1259 El Camino Real, Ste 275, Menlo Park, CA 94025. TEL 415-855-8064. Ed. Sue Swezey.

CHICOREL INDEX SERIES. see *BIBLIOGRAPHIES*

371.9 GBR ISSN 0265-6590
LC4704.5
➤ **CHILD LANGUAGE TEACHING AND THERAPY.** Text in English. 1985. 3/yr. GBP 58 in the European Union to individuals; USD 108 in North America to individuals; GBP 67 elsewhere to individuals; GBP 153 in Europe to institutions; USD 291 in North America to institutions; GBP 170 elsewhere to institutions; GBP 85 in developing nations; GBP 50 per issue in Europe; USD 100 per issue in North America; GBP 56 per issue elsewhere (effective 2006); Subscr. includes online access. adv. bk.rev. back issues avail.; reprints avail. **Document type:** *Journal, Academic/Scholarly.* **Description:** Helps persons involved with children handicapped by an inadequate command of the spoken or written language.
Related titles: Online - full text ed.: ISSN 1477-0865 (from EBSCO Publishing, Gale Group, IngentaConnect, O C L C Online Computer Library Center, Inc., ProQuest Information & Learning, Swets Information Services).
Indexed: ASSIA, BrEdI, CDA, CINAHL, CPE, ChPerI, DIP, ERA, ETA, FamI, IBR, IBZ, L&LBA, LT&LA, MEA, MLA-IB, PCI, PsycInfo, PsycholAb, RHEA, RILM, RefZh, SEA, SENA, SOMA, SOPODA, TEA, e-psyche.
—BLDSC (3172.944690), IE, Infotrieve, ingenta. **CCC.**
Published by: Hodder Arnold Journals (Subsidiary of: Hodder Headline plc.), 338 Euston Rd, London, NW1 3BH, United Kingdom. TEL 44-20-78736000, FAX 44-20-78736367, arnoldjournals@hodder.co.uk, http://www.clttjournal.com, http://www.hodderarnoldjournals.com/. Eds. Carol Miller, Jannet Wright. Adv. contact Mary Attree. B&W page GBP 370; trim 120 x 200. Circ: 900. **Subscr. to:** Extenza - Turpin, Pegasus Dr, Stratton Business Park, Biggleswade, Beds SG18 8TQ, United Kingdom. TEL 44-1462-488900, FAX 44-1462-480947, subscriptions @turpinltd.com.

➤ **CHILD PSYCHIATRY AND HUMAN DEVELOPMENT.** see *MEDICAL SCIENCES—Psychiatry And Neurology*

371.9 JPN ISSN 0916-2682
CHIRYO KYOIKU KENKYU KIYO/GIFU UNIVERSITY. DEPARTMENT OF REMEDIAL EDUCATION. REPORT. Text in Japanese. 1979. a.
Published by: (Chiryo Kyoikugaku Kenkyushitsu), Gifu Daigaku, Kyoikugakubu/Gifu University, Faculty of Education, 1-1 Yanagi-To, Gifu, 501-1112, Japan.

CLINICAL CHILD AND FAMILY PSYCHOLOGY REVIEW. see *PSYCHOLOGY*

371.9142 USA ISSN 0890-409X
RJ496.C67
CLINICAL CONNECTION; idea source for the speech and language specialist working with the young communicator. Text in English. 1986. q. USD 39 domestic; USD 43 in Canada; USD 49 elsewhere. bk.rev. back issues avail. **Document type:** *Academic/Scholarly.* **Description:** Forum for speech and language pathologists to share practical clinical ideas.
Published by: A A D of Northern Virginia, 708 Pendleton St, Alexandria, VA 22314-1819. TEL 703-549-5126, FAX 703-548-5563. Ed. Georgina Ruley Parks. Circ: 6,000.

CLINICAL LINGUISTICS & PHONETICS. see *MEDICAL SCIENCES—Psychiatry And Neurology*

371.9025 USA ISSN 0886-1935
HV1569.5
CLOSING THE GAP. Text in English. 1982. bi-m. USD 34 domestic; USD 49 in Canada & Mexico; USD 66 elsewhere (effective 2005). adv. bk.rev. **Document type:** *Journal, Academic/Scholarly.* **Description:** Aimed at people working with persons with disabilities and those interested in the use of micro-computers in special education and rehabilitation. Each issue contains information emphasizing the practical applications of micro-computers as personal tools and educational aids for the handicapped.
Related titles: Online - full text ed.: (from Northern Light Technology, Inc.).
Indexed: CWI, SoftBase.
Address: PO Box 68, Henderson, MN 56044. TEL 507-248-3294, FAX 507-248-3810, info@closingthegap.com, http://www.closingthegap.com. Ed. Budd Hagen. Adv. contact Maryann Harty. Circ: 10,000.

371.9 371.3 FRA ISSN 0763-949X
COLLECTION C R E S A S. (Centre de Recherche de l'Education Specialisee et de l'Adaptation Scolaire) Text in French. 1969. irreg.
Former titles (until 1982): S R E S A S. Section de Recherche de l'Education Specialisee et de l'Adaptation Scolaire (0247-0942); (until 1976): C R E S A S. Centre de Recherche de l'Education Specialisee et de l'Adaptation Scolaire (0248-6024); (until 1972): Travaux du Centre de Recherche de l'Education Specialisee et de l'Adaptation Scolaire (0247-0993)
Published by: L' Harmattan, 5 rue de l'Ecole Polytechnique, Paris, 75005, France. TEL 33-1-43257651, FAX 33-1-43258203, http://www.editions-harmattan.fr.

371.94 GBR ISSN 0045-7663
COMMUNICATION (LONDON, 1967); the magazine of the National Autistic Society. Text in English. 1967. 3/yr. GBP 11 domestic to members; GBP 16 foreign to members (effective 2001). adv. bk.rev. 32 p./no.; **Document type:** *Magazine.*
Indexed: CurCont, SSCI.
—BLDSC (3354.818000).
Published by: National Autistic Society, 393 City Rd, London, EC1V 1NG, United Kingdom. TEL 44-20-7833-2299, FAX 44-20-7833-9666, communication@nas.org.uk, http://www.nas.org.uk. Ed., R&P Anne Cooper. Circ: 10,000 (paid).

371.9142 USA ISSN 1525-7401
RC423.A1
➤ **COMMUNICATION DISORDERS QUARTERLY.** Text in English. 1977. 4/yr., latest vol.24, Sum. USD 46 in North America to individuals; USD 76 elsewhere to individuals; USD 124 in North America to institutions; USD 156 elsewhere to institutions (effective 2006). adv. bk.rev. 64 p./no.; back issues avail.; reprint service avail. from PSC. **Document type:** *Journal, Academic/Scholarly.* **Description:** Discusses many aspects of communication disorders: speech, hearing, language, and learning disabilities.
Former titles: Journal of Children's Communication Development (1093-5703); (until 1995): Journal of Childhood Communication Disorders (0735-3170)
Related titles: Microform ed.; Online - full text ed.: ISSN 1538-4837 (from EBSCO Publishing, Florida Center for Library Automation, Gale Group, IngentaConnect, ProQuest Information & Learning).
Indexed: CIJE, CINAHL, CPE, ECER, ERA, ETA, MEA, PsycInfo, PsycholAb, RHEA, SEA, SENA, SOMA, SOPODA, TEA, e-psyche.
—BLDSC (3359.821000), IE, ingenta. **CCC.**
Published by: (Council for Exceptional Children), Pro-Ed Inc., 8700 Shoal Creek Blvd, Austin, TX 78757-6897. TEL 512-451-3246, 800-897-3202, FAX 512-302-9129, 800-397-7633, journals@proedinc.com, http://www.proedinc.com/cdq.html. Ed. Kathy Coufal. Pub. Donald D Hammill. R&P, Adv. contact Paula Gonzalez. page USD 400. Circ: 1,900 (paid and free).

➤ **CONSUMER TIMES.** see *HANDICAPPED—Visually Impaired*

371.9 USA ISSN 1053-1386
COUNTERPOINT (HORSHAM). Text in English. q. USD 39.95 (effective 2006). **Document type:** *Newspaper, Trade.* **Description:** Provides teachers and administrators with innovative practices in curriculum and technology, descriptions of new products, publications and videos, meeting and convention information, and a roundup of special education news from the states.
Formerly (until 1985): The Independent Counterpoint (0739-9421)
Published by: (National Association of State Directors of Special Education), L R P Publications, 747 Dresher Rd, PO Box 980, Horsham, PA 19044. TEL 215-784-0860, 800-341-7874, FAX 215-784-9639, custserve@lrp.com, http://www.shoplrp.com/product/p-300025.html, http://www.lrp.com.

371.912 USA
COURAGE NEWS. Text in English. q. free. back issues avail.
Published by: Courage Center, 3915 Golden Valley Rd., Golden Valley, MN 55422. TEL 612-520-0520, FAX 612-520-0577.

371.91 USA ISSN 1059-8243
➤ **CUED SPEECH JOURNAL.** Short title: C S Journal. Text in English. 1985. a. USD 5 to non-members. adv. abstr.; bibl.; charts; stat. 80 p./no.; back issues avail. **Document type:** *Journal, Academic/Scholarly.* **Description:** Discusses professional use of and research on Cued Speech, a system of communication for people with hearing, speech and language needs.
Formerly: Cued Speech Annual (1041-6226)
Published by: National Cued Speech Association, 23970 Hermitage Rd., Shaker Heights, OH 44122. TEL 216-292-6213, 800-459-3529, cuedspdisc@aol.com, http://www.cuedspeech.org/CSJ/index.html. Ed., R&P, Adv. contact Pam Beck. Circ: 500.

➤ **CURRENT EVENTS (LARGE PRINT EDITION).** see *CHILDREN AND YOUTH—For*

➤ **CURRENT SCIENCE (LARGE PRINT EDITION).** see *CHILDREN AND YOUTH—For*

➤ **D B S V JAHRBUCH.** see *HANDICAPPED—Visually Impaired*

371.928 USA
D D D EXPRESS. (Division on Developmental Disabilities) Text in English. 1984. s-a. membership only. **Document type:** *Newsletter.* **Description:** Presents information on the division and its activities. Includes news in the field of mental retardation.
Former titles (until 2002): M R D D Express; C E C - M R Newsletter; C E C - M Report
Related titles: Online - full text ed.
Published by: Council for Exceptional Children, Division on Developmental Disabilities, 1110 N Glebe Rd., Ste 300, Arlington, VA 22201-5704. TEL 703-620-3660, 888-CEC-SPED, FAX 703-264-9494, http://www.mrddcec.org/publications.htm, http://www.dddcec.org/. Ed. Phil Parette. Circ: 7,000 (controlled).

371.9 USA
D L D TIMES. Text in English. 1984. 3/yr. membership only. **Document type:** *Newsletter.* **Description:** Provides information and news in the field of learning disabilities, and the activities of the division.
Published by: (Division for Learning Disabilities), Council for Exceptional Children, 1110 N. Glebe Rd., Ste. 300, Arlington, VA 22201-4795. TEL 703-620-3660, FAX 703-264-9494. Ed. Dr. Kate Garnett. Circ: 12,500.

371.9 USA
D P H D NEWSLETTER. (Division for Physical & Health Disabilities) Text in English. 1980. q. membership only. adv. **Document type:** *Newsletter.* **Description:** Provides information on the division and its activities. Includes news about education for children with physical or health disabilities.
Published by: Council for Exceptional Children, Division for Physical & Health Disabilities, 1110 N. Glebe Rd., Ste. 300, Arlington, VA 22201-4795. TEL 703-620-3660, FAX 703-264-9494, http://www.cec.org, http://www.cec.sped.org. Ed. Sherwood Best. Circ: 1,500.

371.9 DNK ISSN 0908-1755
DANISH CENTRE FOR TECHNICAL AIDS FOR REHABILITATION AND EDUCATION. NEWSLETTER. Text in Danish. 1989. 2/yr. free. bk.rev. **Document type:** *Newsletter.*
Formerly (until 1992): DATCH Information (0905-0221)
Published by: Danish Centre for Technical Aids for Rehabilitation and Special Education, Gregersensvej, Taastrup, 2630, Denmark. TEL 45-43-99-33-22, FAX 45-43-52-70-72. Ed. Joergen Bisgaard.

DEAF - BLIND PERSPECTIVES. see *HANDICAPPED—Visually Impaired*

DEAF WORLDS; international journal of deaf studies. see *HANDICAPPED—Hearing Impaired*

DEAFNESS AND EDUCATION INTERNATIONAL. see *HANDICAPPED—Hearing Impaired*

371.9 DEU ISSN 0939-4702
DEUTSCHE BEHINDERTENZEITSCHRIFT. Abbreviated title: D B Z. Text in German. 1964. bi-m. adv. bk.rev. **Document type:** *Magazine, Consumer.*
Former titles (until 1990): Behindertenzeitschrift (0939-4699); (until 1988): Behinderten-Zeitschrift (0175-5854); (until 1984): Behinderte Kind (0005-7991)
Indexed: RefZh, e-psyche.
—GNLM. **CCC.**
Published by: Reha-Verlag GmbH, Postfach 1460, Remagen, 53404, Germany. TEL 49-2642-992696, FAX 49-2642-992652, http://www.reha-verlag.de. Ed. Leo Sparty. adv.: B&W page EUR 950, color page EUR 1,280; trim 210 x 297. Circ: 10,000 (controlled).

DEVELOPMENTAL DISABILITIES BULLETIN. see *MEDICAL SCIENCES—Psychiatry And Neurology*

DEVELOPMENTAL DISABILITIES SPECIAL INTEREST SECTION QUARTERLY. see *PSYCHOLOGY*

371.95 GBR
DEVON COUNTY COUNCIL. SPECIAL EDUCATIONAL NEEDS SERIES. Text in English. 1993 (no.2). irreg. **Document type:** *Monographic series, Government.*
Indexed: e-psyche.
Published by: Devon County Council, Education, County Hall, Devon County Council, Topsham Rd, Exeter, Devon EX2 4QQ, United Kingdom.

371.95 USA ISSN 0070-5012
LC4007
DIRECTORY FOR EXCEPTIONAL CHILDREN; a listing of educational and training facilities. Text in English. 1954. triennial, latest vol.14, 2001. USD 75 per issue (effective 2004 - 2005). adv. illus.; stat. index. 1056 p./no.; **Document type:** *Directory, Consumer.* **Description:** Includes 3,000 schools, facilities and organizations across the US serving children and young adults with developmental, emotional, physical and medical disabilities.
Indexed: e-psyche.
Published by: Porter Sargent Publishers, Inc., 11 Beacon St, Ste 1400, Boston, MA 02108. TEL 617-523-1670, 800-342-7470, FAX 617-523-1021, info@portersargent.com, http://www.exceptionalchildren.us, http://www.portersargent.com. Ed. Daniel P. McKeever. Pub., Adv. contact John Yonce. page USD 540; 4.25 x 7. Circ: 3,000.

DIRECTORY OF COLLEGE FACILITIES AND SERVICES FOR PEOPLE WITH DISABILITIES. see *EDUCATION—Guides To Schools And Colleges*

371.22 USA ISSN 1077-3282
HV1553
DIRECTORY OF GRANTS FOR ORGANIZATIONS SERVING PEOPLE WITH DISABILITIES; a guide to sources of funding in the United States for programs & services for persons with disabilities. Text in English. 1978. biennial. USD 59.50 per vol.. bk.rev. **Document type:** *Directory.* **Description:** Lists funding sources for programs and services for organizations serving people who are disabled. Provides extensive profiles on foundations and includes essays on grantsmanship to help guide the reader through the intricate process of securing a grant.
Formerly (until 1993): Handicapped Funding Directory (0733-4753)
Published by: Research Grant Guides, PO Box 1214, Loxahatchee, FL 33470. TEL 561-795-6129, FAX 561-795-7794. Ed. Richard M Eckstein.

371.9 USA ISSN 1067-9049
LC4031
DIRECTORY OF SELECTED EARLY CHILDHOOD PROGRAMS. Text in English. 1988. irreg. **Document type:** *Directory.*
Published by: Office of Special Education and Rehabilitative Services, U.S. Department of Education, 400 Maryland Ave SW, Washington, DC 20202. TEL 202-205-5465.

▼ **DISABILITY STUDIES IN EDUCATION.** see *HANDICAPPED*

DIVISION ON VISUAL IMPAIRMENTS QUARTERLY. see *HANDICAPPED—Visually Impaired*

DOWN & UP. see *HANDICAPPED*

371.9144 GBR ISSN 1076-9242
RC394.W6D952 CODEN: DYSLEO
➤ **DYSLEXIA.** Text in English. 1995. q. USD 350 to institutions; USD 358 combined subscription to institutions print & online eds. (effective 2006). adv. back issues avail.; reprint service avail. from PSC. **Document type:** *Journal, Academic/Scholarly.* **Description:** Provides reviews and reports of research, assessment and intervention practice.
Related titles: Microform ed.: (from PQC); Online - full content ed.: ISSN 1099-0909. USD 350 to institutions (effective 2006); Online - full text ed.: (from EBSCO Publishing, Gale Group, IngentaConnect, Swets Information Services, Wiley InterScience).
Indexed: ASSIA, BrEdI, CJA, CPE, CurCont, ERA, ETA, ExcerpMed, IndMed, L&LBA, MEA, MEDLINE, PsycInfo, PsycholAb, RHEA, SEA, SENA, SOMA, SSCI, TEA, e-psyche.
—BLDSC (3637.234000), IE, Infotrieve, ingenta. **CCC.**
Published by: (British Dyslexia Association), John Wiley & Sons Ltd. (Subsidiary of: John Wiley & Sons, Inc.), The Atrium, Southern Gate, Chichester, West Sussex PO19 8SQ, United Kingdom. TEL 44-1243-779777, FAX 44-1243-775878, customer@wiley.co.uk, http://www3.interscience.wiley.com/cgi-bin/jhome/6124, http://www.wiley.co.uk. Ed. A J Fawcett. adv.: B&W page GBP 650, color page GBP 1,550; trim 165 x 248. **Subscr. in the Americas to:** John Wiley & Sons, Inc., 111 River St, Hoboken, NJ 07030-5774. TEL 201-748-6645, 800-225-5945, subinfo@wiley.com.

371.9144 GBR
DYSLEXIA HANDBOOK. Text in English. a.
—BLDSC (3637.237000).
Published by: British Dyslexia Association, 98 London Rd, Reading, RG1 5AU, United Kingdom. TEL 44-118-966-2677, FAX 44-118-966-8271, info@dyslexiahelp-bda.demon.co.uk, http://www.bda-dyslexia.org.uk. Ed. Ian Smythe.

371.9144 GBR ISSN 0308-6275
DYSLEXIA REVIEW. Text in English. 1969. s-a.
Formerly: North Surrey Dyslexia Society Review
—BLDSC (3637.240000), IE, ingenta.
Published by: The Dyslexia Institute, 133 Gresham Rd, Staines, Middx TW18 2Aj, United Kingdom. TEL 44-1784-463851, FAX 44-1784-460747, http://www.dyslexia-inst.org.uk.

EARLY CHILDHOOD LAW AND POLICY REPORTER. see *EDUCATION—Teaching Methods And Curriculum*

371.9 USA ISSN 1058-6482
EARLY CHILDHOOD REPORT; children with special needs and their families. Text in English. 1989. m. USD 175 (effective 2006). back issues avail. **Document type:** *Newsletter.* **Description:** Aims to assist professionals in the early childhood field to avoid litigation and provide proper services to children with special needs.
Related titles: Online - full text ed.: (from LexisNexis).
—**CCC.**
Published by: L R P Publications, 747 Dresher Rd, PO Box 980, Horsham, PA 19044. TEL 215-784-0941, 800-341-7874, FAX 215-784-9014, custserve@lrp.com, http://www.shoplrp.com/product/p-300003.html, http://www.lrp.com. Ed. Judith Malveaux.

371.9 USA ISSN 1058-8396
EARLY INTERVENTION. Text in English. 1986. q. free. bk.rev. back issues avail. **Document type:** *Newsletter.*
Published by: (Illinois Early Childhood Intervention Clearinghouse), Illinois Public Health Association, 223 S Third St, Springfield, IL 62701. TEL 217-522-5687. Ed. Chet Brandt. Circ: 4,900 (controlled). **Subscr. to:** 830 S Spring St, Springfield, IL 62701.

371.9 CAN ISSN 1482-8383
EASTER SEALS - MARCH OF DIMES NATIONAL COUNCIL. ANNUAL REPORT. Text in English, French. 1963. a. free. **Document type:** *Corporate.* **Description:** Information on rehabilitation, fund raising services and the network of organizations improving the quality of life for the disabled.
Formerly: Canadian Rehabilitation Council for the Disabled. Annual Report (0068-9580)
Published by: Easter Seals - March of Dimes National Council, 90 Eglington Ave E, Ste 511, Toronto, ON M4P 2Y3, Canada. TEL 416-932-8382, FAX 416-932-9844, national.council@esmodnc.org, http://www.esmodnc.org. Circ: 2,000.

371.9 ESP ISSN 1139-9899
EDUCACION, DESARROLLO Y DIVERSIDAD. Text in Spanish. 1998. 3/yr.
—CINDOC.
Published by: Asociacion Espanola para la Educacion Especial, Plaza Vicente Risco, s-n, Orense, Galicia 32001, Spain. TEL 34-988-387270, FAX 34-988-219844, X10@uvigo.es. Ed. Jose Manuel Cabada Alvarez.

371.95 GBR ISSN 1367-1960
EDUCATING ABLE CHILDREN. Text in English. 1994. s-a. free with membership. bk.rev. back issues avail. **Description:** Offers teachers and other educators tips and research on providing instruction to exceptional and gifted children.
Formerly (until 1997): Flying High (1357-2377)
Indexed: BrEdI.
—BLDSC (3661.158100), IE, ingenta.
Published by: National Association for Able Children in Education, Arnolds Way, PO Box 242, Oxford, OX2 9FR, United Kingdom. TEL 44-1865-861879, FAX 44-1865-861880, info@nace.co.uk, http://www.nace.co.uk. Ed. Diane Montgomery.

371.95 USA
EDUCATION AND PSYCHOLOGY OF THE GIFTED SERIES. Text in English. irreg. price varies. charts; illus. back issues avail. **Document type:** *Monographic series, Academic/Scholarly.*
Published by: Teachers College Press, Teachers College, Columbia University, 525 W 120th St, Box 303, New York, NY 10027-6694. http://www.teacherscollegepress.com. Pub. Carole Saltz. R&P Amy Detjen. **Dist. by:** Eurospan University Press Group, Order Dept, 3 Henrietta St, London WC2E 8LU, United Kingdom. TEL 44-20-7240-0856, FAX 44-20-7379-0609, http://www.eurospan.co.uk; Pademelon Press, Pty Ltd, 7-10 Anella Ave, PO Box 229, Castle Hill, NSW 2154, Australia. TEL 61-2-9634-2558, FAX 61-2-9680-4634; Transdex International, Pte Ltd, Block 1, Farrer Rd 307-05, Singapore 268817, Singapore. TEL 65-468-6242, FAX 65-462-5457.

371.928 USA ISSN 1547-0350
HV894
EDUCATION AND TRAINING IN DEVELOPMENTAL DISABILITIES. Text in English. 1966. q. USD 30 domestic to individuals; USD 75 domestic to institutions; USD 79.50 foreign; USD 20 newsstand/cover (effective 2005). adv. bk.rev. illus. index. reprint service avail. from PQC. **Document type:** *Journal, Academic/Scholarly.* **Description:** Publishes research into the theory and methodology of teaching students with severe developmental disabilities.
Former titles (until 2003): Education and Training in Mental Retardation and Developmental Disabilities (1079-3917); (until 1994): Education and Training in Mental Retardation (1042-9859); (until Dec. 1986): Education and Training of the Mentally Retarded (0013-1237)
Related titles: Microform ed.: (from PQC); Online - full text ed.: (from H.W. Wilson, O C L C Online Computer Library Center, Inc.).
Indexed: ABIn, AMHA, ASCA, AgeL, BMAb, CIJE, CPE, CurCont, EAA, ECER, EduInd, ExcerpMed, FamI, L&LBA, MEA&I, PsycInfo, PsycholAb, RehabLit, SENA, SOPODA, SSA, SSCI, SWR&A, e-psyche.
—BLDSC (3661.198800), GNLM, IDS, IE, ingenta. **CCC.**
Published by: Council for Exceptional Children, Division on Developmental Disabilities, Special Education Program, PO Box 872011, Tempe, AZ 85287-2011. TEL 480-965-2011, 888-232-7733, FAX 480-965-4942, http://www.dddcec.org/. Ed. Stanley H Zucker. adv.: page USD 500. Circ: 6,500 (controlled).

371.9 USA
➤ **THE EDUCATIONAL THERAPIST.** Text in English. 3/yr. USD 25 to non-members; USD 50 to institutions (effective 2003). **Document type:** *Journal, Academic/Scholarly.* **Description:** Covers learning disabilities issues. For readers on the graduate level in the various disciplines that work with a learning disabled population.
Published by: Association of Educational Therapists, 1804 West Burbank Blvd, Burbank, CA 91506. TEL 818-843-1183, FAX 818-843-7423, aetla@aol.com, http://www.aetonline.org/content.php?PageID=75. Ed. Li Moon.

371.9 GBR ISSN 0964-8690
EDUCATIONAL THERAPY & THERAPEUTIC TEACHING. Text in English. 1985. s-a. GBP 6 to non-members (effective 2000). bk.rev. index. back issues avail. **Document type:** *Academic/Scholarly.* **Description:** Explores the theory of educational therapy, a mode of treatment for persons with learning disabilities. Disseminates knowledge in the field among professionals and students in education, educational psychology, and related disciplines.
Formerly (until 1992): Journal of Educational Therapy (0952-4339)
Indexed: BrEdI, CPE.
—BLDSC (3662.570000), IE, ingenta.
Published by: Forum for the Advancement of Educational Therapy and Therapeutic Teaching, Caspare House, 1 Noel Rd, London, NI 8HQ, United Kingdom. TEL 020 7704 1977. Eds. Lee Marsden, Sue Davies.

371.91 IND
EDUCATOR. Text in English. 1952. s-a. membership. bk.rev. **Document type:** *Newsletter, Trade.*
Former titles (until 1993): I C E V H Educator (8755-9919); International Conference of Educators of Youth. Proceedings (0074-2937)
Indexed: ECER.
—BLDSC (3662.693000).
Published by: International Council for Education of the Visually Handicapped, c/o Nandini Rawal, Jagdish Patel Chowk, Surdas Marg, Vastrapur Ahmedabad, Gujarat, 380 015, India. TEL 91-79-6305082, FAX 91-79-6300106, bpaiceviad1@sancharnet.in, http://www.icevi.org. Circ: 2,200.

EDUCAZIONE DEI SORDI. see *HANDICAPPED—Hearing Impaired*

371.9 USA ISSN 1545-0473
➤ **ELECTRONIC JOURNAL FOR INCLUSIVE EDUCATION**; promoting access to knowledge for all students. Text in English. 1999. irreg. **Document type:** *Academic/Scholarly.*
Media: Online - full content.
Published by: Wright State University, College of Education and Human Services, 3640 Colonel Glenn Hwy., Dayton, OH 45435-0001. TEL 937-775-2821, http://www.ed.wright.edu/~prenick/index.htm. Ed. Patricia R. Renick.

E

▼ new title ➤ refereed ✶ unverified ♦ full entry avail.

371.9 DEU ISSN 1439-8095
ELTERNRUNDBRIEF. Text in German. 1993. 2/yr. bk.rev.
Document type: *Magazine, Consumer.* **Description:** Contains information for parents of children who stutter.
Published by: Bundesvereinigung Stotterer-Selbsthilfe e.V., Zuelpicher Str 58, Cologne, 50674, Germany. TEL 49-221-1391106, FAX 49-221-1391370, info@bvss.de, http://www.bvss.de. Ed. Ruth Heap. Circ: 600 (paid).

371.94 GBR ISSN 1363-2752
RJ506.B44 CODEN: EBDMA2
➤ **EMOTIONAL AND BEHAVIOURAL DIFFICULTIES.** Text in English. 1959. q. GBP 271, USD 515 combined subscription to institutions print & online eds. (effective 2006). adv. bk.rev.
Document type: *Journal, Academic/Scholarly.* **Description:** Covers interests of disturbed children and promotes communication between professional workers involved with them. Regional and national events; monographs on specific topics.
Former titles (until 1996): Therapeutic Care and Education (0968-1728); Maladjustment and Therapeutic Education (0264-4614); New Growth (0261-0477); Therapeutic Education (0305-7860); Association of Workers for Maladjusted Children. Journal
Related titles: Online - full text ed.: ISSN 1741-2692. GBP 258, USD 490 to institutions (effective 2006) (from C S A, EBSCO Publishing, O C L C Online Computer Library Center, Inc., Sage Publications, Inc., Swets Information Services).
Indexed: ASSIA, BrEdI, CINAHL, CPE, ERA, ESPM, ETA, ExcerpMed, FamI, MEA, PsycInfo, PsycholAb, RHEA, RiskAb, SEA, SENA, SFSA, SOMA, SWA, SWR&A, TEA, e-psyche.
—BLDSC (3733.567500), GNLM, IE, Infotrieve. **CCC.**
Published by: (Association of Workers for Children with Emotional and Behavioral Difficulties), Routledge (Subsidiary of: Taylor & Francis Group), 4 Park Sq, Milton Park, Abingdon, Oxon OX14 4RN, United Kingdom. TEL 44-1235-828600, FAX 44-1235-829000, journals@routledge.com, http://www.tandf.co.uk/journals/titles/13632752.asp, http://www.routledge.co.uk. Ed. Paul Cooper TEL 44-1223-369631. Circ: 2,000.

371.928 USA
ENCOR RESPONDENCE. Text in English. q. free (effective 2005).
Document type: *Newsletter, Trade.*
Published by: Eastern Nebraska Community Office of Retardation, 900 S 74th Plz, Ste 200, Omaha, NE 68114. TEL 402-444-6500, FAX 402-444-6504. Ed. Billie Dawson. Circ: 800 (free).

371.92 CAN ISSN 0829-8815
ENTOURAGE; the magazine promoting community living. Text in English, French. 1958. q. CND 19.26. adv. bk.rev. **Document type:** *Magazine, Consumer.* **Description:** Explores the issues affecting people with disabilities, their families and the advocates working for them. Keeps readers up-to-date on developments in the disability movement across Canada and around the world.
Incorporates (in Jun. 1988): Information Exchange Bulletin; Which was formerly (until 1986): Revue Canadienne de la Deficience Mentale - Canadian Journal on Mental Retardation; Deficience Mentale - Mental Retardation (0011-7668)
Indexed: CEI, CIJE, CPerI, ECER, PsycholAb, SENA.
Published by: Roeher Institute at York University, c/o Becker Associates, P O Box 507, Station Q, Toronto, ON M4T 2M5, Canada. TEL 416-661-9611, FAX 416-661-5701. Ed. Marguerite Martindale. Circ: 4,000.

ENVISION; a publication for parents and educators of children with impaired vision. see *HANDICAPPED—Visually Impaired*

371.9 DEU ISSN 0942-8623
CODEN: ERRECQ
ERGOTHERAPIE UND REHABILITATION. Text in German. 1962. m. EUR 76.50; EUR 8.70 newsstand/cover (effective 2005). adv. bk.rev. abstr.; charts; illus. index. back issues avail.
Document type: *Journal, Trade.*
Formerly (until 1993): Beschaeftigungstherapie und Rehabilitation (0340-529X)
Related titles: Online - full text ed.
Indexed: AMED, CINAHL, DIP, ExcerpMed, IBR, IBZ.
—BLDSC (3808.802700), GNLM.
Published by: (Deutscher Verband der Ergotherapeuten e.V.), Schulz - Kirchner Verlag GmbH, Mollweg 2, Idstein, 65510, Germany. TEL 49-6126-93200, FAX 49-6126-932050, info@schulz-kirchner.de, http://www.schulz-kirchner.de/ergotherapie/zeitschrift.htm. Ed. Christa Berting-Hueneke. Adv. contact Tanja Tietz. B&W page EUR 1,205, color page EUR 1,790; trim 180 x 260. Circ: 14,888 (paid and controlled).

371.9 DNK ISSN 1029-8142
EURONEWS ON SPECIAL NEEDS EDUCATION. Text in English. 1998. irreg. free (effective 2005). back issues avail.
Document type: *Newsletter.* **Description:** Provides up to date information about what is happening in the field of special needs education across Europe.
Media: Online - full content. **Related titles:** Icelandic ed.: ISSN 1560-3105; German ed.: ISSN 1560-2354; Finnish ed.: ISSN 1560-2362; Swedish ed.: ISSN 1560-2370; Norwegian ed.: ISSN 1560-2389; Portuguese ed.: ISSN 1560-2397; Dutch ed.: ISSN 1560-2400; French ed.: ISSN 1560-2419; Spanish ed.: ISSN 1560-2427; Italian ed.: ISSN 1560-2435; Latvian ed.: ISSN 1811-8127; Danish ed.: ISSN 1560-3091; Chechen ed.: ISSN 1811-8119; Greek ed.: ISSN 1560-3113; Estonian ed.: ISSN 1811-8100; Lithuanian ed.: ISSN 1811-8135.
Published by: European Agency for Development in Special Needs Education, Teglgaardsparken 102, Middelfart, 5500, Denmark. TEL 45-64-410020, FAX 45-64-412303, adm@european-agency.org, http://www.european-agency.org/. Eds. Amanda Watkins, Joergen Greve, Ole Praem-Nielsen.

371.9 GBR ISSN 0885-6257
LC3986.A2 CODEN: EJSEEB
EUROPEAN JOURNAL OF SPECIAL NEEDS EDUCATION. Text in English. 1986. q. GBP 296, USD 488 combined subscription to institutions print & online eds. (effective 2006). adv. reprint service avail. from PSC. **Document type:** *Journal, Academic/Scholarly.* **Description:** Reflects the dynamic growth of the theory and practice of special needs education as it is emerging worldwide.
Related titles: Online - full text ed.: ISSN 1469-591X. GBP 281, USD 464 to institutions (effective 2006) (from EBSCO Publishing, Gale Group, IngentaConnect, O C L C Online Computer Library Center, Inc., Swets Information Services).
Indexed: ABIn, ASSIA, BrEdI, CPE, CurCont, ECER, ERA, ETA, EduInd, ExcerpMed, FamI, L&LBA, MEA, PsycInfo, PsycholAb, RHEA, RILM, SEA, SENA, SOMA, SOPODA, TEA.
—BLDSC (3829.744000), IE, Infotrieve, ingenta, KNAW. **CCC.**
Published by: (National Foundation for Educational Research), Routledge (Subsidiary of: Taylor & Francis Group), 4 Park Square, Milton Park, Abingdon, Oxon OX14 4RN, United Kingdom. TEL 44-1235-828600, FAX 44-1235-829000, http://www.tandf.co.uk/journals/titles/08856257.asp, http://www.routledge.co.uk. Ed. Dr. Seamus Hegarty. R&P Sally Sweet. adv.: page GBP 150; trim 205 x 126. **Subscr. to:** Taylor & Francis Ltd, Journals Customer Service, Rankine Rd, Basingstoke, Hants RG24 8PR, United Kingdom. TEL 44-1256-813000, FAX 44-1256-330245, enquiry@tandf.co.uk.

EXCEPTIONAL CHILD EDUCATION RESOURCES (ONLINE EDITION). see *EDUCATION—Abstracting, Bibliographies, Statistics*

371.9 155.4 USA ISSN 0014-4029
CODEN: EXCCAJ
➤ **EXCEPTIONAL CHILDREN.** Text in English. 1934. q. USD 70 domestic to individuals; USD 105 foreign to individuals; USD 155 domestic to institutions; USD 185 foreign to institutions; USD 20 newsstand/cover (effective 2005). adv. bibl.; illus. index. 128 p./no.; reprint service avail. from PQC. **Document type:** *Journal, Academic/Scholarly.* **Description:** Publishes current articles on critical and controversial issues in special education, as well as credible articles on research and developments in the field.
Formerly (until 1951): Journal of Exceptional Children (0887-5405)
Related titles: Microfilm ed.: (from PQC); Online - full text ed.: (from bigchalk, EBSCO Publishing, Florida Center for Library Automation, Gale Group, H.W. Wilson, Northern Light Technology, Inc., O C L C Online Computer Library Center, Inc., ProQuest Information & Learning).
Indexed: ABIn, AMHA, ASCA, ASSIA, AcaI, BDM&CN, CIJE, CJA, CPE, CurCont, DIP, EAA, ECER, ERA, ETA, EduInd, ExcerpMed, FamI, IBR, IBZ, IMFL, IndMed, L&LBA, LRI, MEA, MEDLINE, MRD, PsySCDP, PsycInfo, PsycholAb, RehabLit, SEA, SENA, SOMA, SOPODA, SSCI, SWR&A, TEA, e-psyche.
—BLDSC (3835.300000), GNLM, IDS, IE, Infotrieve, ingenta.
Published by: Council for Exceptional Children, 1110 N. Glebe Rd., Ste. 300, Arlington, VA 22201-4795. TEL 703-264-9481, FAX 703-264-1637, cecpubs@cec.sped.org, http://www.cec.sped.org/bk/catalog2/journals.html. Ed. Steve Graham. Adv. contact Victor Erickson. Circ: 54,000 (paid).

371.91 362.4 USA ISSN 0046-9157
EXCEPTIONAL PARENT; the magazine for families and professionals caring for people with special needs. Text in English. 1971. m. USD 34.95 domestic; USD 49.95 in Canada; USD 52.95 elsewhere (effective 2005). bk.rev. illus. Index. 75 p./no.; back issues avail.; reprint service avail. from PQC. **Document type:** *Magazine, Consumer.* **Description:** Source of help and guidance for the parents of children and young adults with disabilities and special health needs and the professionals who serve them.
Related titles: Microfilm ed.: (from PQC); Online - full text ed.: (from Gale Group, H.W. Wilson, Northern Light Technology, Inc., O C L C Online Computer Library Center, Inc., ProQuest Information & Learning).
Indexed: ABIn, CIJE, CINAHL, ECER, EduInd, FamI, HlthInd, IMFL, IndMed, MRefA, PsycholAb, RehabLit, SENA, YAE&RB.
—BLDSC (3835.500000), IE, ingenta. **CCC.**
Address: 65 State Rt 4, River Edge, NJ 07661-1949. TEL 201-489-4111, FAX 201-489-0074, epedit@aol.com, www.eparent.com. Ed. Rick Rader. Pub. Joseph M Valenzano. R&P Bridget M Lyne. Circ: 33,000 (controlled).

371.95 USA ISSN 0936-2835
LC3950 CODEN: EXCEET
➤ **EXCEPTIONALITY**; a special education journal. Text in English. 1990-1997; resumed 1999. q. USD 375 in US & Canada to institutions; USD 405 elsewhere to institutions; USD 395 combined subscription in US & Canada to institutions print & online eds.; USD 425 combined subscription elsewhere to institutions print & online eds. (effective 2006). adv. illus. Index. back issues avail.; reprint service avail. from PSC. **Document type:** *Journal, Academic/Scholarly.* **Description:** Publishes original research and research reviews pertaining to individuals of all ages and disabilities, as well as to those who are gifted and talented.
Related titles: Online - full text ed.: ISSN 1532-7035. USD 355 worldwide to institutions (effective 2006) (from EBSCO Publishing, Gale Group, O C L C Online Computer Library Center, Inc., Swets Information Services).
Indexed: ABIn, CIJE, ECER, EduInd, FamI, PsycInfo, PsycholAb, SOPODA, e-psyche.
—BLDSC (3835.550000), IE, Infotrieve, ingenta. **CCC.**
Published by: (Council for Exceptional Children, Division for Research), Lawrence Erlbaum Associates, Inc., 10 Industrial Ave, Mahwah, NJ 07430-2262. TEL 201-258-2200, 800-926-6579, FAX 201-236-0072, journals@erlbaum.com, http://www.leaonline.com/loi/ex. Ed. Edward J Sabornie. adv.: page USD 475; trim 5 x 8.

371.95 CAN ISSN 1183-322X
➤ **EXCEPTIONALITY EDUCATION CANADA.** Text in English. 1991. 3/yr. CND 40 to individuals; CND 60 to institutions; CND 25 to students (effective 2004). **Document type:** *Journal, Academic/Scholarly.* **Description:** Provides a forum for scholarly exchange among Canadian professionals in education and related disciplines who are involved with students across the spectrum of exceptionality.
Related titles: Microform ed.: (from MML).
Indexed: CEI, ECER.
—BLDSC (3835.570000), IE, ingenta. **CCC.**
Published by: University of Prince Edward Island, Faculty of Education, 550 University Avenue, Charlottetown, PE C1A 4P3, Canada. TEL 902-566-0330, FAX 902-894-2840, eec@upei.ca, http://www.upei.ca/~eecj/. Ed., R&P Vianne Timmons TEL 902-566-0330. Circ: 250.

371.91 USA ISSN 0015-4288
HV1796
FLORIDA SCHOOL HERALD. Text in English. 1891. 6/yr. USD 6. abstr.; illus. **Document type:** *Newsletter.* **Description:** Highlights education of the deaf and blind.
Published by: Florida School for the Deaf and the Blind, 207 North San Marco Ave., St. Augustine, FL 32084-2799. TEL 904-827-2219, FAX 904-827-2218, http://www.fsdb.k12.fl.us. Ed. Kathy Gillespie. Circ: 1,550 (controlled).

FOCAL POINT; a national bulletin on family support and children's mental health. see *HANDICAPPED*

FOCUS. see *SOCIAL SERVICES AND WELFARE*

FOCUS ON AUTISM AND OTHER DEVELOPMENTAL DISABILITIES. see *MEDICAL SCIENCES—Psychiatry And Neurology*

371.95 USA ISSN 0015-511X
LC3950
FOCUS ON EXCEPTIONAL CHILDREN. Text in English. 1969. 9/yr. (Sep.-May). USD 36 to individuals; USD 48 to institutions (effective 2004). adv. bk.rev. illus. Index. 16 p./no.; back issues avail.; reprint service avail. from PQC. **Document type:** *Journal, Academic/Scholarly.*
Related titles: CD-ROM ed.; Microform ed.: (from PQC); Online - full text ed.: (from bigchalk, EBSCO Publishing, Florida Center for Library Automation, Gale Group, H.W. Wilson, Northern Light Technology, Inc., O C L C Online Computer Library Center, Inc., ProQuest Information & Learning).
Indexed: ABIn, ASCA, CIJE, CPE, CurCont, ECER, EduInd, RehabLit, SSCI.
—BLDSC (3964.215000), IDS, IE, ingenta.
Published by: Love Publishing Co., 9101 E Kenyon Ave, Ste 2200, Denver, CO 80237. TEL 303-221-7333, FAX 303-221-7444, lpc@lovepublishing.com, http://www.lovepublishing.com/. Eds. Chriss Walther-Thomas, Edwin S Ellis, Timothy J Lewis. Circ: 3,000.

371.9 USA ISSN 1548-9132
▼ **FOCUS ON INCLUSIVE EDUCATION.** Text in English. 2003 (Fall). q. USD 30 to non-members; USD 15 to members (effective 2004). **Document type:** *Newsletter.*
Published by: Association for Childhood Education International, 17904 Georgia Ave, Ste 215, Olney, MD 20832-2277. TEL 301-570-2111, 800-423-3563, FAX 301-570-2212, http://www.acei.org. Ed. Jerry Aldridge.

FOCUS ON LEARNING PROBLEMS IN MATHEMATICS. see *MATHEMATICS*

E

371.95 DEU ISSN 0947-272X
➤ **FOERDERSCHULMAGAZIN.** Text in German. 1979. m. EUR 70.80; EUR 46.60 to students; EUR 8.90 newsstand/cover (effective 2003). **Document type:** *Journal, Academic/Scholarly.* **Description:** Aimed at teachers working with educationally challenged children. Includes instructional models.
Former titles (until 1995): Sonderschulmagazin (0941-5017); (until 1992): Lehrermagazin Sonderschulmagazin (0930-696X); Sonderschulmagazin (0171-9629)
Indexed: DIP, IBR, IBZ.
—CCC.
Published by: Oldenbourg Schulbuchverlag GmbH und Bayerischer Schulbuch Verlag GmbH (Subsidiary of: Oldenbourg Wissenschaftsverlag GmbH), Rosenheimer Str. 145, Munich, 81671, Germany. TEL 49-89-450510, FAX 49-89-45051200, info@oldenbourg-bsv.de, http://www.oldenbourg-bsv.de. Ed. Stefan Holler. Pub. Ortwin Krieg. Adv. contact Renate Kienzler TEL 49-7141-871670.

➤ **FORUM ERZIEHUNGSHILFEN.** see *SOCIAL SERVICES AND WELFARE*

➤ **FULBRIGHT ASSOCIATION NEWSLETTER.** see *EDUCATION—Higher Education*

➤ **FUTURE REFLECTIONS.** see *HANDICAPPED—Visually Impaired*

371.9 DEU ISSN 0932-934X
G W G - ZEITSCHRIFT. Text in German. 1971. q. EUR 31; EUR 7.75 newsstand/cover (effective 2005). adv. bk.rev. back issues avail. **Document type:** *Journal, Academic/Scholarly.*
Formerly: G W G-Info
—GNLM.
Published by: Gesellschaft fuer Wissenschaftliche Gespraechspsychotherapie e.V., Melatenguertel 125a, Cologne, 50825, Germany. TEL 49-221-9259080, FAX 49-221-251276, gwg@gwg-ev.org, http://www.gwg-ev.org. Eds. Michael Barg, Ursula Reinsch. adv.: page EUR 800; trim 190 x 260. Circ: 4,600 (paid and controlled).

GATHERED VIEW. see *MEDICAL SCIENCES*

371.928 DEU ISSN 0173-9573
GEISTIGE BEHINDERUNG; Fachzeitschrift der Lebenshilfe fuer geistig Behinderte. Text in German. 1962. q. EUR 26 (effective 2005). adv. bk.rev. illus. index. **Document type:** *Journal, Academic/Scholarly.* **Description:** Directed to specialists working with the mentally retarded. Focus is on development, education, social adaptation, special problems. Also lists available positions.
Formerly (until 1980): Lebenshilfe (0023-995X)
Indexed: DIP, IBR, IBZ, e-psyche.
—GNLM.
Published by: Bundesvereinigung Lebenshilfe fuer Menschen mit Geistiger Behinderung e.V., Raiffeisenstr 18, Marburg, 35043, Germany. TEL 49-6421-4910, FAX 49-6421-491167, bundesvereinigung@lebenshilfe.de, http://www.lebenshilfe.de. Ed. Theo Fruehauf. Adv. contact Ursula Dahlstroem. Circ: 8,500.

GEORGIA SCHOOL LAW DECISIONS. see *EDUCATION—School Organization And Administration*

371.95 USA ISSN 0016-9862
LC3991 CODEN: GICQAC
➤ **GIFTED CHILD QUARTERLY.** Text in English. 1957. q. USD 65 domestic membership; USD 75 foreign membership (effective 2005). adv. bk.rev. illus. back issues avail.; reprints avail. **Document type:** *Journal, Academic/Scholarly.* **Description:** For educational researchers, administrators, teachers and parents of gifted children. Publishes research and theoretical papers on the nature and needs of high-ability children.
Related titles: Microfilm ed.: (from PQC); Online - full text ed.: (from ProQuest Information & Learning).
Indexed: ABIn, ASCA, Acal, ArtHuCI, CDA, CIJE, CPE, CurCont, EAA, ECER, EduInd, FamI, IMFL, LRI, PsycInfo, PsycholAb, SFSA, SSCI, e-psyche.
—BLDSC (4175.300000), IE, Infotrieve, ingenta. **CCC.**
Published by: National Association for Gifted Children, 1707 L St, N W, Ste 550, Washington, DC 20036-4201. TEL 202-785-4268, FAX 202-785-4248, nagc@nagc.org, http://www.nagc.org/Publications/GiftedChild/index.html. Ed. Paula L Olszewski-Kubilius. R&P Peter Rosenstein. Adv. contact Cora Powers. page USD 700; trim 11 x 8.5. Circ: 6,500 (paid).

371.95 USA ISSN 1076-2175
LC3991
GIFTED CHILD TODAY MAGAZINE; the nation's leading resource for nurturing talented children . Text in English. 1978. q. USD 35 domestic; USD 45 foreign (effective 2005). bk.rev. bibl.; illus. back issues avail.; reprint service avail. from PQC. **Document type:** *Magazine, Consumer.* **Description:** Designed to meet the needs of parents and teachers of gifted, creative and talented youngsters.
Former titles (until 1993): Gifted Child Today (0892-9580); G C T (Gifted, Creative, Talented Children) (0164-9728)
Related titles: Online - full text ed.: (from bigchalk, EBSCO Publishing, Florida Center for Library Automation, Gale Group, H.W. Wilson, O C L C Online Computer Library Center, Inc., ProQuest Information & Learning).
Indexed: ABIn, CIJE, ECER, EduInd, RILM.
—BLDSC (4175.305000), IE, ingenta.
Published by: Prufrock Press Inc., PO Box 8813, Waco, TX 76714-8813. gct@prufrock.com, info@prufrock.com, http://www.prufrock.com/client/client_pages/prufrock_jm_giftchild.cfm. Eds. Susan Johnsen, Jim Kendrick. Pub. Joel McIntosh. Circ: 20,000.

371.95 GBR ISSN 0261-4294
GIFTED EDUCATION INTERNATIONAL. Text in English. 1982. 3/yr. adv. bk.rev. bibl.; illus. back issues avail. **Document type:** *Journal, Academic/Scholarly.*
Related titles: Microform ed.
Indexed: ASSIA, BrEdI, CIJE, CPE, DIP, ECER, ERA, ETA, IBR, IBSS, IBZ, LT&LA, MEA, PsycholAb, RHEA, RILM, SEA, SENA, SOMA, SWA, TEA, e-psyche.
—BLDSC (4175.320000), IE, Infotrieve, ingenta. **CCC.**
Published by: A B Academic Publishers, PO Box 42, Bicester, Oxon OX26 6NW, United Kingdom. jrnls@abapubl.demon.co.uk. Ed. Ms. Belle Wallace.

371.95 USA ISSN 1064-0053
GIFTED EDUCATION PRESS QUARTERLY. Text in English. 1987. q. USD 22 lifetime subscr. (effective 2005). bk.rev. bibl. 12 p./no.; back issues avail. **Document type:** *Newsletter, Consumer.* **Description:** Covers current problems and issues concerned with educating the gifted, and using the humanities and sciences with the gifted.
Formerly: Gifted Education Press Newsletter
Related titles: Microfiche ed.; Online - full text ed.: 2001.
Indexed: CIJE.
Published by: Gifted Education Press, 10201 Yuma Court, Box 1586, Manassas, VA 20109. TEL 703-369-5017, FAX 703-393-2879, http://www.giftedpress.com/. Ed., Pub., R&P, Adv. contact Maurice D Fisher. Circ: 3,000 (paid and controlled).

371.95 USA ISSN 0740-560X
GIFTED UNLIMITED. Text in English. m. USD 25 includes membership. **Document type:** *Newsletter.*
Published by: Northwest Gifted Child Association, PO Box 1226, Bellevue, WA 98009. TEL 206-649-8546, 800-864-2073. Ed. Howard Modell. Circ: 375.

GONG; mesicnik sluchove postizenych. see *HANDICAPPED—Hearing Impaired*

GOOD AUTISM PRACTICE. see *HANDICAPPED*

371.91 USA ISSN 1090-3364
THE GRAM. Text in English. 1968. q. USD 15 domestic to non-members; USD 30 foreign to non-members; USD 45 membership (effective 2003). adv. bk.rev.; film rev.; software rev. charts. **Document type:** *Newsletter.*
Formerly: C A N H C - Gram (California Association for Neurologically Handicapped Children)
Published by: Learning Disabilities Association of California (L D A - C A), PO Box 601067, Sacramento, CA 95860. TEL 916-725-7881, 866-532-6322, FAX 916-725-8786, Theamclean@aol.com, http://www.ldaca.org/gram/. Ed., Pub., R&P, Adv. contact Betty G Schiemenz. B&W page USD 500; trim 7.5 x 9.25. Circ: 3,600. **Dist. by:** Thea McLean, 6060 Sunrise Vista Dr., Ste.1550, Citrus Heights, CA 95610. TEL 510-352-9469, FAX 510-352-8283.

GUIDE TO TOYS FOR CHILDREN WHO ARE BLIND OR VISUALLY IMPAIRED. see *HANDICAPPED—Visually Impaired*

371.91 NOR
HANDICAP IDRETT. Text in Norwegian. bi-m. adv.
Published by: (Norges Handicapidrettsforbund), Per Sletholt og Co., Postboks 57, Tveita, Oslo 6, Norway.

371.95 CAN ISSN 0846-3522
HEAR OUR WINGS. Text in English. irreg. CND 15; CND 15 foreign (effective 1998). **Document type:** *Monographic series.*
Published by: (Saskatchewan Council for the Education of Gifted Learners), Saskatchewan Teachers' Federation, 2317 Arlington Ave., Saskatoon, SK S7J 2H8, Canada. stf@stf.sk.ca. Ed. Carol Casswell.

HEIDELBERGER BEITRAEGE ZUR GEHOERLOSENBILDUNG UND SCHWERHOERIGENBILDUNG. see *HANDICAPPED—Hearing Impaired*

HEILPAEDAGOGISCHE FORSCHUNG; Zeitschrift fuer Paedagogik und Psychologie bei Behinderungen. see *MEDICAL SCIENCES—Psychiatry And Neurology*

371.95 GBR ISSN 1359-8139
LC3991
➤ **HIGH ABILITY STUDIES.** Text in English. 1990. s-a. GBP 206, USD 338 combined subscription to institutions print & online eds. (effective 2006). reprint service avail. from PSC. **Document type:** *Journal, Academic/Scholarly.* **Description:** Offers a medium of scientific, scholarly and practical communication among researchers and practitioners in the field of giftedness.
Formerly (until vol.7): European Journal for High Ability (0937-4450)
Related titles: Online - full text ed.: ISSN 1469-834X. GBP 196, USD 321 to institutions (effective 2006) (from EBSCO Publishing, Gale Group, IngentaConnect, Northern Light Technology, Inc., O C L C Online Computer Library Center, Inc., ProQuest Information & Learning, Swets Information Services).
Indexed: BrEdI, CPE, CurCont, DIP, ECER, ERA, ETA, IBR, IBZ, MEA, PsycInfo, PsycholAb, RHEA, SEA, SENA, SOMA, SSCI, SWA, TEA, e-psyche.
—BLDSC (4307.283450), IE, Infotrieve, ingenta. **CCC.**
Published by: (European Council for High Ability), Routledge (Subsidiary of: Taylor & Francis Group), 4 Park Sq, Milton Park, Abingdon, Oxon OX14 4RN, United Kingdom. TEL 44-1235-828600, FAX 44-1235-829000, info@routledge.co.uk, http://www.tandf.co.uk/journals/titles/13598139.asp, http://www.routledge.co.uk. Ed. Dr. Albert Ziegler. **Subscr. to:** Taylor & Francis Ltd, Journals Customer Service, Rankine Rd, Basingstoke, Hants RG24 8PR, United Kingdom. TEL 44-1256-813000, FAX 44-1256-330245, enquiry@tandf.co.uk.

371.91 DNK ISSN 1395-1912
HIT. Text in Danish. 1988. 5/yr. (includes 1 book). DKK 375 (effective 2001). adv. bk.rev. **Document type:** *Academic/Scholarly.*
Former titles (until 1995): Via Datch (0903-9821); (until 1988): Mikronyt i Specialundervisningen (0900-6230)
Published by: Danish Centre for Rehabilitation and Special Education, Graham Bells Vej 1 A, Aarhus N, 8200, Denmark. TEL 45-86-78-37-00, FAX 45-86-78-37-30, tb.mikkelsen@hmi.dk. Eds. Marianne Henriksen, Trine Bjerre Mikkelsen. Adv. contact Trine G Bak. Circ: 1,700.

HOERGESCHAEDIGTE KINDER - ERWACHSENE HOERGESCHAEDIGTE. see *HANDICAPPED—Hearing Impaired*

HOME CARE FAMILY NEWSLETTER. see *SOCIAL SERVICES AND WELFARE*

HYDROCEPHALUS NEWS & NOTES. see *MEDICAL SCIENCES—Psychiatry And Neurology*

371.93 AUS ISSN 0810-6398
HYPER ACTIVITIES. Text in English. 1976. 8/yr. AUD 15 (effective 1999). adv. bk.rev. index. back issues avail. **Document type:** *Newsletter.* **Description:** Discusses diet behavior management, medication, hyperactivity, attention deficit disorder.
Indexed: e-psyche.
Published by: Hyperactivity Attention Deficit Association (N.S.W.), 15-29 Bertram St, Chatswood, NSW 2067, Australia. hyperadd@bigpond.com. Ed., Pub., R&P, Adv. contact Roslyn Mitchell. page AUD 200. Circ: 500.

371.91 GBR
I C A N COMMUNICATE. Text in English. irreg. free. adv. back issues avail. **Document type:** *Newsletter.*
Formerly: I C A N Speech and Language Newsletter
Published by: Invalid Children's Aid Nationwide, I CAN, 4 Dyer's Bldgs, Holborn, London, EC1N 2QP, United Kingdom. TEL 44-870-010-4066, FAX 44-870-010-4067. Ed. Neil Cox. adv.: page GBP 500. Circ: 7,000 (controlled).

371.9 USA
I D E A NEWS. (Individuals with Disabilities Education Act) Text in English. m. free. **Document type:** *Newsletter, Government.*
Published by: I D E A Practices, Office of Special Education Programs, US Dept of Education, 400 Maryland Ave, SW, Washington, DC 20202. TEL 202-205-5507, ideapractices@cec.sped.org, http://idea-live.2rad.net/ideanews/index.php, http://idea-live.2rad.net/index.php.

I F H O H JOURNAL. see *HANDICAPPED—Hearing Impaired*

371.928 616.8 USA
I Q: INDEPENDENCE QUARTERLY. Text in English. 2002 (Nov.). q. **Document type:** *Journal, Academic/Scholarly.*
Published by: Hillsborough Association for Retarded Citizens, 220 E Madison St, Ste 1040, Tampa, FL 33602. TEL 813-273-6364, HillsChfdn@aol.com, http://www.hillsarc.com/.

371.95 USA ISSN 1071-605X
LC3991
➤ **IMAGINE (BALTIMORE)**; opportunities and resources for academically talented youth. Text in English. 1993. 5/yr. USD 30 to individuals; USD 35 to institutions (effective 2006). adv. back issues avail. **Document type:** *Journal, Consumer.* **Description:** Offers academically talented students in grades 7-12 tips on opportunities in school, at home, and in the community at large.

E

▼ new title ➤ refereed ✶ unverified ♦ full entry avail.

Related titles: Online - full text ed.: ISSN 1086-3230. 1996. USD 35 (effective 2006) (from EBSCO Publishing, Project MUSE).
—CCC.
Published by: Johns Hopkins University, Center for Talented Youth, 3400 N Charles St, Baltimore, MD 21218. TEL 410-516-0337, FAX 410-516-0804, http://www.press.jhu.edu/journals/imagine/index.html. Ed. Melissa Hartman.

371.9 CAN ISSN 1200-409X
INCLUSION NEWS. Text in English. 1990. a. free (effective 2005).
—CCC.
Published by: (Marsha Forest Centre), Inclusion Press, 24 Thome Crescent, Toronto, ON M6H 2S5, Canada. TEL 416-658-5363, FAX 416-658-5067, inclusionpress@inclusion.com, http://www.inclusion.com/inclusionnews.html.

371.9 USA ISSN 1072-3811
INCLUSION TIMES. Text in English. 1993. 5/yr. USD 59.95 (effective 2005). adv. bk.rev. back issues avail. **Document type:** *Newsletter, Trade.* **Description:** Focuses on issues relating to educating children and youth with disabilities in regular education and other inclusive learning environments.
Published by: Assistive Tek LLC, 174 Stephensburg Rd, Port Murray, NJ 07865. TEL 908-852-3460, FAX 908-979-9196, rhanson@nprinc.com, http://www.nprinc.com. Ed., R&P Brian S Friedlander.

371.91 USA ISSN 1076-8548
INCLUSIVE EDUCATION PROGRAMS; advice on educating students with disabilities in regular education classes. Text in English. 1994. m. USD 160 (effective 2006). Index. back issues avail. **Document type:** *Newsletter, Trade.* **Description:** Covers the legal and practical issues of educating children with disabilities in regular education environments. Provides concise case summaries of the most recent judicial case law.
Related titles: Online - full text ed.: (from LexisNexis).
—CCC.
Published by: L R P Publications, 747 Dresher Rd, PO Box 980, Horsham, PA 19044. TEL 215-784-0860, 800-341-7874, FAX 215-784-9639, custserve@lrp.com, http://www.shoplrp.com/product/p-300027.html, http://www.lrp.com. Ed. Judith Malveaux.

371.9 USA ISSN 1055-520X
KF4210
INDIVIDUALS WITH DISABILITIES EDUCATION LAW REPORT. Text in English. 1978. 2 base vols. plus updates 22/yr. looseleaf. USD 995 (effective 2006). cum.index. back issues avail. **Document type:** *Trade.* **Description:** Provides full-text case reports on special-education judicial decisions, policy rulings and major federal statutes and regulations.
Formerly (until 1991): Education for the Handicapped Law Report (0744-4117)
Related titles: CD-ROM ed.: USD 1,949 includes Special Education Law Monthly (effective 2002); Online - full text ed.
—CCC.
Published by: L R P Publications, 747 Dresher Rd, PO Box 980, Horsham, PA 19044. TEL 215-784-0941, 800-341-7874, FAX 215-784-9014, custserve@lrp.com, http://www.shoplrp.com/product/p-300001.html, http://www.lrp.com.

INFORMATION TECHNOLOGY AND DISABILITIES. see *HANDICAPPED—Computer Applications*

INSIGHT (CHARLESTON). see *COMPUTERS—Computer Assisted Instruction*

371.9 FRA
INTERNATIONAL ASSOCIATION OF WORKERS FOR TROUBLED CHILDREN AND YOUTH. CONGRESS REPORTS. Text in English, French. 1955. quadrennial. USD 30. **Document type:** *Proceedings, Trade.*
Formerly: International Association of Workers for Maladjusted Children. Congress Report (0074-1787)
Published by: International Association of Workers for Troubled Children and Youth, E.E.S., 22 rue Halevy, Lille, 59000, France.

371.91 CAN ISSN 1703-3381
➤ **INTERNATIONAL JOURNAL OF DISABILITY, COMMUNITY & REHABILITATION.** Text in English. 1977. 3/yr. USD 20 (effective 2003). adv. bk.rev. abstr.; illus.; stat. back issues avail. **Document type:** *Journal, Academic/Scholarly.* **Description:** Concerned with disability, practice and applied research in the field of rehabilitation.
Former titles (until 2002): International Journal of Practical Approaches to Disability (1205-4291); (until 1995): Journal of Practical Approaches to Developmental Handicap (0707-7807)
Media: Online - full content. **Related titles:** Microfiche ed.: (from MML); Microform ed.: (from MML).
Indexed: AMED, ASSIA, BrNI, SENA.
—BLDSC (4542.481600). **CCC.**
Published by: University of Calgary, Rehabilitation Studies, c/o Community Rehabilitation & Disability Studies, Education Tower 4th Fl, University of Calgary, 2500 University Dr, N W, Calgary, AB T2N 1N4, Canada. TEL 403-220-3543, FAX 403-284-6494, ijder@calgary.ca, http://www.ijdcr.ca, http://www.crds.org. Ed. Aldred Neufeldt. Circ: 450.
Co-sponsor: Vocational and Rehabilitation Research Institute.

371.91 362.4 GBR ISSN 1034-912X
LC4661 CODEN: IJDEFF
➤ **INTERNATIONAL JOURNAL OF DISABILITY, DEVELOPMENT AND EDUCATION.** Text in English. 1954. q. GBP 284, USD 470 combined subscription to institutions print & online eds. (effective 2006); AUD 321 combined subscription to institutions print & online eds. (effective 2005). adv. bk.rev. bibl.; charts; illus. Index. reprint service avail. from PSC. **Document type:** *Journal, Academic/Scholarly.* **Description:** Reflects a variety of topics, disciplines, research methods and cultural perspectives. Various orientations are represented including special education, psychology, and social work.
Former titles (until 1990): Exceptional Child (0156-6555); Slow Learning Child (0037-704X)
Related titles: Microfilm ed.: (from PQC); Online - full text ed.: ISSN 1465-346X. GBP 270, USD 447, AUD 305 to institutions (effective 2006) (from EBSCO Publishing, Gale Group, H.W. Wilson, IngentaConnect, O C L C Online Computer Library Center, Inc., R M I T Publishing, Swets Information Services).
Indexed: ABIn, AEI, AMED, ASSIA, CIJE, CPE, CurCont, DIP, ECER, ERA, ETA, EduInd, IBR, IBZ, L&LBA, MEA, MEA&I, PsycInfo, PsycholAb, RHEA, SEA, SENA, SOMA, SOPODA, SSCI, SWA, TEA, e-psyche.
—BLDSC (4542.185450), IE, Infotrieve, ingenta. **CCC.**
Published by: (Fred and Eleanor Schonell Educational Research Centre), Routledge (Subsidiary of: Taylor & Francis Group), 4 Park Sq, Milton Park, Abingdon, Oxon OX14 4RN, United Kingdom. TEL 44-1235-828600, FAX 44-1235-829000, info@routledge.co.uk, http://www.tandf.co.uk/journals/titles/1034912x.asp, http://www.routledge.co.uk. Ed. Christa van Kraayenoord. Circ: 1,400. **Subscr. to:** Taylor & Francis Ltd, Journals Customer Service, Rankine Rd, Basingstoke, Hants RG24 8PR, United Kingdom. TEL 44-1256-813000, FAX 44-1256-330245; **Subscr.in N. America to:** Taylor & Francis Inc., Customer Services Dept, 325 Chestnut St, 8th Fl, Philadelphia, PA 19106. TEL 215-625-8900, 800-354-1420, FAX 215-625-8914, customerservice@taylorandfrancis.com.

➤ **INTERNATIONAL JOURNAL OF LANGUAGE AND COMMUNICATION DISORDERS.** see *MEDICAL SCIENCES—Otorhinolaryngology*

➤ **INTERNATIONAL JOURNAL OF REHABILITATION RESEARCH.** see *MEDICAL SCIENCES—Physical Medicine And Rehabilitation*

371.9 CAN
➤ **INTERNATIONAL JOURNAL OF SPECIAL EDUCATION (ONLINE).** Text in English. 1985. s-a. free (effective 2005). adv. back issues avail. **Document type:** *Journal, Academic/Scholarly.* **Description:** Presents experimental research, surveys, reports, philosophical discussions about special education.
Formerly (until 2002): International Journal of Special Education (Print) (0827-3383)
Media: Online - full text.
Indexed: CEI, CPE, ECER, ERA, SENA.
—BLDSC (4542.665000), ingenta. **CCC.**
Published by: International Journal of Special Education, c/o Dr. Marg Csapo, 2889 Highbury St, Vancouver, BC, Canada. TEL 604-228-0086, marcsapo@interchange.ubc.ca, http://www.internationaljournalofspecialeducation.com/. Ed., R&P, Adv. contact Marg Csapo. B&W page USD 100. Circ: 500.

➤ **INTERNATIONAL REVIEW OF RESEARCH IN MENTAL RETARDATION.** see *MEDICAL SCIENCES—Psychiatry And Neurology*

371.9 USA ISSN 1053-4512
LC4001 CODEN: ISCLEP
➤ **INTERVENTION IN SCHOOL AND CLINIC.** Text in English. 1965. 5/yr. USD 41 in North America to individuals; USD 76 elsewhere to individuals; USD 124 in North America to institutions; USD 169 elsewhere to institutions (effective 2006). adv. bk.rev.; software rev.; video rev. bibl.; charts; illus.; abstr. Index. back issues avail.; reprint service avail. from PSC. **Document type:** *Journal, Academic/Scholarly.* **Description:** Interdisciplinary journal directed to an international audience of teachers, parents, educational therapists and specialists in all fields, who deal with the day-to-day aspects of special and remedial education.
Former titles (until 1990): Academic Therapy (0001-396X); (until 1968): Academic Therapy Quarterly (1040-9777)
Related titles: Microfilm ed.: (from PQC); Online - full content ed.: ISSN 1538-4810; Online - full text ed.: (from EBSCO Publishing, Florida Center for Library Automation, Gale Group, H.W. Wilson, IngentaConnect, O C L C Online Computer Library Center, Inc., ProQuest Information & Learning).
Indexed: ABIn, ASCA, ASSIA, ArtHuCI, CIJE, CPE, CurCont, DIP, DSHAb, EAA, ECER, ERA, ETA, EduInd, FamI, IBR, IBZ, L&LBA, MEA, PsycholAb, RHEA, RehabLit, SEA, SENA, SFSA, SOMA, SOPODA, SSCI, SWA, TEA, e-psyche.
—BLDSC (4557.471850), GNLM, IDS, IE, Infotrieve, ingenta. **CCC.**
Published by: Pro-Ed Inc., 8700 Shoal Creek Blvd, Austin, TX 78757-6897. TEL 512-451-3246, 800-897-3202, FAX 512-302-9129, 800-397-7633, journals@proedinc.com, http://www.proedinc.com/isc.html. Ed. Brenda Smith Myles. Pub. Donald D Hammill. R&P, Adv. contact Paula Gonzalez. B&W page USD 400, color page USD 1,000. Circ: 2,500.

➤ **ISBI.COM.** (Independent Schools of the British Isles) see *EDUCATION—Guides To Schools And Colleges*

371.95 USA ISSN 0162-3532
LC3993.9
JOURNAL FOR THE EDUCATION OF THE GIFTED. Text in English. q. USD 44 to individuals; USD 60 to institutions (effective 2005). bk.rev. **Document type:** *Magazine, Trade.*
Related titles: Online - full text ed.: (from H.W. Wilson, O C L C Online Computer Library Center, Inc.).
Indexed: ABIn, ASCA, ArtHuCI, CDA, CIJE, CPE, ChPerI, CurCont, EAA, ERA, ETA, EduInd, FamI, MEA, PsycInfo, PsycholAb, RHEA, SEA, SENA, SOMA, SRRA, SSCI, SWA, TEA, e-psyche.
—BLDSC (4973.140000), IDS, IE, Infotrieve, ingenta.
Published by: (Association for the Gifted), Prufrock Press Inc., PO Box 8813, Waco, TX 76714-8813. info@prufrock.com, http://www.prufrock.com/client/client_pages/prufrock_jm_jeg.cfm. Eds. Laurence J Coleman, Jim Kendrick. Pub. Joel McIntosh. Circ: 2,700.

371.95 AUT ISSN 1681-7001
JOURNAL FUER BEGABTENFOERDERUNG. Text in German. 2001. 2/yr. EUR 25; EUR 14.60 newsstand/cover (effective 2005). **Document type:** *Journal, Academic/Scholarly.*
Published by: StudienVerlag, Amraser Str 118, Innsbruck, 6020, Austria. TEL 43-512-395045, FAX 43-512-39504515, order@studienverlag.at, http://www.studienverlag.at.

JOURNAL OF ABNORMAL CHILD PSYCHOLOGY. see *PSYCHOLOGY*

371.9 USA ISSN 1537-7903
LC3950
➤ **JOURNAL OF APPLIED SCHOOL PSYCHOLOGY.** Text in English. 1984. 2/yr. USD 365 combined subscription domestic to institutions print & online eds.; USD 492.75 combined subscription in Canada to institutions print & online eds.; USD 529.25 combined subscription elsewhere to institutions print & online eds. (effective academic year 2005 - 2006). adv. bk.rev. back issues avail.; reprint service avail. from HAW. **Document type:** *Journal, Academic/Scholarly.* **Description:** Disseminates state-of-the-art material to education professionals of children with special needs in public schools and related educational settings.
Formerly (until 2002): Special Services in the Schools (0739-9820)
Related titles: Microfiche ed.: (from PQC); Microform ed.; Online - full content ed.: ISSN 1537-7911. free to institutions (effective 2003); free with print subs.; Online - full text ed.: (from EBSCO Publishing, O C L C Online Computer Library Center, Inc., Swets Information Services).
Indexed: CDA, CIJE, CPE, DIP, EAA, ECER, ERA, ETA, FamI, IBR, IBZ, MEA, PsycInfo, PsycholAb, RefZh, SEA, SENA, SFSA, SWR&A, e-psyche.
—BLDSC (4947.049000), Haworth, IE. **CCC.**
Published by: Haworth Press, Inc., 10 Alice St, Binghamton, NY 13904-1580. TEL 607-722-5857, 800-429-6784, FAX 607-722-1424, 800-895-0582, getinfo@haworthpress.com, http://www.haworthpress.com/web/JAPPS. Ed. Charles A Maher. Pub. William Cohen. R&P Ruth Ann Heath TEL 607-722-5857 ext 316. Adv. contact Rebecca Miller-Baum TEL 607-722-5857 ext 337. B&W page USD 315, color page USD 550; trim 4.375 x 7.125. Circ: 46 (paid).

➤ **JOURNAL OF ATTENTION DISORDERS.** see *MEDICAL SCIENCES—Psychiatry And Neurology*

371.94 USA ISSN 0162-3257
RJ499.A1 CODEN: JADDDQ
➤ **JOURNAL OF AUTISM AND DEVELOPMENTAL DISORDERS.** Text in English. 1971. bi-m. EUR 898, USD 918, GBP 528 combined subscription to institutions print & online eds. (effective 2005). adv. bk.rev. abstr.; charts; illus.; stat. index. back issues avail.; reprint service avail. from PSC. **Document type:** *Journal, Academic/Scholarly.* **Description:** Includes research covering the psychopathologies in childhood, including autism and childhood schizophrenia. Publishes experimental studies on the biochemical, neurological, and genetic aspects of a particular disorder; the implications for normal development; and the interaction between disordered behavior of individuals and social or group factors.
Formerly (until 1979): Journal of Autism and Childhood Schizophrenia (0021-9185)
Related titles: Microfilm ed.: (from PQC); Online - full text ed.: ISSN 1573-3432 (from EBSCO Publishing, Gale Group, IngentaConnect, Kluwer Online, O C L C Online Computer Library Center, Inc., Ovid Technologies, Inc., Springer LINK, Swets Information Services).
Indexed: ABIn, AMED, ASCA, ASSIA, BDM&CN, BIOSIS Prev, BibLing, BiolAb, CDA, CIJE, CINAHL, CPE, ChemAb, CurCont, ECER, ERA, ETA, EduInd, ExcerpMed, FamI, IMFL, IndMed, MEA, MEA&I, MEDLINE, NSCI, PsySCDP, PsycInfo, PsycholAb, RHEA, RefZh, SEA, SENA, SOMA, SSCI, SWR&A, TEA, e-psyche.
—BLDSC (4949.552000), CISTI, GNLM, IDS, IE, Infotrieve, ingenta, KNAW. **CCC.**

Published by: (Autism Society of America), Plenum US (Subsidiary of: Springer Science+Business Media), 233 Spring St, New York, NY 10013. TEL 212-460-1500, FAX 212-460-1575, service@springer-ny.com, http://springerlink.metapress.com/openurl.asp?genre=journal&issn=0162-3257, http://www.springeronline.com. Ed. Gary B Mesibov.

➤ **JOURNAL OF CHILD AND ADOLESCENT PSYCHIATRIC NURSING.** see *MEDICAL SCIENCES—Nurses And Nursing*

➤ **THE JOURNAL OF DEAF STUDIES AND DEAF EDUCATION.** see *HANDICAPPED—Hearing Impaired*

➤ **JOURNAL OF DEVELOPMENTAL AND PHYSICAL DISABILITIES.** see *HANDICAPPED*

▼ ➤ **JOURNAL OF DRUG EDUCATION AND AWARENESS.** see *DRUG ABUSE AND ALCOHOLISM*

371.95 USA ISSN 1053-8151
LC4019.2
➤ **JOURNAL OF EARLY INTERVENTION.** Text in English. 1979. q. USD 50 domestic to individuals; USD 74 foreign to individuals; USD 70 domestic to institutions; USD 74 foreign to institutions (effective 2004). adv. bk.rev. illus. Index. back issues avail.; reprints avail. **Document type:** *Journal, Academic/Scholarly.* **Description:** Features current research, exemplary practices, family involvement, personnel preparation, collaborative efforts, legislation, and technology for professionals.
Formerly (until 1989): Council of Exceptional Children. Division for Early Childhood. Journal (0885-3460)
Indexed: ASCA, CIJE, CPE, CurCont, ECER, ERA, FamI, MEA, PsycInfo, PsycholAb, SENA, SFSA, SSCI, e-psyche.
—BLDSC (4970.705000), IDS, IE, Infotrieve, ingenta.
Published by: Council for Exceptional Children, Division for Early Childhood, 634 Eddy Ave, Missoula, MT 59812. TEL 406-243-5819, FAX 406-243-4730, dec@selway.unit.org, dec@dec-sped.org, http://alliedhealth.lsuhsc.edu/jei/, http://www.dec-sped.org. Ed., Adv. contact Patricia Snyder. B&W page USD 300. Circ: 7,000. **Subscr. to:** Allen Press Inc., Subscription Fulfillment & Business Services, 810 E 10th St, Lawrence, KS 66044. TEL 785-843-1235, FAX 785-843-1274.

➤ **JOURNAL OF EMOTIONAL AND BEHAVIORAL DISORDERS.** see *MEDICAL SCIENCES—Psychiatry And Neurology*

371.9 GBR ISSN 1744-6309
LC4704 CODEN: JLDOAV
➤ **JOURNAL OF INTELLECTUAL DISABILITIES.** Text in English. 1997. q. GBP 383, USD 669 to institutions; GBP 398, USD 697 combined subscription to institutions print & online eds. (effective 2006). bk.rev. **Document type:** *Journal, Academic/Scholarly.* **Description:** Provides a medium for the exchange of best practice, knowledge, and research between the academic and professional disciplines of education, social and health care, who are committed to the advancement of services for people with learning disabilities.
Former titles (until 2005): Journal of Learning Disabilities (1469-0047); (until 2000): Journal of Learning Disabilities for Nursing, Health and Social Care (1362-0177)
Related titles: Online - full text ed.: ISSN 1744-6295. GBP 379, USD 662 to institutions (effective 2006) (from C S A, EBSCO Publishing, O C L C Online Computer Library Center, Inc., Swets Information Services).
Indexed: BrEdI, BrNI, CINAHL, ExcerpMed, FamI, MLA-IB, PEI, PsycInfo, PsycholAb, SSA, e-psyche.
—BLDSC (5010.230050), Infotrieve, ingenta. **CCC.**
Published by: Sage Publications Ltd. (Subsidiary of: Sage Publications, Inc.), 1 Oliver's Yard, 55 City Rd, London, EC1 1SP, United Kingdom. TEL 44-20-73248500, FAX 44-20-73248600, info@sagepub.co.uk, http://www.sagepub.co.uk/journal.aspx?pid=105663. Ed. Bob Gates. **Subscr. in the Americas to:** Sage Publications, Inc., 2455 Teller Rd, Thousand Oaks, CA 91320. TEL 805-499-0721, FAX 805-499-0871, journals@sagepub.com.

371.91 USA ISSN 0022-2194
LB1134 CODEN: JLDIAD
➤ **JOURNAL OF LEARNING DISABILITIES.** Text in English. 1967. bi-m., latest vol.36. USD 57 in North America to individuals; USD 92 elsewhere to individuals; USD 151 in North America to institutions; USD 177 elsewhere to institutions (effective 2005); USD 58 in North America to individuals; USD 94 elsewhere to individuals; USD 156 in North America to institutions; USD 182 elsewhere to institutions (effective 2006). adv. abstr.; charts; illus. index. back issues avail.; reprint service avail. from PSC. **Document type:** *Journal, Academic/Scholarly.* **Description:** Contains articles on practice, research, and theory related to learning disabilities.
Related titles: Microform ed.: (from PQC); Online - full text ed.: ISSN 1538-4780 (from bigchalk, EBSCO Publishing, Florida Center for Library Automation, Gale Group, H.W. Wilson, IngentaConnect, O C L C Online Computer Library Center, Inc., ProQuest Information & Learning).
Indexed: ABIn, AMED, AMHA, ASCA, ASSIA, BDM&CN, BRI, BiolAb, BrNI, CDA, CIJE, CINAHL, CPE, CurCont, DIP, EAA, ECER, ERA, ETA, EduInd, ExcerpMed, HEA, HECAB, IBR, IBZ, IMFL, INI, IndMed, L&LBA, MEA, MEA&I, MEDLINE, MLA-IB, NSCI, PAIS, PsySCDP, PsycInfo, PsycholAb, RHEA, RehabLit, SEA, SENA, SOMA, SOPODA, SSCI, SWA, TEA, YAE&RB, e-psyche.
—BLDSC (5010.230000), GNLM, IDS, IE, ingenta. **CCC.**
Published by: Pro-Ed Inc., 8700 Shoal Creek Blvd, Austin, TX 78757-6897. TEL 512-451-3246, 800-897-3202, FAX 512-302-9129, 800-397-7633, ltippett@proedinc.com, journals@proedinc.com, http://www.proedinc.com/jld.html. Ed. Lee Swanson. Pub. Donald D Hammill. R&P, Adv. contact Paula Gonzalez. B&W page USD 800, color page USD 1,000. Circ: 4,100 (paid and free).

371.9142 GBR ISSN 1476-9670
RC423.A1
▼ **JOURNAL OF MULTILINGUAL COMMUNICATION DISORDERS.** Text in English. 2003. 3/yr. GBP 186, USD 309 combined subscription to institutions print & online eds. (effective 2006). **Document type:** *Journal, Academic/Scholarly.* **Description:** Encompass research into how communication disorders are manifested in multilingual individuals, how treatment is best undertaken for multilingual clients and provision of multilingual assessments materials.
Related titles: Online - full text ed.: ISSN 1476-9689. GBP 186, USD 294 (effective 2006) (from EBSCO Publishing, Gale Group, IngentaConnect, O C L C Online Computer Library Center, Inc., Swets Information Services).
Indexed: CINAHL.
—BLDSC (5021.061000), IE.
Published by: Taylor & Francis Ltd (Subsidiary of: Taylor & Francis Group), 4 Park Sq, Milton Park, Abingdon, OX14 4RN, United Kingdom. TEL 44-1235-828600, FAX 44-1235-829000, info@tandf.co.uk, http://www.tandf.co.uk/journals/titles/14769670.asp. Ed. Nicole Mueller. **Subscr. to:** Journals Customer Service, Rankine Rd, Basingstoke, Hants RG24 8PR, United Kingdom. TEL 44-1256-813000, FAX 44-1256-330245, enquiry@tandf.co.uk.

371.9 GBR ISSN 1471-3802
LC3950
➤ **THE JOURNAL OF RESEARCH IN SPECIAL EDUCATIONAL NEEDS.** Abbreviated title: J O R S E N. Text in English. 2001 (Mar). 3/yr. GBP 178 in Europe to institutions; USD 329 in the Americas to institutions; GBP 203 elsewhere to institutions (effective 2004); Avail. only with a subscription to the British Journal of Special Education or Support for Learning. back issues avail. **Document type:** *Journal, Academic/Scholarly.* **Description:** Contains scholarly papers based on original research as well as critical reviews and theoretical essays.
Media: Online - full text (from O C L C Online Computer Library Center, Inc.).
—CCC.
Published by: (National Association for Special Educational Needs), Blackwell Publishing Ltd., 9600 Garsington Rd, Oxford, OX4 2ZG, United Kingdom. TEL 44-1865-776868, FAX 44-1865-714591, customerservices@oxon.blackwellpublishing.com, http://www.blackwellpublishing.com. Ed. Lani Florian.

371.95 USA ISSN 1077-4610
➤ **JOURNAL OF SECONDARY GIFTED EDUCATION.** Text in English. q. USD 55 (effective 2005). **Document type:** *Journal, Academic/Scholarly.*
Related titles: Online - full text ed.: (from EBSCO Publishing, Florida Center for Library Automation, Gale Group, O C L C Online Computer Library Center, Inc.).
Indexed: CIJE, PsycInfo, PsycholAb, RILM.
—BLDSC (5062.550000), IE, ingenta.
Published by: Prufrock Press Inc., PO Box 8813, Waco, TX 76714-8813. TEL 800-998-2208, FAX 800-240-0333, info@prufrock.com, http://www.prufrock.com/magazines. Ed. Bonnie Cramond TEL 706-542-4248. Pub. Joel McIntosh. Circ: 800 (paid).

371.9 USA ISSN 0022-4669
LC4001 CODEN: JSPEB9
➤ **THE JOURNAL OF SPECIAL EDUCATION.** Text in English. 1966. q., latest vol.36. USD 45 in North America to individuals; USD 74 elsewhere to individuals; USD 120 in North America to institutions; USD 151 elsewhere to institutions (effective 2006). adv. abstr.; illus.; stat.; charts. index. back issues avail.; reprint service avail. from PSC. **Document type:** *Journal, Academic/Scholarly.* **Description:** Contains research articles in all subspecialities of special education for individuals with disabilities from mild to severe.
Related titles: Microform ed.: (from PQC); Online - full text ed.: ISSN 1538-4764 (from EBSCO Publishing, Florida Center for Library Automation, Gale Group, H.W. Wilson, IngentaConnect, O C L C Online Computer Library Center, Inc., ProQuest Information & Learning).
Indexed: ABIn, ASCA, ASSIA, CDA, CIJE, CIS, CLFP, CPE, CurCont, DIP, EAA, ECER, ERA, ETA, EduInd, ExcerpMed, FamI, HECAB, IBR, IBZ, L&LBA, MEA, MRefA, PAIS, PsycInfo, PsycholAb, RehabLit, SEA, SOPODA, SSA, SSCI, TEA, YAE&RB, e-psyche.
—BLDSC (5066.120000), IDS, IE, Infotrieve, ingenta. **CCC.**
Published by: Pro-Ed Inc., 8700 Shoal Creek Blvd, Austin, TX 78757-6897. TEL 512-451-3246, 800-897-3202, FAX 512-302-9129, 800-397-7633, ltippett@proedinc.com, journals@proedinc.com, http://www.proedinc.com/jse.html. Eds. Charles A MacArthur, Ralph P Ferretti. Pub. Donald D Hammill. R&P, Adv. contact Paula Gonzalez. B&W page USD 400. Circ: 3,600 (paid and free).

371.90285 USA ISSN 0162-6434
LC4023
➤ **JOURNAL OF SPECIAL EDUCATION TECHNOLOGY.** Text in English. 1978. q. USD 40 to individuals; USD 89 to institutions (effective 2005). adv. bk.rev.; software rev.; Website rev. charts; illus. back issues avail.; reprint service avail. from PQC. **Document type:** *Journal, Academic/Scholarly.* **Description:** Features articles on theory and research in the applications of computer-assisted instruction in special education.
Related titles: Microform ed.: (from PQC); Online - full text ed.: 2000. free (effective 2005) (from H.W. Wilson, O C L C Online Computer Library Center, Inc., ProQuest Information & Learning).
Indexed: ABIn, CIJE, CPE, ECER, ETA, EduInd, Inspec, SENA, TEA, e-psyche.
—BLDSC (5066.120500), IE, Infotrieve, ingenta.
Published by: Council for Exceptional Children, Technology and Media Division, 1110 N Glebe Rd Ste 300, Arlington, VA 22201-5704. TEL 703-620-3663, FAX 703-264-9494, http://jset.unlv.edu, http://www.tamcec.org/. Ed. Herbert Rieth. Circ: 2,000.

371.9142 CAN ISSN 0848-1970
CODEN: JSLAEE
➤ **JOURNAL OF SPEECH - LANGUAGE PATHOLOGY AND AUDIOLOGY/REVUE D'ORTHOPHONIE ET D'AUDIOLOGIE.** Short title: J S L P A - R O A. Text in English, French. 1973. q. free to members; CND 45 domestic to individuals; CND 55 foreign to individuals; CND 55 domestic to institutions; CND 65 foreign to institutions; CND 30 domestic to students; CND 40 foreign to students (effective 2005). adv. bk.rev. abstr. **Document type:** *Academic/Scholarly.* **Description:** Aims to disseminate knowledge pertaining to human communication and its related disorders.
Former titles: Journal of Speech Language Pathologists and Audiologists; (until 1989): Human Communication Canada (0822-5486); Which was formed by the 1983 merger of: Human Communication (0319-1419); Hear Here
Indexed: CINAHL, DSHAb, L&LBA, PsycInfo, PsycholAb, SENA, SOPODA, e-psyche.
—BLDSC (5066.175000), CISTI, IE, ingenta. **CCC.**
Published by: Canadian Association of Speech - Language Pathologists and Audiologists/Association Canadienne des Orthophonistes et Audiologistes, 401-200 Elgin St, Ottawa, ON K2P 1L5, Canada. TEL 613-567-9968, 800-259-8519, FAX 613-567-2859, caslpa@caslpa.ca, http://www.caslpa.ca/english/resources/jslpa.asp. Ed. Dr. Phyllis Schneider. Pub., R&P, Adv. contact Suzanne Fraser. Circ: 4,100.

➤ **JOURNAL ON DEVELOPMENTAL DISABILITIES/JOURNAL SUR LES HANDICAPS DU DEVELOPPEMENT.** see *MEDICAL SCIENCES—Psychiatry And Neurology*

371.9 DEU ISSN 0174-3147
DER KIESELSTEIN. Text in German. 1978. m. EUR 30 (effective 2005). adv. bk.rev. illus. index. back issues avail. **Document type:** *Magazine, Consumer.* **Description:** Contains information on speech therapy and self-help for people who stutter.
Published by: Bundesvereinigung Stotterer-Selbsthilfe e.V., Zuelpicher Str 58, Cologne, 50674, Germany. TEL 49-221-1391106, FAX 49-221-1391370, info@bvss.de, http://www.bvss.de/der-kieselstein/. Ed. Michael Koop. Adv. contact Konrad Schaefers. Circ: 1,500 (paid and free).

KNOW YOUR WORLD EXTRA (LARGE PRINT EDITION). see *CHILDREN AND YOUTH—For*

371.9 KOR
KOREA SOCIAL WORK COLLEGE. RESEARCH INSTITUTE FOR SPECIAL EDUCATION. JOURNAL/KWANG-EUNG YEO. Text in Korean. 1978 (vol.6). a.
Published by: Korea Social Work College, Research Institute for Special Education, 2288 Daemyung-dong Nam Gu, Daegu, 634-00, Korea, S.

371.9 USA ISSN 0739-909X
L D A NEWSBRIEFS; items of interest on learning disabilities. Text in English. 1978 (no.118). bi-m. USD 15 domestic; USD 35 foreign; USD 30 membership includes subscr. to L D A Newsbriefs (effective 2003). adv. bk.rev. **Document type:** *Newsletter.* **Description:** Provides information on learning disabilities to the community of educators and others who are interested.
Formerly: A C L D Newsbriefs (Association for Children and Adults with Learning Disabilities)
Published by: Learning Disabilities Association of America, 4156 Library Rd, Pittsburgh, PA 15234. TEL 412-341-1515, FAX 412-344-0224, info@ldaamerica.org, http://www.ldanatl.org/forms/newsbriefs.html. Ed., R&P Lynne Cannon. Adv. contact Andrea Turkheimer. Circ: 50,000.

E

371.91 USA
THE L D READER. (Learning Disabilities) Text in English. 1995. irreg., latest vol.61. free. back issues avail. **Document type:** *Newsletter.* **Description:** Offers persons with learning disabilities and their families support in dealing with their condition. Seeks to foster public awareness and understanding of learning disabilities by disseminating practical information and dispelling common myths.
Media: Online - full text.
Indexed: e-psyche.
Published by: L D Reader, 202 Lake Rd, New, Preston, CT 06777. TEL 860-868-3214, ldr@ldresources.com, richard@ldresources.com, http://www.ldresources.com. Ed. Richard Wanderman.

371.928 USA ISSN 0163-2205
L I N K S. (Living in New Kinds of Situations) Text in English. 1970. m. adv. bk.rev. **Document type:** *Newspaper, Trade.* **Description:** A publication for private providers serving people with disabilities.
Indexed: CPE.
Published by: (American Network for Community Options Resources), A N C O R, 1101 King St. Suite 380, Alexandria, VA 22314. TEL 703-535-7850, FAX 703-535-7860, http://www.ancor.org/links.html. adv.: page USD 600. Circ: 7,000.

LANGUAGE ACQUISITION AND LANGUAGE DISORDERS. see *LINGUISTICS*

LANGUAGE, SPEECH AND HEARING SERVICES IN SCHOOLS. see *MEDICAL SCIENCES—Otorhinolaryngology*

371.9 USA ISSN 1046-6819
LC4705
LEARNING DISABILITIES (PITTSBURGH); a multidisciplinary journal. Text in English. 1989. q. USD 30 (effective 2004). **Document type:** *Journal, Academic/Scholarly.* **Description:** Covers all forms of learning disabilities from a multidisciplinary perspective.
Indexed: CIJE.
—BLDSC (5179.326380), IE, ingenta. **CCC.**
Published by: Learning Disabilities Association of America, 4156 Library Rd, Pittsburgh, PA 15234. TEL 412-341-1515, FAX 412-344-0224, info@ldaamerica.org, http://www.ldanatl.org/. Circ: 800 (paid).

371.9 USA ISSN 0938-8982
CODEN: LDRPE6
LEARNING DISABILITIES RESEARCH AND PRACTICE. Text in English. 1991. q. USD 64 combined subscription in the Americas to individuals & Caribbean, print & online eds.; EUR 72 combined subscription in Europe to individuals print & online eds.; GBP 48 combined subscription elsewhere to individuals print & online eds.; USD 489 combined subscription in the Americas to institutions & Caribbean, print & online eds.; GBP 374 combined subscription elsewhere to institutions print & online eds. (effective 2006). adv. **Document type:** *Journal, Academic/Scholarly.* **Description:** Covers current research of interest to teachers, teacher educators and researchers.
Formed by the merger of (1985-1991): Learning Disabilities Research (0892-502X); (1985-1991): Learning Disabilities Focus (0892-5011)
Related titles: Online - full text ed.: ISSN 1540-5826. 1981. USD 465 in the Americas to institutions & Caribbean; GBP 355 elsewhere to institutions (effective 2006) (from Blackwell Synergy, EBSCO Publishing, Gale Group, IngentaConnect, O C L C Online Computer Library Center, Inc., Ovid Technologies, Inc., Swets Information Services).
Indexed: CIJE, CPE, ECER, ERA, ETA, MEA, MLA-IB, PsycInfo, PsycholAb, RHEA, SEA, SENA, SOMA, TEA, e-psyche.
—BLDSC (5179.326480), IE, Infotrieve. **CCC.**
Published by: (Council for Exceptional Children, Division for Learning Disabilities), Blackwell Publishing, Inc. (Subsidiary of: Blackwell Publishing Ltd.), Commerce Place, 350 Main St, Malden, MA 02148. TEL 781-388-8206, FAX 781-388-8232, subscrip@blackwellpub.com, http://www.blackwellpublishing.com/journal.asp?ref=0938-8982&site=1. Eds. C Addison Stone, Joanne F Carlisle. adv.: page USD 550; trim 7 x 10. Circ: 14,000.

371.9 GBR ISSN 1465-8712
LEARNING DISABILITY PRACTICE. Text in English. 1999. bi-m. GBP 43.50 in Europe to members; GBP 70 elsewhere to members; GBP 52.50 in Europe to non-members; GBP 85 elsewhere to non-members (effective 2004). adv. **Document type:** *Journal, Academic/Scholarly.* **Description:** Provides material that is accessible, topical and jargon-free for the specialist nurse and care giver.
Related titles: Online - full text ed.: (from EBSCO Publishing, Gale Group).
Indexed: BrNI, CINAHL, e-psyche.
—BLDSC (5179.326485), IE, ingenta. **CCC.**
Published by: (Royal College of Nursing), R C N Publishing Co. (Subsidiary of: B M J Publishing Group), R C N Direct, Copse Walk, Cardiff Gate Business Park, Cardiff, CF23 8XG, United Kingdom. TEL 44-29-2054-6450, FAX 44-29-2054-6401, directjournalsteam@rcn.org.uk, http://www.rcn.org.uk/. Ed. John Turnbull. Adv. contact Phil Whomes. Circ: 900 (controlled).

371.9 USA ISSN 0731-9487
LC4704
➤ **LEARNING DISABILITY QUARTERLY.** Text in English. 1978. q. USD 65 domestic to institutions; USD 75 foreign to institutions; USD 55 to individual members; USD 25 to students (effective 2005). adv. bk.rev. illus. index. 80 p./no.; back issues avail.; reprints avail. **Document type:** *Journal, Academic/Scholarly.* **Description:** Reports on techniques in identification, assessment, remediation and programming, advanced theories, research and personnel preparation.
Related titles: Microform ed.; Online - full text ed.: (from EBSCO Publishing, Florida Center for Library Automation, Gale Group, H.W. Wilson, O C L C Online Computer Library Center, Inc., ProQuest Information & Learning).
Indexed: ABIn, ASCA, BehAb, CIJE, CPE, ChPerI, CurCont, ECER, ERA, ETA, EduInd, FamI, MEA, PsycInfo, PsycholAb, RHEA, SEA, SENA, SOMA, SSCI, SSI, SWA, TEA, e-psyche.
—BLDSC (5179.326490), IDS, IE, Infotrieve, ingenta.
Published by: C L D, Box 4014, Leesburg, VA 20177. TEL 571-258-1010, FAX 571-258-1011, http://www.cldinternational.org/c/@zkulSLo4s8G9s/Pages/ldq.html, http://www.cldinternational.com. Ed. David Edgburn. R&P, Adv. contact Kirsten McBride. Circ: 3,500.

371.9 DEU
LEBENSHILFE AKTUELL. Text in German. 1975. bi-m. adv. back issues avail. **Document type:** *Journal, Academic/Scholarly.* **Description:** Provides information about mental handicaps.
Published by: Bundesvereinigung Lebenshilfe fuer Menschen mit Geistiger Behinderung e.V., Raiffeisenstr 18, Marburg, 35043, Germany. TEL 49-6421-4910, FAX 49-6421-491167. Eds. Dr. Bernhard Conrads, Juergen Reuter. Adv. contact Ursula Dahlstroem. Circ: 125,000.

371.9 DEU
LEBENSHILFE-ZEITUNG. Text in German. 1980. q. EUR 12; EUR 3 newsstand/cover (effective 2003). adv. **Document type:** *Newspaper, Academic/Scholarly.*
Published by: Bundesvereinigung Lebenshilfe fuer Menschen mit Geistiger Behinderung e.V., Raiffeisenstr 18, Marburg, 35043, Germany. TEL 49-6421-4910, FAX 49-6421-491167, bundesvereinigung@lebenshilfe.de, http://www.lebenshilfe.de. Ed. Dr. Bernhard Conrads. Adv. contact Ursula Dahlstroem. page EUR 5,871; trim 281 x 412. Circ: 125,000 (paid and controlled).

371.9 DEU ISSN 0720-8316
LERNEN FOERDERN; Zeitschrift fuer Eltern, Lehrer und Erzieher. Text in German. 1981. q. EUR 15.34; EUR 4.60 newsstand/cover (effective 2005). back issues avail. **Document type:** *Journal, Academic/Scholarly.*
Published by: Bundesverband zur Foerderung Lernbehinderter e.V., Gerberstr 17, Stuttgart, 70178, Germany. TEL 49-711-6338438, FAX 49-711-6338439, post@lernen-foerdern.de, http://www.lernen-foerdern.de. Ed., R&P, Adv. contact Rudolf Zelfel. Circ: 5,000.

371.92 DEU ISSN 0722-1843
LERNEN KONKRET. Text in German. 1981. q. EUR 30 (effective 2003). adv. bk.rev. illus. **Document type:** *Journal, Academic/Scholarly.* **Description:** Scientific discussion, reports and experiences on the different aspects of the education of mentally and/or physically handicapped pupils.
Published by: Bildungsverlag EINS GmbH, Sieglarer Str. 2, Troisdorf, 53842, Germany. TEL 49-2241-39760, FAX 49-2241-3976990, service@bildungsverlag1.de, http://www.bildungsverlag1.de. Ed. Karl Heinz Zuber. Circ: 2,500.

LIGHT (WHEATON). see *HANDICAPPED—Visually Impaired*

371.91 FRA ISSN 0182-5437
LIGUE POUR L'ADAPTATION DU DIMINUE PHYSIQUE AU TRAVAIL. CAHIERS. Key Title: Cahiers de LADAPT. Text in French. 1971. q. EUR 5 per issue (effective 2005). **Document type:** *Newspaper, Consumer.*
Formerly (until 1975): Cahiers de LADAPT, Gageure (0182-6611); Which was formed by the merger of (1968-1971): Gageure (0182-6638); (1961-1971): Cahiers de LADAPT (0182-662X)
Published by: Ligue pour l'Adaptation du Diminue Physique au Travail, Tour Essor, 14 rue Scandicci, Pantin, 93508, France. TEL 33-1-48101246, FAX 33-1-48101244, contact@ladapt.net, http://www.ladapt.asso.fr. Circ: 6,000 (paid).

LOGOPEDIE EN FONIATRIE; vaktijdschrift voor logopedie (stem-, spraak-, taal- en gehoorstoornissen). see *HANDICAPPED—Hearing Impaired*

LOGOPEDNYTT. see *MEDICAL SCIENCES—Psychiatry And Neurology*

MAINSTREAM NEWS. see *HANDICAPPED—Hearing Impaired*

MAINTAINING SAFE SCHOOLS. see *EDUCATION—School Organization And Administration*

MANITOBA COUNCIL FOR EXCEPTIONAL CHILDREN. see *CHILDREN AND YOUTH—About*

MARBURGER BUECHERLISTEN. see *HANDICAPPED—Visually Impaired*

371.9 DEU
MARIABERGER BRIEF; Berichte aus unserer Arbeit. Text in German. 1968. 2/yr. adv. **Document type:** *Bulletin.*
Published by: Mariaberger Heime, Klosterhof 1, Gammertingen, 72501, Germany. TEL 49-7124-923-0, FAX 49-7124-923500. Ed. K R Eder. Adv. contact A Martin Steffe. Circ: 18,000.

371.9 DEU
MARIABERGER HEIME; Berichte aus unserer Arbeit. Text in German. 1847. a. adv. **Document type:** *Bulletin.*
Address: Klosterhof 1, Gammertingen, 72501, Germany. TEL 49-7124-923-0, FAX 49-7124-923500. Ed. A Lenkert Hoerrmann. Adv. contact A Martin Steffe. Circ: 20,000.

371.95 USA ISSN 0025-9551
BF412
MENSA RESEARCH JOURNAL. Text in English. 3/yr. USD 21 (effective 2001). adv. bk.rev. back issues avail. **Document type:** *Journal, Academic/Scholarly.* **Description:** Covers research on intelligence; aimed particularly at the gifted.
Published by: Mensa Education and Research Foundation, 1229 Corporate Dr W, Arlington, TX 76006-6103. TEL 817-607-0060, FAX 817-649-5232. Ed. Phyllis Miller. R&P Annette Kovac TEL 817-607-0060. Circ: 1,000.

371.928 USA ISSN 0047-6765
RC569.7 CODEN: MRTDAH
➤ **MENTAL RETARDATION**; a journal of practices, policy and perspectives. Text in English. 1963. bi-m. USD 106 combined subscription domestic to individuals print & online eds.; USD 139 combined subscription foreign to individuals print & online eds.; USD 219 combined subscription domestic to institutions print & online eds.; USD 252 combined subscription foreign to institutions print & online eds. (effective 2005). adv. bk.rev. illus. index. back issues avail.; reprints avail. **Document type:** *Journal, Academic/Scholarly.* **Description:** Seeks effective ways to help people with mental retardation and their families.
Related titles: Microfilm ed.; Online - full text ed.: USD 95 worldwide to individuals; USD 207 worldwide to institutions (effective 2005) (from EBSCO Publishing, H.W. Wilson, O C L C Online Computer Library Center, Inc.).
Indexed: ABIn, AMHA, ASCA, AgeL, BDM&CN, BiolAb, CDA, CIJE, CLFP, CurCont, DentInd, EduInd, ExcerpMed, FamI, HospLI, INI, IndMed, L&LBA, MEA, MEDLINE, PsycInfo, PsycholAb, RehabLit, SENA, SOPODA, SSA, SSCI, SociolAb, e-psyche.
—BLDSC (5678.655000), CISTI, GNLM, IDS, IE, Infotrieve, ingenta, KNAW. **CCC.**
Published by: American Association on Mental Retardation, 444 N Capitol St, Ste 846, Washington, DC 20001-1512. TEL 202-387-1968, 800-424-3688, FAX 202-387-2193, orders@allenpress.com, http://www.aamr.allenpress.com. Ed. Steven Taylor. Pub. M Doreen Croser. R&P Stephen Stidinger. adv.: B&W page USD 920; trim 8.25 x 10.875. Circ: 7,500.
Subscr. to: Allen Press Inc., PO Box 1897, Lawrence, KS 66044.

➤ **MILL NECK FOUNDATION NEWSLETTER.** see *HANDICAPPED—Hearing Impaired*

➤ **MINNESOTA SPEECH - LANGUAGE - HEARING ASSOCIATION. NEWSLETTER.** see *MEDICAL SCIENCES—Otorhinolaryngology*

➤ **MISSOURI RECORD.** see *HANDICAPPED—Hearing Impaired*

371.9 DEU ISSN 0179-3470
MUENCHENER BEITRAEGE ZUR SONDERPAEDAGOGIK. Text in German. 1986. irreg., latest vol.26, 2002. EUR 46.80 per vol. (effective 2003). **Document type:** *Monographic series, Academic/Scholarly.*
Published by: Peter Lang GmbH Europaeischer Verlag der Wissenschaften, Eschborner Landstr 42-50, Frankfurt Am Main, 60489, Germany. TEL 49-69-7807050, FAX 49-69-78070543, zentrale.frankfurt@peterlang.com, http://www.peterlang.de.

371.928 368 USA
N A F I M NEWSLETTER. Text in English. 1971. q. USD 35 domestic (effective 2001). bk.rev. **Document type:** *Newsletter, Consumer.* **Description:** Covers current news, issues and concerns of children and adults with mental retardation and their families, and parish religion programs.
Former titles (until 1997): National Apostolate with People with Mental Retardation. Newsletter; (until 1992): National Apostolate with Mentally Retarded Persons. Newsletter (0889-9592)
Published by: National Apostolate for Inclusion Ministry, PO Box 218, Riverdale, MD 20738-0218. TEL 301-699-9500, 800-736-1280, FAX 240-220-8374, qnafim@aol.com, http://www.nafim.org. Ed. Barbara Lampe. Circ: 1,000.

371.9 371.2012 USA
N A P S A NEWS. Text in English. 1966. q. looseleaf. membership. **Document type:** *Newsletter.* **Description:** Provides information for administrators of pupil services programs.
Published by: National Association of Pupil Services Administration, 7030 Coffman Rd, Dublin, OH 43017. TEL 614-761-5886, FAX 703-359-8973. Ed. Kathleen Lowery. Circ: 500.

E

371.9 USA
N A P S E C MEMBERSHIP DIRECTORY. Text in English. 1980. biennial. USD 32. **Document type:** *Directory.* **Description:** Lists and describes over 200 member schools that have populations of students with disabilities, including day, residential, summer, clinical programs, and hospital affiliated programs.
Published by: National Association of Private Schools for Exceptional Children, 1522 K St, N W, Ste 1032, Washington, DC 20005. TEL 202-408-3338, FAX 202-408-3340. Ed. Sherry L Kolbe. Circ: 500.

371.95 USA
N A P S E C NEWS. Text in English. 3/yr. **Document type:** *Newsletter.*
Published by: National Association of Private Schools for Exceptional Children, 1522 K St; N W, Ste 1032, Washington, DC 20005. TEL 202-408-3338, FAX 202-408-3340. Ed. Sherry L Kolbe. Circ: 300.

371.91 CAN ISSN 0709-1370
NATIONAL (OTTAWA, 1970). Text in English. 1970. q. USD 20 (effective 1998). adv. bk.rev. **Document type:** *Newsletter.* **Description:** Covers the Association's national activities: projects, federal government liaison; reports on provincial, territorial associations' initiatives; includes articles and resources about learning disabilities.
Former titles: Post (0380-7967); Perceptual Post (0380-7975)
Related titles: French ed.
Indexed: CEI.
Published by: Learning Disabilities Association of Canada, Kildare House, 323 Chapel St, Ottawa, ON K1N 7Z2, Canada. TEL 613-238-5721, FAX 613-235-5391, LDACTAAC@fox.nstn.ca, http://educ.queensu.ca/~lda. Ed. P Mantha. Circ: 8,000.

371.928 268 USA ISSN 1534-5297
NATIONAL APOSTOLATE FOR INCLUSION MINISTRY. QUARTERLY PUBLICATION; Supporting the Inclusion of Persons with Mental Retardation in the Catholic Church. Text in English. 1968. q. USD 35 domestic (effective 2001); includes Newsletter. illus. **Document type:** *Journal, Consumer.* **Description:** Covers current news, issues and concerns of children and adults with mental retardation and their families, and parish religion programs.
Former titles (until 1997): National Apostolate with People with Mental Retardation. Quarterly (1088-2715); (until 1992): National Apostolate with Mentally Retarded Persons. Quarterly Publication (0273-9178)
Published by: National Apostolate for Inclusion Ministry, PO Box 218, Riverdale, MD 20738-0218. TEL 301-699-9500, 800-736-1280, FAX 240-220-8374, qnafim@aol.com, http://www.nafim.org. Ed. Ray Daull. Circ: 400 (paid).

371.91 USA ISSN 0884-3643
LC3991
NATIONAL ASSOCIATION FOR GIFTED CHILDREN. COMMUNIQUE. Text in English. 19??. q.
Related titles: Online - full text ed.: (from SoftLine Information).
—BLDSC (3363.545100).
Published by: National Association for Gifted Children, 1707 L St, N W, Ste 550, Washington, DC 20036-4201. TEL 202-785-4268, FAX 202-785-4248, nagc@nagc.org, http://www.nagc.org.

371.91 GBR
NATIONAL ASSOCIATION FOR SPECIAL EDUCATIONAL NEEDS. PUBLICATIONS. Text in English. 1983. irreg. **Document type:** *Monographic series.*
Formerly: National Council for Special Education. Occasional Publications
Published by: National Association for Special Educational Needs, NASEN House, 4-5 Amber Business Village, Amber Village, Amington, Tamworth, Warks B77 4RP, United Kingdom. TEL 44-1827-311500, FAX 44-1827-313005, welcome@nasen.org.uk, http://www.nasen.org.uk.

NATIONAL ASSOCIATION OF JUVENILE CORRECTION AGENCIES. PROCEEDINGS. see *CRIMINOLOGY AND LAW ENFORCEMENT*

NATIONAL DISABILITY LAW REPORTER. see *LAW*

371.9 USA ISSN 1043-2167
LC3981
➤ **NATIONAL FORUM OF SPECIAL EDUCATION JOURNAL - ELECTRONIC.** Abbreviated title: N F S E Journal. Text in English. 1989. a. USD 44 domestic to individuals; USD 88 domestic to institutions (effective 2005); USD 144 foreign to institutions (effective 2002). adv. index. back issues avail. **Document type:** *Journal, Academic/Scholarly.*
Media: Online - full text.
Indexed: ECER.
—CCC.
Published by: (National Forum Society of Educators), National Forum Journals, 17603 Bending Post Dr, Houston, TX 77095. TEL 281-550-5700, http://www.nationalforum.com. Ed., Pub., R&P, Adv. contact Dr. William Kritsonis TEL 337-477-0008. Circ: 7,500.

371.9 JPN ISSN 0387-3528
NATIONAL INSTITUTE OF SPECIAL EDUCATION. BULLETIN/KOKURITSU TOKUSHU KYOIKU SOGO KENKYUJO KENKYU KIYO. Text in Japanese; Summaries in English. 1974. a. free. **Document type:** *Bulletin.*
Published by: National Institute of Special Education/Kokuritsu Tokushu Kyoiku Sogo Kenkyusho, 5-1-1 Nobi, Yokosuka-shi, Kanagawa-ken 239-0841, Japan. TEL 81-468-48-4121. Circ: 1,480.

371.9 JPN
NATIONAL INSTITUTE OF SPECIAL EDUCATION. NEWSLETTER. Text in Japanese. q. **Document type:** *Newsletter.*
Published by: National Institute of Special Education/Kokuritsu Tokushu Kyoiku Sogo Kenkyusho, 5-1-1 Nobi, Yokosuka-shi, Kanagawa-ken 239-0841, Japan. TEL 81-468-48-4121.

371.9 JPN
NATIONAL INSTITUTE OF SPECIAL EDUCATION SEMINAR. FINAL REPORT. Text in Japanese. a. **Document type:** *Corporate.*
Published by: National Institute of Special Education/Kokuritsu Tokushu Kyoiku Sogo Kenkyusho, 5-1-1 Nobi, Yokosuka-shi, Kanagawa-ken 239-0841, Japan. TEL 81-468-48-4121.

371.95 USA
NATIONAL RESEARCH CENTER ON THE GIFTED AND TALENTED NEWSLETTER. Text in English. 1993. s-a. free. **Document type:** *Newsletter.*
Published by: National Research Center on the Gifted and Talented, University of Connecticut, 362 Fairfield Rd. U7, Storrs, CT 06269-2007. TEL 860-486-4826, http://www.ucc.uconn.edu/~wwwgt/nrcgttxt.html. Ed. E Jean Gubbins.

NEW JERSEY. DEVELOPMENTAL DISABILITIES COUNCIL. ANNUAL REPORT. see *SOCIAL SERVICES AND WELFARE*

NEW LITERATURE ON VISUAL IMPAIRMENT. see *HANDICAPPED—Abstracting, Bibliographies, Statistics*

NEW MEXICO PROGRESS. see *HANDICAPPED—Hearing Impaired*

NEWS 'N' NOTES. see *HANDICAPPED—Hearing Impaired*

NORDISK TIDSKRIFT FOER HOERSEL- OCH DOEVUNDERVISNING NTD. see *HANDICAPPED—Hearing Impaired*

NORTH DAKOTA STATE PLAN FOR REHABILITATION FACILITIES AND WORKSHOPS; annual modification. see *MEDICAL SCIENCES—Physical Medicine And Rehabilitation*

371.9 FRA ISSN 1289-0065
LA NOUVELLE REVUE DE L'A I S. (Adaptation, Integration Scolaires et Education Specialisee) Text in French. N.S. 1998. q. EUR 45 (effective 2004).
Formed by the merger of (1967-1997): Le Courrier de Suresnes (0767-2403); (197?-1997): Les Cahiers de Beaumont (0244-1934)
Published by: Centre National d'Etudes et de Formation pour l'Enfance Inadaptee, 58-60 avenue des Landes, Suresnes, 92150, France. TEL 33-1-41443129, FAX 33-1-41443579, vente@cnefei.fr, http://www.cnefei.fr/Ressource/NRAIS/AccueilNRAIS.htm. Ed. Herve Benoit.

371.9142 CAN ISSN 1207-5639
THE O S L A CONNECTION. Text in English. 1960. 3/yr. membership. adv. **Document type:** *Newsletter, Trade.*
Former titles (until 1995): O S L A Newsletter (0836-4362); (until 1987): O.S.H.A. Ontario Speech and Hearing Association (0705-8713); (until 1976): Ontario Speech and Hearing Association. Journal (0705-8888)
Published by: Ontario Association of Speech - Language Pathologists and Audiologists, 410 Jarvis St, Toronto, ON M4Y 2G6, Canada. TEL 416-920-3676, FAX 416-920-6214, http://www.osla.on.ca. Ed. Liz Brady. R&P, Adv. contact Lucy Robinson. Circ: 1,500 (controlled).

371.912 USA ISSN 1544-6751
HV2510 CODEN: PEDEFN
➤ **ODYSSEY: NEW DIRECTIONS IN DEAF EDUCATION.** Text in English. 1982. q. free. adv. bk.rev.; film rev. illus. index. back issues avail.; reprints avail. **Document type:** *Academic/Scholarly.* **Description:** Directed to professionals and families involved with educating deaf and hard-of-hearing students. Provides a forum for exchange of creative approaches to classroom teaching; gives views about current issues in deafness and education.
Former titles (until 2000): Perspectives in Education and Deafness (1051-6204); (until 1989): Perspectives for Teachers of the Hearing Impaired (0735-6315)
Indexed: CIJE, ECER, FamI, SOPODA, SSI.
Published by: Gallaudet University, Laurent Clerc National Deaf Education Center, 800 Florida Ave, NE, Washington, DC 20002-3695. TEL 202-651-5340, 800-526-9105, FAX 202-651-5708, http://clerccenter.gallaudet.edu/Odyssey/index.html. Ed. Cathryn Carroll. Adv. contact Susan Flanigan. Circ: 4,000.

➤ **OKEE.** see *MEDICAL SCIENCES—Psychiatry And Neurology*

371.91 USA ISSN 1041-6234
ONCUE. Text in English. 1984. q. USD 40 membership; USD 65 to institutions; USD 30 to students (effective 2005). adv. bk.rev. illus. 12 p./no.; **Document type:** *Journal, Consumer.* **Description:** Information for professionals and families regarding the use of Cued Speech, a system of communication for people with hearing, speech and language needs.
Former titles: C U E Newsletter; Computer Using Educators (0739-9553)
Published by: Computer Using Educators, Inc., 2150 Mariner Square Dr, Ste 100, Alameda, CA 94501. TEL 510-814-6630, FAX 510-814-0195, cueinc@cue.org, http://www.cue.org. adv: B&W page USD 725. Circ: 11,000 (paid).

ONE IN SEVEN. see *HANDICAPPED—Hearing Impaired*

OREGON OUTLOOK. see *HANDICAPPED—Hearing Impaired*

371.9 USA ISSN 0737-514X
PAEDOPERISSE✶ ; an international journal of comparative special education. Text in English. 1984. q. adv. bk.rev. abstr.; charts; illus. index.
Published by: Eterna International, Inc., PO Box 5731, Hauppauge, NY 11788-0154. Ed. Stephen B Parrish.

371.91 USA ISSN 8756-5811
PALAESTRA; forum of sport, physical education and recreation for those with disabilities. Text in English. 1984. q. USD 19.95 to individuals; USD 26.95 to institutions (effective 2005). adv. bk.rev. illus. index. back issues avail.; reprints avail.
Document type: *Consumer.* **Description:** Provides technical, "how-to" articles and practical research on recreation and physical education activities for individuals with a disability. Covers national and international sports events and looks at equipment and facility modification.
Related titles: Microform ed.: (from PQC); Online - full text ed.: (from Gale Group, Northern Light Technology, Inc., O C L C Online Computer Library Center, Inc., ProQuest Information & Learning).
Indexed: HlthInd, PEI, SPI, SportS.
—BLDSC (6345.214200), IE, ingenta.
Published by: Challenge Publications, Ltd., Circulation Department, PO Box 508, Macomb, IL 61455-0508. challpub@macomb.com, http://www.palaestra.com. Ed. David P Beaver. adv.: B&W page USD 1,270, color page USD 2,045. Circ: 5,500. **Co-sponsors:** Committee on Sports for the Disabled of the United States Olympic Committee; Adapted Physical Activity Council of the American Alliance for Health, Physical Education, Recreation and Dance.

371.9 CHE ISSN 1420-1534
PEDAGOGIE SPECIALISEE. Text in French, Italian. 1995. 4/yr. CHF 30 domestic; CHF 36 foreign (effective 2001). adv. bk.rev. bibl. **Document type:** *Journal, Academic/Scholarly.*
Published by: Schweizerische Zentralstelle fuer Heilpaedagogik, Obergrundstr 61, Luzern, 6003, Switzerland. TEL 41-41-2263040, FAX 41-41-2263041, szh@tic.ch, http://www.spc.ch, http://www.szh.ch. Ed. Alois Buerli.

371.928 USA ISSN 0031-4609
PENNSYLVANIA MESSAGE. Text in English. 1965. q. USD 20. adv. bk.rev. abstr. 16 p./no.; back issues avail.
Indexed: e-psyche.
Published by: The Arc of Pennsylvania, 2001 N Front St, Ste 221, Harrisburg, PA 17102-2104. TEL 717-234-2621, FAX 717-234-7615, komyers@usa.net, http://www.thearcpa.org. Ed. Kristi O'Connell Myers. Circ: 8,500 (controlled).

371.92 USA ISSN 0731-566X
PEOPLE WITH SPECIAL NEEDS - DOWN SYNDROME REPORT✶ . Text in English. 1985. 6/yr. USD 5 (effective 2000). bk.rev.; film rev. bibl.; charts; stat. **Document type:** *Newsletter.*
Published by: The Arc, Upper Valley, PO Box 12420, Grand Forks, ND 58308-2420. Robjohns@sendit.sendit.nodak.edu. Circ: 6,000.

PERSPECTIVES (BALTIMORE). see *MEDICAL SCIENCES—Psychiatry And Neurology*

371.91 USA
PHYSICAL DISABILITIES - EDUCATION & RELATED SERVICES. Text in English. 1978. s-a. membership only. adv. bk.rev. **Document type:** *Directory, Trade.* **Description:** Provides educational and support services information for individuals with physical or health disabilities.
Formerly: D P H Journal
Indexed: CIJE, ECER.
Published by: Council for Exceptional Children, Division for Physical & Health Disabilities, 1110 N. Glebe Rd., Ste. 300, Arlington, VA 22201-4795. TEL 703-620-3660, FAX 703-264-9494, http://www.cec.sped.org. Ed. Barbara Kulik. Circ: 1,500.

PINE CONE. see *MEDICAL SCIENCES—Psychiatry And Neurology*

E

▼ *new title*   ➤ *refereed*   ✶ *unverified*   ♦ *full entry avail.*

PLENUM SERIES ON HUMAN EXCEPTIONALITY. see *PSYCHOLOGY*

371.91 JPN
PRACTICAL EDUCATION FOR THE HANDICAPPED/JISSEN SHOGAIJI KYOIKU. Text in Japanese. 1973. m. JPY 4,800.
Formerly: Education for the Handicapped
Published by: Gakken Co. Ltd., 40-5 Kami-Ikedai 4-chome, Ota-ku, Tokyo, 145-0064, Japan. Ed. Yukio Nakayama.

371.91 USA ISSN 1045-988X
HV888
➤ **PREVENTING SCHOOL FAILURE.** Text in English. 1956. q. USD 54 domestic to individuals; USD 68 foreign to individuals; USD 123 domestic to institutions; USD 137 foreign to institutions; USD 30.75 per issue (effective academic year 2005 - 2006). adv. bk.rev. charts; illus. index. back issues avail.; reprint service avail. from PQC,PSC. **Document type:** *Journal, Academic/Scholarly.*
Formerly (until 1989): Pointer (Washington) (0554-4246)
Related titles: CD-ROM ed.: (from ProQuest Information & Learning); Microform ed.; Online - full text ed.: (from bigchalk, EBSCO Publishing, Florida Center for Library Automation, Gale Group, H.W. Wilson, O C L C Online Computer Library Center, Inc., ProQuest Information & Learning, SoftLine Information).
Indexed: ABIn, BehAb, CIJE, CPE, DIP, ECER, ERA, ETA, EduInd, FamI, IBR, IBZ, MEA, PsycholAb, RHEA, RehabLit, SEA, SENA, SOMA, TEA.
—BLDSC (6612.727400), IE, ingenta. **CCC.**
Published by: (Helen Dwight Reid Educational Foundation), Heldref Publications, 1319 18th St, NW, Washington, DC 20036-1802. TEL 202-296-6267, 800-365-9753, FAX 202-293-6130, psf@heldref.org, subscribe@heldref.org, http://www.heldref.org/psf.php. Adv. contact Chante Douglas. B&W page USD 175; trim 7 x 10. Circ: 444 (paid).

➤ **PURE FACTS.** see *MEDICAL SCIENCES—Psychiatry And Neurology*

➤ **QUALITY OF CARE.** see *MEDICAL SCIENCES—Psychiatry And Neurology*

371.9 ESP ISSN 0212-5943
QUINESIA; revista de educacion especial. Text in Spanish. 1983. 3/yr.
—CINDOC.
Published by: Centro de Educacion Especial "San Rafael", Marques de Valladares, 9, Vigo, Pontevedra 36201, Spain.

371.91 USA
R E S N A NEWS. (Rehabilitation Engineering and Assistive Technology Society of North America) Text in English. 1982. bi-m. USD 25 (effective 2004). adv. bk.rev. back issues avail. **Document type:** *Newsletter, Academic/Scholarly.* **Description:** Aims for the dissemination and utilization of knowledge of rehabilitative and assistive technology.
Formerly (until 1990): Rehabilitation Technology Review (0882-2476)
Published by: R E S N A, 1700 N Moore St, Ste 1540, Arlington, VA 22209-1903. TEL 703-524-6686, FAX 703-524-6630, info@resna.org, http://www.resna.org. Circ: 2,000.

RAAKPUNT. see *MEDICAL SCIENCES—Psychiatry And Neurology*

371.9 IRL ISSN 0790-8695
REACH; journal of special needs education in Ireland. Text in English. 1987. s-a. GBP 8 (effective 2000).
—BLDSC (7300.263540).
Published by: Irish Association of Teachers in Special Education, 27 Upper Mount St, Dublin, 2, Ireland. TEL 353-1-662-3540, FAX 353-1-662-3580, info@principleconcepts.ie. Ed. Patricia Lynch.

371.9144 GBR ISSN 1366-2031
REACH NEWSLETTER. Text in English. 1985. 3/yr. GBP 25 to individuals; GBP 35 to institutions (effective 2001). bk.rev.; software rev. **Document type:** *Newsletter.* **Description:** Contains articles for people who work with children who have reading disabilities.
Former titles (until 1996): National Library for the Handicapped Child. Newsletter (0952-9705); Blyton Handi Read Centre Newsletter
Published by: Reach Advice Centre (Subsidiary of: REACH: National Advice Centre for Children with Reading Difficulties), California Country Park, Nine Mile Ride, Finchampstead, Wokingham, Berks RG40 4HT, United Kingdom. TEL 44-118-973-7575, FAX 44-118-973-7105, reach@reach-reading.demon.co.uk, http://www.reach-reading.demon.co.uk. Ed., R&P Beverley Mathias. Circ: 1,500.

371.9 FRA ISSN 0484-0305
READAPTATION. Text in French. 1954. m. (10/yr.). adv. bk.rev. **Document type:** *Newspaper.*
Indexed: ExcerpMed, PdeR.
Published by: Centre National d'Information pour la Readaptation, 10 rue de Sevres, Paris, 75007, France. TEL 33-1-42222273, FAX 33-1-45480190. Eds. Jean Savy, Monique Vigneron. Pub. M Valdiguie. R&P Jean Savy. Circ: 5,600. **Subscr. to:** ONISEP Diffusion, Paris Cedex 13 75635, France. **Co-sponsor:** Office National d'Information sur les Enseignements et les Professions.

371.914 USA ISSN 1057-3569
LB1050.5 CODEN: RWQUEB
➤ **READING AND WRITING QUARTERLY;** overcoming learning difficulties. Text in English. 1975. q. GBP 251, USD 415 combined subscription to institutions print & online eds. (effective 2006). film rev. abstr.; bibl.; charts; tr.lit.; illus. Index. back issues avail.; reprint service avail. from PQC,PSC. **Document type:** *Journal, Academic/Scholarly.* **Description:** Covers reading, writing, and learning disabilities.
Former titles (until 1992): Journal of Reading, Writing, and Learning Disabilities International (0748-7630); (until 1984): Chicorel Abstracts to Reading and Learning Disabilities (0149-533X)
Related titles: Microform ed.: (from PQC); Online - full text ed.: ISSN 1521-0693. GBP 238, USD 394 to institutions (effective 2006) (from EBSCO Publishing, Gale Group, IngentaConnect, O C L C Online Computer Library Center, Inc., Swets Information Services).
Indexed: CDA, CIJE, CPE, ChPerI, ECER, ERA, ETA, FamI, L&LBA, MEA, PsycInfo, PsycholAb, RHEA, SEA, SENA, SOMA, SOPODA, TEA, e-psyche.
—BLDSC (7300.877000), IE, Infotrieve, ingenta. **CCC.**
Published by: Taylor & Francis Inc. (Subsidiary of: Taylor & Francis Group), 325 Chestnut St, Ste 800, Philadelphia, PA 19016. TEL 215-625-8900, 800-354-1420, FAX 215-625-2940, info@taylorandfrancis.com, http://www.tandf.co.uk/journals/titles/10573569.asp, http://www.taylorandfrancis.com. Ed. Howard Margolis. **Subscr. in Europe to:** Taylor & Francis Ltd, Journals Customer Service, Rankine Rd, Basingstoke, Hants RG24 8PR, United Kingdom. TEL 44-1256-813000, FAX 44-1256-330245, enquiry@tandf.co.uk.

371.9 USA ISSN 0034-0502
LB1050
READING HORIZONS. Text in English. 1960. 4/yr. USD 25 domestic to individuals; USD 30 in Canada to individuals; USD 35 domestic to individuals; USD 30 domestic to institutions; USD 35 in Canada to institutions; USD 40 elsewhere to institutions (effective 2004). adv. bk.rev. abstr.; bibl. reprint service avail. from PQC. **Document type:** *Journal, Academic/Scholarly.* **Description:** Shares reports, research, and ideas about teaching reading at all levels.
Related titles: Microfilm ed.: (from PQC); Online - full text ed.: (from H.W. Wilson, O C L C Online Computer Library Center, Inc., ProQuest Information & Learning).
Indexed: ABIn, CIJE, CPE, EduInd, RILM.
—BLDSC (7300.990000), IE, ingenta.
Published by: Western Michigan University, College of Education, 1903 W Michigan Ave, Kalamazoo, MI 49008. TEL 269-387-3470, FAX 269-387-2882, http://www.wmich.edu/tll/reading/readhorizons.htm. Ed. Karen Thomas. Circ: 1,000.

371.9144 USA ISSN 0034-0510
LB1050.5
➤ **READING IMPROVEMENT;** a journal for the improvement of reading teaching. Text in English. 1963. q. USD 34 domestic to individuals; USD 44 in Canada to individuals; USD 54 elsewhere to individuals; USD 40 to institutions; USD 50 in Canada to institutions; USD 60 elsewhere to institutions (effective 2005). adv. bk.rev. abstr.; illus. index, cum.index. reprint service avail. from PQC. **Document type:** *Journal, Academic/Scholarly.*
Formerly: Reading in High School
Related titles: Microform ed.: (from PQC); Online - full text ed.: (from EBSCO Publishing, Florida Center for Library Automation, Gale Group, H.W. Wilson, O C L C Online Computer Library Center, Inc., ProQuest Information & Learning).
Indexed: ABIn, CIJE, CPE, ERA, EduInd, L&LBA, RILM, SOPODA.
—BLDSC (7301.050000), IE, Infotrieve, ingenta. **CCC.**
Published by: Dr. George E. Uhlig, 1362 Santa Cruz Ct, Chula Vista, CA 91910-7114. TEL 334-633-7802, http://journals825.home.mindspring.com/ri.html. Circ: 1,100 (paid).

371.9 USA ISSN 1080-0220
HV1
➤ **REFLECTIONS;** narratives of professional helping. Text in English. 1995. q. USD 40 domestic to individuals; USD 55 foreign to individuals; USD 55 domestic to institutions; USD 70 foreign to institutions (effective 2004). adv. film rev. index. back issues avail. **Document type:** *Journal, Academic/Scholarly.* **Description:** Publishes personal narratives by and for persons in the helping and academic professions - anyone engaged in bringing about social change.
Related titles: Online - full text ed.
Indexed: SSA, SWR&A, SociolAb, e-psyche.
Published by: California State University, Long Beach, University Press, c/o Dept of Social Work, 1250 Bellflower Boulevard, Long Beach, CA 90840-0902. TEL 562-985-4626, FAX 562-985-5514, reflect@usulb.edu, http://www.csulb.edu/depts/socialwk/reflections/. Ed., R&P Mary Ann Jimenez. Adv. contact Paul Abels.

371.9 USA ISSN 0889-7018
HD7255.5
➤ **REHABILITATION EDUCATION.** Text in English. 1987. q. USD 25 domestic to individuals; USD 40 foreign to individuals; USD 90 domestic to institutions; USD 105 foreign to institutions; USD 10 domestic to students; USD 25 foreign to students. adv. **Document type:** *Academic/Scholarly.* **Description:** Features original contributions dealing with all aspects of rehabilitation education, including curriculum development, information about instruction materials, education media, and issues related to licensing, certification and accreditation.
Indexed: AMED, CINAHL, CPE, MEA, PsycInfo, PsycholAb, SEA, TEA, e-psyche.
—BLDSC (7350.236200), GNLM, IE, ingenta. **CCC.**
Published by: (National Council on Rehabilitation Education), Elliott & Fitzpatrick, Inc., 1135 Cedar Shoals Dr, Athens, GA 30605. TEL 706-548-8161, 800-843-4977, FAX 706-546-8417. Ed. Dr. Douglas C Strohmer. Adv. contact Tim Field. page USD 250; 7.63 x 5.38. Circ: 675.

➤ **REHABILITATION INDUSTRIES CORPORATION. ANNUAL REPORT.** see *MEDICAL SCIENCES—Physical Medicine And Rehabilitation*

371.9 USA ISSN 0741-9325
LC3950
➤ **REMEDIAL AND SPECIAL EDUCATION.** Text in English. 1984. bi-m., latest vol.23. USD 49 in North America to individuals; USD 83 elsewhere to individuals; USD 144 in North America to institutions; USD 170 elsewhere to institutions (effective 2006). adv. bk.rev. illus.; abstr. Index. 64 p./no.; back issues avail.; reprint service avail. from PSC. **Document type:** *Journal, Academic/Scholarly.* **Description:** Features articles on all topics in the field, bridging the gap between theory and practice. Two special issues each year provide in-depth coverage of a single topic.
Formed by the merger of (1981-1984): Topics in Learning and Learning Disabilities (0271-1494); (1980-1984): Exceptional Education Quarterly (0196-6960); (1978-1983): Journal for Special Educators (0197-5323); Which was formed by the 1978 merger of: Special Children (0160-3248); Journal for Special Educators of the Mentally Retarded (0012-2807); Which was formerly: Digest of the Mentally Retarded; Incorporates: Retarded Adult
Related titles: Microfilm ed.: (from PQC); Online - full text ed.: ISSN 1538-4756 (from EBSCO Publishing, Florida Center for Library Automation, Gale Group, H.W. Wilson, IngentaConnect, O C L C Online Computer Library Center, Inc., ProQuest Information & Learning).
Indexed: ABIn, ASCA, ASSIA, CIJE, CJA, CLFP, CPE, CurCont, DIP, EAA, ECER, ERA, ETA, EduInd, FamI, IBR, IBZ, L&LBA, MEA, PsycInfo, PsycholAb, RHEA, SEA, SENA, SOMA, SOPODA, SSCI, TEA, e-psyche.
—BLDSC (7356.760000), IDS, IE, Infotrieve, ingenta. **CCC.**
Published by: Pro-Ed Inc., 8700 Shoal Creek Blvd, Austin, TX 78757-6897. TEL 512-451-3246, FAX 512-302-9129, ltippett@proedinc.com, journals@proedinc.com, http://www.proedinc.com/rase.html. Ed. Dave Edyburn. Pub. Donald D Hammill. R&P, Adv. contact Paula Gonzalez. B&W page USD 400. Circ: 1,700 (paid and free).

➤ **REPORT ON DISABILITY LAW.** see *SOCIAL SERVICES AND WELFARE*

➤ **RESEARCH IN DEVELOPMENTAL DISABILITIES.** see *MEDICAL SCIENCES—Psychiatry And Neurology*

➤ **RIABILITAZIONE E APPRENDIMENTO.** see *MEDICAL SCIENCES—Physical Medicine And Rehabilitation*

➤ **THE ROUNDTABLE (SOUTHFIELD).** see *SOCIAL SERVICES AND WELFARE*

371.9142 GBR
ROYAL COLLEGE OF SPEECH AND LANGUAGE THERAPISTS. BULLETIN. Text in English. 1945. m. GBP 40; GBP 45 overseas; GBP 70 with European Journal of Disorders of Communication; GBP 85 overseas with European Journal of Disorders of Communication (effective 1999). adv. bk.rev. Supplement avail. **Document type:** *Bulletin, Academic/Scholarly.* **Description:** Contains research papers, practice reports, correspondence and Royal College news of interest to students and professionals in speech-language pathology and audiology.
Former titles: College of Speech and Language Therapists. Bulletin (0953-6086); College of Speech Therapists. Bulletin
—BLDSC (2700.250000). **CCC.**
Published by: Royal College of Speech and Language Therapists, 7 Bath Pl, London, EC2 3DR, United Kingdom. TEL 44-20-7613-3855, FAX 44-20-7613-3854. Ed., R&P Jenny Sheridan TEL 44-20-7613-6404. Adv. contact Vivien Robinson. Circ: 8,000 (controlled).

371.9 USA ISSN 8756-8705
RURAL SPECIAL EDUCATION QUARTERLY. Text in English. 1984. q. USD 75 domestic to individual members; USD 81 foreign to individual members; USD 100 domestic to institutional members; USD 106 foreign to institutional members; USD 25 to students membership (effective 2005). illus. Index. back issues avail.; reprints avail. **Document type:** *Academic/Scholarly.* **Description:** Covers pre-service training, administration and curriculum for pre-service educators and direct service providers.
Related titles: Online - full text ed.: (from EBSCO Publishing, H.W. Wilson, ProQuest Information & Learning).
Indexed: Agr, BibAg, CIJE.
—BLDSC (8052.631000), IE, ingenta.
Published by: American Council on Rural Special Education, Kansas State University, 2323 Anderson Ave., Ste. 226, Manhattan, KS 66502-2912. TEL 785-532-2737, FAX 785-532-7732, http://extension.usu.edu/acres/publications.html. Ed. Barbara Ludlow TEL 304-293-3450 ext. 1127. Circ: 650.

371.9 USA
RURALINK. Text in English. 6/yr. membership. **Document type:** *Newsletter.* **Description:** Covers resources and information on rural special education.
Published by: American Council on Rural Special Education, Kansas State University, 2323 Anderson Ave., Ste. 226, Manhattan, KS 66502-2912. TEL 785-532-2737, FAX 785-532-7732, acres@ksu.edu. Ed. Barbara Ludlow TEL 304-293-3450 ext. 1127. Circ: 600.

371.91 JPN ISSN 0036-0538
RYOIKU/REHABILITATION (TOKYO, 1951). Text in Japanese. 1951. a. JPY 2,600.
Published by: Japanese Society for Disabled Children/Nihon Shitai Fujiyuji Kyokai, 1-7 Komone 1-chome, Itabashi-ku, Tokyo, 173-0037, Japan. Circ: 2,000.

371.9 GBR ISSN 1367-2460
➤ **S L D EXPERIENCE.** (Severe Learning Difficulties) Text in English. 1991. 3/yr. GBP 23 domestic to individuals; GBP 29 in Europe to individuals; GBP 38 elsewhere to individuals (effective 2003). adv. bk.rev. **Document type:** *Journal, Academic/Scholarly.* **Description:** Aimed at parents and practitioners working with and caring for children and young people with severe learning disabilities; and contains news information and updates on curriculum matters, research, medical and legal issues.
Indexed: e-psyche.
—BLDSC (8309.428970).
Published by: B I L D, Campion House, Green St, Kidderminster, Worcs DY10 1JL, United Kingdom. TEL 44-1562-723010, FAX 44-1562-723029, enquiries@bild.org.uk, http://www.bild.org.uk. Ed. Dawn Male. Adv. contact Tracey Tindell TEL 44-1562-723020. Circ: 1,500 (paid).

371.9 AUS ISSN 1328-682X
S P E L D BULLETIN. Text in English. 1970. 2/yr. AUD 35 to members (effective 2000). adv. bk.rev. **Document type:** *Bulletin.*
Formerly: D.A.W.A. Bulletin
Indexed: AEI.
Published by: Specific Learning Difficulties Association of Victoria Inc., 494 Brunswick St, Fitzroy North, VIC 3068, Australia. TEL 61-3-94894344, FAX 61-3-94862437, spelvic@telstra.easymail.com.au, http://www.vicnet.net.au/~speld. Ed., R&P, Adv. contact Christopher Davidson TEL 61-3-9826-0371. Circ: 700.

371.9 AUS
S P E L D NEWS. Text in English. 1969. q. AUD 25 membership; AUD 35 foreign membership (effective 1999). bk.rev. back issues avail. **Document type:** *Newsletter.* **Description:** Contains articles relating to recent research into specific learning difficulties and related subjects.
Published by: Specific Learning Difficulties Association of New South Wales, 33-41 Linfield Ave, Lindfield, NSW 2070, Australia. TEL 61-2-9416-9100, FAX 61-2-9416-9277, http://www.edfac.usyd.edu.au/projects/speld. Ed., R&P Valentine Badham. Circ: 1,500.

SAGGI - CHILD DEVELOPMENT DISABILITIES. see *MEDICAL SCIENCES—Psychiatry And Neurology*

SCHOLASTIC ACTION. see *EDUCATION—Teaching Methods And Curriculum*

371.9 371.2 USA ISSN 1094-3749
KF4102
SCHOOL LAW BRIEFINGS. Text in English. m. USD 150 (effective 2006). back issues avail. **Document type:** *Newsletter, Trade.* **Description:** Summaries of general education, special education and early childhood court cases, as well as administrative hearings. Each issue includes a brief overview of all the court cases and administrative hearings.
Formerly: School Law Bulletin
—CCC.
Published by: L R P Publications, 747 Dresher Rd, PO Box 980, Horsham, PA 19044. TEL 215-784-0860, 800-341-7874, FAX 215-784-9639, custserve@lrp.com, http://www.shoplrp.com/product/p-300072.html, http://www.lrp.com.

SCHOOL SOCIAL WORK JOURNAL. see *SOCIAL SERVICES AND WELFARE*

615 USA ISSN 1093-7242
SCHOOL SYSTEM SPECIAL INTEREST SECTION QUARTERLY. Text in English. 1994. q. **Document type:** *Newsletter, Academic/Scholarly.* **Description:** Addresses the needs of school-based practitioners providing educationally related services to infants, preschoolers, children, and adolescents.
Formerly (until 1997): School System Special Interest Section Newsletter (1074-7745)
Indexed: CINAHL.
—CCC.
Published by: American Occupational Therapy Association, Inc., 4720 Montgomery Ln, Bethesda, MD 20814-3425. TEL 301-652-2682, FAX 301-652-7711, http://www.aota.org.

371.9 CHE ISSN 1420-1607
SCHWEIZERISCHE ZEITSCHRIFT FUER HEILPAEDAGOGIK. Text in German. 1995. 11/yr. CHF 59 domestic; CHF 71 foreign (effective 2001). adv. bk.rev. bibl. **Document type:** *Journal, Academic/Scholarly.*
Published by: Schweizerische Zentralstelle fuer Heilpaedagogik, Obergrundstr 61, Luzern, 6003, Switzerland. TEL 41-41-2263040, FAX 41-41-2263041, szh@tic.ch, http://www.szh.ch. Ed. Alois Buerli.

371.9 371.2 USA ISSN 1094-3730
SECTION 504 COMPLIANCE ADVISOR. Text in English. 1997. m. USD 180 (effective 2006). **Document type:** *Newsletter, Trade.* **Description:** Provides information for special-education professionals, law firms, and attorneys specializing in this area.
Related titles: Online - full text ed.: (from LexisNexis).
—CCC.
Published by: L R P Publications, 747 Dresher Rd, PO Box 980, Horsham, PA 19044. TEL 215-784-0860, 800-341-7874, FAX 215-784-9639, custserve@lrp.com, http://www.shoplrp.com/product/p-300065.html, http://www.lrp.com.

SEMINARS IN SPEECH AND LANGUAGE. see *MEDICAL SCIENCES—Otorhinolaryngology*

SERCE I TROSKA. see *HANDICAPPED*

SHARING SOLUTIONS; a newsletter for people with imparied vision and their support networks. see *HANDICAPPED—Visually Impaired*

371.91 JPN ISSN 0037-3990
SHITAI FUJIYU KYOIKU/JAPANESE JOURNAL OF EDUCATION OF THE HANDICAPPED. Text in Japanese. 1970. 5/yr. JPY 3,600. **Description:** Includes rehabilitation techniques.
Published by: Japanese Society for Disabled Children/Nihon Shitai Fujiyuji Kyokai, 1-7 Komone 1-chome, Itabashi-ku, Tokyo, 173-0037, Japan. Circ: 4,500.

SIGHTS AND SOUNDS. see *HANDICAPPED—Hearing Impaired*

THE SILENT ADVOCATE. see *HANDICAPPED—Hearing Impaired*

371.9 GBR
THE SKILL JOURNAL. Text in English. 1976. 3/yr. membership. bk.rev. bibl. cum.index. **Document type:** *Academic/Scholarly.*
Formerly (until 1995): Educare (0141-7282)
Indexed: BrEdI, CPE, SENA.
—BLDSC (8295.780000), ingenta.
Published by: Skill: National Bureau for Students with Disabilities, Chapter House, 18-20 Crucifix Ln, London, SE1 3JW, United Kingdom. TEL 44-20-7450-0620, 0800-328-5050, FAX 44-20-7450-0650, info@skill.org.uk, http://www.skill.org.uk. Ed., Pub., R&P, Adv. contact Barbara Waters. Circ: 1,500.

SMITH - KETTLEWELL TECHNICAL FILE; a biannual technical journal for the blind and visually impaired. see *HANDICAPPED—Visually Impaired*

371.9 DEU ISSN 0342-7366
SONDERPAEDAGOGIK; Vierteljahresschrift ueber aktuelle Probleme der Behinderten in Schule und Gesellschaft. Text in German. 1964. q. adv. bk.rev. reprint service avail. from SCH. **Document type:** *Academic/Scholarly.*
Indexed: DIP, IBR, IBZ.
—CCC.
Published by: Wissenschaftsverlag Volker Spiess GmbH, Gneisenaustr 33, Berlin, 10961, Germany. TEL 49-30-6917073, FAX 49-30-6914067. Ed. Heinz Neukaeter.

371.9 DEU ISSN 1618-6028
SONDERPAEDAGOGIK IN FORSCHUNG UND PRAXIS. Text in German. 2001. irreg., latest vol.10, 2005. price varies. **Document type:** *Monographic series, Academic/Scholarly.*
Published by: Verlag Dr. Kovac, Arnoldstr 49, Hamburg, 22763, Germany. TEL 49-40-3988800, FAX 49-40-39888055, info@verlagdrkovac.de, http://www.verlagdrkovac.de/7-16.htm.

371.9 USA
SOURCE (ST. CHARLES). Text in English. 1987. m. USD 12. adv. bk.rev. **Document type:** *Newspaper.*
Published by: J A G Enterprises, PO Box 1439, St. Charles, MO 63302. TEL 314-949-9456, FAX 314-724-8082. Ed. Julie Ann Groog. Circ: 10,000.

371.9 USA
SOWER. Text in English. 1981. q. free. back issues avail. **Document type:** *Newsletter.*
Formerly: Broadcaster
Published by: Beatrice State Development Center, Department of Public Institutions, 3000 Lincoln Blvd, Beatrice, NE 68310. TEL 402-223-2302. Ed. Jerry Crisp. Circ: 6,000.

371.9 GBR ISSN 0966-4831
SPECIAL. Text in English. 1992. 3/yr. **Document type:** *Academic/Scholarly.*
—CCC.
Published by: National Association for Special Educational Needs, NASEN House, 4-5 Amber Business Village, Amber Village, Amington, Tamworth, Warks B77 4RP, United Kingdom. TEL 44-1827-311500, FAX 44-1827-313005, welcome@nasen.org.uk, http://www.nasen.org.uk.

371.9 362.7 GBR ISSN 0951-6875
SPECIAL CHILDREN. Text in English. 1986. 6/yr. GBP 45 domestic to individuals; GBP 60 foreign to individuals; GBP 60 domestic to institutions; GBP 80 elsewhere to institutions (effective 2004). adv. bk.rev. index. back issues avail.; reprints avail. **Document type:** *Academic/Scholarly.* **Description:** Designed to assist all schools in meeting the educational needs of children with a wide range of abilities and aptitudes.
Related titles: Online - full text ed.: (from Swets Information Services).
Indexed: BrEdI, CPE, ChLitAb.
—BLDSC (8365.799000), IE, ingenta.
Published by: Questions Publishing Company Ltd., 1st Fl, Leonard House, 321 Bradford St, Digbeth, Birmingham, Warks B1 3ET, United Kingdom. TEL 44-121-6667878, FAX 44-121-6667879, rchima@qiis.co.uk, http://www.education-quest.com/. Ed. Mick Archer. Adv. contact Stan Harris. Circ: 11,000 (paid).

THE SPECIAL ED ADVOCATE NEWSLETTER. see *HANDICAPPED*

SPECIAL EDUCATION BIBLE STUDY. see *RELIGIONS AND THEOLOGY—Protestant*

371.9 USA
SPECIAL EDUCATION BULLETIN AND REVIEW✶. Text in English. 1980. m.
Published by: Eterna International, Inc., PO Box 5731, Hauppauge, NY 11788-0154. Ed. Stephen B Parrish.

371.9 USA
SPECIAL EDUCATION LAW AND LITIGATION TREATISE. Text in English. 1992. irreg., latest 2002, 2nd ed. USD 197 per vol. (effective 2006). **Document type:** *Monographic series, Trade.* **Description:** Provides due-process hearings and court proceedings, factors that determine eligibility for special education, and in-depth coverage of the requirements and issues addressed by the I.D.E.A. and Part H.
Related titles: CD-ROM ed.
Published by: L R P Publications, 747 Dresher Rd, PO Box 980, Horsham, PA 19044. TEL 215-784-0860, 800-341-7874, FAX 215-784-9639, custserve@lrp.com, http://www.lrp.com. Ed. Mark C Weber.

371.9 344 USA ISSN 1542-4995
SPECIAL EDUCATION LAW BULLETIN. Variant title: Quinlan's Special Education Law Bulletin. Text in English. 1995 (Sept.). m. USD 147 (effective 2005). **Document type:** *Newsletter, Trade.*
Formerly (until 1999): School Administrator's Special Education Hotline (1084-7634)
Related titles: Online - full text ed.: ISSN 1545-9462.
Published by: Quinlan Publishing Group, Marine Industrial Park, 23 Drydock Ave, 6th Fl, Boston, MA 02210-2387. TEL 617-542-0048, 800-229-2084, FAX 617-345-9646, info@quinlan.com, http://www.quinlan.com. Ed. Heidi Taylor. Pub. Dennis Hofmaier.

371.9 371.3 USA ISSN 1094-3773
SPECIAL EDUCATION LAW MONTHLY. Text in English. m. USD 140 (effective 2006). back issues avail. **Document type:** *Newsletter.* **Description:** Covers court decisions and administrative rulings affecting the education of students with disabilities. Brief overviews and case summaries are included.
Related titles: CD-ROM ed.: USD 1,949 includes Individuals with Disabilities Education Law Report (effective 2002); Online - full text ed.: (from LexisNexis).
—CCC.
Published by: L R P Publications, 747 Dresher Rd, PO Box 980, Horsham, PA 19044. TEL 215-784-0860, 800-341-7874, FAX 215-784-9639, http://www.shoplrp.com/product/p-300073.html, http://www.lrp.com.

E

371.9 USA
SPECIAL EDUCATION LAW UPDATE✶. Text in English. 1983. m. looseleaf. USD 147; USD 167 foreign. cum.index. back issues avail. **Document type:** *Newsletter.* **Description:** Reports the latest school law cases and late-breaking legislation along with the most recent law review articles affecting special education.
Formerly: Special Education and the Handicapped (8756-3746)
Published by: Data Research, Inc., 11975 Portland Ave Ste 110, Burnsville, MN 55337-1530. TEL 651-452-8267, FAX 651-452-8694, http://www.dataresearchinc.com. Ed. Warren Cody. **Subscr. to:** PO Box 409, Rosemount, MN 55068-9987.

371.9 USA
SPECIAL EDUCATION NEWS. Text in English. 1999. w. free. adv. Website rev. stat. back issues avail.; reprints avail. **Document type:** *Magazine, Newspaper-distributed.* **Description:** Answers a need in education for in-depth timely news related to educating students with disabilities. Targets parents, educators, administrators, advocates, disability organizations and government agencies.
Media: E-mail. **Related titles:** Online - full text ed.
Address: 3430 Connecticut Ave, NW, #11168, Washington, DC 20008. info@specialednews.com, http://www.specialednews.com. Pub. Mary Hillebrand TEL 202-320-0521.

371.9 AUS
➤ **SPECIAL EDUCATION PERSPECTIVES.** Text in English. 1975. 2/yr. AUD 35 (effective 2000). adv. bk.rev. illus. **Document type:** *Academic/Scholarly.*
Former titles: Perspectives (1038-6475); N S W Journal of Special Education (0814-0960); (until 1983): A S E T Journal (0814-0952); O A Journal
Indexed: SENA.
—BLDSC (8366.318650), IE, ingenta.
Published by: Australian Association of Special Education Inc., New South Wales Chapter, PO Box 223, Bomaderry, NSW 2541, Australia. TEL 61-2-98508691. Eds. Chris Gordon, Michael Arthur. R&P, Adv. contact Michael Arthur. Circ: 600.

371.9 USA ISSN 1553-4294
LC4031
SPECIAL EDUCATION REPORT; the independent bi-weekly news service on legislation, programs and funding for special education. Text in English. 1975. bi-w. looseleaf. USD 383 (effective 2002). s-a. index. **Document type:** *Newsletter.* **Description:** Covers federal and state legislation and LRE policy issues. Looks at innovations and research in the field.
Formerly (until 1992): Education of the Handicapped (0194-2255)
Related titles: Online - full text ed.: (from EBSCO Publishing, Gale Group).
Indexed: RehabLit.
—**CCC.**
Published by: Aspen Publishers, Inc. (Subsidiary of: Wolters Kluwer N.V.), 111Eighth Ave., 7th Fl, New York, NY 10011. TEL 212-771-0600, FAX 212-771-0885, customer.service@aspenpubl.com, http://www.aspenpublishers.com. Ed. William J Cahir. Pub. Marjorie Weiner. **Dist. by:** Customer Care, 7201 McKinney Circle, Frederick, MD 21704. TEL 800-234-1660, FAX 800-901-9075.

SPECIAL EDUCATION. TEACHER. see *RELIGIONS AND THEOLOGY—Protestant*

371.9 USA ISSN 1524-2765
SPECIAL EDUCATION TECHNOLOGY PRACTICE. Text in English. 1999. 5/yr. USD 29.95 domestic; USD 39.95 foreign (effective 2003). adv. back issues avail.; reprints avail. **Document type:** *Journal, Academic/Scholarly.*
Published by: Knowledge by Design, Inc., 5907 N, Kent Ave, Whitefish Bay, WI 53217-4615. TEL 414-962-0120, FAX 414-962-0120, setpinfo@setp.net, http://www.setp.net/. Ed., Adv. contact David E Edyburn.

371.97 USA ISSN 1080-1375
SPECIAL EDUCATION TODAY. Text in English. q. USD 4.75 per issue (effective 2005). **Document type:** *Magazine, Consumer.* **Description:** Provides information and advice for parents, families, and church leaders with persons with handicaps.
Formerly (until 1995): Special Education Leadership (0896-7784)
Published by: LifeWay Christian Resources, 1 Lifeway Plaza, Nashville, TN 37234. TEL 615-251-2000, 800-458-2772, FAX 615-251-5933, customerservice@lifeway.com, http://www.lifeway.com.

SPECIAL EDUCATIONAL NEEDS ABSTRACTS. see *EDUCATION—Abstracting, Bibliographies, Statistics*

371.9 344.73 USA ISSN 1047-1618
LC4031
THE SPECIAL EDUCATOR. Text in English. 1982. bi-w. (22/yr.). looseleaf. USD 265 (effective 2006). q. index. back issues avail. **Document type:** *Newsletter, Trade.* **Description:** Provides special judicial decisions in special education cases, OSEP and OSERS policy rulings, OCR rulings, SEA decisions, and analysis to aid school administrators.
Related titles: Audio cassette/tape ed.; Online - full text ed.: (from LexisNexis).
—**CCC.**
Published by: L R P Publications, 747 Dresher Rd, PO Box 980, Horsham, PA 19044. TEL 215-784-0860, 800-341-7874, 800-341-7874, FAX 215-784-9639, custserve@lrp.com, http://www.shoplrp.com/product/p-300002.html, http://www.lrp.com. Ed. Jay Kravetz.

371.9 DNK ISSN 0107-0649
➤ **SPECIALPAEDAGOGIK**; tidsskrift for specialundervisning og anden specialpaedagogisk bistand. Text in Danish. 1981. bi-m. DKK 420 (effective 2004). back issues avail. **Document type:** *Journal, Academic/Scholarly.*
Formed by the merger of (1964-1981): Saa Paedagogen (0107-394X); (1966-1981): Dansk tidsskrift for Specialpaedagogik (0106-3936); Which was formerly (until 1979): Hjaelpeskolen (0107-4644); Incorporates (1976-1981): Saerforsorgens Laererforenings Information (0105-7111)
Published by: Danmarks Specialpaedagogiske Forening, c/o Johnna Kragh, Guredevej 17, Holbaek, 4300, Denmark. TEL 45-59467000, FAX 45-40-219095, johnnakragh@yahoo.dk, http://www.specialpaedagogik.dk/om.asp, http://www.dsf.ffw.dk. Ed. Lone Dall. **Co-publisher:** Speciallaererforeningen af 1981.

371.9 SWE ISSN 1650-7231
SPECIALPEDAGOGIK. Text in Swedish. 1983. bi-m. SEK 210 (effective 2003). adv. **Document type:** *Magazine, Trade.*
Former titles (until 2001): Specialpedagogen (1102-1276); (until 1991): Spridaren (0281-5559)
Related titles: Online - full text ed.
Published by: Laerarfoerbundet, Tidningsafdelning, Segelbaatsvaegen 15, Box 12229, Stockholm, 10226, Sweden. TEL 46-8-7376500, FAX 46-8-7376569, kansli@lararforbundet.se, http://www.specialpedagogik.net/default.asp, http://www.lararforbundet.se. Ed. Hasse Hedstroem. Adv. contact Lisen Skeppstedt. B&W page SEK 5,250, color page SEK 7,600; trim 182 x 266. Circ: 12,800.

371.9 DNK ISSN 0907-6069
SPECIALUNDERVISNING. Text in Danish. 1976. biennial. DKK 168.75 (effective 2002).
Former titles (until 1992): Undervisningsmidler til Specialundervisning (0106-7745); (until 1980): Materialer til Specialundervisning (0107-1505)
Published by: Landsforeningen for Laesepaedagoger, Strandstien 18, Thorupstrand, Fjerritslev, 9690, Denmark. TEL 45-96-50-80-90, FAX 45-98-22-58-76.

371.9142 GBR ISSN 1368-2105
SPEECH & LANGUAGE THERAPY IN PRACTICE. Text in English. 1985. q. GBP 24 domestic to individuals; GBP 28 in Europe to individuals; GBP 32 elsewhere to individuals; GBP 40 domestic to institutions; GBP 44 in Europe to institutions. adv. bk.rev. **Document type:** *Academic/Scholarly.* **Description:** Contains practical information for speech and language therapists and associated professionals.
Former titles (until 1997): Human Communication (0968-1108); (until 1991): Speech Therapy in Practice (0269-0527)
—BLDSC (8411.195820), IE, ingenta.
Published by: Avril Nicoll Ed. & Pub., Lynwood Cottage, High St, Drumlithie, Stonehaven, AB39 3YZ, United Kingdom. avrilnicoll@sol.co.uk, http://www.sol.co.uk/s/speechnag. R&P Avril Nicoll. adv.: B&W page GBP 450, color page GBP 600. Circ: 1,300 (paid).

371.9 NLD
SPORTSIGNAAL. Text in Dutch. 1952. s-m. adv. bk.rev. illus. **Document type:** *Bulletin.*
Formerly: Sportparade (0038-8130)
Published by: Nederlandse Katholieke Sportfederatie, Korte Bergstraat 15, Amersfoort, 3811 ML, Netherlands. TEL 31-73-138884, FAX 31-73-145705. Ed. Hidde van der Ploeg. R&P Suzanne Vreven. Adv. contact Eveline Balemans. Circ: 2,500.

371.9 DEU ISSN 0342-0477
➤ **SPRACHE - STIMME - GEHOER**; Zeitschrift fuer Kommunikationsstoerungen. Text in German; Summaries in English, German. 1977. q. EUR 82.80 domestic to institutions; EUR 86.80 in Europe to institutions; EUR 91.80 elsewhere to institutions; EUR 46 to students; EUR 24 newsstand/cover (effective 2006). adv. bk.rev. index. back issues avail.; reprint service avail. from PQC. **Document type:** *Journal, Academic/Scholarly.*
Related titles: Online - full text ed.: ISSN 1439-1260 (from EBSCO Publishing, Swets Information Services).
Indexed: CurCont, ExcerpMed.
—GNLM, IE, Infotrieve. **CCC.**
Published by: Georg Thieme Verlag, Ruedigerstr 14, Stuttgart, 70469, Germany. TEL 49-711-89310, FAX 49-711-8931298, kunden.service@thieme.de, http://www.thieme.de/ssg. Ed. M Ptok. R&P Peter Eich. adv.: B&W page EUR 1,090, color page EUR 2,155; 175 x 250. Circ: 3,000 (paid).

371.9 DEU ISSN 0584-9470
DIE SPRACHHEILARBEIT; Fachzeitschrift fuer Sprachbehindertenpaedagogik. Text in German. 1956. bi-m. EUR 40; EUR 7.50 newsstand/cover (effective 2003). adv. **Document type:** *Journal, Academic/Scholarly.*
Indexed: DIP, IBR, IBZ.
—GNLM.
Published by: Verlag Modernes Lernen Borgmann KG, Hohe Str. 39, Dortmund, 44139, Germany. TEL 49-180-5340130, FAX 49-180-5340120, info@verlag-modernes-lernen.de, http://www.verlag-modernes-lernen.de. Eds. Dr. Ulrike de Langen-Mueller, Dr. Uwe Foerster. adv.: page EUR 645; trim 171 x 252. Circ: 7,200.

371.7 362.4 USA
THE STUDENT ADVOCATE. Text in English. q. USD 25 to non-members (effective 2005); free with membership. back issues avail. **Document type:** *Magazine, Consumer.* **Description:** Addresses issues of concern to students who are blind or visually impaired.
Media: Large Type (16 pt.). **Related titles:** Audio cassette/tape ed.; Braille ed.; Online - full text ed.
Published by: National Alliance of Blind Students, c/o American Council of the Blind, 1155 15th Street, NW, Suite 1004, Washington, DC 20005. TEL 202-467-5081, 800-424-8666, FAX 202-467-5085, http://www.blindstudents.org. Ed. Marketoe Day.

371.9 USA ISSN 1076-0911
KF4210
STUDENTS WITH DISABILITIES AND SPECIAL EDUCATION✶. Text in English. 1983. a. USD 144.95. **Document type:** *Trade.* **Description:** Contains an up-to-date compilation of summarized federal and state appellate court decisions that affect special education.
Published by: Oakstone Business and Legal Publishing, 11975 Portland Ave Ste 110, Burnsville, MN 55337-1530. TEL 651-452-8267, FAX 651-452-8694. Ed., R&P Steve McEllistrem. Pub. Joanne E Fiore.

371.95 DEU
STUDIENSTIFTUNG. JAHRESBERICHT. Text in German. 1970. a. free. illus.; stat. **Document type:** *Corporate.* **Description:** Report of the society which enables specially gifted students to further their education and receive scholarships. Includes report on activities and statistics.
Published by: Studienstiftung des Deutschen Volkes, Mirbachstr 7, Bonn, 53173, Germany. Ed. Klaus H Kohrs. Circ: 35,000.

STUDIES IN SPEECH PATHOLOGY AND CLINICAL LINGUISTICS. see *MEDICAL SCIENCES—Psychiatry And Neurology*

371.9 GBR ISSN 0268-2141
LB1029.R4
SUPPORT FOR LEARNING. Text in English. 1967. q. EUR 71 combined subscription in Europe to individuals print & online eds.; USD 79 combined subscription in the Americas to individuals & Carribean, print & online eds.; GBP 47 combined subscription elsewhere to individuals print & online eds.; GBP 207 combined subscription in Europe to institutions print & online eds.; USD 395 combined subscription in the Americas to institutions & Carribean, print & online eds.; GBP 235 combined subscription elsewhere to institutions print & online eds. (effective 2006). **Document type:** *Journal, Academic/Scholarly.* **Description:** Examines the practical and theoretical issues surrounding the education of pupils with special educational needs in mainstream schools.
Formerly (until 1986): Remedial Education (0034-4214)
Related titles: Microform ed.: (from SWZ); Online - full text ed.: ISSN 1467-9604. GBP 196 in Europe to institutions; USD 375 in the Americas to institutions & Caribbean; GBP 223 elsewhere to institutions (effective 2006) (from Blackwell Synergy, EBSCO Publishing, Gale Group, IngentaConnect, O C L C Online Computer Library Center, Inc., Swets Information Services).
Indexed: BrEdI, CPE, ChLitAb, ECER, ERA, ETA, HECAB, LT&LA, MEA, PsycInfo, PsycholAb, RHEA, SEA, SENA, SOMA, SWA, TEA, e-psyche.
—BLDSC (8547.638300), IE, Infotrieve, ingenta. **CCC.**
Published by: (National Association for Special Educational Needs), Blackwell Publishing Ltd., 9600 Garsington Rd, Oxford, OX4 2ZG, United Kingdom. TEL 44-1865-776868, FAX 44-1865-714591, customerservices@oxon.blackwellpublishing.com, http://www.blackwellpublishing.com/journals/SUFL. Ed. Caroline Roaf. Circ: 5,500.

SWIAT CISZY; czasopismo polskich inwalidow sluchu. see *HANDICAPPED—Hearing Impaired*

371.9 POL ISSN 0137-818X
SZKOLA SPECJALNA. Text in Polish. 1924. bi-m. USD 18. **Description:** Discusses problems of children who are mentally handicapped, or with impaired hearing, speech, or sight, as well as children suffering from chronic illness or who are socially maladjusted. Publishes articles on teaching and care in special schools and institutions. Reports the progress of special education in other countries.
Published by: Wyzsza Szkola Pedagogiki Specjalnej, ul Szczesliwicka 40, Warsaw, 02-353, Poland. TEL 48-22-6580069 ext.152. Ed. Ewa Zabdzynska. **Dist. by:** Ars Polona, Krakowskie Przedmiescie 7, Warsaw, Poland. TEL 48-22-9263914, FAX 48-22-9265334, arspolona@arspolona.com.pl, http://www.arspolona.com.pl. **Co-sponsor:** Ministerstwo Edukacji Narodowej.

T C H I UPDATE. see *HANDICAPPED—Hearing Impaired*

E

371.95   AUS   ISSN 0815-8150
➤ **TALENTED.** Text in English. 1983. 3/yr. AUD 40, USD 30 (effective 2002). bk.rev. 60 p./no.; back issues avail. **Document type:** *Journal, Academic/Scholarly.* **Description:** For teachers and parents on the education of the gifted and talented.
Indexed: AEI.
Published by: (School of Curriculum Studies), University of New England, Armidale, NSW 2351, Australia. TEL 61-67-733832, FAX 61-67-735078, sbailey@metz.une.edu.au. Eds. Linley Lloyd, Stan Bailey. R&P Stan Bailey. Circ: 500 (paid).

371.9   USA   ISSN 0888-4064
➤ **TEACHER EDUCATION AND SPECIAL EDUCATION.** Abbreviated title: T E S E(Teacher Education and Special Education). Text in English. 1977. q. USD 50 domestic to individuals; USD 55 foreign to individuals; USD 62 domestic to institutions; USD 67 foreign to institutions; USD 12.50 per issue to individuals; USD 15.50 per issue to institutions (effective 2004). adv. bk.rev. back issues avail.; reprints avail. **Document type:** *Journal, Academic/Scholarly.* **Description:** Contains reports of original research, evaluations of personnel preparation programs or components thereof, and theoretically based discussions of personnel preparation practices.
Related titles: Microform ed.: (from PQC); Online - full text ed.: (from H.W. Wilson, O C L C Online Computer Library Center, Inc.).
Indexed: ABIn, CIJE, CPE, ECER, ERA, ETA, EduInd, MEA, RHEA, SEA, SENA, SOMA, TEA.
—BLDSC (8613.440000), IE, ingenta.
Published by: Teacher Education Division (Subsidiary of: Council for Exceptional Children), 1110 North Glebe Rd, Suite 300, Arlington, VA 22201-5704. TEL 703-264-9470, FAX 703-620-3660, kath@cec.sped.org, http://www.cec.sped.org/bk/catalog2/divjourn.html, http://www.tedcec.org/. Eds. Fred Spooner, Robert Algozzine. Circ: 3,300. **Subscr. to:** Boyd Printing Co., 49 Sheridan Ave, Albany, NY 12210-1413.

371.92   GBR   ISSN 0040-0572
TEACHING & TRAINING. Text in English. 1962. q. GBP 1.65. adv. bk.rev.; film rev. illus.
Indexed: HECAB.
Published by: National Association of Teachers of the Mentally Handicapped, c/o Edward R.D. Myer, 77 Highfield, Bromham, Chippenham, Wilts SN15 2HT, United Kingdom. Circ: 1,600.

371.95   USA   ISSN 0040-0599
LC3950
➤ **TEACHING EXCEPTIONAL CHILDREN.** Text in English. 1968. bi-m. USD 75 domestic to non-members; USD 110 foreign to non-members; USD 25 per issue to non-members (effective 2005). adv. charts; illus. Index. reprint service avail. from PQC. **Document type:** *Journal, Academic/Scholarly.* **Description:** Designed specifically for teachers of handicapped and gifted children, including therapists, related service personnel, special-education teachers, and teachers who have exceptional children in regular classes. Articles deal with practical methods and materials for classroom use.
Related titles: Microform ed.: (from PQC); ◆ Online - full text ed.: Teaching Exceptional Children Plus. ISSN 1553-9318.
Indexed: ABIn, AMHA, CDA, CIJE, CPE, DIP, ECER, EduInd, IBR, IBZ, RehabLit, SENA, e-psyche.
—BLDSC (8614.120000), IE, Infotrieve, ingenta.
Published by: Council for Exceptional Children, 1110 N. Glebe Rd., Ste. 300, Arlington, VA 22201. http://www.cec.sped.org/. Ed. Chris Jesse. Adv. contact Victor Erickson. Circ: 55,000.

371.9   USA   ISSN 1553-9318
LC3950
▼ **TEACHING EXCEPTIONAL CHILDREN PLUS.** Text in English. 2004. irreg. free (effective 2005). bk.rev. **Document type:** *Journal, Academic/Scholarly.* **Description:** Publishes material which is of particular interest to individuals who work with children with special needs.
Media: Online - full text (from bigchalk, EBSCO Publishing, H.W. Wilson, Northern Light Technology, Inc., O C L C Online Computer Library Center, Inc., ProQuest Information & Learning). **Related titles:** Microform ed.: (from PQC); ◆ Print ed.: Teaching Exceptional Children. ISSN 0040-0599.
Published by: Council for Exceptional Children, 1110 N. Glebe Rd., Ste. 300, Arlington, VA 22201-4795. TEL 703-264-9481, FAX 703-264-1637, http://escholarship.bc.edu/education/tecplus, http://www.cec.sped.org/. Eds. Alec Peck, Stan Scarpati.

TEAM OF ADVOCATES FOR SPECIAL KIDS NEWSLETTER. see *HANDICAPPED*

371.9   USA
TEXAS TALK. Text in English, Spanish. 1952. 3/yr. free (effective 2003); avail. Online in PDF format. adv. **Document type:** *Newsletter.* **Description:** Provides advice, guidance, references, and examples to Arc chapters, members, parents of children with disabilities, and special-education professionals on how to include people with disabilities into society.
Related titles: Online - full content ed.
Published by: Arc of Texas, 1600 W 38th St, Ste 200, Austin, TX 78731. TEL 512-454-6694, 800-252-9729, FAX 512-454-4956, gallan@thearcoftexas.org, http://www.thearcoftexas.org. Ed., R&P, Adv. contact Russell Slaton. Circ: 4,000.

371.9   USA
THEIR WORLD. Text in English. 1970. a. USD 6. adv. bk.rev. abstr.
Published by: National Center for Children with Learning Disabilities, 381 Park Ave S, 1420, New York, NY 10016-8806. TEL 212-545-7510. Ed. Sheldon H Horowitz. Circ: 70,000.

THERAPEUTIC RECREATION JOURNAL. see *MEDICAL SCIENCES—Physical Medicine And Rehabilitation*

371.9   GBR   ISSN 1353-3347
THERAPEUTIC WORK WITH CHILDREN∗ . Text in English. 1995. a. **Document type:** *Academic/Scholarly.*
Published by: Routledge (Subsidiary of: Taylor & Francis Group), 4 Park Square, Milton Park, Abingdon, Oxon OX14 4RN, United Kingdom. TEL 44-20-7583-9855, FAX 44-20-7842-2298. **Subscr. to:** ITPS Ltd., Cheriton House, North Way, Walworth Industrial Estate, Andover, Hants SP10 5BE, United Kingdom. TEL 44-1264-342919, FAX 44-1264-342807.

TITLE I HANDBOOK: UNDERSTANDING AND IMPLEMENTING THE PROGRAM. see *EDUCATION—School Organization And Administration*

371.9   JPN   ISSN 0387-3374
TOKUSHU KYOKUGAKU KENKYU/JAPANESE JOURNAL OF SPECIAL EDUCATION. Text in Japanese. 1964. 3/yr. **Document type:** *Journal, Academic/Scholarly.*
Indexed: L&LBA, PsycInfo, PsycholAb.
—BLDSC (4658.820000), IE. CCC.
Published by: Nihon Tokushu Kyoiku Gakkai/Japanese Association of Special Education, 6-17-9 Hongo, Bunkyo-ku, Hongo Tsuna Bldg, 2F, Tokyo, 113-0033, Japan. TEL 81-3-38141363, FAX 81-3-38141362, http://www1.accsnet.ne.jp/~tokkyou/mag.html.

371.95   JPN   ISSN 0386-3271
LC3987.J3
TOKYO GAKUGEI DAIGAKU TOKUSHU KYOIKU KENKYU SHISETSU HOKOKU/R I E E C REPORT. Text in English, Japanese. 1968. s-a.
Formerly (until 1972): Tokyo Gakugei Daigaku Tokushu Kyoiku Kenkyu Shisetsu Kenkyu Kiyo (0386-3263)
Indexed: SOPODA.
Published by: Tokyo Gakugei Daigaku, Tokushu Kyoiku Kenkyu Shisetsu/Tokyo Gakugei University, Research Institute for the Education of Exceptional Children, Koganeishi, Tokyo-to 184, Japan. TEL 0423-25-2111.

371.9   USA   ISSN 0271-1214
       CODEN: TECEER
➤ **TOPICS IN EARLY CHILDHOOD SPECIAL EDUCATION.** Text in English. 1981. q. USD 45 in North America to individuals; USD 74 elsewhere to individuals; USD 120 in North America to institutions; USD 151 elsewhere to institutions (effective 2006). adv. charts; illus.; abstr. Index. 64 p./no.; back issues avail.; reprint service avail. from PQC,PSC. **Document type:** *Journal, Academic/Scholarly.* **Description:** Presents comprehensive discussion of timely and important issues in the field of early childhood special education.
Related titles: Microform ed.: (from PQC); Online - full text ed.: ISSN 1538-4845 (from bigchalk, EBSCO Publishing, Florida Center for Library Automation, Gale Group, H.W. Wilson, IngentaConnect, O C L C Online Computer Library Center, Inc., ProQuest Information & Learning).
Indexed: ABIn, ASCA, ASSIA, CDA, CIJE, CPE, CurCont, DIP, EAA, ECER, ERA, ETA, EduInd, FamI, IBR, IBZ, IMFL, L&LBA, MEA, PsycInfo, PsycholAb, RHEA, SEA, SENA, SFSA, SOMA, SOPODA, SSCI, SWA, TEA, e-psyche.
—BLDSC (8867.437300), IDS, IE, Infotrieve, ingenta. CCC.
Published by: Pro-Ed Inc., 8700 Shoal Creek Blvd, Austin, TX 78757-6897. TEL 512-451-3246, 800-897-3202, FAX 512-302-9129, ltippett@proedinc.com, journals@proedinc.com, http://www.proedinc.com/tec.html. Ed. Judith Carta. Pub. Donald D Hammill. R&P, Adv. contact Paula Gonzalez. B&W page USD 400. Circ: 1,300 (paid and free).

371.9142   USA   ISSN 0271-8294
RC423.A1
➤ **TOPICS IN LANGUAGE DISORDERS.** Text in English. 1981. q. USD 85 domestic to individuals; USD 147 foreign to individuals; USD 253 domestic to institutions; USD 306 foreign to institutions (effective 2006). adv. bk.rev. illus. reprints avail. **Document type:** *Journal, Academic/Scholarly.* **Description:** Provides information that bridges the gap between theory, research and everyday practice.
Related titles: Online - full text ed.: ISSN 1550-3259 (from bigchalk, EBSCO Publishing, Florida Center for Library Automation, Gale Group, Ovid Technologies, Inc., ProQuest Information & Learning).
Indexed: ABIn, AMED, ASCA, AgeL, CIJE, CINAHL, CurCont, ECER, EduInd, L&LBA, PsycInfo, PsycholAb, SOPODA, SSCI, e-psyche.
—BLDSC (8867.458500), GNLM, IDS, IE, Infotrieve, ingenta. CCC.
Published by: Lippincott Williams & Wilkins (Subsidiary of: Wolters Kluwer N.V.), 530 Walnut St, Philadelphia, PA 19106-3621. TEL 215-521-8300, FAX 215-521-8902, custserv@lww.com, http://www.lww.com/products/?0271-8294. Ed. Katherine G Butler. Circ: 4,550 (paid).

➤ **TOWERS.** see *HANDICAPPED—Visually Impaired*

371.9   CAN   ISSN 0381-9612
THE TRUST. Text in English. 1967. q. free with membership. bk.rev. bibl. back issues avail. **Document type:** *Newsletter.* **Description:** Provides information with intellectual disabilities in the areas of education, housing, recreation and employment for parents and caregivers.
Published by: Regina and District Association for Community Living Inc., 2216 Smith St, Regina, SK S4P 2P4, Canada. TEL 306-790-5680, FAX 306-586-7899, racl@sk.sympatico.ca. Ed., R&P Elyse Fisher. Circ: 500.

371.9025   GBR
U K SPECIAL EDUCATION DIRECTORY. Text in English. 1991. a. GBP 42 (effective 1997). **Document type:** *Directory.* **Description:** Details the provision of special education throughout England, Wales, Scotland and Northern Ireland.
Formerly: U K Special Learning Needs Directory
Published by: School Government Publishing Co. Ltd., Darby House, Bletchingley Rd, Merstham, Redhill, Surrey RH1 3DN, United Kingdom. TEL 44-1737-642223, FAX 44-1737-644283. Ed. M Darby. adv.: page GBP 200; trim 106 x 178. Circ: 2,000.

371.9   USA   ISSN 0070-6736
LC4019
U S C ANNUAL DISTINGUISHED LECTURE SERIES MONOGRAPHS IN SPECIAL EDUCATION AND REHABILITATION. Text in English. 1962. a. price varies. **Document type:** *Monographic series.*
Indexed: CIJE, ECER, RehabLit.
Published by: (University of Southern California, School of Education), University of Southern California Press, c/o Bookstore, University Park, Los Angeles, CA 90007. TEL 213-743-5371. Ed. James F Magary. Circ: 3,000.

371.9   DNK
UDTRYK. Text in Danish. 1977. bi-m. DKK 70 domestic; DKK 100 foreign (effective 2001). adv. bk.rev. **Document type:** *Newsletter.* **Description:** Contains general organisational information and articles contributed by readers and members.
Former titles (until 1999): Stammebladet (0907-5364); (until 1990): P P P (0108-7207)
Published by: Foreningen for Stammere i Danmark/Association for Stutterers in Denmark, c/o D S I, Kloeverprisvej 10 B, Hvidovre, 2650, Denmark. TEL 45-86-86-26-96, FAX 45-86-86-27-96, fsd@fsd.dk, http://www.FSD.dk. Ed. Steen Christensen. Circ: 600.

371.95   USA   ISSN 1040-1350
UNDERSTANDING OUR GIFTED. Text in English. 1988. q. USD 35 to individuals; USD 47 to institutions (effective 2004). **Document type:** *Magazine, Consumer.*
—BLDSC (9090.005250).
Published by: Open Space Communications, Box 18268, Boulder, CO 80308. TEL 303-545-6505, FAX 303-444-7020, dorothy@openspacecomm.com, http://www.our-gifted.com/.

371.9   DNK   ISSN 0107-377X
UNDERVISNINGSMATERIALER TIL BEGYNDER- OG SPECIALUNDERVISNING. Text in Danish. 1980. a. free. illus.
Formerly: Test- og Undervisningsmaterialer
Published by: Special Paedagogisk Forlag, Herning, Denmark.

371.91   SVK
UNIVERZITA KOMENSKEHO. PEDAGOGICKA FAKULTA. KATEDRA SPECIALNEJ PEDAGOGIKY. ZBORNIK. PAEDAGOGICA SPECIALIS. Text in Slovak; Summaries in English, German, Russian. 1969. a. per issue exchange basis. **Document type:** *Monographic series, Academic/Scholarly.* **Description:** Forum for the theory, practice and research of special education for handicapped children.
Formerly: Univerzita Komenskeho. Oddelenie Liecebnej a Specialnej Pedagogiky. Zbornik. Paedagogica Specialis (0083-4211)
Related titles: Microfilm ed.
Indexed: BibLing.
Published by: (Katedra Specialnej Pedagogiky), Univerzita Komenskeho, Pedagogicka Fakulta, Moskovska ul 3, Bratislava, 81334, Slovakia. TEL 07-254-874. Ed. Stefan Vasek. Circ: 500.

371.9   CHE   ISSN 0017-9655
VIERTELJAHRESSCHRIFT FUER HEILPAEDAGOGIK UND IHRE NACHBARGEBIETE. Text in German; Summaries in English, French, German. 1932. q. CHF 52 domestic; EUR 33 Germany & Austria; CHF 56 elsewhere; CHF 28 domestic to students; EUR 18 to students Germany & Austria; CHF 35 elsewhere to students (effective 2003). adv. bk.rev. **Document type:** *Journal, Academic/Scholarly.*
Formerly: Heilpaedagogische Werkblaetter
Indexed: DIP, IBR, IBZ, PsycInfo, PsycholAb, e-psyche.
Published by: Heilpaedagogisches Institut der Universitaet Freiburg, Petrus Kanisius Gasse 21, Fribourg, 1700, Switzerland. TEL 41-26-3007700, FAX 41-26-3009749, christina.amrein@unifr.ch, http://pedcurmac13.unifr.ch/. Ed., Adv. contact Christina Amrein. Pub. Urs Haeberlin. Circ: 1,800 (paid and controlled).

E

▼ *new title*   ➤ *refereed*   ∗ *unverified*   ◆ *full entry avail.*

371.911 362.41   GBR   ISSN 0961-9879
VISABILITY. Text in English. 199?. 3/yr. GBP 10.50 domestic; GBP 15 foreign (effective 2005). illus. **Document type:** *Magazine, Consumer.* **Description:** Offers special-education professionals and parents practical information on teaching children who are blind or visually impaired.
Related titles: Audio cassette/tape ed.; Braille ed.; Diskette ed.
Published by: Royal National Institute for the Blind, Education, Training and Employment Division, 7 Poplar St, Fisher Gate, Nottingham, NG1 1GP, United Kingdom. TEL 44-115-9582322, webmaster@rnib.org.uk, cservices@rnib.org.uk, e&elondon@rnib.org.uk, http://www.rnib.org.uk/xpedio/groups/public/documents/PublicWebsite/public_aboutvis.hcsp. Ed. Joanna Shaw TEL 44-115-8526736. **Subscr. to:** PO Box 173, Peterborough PE2 6WS, United Kingdom. TEL 845-702-3153, 44-1733-238541, exports@rnib.org.uk, cservices@rnib.org.uk.

371.92   FRA   ISSN 1152-6653
VIVRE ENSEMBLE. Text in French. 1962. bi-m. adv. bk.rev.; film rev. bibl.; stat. **Document type:** *Newspaper.*
Formerly (until 1990): Epanouir (0182-4651)
Published by: Union Nationale des Associations de Parents et Amis de Personnes Handicapees Mentales, 15 rue Coysevox, Paris, Cedex 18 75876, France. TEL 33-1-44855050, FAX 33-1-44855060, public@unapei.org, http://www.unapei.org. Ed., Pub., R&P Patrick Gohet. Adv. contact Christophe Magnant. Circ: 75,250 (controlled).

371.9   USA
VOCATIONAL REHABILITATION REVIEW✶ . Text in English. 1982. w. membership.
Published by: National Association of Rehabilitation Facilities, 206 S 6th St, Springfield, IL 62701-1530. Ed. Charles W Harles. Circ: 545. **Subscr. to:** PO Box 17675, Washington, DC 20041.

THE VOLTA REVIEW. see *HANDICAPPED—Hearing Impaired*

VOLTA VOICES. see *HANDICAPPED—Hearing Impaired*

W C E R RESEARCH HIGHLIGHTS. see *EDUCATION—Teaching Methods And Curriculum*

371.9   USA
WASHINGTON (STATE). DIVISION OF VOCATIONAL REHABILITATION. STATE FACILITIES DEVELOPMENT PLAN. Text in English. 1969. every 3 yrs. free.
Former titles: Washington (State). Vocational Rehabilitation Services Division. State Facilities Development Plan; Washington (State). Vocational Rehabilitation Services Division. State Facilities Plan (0092-5543)
Published by: Department of Social and Health Services, Division of Vocational Rehabilitation, OB 2, Olympia, WA 98504. TEL 206-753-0767, FAX 206-586-6505. Circ: 1,000.

WEEKLY READER. GRADE 2 EDITION (LARGE PRINT EDITION). see *CHILDREN AND YOUTH—For*

WEEKLY READER. GRADE 3 EDITION (LARGE PRINT EDITION). see *CHILDREN AND YOUTH—For*

WEEKLY READER. GRADE 4 EDITION (LARGE PRINT EDITION). see *CHILDREN AND YOUTH—For*

WEEKLY READER. SENIOR EDITION (LARGE PRINT EDITION). see *CHILDREN AND YOUTH—For*

371.9   GBR   ISSN 0144-5359
WESSEX STUDIES IN SPECIAL EDUCATION. Text in English. 1981. biennial. looseleaf. GBP 5. bk.rev.
Related titles: Microfiche ed.
Indexed: BrEdI, ECER.
Published by: King Alfred's College, Winchester, Hants SO22 4NR, United Kingdom. Ed. Barny Gray. Circ: 400.

371.9   USA   ISSN 1525-9765
WHAT'S WORKING IN SPECIAL EDUCATION. Text in English. m. USD 130 (effective 2002). **Document type:** *Newsletter.* **Description:** Offers advice to overcome obstacles when providing quality services to students with disabilities. It gives practical ideas, helpful hints and expert advice.
Published by: L R P Publications, 747 Dresher Rd, PO Box 980, Horsham, PA 19044. TEL 800-341-7874, custserve@lrp.com, http://www.lrp.com.

WHICH SCHOOL? FOR SPECIAL NEEDS. see *EDUCATION—Guides To Schools And Colleges*

371.912   USA
THE WISCONSIN TIMES. Text in English. 1878. bi-m. USD 5. **Document type:** *Newsletter.* **Description:** Covers the special education of deaf students and other issues concerning the hearing impaired.
Published by: Wisconsin School for the Deaf, 309 W Walworth Ave, Delavan, WI 53115. TEL 414-728-7120. Eds. James Hansen, William A Wilson.

371.9142   USA   ISSN 1048-3950
WORD OF MOUTH (SAN ANTONIO). Text in English. 1989. 5/yr. USD 28 in North America to individuals; USD 38 elsewhere to individuals; USD 45 in North America to institutions; USD 66 elsewhere to institutions (effective 2006). index. back issues avail.; reprints avail. **Document type:** *Newsletter.* **Description:** Addresses the needs of the school speech pathologist interested in keeping up with trends in working with school-age children.
Related titles: Online - full content ed.
—CCC.
Published by: Pro-Ed Inc., 8700 Shoal Creek Blvd, Austin, TX 78757-6897. TEL 512-451-3246, 800-897-3202, FAX 512-302-9129, 800-397-7633, journals@proedinc.com, http://www.proedinc.com. Ed. Carol Westby. Pub. Donald D Hammill. Circ: 1,700 (paid and free).

371.9   NZL   ISSN 1174-9970
WORK AND PROGRESS. Text in English. 1995. q. free. **Document type:** *Newsletter.*
Published by: Association Supported Employment in New Zealand, Box 1905, Palmerston North, New Zealand. TEL 64-6-354-2088, FAX 64-6-354-2588. Eds. G Bennie, J Taylor. Pub. Roy Wilson. Circ: 500 (paid); 500 (controlled).

371.912   USA   ISSN 0199-8293
WORLD AROUND YOU. Text in English. 1978. 3/yr. free (effective 2003). adv. back issues avail. **Document type:** *Journal, Academic/Scholarly.* **Description:** News magazine for hearing impaired teens.
Related titles: Online - full content ed.; ◆ Special ed(s).: World Around You. Teacher's Edition. ISSN 1059-9894.
Published by: Gallaudet University, National Deaf Educ Network & Clearinghouse, 800 Florida Ave, NE, KDES PAS 6, Washington, DC 20002-3695. TEL 202-651-5340, FAX 202-651-5708, cmcarrol@gallux.gallaudet.edu, http://clerccenter.gallaudet.edu/WorldAroundYou/. Ed. Cathryn Carroll. Adv. contact Susan Flanigan. Circ: 6,500.

371.95   USA
WORLD COUNCIL FOR GIFTED AND TALENTED CHILDREN. YEARBOOK. Text in English. 1981. biennial. USD 15. back issues avail. **Document type:** *Proceedings.* **Description:** Describes the proceedings of the world conferences held by the council.
Published by: World Council for Gifted and Talented Children, PO Box 10034, Beaumont, TX 77710. TEL 409-880-8046, FAX 409-880-8685.

371.9   USA   ISSN 1096-2506
LC4019.3
➤ **YOUNG EXCEPTIONAL CHILDREN.** Text in English. 1997. q. USD 20 domestic to individuals; USD 35 domestic to institutions; USD 40 foreign (effective 2004). adv. bk.rev. 30 p./no.; back issues avail.; reprints avail. **Document type:** *Journal, Academic/Scholarly.* **Description:** Provides practical ideas for teachers, early-care and education personnel, administrators, therapists, family members, and others who work with or on behalf of children from birth through age 8 who have disabilities or developmental delays, are gifted and talented, or are at risk for future developmental problems.
Incorporates: D E C Communicator
Indexed: e-psyche.
—BLDSC (9421.418800).
Published by: Council for Exceptional Children, Division for Early Childhood, 634 Eddy Ave, Missoula, MT 59812. TEL 406-243-5898, FAX 406-243-4730, dec@selway.unit.org, http://www.dec-sped.org. Ed. Eva Horn. Circ: 6,600.

371.9   DEU   ISSN 0513-9066
ZEITSCHRIFT FUER HEILPAEDAGOGIK. Text in German. 1949. m. EUR 8.50 newsstand/cover (effective 2005). adv. bk.rev. cum.index: 1959-1976. back issues avail. **Document type:** *Journal, Academic/Scholarly.*
Formerly (until 1951): Heilpaedagogischer Blaetter (1614-2675)
Indexed: DIP, IBR, IBZ.
Published by: Verband Deutscher Sonderschulen e.V., Ohmstr 7, Wuerzburg, 97076, Germany. TEL 49-931-24020, FAX 49-931-24023, vds.fachverband@t-online.de, http://www.vds-bundesverband.de. Eds. Dr. Ditmar Schmetz, Dr. Peter Wachtel. adv.: B&W page EUR 1,070, color page EUR 1,880; trim 172 x 245. Circ: 12,000 (paid and controlled).

▼ **2E: TWICE-EXCEPTIONAL NEWSLETTER.** see *CHILDREN AND YOUTH—About*

EDUCATION—Teaching Methods And Curriculum

see also specific subjects

610.71   USA   ISSN 0092-0371
R745
A A M C CURRICULUM DIRECTORY. Text in English. 1972. a. USD 35. reprint service avail. from PQC. **Document type:** *Directory.* **Description:** Describes the academic programs of medical schools in the Unites States, Canada, and Puerto Rico. Includes information on curriculum characteristics and current trends and innovations of interest to applicants, other students, faculties, and deans.

Published by: Association of American Medical Colleges, 2450 N St N W, Washington, DC 20037-1126. TEL 202-828-0416, FAX 202-828-1123. R&P Cynthia Bennett.

A A T A NEWSLETTER. see *LINGUISTICS*

A A T F NATIONAL BULLETIN. see *LINGUISTICS*

407.1   USA   ISSN 0147-1236
P10
A C T F L FOREIGN LANGUAGE EDUCATION SERIES. Text in English. 1969. a., latest vol.25, 1995. USD 15.95 to non-members; USD 11.95 to members. **Document type:** *Academic/Scholarly.*
Former titles: A C T F L Review of Foreign Languages Education (0091-2476); A C T F L Annual Review of Foreign Language Education (0068-1180); Britannica Review of Foreign Language Education
Published by: American Council on the Teaching of Foreign Languages, Inc., 700 S. Washington St., Ste 210, Alexandria, VA 22314. TEL 914-963-8830, FAX 914-963-1275, actflhq@aol.com, http://www.actfl.org. R&P C Edward Scebold.

A C T F L NEWSLETTER. see *LINGUISTICS*

A D E BULLETIN. see *EDUCATION—Higher Education*

A D F L BULLETIN. see *EDUCATION—Higher Education*

A D L ON THE FRONTLINE. see *POLITICAL SCIENCE—Civil Rights*

A E C A VOICE. see *CHILDREN AND YOUTH—About*

A E S BUG CLUB NEWS. see *CHILDREN AND YOUTH—For*

707.1   AUS
A E V NEWS. Text in English. q. looseleaf. AUD 60 to individual members (effective 2003). bk.rev.; video rev. 4 p./no.; back issues avail. **Document type:** *Newsletter.* **Description:** Provides news about forthcoming art education activities for teachers.
Formerly: A C T A News (Art Craft Teachers Association) (0155-722X)
Published by: Art Education Victoria, SRC 150 Palmerston St, Carlton, VIC 3053, Australia. TEL 61-3-93495188, FAX 61-3-93492050, enquiries@aev.vic.edu.au, http://www.aev.vic.edu.au. R&P, Adv. contact Marian Strong. Circ: 800.

A I L A NEWSLETTER. (Association Internationale de Linguistique Appliquee) see *LINGUISTICS*

372.4   USA   ISSN 0882-2840
➤ **THE A L A N REVIEW.** (Assembly on Literature for Adolescents) Text in English. 1972. 3/yr. USD 20 to individuals; USD 30 to institutions (effective academic year 2004 - 2005). adv. bk.rev. **Document type:** *Journal, Academic/Scholarly.* **Description:** Features interviews with authors and articles by young adult authors, and provides techniques for integrating young adult literature into the classroom.
Formerly: A L A N Newsletter
Related titles: Microfiche ed.; Online - full text ed.: ISSN 1547-741X (from ProQuest Information & Learning).
Indexed: CIJE, ChLitAb.
—BLDSC (0786.525117), IE, ingenta. CCC.
Published by: National Council of Teachers of English, Assembly on Literature for Adolescents, Florida State University, 209 MCH, Tallahassee, FL 32306-4490. lagoodson@cox.net, James.Blasingame@asu.edu, http://www.alan-ya.org. Eds. James Blasingame, Lori A Goodson. R&P, Adv. contact S Carroll TEL 850-644-2997. Circ: 2,500. **Subscr. to:** 1111 Kenyon Rd, Urbana, IL 61801. TEL 217-328-3870, 877-369-6283.

➤ **A L A NEWS.** see *LAW*

371.3 384 401   FRA   ISSN 1286-4986
A L S I C. (Apprentissage de Langues et Systemes d'Information et de Communication) Text in French. 1998. s-a. free (effective 2005). **Document type:** *Academic/Scholarly.*
Media: Online - full content.
Indexed: MLA-IB.
Published by: Universite de Strasbourg II (Marc Bloch/Sciences Humaines), 22 rue Descartes, Strasbourg, 67084, France. http://alsic.univ-fcomte.fr.

A M C SOLUTIONS AND STATISTICS (YEAR). (Australian Mathematics Competition) see *MATHEMATICS*

371.33   USA
A N J E E NEWSLETTER. Text in English. q. membership. **Document type:** *Newsletter, Trade.* **Description:** Informs school teachers in New Jersey of programs for incorporating environmental studies in their schools' and classroom curricula.

Published by: Alliance for New Jersey Environmental Education, c/o NJ Dept of Environmental Protection, Public Access Center, 401 E State St, 7th Fl, PO Box 402, Trenton, NJ 08625-0402. TEL 609-777-DEP3, FAX 609-777-1781, http://ceaedep.rutgers.edu/ANJEEweb.html, http://www.state.nj.us/dep.

371.3   USA
A S C D CURRICULUM HANDBOOK. Text in English. base vol. plus q. updates. looseleaf. USD 450 to non-members; USD 375 to members. **Document type:** *Trade.* **Description:** Offers more than 1,000 pages of essential information in developing curricula in every area, along with interdisciplinary curricula.
Related titles: Online - full text ed.
Published by: Association for Supervision and Curriculum Development, 1703 N Beauregard St, Alexandria, VA 22311. TEL 703-578-9600, FAX 703-575-5400, member@ascd.org, update@ascd.org, http://www.ascd.org.

A S W E A JOURNAL FOR SOCIAL WORK EDUCATION IN AFRICA. see *SOCIAL SERVICES AND WELFARE*

371.3   USA   ISSN 0044-9687
A T S S BULLETIN. Text in English. 1971 (vol.39). irreg. (5-6/yr.). membership. adv. bk.rev. bibl. **Document type:** *Bulletin.*
Published by: Association of Teachers of Social Studies in the City of New York, c/o Bell Sigelalis, Pres, John Dewey High School, 50 Avenue X, Brooklyn, NY 11223. Ed. William McGinn. Circ: 1,200.

371.3   GBR
A T S S NEWSLETTER. (Association for the Teaching of the Social Sciences) Text in English. 3/yr.
Published by: Association for the Teaching of the Social Sciences, P.O. Box 6079, Leicester, LE2 4DW, United Kingdom. TXL@le.ac.uk.

371.335   JPN   ISSN 0065-0102
A V E IN JAPAN. (Audio-Visual Education) Text in English. 1963. a. JPY 1,220 (effective 2001). **Document type:** *Yearbook, Academic/Scholarly.*
Published by: Japan Audio-Visual Education Association/Nihon Shichokaku Kyoiku Kyokai, 1-17-1 Toranomon, Minato-ku, Tokyo, 105-0001, Japan. TEL 81-3-3591-2186, FAX 81-3-3597-0564, jpn@javea.or.jp, http://www.javea.or.jp/. Ed. Morio Okabe. Circ: 2,000.

371.33   USA   ISSN 0091-360X
LB1044.A2
A V GUIDE; the learning media newsletter. Text in English. 1922. m. USD 15 domestic; USD 18 foreign; USD 2 newsstand/cover (effective 2001). film rev.; software rev.; music rev.; rec.rev.; video rev. illus. index. 4 p./no.; back issues avail.; reprint service avail. from PQC. **Document type:** *Newsletter.* **Description:** Focus on methods of using learning media and related audiovisual products and media such as CD-ROMs, videotapes, and audiotapes.
Former titles: A V Guide Newsletter; Educational Screen and Audio Visual Guide (0013-1938)
Related titles: Microfilm ed.: ISSN 0364-9946 (from PQC). —CCC.
Published by: Educational Screen, Inc., 380 E Northwest Hwy, Des Plaines, IL 60016-2282. FAX 847-390-0408, nferguson@sgcmail.com. Ed. Natalie Ferguson. Pub. H S Gillette. Circ: 1,000 (paid).

371.335   USA   ISSN 1044-0445
LB1043
A V MARKET PLACE; the complete business directory of: audio, audio visual, computer systems, film, video, programming - with industry yellow pages. (Audio Video) Text in English. 1969. a. USD 199.95 (effective 2006). **Document type:** *Directory, Trade.* **Description:** Lists companies that create, supply, or distribute audiovisual equipment and services for business, education, science, government, and libraries.
Former titles (until 1988): Audio Video Market Place (0000-1112); (until 1984): Audiovisual Market Place (0067-0553).
Published by: Information Today, Inc., 143 Old Marlton Pike, Medford, NJ 08055-8750. TEL 609-654-6266, FAX 609-654-4309, custserv@infotoday.com, http://www.infotoday.com.

371.33523   ZAF
A V PRESENTATIONS HANDBOOK. (Audio Visual) Text in English. 1994. bi-m. ZAR 60. illus.
Published by: Doddington Direct, PO Box 3939, Honeydew, 2040, South Africa.

808   USA   ISSN 1079-7025
PN181
A W P OFFICIAL GUIDE TO WRITING PROGRAMS. Text in English. biennial, latest 10th ed. USD 28.45 per issue (effective 2003). adv. **Document type:** *Catalog.* **Description:** Describes over 300 creative writing programs.
Formerly (until 1991): A W P Catalogue of Writing Programs
Published by: Associated Writing Programs, Tallwood House, Mail Stop 1E3, George Mason University, Fairfax, VA 22030. TEL 703-993-4301, FAX 703-993-4302, awp@gmu.edu, http://www.awpwriter.org/bookshelf/guide.htm. Ed. David W Fenza. Adv. contact David Sherwin TEL 703-993-4310.

ACADEMIA VENEZOLANA DE LA LENGUA. BOLETIN. see *LINGUISTICS*

371.3   USA   ISSN 1096-1453
LB1025.3
➤ **ACADEMIC EXCHANGE QUARTERLY.** Abbreviated title: A E Q. Text in English. 1997. q. USD 126 domestic; USD 156 foreign; USD 39 per issue; free to qualified personnel (effective 2005). 300 p./no.; **Document type:** *Journal, Academic/Scholarly.* **Description:** Presents ideas, research, and methodsleading to effective instruction and learning regardless of level or subject.
Related titles: Online - full text ed.: (from Florida Center for Library Automation, Gale Group).
—BLDSC (0570.511280).
Published by: Rapid Intellect Group, PO Box 131, Stuyvesant Falls, NY 12174. TEL 518-731-1336, academicexchange@yahoo.com, http://rapidintellect.com/AEQweb/, http://www.rapidintellect.com/. Ed. Melinda R Pierson. Pub. S Seweryn Pec. Circ: 2,500 (paid).

371.3   USA
▼ **ACADEMIC TESTING MATERIALS: MARKET ANALYSIS & FORECAST (YEAR).** Text in English. 2004. a. USD 2,295 (effective 2006). **Document type:** *Directory, Trade.* **Description:** Provides comprehensive and detailed information on selling educational testing materials to U.S. school systems.
Related titles: Online - full text ed.: USD 2,295 (effective 2005).
Published by: SIMBA Information (Subsidiary of: R.R. Bowker LLC), 60 Long Ridge Rd., Ste 300, Stamford, CT 06902. TEL 203-325-8193, 800-307-2529, FAX 203-325-8915, info@simbanet.com, http://www.simbanet.com/publications/report_atm.htm.

ACADEMIC.WRITING; interdisciplinary perspectives on communication across the curriculum. see *LITERATURE*

371.3   USA   ISSN 1528-2643
➤ **ACADEMY OF EDUCATIONAL LEADERSHIP JOURNAL.** Text in English. s-a. **Document type:** *Journal, Academic/Scholarly.*
Related titles: Online - full text ed.
Published by: Allied Academies, 145 Travis Rd., P. O. Box 2689, Cullowhee, NC 28723. http://www.alliedacademies.org/education/index.html.

372.677   USA
ACORN EARLY YEARS STORYTELLER. Text in English. 1978. q. USD 14.95. adv. bk.rev. **Document type:** *Trade.* **Description:** Contains read-aloud folk tales and stories for the pre-K to grade 3 children's librarian or elementary teacher to use, along with flannel patterns, story props, masks, bulletin board characters, name tags and bookmarks; on such themes as pirates, insects, cowboys, sports, parties and transportation.
Former titles: Acorn Storyteller; Acorn (0274-8762)
Published by: Bur Oak Press, Inc., 8717 Mockingbird Rd, Platteville, WI 53818. TEL 608-348-8662. Ed., Pub., R&P, Adv. contact Susan Pagnucci. Circ: 1,000 (paid).

▼ **ACROSS THE DISCIPLINES.** see *LINGUISTICS*

ACTA UNIVERSITATIS NICOLAI COPERNICI. HUMANITIES AND SOCIAL STUDIES. ENGLISH STUDIES/ACTA UNIVERSITATIS NICOLAI COPERNICI. NAUKI HUMANISTYCZNO-SPOLECZNE. FILOLOGIA ANGIELSKA. see *LINGUISTICS*

ACTA UNIVERSITATIS NICOLAI COPERNICI. NAUKI HUMANISTYCZNO-SPOLECZNE. FILOLOGIA ROSYJSKA. see *LINGUISTICS*

ACTA UNIVERSITATIS NICOLAI COPERNICI. NAUKI HUMANISTYCZNO-SPOLECZNE. STUDIA ROSJOZNAWCZE. see *LINGUISTICS*

371.3   USA
ACTION (CLEARWATER). Text in English. 1962. m. free. adv. bk.rev. illus. **Document type:** *Trade.*
Former titles: New Pinellas Teacher; Pinellas Teacher (0031-9872)
Published by: Pinellas Classroom Teachers Association, Inc., 650 Seminole Blvd, Largo, FL 33770. TEL 727-585-6518. Ed. Jade T Moore. Circ: 5,600.

371.3   AUS
ACTION (POTTS POINT). Text in English. 1970. q. free. **Document type:** *Newsletter.* **Description:** Contains information on company activities, projects.
Formerly (until Nov. 1987): A S E A Action
Published by: A B B Marketing Services, ABB EPT House, 166 William St, Potts Point, NSW 2011, Australia. TEL 61-2-9356-0970, FAX 61-2-9356-0977. Circ: 4,000.

ACTIVE LEARNING IN HIGHER EDUCATION; the journal of the Institute for Learning and Teaching. see *EDUCATION—Higher Education*

ADULT BIBLE STUDIES TEACHER. see *RELIGIONS AND THEOLOGY—Protestant*

371.3   USA
ADVANCES IN EDUCATIONAL PRODUCTIVITY. Text in English. irreg., latest vol.7, 1998. price varies. back issues avail. **Document type:** *Monographic series, Academic/Scholarly.* —BLDSC (0704.590000).
Published by: J A I Press Inc. (Subsidiary of: Elsevier Science & Technology), 360 Park Ave S, New York, NY 10010-1710. TEL 212-989-5800, FAX 212-633-3990, usinfo-f@elsevier.com, http://www.elsevier.com/wps/find/bookdescription.cws_home/BS_EDPROD/description#description. Ed. Herbert J Walberg.

371.3   USA
ADVANCES IN FOREIGN AND SECOND LANGUAGE PEDAGOGY. Text in English. 2000. irreg. price varies. bibl.; charts; illus. back issues avail. **Document type:** *Monographic series, Academic/Scholarly.* **Description:** Examines issues in the teaching of a foreign or second language.
Published by: Ablex Publishing Corporation (Subsidiary of: Greenwood Publishing Group Inc.), 88 Post Rd W, Westport, CT 06881. TEL 203-226-3571, http://info.greenwood.com/books.

613.7   USA   ISSN 0890-4073
RA440.A1
➤ **ADVANCES IN HEALTH EDUCATION: CURRENT RESEARCH.** Text in English. 1988. a. USD 37.50. bk.rev. index. back issues avail. **Document type:** *Academic/Scholarly.* **Description:** Contains original research on current issues, both biological and behavioral, in the field of health education.
Indexed: e-psyche.
Published by: A M S Press, Inc., 63 Flushing Ave., # 417, Brooklyn, NY 11205-1005. TEL 212-777-4700, FAX 212-995-5413. Ed. James H Humphrey.

371.3   GBR   ISSN 1474-7863
ADVANCES IN PROGRAM EVALUATION. Text in English. 1992. irreg., latest vol.9, 2004. back issues avail. **Document type:** *Monographic series, Academic/Scholarly.*
Related titles: Online - full text ed.: (from ScienceDirect).
Published by: J A I Press Ltd. (Subsidiary of: Elsevier Science & Technology), The Boulevard, Langford Ln, Kidlington, Oxford, OX5 1GB, United Kingdom. TEL 44-1865-843000, FAX 44-1865-843010, nlinfo-f@elsevier.com, http://www.elsevier.com/wps/product/cws_home/BS_APE. Ed. R E Stake.

371.3   USA   ISSN 1569-4895
ADVANCES IN RESEARCH ON TEACHING. Text in English. 1989. irreg., latest vol.10, 2003. price varies. back issues avail. **Document type:** *Monographic series, Academic/Scholarly.* **Description:** Intended for scholars who conduct research on teaching and for teacher educators whose practice is informed by this research.
Related titles: Online - full text ed.
—ingenta.
Published by: J A I Press Inc. (Subsidiary of: Elsevier Science & Technology), 360 Park Ave S, New York, NY 10010-1710. TEL 212-989-5800, 800-325-4177, FAX 212-633-3990, jereb@msu.edu, usinfo-f@elsevier.com, http://www.elsevier.com/wps/find/bookdescription.cws_home/BS_ART/description#description. Ed. J Brophy TEL 517-353-6470.

371.3   USA   ISSN 0748-0067
LB1715
ADVANCES IN TEACHER EDUCATION. Text in English. 1984. irreg., latest vol.5, 1999. USD 99.95. **Document type:** *Academic/Scholarly.*
Indexed: e-psyche.
—BLDSC (0711.595800). CCC.
Published by: Ablex Publishing Corporation (Subsidiary of: Greenwood Publishing Group Inc.), 88 Post Rd W, Westport, CT 06881. TEL 203-323-9606, FAX 203-357-8446. Eds. James Raths, Lilian Katz.

296.68   USA   ISSN 1072-1150
LC 701
AGENDA: JEWISH EDUCATION; a journal of public policy magazine. Text in English. 1949. a. USD 18. bk.rev. bibl.
Formerly (until 1992): Pedagogic Reporter (0031-3793)
Indexed: IJP.
Published by: Jewish Education Service of North America, Inc., 111 Eighth Ave, Ste 11E, New York, NY 10011-5201. TEL 212-284-6950, FAX 212-284-6951, info@jesna.org, http://www.jesna.org/. Ed. Arthur Vernon. R&P Amy Stein TEL 212-284-6896. Circ: 2,000.

AIR & SPACE - SMITHSONIAN. see *AERONAUTICS AND SPACE FLIGHT*

371.3   SCG   ISSN 0350-5197
AKTUELNOSTI U VASPITANJU I OBRAZOVANJU. Text in Serbo-Croatian. 1971-1983; resumed 198?. 10/yr. YUN 10,000. USD 50.
Published by: (Sector za Pedagosku Dokumentaciju YUG), Republicki Zavod za Unapredjivanje Vaspitanja i Obrazovanja, Draze Pavlovica 15, Belgrade, 11124. TEL 765-366. Ed. Iskra Maksimovic. Circ: 1,000.

ALAMBIQUE; didactica de las ciencias experimentales. see *SCIENCES: COMPREHENSIVE WORKS*

E

ALIZES. see *LINGUISTICS*

ALLIANCE UPDATE. see *PHYSICAL FITNESS AND HYGIENE*

ALLONS-Y. see *EDUCATION—International Education Programs*

DER ALTSPRACHLICHE UNTERRICHT; Arbeitshefte zu seiner wissenschaftlichen Begruendung und praktischen Gestalt. see *LINGUISTICS*

ALVERNO MAGAZINE. see *EDUCATION—Higher Education*

499.992 USA ISSN 0002-7499
AMERICAN ASSOCIATION OF TEACHERS OF ESPERANTO QUARTERLY BULLETIN/AMERIKA ASOCIO DE INSTRUISTOJ DE ESPERANTO KVARONJARA BULTENO. Text in English, Esperanto. 1963. q. USD 25 to members. bk.rev. **Document type:** *Bulletin.*
Media: Duplicated (not offset).
Published by: American Association of Teachers of Esperanto, c/o Sally Lawton, 12 Stage Rd., Westhampton, MA 01027. TEL 805-967-5241. Ed. Dorothy Holland. Circ: 100.

AMERICAN BAPTIST CURRICULUM SUPPLEMENT. see *RELIGIONS AND THEOLOGY—Protestant*

613.7 USA
LB3401 CODEN: HEEDE4
➤ **AMERICAN JOURNAL OF HEALTH EDUCATION.** Text in English. 1970. bi-m. USD 120 domestic to institutions; USD 128 elsewhere to institutions; USD 20 per issue (effective 2004). adv. bk.rev. charts; stat. index. back issues avail.; reprint service avail. from PQC,ISI. **Document type:** *Journal, Academic/Scholarly.* **Description:** Provides articles on research findings, teaching ideas, community and public health promotion. Each issue contains two CEU self-study articles.
Former titles (until 2003): Journal of Health Education (1055-6699); (until 1991): Health Education (0097-0050); (until 1975): School Health Review (0036-6579)
Related titles: Microform ed.: (from PQC); Online - full text ed.: (from ProQuest Information & Learning).
Indexed: ABIn, AgeL, Agr, CIJE, CINAHL, CPE, ECER, ERA, ESPM, EduInd, H&SSA, MEA, MEDLINE, MRD, PEI, SEA, SOMA, SportS, TEA.
—BLDSC (0824.710000), GNLM, IE, Infotrieve, ingenta, KNAW. **CCC.**
Published by: American Alliance for Health, Physical Education, Recreation, and Dance, 1900 Association Dr, Reston, VA 20191-1599. TEL 703-476-3400, 800-213-7193, FAX 703-476-9527, info@aahperd.org, http://www.aahperd.org/aahe/template.cfm?template=ajhe_main.html. Ed. Becky Smith. Circ: 11,500.

➤ **AMERICAN JOURNAL OF PHYSICS.** see *PHYSICS*

➤ **AMERICAN SECONDARY EDUCATION.** see *EDUCATION—School Organization And Administration*

➤ **AMERICAN SOKOL.** see *PHYSICAL FITNESS AND HYGIENE*

➤ **AMERICAN SUZUKI JOURNAL.** see *MUSIC*

➤ **L'AMITIE/FRIENDSHIP.** see *LINGUISTICS*

E

930.071 NLD ISSN 1571-6511
AMPHORA. Text in Dutch. 1982. q. EUR 15 membership (effective 2005). bk.rev.; play rev. back issues avail. **Document type:** *Newsletter.* **Description:** Promotes classical studies in high schools.
Formerly (until 2003): Vereniging Vrienden van het Gymnasium. Mededelingen (1383-1267)
Published by: Vereniging Vrienden van het Gymnasium, Bergerweg 40, Alkmaar, 1815 AD, Netherlands. info@gymnasiumnu.nl, http://www.gymnasiumnu.nl. Circ: 4,600.

ANNOUNCER. see *PHYSICS*

418 DEU ISSN 0940-7669
PE68.G4
ANNUAL REPORT ON ENGLISH AND AMERICAN STUDIES. Text in German. 1991. s-a. **Document type:** *Journal, Academic/Scholarly.*
Published by: Wissenschaftlicher Verlag Trier, Bergstr 27, Trier, 54295, Germany. TEL 49-651-41503, FAX 49-651-41504, wvt@wvttrier.de, http://www.wvttrier.de. Eds. Joachim Kornelius, Norbert Greiner.

APERTURA. see *EDUCATION*

ARAB JOURNAL OF LANGUAGE STUDIES/AL-MAJALLAH AL-'ARABIYYAH LIL-DIRASAT AL-LUGHAWIYYAH. see *LINGUISTICS*

005.52 DEU
ARCHIV FUER STENOGRAFIE, TEXTVERARBEITUNG, BUEROTECHNIK. Text in German. 1973. q. bk.rev. back issues avail. **Document type:** *Bulletin, Trade.* **Description:** Information for teachers of word processing and shorthand in German speaking countries.
Formerly: Archiv fuer Stenografie, Textverarbeitung, Maschinenschreiben, Buerotechnik
Published by: Forschungs- und Ausbildungsstaette fuer Kurzschrift und Textverarbeitung in Bayreuth e.V., Bernecker Str 11, Bayreuth, 95448, Germany. TEL 49-921-23445, FAX 49-921-7857475, kampfer@forschungsstaette.de, http://www.forschungsstaette.de. Ed. Hans Juergen Baese. Circ: 400 (controlled).

ARIZONA ENGLISH BULLETIN. see *LINGUISTICS*

808.5 DEU ISSN 1616-4768
ARS RHETORICA. Text in German. 1990. irreg., latest vol.12, 2002. EUR 20.90 per vol.. **Document type:** *Monographic series, Academic/Scholarly.*
Published by: Lit Verlag, Grevener Str. 179, Muenster, 48159, Germany. TEL 49-251-235091, FAX 49-251-231972, lit@lit-verlag.de, http://www.lit-verlag.de.

707 GBR ISSN 0262-7035
ART & CRAFT; a magazine for primary teachers. Text in English. 1936. m. GBP 28.20, GBP 37.95; GBP 2.35 newsstand/cover (effective 1999). adv. bk.rev. illus. **Document type:** *Magazine, Consumer.* **Description:** Offers primary-school teachers tips on creating arts and crafts lessons and on dealing with important issues. Includes free materials and pull-out posters.
Formerly (until 1979): Art and Craft in Education (0004-3028)
Related titles: Microform ed.: (from PQC).
—IE.
Published by: Scholastic Ltd., Villiers House, Clarendon Ave, Leamington Spa, Warks CV32 5PR, United Kingdom. TEL 44-1926-887799, FAX 44-1926-883331, scholastic@compuserve.com, enquiries@scholastic.co.uk, http://www.scholastic.co.uk. Ed. Sian Morgan. Adv. contact Chris Pratt. Circ: 15,773. **Subscr. to:** Subscription Department, Westfield Rd, Southam, Leamington Spa, Warks CV33 0JH, United Kingdom. TEL 44-1926-816250.

ART TO ZOO. see *MUSEUMS AND ART GALLERIES*

707.1 AUS
ARTICLE; art education Victoria. Text in English. 1968. 3/yr. AUD 60 to individual members (effective 2003). adv. bk.rev.; video rev.; Website rev. Supplement avail.; back issues avail. **Document type:** *Journal, Academic/Scholarly.* **Description:** For art teachers: curriculum development and educational issues.
Former titles: Interacta (0159-9135); A C T A Magazine; Art Teachers Association of Victoria. Journal (0044-9059)
Related titles: Online - full text ed.
Indexed: AEI.
Published by: Art Education Victoria, SRC 150 Palmerston St, Carlton, VIC 3053, Australia. TEL 61-3-93495188, FAX 61-3-93492050, enquiries@aev.vic.edu.au, http://www.aev.vic.edu.au. R&P, Adv. contact Marian Strong. color page AUD 600. Circ: 800.

ARTICLES DE DIDACTICA DE LA LLENGUA I DE LA LITERATURA. see *LINGUISTICS*

372.6 USA ISSN 0004-3931
L11
ARTS AND ACTIVITIES; the nation's leading arts education magazine. Text in English. 1932. m. (Sep.-June). USD 24.95 domestic; USD 44.95 foreign; USD 3 newsstand/cover (effective 2005). bk.rev.; video rev. illus.; tr.lit. s-a. index. 60 p./no. 3 cols./p.; back issues avail.; reprint service avail. from PQC. **Document type:** *Magazine, Trade.* **Description:** Publishes articles dealing with the theory and practice of art education at the elementary and secondary levels, as well as teacher education and related issues. Reviews useful products, materials and supplies.
Related titles: Microform ed.: (from PQC); Online - full text ed.: (from bigchalk, EBSCO Publishing, Florida Center for Library Automation, Gale Group, H.W. Wilson, O C L C Online Computer Library Center, Inc., ProQuest Information & Learning).
Indexed: ABIn, EduInd, ICM, JHMA, MRD, WBA, WMB.
—BLDSC (1735.400000), IE, ingenta.
Published by: Publishers Development Corp., 12345 World Trade Dr, San Diego, CA 92128. TEL 858-605-0253, FAX 858-605-0247, ed@artsandactivities.com, http://www.artsandactivities.com. Ed. Maryellen Bridge. Pub. Thomas von Rosen. Adv. contact Tracy Brdicko. Circ: 22,000.

ARTS AND HUMANITIES IN HIGHER EDUCATION; an international journal of theory, research and practice. see *HUMANITIES: COMPREHENSIVE WORKS*

ARTS EDUCATION POLICY REVIEW. see *ART*

ASIA PACIFIC JOURNAL OF LANGUAGE IN EDUCATION. see *LINGUISTICS*

371.3 GBR ISSN 1359-866X
➤ **ASIA - PACIFIC JOURNAL OF TEACHER EDUCATION.** Text in English. 1972. 3/yr. GBP 534, USD 885, AUD 878 combined subscription to institutions print & online eds. (effective 2006). bk.rev. back issues avail.; reprint service avail. from PSC. **Document type:** *Journal, Academic/Scholarly.* **Description:** Promotes critical analysis of pedagogy across early childhood, primary, secondary and post compulsory education.
Formerly (until 1995): South Pacific Journal of Teacher Education (0311-2136)
Related titles: Online - full text ed.: ISSN 1469-2945. GBP 507, USD 841, AUD 834 to institutions (effective 2006) (from EBSCO Publishing, Gale Group, IngentaConnect, O C L C Online Computer Library Center, Inc., ProQuest Information & Learning, Swets Information Services).
Indexed: AEI, CPE, EAA, ERA, ETA, L&LBA, MEA, PsycInfo, PsycholAb, REE&TA, RHEA, SEA, SENA, SOMA, SOPODA, SPPI, SWA, TEA.
—BLDSC (1742.260941), IE, Infotrieve, ingenta. **CCC.**
Published by: (Curtin University AUS, Faculty of Education AUS), Routledge (Subsidiary of: Taylor & Francis Group), 4 Park Sq, Milton Park, Abingdon, Oxon OX14 4RN, United Kingdom. TEL 44-1235-828600, FAX 44-1235-829000, info@routledge.co.uk, http://www.tandf.co.uk/journals/titles/1359866X.asp, http://www.routledge.com. Eds. Anne McMaugh, Colin Symes, David Saltmarsh, Jennifer Sumsion. **Subscr. to:** Taylor & Francis Ltd, Journals Customer Service, Rankine Rd, Basingstoke, Hants RG24 8PR, United Kingdom. TEL 44-1256-813000, FAX 44-1256-330245. **Co-sponsor:** Australian Teacher Education Association, Inc.

➤ **ASIAN JOURNAL OF ENGLISH LANGUAGE TEACHING.** see *LINGUISTICS*

371.3 GBR ISSN 1075-2935
PE1404 CODEN: ASWRFM
➤ **ASSESSING WRITING.** Text in English. 1994. 3/yr. EUR 57 in Europe to individuals; JPY 7,600 in Japan to individuals; USD 63 elsewhere to individuals; EUR 218 in Europe to institutions; JPY 28,900 in Japan to institutions; USD 245 elsewhere to institutions (effective 2006). bk.rev. **Document type:** *Journal, Academic/Scholarly.* **Description:** Explores writing assessment issues from diverse perspectives: classrooms, research, institutional, and administrative.
Related titles: Online - full text ed.: (from EBSCO Publishing, Gale Group, IngentaConnect, ScienceDirect, Swets Information Services).
Indexed: MLA-IB, SOPODA.
—BLDSC (1746.635300), IE, ingenta. **CCC.**
Published by: Pergamon (Subsidiary of: Elsevier Science & Technology), The Boulevard, Langford Ln, East Park, Kidlington, Oxford OX5 1GB, United Kingdom. TEL 44-1865-843000, FAX 44-1865-843010, http://www.elsevier.com/locate/asw. Eds. L. Hamp-Lyons, W. Condon. **Subscr. to:** Elsevier BV, PO Box 211, Amsterdam 1000 AE, Netherlands. nlinfo-f@elsevier.nl, http://www.elsevier.nl.

371 340 USA
ASSESSMENT CENTER HANDBOOK. Text in English. 1995. irreg. USD 14.95 per issue (effective 2003). **Document type:** *Academic/Scholarly.* **Description:** Prepared for oral and written assessment center exercises. Includes scoring methodology behind exercises such as group discussion, fact-finding, career interview, reading comprehension and speech, to name a few.
Published by: Gould Publications, Inc. (Subsidiary of: LexisNexis), 1333 North US Hwy 17-92, Longwood, FL 32750-3724. TEL 407-695-9500, 800-717-7917, FAX 407-695-2906, info@gouldlaw.com, http://www.gouldlaw.com/showprod.asp?prodinfoid=5.

418 GBR
ASSESSMENT OF ACHIEVEMENT PROGRAMME ENGLISH. Text in English. 1993. a. **Document type:** *Government.*
—BLDSC (7673.381000).
Published by: (Scotland. Educational Research Unit), Scottish Office, Education and Industry Department, Scottish Office, 1-B Victoria Quay, Edinburgh, EH6 6QQ, United Kingdom. TEL 44-131-244-0154, FAX 44-131-244-5581, dissemination@scotland.gov.uk, http://www.scotland.gov.uk/. Ed. Jane Ogden-Smith. R&P Jane Ogden Smith.

371 USA
ASSOCIATION FOR SUPERVISION AND CURRICULUM DEVELOPMENT. EXECUTIVE DIRECTORS ANNUAL REPORT. Text in English. a. free. **Document type:** *Corporate.* **Description:** Reports on association news and goals for the year.
Related titles: Online - full text ed.
Published by: Association for Supervision and Curriculum Development, 1703 N Beauregard St, Alexandria, VA 22311. TEL 703-578-9600, FAX 703-575-5400, update@ascd.org, http://www.ascd.org.

371.1 IRL ISSN 0790-6560
ASTIR. Text in English. 1970. 9/yr. adv. **Document type:** *Journal, Trade.*

Published by: Association of Secondary Teachers Ireland, Winetavern St., Dublin, 8, Ireland. TEL 353-1-6040160, FAX 353-1-6719280, info@asti.ie, http://www.asti.ie. adv.: B&W page EUR 1,397, color page EUR 1,651. Circ: 17,000 (controlled).

AUDIOCASSETTE & C D FINDER. see *EDUCATION—Abstracting, Bibliographies, Statistics*

371.3 ESP ISSN 1131-995X
AULA DE INNOVACION EDUCATIVA. Text in Spanish. 1992. m. EUR 67 domestic to individuals; EUR 94.50 domestic to institutions (effective 2004). **Document type:** *Monographic series, Academic/Scholarly.* **Description:** Covers teaching in general from infant to high school.
Indexed: RILM.
—CINDOC.
Published by: Institut de Recursos i Investigacio per a la Formacio, S.L., Francesc Tarrega 32-34, Barcelona, 08027, Spain. TEL 34-93-4080464, FAX 34-93-3524337, grao-comercial@jet.es, http://www.grao.com. Ed. Cinta Vidal.

371.3 AUS ISSN 0084-6961
AUSTRALASIAN COMMERCIAL TEACHERS' ASSOCIATION. JOURNAL✶ . Text in English. 1968. a. USD 1.
Published by: Australasian Commercial Teachers' Association, 20 Napoleon St, Rosebery, NSW 2018, Australia.

371.334 AUS ISSN 1449-3098
LB1028.3 CODEN: AETEF6
➤ **AUSTRALASIAN JOURNAL OF EDUCATIONAL TECHNOLOGY.** Text in English. 1976. triennial. AUD 35 in Asia & the Pacific; AUD 45 elsewhere (effective 2005). bk.rev. back issues avail. **Document type:** *Journal, Academic/Scholarly.* **Description:** Publishes research, development and practical articles on all aspects of learning with technology.
Former titles (until 2003): Australian Journal of Educational Technology (0814-673X); (until 1985): Australian Society for Educational Technology. Yearbook (0313-4202)
Related titles: Online - full content ed.: ISSN 1449-5554. free (effective 2005).
Indexed: AEI, CPE, ERA, ETA, Inspec, TEA.
—BLDSC (1794.931000), IE, ingenta.
Published by: A S C I L I T E, c/o ascilite Secretariat, CEDIR, University of Wollongong, Wollongong, NSW 2522, Australia. TEL 61-2-42214895, FAX 61-2-42258312, ajet-editor@ascilite.org.au, info@ascilite.org.au, http://www.ascilite.org.au/ajet/ajet.html. Ed., R&P Catherine McLoughlin. Circ: 600. **Subscr. to:** c/o Dr Roger Atkinson, Unit 5, 202 Coode St., Como, WA 6152. TEL 61-8-93671133, rjatkinson@bigpond.com. **Co-publisher:** Australian Society for Educational Technology.

➤ **AUSTRALIA. BUREAU OF STATISTICS. A DIRECTORY OF EDUCATION AND TRAINING STATISTICS.** see *EDUCATION—Abstracting, Bibliographies, Statistics*

➤ **AUSTRALIA. BUREAU OF STATISTICS. ASPECTS OF LITERACY: ASSESSED SKILL LEVELS, AUSTRALIA.** see *EDUCATION—Abstracting, Bibliographies, Statistics*

➤ **AUSTRALIA. BUREAU OF STATISTICS. ASPECTS OF LITERACY: PROFILES AND PERCEPTIONS, AUSTRALIA.** see *EDUCATION—Abstracting, Bibliographies, Statistics*

➤ **AUSTRALIA. BUREAU OF STATISTICS. AUSTRALIAN STANDARD CLASSIFICATION OF EDUCATION.** see *EDUCATION—Abstracting, Bibliographies, Statistics*

➤ **AUSTRALIA. BUREAU OF STATISTICS. EDUCATION AND TRAINING INDICATORS, AUSTRALIA.** see *EDUCATION—Abstracting, Bibliographies, Statistics*

➤ **AUSTRALIA. BUREAU OF STATISTICS. INFORMATION PAPER: AUSTRALIAN STANDARD CLASSIFICATION OF EDUCATION.** see *EDUCATION—Abstracting, Bibliographies, Statistics*

➤ **AUSTRALIA. BUREAU OF STATISTICS. INFORMATION PAPER: EDUCATION AND TRAINING EXPERIENCE, AUSTRALIA, (YEAR) - CONFIDENTIALISED UNIT RECORD FILE.** see *EDUCATION—Abstracting, Bibliographies, Statistics*

➤ **AUSTRALIAN ART EDUCATION.** see *ART*

371.3 AUS ISSN 0045-0685
➤ **AUSTRALIAN MATHEMATICS TEACHER.** Text in English. 1945. 4/yr. AUD 55 domestic to non-members; AUD 70 foreign to non-members; AUD 27.50 to members (effective 2005). adv. bk.rev.; software rev.; video rev. bibl. back issues avail. **Document type:** *Journal, Academic/Scholarly.* **Description:** Serves as a medium both for the exchange of ideas and experiences in the teaching of elementary mathematics and for the instruction of teachers in the trends and developments of mathematics education at home and abroad. Aimed at teachers of mathematics in years 7-10.
Related titles: Online - full text ed.: (from EBSCO Publishing).
Indexed: AEI, CIJE, CPE, Englnd, TEA.
—BLDSC (1814.150000), Ei, IE, ingenta.
Published by: Australian Association of Mathematics Teachers Inc., GPO Box 1729, Adelaide, SA 5001, Australia. TEL 61-8-83630288, FAX 61-8-83629288, office@aamt.edu.au, http://www.aamt.edu.au/. Eds. Garry Clark, Rosemary Callingham. adv.: B&W page USD 350, color page USD 450. Circ: 3,000.

➤ **AUSTRALIAN REVIEW OF APPLIED LINGUISTICS.** see *LINGUISTICS*

371.33523 AUS ISSN 1443-1629
➤ **AUSTRALIAN SCREEN EDUCATION.** Text in English. 1994. q. AUD 66 domestic to individuals; AUD 96 foreign to individuals; AUD 88 domestic to institutions; AUD 118 foreign to institutions; AUD 55 to students and unemployed (effective 2004). adv. bk.rev.; dance rev.; film rev.; music rev.; play rev.; rec.rev.; software rev.; tel.rev.; video rev.; Website rev. 184 p./no.; back issues avail. **Document type:** *Journal, Academic/Scholarly.* **Description:** Aims to provide information and practical guidelines on how to teach media-related subjects. Includes information on new technologies and their potential applications in the classroom.
Formerly (until 1999): Metro Education (1323-3386)
Related titles: Online - full text ed.: (from bigchalk, EBSCO Publishing, Gale Group).
Indexed: FLI, WBA.
Published by: Australian Teachers of Media, PO Box 2211, St Kilda West Post Office, St Kilda, VIC 3182, Australia. TEL 61-3-95255302, FAX 61-3-95372325, tapp@netspace.net.au, http://www.metromagazine.com.au. Eds. Kate Raynor, Peter Tapp TEL 613-9525-5302. R&P, Adv. contact Peter Tapp TEL 613-9525-5302. B&W page AUD 1,000, color page AUD 1,400; 165 x 260. Circ: 15,000 (paid).

371.3 510.71 AUS ISSN 0819-4564
➤ **AUSTRALIAN SENIOR MATHEMATICS JOURNAL.** Text in English. 1987. s-a. AUD 49.50 domestic; AUD 55 foreign (effective 2002). adv. **Document type:** *Academic/Scholarly.* **Description:** Serves all persons interested in the learning and teaching of mathematics to the secondary school years 11 and 12 and to the first few years of tertiary education at university, college, and TAFE.
Related titles: Online - full text ed.: (from EBSCO Publishing).
Indexed: AEI, CIJE, MASUSE.
—BLDSC (1820.128000).
Published by: Australian Association of Mathematics Teachers Inc., GPO Box 1729, Adelaide, SA 5001, Australia. TEL 61-8-83630288, FAX 61-8-83629288, office@aamt.edu.au, http://www.aamt.edu.au/. Eds. Howard Reeves, Ken Milton. R&Ps Jenny Tayler, Judy Anderson. Circ: 15,000 (paid).

➤ **AUSTRALIAN STYLE (MACQUARIE)**; issues in Australian style and the use of English in Australia. see *LINGUISTICS*

371.12 AUS ISSN 0815-3701
AUSTRALIAN T A F E TEACHER. Text in English. 1969. q. AUD 10.
Formerly: Australian Technical Teacher (0045-0928)
Indexed: AEI, CPE, MEA.
Published by: (Technical and Further Education Teacher's Association), Percival Publishing Co. Pty. Ltd., 862-870 Elizabeth St, Waterloo Dc, NSW 2017, Australia.

AUSTRALIAN VOICE. see *MUSIC*

438 AUT
AUSTRIA (YEAR). Text in German. 1961. a. adv. **Document type:** *Academic/Scholarly.*
Formerly: Deutschkurse (0012-1398)
Published by: Oesterreichischer Austauschdienst/Austrian Exchange Service, Alserstrasse 4-1-3-8, Vienna, W 1090, Austria. TEL 43-1-4277-28180, FAX 43-1-4277-28195, info@oead.ac.at, http://www.oead.ac.at. Circ: 2,000.

AYMARA QHANTATI; cuadernillo educativo de lengua aymara. see *LINGUISTICS*

707.1 DEU ISSN 0005-2981
B D K MITTEILUNGEN. Text in German. 1964. q. adv. bibl.; illus. **Document type:** *Journal, Academic/Scholarly.*
Formerly (until 1976): Bund Deutscher Kunsterzieher. Mitteilungen (0722-530X)
Indexed: DIP, IBR, IBZ.
Published by: Bund Deutscher Kunsterzieher, Jakobistr 40, Hannover, 30163, Germany. TEL 49-511-662229, FAX 49-511-3971843, verlag@bunddeutscherkunsterzieher.de, http://www.bunddeutscherkunsterzieher.de. Ed. Ole Dunkel. Circ: 4,200.

B I N E BASIS ENERGIE. (Burger Information Neue Energietechniken) see *ENERGY*

371.3 DEU ISSN 0944-6028
B L Z. (Bremer Lehrerzeitung) Text in German. 1951. 10/yr. EUR 48 membership (effective 2005). adv. bk.rev. 28 p./no.; back issues avail. **Document type:** *Newsletter, Academic/Scholarly.*
Former titles (until 1985): B L Z - Bremer Lehrerzeitung (0948-1788); (until 1972): Bremer Lehrerzeitung (0407-114X)
Published by: G E W - Gewerkschaft Erziehung und Wissenschaft, Loeningstr 35, Bremen, 28195, Germany. TEL 49-421-337640, FAX 49-421-3376430, info@gew-hb.de, http://www.gew-hb.de/BLZ.html. R&P, Adv. contact Georg Berghorn. B&W page EUR 505; trim 184 x 262. Circ: 4,700 (controlled).

B S C S: THE NATURAL SELECTION; innovative science education. see *BIOLOGY*

375 GBR
B T A DIRECTIONS SERIES. Text in English. 1989. a. looseleaf. back issues avail. **Description:** Contains information on a variety of subjects for national curriculum sponsored by national companies.
Published by: British Trades Alphabet Publications, Abbott House, 1-2 Hanover St, London, W1R 9WB, United Kingdom. TEL 44-20-7495-7945, FAX 44-20-7495-7916. Ed. Alan Rothery. Circ: 7,500.

371.33 GBR
B T A STUDYCARDS; publication of educational projects. Text in English. 1953. a. free to U.K. junior, middle and senior schools. adv.
Formerly: British Trades Alphabet (0068-2632)
Media: Cards.
Published by: British Trades Alphabet Publications, Abbott House, 1-2 Hanover St, London, W1R 9WB, United Kingdom. TEL 44-20-7495-7945, FAX 44-20-7495-7916. Ed. Jools Viner. Circ: 5,000.

418 AUS ISSN 0005-3503
➤ **BABEL.** Text in English. 1950. 3/yr. AUD 60.50 domestic to non-members; AUD 65 foreign to non-members; AUD 66 domestic to institutions; AUD 70 foreign to institutions (effective 2004). adv. bk.rev.; software rev. bibl. cum.index. 40 p./no.; back issues avail. **Document type:** *Journal, Academic/Scholarly.* **Description:** Publishes articles and reviews on the teaching and learning of languages other than English at primary, secondary, and tertiary levels.
Related titles: Online - full text ed.: (from R M I T Publishing).
Indexed: AEI, AusPAIS, CIJE, CPE, LT&LA, MEA&I, MLA, RASB, SOPODA.
—BLDSC (1854.600000), IE, Infotrieve, ingenta.
Published by: Australian Federation of Modern Language Teachers Associations, 2 Rubida Grove, Aldgate, SA 5154, Australia. TEL 61-8-83394089, djvale@ozemail.com.au, http://www.afmlta.asn.au/. Eds. Lesley Harbon, Wendy Venning. Adv. contact David Vale. page AUD 275; 210 x 295. Circ: 2,500 (paid and controlled).

➤ **BAERENREITER STUDIENBUECHER MUSIK.** see *MUSIC*

371.33 USA ISSN 1074-4266
BALANCED READING INSTRUCTION. Text in English. 1994. s-a.
Indexed: L&LBA.
Published by: University of Central Florida, College of Education, 400 Central Florida Blvd, Orlando, FL 32816. TEL 407-823-2000, FAX 407-882-0909, http://www.edcollege.ucf.edu/.

BASE. see *ENGINEERING*

BASKETBALL CASE BOOK. see *SPORTS AND GAMES—Ball Games*

371.33 DEU ISSN 0173-8585
BAUSTEINE KINDERGARTEN. Text in German. 1980. q. looseleaf. EUR 36; EUR 12 newsstand/cover (effective 2005). back issues avail. **Document type:** *Journal, Academic/Scholarly.* **Description:** Written for educators of kindergartens and nursery schools. Provides ideas for projects and activites; learning materials for the classroom.
Published by: Bergmoser und Hoeller Verlag GmbH, Karl-Friedrich-Str 76, Aachen, 52072, Germany. TEL 49-241-93888123, FAX 49-241-93888134, kontakt@buhv.de, http://www.buhv.de. Circ: 29,000.

375 DEU ISSN 0344-9432
DIE BAYERISCHE REALSCHULE. Text in German. 1954. 9/yr. EUR 27 to non-members (effective 2004). adv. bk.rev. **Document type:** *Journal, Academic/Scholarly.*
Formerly (until 1965): Die Bayerische Mittelschule (0344-9521)
Published by: Bayerischer Realschullehrerverband e.V., Dachauerstr. 44b, Munich, 80335, Germany. TEL 49-89-553876, FAX 49-89-553819, gross@vdr.dbb.de, http://www.brlv.de/Verbandszeitschrift/Verbandszeitschrift.htm, http://www.blrv.de. Ed. Claudia Christ. adv.: B&W page EUR 550. Circ: 8,900 (controlled).

370.15 USA
BEHAVIORAL EDUCATOR. Text in English. 1980. q. USD 5 to individuals; USD 3 to students. adv. bk.rev. back issues avail.
Indexed: e-psyche.
Published by: Special Interest Group in Education, c/o Deborah A Shanley, Ed, 330 E 71st St, New York, NY 10021. TEL 212-734-8401. Circ: 110. **Subscr. to:** Theodore A. Hoch, 509 Allen Hall, West Virginia University, Box 6122, Morgantown, WV 26506-6122. **Co-sponsor:** Association for Behavior Analysis in Education.

E

▼ *new title* ➤ *refereed* ✶ *unverified* ♦ *full entry avail.*

371.3 DEU ISSN 0175-2723
BEISPIELE; in Niedersachsen Schule Machen. Text in German. 1983. q. bk.rev. back issues avail. **Document type:** *Journal, Academic/Scholarly.*
Indexed: DIP, IBZ.
—CCC.
Published by: (Niedersaechsisches Kulturministerium), Kallmeyersche Verlagsbuchhandlung GmbH, Im Brande 19, Seelze, 30926, Germany. TEL 49-511-40004175, FAX 49-511-40004176, leserservice@kallmeyer.de, http://www.kallmeyer.de. Circ: 17,000.

BEITRAEGE PAEDAGOGISCHER ARBEIT. see *PHILOSOPHY*

BEITRAEGE ZUR FREMDSPRACHENVERMITTLUNG. see *LINGUISTICS*

371.33 CHE ISSN 0259-353X
➤ **BEITRAEGE ZUR LEHRERBILDUNG**; Zeitschrift zu Theorie und Praxis der Grundausbildung Fort- und Weiterbildung von Lehrerinnen und Lehrern. Text in German. 1982. 3/yr. CHF 60 to individuals; CHF 70 to institutions; CHF 20 per issue (effective 2002). **Document type:** *Journal, Academic/Scholarly.*
Indexed: DIP, IBR, IBZ.
Published by: Schweizerischen Gesellschaft fuer Lehrerinnen- und Lehrerbildung, Postfach, Grosshoechstetten, Switzerland. TEL 41-31-7114344, http://www.bzl-online.ch.

371.3 GBR
BENCHMARK INFORMATION FOR KEY STAGE. Text in English.
—BLDSC (1891.229550).
Published by: Welsh Office Education Department, School Performance Division 3, Cathays Park, Cardiff, CF1 2NQ, United Kingdom. TEL 44-1222-826010, FAX 44-1222-826016.

371.3 USA ISSN 1061-1495
BETTER TEACHING; tips and techniques to improve student learning. Text in English. 1987. s-m. (Sep.-June). USD 98 to individuals (effective 2003). bk.rev. charts; illus. back issues avail. **Document type:** *Newsletter.* **Description:** Offers practical ideas to help teachers improve student learning.
Published by: Teacher Institute, PO Box 397, Fairfax, VA 22039-0397. TEL 703-503-5413, 800-333-0776, FAX 703-323-9173, custsvc@teacher-institute.com, http://www.teacher-institute.com/products/bt/btmain.shtml. Ed., Pub. John H Wherry.

BIBLE DISCOVERERS. TEACHER. see *RELIGIONS AND THEOLOGY—Protestant*

371.3 USA ISSN 1521-7809
BIG 6 NEWSLETTER; teaching technology and information skills. Text in English. 1997. bi-m. USD 39 domestic; USD 55 in Canada; USD 70 elsewhere; USD 7 newsstand/cover. **Document type:** *Newsletter, Trade.* **Description:** Presents vision, strategies and tools for teaching essential skills for the information age. Promotes a 6-stage process for using information.
Published by: Linworth Publishing, Inc., 480 E Wilson Bridge Rd, Ste L, Worthington, OH 43085. TEL 614-436-7107, FAX 614-436-9490, newslin@aol.com, linworth@linworthpublishing.com, http://www.linworth.com. Eds. Bob Berkowitz, Mike Eisenberg. Pub. Marlene Woo Lun.

371.3 DEU ISSN 0944-2979
BILDUNGSARBEIT IN DER ZWEITSPRACHE DEUTSCH. Text in German. 1984. 3/yr. **Document type:** *Academic/Scholarly.*
Formerly (until 1992): Bildungsarbeit mit Auslaendischen Jugendlichen (0179-2598)
Indexed: L&LBA, SOPODA.
Published by: Schneider Verlag Hohengehren GmbH, Wilhelmstr 13, Baltmannsweiler, 73666, Germany. FAX 49-7153-48761, schneider-verlag-hohengehren@t-online.de.

371.3 DEU ISSN 0945-5469
BILDUNGSPRAXIS. Text in German. q. EUR 24; EUR 6.80 newsstand/cover (effective 2004). adv. **Document type:** *Magazine, Trade.*
Published by: Verlag Dr. Ing. Paul Christiani GmbH & Co. KG, Hermann-Hesse-Weg 2, Konstanz, 78464, Germany. TEL 49-7531-580126, FAX 49-7531-580185, info@bildungspraxis.de, info@christiani.de, http://www.bildungspraxis.de, http://www.christiani.de. Ed. Bernd Janowski. adv.: B&W page EUR 2,250, color page EUR 3,150; trim 180 x 265. Circ: 10,000 (paid and controlled).

BIOLOGIA W SZKOLE. see *BIOLOGY*

BIOLOHIYA I KHIMIYA V SHKOLI. see *BIOLOGY*

BIOSCENE; journal of college biology teaching. see *BIOLOGY*

BIT'ON LEMORIM LE'ARAVIT. see *LINGUISTICS*

371.3 CHE
BLAETTER - REVUE - RIVISTA. Text in German. 10/yr. CHF 70; CHF 90 foreign (effective 1999). **Document type:** *Trade.*
Formerly: Schweizerischer Verband fuer Beruflichen Unterricht. Blaetter (0378-7664)
—CCC.
Published by: (Schweizerischer Verband fuer Beruflichen Unterricht), Sauerlaender AG, Laurenzenvorstadt 89, Aarau, 5001, Switzerland. FAX 41-62-8245780. Ed. Willy Nabholz. adv.: B&W page CHF 1,610; trim 264 x 185. Circ: 2,900.

THE BLIND TEACHER. see *HANDICAPPED—Visually Impaired*

BLUEGRASS MUSIC NEWS. see *MUSIC*

BOOK MARK; children's literature in review with related activities for preschoolers through young adults. see *CHILDREN AND YOUTH—About*

613.7 BRA
BRAZIL. MINISTERIO DE EDUCACAO. DEPARTAMENTO DE EDUCACAO FISICA E DESPORTOS. CADERNO CULTURAL. Text in Portuguese. q. BRL 56, USD 48. illus.; charts; bibl. **Document type:** *Government.*
Published by: Ministerio da Educacao, Departamento de Educacao Fisica e Desportos, Brasilia, DF, Brazil.

428 CAN
BRITISH COLUMBIA TEACHERS OF ENGLISH LANGUAGE ARTS. UPDATE. Text in English. 1960. 3/yr. CND 53.50 includes one issue of Student Writing Journal (effective 2005). **Document type:** *Journal, Academic/Scholarly.*
Incorporates (1960-1994): British Columbia English Teachers' Association. Journal (1183-5478); Which was formerly (until 1990): B C E T A Journal (0834-0781); (until 1986): Sandbox (0834-079X); (until 1985): British Columbia English Teachers' Association. Journal (0316-0173); (until 1972): British Columbia English Teacher (0045-2955); Former titles (until 1994): British Columbia English Teachers' Association. Update (0315-2189); (until 1972): British Columbia English Teachers' Association. Newsletter (0315-2170); (until 1971): Satelines (0315-2162)
Indexed: CEI.
—CCC.
Published by: British Columbia Teachers of English Language Arts (Subsidiary of: British Columbia Teachers' Federation), c/o Dave Ellison, W.L. Seaton Secondary School, 2701 41st Ave, Vernon, BC V1T 6X3, Canada. TEL 250-542-3361, FAX 250-542-6076, dellison@sd22.bc.ca, http://www.bctf.ca/BCTELA/update/index.html, http://www.bctf.ca/bctela.

371.3 GBR ISSN 0007-1013
CODEN: BJETDK
➤ **BRITISH JOURNAL OF EDUCATIONAL TECHNOLOGY.** Text in English. 1970. bi-m. GBP 80, EUR 120 combined subscription in Europe to individuals print & online eds.; USD 168 combined subscription in the Americas to individuals & Caribbean, print & online eds.; GBP 100 combined subscription elsewhere to individuals print & online eds.; GBP 420 combined subscription in Europe to institutions print & online eds.; USD 829 combined subscription in the Americas to institutions & Caribbean, print & online eds.; GBP 494 combined subscription elsewhere to institutions print & online eds. (effective 2006). adv. bk.rev. illus. Index. back issues avail.; reprint service avail. from PQC,PSC. **Document type:** *Journal, Academic/Scholarly.* **Description:** Provides with coverage of developments in educational technology word-wide.
Formerly: Journal of Eductional Technology (0022-0698)
Related titles: Microform ed.: (from PQC); Online - full text ed.: ISSN 1467-8535. GBP 399 in Europe to institutions; USD 786 in the Americas to institutions & Caribbean; GBP 468 elsewhere to institutions (effective 2006) (from Blackwell Synergy, EBSCO Publishing, Gale Group, H.W. Wilson, IngentaConnect, O C L C Online Computer Library Center, Inc., Swets Information Services).
Indexed: ABIn, ASCA, BrEdI, CIJE, CPE, CompLI, CurCont, EAA, ERA, ETA, EduInd, EngInd, ErgAb, HECAB, IBR, IBZ, Inspec, L&LBA, MEA, PCI, PsycInfo, PsycholAb, RASB, RHEA, SEA, SENA, SOMA, SOPODA, SSCI, TEA.
—BLDSC (2307.750000), AskIEEE, Ei, IDS, IE, Infotrieve, ingenta. **CCC.**
Published by: (British Educational Communications and Technology Agency), Blackwell Publishing Ltd., 9600 Garsington Rd, Oxford, OX4 2ZG, United Kingdom. TEL 44-1865-776868, FAX 44-1865-714591, customerservices@oxon.blackwellpublishing.com, http://www.blackwellpublishing.com/journals/BJET. Ed. Nick Rushby. Circ: 1,200.

613.7 GBR
➤ **BRITISH JOURNAL OF PHYSICAL EDUCATION. RESEARCH SUPPLEMENT.** Text in English. q. membership. **Document type:** *Academic/Scholarly.* **Description:** Publishes original research on all aspects of physical and health education, outdoor activities, and sports and dance.
Published by: Physical Education Association of the United Kingdom, Ling House, Building 25, London Rd, Reading, Berks RG1 5AQ, United Kingdom. TEL 44-1189-316240, FAX 44-1189-316242, enquiries@pea.uk.com, http://www.pea.uk.com. Ed. Neil Armstrong.

613.7 GBR ISSN 1472-4375
CODEN: BJPEBS
THE BRITISH JOURNAL OF TEACHING PHYSICAL EDUCATION. Text in English. q. membership. adv. bk.rev. bibl.; charts; illus. **Document type:** *Academic/Scholarly.* **Description:** Includes research articles; lists of resources; announcements of conferences and seminars pertaining to all aspects of physical and health education; outdoor activities, sports, and dance in the U.K.
Former titles (until 1999): British Journal of Physical Education (0954-6693); (until 1983): Action (0144-3569); (until 1980): British Journal of Physical Education (0007-120X); Which incorporates: Outdoors (0306-5723); Research in Physical Education; Physical Education; Which was formed by the 1970 merger of: Research in Physical Education; Physical Education Association of Great Britain and Northern Ireland. Leaflet
Related titles: Supplement(s): British Journal of Physical Education. Research Supplement.
Indexed: AMED, BiolAb, BrEdI, CIJE, CPE, ERA, ETA, MEA, PEI, RASB, RHEA, RRTA, SEA, SENA, SOMA, SportS, TEA, WAE&RSA.
—BLDSC (2325.600000), IE, ingenta. **CCC.**
Published by: Physical Education Association of the United Kingdom, Ling House, Building 25, London Rd, Reading, Berks RG1 5AQ, United Kingdom. TEL 44-1189-316240, FAX 44-1189-316242, enquiries@pea.uk.com, http://www.pea.uk.com. Ed. Liz Taplin. R&P John Matthews. Circ: 6,000.

BULLA GYMNASIA VIRTUALIS. see *COMPUTERS—Computer Assisted Instruction*

613.7 GBR ISSN 0007-5043
BULLETIN OF PHYSICAL EDUCATION. Text in English. 1946. 3/yr. GBP 20; GBP 22 foreign (effective 2000). adv. bk.rev. charts; illus.; stat. **Document type:** *Bulletin.*
Related titles: Microform ed.
Indexed: BrEdI, CPE, ERA, SOMA, SportS.
—BLDSC (2882.840000), IE, Infotrieve, ingenta.
Published by: (British Association of Advisers and Lecturers in Physical Education), Studies in Education, Driffield Rd, Nafferton, Driffield, E Yorks YO25 4JJ, United Kingdom. TEL 44-1377-254231, FAX 44-1377-256861. Ed. B Chappell. Circ: 1,500.

BUROS - NEBRASKA SERIES ON MEASUREMENT AND TESTING. see *PSYCHOLOGY*

371.33523 USA
BUSINESS EDUCATION FILMS CATALOG. Text in English. 1950. biennial. free. **Description:** Catalog of business education films available.
Published by: Business Education Films, c/o Paul Weinberg, Ed., Box 449, Clarksville, NJ 08510. TEL 201-462-3522, FAX 908-294-0330. Circ: 20,000.

BUSINESS - EDUCATION INSIDER; how business can reform education. see *BUSINESS AND ECONOMICS—Economic Situation And Conditions*

BUSINESSDATE. see *BUSINESS AND ECONOMICS—Management*

371.0712 USA
C A V E NEWSLETTER. Text in English. 1974. q. looseleaf. free. adv. bk.rev.; film rev. **Document type:** *Newsletter.*
Published by: Catholic Audio-Visual Educators, PO Box 9257, Pittsburgh, PA 15224. TEL 412-683-9996. Ed. John Manear. Circ: 1,000.

C E A CHAP BOOK. (College English Association) see *LITERATURE*

C I I L ADULT LITERACY SERIES. see *EDUCATION—Adult Education*

C I I L - APNI BOLI SERIES. see *LINGUISTICS*

C I I L BILINGUAL EDUCATION SERIES. see *LINGUISTICS*

C I I L BILINGUAL HINDI SERIES. see *LINGUISTICS*

C I I L COMMON VOCABULARY SERIES. see *LINGUISTICS*

C I I L DOCUMENTATION SERIES. see *LINGUISTICS*

C I I L GRAMMAR SERIES. see *LINGUISTICS*

C I I L INTENSIVE COURSE SERIES. see *LINGUISTICS*

C I I L OCCASIONAL BULLETIN SERIES. see *LINGUISTICS*

C I I L OCCASIONAL MONOGRAPH SERIES. see *LINGUISTICS*

C I I L PHONETIC READER SERIES. see *LINGUISTICS*

C I I L PICTORIAL GLOSSARY SERIES. see *LINGUISTICS*

C I I L READING SERIES. see *LINGUISTICS*

E

C I L SECOND LANGUAGE TEXTBOOK SERIES. see *LINGUISTICS*

C I L SOCIOLINGUISTICS SERIES. see *LINGUISTICS*

371.3 USA
C S E MONOGRAPH SERIES IN EVALUATION. (Center for the Study of Evaluation) Text in English. 1973. a. **Document type:** *Monographic series.*
Indexed: CIJE.
Published by: (Graduate School of Education), University of California at Los Angeles, Center for the Study of Evaluation, 300 Charles E. Young Drive North, 301 GSE & IS Bldg, Box 951522, Los Angeles, CA 90095. TEL 310-206-1532. Ed., R&P Ron Dietel TEL 310-794-9168.

C S S JOURNAL. (Computers in the Social Studies) see *EDUCATION—Computer Applications*

371.335 USA ISSN 1054-5409
LB1044.7
CABLE IN THE CLASSROOM; teaching with television. Text in English. 1989. m. USD 18. **Document type:** *Consumer.* **Description:** Directed to teachers interested in bringing television into the classroom as an educational medium.
Formerly (until 1991): Connect (Boston) (1047-7268)
Related titles: Online - full text ed.
Indexed: CPerI.
Published by: Connell Communications, Inc. (Subsidiary of: International Data Group), 86 Elm St, Peterborough, NH 03458-1009. TEL 800-216-2225, FAX 603-924-6838. Ed. Al Race. Circ: 90,000.

CADENZA. see *MUSIC*

371.3 FRA ISSN 1243-6852
LES CAHIERS DE L'ANIMATION, VACANCES, LOISIRS; une publication des C E M E A. Text in French. 1993. q.
Published by: Centre d'Entrainement aux Methodes d'Education Active, c/o Pascale Chesnay, 76 bd. de la Villette, Paris, Cedex 19 75940, France. TEL 33-1-40404341. Ed. Bertrand Chavaroche. Pub. Christian Gautellier.

CAHIERS DE LINGUISTIQUE FRANCAISE. see *LINGUISTICS*

371.3 BEL ISSN 1375-9310
LES CAHIERS DU SERVICE DE PEDAGOGIE EXPERIMENTALE. Text in French. 2000. 4/yr. EUR 25 (effective 2004).
Published by: Universite de Liege, Service de Pedagogie Theorique et Experimentale, Boulevard du Rectorat 5, B32, Liege, 4000, Belgium. TEL 32-4-3662075, FAX 32-4-3662855, pedaexpe@ulg.ac.be, http://www.ulg.ac.be/pedaexpe/cahiers.html.

418 USA ISSN 0279-1161
PE65
CALIFORNIA ENGLISH. Text in English. 1960. q. USD 35. adv. bk.rev. charts. **Document type:** *Academic/Scholarly.* **Description:** Covers topical articles on major issues surrounding the teaching of English in schools and universities.
Indexed: AES.
Published by: California Association of Teachers of English, 15332 Antioch St, Ste 539, Pacific Palisades, CA 90272. TEL 310-459-8435, FAX 310-459-9875, jago@gseis.ucla.edu, http://www.cateweb.org/. Ed., R&P Carol Jago. Adv. contact Don Harrison. Circ: 5,500.

372.4 USA ISSN 0892-6964
➤ **CALIFORNIA READER.** Text in English. 196?. q. USD 30 membership (effective 2005). adv. bk.rev. **Document type:** *Academic/Scholarly.* **Description:** Serves as the voice of literacy educators for students in pre-school through adulthood.
Published by: California Reading Association, 3186 Airway Ave, Ste D, Costa Mesa, CA 92626-4650. TEL 714-435-1983, FAX 714-435-0269, http://www.californiareads.org/. Ed. Janet Towell. R&P, Adv. contact Marilyn Holland TEL 209-667-3292. Circ: 18,000.

371.3 USA ISSN 1082-4448
CALIFORNIA SPECIAL EDUCATION ALERT. Text in English. 1994. 2 base vols. plus updates 22/yr. USD 240 (effective 2006).
Related titles: Online - full text ed.
—CCC.
Published by: L R P Publications, 747 Dresher Rd, PO Box 980, Horsham, PA 19044. TEL 215-784-0910, 800-341-7874, FAX 215-784-9014, custserve@lrp.com, http://www.shoplrp.com/product/p-300033.html, http://www.lrp.com.

418 AUS ISSN 1442-438X
➤ **CALL-EJ ONLINE.** Text in English. 1996. 3/yr. free. bk.rev. **Document type:** *Academic/Scholarly.*
Formerly (until 1999): On-Call Journal (1034-571X)
Media: Online - full text.
Indexed: CIJE, MLA-IB.
Published by: University of Queensland, Centre for Language Teaching and Research, Brisbane, QLD 4072, Australia. TEL 61-7-3656897, FAX 61-7-3657077, on-call@cltr.uq.oz.au, http://www.clec.ritsumei.ac.jp/english/callejonline/. Ed. Michael J Levy. Circ: 250 (controlled).

371.3 ESP ISSN 0213-9529
➤ **CAMPO ABIERTO**; revista de educacion. Text in Spanish. 1982. s-a. adv. bk.rev. **Document type:** *Academic/Scholarly.*
—CINDOC.
Published by: Universidad de Extremadura, Facultad de Educacion, Av. de Elvas s-n, Badajoz, 06071, Spain. TEL 34-924-289501, FAX 34-924-270214, cabierto@unex.es, http://www.unex.es/educacion. Ed. Jose Maria de Peralta y Sosa. Circ: 1,000.

423 CAN ISSN 1707-3960
CANADIAN COUNCIL OF TEACHERS OF ENGLISH LANGUAGE ARTS. NEWS UPDATE. Abbreviated title: C C T E L A News Update. Text in English. 1978. s-a. CND 50 domestic membership to individuals; CND 60 foreign membership to individuals; CND 80 domestic membership to institutions; CND 90 foreign membership to institutions (effective 2003); Membership inclds subscr. to English Quarterly & CCTELA News Update. **Document type:** *Newsletter, Academic/Scholarly.* **Description:** Covers the current issues in education and the activities of the Board of Directors and Executives.
Former titles (until 1999): Canadian Council of Teachers of English Language Arts (1193-9966); (until 1992): Canadian Journal of English Language Arts (0836-5865); (until 1986): Highway One (0045-4613)
Related titles: Online - full text ed.: (from Micromedia ProQuest).
Indexed: CEI.
—CCC.
Published by: Canadian Council of Teachers of English and Language Arts, #10-730 River Rd, University of Manitoba, Winnipeg, MB R2M 5A4, Canada. http://www.cctela.ca.

418 CAN ISSN 0705-386X
CANADIAN COUNCIL OF TEACHERS OF ENGLISH. NEWSLETTER. Text in English. 1968. 3/yr. CND 25 (effective 1999). adv. bk.rev. **Document type:** *Newsletter.* **Description:** Presents a forum for opinions and concerns of membership, practical teaching ideas, and recent research reports.
—CCC.
Published by: Canadian Council of Teachers of English and Language Arts, #10-730 River Rd, University of Manitoba, Winnipeg, MB R2M 5A4, Canada. TEL 204-474-8564, FAX 204-474-7551, watsonm@ms.umanitoba.ca. Ed. Lars Thompson. R&P, Adv. contact Stephanie Purvis. Circ: 500.

CANADIAN JOURNAL OF ENVIRONMENTAL EDUCATION. see *ENVIRONMENTAL STUDIES*

371.3 CAN
LB1028.3
➤ **CANADIAN JOURNAL OF LEARNING AND TECHNOLOGY/REVUE CANADIENNE DE L'APPRENTISSAGE ET DE LA TECHNOLOGIE.** Text in English, French. 1972. 3/yr. CND 80.25 domestic to non-members; CND 101.64 foreign to non-members (effective 1999). adv. bk.rev.; software rev. illus.; charts; bibl. index. **Document type:** *Journal, Academic/Scholarly.* **Description:** Provides Canadian and international focus on educational communication through the application of media and technology.
Former titles (until 2002): Canadian Journal of Educational Communication (0710-4340); (until 1981): Media Message (0380-0199)
Related titles: Microform ed.: (from MML); Online - full text ed.: 2002. free (effective 2005).
Indexed: CEI, CIJE, CPE, ERA, ETA, MEA, RHEA, SEA, SENA, SOMA, TEA.
—BLDSC (3031.275000). **CCC.**
Published by: Association for Media and Technology in Education in Canada (AMTEC), 3 1750 The Queensway, Ste 1318, Etobicoke, ON M9C 5H5, Canada. rlewis@uwindsor.ca, http://www.cjlt.ca/index.html, http://www.amtec.ca. Ed. Richard Lewsi. Circ: 500.

300.71 CAN ISSN 1191-162X
➤ **CANADIAN SOCIAL STUDIES**; the history and social science teacher. Text in English. 1965-1990 (vol.25, no.4); resumed 1991-199?; resumed 1998. q. free (effective 2005). adv. bk.rev.; software rev. illus. back issues avail.; reprint service avail. from PQC. **Document type:** *Journal, Academic/Scholarly.* **Description:** Contains comment and criticism on social education and publishes articles on curricular issues relating to history, geography, social sciences, and social studies.
Former titles (until 1991): History and Social Science Teacher (0316-4969); (until 1974): Canadian Journal of History and Social Science (0316-4977); (until 1969): Canadian Journal of History (Toronto) (0576-5560); (until 1965): History Newsletter
Media: Online - full content. **Related titles:** Microfiche ed.: (from MML); Microfilm ed.: (from MML); Microform ed.: (from MML, PQC); Online - full text ed.: (from H.W. Wilson, Micromedia ProQuest, O C L C Online Computer Library Center, Inc., ProQuest Information & Learning).
Indexed: ABIn, AmH&L, CEI, CIJE, CPE, ERA, EduInd, MEA, SRRA.
—CCC.
Published by: University of Alberta, Faculty of Education, 845 Education South, Edmonton, AB T6G 2G5, Canada. TEL 780-492-3751, FAX 780-492-0236, http://www.quasar.ualberta.ca/css, http://www.education.ualberta.ca/. Ed. George Richardson. Circ: 700.

➤ **CANADIAN UNIVERSITY MUSIC REVIEW/REVUE DE MUSIQUE DES UNIVERSITES CANADIENNES.** see *MUSIC*

➤ **CARLETON PAPERS IN APPLIED LANGUAGE STUDIES.** see *LINGUISTICS*

➤ **CAROLINA TIPS.** see *BIOLOGY*

371.3 URY
CATALOGO DE PUBLICACIONES DIDACTICAS LATINOAMERICANAS DE FORMACION PROFESIONAL. Text in Spanish. 1976. irreg. price varies.
Supersedes (1969-1976): Catalogo de Manuales Latinoamericanos
Published by: Centro Interamericano de Investigacion y Documentacion Sobre Formacion Profesional, Av. Uruguay, 1238, Casilla de Correos 1761, Montevideo, 11106, Uruguay. FAX 921305, dirmvd@cinterfor.org.uy.

CATALYST FOR CHANGE. see *EDUCATION—School Organization And Administration*

CAUCE; revista de filologia y su didactica. see *LINGUISTICS*

CENTRAL STATES CONFERENCE ON THE TEACHING OF FOREIGN LANGUAGES. EDUCATION SERIES. see *LINGUISTICS*

CENTRE FOR SPORTS SCIENCE AND HISTORY. SERIAL HOLDINGS. see *EDUCATION—Abstracting, Bibliographies, Statistics*

371.3 URY
CENTRO INTERAMERICANO DE INVESTIGACION Y DOCUMENTACION SOBRE FORMACION PROFESIONAL. INFORMES. Text in Spanish. 1964. irreg. price varies.
Published by: Centro Interamericano de Investigacion y Documentacion Sobre Formacion Profesional, Av. Uruguay, 1238, Casilla de Correos 1761, Montevideo, 11106, Uruguay. FAX 921305, dirmvd@cinterfor.org.uy.

CENTRO INTERAMERICANO DE INVESTIGACION Y DOCUMENTACION SOBRE FORMACION PROFESIONAL. SERIE BIBLIOGRAFICA. see *EDUCATION—Abstracting, Bibliographies, Statistics*

CHAIN REACTION; stories of science and learning from Arizona state university. see *SCIENCES: COMPREHENSIVE WORKS*

CHALLENGES IN LANGUAGE AND LITERACY. see *LINGUISTICS*

510.71 FRA ISSN 0395-7837
CHANTIERS DE PEDAGOGIE MATHEMATIQUE. Text in French. 1970. 5/yr. EUR 5 (effective 2002). adv. bk.rev. **Document type:** *Bulletin.* **Description:** Covers meetings, appointments, opinions and experiences of the members of the association.
Published by: Association des Professeurs de Mathematiques de l'Enseignement Public, Regionale Ile de France, 26 rue Dumeril, Paris, 75013, France. TEL 33-1-43313405, FAX 33-1-42170877. Adv. contact Valerie Larose. Circ: 1,600.

CHEMIA W SZKOLE. see *CHEMISTRY*

CHILD CARE BRIDGES. see *CHILDREN AND YOUTH—About*

CHILD LANGUAGE TEACHING AND THERAPY. see *EDUCATION—Special Education And Rehabilitation*

372.072 USA ISSN 0009-4056
➤ **CHILDHOOD EDUCATION.** Text in English. 1924. bi-m. USD 65 to institutions non-members (effective 2005). adv. bk.rev.; software rev.; video rev. abstr.; bibl.; charts; illus.; tr.lit. index. 80 p./no.; back issues avail.; reprint service avail. from PQC. **Document type:** *Journal, Trade.* **Description:** Articles cover current research in education from infants to early adolescence.
Incorporates (1981-1991): A C E I Exchange (0732-5371)
Related titles: Microfilm ed.: (from PMC, PQC); Online - full text ed.: (from bigchalk, Florida Center for Library Automation, Gale Group, H.W. Wilson, O C L C Online Computer Library Center, Inc., ProQuest Information & Learning).
Indexed: ABIn, AMHA, AcaI, BRI, CBRI, CDA, CIJE, CPE, ChLitAb, ECER, EduInd, FamI, IMFL, MagInd, NutrAb, PCI, PsycholAb, RASB, RehabLit.
—BLDSC (3172.955000), IE, Infotrieve, ingenta. **CCC.**
Published by: Association for Childhood Education International, 17904 Georgia Ave, Ste 215, Olney, MD 20832-2277. TEL 301-570-2111, 800-423-3563, FAX 301-570-2212, aceimemb@aol.com, aceihq@aol.com, http://www.acei.org. Ed. Anne Watson Bauer. Adv. contact Bruce Herzig. Circ: 11,500 (paid).

E

➤ **CHILDREN'S TECHNOLOGY REVIEW.** see *COMPUTERS—Software*

➤ **CHIMICA NELLA SCUOLA.** see *CHEMISTRY*

➤ **CHRISTIAN EDUCATORS JOURNAL.** see *RELIGIONS AND THEOLOGY*

371.3 USA
➤ **THE CHRISTIAN SCHOOL BUILDER.** Text in English. 1969. m. USD 9.85. back issues avail. **Document type:** *Journal, Academic/Scholarly.* **Description:** Features helps for school boards, teachers and parents to operate a Christian school. Discusses classroom techniques and management.
Published by: Rod and Staff Publishers, Inc., PO Box 3, Crockett, KY 41413-0003. TEL 606-522-4348, FAX 800-643-1244. Ed. J Scott Martin. R&P James L Boll. Circ: 4,000 (paid).

➤ **CHRISTIAN SCHOOL EDUCATION**; enabling christian educators and schools worldwide. see *EDUCATION—School Organization And Administration*

➤ **CHURCH MEDIA LIBRARY MAGAZINE.** see *LIBRARY AND INFORMATION SCIENCES*

372.4 USA ISSN 0886-6880
LB1049.95
CLAREMONT READING CONFERENCE. YEARBOOK. Text in English. 1932. a., latest vol.60, 1996. USD 20 (effective 1997). reprint service avail. from PQC.
Related titles: Microfilm ed.: (from PQC); Online - full text ed.: (from H.W. Wilson, O C L C Online Computer Library Center, Inc.).
Indexed: ABIn, CIJE, EduInd.
—BLDSC (9411.619000).
Published by: (Claremont Reading Conference), Claremont Graduate School, Institute for Development Studies, Harper 200, CGS, 150 E 10th St, Claremont, CA 91711-6160. TEL 909-607-1667, FAX 909-621-8734, readconf@cgu.edu. Ed. Philip H Dreyerass. Circ: 1,200.

CLARITAS. see *LINGUISTICS*

371.33 USA
CLASS ACT. Text in English. 1987. m. (Sep.-May). USD 25 (effective 2003). adv. bk.rev. back issues avail. **Document type:** *Newsletter.* **Description:** Includes practical ideas, activities, lessons, games and assignments for language arts teachers, grades 6-12.
Formerly (until May, 1993): Cottonwood Monthly
Published by: Class Act, Inc., PO Box 802, Henderson, KY 42419. TEL 270-826-1085, classact@lightpower.net, classact@henderson.net, http://www.classactpress.com/, http://www.henderson.net/~classact. Ed., Pub., Adv. contact Susan Thurman. Circ: 300.

371.3 CAN ISSN 0315-906X
CLASSMATE. Text in English. 3/yr. CND 20. bk.rev. **Document type:** *Academic/Scholarly.* **Description:** Presents study and teaching techniques by teachers to teachers.
Indexed: CEI.
Published by: Manitoba Association of Teachers of English, 128 Birchdale Ave, Winnipeg, MB R2H 1S4, Canada. TEL 204-237-9598, FAX 204-231-2040. Eds. Janie McTavish, Stephen Britton. Circ: 600.

371.3 AUS ISSN 0727-1255
CLASSROOM; the magazine for teachers. Text in English. 1981. 7/yr. AUD 45 domestic; AUD 60 foreign (effective 2000). adv. bk.rev. back issues avail. **Document type:** *Trade.*
Incorporates: Classroom Computing
Indexed: AEI, RASB.
—CCC.
Published by: Scholastic Pty. Ltd., Railway Crescent, Lisarow, NSW 2250, Australia. TEL 61-2-4328-3555, FAX 043-23-3827, http://www.scholastic.com.au. Ed. Wendy Rapee. Adv. contact Ken McLachlan. Circ: 6,000. **Subscr. to:** PO Box 579, Gosford, NSW 2250, Australia.

371.33 AUS ISSN 1039-4982
THE CLASSROOM CONNECTION; practical activities for the primary classroom. Text in English. q. AUD 40 domestic; AUD 55 foreign (effective 2003). bk.rev. illus. **Document type:** *Trade.* **Description:** Offers teachers in K-6 classrooms practical ideas and activities for teaching mathematics, language arts, social studies, science, and computers. Contains material that can be photocopied for classroom distribution.
Published by: Research Publications Pty., 27 A Boronia Rd, Vermont, VIC 3133, Australia. TEL 61-3-98748982, FAX 61-3-98730100. Ed. Ted Colville. Circ: 2,000 (paid).

371.3 USA
CLASSROOM LEADERSHIP; the companion newsletter to ASCD's Educational Leadership magazine. Text in English. 1997. 9/yr. USD 23 to non-members (effective 2003). illus. **Document type:** *Newsletter.* **Description:** Reports on trends affecting teachers and school administrators. Offers both groups of professionals practical tips, with the aim of improving education.
Related titles: ♦ Supplement to: Educational Leadership. ISSN 0013-1784.
Published by: Association for Supervision and Curriculum Development, 1703 N Beauregard St, Alexandria, VA 22311. TEL 703-578-9600, FAX 703-575-5400, update@ascd.org, http://www.ascd.org. Eds. Karen Rasmussen, Kathy Checkley. Pub. Nancy Modrak. R&P Chris Richards.

371.3 USA ISSN 1526-5641
LB1576
CLASSROOM NOTES PLUS; a quarterly of practical teaching ideas. Text in English. 1983. q. USD 60 to individuals includes $40 membership fee; USD 60 to institutions (effective 2005). adv. **Document type:** *Newsletter, Trade.* **Description:** Contains teachers' ideas for teaching English at junior high and high school levels.
Formerly (until 1999): Notes Plus (0738-8624)
Related titles: Online - full text ed.: (from EBSCO Publishing).
—CCC.
Published by: National Council of Teachers of English, 1111 W Kenyon Rd, Urbana, IL 61801-1096. TEL 217-328-3870, 800-369-6283, FAX 217-328—9645, cschanche@ncte.org, http://www.ncte.org/pubs/journals/cnp, http://www.ncte.org/notesplus. Ed. Felice A Kaufmann. R&P Felice Kaufmann. Adv. contact Carrie Stewart. Circ: 25,000.

▼ **THE CLINICAL TEACHER.** see *MEDICAL SCIENCES*

COE-MMUNETY. see *EDUCATION—Higher Education*

371.3 URY
COLECCIONES BASICAS C I N T E R F O R. Text in Portuguese, Spanish. 1970. irreg. price varies.
Indexed: CIRFAb.
Published by: Centro Interamericano de Investigacion y Documentacion Sobre Formacion Profesional, Av. Uruguay, 1238, Casilla de Correos 1761, Montevideo, 11106, Uruguay. FAX 921305, dirmvd@cinterfor.org.uy.

COLLECTION C R E S A S. (Centre de Recherche de l'Education Specialisee et de l'Adaptation Scolaire) see *EDUCATION—Special Education And Rehabilitation*

COLLEGE & UNIVERSITY MEDIA REVIEW; a look at practices, trends & research. see *EDUCATION—Higher Education*

808 USA ISSN 0010-096X
PE1001
➤ **COLLEGE COMPOSITION AND COMMUNICATION.** Text in English. 1950. q. USD 25 membership; USD 75 to institutions (effective 2005). adv. bk.rev. illus. index. reprints avail. **Document type:** *Journal, Academic/Scholarly.* **Description:** Contains articles dealing with the theory, practice, research of composition, and the preparation of writing teachers.
Related titles: Microform ed.: (from PQC); Online - full text ed.: (from EBSCO Publishing, JSTOR (Web-based Journal Archive), ProQuest Information & Learning).
Indexed: ABIn, ASCA, AbAn, ArtHuCI, BRI, CBRI, CIJE, CPE, CurCont, DIP, ERA, ETA, EduInd, IBR, IBRH, IBZ, L&LBA, MEA, MLA, MLA-IB, PCI, RASB, RHEA, SEA, SENA, SOMA, SOPODA, SSCI, SWA, TEA.
—BLDSC (3095.847270), IE, Infotrieve, ingenta. **CCC.**
Published by: (Conference on College Composition and Communication), National Council of Teachers of English, 1111 W Kenyon Rd, Urbana, IL 61801-1096. TEL 217-328-3870, FAX 217-328-9645, ccc@niu.edu, membership@ncte.org, http://www.ncte.org/pubs/journals/ccc. Ed. Deborah Holdstein. Circ: 10,000.

➤ **COLLEGE E S L.** (English as a Second Language) see *LINGUISTICS*

810 USA ISSN 0010-0994
PE1
COLLEGE ENGLISH. Text in English. 1939. bi-m. USD 65 membership; USD 75 to institutions (effective 2005). adv. bk.rev. illus. Index. back issues avail.; reprints avail. **Document type:** *Journal, Academic/Scholarly.* **Description:** Examines various study and teaching methods for teachers of college-level English language arts.
Related titles: Microform ed.: (from PMC, PQC); Online - full text ed.: (from Chadwyck-Healey Inc., EBSCO Publishing, JSTOR (Web-based Journal Archive), O C L C Online Computer Library Center, Inc., ProQuest Information & Learning).
Indexed: ABIn, AIPP, ASCA, AbAn, AcaI, AmHI, ArtHuCI, BEL&L, BRI, CIJE, CPE, CurCont, DIP, ECER, EduInd, HumInd, IAPV, IBR, IBRH, IBZ, L&LBA, LIFT, LT&LA, MLA, MLA-IB, PhilInd, RASB, SOPODA, SSCI.
—BLDSC (3311.060000), IE, Infotrieve, ingenta. **CCC.**
Published by: National Council of Teachers of English, 1111 W Kenyon Rd, Urbana, IL 61801-1096. TEL 217-328-3870, 800-369-6283, FAX 217-328-9645, cschanche@ncte.org, cnimz@ncte.org, http://www.ncte.org/pubs/journals/ce. Eds. Carol Schanche, Jeanne Gunner. R&P Barbara Lamar. Adv. contact Carrie Stewart. Circ: 8,000.

371.3 USA
COLLOQUY (SAN FRANCISCO). Text in English. 1980. q. USD 6 out of state (effective 2001); free in state. back issues avail. **Document type:** *Newsletter, Trade.* **Description:** Examines international studies of teaching, teaching methods and curriculum, the humanities, history, and social studies for grades K-12.
Published by: World Affairs Council, 312 Sutter St, Ste 200, San Francisco, CA 94108. TEL 415-982-3263, FAX 415-982-5028, schools@wacsf.org, http://www.wacsf.org. Ed. Heather Murray. R&P Sandra Wulff. Circ: 35,000 (paid and controlled).

COME LEARN BEGINNERS. see *RELIGIONS AND THEOLOGY*

COME LEARN JUNIORS. see *RELIGIONS AND THEOLOGY*

COME LEARN PRIMARIES. see *RELIGIONS AND THEOLOGY*

371.33 USA ISSN 0363-4523
PN4071
➤ **COMMUNICATION EDUCATION.** Text in English. 1952. q. USD 275 combined subscription to institutions print & online eds. (effective 2005); GBP 170 combined subscription to institutions print & online eds. (effective 2006). adv. bk.rev. abstr.; charts; illus. cum.index. reprint service avail. from PQC,PSC. **Document type:** *Journal, Academic/Scholarly.* **Description:** Presents studies and research on communication in instructional settings.
Formerly (until 1976): Speech Teacher (0038-7177)
Related titles: Microform ed.: (from PQC); Online - full text ed.: ISSN 1479-5795. USD 261, GBP 162 to institutions (effective 2006) (from EBSCO Publishing, Gale Group, IngentaConnect, Northern Light Technology, Inc., O C L C Online Computer Library Center, Inc., Swets Information Services).
Indexed: ABIn, ASCA, AcaI, BRI, CBRI, CIJE, CPE, CommAb, CurCont, DIP, EAA, EduInd, IBR, IBZ, IJCS, LISA, MLA, MLA-IB, MRD, PCI, PsycInfo, PsycholAb, RASB, SOPODA, SSA, SSCI, e-psyche.
—BLDSC (3359.830000), IDS, IE, Infotrieve, ingenta. **CCC.**
Published by: (National Communication Association), Routledge (Subsidiary of: Taylor & Francis Ltd), 325 Chestnut St., Suite 800, Philadelphia, PA 19106. TEL 215-625-8900, 800-354-1420, FAX 215-625-8914, comed@uga.edu, journals@routledge.com, http://www.tandf.co.uk/journals/titles/03634523.asp, http://www.routledge.com. Eds. Don Rubin, Joe Ayres. Circ: 3,700. **Subscr. to:** Taylor & Francis Inc.

➤ **COMMUNIQUE (COLUMBUS, 1967).** see *BUSINESS AND ECONOMICS—Management*

➤ **COMPASS (VICTORIA)**; a magazine for peer assistance, mentorship and coaching. see *SOCIAL SERVICES AND WELFARE*

361.740 USA ISSN 1046-0780
HD2769.2.U6
COMPENDIUM OF RESOURCES FOR TEACHING ABOUT THE NONPROFIT SECTOR, VOLUNTARISM AND PHILANTHROPY. Text in English. 1989. a.
Published by: Independent Sector, 1200 Eighteenth St, N W, Ste 200, Washington, DC 20036. TEL 202-467-6100, FAX 202-467-6101, info@indepsec.org, http://www.independentsector.org.

371.33 IND
COMPETITION MASTER. Text in English. 1959. m. INR 200 (effective 2000). adv. index. **Document type:** *Academic/Scholarly.* **Description:** Features current affairs and competition aids.
Published by: Chandika Press Ltd., 126 Industrial Area Phase-1, Chandigarh, Haryana 160 002, India. TEL 91-172-650362, FAX 91-172-657783, desh@competitionmaster.com, http://www.competitionmaster.com. Ed. O P Khanna. Pub. D D Khann. Adv. contact K D Khanna. B&W page INR 20,000, color page INR 40,000. Circ: 115,000.

418 USA ISSN 1542-5894
➤ **COMPOSITION STUDIES.** Text in English. 1972. s-a. USD 15 domestic to individuals; USD 20 foreign to individuals; USD 30 domestic to institutions; USD 30 foreign to institutions; USD 12 to students (effective 2005). adv. bk.rev. back issues avail.; reprint service avail. from PQC. **Document type:** *Academic/Scholarly.* **Description:** Publishes essays on theories of composition and rhetoric, the teaching and administration of writing and rhetoric at all post-secondary levels and disciplinary-institutional issues of interest to the field's teacher-scholars. It includes course designs, an innovative feature on curricular development in writing and rhetoric of interest to teachers at all post-secondary levels.
Former titles (until 1999): Composition Studies - Freshman English News (1534-9322); (until 1992): Freshman English News (0739-4713)
Related titles: Microform ed.: (from PQC); Online - full text ed.: (from ProQuest Information & Learning).
Indexed: CIJE, MLA-IB.
—BLDSC (3366.051000), IE, ingenta.
Published by: DePaul University, English Department, 802 W Belden Ave, Chicago, IL 60614. TEL 773-325-7211, FAX 773-325-7328, composition_studies@wppost.depaul.edu, http://www.compositionstudies.tcu.edu/. Ed., R&P, Adv. contact Peter Vandenberg TEL 773-325-7211. Circ: 900.

E

➤ **COMPUSCHOOL.** see *EDUCATION—Computer Applications*

371.334 AUS
➤ **COMPUTE - ED**; an electronic journal of teaching and learning with and about technology. Text in English. 1995. a.
Document type: *Academic/Scholarly.* **Description:** Concerned with issues and applications in teaching with and about technology in secondary and tertiary education.
Media: Online - full text.
Indexed: AEI.
Published by: University of Technology, Sydney, City Campus, PO Box 123, Broadway, NSW 2007, Australia. TEL 61-2-95145613, FAX 61-2-95145556, j.eklund@UTS.edu.au, j.harvey@edfac.usyd.edu.au, http://www.computed.coe.wayne.edu/index.html. Eds. John Eklund, John Harvey.

➤ **COMPUTER ASSISTED LANGUAGE LEARNING**; an international journal. see *COMPUTERS—Computer Assisted Instruction*

➤ **COMPUTER EDUCATION.** see *COMPUTERS—Computer Assisted Instruction*

➤ **COMPUTER SCIENCE EDUCATION.** see *EDUCATION—Computer Applications*

➤ **COMPUTER UND UNTERRICHT.** see *EDUCATION—Computer Applications*

371.3 USA ISSN 1041-682X
LB1585.3
CONNECT (BRATTLEBORO); teachers' innovations in K - 8 science, math and technology. Text in English. 1987. 5/yr. USD 25 domestic; USD 31 in Canada & Mexico; USD 44 elsewhere (effective 2005). bk.rev. Index. back issues avail.
Document type: *Magazine, Trade.*
Related titles: Online - full text ed.: (from EBSCO Publishing).
Published by: Synergy Learning International, Inc., PO Box 60, Brattleboro, VT 05302-0060. TEL 802-257-2629, 800-769-6199, FAX 802-254-5233, connect@synergylearning.org, http://www.synergylearning.org. Ed., Pub., R&P Casey Murrow. Circ: 1,500 (paid and controlled).

371.3 USA ISSN 1554-4583
LB1044.87
CONNECTED NEWSLETTER. Text in English. 1994. 9/yr. USD 59 (effective 2005). illus. Index. reprints avail. **Document type:** *Journal, Trade.*
Former titles (until 2003): Classroom Connect Newsletter (1526-3673); (until 1999): Classroom Connect (1078-6430)
Published by: Classroom Connect, Inc., 8000 Marina Blvd., Ste. 400, Brisbane, CA 94005-1885. TEL 310-725-0887, FAX 310-725-0899, permission@classroom.com, http://www.classroom.com. Ed. Christine Hofer Borror.

CONSULTING SUCCESS ONLINE. see *ADVERTISING AND PUBLIC RELATIONS*

507.1 AUS
CONTACT (RICHMOND). Text in English. m. AUD 50 (effective 1999). adv. **Document type:** *Newsletter.*
Published by: Science Teachers' Association of Victoria, PO Box 3058, Coburg, VIC 3058, Australia. TEL 61-3-9385-3999, FAX 61-3-9386-6722, stav@netspace.net.au, stav@stav.vic.edu.au, http://www.srl.rmit.edu.au/stav/. Ed. Julie Mills. Adv. contact Danielle Duong.

371.33 USA ISSN 1528-5804
LB1028.3 CODEN: CITTBT
➤ **CONTEMPORARY ISSUES IN TECHNOLOGY & TEACHER EDUCATION.** Text in English. 2000. q. free (effective 2005).
Document type: *Journal, Academic/Scholarly.* **Description:** Includes articles related either to general technology use or discipline-specific technology and educational use.
Media: Online - full text.
Indexed: Inspec.
—CCC.
Published by: Association for the Advancement of Computing in Education, PO Box 3728, Norfolk, VA 23514. TEL 757-623-7588, FAX 703-997-8760, info@aace.org, http://www.citejournal.org/vol4/iss4/, http://www.aace.org. Ed. Jerry Willis.

➤ **CONTEXTOS EDUCATIVOS**; revista de educacion. see *EDUCATION*

371.3 USA ISSN 1057-4190
THE COUNCIL CHRONICLE. Text in English. 1991. 5/yr. (Sept., Nov., Feb., Apr., June). free to members (effective 2005). adv. bk.rev. 20 p./no.; back issues avail. **Document type:** *Newspaper, Trade.* **Description:** Contains news for and about members of the National Council of Teachers.
Published by: National Council of Teachers of English, 1111 W Kenyon Rd, Urbana, IL 61801-1096. TEL 217-328-3870, 800-369-6283, FAX 217-328—9645, 217-328-9645, chronicle@ncte.org, membership@ncte.org, http://www.ncte.org/pubs/chron. Ed. Felice Kaufmann. Adv. contact Carrie Stewart. page USD 1,650; trim 12.75 x 10.38. Circ: 75,000 (paid).

418 USA
COUNCIL-GRAMS. Text in English. 1972. 3/yr. bk.rev. abstr.; bibl.
Published by: National Council of Teachers of English, 1111 W Kenyon Rd, Urbana, IL 61801-1096. TEL 217-328-3870, 800-369-6283, FAX 217-328-9645, lbianchi@ncte.org. Ed. Lori Bianchini. Circ: 3,000.

CRINKLES; because learning makes crinkles in your brain. see *CHILDREN AND YOUTH—For*

CRITICAL ISSUES IN EDUCATIONAL LEADERSHIP SERIES. see *EDUCATION—School Organization And Administration*

371.3 USA
➤ **CRITICAL ISSUES IN TEACHER EDUCATION.** Text in English. 1991. a. membership. bk.rev. **Document type:** *Academic/Scholarly.* **Description:** Focuses on issues related to teacher education, including preservice and inservice teacher education, curriculum and instruction, and policies related to teacher education.
Published by: Illinois Association of Teacher Education, Dept of Student Teaching, Eastern Illinois University, Charleston, IL 61920. TEL 618-242-3454, FAX 217-581-2518, cfmev@eju.edu. Ed. Mary Ellen Varble. Circ: 300.

371.3 ESP ISSN 0213-1269
CUESTIONES PEDAGOGICAS. Text in Spanish. 1984. a., latest vol.14, 1999. EUR 18 per issue (effective 2005). **Document type:** *Journal, Academic/Scholarly.*
—CINDOC.
Published by: (Universidad de Sevilla, Instituto de Ciencias de la Educacion), Universidad de Sevilla, Secretariado de Publicaciones, Porvenir 27, Sevilla, 41013, Spain. TEL 34-95-4487444, FAX 34-95-4487443, secpub10@us.es, http://www.us.es/publius/inicio.html.

371.33 USA ISSN 0199-820X
CURRENT HEALTH 1; the beginning guide to health education. Text in English. 1974. 8/yr. (m., Sep.-May). USD 34.50 per academic year; USD 10.15 per academic year 15 or more subscriptions (effective 2005 - 2006). charts; illus. reprint service avail. from PQC. **Document type:** *Magazine, Consumer.* **Description:** Provides students in grades 4-7 with today's essential health information in a stimulating magazine format. Includes a separate teacher's guide.
Related titles: Online - full text ed.: (from bigchalk, EBSCO Publishing, Northern Light Technology, Inc., ProQuest Information & Learning).
Indexed: ICM, JHMA, MASUSE, MagInd, PMR, RGYP.
Published by: Weekly Reader Corp. (Subsidiary of: W R C Media Inc.), 200 First Stamford Pl, PO Box 120023, Stamford, CT 06912-0023. TEL 203-705-3500, 800-446-3355, FAX 203-705-1662, http://www.weeklyreader.com. Circ: 300,000 (paid).

371.33 USA ISSN 0163-156X
CURRENT HEALTH 2; the continuing guide to health education. Text in English. 8/yr. (m., Sep.-May). USD 34.50 per academic year; USD 10.15 per academic year 15 or more subscriptions (effective 2005). **Document type:** *Magazine, Consumer.* **Description:** Provides middle- and high-school students with today's essential health information in a stimulating magazine format that students relate to. Includes a separate teacher's guide.
Related titles: CD-ROM ed.: (from ProQuest Information & Learning); Online - full text ed.: (from bigchalk, EBSCO Publishing, Florida Center for Library Automation, Gale Group, H.W. Wilson, Northern Light Technology, Inc., O C L C Online Computer Library Center, Inc., ProQuest Information & Learning); ♦ Supplement(s): Human Sexuality Supplement. ISSN 0196-061X.
Indexed: AcaI, HlthInd, JHMA, MASUSE, MagInd, RGAb, RGPR, RGYP, TOM.
Published by: Weekly Reader Corp. (Subsidiary of: W R C Media Inc.), 200 First Stamford Pl, PO Box 120023, Stamford, CT 06912-0023. TEL 203-705-3500, 800-446-3355, FAX 203-705-1662, science@weeklyreader.com, http://www.weeklyreader.com. Circ: 300,000 (paid).

780.71 USA ISSN 0070-198X
CURRENT ISSUES IN MUSIC EDUCATION. Text in English. 1963. irreg., latest vol.5, 1970. price varies.
Published by: Ohio State University, School of Music, Div of Music Education, Columbus, OH 43210. TEL 615-422-6511.

375 AUS ISSN 0726-416X
LB1570
➤ **CURRICULUM AND TEACHING.** Text in English. 1986. s-a. AUD 374 domestic to institutions; AUD 340 in New Zealand to institutions; GBP 168 in Europe to institutions; USD 260 elsewhere to institutions (effective 2005). adv. index.
Document type: *Journal, Academic/Scholarly.* **Description:** Explores current issues in curriculum theory, design, evaluation and development of elementary and secondary schooling. Includes information on instruction, innovation, policy planning and educational administration.
Indexed: AEI, CPE, ERA, ETA, L&LBA, MEA, RHEA, SEA, SENA, SOMA, SOPODA, SRRA, TEA.
—BLDSC (3505.230000), IE, Infotrieve, ingenta.
Published by: James Nicholas Publishers, Pty. Ltd., PO Box 244, Albert Park, VIC 3206, Australia. TEL 61-3-96905955, FAX 61-3-96992040, custservice@jamesnicholaspublishers.com.au, http://www.jamesnicholaspublishers.com.au/ctjrnl.htm. Ed. Dr. Joseph Zajda. Pub. Rea Zajda. R&P Mary Berchmans. Adv. contact Irene Schevchenko.

375 USA ISSN 1538-750X
LB2806.15
CURRICULUM AND TEACHING DIALOGUE. Text in English. 1999. s-a. USD 70 to individuals; USD 115 to institutions; USD 50 to students; USD 25 per issue to individuals; USD 45 per issue to institutions (effective 2006). adv. **Document type:** *Magazine, Trade.*
Related titles: Online - full text ed.: (from EBSCO Publishing, ProQuest Information & Learning).
Published by: Information Age Publishing, Inc., 411 W Putnam Ave, Ste 205, PO Box 4967, Greenwich, CT 06831. TEL 203-661-7602, FAX 203-661-7952, order@infoagepub.com, http://www.infoagepub.com. Ed. Susan C. Brown. Pub., R&P, Adv. contact George F. Johnson. B&W page USD 100.

CURRICULUM FORUM/KECHENG LUNTAN. see *EDUCATION—Higher Education*

371.3 CAN
CURRICULUM HANDBOOK FOR PARENTS. Text in English. 1997. a. **Document type:** *Academic/Scholarly.* **Description:** Covers what Alberta students are expected to learn in each grade, including overviews of subjects and topics.
Related titles: Online - full content ed.; French ed.: Ce que Mon Enfant Apprend a l'Ecole, Manuel a l'Intention des Parents; ♦ Series: Curriculum Handbook for Parents. Grade 1. ISSN 1483-1694; ♦ Curriculum Handbook for Parents. Grade 2. ISSN 1483-1686; ♦ Curriculum Handbook for Parents. Grade 3. ISSN 1483-1678; ♦ Curriculum Handbook for Parents. Grade 4. ISSN 1483-166X; ♦ Curriculum Handbook for Parents. Grade 5. ISSN 1483-1651; ♦ Curriculum Handbook for Parents. Grade 6. ISSN 1483-1643; ♦ Curriculum Handbook for Parents. Grade 7. ISSN 1483-1635; ♦ Curriculum Handbook for Parents. Grade 8. ISSN 1483-1627; ♦ Curriculum Handbook for Parents. Grade 9. ISSN 1483-1619; ♦ Curriculum Handbook for Parents. Senior High School. ISSN 1487-203X; ♦ Curriculum Handbook for Parents. Kindergarten.
Published by: Alberta Education, 108 St NW, Edmonton, AB T5J 5E6, Canada. TEL 780-427-7219, FAX 780-422-1263, curric.contact@learning.gov.ab.ca, comm.contact@learning.gov.ab.ca, http://www.education.gov.ab.ca/parents/handbooks/. **Subscr. to:** Learning Resources Centre, 12360 142 St., Edmonton, AB T5L 4X9, Canada. TEL 780-427-2767, 310-0000, FAX 780-422-9750, http://www.lrc.learning.gov.ab.ca.

230.071 CAN
CURRICULUM HANDBOOK FOR PARENTS (CATHOLIC SCHOOL VERSION). Text in English. 1997. a.
Related titles: Online - full content ed.; ♦ Series: Curriculum Handbook for Parents. Grade 1 (Catholic School Version). ISSN 1483-1783; ♦ Curriculum Handbook for Parents. Grade 2 (Catholic School Version). ISSN 1483-1775; ♦ Curriculum Handbook for Parents. Grade 3 (Catholic School Version). ISSN 1483-1767; ♦ Curriculum Handbook for Parents. Grade 4 (Catholic School Version). ISSN 1483-1759; ♦ Curriculum Handbook for Parents. Grade 5 (Catholic School Version). ISSN 1483-1740; ♦ Curriculum Handbook for Parents. Grade 6 (Catholic School Version). ISSN 1483-1732; ♦ Curriculum Handbook for Parents. Grade 7 (Catholic School Version). ISSN 1483-1724; ♦ Curriculum Handbook for Parents. Grade 8 (Catholic School Version). ISSN 1483-1716; ♦ Curriculum Handbook for Parents. Grade 9 (Catholic School Version). ISSN 1483-1708; ♦ Curriculum Handbook for Parents. Senior High School (Catholic School Version). ISSN 1481-9406; ♦ Curriculum Handbook for Parents. Kindergarten (Catholic School Version).
Published by: Alberta Education, 108 St NW, Edmonton, AB T5J 5E6, Canada. TEL 780-427-7219, FAX 780-422-1263, comm.contact@learning.gov.ab.ca, http://www.education.gov.ab.ca/parents/handbooks/. **Subscr. to:** Learning Resources Centre, 12360 142 St., Edmonton, AB T5L 4X9, Canada. TEL 780-427-2767, 310-0000, FAX 780-422-9750, http://www.lrc.learning.gov.ab.ca.

371.3 CAN ISSN 1483-1694
CURRICULUM HANDBOOK FOR PARENTS. GRADE 1. Text in English. 1997. a. **Document type:** *Academic/Scholarly.*
Related titles: Online - full content ed.; French ed.: Ce que Mon Enfant Apprend a l'Ecole, Manuel a l'Intention des Parents. Premiere Annee. ISSN 1489-811X; ♦ Series of: Curriculum Handbook for Parents.
Published by: Alberta Education, 108 St NW, Edmonton, AB T5J 5E6, Canada. TEL 780-427-7219, FAX 780-422-1263, curric.contact@learning.gov.ab.ca, comm.contact@learning.gov.ab.ca, http://www.education.gov.ab.ca/parents/handbooks/. **Subscr. to:** Learning Resources Centre, 12360 142 St., Edmonton, AB T5L 4X9, Canada. TEL 780-427-2767, 310-0000, FAX 780-422-9750, http://www.lrc.learning.gov.ab.ca.

E

▼ new title ➤ refereed ✶ unverified ♦ full entry avail.

230.071   CAN   ISSN 1483-1783
**CURRICULUM HANDBOOK FOR PARENTS. GRADE 1
(CATHOLIC SCHOOL VERSION).** Text in English. 1997. a.
Document type: *Academic/Scholarly.*
Related titles: Online - full content ed.; ♦ Series of: Curriculum
Handbook for Parents (Catholic School Version).
Published by: Alberta Education, 108 St NW, Edmonton, AB T5J
5E6, Canada. TEL 780-427-7219, FAX 780-422-1263,
comm.contact@learning.gov.ab.ca, http://
www.education.gov.ab.ca/parents/handbooks/. **Subscr. to:**
Learning Resources Centre, 12360 142 St., Edmonton, AB
T5L 4X9, Canada. TEL 780-427-2767, 310-0000, FAX
780-422-9750, http://www.lrc.learning.gov.ab.ca.

371.3   CAN   ISSN 1483-1686
CURRICULUM HANDBOOK FOR PARENTS. GRADE 2. Text in
English. 1997. a. **Document type:** *Academic/Scholarly.*
Related titles: French ed.: Ce que Mon Enfant Apprend a l'Ecole,
Manuel a l'Intention des Parents. Deuxieme Annee. ISSN
1489-8128. 1999; ♦ Series of: Curriculum Handbook for
Parents.
Published by: Alberta Education, 108 St NW, Edmonton, AB T5J
5E6, Canada. TEL 780-427-7219, FAX 780-422-1263,
curric.contact@learning.gov.ab.ca, http://
www.education.gov.ab.ca/parents/handbooks/. **Subscr. to:**
Learning Resources Centre, 12360 142 St., Edmonton, AB
T5L 4X9, Canada. TEL 780-427-2767, 310-0000, FAX
780-422-9750, http://www.lrc.learning.gov.ab.ca.

230.071   CAN   ISSN 1483-1775
**CURRICULUM HANDBOOK FOR PARENTS. GRADE 2
(CATHOLIC SCHOOL VERSION).** Text in English. 1997. a.
Document type: *Academic/Scholarly.*
Related titles: Online - full content ed.; ♦ Series of: Curriculum
Handbook for Parents (Catholic School Version).
Published by: Alberta Education, 108 St NW, Edmonton, AB T5J
5E6, Canada. TEL 780-427-7219, FAX 780-422-1263,
comm.contact@learning.gov.ab.ca, http://
www.education.gov.ab.ca/parents/handbooks/. **Subscr. to:**
Learning Resources Centre, 12360 142 St., Edmonton, AB
T5L 4X9, Canada. TEL 780-427-2767, 310-0000, FAX
780-422-9750, http://www.lrc.learning.gov.ab.ca.

371.3   CAN   ISSN 1483-1678
CURRICULUM HANDBOOK FOR PARENTS. GRADE 3. Text in
English. 1997. a. **Document type:** *Academic/Scholarly.*
Related titles: Online - full content ed.; French ed.: Ce que Mon
Enfant Apprend a l'Ecole, Manuel a l'Intention des Parents.
Troisieme Annee. ISSN 1489-8136. 1999; ♦ Series of:
Curriculum Handbook for Parents.
Published by: Alberta Education, 108 St NW, Edmonton, AB T5J
5E6, Canada. TEL 780-427-7219, FAX 780-422-1263,
comm.contact@learning.gov.ab.ca, http://
www.education.gov.ab.ca/parents/handbooks/. **Subscr. to:**
Learning Resources Centre, 12360 142 St., Edmonton, AB
T5L 4X9, Canada. TEL 780-427-2767, 310-0000, FAX
780-422-9750, http://www.lrc.learning.gov.ab.ca.

230.071   CAN   ISSN 1483-1767
**CURRICULUM HANDBOOK FOR PARENTS. GRADE 3
(CATHOLIC SCHOOL VERSION).** Text in English. 1997. a.
Document type: *Academic/Scholarly.*
Related titles: Online - full content ed.; ♦ Series: Curriculum
Handbook for Parents (Catholic School Version).
Published by: Alberta Education, 108 St NW, Edmonton, AB T5J
5E6, Canada. TEL 780-427-7219, FAX 780-422-1263,
curric.contact@learning.gov.ab.ca, http://
www.education.gov.ab.ca/parents/handbooks/. **Subscr. to:**
Learning Resources Centre, 12360 142 St., Edmonton, AB
T5L 4X9, Canada. TEL 780-427-2767, 310-0000, FAX
780-422-9750, http://www.lrc.learning.gov.ab.ca.

371.3   CAN   ISSN 1483-166X
CURRICULUM HANDBOOK FOR PARENTS. GRADE 4. Text in
English. 1997. a. **Document type:** *Academic/Scholarly.*
Related titles: Online - full content ed.; French ed.: Ce que Mon
Enfant Apprend a l'Ecole, Manuel a l'Intention des Parents.
Quatrieme Annee. ISSN 1489-8144; ♦ Series of: Curriculum
Handbook for Parents.
Published by: Alberta Education, 108 St NW, Edmonton, AB T5J
5E6, Canada. TEL 780-427-7219, FAX 780-422-1263,
comm.contact@learning.gov.ab.ca, http://
www.education.gov.ab.ca/parents/handbooks/. **Subscr. to:**
Learning Resources Centre, 12360 142 St., Edmonton, AB
T5L 4X9, Canada. TEL 780-427-2767, 310-0000, FAX
780-422-9750, http://www.lrc.learning.gov.ab.ca.

230.071   CAN   ISSN 1483-1759
**CURRICULUM HANDBOOK FOR PARENTS. GRADE 4
(CATHOLIC SCHOOL VERSION).** Text in English. 1997. a.
Document type: *Academic/Scholarly.*
Related titles: Online - full content ed.; ♦ Series of: Curriculum
Handbook for Parents (Catholic School Version).

Published by: Alberta Education, 108 St NW, Edmonton, AB T5J
5E6, Canada. TEL 780-427-7219, FAX 780-422-1263,
curric.contact@learning.gov.ab.ca, http://
www.education.gov.ab.ca/parents/handbooks/. **Subscr. to:**
Learning Resources Centre, 12360 142 St., Edmonton, AB
T5L 4X9, Canada. TEL 780-427-2767, 310-0000, FAX
780-422-9750, http://www.lrc.learning.gov.ab.ca.

371.3   CAN   ISSN 1483-1651
CURRICULUM HANDBOOK FOR PARENTS. GRADE 5. Text in
English. 1997. a. **Document type:** *Academic/Scholarly.*
Related titles: Online - full content ed.; French ed.: Ce que Mon
Enfant Apprend a l'Ecole, Manuel a l'Intention des Parents.
Cinquieme Annee. ISSN 1489-8152; ♦ Series of: Curriculum
Handbook for Parents.
Published by: Alberta Education, 108 St NW, Edmonton, AB T5J
5E6, Canada. TEL 780-427-7219, FAX 780-422-1263,
curric.contact@learning.gov.ab.ca, http://
www.education.gov.ab.ca/parents/handbooks/. **Subscr. to:**
Learning Resources Centre, 12360 142 St., Edmonton, AB
T5L 4X9, Canada. TEL 780-427-2767, 310-0000, FAX
780-422-9750, http://www.lrc.learning.gov.ab.ca.

230.071   CAN   ISSN 1483-1740
**CURRICULUM HANDBOOK FOR PARENTS. GRADE 5
(CATHOLIC SCHOOL VERSION).** Text in English. 1997. a.
Document type: *Academic/Scholarly.*
Related titles: Online - full content ed.; ♦ Series of: Curriculum
Handbook for Parents (Catholic School Version).
Published by: Alberta Education, 108 St NW, Edmonton, AB T5J
5E6, Canada. TEL 780-427-7219, FAX 780-422-1263,
comm.contact@learning.gov.ab.ca, http://
www.education.gov.ab.ca/parents/handbooks/. **Subscr. to:**
Learning Resources Centre, 12360 142 St., Edmonton, AB
T5L 4X9, Canada. TEL 780-427-2767, 310-0000, FAX
780-422-9750, http://www.lrc.learning.gov.ab.ca.

371.3   CAN   ISSN 1483-1643
CURRICULUM HANDBOOK FOR PARENTS. GRADE 6. Text in
English. 1997. a. **Document type:** *Academic/Scholarly.*
Related titles: Online - full content ed.; French ed.: Ce que Mon
Enfant Apprend a l'Ecole, Manuel a l'Intention des Parents.
Sixieme Annee. ISSN 1489-8160. 1999; ♦ Series of:
Curriculum Handbook for Parents.
Published by: Alberta Education, 108 St NW, Edmonton, AB T5J
5E6, Canada. TEL 780-427-7219, FAX 780-422-1263,
curric.contact@learning.gov.ab.ca, http://
www.education.gov.ab.ca/parents/handbooks/. **Subscr. to:**
Learning Resources Centre, 12360 142 St., Edmonton, AB
T5L 4X9, Canada. TEL 780-427-2767, 310-0000, FAX
780-422-9750, http://www.lrc.learning.gov.ab.ca.

230.071   CAN   ISSN 1483-1732
**CURRICULUM HANDBOOK FOR PARENTS. GRADE 6
(CATHOLIC SCHOOL VERSION).** Text in English. 1997. a.
Document type: *Academic/Scholarly.*
Related titles: Online - full content ed.; ♦ Series of: Curriculum
Handbook for Parents (Catholic School Version).
Published by: Alberta Education, 108 St NW, Edmonton, AB T5J
5E6, Canada. TEL 780-427-7219, FAX 780-422-1263,
curric.contact@learning.gov.ab.ca, http://
www.education.gov.ab.ca/parents/handbooks/. **Subscr. to:**
Learning Resources Centre, 12360 142 St., Edmonton, AB
T5L 4X9, Canada. TEL 780-427-2767, 310-0000, FAX
780-422-9750, http://www.lrc.learning.gov.ab.ca.

371.3   CAN   ISSN 1483-1635
CURRICULUM HANDBOOK FOR PARENTS. GRADE 7. Text in
English. 1999. a. **Document type:** *Consumer.*
Related titles: Online - full content ed.; French ed.: Ce que Mon
Enfant Apprend a l'Ecole, Manuel a l'Intention des Parents.
Septieme Annee. ISSN 1489-8179. 1999; ♦ Series of:
Curriculum Handbook for Parents.
Published by: Alberta Education, 108 St NW, Edmonton, AB T5J
5E6, Canada. TEL 780-427-7219, FAX 780-422-1263,
curric.contact@learning.gov.ab.ca, http://
www.education.gov.ab.ca/parents/handbooks/. **Subscr. to:**
Learning Resources Centre.

230.071   CAN   ISSN 1483-1724
**CURRICULUM HANDBOOK FOR PARENTS. GRADE 7
(CATHOLIC SCHOOL VERSION).** Text in English. 1997. a.
Document type: *Academic/Scholarly.*
Related titles: Online - full content ed.; ♦ Series of: Curriculum
Handbook for Parents (Catholic School Version).
Published by: Alberta Education, 108 St NW, Edmonton, AB T5J
5E6, Canada. TEL 780-427-7219, FAX 780-422-1263,
curric.contact@learning.gov.ab.ca, http://
www.education.gov.ab.ca/parents/handbooks/. **Subscr. to:**
Learning Resources Centre, 12360 142 St., Edmonton, AB
T5L 4X9, Canada. TEL 780-427-2767, 310-0000, FAX
780-422-9750, http://www.lrc.learning.gov.ab.ca.

371.3   CAN   ISSN 1483-1627
CURRICULUM HANDBOOK FOR PARENTS. GRADE 8. Text in
English. 1997. a. **Document type:** *Academic/Scholarly.*
Related titles: Online - full content ed.; French ed.: Ce que Mon
Enfant Apprend a l'Ecole, Manuel a l'Intention des Parents.
Huitieme Annee. ISSN 1489-8187; ♦ Series of: Curriculum
Handbook for Parents.
Published by: Alberta Education, 108 St NW, Edmonton, AB T5J
5E6, Canada. TEL 780-427-7219, FAX 780-422-1263,
curric.contact@learning.gov.ab.ca, http://
www.education.gov.ab.ca/parents/handbooks/. **Subscr. to:**
Learning Resources Centre, 12360 142 St., Edmonton, AB
T5L 4X9, Canada. TEL 780-427-2767, 310-0000, FAX
780-422-9750, http://www.lrc.learning.gov.ab.ca.

230.071   CAN   ISSN 1483-1716
**CURRICULUM HANDBOOK FOR PARENTS. GRADE 8
(CATHOLIC SCHOOL VERSION).** Text in English. 1997. a.
Document type: *Academic/Scholarly.*
Related titles: Online - full content ed.; ♦ Series of: Curriculum
Handbook for Parents (Catholic School Version).
Published by: Alberta Education, 108 St NW, Edmonton, AB T5J
5E6, Canada. TEL 780-427-7219, FAX 780-422-1263,
curric.contact@learning.gov.ab.ca, http://
www.education.gov.ab.ca/parents/handbooks/. **Subscr. to:**
Learning Resources Centre, 12360 142 St., Edmonton, AB
T5L 4X9, Canada. TEL 780-427-2767, 310-0000, FAX
780-422-9750, http://www.lrc.learning.gov.ab.ca.

371.3   CAN   ISSN 1483-1619
CURRICULUM HANDBOOK FOR PARENTS. GRADE 9. Text in
English. 1997. a. **Document type:** *Academic/Scholarly.*
Related titles: Online - full content ed.; French ed.: Ce que Mon
Enfant Apprend a l'Ecole, Manuel a l'Intention des Parents.
Neuvieme Annee. ISSN 1489-8195. 1999; ♦ Series of:
Curriculum Handbook for Parents.
Published by: Alberta Education, 108 St NW, Edmonton, AB T5J
5E6, Canada. TEL 780-427-7219, FAX 780-422-1263,
comm.contact@learning.gov.ab.ca, http://
www.education.gov.ab.ca/parents/handbooks/. **Subscr. to:**
Learning Resources Centre.

230.071   CAN   ISSN 1483-1708
**CURRICULUM HANDBOOK FOR PARENTS. GRADE 9
(CATHOLIC SCHOOL VERSION).** Text in English. 1997. a.
Document type: *Academic/Scholarly.*
Related titles: Online - full content ed.; ♦ Series of: Curriculum
Handbook for Parents (Catholic School Version).
Published by: Alberta Education, 108 St NW, Edmonton, AB T5J
5E6, Canada. TEL 780-427-7219, FAX 780-422-1263,
curric.contact@learning.gov.ab.ca, http://
www.education.gov.ab.ca/parents/handbooks/. **Subscr. to:**
Learning Resources Centre, 12360 142 St., Edmonton, AB
T5L 4X9, Canada. TEL 780-427-2767, 310-0000, FAX
780-422-9750, http://www.lrc.learning.gov.ab.ca.

371.3   CAN
CURRICULUM HANDBOOK FOR PARENTS. KINDERGARTEN.
Text in English. a. **Document type:** *Academic/Scholarly.*
Related titles: Online - full content ed.; ♦ Series of: Curriculum
Handbook for Parents.
Published by: Alberta Education, 108 St NW, Edmonton, AB T5J
5E6, Canada. TEL 780-427-7219, FAX 780-422-1263,
curric.contact@learning.gov.ab.ca, http://
www.education.gov.ab.ca/parents/handbooks/. **Subscr. to:**
Learning Resources Centre, 12360 142 St., Edmonton, AB
T5L 4X9, Canada. TEL 780-427-2767, 310-0000, FAX
780-422-9750, http://www.lrc.learning.gov.ab.ca.

371.3   CAN
**CURRICULUM HANDBOOK FOR PARENTS. KINDERGARTEN
(CATHOLIC SCHOOL VERSION).** Text in English. a.
Document type: *Academic/Scholarly.*
Related titles: Online - full content ed.; ♦ Series of: Curriculum
Handbook for Parents (Catholic School Version).
Published by: Alberta Education, 108 St NW, Edmonton, AB T5J
5E6, Canada. TEL 780-427-7219, FAX 780-422-1263,
curric.contact@learning.gov.ab.ca, http://
www.education.gov.ab.ca/parents/handbooks/. **Subscr. to:**
Learning Resources Centre, 12360 142 St., Edmonton, AB
T5L 4X9, Canada. TEL 780-427-2767, 310-0000, FAX
780-422-9750, http://www.lrc.learning.gov.ab.ca.

371.3   CAN   ISSN 1487-203X
**CURRICULUM HANDBOOK FOR PARENTS. SENIOR HIGH
SCHOOL.** Text in English. 1999. a. **Document type:**
Academic/Scholarly.
Related titles: Online - full content ed.; ♦ Series of: Curriculum
Handbook for Parents.

E

Published by: Alberta Education, 108 St NW, Edmonton, AB T5J 5E6, Canada. TEL 780-427-7219, FAX 780-422-1263, curric.contact@learning.gov.ab.ca, comm.contact@learning.gov.ab.ca, http://www.education.gov.ab.ca/parents/handbooks/. **Subscr. to:** Learning Resources Centre, 12360 142 St., Edmonton, AB T5L 4X9, Canada. TEL 780-427-2767, 310-0000, FAX 780-422-9750, http://www.lrc.learning.gov.ab.ca.

230.071 CAN ISSN 1481-9406
CURRICULUM HANDBOOK FOR PARENTS. SENIOR HIGH SCHOOL (CATHOLIC SCHOOL VERSION). Text in English. 1999. a. **Document type:** *Academic/Scholarly.*
Related titles: Online - full content ed.; ♦ Series of: Curriculum Handbook for Parents (Catholic School Version).
Published by: Alberta Education, 108 St NW, Edmonton, AB T5J 5E6, Canada. TEL 780-427-7219, FAX 780-422-1263, curric.contact@learning.gov.ab.ca, comm.contact@learning.gov.ab.ca, http://www.education.gov.ab.ca/parents/handbooks/. **Subscr. to:** Learning Resources Centre, 12360 142 St., Edmonton, AB T5L 4X9, Canada. TEL 780-427-2767, 310-0000, FAX 780-422-9750, http://www.lrc.learning.gov.ab.ca.

371.3 375.4 CAN
CURRICULUM HANDBOOKS FOR PARENTS. FRENCH IMMERSION. Text in English. a. **Document type:** *Academic/Scholarly.*
Related titles: Online - full content ed.
Published by: Alberta Education, 108 St NW, Edmonton, AB T5J 5E6, Canada. TEL 780-427-7219, FAX 780-422-1263, curric.contact@learning.gov.ab.ca, comm.contact@learning.gov.ab.ca, http://www.education.gov.ab.ca/parents/handbooks/. **Subscr. to:** Learning Resources Centre, 12360 142 St., Edmonton, AB T5L 4X9, Canada. TEL 780-427-2767, 310-0000, FAX 780-422-9750, http://www.lrc.learning.gov.ab.ca.

375 USA ISSN 0362-6784
LB1570
➤ **CURRICULUM INQUIRY.** Text in English. 1971. q. USD 51 combined subscription in the Americas to individuals & Caribbean (print & online eds.); EUR 77 combined subscription in Europe to individuals print & online eds.; GBP 51 combined subscription elsewhere to individuals print & online eds.; USD 284 combined subscription in the Americas to institutions & Caribbean (print & online eds.); GBP 216 combined subscription elsewhere to institutions print & online eds.; USD 42 combined subscription in the Americas to students print & online eds.; EUR 63 combined subscription in Europe to students & Caribbean (print & online eds.); GBP 42 combined subscription elsewhere to students print & online eds. (effective 2006). adv. bk.rev. bibl.; illus. index. back issues avail.; reprint service avail. from PQC. **Document type:** *Journal, Academic/Scholarly.* **Description:** Studies curriculum research, development and evaluation. Also covers school reform, educational theory and practice, and classrooms and teaching.
Formerly: Curriculum Theory Network (0011-4049)
Related titles: Microform ed.; Online - full text ed.: ISSN 1467-873X. USD 270 in the Americas to institutions & Caribbean; GBP 205 elsewhere to institutions (effective 2006) (from Blackwell Synergy, EBSCO Publishing, Gale Group, IngentaConnect, JSTOR (Web-based Journal Archive), O C L C Online Computer Library Center, Inc., Swets Information Services).
Indexed: ABIn, ASCA, ArtHuCI, CEI, CIJE, CPE, ChLitAb, CurCont, DIP, EAA, ERA, ETA, EduInd, FamI, IBR, IBZ, MEA, RHEA, SEA, SENA, SOMA, SSCI, SWA, TEA.
—BLDSC (3505.276000), IDS, IE, Infotrieve, ingenta. **CCC.**
Published by: (Ontario Institute for Studies in Education CAN), Blackwell Publishing, Inc. (Subsidiary of: Blackwell Publishing Ltd.), Commerce Place, 350 Main St, Malden, MA 02148. TEL 781-388-8206, FAX 781-388-8232, subscrip@blackwellpub.com, http://www.blackwellpublishing.com/journals/CI. Eds. F Michael Connelly TEL 416-923-6641 ext 2630, JoAnn Phillion, Ming Fang He. Circ: 1,700.

375 GBR ISSN 0958-5176
CURRICULUM JOURNAL. Text in English. 1990. q. GBP 296, USD 492 combined subscription to institutions print & online eds. (effective 2006). adv. reprint service avail. from PSC. **Document type:** *Journal, Academic/Scholarly.* **Description:** Concerned with vital issues of curriculum structure, organization, and development.
Related titles: Online - full text ed.: ISSN 1469-3704. GBP 281, USD 467 to institutions (effective 2006) (from EBSCO Publishing, Gale Group, IngentaConnect, O C L C Online Computer Library Center, Inc., Swets Information Services).
Indexed: BrEdI, CPE, ChLitAb, ERA, ETA, MEA, PCI, RHEA, SEA, SENA, SOMA, TEA.
—BLDSC (3505.278300), IE, Infotrieve, ingenta. **CCC.**
Published by: (British Curriculum Foundation), Routledge (Subsidiary of: Taylor & Francis Group), 4 Park Square, Milton Park, Abingdon, Oxon OX14 4RN, United Kingdom. TEL 44-1235-828600, FAX 44-1235-829000, info@routledge.co.uk, http://www.tandf.co.uk/journals/routledge/09585176.asp, http://www.routledge.com. Eds. Bob McCormick, Bob Moon. R&P Sally Sweet. adv.: page GBP 175; trim 190 x 115. **Subscr. addr. in N America:** Taylor & Francis Inc., Customer Services Dept, 325 Chestnut St, 8th Fl, Philadelphia, PA 19106. TEL 215-625-8900, 800-354-1420, FAX 215-625-8914; **Subscr. to:** Taylor & Francis Ltd, Journals Customer Service, Rankine Rd, Basingstoke, Hants RG24 8PR, United Kingdom. TEL 44-1256-813000, FAX 44-1256-330245, enquiry@tandf.co.uk.

371.3 AUS
CURRICULUM PERSPECTIVES (NEWSLETTER EDITION). Text in English. s-a. **Document type:** *Newsletter, Academic/Scholarly.*
Published by: Australian Curriculum Studies Association Inc., PO Box 331, Deakin West, ACT 2600, Australia. TEL 61-2-62605660, FAX 61-2-62605665, acsa@acsa.edu.au, http://www.acsa.edu.au.

375.006 USA
CURRICULUM RESOURCE; stories, poetry and education. Text in English. 1999. m. USD 17.95 domestic; USD 19.50 in Canada; USD 21.95 elsewhere (effective 2001). **Document type:** *Newsletter.* **Description:** Contains information about curricula for schools, home schools, non-profit organizations and other educational institutions.
Published by: Story Time Stories That Rhyme, PO Box 416, Denver, CO 80201-0416. TEL 303-575-5676, a@curriculumresourceonline.com, http://www.curriculumresourceonline.com. Ed. A Doyle TEL 303-575-5676.

375 USA ISSN 0147-2453
Z1035.A1
CURRICULUM REVIEW. Text in English. 1960. m. USD 169 (effective 2004). adv. bk.rev. illus. back issues avail.; reprints avail. **Document type:** *Newsletter, Trade.* **Description:** For teachers of grades K-12. Each issue contains articles, columns, and reports on current trends in curriculum development. Provides analytical reviews of textbooks, supplement materials, multimedia kits, and software.
Former titles (until Dec. 1975): C A S Review; C S Review
Related titles: Microform ed.: (from PQC); Online - full text ed.: (from EBSCO Publishing, Florida Center for Library Automation, Gale Group, H.W. Wilson, O C L C Online Computer Library Center, Inc., ProQuest Information & Learning).
Indexed: ABIn, BRI, CBRI, CPE, ChPerI, EduInd, MRD.
—BLDSC (3505.283000).
Published by: PaperClip Communications, 125 Paterson Ave, Little Falls, NJ 07424. TEL 973-256-1333, FAX 973-256-8088, info@paper-clip.com, http://www.paper-clip.com. Circ: 4,800.

CURRICULUM - TECHNOLOGY QUARTERLY. see *EDUCATION—Computer Applications*

371.3 700 DNK ISSN 0909-5926
D B 3 BILLEDKUNST. Text in Danish. 1978. q. DKK 370 membership (effective 2004). illus. **Document type:** *Academic/Scholarly.*
Formerly (until 1994): D F 3 Formning (0107-9387)
Published by: Danmarks Billedkunstlaerere/Association of Art Teachers in Denmark, c/o Inger Johansen, Kamma Rahbeksvej 48, Aabyhoj, 8230, Denmark. TEL 45-86-158236, ingerjoh@mail1.stofanet.dk. Ed. Inger Johansen.

371.3 USA
D E T C NEWS. Text in English. 1971. s-a. free. bk.rev. illus.; stat. **Document type:** *Newsletter.* **Description:** Describes the council's activities and provides articles on the distance education industry.
Formerly (until 19??): N H S C News (0027-6596)
Published by: Distance Education & Training Council, 1601 18th St, N W, Washington, DC 20009. TEL 202-234-5100. Ed. Sally R Welch. Circ: 1,500.

DANCE TEACHER. see *DANCE*

THE DANGLING MODIFIER. see *LITERATURE*

371.33 469 USA
DE PAR EN PAR. Text mainly in Spanish. 1993. irreg. (approx bi-m). free. illus. back issues avail. **Document type:** *Trade.* **Description:** Provides classroom teachers of Spanish as a foreign language with interesting items to read and study, all of which reflect Spanish cultural heritage.
Media: Online - full content.
Published by: Embajada de Espana en Estados Unidos, Consejeria de Educacion/Spanish Embassy in the US, Education Office, 2375 Pennsylvania Ave, NW, Washington, DC 20037-1736. TEL 202-728-2335, FAX 202-728-2313, http://www.spainembedu.org/deparenpar.

DEUTSCH - BETRIFFT UNS. see *LINGUISTICS*

DEUTSCH: LEHREN UND LERNEN. see *LINGUISTICS*

DER DEUTSCHE LEHRER IM AUSLAND. see *LINGUISTICS*

▼ **DEUTSCHMAGAZIN.** see *LINGUISTICS*

DEYU XUEXI/LEARNING GERMAN. see *LINGUISTICS*

371.3 FRA ISSN 0223-3592
DIALOGUE (IVRY); education, formation recherche. Text in French. 1971. 4/yr. EUR 28 domestic; EUR 31 foreign (effective 2003). bk.rev. illus. 50 p./no.; back issues avail. **Document type:** *Magazine.* **Description:** Publishes articles of interest to parents and teachers.
Published by: Groupe Francais d'Education Nouvelle, 14 Av Spinoza, Ivry-sur-Seine, 94200, France. TEL 33-1-4672-5317, FAX 33-1-4671-6338, gfen@gfen.asso.fr, http://www.gfen.asso.fr. Ed., R&P Marie Serpereau. Circ: 1,500.

DIALOGUES ET CULTURES. see *LINGUISTICS*

375.006 SVN ISSN 0354-0421
➤ **DIDAKTA.** Text in Slovenian. 1991. 5/yr. USD 44; USD 10 newsstand/cover (effective 2005). adv. **Document type:** *Journal, Academic/Scholarly.* **Description:** Contains articles on the theory of education, psychology, and samples of excellent teaching practices aimed at primary school teachers.
Published by: Didakta d.o.o., Gorenjska 33c, Radovljica, 4240, Slovenia. TEL 386-4-5320200, FAX 386-4-5320211, revija@didakta.si, http://www.revija.didakta.si. Ed. Carmen Lasic. Pub. Rudi Zaman. R&P, Adv. contact Jana Babsek. color page USD 1,000. Circ: 1,000 (paid and controlled).

371.334 ITA ISSN 0419-1218
DIDATTICA DELLE SCIENZE E INFORMATICA NELLA SCUOLA. Text in Italian. 1965. bi-m. EUR 44 domestic; EUR 55 in Europe; EUR 70 elsewhere (effective 2005). adv. **Document type:** *Journal, Academic/Scholarly.*
Published by: Editrice La Scuola SpA, Via Luigi Cadorna 11, Brescia, BS 25124, Italy. TEL 39-030-29931, FAX 39-030-2993299, http;//www.lascuola.it. Ed. Luigi Morgano. Circ: 6,000.

DIG. see *ARCHAEOLOGY*

407.1 USA
DIMENSION (YEAR). Text in English. 1966. a. USD 10 (effective 2002). back issues avail. **Document type:** *Proceedings.*
Formerly: Dimension. Languages (Year) (0070-4881)
Related titles: Microfiche ed.
Published by: (Southern Conference on Language Teaching), S C O L T Publications, c/o Lee Bradley, Pub, Valdosta State University, Valdosta, GA 31698. TEL 912-333-7358, FAX 912-333-7389, lbradley@valdosta.edu, http://www.valdosta.edu/scolt/. Eds. C Maurice Cherry, David Alley. R&P Lee Bradley. Circ: 1,000 (paid).

371.3 658.8 USA ISSN 1080-0476
DIMENSIONS (RESTON). Text in English. 1947. 4/school-academic yr. USD 5 (effective 2005). adv. bk.rev. illus. 28 p./no. 2 cols./p.; **Document type:** *Magazine, Trade.* **Description:** Aimed at students enrolled in a marketing education program at the high school through college level, and for college students preparing to teach marketing education. Topics include marketing, entrepreneurship and business.Leadership; career and professional development.
Former titles (until 1994): D E C A Dimensions (1060-6106); (until 1992): New Dimensions (Reston) (0279-473X); (until 1982): D E C A Distributor (0011-4847)
Published by: D E C A, Inc., 1908 Association Dr, Reston, VA 22091-1594. TEL 703-860-5000, FAX 703-860-4013, deca-dimensions@deca.org, decainc@aol.com, http://www.deca.org. Ed. Traci Tavares. adv.: page USD 2,700; 7 x 10. Circ: 161,000 (paid).

327.2 AUT
DIPLOMATISCHE AKADEMIE WIEN. FAVORITA PAPERS. Text in German. 1997. irreg. (4-5/yr.). price varies. **Document type:** *Monographic series, Academic/Scholarly.* **Description:** Contains texts and essays focusing on the practical conduct and training of diplomatic and consular relations, including substantive reports on program items regarding contemporary problems facing Austria and Europe.
Formerly (until 2001): Diplomatische Akademie Wien. Occasional Papers
Published by: Diplomatische Akademie Wien, Favoritenstr 15a, Vienna, W 1040, Austria. TEL 43-1-5057272, FAX 43-1-5042265, diplomat@dak-vienna.ac.at, http://www.da-vienna.ac.at. Ed. Paul Leifer. Adv. contact Gerhard Reiweger.

327.2 AUT ISSN 0419-1722
DIPLOMATISCHE AKADEMIE WIEN. JAHRBUCH. Text in German. 1965. a. EUR 9 (effective 2005). **Document type:** *Journal, Trade.* **Description:** Contains curricula of the international postgraduate training programs, list of public lectures, and abstracts of conferences and seminars.
Published by: Diplomatische Akademie Wien, Favoritenstr 15a, Vienna, W 1040, Austria. TEL 43-1-5057272, FAX 43-1-5042265, info@da-vienna.ac.at, http://www.da-vienna.ac.at. Ed. Paul Leifer. Adv. contact Gerhard Reiweger. Circ: 1,500.

371.334 USA ISSN 1540-0026
DIRECT INSTRUCTION NEWS. Text in English. 2001. s-a. free to members (effective 2003).
Supersedes in part (in 2001): Effective School Practices (1068-7378); Which was formerly (until 1992): Association for Direct Instruction. News (1057-8595)

E

Published by: Association for Direct Instruction, PO Box 10252, Eugene, OR 97440. TEL 541-485-1293, FAX 541-683-7543, info@adihome.org, http://www.adihome.org.

371.358 GBR ISSN 1326-0065
➤ **DISTANCE EDUCATION JOURNAL**✶ . Text in English. s-a. GBP 38, USD 58, AUD 107 to individuals; GBP 117, USD 180, AUD 180 to institutions (effective 2004). bk.rev. **Document type:** *Journal, Academic/Scholarly.*
Media: Online - full text.
Published by: Carfax Publishing Ltd. (Subsidiary of: Taylor & Francis Group), 4 Park Sq, Milton Park, Abingdon, Oxfordshire OX14 4RN, United Kingdom. TEL 44-1235-828600, FAX 44-1235-829000, enquiry@tandf.co.uk, http://www.tandf.co.uk/journals/carfax/01587919.html.

371.334 USA ISSN 1547-4712
▼ **DISTANCE LEARNING.** Text in English. 2004 (Feb.). 6/yr. USD 60 to individuals; USD 160 to institutions; USD 45 to students; USD 25 per issue (effective 2006). **Document type:** *Journal, Academic/Scholarly.* **Description:** Provides information for those who provide instruction to all types of learners, of all ages, using telecommunication technologies of all types.
Related titles: Online - full text ed.: (from ProQuest Information & Learning).
Published by: (United States Distance Learning Association), Information Age Publishing, Inc., 411 W Putnam Ave, Ste 205, PO Box 4967, Greenwich, CT 06831. TEL 203-661-7602, FAX 203-661-7952, info@infoagepub.com, http://www.infoagepub.com. Ed. Michael Simonson.

375 USA
DISTRICT ADMINISTRATION; the magazine for K-12 education leaders. Text in English. 1972. m. (10/yr.). free (effective 2005). adv. bk.rev.; film rev.; play rev. illus.; tr.lit. **Document type:** *Magazine, Trade.*
Former titles (until 2004): Curriculum Administrator (1082-5495); (until 1994): Curriculum Product News (1063-3375); (until 1988): District Educator's Curriculum Product Review (1052-2085); (until 198?): Curriculum Product Review (0273-7418)
Related titles: Online - full text ed.: (from EBSCO Publishing, Florida Center for Library Automation, Gale Group).
Published by: Educational Media, Inc. (Subsidiary of: Hanson Publishing Group, Inc.), 488 Main Ave, Norwalk, CT 06851 . TEL 203-663-0100, FAX 203-663-0149, http://www.districtadministration.com. Ed. Wayne D'Orio. Pub. Dan Kinnaman. Circ: 54,599 (controlled).

DONAIRE. see *EDUCATION—International Education Programs*

372.21 RUS ISSN 0012-561X
➤ **DOSHKOL'NOE VOSPITANIE.** Text in Russian. 1928. m. USD 99 foreign (effective 2005). adv. bk.rev. bibl.; illus. **Document type:** *Magazine, Consumer.* **Description:** Provides information aimed at pre-school and kindergarten teachers.
Related titles: Microfiche ed.: (from EVP).
—East View.
Published by: Redaktsiya Zhurnala Doshkol'noe Vospitanie, Pokrovskii bulv 4-17, str 5, Moscow, 101833, Russian Federation. TEL 7-095-9247512, FAX 7-095-9247620. Ed., Pub. Valentina M Kuzina. R&P Viacheslav M Shurukov TEL 7-095-924-7606. Adv. contact Galina A Trostyanskaya. B&W page RUR 10,000. Circ: 70,000 (paid). **Dist. by:** M K - Periodica, ul Gilyarovskogo 39, Moscow 129110, Russian Federation. TEL 7-095-2845008, FAX 7-095-2813798, info@periodicals.ru, http://www.mkniga.ru.

371.335 027.8 NLD ISSN 1569-9633
DOSSIER KENNIS EN MEDIA. Text in Dutch. 1983. bi-m. EUR 46.32 (effective 2005). bk.rev. illus. **Document type:** *Journal, Trade.* **Description:** Publishes concise articles on using various media in secondary education in teaching and independent study. Discusses the keeping of resources in print and other media in a classroom or a school library.
Formerly (until 2002): Het Studiehuis (1388-3194); Supersedes (in 1998): Selectie Aanschafinformatie Voortgezet Onderwijs (0927-2186)
Related titles: CD-ROM ed.
Published by: Biblion Uitgeverij, Postbus 437, Leidschendam, 2260 AK, Netherlands. info@nbdbiblion.nl, http://www.nbdbiblion.nl/?pagina=7464. Ed. Margreet van den Berg. **Dist in Belgium:** Swets Belgium NV, Eigenlostraat 21, St-Niklaas 9100, Belgium. TEL 32-37-806262, FAX 32-37-806299.

371.3 FRA ISSN 1264-3025
DOSSIERS PEDAGOGIQUES. Text in French. 1994. irreg.
Published by: Institut National de la Jeunesse et de l'Education Populaire, Parc du Val-Flory, Rue Paul Leplat, BP 35, Marly-le-Roi, 78160, France. TEL 33-1-39172727, FAX 33-1-39172790. Ed. Jacques Touzeau.

DRAGON. see *LITERATURE*

DRAGONFLY TEACHER'S COMPANION. see *SCIENCES: COMPREHENSIVE WORKS*

371.3 792 SWE ISSN 1652-9286
▼ **DRAMAFORUM.** Variant title: Drama Forum. Text in Swedish. 2004. q. SEK 240 (effective 2005). **Document type:** *Journal, Trade.*
Published by: Riksorganisationen Auktoriserade Dramapedagoger/Swedish Association of Authorized Drama Pedagogues, c/o Susanne Ruthstroem, Saetrahoejden 144 B, Gaevle, 80638, Sweden. redaktion.rad@dramapedagogen.nu.

DRAMATICS; the magazine for students and teachers of theatre. see *THEATER*

DRUG EDUCATION MATTERS. see *DRUG ABUSE AND ALCOHOLISM*

DYVOSLOVO. see *LINGUISTICS*

E B E JOURNAL. see *BUSINESS AND ECONOMICS*

371.335 ITA ISSN 0393-098X
E D A V. (Educazione Audiovisiva) Text in Italian. 1972. m. (10/yr.). EUR 52 domestic; EUR 63 foreign (effective 2003). back issues avail. **Document type:** *Academic/Scholarly.* **Description:** Covers current news in the field of education and problems that mass media creates related to education.
Related titles: Video ed.
Published by: Centro Internazionale dello Spettacolo e della Comunicazione Sociale (C.I.S.C.S.), Via Giovanni Giolitti 208, Rome, 00185, Italy. TEL 39-06-7027212, edav@edav.it, cisc@edav.it, http://www.edav.it. Ed. Nazareno Taddei.

E L GAZETTE. (English Language) see *LINGUISTICS*

E L T JOURNAL; an international journal for teachers of English to speakers of other languages. (English Language Teaching) see *LINGUISTICS*

371.334 GBR ISSN 1741-8887
▼ ➤ **E-LEARNING.** Text in English. 2004. q. GBP 140 domestic to libraries; USD 205 foreign to libraries (effective 2005). **Document type:** *Journal, Academic/Scholarly.* **Description:** Aims to serve as an international forum to facilitate current research, practice and development of e-learning in education.
Media: Online - full content.
Published by: Symposium Journals (Subsidiary of: wwwords Ltd), PO Box 204, Didcot, Oxford, OX11 9ZQ, United Kingdom. TEL 44-1235-818062, FAX 44-1235-817275, info@symposium-journals.co.uk, subscriptions@symposium-journals.co.uk, http://www.wwwords.co.uk/elea/, http://www.symposium-journals.co.uk/. Eds. Colin Lankshear, James Paul Gee, Michele Knobel.

371.3 USA
E N C FOCUS. Text in English. w. **Document type:** *Journal, Academic/Scholarly.* **Description:** Covers topical issues in math & science education.
Media: Online - full content. **Related titles:** Print ed.
Published by: Eisenhower National Clearinghouse for Mathematics and Science Education, 1929 Kenny Rd., Columbus, OH 43210. TEL 614-292-7784, 800-621-5785, FAX 614-292-2066, editor@enc.org, info@enc.org, http://www.enc.org/features/focus/?ls=fe.

375 AUS ISSN 1320-2944
E Q AUSTRALIA. (Education Quarterly) Text in English. 1993. q. AUD 28 domestic to individuals; AUD 34 foreign to individuals; AUD 68 domestic to institutions; AUD 70 foreign to institutions (effective 2000). adv.
Related titles: Online - full content ed.
Indexed: AEI.
Published by: Curriculum Corporation, Casselden Place, Level 5, 2 Lonsdale St, Melbourne, VIC 3000, Australia. TEL 61-3-9207-9600, FAX 61-3-9639-1616, maree.grace@curriculum.edu.au, http://www.curriculum.edu.au/curriculum/eq_aust/eq_art/eqindex.htm. Ed. Kathy Skelton. R&P, Adv. contact Maree Grace. B&W page AUD 850; trim 230 x 188. Circ: 4,000. **Subscr. to:** PO Box 177, Carlton, VIC 3053, Australia.

E S L MAGAZINE. (English as a Second Language) see *LINGUISTICS*

371.3 USA
EARLY CHILDHOOD DIGEST; families and teachers as partners. Text in English. q. **Document type:** *Trade.* **Description:** Reports on ways that families and schools can work together to help young children learn.
Published by: (National Institute on Early Childhood Development and Education), U.S. Department of Education, Office of Educational Research and Improvement, c/o Holly Kreider, Harvard Family Research Project HFRP, 38 Concord Ave, Cambridge, MA 02138. TEL 617-496-4304, 800-872-5327, http://www.ed.gov/offices/OERI/ECI/publications.html.

379.112 USA ISSN 1055-4157
EARLY CHILDHOOD LAW AND POLICY REPORTER. Text in English. 1991. 2 base vols. plus m. updates. looseleaf. USD 495 (effective 2006). **Document type:** *Trade.* **Description:** Covers federal and state judicial decisions, U.S. Department of Education policy rulings, letters of finding and memoranda, and state administrative decisions.
—CCC.
Published by: L R P Publications, 747 Dresher Rd, PO Box 980, Horsham, PA 19044. TEL 215-784-0860, 800-341-7874, FAX 215-784-9639, custserve@lrp.com, http://www.shoplrp.com/product/p-300008.html, http://www.lrp.com.

371.3 USA
▼ **EARLY CHILDHOOD LEARNING**; resources for successful teaching. Text in English. 2005. a. USD 4.95 per issue (effective 2005). adv. **Document type:** *Magazine, Trade.*
Published by: Education Center, Inc., 3515 W Market St, Ste 200, PO Box 9753, Greensboro, NC 27403. TEL 336-854-0407, 877-696-0825, FAX 336-547-1586, http://www.theeducationcenter.com. Pub. Anne Sumpter. adv.: color page USD 3,000; trim 5.5 x 7.625.

371.33 USA ISSN 1070-1214
CODEN: SDREEG
EARLY CHILDHOOD TODAY. Abbreviated title: E C T. Text in English. 1986. 8/yr. USD 19.95; USD 4 per issue (effective 2005). adv. illus. 3 cols./p.; **Document type:** *Magazine, Trade.* **Description:** Provides teaching tips, curriculum activities, management strategies, and technology updates tailored to the needs of early childhood educators.
Formerly (until 1993): Scholastic Pre-K Today (0888-3009)
Related titles: Online - full text ed.: (from bigchalk, EBSCO Publishing, H.W. Wilson, O C L C Online Computer Library Center, Inc., ProQuest Information & Learning).
Indexed: ABIn, CIJE, EduInd.
Published by: Scholastic Inc., 557 Broadway, New York, NY 10012-0399. TEL 212-343-6100, 800-544-2917, FAX 212-343-4808, ect@scholastic.com, http://www.earlychildhoodtoday.com, http://www.scholastic.com. adv.: B&W page USD 5,445, color page USD 6,010; trim 7 x 9.75. Circ: 55,000 (paid). **Subscr. to:** 2931 E McCarthy St, PO Box 3710, Jefferson City, MO 65102-9957. TEL 800-724-6527, classmags@scholastic.com.

371.3 GBR ISSN 0957-5146
LB1139.2
➤ **EARLY YEARS**; an international journal of research and development. Text in English. 1980. 3/yr. GBP 196, USD 315 combined subscription to institutions print & online eds. (effective 2006). reprint service avail. from PSC. **Document type:** *Journal, Academic/Scholarly.* **Description:** Understanding the early years of education, both scholarly and practical articles.
Related titles: Online - full text ed.: ISSN 1472-4421. GBP 186, USD 299 to institutions (effective 2006) (from EBSCO Publishing, Gale Group, IngentaConnect, O C L C Online Computer Library Center, Inc., Swets Information Services).
Indexed: BrEdI, CPE, ERA, ETA, MEA, RHEA, SEA, SENA, SOMA, TEA.
—BLDSC (3643.002200), IE, Infotrieve, ingenta. **CCC.**
Published by: (Training, Advancement & Co-operation in Teaching Young Children), Routledge (Subsidiary of: Taylor & Francis Group), 4 Park Sq, Milton Park, Abingdon, Oxon OX14 4RN, United Kingdom. TEL 44-1235-828600, FAX 44-1235-829000, info@routledge.co.uk, http://www.tandf.co.uk/journals/titles/09575146.asp, http://www.routledge.com. Eds. Geva Blenkin, Rod Parker-Rees. **Subscr. to:** Taylor & Francis Ltd, Journals Customer Service, Rankine Rd, Basingstoke, Hants RG24 8PR, United Kingdom. TEL 44-1256-813000, FAX 44-1256-330245.

371.3 BRB
EASTERN CARIBBEAN STANDING CONFERENCE ON TEACHER EDUCATION. REPORT. Text in English. 1957. biennial. BBD 30. **Document type:** *Proceedings.*
Formerly: Conference on Teacher Education in the Eastern Caribbean. Report (0069-8695)
Published by: University of the West Indies, Faculty of Education, P.O. Box 64, Bridgetown, Barbados. FAX 246-425-1327, TELEX UNIVADOS WB2257. Ed. W. K. King. Circ: 800.

ECODATE. see *BUSINESS AND ECONOMICS*

448 FRA ISSN 0761-3903
L'ECOLE DES LETTRES DES COLLEGES. Text in French. 1908. 14/yr. **Description:** Serves as a professional review of French language, history and geography.
Former titles (until 1964): Ecole. Cycle d'Observation et Classes de 4e et 3e Enseignement Litteraire (1153-1622); (until 1960): Ecole. Classes du 1er Cycle Enseignement Litteraire (1153-1630)
Published by: Ecole des Loisirs, 11 Rue de Sevres, Paris, Cedex 6 75278, France. TEL 33-1-42229410, FAX 33-1-45480499, http://www.ecoledesloisirs.fr. Ed. Michele Filatoff.

371.3 FRA ISSN 0765-6017
ECOLES DES LETTRES. SECOND CYCLE. Text in French. 1908. 14/yr. adv. **Description:** Acts as a forum for the methods and contents for teaching.
Former titles: Ecole. Classes du Second Cycle Enseignement Litteraire (1153-1649); Revue Pedagogique et Litteraire (0070-7139)
—BLDSC (3648.681800), IE, ingenta. **CCC.**
Published by: Ecole des Loisirs, 11 Rue de Sevres, Paris, Cedex 6 75278, France. TEL 33-1-42229410, FAX 33-1-45480499, http://www.ecoledesloisirs.fr. Ed., R&P, Adv. contact Claude Riva TEL 33-1-44229410.

E

EDITION Q U E M. (Qualifikations Entwicklungs Management) see *BUSINESS AND ECONOMICS—Personnel Management*

371.33 VEN ISSN 0013-1075
L45
EDUCACION✶ ; revista para el magisterio. Text in Spanish. 1975 (vol.37). q. free. bibl.; charts; illus.; stat. cum.index.
Indexed: HistAb.
Published by: Ministerio de Educacion, c/o Ministerio de Relaciones Exteriores, Direccion de Relaciones Culturales, Caracas, Venezuela. Ed. Ligia de Lima de Bianchi. Circ: 30,000.

371.33 GBR
EDUCATE ONLINE. Text in English. 1995. d.
Media: Online - full text.
Published by: Chan Publishing, 45 St Austell Rd, Weston-super-Mare, Somerset, BS22 8LJ, United Kingdom. TEL 44-193-441-9665, FAX 44-193-464-2287, sales@educate.co.uk, http://www.educate.co.uk/. Ed. Jean Smith. Circ: 75,000.

EDUCATING ABLE CHILDREN. see *EDUCATION—Special Education And Rehabilitation*

371.335 FRA ISSN 0768-2662
EDUCATION 2000. Text in French. 1971. q. **Description:** Discusses audio-visual aids.
Published by: Institut Superieur de Paris, 3 rue de l'Abbaye, Paris, 75006, France. Ed. Gilles Delavaud.

EDUCATION ABOUT ASIA. see *ASIAN STUDIES*

371.334 USA ISSN 1360-2357
LB1028.43 CODEN: EITEFA
➤ **EDUCATION AND INFORMATION TECHNOLOGIES.** Text in English. 1996. q. EUR 460, USD 460, GBP 288 combined subscription to institutions print & online eds. (effective 2005). adv. back issues avail.; reprint service avail. from PSC. **Document type:** *Journal, Academic/Scholarly.* **Description:** Publishes articles from all sectors of education on all aspects of information and information systems.
Related titles: Online - full text ed.: ISSN 1573-7608 (from EBSCO Publishing, Gale Group, IngentaConnect, Kluwer Online, O C L C Online Computer Library Center, Inc., Springer LINK, Swets Information Services).
Indexed: BibLing, BrEdI, CPE, CompLI, Inspec.
—BLDSC (3661.188100), IE, Infotrieve, ingenta. **CCC.**
Published by: (I F I P Technical Committee on Education), Springer-Verlag New York, Inc. (Subsidiary of: Springer Science+Business Media), 233 Spring St, New York, NY 10013. TEL 212-460-1500, FAX 212-460-1575, service@springer-ny.com, http://springerlink.metapress.com/openurl.asp?genre=journal&issn=1360-2357, http://www.springer-ny.com. Ed. Deryn M Watson. **Subscr. to:** Journal Fulfillment, PO Box 2485, Secaucus, NJ 07096-2485. TEL 201-348-4033, FAX 201-348-4505, journals@springer-ny.com.

371 USA
EDUCATION BULLETIN. Text in English. 1998. bi-w. free. **Document type:** *Newsletter.* **Description:** Helps teachers and other educators stay informed on a variety of issues affecting education and the K-12 classroom.
Media: Online - full text. **Related titles:** E-mail ed.
Published by: Association for Supervision and Curriculum Development, 1703 N Beauregard St, Alexandria, VA 22311. TEL 703-578-9600, FAX 703-575-5400, member@ascd.org, update@ascd.org, http://www.ascd.org. Circ: 3,000.

EDUCATION IN CHEMISTRY. see *CHEMISTRY*

EDUCATION LEADER; news and views on education. see *EDUCATION—School Organization And Administration*

371.3 USA ISSN 1094-5296
➤ **EDUCATION REVIEW**; a journal of book reviews. Text in English. 1998. irreg. free (effective 2005). bk.rev. back issues avail. **Document type:** *Journal, Trade.* **Description:** Publishes reviews of current books in education.
Media: Online - full text.
Indexed: AEI, BrEdI.
Address: c/o Gene V Glass, Arizona State University, College of Education, Tempe, AZ 85287. TEL 480-965-9644, glass@asu.edu, burbules@uiuc.edu, http://coe.asu.edu/edrev. Ed., R&P Gene V Glass.

371.3 USA
THE EDUCATION STANDARD; independent reporting on education for employment. Text in English. 1994. bi-w. USD 298. charts; maps; stat. back issues avail. **Document type:** *Newsletter.* **Description:** Publishes national, state and local news on education for employment programs, with special reference to grants and funding, curriculum development, program models and research.
Formerly: School to Work (1069-5257)
Published by: M I I Publications, Inc., 773 15th St NW Ste 900, Washington, DC 20005-2112. TEL 202-347-4822, FAX 202-347-4893, service@miipublications.com, http://www.miipublications.com. Eds. Lori Heymann, Cecilio J Morales. Pub. Cecilio J Morales. R&P David Barrows TEL 202-347-4822 ext 101.

EDUCATION TECHNOLOGY LITERATURE REVIEW. see *EDUCATION—School Organization And Administration*

371.3 GBR ISSN 1460-0463
EDUCATION TODAY (MAIDSTONE). Text in English. 1992. m. GBP 32.50 domestic; GBP 50 in Europe; GBP 65 elsewhere (effective 2004). adv. **Document type:** *Magazine, Trade.* **Description:** Provides up-to-the-minute information on the N.C., L. M. S. and the supplies and services available to the 5-16 market. It also helps decision makers plug into the constantly changing elements of technology, equipment, services, teaching methods and aids.
—**CCC.**
Published by: Datateam Publishing Ltd, 15a London Rd, Maidstone, Kent ME16 8LY, United Kingdom. TEL 44-1622-687031, FAX 44-1622-757646, education@datateam.co.uk, info@datateam.co.uk, http://www.datateam.co.uk/business_publications/education_today.htm, http://www.datateam.co.uk/home/home.htm. adv.: B&W page GBP 1,500, color page GBP 1,900; trim 192 x 275.

371.3 USA
EDUCATION WORLD; where educators go to learn. Text in English. w. **Document type:** *Academic/Scholarly.* **Description:** Contains articles on issues that are of interest to educators, parents, and students, including new lesson plans and curriculum ideas.
Media: Online - full text.
Published by: American Fidelity Educational Services webmaster@education-world.com, http://www.education-world.com/. **Co-sponsors:** National Education Association; Vocational Industrial Clubs of America.

371.3 GBR ISSN 0965-0792
LB1028.24 CODEN: EACRE9
➤ **EDUCATIONAL ACTION RESEARCH.** Text in English. 1993. q. GBP 318, USD 491 combined subscription to institutions print & online eds. (effective 2006). bk.rev. abstr.; illus. reprint service avail. from PSC. **Document type:** *Journal, Academic/Scholarly.* **Description:** Covers participatory research and action inquiry in education and across the professions.
Related titles: Online - full text ed.: ISSN 1747-5074. GBP 302, USD 466 to institutions (effective 2006) (from EBSCO Publishing, Swets Information Services).
Indexed: ASSIA, BrEdI, CPE, DIP, EAA, ERA, ETA, IBR, IBZ, MEA, RHEA, SEA, SENA, SOMA, SOPODA, SSA, SWA, TEA.
—BLDSC (3661.356500), IE, Infotrieve, ingenta. **CCC.**
Published by: Routledge (Subsidiary of: Taylor & Francis Group), 4 Park Sq, Milton Park, Abingdon, Oxon OX14 4RN, United Kingdom. TEL 44-1235-828600, FAX 44-1235-829000, journals@routledge.com, http://www.tandf.co.uk/journals/titles/09650792.asp, http://www.routledge.co.uk. Eds. Carol Munn-Giddings, Christopher Day, Julienne Meyer.

371.3 USA ISSN 1047-8248
LA217 CODEN: EDFOF3
➤ **EDUCATIONAL FOUNDATIONS.** Text in English. 1986. 4/yr. USD 50 to individuals; USD 80 to institutions (effective 2005). adv. illus. back issues avail.; reprints avail. **Document type:** *Journal, Academic/Scholarly.* **Description:** Features the social foundations of education.
Related titles: Online - full text ed.: (from H.W. Wilson, O C L C Online Computer Library Center, Inc., ProQuest Information & Learning).
Indexed: ABIn, CIJE, CPE, DIP, ERA, ETA, EduInd, IBR, IBZ, MEA, RHEA, SEA, SENA, SOMA, SOPODA, SSA, TEA.
—BLDSC (3661.414200), IE, ingenta.
Published by: (American Educational Studies Association), Caddo Gap Press, 3145 Geary Blvd,, PMB 275, San Francisco, CA 94118. TEL 415-666-3012, FAX 415-666-3552, info@caddogap.com, http://www.caddogap.com. Ed. William T Pink. Pub., R&P, Adv. contact Alan H Jones. page USD 200; 4.5 x 7. Circ: 400 (paid).

371.3 USA ISSN 0013-1784
L11
EDUCATIONAL LEADERSHIP. Text in English. 1943. 8/yr. (Sep.-May). USD 36 (effective 2005). adv. bk.rev. charts; illus. 96 p./no. 3 cols./p.; back issues avail.; reprint service avail. from PQC. **Document type:** *Journal, Academic/Scholarly.* **Description:** Each issue is devoted to an important contemporary theme in learning and teaching at all levels. Expert researchers and practitioners share diverse insights and viewpoints on social, psychological, and pedagogical topics.
Related titles: Audio cassette/tape ed.; Microform ed.: (from PQC); Online - full text ed.: (from EBSCO Publishing, Florida Center for Library Automation, Gale Group, H.W. Wilson, O C L C Online Computer Library Center, Inc., ProQuest Information & Learning); ♦ Supplement(s): Classroom Leadership.
Indexed: ABIn, ASCA, AcaI, AgeL, BRI, CBRI, CIJE, CPE, CurCont, DIP, EAA, ECER, EduInd, FamI, IBR, IBZ, L&LBA, MASUSE, MEA, PCI, RILM, SENA, SOMA, SOPODA, SSCI.
—BLDSC (3661.427000), IDS, IE, Infotrieve, ingenta. **CCC.**
Published by: Association for Supervision and Curriculum Development, 1703 N Beauregard St, Alexandria, VA 22311. TEL 703-578-9600, FAX 703-575-5400, el@ascd.org, update@ascd.org, http://www.ascd.org/portal/site/ascd/menuitem.a4dbd0f2c4f9b94cdeb3ffdb62108a0c/. Ed. Margaret M Scherer. R&Ps Christine Richards TEL 800-933-2723 ext 5749, Suellen Christopoulos. Adv. contact Teola T Jones. Circ: 175,000 (paid).

EDUCATIONAL MARKETER; the educational publishing industry's voice of authority since 1968. see *PUBLISHING AND BOOK TRADE*

371.335 USA ISSN 8755-2094
LB1028.3
EDUCATIONAL MEDIA AND TECHNOLOGY YEARBOOK. Text in English. 1973. a., latest vol.28, 2003. USD 75 per vol. (effective 2003). **Description:** Provides an up-to-date overview of educational media, technology, and communications; includes information on professional associations, graduate programs, foundations, and funding sources.
Formerly (until 1985): Educational Media Yearbook (0000-037X)
Indexed: CIJE.
—BLDSC (3661.452000), IE, ingenta.
Published by: Libraries Unlimited, Inc. (Subsidiary of: Greenwood Publishing Group Inc.), 88 Post Road W, Westport, CT 06881. TEL 800-225-5800, FAX 203-222-1502, lu-books@lu.com. Eds. Mary Ann Fitzgerald, Robert Maribe Branch.

371.335 GBR ISSN 0952-3987
LB1043
➤ **EDUCATIONAL MEDIA INTERNATIONAL.** Text in English. 1961. q. GBP 251, USD 413 combined subscription to institutions print & online eds. (effective 2006). adv. bk.rev. illus. reprint service avail. from PQC,PSC. **Document type:** *Journal, Academic/Scholarly.* **Description:** Discusses innovations in educational technology.
Former titles (until 1986): Educational Media International (0004-7597); (until 1971): Audio-Visual Media (0571-8716)
Related titles: Microfilm ed.: (from PQC); Online - full text ed.: ISSN 1469-5790. GBP 238, USD 392 to institutions (effective 2006) (from EBSCO Publishing, Gale Group, IngentaConnect, O C L C Online Computer Library Center, Inc., Swets Information Services).
Indexed: ABIn, AHCI, BrEdI, CIJE, CPE, CommAb, ERA, ETA, EduInd, ExcerpMed, HECAB, Inspec, MEA, MEA&I, RHEA, SEA, SENA, SOMA, SWA, TEA.
—BLDSC (3661.454000), IE, ingenta. **CCC.**
Published by: (International Council for Educational Media), Routledge (Subsidiary of: Taylor & Francis Group), 4 Park Square, Milton Park, Abingdon, Oxon OX14 4RN, United Kingdom. TEL 44-1235-828600, FAX 44-1235-829000, http://www.tandf.co.uk/journals/routledge/09523987.asp, http://www.routledge.co.uk. Ed. John Hedberg. R&P Sally Sweet. Circ: 500. **Subscr. in N America to:** Taylor & Francis Inc., Customer Services Dept, 325 Chestnut St, 8th Fl, Philadelphia, PA 19106. TEL 800-354-1420, FAX 215-625-8914; **Subscr. to:** Taylor & Francis Ltd, Journals Customer Service, Rankine Rd, Basingstoke, Hants RG24 8PR, United Kingdom. TEL 44-1256-813000, FAX 44-1256-330245, enquiry@tandf.co.uk.

371.3 AUS ISSN 1323-577X
CODEN: EPTHFY
➤ **EDUCATIONAL PRACTICE AND THEORY.** Text in English. 1978. s-a. AUD 374 domestic to institutions; AUD 340 in New Zealand to institutions; GBP 168 in Europe to institutions; USD 260 elsewhere to institutions (effective 2005). adv. bk.rev. index. back issues avail. **Document type:** *Journal, Academic/Scholarly.* **Description:** Investigates trends in educational practice and theory by focusing on educational reforms, teaching methods, curriculum evaluation and comparative studies in education and social change.
Formerly (until 1995): New Education (0156-0905)
Indexed: AEI, CPE, ERA, ETA, L&LBA, MEA, PCI, REE&TA, RHEA, SEA, SENA, SOMA, SOPODA, SWA, TEA.
Published by: James Nicholas Publishers, Pty. Ltd., PO Box 244, Albert Park, VIC 3206, Australia. TEL 61-3-96905955, FAX 61-3-96992040, custservice@jamesnicholaspublishers.com.au, http://www.jamesnicholaspublishers.com.au/epatjrnl.htm. Ed. Dr. Joseph Zajda. Pub. Rea Zajda. R&P Mary Berchmans. Adv. contact Irene Schevchenko.

371.3 GBR
EDUCATIONAL REVIEW PUBLICATIONS. HEADLINE SERIES✶ Text in English. 1988 (no.14); N.S. 1993. irreg., latest vol.5. GBP 64 in United Kingdom to individuals; GBP 118 foreign to individuals; GBP 218 in United Kingdom to institutions; GBP 528 foreign to institutions. adv. bk.rev. **Document type:** *Monographic series, Academic/Scholarly.*
Formerly: Educational Review Occasional Publication
Published by: Educational Review Publications, University of Birmingham, School of Education, Edgbaston, Birmingham B15 2TT, United Kingdom. Ed. Barrie Wade. Adv. contact Rachel Wage. Circ: 750.

E

EDUCATIONAL TECHNOLOGY; the magazine for managers of change in education. see *COMPUTERS—Computer Assisted Instruction*

EDUCATIONAL TECHNOLOGY & SOCIETY. see *EDUCATION—Computer Applications*

371.33523 USA ISSN 1042-1629
LB1028.3 CODEN: ETRDE5
➤ **EDUCATIONAL TECHNOLOGY RESEARCH & DEVELOPMENT.** Short title: E T R and D. Text in English. 1989. q. USD 75 domestic to individuals; USD 100 foreign to individuals; USD 150 domestic to institutions; USD 175 foreign to institutions (effective 2005). adv. bk.rev. abstr.; charts; illus. index. back issues avail.; reprint service avail. from PQC. **Document type:** *Journal, Academic/Scholarly.* **Description:** Covers research theory and comments on all phases of educational technology and communications.
Formed by the merger of (1977-1989): Journal of Instructional Development (0162-2641); (1953-1989): Educational Communications and Technology Journal (0148-5806); Which was formerly (unil 1978): A V Communication Review (0001-2890); (until 1963): Audio Visual Communication Review (0885-727X)
Related titles: Microform ed.: (from PQC); Online - full text ed.: ISSN 1556-6501 (from EBSCO Publishing, H.W. Wilson, O C L C Online Computer Library Center, Inc., ProQuest Information & Learning).
Indexed: ABIn, ASCA, ArtHuCI, CIJE, CPE, ChPerl, CommAb, CurCont, EAA, ERA, ETA, EduInd, Inspec, L&LBA, MEA, PsycInfo, PsycholAb, RHEA, SEA, SENA, SOMA, SOPODA, SSCI, T&DA, TEA, e-psyche.
—BLDSC (3662.531500), AskIEEE, IDS, IE, Infotrieve, ingenta.
Published by: Association for Educational Communications and Technology, 1800 N Stonelake Dr, Ste 2, Bloomington, IN 47404. TEL 812-335-7675, FAX 812-335-7678, aect@aect.org, http://www.aect.org/. Eds. Michael Spector, Steven M Ross. Circ: 5,000 (paid).

371.3 BEL ISSN 1265-1362
EDUCATIONS; revue de diffusion des savoir en education. Text in French. 1994. q.
Published by: De Boeck Universite, Fond Jean-Paques 4, Louvain-la-Neuve, 1348, Belgium. TEL 32-10-482511, FAX 32-10-482519, info@universite.deboeck.com, http://universite.deboeck.com. Ed. Myriam Matonog.

371.12 USA ISSN 0279-3539
EDUCATOR (CONCORD). Text in English. 1920. 8/yr. USD 3.60 to non-members. adv. bk.rev.; film rev. illus. **Document type:** *Newspaper.*
Formerly (until 1981): New Hampshire Educator (0028-5234)
Published by: National Education Association - New Hampshire, 103 N State St, Concord, NH 03301-4340. TEL 603-224-7751, FAX 603-224-2648, http://www.neanh.org. Ed. Carol Carstarphen. Circ: 7,800.

371.335 USA
LB1044
EDUCATORS GUIDE TO FREE FILMS, FILMSTRIPS AND SLIDES. Text in English. 1941. a., latest 62nd Ed. USD 36.95 per issue (effective 2002 - 2003). index. 162 p./no.; **Document type:** *Directory, Academic/Scholarly.* **Description:** Contains films, filmstrips, slides, and audiotapes available free of cost throughout the United States.
Formed by the merger of: Educators Guide to Free Films (0070-9395); Educators Guide to Free Filmstrips and Slides (1044-5943); Which was formerly: Educators Guide to Free Filmstrips, Slides, and Audiotapes (0070-9409)
Published by: Educators Progress Service, Inc., 214 Center St, Randolph, WI 53956. TEL 920-326-3126, FAX 920-326-3127, http://www.freeteachingaids.com/vfc_877083363.html. Ed. Kathleen Suttles Nehmer.

371.335 USA ISSN 0070-9417
HF5381.A1
EDUCATORS GUIDE TO FREE GUIDANCE MATERIALS. Text in English. 1962. a., latest 41st Ed. USD 34.95 per issue (effective 2002 - 2003). 230 p./no.; **Document type:** *Directory, Academic/Scholarly.* **Description:** Lists free films, filmstrips, slides, videotapes, printed materials and websites.
Published by: Educators Progress Service, Inc., 214 Center St, Randolph, WI 53956. TEL 920-326-3126, FAX 920-326-3127, http://www.freeteachingaids.com/mmr_87708341X.html. Ed. Kathleen Suttles Nehmer.

613.7 USA ISSN 0424-6241
Z6121
EDUCATORS GUIDE TO FREE HEALTH, PHYSICAL EDUCATION & RECREATION MATERIALS. Text in English. 1968. a., latest 35th Ed. USD 34.95 per issue (effective 2002 - 2003). 226 p./no.; **Document type:** *Directory, Academic/Scholarly.* **Description:** Lists free films, filmstrips, slides, videotapes, printed materials, and websites.
Published by: Educators Progress Service, Inc., 214 Center St, Randolph, WI 53956. TEL 920-326-3126, FAX 920-326-3127, http://www.freeteachingaids.com/mmr_877083428.html. Ed. Kathleen Suttles Nehmer.

371.3 USA ISSN 0070-9425
Q181.A1
EDUCATORS GUIDE TO FREE SCIENCE MATERIALS. Text in English. 1960. a., latest 43rd Ed. USD 35.95 per issue (effective 2002 - 2003). index. 214 p./no.; **Document type:** *Directory, Academic/Scholarly.* **Description:** Lists free films, filmstrips, slides, tapes, printed materials, and websites.
Published by: Educators Progress Service, Inc., 214 Center St, Randolph, WI 53956. TEL 920-326-3126, FAX 920-326-3127, http://www.freeteachingaids.com/mmr_877083398.html. Ed. Kathleen Suttles Nehmer.

371.3 USA ISSN 0070-9433
EDUCATORS GUIDE TO FREE SOCIAL STUDIES MATERIALS. Text in English. 1961. a., latest 42nd Ed. USD 35.95 per issue (effective 2002 - 2003). 312 p./no.; **Document type:** *Directory, Academic/Scholarly.* **Description:** Covers free films, filmstrips, slides, tapes, printed materials, and websites.
—Linda Hall.
Published by: Educators Progress Service, Inc., 214 Center St, Randolph, WI 53956. TEL 920-326-3126, FAX 920-326-3127, http://www.freeteachingaids.com/mmr_877083401.html. Ed. Kathleen Suttles Nehmer.

371.3 USA ISSN 1550-3917
LB1043.Z9
EDUCATORS GUIDE TO FREE VIDEOTAPES (ELEMENTARY/MIDDLE SCHOOL ED.). Text in English. a. (3rd Ed.), latest 2002-2003. USD 36.95 per issue (effective 2002). 318 p./no.; **Document type:** *Directory, Academic/Scholarly.*
Supersedes in part (in 2000): Educators Guide to Free Videotapes (1068-9206); Which had former titles (until 1992): Educators Guide to Free Audio and Video Materials (0160-1296); (until 1977): Educators Guide to Free Tapes, Scripts and Transcriptions (0070-9441)
Published by: Educators Progress Service, Inc., 214 Center St, Randolph, WI 53956. TEL 920-326-3126, FAX 920-326-3127, http://www.freeteachingaids.com/vfc_877083460.html. Ed. Kathleen Suttles Nehmer.

371.3 USA
LB1043.Z9
EDUCATORS GUIDE TO FREE VIDEOTAPES (SECONDARY ED.). Text in English. 1954. a., latest 49th Ed. USD 36.95 per issue (effective 2002 - 2003). 305 p./no.; **Document type:** *Directory, Academic/Scholarly.* **Description:** Lists free videotapes specially suited for students in grades K-8.
Supersedes in part (in 2000): Educators Guide to Free Videotapes (1068-9206); Which was formerly (until 1992): Educators Guide to Free Audio and Video Materials (0160-1296); (until 1977): Educators Guide to Free Tapes, Scripts, and Transcriptions (0070-9441)
Published by: Educators Progress Service, Inc., 214 Center St, Randolph, WI 53956. TEL 920-326-3126, FAX 920-326-3127, http://www.freeteachingaids.com/vfc_877083347.html. Ed. Kathleen Suttles Nehmer.

371.3 USA ISSN 1079-610X
EFFECTIVE TEACHING; the Carolina Colloquy's electronic journal of university teaching and learning. Text in English. irreg.
Media: Online - full content.
Published by: University of North Carolina at Wilmington, Institute for College and University Teaching, The Carolina Colloquy for University Teaching, Wilmington, NC 28403. http://cte.uncwil.edu/et/.

371.0712 DEU ISSN 1617-4003
AS182.W655
EICHSTAETTER ANTRITTSVORLESUNGEN. Text in German. 1999. irreg. EUR 8.69 per issue (effective 2002). **Document type:** *Monographic series, Academic/Scholarly.*
Published by: (Universitaet Eichstaett), Verlag Kastner & Zeeb, Schlosshof 2-6, Wolnzach, 85283 , Germany. TEL 49-8442-92530, FAX 49-8442-2289, verlag@kastner.de, http://www.kastner.de.

371.0712 DEU ISSN 0722-1010
EICHSTAETTER MATERIALIEN. Text in German. irreg., latest vol.16. price varies. **Document type:** *Monographic series, Academic/Scholarly.*
Published by: (Universitaet Eichstaett), Verlag Friedrich Pustet, Gutenbergstr 8, Regensburg, 93051, Germany. TEL 49-941-920220, FAX 49-941-948652, verlag@pustet.de, http://www.pustetverlag.de.

EICHSTAETTER UNIVERSITAETSREDEN. see *RELIGIONS AND THEOLOGY—Roman Catholic*

ELEARN MAGAZINE. see *COMPUTERS—Computer Assisted Instruction*

371.358 GBR ISSN 1479-4403
▼ **ELECTRONIC JOURNAL OF E-LEARNING.** Text in English. 2003. s-a. free (effective 2005). **Description:** Provides perspectives on topics relevant to the study, implementation and management of e-Learning initiatives.
Media: Online - full content.
Published by: Management Centre International Ltd., Curtis Farm, Kidmore End, Near Reading, RG4 9AY, United Kingdom. TEL 44-1189-724148, FAX 44-1189-724691, submussions@ejel.org, http://www.ejel.org/index.htm.

ELECTRONIC JOURNAL OF MULTICULTURAL EDUCATION. see *EDUCATION—International Education Programs*

ELECTRONIC LEARNING. see *COMPUTERS—Computer Assisted Instruction*

371.335 USA
ELECTRONIC MEDIA FOR THE SCHOOL MARKET (YEAR): REVIEW, TRENDS & FORECAST. Text in English. a. USD 1,995 (effective 2005). **Document type:** *Directory, Trade.* **Description:** Examines the application of new technologies in education and how they are being integrated into school curricula. Profiles important companies.
Published by: SIMBA Information (Subsidiary of: R.R. Bowker LLC), 60 Long Ridge Rd., Ste 300, Stamford, CT 06902. TEL 203-325-8193, 800-307-2529, FAX 203-325-8915, info@simbanet.com, http://www.simbanet.com/publications/preorder_emsm2004.htm.

372.86 USA ISSN 9874-5832
➤ **ELEMENTARY PHYS-ED NEWSLETTER.** Text in English. 1977. 5/yr. **Document type:** *Newsletter, Academic/Scholarly.* **Description:** Provides tips and advice on teaching physical education at the elementary school level.
Published by: Whitney Publications, Inc., 147 Lake Valley Rd, Morristown, NJ 07960. TEL 908-219-0284, FAX 908-219-0182, gniking@excite.com. Circ: 1,200.

375 USA ISSN 0070-9980
Z5817.2
ELEMENTARY TEACHERS GUIDE TO FREE CURRICULUM MATERIALS. Text in English. 1944. a., latest 59th Ed. USD 36.95 per issue (effective 2002 - 2003). 312 p./no.; **Document type:** *Directory, Academic/Scholarly.* **Description:** Lists free pamphlets, pictures, and chart materials.
Published by: Educators Progress Service, Inc., 214 Center St, Randolph, WI 53956. TEL 920-326-3126, FAX 920-326-3127, http://www.freeteachingaids.com/pm_87708338X.html. Ed. Kathleen Suttles Nehmer.

371.3 CAN
ELIBRARY CANADA CURRICULUM EDITION. Text in English. 1981. d. CND 2,000 to libraries (effective 2005). **Description:** Contains K-12 periodical and multimedia resources for students.
Media: Online - full content.
Published by: Micromedia ProQuest (Subsidiary of: ProQuest Information & Learning), 20 Victoria St, Toronto, ON M5C 2N8, Canada. TEL 416-362-5211, 800-387-2689, FAX 416-362-6161, info@micromedia.ca, http://www.micromedia.ca/products_services/eLibrary/eLibrary_ce.htm.

EMBAJADA DE ESPANA. LONDRES. CONSEJERIA DE EDUCACION Y CIENCIA. BOLETIN. see *EDUCATION—International Education Programs*

371.3 DEU ISSN 0931-5020
➤ **EMPIRISCHE PAEDAGOGIK**; Zeitschrift zu Theorie und Praxis erziehungswissenschaftlicher Forschung. Text in German. 1987. q. EUR 36 (effective 2003). adv. bk.rev. 115 p./no. 1 cols./p.; back issues avail. **Document type:** *Journal, Academic/Scholarly.* **Description:** Presents papers on empirical education.
Indexed: DIP, IBR, IBZ.
Published by: Empirische Paedagogik e.V., Buergerstr. 23, Landau In Der Pfalz, 76829, Germany. TEL 49-6341-906165, FAX 49-6341-906166, ep@vep-landau.de, http://www.vep-landau.de. Ed., Adv. contact R.S. Jaeger TEL 49-6341-906175. Circ: 250.

371.33 USA ISSN 1094-3838
➤ **ENCOUNTER: EDUCATION FOR MEANING AND SOCIAL JUSTICE.** Text in English. 1987. q. USD 39.95 domestic to individuals; USD 48.95 foreign to individuals; USD 85 domestic to institutions; USD 94 foreign to institutions (effective 2005). adv. bk.rev. illus.; abstr. 64 p./no. 2 cols./p.; back issues avail. **Document type:** *Magazine, Trade.* **Description:** Includes information on education from a holistic perspective and focuses its role in helping a student develop a sense of personal meaning and social justice.
Formerly (until Jan. 1998): Holistic Education Review (0898-0926)
Related titles: Online - full text ed.: (from EBSCO Publishing, ProQuest Information & Learning, SoftLine Information).
Indexed: AltPI.
—**CCC.**
Published by: Psychology Press (Subsidiary of: Taylor & Francis Inc.), 39 Pearl St., Brandon, VT 05733. encounter@great-ideas.org, http://www.great-ideas.org/enc.htm. Ed. William Crain. Pub. Charles Jakiela. Circ: 650 (paid and free).
Co-publisher: Holistic Education Press.

371.3 DEU ISSN 0723-3507
ENGAGEMENT; Zeitschrift fuer Erziehung und Schule. Text in German. 1983. q. adv. bk.rev. back issues avail. **Document type:** *Journal, Academic/Scholarly.*
Indexed: DIP, IBR, IBZ.
—**CCC.**

E

Published by: (Zentralstelle Bildung der Deutschen Bischofskonferenz), Aschendorffsche Verlagsbuchhandlung, Soester Str 13, Muenster, 48135, Germany. TEL 49-251-690-0, FAX 49-251-690143, buchverlag@aschendorff.de, http://www.aschendorff.de/buch. Ed. Eckhard Nordhofen. R&P Dirk F Passmann. Adv. contact Petra Landsknecht. Circ: 1,400.

ENGLISCH BETRIFFT UNS. see *LINGUISTICS*

371.3 GBR ISSN 1355-0721
➤ **ENGLISH & MEDIA MAGAZINE.** Text in English. 1979. 3/yr. GBP 56; GBP 29 to libraries (effective 2000). adv. bk.rev.; software rev. back issues avail. **Document type:** *Academic/Scholarly.*
Formerly (until 1993): English Magazine (0144-6487)
Indexed: ChLitAb.
—BLDSC (3772.910000), IE. **CCC.**
Published by: English & Media Centre, 136 Chalton St, London, NW1 1RX, United Kingdom. TEL 44-20-73830488, FAX 44-20-73833688. Ed. Michael Simons. R&P Fran Stowell TEL 44-20-7383-0488. Circ: 7,000. **Dist by:** Nate, 50 Broadfield Rd, Sheffield, S Yorks S8 0XJ, United Kingdom. TEL 44-1142-555419, FAX 44-1142-555296.

418 USA ISSN 0007-8204
LA632
➤ **ENGLISH EDUCATION**; official journal of the Conference on English Education and Communication. Text in English. 1963. 4/yr. USD 45 (effective 2003). adv. bk.rev. illus. index. reprint service avail. from PQC. **Document type:** *Journal, Academic/Scholarly.*
Formerly (until 1968): Conference on English Education. Selected Addresses Delivered (0573-3561)
Related titles: Microfilm ed.: (from PQC); Online - full text ed.: (from EBSCO Publishing, ProQuest Information & Learning).
Indexed: ABIn, CIJE, CPE, CurCont, EduInd, SSCI.
—BLDSC (3773.490000), IE, ingenta. **CCC.**
Published by: (Conference on English Education), National Council of Teachers of English, 1111 W Kenyon Rd, Urbana, IL 61801-1096. TEL 217-328-3870, 800-369-6283, FAX 217-328-9645, rsmith@ncte.org, http://www.ncte.org/pubs/journals/ee. Eds. Cathy Fleischer, Dana Fox. R&P Barbara Lamar. Adv. contact Carrie Stewart. Circ: 3,100.

➤ **ENGLISH FOR SPECIFIC PURPOSES.** see *LINGUISTICS*

371.33 052 808.51 GBR ISSN 1460-5945
ENGLISH FOUR TO ELEVEN. Text in English. 1992. 3/yr. GBP 10, USD 23 (effective 2001). software rev.; bk.rev. bibl.; charts; illus. back issues avail. **Document type:** *Magazine.* **Description:** Deals with all aspects of teaching English language and literatures in the age range of 4 - 11.
Formerly (until 1997): Primary English (0965-5263)
Indexed: CPE.
Published by: The English Association, University of Leicester, University Rd, Leicester, LE1 7RH, United Kingdom. TEL 44-116-252-3982, FAX 44-116-252-2301, engassoc@le.ac.uk. Eds. John Paine, Susanna Garlorth. R&P Helen Lucas. Circ: 500.

371.39 420 AUS ISSN 0155-2147
➤ **ENGLISH IN AUSTRALIA.** Text in English. 1965. 3/yr. AUD 55 domestic; AUD 80 foreign (effective 2005). adv. bk.rev. 96 p./no.; back issues avail. **Document type:** *Journal, Academic/Scholarly.* **Description:** Contains articles of academic interest, and teacher resource materials in the field of English. Includes reviews of new textbooks and fiction relevant to teachers and librarians.
Incorporates (1970-1994): A.A.T.E. Guide to English Books and Resources
Related titles: Online - full text ed.: (from R M I T Publishing).
Indexed: AEI, AusPAIS, BEL&L, CIJE, ChLitAb, SOPODA.
—BLDSC (3772.940000), IE, ingenta.
Published by: Australian Association for the Teaching of English, PO Box 3203, Norwood, SA 5067, Australia. TEL 61-8-3322845, FAX 61-8-3330394, aate@aate.org.au, http://www.aate.org.au. Ed. Wayne Sawyer. R&P, Adv. contact Robyn Cations. Circ: 5,000.

428 GBR ISSN 0425-0494
➤ **ENGLISH IN EDUCATION.** Text in English. 1964. 3/yr. free to members (effective 2005). adv. reprint service avail. from PQC. **Document type:** *Journal, Academic/Scholarly.* **Description:** Presents study and teaching methods.
Related titles: Microform ed.: (from PQC).
Indexed: BrEdI, CIJE, CPE, ChLitAb, ERA, ETA, HECAB, LT&LA, MEA, RHEA, SEA, SENA, SOMA, TEA.
—BLDSC (3773.500000), IE, ingenta. **CCC.**
Published by: National Association for the Teaching of English, 50 Broadfield Rd, Sheffield, S Yorks S8 0XJ, United Kingdom. TEL 44-114-2555419, FAX 44-114-2555296, info@nate.org.uk, http://www.nate.org.uk/. Adv. contact Lyn Fairfax. Circ: 5,500.

372.6 USA ISSN 0425-0508
➤ **ENGLISH IN TEXAS.** Text in English. 1969. 3/yr. USD 30 includes membership (effective 2003). adv. bk.rev. **Document type:** *Academic/Scholarly.* **Description:** Publishes articles on English and language arts instruction from elementary through university levels, as well as poetry and fiction.
Indexed: CIJE, MLA-IB.
—IDS.
Published by: Texas Council of Teachers of English, 1300 San Pedro, San Antonio, TX 78212. TEL 409-294-1151, FAX 409-294-1153, lis_tsl@shsu.edu, http://www.tcte.org/engintx.html. Ed. Kylene Beers. Pub., R&P, Adv. contact Teri Lesesne. Circ: 2,500 (paid).

418 USA ISSN 0013-8274
PE1
➤ **ENGLISH JOURNAL.** Text in English. 1912. bi-m. USD 25 to members; USD 75 to non-members (effective 2005). adv. bk.rev.; rec.rev. illus. index. reprint service avail. from PQC. **Document type:** *Magazine, Academic/Scholarly.* **Description:** Allows for middle- and high-school English teachers to explore important issues in teaching language arts and literature.
Related titles: Microform ed.: (from PMC, PQC); Online - full text ed.: (from EBSCO Publishing, JSTOR (Web-based Journal Archive), O C L C Online Computer Library Center, Inc., ProQuest Information & Learning).
Indexed: ABIn, AES, Acal, BRI, CBRI, CIJE, CPE, ChLitAb, CurCont, ECER, EduInd, FLI, IAPV, JHMA, L&LBA, LIFT, LRI, LT&LA, MLA, MLA-IB, MRD, MagInd, PCI, PSI, RASB, SOPODA, SSCI, TOM, WBA, WMB.
—BLDSC (3775.020000), IE, Infotrieve, ingenta. **CCC.**
Published by: National Council of Teachers of English, 1111 W Kenyon Rd, Urbana, IL 61801-1096. TEL 217-328-3870, 800-369-6283, FAX 217-328-9645, rsmith@ncte.org, membership@ncte.org, http://www.ncte.org/pubs/journals/ej. Ed. Virginia Monseau. R&P Barbara Lamar. Adv. contact Carrie Stewart. Circ: 51,000 (paid).

➤ **ENGLISH LANGUAGE AND ORIENTATION PROGRAMS IN THE UNITED STATES**; including a list of summer programs for training teachers of English as a second language. see *LINGUISTICS*

371.3 370.711 GBR ISSN 1365-3741
ENGLISH LANGUAGE TEACHER EDUCATION AND DEVELOPMENT. Text in English. 1995. s-a. **Description:** Provides a forum for the exchange of ideas and information on theoretical and applied issues pertaining to English language teacher education.
Indexed: L&LBA.
Published by: University of Birmingham, Centre for English Language Studies, Westmere, Edgbaston, Birmingham B15 2TT, United Kingdom. TEL 44-121-4145695, FAX 44-121-4143298, CELS@bham.ac.uk, http://www.cels.bham.ac.uk/ELTED/. Ed. Corony Edwards.

418 371.3 USA ISSN 1054-1578
LB1620.5
ENGLISH LEADERSHIP QUARTERLY. Text in English. 1972 (vol.3). q. USD 65 to individuals includes $40 membership fee; USD 75 to institutions (effective 2005). adv. **Document type:** *Newsletter.* **Description:** Assists educators in supervisory positions in exploring issues in English language arts instruction.
Former titles (until 1991): C S S E D C Quarterly (0738-1409); (until 1979): C S S E D C Newsletter
Related titles: Online - full text ed.: (from EBSCO Publishing, ProQuest Information & Learning).
—CCC.
Published by: (Conference on English Leadership), National Council of Teachers of English, 1111 W Kenyon Rd, Urbana, IL 61801-1096. TEL 217-328-3870, 800-369-6283, FAX 217-328—9645, cschanche@ncte.org, http://www.ncte.org/pubs/journals/elq. Ed. Henry Kiernan. R&P Barbara Lamar. Adv. contact Carrie Stewart. Circ: 2,000.

418 CAN ISSN 0013-8355
PR31
➤ **ENGLISH QUARTERLY.** Text in English. 1968. s-a. bk.rev. illus. index. **Document type:** *Academic/Scholarly.* **Description:** Dedicated to scholarship levels and theory at all levels of English education.
Related titles: Microfiche ed.: (from MML); Microfilm ed.: (from MML); Microform ed.: (from MIM, MML, PQC); Online - full text ed.: (from Micromedia ProQuest).
Indexed: CEI, CIJE, CPE, MEA, SEA.
—BLDSC (3775.113000), IE, ingenta. **CCC.**
Published by: Canadian Council of Teachers of English and Language Arts, #10-730 River Rd, University of Manitoba, Winnipeg, MB R2M 5A4, Canada. TEL 204-474-8564, FAX 204-474-7551, watsonm@ms.umanitoba.ca. Eds. Allan Patenaude, Jon Bradley. Pub. Stephanie Purvis. Circ: 500.

418 ISR ISSN 0333-533X
PE1068.I8
ENGLISH TEACHERS' JOURNAL (ISRAEL). Text in English; Summaries in Hebrew. 1968. s-a. bk.rev.
Incorporates: English Teaching Guidance
Indexed: CIJE, L&LBA, LT&LA, SOPODA.
—BLDSC (3775.147000).
Published by: (Israel. English Inspectorate), Ministry of Education, 34 Shivtei Israel St., P O Box 292, Jerusalem, 91911, Israel. Ed. Raphael Gefen. Circ: 2,000. **Subscr. to:** Eric Cohen Ltd., 5 Hankin St., Raanana, Israel.

L'ENSEIGNEMENT PHILOSOPHIQUE. see *PHILOSOPHY*

371.33 USA
ENTRY POINTS. Text in English. 1998. irreg., latest vol.2. USD 25; USD 5 newsstand/cover (effective 2005). back issues avail. **Document type:** *Consumer.* **Description:** Offers teachers creative ideas they can use in the classroom, elementary, middle school, and secondary.
Published by: Country Road Software, 517 S Fifth St, Goshen, IN 46526-2927. crs1@entrypoints.com, http://entrypoints.com. Ed. Mark Jordan.

ENTWURF; religionspaedagogische Mitteilungen. see *RELIGIONS AND THEOLOGY—Protestant*

EQUINE VETERINARY EDUCATION. see *VETERINARY SCIENCE*

ESCHOOL NEWS. see *EDUCATION—School Organization And Administration*

ESPERANTO-NYTT. see *LINGUISTICS*

371.33 USA ISSN 1499-190X
ESSENTIAL RESOURCES FOR SCHOOLS AND LIBRARIES. Text in English. 1979. 5/yr. looseleaf. USD 20 domestic; CND 21 in Canada; USD 25 elsewhere. adv. **Document type:** *Newsletter, Trade.* **Description:** Provides schools and libraries with a list of recommended free materials and services, websites, research units, unique periodical reviews, and informative articles.
Former titles (until 2001): Free Materials for Schools and Libraries (0836-0073); (until 1987): Free! The Newsletter of Free Materials and Services (0708-4625)
Published by: Connaught Education Services, Box 34069, Dept 349, Seattle, WA 98124. TEL 604-689-1568, FAX 604-689-1767, jclark@smartt.com, http://www.connaughted.com. Ed., Pub., R&P Jim Clark. Adv. contact Sylvia Lim. Circ: 2,500 (paid).

▼ **ESSENTIAL TEACHER.** see *LINGUISTICS*

ESTADISTICAS DE EDUCACION EXTRAESCOLAR. see *EDUCATION—Abstracting, Bibliographies, Statistics*

371.3 USA
ESTES EDUCATOR NEWS. Text in English. 1973. irreg. (3-4/yr.). free to qualified personnel. adv.
Published by: Estes Industries, 1295 H St, Penrose, CO 81240. TEL 719-372-6565, FAX 719-372-3419. Ed. Jim Kranich. Circ: 50,000.

ESTUDIOS BIBLICOS PARA NINOS. MAESTROS. see *RELIGIONS AND THEOLOGY—Protestant*

371.3 AUS ISSN 1448-1324
▼ **ETHOS**; ideas for the classroom discussions & reviews. Text in English. 2003. 3/yr. AUD 70 to individuals; AUD 100 to institutions; AUD 35 to students (effective 2000). adv. bk.rev.
Formed by the merger of (1993-2003): Ethos 7-12 (1328-1941); (1993-2003): Ethos P-6 (1328-1925)
Related titles: Online - full text ed.: (from EBSCO Publishing); ♦ Supplement(s): Ethos (Balaclava). ISSN 1328-1933.
Published by: Victorian Association of Social Studies Teachers Inc., 150 Palmerston St, Carlton, VIC 3053, Australia. TEL 61-3-93494957, FAX 61-3-93492050, vasst@vasst.asn.au, http://www.vasst.asn.au/. Ed., R&P Loretta Glass. Circ: 1,500.

EUCLIDES; maandblad voor de didactiek van de wiskunde. see *MATHEMATICS*

EUFONIA; didactica de la musica. see *MUSIC*

613.7 GBR ISSN 1356-336X
GV243
➤ **EUROPEAN PHYSICAL EDUCATION REVIEW.** Text in English. 1978. 3/yr. GBP 257, USD 449 to institutions; GBP 267, USD 468 combined subscription to institutions print & online eds. (effective 2006). adv. bk.rev. **Document type:** *Journal, Academic/Scholarly.* **Description:** International interdisciplinary journal that seeks to stimulate and present scholarly enquiry in the broad field of physical education, including sport and leisure issues and research.
Formerly (until 1995): Physical Education Review (0140-7708)
Related titles: Online - full text ed.: ISSN 1741-2749. GBP 254, USD 444 to institutions (effective 2006) (from C S A, EBSCO Publishing, O C L C Online Computer Library Center, Inc., Sage Publications, Inc., Swets Information Services).
Indexed: AbHyg, BrEdI, CPE, EAA, ERA, ETA, MEA, NutrAb, PEI, RHEA, RRTA, SEA, SENA, SOMA, SWA, SportS, TEA, WAE&RSA, e-psyche.
—BLDSC (3829.779200), IE, Infotrieve, ingenta. **CCC.**
Published by: (North West Physical Education Authority), Sage Publications Ltd. (Subsidiary of: Sage Publications, Inc.), 1 Oliver's Yard, 55 City Rd, London, EC1 1SP, United Kingdom. TEL 44-20-73248500, FAX 44-20-73248600, info@sagepub.co.uk, http://www.sagepub.co.uk/journal.aspx?pid=105544. Ed. Ken Green. Adv. contact Jenny Kirby. page GBP 195; trim 194 x 114. **Subscr. in the Americas to:** Sage Publications, Inc., 2455 Teller Rd, Thousand Oaks, CA 91320. TEL 805-499-0721, FAX 805-499-0871, journals@sagepub.com.

E

➤ **EVANGELIZING TODAY'S CHILD.** see *RELIGIONS AND THEOLOGY—Protestant*

371.3 USA ISSN 0740-9893
LB1027
EXCELLENCE IN TEACHING. Text in English. 1984. q. bk.rev.; film rev. bibl. **Description:** Contains articles on teaching and the teaching profession, including those describing exemplary programs, projects, and research activities in primary and secondary schools.
Published by: Northern Arizona University, Center for Excellence in Education, PO Box 5774, Flagstaff, AZ 86011-5774. TEL 602-523-3480, FAX 602-523-1929. Ed. Stephen D Lapan. Circ: 800.

EXPLORE THE BIBLE: ADULT COMMENTARY. see *RELIGIONS AND THEOLOGY—Protestant*

371.39 USA ISSN 1534-2808
▼ **EXTREME TEACHING**; rigorous texts for troubled times. Text in English. 2003. irreg., latest 2004. price varies. **Document type:** *Monographic series.*
Published by: Peter Lang Publishing, Inc., 275 Seventh Ave, 28th Fl, New York, NY 10001. TEL 212-647-7700, 800-770-5264, FAX 212-647-7707, customerservice@plang.com, http://www.peterlangusa.com. Eds. Danny Weil, Joe L Kincheloe.

EYU XUEXI/LEARNING RUSSIAN. see *LINGUISTICS*

F F A NEW HORIZONS. (Future Farmers of America) see *AGRICULTURE*

371.3 DEU
FACHHOCHSCHULE KIEL. STUDIENFUEHRER UND PERSONAL VERZEICHNIS. Text in German. 1976. a. **Document type:** *Directory, Trade.*
Published by: Fachhochschule Kiel, Sokratesplatz 1, Kiel, 24149, Germany. TEL 49-431-2100, FAX 49-431-2101900, info@fh-kiel.de, http://www.fh-kiel.de. Circ: 3,000.

613.7 SCG ISSN 0354-4745
FACTA UNIVERSITATIS. SERIES PHYSICAL EDUCATION. Text in English, French, German. 1994. irreg., latest vol.1, no.4, 1997. **Document type:** *Journal, Academic/Scholarly.*
Published by: Univerzitet u Nishu/University of Nis, Univerzitetski Trg 2, P.O. Box 123, Nis, 18000. TEL 381-18-547970, FAX 381-18-547950, znenad@filfak.filfak.ni.ac.yu, facta@ni.ac.yu, http://facta.junis.ni.ac.yu/facta/pe/pe.html, http://ni.ac.yu. Ed. Nenad Zivanovic.

371.3 USA
FAMILY AND CONSUMER SCIENCES EDUCATOR. Text in English. 1927. s-a. membership. bk.rev. **Document type:** *Monographic series.* **Description:** Articles covering the changing times and offering guidelines for the teaching of classroom units.
Former titles: Home Economics Educator; Home Economics Education Association. Newsletter; Home Economics Education Association. Bulletin (0073-3091)
Published by: Family and Consumer Sciences Education Association, 400 E 8th Ave, Ellensburg, WA 98926-7565. TEL 509-963-2766. Circ: 2,000.

FAMILY BIBLE SERIES: ADULT TEACHER. see *RELIGIONS AND THEOLOGY—Protestant*

FAMILY BIBLE SERIES: CHILDREN'S TEACHER. see *RELIGIONS AND THEOLOGY—Protestant*

FAMILY BIBLE SERIES: PRESCHOOL TEACHER. see *RELIGIONS AND THEOLOGY—Protestant*

FAMILY BIBLE STUDY: SINGLE ADULT LEARNER GUIDE. see *RELIGIONS AND THEOLOGY—Protestant*

FAMILY WALK. see *RELIGIONS AND THEOLOGY—Protestant*

371.3 FRA
THE FARNATCHI SERIES. (Consists of: Farnatchi and the Foursome, Farnatchi in the Land of Illusions, Farnatchi and the Masked Ball, Farnatchi and the Mysterious Red Bag) Text in Arabic, English, French. 1995. 3/yr. price varies. **Description:** Teaching aid for the primary-school level with a focus on the dangers of tobacco, alcohol-dependency, drugs and AIDS.
Published by: UNESCO Publishing, 7 place de Fontenoy, Paris, 75352, France. TEL 33-1-45684300, FAX 33-1-45685737, http://www.unesco.org/publications. **Dist. in the U.S. by:** Bernan Associates, Bernan, 4611-F Assembly Dr., Lanham, MD 20706-4391. TEL 800-274-4447, FAX 800-865-3450. **Co-publisher:** Editions Vie et Sante.

FAYU XUEXI/APPRENONS LE FRANCAIS/LEARNING FRENCH. see *LINGUISTICS*

371.3 USA ISSN 0882-4843
LC197
➤ **FEMINIST TEACHER**; a journal of the practices, theories, and scholarship of feminist teaching. Text in English. 1984. 3/yr., latest vol.13. USD 30 domestic to individuals; USD 50 foreign to individuals; USD 75 domestic to institutions; USD 95 foreign to institutions (effective 2005). adv. bk.rev.; video rev. 90 p./no.; back issues avail. **Document type:** *Journal, Academic/Scholarly.* **Description:** Provides a forum for new ideas in the classroom. Includes articles and essays written for and by women teachers.
Related titles: Online - full text ed.: (from Gale Group, Northern Light Technology, Inc., O C L C Online Computer Library Center, Inc., ProQuest Information & Learning, SoftLine Information).
Indexed: ABIn, AltPI, CIJE, CPE, CWI, DYW, EduInd, FemPer, GendWatch, SEA, SWA, WSA, WSI.
—BLDSC (3905.197900).
Published by: Feminist Teacher Editorial Collective, c/o Theresa D. Kemp, Feminist Teacher Editorial Collective, English Department, University of Wisconsin, Eau Claire, PO Box 4004, Eau Claire, WI 54702-4004. feminist-teacher@wheatonma.edu, http://www.uwec.edu/wmns/FeministTeacher/. Circ: 600. **Subscr. to:** University of Illinois Press, 1325 S Oak St, Champaign, IL 61820-6903. TEL 217-244-0626, FAX 217-244-9910.

➤ **FICTION FOCUS**; New Titles for Teenagers. see *LITERATURE*

791.43 GBR ISSN 1367-5141
FILM AND TELEVISION IN EDUCATION. Text in English. 1991. biennial.
Formerly (until 1994): B U F V C Handbook for Film and Television in Education (0963-7478)
—BLDSC (3925.682153).
Published by: British Universities Film and Video Council, 77 Wells St., London, W1T 3QJ, United Kingdom. TEL 44-20-73931500, FAX 44-20-73931555, ask@bufvc.ac.uk, http://www.bufvc.ac.uk.

FILM & VIDEO; Fachinformation ueber Informationsvideos und 16mm Filme. see *COMMUNICATIONS—Video*

FILMSTRIP AND SLIDE SET FINDER. see *EDUCATION—Abstracting, Bibliographies, Statistics*

FIVE OWLS; a publication for readers, personally and professionally involved in children's literature. see *CHILDREN AND YOUTH—About*

FIZIKA V SHKOLE. see *PHYSICS*

FIZYKA W SZKOLE. see *PHYSICS*

375.001 DEU
FLOHS IDEENKISTE; Tipps von Lehrerinnnen und Lehrern fuer Lehrerinnen und Lehrern. Text in German. 4/yr. **Document type:** *Magazine, Academic/Scholarly.* **Description:** Contains information and advice on teaching methods from teachers for teachers.
Published by: Domino Verlag, Menziger Str 13, Munich, 80638, Germany. TEL 49-89-179130, FAX 49-89-1783788, vertrieb@domino-verlag.de, http://www.domino-verlag.de.

371.33 USA
FLORIDA ASSOCIATION FOR MEDIA IN EDUCATION. MEMBERSHIP DIRECTORY. Text in English. a. membership. adv. **Document type:** *Directory.* **Description:** Lists FAME members; describes the organization's activities, including awards and scholarships.
Published by: (Florida Association for Media in Education), Naylor Publications, Inc., 5950 NW 1st Pl, Gainesville, FL 32607-6018. TEL 800-369-6220, http://www.firn.edu/fame, http://www.naylor.com. Ed. Robin D Lamerson. Pub. Mike Winters. Circ: (controlled). **Orders to:** FAME, PO Box 70577, Ft. Lauderdale, FL 33307-0577. TEL 954-566-1312.

371.33 USA ISSN 1085-1976
FLORIDA MEDIA QUARTERLY. Text in English. 1973. q., latest vol.27, no.3. USD 40 membership; USD 50 foreign membership. adv. bk.rev.; film rev. charts; illus. **Document type:** *Newsletter.*
Supersedes (in Sep. 1975): F A M E Newsletter; Which superseded in part: Florida Audiovisual Association. A V A News (0046-4090)
Related titles: Online - full text ed.: (from H.W. Wilson, O C L C Online Computer Library Center, Inc.).
Indexed: CIJE, LibLit.
Published by: Florida Association for Media in Education, AMNI Association Management Network Inc, 320 West Sabal Palm Place, 150, Longwood, FL 32779. TEL 407-834-6688, 407-384-2075, FAX 407-834-4747, http://www.firn.edu/fame/fmq/index.html. Eds. Kathy Katz, Linda Miller. Adv. contacts Deborah Svec, Helen Zientek. B&W page USD 400, color page USD 600. Circ: 1,800.

FLYING TOGETHER. see *MUSIC*

401 430 375.4 DNK ISSN 1397-2340
DET FLYVENDE TAEPPE; nyt om undervisningen af tosprogede boern, unge og voksne. Text in Danish. 1995. q. **Description:** Teaching Danish to children and adult immigrants.
Related titles: Online - full content ed.: ISSN 1601-3409.
Published by: Ministeriet for Flygtninge, Indvandrere og Integration/Ministry of Refugee, Immigration, and Integration, Holbergsgade 6, Copenhagen K, 1057, Denmark. TEL 45-33-923380, FAX 45-33-111239, inm@inm.dk, http://www.inm.dk/Index/mainstart.asp?o=130&n=2&h=19&s=4. Ed. Jette Lou.

371.3 USA
THE FOCUS NEWSLETTER. Text in English. 3/yr. USD 33 membership (effective 2004); includes Focus on Education. **Document type:** *Newsletter, Trade.* **Description:** Keeps members informed with local current news and educational topics.
Published by: New Jersey Association for Supervision and Curriculum Development, 12 Center Dr, Monroe Township, NJ 08831. TEL 609-860-8991, FAX 609-860-6677, http://www.njascd.org. Ed. Scott Taylor.

FOCUS ON BUSINESS EDUCATION. see *BUSINESS AND ECONOMICS*

371.3 USA
➤ **FOCUS ON EDUCATION.** Text in English. 195?. a. USD 33 membership; includes Focus Newsletter. bk.rev. **Document type:** *Journal, Academic/Scholarly.* **Description:** Addresses the curricular, instructional, assessment, and supervisory aspects of education in New Jersey and nationwide.
Published by: New Jersey Association for Supervision and Curriculum Development, 12 Center Dr, Monroe Township, NJ 08831. http://www.njascd.org. R&P Alan Markowitz.

371.3 USA ISSN 1548-9167
FOCUS ON ELEMENTARY. Text in English. q. USD 30 to non-members; USD 15 to members (effective 2003). **Document type:** *Newsletter.* **Description:** Offers elementary-school teachers professional news, along with developmentally appropriate activities and other helpful pedagogical hints they can incorporate in their classroom teaching.
Published by: Association for Childhood Education International, 17904 Georgia Ave, Ste 215, Olney, MD 20832-2277. TEL 301-570-2111, 800-423-3563, FAX 301-570-2212, aceimemb@aol.com, http://www.acei.org/focusel.htm.

371.3 USA ISSN 1548-9140
FOCUS ON INFANTS & TODDLERS. Text in English. q. USD 30 to non-members; USD 15 to members (effective 2003). **Document type:** *Newsletter.* **Description:** Offers teachers working with infants and toddlers helpful news, developmentally appropriate activities, and teaching advice.
Published by: Association for Childhood Education International, 17904 Georgia Ave, Ste 215, Olney, MD 20832-2277. TEL 301-570-2111, 800-423-3563, FAX 301-570-2212, aceimemb@aol.com, http://www.acei.org.

371.3 USA ISSN 1548-9116
FOCUS ON MIDDLE SCHOOL. Text in English. q. USD 30 to non-members; USD 15 to members (effective 2003). **Description:** Offers middle-school teachers professional news and pedagogical hints, along with developmentally appropriate activities they can incorporate into their classroom teaching.
Published by: Association for Childhood Education International, 17904 Georgia Ave, Ste 215, Olney, MD 20832-2277. TEL 301-570-2111, 800-423-3563, FAX 301-570-2212, aceimemb@aol.com, http://www.acei.org/focuslc.htm.

371.3 USA ISSN 1548-9159
FOCUS ON PRE-K & K. Text in English. q. USD 30 to non-members; USD 15 to members (effective 2003). **Document type:** *Newsletter.* **Description:** Offers teachers working with pre-kindergarten and kindergarten children developmentally appropriate activities, news, and helpful pedagogical advice they can use in the classroom.
Formerly (until 1997): Focus on Early Childhood
Published by: Association for Childhood Education International, 17904 Georgia Ave, Ste 215, Olney, MD 20832-2277. TEL 301-570-2111, 800-423-3563, FAX 301-570-2212, aceimemb@aol.com, http://www.acei.org/focusec.htm.

371.3 USA ISSN 1548-9124
FOCUS ON TEACHER EDUCATION. Text in English. 2000. q. looseleaf. USD 30 to non-members; USD 15 to members (effective 2003). **Document type:** *Newsletter, Trade.* **Description:** Provides a forum for teacher educators' research, insights, advice and commentary.
Related titles: Online - full text ed.: ISSN 1548-9450.
Published by: Association for Childhood Education International, 17904 Georgia Ave, Ste 215, Olney, MD 20832-2277. TEL 301-570-2111, FAX 301-570-2212, aceimemb@aol.com, http://www.acei.org/focuste.htm. Ed. Rebecca P. Harlin. R&P Bruce Herzig.

418 USA ISSN 0163-5425
LB1576
FOCUS: TEACHING ENGLISH LANGUAGE ARTS. Text in English. 1974. 2/yr. USD 12. bk.rev. **Document type:** *Academic/Scholarly.*

E

Published by: Southeastern Ohio Council of Teachers of English, 14 Briarwood Dr, Athens, OH 45701-1301. TEL 614-592-2632. Ed. Ron Luce. Circ. 250.

FOOTBAL RULES BOOK. see *SPORTS AND GAMES—Ball Games*

FOOTBALL CASE BOOK. see *SPORTS AND GAMES—Ball Games*

FOREIGN CORRESPONDENT. see *CHILDREN AND YOUTH—For*

FOREIGN LANGUAGE ANNALS. see *LINGUISTICS*

FORM; et fagpedagogisk tidsskrift. see *ARTS AND HANDICRAFTS*

FORUM; English teaching. see *LINGUISTICS*

FORUM DEUTSCH. see *LINGUISTICS*

FORUM MUSIKPAEDAGOGIK. see *MUSIC*

FORUM OSWIATOWE. see *EDUCATION—Adult Education*

FORUM SPRACHLEHRFORSCHUNG. see *LINGUISTICS*

371.3   USA
FOXFIRE NEWS. Text in English. q. bk.rev. **Document type:** *Newsletter.*
Published by: Foxfire Fund, Inc., M 2837, Hwy 441 South, PO Box 541, Mountain City, GA 30562. TEL 706-746-5828, FAX 706-746-5829, foxfire@foxfire.org, http://www.foxfire.org. R&P Ann Moore.

FRANCAIS AU NIGERIA. see *LINGUISTICS*

448   DEU   ISSN 0342-2895
    CODEN: FRHEFO
FRANZOESISCH HEUTE; Informationsblaetter fuer Franzoesischlehrer in Schule und Hochschule. Text in French, German. 1972. q. EUR 26; EUR 8 newsstand/cover (effective 2004). adv. bk.rev. **Document type:** *Journal, Academic/Scholarly.*
Indexed: DIP, IBR, IBZ, L&LBA, MLA, MLA-IB, RILM. —BLDSC (4033.020700), IE, ingenta. **CCC.**
Published by: (Vereinigung der Franzoesischlehrer e.V.), Kallmeyersche Verlagsbuchhandlung GmbH, Im Brande 19, Seelze, 30926, Germany. TEL 49-511-40004175, FAX 49-511-40004176, leserservice@kallmeyer.de, http://www.kallmeyer.de. Circ. 3,500.

371.3   AUT
FREIE MEINUNG. Text in German. q. illus. **Document type:** *Magazine, Trade.*
Published by: Freiheitlicher Oesterreichischer Lehrerverband, Herbeckstr 59, Vienna, W 1180, Austria. postmaster@flv.at, http://www.flv.at/FM-Home/fmhome.htm. Ed. Liselotte Beran.

DER FREMDSPRACHLICHE UNTERRICHT. ENGLISCH; Grundlagen Unterrichtsvorschlaege Materialien. see *LINGUISTICS*

DER FREMDSPRACHLICHE UNTERRICHT. FRANZOESISCH. see *LINGUISTICS*

371.3 401 840   USA   ISSN 0016-111X
PC2001
FRENCH REVIEW. Text in English, French. 1927. 6/yr. USD 38 domestic; USD 43 foreign (effective 2005). adv. bk.rev. bibl. index. back issues avail.; reprint service avail. from PQC. **Document type:** *Journal, Academic/Scholarly.* **Description:** Contains articles and reviews on francophone culture, including literature, language, linguistics, culture, creative works, technology, etc.
Related titles: Fax ed.; Microform ed.: (from PMC, PQC); Online - full text ed.: (from JSTOR (Web-based Journal Archive)); Supplement(s): The French Review. Special Issue. ISSN 0271-3349. 1970.
Indexed: ABIn, ASCA, ArtHuCI, BRI, BibLing, CBRI, CIJE, CurCont, DIP, EduInd, FLI, HumInd, IBR, IBRH, IBZ, L&LBA, LT&LA, MLA, MLA-IB, PCI, RASB, RILM, SOPODA. —BLDSC (4034.450000), IDS, IE, Infotrieve, ingenta. **CCC.**
Published by: American Association of Teachers of French, Mailcode 4510, Dept of Foreign Languages, Southern Illinois University, Carbondale, IL 62901-4510. TEL 618-453-5731, FAX 618-453-5733, abrate@siu.edu, http://www.frenchteachers.org. Ed. Christopher P Pinet TEL 406-994-4448. Pub., R&P Jayne Abrate. Adv. contact Rosalie Vermette. Circ. 12,000 (paid).

371.334   USA
FROM NOW ON - THE EDUCATIONAL TECHNOLOGY JOURNAL∗. Text in English. 1990. m. **Description:** Explores the challenge of introducing new technologies to schools in ways which support the development of students' decision-making and problem-solving skills.
Media: Online - full text.

Address: 500 15th St, Bellingham, WA 98225-6113. TEL 360-637-8759, mckenzie@fromnowon.org, http://fromnowon.org. Ed. Jamieson McKenzie.

613.7   JPN
FUKUI UNIVERSITY. FACULTY OF EDUCATION. MEMOIRS. SERIES 6: PHYSICAL EDUCATION. Text in Japanese. a. free. **Document type:** *Academic/Scholarly.*
Published by: Fukui University, Faculty of Education/Fukui Daigaku Kyoikugakubu, 9-1 Bunkyo 3-chome, Fukui-shi, 910-0017, Japan.

371.3   AUS   ISSN 0313-6825
➤ **FUNCTION.** Text in English. 1977. 5/yr. AUD 20. adv. bk.rev. back issues avail. **Document type:** *Academic/Scholarly.* **Description:** Covers school mathematics.
Published by: Monash University, Department of Mathematics, PO Box 197, Caulfield East, VIC 3145, Australia. TEL 61-3-9903-2337, FAX 61-3-9903-2227, function@maths.monash.edu.au, http://www.maths.monash.edu.au/~cristina/function.html. Ed., R&P Cristina Varsavsky. Adv. contact Barbara Hardie. Circ. 300 (paid).

➤ **FUNMATH**; the annual delight. see *MATHEMATICS*

➤ **GANZTAGSSCHULE.** see *EDUCATION—School Organization And Administration*

371.3   DEU   ISSN 0943-8394
➤ **GEMEINSAM LEBEN**; Zeitschrift fuer integrative Erziehung. Text in German. 1993. q. EUR 45; EUR 12.50 newsstand/cover (effective 2003). adv. **Document type:** *Journal, Academic/Scholarly.*
Indexed: DIP, IBR, IBZ.
Published by: Julius Beltz GmbH & Co. KG, Werderstr 10, Weinheim, 69469, Germany. TEL 49-6201-60070, FAX 49-6201-6007393, info@beltz.de, http://www.beltz.de. Ed. Gabriele Pannwitz. Adv. contact Brigitte Bell. B&W page EUR 375, color page EUR 1,065.

495.6   JPN   ISSN 0912-6015
LB1577.J3
➤ **GENGO TO KYOIKU NO KENKYU/JOURNAL OF JAPANESE LANGUAGE TEACHING.** Text in Japanese. 1986. biennial. JPY 3,800 domestic; JPY 5,000 foreign (effective until 2001). adv. bk.rev. back issues avail. **Document type:** *Academic/Scholarly.*
Related titles: Fax ed.; Online - full text ed.
Published by: Gengo to Kyoiku no Kai, Saitama Daigaku Kyoiku Gakubu, Takenaga Laboratory, 255 Shimo-Okubo, Urawa-shi, Saitama-ken 338-0825, Japan. TEL 81-48-858-3175, FAX 81-48-858-3690. Ed. Yoshimasa Takenaga. R&P, Adv. contact Tadashi Kaneko. Circ. 350 (paid); 150 (controlled). **Dist. by:** Eigyou Itibu Zassika, Nippon Shuppan Boueki Ltd., 1-2-1 Sarugaku-cho, Chiyoda-ku, Tokyo 101-0064, Japan. TEL 81-3-3292-3753, FAX 81-3-3292-0410.

➤ **GEOACTIVE.** see *GEOGRAPHY*

➤ **GEODATE.** see *GEOGRAPHY*

➤ **GEOGRAFIA W SZKOLE.** see *GEOGRAPHY*

➤ **GEOGRAFISKA NOTISER.** see *GEOGRAPHY*

910.71   AUS   ISSN 0085-0969
GEOGRAPHICAL EDUCATION. Text in English. 1969. a. AUD 12 in Australasia; AUD 18 elsewhere. adv. bk.rev. **Document type:** *Academic/Scholarly.*
Related titles: Online - full text ed.: (from R M I T Publishing).
Indexed: AEI, AusPAIS, CIJE.
Published by: Australian Geography Teachers' Association, c/o Tammy Kwan Ed., School of Professional Studies, Queensland University of Technology, Red Hill, Brisbane, Locked Bag 2, Kelvin Grove, QLD 4059, Australia. TEL 61-7-8643454, FAX 61-7-8643986, t.kwan@qut.edu.au. adv.: page AUD 300; 260 x 180. Circ. 2,600. **Subscr. to:** Stephen Matthews, Business Manager, c/o GTAV, Melbourne, PO Box 2066, Camberwell, VIC 3124, Australia. FAX 61-7-95109392.

GEOGRAPHIE UND IHRE DIDAKTIK. see *GEOGRAPHY*

910.71   CHN   ISSN 1000-078X
GEOGRAPHY TEACHING/DILI JIAOXUE. Text in Chinese. 1959-1966; resumed 1980. bi-m. CNY 2.10 per issue. **Document type:** *Academic/Scholarly.*
Published by: (Dili Xi), Huadong Shifan Daxue/East China Normal University, 3663 Zhongshan Beilu, Shanghai, 200062, China. TEL 86-21-2577577, http://www.ecnu.edu.cn. Circ. 18,818.

GEORGIA SCHOOL LAW DECISIONS. see *EDUCATION— School Organization And Administration*

375   DEU   ISSN 1439-9350
GERMANY. BUNDESANSTALT FUER ARBEIT. FOERDERUNG DER BERUFLICHEN WEITERBILDUNG. Text in German. 1970. a. **Document type:** *Government.*

Former titles (until 1994): Germany. Bundesanstalt fuer Arbeit. Foerderung der Beruflichen Weiterfortbildung (1439-9296); (until 1988): Germany. Bundesanstalt fuer Arbeit. Foerderung der Beruflichen Bildung (0173-6876)
Related titles: ◆ Supplement to: Germany. Bundesagentur fuer Arbeit. Amtliche Nachrichten. ISSN 1613-9429.
Published by: Bundesanstalt fuer Arbeit, Regensburger Str 104, Nuernberg, 90478, Germany. TEL 49-911-1790, FAX 49-911-1792123, zentrale@arbeitsagentur.de, http://www.arbeitsagentur.de.

371.3   DEU
GESTALTUNGS-STUNDE; Lehrblaetter fuer bild- und werkhaftes Gestalten in der Grundschule. Text in German. 1971. 3/yr. looseleaf. EUR 13.50 (effective 2005). cum.index: 1990-1999. back issues avail. **Document type:** *Journal, Academic/Scholarly.*
Published by: A L S Verlag GmbH, Voltastr 3, Dietzenbach, 63128, Germany. TEL 49-6074-82160, FAX 49-6074-27322, info@als-verlag.de, http://www.als-verlag.de. Ed. Ingrid Kreide. R&P Maria Landji.

371.3   USA
GHANTA. Text in English. 1990. s-a. free. adv. bk.rev. back issues avail. **Document type:** *Newsletter.* **Description:** Provides information on southern Asia for K-12 teachers. Serves as a forum for an exchange of ideas on teaching about southern Asia. Includes information on available resources for teachers.
Published by: (Outreach Office), University of Wisconsin at Madison, Center for South Asia, 203 Ingraham Hall, 1155 Observatory Dr, Madison, WI 53706. TEL 608-262-4884, FAX 608-265-3062. Ed. Joseph Elder. Circ. 1,500.

GIORNALE DI FISICA. see *PHYSICS*

GO!; das Fahrschuelermagazin. see *TRANSPORTATION— Automobiles*

GO TEACH BEGINNERS. see *RELIGIONS AND THEOLOGY*

GO TEACH JUNIORS. see *RELIGIONS AND THEOLOGY*

GO TEACH PRIMARIES. see *RELIGIONS AND THEOLOGY*

GO TEACH YOUNG TEENS. see *RELIGIONS AND THEOLOGY*

375   GBR   ISSN 0072-7113
GREAT BRITAIN. SCHOOLS COUNCIL PUBLICATIONS. CURRICULUM BULLETINS. Text in English. 1965. irreg. price varies. **Document type:** *Bulletin.*
Published by: (Schools Council), Routledge (Subsidiary of: Taylor & Francis Group), 4 Park Square, Milton Park, Abingdon, Oxon OX14 4RN, United Kingdom. TEL 44-20-7583-9855, FAX 44-207-583-0701.

372.357   CAN   ISSN 1192-1285
GREEN TEACHER; education for planet earth . Text in English. 1991. q. CND 28.04 domestic; USD 26 in United States; USD 33.60 elsewhere; CND 7.95, USD 6.95 per issue (effective 2004). adv. bk.rev.; film rev.; video rev. charts; illus. back issues avail.; reprints avail. **Document type:** *Journal, Academic/Scholarly.* **Description:** Covers teaching methods, philosophy, resources in the areas of environmental and global education for elementary and secondary teachers.
Related titles: Online - full text ed.: (from bigchalk, Micromedia ProQuest, Northern Light Technology, Inc., ProQuest Information & Learning).
Indexed: CEI, CIJE, CPE, CPerl, EnvAb, RefZh. —CIS. **CCC.**
Address: 95 Robert St, Toronto, ON M5S 2K5, Canada. TEL 416-960-1244, 888-804-1486, FAX 416-925-3474, info@greenteacher.com, http://www.greenteacher.com. Eds., Pubs. Gail Littlejohn, Tim Grant. R&P Tim Grant. Adv. contact Gail Littlejohn. page CND 550; trim 7.19 x 9.69. Circ. 6,800.

371.3   DEU
DAS GRUNDSCHUL-HAUSAUFGABENHEFT. Text in German. 2000. a. EUR 2.50 newsstand/cover (effective 2003). adv. **Document type:** *Magazine, Academic/Scholarly.*
Published by: Verlag Reiter & Klingberg GbR, Barer Str. 70, Munich, 80799, Germany. TEL 49-89-2782690, FAX 49-89-27826999. adv.: color page EUR 11,400. Circ. 122,713 (paid and controlled).

371.3   DEU   ISSN 0533-3431
GRUNDSCHULE. Text in German. 1969. 11/yr. EUR 92.95; EUR 68.75 to students; EUR 8.80 newsstand/cover (effective 2003). adv. bk.rev. EUR 64 p./no.; back issues avail. **Document type:** *Journal, Academic/Scholarly.*
Related titles: ◆ Supplement(s): Praxis Grundschule. ISSN 0170-3722.
Indexed: DIP, IBR, IBZ. —CCC.
Published by: Westermann Schulbuchverlag GmbH, Georg-Westermann-Allee 66, Braunschweig, 38104, Germany. FAX 49-531-708209, schulservice@westermann.de, http://www.die-grundschule.de, http://www.westermann.de. Ed. Ursula Flemmer. adv.: B&W page EUR 2,200, color page EUR 3,520; trim 187 x 257. Circ. 13,482 (controlled).

GRUNDSCHULE ENGLISCH. see *LINGUISTICS*

▼ *new title*   ➤ *refereed*   ∗ *unverified*   ◆ *full entry avail.*

375 DEU ISSN 1616-7104
GRUNDSCHULE KUNST. Text in German. 2000. 4/yr. EUR 74; EUR 9 newsstand/cover (effective 2004). **Document type:** *Journal, Academic/Scholarly.*
Indexed: DIP, IBR, IBZ.
Published by: Kallmeyersche Verlagsbuchhandlung GmbH, Im Brande 19, Seelze, 30926, Germany. TEL 49-511-40004175, FAX 49-511-40004176, leserservice@kallmeyer.de, http://www.kallmeyer.de.

GRUNDSCHULE RELIGION. see *RELIGIONS AND THEOLOGY*

375 DEU ISSN 1437-319X
GRUNDSCHULE SACHUNTERRICHT - THEMENHEFT. Text in German. 1999. 4/yr. EUR 68; EUR 8.50 newsstand/cover evening (effective 2004). **Document type:** *Journal, Academic/Scholarly.*
Indexed: IBR, IBZ.
Published by: Kallmeyersche Verlagsbuchhandlung GmbH, Im Brande 19, Seelze, 30926, Germany. TEL 49-511-40004175, FAX 49-511-40004176, leserservice@kallmeyer.de, http://www.kallmeyer.de.

GRUNDSCHULE SPRACHEN. see *LINGUISTICS*

371.3 DEU ISSN 0943-3759
➤ **GRUNDSCHULMAGAZIN**; Impulse fuer kreativen Unterricht. Text in German. 1986. m. EUR 53.40; EUR 42.90 to students; EUR 10.90 newsstand/cover (effective 2003). **Document type:** *Journal, Academic/Scholarly.*
Formerly (until 1992): Lehrerjournal Grundschulmagazin (0930-6943); Which was formed by the merger of (1926-1986): Lehrer Journal (0722-8600); Which was formerly (until 1983): Monatshefte fuer die Unterrichtspraxis (0344-7715); (until 1978): Die Scholle (0344-7693); (1976-1986): Hauptschulmagazin (0724-3502); Which was formerly (until 1983): Ehrenwirth Hauptschulmagazin (0340-580X); (197?-1986): Grundschulmagazin (0724-3499); Which was formerly (until 1983): Ehrenwirth Grundschulmagazin (0340-5842)
Indexed: DIP, IBR, IBZ.
Published by: Oldenbourg Schulbuchverlag GmbH und Bayerischer Schulbuch Verlag GmbH (Subsidiary of: Oldenbourg Wissenschaftsverlag GmbH), Rosenheimer Str. 145, Munich, 81671, Germany. TEL 49-89-450510, FAX 49-89-45051200, info@oldenbourg-bsv.de, http://www.oldenbourg-bsv.de. Ed. Stefan Holler. Adv. contact Renate Kienzler TEL 49-7141-871670.

371.3 DEU ISSN 0932-3910
DIE GRUNDSCHULZEITSCHRIFT. Text in German. 1985. 10/yr. EUR 91; EUR 9.80 newsstand/cover (effective 2005). adv. **Document type:** *Journal, Academic/Scholarly.*
Formerly (until 1986): Grundschullehrer (0178-8523)
Indexed: DIP, IBR, IBZ.
Published by: Erhard Friedrich Verlag GmbH, Im Brande 17, Seelze, 30926, Germany. TEL 49-511-400040, FAX 49-511-40004170, info@friedrich-verlag.de, http://www.friedrich-verlag.de/index.cfm?400EEDB3776D4FC1AC5741379B01B6B8. Ed. Anneli Kessler. adv.: page EUR 2,130. Circ: 7,496 (paid and controlled).

371.3 DEU ISSN 0724-3332
GRUPPE UND SPIEL; Zeitschrift fuer kreative Gruppenarbeit. Text in German. 1983. 6/yr. EUR 41.40; EUR 9 newsstand/cover (effective 2004). adv. bk.rev. **Document type:** *Journal, Trade.*
Former titles (until 1983): Zeitschrift fuer Gruppenpaedagogik (0341-6879); (until 1976): Bulletin uber Gruppenarbeit in Bildung und Erziehung (0341-7018)
Indexed: DIP, IBZ.
Published by: Kallmeyersche Verlagsbuchhandlung GmbH, Im Brande 19, Seelze, 30926, Germany. TEL 49-511-40004175, FAX 49-511-40004176, leserservice@kallmeyer.de, http://www.kallmeyer.de. Ed. Ulrich Baer.

E

745.5 GBR
A GUIDE TO ART & DESIGN COURSES. Text in English. 1975. a. GBP 14.99 domestic (effective 2001). **Document type:** *Directory.* **Description:** Provides details of all UK degree courses in Art and Design.
Former titles (until 1998): Art and Design Courses (1368-633X); (until 1995): Design Courses (0309-4499)
Published by: (Design Council), Trotman & Co. Ltd., 2 The Green, Richmond, Surrey TW9 1PL, United Kingdom. TEL 44-20-8486 1150, FAX 44-20-8486 1161, mail@trotman.co.uk, http://www.trotmanpublishing.co.uk. Ed. Tony Charlton. R&P Amanda Williams. Adv. contact Alistair Rogers. **Dist. by:** Plymbridge Distributors Ltd, Plymbridge House, Estover Rd, Plymouth, Devon PL6 7PY, United Kingdom. TEL 44-1752-202300, FAX 44-1752-202330, enquiries@plymbridge.com.

GUINIGUADA. see *EDUCATION—Adult Education*

371.3 ESP ISSN 0213-8581
GUIX; elements d'accio educativa. Text in Catalan. 1977. m. EUR 69 domestic to individuals; EUR 96.50 domestic to institutions (effective 2005). bk.rev. index. **Document type:** *Monographic series, Academic/Scholarly.* **Description:** Covers teaching in general from infant to high school.
Indexed: RILM.
—CINDOC.
Published by: Institut de Recursos i Investigacio per a la Formacio, S.L., Francesc Tarrega 32-34, Barcelona, 08027, Spain. TEL 34-93-4080464, FAX 34-93-3524337, http://www.grao.com. Ed. Vicenc Oset. Pub. Antoni Zabali. Circ: 7,700 (paid).

GUYANA SCIENCE TEACHERS' ASSOCIATION. NEWSLETTER. see *SCIENCES: COMPREHENSIVE WORKS*

371.076 FRA ISSN 0046-676X
HAMORE; revue trimestrielle des educateurs et enseignants juifs. Text in French, Hebrew. 1957. q. bk.rev. bibl. cum.index. **Document type:** *Academic/Scholarly.* **Description:** For Jewish teachers and educators.
Published by: F S J U, 23 rue Olivier Metra, Paris, 75020, France. Ed. Prosper Elkonby. Pub. Claude Gugenheim. Circ: 1,000.

HANDBOOK OF DISTANCE EDUCATION (YEAR). see *EDUCATION—Computer Applications*

HANDELSSKOLEN. see *BUSINESS AND ECONOMICS*

HANYU XUEXI/CHINESE LANGUAGE LEARNING. see *LINGUISTICS*

HERITAGE LANGUAGE JOURNAL. see *LINGUISTICS*

371.3 ESP ISSN 1137-8573
HEURESIS; revista electronica de investigacion curricular y educativa. Text in English, Italian, Portuguese, Spanish. 1997. s-a. free. bk.rev. back issues avail. **Document type:** *Academic/Scholarly.* **Description:** Presents papers on educational research and innovation.
Media: Online - full text.
Published by: Universidad de Cadiz, Laboratorio para el Analisis del Cambio Educativo, Campus Rio San Pedro, Puerto Real, Cadiz 11510, Spain. TEL 34-95-6831314, FAX 34-95-6835163, heuresis@uca.es, http://www.uca.es/heuresis/. Ed. J Felix Angulo Rasco.

HI HELLO SALUT. see *LINGUISTICS*

375 USA ISSN 0892-5135
HIGH - SCOPE EXTENSIONS; the newsletter of the High-Scope curriculum. Text in English. 1986. 6/yr. looseleaf. USD 30.95 domestic; USD 33.95 foreign. abstr.; charts. back issues avail. **Document type:** *Newsletter.* **Description:** Designed for early childhood education teachers and caregivers, providing information and activity ideas.
Published by: (High Scope Educational Research Foundation), High-Scope Press, 600 N River St, Ypsilanti, MI 48198-2898. TEL 800-407-7377, FAX 800-442-4329, info@highscope.org, http://www.highscope.org/. Ed. Nancy Altman Brickman. R&P Tony Caprarese. Adv. contact Kathy Woodard. Circ: 4,500.

375 USA ISSN 0887-2007
HIGH - SCOPE RESOURCE; a magazine for educators. Text in English. 1981. 3/yr. free domestic; USD 8 foreign. adv. bk.rev. tr.lit. **Document type:** *Magazine.* **Description:** Explores issues, research primarily in early childhood education, focusing on the High-Scope curricula and publications.
Published by: (High-Scope Educational Research Foundation), High-Scope Press, 600 N River St, Ypsilanti, MI 48198-2898. TEL 734-485-2000, FAX 734-485-0704, info@highscope.org, http://www.highscope.org/. Ed. Lynn Spencer Taylor. R&P Tony Caprarese. Adv. contact Kathy Woodard. Circ: 180,000.

371.3 GBR
HILLCOLE GROUP PAPERS. Text in English. 1989. irreg., latest vol.7, 1992. **Document type:** *Monographic series.* **Description:** Intends to influence and improve the quality of schooling based on the ideological principles of the Radical Left.
—BLDSC (4314.831000).
Published by: Tufnell Press, 47 Dalmeny Rd, London, N7 0DY, United Kingdom.

HISPANIA; a journal devoted to the interests of the teaching of Spanish and Portuguese. see *LINGUISTICS*

375 FRA ISSN 0298-5632
HISTOIRE BIOGRAPHIQUE DE L'ENSEIGNEMENT. Text in French. 1985. irreg. price varies. **Document type:** *Monographic series, Academic/Scholarly.*
Published by: (France. Centre National de la Recherche Scientifique), C N R S Editions, 15 Rue Malebranche, Paris, 75005, France. TEL 33-1-53102700, FAX 33-1-53102727, http://www.cnrseditions.fr.

HISTORIE OG SAMTID. see *HISTORY*

907.1 AUS ISSN 0085-1558
HISTORY TEACHERS ASSOCIATION OF NEW SOUTH WALES. NEWSLETTER. Text in English. 1965. 4/yr. AUD 55 to individual members; AUD 95 to institutions (effective 2003). **Document type:** *Newsletter.*
Published by: History Teachers' Association of New South Wales, PO Box W122, Wareemba, NSW 2046, Australia. TEL 61-2-97139376, FAX 61-2-97138259, htansw@tpg.com.au, http://www.htansw.asn.au/. Ed. Bernie Howitt.

HJEMKUNDSKAB (HVALSOE). see *HOME ECONOMICS*

HOCHSCHULE FUER TECHNIK UND WIRTSCHAFT DRESDEN. BERICHTE UND INFORMATIONEN. see *TECHNOLOGY: COMPREHENSIVE WORKS*

371.3 DEU
HOCHSCHULE INNOVATIV. Text in German. s-a. **Document type:** *Journal, Academic/Scholarly.* **Description:** Presents research on educational issues.
Published by: Lemmens Verlags- und Mediengesellschaft mbH, Koenigswinterer Str 95, Bonn, 53227, Germany. TEL 49-228-42137-0, FAX 49-228-4213729, info@lemmens.de, http://www.lemmens.de. Ed. Ulrich Teichler.

371.33 306 USA ISSN 1524-427X
HOLIDAYS & SEASONAL CELEBRATIONS. GRADES 1-3. Text in English. 199?. 5/yr. (during school year). USD 19.95 domestic; USD 24.95 foreign (effective 2001). bk.rev. illus. 64 p./no.; back issues avail. **Document type:** *Trade.* **Description:** Offers teachers in grade 1-3 classrooms ideas for ways in which to have their students learn through hands-on participation about secular and religious holidays from a variety of cultures.
Supersedes in part (in 1998): Holidays and Seasonal Celebrations (1097-4423)
Published by: Teaching & Learning Company (Subsidiary of: Hodges & Reed Services, Inc.), 1204 Buchanan St, PO Box 10, Carthage, IL 62321-0010. TEL 800-852-1234, FAX 217-357-6789, customerservice@teachinglearning.com, http://www.teachingandlearning.com.

371.33 306 USA ISSN 1524-7775
HOLIDAYS & SEASONAL CELEBRATIONS. PRESCHOOL - KINDERGARTEN. Text in English. 199?. 5/yr. (during school year). USD 19.95 domestic; USD 24.95 foreign (effective Jan. 2002). bk.rev. illus. 64 p./no.; back issues avail. **Document type:** *Trade.* **Description:** Offers teachers in preschool and kindergarten classrooms ideas for ways in which to have their students learn through hands-on participation about secular and religious holidays from a variety of cultures.
Supersedes in part (in 1998): Holidays and Seasonal Celebrations (1097-4423)
Published by: Teaching & Learning Company (Subsidiary of: Hodges & Reed Services, Inc.), 1204 Buchanan St, PO Box 10, Carthage, IL 62321-0010. TEL 217-357-2591, 800-852-1234, FAX 217-357-6789, customerservice@teachinglearning.com, http://www.teachingandlearning.com.

371.33523 USA ISSN 1069-3874
PN2078.U6
HOLLYWOOD ACTING COACHES AND TEACHERS DIRECTORY. Text in English. 1984. q. tr.lit. **Document type:** *Directory, Trade.* **Description:** Contains a directory of all Hollywood acting instruction programs; includes biographies of instructors, articles about studying acting.
Published by: Acting World Books, PO Box 3899, Hollywood, CA 90078. TEL 818-905-1345, 800-210-1197. Ed., R&P Lawrence Parke. Circ: 2,600.

371.3 USA ISSN 0888-4633
HOME EDUCATION MAGAZINE. Text in English. 1984. bi-m. USD 32 (effective 2003). adv. bk.rev.; Website rev. illus. back issues avail.; reprints avail. **Document type:** *Magazine, Consumer.* **Description:** Contains articles, interviews with prominent personalities, news analysis, resources and reviews for the home schooling movement.
Address: PO Box 1083, Tonasket, WA 98855. TEL 509-486-1351, 800-236-3278, FAX 509-486-2753, hem@home-ed-magazine.com, hem-editor@home-ed-magazine.com, http://www.home-ed-magazine.com. Ed., R&P Helen E Hegener. Pub. Mark Hegener. Adv. contact Barb Lundgren TEL 817-540-6423. Circ: 28,000.

371.042 USA ISSN 1080-4730
HD9810.U6
HOME SCHOOL MARKET GUIDE; how to sell curriculum, books, educational toys and games, software programs, DVDs and other educational products to the home school market. Text in English. 1990. a. USD 150 per vol. (effective 2003). index. **Document type:** *Directory, Trade.* **Description:** Explains how to reach the estimated 1.2 million home schoolers that make up today's home school education market. Contains more than 500 listings, including names, addresses, telephone numbers, fax numbers, contact people, circulation figures, editorial descriptions, and marketing tips.
Formerly (until 1995): Selling to the Other Educational Markets (1054-4593)
Published by: Bluestocking Press, Dept U, Box 1014, Placerville, CA 95667. TEL 530-621-1123, 800-959-8586, FAX 530-642-9222, uncleric@jps.net, http://www.bluestockingpress.com. Ed., Pub., R&P, Adv. contact Jane A Williams.

HOME SCHOOL RESEARCHER. see *EDUCATION*

371.33 USA ISSN 1535-7260
LC40
HOMESCHOOLER'S GUIDE TO FREE TEACHING AIDS. Text in English. 1999. a., latest 4th Ed. USD 34.95 per issue (effective 2002). 277 p./no.; **Document type:** *Directory, Academic/Scholarly.* **Description:** Covers free teaching aids to home schoolers.
Published by: Educators Progress Service, Inc., 214 Center St, Randolph, WI 53956. TEL 920-326-3126, FAX 920-326-3127, http://www.freeteachingaids.com/hg_877083339.html. Ed. Kathleen Suttles Nehmer.

HONG KONG JOURNAL OF APPLIED LINGUISTICS. see *LINGUISTICS*

378 USA ISSN 1052-8938
HORACE. Text in English. 198?. q. USD 35 (effective 2004). **Document type:** *Journal, Academic/Scholarly.* **Description:** Combines educational research with resources and examples of innovative and effective practices from CES schools from around the country.
Published by: Coalition of Essential Schools, 1814 Franklin St, Ste 700, Oakland, CA 94612. TEL 510-433-1451, FAX 510-433-1455, bbradshaw@essentialschools.org, http://www.essentialschools.org/pub/ces_docs/resources/horace/horace.html. Ed. Jill Davidson.

372.83 CAN ISSN 0315-8527
HORIZON. Text in English. 1961. a. bk.rev.
Formerly (until 1972): British Columbia Social Studies Teachers' Association. Newsletter (0045-3048)
Indexed: Acal, CBPI, CEI.
Published by: British Columbia Social Studies Teachers' Association (Subsidiary of: British Columbia Teachers' Federation), c/o Ellen Ellis, Pres., Nanaimo District Secondary, 6319 Invermere Rd, Nanaimo, BC V9V 1C2, Canada. TEL 250-740-2000, FAX 250-740-2020, eellis@sd68.bc.ca. Circ: 550.

056.1 GBR ISSN 0018-6856
HOY DIA. Text in Spanish. 6/yr. (during school year). USD 7.95 (effective 2003 - 2004). illus. **Description:** Advanced language magazine for students of Spanish.
Supersedes: Listo (1055-1204)
—CCC.
Published by: Mary Glasgow Magazines (Subsidiary of: Scholastic Publications Ltd.), Commonwealth House, 1-19 New Oxford St, London, WC1A 1NU, United Kingdom. TEL 44-20-74219050, FAX 44-20-74219051, http://www.link2english.com. **Subscr. to:** Westfield Rd, Southam, Leamington Spa, Warks CV33 03H, United Kingdom. orders@maryglasgowmags.co.uk; Scholastic Inc., 2931 E McCarthy St, PO Box 3710, Jefferson City, MO 65102-9957. TEL 800-724-6527, classmags@scholastic.com.

371.33 USA ISSN 0196-061X
HUMAN SEXUALITY SUPPLEMENT. Text in English. 8/yr. (m., Sep.-May). USD 4 per academic year 10 or more subscriptions (effective 2004 - 2005). **Document type:** *Magazine, Consumer.* **Description:** Contains current information on the sexual aspects of health and well-being. Includes a separate teacher's guide.
Related titles: ♦ Supplement to: Current Health 2. ISSN 0163-156X.
Published by: Weekly Reader Corp. (Subsidiary of: W R C Media Inc.), 200 First Stamford Pl, PO Box 120023, Stamford, CT 06912-0023. TEL 203-705-3500, 800-446-3355, FAX 203-705-1662, science@weeklyreader.com, http://www.weeklyreader.com. Ed. Charles Piddock. Pub. Peter Esposito. R&P Cathy Pekai TEL 203-705-3426.

HYOGO KYOIKU DAIGAKU KENKYU KIYO. DAI-3-BUNSATSU. SHIZENKEI KYOIKU, SEIKATSU KENKOKEI KYOIKU/HYOGO UNIVERSITY OF TEACHER EDUCATION JOURNAL. SERIES 3: NATURAL SCIENCE, PRACTICAL LIFE STUDIES. see *BIOLOGY*

THE I A L L T JOURNAL OF LANGUAGE LEARNING TECHNOLOGIES. see *LINGUISTICS*

371.3 USA ISSN 1069-5672
LA370
I D R A NEWSLETTER. Text in English. 1973. m. free. bk.rev. back issues avail. **Document type:** *Newsletter.* **Description:** Addresses various educational topics. Disseminates IDRA's research and information.
Published by: Intercultural Development Research Association, 5835 Callaghan Rd, Ste 350, San Antonio, TX 78228-1190. TEL 210-444-1710, FAX 210-444-1714, contact@idra.org, http://www.idra.org. Ed., R&P Christie L Goodman. Circ: 7,600.

I E E E TRANSACTIONS ON EDUCATION. see *ENGINEERING—Electrical Engineering*

I P N - BLAETTER. see *SCIENCES: COMPREHENSIVE WORKS*

I R A L/INTERNATIONALE ZEITSCHRIFT FUR ANGEWANDTE LINGUISTIK IN DER SPRACHERZIEHUNG/REVUE INTERNATIONALE DE LINGUISTIQUE APPLIQUEE: ENSEIGNEMENT DES LANGUES. see *LINGUISTICS*

371.334 USA
I S T E UPDATE; people, events and news in education technology. Text in English. 1988. 10/yr. USD 79 membership (effective 2005). adv. back issues avail. **Document type:** *Newsletter, Academic/Scholarly.* **Description:** Articles on current issues by leaders in the field of technology in education.
Media: E-mail.
Published by: International Society for Technology in Education, 480 Charnelton St, Eugene, OR 97401-2626. TEL 541-434-8917, FAX 541-302-3781, iste@iste.org, http://www.iste.org/Content/NavigationMenu/Membership/Member_Resources/ISTE_Update/ISTE_Update_an_e-mail_news_alert_for_ISTE_members.htm. Ed. Mindy DeForest. R&P Amy Miller. Adv. contact Danielle Larson. Circ: 14,000.

IBER; didactica de las ciencias sociales, geografia e historia. see *SOCIAL SCIENCES: COMPREHENSIVE WORKS*

371.3 USA ISSN 1042-5330
LB1631
IDEAS PLUS. Text in English. 1984. a. price varies. back issues avail. **Document type:** *Monographic series, Trade.* **Description:** Offers teachers of English practical ideas they can use in instruction and assessment.
—CCC.
Published by: National Council of Teachers of English, 1111 W Kenyon Rd, Urbana, IL 61801-1096. TEL 217-328-3870, 800-369-6283, FAX 217-328-9645, 217-328—9645, membership@ncte.org, http://www.ncte.org.

418 AUS ISSN 0046-8568
IDIOM. Text in English. 1963. 7/yr. AUD 45. adv. bk.rev.
Indexed: AEI, ChLitAb.
—BLDSC (4362.482500), IE, ingenta.
Published by: Victorian Association for the Teaching of English, c/o Amanda McGraw, 185 Lygon St, Carlton South, VIC 3053, Australia. FAX 03-347-3918. Ed. Philip Gardner. Circ: 1,400.

418 USA ISSN 0019-2023
PE1011
➤ **ILLINOIS ENGLISH BULLETIN.** Text in English. 1907. bi-m. (Oct.-May). free to members. abstr. **Document type:** *Bulletin, Academic/Scholarly.* **Description:** Features essays and articles pertinent to teaching English in Illinois.
Related titles: Microfiche ed.
Indexed: CIJE, PCI.
Published by: University of Illinois at Urbana-Champaign, English Department, 608 Wright St, Urbana, IL 61801. http://www.iateonline.org/. Ed. Bob Broad. Circ: 2,100.
Co-sponsor: Illinois Association of Teachers.

➤ **ILLINOIS JOURNAL OF TECHNOLOGY EDUCATION.** see *TECHNOLOGY: COMPREHENSIVE WORKS*

➤ **ILLINOIS MUSIC EDUCATOR.** see *MUSIC*

➤ **ILLINOIS SPEECH AND THEATRE ASSOCIATION. JOURNAL.** see *COMMUNICATIONS*

➤ **:IN DEUTSCH.** see *LINGUISTICS*

➤ **:IN ENGLISCH.** see *LINGUISTICS*

➤ **IN MOTION (NORTHBROOK)**; the guide to safe driving. see *TRANSPORTATION—Automobiles*

➤ **:IN RELIGION.** see *RELIGIONS AND THEOLOGY*

372 CAN ISSN 0823-695X
IN THE MIDDLE. Text in English. 1982. 3/yr. CND 20 (effective 2000). adv. **Document type:** *Journal, Academic/Scholarly.*
Indexed: CEI.
Published by: (Saskatchewan Middle Years Association), Saskatchewan Teachers' Federation, 2317 Arlington Ave., Saskatoon, SK S7J 2H8, Canada. TEL 306-373-1660, 800-667-7762, FAX 306-374-1122, http://www.northweb.sk.ca/smya/smyajour.htm, http://www.stf.sk.ca.

INDEPENDENT EDUCATION. see *EDUCATION—Higher Education*

INDIANA ENGLISH. see *LITERATURE*

INDIANA MUSICATOR. see *MUSIC*

372.2 GBR ISSN 0269-9524
INFANT PROJECTS. Text in English. 1974. 6/yr. GBP 18.75 domestic; GBP 24.95 foreign (effective 2001). bk.rev. **Document type:** *Magazine, Academic/Scholarly.* **Description:** Contains information on theme-based curricula for teachers of 4-7 year olds.
Former titles: Child Education Special (0262-7507); Child Education Quarterly (0045-6640)
Related titles: Microform ed.: (from PQC).
Indexed: CPE.
Published by: Scholastic Ltd., Villiers House, Clarendon Ave, Leamington Spa, Warks CV32 5PR, United Kingdom. TEL 44-1926-887799, FAX 44-1926-817727, enquiries@scholastic.co.uk, http://www.scholastic.co.uk. Ed. Jane Morgan. Circ: 34,000. **Subscr. to:** Westfield Rd, Southam, Leamington Spa CV33 0JH, United Kingdom. TEL 44-1926-813910.

371.3 DEU
➤ **INFODIENST SCHULE.** Text in German. 1978. 6/yr. **Document type:** *Newsletter, Government.*
Formerly (until 1999): Schulintern (0179-857X)
Published by: Ministerium fuer Kultus Jugend und Sport, Schlossplatz 4, Stuttgart, 70173, Germany. TEL 49-711-2790, FAX 49-711-2792838, poststelle@km.kv.bwl.de, http://www.km.bwl.de/is. Ed. Carsten Rabe. Circ: 130,000.

375 GBR ISSN 1354-8204
INFORM (LONDON, 1994). Text in English. 1994. 3/yr. free. **Document type:** *Newsletter.*
Indexed: AEI.
Published by: School Curriculum and Assessment Authority, Newcombe House, 45 Notting Hill Gate, London, W11 3JB, United Kingdom. TEL 44-171-229-1234, FAX 44-171-229-8526, http://www.open.gov.uk/scaa/scaahome.htm. **Subscr. to:** SCAA Publications, PO Box 235, Hayes, Mddx UB3 1HF, United Kingdom. TEL 44-181-561-4499, FAX 44-181-813-6432.

INFORM-ACTION; educateurs franco-manitobains. see *LINGUISTICS*

INFORMATIK BETRIFFT UNS. see *COMPUTERS—Information Science And Information Theory*

371.3 DEU ISSN 0930-7672
INFORMATIONEN FUER DEN GESCHICHTS- UND GEMEINSCHAFTSKUNDELEHRER. Text in German. 1967. 2/yr. **Document type:** *Journal, Academic/Scholarly.*
Indexed: DIP, IBR, IBZ.
Published by: Wochenschau Verlag, Adolf Damaschke Str 12, Schwalbach, 65824, Germany. TEL 49-6196-86065, FAX 49-6196-86060, wochenschau-verlag@t-online.de. Eds. Bernward Debus, Ursula Buch. R&P Bernward Debus. Adv. contact Edith Beralli.

371.334 GBR ISSN 1470-3297
LB1028.5 CODEN: IETIF4
➤ **INNOVATIONS IN EDUCATION AND TEACHING INTERNATIONAL.** Variant title: I E T I. Text in English. 1964. q. GBP 261, USD 431 combined subscription to institutions print & online eds. (effective 2006). adv. bk.rev.; film rev. abstr.; charts; illus. back issues avail.; reprint service avail. from PQC,PSC. **Document type:** *Journal, Academic/Scholarly.* **Description:** Presents topics and issues relevant to educational and training technology.
Former titles (until 2000): Innovations in Education and Training International (1355-8005); (until 1995): Educational and Training Technology International (0954-7304); (until 1989): Programmed Learning and Educational Technology (0951-0907); Programmed Learning (0033-0396)
Related titles: Microform ed.: (from PQC); Online - full text ed.: ISSN 1470-3300. GBP 248, USD 409 to institutions (effective 2006) (from EBSCO Publishing, Gale Group, IngentaConnect, O C L C Online Computer Library Center, Inc., ProQuest Information & Learning, Swets Information Services).
Indexed: AHCI, AgeL, BrEdI, CIJE, CMCI, CPE, CompAb, CompC, CurCont, DIP, EAA, ERA, ETA, HECAB, IBR, IBZ, Inspec, MEA, RASB, RHEA, SEA, SENA, SOMA, SSCI, TEA.
—BLDSC (4515.487155), AskIEEE, IDS, IE, Infotrieve, ingenta. CCC.
Published by: (Association for Educational and Training Technology), Routledge (Subsidiary of: Taylor & Francis Group), 4 Park Sq, Milton Park, Abingdon, Oxon OX14 4RN, United Kingdom. TEL 44-1235-828600, FAX 44-1235-829000, info@routledge.co.uk, http://www.tandf.co.uk/journals/titles/14703297.asp, http://www.routledge.co.uk. Eds. Gina Wisker, Philip Barker. R&P Sally Sweet. Circ: 1,200. **Subscr. in US & Canada to:** Taylor & Francis Ltd, Journals Customer Service, Rankine Rd, Basingstoke, Hants RG24 8PR, United Kingdom. TEL 44-1256-813000, FAX 44-1256-330245, enquiry@tandf.co.uk; **Subscr. to:** Taylor & Francis Inc., Customer Services Dept, 325 Chestnut St, 8th Fl, Philadelphia, PA 19106. TEL 800-354-1420, FAX 215-625-8914. **Co-sponsor:** Staff and Educational Development Association.

371.3 USA
INNOVATIONS IN SCIENCE EDUCATION AND TECHNOLOGY. Text in English. 1997. irreg., latest 2003. price varies.
Published by: Springer-Verlag New York, Inc. (Subsidiary of: Springer Science+Business Media), 233 Spring St, New York, NY 10013. TEL 212-460-1500, FAX 212-460-1575, service@springer-ny.com, http://www.springer-ny.com. Ed. Karen C Cohen.

INOSTRANNYE IAZYKI V SHKOLE. see *LINGUISTICS*

INSEGNAMENTO DELLA MATEMATICA E DELLE SCIENZE INTEGRATE. see *MATHEMATICS*

E

INSIGHT (CHARLESTON). see *COMPUTERS—Computer Assisted Instruction*

INSIGHTS ON LAW & SOCIETY. see *LAW*

371.3 NLD ISSN 0020-4277
L11 CODEN: INLSBJ
➤ **INSTRUCTIONAL SCIENCE**; an international journal of learning and cognition. Text in English. 1971. bi-m. EUR 545, USD 558, GBP 338 combined subscription to institutions print & online eds. (effective 2005). adv. bk.rev. illus. index, cum.index. reprint service avail. from PSC. **Document type:** *Journal, Academic/Scholarly.* **Description:** Promotes a deeper understanding of the nature, theory and practice of the instructional process and of the learning to which it gives rise.
Related titles: Microform ed.: (from PQC); Online - full text ed.: ISSN 1573-1952 (from EBSCO Publishing, Gale Group, IngentaConnect, Kluwer Online, O C L C Online Computer Library Center, Inc., Ovid Technologies, Inc., Springer LINK, Swets Information Services).
Indexed: ABIn, ASCA, BibLing, BrEdI, CIJE, CPE, CommAb, CompAb, CompR, CurCont, DIP, EAA, ERA, ETA, EduInd, HEA, IBR, IBSS, IBZ, L&LBA, MEA, PsycInfo, PsycholAb, PsycholRG, RASB, RHEA, SEA, SENA, SOMA, SOPODA, SSCI, TEA, e-psyche.
—BLDSC (4524.950000), IDS, IE, Infotrieve, ingenta, KNAW. **CCC.**
Published by: Springer-Verlag Dordrecht (Subsidiary of: Springer Science+Business Media), Van Godewijckstraat 30, Dordrecht, 3311 GX, Netherlands. TEL 31-78-6576050, FAX 31-78-6576474, http://springerlink.metapress.com/openurl.asp?genre=journal&issn=0020-4277, http://www.springeronline.com. Eds. Patricia A Alexander, Peter Goodyear.

330.071 USA ISSN 1072-1517
INSTRUCTIONAL STRATEGIES: AN APPLIED RESEARCH SERIES. Text in English. q. USD 15; USD 4 newsstand/cover. **Document type:** *Journal, Trade.* **Description:** Provides information, especially teaching tips for business educators on current topics in the business field.
Related titles: Online - full text ed.: (from EBSCO Publishing).
Indexed: BusEdI.
Published by: Delta Pi Epsilon Graduate Business Education Society, National Office, P O Box 4340, Little Rock, AR 72214. TEL 501-562-1233, FAX 501-562-1293.

INSTRUMENTALIST; a magazine for school and college band and orchestra directors, professional instrumentalists, teacher-training specialists in instrumental music education and instrumental teachers. see *MUSIC*

371.3 DEU ISSN 1860-0603
▼ **INTEGRATIONSPAEDAGOGIK IN FORSCHUNG UND PRAXIS.** Text in German. 2005. irreg. price varies. **Document type:** *Monographic series, Academic/Scholarly.*
Published by: Verlag Dr. Kovac, Arnoldstr 49, Hamburg, 22763, Germany. TEL 49-40-3988800, FAX 49-40-39888055, info@verlagdrkovac.de, http://www.verlagdrkovac.de/7-23.htm.

371.335 ESP ISSN 1576-4990
LB1028.3
➤ **INTERACTIVE EDUCATIONAL MULTIMEDIA.** Text mainly in English. 2000. s-a. **Document type:** *Journal, Academic/Scholarly.* **Description:** Forum for intellectual debate about training in the use of information and communication technologies, the application of virtual environments in education, the publication of multimedia materials, the cognitive processes and associated learning, and the emprirical results of its study.
Media: Online - full text.
Published by: Universitat de Barcelona, Multimedia Teaching and Learning Group, Passeig de la Vall d'Hebron, 171, Barcelona, 08035, Spain. mme@d5.ub.es, http://www.ub.es/multimedia/iem. Ed. Jose Luis Rodriguez Illera.

➤ **INTERACTIVE LEARNING ENVIRONMENTS.** see *EDUCATION—Computer Applications*

➤ **INTERCOM (SASKATOON).** see *BUSINESS AND ECONOMICS*

➤ **INTERDISCIPLINARY HUMANITIES.** see *HUMANITIES: COMPREHENSIVE WORKS*

371.3 CHE ISSN 0257-3849
INTERFACE. Text in English. 4/yr. CHF 30. index. **Document type:** *Academic/Scholarly.*
—**CCC.**
Published by: Schweizerischer Informatik Lehrer Verein, Postfach 126, Lenzburg, 5600, Switzerland.

371.393 USA
INTERNATIONAL CONFERENCE ON PIAGETIAN THEORY AND THE HELPING PROFESSIONS. PROCEEDINGS. Text in English. 1978 (8th). a. price varies. **Document type:** *Proceedings.*
Published by: (Children's Hospital of Los Angeles, University Affiliated Program), University of Southern California, Department of Sociology and Social Research, University Park, KAP 352, Los Angeles, CA 90089-2539. TEL 213-740-3533, FAX 213-740-3535. Ed. Barry Glassner.

371.33 310 NLD
INTERNATIONAL CONFERENCE ON TEACHING STATISTICS. PROCEEDINGS. Abbreviated title: I C O T S. Text in English. irreg., latest vol.5, 1998. price varies. back issues avail. **Document type:** *Proceedings, Academic/Scholarly.*
Related titles: CD-ROM ed.: 2002. EUR 25 per issue (effective 2003).
Published by: International Statistical Institute, Princes Beatrixlaan 428, PO Box 950, Voorburg, 2270 AZ, Netherlands. TEL 31-70-3375737, FAX 31-70-3860025, isi@cbs.nl, http://www.cbs.nl/isi/index.htm.

INTERNATIONAL CONSULTATIVE FORUM ON EDUCATION FOR ALL. STATUS AND TRENDS; an annual report on new trends in basic education. see *EDUCATION*

INTERNATIONAL DIRECTORY OF MUSIC EDUCATION; and music education institutions. see *MUSIC*

THE INTERNATIONAL ELECTRONIC JOURNAL OF HEALTH EDUCATION. see *PHYSICAL FITNESS AND HYGIENE*

707.1 GBR ISSN 1476-8062
N81
➤ **INTERNATIONAL JOURNAL OF ART & DESIGN EDUCATION.** Text in English. 19??. 3/yr. EUR 95 combined subscription in Europe to individuals print & online eds.; USD 106 combined subscription in the Americas to individuals & Caribbean (print & online eds.); GBP 63 combined subscription elsewhere to individuals print & online eds.; GBP 433 combined subscription in Europe to institutions print & online eds.; USD 874 combined subscription in the Americas to institutions & Caribbean (print & online eds.); GBP 520 combined subscription elsewhere to institutions print & online eds. (effective 2006). bk.rev. illus. index. back issues avail. **Document type:** *Journal, Academic/Scholarly.*
Former titles (until 2002): Journal of Art and Design Education (0260-9991); (until 1982): National Society for Art Education. Journal
Related titles: Microfiche ed.; Online - full text ed.: ISSN 1476-8070. 1997. GBP 411 in Europe to institutions; USD 830 in the Americas to institutions & Caribbean; GBP 495 elsewhere to institutions (effective 2006) (from Blackwell Synergy, EBSCO Publishing, Gale Group, IngentaConnect, O C L C Online Computer Library Center, Inc., Swets Information Services).
Indexed: ABM, ASCA, ArtHuCI, BHA, BrEdI, CIJE, CPE, CurCont, DAAI, ERA, ETA, RHEA, SOMA, SSCI, SWA, TEA.
—BLDSC (4542.104600), IDS, IE, Infotrieve, ingenta. **CCC.**
Published by: (National Society for Education in Art and Design), Blackwell Publishing Ltd., 9600 Garsington Rd, Oxford, OX4 2ZG, United Kingdom. TEL 44-1865-776868, FAX 44-1865-714591, customerservices@oxon.blackwellpublishing.com, http://www.blackwellpublishing.com/journals/JADE. Ed. Dr. Dennis Atkinson.

370.1163 371.33 USA
➤ **INTERNATIONAL JOURNAL OF CURRICULUM AND INSTRUCTION.** Text in English. 1987. s-a. USD 35 (effective 2002). bk.rev. illus.; stat. 134 p./no.; back issues avail. **Document type:** *Academic/Scholarly.* **Description:** For the purpose of broadening international cooperation among educators.
Formerly (until 1997): W C C I Forum (0116-5461)
Published by: World Council for Curriculum and Instruction, c/o WCCI Secretariat, Alliant International University, 10455 Pomerado Rd, San Diego, CA 92131-1799. TEL 858-635-4718, FAX 858-635-4714, wcci@uc.edu, wcci@alliant.edu, http://www.uc.edu/wcci, http://www.uc.edu/wcci/. Ed., R&P Virginia Floresca Cawagas TEL 780-492-4916. Pub. Estela Matriano. Circ: 1,000.

➤ **INTERNATIONAL JOURNAL OF ELECTRICAL ENGINEERING EDUCATION.** see *ENGINEERING—Electrical Engineering*

371.33 USA ISSN 0092-1815
LB1043
➤ **INTERNATIONAL JOURNAL OF INSTRUCTIONAL MEDIA.** Text in English. 1973. q. USD 186 domestic; USD 196 foreign (effective 2005). bk.rev. abstr.; bibl.; charts; illus. index. reprints avail. **Document type:** *Journal, Academic/Scholarly.* **Description:** Contains articles discussing specific applications and techniques for bringing the advantages of a particular instructional medium to bear on a complete curriculum system or program.
Related titles: Online - full text ed.: (from bigchalk, EBSCO Publishing, Factiva, Florida Center for Library Automation, Gale Group, H.W. Wilson, Northern Light Technology, Inc., O C L C Online Computer Library Center, Inc., ProQuest Information & Learning).
Indexed: ABIn, CIJE, CPE, CompLI, DIP, ERA, ETA, EduInd, IBR, IBZ, MEDLINE, RILM, TEA.
—BLDSC (4542.310000), IE, Infotrieve, ingenta. **CCC.**
Published by: Westwood Press, Inc., 116 E 16th St, New York, NY 10003-2112. TEL 212-420-8008, FAX 212-353-8291, http://www.adprima.com/ijim.htm. Ed. Phillip J Sleeman. R&P Richard Lombard. Circ: 500.

613.7 DEU ISSN 0341-8685
GV201
INTERNATIONAL JOURNAL OF PHYSICAL EDUCATION/ INTERNATIONALE ZEITSCHRIFT FUER SPORTPAEDAGOGIK. Text in English, German; Summaries in French, Spanish. 1963. q. EUR 34, EUR 30; EUR 9 newsstand/cover (effective 2002). adv. bk.rev. charts; illus. index. **Document type:** *Journal, Academic/Scholarly.*
Formerly: Gymnasion
Related titles: Online - full text ed.: (from H.W. Wilson, O C L C Online Computer Library Center, Inc.).
Indexed: ABIn, CPE, DIP, ERA, EduInd, IBR, IBZ, SOMA, SportS, TEA.
—BLDSC (4542.466000), IE, Infotrieve, ingenta. **CCC.**
Published by: Verlag Karl Hofmann, Postfach 1360, Schorndorf, 73603, Germany. TEL 49-7181-402127, FAX 49-7181-402111, info@hofmann-verlag.de, http://www.hofmann-verlag.de. Ed. Herbert Haag. Circ: 2,500.

607.1 NLD ISSN 0957-7572
➤ **INTERNATIONAL JOURNAL OF TECHNOLOGY AND DESIGN EDUCATION.** Text in Dutch. 1989. 3/yr. EUR 230, USD 230, GBP 151 combined subscription to institutions print & online eds. (effective 2005). adv. reprint service avail. from PSC. **Document type:** *Journal, Academic/Scholarly.* **Description:** Seeks to encourage research and scholarly writing about any aspect of technology and design education. Critical, review, and comparative studies are particularly prominent, as are contributions which draw upon other literatures.
Related titles: Online - full text ed.: ISSN 1573-1804 (from EBSCO Publishing, Gale Group, IngentaConnect, Kluwer Online, O C L C Online Computer Library Center, Inc., Springer LINK, Swets Information Services).
Indexed: BibLing, BrEdI, CPE, ERA, ETA, EngInd, Inspec, MEA, RHEA, SEA, SENA, SOMA, TEA.
—BLDSC (4542.693250), AskIEEE, Ei, IE, Infotrieve, ingenta. **CCC.**
Published by: Springer-Verlag Dordrecht (Subsidiary of: Springer Science+Business Media), Van Godewijckstraat 30, Dordrecht, 3311 GX, Netherlands. TEL 31-78-6576050, FAX 31-78-6576474, http://springerlink.metapress.com/openurl.asp?genre=journal&issn=0957-7572, http://www.springeronline.com. Ed. Marc J de Vries.

▼ ➤ **INTERNATIONAL JOURNAL OF WEB-BASED LEARNING AND TEACHING TECHNOLOGIES.** see *COMPUTERS—Computer Assisted Instruction*

➤ **INTERNATIONAL REVIEW FOR BUSINESS EDUCATION/INTERNATIONALE ZEITSCHRIFT FUER KAUFMAENNISCHES BILDUNGSWESEN/REVISTA INTERNACIONAL PARA LA ENSENANZA COMERCIAL/REVUE INTERNATIONALE POUR L'ENSEIGNEMENT COMMERCIAL/RIVISTA INTERNAZIONALE PER LA CULTURA COMMERCIALE.** see *BUSINESS AND ECONOMICS*

➤ **INTERNATIONAL REVIEW OF HISTORY EDUCATION.** see *HISTORY*

➤ **INTERNATIONAL SCHOOLS JOURNAL.** see *EDUCATION—International Education Programs*

306.43 GBR ISSN 0962-0214
CODEN: ISSDED
➤ **INTERNATIONAL STUDIES IN SOCIOLOGY OF EDUCATION.** Text in English. 1991. 3/yr. GBP 256 combined subscription domestic to institutions; USD 407 combined subscription foreign to institutions (effective 2006). bk.rev. abstr.; illus. back issues avail.; reprint service avail. from PSC. **Document type:** *Journal, Academic/Scholarly.* **Description:** Contains material from current research projects and offers insights and ideas on their respective topics.
Related titles: Online - full text ed.: ISSN 1747-5066. GBP 243, USD 387 to institutions (effective 2006) (from EBSCO Publishing, Swets Information Services).
Indexed: ASSIA, BrEdI, CPE, DIP, EAA, ERA, ETA, IBR, IBZ, MEA, RHEA, SEA, SENA, SOMA, SOPODA, SSA, SWA, SociolAb, TEA.
—BLDSC (4549.822000), IE, ingenta. **CCC.**
Published by: Routledge (Subsidiary of: Taylor & Francis Group), 4 Park Sq, Milton Park, Abingdon, Oxon OX14 4RN, United Kingdom. TEL 44-1235-828600, FAX 44-1235-829000, journals@routledge.com, http://www.tandf.co.uk/journals/titles/09620214.asp, http://www.routledge.co.uk. Ed. Suzy Harris.

371.3 DEU ISSN 0172-8237
LB3045
INTERNATIONALE SCHULBUCHFORSCHUNG/ INTERNATIONAL TEXTBOOK RESEARCH. Text in English, French, German. 1951. 4/yr. EUR 26 (effective 2003). bk.rev. abstr. **Document type:** *Journal, Academic/Scholarly.*
Former titles (until 1978): Internationales Jahrbuch fuer Geschichts und Geographieunterricht (0074-9834); (until 1967): Internationales Jahrbuch fuer Geschichtsunterricht (0179-4418)
Indexed: AmH&L, DIP, HistAb, IBR, IBZ, PCI.
—BLDSC (4554.695500), IE, ingenta. **CCC.**

E

Published by: Georg-Eckert-Institut fuer Internationale Schulbuchforschung, Celler Str 3, Braunschweig, 38114, Germany. TEL 49-531-590990, FAX 49-531-5909999, info@gei.de, http://www.gei.de. Ed. Wolfgang Hoepken. Circ: 2,500. **Distr. by:** Verlag Hahnsche Buchhandlung, Leinstr 32, Hannover 30159, Germany. TEL 49-511-80718040, FAX 49-511-363698, order@hahnsche-buchhandlung.de, http://www.hahnsche-buchhandlung.de.

EL INTERPRETE. see *RELIGIONS AND THEOLOGY—Protestant*

EL INTERPRETE. MAESTROS. see *RELIGIONS AND THEOLOGY—Protestant*

507.1 AUS ISSN 0815-9602
➤ **INVESTIGATING.** Text in English. 1985. q. AUD 37.63 domestic to individuals; AUD 44.20 foreign to individuals; AUD 43.70 domestic to institutions; AUD 49.75 foreign to institutions (effective 2003). adv. bk.rev.; software rev.; Website rev. back issues avail. **Document type:** *Journal, Academic/Scholarly.* **Description:** Informs teachers who promote the teaching of science in primary schools.
Related titles: Online - full text ed.: (from EBSCO Publishing).
Indexed: AEI, WBA, WMB.
Published by: Australian Science Teachers Association, PO Box 334, Deakin West, ACT 2600, Australia. TEL 61-2-62829377, FAX 61-2-62829477, asta@asta.edu.au, http://www.asta.edu.au/. Ed. Sharon Russo. Adv. contact Rhonda Porter. Circ: 2,100 (paid).

➤ **INVESTIGATIVE AND OPERATIONAL REPORT WRITING.** see *LAW*

375 USA
IOWA EDUCATIONAL LEADERSHIP. Text in English. 1977. s-a. USD 3 to non-members. **Description:** Articles dealing with all aspects of curriculum, instruction and supervision.
Formerly: Iowa Curriculum Bulletin
Published by: (Iowa Association for Supervision and Curriculum Development), University of Northern Iowa, College of Education, Cedar, IA 50614. TEL 319-273-2167. Ed. Charles R May.

IOWA ENGLISH BULLETIN. see *LINGUISTICS*

371.3 USA
IOWA MIDDLE LEVEL EDUCATORS BULLETIN. Text in English. a. USD 2 to non-members. **Document type:** *Bulletin.*
Published by: (Iowa Association for Middle Level Educators), University of Northern Iowa, College of Education, Cedar, IA 50614. TEL 319-273-2167. Ed. Mary Nan Aldrige.

371.3 RUS ISSN 0869-4966
ISKUSSTVO V SHKOLE. Text in Russian. 1927. bi-m. USD 89 in North America (effective 2000).
Published by: Redaktsiya Iskusstvo v Shkole, Ul Kedrova 8, Moscow, 117804, Russian Federation. TEL 7-095-1256097. Ed. A A Melik-Pashaev. **Dist. by:** East View Information Services, 3020 Harbor Ln. N., Minneapolis, MN 55447. TEL 763-550-0961, FAX 763-559-2931.

910.71 AUS ISSN 0819-8101
ISSUES (CAMBERWELL). Text in English. 1987. q. AUD 77 domestic; AUD 104 foreign (effective 2004). adv. charts; illus.; maps. cum.index: 1987-1989. back issues avail. **Description:** For teachers in geography, history, ecology and other social education subjects.
Related titles: Online - full text ed.: (from ProQuest Information & Learning).
Indexed: EPB, WBA, WMB.
Published by: Australian Council for Educational Research, 347 Camberwell Rd, Private Bag 55, Camberwell, VIC 3124, Australia. TEL 61-3-9835-7447, FAX 61-3-9835-7499, sales@acer.edu.au, http://www.acer.edu.au. Eds. Judy Rogers, Peter Preuss. R&P Deirdre Morris. Adv. contact Mara Bonaccurso. page AUD 250; trim 250 x 172. Circ: 1,600.

371.33 USA ISSN 1536-3031
ISSUES IN TEACHER EDUCATION. Text in English. s-a. USD 25 to individuals; USD 40 to institutions (effective 2004). **Description:** Features articles, commentary, and reviews on the teacher education field.
Indexed: CPE, ERA.
—BLDSC (4584.327416).
Published by: (California Council on the Education of Teachers), Caddo Gap Press, 3145 Geary Blvd,, PMB 275, San Francisco, CA 94118. TEL 415-666-3012, FAX 415-666-3552, caddogap@aol.com, http://www.caddogap.com. Ed. Steve Turley.

371.3 AUS ISSN 1329-2285
ISSUES OF TEACHING AND LEARNING. Text in English. 1995. m. free (effective 2003). 4 p./no.; back issues avail. **Document type:** *Newsletter, Academic/Scholarly.*
Media: Online - full text. **Related titles:** Print ed.
Published by: University of Western Australia, Centre for the Advancement of Teaching and Learning, 35 Stirling Hwy, Crawley, W.A. 6009, Australia. TEL 61-8-98301577, FAX 61-8-93801156, catloffice@catl.uwa.edu.au, http://www.catl.uwa.edu.au/IssuesOfTandL.html. Ed. Kenn Martin.

372.634 USA
ITALIC HANDWRITING NEWSLETTER; a newsletter for people who care about legibility. Text in English. 1988. s-a. looseleaf. free. bk.rev. bibl.; illus. **Document type:** *Newsletter.* **Description:** Handwriting, penmanship using italic method which produces a more legible, rapidly written hand than other commercially available programs.
Published by: (Portland State University, Student Publications Board), Continuing Education Press, 1633 S W Park, Box 1491, Portland, OR 97207. TEL 503-725-4846, FAX 503-725-4840. Ed. Tena Spears. Pub. Tony Midson. Circ: 15,000 (controlled).

418 USA
J A C ONLINE; a journal of composition theory. Text in English. 1994. 3/yr.
Media: Online - full content.
Published by: University of South Florida, Department of English, 4202 E Fowler Ave, Tampa, FL 33620. http://jac.gsu.edu/. Ed. Todd Taylor.

J A C T REVIEW. see *CLASSICAL STUDIES*

375 USA ISSN 1057-896X
LB1570
➤ **J C T.** (Journal of Curriculum Theorizing) Text in English. 1978. q. USD 75 domestic to individuals; USD 95 foreign to individuals; USD 125 domestic to institutions; USD 145 foreign to institutions (effective 2004). adv. bk.rev. back issues avail. **Document type:** *Journal, Academic/Scholarly.* **Description:** Provides an interdisciplinary forum for curriculum studies and issues.
Formerly: Journal of Curriculum Theorizing (0162-8453)
Related titles: Online - full text ed.: (from H.W. Wilson, O C L C Online Computer Library Center, Inc., ProQuest Information & Learning).
Indexed: ABIn, CPE, DIP, EduInd, IBR, IBZ.
—IE, Infotrieve. **CCC.**
Published by: (Corporation for Curriculum Research), Caddo Gap Press, 3145 Geary Blvd,, PMB 275, San Francisco, CA 94118. TEL 415-922-1911, FAX 415-440-4870, caddogap@aol.com, http://www.jctbergamo.com/issues.html. Ed. Marla Morris. Pub., R&P Alan H Jones. adv.: page USD 200; trim 4.5 x 7. Circ: 600 (paid).

➤ **J E T S REPORT**; promoting interest in engineering, technology, mathematics and science to high school students. see *ENGINEERING*

373.245 DEU
JAHRBUCH BILDUNG UND ARBEIT. Text in German. 1996. a. **Document type:** *Journal, Academic/Scholarly.*
Published by: V S - Verlag fuer Sozialwissenschaften (Subsidiary of: Springer Science+Business Media), Abraham-Lincoln-Str 46, Wiesbaden, 65189, Germany. TEL 49-611-78780, FAX 49-611-7878400, info@vs-verlag.de, http://www.vs-verlag.de.

371.3 DEU ISSN 1435-4594
JAHRBUCH GRUNDSCHULFORSCHUNG. Text in German. 1997. a. EUR 19.90 (effective 2004). **Document type:** *Journal, Academic/Scholarly.* **Description:** Contains articles and research on the latest studies involving changes at the elementary school level.
Published by: V S - Verlag fuer Sozialwissenschaften (Subsidiary of: Springer Science+Business Media), Abraham-Lincoln-Str 46, Wiesbaden, 65189, Germany. TEL 49-611-78780, FAX 49-611-7878400, info@vs-verlag.de, http://www.vs-verlag.de.

371.3 DEU
JAHRBUCH MEDIENPAEDAGOGIK. Text in German. 2000. a. EUR 19.90 (effective 2004). **Document type:** *Journal, Academic/Scholarly.*
Published by: V S - Verlag fuer Sozialwissenschaften (Subsidiary of: Springer Science+Business Media), Abraham-Lincoln-Str 46, Wiesbaden, 65189, Germany. TEL 49-611-78780, FAX 49-611-7878400, info@vs-verlag.de, http://www.vs-verlag.de.

375.001 JPN
JAPANESE SOCIETY OF INDUSTRIAL AND TECHNOLOGY EDUCATION. JOURNAL. Text in Japanese. 1954. q. JPY 7,000. **Description:** Covers curriculum development and evaluation, teaching methodology and materials, philosophy and history.
Formerly: Japan Society of Industrial and Technical Education. Bulletin
Published by: Japanese Society of Industrial and Technology Education, c/o Faculty of Education, Kobe University, 2-5-1 Hiratsu, Otsu-shi, Shiga-ken 520-0862, Japan. TEL 0775-33-2774. Circ: 800.

027.5 028.5 371.33 NLD ISSN 1574-1591
JEUGDLITERATUUR IN PRAKTIJK. Text in Dutch. 1996. q. EUR 28.44 (effective 2005). bk.rev. bibl.; charts; illus. 28 p./no.; **Document type:** *Journal, Trade.* **Description:** Offers elementary-school teachers in the first and second grades practical advice on using children's literature in their classroom instruction.
Formerly: Jeugdliteratuur in de Basisvorming (1384-5535)
Related titles: CD-ROM ed.

Published by: Biblion Uitgeverij, Postbus 437, Leidschendam, 2260 AK, Netherlands. info@nbdbiblion.nl, http://www.nbdbiblion.nl/?pagina=7440. Eds. Ger van Hoek, Max Verbeek, Rob van Veen. **Dist in Belgium by:** Swets Belgium NV, Eigenlostraat 21, St-Niklaas 9100, Belgium. TEL 32-37-806262, FAX 32-37-806299.

JEZIK IN SLOVSTVO. see *LINGUISTICS*

371.3 CHN ISSN 0257-2826
JIAOXUE YU YANJIU/TEACHING AND RESEARCH. Text in Chinese. 1953. m. CNY 72 (effective 2004). **Document type:** *Journal, Academic/Scholarly.* **Description:** Contains papers on teaching and research.
Related titles: Online - full text ed.: (from East View Information Services).
Published by: Zhongguo Renmin Daxue, Shubao Zilio Zhongxin/Renmin University of China, Information Center for Social Server, Dongcheng-qu, 3, Zhangzizhong Lu, Beijing, 100007, China. TEL 86-10-84043003, FAX 86-10-64015080, jiaoyuyan@263.net. **Dist. in China by:** China International Book Trading Corp, 35 Chegongzhuang Xilu, Haidian District, PO Box 399, Beijing 100044, China. TEL 86-10-68412045, FAX 86-10-68412023, cibtc@mail.cibtc.com.cn, http://www.cibtc.com.cn; **Dist. in US by:** China Books & Periodicals Inc, 360 Swift Ave., Ste. 48, S San Fran, CA 94080-6220. info@chinabooks.com, http://www.chinabooks.com/.

JOINT ASSOCIATION OF CLASSICAL TEACHERS. BULLETIN. see *CLASSICAL STUDIES*

372.6521 CAN ISSN 0833-1812
LE JOURNAL DE L'IMMERSION/IMMERSION JOURNAL. Text in English, French. 1978. 3/yr.
Formerly (until 1986): Nouvelles de l'A C P I (0822-9333)
Published by: Association Canadienne des Professeurs d'Immersion/Canadian Association of Immersion Teachers, 201-57 Prom. Auriga, Nepean, ON K2E 8B2, Canada. TEL 613-998-0051, FAX 613-998-7094, acpi@sevec.ca, http://acpi.scedu.umontreal.ca.

LE JOURNAL DE MATHS DES ELEVES. see *MATHEMATICS*

510.71 USA ISSN 0021-8251
QA11.A1 CODEN: JRMEDN
➤ **JOURNAL FOR RESEARCH IN MATHEMATICS EDUCATION.** Text in English. 1970. 5/yr. USD 94 to individual members; USD 151 to institutions (effective 2005). adv. bk.rev. illus. annualindex. 120 p./no.; back issues avail.; reprint service avail. from PQC. **Document type:** *Journal, Academic/Scholarly.* **Description:** Research reports and reviews on the teaching and learning of mathematics at all levels.
Related titles: Microform ed.: (from PQC); Online - full text ed.: J R M E Online (from EBSCO Publishing, H.W. Wilson, JSTOR (Web-based Journal Archive), Northern Light Technology, Inc., O C L C Online Computer Library Center, Inc., ProQuest Information & Learning).
Indexed: ABIn, ASCA, CIJE, CIS, CPE, CurCont, ERA, ETA, EduInd, EngInd, PsycInfo, PsycholAb, SSCI, TEA, e-psyche.
—BLDSC (5052.015000), Ei, IDS, IE, Infotrieve, ingenta.
Published by: National Council of Teachers of Mathematics, 1906 Association Dr, Reston, VA 20191-1502. TEL 703-620-9840, 800-235-7566, FAX 703-476-2970, nctm@nctm.org, http://my.nctm.org/eresources/journal_home.asp?journal_id=1, http://www.nctm.org. Ed. Edward T Silver. Pub. Harry B Tunis. Adv. contact Tom Pearson. Circ: 7,000 (paid).

371.3 510.71 USA ISSN 0883-9530
JOURNAL FOR RESEARCH IN MATHEMATICS EDUCATION. MONOGRAPH. Text in English. 1985. irreg., latest vol.12. price varies. **Document type:** *Monographic series, Academic/Scholarly.* **Description:** Reports on research into effective teaching methods in mathematics education across all grade levels.
Related titles: Online - full text ed.: (from JSTOR (Web-based Journal Archive)).
—BLDSC (5052.015050).
Published by: National Council of Teachers of Mathematics, 1906 Association Dr, Reston, VA 20191-1502. TEL 703-620-9840, 800-235-7566, FAX 703-476-2970, nctm@nctm.org, http://nctm.org.

371.3 AUT ISSN 1681-7028
JOURNAL FUER LEHRERINNEN- UND LEHRERBILDUNG. Text in German. 2001. 4/yr. EUR 31; EUR 12.60 newsstand/cover (effective 2005). **Document type:** *Magazine, Trade.*
Published by: StudienVerlag, Amraser Str 118, Innsbruck, 6020, Austria. TEL 43-512-395045, FAX 43-512-39504515, jlb-journal@studienverlag.at, order@studienverlag.at, http://www.studienverlag.at.

372.4 USA
JOURNAL OF CLINICAL READING: RESEARCH AND PROGRAMS. Text in English. 1984. a. USD 6.70 per issue. bk.rev. bibl.; stat. back issues avail. **Document type:** *Academic/Scholarly.*
Published by: (College Reading Association, Clinical Division), Cleveland State University, 2121 Eastwood Ave, University Center, Cleveland, OH 44115. TEL 216-687-4600. Ed. Lillian R Hinds. Circ: 100.

E

▼ new title ➤ refereed ✶ unverified ♦ full entry avail.

JOURNAL OF COMPUTERS IN MATHEMATICS AND SCIENCE TEACHING. see *MATHEMATICS—Computer Applications*

375 USA ISSN 0882-1232
CODEN: JSTSF7

➤ **JOURNAL OF CURRICULUM AND SUPERVISION.** Text in English. 1985. q. USD 49 to non-members; USD 39 to members (effective 2003). bk.rev. charts; abstr.; illus. index. back issues avail.; reprints avail. **Document type:** *Academic/Scholarly.* **Description:** Provides information on what your school should teach, how to teach it, and why.
Related titles: Online - full text ed.: (from EBSCO Publishing, H.W. Wilson, O C L C Online Computer Library Center, Inc., ProQuest Information & Learning).
Indexed: ABIn, CIJE, CPE, ERA, ETA, EduInd, MEA, RHEA, SEA, SENA, SOMA, TEA.
—BLDSC (4965.935000), IE, Infotrieve, ingenta. **CCC.**
Published by: Association for Supervision and Curriculum Development, 1703 N Beauregard St, Alexandria, VA 22311. TEL 703-578-9600, FAX 703-575-5400, update@ascd.org, http://www.ascd.org/cms/index.cfm?TheViewID=365. Ed. Dr. O L Davis Jr.

375 GBR ISSN 0022-0272
L16

➤ **JOURNAL OF CURRICULUM STUDIES.** Text in English. 1968. bi-m. GBP 384, USD 634 combined subscription to institutions print & online eds. (effective 2006). adv. bk.rev. back issues avail.; reprint service avail. from PSC. **Document type:** *Journal, Academic/Scholarly.* **Description:** Contains original contributions to the theory and practice of curriculum and teaching at the national level. Primary focus is on school experience, but the scope extends to any area where the curriculum is researched and debated.
Related titles: Online - full text ed.: ISSN 1366-5839. GBP 365, USD 601 to institutions (effective 2006) (from EBSCO Publishing, Gale Group, IngentaConnect, O C L C Online Computer Library Center, Inc., Swets Information Services).
Indexed: ABIn, ASCA, ArtHuCI, BrEdI, CIJE, CPE, ChLitAb, CurCont, EAA, ERA, ETA, EduInd, HECAB, LT&LA, MEA, RASB, RHEA, SEA, SENA, SOMA, SSCI, SWA, TEA.
—BLDSC (4965.950000), IDS, IE, Infotrieve, ingenta, KNAW. **CCC.**
Published by: Routledge (Subsidiary of: Taylor & Francis Group), 4 Park Sq, Milton Park, Abingdon, Oxon OX14 4RN, United Kingdom. TEL 44-1235-828600, FAX 44-1235-829000, info@routledge.co.uk, http://www.tandf.co.uk/journals/titles/00220272.asp, http://www.routledge.co.uk. Eds. Ian Westbury, Ian Westbury. **Subscr. in N. America to:** Taylor & Francis Inc., Customer Services Dept, 325 Chestnut St, 8th Fl, Philadelphia, PA 19106. TEL 800-354-1420, FAX 215-625-8914; **Subscr. to:** Taylor & Francis Ltd, Journals Customer Service, Rankine Rd, Basingstoke, Hants RG24 8PR, United Kingdom. TEL 44-1256-813000, FAX 44-1256-330245, enquiry@tandf.co.uk, info@tandf.co.uk, http://www.tandf.co.uk/journals.

707.1 GBR ISSN 1360-1431

JOURNAL OF DESIGN & TECHNOLOGY EDUCATION. Text in English. 1968. 3/yr. GBP 45 in United Kingdom to individuals; GBP 50 elsewhere to individuals; GBP 50 in United Kingdom to institutions; GBP 55 elsewhere to institutions (effective 2002). bk.rev. back issues avail.; reprint service avail. from PQC. **Document type:** *Journal, Academic/Scholarly.* **Description:** Developments in design and technology education from art to applied science and technology, including case studies of new approaches in schools and colleges, new research, studies and reviews of new literature.
Former titles: Design & Technology Teaching (0958-3017); Studies in Design, Education Craft and Technology (0142-4807)
Related titles: Microform ed.: (from PQC).
Indexed: BrEdI, CPE, ERA, ETA, HECAB, Inspec, MEA, RHEA, SEA, SENA, SOMA, SWA, TEA.
—BLDSC (4968.797000), AskIEEE, IE, ingenta. **CCC.**
Published by: Trentham Books Ltd., Westview House, 734 London Rd, Stoke-on-Trent, Staffs ST4 5NP, United Kingdom. TEL 44-1782-745567, FAX 44-1782-745553, tb@trentham-books.co.uk, http://www.trentham-books.co.uk. Ed. Richard Kimbell. Circ: 4,500.

371.334 USA ISSN 1540-0077

JOURNAL OF DIRECT INSTRUCTION. Text in English. 1981. s-a. free to members (effective 2003). adv. bk.rev. bibl. back issues avail. **Document type:** *Journal, Academic/Scholarly.* **Description:** Publishes research, training methods, and experiences of teachers in research-based effective technology practices.
Supersedes in part (2001): Effective School Practices (1068-7378); (until 1992): A D I News
Indexed: CPE.
Published by: Association for Direct Instruction, PO Box 10252, Eugene, OR 97440. TEL 541-485-1293, FAX 541-683-7543, amy@adihome.org, erica@adihome.org, http://www.adihome.org. Eds. Amy Griffin, Sara Tarver, Tim Slocum. Adv. contact Bryan Wickman. Circ: 3,000.

JOURNAL OF EARLY INTERVENTION. see *EDUCATION—Special Education And Rehabilitation*

THE JOURNAL OF ECONOMIC EDUCATION. see *BUSINESS AND ECONOMICS*

375 GBR ISSN 1363-9080

JOURNAL OF EDUCATION AND WORK. Text in English. 1987. 5/yr. GBP 430, USD 711 combined subscription to institutions print & online eds. (effective 2006). adv. bk.rev. illus. cum.index every 5 yrs. back issues avail.; reprint service avail. from PSC. **Document type:** *Journal, Academic/Scholarly.* **Description:** Incorporates the curriculum, teaching methods and research about school and college programs linking industry, careers, employment and education.
Formerly (until 1997): British Journal of Education and Work (0269-0004)
Related titles: Online - full text ed.: ISSN 1469-9435. GBP 409, USD 675 to institutions (effective 2006) (from EBSCO Publishing, Gale Group, IngentaConnect, O C L C Online Computer Library Center, Inc., Swets Information Services).
Indexed: BrEdI, CIJE, CPE, ERA, ETA, MEA, PsycInfo, PsycholAb, RHEA, SEA, SENA, SOMA, SSA, SWA, SociolAb, TEA.
—BLDSC (4973.127000), IE, Infotrieve, ingenta. **CCC.**
Published by: Routledge (Subsidiary of: Taylor & Francis Group), 4 Park Sq, Milton Park, Abingdon, Oxon OX14 4RN, United Kingdom. TEL 44-1235-828600, FAX 44-1235-829000, info@routledge.co.uk, http://www.tandf.co.uk/journals/titles/13639080.asp, http://www.routledge.co.uk. Ed. Hugh Lauder. Circ: 750. **Subscr. to:** Taylor & Francis Ltd, Journals Customer Service, Rankine Rd, Basingstoke, Hants RG24 8PR, United Kingdom. TEL 44-1256-813000, FAX 44-1256-330245.

JOURNAL OF EDUCATION FOR LIBRARY AND INFORMATION SCIENCE. see *LIBRARY AND INFORMATION SCIENCES*

371.3 USA ISSN 1082-4669
LC4091

➤ **JOURNAL OF EDUCATION FOR STUDENTS PLACED AT RISK.** Abbreviated title: J E S P A R. Text in English. 1996. q. USD 405 in US & Canada to institutions; USD 435 elsewhere to institutions; USD 425 combined subscription in US & Canada to institutions print & online eds.; USD 455 combined subscription elsewhere to institutions print & online eds. (effective 2006). adv. back issues avail.; reprint service avail. from PSC. **Document type:** *Journal, Academic/Scholarly.* **Description:** Provides information to professionals involved with improving the education of students placed at risk.
Related titles: Online - full text ed.: ISSN 1532-7671. USD 385 worldwide to institutions (effective 2005) (from EBSCO Publishing, Gale Group, O C L C Online Computer Library Center, Inc., Swets Information Services).
Indexed: CIJE, CPE, EAA, ERA, ESPM, ETA, MEA, PsycInfo, PsycholAb, RHEA, RiskAb, SEA, SENA, SOMA, SociolAb, TEA, V&AA, e-psyche.
—BLDSC (4973.152300), IE, Infotrieve, ingenta. **CCC.**
Published by: Lawrence Erlbaum Associates, Inc., 10 Industrial Ave, Mahwah, NJ 07430-2262. TEL 201-258-2200, 800-926-6579, FAX 201-236-0072, journals@erlbaum.com, http://www.leaonline.com/loi/espr. Eds. John H Hollifield, Samuel C Stringfield. adv.: page USD 300; trim 5 x 8.

➤ **JOURNAL OF EDUCATIONAL MEDIA AND LIBRARY SCIENCES.** see *LIBRARY AND INFORMATION SCIENCES*

➤ **JOURNAL OF EDUCATIONAL MULTIMEDIA AND HYPERMEDIA.** see *COMPUTERS—Computer Assisted Instruction*

372.35 507.1 USA ISSN 1090-185X
LB1585

JOURNAL OF ELEMENTARY SCIENCE EDUCATION. Text in English. 1989. s-a. **Document type:** *Academic/Scholarly.* **Description:** Publishes research on learning and teaching science curriculum material.
Related titles: Online - full text ed.: (from Florida Center for Library Automation, Gale Group).
Indexed: CIJE.
—BLDSC (4976.800000), IE, ingenta.
Published by: University of West Florida, College of Education, 11000 University Pkwy, Pensacola, FL 32514.

JOURNAL OF ENGINEERING EDUCATION. see *ENGINEERING*

JOURNAL OF ENGLISH AND FOREIGN LANGUAGES. see *LINGUISTICS*

428 GBR ISSN 1475-1585
PE1128.A2

JOURNAL OF ENGLISH FOR ACADEMIC PURPOSES. Text in English. 2002. 4/yr. EUR 66 in Europe to individuals; JPY 8,700 in Japan to individuals; USD 75 to individuals except Europe and Japan; EUR 478 in Europe to institutions; JPY 63,600 in Japan to institutions; USD 536 to institutions except Europe and Japan (effective 2006). bk.rev. **Document type:** *Journal, Academic/Scholarly.* **Description:** Provides a forum for dissemination of information and views which enables practitioners of and researchers in EAP to keep current with developments in their field and to contribute to its continued updating. Publishes articles, book reviews, conference reports and academic exchanges in the linguistic, sociolinguistic and psycholinguistic description of English as it occurs in the contexts of academic study and scholarly exchange itself.
Related titles: Online - full text ed.: (from EBSCO Publishing, Gale Group, IngentaConnect, ScienceDirect, Swets Information Services).
Indexed: CPE, ERA, ETA, MEA, MLA-IB, RHEA, SEA, SENA, SOMA, TEA.
—BLDSC (4979.247000), IE, ingenta. **CCC.**
Published by: Pergamon (Subsidiary of: Elsevier Science & Technology), The Boulevard, Langford Ln, East Park, Kidlington, Oxford OX5 1GB, United Kingdom. TEL 44-1865-843000, FAX 44-1865-843010, http://www.elsevier.com/locate/jeap. Eds. Ken Hyland, L. Hamp-Lyons. **Subscr. to:** Elsevier BV, PO Box 211, Amsterdam 1000 AE, Netherlands. TEL 31-20-485-3757, FAX 31-20-485-3432, nlinfo-f@elsevier.nl, http://www.elsevier.nl.

371.3 USA ISSN 1053-8259
L11

➤ **JOURNAL OF EXPERIENTIAL EDUCATION.** Text in English. 1978. 3/yr. USD 60 domestic to non-members; USD 66 in Canada & Mexico to non-members; USD 75 foreign to non-members; free to members (effective 2005). bk.rev. cum.index: 1978-1994. 64 p./no.; **Document type:** *Journal, Academic/Scholarly.* **Description:** Academic articles with valuable ideas, practices, and research in the field of experiential education.
Related titles: Microfilm ed.; Online - full text ed.: (from EBSCO Publishing, Northern Light Technology, Inc., ProQuest Information & Learning).
Indexed: ABS&EES, CIJE, CPE, ERA, ETA, MEA, RHEA, SEA, SENA, SOMA, SWA, TEA.
—BLDSC (4979.686000), IE, Infotrieve, ingenta. **CCC.**
Published by: Association for Experiential Education, 3775 Iris Ave, Ste 4, Boulder, CO 80301-2043. TEL 303-440-8844, FAX 303-440-9581, jourexed@indiana.edu, publications@aee.org, http://www.aee.org/pubs/jee/njourn.html. Ed. Alan Ewert TEL 812-855-3528. Circ: 2,500.

371.3 USA ISSN 0022-0973
CODEN: JEXEAI

➤ **JOURNAL OF EXPERIMENTAL EDUCATION.** Text in English. 1932. q. USD 57 domestic to individuals; USD 71 foreign to individuals; USD 124 domestic to institutions; USD 138 foreign to institutions; USD 31 per issue (effective academic year 2005 - 2006). adv. abstr.; charts; illus.; stat. index. reprint service avail. from PSC. **Document type:** *Journal, Academic/Scholarly.* **Description:** Publishes theoretical, laboratory, and classroom research studies that involve a wide range of quantitative and qualitative methodologies.
Related titles: CD-ROM ed.: (from ProQuest Information & Learning); Microform ed.: (from PMC); Online - full text ed.: (from bigchalk, Chadwyck-Healey Inc., EBSCO Publishing, Florida Center for Library Automation, Gale Group, H.W. Wilson, O C L C Online Computer Library Center, Inc., ProQuest Information & Learning).
Indexed: ABIn, AMHA, ASCA, CDA, CIJE, CIS, CPE, CurCont, DIP, EAA, ERA, ETA, EduInd, FamI, HEA, HECAB, IBR, IBZ, L&LBA, MASUSE, MEA, PCI, PsycInfo, PsycholAb, RASB, RHEA, SEA, SENA, SOMA, SOPODA, SSCI, SWA, TEA, e-psyche.
—BLDSC (4981.500000), CINDOC, IDS, IE, Infotrieve, ingenta. **CCC.**
Published by: (Helen Dwight Reid Educational Foundation), Heldref Publications, 1319 18th St, NW, Washington, DC 20036-1802. TEL 202-296-6267, 800-365-9753, FAX 202-293-6130, jxe@heldref.org, subscribe@heldref.org, http://www.heldref.org/jexpe.php. Adv. contact Chante Douglas. B&W page USD 260; trim 5 x 7.5. Circ: 767 (paid).

➤ **JOURNAL OF FAMILY AND CONSUMER SCIENCES EDUCATION.** see *HOME ECONOMICS*

➤ **JOURNAL OF FRENCH LANGUAGE STUDIES.** see *LINGUISTICS*

➤ **JOURNAL OF GEOSCIENCE EDUCATION.** see *EARTH SCIENCES—Geology*

375 GBR ISSN 1367-4587
LB1731 CODEN: JIEDFL

➤ **JOURNAL OF IN-SERVICE EDUCATION.** Text in English. 1974. q. GBP 316, USD 491 to institutions print & online eds. (effective 2006). bk.rev. abstr.; illus. back issues avail.; reprint service avail. from PSC. **Document type:** *Journal, Academic/Scholarly.* **Description:** Publishes original contributions on all aspects of teacher education, including initial preparation as it affects induction, in-service education, staff development, and the work of teachers' centres and advisory services.
Formerly (until 1998): British Journal of In-Service Education (0305-7631)
Related titles: Online - full text ed.: ISSN 1747-5082. GBP 300, USD 466 to institutions (effective 2006) (from EBSCO Publishing, Swets Information Services).
Indexed: BrEdI, CPE, DIP, ERA, ETA, HECAB, IBR, IBZ, LT&LA, MEA, RASB, RHEA, SEA, SENA, SOMA, SWA, TEA.
—BLDSC (5005.101000), IE, ingenta.
Published by: Routledge (Subsidiary of: Taylor & Francis Group), 4 Park Sq, Milton Park, Abingdon, Oxon OX14 4RN, United Kingdom. TEL 44-1235-828600, FAX 44-1235-829000, journals@routledge.com, http://www.tandf.co.uk/journals/titles/13674587.asp, http://www.routledge.co.uk. Ed. Ken Jones.

E

371.334 USA ISSN 1539-3585
CODEN: JITECS

➤ **JOURNAL OF INFORMATION TECHNOLOGY EDUCATION.** Text and summaries in English. 2002. a. USD 53 per issue domestic; USD 56 per issue foreign (effective 2003). abstr.; charts; illus. **Document type:** *Journal, Academic/Scholarly.* **Description:** Covers Issues on teaching information technology.
Related titles: Online - full text ed.: ISSN 1547-9714. free (effective 2005).
Indexed: Inspec.
Published by: Informing Science Institute, 131 Brookhill Court, Santa Rosa, CA 95409-2464. TEL 707-531-4925, FAX 815-352-9100, jite@jite.org, http://jite.org. Ed., R&P Dr. Eli B Cohen. Pub. Elizabeth C Boyd. Circ: 2,000.

371.358 AUS ISSN 1324-0781

➤ **JOURNAL OF INSTRUCTIONAL SCIENCE AND TECHNOLOGY.** Text in English. 1995. irreg. free (effective 2005). **Document type:** *Journal, Academic/Scholarly.* **Description:** Includes original work of practitioners and researchers with specific focus or implementation for the design of instructional materials.
Media: Online - full text.
Indexed: AEI.
Published by: University of Southern Queensland, Distance Education Centre, 61-7 West St, Toowoomba, QLD 4350, Australia. TEL 61-7-4631-2100, jegede@ouhk.edu.hk, http://www.usq.edu.au/electpub/e-jist/homepage.htm. Eds. Olugbemiro J Jegede, Som Naidu.

➤ **JOURNAL OF INTERACTIVE INSTRUCTION DEVELOPMENT.** see *COMPUTERS—Computer Assisted Instruction*

371.3346 USA ISSN 1541-4914
LB1028.5

➤ **JOURNAL OF INTERACTIVE ONLINE LEARNING.** Text in English. 2002. q. free (effective 2005). **Document type:** *Journal, Academic/Scholarly.* **Description:** Focuses on providing a venue for manuscripts, critical essays, and reviews that encompass disciplinary and interdisciplinary perspectives in regards to issues related to higher-level learning outcomes.
Media: Online - full content.
Published by: National Center for Online Learning Research, P. O. Box 870232, Tuscaloosa, AL 35487-0232. TEL 205-348-1401, FAX 205-348-9863, http://www.ncolr.org/journal/current/current.html. Ed. Cynthia Sunal.

➤ **JOURNAL OF INTERNATIONAL AGRICULTURAL AND EXTENSION EDUCATION.** see *AGRICULTURE*

➤ **JOURNAL OF JAPANESE LINGUISTICS.** see *LINGUISTICS*

➤ **JOURNAL OF LANGUAGE FOR INTERNATIONAL BUSINESS.** see *LINGUISTICS*

➤ **JOURNAL OF MARKETING EDUCATION.** see *BUSINESS AND ECONOMICS—Marketing And Purchasing*

➤ **JOURNAL OF MEDIA PRACTICE.** see *COMMUNICATIONS*

➤ **JOURNAL OF MUSIC THEORY PEDAGOGY.** see *MUSIC*

➤ **JOURNAL OF NATURAL RESOURCES AND LIFE SCIENCES EDUCATION**; an international journal. see *BIOLOGY*

➤ **JOURNAL OF PHARMACY TEACHING.** see *PHARMACY AND PHARMACOLOGY*

613.7 USA ISSN 0730-3084

➤ **JOURNAL OF PHYSICAL EDUCATION, RECREATION AND DANCE.** Variant title: J O P E R D. Text in English. 1896. m. (9/yr). USD 73 in US & Canada to non-members; USD 81 elsewhere to non-members; USD 145 in US & Canada libraries & institutions; USD 153 elsewhere libraries & institutions; free to members (effective 2005). illus. index. 64 p./no. 3 cols./p.; back issues avail.; reprint service avail. from PQC,ISI. **Document type:** *Journal, Academic/Scholarly.* **Description:** Features by-lined articles and short features on all aspects of physical education, recreation, dance, athletics and safety education as taught in schools and colleges. Covers administration, curriculum methods, equipment.
Former titles (until May 1981): Journal of Physical Education and Recreation (0097-1170); (until 1974): Journal of Health, Physical Education, Recreation (0022-1473)
Related titles: Microform ed.: (from PMC, PQC); Online - full text ed.: (from Florida Center for Library Automation, Gale Group, O C L C Online Computer Library Center, Inc., ProQuest Information & Learning).
Indexed: ABIn, AEA, AbHyg, CIJE, CPE, EduInd, IDP, IIPA, MRD, NutrAb, PEI, RASB, RILM, RRTA, RehabLit, SportS, WAE&RSA.
—BLDSC (5036.207000), GNLM, IE, Infotrieve, ingenta.
Published by: American Alliance for Health, Physical Education, Recreation, and Dance, 1900 Association Dr, Reston, VA 20191-1599. TEL 703-476-3400, 800-213-7193, FAX 703-476-9527, info@aahperd.org, http://www.aahperd.org/aahperd/template.cfm?template=johperd_main.html. Ed. Michael T Shoemaker. Adv. contact Rob Crowe. Circ: 18,000 (paid).

371.3 USA

▼ **JOURNAL OF RESEARCH IN CHARACTER EDUCATION.** Text in English. 2004. q. USD 85 to individuals; USD 185 to institutions; USD 65 to students; USD 25 per issue to individuals; USD 45 per issue to institutions (effective 2006). **Document type:** *Journal, Academic/Scholarly.* **Description:** Serves an audience of researchers, policy makers, teacher educators, and school practitioners concerned with the development of positive character in young people.
Published by: Information Age Publishing, Inc., 411 W Putnam Ave, Ste 205, PO Box 4967, Greenwich, CT 06831. TEL 203-661-7602, FAX 203-661-7952, info@infoagepub.com, http://www.character.org/files/journal_hp.htm, http://www.infoagepub.com. Eds. Andrew Milson, Marvin Berkowitz.

JOURNAL OF RESEARCH IN MUSIC EDUCATION. see *MUSIC*

371.4 USA ISSN 1554-2998
LB1027.5

▼ ➤ **JOURNAL OF SCHOOL COUNSELING.** Abbreviated title: J S C. Text in English. 2003. q. free (effective 2005). **Document type:** *Journal, Academic/Scholarly.*
Media: Online - full content.
Address: 305 Herrick Hl, Montana State University, Bozeman, MT 59717-3540. http://www.jsc.montana.edu/index.html. Eds. Jill M Thorngren, Mark D Nelson.

510.71 MYS ISSN 0126-7663
Q181.A1

JOURNAL OF SCIENCE AND MATHEMATICS EDUCATION IN SOUTHEAST ASIA. Text in English. 1978. s-a. USD 35. bk.rev. reprint service avail. from PQC. **Description:** Contains articles related to teaching and learning science and math in Southeast Asia.
Indexed: BAS, CIJE, CPE, ERA, ETA, MEA, TEA.
—BLDSC (5054.830000), IE, ingenta.
Published by: Southeast Asian Ministers of Education Organisation, Regional Centre for Education in Science and Mathematics, Glugor, Penang 11700, Malaysia. TEL 604-6583266, FAX 604-6572541. Ed. Michael Lian. Circ: 650.

JOURNAL OF SCIENCE EDUCATION AND TECHNOLOGY. see *SCIENCES: COMPREHENSIVE WORKS*

JOURNAL OF SINGING. see *MUSIC*

JOURNAL OF SOCIAL STUDIES RESEARCH. see *SOCIAL SCIENCES: COMPREHENSIVE WORKS*

JOURNAL OF SOCIAL THEORY IN ART EDUCATION. see *ART*

378 USA

➤ **THE JOURNAL OF STUDENT CENTERED LEARNING.** Text in English. 1990. 3/yr. USD 52 domestic; USD 67 foreign (effective 2005). tr.lit. back issues avail. **Document type:** *Journal, Academic/Scholarly.* **Description:** Devoted to the study and implementation of cooperative learning techniques in higher education institutions. Features informative articles by practitioners experienced in cooperative learning.
Former titles (until 2002): The Journal of Cooperation & Collaboration in College Teaching; (until 2000): The Cooperative Learning and College Teaching Newsletter
Published by: New Forums Press, Inc., 1018 S Lewis St, Stillwater, OK 74074. TEL 800-606-3766, FAX 405-377-2237, info@newforums.com, http://www.newforums.com. Ed. Jim Cooper. Pub. Dr. Douglas O Dollar.

613.7 USA ISSN 0273-5024
GV363

➤ **JOURNAL OF TEACHING IN PHYSICAL EDUCATION.** Text in English. 1981. q. USD 52 domestic to individuals; USD 62 foreign to individuals; USD 208 domestic to institutions; USD 218 foreign to institutions; USD 73 combined subscription domestic to individuals print & online eds.; USD 83 combined subscription foreign to individuals print & online eds.; USD 291 combined subscription domestic to institutions print & online eds.; USD 301 combined subscription foreign to institutions print & online eds. (effective 2005). adv. bk.rev. bibl.; charts; stat.; illus. index. back issues avail.; reprint service avail. from PSC. **Document type:** *Journal, Academic/Scholarly.* **Description:** Designed to stimulate and communicate research and practical applications in the field of physical education. Offers new teaching methods and ideas to help students, teachers, teacher educators, and administrators at all levels.
Related titles: Online - full text ed.: ISSN 1543-2769. USD 62, USD 250 to individuals (effective 2005) (from EBSCO Publishing).
Indexed: ABIn, ASCA, AbHyg, CIJE, CPE, CurCont, DIP, ERA, ETA, EduInd, FoSS&M, IBR, IBZ, MEA, PEI, PsycInfo, PsycholAb, RHEA, RRTA, SEA, SENA, SOMA, SSCI, SWA, SportS, TEA, e-psyche.
—BLDSC (5068.285700), IDS, IE, Infotrieve, ingenta. **CCC.**
Published by: International Association for the Philosophy of Sport/Human Kinetics, 1607 N Market St, PO Box 5076, Champaign, IL 61825-5076. TEL 217-351-5078, 800-747-4457, FAX 217-351-2674, orders@hkusa.com, http://www.humankinetics.com. Eds. Bonnie Tjeerdsma Blankenship, Melinda Solomon. Adv. contact Chad Hoffman. B&W page USD 300. Circ: 1,183 (paid).

362.3071 USA ISSN 0884-1233
HV11

➤ **JOURNAL OF TEACHING IN SOCIAL WORK**; innovations in instruction, training & educational practice. Abbreviated title: J T S W. Text in English. 1987. q. USD 350 combined subscription domestic to institutions print & online eds.; USD 472.50 combined subscription in Canada to institutions print & online eds.; USD 507.50 combined subscription elsewhere to institutions print & online eds. (effective 2006). adv. bk.rev. illus. 120 p./no. 1 cols./p.; back issues avail.; reprint service avail. from HAW. **Document type:** *Journal, Academic/Scholarly.* **Description:** Addresses qualitative, as well as quantitative studies, philosophical and historical insights; focuses on the educational process in social work.
Related titles: Microfiche ed.: (from PQC); Microform ed.; Online - full text ed.: ISSN 1540-7349. free to institutions (effective 2003); free with print subs. (from EBSCO Publishing, O C L C Online Computer Library Center, Inc., Swets Information Services).
Indexed: ASSIA, CPE, DIP, ERA, ETA, FamI, HRA, IBR, IBZ, IMFL, MEA, PAIS, RHEA, RefZh, SEA, SENA, SFSA, SOMA, SOPODA, SSA, SWA, SWR&A, SociolAb, TEA.
—BLDSC (5068.285750), Haworth, IE, ingenta. **CCC.**
Published by: Haworth Press, Inc., 10 Alice St, Binghamton, NY 13904-1580. TEL 607-722-5857, 800-429-6784, FAX 607-722-1424, getinfo@haworthpress.com, http://www.haworthpressinc.com/web/JTSW, http://www.haworthpress.com. Eds. Florence Vigilante, Harold Lewis. Pub. William Cohen. R&P Ruth Ann Heath TEL 607-722-5857 ext 316. Adv. contact Rebecca Miller-Baum TEL 607-722-5857 ext 337. B&W page USD 315, color page USD 550; trim 4.375 x 7.125. Circ: 326 (paid).

371.3 362.29 USA ISSN 1533-2705
HV4999.2

JOURNAL OF TEACHING IN THE ADDICTIONS. Text in English. 2002. s-a. USD 235 combined subscription domestic to institutions print & online eds.; USD 317.25 combined subscription in Canada to institutions print & online eds.; USD 340.75 combined subscription elsewhere to institutions print & online eds. (effective 2006). adv. reprint service avail. from HAW. **Document type:** *Journal, Academic/Scholarly.* **Description:** Covers instructional/educational issues for the drug and alcohol field.
Related titles: Online - full content ed.: ISSN 1533-2713. free to institutions (effective 2003); free with print subs.; Online - full text ed.: (from EBSCO Publishing, O C L C Online Computer Library Center, Inc., Swets Information Services).
Indexed: DIP, IBR, IBZ, RefZh, e-psyche.
—Haworth.
Published by: Haworth Press, Inc., 10 Alice St, Binghamton, NY 13904-1580. TEL 607-722-5857, 800-429-6784, FAX 607-722-1424, 800-895-0582, getinfo@haworthpress.com, http://www.haworthpress.com/web/JTADD. Ed. Michael J Taleff. R&P Ruth Ann Heath TEL 607-722-5857 ext 316. Adv. contact Rebecca Miller-Baum TEL 607-722-5857 ext 337. B&W page USD 315, color page USD 550; trim 4.375 x 7.125. Circ: 60 (paid).

362.3071 338.4791 USA ISSN 1531-3220
G155.7 CODEN: JTTTBD

JOURNAL OF TEACHING IN TRAVEL & TOURISM; the professional journal of the international society of travel & tourism educators. Text in English. 2001. q. USD 240 combined subscription domestic to institutions print & online eds.; USD 324 combined subscription in Canada to institutions print & online eds.; USD 348 combined subscription elsewhere to institutions print & online eds. (effective 2006). adv. reprint service avail. from HAW. **Document type:** *Journal, Academic/Scholarly.* **Description:** Serves as an international interdisciplinary forum and source of reference for travel and tourism education.
Related titles: Online - full text ed.: ISSN 1531-3239. free with subscr. to the print ed. (from EBSCO Publishing, O C L C Online Computer Library Center, Inc., Swets Information Services).
Indexed: CPE, DIP, H&TI, IBR, IBZ, Inspec, RRTA, RefZh, WAE&RSA.
—Haworth. **CCC.**
Published by: Haworth Hospitality Press (Subsidiary of: Haworth Press, Inc.), 10 Alice St, Binghamton, NY 13904-1580. TEL 607-722-5857, 800-429-6784, FAX 607-771-0012, 800-895-0582, getinfo@haworthpress.com, http://www.haworthpress.com/web/JTTT. Ed. Cathy H C Hsu. Pub. William Cohen. R&P Ruth Ann Heath TEL 607-722-5857 ext 316. Adv. contact Rebecca Miller-Baum TEL 607-722-5857 ext 337. B&W page USD 315, color page USD 550; trim 4.375 x 7.125. Circ: 87 (paid).

371.3 AUS ISSN 1030-407X

JOURNAL OF TEACHING PRACTICE. Text in English. 1981. s-a. AUD 22 to individuals; AUD 28 to institutions. adv. bk.rev. back issues avail. **Description:** Provides a forum for people interested in the school-experience programs for student teachers in Australia.

E

Formerly (until 1984): Australian Journal of Teaching Practice
Indexed: AEI.
Published by: Monash University, School of Education, Switchback Rd, Churchill, VIC 3842, Australia. TEL 051-226375, FAX 051-226361. Ed. Len Cairns. Circ: 180.

JOURNAL OF TEACHING WRITING. see *JOURNALISM*

371.425 USA ISSN 1045-1064
T61
➤ **JOURNAL OF TECHNOLOGY EDUCATION.** Text in English. 1989. s-a. USD 12 domestic to individuals; USD 16 foreign to individuals; USD 20 domestic to institutions; USD 25 foreign to institutions (effective 2004). bk.rev. back issues avail. **Document type:** *Journal, Academic/Scholarly.* **Description:** Provides a forum for scholarly discussion of the theory and research related to technology education.
Related titles: Online - full text ed.: free (effective 2005).
Indexed: CIJE, CPE, Inspec.
—BLDSC (5068.560000), IE, ingenta.
Published by: Virginia Polytechnic Institute, Technology Education Program, c/o James E LaPorte, 144 Smyth Hall, Blacksburg, VA 24061-0432. FAX 703-231-4188, http://scholar.lib.vt.edu/ejournals/JTE/, http://scholar.lib.vt.edu/ejournals/JTE/jte.html. R&P James E Laporte TEL 540-231-8169. Circ: 500.

➤ **JOURNAL OF THEORY CONSTRUCTION AND TESTING.** see *MEDICAL SCIENCES—Nurses And Nursing*

➤ **JOURNAL OF VISUAL COMMUNICATION IN MEDICINE.** see *MEDICAL SCIENCES*

371.335 USA ISSN 1051-144X
LB1068
➤ **JOURNAL OF VISUAL LITERACY.** Text in English. 1981. s-a. USD 40 in US & Canada membership; USD 45 elsewhere membership; USD 20 to students. bk.rev. bibl.; illus. **Document type:** *Journal, Academic/Scholarly.* **Description:** Explores empirical, theoretical, practical or applied aspects of visual literacy and communication.
Formerly (until 1988): Journal of Visual-Verbal Languaging (0748-7525)
Related titles: Online - full text ed.: (from EBSCO Publishing).
Indexed: CIJE.
Published by: International Visual Literacy Association, Inc., c/o Darrell Beauchamp, IVLA, Executive Treasurer, c/o Navarro College, 3200 W. 7th Ave, Corsicana, TX 75110. TEL 903-875-7441, FAX 903-874-4636, nknujpferl@ksu.edu, dbeau@nav.cc.tx.us, http://www.cameron.edu/jvl/, http://www.ivla.org/. Ed. Nancy Nelson Knupfer. R&P John Clarke Belland.

375.001 DEU
JOURNAL WIRTSCHAFTSPRAXIS. Text in German. 2001. s-a. **Document type:** *Journal, Academic/Scholarly.*
Published by: Lit Verlag, Grevener Str. 179, Muenster, 48159, Germany. TEL 49-251-235091, FAX 49-251-231972, lit@lit-verlag.de, http://www.lit-verlag.de. Ed. Juergen Bellers.

371.3 GBR ISSN 0966-7113
JUNIOR FOCUS. Text in English. 1927. m. GBP 37.50 domestic; GBP 49.95 foreign (effective 2001). adv. illus. **Document type:** *Journal, Academic/Scholarly.* **Description:** Contains subject-themed information and resources for teachers of 7-11 year olds.
Former titles: Junior Projects (0269-9532); Junior Education Special (0262-7515); (until Mar. 1982): Pictorial Education Special (0142-4963); Pictorial Education Quarterly (0048-413X)
Related titles: Microform ed.: (from PQC).
Published by: Scholastic Ltd., Villiers House, Clarendon Ave, Leamington Spa, Warks CV32 5PR, United Kingdom. TEL 44-1926-887799, FAX 44-1926-817727, enquiries@scholastic.co.uk, http://www.scholastic.co.uk. Ed. Maggie Henley. Adv. contact Chris Pratt. Circ: 17,000.

001.3 371.33 USA ISSN 0022-6688
JUNIOR SCHOLASTIC. Text in English. 1937. 18/yr. (during school year). USD 8.25 for orders of 10 or more copies; USD 12.75 for orders of 1-9 copies; USD 21.75 for teacher's edition (effective 2003 - 2004). adv. bibl.; charts; illus. index. Supplement avail.; reprint service avail. from PQC. **Document type:** *Magazine, Consumer.* **Description:** Covers US and world events, along with other topics for middle-school social studies curricula, for students in grades 6-8.
Related titles: Microfilm ed.: (from PQC); Online - full text ed.: (from bigchalk, EBSCO Publishing, Gale Group, ProQuest Information & Learning).
Indexed: ICM, RGYP.
—IE, Infotrieve.
Published by: Scholastic Inc., 557 Broadway, New York, NY 10012-0399. TEL 212-343-6100, junior@scholastic.com, http://teacher.scholastic.com/scholasticnews/magazines/junior/, http://www.scholastic.com. Ed. Susanne McCabe. Circ: 570,000 (paid). **Subscr. to:** 2931 E McCarthy St, PO Box 3710, Jefferson City, MO 65102-9957. TEL 800-724-6527, classmags@scholastic.com.

372.35 IND ISSN 0971-2453
JUNIOR SCIENTIST. Text in English. 1963. m. INR 45. adv. bk.rev.
Published by: Association for the Promotion of Science Education, 3 First Trust Link St., Mandavelipakkam, Chennai, Tamil Nadu 600 028, India. Ed. G Venkataraman. Circ: 1,500.

418 USA ISSN 1521-2300
PE1404
➤ **KAIROS;** a journal for teachers of writing in webbed environment. Text in English. 1996. 3/yr. free (effective 2005). **Document type:** *Journal, Academic/Scholarly.*
Media: Online - full content.
Indexed: MLA-IB, OTA.
Address: jinman@english.cas.usf.edu, eymand@wilmington.net, http://english.ttu.edu/kairos/, http://129.118.38.138/kairos/default.htm. Eds. Douglas Eyman, James A. Inman.

➤ **KANSAS MUSIC REVIEW.** see *MUSIC*

371.33 USA ISSN 0022-8958
LJ75
➤ **KAPPA DELTA PI RECORD.** Text in English. 1964. q. USD 18 domestic to non-members; USD 21 foreign to non-members; free to members (effective 2005). bk.rev. charts; illus. index. 48 p./no. 3 cols./p.; back issues avail.; reprint service avail. from PQC. **Document type:** *Journal, Academic/Scholarly.* **Description:** Practitioner-oriented articles featuring implementation strategies of the latest theories in elementary and secondary education.
Related titles: Microform ed.: 1964 (from PQC); Online - full text ed.: (from H.W. Wilson, O C L C Online Computer Library Center, Inc., ProQuest Information & Learning).
Indexed: ABIn, CIJE, EAA, ECER, EduInd.
Published by: Kappa Delta Pi, 3707 Woodview Trace, Indianapolis, IN 46268-1158. TEL 317-871-4900, 800-284-3167, FAX 317-704-2323, pubs@kdp.org, http://www.kdp.org/publications/howtosubscriberecord.php. Ed., R&P Kathie-Jo Arnoff. Circ: 55,000 (paid and controlled).

371.3 DEU ISSN 0724-5688
➤ **KARLSRUHER PAEDAGOGISCHE BEITRAEGE.** Text in German. 1979. 3/yr. EUR 13 (effective 2003). adv. bk.rev. 150 p./no.; back issues avail. **Document type:** *Journal, Academic/Scholarly.*
Published by: Paedagogische Hochschule Karlsruhe, Bismarckstr 10, Karlsruhe, 76133, Germany. TEL 49-721-9254016, FAX 49-721-9254000, kpb@ph-karlsruhe.de, http://www.ph-karlsruhe.de. Eds. Juergen Kurtz, Peter Mueller, Walter Kosack. R&P, Adv. contact Ute Potschka.

375 CHN ISSN 1000-0186
➤ **KECHENG - JIAOCAI - JIAOFA/CURRICULUM, TEACHING MATERIALS, AND METHOD.** Text in Chinese. 1981. m. CNY 5 newsstand/cover (effective 2005). adv. bk.rev. **Document type:** *Journal, Academic/Scholarly.* **Description:** Contains domestic and international news about curriculum, teaching materials, research results, reform trends and educational experiences in the fields of normal education, vocational education, adult education and pre-school education.
Related titles: Online - full text ed.: (from East View Information Services).
Published by: (People's Education Press & Curriculum and Teaching Materials Research Institute), Ministry of Education of China, 55 Sha Tan Hou Street, Beijing, 100009, China. TEL 86-10-64050355, FAX 86-10-64003690, http://pep.com.cn, http://ctmri.org.cn. Eds. Da Lu, Guodong Wei. **Dist. in US by:** China Books & Periodicals Inc, 360 Swift Ave., Ste. 48, S San Fran, CA 94080-6220. TEL 415-282-2994; **Dist. overseas by:** China International Book Trading Corp, 35 Chegongzhuang Xilu, Haidian District, PO Box 399, Beijing 100044, China. TEL 86-10-68412045, FAX 86-10-68412023, cibtc@mail.cibtc.com.cn, http://www.cibtc.com.cn/.

➤ **KEJI YINGYU XUEXI/LEARNING ENGLISH FOR SCIENCE & TECHNOLOGY.** see *LINGUISTICS*

371.3 378 USA
➤ **KENTUCKY JOURNAL OF EXCELLENCE IN COLLEGE TEACHING AND LEARNING.** (a. print ed. avail. at annual Kentucky CPE Faculty development conference) Text in English. irreg. free. **Document type:** *Journal, Academic/Scholarly.* **Description:** Covers the professional development of college/university faculty within Kentucky.
Media: Online - full content.
Address: c/o Walt Bower, Department of Sociology, College of Arts & Science, 1519 Patterson Office Tower, University of Kentucky, Lexington, KY 40506-0027. TEL 859-367-0512, http://www.uky.edu/TLC/JournalNEW/Missionpage.htm.

371.33 USA
➤ **KIDS INSIGHT SERIES.** Text in English. 2000. irreg., latest vol.4, 2002. price varies. bibl. back issues avail. **Document type:** *Monographic series, Academic/Scholarly.* **Description:** Explores critical issues K-12 classroom teachers grapple with every day in literacy and language-arts instruction and offers ways in which they can address their students diverse needs.
Published by: International Reading Association, Inc., 800 Barksdale Rd, Newark, DE 19714-8139. TEL 301-731-1600, 800-336-7323, books@reading.org, http://www.reading.org.

➤ **KIDS' MINISTRY IDEAS.** see *RELIGIONS AND THEOLOGY—Protestant*

➤ **DAS KIND.** see *CHILDREN AND YOUTH—About*

375.001 DEU ISSN 0939-7817
KINDERLEICHT. Text in German. 1991. q. EUR 22; EUR 6.60 newsstand/cover (effective 2005). **Document type:** *Journal, Academic/Scholarly.*
Published by: Bergmoser und Hoeller Verlag GmbH, Karl-Friedrich-Str 76, Aachen, 52072, Germany. TEL 49-241-93888123, FAX 49-241-93888134, kontakt@buhv.de, http://www.buhv.de.

KINEMA; a journal for film and audiovisual media. see *MOTION PICTURES*

KLASSE MUSIK. see *MUSIC*

371.3 DEU ISSN 0863-4386
➤ **KLEIN UND GROSS.** Text in German. 1951. 10/yr. EUR 34.80; EUR 19.20 to students; EUR 4 newsstand/cover (effective 2003). adv. **Document type:** *Journal, Academic/Scholarly.*
Former titles (until 1990): Neue Erziehung im Kindergarten (0323-3022); (until 1955): Neue Erziehung in Kindergarten und Heim (0323-8687)
Related titles: Online - full text ed.
Indexed: DIP, IBR, IBZ.
Published by: Julius Beltz GmbH & Co. KG, Werderstr 10, Weinheim, 69469, Germany. TEL 49-6201-60070, FAX 49-6201-6007393, redaktion@kleinundgross.de, info@beltz.de, http://www.kleinundgross.de, http://www.beltz.de. Ed. Eva Grueber. Adv. contact Brigitte Bell. B&W page EUR 1,770, color page EUR 3,000. Circ: 12,000 (paid and controlled).

371.3 430 DNK ISSN 0901-9731
KOEBENHAVNERSTUDIER I TOSPROGETHED/COPENHAGEN STUDIES IN BILINGUALISM. Text in Danish, English. 1985. irreg., latest vol.33, 2002. price varies. **Document type:** *Monographic series, Academic/Scholarly.*
Published by: Danmarks Paedagogiske Universitet/Danish University of Education, Emdrupvej 101, Copenhagen NV, 2400, Denmark. TEL 45-88-889000, FAX 45-88-889001, dpu@dpu.dk, http://www.dpu.dk.

KOMPETENZENTWICKLUNG. see *BUSINESS AND ECONOMICS—Personnel Management*

375.001 USA
KRAUSE CURRICULUM DEVELOPMENT LIBRARY. Abbreviated title: K C D L. Text in English. 1978. a.
Former titles (until 2001): Krause Curriculum Development Library (Micorform) (0740-1868); until (1983): Curriculum Development Library; until (1980): The Fearon-Pitman Curriculum Development Library
Media: Online - full content.
Address: 4611-F Assembly Dr, Lanham, MD 20706. TEL 301-459-2255, 800-416-4374, FAX 301-459-9235, info@kcdlonline.com, http://www.kcdlonline.com.

KUNSTSTUNDE; Unterrichtsbeispiele zur aesthetischen Erziehung. see *ART*

320.071 DEU ISSN 1433-2000
KURSIV; Journal fuer politische Bildung. Text in German. q. **Document type:** *Journal, Academic/Scholarly.*
Indexed: DIP, IBR, IBZ, RefZh.
Published by: Wochenschau Verlag, Adolf Damaschke Str 12, Schwalbach, 65824, Germany. TEL 49-6196-86065, FAX 49-6196-86060, wochenschau-verlag@t-online.de. Eds. Bernward Debus, Ursula Buch. R&P Bernward Debus. Adv. contact Edith Beralli.

KYOIKU ONGAKU, CHUGAKU KOKO-BAN/EDUCATIONAL MUSIC, JUNIOR HIGH AND HIGH SCHOOL. see *MUSIC*

KYOIKU ONGAKU, SHOGAKU-BAN/EDUCATIONAL MUSIC, ELEMENTARY SCHOOL. see *MUSIC*

371.3 JPN ISSN 0287-1122
KYOKA KYOIKU KENKYU✶ . Text in Japanese. 1968. a. illus.
Published by: Kanazawa Daigaku, Kyoikugakubu/Kanazawa University, Faculty of Education, 1-1 Marunochi, Kanazawa-shi, Ishikawa-ken 920-0937, Japan.

371.3 DNK ISSN 0904-2180
L L - NYT. (Laererstuderendes Landskreds) Text in Danish. 1972. 6/yr. adv.
Incorporates (in 1972): Laererstuderendes Landsblad; Which was formerly (until 1964): Seminarieelevernes Landsblad
Published by: Laererstuderendes Landskreds, Vester Voldgade 104, Copenhagen V, 1552, Denmark. TEL 45-33-93-94-24.

507.1 AUS ISSN 0819-0879
LAB LINES. Text in English. q. AUD 40 (effective 1999). **Document type:** *Newsletter.*
Published by: Science Teachers' Association of Victoria, PO Box 3058, Coburg, VIC 3058, Australia. TEL 61-3-9385-3999, FAX 61-3-9386-6722, stav@netspace.net.au, stav@stav.vic.edu.au, http://www.srl.rmit.edu.au/stav/. Ed. Ritva Fazio.

507 AUS ISSN 0159-2033
LAB TALK. Text in English. 1957. bi-m. AUD 60 (effective 1999). adv. bk.rev. **Document type:** *Academic/Scholarly.* **Description:** Provides teachers and educators with latest trends in science education.

E

Indexed: AEI, AusPAIS.
Published by: Science Teachers' Association of Victoria, PO Box 3058, Coburg, VIC 3058, Australia. TEL 61-3-9385-3999, FAX 61-3-9386-6722, stav@netspace.net.au, stav@stav.vic.edu.au, http://www.srt.rmit.edu.au/stav/. Ed. Peter Nelson. R&P Julie Mills. Adv. contact Danielle Duong. Circ: 1,900.

LANGUAGE AND EDUCATION; an international journal. see *LINGUISTICS*

371.3 USA
LANGUAGE AND LEARNING FOR HUMAN SERVICE PROFESSIONS. Text in English. 1984. irreg., latest vol.6, 1990. price varies. **Document type:** *Monographic series, Academic/Scholarly.*
Indexed: e-psyche.
Published by: Ablex Publishing Corporation (Subsidiary of: Greenwood Publishing Group Inc.), 88 Post Rd W, Westport, CT 06881. TEL 203-323-9606, FAX 203-357-8446. Ed. Cynthia Wallat.

371.3 USA ISSN 1556-3073
LANGUAGE AND LITERACY SERIES. Text in English. 1990. irreg. price varies. charts; illus. back issues avail. **Document type:** *Monographic series, Abstract/Index.* **Description:** Examines issues in teaching and learning reading and writing.
Published by: Teachers College Press, Teachers College, Columbia University, 525 W 120th St, Box 303, New York, NY 10027-6694. http://tc-press.tc.columbia.edu. **Dist. by:** Eurospan University Press Group, Order Dept, 3 Henrietta St, London WC2E 8LU, United Kingdom. TEL 44-20-7240-0856, FAX 44-20-7379-0609, http://www.eurospan.co.uk; Pademelon Press, Pty Ltd, 7-10 Anella Ave, PO Box 229, Castle Hill, NSW 2154, Australia. TEL 61-2-9634-2558, FAX 61-2-9680-4634; Transdex International, Pte Ltd, Block 1, Farrer Rd 307-05, Singapore 268817, Singapore. TEL 65-468-6242, FAX 65-462-5457.

371.3 USA ISSN 0360-9170
LB1576.A1
➤ **LANGUAGE ARTS.** Text in English. 1924. bi-m. USD 65 (effective 2005). adv. bk.rev.; film rev. bibl.; illus. Index. reprint service avail. from PQC. **Document type:** *Journal, Academic/Scholarly.* **Description:** Provides a forum for elementary-school language arts study and teaching methods.
Former titles (until 1975): Elementary English (0013-5968); (until 1946): Elementary English Review (0888-1030)
Related titles: Microform ed.: (from PQC); Online - full text ed.: (from EBSCO Publishing, O C L C Online Computer Library Center, Inc., ProQuest Information & Learning).
Indexed: ABIn, Acal, BRI, CBRI, CIJE, CPE, ChLitAb, CurCont, EduInd, L&LBA, LIFT, LT&LA, MLA-IB, MRD, PCI, SOMA, SOPODA.
—BLDSC (5155.708300), IE, Infotrieve, ingenta. **CCC.**
Published by: National Council of Teachers of English, 1111 W Kenyon Rd, Urbana, IL 61801-1096. TEL 217-328-3870, 800-369-6283, FAX 217-328—9645, cschanch@ncte.org, http://www.ncte.org/pubs/journals/la. Eds. Carol Schanche, Gloria Kauffman, Jean Schroeder, Kathy Short, Sandy Kaser. Circ: 11,500.

➤ **LANGUAGE TEACHING RESEARCH.** see *LINGUISTICS*

➤ **LANGUAGES VICTORIA.** see *LINGUISTICS*

➤ **LANGUES MODERNES.** see *LINGUISTICS*

➤ **LATEIN UND GRIECHISCH IN BERLIN UND BRANDENBURG.** see *CLASSICAL STUDIES*

➤ **LAW TEACHER.** see *LAW*

➤ **LEAFLET (ASSONET).** see *LINGUISTICS*

➤ **LEARNING AND LEADING WITH TECHNOLOGY.** see *EDUCATION—Computer Applications*

371.3 USA ISSN 0896-8756
THE LEARNING EDGE; home based education program news. Text in English. 1984. bi-m. USD 15 domestic; USD 20 foreign (effective 2004). bk.rev. illus. 12 p./no.; **Document type:** *Newsletter, Consumer.* **Description:** Features information for families enrolled in a home-based education program, including articles of general interest to home educators. Covers teaching, learning methods and materials.
Published by: Clonlara Publications, 1289 Jewett, Ann Arbor, MI 48104. TEL 734-769-4515, FAX 734-769-9629, info@clonlara.org, http://www.clonlara.org/newsletter.htm. Ed. Susan Andrews. Circ: 2,500 (paid and controlled).

371.33 GBR ISSN 1743-9884
LB1044.7
➤ **LEARNING, MEDIA & TECHNOLOGY.** Text in English. 1975. 4/yr. GBP 562, USD 1,291 combined subscription to institutions print & online eds. (effective 2006). bk.rev. abstr.; illus. index. back issues avail.; reprint service avail. from PSC. **Document type:** *Journal, Academic/Scholarly.* **Description:** Covers the traditional media of print and broadcast television and radio, but has now seamlessly extended through digital broadcasting and into all forms of electronic and computer mediated presentations.
Former titles (until 2005): Journal of Educational Media (1358-1651); (until 1996): Journal of Educational Television (0260-7417); (until 1982): Journal of Educational Television and Other Media
Related titles: Microfiche ed.; Online - full text ed.: ISSN 1743-9892. GBP 534, USD 1,226 to institutions (effective 2006) (from EBSCO Publishing, Gale Group, IngentaConnect, Northern Light Technology, Inc., O C L C Online Computer Library Center, Inc., ProQuest Information & Learning, Swets Information Services).
Indexed: ASCA, AgeL, ArtHuCI, BrEdI, CIJE, CPE, ChLitAb, CommAb, CompLI, CurCont, EAA, ERA, ETA, ErgAb, IIFP, IITV, MEA, PRA, RASB, RHEA, SEA, SENA, SFSA, SOMA, SSCI, SWA, TEA, WBA, WMB.
—BLDSC (4973.157400), IDS, IE, Infotrieve, ingenta. **CCC.**
Published by: (Educational Television Association), Routledge (Subsidiary of: Taylor & Francis Group), 4 Park Sq, Milton Park, Abingdon, Oxon OX14 4RN, United Kingdom. TEL 44-1235-828600, FAX 44-1235-829000, info@routledge.co.uk, http://www.tandf.co.uk/journals/titles/17439884.asp, http://www.routledge.com. Eds. Dr. Cathy Lewin, Dr. Matthew Pearson. **Subscr. to:** Taylor & Francis Ltd, Journals Customer Service, Rankine Rd, Basingstoke, Hants RG24 8PR, United Kingdom. TEL 44-1256-813000, FAX 44-1256-330245.

➤ **LEARNING TECHNOLOGY.** see *EDUCATION—Computer Applications*

➤ **LECTURA Y VIDA**; revista latinoamericana de lectura. see *LINGUISTICS*

➤ **LEGALDATE.** see *LAW*

➤ **LEGISLATIVE AND POLICY UPDATE.** see *MATHEMATICS*

613.7 DEU ISSN 0342-2461
LEHRHILFEN FUER DEN SPORTUNTERRICHT. Text in German. m. EUR 17.40; EUR 1.80 newsstand/cover (effective 2002). **Document type:** *Journal, Academic/Scholarly.*
Related titles: ♦ Supplement to: Sportunterricht. ISSN 0342-2402.
—**CCC.**
Published by: Verlag Karl Hofmann, Postfach 1360, Schorndorf, 73603, Germany. TEL 49-7181-402127, FAX 49-7181-402111, info@hofmann-verlag.de, http://www.hofmann-verlag.de. Ed. Heinz Lang.

371.3 DEU ISSN 1434-9817
LERNCHANCEN. Text in German. 1946. bi-m. EUR 63; EUR 10 newsstand/cover (effective 2005). adv. bk.rev. index. **Document type:** *Journal, Academic/Scholarly.*
Formerly (until 1998): Paedagogische Welt (0342-8257)
Indexed: DIP, IBR, IBZ, RASB.
Published by: (Paedagogische Stiftung Cassianeum), Erhard Friedrich Verlag GmbH, Im Brande 17, Seelze, 30926, Germany. TEL 49-511-400040, FAX 49-511-40004170, info@friedrich-verlag.de, http://www.friedrich-verlag.de/index.cfm?14BA608859864001B1909DE58D9A831A. Ed. Peter Franke. adv.: B&W page EUR 970, color page EUR 1,460. Circ: 4,500 (paid and controlled).

371.3 DEU
LERNENDE SCHULE; fuer die Praxis paedagogischer Schulentwicklung. Text in German. 4/yr. EUR 52; EUR 11 newsstand/cover (effective 2005). adv. **Document type:** *Journal, Academic/Scholarly.*
Published by: Erhard Friedrich Verlag GmbH, Im Brande 17, Seelze, 30926, Germany. TEL 49-511-400040, FAX 49-511-40004170, info@friedrich-verlag.de, http://www.friedrich-verlag.de/index.cfm?5E505CF70B6E405F94E941985E4E389E. adv.: color page EUR 1,370, B&W page EUR 910. Circ: 5,000 (paid and controlled).

LERNSPRACHE DEUTSCH. see *LINGUISTICS*

507.1 AUS
LET'S FIND OUT. Text in English. q. AUD 50 (effective 1999). adv. **Document type:** *Academic/Scholarly.*
Published by: Science Teachers' Association of Victoria, PO Box 3058, Coburg, VIC 3058, Australia. TEL 61-3-9385-3999, FAX 61-3-9386-6722, stav@netspace.net.au, stav@stav.vic.edu.au, http://www.srl.rmit.edu.au/stav. Ed. Kathy Doolan. R&P Julie Mills. Adv. contact Danielle Duong.

371.33 305.868 USA ISSN 1076-6766
LET'S FIND OUT (SPANISH EDITION). Text in Spanish. 1994. 32/yr. (during school year). USD 5.50 (effective 2003 - 2004); with 10 or more student subscr.. illus. index. reprint service avail. from PQC. **Document type:** *Consumer.* **Description:** Invites kindergarten children whose primary language is Spanish to explore their world through stories, poetry, pictures, and activities.
Related titles: ♦ English ed.: Scholastic Let's Find Out. ISSN 0024-1261.
Published by: Scholastic Inc., 557 Broadway, New York, NY 10012-0399. TEL 212-343-6100, http://www.scholastic.com. **Subscr. to:** 2931 E McCarthy St, PO Box 3710, Jefferson City, MO 65102-9957. TEL 800-724-6527, classmags@scholastic.com.

371.3 500 FRA ISSN 0290-6465
LIAISONS SCIENTIFIQUES. Text in French. 1980. irreg. price varies. **Document type:** *Monographic series, Trade.*
Published by: (France. Centre National de la Recherche Scientifique), C N R S Editions, 15 Rue Malebranche, Paris, 75005, France. TEL 33-1-53102700, FAX 33-1-53102727, http://www.cnrseditions.fr.

370 USA ISSN 1544-9092
LIBRARY SPARKS. Text in English. 9/yr. USD 59.95 domestic; USD 69.95 in Canada; USD 79.50 elsewhere (effective 2005). **Document type:** *Magazine, Academic/Scholarly.* **Description:** Covers lesson plans and activities for elementary school and children's librarian that motivate students to read.
Published by: Upstart, W5527 State Rd 106, PO. Box 800, Fort Atkinson, WI 53538-0800. TEL 815-734-5958, librarysparks@highsmith.com, http://www.highsmith.com/webapp/wcs/stores/servlet/Production/LSP/pages/lsp_home.htm.

613.7 NLD ISSN 0024-2810
LICHAMELIJKE OPVOEDING. Text in Dutch. 1912. 14/yr. EUR 55 (effective 2005). adv. bk.rev. illus.
Incorporates (1967-1987): Thomas (0049-3805)
Related titles: ♦ Supplement(s): Thomas Bulletin. ISSN 1381-5377.
—KNAW.
Published by: Koninklijke Vereniging van Leraren Lichamelijke Opvoeding, Postbus 398, Zeist, 3700 AJ, Netherlands. TEL 31-30-6920847, FAX 31-30-6912810, redactie@kvlo.nl, http://www.kvlo.nl. Ed. H Dijkhoff. Circ: 9,250.

LIFE AND WORK PURSUITS: TEACHER EDITION. see *RELIGIONS AND THEOLOGY—Protestant*

LIFE AND WORK VENTURES AND PATHWAYS: TEACHER EDITION. see *RELIGIONS AND THEOLOGY—Protestant*

LIFELINES (SASKATOON). see *PHYSICAL FITNESS AND HYGIENE*

LIMBA SI LITERATURA. see *LINGUISTICS*

▼ **LINGUA (HAMBURG)**; Fremdsprachenunterricht in Forschung und Praxis. see *LINGUISTICS*

LINGUISTIQUE ET ENSEIGNEMENT. see *LINGUISTICS*

371.3 FRA ISSN 0754-1384
LIRE AU COLLEGE. Text in French. 1980. 3/yr. bk.rev. **Description:** Offers methods and activities to encourage young people to read and write.
Published by: Centre Regional de Documentation Pedagogique, 11 av. du General-Champon, Grenoble, Cedex 38031, France. TEL 33-4-76747454, FAX 33-4-76171405, http://www.crdp.ac-grenoble.fr. Ed. Robert Briatte. Pub. Jacques Papadopoulos. **Subscr. to:** CNDP - Abonnement.

372.4 FRA ISSN 1145-0428
LIRE AU LYCEE PROFESSIONNEL. Text in French. 1989. 3/yr. **Description:** Offers articles and activities to promote reading in schools.
Published by: Centre Regional de Documentation Pedagogique, 11 av. du General-Champon, Grenoble, Cedex 38031, France. TEL 33-4-46349000, FAX 33-4-76171405. **Subscr. to:** CNDP - Abonnement, B.P. 750, Sainte Genevieve Cedex 60732, France. FAX 33-4-76171405.

LISHI JIAOXUE/HISTORY TEACHING. see *HISTORY*

LISHI JIAOXUE WENTI. see *HISTORY*

302.224 AUS ISSN 1320-5692
➤ **LITERACY LEARNING: THE MIDDLE YEARS.** Text in English. 3/yr. AUD 82.50 to individual members; AUD 132 to institutional members; AUD 38.50 student members (effective 2004). back issues avail. **Document type:** *Journal, Academic/Scholarly.* **Description:** Provides information to secondary teachers of all subjects who wish to develop students' literacy and learning competencies across the curriculum and beyond.
Published by: Australian Literacy Educators' Association, PO Box 3203, Norwood, SA 5067, Australia. TEL 61-8-83322845, FAX 61-8-83330394, alea@netspace.net.au, http://www.alea.edu.au/llearn.htm. Ed. Claire Wyatt-Smith.

372.412 GBR ISSN 1464-052X
LITERACY TIME YEARS 3/4. Text in English. 1998. bi-m. GBP 52.50 domestic; GBP 70.50 foreign (effective 2001). **Document type:** *Magazine, Academic/Scholarly.* **Description:** Provides notes and worksheets structured to assist in the teaching of literacy.
Published by: Scholastic Ltd., Villiers House, Clarendon Ave, Leamington Spa, Warks CV32 5PR, United Kingdom. TEL 44-1926-887799, FAX 44-1926-817727, enquiries@scholastic.co.uk, http://www.scholastic.co.uk.

E

▼ new title ➤ refereed ✶ unverified ♦ full entry avail.

372.412 GBR ISSN 1465-9018
LITERACY TIME YEARS 5/6. Text in English. 1999. bi-m. GBP 52.50 domestic; GBP 70.50 foreign (effective 2001).
Document type: *Magazine, Academic/Scholarly.* **Description:** Contains texts and worksheets selected to assist in the teaching of literacy.
Published by: Scholastic Ltd., Villiers House, Clarendon Ave, Leamington Spa, Warks CV32 5PR, United Kingdom. TEL 44-1926-887799, FAX 44-1926-817727, enquiries@scholastic.co.uk, http://www.scholastic.co.uk.

428 GBR ISSN 1367-8825
LITERACY TODAY. Text in English. 1994. q. GBP 18 (effective 2003). **Document type:** *Magazine, Academic/Scholarly.*
Description: Offers a comprehensive listing of the latest literacy research, publications and resources.
Related titles: Online - full text ed.: (from EBSCO Publishing).
Indexed: BrEdI.
Published by: National Literacy Trust, Swire House, 59 Buckingham Gate, London, SW1E 6AJ, United Kingdom. TEL 44-20-78282435, FAX 44-20-79319986, contact@literacytrust.org.uk, http://www.literacytrust.org.uk/pubs/literacytoday.html.

371.33 808.8 USA ISSN 0024-4511
AP2
LITERARY CAVALCADE. Text in English. 1948. 8/yr. (during school year). USD 8.95 per academic year (effective 2005); with 10 or more student subscr.. adv. illus. index. reprint service avail. from PQC. **Document type:** *Magazine, Consumer.* **Description:** Features contemporary and modern classic literature: dramatic scripts, stories, essays, poetry and writing lessons for high-school students, grades 9-12.
Related titles: Microfiche ed.: (from MIM, PQC); Online - full text ed.: (from bigchalk, EBSCO Publishing, Northern Light Technology, Inc., ProQuest Information & Learning).
Indexed: MASUSE.
Published by: Scholastic Inc., 557 Broadway, New York, NY 10012-0399. TEL 212-343-6100, 800-544-2917, FAX 212-343-6333, http://teacher.scholastic.com/products/classmags/litcav.htm, http://www.scholastic.com. Ed. Judy Goldberg. Pub. Richard Robinson. Circ: 200,000 (paid). **Subscr. to:** 2931 E McCarthy St, PO Box 3710, Jefferson City, MO 65102-9957. TEL 800-724-6527.

LITERATUR IM UNTERRICHT; Texte der Moderne und Postmoderne in der Schule. see *LITERATURE*

371.3 RUS ISSN 0130-3546
LITERATURA PO PEDAGOGICHESKIM NAUKAM I NARODNOMU OBRAZOVANIYU. Text in Russian. q. USD 85 in United States.
Indexed: RASB.
—East View.
Published by: Gosudarstvennaya Nauchnaya Pedagogicheskaya Biblioteka im. K.D. Ushinskogo, B Tolmachevskii per 3, Moscow, 113184, Russian Federation. TEL 7-095-2319242. Ed. Boris N Sirov. **US dist. addr.:** East View Information Services, 3020 Harbor Ln. N., Minneapolis, MN 55447. TEL 612-550-0961.

LITERATURA V SHKOLE. see *LITERATURE*

613.7 FRA ISSN 0753-6852
LOISIRS SANTE. Text in French. 1973. 5/yr. bk.rev. bibl.
Document type: *Journal, Academic/Scholarly.*
Formerly (until 1982): Gymnastique Volontaire (0335-2986); Which was formed by the merger of (1902-1973): Education Physique (0184-704X); (1890-1973): Homme Sain (0439-4232); Which was formerly (until 1950): Revue Medicale d'Education Physique (0996-262X); (until 1940): Education Physique et Medecine (0996-2611); (until 1935): Revue des Jeux Scolaires (0996-2603)
Indexed: SportS.
Published by: Federation Francaise d'Education Physique et de Gymnastique Volontaire, 2 rue de Valois, Paris, 75001, France.

371.2 GBR
M A R C E T RED GUIDES. SERIES 1: PLACEMENTS. Text in English. irreg., latest vol.8. **Document type:** *Monographic series, Academic/Scholarly.*
Published by: Northumbria University, Materials and Resources Centre for Enterprising Teaching, Sutherland Bldg, Northumberland Rd, Newcastle upon Tyne, Tyne and Wear NE1 8ST, United Kingdom. TEL 44-191-227-4186, FAX 44-191-227-4186, http://www.unn.ac.uk/central/marcet. Ed. Bruce Gilham.

371.3 GBR ISSN 1366-6452
M A R C E T RED GUIDES. SERIES 10: FLEXIBLE LEARNING. Text in English. 1993. irreg., latest vol.6. **Document type:** *Monographic series, Academic/Scholarly.*
Published by: Northumbria University, Materials and Resources Centre for Enterprising Teaching, Sutherland Bldg, Northumberland Rd, Newcastle upon Tyne, Tyne and Wear NE1 8ST, United Kingdom. TEL 44-191-227-4186, FAX 44-191-227-4186, http://www.unn.ac.uk/central/marcet. Eds. Diana Thomas, Tricia Bryans.

371.3 GBR ISSN 1366-6460
M A R C E T RED GUIDES. SERIES 11: GUIDES FOR STAFF. Text in English. 1994. irreg., latest vol.11. GBP 3.50 per issue (effective 2003). **Document type:** *Monographic series, Academic/Scholarly.*
—BLDSC (7331.261035).
Published by: Northumbria University, Materials and Resources Centre for Education and Technology, Library Building, City Campus, Northumberland Rd, Newcastle upon Tyne, Tyne and Wear NE1 8ST, United Kingdom. http://www.northumbria.ac.uk/marcet. R&P Ms. Margaret E Home.

371.3 GBR
M A R C E T RED GUIDES. SERIES 12: THE USE OF TECHNOLOGY IN TEACHING AND LEARNING. Text in English. 1997. irreg., latest vol.4, 1998. GBP 3.50 per issue (effective 2003). **Document type:** *Monographic series, Academic/Scholarly.*
Published by: Northumbria University, Materials and Resources Centre for Education and Technology, Library Building, City Campus, Northumberland Rd, Newcastle upon Tyne, Tyne and Wear NE1 8ST, United Kingdom. http://www.northumbria.ac.uk/marcet. R&P Ms. Margaret E Home.

371.3 GBR
M A R C E T RED GUIDES. SERIES 2: PORTFOLIOS, PROFILES, RECORDS OF ACHIEVEMENT. Text in English. irreg., latest vol.3, 1997. GBP 3.50 per issue (effective 2003).
Document type: *Academic/Scholarly.*
Published by: Northumbria University, Materials and Resources Centre for Education and Technology, Library Building, City Campus, Northumberland Rd, Newcastle upon Tyne, Tyne and Wear NE1 8ST, United Kingdom. http://www.northumbria.ac.uk/marcet. R&P Ms. Margaret E Home.

371.3 GBR ISSN 1367-529X
M A R C E T RED GUIDES. SERIES 3: GUIDES FOR STUDENTS. Text in English. irreg., latest vol.6. GBP 3.50 per issue (effective 2003). **Document type:** *Monographic series, Academic/Scholarly.*
Published by: Northumbria University, Materials and Resources Centre for Education and Technology, Library Building, City Campus, Northumberland Rd, Newcastle upon Tyne, Tyne and Wear NE1 8ST, United Kingdom. http://www.northumbria.ac.uk/marcet. R&P Ms. Margaret E Home.

371.3 GBR
M A R C E T RED GUIDES. SERIES 4: PARTNERSHIP. Text in English. irreg., latest vol.8. GBP 3.50 per issue (effective 2003). **Document type:** *Monographic series, Academic/Scholarly.*
Published by: Northumbria University, Materials and Resources Centre for Education and Technology, Library Building, City Campus, Northumberland Rd, Newcastle upon Tyne, Tyne and Wear NE1 8ST, United Kingdom. http://www.northumbria.ac.uk/marcet. R&P Ms. Margaret E Home.

371.3 GBR ISSN 1367-5303
M A R C E T RED GUIDES. SERIES 5: COMPETENCE, NVQS, LEARNING OUTCOMES. Text in English. 1993. irreg., latest vol.7. GBP 3.50 per issue (effective 2003). **Document type:** *Monographic series, Academic/Scholarly.*
Published by: Northumbria University, Materials and Resources Centre for Education and Technology, Library Building, City Campus, Northumberland Rd, Newcastle upon Tyne, Tyne and Wear NE1 8ST, United Kingdom. http://www.northumbria.ac.uk/marcet. R&P Ms. Margaret E Home.

371.3 GBR
M A R C E T RED GUIDES. SERIES 6: IMPLICATIONS OF GENDER FOR SKILLS DEVELOPMENT. Text in English. irreg., latest vol.2, 1992. **Document type:** *Monographic series, Academic/Scholarly.*
Published by: Northumbria University, Materials and Resources Centre for Enterprising Teaching, Sutherland Bldg, Northumberland Rd, Newcastle upon Tyne, Tyne and Wear NE1 8ST, United Kingdom. TEL 44-191-227-4186, FAX 44-191-227-4186, http://www.unn.ac.uk/central/marcet.

371.3 GBR
M A R C E T RED GUIDES. SERIES 7: THE STUDENT PERSPECTIVE. Text in English. irreg. GBP 3.50 per issue (effective 2003). **Document type:** *Monographic series, Academic/Scholarly.*
Published by: Northumbria University, Materials and Resources Centre for Education and Technology, Library Building, City Campus, Northumberland Rd, Newcastle upon Tyne, Tyne and Wear NE1 8ST, United Kingdom. http://www.northumbria.ac.uk/marcet. R&P Ms. Margaret E Home.

371.3 GBR ISSN 1367-5311
M A R C E T RED GUIDES. SERIES 8: SKILLS DEVELOPMENT. Text in English. irreg., latest vol.6. GBP 3.50 per issue (effective 2003). **Document type:** *Monographic series, Academic/Scholarly.* **Description:** Describes the type of management structure which might be appropriate if there is to be an effective and consistent process of dissertation supervision.
Published by: Northumbria University, Materials and Resources Centre for Education and Technology, Library Building, City Campus, Northumberland Rd, Newcastle upon Tyne, Tyne and Wear NE1 8ST, United Kingdom. http://www.northumbria.ac.uk/marcet. R&P Ms. Margaret E Home.

371.3 GBR ISSN 1366-6444
M A R C E T RED GUIDES. SERIES 9: EXPERIENTIAL LEARNING. Text in English. 1993. irreg., latest vol.8. GBP 3.50 per issue (effective 2003). **Document type:** *Monographic series, Academic/Scholarly.*
—BLDSC (7331.261033).
Published by: Northumbria University, Materials and Resources Centre for Education and Technology, Library Building, City Campus, Northumberland Rd, Newcastle upon Tyne, Tyne and Wear NE1 8ST, United Kingdom. http://www.northumbria.ac.uk/marcet. R&P Ms. Margaret E Home.

M A T S O L CURRENTS. see *LINGUISTICS*

020.71 CAN
➤ **M S L A JOURNAL.** Text in English. 1968. 4/yr. USD 25 to members. adv. bk.rev. illus. index. **Document type:** *Academic/Scholarly.*
Former titles: M S L A V A Journal (Manitoba School Library Audio Visual Association) (0315-9124); Manitoba Association of School Librarians Newsletter (0025-2204)
Indexed: CEI, CPerI.
Published by: Manitoba School Library Association, c/o Manitoba Teachers Society, 191 Harcourt St, Winnipeg, MB R3J 3H2, Canada. TEL 204-888-7961, http://www.mbnet.ca/~msla. Ed., Adv. contact Joan Marshall. page CND 100. Circ: 250 (controlled).

428 PHL ISSN 0047-5289
M S T ENGLISH QUARTERLY. Text in English. 1950. a. price varies. bk.rev.
Indexed: IPP, LT&LA.
Published by: D C S Manila Teachers of Secondary English, Office of the Supervisors of Secondary English, Manila Science High School, Taft Ave., Manila, Philippines. Circ: 700.

MA F L A NEWSLETTER. see *LINGUISTICS*

371.33 USA ISSN 0199-6045
THE MAILBOX; the idea magazine for teachers. (Avail. in 4 different eds.: Preschool; Kindergarten; Primary; Intermediate) Text in English. 1972. bi-m. USD 24.95 domestic; USD 33.95 foreign (effective 2005). adv. illus. Index. reprints avail.
Document type: *Magazine, Academic/Scholarly.* **Description:** Offers teachers at each of four grade levels creative ideas they can use to enhance their classroom teaching.
Related titles: Supplement(s): Mailbox Companion.
Published by: Education Center, Inc., 3515 W Market St, Ste 200, PO Box 9753, Greensboro, NC 27403. TEL 336-854-0309, 800-334-0298, FAX 336-547-1587, http://www.themailboxcompanion.com. Ed. Angie Kutzer. Pub. Anne Credi. Adv. contact Kate Brower. **Subscr. to:** PO Box 51676, Boulder, CO 80323-1676.

371.33 USA ISSN 1088-6397
Z1037.A1
MAILBOX BOOKBAG; literacy ideas for teachers. Text in English. 1996. bi-m. USD 39.95 (effective 2003). illus. reprints avail.
Document type: *Trade.* **Description:** Provides a resource for teachers of grades 1-5 who choose to use literature as a teaching aid in their classroom.
Published by: Education Center, Inc., 3515 W Market St, Ste 200, PO Box 9753, Greensboro, NC 27403. TEL 336-854-0309, 800-334-0298, FAX 336-547-1587, mbookbag@themailboxbookbag.com, http://www.themailboxbookbag.com. Ed. Christine Thuman. Pub. Anne Credi.

MAJALLAH-I FIZIK/IRANIAN JOURNAL OF PHYSICS. see *PHYSICS*

MANITOBA SCIENCE TEACHER. see *SCIENCES: COMPREHENSIVE WORKS*

372 CAN ISSN 0315-9116
MANITOBA SOCIAL SCIENCE TEACHER. Text in English. 1973. q. CND 14 to members. adv. bk.rev. **Document type:** *Academic/Scholarly.*
Indexed: CEI.
Published by: Manitoba Social Science Teachers' Association, 191 Harcourt St, Winnipeg, MB R3J 3H2, Canada. TEL 204-888-7961. Circ: 450.

371.3 CAN ISSN 0318-2118
MANITOBA SPECTRA. Text in English. 1960. s-a. CND 14. adv. bk.rev.
Indexed: CEI.
Published by: Manitoba Business Education Teachers' Association, 191 Harcourt St, Winnipeg, MB R3J 3H2, Canada. TEL 204-888-7961.

E

371.3 USA
▼ **MARKET OPPORTUNITIES FOR PRE-K EDUCATIONAL MATERIALS (YEAR).** Text in English. 2004. a. USD 2,295 (effective 2005). **Document type:** *Directory, Trade.* **Description:** Examines trends fostering market growth and challenges in marketing to the preschool and kindergarten education segment.
Published by: SIMBA Information (Subsidiary of: R.R. Bowker LLC), 60 Long Ridge Rd., Ste 300, Stamford, CT 06902. TEL 203-325-8193, 800-307-2529, FAX 203-325-8915, info@simbanet.com, http://www.simbanet.com/publications/report_mopk.htm.

MARYKNOLL STUDY GUIDE. see *RELIGIONS AND THEOLOGY—Roman Catholic*

418 USA ISSN 0542-8343
CODEN: MEJOFG
➤ **MARYLAND ENGLISH JOURNAL.** Text in English. 1960. s-a. USD 15. adv. bk.rev. bibl. back issues avail. **Document type:** *Academic/Scholarly.* **Description:** Publishes theoretical, practical and pedagogical essays of interest to English and language arts teachers; also creative writing by teachers.
Indexed: SOPODA.
Published by: Maryland Council of Teachers of English Language Arts, c/o Jacqueline Sachs, Catlyn Place, Annapolis, MD 21401. TEL 301-687-4221, FAX 301-687-4495. Adv. contact Judith J Pula. Circ: 500.

371.33 AUS ISSN 0726-9072
MASK. Text in English. 1977. s-a. AUD 110 for membership to individuals; AUD 198 for membership to institutions (effective 2000); subscr. incld. with membership. adv. bk.rev. back issues avail. **Document type:** *Journal, Academic/Scholarly.*
Indexed: AEI.
Published by: Drama Victoria Inc., Office 6, Artshouse, 117 Sturt St., Southbank, VIC 3001, Australia. TEL 61-3-96866829, FAX 61-3-96866839, dramavic@netspace.net.au, http://www.dramavictoria.vic.edu.au. Circ: 359 (paid).

MATEMATIKA V SHKOLE. see *MATHEMATICS*

MATEMATYKA (WARSAW). see *MATHEMATICS*

371.33 469 USA
MATERIALES; para ensenar los estandares. Text mainly in Spanish. irreg. (2-4/yr). free. illus. back issues avail. **Document type:** *Journal, Academic/Scholarly.* **Description:** Provides classroom teachers of Spanish as a foreign language with interesting materials to use in class, all of which reflect Spanish cultural heritage.
Media: Online - full content. **Related titles:** Print ed.
Published by: Embajada de Espana en Estados Unidos, Consejeria de Educacion/Spanish Embassy in the US, Education Office, 2375 Pennsylvania Ave, NW, Washington, DC 20037-1736. TEL 202-728-2335, FAX 202-728-2313, http://www.spainembedu.org/materiales.

510.71 USA
THE MATH - SCIENCE CONNECTOR. Text in English. 1971. q. looseleaf. membership. **Document type:** *Newsletter.* **Description:** Reports on planned events of the association, including conference information, news of other activities of interest to the membership, candidates for association offices and results of elections.
Formerly: S S M Arrt
Published by: School Science and Mathematics Association, Curriculum and Foundations, Ohio Wesleyan University, Department of Education, Delaware, OH 43015. TEL 740-368-3561, FAX 740-368-3553, mggrote@cc.owu.edu. Ed. Michael Grote. Circ: 1,200. **Subscr. to:** Donald Pratt, Curriculum and Foundations, 400 E Second St, Bloomsburg, PA 17815. TEL 717-389-4915, FAX 717-389-3815.

MATHEMATICS CONTESTS; the Australian scene. see *MATHEMATICS*

371.3 510.7 USA
MATHEMATICS EDUCATION DIALOGUES. Text in English. 3/yr. membership. **Document type:** *Academic/Scholarly.*
Indexed: CIJE.
Published by: National Council of Teachers of Mathematics, 1906 Association Dr, Reston, VA 20191-1502. TEL 703-620-9840, 800-235-7566, FAX 703-476-2970, nctm@nctm.org, dialogues@nctm.org, http://nctm.org. Ed. Andy Reeves. Pub. Harry B Tunis. R&P Jean T Carpenter.

371.3 510.7 USA
MATHEMATICS EDUCATION DIALOGUES AND STUDENTS MATH NOTES. Text in English. 5/yr. free to members.
Published by: National Council of Teachers of Mathematics, 1906 Association Dr, Reston, VA 20191-1502. TEL 703-620-9840, FAX 703-476-2970, nctm@nctm.org, http://nctm.org. Ed. Terry Souhrada.

510.71 AUS ISSN 1033-2170
➤ **MATHEMATICS EDUCATION RESEARCH JOURNAL.** Abbreviated title: M E R J. Text in English. 1989. 2/yr. AUD 60 for membership to individuals; AUD 120 for membership to institutions (effective 2005); subscr. incld. with membership. bk.rev. back issues avail. **Document type:** *Journal, Academic/Scholarly.* **Description:** For academics, students, and teachers involved in mathematics education.
Formerly (until 1989): Research in Mathematics Education in Australia (0812-7859)
Indexed: AEI, CIJE.
—BLDSC (5405.917000), IE, ingenta.
Published by: M E R G A, c/o Helen Chick, MERGA VP Membership, Dept Science and Mathematics Education, University of Melbourne, Melbourne, VIC 3010, Australia. TEL 61-2-9498-2774, 61-3-83448324, FAX 61-2-9144-7544, 61-3-83448739, mergapub@tpgi.com.au, h.chick@unimelb.edu.au. Ed. Helen Forgasz. Circ: 400.

➤ **MATHEMATICS EDUCATION REVIEW.** see *MATHEMATICS*

510 371.3 USA ISSN 1062-9017
QA135.5
➤ **THE MATHEMATICS EDUCATOR.** Abbreviated title: T M E. Text in English. 1990. s-a. USD 6 to individuals; USD 10 to institutions (effective 2004). bk.rev.; software rev. bibl.; charts; illus.; stat. 48 p./no.; back issues avail. **Document type:** *Journal, Academic/Scholarly.*
Related titles: Online - full text ed.: 1999. free (effective 2005).
Indexed: CIJE.
Published by: University of Georgia, Mathematics Education Student Association, 105 Aderhold Hall, Athens, GA 30602-7124. TEL 706-542-4194, FAX 706-542-4551, tme@coe.uga.edu, http://jwilson.coe.uga.edu/DEPT/TME/TMEOnline.html, http://jwilson.coe.uga.edu/DEPT/Mesa/MESA.html. Ed. Holly Anthony. Circ: 500.

➤ **MATHEMATICS IN SCHOOL.** see *MATHEMATICS*

➤ **MATHEMATICS RESOURCE GUIDE.** see *MATHEMATICS*

510.71 USA ISSN 0025-5769
QA1
➤ **MATHEMATICS TEACHER.** Text in English. 1908. 9/yr. (Sep.-May). USD 72 domestic to individuals; USD 90 foreign to individuals; USD 99 domestic to institutions; USD 117 foreign to institutions; USD 36 domestic to students; USD 54 foreign to students (effective 2004). adv. bk.rev. bibl.; illus. index, cum.index: 1908-1965, 1966-1975, 1976-1985. back issues avail.; reprint service avail. from PQC. **Document type:** *Journal, Academic/Scholarly.* **Description:** Contains features on the improvement of mathematics instruction in junior and senior high schools, two-year colleges, and teacher education colleges.
Related titles: Microform ed.: (from PQC); Online - full text ed.: (from H.W. Wilson, Northern Light Technology, Inc., O C L C Online Computer Library Center, Inc., ProQuest Information & Learning).
Indexed: ABIn, BRI, CBRI, CIJE, CIS, CPE, ECER, EduInd, LAMP, MRD, MathR, RASB, WBA, WMB, YAE&RB.
—BLDSC (5407.200000), IE, Infotrieve, ingenta, Linda Hall.
Published by: National Council of Teachers of Mathematics, 1906 Association Dr, Reston, VA 20191-1502. TEL 703-620-9840, 800-235-7566, FAX 703-476-2970, nctm@nctm.org, http://my.nctm.org/eresources/journal_home.asp?journal_id=2, http://www.nctm.org. Ed. Nancy Blue Williams. Pub. Harry B Tunis. R&P Jean T Carpenter. Adv. contact Tom Pearson. Circ: 37,274 (paid).

➤ **MATHEMATICS TEACHING.** see *MATHEMATICS*

372.7 510.71 USA ISSN 1072-0839
QA13
➤ **MATHEMATICS TEACHING IN THE MIDDLE SCHOOL.** Text in English. 1994. 9/yr. (Sept. - May). USD 72 domestic to individuals; USD 90 foreign to individuals; USD 99 domestic to institutions; USD 117 foreign to institutions; USD 36 domestic to students; USD 57 foreign to students (effective 2004). bk.rev. illus. index. back issues avail.; reprints avail. **Document type:** *Journal, Academic/Scholarly.* **Description:** Publishes articles, teaching ideas and features on the improvement of mathematics instruction in middle schools.
Related titles: Online - full text ed.: (from H.W. Wilson, Northern Light Technology, Inc., O C L C Online Computer Library Center, Inc., ProQuest Information & Learning).
Indexed: ABIn, CIJE, CPE, EduInd, MRD.
—BLDSC (5407.505000), IE, Infotrieve, ingenta.
Published by: National Council of Teachers of Mathematics, 1906 Association Dr, Reston, VA 20191-1502. TEL 703-620-9840, 800-235-7566, FAX 703-476-2970, ngreen@nctm.org, nctm@nctm.org, http://my.nctm.org/eresources/journal_home.asp?journal_id=3, http://www.nctm.org. Eds. Dolores Pesek, Pamela A Halonen, Kathleen Lay, Andy Reeves. Pub. Harry B Tunis. R&P Jean T Carpenter. Adv. contact Tom Pearson. Circ: 28,026 (paid).

510.71 DEU ISSN 0175-2235
MATHEMATIK LEHREN. Text in German. 1980. bi-m. EUR 66.60; EUR 10 newsstand/cover (effective 2005). adv. **Document type:** *Journal, Academic/Scholarly.*
Formerly (until 1983): Mathematiklehrer (0720-0420)
Indexed: DIP, IBR, IBZ.
Published by: Erhard Friedrich Verlag GmbH, Im Brande 17, Seelze, 30926, Germany. TEL 49-511-400040, FAX 49-511-40004170, info@friedrich-verlag.de, http://www.friedrich-verlag.de. adv.: B&W page EUR 1,100, color page EUR 1,650. Circ: 8,500 (paid and controlled).

DER MATHEMATIKUNTERRICHT; Beitraege zu seiner wissenschaftlichen und methodischen Gestaltung. see *MATHEMATICS*

MATHEMATISCHE LEHRBUECHER UND MONOGRAPHIEN. ABTEILUNG 1: MATHEMATISCHE LEHRBUECHER. see *MATHEMATICS*

MATHEMATISCHE UNTERRICHTSPRAXIS. see *MATHEMATICS*

372.412 GBR ISSN 1467-1352
MATHS & STORY TIME. Text in English. 1999. bi-m. GBP 49.95 domestic; GBP 68 foreign (effective 2001). **Document type:** *Journal, Academic/Scholarly.* **Description:** Contains teaching materials and ideas for fun-filled activities involving literacy and numeracy.
Published by: Scholastic Ltd., Villiers House, Clarendon Ave, Leamington Spa, Warks CV32 5PR, United Kingdom. TEL 44-1926-887799, FAX 44-1926-817727, enquiries@scholastic.co.uk, http://www.scholastic.co.uk.

MEDIA & METHODS; educational products, technologies & programs for schools & universities. see *COMPUTERS—Computer Assisted Instruction*

371.33523 USA ISSN 0146-2091
MEDIA DIGEST✶ ; a bi-monthly media resource for education. Text in English. 1971. bi-m. USD 10 to individuals; USD 8 to students. adv. bk.rev.; film rev. illus. reprint service avail. from PQC.
Formerly: Sneak Preview
Related titles: Microfilm ed.: 1971 (from PQC).
Published by: National Film & Video Center, Inc., c/o Charles H Slingluff, 10510 Brenda Ave, Ijamsville, MD 21754-9606. Circ: 40,000.

371.3 CAN
MEDIA NEWS. Text in English. q. **Document type:** *Newsletter.* **Description:** Covers news in the field, including tips, future conferences, comments on current projects and information about AMTEC members and the AMTEC Board of Directors.
Published by: Association for Media and Technology in Education in Canada (AMTEC), 3 1750 The Queensway, Ste 1318, Etobicoke, ON M9C 5H5, Canada. gkarlsen@sonoptic.com. Ed. Cathie Edmond.

371.33 USA ISSN 0731-3675
MEDIA SPECTRUM. Text in English. 1974. 3/yr. USD 25 domestic; USD 30 foreign (effective 2001). adv. bk.rev. **Document type:** *Academic/Scholarly.*
Supersedes: Forward (0015-8593)
Indexed: LHTB.
Published by: Michigan Association for Media in Education, 6810 South Cedar, Ste 8, Lansing, MI 48911. TEL 517-699-1717, http://www.mame.gen.mi.us. Adv. contact Roger S Ashley. Circ: 1,500.

371.33 DEU ISSN 1434-3436
MEDIEN IN DER WISSENSCHAFT. Text in German. irreg., latest vol.22, 2002. EUR 29.90 per vol. (effective 2003). **Document type:** *Monographic series, Academic/Scholarly.* **Description:** Presents studies on various media, materials and equipment available for teaching and instruction.
Published by: Waxmann Verlag GmbH, Steinfurter Str 555, Muenster, 48159, Germany. TEL 49-251-26504-0, FAX 49-251-2650426, info@waxmann.com, http://www.waxmann.com.

MEDIEN & ERZIEHUNG. see *COMMUNICATIONS—Television And Cable*

371.33 AUT ISSN 1029-3825
MEDIENIMPULSE; Beitraege zur Medienpaedagogik. Text in German. 1962. 4/yr. EUR 15.34 (effective 2003). adv. bk.rev.; film rev.; software rev. illus.; mkt. cum.index. **Document type:** *Journal, Government.*
Former titles (until 1992): Sehen - Hoeren - Bilden; Sehen und Hoeren (0037-0975)
Published by: Bundesministerium fuer Bildung, Wissenschaft und Kultur, Minoritenplatz 5, Vienna, W 1014, Austria. TEL 43-1-531200, FAX 43-1-531203099, ministerium@bmbwk.gv.at. Ed., R&P Susanne Krucsay. Circ: 8,000.

▼ **MEDIENPAEDAGOGIK UND MEDIENDIDAKTIK.** see *COMMUNICATIONS*

THE MEDIUM. see *LIBRARY AND INFORMATION SCIENCES*

MEHRSPRACHIGKEIT IN SCHULE UND UNTERRICHT. see *LINGUISTICS*

MEISTERWERKE DER KUNST. see *ART*

E

371.2 GBR ISSN 1361-1267
➤ **MENTORING & TUTORING**; partnership in learning. Text in English. 1993. 4/yr. GBP 375, USD 618 combined subscription to institutions print & online eds. (effective 2006). bk.rev. reprint service avail. from PSC. **Document type:** *Journal, Academic/Scholarly.* **Description:** Provides information on mentoring and tutoring in all contexts and for newcomers to obtain guidance.
Formerly (until 1994): Mentoring (0968-4654)
Related titles: Online - full text ed.: ISSN 1469-9745. GBP 356, USD 587 to institutions (effective 2006) (from EBSCO Publishing, Gale Group, IngentaConnect, O C L C Online Computer Library Center, Inc., Swets Information Services).
Indexed: BrEdI, CPE, ERA, ETA, LT&LA, MEA, RHEA, SEA, SENA, SOMA, TEA.
—BLDSC (5678.731950), IE, Infotrieve, ingenta. **CCC.**
Published by: Routledge (Subsidiary of: Taylor & Francis Group), 4 Park Sq, Milton Park, Abingdon, Oxon OX14 4RN, United Kingdom. TEL 44-1235-828600, FAX 44-1235-829000, info@routledge.co.uk, http://www.tandf.co.uk/journals/titles/13611267.asp, http://www.routledge.co.uk. Ed. Dr. Carol A Mullen. Circ: 1,500. **Subscr. to:** Taylor & Francis Ltd, Journals Customer Service, Rankine Rd, Basingstoke, Hants RG24 8PR, United Kingdom. TEL 44-1256-813000, FAX 44-1256-330245.

418 AUS
METAPHOR. Text in English. 1962. q. AUD 45 to members. adv. bk.rev. **Document type:** *Newsletter, Academic/Scholarly.*
Formerly (until 1996): Teaching of English (0049-3147)
Indexed: AEI.
Published by: English Teachers Association of N.S.W., c/o Bill Simon, Ed., Newtown High School of the Performing Arts, PO Box 785, Newton, NSW 2042, Australia. TEL 61-2-519-1544, FAX 61-2-519-1657. R&P, Adv. contact Bill Simon. Circ: 1,500.

METRO. see *MOTION PICTURES*

371.3 USA
MICHIGAN TEACHER. Text in English. 1992. 3/yr. membership. bk.rev. **Document type:** *Newsletter, Trade.* **Description:** Contains history related topics, lesson plans and classroom activities suitable for students in grade K-12. Also contains literature concerning Michigan history.
Published by: Historical Society of Michigan, 2117 Washtenaw Ave, Ann Arbor, MI 48104-4599. TEL 734-769-1828, FAX 734-769-4267, hsm@hsofmich.org, http://www.hsofmich.org. Ed. James Cameron. R&P Hugh Gurney. Circ: 200.

MICROMATH. see *MATHEMATICS*

373 USA ISSN 0094-0771
➤ **MIDDLE SCHOOL JOURNAL.** Text in English. 1970. 5/yr. (Sep.-May). USD 40 (effective 2004). adv. bk.rev. charts; illus. Index. back issues avail.; reprints avail. **Document type:** *Journal, Academic/Scholarly.* **Description:** Seeks to further the understanding and the implementation of effective practices at the middle school level.
Formerly: Midwest Middle School Journal
Indexed: ABIn, CIJE, CPE, EduInd.
—BLDSC (5761.406560), IE, ingenta.
Published by: National Middle School Association, 4151 Executive Pkwy, Ste 300, Westerville, OH 43081-3871. TEL 614-895-4730, 800-528-6672, FAX 614-895-4750, info@nmsa.org, http://www.nmsa.org/services/midjournal.htm. Ed. Tom Erb. R&P Joe Ball. Adv. contact Jane Richardson. Circ: 27,000 (paid).

371.3 USA
MIDDLE SCHOOL TEACHERS GUIDE TO FREE CURRICULUM MATERIALS. Text in English. 1998. a. (5th Ed.), latest 2002-2003. USD 39.95 per issue (effective 2002). 336 p./no.; **Document type:** *Directory, Academic/Scholarly.* **Description:** Lists free books, pamphlets, booklets, maps and various printed materials for the middle school level.
Published by: Educators Progress Service, Inc., 214 Center St, Randolph, WI 53956. TEL 920-326-3126, FAX 920-326-3127, http://www.freeteachingaids.com/pm_877083371.html. Ed. Kathleen Suttles Nehmer.

371.3 296 ISR
MIDEI CHODESH BECHODSHO. Text in Hebrew. 1984. 8/yr. free (effective 2005). back issues avail. **Document type:** *Government.* **Description:** Contains games, activities, and source material targeting all age groups, for teachers and youth leaders in informal Jewish education.
Media: Online - full content.
Published by: Ministry of Education, Department of Torah Culture, Jerusalem, 91911, Israel. TEL 972-2-5601345, FAX 972-2-5601370, tarbut-toranit@education.gov.il, http://cms.education.gov.il/EducationCMS/Units/Toranit/Pirsumim/KitvayET/mideichodeshbchodsho.htm, http://cms.education.gov.il/EducationCMS/UNITS/Toranit/. Ed. Rabbi Aryeh Weinberger. R&P Rabbi Aharon Angstreich. Circ: 3,200.

MINISTERIUM FUER BILDUNG, FRAUEN UND JUGEND RHEINLAND-PFALZ. AMTSBLATT. see *EDUCATION—School Organization And Administration*

MINNESOTA ENGLISH JOURNAL. see *LINGUISTICS*

MINNESOTA ENGLISH NEWSLETTER. see *LINGUISTICS*

MISSISSIPPI MUSIC EDUCATOR. see *MUSIC*

MISSOURI ENGLISH BULLETIN. see *LINGUISTICS*

MISSOURI JOURNAL OF RESEARCH IN MUSIC EDUCATION. see *MUSIC*

MISSOURI SCHOOL MUSIC. see *MUSIC*

MITTENDRIN (DILLENBURG). see *RELIGIONS AND THEOLOGY—Protestant*

510.71 AUS
MOBIUS. Text in English. 1967. q. AUD 52.50 to individual members; AUD 105 to institutions (effective 2000).
Formerly: Mathematical Association of South Australia. S.A. Mathematics Teacher (0047-6242)
Indexed: AEI, CINAHL.
Published by: Mathematical Association of South Australia, PO Box 94, Stepney, SA 5069, Australia. TEL 61-8-83624332, FAX 61-8-83639002, masamail@maths.adelaide.edu.au, http://www.maths.adelaide.edu.au/masa. Circ: 500.

428 GBR ISSN 0308-0587
CODEN: MOETF8
MODERN ENGLISH TEACHER; a magazine of practical suggestions for improving the teaching of English as a foreign language. Text in English. 1973. q. GBP 25, EUR 40, USD 40 to individuals; GBP 35, EUR 55, USD 55 to institutions & libraries (effective 2005). adv. bk.rev. illus. index. **Document type:** *Magazine, Trade.* **Description:** Covers all aspects of English language teaching and offers a magazine for teachers and language professionals that is stimulating, challenging and useul for professional development and day-to-day teaching.
Related titles: Online - full text ed.: (from EBSCO Publishing).
Indexed: BrEdI, CPE, L&LBA, LT&LA, SOPODA.
—BLDSC (5886.440000), IE, Infotrieve, ingenta. **CCC.**
Published by: Modern English Publishing, 32-34 Great Peter St, PO Box 50121, London, SW1P 2DB, United Kingdom. TEL 44-20-72221155, FAX 44-20-72221551, info@ModernEnglishPublishing.com, http://www.onlinemet.com/, http://www.modernenglishpublishing.com/. Ed. Dave Francis. Pub. Simon Collin. Adv. contact Sophie Malone TEL 44-1536-747333. Circ: 6,000. **Dist. by:** Marston Distribution, Unit 160, Milton Park, Abingdon, Oxon OX14 4SD, United Kingdom. TEL 44-1235-465537, FAX 44-1235-465556, subscribe@modernenglishpublishing.com.

MODERN LANGUAGE JOURNAL; devoted to research and discussion about the learning and teaching of foreign and second languages. see *LINGUISTICS*

MONATSHEFTE; fuer deutschsprachige literatur und kultur. see *LINGUISTICS*

371.3 POL ISSN 0077-0558
MONOGRAFIE Z DZIEJOW OSWIATY. Text in Polish; Summaries in English, French, Russian. 1957. irreg., latest vol.39, 1998. price varies. **Document type:** *Monographic series.*
Published by: (Pracownia Dziejow Oswiaty), Polska Akademia Nauk, Instytut Historii Nauki, Palac Staszica, ul Nowy Swiat 72, pok 9, Warsaw, 00330, Poland. TEL 48-22-8268754, FAX 48-22-8266137, ihn@ihnpan.waw.pl. Ed. Jozef Miaso.

371.392 GBR ISSN 1470-8647
MONTESSORI INTERNATIONAL; the international Montessori journal. Text in English. 1989. q. GBP 20; GBP 23 in Europe; USD 43 in United States; GBP 25 elsewhere. adv. bk.rev. **Document type:** *Academic/Scholarly.* **Description:** Covers broad child-care issues, educational philosophy and child development.
Former titles (until 1999): Montessori Education (1354-1498); (until 1994): Montessori Courier
Indexed: CPE.
—BLDSC (5928.545000), IE, ingenta.
Published by: Montessori Centre International, 18 Balderton St, London, W1Y 1TG, United Kingdom. TEL 44-171-493-0165, FAX 44-171-629-7808, lmc@montessori.ac.uk, http://www.montessori.ac.uk. Ed., R&P Paul Ryan. Adv. contact Sheila Allen. Circ: 5,000.

371.392 USA ISSN 1054-0040
LB1029.M75
MONTESSORI LIFE. Text in English. 1981. q. USD 82 membership (effective 2005). adv. bk.rev. **Document type:** *Academic/Scholarly.* **Description:** Provides a forum for educational issues and advances and for the promotion of professional development and parent education.
Formerly (until 1989): A M S Constructive Triangle; Which was formed by the merger of (1960-1981): A M S Bulletin (New York); (1965-1981): Constructive Triangle (0010-700X); (1980-1981): A M S Newsletter; Which was formerly (until 1979): A M S News; A M S News Notes (0065-9444); A M S Board Briefs
Related titles: Online - full text ed.: (from bigchalk, H.W. Wilson, O C L C Online Computer Library Center, Inc., ProQuest Information & Learning).
Indexed: ABIn, CIJE, EduInd.
—BLDSC (5928.555000), IE, ingenta.
Published by: American Montessori Society, 281 Park Ave S, 6th Fl, New York, NY 10010-6102. TEL 212-358-1250, FAX 212-358-1256, joyturner@msn.com, http://www.amshq.org. Ed. Joy S Turner. R&P, Adv. contact Joy Turner TEL 714-968-0107. Circ: 13,000.

371.392 USA ISSN 0889-6720
MONTESSORI NEWS. Text in English. 1979. s-a. USD 25 to individuals; USD 30 to institutions (effective 2005). **Document type:** *Newsletter, Academic/Scholarly.* **Description:** Expands awareness and practical application of Montessori principles with children.
Published by: International Montessori Society, 8115 Fenton St, Ste 304, Silver Spring, MD 20910. TEL 301-589-1127, FAX 301-589-0733, havis@erols.com, http://trust.wdn.com/ims/INDEX.HTM. Ed. Lee Havis. Circ: 4,000.

371.392 USA ISSN 0889-5643
MONTESSORI OBSERVER. Text in English. 1980. q. USD 25 to individuals; USD 30 to institutions (effective 2005). adv. bk.rev. **Document type:** *Newsletter, Trade.* **Description:** Constitutes the official journal of the International Montessori Society and provides news and information about the development of Montessori education whlie promoting awareness of its principles.
Published by: International Montessori Society, 8115 Fenton St, Ste 304, Silver Spring, MD 20910. TEL 301-589-1127, FAX 301-589-0733, havis@erols.com, http://www.wdn.com/trust/ims. Ed. Lee Havis. Circ: 2,000.

MOTORIK. see *PHYSICAL FITNESS AND HYGIENE*

371.39 USA
MOVING MIDDLE SCHOOLS SERIES. Text in English. 1996. irreg., latest vol.4, 1999. USD 19.50 per vol.. bibl. back issues avail. **Document type:** *Academic/Scholarly.* **Description:** Discusses cutting-edge teaching techniques across all disciplines at the middle-school level.
Published by: Heinemann, Inc. (Subsidiary of: Greenwood Publishing Group Inc.), 361 Hanover St, Portsmouth, NH 03801-3912. TEL 603-431-7894, 800-541-2086, FAX 603-431-7840, info@heinemann.com, http://www.heinemann.com.

371.3 USA ISSN 1068-3844
LC1099.3 CODEN: MUEDF2
➤ **MULTICULTURAL EDUCATION**; the magazine of the National Association for Multicultural Education Planning. Text in English. 1993. q. USD 50 to individuals; USD 80 to institutions (effective 2005). adv. bk.rev.; film rev. illus. 48 p./no. 3 cols./p.; back issues avail.; reprints avail. **Document type:** *Magazine, Academic/Scholarly.* **Description:** Features articles, interviews, promising practices, and listing of resources in multicultural education.
Related titles: Online - full text ed.: (from Gale Group, H.W. Wilson, Northern Light Technology, Inc., O C L C Online Computer Library Center, Inc., ProQuest Information & Learning).
Indexed: ABIn, CIJE, CPE, DIP, ERA, ETA, EduInd, IBR, IBZ, L&LBA, MEA, MRD, RHEA, SEA, SENA, SOMA, SOPODA, SWA, TEA.
Published by: Caddo Gap Press, 3145 Geary Blvd,, PMB 275, San Francisco, CA 94118. TEL 415-666-3012, FAX 415-666-3552, info@caddogap.com, http://www.caddogap.com. Ed., Pub., R&P Alan H Jones. adv.: page USD 500; 7.5 x 10. Circ: 1,000 (paid).

➤ **MULTICULTURAL EDUCATION SERIES.** see *EDUCATION—International Education Programs*

370.117 USA ISSN 1521-0960
LC1099
MULTICULTURAL PERSPECTIVES. Text in English. 1999. q. USD 260 in US & Canada to institutions; USD 290 elsewhere to institutions; USD 275 combined subscription in US & Canada to institutions print & online eds.; USD 305 combined subscription elsewhere to institutions print & online eds. (effective 2006). adv. bk.rev.; film rev.; music rev. illus. back issues avail.; reprint service avail. from PSC. **Document type:** *Journal, Academic/Scholarly.* **Description:** Promotes the philosophy of social justice, equity, and cultural and racial integration through education.
Related titles: Online - full text ed.: ISSN 1532-7892. USD 250 worldwide to institutions (effective 2006) (from EBSCO Publishing, Gale Group, O C L C Online Computer Library Center, Inc., Swets Information Services).
Indexed: ERA.
—BLDSC (5983.084270), IE, Infotrieve. **CCC.**
Published by: (National Association for Multicultural Education), Lawrence Erlbaum Associates, Inc., 10 Industrial Ave, Mahwah, NJ 07430-2262. TEL 201-258-2200, 800-926-6579, FAX 201-236-0072, journals@erlbaum.com, http://www.leaonline.com/loi/mcp. Ed. Penelope L Lisi. adv.: page USD 500; trim 7 x 10.

MULTICULTURAL REVIEW; dedicated to a better understanding of ethnic, racial and religious diversity. see *EDUCATION—International Education Programs*

E

371.39 153.9   USA
MULTIPLE INTELLIGENCES NEWSLETTER. Text in English.
1999. irreg. (approx s-m.). free. back issues avail. **Document type:** *Newsletter.* **Description:** Explores on ways to apply the theory of multiple intelligences, pioneered by Dr. Howard Gardner, in teaching and assessing students.
Media: Online - full text. **Related titles:** E-mail ed.
Published by: Multiple Intelligences Research and Consulting, 1316 S Lincoln St, Kent, OH 44240. TEL 330-673-8024, mi_news_subscribe@topica.com, http://www.topica.com/t/16. Ed. Clifford Morris. Pub. C Branton Shearer. Circ: 2,600.

MUSIC ALIVE!; bringing today's music to the classroom. see *MUSIC*

780.71   AUS   ISSN 0047-8431
MUSIC AND THE TEACHER. Text in English. 1965. q. USD 34 domestic; USD 40 foreign (effective 2002). adv. bk.rev.
Document type: *Academic/Scholarly.*
Indexed: AEI.
Published by: Victorian Music Teachers Association, 49 Earl St, Kew, VIC 3101, Australia. TEL 61-3-9853-7861, FAX 61-3-9853-7280, vmta@ozemail.com.au. Eds. Alison Kirkpatrick, Anne Uerse. adv.: page AUD 200; 190 x 115. Circ: 1,200.

MUSIC EDUCATION RESEARCH. see *MUSIC*

372.87 780.071   USA   ISSN 1550-9400
MT32
▼ **MUSIC EDUCATION TECHNOLOGY.** Text in English. 2003 (Fall). q. free (effective 2005). adv. **Document type:** *Magazine, Trade.* **Description:** Desinged for musicians who record in personal studios, combines the technical and publishing expertise of EM with the practical classroom savvy of educators who have already made the move to technology-enhanced teaching.
Related titles: Online - full text ed.: (from Gale Group, H.W. Wilson).
Published by: Primedia Business Magazines & Media, Inc. (Subsidiary of: Primedia, Inc.), 9800 Metcalf Ave, Overland Park, KS 66212-2216. TEL 913-341-1300, inquiries@primediabusiness.com, http:// www.metmagazine.com/, http://www.primediabusiness.com. Ed. Steve Oppenheimer. adv.: B&W page USD 2,045, color page USD 2,500.

MUSIC EDUCATORS JOURNAL. see *MUSIC*

MUSIC EXPRESS! INTERMEDIATE; the music resource for growing minds. see *MUSIC*

MUSIC EXPRESS! PRIMARY; the music resource for growing minds. see *MUSIC*

MUSIC K-8. see *MUSIC*

371.2 780.7   GBR   ISSN 0027-4461
ML5
MUSIC TEACHER. Text in English. 1909. m. GBP 42 domestic; GBP 55 foreign; GBP 3.95 per issue (effective 2005). adv. bk.rev.; music rev. **Document type:** *Magazine, Trade.* **Description:** Tackles important issues relevent to people in all areas of music education.
Formerly: Music Teacher and Piano Student
Related titles: Microform ed.: (from PQC); ◆ Supplement(s): Music Teacher Guide to Leisure Courses.
Indexed: BrEdI, CPE, IIMP, MusicInd, RASB, RILM.
—BLDSC (5990.420000), IE, ingenta. **CCC.**
Published by: Rhinegold Publishing Ltd., 241 Shaftesbury Ave, London, WC2H 8TF, United Kingdom. TEL 44-20-73331747, FAX 44-20-73331769, music.teacher@rhinegold.co.uk, subs@rhinegold.co.uk, http://www.rhinegold.co.uk/magazines/ mt/index.cfm. Ed. Lucien Jenkins. Pub. Tony Gamble. Adv. contact John Simpson. **Subscr. to:** Rhinegold Subscriptions, Barnwell, PO Box 64, Peterborough PE8 5XR, United Kingdom. TEL 44-1832-741941, FAX 44-1832-275560, subs@rhinegold.co.uk.

MUSIK ALS MEDIUM. see *MUSIC*

MUSIK UND UNTERRICHT. see *MUSIC*

780.71   DEU   ISSN 0946-5073
MUSIKPAEDAGOGISCHE FORSCHUNGSBERICHTE. Text in German. 1992. a. bk.rev. bibl.; illus. back issues avail.
Document type: *Magazine, Academic/Scholarly.*
Indexed: RILM.
Published by: Wissner Verlag, Im Tal 12, Augsburg, 86179, Germany. TEL 49-821-259890, FAX 49-821-594932, info@wissner.com, http://www.wissner.com. Pub. Bernd Wissner.

MY FIRST A B C & 1 2 3. see *CHILDREN AND YOUTH—For*

371.3 510.71   USA   ISSN 0277-1365
N C T M NEWS BULLETIN. Text in English. 1964. 10/yr. free to members. illus. **Document type:** *Bulletin.* **Description:** Aimed at improving the teaching of mathematics across all grade levels.

Published by: National Council of Teachers of Mathematics, 1906 Association Dr, Reston, VA 20191-1502. TEL 703-620-9840, 800-235-7566, FAX 703-476-2970, newsbulletin@nctm.org, http://nctm.org. Ed. Marcia A Friedman. Pub. Harry B Tunis. R&Ps Jean T Carpenter, Marcia A Friedman. Circ: 105,000 (controlled).

N E A T E NEWSLETTER. see *LINGUISTICS*

N E C T F L REVIEW. see *LINGUISTICS*

N I C E M INDEX TO A V PRODUCERS AND DISTRIBUTORS. see *EDUCATION—Abstracting, Bibliographies, Statistics*

372.4   USA   ISSN 0547-8375
LB2365.R4
N R C YEARBOOK. (National Reading Conference) Text in English. 1958. a. USD 60 domestic; USD 75 foreign.
Document type: *Academic/Scholarly.*
Indexed: PsycholAb.
—BLDSC (9393.500000), IE.
Published by: National Reading Conference, Inc., 7044 S 13th St, Oak Creek, WI 53154. TEL 414-908-4924, customercare@nrconline.org, http://www.nrconline.org/ yearbook.html. Ed. James V Hoffman. Circ: 2,000.

NAEMNAREN; tidskrift foer matematikundervisning. see *MATHEMATICS*

NATION JUNIOR. see *CHILDREN AND YOUTH—For*

371.3   USA
NATIONAL ASSESSMENT OF EDUCATIONAL PROGRESS. ASSESSMENT REPORTS. Text in English. 1970. irreg. (approx. 10-25/yr.). price varies. bibl.; charts; stat.
Formerly: Education Commission of the States. National Assessment of Educational Progress. Assessment Reports
Related titles: Microfiche ed.
Indexed: CIJE.
Published by: (Educational Testing Service), National Assessment of Educational Progress, CN 6710, Princeton, NJ 08541-6710. Circ: 10,000. **Subscr. to:** U.S. Government Printing Office, Superintendent of Documents, PO Box 371954, Pittsburgh, PA 15250-7954. TEL 202-783-3238, FAX 202-512-2233.

428   GBR   ISSN 0143-4136
NATIONAL ASSOCIATION FOR THE TEACHING OF ENGLISH. NEWSLETTER. Text in English. 5/yr. free to members (effective 2005). adv. **Document type:** *Newsletter, Trade.* **Description:** Contains a topical mix of news of NATE activities and views on current issues.
—CCC.
Published by: National Association for the Teaching of English, 50 Broadfield Rd, Sheffield, S Yorks S8 0XJ, United Kingdom. TEL 44-114-2555419, FAX 44-114-2555296, info@nate.org.uk, http://www.nate.org.uk/. Ed. Helen Hancock. Adv. contact Lyn Fairfax.

NATIONAL ASSOCIATION OF BIOLOGY TEACHERS. NEWS AND VIEWS; issues, events, professional development for biology teachers. see *BIOLOGY*

NATIONAL ASSOCIATION OF SCHOOLS OF MUSIC. DIRECTORY. see *MUSIC*

NATIONAL ASSOCIATION OF SCHOOLS OF MUSIC. HANDBOOK. see *MUSIC*

300   USA   ISSN 0077-4049
H62
NATIONAL COUNCIL FOR THE SOCIAL STUDIES. BULLETINS. Text in English. 1964. irreg. free to members (effective 2005); price varies. adv. **Document type:** *Trade.*
Indexed: CurCont, SSCI.
Published by: National Council for the Social Studies, 8555 16th St, Ste 500, Silver Spring, MD 20910. TEL 301-588-1800, ncss@ncss.org, http://www.socialstudies.org/publications/ books, http://www.ncss.org. Ed. Michael Simpson. R&P Kristen Page. Adv. contact Bill Doran TEL 302-644-0546.

371.3   USA
NATIONAL COUNCIL OF TEACHERS OF ENGLISH. TEACHER'S INTRODUCTION SERIES. Variant title: Teacher's Introduction Series. Text in English. 1991. irreg., latest 1996, No. 50098. price varies. back issues avail. **Document type:** *Monographic series, Trade.* **Description:** Intended to provide brief and lucid glimpses into particularly difficult bodies of theory in the field of literary studies, composition studies, or literacy education.
Published by: National Council of Teachers of English, 1111 W Kenyon Rd, Urbana, IL 61801-1096. TEL 217-328-3870, 800-369-3870, FAX 217-328-9645, membership@ncte.org, http://www.ncte.org/pubs/books/series/107684.htm.

510.024372   USA   ISSN 0077-4103
QA1
NATIONAL COUNCIL OF TEACHERS OF MATHEMATICS. YEARBOOK. Text in English. 1926. a., latest 2004. price varies. back issues avail.; reprint service avail. from PQC.
Document type: *Yearbook, Academic/Scholarly.* **Description:** Presents scholarly papers in topics and issues of interest to mathematics teachers and educators.
Related titles: Microform ed.: (from PQC); Online - full text ed.: (from H.W. Wilson, O C L C Online Computer Library Center, Inc.).
Indexed: ABIn, EduInd.
—BLDSC (9391.000000).
Published by: National Council of Teachers of Mathematics, 1906 Association Dr, Reston, VA 20191-1502. TEL 703-620-9840, 800-235-7566, FAX 703-476-2970, nctm@nctm.org, http://nctm.org. Ed. Charles Clements. Pub. Harry B Tunis. R&P Jean T Carpenter. Circ: (controlled).

375   GBR
NATIONAL CURRICULUM ASSESSMENT RESULTS IN WALES. KEY STAGE 2: LOCAL AUTHORITIES SUPPLEMENT/ CANLYNIADAU ASESIADAU'R CWIRCWLWM CENEDLAETHOL YNG NGHYMRU. CYFNOD ALLWEDDOL 2: ATODIAD YR AWDURDODAU LLEOL. Text in English. a.
Document type: *Government.*
—BLDSC (6021.86782).
Published by: Welsh Office, Education Department, Cathays Park, Cardiff, CF1 3NQ, United Kingdom. TEL 44-1222-826010, FAX 44-1222-826016.

371.3   USA
NATIONAL MONITOR OF EDUCATION. Text in English. 1977. 10/yr. looseleaf. USD 25. adv. bk.rev. charts; stat. back issues avail. **Document type:** *Newsletter.*
Formerly: California Monitor of Education
Address: PO Box 402, Alamo, CA 94507. TEL 510-945-6745. Ed. Betty Arras. Circ: 2,000 (paid).

371.33   USA   ISSN 1077-8365
LB2337.4
NATIONAL POSTSECONDARY STUDENT AID STUDY. Text in English. irreg.
Published by: U.S. Department of Education, National Center for Education Statistics, 1990 K St N W, Washington, DC 20006. TEL 202-219-1828, http://nces.ed.gov/.

NATIONAL TEACHING & LEARNING FORUM. see *EDUCATION—Higher Education*

808   USA   CODEN: QNWLE8
NATIONAL WRITING PROJECT. QUARTERLY. Text in English. 1978. q. USD 20 includes subscr. to The Voice (effective 2003). bk.rev. illus. 40 p./no.; back issues avail.; reprints avail. **Document type:** *Journal, Academic/Scholarly.* **Description:** Covers issues in writing and the teaching and learning of writing, literacy and research in writing.
Formerly: National Writing Project. Center for the Study of Writing. Quarterly (0896-3592)
Related titles: Online - full text ed.
Indexed: CIJE, SOPODA.
—BLDSC (7169.757900), IE, ingenta.
Published by: National Writing Project, 2105 Bancroft Way 1042, University of California, Berkeley, CA 94720-1042. TEL 510-642-8886, FAX 510-643-5717, nwp@writingproject.org, editors@writingproject.org, http://www.writingproject.org/ Publications/quarterly/index.html. Eds. Amy Bauman, Arthur Peterson. Adv. contact Roxanne Barber TEL 510-642-8938. Circ: 4,000.

NATUR-RAUM-GESELLSCHAFT. see *GEOGRAPHY*

THE NAVIGATOR (RALEIGH). see *SCIENCES: COMPREHENSIVE WORKS*

371.3   POL   ISSN 0077-653X
LB1043.2.P6
NEODIDAGMATA. Text in Polish; Text occasionally in English, French, German; Summaries in English, French, Russian. 1970. irreg., latest vol.23, 1997. price varies. **Document type:** *Monographic series, Academic/Scholarly.* **Description:** Contains papers of the university's specialists in the field of psychology, pedagogics and sociology.
Indexed: PsycholAb, e-psyche.
Published by: (Uniwersytet im. Adama Mickiewicza w Poznaniu/Adam Mickiewicz University), Wydawnictwo Naukowe Uniwersytetu im. Adama Mickiewicza/Adam Mickiewicz University Press, Nowowiejskiego 55, Poznan, 61-734, Poland. TEL 48-61-527380, FAX 48-61-527701. Ed. Waclaw Strykowski. Pub. Maria Jankowska. R&P Malgorzata Bis. Circ: 400.

371.3   CAN
➤ **NETWORKS: AN ON-LINE JOURNAL FOR TEACHER RESEARCH.** Text in English. q.?. **Document type:** *Journal, Academic/Scholarly.* **Description:** Serves as a forum for educational practitioners at all levels, K to postgraduate, to exchange their experiences and ideas.
Media: Online - full text.

E

▼ *new title*   ➤ *refereed*   ✳ *unverified*   ◆ *full entry avail.*

Published by: University of Toronto, Ontario Institute for Studies in Education, 252 Bloor St W, Toronto, ON M5S 1V6, Canada. networks-j@oise.utoronto.ca, http://www.oise.utoronto.ca/~ctd/networks/. Ed. Gordon Wells.

371.3   CHE   ISSN 0258-9907
NEUE SCHULPRAXIS. Text in French. 1931. 11/yr. CHF 82 domestic to individuals; EUR 55 foreign to individuals; CHF 122 domestic to institutions; EUR 86 foreign to institutions (effective 2003). back issues avail. **Document type:** *Journal, Academic/Scholarly.*
Published by: St. Galler Tagblatt AG, Fuerstenlandstr 122, St Gallen, 9001, Switzerland. TEL 41-71-2727439, FAX 41-71-2727449, http://www.schulpraxis.ch. Adv. contact Markus Turani. Circ: 11,000.

NEVADA. BUREAU OF MINES AND GEOLOGY. EDUCATIONAL SERIES. see *EARTH SCIENCES—Geology*

THE NEW ADVOCATE. see *LITERATURE*

NEW DEAL; a New Deal List for 1929-1952. see *HISTORY—History Of North And South America*

NEW ENGLAND JOURNAL OF HISTORY. see *HISTORY—History Of North And South America*

371.3   FRA   ISSN 1292-8976
NEW STANDPOINTS. Text in English. 1988. 5/yr. (2 plus audio cassettes). bk.rev. **Description:** Covers current events and daily life in the anglophone world. Includes student worksheets and teacher guidelines.
Formerly (until 1999): Standpoints (0987-7622)
Published by: Centre National de Documentation Pedagogique, 29 rue de l'Ulm, Paris, Cedex 5 75230, France. TEL 33-1-46349000, FAX 33-1-46345544. Ed. Elyane Conarteau.
Subscr. to: CNDP - Abonnement, B.P. 750, Sainte Genevieve Cedex 60732, France. FAX 33-3-44033013. **Co-sponsor:** Mission Laique Francaise.

371.335   USA   ISSN 8756-3940
NEWSCURRENTS. Text in English. 1984. 35/yr. (w. during school year). USD 199; USD 274 with online ed.. illus. **Document type:** *Journal, Academic/Scholarly.* **Description:** Offers school teachers and students background information, visuals, and quizzes to spark the curiosity of children and encourage them to learn and discuss important current events, issues, and people in the news.
Related titles: Online - full text ed.: NewsCurrents Online. USD 149; USD 274 with filmstrip ed. (effective 2000).
Published by: Knowledge Unlimited, PO Box 52, Madison, WI 53791-9438. TEL 608-836-6660, 800-356-2303, FAX 800-618-1570, ku-mail@knowledgeunlimited.com, http://www.newscurrents.com.

371.335   USA
NEWSMATTERS. Text in English. 1997. 5/yr. (during school year). USD 199; includes teacher's guide and poster. back issues avail. **Document type:** *Journal, Academic/Scholarly.* **Description:** Brings current events and issues to the grade 5-12 classroom in an informative, objective, and captivating way.
Media: Video.
Published by: Knowledge Unlimited, PO Box 52, Madison, WI 53791-9438. TEL 608-836-6660, 800-356-2303, FAX 800-618-1570, ku-mail@knowledgeunlimited.com, http://www.ku.com.

NEWSPAPER FUND ADVISER UPDATE. see *JOURNALISM*

NIEUWE WISKRANT. see *MATHEMATICS*

NIGERIA ENGLISH STUDIES ASSOCIATION JOURNAL. see *LINGUISTICS*

NIHON GOGAKU. NIHONGO KYOIKU RONSHU/JOURNAL OF JAPANESE LINGUISTICS AND EDUCATION. see *LINGUISTICS*

NIHON RIKAGAKU KYOKAI. KENKYU KIYO. see *PHYSICS*

▼ **NORDINA**; Nordic studies in science education. see *SCIENCES: COMPREHENSIVE WORKS*

NORTH AMERICAN ASSOCIATION FOR ENVIRONMENTAL EDUCATION. PROCEEDINGS. see *ENVIRONMENTAL STUDIES*

NORTH CAROLINA ENGLISH TEACHER. see *LINGUISTICS*

NORTHERN DEVELOPMENT CURRICULUM PROJECT. see *SOCIAL SERVICES AND WELFARE*

375   GBR
NORTHERN IRELAND COUNCIL FOR THE CURRICULUM, EXAMINATIONS AND ASSESSMENT. CORPORATE PLAN. Text in English. irreg. **Document type:** *Corporate.*
—BLDSC (3472.069406).

Published by: Northern Ireland Council for the Curriculum Examinations and Assessment, Beechill House, 42 Beechill Rd, Belfast, BT8 7RS, United Kingdom. TEL 44-1232-704666, FAX 44-1232-799913.

500 510 372   USA
NORTHWEST TEACHER. Text in English. q. **Document type:** *Journal, Academic/Scholarly.*
Published by: Northwest Regional Education Laboratory, 101 S W Main St,, Ste 500, Portland, OR 97204. TEL 503-275-9500, http://www.nwrel.org/msec/nwteacher/index.html.

NOTES A TEMPO. see *MUSIC*

NOTES ON TEACHING ENGLISH. see *LINGUISTICS*

NOTOS. see *LINGUISTICS*

372.412   GBR
NUMERACY TIME YEARS 3/4. Text in English. bi-m. GBP 49.95 domestic; GBP 68 foreign (effective 2001). **Document type:** *Magazine, Academic/Scholarly.* **Description:** Contains resources and materials to help children practice and apply math skills.
Published by: Scholastic Ltd., Villiers House, Clarendon Ave, Leamington Spa, Warks CV32 5PR, United Kingdom. TEL 44-1926-887799, FAX 44-1926-817727, enquiries@scholastic.co.uk, http://www.scholastic.co.uk.

NURSE EDUCATOR. see *MEDICAL SCIENCES—Nurses And Nursing*

372.412   GBR
NURSERY EDUCATION. Text in English. m. GBP 37.50 domestic; GBP 49.95 foreign (effective 2001). **Document type:** *Magazine, Academic/Scholarly.* **Description:** Contains information and resources for planning, managing and delivering early learning goals for children under five.
Published by: Scholastic Ltd., Villiers House, Clarendon Ave, Leamington Spa, Warks CV32 5PR, United Kingdom. TEL 44-1926-887799, FAX 44-1926-817727, enquiries@scholastic.co.uk, http://www.scholastic.co.uk.

NUTRIDATE. see *NUTRITION AND DIETETICS*

O R T E S O L JOURNAL. (Oregon Teachers of English to Speakers of Other Languages) see *LINGUISTICS*

OBUCHENIETO PO GEOGRAFIA. see *GEOGRAPHY*

372.4   USA   ISSN 0030-1035
➤ **OHIO READING TEACHER**; a journal of education whose objective is to improve reading instruction in Ohio schools. Text in English. 1967. s-a. subscr. incld. with membership. adv. bk.rev. bibl. reprint service avail. from PQC. **Document type:** *Journal, Academic/Scholarly.*
Related titles: Microform ed.: 1967 (from PQC); Online - full text ed.: (from ProQuest Information & Learning).
Indexed: CIJE, L&LBA, SOPODA.
—BLDSC (6247.175000), IE, ingenta.
Published by: Ohio Council of the International Reading Association, c/o Kathy Wersell, Toldeo, OH 43606. http://www.reading.org/dir/councils/counc_oh.html. Ed., R&P Evangeline Newton TEL 330-972-6916. Circ: 1,500.

➤ **OKLAHOMA COUNCIL ON ECONOMIC EDUCATION NEWSLETTER.** see *BUSINESS AND ECONOMICS*

372.4   USA   ISSN 0030-1833
OKLAHOMA READER. Text in English. 1966. 3/yr. USD 10 (effective 2000). adv. bk.rev.
Indexed: SOPODA.
Published by: Oklahoma Reading Association, Langston University, School of Education, 700 N Greenwood Ave, Tulsa, OK 74106. TEL 918-594-8070, 918-594-8091, FAX 918-594-8097. Ed. Emily Porter. Circ: 2,500.

613.7   CAN   ISSN 1180-7563
ON THE MOVE. Text in English. 3/yr. CND 25, CND 25 (effective 2000). adv. **Document type:** *Bulletin.*
Indexed: CEI.
Published by: (Saskatchewan Physical Education Association), Saskatchewan Teachers' Federation, 2317 Arlington Ave., Saskatoon, SK S7J 2H8, Canada. stf@stf.sk.ca.

371.3   GBR
THE ONESTOP MAGAZINE; the magazine for English language teachers. Text in English. d.
Media: Online - full content.
Published by: Macmillan Education, Macmillan Oxford, Between Towns Rd, Oxford, OX4 3PP, United Kingdom. TEL 44-1865-405700, FAX 44-1865-405701, onestopenglish@macmillan.com, elt@mhelt.com, http://www.onestopenglish.com, http://www.macmillaneducation.com. Ed. Tim Bowen.

418   USA
ONLINE CHRONICLE OF DISTANCE EDUCATION AND COMMUNICATION. Text in English. 1994. s-a.
Media: Online - full content.

Published by: Nova Southeastern University, Department of Education, Fort Lauderdale, FL 33314. http://www.fcae.nova.edu/disted/.

ONTARIO ASSOCIATION FOR GEOGRAPHICAL & ENVIRONMENTAL EDUCATION. MONOGRAPH. see *GEOGRAPHY*

371.3   USA   ISSN 1079-2562
OPTIONS FOR TEACHING. Text in English. 1975. irreg. price varies. bibl. back issues avail. **Document type:** *Monographic series, Academic/Scholarly.* **Description:** Presents a wide range of viewpoints on an issue or topic related to the teaching of language and literature.
Indexed: MLA-IB.
Published by: (Modern Language Association of America), Modern Language Association, Book Publications Program, 26 Broadway, 3rd Fl, New York, NY 10004-1789. FAX 646 458-0030, joseph.gibaldi@mla.org, http://www.mla.org/store/CID44. Ed. Joseph Gibaldi.

OREGON SCIENCE TEACHER. see *SCIENCES: COMPREHENSIVE WORKS*

371.3   POL   ISSN 1230-2899
OTWARTA SZKOLA; miesiecznik wielkopolskiej oswiaty. Text in Polish. 1992. m. PLZ 12.50, USD 30 (effective 1998). adv. bk.rev. back issues avail.
Published by: Wojewodzki Osrodek Metodyczny w Poznaniu, Al Niepodleglosci 34, Poznan, 61714, Poland. TEL 48-61-8523329, FAX 48-61-8523329. Ed., Adv. contact Stanislawa Lowinska. **Co-sponsor:** Kuratorium Oswiaty w Poznaniu.

371.33   USA
P B S TEACHER PREVIEWS. Text in English. w. free. tel.rev. back issues avail. **Document type:** *Newsletter.* **Description:** Alerts preK-12 teachers and other educators to forthcoming educational programs to be broadcast on PBS stations. Details related resources and professional development opportunities.
Media: E-mail.
Published by: Public Broadcasting Service, 1320 Braddock Pl, Alexandria, VA 22314. TEL 703-739-5000, teachersource@pbs.org, http://www.pbs.org/teachersource/previews/previews.shtm.

371.33 790.1   GBR   ISSN 1470-6121
P E & SPORT TODAY. (Physical Education) Text in English. 1999. 3/yr. GBP 21 domestic to individuals; GBP 35 foreign to individuals; GBP 36 domestic to institutions; GBP 56 foreign to institutions (effective 2003). adv. **Document type:** *Magazine, Trade.* **Description:** Contains articles, features and materials that assist physical education teachers in developing a practical curriculum.
Related titles: Online - full text ed.: (from Swets Information Services).
Published by: Questions Publishing Company Ltd., 1st Fl, Leonard House, 321 Bradford St, Digbeth, Birmingham, Warks B1 3ET, United Kingdom. TEL 44-121-6667878, FAX 44-121-6667879, rchima@qiis.co.uk, http://www.education-quest.com/. Ed. Miles Barter. Adv. contact Stan Harris.

375.001   DEU   ISSN 1436-7793
P M P - A W T. (Planung, Materialien, Praxis - Arbeit, Wirtschaft, Technik) Text in German. 1992. base vol. plus updates 3/yr. EUR 28 updates per issue (effective 2003). **Document type:** *Journal, Academic/Scholarly.*
Published by: Neckar Verlag GmbH, Postfach 1820, Villingen-Schwenningen, 78008, Germany. TEL 49-7721-89870, FAX 49-7721-898750, service@neckar-verlag.de, http://www.neckar-verlag.de.

375.001   DEU   ISSN 1436-7807
P M P GRUNDSCHULE. (Planung, Materialien, Praxis) Text in German. 1976. 2 base vols. plus updates 3/yr. EUR 36 updates per issue (effective 2003). **Document type:** *Journal, Academic/Scholarly.*
Published by: Neckar Verlag GmbH, Postfach 1820, Villingen-Schwenningen, 78008, Germany. TEL 49-7721-89870, FAX 49-7721-898750, service@neckar-verlag.de, http://www.neckar-verlag.de.

375.01   DEU   ISSN 1436-7815
P M P KLASSE 5 - 10. (Planung, Materialien, Praxis) Text in German. 1996. 2 base vols. plus updates 3/yr. EUR 38 updates per issue (effective 2003). **Document type:** *Journal, Academic/Scholarly.*
Published by: Neckar Verlag GmbH, Postfach 1820, Villingen-Schwenningen, 78008, Germany. TEL 49-7721-89870, FAX 49-7721-898750, service@neckar-verlag.de, http://www.neckar-verlag.de.

375   DEU   ISSN 1430-5399
PAED FORUM. Text in German. 1996. bi-m. **Document type:** *Journal, Academic/Scholarly.*

E

Formed by the merger of (1991-1996): Paedagogisches Forum (0942-9581); Which was formed by the merger of (1960-1991): Paedagogische Forschung (0552-7740); (1988-1991): Forum Paedagogik (0933-9922); (1988-1996): Paed Extra (0943-0598); Which was formerly (until 1991): Paed Extra und Demokratische Erziehung (0933-7997); Which was formed by the merger of (1973-1988): Paed Extra (0341-7069); (1975-1988): Demokratische Erziehung (0340-2495)
Indexed: DIP, IBR, IBZ.
Published by: Schneider Verlag Hohengehren GmbH, Wilhelmstr 13, Baltmannsweiler, 73666, Germany. FAX 49-7153-48761, schneider-verlag-hohengehren@t-online.de.

371.3 USA
PAPERS AND RECORDINGS IN EDUCATION. Text in English. 1971. a. looseleaf. USD 5 paper ed.; USD 10 recording ed.. back issues avail.
Related titles: Audio cassette/tape ed.
Indexed: CIJE.
Published by: Arizona State University, College of Education, PO Box 870211, Tempe, AZ 85287-0211. TEL 602-965-3306. Ed. James John Jelinek. Circ: 1,000.

371.3 USA ISSN 1050-1088
PARENTS EXPRESS✶ ; the newspaper for Philadelphia area parents. Text in English. 1990. 11/yr. USD 24. adv. bk.rev. back issues avail. **Document type:** *Newspaper.* **Description:** Deals with family, child-raising, health, emotional health, education, and activities for families of children ages 1-16.
Supersedes (1986-1990): Skip Magazine
Address: 290 Commerce Dr, Fort Washington, PA 19034-2400. TEL 215-629-1774, FAX 215-629-4853. Eds., Pubs. Cynthia Roberts, Sharon Sexton. Adv. contact Louise Haley. Circ: 70,000.

371.3 THA ISSN 0125-2488
PE1068.T5
PASAA JOURNAL. Text in English, Thai. 1970. s-a. THB 30, USD 15. bk.rev. illus. **Description:** Examines language instruction and education in Thailand.
Formerly (until 1973): Bangkok English Language Center. Bulletin
Indexed: L&LBA, LT&LA, MLA, MLA-IB, RILM, SOPODA.
Published by: Chulalongkorn University, Phyathai Rd, Bangkok, 10500, Thailand. FAX 010-662-2554441. Ed. Supanee Tiancharoen. Circ: 500.

371.3 USA ISSN 1554-480X
▼ **PEDAGOGIES.** Text in English. forthcoming 2006 (Jan.). q. USD 240 in US & Canada to institutions; USD 270 elsewhere to institutions; USD 250 combined subscription in US & Canada to institutions print & online eds.; USD 280 combined subscription elsewhere to institutions print & online eds. (effective 2006). **Document type:** *Journal, Academic/Scholarly.* **Description:** Brings together emergent and breaking work on all aspects of pedagogy: classroom teaching and learning in response to new communities and student bodies, curriculum and responses to new knowledge and changing disciplinarity, blends of traditional and new communications media in classrooms, and most importantly, how we might improve and renew the everyday work that teachers and students do in classrooms.
Related titles: Online - full text ed.: ISSN 1554-4818. forthcoming 2006 (Jan.). USD 225 worldwide (effective 2006).
Published by: Lawrence Erlbaum Associates, Inc., 10 Industrial Ave, Mahwah, NJ 07430-2262. TEL 201-258-2200, 800-926-6579, FAX 201-236-0072, journals@erlbaum.com, http://www.leaonline.com/loi/ped, http://www.erlbaum.com. Ed. Allan Luke.

371.3 BGR
PEDAGOGIKA. Text in Bulgarian. m. USD 48 foreign (effective 2002). **Document type:** *Journal, Academic/Scholarly.*
Published by: Ministerstvo na Obrazovanieto i Naukata na Republika Bulgaria/Ministry of Education and Sciences of the Republic of Bulgaria, 125 Tzarigradsko Shosse Blvd., Bl. 5, PO Box 336, Sofia, 1113, Bulgaria. TEL 359-2-705298, http://www.minedu.government.bg. **Dist. by:** Sofia Books, ul Silivria 16, Sofia 1404, Bulgaria. TEL 359-2-9586257, info@sofiabooks-bg.com, http://www.sofiabooks-bg.com.

375 USA ISSN 1531-4200
PE65
➤ **PEDAGOGY**; critical approaches to teaching literature, language, culture and composition. Text in English. 2000. 3/yr. USD 25 to individuals; USD 75 to institutions; USD 83 combined subscription to institutions print & online eds. (effective 2006). adv. back issues avail.; reprint service avail. from PSC. **Document type:** *Journal, Academic/Scholarly.* **Description:** Seeks to create a new discourse surrounding teaching in English studies by fusing theoretical approaches and practical realities.
Related titles: Online - full text ed.: ISSN 1533-6255. 2001. USD 75 to institutions (effective 2006) (from EBSCO Publishing, Gale Group, IngentaConnect, O C L C Online Computer Library Center, Inc., Project MUSE, Swets Information Services).
Indexed: MLA-IB.
—BLDSC (6417.443650), IE, ingenta. **CCC.**
Published by: (Calvin College, Department of English), Duke University Press, 905 W Main St, Ste 18 B, Durham, NC 27701. TEL 919-687-3600, FAX 919-688-4574, pedagogy@calvin.edu, subscriptions@dukeupress.edu, http://www.dukeupress.edu/pedagogy/. Eds. Jennifer L Holberg, Marcy Taylor. adv.: page USD 200; trim 4.3125 x 7.375. Circ: 500.

375 GBR ISSN 1468-1366
LB1570 CODEN: CISDED
➤ **PEDAGOGY, CULTURE AND SOCIETY.** Text in English. 1993. 3/yr. GBP 256 combined subscription domestic to institutions print & online eds.; USD 407 combined subscription foreign to institutions print & online eds. (effective 2006). bk.rev. abstr.; illus. back issues avail.; reprint service avail. from PSC. **Document type:** *Journal, Academic/Scholarly.* **Description:** Provides an international forum for curriculum discussion and debate involving policy, pedagogy, school reform, ideology and cultures.
Formerly (until 2000): Curriculum Studies (0965-9757)
Related titles: Online - full text ed.: ISSN 1747-5104. GBP 243, USD 387 to institutions (effective 2006) (from EBSCO Publishing, Swets Information Services).
Indexed: BrEdI, CPE, DIP, EAA, ERA, ETA, IBR, IBZ, MEA, RHEA, SEA, SENA, SOMA, SOPODA, SSA, SWA, SociolAb, TEA, V&AA.
—BLDSC (6417.443820), IE, ingenta. **CCC.**
Published by: Routledge (Subsidiary of: Taylor & Francis Group), 4 Park Sq, Milton Park, Abingdon, Oxon OX14 4RN, United Kingdom. TEL 44-1235-828600, FAX 44-1235-829000, info@routledge.co.uk, http://www.tandf.co.uk/journals/titles/14681366.asp, http://www.routledge.co.uk.

➤ **THE PEER BULLETIN.** see *SOCIAL SERVICES AND WELFARE*

371.335 FIN ISSN 0783-1781
PEILI; audiovisual culture of children and teachers. Text in Finnish. 1977. q. EUR 22; EUR 18.50 to students; EUR 6 per issue (effective 2005). adv. bk.rev.; film rev.; video rev. back issues avail. **Document type:** *Magazine, Consumer.*
Formerly (until 1986): Sinae Minae Me (0358-7932)
Indexed: FLI.
Published by: Elokuva- ja Televisiokasvatuksen Keskus, Pohjoiranta 20 B 23, Helsinki, 00170, Finland. TEL 358-9-678778, Matvalim@netti.fi, http://www.etkk.fi/peili/. Ed. Matti Valimaki. adv.: page EUR 250; 210 x 267. Circ: 700.

613.7 USA ISSN 0279-0033
PENNSYLVANIA JOURNAL OF HEALTH, PHYSICAL EDUCATION, RECREATION AND DANCE. Text in English. 194?. q. USD 30. adv. bk.rev. **Document type:** *Academic/Scholarly.*
Formerly (until 1981): Pennsylvania Journal of Health, Physical Education and Recreation (0737-7398)
Indexed: PEI.
Published by: Pennsylvania Association for Health, Physical Education, Recreation and Dance, Inc., Pennsylvania State University, Beaver Campus, Brodhead Rd, Monaca, PA 15061. TEL 814-865-4700. Eds. Donna J Kuga, William G Meacci. Circ: 3,500. **Subscr. to:** Linda Huber, 202 E Third Ave, Lititz, PA 17543.

374 USA ISSN 1090-8811
LB1028.5 CODEN: PEISEL
PERFORMANCE IMPROVEMENT. Text in English. 1962. m. (10/yr.). USD 69 in North America to non-members; USD 119 elsewhere to non-members; free to members (effective 2004). adv. bk.rev. reprint service avail. from PQC,ISI. **Document type:** *Journal, Academic/Scholarly.* **Description:** Addresses improving human performance through a wide range of techniques, including incentives and feedback, effective management, performance aids, organizational development, job design and instruction.
Former titles: Performance and Instruction (0884-1985); (until 1985): Performance and Instruction Journal (8750-0191); (until 1983): Performance and Instruction (0273-5326); (until 1980): N S P I Journal (Year) (0147-2747); Incorporates (in Feb. 1980): Improving Human Performance Quarterly (0146-3756); National Society for Programmed Instruction. Journal (0027-7002); National Society for Programmed Instruction. Newsletter (0090-8118)
Related titles: Microform ed.: (from PQC); Online - full text ed.: (from O C L C Online Computer Library Center, Inc., ProQuest Information & Learning).
Indexed: ABIn, AgeL, CIJE, CPE, PersLit, PsycholAb, QAb, SOPODA, T&DA.
—BLDSC (6423.804000), IE, Infotrieve, ingenta.
Published by: International Society for Performance Improvement, 1400 Spring St, Ste 260, Silver Spring, MD 20910. TEL 301-587-8570, FAX 301-587-8573, info@ispi.org, http://www.ispi.org. Ed. Doug Leigh. adv.: page USD 850; trim 7.25 x 9.25. Circ: 6,000.

371.3 USA ISSN 0898-5952
HF5549.5.P37
PERFORMANCE IMPROVEMENT QUARTERLY. Text in English. q. USD 50 domestic; USD 70 foreign (effective 2004). adv. **Document type:** *Journal, Academic/Scholarly.* **Description:** Represents the cutting edge in research and theory in performance technology.
Related titles: Online - full text ed.: (from ProQuest Information & Learning).
Indexed: ABIn, BusEdI, CIJE, CPE, DIP, ERA, ETA, EduInd, ErgAb, IBR, IBZ, MEA, PsycholAb, RHEA, SEA, SENA, SOMA, T&DA, TEA.
—BLDSC (6423.805000), CISTI, IE, ingenta.
Published by: International Society for Performance Improvement, 1400 Spring St, Ste 260, Silver Spring, MD 20910. TEL 301-587-8570, FAX 301-587-8573, info@ispi.org, http://www.ispi.org/publications/piq.htm.

371.3 USA
DR201 CODEN: RCCCEJ
PERFORMANCE XPRESS. Text in English. 1988. 10/yr. adv. **Document type:** *Newsletter, Academic/Scholarly.*
Formerly: News & Notes (Washington) (1044-9752)
Published by: International Society for Performance Improvement, 1400 Spring St, Ste 260, Silver Spring, MD 20910. TEL 301-587-8570, FAX 301-587-8573, info@ispi.org, http://www.ispi.org. Pub. Richard D Battaglia. R&P Amy M Smitherman. Adv. contact Megan Spillane.

PERSPECTIVE (NEW YORK). see *EDUCATION—International Education Programs*

371.3 CAN ISSN 0316-3334
PERSPECTIVES (SASKATOON). Text in English. 1965. 2/yr. CND 20; USD 20 foreign (effective 2000). adv. bk.rev. bibl.; charts; illus. **Document type:** *Bulletin.*
Indexed: CEI.
Published by: (Saskatchewan Council of Social Sciences), Saskatchewan Teachers' Federation, 2317 Arlington Ave., Saskatoon, SK S7J 2H8, Canada. stf@stf.sk.ca. adv.: B&W page CND 100. Circ: 200.

PHARMACY EDUCATION. see *PHARMACY AND PHARMACOLOGY*

PHILOSOPHY OF MUSIC EDUCATION REVIEW. see *MUSIC*

613.7 GBR ISSN 1740-8989
GV201
➤ **PHYSICAL EDUCATION AND SPORT PEDAGOGY.** Text in English. 1996. 3/yr. GBP 142, USD 214 combined subscription to institutions print & online eds. (effective 2006). adv. bk.rev. abstr. 130 p./no. 1 cols./p.; reprint service avail. from PSC. **Document type:** *Journal, Academic/Scholarly.* **Description:** Provides a forum for the dissemination of research in physical education.
Formerly (until 2004): European Journal of Physical Education (1362-7120)
Related titles: Online - full text ed.: ISSN 1742-5786. GBP 135, USD 203 to institutions (effective 2006) (from EBSCO Publishing, Gale Group, IngentaConnect, O C L C Online Computer Library Center, Inc., Swets Information Services).
Indexed: BrEdI, CPE, ERA, ETA, MEA, PEI, RHEA, RRTA, SEA, SENA, SOMA, SWA, TEA.
—BLDSC (6475.411000), IE, Infotrieve, ingenta. **CCC.**
Published by: (Physical Education Association of the United Kingdom), Routledge (Subsidiary of: Taylor & Francis Group), 4 Park Sq, Milton Park, Abingdon, Oxon OX14 4RN, United Kingdom. TEL 44-1235-828600, FAX 44-1235-829000, info@routledge.co.uk, http://www.tandf.co.uk/journals/titles/17408989.asp, http://www.routledge.co.uk. Eds. David Kirk, David Kirk. **Subscr. in N America to:** Taylor & Francis Inc., Customer Services Dept, 325 Chestnut St, 8th Fl, Philadelphia, PA 19106. TEL 215-625-8900, 800-354-1420, FAX 215-625-8914, customerservice@taylorandfrancis.com; **Subscr. to:** Taylor & Francis Ltd, Journals Customer Service, Rankine Rd, Basingstoke, Hants RG24 8PR, United Kingdom. TEL 44-1256-813000, FAX 44-1256-330245.

➤ **PHYSICAL EDUCATION INDEX.** see *EDUCATION—Abstracting, Bibliographies, Statistics*

613.7 NZL ISSN 1172-5958
➤ **PHYSICAL EDUCATION NEW ZEALAND. JOURNAL.** Text in English. 1953. 4/yr. NZD 45 domestic; USD 30 foreign (effective 2000). adv. bk.rev. cum.index: 1953-1967. reprint service avail. from PQC. **Document type:** *Academic/Scholarly.*
Formerly: New Zealand Journal of Health, Physical Education and Recreation (0028-8314)
Related titles: Microform ed.: (from PQC); Online - full text ed.
Indexed: AbHyg, CPE, ERA, ETA, INZP, MEA, PEI, RHEA, RRTA, SEA, SENA, SOMA, SWA, SportS, TEA.
—BLDSC (5036.206500), GNLM, IE, ingenta. **CCC.**
Published by: Physical Education New Zealand Inc., Level 5, Education House, 178-182 Willis St, Wellington, New Zealand. admin@penz.org.nz. Ed. Mike Boyes. R&P Chris Tait. Circ: 800.

613.7 USA ISSN 0031-8981
GV201
➤ **PHYSICAL EDUCATOR**; a magazine for the profession. Text in English. 1940. q. USD 45 domestic; USD 60 foreign; USD 12 per issue (effective 2004). bk.rev. illus. index. reprint service avail. from PQC,PSC. **Document type:** *Journal, Academic/Scholarly.*

E

Related titles: Microfilm ed.: (from PQC); Online - full text ed.: (from EBSCO Publishing, Florida Center for Library Automation, Gale Group, H.W. Wilson, Northern Light Technology, Inc., O C L C Online Computer Library Center, Inc., ProQuest Information & Learning).
Indexed: ABIn, CIJE, CPE, EduInd, PEI, SportS.
—BLDSC (6475.550000), IE, Infotrieve, ingenta. **CCC.**
Published by: Phi Epsilon Kappa Fraternity, 901 W New York St, Indianapolis, IN 46202. TEL 317-637-8431, http://www2.truman.edu/pek/public.html. Ed. William Stier. Pub. Jeffrey Vessely. Circ: 4,000.

➤ **PHYSICS EDUCATION.** see *PHYSICS*

➤ **PHYSICS TEACHER.** see *PHYSICS*

➤ **THE PHYSICS TEACHER.** see *PHYSICS*

➤ **PHYSICS TEACHING/WULI JIAOXUE.** see *PHYSICS*

➤ **PIANO JOURNAL.** see *MUSIC*

371.3 USA
▼ ➤ **PITCH JOURNAL.** Text in English. 2003. irreg. free (effective 2004). **Document type:** *Academic/Scholarly.* **Description:** Focuses on pedagogical, technological, sociological, legal, and moral issues related to opening access to educational opportunity.
Media: Online - full text.
Published by: O S L O Research Group http://pitchjournal.org/, http://oslo.usu.edu/.

371.3 ESP ISSN 1133-8482
PIXEL-BIT; revista de medios y educacion. Text in Spanish. 1994. s-a. EUR 12 domestic; EUR 19.50 foreign (effective 2005). **Document type:** *Magazine, Trade.*
Related titles: Online - full text ed.
—CINDOC.
Published by: Universidad de Sevilla, Secretariado de Publicaciones, Porvenir 27, Sevilla, 41013, Spain. TEL 34-95-4487444, FAX 34-95-4487443, secpub10@us.es, http://www.sav.us.es/pixelbit/pixelbit.htm, http://www.us.es/publius/inicio.html.

PLAYS; the drama magazine for young people. see *THEATER*

371.3 510 ISR ISSN 0771-100X
PME CONFERENCE. PROCEEDINGS. Text in English. 1977. a.
Indexed: L&LBA, MLA-IB.
Published by: The International Group for the Psychology of Mathematics Education, Joop van Dormolen, Rehov Harofeh 48 A, Haifa, 34367, Israel. TEL 972-4-8246239, FAX 972-4-8258071, joop@tx.technion.ac.il, http://igpme.org.

PO SVETU/PO SVETE/PO SWIECIE. see *LINGUISTICS*

375 DEU ISSN 1433-3120
POLIS. Text in German. 1997. q. EUR 25 domestic; EUR 28.50 foreign; EUR 6 newsstand/cover (effective 2004). **Document type:** *Journal, Academic/Scholarly.*
Formerly: D V P B Aktuell
Indexed: DIP, IBR, IBZ.
Published by: (Deutsche Vereinigung fuer Politische Bildung), V S - Verlag fuer Sozialwissenschaften (Subsidiary of: Springer Science+Business Media), Abraham-Lincoln-Str 46, Wiesbaden, 65189, Germany. TEL 49-611-78780, FAX 49-611-7878400, info@vs-verlag.de, http://www.dvpb.de/polis/polis.htm, http://www.vs-verlag.de. Ed. Karl-Peter Fritzsche.

371.3 DEU ISSN 0938-0884
POLITIK BETRIFFT UNS. Text in German. 1977. bi-m. looseleaf. EUR 48; EUR 12 newsstand/cover (effective 2005). back issues avail. **Document type:** *Journal, Academic/Scholarly.* **Description:** Intended for instructional purposes. Covers current political, social, economic and health issues. Each issue is devoted to a single topic.
Formerly (until 1985): Sozialwissenschaften Betrifft Uns (0176-9448)
Published by: Bergmoser und Hoeller Verlag GmbH, Karl-Friedrich-Str 76, Aachen, 52072, Germany. TEL 49-241-93888123, FAX 49-241-93888134, kontakt@buhv.de, http://www.buhv.de. Ed. Frank Dippel. Circ: 5,200.

320.071 DEU ISSN 0554-5455
JA1
POLITISCHE BILDUNG. Text in German. 1967. q. adv. bk.rev. reprints avail. **Document type:** *Journal, Academic/Scholarly.*
Indexed: DIP, IBR, IBZ, PAIS.
—BLDSC (6544.114100). **CCC.**
Published by: Wochenschau Verlag, Adolf Damaschke Str 12, Schwalbach, 65824, Germany. TEL 49-6196-86065, FAX 49-6196-86060, wochenschau-verlag@t-online.de. Eds. Bernward Debus, Ursula Buch. R&P Bernward Debus. Adv. contact Edith Beralli. Circ: 5,000.

371.3 USA
PORTFOLIO NEWS. Text in English. 1990. q. USD 25. bk.rev. **Document type:** *Newsletter.* **Description:** Includes articles and news from educators involved in portfolio assessment, and provides a forum for the exchange of information and ideas about the use of portfolios in schools.
Published by: Portfolio Assessment Clearinghouse, Teacher Education Program 0070, Univ of California at San Diego, 9500 Gilman Dr, La Jolla, CA 92093-0070. TEL 619-534-1681, FAX 619-534-2462. Ed. Winfield Cooper. Circ: 3,000.

PORTICO. see *EDUCATION—International Education Programs*

371.3 BGR ISSN 1310-8751
POSOKI. Text in Bulgarian. 10/yr. USD 40 foreign (effective 2002). **Document type:** *Journal, Academic/Scholarly.*
Published by: Ministerstvo na Obrazovanieto i Naukata na Republika Bulgaria/Ministry of Education and Sciences of the Republic of Bulgaria, 125 Tzarigradsko Shosse Blvd., Bl. 5, PO Box 336, Sofia, 1113, Bulgaria. TEL 359-2-705298, http://www.minedu.government.bg. **Dist. by:** Sofia Books, ul Silivria 16, Sofia 1404, Bulgaria. TEL 359-2-9586257, info@sofiabooks-bg.com, http://www.sofiabooks-bg.com.

POSTGRADUATE INSTITUTE OF MEDICAL EDUCATION AND RESEARCH, CHANDIGARH. BULLETIN. see *MEDICAL SCIENCES*

371.39 USA ISSN 1075-4741
PRACTICAL HOMESCHOOLING. Text in English. 1993. bi-m. USD 19.95 domestic; USD 29.95 foreign; USD 29 to libraries (effective 2002).
Related titles: Online - full text ed.: (from Gale Group).
Indexed: CPerl.
Published by: Home LIfe, Inc., PO Box 1190, Fenton, MO 63026-1190. TEL 800-346-6322, FAX 636-529-0137, svc@home-school.com, editor@home-school.com, http://www.home-school.com/.

371.3 USA
PRACTICAL INTERVENTIONS IN THE SCHOOLS. Text in English. irreg. price varies. **Document type:** *Monographic series, Academic/Scholarly.*
Published by: Guilford Publications, Inc., 72 Spring St, 4th Fl, New York, NY 10012. TEL 212-431-9800, 800-365-7006, FAX 212-966-6708, info@guilford.com, http://www.guilford.com.

302.224 AUS ISSN 1324-5961
LB1140.A1
PRACTICALLY PRIMARY. Text in English. 1995. 3/yr. AUD 82.50 to individual members; AUD 132 to institutional members (effective 2004). **Document type:** *Journal, Academic/Scholarly.* **Description:** Contains practical, informative ideas for primary classroom teachers. Teachers are invited to submit articles about their classroom practice.
Indexed: AEI.
Published by: Australian Literacy Educators' Association, PO Box 3203, Norwood, SA 5067, Australia. TEL 61-8-83322845, FAX 61-8-83330394, alea@netspace.net.au, http://www.alea.edu.au/pprim.htm. Ed. Nicole King.

373.1 USA ISSN 1556-4509
THE PRACTITIONER INQUIRY SERIES. Text in English. irreg. price varies. illus. back issues avail. **Document type:** *Monographic series, Trade.* **Description:** Examines issues of good educational practice and discusses ways in which to incorporate these ideas in classroom teaching.
Published by: Teachers College Press, Teachers College, Columbia University, 525 W 120th St, Box 303, New York, NY 10027-6694. http://www.teacherscollegepress.com. Pub. Carole Saltz. R&P Amy Detjen. **Dist. by:** Eurospan University Press Group, Order Dept, 3 Henrietta St, London WC2E 8LU, United Kingdom. TEL 44-20-7240-0856, FAX 44-20-7379-0609, http://www.eurospan.co.uk; Pademelon Press, Pty Ltd, 7-10 Anella Ave, PO Box 229, Castle Hill, NSW 2154, Australia. TEL 61-2-9634-2558, FAX 61-2-9680-4634; Transdex International, Pte Ltd, Block 1, Farrer Rd 307-05, Singapore 268817, Singapore. TEL 65-468-6242, FAX 65-462-5457.

PRATIQUES; theorie, pratique, pedagogie. see *LINGUISTICS*

PRATT INSTITUTE CREATIVE ARTS THERAPY REVIEW. see *MEDICAL SCIENCES—Physical Medicine And Rehabilitation*

PRAXIS. see *LINGUISTICS*

PRAXIS DER MATHEMATIK IN DER SCHULE. see *MATHEMATICS*

PRAXIS DER NATURWISSENSCHAFTEN - BIOLOGIE IN DER SCHULE. see *BIOLOGY*

PRAXIS DER NATURWISSENSCHAFTEN - CHEMIE IN DER SCHULE. see *CHEMISTRY*

PRAXIS DER NATURWISSENSCHAFTEN - PHYSIK IN DER SCHULE. see *PHYSICS*

PRAXIS DEUTSCH. see *LINGUISTICS*

PRAXIS FUER BEWEGUNG - SPORT UND SPIEL. see *SPORTS AND GAMES*

PRAXIS GEOGRAPHIE. see *GEOGRAPHY*

371.3 DEU ISSN 0933-5374
PRAXIS GESCHICHTE. Text in German. 1988. 6/yr. EUR 50.10; EUR 36.90 to students; EUR 9.30 newsstand/cover (effective 2003). adv. bibl.; charts; illus. 64 p./no.; **Document type:** *Magazine, Academic/Scholarly.*
Indexed: DIP, IBR, IBZ.
Published by: Westermann Schulbuchverlag GmbH, Georg-Westermann-Allee 66, Braunschweig, 38104, Germany. TEL 49-531-7080, FAX 49-531-708209, pgs@westermann.de, schulservice@westermann.de, http://www.praxisgeschichte.de, http://www.westermann.de. Ed. Bernd Bredemeyer. adv.: B&W page EUR 1,350, color page EUR 2,160; trim 187 x 257. Circ: 9,648 (paid and controlled).

371.3 DEU ISSN 0170-3722
PRAXIS GRUNDSCHULE. Text in German. 1976. 6/yr. EUR 62.70; EUR 44.70 to students; EUR 12.30 newsstand/cover (effective 2003). adv. charts; illus. back issues avail. **Document type:** *Magazine, Academic/Scholarly.*
Related titles: ♦ Supplement to: Grundschule. ISSN 0533-3431.
Indexed: DIP, IBR, IBZ.
Published by: Westermann Schulbuchverlag GmbH, Georg-Westermann-Allee 66, Braunschweig, 38104, Germany. TEL 49-531-7080, FAX 49-531-708209, pgru@westermann.de, schulservice@westermann.de, http://www.praxisgrundschule.de, http://www.westermann.de. Ed. Katrin Bokemeyer. adv.: B&W page EUR 3,300, color page EUR 5,280; trim 187 x 257. Circ: 39,634 (paid and controlled).

PRAXIS POLITISCHE BILDUNG. see *POLITICAL SCIENCE*

375 DEU ISSN 0936-6970
PRAXIS SCHULE 5-10. Text in German. 1990. 6/yr. EUR 50.10; EUR 36.90 to students; EUR 9.30 newsstand/cover (effective 2003). adv. bk.rev. charts; illus. 72 p./no.; back issues avail. **Document type:** *Magazine, Academic/Scholarly.*
Indexed: DIP, IBR, IBZ.
Published by: Westermann Schulbuchverlag GmbH, Georg-Westermann-Allee 66, Braunschweig, 38104, Germany. TEL 49-531-7080, FAX 49-531-708209, ps@westermann.de, schulservice@westermann.de, http://www.praxisschule.de, http://www.westermann.de. Ed. Babette Burgtorf. adv.: B&W page EUR 950, color page EUR 1,520; trim 187 x 257. Circ: 6,580 (controlled).

PREPODAVANIE ISTORII V SHKOLE. see *HISTORY*

PRESCHOOL BIBLE TEACHER A. see *RELIGIONS AND THEOLOGY—Protestant*

PRESCHOOLERS AT CHURCH. TEACHER'S GUIDE. see *RELIGIONS AND THEOLOGY—Protestant*

373.2 CAN ISSN 1194-3319
PRESIDENT'S NEWSLETTER. Text in English. 1981. 3/yr. CND 20 (effective 2000). **Document type:** *Newsletter, Trade.*
Published by: (Saskatchewan Middle Years Association), Saskatchewan Teachers' Federation, 2317 Arlington Ave., Saskatoon, SK S7J 2H8, Canada. TEL 306-373-1660, FAX 306-374-1122, http://www.stf.sk.ca.

371.3 GBR ISSN 1350-4991
THE PRIMARY ASSEMBLY FILE. Text in English. 1993. 3/yr. looseleaf. GBP 45; GBP 51.50 in Europe; GBP 62.50 elsewhere. **Document type:** *Academic/Scholarly.* **Description:** Contains themed, easy-to-use, and original assemblies.
Published by: P f P, Grays Inn Rd, London, WC1X 8HG, United Kingdom. TEL 44-171-404-2776, FAX 44-171-404-2766. Ed. Gerald Haigh. Pub. Nick Hutchins. R&P Felicity Rich. Circ: 6,000 (paid).

371.3 GBR ISSN 0952-2921
➤ **PRIMARY FILE.** Text in English. 1987. 3/yr. looseleaf. GBP 45 domestic; GBP 50.50 in Europe; GBP 56.50 rest of world. **Document type:** *Academic/Scholarly.* **Description:** Provides accessible, jargon-free help for headteachers, teachers and everyone concerned with primary schools.
—**CCC.**
Published by: P f P, Grays Inn Rd, London, WC1X 8HG, United Kingdom. TEL 44-171-404-2776, FAX 44-171-404-2766. Ed. Graham Reeves. Pub. Nick Hutchins. R&P Felicity Rich. Circ: 3,000 (paid).

371.3 GBR ISSN 1361-9128
THE PRIMARY SCHOOL - HOME FILE. Text in English. 1996. 3/yr. looseleaf. GBP 47.50; GBP 54 in Europe; GBP 65 elsewhere. **Document type:** *Academic/Scholarly.* **Description:** Promotes parent partnership.
Published by: P f P, Grays Inn Rd, London, WC1X 8HG, United Kingdom. TEL 44-171-404-2776, FAX 44-171-404-2766. Ed. Dinah Starkey. Pub. Nick Hutchins. R&P Felicity Rich. Circ: 1,600 (paid).

371.3 USA ISSN 1058-4749
Z286.T48
PRINT PUBLISHING FOR THE SCHOOL MARKET: (YEAR) REVIEW, TRENDS & FORECAST. Text in English. 1991. biennial. USD 2,095 per issue (effective 2003 & 2004). **Document type:** *Trade.* **Description:** Reports on the state of elementary and high school publishing and the market opportunities for textbooks, supplementary materials, workbooks, and standardized tests.

Published by: SIMBA Information (Subsidiary of: R.R. Bowker LLC), 60 Long Ridge Rd., Ste 300, Stamford, CT 06902. TEL 203-325-8193, 800-307-2529, FAX 203-325-8915, info@simbanet.com, http://www.simbanet.com.

PRISMA CANADA. see *LINGUISTICS*

375 GBR ISSN 0260-5554
PROBLEM - SOLVING NEWS. Text in English. 1980. 3/yr. GBP 2, USD 3.15. adv. bk.rev. back issues avail.
Address: c/o K.F. Jackson, Ed, 16 Campbell Dr, Beaconsfield, Bucks HP9 1TF, United Kingdom. Circ: 500.

407.1 USA ISSN 0740-6959
P57.U7
PROFESSION. Text in English. 1977. a. USD 7.50 per issue. back issues avail.; reprint service avail. from PQC. **Document type:** *Academic/Scholarly.* **Description:** Essays on the current state of the modern language profession and on aspects of the study of the teaching of modern languages and their literatures.
Related titles: Online - full text ed.: (from Gale Group, IngentaConnect).
Indexed: ChLitAb, MLA-IB, RILM.
Published by: Modern Language Association of America, 26 Broadway, 3rd Fl, New York, NY 10004-1789. TEL 646-576-5000, FAX 646-458-0030, profession@mla.org, kathleen.hansen@mla.org, http://www.mla.org/publications/profession. Ed. Phyllis Franklin. Circ: 36,000.

371.3 400 COL ISSN 1657-0790
➤ **PROFILE**; issues in teachers' professional development. Text in English. 2000. a. COP 6,500 domestic; USD 12 foreign (effective 2005). **Document type:** *Journal, Academic/Scholarly.* **Description:** Research and innovations carried out by teachers of English.
Published by: Universidad Nacional de Colombia, Facultad de Ciencias Humanas, Departamento de Lenguas Extranjeras, Ciudad Universitaria, Bogota, Colombia. TEL 57-1-3165000, FAX 57-1-3165233, rprofile_fchbog@unal.edu.co, http://www.humanas.unal.edu.co/publicaciones/publicaseriadas/profile/index.htm. Ed., R&P, Adv. contact Melba Libia Cardenas Beltran.

371.3 ZAF ISSN 0256-8853
➤ **PROGRESSIO**; newsletter for teaching development - nuusbrief vir onderrigontwikkeling. Text in Afrikaans, English. 1978. s-a. free. bk.rev.; software rev.; video rev. abstr.; bibl.; charts; illus.; stat. back issues avail. **Document type:** *Newsletter, Academic/Scholarly.* **Description:** Disseminates information regarding the theory and practice of distance education.
Indexed: ISAP.
Published by: (University of South Africa) Unisa Press, Periodicals, PO Box 392, Pretoria, 0003, South Africa. TEL 27-12-429-3081, FAX 27-12-429-3221, steypjn@alpha.unisa.ac.za, http://www.unisa.ac.za/dept/press/index.html. Ed. P J N Steyn. R&P Phoebe van der Walt TEL 27-12-429-3051. Circ: 1,700.

➤ **QUALITATIVE RESEARCH JOURNAL.** see *SOCIAL SCIENCES: COMPREHENSIVE WORKS*

371.358 USA ISSN 1528-3518
LC5800
QUARTERLY REVIEW OF DISTANCE EDUCATION. Text in English. 2000. q. USD 95 to individuals; USD 200 to institutions; USD 65 to students; USD 25 per issue to individuals; USD 45 per issue to institutions (effective 2006). adv. **Document type:** *Magazine, Trade.*
Related titles: Online - full text ed.: (from EBSCO Publishing, ProQuest Information & Learning).
Indexed: HEA.
—BLDSC (7206.437000). **CCC.**
Published by: Information Age Publishing, Inc., 411 W Putnam Ave, Ste 205, PO Box 4967, Greenwich, CT 06831. TEL 203-661-7602, FAX 203-661-7952, order@infoagepub.com, http://www.infoagepub.com. Eds. Charles Schlosser, Michael Simonson. Pub., R&P, Adv. contact George F. Johnson. B&W page USD 100.

372.35 507.1 AUS
THE QUEENSLAND SCIENCE TEACHER. Text in English. 1961. bi-m. price varies. adv. bk.rev. **Document type:** *Academic/Scholarly.*
Incorporates (1961-1996): Science Teachers Association of Queensland. Newsletter
Published by: Science Teachers Association of Queensland, School of Mathematics Science & Technology Education, QUT - Kelvin Grove Campus, QUT - Kelvin Grove Campus, Victoria Park Rd, Kelvin Grove, QLD 4059, Australia. TEL 61-7-9864-3340, FAX 61-7-9864-3340, staq@qut.edu.au, http://owl.qut.edu.au/stag. Ed. John Hunt. Pub., R&P, Adv. contact Penny Hauenschild. Circ: 750.

371.3 AUS ISSN 1441-6603
QUEENSLAND TEACHING MAGAZINE ONLINE. Text in English. 1998. q. **Document type:** *Academic/Scholarly.* **Description:** Delivers education articles written by leading Queensland, Australian and International educators.
Media: Online - full text.
Published by: Aussie Dot Web Pty Ltd, Ste 403, 15 Albert Ave, Broadbeach, QLD 4218, Australia. TEL 61-7-5579-7043, FAX 61-7-5538-8421, qt@australia.edu, http://www.australia.edu/QueenslandTeaching/.

613.7 USA ISSN 0033-6297
GV201
➤ **QUEST (CHAMPAIGN).** Text in English. 1949. q. USD 52 domestic to individuals; USD 62 foreign to individuals; USD 208 domestic to institutions; USD 218 foreign to institutions; USD 73 combined subscription domestic to individuals print & online eds.; USD 82 combined subscription foreign to individuals print & online eds.; USD 291 combined subscription domestic to institutions print & online eds.; USD 301 combined subscription foreign to institutions print & online eds. (effective 2005). adv. bk.rev. bibl.; charts; illus.; stat. back issues avail.; reprint service avail. from PSC. **Document type:** *Journal, Academic/Scholarly.* **Description:** Examines issues facing today's physical education faculty and students. Synthesizes research in the sports sciences and other subdisciplines of human movement.
Related titles: Microform ed.: (from PQC); Online - full text ed.: ISSN 1543-2750. USD 62 to individuals; USD 250 to institutions (effective 2005) (from EBSCO Publishing).
Indexed: ABIn, AbHyg, CERDIC, CIJE, CPE, CurCont, DIP, ERA, ETA, EduInd, FoSS&M, IBR, IBZ, MEA, NutrAb, PEI, RHEA, RRTA, SEA, SENA, SOMA, SSCI, SportS, TEA, e-psyche.
—BLDSC (7216.146400), IDS, IE, Infotrieve, ingenta. **CCC.**
Published by: (National Association for Physical Education in Higher Education), International Association for the Philosophy of Sport/Human Kinetics, PO Box 5076, Champaign, IL 61825-5076. TEL 800-747-4457, FAX 217-351-2674, orders@hkusa.com, http://www.humankinetics.com. Ed. Joy T DeSensi. Pub. Rainer Martens. Adv. contact Chad Hoffman. B&W page USD 300. Circ: 1,330 (paid and free).
Co-sponsor: American Academy of Physical Education.

➤ **QUESTIONS: PHILOSOPHY FOR YOUNG PEOPLE.** see *PHILOSOPHY*

➤ **QUIDDITY.** see *MOTION PICTURES*

507.1 MYS ISSN 0126-7612
R E C S A M NEWS. (Regional Centre for Education in Science and Mathematics) Text in English. 1967. q. MYR 5. illus. reprint service avail. from PQC. **Description:** Reports on the activities of the center: seminars, workshops, colloquia and research.
Formerly: R E C S A M Newsletter
Published by: Southeast Asian Ministers of Education Organisation, Regional Centre for Education in Science and Mathematics, Glugor, Penang 11700, Malaysia. TEL 604-6583266, FAX 604-6572541. Ed. K Ganeson. Circ: 2,450.

R U; oekumenische Zeitschrift fuer die Praxis des Religionsunterrichts. (Religionsunterricht) see *RELIGIONS AND THEOLOGY—Roman Catholic*

371.334 301 USA ISSN 1524-6345
LB1
➤ **RADICAL PEDAGOGY.** Text in English. 1998. s-a. free (effective 2005). bk.rev. back issues avail. **Document type:** *Journal, Academic/Scholarly.* **Description:** Examines the evolving state of teaching and learning.
Media: Online - full text.
Indexed: PsycInfo, PsycholAb.
Published by: International Consortium for the Advancement of Academic Publishing, c/o Dept. of Sociology, Univ. of Southern Colorado, Pueblo, CO 81001. TEL 719-549-2416, FAX 719-549-2705, mcgett@uscolo.edu, http://radicalpedagogy.icaap.org, http://www.icaap.org. Ed., R&P Timothy McGettigan.

➤ **RADICAL TEACHER**; a socialist and feminist journal on the theory and practice of teaching. see *POLITICAL SCIENCE*

371.335 ITA ISSN 1126-067X
IL RAGAZZO SELVAGGIO; cinema, televisione e linguaggi multimediali nella scuola. Text in Italian. 1985. bi-m. EUR 20 domestic; EUR 65 foreign (effective 2005). **Document type:** *Magazine, Consumer.* **Description:** Discusses the inclusion of multimedia tools in the classroom.
Published by: Moretti e Vitali Editori, Via Sergentini 6a, Bergamo, BG 24128, Italy. TEL 39-035-251300, FAX 39-035-4329409, http://www.morettievitali.it. Ed. Carlo Tagliabue.

REACTIONS. see *ENERGY—Nuclear Energy*

371.3 302.224 USA ISSN 0891-4214
CODEN: REAMFK
READ, AMERICA!; a quarterly newsletter for reading coordinators. Text in English. 1983. q. USD 25 domestic; USD 30 foreign. adv. bk.rev. back issues avail. **Document type:** *Newsletter, Academic/Scholarly.* **Description:** Covers activities and ideas promoting literacy and reading. Serves to instruct and inform adult teachers, librarians and literacy program leaders. Offers poetry and short stories for children and adults, book giveaways, and reports on book awards.
Formerly (until vol.4, no.4, 1986): Supply Side
Published by: Place in the Woods, 3900 Glenwood Ave, Minneapolis, MN 55422-5302. TEL 763-374-2120, readamerica10732@aol.com. Ed., Pub., R&P, Adv. contact Roger Hammer. B&W page USD 900; trim 11 x 8.5. Circ: 10,000 (controlled).

371.33 373 USA ISSN 0034-0359
READ MAGAZINE. Text in English. 1951. 18/yr. USD 34.50 per academic year; USD 9.95 per academic year 10 or more subscriptions (effective 2004 - 2005). illus. reprint service avail. from PQC. **Document type:** *Magazine, Consumer.* **Description:** Offers junior and senior high-school students a language arts reading magazine that turns students into lovers of reading while improving their language, critical thinking, and reading comprehension skills.
Related titles: Online - full text ed.: (from bigchalk, EBSCO Publishing, ProQuest Information & Learning).
Indexed: ICM, SPPI.
Published by: Weekly Reader Corp. (Subsidiary of: W R C Media Inc.), 200 First Stamford Pl, PO Box 120023, Stamford, CT 06912-0023. TEL 203-705-3500, 800-446-3355, FAX 203-705-1665, science@weeklyreader.com, http://www.weeklyreader.com. Ed. Mia Toschi. Pub. Peter Bergen. R&P Aimee Knoller TEL 203-705-3569. Circ: 380,750 (paid).

371.33 USA
READ, SEE AND HEAR. Text in English. 1950. bi-m.
Description: News of educational materials acquired by the library of the Newark Board of Education.
Published by: Newark Board of Education, Office of Educational Media Services, 2 Cedar St, Newark, NJ 07102. Ed. Binnie B McIntosh. Circ: 180.

READERLY - WRITERLY TEXTS. see *LITERATURE*

READING IN A FOREIGN LANGUAGE. see *LINGUISTICS*

418.4 USA ISSN 0886-0246
LB1050
➤ **READING RESEARCH AND INSTRUCTION.** Text in English. 1961. q. USD 50 domestic; USD 55 in Canada; USD 58 elsewhere. adv. bk.rev. abstr.; illus. Index. reprint service avail. from PQC. **Document type:** *Academic/Scholarly.*
Former titles (until vol.25): Reading World (0149-0117); Journal of the Reading Specialist (0022-5126)
Related titles: Microform ed.: 1961 (from PQC); Online - full text ed.: (from H.W. Wilson, O C L C Online Computer Library Center, Inc., ProQuest Information & Learning).
Indexed: ABIn, ASCA, CIJE, CPE, CurCont, EduInd, FamI, PsycInfo, PsycholAb, SSCI, e-psyche.
—BLDSC (7301.293000), IE, Infotrieve, ingenta.
Published by: College Reading Association, c/o Barbara Martin Palmer, Department of Education, Mount Saint Mary's College, Emmitsburg, MD 21727. TEL 301-447-5371, FAX 301-447-5250, http://explorers.tsuniv.edu/cra/. Ed. Diane Allen. R&P, Adv. contact Gary L Shaffer. Circ: 1,200.

371.3 USA
REFIGURING ENGLISH STUDIES. Text in English. 1996. irreg., latest 2002. price varies. back issues avail. **Document type:** *Monographic series, Academic/Scholarly.* **Description:** Provides a forum for scholarship on English studies as a discipline, a profession, and a vocation.
Published by: National Council of Teachers of English, 1111 W Kenyon Rd, Urbana, IL 61801-1096. TEL 817-328-3870, 800-369-6283, FAX 217-328-9645, membership@ncte.org, http://www.ncte.org/pubs/books/series/107765.htm.

REFLECTIONS; the SoL journal on knowledge, learning and change. see *BUSINESS AND ECONOMICS—Management*

510.71 AUS ISSN 0156-7799
REFLECTIONS (NORTH RYDE). Text in English. 1976. q. AUD 25. adv. bk.rev. back issues avail.
Published by: Mathematical Association of New South Wales, PO Box 339, North Ryde, NSW 1670, Australia. TEL 61-2-9878-1487, FAX 61-2-9878-1675, masamail@maths.adelaide.edu.au, http://www.maths.adelaide.edu.au. Ed. Mia Kumar. Circ: 1,000.

REFLECTIONS ONLINE. see *BUSINESS AND ECONOMICS—Management*

RELIGION BETRIFFT UNS. see *RELIGIONS AND THEOLOGY*

RELIGION TEACHER'S JOURNAL; the magazine for Catechists. see *RELIGIONS AND THEOLOGY*

RELIGIOUS EDUCATION; a platform for the free discussion of issues in the field of religion and their bearing on education. see *RELIGIONS AND THEOLOGY*

371.33 USA
RENAISSANCE LEARNING. Text in English. 5/yr. **Document type:** *Journal, Trade.* **Description:** Advises classroom teachers on how they can use Accelerated Reader, STAR Math, and other well-known Advantage Learning Systems programs and products to enhance their instruction.
Formerly: Advantage (Wisconsin Rapids)
Media: CD-ROM.

E

▼ new title ➤ refereed ✶ unverified ♦ full entry avail.

Published by: Reniassance Learning, Inc., 2911 Peach St, PO Box 8036, Wisconsin Rapids, WI 54495-8036. TEL 715-424-3636, 800-338-4204, FAX 715-424-4242, answers@renlearn.com, http://www.renlearn.com.

REPERES (PARIS, 1970); recherches en didactique du francais langue maternelle. see *LINGUISTICS*

372.21 USA ISSN 1544-9157
REPORT ON PRESCHOOL PROGRAMS; the bi-weekly newsletter on federal programs for early childhood development. Text in English. 1968. 25/yr. looseleaf. USD 357 (effective 2005). bibl.; charts; illus.; stat. back issues avail. **Document type:** *Newsletter, Trade.* **Description:** Provides administrators of preschool programs with reports of new studies of the most effective teaching methods.
Incorporates (in 2004): Day Care U S A; Formerly (until 1983): Report on Preschool Education (0034-4702)
Related titles: E-mail ed.: ISSN 1545-4770. USD 297 (effective 2005); Online - full text ed.: (from Gale Group).
—CCC.
Published by: Business Publishers, Inc., 8737 Colesville Rd., Flr. 10, Silver Spring, MD 20910-3976. TEL 800-274-6737, bpinews@bpinews.com, custserv@bpinews.com, http://www.bpinews.com/edu/pages/rpp.cfm. Ed. Charles Dervarics. Pub. Leonard A Eiserer.

RESEARCH AND SCHOLARSHIP IN COMPOSITION. see *LITERATURE*

371.3 USA ISSN 1542-0612
LB1623.5
➤ **RESEARCH IN MIDDLE LEVEL EDUCATION ANNUAL.** Text in English. 1976. a. free (effective 2003). adv. back issues avail. **Document type:** *Academic/Scholarly.*
Former titles (until 2000): Research in Middle Level Education Quarterly (1084-8959); (until 1995): Research in Middle Level Education (1082-5541)
Related titles: Online - full text ed.: (from EBSCO Publishing).
Indexed: CIJE.
—BLDSC (7742.725800).
Published by: National Middle School Association, 4151 Executive Pkwy, Ste 300, Westerville, OH 43081-3871. TEL 614-895-4730, 800-528-6672, FAX 614-895-4750, info@nmsa.org, http://www.nmsa.org. Ed. David Hough. R&P Joe Ball. Adv. contact Jane Richardson. Circ: 300 (paid).

➤ **RESEARCH IN SCIENCE EDUCATION.** see *SCIENCES: COMPREHENSIVE WORKS*

418 USA ISSN 0034-527X
PE1066
➤ **RESEARCH IN THE TEACHING OF ENGLISH.** Text in English. 1967. q. USD 60 to individuals includes $40 membership; USD 60 to institutions (effective 2005). adv. bk.rev. bibl.; stat.; illus. reprint service avail. from PQC. **Document type:** *Journal, Academic/Scholarly.*
Related titles: Microform ed.: (from PQC); Online - full text ed.: (from EBSCO Publishing, ProQuest Information & Learning).
Indexed: ABIn, ArtHuCI, CIJE, CPE, CurCont, ERA, ETA, EduInd, Faml, L&LBA, LT&LA, MEA, RASB, RHEA, SEA, SENA, SOMA, SOPODA, SSCI, TEA.
—BLDSC (7773.707000), IE, Infotrieve, ingenta. **CCC.**
Published by: National Council of Teachers of English, 1111 W Kenyon Rd, Urbana, IL 61801-1096. TEL 217-328-3870, 800-369-6283, FAX 217-328—9645, cschanche@ncte.org, http://www.ncte.org/pubs/journals/rte. Eds. Michael Smith, Peter Smagorinsky. R&P Barbara Lamar. Adv. contact Carrie Stewart. Circ: 4,100.

371.3 JPN ISSN 0385-9746
RESEARCH JOURNAL OF EDUCATIONAL METHODS. Text in Japanese. 1975. a. JPY 1,200.
Published by: National Association for the Study of Educational Methods, 1-1-89 Higashi-Senda-Machi, Naka-ku, Hiroshima-shi, 730-0053, Japan. TEL 082-241-1221.

RESEARCH QUARTERLY FOR EXERCISE AND SPORT. see *PHYSICAL FITNESS AND HYGIENE*

RESEARCH STUDIES IN MUSIC EDUCATION. see *MUSIC*

370 USA ISSN 1050-2130
LB1584
THE REVIEW (COLUMBUS). Key Title: Ohio Council for the Social Studies. Review. Variant title: O C S S Review. Text in English. a. USD 55 to non-members; USD 25 to qualified personnel; USD 5 to students (effective 2005). **Document type:** *Journal, Trade.*
Indexed: CIJE.
Published by: Ohio Council for the Social Studies, 3258 Scioto Farms Dr, Columbus, OH 43026. http://www.ocss.org. Ed. Linda Logan. Circ: 6,500 (free).

REVIEW OF BUSINESS INFORMATION SYSTEMS. see *BUSINESS AND ECONOMICS—Accounting*

REVISTA BRASILEIRA DE ENSINO DE FISICA. see *PHYSICS*

613.7 BRA ISSN 0102-8464
REVISTA DE EDUCACAO FISICA. Text in Portuguese. 1932. s-a. free. **Document type:** *Academic/Scholarly.* **Description:** Covers physical training, sports, physical fitness, health and education.
Related titles: Diskette ed.
Published by: Centro de Capacitacao Fisica do Exercito, Av. Joao Luis s-n - URLA, Rio De Janeiro, RJ 22291-090, Brazil. TEL 55-21-543-3323, FAX 55-21-543-3323. Ed. Maj Josue Morisson de Maraes. Circ: 5,000.

REVISTA DE HISTORIA. see *HISTORY*

▼ **REVISTA EUREKA SOBRE ENSENANZA Y DIVULGACION DE LAS CIENCIAS.** see *SCIENCES: COMPREHENSIVE WORKS*

613.7 BRA ISSN 1678-2577
GV237
➤ **REVISTA MACKENZIE DE EDUCACAO FISICA E ESPORTE.** Text in Portuguese; Abstracts in English, Portuguese. 2002. a. free (effective 2005). **Document type:** *Journal, Academic/Scholarly.*
Published by: Universidade Presbiteriana Mackenzie (Subsidiary of: Instituto Presbiteriano Mackenzie), Rua da Consolacao 896, Pr.2, Sao Paulo-SP, SP 01302-907, Brazil. FAX 55-11-32368302, biblio.per@mackenzie.br, http://www.mackenzie.com.br/universidade/educacaofisica/remefe.htm. Ed., R&P Mr. Marcos Merida.

613.7 BEL ISSN 1376-1854
REVUE DE L'EDUCATION PHYSIQUE. Text in French. 1907. q. EUR 22.30 domestic to individuals; EUR 40.90 foreign to individuals (effective 2004). adv. bk.rev. charts; stat.
Former titles (until 1955): Revue de l'Education Physique (Edition Bilingue) (1376-1846); (until 1929): Revue de l'Education Physique (0035-1377); (until 1923): Revue Gymnastique (1376-1838)
Related titles: ♦ Dutch ed.: Tijdschrift voor Lichamelijke Opvoeding.
Indexed: SportS.
—BLDSC (7898.876500), IE, ingenta.
Published by: Federation d'Education Physique, Bd de la Sauveniere 33, Liege, 4000, Belgium. fed.ep@contactonline.net, http://www.opt.be/informations/wallonie_Sport/FR/A/AS/34057.html. Ed. Maurice Pieron. Circ: 2,300. **Co-sponsor:** Groupement de Professeurs d'Education Physique.

613.7 FRA ISSN 0245-8969
REVUE E P S. Text in French; Summaries in English, French, German, Spanish. 1950. bi-m. adv. bk.rev. illus.; charts; bibl. index. **Document type:** *Academic/Scholarly.* **Description:** Helps in planning secondary school physical education classes.
Formerly (until 1976): Education Physique et Sport (0013-1474)
Indexed: CPE, PdeR, SportS.
—IE, Infotrieve.
Published by: (Comite d'Etudes et d'Informations Pedagogiques de l'Education Physique et du Sport), Editions Revue E P S, 11 av. du Tremblay, Paris, 75012, France. TEL 33-1-48083087, FAX 33-1-43983738, revue@revue-eps.com, http://www.revue-eps.com. Ed. Claudine Leray. Circ: 26,000.

808.5 DEU ISSN 0720-5775
PN171.4
RHETORIK; Ein internationales Jahrbuch. Text in German. 1980. a. EUR 45 (effective 2005). adv. bk.rev. back issues avail. **Document type:** *Journal, Academic/Scholarly.*
Indexed: BibLing, DIP, IBR, IBZ, RI-1, RI-2.
Published by: Max Niemeyer Verlag GmbH, Postfach 2140, Tuebingen, 72011, Germany. TEL 49-7071-98940, FAX 49-7071-989450, info@niemeyer.de, http://www.niemeyer.de. Eds. Gert Ueding, Joachim Dyck, Manfred Beetz, Wolfgang Neuber. Circ: 800.

RIDAI KAGAKU FORAMU. see *TECHNOLOGY: COMPREHENSIVE WORKS*

371.3 USA ISSN 0278-3193
LC3991
➤ **ROEPER REVIEW**; a journal on gifted education. Text in English. 1978. q. USD 50 domestic to individuals; USD 62 in Canada to individuals; USD 85 elsewhere to individuals; USD 80 domestic to institutions; USD 93 in Canada to institutions; USD 115 elsewhere to institutions (effective 2004). adv. bk.rev. illus.; abstr. index. back issues avail.; reprints avail. **Document type:** *Journal, Academic/Scholarly.* **Description:** Focuses on issues, teaching strategies, academic theory and research regarding education for the gifted.
Related titles: Online - full text ed.: (from EBSCO Publishing, Florida Center for Library Automation, Gale Group, H.W. Wilson, Northern Light Technology, Inc., O C L C Online Computer Library Center, Inc., ProQuest Information & Learning).
Indexed: ABIn, CIJE, CPE, DIP, EAA, ECER, ERA, ETA, EduInd, Faml, IBR, IBZ, MEA, PsycInfo, PsycholAb, RASB, RHEA, RILM, SEA, SENA, SOMA, SWA, TEA, e-psyche.
—BLDSC (8019.158000), IE, ingenta. **CCC.**
Published by: Roeper School, PO Box 329, Bloomfield Hills, MI 48303. TEL 248-203-7321, FAX 248-203-7310, roeper@roeperreview.org, http://www.roeperreview.org. Ed., Pub. Ruthan Brodsky. Adv. contact Vicki Rossbach. Circ: 3,000 (paid).

907.1 305.89185 POL ISSN 0867-5872
DK4110
ROTA; kwartalnik dla Polonii i Polakow poza granicami R P. Text in Polish. 1991. q. PLZ 120 domestic; USD 64 foreign (effective 2003). back issues avail. **Document type:** *Journal, Academic/Scholarly.* **Description:** Covers Polish history, literature, folklore and art. For Polish schools abroad Poland especially in former Soviet Union.
Published by: Fundacja Pomocy Szkolom Polskim na Wschodzie im. T. Goniewicza, Ul Jana Sawy 5, Lublin, 20632, Poland. TEL 48-81-5252924, FAX 48-81-5245330, redakcja@fundgon.begin2.com.pl. Ed. Barbara Jedynak. Circ: 10,000.

371.3 NLD ISSN 1386-2863
ROTTERDAMS ONDERWIJS MAGAZINE. Text in Dutch. 1979. m. EUR 50; EUR 5 newsstand/cover (effective 2005). adv. bk.rev. back issues avail.
Formerly (until 1996): Projektkrant (0167-4196)
Published by: Stichting de Meeuw, Postbus 57689, Rotterdam, 3008 BR, Netherlands. TEL 31-10-4863022, FAX 31-10-4866455, http://www.roplein.nl/index_rom.htm, http://www.de-meeuw.nl. Ed. Willem Bijl. adv.: page EUR 500; 210 x 297. Circ: 7,000.

371.3 KAZ ISSN 0234-6834
RUSSKII YAZYK I LITERATURA V KAZAKHSKOI SHKOLE. Text in Russian. bi-m. USD 110 in United States.
Published by: Ministry of Education, Ul Zhambyla 25, Almaty, 480100, Kazakstan. TEL 3272-617851. Ed. B S Mukhanova. **US dist. addr.:** East View Information Services, 3020 Harbor Ln. N., Minneapolis, MN 55447. TEL 612-550-0961.

RUSSKII YAZYK V SHKOLE. see *LINGUISTICS*

375 GBR
S C A A ANNUAL REPORT. Text in English. a. **Document type:** *Corporate.*
Published by: School Curriculum and Assessment Authority, Newcombe House, 45 Notting Hill Gate, London, W11 3JB, United Kingdom. TEL 44-171-229-1234, FAX 44-171-229-8526, http://www.open.gov.uk/scaa/scaahome.htm. **Subscr. to:** SCAA Publications, PO Box 235, Hayes, Mddx UB3 1HF, United Kingdom. TEL 44-181-561-4499, FAX 44-181-813-6432.

371.3 GBR
S C A A DISCUSSION PAPER. Text in English. 1995. irreg., latest vol.7, 1996. GBP 4. **Document type:** *Monographic series, Academic/Scholarly.*
Published by: School Curriculum and Assessment Authority, Newcombe House, 45 Notting Hill Gate, London, W11 3JB, United Kingdom. TEL 44-171-229-1234, FAX 44-171-229-8526, http://www.open.gov.uk/scaa/scaahome.htm. **Subscr. to:** SCAA Publications, PO Box 235, Hayes, Mddx UB3 1HF, United Kingdom. TEL 44-181-561-4499, FAX 44-181-813-6432.

371.3 IND
S C E R T JOURNAL✶. Text in English. 1970. s-a. charts.
Published by: State Council of Educational Research and Training, Dept. of Public Instruction, Hyderabad, Andhra Pradesh, India.

507.1 AUS ISSN 0157-6488
S C I O S. Text in English. 1965. q. AUD 5 per issue. bk.rev. **Document type:** *Academic/Scholarly.*
Indexed: AEI.
Published by: Science Teachers' Association of Western Australia, PO Box 1099, Osborne Park, W.A. 6916, Australia. TEL 61-8-92441987, FAX 61-8-92442601, stawa@info.asn.au, http://www.stawa.asn.au. Ed. J Pearson. Circ: 780.

S D A JOURNAL. see *THEATER*

S H E T A NEWSLETTER. (Saskatchewan Home Economics Teachers' Association) see *HOME ECONOMICS*

S I E C U S REPORT. see *SOCIOLOGY*

371.334 USA
S I G I T E NEWSLETTER. (Special Interest Group Information Technology Education) Text in English. q. USD 23 (effective 2004). **Document type:** *Newsletter.* **Description:** Provides a forum for the interaction of practitioners, educators and others in the field of Information Technology Education. Encourages the exchange of ideas and activities that advance the knowledge of its members, and the curriculum and teaching of Information Technology.
Media: Online - full text. **Related titles:** Print ed.: ISSN 1550-1469.
Published by: Association for Computing Machinery, Inc., 1515 Broadway, 17th Fl, New York, NY 10036-5701. TEL 212-626-0500, 212-626-0520, 800-342-6626, usacm@acm.org, http://www.acm.org/sigite/.

E

418 USA
S L A T E NEWSLETTER. (Support for the Learning and Teaching of English) Text in English. 1975. 3/yr. free (effective 2003). **Document type:** *Newsletter.* **Description:** Directed to K-12 English language art teachers about censorship, writing centers, and composition.
Media: E-mail.
Published by: National Council of Teachers of English, 1111 W Kenyon Rd, Urbana, IL 61801-1096. TEL 217-328-3870, 800-369-6283, FAX 217-328—9645, 217-328-9645, mdavis@ncte.org, membership@ncte.org, http://www.ncte.org/about/issues/slate/newsletters/109676.htm. Ed. Millie Davis. Circ: 1,000.

S P L C REPORT. see *POLITICAL SCIENCE—Civil Rights*

371.3 USA
S S M A CLASSROOM ACTIVITIES MONOGRAPH SERIES. Text in English. 1987. 8/yr. USD 64; USD 76 foreign. adv. back issues avail. **Document type:** *Monographic series, Academic/Scholarly.* **Description:** Covers various topics on developing mathematics and science curricula in elementary schools.
Published by: School Science and Mathematics Association, Bloomsburg University, Department of Curriculum and Foundations, 400 E Second St, Bloomsburg, PA 17815-1301. TEL 570-389-4915, FAX 570-389-3615, ssma314159@aol.com, pratt@bloomu.edu, http://www.ssma.org. Ed. Margaret Niess. R&P, Adv. contact Donald Pratt.

371.3 USA
S S M A TOPICS FOR TEACHERS MONOGRAPH SERIES. Text in English. 1979. irreg., latest vol.7, 1994. price varies. back issues avail. **Document type:** *Monographic series, Academic/Scholarly.* **Description:** Covers teaching techniques and curriculum development for elementary school teachers of science and mathematics.
Published by: School Science and Mathematics Association, Bloomsburg University, Department of Curriculum and Foundations, 400 E Second St, Bloomsburg, PA 17815-1301. TEL 717-389-4915, FAX 717-389-3815, ssma314159@aol.com, pratt@bloomu.edu, www.ssma.org, http://www.hubble.bloomu.edu/~ssma. Pub. Donald Pratt.

510.71 DEU ISSN 0949-6785
SACHE - WORT - ZAHL. Text in German. 1972. 8/yr. EUR 44.80 to individuals (effective 2006). adv. **Document type:** *Journal, Academic/Scholarly.*
Former titles: Sachunterricht und Mathematik in der Primarstufe (0170-0944); (until 1978): Sachunterricht und Mathematik in der Grundschule (0342-7404)
Indexed: DIP, IBR, IBZ.
Published by: Aulis-Verlag Deubner GmbH und Co. KG, Antwerpener Str 6-12, Cologne, 50672, Germany. TEL 49-221-951454-0, FAX 49-221-518443, info@aulis.de, http://www.aulis.de. R&P Wolfgang Deubner. Adv. contact Ulrike Lennertz. Circ: 6,500 (paid).

SAFETY NET NEWSLETTER. see *CHILDREN AND YOUTH—For*

SASKATCHEWAN ASSOCIATION OF TEACHERS OF FRENCH. BULLETIN DE SERVICE. see *LINGUISTICS*

THE SASKATCHEWAN BAND ASSOCIATION JOURNAL; a smooth connection between notes. see *MUSIC*

792.71 CAN ISSN 1208-8765
SASKATCHEWAN DRAMA ASSOCIATION. NEWSLETTER. Text in English. 1980. 2/yr. CND 45; CND 10 to students (effective 2000). **Document type:** *Newsletter, Trade.*
Former titles (until 1996): S D A Newsletter (1200-1600); (until 1989): Saskatchewan Drama Association. Newsletter (0824-2038); (until 1980): S D A Newsletter (0229-0758)
Published by: (Saskatchewan Drama Association), Saskatchewan Teachers' Federation, 2317 Arlington Ave., Saskatoon, SK S7J 2H8, Canada. stf@stf.sk.ca, http://www.stf.sk.ca.

SASKATCHEWAN MATHEMATICS TEACHERS' SOCIETY. JOURNAL; ideas and resources. see *MATHEMATICS*

SCHATZKAMMER; der deutschen Sprache, Dichtung und Geschichte. see *LINGUISTICS*

371.33 371.913 USA ISSN 0163-3570
SCHOLASTIC ACTION. Text in English. 1977. 14/yr. (during school year). USD 7.95 (effective 2005); with 10 or more student subscr.. illus. reprint service avail. from PQC. **Document type:** *Magazine, Consumer.* **Description:** Helps develop basic English skills for remedial and special-needs students in grades 7-12 with reading levels of grades 3-5, using interesting stories and articles to which these children can relate.
Related titles: Microform ed.: (from PQC); Online - full text ed.: (from bigchalk, EBSCO Publishing, Northern Light Technology, Inc., ProQuest Information & Learning).
Indexed: ICM, MASUSE.
Published by: Scholastic Inc., 557 Broadway, New York, NY 10012-0399. TEL 212-343-6100, FAX 212-343-6333, scienceworld@scholastic.com, http://www.scholastic.com. Ed. Janice Behrans. Pub. Ernest Fleishman. Circ: 230,000. **Subscr. to:** 2931 E McCarthy St, PO Box 3710, Jefferson City, MO 65102-9957. TEL 800-724-6527, classmags@scholastic.com.

371.33 USA ISSN 1060-832X
N1
SCHOLASTIC ART. Text in English. 1970. 6/yr. (during school year). USD 8.95 (effective 2005); with 10 or more student subscr.. bibl.; illus. Index. reprint service avail. from PQC. **Document type:** *Magazine, Consumer.* **Description:** Explains painting and other fine art forms in the cultural and historical contexts in which they were created, for middle- and high-school students, grades 7-12.
Formerly (until 1992): Art and Man (0004-3052); Incorporates: Artist Junior (0004-3893)
Related titles: Microfilm ed.: (from PQC); Online - full text ed.: (from bigchalk, Gale Group, Northern Light Technology, Inc., ProQuest Information & Learning); Special ed(s).: Scholastic Art (Teacher's Edition). USD 34.95 per academic year (effective 2001 - 2002).
Indexed: ICM, RGYP.
Published by: (National Gallery of Art NOR), Scholastic Inc., 557 Broadway, New York, NY 10012-0399. TEL 212-343-6100, FAX 212-343-4808, http://www.scholastic.com. Circ: 245,000. **Subscr. to:** 2931 E McCarthy St, PO Box 3710, Jefferson City, MO 65102-9957. TEL 800-724-6527, classmags@scholastic.com.

028.5 USA ISSN 0883-475X
TX1
SCHOLASTIC CHOICES; personal development & living skills. Text in English. 1956. 6/yr. (during school year). USD 8.50 for 10 copies or more (effective 2005). adv. illus. index. reprint service avail. from PQC. **Document type:** *Magazine, Consumer.* **Description:** Allows for high- and middle-school students, grades 7-12, to make informed decisions on health, fitness, drugs, sex, family life, careers, and consumer products.
Incorporates (in 1999): Health Choices (1087-6421); Supersedes (in 1985): Co-Ed (0009-9724); Incorporates (in 1991): Forecast for the Home Economist (0890-9849); Which superseded (in 1986): Forecast for Home Economics (0015-7090); (1963-1966): Practical Forecast for Home Economics (0742-8693)
Related titles: Microform ed.: (from PQC); Online - full text ed.: (from bigchalk, EBSCO Publishing, Gale Group, H.W. Wilson, O C L C Online Computer Library Center, Inc., ProQuest Information & Learning, The Dialog Corporation).
Indexed: ABIn, EduInd, ICM, MASUSE, MRD, MagInd, RGPR, RGYP, RILM.
—CISTI.
Published by: Scholastic Inc., 557 Broadway, New York, NY 10012-0399. TEL 212-343-6100, FAX 212-343-6333, scienceworld@scholastic.com, http://www.scholastic.com. Ed. Maura Christopher. Pub. Richard Robinson. Circ: 180,000 (paid). **Subscr. to:** 2931 E McCarthy St, PO Box 3710, Jefferson City, MO 65102-9957. TEL 800-724-6527, classmags@scholastic.com.

371.33 511.3 USA ISSN 0732-7773
SCHOLASTIC DYNAMATH. Text in English. 8/yr. (during school year). USD 7 (effective 2005); with 10 or more student subscr.. illus. reprint service avail. from PQC. **Document type:** *Magazine, Consumer.* **Description:** Offers upper-elementary school children, grades 3-6, enjoyable mathematics word problems with real-life applications, many in multicultural contexts.
Formerly (until 1982): Scholastic Math Power (1055-1212)
Related titles: Online - full text ed.: (from bigchalk, EBSCO Publishing, ProQuest Information & Learning).
Published by: Scholastic Inc., 557 Broadway, New York, NY 10012-0399. TEL 212-343-6100, FAX 212-343-6333, dynamath@scholastic.com, http://www.scholastic.com. Ed. Jack Silbert. Circ: 200,000 (paid and free). **Subscr. to:** 2931 E McCarthy St, PO Box 3710, Jefferson City, MO 65102-9957. TEL 800-724-6527, classmags@scholastic.com.

371.33 USA ISSN 0024-1261
SCHOLASTIC LET'S FIND OUT. Variant title: Let's Find Out (English Edition). Text in English. 32/yr. (during school year). USD 4.95 (effective 2005); with 10 or more student subscr.. illus. reprint service avail. from PQC. **Document type:** *Magazine, Consumer.* **Description:** Invites kindergarten children to explore their world through stories, poetry, pictures, and activities.
Formerly (until 1995): My First Magazine (1057-1558)
Related titles: ♦ Spanish ed.: Let's Find Out (Spanish Edition). ISSN 1076-6766.
Published by: Scholastic Inc., 557 Broadway, New York, NY 10012-0399. TEL 212-343-6100, FAX 212-343-4808, http://www.scholastic.com. Circ: 615,000. **Subscr. to:** 2931 E McCarthy St, PO Box 3710, Jefferson City, MO 65102-9957. TEL 800-724-6527, classmags@scholastic.com.

510.71 371.33 USA ISSN 0198-8379
SCHOLASTIC MATH. Text in English. 1980. 12/yr. (during school year). USD 8.15 (effective 2005); with 10 or more student subscr.. illus. reprint service avail. from PQC. **Document type:** *Magazine, Consumer.* **Description:** Contains activities and features focusing on consumer math, math on-the-job, and computation to problem-solving, geared to middle-school students in grades 6-9.
Related titles: Microform ed.: (from PQC); Online - full text ed.: (from bigchalk, EBSCO Publishing, ProQuest Information & Learning).
Indexed: MASUSE, RGYP.
Published by: Scholastic Inc., 557 Broadway, New York, NY 10012-0399. TEL 212-343-6100, FAX 212-343-4808, scienceworld@scholastic.com, http://www.scholastic.com. Ed. Jack Silbert. Circ: 200,000 (paid). **Subscr. to:** 2931 E McCarthy St, PO Box 3710, Jefferson City, MO 65102-9957. TEL 800-724-6527, classmags@scholastic.com.

371.33 305.868 USA ISSN 1070-5880
SCHOLASTIC NEWS EN ESPANOL. EDICION 1. Text in Spanish. 199?. 32/yr. (during school year). USD 4.50 (effective 2003 - 2004); with 10 or more student subscr.. illus. index. reprint service avail. from PQC. **Document type:** *Consumer.* **Description:** Invites children in grade 1 whose primary language is Spanish to read about, explore, ponder, and discuss issues in the news and other noteworthy topics.
Related titles: Microform ed.: (from PQC); ♦ English ed.: Scholastic News. Grade 1 Edition.
Indexed: ICM.
Published by: Scholastic Inc., 557 Broadway, New York, NY 10012-0399. TEL 212-343-6100, http://www.scholastic.com. **Subscr. to:** 2931 E McCarthy St, PO Box 3710, Jefferson City, MO 65102-9957. TEL 800-724-6527, classmags@scholastic.com.

371.33 305.868 USA ISSN 1070-1176
SCHOLASTIC NEWS EN ESPANOL. EDICION 2. Text in Spanish. 32/yr. (during school year). USD 4.50 (effective 2003 - 2004); with 10 or more student subscr.. illus. index. reprint service avail. from PQC. **Document type:** *Consumer.* **Description:** Invites children in grade 2 whose primary language is Spanish to read about, explore, ponder, and discuss issues in the news and other noteworthy topics.
Related titles: ♦ English ed.: Scholastic News. Grade 2 Edition.
Indexed: ICM.
Published by: Scholastic Inc., 557 Broadway, New York, NY 10012-0399. TEL 212-343-6100, http://www.scholastic.com. **Subscr. to:** 2931 E McCarthy St, PO Box 3710, Jefferson City, MO 65102-9957. TEL 800-724-6527, classmags@scholastic.com.

371.33 305.868 USA ISSN 1076-8262
SCHOLASTIC NEWS EN ESPANOL. EDICION 3. Text in Spanish. 1994. 12/yr. (during school year). USD 4.50 (effective 2003 - 2004); with 10 or more student subscr.. illus. index. reprint service avail. from PQC. **Document type:** *Consumer.* **Description:** Invites grade 3 children whose primary language is Spanish to read about, explore, ponder, and discuss issues in the news and other noteworthy topics.
Related titles: Microform ed.: (from PQC); ♦ English ed.: Scholastic News. Grade 3 Edition.
Indexed: ICM.
Published by: Scholastic Inc., 557 Broadway, New York, NY 10012-0399. TEL 212-343-6100, http://www.scholastic.com. **Subscr. to:** 2931 E McCarthy St, PO Box 3710, Jefferson City, MO 65102-9957. TEL 800-724-6527, classmags@scholastic.com.

371.33 USA
SCHOLASTIC NEWS. GRADE 1 EDITION. Variant title: Scholastic News. Edition 1. Text in English. 1960. 32/yr. (during school year). USD 375 (effective 2005); with 10 or more student subscr.. illus. Index. reprint service avail. from PQC. **Document type:** *Magazine, Academic/Scholarly.* **Description:** Invites students in grade 1 to read about, explore, ponder, and discuss issues in the news and other noteworthy topics.
Supersedes (in 1998): Scholastic News (Pilot Edition) (0736-0533); Which was formerly (until 1982): Scholastic News Pilot (0028-9329)
Related titles: Microform ed.: (from PQC); Online - full text ed.: Scholastic News Online. Grade 1 (from EBSCO Publishing); ♦ Spanish ed.: Scholastic News en Espanol. Edicion 1. ISSN 1070-5880.
Indexed: ICM.
Published by: Scholastic Inc., 557 Broadway, New York, NY 10012-0399. TEL 212-343-6100, FAX 212-343-4808, http://teacher.scholastic.com/scholasticnews/magazines/edition1/, http://www.scholastic.com. Ed. Rebecca Bondor. Circ: 955,000. **Subscr. to:** 2931 E McCarthy St, PO Box 3710, Jefferson City, MO 65102-9957. TEL 800-724-6527, classmags@scholastic.com.

371.33 USA
SCHOLASTIC NEWS. GRADE 2 EDITION. Variant title: Scholastic News. Edition 2. Text in English. 1960. 32/yr. (during school year). USD 3.75 (effective 2005); with 10 or more student subscr.. illus. Index. reprint service avail. from PQC. **Document type:** *Magazine, Academic/Scholarly.* **Description:** Invites children in grade 2 to read about, explore, ponder, and discuss issues in the news and other noteworthy topics.

E

Supersedes (in 1998): Scholastic News (Ranger Edition) (0736-055X); Which was formerly (until 1982): Scholastic News Ranger (0036-6404)
Related titles: Microform ed.: (from PQC); Online - full text ed.: Scholastic News Online. Grade 2 (from EBSCO Publishing); ♦ Spanish ed.: Scholastic News en Espanol. Edicion 2. ISSN 1070-1176.
Indexed: ICM.
Published by: Scholastic Inc., 557 Broadway, New York, NY 10012-0399. TEL 212-343-6100, FAX 212-343-4808, http://teacher.scholastic.com/scholasticnews/magazines/edition2/, http://www.scholastic.com. Ed. Alyse Sweeney. Circ: 910,000. **Subscr. to:** 2931 E McCarthy St, PO Box 3710, Jefferson City, MO 65102-9957. TEL 800-724-6527, classmags@scholastic.com.

371.33 USA
SCHOLASTIC NEWS. GRADE 3 EDITION. Variant title: Scholastic News. Edition 3. Text in English. 1960. 24/yr. (during school year). USD 3.95 (effective 2005); with 10 or more student subscr.. bibl.; charts; illus.; stat. Index. reprint service avail. from PQC. **Document type:** *Magazine, Academic/Scholarly.* **Description:** Invites third-grade students to read about, explore, ponder, and discuss topics in the news and other noteworthy issues.
Former titles (until 1998): Scholastic News (Trails Edition) (0736-0576); (until 1982): Scholastic News Trails (0028-9361)
Related titles: Microfilm ed.: (from PQC); Online - full text ed.: (from EBSCO Publishing); ♦ Spanish ed.: Scholastic News en Espanol. Edicion 3. ISSN 1076-8262.
Indexed: ICM.
Published by: Scholastic Inc., 557 Broadway, New York, NY 10012-0399. TEL 212-343-6100, FAX 212-343-4808, http://teacher.scholastic.com/scholasticnews/magazines/edition3/, http://www.scholastic.com. Ed. Glenn Greenberg. Circ: 3,500,000. **Subscr. to:** 2931 E McCarthy St, PO Box 3710, Jefferson City, MO 65102-9957. TEL 800-724-6527, classmags@scholastic.com.

371.33 USA
SCHOLASTIC NEWS. GRADE 4 EDITION. Variant title: Scholastic News. Edition 4. Text in English. 1957. 24/yr. (during school year). USD 3.95 (effective 2005); with 10 or more student subscr.. illus. Index. reprint service avail. from PQC. **Document type:** *Magazine, Academic/Scholarly.* **Description:** Invites fourth-grade students to explore noteworthy issues and news items, with questions that challenge them to think about and discuss what they have read.
Former titles (until 1998): Scholastic News (Explorer Edition) (0736-0592); (until 1982): Scholastic News Explorer (0028-9019)
Related titles: Microfilm ed.: (from PQC); Online - full text ed.: (from EBSCO Publishing).
Indexed: ICM.
Published by: Scholastic Inc., 557 Broadway, New York, NY 10012-0399. TEL 212-343-6100, FAX 212-343-4808, http://teacher.scholastic.com/scholasticnews/magazines/edition4/current/index.asp, http://www.scholastic.com. Ed. Jeff Rubin. **Subscr. to:** 2931 E McCarthy St, PO Box 3710, Jefferson City, MO 65102-9957. TEL 800-724-6527, classmags@scholastic.com.

371.33 001.3 USA ISSN 0036-6412
SCHOLASTIC SCOPE. Text in English. 1964. 18/yr. (during school year). USD 8.50 with 10 or more student subscr. (effective 2005). adv. film rev. illus. index. reprint service avail. from PQC. **Document type:** *Magazine, Consumer.* **Description:** Motivates experienced and reluctant readers by means of high-interest stories and articles covering topics in literature, drama, the arts, current events, and personal profiles. Each issue features a play and original and adapted poetry, literature, or short stories for middle-school students in grades 6-8.
Related titles: Microform ed.: (from PQC); Online - full text ed.: (from EBSCO Publishing, Northern Light Technology, Inc., ProQuest Information & Learning).
Indexed: ICM.
Published by: Scholastic Inc., 557 Broadway, New York, NY 10012-0399. TEL 212-343-6100, 800-724-6527, FAX 212-343-4808, scopemag@scholastic.com, http://www.scholastic.com. Ed. Cate Baily. Circ: 424,843. **Subscr. to:** 2931 E McCarthy St, PO Box 3710, Jefferson City, MO 65102-9957.

SCHOOL AGE NOTES; the newsletter for school-age care professionals. see *CHILDREN AND YOUTH—About*

707.1 USA ISSN 0036-6463
N81
SCHOOL ARTS; the art education magazine for teachers. Text in English. 1901. m. (Sep.-May). USD 23.95 domestic; USD 32.95 foreign (effective 2005). adv. bk.rev.; film rev. bibl.; illus.; stat.; tr.lit. index. back issues avail.; reprint service avail. from PQC. **Document type:** *Journal, Academic/Scholarly.*
Related titles: Microfiche ed.: (from NBI, PQC); Online - full text ed.: (from Florida Center for Library Automation, Gale Group).
Indexed: ABIn, ASIP, BRI, BusI, CBRI, CIJE, EduInd, JHMA, MRD, MagInd, PMR, T&II, TOM.
—BLDSC (8092.629000), IE, Infotrieve, ingenta.
Published by: Davis Publications, Inc. (Worcester), 50 Portland St, Printers Bldg, Worcester, MA 01608. TEL 508-754-7201, 800-533-2847, FAX 508-753-3834, contactus@davis-art.com, http://www.davis-art.com/schoolarts/index.asp. Ed. Eldon Katter. Pub. Wyatt Wade. Adv. contact Christina Carelli. page USD 1,660; 7 x 10. Circ: 24,284 (paid and controlled).

SCHOOL LIBRARY MEDIA ACTIVITIES MONTHLY. see *LIBRARY AND INFORMATION SCIENCES*

SCHOOL OF CELTIC STUDIES. NEWSLETTER/SCEALA SCOIL AN LEINN CHEILTIGH. see *LINGUISTICS*

370.15 GBR ISSN 0143-0343
LB1051
➤ **SCHOOL PSYCHOLOGY INTERNATIONAL.** Text in English. 1979. 5/yr. GBP 606, USD 1,061 to institutions; GBP 631, USD 1,105 combined subscription to institutions print & online eds. (effective 2006). adv. bk.rev. illus. back issues avail. **Document type:** *Journal, Academic/Scholarly.* **Description:** Highlights the concerns of those who provide quality mental health, educational, therapeutic and support services to schools and communities throughout the world.
Related titles: Online - full text ed.: ISSN 1461-7374. GBP 600, USD 1,050 to institutions (effective 2006) (from C S A, EBSCO Publishing, O C L C Online Computer Library Center, Inc., Sage Publications, Inc., Swets Information Services).
Indexed: ASCA, ASSIA, BrEdI, CDA, CIJE, CJA, CPE, ChPerI, CurCont, DIP, EAA, ERA, ETA, FamI, IBR, IBZ, L&LBA, MEA, PsycInfo, PsycholAb, RHEA, SEA, SENA, SFSA, SOMA, SOPODA, SSCI, SWA, TEA, V&AA, e-psyche.
—BLDSC (8092.926300), IDS, IE, Infotrieve, ingenta. **CCC.**
Published by: Sage Publications Ltd. (Subsidiary of: Sage Publications, Inc.), 1 Oliver's Yard, 55 City Rd, London, EC1 1SP, United Kingdom. TEL 44-20-73248500, FAX 44-20-73248600, info@sagepub.co.uk, http://www.sagepub.co.uk/journal.aspx?pid=105766. Eds. Caven S McLoughlin, Robert L Burden. Adv. contact Jenny Kirby. page GBP 195; trim 185 x 115. Circ: 700. **Subscr. in the Americas to:** Sage Publications, Inc., 2455 Teller Rd, Thousand Oaks, CA 91320. TEL 805-499-0721, FAX 805-499-0871, journals@sagepub.com.

371.33 USA ISSN 0036-6803
CODEN: SSMAAC
➤ **SCHOOL SCIENCE AND MATHEMATICS;** journal for all science and mathematics teachers. Text in English. 1901. 8/yr. USD 40 domestic to individuals; USD 47 foreign to individuals; USD 70 domestic to institutions; USD 90 foreign to institutions (effective 2003). adv. bk.rev. bibl.; charts; illus.; tr.lit.; abstr. index, cum.index: 1900-1960. back issues avail.; reprint service avail. from PQC. **Document type:** *Journal, Academic/Scholarly.* **Description:** Includes articles on assessment, curriculum, research, teacher education, learning theory, philosophy and history of science, non-traditional instruction, and science/technology/society.
Related titles: Microform ed.: (from PMC, PQC); Online - full text ed.: (from EBSCO Publishing, Florida Center for Library Automation, Gale Group, H.W. Wilson, O C L C Online Computer Library Center, Inc., ProQuest Information & Learning).
Indexed: ABIn, AcaI, CIJE, CIS, CPE, ChemAb, ERA, ETA, EduInd, ExcerpMed, MEA, RASB, RHEA, SEA, SENA, SOMA, TEA.
—BLDSC (8092.950000), IE, Infotrieve, ingenta, Linda Hall.
Published by: School Science and Mathematics Association, Weniger Hall 237, Oregon State University, Corvallis, OR 97331-6508. TEL 541-737-2545, FAX 541-737-1817, ssm.journal@orst.edu, pratt@bloomu.edu, http://osu.orst.edu/pubs/ssm. Eds. Lawrence B Flick, Norman Lederman. R&P, Adv. contact Carolyn Patacconi. Circ: 3,000 (paid). **Subscr. to:** Donald Pratt, Curriculum and Foundations, 400 E Second St, Bloomsburg, PA 17815. TEL 717-389-4915, FAX 717-389-3615.

➤ **SCHOOL SCIENCE REVIEW.** see *SCIENCES: COMPREHENSIVE WORKS*

418 USA
SCHOOL SMART KIDS NEWSLETTER. Text in English. 1996. irreg.
Media: Online - full content.
Published by: Center for New Discoveries in Learning http://www.howtolearn.com. Ed. Pat Wyman.

371.3 USA ISSN 1083-2939
L11
SCHOOL TALK. Text in English. 1995. q. USD 45 to individuals includes $40 membership fee; USD 55 to institutions (effective 2005). **Document type:** *Newsletter, Trade.* **Description:** Focuses on a theoretical or pedogological topic of interest to elementary-school teachers of English language arts.
Related titles: Online - full text ed.: (from bigchalk, EBSCO Publishing, ProQuest Information & Learning).
—**CCC.**
Published by: National Council of Teachers of English, 1111 W Kenyon Rd, Urbana, IL 61801-1096. TEL 217-328-3870, 800-369-6283, FAX 217-328—9645, cschanche@ncte.org, http://www.ncte.org/pubs/journals/st.

371.384 GBR
SCHOOL VISITS GUIDE. Text in English. 1985. a. **Description:** Reference guide for teachers planning school holidays or outings (field trips). Details transportation, accommodations, museums, farms and more.
Published by: British Trades Alphabet Publications, Abbott House, 1-2 Hanover St, London, W1R 9WB, United Kingdom. TEL 44-20-7495-7945, FAX 44-20-7495-7916. Ed. Jools Viner. Circ: 5,000.

▼ **SCHRIFTEN ZUR KUNSTPAEDAGOGIK UND AESTHETISCHEN ERZIEHUNG.** see *ART*

DAS SCHUELER HAUSAUFGABENHEFT. see *CHILDREN AND YOUTH—For*

371.3 DEU ISSN 0172-5408
DER SCHULGEOGRAPH. Text in German. 1968. s-a. membership. bk.rev. **Document type:** *Academic/Scholarly.*
Published by: Verband Deutscher Schulgeographen, Landesverband Hessen, Karl-Gloeckner-Str 21, Giessen, 35394, Germany. TEL 49-641-9936302, FAX 49-641-9936309, haversath@geo.uni-giessen.de. Ed. Johann Bernhard Haversath. Circ: 400.

375 DEU ISSN 0947-2746
➤ **SCHULMAGAZIN 5 BIS 10;** Impulse fuer kreativen Unterricht. Variant title: Schulmagazin Fuenf bis Zehn. Text in German. 1976. 11/yr. EUR 75; EUR 45.80 to students; EUR 9 newsstand/cover (effective 2003). adv. **Document type:** *Journal, Academic/Scholarly.*
Former titles (until 1995): 5 bis 10 Schulmagazin (0939-8376); (until 1991): Lehrerjournal Hauptschulmagazin (0930-6951); Which supersedes in part (in 1986): Lehrer Journal (0722-8600); Which was formed by the merger of: Grundschulmagazin (0724-3499); Which was formerly: Ehrenwirth Grundschulmagazin (0340-5842); Hauptschulmagazin (0724-3502); Which was formerly: Ehrenwirth Hauptschulmagazin (0340-580X)
Indexed: DIP, IBR, IBZ.
Published by: Oldenbourg Schulbuchverlag GmbH und Bayerischer Schulbuch Verlag GmbH (Subsidiary of: Oldenbourg Wissenschaftsverlag GmbH), Rosenheimer Str. 145, Munich, 81671, Germany. TEL 49-89-450510, FAX 49-89-45051200, info@oldenbourg-bsv.de, http://www.oldenbourg-bsv.de. Ed. Stefan Holler. Adv. contact Renate Kienzler TEL 49-7141-871670. page EUR 820.

➤ **SCIENCE ACTIVITIES;** classroom projects and curriculum ideas. see *SCIENCES: COMPREHENSIVE WORKS*

➤ **SCIENCE AND CHILDREN;** the journal for elementary school science teachers. see *SCIENCES: COMPREHENSIVE WORKS*

418 GBR
SCIENCE DIGEST. Text in English. 1996. s-w.
Media: Online - full content.
Published by: First and Best Education, Oundle, Peterborough, PE8 4HJ, United Kingdom. http://www.schools.co.uk.

SCIENCE EDUCATION. see *SCIENCES: COMPREHENSIVE WORKS*

SCIENCE EDUCATION INTERNATIONAL; the ICASE journal. see *SCIENCES: COMPREHENSIVE WORKS*

SCIENCE EDUCATION NEWSLETTER. see *SCIENCES: COMPREHENSIVE WORKS*

372.35 507.2 USA ISSN 1094-3277
➤ **SCIENCE EDUCATOR.** Text in English. 1992. s-a. free to members (effective 2005). adv. **Document type:** *Academic/Scholarly.* **Description:** Disseminates applied and clinical research in the teaching of science.
Related titles: Online - full text ed.: (from ProQuest Information & Learning).
Indexed: CIJE.
Published by: National Science Education Leadership Association, PO Box 99381, Raleigh, NC 27624-9381. TEL 919-848-8171, FAX 919-848-0496, pegholli@bellsouth.net, http://www.nsela.org/. Ed. Jack Rhoton. Adv. contact Patricia J McWethy.

➤ **SCIENCE NOTES AND NEWS.** see *SCIENCES: COMPREHENSIVE WORKS*

➤ **SCIENCE SCOPE;** a journal for middle-junior high science teachers. see *SCIENCES: COMPREHENSIVE WORKS*

372.35 507.1 USA ISSN 0036-8555
Q181
THE SCIENCE TEACHER. Text in English. 1934. 9/yr. USD 72 to members; USD 75 to institutions (effective 2005). adv. bk.rev.; film rev. charts; illus. index. reprint service avail. from PQC. **Document type:** *Magazine, Academic/Scholarly.* **Description:** Geared for science teachers of grades 7-12.
Related titles: Microfilm ed.: (from PQC); Online - full text ed.: (from EBSCO Publishing, Gale Group, H.W. Wilson, O C L C Online Computer Library Center, Inc., ProQuest Information & Learning).

E

Indexed: ABIn, AcaI, BRI, BiolDig, CIJE, CPE, EduInd, MRD, PhilInd.
—BLDSC (8164.750000), IE, Infotrieve, ingenta, Linda Hall. **CCC.**
Published by: National Science Teachers Association, 1840 Wilson Blvd, Arlington, VA 22201. TEL 703-243-7100, FAX 703-243-3924, thescienceteacher@nsta.org, membership@nsta.org, http://www.nsta.org/pubs/tst. Ed. Janet Gerking. R&P Liz Delaney. Adv. contact Paul Kuntzler. B&W page USD 2,295, color page USD 3,455. Circ: 27,000 (paid).

507.1 GBR ISSN 0961-6152
➤ **SCIENCE TEACHER EDUCATION.** Text in English. 1991. 3/yr. GBP 6 to members; GBP 9 to non-members (effective 2005). adv. 12 p./no. 3 cols./p.; **Document type:** *Journal, Academic/Scholarly.* **Description:** Aims to inform and contribute to the development of science teacher education in all phases of education.
—CCC.
Published by: Association for Science Education, College Ln, Hatfield, Herts AL10 9AA, United Kingdom. TEL 44-1707-283000, FAX 44-1707-266532, http://www.ase.org.uk/htm/journals/ste/index.php. Ed. Christine Harrison. R&P Jane Hanrott. Adv. contact Tracy Hague. Circ: 33,000.

➤ **SCIENCE WEEK.** see *SCIENCES: COMPREHENSIVE WORKS*

371.33 372.35 USA ISSN 1041-1410
SCIENCE WORLD. Text in English. 1959. 13/yr. (during school year). USD 9.25 (effective 2005); with 10 or more student subscr.. adv. bk.rev. charts; illus.; tr.lit. index. reprint service avail. from PQC. **Document type:** *Magazine, Consumer.* **Description:** Covers recent developments in science and technology, as well as science experiments and current events for middle-school students in grades 7-10.
Former titles (until 1987): Scholastic Science World (0162-8399); (until 1974): Science World (0036-8601); (until 1965): Senior Science and Science World
Related titles: Microform ed.: (from PQC); Online - full text ed.: (from bigchalk, EBSCO Publishing, Gale Group, Northern Light Technology, Inc., O C L C Online Computer Library Center, Inc., ProQuest Information & Learning); Special ed(s).: Science World (Teacher's Edition). USD 22.95 per academic year (effective 2001 - 2002).
Indexed: ICM, MASUSE, MagInd, RGYP, TOM, WBA, WMB.
—IE, Infotrieve.
Published by: Scholastic Inc., 557 Broadway, New York, NY 10012-0399. TEL 212-343-6100, FAX 212-343-6333, scienceworld@scholastic.com, http://www.scholastic.com. Pub. Hugh Roome. Adv. contact Brook Kindrad. Circ: 390,298. **Subscr. to:** 2931 E McCarthy St, PO Box 3710, Jefferson City, MO 65102-9957. TEL 800-724-6527, classmags@scholastic.com.

371.3 GBR
SCOTTISH OFFICE. EDUCATION DEPARTMENT. WORKING PAPER. Text in English. irreg., latest vol.7, 1991. **Document type:** *Monographic series, Government.*
Published by: Scottish Office, Education Department, New St Andrew's House, Rm 4-14, Edinburgh, Midlothian EH1 3TG, United Kingdom.

371.3 GBR ISSN 1361-6145
THE SECONDARY ASSEMBLY FILE. Text in English. 1996. 3/yr. GBP 59.50; GBP 64.50 in Europe; GBP 74.50 elsewhere. **Document type:** *Academic/Scholarly.* **Description:** Contains 60 themed, ready-to-use and original assemblies.
—CCC.
Published by: P f P, Grays Inn Rd, London, WC1X 8HG, United Kingdom. TEL 44-171-404-2776, FAX 44-171-404-2766. Ed. Larry Hartley. R&P Felicity Rich.

371.3 GBR ISSN 1460-5015
SECONDARY ENGLISH MAGAZINE. Text in English. 1997. 5/yr. GBP 56; GBP 29 to libraries (effective 2000).
Published by: English & Media Centre, 136 Chalton St, London, NW1 1RX, United Kingdom. TEL 44-20-73830488, FAX 44-20-73833688. **Dist. by:** Nate, 50 Broadfield Rd, Sheffield, S Yorks S8 0XJ, United Kingdom. TEL 44-1142-555419, FAX 44-1142-555296.

SECONDARY TEACHERS GUIDE TO FREE CURRICULUM MATERIALS. see *EDUCATION—Abstracting, Bibliographies, Statistics*

371.3 USA
SENDIT NEWSLETTER. Text in English. q. **Document type:** *Newsletter.* **Description:** Contains information about sendit server resources and their potential and current educational use.
Media: Online - full text.
Published by: North Dakota's Education Network helpdesk@sendit.nodak.edu, http://www.sendit.nodak.edu/sendit/newsletter/.

613.7 CHN ISSN 1006-2076
➤ **SHANDONG TIYU XUEYUAN XUEBAO/SHANDONG PHYSICAL EDUCATION INSTITUTE. JOURNAL.** Text in Chinese; Abstracts and contents page in English. 1985. q. **Document type:** *Journal, Academic/Scholarly.*
Related titles: Online - full text ed.: (from East View Information Services).
—BLDSC (4874.730050).
Published by: Shandong Tiyu Xueyuan/Shandong Physical Education Institute, 2 Wenhua Xi Rd, Jinan, Shandong 250063, China. Ed. Zhaobiao Fan.

➤ **SHIJIE HANYU JIAOXUE/CHINESE TEACHING IN THE WORLD.** see *LINGUISTICS*

510.71 CHN ISSN 0488-7387
SHUXUE JIAOXUE/MATHEMATICS TEACHING. Text in Chinese. 1956. bi-m. CNY 9 (effective 1994). adv. bk.rev. **Document type:** *Academic/Scholarly.*
Related titles: Online - full text ed.: (from East View Information Services).
Published by: (Shuxue Xi), Huadong Shifan Daxue/East China Normal University, 3663 Zhongshan Beilu, Shanghai, 200062, China. TEL 86-21-2577577, FAX 86-21-2578367, http://www.ecnu.edu.cn. Ed. Zhang Dianzhou. Circ: 30,000.

371.3 URY
SIRFO FLASH C I N T E R F O R. Text in Spanish. 1993. q. USD 30.
Published by: Centro Interamericano de Investigacion y Documentacion Sobre Formacion Profesional, Av. Uruguay, 1238, Casilla de Correos 1761, Montevideo, 11106, Uruguay. FAX 921305, dirmvd@cinterfor.org.uy.

SKYLARK (SASKATOON). see *LINGUISTICS*

SLAVIC AND EAST EUROPEAN JOURNAL. see *LINGUISTICS*

371.3346 USA ISSN 1541-2806
SLOAN-C VIEW; perspectives in quality online education. Text in English. 2002 (June). 6/yr.
Media: Online - full content.
Published by: Sloan Consortium, Olin College of Engineering and Babson College, 1735 Great Plain Ave., Needham, MA 02492. TEL 781-292-2524, FAX 781-292-2505, publisher@sloan-c.org, http://www.sloan-c.org/publications/view/v1n1/cover.htm. Eds. Janet C. Moore, John R. Bourne. Pub. Kathryn M. Fife.

SLOVENSKY JAZYK A LITERATURA V SKOLE. see *LINGUISTICS*

SMALL COLLEGE CREATIVITY. see *EDUCATION—Higher Education*

306.43 USA ISSN 0037-7724
H62.A1
SOCIAL EDUCATION; the official journal of the National Council for the Social Studies. Text in English. 1937. 7/yr. USD 55 to individual members; USD 75 to institutional members (effective 2005). adv. bk.rev. illus. index. reprint service avail. from PQC. **Document type:** *Magazine, Trade.* **Description:** Offers new ideas and content for social studies instruction across all grade levels.
Related titles: Microform ed.: (from PQC); Online - full text ed.: (from bigchalk, Florida Center for Library Automation, Gale Group, Northern Light Technology, Inc., O C L C Online Computer Library Center, Inc., ProQuest Information & Learning).
Indexed: ABIn, ABS&EES, AMHA, ASSIA, AcaI, AgeL, AmH&L, BAS, BRI, CBRI, CIJE, CPE, CurCont, ERA, ETA, EduInd, HRIR, HistAb, IndIslam, LRI, MEA, MEA&I, MRD, PCI, PhilInd, RASB, RILM, SSCI.
—BLDSC (8318.087000), IE, Infotrieve, ingenta.
Published by: National Council for the Social Studies, 8555 16th St, Ste 500, Silver Spring, MD 20910. TEL 301-588-1800, FAX 301-588-2049, socialed@ncss.org, ncss@ncss.org, http://www.ncss.org. Ed. Michael Simpson. R&P Kristen Page. Adv. contact Bill Doran TEL 302-644-0546. B&W page USD 1,800, color page USD 2,300. Circ: 29,000 (paid).

371.3 GBR ISSN 0309-7544
SOCIAL SCIENCE TEACHER. Text in English. 1971. 3/yr.
—BLDSC (8318.180600), IE, ingenta.
Published by: Association for the Teaching of the Social Sciences, P.O. Box 6079, Leicester, LE2 4DW, United Kingdom. TXL@le.ac.uk. Ed. Stephen Thomas.

371.3 USA ISSN 1056-0300
LB1584
SOCIAL STUDIES AND THE YOUNG LEARNER. Text in English. 1988. q. USD 55 to individual members; USD 75 to institutional members (effective 2005). adv. **Document type:** *Magazine, Trade.* **Description:** Offers K-6 social studies educators practical tips in all aspects of social studies instruction.
Indexed: ABIn, ABS&EES, CIJE, EduInd.
—BLDSC (8318.212300), IE, ingenta.
Published by: National Council for the Social Studies, 8555 16th St, Ste 500, Silver Spring, MD 20910. TEL 301-588-1800, FAX 301-588-2049, ncss@ncss.org, http://www.socialstudies.org/publications/ssyl, http://www.ncss.org. Ed. Kristen Page. Adv. contact Bill Doran TEL 302-644-0546.

370.115 USA ISSN 0886-9286
LB1584
➤ **SOCIAL STUDIES JOURNAL.** Text in English. 1952. a. adv. bk.rev. back issues avail. **Document type:** *Journal, Academic/Scholarly.* **Description:** Publishes reviews and research of interest to teachers of social studies.
Related titles: Microfilm ed.
Indexed: CIJE.
Published by: Pennsylvania Council for the Social Studies, PCSS, PO Box 208, Irwin, PA 15642. TEL 412-828-1800, kskubistek@kcsys.net, http://www.pcss.org. Ed., Adv. contact Leo West TEL 412-243-8186. Pub. Ken Kubistek. B&W page USD 120; trim 8.5 x 5.5. Circ: 1,000 (paid).

300.71 USA ISSN 0586-6235
THE SOCIAL STUDIES PROFESSIONAL. Text in English. 1969. 5/yr. free to members. bibl. reprint service avail. from PQC. **Document type:** *Newsletter.* **Description:** Covers news developments and issues of interest to social studies teachers. Includes calendar of conferences and programs for professional development.
Related titles: Microform ed.: (from PQC).
Indexed: CIJE.
Published by: National Council for the Social Studies, 8555 16th St, Ste 500, Silver Spring, MD 20910. TEL 301-588-1800, FAX 301-588-2049, ncss@ncss.org, http://www.ncss.org. Ed. E Wayne Ross. R&P Wayne Ross.

300 371.3 USA ISSN 1056-4675
➤ **THE SOCIAL STUDIES TEXAN.** Variant title: The Texan. Text in English. 1986. 3/yr. USD 40 domestic to members (effective 2004). adv. bk.rev.; software rev. bibl.; charts; illus. **Document type:** *Journal, Academic/Scholarly.* **Description:** Includes professional articles relating to social studies education, lesson plans, and examines activities that have been used in the classroom. Contains information about opportunities for professional growth, as well as the latest materials available for use in the classroom.
Indexed: CIJE.
Published by: Texas Council for the Social Studies, 4282 FM 730 N, Decatur, TX 76234. TEL 940-627-3837, FAX 940-627-6633, griley@wf.net, http://www.txcss.org. Ed., R&P Gail Riley. adv.: B&W page USD 200, color page USD 300; trim 9.75 x 7.5. Circ: 2,800 (paid).

371.3 BGR ISSN 0861-8291
SOFIISKI UNIVERSITET SV. KLIMENT OHRIDSKI. FAKULTET PO PEDAGOGIKA. GODISHNIK/UNIVERSITE DE SOFIA. FACULTE DE PHILOSOPHIE. ANNUAIRE. Text in Bulgarian; Summaries in Multiple languages. 1975. irreg. price varies. reprint service avail. from IRC.
Formerly (until 1987): Sofiiskii Universitet Sv. Kliment Ohridskii. Filosofskii Fakultet. Kniga Pedagogika (0204-6407); Supersedes in part (in 1982): Sofiiski Universitet. Filosofski Fakultet. Godisnik (1310-5248)
Indexed: RASB.
Published by: (Sofiiski Universitet Sv. Kliment Okhridski, Fakultet po Pedagogika), Universitetsko Izdatelstvo Sv. Kliment Okhridski/Publishing House of the Sofia University St. Kliment Ohridski, Akad G Bonchev 6, Sofia, 1113, Bulgaria. TEL 359-2-9792914. Circ: 555.

SOOCHOW JOURNAL OF JAPANESE LANGUAGE TEACHING/DONGWU RIYU JIAOYU XUEBAO. see *LINGUISTICS*

SOUTH AUSTRALIAN GEOGRAPHER. see *GEOGRAPHY*

SOUTH AUSTRALIA'S FUTURE MATHEMATICIANS. see *MATHEMATICS*

SOUTH DAKOTA MUSICIAN. see *MUSIC*

507.1 MYS ISSN 0126-8155
SOUTHEAST ASIAN MINISTERS OF EDUCATION ORGANISATION. REGIONAL CENTRE FOR EDUCATION IN SCIENCE AND MATHEMATICS. GOVERNING BOARD MEETING. FINAL REPORT. Text in English. a. free. reprint service avail. from PQC.
Published by: Southeast Asian Ministers of Education Organisation, Regional Centre for Education in Science and Mathematics, Glugor, Penang 11700, Malaysia. TEL 604-6583266, FAX 604-6572541. Circ: 150.

SOUTHEAST ASIAN MINISTERS OF EDUCATION ORGANISATION. REGIONAL CENTRE FOR EDUCATION IN SCIENCE AND MATHEMATICS. LIBRARY ACCESSION LIST. see *EDUCATION—Abstracting, Bibliographies, Statistics*

SOUTHERN SOCIAL STUDIES JOURNAL. see *SOCIAL SCIENCES: COMPREHENSIVE WORKS*

SOUTHWESTERN MUSICIAN. see *MUSIC*

SPEAKING ENGLISH; ideas and developments in oral education. see *LINGUISTICS*

SPECIAL EDUCATION LAW MONTHLY. see *EDUCATION—Special Education And Rehabilitation*

E

SPECIAL EDUCATION. TEACHER. see *RELIGIONS AND THEOLOGY—Protestant*

371.33 ZAF ISSN 0257-005X
SPECTRUM; natural science journal for teachers and lecturers. Text in English. 1963. q. bk.rev. illus. **Document type:** *Trade.* **Description:** Provides science teachers guidance in background reading, skills development, evaluation and assessment, curriculum interpretation, and laboratory practice.
Indexed: CIN, ChemAb, ChemTitl, ISAP.
Published by: (Foundation for Education, Science and Technology), South African Bureau for Scientific Publications, PO Box 11663, Pretoria, Hatfield 0028, South Africa. TEL 27-12-322-6404, FAX 27-12-320-7803, bspman@icon.co.za, http://www.safest.org.za/bsp. Circ: 2,500.

371.3 DEU ISSN 1430-6360
SPEKTRUM FREIZEIT. Text in German. 1979. a. **Document type:** *Academic/Scholarly.*
Formerly (until 1995): Freizeitpaedagogik (0721-1244)
Published by: Schneider Verlag Hohengehren GmbH, Wilhelmstr 13, Baltmannsweiler, 73666, Germany. FAX 49-7153-48761, schneider-verlag-hohengehren@t-online.de.

SPOKESMAN. see *TECHNOLOGY: COMPREHENSIVE WORKS*

SPORTGERICHT. see *SPORTS AND GAMES*

613.7 DEU ISSN 0171-4953
SPORTPAEDAGOGIK; zeitschrift fuer Sport- Spiel- und Bewegungserziehung. Text in German. 1977. 6/yr. EUR 66; EUR 10 newsstand/cover (effective 2005). adv. **Document type:** *Journal, Academic/Scholarly.*
Formerly (until Jan. 1979): Zeitschrift fuer Sportpaedagogik (0340-9058)
Indexed: DIP, IBR, IBZ.
Published by: Erhard Friedrich Verlag GmbH, Im Brande 17, Seelze, 30926, Germany. TEL 49-511-400040, FAX 49-511-40004170, info@friedrich-verlag.de, http://www.friedrich-verlag.de. Ed. Werner Roller. adv.: page EUR 1,370. Circ: 8,500 (paid and controlled).

SPORTPRAXIS; die Fachzeitschrift fuer Sportlehrer und Uebungsleiter. see *SPORTS AND GAMES*

SPORTS DOCUMENTATION MONTHLY BULLETIN. see *EDUCATION—Abstracting, Bibliographies, Statistics*

371.71 DEU ISSN 0342-2402
SPORTUNTERRICHT. Text in German. 1951. m. EUR 46.20 to individuals; EUR 40.20 to students; EUR 5 newsstand/cover (effective 2002). adv. bk.rev. illus. index. **Document type:** *Newsletter, Academic/Scholarly.*
Formerly: Leibeserziehung
Related titles: ♦ Supplement(s): Lehrhilfen fuer den Sportunterricht. ISSN 0342-2461.
Indexed: AbHyg, DIP, IBR, IBZ, NutrAb, RRTA, SportS.
—BLDSC (8419.860500), IE, Infotrieve, ingenta. **CCC.**
Published by: (Deutscher Sportlehrerverband e.V.), Verlag Karl Hofmann, Postfach 1360, Schorndorf, 73603, Germany. TEL 49-7181-402127, FAX 49-7181-402111, info@hofmann-verlag.de, http://www.hofmann-verlag.de. Ed. Ulrich Goehner. Circ: 9,800.

SPROGFORUM; tidsskrift for sprog- og kulturpaedagogik. see *LINGUISTICS*

SPROGLAEREREN. see *LINGUISTICS*

STADION; Internationale Zeitschrift fuer Geschichte des Sports. see *SPORTS AND GAMES*

STAGE OF THE ART. see *THEATER*

371.3 USA ISSN 1085-2549
➤ **STATEMENT (FORT COLLINS).** Text in English. 1970. 3/yr. USD 30 (effective 2002). bk.rev. bibl. **Document type:** *Journal, Academic/Scholarly.*
Published by: Colorado Language Arts Society, 2936 Bow Line Pl., Longmont, CO 80503. TEL 303-772-9630, FAX 303-682-7381, larson_jon@stvrain.k12.co.us, http://clem.mscd.edu/~clas. Ed. Jon Larson. Circ: 800 (paid).

371.33 USA
THE STORY BAG; a national storytelling newsletter. Text in English. 1981. bi-m. looseleaf. USD 20 (effective 2003). adv. bk.rev.; rec.rev. illus. cum.index: 1981-1991; 1992-1994. 8 p./no. 3 cols./p.; back issues avail. **Document type:** *Newsletter.* **Description:** Practical tips for any adult, teacher, or librarian about using storytelling for children or adults. Includes stories, reviews, and a listing of storytelling events.
Formerly (until 1995): Storytellers of San Diego Newsletter (0889-8812)
Related titles: E-mail ed.; Fax ed.
Published by: Harlynne Geisler, Ed. & Pub., 5361 Javier St, San Diego, CA 92117-3215. TEL 858-569-9399, FAX 858-569-0205, storybag@juno.com, http://www.swiftsite.com/storyteller. Ed., R&P, Adv. contact Harlynne Geisler. Circ: 300.

372.412 USA ISSN 1068-0292
STORYWORKS. Text in English. 1993. 6/yr. (during school year). USD 6.95 (effective 2005); with 10 or more student subscr.. bk.rev. illus. reprints avail. **Document type:** *Magazine, Consumer.* **Description:** Offers upper-elementary students, grades 3-6, high-quality original literature and skills activities to challenge their problem-solving abilities.
Related titles: Online - full text ed.: (from Florida Center for Library Automation, Gale Group, Northern Light Technology, Inc., ProQuest Information & Learning).
Indexed: BRI, MASUSE.
Published by: Scholastic Inc., 557 Broadway, New York, NY 10012-0399. TEL 212-343-6100, FAX 212-343-4808, http://teacher.scholastic.com/scholasticnews/magazines/storyworks/, http://www.scholastic.com. **Subscr. to:** 2931 E McCarthy St, PO Box 3710, Jefferson City, MO 65102-9957. TEL 800-724-6527, classmags@scholastic.com.

617.1 USA ISSN 0892-4562
GV223
➤ **STRATEGIES (RESTON)**; a journal for physical and sport educators. Text in English. 1987. bi-m. USD 35 domestic to individuals; USD 43 foreign to individuals; USD 100 domestic libraries & institutions; USD 108 foreign libraries & institutions (effective 2005). adv. charts; illus. index, cum.index: 1987-1997. back issues avail.; reprints avail. **Document type:** *Journal, Academic/Scholarly.* **Description:** Geared toward physical and sports educators, including teachers, coaches, administrators, and athletic directors. Emphasis is placed on applying research to daily practice and on the collaboration between practitioners in the field and university-based educators.
Related titles: Online - full text ed.: (from ProQuest Information & Learning).
Indexed: ABIn, CIJE, EduInd, PEI.
—BLDSC (8474.034210), IE, ingenta.
Published by: (National Association for Girls and Women in Sport), American Alliance for Health, Physical Education, Recreation, and Dance, 1900 Association Dr, Reston, VA 20191-1599. TEL 703-476-3400, 800-213-7193, FAX 703-476-9527, strategies@aahperd.org, info@aahperd.org, http://www.aahperd.org/naspe/template.cfm?template=strategies_main.html. Eds. Dora Schield, Judith C Young. Adv. contact Nancy Jones. page USD 700; trim 10 x 7.25. Circ: 7,500 (paid). **Co-sponsor:** National Association for Sport and Physical Education.

➤ **STREETWISE**; magazine of urban studies and environmental education. see *ENVIRONMENTAL STUDIES*

➤ **STUDENT UND PRAKTIKANT**; Forum fuer die Pharmazeutische Ausbildung. see *PHARMACY AND PHARMACOLOGY*

➤ **STUDIES IN AFRICAN LITERATURE SERIES.** see *LITERATURE*

➤ **STUDIES IN EDUCATION AND TEACHING TECHNIQUES.** see *EDUCATION*

371.3 GBR ISSN 0191-491X
LB1570
➤ **STUDIES IN EDUCATIONAL EVALUATION.** Text in English. 1974. 4/yr. EUR 606 in Europe to institutions; JPY 80,500 in Japan to institutions; USD 679 to institutions except Europe and Japan (effective 2006). adv. illus. reprints avail. **Document type:** *Journal, Academic/Scholarly.* **Description:** Reports on aspects of education evaluation, including curriculum evaluation, educational systems and organizations, teaching and learning strategies, and assessment of student performance.
Related titles: Microfilm ed.: (from PQC); Online - full text ed.: (from EBSCO Publishing, Gale Group, IngentaConnect, ScienceDirect, Swets Information Services).
Indexed: ABIn, BrEdI, CIJE, CPE, ERA, ETA, EduInd, HEA, MEA, RASB, RHEA, RILM, SEA, SENA, SOMA, TEA.
—BLDSC (8490.468000), IE, Infotrieve, ingenta, KNAW. **CCC.**
Published by: (University of California at Los Angeles USA, Universitaet Kiel DEU), Pergamon (Subsidiary of: Elsevier Science & Technology), The Boulevard, Langford Ln, East Park, Kidlington, Oxford OX5 1GB, United Kingdom. TEL 44-1865-843000, FAX 44-1865-843010, http://www.elsevier.com/locate/stueduc. Ed. David Nevo. **Subscr. to:** Elsevier BV, PO Box 211, Amsterdam 1000 AE, Netherlands. TEL 31-20-485-3757, FAX 31-20-485-3432, nlinfo-f@elsevier.nl, http://www.elsevier.nl. **Co-sponsor:** Tel Aviv University School of Education.

407.1 GBR
STUDIES IN LANGUAGE TESTING. Text in English. irreg., latest vol.4, 1996. **Document type:** *Monographic series, Academic/Scholarly.*
—BLDSC (8490.828070).
Published by: University of Cambridge, Press Syndicate, The Pitt Bldg, Trumpington St, Cambridge, Cambs CB2 1RP, United Kingdom. TEL 44-1223-315052.

407.1 GBR ISSN 1351-4091
STUDIES IN MODERN LANGUAGES EDUCATION. Text in English. irreg., latest vol.3, 1995. price varies. **Document type:** *Monographic series, Academic/Scholarly.*
Indexed: BrEdI.
—BLDSC (8491.124350).
Published by: University of Leeds, School of Education, Parkinson Court, Leeds, W Yorks LS2 9JT, United Kingdom. Eds. Colin Asher, Jeremy Higham.

507.1 GBR ISSN 0305-7267
Q181.A1
STUDIES IN SCIENCE EDUCATION. Text in English. 1974. s-a. GBP 27 domestic; GBP 33 foreign (effective 2005). **Document type:** *Journal, Academic/Scholarly.* **Description:** Intended for all who are interested in the educational dimensions of science.
Related titles: Online - full text ed.: (from ProQuest Information & Learning).
Indexed: BrEdI, CIJE, CPE.
—BLDSC (8491.560000), IE, Infotrieve, ingenta. **CCC.**
Published by: Studies in Education, Driffield Rd, Nafferton, Driffield, E Yorks YO25 4JJ, United Kingdom. TEL 44-1377-256861, 44-1377-254231, FAX 44-1377-256861, subs@studiesineducation.fsnet.co.uk, http://www.education.leeds.ac.uk/research/scienceed/. Ed. Dr. James F Donnelly TEL 44-113-3434608.

STUDIES IN THEATRE AND PERFORMANCE. see *THEATER*

780.71 AUS ISSN 1324-0633
THE STUDIO (OATLEY). Text in English. 1936. q. AUD 50 (effective 2000). adv. bk.rev. back issues avail. **Document type:** *Trade.*
Formerly: Music Teachers' Association of N.S.W. Quarterly Magazine (0727-8683)
Indexed: RASB.
Published by: Music Teachers' Association of N.S.W. Ltd., PO Box 244, Oatley, NSW 2223, Australia. TEL 61-2-95701436, musicnsw@talent.com.au. Ed., R&P Rita Crews. Circ: 1,000.

SUCCESS IN SOCCER; the teaching magazine for winning soccer. see *SPORTS AND GAMES—Ball Games*

SUHAG GYOYUG/MATHEMATICAL EDUCATION. see *MATHEMATICS*

371.3 USA
SUNSHINE CLASSROOM. Text in English. 1985. 5/yr. USD 11. adv. back issues avail. **Description:** Provides a forum for the exchange of ideas for teachers of pre-kindergarten to high school.
Published by: Sunshine Classroom, Inc., 1222 S Dale Mabry, Ste 637, Tampa, FL 33629. Ed. Shirley Jovanovic. Circ: 5,000.

371.33 500 USA
SUPERSCIENCE. Text in English. 1997. 8/yr. (during school year). USD 6.95 (effective 2005); with 10 or more student subscr.. illus. Index. reprints avail. **Document type:** *Magazine, Consumer.* **Description:** Contains science and technology news and describes science experiments. Geared towards readers in grades 3-6.
Formed by the merger of (1989-1997): SuperScience Blue (1040-144X); (1989-1997): SuperScience Red (1040-1431)
Related titles: Online - full text ed.
Indexed: ICM, MASUSE, RGYP.
Published by: Scholastic Inc., 557 Broadway, New York, NY 10012-0399. TEL 212-343-6100, FAX 212-343-4808, http://teacher.scholastic.com/scholasticnews/magazines/superscience/, http://www.scholastic.com. **Subscr. to:** 2931 E McCarthy St, PO Box 3710, Jefferson City, MO 65102-9957. TEL 800-724-6527, classmags@scholastic.com.

SVENSKLARARFORENINGENS ARSSKRIFT. see *LINGUISTICS*

375 USA
SYCAMORE TREE NEWSLETTER. Text in English. m. membership. **Description:** Provides Bible-centered alternative education programs and curricular materials for home and school teaching.
Published by: Sycamore Tree, 2179 Meyer Place, Costa Mesa, CA 92627. TEL 714-650-4466. Ed. Sandra Gogel.

375 CMR
SYLLABUS. Text in English, French. 1964. q. charts.
Supersedes: Revue Camerounaise de Pedagogie (0556-7262)
Indexed: LRI.
Published by: Universite de Yaounde, Ecole Normale Superieure, BP 47, Yaounde, Cameroon. TEL 23-12-15.

SYLLABUS (CHICAGO). see *LAW*

SYMBOLAE FACULTATIS LITTERARUM LOVANIENSIS. SERIES C. LINGUISTICA. see *LINGUISTICS*

371.3 USA ISSN 1042-6655
CODEN: TPPUDC
SYNTAX IN THE SCHOOLS. Text in English. 1984. q. USD 7.50 (effective 1998). bk.rev. **Document type:** *Newsletter.*
Published by: Assembly for the Teaching of English Grammar, One College Ave, Williamsport, PA 17701. TEL 717-326-3761. Ed. Edward Vavra. Circ: 450.

E

418 GBR ISSN 0346-251X
P51
➤ **SYSTEM.** Text in English. 1979. 4/yr. EUR 164 in Europe to individuals; JPY 21,800 in Japan to individuals; USD 184 to individuals except Europe and Japan; EUR 460 in Europe to institutions; JPY 61,000 in Japan to institutions; USD 514 to institutions except Europe and Japan (effective 2006). adv. bk.rev. illus. reprints avail. **Document type:** *Academic/Scholarly.* **Description:** Features articles on educational technology applications and systems developments for teaching foreign languages.
Related titles: Microfilm ed.: (from PQC); Online - full text ed.: (from EBSCO Publishing, Gale Group, IngentaConnect, ScienceDirect, Swets Information Services).
Indexed: ASCA, BrEdI, CIJE, CPE, DIP, ERA, ETA, IBR, IBZ, L&LBA, LT&LA, MEA, MLA-IB, PCI, RASB, RHEA, RILM, RefZh, SEA, SENA, SOMA, SOPODA, TEA.
—BLDSC (8589.095000), IE, Infotrieve, ingenta. **CCC.**
Published by: Pergamon (Subsidiary of: Elsevier Science & Technology), The Boulevard, Langford Ln, East Park, Kidlington, Oxford OX5 1GB, United Kingdom. TEL 44-1865-843000, FAX 44-1865-843010, http://www.elsevier.com/locate/system. Eds. K Sajavaara, Norman Davies. Circ: 1,000. **Subscr. to:** Elsevier BV, PO Box 211, Amsterdam 1000 AE, Netherlands. TEL 31-20-485-3757, FAX 31-20-485-3432, nlinfo-f@elsevier.nl, http://www.elsevier.nl.

371.3 DEU ISSN 1432-6272
➤ **SYSTEM SCHULE**; Zeitschrift fuer innovative Schulpraxis. Text in German. 1997. q. EUR 19.50; EUR 6 newsstand/cover (effective 2003). adv. bk.rev. 32 p./no. 3 cols./p.; back issues avail. **Document type:** *Journal, Academic/Scholarly.* **Description:** Provides information for teachers in all school types; systematic approach on everyday work in schools.
Related titles: E-mail ed.; Fax ed.
Indexed: IBR, IBZ.
Published by: Verlag Modernes Lernen Borgmann KG, Hohe Str. 39, Dortmund, 44139, Germany. TEL 49-180-5340130, FAX 49-180-5340120, info@verlag-modernes-lernen.de, http://www.verlag-modernes-lernen.de. Ed. Rolf Balgo. Pubs. Dieter Borgmann, Winfried Palmowski. adv.: page EUR 480; trim 171 x 252. Circ: 1,500.

420.7 CAN ISSN 0826-435X
CODEN: TCJOEA
T E S L CANADA JOURNAL/REVUE T E S L DU CANADA. Text in English, French. 1984. s-a. CND 30 to individuals; USD 50 to libraries; USD 150 to institutions; USD 15 to students (effective 2005).
Indexed: CEI, CIJE, L&LBA.
—BLDSC (8796.257000), IE, ingenta. **CCC.**
Published by: T E S L Canada, P O Box 44105, Burnaby, BC V5B 4Y2, Canada. admin@tesl.ca, http://www.tesl.ca/journal.html. Ed. Dr. Sandra Kouritzin.

428 USA ISSN 0886-0661
T E S L REPORTER. (Teaching English as a Second Language) Text in English. 1967. s-a. USD 10 (effective 2005). back issues avail.
Indexed: L&LBA, RILM.
—BLDSC (8796.258000), IE.
Published by: Brigham Young University, Hawaii Campus, Division of Language and Linguistics, 55-220 Kulanui St, Laie, HI 96762. TEL 808-293-2311, campbelm@byuh.edu, http://www.lib.byu.edu/spc/tesl/index.html, http://www.byuh.edu/.

428.007 CAN ISSN 0700-1584
PE1128.A2
T E S L TALK. (Teachers of English as a Second Language) Text in English. 1970. q. USD 33 to individuals; USD 49.50 to institutions (effective 2002).
Indexed: CEI, CIJE.
Published by: Ministry of Citizenship, Citizenship Development Branch, 77 Bloor St W, 5th fl, Toronto, ON M7A 2R9, Canada.

T E S O L IN CONTEXT; journal of A C T A. (Teachers of English to Speakers of Other Languages) see *EDUCATION—International Education Programs*

T E S O L PLACEMENT BULLETIN (ONLINE EDITION). see *LINGUISTICS*

T E S O L QUARTERLY; a journal for teachers of English to speakers of other languages and of standard English as a second dialect. see *LINGUISTICS*

T I E S (ONLINE EDITION); the magazine of design and technology education. (Technology, Innovation and Entrepreneurship for Students) see *TECHNOLOGY: COMPREHENSIVE WORKS*

371.3 TUR ISSN 1303-6521
LB1028.3
➤ **T O J E T**; a quarterly, peer reviewed international electronic journal. Text in English, Turkish. 2002. 4/yr. free (effective 2005).
Media: Online - full text.
Published by: (Sakarya University), The Turkish Online Journal of Educational Technology editor@tojet.net, tojet@sakarya.edu.tr, http://www.tojet.net.

➤ **T O W S.** (The Online Write Stuff) see *CHILDREN AND YOUTH—For*

➤ **T U - ZEITSCHRIFT FUER TECHNIK IM UNTERRICHT.** see *TECHNOLOGY: COMPREHENSIVE WORKS*

613.7 JPN ISSN 0039-8985
CODEN: TAKABO
TAIIKU NO KAGAKU/JOURNAL OF HEALTH, PHYSICAL EDUCATION AND RECREATION. Text in Japanese. 1951. m. JPY 4,800, USD 16.
Formerly: Journal of Health and Physical Education (0022-1457)
Published by: Japanese Society of Physical Education/Nihon Taiiku Gakkai, Kyorin Shoin, 4-2-1 Yushima, Bunkyo-ku, Tokyo, 113-0034, Japan. Ed. Shinshiro Ebashi. Circ: 4,000.

371.3 USA ISSN 1554-3226
▼ **TAKING SIDES: CLASHING VIEWS AND CONTROVERSIAL ISSUES IN CLASSROOM MANAGEMENT.** Text in English. 2005. biennial. USD 18.50 per vol. (effective 2005). **Document type:** *Monographic series.*
Published by: McGraw-Hill - Dushkin (Subsidiary of: McGraw-Hill Higher Education), 2460 Kerper Blvd, Dubuque, IA 52001. TEL 800-243-6532, customer.service@mcgraw-hill.com, http://www.dushkin.com.

418 GBR
TALKING POINT. Text in English. 1995. 3/yr. free. adv. bk.rev. **Document type:** *Newsletter.* **Description:** Newsletter for teachers and students of English as a foreign or second language.
—BLDSC (8601.404900).
Published by: Trinity College London, 16 Park Crescent, London, W1N 4AP, United Kingdom. TEL 44-171-323-2328, FAX 44-171-323-5201. Ed. Brian Cooper. Circ: 6,000 (controlled).

371.3 USA ISSN 1522-6115
LB1576
TALKING POINTS (URBANA). Text in English. 1989. s-a. USD 30 (effective 2004). **Document type:** *Journal, Trade.* **Description:** Offers teachers of English using the whole-language approach peer advice on effective classroom instruction.
Media: Online - full text.
—CCC.
Published by: Whole Language Umbrella (Subsidiary of: National Council of Teachers of English), 1111 W Kenyon Rd, Urbana, IL 61801-1096. TEL 217-369-6283, 800-369-6283, FAX 217-328-9645, membership@ncte.org, http://www.ncte.org/.

371.3 410 ESP ISSN 0214-9753
LA919.P34
TANTAK; Euskal Herriko Unibertsitateko Hezkuntza Aldizkaria. Text in Basque. 1989. s-a. EUR 15 (effective 2003). back issues avail. **Document type:** *Journal, Academic/Scholarly.* **Description:** Focuses on issues related to teachers, teacher training and education students, as well as specific linguistic and political issues in the Basque country.
Related titles: Online - full text ed.
Indexed: BibLing.
—CINDOC.
Published by: (Universidad del Pais Vasco, Departamento de Didactica y Educacion Escolar), Universidad del Pais Vasco, Servicio Editorial, Apartado 1397, Bilbao, 48080, Spain. TEL 34-94-6015126, FAX 34-94-4801314, luxedito@lg.ehu.es, http://www.ehu.es/servicios/se_az/pags/p36.htm. Ed. Mr. Carlos Santiago. R&P, Adv. contact Mr. Juan J Rodriguez.

TANZANIAN MATHEMATICAL BULLETIN. see *MATHEMATICS*

371.3 GHA
THE TEACHER. Text in English. 1931. q. free. adv. bk.rev. **Document type:** *Newsletter.* **Description:** Informs members and the general public about developments in the field of education, pedagogy, and curriculum, as well as news about the association.
Published by: Ghana National Association of Teachers, PO Box 209, Accra, Ghana. TEL 233-21-221515. Ed. Irene Adanusa. Circ: 20,000.

371.3 GBR ISSN 1366-4530
➤ **TEACHER DEVELOPMENT.** Text in English. 1997. 3/yr. GBP 256, USD 407 combined subscription to institutions print & online eds. (effective 2006). abstr.; illus. back issues avail.; reprint service avail. from PSC. **Document type:** *Journal, Academic/Scholarly.* **Description:** International journal that seeks to publish articles on all aspects of teachers' professional development, aiming to act as a medium for critical and reflective attention to practice in teacher development.
Related titles: Online - full text ed.: ISSN 1747-5120. GBP 243, USD 387 to institutions (effective 2006) (from EBSCO Publishing, Swets Information Services).
Indexed: BrEdI, CPE, DIP, EAA, ERA, ETA, IBR, IBZ, L&LBA, MEA, RHEA, SEA, SENA, SOMA, TEA.
—BLDSC (8613.353500), IE, ingenta.
Published by: Routledge (Subsidiary of: Taylor & Francis Group), 4 Park Sq, Milton Park, Abingdon, Oxon OX14 4RN, United Kingdom. TEL 44-1235-828600, FAX 44-1235-829000, journals@routledge.com, http://www.tandf.co.uk/journals/titles/13664530.asp, http://www.routledge.co.uk. Eds. Michelle Selinger, Sue Brindley.

371.3 USA ISSN 0890-6459
LB1707
➤ **TEACHER EDUCATION AND PRACTICE.** Text in English. 1984. q. USD 66 domestic to individuals; USD 110 foreign to individuals; USD 56 domestic to individual members; USD 132 domestic to institutions; USD 172 foreign to institutions (effective 2004). bk.rev. **Document type:** *Journal, Academic/Scholarly.* **Description:** Dedicated to the encouragement and dissemination of research and scholarship related to professional education preparation programs and to learning in the school setting. The journal serves as a forum for the exchange of diverse ideas and points of view.
Indexed: CIJE, FamI.
—BLDSC (8613.435000), IE, ingenta. **CCC.**
Published by: Scarecrow Education (Subsidiary of: Scarecrow Press, Inc.), 4501 Forbes Blvd, Ste 200, PO Box 191, Lanham, MD 20706. TEL 301-459-3366, 800-462-6420, FAX 800-338-4550, custserv@rowman.com, http://www.scarecroweducation.com/journals/JTEP/Index.shtml. Ed. Dr. Patrick M Jenlink. Pub. Dr. Thomas Koerner. R&P Ms. Kelly Rogers.

➤ **TEACHER EDUCATION AND SPECIAL EDUCATION.** see *EDUCATION—Special Education And Rehabilitation*

371.3 USA ISSN 0737-5328
LB1705
➤ **TEACHER EDUCATION QUARTERLY.** Text in English. 1972. 4/yr. USD 60 to individuals; USD 100 to institutions (effective 2005). adv. bk.rev. illus. back issues avail.; reprint service avail. from PQC. **Document type:** *Journal, Academic/Scholarly.* **Description:** Features articles on all aspects of teacher education, with a focus on research and practice and attention to major themes in the field.
Formerly (until 1983): California Journal of Teacher Education (0278-6052)
Related titles: Microform ed.: (from PQC); Online - full text ed.: (from Gale Group, H.W. Wilson, O C L C Online Computer Library Center, Inc., ProQuest Information & Learning).
Indexed: ABIn, CIJE, CPE, DIP, ERA, ETA, EduInd, IBR, IBZ, MEA, RHEA, SEA, SENA, SOMA, TEA.
—BLDSC (8613.465000), IE, ingenta.
Published by: (California Council on the Education of Teachers), Caddo Gap Press, 3145 Geary Blvd,, PMB 275, San Francisco, CA 94118. TEL 415-666-3012, FAX 415-666-3552, info@caddogap.com, http://www.teqjournal.org/, http://www.caddogap.com. Ed. Thomas G Nelson. Pub., R&P Alan H Jones. Circ: 1,000 (paid).

371.3 USA ISSN 1046-6193
TEACHER MAGAZINE. Text in English. 1989. bi-m. USD 17.94 domestic; USD 23.19 in Canada; USD 28.34 elsewhere (effective 2004). adv. bk.rev. illus. reprints avail. **Document type:** *Trade.* **Description:** Provides a national communications network for teachers, enabling them to be better teachers and effective leaders.
Related titles: Microfiche ed.; Online - full text ed.: (from EBSCO Publishing, ProQuest Information & Learning).
Indexed: ABIn, CIJE, ChPerI, EduInd.
—BLDSC (8613.510000), IE, ingenta. **CCC.**
Published by: Editorial Projects in Education Inc., 6935 Arlington Rd, Ste 100, Bethesda, MD 20814-5233. TEL 301-280-3100, 800-346-1834, FAX 301-280-3200, http://www.teachermagazine.org, http://www.edweek.org. Ed., Pub. Ms. Virginia B Edwards. R&Ps Claire Guimbert, Kay Dorko. Adv. contact Cheryl Staab. Circ: 100,000. **Subscr. to:** Kable Fulfillment Services, Trade Fulfillment Services, Kable Sq, Mount Morris, IL 61054-1473. TEL 740-382-3322, 800-728-2753, FAX 740-389-6720, tach@kable.com, http://www.kable.com/.

371.33 IRL
TEACHER MAGAZINE. Text in English. m. adv. **Document type:** *Magazine, Trade.*
Published by: Impact Press, 47 Harrington St., Dublin, 8, Ireland. TEL 353-1-4760031, FAX 353-1-4760033, sales@impact-press.ie. adv.: B&W page EUR 2,000, color page EUR 3,000. Circ: 14,000 (controlled).

371.39 USA
TEACHER TO TEACHER SERIES. Text in English. 1996. irreg., latest vol.8, 1998. price varies. back issues avail. **Document type:** *Monographic series, Trade.* **Description:** Experienced teachers share tips for optimal instruction in the classroom.
Published by: Heinemann, Inc. (Subsidiary of: Greenwood Publishing Group Inc.), 361 Hanover St, Portsmouth, NH 03801-3912. TEL 603-431-7894, 800-541-2086, FAX 603-431-7840, info@heinemann.com, http://www.heinemann.com.

371.3 GBR ISSN 0951-7626
P51
THE TEACHER TRAINER; a practical journal mainly for modern language teacher trainers. Text in English. 1986. 3/yr. GBP 25 (effective 2001). adv. bk.rev. back issues avail. **Document type:** *Academic/Scholarly.*
Related titles: Online - full text ed.
Indexed: CPE, L&LBA, LT&LA, SOPODA.
—BLDSC (8613.560000), IE, ingenta.

E

Published by: Pilgrims Language Courses, Pilgrims House, Orchard St, Canterbury, Kent CT2 8BF, United Kingdom. TEL 44-1227-762111, FAX 44-1227-459027, postmaster@pilgrims.co.uk, http://www.pilgrims.co.uk/campus/trainer. Ed., R&P Tessa Woodward. adv.: page GBP 283.

371.3 USA ISSN 0194-2859
TEACHER UPDATE; ideas for teachers. Text in English. 1977-1989; resumed 1990. q. USD 25. adv. bk.rev. **Document type:** *Newsletter.* **Description:** Contains suggestions for art projects, unit ideas, math and science games, and other projects of interest to teachers of younger children.
Published by: N A R Publications, PO Box 233, Barryville, NY 12719. TEL 914-557-8713, FAX 914-557-6770. Ed. Donna Papalia. Adv. contact Ed Guild. Circ: 7,500.

371.3 GBR
TEACHER UPDATE. Text in English. 1996. m. free to primary school teachers. adv. **Document type:** *Trade.* **Description:** Serves as a resource magazine for primary school teachers.
Published by: British Trades Alphabet Publications, Abbott House, 1-2 Hanover St, London, W1R 9WB, United Kingdom. TEL 44-20-7495-7945, FAX 44-20-7495-7916, rapport@enterprise.net. Ed. Mr. Dan Barley. Pub. A Dunn. Adv. contact Giles Witcomb. Circ: 10,000.

371.3 GBR ISSN 1354-0602
LB2840 CODEN: TTTPFD
➤ **TEACHERS AND TEACHING**; theory and practice. Text in English. 1995. bi-m. GBP 527, USD 871 combined subscription to institutions print & online eds. (effective 2006). bk.rev. reprint service avail. from PSC. **Document type:** *Journal, Academic/Scholarly.* **Description:** Publishes qualitative and quantitative research on teaching from around the world, focusing on the social, political, and historical contexts of teaching as work.
Related titles: Online - full text ed.: ISSN 1470-1278. GBP 501, USD 827 to institutions (effective 2006) (from EBSCO Publishing, Gale Group, IngentaConnect, O C L C Online Computer Library Center, Inc., Swets Information Services).
Indexed: BrEdI, CPE, EAA, ERA, ETA, MEA, PsycInfo, PsycholAb, RHEA, SEA, SENA, SOMA, SOPODA, TEA.
—BLDSC (8613.634000), IE, Infotrieve, ingenta.
Published by: (International Study Association on Teacher Thinking), Routledge (Subsidiary of: Taylor & Francis Group), 4 Park Sq, Milton Park, Abingdon, Oxon OX14 4RN, United Kingdom. TEL 44-1235-828600, FAX 44-1235-829000, journals@routledge.com, http://www.tandf.co.uk/journals/titles/13540602.asp, http://www.routledge.co.uk. Ed. Christopher Day. **Subscr. to:** Taylor & Francis Ltd, Journals Customer Service, Rankine Rd, Basingstoke, Hants RG24 8PR, United Kingdom. TEL 44-1256-813000, FAX 44-1256-330245.

372.62 USA ISSN 0739-0084
LB1576
TEACHERS & WRITERS. Text in English. 1967. 5/yr. USD 35 domestic membership (effective 2005). bk.rev. cum.index: 1967-1992. reprint service avail. from PQC. **Document type:** *Magazine, Consumer.* **Description:** Provides ideas and strategies for the teaching of writing. Includes practical classroom activities, new resources and articles that emphasize a how-to approach usable in the classroom, from first grade through college level.
Former titles (until 1981): Teachers and Writers Magazine (0146-3381); (until 1976): Teachers and Writers Collaborative Newsletter (0496-9936)
Related titles: Microform ed.: (from PQC).
Indexed: CIJE.
—**CCC.**
Published by: Teachers & Writers Collaborative, 5 Union Sq W, New York, NY 10003-3306. TEL 212-691-6590, FAX 212-675-0171, info@twc.org, http://www.twc.org. Eds. Chris Edgar, Christina Davis. R&P Chris Edgar. Circ: 2,200.

371.33 USA ISSN 1533-0362
LB3525
THE TEACHER'S CALENDAR; the day-by-day directory to holidays, historic events, birthdays and special days, weeks and months. Text in English.
Published by: McGraw-Hill Companies, Inc., 1221 Ave of the Americas, New York, NY 10020. TEL 212-512-4634, FAX 212-512-6458, http://www.mcgraw-hill.com.

TEACHERS' CHOICES. see *CHILDREN AND YOUTH—Abstracting, Bibliographies, Statistics*

371.33 USA
TEACHER'S DISCOVERY - ENGLISH EDITION. Text in English. 1969. s-a. **Document type:** *Trade.*
Published by: American Eagle, 2676 Paldan Dr, Auburn Hills, MI 48326-1824. TEL 248-340-7220, FAX 248-276-1652. Ed. Laurie Freeman. Circ: 2,000,000.

371.33 USA
TEACHER'S DISCOVERY - FOREIGN LANGUAGE EDITION. Text in English. 1969. s-a. **Document type:** *Trade.*
Published by: American Eagle, 2676 Paldan Dr, Auburn Hills, MI 48326-1824. TEL 248-340-7220, FAX 248-276-1652. Ed. Laurie Freeman. Circ: 2,000,000.

371.33 USA
TEACHER'S DISCOVERY - SCIENCE EDITION. Text in English. 1969. s-a. **Document type:** *Trade.*
Published by: American Eagle, 2676 Paldan Dr, Auburn Hills, MI 48326-1824. TEL 248-340-7220, FAX 248-276-1652. Ed. Laurie Freeman. Circ: 2,000,000.

371.33 USA
TEACHER'S DISCOVERY - SOCIAL STUDIES EDITION. Text in English. 1969. s-a. **Document type:** *Trade.*
Published by: American Eagle, 2676 Paldan Dr, Auburn Hills, MI 48326-1824. TEL 248-340-7220, FAX 248-276-1652. Ed. Laurie Freeman. Circ: 2,000,000.

371.33 USA ISSN 1078-6570
TEACHER'S HELPER (KINDERGARTEN EDITION); reproducibles for your classroom. Text in English. q. USD 24.95 (effective 2005). adv. **Document type:** *Academic/Scholarly.* **Description:** Offers elementary-school teachers worksheets they can reproduce for their students.
Formerly: Worksheet Magazine
Related titles: Special ed(s).: Teacher's Helper (Grade 1 Edition); Teacher's Helper (Grades 2-3 Edition); Teacher's Helper (Grades 4-5 Edition).
Published by: Education Center, Inc., 3515 W Market St, Ste 200, PO Box 9753, Greensboro, NC 27403. TEL 336-854-0309, 800-334-0298, FAX 336-547-1587. Ed. Margaret Michel. Adv. contact Kate Brower. **Subscr. to:** PO Box 51111, Boulder, CO 80323-1111.

418 USA
TEACHER'S INTERNET PAGES. Text in English. 1996. bi-m.
Media: Online - full content.
Address: http://www.iteachnet.com/Newsb.html.

372 USA ISSN 0887-9486
LB1025.3
➤ **TEACHING AND LEARNING**; journal of natural inquiry and reflective practice. Text in English. 1915. 3/yr., latest vol.14. USD 12 domestic; USD 22 foreign (effective 2004). bk.rev. abstr.; bibl. back issues avail. **Document type:** *Journal, Academic/Scholarly.* **Description:** Presents research on elementary education.
Former titles (until vol.10, no.16 1986): Journal of Teaching and Learning (0360-5027); (until 1975): University of North Dakota. College of Education. Record (0010-1052)
Related titles: Online - full content ed.; Online - full text ed.: (from EBSCO Publishing); Cumulative ed(s).
Indexed: CIJE, HEA, PsycholAb.
—BLDSC (8614.003400), IE, ingenta.
Published by: University of North Dakota, College of Education & Human Development, PO Box 7189, Grand Forks, ND 58202-7189. TEL 701-777-3574, FAX 701-777-4365, editor.tandl@und.nodak.edu, http://www.und.nodak.edu/dept/ehd/journal/, http://www.und.edu/dept/ehd. Ed. Jeanette Bopry. Circ: 200.

428 GBR ISSN 1479-7976
TEACHING AND LEARNING; transforming education. Text in English. 6/yr. GBP 45 domestic; GBP 60 elsewhere (effective 2004). adv. **Document type:** *Bulletin, Academic/Scholarly.* **Description:** Supports teaching professionals involved in the delivery of the math, science and english curriculum to the classroom.
Former titles (until 2003): Literacy & Learning (1460-8138); (until 1997): Language and Learning (0958-3068)
Related titles: Online - full text ed.: (from Swets Information Services).
Indexed: CPE, ChLitAb.
—BLDSC (8614.003460), IE, ingenta.
Published by: Questions Publishing Company Ltd., 1st Fl, Leonard House, 321 Bradford St, Digbeth, Birmingham, Warks B1 3ET, United Kingdom. TEL 44-121-6667878, FAX 44-121-6667879, rchima@qiis.co.uk, http://www.questpub.co.uk, http://www.education-quest.com/. Ed. Juliet Smith. Pub. Howard Sharron. Adv. contacts Jason Rotton, Kam Badesha.

371.3 GBR ISSN 0742-051X
LB1025.2
➤ **TEACHING AND TEACHER EDUCATION.** Text in English. 1985. 8/yr. EUR 889 in Europe to institutions; JPY 118,100 in Japan to institutions; USD 995 to institutions except Europe and Japan; EUR 274 in Europe to qualified personnel; JPY 36,200 in Japan to qualified personnel; USD 305 to qualified personnel except Europe and Japan (effective 2006). abstr.; bibl.; illus. Index. back issues avail.; reprints avail. **Document type:** *Academic/Scholarly.* **Description:** Devoted to the description and analysis of the cognitive, affective and behavioral components of teaching, teacher effectiveness, teacher education, teacher thinking, and social policies affecting teachers.
Related titles: Microfilm ed.: (from PQC); Online - full text ed.: (from EBSCO Publishing, Gale Group, IngentaConnect, ScienceDirect, Swets Information Services).
Indexed: ABIn, ASCA, BrEdI, CIJE, CPE, CurCont, DIP, ERA, ETA, EduInd, IBR, IBZ, MEA, PCI, PsycInfo, PsycholAb, RASB, RHEA, SEA, SENA, SOMA, SSCI, TEA, e-psyche.
—BLDSC (8614.014000), IDS, IE, Infotrieve, ingenta. **CCC.**
Published by: Pergamon (Subsidiary of: Elsevier Science & Technology), The Boulevard, Langford Ln, East Park, Kidlington, Oxford OX5 1GB, United Kingdom. TEL 44-1865-843000, FAX 44-1865-843010, http://www.elsevier.com/locate/tate. Eds. G Morine, Michael J Dunkin, N L Gage. **Subscr. to:** Elsevier BV, PO Box 211, Amsterdam 1000 AE, Netherlands. TEL 31-20-485-3757, FAX 31-20-485-3432, nlinfo-f@elsevier.nl, http://www.elsevier.nl.

510.71 USA ISSN 1073-5836
QA135
➤ **TEACHING CHILDREN MATHEMATICS.** Text in English. 1954; N.S. 1994. m. (Sep.-May). free membership. adv. bk.rev. bibl.; illus. index, cum.index: 1954-1973; 1974-1983. back issues avail.; reprints avail. **Document type:** *Magazine, Academic/Scholarly.* **Description:** Contains articles, teaching ideas, and features of interest to teachers of mathematics in pre-kindergarten through grade 6.
Formerly (until May 1994): Arithmetic Teacher (0004-136X)
Related titles: Microform ed.: N.S. (from PQC); Online - full text ed.: N.S. (from Florida Center for Library Automation, Gale Group, H.W. Wilson, Northern Light Technology, Inc., O C L C Online Computer Library Center, Inc., ProQuest Information & Learning).
Indexed: ABIn, AcaI, BRI, CIJE, CPE, ECER, EduInd, JHMA, LAMP, MRD.
—BLDSC (8614.055500), IE, Infotrieve, ingenta.
Published by: National Council of Teachers of Mathematics, 1906 Association Dr, Reston, VA 20191-1502. TEL 703-620-9840, 800-235-7566, FAX 703-476-2970, stkillmeyer@nctm.org, nctm@nctm.org, http://www.nctm.org, http://nctm.org. Ed. Andy Reeves. Pub. Harry B Tunis. R&P Jean T Carpenter. Adv. contact Thomas Pearson. Circ: 45,000 (paid).

➤ **TEACHING EARTH SCIENCES.** see *EARTH SCIENCES—Geology*

➤ **TEACHING ELEMENTARY PHYSICAL EDUCATION.** see *SPORTS AND GAMES*

➤ **TEACHING ENGLISH FOR SPECIFIC PURPOSES JOURNAL.** see *LINGUISTICS*

371.3 USA ISSN 1084-0427
TEACHING FOR SUCCESS. Text in English. 1989. m. USD 399 (effective 2003). **Document type:** *Newsletter, Academic/Scholarly.* **Description:** Contains tip and ideas for the education faculty, including strategies based on the five Critica Success Factors of good teaching.
Formerly (until 1989): Adjunct Mentor (1043-0857)
Related titles: Online - full content ed.; Online - full text ed.: (from EBSCO Publishing).
Published by: Pentronics Publishing, PO Box 8379, South Lake Tahoe, CA 96158. TEL 530-573-8964, 800-757-1183, FAX 530-573-8965, http://www.teachingforsuccess.com/. Pub. Jack H Shrawder.

907.1 AUS ISSN 0040-0602
TEACHING HISTORY. Text in English. 1960; N.S. 1967. 4/yr. AUD 55 to individual members; AUD 95 to institutions (effective 2003). adv. bk.rev. bibl. index. reprint service avail. from PQC. **Document type:** *Academic/Scholarly.*
Related titles: Microform ed.: N.S. (from PQC); Online - full text ed.: (from Northern Light Technology, Inc.).
Indexed: AEI.
Published by: History Teachers' Association of New South Wales, PO Box W122, Wareemba, NSW 2046, Australia. TEL 61-2-97139376, FAX 61-2-97138259, htansw@tpg.com.au, http://www.htansw.asn.au/. Eds. Denis Mootz, Paul Kiem. Circ: 1,300.

907.1 GBR ISSN 0040-0610
D16.4.G7
➤ **TEACHING HISTORY.** Text in English. 1969. q. USD 42 to individual members; GBP 60 to institutional members; GBP 90 to non-members (effective 2005). bk.rev. bibl.; illus. reprint service avail. from PQC. **Document type:** *Journal, Academic/Scholarly.*
Related titles: Microform ed.: (from PQC); Online - full text ed.: (from EBSCO Publishing, Northern Light Technology, Inc., O C L C Online Computer Library Center, Inc., ProQuest Information & Learning).
Indexed: AmH&L, BrEdI, CPE, ChLitAb, DIP, ERA, ETA, HistAb, IBR, IBZ, MEA, PCI, RHEA, SEA, SENA, SOMA, TEA.
—BLDSC (8614.210000), IE, Infotrieve, ingenta. **CCC.**
Published by: Historical Association, 59a Kennington Park Rd, London, SE11 4JH, United Kingdom. TEL 44-20-77353901, FAX 44-20-75824989, enquiry@history.org.uk, http://194.93.140.245/publications/teachinghistory.htm, http://194.93.140.245/home.htm. Ed. Christine Counsell. Circ: 2,500.

907.1 USA ISSN 0730-1383
➤ **TEACHING HISTORY: A JOURNAL OF METHODS.** Text in English. 1976. s-a. USD 12 (effective 2005). adv. bk.rev.; film rev.; software rev.; video rev. reprints avail. **Document type:** *Journal, Academic/Scholarly.*
Related titles: Online - full text ed.: (from Florida Center for Library Automation, Gale Group).
Indexed: AmH&L, CIJE, DIP, HistAb, IBR, IBZ.

E

Published by: Emporia State University, Division of Social Sciences, PO Box 4032, Emporia, KS 66801. TEL 316-341-5579, FAX 316-341-5143, dickssam@esumail.emporia.edu. Ed. Stephen Kneeshaw. Circ: 750.

371.3 USA CODEN: TRCTER
TEACHING K-8; the professional magazine for teachers. Text in English. 1971. m. (8/yr.). USD 23.97 domestic; USD 33.97 foreign (effective 2005). adv. bk.rev. illus. reprint service avail. from PQC. **Document type:** *Magazine, Trade.* **Description:** Contains articles that emphasize classroom-tested methods and ideas specifically for professional teachers in kindergarten through eighth grade.
Former titles: Teaching Pre K-8 (0891-4508); Early Years - K-8; (until 1987): Early Years (0094-6532)
Related titles: CD-ROM ed.; Microfilm ed.: (from PQC); Online - full text ed.: (from bigchalk, EBSCO Publishing, H.W. Wilson, Northern Light Technology, Inc., O C L C Online Computer Library Center, Inc., ProQuest Information & Learning).
Indexed: ABIn, BRI, CIJE, ECER, EduInd, ICM, RGYP, RehabLit.
—BLDSC (8614.322000), IE, ingenta.
Published by: Early Years, Inc. (Subsidiary of: Highlights for Children, Inc.), 40 Richards Ave, Norwalk, CT 06854-2309. TEL 203-855-2650, 800-249-9363, FAX 203-855-2656, TeachingK8@aol.com, http://www.teachingk-8.com. Ed. Patricia Broderick. Pub. Allen Raymond. Adv. contact Carol Mata. B&W page USD 5,780, color page USD 7,230; trim 7.88 x 10.5. Circ: 101,000.

371.33 CAN ISSN 1188-679X
Z675.S3
THE TEACHING LIBRARIAN. Text in English. 1974. 3/yr. CND 36 (effective 1999). adv. bk.rev. illus. index. **Document type:** *Trade.* **Description:** Presents articles and reviews of new materials for teachers and librarians with emphasis on applications to learning, teaching styles and curriculum.
Formerly: Reviewing Librarian (0318-0948)
Indexed: CPerI.
Published by: (Ontario School Library Association), Ontario Library Association, 100 Lombard St, Ste 303, Toronto, ON M5C 1M3, Canada. TEL 416-363-3388, FAX 416-941-9581. Ed. Sandra Hughes. Pub. Jefferson Gilbert. Adv. contact Ken Parry. Circ: 1,300.

TEACHING MATHEMATICS AND ITS APPLICATIONS; an international journal of I M A. see *MATHEMATICS*

371.3 USA
TEACHING OF ENGLISH. Text in English. q. membership. bibl. back issues avail. **Document type:** *Trade.* **Description:** Examines a variety of teaching methodologies for instructors of English, along with related issues reflecting content, context, process, and language learning.
Published by: National Council of Teachers of English, 1111 W Kenyon Rd, Urbana, IL 61801-1096. TEL 217-328-3870, 800-369-6283, FAX 217-328—9645, membership@ncte.org, http://www.ncte.org.

TEACHING OF PSYCHOLOGY. see *PSYCHOLOGY*

TEACHING PHILOSOPHY. see *PHILOSOPHY*

TEACHING SOCIOLOGY. see *SOCIOLOGY*

TEACHING THEOLOGY AND RELIGION. see *RELIGIONS AND THEOLOGY*

371.3 GBR ISSN 1470-6105
TEACHING THINKING MAGAZINE. Text in English. 3/yr. GBP 28 to individuals; GBP 48 to institutions (effective 2004). **Description:** Dedicated to promoting critical and creative thinking at both primary and secondary level.
Related titles: Online - full text ed.: (from EBSCO Publishing, Swets Information Services).
Published by: Questions Publishing Company Ltd., 1st Fl, Leonard House, 321 Bradford St, Digbeth, Birmingham, Warks B1 3ET, United Kingdom. TEL 44-121-6667878, FAX 44-121-6667879, http://www.teachthinking.com/, http://www.education-quest.com/.

371.3 USA ISSN 1066-2847
BF575.P9
TEACHING TOLERANCE. Text in English. 1991. s-a. free (effective 2004). bk.rev. **Document type:** *Magazine, Trade.* **Description:** Provides teachers with ideas and resources to promote respect for diverse cultures, races, and religions among children. Profiles individuals who have made a difference in fostering social justice.
Indexed: ABIn, CIJE, EduInd, MRD, SRRA.
—CCC.
Published by: Southern Poverty Law Center, 400 Washington Ave., Montgomery, AL 36104. TEL 334-264-0286, FAX 334-264-3121, http://www.splcenter.org/center/tt/teach.jsp. Eds. Elsie Williams, Jim Carnes. Pub. Elsie Williams. Circ: 600,000 (controlled).

371.33 USA ISSN 1062-9351
T61
➤ **TECH DIRECTIONS**; the magazine linking education to careers. Text in English. 1941. m. (Aug.-May), latest vol.62. USD 30 domestic; USD 40 foreign (effective 2005). adv. bk.rev.; software rev.; video rev.; Website rev. charts; illus.; tr.lit. Index. 50 p./no.; back issues avail.; reprint service avail. from PQC. **Document type:** *Magazine, Trade.* **Description:** Includes articles by teachers, teacher educators and professionals in vocational technology and career technical education covering classroom projects, programs, issues, and government activities, new products and resources.
Former titles (until May 1992): School Shop - Tech Directions (1050-3749); (until May 1990): New School Shop - Tech Directions (1049-8818); (until May 1989): School Shop (0036-682X)
Related titles: CD-ROM ed.; Microform ed.: (from PQC); Online - full text ed.: (from bigchalk, EBSCO Publishing, H.W. Wilson, Northern Light Technology, Inc., O C L C Online Computer Library Center, Inc., ProQuest Information & Learning).
Indexed: ABIn, CIJE, EduInd, MRD.
—BLDSC (8614.690000), IE, ingenta, Linda Hall.
Published by: Prakken Publications, Inc., 832 Phoenix Dr, Ann Arbor, MI 48108-2221. susanne@techdirections.com, http://www.techdirections.com/. Pub. George F. Kennedy. R&P Susanne Packham. Adv. contact Alice B. Augustus. B&W page USD 3,976, color page USD 5,026; 8 x 10.875. Circ: 41,989 (paid and controlled).

371.33 USA ISSN 1057-2252
T11 CODEN: TCQEAB
➤ **TECHNICAL COMMUNICATION QUARTERLY.** Text in English. 1973. q. USD 210 in US & Canada to institutions; USD 240 elsewhere to institutions; USD 220 combined subscription in US & Canada to institutions print & online eds.; USD 250 combined subscription elsewhere to institutions print & online eds. (effective 2006). adv. bk.rev.; software rev. bibl.; illus. 120 p./no.; back issues avail.; reprint service avail. from PSC. **Document type:** *Journal, Academic/Scholarly.* **Description:** Includes articles on research, theory, and teaching methods, approaches to teaching, and news items of interest.
Formerly (until 1992): Technical Writing Teacher (0888-4323)
Related titles: Microfilm ed.: (from PQC); Online - full text ed.: ISSN 1542-7625. USD 200 worldwide to institutions (effective 2006) (from EBSCO Publishing, H.W. Wilson, O C L C Online Computer Library Center, Inc., ProQuest Information & Learning, Swets Information Services).
Indexed: ABIn, AbAn, CIJE, EduInd, Inspec, LISA, MLA-IB.
—BLDSC (8655.150000), IE, ingenta.
Published by: (Association of Teachers of Technical Writing), Lawrence Erlbaum Associates, Inc., 10 Industrial Ave, Mahwah, NJ 07430-2262. TEL 201-258-2200, 800-926-6579, FAX 201-236-0072, journals@erlbaum.com, http://www.leaonline.com/loi/tcq, http://www.erlbaum.com. Eds. Charlotte Thralls, Mark Zachry. adv.: B&W page USD 500; trim 5 x 8. Circ: 2,000.

371.3 USA ISSN 0146-0137
T61
TECHNICAL EDUCATION NEWS. Text in English. 1941. s-a. free to qualified personnel. adv. reprint service avail. from PQC. **Document type:** *Trade.*
Related titles: Microform ed.: (from PQC).
Indexed: CIJE.
—CISTI, Linda Hall.
Published by: Glencoe/McGraw-Hill (Subsidiary of: Educational and Professional Publishing Group), 8787 Orion Pl, Columbus, OH 43240-4027. TEL 800-334-7344, FAX 614-755-5682, customer.service@mcgraw-hill.com, http://www.glencoe.com/ps/ee/ten/. Ed. Wendy K Spiegel. Circ: 47,000 (controlled).

373.246 FRA ISSN 0768-9454
TECHNOLOGIE. Text in French. 1950. 6/yr. (includes one double issue). looseleaf. bk.rev. charts; illus.; mkt. **Description:** Teaches current technological and scientific news to young adults.
Former titles: Techniques Industrielles (0013-8576); Enseignement des Techniques Industrielles
—CISTI.
Published by: Centre National de Documentation Pedagogique, 29 rue de l'Ulm, Paris, Cedex 5 75230, France. TEL 33-1-46349000, FAX 33-1-46345544. Ed. Christian Patoz. Circ: 5,000. **Subscr. to:** CNDP - Abonnement, B.P. 750, Sainte Genevieve Cedex 60732, France. FAX 33-3-44033013.

372.35 USA
TECHNOLOGY AND CHILDREN. Text in English. 1996. 4/yr., latest vol.5. USD 30 domestic to non-members; USD 40 foreign to non-members; USD 20 domestic to members; USD 30 foreign to members (effective 2001). adv. 24 p./no.; back issues avail. **Document type:** *Journal, Academic/Scholarly.* **Description:** Contains practical and innovative articles and activities to teach K-6 children about technology.
Related titles: Online - full text ed.
Published by: International Technology Education Association, 1914 Association Dr, Ste 201, Reston, VA 20191-1539. TEL 703-860-2100, FAX 703-860-0353, iteacomm@iris.org, http://www.iteawww.org/F2.html. Ed., R&P Kathleen de la Paz. Pub. Kendall Starkweather. Adv. contact Lee Anne Pirrello.

607.1 AUS ISSN 1034-6902
TECHNOLOGY DESIGN EDUCATION. Text in English. 1960. q. AUD 80, USD 40 (effective 2001). adv. bk.rev. back issues avail.
Supersedes (in Mar. 1990): Industrial Arts Education (0312-9152)
Published by: Institute of Industrial Arts Technology Education, PO Box 52, Forestville, NSW 2087, Australia. Ed. John Barlow. Circ: 1,200.

TECHNOLOGY, INSTRUCTION, COGNITION AND LEARNING. see *PSYCHOLOGY*

371.334 GBR ISSN 1475-939X
➤ **TECHNOLOGY, PEDAGOGY AND EDUCATIONS.** Text in English. 1992. 3/yr. GBP 256 combined subscription to institutions print & online eds.; USD 407 combined subscription to institutions print & online eds (effective 2006). bk.rev. abstr.; illus. back issues avail. **Document type:** *Journal, Academic/Scholarly.* **Description:** Focuses on the implications of teacher education, both preservice and in-service, in all aspects of information technology.
Formerly (until 2003): Journal of Information Technology for Teacher Education (0962-029X)
Related titles: Online - full text ed.: ISSN 1747-5139 (from EBSCO Publishing, Swets Information Services).
Indexed: BrEdI, CIJE, CPE, DIP, EAA, ERA, ETA, IBR, IBZ, Inspec, L&LBA, LISA, MEA, RHEA, SEA, SENA, SOMA, SOPODA, TEA.
—BLDSC (8758.962700), IE, ingenta.
Published by: Routledge (Subsidiary of: Taylor & Francis Group), 4 Park Sq, Milton Park, Abingdon, Oxon OX14 4RN, United Kingdom. TEL 44-1235-828600, FAX 44-1235-829000, journals@routledge.com, http://www.tandf.co.uk/journals/titles/1475939X.asp, http://www.routledge.co.uk. Ed. Avril Loveless.

372.35 USA ISSN 0746-3537
T61
➤ **THE TECHNOLOGY TEACHER.** Text in English. 1939. 8/yr. USD 70 domestic to non-members; free to members (effective 2005). adv. bk.rev. abstr.; bibl.; charts; illus. Index. 44 p./no. 3 cols./p.; back issues avail.; reprints avail. **Document type:** *Journal, Academic/Scholarly.* **Description:** Includes reports of current trends in technology education, technology learning activities, program articles, news, calendar, etc.
Former titles (until 1983): Man - Society - Technology (0022-1813); Journal of Industrial Arts Education
Related titles: Microform ed.: (from PQC); Online - full text ed.: (from EBSCO Publishing, Gale Group, H.W. Wilson, Northern Light Technology, Inc., O C L C Online Computer Library Center, Inc., ProQuest Information & Learning).
Indexed: ABIn, CIJE, CPE, CompD, CurCont, EduInd, MRD.
—BLDSC (8761.024000), IE, Infotrieve, ingenta.
Published by: International Technology Education Association, 1914 Association Dr, Ste 201, Reston, VA 20191-1539. TEL 703-860-2100, FAX 703-860-0353, iteacomm@iris.org, http://www.iteawww.org/F1.html. Ed., R&P Kathleen de la Paz. Pub. Kendall Starkweather. Adv. contact Dora Anderson TEL 703-860-5028. Circ: 5,000 (paid).

➤ **TECHNOS QUARTERLY**; journal of the Agency for Instructional Technology. see *EDUCATION—Computer Applications*

➤ **TECHNOSCENE.** see *CHILDREN AND YOUTH—For*

➤ **TECHTRENDS**; for leaders in education and training. see *EDUCATION—Computer Applications*

➤ **TECLA**; texts for learners and teachers of Spanish. see *EDUCATION—International Education Programs*

371.334 PRI ISSN 1554-9836
TECNE. Text in Spanish. 1994 (Sept.). irreg. free (effective 2005). **Document type:** *Academic/Scholarly.*
Related titles: Online - full content ed.: ISSN 1554-9844.
Published by: University of Puerto Rico, Rio Piedras Campus, Centro de Tecnologia Educativa, P O Box 23304, San Juan, PR 00931-3304. http://www.rrp.upr.edu/educa/educacion_files/virtual/018_cte/tecne.html. Ed. Aida Castaner.

TEEN-SEARCH. see *RELIGIONS AND THEOLOGY*

TELESNA VYCHOVA A SPORT MLADEZE; odborny casopis pro ucitele, trenery a cvicitele. see *SPORTS AND GAMES*

TEMA. see *LINGUISTICS*

613.7 RUS ISSN 0040-3601
CODEN: TPFKAV
TEORIYA I PRAKTIKA FIZICHESKOI KUL'TURY. Text in Russian. 1925. m. USD 132 foreign (effective 2004). bk.rev. bibl.; charts; illus.; stat. index.
Indexed: BiolAb, IAA.
—BLDSC (0178.100000), East View. **CCC.**
Address: Sirenevyi bulv 4, Moscow, 105122, Russian Federation. TEL 7-095-1663774, FAX 7-095-1663774. Ed. L I Lubysheva. Circ: 16,200. **Dist. by:** M K - Periodica, ul Gilyarovskogo 39, Moscow 129110, Russian Federation. TEL 7-095-2845008, FAX 7-095-2813798, info@periodicals.ru, http://www.mkniga.ru.

E

TESTS IN PRINT. see *PSYCHOLOGY*

371.334   USA   ISSN 1546-8992
▼ **THE TEXAS JOURNAL OF DISTANCE LEARNING.** Text in English. 2004 (Win.). s-a. **Document type:** *Journal, Academic/Scholarly.*
Media: Online - full content.
Published by: University of Houston, 315 Farish Hall, Houston, TX 77204. TEL 713-743-4632, http://www.tjdl.org, http://www.uh.edu. Ed. Philip Ruthstrom.

371.33   USA
TEXTBOOK LETTER. Text in English. 1990. bi-m. USD 42. bk.rev. **Document type:** *Newsletter.* **Description:** Focuses on evaluative reviews of textbooks sold nationally for use in public schools.
Published by: The Textbook League, PO Box 51, Sausalito, CA 94966. textbook@earthlink.net, http://www.csulb.edu/~ttl/main.htm. Ed. William J Bennetta. Circ: 1,000.

TEXTIL UND UNTERRICHT. see *TEXTILE INDUSTRIES AND FABRICS*

370.115   USA   ISSN 0093-3104
H1
➤ **THEORY AND RESEARCH IN SOCIAL EDUCATION.** Variant title: Theory and Research. Text in English. 1972. q. USD 39 (effective 2004). adv. bk.rev. **Document type:** *Journal, Academic/Scholarly.* **Description:** Covers all aspects of social studies research, including teacher training, instructional strategies, curriculum development, student involvement and social action.
Related titles: Microform ed.: (from PQC).
Indexed: ABIn, ASCA, CIJE, CPE, CurCont, ERA, ETA, EduInd, IBR, MEA, PsycInfo, PsychAb, SEA, SSCI, e-psyche.
—BLDSC (8814.629000), IDS, IE, Infotrieve, ingenta. **CCC.**
Published by: National Council for the Social Studies, 8555 16th St, Ste 500, Silver Spring, MD 20910. TEL 301-588-1800, FAX 301-588-2049, eyeager@ufl.edu, ncss@ncss.org, http://www.ncss.org. Ed. Elizabeth Yeageu TEL 352-392-9191 ext 242. Circ: 900.

➤ **THINK IN ENGLISH.** see *LINGUISTICS*

371.3   NLD   ISSN 1381-5377
THOMAS BULLETIN. Text in Dutch. 1960. 6/yr. adv. bk.rev.
Document type: *Bulletin.*
Related titles: ◆ Supplement to: Lichamelijke Opvoeding. ISSN 0024-2810.
Published by: Koninklijke Vereniging van Leerkrachten in de Lichamelijke Opvoeding, Postbus 398, Zeist, 3700 AJ, Netherlands. FAX 31-3404-12810.

613.7   BEL
TIJDSCHRIFT VOOR LICHAMELIJKE OPVOEDING. Text in Dutch. 1945. q. USD 13. adv. bk.rev. bibl.; illus. index.
Related titles: ◆ French ed.: Revue de l'Education Physique. ISSN 1376-1854.
Published by: Bond voor Lichamelijke Opvoeding vzw, Waterkluiskaai 16, Sint-Amandberg - Gent, 9040, Belgium. TEL 32-9-218-9120, http://www.bvlo.be/article/view.web?articleId=35&section=LO&sectie=5&item=28&lang=nl. Circ: 1,500.

371.3   NLD   ISSN 0165-0947
TIJDSCHRIFT VOOR ORTHOPEDAGOGIEK. Text in Dutch. 1962. 11/yr. EUR 86; EUR 51 to students; EUR 15.50 newsstand/cover (effective 2005). **Document type:** *Academic/Scholarly.*
Incorporates (in 2000): Inside (Zeist) (1382-5968); Which was formerly (until 1990): Inside I S O (1382-595X)
Indexed: PsychAb.
—IE, Infotrieve, KNAW.
Published by: (Vereniging Ter Bevordering van Ortho-Agogische Aktiviteiten), Uitgeverij Agiel, Eijerdijk 87, Hattem, 8051 MS, Netherlands. orthopedagogiek@xs4all.nl, http://www.agiel.nl/. Ed. Dr. R de Groot.

TIRO. see *LINGUISTICS*

TODAY'S SCHOOL PSYCHOLOGIST. see *PSYCHOLOGY*

TOHOKU - HOKURIKU SUGAKU KYOIKU KISOTEKI KENKYU HOKOKU. see *MATHEMATICS*

TOMORROW'S MORNING CLASSROOM EDITION; born to read. see *CHILDREN AND YOUTH—For*

TOPICS; for today's students in touch with their world. see *CHILDREN AND YOUTH—For*

TRAINING; the magazine covering the human side of business. see *BUSINESS AND ECONOMICS—Management*

TRAINING IN COUNSELLING & PSYCHOTHERAPY. see *PSYCHOLOGY*

371.3   USA   ISSN 1081-2393
TRAINING RESEARCH JOURNAL; the science and practice of training. Abbreviated title: T R J. Text in English. 1995. a. USD 60 (effective 2001). **Document type:** *Journal, Academic/Scholarly.*
—**CCC.**
Published by: Educational Technology Publications, 700 Palisade Ave, PO Box 1564, Englewood Cliffs, NJ 07632-0564. TEL 201-871-4007, 800-952-2665, FAX 201-871-4009, edtecpubs@aol.com, http://www.bookstoread.com/etp/. Pub. Laurence Lipsitz. R&P Charles Renavd.

371.3   USA   ISSN 1527-4233
TRENDS AND ISSUES IN ELEMENTARY LANGUAGE ARTS. Text in English. 1999. a. USD 19.95 per issue to non-members; USD 14.95 per issue to members (effective 2000). **Document type:** *Journal, Trade.* **Description:** Reports and examines trends and issues of importance to teachers of English at all levels.
Published by: National Council of Teachers of English, 1111 W Kenyon Rd, Urbana, IL 61801-1096. TEL 800-369-6283, FAX 217-328-9645, membership@ncte.org, http://www.ncte.org.

371.3   USA   ISSN 1527-4241
TRENDS AND ISSUES IN POSTSECONDARY ENGLISH STUDIES. Text in English. 1999. a.
Indexed: DIP.
Published by: National Council of Teachers of English, 1111 W Kenyon Rd, Urbana, IL 61801-1096. TEL 817-328-3870, FAX 217-328-9645, http://www.ncte.org.

TRIAD (DAYTON). see *MUSIC*

TSJIP - LETTEREN; vaktijdschrift voor literaire vorming, literatuuronderwijs en culturele en kunstzinnige vorming. see *LIBRARY AND INFORMATION SCIENCES*

TU WAS! AUSGABE 1. see *SCIENCES: COMPREHENSIVE WORKS*

TU WAS! AUSGABE 2. see *SCIENCES: COMPREHENSIVE WORKS*

371.358   TUR   ISSN 1302-6488
LC5800
➤ **TURKISH ONLINE JOURNAL OF DISTANCE EDUCATION.** Abbreviated title: T O J D E. Text in English. 2000. q. free (effective 2005). bk.rev.; Website rev. abstr.; bibl.; illus.; maps; stat. back issues avail. **Document type:** *Journal, Academic/Scholarly.* **Description:** Aims to establish new channels of communication for the distance education world in general.
Media: Online - full text. **Related titles:** CD-ROM ed.
Published by: Anadolu University, Yunusemre Campus, Eskisehir, 26470, Turkey. TEL 90-222-335-0581, FAX 90-222-320-4520, tojde@anadolu.edu.tr, http://tojde.anadolu.edu.tr, http://www.tojde.anadolu.edu.tr. Ed., R&P, Adv. contact Ugur Demiray.

375.001   USA
U A B REPORTER. (University of Alabama) Text in English. 1976. w. free. **Document type:** *Newspaper.*
Published by: University of Alabama at Birmingham, Administration Bldg., 701 S. 20th St., Birmingham, AL 35294-0113. TEL 205-934-2040, FAX 205-934-7911, reporter@uab.edu, http://www.uab.edu/reporter. Ed. Linda Gunter. Circ: 15,500 (free).

U K SPACE INDEX. see *AERONAUTICS AND SPACE FLIGHT*

U M A P JOURNAL. (Undergraduate Mathematics Applications Project) see *MATHEMATICS*

UCITELJ/TEACHER. see *EDUCATION—Computer Applications*

613.7   DEU   ISSN 0945-4950
UE; Magazin fuer Uebungsleiterinnen und Uebungsleiter. Text in German. 1992. bi-m. EUR 21; EUR 4 newsstand/cover (effective 2003). adv. 36 p./no. 3 cols./p.; back issues avail. **Document type:** *Magazine, Consumer.* **Description:** Provides information about trends and developments in sports and sport instruction.
Published by: (Deutscher Turner-Bund), Meyer und Meyer Fachverlag GmbH, Von-Coels-Str 390, Aachen, 52080, Germany. TEL 49-241-958100, FAX 49-241-9581010, verlag@meyer-meyer-sports.com, http://www.meyer-meyer-sports.com. Ed. Maike Masurat. Adv. contact Michael Friesing TEL 49-241-9581012. B&W page EUR 1,483, color page EUR 2,818. Circ: 30,000 (paid and controlled).

DER UEBUNGSLEITER; Arbeitshilfen fuer Uebungsleiter im Deutschen Sportbund. see *SPORTS AND GAMES*

523.1   USA   ISSN 0890-6866
THE UNIVERSE IN THE CLASSROOM; a newsletter on astronomy for teachers. Text in English. 1984. m. free to qualified personnel (effective 2000). adv. illus. back issues avail. **Document type:** *Newsletter.* **Description:** For teachers of astronomy for grades 6-college, with information, activities and resource lists.
Media: Online - full text.

Published by: Astronomical Society of the Pacific, 390 Ashton Ave, San Francisco, CA 94112. TEL 415-337-1100, FAX 415-337-5205, schippindale@astrosociety.org, editor@astrosociety.org, http://www.astrosociety.org. Ed. Suzanne Chippindale. Adv. contact Michael Bennett. Circ: 10,000 (controlled and free).

371.33   FRA
UNIVERSITE DE BRETAGNE OCCIDENTALE. GUIDE DE L'ETUDIANT. Text in French. 1971. a. free.
Media: Duplicated (not offset).
Published by: Universite de Bretagne Occidentale, 3 rue des Archives, Brest, Cedex 29285, France. TEL 33-2-98016020, FAX 33-2-98016001, http://www.univ-brest.fr. Circ: (controlled).

448   FRA   ISSN 0077-2712
UNIVERSITE DE NANCY II. CENTRE DE RECHERCHES ET D'APPLICATIONS PEDAGOGIQUES EN LANGUES. MELANGES. Spine title: Melanges CRAPEL. Text in French; Text occasionally in English. 1970. a. back issues avail.
Document type: *Academic/Scholarly.*
Indexed: L&LBA, LT&LA, SOPODA.
—BLDSC (5536.803900).
Published by: Universite de Nancy II, Centre de Recherches et d'Applications Pedagogiques en Langues, B.P. 33-97, Nancy, 54015, France. TEL 33-03-83967130, FAX 33-03-83967132, crapel@univ-nancy,fr, http://www.univ-nancy.fr/recherche/crapel. Eds. F Carton, P Riley. Circ: 1,000.

UNIVERSITY OF MEMPHIS. CENTER FOR RESEARCH ON WOMEN. CURRICULUM INTEGRATION SERIES. see *WOMEN'S STUDIES*

371.3   POL   ISSN 1426-689X
LA840
UNIWERSYTET OPOLSKI. ZESZYTY NAUKOWE. PEDAGOGIKA. Text in Polish; Summaries in English. 1956. irreg., latest 2002. price varies; avail. on exchange basis.
Document type: *Monographic series, Academic/Scholarly.*
Formerly (until 1994): Wyzsza Szkola Pedagogiczna, Opole. Zeszyty Naukowe. Seria A. Pedagogika (0474-2982)
Indexed: RASB.
Published by: Wydawnictwo Uniwersytetu Opolskiego, ul Sienkiewicza 33, Opole, 45037, Poland. TEL 48-77-4410878, wydawnictwo@uni.opole.pl.

UNO; revista de didactica de las matematicas. see *MATHEMATICS*

373.246   USA   ISSN 1057-1043
UNSCHOOLERS NETWORK. Text in English. 1977. irreg. (approx. 4/yr). looseleaf. USD 15 (effective 2000). adv. bk.rev.
Document type: *Newsletter.*
Published by: Nancy Plent, Ed. & Pub., 2 Smith St, Farmingdale, NJ 07727. TEL 732-938-2473. R&P, Adv. contact Nancy Plent. Circ: 350.

371.3   DEU   ISSN 1438-8987
UNTERRICHT ARBEIT UND TECHNIK. Text in German. 1999. 4/yr. EUR 53.60 (effective 2005). adv. bk.rev. charts; illus. index. **Document type:** *Journal, Academic/Scholarly.*
Formed by the merger of (1959-1999): Arbeit und Technik in der Schule (0863-4424); Which was formerly (until 1990): Polytechnische Bildung und Erziehung (0032-4116); (1982-1999): Arbeiten und Lernen. Technik (0941-536X); Which superseded in part (in 1991): Arbeiten und Lernen. Arbeitslehre (0176-3717); Which was formed by the merger of (1979-1982): Arbeiten Plus (0172-7338); (1972-1982): Arbeitslehre (0340-2401)
Indexed: DIP, IBR, IBZ.
—IE. **CCC.**
Published by: Erhard Friedrich Verlag GmbH, Im Brande 17, Seelze, 30926, Germany. TEL 49-511-400040, FAX 49-511-40004170, info@friedrich-verlag.de, http://www.friedrich-verlag.de/index.cfm?BFE56764CAE740B998F71DEBAE3DFC63. Circ: 2,500.

UNTERRICHT BIOLOGIE; Beitraege zu seiner Gestaltung. see *BIOLOGY*

UNTERRICHT PHYSIK; Beitraege zu seinen fachlichen, methodischen und didaktischen Problemen. see *PHYSICS*

URBAN EDUCATOR; the nation's voice for urban education. see *EDUCATION—School Organization And Administration*

371.2   AUS
V A T F NEWSLETTER∗. Text in English. 1976. m. AUD 7. back issues avail. **Document type:** *Newsletter.* **Description:** Covers teaching, conditions of work, curriculum, school organization.
Published by: Victorian Affiliated Teachers' Federation, GPO Box 1700, Hobart, VIC 7001, Australia. TEL 61-3-62-341774, FAX 61-3-62-347349. Circ: 2,000.

VERPLEEGKUNDE; Nederlandse-Vlaams tijdschrift voor verpleegkundigen. see *MEDICAL SCIENCES—Nurses And Nursing*

371.3 CAN ISSN 0707-2511
VIE PEDAGOGIQUE. Text in English. 1979. 4/yr. free. bk.rev. **Document type:** *Government.*
Indexed: CEI, PdeR.
Published by: Ministere de l'Education, 600 rue Fullum, 10th Fl, Montreal, PQ H2K 4L1, Canada. TEL 514-873-8095, FAX 514-864-2294, vie.pedagogique@meq.gouv.qc.ca. Ed. Luce Brossard. Circ: 55,000.

791.43 GBR ISSN 0952-4444
VIEWFINDER. Text in English. 1967. 3/yr. GBP 12 domestic; GBP 20 in Europe; GBP 26 elsewhere (effective 2000). adv. bk.rev.; film rev. abstr. cum.index. **Document type:** *Newsletter.*
Former titles: B U F V C Newsletter (0265-6817); B U F C Newsletter (0308-5376)
Indexed: ABM, AICP, BrArAb, BrEdI, ERA, ETA, HECAB, IIFP, MRD.
Published by: British Universities Film and Video Council, 77 Wells St., London, W1T 3QJ, United Kingdom. TEL 44-20-73931500, FAX 44-20-73931555, ask@bufvc.ac.uk, http://www.bufvc.ac.uk. Ed., Adv. contact Chris Dry. Circ: 5,800.

VIJAYAVEEDHI. see *CHILDREN AND YOUTH—For*

VINCULUM. see *MATHEMATICS*

VIRGINIA GEOGRAPHER. see *GEOGRAPHY*

VISION (GREENSBORO). see *EDUCATION—School Organization And Administration*

VISUAL ARTS RESEARCH; educational, historical, philosophical and psychological perspectives. see *ART*

371.3 USA
VISUAL LITERACY NEWSLETTER. Text in English. 1971. bi-m. USD 25. bk.rev.
Published by: International Visual Literacy Association, Visual Communications 0144, c/o Tom Hergert, Virginia Tech, Blacksburg, VA 24061-0144. TEL 540-231-8710. Circ: 250.

379.24 USA
VISUAL LITERACY REVIEW. Text in English. 5/yr. USD 40 membership; USD 20 to students. back issues avail. **Document type:** *Journal, Academic/Scholarly.*
Published by: International Visual Literacy Association, Inc., c/o Barbara Lockee, Office of Distance Learning, Virginia Tech, Old Security Bldg, Blacksburg, VA 24061-0445. dbeau@nav.cc.tx.us, http://www.ivla.org/. Eds. Barbara Lockee, Tom Hergert.

371.3 USA ISSN 1074-4762
LB1631
VOICES FROM THE MIDDLE. Text in English. 1994. q. USD 60 to individuals includes $40 membership fee; USD 60 to institutions (effective 2005). adv. bk.rev. bibl. index. back issues avail. **Document type:** *Journal, Academic/Scholarly.* **Description:** Explores topics in middle-school English language arts education.
Related titles: Online - full text ed.: (from EBSCO Publishing, ProQuest Information & Learning).
Indexed: ABIn, EduInd.
—CCC.
Published by: National Council of Teachers of English, 1111 W Kenyon Rd, Urbana, IL 61801-1096. TEL 217-328-3870, 800-369-6283, FAX 217-328—9645, cschanche@ncte.org, http://www.ncte.org/pubs/journals/vm. Ed. Kylene Beers. R&P Barbara Lamar. Adv. contact Carrie Stewart. B&W page USD 750; trim 11 x 8.5. Circ: 10,000 (paid).

371.3 RUS ISSN 0130-0776
VOSPITANIE SHKOL'NIKOV. Text in Russian. bi-m. USD 56 foreign (effective 2004).
Indexed: RASB.
—East View.
Published by: Izdatel'stvo Shkola Press, Rustaveli ul 10-3, Moscow, 127254, Russian Federation. TEL 7-095-2198380, FAX 7-095-2195289. Ed. L V Kuznetsova. **Dist. by:** M K - Periodica, ul Gilyarovskogo 39, Moscow 129110, Russian Federation. TEL 7-095-2845008, FAX 7-095-2813798, info@periodicals.ru, http://www.mkniga.ru.

371.3 USA
W C E R RESEARCH HIGHLIGHTS. Text in English. 1970. q. free (effective 2005). 8 p./no.; back issues avail. **Document type:** *Newsletter.* **Description:** Examines university research on teaching methods and curriculum, organization and administration, higher education, special education, mathematics and science education, and studies of English and writing instruction.
Former titles (until 2004): W C E R Highlights (1073-1822); (until 1989): Wisconsin Center for Education Research News
Related titles: Online - full text ed.
Published by: Wisconsin Center for Education Research, University of Wisconsin at Madison, 1025 W Johnston St, Ste 785, Madison, WI 53706. TEL 608-263-4200, FAX 608-263-6448, pbaker@wise.edu, http://www.wcer.wisc.edu/Publications/WCER_Highlights/. Ed., R&P Paul Baker. Circ: 9,000 (free).

371.335 CHN ISSN 1001-5795
WAIYU DIANHUA JIAOXUE/AUDIO-VISUAL TEACHING OF FOREIGN LANGUAGES. Text in Chinese; Summaries in English. 1981. q. CNY 0.90. **Document type:** *Academic/Scholarly.*
Related titles: Online - full text ed.: (from East View Information Services).
Published by: Shanghai Waiyu Dianhua Jiaoxue Guan/Shanghai Foreign Language Audiovisual Publishing House, 550 Dalian Xilu, Shanghai, 200083, China. TEL 86-21-5420787, FAX 86-21-5427900. Eds. Shi Xin, Sun Congyang. Circ: 50,005. **Subscr. to:** China International Book Trading Corp, 35 Chegongzhuang Xilu, Haidian District, PO Box 399, Beijing 100044, China. TEL 86-10-68412045, FAX 86-10-68412023, cibtc@mail.cibtc.com.cn, http://www.cibtc.com.cn.

WAIYU JIAOXUE YU YANJIU/FOREIGN LANGUAGE TEACHING & RESEARCH. see *LINGUISTICS*

371.3 USA
WAYS OF KNOWING IN SCIENCE SERIES. Text in English. 1999. irreg. price varies. charts; illus. back issues avail. **Document type:** *Monographic series, Academic/Scholarly.* **Description:** Examines teaching and learning in the sciences.
Published by: Teachers College Press, Teachers College, Columbia University, 525 W 120th St, Box 303, New York, NY 10027-6694. http://tc-press.tc.columbia.edu. **Dist. by:** Eurospan University Press Group, Order Dept, 3 Henrietta St, London WC2E 8LU, United Kingdom. TEL 44-20-7240-0856, FAX 44-20-7379-0609, http://www.eurospan.co.uk; Pademelon Press, Pty Ltd, 7-10 Anella Ave, PO Box 229, Castle Hill, NSW 2154, Australia. TEL 61-2-9634-2558, FAX 61-2-9680-4634; Transdex International, Pte Ltd, Block 1, Farrer Rd 307-05, Singapore 268817, Singapore. TEL 65-468-6242, FAX 65-462-5457.

371.3 USA
WEB FEET K - 8. Text in English. 1996. 9/yr. USD 50 (effective 2003). illus. back issues avail.; reprints avail. **Document type:** *Bibliography.* **Description:** Explores a theme from all angles, seeking new and exciting ways to approach it that will inspire students to think creatively.
Formerly: Online - Offline (1090-1930)
Media: Online - full content.
Published by: RockHill Communications, 522, Bala Cynwyd, PA 19004-0522. TEL 610-667-2040, 888-762-5445, FAX 610-667-2291, info@webfeetguides.com, http://www.online-offline.com/, http://www.rockhillcommunications.com. Ed. Terry Schneider. Pub. Matt DeJulio. R&P Sophie Socha.

371.33 USA ISSN 1525-4984
WEEKLY READER. GRADE 1 EDITION. Text in English. 1928. 32/yr. (w., during school yr.). USD 24.95 per academic year; USD 3.45 per academic year 10 or more subscriptions (effective 2004 - 2005). reprint service avail. from PQC. **Document type:** *Newspaper, Consumer.* **Description:** Provides first-grade students with stories, photos, and articles. Includes separate teacher's guide and a poster-size version of each issue.
Former titles (until 1999): Weekly Reader, Edition 1 (0890-3220); Buddy's Weekly Reader (0163-4895); My Weekly Reader 1
Related titles: Online - full text ed.: (from Gale Group).
Published by: Weekly Reader Corp. (Subsidiary of: W R C Media Inc.), 200 First Stamford Pl, PO Box 120023, Stamford, CT 06912-0023. TEL 203-705-3500, FAX 203-705-1662, science@weeklyreader.com, http://www.weeklyreader.com. Ed. Charles Piddock. Pub. Peter Esposito. R&P Cathy Pekai TEL 203-705-3426. Circ: 1,359,345 (paid).

372.4 028.5 USA
WEEKLY READER. GRADE 2 EDITION. Text in English. 1929. 25/yr. (w., during school yr.). USD 24.95 per academic year (effective 2005 - 2006). adv. reprint service avail. from PQC. **Document type:** *Newspaper, Consumer.* **Description:** Provides second-grade students with news stories, photos, and articles. Includes separate teacher's guide.
Former titles (until 1999): Weekly Reader, Edition 2 (0890-3212); Weekly Reader News Hunt (0163-4909); (until 1976): My Weekly Reader 2
Related titles: Online - full text ed.: (from EBSCO Publishing, Gale Group).
Published by: Weekly Reader Corp. (Subsidiary of: W R C Media Inc.), 200 First Stamford Pl, PO Box 120023, Stamford, CT 06912-0023. TEL 203-705-3500, 800-446-3355, FAX 203-705-1662, https://www.weeklyreader.com/store/wretwo.asp, http://www.weeklyreader.com. Ed. Andrew Casino TEL 203-705-3569. Pub. Peter Bergen. R&P Aimee Knoller TEL 203-705-3569. Adv. contact Greg Hilbert. Circ: 1,391,835 (paid).

371.33 028.5 USA ISSN 0890-3204
WEEKLY READER. GRADE 3 EDITION. Text in English. 1930. 25/yr. (w., during school yr.). USD 24.95 per academic year (effective 2004 - 2005). reprint service avail. from PQC. **Document type:** *Newspaper, Consumer.* **Description:** Provides third-grade students with news stories, photos, maps, graphs, and charts. Includes separate teacher's guide.
Former titles: Weekly Reader News Patrol (0163-4879); (until 1978): Weekly Reader Whiz; (until 1976): My Weekly Reader 3
Related titles: Online - full text ed.: (from EBSCO Publishing, Gale Group).
Published by: Weekly Reader Corp. (Subsidiary of: W R C Media Inc.), 200 First Stamford Pl, PO Box 120023, Stamford, CT 06912-0023. TEL 203-705-3500, 800-446-3355, FAX 203-705-1662, http://www.weeklyreader.com. Ed. Charles Piddock. Pub. Peter Esposito. R&P Cathy Pekai TEL 203-705-3426. Circ: 1,150,271 (paid).

372.4 028.5 USA ISSN 0890-3190
WEEKLY READER. GRADE 4 EDITION. Text in English. 1934. 25/yr. (w., during school yr.). USD 24.95 per academic year (effective 2004 - 2005). illus. reprint service avail. from PQC. **Document type:** *Newspaper, Consumer.* **Description:** Provides fourth-grade students with news stories, photos, maps, graphs, and charts. Includes separate teacher's guide.
Former titles: Weekly Reader News Parade (0163-4860); (until 1976): My Weekly Reader News Parade Edition 4
Related titles: Online - full text ed.: (from EBSCO Publishing, Gale Group).
Indexed: ICM.
Published by: Weekly Reader Corp. (Subsidiary of: W R C Media Inc.), 200 First Stamford Pl, PO Box 120023, Stamford, CT 06912-0023. TEL 203-705-3500, 800-446-3355, FAX 203-705-1662, science@weeklyreader.com, http://www.weeklyreader.com. Ed. Charles Piddock. Pub. Peter Esposito. R&P Cathy Pekai TEL 203-705-3426. Circ: 850,176 (paid).

371.33 USA ISSN 1525-5093
WEEKLY READER. K EDITION. Text in English. 1959. 28/yr. (w., during school yr.). USD 24.95 per academic year; USD 4.75 per academic year 10 or more subscriptions (effective 2004 - 2005). illus. reprint service avail. from PQC. **Document type:** *Newspaper, Consumer.* **Description:** Provides kindergarten students with stories, photos, and articles. Includes separate teacher's guide and poster-size version of each issue.
Former titles (until 1999): Weekly Reader, Edition K (0890-3166); Weekly Reader Surprise (0163-4887)
Related titles: Online - full text ed.: (from EBSCO Publishing, Gale Group).
Published by: Weekly Reader Corp. (Subsidiary of: W R C Media Inc.), 200 First Stamford Pl, PO Box 120023, Stamford, CT 06912-0023. TEL 203-705-3500, 800-446-3355, FAX 203-705-1662, science@weeklyreader.com, http://www.weeklyreader.com. Ed. Charles Piddock. Pub. Peter Esposito. R&P Cathy Pekai TEL 203-705-3426. Circ: 1,002,911 (paid).

WEEKLY READER. PRE-K EDITION. see *CHILDREN AND YOUTH—For*

371.33 028.5 USA ISSN 0890-3239
WEEKLY READER. SENIOR EDITION. Text in English. 1947. 25/yr. (w., during school yr.). USD 24.95 per academic year (effective 2004 - 2005). illus. reprint service avail. from PQC. **Document type:** *Newspaper, Consumer.* **Description:** Provides news stories, photos, maps, graphs, and charts to fifth- and sixth-grade students. Includes separate teacher's guide.
Incorporates (in 1999): Weekly Reader, Edition 5 (0890-3182); Which was formerly: Weekly Reader Eye (0163-4828); (until 1976): My Weekly Reader Eye 5; (1954-1973): My Weekly Reader 5; Supersedes (in 198?): Senior Weekly Reader (0163-4852)
Indexed: ICM.
Published by: Weekly Reader Corp. (Subsidiary of: W R C Media Inc.), 200 First Stamford Pl, PO Box 120023, Stamford, CT 06912-0023. TEL 203-705-3500, 800-446-3355, FAX 203-705-1662, science@weeklyreader.com, http://www.weeklyreader.com. Ed. Charles Piddock. Pub. Peter Esposito. R&P Cathy Pekai TEL 203-705-3426. Circ: 792,244 (paid).

WESSEX STUDIES IN SPECIAL EDUCATION. see *EDUCATION—Special Education And Rehabilitation*

WESTFIELD CENTER. NEWSLETTER. see *MUSIC*

371.3 USA ISSN 0083-9116
L11
WHAT RESEARCH SAYS TO THE TEACHER SERIES. Text in English. 1953. irreg. price varies. **Document type:** *Monographic series.*
Published by: National Education Association of the United States, 1201 16th St, N W, Washington, DC 20036-3290. TEL 202-822-7207, FAX 202-822-7206. **Subscr. to:** NEA Professional Library, PMDS, 9050 Junction Dr, Annapolis, MD 20701. TEL 800-229-4200.

371.3 USA ISSN 1553-4057
LB1028
WHAT WORKS IN TEACHING AND LEARNING. Text in English. 1968. bi-w. looseleaf. USD 383 (effective 2002). bk.rev. bibl.; charts; illus.; stat. s-a. index. **Document type:** *Newsletter, Academic/Scholarly.* **Description:** For teachers, supervisors, administrators, and professors of education. Aims to help teachers motivate students and find funding for programs. Provides information about curriculum and the use of technology in education.
Formerly (until 1997): Report on Education Research (0034-4699); Incorporates: How to Evaluate Education Programs (0270-157X)
Related titles: Online - full text ed.: (from bigchalk, Gale Group).

E

—CCC.
Published by: Aspen Publishers, Inc. (Subsidiary of: Wolters Kluwer N.V.), 111Eighth Ave., 7th Fl, New York, NY 10011. TEL 212-771-0600, 212-597-0020, FAX 212-771-0885, customer.service@aspenpubl.com, http://www.aspenpublishers.com. Ed. Jonathan Fox. Pub. Marjorie Weiner. R&P Rossette Graham. Circ: 1,200 (paid). **Dist. by:** Customer Care, 7201 McKinney Circle, Frederick, MD 21704. TEL 800-234-1660, FAX 800-901-9075.

371.3 USA ISSN 1069-3866
THE WHOLE IDEA; newsletter for innovative teachers. Text in English. 1990. q. USD 16. bk.rev. charts; illus. **Document type:** *Newsletter.* **Description:** Aimed at teachers of K-6 seeking to apply a whole-learning philosophy to their teaching.
Published by: Wright Group Publishing, Inc. (Subsidiary of: Tribune Company), 19201 120th Ave, N E, Bothell, WA 98011. TEL 206-486-8011, FAX 206-486-7868. Ed. Michael Ford. Pub. Thomas C Wright. R&P Ann Naumann. Circ: 20,000.

371.3 POL ISSN 1425-0772
WIESCI OSWIATOWE; suwalski miesiecznik edukacyjny. Text in Polish. 1992. m. PLZ 20, USD 7; PLZ 2 newsstand/cover (effective 1998 & 1998). adv. back issues avail. **Description:** Provides information for teachers in the region.
Related titles: Diskette ed.
Published by: Kuratorium Oswiaty w Suwalkach, Ul Noniewicza 10, Suwalki, 16432, Poland. TEL 48-87-663760, FAX 48-87-663760. Ed. Jan Bielecki.

658.0071 DEU ISSN 0934-4411
WIRTSCHAFT UND GESELLSCHAFT IM BERUF. Text in German. 1976. bi-m. **Document type:** *Academic/Scholarly.*
Formerly: Wirtschaft und Gesellschaft im Unterricht (0342-6017)
—CCC.
Published by: Verlag Dr. Max Gehlen GmbH und Co. KG, Daimlerstr 12, Bad Homburg, 61352, Germany. TEL 49-6172-1804-148, FAX 49-6172-23055.

418 USA ISSN 0512-1213
WISCONSIN ENGLISH JOURNAL. Text in English. 1959. 3/yr. USD 10. adv. bk.rev. cum.index. back issues avail. **Document type:** *Academic/Scholarly.*
Published by: Wisconsin Council of Teachers of English, c/o Mary Ellen Alea, Department of English, University of Wisconsin, Eau Claire, WI 54702. TEL 715-836-5848, FAX 715-836-5848, aleame@uwec, ruthann.p.wood@uwrf.edu, http://facstaff.uww.edu/wctela/wej.htm. Eds. Mary Ellen Alea, Stephen Fisher. Adv. contact Mary Ellen Alea. Circ: 1,200.

WISCONSIN SCHOOL MUSICIAN. see *MUSIC*

780.71 USA
THE WOMAN CONDUCTOR. Text in English. 1984. 3/yr. (Oct., May, Feb.). membership. adv. bk.rev.; music rev.; video rev. back issues avail. **Document type:** *Newsletter, Trade.* **Description:** Covers news and events of interest to woman conductors of elementary and high school bands.
Published by: (Woman Band Directors National Association), Gladys Wright, Ed. & Pub., 345 Overlook Dr, West Lafayette, IN 47906-1210. TEL 765-463-1738, FAX 765-463-1738. Circ: 400.

WORKING PAPERS IN EDUCATIONAL LINGUISTICS. see *LINGUISTICS*

418 USA
WORKPLACE. Text in English. 1998. s-a.
Media: Online - full content.
Published by: Modern Language Association, 26 Broadway., Flr. 3, New York, NY 10004-1789. http://www.workplace-gsc.com.

371.3 USA
WORLD COUNCIL FOR CURRICULUM AND INSTRUCTION. NEWSLETTER. Text in English. irreg. **Document type:** *Newsletter.*
Published by: World Council for Curriculum and Instruction, c/o WCCI Secretariat, Alliant International University, 10455 Pomerado Rd, San Diego, CA 92131-1799. TEL 858-635-4718, FAX 858-635-4714, wcci@alliant.edu, http://www.uc.edu/wcci/.

300.71 USA ISSN 0193-7871
WORLD EAGLE; the monthly social studies resource. Text in English. 1977. 10/yr. USD 70 domestic to individuals; USD 70 foreign to individuals; USD 125 to institutions (effective 2001). illus.; maps; stat. index. reprints avail. **Document type:** *Magazine, Academic/Scholarly.* **Description:** Presents comparative information for use as a resource and reference tool for social studies teachers, libraries and medical centers.
Related titles: Diskette ed.; E-mail ed.; Online - full text ed.: (from Northern Light Technology, Inc., ProQuest Information & Learning).
Address: 111 King St, Littleton, MA 01460-1527. TEL 978-486-9652, 800-854-8273, FAX 978-486-9652, info@worldeagle.com, http://www.worldeagle.com. Ed. Martine L Crandall Hollick. Pub. Martine Crandall Hollick. R&P Martine Crandall-Hollick.

WRITE IT RIGHT; quarterly for corrections personnel. see *CRIMINOLOGY AND LAW ENFORCEMENT*

THE WRITER'S CHRONICLE. see *JOURNALISM*

371.33 USA ISSN 0279-7208
WRITING (STAMFORD); the magazine of effective communication. Text in English. 1974. 6/yr. (m., during the school year). USD 34.50 per academic year; USD 9.95 per academic year 15 or more subscriptions (effective 2004 - 2005). illus. reprint service avail. from PQC. **Document type:** *Magazine.* **Description:** Builds skills needed to write clearly and effectively and motivates students in grades 6-12 by means of a wide range of high-interest activites with real-world applicability. Includes a teacher's guide.
Formerly (until 1981): Current Media (0194-5475)
Related titles: Online - full text ed.: (from Chadwyck-Healey Inc., EBSCO Publishing, Gale Group, ProQuest Information & Learning).
Published by: Weekly Reader Corp. (Subsidiary of: W R C Media Inc.), 200 First Stamford Pl, PO Box 120023, Stamford, CT 06912-0023. TEL 203-705-3500, 800-446-3355, FAX 203-705-1662, http://www.weeklyreader.com. Ed. Charles Piddock. Pub. Peter Esposito. R&P Cathy Pekai TEL 203-705-3426. Circ: 127,343 (paid).

808.81 USA ISSN 1040-3779
PE1404
➤ **WRITING LAB NEWSLETTER.** Text in English. 1976. 10/yr. USD 15 domestic; USD 20 in Canada; USD 40 elsewhere (effective 2004). bk.rev. index. back issues avail. **Document type:** *Newsletter, Academic/Scholarly.*
Published by: Purdue University, Department of English, 1356 Heavilon, West Lafayette, IN 47907-1356. TEL 765-494-7268, FAX 765-494-3780, harrism@cc.purdue.edu, http://owl.english.purdue.edu/lab/newsletter/, http://owl.english.purdue.edu/Files/newsletter.html. Ed. Muriel Harris. R&P Mary Jo Turley. Circ: 1,000 (paid).

613.7 POL ISSN 0043-9630
WYCHOWANIE FIZYCZNE I SPORT/PHYSICAL TRAINING AND SPORT. Text in Polish; Summaries in English. 1957. q. USD 60 foreign (effective 2003). charts; illus. index. 100 p./no.; **Document type:** *Journal, Academic/Scholarly.* **Description:** Contains original works in the area of physical education sciences and sport, as well as pedagogy, psychology, anthropology and related disciplines.
—BLDSC (9365.410000), IE, ingenta.
Published by: (Polska Akademia Nauk, Komitet Nauk o Kulturze Fizycznej/Polish Academy of Science, Committee of Physical Culture), Wydawnictwo Naukowe P W N SA/Polish Scientific Publishers P W N, ul Miodowa 10, Warsaw, 00251, Poland. TEL 48-22-6954181, FAX 48-22-6954288, ksiegarnia@pwn.pl, http://en.pwn.pl. Ed. H Sozanski. Circ: 1,950. **Co-sponsor:** Akademia Wychowania Fizycznego w Warszawie.

613.7 POL ISSN 0860-8075
WYCHOWANIE FIZYCZNE I ZDROWOTNE. Text in Polish. 1953. 5/yr. **Description:** For teachers of physical education, doctors and nurses working in schools with healthy and disabled students.
Former titles (until 1989): Wychowanie Fizyczne i Higiena Szkolna (0510-9868); (until 1961): Wychowanie Fizyczne w Szkole (0860-8571)
Published by: (Poland. Ministerstwo Edukacji Narodowej), AMOS, ul Zuga 12, Warsaw, 01806, Poland. TEL 48-22-8346521. Ed. Tadeusz Maszczak. **Dist. by:** Ars Polona, Krakowskie Przedmiescie 7, Warsaw, Poland.

WYZSZA SZKOLA PEDAGOGICZNA IM. KOMISJI EDUKACJI NARODOWEJ W KRAKOWIE. ROCZNIK NAUKOWE-DYDAKTYCZNY. PRACE TECHNICZNE. see *TECHNOLOGY: COMPREHENSIVE WORKS*

WYZSZA SZKOLA PEDAGOGICZNA IM. KOMISJI EDUKACJI NARODOWEJ W KRAKOWIE. ROCZNIK NAUKOWO-DYDAKTYCZNY. PRACE EKONOMICZNO-SPOLECZNE. see *BUSINESS AND ECONOMICS*

WYZSZA SZKOLA PEDAGOGICZNA IM. KOMISJI EDUKACJI NARODOWEJ W KRAKOWIE. ROCZNIK NAUKOWO-DYDAKTYCZNY. PRACE FILOZOFICZNE. see *PHILOSOPHY*

WYZSZA SZKOLA PEDAGOGICZNA IM. KOMISJI EDUKACJI NARODOWEJ W KRAKOWIE. ROCZNIK NAUKOWO-DYDAKTYCZNY. PRACE FIZYCZNE. see *PHILOSOPHY*

WYZSZA SZKOLA PEDAGOGICZNA IM. KOMISJI EDUKACJI NARODOWEJ W KRAKOWIE. ROCZNIK NAUKOWO-DYDAKTYCZNY. PRACE GEOGRAFICZNE. see *GEOGRAPHY*

WYZSZA SZKOLA PEDAGOGICZNA IM. KOMISJI EDUKACJI NARODOWEJ W KRAKOWIE. ROCZNIK NAUKOWO-DYDAKTYCZNY. PRACE HISTORYCZNE. see *HISTORY*

WYZSZA SZKOLA PEDAGOGICZNA IM. KOMISJI EDUKACJI NARODOWEJ W KRAKOWIE. ROCZNIK NAUKOWO-DYDAKTYCZNY. PRACE HISTORYCZNOLITERACKIE. see *LITERATURE*

WYZSZA SZKOLA PEDAGOGICZNA IM. KOMISJI EDUKACJI NARODOWEJ W KRAKOWIE. ROCZNIK NAUKOWO-DYDAKTYCZNY. PRACE MATEMATYCZNE. see *MATHEMATICS*

WYZSZA SZKOLA PEDAGOGICZNA IM. KOMISJI EDUKACJI NARODOWEJ W KRAKOWIE. ROCZNIK NAUKOWO-DYDAKTYCZNY. PRACE PSYCHOLOGICZNE. see *PSYCHOLOGY*

WYZSZA SZKOLA PEDAGOGICZNA IM. KOMISJI EDUKACJI NARODOWEJ W KRAKOWIE. ROCZNIK NAUKOWO-DYDAKTYCZNY. PRACE ROMANISTYCZNE. see *LINGUISTICS*

WYZSZA SZKOLA PEDAGOGICZNA IM. KOMISJI EDUKACJI NARODOWEJ W KRAKOWIE. ROCZNIK NAUKOWO-DYDAKTYCZNY. PRACE Z DYDAKTYKI BIOLOGII. see *BIOLOGY*

WYZSZA SZKOLA PEDAGOGICZNA IM. KOMISJI EDUKACJI NARODOWEJ W KRAKOWIE. ROCZNIK NAUKOWO-DYDAKTYCZNY. PRACE Z DYDAKTYKI LITERATURY I JEZYKA POLSKIEGO. see *LINGUISTICS*

WYZSZA SZKOLA PEDAGOGICZNA IM. KOMISJI EDUKACJI NARODOWEJ W KRAKOWIE. ROCZNIK NAUKOWO-DYDAKTYCZNY. PRACE Z DYDAKTYKI MATEMATYKI. see *MATHEMATICS*

WYZSZA SZKOLA PEDAGOGICZNA IM. KOMISJI EDUKACJI NARODOWEJ W KRAKOWIE. ROCZNIK NAUKOWO-DYDAKTYCZNY. PRACE Z RACHUNKU PRAWDOPODOBIENSTWA I JEGO DYDAKTYKI. see *MATHEMATICS*

WYZSZA SZKOLA PEDAGOGICZNA IM. KOMISJI EDUKACJI NARODOWEJ W KRAKOWIE. ROCZNIK NAUKOWO-DYDAKTYCZNY. PRACE Z WYCHOWANIA PLASTYCZNEGO. see *ART*

371.3 CHN
XIAOXUE GEKE JIAOYUXUE/TEACHING AND LEARNING OF ALL SUBJECTS IN PRIMARY SCHOOL. Text in Chinese. 1980. bi-m. USD 57.60 (effective 2004). 112 p./no.; **Document type:** *Journal, Academic/Scholarly.* **Description:** Covers elementary school education, teaching methods and curriculum.
Formerly: Xiaoxue Geke Jiaoxue (1001-2974)
Published by: Zhongguo Renmin Daxue, Shubao Zilio Zhongxin/Renmin University of China, Information Center for Social Server, Dongcheng-qu, 3, Zhangzizhong Lu, Beijing, 100007, China. TEL 86-10-64039458, FAX 86-10-64015080, kyes@163.net, http://www.confucius.cn.net/bkdetail.asp?fzt=G39. **Dist. in US by:** China Publications Service, PO Box 49614, Chicago, IL 60649. TEL 312-288-3291, FAX 312-288-8570; **Dist. by:** China International Book Trading Corp, 35 Chegongzhuang Xilu, Haidian District, PO Box 399, Beijing 100044, China. TEL 86-10-68412045, FAX 86-10-68412023, cibtc@mail.cibtc.com.cn, http://www.cibtc.com.cn.

XIAOXUE SHUXUE JIAOSHI/ARITHMETIC TEACHER. see *MATHEMATICS*

XIAOXUE YUWEN JIAOSHI/ELEMENTARY SCHOOL CHINESE LANGUAGE TEACHER. see *LINGUISTICS*

371.3 CHN ISSN 1004-6720
XIAOXUE YUWEN JIAOXUE/ELEMENTARY SCHOOL CHINESE TEACHING. Text in Chinese. 1980. m. **Document type:** *Academic/Scholarly.*
Related titles: Online - full text ed.: (from East View Information Services).
Published by: (Zhongguo Jiaoyu Xuehui, Quanguo Xiaoxue Yuwen Jiaoxue Yanjiuhui/National Association of Elementary Chinese Teaching), Shanxi Jiaoyu Baokan She, 17 Jiefang Lu, Dongtou Daoxiang, Taiyuan, Shanxi 030009, China. TEL 86-351-3047074. Ed. Li Xanqian. Circ: 120,000 (paid).

XUE HANYU/LEARNING CHINESE. see *LINGUISTICS*

371.3 USA ISSN 1538-6619
LB1140.A1 CODEN: YNGCAJ
➤ **Y C - YOUNG CHILDREN.** Text in English. 1944. bi-m. USD 60 domestic to individuals; USD 80 foreign to individuals; USD 95 domestic to institutions; USD 115 foreign to institutions (effective 2004). adv. bk.rev. bibl.; charts; illus. index. back issues avail.; reprint service avail. from PQC. **Document type:** *Journal, Academic/Scholarly.* **Description:** Directed to early childhood educators who use research and theory for classroom practice.
Formerly (until 2002): Young Children (0044-0728)
Related titles: Microform ed.: (from PQC); Online - full text ed.: (from ProQuest Information & Learning).
Indexed: ABIn, ASCA, AgeL, Agr, CDA, CIJE, CPE, CurCont, DSHAb, EAA, ECER, EduInd, FamI, L&LBA, MRD, PCI, PsycholAb, SFSA, SOPODA, SSCI.
—BLDSC (9421.410000), IDS, IE, Infotrieve, ingenta.

E

Published by: National Association for the Education of Young Children, 1509 16th St, N W, Washington, DC 20036-1426. TEL 202-232-8777, 800-424-1846, FAX 202-328-1846, http://www.naeyc.org. Ed. Polly Greenberg. Circ: 90,000.

371.33 807   USA
YOUNG ADULT LITERATURE SERIES. Text in English. 1992. irreg., latest 2000. price varies. bibl. back issues avail. **Document type:** *Monographic series, Trade.* **Description:** Discusses ways in which to use young adult literature effectively to teach English literature and other subjects. Provides tips for effective classroom instruction.
Published by: Heinemann - Boynton-Cook (Subsidiary of: Greenwood Publishing Group Inc.), 361 Hanover St, Portsmouth, NH 03801-3912. TEL 603-431-7894, 800-793-2154, FAX 603-431-7840, http://www.boyntoncook.com.

YOUNG EXCEPTIONAL CHILDREN. see *EDUCATION—Special Education And Rehabilitation*

THE YOUTH DISCIPLE. see *RELIGIONS AND THEOLOGY—Protestant*

YOUTH IN ACTION. TEACHER. see *RELIGIONS AND THEOLOGY—Protestant*

YOUTH IN DISCOVERY. TEACHER. see *RELIGIONS AND THEOLOGY—Protestant*

YOUTH THEATRE JOURNAL. see *THEATER*

YRKESLAERAREN - RET-INFO. see *EDUCATION—Adult Education*

YUWEN JIAOXUE TONGXUN/BULLETIN OF CHINESE LANGUAGE TEACHING. see *LINGUISTICS*

YUYAN JIAOXUE YU YANJIU/LANGUAGE TEACHING & STUDIES. see *LINGUISTICS*

371.3   DEU   ISSN 0172-2875
➤ **ZEITSCHRIFT FUER BERUFS- UND WIRTSCHAFTSPAEDAGOGIK.** Text in German. 1892. q. EUR 118; EUR 41 newsstand/cover (effective 2006). adv. bk.rev. index. back issues avail. **Document type:** *Journal, Academic/Scholarly.*
Formerly: Deutsche Berufs- und Fachschule (0011-9946)
Related titles: ◆ Supplement(s): Zeitschrift fuer Berufs- und Wirtschaftspaedagogik. Beihefte. ISSN 0174-0830.
Indexed: DIP, IBR, IBZ, RASB.
—CCC.
Published by: Franz Steiner Verlag Stuttgart GmbH, Birkenwaldstr 44, Stuttgart, 70191, Germany. TEL 49-711-25820, FAX 49-711-2582290, service@steiner-verlag.de, http://www.steiner-verlag.de. Ed. Gerhard Hauptmeier. R&P Sabine Koerner. Adv. contact Susanne Szoradi. B&W page EUR 810; trim 170 x 240. Circ: 2,500.

371.3   DEU   ISSN 0174-0830
ZEITSCHRIFT FUER BERUFS- UND WIRTSCHAFTSPAEDAGOGIK. BEIHEFTE. Text in German. 1980. irreg., latest vol.14, 1998. price varies. **Document type:** *Monographic series, Academic/Scholarly.*
Related titles: ◆ Supplement to: Zeitschrift fuer Berufs- und Wirtschaftspaedagogik. ISSN 0172-2875.
Published by: Franz Steiner Verlag Stuttgart GmbH, Birkenwaldstr 44, Stuttgart, 70191, Germany. TEL 49-711-25820, FAX 49-711-2582390, franz.steiner.verlag@t-online.de, http://www.steiner-verlag.de. R&P Sabine Koerner.

ZEITSCHRIFT FUER DIDAKTIK DER PHILOSOPHIE UND ETHIK. see *PHILOSOPHY*

ZENTRALBLATT FUER DIDAKTIK DER MATHEMATIK. see *MATHEMATICS*

ZEPHYR. see *LINGUISTICS*

373.245   CHN   ISSN 1001-2826
ZHIYE JISHU JIAOYU/OCCUPATIONAL AND TECHNICAL EDUCATION. Text in Chinese. bi-m. CNY 34.80 (effective 2004). 72 p./no.; **Document type:** *Journal, Academic/Scholarly.*

Published by: Zhongguo Renmin Daxue, Shubao Zilio Zhongxin/Renmin University of China, Information Center for Social Server, Dongcheng-qu, 3, Zhangzizhong Lu, Beijing, 100007, China. TEL 86-10-64039458, FAX 86-10-64015080, kyes@163.net, http://www.confucius.cn.net/bkdetail.asp?fzt=G53. **Dist. in US by:** China Publications Service, PO Box 49614, Chicago, IL 60649. TEL 312-288-3291, FAX 312-288-8570; **Dist. by:** China International Book Trading Corp, 35 Chegongzhuang Xilu, Haidian District, PO Box 399, Beijing 100044, China. TEL 86-10-68412045, FAX 86-10-68412023, cibtc@mail.cibtc.com.cn, http://www.cibtc.com.cn.

ZHONGXUE HUAXUE JIAOYUXUE/TEACHING AND LEARNING OF CHEMISTRY IN MIDDLE SCHOOL. see *CHEMISTRY*

ZHONGXUE WAIYU JIAOYUXUE/TEACHING AND LEARNING OF FOREIGN LANGUAGE IN MIDDLE SCHOOL. see *LINGUISTICS*

ZHONGXUE YUWEN JIAOYUXUE/TEACHING AND LEARNING OF CHINESE IN MIDDLE SCHOOL. see *LINGUISTICS*

510.71   CHN   ISSN 1001-6953
ZHONGXUESHENG SHU-LI-HUA (GAOZHONG BAN). Text in Chinese. m. USD 24.20. **Description:** Covers mathematics, physics, and chemistry for high school students.
Published by: Henan Jiaoyu She, 11 Shunhe Lu, Zhengzhou, Henan 450004, China. Ed. Yang Zhongxing. **Dist. in US by:** China Books & Periodicals Inc, 360 Swift Ave., Ste. 48, S San Fran, CA 94080-6220. info@chinabooks.com, http://www.chinabooks.com/.

ZHONGXUESHENG WULI YUANDI/PHYSICS FOR MIDDLE SCHOOL STUDENTS. see *PHYSICS*

ZOOM; filmpedagogisk tidskrift. see *MOTION PICTURES*

371.3   ESP   ISSN 1133-6919
20.B-INTE. (20 Boletin de Introduccion a las Nuevas Tecnologias en la Educacion) Text in Spanish. 1993. a.
—CINDOC.
Published by: Centro de Profesores "Costa Granadina", Departamento de Nuevas Tecnologias, Aguas del Hospital, s-n, Motril, Granada 18600, Spain. TEL 34-958-823404, FAX 34-958-822578.

▼ *new title*   ➤ *refereed*   ✳ *unverified*   ◆ *full entry avail.*

E